2025
LexisNexis®
Corporate Affiliations™

Content Operations:
Director-News & Business Content Operations & Metadata: Tammy Bair
Manager-Corporate Affiliations & Entity Management: Elizabeth A. Powers
Lead Content Analysts: Eric Eelman, Kevin Gaven

Production:
Senior Production Specialist: Joseph C. Stewart

Reed Elsevier Philippines-Corporate Affiliations Iloilo Team:
Operations Manager: Timothy J. Vilches
Operations Supervisor: Kristel Faye B. De la Cruz
Product Lead: Raquel G. Gajardo

2025
LexisNexis®
Corporate Affiliations™
U.S. Private Companies

Volume V
K-Z

QUESTIONS ABOUT THIS PUBLICATION?

For CONTENT questions concerning this publication, please call:

Content Operations Department at 800-340-3244
FAX 908-790-5405

For CUSTOMER SERVICE ASSISTANCE concerning shipments, billing or other matters, please call:
Customer Service at 800-340-3244, press 3

For SALES ASSISTANCE, please call:
The Sales Department at 800-340-3244, press 2

No part of this publication may be reproduced or transmitted in any form or by any means sorted in any information storage and retrieval system without prior written permission of LexisNexis, Content Operations, 9443 Springboro Pike, Miamiburg, OH 45342.

Library of Congress Catalog Card Number: 67-22770

U.S. Private Companies Volume 5, ISBN: 979-8-3417-0463-3

Corporate Affiliations 8-Volume Library, ISBN: 979-8-3417-0458-9

©2025 LexisNexis Group.

All Rights Reserved

LexisNexis, the knowledge burst logo and Corporate Affiliations are trademarks of Reed Elsevier Properties Inc., used under license.

The LexisNexis Group has used its best efforts in collecting and preparing material for inclusion in Corporate Affiliations: U.S. Private Companies ™ but does not assume, and hereby disclaims, any liability to any person for any loss or damage caused by errors or omissions in Corporate Affiliations: U.S. Private Companies whether such errors or omissions result from negligence, accident or any other cause.

Corporate Affiliations

Content Operations
9443 Springboro Pike
Miamisburg, OH 45342

www.lexisnexis.com

ISBN 979-8-3417-0463-3

9 798341 704633

CONTENTS

Preface vii
How To Use *Corporate Affiliations*™ ix
Abbreviations..xv
New Listings xvii
Mergers and Acquisitions xxi
U.S. Private Companies..2249

PREFACE

CORPORATE AFFILIATIONS

Corporate Affiliations is a logically organized business reference tool that covers major public and private businesses in the United States and throughout the world. The set consists of eight volumes:

Volume I	Master Index I
Volume II	Master Index II
Volume III	U.S. Public Companies
Volume IV	U.S. Private Companies I
Volume V	U.S. Private Companies II
Volume VI	International Public & Private Companies I
Volume VII	International Public & Private Companies II
Volume VIII	International Public & Private Companies III

The principle of organization for the set is geographical (by parent company) and hierarchical (by company reportage). Subsidiaries of a parent company, no matter where they are located, will be found in the same volume as the ultimate parent.

Please note that guidelines on the organization of the entire set for this edition can be found in the *Master Index* Volume I.

Entry criteria for the set are flexible. Generally speaking, U.S. based companies must demonstrate revenue in excess of $10 million, substantial assets, a work force in excess of 100 persons, or be traded on a major stock exchange. Non-U.S. based companies must demonstrate revenues in excess of $10 million.

THE *U.S. PRIVATE COMPANIES* VOLUME

Corporate Affiliations: U.S. Private Companies contains listings for privately held companies with U.S. located headquarters or holding companies. Subsidiaries for these parent companies are included, whether or not they are located in the United States. Also included are outside service firms attached to the parent companies. These are firms that perform specialized services such as accounting, legal, pension management, etc.

Content and Coverage in Corporate Affiliations-U.S. Private Companies

Listing statistics for this edition of U.S. Private are as follows:

Ultimate parent companies 67,177
U.S. located sub companies 32,903
Non-U.S. located sub companies 17,374
Total entry units listed 117,454

Outside service firms: 4,318

PREFACE

Companies are arranged alphabetically by the name of the parent company. Subsidiary companies follow the parent in order of reporting hierarchy. The bold number in parentheses shows the level of corporate reportage. Each listing can contain an extensive number of informational items. Please refer to the helpful 'How to Use' section for a guide to referencing methods and comprehensive listing samples.

The *U.S. Private* volume also contains several useful features in the frontmatter including 'New Listings' for this edition and 'Mergers and Acquisitions.'

COMPILATION

Corporate Affiliations is compiled and updated from information supplied by the companies themselves, business publications, internet research and annual reports.

RELATED SERVICES

For information on the corporateaffiliations.com web site, please call (800) 340-3244.

Mailing lists compiled from information contained in *Corporate Affiliations* may be ordered from:
R. Michael Patterson, Inside Sales Representative
DM2 Decision Maker
2000 Clearwater Drive, Oak Brook, IL
Tel: (630) 288-8348
E-mail: robert.patterson@dm2decisionmaker.com

Electronic database tapes of the directory in raw data format are available for licensing. For electronic database tapes or alliance opportunities, please contact:
LexisNexis, Corporate Affiliations
9443 Springboro Pike, Miamisburg, OH 45342
Tel: (800) 285-3947
E-mail: information@lexisnexis.com

Companies who wish to add or correct their listings can send information to:
LexisNexis, Corporate Affiliations Content Operations
9443 Springboro Pike
Miamisburg, OH 45342
Tel: (937) 865-6800

In addition to keeping the information in our directories as up to date as possible, we are constantly trying to improve their design, and add useful new features. Any comments or suggestions in this regard can be directed to the Managers of Operations at the above address.

HOW TO USE CORPORATE AFFILIATIONS: *U.S. PRIVATE COMPANIES*

Corporate Affiliations, U.S. Private Companies, contains a vast amount of useful information about firms that are not generally in the public eye. Included in *U.S. Private* are privately owned parent companies located in the United States.

This user guide is divided into three parts.

— **Part A**, 'How to Locate a Company' gives referencing instructions and samples of indexes. It demonstrates many useful methods for getting the information you need from this volume and from the *Corporate Affiliations* set at large.

— **Part B**, 'Sample Entries' shows the various data elements and listing style of companies in *Corporate Affiliations*.

— **Part C**, 'Understanding Levels of Reportage' demonstrates how company reportage structures are simply and clearly presented throughout *Corporate Affiliations*.

PART A: HOW TO LOCATE A COMPANY

1. **If you know the name of the company, but do not know its nationality or ownership status:**

    Look in the 'Master Index of Company Names' in volume I. This index will direct you to the correct volume of the set (i.e. Public, Private or International) and the correct page listing therein.

    KOMAG, INCORPORATED; *U.S. Public*, pg. 1023
    KOMAG MATERIAL TECHNOLOGY INC.—See
      Komag, Incorporated; *U.S. Public*, pg. 1023
    KOMAGANE ELECTRONICS, INC.—See Kenwood
      Corporation; *Int'l*, pg. 638

2. **If you know the company is a privately held parent company:**

    You can turn directly to the company listings in volumes IV and V, all of which are alphabetized by the name of the parent company.

3. **If you cannot find the company's name in the master index:**

It may mean that the company has been acquired or changed its name. To confirm this, try looking in the 'Mergers and Acquisitions' section at the front of this volume.

Sample of Mergers and Acquisitions Section

Alloway Industries–acquired by Code, Hennessy & Simmons, Inc.
Alpha Wire Company–acquired by Belden Inc.
Ambassador Steel Co.–ceased operations (no longer in business)

4. **To locate companies in a given line of business:**

Use the N.A.I.C.S. (North American Industrial Classification System) Master Index in volume II. This index interfiles data from all six volumes of *Corporate Affiliations*, arranging companies by particular products and services according to their primary N.A.I.C.S. code. The index is preceded by two helpful compendia: one sorts the codes alphabetically by the name of the product or service, the other numerically by the code itself.

Sample of Alpha Compendium of N.A.I.C.S. Codes

Description	N.A.I.C.S.
Administration of Conservation Programs	924120
Administration of Education Programs	923110

Sample of Numeric Compendium of N.A.I.C.S. Codes

Code	Description
523120	**SECURITIES BROKERAGE**
523210	Securities and Commodity Exchanges
523910	Miscellaneous Intermediation

Both parent and sub companies are covered in this index; parent companies are printed in bold type, sub companies in regular typeface followed by the name of its ultimate parent. A sample of the N.A.I.C.S. Master Index is shown here:

337211 — WOOD OFFICE FURNITURE MANUFACTURING

ABCO—Jami, Inc.; *Int'l*, pg. 586
ANDERSON HICKEY, INC.—Haworth, Inc.; *U.S. Public*, pg. 516
BELVEDERE COMPANY—Smith Investment Company; *Int'l*, pg. 1019
BRAYTON INTERNATIONAL INC.—Steelcase Inc.; *U.S. Public*, pg. 1048
BRODART COMPANY; *U.S. Private*, pg. 172
COMMUNITY—Jasper Seating Co., Inc.; *U.S. Private*, pg. 589
CRAMER INC.; *U.S. Public*, pg. 288
EAC CORPORATION; *Int'l*, pg. 357

PART B: BASIC COMPONENTS OF A PRIVATE COMPANY LISTING

Following is an example of a typical parent company listing with tags to some of its basic components.

SOUTHWEST PASSAGES, INC.	Company Name
528 S Sandia Dr	Company Address
Denver, CO 86052	
Tel: (303) 555-2156 — DE	Telecommunications Data & State of Incorporation
Web Site: www.spi.com	Electronic Address
Year Founded: 1965	
Assets: $18,000,000	Financial Data
Liabilities: $10,000,000	
Net Worth: $8,000,000	
Earnings: $2,500,000	
Emp.: 398	Number of Employees, Including Subsidiaries
Fiscal Year End: 12/31/24	
Retail Book Stores	
N.A.I.C.S.: 424920	North American Industry Classification System Code
No. of U.S. Offices: 8	
No. of Foreign Offices: 3	
Nelly LaGuardia (*Pres*)	
John Davidson (*COO*)	
Gregory James (*CFO & VP-Fin*)	

Following each parent company listing are the entries for each of that company's divisions, subsidiaries, affiliates, joint ventures, units, etc. Though companies vary widely in their usage of these terms, some of the more common company designations can be defined as follows:

Affiliate   A chartered business owned by the company at less than 50%.

Division   An internal unit of a company, not incorporated.

Joint Venture   A business in which two or more companies share responsibility and ownership.

Subsidiary   A chartered business owned by the company at 50% or more.

PART C: UNDERSTANDING LEVELS OF REPORTAGE

Each sub-unit of the company will have a number in parentheses to the right of the company name. This number represents the level of reportage for that particular company. Any company with a level (1) reports directly to the parent company. Level (2) companies report to the level (1) company immediately above them. Level (3) companies report to the level (2) company immediately above them, etc.

In the example below, Maine Passages, Mass Books, and Western Passages all report directly to the parent company, Southwest Passages, Inc. R.I. Books is a subsidiary of, and reports directly to, Mass Books, and B.C. Books Etc. is a subsidiary of, and reports directly to, R.I. Books.

Subsidiaries:

Maine Passages ——————— (1) ——— **Reports to the Parent Company**
US 1 RR 32   **(Southwest Passages, Inc. from**
Bangor, ME 04402 ——————— ME ——— **previous example)**
Tel: (207) 555-1235   (70%) ——— **Percentage of Ownership**
Sales Range: $20-24.9 Million
Emp: 7
Mail Order Books
N.A.I.C.S.: 454113
Kurt King, Jr. (*CEO*)

Mass Books   (1) ——— **Reports Direct to the**
1 Olympia Dr   **Parent Company**
Boston, MA 02101   MA ——— **State of Incorporation**
Tel: (508) 555-1011
Retail Book Stores
N.A.I.C.S.: 424920
Dan Lagattuta (*Pres*)

Subsidiary:

R.I. Books ——————————— (2) ——— **Reports Direct to Level 1**
100 W 57th St   **Company Above (Mass Books)**
Newport, RI 06001   CT
Tel: (401) 555-4000
Retail Book Stores
N.A.I.C.S.: 424920
Craig Russell (*Pres*)

Non-U.S. Holding:

BC Books Etc. ——————— (3) ——————— **Non-U.S. Based Holding that Reports**
2 Victoria Avenue **Direct to the Level 2 Company on**
Vancouver, BC, L5T 2N5, Canada **Bottom of Previous Page (R.I. Books)**
Tel: (604) 555-8912
Emp.: 11
Retail Book Stores
N.A.I.C.S.: 424920
Jeffery Gilbert *(Pres)*

Western Passages ——————— (1) ——————— **Reports to Parent Company**
1200 Agua Fria Blvd **(Southwest Passages, Inc.)**
Santa Fe, NM 87501
Tel.: (505) 555-7373
Emp.: 46
Retail Book Stores
N.A.I.C.S.: 424920
Laura Maggio *(CEO)*

In addition to keeping the information in our directories as up-to-date as possible, we are constantly trying to improve their design and organization, and to add useful new features. Any comments or suggestions in this regard can be directed to: The LexisNexis Group, Corporate Affiliations Content Operations, 9443 Springboro Pike, Miamisburg, OH 45342.

ABBREVIATIONS

Acct	Account	Matl	Material
Acctg	Accounting	Matls	Materials
Accts	Accounts	Mdse	Merchandise
Acq	Acquisition(s)	Mdsg	Merchandising
Admin	Administration	Mfg	Manufacturing
Admin	Administrative	Mfr	Manufacturer
Adv	Advertising	Mgmt	Management
Assoc	Associate	Mgr	Manager
Asst	Assistant	Mktg	Marketing
Brdcst	Broadcast	Mng	Managing
Bus	Business	Natl	National
CEO	Chief Executive Officer	Ops	Operations
CFO	Chief Financial Officer	Org	Organization
Chm	Chairman of the Board	Pkg	Packaging
CIO	Chief Information Officer	Plng	Planning
CMO	Chief Marketing Officer	Pres	President
Comm	Communication(s)	Prof	Professional
Comml	Commercial	Promo	Promotion
COO	Chief Operating Officer	Promos	Promotions
Coord	Coordinator	Pub	Public
Corp	Corporate/Corporation	Pub Rel	Public Relations
CTO	Chief Technology Officer	Publ	Publishing
Dept	Department	Publr	Publisher
Dev	Development	Pur	Purchasing
Dir	Director	R&D	Research & Development
Distr	Distribution	Reg	Regional
Div	Division	Rep	Representative
DP	Data Processing	Res	Research
Engr	Engineer	Sec	Secretary
Engrg	Engineering	Sls	Sales
Environ	Environmental	Sr	Senior
Exec	Executive	Supvr	Supervisor
Fin	Finance/Financial	Svc	Service
Gen	General	Svcs	Services
Govt	Government	Sys	Systems
Grp	Group	Tech	Technology
HR	Human Resources	Tech	Technical
Indus	Industry/Industrial	Telecom	Telecommunication(s)
Info	Information	Treas	Treasurer
Intl	International	Trng	Training
IR	Investor Relations	Vice Chm	Vice Chairman
IT	Information Technology	VP	Vice President
Jr	Junior		

COMPANY DESIGNATIONS

The following designations indicate the forms of business enterprise in various countries; these forms usually represent the organizations for large enterprises.

AB	Aktiebolag	Finland, Sweden
AG	Aktiengesellschaft	Austria, Germany, Switzerland, Liechtenstein
A/S	Aksjeselskap	Norway
	Aktieselskab	Denmark
B.V.	Besloten Vennootschap	Holland
C.V.	Commanditaire Vennootschap	Holland
Cie.	Compagnie	France, Luxembourg
Co.	Company	United States, France, South Africa, Luxembourg
Ets.	Etablissement(s)	France, Luxembourg
GmbH	Gesellschaft mit beschrankter Haftung	Austria, Germany, Switzerland
I/S	Interessantelskab	Denmark, Norway
KG	Kommanditgesellschaft	Austria, Germany, Switzerland
KK	Kabushiki Kaisha	Japan
K/S	Kommanditselskab	Denmark
Lda.	Limitada	Portugal
Ltd.	Limited	United Kingdom, United States, South Africa
Ltda.	Limitada	Brazil, Portugal
Ltee.	Limitee	Canada
Mij.	Maatschappij	Holland
N.V.	Naamloze Vennootschap	Belgium, Holland
OHG	Offene Handelsgesellschaft	Austria
Oy	Osakeyhtiot	Finland
PLC	Public Limited Company	United Kingdom
P.T.	Perusahaan Terbatas	Indonesia
Pte.	Private	Singapore
Pty.	Proprietary	Australia, South Africa
Pvt.	Private	India, Rhodesia
S.A.	Societe Anonyme	Belgium, France, Luxembourg, Switzerland
Sociedad	Anonima	Spain, Latin America
S.A.C.I.	Sociedad Anonima Comercial e Industrial	Latin America
S.A. de C.V.	Sociedad Anonima de Capital Variable	Mexico
S.A.E.	Sociedad Anonima Espanola	Spain
S.A.I.C.	Sociedad Anonima Industrial y Comercial	Latin America
S.A.R.L.	Sociedad Anonima de Responsabilidade Limitada	Brazil
	Sociedade a Responsabilitie Limitee	France, Luxembourg
S.A.S.	Societa in Accomandita Semplice	Italy
S.C.	Societe en Commandite	France
S.p.A.	Societa per Azioni	Italy
S.P.R.L.	Societe de Personnes a Responsabilitie Limitee	Belgium
S.R.L.	Societa a Responsabilita Limitata	Italy
Sdn. Bhd.	Sendirian Berhad	Malaysia
Ste.	Societe	France, Switzerland
Ste. Cve.	Societe Cooperative	Belgium
V.o.F.	Vennootschap onder firma	Holland

xvi

NEW LISTINGS 2025
Appearing for the first time in this publication

2
26NORTH BDC, INC.; NEW YORK, NY

A
AFM CAPITAL PARTNERS, INC.; INDIANAPOLIS, IN

AGITAL HOLDINGS, LLC; BURLINGTON, MA

AGNO PHARMA; NEW YORK, NY

ALGER ASSOCIATES, INC.; NEW YORK, NY

APEX SERVICE PARTNERS LLC; TAMPA, FL

APG POLYTECH, LLC; APPLE GROVE, WV

APOLLO REALTY INCOME SOLUTIONS, INC.; NEW YORK, NY

APPLIED VALUE LLC; ANDOVER, MD

ARBOL INC.; NEW YORK, NY

ARMADA GROUP, LTD.; PITTSBURGH, PA

ARMADA MATERIALS, LLC; TAMPA, FL

ASC GLOBAL INC.; BRADENTON, FL

ASCEND PLASTIC SURGERY PARTNERS; ATLANTA, GA

ASCENSION ST JOHN FOUNDATION; TULSA, OK

ATSIGN, INC.; SAN JOSE, CA

AUA PRIVATE EQUITY PARTNERS LLC; WEST PALM BEACH, FL

AUSTERLITZ ACQUISITION CORP I; LAS VEGAS, NV

AVION SOLUTIONS, INC.; HUNTSVILLE, AL

B
B&M INDUSTRIAL, INC.; EL PASO, TX

BANSK GROUP LLC; NEW YORK, NY

BARINGS PRIVATE CREDIT CORPORATION; CHARLOTTE, NC

BAY RIDGE PREP; BROOKLYN, NY

BEACON CREDIT UNION; WABASH, IN

BEAN'S BEST LLC; ANN ARBOR, MI

BENDITO RESOURCES INC.; RENO, NV

BHARCAP PARTNERS, LLC; GREENWICH, CT

BIG TREE GROUP, INC.; ROSEVILLE, MI

BINDTECH LLC; NASHVILLE, TN

BIOME MAKERS INC.; DAVIS, CA

BIP VENTURES EVERGREEN BDC; ATLANTA, GA

BLOOM EQUITY PARTNERS MANAGEMENT, LLC; NEW YORK, NY

BLOOM HOLDCO LLC; MIAMI, FL

BLOOMERANG, LLC; INDIANAPOLIS, IN

BLUE CHIP CAPITAL GROUP, INC.; BEVERLY HILLS, CA

BLUE DELTA CAPITAL PARTNERS LLC; MCLEAN, VA

BLUE WATER SHIELD LLC; HOLLYWOOD, CA

BODINE AND COMPANY, LLC; POLAND, OH

BP ENERGY PARTNERS, LLC; DALLAS, TX

BRADDOCKMATTHEWSBARRETT, LLC; NEW YORK, NY

BRAEMONT CAPITAL MANAGEMENT LLC; DALLAS, TX

BRIGHT SHEET METAL COMPANY, INC.; INDIANAPOLIS, IN

BRIGHTWORKS SUSTAINABILITY LLC; PORTLAND, OR

BROADVIEW GROUP HOLDINGS, LLC; ST. LOUIS, MO

C
C2DESIGN; CLEVELAND, OH

CACTUS COMMUNICATIONS, INC.; PRINCETON, NJ

CALIFORNIA NURSES ASSOCIATION; OAKLAND, CA

CALLAWAY CAPITAL MANAGEMENT, LLC; NASHVILLE, TN

CAPITAL MACHINE TECHNOLOGIES, INC.; TAMPA, FL

CAPITAL ONE AUTO RECEIVABLES LLC; MCLEAN, VA

CAPITAL PARTNERS LLC; EDINA, MN

CAPITAL RIVERS COMMERCIAL LLC; SACRAMENTO, CA

CES POWER LLC; MEMPHIS, TN

CHAYAH CONSULTING GROUP LLC; LOVELAND, CO

CHRISTIAN HOSPITAL FOUNDATION; SAINT LOUIS, MO

CITICORP TRUST SOUTH DAKOTA; SIOUX FALLS, SD

CONTAINER SERVICES LLC; CHICAGO, IL

CORK DISTRIBUTORS, LLC; LAS VEGAS, NV

CORPORATE PROPERTY ASSOCIATES 18 GLOBAL INC; NEW YORK, NY

CORROHEALTH, INC.; PLANO, TX

CREDITECH, INC.; BANGOR, ME

CRESCENT PRIVATE CREDIT INCOME CORP.; LOS ANGELES, CA

CROWE LLP; CHICAGO, IL

CRUX CAPITAL LTD; DALLAS, TX

CURATORS OF THE UNIVERSITY OF MISSOURI; COLUMBIA, MO

D
DARK HORSE CONSULTING; WALNUT CREEK, CA

DELCAM HOLDINGS, LLC; HOPEDALE, MA

DEMAND SCIENCE GROUP, LLC; DANVERS, MA

DERMTECH, LLC; SAN DIEGO, CA

DINI SPHERIS; HOUSTON, TX

DIRECT EDGE CAMPAIGNS, LLC; NASHVILLE, TN

New Listings—continued

DOMINION EQUITY LLC; CHICAGO, IL

DRY FLY CAPITAL LLC; LITTLETON, CO

DUNAWAY ASSOCIATES, LLC; FORT WORTH, TX

E

EBC HR & PAYROLL SOLUTIONS, INC.; BUFFALO, NY

EBERLESTOCK USA LLC; BOISE, ID

ELEMENTS HEALTH INVESTORS, LLC; NEW YORK, NY

ELEVATE ORAL CARE, LLC; WEST PALM BEACH, FL

EMED, LLC; MIAMI, FL

EMPEOPLE CREDIT UNION; MOLINE, IL

ENGINEERS WITHOUT BORDERS-USA, INC.; DENVER, CO

ENKO CHEM, INC.; MYSTIC, CT

ENVIROTROL PEST MANAGEMENT SYSTEMS INC.; GRAND PRAIRIE, TX

ERGO-FLEX TECHNOLOGIES, LLC; CONROE, TX

EVANGELICAL LUTHERAN CHURCH IN AMERICA; CHICAGO, IL

F

F&I SENTINEL, LLC; TALLAHASSEE, FL

FACTOR 89 PARTNERS, LLC; CHICAGO, IL

FIDELITY PRIVATE CREDIT COMPANY LLC; BOSTON, MA

FIRELIGHT CAPITAL PARTNERS LLC; FORT LAUDERDALE, FL

FLAG PUBLICATION, INC; OCEAN CITY, MD

FLAGLER BANCSHARES CORPORATION; NORTH PALM BEACH, FL

FLEET TEAM, INC.; INDEPENDENCE, OH

FOREST ROAD SECURITIES, LLC; SANTA MONICA, CA

G

GELLERT GLOBAL GROUP; ELIZABETH, NJ

GEORGE WASHINGTON'S MOUNT VERNON; MOUNT VERNON, VA

GLOBAL REDEMPTION INC.; LANCASTER, PA

GMSS HOLDINGS, LLC; WOBURN, MA

GOLDMAN SACHS PRIVATE CREDIT CORP.; NEW YORK, NY

GOLUB CAPITAL DIRECT LENDING UNLEVERED CORPORATION; NEW YORK, NY

GORHAM BANCORP, MHC; GORHAM, ME

GRADE EIGHT CORP; PLANO, TX

GRANITE BANK; COLD SPRING, MN

GREENOAKS CAPITAL PARTNERS LLC; SAN FRANCISCO, CA

GUARDIAR USA LLC; ENNIS, TX

GUTTMAN HOLDINGS, INC.; BELLE VERNON, PA

H

HALFF ASSOCIATES, INC.; RICHARDSON, TX

HEARTLAND DERMATOLOGY AND SKIN CANCER CENTER, P.A.; SALINA, KS

HIRSCHBACH MOTOR LINES, INC.; DUBUQUE, IA

HOAG HOSPITAL FOUNDATION; NEWPORT BEACH, CA

HOLLEWAY CAPITAL PARTNERS LLC; SAINT LOUIS, MO

HOOD CONTAINER CORPORATION; ATLANTA, GA

HOSPECO BRANDS GROUP; CLEVELAND, OH

I

ICONECTIV, LLC; BRIDGEWATER, NJ

ILION CAPITAL PARTNERS; NEW YORK, NY

ILLUMINATE OPERATIONS LLC; HERNDON, VA

INCODE TECHNOLOGIES, INC.; SAN FRANCISCO, CA

INDIVIDUAL CENTRICITY CORPORATION; SAN RAMON, CA

INFINITY HOME SERVICES; BROOKFIELD, WI

INOVA HEALTH SYSTEM FOUNDATION; FAIRFAX, VA

INTELETRAVEL.COM; DELRAY BEACH, CA

INTERNATIONAL BROTHERHOOD OF TEAMSTERS; WASHINGTON, DC

INTERNATIONAL UNION OF PAINTERS AND ALLIED TRADES; HANOVER, MD

INTERPLAY LEARNING INC.; AUSTIN, TX

IUPAT DISTRICT COUNCIL 21; PHILADELPHIA, PA

IUPAT DISTRICT COUNCIL 9; NEW YORK, NY

J

J RUSSELL & ASSOCIATES LLC; ATHENS, GA

JACMEL GROWTH PARTNERS MANAGEMENT LLC; NEW YORK, NY

JADE STEEL GROUP, LTD.; BEDFORD HEIGHTS, OH

JETS MRO, LLC; DALLAS, TX

JHM FINANCIAL GROUP, LLC; STAMFORD, CT

JOAN PEARCE RESEARCH ASSOCIATES; LOS ANGELES, CA

JUST PLAY PRODUCTS, LLC; BOCA RATON, FL

K

KAYNE DL 2021, INC.; HOUSTON, TX

KFM ENTERPRISES, LLC; TULSA, OK

KIMMERIDGE ENERGY MANAGEMENT COMPANY, LLC; NEW YORK, NY

KIND, INC.; WASHINGTON, DC

KKR PRIVATE EQUITY CONGLOMERATE LLC; NEW YORK, NY

L

LARKIN INGRASSIA, PLLC; NEWBURGH, NY

LARRY MATHIS FINANCIAL PLANNING, LLC; PHOENIX, AZ

LEGACY COMMUNITY HEALTH; HOUSTON, TX

LEPERCQ, DE NEUFLIZE & CO. INC; NEW YORK, NY

LEXAGENE HOLDINGS INC.; BEVERLY, MA

LGAM PRIVATE CREDIT LLC; NEW YORK, NY

LIBERTY 77 CAPITAL, L.P.; WASHINGTON, DC

LIUNA MIDWEST REGION; SPRINGFIELD, IL

LOS ANGELES PUBLIC LIBRARY DOCENTS; LOS ANGELES, CA

LOTUS INFRASTRUCTURE PARTNERS LLC; GREENWICH, CT

LOWER HOLDING COMPANY; COLUMBIA, MD

New Listings—continued

LUCERNE CAPITAL MANAGEMENT, LP.; GREENWICH, CT

M

MAINE COMMUNITY BANCORP, MHC; WESTBROOK, ME

MALLOY AUTOMOTIVE OF WINCHESTER LLC; ALEXANDRIA, VA

MAPR.AGENCY, INC.; BOULDER, CO

MARCUM WEALTH LLC; CLEVELAND, OH

MARILLAC ST. VINCENT FAMILY SERVICES; CHICAGO, IL

MARKQUART INC.; CHIPPEWA FALLS, WI

MASS GENERAL BRIGHAM INCORPORATED; BOSTON, MA

MATTHEWS REAL ESTATE INVESTMENT SERVICES; NASHVILLE, TN

MAURY, DONNELLY & PARR, INC.; BALTIMORE, MD

MAVIK CAPITAL MANAGEMENT, LP; NEW YORK, NY

MAX SOLUTIONS INC.; BRISTOL, CT

MBE CPAS LLP; BARABOO, WI

MD ESTHETICS, LLC; WINDHAM, NH

METEORA CAPITAL LLC; BOCA RATON, FL

METHODIST HOSPITAL FOUNDATION; OMAHA, NE

MHR MANAGEMENT LLC; PORTLAND, ME

MIDWEST BANCORPORATION, INC.; EDEN PRAIRIE, MN

MISSION CRITICAL GROUP; SPICEWOOD, TX

MOCKLER BEVERAGE CO. LP; BATON ROUGE, LA

MODE GLOBAL, LLC; DALLAS, TX

MODIGENT LLC; PHOENIX, AZ

MON SPACE NET INC.; LAS VEGAS, NV

MORRIS COUNTY LIBRARY; WHIPPANY, NJ

MOUNT NITTANY MEDICAL CENTER; STATE COLLEGE, PA

MUNA FEDERAL CREDIT UNION; MERIDIAN, MS

MUSEUM OF NEW MEXICO FOUNDATION; SANTA FE, NM

MUSICTODAY II, LLC; CROZET, VA

MUTUAL BANCORP; HYANNIS, MA

MUTUAL CAPITAL GROUP, INC.; WYALUSING, PA

MYONEX, LLC; HORSHAM, PA

N

NATIONAL FFA FOUNDATION; INDIANAPOLIS, IN

NEW RITE AID, LLC; PHILADELPHIA, PA

NEXT LEVEL BURGER COMPANY, INC.; BEND, OR

NEXTTRIP HOLDINGS, INC.; SUNRISE, FL

NORTH ATLANTIC STATES REGIONAL COUNCIL OF CARPENTERS; BOSTON, MA

NORTH BAY JOBS WITH JUSTICE; SANTA ROSA, CA

NORTH HAVEN PRIVATE INCOME FUND LLC; NEW YORK, NY

NORTH TEXAS FOOD BANK; PLANO, TX

NORTHEAST GROCERY, INC.; SCHENECTADY, NY

NXTLVL MARINE, LLC; AUSTIN, TX

O

O'DONNELL'S TERMITE & PEST CONTROL, INC.; QUINCY, MA

OAKTREE GARDENS OLP, LLC; LOS ANGELES, CA

OBRA CAPITAL, INC.; AUSTIN, TX

ONEMAIN FINANCE CORPORATION; EVANSVILLE, IN

ORCUS TECHNOLOGIES, INC; LUBBOCK, TX

OUTSIDE INTERACTIVE, INC.; BOULDER, CO

P

PALMER JOHNSON ENTERPRISES, INC.; MADISON, WI

PARADIGM CAPITAL PARTNERS; LOS ANGELES, CA

PARIC HOLDINGS, INC.; SAINT LOUIS, MO

PARMAN HOLDING CORPORATION; NASHVILLE, TN

PATHOS AI, INC.; CHICAGO, IL

PCB FINANCIAL, INC; COSTA MESA, CA

PEACH STATE FEDERAL CREDIT UNION.; LAWRENCEVILLE, GA

PERIGON WEALTH MANAGEMENT LLC; SAN FRANCISCO, CA

PERSHING SQUARE SPARC HOLDINGS, LTD.; NEW YORK, NY

PHOENIX CHILDREN'S FOUNDATION; PHOENIX, AZ

PIEZO MOTION CORP.; SARASOTA, FL

PKDW EQUITY PARTNERS, LLC; PITTSBURGH, PA

POLYVENTIVE LLC; CALHOUN, GA

POPS MART FUELS, LLC; COLUMBIA, SC

PRAGER UNIVERSITY FOUNDATION; SHERMAN OAKS, CA

PRESBYTERIAN HEALTHCARE FOUNDATION; ALBUQUERQUE, NM

PSG EQUITY L.L.C.; BOSTON, MA

PULASKI-WHITE RURAL TELEPHONE COOPERATIVE, INC.; BUFFALO, NY

Q

QUAD VIDEO HOLDINGS CORPORATION; HOUSTON, TX

QUANTUM CAPITAL GROUP LLC; HOUSTON, TX

R

RAINFOREST DISTRIBUTION CORP; BAYONNE, NJ

REDYREF INTERACTIVE KIOSKS; RIVERDALE, CA

REEDER-TRAUSCH MARINE; ROCKVILLE, MD

RESULTSCX; FORT LAUDERDALE, FL

REVOLENT CAPITAL SOLUTIONS; TAMPA, FL

RIVAL HOLDINGS, LLC.; FORT WAYNE, IN

RIVER FALLS MUTUAL INSURANCE COMPANY; RIVER FALLS, WI

ROCK SOLID UK LTD.; BENTONVILLE, AR

ROOTS EQUITY GROUP LLC; BEVERLY HILLS, CA

S

SAG-AFTRA HEALTH PLAN; BURBANK, CA

New Listings—continued

SAINT JAMES HOLDING & INVESTMENT COMPANY TRUST; DOVER, NJ

SALLYPORT COMMERCIAL FINANCE, LLC; SUGAR LAND, TX

SALT BLOCKCHAIN INC.; DENVER, CO

SANDERSON BELLECCI, INC.; CONCORD, CA

SCIENS CAPITAL MANAGEMENT LLC; NEW YORK, NY

SECURITY STATE CORPORATION; CENTRALIA, WA

SEMAFOR, INC.; NEW YORK, NY

SENDAYCO, LLC; DAYTON, OH

SENIOR CREDIT INVESTMENTS, LLC; NEW YORK, NY

SG ENTERPRISES II, LLC; BELLEVUE, WA

SIXTH STREET LENDING PARTNERS; DALLAS, TX

SKAN, INC.; MENLO PARK, CA

SMK IMAGING, LLC; ELMSFORD, NY

SOCIAL CAPITAL HEDOSOPHIA HOLDINGS CORP. IV; MENLO PARK, CA

SOCIETY BRANDS, INC.; CANTON, OH

SOUTHEAST ALASKA REGIONAL HEALTH CONSORTIUM; JUNEAU, AK

STIRLING HOTELS & RESORTS, INC.; DALLAS, TX

STO BUILDING GROUP INC.; NEW YORK, NY

STONE POINTE, LLC; NAPERVILLE, IL

STRATEGIC GOVERNMENT RESOURCES INC.; KELLER, TX

STRUCTURA, INC.; BETHESDA, MD

SUBSPLIT SERVICES GROUP, L.P.; MEMPHIS, TN

SUN POWERSPORTS INVESTMENTS, LLC; DENVER, CO

SURGE VENTURES, LLC; MENLO PARK, CA

SURVEYING AND MAPPING, LLC; AUSTIN, TX

SWELL ENERGY INC; SANTA MONICA, CA

SYNAGEX, INC; PITTSFIELD, MA

SYSTM BRANDS, LLC; NEWPORT BEACH, CA

T

TAYLOR ENERGY, LLC; WINDSOR, CT

TEAM SOLUTIONS GROUP, INC.; VAN NUYS, CA

THE BLACK PHOENIX GROUP; CHICAGO, IL

THE CHILDREN'S HOSPITAL OF PHILADELPHIA FOUNDATION; PHILADELPHIA, PA

THE CHOSEN, INC.; HURRICANE, UT

THE INTERNATIONAL SPY MUSEUM; WASHINGTON, DC

THE KENT COMPANIES; MIDLAND, TX

THE LONGHORN COUNCIL, BOY SCOUTS OF AMERICA; HURST, TX

THE METROHEALTH FOUNDATION, INC.; CLEVELAND, OH

THE STEVENS & LEE COMPANIES, LLC; READING, PA

THE UNITED SERVICE ORGANIZATIONS, INC.; WASHINGTON, DC

THOMPSON DISTRIBUTION, LLC; NASHVILLE, TN

TIMONEER STRATEGIC PARTNERS, LLC; NEWPORT BEACH, CA

TOTAL LENDER SOLUTIONS, INC.; SAN DIEGO, CA

TRANSTEX LLC; INDIANAPOLIS, IN

TREND HEALTH PARTNERS LLC; HUNT VALLEY, MD

TROUT UNLIMITED INC.; ARLINGTON, VA

TROUTMAN PEPPER HAMILTON SANDERS LLP; ATLANTA, GA

TTCP MANAGEMENT SERVICES, LLC.; BLOOMINGTON, IN

TXEX ENERGY INVESTMENTS, LLC; HOUSTON, TX

U

UC SAN DIEGO HEALTH; SAN DIEGO, CA

UCI HEALTH; ORANGE, CA

UHY LLP; ALBANY, NY

UKG INC.; WESTON, FL

UNICOIN INC.; NEW YORK, NY

UNITED FOR RESPECT EDUCATION FUND; SACRAMENTO, CA

V

VANGEO TECHNOLOGY GROUP, LLC; SCOTTSDALE, AZ

VARAGON CAPITAL CORPORATION; NEW YORK, NY

VEGAS BRAZIL LLC; LAS VEGAS, NV

VERSE INNOVATION PRIVATE LIMITED; KARNATAKA, IN

VILLAGE HEALTH WORKS; NEW YORK, NY

VIRGIN ORBIT HOLDINGS, INC.; LONG BEACH, CA

VIRGINIA LEAGUE FOR PLANNED PARENTHOOD INC.; RICHMOND, VA

VISTA CREDIT STRATEGIC LENDING CORP.; NEW YORK, NY

VIVENT HEALTH, INC.; MILWAUKEE, WI

VOYAGER INTERESTS, LLC; HOUSTON, TX

W

WALLEYE CAPITAL, LLC; NEW YORK, NY

WAYNE-SANDERSON FARMS; OAKWOOD, CA

WEILL CORNELL MEDICINE; NEW YORK, NY

WEST MAUI CONSTRUCTION, INC.; KAHULUI, HI

WHANAU INTERESTS LLC.; AUSTIN, TX

WILLIAM MACKLOWE COMPANY LLC; NEW YORK, NY

WINDY CITY NOVELTIES, INC.; VERNON HILLS, IL

WOODSON EQUITY LLC; CHICAGO, IL

WORKERS UNITED; PHILADELPHIA, PA

Y

YOUNG & ASSOCIATES; NASHVILLE, TN

Mergers and Acquisitions
January 2024—December 2024
(Parent Companies Only)

1

121 Financial Credit Union—acquired by VyStar Credit Union

A

A S Arbury & Sons, Inc.—acquired by Hellman & Friedman LLC

A&D Maintenance Leasing & Repairs, Inc.—acquired by Custom Truck One Source, Inc.

Aaron Concrete Contractors LP—acquired by Heidelberg Materials AG

Aatrix Software, Inc.—acquired by HgCapital Trust plc

Abelei, Inc—acquired by T. Hasegawa Co. Ltd.

Abpro Corporation—merged with Atlantic Coastal Acquisition Corp. II, to form Abpro Holdings, Inc.

Absolute Mobility Center—acquired by Edwards Capital, LLC

Acclara Solutions, LLC—acquired by R1 RCM Inc.

Accurate Computer Solutions, LLC—acquired by The 20 Msp Group LLC

Acroname Inc.—acquired by Valens Semiconductor Ltd.

Adheso-Graphics, Inc.—acquired by Anderson & Vreeland, Inc.

ADT, LLC—acquired by Q-Lab Corp.

Advanced Cooling Therapy, Inc.—acquired by Haemonetics Corporation

Advanced Industrial Coatings, Inc.—acquired by Crawford United Corporation

Advanced Systems Engineering Corporation—acquired by Sterling Investment Partners, L.P.

Advantix Solutions Group, Inc.—acquired by ScanSource, Inc.

Advent Intermodal Solutions, LLC—acquired by CargoSprint LLC

Aerospace Lubricants, Inc.—acquired by Amsoil Inc.

Agnoli, Barber & Brundage, Inc.—acquired by LJA Engineering, Inc.

AGR International, Inc.—acquired by Clayton, Dubilier & Rice, LLC

Aim Processing, Inc.—acquired by Mcm Capital Partners, LP

Air Filter Supply, Inc.—acquired by Audax Group, Limited Partnership

Airborn Inc.—acquired by Koch Industries, Inc.

Airon Corporation—acquired by Inspiration Healthcare Group Plc

Alarm Specialists, Inc.—acquired by Pye-Barker Fire & Safety, LLC

Albert Frei & Sons Inc.—acquired by Martin Marietta Materials, Inc.

All American Building Products—acquired by Strength Capital Partners, LLC

All New York Title Agency, Inc.—acquired by Stewart Information Services Corporation

All Star Striping LLC—acquired by Investcorp Holdings B.S.C. and Trilantic Capital Management L.P.

AllCool Refrigerant Reclaim, LLC—acquired by Heritage Environmental Services, LLC and BC Partners LLP

Alliance Business & Commercial Insurance Services—acquired by Inszone Insurance Services, LLC

Allied Alloys LP—acquired by Stainless Steel Midwest LLC

Allstate Can Corporation—acquired by The Ohio Art Company, Inc.

Allston Supply Co., Inc.—acquired by Bain Capital, LP

Alpha Imaging, Inc.—acquired by Radon Medical Imaging Corp.

Alt 5 Sigma Inc.—acquired by JanOne Inc.

Altek Electronics Inc.—acquired by Cyient Limited

Amcap Mortgage Ltd.—acquired by Crosscountry Mortgage, LLC

American Cleaning Systems, Inc.—acquired by Valcourt Building Services LLC

American Financial Resources, Inc.—acquired by Proprietary Capital LLC

American Heritage Agency Inc.—acquired by Inszone Insurance Services, LLC

Ameristar Agency, Inc.—acquired by Marsh & McLennan Companies, Inc.

Ammcon Corp.—acquired by Arcline Investment Management LP

Analytic Stress Relieving, Inc.—acquired by The CapStreet Group LLC

Angel City Press—acquired by Los Angeles Public Library Docents

Anillo Industries, Inc.—acquired by KKR & Co. Inc.

Antares Homes, Ltd.—acquired by Landsea Homes Corp.

Apex Integrated Security Solutions, LLC—acquired by GTCR LLC

Apex Plastics Inc.—acquired by Container Services LLC

Mergers and Acquisitions—continued

Applied Felts, Inc.—acquired by Vortex Company, LLC

Applied Thermal Systems—acquired by Gryphon Investors, LLC

Aqua Blasting Corp.—acquired by Battle Investment Group LLC

Arbor-Nomics Turf, Inc.—acquired by Senske Lawn & Tree Care, Inc.

Archerpoint, L.L.C.—acquired by Cherry Bekaert LLP

Arcoplast Inc.—acquired by Germfree Laboratories Inc.

Arnott, Inc.—acquired by MidOcean Partners, LLP

Ascend Clinical LLC—acquired by Eurofins Scientific S.E.

Ascentek, Inc.—acquired by Synagex, Inc

Ascolta, LLC—acquired by Management Science & Innovation LLC

Associated Buyers, LLC—acquired by Rainforest Distribution Corp

Association Headquarters, LLC—acquired by Corridor Capital, LLC

Astrape Consulting LLC—acquired by TA Associates, Inc.

ATEC Systems, Ltd.—acquired by Armada Group, Ltd.

Atlantis Travel & Tours—acquired by The Appointment Group Limited

Atlass Hardware Corporation—acquired by Frontenac Company LLC

Aul Brothers Tool & Die Inc.—acquired by Mursix Corporation

Auroralight, Inc.—acquired by Kuzco Lighting, Inc.

Automatic Entrances of Wisconsin, Inc.—acquired by Alpine Investors

Avian Mobile Ltd.—acquired by Nationwide Fleet Installations Ltd.

Award Solutions, Inc.—acquired by Accenture plc

Aysling LLC—acquired by Valsef Group

Azure Summit Technology, Inc.—acquired by CACI International Inc.

B

Bacon & Graham, Inc.—acquired by Wellspring Capital Management LLC

Bairstow Lifting Products Co., Inc.—acquired by Altamont Capital Partners

Baptist Memorial Health Care Corporation—acquired by Anderson Regional Health System

Barclay Water Management, Inc.—acquired by Ecolab Inc.

Bates Security, LLC—acquired by Pye-Barker Fire & Safety, LLC

Battea - Class Action Services, LLC—acquired by SS&C Technologies Holdings, Inc.

Battlefield Farms Inc.—acquired by Costa Farms, LLC

BC Cannon Co. Inc.—acquired by Investcorp Holdings B.S.C. and Trilantic Capital Management L.P.

BCC Engineering, Inc.—acquired by Parsons Corporation

Bee Equipment Sales, Ltd.—acquired by SMT Belgium NV

BelFlex Staffing Network, LLC—acquired by Elwood Staffing Services, Inc.

Beltz Ianni & Associates—acquired by Crestview Partners, L.P.

Bend Construction Supply, Inc.—acquired by Clayton, Dubilier & Rice, LLC

Benoure Plumbing & Heating Inc—acquired by Empowered Ventures, Inc.

Berliss Bearing Co.—acquired by FICODIS Inc.

Besse Forest Products Group, Co.—acquired by The Hoffmann Family of Companies

Big Tree Organic Farms, Inc.—acquired by Once Again Nut Butter Collective Inc.

Bill Brown Ford Inc.—acquired by Penske Automotive Group, Inc.

Bio-Vet, Inc.—acquired by Anpario plc

BioMatrix Specialty Pharmacy, LLC—acquired by Frazier Management, LLC

BioResource International, Inc.—acquired by Mitsui & Co., Ltd.

BioTechLogic, Inc.—acquired by Dark Horse Consulting

Biscayne Engineering Company, Inc.—acquired by Atwell, LLC

Black Eagle Consulting, Inc.—acquired by OceanSound Partners, LP

Blazer Electric Supply Company of Colorado Springs—acquired by Graybar Electric Company, Inc.

Bloomberg Consulting, Inc.—acquired by YOUNG & Associates

BMC Enterprises, Inc—acquired by Breedon Group plc

Bobby Taylor Oil Co. Inc.—acquired by Parker Holding Company, Inc.

Boston Brace International, Inc.—acquired by Ortho-Pediatrics Corp.

Boyd's Tire & Service—acquired by Greenbriar Equity Group, LLC

BPatt LLC—acquired by Agital Holdings, LLC

Bradford Machine Co—acquired by HC Private Investments LLC

Bradshaw, Fowler, Proctor & Fairgrave, PC—acquired by Dickinson, Mackaman, Tyler & Hagen, P.C.

Brandmark Creative Inc.—acquired by Brandmark Creative Inc.

Mergers and Acquisitions—continued

Braner USA, Inc.—acquired by Holleway Capital Partners LLC

Brayton & Hughes Design Studio—acquired by DLR Holding, LLC

BreathableBaby, LLC—acquired by Transom Capital Group, LLC

Britt Metal Processing, Inc.—acquired by Jets MRO, LLC

Brown Wood Preserving Company Inc.—acquired by Koppers Holdings Inc.

Buddy Moore Trucking, Inc.—acquired by OEP Capital Advisors, L.P.

Bullen Midwest Inc.—acquired by Hospeco Brands Group

Bunting Door & Hardware Co., Inc.—acquired by Platinum Equity, LLC

Burklund Distributors Inc.—acquired by AMCON Distributing Company

C

C J Hensch & Associates, Inc.—acquired by Miovision Technologies, Inc.

C-D Electric, Inc.—acquired by B&M Industrial, Inc.

Cabrera Services, Inc.—acquired by The Toronto-Dominion Bank

Cad Technology Center—acquired by Addnode Group AB

Cal Tec Labs, Inc.—acquired by Medical Technology Associates, LLC

Callaway Jones Funeral Home—acquired by Homesteaders Life Co. Inc.

Campion Insurance Inc.—acquired by Maury, Donnelly & Parr, Inc.

Cannon Fabrication, Inc.—acquired by Vibration Mountings & Controls, Inc.

Capital Region Medical Center Inc.—acquired by Curators of the University of Missouri

Capital Steel Service, LLC.—acquired by Hill & Smith PLC

Capitol Vending & Coffee—acquired by Sodexo S.A.

Cargo-Link International, Inc.—acquired by Gebruder Weiss Gesellschaft m.b.H.

CargoBarn Inc.—acquired by SheerTrans Solutions, LLC

Carpenters Roofing & Sheet Metal, Inc.—acquired by Infinity Home Services

Cascade Insurance Center LLC—acquired by Inszone Insurance Services, LLC

Cascade Transportation, Inc.—acquired by Radiant Logistics, Inc.

Cashco, Inc.—acquired by May River Capital, LLC

Cassidy & Company, LLC—acquired by Galiot Insurance Services, Inc.

Cast-Rite International Inc.—acquired by Perella Weinberg Partners LP

CCRO, LLC—acquired by Susquehanna International Group, LLP

Ceatus Media Group LLC—acquired by Advice Media LLC

Cendrowski Corporate Advisors, LLC—acquired by Unity Partners LP

Central Business Systems Inc.—acquired by Advanced Business Methods Inc.

Central Steel Fabricators Inc.—acquired by Live Ventures Incorporated

Cerimele, Meyer & Wray, LLC—acquired by Bodine and Company, LLC

CF Global Trading, LLC—acquired by State Street Corporation

CFV Solar Test Laboratory, Inc.—acquired by Groundwork Renewables, Inc.

Charles E. Gillman Company—acquired by Behrman Brothers Management Corp.

Chastain-Skillman, Inc.—acquired by White Wolf Capital LLC

Chelsea Green Publishing Company—acquired by Fininvest S.p.A.

Chem Arrow Corp.—acquired by Motul S.A.

CHEMFLOW Products, LLC—acquired by Relevant Industrial LLC

Chicago Switchboard Co., Inc.—acquired by Greenbriar Equity Group, L.P.

Childhaven—acquired by Children'S Home Society Of Washington

ChlorKing, LLC—acquired by Hayward Holdings, Inc.

Churchill Linen Service Inc.—acquired by Alsco Inc.

Cimquest Inc.—acquired by Sandvik AB

Cincom Systems, Inc.—acquired by Partner One Capital, Inc.

Circle City Heat Treating, Inc.—acquired by Incertec Plating Corp.

Citiscape Property Management Group, LLC.—acquired by FirstService Corporation

CitySquare—acquired by The Stewpot

Civitas Public Affairs Group LLC—acquired by O2 Investment Partners, LLC

Classic Protection Systems, Inc.—acquired by The Carlyle Group Inc.

Cleveland Scene Publishing LLC—acquired by Great Lakes Publishing Company

CMS Processing LLC—acquired by Alvarez & Marsal, Inc.

Coast International Services, Inc.—acquired by Olympus Partners

Coastal Engineering Co. Inc.—acquired by Tighe & Bond, Inc.

Cognosante LLC—acquired by Accenture plc

Coker Group Holdings, LLC—acquired by Trinity Hunt Management, L.P.

Cokeva, Inc.—acquired by TD Synnex Corp

Colagio The Painter—acquired by Davis Painting

Mergers and Acquisitions—continued

Combined Benefits Administrators, LLC—acquired by Hellman & Friedman LLC
Compressed Air Technologies, Inc.—acquired by Atlas Copco AB
Computer Systems Plus Inc.—acquired by Robert J. Young Company, LLC
Connective Computing Inc.—acquired by Modern Office Methods Inc.
Connectria LLC—acquired by GI Manager L.P.
Consolidated Container Company LLC—acquired by Stone Canyon Industries, LLC
Consolidated Mechanical, Inc.—acquired by Limbach Holdings, Inc.
Continental Engines, Inc.—acquired by Palmer Johnson Enterprises, Inc.
Cooksey Iron & Metal Co. Inc.—acquired by Reliance Steel & Aluminum Co.
Cooney Brothers Inc—acquired by Vergani & Associates, LLC
Corporate Concepts, Inc.—acquired by PARIC Holdings, Inc.
Cotera Reed Architects Inc.—acquired by Dykema Architects Inc.
Courtesy Acura—acquired by Don Jacobs Automotive Inc.
Cox Fire Protection, Inc.—acquired by Pye-Barker Fire & Safety, LLC
Cram Roofing Company Inc—acquired by New State Capital Partners LLC
Creative Dimensions, Inc.—acquired by Pinnacle Exhibits, Inc.
Credential Leasing Corp.—acquired by Freeman Spogli & Co. Incorporated
Creekside Custom Homes LLC—acquired by United Homes Group, Inc
Creighton Manning Engineering, Llp.—acquired by Comvest Group Holdings LLC
Criado & Associates, Inc.—acquired by Dunaway Associates, LLC
Criteria Labs, Inc.—acquired by Dover Corporation
Croton Watch Company & Nationwide Time—acquired by The Digital Artistry
Crown Capital Securities LP—acquired by LPL Financial Holdings Inc.
Crowther Roofing & Sheet Metal of Florida, Inc.—acquired by FirstService Corporation
Cubic Asset Management, LLC—acquired by CW Advisors LLC
Cupertino Electric, Inc.—acquired by Quanta Services, Inc.
Cureatr, Inc.—acquired by Vora Ventures LLC

D

D'Huy Engineering, Inc. (DEI)—acquired by H.I.G. Capital, LLC
Dacsis LLC—acquired by Pye-Barker Fire & Safety, LLC
Dan-Am Co.—acquired by SATA GmbH & Co. KG
Data Science Automation, Inc.—acquired by Blackford Capital LLC
Datavail Corporation—acquired by CIVC Partners LLC
Daughtridge Sales Co., Inc.—acquired by Frontenac Company LLC
David Barrett Partners LLC.—acquired by Braddock-Matthews LLC
DC Oil Co Inc.—acquired by The Kent Companies
DDK Kitchen Design Group Inc.—acquired by Design First Builders
Decision Research Corp.—acquired by Thoma Bravo, L.P.
Delphix Corp.—acquired by Clearlake Capital Group, L.P. and Francisco Partners Management, LP
Denny's Marina Inc.—acquired by Reeder-Trausch Marine
Design Plastics, Inc.—acquired by Coda Resources, Ltd.
Devenish Nutrition—acquired by Easy Holdings Co., Ltd.
DHL Analytical, Inc—acquired by Sentinel Capital Partners, L.L.C.
Dialogconcepts, Inc.—acquired by Agital Holdings, LLC
Dick Jones Communications, LLC—acquired by Renovus Capital Partners
Dickerson & Bowen, Inc.—acquired by Granite Construction Incorporated
Dickinson Hussman Architects, P.C.—acquired by BLDD Architects, Inc.
Digicom Electronics Inc.—acquired by Kaynes Technology India Limited
Digicorp, Inc.—acquired by Win, LLC
Digiop Technologies, Ltd.—acquired by GTCR LLC
Discovery Door, Inc.—acquired by Platinum Equity, LLC
Document Center Inc—acquired by Nimonik, Inc.
Document Essentials LLC—acquired by Doceo Office Solutions, LLC
DOMA Technologies LLC—acquired by Pleasant Land
Donald F Dickerson Associates—acquired by Coffman Engineers, Inc.
Donatelle Plastics, Inc.—acquired by DuPont de Nemours, Inc.
Douglas Lumber Corporation—acquired by Builders FirstSource, Inc.
Drymaster Restoration—acquired by BMS CAT, Inc.
Dudek Insurance Agency Group—acquired by ABRY Partners, LLC
Dust Free, LP—acquired by CSW Industrials, Inc.
Dynamic Sealing Technologies, Inc.—acquired by Kadant Inc.

Mergers and Acquisitions—continued

E

E&H Certified Public Accountants & Management Consultants P.C.—acquired by Mbe Cpas LLP

E&M International, Inc.—acquired by Chenega Corporation

Eagan Insurance Agency, Inc.—acquired by Galiot Insurance Services, Inc.

Eagle Cornice Co. Inc.—acquired by Altas Partners LP

Earl W. Johnston Roofing Inc.—acquired by Dunes Point Capital, LLC

East Coast Air & Heat, LLC—acquired by Del-Air Heating, Air Conditioning & Refrigeration Corp.

Eastern Sierra Propane—acquired by Ferrellgas Partners, L.P.

Eckhart & Company, Inc.—acquired by BindTech LLC

Eclipse Engineering, P.C.—acquired by Cushing Terrell

Ecs, Inc.—acquired by Coffman Engineers, Inc.

Ed Brown Distributors—acquired by EVI Industries, Inc.

eDot LLC—acquired by CyberAdvisors, Inc.

Electronic Warfare Associates, Inc.—acquired by Sagewind Capital LLC

Elliott Machine Works, Inc.—acquired by Stellar Industries Inc.

Emery Thompson Machine Supply Co.—acquired by The Middleby Corporation

Emily Corporation—acquired by GMSS Holdings, LLC

Engineering World Health—acquired by Engineers Without Borders-USA, Inc.

Envirosafe Services Of Ohio, Inc.—acquired by J.F. Lehman & Company, Inc.

EnviroTech Services Inc.—acquired by Monomoy Capital Partners LLC

Envoi, LLC—acquired by AlTi Global, Inc.

EpiPhotonics Corp.—acquired by Kohoku Kogyo Co., Ltd.

Ericson Insurance Services, LLC—acquired by Arthur J. Gallagher & Co.

Execupay, Inc.—acquired by Vensure Employer Services, Inc.

Executive Business Services, Inc.—acquired by Roper Technologies, Inc.

Exler & Company, Inc.—acquired by Horovitz, Rudoy & Roteman, LLC

Expand, LLC—acquired by DYN365, Inc.

Export-Import Services Inc.—acquired by Share Logistics BV

Exusia Inc.—acquired by Globant S.A.

F

Farmacia De Leo S.r.l.—acquired by Farmacosmo S.p.A.

Farris Bobango PLC—acquired by Phelps Dunbar LLP

Fastfetch Corp.—acquired by ABCO Systems LLC

Federman, Lally & Remis LLC—acquired by Marcum LLP

Ferencik Libanoff Brandt Bustamante & Goldstein, P.A.—acquired by Hinckley, Allen & Snyder LLP

Fidelity Mutual Holding Company—acquired by Mutual Bancorp

Fidelity Roof Company—acquired by HCI Equity Management, L.P.

Fillauer Companies, Inc.—acquired by Patient Square Capital, L.P.

Finance 500, Inc.—acquired by Stifel Financial Corp.

Financial Arts Inc.—acquired by Inszone Insurance Services, LLC

Fire Systems Professionals, LLC—acquired by The Riverside Company

Fiscalsoft Corp.—acquired by Black Mountain Software, LLC

Fishman Center For Total Eye Care—acquired by Ophthalmic Consultants of Long Island and Blue Sea Capital Management LLC

Fitzpatrick Engineering Group, PLLC—acquired by Structura, Inc.

Flavor Producers, LLC—acquired by Glanbia Co-Operative Society Limited

Fleet Equipment LLC.—acquired by Stonepeak Partners L.P.

Fleet Parts & Service, Inc.—acquired by Boyne Capital Management, LLC

Flex-Tec Inc.—acquired by Cerberus Capital Management, L.P.

Flint Hills Music, Inc.—acquired by Ernie Williamson, Inc.

FLOW-TRONIC S.A.—acquired by Sophora Unternehmerkapital GmbH

Folkerson Communications, Ltd.—acquired by Renaissance Systems, Inc.

Force Communications, LLC—acquired by Keystone Group, L.P.

Forensic Resolutions, Inc.—acquired by Kelso & Company, L.P.

Forklift Training Systems, Inc—acquired by Fleet Team, Inc.

Fox Valley Metal Tech, LLC—acquired by Littlejohn & Co., LLC

Frame USA, Inc.—acquired by Craig Frames, Inc.

Fran Corp.—acquired by 302 Rockwell Intellectual Property LLC

Frank Vitale Insurance Agency—acquired by Inszone Insurance Services, LLC

Freeland & Kauffman, Inc.—acquired by LJA Engineering, Inc.

Fromm International, Inc.—acquired by Firelight Capital Partners LLC [et al]

Frontier Community Bank—acquired & absorbed by

xxv

Mergers and Acquisitions—continued

National Bankshares, Inc.
Frontier Fastener Inc.—acquired by Great Lakes Fasteners, Inc.
Frontier Roofing, Inc—acquired by EMP Management, LLC
Future Tech Consultants of New York, Inc.—acquired by Cobepa S.A.

G

Garden Supply Hardscapes—acquired by Trilantic Capital Management L.P.
GCT Semiconductor, Inc.—merged with Concord Acquisition Corp III, to form GCT Semiconductor Holding, Inc.
Gehrki Commercial Real Estate, LLC—acquired by Colliers International Group Inc.
Geiger Excavating, Inc.—acquired by Zemba Bros Inc
Geiger Pump & Equipment Company—acquired by AEA Investors LP
Gemsa Enterprises, LLC—acquired by Marubeni Corporation
General Aviation Flying Services, Inc.—acquired by Blackstone Inc., Cascade Investment LLC and Global Infrastructure Management, LLC
General Body Manufacturing Company—acquired by J.B. Poindexter & Co., Inc.
Genetics & IVF Institute, Inc.—acquired by Amulet Capital Partners, L.P.
George Lay Signs, Inc.—acquired by Miracle Signs, Inc.
Geothermal Supply Co., Inc.—acquired by Core & Main, Inc.
Gerome Technologies, Inc.—acquired by Eis Inc.
Glenn Harris & Associates, Inc.—acquired by Galiot Insurance Services, Inc.
Global Infrastructure Management, LLC—acquired by BlackRock, Inc.
Global Systems Technologies, Inc.—acquired by Broadtree Partners, LLC
Go2 Communications, Inc.—acquired by Gemspring Capital Management, LLC
Golden Harvest, Inc.—acquired by XPV Water Partners
Golden Organics—acquired by Innovative Food Holdings, Inc.
Grand Basket, Inc—acquired by Z Capital Group, LLC
Graphics East, Inc.—acquired by Detroit Legal News Company
Gray Consulting Inc.—acquired by Thoma Bravo, L.P.
Green Equipment Company—acquired by Core & Main, Inc.
Greenery of Charleston, LLC—acquired by Ruppert Landscape, LLC
Greenfield Beverage Company Inc—acquired by Zink Distributing Inc
Greensfelder, Hemker & Gale, P.C.—merged with Ulmer & Berne LLP, to form UB Greensfelder LLP
Gregg Communications Systems, Inc.—acquired by APLJ Capital Management LLC
Greiner Industries, Inc.—acquired by IES Holdings, Inc.
Grette Associates, LLC—acquired by Farallon Consulting, LLC
Gryphon Scientific, LLC—acquired by Deloitte LLP

H

Haedrich & Co., Inc.—acquired by Capital Rivers Commercial LLC
Hall Capital Partners LLC—acquired by Lovell Minnick Partners LLC
Halstead Insurance Agency, Inc.—acquired by GTCR LLC
Harbour Results Inc.—acquired by Wipfli LLP
Harger Inc.—acquired by TE Connectivity Ltd.
Harrick Scientific Products, Inc.—acquired by Ampersand Management LLC
Harris Fire Protection Co Inc.—acquired by Knox Lane LP
Hartwell Environmental Corp.—acquired by DXP Enterprises, Inc.
Healthwise, Incorporated—acquired by KKR & Co, Inc.
Heany Industries, Inc.—acquired by Crawford United Corporation
Hearron Sales, Inc.—acquired by Platinum Equity, LLC
Hearsay Social, Inc.—acquired by Yext, Inc.
Heat-Flo, Inc.—acquired by Bradford-White Corporation
Heath & Associates Inc.—acquired by Warren Equity Partners, LLC
Helgesen Industries Inc.—acquired by Standard Iron & Wire Works Inc.
Hennesy Mechanical Sales, LLC—acquired by DXP Enterprises, Inc.
Heritage Environmental Services, LLC—acquired by EQT AB
Hi-Line Industries Ii, Inc.—acquired by Sciens Capital Management LLC
Highfield Communications LLC—acquired by Kearney O'Doherty Public Affairs, LLC
Hofmann Sausage Co., Inc.—acquired by Trivest Partners, LP
Holmes Landscape Company—acquired by Landscape Developmental Inc.
Homeland Safety Systems Inc.—acquired by Alpine Investors
Homerun Electronics, Inc.—merged with iWired, Inc.,

Mergers and Acquisitions—continued

to form Vangeo Technology Group, LLC

Homestead Building Systems Inc.—acquired by Bain Capital, LP

Horak Insurance, Inc—acquired by Arthur J. Gallagher & Co.

Horizon Services Corporation—acquired by O2 Investment Partners, LLC

Houska Insurance Services Inc.—acquired by New Mountain Capital, LLC

Hugh Wood, Inc.—acquired by Kelso & Company, L.P.

Human Resource Specialties Inc.—acquired by DCI Consulting Group, Inc.

Humm Kombucha, LLC—acquired by SYSTM Brands, LLC

Huntington Pacific Insurance Agency, Inc.—acquired by Inszone Insurance Services, LLC

Hydradyne, LLC—acquired by Applied Industrial Technologies, Inc.

Hydro Consultants Inc.—acquired by Atwell, LLC

Hydromax USA, LLC—acquired by Gallant Capital Partners, LLC

I

I.C. Thomasson Associates, Inc.—acquired by Salas O'Brien Engineers, Inc.

IB Roof Systems, Inc.—acquired by Kingspan Group PLC

Idaho Package Company—acquired by Warburg Pincus LLC and Kelso & Company, L.P.

Ideal Wood Products, Inc.—acquired by Prophet Equity L.P.

iLearningEngines Inc.—merged with Arrowroot Acquisition Corp., to form iLearningEngines, Inc.

Impact 21 Group LLC—acquired by W. Capra Consulting Group, Inc.

Independence RV Sales & Services, Inc—acquired by General RV Center Inc.

Industrial Coil Inc.—acquired by Jay Industrial Repair, Inc.

Industrial Training International, Inc.—acquired by Interplay Learning Inc.

Infinity Laboratories Inc.—acquired by Eurofins Scientific S.E.

Inland Forest Management, Inc.—acquired by F&W Forestry Services Inc.

Innovative Packaging Solutions—acquired by Welch Packaging Group, Inc.

Insight Distributing, Inc.—acquired by Bain Capital, LP

Insurance Management Company—acquired by Hellman & Friedman LLC

Integrated Computer Systems, Inc.—acquired by Banneker Partners, LLC

Inter-Pacific Motors Inc.—acquired by Steve Marshall Group Ltd.

International Cellulose Corp.—acquired by Compagnie de Saint-Gobain SA

International Parking Management, Inc.—acquired by LAZ Parking Ltd, LLC

Internetwork Engineering—acquired by BC Partners LLP

Intricity, LLC—acquired by KKR & Co. Inc.

Irwin Engineers Inc.—acquired by Pennoni Associates Inc.

Isograph Ltd.—acquired by Main Capital Partners B.V.

Italiano Insurance Services, Inc.—acquired by GTCR LLC

Iteam Consulting, LLC—acquired by Netsurit (Pty) Ltd

Ives Equipment Corporation—acquired by Frontenac Company LLC

J

J & J Calibration Services, Inc—acquired by Aldinger Company

JA Kirsch Corporation—acquired by Gellert Global Group

Jacks Tire & Oil Management Co.—acquired by Purcell Tire & Rubber Company Inc.

JAD Corporation—acquired by Bain Capital, LP

Jamco International Inc.—acquired by Littlejohn & Co., LLC

Jamesbeck Global Partners, LLC—acquired by RFE Investment Partners

Janicki Environmental, Inc.—acquired by Environmental Science Associates

JJR Solutions, LLC.—acquired by Logistics Management Institute

JLM Wholesale Inc.—acquired by Dominus Capital, L.P.

Joe & Ross Inc.—acquired by Guggenheim Partners, LLC

Johansen & Anderson, Inc.—acquired by Partners Group Holding AG

Johnson County Bank—acquired by SKYLINE BANKSHARES, INC.

Johnson Engineering, Inc.—acquired by Apex Companies, LLC

Jorgensen Conveyors, Inc.—acquired by Innovance, Inc.

Josam Company—acquired by Watts Water Technologies, Inc.

Judith Heft Associates, LLC—acquired by Aon plc

Juneau Physical Therapy, A Professional Corporation—acquired by SouthEast Alaska Regional Health Consortium

Juno Technologies, Inc.—acquired by Sagewind Capital LLC

Mergers and Acquisitions—continued

K

Kain Automotive, Inc.—acquired by NCM Associates, Inc.
Kamco Supply Corp.—acquired by GMS Inc.
Kappe Associates, Inc.—acquired by DXP Enterprises, Inc.
Keffer of Little River, LLC—acquired by Beach Automotive Group
Kelly & Partners, Inc.—acquired by Keystone Digital Imaging, Incorporated
Kens Tree Care Inc.—acquired by Apax Partners LLP
Kent Island Mechanical, LLC—acquired by Crawford United Corporation
Key Knife Inc.—acquired by Kadant Inc.
Keystone Information Systems—acquired by Valsef Group
Kirsch Kohn & Bridge LLP—acquired by Aprio, LLP
Kleet Lumber Company, Inc.—acquired by Builders FirstSource, Inc.
Knot Standard, LLC—acquired by Billy Reid, Inc.
Koch Industries, Inc.—acquired by Hillman Solutions Corp.
Kovair Software, Inc.—acquired by Surge Ventures, LLC
Kovalsky-Carr Electric Supply Co, Inc.—acquired by United Electric Supply Company, Inc.
Kunzler & Company, Inc.—acquired by Clemens Food Group, LLC
KWS Manufacturing Company, Ltd.—acquired by Kadant Inc.
Kynex Inc—acquired by Genstar Capital, LLC

L

La Marzocco International, LLC—acquired by De'Longhi S.p.A.
Lake City Heat Treating Corp.—acquired by Bodycote plc
Lakeside Painting, Inc.—acquired by Painters USA, Inc.
Landmark Homes of Tennessee, Inc.—acquired by Century Communities, Inc.
Latitude 34 Technologies, LLC—acquired by Team Solutions Group, Inc.
Latter & Blum, Inc.—acquired by Compass, Inc.
Laundry Pro of Florida, Inc.—acquired by EVI Industries, Inc.
Laux Construction, LLC—acquired by Rival Holdings, LLC.
Lead Technologies, Inc.—acquired by Thoma Bravo, L.P.
Ledge Wealth Management, Inc.—acquired by Dakota Wealth Management LLC
Lee Supply Company Inc.—acquired by Core & Main, Inc.

Leith Inc.—acquired by Holman Automotive Group, Inc.
Lenz Therapeutics, Inc.—merged with Graphite Bio, Inc., to form Lenz Therapeutics, Inc.
Leverage Information Systems, Inc.—acquired by American Securities LLC
Lewandowski Engineers—acquired by Round Table Capital Management, LP
LIFE QUOTES, INC.—acquired by Keystone Insurers Group, Inc. and Bain Capital, LP
Lincoln Insurance—acquired by King Insurance Partners, LLC
Linton Engineering LLC—acquired by Bennett & Pless, Inc.
LiveIntent, Inc.—acquired by Zeta Global Holdings Corp.
LMR Disposal LLC—acquired by Casella Waste Systems, Inc.
LMS Manufacturing—acquired by Product Recovery Management
Logic Information Systems, Inc.—acquired by Accenture plc
Lone Star State Bancshares, Inc.—acquired by Prosperity Bancshares, Inc.
Low Voltage Integrated Systems Inc.—acquired by The Carlyle Group Inc.
LS Technologies, LLC.—acquired by Tetra Tech, Inc.
LTi Printing, Inc.—acquired by Max Solutions Inc.
Lupini Construction Inc.—acquired by Valcourt Building Services LLC
Lyons HR, Inc.—acquired by New Mountain Capital, LLC

M

Maassen Oil Company Inc.—acquired by Palmdale Oil Company, Inc.
MAC Equipment, LLC—acquired by Herc Holdings Inc.
Madison Consulting Group, Inc.—acquired by FTI Consulting, Inc.
Madison Financial Advisors, Ltd.—acquired by Keystone Group, L.P.
Magzter Inc.—acquired by VerSe Innovation Private Limited
Mallard Manufacturing Corp.—acquired by MacLean-Fogg Co.
Manhattan Dermatology PA—acquired by Heartland Dermatology and Skin Cancer Center, P.A.
Maple Grove Auto Service, Inc.—acquired by O2 Investment Partners, LLC
Martex Fiber Southern Corporation—acquired by Leigh Fibers, Inc.
Marway Power Systems Inc.—acquired by HEICO Corporation
Mason Blau & Associates, Inc.—acquired by Godspeed Capital Management LP

Mergers and Acquisitions—continued

Master Magnetics Inc.—acquired by Factor 89 Partners, LLC
Mat-Pac Inc.—acquired by HCI Equity Management, L.P.
Maxwell-Reddick & Associates, Inc.—acquired by Palm Beach Capital Partners LLC
Mazars USA LLP—acquired by FORVIS, LLP, to form Forvis Mazar, LLP
Mcbride Door & Hardware, Inc.—acquired by Platinum Equity, LLC
McCrary Daniels Insurance Agency—acquired by PointeNorth Insurance Group LLC
McGee Storage & Handling, Inc.—acquired by Atlanta Forklifts, Inc.
Mclean Engineering Company, Inc.—acquired by EQT AB
McMahon Architects—acquired by RODE Architects Inc
Mcnamara, Co.—acquired by Brown & Brown, Inc.
McVeigh Global Meetings & Events, LLC—acquired by InteleTravel.com
MD Connect, Inc.—acquired by Intellibright Corporation
Mechanical Engineering & Construction Corporation—acquired by Ares Management Corporation
Medata Inc.—acquired by The Carlyle Group Inc.
Megatran Industries Inc.—acquired by American Superconductor Corporation
Metal Trades, LLC—acquired by Arlington Capital Partners LLC
Metamap, Inc.—acquired by Incode Technologies, Inc.
Metcalf Archaeological Consultants, Inc.—acquired by Terracon Consultants, Inc.
Meyer Laboratory, Inc.—acquired by TruArc Partners, L.P.
Michigan Brush Manufacturing Company, Inc.—acquired by Gordon Brush Mfg Co, Inc.
Micron Industries Corp.—acquired by Hammond Power Solutions, Inc.
Microtel LLC—acquired by Arlington Capital Partners LLC
Midwest Box Company, Inc.—acquired by Jamestown Container Corporation
Midwest Glass Fabricators, Inc.—acquired by KPS Capital Partners, LP
Miinc, LP—acquired by SubSplit Services Group, L.P.
Miller Paint Company, Inc.—acquired by Cloverdale Paint Inc.
Millican Nurseries, Inc.—acquired by SiteOne Landscape Supply, Inc.
Mills & Associates, Inc.—acquired by Pennoni Associates Inc.
MIM Software Inc.—acquired by GE HealthCare Technologies Inc.
Mississippi River Bank—acquired by Merchants & Marine Bancorp, Inc.
Mobile Steam Boiler Rental Corp.—acquired by Miller Proctor Nickolas Inc.
Mobotrex, Inc.—acquired by Warren Equity Partners, LLC
Modern Classic Motors Inc.—acquired by Group 1 Automotive, Inc.
Modern Machinery Company—acquired by Capital Machine Technologies, Inc.
MOGAS Industries, Inc.—acquired by Flowserve Corporation
Mohawk Fine Papers, Inc.—acquired by Fedrigoni SpA
Morgan & Myers, Inc.—acquired by Gibbs & Soell, Inc.
Mortgage Lender Services, Inc.—acquired by Total Lender Solutions, Inc.
Morton Photonics, Inc.—acquired by Coldquanta, Inc.
Mott Corp.—acquired by IDEX Corp
Mountain Air Compressor Inc.—acquired by Hitachi, Ltd.
Mullins Building Products, Inc.—acquired by Platinum Equity, LLC
Municipay, LLC—acquired by Stella Point Capital, LP
Mutual Savings Bank—acquired by Oconee Federal Financial Corp.

N

Nacarato Trucks, Inc.—acquired by SF Holding Corp.
National Safety Apparel, Inc.—acquired by Blue Point Capital Partners, LLC
Nations Roof LLC—acquired by AEA Investors LP
ND Industries Inc.—acquired by H.B. Fuller Company
Nda Distributors, LLC—acquired by Elbi S.P.A.
Netranom Communications, Inc.—acquired by Alpine Investors
Network People, Inc.—acquired by Frontenac Company LLC
Neuro-ID, Inc.—acquired by Experian plc
New Technology Investments, Inc.—acquired by RMS Omega Technologies Group, Inc.
NewBold Corporation—acquired by Fort Point Capital, LLC
Newbrook Solutions, Inc.—acquired by Edgesource Corporation
Newman Lawn Care Inc.—acquired by Crux Capital Ltd
Nextera Communications LLC—acquired by Trive Capital Inc.
Nion, Co.—acquired by Bruker Corporation

Mergers and Acquisitions—continued

Norflex, Inc.—acquired by Arsenal Capital Management LP
North Point Geographic Solutions—acquired by Avineon, Inc.
Northeast Air Solutions Inc—acquired by Daikin Industries, Ltd.
Northern California Fertility Medical Center, A Professional, Corp.—acquired by Ivy Fertility
Northern Dry-Bulk, Inc.—acquired by Ontario Municipal Employees Retirement System
Northgate Ready Mix, LLC—acquired by CRH plc
Northtown Motor Homes, Inc.—acquired by Fun Town RV LP
Northwest Pump & Equipment Co.—acquired by H.I.G. Capital, LLC
NuAire Inc.—acquired by Kewaunee Scientific Corporation
NuMSP LLC—acquired by Tonka Bay Equity Partners LLC

O

OCR Services Inc.—acquired by The Descartes Systems Group Inc.
Octopi Brewing, LLC—acquired by Asahi Group Holdings Ltd.
ODC Construction, LLC—acquired by Asahi Kasei Corporation
Oldham Collision Center—acquired by Glaser's Collision Center
Omnica Corp.—acquired by StarFish Product Engineering Inc.
Omnyon LLC—acquired by Alpine Investors
On Time Trucking, Inc.—acquired by The RK Logistics Group, Inc.
One Beat CPR Learning Center, Inc.—acquired by Investor AB
OnKure, Inc.—merged with Reneo Pharmaceuticals, Inc., to form OnKure Therapeutics, Inc.
Open Systems Integrators, Inc.—acquired by The Carlyle Group Inc.
OpenGov, Inc.—acquired by Cox Enterprises, Inc.
Opticolor, Inc.—acquired by Techmer PM, LLC
Optimum Design Associates, Inc.—acquired by Crestview Partners, L.P.
Orange Tree Employment Screening LLC—acquired by Boathouse Capital Management, LLC

P

P2S Inc.—acquired by Blackstone Inc.
Pace Professional Services, Ltd.—acquired by Kelso & Company, L.P.
Pacesetter Steel Service, Inc.—acquired by Flack Steel LLC
Pacific Fire And Security, Inc.—acquired by Pye-Barker Fire & Safety, LLC
Pacific Magnetics Inc.—acquired by Careen, Inc.
Pacific Medical Management Services, Inc—acquired by Constellation Software Inc.
Pacific Paper Tube, Inc.—acquired by Sky Island Capital LLC
Paramount Centre, Inc.—acquired by Susquehanna International Group, LLP
Paresky Flitt & Company, LLP—acquired by UHY LLP
Park 100 Foods Inc.—acquired by OSI Group, LLC
PaymentCloud Inc.—acquired by NCR Voyix Corporation.
Paytronix Systems, Inc.—acquired by Access Technology Group Limited
Peerless Aerospace Fastener Corp.—acquired by Diploma PLC
Personal Strengths Publishing, Inc.—acquired by Leeds Equity Partners, LLC
Peterson Brustad Inc.—acquired by Round Table Capital Management, LP
PG Calc, Inc.—acquired by GTCR LLC
Pharmasite Research Inc.—acquired by KKR & Co. Inc.
Phoenix Fire Systems, Inc.—acquired by Pye-Barker Fire & Safety, LLC
Piermont Wealth Management, Inc.—acquired by TA Associates, Inc.
Pilgrim Screw Corporation—acquired by MEIDOH Co., Ltd
Pinnacle Central Company, Inc.—acquired by Source Capital, LLC
Planbox, Inc.—acquired by Main Capital Partners B.V.
Planned & Engineered Construction, Inc.—acquired by Vortex Company, LLC
Plastiform, Inc.—acquired by Nefab AB
Plutora, Inc.—acquired by TPG Capital, L.P. and TA Associates, Inc.
Plx, Inc.—acquired by SK Capital Partners, LP and Edgewater Capital Partners, L.P.
Point Eight Power Inc.—acquired by Mission Critical Group
Ponte Vedra Plastic Surgery—acquired by Ascend Plastic Surgery Partners
Pontiff & Associates, P.C.—acquired by Aprio, LLP
Port Milford LLC—acquired by Sun Communities, Inc.
Portage Lumber Company, Inc.—acquired by Bliffert Lumber & Fuel Co. Inc.
Potter Equipment Co—acquired by Machine Maintenance, Inc.
POWER Engineers, Inc.—acquired by WSP Global, Inc.
Powers & Sullivan, LLC—acquired by Marcum Wealth LLC
Precision Kidd Steel Co. Inc.—acquired by Jade Steel Group, Ltd. and Standard Horse Nail Company, LLC

Precision Optical Technologies, Inc.—acquired by Belden, Inc.
Precisionpoint Inc.—acquired by Surveying And Mapping, LLC
Prevalent Power, Inc—acquired by Ontario Teachers' Pension Plan
Price Chevrolet Co.—acquired by Malloy Automotive of Winchester LLC
Primal Life Organics, LLC—acquired by Society Brands, Inc.
Pro Products, Inc.—acquired by AFM Capital Partners, Inc.
Professional Foam Insulators Ltd.—acquired by Quad-C Management, Inc.
Professional Risk Associates, Inc.—acquired by Kelso & Company, L.P.
Proheat, Inc.—acquired by Gryphon Investors, LLC
PromoSuite—acquired by Banyan Software, Inc.
Promotional Alliance Inc.—acquired by The Specialty Company
Protect Alarms—acquired by Pye-Barker Fire & Safety, LLC
Prudeo Partners L.L.C.—acquired by Perigon Wealth Management LLC
PSI Services LLC—acquired by Educational Testing Service Inc.
Pure Wafer Inc.—acquired by ZelnickMedia Corp.

Q

Q. Grady Minor & Associates, P.A.—acquired by Palm Beach Capital Partners LLC
Qgiv, Inc.—acquired by Bloomerang, LLC
Quality Air Forwarding, Inc.—acquired by Littlejohn & Co., LLC
Quality Uptime Services, LLC—acquired by ABM Industries, Inc.
QuintEvents LLC—acquired by Liberty Media Corporation
Quintron Systems, Inc.—acquired by Godspeed Capital Management LP
Quotient Inc.—acquired by Jacmel Growth Partners Management LLC
QX Networking & Design, Inc.—acquired by Trive Capital Inc.

R

R V World, Inc.—acquired by Markquart Inc.
Radial Bearing Corp.—acquired by Torque Capital Group, LLC
Ralph C Wilson Agency, Inc.—acquired by Kelso & Company, L.P.
Randall Bearings, Inc.—acquired by Wieland-Werke AG
Ratner & Prestia PC—acquired by Buchanan Ingersoll & Rooney PC
Rayotek Scientific, Inc.—acquired by Artemis Capital Partners Management Co., LLC
RC&E, LLC—acquired by Southfield Capital Advisors, LLC
Readfield Meats Inc.—acquired by Dominion Equity LLC
Ready Welder Corporation—acquired by Broco, Inc.
Reagent Chemical & Research Inc.—acquired by Wynnchurch Capital, L.P.
Renters Legal Liability LLC.—acquired by DOXA Insurance Holdings LLC
Renu Energy Solutions LLC—acquired by Swell Energy Inc
Resource Management Associates, Inc—acquired by Global Infrastructure Solutions, Inc.
Reviva Labs, Inc.—acquired by SenDayCo, LLC
RevLocal, LLC—acquired by H.I.G. Capital, LLC
RH Wealth Advisors, Inc.—acquired by Larry Mathis Financial Planning, LLC
Richmond Master Distributors Inc.—acquired by AMCON Distributing Company
Rips Professional Lawn Care, Inc.—acquired by Juniper Landscaping, Inc.
Risk International Services Inc.—acquired by Arthur J. Gallagher & Co.
Riskpoint Insurance Advisors, LLC—acquired by IMA Financial Group, Inc.
River States Truck & Trailer—acquired by Penske Automotive Group, Inc.
Rizzetta & Company, Inc.—acquired by FirstService Corporation
RMB Capital Management, LLC—acquired by Curi Holdings, Inc.
Robbins, Inc.—acquired by L2 Capital Partners
Robertson Tire Co. Inc.—acquired by Big Brand Tire & Service
Robinson Paving Company—acquired by Construction Partners, Inc.
Rocky Mountain Advisory, LLC—acquired by Marshall & Stevens Inc.
Rocky Mountain Industrial Supply, Inc—acquired by Mallory Safety & Supply LLC
Rogan Shoes Incorporated—acquired by Shoe Carnival, Inc.
Roofers Mart of Southern California, Inc.—acquired by Beacon Roofing Supply, Inc.
Roofers' Supply of Greenville, Inc.—acquired by Beacon Roofing Supply, Inc.
Rose Electronics Distributing Co, Inc.—acquired by Tropical Battery Company Limited
Rossdruliscusenbery Architecture, Inc.—acquired by DLR Holding, LLC
RWR Trucking Inc.—acquired by Source Energy Services Ltd.
RxSafe LLC—acquired by Illinois Tool Works Inc.

Mergers and Acquisitions—continued

S

Saint Luke's Health System, Inc.—acquired by BJC Health System

Sale Insurance Agency, Inc.—acquired by Hellman & Friedman LLC

Salm Partners, LLC.—acquired by Johnsonville, LLC

Sam Asher Computing Services Inc.—acquired by Valsef Group

San Fernando Valley Alarm, Inc.—acquired by Armet Alarm & Electronics Inc.

Sandy Hill Kennels, Inc.—acquired by General Atlantic Service Company, L.P.

SaveWay Compounding Pharmacy, LLC—acquired by Myonex, LLC

Scale Finance LLC—acquired by Belay, Inc.

Scientific Boiler Water Conditioning Co, Inc.—acquired by Nolan Capital, Inc.

Scienture, Inc.—merged with TRxADE HEALTH, Inc., to form Scienture Holdings, Inc.

Scout Bio, Inc.—acquired by Ceva Sante Animale SA

SCS Software, Inc.—acquired by CrossCountry Consulting LLC

Seaford Consulting, LLC—acquired by Godspeed Capital Management LP

Securicon, LLC.—acquired by Risk Mitigation Consulting Inc.

SecuriGence LLC—acquired by Chenega Corporation

Serina Therapeutics, Inc.—merged with AgeX Therapeutics, Inc., to form Serina Therapeutics, Inc.

Shapiro, Lifschitz and Schram, P.C.—acquired by Barclay Damon, LLP

Shearman & Sterling LLP—merged with Allen & Overy LLP, to form Allen Overy Shearman Sterling LLP

Sherex Fastening Solutions, LLC—acquired by Tinicum Enterprises, Inc.

Sierra Auction Management, Inc.—acquired by Liquidity Services, Inc.

Signallamp Health Inc.—acquired by Sunstone Partners Management LLC

Silvertip Associates, Inc.—acquired by Vance Street Capital LLC

Singhofen & Associates, Inc.—acquired by Halff Associates, Inc.

Sitex Corporation—acquired by Cintas Corporation

Skin, A Medical Spa—acquired by MD Esthetics, LLC

Skuid, Inc.—acquired by TPG Capital, L.P.

Skyline Steel, Inc.—acquired by Endres Manufacturing Co, Inc.

Skytap, Inc.—acquired by Kyndryl Holdings Inc.

SL Investment Corp.—acquired by North Haven Private Income Fund LLC

Smart Software, Inc.—acquired by Clayton, Dubilier & Rice, LLC

Smart Source, LLC—acquired by Guggenheim Partners, LLC

Smith Consulting Architects—acquired by Godspeed Capital Management LP

SNC Manufacturing Company, Inc.—acquired by Allient Inc.

Snow, Christensen & Martineau, P.C.—acquired by Spencer Fane LLP

Snugg Home LLC—acquired by ABRY Partners, LLC

Softrams LLC—acquired by Sagewind Capital LLC

Softtech Solutions, Inc.—acquired by Falfurrias Capital Partners, LP

Soil-Away Cleaning & Restoration Services—acquired by Insurcomm Construction, Inc.

Solid Restoration Inc.—acquired by Timoneer Strategic Partners, LLC and Grays Peak Capital LP [et al]

Somers Oil Service, Inc.—acquired by Taylor Energy, LLC

Southeast Mower & Saw Shop—acquired by Ag-Pro, LLC

Southern Anchor Bolt Co.—acquired by Portland Bolt & Manufacturing Co., LLC

Southern California Fleet Services, Inc.—acquired by Velocity Vehicle Group

Southern Tooling, Inc.—acquired by LFM Capital LLC

Southern Tractor & Outdoors—acquired by Sumitomo Corporation

Southwest Beverage Co. Inc.—acquired by Mockler Beverage Co. LP

Southwest Heater & Controls, Inc.—acquired by Gryphon Investors, LLC

Space Age Electronics, Inc.—acquired by DelCam Holdings, LLC

Spalding Consulting Inc.—acquired by Saalex Corp.

Spartan Tool Supply Company, Inc.—acquired by Foundation Investment Partners, LLC

Spectra Color, Inc.—acquired by Arsenal Capital Management LP

Speece Lewis Engineers, Inc.—acquired by Bowman Consulting Group Ltd.

Speechcenter Inc.—acquired by Sidekick Therapy Partners

SpinDance, Inc.—acquired by Century Technology Group

SproutLoud Media Networks, LLC—acquired by Ansira Partners, Inc.

Stan's Heating & Air Conditioning, Inc.—acquired by Catterton Management Company, LLC

Stanley M. Proctor Company, LLC—acquired by Applied Industrial Technologies, Inc.

State Alarm, Inc.—acquired by Redwire LLC

Storage Systems Unlimited, Inc.—acquired by Cme Corporation

Strausser Insurance Agency, Inc.—acquired by Key-

Mergers and Acquisitions—continued

stone Agency Partners, LLC

Strong Systems International, Inc.—acquired by RAF Industries, Inc.

Structural Engineering Associates, Inc.—acquired by Johnson, Mirmiran & Thompson, Inc.

Studio Four Design Inc.—acquired by Michael Graves & Associates, Inc.

Sumter Packaging Corporation—acquired by Hood Container Corporation

Sun Enterprises Incorporated—acquired by Sun Powersports Investments, LLC

Sunbelt Asphalt Surfaces, Inc—acquired by Construction Partners, Inc.

Sunbelt Modular, Inc.—acquired by Littlejohn & Co., LLC

Suncoast Bakeries, Inc.—acquired by Shoreline Equity Partners, LLC

Sunshine Answering Service, Inc.—acquired by ECI Partners LLP

Sunstar Insurance Group, LLC—acquired by Reverence Capital Partners LLC

Superior Controls, Inc.—acquired by Lincoln Electric Holdings, Inc.

Superior Iron Works Inc.—acquired by Extreme Steel, Inc

Superior Systems & Technologies, Llp.—acquired by Mission Critical Group

Surdex Corp.—acquired by Bowman Consulting Group Ltd.

Surgical Product Solutions LLC—acquired by Shore Capital Partners, LLC

Surveyconnect Inc.—acquired by Orcus Technologies, Inc

Sw Resources, Inc.—acquired by Goodwill Industries of Kanawha Valley, Inc.

Swafford Warehousing, Inc.—acquired by Peoples Services Inc.

Sydell Group Ltd.—acquired by Hilton Worldwide Holdings Inc.

Synectic Research & Analysis, Inc.—acquired by Avion Solutions, Inc.

SyQwest, Inc.—acquired by CTS Corporation, and name changed to SyQwest, LLC

Systems Design Group LLC—acquired by Pye-Barker Fire & Safety, LLC

T

Takenaka Partners, LLC—acquired by YAMADA Consulting Group Co., Ltd.

Tampa Bay Steel Corporation—acquired by Russel Metals Inc.

Tara Toy Corp.—acquired by Just Play Products, LLC

Target Marketing Group—acquired by Banyan Technologies Group, LLC

Team Epiphany—acquired by Stagwell, Inc.

Tec Laboratories, Inc.—acquired by Promus Holdings, LLC

Technifab Products, Inc.—acquired by Crane Company

Technology Solutions Provider Inc.—acquired by Abt Associates Inc.

Tekmasters LLC—acquired by Godspeed Capital Management LP

Terminus Software, Inc.—acquired by Demand Science Group, LLC

Texplor of Dallas, Inc.—acquired by Terracon Consultants, Inc

The A.G. Mauro Company—acquired by Dunes Point Capital, LLC

The Connable Office, Inc.—acquired by Cresset Asset Management, LLC

The Durbin Group, LLC—acquired by The Goldman Sachs Group, Inc.

The Expo Group, Inc.—acquired by New State Capital Partners LLC

The Horton Group Inc.—acquired by Marsh & McLennan Companies, Inc.

The Patterson Capital Corporation—acquired by Estancia Capital Management, LLC

THEDACARE INC.—acquired by Froedtert Memorial Lutheran Hospital, Inc.

Theoris Inc.—acquired by Asseco Poland S.A.

Thermal Devices, Inc.—acquired by Gryphon Investors, LLC

Times Publishing Newspapers Inc.—acquired by O'Rourke Media Group, LLC

Tlc Ingredients, Inc.—acquired by Gemspring Capital Management, LLC

Toepfer Security Corp.—acquired by Alpine Investors

Tomar Computer Integration, Inc.—acquired by Trinity Hunt Management, L.P.

Total Machine Solutions, Inc.—acquired by Applied Industrial Technologies, Inc.

TPG Software, Inc.—acquired by The Carlyle Group Inc.

TR3 Solutions, Inc.—acquired by Rock Solid UK Ltd.

TraceGains, Inc.—acquired by Veralto Corporation

Trade Lake Mutual Insurance Co, Inc.—acquired by River Falls Mutual Insurance Company

Transitions Wealth Management LLC—acquired by Keystone Group, L.P. and Genstar Capital, LLC

Treasure Valley Fire Protection, Inc.—acquired by Pye-Barker Fire & Safety, LLC

Trew Auto Body, Inc.—acquired by Susquehanna International Group, LLP

Tri City Supply, Inc.—acquired by Freeman Spogli & Co. Incorporated

Tri-County Mental Health Services—acquired by Spurwink Services Incorporated

Tri-Excellence, Inc.—acquired by Gulfside Supply Inc.

Triad RF Systems Inc.—acquired by Comrod Inc.

Mergers and Acquisitions—continued

Trinisys, LLC—acquired by Novacap Management Inc.
Trinity Supply & Installation, LLC—acquired by Lezzer Lumber, Inc.
Triumph Geo-Synthetics, Inc.—acquired by Clayton, Dubilier & Rice, LLC
Trudell Consulting Engineers, Inc.—acquired by Bowman Consulting Group Ltd.
Truss-T Structures, Inc.—acquired by Roots Equity Group LLC
Tulkoff Food Products, Inc.—acquired by The Graham Group, Inc.
Turbine Controls, Inc.—acquired by VSE Corporation
Tuttle, Inc.—acquired by LFM Capital LLC
Twin City Crane & Hoist Inc.—acquired by Balance Point Capital Advisors, LLC

U

U.S. Toy Co., Inc.—acquired by Windy City Novelties, Inc.
Ultra Pet Company, Inc.—acquired by Oil-Dri Corporation of America
Unified Life Insurance Company—acquired by Obra Capital, Inc.
United Language Group, Inc.—acquired by Leonard Green & Partners, L.P. and TTCP Management Services, LLC.
United Medco, LLC—acquired by Medline Industries, LP
Utility Coatings & Fabrication, Inc.—acquired by Victaulic Company

V

V.A. Anderson Enterprises, Inc.—acquired by Apax Partners LLP
Valley Solvent Company, Inc.—acquired by Apollo Global Management, Inc.
Valley Supply, Inc.—acquired by Clayton, Dubilier & Rice, LLC
Valley Transformer Co—acquired by Trilantic Capital Management L.P.
Value Logic, Inc.—acquired by MPAC Group PLC
Vanner, Inc.—acquired by Havis, Inc.
Varni Brothers Corporation—acquired by KKR & Co. Inc.
Veggie Grill, Inc.—acquired by Next Level Burger Company, Inc.
Velocity Dynamics, LLC—acquired by Baird Financial Group, Inc.
Ventera Corporation—acquired by CI Capital Partners LLC
Veritas Total Solutions, LLC—acquired by Marsh & McLennan Companies, Inc.
Vertos Medical Inc.—acquired by Stryker Corporation
Veth Research Associates LLC—acquired by AEVEX Aerospace
VIA Technical, LLC—acquired by Stone Point Capital LLC
Vian Enterprises, Inc.—acquired by Crane Company
Vigilanz Corporation—acquired by Inovalon Holdings, Inc.
Vistacom, Inc.—acquired by Conference Technologies, Inc.
Visual Lease, LLC—acquired by CoStar Group, Inc.
VonLehman & Co. Inc.—acquired by Dean Dorton Allen Ford, PLLC
VSee Lab, Inc.—acquired by Digital Health Acquisition Corp., to form VSee Health, Inc.

W

W C P, Inc.—acquired by AGNORA Ltd
Wallace Welch & Willingham, Inc.—acquired by IMA Financial Group, Inc.
WealthSource Partners, LLC—acquired by New Mountain Capital, LLC
Webster Industries Inc.—acquired by MPE Partners, LLC [et al]
West Virginia National Auto Insurance Co, Inc.—acquired by Warrior Insurance Network, Inc
Western Heritage Bank—acquired by Nusenda Credit Union
Wharton Lyon & Lyon—acquired by GCP Capital Partners Holdings LLC
Whitco Supply, LLC—acquired by DNOW Inc.
White Crane Co, Inc.—acquired by Barnhart Crane & Rigging Co.
Wholesale Supply Inc.—acquired by Freeman Spogli & Co. Incorporated
Wilbanks, Smith & Thomas Asset Management, LLC.—acquired by Edwards Capital, LLC
Willbrook Solutions, Inc.—acquired by Godspeed Capital Management LP
Wisconsin Title Service Company, Inc.—acquired by First American Financial Corporation
Woodbridge International LLC—acquired by Mariner Wealth Advisors, LLC
Woodhill Supply Inc.—acquired by The Macomb Group, Inc.
Work & Co—acquired by Accenture plc
WR Sims Agency Incorporated—acquired by Bain Capital, LP and Keystone Insurers Group, Inc.
Wright Paving Contractors Inc—acquired by Armada Materials, LLC
WTW Architect, Inc.—acquired by AE Works Ltd.
Wyatt Insurance Services, Inc.—acquired by Hellman & Friedman LLC
Wyoming Millwork Co.—acquired by Builders FirstSource, Inc.

Y

Yellowstone Tree Surgeons, Inc.—acquired by Apax Partners LLP

Z

Zahroof Valves, Inc.—acquired by Atlas Copco AB

Zavda Technologies, LLC—acquired by Acacia Capital NL LLC

Zepnick Solutions, Inc.—acquired by Salas O'Brien Engineers, Inc.

Zubatkin Owner Representation, LLC—acquired by Cumming Construction Management, Inc.

COMPANIES

K & D INDUSTRIAL SERVICES INC.
30105 Beverly Rd, Romulus, MI 48174
Tel.: (734) 722-8922
Web Site: http://www.kdigroup.com
Year Founded: 1974
Rev.: $18,000,000
Emp.: 50
Sewer Cleaning & Rodding
N.A.I.C.S.: 562991
Ken Liabenow *(Pres)*

K & E EXCAVATING INC.
3871 Langley St SE, Salem, OR 97317
Tel.: (503) 399-4833
Web Site: http://www.keex.net
Year Founded: 1998
Sales Range: $10-24.9 Million
Emp.: 100
Site Preparation Services
N.A.I.C.S.: 238910
Kerry Kuenzi *(Owner)*
Jedidiah Percher *(Mgr)*

K & F BUSINESS BROKERS
15200 Shady Grove Rd, Rockville, MD 20850
Tel.: (301) 670-2823
Year Founded: 1987
Sales Range: $10-24.9 Million
Emp.: 15
Nonresidential Construction Services
N.A.I.C.S.: 236220
Michael Doyle *(Pres)*

K & J CHEVROLET, INC.
3051 Franklin St, Carlyle, IL 62231-2406
Tel.: (618) 594-3113
Web Site: http://www.kandjchevrolet.com
Sales Range: $10-24.9 Million
Emp.: 16
Car Whslr
N.A.I.C.S.: 441110
Tony Jansen *(Principal)*

K & L DISTRIBUTORS, INC.
3215 Lind Ave SW, Renton, WA 98057
Tel.: (206) 808-6000
Year Founded: 1940
Alcoholic & Non-Alcoholic Beverage Distr
N.A.I.C.S.: 424820
Daniel B. Levine *(Owner, Pres & CEO)*
Bonnie Pemble *(Mgr-Telecom)*

K & S TOOL, DIE & MANUFACTURING, INC.
N8145 Maple St, Ixonia, WI 53036
Tel.: (920) 261-4663
Web Site: http://www.kstooldie.com
Rev.: $13,300,000
Emp.: 90
Special Die & Tool Die Set Jig & Fixture Mfr
N.A.I.C.S.: 333514
Jay Eschrich *(COO & Exec VP)*

K BHINDI INTERNATIONAL
18508 Pioneer Blvd, Artesia, CA 90701
Tel.: (562) 402-8755
Web Site: http://www.bhindi.com
Rev.: $20,000,000
Emp.: 14
Jewelry Stores
N.A.I.C.S.: 458310
Sanat Bhindi *(Office Mgr)*

K CAPITAL CORPORATION
1 E Pratt St Ste 800, Baltimore, MD 21202-1127
Tel.: (410) 363-7050
Sales Range: $25-49.9 Million
Emp.: 210
Bank Holding Company
N.A.I.C.S.: 551111
Bill Knight *(VP)*

Subsidiaries:

K Bank (1)
11407 Cronhill Dr Ste N, Owings Mills, MD 21117-6218
Tel.: (410) 363-7050
Sales Range: $25-49.9 Million
Emp.: 250
Commercial Banking Services
N.A.I.C.S.: 522110

K I LIPTON INC.
132 Welsh Rd Ste 120, Horsham, PA 19044
Tel.: (267) 893-5671
Year Founded: 1980
Sales Range: $100-124.9 Million
Emp.: 14
N.A.I.C.S.: 541810
Ken Lipton *(Acct Exec)*
H. Raymond DeMoss *(Pres)*
Christi Schofield *(Dir-Graphics & Production)*
Linda Barker *(VP-Editorial Svcs)*
Steven Everly *(VP-Sls & Strategic Devel)*
Frank Vivian *(Acct Rep)*
Amy Jackson *(Acct Mgr)*
Erin McNelis *(Assoc Copy Editor)*
Chris Opdyke *(Mgr-Graphics & Production)*

Subsidiaries:

MedMedia (1)
132 Welsh Rd Ste 120, Horsham, PA 19044
Tel.: (267) 893-5686
Emp.: 5
N.A.I.C.S.: 541810
Steve Everly *(Sr VP-Sls & Strategic Devel)*
John McHale *(CFO)*
Frank Vivian *(Acct Rep)*
Joseph Rowan *(Acct Exec)*
Chris Opdyke *(Mgr-Graphics & Production)*

K LOGIX, LLC
233 Harvard St Ste 308, Brookline, MA 02446
Tel.: (617) 731-2314
Year Founded: 2001
Sales Range: $10-24.9 Million
Emp.: 7
Custom Computer Programming Services
N.A.I.C.S.: 541511
Kevin West *(CEO)*
Kevin Pouche *(COO)*
Rick Grimaldi *(Chief Strategy Officer)*
Anand Pandey *(Mgr-Bus Dev)*
Danielle Cameron *(Acct Exec)*
Gabby Jockers *(Acct Exec)*
James Haughton *(Acct Exec)*
Katie Haug *(Mgr-Mktg Programs)*
Kelsey Moulton *(Project Coord)*

K MICRO INC.
2050 S Westgate Ave, Los Angeles, CA 90025-6119
Tel.: (310) 442-3200
Web Site: http://www.corpinfo.com
Year Founded: 1983
Sales Range: $25-49.9 Million
Emp.: 150
IT Infrastructure Services
N.A.I.C.S.: 541512
Michael Sabourian *(Pres)*

K ROAD POWER, INC.
295 Madison Ave 37th Fl, New York, NY 10017
Tel.: (212) 351-0535
Web Site: http://www.kroadpower.com
Year Founded: 2008
Sales Range: $10-24.9 Million
Emp.: 8
Acquisitions & Investments in the U.S. Power Industry
N.A.I.C.S.: 523999
William V. Kriegel *(Founder, Chm & CEO)*
Mark Friedland *(Co-Partner)*
Karl Olsoni *(Partner)*

K&B TRANSPORTATION
4700 Dakota Ave, South Sioux City, NE 68776
Tel.: (402) 494-3459
Web Site: http://www.kbtransportation.com
Year Founded: 1986
Sales Range: $50-74.9 Million
Emp.: 700
Trucking Services
N.A.I.C.S.: 484121
Ken Ackerman *(Pres)*
Bill Haberman *(CFO)*
Mike Ratkiewicz *(Exec VP)*

K&F DISTRIBUTORS INC.
100 W Main St, Lincolnville, KS 66858
Tel.: (620) 924-5202
Sales Range: $10-24.9 Million
Emp.: 30
Petroleum Bulk Stations
N.A.I.C.S.: 424710

K&K EXPRESS LLC
2980 Commers Dr Ste 100, Eagan, MN 55121
Tel.: (651) 209-8771
Web Site: http://www.k2logistics.com
Sales Range: $10-24.9 Million
Emp.: 40
Provider of Freight Forwarding Services
N.A.I.C.S.: 488510
Briant Stiernagle *(Acct Mgr)*
Dion Anderson *(VP-Ops)*
Jon Hill *(VP-Logistics & Transportation)*

K&K IRON WORKS INC.
5100 S Lawndale Ave, McCook, IL 60525
Tel.: (708) 924-0000
Web Site: http://www.kkironworks.com
Year Founded: 1976
Sales Range: $10-24.9 Million
Emp.: 100
Steel Products Mfr
N.A.I.C.S.: 332312
Kevin Breen *(Pres & Chief Estimator)*

K&L FREIGHT MANAGEMENT, INC.
745 S Rohlwing Rd, Addison, IL 60101
Tel.: (630) 607-1500
Web Site: http://www.kandlfreight.com
Year Founded: 1997
Sales Range: $10-24.9 Million
Emp.: 50
Expedited Freight Logistics
N.A.I.C.S.: 488510
Russ Gallemore *(Owner)*

K&L GATES LLP
K L Gates Ctr 210 6th Ave, Pittsburgh, PA 15222-2613
Tel.: (412) 355-6500
Web Site: http://www.klgates.com
Year Founded: 1946
Sales Range: $1-4.9 Billion
Emp.: 1,800
Law firm
N.A.I.C.S.: 541110
Charles A. Hokanson *(CFO)*
Jeffrey Nevill *(Deputy COO-Australia)*
Robert Wymond *(Deputy CFO-Australia)*
Cameron Abbott *(Partner-Melbourne)*
Stacy G. Ackermann *(Partner-Fin-Charlotte)*
Jeffrey W. Acre *(Partner)*
David B. Allen *(Partner-Orange County)*
R. Bruce Allensworth *(Partner-Boston)*
John D. Allison *(Partner-Charlotte)*
Joel D. Almquist *(Partner-Boston)*
Susan P. Altman *(Partner)*
Vincent N. Avallone *(Partner-Newark)*
David Benson *(Partner)*
David Hattery *(Partner)*
Carla DewBerry *(Partner)*
Christa Lenard *(Partner-Workplace Rels-Sydney)*
Betsy-Ann Howe *(Partner-Tax-Sydney)*
Alan Maclean *(Partner-Fin-Melbourne)*
Nick Ruskin *(Partner-Labor, Employment & Workplace Safety Practice-Melbourne)*
David J. Raphael *(Partner-Environment, Land & Natural Resources Practice-Harrisburg)*
Takahiro Hoshino *(Partner-Comml Disputes-Tokyo)*
Michael Freno *(Partner-Seattle)*
Peter Giunta *(Partner-New York)*
Elisa D'Amico *(Partner)*
Susan K. Hackney *(Partner-Res Triangle Park)*
Mackenzie Morse *(Partner)*
Sarah Bowman *(Partner)*
Rhys Hefta *(Partner)*
John E. Garda *(Mng Partner-Dallas)*
Jeffrey S. Patterson *(Partner-Boston)*
Christopher S. Finnerty *(Partner-Boston)*
Morgan T. Nickerson *(Partner-Boston)*
Michael T. Murphy *(Mng Partner-Houston)*
David Fialkow *(Partner-Boston)*
Sean R. Higgins *(Partner-Boston)*
Daniel J. Stephenson *(Partner-Raleigh)*
Brian Graham *(Partner)*
Edward Dartley *(Partner-Investment Mgmt, Hedge Funds & Alternative Investments)*
Richard Kerr *(Partner)*
Bruce MacLennan *(Partner)*
Todd W. Betke *(Partner-Washington)*
Michelle Repp *(Partner)*
Ian M. Liao *(Partner-Shanghai)*
Robert J. Grey *(Partner-Energy-Washington)*
Stephanie Moot *(Partner)*
Lindsay Sampson Bishop *(Partner-Boston)*
David D. Christensen *(Partner-Boston)*
Jennifer Janeira Nagle *(Partner-Boston)*
Tara L. Pehush *(Partner-New York)*
Grace Fan-Delatour *(Partner-Beijing)*
Anja Rosch *(Partner-Berlin)*
Jennifer H. Thiem *(Partner-Charleston)*
Brian A. Wildstein *(Partner-Charleston)*
Lauren Norris Donahue *(Partner-Chicago)*
Nolan R. Hubbard *(Partner-Chicago)*
Benjamin E. Weed *(Partner-Chicago)*
Desiree F. Moore *(Partner-Doha)*
Phi Lan Tinsley *(Partner-Boston)*

K&L GATES LLP

K&L Gates LLP—(Continued)
Christina N. Goodrich (Partner-Los Angeles)
Feroze Abbas (Partner-London)
Rajeev Joshi (Partner-London)
Andrew J. Massey (Partner-London)
Steven Wulff (Partner-Melbourne)
Vittorio Salvadori Di Wiesenhoff (Partner-Milan)
George P. Barbatsuly (Partner-Newark)
Dawn M. Lamparello (Partner-Newark)
Loly Garcia Tor (Partner-Newark)
Caitlin C. Blanche (Partner-Orange County)
Karishma Shah Page (Partner-Washington)
Sonia R. Gioseffi (Partner-San Francisco)
Rikki A. Sapolich-Krol (Partner-San Francisco)
Brent Johnson (Partner-Orange County)
Jackson Ho (Partner-Litigation-Palo Alto)
Claude-Etienne Armingaud (Partner-Paris)
David Fusco (Partner)
Suzanne B. Allaire (Partner-Real Estate Investment, Dev & Fin-Raleigh)
Darlene S. Davis (Partner-Research Triangle Park)
J. Timothy Hobbs (Partner-Seattle)
Ankur Tohan (Partner)
Henry Wang (Partner)
Simone Mitchell (Partner-Sydney)
Nick Nichola (Mng Partner-Australia)
Sang-Yul Lee (Partner-Labor, Employment & Workplace Safety Practice-Chicago)
Michael E. Martinez (Mng Partner-Chicago)
Christopher J. Voss (Partner-Seattle)
Nickolas G. Spiliotis (Partner-Labor, Employment & Workplace Safety Practice-Houston)
Barry B. Cosgrave (Partner-Global Fin Practice-London)
Tony Griffiths (Partner-Admin-London)
Mayank Gupta (Partner-Global Fin Practice-London)
Olivia S. Byrne (Partner-Washington)
Steven F. Hill (Partner)
Sasha Burstein (Partner-Investment Mgmt-San Francisco)
Edward P. Sangster (Partner-Admin-San Francisco)
Ted Lotchin (Partner-Research Triangle Park)
Pam Kohli Jacobson (Partner)
Michael Dyson (Partner-Washington)
Philip Kunz (Partner)
Molly Suda (Partner-Washington)
Dennis Kiely (Partner)
Mounir Letayf (Partner-Banking & Asset Fin Practice)
Elias Hinckley (Partner-Washington)
Joseph P. Regan (Partner-Fort Worth)
Adam L. Plumbley (Partner-Fort Worth)
Adam F. Kelson (Partner-Emerging Growth & Venture Capital Practice)
Thomas Smith (Partner-Admin)
John Rothermich (Partner-Portland)
Daniel Eliades (Partner-Newark)
Liz Boydston (Partner-Restructuring & Insolvency Practice-Dallas)
Jack M. Erskine (Mng Partner-Austin)
Jay C. Chiu (Partner-Beijing)
Yujing Shu (Partner-Beijing)
Vincent R. Tso (Partner-Beijing)
Frank Voon (Partner-Beijing)
Linda Zhou (Partner-Beijing)
Jonathan M. Barron (Partner-New York)
Calvina Bostick (Partner-New York)
Douglas F. Broder (Partner-New York)
Eric R. I. Cottle (Partner-New York)
Roger R. Crane (Partner-New York)
Amanda L. Darling (Partner-New York)
Michael DeMarco (Partner-New York)
Joanna Diakos (Partner-New York)
Peter N. Flocos (Partner-New York)
Andrew L. Gespass (Partner-New York)
Randy M. Goodman (Partner-New York)
Martin F. Gusy (Partner-New York)
Holly D. Hatfield (Partner-New York)
Peter J. Kalis (Partner-New York)
Brian D. Koosed (Partner-New York)
Jamie Lavergne Bryan (Partner-Houston)
Michael D. Cuda (Partner-Houston)
Robert H. George (Partner-Houston)
Kirstie Richards (Partner-Washington)
Lucy Shanahan (Partner-Washington)
Kjersten Turpen (Partner-Portland)
Eugene Yeung (Partner-Fin Practice-Hong Kong)
A. Lee Hogewood III (Mng Partner-Raleigh)
John Owens III (Partner)
Robert H. McCarthy Jr. (Partner-Austin)

K&M ELECTRIC SUPPLY INC.
7641 Central Industrial Dr, Riviera Beach, FL 33404
Tel.: (561) 842-4911
Web Site: http://www.kmelectric.com
Sales Range: $10-24.9 Million
Emp.: 75
Wire & Cable
N.A.I.C.S.: 423610
William K. Mooney (Owner)
Mike Ritchie (Mgr-Accts Payable)
Derrick E. Hoskins (Pres)

K&M TIRE, INC.
965 Spencerville Rd, Delphos, OH 45833-0279
Tel.: (419) 695-1061   OH
Web Site: http://www.kmtire.com
Year Founded: 1970
Automotive Tires & Tubes Distr
N.A.I.C.S.: 423130
Kenneth Langhals (Founder & CEO)
Cheryl Gossard (Pres)
Jill Cilmi (VP)

K&N ELECTRIC INC.
4909 Rondo Dr, Fort Worth, TX 76106
Tel.: (817) 626-2885
Web Site: http://www.kandnmobile.com
Sales Range: $10-24.9 Million
Emp.: 30
Electrical Supplies Sales
N.A.I.C.S.: 423610
Curtis Nelson (Pres)
Audie Jones (Mgr-Inventory Control & Pur)

K&N ELECTRIC MOTORS INC.
415 N Fancher Rd, Spokane Valley, WA 99212
Tel.: (509) 838-8000
Web Site: http://www.knelectric.com
Sales Range: $10-24.9 Million
Emp.: 95
Electrical Apparatus & Equipment Wiring Supplies & Related Equipment Merchant Whslr
N.A.I.C.S.: 423610

K&N ENGINEERING INC.
1455 Citrus St, Riverside, CA 92507
Tel.: (951) 826-4000
Web Site: http://www.knfilters.org
Year Founded: 1967
Sales Range: $25-49.9 Million
Emp.: 600
Mfr of Oil Filters
N.A.I.C.S.: 336390
Caitlin Clement (Coord-Mktg)
Dena Daniel (Mgr-Customer Quality)
Jerry Mailloux (Supvr-Production)
Kevin Floody (Mgr-Intl Bus)
Tim Martin (VP)
Dino Marutsos (Mgr-Heavy Duty Tech Sls)
Norman Cole (Acct Mgr-Natl)
Rick Shelman (Mgr-Maintenance)
Liz Sanders (Mgr-Acctg)
Jere Wall (Sr Mgr-PD&E)
Craig A. Scanlon (CEO)
Brian Horvath (Sls Mgr-Half West)
Matt Kenefick (Sls Mgr-East)
Jesse Spungin (Pres)
Manny Perez (Sls Mgr-Govt & Fleet)
Mo Ayad (VP-New Product Dev Mktg)
J. R. Badian (CMO)

K&R INDUSTRIES INC.
14110 Sullyfield Cir, Chantilly, VA 20151
Tel.: (703) 631-4200
Sales Range: $100-124.9 Million
Emp.: 25
Advertising Promotion Services
N.A.I.C.S.: 423940
Mark Eagen (Pres)
Nancy Gisin (Gen Mgr)

K&S MARKET INC.
650 San Benito St Ste 210, Hollister, CA 95023
Tel.: (831) 637-5821
Sales Range: $25-49.9 Million
Emp.: 4
Provider of Grocery Services
N.A.I.C.S.: 445110
Lily Klauer (Pres)

K&S SERVICES INC.
15677 Noecker Way, Southgate, MI 48195
Tel.: (734) 374-0400
Web Site: http://www.k-and-s.com
Rev.: $60,631,273
Emp.: 181
Professional Instrument Repair Services
N.A.I.C.S.: 811210
Terri Desselles (Acct Mgr)
Jeff Truitt (VP-Ops)

K&W CAFETERIAS INC.
1391 Plaza W Rd, Winston Salem, NC 27103
Tel.: (336) 760-0526   NC
Web Site: http://www.kwcafeterias.com
Year Founded: 1940
Sales Range: $100-124.9 Million
Emp.: 2,500
Cafeteria Owner & Operator
N.A.I.C.S.: 722514
Leslie Allred-Yates (Coord-Catering)
Donald C. Allred (Chm & CEO)
Todd Smith (Exec VP)
R. Leo Sasaki (VP-Fin & Admin)
Katie Kispert (VP-HR)
David Estess (VP-Ops)
John Keeter (Dir-IT & ECommerce)

K&W TIRE COMPANY INC.
735 N Prince St, Lancaster, PA 17603
Tel.: (717) 397-3596
Web Site: http://www.kwtire.com
Sales Range: $25-49.9 Million
Emp.: 70
Automobile Tires & Tubes
N.A.I.C.S.: 423130
Richard J. Kline (Chm)

K-1 TECHNOLOGIES
10901 Roosevelt Blvd Ste 800B, Saint Petersburg, FL 33716
Tel.: (727) 342-1111
Web Site: http://www.k-1tech.com
Rev.: $17,500,000
Emp.: 14
Electronic Parts & Equipment Merchant Whslr
N.A.I.C.S.: 423690
Winston Worth (Gen Mgr)

K-B CORPORATION
122 Penny Rd, Old Town, ME 04468
Tel.: (207) 827-6060
Web Site: http://www.kbcorp.us
Sales Range: $10-24.9 Million
Emp.: 75
General Freight Trucking Services
N.A.I.C.S.: 484110
Greg Kitchen (VP)
Jason Bond (Mgr-Parts & Svc)
Melonie Bond (Mgr-Fleet)

K-BOB'S USA INC.
135 W Palace Ave Ste300, Santa Fe, NM 87501
Tel.: (505) 892-3438   NM
Web Site: http://www.k-bobs.com
Year Founded: 1966
Sales Range: $25-49.9 Million
Emp.: 12
Restaurant
N.A.I.C.S.: 722511
Ed Tinsley (Pres)

K-D SUPPLY CORPORATION
245 Cooper Ave Ste 100, Tonawanda, NY 14150
Tel.: (716) 693-7600
Web Site: http://www.kdsupply.com
Sales Range: $10-24.9 Million
Emp.: 100
Industrial Machinery & Equipment
N.A.I.C.S.: 423830
Greg Brun (Pres & CEO)

K-F MANAGEMENT COMPANY, INC.
511 Sixteenth St Ste 600, Denver, CO 80202
Tel.: (303) 571-0100   DE
Web Site: http://www.chbcapital.com
Year Founded: 1995
Equity Investment Firm
N.A.I.C.S.: 523999
John W. Flanigan (Mng Partner)
J. Blake Morris (Partner)
David Anderson (CFO)
Katie Henning (Office Mgr)
Sean McClenaghan (Partner-Atlanta)
Samantha Sigler (Chief Admin Officer-Denver)
Thomas L. Kelly II (Gen Partner)

Subsidiaries:

CT Systems   (1)
11064 Strang Line Road, Lenexa, KS 66215
Tel.: (913) 469-6400
Sales Range: $25-49.9 Million
Integrated Systems, Assemblies & Turn-Key Products for Aerospace & Electrical Businesses
N.A.I.C.S.: 332721

COMPANIES

K-FIVE CONSTRUCTION CORPORATION
13769 Main St, Lemont, IL 60439-9371
Tel.: (630) 257-5600   IL
Web Site: http://www.k-five.net
Year Founded: 1977
Sales Range: $100-124.9 Million
Emp.: 500
Construction Services
N.A.I.C.S.: 237310
Dennis DeVitto *(VP)*
George B. Krug Jr. *(CEO)*
Mark Sniegowski *(CFO & VP)*
Rick Sniegowski *(VP)*

Subsidiaries:

B-K Concrete Products Inc. (1)
999 Oak Mont Plaza Dr Ste 200, Westmont, IL 60559
Tel.: (630) 257-5600
Web Site: http://www.k-five.com
Sales Range: $10-24.9 Million
Emp.: 4
Concrete Contractor
N.A.I.C.S.: 238110
Robert G. Krug *(Pres)*

Chicago Materials Corporation (1)
13769 Main St, Lemont, IL 60439-9371   (100%)
Tel.: (630) 257-5600
Construction Machinery
N.A.I.C.S.: 333120

K-Five Construction Corporation - Chicago Plant (1)
12800 S Cottage Grove Ave, Chicago, IL 60628
Tel.: (773) 264-0189
Construction Engineering Services
N.A.I.C.S.: 541330

K-Five Construction Corporation - Elmhurst Plant (1)
1 N 550 Route 83, Elmhurst, IL 60126
Tel.: (630) 832-4213
Construction Engineering Services
N.A.I.C.S.: 541330

K-Five Construction Corporation - Markham Plant (1)
16222 S Western Ave, Markham, IL 60428
Tel.: (708) 331-1775
Construction Engineering Services
N.A.I.C.S.: 541330

K-Five Construction Corporation - Naperville Plant (1)
29 W 255 N Aurora Rd, Naperville, IL 60563
Tel.: (630) 355-0201
Emp.: 4
Construction Engineering Services
N.A.I.C.S.: 541330
Robert Krug *(Gen Mgr)*

K-FOODS INC.
405 Washington St W, Charleston, WV 25302
Tel.: (304) 343-1979
Web Site: http://www.faschek.com
Sales Range: $1-9.9 Million
Emp.: 300
Grocery Stores
N.A.I.C.S.: 445110
Don Tate *(Pres)*

K-O-I ENTERPRISES INC.
2701 Spring Grove Ave, Cincinnati, OH 45225
Tel.: (513) 357-2427
Web Site: http://www.koiautoparts.com
Rev.: $101,900,000
Emp.: 900
Automotive Supplies & Parts
N.A.I.C.S.: 423120
David Wesselman *(Pres)*

K-SOLV GROUP, LLC
952 Echo Ln, Ste 400, Houston, TX 77024
Tel.: (713) 468-5768
Web Site: https://www.ksolvgroup.com
Year Founded: 2018
Chemicals Mfr
N.A.I.C.S.: 325998
Russell Allen *(Owner & CEO)*
Todd Riddle *(COO)*

Subsidiaries:

TurnKey Industries, LLC (1)
29708 Fm 2978 Rd, Magnolia, TX 77354
Tel.: (281) 356-1386
Web Site: http://tkind.com
Sales Range: $1-9.9 Million
Emp.: 14
Recreational Vehicle Dealers
N.A.I.C.S.: 441210
Jeff Conter *(Exec VP)*

K-TEC INCORPORATED
1206 S 1680 W, Orem, UT 84058
Tel.: (801) 222-0888
Web Site: http://www.blendtec.com
Year Founded: 1988
Electric Household Cooking Utensils
N.A.I.C.S.: 335210
Gina Bickery *(Controller)*

K-TECH CORP.
1661 Jody Industrial Ct, Saint Louis, MO 63132
Tel.: (314) 644-4700   MO
Web Site: http://www.schneiderelectricco.com
General Electrical Contractor
N.A.I.C.S.: 238210
Jamie Lancaster *(CFO)*
Mark Wiesehan *(Dir-Manpower & Safety)*
Brian Oehler *(Mgr-Project)*
John Hunerlach *(Mgr-Project)*
Carson Vandorn *(Mgr-Project)*
Ken Brandt *(Mgr-Project)*
Luke Meyer *(Mgr-Project)*
Mike Hawf *(Mgr-Project)*
Greg Lynch *(Mgr-Warehouse)*
Sam Wattle *(Supvr-Svc)*
Robert J. Unterriner *(Pres & CEO)*
Gary E. Rickerd *(Exec VP)*

K-TECHNOLOGIES, INC.
4090 Jeffrey Blvd, Buffalo, NY 14219
Tel.: (716) 649-5460   NY
Web Site: http://www.k-technologies.com
Year Founded: 1997
Sales Range: $1-9.9 Million
Emp.: 20
Fluid Meters & Counting Devices Mfr
N.A.I.C.S.: 334514
Larry Mentkowski *(Gen Mgr)*

K-TOOL CORPORATION MICHIGAN
31111 Wixom Rd, Wixom, MI 48393
Tel.: (248) 669-5000
Web Site: http://www.ktoolinternational.com
Sales Range: $10-24.9 Million
Emp.: 80
Tools & Equipment, Automotive
N.A.I.C.S.: 423120
Bob Geisinger *(Pres)*

K-VA-T FOOD STORES, INC.
151 Cook St, Abingdon, VA 24210
Tel.: (276) 628-3654   VA
Web Site: https://www.foodcity.com
Year Founded: 1955
Sales Range: Less than $1 Million
Emp.: 15,000
Supermarkets & Other Grocery Retailers (except Convenience Retailers)
N.A.I.C.S.: 445110
Jack C. Smith *(Founder)*

Subsidiaries:

Food City Distribution Center (1)
396 Towne Centre Dr, Abingdon, VA 24210-7619
Tel.: (276) 628-3654
Web Site: http://www.foodcity.com
Sales Range: $25-49.9 Million
Emp.: 100
Warehousing & Distribution Services
N.A.I.C.S.: 531130
Dan Glei *(Exec VP-Mktg & Mdsg)*

Misty Mountain Spring Water Co. LLC (1)
26331 Hillman Hwy, Abingdon, VA 24210-7619
Tel.: (276) 623-5000
Web Site: http://www.mistyh2o.com
Bottled Water Mfr & Distr
N.A.I.C.S.: 312112
Steven Miller *(Ops Mgr)*

Super Dollar Discount Foods (1)
26331 Hillman Hwy, Abingdon, VA 24210-7619
Tel.: (276) 628-2053
Food Store
N.A.I.C.S.: 445298
Richard Gunn *(Dir-Grocery Ops)*

K. BARGER REALTY, LLC
3071 118th Ave N, Saint Petersburg, FL 33716
Tel.: (727) 520-7711
Web Site: http://www.kbargerrealty.com
Year Founded: 2003
Sales Range: $1-9.9 Million
Commercial Real Brokerage, Consulting, Investment & Management
N.A.I.C.S.: 531210
Kim Barger *(Partner)*
Mike Barger *(Partner)*
Judy Humbarger *(Partner)*

K. COATINGS, LLC
PO Box 241037, Cleveland, OH 44124-8937
Tel.: (440) 248-8288
Web Site: http://www.poxycoat.com
Sales Range: $25-49.9 Million
Emp.: 45
Epoxy & Specialty Coating Materials Mfr
N.A.I.C.S.: 332812
Neil Koppelman *(Pres)*

K. HEEPS INC.
5239 W Tilghman St, Allentown, PA 18104
Tel.: (610) 530-8010
Web Site: http://www.heeps.com
Sales Range: $25-49.9 Million
Emp.: 70
Meat Sales
N.A.I.C.S.: 424470
James W. Heeps *(Chm)*
Beau J. Heeps *(Pres)*
Ted L. Heeps *(VP)*

K. NEAL INTERNATIONAL TRUCKS, INC.
5000 Tuxedo Rd, Hyattsville, MD 20781
Tel.: (301) 772-5100   DE
Web Site: http://www.knealinternational.com
Sales Range: $25-49.9 Million
Emp.: 100
Trucks, Tractors & Trailers: New & Used
N.A.I.C.S.: 441110
Stephen Neal *(Pres)*
Larry Hurwitz *(Gen Mgr-Bus Dev & Idealease)*
Sharon Calomese *(CFO & Sr VP)*

Subsidiaries:

Powell's Truck & Equipment Inc. (1)
13260 Wards Rd, Lynchburg, VA 24501-7130
Tel.: (434) 482-5935
Web Site: http://www.powelltruck.com
New Car Dealers
N.A.I.C.S.: 441110

K.B. SOCKS, INC.
550 N Oak St, Inglewood, CA 90302
Tel.: (310) 670-3235
Web Site: http://www.kbellsocks.com
Year Founded: 1978
Rev.: $14,000,000
Emp.: 100
Socks
N.A.I.C.S.: 315120
Karen Sue Bell *(Founder)*

K.B.C. GROUP INC.
3400 109th St, Des Moines, IA 50322
Tel.: (515) 270-2417
Web Site: http://www.bratney.com
Sales Range: $10-24.9 Million
Emp.: 100
Agricultural Building Contractors
N.A.I.C.S.: 236220
Joe Gasmen *(Coord-IT)*

Subsidiaries:

Bratney Equipment Company Inc (1)
3400 109th St, Urbandale, IA 50322
Tel.: (515) 270-2417
Web Site: http://www.bratney.com
Rev.: $9,869,599
Emp.: 25
Agricultural Machinery & Equipment
N.A.I.C.S.: 423820

Cimbria Bratney Co. (1)
3400 109th St, Des Moines, IA 50322
Tel.: (515) 270-2417
Web Site: http://www.bratney.com
Emp.: 65
Agricultural Machinery & Equipment
N.A.I.C.S.: 423820
Peter Bratney *(Pres & CEO)*

Ken Bratney Company (1)
3400 109th St, Des Moines, IA 50322
Tel.: (515) 270-2417
Web Site: http://www.bratney.com
Industrial Buildings & Warehouses
N.A.I.C.S.: 236220
Peter K. Bratney *(CEO)*

K.C. PETROLEUM, INC.
650 Talleyrand Ave, Jacksonville, FL 32202
Tel.: (904) 693-3200
Web Site: http://www.kcpetroleum.com
Rev.: $16,900,000
Emp.: 50
All Other Specialty Trade Contractors
N.A.I.C.S.: 238990
Kevin Cormier *(Pres)*
Laura Cormier *(Treas & Sec)*
Charlotte Freeman *(Mgr-Svc)*

K.D. STEEL, INC.
7004 N Altamont Ste A, Spokane, WA 99217
Tel.: (509) 467-5309
Web Site: http://www.kdsteel.com
Year Founded: 1988
Rev.: $14,000,000
Emp.: 40
Steel Erection Services
N.A.I.C.S.: 238120
Sage Williamson *(VP-Ops)*

K.D. TIMMONS INC.
308 W Dodge St, Bryan, TX 77803

K.D. TIMMONS INC.

K.D. Timmons Inc.—(Continued)
Tel.: (979) 822-1394
Web Site: http://www.timmonsoil.net
Sales Range: $10-24.9 Million
Emp.: 12
Petroleum Bulk Stations
N.A.I.C.S.: 424710
Ken D. Timmons (Pres)
Lee Ball (VP)

K.E. MCKAY'S MARKET OF COOS BAY

226 Hall St, Coos Bay, OR 97420
Tel.: (541) 269-5921
Sales Range: $25-49.9 Million
Emp.: 280
Independent Supermarket
N.A.I.C.S.: 445110
William Coldwell (Pres)

K.L. MCCOY & ASSOCIATES

13200 Levan Rd, Livonia, MI 48150
Tel.: (734) 452-8230
Web Site: http://www.klmccoy.com
Sales Range: $10-24.9 Million
Emp.: 45
Plumbing & Hydronic Heating Supplies
N.A.I.C.S.: 423720
John McCoy (Pres)
Kyle Tevault (Engr-Sls)

K.R. ANDERSON CO. INC.

18330 Sutter Blvd, Morgan Hill, CA 95037-2841
Tel.: (408) 825-1800
Web Site: http://www.kranderson.com
Year Founded: 1968
Sales Range: $25-49.9 Million
Emp.: 45
Specialty Chemicals & Allied Products
N.A.I.C.S.: 424690
Dennis Wagner (Pres)
Eric Arnold (Engr-Sls)
Lisa Cummings (Asst Controller)

K.TEK SYSTEMS, INC.

2536 Countryside Blvd Ste 200, Clearwater, FL 33763
Tel.: (727) 726-1700
Web Site: http://www.ktek.com
Year Founded: 1993
Sales Range: $10-24.9 Million
Emp.: 50
Web Based Solutions Including Custom Web Design & Development, Hosting & Internet Application Management
N.A.I.C.S.: 513210
Kimberly K. During (Founder & CEO)
Ron During (CIO)

K.W. REESE INC.

9486 Buchanan Trl W, Mercersburg, PA 17236
Tel.: (717) 328-5211
Web Site: http://www.kwreese.com
Rev.: $10,000,000
Emp.: 125
Land Clearing Contractor
N.A.I.C.S.: 236210
Carl Calfo (Mgr)
Jeff Reese (Pres)

K/E ELECTRIC SUPPLY CORP.

146 N Groesbeck Hwy, Mount Clemens, MI 48043
Tel.: (586) 469-3005
Web Site: http://www.keelectricsupplycorp.com
Year Founded: 1988
Electrical Construction Materials
N.A.I.C.S.: 423610
John White (Gen Mgr)

K/P CORPORATION

13951 Washington Ave, San Leandro, CA 94577
Tel.: (510) 351-5400 OR
Web Site: http://www.kpcorporation.com
Year Founded: 1967
Sales Range: $75-99.9 Million
Emp.: 550
Commercial Lithographic Printing Services
N.A.I.C.S.: 323111
Brett Olszewski (Chief Sls & Mktg Officer)
Joe Atturio (Pres & CEO)
Thomas Middleton (CIO)
Paul Braverman (COO)

K1 INVESTMENT MANAGEMENT, LLC

875 Manhattan Beach Blvd, Manhattan Beach, CA 90266
Web Site: http://www.k1capital.com
Single-Family Housing
N.A.I.C.S.: 236115
Hasan Askari (Mng Partner)
Taylor Beaupain (Mng Partner)
Ron Cano (Mng Dir)
Dan Ghammachi (Mng Dir)
Sujit Banerjee (Mng Dir)
George Mansour (Principal)

Subsidiaries:

Certify, LLC (1)
20 York St, Portland, ME 04101-3905 (100%)
Tel.: (207) 773-6100
Web Site: http://www.certify.com
Software Publisher
N.A.I.C.S.: 513210
Heath MacArthur (Chief Revenue Officer)

Subsidiary (Domestic):

Chrome River Technologies, Inc. (2)
SAG-AFTRA Plaza 5757 Wilshire Blvd Ste 270, Los Angeles, CA 90036
Tel.: (323) 857-5800
Web Site: http://www.chromeriver.com
Sales Range: $10-24.9 Million
Emp.: 98
Online Expense Reporting & Invoice Automation Platforms
N.A.I.C.S.: 513210
Anne Becknell (Sr VP-Customer Success)
Alan Rich (Founder & CEO)
Julie Norquist Roy (CMO)
Aviva Kram (VP-Quality Assurance & Support Ops)
Daniel Machock (CFO)
Matt Gahr (Chief Sls Officer)
Sunil Kayiti (CTO)
Dave Terry (COO)
Nancy Dushkin (Sr VP-Client Svcs)

Clarizen, Inc. (1)
691 S Milpitas Blvd Ste 212, Milpitas, CA 95035
Tel.: (650) 227-0300
Web Site: http://www.clarizen.com
Enterprise Collaborative Work Management Software Developer
N.A.I.C.S.: 513210
Avinoam Nowogrodski (Founder)
Matt Zilli (CEO)
Boaz Chalamish (Chm)

Damballa, Inc. (1)
817 W Peachtree St NW Ste 800, Atlanta, GA 30308
Tel.: (404) 961-4049
Web Site: http://www.damballa.com
Computer & Electronic Equipment Distr
N.A.I.C.S.: 423690
David Scholtz (CEO)
Tom Savini (CFO)
David Fortune (VP-Ops)
Stephen Newman (CTO)
Joseph Ward (VP-Products)
Dale Gonzalez (Chief Product Officer)
Francis A. Dramis (Chm)

ELMO Software Limited (1)
Level 27 580 George Street, Sydney, 2000, NSW, Australia
Tel.: (61) 283054600
Web Site: https://www.elmosoftware.com.au
Rev.: $35,005,169
Assets: $172,272,346
Liabilities: $46,908,087
Net Worth: $125,364,259
Earnings: ($13,019,844)
Emp.: 384
Fiscal Year-end: 06/30/2020
Software Development Services
N.A.I.C.S.: 541511
James Haslam (CFO & COO)
Gordon Starkey (COO & Chief Revenue Officer)
Joseph Lyons (CEO)
Sarah Dart (Chief Customer Officer)
Katherine Landon (Sr VP-Finance)
Joshua McKenzie (CTO)
Gareth Burrows (Mng Dir-Breathe HR)

Subsidiary (Non-US):

Pivot Remesys Limited (2)
23 Sir William Pickering Drive, Burnside, Christchurch, 8053, New Zealand
Tel.: (64) 33591707
Web Site: http://www.pivotsoftware.com
Software Development Services
N.A.I.C.S.: 541511
Jared Cameron (Gen Mgr)
Robin Dickie (Head-Dev & Infrastructure)
Stacey Hill (Product Mgr)
Kristy Lane (Head-Client Relationships)

Subsidiary (Domestic):

Pivot Remesys Pty. Limited (2)
Level 27 580 George Street, Sydney, 2000, NSW, Australia
Tel.: (61) 1300316879
Software Development Services
N.A.I.C.S.: 541511

Subsidiary (Non-US):

Safety Business Learning Limited (2)
Whitehouse 111 New Street, Birmingham, B2 4EU, United Kingdom
Tel.: (44) 1212005810
Web Site: http://www.safetybusinesslearning.co.uk
Education Management Services
N.A.I.C.S.: 611710

Jobvite, Inc. (1)
270 E Ln Ste 3, Burlingame, CA 94010
Tel.: (650) 376-7200
Web Site: http://www.jobvite.com
Sales Range: $10-24.9 Million
Emp.: 120
Webpage Design Services
N.A.I.C.S.: 541511
Dan Finnigan (CEO)
Skip Hilton (VP-Bus Dev)
Adam Hyder (CTO)
David Lahey (VP-Intl)
Tim Lambert (Chief Revenue Officer)
Kevin Nanney (VP-Product)
Rachel Bitte (Chief People Officer)
Bill Loller (Chief Product Officer)
Robert Tsao (Co-Chief Product Officer)
Matt Singer (VP-Mktg)
Matt McLaughlin (VP-Mid Market & Enterprise Sls)
Paul Turner (VP-Customer Success)

MariaDB plc (1)
1900 McCarthy Blvd Ste 301, Milpitas, CA 95035
Web Site: https://www.mariadb.com
Rev.: $53,113,000
Assets: $29,792,000
Liabilities: $75,311,000
Net Worth: ($45,519,000)
Earnings: ($51,857,000)
Emp.: 303
Fiscal Year-end: 09/30/2023
Custom Computer Programming Services
N.A.I.C.S.: 541511
Rohit De Souza (CEO)

Panopto, Inc. (1)
2000 E Carson St Ste 300, Pittsburgh, PA 15203
Web Site: http://www.panopto.com
Software Publisher
N.A.I.C.S.: 513210

Brad Winney (Pres)
Rob Hughes (VP-Sls)
Sean Gorman (COO)
Eric Burns (Founder & CEO)
Dave Neway (VP-Mktg)
Will Wyatt (Chief Sls Officer)
Christina Mautz (CMO)

Reveal Data Corporation (1)
318 W Adams St Ste 1607, Chicago, IL 60606
Tel.: (614) 705-1515
Web Site: http://www.revealdata.com
Cloud-based eDiscovery Software Solutions & Services
N.A.I.C.S.: 513210
Wendell Jisa (Founder & CEO)

Subsidiary (Domestic):

IPRO Tech, LLC (2)
1700 N Desert Dr Ste 101, Tempe, AZ 85281
Tel.: (602) 324-4776
Web Site: http://www.iprotech.com
Sales Range: $1-9.9 Million
Emp.: 55
Software Development Services
N.A.I.C.S.: 541511
Steve Moore (Dir-Corp Bus Dev)
Greg Horne (CFO)

Mindseye Solutions LLC (2)
2301 Columbia Pike Ste 121, Arlington, VA 22204-4451
Tel.: (202) 349-0177
Web Site: http://www.mindseyesolutions.com
eDiscovery Software Services
N.A.I.C.S.: 513210
Bob Krantz (Founder & CEO)

Smarsh Inc. (1)
851 SW 6th Ave Ste 800, Portland, OR 97204
Tel.: (503) 946-5980
Web Site: http://www.smarsh.com
Sales Range: $10-24.9 Million
Emp.: 230
Email Archiving & Compliance Solutions
N.A.I.C.S.: 513210
Stephen Marsh (Founder & Chm)
Justin Parker (VP-Product Dev)
Sam Kolbert-Hyle (VP-Bus Dev & Strategic Initiatives)
Vinay Mehta (CTO)
Suzanne Rudnitzki (COO)
Laurie Ehrbar (CMO)
Goutam Nadella (Chief Product Officer)
Kim Crawford Goodman (CEO)

Subsidiary (Domestic):

Actiance, Inc. (2)
900 Veterans Blvd 5th Fl, Redwood City, CA 94063
Tel.: (503) 946-5980
Web Site: http://www.smarsh.com
Software Publisher
N.A.I.C.S.: 513210
Naresh Bansal (CFO)

Subsidiary (Non-US):

Actiance Europe Limited (3)
Asmec Centre Merlin House, Brunel Road, Theale, RG7 4AB, Berkshire, United Kingdom
Tel.: (44) 118 902 6464
Web Site: http://www.actiance.com
Software Publisher
N.A.I.C.S.: 513210

Actiance India Pvt. Ltd. (3)
Le Parc Richmonde 51 Richmond Road, Bengaluru, 560 025, India
Tel.: (91) 80 41125250
Emp.: 140
Software Publisher
N.A.I.C.S.: 513210
Sridhar Vutukuri (VP & Head-India)

Subsidiary (Domestic):

Entreda, Inc. (2)
3211 Scott Blvd Ste 204, Santa Clara, CA 95054
Tel.: (605) 308-4269
Web Site: http://www.entreda.com
Software Publisher

N.A.I.C.S.: 513210
Sid Yenamandra (Co-Founder & CEO)

K1 SPEED, LLC
6212 Corte Del Abeto, Carlsbad, CA 92011
Tel.: (760) 929-2225
Web Site: http://www.k1speed.com
Year Founded: 2004
Sales Range: $1-9.9 Million
Emp.: 100
Amusement/Recreation Services
N.A.I.C.S.: 532284
Bengen Ma (VP)

Subsidiaries:

Pole Position Raceway, Inc. (1)
1594 E Bentley Dr, Corona, CA 92879
Tel.: (951) 817-5032
Web Site:
    http://www.polepositionraceway.com
Rev.: $1,700,000
Emp.: 100
Offices of Other Holding Companies
N.A.I.C.S.: 551112
Jason Williams (Co-Founder)
Ken Faught (Co-Founder)

K2 DESIGN & STRATEGY, INC.
9654 W 131 St Ste 202, Palos Park, IL 60464
Tel.: (800) 501-2057　　DE
Year Founded: 2014
Analytics Software & Services
N.A.I.C.S.: 513210
George C. Pell (Co-Founder, Pres, CEO, CFO, Treas & Sec)
Mishe C. Harvey (Co-Founder & Chief-Innovation & Strategy)
Jeffrey K. Koranda (Co-Founder & Specialist-Optimal Performance)

K2 DIAMOND COMPANY
23911 Garnier St Ste C, Torrance, CA 90505
Tel.: (310) 539-6116
Web Site: http://www.k2diamond.com
Diamond Blades, Diamond Bits, Diamond Wire & Equipment Mfr
N.A.I.C.S.: 332216
Michael Nunez (Specialist-Core & Tubing Specialist)

Subsidiaries:

Sanders Saws, Inc. (1)
2470 Conestoga Ave, Honey Brook, PA 19344
Tel.: (610) 273-3733
Web Site: http://www.sanderssaws.com
Diamond Cutting Products Mfr
N.A.I.C.S.: 333517

K2 ENERGY SOLUTIONS, INC.
7461 Eastgate Rd, Henderson, NV 89011
Tel.: (702) 478-3590　　NV
Web Site: http://www.k2battery.com
Year Founded: 2006
Sales Range: $10-24.9 Million
Emp.: 71
Rechargeable Battery Systems Developer, Mfr & Distr
N.A.I.C.S.: 335910
Johnnie M. Stoker (Pres)
James D. Hodge (CTO)
Nicholas Smith (Engr-Battery Pack)
Joe Turner (Engr-Dev)
Sean Campbell (CEO)
Robert Licha (CFO)

K2 PARTNERING SOLUTIONS, INC.
235 Promenade St Ste 104, Providence, RI 02908
Tel.: (617) 263-3200
Web Site:
    http://www.k2partnering.com
Temporary Help Service
N.A.I.C.S.: 561320
Peter Abreu (Treas)

Subsidiaries:

Openlogix Corp. (1)
28345 Beck Rd Ste 308, Wixom, MI 48393
Tel.: (248) 869-0080
Web Site: http://www.open-logix.com
Computer System Design Services
N.A.I.C.S.: 541512
Krista Valentine (Mgr-Sls Acct)

K2 SOLUTIONS, INC.
5735 US Hwy 1 N, Southern Pines, NC 28388
Tel.: (910) 692-6898
Web Site: http://www.k2si.com
Year Founded: 2003
Sales Range: $25-49.9 Million
Emp.: 268
Security Software Development Services
N.A.I.C.S.: 541511
Lane Kjellsen (Chm & CEO)
Jim Lynch (Pres & CFO)
Randy Rhynes (VP-Canine Svcs)
Rodger Moore (VP-Bus Dev)
Nancy Mills-Smith (VP-Ops)

K2SHARE, LLC.
1005 University Dr E, College Station, TX 77840
Tel.: (979) 260-0030　　TX
Web Site: http://www.k2share.com
Year Founded: 2000
Sales Range: $1-9.9 Million
Emp.: 65
Information Technology Services
N.A.I.C.S.: 518210
Jefferson H. England (CFO)

K3 CONSTRUCTION GROUP, INC.
1910 Association Dr Ste 200, Reston, VA 20190
Tel.: (703) 736-1000　　VA
Web Site: http://www.k3cg.com
Year Founded: 1982
Nonresidential Construction & Commercial Contractor
N.A.I.C.S.: 236220
Jeff Martello (Pres)

K3 ENTERPRISES INC.
225 Ray Ave Ste 300, Fayetteville, NC 28301
Tel.: (910) 307-3017
Web Site: http://www.k3-enterprises.com
Year Founded: 2005
Sales Range: $10-24.9 Million
Emp.: 39
Business Management Services
N.A.I.C.S.: 561499
Genea Closs (Mgr-Contracts)
Mark Wamsher (VP-Ops)

K4 SOLUTIONS, INC.
8300 Boone Blvd Ste 200, Vienna, VA 22182
Tel.: (703) 448-4860
Web Site: http://www.k4solutions.com
Year Founded: 2001
Sales Range: $75-99.9 Million
Emp.: 200
Information Technology Services for Federal Government
N.A.I.C.S.: 541519
Sumi Krishnan (Pres & CEO)
Sean Tighe (Project Mgr)
Wynsome Hay (Coord-Policy)
Nat Krishnan (COO)

KA INDUSTRIES INC.
16805 Central Ave, Carson, CA 90746
Tel.: (310) 668-2105
Sales Range: Less than $1 Million
Emp.: 100
Bakery Products Production & Sales
N.A.I.C.S.: 445291
Kenneth Harris (Pres & CEO)
Jeffrey Beasley (Exec VP-Ops)
Victor Deyman (VP & Controller)

Subsidiaries:

Mrs. Beasleys LLC (1)
16803 Central Ave, Carson, CA 90746
Tel.: (310) 668-2105
Web Site: http://www.mrsbeasleys.com
Retail Bakeries
N.A.I.C.S.: 445291

KABAM, INC.
795 Folsom St Ste 600, San Francisco, CA 94107
Tel.: (415) 391-0817
Web Site: http://www.kabam.com
Year Founded: 2006
Sales Range: $150-199.9 Million
Emp.: 501
Online Game Development Services
N.A.I.C.S.: 541511
Kevin Chou (Co-Founder)
Steve Klei (CFO)
Michael Li (Co-Founder & Gen Mgr-China)
Holly Liu (Co-Founder)
Kent Wakeford (COO)
Mike DeLaet (Sr VP-Worldwide Bus Dev)
Jordan Edelstein (VP-Mktg)
Jeff Howell (CIO)
Seungwon Lee (CEO)

KABANA INC.
616 Indian School Rd NW, Albuquerque, NM 87102
Tel.: (505) 843-9330
Web Site: http://www.kabana.net
Sales Range: $10-24.9 Million
Emp.: 130
Jewelry Mfr & Sales
N.A.I.C.S.: 339910
Stavros Eleftheriou (Pres)
Bill Thompson (VP)
Amanda Garcia (Asst Mgr)
Eileen Jordan (Mgr-Credit & Collection)
Sue Kabana (Mgr-Customer Svc)
Eric Anderson (Mgr-Sls-Intl)
Marjory Schneider (Mgr-Acctg)
Carol Jenkins (Mgr-Inventory Control & Trade Show)

KABCORP, INC.
8411 Glenwood Ave, Raleigh, NC 27612
Tel.: (919) 783-7100　　NC
Web Site:
    http://www.kandbgalleries.com
Year Founded: 1997
Appliances, Cabinetry, Countertops, Hardware, Plumbing Fixtures & Tile Mfr
N.A.I.C.S.: 423620
Stephen Vaughn (Pres & CEO)

KABELIN HARDWARE COMPANY INC.
1010 1/2 Lincolnway, La Porte, IN 46350
Tel.: (219) 362-7838　　IN
Web Site:
    http://www.kabelinacehardware.com
Year Founded: 1912
Sales Range: $10-24.9 Million
Emp.: 180
Building Materials & Products
N.A.I.C.S.: 444140
Diane Corlay (Pres & CEO)

KABLE STAFFING RESOURCES LLC
6584 Sosna Dr, Fairfield, OH 45014
Tel.: (513) 829-7823　　DE
Web Site:
    http://www.kablestaffing.com
Year Founded: 2006
Staffing Services
N.A.I.C.S.: 561320
S. Joshua Guttman (Owner)

KABOOM!, INC.
4301 Connecticut Ave NW Ste ML-1, Washington, DC 20008
Tel.: (202) 659-0215　　DC
Web Site: http://www.kaboom.org
Year Founded: 1996
Sales Range: $25-49.9 Million
Emp.: 121
Play Space Construction Services
N.A.I.C.S.: 237990
Gerry Megas (CFO)
Darell Hammond (Founder & CEO)
Bruce Bowman (Pres)
Richard Devaney (Treas)
Timothy M. Fesenmyer (Sec)
James Siegal (Pres)
Roopal Saran (Dir-Client Svcs Acct Mgmt)
Dave Flanigan (Dir-Grants)
Kathryn Lusk (Dir-Project Mgmt)
Carlyne Cardichon (VP-Fin)
Sharon Price John (CEO)
Sally McConnell (Chief Revenue & Mktg Officer)
Sarah Rose Pinsky (Dir-Client Svcs Acct Mgmt)
Joy Hathaway (Dir-Project Mgmt)
Roxane Rucker (VP)

KADDIS MANUFACTURING CORP.
293 Patriot Way, Rochester, NY 14624
Tel.: (585) 464-9000
Web Site: http://www.kaddis.com
Sales Range: $10-24.9 Million
Emp.: 100
Screw Machine Products Mfr
N.A.I.C.S.: 332721
Jim Mac Ann (Pres)

KADES CORP.
5621 Red Bluff Rd, Pasadena, TX 77505
Tel.: (281) 479-4700
Web Site: http://www.kadescorp.com
Sales Range: $10-24.9 Million
Emp.: 35
Fast-Food Restaurants & Supermarkets Owner & Operator
N.A.I.C.S.: 722513
Ken Kades (Pres)

KADLEC REGIONAL MEDICAL CENTER
888 Swift Blvd, Richland, WA 99352
Tel.: (509) 946-4611　　WA
Web Site: http://www.kadlec.org
Year Founded: 1947
Sales Range: $350-399.9 Million
Emp.: 2,841
Medical Care Services
N.A.I.C.S.: 622110
Dave Roach (CIO)
Rand Wortman (Pres & CEO)
Glenn Welch (VP-Resource Dev & Exec Dir)
Kirk Harper (VP-Nursing)
Julie Meek (VP-Fin)
Jeffrey Clark (VP-Support Svcs)
Bill Wingo (VP-Corp Council)
Dale Hoekema (VP-Medical Affairs)
Lane Savitch (Pres & CEO)

KAEREK HOMES, INC.

KAEREK HOMES, INC.   U.S. PRIVATE

Kaerek Homes, Inc.—(Continued)
11600 W Lincoln Ave, West Allis, WI 53227
Tel.: (414) 321-5300
Web Site: http://www.kaerekhomes.com
Sales Range: $10-24.9 Million
Emp.: 50
New Construction, Single-Family Houses
N.A.I.C.S.: 236115
Michael J. Kaerek (Pres)
Karen Bova (Mgr-Acctg)
Jan Francki (Exec VP)
Janine Frank (Coord-Field Ops)
Dan Pelon (VP-Ops)
Melissa Schlei-Peters (Mgr-Sls & Mktg)
Amanda Ameen (Coord-Design Center)
Carol Ameen (Coord-Design Center)
Mary Rantala (Coord-Showroom)
Jakki Brunn (Mgr-Design Center)

KAESER & BLAIR INCORPORATED
4236 Grissom Dr, Batavia, OH 45103
Tel.: (513) 732-6400   OH
Web Site: http://www.kaeser-blair.com
Year Founded: 1894
Sales Range: $75-99.9 Million
Emp.: 140
Promotional Advertising Products Distr
N.A.I.C.S.: 541890
Kurt R. Kaeser (Co-Owner, Chm, Pres & CEO)
Scott Graber (CFO)
Gregg Emmer (CMO)
Robert Lewellen (Dir-Dealer Rels)
Christy Kaeser (Co-Owner & Mng Dir-Special Projects)

KAESER COMPRESSORS INC.
511 Sigma Dr, Fredericksburg, VA 22408
Tel.: (540) 898-5500
Web Site: http://www.kaeser.com
Sales Range: $25-49.9 Million
Emp.: 120
Compressor Mfr
N.A.I.C.S.: 423830
Alfred Underwood (Branch Mgr)
Adam Sutton (Coord-Natl Sls)
Tim Dalton (Engr-Natl Svs)
Alex Wuenderling (Mgr-CRM)
Roy Stuhlman (VP-Sls)
Matt McCorkle (Branch Mgr)
Angela Kelly (Dir-Comm)

KAFFENBARGER TRUCK EQUIPMENT CO.
10100 Ballentine Pike, New Carlisle, OH 45344
Tel.: (937) 845-3804
Web Site: http://www.kaffenbarger.com
Sales Range: $10-24.9 Million
Emp.: 110
Truck Bodies Mfr
N.A.I.C.S.: 336211
Larry Kaffenbarger (Pres)
Tim Schuler (VP)

KAHALA CORP.
9311 E Via De Ventura, Scottsdale, AZ 85258
Tel.: (480) 362-4800   DE
Web Site: http://www.kahalamgmt.com
Holding Company; Restaurant Owner, Operator & Franchisor
N.A.I.C.S.: 551112

Subsidiaries:

Cold Stone Creamery, Inc.   (1)
9311 E Via De Ventura, Scottsdale, AZ 85258
Tel.: (480) 362-4800
Web Site: http://www.coldstonecreamery.com
Emp.: 195
Ice Cream Restaurant Operator & Franchisor
N.A.I.C.S.: 722515
Michael Serruya (Chm & Co-CEO)

Tasti D-Lite LLC   (1)
9311 E Via de Ventura, Scottsdale, AZ 85258
Tel.: (480) 362-4800
Web Site: http://www.tastidlite.com
Snack & Nonalcoholic Beverage Bars
N.A.I.C.S.: 722515
Kevin Blackwell (CEO)

KAHALA SENIOR LIVING COMMUNITY, INC.
4389 Malia St, Honolulu, HI 96821
Tel.: (808) 218-7200   HI
Web Site: http://www.kahalanui.com
Year Founded: 1989
Sales Range: $25-49.9 Million
Emp.: 375
Senior Living Services
N.A.I.C.S.: 623311
Patrick Duarte (Pres & CEO)

KAHLE ENGINEERING CO.
89 Headquarters Plz N Ste 355, Morristown, NJ 07960
Tel.: (973) 993-1850   NJ
Web Site: http://www.kahleautomation.com
Year Founded: 1930
Sales Range: $10-24.9 Million
Healthcare Industry Automation Systems Mfr
N.A.I.C.S.: 333998
Julie Logothetis (Pres)

KAHLER AUTOMATION CORPORATION
808 Timberlake Rd, Fairmont, MN 56031
Tel.: (507) 235-6648   MN
Web Site: http://www.kahlerautomation.com
Year Founded: 1990
Sales Range: $1-9.9 Million
Emp.: 70
Custom Integrator of Industrial Control Systems
N.A.I.C.S.: 335314
Wayne Kahler (Pres)
Eric Henderson (Engr-Software)

KAHLER-SENDERS GROUP INC.
523 SE 9th Ave, Portland, OR 97214
Tel.: (503) 236-7363
Web Site: http://www.kahler-senders.com
Sales Range: $10-24.9 Million
Emp.: 42
Confectionery
N.A.I.C.S.: 424450
Rod Hatch (Controller)
Nathan Woods (Branch Mgr)
Kevin Jenkins (Pres)

KAHLIG ENTERPRISES INC.
351 IH 35 S, New Braunfels, TX 78130
Tel.: (830) 606-8011
Web Site: http://www.bluebonnetfordmerc.com
Rev.: $133,692,112
Emp.: 200
New & Used Car Sales
N.A.I.C.S.: 441110

Fred Scheel (Mgr-Parts)
Alan Gullett (Mgr-Sls)
Karen Nance (Mgr-Customer Rels)
Wes R. Studdard (Gen Mgr)
Joe DeLeon (Gen Mgr-Sls)
Christine McKinley (Mgr-Sls)
Clarence Kahlig II (Owner)

KAHLO CHRYSLER JEEP DODGE RAM
9900 Pleasant St, Noblesville, IN 46060
Tel.: (317) 773-6363
Web Site: http://www.kahlochryslerjeepdodge.com
Sales Range: $10-24.9 Million
Emp.: 75
New Car Retailer
N.A.I.C.S.: 441110
Kevin Kahlo (Owner)
Barbara Dorsey (Dir-Fin)
John Fogleman (Gen Mgr-Sls)

KAHLO JEEP CHRYSLER DODGE
9900 Pleasant St, Noblesville, IN 46060
Tel.: (765) 345-5731
Web Site: http://www.kahlojeep.com
Sales Range: $25-49.9 Million
Emp.: 52
Sales of New & Used Automobiles
N.A.I.C.S.: 441110
Kevin Kahlo (Pres)

KAHN-LUCAS-LANCASTER INC.
100 W 33rd St Ste 921, New York, NY 10001
Tel.: (212) 244-4500
Web Site: http://www.kahnlucas.com
Sales Range: $25-49.9 Million
Emp.: 50
Children's Clothing Mfr
N.A.I.C.S.: 315250
Howard L. Kahn (Chm)
John Zander (Controller)
Dor Sela (CEO)

Subsidiaries:

Alexander Doll Company, Inc.   (1)
615 W 131st St, New York, NY 10027-7922
Tel.: (212) 283-5900
Web Site: http://www.madamealexander.com
Sales Range: $10-24.9 Million
Emp.: 100
Dolls Mfr
N.A.I.C.S.: 339930
Gale Jarvis (Pres)

KAI POLU SERVICES LLC
137 N Washington St Ste 301, Falls Church, VA 22046-4576
Tel.: (703) 533-0039
Web Site: http://www.polukaiservices.com
Year Founded: 2003
Sales Range: $1-9.9 Million
Emp.: 31
Management Consulting Services
N.A.I.C.S.: 541611
Barbara Parks (Mgr-Admin)
Sean Jensen (Pres & CEO)

KAIBAB INDUSTRIES, INC.
532 E Flynn Ln, Phoenix, AZ 85012
Tel.: (602) 840-5555
Web Site: http://www.kaibabindustries.com
Lumber Milling Services
N.A.I.C.S.: 321113
M. Barry Whiting (Sec & Treas)

KAIN CAPITAL, LLC
360 Madison Ave 20th Fl, New York, NY 10017
Tel.: (949) 649-2288   DE
Web Site: http://www.kaincap.com
Investment Services
N.A.I.C.S.: 523999
Kunal kain (Founder & Mng Partner)
Ben Kraus (Mng Dir)
Chris Chen (VP)
Telly Hoimes (Mng Partner)
Jimmy Qiu (Principal)
Bret Cummings (CFO & Chief Compliance Officer)
Harry Zirinsky (Head-Bus Dev)
Idan Eidlman (VP)

Subsidiaries:

Akeso Medical Holdings, LLC   (1)
7700 Irvine Ctr Dr Ste 870, Irvine, CA 92618
Tel.: (949) 649-2288
Web Site: http://www.akesomedical.com
All Other Miscellaneous Ambulatory Health Care Services
N.A.I.C.S.: 621999
Greg Moore (CEO)
Michael Byer (COO)

Subsidiary (Domestic):

Coastal Occupational Medical Group   (2)
1901 Outlet Ctr Dr Ste 100, Oxnard, CA 93036-0669
Tel.: (805) 988-3200
Web Site: http://www.coastalomg.com
Offices of Physicians (except Mental Health Specialists)
N.A.I.C.S.: 621111
Rosie Martinez (Office Mgr)

KAIN MANAGEMENT GROUP
30 Oakwood Dr, Norwalk, CT 06850
Tel.: (203) 951-0266
Web Site: http://www.kainmg.com
Year Founded: 2002
Sales Range: $1-9.9 Million
Emp.: 8
Human Resource Consulting Services
N.A.I.C.S.: 541612
Syd Kain (Mng Partner)
John Colasanto (Mng Partner)

KAINOS CAPITAL, LLC
2100 McKinney Ave Ste 1600, Dallas, TX 75201
Tel.: (214) 740-7300   DE
Web Site: http://www.kainoscapital.com
Rev.: $120,000,000
Equity Investment Firm
N.A.I.C.S.: 523999
Daniel J. Hopkin (Partner)
Andrew Rosen (Mng Partner)
Robert W. Sperry (Partner)
Jerry Neisel (Chief Compliance Officer & Treas)
Alisha Barbera (Controller)
Kevin Elliott (Partner)
Jay Desai (Partner)
Robin Olsson (Mng Dir)
Jeff Moredock (Principal)
Rob Ruegger (Mng Dir)

Subsidiaries:

Arena Brands Inc.   (1)
601 Marion Dr, Garland, TX 75042-7930   (100%)
Tel.: (972) 494-0511
Web Site: http://www.stetsonhat.com
Sales Range: $75-99.9 Million
Mfr of Western Hats
N.A.I.C.S.: 315990

Subsidiary (Domestic):

Lucchese, Inc.   (2)
40 Walter Jones Blvd, El Paso, TX 79906
Tel.: (915) 778-3066
Web Site: http://www.lucchese.com

COMPANIES

Sales Range: $25-49.9 Million
Western Boots Mfr
N.A.I.C.S.: 316210
Doug Kindy (Pres)

Culinarte Marketing Group, LLC (1)
808 Packerland Dr, Green Bay, WI 54303
Tel.: (920) 498-3004
Web Site:
http://www.bonewerksculinarte.com
Dried & Dehydrated Food Mfr
N.A.I.C.S.: 311423
Tom Sausen (Founder & Pres)
Clint Klimek (Mgr-Ops)

Evriholder Products LLC (1)
1500 S Lewis St, Anaheim, CA 92805
Tel.: (714) 490-7878
Web Site: http://www.evriholder.com
Sales Range: $25-49.9 Million
Emp.: 25
Consumer Products Mfr & Distr
N.A.I.C.S.: 423620
Ivan Stein (Co-Founder & CEO)

Subsidiary (Domestic):

Progressive International Corp. (2)
6111 S 228th St, Kent, WA 98032-1849
Tel.: (253) 850-6111
Web Site: http://www.progressiveintl.com
Distribute Kitchen Ware
N.A.I.C.S.: 423220
Kurt Bergquist (CEO)
Rob Foster (Mgr-Warehouse)
Patrick Klein (VP-Logistics)

Kettle Cuisine, LLC (1)
270 2nd St, Chelsea, MA 02150
Tel.: (617) 409-1100
Web Site: http://www.kettlecuisine.com
Sales Range: $10-24.9 Million
Emp.: 125
Soup Mfr
N.A.I.C.S.: 311422
Jerry Shafir (Founder & Pres)
Alan Gilbert (Mgr-Warehouse)
Lillian Caires (Mgr-HR)
Julie Bonney (VP)
Tony Fufco (Mgr-IT)
Jose Sanchez (Mgr-Production)
Liam McClennon (CEO)
Mike Illum (Exec VP-Sls)
Jeremy Kacuba (COO)

Subsidiary (Domestic):

Del Monaco Foods, Inc. (2)
18675 Madrone Pkwy Ste 150, Morgan Hill, CA 95037 (100%)
Tel.: (408) 500-4100
Web Site: http://www.delmonacofoods.com
Sales Range: $1-9.9 Million
Emp.: 200
Custom Food Manufacturing
N.A.I.C.S.: 311991
Mona Heffernan (CFO)
Vic Del Monaco (CEO)
Mike Wargocki (VP-Ops)

The Harris Soup Company (2)
17711 NE Riverside Pkwy, Portland, OR 97230
Tel.: (503) 257-7687
Web Site: http://www.harrysfresh.com
Sales Range: $1-9.9 Million
Emp.: 125
Prepared Foods Mfr & Whslr
N.A.I.C.S.: 311991
Jamie Colbourne (CEO)

Mills & Partners (1)
8235 Forsyth Blvd Ste 300, Saint Louis, MO 63105-3406
Tel.: (314) 727-1701
Web Site: http://www.mills-partners.com
Sales Range: $75-99.9 Million
Emp.: 3
Holding Company
N.A.I.C.S.: 523910
James N. Mills (Chm & CEO)

Muenster Milling Company, LLC (1)
202 South Main St, Muenster, TX 76252
Tel.: (940) 759-2287
Web Site: http://www.muenstermilling.com
Pet Food Mfr
N.A.I.C.S.: 311119
Ronnie Felderhoff (Mgr)
Mitch Felderhoff (Pres)

NutriSystem, Inc. (1)
Fort Washington Executive Center 600 Office Center Dr, Fort Washington, PA 19034
Tel.: (215) 706-5300
Web Site: http://www.nutrisystem.com
Weight Loss Centers, Services & Products
N.A.I.C.S.: 812191
Adam Holland (Pres)

Subsidiary (Domestic):

SBD Enterprises, LLC (2)
3804 Radium Springs Rd, Albany, GA 31705
Tel.: (229) 883-7913
Business Support Services
N.A.I.C.S.: 561990

Slim & Tone (2)
10 Penn Vly Dr, Yardley, PA 19067 (100%)
Tel.: (215) 321-8664
Sales Range: $50-74.9 Million
Weight Loss & Dietary Centers
N.A.I.C.S.: 812191

Phone Directories Company (1)
135 S Mtn Way Dr, Orem, UT 84058
Tel.: (801) 225-0801
Printed Telephone Directory Publisher
N.A.I.C.S.: 513140
Mike Bynum (CEO)

Sun Rich Fresh Foods, Inc. (1)
22151 Fraserwood Way, Richmond, V6W 1J5, BC, Canada
Tel.: (604) 244-8800
Web Site: http://www.freshfoodgroup.com
Fresh-cut Fruit Products
N.A.I.C.S.: 311421
Grant Longstreet (Dir-Sls)

Subsidiary (US):

Sun Rich Fresh Foods (USA) Inc. (2)
515 E Rincon St, Corona, CA 92879-1353
Tel.: (951) 735-3800
Fresh Fruit Mfr
N.A.I.C.S.: 311991

Plant (Domestic):

Sun Rich Fresh Foods (USA) Inc. - Eastern Fresh Facility (3)
425 Gateway Dr, Reading, PA 19601
Tel.: (610) 320-8100
Fresh Fruit Mfr
N.A.I.C.S.: 311991

Plant (Domestic):

Sun Rich Fresh Foods, Inc. - Northeast Fresh Facility (2)
35 Bramtree Court Unit 1, Brampton, L6S 6G2, ON, Canada
Tel.: (905) 789-0200
Web Site: http://www.sun-rich.com
Fresh Fruit Mfr
N.A.I.C.S.: 311991

KAIROS AR, INC.
400 NW 26th St, Miami, FL 33127
Tel.: (888) 440-1005 DE
Web Site: http://www.kairos.com
Year Founded: 2012
Face Recognition & Emotion Analysis Software Developer
N.A.I.C.S.: 513210
Stephen Moore (Chief Scientific Officer)
Cole Calistra (CTO)
Alessandra Szul (Dir-Acct)
Mary Wolff (COO)

KAISER MARKETING, INC.
27856 Winding Way, Malibu, CA 90265-4457
Tel.: (310) 479-8999 CA
Year Founded: 1970
Rev.: $25,000,000
Emp.: 30
Advetising Agency
N.A.I.C.S.: 541810
Michael Kaiser (Chm & CEO)
Rob Edwards (VP & Dir-Creative & Art)
Silvia Rodriguez (Office Mgr)

KAISER PERMANENTE

10163 SE Sunnyside ste 490, Clackamas, OR 97015
Tel.: (503) 249-3434
Web Site:
http://www.healthy.kaiserpermanente.org
Year Founded: 1945
Sales Range: $50-74.9 Billion
Emp.: 175,668
Hospital & Medical Service Plan Services Organization
N.A.I.C.S.: 813920
Paul Swenson (Chief Admin Officer & Exec VP)
Julie Miller-Phipps (Pres-Southern California, Hawaii Health Plan & Hospitals)
Kimberly Horn (Grp Pres-Markets Outside California & Exec VP)
Ruth E. Williams-Brinkley (Pres-Mid-Atlantic States)
Ruth Williams-Brinkley (Pres-Mid-Atlantic States)
Kathy Lancaster (CFO & Exec VP)
Janet A. Liang (Grp Pres, COO-Care Delivery & Exec VP)
Anthony A. Barrueta (Executives)
Jeff Collins (Reg Pres-Northwest)
Vanessa M. Benavides (Chief Legal Officer & Sr VP)
Carrie Owen Plietz (Reg Pres-Northern California)
Gregory A. Adams (Chm & CEO)
Christian Meisner (Chief HR Officer & Sr VP)
Catherine Hernandez (Chief Comm Officer & Sr VP)
Diane Comer (Chief IT Officer & Exec VP)
Yazdi Bagli (Exec VP-Enterprise Bus Svcs)
Andrew B. Bindman (Chief Medical Officer & Exec VP)
Linda Horne (Sr VP-Bus Optimization & Redesign)
Shakeya A. McDow (Chief Compliance & Privacy Officer & Interim Sr VP)
Michael Ramseier (Pres-Colorado)
Pamela Shipley (Pres-Georgia)
Ron Vance (Interim Pres-Washington)
Ruth E. Williams-Brinkley (Pres-Mid-Atlantic States)
Murtaza Sanwari (Sr VP & Mgr-Woodland Hills)
Payman Roshan (Sr VP-Orange County & Area Mgr-Orange County)
C. J. Bhalla (CFO/Sr VP-Northern California)
Janet Liang (Pres-Northern California)
Laura Gallardo (COO-Kaiser Foundation Health Plan & Hospitals)
Bridget E. Karlin (Sr VP-IT)
Kimberly Menzel (CEO-Hospital-Roseville, Sr VP & Area Mgr-Roseville)
Patricia Clausen (Sr VP, Area Mgr-Kaiser Foundation Health Plan & Hospitals & Mgr-Panorama City & Antelope Valley)
Kenneth Rivers (COO-External Networks)

Subsidiaries:

Kaiser Foundation Health Plan of Washington (1)
601 Union St Ste 3100, Seattle, WA 98101-1374
Tel.: (206) 630-4636
Web Site: http://wa.kaiserpermanente.org
Health Care Srvices
N.A.I.C.S.: 621610
Susan Mullaney (Pres-Kaiser Permanente Washington)
Stephen Tarnoff (Pres & CEO-Washington Permanente Med Grp)

Kaiser Foundation Health Plan, Inc. (1)
1 Kaiser Plz, Oakland, CA 94612
Tel.: (510) 271-5910
Web Site: http://www.kp.org
Medical Insurance & Services
N.A.I.C.S.: 524114
Paul Swenson (Chief Admin Officer & Exec VP)
Julie Miller-Phipps (Executives)
Ruth E. Williams-Brinkley (Pres-Mid-Atlantic States)
Ruth Williams-Brinkley (Pres-Mid-Atlantic States)
Kathy Lancaster (CFO & Exec VP)
Donna Lynne (Grp Pres-Colorado, Northwest & Hawaii & Exec VP)
Janet A. Liang (Grp Pres, COO-Care Delivery & Exec VP)
Anthony A. Barrueta (Executives)
Jeff Collins (Reg Pres-Northwest)
Carrie Owen Plietz (Reg Pres-Northern California)
Bechara Choucair (Chief Health Officer & Sr VP)
Gregory A. Adams (Chm & CEO)
Christian Meisner (Chief HR Officer & Sr VP)
Catherine Hernandez (Chief Comm Officer & Sr VP)
Diane Comer (Chief IT Officer & Exec VP)
Yazdi Bagli (Exec VP-Enterprise Bus Svcs)
Andrew B. Bindman (Chief Medical Officer & Exec VP)
Linda Horne (Sr VP-Bus Optimization & Redesign)
Shakeya A. McDow (Chief Compliance & Privacy Officer & Interim Sr VP)
Michael Ramseier (Pres-Colorado)
Pamela Shipley (Pres-Georgia)
Ron Vance (Interim Pres-Washington)
Ruth E. Williams-Brinkley (Pres-Mid-Atlantic States)
Arthur M. Southam (Chief Growth Officer & Exec VP-Health Plan Ops)
Patrick Courneya (Chief Medical Officer & Exec VP)
Alek Logutenkov (Sr Mgr)
Roland Lyon (Pres-Colorado)
Gregory A. Adams (Exec VP)
Dave Underriner (Pres-Oahu)
Christian Meisner (Chief HR Officer & Sr VP)

Subsidiary (Domestic):

Kaiser Foundation Health Plan of Georgia, Inc. (2)
9 Piedmont Ctr 3495 Piedmont Rd NE, Atlanta, GA 30305
Tel.: (404) 364-7000
Health Insurance Services
N.A.I.C.S.: 524114
Julie Miller-Phipps (Pres)

Kaiser Foundation Health Plan of the Mid-Atlantic States, Inc. (2)
2101 E Jefferson St, Rockville, MD 20852
Tel.: (301) 816-2424
Web Site: http://www.kp.org
Emp.: 1,000
HMO Plan
N.A.I.C.S.: 524114
Kimberly Horn (Pres)
Ruth E. Williams-Brinkley (Pres)
Ruth Williams-Brinkley (Pres)
Susan Ayres (Mgr-Mktg)
Herman Weil (Sr VP)
Keith Montgomery (Dir-Mktg Comm)
Beth Jaeger (VP-HR)

Kaiser Foundation Health Plan of the Northwest (2)
500 NE Multnomah St Ste 100, Portland, OR 97232
Tel.: (503) 813-2800
Health Insurance Services
N.A.I.C.S.: 524114
Chad Melvin (Dir-Strategic Market Plng)
Julie Posch (Mgr-Large Grp Acct Mgmt)
Rebecca Sherlock (Reg Mgr-Privacy Program)

KAISER PERMANENTE

Kaiser Permanente—(Continued)
Kenneth Wright (VP-Dental Care Svcs)
Andrew McCulloch (Pres & CEO)
Christopher Smith (Chief Engr)

Kaiser Health Plan Asset Management, Inc. (2)
1 Kaiser Plz Ste 1550L, Oakland, CA 94612-3610
Tel.: (510) 271-5910
Asset Management Services
N.A.I.C.S.: 523940

Kaiser Permanente Insurance Company (2)
1 Kaiser Plz, Oakland, CA 94612-3610
Tel.: (800) 464-4000
Health Insurance Services
N.A.I.C.S.: 524114

Kaiser Foundation Hospitals (1)
1 Kaiser Plz, Oakland, CA 94612
Tel.: (510) 271-5910
Web Site: http://www.kp.org
Hospital Operator
N.A.I.C.S.: 622110
Donna Lynne (Grp Pres-Colorado, Northwest & Hawaii & Exec VP)
Bechara Choucair (Chief Health Officer & Sr VP)
Patrick Courneya (Chief Medical Officer & Exec VP)
Vanessa Benavides (Chief Compliance & Privacy Officer & Sr VP)
Bechara Choucair (Chief Community Health Officer & Sr VP-Community Health)
Catherine Hernandez (Chief Comm Officer & Sr VP)

Subsidiary (Domestic):

Kaiser Hospital Asset Management, Inc. (2)
1 Kaiser Plz 19L, Oakland, CA 94612-3610
Tel.: (510) 271-5800
Asset Management Services
N.A.I.C.S.: 523940

Kaiser Permanente, Colorado Region (1)
10350 E Dakota Ave, Denver, CO 80231-1314
Tel.: (303) 344-7200
HMO Plan
N.A.I.C.S.: 524114
Troy Stubbings (Dir-Bus Ops & Market Expansion-Health Plan-South)
Patrick Kusek (Dir-Market Medical-North)
Kathleen Westcoat (Sr Dir-Medicaid)
Mike Ramseier (Pres)

Kaiser Permanente, Georgia Region (1)
3495 Piedmont Rd NE, Atlanta, GA 30305
Tel.: (404) 364-7000
Web Site: http://thrive.kaiserpermanente.org
Sales Range: $1-4.9 Billion
Emp.: 3,500
HMO Plan
N.A.I.C.S.: 524114
Phil Jones (Dir-Sls Ops & Support)
Madelyn R. Adams (Dir-Community Benefit)

Kaiser Permanente, Hawaii Region (1)
711 Kapiolani Blvd, Honolulu, HI 96813-5237
Tel.: (808) 432-5955
Web Site: http://www.kaiserpermanente.org
Sales Range: $10-24.9 Million
Emp.: 100
HMO Plan
N.A.I.C.S.: 621111
Janet A. Liang (Executives)
Joy Barua (Sr Dir-Govt, Community Rels & Community Benefit)
Janna Muscare (VP-Quality, Safety & Patient Experience)
Terrance Muldoon (Chief Energy Officer & Exec Dir-Natl Facility Svcs)
Patricia Bazin (Sr Dir-Community-Based Care)
Kimberly Zeltsar (Exec Dir-Revenue Cycle Mgmt)
Darren Kasai (Sr Dir-Clinic Ops)
Donna Scannell (VP-IT Ops)
Allan Gold (Dir-Actuarial Svcs)
Noe Foster (Dir-Strategic Comm)

Jaclyn Sadoyama (Asst Controller)
Julianne Chun (Dir-Corp Compliance & Assoc Gen Counsel)
Andrew Yeh (Dir-Analytics)
James Preusser (Dir-Employee & Labor Rels)
Garret Sugai (VP-Health Plan Svcs & Admin)
Linda Puu (VP-Quality, Safety & Patient Experience)
Maribel Avila-Kunkel (VP-Ambulatory Care & Clinical Svcs)
Greg Christian (Pres-Health Plan & Hospitals)

Kaiser Permanente, Northwest Region (1)
500 NE Multnomah, Portland, OR 97232
Tel.: (503) 813-2000
Web Site: http://www.kp.org
Sales Range: $650-699.9 Million
Emp.: 7,000
Health Maintenance Organization
N.A.I.C.S.: 621610

The Permanente Federation, LLC (1)
1 Kaiser Plz 22nd Fl, Oakland, CA 94612
Tel.: (510) 267-2194
Web Site: http://www.permanente.org
Medical Practitioners Organization
N.A.I.C.S.: 813920
Scott S. Young (Assoc Editor)
David Bell (Exec VP-People & Leadership Strategy)
Patricia Conolly (CIO & Exec VP-IT)
Edward M. Ellison (Co-CEO)
Pauline Fox (Chief Legal Officer & Exec VP)
Chris Grant (COO & Exec VP)
Richard S. Isaacs (Co-CEO)
Michael Kanter (Chief Quality Officer & Exec VP-Quality)
Daryl Kurozawa (Exec VP-Products, Sls & Mktg)
Paul Minardi (Exec VP-Fin & Strategy)
Stephen Parodi (Exec VP-External Affairs, Comm & Brand)
Geoffrey S. Sewell (Chm-NPEC)
Richele Thornburg (Exec VP-People & Leadership Strategy)

Subsidiary (Domestic):

Mid-Atlantic Permanente Medical group, P.C. (2)
2101 E Jefferson St, Rockville, MD 20852-4908
Tel.: (301) 816-6520
Health Care Insurance Services
N.A.I.C.S.: 524114
Nancy Doellgast (Dir-Compliance)
Michael Horberg (Exec Dir-Res)
Richard S. Isaacs (Pres & CEO)

Northwest Permanente P.C. (2)
13705 NE Airport Way Ste C, Portland, OR 97230
Tel.: (503) 258-6800
Health Care Srvices
N.A.I.C.S.: 621999
Shana Klemchuk (Mgr-Speciality Care Recruitment)
Imelda Dacones (Pres & Exec Dir-Medical)
Ajay Doshi (Asst VP-Fin)

Permanente Dental Associates, PC (2)
500 NE Multnomah St Ste 100, Portland, OR 97232-2099
Tel.: (503) 286-6867
Web Site: http://www.pda-dental.com
Rural Health Care Services
N.A.I.C.S.: 621999

The Permanente Medical Group, Inc. (2)
1950 Franklin St 18th Fl, Oakland, CA 94612-5190
Tel.: (510) 987-2712
Web Site: http://mydoctor.kaiserpermanente.org
Health Care Srvices
N.A.I.C.S.: 621999
Jerry Bajada (CFO)
Barry Scurran (Chief Compliance Officer)
Bo Chau (Coord-Recruitment)
Barbara Mora (Mgr)
Eddie Huang (Mgr-Consulting)

Jeff Keyes (Mgr-Physician HR Res)
Bela Goncalves (Mgr-Support Svcs)
Chris Palkowski (Chm)
Richard S. Isaacs (CEO)

The Southeast Permanente Medical Group, Inc. (2)
3495 Piedmont Rd NE Bldg 9, Atlanta, GA 30305
Tel.: (800) 877-0409
Web Site: http://www.tspmg.com
Health Care Insurance Services
N.A.I.C.S.: 524114
Michael Doherty (Assoc Dir-Medical-Bus Systems)
Martha Wilber (Assoc Dir-Medical-Hospital & Acute Care)
Debra Carlton (Assoc Dir-Medical-Patient Care Experience)
Jeff Hoffman (COO-Ambulatory Ops)
Ed Ellison (Chm)
Mary Wilson (Exec Dir-Medical)

KAISER WHOLESALE, INC.
415 E Oak St, New Albany, IN 47150   IN
Tel.: (812) 945-2651
Year Founded: 1956
Sales Range: $25-49.9 Million
Emp.: 35
Wholesale Distribution of Tobacco & Tobacco Products; Confectionery; Paper & Plastic Productss; Health & Beauty; Janitorial Supplies
N.A.I.C.S.: 424940
Mark Kaiser (VP)

Subsidiaries:

Kaiser Tobacco Store (1)
326 Pearl St, New Albany, IN 47150-3418
Tel.: (812) 945-5671
Sales Range: $10-24.9 Million
Emp.: 2
Tobacco Products Distr
N.A.I.C.S.: 459991
Gene Harris (Mgr)

KAISER-FRANCIS OIL COMPANY
6733 S Yale Ave, Tulsa, OK 74136-3302
Tel.: (918) 494-0000   DE
Web Site: http://www.kfoc.net
Sales Range: $75-99.9 Million
Oil & Gas Exploration & Extraction
N.A.I.C.S.: 211120
Don P. Millican (CFO)
Robert A. Waldo (Pres)
Henry G. Kleemeier (CEO)
George B. Kaiser (VP)

KAIZEN TECHNOLOGIES, INC.
76 NorthEastern Blvd Ste 29A/A-9, Nashua, NH 03062
Tel.: (603) 589-2580
Web Site: http://www.kaizentek.com
Year Founded: 1995
Sales Range: $10-24.9 Million
Emp.: 200
Computer Design & Software Development Services
N.A.I.C.S.: 541512
Ashok Krishnaswamy (Pres)

KAJEET, INC.
7901 Jones Branch Dr Ste 350, McLean, VA 22102
Tel.: (240) 482-4363
Web Site: http://www.kajeet.com
Rev: $3,700,000
Emp.: 27
Radio & Television Broadcasting & Wireless Communications Equipment Mfr
N.A.I.C.S.: 334220
Daniel J. W. Neal (Co-Founder & Chm)
Ben Weintraub (Co-Founder & CEO)
David Pinto (VP-Engrg)

U.S. PRIVATE

Michael Flood (Sr VP/Gen Mgr-Education)
Michael Cooley (Sr VP/Gen Mgr-Enterprise Solutions Bus)
Guy Abramovitz (CFO)
Linda Jennings (Dir-Corp Comm)
Zack Kowalski (Chief Revenue Officer)

Subsidiaries:

Red Rover Ltd. (1)
787 Foothill Rd, Reno, NV 89511-9426
Tel.: (775) 851-3314
Web Site: http://www.redroverltd.com
Business to Business Electronic Markets
N.A.I.C.S.: 425120
Kevin Prentiss (CEO)

KAJUN KETTLE FOODS, INC.
PO Box 23722, New Orleans, LA 70183
Tel.: (504) 733-8800
Web Site: http://www.kajunkettle.com
Sales Range: $10-24.9 Million
Emp.: 40
Soup & Sauce Mfr
N.A.I.C.S.: 311412
Pierre Hilzim (Pres)
Melissa Isom (Mgr-Culinary)
Monica Davidson (Partner)

KAKTUS SPORTSWEAR INC.
1407 Broadway Ste 1415, New York, NY 10018
Tel.: (201) 372-0004
Web Site: http://www.kaktussportswear.com
Rev.: $10,000,000
Emp.: 9
Sportswear for Women & Children Mfr
N.A.I.C.S.: 424350
Prakash Tewani (Pres)

KAL KUSTOM ENTERPRISES
43289 Osgood Rd, Fremont, CA 94539
Tel.: (510) 651-8400
Web Site: http://www.reinell.com
Sales Range: $50-74.9 Million
Emp.: 15
Motorboats, Inboard Or Outboard; Building & Repairing
N.A.I.C.S.: 423910
Karl Koster (Pres)

KALALOU INC.
3844 W Northside Dr, Jackson, MS 39209
Tel.: (601) 366-4229
Web Site: http://www.kalalou.com
Sales Range: $10-24.9 Million
Emp.: 60
Home Furnishing Merchant Whslr
N.A.I.C.S.: 423220
Susan Williams (Co-Founder & VP)
Douglas Williams (Co-Founder & Pres)

KALAMA EXPORTS LLC
200 SW Market St Ste 1930, Portland, OR 97201
Tel.: (503) 274-1410
Sales Range: $25-49.9 Million
Emp.: 56
Exporter of Grains
N.A.I.C.S.: 424510
David Northrop (Pres)

KALAMAZOO HOLDINGS, INC.
3713 W Main St PO Box 50511, Kalamazoo, MI 49006-2842
Tel.: (269) 349-9711   MI
Web Site: http://www.kalsec.com
Year Founded: 1979
Sales Range: $100-124.9 Million
Emp.: 250

Holding Company
N.A.I.C.S.: 311942
Subsidiaries:

Kalsec, Inc. (1)
3713 W Main St Dr, Kalamazoo, MI
49006-2842 (100%)
Tel.: (269) 349-9711
Web Site: http://www.kalsec.com
Food Flavors & Natural Colors Hop Extractives
N.A.I.C.S.: 311942
George Todd (Chm)
Scott Nykaza (CEO)
Julie Heine (Exec VP-Sls)
Lisa Patel (Exec Dir-Regulatory Affairs-Global)
Don Berdahl (CTO & Exec VP-Res Strategy)
Roger Naha (VP-Res & Dev-Global)
Martha Todd (Vice Chm)
Paul Todd Jr. (Founder)

KALAMAZOO TRUCK SALES INC.
1949 Olmstead Rd, Kalamazoo, MI 49048
Tel.: (269) 381-5600
Sales Range: $10-24.9 Million
Emp.: 20
Sells Commercial Vehicles
N.A.I.C.S.: 423110
Charles Watson (Pres)
John Wagner (VP)

KALAS MANUFACTURING, INC.
167 Greenfield Rd, Lancaster, PA 17601
Tel.: (717) 336-5575 PA
Web Site: http://www.kalaswire.com
Year Founded: 1958
Sales Range: $150-199.9 Million
Emp.: 500
Wire Product Mfr
N.A.I.C.S.: 332618
Dennis Melnyk (CFO)
Jack Witweer (Pres & COO)

KALEIDA HEALTH
100 High St, Buffalo, NY 14203
Tel.: (716) 859-5600 NY
Web Site:
 http://www.kaleidahealth.org
Year Founded: 1998
Sales Range: $1-4.9 Billion
Emp.: 9,344
Community Health Care Services
N.A.I.C.S.: 621498
Michael P. Hughes (Sr VP-Pub Affairs & Mktg)
Toni L. Booker (Chief HR Officer & Exec VP)
Donald Boyd (Sr VP-Bus Dev)
David P. Hughes (Chief Medical Officer & Exec VP)
Allegra C. Jaros (Pres-Oishei Children's Hospital)
Cheryl Klass (Exec VP)
Jamal A. Ghani (COO & Exec VP)
Lisa Schmidt (COO-Core Svcs & VP-Buffalo Gen Medical Center)
Lorraine Duthe (VP & Assoc Gen Counsel)
Andrew DiLuca (Dir-Pharmacy Svcs)
Aven Rennie (Assoc Gen Counsel)

KALEIDESCAPE, INC.
440 Potrero Ave, Sunnyvale, CA 94085
Tel.: (650) 625-6100 DE
Web Site:
 http://www.kaleidescape.com
Year Founded: 2001
Sales Range: $50-74.9 Million
Emp.: 151
High Definition Audio & Video Systems

N.A.I.C.S.: 334310
Henry Tayloe Stansbury (CEO)
Tayloe Stansbury (CEO)
Michael Malcolm (Co-Founder & Chm)
Rusty Johnson (Engr-Support)
Cheena Srinivasan (Co-Founder & CEO)
Mark McKenzie (Sr Dir-Software Engrg)
Craig McKinley (Sr Dir-Store Engrg)
Kevin Smyth (VP-Mfg)

KALIAN CORPORATION
2 Hennessey Blvd, Atlantic Highlands, NJ 07716
Tel.: (732) 741-0054
Web Site: http://www.kalian.com
Year Founded: 1986
Construction & Contracting Services
N.A.I.C.S.: 236115
Patrick Kalian (Owner & Pres)
Lou Bianchini (VP-Construction)

KALIHI-PALAMA HEALTH CENTER
915 N King St, Honolulu, HI 96817
Tel.: (808) 848-1438 HI
Web Site: http://www.kphc.org
Year Founded: 1975
Sales Range: $10-24.9 Million
Emp.: 260
Health Care Srvices
N.A.I.C.S.: 622110
Darrin Sato (COO)
Liane Sugimoto (CFO)
Keith Larson (Dir-Dental)
Emmanuel Kintu (CEO & Exec Dir)
Vernon Nakamura (Pres)

KALIL BOTTLING CO., INC.
931 S Highland Ave, Tucson, AZ 85719-6726
Tel.: (520) 624-1788 AZ
Web Site: http://www.kalilbottling.com
Year Founded: 1946
Sales Range: $25-49.9 Million
Emp.: 750
Bottled & Canned Soft Drinks Distr
N.A.I.C.S.: 312111
Subsidiaries:

Southwest Canning & Packaging Inc (1)
931 S Highland Ave, Tucson, AZ
85719-6726 (100%)
Tel.: (520) 622-5811
Web Site: http://www.swcpaz.com
Bottled And Canned Soft Drinks, Nsk
N.A.I.C.S.: 312111
George Kalil (Pres)

KALIN ENTERPRISES, INC.
5252 S Tamiami Trl, Sarasota, FL 34231-4233
Tel.: (941) 924-1271 FL
Web Site:
 http://www.kanesfurniture.com
Year Founded: 1950
Sales Range: $10-24.9 Million
Emp.: 75
Holding Company; Retail & Real Estate Services
N.A.I.C.S.: 551112
Edward L. Kalin (Pres)
Jeffrey M. Kalin (Sr VP)
Phyllis K. Kessler (CFO & VP-Fin)
Subsidiaries:

Kalin Financial Division (1)
5252 S Tamiami Trl, Sarasota, FL
34231-4233 (100%)
Tel.: (941) 923-5638
Web Site: http://www.kanessarasota.com
Mortgage & Real Estate Investment Services
N.A.I.C.S.: 522310

Edward L. Kalin (Pres)
Phyllis K. Kessler (VP-Fin)

KALIO, INC.
19330 Stevens Creek Blvd Ste 100, Cupertino, CA 95014
Tel.: (408) 996-1813 KY
Web Site: http://www.kalioinc.com
Year Founded: 1999
Sales Range: $10-24.9 Million
Emp.: 70
E-Commerce Site Improvement Services
N.A.I.C.S.: 541519
Jonathan Lee (Chm)
Bill Kim (CIO)
Mark Richards (CEO)
Harry Dressler (VP-Customer Svcs)
Mayank Vadodaria (VP-Engrg)
Subsidiaries:

Moyo Group, Inc. (1)
19330 Stevens Creek Blvd Ste 100, Cupertino, CA 95014
Tel.: (408) 550-8000
Web Site: http://www.moyogroup.com
Information Technology Security & Application Services
N.A.I.C.S.: 541511

KALITTA AIR, LLC
818 Willow Run Airport, Ypsilanti, MI 48198-0899
Tel.: (734) 484-0088 MI
Web Site: http://www.kalittaair.com
Year Founded: 2000
Sales Range: $75-99.9 Million
Emp.: 500
Provider of Air Cargo Carriers & Package Delivery Services
N.A.I.C.S.: 492110
Pete Sanderlin (VP, Gen Mgr & Dir-Ops)
Conrad Kalitta (Owner & CEO)
Brian Coughlin (Mgr-Power Plants)
Gregory Strzynski (CFO)
Laurie Stockton (Dir-HR)
Mark Nolff (Dir-Maintenance)
Zoltan Kocis (Dir-Quality Control & Aircraft Transactions)
George Kelsey (Gen Counsel)
Subsidiaries:

DK Turbines, LLC. (1)
210 Skylane Dr, Hollister, CA 95023
Web Site:
 http://www.kalittamaintenance.com
Emp.: 6
Aircraft Turbine Mfr
N.A.I.C.S.: 336412
Steve Elia (Mgr-Pur)

Kalitta Charters, LLC. (1)
843 Willow Run Airport, Ypsilanti, MI 48198
Tel.: (734) 544-3400
Web Site: http://www.kalittacharters.com
Sales Range: $1-9.9 Million
Passenger Air Transportation Services
N.A.I.C.S.: 481211
Louis Birurakis (Gen Mgr)

Kalitta Turbine Leasing, LLC (1)
2850 Tyler Rd, Ypsilanti, MI 48198
Tel.: (734) 926-4163
Web Site:
 http://www.kalittamaintenance.com
Aircraft Turbine Leasing Services
N.A.I.C.S.: 532411

KALIX
605 27th St SE, Minot, ND 58701-1030
Tel.: (701) 852-1014 ND
Web Site: http://www.kalixnd.org
Year Founded: 1960
Sales Range: $10-24.9 Million
Emp.: 479
Disability Assistance Services
N.A.I.C.S.: 624120

Roland Arrayan (Dir-Residential Svcs)
Borgi Beeler (Pres & CEO)
Blaine Deslauriers (Vice Chm)
John Stewart (Treas)
Rich Campbell (Sec)
Roger Tollefson (Chm)

KALKREUTH ROOFING & SHEETMETAL INC.
6314th St, Wheeling, WV 26003
Tel.: (304) 232-8540
Web Site: http://www.krsm.net
Sales Range: $25-49.9 Million
Emp.: 300
Roofing Contractors
N.A.I.C.S.: 238160
John L. Kalkreuth (Pres)
Patrick Hurley (Project Mgr)
James J. Hurley (Exec VP)
Wes Nickell (VP-Fin & Controller)
David A. Hesse III (VP-Maryland)

KALLIDUS INC.
555 Mission St Ste 1950, San Francisco, CA 94111
Tel.: (877) 554-2176
Web Site: http://www.skava.com
Sales Range: $10-24.9 Million
Emp.: 250
E-Commerce Software Applications
N.A.I.C.S.: 513210
Sudha Varadarajan (Co-Founder & CTO)
Arish Ali (Co-Founder & CEO)
Vivek Agrawal (Global VP-Ops)
Manu Gupta (VP-Solutions Delivery)

KALMAN FLOOR COMPANY
1202 Bergen Pkwy Ste 110, Evergreen, CO 80439
Tel.: (303) 674-2290
Web Site:
 http://www.kalmanfloor.com
Sales Range: $10-24.9 Million
Emp.: 150
Flooring Contractors
N.A.I.C.S.: 238990
Carl N. Ytterberg (Pres & CEO)
Scott Vogeler (Controller)

KALMBACH FEEDS, INC.
7148 State Hwy 199, Upper Sandusky, OH 43351-3351
Web Site:
 http://www.kalmbachfeeds.com
Animal Feed Mfr
N.A.I.C.S.: 311119
Austin Beach (Mgr-Recruiting)
Subsidiaries:

Ware Milling, Inc (1)
150 A F L Dr, Houston, MS 38851
Tel.: (662) 456-9032
Web Site: http://www.waremilling.com
Rev: $4,655,000
Emp.: 7
Nursery & Garden Centers
N.A.I.C.S.: 444240
Richard Ware (Owner)

KALMBACH PUBLISHING CO.
21027 Crossroads Cir, Waukesha, WI 53187-1612
Tel.: (262) 796-8776 WI
Web Site: http://www.kalmbach.com
Year Founded: 1934
Sales Range: $50-74.9 Million
Emp.: 275
Book & Magazine Publisher
N.A.I.C.S.: 513120
Sarah Horner (VP-HR)
Dan Hickey (CEO)
Subsidiaries:

Discover Magazine (1)
21027 Crossroads Cir, Waukesha, WI
53186

KALMBACH PUBLISHING CO.

Kalmbach Publishing Co.—(Continued)
Tel.: (262) 796-8776
Web Site: http://www.discovermagazine.com
Sales Range: $10-24.9 Million
Scientific Magazine Publisher
N.A.I.C.S.: 513120
Corey S. Powell *(Editor)*
Dan Bishop *(Dir-Design)*
Stephen C. George *(VP-Content)*
Kathy Kube *(Mng Editor)*
Diane Bacha *(Dir-Editorial)*
Daniel R. Lance *(Sr VP-Sls & Mktg)*
Alison Mackey *(Assoc Dir-Art)*
Ernie Mastroianni *(Editor-Photo)*
James R. McCann *(VP-Fin)*
Nicole McGuire *(VP-Consumer Mktg)*
Steve Meni *(Mgr-Adv Sls)*
Maureen M. Schimmel *(Dir-Corp Art)*
James Schweder *(VP-Tech)*
Ann E. Smith *(Dir-Corp Adv)*

KALNIN VENTURES LLC
1200 17th St Ste 1850, Denver, CO 80202
Tel.: (720) 375-9680   CO
Web Site:
  http://www.kalninventures.com
Year Founded: 2013
Oil & Natural Gas Property Investment Firm
N.A.I.C.S.: 531390
Christopher Kalnin *(Co-Founder & Mng Dir)*
Rebecca Kalnin *(Co-Founder)*
Joseph Davis *(Partner & Sr VP-Geosciences)*
Ethan Ngo *(Partner & Sr VP-Engrg)*
Matthew Johnson *(VP-Corp Dev & Partner)*
Kathleen Neuheardt *(Vp-Fin, Controller & Partner)*
Daniel Androphy *(VP-Mktg)*
Mahesh Anandan *(VP-Information Systems)*
Thomas Mattern *(VP-Ops)*

KALO, INC.
13200 Metcalf Ave Ste 250, Overland Park, KS 66213
Tel.: (913) 491-9125   KS
Web Site: http://www.kalo.com
Year Founded: 1932
Sales Range: $10-24.9 Million
Emp.: 9
Agricultural Specialty Chemicals Mfr
N.A.I.C.S.: 325320
Chuck Champion *(Pres)*
Bart Wise *(VP-Ops)*
Doug John *(Dir-Sls & Mktg)*

KALONA COOPERATIVE TELEPHONE COMPANY
510 B Ave, Kalona, IA 52247
Tel.: (319) 656-3668   IA
Web Site: http://www.kctc.net
Year Founded: 1947
Rev.: $4,557,624
Assets: $13,292,569
Liabilities: $7,404,751
Net Worth: $5,887,818
Earnings: $357,476
Emp.: 17
Fiscal Year-end: 12/31/13
Telecommunication Support Services
N.A.I.C.S.: 517810
Steve Rich *(VP)*
Steve Yotty *(Pres)*
Atlee Yoder *(Sec)*
Casey L. Peck *(CFO & Gen Mgr)*

Subsidiaries:

Communications Network Inc   (1)
510 B Ave., Kalona, IA 52247
Tel.: (319) 656-3668
Wireless Telecommunications
N.A.I.C.S.: 517112

Subsidiary (Domestic):

The Farmers & Merchants Mutual Telephone Co. of Wayland, Iowa   (2)
210 W Main St, Wayland, IA 52654-9760
Tel.: (319) 256-2736
Sales Range: $1-9.9 Million
Emp.: 7
Telephone Communications, except Radio Telephone
N.A.I.C.S.: 517111
Rex McGuire *(Mgr)*

KALOTI ENTERPRISES INC.
5475 S Westridge Ct, New Berlin, WI 53151
Tel.: (262) 641-2060
Rev.: $38,650,663
Emp.: 45
Owner & Operator of Grocery Stores
N.A.I.C.S.: 424410

KALTY & SALIOS SALES INC.
12833 Monarch St, Huntington Beach, CA 92841
Tel.: (714) 933-9300   CA
Web Site: http://www.kaltysalios.com
Year Founded: 1977
Sales Range: $10-24.9 Million
Emp.: 60
Hardware & Home Improvement Products Distr
N.A.I.C.S.: 423710
Bill Kemple *(Controller)*

KALWALL CORPORATION
1111 Candia Rd, Manchester, NH 03109
Tel.: (603) 627-3861
Web Site: http://www.kalwall.com
Sales Range: $50-74.9 Million
Emp.: 400
Building Product Mfr
N.A.I.C.S.: 326199
Richard Keller *(Pres & CEO)*
Bruce Keller *(VP-Adv & Mktg)*
Bill Wilder *(Gen Mgr-Installation & Svc)*
John Graham *(Mgr-R&D)*
Michael Martin *(Supvr-Aluminum Assembly)*
Nancy Garneau *(Project Coord)*

KAM PLASTICS CORPORATION
611 Ottawa Ave, Holland, MI 49423-4068
Tel.: (616) 355-5900   MI
Web Site:
  http://www.kamplastics.com
Year Founded: 1994
Heavy Truck Mirrors Mfr
N.A.I.C.S.: 326199
Pete Prouty *(Pres)*

KAMAAINA KIDS
156 Hamakua Dr Ste C, Kailua, HI 96734
Tel.: (808) 262-4538   HI
Web Site:
  http://www.kamaainakids.com
Year Founded: 1987
Sales Range: $10-24.9 Million
Emp.: 1,359
Child Care Services
N.A.I.C.S.: 624110
Mark Nishiyama *(VP)*
Raymond C. Sanborn *(Pres & CEO)*
Barbara Owens *(VP)*
Kathleen G. Hew *(VP)*
Charlene Yamasaki *(Treas)*

KAMALI LEATHER LLC
44 Hillside Ave, Manhasset, NY 11030
Tel.: (516) 627-6505   NY

Web Site:
  http://www.kamalileather.com
Year Founded: 1951
Rev.: $20,000,000
Emp.: 10
Leather Tanning & Whslr
N.A.I.C.S.: 316110
Bob Kamali *(VP)*

KAMAN'S ART SHOPPES INC.
16838 Park Circle Dr, Chagrin Falls, OH 44023-4516
Tel.: (440) 708-1909
Web Site: http://www.kamansart.com
Year Founded: 1971
Rev.: $17,408,587
Amusement & Theme Park Concessionaire; Graphic Design Services; Sign Mfr
N.A.I.C.S.: 713990
Tricia Kaman *(Pres)*
Rich Kaman *(Exec VP)*
Ben Kaman *(VP)*

KAMCO SUPPLY CORPORATION
80 21st St, Brooklyn, NY 11232
Tel.: (718) 768-1234
Web Site: http://www.kamco.com
Rev.: $19,800,000
Emp.: 30
Lumber: Rough, Dressed & Finished
N.A.I.C.S.: 423310
Allan B. Swerdlick *(Pres)*
Brendan McKenna *(Branch Mgr)*
Anthony Gentile *(Acct Mgr)*
Mayda Idone *(Treas)*

Subsidiaries:

Kamco Building Supply Corporation of Pennsylvania   (1)
1100 Township Line Rd, Chester, PA 19013
Tel.: (610) 872-5000
Web Site: http://www.kamcosupply.com
Building Materials Distr
N.A.I.C.S.: 423310
Charles P. Dougherty *(Pres)*

Kamco Supply Corporation of Boston   (1)
181 New Boston St, Woburn, MA 01801
Tel.: (781) 938-0909
Web Site: http://www.kamcoboston.com
Distr of Brick, Stone & Related Material
N.A.I.C.S.: 423320
James F. Scaia *(Pres & CEO)*
Scott Foote *(Mgr)*

Division (Domestic):

Kamco Supply Corporation of Boston - Kamco/O'Connor Door Division   (2)
40 A St, Needham, MA 02492
Tel.: (781) 444-3902
Building Materials Distr
N.A.I.C.S.: 423390

Kamco Supply Corporation of Boston - Maine Door Division   (2)
69 Freedom Pkwy Bldg 2 Ste 3, Hermon, ME 04401
Tel.: (207) 848-3060
Building Materials Distr
N.A.I.C.S.: 423390

Kamco Supply Corporation of Boston - Massachusetts Door Division   (2)
4 Samoset Ave, Mansfield, MA 02048
Tel.: (508) 339-3315
Web Site: http://www.kamcoboston.com
Emp.: 4
Building Materials Distr
N.A.I.C.S.: 423390
Brian Messina *(Dir-Ops)*

Kamco Supply Corporation of New England   (1)
2 Barnes Industrial Rd S, Wallingford, CT 06492
Tel.: (203) 284-1968
Web Site: http://www.kamco.com
Building Materials, Interior
N.A.I.C.S.: 423310

U.S. PRIVATE

Paul Taylor *(Owner)*

Kamco Supply of NJ, LLC   (1)
845 E 25th St, Paterson, NJ 07513
Tel.: (973) 247-1234
Web Site: http://www.kamconj.com
Building Materials Distr
N.A.I.C.S.: 423390

KAMEDDATA.COM, INC
4400 Bayou Blvd Ste 12, Pensacola, FL 32503
Tel.: (850) 477-2475   FL
Web Site: http://www.kameddata.com
Year Founded: 2001
Sales Range: $10-24.9 Million
Emp.: 207
Health Care Business Consulting Services
N.A.I.C.S.: 541618
Niels K. Andersen *(Pres & CEO)*
Brenda Walker *(CFO)*

KAMEN & CO.
626 RXR Plz W Twr 6th Fl, Uniondale, NY 11556
Tel.: (516) 379-2797
Web Site:
  http://www.kamengroup.com
Sales Range: $1-9.9 Million
Investment Management & Consulting Services
N.A.I.C.S.: 523150
Kevin B. Kamen *(Pres & CEO)*

KAMEN INDUSTRIAL TECHNOLOGIES
5551 Parkwest Dr Ste 185, Bessemer, AL 35022
Tel.: (205) 942-0111   DE
Web Site: http://www.kaman-ind-tech.com
Year Founded: 1946
Sales Range: $10-24.9 Million
Emp.: 18
Bearing, Conveyor, Electrical, Fluid Power & Power Transmission Components
N.A.I.C.S.: 423840
Scott Mitchell *(Supvr-Customer Svcs)*

Subsidiaries:

Kamen Industrial Supplies Inc.   (1)
Hwy 20 W, Decatur, AL 35601   (100%)
Tel.: (256) 353-3600
Sales Range: $10-24.9 Million
Emp.: 5
Industrial Supplies
N.A.I.C.S.: 423840

KAMIND IT INC.
5200 Meadows Rd Ste 150, Lake Oswego, OR 97035
Tel.: (503) 406-4599
Web Site: http://www.kamind.com
Year Founded: 2009
Sales Range: $1-9.9 Million
Emp.: 9
Information Technology Services
N.A.I.C.S.: 541512
Matt Katzer *(Founder & CEO)*

KAMMINGA & ROODVOETS INC.
3435 Broadmoor Ave SE, Grand Rapids, MI 49512
Tel.: (616) 949-0800
Sales Range: $75-99.9 Million
Emp.: 240
Excavation Work
N.A.I.C.S.: 238910
Joanne Forseca *(Controller)*
Kurt Poll *(Pres)*

KAMO ELECTRIC COOPERATIVE
500 S Kamo Dr, Vinita, OK 74301

Tel.: (918) 256-5551
Web Site:
  http://www.kamopower.com
Sales Range: $150-199.9 Million
Emp.: 155
Transmission, Electric Power
N.A.I.C.S.: 221121
J. Chris Cariker (CEO)

KAMRAN & COMPANY, INC.
411 E Montecito St, Santa Barbara, CA 93101
Tel.: (805) 963-3016 CA
Web Site: http://www.kamranco.com
Year Founded: 1988
Sales Range: $10-24.9 Million
Emp.: 40
Bakery & Restaurant Equipment
N.A.I.C.S.: 238990
Faye Amiri (Pres)

KAN EQUIPMENT INC.
18035 E United States Hwy 24, Wamego, KS 66547
Tel.: (785) 456-2041
Web Site: http://www.kanequip.com
Sales Range: $1-9.9 Million
Emp.: 60
Farm Implements
N.A.I.C.S.: 444230
Craig Goff (Gen Mgr)
Jaimee Hoobler (Mgr-HR)
Trent Giles (Mgr-Wholegoods Program)
Grant Meinhardt (Mgr-Pub Sector Sls)
Ken Roberts (Mgr-Warranty)
Beth Ernst (Mgr-Mktg)
April Goff (Controller)

KANA PIPELINE, INC.
1639 E Miraloma Ave, Placentia, CA 92870
Tel.: (714) 986-1400
Web Site:
  http://www.kanapipeline.com
Year Founded: 1984
Sales Range: $10-24.9 Million
Emp.: 100
Water & Sewer Line Structures Construction Services
N.A.I.C.S.: 237110
Daniel Locke (Founder)
Austin Locke (Dir-Pur)

KANAN ENTERPRISES, INC.
31900 Solon Rd, Solon, OH 44139 OH
Web Site: http://www.kingnut.com
Year Founded: 1927
Processor, Retailer & Distr Nuts & Other Snacks
N.A.I.C.S.: 311911
Matthew R. Kanan (CMO & Exec VP)
Martin Kanan (Pres & CEO)
Michael Kanan (Chm)
Joseph A. Valenza (CFO & Sr VP)
Michael Smith (VP-Mfg & Plant Ops)
Justin Rosenberg (VP & Controller)
Richard Keay (Mng Dir-Quality Assurance & Product Dev)

KANAN, CORBIN, SCHUPAK & ARONOW, INC.
420 5th Ave 3rd Fl, New York, NY 10018
Tel.: (212) 682-6300 NY
Web Site: http://www.kcsa.com
Year Founded: 1969
Sales Range: $1-9.9 Million
Emp.: 35
Public Relations Agency
N.A.I.C.S.: 541820
Todd Fromer (Mng Partner)
Anne G. Donohoe (Mng Dir-PR)
Lewis Goldberg (Mng Partner)
Jeffrey Goldberger (Mng Partner)
Joseph Septon (CFO)
Cynthia Salarizadeh (Mng Partner)
Philip Carlson (Mng Dir-IR)
Danielle DeVoren (Mng Dir-PR)
Valter Pinto (Mng Dir)
Jon Goldberg (Sr VP & Dir-Media-PR)
Caitlin Kasunich (Sr VP-PR)
Alessandra Nagy (Sr VP-PR)

KANAWHA HOSPICE CARE, INC.
1606 Kanawha Blvd W, Charleston, WV 25387-2536
Tel.: (304) 768-8523 WV
Web Site:
  http://www.hospicecarewv.org
Year Founded: 1981
Sales Range: $10-24.9 Million
Emp.: 310
Health Care Srvices
N.A.I.C.S.: 622110
Kendra Prine (Dir-HR)
Larry Robertson (Exec Dir)
Vickie Powell (Dir-Palliative Care)
Brian Rumberg (Dir-Quality Assessment & Performance Improvement)
Jeff Sikorovsky (Dir-Mktg)
Melanie Allen (Dir-Volunteer Svcs)
Michael Dupay (Dir-Bereavement & Spiritual Care)
Michael Morris (Dir-Fin & IT)
Richie Hills (Dir-Social Svcs)
Shellie Powell (Dir-Clinical Svcs)

KANAWHA MANUFACTURING COMPANY
1520 Dixie St, Charleston, WV 25311
Tel.: (304) 342-6127
Web Site:
  http://www.kanawhamfg.com
Sales Range: $25-49.9 Million
Emp.: 125
Plate Work for the Metalworking Trade
N.A.I.C.S.: 332313
William B. Davis (Pres)
Emmett Hedrick (Mgr-Pur)
William Lively (VP-Sls)

KANAWHA SCALES & SYSTEMS INC.
111 Jacobson Dr, Poca, WV 25159
Tel.: (304) 755-8321
Web Site:
  http://www.kanawhascales.com
Rev.: $52,600,000
Emp.: 421
Commercial Equipment Merchant Whslr
N.A.I.C.S.: 423440
James Bradbury (Chm & CEO)
Mike Cook (Dir-Utility Svcs)
James Freeman (Dir-Tech Svcs)
William J. McHale (VP-Sls-Intl)
John Holt (Mgr)
John Steele (Mgr)

KANAWHA STONE COMPANY INC.
401 Jacobson Dr, Poca, WV 25159
Tel.: (304) 755-8271
Web Site:
  http://www.kanawhastone.com
Sales Range: $10-24.9 Million
Emp.: 100
Highway, Street & Bridge Construction
N.A.I.C.S.: 237310
Virginia L. King (VP)
Arthur L. King (Owner)

KANDERS & COMPANY, INC.
1 Landmark Sq Fl 22, Greenwich, CT 06830
Tel.: (203) 552-9600 DE
Investment Holding Company
N.A.I.C.S.: 551112
Warren B. Kanders (Pres & CEO)

Subsidiaries:

Safariland, LLC (1)
13386 International Pkwy, Jacksonville, FL 32218-2383
Tel.: (904) 741-5400
Web Site: http://www.safariland.com
Sales Range: $200-249.9 Million
Emp.: 1,700
Body Armor Products for Law Enforcement Personnel, Correctional Officers & Military Personnel
N.A.I.C.S.: 339999
Warren B. Kanders (Chm & CEO)
Scott O'Brien (Pres)
Brad E. Williams (COO)

Co-Headquarters (Domestic):

Safariland, LLC - Ontario Office (2)
3120 E Mission Blvd, Ontario, CA 91761
Tel.: (909) 923-7300
Web Site: http://www.safariland.com
Law Enforcement & Military Equipment Including Ballistic Resistant Vests & Duty Gear, Including Belts, Holsters, Handcuffs & Flashlight Holders & Related Accessories
N.A.I.C.S.: 332999
Scott O'Brien (Co-Pres)
Scott Carnahan (VP-Equipment Category)
Brad E. Williams (Co-Pres)

Subsidiary (Non-US):

Aegis Engineering Limited (3)
Unit 5 Chesford Grange, Woolston, Warrington, WA1 4RQ, Cheshire, United Kingdom
Tel.: (44) 1925840048
Web Site: http://www.aegis-eng.com
Body Armour Systems & Other Homeland Security Products Mfr & Distr
N.A.I.C.S.: 315210

Subsidiary (Domestic):

Atlantic Tactical, Inc. (3)
772 Corporate Cir, New Cumberland, PA 17070
Tel.: (717) 774-3339
Web Site: http://www.atlantictactical.com
Sales Range: $1-9.9 Million
Public Safety Professional Equipment & Uniform Distr & Retailer
N.A.I.C.S.: 423490
Sean Conville (Pres)

Lawmen's Safety Supply Inc. (3)
3319 Anvil Pl, Raleigh, NC 27603
Tel.: (919) 779-6141
Web Site: http://www.lawmens.com
Sales Range: $1-9.9 Million
Emp.: 18
Distr of Equipment & Uniforms for Law Enforcement & Public Safety
N.A.I.C.S.: 459999
Al Sutton (Pres)
Patrice Mann-Sutton (CFO)
Ryan Lilly (VP-Ops)
Austin Keaton (Mgr-Ops)
Mindy Blalock (Mgr-Acctg)

Subsidiary (Non-US):

Med-Eng Systems Inc. (3)
2400 Saint Laurent Blvd, Ottawa, K1G 6C4, ON, Canada
Tel.: (613) 482-8835
Web Site: http://www.med-eng.com
Military & Law Enforcement Personal Protection & Bomb Disposal Equipment Mfr
N.A.I.C.S.: 339113
Rob Reynolds (VP & Gen Mgr)

Subsidiary (US):

Med-Eng, LLC (4)
835 Commerce Park Dr, Ogdensburg, NY 13669
Tel.: (613) 739-9646
Web Site: http://www.med-eng.com
Sales Range: $1-9.9 Million
Emp.: 60
Military & Law Enforcement Personal Protection & Bomb Disposal Equipment Mfr & Whslr
N.A.I.C.S.: 339113

Unit (Domestic):

Safariland LLC - Defense Technology (3)
1855 S Loop Ave, Casper, WY 82001
Tel.: (307) 235-2136
Web Site: http://www.defense-technology.com
Sales Range: $50-74.9 Million
Emp.: 85
Gas Masks, Hand-Held Pepper Spray, Specialty Impact Munitions & Related Accessories Mfr & Distr
N.A.I.C.S.: 339999
John Kapeles (Dir-Ops & Engrg)
Michael Kramer (Mgr-Ops)

Subsidiary (Domestic):

Tactical Command Industries, Inc. (3)
1872 Verne Roberts Cir, Antioch, CA 94509
Tel.: (925) 756-7354
Web Site: http://www.safariland.com
Sales Range: $1-9.9 Million
Military & Law Enforcement Communications Equipment Mfr & Whslr
N.A.I.C.S.: 334220

United Uniform Co., Inc. (3)
495 N French Rd, Buffalo, NY 14228
Tel.: (716) 691-4400
Web Site: http://www.uniteduniform.com
Sales Range: $1-9.9 Million
Emp.: 115
Retails & Distributes Equipment, Tactical Gear & Uniforms for Law Enforcement & Public Safety Professionals
N.A.I.C.S.: 458110
Josh Muskat (Pres)

KANE & FINKEL HEALTHCARE COMMUNICATIONS
534 4th St, San Francisco, CA 94107
Tel.: (415) 777-4990 CA
Year Founded: 1997
Sales Range: $50-74.9 Million
Emp.: 70
Advertising Agencies
N.A.I.C.S.: 541810
John Kane (Mng Dir & Principal)
Robert Finkel (Principal, Chief Creative Officer)
Deborah Kessler (Chief Science Liaison & Sr VP)
Jonathan Peischl (Sr VP & Dir-Creative)
Jon Meisner (VP & Dir-Medical)
Bob Finkel (Principal & Chief Creative Officer)

KANE COMMUNICATIONS GROUP, LLC
250 E Wisconsin Ave, Ste 1200, Milwaukee, WI 53202
Tel.: (414) 635-7000
Web Site:
  https://www.kanecommgroup.com
Advertising Services
N.A.I.C.S.: 541810

Subsidiaries:

Leonard & Finco Public Relations Inc. (1)
1039 W Mason St, Green Bay, WI 54303-1842
Tel.: (920) 965-7750
Web Site: http://www.lfpublicrelations.com
Public Relations Agencies
N.A.I.C.S.: 541820
Susan Finco (Pres)

KANE FURNITURE CORPORATION
5700 70th Ave, Pinellas Park, FL 33781-4238
Tel.: (727) 545-9555 FL

KANE FURNITURE CORPORATION   U.S. PRIVATE

Kane Furniture Corporation—(Continued)
Web Site:
http://www.kanesfurniture.com
Year Founded: 1948
Sales Range: $100-124.9 Million
Emp.: 600
Furniture Retailer
N.A.I.C.S.: 449110
Erwin Novack (Pres & CEO)
Chuck Schaffer (Controller)
Wayne Liburdhas (Mgr-IT)
Danielle Tichio (Mgr-Mdse-Case Goods)
Dan Kennedy (COO)

KANE IS ABLE, INC.
Stauffer Indus Pk, Taylor, PA 18517
Tel.: (570) 344-9801   PA
Web Site: http://www.kaneisable.com
Year Founded: 1985
Sales Range: $50-74.9 Million
Emp.: 1,000
Provider of Trucking Services
N.A.I.C.S.: 484121
Rich Bourque (Dir-Bus Dev-Transportation)

Subsidiaries:

Kalstar Enterprises LLC   (1)
PO Box 931, Scranton, PA 18501-0931
Tel.: (855) 492-3375
Web Site: http://www.kalstar.com
Logistics Consulting Servies
N.A.I.C.S.: 541614

Kane Freight Lines Inc.   (1)
Stauffer Industrial Park, Taylor, PA 18517
Tel.: (570) 344-9801
Sales Range: $25-49.9 Million
Emp.: 155
Provider of Trucking Services
N.A.I.C.S.: 484230

Kane Traffic Services Inc.   (1)
3 Stauffer Industrial Park, Scranton, PA 18504
Tel.: (570) 344-9801
Web Site: http://www.kaneisable.com
Provider of Trucking Services
N.A.I.C.S.: 488510

Kane Warehousing Inc.   (1)
3 Stauffer Industrial Park, Taylor, PA 18517
Tel.: (570) 344-9801
Sales Range: $25-49.9 Million
Emp.: 800
Provider of Refrigerated Warehousing Services
N.A.I.C.S.: 493110
Christine Skutnick (Mgr-HR)

KANE-MILLER CORP.
1991 Main St Ste 260, Sarasota, FL 34236
Tel.: (941) 906-7700   DE
Year Founded: 1920
Sales Range: $75-99.9 Million
Emp.: 3
Provider of Food Processing Services
N.A.I.C.S.: 311613
Robert Weninger (CFO)

Subsidiaries:

HRR Enterprises, Inc.   (1)
1755 Genesis Dr, La Porte, IN 46350   (100%)
Tel.: (219) 362-9050
Web Site: http://www.hrrenterprises.com
Sales Range: $25-49.9 Million
Rendering Plant
N.A.I.C.S.: 449210

KANEBRIDGE CORPORATION
153 Bauer Dr, Oakland, NJ 07436
Tel.: (201) 337-3200
Web Site: http://www.kanebridge.com
Sales Range: $25-49.9 Million
Emp.: 50
Distr Fasteners
N.A.I.C.S.: 423710

Robert Williams (VP)
Nick Peles (Mgr-Ops)
Pat Lang (Mgr-Sls)
Vic LaPoma (Mgr-Mktg)
Mike Sutphin (Controller)

KANEQUIP, INC.
18035 East Hwy 24, Wamego, KS 66547
Tel.: (785) 456-2041
Web Site: http://www.kanequip.com
Year Founded: 1999
Rev.: $1,300,000
Emp.: 12
Farm & Garden Machinery & Equipment
N.A.I.C.S.: 423820
Jim Meinheirt (Pres)
Craig Goff (Gen Mgr)
Danny Starnes (Mgr-Parts-Dodge City)
Bryce Davis (Mgr-Parts-Ellsworth)
Bryndon Meinhardt (Mgr-Marysville)
Chad Frick (Mgr-Store-Garden City)
Darren Thomas (Mgr-Store-Dodge City)
Debbie Colpetzer (Mgr-Svc-Garden City)
April Goff (Controller)
Beth Ernst (Mgr-Mktg)
Bill Enstrom (Mgr-Svc-Dodge City)
Doug Loewen (Mgr-Clay Center)
Grant Meinhardt (Mgr-Pub Sector Sls)
Heath Ehrlich (Mgr-Svc-Ellsworth)
Jaimee Hoobler (Mgr-HR)
Trent Giles (Program Mgr-Wholegoods)

Subsidiaries:

Straub International Inc.   (1)
214 Sw 40 Avenue, Great Bend, KS 67530
Tel.: (620) 792-5256
Web Site: http://www.straubint.com
Agricultural Machinery & Equipment
N.A.I.C.S.: 423820
Ronald Straub (Pres)
Kathy Straub (CFO)
Larry Straub (CEO)

KANEY AEROSPACE, INC.
1321 Capital Dr, Rockford, IL 61109-2945
Tel.: (815) 986-4359
Web Site:
http://www.kaneyaerospace.com
Engineeering Services
N.A.I.C.S.: 541330
Ron Soave (Pres)
Andrew Mealey (Exec VP)
Daniel E. Brady (VP-Technical Ops)
Heather Spillare (CFO)
Dawn Johnson (Dir-HR)
Rick Ludwig (Dir-Sls & Contracts)
Dave Nemeth (Dir-Quality)
Craig Legault (Dir-Bus Dev)
Jennifer Aurelien (Deputy CFO)
Jeffrey J. Kaney Sr. (CEO)

Subsidiaries:

BVR Technologies Co.   (1)
3358-60 Publishers Dr, Rockford, IL 61109
Tel.: (815) 874-2471
Web Site: http://www.kaneyaerospace.com
Motion Control & Avionics Products Mfr
N.A.I.C.S.: 334511

KANGAROO BRANDS, INC.
7620 N 81st St, Milwaukee, WI 53223
Tel.: (414) 355-9696   WI
Web Site:
http://www.kangaroobrands.com
Year Founded: 1979
Sales Range: $50-74.9 Million
Pita Bread & Food Products Mfr
N.A.I.C.S.: 311812

George Kashou (Owner)

KANGAS & ASSOCIATES, LLC
4545 Mariotti Ct Unit J, Sarasota, FL 34233
Tel.: (941) 922-9646
Web Site: http://www.kangastel.com
Year Founded: 1981
Sales Range: $1-9.9 Million
Emp.: 12
Telecommunications Equipment
N.A.I.C.S.: 423620
Craig A. Flynt (Owner & Pres)

KANSAS CHILDREN'S SERVICE LEAGUE
1365 N Custer St, Wichita, KS 67203
Tel.: (316) 942-4261   KS
Web Site: http://www.kcsl.org
Year Founded: 1893
Sales Range: $10-24.9 Million
Emp.: 319
Child Care Services
N.A.I.C.S.: 624110
Paula Wischnack (Treas)

KANSAS CITY CHIEFS FOOTBALL CLUB, INC.
1 Arrowhead Dr, Kansas City, MO 64129-1651
Tel.: (816) 920-9300   MO
Web Site: http://www.kcchiefs.com
Year Founded: 1960
Sales Range: $50-74.9 Million
Emp.: 150
Professional Football Franchise
N.A.I.C.S.: 711211
Clark Hunt (Chm & CEO)
Gary Spani (Dir-Special Events)
Ken Radino (Asst Dir-Video Ops)
Jeremy Slavens (Dir-Mktg & Event Acq)
Jayne Martin (VP-Fan Experience)
Pat Brazil (Dir-Video Ops)
Chuck Castellano (Dir-Community Outreach)
Mark Donovan (Pres)
Bill Chapin (Sr VP-Bus Ops)
Dan Crumb (CFO)
Kirsten Krug (VP-Admin)
B. J. Stabler (Mgr-Player Engagement)
Brian Dunn (VP-Acctg & Controller)
John Dorsey (Gen Mgr)
Kristin Conlon (Mgr-Payroll)
Mike Borgonzi (Dir-Player Personnel)
Tyler Epp (VP-Bus Dev)
Ted Crews (VP-Comm)
Lara Krug (CMO & Exec VP)
Michael Ragsdale (VP-Fin, Strategy & Analytics)
Shaun Tyrance (VP-Player Svcs & Assessment)

KANSAS CITY ELECTRICAL SUPPLY CO.
10900 MidAmerica Ave, Lenexa, KS 66219
Tel.: (913) 541-1717
Web Site:
http://www.kcelectricalsupply.com
Sales Range: $10-24.9 Million
Emp.: 40
Electrical Supplies
N.A.I.C.S.: 423610
Jimmy Jones (Branch Mgr)
John Owens (Treas & Mgr-Fin)
Gary Williams (Gen Mgr)
Colin Hinkley (Mgr-Sls)

KANSAS CITY HOME CARE, INC.
6400 W 110th St Ste 200, Overland Park, KS 66211
Tel.: (913) 341-4800

Web Site:
http://www.kchomecare.com
Year Founded: 1989
Rev.: $3,000,000
Emp.: 100
Health Services
N.A.I.C.S.: 621610
Leslie Griffith (Mgr-Care)

KANSAS CITY HOSPICE & PALLIATIVE CARE
1500 Meadow Lake Pkwy Ste 200, Kansas City, MO 64114
Tel.: (816) 363-2600   MO
Web Site:
http://www.kansascityhospice.org
Year Founded: 1980
Sales Range: $10-24.9 Million
Emp.: 384
Hospice & Palliative Care Services
N.A.I.C.S.: 621610
Bill Tammeus (Vice Chm)
Michelle Stark Kaufman (Sec)
Donna Payne (Chm)
Al Biggs (Treas)
Jody Abbott (Vice Chm)
David Wiley (Pres & CEO)
Gloria Soendker (Dir-Clinical Svcs)
Tom Raupp (Vice Chm)
Kiran Chandra (Dir-Corp & Community Engagement)
Mark Wiles (Assoc Dir-Medical)

KANSAS CITY PETERBILT INC.
8915 Woodend Rd, Kansas City, KS 66111
Tel.: (913) 441-2888
Web Site: http://www.kcpete.com
Sales Range: $50-74.9 Million
Emp.: 180
Sell Commercial Trucks; Service Trucks & Sell Parts
N.A.I.C.S.: 423110
Chris Geis (Pres)
Dwight Mann (Mgr-Parts)
Mike Carothers (Mgr-Sls)
Steve Hahn (Mgr)

KANSAS CITY ROYALS BASEBALL CORPORATION
1 Royal Way, Kansas City, MO 64129
Tel.: (816) 504-4040   MO
Web Site:
http://kansascity.royals.com
Year Founded: 1969
Sales Range: $75-99.9 Million
Emp.: 75
Professional Baseball Club
N.A.I.C.S.: 711211
Toby Cook (VP-Community Affairs & Publicity)
Kevin Uhlich (Sr VP-Bus Ops)

KANSAS CITY SAUSAGE COMPANY
8001 NW 106th St, Kansas City, MO 64153
Tel.: (816) 891-9600
Web Site:
http://www.kcsausageco.com
Year Founded: 2008
Sales Range: $10-24.9 Million
Emp.: 150
Sausage Mfr
N.A.I.C.S.: 424470
Bruce Ginn (CEO)
Paul Forde (VP-Sls & Mktg)

KANSAS ELECTRIC POWER COOPERATIVE, INC.
600 SW Corporate View, Topeka, KS 66615
Tel.: (785) 273-7010   KS
Web Site: http://www.kepco.org

Year Founded: 1975
Rev.: $162,619,958
Assets: $280,168,485
Liabilities: $59,399,889
Net Worth: $220,768,596
Earnings: $2,710,302
Fiscal Year-end: 12/31/18
Generation & Transmission Cooperative
N.A.I.C.S.: 813990
Coleen Wells (CFO & Sr VP)
Shawn Geil (Exec Dir-Technical Energy Svcs)
Mark Barbee (Sr VP-Engrg & Ops)
Mark Doljac (Exec Dir-Regulatory Affairs & Plng)
Phil Wages (Dir-Member Svcs, Govt Affairs & Bus Dev)
John Payne (Sr Engr)
Suzanne Lane (CEO & Exec VP)
Susan Cunningham (Gen Counsel & Sr VP-Regulatory & Govt Affairs)

KANSAS ELKS TRAINING CENTER FOR THE HANDICAPPED, INC.
1006 E Waterman St, Wichita, KS 67211
Tel.: (316) 383-8700   KS
Web Site: http://www.ketch.org
Year Founded: 1964
Sales Range: $10-24.9 Million
Emp.: 535
Disability Assistance Services
N.A.I.C.S.: 624120
Sallie Jensen (VP-Quality Assurance)
Pattie Knauff (VP-HR)
Sheila Brown (VP-Fin)
Ron Pasmore (Pres & CEO)
Laura Roberds (VP-Community Svcs)

KANSAS FEEDS, INC.
1110 E Trail St, Dodge City, KS 67801-9062
Tel.: (620) 225-3500   KS
Web Site: http://www.kansasfeedsinc.net
Year Founded: 1983
Sales Range: $10-24.9 Million
Emp.: 22
Animal Feed Sales
N.A.I.C.S.: 311119
Brad Smith (Mgr-Distr)

KANSAS LIVESTOCK ASSOCIATION
6031 SW 37th St, Topeka, KS 66614
Tel.: (785) 273-5115   KS
Web Site: http://www.kla.org
Year Founded: 1969
Sales Range: $10-24.9 Million
Emp.: 25
Livestock Association
N.A.I.C.S.: 813910
Mike Beam (Sr VP)
Aaron Popelka (VP-Legal & Govt Affairs)
Andrew Sylvester (Dir-Mktg & Promos)
Tammy Houk (Mgr-Adv)
Todd Domer (VP-Comm)
Rich McKee (Sr VP)
Scarlett Hagins (Mgr-Comm Program)
Matt Teagarden (CEO)
Jaret Moyer (Pres)

KANSAS LUMBER HOMESTORE INC.
217 S 4th St, Manhattan, KS 66502
Tel.: (785) 776-5353
Web Site: http://www.homestoredirects.com
Sales Range: $10-24.9 Million
Emp.: 70
Lumber: Rough, Dressed & Finished
N.A.I.C.S.: 423310

Kent Glasscock (Chm)
Amy Abitz (CFO)

KANSAS MASONIC HOME
401 S Seneca St, Wichita, KS 67213
Tel.: (316) 269-7500   KS
Web Site: http://www.ksmasonic.org
Year Founded: 1893
Sales Range: $10-24.9 Million
Emp.: 326
Community Care Services
N.A.I.C.S.: 624190
Matthew Bogner (CEO)
Arien Reeves (Dir-Assisted Living)
Hervey Wright (Dir-Dev)
Mike Miller (COO)
Ashley Ross (Dir-Mktg)
Caryn Clothier (Dir-HR)

KANSAS MEDICAL MUTUAL INSURANCE CO
623 SW 10th Ave, Topeka, KS 66612
Tel.: (785) 232-2224
Web Site: http://www.kammco.com
Year Founded: 1989
Accident & Health Insurance
N.A.I.C.S.: 524114
Kurtis L. Scott (Pres & CEO)
Melissa Atkins (CEO-Graham County Hospital)
Thomas Bell (Pres-KHA)
Jon Rosell (Exec Dir)
Jerry Slaughter (Exec VP)

KANSAS TURNPIKE AUTHORITY
9401 E Kellogg Dr, Wichita, KS 67207
Tel.: (316) 682-4537   KS
Web Site: http://www.ksturnpike.com
Year Founded: 1953
Sales Range: $100-124.9 Million
Highway Maintenance Services
N.A.I.C.S.: 488490
Eric J. Becker (Dir-Roadway Ops)
David Lindstrom (Chm)
Jennifer Szambecki (Dir-Innovation & Partnerships)
Alan E. Streit (Gen Counsel)
David E. Jacobson (Dir-Engrg)
Rachel Bell (Dir-Mktg & Comm)
Steve Hewitt (CEO)
Bruce Meisch (Dir-Tech)
Kent Olson (Dir-Fin)

KANSAS/OKLAHOMA MACHINE TOOLS, INC.
3427 W 30th St, Wichita, KS 67217
Tel.: (316) 945-6800
Web Site: http://www.komt.com
Year Founded: 1962
Sales Range: $10-24.9 Million
Emp.: 24
Distr & Servicer of Machine Tools & Accessories
N.A.I.C.S.: 423830
Lynn Ungles (Mgr-Customer Support)

KANTO CORPORATION
13424 N Woodrush Way, Portland, OR 97203
Tel.: (503) 283-0405
Web Site: http://www.kantocorp.com
Year Founded: 1944
Sales Range: $10-24.9 Million
Emp.: 65
Provider of Chemicals & Allied Products
N.A.I.C.S.: 424690
Rey Castino (Mgr-Lab)
Alan Wickizer (Mgr-HR)
Richard Robideau (Dir-Sls)
Rick Schellenger (Mgr-Engrg)
Kyle Hamar (Plant Mgr)
Robert Alipio (Mgr-Bus Dev)

KANTORWASSINK
330 Market Ave SW, Grand Rapids, MI 49503
Tel.: (616) 233-3118
Web Site: http://www.kantorwassink.com
Year Founded: 2006
Sales Range: $1-9.9 Million
Emp.: 8
Brand Strategy, Awareness & Development
N.A.I.C.S.: 541613
Wendy Wassink (Principal & Dir-Strategy)

KAPCO INCORPORATED
1000 Badger Cir, Grafton, WI 53024
Tel.: (262) 377-6500
Web Site: http://www.kapcoinc.com
Rev.: $20,019,786
Emp.: 50
Stamping Metal
N.A.I.C.S.: 332119
Jim Kacmarcik (Pres)
Charles Minor (Supvr-Quality)
Dean Rennicke (VP-Mktg)
Kiki Nimtz (Dir-Sls)
Todd Etzel (Product Mgr-Dev)
John Steger (VP-Mfg)
Jennifer Wenger (Dir-Talent & Org Dev)
Mitchell Kessenich (Engr-Safety)

KAPLAN AUTO GROUP
449 Neponset St, Norwood, MA 02062
Tel.: (781) 619-9000
Web Site: http://www.jakekaplans.com
Deep Sea Freight Transportation
N.A.I.C.S.: 483111
Sheree Kaplan-Allen (Pres)

Subsidiaries:

Mercedes-Benz of Portsmouth   (1)
309 Portsmith Ave, Greenland, NH 03840
Tel.: (603) 431-8585
Web Site: http://www.mbportsmouth.com
Car Dealership
N.A.I.C.S.: 441110
Eddy Allen (Gen Mgr)
Jose Silva (Gen Sls Mgr)
Jeremy Copp (Sls Mgr)
Bethany Juneau (Dir-Bus Dev)
Richard Murray (Dir-Svc)

KAPLAN COMPANIES INC.
1310 Lewisville Clemmons Rd, Lewisville, NC 27023-9635
Tel.: (336) 766-7374   NC
Web Site: http://www.kaplanco.com
Year Founded: 1968
Sales Range: $25-49.9 Million
Emp.: 190
Educational Products
N.A.I.C.S.: 423490
Hal Kaplan (Pres & CEO)
Wes Wooten (Gen Mgr-Playgrounds)
Jeff Hancock (Mgr-Reg)
Julie Spencer (Mng Dir)

Subsidiaries:

Kaplan Early Learning Company   (1)
1310 Lewisville Clemmons Rd, Lewisville, NC 27023-9635
Tel.: (336) 766-7374
Web Site: http://www.kaplanco.com
Sales Range: $25-49.9 Million
Catalog & Mail-Order Houses
N.A.I.C.S.: 423490
Hal Kaplan (Chm)
Matthew Marceron (Pres & CEO)

KAPLAN CORPORATION
116 Harvard St, Brookline, MA 02446
Tel.: (617) 232-3300
Web Site: http://www.kaplanconstructs.com

Year Founded: 1976
Sales Range: $10-24.9 Million
Emp.: 25
Nonresidential Construction Services
N.A.I.C.S.: 236220
Kenneth Kaplan (Founder & Chm)
Paul Pavao (Superintendent-Construction)
Melissa Bullock (Coord-Mktg & Admin)
Nathan Peck (Pres)
Jane Kaplan Peck (COO)
Laura Boule (VP-Investments)
Barry Markham (Founder)

KAPLAN TRUCKING COMPANY
6600 Bessemer Ave, Cleveland, OH 44127-1804
Tel.: (216) 341-3322
Web Site: http://www.kaplantrucking.com
Year Founded: 1983
Sales Range: $50-74.9 Million
Emp.: 104
Long Distance Trucking Services
N.A.I.C.S.: 484121
Wendy Shuler-Kohl (Mgr-Rate)

Subsidiaries:

Kaplan Trucking   (1)
1901 Finley Blvd Ste 10, Birmingham, AL 35234
Tel.: (205) 324-5432
Sales Range: $10-24.9 Million
Emp.: 3
Provides Trucking Services
N.A.I.C.S.: 484110

KAPLANSKY INSURANCE AGENCY, INC.
10 Kearney Rd, Needham, MA 02494
Tel.: (781) 453-2552
Web Site: http://www.kaplansky.com
Year Founded: 1974
Insurance Services
N.A.I.C.S.: 524128
Ely Kaplansky (Pres)
Patty Foley (Sr VP)
Robert Cuzzupe (CFO)

Subsidiaries:

Brooklawn Insurance Agency, Inc.   (1)
696 Ashley Blvd, New Bedford, MA 02745
Tel.: (508) 995-8351
Insurance Related Activities
N.A.I.C.S.: 524298
Suzanne Rebeiro (Pres)

KAPOOR ENTERPRISES
461 S Milpitas Blvd Ste 1, Milpitas, CA 95035
Tel.: (408) 933-4422
Web Site: http://www.bonfaremarkets.com
Grocery & Convenience Store Owner & Operator
N.A.I.C.S.: 561110
Jagjeet Kapoor (Chm)

Subsidiaries:

Bonfare Markets Inc.   (1)
461 S Milpitas Blvd Ste 1, Milpitas, CA 95035   (100%)
Tel.: (408) 933-4422
Web Site: http://www.bonfaremarkets.com
Rev.: $18,000,000
Emp.: 10
Grocery Store Operator
N.A.I.C.S.: 445110

Stop n Save, Inc.   (1)
461 S Milpitas Blvd, Milpitas, CA 95035   (100%)
Tel.: (408) 933-4422
Web Site: http://www.bonfaremarkets.com
Rev.: $12,500,000

KAPOOR ENTERPRISES

Kapoor Enterprises—(Continued)
Emp.: 8
Convenience Store
N.A.I.C.S.: 445131

KAPP ADVERTISING SERVICE INCORPORATED
100 E Cumberland St, Lebanon, PA 17042
Tel.: (717) 273-8127
Web Site:
http://www.themerchandiser.com
Sales Range: $10-24.9 Million
Emp.: 90
Shopping News: Publishing & Printing
N.A.I.C.S.: 513199
Robert S. Kapp *(Founder, Owner & Pres)*
Valerie Stokes *(Gen Mgr)*
Randy Miller *(Gen Mgr-Sls)*

KAPP CONSTRUCTION COMPANY, INC.
329 Mount Vernon Ave, Springfield, OH 45503
Tel.: (937) 324-0134
Web Site:
http://www.kappconstruction.com
Sales Range: $75-99.9 Million
Emp.: 60
Nonresidential Construction Services
N.A.I.C.S.: 236220
Randy Kapp *(Pres)*

KAPPA GRAPHICS, LP
50 Rock St, Pittston, PA 18640-3028
Tel.: (570) 655-9681   DE
Web Site:
http://www.kappagraphics.com
Year Founded: 1970
Sales Range: $25-49.9 Million
Emp.: 160
Magazine Printing Services
N.A.I.C.S.: 323111
Nick G. Karabots *(Chm)*
Andrea Duloc *(Dir-HR)*

KAPPA KAPPA GAMMA
530 E Town St, Columbus, OH 43216
Tel.: (614) 228-6515
Web Site:
http://www.kappakappagamma.org
Year Founded: 1870
Sales Range: $25-49.9 Million
Emp.: 40
Women Fraternity Services
N.A.I.C.S.: 721310
Ashley Moyer *(Dir-Mktg & Comm)*
Heather Root *(Dir-Fin)*
Jane Steiner *(Dir-Membership Svcs)*

KAPPA MAP GROUP, LLC
124B S Amelia Ave Ste 201, Deland, FL 32724
Tel.: (366) 873-3010   PA
Web Site:
http://www.kappamapgroup.com
Year Founded: 1916
Map & Atlas Mfr & Sales
N.A.I.C.S.: 424990
Paul Kolkka *(Pres)*

KAPPA PUBLISHING GROUP, INC.
6198 Butler Pike Ste 200, Blue Bell, PA 19422
Tel.: (215) 643-6385
Web Site:
http://www.kappapublishing.com
Sales Range: $10-24.9 Million
Emp.: 75
Periodical Publishers
N.A.I.C.S.: 513120
Nick Karabots *(Chm & CEO)*
Dave Tyler *(Dir-Newsstand Circulation)*

Subsidiaries:

Kappa Books Publishers LLC   (1)
6198 Butler Pike Ste 200, Blue Bell, PA 19422
Tel.: (215) 643-5800
Web Site: http://www.kappapublishing.com
Book Publishers
N.A.I.C.S.: 513130

Subsidiary (Domestic):

Modern Publishing, Inc.   (2)
155 E 55th St Ste 203, New York, NY 10022-4038   **(100%)**
Tel.: (212) 826-0850
Web Site: http://www.modernpublishing.com
Children's Puzzle, Educational, Coloring & Activity Book Publisher
N.A.I.C.S.: 513130

KAPPEL & KAPPEL INC.
355 Main St, Vacaville, CA 95688
Tel.: (707) 446-0600
Web Site: http://www.kappels.com
Rev.: $13,534,692
Emp.: 48
Real Estate Brokers & Agents
N.A.I.C.S.: 531210
Steven T. Kappel *(Pres)*

KAPTYN, INC.
6312 W Cheyenne Ave, Las Vegas, NV 89108
Tel.: (702) 462-2182
Web Site: http://www.kaptyn.com
Taxicabs; For-Hire Transportation & Fleet Management Services
N.A.I.C.S.: 485310
Anrew Meyers *(Co-Founder & CEO)*
Jeff Burton *(Co-Founder & CFO)*

KARAS & KARAS GLASS CO. INC.
455 Dorchester Ave, Boston, MA 02127-2707
Tel.: (617) 268-8800   MA
Web Site: http://www.karasglass.com
Year Founded: 1924
Sales Range: $25-49.9 Million
Emp.: 175
Glass Suppliers & Contract Layers Whslr
N.A.I.C.S.: 238130
Joseph Karas *(Pres)*
Patti Finlayson *(Mgr-Acctg)*
Armand Brunelle *(Project Mgr)*
Stephen Clark *(Project Mgr)*
Kevin Drew *(Supvr)*

KARAVAN TRAILERS INC.
100 Karavan Dr, Fox Lake, WI 53933
Tel.: (920) 928-6200
Web Site:
http://www.karavantrailers.com
Year Founded: 1986
Sales Range: $10-24.9 Million
Emp.: 150
Sales of Trailers & Trailer Equipment
N.A.I.C.S.: 336214
Chip Detuncq *(Controller)*
Gail Lindsey *(Head-HR)*

KARBON BEAUTY LLC
4640 Admiralty Way Ste 500, Marina Del Rey, CA 90292
Tel.: (310) 966-6780
Web Site:
http://www.beautychoice.com
Year Founded: 2007
Sales Range: $1-9.9 Million
Emp.: 5
Online Retailer of Cosmetics, Skincare, Fragrances & Hair Products
N.A.I.C.S.: 456120
Jordan Blum *(Pres)*

KAREN MILLER LTD.
60 W 38th St Fl 2, New York, NY 10018   NY
Year Founded: 1987
Sales Range: $10-24.9 Million
Emp.: 18
Ensemble Dresses Mfr
N.A.I.C.S.: 315250
Mehrdad Sarraf *(Pres)*

KAREN MORSTAD & ASSOCIATES LLC.
79 E Putnam Ave, Greenwich, CT 06830
Tel.: (203) 661-1090
Web Site:
http://www.karenmorstad.com
Year Founded: 2004
Sales Range: $10-24.9 Million
Emp.: 52
N.A.I.C.S.: 541810
Karen Morstad *(Pres)*
Dean Topo *(Art Dir)*

KAREN RADLEY ACURA VOLKSWAGEN
14700 Jefferson Davis Hwy, Woodbridge, VA 22191
Tel.: (703) 497-0900
Web Site:
http://www.karenradleyacura.com
Sales Range: $10-24.9 Million
Emp.: 24
Car Whslr
N.A.I.C.S.: 441110
Rod Emmons *(Gen Mgr)*

KAREO, INC.
3353 Michelson Ste 400, Irvine, CA 92612   CA
Web Site: http://www.kareo.com
Year Founded: 2004
Sales Range: $25-49.9 Million
Emp.: 500
Software Development Services
N.A.I.C.S.: 541511
Dan Rodrigues *(Founder, Chm & CEO)*
Robert Pickell *(CMO)*
Thomas Giannulli *(Chief Medical Information Officer)*
David Mitzenmacher *(VP-Customer Success)*
Nitin Somalwar *(VP & Gen Mgr-Billing Company Channel)*
Drew Hamilton *(Chief Sls Officer)*
Gregg A. Waldon *(CFO)*
Bryan Koch *(Gen Mgr-Managed Billing)*
Robert Fosmire *(VP-Customer Success)*
Chris Lankford *(VP-Engrg)*
Clarissa Riggins *(VP-Product)*
Kyle Ryan *(CTO)*
Brian Tran *(Gen Counsel)*

Subsidiaries:

DoctorBase, Inc.   (1)
576 Sacramento St 3rd & 7th Fl, San Francisco, CA 94111
Tel.: (415) 205-4111
Web Site: http://www.doctorbase.com
Emp.: 27
Develops Software for Practice Marketing & Patient Communications
N.A.I.C.S.: 513210
Mischa Spiegelmock *(CTO)*
John Sung Kim *(CEO)*
Joshua Angeles *(VP-Sls)*
Sean Cottrell *(VP-Ops)*
Emily Novosel *(Mgr-Mktg)*

KARGA SEVEN PICTURES, LLC
1201 W 5th St Ste T-1200, Los Angeles, CA 90017
Tel.: (323) 570-0507
Web Site: https://karga7la.com

U.S. PRIVATE

TV Entertainment Services
N.A.I.C.S.: 512110
Brett Boydstun *(Head-Production & Ops & Exec VP)*
Jason Wolf *(Sr VP & Head-Programming)*
Dan Johnson *(CFO)*
Marianna Cerulle *(VP-Production Acct)*
Ted Garvey *(Dir-Post Production)*

KARIMS INTERNATIONAL USA
10408 W State Rd 84 Ste 101, Davie, FL 33324
Tel.: (305) 620-5466
Web Site: http://www.karims.com
Year Founded: 1991
Sales Range: $10-24.9 Million
Emp.: 30
Import & Export Services
N.A.I.C.S.: 561499
Mohammed Amdani *(Pres)*
Saleem Waldes *(Controller)*

KARINS ENGINEERING GROUP, INC.
2017 Fiesta Dr, Sarasota, FL 34231
Tel.: (941) 927-8525   FL
Web Site: http://www.keg-engineering.com
Year Founded: 1999
Sales Range: $1-9.9 Million
Emp.: 30
Civil, Structural & Mechanical Engineering Services
N.A.I.C.S.: 541330
David G. Karins *(Co-Founder & Pres)*
John F. Bonacci *(Dir-Structural Engrg Design)*
F. Carter Karins *(Co-Founder & CEO)*
Arthur C. Schoenewaldt III *(Dir-Restoration)*

Subsidiaries:

Karins Engineering Group, Inc. - St. Petersburg Office   (1)
290 9th St N Ste 203, Saint Petersburg, FL 33705
Tel.: (727) 895-9119
Web Site: http://www.keg-engineering.com
Emp.: 9
Civil Structural & Mechanical Engineering Services
N.A.I.C.S.: 541330
Christina Grubbs *(Mgr-Reg)*

KARL FLAMMER FORD, INC.
41975 US Hwy 19 N, Tarpon Springs, FL 34689-4115
Tel.: (727) 937-5131
Web Site:
http://www.karlflammerford.com
Sales Range: $25-49.9 Million
Emp.: 50
Car Whslr
N.A.I.C.S.: 441110
Jim Flammer *(Gen Mgr)*
Nancy J. Flammer *(Sec)*
Dawn Galla *(Mgr-Customer Rels)*
Matt Stuecher *(Principal)*

KARL KNAUZ MOTORS INC.
409 Skokie Hwy, Lake Bluff, IL 60044
Tel.: (847) 234-1700
Web Site: http://www.knauz.com
Rev.: $51,500,000
Emp.: 300
Automobiles, New & Used
N.A.I.C.S.: 441110
William Madden *(Pres)*
Ron Lofchie *(CFO)*

KARL R. JOHNSON TRUCKING, INC.
2627 E 139 St, Burnham, IL 60633
Tel.: (708) 868-0059
Web Site: http://www.mrbults.com

Year Founded: 1984
Sales Range: $10-24.9 Million
Emp.: 66
Trucking Transport of Solid Waste & Raw Materials
N.A.I.C.S.: 484220
Karl R. Johnson *(Founder, Pres & CEO)*

KARL'S RENTAL CENTER INC.
7000 S Tenth St, Oak Creek, WI 53154-1421
Tel.: (414) 831-7069
Web Site: http://www.karls.com
Year Founded: 1966
Rev.: $6,000,000
Emp.: 300
Party & Event Equipment Rental
N.A.I.C.S.: 532289
Ron Creten *(Pres & COO)*

KARLEN WILLIAMS GRAYBILL ADVERTISING
512 7th Ave 41st Fl, New York, NY 10018
Tel.: (212) 414-9000
Web Site: http://www.kwgadv.com
Year Founded: 1967
Rev.: $44,000,000
Emp.: 20
N.A.I.C.S.: 541810
Jim Williams *(Pres)*
Jeff Graybill *(Partner)*

KARLIN+PIMSLER
1375 Broadway Ste 1400, New York, NY 10018
Tel.: (212) 779-2111   NY
Web Site:
   http://www.karlinpimsler.com
Year Founded: 1995
Rev.: $17,000,000
Emp.: 10
Business-To-Business, Collateral, Consulting, Consumer Marketing, Corporate Identity, Direct Marketing, Internet/Web Design, Logo & Package Design, Sales Promotion, Strategic Planning/Research, T.V.
N.A.I.C.S.: 541810
Malcolm T. Karlin *(Pres, Chief Creative Officer)*
Stephen Pimsler *(VP & Dir-Creative)*

KARMAK INC.
1 Karmak Plz, Carlinville, IL 62626
Tel.: (217) 854-4721
Web Site: http://www.karmak.com
Year Founded: 1974
Rev.: $15,200,000
Emp.: 175
Turnkey Vendors, Computer Systems
N.A.I.C.S.: 541512
J. Richard Schien *(Chm)*
Gail Wilkinson *(VP-HR)*
John Lebel *(CTO)*
Scott Elbring *(VP-Sls & Mktg)*
Jim Allen *(VP-Client Svcs)*
Adam Madsen *(VP-Bus Solutions)*
Linda Schien *(Treas & Sec)*
John Pacione *(Pres & CEO)*

Subsidiaries:

Adam Systems   (1)
30500 State Hwy 181 Ste 462, Spanish Fort, AL 36527-5824
Web Site: http://www.adamdms.com
Process, Physical Distribution & Logistics Consulting Services
N.A.I.C.S.: 541614
Mike Riley *(Gen Mgr)*

KARMART CHRYSLER DODGE VOLKSWAGEN MITSUBISHI
660 Auto Blvd, Burlington, WA 98233
Tel.: (360) 757-2273

Web Site: http://www.karmartusa.com
Rev.: $95,000,000
Emp.: 100
Automobiles, New & Used
N.A.I.C.S.: 441110
Jim Draper *(Gen Mgr)*

KARMASPHERE, INC.
19200 Stevens Creek Blvd Ste 130, Cupertino, CA 95014
Tel.: (650) 292-6100
Web Site:
   http://www.karmasphere.com
Sales Range: $1-9.9 Million
Software Developer
N.A.I.C.S.: 513210
Gail Ennis *(CEO)*
Martin Hall *(Chm & Exec VP-Corp Dev)*
Mike Azevedo *(VP-Worldwide Sls & Channels)*
Richard J. Guth *(CMO & VP-Mktg)*
Abe Taha *(VP-Engrg)*

KARNAK CORPORATION
330 Central Ave, Clark, NJ 07066-1108
Tel.: (732) 388-0300   NJ
Web Site: http://www.karnakcorp.com
Year Founded: 1932
Sales Range: $150-199.9 Million
Emp.: 90
Sealants, Adhesives & Coatings for Roofing & Waterproofing Mfr & Whslr
N.A.I.C.S.: 325520
James D. Hannah *(Pres)*
Chris Salazar *(COO)*
Sean Smith *(Dir-Mfg)*
Sarah J. Jelin *(Chm & Pres)*
John McDermott *(VP-Sls)*
Joe Eckstein *(Mgr-Sls-Midwest)*
Chris Huettig *(Dir-Technical Sls-Natl)*
Johnny Smith *(Mgr-Sls-Southwest)*
David Gritz *(CFO)*
Ansil Dyal *(Mgr-Technical Svcs)*
Todd Harris *(Mgr-Sls-Eastern)*
Jim Grauer *(Mgr-Southeast)*

KARNS PRIME AND FANCY FOOD
675 Silver Spring Rd, Mechanicsburg, PA 17050
Tel.: (717) 766-6477
Web Site: http://www.karnsfoods.com
Sales Range: $75-99.9 Million
Emp.: 900
Grocery Store Operator
N.A.I.C.S.: 445110
Ruth Karns Rudderow *(VP)*
D. Scott Kerns *(Pres)*
Ted Kintz *(VP-Perishables)*

KARPREILLY, LLC
104 Field Point Rd, Greenwich, CT 06830
Tel.: (203) 504-9900   DE
Web Site: http://www.karpreilly.com
Privater Equity Firm
N.A.I.C.S.: 523999
Allan W. Karp *(Co-Founder & Partner)*
Christopher K. Reilly *(Co-Founder & Partner)*
Billy Logan *(Partner)*
Adam Burgoon *(Partner)*
Ajay Natrajan *(CFO)*
Andrew Keating *(Partner)*
Hank Spring *(Principal)*
Ryan Greene *(VP)*
Rich Reuter *(VP)*

Subsidiaries:

XS Cargo   (1)
15435 131 Avenue, Edmonton, T5V 0A4, AB, Canada
Tel.: (780) 413-4296
Web Site: http://www.shopxscargo.com

Sales Range: $100-124.9 Million
Emp.: 113
Discount Merchandise Retailer
N.A.I.C.S.: 455110
Michael J. McKenna *(Pres & CEO)*

Zola   (1)
1501-A Vermont St, San Francisco, CA 94107
Tel.: (415) 775-6355
Web Site: http://www.livezola.com
Sales Range: $1-9.9 Million
Beverage & Confection Mfr & Marketer
N.A.I.C.S.: 312111
Rosa Compean *(VP-Mktg)*

KARR BARTH ASSOCIATES INC.
40 Monument Rd, Bala Cynwyd, PA 19004
Tel.: (610) 660-4600
Web Site: http://www.karr-barthassociates.com
Year Founded: 1967
Sales Range: $50-74.9 Million
Emp.: 300
Business & Investment Planning Services
N.A.I.C.S.: 523940
David D. Brain *(Dir-Advanced Plng)*
James Frank *(Dir-Fin Plng)*
Matthew Crane *(Div VP)*
Robert F. Cranshaw *(COO)*
Christopher Faust *(Div VP)*
Brad Minor *(Div VP)*
Andrew J. Pompe *(Div VP)*

KARRIERS INC.
809 S 48th St, Grand Forks, ND 58201
Tel.: (701) 746-8307
Sales Range: $10-24.9 Million
Emp.: 14
Trucking Service
N.A.I.C.S.: 484121
Wayne Anderson *(VP)*
Brooky Anderson *(Pres)*

KARSTEN MANUFACTURING CORPORATION
2201 W Desert Cove Ave, Phoenix, AZ 85029
Tel.: (800) 474-6434   AZ
Web Site: http://www.ping.com
Year Founded: 1959
Golf Equipment Mfr
N.A.I.C.S.: 339920
John A. Solheim *(CEO)*
Rawleigh Grove *(VP & Gen Counsel)*

Subsidiaries:

Dolphin, Inc.   (1)
740 S 59th Ave, Phoenix, AZ 85043-4509
Tel.: (602) 272-6747
Web Site: http://www.dolphincasting.com
Sales Range: $10-24.9 Million
Emp.: 70
Precision Castings
N.A.I.C.S.: 331524
Pete Poleon *(Gen Mgr)*

Ping Canada Corporation   (1)
2790 Brighton Road, Oakville, L6H 5T4, ON, Canada   (100%)
Tel.: (905) 829-8004
Sales Range: $10-24.9 Million
Emp.: 30
Wholesale Golf Equipment
N.A.I.C.S.: 459110

Ping Inc.   (1)
2201 W Desert Cove Ave, Phoenix, AZ 85029-4912
Tel.: (602) 687-5000
Web Site: http://www.ping.com
Sales Range: $50-74.9 Million
Golf Irons Wood Putter Bag Carry Bag & Wood Cover Mfr
N.A.I.C.S.: 423440
John K. Solheim *(Pres)*

Division (Domestic):

Maximet   (2)
5923 W Monroe, Phoenix, AZ 85043
Tel.: (602) 272-3241
Mfr of Specialized Ferrous & Non-Ferrous Components & Assemblies Requiring Brazing or Metal Joining
N.A.I.C.S.: 811490

KAS INVESTMENT CO. INC.
3121 40th Ave NW Ste 100, Rochester, MN 55901
Tel.: (507) 280-4314
Web Site:
   http://www.kasinvestment.com
Sales Range: $10-24.9 Million
Emp.: 5
Glass & Glazing Work
N.A.I.C.S.: 238150
Kevin J. Swanson *(Pres)*
Michelle Howard *(Controller & VP)*
Peter Foley *(Mgr-Pur)*
Mitchell Swanson *(VP & Mgr-Sls)*

KASA COMPANIES INC.
418 E Ave B, Salina, KS 67401
Tel.: (785) 404-3600
Web Site:
   http://www.kasacompanies.com
Year Founded: 1974
Sales Range: $25-49.9 Million
Emp.: 170
Investment Management Service
N.A.I.C.S.: 523940
Dan Stutterheim *(Pres)*

KASA INDUSTRIAL CONTROLS INC.
418 E Ave B, Salina, KS 67401
Tel.: (785) 825-7181
Web Site:
   http://www.kasacontrols.com
Year Founded: 1974
Sales Range: $10-24.9 Million
Emp.: 160
Control Panels, Electric
N.A.I.C.S.: 335313
Dan Stutterheim *(Pres)*

KASBAR NATIONAL INDUSTRIES, INC.
370 Reed Rd Ste 200, Broomall, PA 19008
Tel.: (610) 544-7117
Web Site:
   http://www.kasbarnational.com
Year Founded: 1942
Textile Products Mfr
N.A.I.C.S.: 314999
Stephen Derman *(Pres, CFO & COO)*
Jeffrey Shapiro *(Chm & CEO)*
Larry Wright *(VP-Mktg)*
Daniel Fisher *(Dir-Ops)*
Linda Long *(Acctg Mgr)*
Charles Noone *(Sr Acct Exec)*
Kenneth Bigelow *(Sr Acct Exec)*
Scott Mauney *(Dir-Mfg-Nonwovens-Columbia)*

KASCO CORPORATION
1600 E 4th Ave, El Paso, TX 79901
Tel.: (915) 544-1210
Web Site:
   http://www.kascoventures.com
Year Founded: 1976
Sales Range: $10-24.9 Million
Emp.: 10
Developer & Manager of Commercial & Industrial Real Estate Properties: Real Estate Investment Trusts
N.A.I.C.S.: 525990
William F. Kastrin *(Pres)*
Veronica K. Callaghan *(VP-Mktg)*

Subsidiaries:

Kasco Ventures Inc.   (1)

KASCO CORPORATION

Kasco Corporation—(Continued)
1600 E 4th Ave, El Paso, TX 79901
Tel.: (915) 544-1210
Web Site: http://www.kascoventures.com
Subdividers & Developers
N.A.I.C.S.: 237210
William F. Kastrin (Pres)
Veronica K. Callaghan (VP-Mktg)

Southwest Growth Corporation (1)
1600 E 4th Ave, El Paso, TX 79901
Tel.: (915) 533-7483
Web Site: http://www.elpasosteel.com
Steel Mfrs
N.A.I.C.S.: 331110

KASON INDUSTRIES INCORPORATED
57 Amlajack Blvd, Newnan, GA 30265
Tel.: (770) 251-1422
Web Site: http://www.kasonind.com
Year Founded: 1926
Sales Range: $50-74.9 Million
Emp.: 260
Hardware Mfr
N.A.I.C.S.: 332510
Alexander Katz (Treas)
Peter Katz (Pres)
Sean Leroux (Plant Mgr)
Tracy Dunsmore (Supvr-Production)
Rick Truskolaski (Mgr-Mfg)
David Ring (VP-Sls & Mktg)

KASOWITZ BENSON TORRES & FRIEDMAN LLP
1633 Broadway, New York, NY 10019
Tel.: (212) 506-1700
Web Site: http://www.kasowitz.com
Year Founded: 1993
Sales Range: $200-249.9 Million
Emp.: 340
Law firm
N.A.I.C.S.: 541110
Daniel Fetterman (Partner)
John Berlinski (Partner)
Andrew K. Glenn (Partner)
Michael Bowen (Partner)
Mitchell R. Schrage (Mng Partner-Ops & Partner)
Sheron Korpus (Partner)
Trevor Welch (Partner)
Wallace Schwartz (Partner)
David W. Fermino (Partner-San Francisco)

KASPER MACHINE CO.
29275 Stephenson Hwy, Madison Heights, MI 48071-2316
Tel.: (248) 547-3150
Precision Boring & Turning Machines Mfr
N.A.I.C.S.: 333517
Elizabeth Smith (Office Mgr)

KASS BROS INC.
PO Box 487, Westwego, LA 70096
Tel.: (504) 348-9018
Web Site: http://www.kassbros.com
Rev.: $10,679,065
Emp.: 78
Excavation & Grading, Building Construction
N.A.I.C.S.: 238910
Calvin Kass (Co-Pres)
Gene Kass (Co-Pres)
Patty Guidry (Office Mgr)

KASS INDUSTRIAL SUPPLY CORP.
1715 Washington Ave, Bronx, NY 10457
Tel.: (718) 299-6060
Web Site: http://www.kassind.com
Rev.: $16,000,000
Emp.: 35
Hardware

N.A.I.C.S.: 423710
Allen Kass (Pres)
Marty Kass (Owner & Co-Pres)

KASSEL EQUITY GROUP, LLC
7686 Fishel Dr N Ste B, Dublin, OH 43016
Tel.: (614) 310-4060
Web Site: http://www.kasselequity.com
Year Founded: 2010
Private Investment Firm
N.A.I.C.S.: 523999
Thomas Werner (CEO & Mng Partner)
Brett Motherwell (Mng Partner, CFO & Exec VP)
David Covert (CTO)
Aja De Los Santos (Mng Dir)
Felipe Gonzalez (Mng Dir-Real Estate Ops)
Brenda Werner (Pres-Real Estate)

Subsidiaries:

KE Gutridge, LLC (1)
88 S 2nd St, Newark, OH 43055
Tel.: (740) 349-9411
Web Site: http://www.gutridge.com
Plumbing, Heating & Air-Conditioning Contractor
N.A.I.C.S.: 238220

Purdy Electric, Inc. (1)
2510 Englewood Dr, Columbus, OH 43219
Tel.: (614) 471-5999
Electronic Services
N.A.I.C.S.: 238210
John Purdy (Pres)

KASSIK MILLING CO.
309 Main St, Milligan, NE 68406
Tel.: (402) 629-4241
Web Site: http://www.kassikmilling.com
Sales Range: $10-24.9 Million
Emp.: 16
Animal Feed Mfr
N.A.I.C.S.: 311119
Michael Kassik (Pres)

KASSOY, LLC
101 Commercial St Ste 200, Plainview, NY 11803
Tel.: (516) 942-0560
Web Site: http://www.kassoy.com
Rev.: $10,000,000
Emp.: 30
Jewelry Tools & Supplies
N.A.I.C.S.: 332216
Jaclyn Smutny (Supvr-Customer Svc)
Alan Berner (Supvr-Pur)
Catherine Dugan (Dir-Mktg)
Hans E. R. Bosch (Interim Pres)
David Allen (Gen Mgr)

KAST CONSTRUCTION COMPANY, LLC
701 S Olive Ave Ste 105, West Palm Beach, FL 33401
Tel.: (561) 689-2910
Web Site: http://www.kastbuild.com
Sales Range: $25-49.9 Million
Emp.: 60
Construction Services
N.A.I.C.S.: 236220
Mike Neal (Pres & CEO)
Eric Plotke (VP-Ops)
Dave DeMay (VP)
Roger Whitman (CFO)
Chandler Aden (Dir-Preconstruction Svcs)
Ashlee Figg (Dir-Bus Dev)
Page McKee (VP-Tampa)
Ashlee Kinback (VP-Bus Dev-Bus Unit-Tampa)

Sean Ouellette (VP-Ops-Bus Unit-Tampa)
Kristine Retetagos (VP-Preconstruction Svcs)

KASTEEL ENTERPRISES, INC.
552 Vandiviere Rd, Dawsonville, GA 30534
Tel.: (706) 265-2944
Sales Range: $10-24.9 Million
Emp.: 13
Commercial & Institutional Building Construction Services
N.A.I.C.S.: 236220
Chad Muilenburg (CEO)
Tiffany Muilenburg (CFO & Sec)

KASTEN MASONRY SALES INC.
713 Kasten Dr, Jackson, MO 63755
Tel.: (573) 243-3591
Web Site: http://www.kastenmasonry.com
Rev.: $13,282,445
Emp.: 43
Brick & Construction Product Sales
N.A.I.C.S.: 423320

KASTLE ELECTRIC COMPANY
4501 Kettering Blvd, Dayton, OH 45439
Tel.: (513) 360-2901
Web Site: http://www.kastle-group.com
Sales Range: $10-24.9 Million
Emp.: 55
General Electrical Contractor
N.A.I.C.S.: 238210
K. Andrew Stuhlmiller (CEO)
Gregory Brush (Pres)

KASTLE SYSTEMS INTERNATIONAL LLC
6402 Arlington Blvd, Falls Church, VA 22042
Tel.: (855) 527-8531
Web Site: http://www.kastle.com
Year Founded: 1972
Office Security Systems
N.A.I.C.S.: 561621
Piyush Sodha (Co-Chm)
Haniel Lynn (CEO)
Mark Erin (CO-Chairman)
Tom Radigan (Chief Customer Officer)
Mohammad Soleimani (Chief Innovation Officer)
Ralph Masino (CFO)
Jake Heinz (CMO)
Bob Ryan (Chief Sls Officer)
Todd Burner (Sr VP-Product)
Mike Slauson (Gen Mgr-South Region)
Andrea Kuhn (Gen Mgr-Midwestern Region)
Harry Choi (Gen Mgr-Enterprise Accts)
David Fisher (Gen Mgr-Remote Video Monitoring)
John Gellei (Gen Mgr-Australia)
Robert Kieffer (Gen Mgr-Philadelphia)
Al Valvano (CTO)

Subsidiaries:

Kastle Systems LLC (1)
6402 Arlington Blvd, Falls Church, VA 22042
Tel.: (855) 527-8531
Web Site: http://www.kastle.com
Designer, Retailer, Installer & Servicer Electronic Security Systems
N.A.I.C.S.: 561621

Subsidiary (Domestic):

CheckVideo, LLC (2)
6402 Arlington Blvd Ste 200, Falls Church, VA 22042

Tel.: (571) 418-7230
Web Site: http://www.checkvideo.com
Security System Services
N.A.I.C.S.: 561621
Nik Gagvani (Pres & Gen Mgr)

Mutual Central Alarm Service Inc. (2)
10 W 46th St, New York, NY 10036
Tel.: (212) 768-0808
Web Site: http://www.4mutual.com
Security System Services
N.A.I.C.S.: 561621

KASTNER & PARTNERS
150 Pico Blvd, Santa Monica, CA 90405
Tel.: (310) 458-2000
Web Site: http://www.kastnernetwork.us
Sales Range: $100-124.9 Million
Emp.: 60
Advertising Agencies
N.A.I.C.S.: 541810
Tim Braybrooks (Dir-Creative)
Brandon Rochon (Chief Creative Officer)

Subsidiaries:

Kastner & Partners - Saint Louis (1)
612 N 2nd St Ste 401, Saint Louis, MO 63102-2553
Tel.: (314) 735-7900
Web Site: http://www.kastnernetwork.us
Sales Range: Less than $1 Million
Emp.: 10
Advertising Agencies
N.A.I.C.S.: 541810
Tim Braybrooks (Dir-Creative)

KATAHDIN INDUSTRIES, INC.
63 Sprague St, Boston, MA 02136
Tel.: (781) 329-1420
Web Site: http://www.katahdin-inc.com
Year Founded: 1969
Sales Range: $25-49.9 Million
Support Services
N.A.I.C.S.: 561499
Tim Cabot (CEO)
Robert DeAngelis (Treas)
Steven Schaepe (CFO & Exec VP)

Subsidiaries:

Precision Coating Co., Inc. (1)
51 Parmenter Rd, Hudson, MA 01749
Tel.: (978) 562-7561
Web Site: http://www.precisioncoating.com
Rev.: $2,333,333
Emp.: 50
Metal Coating, Engraving, except Jewelry & Silverware & Allied Services to Manufacturers
N.A.I.C.S.: 332812
Craig Jones (Mgr-Sls-Reg)

KATALYST PARTNERS, LLC
111 Dunnell Rd Ste 201, Maplewood, NJ 07040
Tel.: (973) 500-6669
Web Site: http://www.katalystpartners.com
Business Technical Support Services
N.A.I.C.S.: 561499
Boris Katsnelson (Mng Partner)

KATHERINE'S COLLECTION INC.
370 Falls Commerce Pkwy, Cuyahoga Falls, OH 44224
Tel.: (330) 572-2780
Web Site: http://www.katherinescollection.com
Rev.: $10,758,083
Emp.: 50
Maps & Charts
N.A.I.C.S.: 424990
Fran Folwarczny (Controller)
Gary Giller (CEO)

KATOM RESTAURANT SUPPLY INC
305 KaTom Dr, Kodak, TN 37764
Tel.: (423) 586-5758
Web Site: http://www.katom.com
Year Founded: 1987
Sales Range: $25-49.9 Million
Emp.: 75
Kitchen Equipment Supplies
N.A.I.C.S.: 423740
Patricia Bible *(Founder, Pres & CEO)*
Dawn Conner *(Dir-Bid)*
Birdie Eslinger *(Office Mgr)*

KATTEN MUCHIN ROSENMAN LLP
525 W Monroe St, Chicago, IL 60661-3693
Tel.: (312) 902-5200   IL
Web Site: http://www.kattenlaw.com
Year Founded: 1974
Sales Range: $450-499.9 Million
Emp.: 1,001
Legal Advisory Services
N.A.I.C.S.: 541110
Geoff AuYeung *(Partner)*
Kristin J. Achterhof *(Partner)*
Sheldon I. Banoff *(Partner)*
Seth M. Aigner *(Partner)*
Gil M. Soffer *(Mng Partner)*
Christopher S. Atkinson *(Partner)*
Karin H. Berg *(Partner)*
David C. Bohan *(Partner)*
Cathleen A. Booth *(Partner)*
Gregory K. Brown *(Partner)*
Matthew S. Brown *(Partner)*
Robert T. Smith *(Partner)*
Gregory C. Dillard *(Mng Partner-Houston)*
Ben Patton *(Partner)*
Kimberly T. Smith *(Partner)*
Joshua Yablonski *(Partner)*
Andrew J. Demko *(Partner)*
Roger P. Furey *(Chm)*
Julia Schmidt *(Partner)*
Michael Justus *(Partner)*
Brandon Hadley *(Partner)*
Polly Sprenger *(Partner-London)*
Peter Sugden *(Mng Partner-UK)*
Craig Courter *(COO)*
Michelle A. Gyves *(Partner-Corp & Private Equity Practice-New York)*
Renee Lercher *(CFO)*

KATZ & KATZ TRANSFER, INC.
2044 NW 25th Ave, Pompano Beach, FL 33069
Tel.: (954) 927-0104
Web Site: http://www.kktransfer.com
Year Founded: 1987
Sales Range: $1-9.9 Million
Emp.: 20
Moving, Delivery, Storage & Warehousing
N.A.I.C.S.: 484220
Steven Katz *(Pres)*

KATZ SAPPER & MILLER LLP
800 E 96th St Ste 500, Indianapolis, IN 46240
Tel.: (317) 580-2000
Web Site: http://www.ksmcpa.com
Year Founded: 1993
Sales Range: $10-24.9 Million
Emp.: 240
Certified Public Accountants
N.A.I.C.S.: 541211
Donna Niesen *(Partner)*
Tim Almack *(Partner)*
Timothy J. Duvall *(Partner)*
Mark Flinchum *(Partner)*
Mike Lee *(Partner)*
Scott Schuster *(Partner)*
Corey Massella *(Partner)*
Curtis Miller *(Chm)*
David B. Charles *(Partner)*
Jay D. Benjamin *(Partner)*
John R. Bruch *(Partner)*
Mark N. Bernstein *(Partner)*
Patrick R. Brauer *(Partner)*
Rosanne E. Ammirati *(Partner)*
Tim C. Cook *(Partner)*
Jamie S. Ellis *(COO & Partner)*
Chris Lane *(Mgr-Tax)*
Kevin Newingham *(Dir-Healthcare Consulting)*
Jennifer Moore *(CMO)*
Ryan Elpers *(Chief Growth Officer)*
Charles C. Brandt III *(Partner)*

KATZMAN FAMILY SUPPORT FOUNDATION
6735 Telegraph Rd, Bloomfield Hills, MI 48301
Tel.: (248) 642-4260   MI
Year Founded: 2002
Rev.: $9,259,271
Fiscal Year-end: 05/31/14
Community Welfare Services
N.A.I.C.S.: 624190
David Katzman *(Pres)*
Dorothy Benyas *(Treas)*
Howard Neistein *(Asst Sec)*
Scott Kaufman *(Sec & VP)*

KATZSON BROS, INC.
960 Vallejo St, Denver, CO 80204-3843
Tel.: (303) 893-3535
Web Site: http://www.katzson.com
Year Founded: 1960
Sales Range: $10-24.9 Million
Emp.: 32
Hotel Supplies, Laundry & Dry Cleaning Supplies Distr
N.A.I.C.S.: 423850
Richard H. Right *(Owner)*

KAUFFMAN POULTRY FARMS, INC.
8519 Leland Rd, Waterman, IL 60556
Tel.: (815) 264-3470   IL
Web Site: http://www.hokaturkeys.com
Year Founded: 1933
Sales Range: Less than $1 Million
Emp.: 7
Poultry Grower & Processor
N.A.I.C.S.: 112330
Robert Kauffman *(Pres)*
Tom Klopfenstein *(Gen Mgr)*

KAUFFMAN TIRE INC.
2832 Anivelle Block Rd, Ellenwood, GA 30294-6009
Tel.: (404) 762-4944   GA
Web Site: http://www.kauffmantire.com
Year Founded: 1936
Sales Range: $25-49.9 Million
Emp.: 300
Supplier of Tires
N.A.I.C.S.: 423130
Andy Peterman *(Dir-Online & Special Channel Sls)*
Gwen Rimes *(Mgr-Credit)*
Michael Stine *(Mgr-Store)*
Mickey Payne *(Mgr-Sls)*
Mondrella Glenn *(Mgr-Sls)*
Rob Salter *(Mgr-HR)*
Brian Wilhite *(Dir-Mktg)*
Korey Smith *(Gen Mgr)*

Subsidiaries:

Kauffman Tire Service of Cincinnati Inc.   (1)
12000 Mosteler Rd Ste 100, Cincinnati, OH 45241
Tel.: (513) 772-8473
Web Site: http://www.kauffmantire.net
Sales Range: $10-24.9 Million
Emp.: 5
Wholesale Of Tires & Tubes
N.A.I.C.S.: 423130

KAUFMAN ADVERTISING AGENCY
412 W 10th St, Kansas City, MO 64105-1459
Tel.: (816) 221-8840
Web Site: http://www.batteryoperatedcandles.net
Year Founded: 1950
Sales Range: $10-24.9 Million
Emp.: 13
In House Advertising Agency
N.A.I.C.S.: 541810
H.G. Kaufman *(Owner)*

KAUFMAN COMPANY INC.
19 Walkhall Rd, Norwood, MA 02062
Tel.: (617) 491-5500
Web Site: http://www.kaufmanco.com
Sales Range: $10-24.9 Million
Emp.: 50
Industrial Tools
N.A.I.C.S.: 541618
Norman Kaufman *(Pres)*

KAUFMAN CONTAINER CO.
1000 Keystone Pkwy Ste 100, Cleveland, OH 44135
Tel.: (216) 898-2000
Web Site: http://www.kaufmancontainer.com
Rev.: $14,700,000
Emp.: 160
Industrial Supplies
N.A.I.C.S.: 423840
Roger Seid *(CEO)*

KAUFMAN LYNN CONSTRUCTION, INC.
4850 T-Rex Ave Ste 300, Boca Raton, FL 33431
Tel.: (561) 361-6700
Web Site: http://www.kaufmanlynn.com
Year Founded: 1989
Sales Range: $50-74.9 Million
Emp.: 75
Commercial Construction Services
N.A.I.C.S.: 236220
Michael Kaufman *(Pres & CEO)*
Neil J. Carson *(Mng Dir-Multifamily Dev)*
Douglas Simms *(CFO)*
Chris Long *(COO)*
Sam Doggart *(Exec VP-Preconstruction)*
Frank White *(Sr VP-Multifamily Dev)*
Garret Southern *(VP-Ops)*
Derek Wolfhope *(VP-Ops)*
Dan Root *(VP-Ops)*
Tom Thrasher *(VP-Ops-South Florida)*
Jeff Zalkin *(VP-Dev)*
Tayler Novick *(Mgr-HR)*
Joshua M. Atlas *(Chief Legal Officer)*

KAUFMAN MFG. COMPANY
547 S 29th St, Manitowoc, WI 54220
Tel.: (920) 684-6641
Web Site: http://www.kaufmanmfg.com
Year Founded: 1927
Sales Range: $50-74.9 Million
Emp.: 100
Metal Cutting Tool Mfr
N.A.I.C.S.: 333517
Mike Kurtem *(VP-Engrg)*
Robert E. Kaufman *(Owner)*
Tyler Bowring *(Engr-Application)*
Dan Meneau *(Mgr-Mfg)*

KAUFMAN, ROSSIN & CO., PROFESSIONAL ASSOCIATION
2699 S Bayshore Dr Ste 500, Miami, FL 33133
Tel.: (305) 858-5600   FL
Web Site: http://www.kaufmanrossin.com
Year Founded: 1962
Sales Range: $10-24.9 Million
Emp.: 300
Certified Public Accountants
N.A.I.C.S.: 541211
Cary Valdes-Perez *(Mgr-Assurance & Advisory Svcs Dept)*
Kenneth Rios *(Principal-Tax)*
Paul Blackwell *(Assoc Principal-Assurance)*
Jennifer Newton *(Dir-Consumer Fin Svcs Compliance)*
Ricardo Gomez *(Principal-Risk Advisory Svcs Practice)*

KAUTEX MACHINES, INC.
25 Columbia Rd, North Branch, NJ 08876
Tel.: (908) 252-9350
Web Site: http://www.kautex-group.com
Emp.: 400
Plastics & Machinery Equipments Mfr
N.A.I.C.S.: 333998
Chuck Flammer *(VP-Sls)*
Andreas Lichtenauer *(Partner & Mng Dir)*
Olaf Weiland *(CEO & Partner)*
Frank Rohrlein *(Partner & CFO)*
Andras Schulz *(Partner & Dir-Strategic Pur Logistics)*

KAVALA, INC.
645 E Dania Beach Blvd, Dania Beach, FL 33004
Tel.: (954) 922-6700   FL
Sales Range: $10-24.9 Million
Emp.: 20
Real Estate
N.A.I.C.S.: 531210
Ace J. Blackburn Jr. *(Pres)*

KAVANAUGH, INC.
1025 N Sherman Ave, Madison, WI 53704
Tel.: (608) 249-0193   WI
Web Site: http://www.kavanaughsesquire.club
Full-Service Restaurants
N.A.I.C.S.: 722511
John Kavanaugh *(Owner)*

KAW VALLEY COMPANIES, INC.
5600 Kansas Ave, Kansas City, KS 66106-1147
Tel.: (913) 281-9950
Web Site: http://www.kawvalleyco.com
Year Founded: 1984
Sales Range: $10-24.9 Million
Emp.: 69
Construction Materials Whslr
N.A.I.C.S.: 423320
Brad George *(Project Mgr)*

KAWA CAPITAL MANAGEMENT, INC.
21500 Biscayne Blvd Ste 700, Aventura, FL 33180
Tel.: (305) 560-5200
Web Site: http://www.kawa.com
Year Founded: 2007
Rev.: $600,000,000
Private Equity & Portfolio Management
N.A.I.C.S.: 523999
Daniel Ades *(Mng Partner & Chief Investment Officer)*

KAWA CAPITAL MANAGEMENT, INC.

Kawa Capital Management, Inc.—(Continued)
Felipe Lemos (Partner & COO)
Alexandre Saverin (Partner-Portfolio Mgmt)
Luciano Lautenberg (Partner-IR)
James Ivo Almuli (Partner-IR)
Jeremy Traster (Chief Compliance Officer & Gen Counsel)
Cristina Baldim (Partner-Investments)
Chris Chakford (Mng Dir-Investments)

Subsidiaries:

Conergy Global Solutions GmbH (1)
Anckelmannsplatz 1, 20537, Hamburg, Germany
Tel.: (49) 40271421000
Web Site: http://www.conergy-group.com
Sales Range: $600-649.9 Million
Emp.: 300
Holding Company; Regenerative Energy Systems Mfr
N.A.I.C.S.: 551112
Alexander Gorski (COO & Member-Mgmt Bd)
R. Andrew dePass (Chm)
Anthony Fotopoulos (CEO-America & Member-Mgmt Bd)

Subsidiary (Domestic):

Conergy Deutschland GmbH (2)
Bleichenbrucke 10, 20354, Hamburg, Germany
Tel.: (49) 40 236 208 0
Web Site: http://www.conergy.com
Solar Panels Whslr
N.A.I.C.S.: 423440

Subsidiary (Domestic):

Mounting Systems GmbH (3)
Mittenwalder Strasse 9A, 15834, Rangsdorf, Brandenburg, Germany
Tel.: (49) 337085290
Web Site: http://www.mounting-systems.de
Sales Range: $25-49.9 Million
Emp.: 200
Solar Mounting System Mfr
N.A.I.C.S.: 335132
Stefan Spork (Mng Dir)

Subsidiary (Non-US):

Conergy India (2)
660/1 100 Feet Road, Indiranagar, Bengaluru, 560 038, Karnataka, India
Tel.: (91) 8041880900
Sales Range: $25-49.9 Million
Emp.: 90
Solar Integrated Equipments Mfr
N.A.I.C.S.: 333414
Angel Bernardo (Coord-Sls Support)

Conergy Italia SpA (2)
Via Zamenhof 200, 36100, Vicenza, Italy
Tel.: (39) 0444380131
Web Site: http://www.conergy.it
Photovoltaic Modules Whslr
N.A.I.C.S.: 423690
Giuseppe Sofia (CEO)

Conergy Pte Ltd (2)
120 Robinson Road 12-01 Parakou Building, Singapore, 068913, Singapore
Tel.: (65) 6849 5540
Renewable Energy System Mfr
N.A.I.C.S.: 334413

Subsidiary (Domestic):

Conergy Asia & ME Pte Ltd (3)
120 Robinson Road #12-01, Singapore, 068913, Singapore
Tel.: (65) 68495540
Web Site: http://asia.conergy.com
Solar Power Solutions
N.A.I.C.S.: 221114
Alexander Lenz (Pres)

Subsidiary (Non-US):

Conergy Pty Limited (2)
Unit 6 44-48 O'Dea Avenue, Waterloo, 2017, NSW, Australia
Tel.: (61) 285072222
Web Site: http://www.conergy.com.au
Photovoltaic Systems Distr
N.A.I.C.S.: 423490

Conergy SAS (2)
ZAC Nicopolis - Route Nationale 7, 83170, Brignoles, Var, France
Tel.: (33) 4 9477 5400
Web Site: http://www.conergy.fr
Sales Range: $25-49.9 Million
Emp.: 17
Solar Panels Distr
N.A.I.C.S.: 423690

Subsidiary (US):

Conergy, Inc. (2)
2460 W 26th Ave Ste 280C, Denver, CO 80211
Tel.: (888) 396-6611
Sales Range: $10-24.9 Million
Emp.: 18
Solar Power Products Whslr
N.A.I.C.S.: 423440
Anthony Fotopoulos (CEO-Americas)

Subsidiary (Domestic):

EPURON GmbH (2)
Anckelmannsplatz 1, 20537, Hamburg, Germany
Tel.: (49) 40 2714 23000
Web Site: http://www.epuron.de
Energy Projects Development Services
N.A.I.C.S.: 237130
Michael Weibflog (Mng Dir)

Subsidiary (Non-US):

EPURON EPE (2)
Vouliagmenis 4, Glyfada, 166 75, Athens, Greece
Tel.: (30) 2109604205
Web Site: http://www.epuron.de
Photovoltaic Device Mfr
N.A.I.C.S.: 334413

EPURON Pty Ltd (3)
Level 11 75 Miller Street, North Sydney, Sydney, 2060, NSW, Australia
Tel.: (61) 284567400
Web Site: http://www.epuron.com.au
Emp.: 20
Power Plant Management Services
N.A.I.C.S.: 541618
Andrew Durran (Co-Founder & Exec Dir)
Martin Poole (Co-Founder & Exec Dir)
Andrew Wilson (Gen Mgr-Wind)
Anthony Melov (Sr Project Mgr)
Daniel Gilbert (Mgr-Solar Asset)
Donna Bolton (Sr Project Mgr)
Michelle Willis-Davis (Sec & Mgr-Fin & Admin)

EPURON SARL (3)
9 Avenue de Paris, Vincennes, 94300, Val-de-Marne, France
Tel.: (33) 1 4174 7040
Web Site: http://www.epuron.fr
Emp.: 10
Eletric Power Generation Services
N.A.I.C.S.: 221118
Jean-Baptiste Godmet (Mng Dir)

EPURON Spain SLU (3)
C Jazminero 1 1-6, Aguadulce, 04720, Almeria, Spain
Tel.: (34) 950 55 1408
Web Site: http://www.epuron.es
Power Plant Financing & Development Services
N.A.I.C.S.: 237130

KAY & ASSOCIATES INC.
165 N Arlington Hts Rd Ste 150, Buffalo Grove, IL 60089
Tel.: (847) 255-8444 DE
Web Site: http://www.kayinc.com
Year Founded: 1960
Sales Range: $25-49.9 Million
Emp.: 850
Engineeering Services
N.A.I.C.S.: 541330
Gregory G. Kay (Pres)

KAY PACKING COMPANY INC.
PO Box 10874, Houston, TX 77206
Tel.: (713) 751-3020 TX
Year Founded: 1946
Sales Range: $10-24.9 Million
Emp.: 15

Food Packaging Services
N.A.I.C.S.: 424420
Sophia Gerscszen (Pres)

Subsidiaries:

Kay Foods Inc. (1)
611 W Crosstimbers Rd, Houston, TX 77022 (100%)
Tel.: (713) 751-3020
Supplier of Meat Products
N.A.I.C.S.: 424470

KAY SCREEN PRINTING, INC.
57 Kay Indus Dr, Lake Orion, MI 48361
Tel.: (248) 377-4999 DE
Web Site:
http://www.kayautomotive.com
Year Founded: 1968
Sales Range: $25-49.9 Million
Emp.: 325
Commercial Printing
N.A.I.C.S.: 323111
Joseph Kowalczyk (Owner & Pres)

Subsidiaries:

Kay Graficas Automotrices S.A. DE C.V. (1)
Calle 17 No 3272 Parques Industriales Amistad, 25017, Saltillo, Mexico
Tel.: (52) 84 4438 4300
Commercial Printing Services
N.A.I.C.S.: 323111

Kay Premium Marking Films, Ltd. (1)
Oakwood Close Penyfan Industrial Park, Crumlin, Newport, NP11 3HY, Wales, United Kingdom
Tel.: (44) 1495 242300
Web Site: http://www.kpmf.com
Emp.: 75
Graphic Design Services
N.A.I.C.S.: 541430
Mitch Backenstose (Mng Dir)

Subsidiary (US):

KPMF USA Inc (2)
57 Kay Industrial Dr, Lake Orion, MI 48361
Tel.: (248) 377-4999
Web Site: http://www.kpmfusa.com
Graphic Design Services
N.A.I.C.S.: 541430

KAY UPHOSTERY
1201 W Bankhead, New Albany, MS 38652
Tel.: (662) 534-4762
Sales Range: $300-349.9 Million
Emp.: 600
Investment Holding Companies, Except Banks
N.A.I.C.S.: 337121
Herb Hester (CEO)

KAYA ASSOCIATES INC.
101 Quality Cir Ste 120, Huntsville, AL 35806
Tel.: (256) 382-8084
Web Site: http://www.kayacorp.com
Sales Range: $25-49.9 Million
Emp.: 100
Administrative Management & General Management Consulting Services
N.A.I.C.S.: 541611
John Prince (Co-Founder & CEO)

KAYE CORPORATION
1910 Lookout Dr, North Mankato, MN 56003
Tel.: (507) 625-5293
Web Site: http://www.kayecorp.com
Sales Range: $10-24.9 Million
Emp.: 26
Lawn & Garden Machinery & Equipment
N.A.I.C.S.: 423820

Mike Lloyd (VP-Fin & Controller)
Warren Wilking (Product Mgr)
Steve Lloyd (Product Mgr)
Kevin Lloyd (Pres)

KAYE PUBLISHING CORPORATION
89 5th Ave Ste 901, New York, NY 10003
Tel.: (212) 696-4380
Web Site: http://www.gdusa.com
Emp.: 8
Magazine Publisher
N.A.I.C.S.: 513120
Gordon Kaye (Publr)

Subsidiaries:

Graphic Design USA (1)
89 5th Ave Ste 901, New York, NY 10003
Tel.: (212) 696-4380
Web Site: http://www.gdusa.com
Emp.: 7
Graphic Design Magazine
N.A.I.C.S.: 513120
Gordon Kaye (Publr & Editor)
Ilana Greenberg (Dir-Creative)
Rachel Goldberg (Dir-Production)
Althea Edwards (Mgr-Accts)
Ron Andriani (Sr VP-Sls)

KAYE-SMITH
700 112th Ave NE Ste 302, Bellevue, WA 98004-5106
Tel.: (425) 455-0923 OR
Web Site: http://www.kayesmith.com
Year Founded: 1964
Sales Range: $10-24.9 Million
Emp.: 140
Document Processing Services
N.A.I.C.S.: 323111
Joan St. Marie (CFO)
Alexandria Smith (CEO)
Randy Gifford (VP & Gen Mgr)

KAYEM FOODS, INC.
75 Arlington St, Chelsea, MA 02150
Tel.: (617) 889-1600 MA
Web Site: http://www.kayem.com
Year Founded: 1909
Sales Range: $100-124.9 Million
Emp.: 500
Meats Processor
N.A.I.C.S.: 311611
Carl Colson (Dir-Procurement)
Ralph Smith (Pres & CEO)
John Gary (VP-Ops)
Matt Monkiewicz (VP-Mktg)
Stephan Monkiewicz (Treas)

Subsidiaries:

McKenzie Country Classics (1)
160 Flynn Ave, Burlington, VT 05401
Tel.: (802) 864-4585
Web Site:
http://www.mckenziecountryclassics.com
Sales Range: $10-24.9 Million
Emp.: 10
Sausage Products Mfr
N.A.I.C.S.: 424470
Greg Rouille (Dir-Sls & Retail)

KAYNE & SON CUSTOM HARDWARE INC.
100 Daniel Ridge Rd, Candler, NC 28715
Tel.: (828) 667-8868
Web Site:
http://www.blacksmithsdepot.com
Emp.: 4
Custom Hardware & Blacksmithing Mfr
N.A.I.C.S.: 332510
Shirley Kayne (Owner & Pres)
David Kayne (CEO & Dir-Ops)

Subsidiaries:

Blacksmiths Depot (1)

100 Daniel Ridge Rd, Candler, NC
28715 **(100%)**
Tel.: (828) 667-8868
Web Site: http://www.blacksmithsdepot.com
Sales Range: Less than $1 Million
Mfr & Distr of Quality Blacksmithing Tools
N.A.I.C.S.: 332510

KAYNE ANDERSON BDC, INC.
150 N Riverside Plz Ste 2010, Chicago, IL 60606
Tel.: (312) 994-8430 DE
Web Site: https://www.kaynebdc.com
Year Founded: 2018
Rev.: $74,829,000
Assets: $1,194,394,000
Liabilities: $602,353,000
Net Worth: $592,041,000
Earnings: $40,179,000
Fiscal Year-end: 12/31/22
Investment Services
N.A.I.C.S.: 523940

KAYNE ANDERSON CAPITAL ADVISORS, L.P.
1800 Avenue of the Stars 3rd Fl, Los Angeles, CA 90067
Tel.: (310) 282-7900 CA
Web Site:
http://www.kaynecapital.com
Year Founded: 1984
Rev.: $13,100,000,000
Emp.: 147
Equity Investment Firm
N.A.I.C.S.: 523999
James C. Baker *(Sr Mng Dir)*
David J. Shladovsky *(Gen Counsel)*
Robert Vose Sinnott *(Co-Chm)*
Richard Kayne *(Founder & Co-Chm)*
Terrence Quinn *(Vice Chm)*
Gary Ghazarian *(Partner & Dir-Ops)*
Stephen Smith *(Sr Mng Dir & Partner)*
Kevin Welsh *(Sr Mng Dir & Partner)*
Marilynn Moscrip *(Partner)*
Felice Rosen *(Dir-Admin & Benefits)*
Frank Arentowicz *(Sr Mng Dir-Client Rels Mktg)*
Bill Claybaugh *(Mng Dir-Client Rels Mktg)*
David Selznick *(CIO)*
Paul Blank *(Partner & COO)*
Paul Stapleton *(CFO)*
Mike Levitt *(CEO)*
Terry Hart *(CFO & Treas)*
Jody Meraz *(Partner & Mng Dir)*
Alan Boswell *(Mng Dir)*
Michael O'Neil *(Chief Compliance Officer)*
Oren Marouni *(Sr VP)*
Eric Pregler *(Sr VP)*
Daniel Weingeist *(Mng Partner)*
Chuck Yates *(Mng Partner)*
Cory Christofferson *(Mng Partner)*
Buddy Clarke *(Mng Dir)*
Patrick Lissonnet *(Mng Dir)*
Kevin Brophy *(Gen Counsel)*
Bradford Witmer *(Chief Admin Officer)*
Todd Burgamy *(Sr VP)*
Nick Christ *(Sr VP)*
Jack Foster *(Sr VP)*
Ryan Sauer *(Mng Dir)*
Gifford Wilkerson *(Mng Dir)*
David Walsh *(Mng Partner)*
Nathan Locke *(Partner)*
Nishita Cummings *(Partner)*
Leon Chen *(Partner)*
Michael Heinz Jr. *(Mng Partner)*

Subsidiaries:

KA Fund Advisors LLC **(1)**
717 Texas Ave Ste 3100, Houston, TX 77002
Tel.: (713) 493-2000
Web Site: http://www.kaynefunds.com
Closed-End Fund Investment Advisory & Portfolio Management Services
N.A.I.C.S.: 523940
James C. Baker *(Co-Mng Partner)*

Affiliate (Domestic):

Kayne Anderson Energy Infrastructure Fund, Inc. **(2)**
811 Main St 14th Fl, Houston, TX 77002
Tel.: (877) 657-3863
Web Site: http://www.kaynefunds.com
Closed-End Investment Fund
N.A.I.C.S.: 525990
James C. Baker *(Chm, Pres, CEO & Officer)*
Kevin S. McCarthy *(Chm)*
David J. Shladovsky *(Sec)*

Subsidiary (Domestic):

Kayne Anderson NextGen Energy & Infrastructure, Inc. **(3)**
2121 Ave of the Stars 9th Fl, Los Angeles, CA 90067
Rev.: $19,286,000
Assets: $812,980,000
Liabilities: $279,023,000
Net Worth: $533,957,000
Earnings: ($4,606,000)
Fiscal Year-end: 11/30/2019
Investment Management Service
N.A.I.C.S.: 525990
James C. Baker *(CEO)*

Affiliate (Domestic):

Kinetik Holdings Inc. **(2)**
2700 Post Oak Blvd Ste 300, Houston, TX 77056-4400
Tel.: (713) 621-7330
Web Site: https://www.kinetik.com
Rev.: $1,213,490,000
Assets: $5,919,711,000
Liabilities: $6,759,486,000
Net Worth: ($839,775,000)
Earnings: $135,518,000
Emp.: 300
Fiscal Year-end: 12/31/2022
Investment Services
N.A.I.C.S.: 523999
Jamie Welch *(Pres & CEO)*
Steve Stellato *(Chief Admin Officer, Chief Acctg Officer & Exec VP)*
Kris Kindrick *(Sr VP-Comml)*
Tyler Milam *(Sr VP-Crude, Water, and New Energy Ventures)*
Trevor Howard *(CFO & Sr VP)*
Matt Wall *(COO & Exec VP)*
Todd Carpenter *(Chief Compliance Officer & Gen Counsel)*
Anne Psencik *(Chief Strategy Officer)*

Subsidiary (Domestic):

EagleClaw Midstream Ventures, LLC **(3)**
500 W Illinois Ste 700, Midland, TX 79701
Tel.: (432) 789-1333
Web Site:
http://www.eagleclawmidstream.com
Oil & Natural Gas Transportation Management Services
N.A.I.C.S.: 541990

Terra Energy Partners LLC **(1)**
4828 Loop Central Dr Ste 900, Houston, TX 77081
Tel.: (281) 936-0355
Web Site: http://www.terraep.com
Oil & Gas Exploration & Production
N.A.I.C.S.: 211120
Michael S. Land *(CEO)*

KAYNE DL 2021, INC.
717 Texas Ave Ste 2200, Houston, TX 77002
Tel.: (713) 493-2020 DE
Year Founded: 2021
Rev.: $17,746,000
Assets: $189,819,000
Liabilities: $5,268,000
Net Worth: $184,551,000
Earnings: $16,654,000
Fiscal Year-end: 12/31/23
Investment Management Service
N.A.I.C.S.: 523999

KAYO OF CALIFORNIA, INC.
161 W 39th St, Los Angeles, CA 90037
Tel.: (323) 233-6107
Web Site:
http://www.kayoofcalifornia.com
Year Founded: 1968
Sales Range: $10-24.9 Million
Emp.: 55
Mfr & Sales of Women's, Misses' & Juniors' Clothing
N.A.I.C.S.: 315250
Jeffrey Michaels *(Pres & CEO)*
Jonathan M. Kaye *(Exec VP)*
Annabelle Wall *(CFO)*
Cassie Frye *(Dir-Design)*
Stephen Levinsohn *(Controller)*
Peggy Alvarez *(Office Mgr)*

KAYSER AUTOMOTIVE GROUP, LLC
2303 W Beltline Hwy, Madison, WI 53713
Tel.: (608) 271-6000 WI
Web Site:
http://www.kayseronline.com
Year Founded: 1925
Sales Range: $100-124.9 Million
Emp.: 235
Holding Company New & Used Car Distr
N.A.I.C.S.: 551112
Sean P. Baxter *(Pres)*

Subsidiaries:

Kayser Chrysler Center Stoughton **(1)**
1411 Hwy 51, Stoughton, WI 53589
Tel.: (608) 873-5621
Web Site: http://www.danecountyauto.com
New & Used Car Dealership
N.A.I.C.S.: 441110
Danton Walthers *(Gen Mgr)*

Kayser Chrysler Center of Watertown, Inc. **(1)**
105 Hwy 16 Frontage Rd, Watertown, WI 53094
Tel.: (920) 261-3870
Web Site:
http://www.kayserchryslercenterofwatertown.com
Sales Range: $25-49.9 Million
Emp.: 20
New & Used Car Dealership
N.A.I.C.S.: 441110
Michelle Chroeter *(Office Mgr)*

Kayser Chrysler Center, Inc. **(1)**
866 Phillips Blvd, Sauk City, WI 53583
Tel.: (608) 729-4923
Web Site:
http://www.kayserchryslercenter.com
Sales Range: $10-24.9 Million
Emp.: 35
New & Used Car Distr
N.A.I.C.S.: 441110
Todd Klais *(Asst Mgr-Body Shop)*

Kayser Ford, Inc. **(1)**
2303 W Beltline Hwy, Madison, WI 53713
Tel.: (608) 271-6000
Web Site:
http://www.kayserford.dealerconnection.com
Sales Range: $50-74.9 Million
Emp.: 220
New & Used Car Dealership
N.A.I.C.S.: 441110
Patrick J. Baxter *(Pres & CEO)*
Greg Ericson *(VP)*
Linda Brown *(CFO)*
Tim Askey *(Mgr-Comml Sls)*

KAYSUN CORPORATION
5500 W Dr, Manitowoc, WI 54220
Tel.: (920) 682-6388
Web Site: http://www.kaysun.com
Sales Range: $50-74.9 Million
Emp.: 204
Injection Molding Of Plastics
N.A.I.C.S.: 326199

Benjamin G. Harrison *(Pres & CEO)*
Karen Schoenborn *(Controller)*
Don Pantzlaff *(Mgr-Pur)*
Mary Stuiber *(Mgr-Customer Svc)*
Ray Dorow *(Mgr-Quality)*
Ken Glassen *(VP-Engrg)*

KAYTON INTERNATIONAL, INC.
2630 State Hwy 14, Albion, NE 68620
Tel.: (402) 395-2181 NE
Web Site: http://www.kaytonint.com
Year Founded: 1985
Rev.: $16,000,000
Emp.: 50
Farm Implements
N.A.I.C.S.: 423820
Roger Turnus *(Pres)*
Tim Kayton *(Mgr-Ops)*
Ray Docler *(Parts Mgr)*
Ben Edward *(Mgr-Sls)*

KAZAN INTERNATIONAL, INC.
1430 US Hwy 206 Ste 110, Bedminster, NJ 07921
Tel.: (908) 901-0900 NJ
Web Site:
http://www.kazansearch.com
Year Founded: 1989
Sales Range: $10-24.9 Million
Emp.: 5
Life Science & Healthcare Executive Search Services
N.A.I.C.S.: 541612
J. Neil Kazan *(Founder & CEO)*

Subsidiaries:

Kazan International **(1)**
601 108th Ave NE 19th Fl, Bellevue, WA 98004
Tel.: (425) 943-7709
Web Site: http://www.kazansearch.com
Life Science & Healthcare Executive Search Services
N.A.I.C.S.: 541612

KAZI FOODS INC.
3671 Sunswept Dr, Studio City, CA 91604-2325
Tel.: (818) 761-7202
Web Site: http://www.kazifoods.com
Year Founded: 1977
Sales Range: $150-199.9 Million
Emp.: 2,450
Operator of Restaurants
N.A.I.C.S.: 722513
Zubair Kazi *(Pres)*

Subsidiaries:

Kazi Foods Corp. of Hawaii **(1)**
560 N Nimitz Hwy Ste 214, Honolulu, HI 96817
Tel.: (808) 550-4100
Rev.: $26,941,051
Emp.: 12
Fast Food Restaurants
N.A.I.C.S.: 722513
Jose Djavadi *(Gen Mgr)*

KAZOO & COMPANY
2930 E 2nd Ave, Denver, CO 80206
Tel.: (303) 322-0973
Web Site: http://www.kazootoys.com
Sales Range: $10-24.9 Million
Emp.: 30
Educational Toys, Games & Puzzles Online & Store Retailer
N.A.I.C.S.: 459120
Diana Nelson *(Pres)*

KAZOO, INC.
4900 9th St, Kalamazoo, MI 49009
Tel.: (269) 375-4900 OK
Web Site:
http://www.edwardsgarment.com
Sales Range: $100-124.9 Million
Emp.: 200
Men's & Women's Clothing Mfr
N.A.I.C.S.: 315250

KAZOO, INC.

Kazoo, Inc.—Continued
Gary Schultz (Pres)
Carol King (Mgr-Payroll)
Denise Jacobs (Mgr-Demand)
Dawn Rowley (Mgr-HR)

Subsidiaries:
Kazoo, Inc. - Edwards Garment Division (1)
4900 S 9th St, Kalamazoo, MI 49009
Tel.: (800) 253-9885
Apparels Mfr
N.A.I.C.S.: 315250

KAZTRONIX, LLC
8260 Greensboro Dr Ste 150, McLean, VA 22102-3806
Tel.: (703) 356-5440
Web Site: http://www.kaztronix.com
Year Founded: 2002
Rev.: $22,400,000
Emp.: 250
Employment Placement Agencies
N.A.I.C.S.: 561311
Michael Kasmir (Co-Founder)

KB BUILDING SERVICES, INC.
10101 J St, Omaha, NE 68127
Tel.: (402) 330-8243 NE
Web Site: http://www.kbbldservices.com
Year Founded: 1984
Sales Range: $1-9.9 Million
Emp.: 240
Building Cleaning Services
N.A.I.C.S.: 561720
Dana Rezac (Owner & Pres)
Henrietta Morse (Dir-Fin)
Gordon Wehner (Mgr-Div)
Lucina Tlatenchi (Dir-Field Ops)

KB ENGINEERING, PC
100 Great Oaks Blvd Ste 114, Albany, NY 12203
Tel.: (518) 382-1774
Web Site: http://www.mcdonaldengineers.com
Engineeering Services
N.A.I.C.S.: 541330
Kumar Buvanendaran (Pres & CEO)
William Taylor (VP & Reg Mgr)

Subsidiaries:
Ward Associates, PC (1)
1500 Lakeland Ave, Bohemia, NY 11716
Tel.: (631) 563-4800
Landscape Architectural Services
N.A.I.C.S.: 541320

KB INSURANCE COMPANY LTD.
400 Kelby St 15th Fl, Fort Lee, NJ 07024
Tel.: (201) 720-2100
Web Site: http://www.kbicus.com
Insurance Services
N.A.I.C.S.: 524298
Charles Park (Pres-KBIC US branch)
Kevin Lee (Dir-Corporate Mktg)
KC Lee (Dir-Mktg)
Shashi Galav (CFO)
Kyunghwan Cho (Dir-IT)
Michael S. Fragner (Gen Counsel & Dir-Compliance & Internal Audit)

KB OF BALTIMORE INC.
1937 Greenspring Dr, Lutherville Timonium, MD 21093-4113
Tel.: (410) 561-3100
Rev.: $20,804,448
Emp.: 7
Fast Food Restaurants Franchisor
N.A.I.C.S.: 722513
Philip Hoag (Pres)

KB STAFFING
1560 6th St SE, Winter Haven, FL 33880
Tel.: (863) 875-5721
Web Site: http://www.kbstaffing.com
Sales Range: $1-9.9 Million
Staffing Services
N.A.I.C.S.: 561320
Kelly Braaten (Pres)

KBA DOCUSYS, INC.
32900 Alvarado Niles Rd Ste 100, Union City, CA 94587
Tel.: (510) 214-4040
Web Site: http://www.kbadocusys.com
Year Founded: 2007
Sales Range: $10-24.9 Million
Emp.: 50
Copier Distribution Services
N.A.I.C.S.: 423830
Todd Moody (Pres & COO)
Jim Graf (CEO)
Todd Court (CFO)
Rod Manning (VP-Bus Dev)

KBC TOOLS INCORPORATED
6300 18 Mile Rd, Sterling Heights, MI 48314-4208
Tel.: (586) 979-0500 MI
Web Site: http://www.kbctools.com
Year Founded: 1964
Sales Range: $25-49.9 Million
Emp.: 145
Industrial Machinery & Equipment
N.A.I.C.S.: 423830
Shiela Bass (Chm)
Paula Bass (Owner & Pres)

Subsidiaries:
KBC Tools Incorporated - MACHINERY DIVISION (1)
6465 18 Mile Rd, Sterling Heights, MI 48314
Tel.: (586) 737-3600
Industrial Machinery Mfr & Distr
N.A.I.C.S.: 333515

KBC, INC.
4444 S 108th St, Omaha, NE 68137
Tel.: (402) 339-2342 NE
Web Site: http://www.johnstonesupply.com
Year Founded: 1953
Heating, Air Conditioning, Ventilation & Refrigeration Parts Distr
N.A.I.C.S.: 423730
Kim B. Cafferty (Pres)
Katherine Fletcher (Sec)

KBE BUILDING CORPORATION
30 Batterson Park Rd, Farmington, CT 06032-2579
Tel.: (860) 284-7110
Web Site: http://www.kbebuilding.com
Year Founded: 1959
Sales Range: $200-249.9 Million
Emp.: 120
Construction Services
N.A.I.C.S.: 236220
Michael Kolakowski (Pres, CEO & Principal)
Eric Brown (Principal & Sr VP-Ops)
Robert G. Dunn (Principal, Gen Counsel & VP)
Allan Kleban (VP-Bus Dev)
Jim Culkin (VP-Preconstruction & Estimating)
Anthony Maselli (VP-Field Ops-Northeast)
Antonio Mancini (Principal & VP-Field Ops-Northeast)
Kristen Schrader (Mgr-Bus Dev-Maryland)
Robert Baumann (Dir-Field Ops-Columbia)
Simon F. Etzel Jr. (Sr VP-Procurement)

KBHL LLC
2525 Kaanapali Pkwy, Lahaina, HI 96761
Tel.: (808) 661-0011
Web Site: http://www.kbhmaui.com
Year Founded: 1964
Sales Range: $25-49.9 Million
Emp.: 300
Resort Hotel
N.A.I.C.S.: 721110
Mike White (Gen Mgr)
Nore Rabaago (Controller)

KBK TECHNOLOGIES, INC.
1310 S Powerline Rd, Deerfield Beach, FL 33442
Tel.: (954) 596-8781
Web Site: http://www.poolworldsupplies.com
Year Founded: 2004
Sales Range: $10-24.9 Million
Emp.: 35
Swimming Pool Equipment Manufacturer
N.A.I.C.S.: 459110
Rene Valdez (Controller)

KBM ENTERPRISES INC.
Executive Park 639 E Main St Ste B 203, Hendersonville, TN 37075
Tel.: (615) 826-5111
Web Site: http://www.kbm-inc.com
Sales Range: $10-24.9 Million
Emp.: 20
Commercial Physical Research & Information Technology Services
N.A.I.C.S.: 541715
Sherry Knight (Pres)
Travis Black (Exec Dir)
Steve Tofflemire (Engr)

KBM GROUP, INC.
2096 Gaither Rd Ste 220, Rockville, MD 20850
Tel.: (301) 587-7333
Web Site: http://www.kbmgroup.com
Year Founded: 1985
Rev.: $5,900,000
Emp.: 20
Computer System Design Services
N.A.I.C.S.: 541512
Brenda Joseph (Pres)

KBM-HOGUE
160 W Santa Clara St, San Jose, CA 95113
Tel.: (408) 351-7100 CA
Web Site: http://www.kbm-hogue.com
Year Founded: 1946
Office & Public Building Furniture
N.A.I.C.S.: 423210
Stan Vuckovich (CEO)
Mark Dailey (Pres)
Matt Denning (VP & Gen Mgr-San Francisco)
Michelle Bravin (VP-San Jose)
Kristi Rolak (VP & Gen Mgr-Sacramento)
Jennifer Merritt (VP-Ops)
Jill Marsh (Dir-Acct Mgmt)

KBO ENTERPRISES INC.
1813 Cleveland St Ext, Greenville, SC 29607
Tel.: (864) 234-5806
Sales Range: $50-74.9 Million
Emp.: 40
Frozen Dairy Desserts
N.A.I.C.S.: 424430
Betty Crow (Pres)
Patsy Gray (Office Mgr)

U.S. PRIVATE

KBR, INC.
2000 W Gaylord St, Long Beach, CA 90813
Tel.: (562) 436-9281 NY
Web Site: http://www.etmgraphite.com
Year Founded: 1968
Sales Range: $10-24.9 Million
Carbon & Graphite Product Mfr
N.A.I.C.S.: 335991
David R. McMahon (Pres & CEO)

Subsidiaries:
MWI, Inc. (1)
1269 Brighton Henrietta Town Line Rd, Rochester, NY 14623
Tel.: (585) 424-4204
Sales Range: $10-24.9 Million
Emp.: 72
Carbon & Graphite Products
N.A.I.C.S.: 335991
David R. McMahon (Chm)
Dale Campisi (Suprv-Maintenance)
Patrick Condon (Plant Mgr)
John Villareale (Mgr-Sls)

KBS CONSTRUCTION, INC.
3841 Kipp St, Madison, WI 53718
Tel.: (608) 838-6100
Web Site: http://www.kbsconstruction.com
Rev.: $46,900,000
Emp.: 250
Commercial & Institutional Building Construction
N.A.I.C.S.: 236220
Dennis Klein (Chm)
Tom Schuchardt (Pres)
Pat Babe (VP)
Larry Breneman (VP)

KBS LEGACY PARTNERS APARTMENT REIT, INC.
800 Newport Center Dr Ste 700, Newport Beach, CA 92660
Tel.: (949) 417-6500 MD
Web Site: http://www.kbslegacyreit.com
Year Founded: 2009
Sales Range: $25-49.9 Million
Real Estate Investment Trust
N.A.I.C.S.: 523999
Jeffrey K. Waldvogel (CFO)
Hans Henselman (COO & Chief Compliance Officer)
Jeffrey Kremin (Exec VP & Mgr-Natl Sls)
Jonathan Thomas (Chief Mktg Officer)
Mick Manning (Pres & CEO)
Rustyn L. Osier (Chief Acctg Officer)

KBS REALTY ADVISORS, LLC
800 Newport Center Dr Ste 700, Newport Beach, CA 92660
Tel.: (949) 417-6500 DE
Web Site: http://www.kbs.com
Year Founded: 1992
Sales Range: $10-24.9 Million
Emp.: 100
Real Estate Investment Advisory & Asset Management Services
N.A.I.C.S.: 531390
Charles Jay Schreiber Jr. (CEO)
Robert Durand (Exec VP-Fin)
Stephen Close (Sr VP & Mgr-Asset-Eastern)
Brent Carroll (Sr VP & Mgr-Asset-Western)
Brett Merz (Sr VP & Mgr-Asset-Western)
Giovanni Cordoves (Sr VP & Mgr-Asset-Western)
Timothy Helgeson (Sr VP & Mgr-Asset-Western)
David Zamudio (Sr VP-HR)
Michael Potter (VP)

COMPANIES

KCI HOLDINGS INC.

Mimi Nguyen *(Exec VP-Underwriting)*
Ken Robertson *(Pres-Central Reg)*
Rodney Richerson *(Pres-Western Reg)*
David Meltz *(Sr VP & Dir-Portfolio Acctg)*
Allen Aldridge *(Sr VP & Mgr-Asset-Eastern Reg)*
Shannon Hill *(Sr VP & Mgr-Asset-Eastern Reg)*
Clint Copulos *(Sr VP & Mgr-Asset-Western Reg)*
David Jenkins *(VP & Mgr-Capital Project)*
Rachel Umipig *(Chief Compliance Officer)*
Dan Park *(Sr VP & Mgr-Asset-Eastern)*
Stacie Yamane *(Chief Acctg Officer)*
Marc DeLuca *(Pres-Eastern Reg)*

Subsidiaries:

KBS Capital Advisors, LLC (1)
620 Newport Center Dr Ste 1300, Newport Beach, CA 92660
Tel.: (949) 797-0305
Web Site: http://www.kbscapitaladvisors.com
Real Estate Investment Advisory & Asset Management Services
N.A.I.C.S.: 531390
Peter B. McMillan III *(Treas)*
Charles Jay Schreiber Jr. *(CEO)*
Keith D. Hall *(Exec VP)*
Stephen Close *(Sr VP-Mid Atlantic)*
Brian Ragsdale *(Exec VP-Transaction Mgmt)*
David Moore *(Sr VP & Mgr-Asset)*
Geoff Hawkins *(Mng Dir)*
Holden Slusher *(VP)*
Jeff Rader *(Sr VP & Mgr-Asset)*
James Rodgers *(Exec VP & Head-Acq)*
Michael Potter *(VP)*
Robert Durand *(Sr VP)*
Jeff Waldvogel *(CFO)*
Stacie Yamane *(Chief Acctg Officer)*

KBS Capital Markets Group, LLC (1)
660 Newport Center Dr, Newport Beach, CA 92660
Tel.: (949) 640-7074
Web Site: http://www.kbs-cmg.com
Real Estate Investment Products Distr
N.A.I.C.S.: 531210
Luke A. Bobey *(VP-Ohio River Reg)*
Dominic Alto *(VP-Florida)*
Hans Henselman *(Chief Operating & Compliance Officer)*
Jeffrey Kremin *(Exec VP & Mgr-Natl Sls)*
Mick Manning *(Pres & CEO)*
Rustyn L. Osier *(Chief Acctg Officer)*
Mark Saukkola *(Mgr-Sls Desk)*
Megan Smith *(Exec VP & Mgr-Natl Accts)*
Jonathan Thomas *(CMO)*
Mike Yee *(Dir-Ops)*
Drew Schenk *(Sr VP-Lower Midwest)*
Bruce Stewart *(Sr VP-Texas)*

KC BELL, INC.
8100 E 22nd St N Bldg 300 Ste 100, Wichita, KS 67226
Tel.: (316) 684-8100   KS
Rev.: $10,900,000
Emp.: 9
Franchise Fast-Food Restaurants Owner & Operator
N.A.I.C.S.: 722513
Paul R. Hoover *(Pres)*
Travis Jasnoski *(Controller)*

KC COMPANY INC.
12100 Baltimore Ave Ste 1, Beltsville, MD 20705
Tel.: (301) 419-2200
Web Site: http://www.kc-pella.com
Sales Range: $25-49.9 Million
Emp.: 180
Lumber, Plywood & Millwork
N.A.I.C.S.: 423310
Kevin Cassidy *(Chm & CEO)*
Terry Sheehan *(CFO)*

KC ELECTRIC ASSOCIATION
422 3rd Ave, Hugo, CO 80821
Tel.: (719) 743-2431
Rev.: $11,436,311
Emp.: 28
Electric Power Distr
N.A.I.C.S.: 221122
Kevin Penny *(Pres)*
David Churchwell *(Gen Mgr)*

KC MART INC.
955 N Adams, Papillion, NE 68046
Tel.: (402) 593-0488
Rev.: $11,088,169
Emp.: 4
Convenience Store
N.A.I.C.S.: 445131
Karen Crandall *(Pres)*

KC TRANSPORTATION INC.
888 Will Carleton Rd, Carleton, MI 48117
Tel.: (734) 654-0010
Web Site: http://www.kctrans.com
Year Founded: 1986
Rev.: $25,493,592
Emp.: 300
Local Trucking Services
N.A.I.C.S.: 484110
Kenyon S. Calender *(CEO)*
Dale Tanner *(Pres)*
Terry Coleman *(Mgr)*

KCA PARTNERS, LTD.
1 Sansome St Ste 3500, San Francisco, CA 94104
Tel.: (415) 433-4494
Web Site: http://www.kcapartners.com
Year Founded: 1993
Sales Range: $10-24.9 Million
Emp.: 100
Plastics Material & Resin Mfr
N.A.I.C.S.: 325211
Sedge Dienst *(Co-Partner)*
P. J. Nora *(Co-Partner)*

KCB MANAGEMENT LLC
117 E Colorado Blvd Ste 400, Pasadena, CA 91103
Tel.: (626) 356-0944   CA
Web Site: http://www.kcbm.com
Year Founded: 1986
Emp.: 20
Private Equity & Real Estate Investment Services
N.A.I.C.S.: 523999
Harvey G. Knell *(Founder & Pres)*
Peter Knell *(Mng Dir)*
Lorin Knell *(Mng Dir)*

Subsidiaries:

Integrated Systems Improvement Services, Inc. (1)
4116 Avenida Cochise Ste Q, Sierra Vista, AZ 85635
Tel.: (520) 459-5012
Web Site: http://www.isishq.com
Government Services Contractor; Intelligence, Instructional & Training Support & Technical Services Support
N.A.I.C.S.: 921190
Steve Walters *(Mgr-Intel Program)*
Luis Vega *(VP-Bus Dev)*
Mark Benedict *(Mgr-Site-Bus Dev)*
Alicia Burdick *(Controller)*
Martin Kesner *(Mgr-Recruiting)*
Donald A. Wright *(Pres & CEO)*

Spiral Binding LLC (1)
1 Maltese Dr, Totowa, NJ 07511
Tel.: (973) 256-0666
Web Site: http://www.spiralbinding.com
Sales Range: $25-49.9 Million
Emp.: 260
Print Finishing, Graphic Arts & Presentation Products Mfr & Services
N.A.I.C.S.: 424120
Robert Matthew Roth *(Pres & CEO)*
Ann Marie Boggio *(VP-Strategic Accts)*

Doris Dytchel *(Dir-HR)*
Richard Christmas *(Dir-Ops)*
Bob Cooke *(Gen Mgr-Larger Equipment Div)*

KCC CONTRACTOR INC.
2664 E Kearney, Springfield, MO 65803-2518
Tel.: (417) 883-6088   MO
Web Site: http://www.killco.com
Year Founded: 1985
Sales Range: $10-24.9 Million
Emp.: 65
Nonresidential Construction Services
N.A.I.C.S.: 236220
William F. Killian *(CEO)*

KCD, INC.
450 W 15th St Ste 604, New York, NY 10011
Tel.: (212) 590-5100
Web Site: http://www.kcdworldwide.com
Year Founded: 1985
Sales Range: $1-9.9 Million
Emp.: 80
Public Relations Agency
N.A.I.C.S.: 541820
Rachna Shah *(VP)*
Ed Filipowski *(Pres & CEO)*
Julie Mannion *(Mng Partner)*

KCEOC COMMUNITY ACTION PARTNERSHIP, INC.
5448 N US 25 E Ste A, Gray, KY 40734
Tel.: (606) 546-3152
Web Site: http://www.kceoc.com
Year Founded: 1964
Sales Range: $10-24.9 Million
Emp.: 260
Community Action Service Agency
N.A.I.C.S.: 624190
Tish Coldiron *(Dir-Child Dev)*
Paul Dole *(Pres & CEO)*
Paulette Turpin *(Coord-Civic Involvement)*

KCG, INC.
15720 W 108th St Ste 100, Shawnee Mission, KS 66219-1472
Tel.: (913) 438-4142   AZ
Web Site: http://www.rewmaterials.com
Year Founded: 1980
Sales Range: $50-74.9 Million
Emp.: 600
Brick Stone & Related Material, Drywall Related
N.A.I.C.S.: 423320
Jeff Butts *(Dir-HR)*
John Thomas *(Dir-Mktg)*

KCI CONSTRUCTION CO.
10315 Lake Bluff Dr, Saint Louis, MO 63123
Tel.: (314) 894-8888
Web Site: http://www.kciconstruction.com
Sales Range: $25-49.9 Million
Emp.: 150
Specialized Public Building Contractors
N.A.I.C.S.: 236220
Matt Willingham *(Dir-Safety)*
Ron Webelhuth *(Project Mgr)*
Mark Stewart *(Mgr-Equipment)*
Carrol Tauser *(Sec & Office Mgr-St. Louis)*
Jon Schenk *(VP)*
Brett Brinkmann *(Mgr-Equipment & Warehouse)*
Don Recar *(Mgr-Field Ops)*
Justin Cline *(Project Mgr)*
Jason Diekemper *(Project Mgr)*
Kyle Nieman *(Project Mgr)*

Mike Opels *(Project Mgr)*
Darrell Vankygrifka *(Project Mgr)*
Tom Huster *(VP)*
Brent Krueger *(VP)*

KCI HOLDINGS INC.
936 Ridgebrook Rd, Sparks, MD 21152
Tel.: (410) 316-7800   MD
Web Site: http://www.kci.com
Year Founded: 1988
Sales Range: $75-99.9 Million
Emp.: 1,000
Engineeering Services
N.A.I.C.S.: 541330
Terry F. Neimeyer *(Chm & CEO)*
Charles A. Phillips *(Sr VP & Mgr-Site & Facilities Discipline)*
Christopher J. Griffith *(Exec VP)*
Nathan J. Beil *(Pres)*
Harvey M. Floyd *(Exec VP & Mgr-Transportation Discipline)*
Thomas G. Sprehe *(Sr VP & Mgr-Environmental Discipline)*
G. Scott Lang *(Sr VP & Mgr-Construction Management Discipline)*
Jeffrey C. Lookup *(VP & Dir-Growth & Dev)*
Gary M. Mryncza *(VP-Resource Mgmt)*
Christine Koski *(CFO & VP)*
Michael G. Perez *(VP & Mgr-Textile Market)*
David J. Eberspeaker *(VP)*
Scott D. Riddle *(VP & Mgr-Utilities Discipline)*
Christina Stevenson *(Chief HR Officer & VP)*

Subsidiaries:

KCI Technologies Inc. (1)
936 Ridgebrook Rd, Sparks, MD 21152
Tel.: (410) 316-7800
Web Site: http://www.kci.com
Construction Engineering Services
N.A.I.C.S.: 541330
Terry F. Neimeyer *(Chm)*

Subsidiary (Domestic):

Armeni Consulting Services, LLC (2)
4411 Suwanee Dam Rd Ste 750, Suwanee, GA 30024
Tel.: (770) 904-4178
Web Site: http://www.armeniconsulting.com
Professional, Scientific & Technical Services
N.A.I.C.S.: 541990
John Armeni *(Founder & Pres)*

Espa Corp, Inc. (2)
7120 Grand Blvd, Houston, TX 77054
Tel.: (713) 680-0080
Web Site: http://www.espa-corp.com
Sales Range: $1-9.9 Million
Emp.: 40
Engineeering Services
N.A.I.C.S.: 541330
Willie Jordan *(Head-Architecture)*

KCI Associates of North Carolina, P.A. (2)
9741 Southern Pine Bllvd Ste J, Charlotte, NC 28273
Tel.: (704) 499-9452
Construction Engineering Services
N.A.I.C.S.: 541330
Elizabeth Phipps *(VP)*

KCI Associates of Ohio, P.A. (2)
441 Wolls ledges Pkwy, Akron, OH 44311
Tel.: (330) 564-9100
Web Site: http://www.kci.com
Construction Engineering Services
N.A.I.C.S.: 541330

KCI Associates of the District of Columbia, P.C. (2)
122 C St NW Ste 500, Washington, DC 20001
Tel.: (202) 470-6382
Construction Engineering Services
N.A.I.C.S.: 541330

KCI HOLDINGS INC.

U.S. PRIVATE

KCI Holdings Inc.—(Continued)

KCI Communications Infrastructure (2)
921 Mercantile Dr Ste H, Hanover, MD 21076
Tel.: (410) 309-7902
Construction Engineering Services
N.A.I.C.S.: 541330
Brian Skimmons *(VP & Head-Discipline)*
Ronald Hubbell Jr. *(Mgr-Warehouse)*

KCI Protection Technologies LLC (2)
1352 Marrows Rd Ste 100, Newark, DE 19711
Tel.: (302) 731-9176
Web Site: http://www.kci-pt.com
Construction Engineering Services
N.A.I.C.S.: 541330

Landair Surveying Company of Georgia (2)
1875 Old Alabama Rd Ste 1120, Roswell, GA 30076
Tel.: (770) 730-9950
Web Site: http://www.kci.com
Engineeering Services
N.A.I.C.S.: 541330
Tate H. Jones *(VP)*

KCM CAPITAL PARTNERS, LLC
525 W Monroe St Ste 1300, Chicago, IL 60661-3693
Tel.: (312) 577-8506
Web Site: http://www.kcmcap.com
Privater Equity Firm
N.A.I.C.S.: 523999
Emmett Mosley IV *(Partner)*
Derek Ferguson *(Partner)*

Subsidiaries:

Icat Logistics, Inc. (1)
6805 Douglas Legum Dr, Elkridge, MD 21075
Tel.: (443) 891-2000
Web Site: https://www.icatlogistics.com
Sales Range: $25-49.9 Million
Emp.: 35
Freight Forwarding Services
N.A.I.C.S.: 488510
Rick Campbell *(Founder & CEO)*
Jim Vespa *(VP-Fin)*
Ray Smith *(Sr VP)*
Hann Livinston *(Chief Growth Officer)*

KCOE ISOM, LLP
3030 Cortland Cir, Salina, KS 67401
Tel.: (785) 825-1561 KS
Web Site: https://www.pinionglobal.com
Year Founded: 1932
Sales Range: $50-74.9 Million
Emp.: 400
Accounting, Tax, Consulting & Wealth Management Services
N.A.I.C.S.: 541211
Jeannie Blue *(Mgr-HR)*
Jeff Wald *(Principal)*
Brian Wurst *(Principal)*
Christina Ricke *(Principal)*
Greg Davis *(Principal)*
Chris Bonacorsi *(Principal)*
Dawn Buchanan *(Principal)*
Joan Porsch *(Principal)*
Michelle Golden *(Principal)*
Leslie Thole *(Principal)*
Chris Pfannenstiel *(Mgr)*
Clinton Baker *(Principal)*
Corlene Lange *(Mgr)*
Travis Lank *(Mgr)*
Wayne Myers *(Principal)*
Brad Palen *(Principal)*
Bryce Gibbs *(Principal)*
Carol Medeiros *(Principal)*
Christy Norton *(Principal)*
Craig Duncan *(Principal)*
Dave Burger *(Principal)*
Dean Bretney *(Principal)*
Donna Funk *(Principal)*
Doug Claussen *(Principal)*
Doug Mitchell *(Principal)*
Jill Eberhart *(Principal)*
Julie Kauffman *(Principal)*
Kevin Bearley *(Principal)*
Kevin Mills *(Principal)*
Marc Johnson *(Principal)*
Mark Boyer *(Principal)*
Michelle Ellis *(Principal)*
Peter Martin *(Principal)*
Ralph Mathes *(Principal)*
Shellee Callahan *(Principal)*
Tommy Irvine *(Principal)*
Tracy Garone *(Principal)*
Emily Johannes *(Principal & Dir-ResourceMAX)*

Subsidiaries:

AgKnowledge, LLC (1)
1308 N Lamar Ste 5, Oxford, MS 38655
Tel.: (662) 234-0203
Web Site: http://www.ag-knowledge.com
Agricultural Finance & Credit Management, Commodity Risk Management, Crop Insurance & Related Consulting Services
N.A.I.C.S.: 541611
Alan Grafton *(Principal)*

Kennedy & Coe Wealth Management, LLC (1)
1605 N Waterfront Pkwy Ste 200, Wichita, KS 67206
Tel.: (316) 685-0222
Web Site: http://www.kcoewm.com
Wealth Management Services
N.A.I.C.S.: 523940
Jeff Wald *(CEO)*

Noell, Agnew & Morse (1)
1001 N Demaree St, Visalia, CA 93291
Tel.: (559) 733-5500
Web Site: http://www.namcpa.com
Sales Range: $1-9.9 Million
Emp.: 30
Accounting Services
N.A.I.C.S.: 541219
Kevin Noell *(Partner)*
Glen D. Teter *(Mng Partner)*

KCP HOLDCO, INC.
603 W 50th St, New York, NY 10019
Tel.: (212) 265-1500 DE
Web Site: http://www.kennethcole.com
Year Founded: 2012
Holding Company
N.A.I.C.S.: 551112
Kenneth D. Cole *(Owner, Chm & Chief Creative Officer)*

Subsidiaries:

Kenneth Cole Productions, Inc. (1)
603 W 50th St, New York, NY 10019
Tel.: (212) 265-1500
Web Site: http://www.kennethcole.com
Sales Range: $200-249.9 Million
Emp.: 1,600
Apparels, Handbags & Footwear Whslr
N.A.I.C.S.: 424350
Kenneth D. Cole *(Founder, Chm & Chief Creative Officer)*
David P. Edelman *(CFO)*
Chris Nakatani *(Pres-Wholesale)*
Elana Drell Szyfer *(Exec VP-Global Brand Strategy)*
Roberto Zamarra *(Grp Pres-Footwear)*

KCTS TELEVISION
401 Mercer St, Seattle, WA 98109
Tel.: (206) 728-6463
Web Site: http://www.kcts9.org
Sales Range: $10-24.9 Million
Emp.: 100
Provider of Television Broadcasting Station Services
N.A.I.C.S.: 516120
Rob Dunlop *(Pres & CEO)*
Lisa Moore *(Dir-Design)*
Amy Jolley *(Mgr-Legal Affairs)*
Anna Rhodes *(Mgr-Direct Mktg)*
Sara Elward *(Mgr-Gift Plng)*
Meredith Easton Brown *(Dir-Major Giving)*

KD ACQUISITION I, LLC.
PO Box 5935, Gainesville, GA 30504
Tel.: (770) 536-5177
Sales Range: $75-99.9 Million
Emp.: 837
Frozen Fruit, Juice & Vegetable Mfr
N.A.I.C.S.: 311411
Barry J. Cooley *(CEO)*
Rick Morris *(Mgr-IT)*
Gale Dale *(Dir-HR)*
John Hester *(Plant Mgr)*

KDC REAL ESTATE DEVELOPMENT & INVESTMENTS
8115 Preston Rd Ste 700, Dallas, TX 75225-6344
Tel.: (214) 696-1700
Web Site: http://www.kdc.com
Year Founded: 1962
Sales Range: $200-249.9 Million
Emp.: 36
Real Estate Development & Contracting Services
N.A.I.C.S.: 237210
Tracie Frazier *(Dir-Mktg)*
Tobin C. Grove *(Pres)*
Scott Ozymy *(Chief Investment Officer & Exec VP)*
Don Mills *(Exec VP)*
Mike Rosamond *(Exec VP)*
James Williams *(VP)*
Kurt Petersen *(Exec VP)*
John Dwyer *(VP)*
Phillip Sharp *(Sr VP-Design & Construction)*
A. B. Atkins *(Partner & Sr VP)*
Kim Bonfield *(CFO)*
Alex Chambers *(Reg VP)*
Michael Alost *(Sr VP)*
Bret Creel *(Sr VP-Design & Construction)*
Chad Jackson *(VP)*
Colin Fitzgibbons *(VP)*
Robert Maddux *(VP)*
Rick Sweat *(VP & Controller)*
David Fisk *(VP-Design & Construction)*
Gary Steele *(VP-Design & Construction)*
Jeff Innmon *(VP-Design & Construction)*
Marc Flores *(VP-Design & Construction)*

Subsidiaries:

KDC Real Estate Development & Investments - Southeast Division (1)
4201 Congress Ste 155, Charlotte, NC 28209
Tel.: (704) 554-6111
Web Site: http://www.kdc.com
Emp.: 4
Real Estate & Construction Services
N.A.I.C.S.: 531390
Larry Wilson *(Pres-Div)*

KDE INC.
1033 River St Ste 3, Port Huron, MI 48060
Tel.: (810) 987-3363
Sales Range: $10-24.9 Million
Emp.: 5
Management Office for Fast-Food Restaurants
N.A.I.C.S.: 722513
Markus Schulz *(Pres)*
Bobbie Lane *(Office Mgr)*

KDI ELEMENTS
PO Box 14150, Palm Desert, CA 92255-4150
Tel.: (760) 345-9933
Web Site: http://www.kdielements.com
Sales Range: $25-49.9 Million
Emp.: 250
Tile & Terrazzo Contractor Services

N.A.I.C.S.: 238340
Dana Nichols *(Pres)*

KDNY ENTERPRISE
1001 6th Ave, New York, NY 10018
Tel.: (212) 719-3700
Year Founded: 2004
Sales Range: $10-24.9 Million
Emp.: 20
N.A.I.C.S.: 541810

KDR PRODUCTIONS/DOLLARWISE PUBLICATIONS
2500 W Higgins Rd, Hoffman Estates, IL 60169
Tel.: (630) 894-0934
Web Site: http://moneysavermagazine.net
Year Founded: 1992
Rev.: $2,500,000
Emp.: 20
Fiscal Year-end: 12/31/03
N.A.I.C.S.: 541810
Kenneth W. Goldman *(Pres)*
Dino A. Thanos *(Publr)*
Greta Goldman *(Classified Sls Dir)*

KDR SUPPLY, INC.
3112 Beaumont Ave, Liberty, TX 77575
Tel.: (936) 336-6267
Web Site: http://www.kdrsupply.com
Year Founded: 1981
Sales Range: $10-24.9 Million
Emp.: 58
Construction & Mining Machinery & Equipment Whslr
N.A.I.C.S.: 423810
Kenny Simmons *(Gen Mgr)*
Johnnie Johnson *(Mgr-Credit)*

KDS INTERIORS, INC.
306 E Oak Ave, Tampa, FL 33602
Tel.: (813) 767-9901
Web Site: http://www.kdsinteriors.com
Sales Range: $1-9.9 Million
Interior Design Services
N.A.I.C.S.: 541410
Katie Kirby *(Pres)*
Heather Oskey *(VP)*
Heidi Clemmensen *(VP)*

KDV LABEL CO., INC.
431 W Newhall Ave, Waukesha, WI 53187
Tel.: (262) 544-5891
Web Site: http://www.kdvlabel.com
Sales Range: $25-49.9 Million
Emp.: 90
Coated & Laminated Paper Mfr
N.A.I.C.S.: 322220
Dick Vaughn *(CEO)*
Andrew J. Hulen *(CFO)*
Nick Scharber *(Mgr-Pre-Press)*
Shane Vaughn *(Pres)*
Harry Frank *(VP-Sls)*
Karen Vaughn *(VP)*
Keith Seidel *(VP-Ops)*

KE TUBE INC.
79 Wilkins Rd, Gardner, MA 01440
Tel.: (978) 630-1436
Web Site: http://www.kirkeastern.com
Sales Range: $10-24.9 Million
Emp.: 20
Wrought Pipes & Welded Lock Joints Mfr
N.A.I.C.S.: 331210
Peter Lord *(Pres)*

KE&G DEVELOPMENT LLC
1601 Paseo San Luis Ste 202, Sierra Vista, AZ 85635-2827
Tel.: (520) 458-9594 AZ

COMPANIES

Web Site: http://www.kegtusv.com
Year Founded: 1979
Sales Range: $25-49.9 Million
Emp.: 210
Commercial Construction
N.A.I.C.S.: 513199
Karol George *(Pres)*
Kent Hoover *(VP & Controller)*
Debbi Sanders *(Controller)*

KEA ADVERTISING
217 Rte 303 Ste 1, Valley Cottage, NY 10989-2534
Tel.: (845) 268-8686   NY
Web Site:
  http://www.keaadvertising.com
Year Founded: 1995
Sales Range: $10-24.9 Million
Emp.: 16
Advertising Services
N.A.I.C.S.: 541810
Henry Kwartler *(Pres)*
Lorrie Kwartler *(VP-Ops)*
Dean Errigo *(VP & Art Dir)*
Brandon Hoffman *(Dir-Internet Mktg)*

KEANE GROUP HOLDINGS, LLC
2121 Sage Rd, Houston, TX 77056
Tel.: (713) 960-0381   DE
Web Site: http://www.keanegrp.com
Emp.: 3,000
Holding Company; Hydraulic Fracturing & Drilling Services
N.A.I.C.S.: 551112
James C. Stewart *(CEO)*

Subsidiaries:

Keane Frac, LP   (1)
14235 Rte 6, Mansfield, PA 16933
Tel.: (570) 302-4050
Web Site: http://www.keanefrac.com
Emp.: 50
Hydraulic Fracturing & Drilling Services
N.A.I.C.S.: 213112
James Stewart *(CEO)*

KEARNEY ELECTRIC, INC.
3609 E Superior Ave, Phoenix, AZ 85040
Tel.: (602) 437-0235
Web Site: http://www.kearneyaz.com
Year Founded: 1977
Sales Range: $25-49.9 Million
Emp.: 300
Electronic Services
N.A.I.C.S.: 238210
Greg Frost *(Treas)*

KEARNEY O'DOHERTY PUBLIC AFFAIRS, LLC
111 S Calvert St Ste 2820, Baltimore, MD 21202
Tel.: (410) 685-7080   MD
Web Site:
  http://www.kopublicaffairs.com
Year Founded: 2008
Strategic Communication Services
N.A.I.C.S.: 517810
Damian O'Doherty *(Co-Founder & Principal)*
Steve Kearney *(Co-Founder & Mng Partner)*
Rick Abbruzzese *(Partner)*
Elisabeth Feldman *(Head-Consumer Mktg & PR)*

Subsidiaries:

Highfield Communications LLC   (1)
1122 Kenilworth Dr Ste 303, Towson, MD 21204-2146
Tel.: (410) 339-5100
Web Site: http://www.hillmanpr.com
Public Relations Agencies
N.A.I.C.S.: 541820
Sandy Hillman *(Pres)*

KEARNS-TRIBUNE, LLC
90 S 400 W Ste 700, Salt Lake City, UT 84101
Tel.: (801) 257-8742   DE
Web Site: http://www.sltrib.com
Sales Range: $10-24.9 Million
Emp.: 100
Newspaper Publishers
N.A.I.C.S.: 513110
Tim Fitzpatrick *(Exec VP)*
Gordon L. Harman *(Dir-IT)*
Michael Nakoryakov *(Dir-Print)*
Matt Canham *(Sr Mng Editor)*
Sheila R. McCann *(Mng Editor)*
Lauren Gustus *(Editor)*
Chris Stegman *(Chief Revenue Officer)*
Jon M. Huntsman Jr. *(Chm)*

KEARNY MESA INFINITI
4670 Convoy St, San Diego, CA 92111
Tel.: (858) 573-1700
Web Site:
  http://www.kearnymesainfiniti.com
Sales Range: $10-24.9 Million
Emp.: 42
Automobiles, New & Used
N.A.I.C.S.: 441110
Richard Newendyke *(Gen Mgr)*
Tommy Wanless *(Mgr-Svcs)*

KEATING & CO.
285 West Broadway 4th Fl, New York, NY 10013
Tel.: (212) 925-6900
Web Site: http://www.keatingco.com
Year Founded: 1968
Public Relations Agency
N.A.I.C.S.: 541820
Rick Keating *(CEO & Chief Strategist)*
Bill Fallon *(Exec VP)*
Steve Finnern *(COO & Exec VP)*

KEATING MAGEE MARKETING COMMUNICATIONS
706 Papworth Ave, Metairie, LA 70005
Tel.: (504) 299-8000   LA
Web Site:
  http://www.keatingmagee.com
Year Founded: 1981
Sales Range: $10-24.9 Million
Emp.: 26
Health Care, Leisure
N.A.I.C.S.: 541810
Jennifer Keating Magee *(CEO)*
Ann Wills *(Dir-Comm)*

KEATING, MUETHING & KLEKAMP PLL
1 E 4th St Ste 1400, Cincinnati, OH 45202
Tel.: (513) 579-6400
Web Site: http://www.kmklaw.com
Year Founded: 1954
Sales Range: $25-49.9 Million
Emp.: 400
Law firm
N.A.I.C.S.: 541110
Paul V. Muething *(Mng Partner)*
Rachael A. Rowe *(Partner)*
Lori S. Moser *(Dir-HR)*
Jeffrey R. Starnes *(Dir-Fin)*
Richard E. Wills *(CIO)*
Kasey L. Bond *(Partner)*
Julie Muething *(Partner)*
Cole Bond *(Partner)*
Kelley Brandstetter Tracy *(Partner)*
Helana A. Darrow *(Partner)*
Kathy L. Stanley *(Mgr-Clerk's Dept)*
Meribeth H. Sewell *(Dir-Info Resources)*
Craig Hopewell *(Gen Counsel)*
Julie Mulhern *(Dir-Legal Recruiting & Professional Dev)*
Alan S. Fershtman *(Partner)*
Anthony M. Verticchio *(Partner)*
Barrett P. Tullis *(Partner)*
Benjamin G. Stewart *(Partner)*
Bryce J. Yoder *(Partner)*
D. Brock Denton *(Partner)*
Don R. Gardner *(Partner)*
G. Randall Ayers *(Partner)*
J. Neal Gardner *(Partner)*
James H. Brun *(Partner)*
James E. Burke *(Partner)*
Jill A. Weller *(Partner)*
Louis F. Gilligan *(Partner)*
Mark J. Chumley *(Partner)*
Mark E. Sims *(Partner)*
Mary Ellen Malas *(Partner)*
Michael T. Cappel *(Partner)*
Nicholas L. Simon *(Partner)*
Philip A. Tracy *(Partner)*
Ross J. Bextermueller *(Partner)*
Steven C. Coffaro *(Partner)*
James J. McGraw Jr. *(Partner)*
Robert C. Lesan III *(Partner)*
Thomas M. Tepe Jr. *(Partner)*

Subsidiaries:

KMK Consulting Company, LLC   (1)
1 E 4th St Ste 1400, Cincinnati, OH 45202
Tel.: (513) 579-6932
Web Site: http://www.kmkconsulting.com
Emp.: 2
Consulting Services
N.A.I.C.S.: 541611
James J. McGraw Jr. *(Pres & CEO)*

KEATS MANUFACTURING COMPANY
350 Holbrook Dr, Wheeling, IL 60090
Tel.: (847) 520-1133
Web Site: http://www.keatsmfg.com
Rev.: $17,168,666
Emp.: 126
Clips & Fasteners Mfr
N.A.I.C.S.: 332618
Herbert A. Keats *(Chm)*
Donna Brand *(Exec VP)*

KEB ENTERPRISES LP
384 S 400 West Ste 100, Lindon, UT 84042
Tel.: (801) 764-9999
Holding Company
N.A.I.C.S.: 551112
Kenneth E. Brailsford *(Owner)*
Kyle Standifird *(CFO)*

KECK INC.
501 SW 7th St Ste D, Des Moines, IA 50309-4420
Tel.: (515) 244-5646   DC
Web Site:
  http://www.keckenergy.com
Year Founded: 1928
Sales Range: $10-24.9 Million
Emp.: 15
Petroleum Products Distr
N.A.I.C.S.: 424720
Mark Meyer *(Pres-Sls)*
Joleen Wirth *(Asst Controller)*

KECKLEY COMPANY
3400 Cleveland St, Skokie, IL 60076
Tel.: (847) 674-8422   IL
Web Site: http://www.keckley.com
Year Founded: 1914
Valves & Fittings Mfr
N.A.I.C.S.: 423830

KEDREN COMMUNITY HEALTH CENTER, INC.
4211 S Avalon Blvd, Los Angeles, CA 90011
Tel.: (323) 233-0425   CA

KEECO, LLC

Web Site:
  http://www.kedrenmentalhealth.com
Year Founded: 1965
Sales Range: $50-74.9 Million
Emp.: 751
Mental Health Care Services
N.A.I.C.S.: 621420
Emma J. Conner *(Dir-Social Svcs)*
Ethel Rasdale *(Dir-Support Svcs)*
Shaun Allen *(Program Dir-Children, Youth & Family Svcs)*
Lori McMillan *(Dir-HR)*
John H. Griffith *(Pres & CEO)*
Frank L. Williams *(Exec VP & Dir-Medical)*
Marcia Mills *(Sec)*
Vera Patterson *(Co-Treas)*
Kathy Gibbons *(Chm)*
Robert Lawson *(Treas)*

KEE ACTION SPORTS LLC
570 Mantua Blvd, Sewell, NJ 08080
Tel.: (856) 464-1068
Web Site:
  http://www.keeactionsports.com
Sales Range: $50-74.9 Million
Emp.: 2,000
Sporting Goods Supply
N.A.I.C.S.: 423910
Jason Kreisman *(Mgr-Product Mktg)*
Bryan Stowe *(Dir-Creative)*
Jamirsen Ezell *(Engr-Electronics)*

Subsidiaries:

KEE Action Sports Canada   (1)
98 Bessemer Court Unit 4, London, N6E 1k7, ON, Canada
Tel.: (519) 685-0030
Web Site: http://www.keeactionsports.com
Sales Range: $25-49.9 Million
Emp.: 100
Sporting Goods Supply
N.A.I.C.S.: 423910

KEE Action Sports Europe   (1)
Unit 3 Easter Park Cockoo Farm Business Park, Axial Way, Colchester, CO4 5WY, Essex, United Kingdom
Tel.: (44) 1206756241
Emp.: 8
Sporting Goods Supply
N.A.I.C.S.: 423910
Jackie Sosta *(Gen Mgr)*

KEE REAL ESTATE CO. OF DETROIT, INC
30800 Van Dyke Ave, Warren, MI 48093
Tel.: (586) 573-8600
Web Site: http://www.century21.com
Rev.: $10,489,099
Emp.: 13
Real Estate Brokers & Agents
N.A.I.C.S.: 531210
John Meeseman *(Pres)*

KEE SAFETY, INC.
100 Stradtman St, Buffalo, NY 14206
Tel.: (716) 896-4949
Web Site: http://www.keesafety.com
Year Founded: 1934
Rev.: $9,800,000
Emp.: 30
Supplier of Components & Custom Systems for Railings, Barriers, Roof Edge Protection & Fall Prevention
N.A.I.C.S.: 238160
David Wolff *(Mgr)*
Mike Mumau *(Pres)*
Charles Badding *(CFO)*

KEECO, LLC
30736 Wiegman Rd, Hayward, CA 94544
Tel.: (510) 324-8800   CA
Web Site: http://www.lkeeco.com
Year Founded: 1977
Sales Range: $25-49.9 Million

KEECO, LLC

Keeco, LLC—(Continued)
Emp.: 280
Home Furnishing Whslr
N.A.I.C.S.: 423220
Kevin Lawrence *(COO)*
Kristine Igoe *(Dir-HR & AR & Mgr-Claims)*
Martin Berry *(VP-Fin)*
Darren Raleigh *(Mgr-Ops)*
Chris Grassi *(CEO)*
Brett Rife *(VP/Sls Mgr-Hospitality-Chicago)*

KEEFE CONSTRUCTION SERVICES
16229 Hwy 52, Wiggins, CO 80654
Tel.: (970) 483-5295
Year Founded: 2006
Sales Range: $10-24.9 Million
Emp.: 13
Nonresidential Construction Services
N.A.I.C.S.: 236220
Paula Keefe *(Owner)*

KEELER MOTOR CAR COMPANY, INC.
1111 Troy Schenectady Rd, Latham, NY 12110-1002
Tel.: (518) 785-4197 NY
Web Site: http://www.keeler.com
Year Founded: 1967
Sales Range: $125-149.9 Million
Emp.: 200
Sales of Automobiles
N.A.I.C.S.: 441110
Alexander Keeler *(Owner)*

KEELING COMPANY
PO Box 15310, North Little Rock, AR 72231
Tel.: (501) 945-4511
Web Site:
  http://www.keelingcompany.com
Year Founded: 1965
Sales Range: $10-24.9 Million
Emp.: 60
Liquid Handling Products Whslr
N.A.I.C.S.: 423720
James Keeling *(VP)*
Helen Keeling *(Treas & Sec)*
Joe E. Keeling Jr. *(Pres)*

KEEN BATTLE MEAD & CO.
7850 NW 146th St Ste 200, Hialeah, FL 33016
Tel.: (305) 558-1101
Web Site: http://www.kbmco.com
Rev.: $16,000,000
Emp.: 52
Automobile Insurance
N.A.I.C.S.: 524126
Claudia Reutlinger *(Acct Exec)*

KEEN BRANDING
30616 Overbrook Ctr Way, Milton, DE 19969
Tel.: (302) 644-6885
Web Site:
  http://www.keenbranding.com
Year Founded: 2000
Emp.: 15
Advertising Agencies
N.A.I.C.S.: 541810
Alicia Stack *(Partner)*
Jan Walker *(Sr Consultant)*
Dave Sharpe *(Dir-Design)*
Andy Modlin *(Dir-Strategy)*

Subsidiaries:

Keen Branding (1)
310 Arlington Ave Ste 303, Charlotte, NC 28203
Tel.: (704) 295-1100
Web Site: http://www.keenbranding.com
Advertising Agencies
N.A.I.C.S.: 541810

Keen Branding-West Coast (1)
303 Almaden Blvd Ste 600, San Jose, CA 95110
Tel.: (408) 241-9800
Advertising Agencies
N.A.I.C.S.: 541810

KEEN COMPRESSED GAS COMPANY
4063 New Castle Ave, New Castle, DE 19720
Tel.: (302) 594-4545 DE
Web Site: http://www.keengas.com
Year Founded: 1919
Sales Range: $75-99.9 Million
Emp.: 90
Wholesale Distributor of Compressed & Liquified Gases; Welding Supplies; Bottle Propane Gas
N.A.I.C.S.: 423840

Subsidiaries:

Keen Compressed Gas (1)
4063 New Castle Ave, New Castle, DE 19720-1414 (100%)
Tel.: (302) 594-4545
Web Site: http://www.keengas.com
Sales Range: $25-49.9 Million
Emp.: 40
Industrial Gases Sales
N.A.I.C.S.: 423840

KEEN HEALTHCARE COMPANY
5457 SW Canyon Ct, Portland, OR 97221
Tel.: (503) 285-9090
Web Site:
  http://www.keenhealthcare.com
Year Founded: 2002
Rev.: $2,600,000
Emp.: 46
Healthcare & Distributes Products Design
N.A.I.C.S.: 518210
Vail Horton *(Founder & CEO)*

KEEN INFOTEK INC.
710 E Ogden Ave Ste 100, Naperville, IL 60563
Tel.: (630) 544-5710
Web Site:
  http://www.keeninfotek.com
Year Founded: 2005
Sales Range: $1-9.9 Million
Emp.: 50
Consulting & IT Services
N.A.I.C.S.: 541618
Harpal Singh *(CTO)*

KEEN TECHNICAL SOLUTIONS LLC
800 Cottageview Dr, Traverse City, MI 49684
Web Site: http://www.keen-minds.com
Year Founded: 2008
Sales Range: $1-9.9 Million
Emp.: 11
Energy Conservation Strategies
N.A.I.C.S.: 924120

KEENAN ENERGY COMPANY INCORPORATED
3923 W Beltline Blvd, Columbia, SC 29204
Tel.: (803) 256-0667
Web Site:
  http://www.keenanenergy.com
Sales Range: $50-74.9 Million
Emp.: 3
Petroleum Bulk Stations
N.A.I.C.S.: 424710
William J. Keenan II *(Pres)*

KEENAN, HOPKINS, SCHMIDT & STOWELL CONTRACTORS INC.
5422 Bay Center Dr Ste 200, Tampa, FL 33609
Tel.: (813) 628-9330 DE
Web Site: http://www.khss.com
Year Founded: 1984
Sales Range: $125-149.9 Million
Emp.: 500
Commerical Construction Services
N.A.I.C.S.: 236220
Mike Cannon *(Pres)*
Lynda Licht *(CFO)*

KEENAN-NAGLE ADVERTISING
1301 S 12th St, Allentown, PA 18103-3814
Tel.: (610) 797-7100 PA
Web Site:
  http://www.keenannagle.com
Year Founded: 1985
Sales Range: $1-9.9 Million
Emp.: 14
Advertising Agencies
N.A.I.C.S.: 541810
Gena Cavallo *(Mgr-Production)*
Michael C. Keenan *(Owner & Pres)*
Kathryn M. Minzola *(Assoc Mgr-Media Svcs)*

KEENE BUILDING PRODUCTS COMPANY, INC.
23750 St Claire Ave, Euclid, OH 44117
Tel.: (440) 605-1020
Web Site:
  http://www.keenebuilding.com
Year Founded: 2002
Clay Building Material & Refractories Mfr
N.A.I.C.S.: 327120
Melanie Debelak *(Dir-Mktg)*

Subsidiaries:

The Continental Products Company, Inc. (1)
1150 E 222nd St, Euclid, OH 44117
Tel.: (216) 531-0710
Web Site: http://www.continentalprod.com
Allied Products Mfg
N.A.I.C.S.: 325510
Robert Lesher *(Mgr-Market-Wood Coatings & Greenhouse Products)*

Village Plastics Co. (1)
100 16th St SW, Barberton, OH 44203
Tel.: (330) 753-0100
Web Site: https://www.villageplastics.com
Polyester Fiber & Filament Yarn Mfr
N.A.I.C.S.: 313110

KEENE CHRYSLER, INC.
410 Winchester St, Keene, NH 03431
Tel.: (603) 357-0808
Web Site:
  http://www.keenechryslerdodgejeep.com
Sales Range: $10-24.9 Million
Emp.: 50
Car Whslr
N.A.I.C.S.: 441110
Larry Monson *(Gen Mgr)*
Erik Johnson *(Dir-Svc)*

KEENE DODGE CO. INC.
3707 Norrisville Rd, Jarrettsville, MD 21084
Tel.: (410) 692-5111 MD
Web Site:
  http://www.keenedodge.com
Year Founded: 1985
Sales Range: $25-49.9 Million
Emp.: 120
Sales of New & Used Automobiles
N.A.I.C.S.: 441110
Tony Bisesi *(Mgr-Svc)*

KEENE PROMOTIONS, INC.
450 Lexington St Ste 102, Newton, MA 02466
Tel.: (617) 243-0101
Web Site:
  http://www.keenepromotions.com
Year Founded: 1949
Sales Range: Less than $1 Million
Emp.: 12
Marketing & Brand Promotional Services
N.A.I.C.S.: 541820
Michael Keene *(CEO)*

Subsidiaries:

Keene Promotions, Inc. (1)
663 N Sangamon St, Chicago, IL 60622
Tel.: (312) 953-6161
Web Site: http://www.keenepromotions.com
Emp.: 2
Brand Marketing & Promotional Services
N.A.I.C.S.: 541820
Leila Keene *(Dir-Sls)*

Keene Promotions, Inc. (1)
20560 Shelburne Rd, Shaker Heights, OH 44122
Tel.: (216) 932-1989
Web Site: http://www.keenepromostore.com
Emp.: 11
Brand Marketing & Promotional Services
N.A.I.C.S.: 541820
Judith Greenspan *(Mgr-Reg)*

KEENELAND ASSOCIATION INC.
4201 Versailles Rd, Lexington, KY 40510
Tel.: (859) 254-3412 KY
Web Site: http://www.keeneland.com
Year Founded: 1936
Sales Range: $750-799.9 Million
Emp.: 160
Racer & Retailer of Thoroughbred Horses
N.A.I.C.S.: 424520
Geoffrey Russell *(Dir-Sls Ops)*
D. Ben Huffman *(Sec)*
Amy Gregory *(Dir-Comm)*
Bill Thomason *(Pres & CEO)*
Robert N. Elliston *(VP-Racing & Sls)*
Shannon Bishop Arvin *(Pres & CEO)*

Subsidiaries:

Keeneland Association Inc. - The Thoroughbred Center Division (1)
3380 Paris Pike, Lexington, KY 40511
Tel.: (859) 293-1853
Web Site: http://www.thoroughbred-center.com
Emp.: 50
Horse Training Services
N.A.I.C.S.: 327910

KEENER LUMBER COMPANY INC.
1209 W Market St, Smithfield, NC 27577
Tel.: (919) 934-1087 NC
Year Founded: 1963
Sales Range: $10-24.9 Million
Emp.: 62
Sawmills & Planing Mills General
N.A.I.C.S.: 321113
Wade M. Stewart *(Pres)*
Charles Kenley *(CFO)*
Reid Stewart *(Owner)*

KEEP ENTERPRISES, INC.
3120 Hwy 332, International Falls, MN 56649
Tel.: (218) 283-4477
Oil & Natural Gas Distr
N.A.I.C.S.: 221210
Larry Keep *(Pres)*

KEEP ON TRUCKING COMPANY INCORPORATED

11355 Arrow Rte, Rancho Cucamonga, CA 91730
Tel.: (909) 987-3939
Web Site: http://www.kot.com
Sales Range: $10-24.9 Million
Emp.: 120
Local Trucking with Storage
N.A.I.C.S.: 484110
John Hallaway *(Pres-Ops)*
Paul Bojanower *(Chm)*
George Gruenwald *(Mgr-Ops)*

KEEP SERVICES, INC.
27 Cleveland St, Valhalla, NY 10595
Tel.: (914) 220-1400   NY
Web Site:
http://www.keepinsurance.com
Year Founded: 1983
Sales Range: $50-74.9 Million
Emp.: 50
Insurance Agents, Brokers & Service
N.A.I.C.S.: 524210
Joe Cantarella *(VP)*
Thomas Patrick Kelly *(Pres)*

KEEPING CURRENT MATTERS, INC.
7204 Glen Forest Dr Ste 204, Richmond, VA 23226
Tel.: (631) 787-6200
Web Site:
http://www.keepingcurrentmatters.com
Year Founded: 2007
Sales Range: $1-9.9 Million
Emp.: 19
Real Estate Agency Services
N.A.I.C.S.: 531210
Steve Harney *(Founder)*
Bill Harney *(Pres & CEO)*
Beth Frank *(Chief People Officer)*
Charlotte Parrish *(VP-Member Success & Product)*
David Childers *(VP-Content & Mktg)*

KEEPING KIDS SAFE INC.
124 W Front St Ste 102, Findlay, OH 45840
Tel.: (567) 525-4520   OH
Web Site:
http://www.keepingkidssafe.org
Year Founded: 2010
Rev.: $1,162,569
Assets: $490,855
Liabilities: $123,248
Net Worth: $367,607
Earnings: $31,636
Emp.: 13
Fiscal Year-end: 06/30/14
Child Foster Care Services
N.A.I.C.S.: 623990
Judith Hutton *(Pres)*

KEEPING TRADITIONS INC.
850 Santa Cruz Ave, Menlo Park, CA 94025
Tel.: (650) 325-4849
Web Site: http://www.traditionsforthehome.com
Rev.: $10,000,000
Emp.: 85
Furniture Retailer
N.A.I.C.S.: 449110
Roland K. Wentzel *(Pres)*

KEEPRS, INC.
305 4th Ave S, Sauk Rapids, MN 56379
Tel.: (320) 529-9585
Web Site: http://www.keeprs.com
Year Founded: 1998
Sales Range: $10-24.9 Million
Emp.: 20
Retailer of Uniforms & Equipment for Public Safety Groups
N.A.I.C.S.: 459999

Wendy Klinefelter Tragiai *(Owner)*
John Tragiai *(Pres)*

KEESEE MOTOR CO.
111 S Broadway St, Cortez, CO 81321
Tel.: (970) 565-8431
Web Site:
http://www.keeseemotorcompany.com
Sales Range: $10-24.9 Million
Emp.: 40
Car Whslr
N.A.I.C.S.: 441110
Larry Pickens *(Gen Mgr)*

KEETER MOTORS INC.
1775 E Dixon Blvd, Shelby, NC 28152-6946
Tel.: (704) 482-6791
Sales Range: $10-24.9 Million
Emp.: 65
Car Whslr
N.A.I.C.S.: 441110
Missy Darnell *(Mgr-Ops)*
David Mull *(Dir-Svc)*
Keeter Owner *(Principal)*

KEETON'S OFFICE & ART SUPPLY CO.
817 Manatee Ave W, Bradenton, FL 34205
Tel.: (941) 747-2995
Web Site:
http://www.keetonsonline.com
Rev.: $11,700,000
Emp.: 38
Office Supplies & Stationery Stores
N.A.I.C.S.: 459410
Brice Hoopingarner *(Pres & CEO)*
Patricia A. Hoopingarner *(Treas)*
Margaret A. Keeton *(Sec)*

KEFFER HYUNDAI
9010 E Independence Blvd, Matthews, NC 28105-4506
Tel.: (704) 714-4700
Web Site:
http://www.kefferhyundai.com
Year Founded: 1982
Sales Range: $10-24.9 Million
Emp.: 38
Car Whslr
N.A.I.C.S.: 441110
Melanie Murrill *(Dir-Mktg)*
Jacob Franklin *(Mgr-Parts)*
Rose Reyes *(Coord-Bus Dev)*
Tony Shinault *(Mgr-Used Car)*

KEGEL COMPANY INC.
1951 Longleaf Blvd, Lake Wales, FL 33859
Tel.: (863) 734-0200
Web Site: http://www.kegel.net
Rev.: $10,488,698
Emp.: 81
Bowling Facility Cleaning Products & Maintenance Equipment Mfr & Distr
N.A.I.C.S.: 333310
Larry Klemme *(Pres)*

KEHE DISTRIBUTORS, LLC
1245 E Diehl Rd Ste 200, Naperville, IL 60563
Tel.: (630) 343-0000   DE
Web Site: https://www.kehe.com
Year Founded: 1952
Sales Range: $250-299.9 Million
Emp.: 6,800
Other Grocery & Related Products Merchant Wholesalers
N.A.I.C.S.: 424490
Gene Carter *(COO)*
Annette Roder *(Chief Talent Officer & Sr VP-HR)*
Joel Jorgensen *(Chief Acctg Officer)*

Mike Leone *(Chief Comml Officer)*
Brian Wilkinson *(CFO)*
Larry Hartley *(Exec VP-Warehouse Ops)*
Deb Conklin *(Pres)*
Subsidiaries:

DPI Specialty Foods, Inc.   (1)
601 Rockefeller Ave, Ontario, CA 91761
Tel.: (909) 975-1019
Web Site: http://www.distribution-plus.com
Specialty Foods Distr
N.A.I.C.S.: 424410
John Jordan *(CEO)*
Francis Haren *(COO)*
Conor Crowley *(CFO)*
Russ Blake *(Pres & Chief Comml Officer)*
Nadia Rosseels *(VP-IT)*
Kristen Flynn *(VP-HR)*

Division *(Domestic)*:

DPI Mid Atlantic   (2)
1200 Claybrick Rd Ste 100, Capitol Heights, MD 20743
Tel.: (301) 430-2200
Web Site: http://www.dpispecialtyfoods.com
Food Distr
N.A.I.C.S.: 424490

DPI Midwest   (2)
600 E Brook Dr, Arlington Heights, IL 60005
Tel.: (847) 364-9704
Web Site: http://www.distribution-plus.com
Food Distr
N.A.I.C.S.: 424490
Dan Plattner *(CFO)*

DPI Northwest   (2)
12360 SW Leveton Dr, Tualatin, OR 97062-6001
Tel.: (503) 692-0662
Web Site: http://www.distribution-plus.com
Imported Foods Distr
N.A.I.C.S.: 424490

DPI Rocky Mountain   (2)
8125 E 88th Ave, Henderson, CO 80640
Tel.: (303) 301-1226
Web Site: http://www.distribution-plus.com
Food Distr
N.A.I.C.S.: 424490
Dan Dahm *(VP-Procurement)*
Joe Moseley *(VP-Warehouse & Transportation)*
Gary Elings *(CFO)*
Ralph Howell *(VP-Sls & Mktg)*

DPI West   (2)
601 Rockefeller Ave, Ontario, CA 91761
Tel.: (909) 975-1019
Web Site: http://www.distribution-plus.com
Food Distr
N.A.I.C.S.: 424410
Jeff Mejia *(Gen Mgr-Ops)*
Alan Stock *(VP-Sls)*
Gary Elings *(CFO)*
Clive Baravilala *(VP-Procurement)*

Monterrey Provision Company, Inc.   (1)
7850 Waterville Rd, San Diego, CA 92154-8205   (100%)
Tel.: (619) 294-2222
Web Site: http://www.monprov.com
Food Products Whslr & Distr
N.A.I.C.S.: 424470
Luke Abbott *(Pres)*

Nature's Best, Inc.   (1)
6 Pointe Dr Ste 300, Brea, CA 92821
Tel.: (714) 255-4600
Web Site: http://www.naturesbest.net
Health & Natural Food Products Whslr & Distr
N.A.I.C.S.: 424490
James Beck *(CEO)*
Tim Groff *(CFO, COO & Exec VP)*
Tom Echolds *(Pres)*

Peters Imports, Inc.   (1)
3040 Remico St SW, Grandville, MI 49418
Tel.: (616) 261-5405
Web Site: http://www.petersimports.com
Sales Range: $1-9.9 Million
Emp.: 55
Importer & Distr of Specialty Foods
N.A.I.C.S.: 424490
Edwin Peters *(Pres)*

KEHM OIL COMPANY
1600 Oakdale Rd, Oakdale, PA 15071
Tel.: (412) 921-5200
Sales Range: $10-24.9 Million
Emp.: 25
Petroleum Bulk Stations
N.A.I.C.S.: 424710
George M. Kehm *(Pres)*

KEHOE COMPONENT SALES INC.
34 Foley Dr, Sodus, NY 14551-0067
Tel.: (315) 483-9122
Web Site:
http://www.paceelectronics.com
Year Founded: 1969
Sales Range: $10-24.9 Million
Emp.: 20
Capacitors, Electronic
N.A.I.C.S.: 423690
Alan Zimmer *(CFO)*
Peter Yang *(Mng Dir)*
Peter Wang *(Gen Mgr-Mfg)*

KEIKA VENTURES LLC
PO Box 4704, Chapel Hill, NC 27515
Tel.: (919) 933-9569
Web Site:
http://www.keikaventures.com
Year Founded: 2001
Sales Range: $1-9.9 Million
Emp.: 7
Products, Supplies & Equipment for Environmental Testing
N.A.I.C.S.: 541620
Allyson Porter *(Mng Partner)*

KEILER & COMPANY
304 Main St, Farmington, CT 06032-2985
Tel.: (860) 677-8821   CT
Web Site: http://www.keiler.com
Year Founded: 1973
Sales Range: $1-9.9 Million
Emp.: 50
Advertising Agencies
N.A.I.C.S.: 541810
Bill Smith *(Mng Partner)*
Mel Maffei *(Mng Partner)*
Lynn Taylor *(Pres & CEO)*
Lisa Geissler *(Dir-Media)*
Corinna Tamburini *(Dir-Media Svcs)*
Sheli Chiaradio *(CFO)*
Gini Kramer *(Exec Dir-Creative)*
Kim Prauda *(Acct Supvr)*
Lucas McHale *(Dir-Creative Interactive)*
Paul Emery *(Assoc Dir-Creative)*
Wayne Waaramaa *(Assoc Dir-Creative)*
Scott Fitzgerald *(Dir-New Bus)*
Michael Feinberg *(Dir-Creative)*
Ashleigh Karnilowicz *(Asst Acct Mgr)*
Henrietta Sabel *(Coord-Media)*
Jon Brody *(Exec Dir-Healthcare)*
Jerome Barrillon *(Exec Dir-Indus Accts)*

KEIM CHEVROLET INC.
3265 Lincoln Hwy E, Paradise, PA 17562
Tel.: (717) 768-8225
Web Site: http://www.keimchevy.com
Rev.: $14,970,010
Emp.: 26
Automobiles, New & Used
N.A.I.C.S.: 441110
Alan Keim *(Pres)*

KEIM CORP.
823 Sunflower Dr, Geneva, IL 60134
Tel.: (630) 232-1400
Web Site: http://www.keimcorp.com
Year Founded: 1956
Sales Range: $25-49.9 Million

KEIM CORP.

Keim Corp.—(Continued)
Emp.: 20
Single-Family Custom Home Construction Services
N.A.I.C.S.: 236115
Joseph A. Keim (Pres)
Judith Dimonte (Exec VP)
Helen Keim (Treas & Sec)

KEIM LUMBER COMPANY
State Rte 557, Charm, OH 44617
Tel.: (330) 893-2251   OH
Web Site:
   http://www.keimlumber.com
Year Founded: 1968
Sales Range: $25-49.9 Million
Emp.: 178
Distr of Lumber & Other Building Materials
N.A.I.C.S.: 423310
Bill Keim (Owner & Pres)

KEIM TS INC.
1249 N 9th St, Sabetha, KS 66534
Tel.: (785) 284-2147
Web Site: http://www.keimts.com
Sales Range: $10-24.9 Million
Emp.: 225
Trucking Service
N.A.I.C.S.: 484121
Stan Keim (Pres)
Paul Herle (Controller)
Paul Herl (CFO)
Stuart Burton (Exec Dir-Maint & Equip Sls)

KEITH BAKER HOMES INC.
122 E James Campbell Blvd, Columbia, TN 38401
Tel.: (931) 381-5035
Web Site:
   http://www.keithbakerhomes.com
Year Founded: 1976
Sales Range: $10-24.9 Million
Emp.: 40
Mobile Home Dealers
N.A.I.C.S.: 459930
Ralph Keith Baker (Pres)
Wanda H. Smith (Gen Mgr)
Ron Kelley (Mgr-Sls)

KEITH DOYLE & ASSOCIATES INC.
9 Town Forest Rd, Oxford, MA 01540
Tel.: (508) 987-8518
Sales Range: $10-24.9 Million
Emp.: 5
Keith Doyle & Associates Inc.
N.A.I.C.S.: 424990
Keith J. Doyle (Pres)
Cynthia Doyle (VP)

KEITH HAWTHORNE FORD
617 N Main St, Belmont, NC 28012
Tel.: (704) 825-5186
Web Site:
   http://www.fordofbelmont.com
Year Founded: 1922
Sales Range: $10-24.9 Million
Emp.: 66
New Car Whslr
N.A.I.C.S.: 441110
Scott Baucom (Gen Mgr)

KEITH SMITH COMPANY, INC.
130 K Tech Ln, Hot Springs, AR 71913
Tel.: (501) 760-0100   AR
Web Site: http://www.keith-smith.com
Year Founded: 1948
Sales Range: $75-99.9 Million
Emp.: 76
Provider of Poultry & Egg Products
N.A.I.C.S.: 424440
Wayne Freeman (VP-Transportation & Dedicated Contract Svcs)

Keith Smith (VP-Sls)
Syd Tatum (Mgr-Live Production)
James Keith Smith II (Pres & CEO)

KEITH TITUS CORPORATION
2758 Trombley Rd, Weedsport, NY 13166-9510
Tel.: (315) 834-6681   NY
Web Site:
   http://www.pagetrucking.com
Year Founded: 1975
Rev.: $115,000,000
Emp.: 55
Provider of Trucking Services
N.A.I.C.S.: 484121

Subsidiaries:

Page Transportation Inc.   (1)
2758 Trombley Rd, Weedsport, NY 13166-9510
Tel.: (315) 834-6681
Web Site: http://www.pagetrucking.com
Sales Range: $10-24.9 Million
Emp.: 40
Provide State To State Trucking Services
N.A.I.C.S.: 484121
Daniel K. Titus (Pres)
Christopher Jorolemon (VP-Ops)
Piper Titus (CFO)
Mary Birchfield (Mgr-Terminal)
Mel Clawson (Mgr-Terminal)
Mark Gleason (Mgr-Terminal)
Denise Hinman (Office Mgr)
Donna Keysor (Mgr-Terminal)
Jacquie Moore (Mgr-HR & Insurance)
Tom Schrader (Mgr-Terminal)

KEITH ZARS POOLS
17427 San Pedro Ave, San Antonio, TX 78232
Tel.: (210) 494-0800
Web Site:
   http://www.keithzarspools.com
Year Founded: 1985
Sales Range: $25-49.9 Million
Emp.: 250
Specialty Trade Contractors
N.A.I.C.S.: 238910
Keith Zars (Pres)

KEITHLY-WILLIAMS SEEDS INC.
420 Palm Ave, Holtville, CA 92250-1156
Tel.: (760) 356-5533   CA
Web Site:
   http://www.keithlywilliams.com
Year Founded: 1981
Sales Range: $10-24.9 Million
Emp.: 39
Farm Supplies; Vegetable Seeds
N.A.I.C.S.: 424910
Kevin Ford (Mgr-Quality Assurance)

KEJR, INC.
1835 Wall St, Salina, KS 67401
Tel.: (785) 825-1842
Web Site: http://geoprobe.com
Year Founded: 1986
Sales Range: $10-24.9 Million
Emp.: 100
Professional, Scientific & Technical Services
N.A.I.C.S.: 541990
Tom Christy (VP)
John Robb (Mgr-Fabrication Production)

KELBE BROS EQUIPMENT CO. INC.
12770 West Silver Spring Dr, Butler, WI 53007
Tel.: (262) 781-4970
Web Site: http://www.kelbebros.com
Sales Range: $10-24.9 Million
Emp.: 40
General Construction Machinery & Equipment

N.A.I.C.S.: 423810
Larry R. Miller (Pres)
Tom Schilling (Mgr-Product Support)
Tim Stummer (Controller)

KELBY MEDIA GROUP, INC.
333 Douglas Rd E, Oldsmar, FL 34677-2922
Tel.: (813) 749-4000
Web Site:
   http://www.kelbymediagroup.com
Sales Range: $25-49.9 Million
Emp.: 90
Creative Professionals Education & Information Services Including Magazines, Books, DVDs, Online Training, Videos, Conferences & Seminars
N.A.I.C.S.: 611699
Scott Kelby (Pres)
Kevin Agren (VP-Sls)
Jeanne Jilleba (Coord-Adv)

Subsidiaries:

Kelby Training Inc.   (1)
333 Douglas Rd E, Oldsmar, FL 34677-2922
Tel.: (813) 433-5000
Web Site: http://www.kelbyone.com
Emp.: 80
Online Photography, Photoshop & Web Design Training Courses
N.A.I.C.S.: 611699
Scott Kelby (Pres)

KELCO INDUSTRIES INC.
1425 Lk Ave, Woodstock, IL 60098
Tel.: (815) 334-3600
Sales Range: $50-74.9 Million
Emp.: 842
Flexible Metal Hose, Tubing & Bellows
N.A.I.C.S.: 333998
Kevin Kelly (Pres & Treas)

Subsidiaries:

Guardian Electric Manufacturing Company   (1)
1425 Lk Ave, Woodstock, IL 60098-7419
Tel.: (815) 334-3600
Web Site: http://www.guardian-electric.com
Sales Range: $1-9.9 Million
Emp.: 80
Relays, Solenoids, Switches, Steppers & Controls, Aero Products, Grips & Military Relays Mfr
N.A.I.C.S.: 334419

KELCO LIMITED
114 Joy St, Sevierville, TN 37862
Tel.: (865) 453-4666
Sales Range: $10-24.9 Million
Emp.: 2
Provider of Petroleum Products
N.A.I.C.S.: 424720
Gary R. Wade (Partner)

KELLEN COMMUNICATIONS
1100 Johnson Ferry Rd Ste 300, Atlanta, GA 30342
Tel.: (404) 252-3663
Web Site:
   http://www.kellencompany.com
Year Founded: 1945
Public Relations Agency
N.A.I.C.S.: 541820
Russell A. Lemieux (Grp VP)
Richard E. Cristol (Pres)
Michael Brooks (CFO, Treas & Exec VP)
Eric Allen (VP)
Michael Cummings (VP)
Jim Fowler (VP)
Katherine Bennett (Sr Acct Supvr)

Subsidiaries:

John Adams Associates Inc.   (1)
750 National Press Bldg, Washington, DC 20045-1601

U.S. PRIVATE

Tel.: (202) 737-8400
Web Site: http://www.johnadams.com
Emp.: 25
Fiscal Year-end: 12/31/2000
Full Service
N.A.I.C.S.: 541810

Kellen Communications   (1)
355 Lexington Ave Ste 1515, New York, NY 10017
Tel.: (212) 297-2100
Emp.: 45
Public Relations Agency
N.A.I.C.S.: 541820
Greg Sherry (Exec VP-Comm)

Kellen Communications
1156 15th St NW Ste 900, Washington, DC 20005
Tel.: (202) 207-0915
Sales Range: $10-24.9 Million
Emp.: 25
Public Relations Agency
N.A.I.C.S.: 541820

Kellen Communications   (1)
1604 N Country Club Rd, Tucson, AZ 85716
Tel.: (520) 325-1055
Emp.: 10
Public Relations Agency
N.A.I.C.S.: 541820

Kellen Europe   (1)
Avenue Marcel Thiry 204, B-1200, Brussels, Belgium
Tel.: (32) 2 774 96 10
Web Site: http://www.kelleneurope.com
Public Relations Agency
N.A.I.C.S.: 541820

KELLER BROS MOTOR CO.
1030 Schaeffer Rd, Lebanon, PA 17042
Tel.: (717) 949-6501   PA
Web Site:
   http://www.kellerbrosford.com
Year Founded: 1918
Sales Range: $10-24.9 Million
Emp.: 67
Sales of New & Used Automobiles
N.A.I.C.S.: 441110
Gregory Lessig (Gen Mgr)
Jeremy Weaver (Asst Gen Mgr)

KELLER CONSTRUCTION INC.
2412 S 3400 W, Salt Lake City, UT 84119
Tel.: (801) 972-1018
Web Site:
   http://www.kellerconstruct.com
Sales Range: $1-9.9 Million
Emp.: 20
Commercial & Office Building Construction Services
N.A.I.C.S.: 236220
Ferris Keller (Pres)

KELLER ELECTRICAL INDUSTRIES, INC.
1881 E University Dr, Phoenix, AZ 85034
Tel.: (602) 437-3015   AZ
Web Site:
   http://www.kellerelectrical.com
Year Founded: 1980
Sales Range: $25-49.9 Million
Emp.: 88
Electronic & Precision Equipment Repair & Maintenance
N.A.I.C.S.: 811210
Don Anderson (Pres & CEO)
Jim Everson (VP & CFO)
Danny Morone (VP-Repairs Ops)
Cody Eslick (VP-Ops)
Dwight Groth (VP-Sls)

KELLER ENTERPRISES, INC.
1514 Main St, Northampton, PA 18067
Tel.: (610) 262-3975
Web Site: http://www.kellerent.com

Year Founded: 1994
Wood Pellets & Petroleum Products;
Heating & Cooling Equipment Installation, Service & Maintenance
N.A.I.C.S.: 324199
Frank I. Keller III *(Pres)*

KELLER GRAIN & FEED INC.
7977 Main St, Greenville, OH 45331-9255
Tel.: (937) 448-2284 OH
Web Site: http://www.kellergrain.com
Year Founded: 1974
Sales Range: $10-24.9 Million
Emp.: 33
Grain & Field Beans
N.A.I.C.S.: 424510
David W. Keller *(Pres)*
John Keller *(Treas & Sec)*

KELLER GROUP INC.
1 Northfield Plz Ste 510, Northfield, IL 60093-1216
Tel.: (847) 446-7550 OH
Year Founded: 1971
Sales Range: $25-49.9 Million
Emp.: 650
Provider of Mining Products & Services
N.A.I.C.S.: 332111
John P. Keller *(Chm)*
David Spada *(VP-Fin)*

Subsidiaries:

Meadville Forging Company Inc. (1)
15309 Baldwin St Ext, Meadville, PA 16335
Tel.: (814) 332-8200
Web Site: http://www.meadforge.com
Sales Range: $25-49.9 Million
Emp.: 330
Designer & Producer of Custom Forged Iron & Steel Parts
N.A.I.C.S.: 332111
Jack Keller *(Owner)*

KELLER INC.
N216 State Hwy 55, Kaukauna, WI 54130-8401
Tel.: (920) 766-5795 WI
Web Site: http://www.kellerbuilds.com
Year Founded: 1960
Sales Range: $50-74.9 Million
Emp.: 185
Nonresidential Construction Services
N.A.I.C.S.: 236220
Doug Stecker *(CFO & VP-Fin)*
Jerry Cohen *(VP-Ops)*
Scott Krueger *(Project Mgr)*
Vern Nystrom *(Project Mgr)*
Dale Hulce *(Mgr-Project Sls)*
Weston Zuleger *(Mgr-Project Sls-Green Bay)*
Corey Trcka *(Project Mgr-Wausau)*
Pete Read *(Project Mgr-Madison)*
Nate Sparbel *(Asst Project Mgr-Madison)*
Sam Winterfeldt *(Asst Project Mgr-Kaukauna)*
Scott Lausten *(Asst Project Mgr-Milwaukee)*
Jesse Hall *(Project Mgr-Green Bay)*

KELLER KITCHEN CABINETS, INC.
2526 State Rd 44 W, Deland, FL 32721
Tel.: (386) 734-1984 FL
Year Founded: 1993
Sales Range: $75-99.9 Million
Emp.: 35
Mfr & Distributor of Kitchen & Bath Cabinets
N.A.I.C.S.: 321999
Steve Toland *(VP-Sls)*

KELLER SUPPLY COMPANY INC.
3209 17th Ave W, Seattle, WA 98119-1708
Tel.: (206) 285-3300 WA
Web Site: http://www.kellersupply.com
Year Founded: 1945
Sales Range: $125-149.9 Million
Emp.: 80
Plumbing Fixtures, Equipment & Supplies
N.A.I.C.S.: 423720
Nick Keller *(CEO)*

KELLER TECHNOLOGY CORPORATION
2320 Military Rd, Tonawanda, NY 14150
Tel.: (716) 693-3840 NY
Web Site: http://www.kellertechnology.com
Year Founded: 1918
Sales Range: $10-24.9 Million
Emp.: 215
Industrial Machinery Mfr
N.A.I.C.S.: 332710
Mike Keller *(Pres)*
Dan Dirrigl *(Controller)*

KELLER WILLIAMS CAPITAL PROPERTIES
801 D St NE, Washington, DC 20002
Tel.: (202) 243-7700
Web Site: http://www.kellerwilliamsdc.com
Sales Range: $10-24.9 Million
Emp.: 16
Real Estate Brokerage Services
N.A.I.C.S.: 531210
Brandon Green *(Mng Partner)*
Bo Menkiti *(Founder & CEO)*
Bob Dillard *(Mng Dir-Fairfax)*
Dontae Carroll *(COO)*

KELLER WILLIAMS LEGACY BROKERAGE GROUP
1515 Reisterstown Rd 2nd Fl, Pikesville, MD 21208
Tel.: (443) 660-9229
Web Site: http://www.kwlegacypikesville.com
Year Founded: 2014
Sales Range: $10-24.9 Million
Emp.: 420
Real Estate Agency Services
N.A.I.C.S.: 531210
Metta Edwards *(Coord-Agent Svc)*
Pam Lloyd *(Acct Coord)*
Courtney Chase *(Coord-Compliance)*
Elana Royfer *(Coord-MC)*
Seth Campbell *(Principal-Ops)*

KELLER WILLIAMS PLATINUM PARTNERS, INC.
1201 NE Windsor Dr, Lees Summit, MO 64086
Tel.: (816) 525-7000
Web Site: http://www.kwleessummit.com
Rev.: $200,000,000
Emp.: 4
Real Estate Agents & Managers
N.A.I.C.S.: 531210
Locas Sheridan *(Pres)*

KELLER WILLIAMS REALTY, INC.
1221 S Mopac Expy Ste 400, Austin, TX 78746
Tel.: (512) 327-3070
Web Site: http://www.kw.com
Sales Range: $25-49.9 Million
Emp.: 150
Real Estate Brokerage Services
N.A.I.C.S.: 531210

Gary Keller *(Founder & Exec Chm)*
Mo Anderson *(Vice Chm)*
Mark Willis *(CEO)*
Ann Yett *(CFO)*
Dianna Kokoszka *(CEO-MAPS Coaching)*
Jay Papasan *(VP-Publ)*
Sharon Gibbons *(VP-Philanthropic Admin)*
Josh Team *(Pres)*
Darrell King *(COO)*
Ellen Curtis *(COO-Worldwide)*
Jim Talbot *(Dir-Res)*
Tamara Hurwitz *(Exec Dir-Ops)*
Tom Freireich *(Dir-Vendor Rels)*
Jamie Jatzlau *(Gen Counsel)*
Neil Dholakia *(Chief Product Officer)*
Mindy Grubb *(Exec Dir-Events)*
Annie Switt *(Exec Dir-Mktg & Comm)*
Debbie Gardner *(Dir-Commitment-Franchise Sys)*
Darryl G. Frost *(Dir-PR & Media Rels)*

KELLER-SMITH SUPPLY, INC.
855 E Lakeside Dr, Mobile, AL 36693
Tel.: (251) 666-7210 FL
Web Site: http://www.keller-smith.com
Year Founded: 1967
Sales Range: $10-24.9 Million
Emp.: 30
Specialty Building Products, Vinyl Floors, Steel Doors, Aluminum Windows & Other Products Whslr
N.A.I.C.S.: 423310
John Calder *(Mgr-Sls)*

KELLEY & COMPANY
1050 Winter St Ste 1000, Waltham, MA 02451
Tel.: (781) 239-8092 MA
Year Founded: 1993
Rev.: $11,300,000
Emp.: 9
Automotive, Brand Development, Consumer Marketing, Education, Financial, Leisure, Retail, Sports Marketing, Travel & Tourism
N.A.I.C.S.: 541810
Glenn C. Kelley *(Pres & CEO)*

KELLEY AUTOMOTIVE GROUP
633 Ave of Autos, Fort Wayne, IN 46804
Tel.: (260) 434-4600 IN
Web Site: http://www.drivekelley.com
Year Founded: 1952
Sales Range: $350-399.9 Million
Emp.: 500
New & Used Automobile Dealer & Servicer
N.A.I.C.S.: 441110
Thomas Kelley *(Pres)*
Jeff Johnson *(Mgr-Fin)*
Trent Waybright *(Dir-Pre-Owned Ops)*
Adam Brueggeman *(Controller)*
Brian Lytle *(VP-Sls)*

KELLEY BEAN CO., INC.
2407 Circle Dr, Scottsbluff, NE 69361
Tel.: (308) 635-6438 NE
Web Site: http://www.kelleybean.com
Year Founded: 1927
Sales Range: $125-149.9 Million
Emp.: 200
Processor & Whslr of Agricultural Products; Dry Edible Beans
N.A.I.C.S.: 424510
Gary L. Kelley *(Chm)*
Lee Glenn *(Pres, CFO & Treas)*
Robert L. Kelley *(Pres)*
Kevin Kelley *(VP-Trading Mktg)*

KELLEY BROS
317 E Brighton Ave, Syracuse, NY 13210
Tel.: (315) 478-2151
Web Site: http://www.kelleybros.com
Sales Range: $25-49.9 Million
Emp.: 60
Builders' Hardware, Nec
N.A.I.C.S.: 423710
Ellen Tracy *(Project Mgr)*
Brian Binder *(Project Mgr)*
Jim Tartre *(Mgr-Sls-Natl)*
Marco Dougherty *(Project Mgr)*
Tom Reid *(Project Mgr)*

KELLEY CAWTHORNE, LLC
208 N Capitol Ave Ste 3, Lansing, MI 48933-1356
Tel.: (517) 371-1400
Web Site: http://www.kelley-cawthorne.com
Law firm
N.A.I.C.S.: 541110

Subsidiaries:

Thomas P. Pappas & Associates (1)
66 E Lynn St, Columbus, OH 43215-3541
Tel.: (614) 621-2000
Web Site: http://www.tompappas.com
Law firm
N.A.I.C.S.: 541110

KELLEY CHEVROLET INC.
633 Avenue Of Autos, Fort Wayne, IN 46804-1184
Tel.: (260) 484-5566 IN
Web Site: http://www.jimkelleychevrolet.com
Year Founded: 1955
Sales Range: $25-49.9 Million
Emp.: 210
Sales of New & Used Cars
N.A.I.C.S.: 441110
Ken Runyan *(Mgr-Truck Svc)*

KELLEY CONNECT CO.
22710 72nd Ave S, Kent, WA 98032
Tel.: (206) 284-9100
Web Site: https://kelleyconnect.com
Year Founded: 1974
Application Development, Network Integration, Mobility Solutions, Website Development, Infrastructure Design, Security Technology, Managed Services IT Outsourcing Services
N.A.I.C.S.: 518210
Aric Manion *(Pres)*

KELLEY DRYE & WARREN LLP
101 Park Ave, New York, NY 10178
Tel.: (212) 808-7800 NY
Web Site: http://www.kelleydrye.com
Year Founded: 1836
Legal Advisory Services
N.A.I.C.S.: 541110
Joseph B. Hoffman *(Partner)*
Michael A. Adelstein *(Partner)*
Michael Kosmas *(Partner)*
Cliff Katz *(Partner)*
Tim Lavender *(Partner)*
Michael C. Lynch *(Partner)*
Joseph Hoffman *(Partner)*

Subsidiaries:

Jackson Gilmour & Dobbs, P.C. (1)
3900 Essex Ln Ste 700, Houston, TX 77027
Tel.: (713) 552-0325
Law Firm
N.A.I.C.S.: 541199

KELLEY HABIB JOHN
1 Constitution Ctr, Boston, MA 02129-2025
Tel.: (617) 241-8000 MA
Web Site: http://www.khj.com

KELLEY HABIB JOHN

Kelley Habib John—(Continued)
Year Founded: 1986
Rev.: $34,700,000
Emp.: 20
Advetising Agency
N.A.I.C.S.: 541810
Gregory P. John *(Chm & Chief Creative Officer)*
Judy A. Habib *(Pres & CEO)*
Adam Cramer *(Partner & Dir-Art & Creative)*
Sylvie Askins *(Principal & Exec VP-Strategy & Plng)*

KELLEY HOLDINGS INC.
7220 Division St, Cleveland, OH 44146-5406
Tel.: (440) 232-9595
Web Site: http://www.kelleysteel.com
Year Founded: 1993
Sales Range: $25-49.9 Million
Emp.: 280
Steel Contracting Services
N.A.I.C.S.: 236115
Subsidiaries:

Kelley Steel Erectors Inc.   (1)
7220 Division St, Cleveland, OH 44146
Tel.: (440) 232-9595
Web Site: http://www.kelleysteel.com
Sales Range: $50-74.9 Million
Emp.: 200
Structural Steel Erection Services
N.A.I.C.S.: 238120
Michael J. Kelley *(Chm & Pres)*
Dan Gold *(CEO)*

KELLEY SWOFFORD ROY, INC.
50 NE 29th St, Miami, FL 33137
Tel.: (305) 444-0004   FL
Web Site:
   http://www.ksrmarketing.com
Year Founded: 1983
Rev.: $18,800,000
Emp.: 12
Advetising Agency
N.A.I.C.S.: 541810
Susan P. Kelley *(Chm & CEO)*
William R. Roy *(Sr Partner)*
Vivian Villalba *(Art Dir & Mgr-Production)*
Jesus Salinas *(Controller)*
Clarice MacGarvey *(Dir- PR)*
Melisa Garcia *(Acct Exec)*
Jose Wilches *(Mgr-IT)*
Marcy Rusillo *(Dir-Media)*

KELLEY TRUCKING, INC.
6201 McIntyre St, Golden, CO 80403
Tel.: (303) 279-4150   CO
Web Site:
   http://www.kelleytruckinginc.com
Year Founded: 1981
Trucking Service
N.A.I.C.S.: 484110
John Kelley *(Founder & Pres)*
Dave Hayner *(Mgr-Fleet)*
Diane Amico *(Controller)*

KELLEY-WILLIAMSON COMPANY INC.
1132 Harrison Ave, Rockford, IL 61104-7262
Tel.: (815) 397-9410   IL
Web Site: http://www.kw-oil.com
Year Founded: 1975
Sales Range: $50-74.9 Million
Emp.: 460
Gasoline Service Stations
N.A.I.C.S.: 457120
John Griffin *(Pres)*
Kim Schmidt *(Controller)*
Neil Jasinski *(Engr-Sls)*
Bob Sanders *(Mgr-Retail Ops)*

KELLIHER SAMETS VOLK
212 Battery St, Burlington, VT 05401-5281
Tel.: (802) 862-8261   VT
Web Site: http://www.ksvc.com
Year Founded: 1977
Rev.: $40,000,000
Emp.: 65
Advetising Agency
N.A.I.C.S.: 541810
Bob Smith *(VP & Dir-Contact Grp)*
Yoram Samets *(Mng Dir)*
Cheryl Eaton *(Partner & Dir-Strategy)*
Claudia Renchy Morton *(Dir-PR)*
Linda Kelliher *(Creative Dir)*
Maryanne De Presco *(Grp Dir-Brand)*
John Marcoe *(Ops Mgr)*
Meghan Haley *(Dir-Digital Strategy)*
Frank Sampogna *(Pres-NY)*
King Borman *(Mng Partner-Boston)*
Doug Chapman *(Partner & Creative Dir)*
Lori Roberts *(Assoc Dir-Creative)*
Dianne Hanlon-Druyff *(Dir-Client Svcs)*
Matt Ogelby *(Copywriter)*
Janine Allo *(Pres)*
Mary Stewart *(Dir-Strategic Partnerships)*

Subsidiaries:

Kelliher Samets Volk   (1)
500 Harrison Ave Ste 403, Boston, MA 02118
Tel.: (617) 832-7900
Sales Range: $10-24.9 Million
Emp.: 20
N.A.I.C.S.: 541820
Doug Chapman *(Partner & Creative Dir)*
Kimberly E. Borman *(Owner & Mng Partner)*
Rebecca Tehrani *(Mgmt Supvr)*
Pete Valle *(Assoc Dir-Creative)*
Dotsy Evans *(Dir-Creative)*
Lawrence O'Toole *(Copywriter)*

Kelliher Samets Volk NY   (1)
337 Broome St 3rd Fl, New York, NY 10002
Tel.: (212) 366-4000
Web Site: http://www.ksvc.com
Sales Range: Less than $1 Million
Emp.: 4
N.A.I.C.S.: 541810
Estee Pouleris *(Project Mgr)*
Frank Sampogna *(Pres)*
Linda Kelliher *(Creative Dir)*
Yoram Samets *(Mng Dir)*
Tim Volk *(Pres)*
Cheryl Eaton *(Partner & Dir-Strategy)*
Lori Roberts *(Assoc Dir-Creative)*
Bob Smith *(VP & Dir-Contact Grp)*

KELLOGG & KIMSEY, INC.
6077 Clark Center Ave, Sarasota, FL 34238
Tel.: (941) 927-7700
Web Site:
   http://www.kelloggkimsey.com
Year Founded: 1986
Sales Range: $25-49.9 Million
Emp.: 43
Commercial & Institutional Building Construction
N.A.I.C.S.: 236220
Ed Doughty *(CFO)*
Melanie Lehmann *(Dir-Safety)*
Charles B. Kimsey *(Exec VP-Mktg)*
Philip A. Kellogg *(Pres)*
Brent Bobo *(VP-Bus Dev)*
David Pfeil *(VP-Ops)*

KELLOGG SUPPLY CO. INC.
917 Burnside Rd, Manteo, NC 27954
Tel.: (252) 473-2167
Web Site:
   http://www.kelloggsupplyco.com
Sales Range: $10-24.9 Million
Emp.: 75
Lumber & Other Building Materials
N.A.I.C.S.: 423310
Steve Garza *(Mgr-Store)*

KELLOGG SUPPLY INC.
350 W Sepulveda Blvd, Carson, CA 90745
Tel.: (310) 830-2200   CA
Web Site:
   http://www.kellogggarden.com
Year Founded: 1925
Emp.: 100
Nitrogenous Fertilizer
N.A.I.C.S.: 325311
Renna Howard *(Sr Dir-HR)*
Stan Gibbs *(CFO)*
Tracy Oyama *(Controller)*
Andrew Godfrey *(Dir-Qty Assurance & Control)*

KELLY & ASSOCIATES INSURANCE GROUP, INC.
1 Kelly Way, Sparks, MD 21152
Tel.: (410) 527-3400
Web Site: http://www.kaig.com
Year Founded: 1976
Sales Range: $10-24.9 Million
Emp.: 350
Insurance Agency & Brokerage Services
N.A.I.C.S.: 524210
Laurie McGonigle *(Sr VP-Admin)*
Bryan Kelly *(Pres-Mktg Svcs & Chief People Officer)*
Craig Horner *(CFO & Treas)*
Joe Seifert *(Dir-Broker Sls)*
Sandy Walters *(Chief Indus Info Officer & Exec VP)*
Rasoul Motavalli *(CTO)*
Jennifer Silberzahn *(Sr VP-Comm, Mktg & Compliance)*
Wes Mace *(COO)*
Trish Backer-Miceli *(VP-HR)*
Francis X. Kelly Jr. *(Co-Founder & Chm)*
Francis X. Kelly III *(CEO)*

KELLY AUTOMOTIVE GROUP
155 Andover St Rt 114, Danvers, MA 01923
Tel.: (855) 885-3559
Web Site: http://www.kellyauto.com
Year Founded: 1965
New & Used Car Dealers
N.A.I.C.S.: 441110
Brian Heney *(COO)*

Subsidiaries:

Infiniti of Melbourne   (1)
901 S Apollo Blvd, Melbourne, FL 32901-1931
Tel.: (220) 220-2250
Web Site:
   http://www.infinitiofmelbourne.com
New Car Dealers
N.A.I.C.S.: 441110
Tom Simms *(Mgr)*

KELLY BMW
4050 Morse Rd, Columbus, OH 43230
Tel.: (614) 471-2277
Web Site: http://www.kellybmw.com
Year Founded: 1978
Sales Range: $10-24.9 Million
Emp.: 40
Car Whslr
N.A.I.C.S.: 441110
Jody Wenger *(Bus Mgr)*
Brian Carter *(Asst Mgr-Svc)*
Eric Robare *(Mgr-New Car Sls)*
Kelly Marsh *(Owner)*

KELLY BOX & PACKAGING CORP.
2801 Covington Rd, Fort Wayne, IN 46802
Tel.: (260) 432-4570
Web Site: http://www.kellybox.com
Sales Range: $10-24.9 Million
Emp.: 55

U.S. PRIVATE

Boxes Corrugated: Made From Purchased Materials
N.A.I.C.S.: 322211
Roquel Beachy *(Controller)*
Doug Cope *(Mgr-Sls)*

KELLY CAPITAL, LLC
NBC Twr 225 Broadway 18th Fl, San Diego, CA 92101
Tel.: (619) 687-5000   CA
Web Site: http://www.kellycapital.com
Year Founded: 1993
Privater Equity Firm
N.A.I.C.S.: 523999
Michael R. Kelly *(Co-Founder & CEO)*
Richard Kelly *(Co-Founder)*

KELLY FOODS CORPORATION
3337 Medina Rd, Medina, OH 44256-9631
Tel.: (330) 722-8855
Sales Range: $10-24.9 Million
Emp.: 70
Animal Feed Mfr
N.A.I.C.S.: 311119
Robert Kelly *(Pres)*
Joanne Sanford *(CFO)*
Neal Connors *(Plant Mgr)*
Jerry McRoberts *(Plant Mgr)*
Chris Gee *(Mgr-Maintenance)*

KELLY IMPORTS INC.
501-23 State Rd, Emmaus, PA 18049
Tel.: (610) 967-2101
Sales Range: $10-24.9 Million
Emp.: 50
Car Whslr
N.A.I.C.S.: 441110
Tom Carey *(Gen Mgr)*

KELLY MANAGEMENT CORPORATION
1202 Malabar Rd, Palm Bay, FL 32907
Tel.: (321) 768-2424   FL
Web Site: http://www.kellycar.com
Year Founded: 1934
Sales Range: $10-24.9 Million
Emp.: 100
Sales of New & Used Automobiles
N.A.I.C.S.: 441110
Eric Frechette *(CEO)*

KELLY MEDIA GROUP
2022 W 11th St, Los Angeles, CA 91786
Tel.: (909) 621-4737
Web Site:
   http://www.kellymediagroup.com
Year Founded: 2002
Rev.: $27,000,000
Emp.: 72
Advetising Agency
N.A.I.C.S.: 541810

KELLY NISSAN INC.
4300 W 95th St, Oak Lawn, IL 60453
Tel.: (708) 499-1000
Web Site: http://www.kellynissan.com
Sales Range: $10-24.9 Million
Emp.: 55
Sales & Service Of New & Used Automobiles
N.A.I.C.S.: 441110
Arthur Kelly *(Pres)*
Ryan Kelly *(Co-Owner & VP)*
Dave Campbell *(Gen Mgr)*

KELLY RYAN EQUIPMENT COMPANY
900 Kelly Ryan Dr, Blair, NE 68008
Tel.: (402) 426-2151   NE
Web Site: http://www.kryan.com
Year Founded: 1945
Sales Range: $1-9.9 Million

Emp.: 50
Mfr of Farming Machinery & Equipment
N.A.I.C.S.: 333111
James P. Ryan (CEO)
Steven L. Cook (Pres)
R. J. Ryan (VP)

KELLY SUBARU & MITSUBISHI
900 Riverfront Pkwy, Chattanooga, TN 37402
Tel.: (423) 490-0181
Web Site:
http://www.kellysubaru.com
Year Founded: 1992
Sales Range: $10-24.9 Million
Emp.: 45
Car Whslr
N.A.I.C.S.: 441110
Eric Horn (Mgr-Parts)
Jim Higdon (Mgr-Fin)
Keith Aviles (Mgr-Internet Sls)
Steve Marlin (Gen Mgr)
Susan Norton (Controller)

KELLY SUPPLY COMPANY
1004 W Oklahoma Ave, Grand Island, NE 68801
Tel.: (308) 382-5670
Web Site: http://www.kellysupply.com
Sales Range: $10-24.9 Million
Emp.: 102
Industrial Supplies
N.A.I.C.S.: 423840
Don Meyer (Office Mgr)

KELLY TRACTOR CO. INC.
8255 NW 58th St, Miami, FL 33166-3406
Tel.: (305) 592-5360   FL
Web Site: http://www.kellytractor.com
Year Founded: 1933
Sales Range: $50-74.9 Million
Emp.: 500
Heavy Construction Equipment Rental
N.A.I.C.S.: 532412
Nick Kelly (VP)
John Willis (Mgr)

KELLY'S CAJUN GRILL FRANCHISE
4531 Ponce de Leon Blvd Ste 300, Coral Gables, FL 33146
Tel.: (305) 476-1611
Emp.: 25
Lunchrooms & Cafeterias
N.A.I.C.S.: 722514
Hoi Sang Yeung (Chm & Pres)

KELLY'S KIDS
391 Liberty Rd, Natchez, MS 39120
Tel.: (601) 442-5332
Web Site: http://www.kellyskids.com
Sales Range: $10-24.9 Million
Emp.: 40
Girl's & Children's Dresses, Blouses; Childrenswear
N.A.I.C.S.: 315250
Lynn James (Owner & Founder)
Ashton James (CEO)
Sally Chatman (Dir-Personnel)

KELLY, SCOTT & MADISON
303 E Wacker Dr 14th Fl, Chicago, IL 60601-2314
Tel.: (312) 977-0772   DE
Web Site: http://www.ksmmedia.com
Year Founded: 1966
Sales Range: $250-299.9 Million
Emp.: 190
Media Buying Services
N.A.I.C.S.: 541830
Jonathan Lichter (Chief Strategy Officer & Partner)
Joni Williams (Pres & Partner)
Sy Chaba (Exec VP & Dir-Strategic Plng & Acct Svcs)
David Warso (Partner & Treas)
Mel Greve (Sr VP & Dir-Brdcst)
Mark Sloane (CFO)
Elizabeth Amstutz (Sr VP & Grp Dir-Media)
Mark Willson (Sr VP & Dir-New Bus Dev)
Donna Kleinman (VP & Dir-Media Rels)
Elizabeth Kalmbach (VP & Dir-Grp Media)
Kay Wesolowski (VP & Dir-Digital Media)
Rachael Muhlenbeck (Mgr-Promotions)

Subsidiaries:

Kelly, Scott & Madison   (1)
7 Piedmont Ctr Ste 300, Atlanta, GA 30305
Tel.: (312) 977-0772
Web Site: http://www.ksmmedia.com
Emp.: 1
N.A.I.C.S.: 541830
Toby Steinberg (VP-Bus Dev)
Joni Williams (Pres & Partner)
Jonathan Lichter (Chief Strategy Officer & Partner)
David Warso (Partner & Treas)
Sy Chaba (Exec VP & Dir-Strategic Plng & Acct Svcs)
Mark Willson (Sr VP & Dir-New Bus Dev)
Donna Kleinman (VP & Dir-Media Rels)
Kay Wesolowski (VP & Dir-Digital Media)
Mel Greve (Sr VP & Dir-Brdcst)
Rachael Muhlenbeck (Mgr-Promos)

KELLY-MOORE PAINT COMPANY, INC.
987 Comml St, San Carlos, CA 94070
Tel.: (650) 592-8337   CA
Web Site: http://www.kellymoore.com
Year Founded: 1946
Sales Range: $250-299.9 Million
Emp.: 1,400
Paint & Paint Sundries Mfr & Retailer
N.A.I.C.S.: 325510
Steve Devo (Chm, Pres & CEO)
Jim Albert (VP-Sls)
Bruce McGregor (Sr VP-Mfg)

KELLYCO METAL DETECTOR SUPERSTORE
1085 Belle Ave, Winter Springs, FL 32708
Tel.: (407) 699-8700
Web Site:
http://www.kellycodetectors.com
Sales Range: $10-24.9 Million
Emp.: 51
Metal Detector Distr
N.A.I.C.S.: 423510
Stu Auerbach (Pres)
John Fetner (VP)

KELLYMITCHELL GROUP, INC.
8229 Maryland Ave, Saint Louis, MO 63105
Tel.: (314) 727-1700
Web Site:
http://www.kellymitchell.com
Year Founded: 1998
Sales Range: $10-24.9 Million
Emp.: 500
Software Development, Enterprise Resource Planning & E-Commerce Consulting Services
N.A.I.C.S.: 561499
Mark LoCigno (Co-Founder & Pres)
Rebecca Boyer (CFO)
Cassandra R. Sanford (Co-Founder & CEO)

KELLYTOY USA INC.
4811 S Alameda St, Vernon, CA 90058
Tel.: (323) 923-1300   CA
Web Site: http://www.kellytoy.com
Year Founded: 1986
Sales Range: $1-9.9 Million
Emp.: 20
Toys & Hobby Goods & Supplies
N.A.I.C.S.: 423920
Jeanne Yoon (VP-Sls & Dev)
Rami Hajeb (CFO)
Victor Garcia (Mgr-Warehouse)

KELMSCOTT COMMUNICATIONS, INC.
5656 McDermott Dr, Berkeley, IL 60163
Tel.: (630) 898-4261
Web Site:
http://www.kelmscottcommunications.com
Sales Range: $10-24.9 Million
Emp.: 80
Graphic Design Services
N.A.I.C.S.: 541430
Scott Voris (Pres)
Jason M. Tews (Exec VP)
Bill Barta (Principal)
Jennifer Cox (VP-Strategy & Client Svcs)

Subsidiaries:

Graphix Products, Inc.   (1)
399 Wegner Dr, West Chicago, IL 60185-2673
Tel.: (630) 231-2425
Sales Range: $10-24.9 Million
Commercial Flexographic Printing
N.A.I.C.S.: 323111
Henry Tews (Treas, Sec & VP)

KELPE CONTRACTING, INC.
17955 Manchester Rd, Glencoe, MO 63038
Tel.: (636) 458-1400
Web Site: http://www.kelpe.com
Year Founded: 1960
Sales Range: $10-24.9 Million
Emp.: 75
Excavation & Grading, Building Construction
N.A.I.C.S.: 238910
Tom Kelpe (Owner & Pres)
Jeff Hancock (Project Mgr)
Terry Schott (VP)
Dave Fuszner (VP)
Todd Fulsom (Mgr-Scheduling)
David Callies (Dir-Safety)
Rick Burke (Project Mgr)
Nick Collins (Mgr-Shop)

KELSER CORPORATION
111 Roberts St Ste D, East Hartford, CT 06108-3653
Tel.: (860) 528-9819   DE
Web Site: http://www.kelsercorp.com
Year Founded: 1981
Sales Range: $50-74.9 Million
Emp.: 52
Technology Solutions to the Insurance & Financial Services Markets Worldwide
N.A.I.C.S.: 423430
Barry Kelly (Pres & CEO)
Jonathan Stone (COO & CTO)
Matt Hoskin (Controller)
Howard Steinman (VP-Enterprise Sls)
Tom Sharp (VP-Ops)
Devin Kelly (Officer-Relationship)

KELSEY CONSTRUCTION, INC.
306 E Princeton St, Orlando, FL 32804-5547
Tel.: (407) 898-4101   FL
Web Site:
http://www.kelseyconstruction.com
Year Founded: 1920
Sales Range: $75-99.9 Million
Emp.: 45
Commercial Construction Contractors
N.A.I.C.S.: 236220
Courtney Kelsey (Dir-Bus Dev)

KELSO & COMPANY, L.P.
320 Park Ave 24th Fl, New York, NY 10022-6815
Tel.: (212) 350-7700   DE
Web Site: http://www.kelso.com
Year Founded: 1971
Equity Investment Services
N.A.I.C.S.: 523999
Frank T. Nickell (Chm)
Howard A. Matlin (Sr Partner-Advisory)
Frank Loverro (Co-CEO)
Thomas R. Wall (Sr Partner-Advisory)
Michael B. Goldberg (Sr Partner-Advisory)
David I. Wahrhaftig (Sr Partner-Advisory & Mng Dir)
Philip Berney (Co-CEO)
Church M. Moore (Partner-Investment)
Barbara Alechman (VP & Controller)
Renee Schwidel (Controller)
Chris Collins (Partner-Investment)
Lynn Alexander (Partner-IR & Mktg)
Tim M. Ding (Dir-Tax)
Rosanna T. Leone (VP-Compliance & Legal Affairs)
Steve Dutton (Partner-Investment)
Allie Condon (VP-IR)
Keith Castaldi (Principal)
Karen Cipriano (Coord-Legal & Compliance)
Forrest Compton (VP)
Bill Frayer (Principal)
Alec Hufnagel (Partner-Investment)
Hank Mannix (Partner-Investment)
Hugh McBride (Principal)
Michael Nichols (Partner-Capital Markets)
Tamara O'Leary (Coord-Tech)
Sandy Osborne (Partner-Investment)
Dominic Thelliyankal (Senior Controller)
James J. Connors II (Sr Partner-Advisory)
Frank K. Bynum Jr. (Sr Partner-Advisory)
Frank K. Bynum Jr. (Sr Partner-Advisory)

Subsidiaries:

Bridgenext, Inc.   (1)
Tel.: (973) 376-4242
Web Site: https://www.bridgenext.com
Sales Range: $200-249.9 Million
Information Technology Consultancy & Support Services
N.A.I.C.S.: 541519
Samir R. Bhatt (VP-Fin & Head-Bus Process Outsourcing)
Dinesh R. Desai (Founder & Chm)
Sunil Misra (Pres & CEO)
Siva Arunachalam (CTO & Mng Dir-Managed Svcs-Global)
Rachana Jain (VP-HR)
Don Sweeney (Mng Dir-Bus Svcs)
Dave Krauthamer (Exec VP-Digital Svcs)
Scott Curry (VP-Sls-Bus Svcs)
Rich Reid (Mng Dir-Advisory Svcs)
Colwyn Warner (VP-Strategic Client Solutions)
Rick Johnson (CFO)
Ravi Chennupati (Chief Acctg Officer)
Larry Gordon (Mng Dir-Go-To-Market-Emtec Digital)

Subsidiary (Domestic):

Definition 6, LLC   (2)
420 Posters Ave, Atlanta, GA 30324
Tel.: (404) 870-0323
Web Site: https://www.definition6.com

KELSO & COMPANY, L.P.

Kelso & Company, L.P.—(Continued)

Sales Range: $25-49.9 Million
Emp.: 200
Marketing Agency
N.A.I.C.S.: 541810
Jeff Katz (CEO)
Paul McClay (Chief Digital Officer)
Stewart Brooks (CFO)
Diana Lochridge (Dir-Creative-Entertainment Div)
Rob Ortiz (Exec VP-Entertainment & Integrated Media)
Matt Thomson (Mng Dir-News Market)
Laura Pair (Mng Dir-Synaptic Digital)
Ivy Garcia (VP & Dir-Acct)
M. P. Holt (VP & Dir-Acct)

Emtec Federal, Inc. (2)
11 Diamond Rd, Springfield, NJ 07081-3101
Tel.: (703) 961-1125
Web Site: http://www.emtec.com
Sales Range: $50-74.9 Million
Emp.: 85
Military & Government Technical Consulting & Information Technology Services
N.A.I.C.S.: 541519

Branch (Domestic):

Emtec Federal, Inc. (3)
352 7th Ave, New York, NY 10001-5012
Tel.: (703) 961-1125
Web Site: http://www.emtecinc.com
Sales Range: $25-49.9 Million
Emp.: 12
Military & Government Technical Consulting & Information Technology Services
N.A.I.C.S.: 541519

Subsidiary (Domestic):

Lucidity Consulting Group LP (2)
2435 N Central Expressway Ste 1200, Richardson, TX 75080
Tel.: (214) 451-2500
Administrative Management & General Management Consulting Service
N.A.I.C.S.: 541611

Secure Data, Inc. (2)
612 Pierce Blvd, O'Fallon, IL 62269-2141
Tel.: (618) 726-5200
Web Site: http://www.securedatainc.com
Sales Range: $1-9.9 Million
Emp.: 24
Online Systems Integration Services
N.A.I.C.S.: 541512

Carecycle Solutions, LLC (1)
3406 Main St, Dallas, TX 75226
Tel.: (855) 746-4325
Web Site: http://www.carecyclesolutions.net
Women Healthcare Services
N.A.I.C.S.: 621610
Wayne Bazzle (CEO)

Cronos Holding Co Ltd. (1)
Clarendon House 2 Church Street, Hamilton, HM11, Bermuda
Tel.: (441) 2362478
Container Equipment Leasing Services
N.A.I.C.S.: 532411

Subsidiary (Domestic):

Cronos Ltd. (2)
Canon's Court 22 Victoria Street, Hamilton, HM12, Bermuda
Tel.: (441) 4412362478
Container Equipment Leasing Services
N.A.I.C.S.: 532411

Eagle Family Foods Group LLC (1)
4020 Kinross Lakes Pkwy, Richfield, OH 44286
Tel.: (330) 382-3725
Web Site: http://www.eaglefamilyfoods.com
Condensed & Evaporated Canned Milk Products Mfr & Marketer
N.A.I.C.S.: 311514
Paul Smucker Wagstaff (CEO)

Subsidiary (Domestic):

Cornfields, Inc. (2)
3898 Sunset Ave, Waukegan, IL 60087
Tel.: (847) 263-7000
Web Site: http://www.cornfieldsinc.com
Snack Food Mfr & Whslr
N.A.I.C.S.: 311919

Ferraro Foods Inc. (1)
287 S Randolphville Rd, Piscataway, NJ 08854
Tel.: (732) 424-3400
Web Site: http://www.ferrarofoods.com
Pizzeria & Restaurant Supplier
N.A.I.C.S.: 722511
Michael Giammarino (CEO)

Subsidiary (Domestic):

GDS Foods Incorporated (2)
PO Box 728, Sussex, NJ 07461
Web Site: http://www.gdsfoods.com
General Line Grocery Merchant Whslr
N.A.I.C.S.: 424410
Shawn P. Callahan (Territory Mgr)

J.S. Held LLC (1)
50 Jericho Quadrangle Ste 117, Jericho, NY 11753
Tel.: (516) 621-2900
Web Site: http://www.jsheld.com
Construction Consulting Services
N.A.I.C.S.: 541618
Randy Ison (Exec VP-Client Svcs-Natl)
Jonathon Held (CEO)
Brian Beatty (Mgr-Ops-Greenwood Village)
Christy Ball (Dir-Alpharetta)
Derek Boggi (Asst VP-Philadelphia)
David McLaughlin (Sr VP & Mgr-South Central)
Jeff Nicholson (VP & Mgr-Ops-Phoenix)
John Schneider (Asst VP-Charlotte)
Monica Christopher (CMO)
Douglas G. DePhillips (Sr Exec VP-Svcs-Global)
David Held (Exec VP-Corp Dev)
Sean P. Donohue (Sr VP-Advisory Svcs)
Adrian Frank (Sr Exec VP-Insurance Svcs)
Andrew Englehart (Sr VP)
Charles Kandrach (Partner-HR Bus)
Douglas MacKinney (Exec VP & Mgr-Philadelphia)
Erik Jaeger (Exec VP-Quality Assurance & Control)
Felipe A. I. Gutierrez (Sr VP)
Frederic Samelian (Mng Dir-Strategy & Dev)
Granger Stuck (Exec VP)
John Gillen (Sr VP-Learning & Dev)
John Lovett (Sr VP & Dir-Surety Svcs-Natl)
Kim Ash (Partner-HR Bus)
Leonard Alexander (Sr VP-Client Svcs-Global)
Lisa Enloe (Chief Quality Officer)
Mark Cohen (Sr VP)
Michael Collins (Sr VP)
Raul Losana Alvarado (Sr VP)
Robert I. Leighton (Sr VP)
Russell Polin (CFO)
Scott Cushing (Sr VP)
Scott Katcher (Chief HR Officer & Gen Counsel)
Tracey Dodd (Exec VP-Environmental, Health & Safety)
Troy Wilson (Sr VP-Insurance Svcs Ops-US)
William C. Bracken (Exec VP-Forensic Architecture & Engrg)
Kathryn Johnson (VP-Forensic Acctg & Economics)
Frank Antonucci Sr. (Sr VP)

Subsidiary (Domestic):

Forensic Resolutions, Inc. (2)
17 Mechanic St, Haddonfield, NJ 08033
Tel.: (856) 857-9000
Web Site: http://www.forensicresolutions.com
Forensic & Investigative Accounting Services
N.A.I.C.S.: 541219
James Stavros (Co-Founder)
Howard Silverstone (Co-Founder)

Leighton Associates, Inc. (2)
7020 Austin St Ste 115, Forest Hills, NY 11375
Tel.: (718) 268-6314
Business Consulting Services Trade Contractor
N.A.I.C.S.: 541690

Lovett, Silverman Construction Consultants, Inc. (2)
888 Veterans Memorial Hwy Suite 500, Hauppauge, NY 11788 **(100%)**
Tel.: (631) 979-7600
Web Site: http://www.lovett-silverman.com
Sales Range: $1-9.9 Million
Emp.: 5
Management & Construction Consulting Services
N.A.I.C.S.: 541618
John J. Lovett (Sr VP & Natl Dir-Surety Svcs)
Anthony Lardaro (VP-New York)
Richard Sexton (VP-Orlando)

TBG Security Inc. (2)
31 Hayward St, Franklin, MA 02038
Tel.: (877) 233-6651
Web Site: http://www.tbgsecurity.com
Sales Range: $1-9.9 Million
Information Technology Security Services
N.A.I.C.S.: 541511
Frank Murphy (Principal)

Twenty First Century Engineering Corp. (2)
836 Bougainvillea Ln, Vero Beach, FL 32963
Tel.: (954) 522-6446
Web Site: http://www.21st-centuryengineering.com
Rev.: $1,580,000
Emp.: 10
Engineeering Services
N.A.I.C.S.: 541330
John Carroll Jr. (Principal)

Vtgte Inc. (2)
18372 Redmond Way, Redmond, WA 98052
Tel.: (425) 556-5555
Toxicology, Industrial Hygiene & Risk Assessment
N.A.I.C.S.: 621511

Wakelee Associates LLC (2)
407 State St, Hackensack, NJ 07601 **(100%)**
Tel.: (201) 387-7711
Web Site: http://www.jsheld.com
Emp.: 18
Construction & Mitigation Consulting Services
N.A.I.C.S.: 236210
Timothy Woods (VP)
Nick Sommerfeld (Dir)
Peter McCabe (VP)
Pete Cornet (VP)

Jordan Health Services, Inc. (1)
14295 Midway Rd Ste 400, Addison, TX 75001
Tel.: (800) 646-8773
Web Site: http://www.elara.com
Health Care Srvices
N.A.I.C.S.: 621999
Jeff Bonham (Pres-Markets)
Scott Powers (CEO)
Bruce Jarvie (CFO)
Ian Gordon (Pres-Ops)
Dave Marchand (CIO)
Patricia Bradford (Chief HR Officer)
Christine Weir (Chief Compliance officer)
Joseph Jasser (Chief Medical Officer)

LRI Holdings, Inc. (1)
3011 Armory Dr Ste 300, Nashville, TN 37204
Tel.: (615) 885-9056
Web Site: http://www.logansroadhouse.com
Rev.: $614,309,000
Assets: $389,524,000
Liabilities: $521,436,000
Net Worth: ($131,912,000)
Earnings: ($144,786,000)
Emp.: 14,885
Fiscal Year-end: 08/02/2015
Holding Company; Restaurant Owner & Operator
N.A.I.C.S.: 551112

Novvia Group (1)
675 Hartman Rd Ste 100, Austell, GA 30168
Tel.: (800) 646-6275
Web Site: http://www.novviagroup.com
Holding Company
N.A.I.C.S.: 551112
Sarah Macdonald (CEO)
Ken Roessler (Chm)

Subsidiary (Domestic):

Duval Container Company (2)

U.S. PRIVATE

91 S Myrtle Ave, Jacksonville, FL 32204
Tel.: (904) 355-6591
Web Site: http://www.duvalcontainer.com
Sales Range: $1-9.9 Million
Emp.: 45
Industrial Supplies, Nsk
N.A.I.C.S.: 423840
Joe Thornhill (Sls Mgr)

Fox Valley Containers, Inc. (2)
300 Exchange Dr Ste A, Crystal Lake, IL 60014
Tel.: (847) 836-2203
Web Site: http://www.foxvalleycontainers.com
Rev.: $8,280,000
Emp.: 10
Industrial & Personal Service Paper Merchant Whslr
N.A.I.C.S.: 424130
Don Brown (VP)

Inmark, LLC (2)
675 Hartman Rd Ste 100, Austell, GA 30168
Tel.: (770) 373-3300
Web Site: http://www.inmarkpackaging.com
Emp.: 200
Packaging & Paper Products Mfr
N.A.I.C.S.: 322211
Brad Crouch (CFO)
Harry Franze (CEO)

Subsidiary (Domestic):

Container Resources Inc. (3)
219 Commerce Rd, Greenville, SC 29611
Web Site: http://www.containerresources.com
Containers & Packaging Materials Distr
N.A.I.C.S.: 423840

Division (Domestic):

Inmark, LLC - Biomedical Packaging Division (3)
675 Hartman Rd Ste 100, Austell, GA 30168
Tel.: (770) 373-3300
Web Site: http://www.inmarkinc.com
Mfr & Supplier of Biomedical Packaging
N.A.I.C.S.: 423840
Dave Oler (Pres)

Subsidiary (Non-US):

Saf-T-Pak Inc. (3)
Ste 201 C 17220 Stony Plain Rd, Edmonton, T5S 1K6, AB, Canada
Tel.: (780) 486-0211
Web Site: http://www.saftpak.com
Emp.: 3
Infectious & Biological Specimen Packaging Products Mfr & Regulatory Training Services
N.A.I.C.S.: 326160
Jay Colville (Gen Mgr)

Subsidiary (Domestic):

J.F. Shelton Co., Inc. (2)
19516 62nd Ave S, Kent, WA 98032
Tel.: (253) 872-6363
Web Site: http://www.jfshelton.com
Chemical & Allied Products Merchant Whslr
N.A.I.C.S.: 424690
Dan Kiefel (Pres)

Rahway Steel Drum Company, Inc. (2)
26 Brick Yard Rd, Cranbury, NJ 08512
Tel.: (732) 382-0113
Web Site: http://www.rahwaysteeldrum.com
Sales Range: $1-9.9 Million
Emp.: 27
Whol Industrial Supplies
N.A.I.C.S.: 423840
Anthony Foglia (Pres)

Southern Container LLC (2)
150 Howell Dr, Dalton, GA 30721-1512
Tel.: (706) 277-6144
Web Site: http://www.southerncontainerllc.com
Corrugated & Solid Fiber Box Mfr
N.A.I.C.S.: 322211
Billy Smith (Pres)

Perrin Bernard Supowitz, LLC (1)
5496 Lindbergh Ln, Bell, CA 90201
Tel.: (323) 981-2800

COMPANIES

KELSO & COMPANY, L.P.

Web Site:
http://www.individualfoodservice.com
Rev.: $7,500,000
Emp.: 32
Paper, Plastic, Packaging, Janitorial & Small Wares Products Distr
N.A.I.C.S.: 424130
Kenneth Sweder (Chm & CEO)

Joint Venture (Domestic):

Brady Industries Inc. (2)
7055 Lindell Rd, Las Vegas, NV 89118
Tel.: (702) 876-3990
Web Site: http://www.bradyindustries.com
Sales Range: $50-74.9 Million
Emp.: 420
Sanitation Preparations
N.A.I.C.S.: 424690
Eric Brady (CFO)
Travis Brady (Pres)
Michelle Harrison (Dir-Mktg)
Ryan Banks (Corp VP-Sls & Mktg)

Subsidiary (Domestic):

Envoy Solutions LLC (3)
2101 Claire Ct, Glenview, IL 60025
Tel.: (800) 508-5830
Web Site: http://www.envoysolutions.com
Janitorial Supply, Packaging Solutions & Specialty Products Distr
N.A.I.C.S.: 423850
Mark Fisher (CEO)

Subsidiary (Domestic):

Delta Packaging & Supply, LLC (4)
500 Gulf South Dr, Flowood, MS 39232
Tel.: (601) 354-8986
Web Site: http://www.deltapackaging.net
Rev.: $4,140,000
Emp.: 5
Industrial & Personal Service Paper Merchant Whslr
N.A.I.C.S.: 424130
Johnie Weems (Pres & CEO)

GPMI Company (4)
1051 N Fiesta Blvd, Gilbert, AZ 85233
Tel.: (480) 503-0006
Web Site: http://www.gpmicompany.com
Sales Range: $1-9.9 Million
Emp.: 100
Home Care & Automotive Products Mfr
N.A.I.C.S.: 423220
Chuck Tornabene (COO)
Leslie Bendor (Dir-Mktg)

H.T. Berry Co. Inc. (4)
50 N St, Canton, MA 02021
Tel.: (781) 828-6000
Web Site: http://www.htberry.com
Sales Range: $10-24.9 Million
Emp.: 50
Wholesale Distributor of Food Service, Janitorial/Sanitary & Industrial Packaging Products
N.A.I.C.S.: 424130
Chris Nolan (Pres)
James Berry (VP)

Sunbelt Packaging, LLC. (4)
7826 Park Place Rd, York, SC 29745
Tel.: (803) 684-2286
Web Site:
http://www.sunbeltpackagingllc.com
Packaging Materials Mfr & Distr
N.A.I.C.S.: 423990
Jade Boling (COO)

Superior Supply Co., Inc. (4)
1331 Wisconsin Ave, Sheboygan, WI 53081
Tel.: (920) 457-4481
Web Site: http://www.northwoodstm.com
Sales Range: $1-9.9 Million
Emp.: 50
Chemical & Allied Products Merchant Whslr
N.A.I.C.S.: 424690
Tim Junior (Office Mgr)
Terry Schaller (Pres)

Swish White River Ltd. (4)
1118 Route 14, Hartford, VT 05047
Tel.: (800) 639-7226
Web Site: http://www.swishusa.com
Janitorial Equipment Distr & Mfr
N.A.I.C.S.: 561720
Anthony W. Ambler (Pres)
Peter Crouse (CEO)

United Packaging Supply Co. (4)
102 Wharton Rd, Bristol, PA 19007
Tel.: (215) 633-0700
Web Site: http://www.unitedpkg.com
Sales Range: $1-9.9 Million
Emp.: 40
Packaging & Shipping Supplies Distr
N.A.I.C.S.: 424990
Scott Paul (Mgr-Distr Center)
Jeff Seidel (Pres & CEO)

Subsidiary (Domestic):

FPC Holdings, Inc. (3)
6630 Amberton Dr, Elkridge, MD 21075
Tel.: (410) 579-1000
Web Site: http://www.fpcsolutions.com
Motor Vehicle & Engine Parts Mfr
N.A.I.C.S.: 336310
Richard W. Roe (Pres)

Subsidiary (Domestic):

FPC Distribution, Inc. (4)
6630 Amberton Dr Ste A, Elkridge, MD 21075-6246
Tel.: (410) 579-1000
Web Site: http://www.fpcdistribution.com
Industrial & Personal Service Paper Merchant Whslr
N.A.I.C.S.: 424130
Richard Roe (Pres)

Subsidiary (Domestic):

Gorm, Inc. (3)
150 S Hudson Ave, Ontario, CA 91761
Tel.: (909) 292-1400
Web Site: http://www.gorminc.com
Sales Range: $1-9.9 Million
Emp.: 20
Service Establishment Equipment & Supply Whslr
N.A.I.C.S.: 423850
Ron Johnson (VP-Sls)

Idaho Package Company (3)
2140 Heyrend Way, Idaho Falls, ID 83402
Tel.: (208) 529-0891
Web Site: http://www.idahopackage.com
Sales Range: $10-24.9 Million
Emp.: 30
Packaging Solutions Services
N.A.I.C.S.: 424990
Conn Hix (Pres & CEO)

PFS Sales Company (3)
4701 Beryl Rd, Raleigh, NC 27606
Tel.: (919) 829-1116
Web Site: http://www.pfssales.com
Sales Range: $1-9.9 Million
Emp.: 26
Industrial & Personal Service Paper Whslr
N.A.I.C.S.: 424130

YPV Distribution, Inc. (3)
160 Scott St, Elk Grove Village, IL 60007-1211
Tel.: (847) 718-1100
Web Site: http://www.ypvdist.com
Industrial & Personal Service Paper Merchant Whslr
N.A.I.C.S.: 424130
John Bouzas (Pres)

Subsidiary (Domestic):

Central Sanitary Supply Company (2)
416 N 9th St, Modesto, CA 95350
Tel.: (209) 523-3002
Web Site: http://www.centralsanitary.com
Sales Range: $1-9.9 Million
Emp.: 35
Service Establishment Equipment & Supplies Merchant Whslr
N.A.I.C.S.: 423850
Dave Martini (Pres)

Physicians Endoscopy, LLC (1)
2500 York Rd Ste 300, Jamison, PA 18929
Tel.: (215) 589-9000
Web Site: http://www.endocenters.com
Endoscopic Healthcare Organization
N.A.I.C.S.: 813920
Barry Tanner (Founder & Chm)
David Young (CEO)
James O'Brien (Sr Dir-Mktg)

Subsidiary (Domestic):

The Endoscopy Center of West Central Ohio, LLC (2)
2793 Shawnee Rd, Lima, OH 45806
Tel.: (419) 879-3636
Medical Devices
N.A.I.C.S.: 621112

Premia Holdings Ltd (1)
Waterloo House 100 Pitts Bay Road, First Floor, Pembroke, HM08, Bermuda
Tel.: (441) 278-9176
Web Site: https://premiaholdings.com
Financial Services
N.A.I.C.S.: 523999

RSC Insurance Brokerage, Inc. (1)
160 Federal St, Boston, MA 02110
Tel.: (617) 330-5700
Web Site: http://www.risk-strategies.com
Specialty Insurance Brokerage & Risk Management Services
N.A.I.C.S.: 524210
Thomas O'Rourke Maggs (Pres)
John Vaglica (Chief M&A Officer)
Michael B. Christian (Chm)
John Mina (CEO)
Mike Christian (Chm)
Bob Dubraski (Chief Growth Officer)
John Mina (CEO)
Sharon Edwards (CFO)
Natalie Logan (Chief Legal Officer)
Jennifer J. Johnston (CMO)
Tracy Hoffman (Mng Dir)
Matthew Smith (Mng Dir)
Eric Levy (COO)
Steve Bryant (Mng Dir)
Patrick Roth (Sr VP-Central & West)
Amanda E. Mullan (Chief HR Officer)
Alison Murphy (Mng Dir)
J. C. Fulse (Sr VP)
Steve Trimarchi (Sr VP-New England)
Ali Rana (Mng Dir-Education Practice-Student Health & Wellness)

Subsidiary (Domestic):

Advanced Insurance Underwriters LLC (2)
3250 N 29th Ave, Hollywood, FL 33020
Tel.: (954) 963-6666
Web Site: http://www.risk-strategies.com
Insurance Services
N.A.I.C.S.: 524210

Bisnett Insurance, Inc. (2)
310 N State St Ste 220, Lake Oswego, OR 97034
Tel.: (503) 635-4482
Web Site: http://www.bisnett.com
Insurance Agencies & Brokerages
N.A.I.C.S.: 524210
Kent Bergstedt (VP-Sls & Mktg)

Bonds, Inc. (2)
1 N Park Dr Ste 204, Hunt Valley, MD 21030
Tel.: (410) 527-9881
Web Site: http://www.bondsinc.com
Insurance Agencies & Brokerages
N.A.I.C.S.: 524210

Burke Insurance Group, LLC (2)
1691 S Telnor Blvd, Las Cruces, NM 88011
Tel.: (575) 524-2222
Web Site: http://www.burke-insurance.com
Insurance Agencies & Brokerages
N.A.I.C.S.: 524210
Will Burke (Founder)

Cambridge Advisory Group, Inc. (2)
1400 S Trooper Rd Ste 210, Eagleville, PA 19403
Tel.: (610) 755-3871
Web Site: http://www.camadvgrp.com
Rev.: $1,400,000
Emp.: 22
All Other Business Support Services
N.A.I.C.S.: 561499

Combined Underwriters Of Miami (2)
7950 NW 53rd St Ste 201, Miami, FL 33166-4681
Tel.: (305) 477-0444
Web Site: http://www.combinedmiami.com
Insurance Related Activities
N.A.I.C.S.: 524298

Dash & Love, Inc. (2)
One Belmont Ave Ste 500, 19004, Bala Cynwyd, PA
Tel.: (610) 667-2244

Web Site: http://www.dashlove.com
Insurance & Risk Management Services
N.A.I.C.S.: 524298
Ken Dash (Pres)

Delmarva Surety Associates, Inc. (2)
303 International Cir Ste 160, Hunt Valley, MD 21030
Tel.: (410) 561-3593
Web Site: http://www.delmarvasurety.com
Insurance Agencies & Brokerages
N.A.I.C.S.: 524210

Dickstein Associates Agency LLC (2)
4001 Asbury Ave 2nd FL, Tinton Falls, NJ 07753
Tel.: (732) 566-0700
Web Site:
http://www.dicksteininsurance.com
Provider of Insurance Services
N.A.I.C.S.: 524210
Allison Antonelli (Acct Mgr-Comml Insurance)
Carolyn Windrem (Acct Mgr-Personal Lines)
Vicky Grande (VP-Ops)

Dubraski & Associates Insurance Services, LLC (2)
11622 El Camino Real Ste 100, San Diego, CA 92130
Tel.: (858) 792-4000
Web Site: http://www.dubraski.com
Insurance Brokerage & Consulting Services
N.A.I.C.S.: 524210
Robert J. Dubraski (Pres & CEO)
Jonathan Hageman (Dir-Ops)
Mark E. Manzi (Mng Dir)
Riggs Stephenson (Mng Dir)
Richard V. Bailey (CFO)
Douglas J. Dalrymple (Principal)
Tracy Hoffman (Principal)
Dave Kalb (Principal)
Joe Levy (Principal)
Sharon Scheuermann (Principal)
Cathy Sussman (Principal)
Chris Williams (Principal)
Bob Dubraski (Founder)

First Insurance Group of the Midwest, Inc. (2)
511 5th St, Defiance, OH 43512
Tel.: (419) 784-5431
Web Site: http://www.firstinsurancegrp.com
Emp.: 20
Investment & Financial Benefit Services
N.A.I.C.S.: 524210
Larry Woods (Exec VP-Property & Casualty)
Timothy S. Whetstone (Exec VP-Property & Casualty)
Kenneth G. Keller (Exec VP)
Luke J. Shipp (VP-Comml Lines)
Nick Mehdikhan (Pres & Chief Admin Officer)
Barb Gerken (Dir-Employee Benefits Compliance)
Jaclyn Arbogast (Acct Mgr-Benefits)
Camille Kimes (Acct Mgr-Benefits)
Carrie Hunter (Accountant)
Mike Klein (Pres & COO)
Lori A. Hall (Dir-HR Consulting & Health Mgmt)
Ron Burns (Exec VP)
John Payak III (Exec VP-Property & Casualty)

Friedman & Friedman (2)
900 5th Ave, Pittsburgh, PA 15219-4737
Tel.: (412) 261-5834
Web Site: http://www.friedman-law.com
Accounting Services
N.A.I.C.S.: 541219
Jacob Friedman (Atty)

Geo V Bullen & Son, Inc. (2)
3333 New Hyde Park Rd Ste 300, New Hyde Park, NY 11042
Tel.: (516) 482-7200
Sales Range: $1-9.9 Million
Emp.: 30
Insurance Agencies & Brokerages
N.A.I.C.S.: 524210
Matt Fox (Pres)

Gerard B Tracy Associates, Inc. (2)
1261 Post Rd Ste 201, Fairfield, CT 06824-6072
Tel.: (203) 222-0900

KELSO & COMPANY, L.P.

Kelso & Company, L.P.—(Continued)
Insurance Agencies & Brokerages
N.A.I.C.S.: 524210

Hugh Wood, Inc.
55 Broadway Fl 24, New York, NY 10006
Tel.: (212) 509-3777
Sales Range: $1-9.9 Million
Emp.: 52
Insurance Agencies & Brokerages
N.A.I.C.S.: 524210
Hugh W. Wood (Chm)
Jack Fisher (Exec VP)

International Insurance Brokers, Ltd. (2)
303 Runion Ctr 9 E 4th St, Tulsa, OK 74103
Tel.: (918) 592-4200
Web Site: http://www.iibltd.com
Sales Range: $1-9.9 Million
Emp.: 46
Insurance Brokerage Services
N.A.I.C.S.: 524210
Matthew F. Coughlin (Mng Partner)
Cyndi Benson (Partner)
Deborah Crall (Partner)
Caroline Sniff (Mng Partner)

JW Bond Consultants, Inc. (2)
6023 A Kellers Church Rd, Pipersville, PA 18947
Web Site: http://www.jwsuretybonds.com
Depository Credit Intermediation
N.A.I.C.S.: 522180
Michael Weisbrot (VP)
J.D. Weisbrot (Pres & Chief Underwriting Officer)

John Buttine Inc. (2)
420 Lexington Ave Ste 2700, New York, NY 10170
Tel.: (212) 697-1010
Web Site: http://www.buttine.com
Insurance Brokerage/Financial Management Services
N.A.I.C.S.: 524210
Joseph A. Panasci (CFO)
Nancy Buttine (Mgr-Personal Insurance)
Jack M. Buttine (Pres)
Sandra Carey (Sr Acct Exec)
Ian Heitner (Acct Exec)
Kamaria Lawrence (Acct Exec)
Bryan Levey (Sr Acct Exec)
Marina Raskhovsky (Acct Exec)
Mary Beth Ryan (Exec VP)

Kahn-Carlin + Co., Inc. (2)
3350 S Dixie Hwy, Miami, FL 33133
Tel.: (305) 446-2271
Web Site: http://www.kahn-carlin.com
Emp.: 49
Insurance Agencies & Brokerages
N.A.I.C.S.: 524210
Roy Fabry (Sr VP)

Krauter & Company, LLC (2)
1350 Avenue of the Americas Fl 18 & 19, New York, NY 10019
Tel.: (212) 596-3400
Insurance Agency Services
N.A.I.C.S.: 524210

Mahorsky Group, Inc. (2)
2100 Quaker Pointe Dr, Quakertown, PA 18951
Tel.: (215) 536-0253
Web Site: http://www.mahorskygroup.com
Women's, Girls & Infants Cut & Sew Apparel Contractors
N.A.I.C.S.: 315210
Scott Mahorsky (Pres)

May, Bonee & Clark Insurance (2)
180 Glastonbury Blvd, Glastonbury, CT 06033
Tel.: (860) 430-3700
Web Site: http://www.mayboneewalsh.com
Insurance Brokerage Services
N.A.I.C.S.: 524210

McLaughlin Brunson Insurance Agency, LLP (2)
12801 N Central Expy Ste 1710, Dallas, TX 75243
Tel.: (214) 503-1212
Web Site: http://www.mclaughlinbrunson.com
Insurance Agencies & Brokerages

N.A.I.C.S.: 524210
John Krantz (Partner)
Joe A. Bryant (Partner)
Hillary Williams (Acct Mgr)
Jeremy Mahoney (Acct Exec)

Oakbridge Advisors, Inc. (2)
4000 MacArthur Blvd Ste 550, Newport Beach, CA 92660
Tel.: (866) 532-7490
Web Site: http://www.oakbridgeadvisors.com
Financial Investment Activities
N.A.I.C.S.: 522320
Edward D. Kirkwood (CEO & Co-Founder)
Lawrence Hartley (Pres & Co-Founder)

Pace Professional Services, Ltd. (2)
585 Stewart Ave Ste 600, Garden City, NY 11530-4767
Tel.: (516) 222-6006
Web Site: http://www.pacebd.com
Insurance Agencies & Brokerages
N.A.I.C.S.: 524210
Kenneth Gross (Owner)

Parady Financial Group, Inc. (2)
340 Heald Way Ste 226, The Villages, FL 32163-6088
Tel.: (352) 751-3016
Web Site: http://www.paradyfinancial.com
Sales Range: $1-9.9 Million
Emp.: 32
Investment Consulting Services
N.A.I.C.S.: 523940
Gregory J. Parady (CEO)
Brent Mauriell (Dir-Client Svcs)
Cindy Nazzaro (Mng Partner)
Julie Duvall (COO & Partner)
Kelly Sandro (VP-Member Svcs)
Kathie Laseter (Partner & VP)

Pro Safety Services, LLC (2)
20 Cedar St Ste 103, New Rochelle, NY 10801
Tel.: (914) 654-4870
Web Site: http://www.prosafetyllc.com
Safety & Loss Control Services
N.A.I.C.S.: 922190
John McCarthy (Pres)

Professional Risk Associates, Inc. (2)
2909 Polo Pkwy 100, Midlothian, VA 23113
Tel.: (804) 794-0574
Web Site: http://www.profrisk.com
Rev.: $2,100,000
Emp.: 18
Insurance Agencies & Brokerages
N.A.I.C.S.: 524210
Robert Meadows (Exec VP)
John Glander (Pres)

Prosurance/Redeker Group Ltd. (2)
111 Broadway 14th Fl, New York, NY 10006-1901
Tel.: (212) 693-1550
Web Site: http://www.ae-insurance.com
Insurance Agencies & Brokerages
N.A.I.C.S.: 524210

Ralph C Wilson Agency, Inc. (2)
26026 Telegraph Rd Ste 100, Southfield, MI 48034
Tel.: (248) 355-1414
Web Site: http://www.rcwa.net
Sales Range: $1-9.9 Million
Emp.: 30
Insurance Brokerage Services
N.A.I.C.S.: 524210
Jay Poplawski (Sr VP)
Dave Palmeri (VP)
Robert J. Farris (Pres & CEO)

Reiff & Associates, LLC (2)
254 W 54th St 12th Fl, New York, NY 10019-3705
Tel.: (212) 603-0231
Web Site: http://www.reiffinsurance.com
Insurance Agencies & Brokerages
N.A.I.C.S.: 524210

Risk Management Advisors, Inc. (2)
2040 Main St Ste 450, 92614, Irvine, CA
Tel.: (562) 472-2846
Web Site: http://www.riskmgmtadvisors.com
Captive Insurance Companies, Asset Protection & Wealth Management,
N.A.I.C.S.: 525120

Robert Alan Agency, Inc. (2)
115 N Main St, New City, NY 10956
Tel.: (845) 638-2206
Web Site: http://www.robertalanagency.com
Sales Range: $1-9.9 Million
Emp.: 10
Insurance Agencies & Brokerages
N.A.I.C.S.: 524210
Robert Carlucci (Principal)

Setnor, Byer, Bogdanoff, Inc. (2)
7901 SW 6th Ct Ste 430, Fort Lauderdale, FL 33324
Tel.: (954) 382-4350
Web Site: http://www.setnorbyer.com
Sales Range: $1-9.9 Million
Emp.: 15
Insurance Agencies & Brokerages
N.A.I.C.S.: 524210
Anita Byer (Pres)

Singer Nelson Charlmers (2)
1086 Teaneck Rd, Teaneck, NJ 07666
Tel.: (201) 837-1100
Web Site: http://www.singernelson.com
Insurance Agents, Brokers & Service
N.A.I.C.S.: 524210
Joshua Lluch (Mgr-Bus Dev)

Tanenbaum Harber of Florida, LLC (2)
2900 SW 149th Ave, Ste 100, Miramar, FL 33027-6605
Tel.: (954) 763-3144
Web Site: http://www.thflorida.com
Sales Range: $1-9.9 Million
Emp.: 50
Insurance Agencies & Brokerages
N.A.I.C.S.: 524210
Alina Larraz (VP)
Efrain Jove (Pres)
Jerry A. Skidmore (VP-Ops)

The Gehring Group, Inc. (2)
11505 Fairchild Grdns 202, Palm Beach Gardens, FL 33410
Tel.: (561) 626-6797
Web Site: http://www.gehringgroup.com
Insurance Agencies & Brokerages
N.A.I.C.S.: 524210
Kurt Gehring (Founder, Pres & CEO)

Transport Risk Management Inc. (2)
12424 Big Timber Dr Ste 5, Conifer, CO 80433-6410
Tel.: (202) 647-4000
Web Site: http://www.transportrisk.com
Marketing Consulting Services
N.A.I.C.S.: 541613
Terry Miller (Pres)

UNIRISC, Inc. (2)
2000 N 14th St Ste 500, Arlington, VA 22201
Tel.: (703) 797-3300
Web Site: http://www.unirisc.com
Insurance Related Services
N.A.I.C.S.: 524210
Claire Ryan (Sr Acct Exec)
Charles Sharpe (Engr-Software Sys)
Bob Wohlfort (Dir-IT)

United Health Actuarial Services, Inc. (2)
11611 N Meridian St Ste 330, Carmel, IN 46032
Tel.: (317) 575-7671
Web Site: http://www.uhasinc.com
Health Actuarial, Management & Underwriting Consulting Services
N.A.I.C.S.: 541618

University Health Plans, Inc (2)
15 Pacella Park Dr, Randolph, MA 02368
Tel.: (617) 472-5324
Web Site: http://www.universityhealthplans.com
Student Health Insurance Programs
N.A.I.C.S.: 524298
Steve Grabowski (Acct Mgr)
William Devine (Mng Dir)
Kristen Devine (Sr Acct Mgr)
Marcia O'Neill (Sr Acct Mgr)
Erin Devine (Sr Acct Mgr)
Tien Lam (Acct Mgr)
Liz Bonomi (Acct Mgr)
Christina Echelle (Acct Mgr)
Ashley White (Acct Mgr)
Patti Dahlquist (Acct Mgr)
Callie Hall (Acct Mgr)
Julia Regan (Acct Mgr)
Boyce Morin (VP)

U.S. PRIVATE

Wallace Specialty Insurance Group, LLC (2)
640 James Dr., Richardson, TX 75080
Tel.: (972) 663-5190
Web Site: https://www.insurance4dds.com
Insurance Agencies & Brokerage Services
N.A.I.C.S.: 524210
Holly M. Black (Mgr-Sls)
Terri Wallace (Co-Owner)
Kyle Wallace (Co-Owner)

Weaver Bros. Insurance Associates, Inc. (2)
7315 Wisconsin Ave Ste 900E, Bethesda, MD 20814
Tel.: (610) 793-1700
Web Site: http://www.weaverbros.com
Insurance Related Activities
N.A.I.C.S.: 524298
Sandy Colangelo (VP)

Winter Group, Inc. (2)
16935 W Bernardo Dr Ste 100, San Diego, CA 92127
Tel.: (800) 211-2860
Web Site: http://truckinsure.agency
Insurance Services
N.A.I.C.S.: 524210
Jared Duncan (Chm & CEO)

Zito Insurance Agency, Inc. (2)
8339 Tyler Blvd, Mentor, OH 44060
Tel.: (440) 205-7400
Web Site: http://www.zitoinsurance.com
Insurance Agencies & Brokerages
N.A.I.C.S.: 524210
Chris Zito (Mng Dir)
Bertha Barresi (Principal, VP-Ops & Office Mgr)
Jacqui Smith (Acct Mgr)
Jennifer McGreal (Acct Mgr)
Karen Berendsen (Acct Mgr)
Kathy Mamie (Acct Mgr)
Kelly Beebe (Acct Mgr)
Kim Hollister (Acct Mgr)
Mary Moore (Acct Mgr)
Michele Hanzak (Sr Acct Exec-Grp Benefits)
Nicci Vanjo (Acct Mgr)
Ranee Jackson (Acct Exec-Grp Benefits)
Sue Baker (Acct Mgr-Small Bus Unit)
Tammie Vicini (Acct Mgr)
Greg Zito (VP-Life Svcs)
Rosalyn Baum (Mgr-Acct)
Tracy Alexander (Mgr-Acct)

Resolute Investment Managers, Inc. (1)
220 E Las Colinas Blvd Ste 1200, Irving, TX 75039
Tel.: (817) 391-6100
Web Site: http://www.resolutemanagers.com
Investment Services
N.A.I.C.S.: 523940
Jeffrey K. Ringdahl (Pres & CEO)
Erica B. Duncan (VP-Mktg)
Rebecca L. Harris (Sr VP-Corp Dev & Product Mgmt)
Terri L. McKinney (Sr VP-Enterprise Svcs)
Rosemary K. Behan (VP & Gen Counsel)
Melinda G. Heika (VP & CFO)
Christina E. Sears (VP-Compliance)

Subsidiary (Domestic):

SSI Investment Management, Inc. (2)
9440 Santa Monica Blvd Ste 800, Beverly Hills, CA 90210
Tel.: (310) 595-2000
Web Site: http://www.ssi-invest.com
Investment Advice
N.A.I.C.S.: 523940
Syed Mehdi (Pres & Chief Compliance Officer)
George M. Douglas (Chief Investment Officer & Mng Principal)
Judy Wang (Mng Dir-Ops)
Maria Ruiz (Dir-Fin)
Ravi Malik (Principal & Portfolio Mgr)

Southeast Connections LLC (1)
2720 Dogwood Dr SE, Conyers, GA 30013
Tel.: (404) 659-1422
Web Site: http://www.seconnections.com
Underground Construction Services
N.A.I.C.S.: 237990
Billy Campbell (Pres & CEO)
Scott Warren (COO)

COMPANIES

Keith Plemons (Dir-Safety)
Kevin Adams (VP-Ops)
Kyle Ormsby (Sr VP)

WilliamsMarston LLC (1)
800 Boylston St 16th Fl, Boston, MA 02199
Tel.: (617) 982-6699
Web Site: http://www.williamsmarston.com
Management Consulting Services
N.A.I.C.S.: 541611
Jonathan Marston (Co-Founder & Mng Partner)
Landen Williams (Co-Founder & Mng Partner)

Subsidiary (Domestic):

Bay Valuation Advisors, LLC (2)
1 Kaiser Plz Ste 1475, Oakland, CA 94612
Tel.: (510) 879-7670
Web Site: http://www.bayvaluation.com
All Other Support Services
N.A.I.C.S.: 561990
Long Aeneas (Founder & Partner)

KELSO-BURNETT COMPANY
5200 Newport Dr, Rolling Meadows, IL 60008
Tel.: (847) 259-0720 DE
Web Site: http://www.kelso-burnett.com
Year Founded: 1908
Sales Range: $200-249.9 Million
Emp.: 300
Provider of Electrical Contracting Services
N.A.I.C.S.: 238210
Stefan Lopata (Pres & CEO)
John Ryder (COO & Exec VP)

Subsidiaries:

Contech MSI Co. (1)
5200 Newport Dr, Rolling Meadows, IL 60008
Tel.: (847) 342-9932
Web Site: http://www.contechco.com
Fire Alarm Installation Services
N.A.I.C.S.: 238210
Bryan Nordlund (Pres)
Scotty Nordlund (Project Mgr-Inspections Asst)

KELTA, INC.
80 Skyline Dr Ste 101, Plainview, NY 11803
Tel.: (516) 433-1423 DE
Year Founded: 2003
Electrical & Communications Products Mfr
N.A.I.C.S.: 334419
Parag Mehta (Pres & CEO)

Subsidiaries:

Tii Network Technologies, Inc. (1)
141 Rodeo Dr, Edgewood, NY 11717-8378
Tel.: (631) 789-5000
Web Site: http://www.tiinetworktechnologies.com
Emp.: 78
Communications Equipment Components Designer, Mfr & Distr
N.A.I.C.S.: 335313
David E. Foley (VP-Tech Dev)

Subsidiary (Domestic):

Tii Fiber Optics, Inc. (2)
141 Rodeo Dr, Edgewood, NY 11717
Tel.: (631) 789-5000
Web Site: http://www.tiitech.com
Sales Range: $10-24.9 Million
Emp.: 9
Fiber Optic Equipment Mfr
N.A.I.C.S.: 335921
Alex Feezer (VP)

KELTRON ELECTRONICS CORP.
1505 Sara Cir, Port Jefferson Station, NY 11776
Tel.: (631) 567-6300
Web Site: http://www.keltron.com
Year Founded: 1980
Sales Range: $25-49.9 Million
Emp.: 20
Electronic Components
N.A.I.C.S.: 334419
David Levison (CEO)

Subsidiaries:

Keltron Connectors (1)
3385 Veterans Hwy Ste E, Ronkonkoma, NY 11779
Tel.: (631) 567-0500
Web Site: http://www.keltronconnectors.com
Mfr of Electronic Parts & Equipment
N.A.I.C.S.: 423690

KELVYN PRESS INC.
2910 S 18th Ave, Broadview, IL 60155
Tel.: (708) 343-0448
Web Site: http://www.fgraphic.com
Rev.: $11,400,000
Emp.: 700
Commercial Lithographic Printing
N.A.I.C.S.: 323111
Jeff Badali (Mgr)
Nancy Overholt (CFO)
Gary Malacine (Gen Mgr)
Tony Malacina (VP & Gen Mgr)
Anthony Malacina (VP-Ops)
Michael Price (Mgr)
Richard Malacina Sr. (Pres & CEO)
Richard Malacina Jr. (VP)

KEM KREST CORPORATION
3221 Magnum Dr, Elkhart, IN 46516
Tel.: (574) 389-2650
Web Site: http://www.kemkrest.com
Year Founded: 1979
Supply Chain, Warehousing & Logistics Services
N.A.I.C.S.: 488510
Amish Shah (CEO)
David Weaver (Pres & Co-Owner)
Andrew Hauser (Acct Mgr)
Neil Chilberg (Dir-Sls)
Brian McMahon (Dir-Supply Chain)
Bill Crosby (Dir-Aftersales)

KEMBA CREDIT UNION, INC.
8763 Union Centre Blvd, West Chester, OH 45069
Tel.: (513) 762-5070 OH
Web Site: http://www.kemba.com
Year Founded: 1934
Sales Range: $25-49.9 Million
Emp.: 217
Credit Union Operator
N.A.I.C.S.: 522130
Steve Behler (Pres & CEO)

KEMBA FINANCIAL CREDIT UNION
555 Officenter Pl, Gahanna, OH 43230
Tel.: (614) 235-2395 OH
Web Site: http://www.kemba.org
Year Founded: 1933
Sales Range: $25-49.9 Million
Emp.: 275
Financial Management Services
N.A.I.C.S.: 522130
Jerry Guy (Pres & CEO)
Mark Decello (COO & Exec VP)
Mark Seymour (VP-Lending & Risk)
Kevin Russo (VP-Tech)
Jeff Gale (Vice Chm)
Mark Solomon (Chm)
Marjorie Brant (Sec)
Steve Perdue (Treas)
Lynn McNabb (VP-HR)
John Zajac (CFO)

KEMCO INDUSTRIES INC.
70 Keyes Ct, Sanford, FL 32773
Tel.: (407) 322-1230
Web Site: http://www.kemco.com
Sales Range: $10-24.9 Million
Emp.: 65
Fabricated Structural Metal Mfr
N.A.I.C.S.: 332312
Terri Booth (CFO)
Ty Kracht (Owner & Pres)

KEMIN INDUSTRIES, INC.
1900 Scott Ave, Des Moines, IA 50317
Tel.: (515) 559-5100
Web Site: http://www.kemin.com
Sales Range: $75-99.9 Million
Emp.: 1,000
Food Ingredient & Pharmaceutical Manufacturer
N.A.I.C.S.: 325412
Christopher E. Nelson (Pres & CEO)
Elizabeth Nelson (Gen Counsel & VP)
R. W. Nelson (Chm)
Yannick Riou (Pres-Kemin Nutrisurance)
Leo Xie-Lei (Pres-Kemin AquaScience-Shanghai)
Vinoth Kumar R. (Comm Mgr)
Haley Stomp (Sr VP-Worldwide Mktg)
Lauren Burt (Head-Worldwide Comm)
Rebecca Lucas (Dir-R&D-Human Nutrition & Health Bus)
Joao Marcelo Gomes (Pres-Kemin Food Technologies-Europe, Middle East & Africa)
Giuseppe Abrate (Pres-Food & Human-Global)
Marsha Bro (Dir-Worldwide Acq & Licensing)
Caroline Ecoffard (Mgr-Product Platform)

Subsidiaries:

Bio-Cide International, Inc. (1)
2845 Broce Dr Ste D, Norman, OK 73072
Tel.: (405) 329-5598
Web Site: http://www.bio-cide.com
Sales Range: $1-9.9 Million
Emp.: 28
Basic Inorganic Chemical Mfr
N.A.I.C.S.: 325180
Scott Owens (VP-Sls & Mktg)
Jim Ringo (Dir-Regulatory Affairs)

KEMLON PRODUCTS & DEVELOPMENT CO.
1424 N Main St, Pearland, TX 77581
Tel.: (281) 997-3300
Web Site: http://www.kemlon.com
Rev.: $11,500,000
Emp.: 126
Connectors & Terminals for Electrical Devices
N.A.I.C.S.: 335931
John Ring (Pres)
David Wright (Mgr-Sls)

KEMMONS WILSON, INC.
8700 Trial Lk Dr W Ste 300, Memphis, TN 38125
Tel.: (901) 346-8800 TN
Web Site: http://www.kwilson.com
Year Founded: 1965
Sales Range: $300-349.9 Million
Emp.: 500
Investment Holding Company
N.A.I.C.S.: 551112
C. Kemmons Wilson Jr. (Vice Chm)
Spence L. Wilson (Chm)
Robert A. Wilson (Vice Chm)
William R. Batt (CFO & Pres-Wilson Family Office Svcs)
McLean T. Wilson (Principal)
D. Webb Wilson (Principal)
Tony Graves (Chief Investment Officer)
Rebecca Wilson Macsovits (Chief Brand Officer)

KEMNA MOTOR CO.

Cecil E. Carney III (Pres-Private Investments)
C. Kemmons Wilson III (Principal)
Spence Wilson Jr. (Principal)

Subsidiaries:

Wilson Hotel Management Company, Inc. (1)
8700 Trl Lk Dr W Ste 300, Memphis, TN 38125
Tel.: (901) 346-8800
Web Site: http://www.wilsonhotels.com
Home Management Services
N.A.I.C.S.: 721110
C. Kemmons Wilson Jr. (Chm & Pres)
Edward E. Crenshaw (Controller)
Vicki M. Bradley (Dir-HR)
James M. O'Brien (Exec VP)
Robert A. Wilson (VP)
Jerry Jacocks (Asst Controller)
Sybil Sides (Reg Dir-Sls)

Wilson Resort Management Corp. (1)
8505 W Irlo Bronson Memorial Hwy, Kissimmee, FL 34747-8217
Tel.: (407) 239-0000
Web Site: http://www.orangelake.com
Sales Range: $75-99.9 Million
Resort Management Services
N.A.I.C.S.: 713910
C. Kemmons Wilson Jr. (Founder)
Brian T. Lower (Gen Counsel & Exec VP)
Don L. Harrill (Vice Chm)
Thomas Nelson (Pres & CEO)
Denise Godreau (Chief Brand & Innovation Officer)

Holding (Domestic):

Orange Lake Country Club, Inc. (2)
8505 W Irlo Bronson Memorial Hwy, Kissimmee, FL 34747-8201
Tel.: (407) 239-0000
Web Site: http://www.orangelake.com
Country Club & Resort Developer & Operator
N.A.I.C.S.: 713910
Spence L. Wilson (Chm)
Don L. Harrill (Vice Chm)
Thomas Nelson (Pres & CEO)
Brian T. Lower (Gen Counsel & Exec VP)
Patrick Connolly (Chief Customer Officer & Sr VP)
Michael Thompson (Sr VP-Legal Svcs)
Barbara Wilcox (Chief Talent Officer & Sr VP)
Sonya Dixon (CFO & Sr VP)
Steve Pflugner (Sr VP-Capital Mgmt)
Denise Godreau (Chief Brand & Innovation Officer)
John A. Sutherland II (Exec VP-Sls & Mktg)

Subsidiary (Domestic):

Orange Lake Country Club Realty, Inc. (3)
8505 W Irlo Bronson Hwy, Kissimmee, FL 34747
Tel.: (407) 239-0000
Web Site: http://www.orangelake.com
Real Estate Investment, Development, Property Management & Leasing Services
N.A.I.C.S.: 531390
Dennis DeLorenzo (Sr VP-Mktg)
John Alvarez (VP-Acq)
John Sutherland (Sr VP)
Michael Thompson (Sr VP-Legal Svcs)
Ralph Bailey (Sr VP-Construction)
Spence Wilson (Chm)
Steve Pflugner (Sr VP-Capital Mgmt)
Thomas Nelson (Pres & COO)
Bob Albertson (Exec VP)
Brian Lower (Gen Counsel & Exec VP-Plng & Dev)

Silverleaf Resorts, Inc. (3)
6321 Blvd 26 Ste 400 N, Richland Hills, TX 76180
Tel.: (817) 284-2390
Web Site: http://www.silverleafresorts.com
Timeshare Resorts Developer, Operator & Marketer
N.A.I.C.S.: 531210
Tom Nelson (Pres)

KEMNA MOTOR CO.

KEMNA MOTOR CO.   U.S. PRIVATE

Kemna Motor Co.—(Continued)
617 Hwy 18 W, Algona, IA 50511
Tel.: (515) 295-2406
Web Site: http://www.kemna.com
Year Founded: 1956
Sales Range: $10-24.9 Million
Emp.: 100
Sales of New & Used Automobiles
Including Service & Parts
N.A.I.C.S.: 441120
Kenneth Kemna *(Pres)*

KEMP & RUGE LAW GROUP
2049 Wellbilt Blvd, Trinity, FL 34655
Tel.: (727) 847-4878
Web Site:
http://www.kemprugegreen.com
Sales Range: $1-9.9 Million
Emp.: 9
Law firm
N.A.I.C.S.: 541110
Stacy Kemp *(Owner)*

KEMP MANUFACTURING COMPANY
4310 N Voss St, Peoria, IL 61616
Tel.: (309) 682-7292
Sales Range: $10-24.9 Million
Emp.: 45
Machine Shop, Jobbing & Repair
N.A.I.C.S.: 332710
Hylee F. Kemp *(Pres)*
Matt Kemp *(VP)*
Susan Alwan *(Mgr-Fin)*

KEMPER CPA GROUP LLP
505 N 6th St, Vincennes, IN 47591
Tel.: (812) 882-7730
Web Site: http://www.kcpag.com
Year Founded: 1958
Sales Range: $10-24.9 Million
Emp.: 100
Certified Public Accountants
N.A.I.C.S.: 541211
Curtis Benson *(Partner)*

Subsidiaries:
KCPAG Financial Advisors LLC (1)
302 E Walnut St, Robinson, IL 62454
Tel.: (618) 544-4993
Financial Management Services
N.A.I.C.S.: 541611
Brian Bradbury *(Partner)*

Kemper Capital Management
LLC (1)
7200 Eagle Crest Blvd, Evansville, IN 47715
Tel.: (812) 421-8000
Emp.: 5
Financial Management Services
N.A.I.C.S.: 541611
John Porter *(Gen Mgr)*

Kemper Technology Consulting (1)
121 W Walnut St, Robinson, IL 62454
Tel.: (618) 546-5633
Web Site: http://www.kempertc.com
Emp.: 5
Office Computer Technology Consultants
N.A.I.C.S.: 541211
Mike Gibsin *(Gen Mgr)*

KEMPER EQUIPMENT INC.
5051 Horseshoe Pike Ste 200, Honey Brook, PA 19344-1365
Tel.: (610) 273-2066
Web Site:
http://www.kemperequipment.com
Sales Range: $10-24.9 Million
Emp.: 45
Mining Machinery & Equipment, Except Petroleum
N.A.I.C.S.: 423810
Greg Donecker *(Pres)*
Tom McDonald *(Controller)*
Chris Rettew *(Dir-Sls)*

KEMPER SPORTS, INC.
500 Skokie Blvd Ste 444, Northbrook, IL 60062
Tel.: (847) 850-1818
Web Site:
http://www.kempersports.com
Year Founded: 1998
Sales Range: $250-299.9 Million
Emp.: 4,200
Golf Courses & Country Clubs
N.A.I.C.S.: 713910
Steven H. Lesnik *(Chm)*
Steven K. Skinner *(CEO)*
Josh W. Lesnik *(Pres)*
Ben Blake *(Exec VP-Bus Dev)*
Jim Stegall *(Exec VP)*
Andrew Fleming *(Sr VP)*
Dan Cunningham *(VP)*
Douglas Hellman *(Sr VP)*
Hank Hickox *(VP)*
Heather Margulis *(VP)*
Jim Lawler *(CFO)*
Keith Hanley *(VP)*
Mark Hoesing *(Sr VP)*
Steve Kelley *(Gen Counsel & VP)*
Matt Lindley *(Sr VP-Ops-Southeast)*
Jeremy Goldblatt *(COO)*
Steve Goris *(Sr VP-Venues)*

KEMPERCONNECT
308 E 8th St, Cincinnati, OH 45202-2204
Tel.: (513) 352-0991
Year Founded: 1966
Sales Range: $75-99.9 Million
Emp.: 12
Advetising Agency
N.A.I.C.S.: 541810
Robert B. Kemper *(CEO & Dir-Creative)*

KEMPERLESNIK
500 Skokie Blvd 4th Fl, Northbrook, IL 60062
Tel.: (847) 850-1818
Web Site:
http://www.kemperlesnik.com
Year Founded: 1979
Sales Range: $1-9.9 Million
Emp.: 30
Public Relations Agency
N.A.I.C.S.: 541820
Steve Skinner *(CEO)*
Tom Valdiserri *(Mng Dir & VP)*
Cybil Rose *(VP)*
Christie Zielinski *(Grp Acct Dir)*
Josh Lesnik *(Pres)*
Mark Starsiak *(Dir-Event Ops)*
Eric Jonke *(Sr VP)*
John Knebel *(VP-Sls)*
Gretchen Muller *(Sr VP-PR)*
David Prosperi *(Mng Dir & Exec VP)*
Doug Manning *(Sr VP-Bus Dev)*

KEMPSMITH MACHINE COMPANY
1819 S 71st St, Milwaukee, WI 53214-4836
Tel.: (414) 256-8160
Web Site: http://www.kempsmith-dl.com
Year Founded: 1888
Sales Range: $50-74.9 Million
Emp.: 50
Designer & Mfr Paper Folding, Converting, Cutting & Creasing Machinery & Flexographic Printers
N.A.I.C.S.: 333243
Robert Burris *(Owner & CEO)*
Brett Burris *(Pres)*

KEMPTHORN MOTORS INC.
1449 Cleveland Ave NW, Canton, OH 44703
Tel.: (330) 452-6511
Web Site: http://www.kempthorn.com
Year Founded: 1938

Sales Range: $10-24.9 Million
Emp.: 160
Sales of New & Used Automobiles
N.A.I.C.S.: 522220
Richard Kempthorn *(Owner)*
Eric Kempthorn *(CEO)*
James Kempthorn *(VP)*

KEMPTON CHEVROLET BUICK LTD
715 5th St, Safford, AZ 85546
Tel.: (928) 428-0252
Web Site:
http://www.kemptonchevrolet.com
Rev.: $13,850,000
Emp.: 37
Dealer of New & Used Automobiles
N.A.I.C.S.: 441110

KEMRON ENVIRONMENTAL SERVICES, INC.
8521 Leesburg Pike Ste 175, Vienna, VA 22182-2228
Tel.: (703) 893-4106
Web Site: http://www.kemron.com
Year Founded: 1975
Sales Range: $25-49.9 Million
Emp.: 140
Environmental Consulting, Remediation & Analytical Services
N.A.I.C.S.: 541620
Juan J. Gutierrez *(Chm, Pres & CEO)*
John Dwyer *(Exec VP)*
Tracy Bergquist *(VP-Federal Programs)*

KEN CLARK INTERNATIONAL
989 Lenox Dr Ste 304, Lawrence, NJ 08648-2315
Tel.: (609) 308-5200
Web Site: http://www.kenclark.com
Sales Range: $10-24.9 Million
Emp.: 32
Executive Placement
N.A.I.C.S.: 541612
Kenneth Michael Clark *(Founder, Chm & CEO)*
Ray Clark *(Controller)*
Chris Headle *(VP)*

KEN COOK CO.
9929 W Silver Spring Dr, Milwaukee, WI 53225
Tel.: (414) 466-6060
Web Site: http://www.kencook.com
Rev.: $11,600,000
Emp.: 50
Publisher
N.A.I.C.S.: 513199
Robert T. Haukohl *(VP)*
Kenneth J. Cook *(Pres, CEO & Mgr-Sls)*
John C. Poelzer *(Treas)*
Bill Duncan *(Dir-Writing & Graphic Svcs)*
Brad Uelmen *(VP)*
Brian McGowan *(VP)*
Greg King *(VP)*

KEN DIXON AUTOMOTIVE GROUP
2298 Crain Hwy, Waldorf, MD 20601
Tel.: (301) 645-7000
Web Site:
http://www.waldorfchevycadillac.com
Year Founded: 1961
Sales Range: $10-24.9 Million
Emp.: 150
Used Car Retailer
N.A.I.C.S.: 441120
Tom Kody *(Owner)*
Floyd Alexander *(Gen Mgr)*

KEN FOWLER MOTORS INC.
1265 Airport Park Blvd, Ukiah, CA 95482

Tel.: (707) 468-0101
Web Site:
http://www.fowlerautocenter.com
Sales Range: $10-24.9 Million
Emp.: 44
Automobile Sales, New & Used
N.A.I.C.S.: 441110
Kenneth Fowler *(Pres)*

KEN GRODY FORD
6211 Beach Blvd, Buena Park, CA 90621
Tel.: (714) 521-3110
Web Site:
http://www.kengrodyford.com
Sales Range: $125-149.9 Million
Emp.: 300
Automobiles, New & Used
N.A.I.C.S.: 441110
Ken Grody *(Owner-Buena Park)*
James Ramos *(Mgr-Sls)*
Eric Romanoff *(Dir-Parts & Svc)*
Travis White *(Mgr-Fleet)*
Louis Rubalcava *(Dir-Fleet Svc)*
Rafael Alvarez *(Mgr-Parts Wholesale)*

KEN KOJAIAN HOMES, INC.
189 W Merrill St, Birmingham, MI 48009
Tel.: (248) 723-8055
Web Site:
http://www.kenkojaianhomes.com
Year Founded: 1993
Sales Range: $10-24.9 Million
Emp.: 3
Housing Construction Services
N.A.I.C.S.: 236117
Ken J. Kojaian *(Pres)*

KEN LUNEACK CONSTRUCTION CO.
721 E Washington St, Saint Louis, MI 48880
Tel.: (989) 681-5774
Sales Range: $10-24.9 Million
Emp.: 220
Truss & Wooden Roof Manufacturing
N.A.I.C.S.: 321215
Paul Luneak *(Pres)*

KEN NELSON AUTO PLAZA INC.
1000 N Galena Ave, Dixon, IL 61021
Tel.: (815) 288-4455
Web Site:
http://www.kennelsonauto.com
Sales Range: $50-74.9 Million
Emp.: 110
Automobiles; New & Used
N.A.I.C.S.: 441110
Kenneth A. Nelson *(Founder & Owner)*
Rick Curia *(Pres)*
Michael Freeman *(Gen Mgr-Sls)*
Jeremy Jahn *(Dir-Svcs)*

KEN WEAVER MEATS INC.
47 N St, Wellsville, PA 17365
Tel.: (717) 432-4146
Web Site:
http://www.weaversofwellsville.com
Year Founded: 1889
Sales Range: $25-49.9 Million
Emp.: 24
Meat Product Production & Distribution Services
N.A.I.C.S.: 424470
Craig Weaver *(Pres)*
Kimberly Weaver *(Sec)*

KEN WILSON FORD INC.
769 Champion Dr, Canton, NC 28716
Tel.: (828) 648-2313
Web Site:
http://www.kenwilsonford.net
Rev.: $110,000,000

Emp.: 135
New & Used Automobiles
N.A.I.C.S.: 441110
Kenneth Wilson (Pres)
Lisa Hynes (Controller)
Conley Smith (Mgr-Comml)
David Williams (Dir-Fin Svcs)

KEN'S FOODS, INC.
1 Dangelo Dr, Marlborough, MA 01752
Tel.: (508) 485-7540   MA
Web Site: http://www.kensfoods.com
Year Founded: 1958
Sales Range: $150-199.9 Million
Emp.: 500
Salad Dressing, Mayonnaise, Vinegar, Sauces & Syrups Mfr
N.A.I.C.S.: 311941
Brian Crowley (Pres-Food Svc Sls)
Joseph F. Shay (Treas)
James Sutherby (CFO)

KEN'S SUPERFAIR FOODS
2105 6th Ave SE, Aberdeen, SD 57401
Tel.: (605) 225-6671
Web Site: http://www.kensuperfair.com
Sales Range: $1-9.9 Million
Emp.: 250
Independent Supermarket
N.A.I.C.S.: 445110
Kenneth Fiedler (Owner)
Kevin Fiedler (Pres)

KEN-API SUPPLY INC.
11360 Enterprise Park Dr, Cincinnati, OH 45241-1885
Tel.: (513) 771-3555   OH
Web Site: http://www.kenapi.com
Year Founded: 1982
Sales Range: $25-49.9 Million
Emp.: 50
Dry Wall Sealings Specialties & Metal
N.A.I.C.S.: 423310
Jonathan Votel (Pres)
Ben Guess (VP)
Jim Leisureman (Controller)

KEN-TRON MANUFACTURING INC.
610 Indus Dr, Owensboro, KY 42301
Tel.: (270) 684-0431
Web Site: http://www.ken-tron.com
Sales Range: $10-24.9 Million
Emp.: 75
Electronic Enclosures Wire Division
N.A.I.C.S.: 332119
Robert D. Hudson (Pres)

KENAI DRILLING LIMITED
6430 Cat Canyon Rd, Santa Maria, CA 93454
Tel.: (805) 937-7871
Web Site: http://www.kenaidrilling.com
Rev.: $19,600,000
Emp.: 271
Drilling Oil & Gas Wells
N.A.I.C.S.: 213111
Gene Kramer (Gen Mgr)
Mike Peterson (Mgr-Ops)
Carl Hathaway (Mgr-Engrg)
Donna Marier (Mgr-Acctg)
Tim Crist (Pres)
David Uhler (CFO)
Rex Northern (VP & Gen Mgr)
David Arias (COO & VP)

KENBAR SERVICES INC.
1817 Ailor Ave, Knoxville, TN 37921-5845
Tel.: (865) 523-5166
Rev.: $19,000,000
Emp.: 42
Employee Leasing Svcs
N.A.I.C.S.: 561330
Ronald Garrett (Sec & VP-Personnel)
Barbara Garrett (Pres)
Marlene Deal (Mgr-Acctg)
William Yarberry (Treas & VP-Fin & Personnel)

KENCO GROUP INC.
2001 Riverside Dr, Chattanooga, TN 37406-4324
Tel.: (423) 622-1113   TN
Web Site: http://www.kencogroup.com
Year Founded: 1950
Sales Range: $50-74.9 Million
Emp.: 3,000
General Warehousing & Storage
N.A.I.C.S.: 493110
Sean Coakley (Sr VP-Sls & Mktg)
Frazer Middleton (CIO)
Jane Kennedy Greene (Chm)
David Caines (COO)
Denis Reilly (Pres & CEO)
Mike McClelland (Sr VP-Transportation)

Subsidiaries:

JDK Real Estate, LLC   (1)
2001 Riverside Dr, Chattanooga, TN 37406
Tel.: (423) 643-3258
Web Site: http://www.jdkrealestategroup.com
Janitorial Services
N.A.I.C.S.: 561720

Kenco Logistic Services Inc.   (1)
195 King Mill Rd, McDonough, GA 30253
Tel.: (404) 608-7400
Web Site: http://www.kenco.com
Rev.: $18,366,562
Emp.: 200
Trucking Except Local
N.A.I.C.S.: 488490
Gerald Perritt (Pres & CEO)

KENCO INC.
1821 Spring Arbor Rd, Jackson, MI 49203-2703
Tel.: (517) 787-6081   MI
Web Site: http://www.country-markets.com
Year Founded: 1983
Sales Range: $50-74.9 Million
Emp.: 600
Owner & Operator of Grocery Stores
N.A.I.C.S.: 445110
Kim Kennedy (Pres)

KENCOIL INC.
2805 Engineers Rd, Belle Chasse, LA 70037
Tel.: (504) 394-4010
Web Site: http://www.kencoil.com
Year Founded: 1981
Sales Range: $10-24.9 Million
Emp.: 110
Coils for Electric Motors or Generators Mfr
N.A.I.C.S.: 335312
John Lazarski (Gen Mgr)
Scott Key (Pres & CEO)
Frank Divincenti (Mgr-EHS&Q)

KENDAL KING GROUP
1925 Central, Kansas City, MO 64108
Tel.: (816) 569-6651
Web Site: http://www.kendalking.com
Year Founded: 1987
Rev.: $15,000,000
Emp.: 32
Sign Mfr
N.A.I.C.S.: 339950
Phil Gyori (VP-Mktg)
Scott King (CEO)
Landon Nobles (VP-Ops)
Tom Hauge (Dir-Category Solutions)

Charlene Kelley (Dir-Accts & Bus Dev-Bentonville)
Madison Jackson (Program Mgr-Soapbox Influencer Mktg-Bentonville)

KENDALE INDUSTRIES, INC.
7600 Hub Pkwy, Valley View, OH 44125
Tel.: (216) 524-5400   OH
Web Site: http://www.kendaleinc.com
Year Founded: 1960
Sales Range: $75-99.9 Million
Emp.: 100
Metal Stampings, Washers & Semi-Precision Ball Bearings Mfr
N.A.I.C.S.: 332991
Patrick Honroth (VP-Sls)
Antonio Viscomi (Gen Mgr)

Subsidiaries:

KD Industries Inc.   (1)
355 Industry Dr, Auburn, AL 36832-4274   (100%)
Tel.: (334) 887-8886
Sales Range: $10-24.9 Million
Emp.: 19
Assembler of Semi Precision Ball Bearings
N.A.I.C.S.: 332991

KENDALL AUTOMOTIVE GROUP INC.
344 Goodpasture Island Rd, Eugene, OR 97401
Tel.: (541) 357-8918   OR
Web Site: http://www.kendallautogroup.com
Holding Company; Car Dealerships Owner & Operator
N.A.I.C.S.: 551112
David E. Blewett (Pres)

Subsidiaries:

Kendall H LLC   (1)
846 Goodpasture Island Rd, Eugene, OR 97401-2435
Tel.: (541) 485-6111
Web Site: http://www.kendallhonda.com
Sales Range: $10-24.9 Million
Emp.: 76
New & Used Car Distr
N.A.I.C.S.: 441110
Matt Bodine (Gen Mgr)

Kendall L LLC   (1)
344 Goodpasture Is Rd, Eugene, OR 97401
Tel.: (541) 683-5181
Web Site: http://www.kendalllexuseugene.com
Sales Range: $1-9.9 Million
New & Used Car Dealer
N.A.I.C.S.: 441110
Scott Kletzok (Mgr-Auto Parts)
Mike McKean (Gen Mgr)

KENDALL IMPORTS LLC
10943 S Dixie Hwy, Miami, FL 33156
Tel.: (305) 665-6581
Web Site: http://www.kendalltoyota.com
Sales Range: $50-74.9 Million
Emp.: 1,300
Car Dealership
N.A.I.C.S.: 441110
Frank Marsala (Gen Mgr)
Nomi Paracha (Mgr-Fin)
George Weitz (Controller)

KENDALL MOULDING & FRAMES, INC.
5838 Research Park Blvd, Huntsville, AL 35806
Tel.: (256) 859-5533   AL
Web Site: http://www.kmaf.com
Year Founded: 1974
Rev.: $34,143,574
Emp.: 50
Frames & Framing, Picture & Mirror
N.A.I.C.S.: 423220
Wes Kendall (Pres)

KENDALL PACKAGING CORPORATION
10335 N Port Washington Rd Ste 200, Mequon, WI 53092
Tel.: (262) 404-1200
Web Site: http://www.kendallpkg.com
Year Founded: 1948
Sales Range: $10-24.9 Million
Emp.: 160
Provider of Laminated Packaging Services
N.A.I.C.S.: 322220
Eric G. Erickson (CEO)
Nate Freidl (Dir-Mfg)
Deanna Einwalter (Supvr-Acctg)
Randy Mjelde (Area Mgr-Sls)
Dave Carpentier (Mgr-Ink Dept)
Tim Brucker (Product Mgr-Dev)
Michael Sallmann (CFO)
Stewart Landy (Dir-Sls)

Subsidiaries:

Kendall Packaging Corporation - Jefferson   (1)
707 N Parkway St, Jefferson, WI 53549
Tel.: (920) 674-3220
Web Site: http://www.kendallpkg.com
Emp.: 55
Laminated Packaging Services
N.A.I.C.S.: 322220
Nathan Friedl (Dir-Mfg & Mgr-Ops)

Kendall Packaging Corporation - Pittsburg Facility   (1)
1901 E 27th St Ter, Pittsburg, KS 66762
Tel.: (620) 231-9804
Packaging Services
N.A.I.C.S.: 561910

KENDALL/HUNT PUBLISHING COMPANY INC.
4050 Westmark Dr, Dubuque, IA 52004-1840
Tel.: (563) 589-1000   IA
Web Site: http://www.kendallhunt.com
Year Founded: 1944
Sales Range: $25-49.9 Million
Emp.: 200
Book Publishing
N.A.I.C.S.: 513130
Ron Cavanagh (CFO)
Mark C. Falb (Chm & CEO)
Chad M. Chandlee (Pres & COO)

KENDRA SCOTT DESIGN, INC.
1400 S Congress Ave Ste A-170, Austin, TX 78704
Tel.: (512) 499-8400
Web Site: http://www.kendrascott.com
Year Founded: 2002
Sales Range: $10-24.9 Million
Emp.: 82
Jewelry Mfr & Retailer
N.A.I.C.S.: 339910
Kendra Scott (Pres & CEO)
Jana Waller (Mgr-Community Rels & Event)

KENDRICK OIL CO. INC.
801 Main St, Friona, TX 79035-2039
Tel.: (806) 250-3991   TX
Web Site: http://www.kendrickoil.com
Year Founded: 1982
Sales Range: $10-24.9 Million
Emp.: 100
Petroleum Products Mfr
N.A.I.C.S.: 424720
Daniel M. Kendrick (Pres)
Greg Lewellen (Controller)

KENERGY CORP.
6402 Old Corydon Rd, Henderson, KY 42420
Tel.: (270) 826-3991

KENERGY CORP.

Kenergy Corp.—(Continued)
Web Site:
http://www.kenergycorp.com
Year Founded: 1999
Sales Range: $250-299.9 Million
Emp.: 175
Distribution, Electric Power
N.A.I.C.S.: 221122
John Newland (VP-Engrg)
Steve Thompson (VP-Fin)
Ken Stock (VP-Ops)
Keith Ellis (VP-HR)

KENEX HOLDINGS LLC
150 N Wacker Ste 3025, Chicago, IL 60606
Tel.: (312) 675-4314
Web Site:
http://www.kenexholdings.com
Year Founded: 2013
Investment Holding Company
N.A.I.C.S.: 551112
Nick Kuneman (Partner)
Mike Kenefick (Partner)

Subsidiaries:

Bubbies Homemade Ice Cream & Desserts, Inc. (1)
99-1267 Waiua Pl Unit B, Aiea, HI 96701-3277
Tel.: (808) 487-7218
Web Site: http://www.bubbiesicecream.com
Ice Cream & Frozen Dessert Mfr
N.A.I.C.S.: 311520
Rick Schaffer (CEO)

KENILWORTH STEEL CO. INC.
106 E Market St Ste 809, Warren, OH 44481-1103
Tel.: (330) 373-1885   OH
Web Site:
http://www.kenilworthsteel.com
Year Founded: 1981
Sales Range: $10-24.9 Million
Emp.: 25
Metals Service Centers & Offices
N.A.I.C.S.: 423510
Bill Campbell (Controller)
Scott Pape (Pres)

KENJO INC.
806 High St, Maryville, TN 37804-5031
Tel.: (865) 982-2192   TN
Web Site: http://www.downeyoil.com
Year Founded: 1978
Sales Range: $25-49.9 Million
Emp.: 375
Provider of Gasoline Services
N.A.I.C.S.: 457120
Charles W. Carruthers (Pres)

KENKO UTILITY SUPPLY INC.
639 Quinn Ave, San Jose, CA 95112
Tel.: (408) 294-7700
Sales Range: $10-24.9 Million
Emp.: 25
Whslr of Pipe Valves & Fittings
N.A.I.C.S.: 423830
Pamela C. Koziar (Pres)
Carolyn Barela (Controller)

KENLEE PRECISION CORPORATION
1701 Inverness Ave, Baltimore, MD 21230
Tel.: (410) 525-3800
Web Site: http://www.kenlee.com
Sales Range: $10-24.9 Million
Emp.: 90
Mfr of Precision Crafted Parts & Assemblies
N.A.I.C.S.: 332710
Gary LeCompte (VP & Gen Mgr)
Darla Stanley (Pres & CEO)

KENLOC, INC.
1100 Town & Country Rd Ste 1250, Orange, CA 92868
Tel.: (657) 235-5016   NV
Web Site: http://www.kenloc.net
Year Founded: 2018
Assets: $90,454
Liabilities: $120,986
Net Worth: ($30,532)
Earnings: ($80,411)
Fiscal Year-end: 03/31/20
Real Estate Asset Management Services
N.A.I.C.S.: 531390
Fei Hao (Chm, Pres & CEO)
Lixin He (CFO & Treas)
Michael Aniff (Sec)

KENMAR CORPORATION
17515 W 9 Mile Rd Ste 1200, Southfield, MI 48075
Tel.: (248) 424-8200
Web Site: http://www.ekenmar.com
Year Founded: 1960
Sales Range: $10-24.9 Million
Emp.: 25
Automotive Supplies & Parts
N.A.I.C.S.: 423120
Mary C. Elliott (Chm)
Aric Rusk (Pres)
John Klein (Controller)
Maria Kalina (Coord-Program-Interior Trim Grp)
Mark Kalina (Sr Mgr-Sls)

KENMOR ELECTRIC CO. LP
8330 Hansen Rd, Houston, TX 77075-1004
Tel.: (713) 869-0171   TX
Web Site: http://www.kenmor.com
Year Founded: 1976
Sales Range: $25-49.9 Million
Emp.: 300
Electrical Contractor
N.A.I.C.S.: 238210
Joe G. Martin (Exec VP)
Jeff Hinton (VP-Estimating)
Kip Farrington (Pres)

KENMORE AIR HARBOR INC.
6321 NE 175th St, Kenmore, WA 98028
Tel.: (425) 486-1257
Web Site: http://www.kenmoreair.com
Sales Range: $10-24.9 Million
Emp.: 95
Airport Service Center
N.A.I.C.S.: 488119
Rob Richey (Dir-Maintenance)
Ty Edwards (Dir-Customer Svc)

KENMORE CONSTRUCTION CO., INC.
700 Home Ave, Akron, OH 44310-4104
Tel.: (330) 762-9373   OH
Web Site:
http://www.kenmorecompanies.com
Year Founded: 1956
Sales Range: $25-49.9 Million
Emp.: 210
Highway & Street Construction
N.A.I.C.S.: 237310
William A. Scala (Pres)
Amy Adams (Sec)

KENNEBEC SAVINGS BANK, MHC
150 State St, Augusta, ME 04332
Tel.: (207) 622-5801
Web Site:
http://www.kennebecsavings.bank
Year Founded: 2014
Bank Holding Company
N.A.I.C.S.: 551111
Andrew Silsby (Pres & CEO)

Subsidiaries:

Kennebec Savings Bank (1)
150 State St, Augusta, ME 04330
Tel.: (207) 622-5801
Web Site: http://www.kennebecsavings.com
Sales Range: $25-49.9 Million
Emp.: 71
Federal Savings Bank
N.A.I.C.S.: 522110
William S. Hill (Reg VP)
David J. Roy (Officer-Loan & Reg VP)
Andrew E. Silsby (Pres & CEO)
Gary Lapierre (Officer-Loan & VP)
James R. Lagasse (CTO & VP)
Matthew W. Dwyer (VP & Branch Mgr)
Mary A. Hammond (Officer-HR)
Kelley I. Madore (Asst VP & Officer-Risk & Security)
Debra A. Getchell (CFO & Sr VP)
Kevin Healey (Chief HR Officer & Sr VP)
Craig J. Garofalo (COO & Sr VP)
Russ L. Donahue (Officer-Comm & Dir-Mktg)
George W. Diplock Jr. (VP & Officer-Collections)

KENNEBUNK SAVINGS BANK
104 Main St, Kennebunk, ME 04043
Tel.: (207) 985-4903
Web Site:
http://www.kennebunksavings.com
Year Founded: 1871
Sales Range: $25-49.9 Million
Emp.: 250
Mutual Savings & Community Bank
N.A.I.C.S.: 522180
Jill Peter (Sr VP-Credit Admin)
Jamie Thompson (VP-Corp Lending)
Len Guerra (VP & Coord-Risk)
Lisa Randall (VP & Mgr-Asset & Liability)
James N. Carrigan (VP & Branch Mgr)
Dick Carmichael (Sr VP)
Erik N. Bergeron (Mgr-Comml & Portfolio)
Mark Roller (VP)
Michelle Nappi (VP & Mgr-Retail Credit Admin)
Susan Benson (VP-Mktg)
Toby Boyd (Asst VP)
Lorraine Boston (Exec VP)
Bradford Paige (Pres & CEO)
Bryan Daley (Asst VP)
Steve Soubble (CFO)
Paul Wolf (Sr VP)
Helene Plourde (VP & Mgr)
Jessica Bollotta (VP & Mgr-Customer Care)
Judy DesMeules (VP & Mgr-Wells)
Rhonda Hebert (VP & Mgr-Lower Village)

KENNEDY ASSOCIATES/ARCHITECTS, INC.
2060 Craigshire Rd, Saint Louis, MO 63146
Tel.: (314) 241-8188   MO
Web Site: http://www.kai-db.com
Year Founded: 1980
Sales Range: $10-24.9 Million
Emp.: 90
Architectural, Interior Design & Engineering Services
N.A.I.C.S.: 541310
Michael E. Kennedy (Chm)
Bruce L. Wood (COO)
Darren B. James (Pres)
Michael B. Kennedy Jr. (CEO)

Subsidiaries:

Volk Construction Company (1)
1737 Macklind Ave, Saint Louis, MO 63110
Tel.: (314) 776-8655
Single-Family Housing
N.A.I.C.S.: 236115

KENNEDY AUTOMOTIVE GROUP INC.
620 Bustleton Pke, Feasterville Trevose, PA 19053
Tel.: (215) 357-6600
Web Site:
http://www.kennedyauto.com
Sales Range: $75-99.9 Million
Emp.: 90
Automobiles, New & Used
N.A.I.C.S.: 441110
Stell Mach (Gen Mgr)

Subsidiaries:

John Kennedy Ford Lincoln Mercury (1)
3189 W Rdg Pike, Pottstown, PA 19464
Tel.: (610) 495-7172
Web Site: http://www.kennedyauto.com
Rev.: $37,402,607
Emp.: 55
Automobiles, New & Used
N.A.I.C.S.: 441110
Matt Armstrong (Gen Mgr)

John Kennedy Ford of Phoenixville (1)
730 Valley Forge Rd, Phoenixville, PA 19460
Tel.: (610) 933-5811
Web Site: http://www.fordofphoenixville.com
Rev.: $18,900,000
Emp.: 55
New & Used Car Dealer Distr
N.A.I.C.S.: 441110

Kennedy Advertising (1)
365 St Rd, Southampton, PA 18966
Tel.: (215) 364-1710
Web Site: http://www.kennedyauto.com
Rev.: $280,000
Emp.: 2
Advertising Agencies
N.A.I.C.S.: 541810

KENNEDY CAPITAL MANAGEMENT, INC.
10829 Olive Blvd, Saint Louis, MO 63141
Tel.: (314) 432-0400
Web Site:
http://www.kennedycapital.com
Rev.: $9,654,600
Emp.: 64
Portfolio Management
N.A.I.C.S.: 523940
Richard Oliver (CFO)
Stephen Mace (COO & VP)
Chuck Bryant (Mng Dir-Sls & Mktg)
Richard Hibbs (Mng Dir-Sls & Mktg)
Marilyn Lammert (Chief Compliance Officer & VP)
Richard Sinise (Exec VP)
Kimberly Wood (Chm, Pres & CEO)
Jean Barnard (Dir-Res)
Frank Latuda Jr. (VP)

KENNEDY CONTRACTORS, INC.
2465 Mercer Ave Ste 107, West Palm Beach, FL 33401
Tel.: (561) 434-1300   FL
Web Site:
http://www.kennedycompanies.com
Year Founded: 1994
Sales Range: $10-24.9 Million
Emp.: 15
Nonresidential Construction Services
N.A.I.C.S.: 236220
Michael Carp (Pres)

KENNEDY ENGINE CO., INC.
980 Motsie Rd, Biloxi, MS 39532-2202
Tel.: (228) 392-2200
Web Site:
http://www.kennedyengine.com
Sales Range: $10-24.9 Million
Emp.: 25

Industrial Engine & Fire Pump Package Distr
N.A.I.C.S.: 423830
Tommy Kennedy *(Pres)*
Robbie Robertson *(Mgr-Svc)*

KENNEDY GROUP INC.
38601 Kennedy Pkwy, Willoughby, OH 44094
Tel.: (440) 951-7660
Web Site:
http://www.kennedygrp.com
Rev.: $20,000,000
Emp.: 70
Gummed Tape Mfr
N.A.I.C.S.: 322220
Michael R. Kennedy *(Pres)*

KENNEDY HEALTH SYSTEM
1099 White Horse Rd, Voorhees, NJ 08043
Tel.: (856) 566-5200
Web Site:
http://www.kennedyhealth.org
Year Founded: 1965
Sales Range: $300-349.9 Million
Emp.: 4,000
Health Care Srvcs
N.A.I.C.S.: 622110
Christopher J. Barone *(VP-Medical Affairs & GME)*
Albert E. Smith *(Chm)*
Anneliese McMenamin *(VP-HR)*
Bruce Paparone *(Vice Chm)*
Lisa Morina *(VP-Govt & External Rels)*
Kelly Walenda *(VP & Asst Gen Counsel)*
Glenn A. Zirbser *(CFO & Sr VP)*
H. Timothy Dombrowski *(Chief Medical Officer)*
Robert DiStanislao *(Treas)*
Ronald L. Caputo *(Sec)*
Robert Davis *(VP-Product Lines)*
Laurie Grey *(VP-Revenue Cycle)*
Carman Ciervo *(Exec VP)*
Daniel Tarditi *(Co-Treas)*
David V. Condoluci *(Chief Patient Safety & Quality Officer & Sr VP)*
Edward Sullivan *(Chief Legal Officer & Sr VP)*
Helene Burns *(VP-Clinical Svcs)*
James Huynh *(VP-Facilities Mgmt)*
Jill C. Ostrem *(Sr VP-Ops)*
Kim Alliano *(VP-Fin)*
Maryann Lauletta *(VP-Medical Ops)*
Tammy Curren *(CIO & VP-Information Sys & Tech)*

KENNEDY INK CO, INC.
5230 Wooster Rd., Cincinnati, OH 45226
Tel.: (513) 871-2515
Year Founded: 1956
Rev.: $1,700,000
Emp.: 15
Fiscal Year-end: 12/31/10
Printing Ink Mfr
N.A.I.C.S.: 325910

KENNEDY LEWIS INVESTMENT MANAGEMENT LLC
111 W 33rd St, Ste 1910, New York, NY 10120
Tel.: (212) 782-3480
Web Site: http://www.klimllc.com
Year Founded: 2017
Investment Firm
N.A.I.C.S.: 523999
Darren L. Richman *(Co-Founder)*
Dik Blewitt *(Partner, Head-Tactical Opportunities & Co-Head-ESG)*
David Valiaveedan *(Mng Dir)*
Brieanne Nikrandt *(Mng Dir)*

Doug Logigian *(Pres & Co-Mng Partner)*
David K. Chene *(Co-Founder, Co-Mng Partner & Co-Portfolio Mgr)*

KENNEDY MANUFACTURING COMPANY
1260 Industrial Dr, Van Wert, OH 45891
Tel.: (419) 238-2442
Web Site:
http://www.kennedymfg.com
Year Founded: 1911
Sales Range: $50-74.9 Million
Emp.: 70
Tool Box Chest Roller Cabinet & Work Bench Mfr
N.A.I.C.S.: 332119
Craig Martin *(VP-Sls & Mktg)*

Subsidiaries:

Blue Bell Bio-Medical (1)
1260 Industrial Dr, Van Wert, OH 45891-1350 (100%)
Tel.: (419) 238-4442
Web Site: http://www.bluebellcarts.com
Sales Range: $25-49.9 Million
Emp.: 5
Medical Storage Products Mfr
N.A.I.C.S.: 423450

KENNEDY RICE DRYERS LLC
610 N Hwy 165, Mer Rouge, LA 71261
Tel.: (318) 647-5744
Sales Range: $10-24.9 Million
Emp.: 10
Rice, Unpolished
N.A.I.C.S.: 424510
William E. Kennedy *(Pres & Dir-Personnel)*
Wes Bolton *(Controller)*

KENNEDY TANK & MANUFACTURING COMPANY, INC.
833 E Sumner Ave, Indianapolis, IN 46227-1345
Tel.: (317) 787-1311
Web Site:
http://www.kennedytank.com
Year Founded: 1898
Sales Range: $10-24.9 Million
Emp.: 150
Carbon, Stainless Steel & other Alloy Plates & Sheets Mfr; Storage Tanks Mfr; Pressure Vessels & Heat Exchangers Mfr; Boilers & Powerhouse Equipment Mfr & Distr
N.A.I.C.S.: 332313
Patrick W. Kennedy *(Pres)*
Scot Evans *(VP-Reg Field Svc)*
Gerald A. Hemmelgarn *(VP-Fin)*
John Cochran *(VP-Engrg)*

Subsidiaries:

Southern Petroleum Equipment Company, Inc. (1)
1521 Sweeney St PO Box 488 42302, Owensboro, KY 42303-1020
Tel.: (270) 683-0753
Rev.: $1,800,000
Emp.: 4
Industrial Machinery & Equipment Whslr
N.A.I.C.S.: 423830

Southern Tank & Manufacturing Inc (1)
1501 Haynes Ave, Owensboro, KY 42303-1019
Tel.: (270) 684-2321.
Web Site: http://www.southerntank.net
Sales Range: $1-9.9 Million
Emp.: 24
AG & VG Storage Tanks Mfr
N.A.I.C.S.: 332313
Patrick W. Kennedy *(Pres)*
Phil Higdon *(VP & Gen Mgr)*
Charlie Mackey *(Plant Mgr)*

Steel Tank & Fabricating Corporation (1)
365 S James St, Columbia City, IN 46725
Tel.: (260) 248-8971
Emp.: 25
Storage Tanks, Pressure Tanks & Custom Fabricated Carbon & Alloy Plates & Steel Sheets Mfr
N.A.I.C.S.: 332313
Mike Reed *(Gen Mgr)*

KENNEDY TRANSPORTATION
8 Greenwood Ave, Romeoville, IL 60446
Tel.: (815) 372-9898
Web Site:
http://www.kennedytransportation.com
Sales Range: $25-49.9 Million
Emp.: 20
Trucking, Warehousing & Transportation Brokerage Services
N.A.I.C.S.: 484121
Norm Breyer *(CFO)*
Ben Weyenberg *(Pres)*
Frank Galman *(Pres)*

Subsidiaries:

Kennedy Transportation (1)
8 Greenwood Ave, Romeoville, IL 60446
Tel.: (815) 372-9898
Web Site:
http://www.kennedytransportation.com
Sales Range: Less than $1 Million
Trucking Except Local
N.A.I.C.S.: 484121

KENNEDY WIRE ROPE & SLING CO.
302 Flato Rd, Corpus Christi, TX 78405
Tel.: (361) 289-1444
Web Site: http://www.kwrs.com
Sales Range: $10-24.9 Million
Emp.: 100
Wire & Rope Mfr
N.A.I.C.S.: 423510
Jacqueline Kennedy *(CEO)*
Arnold Lopez *(Mgr-Synthetic Web)*

KENNEDY-DONOVAN CENTER, INC.
1 Commercial St, Foxboro, MA 02035
Tel.: (508) 772-1211
Web Site: http://www.kdc.org
Year Founded: 1969
Sales Range: $25-49.9 Million
Emp.: 600
Developmental Disability Assistance Services
N.A.I.C.S.: 623210
Patricia Forts *(Vice Chm)*
Aubrey Macfarlane *(Pres & CEO)*
Stephen Sanford *(Treas)*
Larry Sauer *(Chief Program Officer)*
Robert Panessiti *(Chm)*
Frank Maher *(VP-Dev & PR)*
Kate Fontana *(VP-Ops & Organizational Dev)*

KENNEDY-WILSON PROPERTIES, LTD.
9701 Wilshire Blvd Ste 700, Beverly Hills, CA 90212
Tel.: (310) 887-6495
Year Founded: 1998
Real Estate Services
N.A.I.C.S.: 531120

KENNEDY/JENKS CONSULTANTS INC.
303 Second St Ste 300 S, San Francisco, CA 94107-1305
Tel.: (415) 243-2150
Web Site:
http://www.kennedyjenks.com
Year Founded: 1919

Sales Range: $50-74.9 Million
Emp.: 500
Engineering Consultancy Services
N.A.I.C.S.: 541330
Keith London *(Pres & CEO)*
Larry Catalano *(Mgr-Client Svc-Colorado)*
Gary Carlton *(Chm)*

KENNEL VACCINE VET SUPPLY CO.
3190 N Rd, David City, NE 68632
Tel.: (402) 367-6047
Web Site: http://www.kvvet.com
Sales Range: $10-24.9 Million
Emp.: 90
Mail-Order Houses
N.A.I.C.S.: 541940
Karen Fendrich *(Treas)*
Tracy Loyd *(Gen Mgr & Office Mgr)*

KENNER & COMPANY, INC.
437 Madison Ave Fl 36, New York, NY 10022-7019
Tel.: (212) 319-2300
Year Founded: 1986
Privater Equity Firm
N.A.I.C.S.: 523999
Jeffrey Kenner *(Pres)*
Oneida Fernandez *(Office Mgr)*

Subsidiaries:

Atrium Corporation (1)
3890 W NW Hwy Ste 500, Dallas, TX 75220
Tel.: (214) 630-5757
Web Site: http://www.atrium.com
Sales Range: $50-74.9 Million
Emp.: 100
Holding Company; Window & Door Mfr
N.A.I.C.S.: 551112
Gregory T. Faherty *(Pres)*
Chris Reilly *(VP-Mktg-Retail & Distr)*
Steven Monks *(Sr VP-Ops)*

Subsidiary (Domestic):

Atrium Companies, Inc. (2)
3890 W NW Hwy Ste 500, Dallas, TX 75220
Tel.: (214) 630-5757
Web Site: http://www.atrium.com
Doors & Windows Mfr & Distr
N.A.I.C.S.: 332321

Subsidiary (Domestic):

Aluminum Screen Manufacturing Co. (3)
610 N Wildwood Dr, Irving, TX 75061
Tel.: (972) 579-4951
Sales Range: $10-24.9 Million
Solar Window Screen Mfr
N.A.I.C.S.: 332321

Atrium Door & Window Co. (3)
3890 NW Hwy Ste 500, Dallas, TX 75220
Tel.: (214) 630-5757
Web Site: http://www.atrium.com
Sales Range: $100-124.9 Million
Mfr of Aluminum Windows & Doors
N.A.I.C.S.: 332321

Atrium Windows & Doors, Inc. (3)
9001 Ambassador Row, Dallas, TX 75247-4509
Tel.: (904) 355-1476
Web Site: http://www.atriumcomp.com
Design & Installation of Household Windows & Doors
N.A.I.C.S.: 321911
Donna Manchester *(VP-HR)*

Superior Engineered Products Corp. (3)
1650 S Archibald Ave, Ontario, CA 91761-7604
Tel.: (909) 930-1800
Sales Range: $100-124.9 Million
Door & Window Mfr
N.A.I.C.S.: 332321

Thermal Industries, Inc. (3)
5450 2nd Ave, Pittsburgh, PA 15207
Tel.: (412) 244-6400
Web Site: http://www.thermalindustries.com

KENNER & COMPANY, INC.   U.S. PRIVATE

Kenner & Company, Inc.—(Continued)

Sales Range: $75-99.9 Million
Mfr of Vinyl Windows, Patio Doors & Enclosures, Decks, Docks & Railing Systems
N.A.I.C.S.: 332321
Scott Jeffreys (VP-Sls)

Pace Industries, Inc. (1)
481 S Shiloh Dr, Fayetteville, AR 72704
Tel.: (479) 443-1455
Web Site: http://www.paceind.com
Sales Range: $700-749.9 Million
Aluminum Die-Castings
N.A.I.C.S.: 331523
Yan Zhu (Chief Engr-Design)
Kevin Roberts (Mgr-Ops)
Arnie Fulton (VP-Engrg)
John Marshall Haines (VP-Pur)
Joseph Wempe (Controller & VP-Acctg Ops)

Division (Domestic):

Pace Industries - B & C Division (2)
513 Hwy 62/65 Bypass N, Harrison, AR 72601
Tel.: (870) 741-8255
Web Site: http://www.paceind.com
Sales Range: $10-24.9 Million
Zinc Die Castings
N.A.I.C.S.: 331529

Pace Industries - St. Paul Division (2)
3737 Lexington Ave N, Arden Hills, MN 55126
Tel.: (651) 483-6641
Web Site: http://www.paceind.com
Sales Range: $50-74.9 Million
Aluminum Die-Castings Mfr
N.A.I.C.S.: 331523
Jeff Rivers (Plant Mgr)

Subsidiary (Non-US):

Pace Industries de Mexico, S.A. de C.V. (2)
Blvd Vito Alessio Robles No 2451, Saltillo, Coahuila, Mexico
Tel.: (52) 8444387800
Web Site: http://www.paceind.com
Sales Range: Less than $1 Million
Industrial Aluminum Die Castings
N.A.I.C.S.: 332911
Roberto Eftama (Pres)

Subsidiary (Domestic):

Pace Industries de Chihuahua, S.A. de C.V. (3)
Alejandro Dumas 11326, Complejo Industrial Chihuahua, 31109, Mexico
Tel.: (52) 6144421010
Web Site: http://www.paceind.com
Sales Range: $250-299.9 Million
Emp.: 600
Aluminum Die Cast
N.A.I.C.S.: 331523
Max Vargas (Gen Mgr)

KENNERLEY-SPRATLING INC.
2116 Farallon Dr, San Leandro, CA 94577
Tel.: (510) 351-8230
Web Site: http://www.ksplastic.com
Sales Range: $25-49.9 Million
Emp.: 180
Injection Molding Of Plastics
N.A.I.C.S.: 326199
Timothy Arambula (Plant Mgr)
Noel Ordiz (Mgr-QA)
Kevin Ahern (Gen Mgr)

Subsidiaries:

KS Automotive Inc (1)
14801 Catalina St, San Leandro, CA 94577
Tel.: (510) 667-9716
Web Site: http://www.ksautomotive.com
Automotive Part Whslr
N.A.I.C.S.: 423120
Ed Lopez (Pres)
Kevin Ahern (VP-Sls)
Tracey Bacho (Mgr-Customer Svc)

MOS Plastics Inc. (1)
2308 Zanker Rd, San Jose, CA 95131

Tel.: (408) 944-9407
Web Site: http://www.mosinc.com
Rev.: $11,200,000
Emp.: 134
Biometric, Electronic & Medical Device Supply Chain Management
N.A.I.C.S.: 326199
Jason McLoud (Dir-Sls)
Pete Yager (Gen Mgr)
Robert Zimmerman (Mgr-Engrg)
Ernest Harper (Mgr-Production Control)
Sunil Behl (Mgr-Quality Dept)

KENNESAW MOTOR SALES, INC.
2111 Barrett Lakes Blvd NW, Kennesaw, GA 30144
Tel.: (770) 422-8555
Web Site: http://www.cobbcountyscion.com
Sales Range: $10-24.9 Million
Emp.: 130
New Car Dealers
N.A.I.C.S.: 441110
Barbara W. Evans (CFO & Sec)
Michael A. Perrin (CEO)

KENNETH FOX SUPPLY CO.
2200 Fox Dr, McAllen, TX 78504
Tel.: (956) 682-6176
Web Site: http://www.foxbag.com
Year Founded: 1962
Bags & Containers, Except Sleeping Bags: Textile
N.A.I.C.S.: 314910

KENNEWICK INDUSTRIAL & ELECTRICAL SUPPLY INC.
113 E Columbia Dr, Kennewick, WA 99336
Tel.: (509) 582-5156
Web Site: http://www.kiesupply.com
Rev.: $22,600,000
Emp.: 70
Electrical Apparatus & Equipment Wiring Supplies & Related Equipment Merchant Whslr
N.A.I.C.S.: 423610
Augustan Kittson (Pres)
George Peterson (VP)
Charles Claybrook (Dir-IT)
Richard Cox (Mgr-Sls)

KENNEY MACHINERY CORPORATION
8420 Zionsville Rd, Indianapolis, IN 46268
Tel.: (317) 872-4793
Web Site: http://www.kmuturf.com
Sales Range: $25-49.9 Million
Emp.: 60
Lawn & Garden Machinery & Equipment
N.A.I.C.S.: 423820
James E. Kenney (CEO)
Mike Kenney (Pres)

KENNEY MANUFACTURING COMPANY
1000 Jefferson Blvd, Warwick, RI 02886
Tel.: (401) 739-2200
Web Site: http://www.kenney.com
Year Founded: 1914
Sales Range: $150-199.9 Million
Emp.: 350
Household Consumer Products Mfr & Distr
N.A.I.C.S.: 337920
Bruce Bialy (CFO)
Sally Voas (VP-Mktg)
Karlton Lough (Controller)
Jerson Taveras (Coord-Import & Export)
Tasha Shepard (Coord-Ops)

KENNICOTT BROS CO. INC.
452 N Ashland Ave, Chicago, IL 60622
Tel.: (312) 492-8200
Web Site: http://www.kennicott.com
Rev.: $36,933,119
Emp.: 104
Flowers, Fresh
N.A.I.C.S.: 424930
Gary Doran (VP)

KENNIE'S MARKETS INC.
217 W Middle St, Gettysburg, PA 17325
Tel.: (717) 334-2179
Web Site: http://www.kenniesmarket.com
Year Founded: 1959
Sales Range: $10-24.9 Million
Emp.: 350
Independent Food Market
N.A.I.C.S.: 445110
Paul K. Hoover Jr. (Pres)

KENNINGTON LTD., INC.
28128 Pacific Coast Hwy Spc 254, Malibu, CA 90265-8254
Tel.: (818) 994-2476
Year Founded: 1962
Sales Range: $10-24.9 Million
Emp.: 12
Men's, Boys' & Youths' Shirts
N.A.I.C.S.: 315250
Lance Tendler (Pres)
Stanley Tendler (Chm & CEO)
Jerome Janger (Sec & Legal Counsel)

Subsidiaries:

ComCorp Factors, Inc. (1)
28128 Pacific Coast Hwy Spc 254, Malibu, CA 90265-8254 (100%)
Tel.: (818) 994-2476
Men's & Boys' Shirts
N.A.I.C.S.: 513120

Stanleigh International, Inc. (1)
14761 Califa St, Van Nuys, CA 91411-3107 (100%)
Tel.: (818) 994-2476
Sales Range: $10-24.9 Million
Mens & Boys Sportshirts & Sweaters Mfr; Buying Office for Kennington
N.A.I.C.S.: 315210

KENNY ELECTRIC SERVICE INC.
595 Quivas St, Denver, CO 80204
Tel.: (303) 605-2100
Web Site: http://www.kenny-electric.com
Year Founded: 1974
General Electrical Contractor
N.A.I.C.S.: 238210
Becky Wagner (Office Mgr)
Dave Pavelka (Pres)

KENNY INDUSTRIES INC.
2215 Sanders Rd Ste 400, Northbrook, IL 60062
Tel.: (847) 541-8200
Web Site: http://www.kennyconstruction.com
Year Founded: 1985
Sales Range: $400-449.9 Million
Emp.: 410
Highway, Tunnel & Street Construction Services
N.A.I.C.S.: 237310
Gene Hugbner (CFO)

Subsidiaries:

Kenny Construction Company Inc. (1)
2215 Sanders Rd Ste 400, Northbrook, IL 60062-2668
Tel.: (847) 541-8200
Web Site: http://www.kennyconstruction.com
Sales Range: $10-24.9 Million
Emp.: 40

Provider of Bridge, Tunnel & Highway Construction Services
N.A.I.C.S.: 237310
Patrick Kenny (Pres)
Bryan Fulther (VP-Tunnels)

Seven K Construction Company Inc. (1)
144 Green Bay Rd, Winnetka, IL 60093-4007
Tel.: (847) 446-7224
Sales Range: $10-24.9 Million
Emp.: 2
Provider of Bridge, Tunnel & Highway Construction Services
N.A.I.C.S.: 237310

KENNY KENT CHEVROLET CO. INC.
4600 Division St, Evansville, IN 47715
Tel.: (812) 477-4600
Web Site: http://www.kennykentchev.com
Sales Range: $25-49.9 Million
Emp.: 90
Sales of New & Used Automobiles
N.A.I.C.S.: 441110
Cecil Van Puyl (Pres)

KENNY PIPE & SUPPLY, INC.
715 Cowan St, Nashville, TN 37207-5621
Tel.: (615) 255-4810
Web Site: http://www.kennypipe.com
Year Founded: 1992
Sales Range: $25-49.9 Million
Emp.: 190
Plumbing Fixtures Equipment & Supplies
N.A.I.C.S.: 423720
Tommy Spinks (Branch Mgr)
Paul Langston (Branch Mgr)
Steve Burkhalter (Dir-Indus Sls)
Chris Finley (Mgr-Bridgeport)

Subsidiaries:

Eagle Equipment Company Inc. (1)
2 Villa Dr, Rome, GA 30165
Tel.: (706) 232-0821
Web Site: http://www.eaglekps.com
Pipe, Fitting & Valve Distr
N.A.I.C.S.: 423720
David Gordon (VP)
Tim Morgan (Mgr-Warehouse)
Sharyn Gillaspie (Mgr-Admin)

Kenny & Company (1)
303 11th Ave S, Nashville, TN 37203
Tel.: (615) 782-8000
Web Site: http://www.kennycompany.com
Kitchen & Bathroom Accessory Distr
N.A.I.C.S.: 423220

KENNY ROSS BUICK-GMC, INC.
11250 Rte 30, North Huntingdon, PA 15642
Tel.: (412) 436-1272
Web Site: http://www.kennyrosschevybuickgmc.com
Sales Range: $25-49.9 Million
Emp.: 65
Car Dealership Owner & Operator
N.A.I.C.S.: 441110
Jim Ross (Owner)

KENNY THOMAS ENTERPRISES INC.
685 N Rawhide Rd, Olathe, KS 66061
Tel.: (913) 780-9919
Web Site: http://www.olathetoyota.com
Sales Range: $50-74.9 Million
Emp.: 150
New & Used Automobiles
N.A.I.C.S.: 441110
Kenny Thomas (Pres)

KENNY'S TILE & FLOORING, INC.
3303 Main St, Grandview, MO 64030
Tel.: (816) 765-0400
Web Site: http://www.kennystile.com
Year Founded: 1954
Sales Range: $10-24.9 Million
Emp.: 160
Flooring Contracting Services
N.A.I.C.S.: 238330
Tony Siebert (Pres)
Randy Kesler (CFO)
Brad Barlow (Gen Mgr)
Mark Perschau (Project Mgr)

KENO AUCTIONS LLC
127 E 69th St, New York, NY 10021
Tel.: (212) 734-2381
Web Site:
  http://www.kenoauctions.com
Sales Range: $1-9.9 Million
Emp.: 4
Antique Dealer
N.A.I.C.S.: 459510
Leigh Keno (Pres)

KENOSHA BEEF INTERNATIONAL LTD. INC.
3111 152nd Ave, Kenosha, WI 53144-7630
Tel.: (262) 859-2272 WI
Web Site: http://www.bwfoods.com
Year Founded: 1960
Sales Range: $25-49.9 Million
Emp.: 755
Provider of Trucking Services & Meat Products
N.A.I.C.S.: 484121
Dennis Vignieri (Pres & CEO)
Jerry King (CFO)
Ottavio Ruffolo (Exec VP-Ops & Procurement)
Mike Marquardt (VP-Birchwood Transport)
Phyllis Murray (VP-HR & Safety)

Subsidiaries:

Birchwood Foods (1)
3111 152nd Ave, Kenosha, WI 53144-7630
Tel.: (262) 859-2272
Web Site: http://www.bwfoods.com
Sales Range: $25-49.9 Million
Emp.: 300
Meat Plant
N.A.I.C.S.: 484121
John Ruffel (VP-Ops)
Rick Kieffer (Mgr-Maintenance)
Roxanne Patrick (Mgr-Customer Svc)
Wayne Wehking (VP-Sls & Mktg)

Birchwood Foods (1)
1821 Dividend Dr, Columbus, OH 43228-3848 (100%)
Tel.: (614) 771-1330
Web Site: http://www.birchwoodfoods.com
Sales Range: $25-49.9 Million
Emp.: 130
Mfr of Food Items
N.A.I.C.S.: 424470
Kan Fude (Dir-Ops)
Martin G. Roberts (Mgr-Acctg)

Birchwood Transport Inc. (1)
3111 152nd Ave, Kenosha, WI 53144-7630 (100%)
Tel.: (262) 859-3018
Web Site: http://www.bwfoods.com
Sales Range: $10-24.9 Million
Emp.: 70
Trucking Company
N.A.I.C.S.: 484230
Michael Marquardt (VP)
Dennis Vignieri (Pres & CEO)

KENOSIA CONSTRUCTION INC.
PO Box 2269, Danbury, CT 06813
Tel.: (203) 748-3113
Web Site:
  http://www.kenosiaconstruction.com
Year Founded: 1992
Sales Range: $1-9.9 Million
Emp.: 10
Commercial & Institutional Building Construction
N.A.I.C.S.: 236220
Ellis A. Tarlton III (Principal)
Ellis A. Tarlton Jr. (Principal)
Christian DaCunha (Principal)
Christopher Paul (Principal)
Brian Cleveland (Project Mgr)

KENRY HOME IMPROVEMENT NETWORK, INC.
7427 N Lamar Blvd ste 100, Austin, TX 78752
Web Site: http://www.mainfaucet.com
Year Founded: 1999
Sales Range: $1-9.9 Million
Emp.: 12
Sales of Faucets & Lighting Fixtures
N.A.I.C.S.: 335132
Mathew Sotelo (Mgr-Sls)

Subsidiaries:

MainFaucet.com (1)
7427 N Lamar Blvd Ste 100, Austin, TX 78752 (100%)
Tel.: (877) 203-3858
Web Site: http://www.mainfaucet.com
Emp.: 10
Faucet Distr & Sales
N.A.I.C.S.: 332913
Mathew Sotelo (Mgr-Sls)

KENSINGTON CAPITAL PARTNERS, LLC
3 Greenacre Ct, Great Neck, NY 11021
Tel.: (646) 382-5153
Web Site: http://www.kensington-cap.com
Year Founded: 1999
Privater Equity Firm
N.A.I.C.S.: 523999
Justin E. Mirro (Pres)

KENSINGTON PUBLISHING CORP.
119 W Forty St 21st Fl, New York, NY 10018
Tel.: (212) 407-1500 NY
Web Site:
  http://www.kensingtonbooks.com
Year Founded: 1972
Sales Range: $10-24.9 Million
Emp.: 75
Book Publishers
N.A.I.C.S.: 513130
Steven Zacharius (Pres & CEO)
Mike Rosamilia (CFO & VP)
Michaela Hamilton (Editor-in-Chief Citadel & Editor-Kensington)
Selena James (Exec Editor)
Wendy McCurdy (Dir-Editorial)

KENT BEVERAGE COMPANY
4490 60th St SE Grand Rapids, Wyoming, MI 49512
Tel.: (616) 241-5022 MI
Web Site:
  http://www.kentbeverage.com
Year Founded: 1962
Sales Range: $10-24.9 Million
Emp.: 450
Beer & Other Fermented Malt Liquors Distr
N.A.I.C.S.: 424810
Lisa Wilson (Mgr-HR)

KENT BUSINESS SYSTEMS CORP.
1131 E 1st St N, Wichita, KS 67214
Tel.: (316) 262-4487
Web Site: http://www.kentav.com
Year Founded: 1975
Video & Audio Equipment Rental & Sales
N.A.I.C.S.: 423990
Maddie Nevins (General Mgr)

KENT CHEVROLET, CADILLAC, INC.
1413 Hwy 62 E, Mountain Home, AR 72653
Tel.: (870) 425-6262
Web Site:
  http://www.kentchevrolet.com
Sales Range: $10-24.9 Million
Emp.: 50
Car Whslr
N.A.I.C.S.: 441110
Barbara Graham (Owner)

KENT COMPANIES INC.
130 60th St SW Ste 1, Grand Rapids, MI 49548
Tel.: (616) 534-4909
Web Site:
  http://www.kentcompanies.com
Year Founded: 1957
Commercial, Industrial & Residential Construction Services
N.A.I.C.S.: 238110
Randy Brink (CFO)
Jeff Vanderlaan (CEO)
Angel Alvarez (Exec VP-Multi Family Div)

KENT CORPORATION
2905 Hwy 61 N, Muscatine, IA 52761
Tel.: (563) 264-4211 IA
Web Site: http://www.kentww.com
Year Founded: 1927
Emp.: 2,000
Holding Company
N.A.I.C.S.: 551112
Gage A. Kent (Chm & CEO)
Carol A. Reynolds (VP-HR & Comm)
John Thorpe (Pres & COO)

Subsidiaries:

Grain Processing Corporation (1)
1600 Oregon St, Muscatine, IA 52761-1494 (100%)
Tel.: (563) 264-4265
Web Site: http://www.grainprocessing.com
Emp.: 5,000
Wet Corn Milling
N.A.I.C.S.: 311221
Gage A. Kent (CEO)
Diane Rieke (Mgr-Mktg Comm)
Mark Ricketts (VP-Alcohol Products)
Kevin Garrison (Dir-Safety Div)
Patrick Homoelle (Pres)
Kevin Schilling (Sr VP-R&D)
Ron Zitzow (Sr VP-Ops)
Stu Mabee (VP-Sls-Intl)
Pete Miller (VP-Sls)
Rani Thomas (VP-Quality & Regulatory Affairs)
Jimmy Kent Sr. (Sr VP)
Kevin Halstead (VP-Engrg)

Subsidiary (Domestic):

Natural Products, Inc. (2)
2211 Sixth Ave, Grinnell, IA 50112
Tel.: (641) 236-0852
Web Site: http://www.npisoy.com
Full Fat Soy Ingredients Mfr
N.A.I.C.S.: 311119
Michael Soderstrom (Asst Mgr)
Ray Lang (Gen Mgr)
Janna Stoker (Mgr-Office & Export Shipping)

Kent Nutrition Group, Inc. (1)
2905 Hwy 61 N, Muscatine, IA 52761 (100%)
Tel.: (563) 264-4211
Web Site: http://www.kentnutritiongroup.com
Sales Range: $100-124.9 Million
Emp.: 1,000
Livestock & Poultry Feeds & Animal-Care & Pet-Food Products Mfr
N.A.I.C.S.: 311119

Gage A. Kent (Chm)
Michael Edmonds (VP-Swine & Poultry Nutrition)
Mark Krieger (VP-Mktg)
Paul Zobel (Dir-Brand & Mktg Svcs)
Tiffany Briggs (Mgr-Sls-Southern New Hampshire & Massachusetts)
Melanie Locke (Mgr-Windham)

Kent Pet Group, Inc. (1)
2905 Hwy 61, Muscatine, IA 52761
Tel.: (563) 264-4211
Web Site: http://www.kentpetgroup.com
Marketer of Dog & Cat Food & Product Mfr
N.A.I.C.S.: 311111
Jean Broders (Brand Mgr)

Kent Precision Foods Group, Inc. (1)
11457 Olde Cabin Rd, Saint Louis, MO 63141-7139
Tel.: (314) 567-7400
Web Site: http://www.precisionfoods.com
Sales Range: $25-49.9 Million
Emp.: 30
Food Products Mfr
N.A.I.C.S.: 311423
Gage A. Kent (Co-Chm)
Jerry L. Fritz (Co-Chm)
Connie Huck (Pres)
Debbie Rudy (Mgr-Credit)
Jennifer Kent (Customer Svc)
Joseph Buchanan (VP-Ops)
Mike Saniat (VP-Technical Svcs)
Steve Barnes (Sr Dir-Ops)

PouchTec Industries, LLC (1)
347 Glen St, Foley, MN 56329
Tel.: (800) 800-2038
Web Site: http://www.pouchtec.com
Soft Drink Soft Pouches Mfr
N.A.I.C.S.: 312111
Robert Jones (Sr VP-Liquid Pkg Innovation)
Karmen O'Bando (Dir-Sls & Mktg)

KENT DISTRIBUTORS INC.
2408 N Bigspring St, Midland, TX 79705
Tel.: (432) 520-4000
Web Site: http://www.kentoil.com
Year Founded: 1984
Sales Range: $25-49.9 Million
Emp.: 400
Petroleum Products Mfr & Distr
N.A.I.C.S.: 445131
William B. Kent (Pres)
Benet Robb (VP-Fin & Admin)
Bobby Barrett (Dir-Maintenance)
Julie Bixler (VP-Adv)
Marylou Poulido (VP-HR)

Subsidiaries:

Parsons Oil Company Inc (1)
105 Algeria St, Fayetteville, TN 37334
Tel.: (931) 433-4584
Rev.: $9,101,000
Emp.: 10
Petroleum Bulk Stations & Terminals
N.A.I.C.S.: 424710
William J. Parsons (Pres)

KENT GYPSUM SUPPLY INC.
10720 26th Ave S, Lakewood, WA 98499-8719
Tel.: (253) 722-1234
Web Site:
  http://www.kentgypsum.com
Sales Range: $10-24.9 Million
Emp.: 15
Wallboard Mfr
N.A.I.C.S.: 423310
Matthew Klein (Owner & CEO)
Greg Erwin (VP)
Glenn Oglesbee (Mgr-Lakewood)
Gregg Mathisen (Mgr-Bothell)
Jon Horner (Owner)
Bonnie Vanderwaal (VP)
Harry Stanley (VP)

KENT INTERNATIONAL INC.
60 E Halsey Rd, Parsippany, NJ 07054
Tel.: (973) 402-1414

KENT INTERNATIONAL INC.

Kent International Inc.—(Continued)
Web Site:
http://www.kentbicycles.com
Rev.: $10,700,000
Emp.: 35
Bicycles
N.A.I.C.S.: 423910
Arnold B. Kamler *(Chm)*
John Levi *(VP)*
Diane Caropreso *(Accountant)*

KENT M. LIM & COMPANY, INC.
1260 Egbert Ave, San Francisco, CA 94127
Tel.: (415) 822-1232
Web Site: http://www.kentlimco.com
Sales Range: $10-24.9 Million
Emp.: 110
Commercial HVAC Contractor
N.A.I.C.S.: 238220
Kent M. Lim *(Pres)*

KENT RYLEE CHEVROLET-OLDSMOBILE, INC.
2100 S 8th St, Rogers, AR 72758
Tel.: (479) 636-3333
Web Site: http://www.kentrylee.com
Rev.: $24,000,000
Emp.: 55
New & Used Car Dealers
N.A.I.C.S.: 441110
Kent Rylee *(Pres)*
Tracy Everhart *(Gen Mgr-Sls)*

KENT SPORTING GOODS COMPANY
433 Park Ave, New London, OH 44851
Tel.: (419) 929-7021
Web Site:
http://www.kentwatersports.com
Rev.: $51,300,000
Emp.: 35
Distribute Water Sports Equipment
N.A.I.C.S.: 339920
Russell Gaskill *(Controller)*

KENT-MICHAEL ENTERPRISES INC.
15000 SE Eastgate Way, Bellevue, WA 98007
Tel.: (425) 641-2002
Web Site: http://www.chaplins.com
Rev.: $81,312,088
Emp.: 120
Automobiles, New & Used
N.A.I.C.S.: 441110
Kent P. Chaplin *(Pres)*
Gale Caroon *(Controller)*

KENTCO INC.
300 E Main St, Tremonton, UT 84337
Tel.: (435) 257-7014   UT
Year Founded: 1982
Sales Range: $25-49.9 Million
Emp.: 200
Operator of Independent Supermarket
N.A.I.C.S.: 445110
Kent Beckstrom *(Pres)*

KENTMERE REHABILITATION AND HEALTHCARE CENTER
1900 Lovering Ave, Wilmington, DE 19806-2123
Tel.: (302) 652-3311   DE
Web Site:
http://www.kentmererehab.com
Year Founded: 1901
Sales Range: $10-24.9 Million
Emp.: 177
Medical Care Services
N.A.I.C.S.: 622110

Jerome Rhodes *(Pres)*
Eileen Mahler *(Exec Dir)*
Robert Beste *(Sec)*
Kris Kowal *(Treas)*

KENTUCKIANA COMFORT CENTER, INC.
2716 Grassland Dr, Louisville, KY 40299
Tel.: (502) 491-9880
Web Site: http://www.kycomfort.com
Year Founded: 1987
Sales Range: $10-24.9 Million
Emp.: 75
Plumbing, Heating & Air-Conditioning Contracting Services
N.A.I.C.S.: 238220
Rebecca Slahta *(Coord-Svc)*
David Denny *(Mgr-Comml Production)*

KENTUCKY APPAREL LLP
13105 Spivey Dr, Laredo, TX 78045-1811
Tel.: (270) 487-6723
Sales Range: $25-49.9 Million
Emp.: 40
Jeans: Girls', Children's & Infants'
N.A.I.C.S.: 315210

KENTUCKY ASSOCIATION OF ELECTRIC COOPERATIVES, INC.
4515 Bishop Ln, Louisville, KY 40218
Tel.: (502) 451-2430
Web Site: http://www.kaec.com
Rev.: $75,658,251
Emp.: 185
Power Transformers, Electric
N.A.I.C.S.: 335311
Barbara Prather *(Mgr-Fin Svcs)*
David Kimbell *(Chm)*
Chase Crigler *(Dir-Community & Govt Affairs)*
Clarence Greene *(Dir-Safety & Loss Prevention)*
Anita Travis Richter *(Editor-Kentucky Living-Comm & Member Rels Div)*
Chris Perry *(Pres & CEO)*
Richard Lacy *(CFO)*
Joe Arnold *(VP-Strategic Comm)*

KENTUCKY AUTOMOTIVE CENTER OF GRAYSON
333 C W Stevens Blvd, Grayson, KY 41143
Tel.: (606) 474-5414
Web Site: http://yourautocentres.com
Year Founded: 2007
Sales Range: $10-24.9 Million
Emp.: 38
New Car Whslr
N.A.I.C.S.: 441110
Greg Crawford *(Gen Mgr)*
Lydia Crawford *(Principal)*
E. B. Lowman II *(Principal)*

KENTUCKY EAGLE BEER INC.
2440 Innovation Dr, Lexington, KY 40511-8515
Tel.: (859) 252-3434   KY
Web Site: http://www.kyeagle.net
Year Founded: 1948
Sales Range: $25-49.9 Million
Emp.: 165
Beer & Ale
N.A.I.C.S.: 424810
David Stubblefield *(VP-Sls)*
Terry Hartfel *(Office Mgr)*
Ann McBrayer *(Pres & CEO)*

KENTUCKY EDUCATION ASSOCIATION
401 Capital Ave, Frankfort, KY 40601
Tel.: (502) 875-2889   KY

Web Site: http://www.kea.org
Year Founded: 1907
Sales Range: $10-24.9 Million
Emp.: 88
Educational Support Services
N.A.I.C.S.: 611710
Ann Eads *(Accountant)*
Stephanie Winkler *(Pres)*
Eddie Campbell *(VP)*

KENTUCKY EMPLOYERS MUTUAL INSURANCE
250 W Main St Ste 900, Lexington, KY 40507
Tel.: (859) 425-7800
Web Site: http://www.kemi.com
Sales Range: $25-49.9 Million
Emp.: 180
Workers Compensation Insurance
N.A.I.C.S.: 524126
Roger Fries *(CEO)*
Kim Friend *(Dir-Claims)*
Jon Stewart *(CFO)*
Randy Garland *(CIO & VP-IT)*
Jenny Whitis *(VP-HR)*
Paul Dillon *(Dir-Special Investigations)*
W. Kevin Ickes Jr. *(Dir-Legal Svcs)*

KENTUCKY FARM BUREAU MUTUAL INSURANCE COMPANY INC.
9201 Bunsen Pkwy, Louisville, KY 40220-3792
Tel.: (502) 495-5000
Web Site: http://www.kyfb.com
Year Founded: 1943
Sales Range: $450-499.9 Million
Emp.: 400
Fire, Marine & Casualty Insurance
N.A.I.C.S.: 524126
Mark Haney *(Pres)*
Eddie Melton *(VP)*
Jena Stone *(VP-Acctg & Fin)*
Kathy Grider *(Dir-Policy Svcs)*
Greg Padgett *(Dir-Acctg & Taxes)*
Drew Graham *(Exec VP)*

Subsidiaries:

Kentucky Farm Bureau Insurance Agency Inc.   (1)
9201 Bunsen Pkwy, Louisville, KY 40220-3792   (100%)
Tel.: (502) 495-5000
Web Site: http://www.kyfbins.com
Sales Range: $600-649.9 Million
Emp.: 679
Insurance Agents
N.A.I.C.S.: 524210
David Beck *(Exec VP-Federation)*
Christopher French *(Mgr-Agency Support & Mktg)*
Jena Stone *(Dir-Acctg & Taxes)*
Bryan Regenauer *(Dir-Support Svcs)*

The FB Insurance Company Inc.   (1)
9201 Bunsen Pkwy, Louisville, KY 40220
Tel.: (502) 495-5000
Web Site: http://www.kyfb.com
Sales Range: $1-9.9 Million
Emp.: 500
Fire, Marine & Casualty Insurance
N.A.I.C.S.: 524126
Bradley Smith *(CEO & Exec VP)*

KENTUCKY FARMERS BANK CORPORATION
2500 Broadway St, Catlettsburg, KY 41129
Tel.: (606) 929-5000
Web Site:
http://www.kentuckyfarmersbank.com
Year Founded: 1931
Commericial Banking
N.A.I.C.S.: 522110
April Russell Perry *(Chm & CEO)*
Donald J. Perry *(Sr VP & Mgr-Investments)*

Stuart Webb *(Sr VP & Mgr-Wealth & Investments)*
Shawn Heck *(Pres)*

KENTUCKY HIGHLANDS INVESTMENT CORP.
PO Box 1738, London, KY 40743
Tel.: (606) 864-5175   KY
Web Site: http://www.khic.org
Year Founded: 1968
Sales Range: $1-9.9 Million
Emp.: 20
Economic Development Company
N.A.I.C.S.: 523999
Brenda McDaniel *(CFO & Exec VP)*
Jerry Rickett *(Pres & CEO)*

KENTUCKY LAKE OIL CO. INC.
620 S 4th St, Murray, KY 42071-2680
Tel.: (270) 753-1323   KY
Year Founded: 1973
Sales Range: $25-49.9 Million
Emp.: 130
Gasoline Service Stations
N.A.I.C.S.: 457120
Chuck Baker *(CEO)*

KENTUCKY MANUFACTURING CO.
7201 Logistics Dr, Louisville, KY 40258-3187
Tel.: (502) 637-2551   KY
Web Site: http://www.kytrailers.com
Year Founded: 1936
Sales Range: $150-199.9 Million
Emp.: 500
Commercial Truck Trailers Mfr
N.A.I.C.S.: 336212
Larry Roy *(CFO & Exec VP)*
Dan Murphy *(Sr VP-Ops)*

KENTUCKY MEDICAL SERVICES FOUNDATION INC.
2333 Alumni Park Plz Ste 200, Lexington, KY 40517
Tel.: (859) 257-7910
Web Site: http://www.kmsf.org
Sales Range: $100-124.9 Million
Emp.: 150
Billing & Bookkeeping Service
N.A.I.C.S.: 541219
Peggy Halcomb *(Dir-Bus Ops)*
Annette Fischer *(Mgr-Revenue Cycle)*
Cindy White *(Mgr-Billing Svcs)*

KENTUCKY OIL & REFINING COMPANY
156 Kentucky Oil Village, Betsy Layne, KY 41605
Tel.: (606) 478-9501
Web Site: http://www.teamkore.com
Sales Range: $600-649.9 Million
Emp.: 200
Petroleum Bulk Stations & Terminals
N.A.I.C.S.: 424710
Chris Tomlinson *(Pres)*
Thomas Scott Stanley III *(VP)*

KENTUCKY ORGAN DONOR AFFILIATES
10160 Linn Sta Rd, Louisville, KY 40223
Tel.: (502) 581-9511   KY
Web Site:
http://www.kyorgandonor.org
Year Founded: 1987
Sales Range: $10-24.9 Million
Emp.: 79
Organ Donation Services
N.A.I.C.S.: 621991
Paul O'Flynn *(Exec Dir)*

KENTUCKY PETROLEUM SUPPLY, INC.

1225 Early Dr, Winchester, KY 40391
Tel.: (859) 744-7778 KY
Web Site:
http://www.triplecrownfeed.com
Year Founded: 1991
Sales Range: $10-24.9 Million
Emp.: 30
Petroleum Bulk Stations & Terminals
N.A.I.C.S.: 424710
George Stamper (Owner)

KENTUCKY TEXTILES INC.
1 W 20th St, Paris, KY 40361
Tel.: (859) 987-5228 KY
Year Founded: 1987
Sales Range: $10-24.9 Million
Emp.: 557
Sales Of Womens & Misses Apparel
N.A.I.C.S.: 315250
Clifford Shumate (Pres)
Ricky Hicks (CFO)

KENTUCKY-TENNESSEE CLAY COMPANY
304 N 7th St, Paducah, KY 42001
Tel.: (270) 841-0607 DE
Sales Range: $50-74.9 Million
Emp.: 198
Ball Clay, Kaolin & Feldspar Mining
N.A.I.C.S.: 212323
Brad Lynne (Mgr-Ceramic Tile)

KENTWOOD OFFICE FURNITURE INC.
3063 Breton Rd SE, Grand Rapids, MI 49512-5655
Tel.: (616) 957-2320
Web Site:
http://www.kentwoodoffice.com
Year Founded: 1976
Rev.: $22,600,000
Emp.: 50
Office & Public Building Furniture
N.A.I.C.S.: 423210
Art Hasse (Pres)
Jim Doenges (Pres-Chicago)
Jack Gezon (Sr Acct Exec-Furniture Team-Grand Rapids)
Bruce Brower (Mgr-Wholesale & Brokerage)
James Porter (VP-Ops)
Bob Koehne (Pres-Indianapolis)
Bob Von Kaenel (Pres)

KENTWOOL COMPANY
671 Runnymede Rd, Pickens, SC 29671
Tel.: (864) 878-6367 PA
Web Site: http://www.kentwool.com
Year Founded: 1843
Sales Range: $75-99.9 Million
Emp.: 120
Yarn Mfr
N.A.I.C.S.: 313110
Mark B. Kent (CEO)
Tom Perkinson (Dir-Sls)
Steve Haire (Plant Mgr)
Cecelia Colangelo (CFO)
Dan Murphy (Pres)

KENVIN INCORPORATED
4826 Gregg Rd, Pico Rivera, CA 90660
Tel.: (562) 699-8300
Rev.: $22,371,089
Emp.: 25
Men's & Boy's Clothing
N.A.I.C.S.: 424350
David Sim (Pres)

KENWAL STEEL CORP.
8223 W Warren Ave, Dearborn, MI 48126-1615
Tel.: (313) 739-1000 MI
Web Site: http://www.kenwal.com
Year Founded: 1947
Sales Range: $10-24.9 Million
Emp.: 150
Steel Service Center
N.A.I.C.S.: 423510
David Bazzy (Pres & COO)
Brian Eisenberg (VP)
Jon Davidson (VP-Automotive)
Kenneth Eisenberg (Chm)
Stephen Eisenberg (Pres-Burns Harbor)
Subsidiaries:
Kenwal Canada, Inc. (1)
1100 S Service Rd Ste 317, Stoney Creek, L8E 0C5, ON, Canada (100%)
Tel.: (905) 643-8930
Sales Range: $10-24.9 Million
Emp.: 7
Steel Traders
N.A.I.C.S.: 423510

Kenwal Steel Corp. (1)
307 Tech Dr, Chesterton, IN 46304-8843 (100%)
Tel.: (219) 880-1100
Web Site: http://www.kenwal.com
Sales Range: $10-24.9 Million
Emp.: 60
Steel Service Center
N.A.I.C.S.: 423510

KENWAY DISTRIBUTORS INC.
6320 Strawberry Ln, Louisville, KY 40214
Tel.: (502) 367-2201
Web Site: http://www.kenway.net
Rev.: $17,213,289
Emp.: 50
Janitors' Supplies
N.A.I.C.S.: 423850
James W. Crutcher (Chm)
Ken Crutcher (Pres)
Jack Ledogar (VP-Sls)
John Parrott (VP-Ops)
Steve Dukes (Mgr)
Jimmy Thomas (Mgr)
Lee Hopewell II (Mgr)

KENWOOD DEALER GROUP, INC.
4780 Socialville Foster Rd, Mason, OH 45040
Tel.: (513) 683-5484
Sales Range: $10-24.9 Million
Emp.: 50
Sales of Automobiles
N.A.I.C.S.: 441110
Robert C. Reichert (Pres)
Dewayne Vaught (CFO)
Subsidiaries:
Kings Toyota (1)
9500 Kings Auto Mall Rd, Cincinnati, OH 45249-8238
Tel.: (513) 683-5440
Web Site: http://www.kingstoyota.com
Automobile Sales, Service & Leasing
N.A.I.C.S.: 441110
Kevin McHone (Asst Gen Mgr)
Dave Caddell (Sr Mgr-Used Car Sls)

Northgate Ford Lincoln Mercury (1)
8940 Colerain Ave, Cincinnati, OH 45251 (100%)
Tel.: (513) 385-1414
Web Site:
http://www.northgatefordcincinnati.com
Automobile Dealership
N.A.I.C.S.: 441110
Steve Reichert (Gen Mgr)

KENWOOD LINCOLN MERCURY INC.
9620 Montgomery Rd, Cincinnati, OH 45242
Tel.: (513) 683-3800 OH
Year Founded: 1976
Sales Range: $10-24.9 Million
Emp.: 50
Sales of New & Used Automobiles
N.A.I.C.S.: 441110
Robert C. Reichert (Pres)
Mike Molzberger (Gen Mgr)

KENWOOD LIQUORS
10750 S Cicero Ave, Oak Lawn, IL 60453
Tel.: (708) 424-3580 IL
Web Site:
http://www.kenwoodliquors.com
Year Founded: 1948
Sales Range: $10-24.9 Million
Liquor & Alcoholic Beverages Dist
N.A.I.C.S.: 445320
Thomas J. Galateo (Pres & CEO)

KENWOOD PAINTED METALS, INC
20200 Governors Dr Ste 202, Olympia Fields, IL 60461
Tel.: (708) 957-4443
Web Site:
http://www.kenwoodpainted.com
Rev.: $26,000,000
Emp.: 21
Metals Service Centers & Offices
N.A.I.C.S.: 423510
Greg Underwood (Pres)

KENWORTH NORTHWEST, INC.
20220 International Blvd S, Seattle, WA 98198
Tel.: (206) 433-5911
Web Site:
http://www.kenworthnorthwest.com
Rev.: $65,600,000
Emp.: 180
Automobile & Other Motor Vehicle Merchant Whslr
N.A.I.C.S.: 423110
Marshall Cymbaluk (Pres)

KENWORTH OF CENTRAL FLORIDA
1800 North Orange Blossom Trl, Orlando, FL 32804
Tel.: (407) 425-3170
Web Site:
http://www.kenworthcentfl.com
Sales Range: $25-49.9 Million
Emp.: 115
Trucks
N.A.I.C.S.: 441110
Bob Glass (Mgr)
Clayton Carter (Branch Mgr)
Eric Johns (Mgr-Sls-Gen Used Trucks)
Joe Calo (Dir-Fleet Sls)
Rob Robinson (Mgr-Used Truck)
Mike O'Brien (CFO)

KENWORTH OF CINCINNATI INC.
11155 Mosteller Rd, Cincinnati, OH 45241-1823
Tel.: (513) 771-5831
Web Site:
http://www.kenworthofcincinnati.com
Year Founded: 1978
Sales Range: $10-24.9 Million
Emp.: 100
Automobiles & Truck Sales & Repairs
N.A.I.C.S.: 423110
Jeff Gauger (Controller)
Greg Mills (Gen Mgr)
Steve Hedger (Mgr-Body Shop)

KENWORTH OF INDIANAPOLIS INC.
2929 S Holt Rd, Indianapolis, IN 46241-6021
Tel.: (317) 247-8421 IN
Web Site:
http://www.palmertrucks.com
Year Founded: 1965
Sales Range: $200-249.9 Million
Emp.: 600
Provider of Retail & Service of New & Used Heavy-Duty Trucks
N.A.I.C.S.: 441110
John Edward (Pres)
Kurt Palmer (Dir-Sls)

KENWORTH OF JACKSON INC.
421 Hwy 49 S, Richland, MS 39218
Tel.: (601) 939-5300
Year Founded: 1986
Sales Range: $10-24.9 Million
Emp.: 40
Truck Products Mfr & Related Services
N.A.I.C.S.: 532120
Susan Bailey (Controller)
Barry Willoughby (Branch Mgr)

KENWORTH OF JACKSONVILLE, INC.
833 Pickettville Rd, Jacksonville, FL 32220
Tel.: (904) 739-2296
Web Site: http://www.kwjax.com
Sales Range: $25-49.9 Million
Emp.: 50
Trucks, Tractors & Trailers Retailer
N.A.I.C.S.: 441227
Denis Ross (Pres)
David Butler (CFO)

KENWORTH OF ST. LOUIS INC.
185 Soccer Park Rd, Fenton, MO 63026
Tel.: (636) 343-6900
Web Site:
http://www.kenworthstl.com
Rev.: $23,600,000
Emp.: 70
Trucks, Commercial
N.A.I.C.S.: 423110
Jerry Ackerman (Chm)
Mike Cardinale (Mgr-Parts)

KENWORTH SALES COMPANY, INC.
2125 S Constitution Blvd, West Valley City, UT 84119
Tel.: (801) 487-4161 UT
Web Site:
http://www.kenworthsalesco.com
Year Founded: 1945
Sales Range: $150-199.9 Million
Emp.: 100
Automobile Sales & Services
N.A.I.C.S.: 423110
Kyle Treadway (Pres)
Kip Ekker (COO)
Mike McKay (Mgr-District 1-Chicago)
Terry Spencer (District Mgr-Svc)
Lance Jorgensen (CFO)
Bob Sant (Dir-HR)
Martha Mills (Dir-Mktg)
Susan Lujan (Dir-Corp Credit)
Ryan Colby (Dir-Mktg)

KENYAN ENTERPRISES INC.
543 S Main St, Springhill, LA 71075
Tel.: (318) 539-9116
Sales Range: $25-49.9 Million
Emp.: 300
Grocery Stores
N.A.I.C.S.: 445110
Edwin L. Kenyan (Pres)
David Scruggs (Controller)

KENYON COMPANIES
4001 W Indian School Rd, Phoenix, AZ 85019
Tel.: (602) 233-1191
Sales Range: $75-99.9 Million
Emp.: 1,400

KENYON COMPANIES U.S. PRIVATE

Kenyon Companies—(Continued)
Plastering Services
N.A.I.C.S.: 238310
Dave Barry (Pres)

KENYON CONSTRUCTION, INC.
4001 W Indian School Rd, Phoenix, AZ 85019-3314
Tel.: (602) 233-1191
Web Site:
http://www.kenyonweb.com
Year Founded: 1978
Sales Range: $75-99.9 Million
Emp.: 2,000
Mfr of Plastering Drywall & Insulation
N.A.I.C.S.: 238310
Dave Berry (Pres)

KENYON POWER BOATS INC.
36851 US Hwy 19 N, Palm Harbor, FL 34684
Tel.: (727) 942-7767 FL
Web Site:
http://www.kenyonpowerboats.com
Year Founded: 1985
Sales Range: $10-24.9 Million
Emp.: 40
Seller of Fishing Boats, Pontoons, Runabouts, Catamarans, Flat & Bass Boats & Performance Boats
N.A.I.C.S.: 441222
Mark Carlson (Pres & Mgr-Sls)
Jim Gorman (Mgr-Parts)

KEO MARKETING INC.
4809 E Thistle Landing Dr Suite 100, Phoenix, AZ 85044
Tel.: (480) 413-2090
Web Site:
http://www.keomarketing.com
Year Founded: 2000
Sales Range: $1-9.9 Million
B2B Marketing Strategies
N.A.I.C.S.: 541820
Sheila Kloefkorn (Pres & CEO)
Jennifer McQuesten (Dir-Inbound Mktg & Project Mgmt)
Ryan Grimes (Dir-Bus Intelligence Adv)

KEPCO INC.
13138 Sanford Ave, Flushing, NY 11355
Tel.: (718) 461-7000 DE
Web Site:
http://www.kepcopower.com
Year Founded: 1946
Sales Range: $10-24.9 Million
Emp.: 270
Power Distribution & Specialty Transformers
N.A.I.C.S.: 335311
Morton Kupferberg (Pres)

KEPHART TRUCKING COMPANY
983 Woodland Bigler Hwy, Woodland, PA 16825
Tel.: (814) 857-7704
Web Site:
http://www.kepharttrucking.com
Year Founded: 1950
Sales Range: $50-74.9 Million
Emp.: 250
Provider of Trucking Services
N.A.I.C.S.: 484121
Timothy Kephart (Pres)
Tom Hampton (Mgr-Ops)

KEPNER-TREGOE, INC.
Princeton Forrestal Vlg 116 Vlg Blvd Ste 300, Princeton, NJ 08540
Tel.: (609) 921-2806 DE
Web Site: http://www.kepner-tregoe.com
Year Founded: 1958
Sales Range: $100-124.9 Million
Emp.: 200
Management Consulting & Human Resource Development Services
N.A.I.C.S.: 541611
Bill Baldwin (CEO)
Barbara Stoeber (CIO)
Samuel M. Bernstine (Partner)
Kevin Duffy (VP-Strategic Dev)
Andrew Graham (Pres)
Christoph Goldenstern (VP-Global Strategy & Mktg)
David Kossoss (VP-Mktg)
Andy Cook (Chm)
Michael Kutner (Mng Dir-North America)
Belinda Bright (Dir-Org Transformation)
Anthony Friedli (Mng Dir-Australia & New Zealand)
Albert Chan (Mng Dir-Southeast Asia)
Patrick Browne (Reg Mng Dir)

Subsidiaries:
KT Andina S.A.C. (1)
Manuel Olguin 1060-14 Surco, Lima, Peru
Tel.: (51) 1 222 5104
Consulting & Training Services
N.A.I.C.S.: 611430

Kepner-Tregoe (Malaysia) Sdn. Bhd. (1)
Unit 1301 Level 13 Uptown 1 1 Jalan SS21/58 Damansara Uptown, Off Jalan Damansara, 47400, Petaling Jaya, Selangor, Malaysia
Tel.: (60) 3 7660 9128
Sales Range: $10-24.9 Million
Emp.: 10
Management Consulting & Training Services
N.A.I.C.S.: 541618

Kepner-Tregoe Australasia Pty Ltd (1)
Suite 2 Level 13 20 Berry Street, North Sydney, 2060, NSW, Australia
Tel.: (61) 2 9955 5944
Web Site: http://www.kepner-tregoe.com
Sales Range: $10-24.9 Million
Emp.: 20
Management Consulting & Training Services
N.A.I.C.S.: 541618
Anthony Friedli (Mng Dir)

Kepner-Tregoe Deutschland, LLC. (1)
Gerichtsstrasse 3, Wiesbaden, 65815, Germany
Tel.: (49) 611 41149 15
Web Site: http://www.kepner-tregoe.de
Emp.: 20
Consulting & Training Services
N.A.I.C.S.: 541618
Patrick Drown (Gen Mgr)

Kepner-Tregoe Japan, LLC (1)
Nissei Moto-Akasaka Building 7-18 Moto-Akasaka 1-chome, Minato-ku, Tokyo, 107, Japan
Tel.: (81) 3 3401 9521
Web Site: http://www.kepner-tregoe.co.jp
Sales Range: $10-24.9 Million
Emp.: 15
Management Consulting & Training Services
N.A.I.C.S.: 541618
Takesi Sato (Pres)

Kepner-Tregoe Ltd. (1)
Moorbridge Court Moorbridge Road, Maidenhead, SL6 8LT, Berkshire, United Kingdom
Tel.: (44) 1628 778776
Web Site: http://www.kepner-tregoe.com
Emp.: 12
Management Consulting & Training Services
N.A.I.C.S.: 541618
Jens Refflinghaus (Dir)

Kepner-Tregoe Sarl (1)
59 rue des Petits Champs, Paris, 75001, France
Tel.: (33) 1 42 97 42 00
Web Site: http://www.kepner-tregoe.com
Emp.: 10
Management Consulting & Training Services
N.A.I.C.S.: 541618

Kepner-Tregoe Southeast Asia Limited. (1)
80 Raffles Place 36-01 UOB Plaza 1, Singapore, 48624, Singapore
Tel.: (65) 6256 6492
Web Site: http://www.kepner-tregoe.com
Management Consulting & Training Services
N.A.I.C.S.: 541618
Albert Chan (Mng Dir)

Kepner-Tregoe Southeast Asia Ltd (1)
Level 19 Two International Finance Centre 8 Finance Street, Central, Hong Kong, China (Hong Kong)
Tel.: (852) 2251 1581
Web Site: http://www.kepner-tregoe.com
Management Consulting & Training Services
N.A.I.C.S.: 541618

Kepner-Tregoe Thailand, LLC (1)
230 CS Tower 9th Floor, Rajchadaphisaek Road Huaykwang, Bangkok, 10320, Thailand
Tel.: (66) 2 274 0646
Web Site: http://www.kepner-tregoe.com
Consulting & Training Services
N.A.I.C.S.: 541618

Kepner-Tregoe, SA (1)
8 Avenue Jomini, Case Postale 5412, 1002, Lausanne, Switzerland
Tel.: (41) 22 361 2131
Management Consulting & Training Services
N.A.I.C.S.: 541618

KER, INC.
7491 Ulmerton Rd Ste B, Largo, FL 33771
Tel.: (727) 535-2939
Web Site: http://www.winghouse.com
Year Founded: 1994
Restaurant Owner & Operator
N.A.I.C.S.: 722511

KERBECK CADILLAC PONTIAC CHEVROLET, INC.
430 N Albany Ave, Atlantic City, NJ 08401
Tel.: (609) 344-2100
Web Site: http://www.kerbeck.com
Rev.: $150,000,000
Emp.: 92
Car Dealership
N.A.I.C.S.: 441110
Charles Kerbeck (Pres)
George Kerbeck (VP)

KERBER BROS. POOL PLASTERING, INC.
14006 Gracebee Ave, Norwalk, CA 90650-4599
Tel.: (562) 921-3447
Web Site:
http://www.kerberbrothers.com
Year Founded: 1952
Sales Range: $25-49.9 Million
Emp.: 236
Other Specialty Trade Contracting Services
N.A.I.C.S.: 238990
Skip Hawkins (Owner)

KERBS OIL COMPANY INC.
2307 W Main St, Burley, ID 83318
Tel.: (208) 678-8256
Sales Range: $10-24.9 Million
Emp.: 25
Convenience Stores; Independent
N.A.I.C.S.: 445131

KERI SYSTEMS INC.
1530 Old Oakland Rd # 100, San Jose, CA 95131
Tel.: (408) 435-8400
Web Site: http://www.kerisys.com
Sales Range: $10-24.9 Million
Emp.: 60
Security Control Equipment & Systems
N.A.I.C.S.: 335999
Scott Bidochka (Mgr-Facilities)
Vince Deiuliis (Dir-Sls & Mktg)
Dennis Geiszler (VP-Mktg & Sls-Intl)
Adrian Gonzalez (Reg Mgr-Sls)
David J. Bell (Mgr-Sls-Southern Central)
Vickie Carr (Supvr-Inside Sls)
Edward P. Hendricks Jr. (Mgr-Sls-Natl)

KERKERING, BARBERIO & CO.
1990 Main St Ste 801, Sarasota, FL 34236
Tel.: (941) 365-4617 FL
Web Site: http://www.kbgrp.com
Year Founded: 1972
Sales Range: $10-24.9 Million
Emp.: 110
Accounting Services
N.A.I.C.S.: 541211
Robert P. Clarke (CFO)
Tracy O'Neill (Chief Admin Officer)

Subsidiaries:
KB Pension Services, Inc. (1)
1990 Main St Ste 801, Sarasota, FL 34236
Tel.: (941) 365-4617
Pension Services
N.A.I.C.S.: 524292
John Cotterman (Pres)
Kathy Rice (Mgr-Admin)

Kerkering Barberio Financial Services, Inc. (1)
1990 Main St Ste 801, Sarasota, FL 34236
Tel.: (941) 365-3745
Web Site:
http://www.kerkeringbarberiofinancial.com
Financial Planning & Investment Advisory Services
N.A.I.C.S.: 523940
Martin Kossoff (Pres)

KERMANS FINE FLOORING, INC.
4505 E 82nd St, Indianapolis, IN 46250
Tel.: (317) 842-5700
Web Site: http://www.kermans.com
Sales Range: $10-24.9 Million
Emp.: 30
Floor Coverings Whslr
N.A.I.C.S.: 449121
Dave Amsler (Mgr)

KERN & ASSOCIATES
10000 Riverside Dr, Toluca Lake, CA 91602
Tel.: (818) 766-0006 CA
Year Founded: 1982
Sales Range: $75-99.9 Million
Emp.: 70
Steel Cans & Related Tomato Products Mfr
N.A.I.C.S.: 561110

KERN FOOD DISTRIBUTING INC.
2711 Wagel Rd, Brooksville, KY 41004
Tel.: (606) 756-2255
Web Site:
http://www.webberfarms.com
Sales Range: $10-24.9 Million
Emp.: 35
Meats & Meat Products
N.A.I.C.S.: 424470

Edward B. Kern (Pres)

KERN MACHINERY
520 S Mt Vernon Ave, Bakersfield, CA 93307
Tel.: (661) 833-9900
Web Site: http://www.kernmachinery.com
Year Founded: 1971
Sales Range: $10-24.9 Million
Emp.: 50
Farm Machinery
N.A.I.C.S.: 333111
Clayton Camp (Pres & Gen Mgr)

KERN REGIONAL CENTER
3200 N Sillect Ave, Bakersfield, CA 93308-6333
Tel.: (661) 327-8531   CA
Web Site: http://www.kernrc.org
Year Founded: 1971
Sales Range: $10-24.9 Million
Emp.: 183
Individual & Family Services
N.A.I.C.S.: 624120
Duane Law (CEO)

KERNEY SERVICE GROUP INC.
1721 Pennsylvania Ave, Linden, NJ 07036-1762
Tel.: (908) 486-2644
Web Site: http://www.kerneyservice.com
Sales Range: $10-24.9 Million
Emp.: 75
Shipbuilding & Repairing
N.A.I.C.S.: 336611
Frank Kerney Sr. (Pres)
Frank Kerney Jr. (VP)

KERNS MANUFACTURING CORP.
3714 29th St, Long Island City, NY 11101
Tel.: (718) 784-4044
Web Site: http://www.kernsmfg.com
Rev.: $23,000,000
Emp.: 125
Aircraft Engines & Engine Parts
N.A.I.C.S.: 336412
Behnam Movaseghi (Treas & Sec)
Joshua L. Markowitz (Executives)

KERNS TRUCKING INC.
703 S Battleground Ave, Grover, NC 28073
Tel.: (704) 739-4747
Web Site: http://www.kernstrucking.com
Year Founded: 1933
Rev.: $20,200,000
Emp.: 70
Logistics & Transportation Services
N.A.I.C.S.: 484121
Doug Prestwood (VP)
Carol Canipe (Mgr)

KERR LAKESIDE INC.
26841 Tungsten Rd, Euclid, OH 44132
Tel.: (216) 261-2100
Web Site: http://www.kerrlakeside.com
Sales Range: $10-24.9 Million
Emp.: 75
Mfr of Bolts & Special Cold Head Components
N.A.I.C.S.: 332722
Richard W. Kerr (Chm)
Angela Rivera (Treas)
John Gervasi (VP-Ops)

KERR PACIFIC CORP.
1211 SW 6th Ave, Portland, OR 97204-3340
Tel.: (503) 221-1301   OR
Web Site: http://www.kerrpacific.com
Year Founded: 1963
Sales Range: $25-49.9 Million
Emp.: 200
Food Distribution & Flour Mills
N.A.I.C.S.: 424410
Randolph E. Labbe (CEO)

KERR PUMP AND SUPPLY INC.
12880 Cloverdale St, Oak Park, MI 48237
Tel.: (248) 543-3880
Web Site: http://www.kerrpump.com
Rev.: $13,819,459
Emp.: 48
Water Pumps (Industrial)
N.A.I.C.S.: 423830
John A. Sloan (Pres)
Daryl Reddick (Plant Mgr)

KERRY FORD INC.
155 W Kemper Rd, Cincinnati, OH 45246
Tel.: (513) 671-6400
Web Site: http://www.buykerryford.com
Rev.: $76,000,000
Emp.: 100
Owner & Operator of Car Dealerships
N.A.I.C.S.: 441110
Patrick DeCastro (Pres)
Rod Henderson (CEO)

KERRY TOYOTA TOWNE
6050 Hopeful Church Rd, Florence, KY 41042
Tel.: (859) 371-3939
Web Site: http://www.kerrytoyota.com
Sales Range: $50-74.9 Million
Emp.: 102
New & Used Car Dealers
N.A.I.C.S.: 441110
Mark Stein (Gen Mgr)

KERRY VOLKSWAGEN
1010 Burlington Pike, Florence, KY 41042
Tel.: (859) 371-8191
Web Site: http://www.kerryvw.com
Year Founded: 2010
Sales Range: $50-74.9 Million
Emp.: 92
Car Whslr
N.A.I.C.S.: 441110
Doy Baker (Pres)

KERSHNER OFFICE FURNITURE
600 Clark Ave, King of Prussia, PA 19406
Tel.: (610) 768-0200
Web Site: http://www.kershneroffice.com
Year Founded: 2002
Rev.: $7,200,000
Emp.: 20
Furniture Merchant Whslr
N.A.I.C.S.: 423210
Carla Grabowski (Dir-Ops)
Carolyn DiStefano (Project Mgr)
Bruer Kershner (CEO)
Mitchell Berman (Pres)
Sandy Arnell (Project Mgr)

KERUSSO ACTIVEWEAR, INC.
402 Hwy 62 Spur, Berryville, AR 72616
Tel.: (870) 423-6242   AR
Web Site: http://www.kerusso.com
Year Founded: 1987
Sales Range: $10-24.9 Million
Emp.: 100
Christian Themed Apparel & Gifts
N.A.I.C.S.: 323113

Vic Kennett (Founder & CEO)
Michelle Amundson (Dir-Bus Process Improvement)
Chris Rainey (Mktg Dir)
Nik Kennett (VP-Mktg)
Matthew Haley (Sls Dir-Natl)

KESSEL CONSTRUCTION INC.
345 High St, Bradford, PA 16701
Tel.: (814) 362-4696
Web Site: http://www.kesselco.com
Year Founded: 1979
Sales Range: $10-24.9 Million
Emp.: 50
Commercial & Office Building, New Construction
N.A.I.C.S.: 236220
Richard L. Kessel (CEO)
Timothy J. Asinger (Pres)
Steve Borowski (Territory Mgr-Sls)
Ann Kessel (Treas)
Clark Johnson (Territory Mgr-Sls)
Jim Curcio (Project Mgr)
Margie Spencer (Mgr-HR)
Tina Baker (Controller)

KESSINGER/HUNTER & CO. LC
2600 Grand Blvd Ste 700, Kansas City, MO 64108
Tel.: (816) 842-2690
Web Site: http://www.kessingerhunter.com
Sales Range: $10-24.9 Million
Emp.: 200
Real Estate Brokers & Agents
N.A.I.C.S.: 531210
Charles H. Hunter (Principal-Indus Brokerage)
Debbie Jarrett (Office Mgr)
Pat McGannon (Pres & Principal-Indus Brokerage)
Jerry P. Fogel (Principal)
Darold Frenzen (CFO & Dir-Acctg Dept)
Leland Hawley (Mgr-Property)
Vaughn L. Tribble (Mgr-Property)
Gregory W. Swetnam (Principal & Dir-Office Brokerage)
Leslie S. Perkins (Mgr-Property)
William B. Kessinger (Principal)
John DeHardt (Mng Principal)
Kimberlin Gartman (Controller-Acctg Dept)
Kenneth M. Nicolay (Principal)
Kise Randall (Exec Dir-Sunflower Redevelopment)
Gary Schlotzhauer (Dir-Energy & Engrg)
Daniel B. Jensen (Principal-Indus Brokerage Dev)
Deborah F. Schulte (Principal-Office Brokerage)
Tim Sweeten (Mgr-Construction)

KESSLER GROUP INCORPORATED
410 White Spruce Blvd, Rochester, NY 14623
Tel.: (585) 424-5277
Web Site: http://www.kesslerrestaurants.com
Sales Range: $75-99.9 Million
Emp.: 1,000
Fastfood Chain
N.A.I.C.S.: 722511
Howard J. Kessler (Founder, Chm & CEO)
Carl Rutstein (Pres)
Ray Fischer (Vice Chm & Chief Admin Officer)
Keryn Brunner (Mng Dir-Intl)
Kurt Campisano (Mng Dir-Kessler Capital)
Dax Cummings (Mng Dir-Bus Dev)
Carl Erickson (Sr Exec VP-Strategy)

Felix Riccio (Sr Exec VP)
Scott W. Shaw (COO)
David Smith (Mng Dir-Mergers & Acq Advisory Solutions & Sr Exec VP)
Frank Spellman (CFO)
Al Tringali (Pres-Fin Institutions Grp)
Patrick Aylmer (Exec VP-Mergers & Acq Advisory Solutions)
Robert Curry (Exec VP-Mergers & Acq Advisory Solutions)
Todd DaCosta (Exec VP-Fin Institutions Grp)
Greg Fisher (Sr VP-New Bus Dev)
Sandi Goodman-Brown (Sr VP-Mktg & Consulting Solutions)
Kevin Mulligan (Sr VP-Fin Institutions Grp)
Andrea Perry (Sr VP-Mktg & Consulting Solutions)
George Tsiklauri (Sr VP-Mergers & Acq Advisory Solutions)

KESSLER INDUSTRIES INC.
8600 Gateway Blvd E, El Paso, TX 79907
Tel.: (915) 591-8161
Web Site: http://www.kesslerind.com
Sales Range: Less than $1 Million
Emp.: 2
Novelty Furniture, Household: Metal
N.A.I.C.S.: 337126
Neil Kessler (Pres)

KESSLER-ELLIS PRODUCTS CO. INC.
10 Indus Way E, Eatontown, NJ 07724
Tel.: (732) 935-1320
Web Site: http://www.kep.com
Sales Range: $10-24.9 Million
Emp.: 50
Controls, Revolution & Timing Instruments
N.A.I.C.S.: 334514
Peter Sabat (Pres)
Barbara Meisler (Mgr-HR)
Rich Woods (Mgr-Sls)
Corson E. Ellis III (Owner)

KESSLERS INCORPORATED
1201 Hummel Ave, Lemoyne, PA 17043
Tel.: (717) 763-7162
Web Site: http://www.kesslerfoods.com
Sales Range: $10-24.9 Million
Emp.: 40
Poultry & Poultry Products Mfr
N.A.I.C.S.: 424440
Robert E. Kessler Jr. (Pres)

KESTREL CORP.
3815 Osuna Rd NE, Albuquerque, NM 87109
Tel.: (505) 345-2327   NM
Web Site: http://www.kestrelcorp.com
Year Founded: 1993
Sales Range: $1-9.9 Million
Emp.: 26
Engineering Services
N.A.I.C.S.: 541330
Elinor Reiners (VP)

KETCHAM FOREST PRODUCTS, INC.
2811 E Madison St Ste 204, Seattle, WA 98112-4868
Tel.: (206) 329-2700   WA
Year Founded: 1991
Sales Range: $10-24.9 Million
Emp.: 20
Lumber Plywood & Millwork
N.A.I.C.S.: 423310
Sam Howard (Pres & CEO)

KETT ENGINEERING CORPORATION

Kett Engineering Corporation—(Continued)

KETT ENGINEERING CORPORATION
15500 Erwin St Ste 1029, Van Nuys, CA 91411-1028
Tel.: (818) 908-5388 CA
Web Site: http://www.ketteng.com
Year Founded: 1973
Sales Range: $25-49.9 Million
Emp.: 500
Testing Laboratories for Cars
N.A.I.C.S.: 541380
Eric Stromsborg *(Pres)*
Brett Bergman *(CFO)*
Jan Derek Stoetzer *(Mgr-Mktg)*

KETTELHUT CONSTRUCTION, INC.
740 Sagamore Pkwy S, Lafayette, IN 47905
Tel.: (765) 447-2181
Web Site: http://www.kettelhut.com
Year Founded: 1935
Sales Range: $10-24.9 Million
Emp.: 45
Commercial & Institutional Building Construction Services
N.A.I.C.S.: 236220
Steve Habben *(Pres)*
Rick Olson *(Sec & VP)*
Matt Shultz *(Project Mgr)*

KETTERING ADVENTIST HEALTHCARE
2110 Leiter Rd, Miamisburg, OH 45342
Tel.: (937) 384-4550 OH
Web Site:
http://www.ketteringhealth.org
Year Founded: 1982
Sales Range: $25-49.9 Million
Emp.: 52
Health Care Srvices
N.A.I.C.S.: 622110
Terri Day *(Pres)*
Roy Chew *(Exec VP)*
Fred Manchur *(CEO)*
George Lewis *(Exec VP-Physician Enterprise)*
Tim Dutton *(Chief HR Officer, Exec VP-Mission, Mktg & People & Sr VP)*

KETTLE-LAKES COOPERATIVE
505 S Main St, Cedar Grove, WI 53013
Tel.: (920) 668-8561
Web Site:
http://www.kettlelakescoop.com
Sales Range: $10-24.9 Million
Emp.: 35
Hardware Stores
N.A.I.C.S.: 444140
Mark Mentink *(CEO & Gen Mgr)*

KETTLEY & COMPANY REALTORS INC.
503 W Galena Blvd, Aurora, IL 60506-3847
Tel.: (630) 896-5000 IL
Web Site:
http://www.kettleyhomes.com
Year Founded: 1982
Sales Range: $10-24.9 Million
Emp.: 5
Realty Services
N.A.I.C.S.: 531210
Edward Kettley *(Pres)*

Subsidiaries:

Kettley & Company Realtors-Batavia (1)
125 S Batavia Ave, Batavia, IL 60510-2450   (100%)
Tel.: (630) 879-9555

Web Site: http://www.kettleyhomes.com
Real Estate Services
N.A.I.C.S.: 531210
Edward Kettley *(Mgr)*

Kettley & Company Realtors-Commercial (1)
58 Chicago Rd, Oswego, IL 60543
Tel.: (630) 896-3500
Web Site: http://www.kettleyrealtors.com
Provider of Realty Services
N.A.I.C.S.: 531210

Kettley & Company Realtors-Oswego (1)
58 Chicago Rd, Oswego, IL 60543-8611
Tel.: (630) 554-8700
Web Site: http://www.kettleyhomes.com
Emp.: 25
Provider of Realty Services
N.A.I.C.S.: 531210
Ed Kettley Jr. *(Gen Mgr)*

Kettley & Company Realtors-Saint Charles (1)
203 W Main St, Saint Charles, IL 60174-1811
Tel.: (630) 584-7000
Web Site: http://www.kettleyhomes.com
Emp.: 15
Provider of Realty Services
N.A.I.C.S.: 531210
Margie Thorgesen *(Office Mgr)*

Kettley & Company Realtors-Sandwich (1)
903 E Church St, Sandwich, IL 60548-2004
Tel.: (815) 786-3200
Web Site: http://www.kettleyhomes.com
Provider of Realty Services
N.A.I.C.S.: 531210
Ed Kettley Jr. *(Gen Mgr)*

Kettley & Company Realtors-Sugar Grove (1)
36 Terry Dr, Sugar Grove, IL 60554
Tel.: (630) 466-4600
Web Site: http://www.kettleyhomes.com
Sales Range: $10-24.9 Million
Realty Services
N.A.I.C.S.: 621310
Patricia Midgley *(Gen Mgr)*

Kettley & Company Realtors-Yorkville (1)
720 N Bridge St, Yorkville, IL 60560-1108
Tel.: (630) 553-5060
Web Site: http://www.kettleyhomes.com
Provider of Realty Services
N.A.I.C.S.: 531210

Kettley Realtors (1)
313 N Main St, Elburn, IL 60119-9207
Tel.: (815) 286-7300
Web Site: http://www.kettleyhomes.com
Provider of Realty Services
N.A.I.C.S.: 531210

KEVIN WHITAKER CHEVROLET INC.
2320 Laurens Rd, Greenville, SC 29607
Tel.: (864) 271-2277 SC
Web Site:
http://www.kevinwhitaker.net
Year Founded: 1989
Sales Range: $10-24.9 Million
Emp.: 80
Buying & Selling of New & Used Cars
N.A.I.C.S.: 441110
Kevin Whitaker *(Pres)*

KEVIN'S WHOLESALE LLC
710 Capouse Ave, Scranton, PA 18509
Tel.: (570) 344-9055
Web Site: http://www.kevins.biz
Year Founded: 1994
Rev.: $6,400,000
Emp.: 48
Business Products & Services
N.A.I.C.S.: 424350
Larry Tinkelman *(Pres)*
Sally Stolarcyk *(Head-HR)*
Scott Tinkelman *(VP-Sls & Mktg)*
Kevin Tinkelman *(VP-Ops)*

KEWEENAW BAY INDIAN COMMUNITY
16429 Bear Town Rd, Baraga, MI 49908
Tel.: (906) 353-6623
Web Site:
http://www.ojibwacasino.com
Rev.: $23,900,000
Emp.: 75
Gambling Establishment
N.A.I.C.S.: 713290
Francis LaPointe *(CFO)*
Donald Shalifoe *(Chm & Pres)*
Don Wren *(Gen Mgr-Marquette & Baraga Properties)*

KEY & ASSOCIATES PC
8630 Fenton St Ste 402, Silver Spring, MD 20910
Tel.: (301) 608-3033
Web Site: http://www.bkeycpa.com
Year Founded: 2002
Sales Range: $1-9.9 Million
Emp.: 16
Accounting & Tax Preparation
N.A.I.C.S.: 541211
Beatrice A. Key *(Founder)*

KEY AUTO GROUP
221 Rte 108, Somersworth, NH 03878
Tel.: (603) 742-7485
Web Site: http://www.keyauto.com
Sales Range: $75-99.9 Million
Emp.: 300
Holding Company; New & Used Car Dealerships Owner & Operator
N.A.I.C.S.: 551112
Anthony DiLorenzo *(Owner & Pres)*
Jacob Lampert *(Bus Mgr)*
Chris Stromberg *(Mgr)*
Morgan Booth *(Mgr-Bus & Fin)*
Jordan Perry *(Mgr-Bus Dev)*
Peter Leonardi *(Gen Mgr-Sls)*
Melissa Forbes *(Mgr-Sls)*

Subsidiaries:

Key Auto Center (1)
549 US Hwy Portsmouth, Somersworth, NH 03801
Tel.: (603) 742-7400
Web Site: http://www.keyauto.net
Sales Range: $10-24.9 Million
Emp.: 10
New & Used Car Dealer
N.A.I.C.S.: 441110
Marie Bundy *(Gen Mgr)*

Portsmouth Chevrolet, Inc. (1)
549 US Hwy 1 Bypass, Portsmouth, NH 03801
Tel.: (603) 436-5010
Web Site:
http://www.portsmouthchevrolet.com
Sales Range: $50-74.9 Million
Emp.: 60
New & Used Car Dealer
N.A.I.C.S.: 441110
Anthony DiLorenzo *(Pres)*

KEY BRAND ENTERTAINMENT, INC.
1619 Broadway 9th Fl, New York, NY 10019
Tel.: (917) 421-5942
Web Site: http://www.kbeinc.net
Promoter & Producer of Live Theatrical Events
N.A.I.C.S.: 711310
John Gore *(CEO)*
Peter Schneider *(Chm)*
Miles Wilkin *(COO & Exec VP)*
Kumiko Yoshii *(Exec VP & Head-Intl Bus Dev)*
Pail Dietz *(CFO)*
Robert Brandon *(Gen Counsel)*

Subsidiaries:

Broadway Across America (1)

1619 Broadway 9th Fl, New York, NY 10019
Tel.: (917) 421-5942
Web Site:
http://www.broadwayacrossamerica.com
Sales Range: $200-249.9 Million
Promoter & Producer of Live Theatrical Events
N.A.I.C.S.: 711320
Jeff Daniel *(Exec VP-Bus Ops)*

Branch (Domestic):

Broadway Across America - Minneapolis (2)
615 Hennepin Ave Ste 140, Minneapolis, MN 55403
Tel.: (612) 455-9500
Web Site:
http://www.broadwayacrossamerica.com
Theatrical Production & Services
N.A.I.C.S.: 711110
Mike Brand *(Exec Dir)*

Broadway Across America - Salt Lake City (2)
610 SE Temple Ste 20, Salt Lake City, UT 84102
Tel.: (801) 355-2200
Web Site: http://www.magicspace.net
Sales Range: $25-49.9 Million
Emp.: 20
Concert & Theatrical Promotion
N.A.I.C.S.: 711310

Broadway Across America - Seattle (2)
2033 6th Ave Ste 995, Seattle, WA 98121
Tel.: (206) 622-2733
Web Site:
http://www.broadwayacrossamerica.com
Sales Range: $25-49.9 Million
Emp.: 7
Theatrical Companies
N.A.I.C.S.: 711110
Kathleen Maki *(Mgr-Grp Sl & Promo)*

KEY BUICK COMPANY
4660 Southside Bl, Jacksonville, FL 32216
Tel.: (904) 642-6060
Web Site:
http://www.keybuickgmc.com
Sales Range: $25-49.9 Million
Emp.: 95
Car Whslr
N.A.I.C.S.: 441110
Maureen Burnett *(Pres)*

KEY CADILLAC, INC.
6825 York Ave S, Edina, MN 55435-2516
Tel.: (952) 920-4300 MN
Web Site: http://www.keycadillac.com
Year Founded: 1973
Sales Range: $100-124.9 Million
Emp.: 65
Sales & Service of New & Used Automobiles
N.A.I.C.S.: 441110
Dennis A. Burg *(Gen Mgr)*
Michael Stanzak *(Owner)*
Pam Thompson *(Controller)*

KEY CITY FURNITURE COMPANY
1804 River St, Wilkesboro, NC 28697
Tel.: (336) 838-4191
Web Site: http://www.keycityfurn.com
Sales Range: $10-24.9 Million
Emp.: 225
Upholstered Living Room Furniture Mfr
N.A.I.C.S.: 449110
Lloyd Coley *(VP-Mdsg)*

KEY COMMUNICATIONS, INC.
20 PGA Dr Ste 201, Stafford, VA 22554
Tel.: (540) 720-5584
Web Site: http://www.key-com.com
Year Founded: 1993

KEY PROGRAM INCORPORATED

Sales Range: $1-9.9 Million
Emp.: 19
Periodical Publishers
N.A.I.C.S.: 513120
Dawn Campbell *(Dir-Art)*
Chris Bunn *(Dir-Video Production)*
Janeen Mulligan *(Mgr-Customer Rels)*
Tara Taffera *(VP-Editorial Svcs)*
Tina Czar *(Mgr-Events)*

KEY CONSTRUCTORS INC.
219 Key Dr, Madison, MS 39110
Tel.: (601) 898-9892
Web Site:
  http://www.keyconstructors.com
Sales Range: $10-24.9 Million
Emp.: 75
General Contractor, Highway & Street Construction
N.A.I.C.S.: 237310
David Trevathan *(Pres)*
Rick Webster *(CEO)*

KEY CONTAINER CORPORATION
21 Campbell St, Pawtucket, RI 02861-4005
Tel.: (401) 723-2000 RI
Web Site:
  http://www.keycontainercorp.com
Year Founded: 1960
Sales Range: $100-124.9 Million
Emp.: 150
Corrugated Shipping Containers Mfr
N.A.I.C.S.: 322211
David Strauss *(Pres & CEO)*
Ronald R. Faria *(VP-Sls)*
Dominique Lapati *(Controller)*

KEY COOPERATIVE
13585 620th Ave, Roland, IA 50236
Tel.: (515) 388-4341
Web Site: http://www.keycoop.com
Sales Range: $50-74.9 Million
Emp.: 180
Grains & Feed Mfr
N.A.I.C.S.: 424510
David Hassebrock *(Sec)*
Rick Fopma *(VP-Lynnville)*
Dave Vander Pol *(Treas)*
Bryan Bandstra *(Mgr-HR & Safety)*
Boyd Brodie *(Gen Mgr)*
Sara Clausen *(Dir-Comm & Member Rels)*
Brian Gates *(Mgr-IT)*
Scott Stabbe *(Mgr-Grain Dept)*
Rick Weigel *(Mgr-Feed Dept)*
Michael Thomas *(CFO)*
Michael Thomas *(CFO)*

KEY EQUIPMENT & SUPPLY COMPANY
13507 NW Industrial Dr, Bridgeton, MO 63044
Tel.: (314) 298-8330
Web Site:
  http://www.keyequipment.com
Sales Range: $10-24.9 Million
Emp.: 44
Industrial Machinery & Equipment
N.A.I.C.S.: 423830
Steve Hyink *(Pres & Mgr-Mktg)*
Mary Hyink *(Mgr-Bridgeton)*
Jeff Miles *(Mgr-Kansas City)*
Don O'Dell *(Mgr-Svc-Bridgeton)*
Jerry Woods *(Mgr-Svc-Kansas City)*

KEY FAMILY OF COMPANIES
8330 Allison Pointe Trl, Indianapolis, IN 46250
Tel.: (317) 284-7100 IN
Web Site: http://www.keybenefit.com
Year Founded: 1979
Sales Range: $100-124.9 Million
Emp.: 485
Third Party Administrator
N.A.I.C.S.: 525120
Larry Dust *(Owner)*
Brad Ray *(CFO)*
Anita Dust *(VP)*
Subsidiaries:

Flex Support Group, Inc. (1)
8330 Allison Pt Trl, Indianapolis, IN 46250-1682 (100%)
Tel.: (317) 284-7120
Web Site: http://www.keyfamily.com
Sales Range: $25-49.9 Million
Emp.: 200
Provider of Software Development Services
N.A.I.C.S.: 541512

Health Care Management, Inc. (1)
8330 Allison Pointe Trl, Indianapolis, IN 46250-1682
Tel.: (317) 284-7100
Web Site: http://www.keyfamily.com
Provider of Health Care Management Services
N.A.I.C.S.: 561110

Key Benefit Administrators (1)
534 Rivercrossing Rd, Fort Mill, SC 29715
Tel.: (803) 396-4600
Web Site: http://www.keybenefit.com
Employee Benefit Administration Services
N.A.I.C.S.: 525120
Floretha Worley *(Coord-New Case Implementation)*
Robert Farmer *(Coord-New Case Implementation)*
Eugenia Mitchell *(Mgr-Claims)*
Jeff Dieker *(Mgr-Facility)*
Carolyn Allen *(Mgr-HR)*
Craig Phillips *(Mgr-New Case & Relationship)*
Dale Kaliser *(VP-Client Rels)*
Lisa Norton *(VP-Client Svc)*

Key Benefit Administrators, Inc. (1)
8330 Allison Pointe Trl, Indianapolis, IN 46250 (100%)
Tel.: (317) 284-7100
Web Site: http://www.keyfamily.com
Sales Range: $125-149.9 Million
Emp.: 400
Provider of Benefit Administration Services
N.A.I.C.S.: 525120

Key Financial Administrators, Ltd. (1)
8330 Allison Pointe Trl, Indianapolis, IN 46250-1682
Tel.: (317) 284-7150
Sales Range: $50-74.9 Million
Emp.: 200
Provider of Pension & Human Resource Services
N.A.I.C.S.: 525120

Key Partners, Inc. (1)
8330 Allison Pointe Trl, Indianapolis, IN 46250-1682 (100%)
Tel.: (317) 284-7171
Web Site: http://www.keypartnersinc.com
Sales Range: $50-74.9 Million
Emp.: 120
Provider of Healthcare Administration Services
N.A.I.C.S.: 525120

TurnKey Benefits Inc. (1)
534 Rivercrossing Rd, Fort Mill, SC 29715
Tel.: (877) 396-7317
Web Site: http://www.turnkeybenefits.com
Employee Benefit Consulting Services
N.A.I.C.S.: 541612

KEY FOOD STORES CO-OPERATIVE, INC.
1200 S Ave, Staten Island, NY 10314
Tel.: (718) 370-4200 NY
Web Site:
  http://www.keyfoodstores.com
Year Founded: 1937
Wholesale Food Co-Operative
N.A.I.C.S.: 424410
Greg O'Donnell *(Mgr-Acctg)*
Dean Janeway *(CEO)*

KEY GLASS LLC
2312 58th Ave E, Bradenton, FL 34203
Tel.: (941) 755-3414
Web Site: http://www.keyglass.com
Year Founded: 1992
Sales Range: $1-9.9 Million
Emp.: 46
Glass & Glazing Contractor
N.A.I.C.S.: 238150
Keith Harrison *(Sr Mgr-Production)*
Ladina Badraun *(Mgr-CAD Engrg Svc)*

KEY HANDLING SYSTEMS, INC.
137 W Commercial Ave, Moonachie, NJ 07074-1704
Tel.: (201) 933-9333 NJ
Web Site:
  http://www.keyhandling.com
Year Founded: 1965
Sales Range: $25-49.9 Million
Emp.: 40
Material Handling Systems Integration
N.A.I.C.S.: 333922
William E. Stefan *(Pres)*
Ron Baptista *(Sr VP)*
Paul Hendrikse *(Dir-Sys Sls)*

KEY IMPACT & SALES SYSTEMS, INC.
1701 CrossRds Dr, Odenton, MD 21113
Tel.: (410) 381-1239 MD
Web Site: http://www.kisales.com
Year Founded: 2000
Sales Range: $10-24.9 Million
Emp.: 600
Food Packaging & Sales Services
N.A.I.C.S.: 311999
Dan Cassidy *(CEO)*
Joe Hargadon *(Sr VP)*
Kathy Mooy *(CFO)*
Butch Cassidy *(Sr VP-Sysco Sls Div)*
Brenda Lotesta *(CMO)*
Chuck Paradowski *(Sr VP-Central Zone)*
Neil Johnson *(CIO)*
Rob Monroe *(Exec VP-Client Mgmt)*
Randy Wieland *(Pres)*
Carl Benkovich *(COO)*
Todd Gordon *(Sr VP-Western Zone)*
Keith Dwyer *(VP-Food Svc-Retail)*
T. J. Lynch *(VP-C-Stores)*
Subsidiaries:

PAMS, Inc. (1)
3361 Pomona Blvd, Pomona, CA 91768
Tel.: (800) 621-1662
Web Site: http://www.pamsinc.com
Food Service, Janitorial Supply & Hospitality
N.A.I.C.S.: 541618

KEY INDUSTRIES, INC.
400 Marble Rd, Fort Scott, KS 66701-8639
Tel.: (620) 223-2000 KS
Web Site:
  http://www.keyindustriesinc.com
Year Founded: 1908
Sales Range: $75-99.9 Million
Emp.: 46
Overalls, Work Clothes & Jeans Mfr
N.A.I.C.S.: 315250
William K. Pollock *(Chm)*
Jeff Sweetser *(CIO & VP)*
Michael Johnson *(Sr VP-Ops)*

KEY INFORMATION SYSTEMS, INC.
21700 Oxnard St Ste 250, Woodland Hills, CA 91367-7565
Tel.: (818) 992-8950 CA
Web Site: http://www.keyinfo.com
Year Founded: 1995
Sales Range: $50-74.9 Million
Emp.: 60
Systems Integration Services
N.A.I.C.S.: 541512
Lief Morin *(Pres)*
Pete Elliot *(Dir-Mktg)*
Terry Boulais *(Dir-Bus Dev)*
Mark Laughlin *(Dir-Natl Tech)*
Rob Kent *(Sr Dir-Sls & Sls-Distr)*
Brian Levine *(Dir-Sls)*
John McGreevy *(CFO)*
Gina Peterson *(VP-Ops)*
Paul Holcomb *(VP-Sls & Mktg)*
Scott Pond *(CTO)*
Scott Youngs *(CIO)*

KEY INTERNATIONAL, INC.
848 Brickell Ave Ste 1100, Miami, FL 33131
Tel.: (305) 377-1001
Web Site: http://www.key-international.com
Rev.: $88,300,000
Emp.: 20
Real Estate Investor, Developer, Owner & Lessor
N.A.I.C.S.: 531390
Jose Ardid *(Pres & CEO)*
Inigo Ardid *(Founder)*
Diego Ardid *(VP)*
Dan Mathason *(VP-Intl Dev)*
Liliana Paez *(CEO-Sls-Intl)*
Maribel Garcia *(Dir-Leasing)*
Shawn Gracey *(Exec VP-Hospitality)*

KEY MECHANICAL COMPANY
19430 68th Ave Ste B, Kent, WA 98032
Tel.: (253) 872-7392
Web Site:
  http://www.keymechanical.com
Sales Range: $10-24.9 Million
Emp.: 60
Heating & Air Conditioning Contractors
N.A.I.C.S.: 238220
Frank Leonard *(Pres)*

KEY POINT HEALTH SERVICES, INC.
135 N Parke St, Aberdeen, MD 21001
Tel.: (443) 625-1600 MD
Web Site: http://www.keypoint.org
Year Founded: 1983
Sales Range: $10-24.9 Million
Emp.: 391
Health Care Srvices
N.A.I.C.S.: 622110
Rajendra Sanikop *(Dir-Medical)*
Tessa Worsham *(Dir-Clinic)*
Shanda Owens *(Dir-Clinic)*
Shawn Cassady *(Dir-Medical)*

KEY PROFESSIONAL MEDIA, INC.
225 S 6th St Ste 5200, Minneapolis, MN 55402-4501
Web Site:
  http://www.keypromedia.com
Sales Range: $10-24.9 Million
Emp.: 90
Publishing Company
N.A.I.C.S.: 513120
Charles Thell *(Pres)*

KEY PROGRAM INCORPORATED
670 Old Connecticut Path, Framingham, MA 01701-4548
Tel.: (508) 877-3690 MA
Web Site: http://www.key.org
Year Founded: 1974

KEY PROGRAM INCORPORATED

Key Program Incorporated—(Continued)
Sales Range: $25-49.9 Million
Emp.: 500
Individual & Family Services
N.A.I.C.S.: 624190
William Lyttle (Pres)
Cynthia Hay (Dir-HR)
Carol Malone (Mgr-Recruitment & Trng)

KEY PROPERTY SOLUTIONS, LLC
1090 Northchase Pkwy SE Ste 300, Marietta, GA 30067
Tel.: (678) 324-1363
Web Site:
  http://www.keypropertyhomes.com
Year Founded: 2001
Sales Range: $10-24.9 Million
Emp.: 72
Real Estate Investment Services
N.A.I.C.S.: 531390
Jeff W. Brock (Founder & CEO)
Jim Mauck (CFO)
Brian Johnson (CIO)
Bruce Douglas (Gen Counsel)

KEY PUNCH COMPUTER TEMPORARIES
936 Broadway, New York, NY 10010
Tel.: (212) 979-1400
Web Site:
  http://www.keysystems.com
Sales Range: $10-24.9 Million
Emp.: 160
Computer & Software Stores
N.A.I.C.S.: 449210
Sara Mallow (Chm)
Jay Geffen (Controller)

KEY SOLUTIONS REAL ESTATE GROUP
6021 Midnight Pass Rd, Sarasota, FL 34242
Tel.: (941) 894-1255
Web Site:
  http://www.keysolutionsrealestate.com
Sales Range: $10-24.9 Million
Emp.: 20
Real Estate Broker
N.A.I.C.S.: 531210
Francis Saltalamacchia (Owner)

KEY WEST BOATS INC.
593 Ridgeville Rd, Ridgeville, SC 29472
Tel.: (843) 873-0112
Web Site:
  http://www.keywestboatsinc.com
Sales Range: $10-24.9 Million
Emp.: 80
Fishing Vessels Mfr
N.A.I.C.S.: 336611
William Holseberg (Pres & CEO)
Walter Renken (Mgr)
Ron Inabinett (Controller)

KEY WEST LAMP COMPANY INC.
5223 S 16th Ave, Tampa, FL 33619
Tel.: (813) 241-0241   FL
Year Founded: 1990
Sales Range: $10-24.9 Million
Emp.: 150
Lamp & Other Household Lighting Products Mfr
N.A.I.C.S.: 423610
Jeffrey Marple (Pres)

KEYAD, LLC
1723 N Loop 1604 E Ste 211, San Antonio, TX 78232
Tel.: (210) 363-2861   TX
Year Founded: 1998
Sales Range: Less than $1 Million
Emp.: 25
Advetising Agency
N.A.I.C.S.: 541810
Mike Pilkilton (Owner)

KEYBOARD CONCEPTS INC.
5539 Van Nuys Blvd, Sherman Oaks, CA 91401
Tel.: (818) 787-0201
Web Site:
  http://www.keyboardconcepts.com
Year Founded: 1983
Piano Retailer & Whslr
N.A.I.C.S.: 459140
Dennis M. Hagerty (Founder & Pres)
Jeff Falgien (VP)
Adam Chester (Sls Mgr--Sherman Oaks)
Todd Peterson (Store Mgr-Fountain Valley)
John Mila De La Roca (Asst Store Mgr-Fountain Valley)
Michael Chan Williamson (Store Mgr-Pasadena)

KEYCO DISTRIBUTORS, INC.
625 New Commerce Blvd, Wilkes Barre, PA 18706-1433
Tel.: (570) 825-9445   DE
Year Founded: 1949
Sales Range: $10-24.9 Million
Emp.: 73
Retail Groceries
N.A.I.C.S.: 424410
Rose McKenzie (Controller)
Francis X. Kowalski Jr. (Pres)

KEYEDIN SOLUTIONS, INC.
5001 American Blvd W Ste 1010, Minneapolis, MN 55437
Tel.: (952) 835-1041   DE
Web Site: http://www.keyedin.com
Software-as-a-Service & Consulting Services
N.A.I.C.S.: 541690
Lauri Klaus (Founder & CEO)
Sheldon Scheu (VP-Dev)
Kevin Hurley (CTO)
Ian Needs (VP-Mktg)
Jessica Guevara (VP-Mktg & Sls Ops)
Lynda Dahlheimer (Sr VP-Mktg)
Martin Philips (VP-Dev)
Paul Gleghorn (VP-SaaS Infrastructure)

Subsidiaries:
KeyedIn (UK) Limited (1)
Maple House Woodland Park, Cleckheaton, BD19 6BW, West Yorkshire, United Kingdom
Tel.: (44) 1274 863 300
Web Site: http://www.keyedin.com
Emp.: 27
Software-as-a-Service & Consulting Services
N.A.I.C.S.: 541690
Lauri Klauss (CEO)

Subsidiary (Domestic):
KeyedIn Solutions Holdings Limited (2)
Maple House Woodland Park, Cleckheaton, BD19 6BW, West Yorkshire, United Kingdom
Tel.: (44) 1274863300
Web Site: http://www.keyedin.com
Sales Range: $1-9.9 Million
Holding Services
N.A.I.C.S.: 551112
Paul Gleghorn (Dir-Product Dev)

Subsidiary (Domestic):
KeyedIn Solutions Limited (3)
Maple House, Woodland Park, Cleckheaton, BD19 6BW, W Yorkshire, United Kingdom
Tel.: (44) 1274 863 300
Web Site: http://www.keyedin.com
Software Development Services
N.A.I.C.S.: 541511

KEYES MOTORS, INC.
5855 Van Nuys Blvd, Van Nuys, CA 91401
Tel.: (818) 907-4456   CA
Web Site: http://www.keyescars.com
Year Founded: 1960
Sales Range: $100-124.9 Million
Emp.: 1,300
Retailer of New & Used Automobiles & Automobile Parts
N.A.I.C.S.: 441110
Howard Keyes (Pres)
Mollie Heitzig (CFO)
Howard Tenenbaum (Sr Dir-Mktg)

Subsidiaries:
Keyes Lexus (1)
5905 Van Nuys Blvd, Van Nuys, CA 91401-3624
Tel.: (818) 379-4000
Web Site: http://www.keyeslexus.com
Sales Range: $25-49.9 Million
Emp.: 100
New Car Whslr
N.A.I.C.S.: 441110
Matt Zanjani (Mgr-Sls)

Keyes Toyota (1)
5855 Van Nuys Blvd, Van Nuys, CA 91401
Tel.: (818) 782-0122
Sales Range: $10-24.9 Million
Emp.: 70
Car Whslr
N.A.I.C.S.: 441110
Howard Tenenbaum (Principal)
Shane Gorgen (Dir-Fin)

KEYGENT LLC
999 N Sepulveda Blvd Ste 500, El Segundo, CA 90245-2716
Tel.: (310) 322-4222   CA
Web Site:
  http://www.keygentcorp.com
Sales Range: $1-9.9 Million
Strategic & Technical Consulting Services
N.A.I.C.S.: 541618
Tony Hsieh (Mng Dir)
Chet Wang (Mng Dir)
Chris Hiatt (VP)

KEYLIMETIE, LLC.
3011 Butterfield Rd Ste 250, Oak Brook, IL 60523
Tel.: (630) 598-9000
Web Site: http://www.keylimetie.com
Year Founded: 2007
Sales Range: $1-9.9 Million
Emp.: 36
Mobile Application Software Development Services
N.A.I.C.S.: 541511
Chris Pautsch (Co-Founder & CEO)
Brian Pautsch (Co-Founder & Pres)
Christen Blaze (Dir-HR)
Dave Bost (CTO)

KEYMARK CORPORATION
1188 Cayadutta Rd, Fonda, NY 12068
Tel.: (518) 853-3421   NY
Web Site:
  http://www.keymarkcorp.com
Year Founded: 1965
Sales Range: $150-199.9 Million
Emp.: 1,000
Aluminum Extrusions
N.A.I.C.S.: 331318
Gus Brotsis (VP-Engrg)
Bob Channell (VP-Ops-New York)
William L. Keller III (Pres)

Subsidiaries:
Kasson & Keller (1)
60 School Ln, Fonda, NY 12068   (100%)
Tel.: (518) 853-3421
Web Site: http://www.kas-kel.com
Sales Range: $25-49.9 Million
Emp.: 275
Mfr Windows
N.A.I.C.S.: 326199
David D. Klopp (Ops Officer-Mfg)

KEYMARK, INC.
105 Tech Ln, Liberty, SC 29657
Tel.: (864) 343-0500   SC
Web Site:
  http://www.keymarkinc.com
Year Founded: 1996
Sales Range: $10-24.9 Million
Emp.: 150
Document Management Software
N.A.I.C.S.: 513210
James D. Wanner (Founder & Chief Expectations Officer)
Jami Mullikin (VP-Mktg)
Cameron Boland (VP-Ops)
Dan Christie (VP-Fin & Legal)
Victoria Pruitt (VP-Sls)

Subsidiaries:
Keymark, Inc. - Northeast (1)
3 Werner Way Ste 300, Lebanon, NJ 08833
Tel.: (908) 236-6505
Sales Range: $1-9.9 Million
Emp.: 16
Document Management Services
N.A.I.C.S.: 561499
Cindy Knowles (CEO)
Wes Knowles (Reg Dir-Sls-Northeast)

KEYNETICS, INC.
917 Lusk St Ste 300, Boise, ID 83706
Tel.: (208) 489-3300   DE
Web Site: http://www.keynetics.com
Year Founded: 1998
Sales Range: $200-249.9 Million
Emp.: 70
Internet-Based Businesses Developer
N.A.I.C.S.: 541511
Bradley J. Wiskirchen (CEO)
Timothy P. Barber (Co-Founder)
Geoffrey Hoyl (Co-Founder & Chm)
Eileen Langan Barber (Co-Founder)

Subsidiaries:
Click Sales Inc. (1)
917 S Lusk St Ste 200, Boise, ID 83706
Tel.: (208) 489-3300
Web Site: http://www.clickbank.com
Online Retailer
N.A.I.C.S.: 541613
Jennifer Johannsen (VP-Ops)
Kate Wallace (VP-Client Dev)
Geoffrey Hoyl (Chm)
Eileen Langan Barber (Co-Founder & Dir-Keynetics)
Timothy P. Barber (Founder)
Chris McClave (VP-Product Mgmt)
Glenn Michael (CFO)
Alex Moore (VP-Sls & Acct Mgmt)
Bill Wynne (VP-Mktg)
Mick Wiskerchen (COO)
David Lewis (Chief Strategy Officer)
Kelly Householder (CEO)
Jason Scherer (CTO)

KEYPATH EDUCATION LLC
933 N Meacham Rd Ste 400, Schaumburg, IL 60173
Tel.: (224) 419-7988
Web Site:
  http://www.keypathedu.com
Year Founded: 2014
Sales Range: $25-49.9 Million
Emp.: 295
Education Training Services
N.A.I.C.S.: 611710
Steve Fireng (CEO)
Jon Gaunt (COO)
Eric Israel (Gen Counsel & Sec)
Peter Vlerick (CFO)
Daniel Baresic (VP-Mktg)

KEYS ENERGY SERVICES
1001 James St, Key West, FL 33040
Tel.: (305) 295-1000
Web Site:
http://www.keysenergy.com
Rev.: $93,700,000
Emp.: 145
Power & Communication Line & Related Structures Construction
N.A.I.C.S.: 237130
Suzanne Greager *(Dir-HR)*
Lynne E. Tejeda *(CEO & Gen Mgr)*
John Wetzler *(CFO & Asst Gen Mgr)*

KEYSER & MILLER FORD INC.
8 E Main St, Collegeville, PA 19426
Tel.: (610) 489-9366
Web Site:
http://www.keysermillerford.com
Sales Range: $25-49.9 Million
Emp.: 43
Automobiles, New & Used
N.A.I.C.S.: 441110
Kathy Krall *(Controller)*
Ron Keyser *(Owner & Pres)*

KEYSER BROTHERS CADILLAC INC.
4130 Sheridan Dr, Williamsville, NY 14221
Tel.: (716) 634-4100
Web Site: http://www.keysercars.com
Sales Range: $25-49.9 Million
Emp.: 40
New & Used Car Dealer
N.A.I.C.S.: 441110
Randy Helf *(Pres)*

KEYSER, LLC
4141 N Scottsdale Rd Ste 150, Scottsdale, AZ 85251
Tel.: (602) 953-9737
Web Site: http://www.keysrco.com
Year Founded: 2013
Sales Range: $10-24.9 Million
Emp.: 50
Real Estate Services
N.A.I.C.S.: 531390
Jonathan Keyser *(Founder)*

KEYSOURCE MEDICAL, INC.
7820 Palace Dr, Cincinnati, OH 45249
Tel.: (513) 469-7881 OH
Web Site:
http://www.keysourcemedical.com
Year Founded: 1996
Sales Range: $10-24.9 Million
Emp.: 50
Generic Pharmaceutical Wholesale Distr
N.A.I.C.S.: 424210
Stephanie Ring *(Co-Founder, Pres & CEO)*
Dave Hoffman *(VP)*

KEYSTON BROS. INC.
2801 Academy Way, Sacramento, CA 95815
Tel.: (916) 927-5851 CA
Web Site:
http://www.keystonbros.com
Year Founded: 1868
Sales Range: $25-49.9 Million
Emp.: 210
Distr of Nondurable Goods
N.A.I.C.S.: 424990
Dee Duncan *(CEO)*
Ann S. Duncan *(Sr VP-HR)*
Dennis Bueker *(Mgr-Sls)*

KEYSTONE AGENCY INVESTORS LLC
2600 Commerce Dr, Harrisburg, PA 17110
Tel.: (570) 473-4362
Web Site:
http://www.kaiagencies.com
Insurance & Brokerages Services
N.A.I.C.S.: 524210
Dan Girardi *(Chief Acq Officer)*
Angela Pacheco *(Chief HR Officer)*
David E. Boedker Sr. *(CEO)*

Subsidiaries:

Bowersox Insurance Agency Company (1)
12647 Olive Blvd Ste 400, Creve Coeur, MO 63141
Tel.: (314) 832-8010
Web Site: http://www.biaco.com
Sales Range: $1-9.9 Million
Emp.: 24
Insurance Services
N.A.I.C.S.: 524210
Douglas S. Clift *(Pres)*

Cartier Agency, Inc. (1)
2631 W Superior St, Duluth, MN 55806
Tel.: (218) 727-5992
Web Site: http://www.caduluth.com
Sales Range: $1-9.9 Million
Emp.: 18
Insurance Agents, Brokers, And Service, N
N.A.I.C.S.: 524210
Cory Cartier *(VP)*
Matthew Cartier *(Pres)*
Jeremy Jeannette *(VP-Life & Health Sls)*
Joe Jeannette *(Pres-Cartier Fin Svcs)*

KEYSTONE BANCSHARES, INC.
11500 Bee Caves Rd Ste 150, Austin, TX 78738
Tel.: (512) 982-9150 TX
Web Site:
http://www.bankkeystone.com
Year Founded: 2017
Sales Range: $1-9.9 Million
Bank Holding Company
N.A.I.C.S.: 551111
Jeffrey A. Wilkinson *(Founder, Chm & CEO)*

Subsidiaries:

Keystone Bank, National Association (1)
11500 Bee Caves Rd Ste 150, Austin, TX 78738
Tel.: (512) 982-9150
Web Site: http://www.bankkeystone.com
Sales Range: $1-9.9 Million
Commericial Banking
N.A.I.C.S.: 522110
Jeffrey A. Wilkinson *(Chm & CEO)*
Bryan St. George *(Pres)*
Mark Few *(COO)*

KEYSTONE BUILDERS RESOURCE GROUP, INC.
1207 Roseneath Rd Ste 200, Richmond, VA 23230-4621
Tel.: (804) 354-8830 DE
Year Founded: 1973
Sales Range: $10-24.9 Million
Emp.: 27
Single-Family Housing Construction
N.A.I.C.S.: 236115
Earl Dickinson *(Pres)*
Teresa Dowdy *(VP)*

KEYSTONE CAPITAL, INC.
155 N Wacker Dr Ste 4150, Chicago, IL 60606
Tel.: (312) 219-7900 IL
Web Site:
http://www.keystonecapital.com
Year Founded: 1994
Privater Equity Firm
N.A.I.C.S.: 523999
Scott L. Gwilliam *(Co-Founder & Mng Dir)*
David A. Greer *(Mng Dir)*
Brian C. Chung *(CFO)*
Dennis J. Howe *(Principal)*
Chaoran Jin *(Mng Dir)*
Bill A. Sommerschield *(Principal)*
Jason S. Van Zant *(Mng Dir)*
Andrew C. Wehr *(Principal-Fin)*
Megan C. Anderson *(Office Mgr)*
Kent P. Dauten *(Chm)*

Subsidiaries:

CONSOR Engineers, LLC (1)
15310 Park Row, Houston, TX 77084
Tel.: (281) 493-4140
Transportation & Water Resources Engineering Services
N.A.I.C.S.: 541330
Scott Gwilliam *(Pres & CEO)*

Subsidiary (Domestic):

TKW Consulting Engineers Inc. (2)
5621 Banner Dr, Fort Myers, FL 33912
Tel.: (239) 278-1992
Web Site: http://www.tkwonline.com
Sales Range: $1-9.9 Million
Emp.: 20
Engineeering Services
N.A.I.C.S.: 541330
Trudi K. Williams *(Owner & CEO)*
Douglas Eckmann *(COO & Mgr-Engrg)*
Patrick Day *(Project Mgr)*
Brett Rosenblum *(Mgr-Civil Engrg)*

Cherry Hill Programs, Inc. (1)
4 E Stow Rd Ste #1, Marlton, NJ 08053
Tel.: (856) 663-1616
Web Site: http://www.cherryhillphoto.com
Sales Range: $1-9.9 Million
Emp.: 50
Holiday Photography Services
N.A.I.C.S.: 541921
Gail Hargaden *(Dir-Special Events)*
Jackie Abate *(Dir-HR)*
James Hershberger *(Dir-Ops-Warehouse)*
Jennifer Mullin *(Mgr-Ops-Digital)*
Lauren Oswald *(Mgr-Mktg & Partner Rels)*
Dianne K. Plover *(Dir-Contract Talent)*

Subsidiary (Domestic):

Photogenic, Inc. (2)
230 E Ohio St Ste 600, Chicago, IL 60611
Tel.: (312) 836-5420
Web Site: https://cherryhillprograms.com
Rev.: $7,400,000
Emp.: 600
Commercial Photography
N.A.I.C.S.: 541922
Lynn Talamonti Nield *(Mgr-Sls)*

Merge Design & Interactive, Inc. (1)
200 E Randolph St Ste 3450, Chicago, IL 60601
Tel.: (312) 787-7667
Web Site: http://www.mergeworld.com
Digital Marketing & Advertising Services
N.A.I.C.S.: 541810
Riley Sheehan *(CTO)*
Lauren Sheehan *(Exec VP & Head-Design)*
Ron Bess *(Chm)*
Kellie Bliss *(Pres/Mng Dir-Chicago)*
Kevin Houlihan *(Pres/Chief Creative Officer-Chicago)*
Lauren Tucker *(Chief Strategy Officer)*
Troy Mastin *(CFO)*
Kerry Griffin *(Chief Talent Officer)*
Bob Bernstein *(Exec VP & Dir-Media)*
Andrew Pelosi *(Pres-Boston)*
Pat McGloin *(Pres-Specialty Health)*
Bob Minihan *(Chief Creative Officer & Exec VP)*
Stephanie Rogers *(Exec VP-Strategy & Analytics)*
Rob Powers *(Exec VP-Fin Svcs Practice Area)*
Justine Fedak *(CMO)*

Subsidiary (Domestic):

The Sandbox Group LLC (2)
1 E Wacker Dr Ste 3200, Chicago, IL 60601
Tel.: (312) 803-1900
Advertising Services
N.A.I.C.S.: 541810
Joseph E. Kuchta *(Principal & Chief Client Officer)*
Mark Goble *(Principal)*
Nancy Finigan *(Dir)*
John Hilbrich *(CEO)*
Jack Federico *(CFO)*
Angela Potts *(Sr VP-Client Svcs)*
Angelo Pizzuto *(VP & Dir-Fin Integration)*
Brian Rose *(Sr VP-Project Mgmt)*
Chad Smith *(Mng Dir)*
Chhavi Saxena *(VP-Fin)*
Chris Gavazzoni *(VP-Creative Svcs)*
Chris Weber *(Sr VP-Strategy)*
Christina Hillestad *(VP)*
Ryan Van Pelt *(Exec VP-Client Svcs)*
Roya Partovi *(Chief Creative Officer-New York)*
Barry Vuckso *(Sr VP & Grp Acct Dir-Client Svc)*

Branch (Domestic):

yMarketing, LLC (3)
4000 MacArthur Blvd Ste 350, Newport Beach, CA 92660
Tel.: (714) 545-2550
Digital Advertising Agency
N.A.I.C.S.: 541810
Falon Fischmann *(Assoc Dir)*

Nature Soy LLC (1)
713 N 10th St, Philadelphia, PA 19123
Tel.: (215) 765-8889
Web Site: http://naturesoy.com
Soy & Vegetarian Food Products Producer & Distr
N.A.I.C.S.: 311224

Vista International Packaging, LLC. (1)
1126 88th Pl, Kenosha, WI 53143
Tel.: (262) 694-2276
Web Site: http://www.vistapackaging.com
Food Packaging Supplier
N.A.I.C.S.: 561910
Mark Baxter *(VP-Supply Chain & Category Mgmt)*
Kevin G. Lewis *(Mgr-Product)*

KEYSTONE CHEVROLET INC.
8700 Charles Page Blvd, Sand Springs, OK 74063
Tel.: (918) 245-2201
Web Site:
http://www.keystonechevrolet.com
Sales Range: $50-74.9 Million
Emp.: 74
New & Used Car Dealers
N.A.I.C.S.: 441110
Michael Henry *(Pres)*
Michael Farley *(Sec)*
Debbie Stewart *(Controller)*

KEYSTONE CLEARWATER SOLUTIONS, LLC
34 Northeast Dr, Hershey, PA 17033
Tel.: (717) 508-0550 DE
Web Site:
http://www.keystoneclear.com
Year Founded: 2009
Wastewater Pipeline Construction Services
N.A.I.C.S.: 237110
Daniel Dalton *(Pres & COO)*
Jeffrey Wehler *(Sr VP)*
Jay Heckman *(VP-Eastern Appalachia)*
Michael Katz *(CFO)*
Adam R. McDonough *(COO)*
Andrew Strassner *(VP-Construction & Engrg)*

KEYSTONE COFFEE COMPANY
2230 Will Wool Dr Ste 100, San Jose, CA 95112
Tel.: (408) 998-2221 CA
Web Site:
http://www.keystonecoffee.com
Year Founded: 1867
Sales Range: $75-99.9 Million
Emp.: 11
Coffee Roaster & Retailer
N.A.I.C.S.: 445298
Tim Wright *(Owner & Pres)*

KEYSTONE CONSULTING ENGINEERS, INC.

KEYSTONE CONSULTING ENGINEERS, INC.   U.S. PRIVATE

Keystone Consulting Engineers, Inc.—(Continued)
2870 Emrick Blvd, Bethlehem, PA 18020-8014
Tel.: (610) 865-4555
Web Site: http://www.kceinc.com
Year Founded: 1972
Sales Range: $1-9.9 Million
Emp.: 85
Consulting Engineers & Surveyors
N.A.I.C.S.: 541618
Albert R. Kortze *(Pres & CEO)*
Kevin D. Harwick *(Treas)*
J. Scott Stenroos *(VP)*
Kevin J. Horvath *(Asst Treas)*
Frank J. Clark *(Sec)*

Subsidiaries:

Keystone Consulting Engineers, Inc. (1)
6235 Hamilton Blvd, Wescosville, PA 18106-9797   (100%)
Tel.: (610) 395-0971
Web Site: http://www.keystoneconsultingengineers.com
Civil & Structural Engineering & Consulting Services
N.A.I.C.S.: 237990
Frank Clark *(Office Mgr)*

Keystone Consulting Engineers, Inc. (1)
865 Interchange Rd, Kresgeville, PA 18333-0639   (100%)
Tel.: (610) 681-5233
Web Site: http://www.keystoneconsultingengineers.com
Emp.: 25
Civil & Structural Engineering & Consulting Services
N.A.I.C.S.: 541330
Eric S. Snyder *(Office Mgr)*

KEYSTONE CORPORATION
5410 Trinity Rd Ste 215, Raleigh, NC 27607
Tel.: (919) 747-7910
Web Site: http://www.keystonecorporation.com
Year Founded: 1979
Land Subdividers & Developers, Commercial
N.A.I.C.S.: 237210
J. Patrick Gavaghan *(Pres & CEO)*
Keith Schneider *(Exec VP & Project Mgr)*
James C. Little *(CFO & COO)*
Michael Blount *(Exec VP-Dev & Construction)*
Charles Wilson *(Dir-Fin)*
David Williams *(Mgr-Property & Mgr-Construction)*

KEYSTONE DEDICATED LOGISTICS
800 N Bell Ave Bldg 6 Ste 100, Carnegie, PA 15106
Tel.: (412) 429-2141
Web Site: http://www.kdlog.com
Year Founded: 1999
Sales Range: $10-24.9 Million
Emp.: 41
Freight Transportation Services
N.A.I.C.S.: 488510
Robert Hammel *(Pres)*
Richard Coyner *(VP)*
Raymond Sevacko *(Coord-Auditor & Invoicing)*

KEYSTONE DENTAL, INC.
144 Middlesex Tpke, Burlington, MA 01803
Tel.: (781) 328-3490
Web Site: http://www.keystonedental.com
Sales Range: $25-49.9 Million
Emp.: 100

Surgical Dental Implant Mfr
N.A.I.C.S.: 339114
Bob Goulet *(Mgr-Inside Sls)*
Daniel J. Levangie *(Chm)*

Subsidiaries:

Keystone Dental AB (1)
Furubergsvagen 3, Saro, 42911, Kungsbacka, Sweden
Tel.: (46) 31936823
Web Site: http://www.keystonedental.eu
Sales Range: $25-49.9 Million
Emp.: 2
Implantable Medical Devices Mfr
N.A.I.C.S.: 339112
Hajan Pletjer *(Mgr)*

Keystone Dental GmbH (1)
Jagerstrasse 66, Alfter, 53347, Bonn, Germany
Tel.: (49) 222292940
Web Site: http://www.keystonedental.com
Sales Range: $25-49.9 Million
Emp.: 15
Implantable Medical Devices Mfr
N.A.I.C.S.: 339112

Keystone Dental S.A.S. (1)
8 Rte des bois, 38500, Voiron, France
Tel.: (33) 562214045
Web Site: http://www.keystonedental.eu
Sales Range: $25-49.9 Million
Emp.: 8
Implantable Medical Devices Mfr
N.A.I.C.S.: 339112

Keystone Dental SpA (1)
Via A Fleming 19, 37135, Verona, 37135, Italy
Tel.: (39) 045 8230294
Web Site: http://www.keystonedental.com
Emp.: 10
Implantable Medical Devices Mfr
N.A.I.C.S.: 339112
Frank Currenti *(Mng Dir)*

KEYSTONE DIGITAL IMAGING, INCORPORATED
200 Racoosin Dr, Aston, PA 19014
Tel.: (610) 604-0300
Web Site: http://www.kdi-inc.com
Rev.: $5,000,000
Emp.: 100
Computer System Design Services
N.A.I.C.S.: 541512
Ricardo Salcedo *(Pres & CEO)*
Greg Bryan *(CTO)*
Don Schatzman *(Pres-Sls)*

Subsidiaries:

Kelly & Partners, Inc. (1)
1500 Market St, Philadelphia, PA 19102
Tel.: (215) 569-3600
Web Site: http://www.kellyandpartners.com
Rev.: $1,700,000
Emp.: 100
Agents & Managers for Artists, Athletes, Entertainers & Other Public Figures
N.A.I.C.S.: 711410
Kevin P. Kelly *(Pres)*
Mike FitzPatrick *(VP-Sls)*

KEYSTONE DODGE, INC.
2350 Lehigh St, Allentown, PA 18103
Tel.: (610) 791-1900
Sales Range: $10-24.9 Million
Emp.: 50
Car Whslr
N.A.I.C.S.: 441110
Charles Merrill *(Pres)*

KEYSTONE ELECTRICAL MANUFACTURING COMPANY
2511 Bell Ave, Des Moines, IA 50321
Tel.: (515) 283-2567
Web Site: http://www.keystoneemc.com
Year Founded: 1964
Sales Range: $10-24.9 Million
Emp.: 100
Protection & Control Switchboards & Switchgear Mfr

N.A.I.C.S.: 335313
Frederick V. Buie *(Pres)*

KEYSTONE FORD
301 Walker Rd, Chambersburg, PA 17201
Tel.: (717) 264-5104
Web Site: http://www.keystoneford.com
Rev.: $25,800,000
Emp.: 50
New & Used Automobile Dealer
N.A.I.C.S.: 441110
Aldine Martin *(Pres)*
Clayton Black *(Gen Mgr)*
Claudia Place *(Office Mgr)*
Gary Paolini *(Mgr-Bus Dev)*

KEYSTONE FRICTION HINGE CO.
520 Matthews Blvd, Williamsport, PA 17702
Tel.: (570) 323-9479
Web Site: http://www.kfhinge.com
Sales Range: $10-24.9 Million
Emp.: 55
Metal Products Mfr & Distr
N.A.I.C.S.: 332119
Edward J. Hannan *(Pres)*

KEYSTONE FUELS, INC.
2432 Emrick Blvd, Bethlehem, PA 18020-8006
Tel.: (610) 867-4620
Web Site: http://www.keystonefuels.com
Gasoline & Diesel Motor Fuel Distr
N.A.I.C.S.: 457210
Gary A. Dell'Alba *(Pres)*
Jonathan P. Krum *(COO)*
Tom E. Donovan *(Sls Mgr)*

KEYSTONE FUNDING, INC.
519 S Red Haven Ln, Dover, DE 19901
Tel.: (302) 508-6111
Web Site: http://www.keystonefunding.com
Year Founded: 2006
Sales Range: $1-9.9 Million
Emp.: 50
Mortgage Banking Services
N.A.I.C.S.: 522292
Tim Paret *(CEO)*

KEYSTONE GROUP HOLDINGS INC.
400 N Ashley Dr Ste 1900, Tampa, FL 33602
Tel.: (813) 225-4650
Sales Range: $50-74.9 Million
Emp.: 25
Memories Through Pictures, Belongings & Keepsakes Funeral Services
N.A.I.C.S.: 541990
Steve Shaffer *(Founder & Chm)*
James Price *(COO)*

KEYSTONE GROUP, L.P.
201 Main St Ste 3100, Fort Worth, TX 76102-3115
Tel.: (817) 390-8400
Year Founded: 1985
Investment Holding Company
N.A.I.C.S.: 551112
Jay H. Herbert *(Gen Counsel)*
Bryan Barrett *(VP & CFO)*

Subsidiaries:

Aerion Corporation (1)
5190 Neil Rd Ste 500, Reno, NV 89502
Tel.: (775) 337-6682
Web Site: http://www.aerionsupersonic.com
Sales Range: $50-74.9 Million
Emp.: 11
Aeronautical Engineering
N.A.I.C.S.: 541715

Jim Chase *(Chief Engr)*
Andres Garzon *(Engr)*
Jason Matisheck *(Engr)*
Ernest Edwards *(Chief Comml Officer & Sr VP)*
Catherine D. Rice *(VP-Bus Mgmt)*
Roger Noble *(VP-Sls-East)*
Steve Berroth *(Sr VP-Ops)*
Tom Vice *(Chm, Pres & CEO)*
Douglas Coleman *(Gen Counsel & Exec VP-Governance & Compliance)*
Scott Kalister *(VP-Worldwide Support & Logistics)*
Gene Holloway *(VP-Boomless Cruise & Environmental Responsibility)*
Andrew Hellen *(VP-Cockpit & Subsystems)*

Bass Enterprises Production Co. (1)
201 Main St Ste 2700, Fort Worth, TX 76102-3105
Tel.: (817) 390-8400
Holding Company; Petroleum & Natural Gas Drilling & Extraction
N.A.I.C.S.: 551112
Frank McCreight *(Sr VP)*

L3 Mobile-Vision, Inc. (1)
400 Commons Wy, Rockaway, NJ 07866
Tel.: (800) 336-8475
Web Site: http://www.mobile-vision.com
In-Vehicle Video Recording Systems for Law Enforcement Agencies Mfr & Supplier
N.A.I.C.S.: 334310
Gautam Gole *(Interim VP & Gen Mgr)*

Oak Hill Capital Partners, L.P. (1)
65 E 55th St 32 Fl, New York, NY 10022
Tel.: (212) 527-8400
Web Site: http://www.oakhillcapital.com
Sales Range: $200-249.9 Million
Privater Equity Firm
N.A.I.C.S.: 523999
J. Taylor Crandall *(Mng Partner)*
Tyler J. Wolfram *(CEO & Mng Partner)*
John R. Monsky *(Partner & Gen Counsel)*
Scott A. Baker *(Partner)*
David S. Scott *(Partner)*
Benjamin Diesbach *(Partner)*
William J. Pade *(Partner)*
John P. Rachwalski *(Partner)*
Brian N. Cherry *(Partner)*
Jon Zagrodzky *(Mng Dir & Chief Compliance Officer)*
Andrew M. Burdick *(Mng Dir & Head-Mktg)*
Steven G. Puccinelli *(Partner)*
James Tarnok *(Controller)*
Christopher Taylor *(CFO)*
Christopher M. Williams *(Principal)*
Ken DiPietro *(Chief Talent Officer)*
Ennio Montinaro *(Chief Admin Officer)*
Adam W. Hahn *(Principal)*
Allan I. Kahn *(Chief Compliance Officer & Assoc Gen Counsel)*
Jeffery R. Mettam *(Principal)*
Stratton R. Heath III *(Partner)*
Steven B. Gruber *(Mng Partner-Advisory)*

Holding (Domestic):

Alibris, Inc. (2)
1250 45th St Ste 100, Emeryville, CA 94608
Tel.: (510) 594-4500
Web Site: http://www.alibris.com
Sales Range: $25-49.9 Million
Online Books, Movies, Music Services
N.A.I.C.S.: 424920
Mark Nason *(VP-Ops)*
Liz Derr *(COO)*
Richard M. Weatherford *(Founder)*

Berlin Packaging LLC (2)
525 W Monroe St, Chicago, IL 60661
Tel.: (312) 876-9292
Web Site: https://www.berlinpackaging.com
Emp.: 2,200
Industrial Supplies Merchant Wholesalers
N.A.I.C.S.: 423840
Robert Goldberg *(Chief Legal Officer & Exec VP-Strategic Partnerships)*
Michael Grebe *(Chm)*
Balaji Jayaseelan *(VP-Sustainability)*
Scott Jost *(VP-Innovation & Design)*

Plant (Domestic):

Berlin Packaging - Fort Lee (3)
1 Bridge Plz 4th Fl Ste 419, Fort Lee, NJ 07024
Tel.: (201) 947-7744

Web Site: http://www.berlinpackaging.com
Sales Range: $50-74.9 Million
Emp.: 10
Packaging Products Whslr & Distr
N.A.I.C.S.: 423840
Jonathan Rabinowitz *(Dir-Bus Dev)*

Berlin Packaging - Pittsburgh (3)
1195 Washington Pike, Bridgeville, PA 15017-2858
Tel.: (412) 257-3000
Web Site: http://www.berlinpackaging.com
Packaging Product Distr
N.A.I.C.S.: 423840
Elaine McDermott *(Mgr-Ops)*

Berlin Packaging - Rancho Cucamonga (3)
11096 Jersey Blvd Ste 102, Rancho Cucamonga, CA 91730
Tel.: (909) 987-6000
Web Site: http://www.berlinpackaging.com
Emp.: 15
Plastic & Tin Industrial Containers Distr
N.A.I.C.S.: 423840

Subsidiary (Non-US):

Consolidated Bottle Corporation (3)
77 Union Street, Toronto, M6N 3N2, ON, Canada
Tel.: (416) 656-7777
Web Site: http://www.consbottle.com
Injection Molding & Decorating Services
N.A.I.C.S.: 333248
Jonathan Rutman *(Pres)*

Subsidiary (Domestic):

Diablo Valley Packaging Inc. (3)
2373 N Watney Way, Fairfield, CA 94533-6746
Tel.: (707) 422-4300
Web Site: http://www.dvpackaging.com
Emp.: 70
Packaged Materials Including Glass & Plastic
N.A.I.C.S.: 424990
Bruce Gardner *(Controller)*
Bill Otwell *(Dir-Ops)*
Rodrigo Melo *(Dir-Bus Dev)*

Subsidiary (Non-US):

H. Erben Limited (3)
Lady Lane Hadleigh, Ipswich, IP7 6AS, United Kingdom
Tel.: (44) 1473 823011
Web Site: http://www.erben.co.uk
Packaging Machinery Mfr
N.A.I.C.S.: 333993
Sasha Erben *(CEO)*

Joint Venture (Domestic):

Charter NEX Films, Inc. (2)
1246 E High St, Milton, WI 53563
Tel.: (608) 868-5757
Web Site: http://charternex.com
Specialty Films Mfr
N.A.I.C.S.: 325992
Kathy Bolhous *(CEO)*

Clarity Telecom, LLC (2)
5100 S Broadband Ln, Sioux Falls, SD 57108
Tel.: (605) 965-9393
Holding Company; Cable Television, Internet & Telephone Services
N.A.I.C.S.: 551112
Jim Gleason *(CEO)*
Keith Davidson *(CFO)*
Larry Eby *(COO)*

Subsidiary (Domestic):

NTS, Inc. (3)
1220 Broadway, Lubbock, TX 79401
Tel.: (806) 771-5212
Web Site: http://www.ntscom.com
Sales Range: $50-74.9 Million
Emp.: 200
Holding Company; Long Distance Voice & Data Communications Services
N.A.I.C.S.: 551112
Cyrus Driver *(Pres & CEO)*

Subsidiary (Domestic):

NTS Communications, Inc. (4)
1220 Broadway St, Lubbock, TX 79401-1610
Tel.: (806) 797-0687
Web Site: http://www.ntscom.com
Sales Range: $50-74.9 Million
Telephone, Internet, Data Products, Point to Point & Voice Mail Communications Services
N.A.I.C.S.: 517810
Cyrus Driver *(Pres & CEO)*
Deborah Crawford *(Exec VP & COO)*
Don Pittman *(Exec VP & CFO)*
Michael McDaniel *(VP-Svc Delivery & IT Strategy)*
Priscilla Rivas *(VP-Network Admin)*
Roberto Chang *(VP-Products & Mktg)*
Wendy J. Lee *(VP-HR)*
Daniel Wheeler *(Gen Counsel & VP)*

Subsidiary (Domestic):

Communications Brokers, Inc. (5)
2305 129th Pl SE, Everett, WA 98208-7131
Tel.: (425) 483-8882
Communication Equipment Repair & Maintenance Services
N.A.I.C.S.: 811210

Subsidiary (Domestic):

Xfone USA, Inc. (4)
1220 Broadway, Lubbock, TX 79401
Tel.: (806) 797-0687
Web Site: http://www.ntscom.com
Sales Range: $50-74.9 Million
Emp.: 200
Communications Services Including Local, Long Distance & Data/Internet Solutions
N.A.I.C.S.: 517810

Subsidiary (Domestic):

Gulf Coast Utilities, Inc. (5)
2833 A Brakley Dr, Baton Rouge, LA 70816
Tel.: (800) 565-1536
Integrated Telecommunication Services
N.A.I.C.S.: 517111

Holding (Domestic):

Dave & Buster's Entertainment, Inc. (2)
1221 S Beltline Rd Ste 500, Coppell, TX 75019
Tel.: (214) 357-9588
Web Site: https://www.daveandbusters.com
Rev.: $1,964,427,000
Assets: $3,760,993,000
Liabilities: $3,350,458,000
Net Worth: $410,535,000
Earnings: $137,135,000
Emp.: 2,089
Fiscal Year-end: 01/29/2023
Restaurant & Arcade Owner & Operator
N.A.I.C.S.: 722511
Darin E. Harper *(CFO)*
Chris Morris *(CEO)*
Kevin M. Sheehan *(Chm & Interim CEO)*
John B. Mulleady *(Sr VP-Real Estate & Dev)*
Antonio Bautista *(Sr VP & Head-Intl Dev)*
Michael Alan Quartieri *(CFO)*
Christopher Morris *(CEO)*
Tony Wehner *(COO & Sr VP)*
Steve Klohn *(CIO)*
Megan Tobin *(CMO)*
Les Lehner *(Head-Main Event Dev & Officer)*

Subsidiary (Domestic):

Dave & Buster's, Inc. (3)
2481 Manana Dr, Dallas, TX 75220
Tel.: (214) 357-9588
Web Site: http://www.daveandbusters.com
Rev.: $635,579,000
Assets: $851,386,000
Liabilities: $577,126,000
Net Worth: $274,260,000
Earnings: $12,496,000
Emp.: 200
Fiscal Year-end: 02/02/2014
Entertainment Complex & Restaurant Builder & Operator
N.A.I.C.S.: 722511
Margo L. Manning *(COO)*
J. Michael Plunkett *(Sr VP-Pur & Intl Ops)*
Michael J. Metzinger *(VP-Acctg & Controller)*
Jay L. Tobin *(Gen Counsel, Sec & Sr VP)*
Sean Gleason *(CMO)*
Kevin Bachus *(Sr VP-Entertainment & Game Strategy)*

Main Event Entertainment LP (3)
2070 S Stemmons Fwy, Lewisville, TX 75067-8761
Tel.: (972) 459-7770
Web Site: http://www.mainevent.com
Sales Range: $50-74.9 Million
Emp.: 100
Entertainment Services
N.A.I.C.S.: 711310
Darin Harper *(CFO)*
Les Lehner *(Chief Dev Officer)*

Subsidiary (Domestic):

Edgewood Partners Insurance Center (2)
1 California St, Ste 400, San Francisco, CA 94111
Tel.: (415) 356-3900
Web Site: https://www.epicbrokers.com
Sales Range: $50-74.9 Million
Emp.: 150
Insurance Brokerage, Consulting & Claims Management Services
N.A.I.C.S.: 524210
John Hahn *(Exec Chm-Galway Holdings)*
Derek Thomas *(Chief Strategy Officer)*
Thomas E. O'Neil *(Pres-Northeast)*
Dan Crawford *(Gen Counsel & Exec VP)*
Scott Gunnison *(Mng Principal-Northeast Reg)*
Frani Smith *(VP-Corp Svcs & Facilities)*
Michael Gonthier *(Chief Admin Officer)*
Jim Gillette *(Pres-Pacific South)*
John Connell *(Pres-Employee Benefits-California)*
Peter Garvey *(Vice Chm-Galway Holdings)*
Denise Walsh *(Asst Gen Counsel & VP)*
Josh Close *(Coord-Client Svcs-Energy Construction Practice-Natl)*
Brian Tanner *(Principal)*
Bob Simpson *(Dir-Comm & Engagement-Houston)*
John Gaffney *(VP-Benefits Ops-Natl)*
Todd Randolph *(Principal-Southeast Employee Benefits Practice-Atlanta)*
Ed Oravetz *(Mng Principal)*
Steve Needle *(Mng Principal-Southeast)*
Scott Schanen *(Pres-Employer Consulting Practice-Natl)*
Robert Johnson *(Principal)*
Sapana Nanuwa *(CMO)*
Steve Denton *(CEO)*
Crawford McInnis *(Chief Sls Officer)*
Philip Moyles *(Chief Growth Officer)*
Parker Rains *(Mng Principal-Property & Casualty Practice)*
Adam Meyerowitz *(Pres-Midwest & Southeast)*

Subsidiary (Domestic):

Frenkel & Company (3)
350 Hudson St 4th Fl, New York, NY 10014
Tel.: (212) 488-0200
Web Site: http://www.frenkel.com
Insurance Services
N.A.I.C.S.: 524210
John F. Kelly *(Pres & CEO)*
Joseph Valenza *(COO & Exec VP)*
Craig Hasday *(Pres-Frenkel Benefits & Sr Exec VP)*
Jacqueline Beaudet *(Gen Counsel)*
Tandis Nili *(Sr VP)*

Subsidiary (Domestic):

Frenkel & Company - Boston (4)
1 Mckinley Sq, Boston, MA 02109
Tel.: (617) 742-2444
Web Site: http://www.frenkel.com
General Insurance Services
N.A.I.C.S.: 524210
John Kelly *(Pres & CEO)*

Frenkel & Company - Jersey City (4)
210 Hudson St Ste 601, Jersey City, NJ 07311
Tel.: (201) 356-3400
Web Site: http://www.frenkel.com
General Insurance Services
N.A.I.C.S.: 524210

Frenkel Benefits, LLC (4)
633 W 5th St 28th Fl, Los Angeles, CA 90071-5422
Tel.: (213) 787-1144
Web Site: http://frenkelbenefits.com
Insurance Services
N.A.I.C.S.: 524210
Craig Hasday *(Pres)*
Nicholas Tunno *(Principal)*
Joseph Ferber *(Principal)*

Subsidiary (Domestic):

Gundermann & Gundermann (3)
175 W Carver St, Huntington, NY 11743
Tel.: (631) 271-0600
Insurance Agents Brokers And Service
N.A.I.C.S.: 524210
Joseph Gundermann *(Pres & CEO)*

Integro USA Inc. (3)
1 State St Plz 9th Fl, New York, NY 10004
Tel.: (212) 295-8000
Web Site: http://www.integrogroup.com
Risk Management & Insurance Services
N.A.I.C.S.: 524298
John Sutton *(Pres-Ops-Intl)*
Toby Humphreys *(Chm-Integro Insurance Brokers-UK)*
Marc Kunney *(Pres-North America Ops)*
William Goldstein *(CEO)*

MAI Capital Management, LLC (3)
1360 E 9th St Ste 1100, Cleveland, OH 44114
Tel.: (216) 920-4800
Web Site: http://www.mai.capital
Financial Services
N.A.I.C.S.: 523999
Jason Putman *(Mng Dir)*
Rick Buoncore *(Mng Partner)*
Steve Trax *(Mng Dir)*
John Dovich *(Sr Mng Dir & Reg Pres-Cincinnati)*
Bill Bruns *(Mng Dir)*
Tom Lalley *(Mng Dir)*
Jordan Press *(Sr Mng Dir & Reg Pres-New York)*
William Jones *(Dir & Portfolio Mgr)*
Matthew Mathias *(Sr Mng Dir & Reg Pres-Naples)*
Richard Beebe *(Mng Dir)*
Biff Baker *(Partner & Mng Dir)*
Mark Q. Haley *(Partner & Mng Dir)*

Subsidiary (Domestic):

J.M. Hartwell L.P. (4)
515 Madison Ave, New York, NY 10022
Tel.: (212) 308-3355
Web Site: http://www.jmhartwell.com
Investment Management & Advisory Services
N.A.I.C.S.: 523940
William D. Jones *(Principal & Portfolio Mgr)*
Jordan S. Press *(Principal & Portfolio Mgr)*
William C. Miller IV *(Principal & Portfolio Mgr)*

John D. Dovich & Associates, LLC (4)
625 Eden Park Dr Ste 310, Cincinnati, OH 45202
Tel.: (513) 579-9400
Financial Investment Services
N.A.I.C.S.: 523999

MTX Wealth Management, LLC (4)
11710 Plz America Dr Ste 1010, Reston, VA 20190
Tel.: (571) 665-5270
Financial Investment Services
N.A.I.C.S.: 523999

MWM Investment Consulting, LLC (4)
2390 Tamiami Trl N Ste 108, Naples, FL 34103-4483
Tel.: (239) 430-0735
Web Site: http://www.mwminvestmentconsulting.com
Investment Advice
N.A.I.C.S.: 523940
Matthew W. Mathias *(Founder)*

Madison Financial Advisors, Ltd. (4)
106 Harrison St, SE, Ste 300, Leesburg, VA 20175
Tel.: (703) 669-6234
Web Site: http://www.madisonadvisors.com

KEYSTONE GROUP, L.P.

Keystone Group, L.P.—(Continued)
Customized Financial Planning, Investment Management, Retirement, Business & Succession Planning & Estate Planning Assistance
N.A.I.C.S.: 523940
James McDermott (Pres)

Wiener Financial Management (4)
12276 Greenleaf Ave, Potomac, MD 20854
Tel.: (301) 762-0030
Web Site: http://www.wienerfinancial.com
Professional, Scientific & Technical Services
N.A.I.C.S.: 541990
Bruce M. Wiener (Principal)

Winfield Associates, Inc. (4)
700 W St Clair Ave, Cleveland, OH 44113
Tel.: (216) 241-2575
Web Site: http://www.winfieldinc.com
Financial Investment Activities
N.A.I.C.S.: 523999
William W. Baker (Pres)

Joint Venture (Domestic):

Protector Holdings LLC (3)
135 Main St 21st Fl, San Francisco, CA 94105
Tel.: (818) 482-6917
Web Site: http://www.protectorholdings.com
Insurance Services
N.A.I.C.S.: 524210
Paul Areida (CEO)
Vince Trapani (CFO)
Paul Woodward (CIO)

Subsidiary (Domestic):

Big Savings Insurance Agency Inc. (4)
7838 Stockton Blvd Ste 300, Sacramento, CA 95823
Tel.: (916) 830-9200
Web Site: http://www.bigsavingsinsurance.com
Insurance Agencies & Brokerages
N.A.I.C.S.: 524210
Sunny Singh (Pres)

Premier Insurance Services Inc. (4)
829 Main St Ste A, Delano, CA 93215
Tel.: (661) 721-8300
Web Site: https://www.prontoinsurance.com
Insurance Services
N.A.I.C.S.: 524210
Rick Genest (Pres)

Subsidiary (Domestic):

Oasis South Insurance Services Inc. (5)
1295 Broadway 209, Chula Vista, CA 91911
Tel.: (619) 425-9696
Web Site: http://www.oasissouth.com
Insurance Services
N.A.I.C.S.: 524210
Trey Nelson (Gen Mgr)

Subsidiary (Domestic):

Sorci Insurance Brokerage, Inc. (3)
15495 Los Gatos Blvd Ste 7, Los Gatos, CA 95032
Tel.: (408) 356-3399
Web Site: http://www.sorciinsurance.com
Insurance Services
N.A.I.C.S.: 524210
Tom Sorci (Owner)

Vanbridge LLC (3)
1185 Ave of the Americas 32nd Fl, New York, NY 10036
Tel.: (646) 572-9366
Web Site: http://www.vanbridge.com
Emp.: 45
Insurance Intermediary, Capital Advisory & Insurance Management Services
N.A.I.C.S.: 524292
Barbara A. Bell (Mng Principal)
Donald M. Callahan (Mng Principal)
Jonathan Legge (Founder)
Kenneth R. Pierce (Mng Principal)
Kyle D. Binnington (Principal)
Michael Fitzsimmons (Principal)
Monica Rodriguez Greene (Principal)
Quentin Hills (Principal)
Scott Guiliana (Principal)
Julie Smith (Sr VP & Dir-Mktg)
Philip V. Moyles Jr. (CEO & Mng Principal)

Subsidiary (Domestic):

Universal Insurance Services of Florida, Inc. (4)
225 NE Mizner Blvd Ste 675, Boca Raton, FL 33432
Tel.: (800) 878-8280
Web Site: http://www.uiservices.com
Insurance Brokerage Services
N.A.I.C.S.: 524210
Michael C. Sorensen (Mng Principal)
Mitchell K. Smith (Mng Principal)
Kelley Sorensen (Dir-LTC Sls & Mktg)
Pete Dressler (Dir-Product & Illustration)
Vince Jenkins (Principal & Dir-Corp & Institutional Insurance)
Amanda Pogrell (Dir-Concierge & Advanced New Bus)
Jessica Schmidt (Dir-Licensing & Contracting)
Priscilla Hazan (Mgr-Case)
Marcelo Nascimento (Mgr-Case)
Ryan Perna (Principal)
Adam Spring (Principal)
Jim Sibson (Principal-Institutional Relationships)

Holding (Domestic):

Imagine! Print Solutions, Inc. (2)
1000 Valley Park Dr, Minneapolis, MN 55379
Tel.: (952) 903-4400
Web Site: http://www.imagineps.com
Commercial Printing Services
N.A.I.C.S.: 323111
Shawn Boyce (VP-Sales)

Subsidiary (Domestic):

Classic Graphics, LLC (3)
8335 Classic Dr, Charlotte, NC 28262-4551
Tel.: (704) 597-9015
Web Site: http://www.knowclassic.com
Graphic Communication Services
N.A.I.C.S.: 541430
David C. Pitts (Founder & Pres)
Jim O'Rourke (Pres-Triangle)
Ed Brown (Mgr-Bus Analysis)
Bill Kwiatkowski (VP-Ops)

GFX International Inc. (3)
333 Barron Blvd, Grayslake, IL 60030
Tel.: (847) 543-4600
Web Site: http://www.gfxi.com
Screen Printing
N.A.I.C.S.: 323113

Joint Venture (Domestic):

Mercer Advisors Inc. (2)
1200 17th St Ste 500, Denver, CO 80202
Tel.: (888) 885-8101
Web Site: https://www.merceradvisors.com
Wealth Management & Advisory Services
N.A.I.C.S.: 523940
Loren Pierson (COO)
Dave Welling (CEO)
Daniel Gourvitch (Pres)

Subsidiary (Domestic):

Bell Wealth Management Inc. (3)
2901 Bee Cave Rd Ste F, Austin, TX 78746
Tel.: (512) 347-9500
Wealth Management & Investment Consulting Services
N.A.I.C.S.: 523940
Colin A. Bell (Pres)

Day & Ennis LLC (3)
125 Plantation Centre S Ste 400B, Macon, GA 31210-1906
Tel.: (478) 474-7480
Web Site: http://www.dayandennis.com
Investment Advice
N.A.I.C.S.: 523940

Jackson Financial Management, Inc. (3)
151 Kalmus Dr Ste H-7, Costa Mesa, CA 92626
Tel.: (714) 434-6900
Web Site: https://www.merceradvisors.com
Portfolio Management
N.A.I.C.S.: 523940

Kanaly Trust (3)
5555 San Felipe St Ste 200, Houston, TX 77056-2760 (100%)
Tel.: (713) 561-9300
Web Site: http://www.kanaly.com
Investment Management & Financial Planning Services
N.A.I.C.S.: 523999
Drew Kanaly (Mgr-Relationship)
Betty Keddington (COO & Chief Compliance Officer)
Linda Halcomb (Sr VP & Mgr-Trust Ops)
Todd Hunter (VP & Controller)

Mercer Global Advisors Inc. (3)
200 17th St Ste 500, Denver, CO 80202
Tel.: (805) 565-1681
Web Site: http://www.merceradvisors.com
Investment Advisory Services
N.A.I.C.S.: 523940
Deb Atwater-Robles (Dir-Incentive Compensation)
Aaron Langston (Reg VP)
Bryan Powers (Sr VP)
David Barton (Vice Chm)
Donald Calcagni (Chief Investment Officer)
Dave Welling (CEO)

Subsidiary (Domestic):

Adam Financial Associates Inc. (3)
2500 N Military Trl Ste 306, Boca Raton, FL 33431
Tel.: (561) 417-0001
Web Site: http://www.adamfinl.com
Financial Planning & Wealth Management Services
N.A.I.C.S.: 523940
Mari Adam (Founder & Pres)

Atlanta Financial Associates Inc. (4)
5901 Peachtree Dunwdy NE Ste B275, Atlanta, GA 30328-7148
Tel.: (770) 261-5380
Web Site: http://www.atlantafinancial.com
Investment Advice
N.A.I.C.S.: 523940
Julianne F. Andrews (Principal)

ClearRock Capital, LLC (4)
131 4th St E, Ketchum, ID 83340
Tel.: (208) 726-8858
Web Site: http://www.clearrockcapital.com
Investment Advice
N.A.I.C.S.: 523940
Mark Eshman (Chm & CEO)

Empyrion Wealth Management, Inc. (4)
3741 Douglas Blvd 130, Roseville, CA 95661
Tel.: (916) 786-7626
Web Site: http://www.empyrionwealth.com
Investment Management Service
N.A.I.C.S.: 523999
Renee Morrison (Dir-Client Svcs)
Kimberly Foss (Founder & Pres)
Marcy Gorton (Mgr-Ops)

Fure Financial Corp. (4)
8500 Normandale Lake Blvd Ste 950, Bloomington, MN 55437
Tel.: (952) 944-8250
Web Site: http://www.furefinancial.com
Portfolio Management
N.A.I.C.S.: 523940
Dale L. Acton (VP)
Johannes C. Fure (Founder, Pres & Chief Investment Officer)
Grant A. Meyer (Mgr-IT)

Goldstein Munger & Associates (4)
18 Crow Canyon Ct Ste 250, San Ramon, CA 94583
Tel.: (925) 552-1400
Web Site: http://www.goldsteinmunger.com
Investment Advice
N.A.I.C.S.: 523940
Bob Munger (Owner)

HawsGoodwin Investment Management, LLC (4)
5000 Meridian Blvd Ste 530, Franklin, TN 37067
Tel.: (615) 771-1012
Web Site: http://www.hawsgoodwin.com
Financial Services
N.A.I.C.S.: 523940
C. Arthur Haws (Co-Founder, CEO & Mng Partner)
W. Cam Goodwin (Co-Founder, Pres & Mng Partner)
Lisa Butler (Dir-Client Relationships)
Tom Weatherman (Dir-Insurance Svcs)

U.S. PRIVATE

Kingfisher Capital, LLC (4)
201 S College St, Charlotte, NC 28244
Tel.: (704) 333-1710
Web Site: http://www.kingfishercapital.com
Securities Brokerage Services
N.A.I.C.S.: 523150
Chad Frk (Dir-AS)

M.J. Smith & Associates, Inc. (4)
5613 DTC Pkwy Ste 650, Greenwood Village, CO 80111
Tel.: (303) 768-0007
Web Site: http://www.mj-smith.com
Emp.: 11
Portfolio Management
N.A.I.C.S.: 523940
Mark J. Smith (Pres)

Private Asset Management, Inc. (4)
11995 El Camino Real, San Diego, CA 92130
Tel.: (858) 792-3800
Web Site: http://www.pamgmt.com
Sales Range: $1-9.9 Million
Emp.: 28
Investment Advice
N.A.I.C.S.: 523940
Gary Pulford (Sr VP & Portfolio Mgr)
Jeff Witt (Dir-Res)
Jonathan Elsberry (Corp VP & Mgr)
Michael D. Berlin (Gen Counsel & VP)
Stephen Cohen (Mgr-Asset)
John Harrington (Sr VP & Portfolio Mgr)
Michael Love (Portfolio Mgr)
Michael N. McGreevy (Mng Dir-Indian Wells)
Michael Ramirez (Portfolio Mgr)
Teresa Whorton (Mgr-Acctg)
Victor Calise (Sr VP-Mktg)

Quest Capital Management Inc (4)
8235 Douglas Ave, Dallas, TX 75225
Tel.: (214) 691-6090
Web Site: http://questadvisor.com
Rev.: $4,400,000
Emp.: 30
Portfolio Management
N.A.I.C.S.: 523940
Dennis J. Moore (Mgr)

Resource Planning Group Ltd. (4)
10 Glenlake Pkwy S Tower, Ste 150, Atlanta, GA 30328
Tel.: (770) 671-9500
Web Site: http://www.rpgplanner.com
Rev.: $2,490,000
Emp.: 6
Portfolio Management
N.A.I.C.S.: 523940
John E. Howard (Owner)

Starks Financial Group Inc. (4)
56 Clayton St, Asheville, NC 28801-2424
Tel.: (828) 285-8777
Web Site: http://www.starksfinancial.com
Miscellaneous Financial Investment Activities
N.A.I.C.S.: 523999
Dawn Starks (Pres)

The Asset Advisory Group, Inc. (4)
4600 McAuley Pl Ste 140, Cincinnati, OH 45242-4765
Tel.: (513) 771-7222
Web Site: http://www.taaginc.com
Miscellaneous Financial Investment Activities
N.A.I.C.S.: 523999
Gregg Jones (Mgr-Ops)
Chip Workman (Pres)

Transitions Wealth Management LLC (4)
8101 E Prentice Ave, Greenwood Village, CO 93550-4036
Tel.: (303) 221-4867
Web Site: https://transitionswm.com
Miscellaneous Intermediation
N.A.I.C.S.: 523910

Wrenn Financial Strategies, Inc. (4)
8352 6 Forks Rd Ste 201, Raleigh, NC 27615
Tel.: (919) 848-9999
Web Site: http://www.wrennfinancial.com
Financial Investment Activities
N.A.I.C.S.: 523999
Janice Wrenn (Co-Founder & VP)
Maxie E. Wrenn Jr. (Co-Founder & Pres)

COMPANIES KEYSTONE GROUP, L.P.

Subsidiary (Domestic):

Regis Management Company LLC (3)
873 Santa Cruz Avenue, Ste 206, Menlo Park, CA 94025
Tel.: (650) 838-1030
Web Site: http://www.regisllc.com
Intermediation
N.A.I.C.S.: 523910
Steven Go *(COO & Chief Compliance Officer)*

Holding (Domestic):

MetroNet Holdings, LLC (2)
3701 Communications Way, Evansville, IN 47715
Tel.: (877) 407-3224
Web Site: http://www.metronetinc.com
Holding Company
N.A.I.C.S.: 551112
David L. Heimbach *(Pres & CEO)*
John Cinelli *(Exec Chm)*
Jerry Dow *(CMO & Exec VP)*
Eddie Massengale *(Dir-Bus Dev)*
Bill Gilliam *(VP-Florida & Gen Mgr-Florida)*
Sarah Overbaugh *(CFO)*
Lohn Weber *(Exec VP-Capital Markets)*

Subsidiary (Domestic):

Metro FiberNet, LLC (3)
3701 Communications Way, Evansville, IN 47715
Tel.: (877) 407-3224
Web Site: http://www.metronetinc.com
Fiber Optic Communication Services
N.A.I.C.S.: 335921

Holding (Domestic):

OTELCO Inc. (2)
505 Third Ave E, Oneonta, AL 35121
Tel.: (205) 625-3580
Web Site: http://www.otelcoinc.com
Telephone Communication Services
N.A.I.C.S.: 517121
Jerry C. Boles *(Controller)*
Trina M. Bragdon *(Gen Counsel, Asst Sec & VP-HR & Regulatory)*
Richard Clark *(Pres & CEO)*
Curtis L. Garner Jr. *(CFO)*

Subsidiary (Domestic):

I-Land Internet Services LLC (3)
215 S Ohio Ave, Sedalia, MO 65301
Tel.: (660) 829-4638
Web Site: http://www.iland.net
Emp.: 25
Internet Service Provider
N.A.I.C.S.: 517111

OTT Communications (3)
890 Hammond St, Bangor, ME 04401
Tel.: (207) 992-9911
Web Site: http://www.ottcommunications.com
Sales Range: $10-24.9 Million
Emp.: 106
Telephone Communication Services
N.A.I.C.S.: 517121

Subsidiary (Domestic):

Shoreham Telephone LLC (4)
3167 Rt 22 A, Shoreham, VT 05770
Tel.: (802) 897-9911
Web Site: http://www.otelco.com
Wired Telecommunications Carriers
N.A.I.C.S.: 517111

Subsidiary (Domestic):

Otelco Telecommunications LLC (3)
215 Roe St, Pilot Grove, MO 65276
Tel.: (660) 834-3311
Emp.: 15
Telecommunication Servicesb
N.A.I.C.S.: 517121
Todd Wessing *(VP)*

Saco River Telephone LLC (3)
56 Campus Dr, New Gloucester, ME 04260
Tel.: (207) 992-9935
Web Site: http://www.ottcommunications.com
Emp.: 100
Telecommunication Servicesb
N.A.I.C.S.: 517121

Subsidiary (Domestic):

Oak Hill Capital Management, LLC (2)
65 E 55th St 32nd Fl, New York, NY 10022
Tel.: (212) 527-8400
Web Site: http://www.oakhillcapital.com
Private Equity Investment & Portfolio Management Services
N.A.I.C.S.: 523999
J. Taylor Crandall *(Mng Partner)*
Tyler J. Wolfram *(Mng Partner)*
Brian N. Cherry *(Partner)*
Steven G. Puccinelli *(Partner)*

Subsidiary (Domestic):

Checkers Drive-In Restaurants, Inc. (3)
4300 W Cypress St Ste 600, Tampa, FL 33607
Tel.: (813) 283-7000
Web Site: http://www.checkers.com
Drive-Through Hamburger Restaurants
N.A.I.C.S.: 722513
Terri Snyder *(CMO & Exec VP)*
Marc Mediate *(Sr VP-Franchise & Restaurant Ops)*
Frances L. Allen *(Pres & CEO)*
Adam Noyes *(Chief Admin Officer & Exec VP)*

Holding (Domestic):

Force Communications, LLC (3)
900 E 96th St Ste 125, Indianapolis, IN 46240
Tel.: (317) 844-3517
Web Site: http://www.forcemed.com
Professional, Scientific & Technical Services
N.A.I.C.S.: 541990
Jay Greenzweig *(Chief Exec & Scientific Officer)*

Holding (Domestic):

Ontario Telephone Company, Inc. (2)
75 Main St, Phelps, NY 14532
Tel.: (315) 548-2411
Web Site: http://www.ottctel.com
Telephone Communications
N.A.I.C.S.: 517121

Prime Risk Partners Inc. (2)
8025 Westside Pkwy Ste 200, Alpharetta, GA 30009
Tel.: (770) 800-7873
Web Site: http://www.primeriskpartners.com
Holding Company; Insurance Agencies
N.A.I.C.S.: 551112
Bret Quigley *(Co-Founder, Chm & CEO)*
Adam Meyerowitz *(Co-Founder & Pres)*
Steven Germundson *(Sr VP-Corp Dev)*
Matthew McKenna *(Sr VP-Corp Dev)*
Scot Kees *(Gen Counsel & Exec VP)*
Robert C. Smith *(COO & Exec VP)*
J. Scott Tofil *(CFO & Exec VP)*
Tod Ashby *(CIO)*
Lesley Dresch *(Sr VP-HR)*

Subsidiary (Domestic):

Gunn, Steers & Company, LLC (3)
30 E 39th St Fl 3, New York, NY 10016
Tel.: (212) 883-8400
Web Site: http://www.gunnsteers.com
Insurance Related Activities
N.A.I.C.S.: 524298
William M. Steers *(CEO)*
Abbe Case Ellam *(Sr VP)*
Magdeline Wills *(Mgr-Personal Lines)*
Ruth Seale *(Controller)*

ONI Risk Partners, Inc. (3)
600 E 96th St Ste 400, Indianapolis, IN 46240
Tel.: (317) 706-9500
Web Site: http://www.onirisk.com
Insurance Agency & Risk Management Consultancy Services
N.A.I.C.S.: 524210
Thomas A. Flynn *(Pres)*
Jim Hynes *(COO & VP)*
John Flynn *(Reg Pres)*
Mike Gilbert *(Reg Pres)*
Tim Bender *(VP-Personal & Small Bus)*
Tom Dickman *(Sr VP-TPA)*
Peter Forsee *(VP-Acctg)*
Pat Carney *(VP-Employee Benefits)*

Steve Danielson *(Reg Pres)*
Frank Krisanits *(Reg Pres)*
Linda Kalber *(Dir-Client Resources & Engagement-Employee Benefits Div)*
Calvin Conerly *(Dir-Client Experience-Employee Benefits Div)*

Subsidiary (Domestic):

Green-Owens Insurance (4)
1111 N Main St, Franklin, IN 46131
Tel.: (317) 736-5522
Web Site: http://www.green-owensins.com
Insurance Agencies & Brokerages
N.A.I.C.S.: 524210
Jim Wise *(Principal & Partner)*
Connie Hawkins *(Partner & Principal)*

Subsidiary (Domestic):

Roblin Insurance Agency, Inc. (3)
144 Gould St, Needham, MA 02494
Tel.: (781) 455-0700
Web Site: http://www.roblininsurance.com
Insurance Brokerage Services
N.A.I.C.S.: 524210
Evan Levine *(VP-Comml Lines)*
Chuck Quealy *(VP-Ops)*
Peter Roblin *(Pres)*
Jim Roblin *(Exec VP)*
Scott Small *(CFO & VP)*

Holding (Non-US):

Pulsant Limited (2)
Cadogan House Rose Kiln Lane, Reading, RG2 0HP, United Kingdom
Tel.: (44) 845 119 9900
Web Site: http://www.pulsant.com
Sales Range: $25-49.9 Million
Emp.: 150
Internet Application Development Services
N.A.I.C.S.: 541511
Pieter Knook *(Deputy Chm)*
Graeme MacKenzie *(CFO)*
Nigel Shaw *(COO)*
Rob Davies *(Dir-Sls & Mktg)*
Chris Roberts *(Dir-Channel)*
Mike Tobin *(Chm)*
Nick Hayne *(Mgr-Bus Dev)*
Adam Eaton *(Dir-Sls)*
Rob Spamer *(Dir-Data Centres)*
Demyon Wright *(Head-Svc Mgmt)*
Rob Coupland *(CEO)*
Stephen Ball *(Chief Sls Officer)*
Simon Michie *(CTO)*

Subsidiary (Domestic):

Pulsant (Scotland) Limited (3)
Sirius House The Clocktower Flassches Yard South Gyle Crescent, Edinburgh, EH12 9LB, United Kingdom
Tel.: (44) 3451199900
Web Site: http://www.pulsant.com
Emp.: 180
Information Technology Support Services
N.A.I.C.S.: 518210

Holding (Domestic):

Trinity Consultants, Inc. (2)
12700 Park Central Dr Ste 2100, Dallas, TX 75251
Tel.: (972) 661-8100
Web Site: http://www.trinityconsultants.com
Environmental Consulting Services
N.A.I.C.S.: 541620
Jay Hofmann *(Pres & CEO)*
Chris Price *(Dir-HR)*
Dave Larsen *(CFO)*
Shishir Mohan *(Mng Dir-South & Gulf Coast)*
Laura Redmon *(Dir-Mktg)*
Mike Remsberg *(Mng Dir-Eastern Reg)*
Cynthia Russel *(Mng Dir-Minnow Environmental)*

Subsidiary (Domestic):

Cerami & Associates, Inc. (3)
404 5th Ave, New York, NY 10018
Tel.: (212) 370-1776
Web Site: http://www.ceramiassociates.com
Sales Range: $1-9.9 Million
Emp.: 48
Engineering Services
N.A.I.C.S.: 541330
James Perry *(Mng Partner)*
Vanessa Crews *(Dir-Bus Dev)*

Sarah Nolan Hoff *(Principal)*
Benjamin K. Joseph *(Principal)*
Justin Y. Lau *(Assoc Principal)*
Albert Maniscalco *(Partner)*
Christopher Peltier *(Principal)*
Christopher Pollock *(Partner)*
Geoffrey Sparks *(Principal)*
Don Walters *(Assoc Principal)*
Michael Ferrara *(COO)*
Victoria Cerami *(CEO)*

Subsidiary (Non-US):

Minnow Environmental, Inc. (3)
2 Lamb St, Georgetown, L7G 3M9, ON, Canada
Tel.: (905) 873-3371
Web Site: https://www.trinityconsultants.com
Environmental Effects Monitoring & Evaluation Services
N.A.I.C.S.: 541620
Pierre Stecko *(Mng Principal)*

Subsidiary (Domestic):

Provenance Consulting LLC (3)
301 W 6th St Ste 200, Borger, TX 79007
Tel.: (806) 273-5100
Web Site: http://www.provenanceconsulting.com
Engineering Consulting
N.A.I.C.S.: 541330
Justin Adams *(Mng Partner)*
Patrick Nonhof *(Mng Partner)*
Tony Powell *(Mng Partner)*

SESPE Consulting, Inc. (3)
468 Poli St Ste 2E, Ventura, CA 93001-5692
Tel.: (805) 275-1515
Web Site: http://www.sespeconsulting.com
Environmental Consulting & Engineering Services
N.A.I.C.S.: 541330
Joe King *(VP)*
Rob Dal Farra *(VP)*
Scott D. Cohen *(Project Mgr)*
Maya Rohr *(Project Mgr)*
John Hecht *(Pres)*
Doug Mason *(Project Mgr)*
Garrett Zuleger *(Project Mgr)*
Jane Farkas *(Project Mgr)*

Soundview Consultants LLC (3)
2907 Harborview Dr Ste D, Gig Harbor, WA 98335-1924
Tel.: (253) 514-8952
Web Site: http://www.soundviewconsultants.com
Environmental Consulting Services
N.A.I.C.S.: 541620
Kim Robinson *(Controller)*

Waid Corp. (3)
14205 Burnet Rd Ste 600, Austin, TX 78728
Tel.: (512) 255-9999
Web Site: http://www.waid.com
Sales Range: $1-9.9 Million
Emp.: 28
Engineeering Services
N.A.I.C.S.: 541330
Jason Graves *(Principal Engr)*
Sara Hutson *(Principal Engr)*

Westland Resources, Inc. (3)
4001 E Paradise Falls Dr, Tucson, AZ 85712
Tel.: (520) 206-9585
Web Site: http://www.westlandresources.com
Sales Range: $10-24.9 Million
Engineeering Services
N.A.I.C.S.: 541330
Brian S. Lindenlaub *(VP-Environmental Svcs)*
Fred W. Huntington *(Principal & Sr Consultant-Cultural Resources)*
Rick W. Schonfeld *(Mgr-Landscape Architecture)*
Kara D. Festa *(VP-Ops & Bus Dev-Tucson)*
Mark F. Taylor *(Sr VP)*
James A. Tress Jr. *(Pres & CEO)*

Working Buildings, LLC (3)
1230 Peachtree St NE 300 Promenade, Atlanta, GA 30309
Tel.: (678) 990-8001
Web Site: http://www.workingbuildings.com

KEYSTONE GROUP, L.P.   U.S. PRIVATE

Keystone Group, L.P.—(Continued)

Sales Range: $1-9.9 Million
Emp.: 69
Building Commissioning Services
N.A.I.C.S.: 925110
Michael L. Weiss *(Pres & CEO)*
John McFarland *(Principal)*
Michael Clements *(Dir-Life Sciences)*
Erin C. Hendrick *(Sr Dir-Pharmacy-Clinical Div)*

Holding (Domestic):

Trumansburg Telephone Company, Inc. (2)
1 Union St, Trumansburg, NY 14886
Tel.: (315) 548-2411
Web Site: http://www.trumansburgtel.com
Sales Range: $1-9.9 Million
Emp.: 31
Telecommunications Resellers
N.A.I.C.S.: 517121
Robert Griswold *(Chm)*

Holding (Non-US):

Vertex Data Science Limited (2)
Office B223 The Heath Business & Technical Park, Runcorn, WA7 4QX, Cheshire, United Kingdom
Web Site: http://www.vertexgroup.com
Business Process & Customer Management Outsourcing Services
N.A.I.C.S.: 561499
Andrew Jornod *(CEO)*

Subsidiary (US):

Vertex Business Services LLC (3)
501 W President George Bush Hwy Ste 350, Richardson, TX 75080
Tel.: (214) 576-1000
Web Site: http://www.vertexone.com
Business Process & Customer Management Outsourcing Services
N.A.I.C.S.: 561499
Andrew Jornod *(CEO)*
Brad Almond *(CFO & Sr VP-Corp Svcs)*
Jesper Olesen *(COO)*
James Riley *(Chief Strategy Officer)*
Todd Buchardt *(Gen Counsel & Exec VP)*

Subsidiary (Non-US):

Vertex Customer Services India Private Limited (3)
First India Place Block-A, First Floor MG Road, 122001, Gurgaon, India
Tel.: (91) 1244106600
Business Process & Customer Management Outsourcing Services
N.A.I.C.S.: 561499
Sanjoy Lodha *(CEO)*

KEYSTONE INSURERS GROUP, INC.

1995 Point Township Dr, Northumberland, PA 17857
Tel.: (570) 473-4302   DE
Web Site:
   http://www.keystoneinsgrp.com
Year Founded: 1983
Holding Company; Insurance Agencies
N.A.I.C.S.: 551112
Elizabeth Schenk *(VP-Sls & Geographic Expansion)*
Lea Ann Hawk *(COO)*
Linda Neff *(Dir-School Trasportation)*
Brian Brusoski *(Sr VP-Property & Casualty)*
Mark Maurer *(VP-Michigan)*
Mike Reddy *(Pres-Employee Benefits)*
Jeremiah Hale *(VP-Kentucky)*
Alex Meiring *(VP-Ohio)*
Margo Mackedanz *(Exec Dir-Franchise Expansion)*
J. R. Fasy *(Dir-Franchise Expansion)*
Tony Rhodes *(Exec VP-Property & Casualty)*
Charles A. Craig III *(Dir-Bus Dev)*

Subsidiaries:

Coverra Insurance Services, Inc. (1)

535 Industrial Dr, Sparta, WI 54656
Tel.: (608) 269-2127
Web Site: http://coverrainsurance.com
Insurance Agencies & Brokerage Services
N.A.I.C.S.: 524210
Gary G. Ascher *(CFO)*
Joyce Putman *(Accountant)*
Jeffrey Ascher *(CEO)*

Keystone Agency Partners, LLC (1)
2600 Commerce Dr, Harrisburg, PA 17110
Tel.: (570) 473-4362
Web Site:
   https://keystoneagencypartners.com
All Other Insurance Related Activities
N.A.I.C.S.: 524298

Subsidiary (Domestic):

Kai Yurconic Insurance Agency, LLC (2)
5910 Hamilton Blvd, Allentown, PA 18106
Tel.: (610) 770-6600
Web Site: http://www.yurconic.com
Sales Range: $1-9.9 Million
Emp.: 65
Auto, Home, Business, Life & Health Insurance Services
N.A.I.C.S.: 524210
John T. Yurconic *(Pres)*
Helena E. Yurconic *(VP)*
Richard V. Leonzi *(CFO)*
Ronald J. Hanna *(Mgr-IT)*
Jeff Boardman *(Mgr-Bus Lines)*
Kim Brown *(Mgr-Vehicle Registration & Driver's License)*
Christy Buchman *(Mgr-Personal Lines)*
Colleen Driscoll *(COO)*
Brenda Laughead *(Mgr-Vehicle Registration & Driver's License)*

Subsidiary (Domestic):

WR Sims Agency Incorporated (3)
1036 Washington Blvd, Williamsport, PA 17701
Tel.: (570) 326-4188
Web Site: http://www.wrsimsagency.com
Insurance Related Activities
N.A.I.C.S.: 524298
Cross Sam *(Mgr-Comml Lines)*

Subsidiary (Domestic):

LIFE QUOTES, INC. (2)
8205 S Cass Ave Ste 102, Darien, IL 60561
Tel.: (630) 515-0170
Web Site: http://www.lifequotes.com
Sales Range: $10-24.9 Million
Emp.: 106
Insurance Agency & Brokerage; Online Consumer Insurance Information Services
N.A.I.C.S.: 524210
Robert S. Bland *(Founder & CEO)*

Miller Insurance, Inc. (1)
36 S Briel Blvd, Middletown, OH 45044
Tel.: (513) 422-3621
Web Site: http://www.millerinsinc.com
Sales Range: $10-24.9 Million
Emp.: 11
Insurance Agents
N.A.I.C.S.: 524210
Michael D. Miller *(Pres)*

KEYSTONE LABORATORIES, INC.

1103 Kansas St, Memphis, TN 38106
Tel.: (901) 774-8860
Web Site: http://www.keystone-labs.com
Year Founded: 1923
Sales Range: $450-499.9 Million
Emp.: 20
Hair Care Products & Toiletries Mfr
N.A.I.C.S.: 325620
Melinda Burns *(Owner)*

Subsidiaries:

Apex Products Company (1)
305 W Trigg Ave, Memphis, TN 38106-2510
Tel.: (901) 774-7614
Contract Heat Transfer Labeling
N.A.I.C.S.: 561910

KEYSTONE LIME COMPANY

1156 Zehner Rd, Springs, PA 15562
Tel.: (814) 662-2711
Web Site:
   http://www.keystonelime.com
Sales Range: $10-24.9 Million
Emp.: 100
Highway & Street Construction
N.A.I.C.S.: 237310
Melinda Gibson *(Pres & CEO)*

KEYSTONE NATIONAL GROUP LLC

5000 Executive Pkwy Ste 445, San Ramon, CA 94583-4282
Tel.: (925) 480-6050
Web Site:
   http://www.keystonenational.net
Year Founded: 2006
Private Equity Company
N.A.I.C.S.: 523999
John Earl *(Mng Partner)*
Brandon Nielson *(Mng Partner)*
Zach Cleff *(Controller)*
Michelle Larsen *(Mgr-Ops)*
Heston Nielson *(VP)*
Brad Allen *(CFO)*
Raymond Chan *(Principal)*
Chris Johnson *(Principal)*

KEYSTONE PRINTING INK CO.

2700 Roberts Ave, Philadelphia, PA 19129
Tel.: (215) 228-8100
Sales Range: $10-24.9 Million
Emp.: 35
Printing Ink Mfr
N.A.I.C.S.: 325910
Robert B. Chamness *(Pres)*
Philip Chamness *(VP-Sls)*

KEYSTONE PROPERTY GROUP

1 Presidential Blvd Ste 300, Bala Cynwyd, PA 19004
Tel.: (610) 980-7000
Web Site:
   http://www.keystoneproperty group.com
Year Founded: 1991
Rev.: $50,800,000
Emp.: 70
Commercial Real Estate
N.A.I.C.S.: 531210
Aimee L. Alexander *(Dir-IR)*
Herman M. Gerwitz *(Treas)*
William H. Glazer *(CEO)*
Richard S. Gottlieb *(Pres & COO)*
David McLaughlin *(Gen Counsel)*
Charles J. Walters *(Chief Investment Officer)*
Timothy A. Criger *(CFO)*
Marc Rash *(Exec VP)*

KEYSTONE SHIPPING CO.

1 Bala Plaza E Ste 600, Bala Cynwyd, PA 19004-1496
Tel.: (610) 617-6800
Web Site: http://www.keyship.com
Sales Range: $300-349.9 Million
Emp.: 3
Intercoastal Freight Transportation Operations
N.A.I.C.S.: 483113
Tim Callahan *(Mgr-Acctg)*
Michael Westergom *(Mgr-Comm)*
Bob Hawke *(Engr-Fleet)*
Bruce Fernie *(VP-Ops)*
Mitch Koslow *(VP-Engrg)*

KEYSTOPS LLC

376 Reasonover Ave, Franklin, KY 42134
Tel.: (270) 586-8283
Web Site: http://www.keystops.com
Sales Range: $200-249.9 Million
Emp.: 300

Petroleum Bulk Stations
N.A.I.C.S.: 424710
Lester Key *(Chm)*
Tammy Motley *(Asst Mgr-Credit)*

KEYSTROKES TRANSCRIPTION SERVICE, INC.

220 Garden St, Yorkville, IL 60560
Tel.: (630) 553-3680
Web Site:
   http://www.keystrokestranscription.com
Year Founded: 1997
Rev.: $11,100,000
Emp.: 472
Health Care Srvices
N.A.I.C.S.: 518210
Lee Tkachuk *(CEO)*
Jeff Tkachuk *(VP-Ops)*
Karyn Binter *(Exec Dir-Ops)*
Becky Bombacino *(Dir-Client Svcs)*
David Miller *(Mgr-IT & Security)*

KEYSTRUCT CONSTRUCTION, INC.

30 Marianne Dr, York, PA 17406-8406
Tel.: (717) 764-1326
Web Site: http://www.keystruct.com
Sales Range: $10-24.9 Million
Emp.: 60
Commercial & Institutional Building Construction Services
N.A.I.C.S.: 236220
Jerry L. Watson *(Pres)*
Doug Leister *(VP)*
Deanna Copp *(Controller)*

KEYWELL LLC

11900 S Cottage Grove Ave, Chicago, IL 60628
Tel.: (773) 660-2060   IL
Web Site: http://www.keywell.com
Year Founded: 1924
Sales Range: $400-449.9 Million
Emp.: 320
Holding Company
N.A.I.C.S.: 423930
Mark Lozier *(Sr VP)*
Michael Rosenberg *(Sr VP)*
Karen Deninato *(Controller)*

Subsidiaries:

Keywell LLC - Falconer Processing Facility (1)
1873 Lyndon Blvd, Frewsburg, NY 14733
Tel.: (716) 922-9100
Metal & Steel Recovery Services
N.A.I.C.S.: 562920

Keywell LLC - West Mifflin Processing Facility (1)
890 Noble Rd, West Mifflin, PA 15122
Tel.: (412) 462-5555
Metal & Steel Recovery Services
N.A.I.C.S.: 562920

KFM ENTERPRISES, LLC

3621 W 5th St, Tulsa, OK 74127
Tel.: (918) 583-1155   OK
Web Site:
   https://www.kfm.enterprises
Year Founded: 2015
Holding Company
N.A.I.C.S.: 551112
Hester Mans *(Treas)*

Subsidiaries:

Adjuvants Unlimited, LLC (1)
3621 W 5th St, Tulsa, OK 74127
Tel.: (918) 583-1155
Web Site:
   https://www.adjuvantsunlimited.com
Sales Range: $10-24.9 Million
Emp.: 15
Whslr of Chemicals & Agricultural Products
N.A.I.C.S.: 424910
John Webber *(Pres)*
Amber Factor *(Coord-Logistics)*

Industrial Oils Unlimited, LLC (1)
3633 Charles Page Blvd, Tulsa, OK 74127
Tel.: (918) 583-1155
Web Site:
   https://www.industrialoilsunlimited.com
Sales Range: $1-9.9 Million
Emp.: 40
Petroleum Lubricating Oil & Grease Mfr
N.A.I.C.S.: 324191
Johnnie Walker (Mgr-Sls)
Greg Hutchison (Mgr-Technical Svcs)
Kelley Evans (Mgr-HR)
Rick Page (Controller)
Shanin Kenney (Mgr-Admin)
Terry Livingston (Mgr-Ops)

KFS INC.
186 Intermodal Pkwy, Fort Worth, TX 76177
Tel.: (817) 488-4115
Web Site: http://www.kfsinc.com
Year Founded: 1989
Air Freight Handling At Airports
N.A.I.C.S.: 488119
James Keller (Pres)
Mark Irwin (CEO)
Richard Jones (Dir-Ops)
Matthew J. Keller (VP)

KG CREATIVE
395 Del Monte Ctr Ste 243, Monterey, CA 93940
Tel.: (831) 333-6294
Web Site: http://www.kgcreative.com
Year Founded: 2008
Sales Range: Less than $1 Million
Emp.: 2
Advertising, Brand Development & Integration, Corporate Identity, Graphic Design, Production (Print), Web (Banner Ads, Pop-ups, etc.)
N.A.I.C.S.: 541810
Kevin Garcia (Principal)

KG TECHNOLOGIES, INC.
429 E Cotati Ave, Cotati, CA 94931-7089
Web Site:
   http://www.kgtechnologies.net
Sales Range: $25-49.9 Million
Emp.: 10
Latching Relays Mfr
N.A.I.C.S.: 335314
Philipp Gruner (Pres & Dir-Engrg)
Thomas Gruner (CEO)

KGB USA, INC.
3864 Courtney St Ste 411, Bethlehem, PA 18017-8987
Tel.: (610) 997-1000   DE
Web Site: http://www.kgbusa.com
Year Founded: 1992
Sales Range: $300-349.9 Million
Emp.: 80
Solutions For Wireless Carriers
N.A.I.C.S.: 517810
Michelle Castillo (Exec VP-Global Ops & Client Svcs)
Alan Superfine (Gen Mgr-Ops & Client Svcs-North America)
Declan Maguire (Gen Mgr-Ops & Client Svcs-Europe)
Derek Rieger (Assoc Gen Counsel)
Glenn Haddock (CTO)
Stacie Smith (Head-Global Workforce Mgmt)
Subsidiaries:
The Number UK Ltd.   (1)
Fusion Point Tresillian Terrace, Cardiff Gate Business Park, Cardiff, CF10 5PF, United Kingdom
Tel.: (44) 2920548000
Web Site: http://www.thenumber.com
Sales Range: $25-49.9 Million
Telephone Directory Assistance
N.A.I.C.S.: 513140

KGEN POWER CORPORATION
4 Oaks Pl 1330 Post Oak Blvd Ste 1500, Houston, TX 77056-3017
Tel.: (713) 979-1900   DE
Web Site: http://www.kgenpower.com
Year Founded: 2006
Sales Range: $50-74.9 Million
Emp.: 17
Power Generation Plants Acquirer, Owner & Operator; Electricity & Electrical Generation Sales & Distr
N.A.I.C.S.: 221118
W. Kevin Redmond (Chief Acctg Officer & Controller)
Thomas B. White (Pres & CEO)
Daniel Hudson (Chm)

KGP GROUP, INC.
1404 Everman Pkwy, Fort Worth, TX 76140
Tel.: (817) 354-0766   TX
Web Site: http://www.speqtrum-pps.com
Sales Range: $10-24.9 Million
Emp.: 115
Prepress Production & Packaging Graphics Printing Services
N.A.I.C.S.: 323120
Kelly Vaughn (Pres)
Gregory D. Burger (Chm & CEO)

KGP TELECOMMUNICATIONS, INC.
3305 Hwy 60 W, Faribault, MN 55021
Tel.: (507) 334-2268   MN
Web Site:
   http://www.kgplogistics.com
Year Founded: 1975
Sales Range: $25-49.9 Million
Emp.: 200
Communications Products Supply Chain Management Services
N.A.I.C.S.: 423690
Kathleen G. Putrah (Chm & CEO)
Stuart Romenesko (CFO & Exec VP)
Trevor Putrah (Pres)
Desi O'Grady (Sr VP-Broadband Network Sls)
Peter Wraight (Chief Strategy Officer & Exec VP)
Megan VonRuden (Mng Dir)
Matt Glass (Chief Svcs Officer & Exec VP)
Tom Grahek (CIO)
Subsidiaries:
BlueStream Professional Services, LLC   (1)
3065 Chastain Meadows Pkwy Ste 100, Marietta, GA 30066
Tel.: (678) 355-6200
Web Site: http://www.bluestreampro.com
Telecommunication Servicesb
N.A.I.C.S.: 517112
Eric McWhorter (Dir-Program Mgmt)
Kathleen G. Putrah (Chm & CEO)
Ken Marcotte (VP-Ops)
Lydia McGregor (Dir-Quality, Trng, LEAN & EHS)
Roger Oettinger (Sr Dir-Fin)
Trevor Putrah (Pres)
Braxton Dougherty (Asst VP-Site Dev-Mobility Svcs)
Matthew Glass (COO)
Stuart Romenesko (CFO)

KGS ELECTRONICS
418 E Live Oak Ave, Arcadia, CA 91006
Tel.: (626) 574-1175
Web Site:
   http://www.kgselectronics.com
Rev.: $10,000,000
Emp.: 70
Power Conversion Units, A.C. To D.C.: Static-Elect
N.A.I.C.S.: 423430

Alex Morales (Mgr)
Le Au (Mgr-Acctg)
Sem Lenh (Mgr-Pur)
Nathan Sugimoto (Pres)
Nick Sukanchi (Engr)

KGS STEEL INC.
3725 Pine Ln, Bessemer, AL 35022
Tel.: (205) 425-0800
Web Site: http://www.kgssteel.com
Sales Range: $10-24.9 Million
Emp.: 50
Iron & Steel Products Mfr
N.A.I.C.S.: 423510
Alfred Boohaker (Controller)
Jeff Hubbard (Plant Mgr)

KH ADVERTISING
245 Main St Ste 202, Chester, NJ 07930
Tel.: (908) 879-3757
Year Founded: 1985
Rev.: $1,500,000
Emp.: 5
Fiscal Year-end: 12/31/03
N.A.I.C.S.: 541810
Kathleen Bodnar Konsulis (Dir-Art)
Kathy Phillips (Acct Mgr)
Kathy Moskowitz (Office Mgr)

KHAN ACADEMY, INC.
PO Box 1630, Mountain View, CA 94042
Tel.: (650) 336-5426   CA
Web Site:
   http://www.khanacademy.org
Year Founded: 2007
Educational Support Services
N.A.I.C.S.: 611710
Ann Doerr (Chm)
Sal Khan (Founder & CEO)
Elizabeth Slavitt (CMO)
Subsidiaries:
Duck Duck Moose, Inc.   (1)
1 Water Park Dr Ste 101, San Mateo, CA 94303   (100%)
Tel.: (650) 336-5426
Web Site:
   http://www.duckduckmoosedesign.com
Software Publisher
N.A.I.C.S.: 513210
Caroline Hu Flexer (Founder & CEO)

KHERA COMMUNICATIONS INC.
1395 Piccard Dr Ste 360, Rockville, MD 20850
Tel.: (301) 825-5658
Web Site:
   http://www.mailermailer.com
Sales Range: $1-9.9 Million
Emp.: 14
List Management Services
N.A.I.C.S.: 513140
Raj Khera (Partner)
Vivek Khera (Partner)
Subsidiaries:
MailerMailer, LLC   (1)
1395 Piccard Dr Ste 360, Rockville, MD 20850
Tel.: (301) 825-5658
Web Site: http://www.mailermailer.com
Emp.: 8
Email Marketing Services
N.A.I.C.S.: 513140
Vivek Khera (Co-Founder & CTO)
Raj Khera (Co-Founder & CEO)

KHI MECHANICAL SERVICES
2630 S 3270 W Ste B, West Valley City, UT 84119-1187
Tel.: (801) 972-2680
Web Site:
   http://www.khimechanical.net
Year Founded: 2002
Sales Range: $10-24.9 Million

Emp.: 95
Air Conditioning System Installation Services
N.A.I.C.S.: 238220
Kelly Kemp (Pres)

KHN SOLUTIONS LLC
300 Bdwy Ste 26, San Francisco, CA 94133
Tel.: (415) 693-9756
Web Site: http://www.bactrack.com
Year Founded: 2001
Rev.: $3,600,000
Emp.: 9
Measuring & Controlling Device Mfr
N.A.I.C.S.: 334519
Keith Nothacker (Founder & Pres)
Brad Burdic (Mgr-Mktg Staff-Sls Staff)

KHOSLA VENTURES, LLC
2128 Centre Rd, Menlo Park, CA 94025
Tel.: (650) 376-8500   CA
Web Site:
   http://www.khoslaventures.com
Year Founded: 2004
Privater Equity Firm
N.A.I.C.S.: 523999
Vinod Khosla (Co-Founder & Partner)
Samir Kaul (Co-Founder & Gen Partner)
David Weiden (Partner)
Keith Rabois (Partner)
Bruce W. Armstrong (Operating Partner)
Amit Soman (Pres)
Keith Rabois (Partner)

KHOURY INC.
1600 W Breitung Ave, Kingsford, MI 49802-1629
Tel.: (906) 774-6333   DE
Year Founded: 1954
Sales Range: $25-49.9 Million
Emp.: 238
Wood Household Furniture Mfr
N.A.I.C.S.: 449129
Daniel Khoury (CEO)

KHS&S CONTRACTORS
5422 Bay Center Dr Ste 200, Tampa, FL 33609
Tel.: (813) 628-9330
Web Site: http://www.khss.com
Year Founded: 1984
Sales Range: $250-299.9 Million
Emp.: 1,300
Construction Services
N.A.I.C.S.: 236220
Dennis Norman (CFO-West Coast)
David Suder (Co-Pres & Co-CEO-West Coast)
Robert Luker (Sr VP-East Coast)
Mark Keenan (Co-Founder & Chm)
Michael Cannon (Co-Pres & Co-CEO-East Coast)
Tom Gibbons (Principal & Sr VP-East Coast)
Tony Hemgesberg (Sr VP-East Coast)
Lynda Licht (CFO-East Coast & Principal)
Philip Cherne (COO-West Coast)
Shawn Martin (Principal & Sr VP-West Coast)
Bruce Holleran (Dir-Bus Dev)

KIA OF SANTA FE
1701 Saint Michael's Dr, Santa Fe, NM 87505-7616
Tel.: (505) 982-1957   NM
Web Site: http://www.kiaofsantafe.net
Year Founded: 1980
Sales Range: $75-99.9 Million
Emp.: 30
Automobile Dealership
N.A.I.C.S.: 441110

KIAN CAPITAL PARTNERS, LLC

Kian Capital Partners, LLC—(Continued)

KIAN CAPITAL PARTNERS, LLC
4201 Congress St Rotunda Bldg Ste 440, Charlotte, NC 28209
Tel.: (704) 943-2500 NC
Web Site: http://www.kiancapital.com
Year Founded: 2010
Privater Equity Firm
N.A.I.C.S.: 523999
Rick Cravey (Co-Founder & Partner-Atlanta Office)
Kevin McCarthy (Co-Founder & Partner)
Scott Buschmann (Partner-Atlanta Office)
Matt Levenson (Partner)
Charlie Edmondson (CFO)
Caldwell Zimmerman (VP)

Subsidiaries:

Motor City Industrial LLC (1)
1600 E 10 Mile Rd, Hazel Park, MI 48030
Tel.: (248) 399-2830
Web Site: http://www.motorcityindustrial.com
Fasteners & Related Products Distr
N.A.I.C.S.: 339993
Joe Stephens (CEO)

Subsidiary (Domestic):

Motor City Fastener, LLC (2)
1600 E 10 Mile Rd, Hazel Park, MI 48030
Tel.: (248) 399-2830
Web Site:
    http://www.motorcityfasteners.com
Hardware Distr
N.A.I.C.S.: 423710
Joe Stephens (CEO)

Quality Fasteners & Supply Co. (2)
3100 Adventure Ln, Oxford, MI 48371
Tel.: (248) 628-0892
Hardware Stores; Industrial Consumables & Ancillary Products Distr
N.A.I.C.S.: 444110
Jim Hiatt (Gen Mgr)
John Shepard (Mgr-Warehouse)

Smith Fastener Co., Inc. (2)
30 INDUSTRIAL WAY, PO BOX 8555, Charleston, WV 25303
Tel.: (304) 925-4787
Web Site: http://www.smithfastener.com
Industrial Supplies Merchant Whslr
N.A.I.C.S.: 423840

Southern Pump & Tank Company (1)
4800 N Graham St, Charlotte, NC 28269-4823
Tel.: (704) 596-4373
Web Site: http://www.spatco.com
Sales Range: $25-49.9 Million
Emp.: 210
Gasoline Equipment Construction & Installation Services; Industrial Pumps, Tanks & Metering Devices Sales; General Contracting Services
N.A.I.C.S.: 423830
John Force (VP-Mktg)
Kent Reed (Branch Mgr-Charlotte)
Jeff Bailey (Pres)

Subsidiary (Domestic):

K&K Electric, Inc. (2)
2517 Country Club Rd, Sanford, FL 32771
Tel.: (407) 323-6300
Web Site: http://www.kkelectric.com
Sales Range: $1-9.9 Million
Emp.: 50
Electrical Contractor
N.A.I.C.S.: 238210
Chris Ferrara (Pres)
Pete Hodges (Mgr-Construction)
Susan Logan (Pres-HR)

Mckinney Petroleum Equipment, Inc. (2)
3926 Halls Mill Rd, Mobile, AL 36693
Tel.: (251) 661-8800
Web Site:
    http://www.mckinneypetroleum.com
Sales Range: $1-9.9 Million
Emp.: 21
Industrial Machinery & Equipment Whslr

N.A.I.C.S.: 423830
Mike Johnson (Mgr-Svc)

The Eastwood Company (1)
263 Shoemaker Rd, Pottstown, PA 19464
Tel.: (800) 343-9353
Web Site: http://www.eastwood.com
Professional-grade Automotive tools, Equipment & Supplies Provider
N.A.I.C.S.: 441330
Brian Huck (CEO)

Subsidiary (Domestic):

Yost Vises, LLC (2)
388 W 24th St, Holland, MI 49423-4037
Tel.: (616) 396-2063
Web Site: http://www.yostvises.com
Saw Blade & Handtool Manufacturing
N.A.I.C.S.: 332216
Pat Nelis (Pres)

KIAWAH ISLAND COMMUNITY ASSOCIATION, INC.
23 Beachwalker Dr, Kiawah Island, SC 29455
Tel.: (843) 768-9194 SC
Web Site: http://www.kica.us
Year Founded: 1976
Sales Range: $10-24.9 Million
Emp.: 173
Community Welfare Services
N.A.I.C.S.: 624190
Ben Cheatham (Chm)
Cathy Pumphrey (Vice Chm)
Mike Feldmann (Treas)
Holly Newman (Sec)
Jimmy Bailey (COO)

KIAWAH ISLAND GOLF RESORTS
1 Sanctuary Beach Dr, Kiawah Island, SC 29455-5677
Tel.: (843) 768-2121 SC
Web Site:
    http://www.kiawahresort.com
Year Founded: 1993
Sales Range: $50-74.9 Million
Emp.: 1,250
Hotels, Motels & Resorts
N.A.I.C.S.: 721110
Russell Burnett (Controller)
Thomas J. Bewley (Dir-Sls-Mktg)
Roger Warren (Pres)

KIAWAH PARTNERS
1 Kiawah Island Pkwy, Kiawah Island, SC 29455
Tel.: (843) 768-3400
Web Site:
    http://www.kiawahisland.com
Year Founded: 1987
Sales Range: $25-49.9 Million
Emp.: 500
Resort & Golf Courses
N.A.I.C.S.: 721110
Townsend Clarkson (COO)

KICE INDUSTRIES INC.
5500 Mill Hts Dr, Wichita, KS 67219
Tel.: (316) 744-7151
Web Site: http://www.kice.com
Sales Range: $10-24.9 Million
Emp.: 190
Sheet Metalwork
N.A.I.C.S.: 332322
Edward M. Kice (Chm & VP-Production-Wichita)
Deanna Puckett (Project Coord)
Adam Ybarra (Engr-Automation Sys)
Stephen Pederson (Engr-Design)
David Wolf (Mgr)

KICKAPOO TRIBE IN KANSAS
824 111th Dr, Horton, KS 66439
Tel.: (785) 486-2131
Web Site: http://www.ktik-nsn.gov
Sales Range: $10-24.9 Million
Emp.: 150

Tribe
N.A.I.C.S.: 722511
Lester Randall (Chm)

KICKAPOO VALLEY CHEESE CORP.
9285 3rd St, Milladore, WI 54454
Tel.: (715) 652-2173
Web Site:
    http://www.kickapoocheese.com
Sales Range: $50-74.9 Million
Emp.: 115
Dairy Product Merchant Whslr
N.A.I.C.S.: 424430
Richard Wyman (CFO & Controller)

KICKHAEFER MANUFACTURING COMPANY INC.
1221 S Pk St, Port Washington, WI 53074-2127
Tel.: (262) 284-3424
Web Site:
    http://www.kmcstampings.com
Year Founded: 1908
Sales Range: $10-24.9 Million
Emp.: 170
Metal Stampings
N.A.I.C.S.: 332119
Gerry Schwarz (Pres)

KIDD & COMPANY LLC
1455 E Putnam Ave, Old Greenwich, CT 06870
Tel.: (203) 661-0070 CT
Web Site:
    http://www.kiddcompany.com
Year Founded: 1976
Privater Equity Firm
N.A.I.C.S.: 523999
William J. Kidd (Founder & Partner)
Gerard A. DeBiasi (Partner)
James G. Benedict (Principal)
Kenneth J. Heuer (Principal)
Matthew A. Cook (Principal)

Subsidiaries:

BRH Garver Construction, L.P. (1)
7600 S Santa Fe Bldg A1 E, Houston, TX 77061
Tel.: (713) 921-2929
Web Site: http://www.brhgarver.com
Water; Sewer & Utility Lines
N.A.I.C.S.: 531210
C. Mike Garver (Founder)
Fred Gular (Treas, Sec & Controller)
David Elett (VP)
Todd Hendricks (VP)
Alan Pate (Pres)
Phil Reed (VP-Estimating & Project Mgmt)
Leslie Hess (CFO)
Gene Kemp (CEO)

Imaginetics LLC (1)
3410 A St SE, Auburn, WA 98002
Tel.: (253) 735-0156
Web Site: http://www.imaginetcsinc.com
Sales Range: $1-9.9 Million
Emp.: 90
Sheet Metal Fabrication, CNC Machining & Assembly Services
N.A.I.C.S.: 332322
Scott Strong (CEO)
Pat Prince (COO)

NextPhase Medical Devices LLC (1)
150 Hopper Ave, Waldwick, NJ 07463
Tel.: (877) 639-2673
Web Site: http://www.nextphasemed.com
Medical Device Mfr
N.A.I.C.S.: 339112
Carlo W. Colesanti (Pres & CEO)
James V. DiVizio (CFO & Sr VP)

Subsidiary (Domestic):

Proven Process Medical Devices, Inc. (2)
110 Forbes Blvd, Mansfield, MA 02048-1145
Tel.: (508) 261-0800
Web Site: http://www.provenprocess.com

Research & Development in the Physical, Engineering & Life Sciences
N.A.I.C.S.: 541715
Charles Aubin (VP-Mechanical Engrg)

KIDD CONSTRUCTION CO., INC.
6885 Cliffdale Rd, Fayetteville, NC 28314
Tel.: (910) 864-9727
Sales Range: $10-24.9 Million
Emp.: 125
Industrial Building Construction Services
N.A.I.C.S.: 236210
Harold J. Kidd (Pres)

KIDD GROUP
2074 Centre Point Blvd Ste 200, Tallahassee, FL 32308
Tel.: (850) 878-5433
Web Site: http://www.kidd.com
Year Founded: 1980
Sales Range: $10-24.9 Million
Emp.: 18
Communications, Education, Financial, Government/Political/Public Affairs, Health Care, Retail
N.A.I.C.S.: 541810
William J. Kidd (Pres & Creative Dir)
Patricia Rodriguez (Agency Dir & Sr Acct Mgr)
Jeremy Spinks (Dir-Web Studio-Tallahassee)
Michael Chiaro (Reg Dir)
Mary Liz Moody (Art Dir & Sr Graphic Designer)
Cindy Martin (Office Mgr)
Blair Berlow (Acct Mgr)
Oliver Debon (Web Designer)
Rodney Johnson (Web Designer)
Ivette Marques (Dir-PR)

KIDD JONES HENDERSON COUNTY
535 W Tyler St, Athens, TX 75751
Tel.: (903) 675-5789
Sales Range: $10-24.9 Million
Emp.: 70
Petroleum Bulk Stations
N.A.I.C.S.: 424710

KIDD ROOFING
1212 E Anderson Ln Ste 200, Austin, TX 78752
Tel.: (512) 671-7791
Web Site: http://www.kiddroof.com
Year Founded: 1982
Sales Range: $10-24.9 Million
Emp.: 65
Roofing Contractor Services
N.A.I.C.S.: 238160
Corey Wilson (Pres)

KIDDER MATHEWS
601 Union St Ste 4720, Seattle, WA 98101
Tel.: (206) 296-9600
Web Site:
    http://www.kiddermathews.com
Year Founded: 1969
Sales Range: $75-99.9 Million
Emp.: 451
Real Estate Development Services
N.A.I.C.S.: 531320
Brian Hatcher (Exec VP-Brokerage-Pacific Northwest)
Caryl Brown (VP-Portland)
Peter K. Shorett (Pres-Valuation Advisory Svcs)
Gregg Domanico (Mng Dir-Northern California & Exec VP)
Bruce McLellan (Partner & Exec VP)
Jaclyn Marshall (VP)
Joe Malaspino (Sr VP & Dir-Engrg, Sustainability & Property Mgmt)

James K. Bennett *(Mng Partner & Exec VP)*
Mike Denevi *(Sr VP-San Jose)*
Kevin Sheehan *(Mng Partner)*
Tom Bacci *(Sr VP)*
Bob Pechal *(VP)*
Stephen Tyrrell *(Partner & Sr VP)*
Jon R. Walker *(Partner & Sr VP)*
Lezlie Plastino *(Sr Mgr-Property)*
Nancy Jameson *(Mgr-Property)*
D. William Frame *(Pres)*
John Booth *(Sr VP)*
Dean Krieger *(Sr VP-Irvine)*
John Austin *(Sr VP-Roseville)*
Eric M. Thies *(Sr VP)*
William R. Boyd *(Exec VP)*
Linda P. Lee *(Exec VP)*
Scott Unger *(Sr VP)*
C. J. Collins *(Sr VP)*
Carter McFarland *(VP)*
Mark McFarland *(Exec VP)*
Christopher J. Corr *(Exec VP)*

KIDDER MATTHEW, LLC
601 S Figueroa St Ste 2700, Los Angeles, CA 90017
Tel.: (877) 454-3337 WA
Web Site: http://kidder.com
Year Founded: 1969
Brokerage & Property Management Consulting Services
N.A.I.C.S.: 531210
Jeffrey S. Lyon *(Bd of Dirs, Executives)*

Subsidiaries:

Wessex Service Co., Inc. (1)
3295 N Drinkwater Blvd Ste 11, Scottsdale, AZ 85251
Tel.: (602) 285-9010
Web Site: http://www.wessexco.com
Lessors of Nonresidential Buildings (except Miniwarehouses)
N.A.I.C.S.: 531120
Michael J. DiDomenico *(Pres & CEO)*
Kathryn E. Taylor *(Controller)*

KIDS IN NEED FOUNDATION
3055 Kettering Blvd Ste 119, Moraine, OH 45439
Tel.: (937) 296-1230 OH
Web Site: http://www.kinf.org
Year Founded: 1995
Sales Range: $25-49.9 Million
Emp.: 8
School Supplies Distr
N.A.I.C.S.: 611710
Phil Wenzell *(Treas)*
Stacia Andersen *(Vice Chm)*
Corey Funkey *(Sec)*
Dave Smith *(Chm)*
Renay Dossman *(Exec Dir)*

KIDS IN THE GAME LLC
132 Nassau St Ste 310, New York, NY 10038
Tel.: (212) 634-7262 NY
Web Site: http://www.kidsinthegame.com
Year Founded: 2013
Sales Range: $1-9.9 Million
Emp.: 150
Educational Support Services
N.A.I.C.S.: 611710
Michael Murphy *(Founder & Chief Program Officer)*
Matt Murphy *(CEO)*
Wilson Rose *(COO)*
Sandy Persaud *(Chief People Officer)*
Cara Hudson *(Dir-People & Culture)*

KIDS PREFERRED INC.
81 Twin Rivers Dr E, Windsor, NJ 08520
Tel.: (732) 274-1144
Web Site: http://www.kidspreferred.com

Year Founded: 1992
Rev.: $30,000,000
Emp.: 35
Plush Toys Whslr
N.A.I.C.S.: 423920
Louis Premselaar *(Pres)*

KIDS STUFF, INC.
7090 Whipple Rd NW, Canton, OH 44720
Tel.: (330) 649-5700 DE
Web Site: http://www.kidsstuff.com
Year Founded: 1977
Sales Range: $10-24.9 Million
Emp.: 20
Child Safety Product Natural & Organic Infant & Children Clothing Wooden Toy Cotton & Organic Diaper & Diaper Cover Mfr
N.A.I.C.S.: 459120
William Miller *(Pres)*
Jennifer Thames *(Gen Mgr)*

Subsidiaries:

Jeannie's Kids Club (1)
7090 Whipple Ave NW, North Canton, OH 44720-7134
Tel.: (330) 649-5700
Web Site: http://www.kidsstuff.com
N.A.I.C.S.: 425120
Jen Thames *(Gen Mgr)*

The Natural Baby Catalog (1)
7090 Whipple Ave NW, Canton, OH 44720-1546
Tel.: (330) 492-8090
Web Site: http://www.kidstuff.com
Sales Range: $10-24.9 Million
Emp.: 6
N.A.I.C.S.: 456199
William Miller *(Pres)*

The Perfectly Safe Catalog (1)
7090 Whipple Ave, North Canton, OH 44720-7134
Tel.: (330) 649-5700
Sales Range: $10-24.9 Million
Emp.: 15
Catalog of Safety Products for Parents with Toddlers & Infants
N.A.I.C.S.: 449129

KIDS2, INC.
3333 Piedmont Rd NE Ste 1800, Atlanta, GA 30305
Tel.: (770) 751-0442
Web Site: http://www.kidsii.com
Sales Range: $10-24.9 Million
Emp.: 140
Blow-Molded Finished Plastics Products
N.A.I.C.S.: 326199
Ryan Gunnigle *(CEO)*
Rick Ayers *(Dir-Pkg & Gear)*
Hector King *(Mgr-Post Production)*
Jeff Lanford *(Sr Mgr-e-Commerce)*
Mark Williams *(Sr VP-Global Distr)*
Jeff Cheslik *(Dir-Domestic Sls)*
Kyli Owen *(Mgr-Channel Mktg)*
Caroline Kogan *(Mgr-Digital Mktg)*
Jessica Kostyniak *(VP-Product Mgmt)*
Katie Walters *(Mgr-Web)*
Russ Coddington *(VP-Infant Toy Div)*
Adam Bain *(Dir-Design & Art-Mktg Creative & Imaging)*
Kerri Braun *(Deputy Gen Counsel-Intellectual Property & Litigation)*
Matthew Smith *(Gen Counsel)*
Mark Zeige *(Sr VP-Global Home & Play Bus Units)*
Aaron Vollrath *(VP-Customer Solutions)*

Subsidiaries:

Summer Infant, Inc. (1)
1275 Park E Dr, Woonsocket, RI 02895
Tel.: (401) 671-6550
Web Site: http://www.summerinfant.com
Rev.: $143,665,000
Assets: $91,230,000

Liabilities: $88,655,000
Net Worth: $2,575,000
Earnings: ($2,898,000)
Emp.: 112
Fiscal Year-end: 01/01/2022
Retailer of Infant Health, Safety & Wellness Products
N.A.I.C.S.: 551112
Chris Witty *(VP-IR)*
Bruce Meier *(Interim CFO)*

Subsidiary (Domestic):

Butterfly Living LLC (2)
251 1st Ave N Fl 2, Minneapolis, MN 55401-1644
Tel.: (610) 286-1742
Sales Range: $10-24.9 Million
Emp.: 4
Nursery Furniture Mfr
N.A.I.C.S.: 337122

KIDSPEACE
4085 Independence Dr, Schnecksville, PA 18078-2574
Tel.: (800) 257-3223 PA
Web Site: http://www.kidspeace.org
Year Founded: 1991
Sales Range: $10-24.9 Million
Emp.: 331
Behavioral Health Rehabilitation Services
N.A.I.C.S.: 621420
Andrew R. Clark *(Dir-Medical)*
Michael Slack *(Pres & CEO)*
Susan Mullen *(Exec VP- Pennsylvania Programs)*
Susan Leyburn *(Exec VP- Programs & Quality)*
Scott Reines *(Chm)*
J. Jackson Eaton III *(Gen Counsel)*

KIDSPEACE CORPORATION
4085 Independence Dr, Schnecksville, PA 18078-2574
Tel.: (610) 799-8110 PA
Web Site: http://www.kidspeace.org
Year Founded: 1886
Sales Range: $25-49.9 Million
Emp.: 500
Behavioral Healthcare Services
N.A.I.C.S.: 623220

KIDVERTISERS, INC.
1133 Broadway Ste 1000, New York, NY 10010
Tel.: (212) 966-2345 NY
Web Site: http://www.kidvertisers.com
Year Founded: 1989
Sales Range: $1-9.9 Million
Emp.: 8
Broadcast, Cable T.V., Children's Market, Collateral, Consumer Publications, Education, Entertainment, Graphic Design, Leisure, Magazines, Teen Market
N.A.I.C.S.: 541810
Deyna Vesey *(Co-Pres & Dir-Creative)*
Larry Nunno *(Co-Pres)*
Mitch Koffler *(Assoc Dir-Creative)*
Nona Bleetstein *(Office Mgr)*

KIDWELL INC.
3333 Folkways Cir, Lincoln, NE 68504
Tel.: (402) 475-9151
Web Site: http://www.kidwell.us.com
Year Founded: 1945
Sales Range: $10-24.9 Million
Emp.: 105
Electrical Wiring Services
N.A.I.C.S.: 238210
Tim Jonas *(Mgr-Estimation)*
David Black *(Dir-Special Sys)*

KIDZMATTER INC.
432 Val Lane, Marion, IN 46952

Tel.: (765) 664-6968 IL
Web Site: http://www.kidzmatter.com
Year Founded: 2010
Sales Range: $1-9.9 Million
Emp.: 100
Child & Family Welfare Services
N.A.I.C.S.: 624190
Tina Houser *(Exec Editor & Sr Dir-Publications)*
Beth Frank *(Chief Creative Officer)*
Dave Condiff *(Dir-Sls)*
Ryan Frank *(CEO)*
Jack Eggar *(Chm)*
Holly Yonamine *(Treas & Sec)*

KIEFER SPECIALTY FLOORING, INC.
2910 Falling Waters, Lindenhurst, IL 60046
Tel.: (847) 245-8450
Web Site: http://www.kieferfloors.com
Year Founded: 1946
Sales Range: $10-24.9 Million
Emp.: 35
Floor Coverings Whslr
N.A.I.C.S.: 423220
Brion Rittenberry *(Pres & CEO)*
Joy Gauthier *(Controller)*
Don Traska *(Project Mgr)*
Barb Miller *(Project Coord-Pur)*

KIEFFER & CO., INC.
3322 Washington Ave, Sheboygan, WI 53081
Tel.: (920) 458-4394
Web Site: http://www.kieffersigns.com
Rev.: $23,300,000
Emp.: 100
Sign Mfr
N.A.I.C.S.: 339950
Mark Stefen *(Controller)*
Jeff Fuhrmann *(VP)*
Larry Caraccilo *(VP)*

KIEFNER BROTHERS, INC.
1459 N Kings Hwy St, Cape Girardeau, MO 63701-2116
Tel.: (573) 334-0707
Web Site: http://www.kiefnerbrothers.com
Sales Range: $25-49.9 Million
Emp.: 60
Nonresidential Construction Services
N.A.I.C.S.: 236220
Thomas Kiefner *(CEO)*

KIEMLE-HANKINS COMPANY
94 H St, Perrysburg, OH 43551
Tel.: (419) 666-0660
Web Site: http://www.kiemlehankins.com
Rev.: $50,000,000
Emp.: 120
Electrical Apparatus & Equipment
N.A.I.C.S.: 811310
A. Stephen Martindale *(Chm)*
Timothy Martindale *(Pres)*
Daniel D'Amico *(CFO & VP)*

KIER CONSTRUCTION CORPORATION
3710 Quincy Ave, Ogden, UT 84403-1934
Tel.: (801) 627-1414
Web Site: http://www.kier.org
Sales Range: $25-49.9 Million
Emp.: 60
Residential Construction Services
N.A.I.C.S.: 236118
Margo L. Culwell *(Dir-HR)*
Stephen J. Kier *(Pres)*
Scott J. Kier *(VP)*

KIER GROUP HOLDINGS, LLC

KIER GROUP HOLDINGS, LLC   U.S. PRIVATE

Kier Group Holdings, LLC—(Continued)
1330 Ave of the Americas, New York, NY 10019-5400
Tel.: (212) 397-7200
Year Founded: 1993
Sales Range: $100-124.9 Million
Emp.: 5
Holding Company; Private Investment Firm
N.A.I.C.S.: 523999

Subsidiaries:

The San Francisco Music Box Company (1)
3113 Woodcreek Dr, Downers Grove, IL 60515
Web Site: http://www.sfmusicbox.com
Sales Range: $100-124.9 Million
Retailer of Musical Gift Items
N.A.I.C.S.: 424930

KIESLER POLICE SUPPLY INC.
2802 Fable Mill Rd, Jeffersonville, IN 47130-9634
Tel.: (812) 288-5740   IN
Web Site: http://www.kiesler.com
Year Founded: 1973
Sales Range: $10-24.9 Million
Emp.: 30
Sporting & Recreation Goods, Police Supply & Ammunition Company
N.A.I.C.S.: 423910
Douglas M. Kiesler (Owner, Chm & CEO)
Tony Chambers (Pres)
Jeffrey Blain (CFO)

KIEWIT CORP.
5002 Cabrillo Hwy, Montara, CA 94037
Tel.: (650) 728-7564
Web Site: http://www.kiewit.com
Emp.: 100
Heavy & Civil Engineering Construction
N.A.I.C.S.: 237990
Paul Madsen (Mgr)

Subsidiaries:

Weeks Marine, Inc. (1)
4 Commerce Dr 2nd Fl, Cranford, NJ 07016-3509
Tel.: (908) 272-4010
Web Site: http://www.weeksmarine.com
Rev: $210,000,000
Emp.: 1,400
Marine Construction & Dredging
N.A.I.C.S.: 236210
Richard S. Weeks (Pres)
Carolina Palmer (Project Mgr)
Michael Paci (Mgr-Heavy Lift, Salvage & Marine Transportation)
Teresa Olivo (Mgr-Corp Claims)
Douglas Nelson (Project Mgr)
John Ghiretti (Dir-Tax)
Edward Herrmann (Engr-Port)
Rod Ridolfo (Mgr-Pur)
Rick MacDonald (Sr VP)
Eric Ellefsen (Pres & CEO)

Subsidiary (Domestic):

Healy Tibbitts Builders, Inc. (2)
99-994 Iwaena St Ste A, Aiea, HI 96701
Tel.: (808) 487-3664
Web Site: http://www.weeksmarine.com
Sales Range: $25-49.9 Million
Emp.: 105
Construction of Piers & Wharves, Submarine Pipelines & Cables, Offshore Structures, Dredging, Pile Driving, Marine Heavy Lifts, Bulk Stevedoring & Marine Transportation
N.A.I.C.S.: 541330
Rick Heltzel (Pres)

Subsidiary (Non-US):

McNally International Inc. (2)
1855 Barton Street East, Hamilton, L8H 2Y7, ON, Canada
Tel.: (905) 549-6561
Web Site: http://www.mcnallycorp.com
Tunnel Construction Services
N.A.I.C.S.: 237990
Murray Malott (Pres)

KIEWIT INFRASTRUCTURE SOUTH CO.
13119 Old Denton Rd, Fort Worth, TX 76177
Tel.: (817) 337-7000
Web Site: http://www.kiewit.com
Sales Range: $25-49.9 Million
Emp.: 559
Highway & Street Construction Services
N.A.I.C.S.: 237310
John Gartner (CFO)
William D. Glaser (Sr VP)

KIGHT LUMBER CO. INC.
5521 Boonville Hwy, Evansville, IN 47715
Tel.: (812) 479-8281   IN
Web Site: http://www.kighthomecenter.com
Year Founded: 1957
Sales Range: $25-49.9 Million
Emp.: 150
Lumber & other Building Materials
N.A.I.C.S.: 444110
Kent R. Bernhardt (Pres)
Mike Lacer (CFO)

KIK POOL ADDITIVES INC.
5160 E Airport Dr, Ontario, CA 91761-7824
Tel.: (909) 390-9912
Web Site: http://www.kem-tek.com
Year Founded: 1958
Sales Range: $10-24.9 Million
Emp.: 130
Chemicals & Allied Products Mfr
N.A.I.C.S.: 325998
John Christensen (Pres)
Kim Munoz (Mgr-Credit)
Brian Patterson (CFO)

KILGORE INDUSTRIES
10050 Houston Oaks Dr, Houston, TX 77064
Tel.: (713) 924-4900
Web Site: http://www.kilgoremechanical.com
Year Founded: 2000
Sales Range: $10-24.9 Million
Emp.: 600
Construction, Plumbing & Electrical Services
N.A.I.C.S.: 236210
Jeff Kilgore (Co-Founder & Co-Owner)
Ken Kilgore Jr. (Co-Founder & Co-Owner)

KILLAM OIL CO. LTD.
4320 University Blvd, Laredo, TX 78041
Tel.: (956) 724-7141
Web Site: http://www.killamcompanies.com
Rev.: $13,000,000
Emp.: 30
Oil & Gas Exploration
N.A.I.C.S.: 213112
Radcliffe Killam (Partner)
David Killam (Partner)
Sara Narvaez (Supvr-Production)

KILLEARN PROPERTIES, INC.
300 Lester Mill Rd Ste 110, Locust Grove, GA 30248
Tel.: (770) 389-2020   FL
Web Site: http://www.killearn.com
Year Founded: 1964
Sales Range: $50-74.9 Million
Emp.: 20
Land Development
N.A.I.C.S.: 531210
William E. Daniels Jr. (CFO)

Subsidiaries:

Killearn Construction, Inc. (1)
135 N Park Pl Ste 100, Stockbridge, GA 30281-6380
Tel.: (770) 389-2020
Web Site: http://www.killearn.org
Home Construction Operations
N.A.I.C.S.: 236115

Killearn Properties of Georgia (1)
135 N Pk Pl Ste 100, Stockbridge, GA 30281-6380
Tel.: (770) 389-2020
Web Site: http://www.killearn.org
Sales Range: $10-24.9 Million
Land Development
N.A.I.C.S.: 531210
J. T. Williams Jr. (COO)

KILLEEN FURTNEY GROUP, INC.
149 S Barrington Ave Ste 800, Los Angeles, CA 90049-3310
Tel.: (310) 476-6941
Web Site: http://www.killeenfurtneygroup.com
Sales Range: Less than $1 Million
Emp.: 10
Advetising Agency
N.A.I.C.S.: 541810
Joann E. Killeen (Pres)
Michael J. Furtney (Partner)

KILLER FILMS INC.
18 E 16th St, New York, NY 10003
Tel.: (212) 473-3950   NY
Web Site: http://www.killerfilms.com
Year Founded: 1997
Sales Range: $10-24.9 Million
Emp.: 5
Producers of Motion Picture Films
N.A.I.C.S.: 512110
Christine Vachon (Partner)
Pam Koffler (Partner)

KILLER INTERACTIVE, LLC
23 E Third St 2nd Floor, Bethlehem, PA 18015
Tel.: (484) 619-3323
Web Site: http://www.wearekiller.com
Year Founded: 1999
Sales Range: $1-9.9 Million
Emp.: 8
Website Design & Development, E-Commerce, Social Media & Email Marketing
N.A.I.C.S.: 541613
Jason Pijut (Creative Dir)
Nick Volchko (Head-Programmer)

KILLIAN BRANDING
322 S Green St Ste 510, Chicago, IL 60607
Tel.: (312) 836-0050
Web Site: http://www.killianbranding.com
Year Founded: 1987
Rev.: $15,200,000
Emp.: 13
Advetising Agency
N.A.I.C.S.: 541810
Bob Killian (Pres)
Katie Scully (Dir-Art)
Mike Adamson (Copywriter)
Amanda Tacker (Acct Exec)

KILLION INDUSTRIES INC.
1380 Poinsettia Ave, Vista, CA 92081
Tel.: (760) 727-5102
Web Site: http://www.killionindustries.com
Sales Range: $10-24.9 Million
Emp.: 121

Counters Or Counter Display Cases, Wood
N.A.I.C.S.: 337110
Richard W. Killion (Pres)
Larry Edwards (Controller)

KILOP USA, INC.
4100 Mendenhall Oaks Pkwy Ste 260, High Point, NC 27265
Tel.: (336) 885-4100
Web Site: http://www.kilopusa.com
Year Founded: 1988
Rev.: $26,300,000
Emp.: 8
Business Products & Services
N.A.I.C.S.: 424610
Christina Yumei Chen (Co-Founder)

KILPATRICK COMPANY INC.
7700 High Rdg Rd, Boynton Beach, FL 33426
Tel.: (561) 533-1450
Web Site: http://www.kilpatrickco.com
Year Founded: 1958
Sales Range: $25-49.9 Million
Emp.: 57
Lawn & Garden Machinery & Equipment Whslr
N.A.I.C.S.: 423820
Don Salter (Gen Mgr-Irrigation Sls & Svc)

Subsidiaries:

Kilpatrick Turf & Industrial Equipment (1)
7700 High Rdg Rd, Boynton Beach, FL 33426-5026
Tel.: (561) 533-1450
Web Site: http://www.kilpatrickco.com
Sales Range: $25-49.9 Million
Provider of Residential & Commercial Irrigation Contracts
N.A.I.C.S.: 423820

KILPATRICK LIFE INSURANCE CO.
1818 Marshall St, Shreveport, LA 71101
Tel.: (318) 222-0555
Web Site: http://www.klic.com
Sales Range: $25-49.9 Million
Emp.: 147
Life Insurance Carrier
N.A.I.C.S.: 524113
Virginia K. Shehee (Chm)
Dona Wilson (CFO)

KILPATRICK SALES INC.
2920 114th St Ste 100, Grand Prairie, TX 75050-8606
Tel.: (214) 634-7271
Web Site: http://www.baldor.com
Sales Range: $25-49.9 Million
Emp.: 12
Motors, Electric
N.A.I.C.S.: 423610

KILPATRICK TOWNSEND & STOCKTON LLP
Ste 2800 1100 Peachtree St NE, Atlanta, GA 30309-4528
Tel.: (404) 815-6500
Web Site: http://www.kilpatricktownsend.com
Year Founded: 1997
Sales Range: $400-449.9 Million
Emp.: 1,001
Law Firm
N.A.I.C.S.: 541110
Miles J. Alexander (Partner)
Olivia Maria Baratta (Partner)
John W. Alden (Partner)
Gary D. Dacey (COO)
Kathy R. Mitchell (Chief Dept Operating Officer & Officer-Intellectual Property Dept)
Ramona P. Moody (Chief HR Officer)

John B. Murphy *(CFO)*
James S. Usher *(CIO)*
W. Benjamin Barkley *(Partner)*
Colin M. Bernardino *(Partner)*
Michael A. Bertelson *(Partner)*
Taylor Higgins Ludlam *(Partner)*
Susan M. Spaeth *(Mng Partner-Global)*
Brian C. Colucci *(CMO & Chief Bus Dev Officer)*
Karly Rodine *(Mng Partner-Dallas)*
John Neeleman *(Partner)*
Gwendolyn Payton *(Partner)*
B. Ford Robertson *(Mng Partner)*
Catherine F. Munson *(Mng Partner)*
Lois W. Colbert *(Mng Partner)*
Kate Gaudry *(Partner-Washington)*
Lindsay Kaplan *(Partner-Washington)*
J. Henry Walker IV *(Chm)*

KIM & SCOTT'S, INC.
2107 W Carroll Ave, Chicago, IL 60612
Tel.: (312) 243-9971
Web Site: http://www.kimandscotts.com
Year Founded: 1995
Sales Range: $1-9.9 Million
Emp.: 78
Gourmet Pretzels
N.A.I.C.S.: 311812
Scott Holstein *(COO)*
Kimberly Holstein *(Pres, CEO & Chief Inspiration Officer)*

KIM HANSEN CHEVROLET-OLDS
1221 W Main St, Burley, ID 83318
Tel.: (208) 678-2221
Web Site: http://www.kimhansen.com
Rev.: $12,702,253
Emp.: 32
Automobiles, New & Used
N.A.I.C.S.: 441110
Kim Hansen *(Pres & CEO)*

KIM KING ASSOCIATES, LLC
1819 Peachtree Rd Ste 575, Atlanta, GA 30309
Tel.: (404) 419-9400   GA
Web Site: http://www.kimkingassoc.com
Year Founded: 1972
Real Estate Development
N.A.I.C.S.: 237210
Kevin T. Byrne *(CFO)*
D. Kimbrough King Jr. *(Pres & CEO)*

Subsidiaries:

Fifth Street Management Company, LLC   (1)
1819 Peachtree Rd NE Ste 575, Atlanta, GA 30309
Tel.: (404) 419-9600
Web Site: http://www.gofifthstreet.com
Emp.: 4
Residential, Commercial & Institutional Property Management Services
N.A.I.C.S.: 531312
Chris McCall *(Sr Mgr-Office Properties)*
Angela King *(Dir-HR)*
D. Kimbrough King Jr. *(Pres)*

KIM'S HOME CENTER INC.
2940 W Olympic Blvd, Los Angeles, CA 90006
Tel.: (213) 386-4882
Web Site: http://www.kimshome.com
Rev.: $11,636,485
Emp.: 35
Electric Household Appliances
N.A.I.C.S.: 449210
Dae Soon Kim *(Pres)*

KIM'S TOYOTA
1030 Highway 15 N, Laurel, MS 39440
Tel.: (601) 425-4701
Web Site: http://www.kimstoyota.com
Sales Range: $10-24.9 Million
Emp.: 50
Used Car Distr
N.A.I.C.S.: 441120
Michael Fielder *(Gen Mgr-Sls)*
Mike Johnson *(Mgr-Sls)*
Cliff Hughes *(Mgr-Fin)*
Brent Hobbs *(Mgr-Sls)*
Tarah Hernderson *(Coord-Internet Sls)*
Theresa McMillan *(Coord-Internet Sls)*
Debbie Myers *(Coord-Internet Sls)*
Sandi Patterson *(Coord-Internet Sls)*
Greg Garcia *(Mgr-Internet Sls)*

KIMBALL ELECTRONICS INC.
2233 S 300 E, Salt Lake City, UT 84115
Tel.: (801) 466-0569
Web Site: http://www.kimballinc.com
Rev.: $49,720,964
Emp.: 50
Electronic Parts & Equipment
N.A.I.C.S.: 423690
Richard A. Kimball Jr. *(Pres)*

KIMBALL EQUIPMENT COMPANY
2839 California Ave, Salt Lake City, UT 84104
Tel.: (801) 972-2121
Web Site: http://www.kimballequipment.com
Sales Range: $10-24.9 Million
Emp.: 32
General Construction Machinery & Equipment
N.A.I.C.S.: 423810
John Kimball *(Owner)*
Mike Brundage *(Mgr-Svc)*
Dave Barton *(Mgr-Svc)*

KIMBER MFG. INC.
555 Taxter Rd Ste 235, Elmsford, NY 10523
Tel.: (406) 758-2222
Web Site: http://www.kimberamerica.com
Year Founded: 1979
Sales Range: $10-24.9 Million
Emp.: 330
Machine Shops
N.A.I.C.S.: 332710
Leslie Edelman *(Owner & CEO)*
Abdool Jamal *(Mgr)*
Winslow Potter *(Dir-Product Mgmt)*
Jerry Kehoe *(Dir-IT)*
Ronald Dudzic *(Product Mgr-Less-Lethal)*
Christopher Lau *(Supvr-CNC)*
Jordan Hunter *(Dir-Mktg Comm)*
Greg Grogan *(COO)*

KIMBER PETROLEUM CORP.
545 Martinsville Rd, Liberty Corner, NJ 07938
Tel.: (908) 903-9600   NJ
Year Founded: 1938
Sales Range: $100-124.9 Million
Emp.: 241
Gas Station Operator
N.A.I.C.S.: 424720
John Maloney *(Supvr)*

KIMBERLITE CORP.
3621 W Beechwood Ave, Fresno, CA 93711-0648
Tel.: (559) 264-9730
Web Site: http://www.sonitrolsecurity.com
Security Guards & Patrol Services
N.A.I.C.S.: 561612
Tom Patterson *(CEO)*

Subsidiaries:

Security First Alarm King   (1)
635 N Plaza Dr, Visalia, CA 93291
Tel.: (559) 734-7761
Web Site: http://www.securityfirstalarmking.com
Sales Range: $1-9.9 Million
Emp.: 20
Security System Product Distr
N.A.I.C.S.: 423610
Susanne Hatzman *(Mgr)*
Robert Shahan *(Owner)*

KIMBLE COMPANIES INC.
3596 State Rte 39 NW, Dover, OH 44622
Tel.: (330) 343-1226
Web Site: http://www.kimblecompanies.com
Holding Company; Mining, Recycling & Waste Disposal Services
N.A.I.C.S.: 551112
Keith B. Kimble *(Pres)*
Mike Yates *(Mgr-IT)*

Subsidiaries:

Penn-Ohio Coal Co.   (1)
3596 State Rte 39 NW, Dover, OH 44622
Tel.: (330) 343-1226
Web Site: http://www.kimblecompanies.com
Sales Range: $10-24.9 Million
Emp.: 150
Coal Mining
N.A.I.C.S.: 212114
Keith B. Kimble *(Pres)*

KIMBRO OIL COMPANY INC.
2200 Clifton Ave, Nashville, TN 37203-1914
Tel.: (615) 320-7484   TN
Web Site: http://www.kimbrooil.com
Year Founded: 1983
Sales Range: $10-24.9 Million
Emp.: 42
Retailer of Petroleum Products
N.A.I.C.S.: 424720
Michael Cameron *(Mgr-Sls)*
Kelly Dalton-Drye *(VP-Fin & Gen Mgr)*
Kevin Cortner *(Mgr-Retail Sls)*
Jeremy Lockhart *(Mgr-Warehouse)*

KIMCO STAFFING SERVICES INC.
17872 Cowan Ave, Irvine, CA 92614-6010
Tel.: (949) 757-4600   CA
Web Site: http://www.kimco.com
Year Founded: 1986
Sales Range: $25-49.9 Million
Emp.: 180
Temporary Help Staffing Services
N.A.I.C.S.: 561320
Kim I. Megonigal *(Founder, Chm & CEO)*
Stephen Bradley *(CFO & VP)*

Subsidiaries:

Advantex Professional Services   (1)
17872 Cowan Ave, Irvine, CA 92614-6010
Tel.: (949) 752-6996
Web Site: http://www.advantexps.com
Emp.: 60
Recruiting Services
N.A.I.C.S.: 561311
Bob Bishop *(Mgr-Client Svcs)*

KIMLEY-HORN AND ASSOCIATES, INC.
3001 Weston Pkwy, Cary, NC 27513-2301
Tel.: (919) 677-2000
Web Site: http://www.kimley-horn.com
Year Founded: 1967
Sales Range: $200-249.9 Million
Emp.: 1,745
Engineering & Environmental Consulting Services
N.A.I.C.S.: 541330
Kent VanRiper *(Sr VP)*
Mandy Bowers *(Coord-Mktg)*
Luke Carraway *(Project Mgr-South Austin)*

Subsidiaries:

Kimley-Horn and Associates, Inc.   (1)
801 Cherry St Unit 11 Ste 950, Fort Worth, TX 76102
Tel.: (817) 335-6511
Web Site: http://www.kimley-horn.com
Sales Range: $1-9.9 Million
Emp.: 25
Engineering & Environmental Consulting Services
N.A.I.C.S.: 541330
Jeff James *(Sr VP)*
Mark Goode III *(Sr Project Mgr)*

Kimley-Horn and Associates, Inc.   (1)
655 N Franklin Ste Ste 150, Tampa, FL 33602
Tel.: (813) 620-1460
Sales Range: $10-24.9 Million
Emp.: 65
Engineering & Environmental Consulting Services
N.A.I.C.S.: 541330
Christopher Hatton *(Sr VP)*

KIMMEL & ASSOCIATES
25 Page Ave, Asheville, NC 28801
Tel.: (828) 251-9900
Web Site: http://www.kimmel.com
Year Founded: 1981
Sales Range: $10-24.9 Million
Emp.: 100
Executive Search Firm Specializing in Solid Waste, Freight Forwarding, Supply Chain & Transportation Industries
N.A.I.C.S.: 541612
Joe Kimmel *(Founder & Chm)*
Charlie Kimmel *(Pres & CEO)*
Alan Macnair *(Exec VP)*
Debbie Eckart *(Exec VP)*
Guy Ross *(Exec VP)*
Todd Chandler *(Mgr-Recruiting)*
Jerry Wilkins *(VP)*
Jim Coddington *(Exec VP)*
Mark Jones *(Exec VP)*
Meredith Love *(VP)*
David Goodrum *(Exec VP)*
Lynn Failing *(Exec VP)*
Paul Samuels *(Exec VP)*
Tim LaBruyere *(Exec VP)*

KIMMERIDGE ENERGY MANAGEMENT COMPANY, LLC
15 Little W12th St, 4th Fl., New York, NY 10014
Tel.: (646) 424-4317
Web Site: https://kimmeridge.com
Year Founded: 2011
Investment Managment Company
N.A.I.C.S.: 523999
Ben Dell *(Mng Partner)*

Subsidiaries:

Kimmeridge Texas Gas, LLC   (1)
840 W Sam Houston Pkwy N, Ste 400, Houston, TX 77024
Tel.: (713) 600-6000
Web Site: https://www.ktgllc.com
Gas Exploration
N.A.I.C.S.: 211130

KIMMINS CONTRACTING CORP.
1501 E 2nd Ave, Tampa, FL 33605
Tel.: (813) 247-0147   FL
Web Site: http://www.kimmins.com
Year Founded: 1923
Sales Range: $25-49.9 Million
Emp.: 230

KIMMINS CONTRACTING CORP.

Kimmins Contracting Corp.—(Continued)
Contract Construction & Demolition Services
N.A.I.C.S.: 238990
John Zemina *(VP-Ops)*
Joseph M. Williams *(Pres)*
Jeff Meigs *(VP-Demolition Estimating)*

KIMRAD TRANSPORT, LP.
371 W Loop 335 S, Amarillo, TX 79118
Tel.: (806) 359-3882
Web Site: http://www.kimrad.com
Year Founded: 2003
Sales Range: $10-24.9 Million
Emp.: 95
Freight Transportation Arrangement Services
N.A.I.C.S.: 488510
Curt Pohlmeier *(Gen Mgr)*
Charlie Friederich *(Mgr-Acctg)*

KIMRAY, INC.
52 NW 42nd St, Oklahoma City, OK 73118
Tel.: (405) 525-6601 OK
Web Site: http://www.kimray.com
Year Founded: 1948
Sales Range: $150-199.9 Million
Emp.: 800
Oil Field Machinery & Equipment Mfr
N.A.I.C.S.: 333132

KIN-KO ACE STORES INC.
6216 Main St, Downers Grove, IL 60516
Tel.: (630) 963-7810
Web Site: http://www.acehardware.com
Sales Range: $10-24.9 Million
Emp.: 125
Hardware Stores
N.A.I.C.S.: 444140
Ralph T. Kindred *(Chm)*
John Tikalsky *(Pres)*
Sharon Kindred *(VP)*

KINCAID PRODUCTS, INC.
PO Box 675, Trenton, FL 32693
Tel.: (352) 463-7027
Sales Range: $10-24.9 Million
Emp.: 10
Miscellaneous Wood Product Mfr
N.A.I.C.S.: 321999
Bob Kincaid *(Pres)*
Violet Kincaid *(VP)*

KINCO CONSTRUCTORS LLC
12600 Lawson Rd, Little Rock, AR 72210
Tel.: (501) 225-7606
Web Site: http://www.kincoconstructors.com
Sales Range: $50-74.9 Million
Emp.: 140
Nonresidential Construction Services
N.A.I.C.S.: 236220
Doug Wasson *(Pres & CEO)*
Gary Furrer *(CFO & VP)*
William Fletcher *(COO & Exec VP)*
Clay Gordon *(VP-Bus Dev)*

KINCO, LLC
18792 NE Portalway, Portland, OR 97230
Web Site: http://www.kinco.com
Year Founded: 1975
Sales Range: $10-24.9 Million
Emp.: 30
Work, Safety, Leather, Coated & Textile Gloves Mfr
N.A.I.C.S.: 315990
Travis Kindler *(Owner)*

KIND CAMPAIGN
10350 Santa Monica Blvd Ste 130, Los Angeles, CA 90025-5073
Tel.: (949) 275-7930 CA
Web Site: http://www.kindcampaign.com
Year Founded: 2009
Sales Range: $1-9.9 Million
Emp.: 3
Crime Prevention Services
N.A.I.C.S.: 813410
Lauren Sturtevant *(Pres)*
Molly Thompson *(VP)*

KIND LLC
55 W 21st St, New York, NY 10010-6809
Tel.: (212) 616-3006
Web Site: http://www.kindsnacks.com
Year Founded: 2003
Rev.: $120,000,000
Emp.: 100
Nut & Fruit Bar Mfr & Distr
N.A.I.C.S.: 311351
Daniel Lubetzky *(Founder & Chm)*
Doug Behrens *(Pres & Chief Customer Officer)*

Subsidiaries:

Creative Snacks Co., LLC (1)
4165 Mendenhall Oaks Pkwy, High Point, NC 27265
Tel.: (336) 668-4151
Web Site: http://www.creativesnacks.com
Confectionery Merchant Whslr
N.A.I.C.S.: 424450

KIND, INC.
PO Box 27839, Washington, DC 20038
Tel.: (202) 824-8680
Web Site: https://www.supportkind.org
Year Founded: 2008
Law Firm
N.A.I.C.S.: 541199

KINDEL FURNITURE COMPANY
4047 Eastern Ave Se, Grand Rapids, MI 49508-3401
Tel.: (616) 243-3676 MI
Web Site: http://www.kindelfurniture.com
Year Founded: 1901
Sales Range: $10-24.9 Million
Emp.: 75
Furniture Mfr
N.A.I.C.S.: 337122
Dennis Patterson *(VP-Fin & Ops)*
Amy Wolbert *(Dir-Mktg)*
Moore Councill *(Sr VP-Sls)*
Rob Burch *(CEO)*

KINDER ELECTRIC COMPANY INC.
9087 Technology Ln, Fishers, IN 46038
Tel.: (317) 842-0809
Web Site: http://www.kinderelectric.com
Sales Range: $10-24.9 Million
Emp.: 100
Electrical Wiring Services
N.A.I.C.S.: 238210
David Kinder *(Pres)*

KINDER REESE
3011 Internet Blvd Ste 116, Frisco, TX 75034
Tel.: (972) 668-5090
Web Site: http://www.naea.com
Year Founded: 2006
Sales Range: $1-9.9 Million
Emp.: 16
Real Estate Training
N.A.I.C.S.: 531390

Jay Kinder *(Co-Founder)*
Michael Reese *(Co-Founder)*

KINDERHOOK INDUSTRIES, LLC
505 5th Ave 25th Fl, New York, NY 10017
Tel.: (212) 201-6780
Web Site: http://www.kinderhook.com
Year Founded: 2003
Privater Equity Firm
N.A.I.C.S.: 523999
Thomas L. Tuttle *(Mng Dir)*
Paul G. Cifelli *(Mng Dir)*
Corwynne C. Carruthers *(Mng Dir)*
Michael Zoch *(Principal)*
Nate Druckenmiller *(VP)*
David Merrell *(VP-Natl Sls-Original One Parts)*
Brian Driehorst *(Sr VP-Global Procurement-Original One Parts)*
Rick Keister *(Chm-Original One Parts)*

Subsidiaries:

Adell Corporation (1)
200 Adell Blvd, Sunnyvale, TX 75182
Tel.: (972) 226-4600
Web Site: http://www.adellcorporation.com
Protective Automotive Door Edge Guards Mfr
N.A.I.C.S.: 336390

Powerflow, Inc. (2)
1714 Broadway St, Buffalo, NY 14212
Tel.: (716) 892-1014
Web Site: http://www.powerflowinc.com
Sales Range: $1-9.9 Million
Emp.: 66
Motor Vehicle Parts Mfr
N.A.I.C.S.: 336390

Adler Tank Rentals, LLC (1)
260 Mack Pl, South Plainfield, NJ 07080
Tel.: (908) 223-5044
Web Site: https://www.adlertankrentals.com
Tanker & Container Rental Services
N.A.I.C.S.: 532411

All States Ag Parts, LLC (1)
10 Ellefson Dr, De Soto, IA 50069
Tel.: (866) 609-1260
Web Site: http://www.tractorpartsasap.com
Tractor Parts Mfr
N.A.I.C.S.: 238990

Subsidiary (Domestic):

H&R Construction Parts & Equipment, Inc. (2)
20 Milburn St, Buffalo, NY 14212
Tel.: (716) 891-4311
Web Site: http://www.hrparts.com
Construction & Mining Machinery & Equipment Whslr
N.A.I.C.S.: 423810
John Gaulin *(Gen Mgr)*
Patrick Kelly *(Mgr-Pur-Construction Equipment)*
David Sorci *(Dir-Classic Parts)*
Tadashi Nakatsuka *(Chm)*
Aaron B. Lian *(Pres & CEO)*

John F Mahaney, Co. (2)
113 Commerce Cir, Sacramento, CA 95815
Tel.: (800) 999-3929
Web Site: http://www.mahaneyhardware.com
Hardware Merchant Whslr
N.A.I.C.S.: 423710

Kern County Tractor Parts, Inc. (2)
29527 Pond Rd, McFarland, CA 93250
Tel.: (661) 792-2188
Web Site: http://www.kerncountytractor.com
Rev.: $4,500,000
Emp.: 20
Fiscal Year-end: 12/31/2006
Tractor Parts Whslr
N.A.I.C.S.: 423830

Romac Industrial Parts, Inc. (2)
607 Bell Park Cir, Woodstock, GA 30188
Tel.: (770) 466-1340

U.S. PRIVATE

Web Site: https://romacparts.com
Rev.: $1,000,000
Emp.: 12
All Other Industrial Machinery Mfr
N.A.I.C.S.: 333248
James Lehman *(VP)*

American Accessories Inc. (1)
11100 Hope St, Cypress, CA 90630
Tel.: (949) 240-1418
Web Site: http://www.americanaccessoriesinc.com
Men's & Women's Accessories Mfr & Distr
N.A.I.C.S.: 315990
Adam Yuzuk *(Pres)*

Bestop, Inc. (100%)
333 Centennial Pkwy Ste B, Louisville, CO 80027
Tel.: (303) 465-1755
Web Site: http://www.bestop.com
Sales Range: $50-74.9 Million
Emp.: 500
Mfr & Supplier of Soft Tops & Accessories for Small Sport Utility Vehicles
N.A.I.C.S.: 336390
Jim Chick *(Dir-Sls & Mktg)*
Paul Dawson *(Dir-Ops)*
Richard E. Sabourin *(Pres)*

CSDVRS, LLC (1)
595 Menlo Dr, Rocklin, CA 95765
Tel.: (866) 932-7891
Web Site: http://www.zvrs.com
Video Phone Hardware, Software & Accessories for the Deaf & Hard of Hearing
N.A.I.C.S.: 517810
Michael Flanagan *(CFO)*

Subsidiary (Domestic):

Optimal Phone Interpreters, Inc. (2)
755 Clay St, Winter Park, FL 32789-4515
Tel.: (407) 478-9500
Web Site: http://www.callopi.com
Translation & Interpretation Services
N.A.I.C.S.: 541930
Greg Engelman *(CEO)*

Purple Communications, Inc. (2)
595 Menlo Dr, Rocklin, CA 95765-3708
Tel.: (877) 885-3172
Web Site: http://www.purple.us
Relay & Wireless Communications & Professional Interpreter Services for Deaf Hard-of-Hearing & Speech-Impaired Consumers
N.A.I.C.S.: 517112
Francine Cummings *(COO-VI Ops)*
Caryn Bain *(Chief Admin Officer)*
Chris Wagner *(COO)*
Greg Hlibok *(Chief Legal Officer)*
Mike Flanagan *(CFO)*
Sherri Turpin *(CEO)*

Subsidiary (Domestic):

Wynd Communications Corporation (3)
433 Hackensack Ave 3rd Fl, Hackensack, NJ 07601
Tel.: (201) 996-1717
Sales Range: $10-24.9 Million
Emp.: 30
Wireless Data Solutions & Services
N.A.I.C.S.: 517112

Subsidiary (Domestic):

Stratus Video, LLC (2)
33 N Garden Ave Ste 1000, Clearwater, FL 33755
Tel.: (727) 451-9766
Web Site: http://www.stratusvideo.com
Language Interpretation Services
N.A.I.C.S.: 541930
David Fetteroff *(CFO)*
Maureen Huber *(CFO & COO)*
William Cobb *(VP-Sls Engrg)*
Kathryn Jackson *(VP-Language Ops)*
Chris Downing *(VP-Engrg)*
Jenny Esno *(VP-Acct Mgmt)*
Kate Pascucci *(VP-Mktg)*
Paivi Smith *(VP-Fin)*
Ehab AbuShmais *(VP-Customer Success)*

Subsidiary (Domestic):

Systematech Technical Management Services, Inc. (3)
555 Andover Park W Suite 201, Tukwila, WA 98188

Tel.: (509) 888-3824
Web Site:
    http://www.indemandinterpreting.com
Video Interpreting Services For Hospitals,
Clinics & Emergency Rescue Personnel
N.A.I.C.S.: 541930
Mary Kate Salley *(COO)*

Extang Corporation (1)
5400 S State Rd, Ann Arbor, MI 48108
Tel.: (734) 677-0444
Web Site: http://www.extang.com
Sales Range: $10-24.9 Million
Motor Vehicle Parts & Accessory Service
N.A.I.C.S.: 336390
Steve Kelley *(VP-Sls & Mktg)*
Bill Reminder *(Pres & CEO)*
Chris Greer *(Mgr-Sls-Eastern Canada Reg)*
Dieter Faerber *(CFO)*
Kelly Kneifl *(COO)*
Laurel Brown *(Mgr-Sls-Southeast Reg)*
Todd Lindblade *(Reg Mgr-Sls)*

Gold Medal Services, LLC (1)
309 Salina Rd, Sewell, NJ 08080
Tel.: (856) 784-5050
Web Site: http://www.goldmedal.net
Waste Disposal Management Services
N.A.I.C.S.: 562998
Pat Angelastro *(VP)*

Subsidiary (Domestic):

Earthtech Contracting, Inc. (2)
2101 Dennisville-Petersburg Rd, Woodbine, NJ 08270
Tel.: (609) 390-2127
Web Site: http://www.earthtech.biz
Real Estate Investment Trust
N.A.I.C.S.: 525990
Douglas Fagerstrom *(Ops Mgr)*

KN Rubber, LLC (1)
521 5th Ave 34th Fl, New York, NY 10175
Tel.: (212) 201-6780
Web Site: http://www.kinderhook.com
Sales Range: $50-74.9 Million
Holding Company
N.A.I.C.S.: 551112

Subsidiary (Domestic):

Koneta, Inc. (2)
1400 Lunar Dr, Wapakoneta, OH 45895-0150
Tel.: (419) 739-4200
Web Site: http://www.konetainc.com
Sales Range: $25-49.9 Million
Emp.: 140
Rubber & Plastic Splash Guards & Body Bumpers for Trucking Industry
N.A.I.C.S.: 326299
Bob Lightle *(Mgr-Sls)*

Subsidiary (Non-US):

National Rubber Technologies (2)
35 Cawthra Ave, Toronto, M6M 5B3, ON, Canada
Tel.: (416) 657-1111
Web Site: https://www.knrubber.com
Sales Range: $25-49.9 Million
Recycled Rubber Plant
N.A.I.C.S.: 326299

Mongolian Operating Co. LLC (1)
12281 Nicollet Ave, Burnsville, MN 55337
Tel.: (952) 288-2363
Web Site: http://www.gomongo.com
Sales Range: $25-49.9 Million
Restaurant
N.A.I.C.S.: 722511
Tom Ragan *(VP-Franchising)*

NACT Telecommunications, Inc. (1)
191 W 5200 N, Provo, UT 84604 (100%)
Tel.: (801) 802-3000
Web Site: http://www.nact.com
Sales Range: $25-49.9 Million
Integrated Switching & Billing Systems for Specialty Telecommunications Applications
N.A.I.C.S.: 517810
Scott Raffensparger *(Engr-Software)*

Subsidiary (Non-US):

NACT Europe Ltd. (2)
Suite 1 Second Floor, 12 Station Street, Brighton, BN41 1AG, East Sussex, United Kingdom
Tel.: (44) 800 012 2000

Integrated Switching & Billing Systems for Specialty Telecommunications Applications
N.A.I.C.S.: 517810

National Truck Protection Co., Inc. (1)
6 Commerce Dr Suite 200, Cranford, NJ 07016 (100%)
Tel.: (908) 592-0108
Web Site: http://www.ntpwarranty.com
Sales Range: $1-9.9 Million
Emp.: 20
Offers Warranty & Service Contracts to the Trucking Industry
N.A.I.C.S.: 524128
Robert S. Amico *(Pres & CEO)*
Justin Hoyt *(Mgr-Mktg)*

Primeritus Financial Services, Inc (1)
435 Metroplex Dr, Nashville, TN 37211
Tel.: (615) 932-6727
Web Site: http://www.primeritus.com
Auto Repossession Managment Services
N.A.I.C.S.: 561499
Chris McGinness *(COO)*
Mike Thomas *(CEO)*
Wesley T. Pollard *(CFO)*

Subsidiary (Domestic):

Consolidated Asset Recovery Systems, Inc. (2)
4800 Six Forks Road Ste 350, Raleigh, NC 27607
Tel.: (919) 518-2277
Web Site: http://www.ez-recovery.com
Asset Recovery Services in Auditing, Tracking & Liquidation
N.A.I.C.S.: 523910
Steve Norwood *(Co-Founder & CEO)*
Terry Groves *(Sr VP)*
Matthew Yoo *(VP-Ops & ReMtkg)*
Jim Wilmsen *(CTO)*
Hope Carroll *(CFO)*

Global Investigative Services, LLC (2)
1203 Sigma Ct, Rockwall, TX 75087-4915
Tel.: (972) 771-6111
Web Site: http://www.gis-investigations.com
Investigation Services
N.A.I.C.S.: 561611
Greg Hill *(Co-Founder & Pres)*
Danny Tolbert *(Co-Founder)*

Roquemore & Roquemore Inc. (2)
310 E I-30 Ste 200, Garland, TX 75043
Tel.: (972) 226-9266
Web Site: http://www.roquemore.com
Collateral Repossession Management & Skiptracing Services
N.A.I.C.S.: 561499
Mike Postlethwait *(Pres)*
Jose Paulino *(CTO)*

Radiant Research Inc. (1)
11500 Northlake Dr Ste 320, Cincinnati, OH 45249
Tel.: (513) 247-5500
Web Site: http://www.radiantresearch.com
Sales Range: $75-99.9 Million
Research Services
N.A.I.C.S.: 541910
Julie L. McHugh *(CEO)*
Michael Kritschgau *(VP-Ops)*
Troy Atwood *(VP-IT)*
Suzanne Bonanza *(VP-Ops-Northeast)*
Michael Clay *(Pres & COO)*
Andrea Garcia *(VP-Ops-Mountain)*
Joanne Mashburn *(Exec VP-Quality Assurance)*
Craig Smith *(CFO)*

Reborn Products Co., Inc. (1)
1355 Adams Rd, Bensalem, PA 19020
Tel.: (215) 639-8000
Web Site: http://www.americanbelt.com
Sales Range: $10-24.9 Million
Men's Belts, Wallets & Other Accessories Distr
N.A.I.C.S.: 424350

Rental Equipment Investment Corp. (1)
250 Palm Ave, Miami Beach, FL 33139
Tel.: (786) 238-7313
Web Site: https://reicorporation.com
Commercial & Industrial Equipment Rental
N.A.I.C.S.: 532120

Kevin Fitzgerald *(CEO)*

Subsidiary (Domestic):

Aim High Equipment Rentals, Inc. (2)
10151 E 107th Pl, Brighton, CO 80601-7175
Tel.: (303) 288-9330
Web Site:
    http://www.aimhighequipment.com
General Rental Centers
N.A.I.C.S.: 532310
Amy Lagerholm *(Pres)*

Superwinch, LLC (1)
359 Lake Rd, Dayville, CT 06241
Tel.: (860) 928-7787
Web Site: http://www.superwinch.com
Sales Range: $10-24.9 Million
Emp.: 50
Electric & Hydraulic Winches, Power Drives & Related Accessories Mfr
N.A.I.C.S.: 333120
Stacy Dimock *(Supvr-Acctg)*
David Burns *(CEO)*

Subsidiary (Non-US):

Superwinch Ltd. (2)
Union Mine Road, Pitts Cleave Industrial Estate, Tavistock, PL19 0NS, Devon, United Kingdom
Tel.: (44) 1822 614101
Web Site: http://www.superwinch.com
Emp.: 20
Electric & Hydraulic Winches, Power Drives & Related Accessories Mfr
N.A.I.C.S.: 333120
David Burns *(Gen Mgr)*

Subsidiary (US):

Healthy Pet, L.P. (3)
6960 Salashan Pkwy, Ferndale, WA 98248
Tel.: (360) 734-7415
Web Site: http://www.healthy-pet.com
Animal Food Products Mfr & Marketer
N.A.I.C.S.: 311119
Ted Mishiakov *(CEO)*
Jesse Henman *(Mgr-Natl Accts)*
James Gorrell *(Mgr-Brand)*
Gary Hardwick *(Mgr-Customer Mktg)*

Subsidiary (Domestic):

Romac Industrial Parts, Inc. (2)
607 Bell Park Cir, Woodstock, GA 30188
Tel.: (770) 466-1340
Web Site: https://romacparts.com
Rev.: $1,000,000
Emp.: 12
All Other Industrial Machinery Mfr
N.A.I.C.S.: 333248
James Lehman *(VP)*

KINDLON ENTERPRISES, INC.
2300 Raddant Rd Ste B, Aurora, IL 60504
Tel.: (630) 585-1800
Year Founded: 1997
Sales Range: $25-49.9 Million
Emp.: 250
Holding Company; Corrugated & Solid Fiber Boxes
N.A.I.C.S.: 322211
Randall Mohler *(CEO)*

Subsidiaries:

South Haven Packaging, Inc. (1)
73475 8th Ave, South Haven, MI 49090
Tel.: (269) 639-1567
Sales Range: $10-24.9 Million
Emp.: 15
Corrugated & Solid Fiber Boxes Mfr
N.A.I.C.S.: 322211

KINECT SOLAR, LLC
828 Airport Blvd, Austin, TX 78702
Web Site: http://kinectsolar.com
Year Founded: 2015
Sales Range: $10-24.9 Million
Emp.: 50
Solar Equipment Distr
N.A.I.C.S.: 423720

Lauren Carson *(CEO)*
Hollis Miles *(COO)*
Rhonda Blum *(Ops Mgr)*
Steve Hernandez *(Ops Mgr)*
Annie Carson *(Reg Mgr-Acct)*

KINECTIQ INC.
12854 E Florence Ave, Santa Fe Springs, CA 90670
Tel.: (310) 884-9991
Web Site: http://www.kinect-iq.com
Electronic Parts Mfr
N.A.I.C.S.: 334419

KINEDYNE CORPORATION
151 Industrial Pkwy, Somerville, NJ 08876-3451
Tel.: (908) 231-1800   DE
Web Site: http://www.kinedyne.com
Year Founded: 1968
Sales Range: $25-49.9 Million
Emp.: 380
Motor Vehicle Parts & Accessories
N.A.I.C.S.: 336390
Dan Schlotterbeck *(Pres)*
John Seliga *(VP-Fin)*
Eric Sorensen *(Mgr-HR-North America)*

Subsidiaries:

Kinedyne Canada Limited (1)
10 Maybrook Dr, Toronto, M1V 4B6, ON, Canada
Tel.: (416) 291-7168
Web Site: http://www.kinedyne.com
Emp.: 25
Cargo Product Mfr & Distr
N.A.I.C.S.: 336390
Robert Spooner *(Mgr-Sls)*

Nantong Kinedyne Limited (1)
26-1 South Tongshen Road, Nantong, 226017, Jiangsu, China
Tel.: (86) 513 8599 6100
Web Site: http://www.kinedyne.com
Cargo Product Mfr
N.A.I.C.S.: 336390

Sistemas Kinedyne, S.A. de C.V. (1)
Calzada de Las Armas No 130-A Col Industrial Las Armas, Tlalnepantla, 54080, Mexico
Tel.: (52) 55 5318 4844
Cargo Product Mfr
N.A.I.C.S.: 336390

KINEMED, INC.
5980 Horton St Ste 470, Emeryville, CA 94608
Tel.: (510) 655-6525   DE
Web Site: http://www.kinemed.com
Year Founded: 2001
Sales Range: $1-9.9 Million
Biomarker Researcher & Developer
N.A.I.C.S.: 541715
David M. Fineman *(Co-Founder, Chm, Pres & CEO)*
Marc K. Hellerstein *(Co-Founder & Chm-SAB)*
Karen S. Carothers *(VP-Fin)*
Alexander J. Glass *(COO)*
Scott Turner *(Exec VP-R&D)*
William J. Evans *(Pres-Muscle & Health Div)*
Patrick James Doyle *(Chief Bus Officer)*

KINESYS INC.
23823 Malibu Rd Unit 457, Malibu, CA 90265
Tel.: (415) 453-0747
Web Site: http://www.kinesys.com
Year Founded: 1994
Sales Range: $1-9.9 Million
Emp.: 6
Bodycare & Suncare Products Retailer
N.A.I.C.S.: 456120

KINESYS INC.

U.S. PRIVATE

Kinesys Inc.—(Continued)
Jeff Kletter (Co-Founder)
Josie Kletter (Co-Founder)
Andrea Lupinek (Gen Mgr)
Tracey Anderson (Mgr-Atlanta & Georgia)

KINETEK CONSULTING, LLC
304 Indian Trace 700, Weston, FL 33326
Tel.: (503) 341-0253
Web Site: http://www.kinetekconsulting.com
Year Founded: 2002
Sales Range: $1-9.9 Million
Emp.: 23
Computer Related Consulting Services
N.A.I.C.S.: 541690
David Delaney (Partner)
John Arhancet (Partner)
Shimi Minhas (Partner)
Steve Fruitman (Partner)

KINETIC
200 Distillery Commons Ste 200, Louisville, KY 40206
Tel.: (502) 719-9500
Web Site: http://www.thetechnologyagency.com
Year Founded: 1968
Sales Range: $1-9.9 Million
Emp.: 88
Translation Management Software
N.A.I.C.S.: 513210
G. Raymond Schuhmann (Pres & CEO)

KINETIC TECHNOLOGIES, INC.
6399 San Ignacio Ave Ste 250, San Jose, CA 95119
Tel.: (408) 701-2558
Web Site: http://www.kinet-ic.com
Year Founded: 2006
Semiconductor Mfr
N.A.I.C.S.: 334413
Kin Shum (CEO)

Subsidiaries:

Akros Silicon, Inc. (1)
6399 San Ignacio Ave Ste 250, San Jose, CA 95119
Tel.: (408) 746-9000
Web Site: http://www.akrossilicon.com
Semiconductor Machinery Mfr
N.A.I.C.S.: 333242
Elias Antoun (Pres & CEO)
John Camagna (VP-Engrg)
Peter Klessel (VP-Sls-WW)
Faisal Ahmad (VP-Mktg)
Carl W. Jasper (VP-Fin)

KINETICOM, INC.
8885 Rio San Diego Ste 210, San Diego, CA 92108
Tel.: (619) 330-3100
Web Site: http://www.kineticom.com
Sales Range: $50-74.9 Million
Emp.: 35
Technology Staffing Services for Telecom Companies
N.A.I.C.S.: 561320
Jennifer Hawk (CFO)

Subsidiaries:

Kineticom Ltd. (1)
Elsinore House 43 Buckingham Street, Aylesbury, HP20 2NQ, Bucks, United Kingdom
Tel.: (44) 1296 332411
Technology Staffing Services for Telecom Companies
N.A.I.C.S.: 561320

KINETICS MECHANICAL ENERGY
3083 Independence Dr, Livermore, CA 94551-7676
Tel.: (925) 245-6200
Sales Range: $10-24.9 Million
Emp.: 100
Plumbing Services
N.A.I.C.S.: 238220
Craig Kirk (Dir-IT)

KING & COMPANY INC.
639 N Dupre St, New Orleans, LA 70119
Tel.: (504) 486-9195 LA
Web Site: http://www.kingcolp.com
Year Founded: 1954
Rev: $40,000,000
Emp.: 500
Plastering, Drywall & Insulation
N.A.I.C.S.: 238310
Warren Jaubert (CFO)
Cyril P. Geary III (Pres)

KING & SPALDING LLP
1180 Peachtree St NE Ste 1600, Atlanta, GA 30309
Tel.: (404) 572-4600
Web Site: https://www.kslaw.com
Year Founded: 1885
Sales Range: $750-799.9 Million
Emp.: 1,500
Law firm
N.A.I.C.S.: 541110
Derek J. Hardesty (COO & Partner)
Pete G. Nolan (CFO)
Timothy T. Scott (Mng Partner-Silicon Valley)
Nathan E. Clukey (Partner-Tax-Washington)
Robert K. Hur (Partner-Special Matters & Govt Investigations Practice-Washington)
Samuel S. Choy (Partner-Tax, Employee Benefits & Exec Compensation Practices)
Smitha G. Stansbury (Partner-FDA & Life Sciences Practice-Washington)
Thomas E. Duley (Partner-Silicon Valley)
Ye Cecilia Hong (Partner-New York)
Linda Lorenat (Partner-Silicon Valley)
Stephen Vaughn (Partner-Intl Trade Team-Washington)
Jason P. Huff (Partner-Fin Practice-Charlotte)
Phillip H. Street (Partner)
Sheldon Bradshaw (Partner-FDA & Life Sciences Practice)
Jacqueline Glassman (Partner-Tort & Environmental Practice-Washington)
Paul Ferdinands (Head-Fin Restructuring & Bankruptcy Practice)
Allison Altersohn (Partner-New York)
Carolyn Zander Alford (Head-Fin Svcs Industry Team)
David L. Balser (Partner-Atlanta)
Jeremiah J. Anderson (Partner-Houston)
Marcia L. Augsburger (Partner-Sacramento)
Anne Voigts (Partner-Appellate, Constitutional & Administrative Law Practice-S)
Jennifer Daly (Partner-Fin Practice-New York)
Steven Kupka (Partner-Govt Advocacy & Pub Policy Practice-Washington)
Wick Sollers (Head-Govt Matters Practice Grp)
Tom Spulak (Chm-Govt Advocacy & Pub Policy Practice)
Robert E. Meadows (Head-Natl Bus Litigation Practice)
Joseph Akrotirianakis (Partner-Bus Litigation Practice-Los Angeles)
Aaron Craig (Partner-Los Angeles)
Peter Strotz (Head-Los Angeles)
Lana Varney (Partner-Life Sciences Practice-Austin)
Lisa Horvath Shub (Partner-Life Sciences Practice-Austin)
Stephen Huffaker (Partner-Life Sciences Practice-Austin)
Andy Bayman (Head-Trial & Global Disputes Practice Grp)
Mike Stenglein (Mng Partner-Austin)
James Woolery (Head-M&A & Corp Governance Practices)
Peter Hays (Partner-Houston)
Tracie Renfroe (Mng Partner-Houston & Head-Energy Practice)
Brian R. Michael (Partner-Los Angeles)
Lee Taylor (Head-Corp Practice-Asia Pacific)
Meredith Redwine (Partner-Singapore)
Jeffrey D. Pawlitz (Partner-New York)
Zachary Fardon (Mng Partner/Head-Litigation-Chicago)
Bradley T. Giordano (Partner-Fin Restructuring Practice-Chicago)
Michael Rupe (Head-Fin Restructuring Practice)
Kevin Glenn (Partner-Corp, Fin & Investments Practice Grp-New York)
Todd Holleman (Head-Corp, Fin & Investments Practice Grp-New York City)
Jessica Corley (Partner-Trial & Global Disputes Practice)
Tom Friel (Partner-Patent Litigation)
Lori Gordon (Partner-Trial & Disputes Practice Grp-Global)
Lisa Bugni (Partner-Trial & Disputes Practice-Global)
Thomas E. Keim (Partner-Corp, Fin & Investments Practice-Chicago)
Patrick Montgomery (Partner-Special Matters Team-Washington)
Amy Peters (Partner-Corp, Fin & Investments Practice Grp-Chicago)
Russ Ryan (Partner-Special Matters & Govt Investigations Team-Washington)
Scott Ferber (Partner-Data, Privacy & Security Team-Washington)
Robert Dedman (Partner-Special Matters & Govt Investigations Team-London)
Matthew W. Nichols (Partner-Corp, Fin & Investments Practice Grp)
Josh Kamin (Mng Partner)
Scott Edson (Partner-Washington)
Nikesh Jindal (Partner-Washington)
Elizabeth Lindquist (Partner-Washington)
Alan Noskow (Partner-Corp, Fin & Investments Practice Grp-Washington)
David Lang (Partner-Corp, Fin & Investments-Houston)
Stephen Baskin (Partner-Intellectual Property-Washington)
Dara Kurlancheek (Partner-Intellectual Property-Washington)
Chris Campbell (Partner-Intellectual Property-Washington)
Mark Jensen (Mng Partner-Washington)
Alicia O'Brien (Partner-Govt Matters Practice Grp-Washington)
Jonathan Arkins (Partner-Corp, Fin & Investments Practice Grp-New York)
Steven Rizzi (Partner-New York)
Ramy Hanna (Partner-Intellectual Property-New York)
Bernhardt Nadell (Partner-Private Equity-New York)
Peter Montoni (Partner-Fin Restructuring-New York)
Roger Schwartz (Partner-Fin Restructuring-New York)
Scott Levin (Partner-Real Estate-New York)
Christine O'Connell (Partner-Real Estate-New York)
Ed Holzwanger (Partner-Labor & Employment Team-Washington)
Sumon Dantiki (Partner-Special Matters & Govt Investigations Team-Washington)
Zack Harmon (Partner-Special Matters-Washington)
Joel McElvain (Partner-Healthcare-Washington)
Marcella Burke (Partner-Govt Matters Practice-Washington)
Lawrence Yanowitch (Partner-Corp, Fin & Investments Practice Grp)
Thomas Knox (Partner-Corp, Fin & Investments Practice Grp)
Charles Katz (Partner-Corp, Fin & Investments Practice Grp)
Jeremy Schropp (Partner-Corp, Fin & Investments Practice Grp)
David Lesser (Partner-Trial & Global Disputes Practice Grp-New York)
Edward Kehoe (Mng Partner-New York)
Suzanne Murray (Partner-Environmental, Health & Safety-Govt Matters Grp)
Robert D. Hays Jr. (Chm)
Norman Armstrong Jr. (Partner-Washington)

KING + COMPANY
72 Madison Ave 10th Fl, New York, NY 10016
Tel.: (212) 561-7450
Web Site: http://kingcompr.com
Emp.: 12
Strategic Marketing, Branding & Public Relations
N.A.I.C.S.: 541820
Judith R. King (Owner & Founder)
Caren Browning (Partner & Exec VP)
Micheal Richards (COO & Partner)
Esha Pai (VP)

KING APPLIANCE CENTER INC.
5010 Vogel Rd, Evansville, IN 47715
Tel.: (812) 473-5464
Web Site: http://www.kingsgreatbuys.com
Sales Range: $10-24.9 Million
Emp.: 20
Electric Household Appliances
N.A.I.C.S.: 449210
Terry Oates (Founder & CEO)

KING ARCHITECTURAL METALS, INC.
9611 E RL Thornton Fwy, Dallas, TX 75228
Tel.: (214) 388-9834
Web Site: http://www.kingmetals.com
Sales Range: $10-24.9 Million
Emp.: 350
Construction Material Merchant Whslr
N.A.I.C.S.: 423390
Stewart E. King (Pres & CEO)

KING AUTO CENTER, INC.
4330 Kukui Grove St, Lihue, HI 96766
Tel.: (808) 245-4788
Web Site: http://www.kingautocenter.com
Sales Range: $10-24.9 Million
Emp.: 55
New Car Distr
N.A.I.C.S.: 441110

Jose Aguayo *(VP & Gen Mgr)*
Roy Yamashita *(Mgr-Sls)*
Anatalio Ramos Jr. *(Mgr-Parts)*

KING BEVERAGE INC.
6715 E Mission Ave, Shelton, WA 99212
Tel.: (509) 444-3700
Web Site: http://www.kingbeverage.com
Rev.: $15,000,000
Emp.: 200
Beverage Distribution
N.A.I.C.S.: 424820
Robyn Sciuchetti *(Mgr-Bus Dev)*

KING BUICK GMC
4175 Byrd Dr, Loveland, CO 80538
Tel.: (970) 667-8905
Web Site: http://www.kinggm.com
Year Founded: 1970
Sales Range: $10-24.9 Million
Emp.: 50
Car Whslr
N.A.I.C.S.: 441110
Rex King *(Pres)*

KING BUSINESS FORMS CORP.
531 Straight Creek Rd, New Tazewell, TN 37825
Tel.: (423) 626-7700
Web Site: http://www.kbfcorp.com
Year Founded: 1972
Sales Range: $10-24.9 Million
Emp.: 35
Forms, Business: Lithographed
N.A.I.C.S.: 323111
Darlene Hacker *(Mgr-Sls)*
Lori King Scott *(Asst Treas & Sec)*

KING CANNON, INC
66 Cherry Hill Dr, Beverly, MA 01915-1054
Tel.: (978) 778-1300
Sales Range: $25-49.9 Million
Emp.: 2,075
Restaurant Operators
N.A.I.C.S.: 722511
Bryce L. King *(Pres)*
Keith Shutz *(Sec)*

KING CAPITAL CORP.
3001 Broadway St Ne Ste 665, Minneapolis, MN 55413-2297
Tel.: (763) 593-1904 MN
Web Site: http://www.kingcapitalcorp.com
Year Founded: 2000
Sales Range: $150-199.9 Million
Emp.: 10
Holding Company
N.A.I.C.S.: 532490
Peter King *(CEO & CFO)*
Russell King *(Sec)*

KING COTTON MOTOR COMPANY OF COVINGTON
959 Hwy 51 N, Covington, TN 38019
Tel.: (901) 475-6080
Year Founded: 1992
Sales Range: $10-24.9 Million
Emp.: 30
New Car Whslr
N.A.I.C.S.: 441110

KING ESTATE OREGON WINES
80854 Territorial Rd, Eugene, OR 97405
Tel.: (541) 942-9874
Web Site: http://www.kingestate.com
Sales Range: $75-99.9 Million
Emp.: 100
Winery & Restaurant
N.A.I.C.S.: 312130

Steve Thomson *(Exec VP)*
Doyal Eubank *(CFO & VP)*
Edward King III *(Reg Mgr-Northwest)*

KING ESTATE WINERY
80854 Territorial Hwy, Eugene, OR 97405
Tel.: (541) 942-9874
Web Site: http://www.kingestate.com
Sales Range: $10-24.9 Million
Emp.: 100
Wine Mfr
N.A.I.C.S.: 312130
Ed King *(Co-Founder & CEO)*
Rick Durette *(Sr VP-Global Sls)*
Jeff Brooks *(Mgr-Northeast)*
Kevin Graham *(Mgr-Central)*
Jim Mauceri *(Dir-Accts-Natl)*
Ray Nuclo *(Dir-Viticulture)*
Edward Holmes *(Mgr-Northwest Reg)*
David Kouzmanoff *(Mgr-South Central)*
Cameron Scott *(Mgr-Southeast)*
Spencer Cole *(Mgr-Southwest)*
Meliton Martinez *(Mgr-Vineyard)*
Randy Ford *(VP-Sls-Eastern Div)*

KING HENRY'S INC.
29124 Hancock Pkwy, Valencia, CA 91355-1066
Tel.: (661) 295-5566 CA
Web Site: http://www.kinghenrys.com
Year Founded: 1989
Sales Range: $50-74.9 Million
Emp.: 40
Nuts & Snack Foods Mfr & Whslr
N.A.I.C.S.: 311911
Henry Davidian *(Pres & CEO)*
Joseph A. DeFelice *(Mgr-Sls-Western Reg)*
Trina Davidian *(CFO)*

KING HICKORY FURNITURE COMPANY INC.
1820 Main Ave SE, Hickory, NC 28603
Tel.: (828) 322-6025 NC
Web Site: http://www.kinghickory.com
Year Founded: 1958
Sales Range: $10-24.9 Million
Emp.: 250
Upholstered Household Furniture
N.A.I.C.S.: 337121
Robert E. Palmer *(Chm & Pres)*

KING INDUSTRIES
3945 Cromwell Rd, Chattanooga, TN 37421
Tel.: (423) 622-4500
Web Site: http://www.king-industries.com
Year Founded: 1987
Rev.: $27,000,000
Emp.: 250
Provider of Industrial Mechanical Design & Construction Services
N.A.I.C.S.: 238220
Bill King *(Pres)*
Bart Bledsoe *(VP)*
Krista Marter *(CFO)*

KING INDUSTRIES, INC.
Science Rd, Norwalk, CT 06852
Tel.: (203) 866-5551 CT
Web Site: http://www.kingindustries.com
Year Founded: 1932
Sales Range: $100-124.9 Million
Emp.: 175
Coating & Lubricant Additives Mfr
N.A.I.C.S.: 325998
Richard S. King *(Pres)*
F. Abi Karam *(Exec VP)*
Robert Dipanni *(CFO)*

KING INSURANCE PARTNERS, LLC
2321 NW 41 St B, Gainesville, FL 32606
Tel.: (352) 377-0420 FL
Web Site: https://www.king-insurance.com
Year Founded: 1974
Insurance Services
N.A.I.C.S.: 524210
Chad King *(CEO)*

Subsidiaries:

Lincoln Insurance (1)
510 E Main St, Lincolnton, NC 28092-3410
Tel.: (704) 735-4122
Web Site: http://www.lincolninsuranceagencyinc.com
Insurance Agencies & Brokerages
N.A.I.C.S.: 524210
Jill Howard *(Owner)*

Pavese-Mccormick Agency, Inc. (1)
3759 US Highway 1, Monmouth Junction, NJ 08852
Tel.: (732) 247-9800
Web Site: http://www.pavesemccormick.com
Sales Range: $1-9.9 Million
Emp.: 14
Insurance Agencies & Brokerages
N.A.I.C.S.: 524210
Raymond Pavese *(Principal & VP)*
Michael McCormick *(Pres & Principal)*
Christine Longhi-Drake *(Mgr-Claims)*
Eric Anderson *(Mgr-Acctg)*

KING KOIL LICENSING COMPANY INC.
7501 S Quincy St Ste 130, Willowbrook, IL 60527
Tel.: (630) 230-9744 DE
Web Site: http://www.comfortsolutions.com
Year Founded: 1898
Sales Range: Less than $1 Million
Emp.: 15
Mattress Mfr
N.A.I.C.S.: 337910
Garret Weyand *(Chm)*
Ross Linsky *(VP-Mfg)*

KING KULLEN GROCERY COMPANY, INC.
185 Central Ave, Bethpage, NY 11714
Tel.: (516) 733-7100 NY
Web Site: http://www.kingkullen.com
Year Founded: 1930
Sales Range: $800-899.9 Million
Emp.: 4,200
Grocery Store Operator
N.A.I.C.S.: 445110
Joseph W. Brown *(Pres & COO)*
Michael Simco *(VP-Admin & Benefits)*
Bernard P. Kennedy *(Chief Admin Officer, Sec & Exec VP)*
Tracey Cullen *(VP-Corp Strategy & Initiatives)*
Albert Hesse *(VP-Pharmacies)*

KING LOGISTICS, INC.
6002 Benjamin Rd, Tampa, FL 33634
Tel.: (813) 881-1799 MI
Web Site: http://www.kinglogistics.com
Year Founded: 2000
Sales Range: $1-9.9 Million
Emp.: 8
Supply Chain Management & Logistics
N.A.I.C.S.: 484110
Marie Davis *(Mgr-Ops)*

KING MANUFACTURING CO. INC.
714 Fulton Dr, Corinth, MS 38834
Tel.: (662) 286-5504
Web Site: http://kingmfgco.com

Sales Range: $10-24.9 Million
Emp.: 120
Metal Stamping Services
N.A.I.C.S.: 332119
Thomas E. Robertson *(CEO)*

KING MILLING COMPANY
115 S Bdwy, Lowell, MI 49331-1601
Tel.: (616) 897-9264 MI
Web Site: http://www.kingflour.com
Year Founded: 1890
Sales Range: $75-99.9 Million
Emp.: 38
Miller of Wheat Flour
N.A.I.C.S.: 311211
Brian K. Doyle *(Pres)*

KING MOTOR CO. INC.
PO Box 1288, Anniston, AL 36202
Tel.: (256) 831-5300
Web Site: http://www.sunnykingford.com
Rev.: $46,542,220
Emp.: 95
Automobiles, New & Used
N.A.I.C.S.: 441110
Patricia M. King *(Pres)*
John Bryan *(VP)*

KING MOTOR COMPANY
1399 S Federal Hwy, Deerfield Beach, FL 33441-7248
Tel.: (954) 421-3330
Web Site: http://www.king-motor-company.com
Sales Range: $10-24.9 Million
Emp.: 100
Car Dealership
N.A.I.C.S.: 441110
Clay King *(Pres)*

KING O'ROURKE CADILLAC
756 Smithtown Bypass, Smithtown, NY 11787
Tel.: (631) 724-4700
Web Site: http://www.kingorourke.com
Rev.: $35,400,000
Emp.: 95
Automobiles, New & Used
N.A.I.C.S.: 441110
Stephen King *(Pres)*

KING OCEAN SERVICES LIMITED
11000 NW 29th St Ste 201, Miami, FL 33172
Tel.: (305) 591-7595
Web Site: http://www.kingocean.com
Year Founded: 2001
Sales Range: $1-9.9 Million
Emp.: 27
Agents & Managers for Artists, Athletes, Entertainers & Other Public Figures
N.A.I.C.S.: 711410
Carlos Perdomo *(Principal)*

KING OF FANS, INC.
1951 Nw 22nd St, Fort Lauderdale, FL 33311
Tel.: (954) 484-7500
Web Site: http://www.kingoffans.com
Sales Range: $100-124.9 Million
Emp.: 30
Ceiling Fans, Interior/Exterior Lighting, High-Velocity Fans, Heaters & Solar Products Mfr & Distr
N.A.I.C.S.: 423620
Tien Lowe *(Pres)*

KING PAR CORPORATION
G 5140 Flushing Rd, Flushing, MI 48433
Tel.: (810) 732-0426
Web Site: http://www.kingpar.com

KING PAR CORPORATION

King Par Corporation—(Continued)
Sales Range: $75-99.9 Million
Emp.: 300
Golfing Supplies
N.A.I.C.S.: 423910
Gordon Coleman (Mgr-Natl Sls)

KING PLASTIC CORPORATION
1100 N Toledo Blade Blvd, North Port, FL 34288-8694
Tel.: (941) 493-5502
Web Site: http://www.kingplastic.com
Year Founded: 1968
Sales Range: $10-24.9 Million
Emp.: 100
Polymer Sheets, Slabs & Massive Shapes Mfr
N.A.I.C.S.: 326199
Jeffrey King (Pres)
Michael Fabbri (Mgr-Natl Sls)
Veronica Rosas (Mgr-Mktg)

KING PLASTICS, INC.
840 N Elm St, Orange, CA 92867
Tel.: (714) 997-7540
Web Site:
http://www.kingplastics.com
Year Founded: 1962
Sales Range: $10-24.9 Million
Emp.: 96
Plastics Pipe & Pipe Fitting Mfr
N.A.I.C.S.: 326122

KING RANCH, INC.
3 Riverway Ste 1600, Houston, TX 77056-1967
Tel.: (832) 681-5700 TX
Web Site: http://www.king-ranch.com
Year Founded: 1853
Sales Range: $300-349.9 Million
Emp.: 663
Livestock, Pecans, Sod & Horse Farming & Retail
N.A.I.C.S.: 112130
Bill Gardiner (CFO & VP)
James H. Clement (Chm)
Dave Delaney (VP & Gen Mgr-Livestock & Ranching Ops)
Robert J. Underlink (Pres & CEO)

Subsidiaries:

Kingsville Publishing Company (1)
1831 W Santa Gertrudis St, Kingsville, TX 78363
Tel.: (361) 592-4304
Newspaper Publishers
N.A.I.C.S.: 513110

Young Pecan, Inc. (1)
1831 W Evans St Ste 200, Florence, SC 29501-2827
Tel.: (843) 664-2330
Web Site: http://www.youngpecan.com
Sales Range: $75-99.9 Million
Emp.: 183
Pecan Farming & Distr
N.A.I.C.S.: 111335
Helen M. Watts (Exec VP)

Plant (Domestic):

Young Pecan - Las Cruces Processing Plant (2)
2455 Entrada Del Sol, Las Cruces, NM 88001-3972
Tel.: (575) 524-4321
Web Site: http://www.youngpecan.com
Sales Range: $50-74.9 Million
Emp.: 30
Shelling Facility
N.A.I.C.S.: 311911

KING SOLUTIONS, INC.
11011 Holly Ln N, Dayton, MN 55369-9203
Tel.: (763) 428-5464
Web Site:
http://www.kingsolutionsglobal.com
Rev.: $23,000,000
Emp.: 20
Freight Forwarding
N.A.I.C.S.: 488510
Michael Patterson (Pres)

KING STEEL, INC.
353 Swanson Dr, Lawrenceville, GA 30043
Tel.: (770) 963-3888
Sales Range: $1-9.9 Million
Emp.: 47
Fabricated Structural Metal Mfr
N.A.I.C.S.: 332312
Charles A. King (CEO & CFO)
Jerry L. Sudderth (Sec)

KING STREET CAPITAL MANAGEMENT, L.P.
65 E 55th St 30th Fl, New York, NY 10022
Tel.: (212) 812-3100
Privater Equity Firm
N.A.I.C.S.: 523999
Brian J. Higgins (Mng Principal)
Bruce S. Darringer (COO)
Jay Ryan (CFO)
O. Francis Biondi Jr. (Mng Partner)

KING STREET REAL ESTATE GP, L.L.C
800 Boylston St, Boston, MA 02199
Tel.: (617) 910-5500
Web Site:
http://kingstreetproperties.com
Real Estate Services
N.A.I.C.S.: 531390
Thomas Ragno (Founder & Principal)
Stephen Lynch (Principal)

Subsidiaries:

Shelborne South Beach Hotel (1)
1801 Collins Ave, Miami Beach, FL 33139
Tel.: (305) 531-1271
Web Site: http://www.shelborne.com
Hotel
N.A.I.C.S.: 721110

KING TACO RESTAURANT INC.
3421 E 14th St, Los Angeles, CA 90023
Tel.: (323) 268-2267
Web Site: http://www.kingtaco.com
Rev.: $23,000,000
Emp.: 400
Fast Food Restaurants
N.A.I.C.S.: 722513
Raul O. Martinez Sr. (Pres)

KING VENTURE INC.
17800 N Laurel Park Dr Ste 200C, Livonia, MI 48152
Tel.: (248) 262-1000
Web Site: http://www.schostak.com
Year Founded: 1981
Sales Range: $50-74.9 Million
Emp.: 250
Provider of Fast-Food Restaurant Services
N.A.I.C.S.: 722513
Mark S. Schostak (Pres & CEO)

KING WIRE INC.
2500 Commonwealth Ave, North Chicago, IL 60064-3310
Tel.: (847) 688-1100 IL
Web Site: http://www.kingwire.com
Year Founded: 1995
Sales Range: $75-99.9 Million
Emp.: 62
Wholesale Distribution of Wire & Cable
N.A.I.C.S.: 423610
Doug Kessel (VP-Eastern Reg)
Bill O'Reilly (VP-Sls)

KING'S COLONIAL FORD
3565 Community Rd, Brunswick, GA 31520
Tel.: (912) 264-6400
Web Site:
http://www.kingscolonialford.com
Sales Range: $10-24.9 Million
Emp.: 40
Car Whslr
N.A.I.C.S.: 441110
Lee N. King (Owner)

KING'S CONSTRUCTION CO., INC.
205 Walnut St, Oskaloosa, KS 66066-4000
Tel.: (785) 863-2534
Web Site: http://www.kings-const.com
Year Founded: 1955
Sales Range: $10-24.9 Million
Emp.: 65
Civil Engineering Services
N.A.I.C.S.: 237310
Kent King (Pres)
Dan C. King (VP)

KING'S FAMILY RESTAURANTS INC
1180 Long Run Rd Ste A, McKeesport, PA 15131
Tel.: (412) 751-0700
Web Site: http://www.kingsfamily.com
Sales Range: $50-74.9 Million
Emp.: 3,000
Family Restaurant Operator
N.A.I.C.S.: 722511
Hartley C. King (Founder & Pres)
Chris Whalen (Pres-KCS Mgmt)

KING'S HAWAIIAN HOLDING COMPANY, INC.
19161 Harborgate Way, Torrance, CA 90501-1316
Tel.: (310) 533-3250 CA
Web Site:
http://www.kingshawaiian.com
Year Founded: 1970
Sales Range: $25-49.9 Million
Emp.: 278
Mfr of Bread, Cake & Related Products
N.A.I.C.S.: 311812
Kevin Shimabukuro (Supvr-Production)
Dan Raatjes (VP-Ops)
Jesse C. Rodriguez (Plant Mgr)
Tommy Saiyasombat (Coord-Recruiting)

Subsidiaries:

King's Hawaiian Retail, Inc. (1)
2808 W Sepulveda Blvd, Torrance, CA 90505-2803
Tel.: (310) 530-0050
Sales Range: $10-24.9 Million
Emp.: 100
Eating Place
N.A.I.C.S.: 722511

Kings Hawaiian Bakery West, Inc. (1)
19161 Harborgate Way, Torrance, CA 90501
Tel.: (310) 533-3250
Web Site: http://www.kingshawaiian.com
Sales Range: $10-24.9 Million
Emp.: 3
Mfr & Retail of Bread, Cake & Related Products
N.A.I.C.S.: 424420
Mark Taira (CEO)

KING'S RESTAURANT & SUPERMARKET, INC.
405 E New Bern Rd, Kinston, NC 28504
Tel.: (252) 527-2101
Web Site: http://www.kingsbbq.com

U.S. PRIVATE

Sales Range: $10-24.9 Million
Emp.: 100
Restaurant Operators
N.A.I.C.S.: 722511
Joe Hargitt (Pres)
Wilbur F. King Jr. (VP)

KING-LAR COMPANY
2020 E Olive St, Decatur, IL 62526
Tel.: (217) 429-2323
Web Site: http://www.kinglar.com
Sales Range: $10-24.9 Million
Emp.: 100
Warm Air Heating & Air Conditioning Contractor
N.A.I.C.S.: 238220
Robert Lamb Jr. (VP)

KINGDOM INC.
719 Lambs Creek Rd, Mansfield, PA 16933-9001
Tel.: (570) 662-7515 PA
Web Site: http://www.kingdom.com
Year Founded: 1980
Sales Range: $25-49.9 Million
Emp.: 80
Computers, Peripherals & Software
N.A.I.C.S.: 423430
Johnny Berguson (Founder & Pres)
Dan Berguson (Dir-Fin)

KINGDOMWAY NUTRITION, INC.
18100 Von Karman Ave Ste 800, Irvine, CA 92612
Tel.: (800) 333-6977 CA
Web Site: http://www.kdw-usa.com
Nutrition Fortifiers & Medical Products Mfr
N.A.I.C.S.: 325412
Melissa Shearer (Sls Mgr)
Forrest Zhang (Mgr-Natl Accts)

Subsidiaries:

Vit-Best Nutrition, Inc. (1)
2802 Dow Ave, Tustin, CA 92780-7212
Tel.: (714) 832-9700
Web Site: http://www.vit-best.com
Nutritional Product Mfr
N.A.I.C.S.: 325412
David Jiang (Dir-Technical Svcs)
Thomas Mooy (CEO)
Katty Watts (VP-Supply Chain)

KINGDON-NICHOLS LLC
5272 W Sunrise Canyon Pl, Marana, AZ 85658
Tel.: (520) 820-3498
Web Site: http://www.kingdon-nichols.com
Strategic Communication Development, Crisis Communication, Executive Coaching & Public Relations
N.A.I.C.S.: 541820
Robert Kingdon Berry (CEO)

KINGERY PRINTING COMPANY
3012 S Banker St, Effingham, IL 62401
Tel.: (217) 347-5151
Web Site:
http://www.kingeryprinting.com
Year Founded: 1968
Sales Range: $25-49.9 Million
Emp.: 160
Offset Printing Services
N.A.I.C.S.: 323111
Steve Shedelbower (Mgr-Sls)
Tom Kingery (Pres)
Mike Kingery (Pres)

KINGFISH INC.
7400 New Lagrange Rd Ste 405, Louisville, KY 40222
Tel.: (502) 339-0565

Web Site:
http://www.kingfishrestaurants.com
Sales Range: $10-24.9 Million
Emp.: 50
Seafood Restaurants
N.A.I.C.S.: 722511
Greg Wortham *(Controller)*

KINGFISHER REGIONAL HOSPITAL
1000 Kingfisher Regional Hospital Dr, Kingfisher, OK 73750
Tel.: (405) 375-3141   OK
Web Site:
http://www.kingfisherhospital.com
Year Founded: 1950
Sales Range: $10-24.9 Million
Emp.: 163
Healthcare Services
N.A.I.C.S.: 622110
Nancy Schmid *(CEO)*

KINGFISHER SYSTEMS, INC.
3110 Fairview Park Dr Ste 1250, Falls Church, VA 22042
Tel.: (703) 820-7970
Web Site:
http://www.kingfishersys.com
Year Founded: 2005
Sales Range: $10-24.9 Million
Emp.: 235
National Security System Services
N.A.I.C.S.: 928110
Roy Reed *(Pres & COO)*
Pete Howton *(CEO)*
Joe Swick *(Sr VP)*

KINGLAND SYSTEMS CORP.
1401 6th Ave S, Clear Lake, IA 50428
Tel.: (641) 355-1000
Web Site: http://www.kingland.com
Year Founded: 1992
Sales Range: $10-24.9 Million
Emp.: 137
Risk Management Software
N.A.I.C.S.: 513210
David J. Kingland *(Chm & CEO)*
Phil Birkedal *(Partner)*
Tony Brownlee *(Pres)*
Jeff Jacobs *(Controller)*
Tim Rourk *(Principal)*
Jason Toyne *(Mng Dir & CTO)*
Patrick Rundall *(Sr Project Mgr)*
Amanda Kasten *(Dir-Project Mgmt)*
Courtney Hiveley *(COO)*

KINGMAN HOSPITAL, INC.
3269 Stockton Hill Rd, Kingman, AZ 86409
Tel.: (928) 757-2101   AZ
Web Site: http://www.azkrmc.com
Year Founded: 1980
Sales Range: $200-249.9 Million
Emp.: 1,924
Healthcare Services
N.A.I.C.S.: 622110
Ryan Kennedy *(COO)*
Brian Turney *(CEO)*
Dave French *(Chm)*
Krystal Burge *(Sec)*
Don Vawter *(Vice Chm)*

KINGMAN REGIONAL MEDICAL CENTER
3629 N Stockton Hill Rd, Kingman, AZ 86409
Tel.: (928) 757-2101
Web Site: http://www.azkrmc.com
Year Founded: 1882
Emp.: 1,800
Health Care Srvices
N.A.I.C.S.: 622110
Krystal Burge *(Sec)*
Jim Baker *(Treas)*

David French *(Chm)*
Don Vawter *(Vice Chm)*
C. William McConnell *(CEO)*

KINGS & CONVICTS BREWING CO.
523 Bank Ln, Highwood, IL 60040
Tel.: (224) 707-0117
Web Site:
http://www.kingsandconvicts.com
Craft Brewery
N.A.I.C.S.: 312120
Brendan Watters *(CEO)*

Subsidiaries:

Ballast Point Brewing & Spirits, Inc.   (1)
9045 Carroll Way, San Diego, CA 92121
Tel.: (858) 790-6900
Web Site: http://www.ballastpoint.com
Beer Breweries & Distilleries Operator; Home Brewing Supplies Retailer; Restaurant & Bar Operator
N.A.I.C.S.: 312120
Laura Slayter *(VP-Natl Accts)*

Subsidiary (Domestic):

Home Brew Mart, Inc.   (2)
5401 Linda Vista Rd Ste 406, San Diego, CA 92110
Tel.: (619) 295-2337
Web Site: http://www.homebrewmart.com
Home Brewing Equipment & Supplies Retailer; Beer Brewery Operator
N.A.I.C.S.: 459999
Jack White Jr. *(Founder)*

KINGS CHRYSLER JEEP DODGE
4486 Kings Water Dr, Cincinnati, OH 45249
Tel.: (513) 683-3000
Sales Range: $10-24.9 Million
Emp.: 100
Car Whslr
N.A.I.C.S.: 441110
Mark Pittman *(Gen Mgr)*
Robert Reichert *(Pres)*

KINGS COMMUNITY ACTION ORGANIZATION
1130 N 11th Ave, Hanford, CA 93230-5901
Tel.: (559) 582-4386   CA
Web Site: http://www.kcao.org
Year Founded: 1965
Sales Range: $10-24.9 Million
Emp.: 267
Community Action Services
N.A.I.C.S.: 624190
Jeff Garner *(Exec Dir)*
Joey Cox *(Dir-IPSS)*
Ron Torres *(Dir-HR)*
Glenda Stephens *(Deputy Exec Dir)*
Michel Dove *(Dir-Child Dev)*
Ruth Rodriguez *(Program Dir-Child Care Assistance)*
Angelina Soper *(Dir-Home & Energy)*
Debra Wood *(Dir-Nutrition Education & Hunger Prevention)*

KINGS CREEK PLANTATION LLC
191 Cottage Cove Ln, Williamsburg, VA 23185
Tel.: (757) 345-6760
Web Site:
http://www.kingscreekplantation.com
Sales Range: $10-24.9 Million
Emp.: 110
Time-Sharing Real Estate Sales, Leasing & Rentals
N.A.I.C.S.: 531390
Kevin Jones *(Owner)*
Joanne Hintz *(Dir-HR)*

KINGS DELIGHT LTD., INC.
2069 Memorial Park Rd, Gainesville, GA 30504-5801
Tel.: (770) 532-3210   GA
Web Site:
http://www.kingsdelight.com
Year Founded: 1986
Sales Range: $25-49.9 Million
Emp.: 400
Poultry Slaughtering & Processing
N.A.I.C.S.: 311615
Barry Jan Cooley *(Chm & CEO)*
Larry Miller *(Pres)*

KINGS FORD INC.
9555 Kings Auto Mall Rd, Cincinnati, OH 45249
Tel.: (513) 683-0220   OH
Web Site:
http://www.kingsfordinc.com
Year Founded: 1979
Sales Range: $50-74.9 Million
Emp.: 85
Sales of New & Used Automobiles
N.A.I.C.S.: 441110
Robert N. Ring *(Owner & Pres)*
Doug Fuller *(Gen Mgr)*
Mike Wheeler *(Mgr-Sls)*

KINGS NISSAN INC.
2758 Coney Is Ave, Brooklyn, NY 11230
Tel.: (718) 376-0538
Web Site:
http://www.kingsnissan.com
Rev.: $29,400,000
Emp.: 45
Automobiles, New & Used
N.A.I.C.S.: 441110
Sal Trantino *(Pres)*
Dave Ivnitsky *(Mgr-Fin)*

KINGS SEAFOOD COMPANY
3185J Airway Ave, Costa Mesa, CA 92626
Tel.: (714) 432-0400
Web Site:
http://www.kingsseafood.com
Year Founded: 1983
Rev.: $25,600,000
Emp.: 25
Eating Place
N.A.I.C.S.: 722511
Matt Stein *(Chief Seafood Officer)*
Malia Cappuccio *(Gen Mgr)*
Steve Ewing *(Gen Mgr)*
Chris Hopgood *(Gen Mgr)*
Zovig Sarkissian *(Gen Mgr)*
Roger Doan *(Chief People Officer)*
Kristin Wojcik *(Dir-Ops)*
Corey Gresham *(Dir-Ops-Water Grill)*

KINGS WAY HOMES INC.
700 Pilgrim Pkwy Ste 100, Elm Grove, WI 53122-2063
Tel.: (262) 797-3636   WI
Web Site:
http://www.kingswayhomes.com
Year Founded: 1972
Sales Range: $10-24.9 Million
Emp.: 25
Single-Family Housing Construction
N.A.I.C.S.: 236115
Beckie Alaimo-Cheng *(Controller & Mgr-HR)*
Deb Olson *(Dir-Pre-Construction)*

KINGSBRIDGE HOLDINGS LLC
150 N Field Dr Ste 193, Lake Forest, IL 60045
Tel.: (847) 693-4100
Web Site:
http://kingsbridgeholdings.com
Holding Company
N.A.I.C.S.: 551112
Dan Flagstad *(Founder & Co-CEO)*

Subsidiaries:

Tech. Finance Co., LLC   (1)
16430 N. Scottsdale Rd, Ste 170, Scottsdale, 85254, AZ
Tel.: (480) 281-1548
Web Site: https://www.techfinanceco.com
Management Consulting Services
N.A.I.C.S.: 541618

KINGSBROOK JEWISH MEDICAL CENTER
585 Schenectady Ave, Brooklyn, NY 11203
Tel.: (718) 604-5000   NY
Web Site: http://www.kingsbrook.org
Year Founded: 1926
Sales Range: $150-199.9 Million
Emp.: 2,690
Health Care Srvices
N.A.I.C.S.: 622110
Jane Lederer *(Chief Nursing Officer & VP)*
Sibte Burney *(Chief Medical Officer)*
Jay Lee *(Chm-Anesthesiology)*
Firozali Panjvani *(Chm-Laboratories)*
Marc Ross *(Chm-Physical Medicine & Rehabilitation)*
Bruce Campbell *(Chm-Radiology)*
Vijay Akkapeddi *(Chm-Emergency Medicine Dept)*
Behame Wubshet *(Chm-Long Term Care Medicine)*
Ellen Tabor *(Chm-Psychiatry Dept)*
William Lois *(Chm-Surgical Svcs)*

KINGSBURY INC.
10385 Drummond Rd, Philadelphia, PA 19154-3803
Tel.: (215) 824-4000   DE
Web Site: http://www.kingsbury.com
Year Founded: 1912
Sales Range: $200-249,9 Million
Emp.: 150
Mfr of Bearings & Related Equipment
N.A.I.C.S.: 333613
William S. Strecker *(Pres & CEO)*
Joseph J. Wilkes *(VP-Engrg)*
Michael Brawley *(VP-Repair & Svc Div)*
Morched Medhioub *(Mng Dir-Kingsbury GmbH)*
Mick McCann *(VP-Sls & Mktg)*
Scan DeCamillo *(Mgr-R&D)*

Subsidiaries:

Kingsbury GmbH   (1)
Wilhelm-Lambrecht-Strasse 2, 37079, Gottingen, Germany
Tel.: (49) 551 999553 0
Bearing Mfr
N.A.I.C.S.: 333613

KINGSGATE TRANSPORTATION SERVICES, LLC
8917 Eagleridge Court, West Chester, OH 45069
Tel.: (513) 874-7447   OH
Web Site:
http://www.kingsgatetrans.com
Year Founded: 1986
Sales Range: $10-24.9 Million
Emp.: 27
Third Party Transportation & Logistics Services
N.A.I.C.S.: 488510
Jeffrey E. Beckham *(Owner, Pres & Partner)*

KINGSLEY CONSTRUCTORS INC.
25250 Borough Park Dr Ste 106, The Woodlands, TX 77380
Tel.: (281) 363-1979
Web Site: http://kci.cc
Sales Range: $50-74.9 Million
Emp.: 100

KINGSLEY CONSTRUCTORS INC.   U.S. PRIVATE

Kingsley Constructors Inc.—(Continued)
General Contractor, Highway & Street Construction
N.A.I.C.S.: 237310
Brad Kingsley (Sr VP)
Jon D. Kingsley Sr. (Pres)

KINGSMEN SOFTWARE LLC
500 W 5th St, Charlotte, NC 28202
Tel.: (704) 997-2755
Web Site: http://www.kingsmensoftware.com
Year Founded: 2013
Sales Range: $1-9.9 Million
Emp.: 45
Software Development Services
N.A.I.C.S.: 541511
Micah Minarik (Mng Partner)
Greg Hart (Mng Partner)
Bill Clerici (CEO)
Kevin Carney (Mng Partner)
David Taylor (Head-Sls & Mktg)
Denise Beachley (Partner & CIO)

KINGSTON COMPANIES
477 Shoup Ave Ste 207, Idaho Falls, ID 83402
Tel.: (208) 522-2365
Web Site: http://www.kingstoncorp.com
Sales Range: $25-49.9 Million
Emp.: 30
Vegetables, Quick Frozen & Cold Pack, Excluding Potato Products
N.A.I.C.S.: 311411
Dave Kingston (Chm & CEO)
Jody Boline (VP-Food Svc & Customer Svc)
Patty Clemons (Controller)

KINGSTON ENVIRONMENTAL SERVICES, INC.
15450 Hanger Rd, Kansas City, MO 64147
Tel.: (816) 524-8811
Web Site: http://www.kingstonenv.com
Year Founded: 1987
Sales Range: $10-24.9 Million
Emp.: 25
Environmental Consulting Services
N.A.I.C.S.: 541620
Chad Tipton (Mgr-HR)

KINGSTON TECHNOLOGY COMPANY, INC.
17600 Newhope St, Fountain Valley, CA 92708-4220
Tel.: (714) 435-2600   CA
Web Site: https://www.kingston.com
Year Founded: 1987
Sales Range: $1-4.9 Billion
Emp.: 3,000
Computer Terminal & Other Computer Peripheral Equipment Manufacturing
N.A.I.C.S.: 334118
David Sun (Co-Founder)
Vishal Parekh (Dir-Mktg-India)

KINGSVIEW LLC
111 W Jackson Blvd Ste 3636, Chicago, IL 60604
Tel.: (312) 819-5910
Web Site: http://www.kingsview.com
Emp.: 65
Securities Brokerage Services
N.A.I.C.S.: 523150
Josh Lewis (CEO)
Terry Morris (Sr VP-Risk & Execution)

KINGSWAY CHARITIES, INC.
1119 Commonwealth Ave, Bristol, VA 24201-4201
Tel.: (276) 466-3014   VA

Web Site: http://www.kingswaycharities.org
Year Founded: 1993
Sales Range: $100-124.9 Million
Emp.: 9
Grantmaking Services
N.A.I.C.S.: 813211
Albert Hester (Dir-Ops & Procurement)
Joan P. Gregory (Sec)
Gregory J. Tebeau (Treas)
John M. Gregory (Chm & CEO)
Mary Ann Gregory Blessing (Pres & COO)

KINGSWAY ENTERPRISES INC.
901 N Marietta St, Gastonia, NC 28054
Tel.: (704) 864-0401
Sales Range: $10-24.9 Million
Emp.: 100
Convenience Store
N.A.I.C.S.: 445131
James T King (Pres)
Mark King (Pres)

KINGSWOOD CAPITAL MANAGEMENT LLC
11812 San Vicente Blvd., Ste 604, Los Angeles, CA 90049
Tel.: (424) 200-6600
Web Site: https://www.kingswood-capital.com
Year Founded: 2013
Private Investment Firm
N.A.I.C.S.: 523999
Ivane Chou (CFO & Chief Compliance Officer)
Alex Wolf (Mng Partner)
James Renna (Partner-Lead Operating)
Michael Niegsch (Partner)
Andrew Kovach (Mng Dir)
Clayton Lechleiter (Principal)
Viswa Maramreddy (VP)
Daniel Lisowski (VP)
Derrek Ross (VP)
Oliver Quintero (Senior Associate)

Subsidiaries:

AVAD LLC   (1)
8501 E Princess DR., Ste 190, Scottsdale, AZ 85255
Tel.: (866) 367-2823
Audio & Video Equipment Distr
N.A.I.C.S.: 423690
Jim Annes (VP & Gen Mgr)
Seth Evenson (Dir-Customer Experience Mgmt)
Rich Turner (Dir-Sls-North America)
Jon Zabel (VP-Sls & Vendor Mgmt)
Tom Jacoby (CEO)
Gary Grant (Sr Branch Mgr-Bellevue)
Dustin Jansen (Mgr-Sls-North America)
Kevin Pass (Sr Branch Mgr-Gaithersburg)
Mark Spector (Sr Branch Mgr-Woburn)
Clark Broyles (Dir-Sls, Pro, and Comml A/V)
Jesse Travis (VP-Ops)
Phillip Parrish (Mgr-Pro AV)
Ron Evans (Mgr-Sls-North America)

Subsidiary (Domestic):

WAVE Electronics   (2)
8648 Glenmont Dr, #130, Houston, TX 77036
Tel.: (713) 466-9283
Web Site: https://www.wave-electronics.com
Radio, Television, And Electronic Stores
N.A.I.C.S.: 449210
Mark Fukuda (CEO)

AutoAnything, Inc.   (1)
6602 Convoy Ct Ste 200, San Diego, CA 92111
Tel.: (858) 569-8111
Web Site: http://www.autoanything.com
Automotive Products Online Reseller
N.A.I.C.S.: 441330

Selwyn Klein (Pres)
Drew Sanocki (CEO)
Michael Epstein (CMO)

Cost Plus, Inc.   (1)
200 4th St, Oakland, CA 94607-4312
Tel.: (510) 893-7300
Web Site: http://www.worldmarket.com
Sales Range: $500-549.9 Million
Emp.: 1,941
Holding Company; Casual Home Decorating & Entertaining Products Retailer
N.A.I.C.S.: 551112
Alexander W. Smith (Chm)

Subsidiary (Domestic):

Cost Plus Management Services, Inc.   (2)
200 4th St, Oakland, CA 94607
Tel.: (510) 893-7300
Web Site: http://www.worldmarket.com
Sales Range: $75-99.9 Million
Emp.: 300
Retail Store Management & Administrative Services
N.A.I.C.S.: 561110

Cost Plus of Texas, Inc.   (2)
1201 Marina Village Pkwy, Alameda, CA 94501
Tel.: (510) 893-7300
Web Site: http://www.worldmarket.com
Sales Range: $75-99.9 Million
Emp.: 300
Retailer of Casual Home Decorating & Entertaining Products
N.A.I.C.S.: 449110

Covenant Testing Technologies, LLC   (1)
1600 Hwy 6 Ste 360, Sugar Land, TX 77478
Tel.: (832) 500-3107
Web Site: http://www.ctest.com
Oil & Energy Flow Management Company
N.A.I.C.S.: 333132
Michael Morreale (CFO)
James Stewart (Chm & CEO)

Kichler Lighting LLC   (1)
7711 E Pleasant Valley Rd, Cleveland, OH 44161-8010
Web Site: https://www.kichler.com
Lighting Product Mfr
N.A.I.C.S.: 335139
Mark J. Macioce (CIO & VP)

Senture, LLC   (1)
460 Industrial Blvd, London, KY 40741
Tel.: (606) 877-6670
Web Site: http://www.senture.com
Telemarketing Bureaus & Other Contact Centers
N.A.I.C.S.: 561422
Christopher Deaton (CEO)
Jim Gayhart (Pres)

The Save Mart Companies, LLC   (1)
2100 Standiford Ave, Modesto, CA 95350
Tel.: (209) 577-0545
Web Site: https://www.savemart.com
Emp.: 14,000
Offices of Other Holding Companies
N.A.I.C.S.: 551112
Tamara Pattison (Chief Digital Officer & Sr VP)
Shane Sampson (Exec Chm)

Subsidiary (Domestic):

Save Mart Supermarkets   (2)
1800 Standiford Ave, Modesto, CA 95350-0180
Tel.: (209) 577-1600
Web Site: http://www.savemart.com
Sales Range: $1-4.9 Billion
Emp.: 16,000
Supermarkets, Chain
N.A.I.C.S.: 445110
Chris McGarry (Chief Admin Officer)
Greg Hill (Co-Pres & CFO)
Nicole Pesco (Co-CEO)

Subsidiary (Domestic):

Yosemite Express Co.   (3)
2400 Louise Ave, Lathrop, CA 95330
Tel.: (209) 858-2212
Web Site: http://www.savemart.com

Sales Range: $25-49.9 Million
Emp.: 150
Transportation
N.A.I.C.S.: 484121

Turbo Wholesale Tires, Inc.   (1)
5793 Martin Rd, Irwindale, CA 91706
Tel.: (626) 856-1400
Web Site: http://www.turbotires.net
Automotive Tire Whslr
N.A.I.C.S.: 441340
Ross T. Kogel Jr. (COO)
Sarkis Sepetjian (Founder)

Subsidiary (Domestic):

Tire Wholesalers Company, LLC   (2)
1783 E 14 Mile Rd, Troy, MI 48083
Tel.: (248) 589-9910
Web Site: http://twitire.tireweb.com
Sales Range: $10-24.9 Million
Emp.: 35
Whslr of Tires
N.A.I.C.S.: 423130
Ross T. Kogel Jr. (CEO)
Ross Kogel Sr. (Founder)

Versar, Inc.   (1)
6850 Versar Ctr, Springfield, VA 22151
Tel.: (703) 750-3000
Web Site: http://www.versar.com
Engineeering Services
N.A.I.C.S.: 541330
James M. Jaska (CEO)
Christine B. Tarrago (CFO)
Daniel M. Patton (Sr VP-Program & Construction Mgmt & Military Programs)
Suzanne J. Bates (Sr VP-Environmental Svcs & Security Sys)

Subsidiary (Domestic):

BayFirst Solutions, LLC   (2)
1025 Vermont Ave NW, Washington, DC 20005
Tel.: (202) 541-1010
Web Site: http://www.bayfirst.com
General Management Consulting Services
N.A.I.C.S.: 541611
Robert W. Rice (Co-Founder & Pres)
Kevin Gooch (CEO)

GEOMET Technologies, LLC   (2)
20251 Century Blvd 300, Germantown, MD 20874-1162   (100%)
Tel.: (301) 428-9898
Environmental Services
N.A.I.C.S.: 541690

Geo-Marine, Inc.   (2)
2201 K Ave Ste Ste A2, Plano, TX 75074-5977
Tel.: (972) 423-5480
Web Site: http://www.geo-marine.com
Engineering Design, Environmental Planning & Archeological Services
N.A.I.C.S.: 541330

Louis Berger Services Inc.   (2)
125 The Pkwy Ste 250, Greenville, SC 29615-6626
Tel.: (202) 303-2791
Web Site: https://www.lbs-inc.com
Emp.: 1,400
Search, Detection, Navigation, Guidance, Aeronautical & Nautical System & Instrument Mfr
N.A.I.C.S.: 334511

Subsidiary (Non-US):

Professional Protection Systems Ltd.   (2)
Protection House Sherbourne Drive, Tilbrook, Milton Keynes, MK7 8HX, United Kingdom
Tel.: (44) 1908272240
Web Site: http://www.ppsgb.com
Personal & Respiratory Protective Equipment Mfr
N.A.I.C.S.: 326199
Bill Vernazza (Mng Dir)
Mark Taylor (Mgr-Logistics)

Subsidiary (Domestic):

Versar ESM Operations   (2)
9200 Rumsey Rd, Columbia, MD 21045-1934
Tel.: (410) 964-9200
Web Site: http://www.versar.com

Environmental Risk Management
N.A.I.C.S.: 541690

Versar Risk Management, Inc. (2)
6850 Versar Ctr Ste 201, Springfield, VA 22151-4148
Tel.: (703) 750-3000
Web Site: http://www.versar.com
Environmental Consulting Services
N.A.I.C.S.: 541690

Versar-Denver (2)
3575 Ringsby Ct Ste 304 & 306, Denver, CO 80216 (100%)
Tel.: (303) 452-5700
Web Site: http://www.versar.com
N.A.I.C.S.: 541330

KINNEY BONDED WAREHOUSE INC.
102 N 13th St, Donna, TX 78537
Tel.: (956) 464-4491
Web Site: http://www.kinneybonded.com
Sales Range: $10-24.9 Million
Emp.: 30
Fertilizers & Agricultural Chemicals
N.A.I.C.S.: 424910
Gary Maurice Kinney *(Pres)*
Todd Kinney *(VP)*
Claudia Vera *(Office Mgr)*

KINNEY DRUGS INC.
520 E Main St, Gouverneur, NY 13642-3360
Tel.: (315) 287-1500 NY
Web Site: http://www.kinneydrugs.com
Year Founded: 1965
Sales Range: $550-599.9 Million
Emp.: 1,800
Drug Stores & Proprietary Stores
N.A.I.C.S.: 456110
Richard A. Cognetti *(VP-Mktg & Mdsg)*
Bridget-Ann Hart *(Pres & CEO-KPH Healthcare Svcs)*
Michael Burgess *(VP-Fin Plng & Treasury)*
Pavi Chigateri *(CTO)*

KINNEY MOTORS
176 US Route 7 S, Rutland, VT 05701
Tel.: (802) 775-6900
Web Site: http://www.kinneymotors.com
Sales Range: $10-24.9 Million
Emp.: 60
Car Whslr
N.A.I.C.S.: 441110
Stephan Maeder *(Pres)*

KINNICKINNIC REALTY CO.
7700 E Arapahoe Rd, Centennial, CO 80112
Tel.: (303) 220-7676
Sales Range: $10-24.9 Million
Emp.: 100
Apartment Building Operators & Owners
N.A.I.C.S.: 531110
E. Gregg Jackson *(Pres)*

KINNSER SOFTWARE, INC.
2600 Via Fortuna Dr Ste 300, Austin, TX 78746
Tel.: (512) 879-3135
Web Site: http://www.kinnser.com
Year Founded: 2003
Sales Range: $1-9.9 Million
Emp.: 37
Electronic Medical Record Keeping
N.A.I.C.S.: 513210
Christopher Hester *(Founder & CEO)*
Brian Thomson *(CFO)*
George D. Santillan *(CIO)*
Ben Chapman *(VP-Sls)*
Scott Chlebos *(VP-HR)*

Matt Curtin *(Chief Revenue Officer)*
Joel Dolisy *(CTO)*
Becky Richardson *(Owner & VP)*
Nick Williams *(COO)*

KINO INTERNATIONAL CORP.
333 W 39th St, New York, NY 10018
Tel.: (212) 629-6880 NY
Web Site: http://www.kino.com
Year Founded: 1977
Sales Range: $1-9.9 Million
Emp.: 21
Classic & Foreign Language Art Films Distr
N.A.I.C.S.: 512120
Richard Lorber *(Pres)*

KINPLEX CORP.
200 Heartland Blvd, Edgewood, NY 11717-8380
Tel.: (631) 242-4800 DE
Web Site: http://www.advancetabco.com
Year Founded: 1990
Rev.: $35,000,000
Emp.: 285
Holding Company; Metal Sinks, Cabinets, Tables & Shelving Mfr & Whslr
N.A.I.C.S.: 551112
Penny Hutner *(Pres)*

Subsidiaries:

Advance Tabco, Inc. (1)
200 Heartland Blvd, Edgewood, NY 11717-8379 (100%)
Tel.: (631) 242-4800
Web Site: http://www.advancetabco.com
Rev.: $10,900,000
Emp.: 85
Metal Sinks, Cabinets, Tables & Shelving Mfr & Whslr
N.A.I.C.S.: 332999
Penny Hutner *(Pres)*

Unit (Domestic):

Advance Tabco, Inc. - Texas (2)
2000 S Houston St, Kaufman, TX 75142-3602
Tel.: (972) 932-4148
Web Site: http://www.advancetabco.com
Sales Range: $25-49.9 Million
Metal Sinks, Cabinets, Tables & Shelving Mfr & Whslr
N.A.I.C.S.: 332999
Chuck Underwood *(Dir-Mfg)*

Subsidiary (Domestic):

Toga Manufacturing, Inc. (2)
1003 GA-42, Jackson, GA 30233
Tel.: (770) 775-2106
Rev.: $1,400,000
Emp.: 15
Metal Sinks, Cabinets, Tables & Shelving Mfr & Whslr
N.A.I.C.S.: 332999

Wesko Industries, Inc. (2)
14400 Lear Blvd, Reno, NV 89506-2606
Tel.: (775) 972-1500
Web Site: http://www.advancetabco.com
Sales Range: $10-24.9 Million
Emp.: 2
Metal Sinks, Cabinets, Tables & Shelving Mfr & Whslr
N.A.I.C.S.: 332999

KINSEL MOTORS INC.
3355 Eastex Fwy, Beaumont, TX 77706
Tel.: (409) 899-4000
Web Site: http://www.kinselmotors.com
Rev.: $68,000,000
Emp.: 235
Automobiles, New & Used
N.A.I.C.S.: 441110
Jamie Frederick *(Controller)*
Craig Kinsel *(CEO)*
James McNutt *(Gen Mgr-Sls)*
Joe Bob Kinsel II *(Owner)*

KINSETH HOSPITALITY COMPANY
2 Quail Creek Cir, North Liberty, IA 52317
Tel.: (319) 626-5600
Web Site: http://www.kinseth.com
Year Founded: 1963
Sales Range: $100-124.9 Million
Emp.: 40
Motel, Franchised
N.A.I.C.S.: 721110
Leslie Kinseth *(Pres)*
Bruce Kinseth *(Exec VP)*
Brian Ossian *(Dir-Ops)*

KINSLEY CONSTRUCTION INC.
2700 Water St, York, PA 17403
Tel.: (717) 741-3841 PA
Web Site: http://www.rkinsley.com
Year Founded: 1963
Sales Range: $200-249.9 Million
Emp.: 1,300
Provider of Industrial Building New Construction
N.A.I.C.S.: 236210
Robert A. Kinsley *(Founder, Chm & CEO)*
Jonathan Kinsley *(Pres & COO)*
Jerry Caslow *(Controller)*
Jarrod Schiding *(Dir-Bus Dev)*

Subsidiaries:

Kinsley Industrial (1)
1110 E Princess St PO Box 2886, York, PA 17403 (100%)
Tel.: (717) 815-6936
Web Site: http://www.kinsleyindustrial.com
Demolition, Structural Concrete & In-Plant Renovation Services
N.A.I.C.S.: 238120
Mike Leiphart *(Mgr-PR)*

Kinsley Manufacturing-Steel Fabrication & Erection (1)
3900 E Market St, York, PA 17402 (100%)
Tel.: (717) 757-8761
Web Site: http://www.kinsleysteel.com
Structural Steel & Miscellaneous Metal Projects
N.A.I.C.S.: 238120
Bobby Chenault *(Gen Mgr)*
Ryan Butler *(Asst Gen Mgr)*
Wendy Ebersole *(Officer-EEO & Dir-HR)*

KINSLEY GROUP, INC.
14 Connecticut S Dr, East Granby, CT 06026
Tel.: (860) 844-6100
Web Site: http://www.kinsleypower.com
Year Founded: 1964
Emp.: 100
Power Systems & Industrial Generators Distr
N.A.I.C.S.: 423610
David Kinsley *(Pres)*
Tom Walbridge *(VP-Ops-Kinsley Power Sys)*
Shari Blackman *(Dir-HR)*
Nati Olin *(Dir-IT)*

KINZIE CAPITAL PARTNERS LP
20 N Clark St 36th Fl, Chicago, IL 60602
Tel.: (312) 809-2490 DE
Web Site: http://www.kinziecp.com
Year Founded: 2017
Privater Equity Firm
N.A.I.C.S.: 523999
Suzanne Yoon *(Co-Founder & Mng Partner)*
David Namkung *(Co-Founder & Partner-Ops)*
Suzanne Yoon *(Founder & Mng Partner)*

Subsidiaries:

Chelsea Lighting NYC, LLC (1)
225 W 34th St, New York, NY 10122
Tel.: (212) 643-3337
Sales Range: $25-49.9 Million
Emp.: 19
Electrical Apparatus & Equipment, Wiring Supplies & Related Equipment Merchant Whslr
N.A.I.C.S.: 423610
Thomas Ike *(Pres)*

Colony Display LLC (1)
2500 Galvin Dr, Elgin, IL 60124
Tel.: (847) 426-5300
Web Site: http://www.colonydisplay.com
Sales Range: $75-99.9 Million
Emp.: 170
Customized Fixtures Designer & Mfr
N.A.I.C.S.: 321999
Joe Galante *(Project Mgr)*
Chuck Zich *(CEO)*

GT Golf Holdings, Inc (1)
1345 Specialty Dr E, Vista, CA 92081
Tel.: (760) 599-9258
Web Site: http://www.ggolf.com
Rev.: $4,920,000
Emp.: 8
Sporting Goods Retailer
N.A.I.C.S.: 459110
Brian Van De Veere *(Pres)*

Subsidiary (Domestic):

Proactive Sports Inc. (2)
1200 SE 2nd Ave, Canby, OR 97013
Tel.: (503) 263-8583
Web Site: http://www.proactivesports.com
Rev.: $9,225,000
Emp.: 15
Sporting Goods Retailer
N.A.I.C.S.: 459110

KIOLBASSA
1325 S Brazos St, San Antonio, TX 78207
Tel.: (210) 226-8127
Web Site: http://www.kiolbassa.com
Year Founded: 1949
Sales Range: $10-24.9 Million
Emp.: 115
Meat Product Production & Distribution Services
N.A.I.C.S.: 424470
John Canales *(Mgr-Production)*
Tary Ramos *(Gen Mgr-Engrg)*

KIONA VINEYARDS & WINERY
44612 N Sunset Rd, Benton City, WA 99320
Tel.: (509) 588-6716
Web Site: http://www.kionawine.com
Sales Range: $1-9.9 Million
Emp.: 12
Wineries
N.A.I.C.S.: 312130
Ann Williams *(Co-Owner)*
John J. Williams *(Founder & Mgr-Sls)*
Lorne Jacobson *(Mgr-Sls-Natl)*

KIOR, INC.
13001 Bay Park Rd, Pasadena, TX 77507
Tel.: (281) 694-8700 DE
Web Site: http://www.kior.com
Year Founded: 2007
Sales Range: $1-9.9 Million
Emp.: 183
Renewable Fuel Producer
N.A.I.C.S.: 324199
Samir Kaul *(Co-Founder)*
Fred Cannon *(CEO)*
John Kasbaum *(Sr VP-Comml)*
Christopher A. Artzer *(Pres, Interim CFO & Gen Counsel)*
John Hacskaylo *(VP-R&D)*
Edward J. Smith *(VP-Engrg & Construction)*
Daniel J. Strope *(VP-Tech)*
George E. Staggs *(Treas & Controller)*

KiOR, Inc.—(Continued)

KIP-CRAFT INCORPORATED
4747 W 160th St, Cleveland, OH 44135
Tel.: (216) 898-5500
Web Site: http://www.schoolbells.com
Sales Range: $25-49.9 Million
Emp.: 50
Uniforms Mfr
N.A.I.C.S.: 458110
Bruce J. Carroll *(Owner)*
Elaine Stephens *(VP)*
Kathleen Luchansky *(Controller)*

KIPER DEVELOPMENT, INC.
3200 Danville Blvd #200, Alamo, CA 94507
Tel.: (925) 648-8888
Web Site:
   http://www.kiperhomes.com
Year Founded: 1978
Sales Range: $25-49.9 Million
Emp.: 25
Housing Construction Services
N.A.I.C.S.: 236117
Edward R. Hobaugh *(Principal)*
Rick Kiper *(Pres)*

KIPSU, INC.
510 1st Ave N, Minneapolis, MN 55403
Tel.: (612) 503-4000
Web Site: http://www.kipsu.com
Year Founded: 2011
Sales Range: $1-9.9 Million
Emp.: 58
Software Development Services
N.A.I.C.S.: 541511
Chris Smith *(Founder & CEO)*
Anna Schaefer *(CFO)*
Eva Dixon *(Mktg Dir)*
Charlie Lehmann *(Dir-Customer Engagement)*
Justin Porter *(VP-Ops)*

KIRBERG ROOFING INC.
1400 S 3rd St, Saint Louis, MO 63104
Tel.: (314) 534-4444
Web Site: http://www.kirberg.com
Rev.: $17,256,993
Emp.: 132
Roofing Contractors
N.A.I.C.S.: 238160
Eric Kirberg *(VP-Mktg)*

KIRBY AGRI INC.
500 Running Pump Rd, Lancaster, PA 17601-2241
Tel.: (717) 299-2541　　　　FL
Web Site: http://www.kirbyagri.com
Year Founded: 1991
Sales Range: $75-99.9 Million
Emp.: 49
Wholesale Fertilizer & Fertilizer Raw Materials
N.A.I.C.S.: 325314
Carroll R. Kirby *(Pres)*
Rick Kirby *(Sr VP)*
Walt Honsinger *(Controller)*
Mary Kirby *(Office Mgr)*

Subsidiaries:

Kirby Agri Inc. - Kirby Agri Ingredients Facility　　　　(1)
1020 Millersville Rd, Lancaster, PA 17603
Tel.: (717) 872-4791
Feed Ingredient Mfr
N.A.I.C.S.: 311119

Kirby Agri Services　　　　(1)
500 Running Pump Rd, Lancaster, PA 17607
Tel.: (717) 299-2541
Web Site: http://www.kirbyagri.com

Sales Range: $10-24.9 Million
Public Storage of Agricultural Products
N.A.I.C.S.: 325314
Walt Honsinger *(Controller)*
John Charles *(Mgr-Feed Ingredients)*
John Gettle *(Mgr)*
Michael King *(Mgr)*
Mary Kirby *(Office Mgr)*
Jeremy Young *(Mgr-Mill)*
Gary Forry *(Mgr)*

KIRBY FOODS INC.
4102 Fieldstone Rd, Champaign, IL 61822
Tel.: (217) 352-2600
Web Site: http://www.kirbyfoods.com
Sales Range: $100-124.9 Million
Emp.: 15
Independent Supermarket
N.A.I.C.S.: 445110

KIRBY KANOY & ASSOCIATES, INC.
1120 Randolph St Ste 31, Thomasville, NC 27360
Tel.: (336) 476-0044
Sales Range: $1-9.9 Million
Emp.: 24
Insurance Brokerage Services
N.A.I.C.S.: 524210
Richard Kirby Kanoy *(Pres)*

KIRBY MANUFACTURING INC.
484 S Hwy 59, Merced, CA 95340
Tel.: (209) 723-0778
Web Site: http://www.kirbymfg.com
Rev.: $11,136,091
Emp.: 85
Cattle Feeding, Handling & Watering Equipment
N.A.I.C.S.: 333111
Richard Kirby *(Pres)*
Richard Mendonca *(Plant Mgr)*
Art Burrows *(Gen Mgr)*

KIRBY MEDICAL CENTER
1000 Medical Center Dr, Monticello, IL 61856
Tel.: (217) 762-2115　　　　IL
Web Site: http://www.kirbyhealth.org
Year Founded: 1939
Sales Range: $10-24.9 Million
Emp.: 271
Health Care Srvices
N.A.I.C.S.: 622110
Alexander Nazarian *(CFO)*
Jennifer Moss *(Chief Clinical Officer)*
Ann Collins *(Dir-Surgical Svcs)*
Jody Bettis *(Dir-Environmental Svcs)*

KIRBY NAGELHOUT CONSTRUCTION CO.
20635 Brinson Blvd, Bend, OR 97701
Tel.: (541) 389-7119
Sales Range: $25-49.9 Million
Emp.: 100
Civil Engineering Services
N.A.I.C.S.: 237310
Cathy Nagelhout *(Co-Owner)*

KIRBY RISK CORPORATION
PO Box 5089, Lafayette, IN 47903-5089
Tel.: (765) 448-4567　　　　IN
Web Site: http://www.kirbyrisk.com
Year Founded: 1926
Sales Range: $100-124.9 Million
Emp.: 1,120
Electrical Apparatus & Equipment
N.A.I.C.S.: 423610
Jason Bricker *(CFO)*
Stephanie Mader *(Controller)*
James K. Risk III *(Pres & CEO)*

KIRBY-SMITH MACHINERY INC.

6715 W Reno Ave, Oklahoma City, OK 73127-6590
Tel.: (405) 495-7820　　　　OK
Web Site: http://www.kirby-smith.com
Year Founded: 1983
Sales Range: $25-49.9 Million
Emp.: 300
Heavy Construction Equipment Rental
N.A.I.C.S.: 532412
David Baker *(Sr VP & Mgr-Oklahoma City)*
Lonnie Kilgore *(Mgr-Retail Fin)*
Greg Otts *(VP & Mgr-Major Accts)*
Chris Kirby *(Mgr-Used Equipment)*
Rick Nielsen *(Mgr-Internet Sls)*
Gary Corley *(Mgr-Paving)*
Jeff Weller *(COO & Exec VP)*
Brent Snapp *(Mgr-Lubbock)*
Tom Montgomery *(VP-Customer Care)*
Chris Ware *(Acct Mgr-Crane Div-St. Louis)*
Rickey Bailey *(VP-Crane Div)*
Tim Yauilla *(Mgr-Ops-Kansas City)*
David Marston *(Mgr-Product Support Sls)*
Kelly Shuffield *(Mgr-Gen Svc-Crane Div)*
Vern Gunderson *(VP-Road Construction & Minerals Div)*
Hoyt Edgar Kirby Jr. *(Pres)*

KIRCO
101 W Big Beaver Rd No 200, Troy, MI 48084
Tel.: (248) 680-7180
Web Site: http://www.kirco.com
Sales Range: $25-49.9 Million
Emp.: 90
Industrial Buildings, New Construction, Nec
N.A.I.C.S.: 236210
Steve Zamanski *(CFO)*
Mary Fogo *(Controller)*
Maggie Donius *(Gen Mgr)*
Cheryl Grosscup *(Mgr-Property)*
Dave Hales *(VP-Property Mgmt)*
A. Mathew Kiriluk II *(Pres)*

KIRILA CONTRACTORS INC.
505 Bedford Rd SE, Brookfield, OH 44403
Tel.: (330) 448-4055
Web Site: http://www.kirila.com
Rev.: $25,400,000
Emp.: 45
Highway & Street Paving Contractor
N.A.I.C.S.: 237310
David Pringle *(Controller)*

KIRK & MATZ LTD.
3390 Denver Dr, Denver, NC 28037
Tel.: (704) 489-8490　　　　CT
Web Site: http://www.kirk-matz.com
Year Founded: 1946
Sales Range: $10-24.9 Million
Emp.: 15
Trophies & Awards Whslr
N.A.I.C.S.: 423990
Victor Matz *(Pres)*

KIRK BROTHERS FORD-LINCOLN, LLC
1512 Hwy 82 W, Greenwood, MS 38930
Tel.: (662) 453-6131　　　　MS
Web Site:
   http://www.kirkbrothersford.com
Sales Range: $10-24.9 Million
Emp.: 44
New & Used Car Dealer
N.A.I.C.S.: 441110
Cannon Kirk *(Co-Owner)*
Kevin Evans *(Gen Mgr)*

Heather Lott *(Mgr-Internet Sls)*
Bill Hammons *(Mgr-Fin)*
J. S. Kirk Sr. *(Co-Owner)*

KIRKHILL AIRCRAFT PARTS CO.
3120 E Enterprise St, Brea, CA 92821-6237
Tel.: (714) 223-5400　　　　CA
Web Site: http://www.kapco-global.com
Year Founded: 1972
Emp.: 600
Aircraft Component Distr
N.A.I.C.S.: 423860
Andrew Todhunter *(Pres & CEO)*
Terry Vieira *(VP-Corp Dev)*

Subsidiaries:

Avio-Diepen B.V.　　　　(1)
J Keplerweg 16, 2408 AC, Alphen aan den Rijn, Netherlands
Tel.: (31) 172 449 777
Web Site: http://www.avio-diepen.com
Emp.: 130
Aircraft Parts Distr
N.A.I.C.S.: 423860
Kees Burger *(Dir-Product Mgmt)*

Subsidiary (US):

Avio-Diepen Inc.　　　　(2)
561 Airport S Pkwy Ste 500, Atlanta, GA 30349
Tel.: (770) 996-6430
Web Site: http://www.avio-diepen.com
Aircraft Parts Distr
N.A.I.C.S.: 423860
Claire Stout *(Dir-Sls)*

KIRKLAND & ELLIS LLP
333 Wolf Point Plz, Chicago, IL 60654
Tel.: (312) 862-2000　　　　DE
Web Site: https://www.kirkland.com
Year Founded: 1938
Sales Range: $75-99.9 Million
Emp.: 6,500
Law firm
N.A.I.C.S.: 541110
Jay P. Lefkowitz *(Partner)*
Mark C. Holscher *(Partner-Los Angeles)*
Taj J. Clayton *(Executives)*
David Fox *(Partner-New York)*
Matthew R. Pacey *(Partner-Houston)*
Ryan D. Harris *(Partner-Chicago)*
Adam D. Larson *(Partner-Houston)*
Andrew Calder *(Partner-Houston)*
Sarah E. Stasny *(Partner-New York)*
Michael E. Weisser *(Partner-New York)*
Erin Nealy Cox *(Partner-Gov, Regulatory & Internal Investigations Grp)*
Javier Rubinstein *(Partner-Chicago)*
Mark Filip *(Partner-Chicago)*
Douglas E. Bacon *(Partner-Houston)*
Jonathan L. Davis *(Partner-New York)*
Matthew Elliott *(Partner-London)*
Shubi Arora *(Partner-Houston & Dallas)*
Lee Morlock *(Partner-Chicago)*
Aaron Marks *(Partner-New York)*
Paul Brinkman *(Partner-Intellectual Property-Washington)*
Julian J. Seiguer *(Partner-Houston)*
Erica Berthou *(Partner-Investment Funds Grp-New York)*
Jordan Murray *(Partner-New York)*
Eric L. Schiele *(Partner-New York)*
Roald Nashi *(Partner-Debt Fin Practice Grp-Washington)*
Richard Sharpe *(Partner-Hong Kong)*
Cori Lable *(Partner-Hong Kong)*
Benjamin Adelson *(Partner-Dallas)*
Katherine V. Coverdale *(Partner-Boston)*

Amanda C. Border *(Partner-Boston)*
Brooksany Barrowes *(Partner-Washington)*

Subsidiaries:

Kirkland & Ellis International LLP (1)
29th Floor China World Office 2 No 1 Jian Guo Men Wai Avenue, Beijing, 100004, China
Tel.: (86) 10 5737 9300
Web Site: http://www.kirkland.com
Emp.: 25
Law firm
N.A.I.C.S.: 541199
Stuart Boyd *(Partner-Corp Practice-London)*
Paula Liu *(Partner-Corp Practice Grp-Shanghai)*
David Zhang *(Sr Partner-Corp Practice Grp-Asia)*
Sean Lacey *(Partner-Restructuring Practice Grp-London)*
Daniel Dusek *(Partner-Corp Practice Grp)*
Attila Oldag *(Partner-Munich)*
Anand Damodaran *(Partner-Investment Funds Grp-London)*
Richard Watkins *(Partner-Investment Funds-London)*
David Higgins *(Partner-Private Equity)*
Adrian Maguire *(Partner-London)*
Chuan Li *(Partner)*
Jing Li *(Partner)*
Steve Lin *(Partner)*

KIRKS AUTOMOTIVE INC.

9330 Roselawn St, Detroit, MI 48204
Tel.: (313) 933-7030 MI
Web Site: http://www.kirksauto.com
Year Founded: 1946
Sales Range: $10-24.9 Million
Emp.: 32
Distr of Automotive Supplies & Parts
N.A.I.C.S.: 423120
Robert E. Kirkman *(Pres)*
Stephen Allen Benish *(VP-Sls)*
Robert R. Kirkman *(CEO)*

KIRKSVILLE MOTOR COMPANY

3607 N Baltimore St, Kirksville, MO 63501
Tel.: (660) 665-2805
Web Site: http://www.kirksvillemotorco.com
Emp.: 60
New & Used Automobile Dealers
N.A.I.C.S.: 441110
Dan Anderson *(Exec Mgr)*
Hector Contreras *(Mgr-BDC)*
Richie Tipton *(Sls Mgr-New Car)*
Kathy Darling *(Office Mgr)*
Charlie Marlay *(Dir-Fin & Leasing)*
Jim Groom *(Dir-Fixed Ops)*

KIRKWOOD BANCORPORATION CO.

2911 N 14th St, Bismarck, ND 58503
Tel.: (701) 258-6550 ND
Web Site: http://www.kirkwoodbank.com
Year Founded: 1990
Bank Holding Company
N.A.I.C.S.: 551111
Peter Jahner *(Pres-Kirkwood Bank & Trust)*
Gerald P. Willer *(Chm & CEO)*

Subsidiaries:

Kirkwood Bank & Trust Co. (1)
2911 N 14th St, Bismarck, ND 58503
Tel.: (701) 258-6550
Web Site: http://www.kirkwoodbank.com
Sales Range: $10-24.9 Million
Emp.: 56
Commericial Banking
N.A.I.C.S.: 522110
Peter Jahner *(Pres)*
Shelley Trolliey *(Officer-Loan & Branch Mgr-South)*
Gerald P. Willer *(Chm & CEO)*

KIRKWOOD HOLDING, INC.

1239 Rockside Rd, Pampa, OH 44134
Tel.: (216) 267-6200 OH
Web Site: http://www.kirkwood-ind.com
Year Founded: 1944
Sales Range: $100-124.9 Million
Emp.: 130
Motor Commutators, Carbon Brushes, Springs & Related Products Mfr
N.A.I.C.S.: 335312
L. Thomas Koechley *(Pres)*

Subsidiaries:

Colorado Fabrication LLC (1)
7210 W 116th Ave, Broomfield, CO 80020
Tel.: (303) 460-9908
Web Site: http://www.coloradofabrication.com
Emp.: 10
Lathe Machine Mfr
N.A.I.C.S.: 333517
Michelle Beston *(Office Mgr)*

Kirkwood Digital LLC (1)
904 Main St, Wilmington, MA 01887
Tel.: (978) 658-4200
Web Site: http://www.kirkwooddigital.com
Graphic Design Services
N.A.I.C.S.: 541430
Wayne Moda *(Exec VP)*
Bob Coppinger *(CEO)*
Chuck Colvin *(Exec VP)*
Craig Wenrich *(Sr VP)*
Eddie Kelley *(Pres)*
Gidge Farraher *(COO)*
Mark Nappa *(Chief Sls Officer)*
Nigel Donovan *(CFO)*
Robert Brown *(Sr VP)*
Will Winship *(Exec VP)*

Techniques LLC (1)
465 South Pierce Ave, Louisville, CO 80027
Tel.: (720) 457-7201
Web Site: http://www.techniquesswiss.com
Precision Component Mfr
N.A.I.C.S.: 332721

Toledo Commutator Co. (1)
1101 S Chestnut, Owosso, MI 48867-4096
Tel.: (989) 725-8192
Web Site: http://www.toledocommutator.com
Sales Range: $25-49.9 Million
Electrical Machinery, Slip Rings & Brush Springs Mfr
N.A.I.C.S.: 335312
Paul Hansen *(Pres)*
Tim Kildea *(VP-Sls)*
Tom Koechley *(CEO)*

KIRKWOOD PRINTING COMPANY, INC.

904 Main St, Wilmington, MA 01887-3319
Tel.: (978) 658-4200
Web Site: http://www.kirkwoodprinting.com
Emp.: 100
Printing
N.A.I.C.S.: 323111
Bob Coppinger *(Pres & CEO)*

Subsidiaries:

DGI Communications, LLC (1)
73 Second Ave, Burlington, MA 01803
Tel.: (781) 270-3670
Web Site: http://www.dgi-invisuals.com
Rev.: $6,666,666
Emp.: 100
Commercial Flexographic Printing
N.A.I.C.S.: 323111

KIRKWOODS INC.

719 2nd St, Chetek, WI 54728
Tel.: (715) 924-3132
Year Founded: 1977
Sales Range: $10-24.9 Million
Emp.: 75
Grocery Stores, Independent
N.A.I.C.S.: 445110
Tom Kurschner *(Pres)*

KIRLIN CUSTOM HOMES INC.

4401 Belvedere Dr, Plano, TX 75093-6968
Tel.: (972) 423-8751
Web Site: http://www.kirlincustomhomes.com
Sales Range: $10-24.9 Million
Emp.: 8
New Construction, Single-Family Houses
N.A.I.C.S.: 236115
Mike Kirlin *(Pres)*

KIRLIN'S INC.

532 Maine St, Quincy, IL 62301
Tel.: (217) 224-8953
Web Site: http://www.hallmark.com
Year Founded: 1948
Rev.: $95,350,401
Emp.: 35
Retail Greeting Card & Gift Stores Owner & Operator
N.A.I.C.S.: 459420
Gary Kirlin *(Pres)*
Dale T. Kirlin Jr. *(Chm)*

KIRTLAND CAPITAL PARTNERS LLC

3201 Enterprise Pkwy Ste 200, Beachwood, OH 44122
Tel.: (216) 593-0100 OH
Web Site: http://www.kirtlandcapital.com
Year Founded: 1977
Sales Range: $150-199.9 Million
Emp.: 11
Privater Equity Firm
N.A.I.C.S.: 523999
Thomas N. Littman *(Pres & Mng Partner)*
James A. Foley *(Partner)*
John N. Heckman *(VP-Fin)*
Corrine Menary *(Principal)*
John G. Nestor *(Chm & Mng Partner)*

KIRTLEY-COLE ASSOCIATES, LLC.

1010 SE Everett Mall Way Ste 102, Everett, WA 98208
Tel.: (425) 609-0400
Web Site: http://www.kirtley-cole.com
Year Founded: 1973
Sales Range: $10-24.9 Million
Emp.: 60
Commercial & Institutional Building Construction Services
N.A.I.C.S.: 236220
Mark Lewinski *(Pres & CEO)*
Todd Nelson *(VP-Preconstruction)*
Debra Sager *(CFO, Sec & Treas)*
Scott Wendlandt *(Dir-Ops)*

KISINGER CAMPO & ASSOCIATES CORP.

201 N Franklin St Ste 400, Tampa, FL 33602
Tel.: (813) 871-5331
Web Site: http://www.kisingercampo.com
Year Founded: 1976
Sales Range: $25-49.9 Million
Emp.: 190
Engineeering Services
N.A.I.C.S.: 541330
Stephen H. McGucken *(CEO)*
Thomas Locicero *(Engr-Bridge Structures)*
Julian Gutierrez *(Chief Engr-Structures)*
Richard Harrison *(Mgr-Roadway Dept)*
Michael Campo *(Engr-Roadway)*
John Burton *(Project Mgr)*

KISMET INTERNATIONAL LIMOUSINE SERVICE INC.

800 Cedar Ln, Teaneck, NJ 07666
Tel.: (201) 986-1700
Web Site: http://www.kismetlimousine.com
Year Founded: 2006
Sales Range: $1-9.9 Million
Emp.: 160
Limousine Services to Corporate, Private & Public Sector Markets
N.A.I.C.S.: 485320
Emin Kahyaoglu *(Pres)*

Subsidiaries:

Rezman Express Inc. (1)
211 N Governor Printz Blvd, Essington, PA 19029 (100%)
Tel.: (215) 695-5001
Limousine & Taxi Services
N.A.I.C.S.: 485320
Emin Kahyaoglu *(Founder & Pres)*

KISMET RUBBER PRODUCTS INC.

215 Industrial Blvd, Blue Ridge, GA 30513-4605
Tel.: (706) 632-2261
Web Site: http://www.kismetrubberproducts.com
Sales Range: $1-9.9 Million
Emp.: 32
Mechanical Rubber Goods
N.A.I.C.S.: 326291

KISSELBACK FORD

1118 13th St, Saint Cloud, FL 34769
Tel.: (407) 892-2141
Web Site: http://www.kisselbackford.com
Emp.: 100
Automobile & Truck Dealership
N.A.I.C.S.: 441110
Bobby Kisselback *(Pres)*

KISSIMMEE UTILITY AUTHORITY

1701 W Carroll St, Kissimmee, FL 34741-6804
Tel.: (407) 933-7777
Web Site: http://www.kua.com
Year Founded: 1985
Sales Range: $150-199.9 Million
Emp.: 300
Electric Power Distribution & Generation Services
N.A.I.C.S.: 221122
Kenneth L. Davis *(VP-Egrng & Ops)*
Chris M. Gent *(VP-Corp Comm)*
Jeffery S. Gray *(VP-IT)*
Wilbur Hill *(VP-HR)*
Grant Lacerte *(Gen Counsel & VP)*
Larry Mattern *(VP-Power Supply)*
Susan Postans *(VP-Customer Svc)*
Greg Woessner *(VP-Sys Compliance & Ops)*
Reginald L. Hardee *(Chm)*
George Gant *(Sec)*
Kathleen Thacker *(Asst Sec)*
Jeanne Van Meter *(Vice Chm)*
Kevin E. Crawford *(VP-Fin & Admin)*
Brian Horton *(Pres, CEO & Gen Mgr)*

KISSIN FRESH MEATS INC.

140 Richmond St, Philadelphia, PA 19125
Tel.: (215) 739-4242
Web Site: http://www.kissinfreshmeats.com
Sales Range: $10-24.9 Million
Emp.: 8
Meat & Meat Product Whslr
N.A.I.C.S.: 424470
Stephen Verica *(Pres & Treas)*

KISSTIXX, LLC

PO Box 971284, Orem, UT 84097
Tel.: (801) 855-6019

Kisstixx, LLC—(Continued)

Web Site: http://www.kisstixx.com
Sales Range: $1-9.9 Million
Lip Balm Mfr
N.A.I.C.S.: 325620
Dallas Robinson (Owner)

KITAHARA PONTIAC-BUICK-GMC, INC.
5515 N Blackstone Ave, Fresno, CA 93710-5017
Tel.: (559) 431-2020
Year Founded: 1998
Sales Range: $25-49.9 Million
Emp.: 90
Car Whslr
N.A.I.C.S.: 441110
Jerald Marks (Gen Mgr-Sls)

KITANO ARMS CORPORATION
66 Park Ave, New York, NY 10016
Tel.: (212) 885-7000
Web Site: http://www.kitano.com
Year Founded: 1973
Sales Range: $10-24.9 Million
Emp.: 60
Hotel
N.A.I.C.S.: 721110
Tsugoto Kitano (Pres)
Maria C. Clotter (Mgr-Corp Sls)
Glenn Ham (Mgr-Room Div)
Natalie Rainford (Mgr-Reservations)
Tania Lavandeira (Mgr-Corp Sls)
Zag Zaharan (Gen Mgr)

KITCHELL CORPORATION
1707 E Highland, Phoenix, AZ 85016
Tel.: (602) 264-4111   AZ
Web Site: http://www.kitchell.com
Year Founded: 1950
Sales Range: $200-249.9 Million
Emp.: 700
Holding Company; Industrial & Public Construction Manager; Luxury Custom Home Builder; Real Estate Developer
N.A.I.C.S.: 236220
Steve Whitworth (Pres-Kitchell Contractors)
Julie Garcia (Dir-Preconstruction)
Arturo Taboada (Exec Dir-Bay Area)
Jim Swanson (Pres & CEO)
Wendy Cohen (VP-Northern California)

Subsidiaries:

American Refrigeration Supplies, Inc.   (1)
2632 E Chambers St, Phoenix, AZ 85040-3601   (88%)
Tel.: (602) 243-2792
Web Site: http://www.store.arsnet.com
Sales Range: $25-49.9 Million
Emp.: 200
Refrigeration & Air Conditioning Parts Whslr
N.A.I.C.S.: 423740
Stephen Martin (CEO)
John White (Pres)

FDI Planning Consultants, Inc.   (1)
505 N Brand Blvd Ste 815, Glendale, CA 91203
Web Site: http://www.fdiplan.com
Emp.: 25
Clinical Technology Planning Services
N.A.I.C.S.: 541614
Donna Nagaoka (Mgr-Ops)

Kitchell CEM, Inc.   (1)
1707 E Highland, Phoenix, AZ 85016-4693   (100%)
Tel.: (602) 266-1970
Sales Range: $10-24.9 Million
Emp.: 30
Program, Project & Construction Management Services to Federal, State, Local & Quasi-Public Agencies
N.A.I.C.S.: 541618

Russ Fox (Pres)
Nicole Maas (Mgr-Mktg)
Patrick McGrath (Mgr-Trng-Facilities Mgmt)

Kitchell Contractors, Inc. of Arizona   (1)
1707 E Highland Ave Ste 200, Phoenix, AZ 85016-4659   (100%)
Tel.: (602) 222-5300
Web Site: http://www.kitchell.com
Sales Range: $25-49.9 Million
Emp.: 150
Construction Management & General Contracting Firm
N.A.I.C.S.: 236220
Dan Pierce (Pres)
Priscilla Iden (Dir-Bus Dev)

Kitchell Development Company   (1)
1707 E Highland Ave Ste 100, Phoenix, AZ 85016-4658   (100%)
Tel.: (602) 264-4411
Web Site: http://www.kitchell.com
Sales Range: $10-24.9 Million
Emp.: 12
Real Estate Development
N.A.I.C.S.: 237210
Jeff Allen (Pres)

hardison/downey, inc.   (1)
6150 N 16th St Ste A, Phoenix, AZ 85016
Tel.: (602) 861-0044
Web Site: http://www.hardisondowney.com
Emp.: 30
Heavy Construction Services
N.A.I.C.S.: 236220
Pat Downey (Pres)
Jim Kurtzman (VP-Client Dev)
Jessica Erts (Dir-Fin)
Conrad Muhleman (Dir-Ops)

KITCHEN FRESH FOODS INC.
1375 Gruber Rd, Green Bay, WI 54313
Tel.: (920) 434-8874
Web Site: http://www.kffoods.com
Rev.: $13,000,000
Emp.: 150
Perishable Prepared Food Mfr
N.A.I.C.S.: 311991
Steven Neerdaels (Sec & VP)
Timothy Neerdaels (Pres & Treas)
Greg Hill (Mgr-Whole Sale)

KITCHEN INVESTMENT GROUP
8413 Excelsior Dr Ste 160, Madison, WI 53717-1970
Tel.: (608) 833-9633   MN
Web Site: http://www.countrykitchenrestaurants.com
Year Founded: 1977
Sales Range: $75-99.9 Million
Emp.: 80
Holding Company
N.A.I.C.S.: 533110
Dennis LaVenture (Exec VP-Ops)

Subsidiaries:

Country Kitchen International, Inc.   (1)
801 Deming Way, Madison, WI 53717-1918   (100%)
Tel.: (608) 833-9633
Web Site: http://www.countrykitchenrestaurants.com
Sales Range: $10-24.9 Million
Emp.: 25
Country Kitchen Restaurant & Franchiser
N.A.I.C.S.: 722310
Charles Myers (Pres & CEO)
Chris McGrath (VP-Mktg)

KITCHEN KABOODLE II INC.
2344 NW 21st Ave, Portland, OR 97209
Tel.: (503) 243-5043
Web Site: http://www.kitchenkaboodle.com
Sales Range: $10-24.9 Million
Emp.: 60
Furniture Retailer

N.A.I.C.S.: 449110
Lynn Becraft (Pres)
Jerome Faulkner (Controller)
John Stuhr (Mgr-Warehouse)

KITCHEN KOMPACT, INC.
911 E 11th St, Jeffersonville, IN 47131
Tel.: (812) 282-6681   KY
Web Site: http://www.kitchenkompact.com
Year Founded: 1937
Sales Range: $125-149.9 Million
Emp.: 275
Kitchen Cabinet Mfr
N.A.I.C.S.: 337110
Dwight Gahm (Founder)

KITCHEN SUPPLIERS INCORPORATED
6680 Whitmore Lake Rd, Brighton, MI 48116-8213
Tel.: (810) 220-8730   MI
Web Site: http://www.ksikitchens.com
Year Founded: 1971
Sales Range: $25-49.9 Million
Emp.: 171
Designers of Kitchens & Bathrooms
N.A.I.C.S.: 337110
Dan Romback (Pres)

KITCHEN-QUIP, INC.
405 E Marion St, Waterloo, IN 46793
Tel.: (260) 837-8311
Web Site: http://www.kqcasting.com
Year Founded: 1946
Sales Range: $10-24.9 Million
Emp.: 20
Aluminum & Zinc Die-Casting Services
N.A.I.C.S.: 331523
Steve Sparling (Pres)
Jeffrey D. Musick (VP)

KITCHNER & PIERRO COMPANY, INC.
5550 26th St W Ste 7, Bradenton, FL 34207-3514
Tel.: (941) 753-3053
Web Site: http://www.kitchnerandpierro.com
Year Founded: 1975
Sales Range: $1-9.9 Million
Employee Benefits & Executive Financial Services
N.A.I.C.S.: 561499
A.H. Skip Kitchner (Partner)
Richard M. Pierro (Pres & Partner)
Josh Kitchner (VP)

KITSAP TOWING
5901 NE Minder Rd, Poulsbo, WA 98370-5804
Tel.: (206) 842-6232
Web Site: http://www.kitsaptowing.com
Motor Vehicle Towing
N.A.I.C.S.: 488410
Deanie Madler (Pres)

Subsidiaries:

Kitsap Public Services, Inc.   (1)
130 Tweed Ln 2, Bremerton, WA 98312
Tel.: (360) 479-7500
Web Site: http://www.chicotowing.com
Motor Vehicle Towing
N.A.I.C.S.: 488410
Gary Hlebechuck (VP)

KITSON & PARTNERS, LLC
4500 PGA Blvd Ste 400, Palm Beach Gardens, FL 33418
Tel.: (561) 624-4000
Web Site: http://www.kitsonpartners.com
Year Founded: 2002
Sales Range: $1-9.9 Million

Emp.: 50
Real Estate Development
N.A.I.C.S.: 237210
Sidney W. Kitson (Chm & CEO)
Richard Brockway (Co-Founder & Vice Chm)
Charles Desanti (Partner-New Bus Mgmt & Dev)
Thomas Hoban (Pres, Partner & Chief Investment Officer)
Al Dougherty (COO-Communities)
Glenn Geiger (Gen Counsel & Sr VP)
Patrice Bishop (Exec VP-HR & Risk Mgmt)
Rick Severance (Pres-Babcock Ranch)

Subsidiaries:

Kitson & Partners Clubs   (1)
4500 PGA Blvd Ste 400, Palm Beach Gardens, FL 33418
Tel.: (561) 624-4000
Web Site: http://www.kitsonpartners.com
Emp.: 40
Golf Courses & Country Clubs Management
N.A.I.C.S.: 531312
Rich Hohman (Pres)

Kitson & Partners Commercial   (1)
4500 PGA Blvd Ste 400, Palm Beach Gardens, FL 33418
Tel.: (561) 624-4000
Web Site: http://www.kitsonpartners.com
Commercial Development
N.A.I.C.S.: 237210

Kitson & Partners Communities   (1)
4500 PGA Blvd Ste 400, Palm Beach Gardens, FL 33418
Tel.: (561) 624-4000
Residential Development
N.A.I.C.S.: 237210

KITTLE'S HOME FURNISHINGS CENTER INC.
8600 Allisonville Rd, Indianapolis, IN 46250-1533
Tel.: (317) 849-5300   IN
Web Site: http://www.kittles.com
Year Founded: 1949
Sales Range: $10-24.9 Million
Emp.: 640
Furniture Retailer
N.A.I.C.S.: 449110
Jim Kittles (Chm)
Eric Easter (Pres)

KITTRICH CORPORATION
1585 W Mission Blvd, Pomona, CA 91766
Tel.: (714) 736-1000
Web Site: http://www.kittrich.com
Year Founded: 1978
Sales Range: $25-49.9 Million
Emp.: 200
Housewares, Yard Goods, Stationery & Writing Instruments, Window Fashions & Organic Bath Products Mfr & Distr
N.A.I.C.S.: 423220
Robert Friedland (Pres)
Marissa De Las Alas (Mgr-Internal Control)
Clara Jurdi (Mgr-Sls)
Jan Meere (Mgr-Sls)
Lazara Morales (Mgr-Ops)
Gary Scherlag (Mgr-Sls)
Edgar Carrasco (Product Mgr)

Subsidiaries:

Kittrich LLC   (1)
5070 Phillip Lee Dr, Atlanta, GA 30336
Tel.: (404) 691-9500
Web Site: http://www.vantagekittrich.com
Sales Range: $75-99.9 Million
Emp.: 50
Mfr of PVC Coated Polyester Substrates Used for Non-Slip Rug Underlay Products
N.A.I.C.S.: 326199

Robert Friedman *(Pres-California)*

KITWARE, INC.
28 Corporate Dr, Clifton Park, NY 12065
Tel.: (518) 371-3971 — NY
Web Site: http://www.kitware.com
Year Founded: 1998
Sales Range: $1-9.9 Million
Emp.: 115
Software Developer
N.A.I.C.S.: 513210
Bob Ahl *(Controller)*
Lisa Sobierajski Avila *(CEO)*
Bill Hoffman *(Chm, CTO & VP)*
Charles Law *(Founder, VP-Strategic Growth & Engr)*
Ken Martin *(Co-Founder)*
Will Schroeder *(Co-Founder)*
Stephen Aylward *(Sr Dir-Medical Res & Ops)*
Berk Geveci *(Sr Dir-Scientific Computing)*
Anthony Hoogs *(Sr Dir-Computer Vision)*
Jeffrey Baumes *(Asst Dir-Scientific Computing)*
Keith Fieldhouse *(Asst Dir-Computer Vision)*
Brad Davis *(Asst Dir-Bus Dev)*
Claudine Hagen *(CFO)*

KITZ & PFEIL INC.
427 N Main St, Oshkosh, WI 54901
Tel.: (920) 236-3340
Web Site: http://www.kitzandpfeil.com
Sales Range: $10-24.9 Million
Emp.: 150
Hardware Stores
N.A.I.C.S.: 444140
Jim Stapel *(Pres)*
Jeni Faust *(Mgr-Acctg & Travel Div)*

KITZMANS LTD.
1616 Windsor Rd, Loves Park, IL 61111-4252
Tel.: (815) 965-6865
Year Founded: 1979
Sales Range: $10-24.9 Million
Emp.: 20
Lumber & Building Material Whslr
N.A.I.C.S.: 444110
Richard A. Kitzman *(Pres)*
Scott Kitzman *(Principal)*

KIWIBOX.COM, INC.
330 W 38th St Ste 1602, New York, NY 10018
Tel.: (347) 836-4727 — DE
Web Site: https://www.kiwibox.com
KIWB—(OTCBB)
Sales Range: Less than $1 Million
Emp.: 3
Online Social Networking Services
N.A.I.C.S.: 516210
Andre S. Scholz *(Pres & CEO)*
Joseph J. Tomasek *(Gen Counsel)*

KIYONNA CLOTHING, INC.
1315 N Brasher St, Anaheim, CA 92807
Tel.: (714) 956-5588
Web Site: http://www.kiyonna.com
Year Founded: 1996
Sales Range: $10-24.9 Million
Emp.: 12
Plus Size Women's Clothing
N.A.I.C.S.: 315250
Kim Khanbeigi *(Founder & Pres)*

KIZAN INTERNATIONAL INC.
100 W Hill Dr, Brisbane, CA 94005
Tel.: (415) 468-7360 — CA
Web Site: http://www.louisraphael.com
Year Founded: 1972
Sales Range: $10-24.9 Million
Emp.: 120
Mens & Boys Clothing
N.A.I.C.S.: 424350
Bill S. Kim *(Pres)*
Kathy Lou *(CFO)*

KIZAN TECHNOLOGIES
1831 Williamson Ct, Louisville, KY 40223
Tel.: (502) 327-0333
Web Site: http://www.kizan.com
Year Founded: 1991
Technology Consulting Services
N.A.I.C.S.: 541512
Shelli Calhoun *(Partner & Acct Exec)*
Debbie Huff *(Office Mgr)*
Denise Poe *(Mgr-Louisville)*
Robert Steele *(VP-Consulting Svcs)*
Roger Kobel *(CEO)*
Nathan Fornwalt *(VP-Intellectual Property)*
Jackie Roberts *(CFO)*
Mike Spence *(VP-Relationship Svcs)*
Michelle Carson *(VP-Project Svcs)*

KJ TECHNOLOGY CONSULTING, INC.
247 W 36th St 5th F, New York, NY 10018
Tel.: (646) 556-6500
Web Site: http://www.kjtechnology.com
Sales Range: $1-9.9 Million
Emp.: 10
Proactive Software Consulting Services
N.A.I.C.S.: 541512
Kenneth Hackel *(Pres)*

KJDE CORP.
5894 E Molloy Rd, Syracuse, NY 13211
Tel.: (315) 454-5535
Web Site: http://www.kjelectric.com
Rev.: $25,000,000
Emp.: 200
Electric Motors, Drives, Controls & Power Transmission Products Distr
N.A.I.C.S.: 423610
Ben Nordmark *(VP-Engrg)*
Richard Maestri *(CFO)*
Jeff Lawrence *(VP-Sls)*
Jessica Durc *(Mgr-Mktg)*

KJELLSTROM & LEE, INC.
1607 Ownby Ln, Richmond, VA 23220
Tel.: (804) 288-0082 — VA
Web Site: http://www.kjellstromandlee.com
Year Founded: 1961
General Contractor; Pre-construction, Construction & Construction Management
N.A.I.C.S.: 236210
Peter S. Alcorn *(Pres & Owner)*

KJT GROUP, INC.
Six E St, Honeoye Falls, NY 14472
Tel.: (888) 623-8050
Web Site: http://www.kjtgroup.com
Year Founded: 2007
Sales Range: $1-9.9 Million
Emp.: 32
Research & Consulting Services
N.A.I.C.S.: 541715
Lynn Clement *(Chief Res Officer)*
Kenneth J. Tomaszewski *(Founder & Chm)*
Thomas Richardson *(Sr VP-Consulting)*
David A. Luery *(Mng Dir-Global Res)*
Kimberly DeYoung *(CFO)*
Danielle Zammit *(VP-Global Access)*
Alex Castello *(Mgr-Res)*
Amy Allen *(VP)*
Chris Claeys *(Dir-Analytics)*
Craig Radley *(Mgr-Res)*
Dan Wasserman *(Mgr-Bus Ops)*
Jessica Spilman *(Dir-Res)*
Johan Mohd Sani *(Mgr-Res)*
Josh Butler *(VP-Ops)*
Jim Bonham *(Dir-Sls)*
Troy Allen *(Mgr-Mktg)*
Scott Kirklin *(Dir-Qualitative Res)*
Michaela Gascon *(CEO)*
Heidi Wirth *(Mktg Dir)*
Andrea Stoltz *(VP-Res)*

KK BOLD
505 E Main Ave Ste 250 PO Box 693, Bismarck, ND 58502-4412
Tel.: (701) 255-3067 — ND
Web Site: http://www.kkbold.com
Year Founded: 1969
Sales Range: $10-24.9 Million
Emp.: 29
Advetising Agency
N.A.I.C.S.: 541810
LaRoy Kingsley *(Pres)*
Wayne Kranzler *(CEO)*
Jackie Hawkinson *(Mgr-Office)*
Tamara Ubl *(Art Dir)*
Marci Goldalde *(Dir-Media)*
Darla Miller *(Acct Mgr)*
Courtenay Crane *(Copywriter)*
Janine Johnson *(Production Artist)*
Candace Christopherson *(Acct Exec)*
Clay Hove *(Dir-Creative)*
Stephanie Schoenrock *(VP)*
Jason Matthews *(Dir-PR)*
Mark Gray *(Editor & Producer-Audio/Visual)*
Ted Hanson *(Dir-Bus Rels)*
Nikki Sims *(Mgr-Production)*
Kalvin Kingsley *(Dir-Ops)*
Alison Moser *(Acct Exec)*

KKR PRIVATE EQUITY CONGLOMERATE LLC
30 Hudson Yards, New York, NY 10001
Tel.: (212) 750-8300 — DE
Web Site: https://www.kkrpec.com
Year Founded: 2022
Rev.: $4,148,000
Assets: $746,536,000
Liabilities: $78,500,000
Net Worth: $668,036,000
Earnings: $9,793,000
Fiscal Year-end: 12/31/23
Investment Management Service
N.A.I.C.S.: 523999

KKW TRUCKING, INC.
3100 E Pomona Blvd, Pomona, CA 91768
Tel.: (909) 869-1200
Web Site: http://www.kkwtrucks.com
Year Founded: 1962
Rev.: $35,000,000
Emp.: 300
Provider of Trucking Services
N.A.I.C.S.: 484121
Dennis W. Firestone *(Pres & CEO)*
Steve Benninghoff *(VP)*
Pete Carlson *(Dir-Sls & Mktg)*

KL OUTDOOR LLC
1790 Sun Dolphin Rd, Muskegon, MI 49444
Tel.: (231) 733-2725
Web Site: http://www.kloutdoor.com
Year Founded: 1982
Outdoor Lifestyle/Recreational & Outdoor Events Products Mfr & Designer
N.A.I.C.S.: 713990
Shelly Trombley *(Acct Mgr)*

Subsidiaries:

GSC Technologies Inc. (1)

160 Vanier Street, Saint-Jean-sur-Richelieu, J3B 3R4, QC, Canada
Tel.: (450) 357-9745
Web Site: http://www.gsctechnology.com
Plastics Materials & Basic Forms & Shapes Merchant Whslr
N.A.I.C.S.: 424610

KLABEN CHRYSLER JEEP DODGE RAM
1106 W Main St, Kent, OH 44240
Tel.: (330) 673-2122
Web Site: http://www.klabenchryslerjeepdodge.com
Sales Range: $10-24.9 Million
Emp.: 75
New Car Dealers
N.A.I.C.S.: 441110
Richard Klaben *(Pres)*
Steve Stephens *(Gen Mgr)*
Tracy Tucci *(Dir-Adv)*
Thomas Wysocki *(Controller)*

KLABZUBA OIL & GAS
100 Lexington St Ste 50, Fort Worth, TX 76102
Tel.: (817) 336-5757
Web Site: http://www.klabzuba.com
Rev.: $16,455,948
Emp.: 18
Crude Petroleum Production
N.A.I.C.S.: 211120
Robert W. Park *(Chm & CEO)*

KLAFF REALTY, L.P.
35 E Wacker Dr Ste 2900, Chicago, IL 60601
Tel.: (312) 360-1234
Web Site: http://www.klaffrealty.com
Year Founded: 1995
Sales Range: $10-24.9 Million
Emp.: 25
Real Estate Investment Firm
N.A.I.C.S.: 525990
Hersch Klaff *(Mng Dir)*
Ryan Levy *(VP)*

KLAFF'S, INC.
28 Washington St, Norwalk, CT 06854-2705
Tel.: (203) 866-1603 — CT
Web Site: http://www.klaffs.com
Year Founded: 1921
Sales Range: $75-99.9 Million
Emp.: 150
Miscellaneous Homefurnishings Stores
N.A.I.C.S.: 449129
Mollie K. Passero *(Pres)*
Joseph Klaff Passero *(Chm & COO)*
John Petito *(CFO)*
Debby Katz *(Treas)*
Lorenzo Muratore *(CFO)*

KLAFTERS INC.
216 N Beaver St, New Castle, PA 16101
Tel.: (724) 658-6561
Web Site: http://www.cigarexpress.com
Sales Range: $10-24.9 Million
Emp.: 22
Cigars & Related Products Mfr
N.A.I.C.S.: 424940
Lee Silverman *(Pres)*
Randy Silverman *(VP)*

KLASS INGREDIENTS INC.
3885 N Buffalo St, Orchard Park, NY 14127-1839
Tel.: (716) 662-6665 — NY
Web Site: http://www.klassingredients.com
Year Founded: 1984
Sales Range: $10-24.9 Million
Emp.: 20

KLASS INGREDIENTS INC.

Klass Ingredients Inc.—(Continued)
Bond Brokers
N.A.I.C.S.: 424410
Patrick Backman (Owner & Pres)
Kelly Wimmer (Mgr-Customer & Principal Svc)

KLASSEN CORPORATION
2021 Westwind Dr, Bakersfield, CA 93301
Tel.: (661) 324-3000   CA
Web Site:
   http://www.klassencorp.com
Year Founded: 1977
Sales Range: $50-74.9 Million
Emp.: 63
Nonresidential Construction
N.A.I.C.S.: 236220
Jerry D. Klassen (Pres & CEO)
Mark Delmarter (VP)
Robert A. Klassen (Principal)
L. Phil Klassen (Principal)
Ed Childres (VP)

KLAUBER BROTHERS INC.
980 Avenue of the Americas, New York, NY 10018
Tel.: (212) 686-2531
Web Site:
   http://www.klauberlace.com
Sales Range: $10-24.9 Million
Emp.: 40
Lace, Knit
N.A.I.C.S.: 313240
Mark Klauber (Pres)
Andy Larivee (Mgr-Production)
Betty Nicolson (Mgr-AR)
Jack Silverman (Mgr-Warehouse)
Zulaimy Fenty (Coord-Production)

KLAUER MANUFACTURING COMPANY
1185 Roosevelt St, Dubuque, IA 52001-8335
Tel.: (563) 582-7201   IA
Web Site: http://www.klauer.com
Year Founded: 1870
Sales Range: $25-49.9 Million
Emp.: 250
Mfr of Sheet Metal Building Products
N.A.I.C.S.: 332322
William R. Klauer (Pres)
Michael Igo (Gen Mgr)
Robert E. Klauer (VP)
James F. Klauer (VP)

KLC HOLDINGS, LTD.
2712 S 16th Ave, Yakima, WA 98903
Tel.: (509) 248-4770   WA
Web Site: http://www.kwiklok.com
Rev.: $18,200,000
Emp.: 100
Holding Company; Plastic Closures Mfr
N.A.I.C.S.: 551112
Jerre Paxton (Pres)
Don Carrell (CEO)
John K. Rothenbueler (Chm)

Subsidiaries:

Kwik Lok (Ireland) Ltd   (1)
Bay 72 Shannon Industrial Estate, Shannon Airport Co, Shannon, Ireland
Tel.: (353) 6 147 1193
Web Site: http://www.kwiklok.ie
Emp.: 30
Plastic Bag Closure & Label Mfr
N.A.I.C.S.: 326199
Jim Coonerty (Accountant-Fin)

Kwik Lok Australia Pty Ltd   (1)
2 Brixton Rd, Cheltenham, 3192, VIC, Australia
Tel.: (61) 3 85819700
Plastic Bag Closure & Label Mfr
N.A.I.C.S.: 322220
Ray Crick (Mgr-Shipping)

Kwik Lok Corporation   (1)
2712 S 16th Ave, Yakima, WA 98903
Tel.: (509) 248-4770
Web Site: http://www.kwiklok.com
Rev.: $17,900,000
Closures, Plastics
N.A.I.C.S.: 326199
Jeff Buege (CFO)
Ron L. Cardey (VP-Sls & Mktg)
Xiuming Bai (Sls Dir-China)

Plant (Domestic):

Kwik Lok Corp. - New Haven   (2)
1222 Ryan Rd, New Haven, IN 46774
Tel.: (260) 493-4429
Web Site: http://www.kwiklok.com
Rev.: $3,100,000
Emp.: 55
Closures, Plastics
N.A.I.C.S.: 326199
Nathan Killworth (Plant Mgr)

Kwik Lok Japan Ltd.   (1)
4-12 Motogo 2-Chome, Saitama, Kawaguchi, 332 0011, Japan
Tel.: (81) 48 224 1804
Web Site: http://www.kwiklok.co.jp
Plastic Bag Closure & Label Mfr
N.A.I.C.S.: 322220

Kwik Lok Ltd.   (1)
176 Sheldon Drive, Cambridge, N1R 7K1, ON, Canada
Tel.: (519) 623-5140
Web Site: http://www.kwiklok.com
Emp.: 330
Plastic Bag Closure & Label Mfr
N.A.I.C.S.: 322220

KLEANGAS ENERGY TECHNOLOGIES, INC.
3001 N Rocky Point Rd Ste 200, Tampa, FL 33771
Tel.: (888) 720-0806   DE
Web Site: http://www.kleangas.com
Gasoline Production Systems Mfr
N.A.I.C.S.: 333132
Bo Linton (Pres, CEO, CFO, Treas & Sec)

KLEAR-VU CORPORATION
600 Airport Rd, Fall River, MA 02723
Tel.: (508) 674-5723
Web Site: http://www.klearvu.com
Rev.: $14,500,000
Emp.: 257
Household Furnishings
N.A.I.C.S.: 314120
Bob Cooper (Pres)

KLEBERG & COMPANY BANKERS, INC.
100 E Kleberg Ave, Kingsville, TX 78363
Tel.: (361) 592-8501   TX
Web Site:
   http://www.klebergbank.com
Year Founded: 1979
Bank Holding Company
N.A.I.C.S.: 551111
Gabriel Guerra (Pres & CEO)

Subsidiaries:

Kleberg Bank, N.A.   (1)
100 E Kleberg Ave, Kingsville, TX 78363
Tel.: (361) 592-8501
Web Site: http://www.klebergbank.com
Sales Range: $10-24.9 Million
Emp.: 85
National Commercial Banks
N.A.I.C.S.: 522110
Brad Womack (Controller)
Gabriel Guerra (Pres & CEO)

KLEEN-TECH BUILDING SERVICES
7100 Broadway Ste 6-L, Denver, CO 80221
Tel.: (303) 428-1873   CO
Web Site: http://www.k-tservices.com
Year Founded: 1993
Sales Range: $10-24.9 Million
Emp.: 700
Janitorial Service, Contract Basis
N.A.I.C.S.: 561720
Kathy J. Hughes (CEO)

KLEEN-TEX INDUSTRIES, INC.
101 N Greenwood St Ste C, Lagrange, GA 30240
Tel.: (706) 882-0111
Web Site: http://www.kleen-tex.com
Year Founded: 1967
Sales Range: $75-99.9 Million
Emp.: 350
Textiles & Rubber Products Mfr
N.A.I.C.S.: 314110
Bruce K. Howard (Pres)
Philip Still (Mgr-Intl Project Dev)

Subsidiaries:

Kleen-Tex Industries GmbH   (1)
Munchner Strasse 21, 6330, Kufstein, Austria   (100%)
Tel.: (43) 537261380
Web Site: http://www.kleen-tex.at
Sales Range: $1-9.9 Million
Emp.: 75
Mfr of Textiles & Rubber Products
N.A.I.C.S.: 314110

Kleen-Tex Industries Ltd.   (1)
Causeway Mill Express Trading Estate Stone Hill Rd, Farnworth, Bolton, BL4 9TP, United Kingdom   (100%)
Tel.: (44) 204863000
Web Site: http://www.kleentex.co.uk
Sales Range: $1-9.9 Million
Emp.: 12
Mfr of Textiles & Rubber Products
N.A.I.C.S.: 314110

Kleen-Tex Japan, Inc.   (1)
1 11 Takasukadai 2 Chome Nishi Ku, Kobe, Hyogo, 651 2271, Japan
Tel.: (81) 789913300
Web Site: http://www.kleen-tex-japan.co.jp
Sales Range: $10-24.9 Million
Emp.: 100
Mfr of Textiles & Rubber Products
N.A.I.C.S.: 314110
Akira Sukuhara (Pres)

Kleen-Tex Polska, Sp. Z.o.o.   (1)
ul Fabryczna 5/12, 26-130, Suchedniow, Poland
Tel.: (48) 412672500
Web Site: http://www.kleen-tex.pl
Sales Range: $10-24.9 Million
Emp.: 100
Mfr of Textiles & Rubber Products
N.A.I.C.S.: 314110
Peter Stehr (Dir-Mgmt Bd)

Kleen-Tex South Africa (Pty) Ltd.   (1)
14-24 Cypress Drive Glen Anil, Durban, 4051, KZN, South Africa   (75%)
Tel.: (27) 31 569 5190
Web Site: http://www.kleen-tex.co.za
Sales Range: $1-9.9 Million
Emp.: 30
Mfr of Textile & Rubber Products
N.A.I.C.S.: 325212
John Cherry (Mgr-Ops)

Kleen-Tex Thailand Co. Ltd.   (1)
789/76 Moo1 Pinthong Industrial Estate Nongkoh-Laemchabang Rd, Nongkham Sriracha, Chon Buri, 20230, Thailand
Tel.: (66) 3 829 6891
Web Site: http://www.kleen-tex.co.th
Rubber Products Mfr
N.A.I.C.S.: 326299
Akira Fukuhara (Chm)
Saisei Oyama (Mng Dir)
Praphol Jomsiriwattana (Dir-Ops)
Panurat Tangbuncheardsuk (Mgr-Mktg)
Saichol Chaosuan (Dir-Fin)

Kleen-Tex do Brazil   (1)
Av Presidente Juscelino, 165 Diadema, Sao Paulo, CEP 09950 370, Brazil   (100%)
Tel.: (55) 1140751050
Web Site: http://www.kleen-tex.com.br
Sales Range: Less than $1 Million
Emp.: 10
Mfr of Textiles & Rubber Products
N.A.I.C.S.: 314110

KLEENMARK SERVICES CORP.
1210 Ann St, Madison, WI 53713
Tel.: (608) 258-3121   WI
Web Site: http://www.kleenmark.com
Year Founded: 1961
Sales Range: $10-24.9 Million
Emp.: 625
Commercial Cleaning Services & Cleaning Supplies
N.A.I.C.S.: 561720
Scott Stevenson (Pres & CEO)
Kent Sheppard (Mgr-Warehouse)
Tina Sirtoff (Mgr-Acct)
Tim Waldsmith (COO)
Trina Keller (VP-Fin)

KLEIDON & ASSOCIATES
320 Springside Dr, Akron, OH 44333
Tel.: (330) 666-5984
Web Site: http://www.kleidon.com
Year Founded: 1975
Sales Range: Less than $1 Million
Emp.: 8
Advetising Agency
N.A.I.C.S.: 541810
Tim Klinger (Dir-Creative)
Rose A.O. Kleidon (Exec VP)
Peggy Schobert (Dir-Ops & Media Rels)
Dennis A. Kleidon (Pres & CEO)
Kurt Kleidon (VP & Gen Mgr)
Diana Lueptow (Dir-Strategic Comm)
Rosella Groves (Dir-Art)

KLEIN & HEUCHAN, INC.
1744 N Belcher Rd Ste 200, Clearwater, FL 33765
Tel.: (727) 441-1951
Web Site:
   http://www.kleinandheuchan.com
Year Founded: 1983
Sales Range: $75-99.9 Million
Emp.: 8
Real Estate Services
N.A.I.C.S.: 531210
Mark S. Klein (Owner)
Steven Klein (VP)

KLEIN BROS. HOLDINGS, LTD.
1515 S Fresno Ave, Stockton, CA 95206-1179
Tel.: (209) 942-1020   CA
Year Founded: 1977
Sales Range: $10-24.9 Million
Emp.: 75
Holding Company; Warehousing & Transportation Services; Contract Packaging Services; Packaged Nuts, Seeds & Fruit Snacks Distr
N.A.I.C.S.: 551112
Jim Olson (Gen Mgr)

Subsidiaries:

Klein Bros. - Snack & Packaged Nut Divison   (1)
1515 S Fresno Ave, Stockton, CA 95206-1179
Tel.: (209) 942-1020
Web Site: http://www.jumbosnacks.net
Packaged Nut Seed & Fruit Snack Distr
N.A.I.C.S.: 424490
Mark K. Lloret (Mgr-Natl Sls)
Sean Lloret (Reg Mgr-Sls)

KLEIN FOODS INC.
11455 Old Redwood Hwy, Healdsburg, CA 95448-9523
Tel.: (707) 433-6511   CA
Web Site:
   http://www.rodneystrong.com
Year Founded: 1989
Sales Range: $10-24.9 Million
Emp.: 120
Vineyard
N.A.I.C.S.: 111332
Thomas B. Klein (Owner)

KLEIN STEEL SERVICE INC.
105 Vangaurd Pkwy, Rochester, NY 14606
Tel.: (585) 328-4000
Web Site: http://www.kleinsteel.com
Year Founded: 1970
Sales Range: $25-49.9 Million
Emp.: 200
Provider of Metals Services
N.A.I.C.S.: 423510
Joe Klein *(Chm & CEO)*
Pauline Malone *(VP-Procurement)*
Pat DiLaura *(Chief Talent Officer)*
Mike Young *(Pres & COO)*

Subsidiaries:

Klein Steel Direct Rochester (1)
105 McLaughlin Rd, Rochester, NY 14615
Tel.: (585) 458-8100
Web Site: http://www.kleinsteeldirect.com
Sales Range: $10-24.9 Million
Emp.: 100
Metal Services
N.A.I.C.S.: 423510

Klein Steel of Syracuse (1)
1 General Motors Dr Ste 14, Syracuse, NY 13206
Tel.: (315) 454-3102
Web Site: http://www.kliensteel.com
Sales Range: $25-49.9 Million
Emp.: 4
Provider of Metals Services
N.A.I.C.S.: 423510
Jon Kleinman *(Gen Mgr)*

Klein Steel of Western New York (1)
1050 Military Rd, Buffalo, NY 14217
Tel.: (716) 826-6060
Web Site: http://www.kleinsteel.com
Rev.: $3,000,000
Emp.: 50
Steel
N.A.I.C.S.: 423510

KLEIN TOOLS INC.
450 Bond St, Lincolnshire, IL 60069-0350
Tel.: (847) 821-5500 DE
Web Site: http://www.kleintools.com
Year Founded: 1857
Sales Range: $150-199.9 Million
Emp.: 1,100
Hand Tools & Occupational Protective Equipment Mfr
N.A.I.C.S.: 332216
Thomas R. Klein *(Chm, Treas & Sec)*
Mark Klein *(Pres-Sls & Mktg)*
Tom Klein Jr. *(Pres-Ops & R&D)*

Subsidiaries:

Civitella & Cia Ltda (1)
R Inacio Borba 749 - Granja Julieta, Sao Paulo, 04715-020, Brazil
Tel.: (55) 11 5182 9577
Web Site: http://www.civitella.com.br
Sales Range: $10-24.9 Million
Emp.: 30
Telecommunication Equipment & Tool Mfr
N.A.I.C.S.: 334210

Harramientas Tultitlin S.A. (1)
Avenida 1 No 3 Parque Indus Cartagena, 54918, Tultitlan, Mexico **(100%)**
Tel.: (52) 5555606633
Web Site: http://www.turlmax.com
Sales Range: $25-49.9 Million
Emp.: 300
Mfr of Hand Tools & Safety Equipment
N.A.I.C.S.: 332216

Klein Cutlery, LLC (1)
7971 Refinery Rd, Bolivar, NY 14715-9605
Tel.: (585) 928-2500
Web Site: http://www.kleincutlery.com
Sales Range: $10-24.9 Million
Emp.: 55
Scissors & Shears Mfr
N.A.I.C.S.: 332215
Rick Gould *(Mgr-Bus Unit)*

Klein Tools de Mexico S de R.L de C.V. (1)
Av Uno No 3 Parque Industrial Cartagena,
Tultitlan, 54918, Mexico
Tel.: (52) 55 5899 5660
Web Site: http://www.kleintools.com.mx
Hand Tool Mfr
N.A.I.C.S.: 332216

KLEIN'S INC.
2011 Klein Plz Dr, Forest Hill, MD 21050-2600
Tel.: (410) 515-9303 DE
Web Site: http://www.kleinsonline.com
Year Founded: 1992
Sales Range: $100-124.9 Million
Emp.: 1,400
Supermarket Management & Services
N.A.I.C.S.: 445110
Andy Klein *(Owner)*

Subsidiaries:

Kleins SuperMarkets Inc. (1)
2011 Klein's Plaza Dr Ste 2-B, Forest Hill, MD 21050
Tel.: (410) 515-9303
Web Site: http://www.kleinsonline.com
Rev.: $14,838,829
Emp.: 40
Independent Supermarket
N.A.I.C.S.: 445110

KLEIN-DICKERT CO. INC.
1402 Emil St, Madison, WI 53713-2326
Tel.: (608) 258-3310
Web Site: http://www.klein-dickert.com
Sales Range: $10-24.9 Million
Emp.: 100
Paint Contracting
N.A.I.C.S.: 238320
Francis X. Dickert *(CEO)*
Amy Olson *(Controller)*

KLEIN-KAUFMAN CORP.
134 W Hills Rd, Huntington Station, NY 11746
Tel.: (631) 271-8055
Sales Range: $10-24.9 Million
Emp.: 10
Fast-Food Restaurant, Chain
N.A.I.C.S.: 722513
Jonah Kaufman *(Owner)*

KLEINE EQUIPMENT
1910 Knox Rd 560 E, Galesburg, IL 61401
Tel.: (309) 342-3188
Web Site: http://www.kleine-eq.com
Sales Range: $10-24.9 Million
Emp.: 35
Agricultural Machinery & Equipment
N.A.I.C.S.: 423820
Jay Haynes *(Pres)*
Lindsey Hankes *(Mgr-Mktg)*
John Hawkins *(Mgr-Remarketing)*
Bill Sullivan *(Owner & CEO)*
Gary Rogers *(Mgr-HR)*
Jason Denham *(Mgr-Corp Svc)*
Tim Tillman *(Mgr-IT)*

KLEINER PERKINS CAUFIELD & BYERS
2750 Sand Hill Rd, Menlo Park, CA 94025
Tel.: (650) 233-2750
Web Site: http://www.kpcb.com
Year Founded: 1972
Sales Range: $25-49.9 Million
Emp.: 60
Venture Capital Firm
N.A.I.C.S.: 523999
Aileen Lee *(Partner)*
K. R. Sridhar *(Partner-Strategic Limited)*
Scott Ryles *(COO)*
Paul Vronsky *(Gen Counsel)*
Susan Biglieri *(CFO)*
Noah Knauf *(Gen Partner-Digital Growth Practice)*
Mamoon Hamid *(Gen Partner)*
Theodore E. Schlein *(Gen Partner)*
Beth C. Seidenberg *(Partner)*
Wen Hsieh *(Gen Partner)*
Albert Arnold Gore Jr. *(Sr Partner)*
Brook H. Byers *(Mng Partner)*
Brook H. Byers *(Mng Partner)*

KLEINKNECHT ELECTRIC CO. INC.
19 W 44th St Ste 500, New York, NY 10036
Tel.: (212) 728-1800
Web Site: http://www.kecny.com
Year Founded: 1916
Sales Range: $25-49.9 Million
Emp.: 20
General Electrical Contractor
N.A.I.C.S.: 238210
Mark Kleinknecht *(Pres)*
Joe Delarosa *(Acct Exec)*

KLEINPARTNERS CAPITAL CORP.
400 Continental Blvd Ste 600, El Segundo, CA 90245
Tel.: (310) 426-2055
Web Site: http://www.kleinpartners.com
Private Investment Firm
N.A.I.C.S.: 523999
Norman Gidney *(Mng Partner)*
Greg M. Klein *(Founder & Mng Partner)*
Edward McMahon *(Mng Partner)*

Subsidiaries:

Spire Payments Espana (1)
Calle de la Plaza 13, 28043, Madrid, Spain
Tel.: (34) 917227700
Web Site: http://www.spirepayments.com
Sales Range: $1-9.9 Million
Emp.: 20
Credit & Debit Card Payment Processing Services
N.A.I.C.S.: 522320

Spire Payments Ltd. (1)
Units 3 & 6 Milford Trading Estate, Blakey Road, Salisbury, SP1 2UD, Wiltshire, United Kingdom
Tel.: (44) 1722 332255
Web Site: http://www.spirepayments.com
Sales Range: $25-49.9 Million
Emp.: 20
End-to-End Electronic Payment Solutions, Including Card Payment Systems, Peripherals, Network Products, Ascendent Software & E-Commerce Payment Solutions
N.A.I.C.S.: 541519
Dave Millener *(Mng Dir)*

KLEINPETER DAIRY FARM INC.
14444 Airline Hwy, Baton Rouge, LA 70817
Tel.: (225) 753-2121
Web Site: http://www.kleinpeterdairy.com
Sales Range: $10-24.9 Million
Emp.: 88
Milk Processing
N.A.I.C.S.: 311511
Jeff Kleinpeter *(Pres)*

KLEINSCHMIDT INC.
450 Lk Cook Rd, Deerfield, IL 60015-4919
Tel.: (847) 945-1000 IL
Web Site: http://www.kleinschmidt.com
Year Founded: 1985
Sales Range: $50-74.9 Million
Emp.: 45
Electronic Data Interchange Software Developers
N.A.I.C.S.: 541512
Harry S. Gaples *(Pres)*
Dale Kaplan *(Controller)*

KLETT CONSTRUCTION COMPANY
46046 Red Arrow Hwy, Paw Paw, MI 49079
Tel.: (269) 655-1394
Web Site: http://www.michiganpaving.com
Sales Range: $25-49.9 Million
Emp.: 6
Highway & Street Paving Contractor
N.A.I.C.S.: 237310
Al Lindstrom *(Area Mgr)*

KLEWIN CONSTRUCTION INC.
444 Brickell Ave Ste 900, Miami, FL 33131
Tel.: (561) 683-5400 CT
Web Site: http://www.klewin.com
Year Founded: 1997
Sales Range: $10-24.9 Million
Emp.: 30
Industrial Buildings & Warehouses
N.A.I.C.S.: 236210
Kyle Klewin *(VP)*
Shani Wyant *(Office Mgr)*
Byron Tramonte *(Project Mgr)*

Subsidiaries:

C.R. Building Company (1)
40 Connecticut Ave, Norwich, CT 06360-1502
Tel.: (860) 886-2491
Web Site: http://www.klewin.com
Sales Range: $10-24.9 Million
Industrial Buildings & Warehouses
N.A.I.C.S.: 236210

C.R. Klewin Southeast (1)
444 Brickell Ave Ste 900, Miami, FL 33131
Tel.: (561) 683-5400
Web Site: http://www.klewin.com
Sales Range: $10-24.9 Million
Emp.: 25
Industrial Buildings And Warehouses
N.A.I.C.S.: 236210

KLH CAPITAL L.P.
601 Bayshore Blvd Ste 850, Tampa, FL 33606
Tel.: (813) 222-0160
Web Site: http://www.klhcapital.com
Sales Range: $150-199.9 Million
Emp.: 14
Private Investment Firm
N.A.I.C.S.: 523999
John F. Kirtley *(Co-Founder)*
P. Jeffrey Leck *(Co-Founder)*
William L. Dowden *(Partner)*
James B. Darnell *(Partner)*
Christopher T. Hart *(Partner)*
Kyle P. Madden *(Partner)*

Subsidiaries:

Federal Resources Supply Company (1)
235 G Log Canoe Cir, Stevensville, MD 21666
Tel.: (410) 643-7810
Web Site: http://www.federalresources.com
Sales Range: $10-24.9 Million
Emp.: 130
Military & First Responder Equipment Mfr
N.A.I.C.S.: 423990
Robert M. William *(Mgr-Sls)*

Selinsky Force, LLC (1)
4015 23rd St SW, Canton, OH 44706
Web Site: http://www.selinskyforce.com
Industrial Engineering Services & Construction Contractor
N.A.I.C.S.: 541330
Lori Scott *(CEO)*

KLICK-LEWIS INC.
720 E Main St, Palmyra, PA 17078
Tel.: (717) 838-1353
Web Site: http://www.klicklewis.com

KLICK-LEWIS INC.

Klick-Lewis Inc.—(Continued)
Sales Range: $25-49.9 Million
Emp.: 200
Sales of New & Used Automobiles
N.A.I.C.S.: 441110
Tom Risser (Mng Partner)
Eric King (Mgr-IT)
Warren L. Lewis Jr. (Pres)

KLIGER-WEISS INFOSYSTEMS, INC.
2200 Northern Blvd, Greenvale, NY 11548
Tel.: (516) 621-2400 NY
Web Site: http://www.kwi.com
Year Founded: 1985
Sales Range: $10-24.9 Million
Emp.: 125
Custom Computer Programming Services
N.A.I.C.S.: 541511
Samuel Kliger (Founder & CEO)
Robert Schildkraut (CFO)
Gary Brill (VP-Bus Dev)
Stuart Levine (Pres-Loss Prevention Div)
Peter George (VP-Client Svcs)
Michael Lazard (CFO)
Steven Tillinger (VP-Tech & Infrastructure)

KLIKLOK CORPORATION
5224 Snapfinger Woods Dr, Decatur, GA 30035-4023
Tel.: (770) 981-5200 GA
Web Site: http://www.kliklok.com
Year Founded: 1947
Sales Range: $75-99.9 Million
Emp.: 300
Mfr of Packaging Machinery
N.A.I.C.S.: 333993
Peter E. Black (Pres & CFO)
William L. Crist (Chm & CEO)
T. Ross Long (VP-Sls)
Simon Taylor (Dir-Comml)

Subsidiaries:

Kliklok International (1)
Western Dr, Hengrove Pk Estate, Bristol, BS14 0AY, Whitchurch, United Kingdom (100%)
Tel.: (44) 1275836131
Web Site: http://www.kliklok-woodman-int.com
Sales Range: $10-24.9 Million
Emp.: 70
N.A.I.C.S.: 333993
Nigel Fox (Dir-Bus Dev)

KLIMAN SALES INC.
1245 N 5th St, San Jose, CA 95116
Tel.: (408) 275-1784
Web Site: http://www.klimansales.com
Rev.: $20,000,000
Emp.: 9
Plumbing & Hydronic Heating Supplies
N.A.I.C.S.: 423720
Brad Kliman (Owner)

KLINE HILL PARTNERS LLC
125 Mason St Fl 1, Greenwich, CT 06830
Tel.: (203) 987-6120
Web Site: http://klinehill.com
Privater Equity Firm
N.A.I.C.S.: 523999
Michael Bego (Mng Partner)
Jared Barlow (Partner)
Danielle Buccola (Mgr-Fin & Ops)

KLINE VOLVO INC.
3040 N Hwy 61, Maplewood, MN 55109
Tel.: (651) 481-9600
Web Site: http://www.klinevolvo.com
Rev.: $25,000,000
Emp.: 100
Automobiles, New & Used
N.A.I.C.S.: 441110
Rick Kline (Owner & Pres)
Jan Sholtee (VP)

KLINGBEIL CAPITAL MANAGEMENT
200 California St Ste 300, San Francisco, CA 94111
Tel.: (415) 398-0106 OH
Web Site: http://www.kcmgt.com
Year Founded: 1959
Sales Range: $25-49.9 Million
Emp.: 50
Property Management & Real Estate Services
N.A.I.C.S.: 531210
James D. Klingbeil (Chm & CEO)

KLINGENSTEIN, FIELDS & CO., L.P.
125 Park Ave Ste 1700, New York, NY 10017-5529
Tel.: (212) 492-7000
Web Site: http://www.klingenstein.com
Year Founded: 1989
Financial Investment Activities
N.A.I.C.S.: 523999
Kenneth H. Fields (Co-Exec Chm & Partner)
Andrew Crofton (Mng Dir)
Kenneth D. Pollinger (Co-Chm, CEO & Partner)

KLINGER COMPANIES INCORPORATED
2015 E 7th St, Sioux City, IA 51101
Tel.: (712) 277-3900
Web Site: http://www.klingercompanies.com
Sales Range: $100-124.9 Million
Emp.: 50
Commercial & Office Building Contractors
N.A.I.C.S.: 236220
Robert Desmidt (CFO)
John W. Gleeson (Pres)

KLINGSHIRN WINERY
33050 Weber Rd, Avon Lake, OH 44012
Tel.: (440) 933-6666
Web Site: http://www.klingshirnwine.com
Year Founded: 1935
Sales Range: $10-24.9 Million
Emp.: 6
Vineyard & Wine Mfr
N.A.I.C.S.: 111332
Allan Klingshirn (Mgr-Quality Control & Engrg)

KLINKE BROTHERS ICE CREAM CO.
2450 Scaper Cove, Memphis, TN 38114
Tel.: (901) 743-8250
Rev.: $21,939,312
Emp.: 69
Ice Cream, Bulk
N.A.I.C.S.: 311520
John P. Klinke (Pres)
Russell Klinke (VP)

KLLM TRANSPORT SERVICES, INC.
134 Riverview Dr, Richland, MS 39218
Tel.: (601) 939-2545 DE
Web Site: http://www.kllm.com
Year Founded: 1963
Sales Range: $25-49.9 Million
Emp.: 2,100
Truckload Transportation & Dedicated Logistics Services to North America
N.A.I.C.S.: 484121
James M. Richards (Pres & CEO)
Vince Schott (VP-Maintenance & Mgmt Info Svcs)
Kevin Adams (CFO)
Steve Szado (VP-HR)

KLM BUILDERS INC.
PO Box 526, Richmond, IL 60071
Tel.: (815) 678-4018
Web Site: http://www.klmbuildersinc.com
Year Founded: 1987
Sales Range: $10-24.9 Million
Emp.: 15
Residential Construction
N.A.I.C.S.: 236115
Kim L. Meier (Founder & Pres)

KLM LABORATORIES, INC.
28280 Alta Vista Ave, Valencia, CA 91355
Tel.: (661) 295-2600 CA
Web Site: http://www.klmlabs.com
Year Founded: 1973
Sales Range: $1-9.9 Million
Emp.: 71
Orthopedic Appliances
N.A.I.C.S.: 423450
Kent Marshall (Co-Owner & VP)
Kirk Marshall (Co-Owner & Pres)
Scott Marshall (Co-Owner, Sec & Treas)

KLN ENTERPRISES INC.
800 4th St NW, Perham, MN 56573
Tel.: (218) 346-7000
Sales Range: $25-49.9 Million
Emp.: 300
Potato Chips & Other Potato-Based Snacks
N.A.I.C.S.: 311919
Mike Cooper (CEO)
Kurt Nelson (Gen Mgr)

Subsidiaries:

Barrel O'Fun Snack Foods Co. (1)
400 Lakeside Dr, Perham, MN 56573-1226
Tel.: (218) 346-7000
Web Site: http://www.barrelofunsnacks.com
Sales Range: $50-74.9 Million
Emp.: 800
Mfr of Potato Chips & Snacks
N.A.I.C.S.: 311919
Randy Johnson (VP-Sls)
Ron Deaver (Gen Mgr)

Kenny's Candy Company Inc. (1)
609 Pinewood Ln, Perham, MN 56573
Tel.: (218) 346-2340
Rev.: $10,700,000
Emp.: 150
Licorice Candy
N.A.I.C.S.: 311340
Kenneth Nelson (Owner & Pres)

Tuffys Pet Foods Inc (1)
145 1st Ave N, Perham, MN 56573
Tel.: (218) 346-7500
Web Site: http://www.tuffyspetfoods.com
Sales Range: $10-24.9 Million
Emp.: 150
Dog & Cat Food
N.A.I.C.S.: 311111

KLNB, LLC
8027 Leesburg Pike Ste 300, Vienna, VA 22182-2701
Tel.: (703) 288-4000
Web Site: http://www.klnb.com
Offices of Real Estate Agents & Brokers
N.A.I.C.S.: 531210
Marc Menick (Pres & CEO)
Harry Dematatis (Sr VP-Office Advisory Grp Team-Downtown)
Joe Fleischmann (Principal-Northern Virginia)
Marc A. Menick (Pres)

Subsidiaries:

Edge Commercial Real Estate LLC (1)
6931 Arlington Rd Ste 550, Bethesda, MD 20814-7217
Tel.: (202) 222-0022
Web Site: http://www.edgecre.com
Residential Property Managers
N.A.I.C.S.: 531311
Marc Balamaci (Partner)

KLONDIKE CHEESE COMPANY
W7839 Hwy 81, Monroe, WI 53566
Tel.: (608) 325-3021
Web Site: http://www.klondikecheese.com
Sales Range: $10-24.9 Million
Emp.: 87
Natural Cheese
N.A.I.C.S.: 722410
Ronald A. Buholzer (Pres)
Tammy Fetterolf (Bus Mgr)
Stan Woodworth (Mgr-Natl Sls)
Jon Brunner (Mgr-Production)

KLOTE INTERNATIONAL CORP.
992 Industrial Park Rd, Dandridge, TN 37725
Tel.: (865) 397-1173
Web Site: http://www.kloteinternational.com
Sales Range: $10-24.9 Million
Emp.: 70
Living Room Furniture: Upholstered On Wood Frames
N.A.I.C.S.: 337121
Carl Eric Klote (Pres)

KLSS INC
4027 Colonel Glenn Hwy Ste 300, Beavercreek, OH 45431-1601
Tel.: (937) 879-3483
Web Site: http://www.klssinc.com
Year Founded: 1997
Sales Range: $1-9.9 Million
Emp.: 10
Computer System Design Services
N.A.I.C.S.: 541512
Nicholas T. Borton (Mng Partner)
Minda L. Moore (Mng Partner)

KLUKWAN INC.
425 Sawmill Rd, Haines, AK 99827
Tel.: (907) 766-2211 AK
Web Site: http://www.klukwan.com
Year Founded: 1973
Rev.: $1,599,843
Emp.: 5
Highway & Street Construction
N.A.I.C.S.: 237310
Les Katzeek (Mng Dir)

KLUMB LUMBER COMPANY INC.
1080 River Oaks Dr Ste A 200, Flowood, MS 39232
Tel.: (601) 932-6080 MS
Web Site: http://www.klumblumber.com
Year Founded: 1945
Sales Range: $25-49.9 Million
Emp.: 145
Lumber & Plywood
N.A.I.C.S.: 423310
Randy Hudson (CFO)
Charles E. Klumb Jr. (Pres)

Subsidiaries:

Klumb Lumber Company Inc. - International Division (1)
29000 Highway 98 A-100, Daphne, AL 36526

Tel.: (251) 626-1716
Web Site: http://www.klumblumber.com
Emp.: 4
Lumber Distr
N.A.I.C.S.: 423310
Stewart O'Neill (Mgr)
Johnny Hudson (Mgr)

KLUNK & MILLAN ADVERTISING INC.
9999 Hamilton Blvd, Allentown, PA 18031
Tel.: (610) 973-2400
Web Site: http://www.klunkmillan.com
Year Founded: 1989
Sales Range: $1-9.9 Million
Emp.: 24
Consumer Marketing, Internet, Print & Emerging Media
N.A.I.C.S.: 541830
Jim Klunk (Founder & Pres)

KLUTTS PROPERTY MANAGEMENT, INC.
1433 Emerywood Dr, Charlotte, NC 28210
Tel.: (704) 544-1111
Web Site: http://www.kluttspropertymanagement.com
Year Founded: 1972
Sales Range: $10-24.9 Million
Emp.: 10
Construction Management Services
N.A.I.C.S.: 236115
Barrett Klutts (COO)

KM INTERNATIONAL CORPORATION
320 N Main St, Kenton, TN 38233
Tel.: (731) 749-8700 AL
Year Founded: 1987
Sales Range: $10-24.9 Million
Emp.: 30
Plastics Raw Materials Mfr
N.A.I.C.S.: 424610
Kourosh Kevin Vakili (Pres)

KM INVESTMENT CORPORATION
475 Steamboat Rd, Greenwich, CT 06830-6478
Tel.: (203) 625-9200
Year Founded: 1987
Sales Range: $25-49.9 Million
Emp.: 278
Investment Services
N.A.I.C.S.: 423520
Fritz Kundrun (CEO)
Hans Mende (Pres)

Subsidiaries:

AMCI International Inc. (1)
475 Steamboat Rd, Greenwich, CT 06830-6478
Tel.: (203) 625-9200
Web Site: http://www.amci-capital.net
Sales Range: $10-24.9 Million
Emp.: 8
Coal Mining Services
N.A.I.C.S.: 423520

American Metals Coal Intrnational (1)
475 Steamboat Rd, Greenwich, CT 06830-6478
Tel.: (203) 625-9200
Rev.: $1,500,000
Emp.: 6
Coal, Ores & Other Minerals Distr
N.A.I.C.S.: 423520
John Albarran (Gen Mgr)

KM KELLY, INC.
106 Huntoon Memorial Hwy, Rochdale, MA 01542
Tel.: (508) 892-8117
Web Site: http://www.kmkellyinc.com
Year Founded: 2006

Sales Range: $10-24.9 Million
Emp.: 15
Electrical Contracting Services
N.A.I.C.S.: 238210
Kevin Menard (Pres)

KMA SUNBELT TRADING CORP.
3696 Ulmerton Rd, Clearwater, FL 33762
Tel.: (727) 572-7258
Web Site: http://www.shopidc.com
Year Founded: 1987
Sales Range: $10-24.9 Million
Emp.: 80
Jewelry Stores
N.A.I.C.S.: 458310
Keith Leclerc (Pres)

KMBH ADVERTISING
3540 Hidden Forest Ct, Lake Orion, MI 48359
Tel.: (248) 481-9391
Web Site: http://www.kmbhadvertising.com
Year Founded: 2003
Sales Range: $10-24.9 Million
Emp.: 1
Media Buying Services
N.A.I.C.S.: 541830
Stephanie Beer Howcroft (Owner)

KMC CONTROLS
19476 Industrial Dr, New Paris, IN 46553
Tel.: (574) 831-5250
Web Site: http://www.kmc-controls.com
Rev.: $21,942,652
Emp.: 200
Control Equipment, Electric
N.A.I.C.S.: 335314
Ben Dorsey (Dir-Mktg)
Bob Rich (Dir-HR)
Jan Baker (Controller)
Mitch Kehler (Pres & CEO)
Ken Kreuter (Founder)

KMG ENTERPRISES INC.
17619 W 66th Ter, Shawnee Mission, KS 66217
Tel.: (913) 962-1816
Sales Range: $10-24.9 Million
Emp.: 400
Restaurant, Family: Chain
N.A.I.C.S.: 722511
Karen Garrett (Pres)

KMG HAULING, INC.
14 Bryant Ct, Sterling, VA 20166
Tel.: (703) 961-1100
Web Site: http://www.kmghauling.com
Year Founded: 2001
Sales Range: $10-24.9 Million
Emp.: 82
Hazardous Waste Treatment & Disposal
N.A.I.C.S.: 562211
Hugo M. Garcia (Pres)
Leon Polite (Dir-Fleet Maintenance)

KMH SYSTEMS, INC.
6900 Poe Ave, Dayton, OH 45414-2531
Tel.: (937) 890-0711 OH
Web Site: http://www.kmhsystems.com
Year Founded: 1976
Sales Range: $10-24.9 Million
Emp.: 125
Industrial Machinery & Equipment
N.A.I.C.S.: 423830
John Guenin (CEO)
Michael Guenin (Pres)
Ron Bedwell (VP-Ops)

KMI SYSTEMS INC.
4704 3 Oaks Rd, Crystal Lake, IL 60014
Tel.: (815) 459-5255
Web Site: http://www.kmisystemsinc.com
Sales Range: $10-24.9 Million
Emp.: 33
Industrial Coatings For Burners
N.A.I.C.S.: 333998
Kevin Coursin (Pres)
Chris Meid (Mgr-Field Svc)
Jim Polizzi (Mgr-Indus Product Sls)
Terry Ray (VP)
Steve Sarver (Mgr-Pur)
Reza Mirza (Engr-Mechanical)

KMJ CONVENIENCE COMPANY
1102 Benson Rd, Montevideo, MN 56265-1108
Tel.: (320) 269-6424 MN
Web Site: http://www.food-n-fuel.com
Year Founded: 1976
Sales Range: $25-49.9 Million
Emp.: 50
Petroleum Bulk Station & Terminal Services
N.A.I.C.S.: 424710
Mark Jaspersen (Pres)

KML SALES INC.
960 French Rd, Buffalo, NY 14227
Tel.: (716) 668-1353 NY
Year Founded: 1961
Sales Range: $25-49.9 Million
Emp.: 100
Owner & Operator of Furniture Stores
N.A.I.C.S.: 449110

KMM TELECOMMUNICATIONS
9 Law Dr, Fairfield, NJ 07004
Tel.: (973) 244-1261
Web Site: http://www.kmmtel.com
Year Founded: 1991
Rev.: $13,200,000
Electrical Apparatus & Equipment
N.A.I.C.S.: 423610
Chris Marcin (VP-Sls & Mktg)

KMRD PARTNERS, INC.
2600 Kelly Rd Ste 300, Warrington, PA 18976
Tel.: (866) 957-5673
Web Site: http://www.kmrdpartners.com
Year Founded: 2005
Casualty Insurance Carrier
N.A.I.C.S.: 524126
Lisa Pascoe (Office Mgr)
Robert Lickfeld (Partner)
Steve Macauley (Partner & Mgr-Risk)
Kevin McPoyle (Pres)
Allison Hill (Acct Mgr)
Bob Dietzel (Founder & Principal)
Brian Heun (Partner)
Debbie Prein (Acct Mgr)
Jeff Brown (Partner)
Keith Boyer (Mng Partner)
Kim Kraus (Controller)
Lisa Simon (Acct Mgr)
Mike Brown (Partner)
Karl Granlun (Mgr-Risk)
Greg Gerber (Mgr-Assoc Account)
Terri Quinn (Acct Mgr)
Andrew Laurie (Acct Mgr)
Jeremy Hahn (Acct Mgr-Limerick)
John Garber Jr. (Mng Dir & Mgr-Risk)

KMS ENTERPRISES, INC.
1401 Mercantile Ln Ste 200-J, Largo, MD 20774
Tel.: (301) 429-5155
Web Site: http://www.kmscorp.com
Sales Range: $10-24.9 Million
Emp.: 16

Administrative Management & General Management Consulting Services
N.A.I.C.S.: 541611
Kenneth J. Graves (Pres)
Steven Walker (Dir-Comml Logistics)

KN PROPERTIES
210 San Mateo Rd, Half Moon Bay, CA 94019-7111
Tel.: (650) 726-4402 CA
Year Founded: 1970
Sales Range: $25-49.9 Million
Emp.: 200
Gasoline Service Stations
N.A.I.C.S.: 457120
Keet Nerhan (Owner)
Gabriel Ronen (Atty)

KNAPP FOODS INC.
275 Ctr St, Newton, MA 02458
Tel.: (617) 965-8244
Year Founded: 1971
Sales Range: $10-24.9 Million
Emp.: 20
Independent Supermarket
N.A.I.C.S.: 445110
Steven Knapp (Pres)

KNAPP OIL CO. INC.
220 Frnt St, Xenia, IL 62899
Tel.: (618) 678-2211
Web Site: http://knappoil.com
Rev.: $14,500,000
Emp.: 15
Petroleum Bulk Stations
N.A.I.C.S.: 424710
Chuck Knapp (VP)

KNECHT'S OF SPRINGFIELD INC.
3400 Main St, Springfield, OR 97478
Tel.: (541) 746-4446
Web Site: http://www.knechts.com
Sales Range: $10-24.9 Million
Emp.: 225
Automotive Parts
N.A.I.C.S.: 441330
Wallis N. Knecht (Pres)

KNESTRICK CONTRACTOR INC.
2964 Sidco Dr, Nashville, TN 37204
Tel.: (615) 259-3755 TN
Web Site: http://www.knestrick.com
Year Founded: 1969
Sales Range: $50-74.9 Million
Emp.: 23
Nonresidential Construction
N.A.I.C.S.: 236220
William Knestrick (Pres & CEO)
Hubert Mitchell (COO)
Jerry Thurman (VP-Ops)
Bill Knestrick (VP-Bus Dev)

Subsidiaries:

Knestrick Properties, LLC (1)
2617 Grandview Ave, Nashville, TN 37211
Tel.: (615) 346-0288
Real Estate Manangement Services
N.A.I.C.S.: 531390

KNEZ BUILDING MATERIALS CO. INC.
8185 SW Hunziker St, Tigard, OR 97223-8229
Tel.: (503) 620-6142 OR
Web Site: http://www.knezinc.com
Year Founded: 1975
Sales Range: $25-49.9 Million
Emp.: 150
Lumber, Plywood & Millwork Services
N.A.I.C.S.: 423310
John S. Knez Jr. (Pres & Mgr-Ops)

KNICHEL LOGISTICS

Knichel Logistics—(Continued)

KNICHEL LOGISTICS
5347 William Flynn Hwy, Gibsonia, PA 15044
Tel.: (724) 449-3300
Web Site: http://www.knichellogistics.com
Year Founded: 2003
Rev.: $34,900,000
Emp.: 36
Freight Transportation Arrangement
N.A.I.C.S.: 488510
Robert D. Thomas (VP-Sls)
Nicole Papinchak (Mgr-Fin)
Terry Rosky (Dir-Carrier & Customer Dev)
Kandy Knichel-Barkley (VP-Admin)
Dana Lion (Mgr-Intermodal Customer Svcs)
Cheryl Pastucha (Mgr-Intermodal Ops)
David Mudd (COO)
Jim Berzonski (Dir-Sls)
Jay Fechter (Sr Acct Mgr)
Keith Eichler (Dir-MIS & IT)
Marc Russell (Dir-Sls)

KNICK KNACK, INC.
20 Henry St, Teterboro, NJ 07608
Tel.: (201) 727-9339   NY
Sales Range: $10-24.9 Million
Emp.: 25
Shirts, Men's & Boys'
N.A.I.C.S.: 424350
Scott Banks (Pres)

KNICKERBOCKER PARTITION CORPORATION
193 Hanse Ave, Freeport, NY 11520
Tel.: (516) 546-0550
Web Site: http://www.knickerbockerpartition.com
Year Founded: 1951
Sales Range: $10-24.9 Million
Emp.: 108
Mfr of Commercial Restroom Partitions
N.A.I.C.S.: 337126
Stewart Markbreiter (Pres)
Mark Reiss (VP-Production)
Albert Giorgianni (VP)

KNIGHT ENTERPRISES INC.
40600 Grand River Ave, Novi, MI 48375
Tel.: (248) 478-3651
Web Site: http://knightdealers.com
Sales Range: $10-24.9 Million
Emp.: 26
Petroleum Bulk Stations
N.A.I.C.S.: 424710

KNIGHT INDUSTRIES & ASSOCIATES INC.
1160 Center Rd, Auburn Hills, MI 48326-2602
Tel.: (248) 377-4950   MI
Web Site: http://www.knight-ind.com
Year Founded: 1984
Sales Range: $50-74.9 Million
Emp.: 141
Lift Tables, Balancers, Conveyers & Specialized Rail Material Handling Equipment
N.A.I.C.S.: 333922
John Lass (Controller)
James Zaguroli Jr. (Pres & CFO)

KNIGHT MARKETING ASSOCIATES, INC.
2032 Hawthorne St, Sarasota, FL 34239
Tel.: (941) 361-3070
Web Site: http://www.knightmarketing.com
Sales Range: $1-9.9 Million
Emp.: 10
Advertising Agencies
N.A.I.C.S.: 541810
Tracy Knight (Pres & Principal)
Ticia Mahler (Exec VP)
Rick Sandler (Dir-Res)
Anne Elhajoui (Dir-Creative)
Jennifer O'Brien (Acct Dir)
Renee Cseresznye (Office Mgr & Acct Coord)
Candice McElyea (Dir-PR & Social Media)

KNIGHT PAPER BOX COMPANY
4651 W 72nd St, Chicago, IL 60629
Tel.: (773) 585-2035
Web Site: http://www.knightpaperbox.com
Sales Range: $10-24.9 Million
Emp.: 60
Setup Paperboard Boxes
N.A.I.C.S.: 322219
Don McCann (Pres)

KNIGHT PROTECTIVE SERVICE, INC.
4200 Parliament Pl, Lanham, MD 20706
Tel.: (301) 808-4669
Web Site: http://www.knightprotectiveservice.com
Sales Range: $50-74.9 Million
Emp.: 1,500
Security Guards & Patrol Services
N.A.I.C.S.: 561612
Macon Sims Jr. (Pres & CEO)
Leonard Raab (VP)
Steve Barnett (CFO)

KNIGHT SEED COMPANY INC.
12550 W Frontage Rd Ste 203, Burnsville, MN 55337-3088
Tel.: (952) 894-8080   MN
Web Site: http://www.knightseed.com
Year Founded: 1975
Sales Range: $50-74.9 Million
Emp.: 15
Farm Supplies
N.A.I.C.S.: 424910
David Bornacker (Pres)
Jeff Pricco (Export Mgr)
Kent Welch (Controller)

KNIGHT SOLUTIONS
208 S King St Ste 104, Leesburg, VA 20175
Tel.: (703) 779-0900
Web Site: http://www.knightsolutionsfirst.com
Year Founded: 2005
Sales Range: $10-24.9 Million
Emp.: 150
Landscape & General Construction Services
N.A.I.C.S.: 561730
Kevin Knight (CEO)
Marina Manguiri (Office Mgr-Proposals)
Richard Fernandez (Coord-Field Ops Admin)

KNIGHT'S ARMAMENT COMPANY
701 Columbia Blvd, Titusville, FL 32780
Tel.: (321) 607-9900
Web Site: http://www.knightarmco.com
Sales Range: $10-24.9 Million
Emp.: 280
Firearms Mfr
N.A.I.C.S.: 332994
C. Reed Knight Jr. (Owner)

KNIGHT'S INC.
1701 W Dewitt Henry Dr, Beebe, AR 72012-2024
Tel.: (501) 882-5328   AR
Web Site: http://www.knightssuperfoods.net
Year Founded: 1971
Sales Range: $50-74.9 Million
Emp.: 140
Grocery Stores
N.A.I.C.S.: 445110
Kent Knight (Owner)
Sandra Knight (Pres)

KNIGHTHEAD CAPITAL MANAGEMENT LLC
280 Park Ave 22nd Fl, New York, NY 10017
Tel.: (212) 356-2900
Web Site: https://www.knighthead.com
Year Founded: 2008
Privater Equity Firm
N.A.I.C.S.: 523999
Thomas Wagner (Co-Founder)
Andrew Shannahan (Partner & Head-Research)
Tom Wagner (Co-Founder)
Ara D. Cohen (Co-Founder)
Adam Cantor (Partner)
Adam Zirkin (Partner)

KNIGHTS OF COLUMBUS
1 Columbus Plz, New Haven, CT 06510-3326
Tel.: (203) 752-4000   CT
Web Site: http://www.kofc.org
Year Founded: 1882
Rev.: $2,431,000,000
Assets: $26,861,000,000
Liabilities: $24,054,000,000
Net Worth: $2,807,000,000
Earnings: $148,000,000
Emp.: 1,500
Fiscal Year-end: 12/31/19
Insurance Services
N.A.I.C.S.: 524210
Michael J. O'Connor (Sec)
Ronald F. Schwarz (Treas)
Michael J. McGivney (Founder)

KNIGHTS' MARINE & INDUSTRIAL SERVICES, INC.
3421 Industrial Rd, Pascagoula, MS 39581
Tel.: (228) 769-5550
Web Site: http://www.knightsmarine.com
Year Founded: 1999
Sales Range: $10-24.9 Million
Emp.: 242
Structural Metal Mfr
N.A.I.C.S.: 332312
Brian Knight (Pres)
David E. Knight (VP)
Melissa Wallis (Gen Mgr)

KNIT-RITE INC.
120 Osage Ave, Kansas City, KS 66105
Tel.: (913) 281-4600
Web Site: http://www.knitrite.com
Year Founded: 1923
Sales Range: $10-24.9 Million
Emp.: 100
Mfr of Prosthetic Socks & Orthotic Textile Interfaces
N.A.I.C.S.: 334510
Mark Smith (Owner)
Chris Vering (Pres)

KNITCRAFT CORPORATION
4020 W 6th St, Winona, MN 55987
Tel.: (507) 454-1163
Web Site: http://www.stcroixknits.com
Sales Range: $10-24.9 Million
Emp.: 100
Sweaters & Sweater Coats, Knit
N.A.I.C.S.: 315120
Bernhard J. Brenner (Pres & CEO)
Lisa Czaplewski (Mgr-Production)
Dennis Meyer (VP)

KNITWORK PRODUCTIONS CORP.
1400 Broadway Rm 1209, New York, NY 10018-0684
Tel.: (718) 821-2201
Web Site: http://www.knitwork.com
Sales Range: $10-24.9 Million
Emp.: 22
Men's & Boys' Sweater Mfr
N.A.I.C.S.: 424350
Izzy Pnini (Founder & Pres)

KNITWORKS DESIGN ZONE, INC.
337 S Anderson St, Los Angeles, CA 90033-3742
Tel.: (323) 526-3526
Year Founded: 1982
Sales Range: $10-24.9 Million
Emp.: 75
Women's, Children's & Infants' Clothing Distr
N.A.I.C.S.: 424350
Vera R. Campbell (Pres)
Gene Bonilla (Controller)

KNL HOLDINGS INC.
3885 W Michegan, Sidney, OH 45365-4369
Tel.: (937) 498-1151
Web Site: http://www.knl.cc
Year Founded: 1995
Sales Range: $25-49.9 Million
Emp.: 300
Truck Rental & Leasing Service
N.A.I.C.S.: 551112
Jeff Philpot (Pres)

Subsidiaries:
Kirk Nationalease Co. Inc.   (1)
3885 W Michegan St, Sidney, OH 45365-4369   (100%)
Tel.: (937) 498-1151
Web Site: http://www.knl.com
Rev.: $16,000,000
Emp.: 50
Truck Rental And Leasing
N.A.I.C.S.: 532120
Jeff Lippo

KNL HOLDINGS, LLC
603 N 3rd Ave, Paragould, AR 72450-3085
Tel.: (870) 236-7753
Web Site: http://www.knlllc.com
Year Founded: 1989
Sales Range: $10-24.9 Million
Emp.: 25
Trailer Mfr
N.A.I.C.S.: 333924
Fred Workman (Pres & CEO)

Subsidiaries:
STECO, LLC   (1)
2215 S Van Buren St, Enid, OK 73703-8218   (100%)
Tel.: (580) 237-7433
Truck Trailer Mfr
N.A.I.C.S.: 333924
Brian Hinrichs (Gen Mgr)

KNL INCORPORATED
151 W Rosecrans Ave, Gardena, CA 90248-1829
Tel.: (310) 851-4772
Rev.: $30,000,000
Emp.: 45
Sportswear, Women's & Children's
N.A.I.C.S.: 424350

COMPANIES

Lars Viklund *(Pres)*

KNOBBE MARTENS OLSON & BEAR LLP
2040 Main St 14th Fl, Irvine, CA 92614
Tel.: (949) 760-0404
Web Site: http://www.knobbe.com
Year Founded: 1962
Sales Range: $150-199.9 Million
Emp.: 265
Intellectual Property Law
N.A.I.C.S.: 541110
Steven J. Nataupsky *(Mng Partner-Orange County)*
Jeremy J. Carney *(Partner & Atty)*
Daniel E. Altman *(Partner & Atty)*
Jared Bunker *(Partner)*
Mark R. Benedict *(Partner)*
Salima Merani *(Partner)*
Ted M. Cannon *(Partner)*
Michelle Armond *(Partner)*
Benjamin J. Everton *(Partner & Atty)*
Gregory A. Hermanson *(Partner)*
William Shreve *(Partner)*
Boris Zelkind *(Partner)*
Bryan W. Wahl *(Partner)*
Chris Steinhardt *(Partner)*
Craig Summers *(Partner)*
Ed Schlatter *(Partner)*
Jason J. Jardine *(Partner)*
Joseph Mallon *(Partner)*
John Sganga *(Partner)*
Jon Gurka *(Partner)*
Joseph Reisman *(Partner)*
Joshua Stowell *(Partner)*
Kerry Taylor *(Partner)*
Kimberly J. Miller *(Partner)*
Lauren Keller Katzenellenbogen *(Partner)*
Michael Trenholm *(Partner)*
Mincheol Kim *(Partner)*
Thomas Yee *(Partner)*
Lori Lee Yamato *(Partner)*
Christy G. Lea *(Partner)*
Adeel S. Akhtar *(Mng Partner-San Francisco)*
David Weiss *(Mng Partner-Los Angeles)*
Michael L. Fuller *(Mng Partner-San Diego)*
Robert J. Roby *(Mng Partner-New York)*
Thomas R. Arno *(Mng Partner-San Diego)*
Wendy Peterson *(Gen Counsel & Atty)*
William R. Zimmerman *(Mng Partner-Washington)*

KNOBIAS, INC.
875 Northpark Dr Bldg 2 Ste 500, Ridgeland, MS 39157
Web Site: http://www.knobias.com
Year Founded: 1968
Sales Range: $1-9.9 Million
Emp.: 25
Internet Financial Information Publisher
N.A.I.C.S.: 513199
Kenneth L. Ivey *(COO & Exec VP)*

KNOCK, INC.
1315 Glenwood Ave, Minneapolis, MN 55405
Tel.: (612) 333-6511
Web Site: http://www.knockinc.com
Year Founded: 2003
Sales Range: $10-24.9 Million
Emp.: 100
Motion Picture & Video Production
N.A.I.C.S.: 512110
Lili Hall *(Founder & CEO)*
Dan Weston *(VP & Dir-Creative)*
Sara Nelson *(VP & Dir-Creative)*
Talia Camarena *(Dir-Strategy)*

Jillian Froehlich *(VP & Head-Digital)*
Todd Paulson *(Chief Creative Officer & Partner)*
Tom Newton *(VP-Bus Dev)*

KNOEPFLER CHEVROLET CO.
100 Jackson St, Sioux City, IA 51101
Tel.: (712) 279-7100
Web Site: http://www.kchev.com
Sales Range: $25-49.9 Million
Emp.: 90
Automobiles, New & Used
N.A.I.C.S.: 441110
Bill Knoepfler *(Co-Owner & Parts Mgr)*
Frank Denton *(Controller & Mgr)*
Jerry Felix *(Mgr-Sls)*
Curt Blankenburg *(Asst Mgr-Svc)*

KNOPF AUTOMOTIVE PARTS
93 Shrewsbury Ave, Red Bank, NJ 07701-1131
Tel.: (732) 212-0444
Web Site: http://www.mmknopf.com
Year Founded: 1948
Sales Range: $10-24.9 Million
Emp.: 120
New & Remanufactured Motor Vehicle Parts Distr
N.A.I.C.S.: 423120
Marshall Knopf *(Founder)*

Subsidiaries:

Knopf Automotive do Brasil Ltda (1)
Da Oti 162 Cj 104 Rua, Porto Alegre, 90680-060, Brazil
Tel.: (55) 51 3373 7523
Automotive Part Whslr
N.A.I.C.S.: 423120
Marcos V. Teixeira *(Dir-Ops)*

KNOPF MOTORS INC.
717 N Bethlehem Pike, Ambler, PA 19002-2502
Tel.: (215) 646-2080
Year Founded: 1965
Sales Range: $10-24.9 Million
Emp.: 30
Owner & Operator of Car Dealerships
N.A.I.C.S.: 441110
Ed Karslo *(Gen Mgr-Sls)*
Tony Satterthwaite *(Co-Owner)*
James Satterthwaite *(Co-Owner)*

KNOTTS CO. INC.
350 Snyder Ave, Berkeley Heights, NJ 07922
Tel.: (908) 464-4800
Web Site: http://www.knottsco.com
Sales Range: $10-24.9 Million
Emp.: 35
Industrial Supplies
N.A.I.C.S.: 423840
Richard Howe *(Owner & Pres)*
Fred Heimall *(Mgr-Tech Svcs)*

KNOUSE FOODS COOPERATIVE INC.
800 Peach Glen Rd - Idaville Rd, Peach Glen, PA 17375
Tel.: (717) 677-8181 DE
Web Site: http://www.knouse.com
Year Founded: 1949
Sales Range: $700-749.9 Million
Emp.: 415
Fruit Product Mfr
N.A.I.C.S.: 111331
Richard Esser *(VP-Sls)*
Michael A. Binkley *(VP-Mfg & Gen Mgr)*
Edward S. Surotchak *(Controller)*

Subsidiaries:

Knouse Foods Cooperative Inc. - Biglerville, Pa. Plant (1)
53 E Hanover St, Biglerville, PA 17307-0807

Tel.: (717) 677-9115
Web Site: http://www.knouse.com
Sales Range: $50-74.9 Million
Emp.: 220
Processed Fruit Product Mfr
N.A.I.C.S.: 311421
Kenneth Guise *(Pres)*

Knouse Foods Cooperative Inc. - Chambersburg, Pa. Plant (1)
421 E Grant St, Chambersburg, PA 17201-1675
Tel.: (717) 263-9177
Web Site: http://www.knosefoods.com
Sales Range: $50-74.9 Million
Emp.: 180
Processed Fruit Product Mfr
N.A.I.C.S.: 311421
Mark Burkhart *(Gen Mgr)*

Knouse Foods Cooperative Inc. - Gardners, Pa. Plant (1)
450 Gardners Station Rd, Gardners, PA 17324-0097
Tel.: (717) 677-7126
Web Site: http://www.knousefoods.com
Sales Range: $50-74.9 Million
Emp.: 150
Processed Fruit Product Mfr
N.A.I.C.S.: 311421
Lisa Baughn *(Mgr)*

Knouse Foods Cooperative Inc. - Orrtanna, Pa. Plant (1)
1505 Orrtanna Road, Orrtanna, PA 17353-0308
Tel.: (717) 642-8291
Sales Range: $50-74.9 Million
Emp.: 240
Processed Fruit Product Mfr
N.A.I.C.S.: 311421

KNOVATION, INC.
3630 Park 42 Dr Ste 170F, Cincinnati, OH 45241
Tel.: (513) 731-4090
Web Site: http://www.nettrekker.com
Year Founded: 2000
Sales Range: $10-24.9 Million
Emp.: 50
K-12 Education Digital Content Solutions
N.A.I.C.S.: 541512
Randy L. Wilhelm *(Co-Founder & CEO)*

KNOVEL CORPORATION
489 Fifth Ave 9th Fl, New York, NY 10017
Tel.: (210) 340-1944
Web Site: http://why.knovel.com
Sales Range: $10-24.9 Million
Emp.: 60
Online Science & Technology Reference Services
N.A.I.C.S.: 513140
Richard J. Harrington *(Chm)*
Sasha Gurke *(Sr VP & Co-Founder)*

KNOWBE4, LLC
601 Cleveland St Ste 230, Clearwater, FL 33755
Web Site: http://www.knowbe4.com
Internet Security Services
N.A.I.C.S.: 561621
Stu Sjouwerman *(Founder & CEO)*
Perry Carpenter *(Chief Evangelist & Strategy Officer)*
Joanna G. Huisman *(Sr VP-Strategic Insights & Res)*
Karina Mansfield *(Mng Dir-Australia)*
Mark Patton *(Sr VP-Engrg)*

KNOWLAN'S SUPER MARKETS INC.
14775 Victor Hugo Blvd, Hugo, MN 55038
Tel.: (651) 483-9242 MN
Web Site: http://www.festy.com
Year Founded: 1989
Sales Range: $50-74.9 Million

Emp.: 600
Grocery Services
N.A.I.C.S.: 445110
Mike Brantner *(Mgr-Meat Dept)*
Debra Brei *(CFO)*

KNOWLAND GROUP INC.
115 W Market St, Lewes, DE 19958
Tel.: (302) 645-9777
Web Site: http://www.knowlandgroup.com
Year Founded: 2004
Sales Range: $1-9.9 Million
Emp.: 38
Marketing Products Supporting the Hospitality Industry
N.A.I.C.S.: 561599
Tim Hart *(CEO)*
Amy Earn *(Dir-HR)*
Jim Vandevender *(Chief Mktg Officer)*
Erika Bucsi *(Dir-Enterprise-Sls-Europe)*
Mattia Melillo *(Dir-Sls-Intl)*
Betty Huang *(Mgr-Sls & Svc-Intl)*
Carleigh Dworetzky *(Dir-Destination Solutions-Rosslyn)*

KNOWLEDGE ADVANTAGE INC.
704 Quince Orchard Rd Ste 225, Gaithersburg, MD 20878
Tel.: (301) 740-8608
Web Site: http://www.kaiglobal.com
Year Founded: 1999
Sales Range: $1-9.9 Million
Emp.: 20
Business Support Services
N.A.I.C.S.: 561439
Danny Aranza *(VP-Bus Dev)*
Georganna Murto *(Dir-Requirements & Analysis)*

KNOWLEDGE ANYWHERE, INC.
170 120th Ave NE Ste 201, Bellevue, WA 98005
Tel.: (425) 454-4454 WA
Web Site: http://www.knowledgeanywhere.com
Year Founded: 2000
Sales Range: $10-24.9 Million
Emp.: 20
Information Retrieval Services Management Consulting Services
N.A.I.C.S.: 611430
Charlie Gillette *(Pres & CEO)*

Subsidiaries:

Labelle Strategic Resources, Inc. (1)
473 Hildebidle Rd, Collegeville, PA 19426
Tel.: (610) 409-2770
Web Site: http://www.lsriagents.com
Sales Range: $10-24.9 Million
Data Processing, Hosting & Related Services
N.A.I.C.S.: 518210

KNOWLEDGE INFORMATION SOLUTIONS, INC.
2877 Guardian Ln Ste 201, Virginia Beach, VA 23452-7330
Tel.: (757) 463-0033
Web Site: http://www.kisinc.net
Year Founded: 1983
Sales Range: $50-74.9 Million
Emp.: 86
IT Products & Services
N.A.I.C.S.: 541512
Augustine G. Riolo *(COO)*
David Testa *(VP-Products)*

KNOWLEDGEBANK, INC.
1 Loudoun 20365 Exchange St, Ashburn, VA 20147
Tel.: (703) 448-8070

KNOWLEDGEBANK, INC.

KnowledgeBank, Inc.—(Continued)
Web Site:
http://www.knowledgebank.us.com
Year Founded: 2003
Outsourced Human Resource Services
N.A.I.C.S.: 561499
Kevin Antler (Pres & CEO)
Michele Borg (VP-Federal Consulting Practice)
Julia Whitcup (CFO)
Ed Kovac (Dir-Bus Dev)
Jim Muscar (Dir-Project Mgmt Ops)

KNOWLEDGELAKE INC.

6 City Place Dr, Ste 500, Saint Louis, MO 63141
Tel.: (314) 898-0500 MO
Web Site:
http://www.knowledgelake.com
Year Founded: 1999
Computer Related Services, Nec, Nsk
N.A.I.C.S.: 541512
Jason Burian (Dir-Product Mgmt)
Ron Cameron (CEO)
David Arthur (Chief Revenue Officer)

KNOWLES ASSOCIATES, LLC

316 Penn Ave, Scranton, PA 18503
Tel.: (570) 342-3214
Web Site: http://www.knowlesins.com
Year Founded: 1963
Insurance Agents
N.A.I.C.S.: 524210
Susan M. Kelly (VP-Sls)
Robert J. Knowles Jr. (Principal)

Subsidiaries:

Welch Insurance LLC (1)
2 E Main St, Canton, PA 17724-1507
Tel.: (570) 673-5781
Web Site:
http://www.mywelchinsurance.com
Insurance Agencies & Brokerages
N.A.I.C.S.: 524210
Carol K. Welch (Owner)

KNOWLOGY CORPORATION

1934 Old Callows Rd, Vienna, VA 22182
Tel.: (703) 532-1000 DE
Web Site: http://www.knowlogy.com
Year Founded: 1986
Computer Technical Training
N.A.I.C.S.: 624310
Hassan Judah (Pres)
Mori Ghazzawi (VP-Ops)
Rob Stewart (VP)

KNOWN GLOBAL LLC

5 Bryant Park, New York, NY 10036
Tel.: (212) 257-5530
Web Site: http://www.known.is
Year Founded: 2020
Marketing & Advertising Services
N.A.I.C.S.: 541613
Kern Schireson (Chm & CEO)
Sarah Broderick (CFO)
Jeff Kingsley (Pres & COO)

Subsidiaries:

Schireson Associates, Inc. (1)
5 Bryant Park Fl 33, New York, NY 10018
Tel.: (212) 257-5530
Web Site: http://www.known.is
Marketing & Data Stragety Services
N.A.I.C.S.: 541910
Kern Schireson (CEO)

Stun Creative, LLC (1)
5757 Wilshire Blvd Ste 600, Los Angeles, CA 90036
Tel.: (323) 460-4035
Marketing & Adversiting Services
N.A.I.C.S.: 541810
Mark Feldstein (Co-Founder & Principal)
Brad Roth (Co-Founder & Principal)
Michael Vamosy (Chief Creative Officer)

Galen Newton (Head-Digital & Social Content)
Holly Gray (Dir-Digital & Strategic Partnerships)

KNOWNHOST LLC

500 S Australian Ave Ste 600 #1042, West Palm Beach, FL 33401
Tel.: (205) 690-1625
Web Site:
https://www.knownhost.com
Year Founded: 2006
Emp.: 100
Data Processing & Hosting Services
N.A.I.C.S.: 518210

KNOX AREA RESCUE MINISTRIES

418 N Broadway, Knoxville, TN 37917
Tel.: (865) 673-6540 TN
Web Site: http://www.karm.org
Year Founded: 1960
Sales Range: $10-24.9 Million
Emp.: 87
Christian Ministry Services
N.A.I.C.S.: 813110
Cynthia Russell (VP-Serenity Ministries)
Joe Haas (VP-Fin)
Betsy Martin (VP-Strategic Initiatives)
Burt Rosen (Pres & CEO)
Steve Clabough (VP-Ops)

KNOX ASSOCIATES, INC.

1601 W Deer Valley Rd, Phoenix, AZ 85027-2112
Tel.: (623) 687-2300 AZ
Web Site: http://www.knoxbox.com
Year Founded: 1975
Fire & Safety Lockbox Mfr
N.A.I.C.S.: 332999
Dohn J. Trempala (Pres & CEO)

KNOX ATTORNEY SERVICE INC.

2250 4th Ave Ste 200, San Diego, CA 92101
Tel.: (619) 233-9700
Web Site:
http://www.knoxservices.com
Sales Range: $10-24.9 Million
Emp.: 205
Photocopying & Duplicating Services
N.A.I.C.S.: 323111
Steve Knox (Owner)
Tracey Oakley (Mgr-Acctg)

KNOX CAPITAL HOLDINGS, LLC

212 W Kinzie St 6th Fl, Chicago, IL 60654
Tel.: (312) 402-1425
Web Site: http://www.knox-cap.com
Private Investment Firm
N.A.I.C.S.: 523999
Alex Gregor (Founder & Partner)
Tom Nugent (Principal)

Subsidiaries:

Lenders Title Company (1)
1 Allied Dr Ste 1710, Little Rock, AR 72202
Tel.: (501) 225-3519
Web Site: http://www.lenderstitlegroup.com
Title Insurance Services
N.A.I.C.S.: 524127
B. J. Fast (Pres & CEO)
Teana Bradford (CFO)
Audreya Brown (Mgr-Admin)

Subsidiary (Domestic):

United Title of Louisiana, Inc. (2)
6425 Youree Dr Ste 140, Shreveport, LA 71105
Tel.: (318) 797-3900
Web Site: http://www.lenderstitlegroup.com
Real Estate Closing & Title Services
N.A.I.C.S.: 524127

Christine Young (Mgr-Bossier Residential)
Janet Brown (Mgr-Shreveport Residential)
Leena Logsdon (Mgr-Shreveport)
Bruce Poynter (Mgr-Ops)
Clint Simon (Mgr-Comml)
Heidi Trant (Mgr-Comml)

TRS Global Services, LLC (1)
2105 Skinner Rd, Houston, TX 77093
Tel.: (713) 692-2930
Web Site: http://www.trsglobal.com
Sales Range: $1-9.9 Million
Emp.: 50
Repair & Maintenance of Components for Heavy Industrial Gas Turbines
N.A.I.C.S.: 811210
Peter Sobieski (COO)
Shawn Smith (Exec VP)
Peggy Prince (Bus Mgr)
Greg Gaul (Mgr-Quality)
Rick Richardson (Mgr-Production)
Christopher Salazar (Engr-Production)
David Theis (Pres & CEO)
Lee Wood (Dir-Sls & Mktg)
Joe Phelan (VP-Ops-Europe)

KNOX COMMUNITY HOSPITAL

1330 Coshocton Ave, Mount Vernon, OH 43050
Tel.: (740) 393-9000 OH
Web Site:
http://www.knoxcommhosp.org
Year Founded: 1977
Sales Range: $125-149.9 Million
Emp.: 1,018
Health Care Srvices
N.A.I.C.S.: 622110
Michael V. Ambrosiani (CFO)
Bruce White (CEO)
Lisa Bragg (VP-HR)
Bruce M. Behner Jr. (COO)

KNOX ENERGY COOPERATIVE ASSOCIATION INC.

4100 Holiday St NW Ste 201, Canton, OH 44718
Tel.: (330) 498-9130 OH
Web Site: http://www.knoxenergy.org
Year Founded: 1998
Sales Range: $10-24.9 Million
Natural Gas Service Provider
N.A.I.C.S.: 221210
Marv Vanatta (Treas)
Lester Iceman (VP)
William Platt (Sec)
Andrew Buckworth (Pres)

KNOX ENTERPRISES INC.

33 Riverside Ave, Westport, CT 06880
Tel.: (203) 226-6288
Web Site: http://www.knoxandco.com
Sales Range: $10-24.9 Million
Emp.: 8
Rolled Paper Products & Wire & Steel Products Mfr
N.A.I.C.S.: 322220
Lee Marino (Owner)

Subsidiaries:

Jackburn Manufacturing Inc. (1)
438 Church St, Girard, PA 16417
Tel.: (814) 774-3573
Web Site: http://www.jackburn.com
Fabricated Wire Product Mfr
N.A.I.C.S.: 332618
Ron Brewer (Mgr-Engrg & Quality)
Michael Vadzemnieks (Controller)

KNOX LANE LP

655 Montgomery St., San Francisco, CA 94111
Tel.: (415) 651-2279
Web Site: https://www.knoxlane.com
Year Founded: 2019
Private Equity
N.A.I.C.S.: 523999
John Bailey (Founder & Mng Partner)

U.S. PRIVATE

Subsidiaries:

Fingerpaint Marketing, Inc. (1)
395 Broadway, Saratoga Springs, NY 12866
Tel.: (518) 693-6960
Web Site:
http://www.fingerpaintmarketing.com
Sales Range: $10-24.9 Million
General Marketing Services
N.A.I.C.S.: 541613
Ed Mitzen (Founder)
Nicole Holland (Head-People & Culture)
Josh Koopman (Acct Exec)
Kevin Kish (Head-Fin & Acctg)
Lori Thatch (Head-Acct Svc)
Bill McEllen (Partner)

Subsidiary (Domestic):

1798, LLC (2)
888 Prospect St Ste 105, La Jolla, CA 92037
Tel.: (855) 777-1798
Web Site: http://www.1798consultants.com
Sales Range: $1-9.9 Million
Health Consulting Services
N.A.I.C.S.: 541618
Roshawn A. Blunt (Founder & Mng Dir)

Fingerpaint Medical Communications (2)
1 Cattano Ave, Morristown, NJ 07960
Web Site:
https://www.fingerpaintmedcomms.com
Sales Range: $1-9.9 Million
Emp.: 50
Health Care Srvices
N.A.I.C.S.: 621610

Guardian Fire Protection Service, LLC (1)
7668 Standish Place, Rockville, MD 20855
Tel.: (301) 970-3007
Web Site:
https://www.guardianfireprotection.com
Security System Services
N.A.I.C.S.: 561621

Subsidiary (Domestic):

Harris Fire Protection Co Inc. (2)
7974 E Baltimore St, Baltimore, MD 21224
Tel.: (410) 285-7272
Web Site: https://www.harrisfire.com
Rev: $9,440,000
Emp.: 10
Other Miscellaneous Durable Goods Merchant Whslr
N.A.I.C.S.: 423990
Coreen Miller (Mgr)
Stephen Cieslak (VP)

KNOX OIL OF TEXAS, INC.

2221 Irving Blvd, Dallas, TX 75207-6511
Tel.: (972) 960-9663 DE
Web Site: http://www.knoxoil.com
Year Founded: 1860
Sales Range: $125-149.9 Million
Emp.: 200
Petroleum Production & Marketing Services
N.A.I.C.S.: 457120
Richard Knox (Pres)
Bob Knox (Exec VP)

KNOXVILLE HOSPITAL & CLINICS

1002 S Lincoln St, Knoxville, IA 50138
Tel.: (641) 842-2151 IA
Web Site:
http://www.knoxvillehospital.org
Year Founded: 1981
Sales Range: $25-49.9 Million
Emp.: 292
Health Care Srvices
N.A.I.C.S.: 622110
Kevin Kincaid (CEO)
Maggie Hamilton-Beyer (CFO)
MaryJane Applegate (Chief Clinical Officer)

COMPANIES

KNOXVILLE WHOLESALE FURNITURE CO. INC.
10461 Parkside Dr, Knoxville, TN 37922
Tel.: (865) 671-5300
Web Site: http://www.knoxvillewholesalefurniture.com
Rev.: $19,168,455
Emp.: 75
Furniture Retailer
N.A.I.C.S.: 449110
Jane Wear (VP-Mdsg)

KNOXVILLE'S COMMUNITY DEVELOPMENT CORP.
901 Broadway, Knoxville, TN 37917
Tel.: (865) 403-1100
Web Site: http://www.kcdc.org
Year Founded: 1936
Sales Range: $25-49.9 Million
Emp.: 275
Housing Authority Operator
N.A.I.C.S.: 531390
R. Culver Schmid (Vice Chm)

KNT MANUFACTURING INC.
4220 Business Center Dr, Fremont, CA 94538
Tel.: (510) 651-7163
Web Site: http://www.kntmfg.com
Sales Range: $25-49.9 Million
Emp.: 150
Precision Machined Components Mfr
N.A.I.C.S.: 332721
Keith Ngo (Pres & CEO)
Loi Ngo (VP-Mktg)

KNUD NIELSEN COMPANY INC.
217 Park St, Evergreen, AL 36401
Tel.: (251) 578-2900
Web Site: http://www.knudnielsen.com
Rev.: $23,000,000
Emp.: 85
Flowers, Artificial & Preserved
N.A.I.C.S.: 339999
Knud Nielsen III (Chm)

KNUDSEN, GARDNER & HOWE, INC.
2103 Saint Clair Ave NE, Cleveland, OH 44114-4018
Tel.: (216) 781-5000   OH
Web Site: http://www.kghinc.com
Year Founded: 1967
Sales Range: $10-24.9 Million
Emp.: 4
Full Service
N.A.I.C.S.: 541810
Tim Knudsen (Pres)
Greg Beckner (Dir-Creative)

KNUDSON MANUFACTURING, INC.
10401 W 120th Ave, Broomfield, CO 80021
Tel.: (303) 469-2101   CO
Web Site: http://www.knudsonmfg.com
Year Founded: 1966
Sales Range: $50-74.9 Million
Emp.: 12
Metal Roll Machines Mfr
N.A.I.C.S.: 333517
Clete Zakrzewski (Plant Mgr)

KNUDTSEN CHEVROLET COMPANY
1900 E Polston Ave, Post Falls, ID 83854
Tel.: (208) 664-8107
Web Site: http://www.knudtsen.com
Year Founded: 1939
Sales Range: $10-24.9 Million
Emp.: 70
Car Whslr
N.A.I.C.S.: 441110
Eve L. Knudtsen (Pres)

KNUPP & WATSON & WALLMAN
5201 Old Middleton Rd, Madison, WI 53705-2715
Tel.: (608) 232-2300   WI
Year Founded: 1986
Sales Range: $10-24.9 Million
Emp.: 27
N.A.I.C.S.: 541810
Theodore H. Knupp (Chm)
James Peltier (Dir-Res)
Andy Wallman (Pres & Exec Dir-Creative)
Jennifer Savino (VP & Dir-Client Svcs)

KNUTSON CONSTRUCTION SERVICES
7515 Wayzata Ave, Minneapolis, MN 55426
Tel.: (763) 546-1400   MN
Web Site: http://www.knutsonconstruction.com
Year Founded: 1911
Sales Range: $200-249.9 Million
Emp.: 300
General Contracting Services
N.A.I.C.S.: 236210
Dave Bastyr (Exec VP-Ops-Minnesota)
Brad Johnson (VP & Gen Mgr)
Chris Terry (VP-Bus Dev)
Jennifer Green (CFO)
Brendan Moore (Pres)
John Curry (CEO)

Subsidiaries:

Knutson Construction Services Midwest Inc. (1)
PO Box 2058, Iowa City, IA 52244
Tel.: (319) 351-2040
Web Site: http://www.knutson.com
Sales Range: $10-24.9 Million
Emp.: 15
Provider of Nonresidential Construction Services
N.A.I.C.S.: 236220
Brad Johnson (VP)

Knutson Construction Services, Inc. (1)
7515 Wayzata Blvd, Minneapolis, MN 55426
Tel.: (763) 546-1400
Web Site: http://www.knutsonconstructionservices.com
Sales Range: $200-249.9 Million
Provider of Industrial Building Services
N.A.I.C.S.: 236210

KNW HOLDINGS, INC.
2020 52nd Ave, Moline, IL 61265
Tel.: (662) 420-7378
Web Site: http://www.ecogistics.org
Year Founded: 2009
Sales Range: $10-24.9 Million
Emp.: 25
Logistics Consulting Servies
N.A.I.C.S.: 541614
Kevin Nolan (Founder)

KO HUTS, INC.
8100 E 22nd St N Bldg 200, Wichita, KS 67226
Tel.: (316) 685-9278   KS
Year Founded: 1969
Sales Range: $25-49.9 Million
Emp.: 600
Holding Company; Franchise Pizza Chain Restaurants Owner & Operator
N.A.I.C.S.: 551112

KO-AMEX GENERAL WHOLESALE INC.
18965 San Jose Ave, City of Industry, CA 91748-1328
Tel.: (626) 854-9848   CA
Web Site: http://www.koamex.com
Year Founded: 1978
Sales Range: $10-24.9 Million
Emp.: 45
Grocery Products Whslr
N.A.I.C.S.: 424490
Yong Hwan Kim (Founder & CEO)
Patrick Kim (Pres)

Subsidiaries:

Major Cash & Carry Inc. (1)
18965 San Jose Ave, City of Industry, CA 91748-1328
Tel.: (626) 854-0854
Web Site: http://www.koamex.com
Sales Range: $10-24.9 Million
Emp.: 20
Sales of Groceries
N.A.I.C.S.: 424410

KO-REC-TYPE CORP.
67 Kent Ave, Brooklyn, NY 11211-1991
Tel.: (718) 782-2601   NY
Web Site: http://www.korectype.com
Year Founded: 1955
Sales Range: $75-99.9 Million
Emp.: 100
Inked Ribbons, Typewriter Correction Materials, Carbon Paper, Inkjet Cartridges & Laser Toner Cartridges Mfr
N.A.I.C.S.: 339940
Andrea Barouh (Pres)

Subsidiaries:

BAROUH EATON (CANADA) LTD. (1)
6039 Ordan Drive, Mississauga, L5T 2M7, ON, Canada
Tel.: (905) 670-1800
Printing Equipment Whslr
N.A.I.C.S.: 423830

Korectype Corporation (1)
67 Kent Ave, Brooklyn, NY 11211-1926
(100%)
Tel.: (718) 782-2601
Web Site: http://www.korectype.com
Sales Range: $10-24.9 Million
Emp.: 20
Mfr of Correction Materials Printer & Typewriter Ribbon
N.A.I.C.S.: 339940
Robert Borough (Mgr)

KOA CAPITAL PARTNERS LLC
820 W Hind Dr Ste 1293, Honolulu, HI 96821
Tel.: (808) 373-3000   HI
Web Site: http://www.koacapitalpartners.com
Privater Equity Firm
N.A.I.C.S.: 523999
Dustin Sellers (Mng Partner)
Chris Eldridge (Operating Partner)

Subsidiaries:

Premier Restoration Hawaii (1)
2815 Kaihikapu St Unit 104, Honolulu, HI 96819
Tel.: (808) 201-2140
Web Site: http://www.premhi.com
Water Damage Restoration, Mold Remediation & Reconstruction Services
N.A.I.C.S.: 237110

KOA HOLDINGS INC.
551 5th Ave Fl 33, New York, NY 10176-3399
Tel.: (212) 830-5200   DE
Holding Company
N.A.I.C.S.: 533110

Subsidiaries:

Franchise Services, Inc. (1)
26722 Plz, Mission Viejo, CA 92691-6390
Tel.: (949) 348-5400
Web Site: http://www.sirspeedy.com
Sales Range: $10-24.9 Million
Emp.: 50
Holding Company
N.A.I.C.S.: 533110
Don F. Lowe (CEO)
Dan Conger (CFO)
Diane Vu (Controller)

Subsidiary (Domestic):

PIP Printing, Inc. (2)
26722 Plz Dr, Mission Viejo, CA 92691
Tel.: (949) 282-3800
Web Site: http://www.pip.com
Business Printing Franchises
N.A.I.C.S.: 323111
David Rovivoux (VP-Mktg)

Sir Speedy, Inc. (2)
26722 Plz, Mission Viejo, CA 92691
Tel.: (949) 348-5000
Web Site: http://www.sirspeedy.com
Emp.: 50
Franchisor of Printing & Digital Networking Centers
N.A.I.C.S.: 533110
Don F. Lowe (CEO)
Richard Lowe (Pres & COO)
Denise Denton (VP-Mktg)
David Robidoux (CMO)
John Bowen (VP-Bus Dev-Intl)
Kelly Kimberlin (VP-Mktg)
David C. Rice (VP-Franchise Support)
Dan Conger (CFO)

Kampgrounds of America, Inc. (1)
TWIII Building 4th Fl, Billings, MT 59101
(100%)
Tel.: (406) 248-7444
Web Site: http://www.koa.com
Sales Range: $25-49.9 Million
Emp.: 333
Campground Franchisor
N.A.I.C.S.: 721214
Pat Hittmeier (Chm)
Toby L. O'Rourke (Pres & CEO)
Yolawnda Henry (VP-HR)
Chris Scheer (CFO)
Lyndsey Geering (Controller)
Billie Gunn (Exec Dir-Acctg & Fin)

Division (Domestic):

West Advertising/Public Relations, Inc. (2)
TWIII Bldg 4th Fl, Billings, MT 59101
Tel.: (406) 248-7444
Web Site: http://www.koa.com
Advertising & Public Relations
N.A.I.C.S.: 541810

KOALA TEE, INC.
2160 17th St, Sarasota, FL 34234
Tel.: (941) 954-7700
Web Site: http://www.koalatee.com
Year Founded: 1983
Sales Range: $1-9.9 Million
Emp.: 31
Screen Printing & Embroidery Services
N.A.I.C.S.: 323113
Rob Harman (Acct Mgr)
Greg Emenecker (Acct Mgr)
Jessica Fox (Acct Mgr-Military)
Barry Fox (VP & Acct Mgr-Military)
Jeff Manley (Pres)
Carmen Manley (Dir-Mktg & Comm)
Liz Davis (Mgr-HR)
Sheri Hirschberg (Supvr-Acct)

KOAM ENGINEERING SYSTEMS INC.
9325 Sky Park Ct Ste 300, San Diego, CA 92123
Tel.: (858) 292-0922
Web Site: http://www.kes.com
Year Founded: 1994
Sales Range: $10-24.9 Million
Information Technology Services

KOAM ENGINEERING SYSTEMS INC.

Koam Engineering Systems Inc.—(Continued)
N.A.I.C.S.: 541512
James Meadows *(Dir-Engrg)*
John Yi *(Founder, Chm & CEO)*
Erica Tofson *(VP-HR & Admin Ops)*
Jonathan Kuo *(VP-Corp Strategy)*
Richard Comber *(VP-Tech Ops)*
Kimberly Lanfersieck *(Dir-Fin & Admin)*
Mark Cook *(Dir-Contracts Admin)*
Bob Tilton *(Dir-Shipboard Design, Integration & Installation)*
Jerry Giacalone *(Dir-Logistics)*

KOBAYASHI TRAVEL SERVICE LTD. INC.
650 Iwilei Rd Ste 410, Honolulu, HI 96817
Tel.: (808) 593-9387
Web Site: http://www.ktshawaii.com
Year Founded: 1945
Sales Range: $10-24.9 Million
Emp.: 100
Travel Agencies
N.A.I.C.S.: 561510
Michael Kobayashi *(Pres)*
Lawson Teshima *(Treas & Sec)*

Subsidiaries:

PHT Inc. (1)
330 Pacific St, Honolulu, HI 96813-5037
Tel.: (524) 504-0240
Web Site: http://www.phthawaii.com
Sales Range: $10-24.9 Million
Emp.: 70
Local Transportation
N.A.I.C.S.: 485999

KOBIE MARKETING, INC.
100 2nd Ave S Ste 1000, Saint Petersburg, FL 33701
Tel.: (727) 822-5353
Web Site: http://www.kobie.com
Year Founded: 1990
Sales Range: $10-24.9 Million
Emp.: 70
Loyalty Marketing
N.A.I.C.S.: 541890
Bonnie Hechtkopf *(Chm)*
Selena McLaughlin *(Sr Dir-HR & Admin)*
Bram Hechtkopf *(CEO)*
Pamela Sullins *(Sr Dir-Client Svcs)*
Nicolle Schreiber *(Sr Dir-Client Svcs)*
Carlos Dunlap *(Dir-Bus Dev & Strategy)*
Nancy Berg *(VP-Client Svcs & Partnerships)*
William Molina *(Sr Dir-Loyalty Ops)*
G. Ashby Green *(VP-Fin & Admin)*
Margaret Meraw *(VP-Loyalty Ops)*
Michael Foukarakis *(Project Mgr)*
David Andreadakis *(VP-Loyalty Strategy)*
Angie Tran *(Sr Mgr-Partnerships)*
Donna Langer *(Sr Acct Mgr)*
Matt Stein *(VP-Customer Experience & Agency Svc)*
Jean-Louis Casabonne *(CFO)*
Mark Chronister *(Chief Growth Officer)*
Larry Roos *(CIO)*
Marti Beller *(Pres)*

KOBRA INTERNATIONAL LTD.
525 7th Ave 20th Fl, New York, NY 10018-4901
Tel.: (212) 719-9200 NY
Web Site: http://www.nicolemiller.com
Year Founded: 1982
Sales Range: $75-99.9 Million
Emp.: 120
Dresses, Blouses, Shirts, Slacks & Accessories Mfr
N.A.I.C.S.: 315250

KOBRAND CORPORATION
1 Manhattanville Rd Fl 4, Purchase, NY 10577-2126
Tel.: (212) 490-9300 NY
Web Site: http://www.kobrand.com
Year Founded: 1944
Sales Range: $125-149.9 Million
Emp.: 200
Wine & Distilled Beverage Mfr, Importer & Retailer
N.A.I.C.S.: 424820
Tom Congdon *(VP & Dir-Spirits)*
Robert De Roose *(Pres & CEO)*

Subsidiaries:

Kobrand/Western Division (1)
4 Venture Ste 280, Irvine, CA 92618
Tel.: (949) 417-0694
Web Site: http://www.kobrandwineandspirits.com
Sales Range: $25-49.9 Million
Emp.: 2
Wines & Spirits Distiller
N.A.I.C.S.: 445320
Kirk Walker *(VP & Mgr-Western Div)*

KOCH & LOWY, INC.
481 W Main St, Avon, MA 02322
Tel.: (508) 588-4700 MA
Year Founded: 1945
Sales Range: $50-74.9 Million
Emp.: 25
Lamps, Fixtures, Furniture & Accessories Mfr
N.A.I.C.S.: 335131
Tom Ruskin *(CEO)*
Rosanne Regent *(VP)*

KOCH DEVELOPMENT CORPORATION
452 E Christmas Blvd, Santa Claus, IN 47579
Tel.: (812) 937-4401 IN
Web Site: http://www.holidayworld.com
Year Founded: 1946
Sales Range: $10-24.9 Million
Emp.: 1,150
Theme Parks
N.A.I.C.S.: 713110
Matt Eckert *(Gen Mgr)*

KOCH ENTERPRISES, INC.
14 S 11th Ave, Evansville, IN 47712
Tel.: (812) 465-9800 IN
Web Site: http://www.kochenterprises.com
Year Founded: 1873
Sales Range: $700-749.9 Million
Emp.: 2,000
Holding Company; Automotive Parts & Accessories & Heating & Air-Conditioning Products
N.A.I.C.S.: 331523
Robert L. Koch II *(Chm)*
Susan E. Parsons *(CFO, Treas & Sec)*
James H. Muehlbauer *(Vice Chm)*
Jennifer Slade *(Dir-Mktg)*
Kevin R. Koch *(Pres & CEO)*

Subsidiaries:

Audubon Metals LLC (1)
3055 Ohio Dr, Henderson, KY 42420-4394 (51%)
Tel.: (270) 830-6622
Web Site: http://www.audubonmetals.com
Producer of Secondary Specification Aluminum Alloy & Heavy-media Separator
N.A.I.C.S.: 331314
Rob Harris *(VP-Raw Materials)*
Brian Hawkes *(Pres)*

Brake Supply Co. (1)
5501 Foundation Blvd, Evansville, IN 47725 (100%)
Tel.: (812) 467-1000
Web Site: http://www.brake.com

Sales Range: $25-49.9 Million
Emp.: 175
Distribution of Machinery & Air Conditioners
N.A.I.C.S.: 423810
Tom Berkley *(Exec VP)*
John Breeden *(Mgr-Inside Sls)*
Jon Umphlett *(Mgr-Sls-Western Div)*
Kevin Koch *(Chm)*
David Koch *(Pres & CEO)*
Richard Barron *(Dir-HR)*
Mike Brown *(Mgr-Mktg & Pricing)*
Jeff Garner *(Mgr-Marine Product)*
Tony Hammel *(Mgr-Quality Sys)*
Barry Heichelbech *(CFO)*

George Koch Sons Europe Ltd. (1)
City House Davidson Road, Lichfield, WS14 9DZ, Staffordshire, United Kingdom
Tel.: (44) 1543444001
Web Site: http://www.kochllc.com
Sales Range: $10-24.9 Million
Emp.: 22
Automated Finishing System Mfr
N.A.I.C.S.: 332813
Tom Mercer *(Mng Dir)*

George Koch Sons LLC (1)
10 S 11th Ave, Evansville, IN 47744 (100%)
Tel.: (812) 465-9600
Web Site: http://www.kochllc.com
Sales Range: $25-49.9 Million
Emp.: 140
Engineering & Building of Industrial Painting Systems & Specialized Coating & Drying Systems
N.A.I.C.S.: 333519

George Koch Sons de Mexico S. de R.L. de C.V. (1)
Av Pirineos 535 Bodegas 7 Y 8 Zona Industrial Benito Juarez, Col El Campanario, 76120, Queretaro, Mexico
Tel.: (52) 4422510500
Automated Finishing System Distr
N.A.I.C.S.: 423830

Gibbs Die Casting Corp. (1)
369 Community Dr, Henderson, KY 42420-4336 (100%)
Tel.: (270) 827-1801
Web Site: http://www.gibbsdc.com
Sales Range: $25-49.9 Million
Emp.: 900
Custom Aluminum Die Casting Mfr
N.A.I.C.S.: 331523
Steve A. Church *(Pres & CEO)*

Gibbs-Hungary Die Casting Kft. (1)
Ipari Park 4, Retsag, 2651, Hungary
Tel.: (36) 35551100
Emp.: 130
Die Casting Component Mfr
N.A.I.C.S.: 333517
Lajos Decsei *(Gen Mgr)*

Koch Air (1)
3141 Riverport Technical Center Dr, Maryland Heights, MO 63043 (100%)
Tel.: (314) 768-4200
Web Site: http://www.kochair.com
Sales Range: $10-24.9 Million
Emp.: 80
Distr of Air-Conditioning, Heating & Ventilating Equipment, Parts & Supplies
N.A.I.C.S.: 423730
Francis Leisure *(Mgr-Comml Sls)*

Koch Air LLC (1)
1900 W Lloyd Expy PO Box 1167 47706, Evansville, IN 47744-0001 (100%)
Tel.: (812) 962-5200
Web Site: http://www.kochair.com
Sales Range: $25-49.9 Million
Emp.: 200
HVAC Equipment, Parts & Supplies Distr
N.A.I.C.S.: 423730
David Koch *(VP-Residential Sls & Mktg)*
Brad Muehlbauer *(Pres)*

Subsidiary (Domestic):

Lathrop-Trotter Co, Inc. (2)
5006 Barrow Ave, Cincinnati, OH 45209
Tel.: (513) 731-5000
Web Site: http://www.lathroptrotter.com
Sales Range: $1-9.9 Million
Emp.: 13
Industrial Machinery & Equipment Merchant Whslr

U.S. PRIVATE

N.A.I.C.S.: 423830
Steve Schneider *(VP)*
Rick Sparrow *(Pres)*
Jon Green *(Engr-Sls)*
T. J. Mueller *(Engr-Sls)*

South Western Communications, Inc. (1)
4871 Rosebud Ln, Newburgh, IN 47630
Tel.: (812) 477-6495
Web Site: http://www.swc.net
Sales Range: $10-24.9 Million
Emp.: 35
Business Support Services
N.A.I.C.S.: 561499
Todd Lucy *(Pres)*

KOCH EXPLORATION COMPANY LLC
950 17th St Ste 1900, Denver, CO 80202
Tel.: (303) 325-2581
Web Site: http://www.kochexploration.com
Sales Range: $10-24.9 Million
Emp.: 20
Crude Petroleum Production
N.A.I.C.S.: 324110
Bryan Kissick *(VP-Exploration)*

KOCH FOODS, INC.
1300 W Higgins Rd Ste 1000, Park Ridge, IL 60068-5743
Tel.: (847) 384-5940 IL
Web Site: https://www.kochfoods.com
Year Founded: 1959
Sales Range: $1-4.9 Billion
Emp.: 14,000
Packaged Frozen Food Merchant Whslr
N.A.I.C.S.: 424420

Subsidiaries:

Aspen Foods (1)
1115 W Fulton Market, Chicago, IL 60607-1213
Tel.: (847) 384-5940
Web Site: http://www.kochfoods.com
Sales Range: $25-49.9 Million
Emp.: 160
Processor of Poultry
N.A.I.C.S.: 311615

Koch Foods LLC (1)
329 Oak St NW Ste 001, Gainesville, GA 30501
Tel.: (770) 536-8818
Sales Range: $50-74.9 Million
Emp.: 700
Processor of Poultry
N.A.I.C.S.: 311615
Peter Gress *(VP-Intl Sls)*
Bill Fasulo *(Dir-Pur)*

Koch Foods LLC (1)
1835 Kerr St, Chattanooga, TN 37401-0749 (100%)
Tel.: (423) 266-0351
Sales Range: $10-24.9 Million
Emp.: 3
Sausages & Other Prepared Meats Distr
N.A.I.C.S.: 424440
Gary Talley *(Gen Mgr)*

Koch Poultry (1)
1300 Higgins Rd, Park Ridge, IL 60668
Tel.: (847) 384-5940
Rev: $33,400,000
Emp.: 40
Poultry Products
N.A.I.C.S.: 424420

KOCH INDUSTRIES, INC.
4111 E 37th St N, Wichita, KS 67220
Tel.: (316) 828-5500 KS
Web Site: http://www.kochind.com
Year Founded: 1940
Sales Range: Less than $1 Million
Emp.: 120,000
Offices of Other Holding Companies
N.A.I.C.S.: 551112
Richard Kevin Dinkel *(CFO & Sr VP)*

COMPANIES

KOCH INDUSTRIES, INC.

Subsidiaries:

Flint Group SA (1)
26b Boulevard Royal, 2449, Luxembourg, Luxembourg
Web Site: http://www.flintgrp.com
Sales Range: $1-4.9 Billion
Emp.: 6,800
Holding Company; Printing Inks & Colourants Mfr & Distr
N.A.I.C.S.: 551112
William B. Miller *(Pres-Print Media-Transatlantic & Japan)*
Doug Aldred *(Pres-Packaging & Narrow Web-EMEA & North America)*
Jan Paul van der Velde *(Sr VP-Procurement, Sustainability, Regulatory & IT)*
Adhemur Pilar *(Pres-Flint Grp-Latin America)*
Rico Hagedorn *(Sr Mgr-Technical Svcs Plates-Flexographic Products)*
Benoit Chatelard *(Pres/CEO-Digital Solutions)*
Dagmar Schmidt *(Pres-Flexographic)*

Subsidiary (Non-US):

Flint Group GmbH (2)
Siegle Strasse 25, 70469, Stuttgart, Germany
Tel.: (49) 71198160
Web Site: https://www.flintgrp.com
Sales Range: $1-4.9 Billion
Emp.: 1,040
Printing Ink, Plate & Colorant Mfr
N.A.I.C.S.: 551114

Subsidiary (US):

Flint Group, Inc. (3)
4550 Main St Ste 220, Kansas City, MO 64111
Tel.: (816) 226-6924
Web Site: http://www.flintgrp.com
Sales Range: $1-4.9 Billion
Emp.: 150
Ink & Coating Mfr
N.A.I.C.S.: 325910
Adhemur Pilar *(Pres)*
Benoit Chatelard *(Pres-Digital Solutions)*
Pierre-Marie De Leener *(Chm)*
Michael Fien *(Chief Digitalisation Officer)*

Subsidiary (Domestic):

Cranney Companies, Inc. (4)
24 Water St, Danvers, MA 01923
Tel.: (978) 716-5698
Web Site: http://www.cranneyhomeservices.com
Electrical Contractor
N.A.I.C.S.: 238210
Joe Ciampa *(Gen Mgr)*
Brian Cranney *(Owner)*

Southwest Plumbing & Water Heaters, Inc. (4)
2401 SW Alaska St, Seattle, WA 98106
Tel.: (206) 932-1777
Web Site: http://www.southwestplumbing.biz
Plumbing, Heating & Air-Conditioning Contractors
N.A.I.C.S.: 238220

Subsidiary (Non-US):

Xeikon NV (3)
Brieversstraat 70, 4529 GZ, Ede, Netherlands
Tel.: (31) 117 37 50 20
Web Site: http://www.xeikon.com
Digital Printing Machinery Mfr & Marketer
N.A.I.C.S.: 333248
Benoit Chatelard *(Pres & CEO)*
Vlad Sljapic *(VP-Sls-Global)*
Robert Welford *(VP-R&D)*

Subsidiary (US):

Xeikon America, Inc. (4)
1375 E Irving Park Rd, Itasca, IL 60143
Tel.: (630) 438-7900
Web Site: https://www.xeikon.com
Developer, Mfr & Distr of High Quality Digital Printing Systems
N.A.I.C.S.: 333248

Subsidiary (Non-US):

Xeikon Japan Co., Ltd. (4)
3-1-3 Yushima, Bunkyo-Ku, Tokyo, 113-0034, Japan
Tel.: (81) 358070210
Web Site: http://www.xeikon.jp
Digital Color Printing Solutions
N.A.I.C.S.: 323111

Xeikon Manufacturing and R&D Center (4)
Duwijckstraat 17, 2500, Lier, Belgium
Tel.: (32) 34431311
Web Site: http://www.xeikon.com
Provider of Digital Color Printing Solutions
N.A.I.C.S.: 323111

Flint Hills Resources, LLC (1)
4111 E 37th St N, Wichita, KS 67220
Tel.: (316) 828-3477
Web Site: http://www.fhr.com
Holding Company; Petroleum Refinery & Terminal Operator; Petroleum Products, Chemicals & Biofuels Mfr & Whslr
N.A.I.C.S.: 457120
Alan D. Hallock *(Gen Counsel, Sec & exec VP)*
Anthony J. Sementelli *(CFO & Exec VP)*
David C. Dotson *(Exec VP-Ops)*
Jeffrey P. Ramsey *(Exec VP-Mktg)*
James B. Urban *(Exec VP-Supply & Trading)*
Patricia A. Calvert *(Sr VP-HR)*
Sheryl Corrigan *(Sr VP-Environment, Health & Safety)*
Marji McNeill *(VP-Compliance & Ethics)*
Jeremy Morse *(Mgr-Production)*

Subsidiary (Domestic):

FHR Propylene LLC (2)
9822 La Porte Fwy, Houston, TX 77017
Tel.: (713) 740-3900
Web Site: http://www.fhr.com
Sales Range: $750-799.9 Million
Emp.: 110
Propylene Mfr
N.A.I.C.S.: 325110
Peter Hentges *(Ops Mgr)*

Subsidiary (Non-US):

Flint Hills Resources Canada, LP (2)
111 5th Ave SW Ste 1510, Calgary, T2P 3Y6, AB, Canada (100%)
Tel.: (403) 716-7600
Web Site: http://www.fhr.com
Emp.: 15
Petroleum Wholesale Trade Broker
N.A.I.C.S.: 425120

Subsidiary (Domestic):

Flint Hills Resources Chemical Intermediates, LLC (2)
1 Michigan St, Joliet, IL 60432
Tel.: (815) 467-3200
Web Site: http://www.fhr.com
Emp.: 250
Chemical Intermediates Mfr
N.A.I.C.S.: 325199

Flint Hills Resources, LP (2)
4111 E 37th St N, Wichita, KS 67220-3203
Tel.: (316) 828-5755
Web Site: http://www.fhr.com
Petroleum Bulk Terminal Operator
N.A.I.C.S.: 424710
Bradley J. Razook *(Pres & CEO)*
Jeff Cook *(Dir-External Affairs)*
David C. Dotson *(Exec VP-Ops)*
James B. Urban *(Exec VP-Supply & Trading)*

Georgia-Pacific LLC (1)
133 Peachtree St NE, Atlanta, GA 30303
Tel.: (404) 652-4000
Web Site: http://www.gp.com
Sales Range: $1-4.9 Billion
Emp.: 50,000
Pulp, Paper, Packaging, Building Products & Related Chemicals Mfr
N.A.I.C.S.: 424130
Shiela M. Weidman *(Sr VP-Comm, Govt & Pub Affairs)*
Tyler Woolson *(CFO & Sr VP)*
Julie Brehm *(Sr VP-HR)*
Tye Darland *(Gen Counsel & Sr VP)*
Mark Luetters *(Exec VP-Building Products)*
David Park *(Sr VP-Strategy & Bus Dev)*
Randal Robison *(Sr VP)*
W. Wesley Jones *(Sr VP-Ops Excellence & Compliance)*
Mike E. Adams *(Sr VP-Sourcing)*
Terry Cinotte *(Pres-Pkg)*
Christian Fischer *(Pres & CEO)*
Rob Barger *(Chief Digital Officer)*
Steve Clancey *(CIO)*
Scott Light *(Exec VP-Pkg & Cellulose)*
Barbara Whiteside *(Sr VP-Compliance & Ethics)*
Jeff Koeppel *(Sr VP-Ops)*
Kevin Heath *(VP-Strategic Sourcing, Procurement, Capital, MRO & Direct Matls)*
Lori Chennault *(Sr VP-Sourcing & Procurement)*
Curley M. Dossman Jr. *(Pres-Foundation)*

Joint Venture (Non-US):

Canfor Georgia-Pacific Japan Corporation (2)
Arco Tower 16F I-8-1 Shimo-Meguro, Meguro-ku, Tokyo, 153-0064, Japan (50%)
Tel.: (81) 354345778
Web Site: http://www.canforpulp.com
Sales Range: $50-74.9 Million
Marketing Consulting Services
N.A.I.C.S.: 541613

Subsidiary (Domestic):

Dixie Consumer Products LLC (2)
133 Peachtree St NE, Atlanta, GA 30303
Tel.: (404) 652-4000
Web Site: http://www.dixie.com
Tabletop Products Mfr
N.A.I.C.S.: 322299

Plant (Domestic):

G-P Gypsum Corp. - Acme (3)
Loop 285 PO Box 330, Quanah, TX 79252
Tel.: (940) 663-6111
Sales Range: $100-124.9 Million
Emp.: 130
Gypsum Product Mfr
N.A.I.C.S.: 327420

G-P Gypsum Corp. - Antioch (3)
801 Minaker Dr, Antioch, CA 94509
Tel.: (925) 757-2870
Sales Range: $100-124.9 Million
Emp.: 105
Gypsum Product Mfr
N.A.I.C.S.: 327420

G-P Gypsum Corp. - Blue Rapids (3)
2127 US Hwy 77, Blue Rapids, KS 66411
Tel.: (785) 363-7767
Web Site: http://www.gp.com
Sales Range: $100-124.9 Million
Emp.: 115
Gypsum Product Mfr
N.A.I.C.S.: 327420

G-P Gypsum Corp. - Camden (3)
1101 S Front St, Camden, NJ 08103
Tel.: (856) 966-7600
Sales Range: $100-124.9 Million
Emp.: 100
Gypsum Product Mfr
N.A.I.C.S.: 327420

G-P Gypsum Corp. - Newington (3)
170 Shattuck Way, Newington, NH 03801
Tel.: (603) 433-8000
Sales Range: $125-149.9 Million
Emp.: 150
Gypsum Product Mfr
N.A.I.C.S.: 327420

G-P Gypsum Corp. - San Leandro (3)
1988 Marina Blvd, San Leandro, CA 94577
Tel.: (510) 483-7580
Web Site: http://www.gp.com
Sales Range: $100-124.9 Million
Emp.: 110
Gypsum Product Mfr
N.A.I.C.S.: 327420

G-P Gypsum Corp. - Savannah (3)
151 Wahlstrom Rd, Savannah, GA 31404
Tel.: (912) 233-4951
Sales Range: $100-124.9 Million
Emp.: 100
Gypsum Product Mfr
N.A.I.C.S.: 327420

G-P Gypsum Corp. - Wheatfield (3)
484 E County Rd 1400 N, Wheatfield, IN 46392-8817
Tel.: (219) 956-3100
Sales Range: $100-124.9 Million
Emp.: 110
Gypsum Product Mfr
N.A.I.C.S.: 327420

Subsidiary (Domestic):

G-P Gypsum Corporation (3)
133 Peachtree St NE, Atlanta, GA 30303 (100%)
Tel.: (404) 652-4000
Web Site: http://www.buildgp.com
Gypsum Product Mfr
N.A.I.C.S.: 327420
Brent Paugh *(Pres)*

Insulair, Inc. (3)
35275 Welty Rd, Vernalis, CA 95385
Tel.: (209) 839-0911
Sales Range: $1-9.9 Million
Emp.: 60
Insulated Drinking Cup Mfr
N.A.I.C.S.: 322299

Subsidiary (Domestic):

Encadria Staffing Solutions, Inc. (2)
133 Peachtree St NE Ste 200, Atlanta, GA 30303-1808 (100%)
Tel.: (404) 652-5493
Web Site: http://www.encadria.com
Sales Range: $25-49.9 Million
Emp.: 10
Staffing Services
N.A.I.C.S.: 561311
Eddie Ray *(Gen Mgr)*

G-P Wood & Fiber Supply, LLC (2)
133 Peachtree St NE, Atlanta, GA 30303-1808 (100%)
Tel.: (404) 652-3552
Web Site: http://www.gp.com
Sales Range: $25-49.9 Million
Emp.: 100
Logs, Wood Fiber & Chips Mfr
N.A.I.C.S.: 321999

Plant (Domestic):

Georgia Pacific Pulp & Paper Mill (3)
Hwy 273 W PO Box 44, Cedar Springs, GA 31732
Tel.: (404) 652-6878
Sales Range: $75-99.9 Million
Softwood & Hardwood Pulpwood Mfr
N.A.I.C.S.: 322120

Georgia-Pacific Corporation (3)
223 Gordon Chapel Rd, Hawthorne, FL 32640-5426
Tel.: (352) 481-4311
Sales Range: $25-49.9 Million
Emp.: 6
Hardwood & Plywood Mfr
N.A.I.C.S.: 321211

Georgia-Pacific Corporation (3)
1400 Woodkraft Rd, Madison, GA 30650-3944
Tel.: (706) 342-4300
Sales Range: $75-99.9 Million
Sawmills
N.A.I.C.S.: 321113
Kenneth Baas *(Office Mgr)*

Georgia-Pacific Corporation (3)
106 Old Augusta Rd Hwy 29, New Augusta, MS 39462
Tel.: (601) 964-7400
Web Site: http://www.gp.com
Sales Range: $25-49.9 Million
Emp.: 1
Saw & Planing Mill
N.A.I.C.S.: 321113

Georgia-Pacific Corporation (3)
11795 Hwy 501 S, Gladys, VA 24554
Tel.: (434) 283-1066
Web Site: http://www.gp.com
Sales Range: $25-49.9 Million
Pine & Hardwood Mfr
N.A.I.C.S.: 321211
Morgan Thomas *(Plant Mgr)*

Georgia-Pacific Corporation (3)
Hwy 51 S, Duck Hill, MS 38925

KOCH INDUSTRIES, INC.

U.S. PRIVATE

Koch Industries, Inc.—(Continued)
Tel.: (662) 226-8634
Sales Range: $50-74.9 Million
Pine & Hardwood Mfr
N.A.I.C.S.: 321211

Georgia-Pacific Fayette Lumber Plant (3)
545 County Rd 6, Belk, AL 35545
Tel.: (205) 932-3243
Sales Range: $25-49.9 Million
Emp.: 80
Pine Sawmill Products Mfr
N.A.I.C.S.: 321113
David Clemen *(Mgr)*

Georgia-Pacific Monticello Pre-Finished MDF Plant (3)
791 Georgia Pacific Rd, Monticello, GA 31064-0386
Tel.: (706) 468-8811
Web Site: http://www.gp.com
Sales Range: $25-49.9 Million
Emp.: 100
Plywood & Hardboard Mfr
N.A.I.C.S.: 321211

Georgia-Pacific Oriented Strand Board Plant (3)
79 N Pax Ave, Mount Hope, WV 25880
Tel.: (304) 877-5656
Web Site: http://www.gp.com
Sales Range: $50-74.9 Million
Pine & Hardwood Mfr
N.A.I.C.S.: 321211

Georgia-Pacific Oriented Strand Board Plant (3)
Hwy 301 S, Skippers, VA 23879
Tel.: (804) 634-8366
Web Site: http://www.gp.com
Sales Range: $50-74.9 Million
Pine & Hardwood Mfr
N.A.I.C.S.: 321211

Georgia-Pacific Palatka Pulp & Paper Operations (3)
215 County Rd 216, Palatka, FL 32177
Tel.: (386) 325-2001
Web Site: http://www.gp.com
Sales Range: $250-299.9 Million
Emp.: 1,200
Pulp & Paper Mfr
N.A.I.C.S.: 322120

Georgia-Pacific Pine Chip & Saw Mill (3)
134 Buck Creek Rd PO Box 329, New Augusta, MS 39462
Tel.: (601) 964-7136
Web Site: http://www.gp.com
Sales Range: $25-49.9 Million
Pine Chip & Saw Wood Mfr
N.A.I.C.S.: 321113

Georgia-Pacific Plywood Plant (3)
100 Mill Supply Rd PO Box 3333, Crossett, AR 71635
Tel.: (870) 567-5014
Web Site: http://www.gp.com
Plywood Mfr
N.A.I.C.S.: 321211

Georgia-Pacific Plywood Plant (3)
634 Davis St, Emporia, VA 23847-6460
Tel.: (434) 634-5123
Sales Range: $75-99.9 Million
Plywood Products Mfr
N.A.I.C.S.: 321211
Steve Russo *(Dir-HR)*

Georgia-Pacific Plywood Plant (3)
139 Bluenton Rd, Dudley, NC 28333-0308
Tel.: (919) 736-4385
Sales Range: $50-74.9 Million
Plywood Mfr
N.A.I.C.S.: 334515

Georgia-Pacific Pulp & Paper Mill (3)
1400 SE Butler Bridge Rd, Toledo, OR 97391-1900
Tel.: (541) 336-2211
Web Site: http://www.gp.com
Sales Range: $75-99.9 Million
Emp.: 300
Softwood & Hardwood Pulpwood Mfr
N.A.I.C.S.: 322120
Ken Li *(Mgr-Mill)*

Georgia-Pacific Pulp & Paper Mill (3)
9363 Lee Jackson Hwy, Big Island, VA 24526
Tel.: (434) 299-5911
Web Site: http://www.gp.com
Sales Range: $25-49.9 Million
Softwood & Hardwood Pulpwood Mfr
N.A.I.C.S.: 322120

Georgia-Pacific Pulp & Paper Mill (3)
401 Northeast Adams, Camas, WA 98607
Tel.: (360) 834-3021
Web Site: http://www.gp.com
Sales Range: $75-99.9 Million
Softwood & Hardwood Pulpwood Mfr
N.A.I.C.S.: 322120

Georgia-Pacific Saw Mill (3)
63779 Mullen Rd, Coos Bay, OR 97420-4030
Tel.: (541) 269-1171
Web Site: http://www.gp.com
Sales Range: $25-49.9 Million
Emp.: 80
Softwood & Hardwood Pulpwood Mfr
N.A.I.C.S.: 322120
Ron Partin *(Mgr-Mfg)*

Georgia-Pacific Softwood Sawmill (3)
24808 Alsea Hwy, Philomath, OR 97370-9529
Tel.: (541) 929-2323
Web Site: http://www.gp.com
Sales Range: $25-49.9 Million
Softwood Mfr
N.A.I.C.S.: 321113

Subsidiary (Domestic):

GP Cellulose, LLC (2)
1400 W 9th St, Brunswick, GA 31520
Tel.: (912) 279-2660
Web Site: http://www.gpcellulose.com
Sales Range: $50-74.9 Million
Emp.: 785
Pulp Mfr
N.A.I.C.S.: 322110

Subsidiary (Domestic):

Brunswick Cellulose (3)
1400 W 9th St, Brunswick, GA 31520
Tel.: (912) 265-5780
Web Site: http://www.gppackaging.com
Sales Range: $50-74.9 Million
Emp.: 600
Mfr of Pulp, Sawmill & Planing Products
N.A.I.C.S.: 322110

Subsidiary (Non-US):

Georgia-Pacific Canada, Inc. (2)
319 Allanburg Rd, Thorold, L2V 5C3, ON, Canada (100%)
Tel.: (905) 227-6651
Web Site: http://www.gp.com
Sales Range: $50-74.9 Million
Emp.: 640
Gypsum Product Mfr
N.A.I.C.S.: 327420

Subsidiary (Domestic):

Georgia-Pacific Consumer Products LP (2)
133 Peachtree St NE, Atlanta, GA 30303
Tel.: (404) 652-6630
Web Site: http://www.gppro.com
Tissue Mfr
N.A.I.C.S.: 322220
Dwayne Hooper *(Mgr-Print Production-Tissue/Towel Div)*

Georgia-Pacific Containerboard LLC (2)
9363 Lee Jackson Hwy, Big Island, VA 24526
Tel.: (434) 299-5911
Packaging Container Mfr
N.A.I.C.S.: 322219

Plant (Domestic):

Georgia-Pacific Corporation Pryor (2)
Hwy 69a PO Box 578, Pryor, OK 74362
Tel.: (918) 825-4100

Sales Range: $50-74.9 Million
Emp.: 125
Gypsum Product Mfr
N.A.I.C.S.: 327420

Georgia-Pacific Green Bay Operations (3)
1919 S Broadway, Green Bay, WI 54304
Tel.: (920) 435-8821
Web Site: http://www.gp.com
Sales Range: $750-799.9 Million
Emp.: 3,636
Bath Tissue, Towels & Napkins Mfr; Tissue Recycling Services
N.A.I.C.S.: 322291
Sandee Laundre *(Dir-Procurement Ops Excellence)*
Glenn Busch *(Mgr-Mechanical Engrg)*
Donn Clermont *(Mgr-Transportation)*

Subsidiary (Domestic):

Georgia-Pacific Gypsum LLC (2)
133 Peachtree St NE, Atlanta, GA 30303
Tel.: (404) 652-4000
Web Site: http://www.gp.com
Emp.: 35,000
Gypsum Mfr
N.A.I.C.S.: 327420
Tim Murphy *(Dir-Plng & Analysis)*

Plant (Domestic):

Georgia-Pacific Gypsum LLC - Las Vegas Toughrock Plant (3)
114 US Highway 91, North Las Vegas, NV 89165
Tel.: (702) 643-8100
Web Site: http://buildgp.com
Emp.: 140
Gypsum Product Mfr
N.A.I.C.S.: 327420

Subsidiary (Domestic):

Georgia-Pacific Packaging Division (2)
133 Peachtree St NE, Atlanta, GA 30303-1808
Tel.: (404) 652-4000
Web Site: http://www.gp.com
Corrugated Containers & Specialty Packaging Products Mfr
N.A.I.C.S.: 322211

Plant (Domestic):

Georgia-Pacific Corporation (3)
133 Peachtree St NE, Atlanta, GA 30303
Tel.: (610) 617-0600
Sales Range: $25-49.9 Million
Emp.: 125
Corrugated Containers Mfr
N.A.I.C.S.: 322211

Georgia-Pacific Corporation (3)
PO Box 35806, West Monroe, LA 71294-5806
Tel.: (318) 387-4444
Web Site: http://www.gp.com
Sales Range: $50-74.9 Million
Emp.: 200
Corrugated Containers Mfr
N.A.I.C.S.: 322211

Georgia-Pacific Corporation (3)
2850 Owens Rd, Circleville, OH 43113
Tel.: (740) 477-3347
Web Site: http://www.gp.com
Sales Range: $25-49.9 Million
Emp.: 130
Corrugated Containers Mfr
N.A.I.C.S.: 322211

Georgia-Pacific Corporation (3)
6300 Regio Ave, Buena Park, CA 90620
Tel.: (714) 521-4270
Web Site: http://www.gp.com
Sales Range: $50-74.9 Million
Emp.: 225
Corrugated Containers Mfr
N.A.I.C.S.: 322211

Georgia-Pacific Corporation (3)
8600 NE 38th St, Kansas City, MO 64161
Tel.: (816) 455-4160
Sales Range: $25-49.9 Million
Emp.: 125
Corrugated Containers Mfr
N.A.I.C.S.: 322211

Georgia-Pacific Corporation (3)
24600 Ave 13, Madera, CA 93637
Tel.: (559) 673-5111
Web Site: http://www.gppackaging.com
Sales Range: $50-74.9 Million
Emp.: 150
Corrugated Containers Mfr
N.A.I.C.S.: 322211

Georgia-Pacific Corporation (3)
623 Riegelsville Rd, Milford, NJ 08848
Tel.: (908) 995-2228
Web Site: http://www.gp.com
Sales Range: $25-49.9 Million
Emp.: 112
Corrugated Containers Mfr
N.A.I.C.S.: 322211
Dave Baily *(Gen Mgr)*

Georgia-Pacific Corporation (3)
900 S Rte 66, Mount Olive, IL 62069
Tel.: (217) 999-2511
Web Site: http://www.gp.com
Sales Range: $50-74.9 Million
Emp.: 150
Corrugated Containers Mfr
N.A.I.C.S.: 322211

Georgia-Pacific Corporation (3)
4200 Old Tasso Rd, Cleveland, TN 37312
Tel.: (423) 476-0236
Web Site: http://www.gp.com
Sales Range: $25-49.9 Million
Emp.: 100
Corrugated Containers Mfr
N.A.I.C.S.: 322211
Clay Reif *(Gen Mgr)*

Georgia-Pacific Corporation (3)
5800 N Hwy 35E, Waxahachie, TX 75165
Tel.: (940) 381-0137
Sales Range: $50-74.9 Million
Emp.: 130
Corrugated Containers Mfr
N.A.I.C.S.: 322211

Georgia-Pacific Corporation (3)
951 County St, Milan, MI 48160
Tel.: (734) 439-2441
Sales Range: $25-49.9 Million
Emp.: 100
Corrugated Containers Mfr
N.A.I.C.S.: 322211

Georgia-Pacific Corporation (3)
1 Owens Way, Bradford, PA 16701
Tel.: (814) 368-8700
Sales Range: $25-49.9 Million
Emp.: 111
Corrugated Containers Mfr
N.A.I.C.S.: 322211

Georgia-Pacific Corrugated-Martinsville Facility (3)
25 Industrial Park Dr, Ridgeway, VA 24148
Tel.: (276) 632-6301
Web Site: http://www.gppackaging.com
Sales Range: $50-74.9 Million
Emp.: 200
Corrugated Containers Mfr
N.A.I.C.S.: 322211
Curtis Hall *(Mgr)*

Georgia-Pacific Packaging - Augusta (3)
1745 Doug Barnard Pkwy, Augusta, GA 30906
Tel.: (706) 798-7420
Web Site: http://www.gp.com
Sales Range: $50-74.9 Million
Emp.: 180
Corrugated Containers Mfr
N.A.I.C.S.: 322211

Subsidiary (Domestic):

Georgia-Pacific Paper Division (2)
133 Peachtree St NE, Atlanta, GA 30303-1808
Tel.: (404) 652-4000
Web Site: http://www.gp.com
Sales Range: $150-199.9 Million
Emp.: 2,000
Paper Mfr
N.A.I.C.S.: 322120

Plant (Domestic):

Georgia Pacific Gurdon Wood Products Complex (3)

COMPANIES

Hwy 67, Gurdon, AR 71743
Tel.: (870) 353-4474
Web Site: http://www.gt.com
Sales Range: $75-99.9 Million
Emp.: 550
Lumber Mill
N.A.I.C.S.: 321113
Anne M. McGeorge *(Mng Partner-Health Care-Natl)*
Jeff T. French *(Mng Partner-Consumer & Indus Products-Natl)*
Mary Moore Hamrick *(Mng Principal-Pub Policy-Natl)*
Mike McGuire *(CEO)*
Srikant Sastry *(Mng Principal-Advisory Svcs-Natl)*
Mike Ward *(Mng Principal-Bus Advisory Svcs-Natl)*
Greg Davis *(Principal-Tech Solutions)*
Enzo Santilli *(Partner)*
Jeffrey L. Burgess *(Mng Partner-Audit Svcs-Natl)*
Randy D. Robason *(Mng Partner-Tax Svcs-Natl)*

Georgia-Pacific Corporation (3)
149 Hamilton St, Leominster, MA 01453-2342
Tel.: (323) 720-8500
Web Site: http://www.gp.com
Sales Range: $50-74.9 Million
Emp.: 300
Coated & Laminated Paper Mfr
N.A.I.C.S.: 322220

Georgia-Pacific Corporation (3)
1915 Marathon Ave, Neenah, WI 54956-4067
Tel.: (920) 729-8000
Web Site: http://www.gp.com
Sales Range: $50-74.9 Million
Emp.: 170
Paper Mfr
N.A.I.C.S.: 322120
Joseph A. Miller *(Gen Mgr)*

Georgia-Pacific Corporation (3)
400 Island Ave, Kalamazoo, MI 49004
Tel.: (269) 226-2200
Web Site: http://www.gp.com
Sales Range: $50-74.9 Million
Emp.: 200
Paper Mfr
N.A.I.C.S.: 322120
Erica Hauser *(Mgr-HR)*

Georgia-Pacific Muskogee (3)
4901 Chandler Rd, Muskogee, OK 74403-4945
Tel.: (918) 683-7671
Web Site: http://www.georgiapacific.com
Sales Range: $200-249.9 Million
Emp.: 1,200
Tissue Paper Mfr
N.A.I.C.S.: 322120
Rodney Bond *(Plant Mgr)*

Subsidiary (Domestic):

Georgia-Pacific Resins, Inc. (2)
133 Peachtree St NE, Atlanta, GA 30303 (100%)
Tel.: (404) 652-4000
Web Site: http://www.gp.com
Sales Range: $150-199.9 Million
Emp.: 1,300
Chemical Products Mfr For the Paper, Pulp & Building Products Industries
N.A.I.C.S.: 424690
Rick Urschel *(Pres)*
Dennis Easter *(VP/Gen Mgr-Thermosets)*

Plant (Domestic):

Georgia-Pacific Resins Taylorsville (3)
Hwy 28 W, Taylorsville, MS 39168
Tel.: (601) 785-6523
Sales Range: $25-49.9 Million
Emp.: 60
Formaldehyde & Wood Adhesives Mfr
N.A.I.C.S.: 325998
Steve Harriman *(Plant Mgr)*

Georgia-Pacific Resins Vienna (3)
7th St S, Vienna, GA 31092
Tel.: (229) 268-4181
Web Site: http://www.gp.com
Sales Range: $50-74.9 Million
Emp.: 150
Formaldehyde, Wood Adhesives & Industrial Resins Mfr
N.A.I.C.S.: 325998

Subsidiary (Domestic):

Georgia-Pacific Resins, Inc. (3)
2883 Miller Rd, Decatur, GA 30035
Tel.: (770) 593-6800
Web Site: http://www.gp.com
Sales Range: $25-49.9 Million
Emp.: 100
Commercial Physical Research & Technical Center
N.A.I.C.S.: 541715

Subsidiary (Domestic):

Georgia-Pacific West, Inc. (2)
401 NE Adam St, Camas, WA 98607-2090 (100%)
Tel.: (360) 834-8300
Web Site: http://www.gpcamas.com
Sales Range: $50-74.9 Million
Emp.: 700
Towels, Tissue & Communication Papers Mfr
N.A.I.C.S.: 322299

Georgia-Pacific Wood Products LLC (2)
1220 W Railroad St, Duluth, MN 55802-2647
Tel.: (218) 727-6891
Sales Range: $25-49.9 Million
Emp.: 150
Hardboard Mfr
N.A.I.C.S.: 321211

Old Augusta Railroad Company (2)
134 Buck Creek Rd, New Augusta, MS 39462
Tel.: (601) 964-8411
Sales Range: $25-49.9 Million
Emp.: 9
Industrial Short Line Rail Services
N.A.I.C.S.: 482112

Reliable Container Corporation (2)
9206 Santa Fe Springs Rd, Santa Fe Springs, CA 90670
Tel.: (562) 861-6226
Web Site: http://www.reliablecontainer.com
Sales Range: $25-49.9 Million
Emp.: 100
Distr of Industrial & Personal Service Paper
N.A.I.C.S.: 424130
Dan E. Brough Sr. *(Pres)*

Guardian Industries Corp. (1)
2300 Harmon Rd, Auburn Hills, MI 48326-1714
Tel.: (248) 340-1800
Web Site: http://www.guardian.com
Emp.: 18,000
Insulation, Glass & Automotive Parts Mfr
N.A.I.C.S.: 327211
Ron Vaupel *(Pres & CEO)*
Luisa Delclaux *(Mng Dir-Glass Svcs)*

Subsidiary (Non-US):

Guardian Africa Corp (Pty) Ltd. (2)
The Burns Industrial Park Unit 2 12 Jet Park Road, Boksburg, 1459, South Africa
Tel.: (27) 11 826 6019
Web Site: http://www.guardianglass.com
Automotive Glass Mfr
N.A.I.C.S.: 327215

Guardian Europe S.a.r.l. (2)
Zone Industrielle Wolser, Dudelange, L-3452, Luxembourg
Tel.: (352) 521111
Web Site: http://www.guardianglass.com
Glass Mfr
N.A.I.C.S.: 327215

Guardian Flachglas GmbH (2)
Guardianstrasse 1, 06766, Thalheim, Germany
Tel.: (49) 3494 361 500
Web Site: http://www.guardianglass.com
Glass Mfr
N.A.I.C.S.: 327215

Subsidiary (Domestic):

Guardian Glass Company (2)
2300 Harmon Rd, Auburn Hills, MI 48326
Tel.: (248) 340-1800
Web Site: http://www.guardianglass.com
Glass Mfr

N.A.I.C.S.: 327211

Plant (Domestic):

Guardian Glass Co. - Corsicana Plant (3)
3801 S US Hwy 287, Corsicana, TX 75109-9373
Tel.: (903) 872-4871
Web Site: http://www.guardianglass.com
Flat Glass Mfr
N.A.I.C.S.: 327211

Guardian Glass Co. - Kingsbury Plant (3)
11535 E Mountain View, Kingsburg, CA 93631
Tel.: (559) 896-6400
Web Site: http://www.guardianglass.com
Flat Glass Mfr
N.A.I.C.S.: 327211

Guardian Glass Co. - Millbury Plant (3)
24145 W Moline Martin Rd, Millbury, OH 43447-9524
Tel.: (419) 855-7706
Web Site: http://www.guardianglass.com
Glass Mfr
N.A.I.C.S.: 327211

Subsidiary (Non-US):

Guardian Glass Espana Central Vidriera S.L. (2)
Avda Egas Moniz Area de Villafranca de Xira-Porto Alta, Samora Correia, 2135-402, Lisbon, Portugal
Tel.: (351) 263 654495
Web Site: http://www.guardianglass.com
Glass Mfr
N.A.I.C.S.: 327215

Guardian Industrie France SAS (2)
8 Rue des Emerauldes, 38280, Villette, France
Tel.: (33) 4 28 67 89 56
Sales Range: $10-24.9 Million
Glass Product Warehousing & Distr
N.A.I.C.S.: 423390

Unit (Domestic):

Guardian Industries Corp - Richburg Plant (2)
610 L & C Railway District Park, Richburg, SC 29729
Tel.: (803) 789-6100
Web Site: http://www.guardianglass.com
Flat Glass Mfr
N.A.I.C.S.: 327211

Subsidiary (Non-US):

Guardian Industries Corp. Ltd. (2)
42 Moo 7 Nongplamoh Sub District, Siam Cement Industrial Estate, 18140, Nongkhae, Saraburi, Thailand
Tel.: (66) 36373373
Web Site: http://www.guardian-thailand.com
Flat Glass Mfr
N.A.I.C.S.: 327212

Guardian Industries Poland Sp.z.o.o. (2)
ul W Korfantego 31/35, 42-200, Czestochowa, Poland
Tel.: (48) 34 323 9 200
Web Site: http://www.guardianglass.com
Glass Mfr
N.A.I.C.S.: 327215

Guardian Industries UK LTD (2)
Tom Pudding Way, Goole, DN14 8GA, East Yorkshire, United Kingdom
Tel.: (44) 1405 726800
Web Site: http://www.guardianglass.com
Flat Glass Mfr
N.A.I.C.S.: 327211

Guardian Industries Vp, S. De R.L. De C.V. (2)
Carretera a Chichimequillas Km 9.6 La Griega, El Marques, 76249, Mexico
Tel.: (52) 442 278 1700
Web Site: http://www.guardianglass.com
Flat Glass Mfr
N.A.I.C.S.: 327211

Guardian Llodio Uno, S.L. (2)

KOCH INDUSTRIES, INC.

Jose Matia No 36, 01400, Llodio, Alava, Spain
Tel.: (34) 94 671 9509
Web Site: http://www.guardianglass.com
Flat Glass Mfr
N.A.I.C.S.: 327211

Guardian Luxguard I S.A. (2)
8 rue Bommel, Grande-Duchy, Bascharage, 4940, Luxembourg
Tel.: (352) 50 301
Web Site: http://www.guardianglass.com
Flat Glass Mfr
N.A.I.C.S.: 327215

Guardian Navarra S.L. (2)
Poligono Industrial Montes de Cierzo CN 232 Km 86, Apdo Correos 366, Navarra, 31500, Tudela, Spain
Tel.: (34) 948 81 7209
Web Site: http://www.guardianglass.com
Glass Mfr
N.A.I.C.S.: 327215

Guardian Oroshaza Co. Ltd. (2)
Csorvasi ut 31, Oroshaza, 5900, Hungary
Tel.: (36) 68 887 200
Web Site: http://www.guardianglass.com
Glass Mfr
N.A.I.C.S.: 327215

Guardian Steklo Rostov LLC (2)
1 Ul Sodruzhestva, Krasnosulinsky District, Krasny Sulin, 346353, Russia
Tel.: (7) 86367 50900
Web Site: http://www.guardianglass.com
Glass Mfr
N.A.I.C.S.: 327215

Guardian Steklo Ryazan LLC (2)
Yuzhny Promuzel District 17a, Ryazan, 390011, Russia
Tel.: (7) 4912 95 66 00
Web Site: http://www.guardian-russia.ru
Glass Mfr
N.A.I.C.S.: 327215

Guardian Zoujaj International Float Glass Co. LLC (2)
Al-Jazirah Al-Hamra, PO Box 6297, Ras al Khaimah, United Arab Emirates
Tel.: (971) 7 205 8000
Web Site: http://www.guardianglass.com
Glass Mfr
N.A.I.C.S.: 327215

Guardian do Brasil Vidros Planos Ltda (2)
Rua Fernando Bernardelli NR 2000, Porto Real, Rio de Janeiro, Brazil
Tel.: (55) 24 3355 9000
Web Site: http://www.guardianglass.com
Automotive Glass Mfr
N.A.I.C.S.: 327215

Joint Venture (Non-US):

Gujarat Guardian Ltd. (2)
State Highway- 13 Village Kondh Valia Road, Ankleshwar, 393001, Gujarat, India
Tel.: (91) 2643 275106
Web Site: http://www.gujaratguardianglass.com
Flat Glass Mfr
N.A.I.C.S.: 327215
Vinay Kumar Modi *(Chm)*
Alok Kumar Modi *(Mng Dir)*
Ajit Mal Surana *(Fin Dir)*

Subsidiary (Domestic):

SRG Global, Inc. (2)
800 Stephenson Hwy, Troy, MI 48083
Tel.: (248) 509-1100
Web Site: http://www.srgglobal.com
Holding Company; Automotive & Household Appliance Chrome Plated Plastic Components Mfr & Whslr
N.A.I.C.S.: 551112
Dave Prater *(Pres & CEO)*

Subsidiary (Domestic):

SRG Global Automotive, LLC (3)
800 Stephenson Hwy, Troy, MI 48083
Tel.: (248) 509-1100
Automotive Chrome Plated Plastic Mouldings Mfr & Whslr
N.A.I.C.S.: 326199

KOCH INDUSTRIES, INC.

U.S. PRIVATE

Koch Industries, Inc.—(Continued)

Subsidiary (Non-US):

Siegel-Robert Automotive (Suzhou) Co., Ltd. (3)
Suzhou Industrial Park, Suzhou, 215021, China
Tel.: (86) 512 6262 200
Web Site: http://www.srgglobal.com
Glass Mfr
N.A.I.C.S.: 327215

Subsidiary (Non-US):

Vitrerie Novy Glass (2)
415 Rue 1, Shippagan, E8S 3H9, NB, Canada
Tel.: (506) 336-8202
Glass Mfr
N.A.I.C.S.: 327215

INVISTA S.a.r.l. (1)
4123 E 37th St N, Wichita, KS 67220
Tel.: (316) 828-1000
Web Site: http://www.invista.com
Textile & Polymer Mfr
N.A.I.C.S.: 325211
Jeffrey N. Gentry (CEO)
Chris Lorge (Mgr-Nylon Mfg Plant-Chattanooga)

Branch (Domestic):

INVISTA (2)
175 TownPark Ste 200, Kennesaw, GA 30144-5801
Tel.: (770) 420-7700
Sales Range: $25-49.9 Million
Emp.: 100
Floor Laying & Floor Work
N.A.I.C.S.: 238330
Nancy Kowalski (Dir-Fin)
Maggie Bidlingmaier (VP-Retail Channel)
Anthony Green (VP-Global Comml Solutions)

Subsidiary (Non-US):

INVISTA GmbH (2)
Philipp Reis Strasse 2, Hattersheim, 65795, Germany
Tel.: (49) 693056400
Web Site: http://www.invista.com
Sales Range: $25-49.9 Million
Emp.: 79
Polyethylene Resins Mfr
N.A.I.C.S.: 325211

Infor, Inc. (1)
641 Avenue of the Americas, New York, NY 10011 (70%)
Tel.: (646) 336-1700
Web Site: http://www.infor.com
Rev.: $3,171,200,000
Assets: $6,752,700,000
Liabilities: $7,310,800,000
Net Worth: ($558,100,000)
Earnings: $142,000,000
Emp.: 17,000
Fiscal Year-end: 04/30/2019
Enterprise Software Publisher, Whslr & Services
N.A.I.C.S.: 541511
Gregory M. Giangiordano (Gen Counsel, Sec & Sr VP)
Kevin Samuelson (CEO)
Corey Tollefson (Sr VP & Gen Mgr-Retail)
Helen Masters (Sr VP & Gen Mgr-Asia Pacific)
Soma Somasundaram (CTO & Pres-Products)
Mayumi Hiramatsu (Sr VP-Cloud Ops Engrg & Security)
Ashley Hart (CMO)
Anne Benedict (Sr VP-HR)
Wesley Kowalski (Head-ASEAN)
Susan Beal (Chief Customer Officer)
Cormac Watters (Gen Mgr & Head-Intl Markets)
Rod Johnson (Gen Mgr & Head-Americas)
Bill Sullivan (Sr VP & Gen Mgr-Public Sector)
Ziad Nejmeldeen (Sr VP)

Unit (Domestic):

AMSI Property Management (2)
401 E Jackson St Ste 1500, Tampa, FL 33607
Tel.: (813) 383-1290
Web Site: http://www.amsi.com
Business Management Software Mfr
N.A.I.C.S.: 513210

Branch (Domestic):

AMSI Property Management - Houston Office (3)
13831 NW Fwy Ste 550, Houston, TX 77040-5243
Tel.: (713) 690-2674
Web Site: http://www.amsi.com
Sales Range: $25-49.9 Million
Business Administration Software
N.A.I.C.S.: 541511

Subsidiary (Domestic):

Birst, Inc. (2)
45 Fremont St 18th Fl, San Francisco, CA 94105
Tel.: (415) 766-4800
Web Site: http://www.birst.com
Software Publisher
N.A.I.C.S.: 518210

Unit (Domestic):

EnRoute Emergency Systems (2)
3501 E Frontage Rd Ste 350, Tampa, FL 33607
Tel.: (813) 207-6911
Web Site: http://www.enroute911.com
Emp.: 20
Computer-Aided Dispatch & Records Management Systems
N.A.I.C.S.: 334610
Nick Gettino (Dir-Dev)
Margaret Moran (Dir-Sls)

Subsidiary (Domestic):

GT Nexus, Inc. (2)
1111 Broadway 5th Fl, Oakland, CA 94607
Tel.: (510) 808-2222
Web Site: http://www.gtnexus.com
Online Business-to-Business Supply Chain Software Services
N.A.I.C.S.: 541511
Kurt Cavano (Founder & Pres)
David Adams (Exec VP-Field Ops)
Mac McGary (Exec VP-Global Sls)

Branch (Domestic):

GT Nexus, Inc. - New York Office (3)
641 6th Ave 4th Fl, New York, NY 10011
Tel.: (646) 336-1700
Web Site: http://www.gtnexus.com
Online Business-to-Business Supply Chain Software Services
N.A.I.C.S.: 541511
Kurt Cavano (Founder & Pres)
Natalie Lindsey (Dir-Talent Acq)
Bryan Nella (Dir-Corp Comm)

Subsidiary (Domestic):

Grasp Systems International Inc. (2)
608 E Harmony Rd, Fort Collins, CO 80525
Tel.: (970) 282-4436
Web Site: http://www.graspinc.com
Sales Range: $1-9.9 Million
Emp.: 25
Workload Management & Patient Assignment Systems
N.A.I.C.S.: 541618
Faiza Abji (VP)
Michael Wellborn (Dir-IT)
Noora Kuusivuori (Dir-Bus Dev)
Penny Meenan (Pres & CEO)
Brian Rubick (VP-Bus Dev)
Laurie Champ (Dir-Canadian Ops)
Debbie Reid (Dir-Tech Support)

Subsidiary (Non-US):

Infor BV (2)
Helftheuvelpassage 18, 5224 AP, 's-Hertogenbosch, Netherlands
Tel.: (31) 736243400
Web Site: http://www.infor.com
Sales Range: $25-49.9 Million
Emp.: 25
Business Administration Software Mfr
N.A.I.C.S.: 334610
Kris Kluiters (Mng Dir)

Unit (Domestic):

Infor Enterprise Asset Management (2)
13560 Morris Rd Ste 4100, Alpharetta, GA 30004
Tel.: (678) 319-8000
Web Site: http://www.infor.com
Sales Range: $100-124.9 Million
Enterprise Asset Management Software & Services
N.A.I.C.S.: 513210

Branch (Non-US):

Infor Global Solutions - Bangkok (2)
21st Fl Unit 2104, 142 Pacific Pl Bldg Sukhumvit, Bangkok, 10110, Thailand
Tel.: (66) 26531304
Sales Range: $25-49.9 Million
Emp.: 20
Provider of Enterprise Resource Planning Software Applications
N.A.I.C.S.: 334610

Infor Global Solutions - Birmingham (2)
The Phoenix Building Central Boulevard, Blythe Valley Park, Solihull, B90 8BG, W Midlands, United Kingdom
Tel.: (44) 1216158000
Web Site: http://www.infor.com
Sales Range: $25-49.9 Million
Enterprise Resource Planning Software Applications
N.A.I.C.S.: 334610
Jim Schaper (Founder & CEO)

Infor Global Solutions - Buenos Aires (2)
Juana Manso 205, 1107, Buenos Aires, Argentina
Tel.: (54) 1140108000
Web Site: http://www.infor.net
Sales Range: $25-49.9 Million
Emp.: 30
Prepackaged Software
N.A.I.C.S.: 334610
Jim Schapper (CEO)

Infor Global Solutions - Capelle aan den IJssel (2)
Baron van Nagellstraat 89, 2909 LK, Barneveld, Netherlands
Tel.: (31) 102064700
Web Site: http://www.infor.com
Sales Range: $25-49.9 Million
Prepackaged Software
N.A.I.C.S.: 334610
Theo Koster (Mgr-Sls)

Infor Global Solutions - Guangzhou (2)
Unit 6302 CITIC Plaza 233 Tianhe North Road, Guangzhou, 510613, China
Tel.: (86) 2038772921
Web Site: http://www.infor.cn
Emp.: 20
Provider of Enterprise Resource Planning Software Application Mfr
N.A.I.C.S.: 334610

Infor Global Solutions - Hong Kong (2)
18th Floor Sino Plaza 255-257 Gloucester Road, Causeway Bay, China (Hong Kong)
Tel.: (852) 25212100
Web Site: http://www.infor.com
Business Administration Software Mfr
N.A.I.C.S.: 334610

Infor Global Solutions - Melbourne (2)
Level 17 357 Collins St, Melbourne, 3000, VIC, Australia
Tel.: (61) 3 8608 8500
Emp.: 60
Workforce Management Software Solutions
N.A.I.C.S.: 541511
Sophie Baldwin (Dir-Mktg)

Infor Global Solutions - Munich (2)
Am Moosfeld 3, 81829, Munich, Germany
Tel.: (49) 898006110
Web Site: http://www.datastream.net
Sales Range: $25-49.9 Million
Emp.: 13
Prepackaged Software
N.A.I.C.S.: 334610

Infor Global Solutions - Petaling Jaya (2)
Centrepoint South Suite 22 01 The Boulevard Mid Valley City, Lingkaran Syed Putra, 59200, Kuala Lumpur, Malaysia
Tel.: (60) 320844808
Web Site: http://www.infor.com
Sales Range: $25-49.9 Million
Emp.: 10
Software Program Services
N.A.I.C.S.: 541511
Fan Siewcheng (Mgr-Fin)

Infor Global Solutions - Santiago (2)
Santio X 2460 Oficina 203, Providencia, Santiago, Chile
Tel.: (56) 22340036
Web Site: http://www.datastream.net
Software Producer
N.A.I.C.S.: 334610

Infor Global Solutions - Sao Paolo (2)
Av Dr Chucri Zaidan 150 11 Andar, Brooklin Novo, Sao Paulo, 04583-110, SP, Brazil
Tel.: (55) 1155088800
Web Site: http://www.brasil.infor.com
Sales Range: $50-74.9 Million
Business Software
N.A.I.C.S.: 541511
Fernando Gordi (Mng Dir)

Infor Global Solutions - Singapore (2)
101 Thomson Rd, 09-03 United Sq, Singapore, 307591, Singapore
Tel.: (65) 63583313
Sales Range: $25-49.9 Million
Emp.: 10
Provider of Enterprise Resource Planning Software Applications
N.A.I.C.S.: 334610

Infor Global Solutions - Sydney (2)
Level 13 Tower A Zenith Centre, 821-843 Pacific Highway, Chatswood, 2067, NSW, Australia
Tel.: (61) 298759100
Web Site: http://www.info.com
Business & Financial Software Mfr
N.A.I.C.S.: 334610
James Brackenrig (Gen Mgr)

Infor Global Solutions - Toronto (2)
250 Ferrand Drive Suite 1200, Toronto, M3C 3G8, ON, Canada
Tel.: (647) 951-8248
Sales Range: $75-99.9 Million
Workforce Management Software Solutions
N.A.I.C.S.: 541511

Branch (Domestic):

Infor Global Solutions, Inc. - Chicago (2)
500 W Madison St Ste 2100, Chicago, IL 60661
Tel.: (312) 258-6000
Web Site: http://www.infor.com
Enterprise Resource & Supply Chain Management Software Developer
N.A.I.C.S.: 541511

Infor Global Solutions, Inc. - Colorado Springs (2)
5555 Tech Ctr Dr Ste 300, Colorado Springs, CO 80919-2372
Tel.: (719) 264-4820
Web Site: http://www.infor.com
Sales Range: $50-74.9 Million
Mfr of Business Information Software
N.A.I.C.S.: 523999

Infor Global Solutions, Inc. - Dallas (2)
8777 N Stemmons Fwy, Dallas, TX 75247-3702
Tel.: (214) 775-6000
Sales Range: $75-99.9 Million
Business Oriented Computer Software
N.A.I.C.S.: 513210

Infor Global Solutions, Inc. - East Greenwich (2)
1351 S County Trl Ste 300, East Greenwich, RI 02818-1622
Tel.: (678) 319-8000
Web Site: http://www.infor.com
Sales Range: $10-24.9 Million
Provider of E-Commerce Enabled Enterprise Solutions to Distribution Organization Services

N.A.I.C.S.: 541511

Infor Global Solutions, Inc. - Grand Rapids (2)
3855 Sparks Dr SE, Grand Rapids, MI 49546-2427
Tel.: (678) 319-8000
Sales Range: $25-49.9 Million
Emp.: 5
Custom Computer Programming Services
N.A.I.C.S.: 541511

Infor Global Solutions, Inc. - Hampton (2)
500 Lafayette Rd, Hampton, NH 03842-3347
Tel.: (603) 926-9696
Web Site: http://www.infor.com
Sales Range: $50-74.9 Million
Emp.: 160
Software Marketer & Developer
N.A.I.C.S.: 541511

Unit (Domestic):

Infor Global Solutions, Inc. - Operations Center (2)
13560 Morris Rd Ste 4100, Alpharetta, GA 30004
Tel.: (678) 319-8000
Web Site: http://www.infor.com
Workforce Management Software Solutions
N.A.I.C.S.: 541511
Duncan B. Angove (Pres)

Subsidiary (Non-US):

Infor Japan K.K. (2)
Tokyo Takarazuka Building 16th Floor 1-1-3 Yurakucho, Chiyoda-ku, Tokyo, 100-0006, Japan
Tel.: (81) 3 4520 0700
Web Site: http://www.infor.jp
Sales Range: $25-49.9 Million
N.A.I.C.S.: 541511

Infor S.A. (2)
142 avenue Jules Bordet / J Bordetlaan, 1140, Brussels, Belgium
Tel.: (32) 27277899
Web Site: http://www.infor.com
Sales Range: $25-49.9 Million
Emp.: 60
Business & Financial Software Publisher
N.A.I.C.S.: 513210

Division (Domestic):

Infor Library & Information Solutions (3)
42 Ave Bourget, Brussels, 1130, Belgium
Tel.: (32) 27277811
Web Site: http://www.nl.infor.com
Sales Range: $25-49.9 Million
Emp.: 11
Custom Computer Programing
N.A.I.C.S.: 541511
Ann Melaerts (Mng Dir)

Branch (US):

Infor Library & Information Solutions - USA (4)
492 Old Connecticut Path, Framingham, MA 01701
Tel.: (508) 598-4063
Web Site: http://www.vubis-smart.com
Sales Range: $75-99.9 Million
Business Management Software Mfr
N.A.I.C.S.: 513210
Ann Melaerts (Mng Dir)

Subsidiary (Domestic):

Intelligent Insites, Inc. (2)
102 Broadway Ste 200, Fargo, ND 58102
Tel.: (701) 893-2000
Web Site: http://www.intelligentinsites.com
Computer System Design Services
N.A.I.C.S.: 541512
Carol Tweten (VP-Govt Programs)

Starmount Co. (2)
3300 Duval Rd Suite 200, Austin, TX 78759
Web Site: http://www.starmount.com
Rev.: $2,800,000
Emp.: 50
Point-of-Sale, Mobile Shopping & Store Inventory Management Products & Services
N.A.I.C.S.: 449210

Joe Pisano (Exec VP-Bus Dev & Chief Revenue Officer)
Joe Halloum (CEO)
Myron G. Mixon (CFO)
Gregory Davis (VP-Product Strategy)
Sudhir Madyastha (VP-R&D)
Kerry Nelson (VP-Mktg)
Jerry Rightmer (Chief Product & Strategy Officer & Exec VP)

TDCI, Inc. (2)
8760 Orion Pl, Columbus, OH 43240
Tel.: (614) 781-2325
Web Site: http://www.tdci.com
Sales Range: $10-24.9 Million
Management Consulting Services
N.A.I.C.S.: 541611
Dinesh Dhamija (Principal)
Dan DeMuth (CEO)
Rhonda J. DeMuth (Chm)
Bob Irwin (Pres)

KCBX (1)
10730 S Burley Ave, Chicago, IL 60617
Tel.: (773) 375-3700
Web Site: http://www.kochind.com
Sales Range: $10-24.9 Million
Emp.: 25
Petroleum
N.A.I.C.S.: 324110
Mike Estadt (Mgr-Terminal)

Koch Agriculture Company (1)
4111 E 37th St N, Wichita, KS 67220-3203
Tel.: (316) 828-5500
Animal Feed Mfr
N.A.I.C.S.: 311119

Koch Alaska Pipeline Company, LLC (1)
4111 E 37th St N, Wichita, KS 67220
Tel.: (316) 828-7082
Pipeline Transportation Services
N.A.I.C.S.: 486110
Steve Kromer (Pres)

Koch Asphalt Solutions (1)
PO Box 2209, Peoria, AZ 85380
Tel.: (623) 939-3311
N.A.I.C.S.: 324110

Koch Business Solutions, LP (1)
55 Park Pl NE, Atlanta, GA 30303-2529
Tel.: (404) 652-8016
Web Site: http://www.kbslp.com
Business Management Services
N.A.I.C.S.: 541618
Scott Farber (Mgr-Wireless & Access Mgmt)

Koch Carbon, LLC (1)
4111 E 37th St N, Wichita, KS 67220-3203
Tel.: (316) 828-5500
Web Site: http://www.kochcarbon.com
Petroleum Product Mfr
N.A.I.C.S.: 324199
Shane Wagnon (VP-Trading & Terminals)

Koch Chemical Technology Group, LLC (1)
PO Box 2256, Wichita, KS 67201-2256
Tel.: (316) 828-8215
Web Site: http://www.kochind.com
Design, Manufacture, Sell, Install & Service Process & Pollution Control Equipment
N.A.I.C.S.: 333248

Subsidiary (Non-US):

Iris Power LP (2)
3110 American Drive, Mississauga, L4V 1T2, ON, Canada (100%)
Tel.: (905) 677-4824
Web Site: https://www.irispower.com
Sales Range: $25-49.9 Million
Emp.: 80
Distribution of Instruments to Measure Electricity
N.A.I.C.S.: 334513

Koch Chemical Technology Group India Pvt. Ltd. - Koch-Glitsch Baroda Division (2)
315-317 Sankarda-Bhadarva Road, Moxi Savli, Baroda, 391780, India
Tel.: (91) 2667244344
Web Site: http://www.koch-glitsch.com
Mass Transfer Equipment Mfr
N.A.I.C.S.: 325998
Prakash Tilekar (Mgr-HR)

Plant (Domestic):

Koch Chemical Technology Group India Pvt. Ltd. - Koch-Glitsch Mumbai Division (3)
Seawoods Station Road, Mumbai, 400706, India
Tel.: (91) 2267717171
Web Site: http://www.kochglitsch.com
Chemical Engineering Mfr
N.A.I.C.S.: 424690

Subsidiary (Non-US):

Koch Chemical Technology Group S.A. de C.V. (2)
Calle 11 Manzana 8 Lote 5, Col Petrolera Cp, Minatitlan, 96850, Veracruz, Mexico
Tel.: (52) 9222230548
Emp.: 3
Chemical Products Mfr
N.A.I.C.S.: 325998
Jorge Ortiz (Gen Mgr)

Koch Chemical Technology Group S.L. Koch-Glitsch division (2)
Calle Isla De Graciosa 3-Oficina 7, San Sebastian De Los Reye, Madrid, Spain
Tel.: (34) 917454386
Chemical Product Whslr
N.A.I.C.S.: 325998

Subsidiary (Domestic):

Koch Knight LLC (2)
5385 Orchard View Dr SE, Canton, OH 44730
Tel.: (330) 488-1651
Web Site: http://www.kochknight.com
Sales Range: $25-49.9 Million
Emp.: 70
Chemical Equipment & Corrosion-Proof Materials Mfr
N.A.I.C.S.: 325998
Wiandt Michelle (Mgr-Acctg)
P. J. Hacker (Mgr-Sls)
Kevin Brooks (Pres)

Koch-Glitsch, LP (2)
4111 E 37th St N, Wichita, KS 67220 (100%)
Tel.: (316) 828-5110
Web Site: http://www.koch-glitsch.com
Sales Range: $125-149.9 Million
Emp.: 1,171
Mass Transfer Equipment Mfr
N.A.I.C.S.: 332313
Randy Peck (Engr-Tool & Die Design)
Pam Roney (Mgr-HR)
Kathy Mccoy (Mgr-Inside Sls & Replacement)

Subsidiary (Domestic):

John Zink Company LLC (3)
11920 E Apache, Tulsa, OK 74116-1309
Tel.: (918) 234-1800
Web Site: http://www.johnzink.com
Sales Range: $100-124.9 Million
Emp.: 1,100
Pollution Control Equipment Mfr
N.A.I.C.S.: 332322
Casey Chambers (CFO)
Dan Brennan (VP-Project Mgmt)
Melissa Edmonsond (Project Coord)
Thomas Flynn (Project Mgr)

Subsidiary (Domestic):

Chentronics Corporation (4)
115 County Rd 45 Airport Industrial Park RT 12, Norwich, NY 13815 (100%)
Tel.: (607) 334-5531
Web Site: http://www.chentronics.com
Sales Range: $50-74.9 Million
Emp.: 20
Industrial Combustion Equipment Mfr
N.A.I.C.S.: 333994
J. Killean (Pres)

Coen Company, Inc. (4)
2151 River Plaza Dr Ste 200, Sacramento, CA 95833-4133
Tel.: (530) 668-2100
Web Site: http://www.coen.com
Sales Range: $50-74.9 Million
Emp.: 30
Heating Equipment Mfr
N.A.I.C.S.: 333414
Steve Louderville (CTO & VP-R&D)

Subsidiary (Non-US):

Hamworthy Combustion Engineering Limited (4)
Fleets Corner, Poole, BH17 0LA, Dorset, United Kingdom
Tel.: (44) 1202662700
Web Site: http://www.hamworthy-combustion.com
Industrial Combustion Technologies Developer, Mfr & Whslr
N.A.I.C.S.: 333994
Tony Saia (CEO)

Subsidiary (Non-US):

Hamworthy Combustion Engineering (Korea) Co. Ltd. (5)
World Meridian Bldg No 1307 Gasan-dong, Geumcheon-gu, Seoul, 153-801, Korea (South)
Tel.: (82) 221138181
Web Site: http://www.hamworthy-combustion.com
Sales Range: $25-49.9 Million
Emp.: 25
Industrial Combustion Equipment Mfr
N.A.I.C.S.: 333994

Hamworthy Combustion Engineering S.r.l. (5)
Via Gramsci 11, IT-20851, Lissone, MI, Italy
Tel.: (39) 0392434010
Web Site: http://www.hamworthy-combustion.com
Sales Range: $25-49.9 Million
Emp.: 50
Industrial Combustion Equipment Mfr
N.A.I.C.S.: 333994

Subsidiary (Domestic):

Hamworthy Peabody Combustion Inc. (4)
70 Shelton Technology Ctr, Shelton, CT 06484-6406
Tel.: (203) 922-1199
Web Site: http://www.hamworthy-peabody.com
Sales Range: $50-74.9 Million
Emp.: 30
Industrial Combustion Equipment Mfr
N.A.I.C.S.: 333994

Subsidiary (Non-US):

John Zink International Luxembourg S.A.r.l. (4)
Zone Industrielle Riedgen, 3401, Dudelange, Luxembourg
Tel.: (352) 518991
Sales Range: $50-74.9 Million
Emp.: 200
Heating Equipment Mfr
N.A.I.C.S.: 333414

John Zink KEU GmbH (4)
Hulser Strasse 410, Krefeld, 47803, Germany
Tel.: (49) 21518990
Web Site: http://www.johnzink.com
Sales Range: $50-74.9 Million
Emp.: 60
Heating Equipment Mfr
N.A.I.C.S.: 333414
Norbert Baensch (Mng Dir)

Subsidiary (Non-US):

KG Process Innovations, s.r.o. (3)
Prikop 8, 60200, Brno, Czech Republic
Tel.: (420) 545427111
Sales Range: $10-24.9 Million
Emp.: 20
Engineering Component Mfr
N.A.I.C.S.: 339999
David Britton (Mng Dir)

Subsidiary (Domestic):

Koch Heat Transfer Company, LP (3)
12602 FM 529, Houston, TX 77041
Tel.: (713) 466-3535
Web Site: http://www.kochheattransfer.com
Emp.: 100
Custom Heat Exchanger Mfr
N.A.I.C.S.: 333248
Vince Dialey (Pres)

KOCH INDUSTRIES, INC.

U.S. PRIVATE

Koch Industries, Inc.—(Continued)

Subsidiary (Non-US):

Koch Heat Transfer Canada, LP (4)
4750 Sheppard Avenue East, Toronto, M1S
3V7, ON, Canada
Tel.: (416) 293-3659
Heating Equipment Mfr
N.A.I.C.S.: 333414

Koch Heat Transfer Company, S.r.l. (4)
Strada Paullese 2, 26010, Bagnolo Cremasco, Italy
Tel.: (39) 0373237611
Web Site: http://www.kochheattransfer.com
Sales Range: $50-74.9 Million
Emp.: 120
Custom Heat Exchanger Mfr
N.A.I.C.S.: 333248
Giovanni Chisari (Gen Mgr)

Koch Heat Transfer Technology Co. (4)
580 Nan Jong Road (W) #48-08/10, Nan Zheng Building, Shanghai, 200041, China
Tel.: (86) 21 6267 4742
Custom Heat Exchanger Mfr
N.A.I.C.S.: 333248

Subsidiary (Domestic):

Koch Membrane Systems, Inc. (3)
850 Main St, Wilmington, MA 01887-3388 (100%)
Tel.: (978) 694-7000
Web Site: http://www.kochmembrane.com
Sales Range: $25-49.9 Million
Emp.: 260
Mfr of Filtering Equipment
N.A.I.C.S.: 333998
Manny Singh (Pres)

Subsidiary (Non-US):

Koch Australia Pty. Ltd. (4)
Suite 6 Level 1 186-190 Church Street, Parramatta, 2150, NSW, Australia
Tel.: (61) 288334650
Industrial Machinery & Equipment Whslr
N.A.I.C.S.: 423830

Koch Chemical Technology Group Limited (4)
The Granary Telegraph Street, Stafford, ST17 4AT, United Kingdom
Tel.: (44) 1785272500
Industrial Machinery Mfr
N.A.I.C.S.: 333248

Division (Domestic):

Koch Chemical Technology Group Limited - Koch-Glitsch UK Division (5)
First Floor Three Counties House Festival Way Hanley, Stoke-on-Trent, ST1 5PX, Staffordshire, United Kingdom
Tel.: (44) 1782744561
Web Site: http://www.kochglitsch.com
Emp.: 100
Industrial Machinery Mfr
N.A.I.C.S.: 333248
Jane Tellwright (Dir-Fin)

Subsidiary (Non-US):

Koch International B.V (4)
Bijkhoevelaan 26, Wijnegem, 32, Belgium
Tel.: (32) 36416583
Industrial Machinery Mfr
N.A.I.C.S.: 333248

Koch Refining International Pte, Ltd. (4)
260 Orchard Road Ste 11-01/09 The Heeren, Singapore, 238855, Singapore
Tel.: (65) 68316566
Commodity Trading & Risk Management Services
N.A.I.C.S.: 541990

Subsidiary (Non-US):

Koch Tecnologia Quimica Ltda. (3)
Rua Tanabi 276, Parque Agua Branca, 05002-010, Sao Paulo, Brazil
Tel.: (55) 1138755655
Industrial Machinery & Equipment Whslr
N.A.I.C.S.: 423830

Koch-Asia Pacific, Inc. (3)
4th Floor Takanawa Muse Bldg 3-14-13 Higashi, Gotanda Shinagawa ku, Tokyo, 141-0022, Japan
Tel.: (81) 343325560
Web Site: http://www.koch-glitsch.com
Engineering Component Mfr
N.A.I.C.S.: 339999

Division (Domestic):

Koch-Asia Pacific, Inc. - John Zink Asia-Pacific Division (4)
4th Floor Takanawa Muse Bldg 3-14-13 Higashi-Gotanda, Shinagawa-ku, Tokyo, 141-0022, Japan
Tel.: (81) 343325550
Web Site: http://www.johnzink.com
Sales Range: $50-74.9 Million
Emp.: 20
Emission Control Component Mfr
N.A.I.C.S.: 333414
Akio Naito (Mng Dir)

Subsidiary (Non-US):

Koch-Glitsch B.V.B.A. (3)
Zone 1 De Hoek Bijkhoevelaan 26, Wijnegem, 2110, Belgium
Tel.: (32) 3 647 28 47
Web Site: http://www.koch-glitsch.com
Sales Range: $25-49.9 Million
Emp.: 16
Industrial Machinery Mfr
N.A.I.C.S.: 333248
Massimo Bizzi (Mng Dir)

Koch-Glitsch Canada, LP (3)
18 Dallas St, Uxbridge, L9P 1C6, ON, Canada
Tel.: (905) 852-3381
Web Site: http://www.koch-glitsch.com
Industry Machinery Mfr
N.A.I.C.S.: 333248

Koch-Glitsch Canada, LP (3)
1829 Ranchlands Blvd NW Unit 209, Calgary, T3G2A7, AB, Canada
Tel.: (403) 266-1830
Sales Range: $25-49.9 Million
Emp.: 2
Mass Transfer Equipment Whslr
N.A.I.C.S.: 423830

Subsidiary (Domestic):

Koch-Glitsch Field Service (3)
12221 E Sam Houston Pkwy N, Houston, TX 77044-5094
Tel.: (713) 427-7700
Web Site: http://www.kochservices.com
Sales Range: $10-24.9 Million
Emp.: 130
Industrial Machinery & Equipment Repair
N.A.I.C.S.: 811210
Craig Alexander (Pres)
Norman Funderburk (VP)

Subsidiary (Non-US):

Koch-Glitsch Italia S.r.l. (3)
Ss 148 Pontina Km 52, 4011, Campoverde di Aprilia, Italy
Tel.: (39) 06928911
Web Site: http://www.koch-glitsch.com
Sales Range: $25-49.9 Million
Emp.: 150
Industrial Machinery Mfr
N.A.I.C.S.: 333248
Cherenkova Natalia (Mng Dir)

Subsidiary (Domestic):

Koch-Otto York Co., Inc. (3)
6611 Killough Rd, Houston, TX 77086-3817
Tel.: (281) 445-7026
Web Site: http://www.koch-ottoyork.com
Sales Range: $10-24.9 Million
Emp.: 40
Mist Elimination Filters Mfr
N.A.I.C.S.: 332618
Thomas Lorato (Mgr)

Subsidiary (Domestic):

Optimized Process Designs Inc. (2)
25610 Clay Rd, Katy, TX 77493-7898
Tel.: (281) 371-7500
Web Site: http://www.opd-inc.com
Sales Range: $50-74.9 Million
Emp.: 40
Engineering Consulting Services
N.A.I.C.S.: 541330
James K. Kuehler (Pres)
Gary Thompson (Exec VP)

Koch Engineered Solutions, LLC (1)
4111 E 37th St N, Wichita, KS 67220
Tel.: (316) 858-6000
Oil & Energy Distr
N.A.I.C.S.: 333132
Don Brown (VP-Bus Dev)

Subsidiary (Domestic):

Sentient Energy, Inc. (2)
880 Mitten Rd, Burlingame, CA 94010
Tel.: (650) 523-6680
Web Site: http://www.sentient-energy.com
Electronic Parts & Equipment Merchant Whslr
N.A.I.C.S.: 423690
Michael Kast (Founder & VP-Engrg)
John Costello (Sr VP-Global Sls)
Rick Joyce (VP-Sls-North America)
David Boone (VP-Product Mgmt)
Bob Karschnia (CEO)

Koch Equity Development LLC (1)
4111 E 37th St N, Wichita, KS 67220
Tel.: (316) 828-5500
Web Site: http://www.kochequity.com
Investment Services
N.A.I.C.S.: 523999
Brett Watson (Pres)

Subsidiary (Domestic):

MIWD Holding Company LLC (2)
1010 54th Ave E, Fife, WA 98424
Tel.: (717) 365-3300
Web Site: https://www.miterbrands.com
Windows & Doors Mfr
N.A.I.C.S.: 321911

Subsidiary (Domestic):

MI Windows and Doors, LLC (3)
650 W. Market St, Gratz, PA 17030
Tel.: (717) 365-3300
Web Site: http://www.miwindows.com
Windows & Doors Mfr
N.A.I.C.S.: 321911
Matthew G. DeSoto (Pres & CEO)
Larry Curran (CFO)

Subsidiary (Domestic):

Milgard Manufacturing Incorporated (4)
1010 54th Ave E, Tacoma, WA 98424-2731
Tel.: (253) 922-2030
Web Site: http://www.milgard.com
Windows
N.A.I.C.S.: 326199

Sunrise Windows Ltd. (4)
200 Enterprise Dr, Temperance, MI 48182
Tel.: (734) 847-8778
Web Site: http://www.sunrisewindows.com
Lumber, Plywood, Millwork & Wood Panel Merchant Whslr
N.A.I.C.S.: 423310
Cliff Langdon (VP-Ops)
Carl Will (Pres & CEO)

Subsidiary (Domestic):

PGT Innovations, Inc. (3)
1070 Technology Dr, North Venice, FL 34275
Tel.: (941) 480-1600
Web Site: http://www.pgtinnovations.com
Rev.: $1,161,464,000
Assets: $1,460,610,000
Liabilities: $931,513,000
Net Worth: $529,097,000
Earnings: $32,878,000
Emp.: 5,300
Fiscal Year-end: 01/01/2022
Holding Company; Impact-Resistant Windows & Doors Mfr
N.A.I.C.S.: 551112
Matthew G. DeSoto (Pres & CEO)
Jeffrey T. Jackson (Pres & CEO)
David McCutcheon (Sr VP-Bus Integration)
Eric Kowalewski (Pres-Ops-Florida Div)
Mike Wothe (Exec VP-Ops)
Amy Rahn (Pres-Window Solutions-Newsouth)

John E. Kunz (CFO & Sr VP)
Rachel Evans (Sr VP-HR)
Eric Kowalewsk (Pres-Ops-Southeast)
Mark Yeandle (Pres-Ops-West)
Craig Henderson (CFO & Sr VP)
Christy Sackett (VP)
Joe Person (Treas)

Subsidiary (Domestic):

ECO Glass Production, LLC (4)
9101 NW 87th Ave, Medley, FL 33166
Tel.: (786) 452-7811
Web Site: https://www.ecoglassproduction.com
Glass Products Mfr
N.A.I.C.S.: 327215

Eco Window Systems LLC (4)
8502 NW 80th St Ste 103, Miami, FL 33166 (75%)
Tel.: (305) 885-5299
Web Site: http://www.ecowindowsystems.com
Other Services to Buildings & Dwellings
N.A.I.C.S.: 561790
Frank Mata (Owner)

NewSouth Window Solutions of Orlando, LLC (4)
820 E Altamonte Dr, Altamonte Springs, FL 32701
Tel.: (407) 261-2277
Window & Door Mfr
N.A.I.C.S.: 332321

NewSouth Window Solutions of Pensacola, LLC (4)
6235 N Davis Hwy Unit 108, Pensacola, FL 32504
Tel.: (850) 738-6400
Wood Window & Door Mfr
N.A.I.C.S.: 321911

NewSouth Window Solutions, LLC (4)
10741 Crossroads Commerce Blvd, Tampa, FL 33610
Tel.: (813) 626-6000
Web Site: https://www.newsouthwindow.com
Vinyl Window & Door Mfr
N.A.I.C.S.: 321911
Earl Rahn (Co-Founder & Pres)

Subsidiary (Domestic):

Doers Window Manufacturing, LLC (5)
10741 Crossroads Commerce Blvd, Tampa, FL 33610
Tel.: (813) 626-6000
Web Site: https://www.doerswindow.com
Window & Door Mfr
N.A.I.C.S.: 332321
Dan Ochstein (CEO)
Earl Rahn (Pres)
Margaret Sillart (Mgr-Doers Acctg)

NewSouth Window Solutions of Bonita Springs, LLC (5)
3300 Bonita Beach Rd Unit 160, Bonita Springs, FL 34134
Tel.: (239) 949-4300
Window & Door Mfr
N.A.I.C.S.: 332321
Rob Sydnes (Pres-South West Florida Market)

NewSouth Window Solutions of Charleston, LLC (5)
2049 Savannah Hwy Ste 90, Charleston, SC 29407
Tel.: (843) 699-2300
Window & Door Mfr
N.A.I.C.S.: 332321

NewSouth Window Solutions of Ft. Lauderdale, LLC (5)
1401 S State Rd 7, North Lauderdale, FL 33068
Tel.: (954) 935-8300
Window & Door Mfr
N.A.I.C.S.: 332321
Mark Hudak (Pres-Affiliate)

NewSouth Window Solutions of Jacksonville, LLC (5)
8590 Philips Hwy, Jacksonville, FL 32256
Tel.: (904) 717-5400
Window & Door Mfr

COMPANIES

KOCH INDUSTRIES, INC.

N.A.I.C.S.: 332321

NewSouth Window Solutions of West Palm Beach, LLC (5)
2526 Okeechobee Blvd, West Palm Beach, FL 33409
Tel.: (561) 712-9000
Window & Door Mfr
N.A.I.C.S.: 332321
Marcus A. Smith (Mgr-Svc)

Subsidiary (Domestic):

PGT Industries, Inc. (4)
1070 Technology Dr, North Venice, FL 34275 (100%)
Tel.: (941) 480-1600
Web Site: http://www.pgtindustries.com
Impact-Resistant Windows & Doors Mfr
N.A.I.C.S.: 332321
Rodney Hershberger (Chm)
Jeffrey T. Jackson (Pres & COO)

Subsidiary (Domestic):

CGI Windows and Doors, Inc. (5)
3780 W 104th St, Hialeah, FL 33018
Tel.: (305) 593-6590
Web Site: https://www.cgiwindows.com
Emp.: 30
Windows & Door Mfr
N.A.I.C.S.: 332321

Subsidiary (Domestic):

CGI Commercial, Inc. (6)
2970 Nw 75th Ave, Miami, FL 33122
Tel.: (305) 718-8890
Impact-resistant Window & Door Mfr
N.A.I.C.S.: 332321

Subsidiary (Domestic):

WinDoor, Inc. (5)
7500 Amsterdam Dr, Orlando, FL 32832
Tel.: (407) 481-8400
Web Site: http://www.windoorinc.com
Sales Range: $10-24.9 Million
Emp.: 250
Sliding Glass Door Mfr
N.A.I.C.S.: 327215

Subsidiary (Domestic):

WWS Acquisition LLC (4)
2200 E Riverview Dr, Phoenix, AZ 85034
Tel.: (877) 398-9643
Web Site: http://www.westernwindowsystems.com
Aluminum Windows & Doors Mfr
N.A.I.C.S.: 332321

Subsidiary (Domestic):

TNS, Inc. (2)
10740 Parkridge Blvd Ste 100, Reston, VA 20191-1406
Tel.: (703) 453-8300
Web Site: http://www.tnsi.com
Sales Range: $500-549.9 Million
Emp.: 1,303
Financial Transaction Services
N.A.I.C.S.: 522320
Michael Q. Keegan (CEO)
Mark G. Cole (Chief Network Officer)
Alan R. Schwartz (Pres-Fin Svcs Div)
James T. McLaughlin (Gen Counsel, Sec & Exec VP)
Alex N. Walker (Sr VP & Gen Mgr-FSD Div)
Jo Moorwood (Sr Dir-Mktg Comm)
Lisa Shipley (Exec VP & Mng Dir-Payment Network Solutions Bus)
Joe Lueckenhoff (Exec VP & Gen Mgr-Telecomm Svcs)
Bill Versen (Chief Product Officer & Pres-Comm Market)
Dennis L. Randolph Jr. (CFO & Treas)

Subsidiary (Non-US):

SC Connet Ro SRL (3)
P ta Alba Iulia Nr 6 Bl I5 Sc 3 Et 7 Ap 37 Sector 3, Bucharest, Romania
Tel.: (40) 314909999
Web Site: http://www.connet-ro.com
Telecommunication Servicesb
N.A.I.C.S.: 517111

Transaction Network Services (India) Private Ltd (3)
Ste C 12A/14 3rd Fl 78 Tardeo Rd, Commerce Center Building, Mumbai, 400034, India
Tel.: (91) 2240159995
Computer System Design Services
N.A.I.C.S.: 541512

Transaction Network Services (UK) Limited (3)
4th Floor 80 Clerkenwell Road, London, EC1M 5RJ, United Kingdom
Tel.: (44) 2073361510
Web Site: http://www.tnsi.com
Computer System Design Services
N.A.I.C.S.: 541512

Transaction Network Services PTY Limited (3)
Level 10 123 Pitt Street, Sydney, 2000, NSW, Australia
Tel.: (61) 299590800
Web Site: http://www.tnsi.com
Computer System Design Services
N.A.I.C.S.: 541512
John VanField (Mng Dir)

Transaction Network Services SG Pte Limited (3)
Level 18 Republic Plz II 9 Raffles Pl, Singapore, 48619, Singapore
Tel.: (65) 68236814
Computer System Design Services
N.A.I.C.S.: 541512
Juhan Png (Dir-Sls)

Subsidiary (Domestic):

Transaction Network Services, Inc. (3)
1939 Roland Clarke Pl, Reston, VA 20191-1406 (100%)
Tel.: (703) 453-8300
Web Site: http://www.tnsi.com
Sales Range: $100-124.9 Million
Financial Transaction Services
N.A.I.C.S.: 522320
Dennis Randolph (CFO)
David Neal (Chief Acctg Officer)
David Durst (Engr-IP Implementations)
Joe Lueckenhoff (Exec VP & Gen Mgr)

Subsidiary (Domestic):

West Highland Support Services, LLC (4)
108 Mill Plain Rd Ste 250, Danbury, CT 06811
Tel.: (212) 867-1848
Web Site: http://www.westhighland.net
Custom Computer Programming Services
N.A.I.C.S.: 541511
Mark Bouges (Mgr)
Roger Peterkin (VP-Sls)

Koch Fertilizer, LLC (1)
4111 E 37th St N, Wichita, KS 67220
Tel.: (316) 828-8207
Holding Company; Nitrogenous Fertilizer Mfr & Distr
N.A.I.C.S.: 551112
Marci Booth (VP-Intl Logistics)

Subsidiary (Domestic):

Koch Agronomic Services, LLC (2)
4111 E 37th St N, Wichita, KS 67220
Tel.: (316) 828-7084
Fertilizer Distr
N.A.I.C.S.: 212390
Greg Schwab (Dir-Agronomy)

Subsidiary (Non-US):

Koch Fertiliser Australia Pty Ltd (2)
Level 10 409 St Kilda Road, PO Box 7024, Melbourne, 3004, VIC, Australia
Tel.: (61) 398768800
Fertilizer Mfr
N.A.I.C.S.: 325314
Jim Cass (Mgr-Territory)
Ross Warren (Territory Mgr)

Koch Fertiliser, Ltd (2)
1 Woodstock Court Blenheim Rd, Marlborough, SN84AN, Wiltshire, United Kingdom
Tel.: (44) 1672518290
Web Site: http://www.kochfertilizer.com
Fertilizer Mfr & Distr
N.A.I.C.S.: 325314

Koch Fertilizer Canada, ULC (2)
1400 17th Street East, Brandon, R7A 7C4, MB, Canada
Tel.: (204) 729-2900
Fertilizer Mfr
N.A.I.C.S.: 325314

Koch Minerals S.A.. (2)
Chemin Des Primeveres 4545, 1700, Fribourg, Switzerland
Tel.: (41) 919110666
Investment Management Service
N.A.I.C.S.: 523940

Subsidiary (Domestic):

Koch Nitrogen Company, LLC (2)
4111 E 37th St N, Wichita, KS 67220 (100%)
Tel.: (316) 828-8207
Web Site: http://www.kochfertilizer.com
Sales Range: $25-49.9 Million
Emp.: 200
Nitrogenous Fertilizer Mfr & Distr
N.A.I.C.S.: 325311
Steve Packebush (Pres)
Mak Soucie (CFO)

Joint Venture (Non-US):

Point Lisas Nitrogen Limited (3)
North Caspian Drive, Point Lisas Industrial Estate, Point Lisas, Trinidad & Tobago (50%)
Tel.: (868) 6363776
Web Site: https://www.plnltt.com
Ammonia Mfr & Distr
N.A.I.C.S.: 325311

Koch Minerals, LLC (1)
4111 E 37th St N, Wichita, KS 67220
Tel.: (316) 828-5500
Petroleum Product Mfr & Whslr
N.A.I.C.S.: 324199
Mike Sackett (Mgr-Comml Compliance)
Dave Seiler (VP-Ops & Compliance)
Shara Brown (Dir-Compliance)
Joseph Hand (VP)

Subsidiary (Domestic):

KM Proppants, LLC (2)
4111 E 37th St N, Wichita, KS 67220-3203
Tel.: (316) 828-5500
Logistics Consulting Servies
N.A.I.C.S.: 541614

The C. Reiss Coal Company (2)
703 N 8th St Ste 301, Sheboygan, WI 53081
Tel.: (920) 451-8910
Coal & Salt Distr
N.A.I.C.S.: 424690

Koch Oil Company (1)
PO Box 1965, Sebring, FL 33871-1965
Tel.: (863) 385-6188
Sales Range: $10-24.9 Million
Emp.: 5
Oil & Petroleum Operations
N.A.I.C.S.: 324110

Koch Pipeline Company, L.P (1)
PO Box 2913, Wichita, KS 67201-2913
Tel.: (316) 828-5755
Web Site: http://www.kochpipeline.com
Pipeline Transportation Services
N.A.I.C.S.: 486110

Koch Supply & Trading, LP (1)
4111 E 37th St N, Wichita, KS 67220
Tel.: (316) 828-5500
Web Site: http://www.ksandt.com
Oil, Natural Gas, Metals & Other Allied Products Wholesale Trade Distr
N.A.I.C.S.: 425120

Subsidiary (Non-US):

Koch HC Partnership BV (2)
Neckarweg 5, Europoort, 3198 LT, Rotterdam, Netherlands
Tel.: (31) 181240150
Web Site: http://www.ksnt.com
Commodity Trading Services
N.A.I.C.S.: 213112

Koch Supply & Trading Company Ltd. (2)
20 Gresham Street 4th Floor, London, EC2V 7JE, United Kingdom (100%)
Tel.: (44) 2076486300

Web Site: http://www.ksandt.com
Emp.: 70
Oil, Natural Gas & Other Resource Commodities Wholesale Trade Distr
N.A.I.C.S.: 425120
Peter Leoni (Head-Structuring & Analytics)

Subsidiary (Domestic):

Koch Metals Trading Limited (3)
20 Gresham Street 4th Floor, London, EC2V 7JE, United Kingdom
Tel.: (44) 2076486300
Web Site: http://www.ksandt.com
Sales Range: $75-99.9 Million
Emp.: 60
Commodity Trading & Risk Management Services
N.A.I.C.S.: 523160

Molex LLC (1)
2222 Wellington Ct, Lisle, IL 60532
Tel.: (402) 458-8665
Web Site: http://www.molex.com
Rev.: $3,620,447,000
Assets: $3,586,854,000
Liabilities: $1,063,691,000
Net Worth: $2,523,163,000
Earnings: $243,623,000
Emp.: 40,000
Fiscal Year-end: 06/30/2013
Electrical, Electronic & Fiber Optic Devices Mfr & Sales
N.A.I.C.S.: 334417
Joseph Nelligan (CEO)
Paul Chaffin (Sr VP-Medical & Pharmaceutical Solutions)

Subsidiary (Domestic):

Affinity Medical Technologies, LLC (2)
3545 Harbor Blvd, Costa Mesa, CA 92626
Tel.: (949) 477-9495
Web Site: http://www.affinitymed.com
Sales Range: $1-9.9 Million
Emp.: 411
Surgical & Medical Instrument Mfr
N.A.I.C.S.: 339112
Bob Frank (Gen Mgr)
Jennifer Bird (Mgr-HR)
Jim Itkin (Mgr-Bus Dev)
Matt Pathmajeyan (Mgr-Product Dev)
Juan Jaquez (Mgr-Mfg & Facilities)

Airborn Inc. (2)
3500 AirBorn Cir, Georgetown, TX 78626
Tel.: (512) 863-5585
Web Site: http://www.airborn.com
Sales Range: $25-49.9 Million
Emp.: 500
Electronic Connector Mfr
N.A.I.C.S.: 334417
Michael Cuff (CTO & Sr VP-Engrg & New Product Dev)
Vicki Besch (Sr VP-HR)
Bill Pitchford (VP-Intl Bus)
Chris Wegmann (Chief Compliance Officer & VP-Corp Strategic Program Mgmt)
Bob Guck (Pres-Little Falls Div)
Michael Cole (Pres & COO)
Bill McManus (CFO)
Robert Kleinschmidt (Sr VP-Mktg & Sls)

BittWare, Inc. (2)
45 South Main St, Concord, NH 03301
Tel.: (603) 226-0404
Web Site: http://www.bittware.com
Scientific & Technical Consulting Services
N.A.I.C.S.: 541690
Jeffry Milrod (Pres & CEO)

Fiberguide Industries Inc. (2)
3409 East Linden St, Caldwell, ID 83605
Tel.: (208) 454-1988
Web Site: http://www.fiberguide.com
Optical Fiber Assembly & Component Mfr
N.A.I.C.S.: 335921
Patricia Seniw (Pres)
Devinder Saini (VP-Tech)

Subsidiary (Non-US):

MI European Holdings CV (2)
Parmentierweg 2, Eindhoven, 5657EL, Netherlands
Tel.: (31) 402958295
Sales Range: $25-49.9 Million
Emp.: 150
Investment Management Service

KOCH INDUSTRIES, INC.   U.S. PRIVATE

Koch Industries, Inc.—(Continued)
N.A.I.C.S.: 551112
Liam Bucklei *(Gen Mgr)*

Subsidiary (Domestic):

Molex Automotive (2)
2025 Taylor Rd, Auburn Hills, MI
48326 **(100%)**
Tel.: (248) 371-9700
Web Site: http://www.molex.com
Sales Range: $50-74.9 Million
Emp.: 150
Automotive Controls Mfr
N.A.I.C.S.: 335314

Subsidiary (Non-US):

Molex European Holdings BV (2)
Parmentierweg 2, 5657 EH, Eindhoven,
Netherlands
Tel.: (31) 402958200
Web Site: http://www.molex.com
Investment Management Service
N.A.I.C.S.: 551112

Subsidiary (Non-US):

Molex Zetronic S.r.l. Unico Socio (3)
Via Ix Strada, Padua, 35129, Italy
Tel.: (39) 0497912200
Electronic Connector & Component Mfr
N.A.I.C.S.: 334417

Subsidiary (Domestic):

Molex International, Inc. (2)
2222 Wellington Ct, Lisle, IL
60532-1682 **(100%)**
Tel.: (630) 969-4550
Web Site: http://www.molex.com
Sales Range: $350-399.9 Million
Emp.: 1,000
Holding Company
N.A.I.C.S.: 334417

Subsidiary (Non-US):

Dongguan Molex South-China Connector Co. Ltd. (3)
C Zone Ming Hua Road No 3 Industrial
Area Juzhou, Shijie Town, Dongguan,
523298, Guangdong, China **(95%)**
Tel.: (86) 76986310328
Electronic Connectors & Components Mfr
N.A.I.C.S.: 334417

Division (Non-US):

Molex Hong Kong/China Ltd. (4)
2 F Blk A 5 7 Yuen Shun Circuit, Shatin Ind
Ctr Siu Lek Yuen, Hong Kong, China (Hong
Kong) **(100%)**
Tel.: (852) 26373111
Sales Range: $900-999.9 Million
Wire Harnesses Mfr
N.A.I.C.S.: 332618

Division (Domestic):

**Molex Interconnect (Beijing) Co.,
Ltd.** (4)
Room 1311 Tower B COFCO Plaza, No 8
Jian Guo Men Nei Street, 100005, Beijing,
China
Tel.: (86) 1065269628
Sales Range: $900-999.9 Million
Emp.: 20
Wire Harnesses Mfr
N.A.I.C.S.: 332618

**Molex Interconnect (Shanghai) Co.,
Ltd.** (4)
No 889 Ying Lun Road, WaiGaoQiao Free
Trade Zone, Shanghai, 200131, Pudong,
China **(100%)**
Tel.: (86) 21 5048 0889
Web Site: http://www.molex.com
Sales Range: $900-999.9 Million
Wire Harnesses Mfr
N.A.I.C.S.: 332618

Subsidiary (Non-US):

Molex (India) Ltd. (3)
Plot No 6 A Sadaramangala Industrial Area,
Kadugodi, Bengaluru, 560 067,
India **(91.74%)**
Tel.: (91) 8041293500
Sales Range: $25-49.9 Million
Emp.: 350
Electronic Connectors & Components Seller
N.A.I.C.S.: 449210
Eric Doesburg *(Mng Dir)*

Molex (Malaysia) Sdn. Bhd. (3)
2607 Jalan Perusahaan, 13600, Perai, Penang, Malaysia **(100%)**
Tel.: (60) 45078788
Web Site: http://www.molex.com
Sales Range: $200-249.9 Million
Emp.: 750
Electronic Connector Mfr
N.A.I.C.S.: 441330
Hidekih Tonaka *(Plant Mgr)*
Tonaka Hideki *(Plant Mgr)*

Molex (Thailand) Ltd. (3)
71 Flat4 Moo 5 Bangpakong Ind Pk, 24130,
Bang Pakong, 24130, Chachoengsao,
Thailand **(94%)**
Tel.: (66) 38573020
Sales Range: $50-74.9 Million
Emp.: 300
onnectors & Components Mfr
N.A.I.C.S.: 449210
Marc Sessare *(Mng Dir)*
Chutima Chamanon *(Mgr-Fin)*

Molex B.V. (3)
Parmentierweg 6, PO BOX 6082, 5657 EH,
Eindhoven, Netherlands **(100%)**
Tel.: (31) 402958295
Sales Range: $10-24.9 Million
Emp.: 5
Electronic Connectors & Components Mfr
N.A.I.C.S.: 449210
Octavio Olvera *(Controller)*
Liam Buckley *(Dir-Ops)*

Unit (Non-US):

Molex B.V. - Espana (4)
Valencia 307 4 4, 8009, Barcelona, Spain
Tel.: (34) 934766880
Web Site: http://www.molex.es
Sales Range: $10-24.9 Million
Emp.: 5
Electronic Components Mfr
N.A.I.C.S.: 449210
Alejandro Vilagut *(Mgr-Sls)*

Subsidiary (Non-US):

Molex Brazil Ltda. (3)
Rua Gal Furtado Nascimento, 05465-070,
Sao Paulo, Brazil **(100%)**
Tel.: (55) 1130242710
Web Site: http://www.molex.com
Sales Range: $1-9.9 Million
Emp.: 10
Electronic Connectors & Components Mfr
N.A.I.C.S.: 334417
Geraldo Barros *(Gen Mgr)*

Molex Electronics Ltd. (3)
610 Alden Road Suite 105, Markham, L3R
9K1, ON, Canada **(100%)**
Tel.: (905) 944-1415
Web Site: http://www.molex.com
Sales Range: $1-9.9 Million
Emp.: 45
Electronic Connectors & Components Mfr
N.A.I.C.S.: 334417
Tony Ianetta *(Mgr-Sls)*

Molex Electronics Ltd. (3)
Molex House Millennium Centre, Farnham,
GU9 7XX, Surrey, United Kingdom **(100%)**
Tel.: (44) 1252720720
Web Site: http://www.molex.com
Sales Range: $10-24.9 Million
Emp.: 25
Electronic Interconnection Equipment Mfr
N.A.I.C.S.: 449210

Molex France (3)
18 Parc Burospace, 91571, Bievres, Cedex,
France **(100%)**
Tel.: (33) 169354900
Sales Range: $25-49.9 Million
Emp.: 50
Electronic Interconnection Equipment Mfr
N.A.I.C.S.: 441330
Steve Updegraff *(Gen Mgr)*

Molex Holding GmbH (3)
Walltorf Str 244, 80807, Munich,
Germany **(100%)**
Tel.: (49) 894130920

Sales Range: $25-49.9 Million
Emp.: 30
Holding Company
N.A.I.C.S.: 551112

Subsidiary (Domestic):

Molex Connectivity GmbH (4)
Gewerbestrasse 60, 75015, Bretten, Germany
Tel.: (49) 725294960
Web Site: http://www.woodhead.com
Sales Range: $50-74.9 Million
Emp.: 75
Network Connectivity Sservices
N.A.I.C.S.: 423620
Andreas Vogg *(Mgr-HR)*

Plant (Domestic):

**Molex Connectivity GmbH
Leinfelden-Echterdingen** (5)
Im Gassle 9, 70771, Leinfelden-Echterdingen, Germany
Tel.: (49) 711 782374 0
Sales Range: $10-24.9 Million
Emp.: 20
Electronic Components Mfr
N.A.I.C.S.: 334419

Subsidiary (Domestic):

S-Team Elektronik GmbH (5)
Schleifweg 2, PO Box 11 21, 74257, Untereisesheim, Germany
Tel.: (49) 7132156830
Web Site: http://www.s-team.de
Sales Range: $10-24.9 Million
Emp.: 10
Electronic Components Mfr
N.A.I.C.S.: 334419
Michael Hartmann *(Mng Dir)*

Subsidiary (Domestic):

Molex Elektronik GmbH (4)
Grashofstr 17, 76275, Ettlingen, 76275,
Germany **(100%)**
Tel.: (49) 72433350
Sales Range: $75-99.9 Million
Computer Cables, Keyboards, Plug Connectors for Circuits, Tube Sockets & Caps,
Switches & Plugs Mfr
N.A.I.C.S.: 334419
Kurt Rahner *(Gen Mgr)*

Molex Services GmbH (4)
Dingolfinger Str 4, D-81673, Munich,
Germany **(100%)**
Tel.: (49) 894130920
Sales Range: $10-24.9 Million
Emp.: 30
Electronic Parts Mfr
N.A.I.C.S.: 811210

Subsidiary (Non-US):

Molex Interconnect GmbH (3)
Parmentierts weg, Eindhoven, 5657 EH,
Netherlands **(100%)**
Tel.: (31) 402958295
Sales Range: $25-49.9 Million
Emp.: 125
European Distribution Center
N.A.I.C.S.: 334417
Liam Buckley *(Mng Dir)*

Molex Ireland Ltd. (3)
Site 1 Shannon Industrial Estates, Shannon
Free Airport, Shannon, V14H N40,
Ireland **(100%)**
Tel.: (353) 61702400
Web Site: http://www.molex.com
Sales Range: $150-199.9 Million
Emp.: 420
Electronic Connectors & Components Mfr
N.A.I.C.S.: 334417
John O'Brien *(Mng Dir)*

Molex Japan Co., Ltd. (3)
1-5-4 Fukami-Higashi, Yamato, 242-8585,
Kanagawa, Japan **(100%)**
Tel.: (81) 462652324
Web Site: http://www.molex.co.jp
Sales Range: $300-349.9 Million
Electronic Connectors & Components Mfr
N.A.I.C.S.: 449210

Subsidiary (Domestic):

S'Next Japan Co. Ltd. (4)

Meguro TS Building 2-7-5 Kamiosaki,
Shinagawa-ku, Tokyo, 141-0021, Japan
Tel.: (81) 364593122
Web Site: http://www.s-next.co.jp
Speaker & Headphone Mfr
N.A.I.C.S.: 334310
Atsuhito Horino *(VP-Tech Innovation & Dev)*

Subsidiary (Non-US):

S'Next Philippines (5)
7170 Blue Diamond Street Clark Freeport
Zone, Candaba, 2023, Pampanga, Philippines
Tel.: (63) 454991300
Web Site: http://www.s-next.com.ph
Sales Range: $25-49.9 Million
Emp.: 200
Speaker & Headphone Mfr
N.A.I.C.S.: 334310
Kiyohiko Hathiya *(Pres)*

Affiliate (Non-US):

Molex Knutsen Danmark A/S (3)
Paul Bergsoes Vej 20A, 2600, Glostrup,
Denmark
Tel.: (45) 43431030
Web Site: http://www.molex.dk
Sales Range: $10-24.9 Million
Emp.: 10
Electronic Components Mfr & Distr
N.A.I.C.S.: 334419
Rene Zweibler *(CFO)*
Stig Andreasen *(Engr-Sls)*
Christian Smith *(Mgr-Sls)*

Molex Knutsen Norge AS (3)
Brynshogda 9, PO Box 6104, 601, Oslo,
Norway **(100%)**
Tel.: (47) 23039100
Web Site: http://www.molexgk.com
Sales Range: $10-24.9 Million
Emp.: 10
Electronic Components Mfr
N.A.I.C.S.: 449210
Kjell Gummar *(Mng Dir)*

Subsidiary (Non-US):

Molex Korea Co., Ltd. (3)
726 3 Wonsi Dong, Ansan, 425090,
Gyunggi Do, Korea (South) **(100%)**
Tel.: (82) 314929000
Web Site: http://www.molex.co.kr
Sales Range: $100-124.9 Million
Emp.: 400
Electronic Connector & IC Socket Mfr
N.A.I.C.S.: 334417

Molex Polska Sp. z o.o. (3)
ul. Zytnia 15, lok.13A, Warsaw, 01-014,
Poland **(100%)**
Tel.: (48) 228621473
Web Site: http://www.molex.pl
Sales Range: $150-199.9 Million
Automotive Equipment Sales
N.A.I.C.S.: 441330

Molex Singapore Pte. Ltd. (3)
No 110 International Rd, Jurong, 629174,
Singapore **(100%)**
Tel.: (65) 62686868
Sales Range: $125-149.9 Million
Emp.: 500
High Speed Progressive Dies, Semiconductor Tooling, Jigs & Fixture Mfr
N.A.I.C.S.: 333514
Jo Nelligen *(Pres)*

Molex Sweden (3)
Farogatan 33, 164 51, Stockholm,
Sweden **(100%)**
Tel.: (46) 859421100
Sales Range: $10-24.9 Million
Emp.: 6
Electronic Connectors & Components Sales
N.A.I.C.S.: 449210
Mekael Sigsridsson *(Mgr)*

Molex Taiwan Ltd. (3)
100-3 Shia Kwei Rou Shan Tamshui, Taipei,
Taiwan **(100%)**
Tel.: (886) 2 2620 2300
Web Site: http://www.molex.com
Sales Range: $75-99.9 Million
Emp.: 200
Electronic Connectors & Components Whslr
N.A.I.C.S.: 334417

COMPANIES

KODA ENTERPRISES GROUP, LLC

Subsidiary (Domestic):

Land Win Electronic Corp. (4)
2F 2 Aly 18 Ln 330 Sec 6 Nanjing E Rd,
Neihu Dist, Taipei, 114, Taiwan
Tel.: (886) 227923756
Web Site: http://www.landwin.com.tw
Sales Range: $50-74.9 Million
Emp.: 250
Electronic Connector & Component Mfr
N.A.I.C.S.: 334417
G. W. Lee (Gen Mgr)

Subsidiary (Non-US):

Molex Turkey (3)
Ataturk Mh Sedef Cd No 15 ATa 3-2 Daire
119 Atasehir, 34758, Istanbul,
Turkiye (100%)
Tel.: (90) 216 580 83 70
Web Site: http://www.molex.com
Sales Range: $10-24.9 Million
Emp.: 15
Electronic Components Mfr
N.A.I.C.S.: 449210

Molex de Mexico S.A. de C.V. (3)
Av De La Productividad Ote 305 Parque
Industrial Guadalajara, KM 7 Carretera A
Chapala, Guadalajara, CP 45690, Jalisco,
Mexico (100%)
Tel.: (52) 36681400
Sales Range: $350-399.9 Million
Emp.: 1,500
Electronic Interconnection Equipment Mfr
N.A.I.C.S.: 449210

SDP Telecom Inc. (3)
119 Brunswick Blvd Unit 600, Pointe-Claire,
H9R 5N2, QC, Canada
Tel.: (514) 428-7070
Web Site: http://www.sdptelecom.com
Telecommunications Equipment Mfr
N.A.I.C.S.: 334290

Subsidiary (Domestic):

Molex Premise Networks, Inc. (2)
2222 Wellington Ct, Lisle, IL
60532 (100%)
Tel.: (630) 969-4550
Web Site: http://www.molexpn.com
Sales Range: $25-49.9 Million
Emp.: 100
Voice, Data & Video-Imaging Signal Transmission Products Mfr
N.A.I.C.S.: 334290
Ljupco Micevski (Mgr)

Division (Domestic):

Molex Fiber Optics (3)
5224 Katrine Ave, Downers Grove, IL
60515 (100%)
Tel.: (630) 512-8787
Web Site: http://www.molex.com
Sales Range: $25-49.9 Million
Emp.: 49
Fiber Optic Device Connector Mfr
N.A.I.C.S.: 335921

Subsidiary (Non-US):

Molex S.A. de C.V. (2)
Av de la Productividad Ote 305 Parque Industrial Guadalajara Km 7 Carr, Guadalajara, 45690, Jalisco, Mexico
Tel.: (52) 3336681400
Sales Range: $200-249.9 Million
Emp.: 1,000
Electronic Connector & Component Mfr
N.A.I.C.S.: 334417
Jesus Amarillas (Mgr-Fin)

Subsidiary (Domestic):

Molex, Inc. - Tampa Bay Operations (2)
4650 62nd Ave, Pinellas Park, FL
33781-5944 (100%)
Tel.: (727) 521-2700
Sales Range: $125-149.9 Million
Emp.: 350
Electronic Connector Mfr
N.A.I.C.S.: 335931

Phillips-Medisize, LLC (2)
1201 Hanley Rd, Hudson, WI 54016
Tel.: (715) 381-3344
Web Site: http://www.phillipsmedisize.com
Emp.: 5,400

Injection Molded Plastic Products Mfr
N.A.I.C.S.: 326199
Matthew J. Jennings (Chm, Pres & CEO)
Dave Thoreson (VP & Gen Mgr)
Bill Welch (CTO)
Arnie DeWitt (CIO & VP)
Cheryl Norder (Dir-Quality Design Assurance)
Iran Bateman (VP-Engrg-Europe)
Paul Chaffin (Pres-Medical & Pharmaceutical Solutions Div & Sr VP)

Polymicro Technologies, LLC (2)
18019 N 25th Ave, Phoenix, AZ 85023-1200
Tel.: (602) 375-4100
Web Site: http://www.molex.com
Emp.: 110
Electronic & Fiber Optic Device Mfr
N.A.I.C.S.: 334417
Kevin O'Connor (Mgr-Sls)
Jim Clarkin (Gen Mgr)

Division (Domestic):

Woodhead Industries, Inc. (2)
333 Knightsbridge Pkwy Ste 200, Lincolnshire, IL 60069
Tel.: (847) 353-2500
Web Site: http://www.woodhead.com
Sales Range: $200-249.9 Million
Emp.: 1,500
Heavy-Duty Electrical Plugs & Connectors
N.A.I.C.S.: 334220

Subsidiary (Domestic):

Central Rubber Company (3)
844 E Jackson St, Belvidere, IL 61008-2332
Tel.: (815) 544-2191
Web Site:
  http://www.centralrubbercompany.com
Sales Range: $25-49.9 Million
Emp.: 50
Custom Molded Parts Mfr
N.A.I.C.S.: 326299
Lynn Baughman (Controller)

Subsidiary (Non-US):

I.M.A. S.r.l. (3)
Piazza Della Vittoria 10 Int 6, 16121,
Genoa, Italy
Tel.: (39) 010593077
Sales Range: $100-124.9 Million
Electrical Component Mfr
N.A.I.C.S.: 334419

Molex Canada Limited (3)
216 Bathurst Drive, Waterloo, N2V 2L7,
ON, Canada
Tel.: (519) 725-5136
Web Site: http://www.woodhead.ca
Sales Range: $10-24.9 Million
Emp.: 35
Electronic Connector Mfr
N.A.I.C.S.: 335999

Woodhead Asia Pte. Ltd. (3)
Marokono Logistics Building, No 4 Toh Tuck
Link, Singapore, 596 226, Singapore
Tel.: (65) 6261 6533
Sales Range: $10-24.9 Million
Emp.: 15
Electrical Connector Distr
N.A.I.C.S.: 423610

Woodhead Connectivity S.A.S.U. (3)
57 rue Jacquard, PO Box 523, 77465, Lagny, Cedex, France
Tel.: (33) 164309136
Web Site: http://www.woodhead.com
Sales Range: $10-24.9 Million
Emp.: 10
Electrical Component Mfr
N.A.I.C.S.: 335999
Leterrier Damien (Gen Mgr)

Woodhead Software & Electronics S.A.S.U. (3)
43 rue Mazagran, 76320, Caudebec-les-Elbeuf, France
Tel.: (33) 232960420
Web Site: http://www.woodhead.com
Sales Range: $100-124.9 Million
Electronic Components Mfr
N.A.I.C.S.: 334419

Woodhead de Mexico S.A. de C.V. (3)
Parque Industrial Internacional Mexicano,

Calle Intermex No 1351, Ciudad Juarez,
32575, Chihuahua, Mexico
Tel.: (52) 6566242504
Web Site: http://www.woodhead.com
Sales Range: $200-249.9 Million
Emp.: 750
Electrical Products Mfr
N.A.I.C.S.: 335999

mPm S.r.l. (3)
Via Zucchi 39 int G, 20095, Cusano
Milanino, MI, Italy
Tel.: (39) 02 664 00321
Web Site: http://www.woodhead.com
Sales Range: $10-24.9 Million
Emp.: 50
Electronic Components Mfr, Marketing & Sales
N.A.I.C.S.: 335931

Oplink Communications, LLC. (1)
46335 Landing Pkwy, Fremont, CA 94538
Tel.: (510) 933-7200
Web Site: http://www.oplink.com
Sales Range: $200-249.9 Million
Fiber Optic Components & Integrated Optical Modules Mfr
N.A.I.C.S.: 334210
Peter Lee (Pres & COO)
Shawn Lin (VP-Mktg)
Rang-Chen Yu (VP-Bus Dev & Gen Mgr-Active Product Line)

Subsidiary (Non-US):

OCP Asia, Inc. (2)
No 26 Industry E 4th Rd Science Based
Industrial Park, Hsin-chu, 300, Taiwan
Tel.: (886) 36666850
Optical Component Mfr
N.A.I.C.S.: 333310

Taiwan Oplink Communications, Inc. (2)
5F No 8 Lane 235 Pao-Chiao Rd, Hsin
Tien, New Taipei City, Taiwan
Tel.: (886) 229126618
Web Site: http://www.oplink.com
Optical Component Mfr
N.A.I.C.S.: 333310

Zhu Hai Oplink Communications, Inc (2)
No 5 Lianfeng Ave Zhuhai Free Trade
Zone, Zhuhai, 519030, China
Tel.: (86) 7568686865
Web Site: http://www.oplink.com
Emp.: 3,000
Fiber Optic Components & Integrated Optical Modules Designer, Mfr & Marketer
N.A.I.C.S.: 335921

KOCHAVA, INC.
201 Church St, Sandpoint, ID 83864
Tel.: (855) 562-4282 DE
Web Site: http://www.kochava.com
Year Founded: 2011
Mobile Ad Analytics
N.A.I.C.S.: 541890
Charles Manning (CEO)
Jason Hicks (VP-Mktg & Client Svcs)
Seth Samuels (VP-R&D)
Eric Mann (Dir-Product Engrg)
Grant Cohen (Gen Mgr-Kochava Collective)
Grant Simmons (Head-Client Analytics)
Ben Stein (VP-Mktg)
Steve Bair (Head-Sls-North America)
Nic Beraudo (Chief Revenue Officer)
Arthur Novarina (Reg VP-Europe, Middle East & Africa)
Leslie Amadio (Dir-PR)

KOCOLENE MARKETING, LLC
2060 1st Ave, Seymour, IN 47274
Tel.: (812) 522-2224 IN
Web Site: http://www.kocolene.com
Year Founded: 1973
Retail Petroleum Products
N.A.I.C.S.: 457120

Subsidiaries:

Shadowood Golf Inc. (1)

333 N Sandy Creek Dr, Seymour, IN
47274 (100%)
Tel.: (812) 522-8164
Web Site: http://www.shadowoodgolf.com
Sales Range: $10-24.9 Million
Emp.: 4
Public Golf Course
N.A.I.C.S.: 713910

KOCOUREK AUTOMOTIVE GROUP
1500 Morning Glory Ln, Wausau, WI
54401-7687
Tel.: (715) 359-0303
Web Site:
  http://www.kocourekauto.com
Sales Range: $50-74.9 Million
Emp.: 150
Automobile Dealership Operator
N.A.I.C.S.: 441110
Keith Kocourek (Pres)

Subsidiaries:

Kocourek Wausau Imports (1)
1501 Morning Glory Ln, Wausau, WI 54401
Tel.: (715) 842-5636
Web Site:
  http://www.kocourekwausauimports.com
Sales Range: $10-24.9 Million
Emp.: 38
Automobile Dealership
N.A.I.C.S.: 441110
Mike Walik (Mgr-Sls)

KOCOUREK CHEVROLET, INC.
1500 Morning Glory Ln, Wausau, WI
54401
Tel.: (715) 359-7200
Web Site:
  http://www.kocourekauto.com
Year Founded: 1987
Sales Range: $10-24.9 Million
Emp.: 51
Car Whslr
N.A.I.C.S.: 441110
Keith A. Kocourek (Pres)

KODA ENTERPRISES GROUP, LLC
2 University Ofc Park 51 Sawyer Rd
Ste 420, Waltham, MA 02453
Tel.: (781) 891-3066 DE
Web Site: http://www.koda.com
Year Founded: 1989
Sales Range: $25-49.9 Million
Emp.: 250
Holding Company
N.A.I.C.S.: 551112
William S. Karol (Pres & CEO)
William J. Leaver (CFO & Exec VP)
Kathleen A. Nee (Office Mgr)
James H. Peden (COO)

Subsidiaries:

KODA Specialty Products Group (1)
750 Marrett Rd Ste 401, Lexington, MA
02421
Tel.: (781) 891-3066
Web Site: http://www.koda.com
Sales Range: $10-24.9 Million
Emp.: 4
Specialty Products Mfr
N.A.I.C.S.: 541613

Subsidiary (Domestic):

KLW Plastics, Inc. (2)
980 Deneen Ave, Monroe, OH 45050
Tel.: (513) 539-2673
Web Site: http://www.klwplastics.com
Sales Range: $1-9.9 Million
Plastic Products Mfr
N.A.I.C.S.: 326199

Proair, LLC (2)
28731 County Rd 6, Elkhart, IN 46514-9512
Tel.: (574) 264-5494
Web Site: http://www.proairllc.com
Air Conditioning & Heating Equipment
N.A.I.C.S.: 336390

KODA ENTERPRISES GROUP, LLC

KODA Enterprises Group, LLC—(Continued)
Jeff Armstead (VP-Sls & Mktg)
Dennis Mitchell (Pres)

Marcor Development Corp. (1)
154 Pioneer Dr, Leominster, MA 01453
Tel.: (201) 935-2111
Web Site: http://www.marcordev.com
Sales Range: $1-9.9 Million
Emp.: 16
Chemicals And Allied Products
N.A.I.C.S.: 424690
Holly Daley (Gen Mgr)

KODA FARMS, INC.
22540 Russell Ave, South Dos Palos, CA 93665
Tel.: (209) 392-2191
Web Site: http://www.kodafarms.com
Year Founded: 1928
Sales Range: $10-24.9 Million
Emp.: 50
Rice Milling Services
N.A.I.C.S.: 311212
Keisaburo Koda (Founder)
Koda Ross (Pres)

KODIAK BUILDING PARTNERS LLC
1745 Shea Ctr Dr Ste 130, Highlands Ranch, CO 80129
Tel.: (303) 576-2230
Web Site: http://www.kodiakbp.com
Year Founded: 2011
Holding Company; Building Materials Industry
N.A.I.C.S.: 551112
Steve Swinney (CEO)
Brad Becker (CIO)
Cally Fromme (VP-Comm & Culture)
Doug Rapier (Pres-Kodiak Interiors Grp)
Scott Barton (VP-Bus Dev)
Jeff Smith (CFO)
Sue Lords (Chief Human Capital Officer)
Matt LaScola (VP- Corp Dev & Real Estate)
Brian Huss (VP-Fin & Treas)
Darius McCurty (Corp Controller)
Carlos Dominguez (Dir-Risk Mgmt Claims & Safety)
Tom Kostelecky (Sr VP-Bus Dev)
Mark Garboski (Pres-LBM)
Paul W. Hylbert Jr. (Chm)

Subsidiaries:

AO, Inc. (1)
1841 Monetary Ln Ste 130, Carrollton, TX 75006
Tel.: (972) 446-1900
Web Site: http://www.aoinc.net
Emp.: 38
Commercial Doors, Frames & Hardware Mfr & Distr
N.A.I.C.S.: 332321
Linda Hawkins (VP-Ops)
Steve Joyce (VP-Sls)
Heather Wright (Dir-Project Mgmt)

American Builders Supply, Inc. (1)
2801 W Airport Blvd, Sanford, FL 32771
Tel.: (407) 321-3667
Web Site: http://www.americanbuildsupply.com
Lumber & Other Building Materials Whslr
N.A.I.C.S.: 423310
Cliff Shimer (Pres)

Branch (Domestic):

American Builders Supply, Inc. - Clermont (2)
1000 Carroll St, Clermont, FL 34711
Tel.: (352) 394-2116
Web Site: http://www.americanbuilderssupplyco.com
Lumber & Other Building Materials Whslr
N.A.I.C.S.: 423310

Barnsco Inc. (1)
2609 Willowbrook Rd, Dallas, TX 75220-4422
Tel.: (214) 352-9091
Construction Product Distr
N.A.I.C.S.: 423320
Randy Dues (CEO)
Roger Gowan (Mgr-Sls)

Subsidiary (Domestic):

Barnsco Fleet Maintenance, Inc. (2)
7125 Harry Hines Blvd, Dallas, TX 75235
Tel.: (972) 241-9111
Web Site: http://www.barnscofleet.com
Emp.: 11
Truck Trailer Repair & Maintenance Services
N.A.I.C.S.: 811121
Mike Miller (Mgr-HR)
Billy Arnold (Mgr-HR)

Christensen Lumber, Inc. (1)
714 S Main St, Fremont, NE 68025
Tel.: (402) 721-3212
Web Site: http://www.logger.com
Emp.: 250
Lumber & Other Building Materials
N.A.I.C.S.: 423310
Tom Christensen (Pres & CEO)
Marlon Nelson (Mgr-Ops)

Diamond Home Hardware & Garden, LLC (1)
2380 S 6th St, Klamath Falls, OR 97603-4340
Tel.: (541) 471-4300
Lumber, Plywood, Millwork & Wood Panel Merchant Whslr
N.A.I.C.S.: 423310
James Rivera (Asst Mgr)
John Steiner (Gen Mgr)

Don's Appliances LLC (1)
2335 Washington Rd, Canonsburg, PA 15317
Tel.: (724) 916-0100
Web Site: http://www.donsappliances.com
Household Appliances, Electric Housewares & Consumer Electronics Merchant Whslr
N.A.I.C.S.: 423620
Matt Hillebrand (Partner & Principal)

Goodrich Lumber Co. (1)
40 Independence Rd, Kingston, MA 02364
Tel.: (781) 422-0131
Web Site: http://www.goodrichlumber.com
Rev.: $5,160,000
Emp.: 20
Home Center Operator
N.A.I.C.S.: 444110
Kevin Medeiros (Pres)

Gulf & Basco (1)
2425 Broad St, Houston, TX 77087
Tel.: (713) 645-6611
Web Site: http://www.gulfbasco.com
Emp.: 75
Miscellaneous Durable Goods Merchant Whslr
N.A.I.C.S.: 423990
Eileen Levy (Coord-Customer Response)
Dave Smith (Pres)

Mandere Construction, Inc. (1)
13964 N Ohio St, Rathdrum, ID 83858
Tel.: (208) 687-3308
Web Site: http://www.mandere.com
Rev.: $7,258,000
Emp.: 60
Construction Services
N.A.I.C.S.: 238130
John D. Mandere (Pres)
Largent Homes (Mgr)

Zarsky Lumber Co., Inc. (1)
604 E Rio Grande St, Victoria, TX 77901-6035
Tel.: (361) 573-2479
Web Site: http://www.zarsky.com
Sales Range: $25-49.9 Million
Emp.: 250
Lumber & Other Building Materials Retailer
N.A.I.C.S.: 423310
Phillip Steffy (Pres)

KODIAK ELECTRIC ASSOCIATION, INC.
515 Marine Way, Kodiak, AK 99615
Tel.: (907) 486-7700
Web Site: http://www.kodiakelectric.com
Year Founded: 1941
Sales Range: $10-24.9 Million
Emp.: 48
Generator & Distributor of Electrical Power
N.A.I.C.S.: 221121
Darron Scott (Pres & CEO)
Alice Job (Mgr-Fin & Admin)

KODIAK FISHMEAL COMPANY
915 Gibson Cove Rd, Kodiak, AK 99615
Tel.: (907) 486-3171
Year Founded: 1995
Sales Range: $10-24.9 Million
Emp.: 22
Fish Meal Mfr
N.A.I.C.S.: 311710
Dan James (Pres)
Gary Anthony (Plant Mgr)
Ralph Amojedo (Supvr-Production)
Tom Saunders (Mgr-Maintenance)

KODIAK VENTURE PARTNERS, L.P.
PO Box 550225, Waltham, MA 02455
Tel.: (781) 214-6855   DE
Web Site: http://www.kodiakvp.com
Year Founded: 1999
Sales Range: $650-699.9 Million
Emp.: 10
Equity Investment Firm
N.A.I.C.S.: 523999
Dave Furneaux (Founder & Mng Partner)
Chip Meakem (Mng Partner)
Lou Volpe (Mng Partner)
Andrey Zarur (Partner)
Penny Breen (VP-Fin)

KOECKRITZ RUGS, INC.
1910 E Devon Ave, Elk Grove Village, IL 60007
Tel.: (847) 859-5459
Web Site: http://www.koeckritzrugs.com
Sales Range: $400-449.9 Million
Emp.: 30
Carpets & Flooring Products
N.A.I.C.S.: 423220
George Koeckritz (Chm & Pres)
Tom Koeckritz (Controller)

KOEDYKER & KENYON CONSTRUCTION, INC.
901 W Calle Progreso, Tucson, AZ 85705-6452
Tel.: (520) 882-7006
Year Founded: 1986
Sales Range: $25-49.9 Million
Emp.: 250
Fence Installation Services
N.A.I.C.S.: 238990
Daniel Bang (Sec)
John W. Kenyon (Pres)
James Koedyker (VP)

KOEGEL MEATS INC.
3400 W Bristol Rd, Flint, MI 48507
Tel.: (810) 238-3685
Web Site: http://www.koegelmeats.com
Sales Range: $25-49.9 Million
Emp.: 80
Frankfurters Mfr & Distr
N.A.I.C.S.: 311612
John C. Koegel (Pres)
James Lay (Mgr)

KOENIG COMPANY INC.
50 E 7 Mile Rd, Detroit, MI 48203
Tel.: (313) 368-1870   MI
Year Founded: 1870
Sales Range: $10-24.9 Million
Emp.: 110

U.S. PRIVATE

Provider of Construction Products & Equipment
N.A.I.C.S.: 327320

Subsidiaries:

Koenig Fuel & Supply Co. Inc. (1)
12100 Wayne Rd, Romulus, MI 48174-3776
Tel.: (313) 368-1870
Sales Range: $10-24.9 Million
Emp.: 40
Central-Mixed Concrete
N.A.I.C.S.: 327320

Koenig Sand & Gravel LLC (1)
1955 Lakeville Rd, Oxford, MI 48371
Tel.: (248) 628-2711
Provider of Sand & Gravel
N.A.I.C.S.: 212321

KOENIG EQUIPMENT INC.
306 N Main, Botkins, OH 45306
Tel.: (937) 693-2201   OH
Web Site: http://www.koenigequipment.com
Year Founded: 1904
Lawn, Garden & Agricultural Equipment Solutions Provider
N.A.I.C.S.: 333112
Aaron Koenig (Pres & CEO)

KOEPPEL MAZDA
57-01 Northern Blvd, Woodside, NY 11377
Tel.: (718) 721-9100
Web Site: http://www.koeppelmazda.com
Year Founded: 2004
Sales Range: $25-49.9 Million
Emp.: 27
Car Whslr
N.A.I.C.S.: 441110
Diane Alongi (Mgr)

KOERNER DISTRIBUTOR INC.
1305 W Wabash Ave, Effingham, IL 62401
Tel.: (217) 347-7113
Web Site: http://www.koernerdistributor.com
Rev.: $33,000,000
Emp.: 100
Beer & Other Fermented Malt Liquors Distr
N.A.I.C.S.: 424810
Paul Koerner (Pres)
Dan Woltman (Mgr-Sls)
Mike Austin (Mgr-Sls)

KOERNER FORD OF SYRACUSE, INC.
805 W Genesee St, Syracuse, NY 13204
Tel.: (315) 474-4275
Web Site: http://www.koernerford.com
Sales Range: $10-24.9 Million
Emp.: 75
Car Whslr
N.A.I.C.S.: 441110
Thomas Licciardello (Owner)

KOETTER WOODWORKING INC.
533 Louis Smith Rd, Borden, IN 47106
Tel.: (812) 923-8875
Web Site: http://www.koetterwoodworking.com
Sales Range: $25-49.9 Million
Emp.: 200
Doors & Door Parts & Trim, Wood
N.A.I.C.S.: 321911
Randall Koetter (Pres)
Brian Koetter (VP)
Steve Whitlow (Controller)

KOETTING FORD, INC.

3465 Progress Pkwy, Granite City, IL
62040-6817
Tel.: (618) 452-5400
Web Site:
 http://www.koettingford.com
Sales Range: $10-24.9 Million
Emp.: 40
Car Whslr
N.A.I.C.S.: 441110
Marty McCabe *(Pres)*

KOFFLER SALES, LLC
785 Oakwood Rd Ste C-100, Lake
Zurich, IL 60047-1524
Tel.: (847) 438-1152
Web Site: http://www.kofflersales.com
Year Founded: 1948
Sales Range: $1-9.9 Million
Emp.: 8
Floor & Wall Protection Product Distr
N.A.I.C.S.: 423850
Pat Starr *(CEO)*
Ron Starr *(Pres)*

KOGA ENGINEERING & CON-STRUCTION, INC.
1162 Mikole St, Honolulu, HI 96820
Tel.: (808) 845-7829
Web Site:
 http://www.kogaengineering.com
Rev.: $21,629,947
Emp.: 60
General Contractor; Highway & Street
Construction
N.A.I.C.S.: 237310
Malcolm T. Koga *(Chm)*
Clay Asato *(Pres)*
Gregg Ichimura *(Project Mgr)*
Hye Jin Warren *(Project Mgr)*

KOGOK CORPORATION
4011 Penn Belt Pl, Forestville, MD
20747
Tel.: (301) 736-5300
Web Site: http://www.kogok.com
Rev.: $15,000,000
Emp.: 85
Sheet Metalwork
N.A.I.C.S.: 332322
Jeffrey W. Kogok *(Co-Pres)*
Ezio Rebechi *(Co-Pres)*
Nick Malizia *(Project Mgr)*
Sean Malott *(Project Coord)*

KOHL ROOFING & SIDING CO., INC.
1047 Old Bernville Rd, Reading, PA
19605
Tel.: (610) 926-8800   PA
Web Site: http://www.kohlbp.com
Year Founded: 1947
Roofing Siding & Insulation Services
N.A.I.C.S.: 423330
Mike Bach *(CFO)*

KOHLBERG & COMPANY, LLC
111 Radio Cir Dr, Mount Kisco, NY
10549-2609
Tel.: (914) 241-7430   DE
Web Site: http://www.kohlberg.com
Year Founded: 1987
Privater Equity Firm
N.A.I.C.S.: 523999
Shant Mardirossian *(COO & Partner)*
Samuel P. Frieder *(Mng Partner)*
Seth H. Hollander *(Partner)*
Benjamin J. Mao *(Partner-Investment)*
Christopher W. Anderson *(Partner-Investment)*
Gordon H. Woodward *(Chief Investment Officer & Partner)*
James D. Wiggins *(Partner-Ops)*
Andrew P. Bonanno *(Partner-Investment)*
Ahmed Wahla *(Partner-Investment)*
Scott M. Birnbaum *(Partner-Ops)*
Roger M. Prevot *(Partner-Ops)*
Evan D. Wildstein *(Partner-Investment)*
Robert G. Isaman *(Operating Partner)*
Jessica Hoffman Brennan *(Partner & Head-Strategy & IR)*
James M. Better *(Partner-Ops)*
Joseph C. Lawler *(Partner-Ops)*
Matt Jennings *(Chm & Operating Partner)*
Jonathan P. Ward *(Operating Partner)*
Robert A. Cucuel Jr. *(Partner-Ops)*
George B. DeHuff III *(Partner-Ops)*
James A. Kohlberg *(Chm)*

Subsidiaries:

AM Conservation Group, Inc.   (1)
2301 Charleston Regional Pkwy, Charleston, SC 29492
Tel.: (843) 971-1414
Web Site:
 http://www.amconservationgroup.com
Emp.: 100
Energy & Water Conservation Product Mfr
N.A.I.C.S.: 334512
Jeff Cagle *(CFO)*
Kristi Mailloux *(CMO)*
John Bailes *(Pres)*
Jim Koches *(VP-Ops)*
Danielle Marquis *(Dir-Strategy)*
Dave Poole *(Dir-IT)*
Jim Madej *(CEO)*
Marisa Uchin *(Chief Comml Officer)*

AWP, Inc.   (1)
4244 Mount Pleasant S NW, North Canton, OH 44720
Web Site: http://www.awptrafficsafety.com
Traffic Control Equipment Mfr
N.A.I.C.S.: 334419
Robert Sehnert *(Pres & CEO)*
Ron Brotherton *(Chief Security & Safety Officer)*
Jack Peak *(Chief Legal Officer & Exec VP)*
Rick Sheafer *(Chief Admin Officer)*
Jeff Gilfand *(CFO)*
Kristina Schnepf *(Chief Comml Officer)*

Subsidiary (Domestic):

Advantage Barricade and Road-Marks, LLC   (2)
2231 Phoenix Ave NE, Albuquerque, NM 87107
Tel.: (505) 883-5114
Web Site: http://advantagebarricade.com
Highway, Street & Bridge Construction
N.A.I.C.S.: 237310

Allstate Traffic Control, LLC   (2)
912 Terryville Ave, Bristol, CT 06010   (100%)
Tel.: (860) 584-5949
Web Site:
 http://www.allstatetrafficcontrol.com
Sales Range: $1-9.9 Million
Emp.: 75
Traffic Control Support Services
N.A.I.C.S.: 561990
Susan Koshier *(Pres)*

Northern Colorado Traffic Control, Inc.   (2)
1712 1st Ave, Greeley, CO 80632
Tel.: (970) 356-6881
Web Site: http://www.nocotraffic.com
Specialty Trade Contractors
N.A.I.C.S.: 238990
Trisha J. Sandau *(Founder & Pres)*
Bill Moran *(Mgr)*

Warning Lites Inc of Colorado   (2)
2200 W Bates Ave, Englewood, CO 80110
Tel.: (303) 936-2990
Sales Range: $1-9.9 Million
Emp.: 60
Consumer Goods Rental
N.A.I.C.S.: 532289
Barbara Barron *(Pres)*

Amendia, Inc.   (1)
1755 W Oak Pkwy, Marietta, GA 30062-2260
Tel.: (877) 774-6255
Web Site: http://www.spinalelements.com
Surgical & Medical Instrument Mfr
N.A.I.C.S.: 339112
Jeff Smith *(Pres & CEO)*

Subsidiary (Domestic):

Spinal Elements, Inc.   (2)
3115 Melrose Dr Ste 200, Carlsbad, CA 92010
Tel.: (760) 607-0121
Web Site: http://www.spinalelements.com
Medical Device Mfr
N.A.I.C.S.: 339112
Jason Blain *(Founder)*
Steve McGowan *(CFO)*
Paul Graveline *(Chief Comml Officer & Exec VP)*
Matt Copp *(VP-Mktg)*
Ronald Lloyd *(Pres & CEO)*

Subsidiary (Domestic):

Benvenue Medical, Inc.   (3)
4590 Patrick Henry Dr, Santa Clara, CA 95054
Tel.: (408) 454-9300
Web Site: http://www.benvenuemedical.com
Health Care Equipment Mfr & Whslr
N.A.I.C.S.: 423490
Robert Weigle *(CEO)*
Laurent Schaller *(Founder & CTO)*
Victor Barajas *(VP-Ops)*
Oliver Brouse *(VP-Fin)*
Eric W. Gilbert *(VP-Sls & Mktg)*
Rick Simmons *(VP-Sls & Mktg)*

Bemis Packaging U.K. Ltd.   (1)
The Flarepath, Elsham Wold Industrial Estate, Brigg, DN20 0SP, North Lincolnshire, United Kingdom
Tel.: (44) 1652680680
Web Site: http://www.bemis.com
Emp.: 100
Packaging Materials Mfr
N.A.I.C.S.: 322220
Damian Harris *(Mgr-Sls)*

Subsidiary (Non-US):

Bemis Healthcare Packaging Ireland Limited   (2)
Kilbeggan Road, Clara, Ireland
Tel.: (353) 579331888
Packaging Products Mfr
N.A.I.C.S.: 326199

Subsidiary (Domestic):

Bemis Swansea Ltd.   (2)
Siemens Way Swansea Enterprise Park, Swansea, SA7 9BB, West Glamorgan, United Kingdom
Tel.: (44) 1792784700
Web Site: http://www.bemis.com
Sales Range: $75-99.9 Million
Emp.: 250
Mfr of Flexible Packaging
N.A.I.C.S.: 322220
Mike Bird *(Plant Mgr)*

BluSky Restoration Contractors, LLC   (1)
9110 E Nicholas Ave Ste 180, Centennial, CO 80112
Tel.: (303) 789-4258
Web Site: http://www.goblusky.com
Commercial & Residential Restoration, Renovation, Environmental & Roofing Services
N.A.I.C.S.: 236220
Daniel F. Flanagan *(Chief Sls Officer)*
Drew Bisping *(CEO)*
Jason Cain *(Exec VP)*
Troy Berns *(VP-Bus Dev)*
Steve Brown *(Dir-Natl Restoration)*
Andy James *(Dir-Natl Restoration)*
Phillip Hammet *(VP-Comml Roofing)*
Jon Easley *(VP-Ops-Southeast)*
Jeffrie A. Thornsbury *(VP-HR)*
Bob Curtis *(VP-Little Rock)*
Aaron Rich *(CIO)*
Chris Howard *(CFO)*
Simone Kelly *(VP-Leadership Dev)*
David Lange *(VP-Columbia)*
Travis Vogt *(Reg VP)*
Alisa Culverhouse *(VP-HR)*
Jeff Thornsbury *(Chief HR Officer)*
Ryan Pollock *(VP-Boston, Stoughton & Bedford)*
Jeremy Rakers *(VP-Champaign)*
Jason Todd *(VP-Plymouth)*
David Moll *(Exec VP)*
Chris Elliott *(VP-Greensboro)*
Michael Clarke *(VP-Western Slope)*
Ashley Fullenkamp *(VP-Insurance Svcs)*
Derek Ewigleben *(VP-Sls Ops)*
Jeff Garza *(VP-Houston)*
Art Eunson *(COO)*
Justin Reiske *(Dir-Safety)*
Jeff Neihouser *(Sr VP-Operational Growth)*
Robert Iwema *(VP-Chicago)*

Subsidiary (Domestic):

J & R Contracting Co. Inc.   (2)
1300 Michigan Ave, Waterville, OH 43566
Tel.: (419) 843-3473
Sales Range: $1-9.9 Million
Emp.: 24
Residential Remodeling Services
N.A.I.C.S.: 236118
Michael J. Bostdorff *(Pres)*

Weston American, Inc.   (2)
13701 Green Ash Ct, Earth City, MO 63045
Tel.: (314) 298-2701
Web Site: http://www.usstl.com
Residential Remodeler
N.A.I.C.S.: 236118

CIBT, Inc.   (1)
1600 Intl Dr Ste 600, McLean, VA 22102
Tel.: (703) 903-1400
Web Site: http://www.cibt.com
Concierge Services
N.A.I.C.S.: 812990
John Donoghue *(Chm)*
Steven Diehl *(Mng Dir-Global-Immigration)*
Pete Fox *(CIO)*
Bill Garrahan *(CFO)*
Nicolas Derbyshire *(Mng Dir-Asia Pacific)*
Sandra Woznitski *(Sr VP-North American Ops)*
Florent Frapolli *(Mng Dir-Europe)*
Lee A. Spirer *(Pres & CEO)*

Cadence, Inc.   (1)
9 Technology Dr, Staunton, VA 24401
Tel.: (540) 248-2200
Web Site: http://www.cadenceinc.com
Surgical & Medical Device Mfr
N.A.I.C.S.: 339112
Alan Connor *(Pres & CEO)*
Ken Cleveland *(CFO)*
Chip Harvill *(VP)*
Jeff Crist *(VP-Pre Production)*
Brian Plummer *(VP-Mfg-Rhode Island)*
Jeff Kelly *(VP & Gen Mgr)*
Keri Rankin *(VP-HR)*
Sandy Sekadlo *(VP-Mfg-Wisconsin)*
Tom Nelli *(VP-Mfg-Virginia)*
Chris McHugh *(VP-Ops)*

Concrete Technologies Worldwide, Inc.   (1)
506 S Wapello St, Mediapolis, IA 52637
Tel.: (319) 394-3197
Web Site:
 http://www.hawkeyepedershaab.com
Concrete Pipe Mfr
N.A.I.C.S.: 327332
Aaron Schmidgall *(VP-Ops)*
Brad Schmidgall *(Pres)*
Darrell Haar *(VP-Sls)*
Jorn Hoffmann *(VP-Sls)*
Vernon Cameron *(CEO)*
Ryan Gable *(CEO)*

Subsidiary (Non-US):

Pedershaab Concrete Technologies A/S   (2)
Saltumvej 25, 9700, Bronderslev, Denmark
Tel.: (45) 9645 4000
Concrete Pipe Mfr
N.A.I.C.S.: 327332
Carfcen Millson *(CEO)*

Decopac, Inc.   (1)
3500 Thurston Ave, Anoka, MN 55303
Tel.: (763) 574-0091
Web Site: http://www.decopac.com
Rev.: $15,200,000
Emp.: 180
Cake & Bakery Decorating Products Supplier
N.A.I.C.S.: 311340

KOHLBERG & COMPANY, LLC

Kohlberg & Company, LLC—(Continued)
John Anderson (VP)
Jill Norberg (Asst Mgr-Pur)
Leo Varley (Sr VP-HR)
Mark Meyers (Dir-Art)

Subsidiary (Domestic):

Jack Guttman, Inc. (2)
9300 Allen Rd, West Chester, OH 45069
Tel.: (513) 942-0862
Web Site: http://www.bakerycrafts.com
Sales Range: $1-9.9 Million
Emp.: 175
Cake Decorations & Baking Supplies Mfr
N.A.I.C.S.: 311999
Sam Guttman (Pres)

Engage PEO, LLC (1)
4000 Hollywood Blvd Ste 400-N, Hollywood, FL 33021
Tel.: (888) 780-8807
Web Site: http://www.engagepeo.com
Sales Range: $10-24.9 Million
Human Resource Consulting Services
N.A.I.C.S.: 541612
Jay Starkman (CEO)
Midge Seltzer (Pres)
Denise Stefan (Pres-Engage Insurance)
Craig Hill (CFO)
Steve Scott (COO)
Ralph Labarta (CTO)
Alex Pisani (Gen Counsel & VP-Strategic Dev)
Dorothy Miraglia-King (Exec VP)
Brittany Galvin (VP-North Florida)
Tiffany Creter (VP-Sls)
Alison Brennen (VP-Sls-Texas)
Farrah Fielder (Exec VP)
John Cataldo (Sr VP-Sls)

Ground Penetrating Radar Systems, LLC (1)
7540 New West Rd, Toledo, OH 43617
Tel.: (419) 843-9804
Web Site: http://www.gp-radar.com
Sales Range: $10-24.9 Million
Emp.: 80
Ground-Penetrating Radar Services to Construction Industries
N.A.I.C.S.: 334511
Mary Anderson (Mgr-HR)
Matt Aston (CEO)
Kyle Sareyka (Reg Dir-Northeast Reg)

Home Decor Holding Company (1)
Highway 63 North, Bono, AR 72416
Tel.: (800) 463-0092
Web Site: http://www.thehomedecorcompanies.com
Home Furnishing Mfr & Distr
N.A.I.C.S.: 423220
Don Harmon (CEO)

Subsidiary (Domestic):

Jimco Lamp & Manufacturing, Co. (2)
11759 Hwy 63n, Bono, AR 72416
Tel.: (870) 935-6820
Web Site: http://www.jimcolamp.com
Residential Electric Lighting Fixture Mfr
N.A.I.C.S.: 335131

Patton Picture Company (2)
207 Lynndale Court Mercha, Mechanicsburg, PA 17050
Tel.: (717) 796-1508
Web Site: http://www.pattonpictures.com
Sales Range: $1-9.9 Million
All Other Miscellaneous Wood Product Mfr
N.A.I.C.S.: 321999
William A. Patton (Pres)
Craig McAlister (Mgr-HR)
Jessica Rabuck (Acct Mgr)
Lindsey Kolaric (Product Mgr-Art)

Thro, Ltd. (2)
181 Freeman Ave, Islip, NY 11751
Tel.: (631) 218-2152
Web Site: http://www.thro.com
Home Decor Whslr
N.A.I.C.S.: 423220
Marlo Lorenz (CEO)

K2-MDV Holdings, LP (1)
413 Pine St 3rd Fl, Seattle, WA 98101
Tel.: (800) 426-1617

Holding Company; Winter Sporting Goods Designer, Mfr & Whslr
N.A.I.C.S.: 551112
Joe Lawler (Chm)
Christoph Bronder (Pres & CEO)
Michael Quinn (CFO)
Jonathan Wiant (Head-Marker, Dalbello & Volkl Brands)
Andrea Bergamin (Head-Ops-Brands)

Subsidiary (Domestic):

K-2 Sports, LLC (2)
413 Pine St 3rd Fl, Seattle, WA 98101
Tel.: (206) 805-4800
Web Site: http://www.k2sports.com
Skis, Snowboards & In-Line Skates Mfr
N.A.I.C.S.: 339920
John Colonna (Pres)

Subsidiary (Non-US):

K2 Corporation of Canada (3)
1 Westside Dr Unit 7, Toronto, M9C 1B2, ON, Canada
Tel.: (416) 679-1217
Web Site: http://www.k2canada.com
Emp.: 20
Sports & Recreational Products Whslr
N.A.I.C.S.: 611620
Brent Allen (Controller)
Dominic McKenna (VP & Gen Mgr)

K2 Sports Europe GmbH (3)
Seeshaupter Str 62, 82377, Penzberg, Germany
Tel.: (49) 8856 901 0
Web Site: http://www.k2sports.de
Sales Range: $25-49.9 Million
Emp.: 66
Sporting & Recreational Goods Whslr
N.A.I.C.S.: 423910
Peter Kuba (Gen Mgr)

Madshus A/S (3)
Industriveien 29, 2836, Biri, Norway
Tel.: (47) 61134300
Web Site: http://www.madshus.com
Sales Range: $25-49.9 Million
Emp.: 100
Skis Mfr
N.A.I.C.S.: 339920
Nils Hult (Gen Mgr)

Subsidiary (Domestic):

Tubbs Snowshoe Company (3)
4201 6th Ave S, Seattle, WA 98108
Tel.: (800) 987-1051
Web Site: http://www.tubbssnowshoes.com
Sales Range: $10-24.9 Million
Emp.: 100
Snowshoes Mfr
N.A.I.C.S.: 339920
Doug Centre (Mgr-Customer Svcs)

Subsidiary (Non-US):

Marker Dalbello Volkl Austria GmbH (2)
Hauptstr 36, 4770, Andorf, Austria
Tel.: (43) 776640700
Web Site: http://www.voelkl.com
Emp.: 10
Miscellaneous Nondurable Goods Whslr
N.A.I.C.S.: 424990
Hans Doblhammer (Mng Dir)

Marker Volkl (International) Sales GmbH (2)
Brunfeldstrasse 4, 94327, Bogen, Germany
Tel.: (49) 94213200
Sportswear Distr
N.A.I.C.S.: 424350

Volkl Sports GmbH & Co. KG (2)
Europaring 8, Straubing, 94315, Germany
Tel.: (49) 94213200
Web Site: http://www.voelkl.com
Sales Range: $150-199.9 Million
Emp.: 400
Sporting Equipments Services
N.A.I.C.S.: 423910
Christoph Bronder (Pres & CEO)

MarketCast Inc. (1)
5900 Wilshire Blvd Fl 2700, Los Angeles, CA 90036
Tel.: (323) 617-9456
Web Site: http://www.marketcast.com

Entertainment Industry Market Research Services
N.A.I.C.S.: 541910
Greg Ferland (Mng Dir)
Jeremy Radisich (Pres)
Frank Romo (Founder & Chief Research Methodologist)
Henry Shapiro (Chm)
Henry Piney (Mng Dir-Intl)
David Breihan (Exec Dir-Ops)
Rachel Krauss (Sr VP & Gen Mgr-Franchise & Content Strategy)
John Pietrolungo (CFO)
Chris Rethore (COO)
Kathleen Sauve (Sr Dir-Intl)
Bart Story (Sr Dir-Res Analysis)
Lee Doyle (Exec VP-Client Strategy-Global)
Jenny Matkovich (Dir-Mktg)
Andrea Marker (Sr Dir-Franchise & Content Strategy)
Chris Rabey (Exec Dir-Intl)
John Batter (CEO)
Zoe Friend (Sr VP-Custom Res & Insights)
Regina Johnson (Chief HR Officer)
Graham McKenna (CMO)

Subsidiary (Domestic):

Fizziology LLC (2)
6161 N Hillside Ave, Indianapolis, IN 46220
Tel.: (323) 476-1823
Web Site: http://www.fizziology.com
Social Media & Entertainment Research Services
N.A.I.C.S.: 541910
Jen Handley (Co-Founder & Co-Pres)
Ben Carlson (Co-Founder & Co-Pres)
Rich Calabrese (VP-Accts & Strategy)
Joe Matas (Mgr-Acct-Entertainment)
Kimberly Gerhart (Mgr-Acct-Brands)
Lauren Brownowski (Project Coord)
Karen Woods (Mgr-Accts-Intl)
Brina Dokich (Coord-Acct)
Logan Dodd (Acct Mgr-Entertainment)

Invoke Solutions, Inc. (2)
395 Totten Pond Rd Ste 403, Waltham, MA 02451
Tel.: (781) 810-2700
Web Site: http://www.invoke.com
Market Research Solutions
N.A.I.C.S.: 541910
Gigi Wang (CEO)
Iqbal Mutabanna (CTO)
Kevin Hughes (CFO)
Kathy Alexander (VP-Res & Insights)
Jennafer Stahl (VP-Res & Product Mgmt)
Grant Ligon (VP-Sls)
Charles Weiblen (VP-Engrg)

Nelipak Corporation, Inc. (1)
21 Amflex Dr, Cranston, RI 02921
Tel.: (401) 946-2699
Web Site: http://www.nelipak.com
Thermoformed Healthcare Packaging Products Mfr
N.A.I.C.S.: 326199
Sean J. Egan (Mgr-Grp Mktg)
Rolando Salas (Dir-Quality-Americas)
Pat Chambliss (CEO)
Roger Prevot (Chm)

Subsidiary (Domestic):

Flexpak Corporation (2)
3720 W Washington St, Phoenix, AZ 85009
Tel.: (602) 269-7648
Web Site: http://www.flexpakcorp.com
Rev.: $10,000,000
Emp.: 75
Packaging & Shipping Materials; Formed Plastics; Thermoforming Mfr
N.A.I.C.S.: 326199
Wanda Guerra (Mgr-Acctg)
Jim Meyer (Dir-Mfg)
Dean Draper (Dir-Matls)

Subsidiary (Non-US):

Nelipak B.V. (2)
Maasheseweg 75, 5804 AB, Venray, Netherlands
Tel.: (31) 478529000
Web Site: http://www.nelipak.com
Emp.: 250
Thermoforming Company
N.A.I.C.S.: 322299
Bert Verheugen (Gen Mgr)

Nellson Nutraceutical, LLC (1)

U.S. PRIVATE

5801 Ayala Ave, Irwindale, CA 91706
Tel.: (626) 812-6522
Web Site: http://www.nellsonllc.com
Nutritional Protein Bars Dry Blend & Healthy Snack Mfr
N.A.I.C.S.: 311919
Jamie Better (CEO)

Subsidiary (Domestic):

Nellson-Salt Lake City Powder Division (2)
391 Orange St, Salt Lake City, UT 84104
Tel.: (801) 954-0471
Web Site: http://www.nellsonllc.com
Turn-key Powder Mfr
N.A.I.C.S.: 311999

Ob Hospitalist Group, Inc. (1)
777 Lowndes Hill Rd Building 1, Greenville, SC 29607
Tel.: (864) 908-3530
Web Site: http://www.obhg.com
Development of OB/GYN Hospital Programs
N.A.I.C.S.: 621111
Christopher C. Swain (Co-Founder)
David C. Swain (Co-Founder)
Marc Kerlin (Chief Growth Officer)
Leonard Castiglione (CEO)
Christie Cook Buchholz (VP-Customer Strategy)
Tama LeBlanc (VP-IT)
Kevin Krenzke (CFO)
Mark N. Simon (Chief Medical Officer)
Barbara Fry (VP-Hospital Ops)
Heather Moore (VP-Risk Mgmt, Quality & Compliance)
Clifford J. Lawrence (Gen Counsel)
Charlie Jaynes (Sr Dir-Medical Ops)
Jane van Dis (Dir-Medical-Bus Dev)
Charles Rollison (Dir-Medical-Ops)
Donna Vaughan (VP-Fin Plng & Analysis)
Cheryl Slack (Chief HR Officer)

PPC Industries Inc. (1)
10101 78th Ave, Pleasant Prairie, WI 53158
Tel.: (262) 947-0900
Web Site: http://www.ppcind.com
Emp.: 500
Plastic Packaging Products Mfr
N.A.I.C.S.: 326112

Subsidiary (Domestic):

VitalMED, Inc. (2)
200 Kenneth Welch Dr, Lakeville, MA 02347 (100%)
Tel.: (508) 563-6437
Web Site: http://www.vitalmedinc.com
Rev.: $2,200,000
Emp.: 20
Medical, Dental & Hospital Equipment & Supplies Merchant Whslr
N.A.I.C.S.: 423450
Andrew Lanciano (Pres)
Don Morrill (Dir-Ops)
Steve Walsh (VP-Mktg)

Xeridiem Medical Devices, Inc. (2)
4700 S Overland Dr, Tucson, AZ 85714
Tel.: (520) 882-7794
Web Site: http://www.spectrumplasticsgroup.com
Catheters & Medical Plastic Device Design, Development & Mfr
N.A.I.C.S.: 339112

Packaging Coordinators, Inc. (1)
3001 Red Lion Rd, Philadelphia, PA 19114
Tel.: (215) 613-3600
Web Site: http://www.pciservices.com
Pharmaceutical & Biotechnology Packaging Services
N.A.I.C.S.: 561910
William Mitchell (Pres)
Bill Bolding (COO)
Phil DiGiacomo (Sr VP-Sls & Mktg)
Mitch Blumenfeld (CFO)
Tim Enterline (Acct Dir)
Alison Burns (Mgr-HR)
Laura Zurlinden (Dir-Bus Dev-Comml Pkg-West Coast)
Jeannie Metzinger (VP-Quality)
Melissa Ertl (Exec Dir-Quality)
Brad Payne (Sr VP-Ops-Global)
Chris Blanton (VP-Ops Strategy & Program Management Office-Global)
Mark Shepanski (Exec Dir-Ops)

COMPANIES

Angi Calkins *(Chief HR Officer & Sr VP)*
Salim Haffar *(CEO)*
John Cullivan *(Chief Corp Dev Officer)*

Subsidiary (Domestic):

Lyophilization Services of New England, Inc. (2)
23 Commerce Drive West, Bedford, NH 03110
Tel.: (603) 626-5763
Web Site: http://www.lyophilization.com
Sales Range: $1-9.9 Million
Emp.: 215
Biological Products Mfr
N.A.I.C.S.: 325414
Matthew Halvorsen *(Founder & Pres)*
Thomas McGrath *(VP-Quality & Regulatory)*
Shawn Cain *(COO)*
Christine Palus *(VP-Sls & Mktg)*
Aimee Hodge *(VP-Ops)*
Joseph Kiely *(CFO)*
Jay Bonewit *(Sr Dir-Quality)*
Chad Bovero *(Dir-Ops)*

Branch (Non-US):

PCI Pharma Services (2)
Wye Valley Business Park, Hay-on-Wye, HR3 5PG, United Kingdom
Tel.: (44) 1497820829
Web Site: http://www.pciservices.com
Pharmaceutical Products Packaging & Clinical Trial Materials Services
N.A.I.C.S.: 561910

PCI Pharma Services (2)
23-24 Tafarnaubach Industrial Estate, Tafarnaubach, Tredegar, NP22 3AA, Wales, United Kingdom
Tel.: (44) 1495 711222
Web Site: http://pciservices.com
Drug Development, Clinical Trial Supply & Manufacturing Services
N.A.I.C.S.: 423450
Jim Neville *(Dir-Ops)*
Norman Barras *(Mng Dir)*

Branch (Domestic):

PCI Pharma Services - Rockford (2)
4545 Assembly Dr, Rockford, IL 61109
Tel.: (815) 484-8900
Web Site: http://pciservices.com
Pharmaceutical & Personal Care Industries Packaging Services
N.A.I.C.S.: 561910
Mitch Lewandowski *(Exec Dir-Quality)*
Brian Keesee *(VP & Gen Mgr-Clinical Ops & Supply-Global)*

Riveron Consulting, LLC (1)
2515 McKinney Ave, Dallas, TX 75201-2099
Tel.: (202) 719-0231
Web Site: http://www.riveronconsulting.com
Process, Physical Distribution & Logistics Consulting Services
N.A.I.C.S.: 541614
Levi Preston *(Principal-Atlanta)*
Scott Gorrell *(Dir-Client Serving)*
Sam Shaw *(CFO)*

Subsidiary (Domestic):

Clermont Partners (2)
150 N Wacker, Suite 1200, Chicago, IL 60606
Tel.: (518) 537-2130
Web Site: http://www.clermontpartners.com
Land Subdivision
N.A.I.C.S.: 237210
Elizabeth Saunders *(Partner)*

SpecialtyCare, Inc. (1)
3 Maryland Farms Ste 200, Nashville, TN 37027-5005
Tel.: (615) 345-5400
Web Site: http://www.specialtycare.net
Hospital Clinical Srvics
N.A.I.C.S.: 622310
Jeff Gray *(CFO, Chief Admin Officer & Exec VP)*
Susan M. Byrd *(Sr VP-People)*
Gary Stephen Guidry *(Pres-Perfusion Svcs)*
Samuel Weinstein *(CEO)*
Jonathan Walters *(Pres-Intraoperative Neuromonitoring)*
John Arena *(Gen Counsel)*
Dan Farrell *(Grp Sr VP-Sls & Mktg)*
Bill Bynum *(Pres-Surgical Svcs)*

Stanadyne Corporation (1)
92 Deerfield Rd, Windsor, CT 06095-4209
Tel.: (860) 525-0821
Web Site: http://www.stanadyne.com
Motor Vehicle Fuel Filtration Components Mfr
N.A.I.C.S.: 336390
David P. Galuska *(CEO)*
John A. Pinson *(Pres)*
Costas Loukellis *(CFO & VP)*
Brad Stroia *(CTO)*

Trinity Partners, LLC (1)
230 3rd Ave, Waltham, MA 02451-7528
Tel.: (781) 577-6300
Web Site: http://www.trinitypartners.com
Administrative Management & General Management Consulting Services
N.A.I.C.S.: 541611
Kevin Francis *(Dir-Analytics & Insights)*
John Corcoran *(Founder & Pres)*
Fotios Kokkotos *(Partner & Head-Advanced Analytics)*
Yogesh Soneji *(Partner)*
Neal Dunn *(Partner)*
Stephen Fleming *(Partner)*
Aparna Deshpande *(Partner)*
Lauren Grant *(Principal)*
Eric Sholk *(Principal)*
Jillian Godfrey Scaife *(Principal)*
Nandini Hadker *(Principal)*
Herman Sanchez *(Sr Partner)*
Paul R. Lucchese *(Gen Counsel)*
Rebecca McNamara *(CFO & Head-Corp Ops)*

Subsidiary (Domestic):

TGaS Advisors, LLC (2)
301 E Germantown Pike, East Norriton, PA 19401
Tel.: (610) 233-1210
Web Site: http://www.tgas.com
Medical Industry Advisory Services
N.A.I.C.S.: 541611
Jeff Wojcik *(Sr VP-Exec Comml Ops)*
Stephen E. Gerard *(Founder, Chm & CEO)*
Carolyn Subers *(Dir-Mktg)*
James Castello *(Exec Dir)*
John Carro *(Sr VP)*
Gary McWalters *(Pres)*
Peter Bittinger *(Sr VP-Ops & Analytics)*
Curt Staab *(Sr VP-Emerging Life Sciences Network)*
Joe Falcon *(Sr VP-Market Access)*
Gary Warner *(VP-Emerging Life Sciences Network)*
Karl Kraft *(VP-Mktg Ops & Med/Reg/Legal)*
Chris Stratton *(CFO)*
Rich Waite *(VP-Comml Learning & Dev)*
Tim Wohlgemut *(Sr VP-TGaS Insights)*

U.S. Retirement Partners, Inc. (1)
99 Wood Ave S Ste 501, Iselin, NJ 08830
Tel.: (732) 321-8300
Web Site: http://www.usretirementpartners.com
Financial Services; Public School, Governmental, Not-for-profit Employee Benefits Plan & Employer-sponsored Retirement Plans
N.A.I.C.S.: 523999
Mark M. Skinner *(Pres & CEO)*
Megan Schneider *(COO)*
Courtney E. Munoz *(Sr VP-Strategic Initiatives)*

e+CancerCare (1)
104 Woodmont Blvd Ste 500, Nashville, TN 37205
Tel.: (877) 392-7226
Web Site: http://www.epluscancercare.com
Health Care Srvices
N.A.I.C.S.: 621999
Tom Weiss *(CEO)*
Robert B. Rhymer *(Chief Clinical Ops Officer)*
George B. DeHuff III *(Chm)*

Subsidiary (Domestic):

Oncologics, Inc. (2)
210 Coolidge St, Lafayette, LA 70501
Tel.: (337) 237-2057
Web Site: http://www.oncologics.net
Health Care Srvices
N.A.I.C.S.: 621999
M. Maitland DeLand *(Pres & CEO)*
Matt Daigle *(Mgr-Market Dev)*

KOHLER COMPANY

KOHLER COMPANY
444 Highland Dr, Kohler, WI 53044-1515
Tel.: (920) 457-4441   WI
Web Site:
https://www.kohlercompany.com
Year Founded: 1873
Sales Range: $1-4.9 Billion
Emp.: 40,000
All Other Miscellaneous Fabricated Metal Product Manufacturing
N.A.I.C.S.: 332999
K. David Kohler *(Chm, Pres & CEO)*
Anddria Clack-Rogers Varnado *(Head-Consumer Bus & Gen Mgr)*
Larry Yuen *(Pres-Kitchen & Bath)*
Paul Ryan *(CIO)*
Steve Bissell *(Pres-Decorative Products-Interiors)*
Stephen Maliszewski *(Dir-PR)*
Todd Weber *(Dir-PR-Comm)*
Laura E. Kohler *(Sr VP-HR, Stewardship, and Sustainability)*

Subsidiaries:

Ann Sacks Tile & Stone, Inc. (1)
8120 NE 33rd Dr, Portland, OR 97218-2018   **(100%)**
Tel.: (503) 281-7751
Web Site: http://www.annsacks.com
Sales Range: $25-49.9 Million
Emp.: 150
Ceramic Tile, Marble & Stone
N.A.I.C.S.: 444180
Ted Chappell *(Pres)*

Baker Knapp & Tubbs Inc. (1)
222 Merchandise Mart Plz Ste 952, Chicago, IL 60654   **(100%)**
Tel.: (312) 329-9410
Web Site: http://www.bakerfurniture.com
Sales Range: $10-24.9 Million
Emp.: 35
Reproduction Traditional & Contemporary Furniture Mfr
N.A.I.C.S.: 337122
Rachel D. Kohler *(Pres-Interiors Grp)*
James Nauyok *(VP-Mktg-Visual Display)*
Austin Rothbard *(Pres)*
Tanu Grewal *(VP-Mktg-Visual Display)*

KLAFS GmbH & Co. KG (1)
Erich-Klafs-Strasse 1-3, 74523, Schwabisch Hall, Germany
Tel.: (49) 7915010
Web Site: http://www.klafs.com
Sales Range: $75-99.9 Million
Emp.: 650
Saunas, Steambaths, Whirlpools & Suntanning Equipment Mfr
N.A.I.C.S.: 335210
Philip Rock *(CEO)*

Subsidiary (Non-US):

KLAFS Technical Limited (2)
8 Century Building Tower Street, Liverpool, L3 4BJ, United Kingdom
Tel.: (44) 3333058567
Web Site: http://www.sauna-spa.co.uk
Sauna, Steam Room & Sanarium Sales & Installation Services
N.A.I.C.S.: 321992

Klafs AG (2)
Oberneuhofstrasse 11, 6340, Baar, Switzerland
Tel.: (41) 417602242
Web Site: http://www.klafs.ch
Sales Range: $25-49.9 Million
Emp.: 43
Sauna, Steam Bath & Spa Equipment Sales & Installation Services
N.A.I.C.S.: 423910

Subsidiary (US):

Klafs Americas (2)
715 Discovery Blvd Unit no 408 Cedar Pk, Cedar Park, TX 78613
Tel.: (702) 430-7015
Web Site: http://www.klafsamericas.com
Sauna, Steam Bath & Spa Equipment Sales & Installation Services
N.A.I.C.S.: 423910

Subsidiary (Non-US):

Klafs GmbH (2)
Sonnwiesenweg 19, 6361, Hopfgarten im Brixental, Austria
Tel.: (43) 533523300
Web Site: http://www.klafs.at
Sales Range: $50-74.9 Million
Emp.: 56
Sauna, Steam Bath & Spa Equipment Sales & Installation Services
N.A.I.C.S.: 423910

Subsidiary (Domestic):

SSF Schwimmbad GmbH (2)
Otto-Hahn-Strasse 8, 40670, Meerbusch, Germany
Tel.: (49) 215996990
Web Site: http://www.ssf-pools.de
Sales Range: $50-74.9 Million
Emp.: 24
Sauna Steam Bath Spa Equipment & Installation Distr
N.A.I.C.S.: 423910
Jens Petersen *(CEO)*
Rolf Petersen *(Dir-Sls)*
Detlef Tuemmermann *(Mgr-Technical)*
Thomas Alberding *(Mgr-Technical Site)*

Kallista, Inc. (1)
1227 N 8th St Ste 2, Sheboygan, WI 53081   **(100%)**
Tel.: (920) 453-6300
Web Site: http://www.kallista.com
Sales Range: $10-24.9 Million
Emp.: 11
Luxury Designer Bathroom & Kitchen Products Mfr
N.A.I.C.S.: 332913
Herbert V. Kohler Jr. *(Pres & CEO)*

Kohler (Thailand) Public Co. Ltd. (1)
15 Fl Jasmine City Bldg, Bangkok, 10110, Thailand   **(81%)**
Tel.: (66) 22046000
Web Site: http://www.kohler.com
Sales Range: $10-24.9 Million
Emp.: 92
Sanitary Ware for the Consumer, Pharmaceutical & Medical Industries Mfr
N.A.I.C.S.: 332999
Kamol Lertsattha *(Mng Dir)*

Kohler - Generator Division (1)
N7650 County Trunk LS, Sheboygan, WI 53083
Tel.: (920) 457-4441
Web Site: http://www.kohler.com
Sales Range: $50-74.9 Million
Emp.: 600
Generator Sets, Transfer Switches, Switchgear & Accessories Mfr
N.A.I.C.S.: 333611

Kohler Australia (1)
327 341 Chisholm Rd, Auburn, 2144, NSW, Australia   **(100%)**
Tel.: (61) 297143900
Web Site: http://www.kohler.com.au
Sales Range: $10-24.9 Million
Emp.: 50
Branch Sales Office of Plumbing & Specialty Products International
N.A.I.C.S.: 423720

Kohler Canada Ltd. (1)
180 Credit View Rd, Vaughan, L4L 9N4, ON, Canada   **(100%)**
Tel.: (905) 762-6599
Web Site: http://www.kohler.com
Sales Range: $10-24.9 Million
Emp.: 5
Sale of Acrylic & Fibreglass Plumbing Product Mfr
N.A.I.C.S.: 332913

Unit (Domestic):

Canac Kitchens (2)
360 John St, Thornhill, L3T 3M9, ON, Canada   **(100%)**
Tel.: (905) 881-2153
Web Site: http://www.canackitchens.com
Wood Kitchen Cabinets Mfr
N.A.I.C.S.: 337110

Division (Domestic):

Kohler Canada Co. - Hytec Plumbing Products Division (2)

KOHLER COMPANY
U.S. PRIVATE

Kohler Company—(Continued)
4150 Spallumcheen Drive, Armstrong, V0E 1B6, BC, Canada
Tel.: (250) 546-3067
Web Site: http://www.hytec.ca.com
Plumbing Products Mfr
N.A.I.C.S.: 327110

Kohler France S.A.S. (1)
Immeuble Le Cap 3 Rue De Brennus, 93631, Saint Denis, Cedex, France (100%)
Tel.: (33) 149173737
Web Site: http://www.jacobdelafon.com
Sales Range: $10-24.9 Million
Emp.: 120
Full-Line Plumbing Products Manufacturer-Vitreous China, Enameled Cast Iron, Stainless Steel & Acrylic Plumbing Fixtures, Brass Faucets & Vanity Cabinets
N.A.I.C.S.: 332913
Jerome Mitchell (Gen Mgr)

Kohler Japan K.K. (1)
Azabutakahasi Bldg 7 Fl 4 13 2 Minami Azabu, Minanto-Ku, Tokyo, 106-0047, Japan (100%)
Tel.: (81) 334404440
Web Site: http://www.kohler.com
Sales Range: $10-24.9 Million
Emp.: 5
Plumbing Products Sales & Showroom
N.A.I.C.S.: 332913

Kohler de Mexico, S.A. de C.V. (1)
Calle Norte 45 No 836, 2300, Mexico, DF, Mexico (100%)
Tel.: (52) 5553683069
Web Site: http://www.kohlermexico.com
Sales Range: $10-24.9 Million
Emp.: 100
Mfr of Engines
N.A.I.C.S.: 333618

Lombardini S.r.l. (1)
Via Cav Del Lavoro Adelmo Lombardini N 2, Reggio Emilia, Reggio nell'Emilia, 42124, Italy
Tel.: (39) 0 522 3891
Web Site: http://www.lombardini.it.com
Emp.: 700
Diesel Engine Mfr & Distr
N.A.I.C.S.: 333618
Herbert KohlerJr. (Pres)

Robern, Inc. (1)
701 N Wilson Ave, Bristol, PA 19007-4515 (100%)
Tel.: (215) 826-9800
Web Site: http://www.robern.com
Sales Range: $10-24.9 Million
Emp.: 50
Mfr of High Quality Mirrored Bathroom Cabinets, Lighting Fixtures & Aluminum Railings for Stairways
N.A.I.C.S.: 337126
Thomas Penner (Pres)

SDMO GENERATING SETS Inc. (1)
3801 Commerce Pkwy, Miramar, FL 33025
Tel.: (305) 863-0012
Web Site: http://us.sdmo.com
Emp.: 30
Power Generator Mfr
N.A.I.C.S.: 335312
Jacky Pluchon (Pres)

SDMO Industries (1)
12 bis rue de la Villeuneuve, 29228, Brest, France
Tel.: (33) 2 98 41 41 41
Web Site: http://www.sdmo.com
Sales Range: $25-49.9 Million
Emp.: 800
Power Generator Mfr
N.A.I.C.S.: 335312
Jean-Marie Soula (Mng Dir)
Thierry Berquez (Mgr-Ops)
David Mallon (Gen Mgr-SDMO Energy Limited)

Subsidiary (Non-US):

SDMO GMBH (2)
Am Funkturm 8, 66482, Zweibrucken, Germany
Tel.: (49) 6332 97 15 00
Web Site: http://www.de.sdmo.com
Emp.: 17

Power Generator Mfr
N.A.I.C.S.: 335312
Ralf Stueber (Gen Mgr)

SDMO INDUSTRIES IBERICA (2)
Carrer Els Argenters 5 Modulo 1 1a planta Parc Tecnologic del Valles, Cerdanyola del Valles, 08290, Barcelona, Spain
Tel.: (34) 900802299
Web Site: http://es.sdmo.com
Power Generator Mfr
N.A.I.C.S.: 335312

SDMO NV/SA (1)
Wijnegembaan 2, Schoten, 2900, Belgium
Tel.: (32) 3 646 04 15
Web Site: http://www.sdmo.com
Sales Range: $10-24.9 Million
Emp.: 15
Power Generator Mfr
N.A.I.C.S.: 335312
Serge Pecher (Mgr)

SOREEL (1)
18 rue de la Gatine Parc d, Cholet, 49304, France
Tel.: (33) 2 41 64 52 00
Web Site: http://www.soreel.com
Sales Range: $25-49.9 Million
Emp.: 200
Electrical Wiring System Design & Implementation Services
N.A.I.C.S.: 238210
John Pan (Gen Mgr)

Sterling Plumbing, Inc. (1)
444 Highland Dr, Kohler, WI 53044
Tel.: (800) 783-7546
Web Site: http://www.sterlingplumbing.com
Sink & Bathroom Accessory Mfr
N.A.I.C.S.: 327110
Jennifer Diener (VP)

The McGuire Furniture Company (1)
1201 Bryant St, San Francisco, CA 94103-4306 (100%)
Tel.: (415) 626-1414
Web Site: http://www.mcguirefurniture.com
Sales Range: $25-49.9 Million
Emp.: 170
Mfr of Rattan Furniture
N.A.I.C.S.: 337126

KOHLERS INC.
300 E Main St, Lehi, UT 84043
Tel.: (801) 768-3578
Web Site: http://kohlers.givingyoumore.net
Rev: $10,100,000
Emp.: 300
Grocery Stores, Independent
N.A.I.C.S.: 445110
Chase Kohler (Pres)

KOHLS-WEELBORG FORD
1307 E Bridge St, Redwood Falls, MN 56283
Tel.: (507) 644-2931
Web Site: http://www.mykwford.com
Sales Range: $10-24.9 Million
Emp.: 25
New Car Retailer
N.A.I.C.S.: 441110
Tina Klinkner (Mgr-F&I)
Doug Kopischke (Mgr-Sls)
Wayne Hanson (Gen Mgr)

KOHR BROTHERS, INC.
2151 Richmond Rd Ste 200, Charlottesville, VA 22911
Tel.: (434) 975-1500
Web Site: http://www.kohrbros.com
Year Founded: 1919
Sales Range: $1-9.9 Million
Emp.: 250
Eating Places; Frozen Custard Stand Franchises
N.A.I.C.S.: 722513
Randolph Kohr (CEO)
Lisa Carter (Dir-Mktg)
Randolph Kohr II (Pres)

KOI AUTO PARTS
2701 Spring Grove Ave, Cincinnati, OH 45225
Tel.: (513) 357-2400
Web Site: http://www.koiautoparts.com
Year Founded: 1946
Sales Range: $150-199.9 Million
Emp.: 705
Automotive Parts & Accessories
N.A.I.C.S.: 441330
Denny Shroats (Coord-Trng)
Mark Wessendorf (Mgr-Sls)
John Burns (Mgr-Inventory)
Cathy Neumann (Mgr-HR)
Dennis Beyer (Coord-Mktg)
Jesse Stone (Mgr)
George Webb (Mgr)
Jim Busick (Mgr)
Micheal Desurne (Mgr)
Mandy Clevenger (Office Mgr)
Kenny Kay (Reg Mgr)
Karrie Winship (Reg Mgr)
Nathan Spradlin (Reg Mgr-Sls)
Don Spath (Sr Acct Mgr)

Subsidiaries:

KOI Auto Parts-Louisville (1)
4001 Produce Rd, Louisville, KY 40218
Tel.: (502) 969-5300
Web Site: http://www.koiautoparts.com
Sales Range: $25-49.9 Million
Emp.: 10
Automotive Supplies & Parts
N.A.I.C.S.: 423120
Al Elliott (Office Mgr)

KOINONIA FOSTER HOMES, INC.
Magnolia St, Loomis, CA 95650
Tel.: (916) 652-5802
Web Site: http://www.kfh.org
Year Founded: 1982
Sales Range: $10-24.9 Million
Foster Care & Social Services
N.A.I.C.S.: 624110
Denna Spann (Dir-Acctg)

KOIS BROTHERS EQUIPMENT CO.
5200 Colorado Blvd, Commerce City, CO 80022
Tel.: (303) 298-7370
Web Site: http://www.koisbrothers.com
Year Founded: 1968
Sales Range: $10-24.9 Million
Emp.: 35
Truck Equipment Whslr
N.A.I.C.S.: 423830
George Kois (Co-Founder & Pres)
Greg Kuch (Reg Mgr)

KOKOMO GRAIN CO., INC.
1002 W Morgan St, Kokomo, IN 46901
Tel.: (765) 457-7536
Web Site: http://www.kokomograin.com
Year Founded: 1950
Sales Range: $75-99.9 Million
Emp.: 50
Agricultural Services
N.A.I.C.S.: 424510

Subsidiaries:

Kokomo Grain Co., Inc. - Winamac (1)
1700 S 50 E, Winamac, IN 46996
Tel.: (574) 946-6101
Web Site: http://www.kokomograin.com
Grain & Field Beans Distr
N.A.I.C.S.: 424510
Rhonda Parcel (Mgr)

KOKOSING CONSTRUCTION COMPANY, INC.
6235 Westerville Rd Ste 200, Westerville, OH 43081
Tel.: (740) 694-6315
Web Site: http://www.kokosing.biz
Year Founded: 1951
Sales Range: $200-249.9 Million
Emp.: 1,500
General Contractor; Highway, Heavy Construction & Utilities, Building, Treatment, Power Plant & Asphalt
N.A.I.C.S.: 237310
William Brian Burgett (Pres & CEO)
W. Barth Burgett (VP-Equipment & Maintenance)

Subsidiaries:

Durocher Marine (1)
958 N Huron St, Cheboygan, MI 49721 (100%)
Tel.: (231) 627-5633
Sales Range: $10-24.9 Million
Emp.: 35
Provider of Heavy Construction Services
N.A.I.C.S.: 236210
Brian Burgette (CEO)
Donald Cobb (CFO)

Kokosing Construction Company Inc (1)
17531 Waterford Rd, Fredericktown, OH 43019 (100%)
Tel.: (740) 694-6315
Sales Range: $25-49.9 Million
Emp.: 100
Highway Construction Services
N.A.I.C.S.: 237310
Zach Wysong (Engr-Design)
Mike Hullinger (Project Mgr)
Kirby Fountaine (Project Mgr)

Kokosing Construction Company, Inc. - Heavy Industrial Division (1)
6235 Westerville Rd Ste 200, Westerville, OH 43081-4071
Tel.: (614) 212-5700
Structural Steel & Concrete Product Mfr
N.A.I.C.S.: 238120

Kokosing Construction Company, Inc. - Highway Division (1)
6235 Westerville Rd, Westerville, OH 43081
Tel.: (614) 228-1029
Highway Construction Services
N.A.I.C.S.: 237310

Kokosing Materials, Inc. (1)
PO Box 334, Fredericktown, OH 43019-0334
Tel.: (740) 694-9585
Web Site: http://www.kokosing-inc.com
Sales Range: $10-24.9 Million
Emp.: 30
Mfr & Retailer of Asphalt Products
N.A.I.C.S.: 324121
Robert D. Bailey (Pres)

Plant (Domestic):

Kokosing Materials, Inc. - Cleveland Plant (2)
3000 Independence Rd, Cleveland, OH 44115
Tel.: (216) 441-8892
Asphalt Mfr
N.A.I.C.S.: 324121
Pat Meisner (Gen Mgr)

Kokosing Materials, Inc. - Columbia Station Plant (2)
13315 Hawke Rd, Columbia Station, OH 44028
Tel.: (440) 236-3933
Asphalt Shingle Mfr
N.A.I.C.S.: 324121

Kokosing Materials, Inc. - Columbus Plant (2)
4755 S High St, Columbus, OH 43207
Tel.: (614) 491-1199
Asphalt Mfr
N.A.I.C.S.: 324121

Kokosing Materials, Inc. - East Claridon Plant (2)
14948 Mayfield Rd, Claridon, OH 44033
Tel.: (440) 635-5063
Web Site: http://www.kokosing.biz

COMPANIES

Emp.: 3
Asphalt Mfr
N.A.I.C.S.: 324121

Kokosing Materials, Inc. - Garfield Plant (2)
13700 McCracken Rd, Cleveland, OH 44125
Tel.: (216) 587-4900
Asphalt Mfr
N.A.I.C.S.: 324121

Kokosing Materials, Inc. - Sheffield Plant (2)
4140 E River Rd, Sheffield Lake, OH 44054
Tel.: (440) 277-9740
Asphalt Shingle Mfr
N.A.I.C.S.: 324122
Dave Armold (Plant Mgr)

McGraw/Kokosing, Inc. (1)
101 Clark Blvd, Middletown, OH 45044-3216
Tel.: (513) 422-4521
Web Site: http://www.mcgrawkokosing.com
Sales Range: $25-49.9 Million
Emp.: 300
Steel Mill Maintenance
N.A.I.C.S.: 236220
Chris A. Bergs (Sr VP-Sls & Gen Mgr)
Dan Walker (Pres)
Mike Price (Project Mgr)

Olen Corporation (1)
4755 S High St, Columbus, OH 43207-4028 (100%)
Tel.: (614) 491-1515
Web Site: http://www.kokosing-inc.com
Sales Range: $10-24.9 Million
Emp.: 100
Aggregate Plant
N.A.I.C.S.: 423320

KOL BIOMEDICAL INSTRUMENTS INC.
13901 Willard Rd, Chantilly, VA 20153
Tel.: (703) 378-8600   VA
Web Site: http://www.kolbio.com
Year Founded: 1971
Sales Range: $10-24.9 Million
Emp.: 30
Provider of Medical Services
N.A.I.C.S.: 423450
Kevin P. Clark (Mgr-Info Sys)

KOLBE & KOLBE MILLWORK CO., INC.
1323 S 11th Ave, Wausau, WI 54401-5980
Tel.: (715) 842-5666   WI
Web Site: http://www.kolbewindows.com
Year Founded: 1946
Sales Range: $400-449.9 Million
Emp.: 1,900
Mfr of Windows & Doors
N.A.I.C.S.: 321911
Jeffrey De Lonay (Pres)
Michael Tomsyck (VP-Fin)
Judy Gorski (CEO)
Robert Kasten (VP-Sls)
Keith Koenig (VP-Mfg)

Subsidiaries:

Point Five Windows, Inc. (1)
1001 Buckingham St, Fort Collins, CO 80524
Tel.: (970) 482-6971
Web Site: http://www.pointfivewindows.com
Sales Range: $1-9.9 Million
Window & Door Mfr
N.A.I.C.S.: 321911
Jeffrey De Lonay (Pres)
Randy Helzer (Exec VP)
Jerry Jaycox (Dir-Engrg)
Keith Andrews (Mgr-Svc)

KOLCRAFT ENTERPRISES, INC.
1100 W Monroe St, Chicago, IL 60607

Tel.: (312) 361-6315
Web Site: http://www.kolcraft.com
Year Founded: 1946
Sales Range: $25-49.9 Million
Emp.: 450
Games, Toys, Children's Furniture & Mattresses
N.A.I.C.S.: 339930
Sanfred Koltun (Chm & CEO)
Tom Koltun (Pres)
Andy Newmark (Sr VP-Sls & Mktg)
Barry Tsai (Mgr-Import)
Chris Hering (VP-Sls)
Gary Klosak (Dir-IT)
Andrea Ostapa (Sr Mgr-Mktg & Product Mgmt)

KOLE CONSTRUCTION COMPANY, INC.
1235 Naperville Dr, Romeoville, IL 60446-1041
Tel.: (630) 378-2006
Web Site: http://www.koleconstruction.com
Sales Range: $10-24.9 Million
Emp.: 190
Carpentry Services
N.A.I.C.S.: 238350
Susan Janasik (Mgr)

KOLETZKY IMPLEMENT, INC.
2302 E Hwy 50, Yankton, SD 57078
Tel.: (605) 665-3872
Web Site: http://www.koletzkyimplement.com
Year Founded: 1962
Sales Range: $10-24.9 Million
Emp.: 15
Farm & Garden Machinery & Equipment Whslr
N.A.I.C.S.: 423820
Alan Feilmeier (Mgr-Parts)
Russ Robb (Mgr-Svc)
Jae A. Koletzky (Owner & Gen Mgr)
Ruth Robinson (Office Mgr)

KOLKHORST PETROLEUM COMPANY
1685 E Washington Ave, Navasota, TX 77868
Tel.: (936) 825-6868
Web Site: http://www.kolkhorst.com
Sales Range: $10-24.9 Million
Emp.: 10
Petroleum Bulk Stations
N.A.I.C.S.: 424710
Jim Kolkhorst (Pres)
Mark Jackson (VP)

KOLLER ENTERPRISES, INC.
1400 S Old Hwy 141, Fenton, MO 63026-5733
Tel.: (636) 343-9220   MO
Web Site: http://www.koller-craft.com
Year Founded: 1941
Sales Range: $50-74.9 Million
Emp.: 350
Injection Molded Finished Plastic Product Vacuum Plating of Plastic Louvres for Commercial Lighting Mfr
N.A.I.C.S.: 326199
James R. Wyrsch (CFO)
Alois J. Koller Jr. (Pres & CEO)
Alois J. Koller III (VP & Sec)

Subsidiaries:

Koller Enterprises, Inc. - Koller-Craft South Division (1)
2620 E Meighan Blvd, Gadsden, AL 35903
Tel.: (256) 492-8997
Web Site: http://www.koller-craftsouth.com
Plastics Product Mfr
N.A.I.C.S.: 326199

Paramount Metalizing Div. (1)
1005 W N Service Rd, Sullivan, MO 63080 (100%)

Tel.: (573) 468-3181
Web Site: http://www.scientific-lighting.com
Sales Range: $25-49.9 Million
Emp.: 12
Vacuum Metallizing of Plastic & Metal Articles
N.A.I.C.S.: 313320

SLP UK LTD. (1)
Unit 11 Faraday Road, Rabans Lane Industrial Estate, Aylesbury, HP19 8RY, Bucks, United Kingdom
Tel.: (44) 1296428822
Web Site: http://www.slpuk.com
Sales Range: $10-24.9 Million
Emp.: 12
Lighting & Ceiling Component Whslr
N.A.I.C.S.: 423610
Steve Flynn (Mng Dir)
Jackie Armstrong (Acct Mgr)

KOLLMAN LABEL GROUP, LLC
c/o Dixie Printing & Packaging
7354-58 Baltimore-Annapolis Blvd, Glen Burnie, MD 21061
Tel.: (410) 766-1944   PA
Web Site: http://www.crimepkg.com
Year Founded: 2008
Emp.: 50
Holding Company; Packaging Products Mfr
N.A.I.C.S.: 551112
Kevin J. Kollman (Owner, Pres & CEO)

Subsidiaries:

Dixie Printing & Packaging, LLC (1)
7354-58 Baltimore-Annapolis Blvd, Glen Burnie, MD 21061
Tel.: (410) 766-1944
Web Site: http://www.dixiebox.com
Sales Range: $10-24.9 Million
Consumer Product Carton Mfr
N.A.I.C.S.: 322212
Kevin J. Kollman (COO)
Renee Dunleavy (Acct Mgr-In-House Sls)

Prime Label & Packaging, LLC (1)
501 N Central Ave, Wood Dale, IL 60191
Tel.: (630) 227-1300
Web Site: http://www.primelabelpkg.com
Sales Range: $10-24.9 Million
Emp.: 60
Commercial Packaging Printing Services
N.A.I.C.S.: 323111
Kevin J. Kollman (CEO)

KOLOGIK LLC
3837 Plz Tower Dr Ste C, Baton Rouge, LA 70816
Tel.: (225) 291-5440   LA
Web Site: http://www.kologik.com
Year Founded: 2015
Software Publisher
N.A.I.C.S.: 513210
Matt Teague (CEO)
Sean Murphy (VP-Product Dev)
Cameron Cotrill (VP-Engrg)

Subsidiaries:

Kologik Capital, LLC (1)
3837 Plz Tower Dr Ste C, Baton Rouge, LA 70816
Tel.: (225) 291-5440
Web Site: http://www.kologik.com
Software Publisher
N.A.I.C.S.: 513210
Paul San Soucie (CIO)

KOLOSSO AUTO SALES INC.
3000 W Wisconsin Ave, Appleton, WI 54914
Tel.: (920) 738-3666
Web Site: http://www.kolossotoyota.com
Sales Range: $10-24.9 Million
Emp.: 50
Car Dealership
N.A.I.C.S.: 441110
William Kolosso (Owner)

KOLTOV INC.
300 S Lewis Rd Ste A, Camarillo, CA 93012
Tel.: (805) 764-0280   CA
Year Founded: 1983
Sales Range: $10-24.9 Million
Emp.: 25
Personal Leather Goods Mfr
N.A.I.C.S.: 316990
Joe Covrigaru (CEO)
Jeff Drake (Pres)
Berenicy Alvarez (Gen Mgr)

KOMA PRECISION INC.
20 Thompson Rd, East Windsor, CT 06088
Tel.: (860) 627-7059
Web Site: http://www.komaprecision.com
Year Founded: 1983
Sales Range: $10-24.9 Million
Emp.: 20
Machine Tools & Accessories
N.A.I.C.S.: 423830
Barry Agosti (VP)
Jurgen Bettray (Mgr-Sls-Central)
David Lynch (Mgr-Sls-Mid West)
William T. Meo Jr. (Pres)

KOMAN INC.
2700 Gambell St Ste 401, Anchorage, AK 99503
Tel.: (907) 569-9130
Web Site: http://www.komaninc.com
Year Founded: 2002
Sales Range: $10-24.9 Million
Emp.: 20
Civil Engineering Services
N.A.I.C.S.: 237310
Laurence Anderson (Sec)
Michael L. Kelly (Pres & CEO)
David Anderson (VP)

KOMAN SPORTSWEAR MANUFACTURING CORP.
380 N St, Teterboro, NJ 07608-1204
Tel.: (201) 438-2211
Web Site: http://komanusa.com
Sales Range: $10-24.9 Million
Emp.: 18
Whslr of Men's & Boys' Sportswear
N.A.I.C.S.: 424350
Ilhwan Cho (Pres)

KOMAR COMPANY
90 Hudson St, Jersey City, NJ 07302
Tel.: (212) 725-1500
Web Site: http://www.komarbrands.com
Year Founded: 1908
Sales Range: $500-549.9 Million
Emp.: 150
Holding Company; Women's Nightwear Designer & Whslr
N.A.I.C.S.: 551112
Charles E. Komar (Pres)

Subsidiaries:

L.S.C., LLC (1)
2222 Palou Ave, San Francisco, CA 94124
Tel.: (415) 957-9378
Web Site: http://www.eileenwest.com
Women's Nightwear Designer & Whslr
N.A.I.C.S.: 424350
Eileen West (Pres)
Laney Thornton (Chm)
Julia Westerbeke (Dir-Creative)

St. Eve International, Inc. (1)
180 Madison Ave Ste 1002, New York, NY 10016-5267
Tel.: (212) 684-4684
Web Site: http://www.sainteve.com
Sales Range: $75-99.9 Million
Emp.: 100
Womens, Childrens & Infants Clothing
N.A.I.C.S.: 424350

KOMAR INDUSTRIES, LLC

Komar Company—(Continued)

KOMAR INDUSTRIES, LLC
4425 Marketing Pl, Groveport, OH 43125
Tel.: (614) 836-2366
Web Site:
http://www.komarindustries.com
Year Founded: 1978
Sales Range: $75-99.9 Million
Emp.: 50
Mfr of Sewage & Water Treatment Equipment
N.A.I.C.S.: 333310
Larry Koenig *(Founder & CEO)*

Subsidiaries:

Maren Engineering Corporation (1)
111 W Taft Dr, South Holland, IL 60473
Tel.: (708) 333-6250
Web Site: http://www.marenengineering.com
All Other Industrial Machinery Mfr
N.A.I.C.S.: 333248
Todd Wondrow *(Pres)*

PTR Baler & Compactor Company (1)
2207 E Ontario St, Philadelphia, PA 19134-2615
Tel.: (215) 533-5100
Web Site: http://www.ptrco.com
Sales Range: $10-24.9 Million
Emp.: 160
Mfr & Distribute Recycling Equipment & Waste Disposal Equipment
N.A.I.C.S.: 333998
Robert J. Riethmiller Jr. *(Chm)*
Michael Savage *(Pres & CEO)*
James Buccella *(Treas)*

Subsidiary (Domestic):

PTR Baler & Compactor Service Inc. (2)
2207 E Ontario St, Philadelphia, PA 19134-2614
Tel.: (215) 533-5100
Web Site: http://www.ptrco.com
Baler & Compactor Sales & Services
N.A.I.C.S.: 811210
James Bucella *(Controller)*

KOMAR SCREW CORP.
7790 N Merrimac Ave, Niles, IL 60714
Tel.: (847) 965-9090
Web Site:
http://www.komarscrew.com
Year Founded: 1969
Sales Range: $10-24.9 Million
Emp.: 50
Mfr of Screws
N.A.I.C.S.: 423710
Marvin Kocian *(Founder, Owner & Pres)*
Rob R. Matthews *(Branch Mgr)*
Branden Jones *(Branch Mgr)*

KOMAX CORPORATION
1100 Corporate E Grove Dr, Buffalo Grove, IL 60089-4543
Tel.: (847) 537-6640 IL
Web Site:
http://www.komaxgroup.com
Year Founded: 1994
Sales Range: $10-24.9 Million
Emp.: 45
Suppliers of Industrial Machinery & Wire Processing
N.A.I.C.S.: 332710
Peter Everham *(Controller)*
Beat Kalin *(Chm)*
Daniel Hirschi *(Vice Chm)*

KOMBI, LTD.
6 Thompson Dr, Essex Junction, VT 05452-3405
Tel.: (802) 879-3369 CT
Web Site:
http://www.kombisports.com
Year Founded: 1969
Sales Range: $75-99.9 Million
Emp.: 20
Ski Gloves & Accessories; Thermal Underwear, Socks & Turtlenecks; Snowboard Gloves & Mitts Distr
N.A.I.C.S.: 423910
Phil Gellis *(CEO)*
Anne Larner *(Mgr-Pur-Import & Export)*

KOMLINE-SANDERSON CORPORATION
12 Holland Ave, Peapack, NJ 07977-0257
Tel.: (908) 234-1000 NJ
Web Site: http://www.komline.com
Year Founded: 1946
Sales Range: $50-74.9 Million
Emp.: 130
Liquid-Solids Separation Equipment, Pumps & Drying Equipment Mfr
N.A.I.C.S.: 333998
Annette Oswald *(Dir-Mktg & HR)*
Russell Komline *(Pres)*
Kerry Kovacs *(VP)*
Danai Brooks *(CEO)*

Subsidiaries:

AquaShield, Inc. (1)
2733 Kanasita Dr Ste 111, Chattanooga, TN 37343
Tel.: (423) 870-8888
Web Site: http://www.aquashieldinc.com
Stormwater Runoff & Rainwater Harvesting Services
N.A.I.C.S.: 561990
Kelly Williamson *(Founder)*

Barnes International, Inc. (1)
814 Chestnut St, Rockford, IL 61105-1203
Tel.: (815) 964-8661
Web Site: http://www.barnesintl.com
Machine Tools, Super Abrasive Honing Systems, Honing Machines, Honing Tools, Coolant Filtration Equipment & Gantry Robotics Mfr
N.A.I.C.S.: 333517
William Kirchner *(Pres)*
David Gollob *(CEO)*

Subsidiary (Domestic):

Advanced Filtration Concepts, Inc. (2)
3211 Grant Line Rd Summit Sq Ste 7, New Albany, IN 47150
Tel.: (812) 949-4711
Web Site: http://www.afcbarnes.com
Coolant Filtration Equipment Distr
N.A.I.C.S.: 423730

Subsidiary (Non-US):

Barnes International Srl (2)
Corso Giulio Cesare 338 5F Int 26, 10154, Turin, Italy
Tel.: (39) 011 246 7380
Machine Tool Coolant Filtration Systems Distr
N.A.I.C.S.: 423840
Nigel Owens *(Mng Dir)*
Giuseppe Zaccari *(Mgr-Site & Svc)*
Anna Baracco *(Office Mgr)*

Subsidiary (Domestic):

H.R. Black Co. Inc. (2)
555 Van Camp Rd, Bowling Green, OH 43402
Tel.: (419) 352-7501
Emp.: 60
Environmental Systems & Automation & Conveyor Systems
N.A.I.C.S.: 333998
Steve Vollmar *(VP)*

Henry Filters, Inc. (2)
555 Van Camp Rd, Bowling Green, OH 43402
Tel.: (419) 352-7501
Web Site: http://www.henryfilters.com
Emp.: 65
Environmental Systems & Automation & Conveyor Systems
N.A.I.C.S.: 333998

Matt Kerwin *(Mgr-Sls)*
Steve Vollmar *(VP-Ops)*

Harn R/O Systems, Inc. (1)
310 Center Ct, Venice, FL 34285
Tel.: (941) 488-9671
Web Site: http://www.harnrosystems.com
Commercial & Service Industry Machinery Mfr
N.A.I.C.S.: 333310
James A. Harn *(Pres)*
Julie Nemeth *(VP)*
Jon Harn *(Project Engr)*
Kyle Jennings *(Project Engr)*
Ronald J. Castle *(Mgr-Process Design)*
Vito Trupiano *(Project Engr)*
Julia E. Nemeth-Harn *(VP)*

The Haselden Company, Inc. (1)
474 Deanna Ln, Charleston, SC 29492
Tel.: (843) 884-6679
Web Site: http://www.haseldenco.com
Sales Range: $1-9.9 Million
Emp.: 20
Industrial Machinery And Equipment
N.A.I.C.S.: 423830
O'Dell Haselden *(Pres)*

KOMO MACHINE INC.
1 Komo Dr, Lakewood, NJ 08701-5923
Tel.: (732) 719-6222 MN
Web Site: http://www.komo.com
Year Founded: 1981
Sales Range: $25-49.9 Million
Emp.: 105
Machine tools, Metal Cutting Type
N.A.I.C.S.: 333517
Jeff Erickson *(VP-Sls & Svcs)*
Mike Kolibas *(Pres)*

KOMODIDAD DISTRIBUTORS INC.
Km 58 HM 8 RR 156, Caguas, PR 00727
Tel.: (787) 746-3188
Web Site:
http://www.gatsbyworld.com
Sales Range: $25-49.9 Million
Emp.: 400
Mens' & Boy's, Women's & Girl's Clothing
N.A.I.C.S.: 424350
Jorge Galliano Artime *(Pres)*

KOMODO HEALTH, INC.
680 Folsom St 5th Fl, San Francisco, CA 94017
Tel.: (415) 805-1425
Web Site:
http://www.komodohealth.com
Year Founded: 2014
Software Publisher for Healthcare Industry
N.A.I.C.S.: 513210
Arif Nathoo *(Co-Founder & CEO)*
Laurent Bride *(CTO)*
Christine Douglass *(Dir-Comm)*
Sarah Shin *(Chief HR Officer)*
Web Sun *(Co-Founder & Pres)*
Bill Madigan *(Chief Revenue Officer)*
Aswin Chandrakantan *(Chief Comml Officer)*
Lauren Stahl *(VP & Head-Sls)*
Vikas Mehta *(CFO)*

Subsidiaries:

Mavens Consulting Services, Inc. (1)
185 N Franklin St Ste 400, Chicago, IL 60606
Tel.: (312) 725-8528
Web Site: http://www.mavens.com
Sales Range: $10-24.9 Million
Information Technology Consulting Services
N.A.I.C.S.: 541512
Prasad Kanumury *(Co-Founder)*
Billy Ho *(Co-Founder)*

KOMPANI GROUP
4981 SW 74th Ct, Miami, FL 33155-4471
Tel.: (786) 594-0435
Web Site:
http://www.kompanigroup.com
Marketing Consulting Services
N.A.I.C.S.: 541613
Gianni D'Alerta *(Partner)*

KONA HR CONSULTING GROUP LLC
4469 Winding Creek Rd, Manlius, NY 13104
Tel.: (315) 256-9532
Web Site: http://konahr.com
Year Founded: 2005
Sales Range: $1-9.9 Million
Emp.: 6
Human Resources Consulting
N.A.I.C.S.: 541612
Sarah L. Kelly *(Partner)*
Vincent J. Kelly Jr. *(Partner)*
Robert F. Toole Jr. *(Partner)*

KONCEPT TECHNOLOGIES INC
429 E Huntington Dr, Monrovia, CA 91016
Tel.: (323) 261-8999
Web Site:
http://www.konceptech.com
Year Founded: 2002
Sales Range: $1-9.9 Million
Emp.: 8
LED Lighting Products
N.A.I.C.S.: 335139
Kenneth Ng *(Co-Founder)*
Edmund Ng *(Co-Founder)*
Peter Ng *(Co-Founder)*

KONIAG INC.
3800 Ctr Point Dr Ste 502, Anchorage, AK 99503
Tel.: (907) 561-2668
Web Site: http://www.koniag.com
Year Founded: 1972
Investment Services
N.A.I.C.S.: 523999
Ronald Unger *(Chm & CEO)*
Conrad Peterson *(Sec)*
Shauna Hegna *(Pres)*
Sharon Beeson *(CFO)*
Peter Boskofsky *(Gen Counsel)*
Memry Dahl *(Sr Dir-HR & Admin)*
Tyan Hayes *(Vice Chm)*
Gordon Olsen *(Treas)*

Subsidiaries:

Glacier Services, Inc. (1)
11921 E Palmer Wasilla Hwy, Palmer, AK 99645
Tel.: (907) 745-6487
Web Site: http://www.glcr.com
Process Automation Services
N.A.I.C.S.: 518210
Troy A. Johnson *(VP)*
Art Garrod *(Pres)*

KONING RESTAURANTS INTERNATIONAL, LTD.
1000 Park Ctr Blvd Ste 134-136, Miami, FL 33169
Tel.: (305) 430-1200
Year Founded: 1999
Sales Range: $50-74.9 Million
Emp.: 3,000
Restaurant Operators
N.A.I.C.S.: 722513
Al Salas *(Owner)*
Robert Wyockkin *(VP)*

KONTAGENT INC.
201 Mission St 25th Fl, San Francisco, CA 94105
Tel.: (415) 766-6500
Web Site: http://www.kontagent.com
Year Founded: 2007

Sales Range: $25-49.9 Million
Emp.: 150
Mobile Analytics Software
N.A.I.C.S.: 513210
Josh Williams *(CEO & Chief Scientfic Officer)*
Charles Marker *(Head-Engrg)*
Jimmy Fan *(Head-Ops)*
Catherine Mylinh *(Head-Mktg & Gen Mgr-New Mobile Markets)*
Anthony Yoo *(Gen Mgr-Channel Dev)*

KONY SOLUTIONS, INC.
7380 W Sand Lake Rd Ste 390, Orlando, FL 32819
Tel.: (321) 293-5669
Web Site: http://www.kony.com
Sales Range: $10-24.9 Million
Mobile Applications Mfr
N.A.I.C.S.: 513210
Sriram Ramanathan *(CTO)*
Blake P. Salle *(Pres-Field Ops)*
Pat Robison *(Chief HR Officer)*
Todd Miller *(Mng Dir)*
John Joyce *(Vice Chm)*

KONZA VALLEY CAPITAL INC.
40 Corporate Woods Ste 200 9401 Indian Creek Pkwy, Overland Park, KS 66210
Tel.: (913) 262-7117
Web Site: http://www.kvci.com
Investment Services
N.A.I.C.S.: 523999
Marshall D. Parker *(Pres & CEO)*
Brian Lueger *(Principal)*

KOOL AUTOMOTIVE
1313 High St, Portsmouth, VA 23704
Tel.: (757) 393-0020
Web Site: http://www.koolautomotive.com
Sales Range: $10-24.9 Million
Emp.: 20
Automobile Service & Collision Center
N.A.I.C.S.: 811111
John Kool *(Pres)*
Ross Kool *(VP & Gen Mgr)*

KOOL CHEVROLET, OLDSMOBILE, CADILLAC, INC.
810 W Chicago Rd, Sturgis, MI 49091
Tel.: (269) 651-9304   MI
Web Site: http://www.koolsturgis.com
Year Founded: 1984
Sales Range: $10-24.9 Million
New & Used Car Dealer
N.A.I.C.S.: 441110
Tom Kool *(Principal)*
Randy Garmire *(Mgr-Fin)*

KOONS FORD INC.
1051 E Broad St, Falls Church, VA 22044
Tel.: (703) 241-7200
Web Site: http://www.koons.com
Rev.: $115,000,000
Emp.: 275
Automobiles, New & Used
N.A.I.C.S.: 441110
James E. Koons *(Pres)*
Steve Meek *(Controller)*

KOONS LINCOLN MERCURY, INC.
9610 Reisterstown Rd, Owings Mills, MD 21117-4128
Tel.: (410) 363-3333
Year Founded: 1987
Sales Range: $10-24.9 Million
Emp.: 70
New Car Whslr
N.A.I.C.S.: 441110

Courtney Moser *(Mgr-Customer Rels)*
Al Riddick *(Mgr-Sls)*
Todd Ruprecht *(Gen Mgr)*
Rudy Schmidt *(Principal)*

KOONS OF MANASSAS INC.
10660 Automotive Dr, Manassas, VA 20109
Tel.: (703) 368-9100
Web Site: http://www.joycekoons.com
Sales Range: $25-49.9 Million
Emp.: 200
Automobiles, New & Used
N.A.I.C.S.: 441110
Joyce Koons *(Owner & Pres)*

KOONS SILVER SPRING FORD LINCOLN
3111 Automobile Blvd, Silver Spring, MD 20904-4902
Tel.: (301) 474-5100
Web Site: http://www.koonssilverspringfordlincoln.com
Sales Range: $100-124.9 Million
Emp.: 72
Automobile Dealership
N.A.I.C.S.: 441110
Christina Irby *(Controller)*

KOONS WESTMINSTER TOYOTA
375 Baltimore Blvd, Westminster, MD 21157
Tel.: (410) 857-1400
Web Site: http://www.koonstoyotawestminster.com
Year Founded: 1989
Sales Range: $10-24.9 Million
Emp.: 100
New Car Retailer
N.A.I.C.S.: 441110
Nigel Hayes *(Gen Mgr)*

KOONTZ-WAGNER ELECTRIC COMPANY
3801 Voorde Dr ste B, South Bend, IN 46628
Tel.: (574) 232-2051
Web Site: http://www.koontz-wagner.com
Rev.: $60,786,432
Emp.: 100
Solenoid Valves
N.A.I.C.S.: 332911

KOOPMAN LUMBER CO. INC.
665 Church St, Whitinsville, MA 01588
Tel.: (508) 234-4545   MA
Web Site: http://www.koopmanlumber.com
Year Founded: 1938
Sales Range: $10-24.9 Million
Emp.: 50
Mfr & Distributor of Lumber & Other Building Materials
N.A.I.C.S.: 423310
Denise Brookhouse *(CFO)*
Anthony Brookhouse *(COO)*

KOOPMAN OSTBO
412 NW 8th Ave, Portland, OR 97209
Tel.: (503) 223-2168
Web Site: http://www.koopmanostbo.com
Rev.: $30,000,000
Emp.: 15
Advertising, Public Relations
N.A.I.C.S.: 541810
Ken Koopman *(Principal)*
Craig Ostbo *(Principal)*
Joe Parker *(Dir-Bus Dev)*
Ashley Bernard *(Acct Mgr-PR)*
Deborah Houston *(VP-Fin)*

Robert Shepard *(Dir-Creative)*
Ted Morgan *(Dir-Acct Svcs)*
Tracy Pokarney *(Dir-Media)*

KOORSEN PROTECTION SERVICES
2719 N Arlington Ave, Indianapolis, IN 46218
Tel.: (317) 542-1800   IN
Web Site: http://www.koorsen.com
Year Founded: 1946
Sales Range: $50-74.9 Million
Emp.: 200
Provider of Loss Prevention Services
N.A.I.C.S.: 423990
Randall R. Koorsen *(Pres)*
Skip Sampson *(VP)*

KOPCO INC.
Caney Industrial Pk 107 A St, Caney, KS 67333
Tel.: (620) 879-2117
Web Site: http://www.kopcoinc.com
Sales Range: $10-24.9 Million
Emp.: 60
Offset Printing
N.A.I.C.S.: 323111
Reba George *(CFO & Co-Owner)*
Kenneth K. George Sr. *(CEO & Co-Owner)*

KOPLAR COMMUNICATIONS INTERNATIONAL, INC.
50 Maryland Dr Ste 300, Saint Louis, MO 63108
Tel.: (314) 345-1000
Web Site: http://www.koplar.com
Year Founded: 1958
Sales Range: $10-24.9 Million
Emp.: 20
Television Broadcasting Stations & Interactive Programming
N.A.I.C.S.: 517810
Edward J. Koplar *(Pres & CEO)*
Caitlin Mindel *(Head-Recruiting)*

Subsidiaries:

Koplar Properties Inc   (1)
50 Maryland Plz Ste 300, Saint Louis, MO 63108-1553
Tel.: (314) 345-1000
Web Site: http://www.koplarproperties.com
General Construction Services
N.A.I.C.S.: 236220

World Events Productions, Ltd.   (1)
50 Maryland Plz Ste 300, Saint Louis, MO 63108-1553
Tel.: (314) 345-1000
Web Site: http://www.wep.com
Producer of Television Programming, Motion Pictures & Videos
N.A.I.C.S.: 512110

KOPPER GLO MINING, LLC
144E Market Pl Blvd, Knoxville, TN 37922
Tel.: (865) 247-4382   DE
Web Site: http://www.kopperglo.com
Year Founded: 1959
Underground Coal Mining
N.A.I.C.S.: 212115
Hunter Hobson *(Pres)*

KOPY KWEEN INCORPORATED
2 42 Broadway, New York, NY 10004-1617
Tel.: (212) 514-6500   NY
Web Site: http://www.thesuperiorgroup.com
Year Founded: 1975
Sales Range: $10-24.9 Million
Emp.: 200
Provider of Photocopying & Duplicating Services
N.A.I.C.S.: 323111

Morris Friedman *(VP)*
Ben Fried *(Pres)*

KORE POWER, INC.
1875 N Lakewood Dr Suite 200, Coeur d'Alene, ID 83814
Tel.: (802) 496-2955
Web Site: https://korepower.com
Emp.: 100
Battery & Energy Storage Mfr
N.A.I.C.S.: 335910
Lindsay Gorrill *(Founder & CEO)*
Paul Coombs *(Founder & Chief Strategy Officer)*
Jay Bellows *(Pres)*
Alexander Nickolatos *(CFO)*

Subsidiaries:

Northern Reliability Inc.   (1)
340 Mad River Pk, Waitsfield, VT 05673-7343
Tel.: (802) 496-2955
Web Site: http://www.northernreliability.com
Other Electric Power Generation
N.A.I.C.S.: 221118

KORE WIRELESS GROUP, INC.
3700 Mansell Rd Ste 250, Alpharetta, GA 30022
Tel.: (866) 710-4028
Web Site: http://www.koretelematics.com
Year Founded: 2003
Holding Company: Wireless Network Services
N.A.I.C.S.: 551112
Robert Metzler *(Exec VP-Sls)*
Danny Thomas *(VP-Ops)*
Chuck Horne *(VP-Product & Svc Mgmt)*
Daniel To *(VP-Fin)*
Terence Jarman *(Chm)*
Richard Burston *(Vice Chm)*
Stephen Healy *(Exec VP-Product)*
Ariel Gonzalez *(VP-Customer Svc)*
Chris Francosky *(VP-IT Ops & Network Engrg)*
Romil Bahl *(Pres & CEO)*
Paul Holtz *(Interim CFO)*
Vik Vijayvergiya *(VP-IR)*

Subsidiaries:

Jazz Wireless Data Inc.   (1)
8480 Honeycutt RdÂ Ste 200, Raleigh, NC 27615
Tel.: (919) 794-4434
Web Site: http://www.jazzwirelessdata.com
Emp.: 11
Wireless Telecommunication Services
N.A.I.C.S.: 517112
Daniel Cebula *(Mgr-Acct-Natl)*
Gregor Bleiman *(Pres)*

Kore Telematics   (1)
3700 Mansell Rd Suite 250, Alpharetta, GA 30022   (100%)
Tel.: (866) 710-4028
M2M Networking Services
N.A.I.C.S.: 519290
Terence Jarman *(Chm)*
Danny Thomas *(Exec VP-Ops & Tech Svcs)*
Robert Metzler *(Exec VP-Sls & Mktg)*
Daniel To *(VP-Fin)*
Chuck Horne *(VP-Product & Svc Mgmt)*

KOREAN WOMEN'S ASSOCIATION
123 E 96th St, Tacoma, WA 98445
Tel.: (253) 535-4202   WA
Web Site: http://www.kwacares.org
Year Founded: 1979
Sales Range: $10-24.9 Million
Emp.: 1,583
Woman Welfare Services
N.A.I.C.S.: 813410
Kyong Arbeeny *(Chm)*

KOREY KAY & PARTNERS

KOREY KAY & PARTNERS

Korey Kay & Partners—(Continued)
130 5th Ave, New York, NY 10011-4306
Tel.: (212) 620-4300   DE
Web Site: http://www.koreykay.com
Year Founded: 1982
Rev.: $57,600,000
Emp.: 41
N.A.I.C.S.: 541810
Milda Misevicius (Exec VP)
Brian Alter (Sr VP & Dir-Media)
Allen Kay (Chm & CEO)

KORMAN SERVICES, L.P.
2 Neshaminy Interplex Dr Ste 301, Trevose, PA 19053-6933
Tel.: (215) 245-0700   PA
Year Founded: 1909
Sales Range: $75-99.9 Million
Emp.: 6
Commercial & Industrial Development & Management Services
N.A.I.C.S.: 531210
Berton E. Korman (Partner)
Steven H. Korman (Partner)
Jeanne Landgraf (Mng Dir)
Leonard I. Korman (Partner)

Subsidiaries:

Korman Residential Properties, Inc.   (1)
2 Neshaminy Interplex Ste 301, Trevose, PA 19053
Tel.: (215) 244-5160
Web Site: http://www.kormanresidential.com
Sales Range: $50-74.9 Million
Emp.: 200
Residential Property Management & Development
N.A.I.C.S.: 531311
John P. Korman (CEO)
James S. Korman (Pres)
Christian M. Troll (CFO)
Pete Rushing (Dir-Mktg)
Deborah Downs (Dir-Fin Reporting)
Colleen Mazzoni (Dir-Customer Rels)
Julie Procaccino (Mgr-Pur)

KOROBERI INC.
1506 E Franklin St Ste 300, Chapel Hill, NC 27514
Tel.: (919) 960-9794
Web Site: http://www.koroberi.com
Sales Range: $1-9.9 Million
Emp.: 12
Advetising Agency
N.A.I.C.S.: 541810
Bruce Olive (Co-Founder & CEO)
Natalie Fioto (Acct Exec-Mktg)
Kathryn Olive (Co-Founder & Pres)
Matt Murphy (Dir-Client Svcs)

KOROTKIN-SCHLESINGER & ASSOCIATES, INC.
26877 Northwestern Hwy Ste 400, Southfield, MI 48033-8418
Tel.: (248) 352-5140   MI
Web Site: http://www.korotkin.com
Year Founded: 1911
Sales Range: $10-24.9 Million
Emp.: 45
Insurance Agents
N.A.I.C.S.: 524210
Kenneth M. Korotkin (Pres)
Glenn H. Warsh (Exec VP)
Jackie Sefferman (VP)
J. J. Reifler (VP)
Sandy Zurcher (Mgr-Acctg)
Lisa Potter (Mgr-Automation & Personal Lines)
Gloria Doster (Mgr-HR)
Kyle Fenton (VP)
Emily M. Korotkin (VP)
Jeffrey S. Belen (VP)
Matt H. Warsh (VP)

KORR MEDICAL TECHNOLOGIES INC.
3487 W 2100 S, Salt Lake City, UT 84119
Tel.: (801) 483-2080
Web Site: http://www.korr.com
Sales Range: $1-9.9 Million
Emp.: 18
Metabolic Testing Products Mfr
N.A.I.C.S.: 541715
Stephen P. Smith (VP-Ops & Controller)
Brent Jones (VP-Sls)
Julie K. Kofoed (VP-Mktg)

KORTE CONSTRUCTION
333 S 18th St Ste 700, Saint Louis, MO 63103-2256
Tel.: (314) 231-3700
Web Site: http://www.korteco.com
Year Founded: 1958
Sales Range: $100-124.9 Million
Emp.: 18
Nonresidential Construction Services
N.A.I.C.S.: 236220
Vernon Eardley (Pres)

KORTE CONSTRUCTION COMPANY INC.
5700 Oakland Ave Ste 275, Saint Louis, MO 63110-2256
Tel.: (314) 231-3700
Web Site: http://www.korteco.com
Year Founded: 1958
Sales Range: $200-249.9 Million
Emp.: 250
Provider of Industrial Buildings & Warehouses
N.A.I.C.S.: 236220
Todd Korte (Pres & CEO)
Alan Schorfheide (Exec VP-Bus Dev)
Brent Korte (Exec VP)
Greg Korte (Pres-Las Vegas)
Mike Tubbs (Exec VP-Bus Dev)
Scott Schmidt (CIO & Exec VP)

Subsidiaries:

Korte Designs, Inc.   (1)
12441 US Hwy 40, Highland, IL 62249-3807   (100%)
Tel.: (618) 654-4800
Web Site: http://www.kortedesign.com
Rev.: $100,000,000
Emp.: 100
Provider of Architectural Services
N.A.I.C.S.: 541310
Darlene Hanks (Principal)

KORTE DOES IT ALL
10920 Stellhorn Rd, New Haven, IN 46774-9775
Tel.: (260) 493-2596
Web Site: http://www.kortedoesitall.com
Year Founded: 1965
Sales Range: $10-24.9 Million
Emp.: 80
Plumbing Services
N.A.I.C.S.: 238220
David Korte (VP)
Kevin Kratzman (VP)
Jerry A. Korte (Pres)

KORTEC, INC.
428 Newburyport Turnpike, Rowley, MA 01938
Tel.: (978) 238-7100
Web Site: http://www.kortec.com
Year Founded: 1996
Sales Range: $25-49.9 Million
Emp.: 30
Designer & Manufacturer of Industrial Injection Mold Machinery to Make Air-Tight Plastic & Glass Bottles for Beverages & Chemicals
N.A.I.C.S.: 541690
Paul Swenson (Pres & CEO)
Gloria Curley (VP-Ops)
Scott Ludwig (Mgr-Bus Dev)

KORTH DIRECT MORTGAGE INC.
135 San Lorenzo Ave Ste 600, Coral Gables, FL 33146
Tel.: (305) 668-8485   FL
Web Site: http://www.korthdirect.com
Year Founded: 2009
Rev.: $9,862,033
Assets: $507,549,161
Liabilities: $475,185,200
Net Worth: $32,363,961
Earnings: $1,607,939
Emp.: 26
Fiscal Year-end: 12/31/22
Mortgage Lending Services
N.A.I.C.S.: 522292
James W. Korth (Chm)
Holly C. MacDonald-Korth (Pres, CEO & CFO)
Daniel Llorente (Chief Lending Officer)
Pamela J. Hipp (Dir-Securities Mktg)
Jonathan L. Shepard (Sec)

KORTX, LLC
415 S Center St, Royal Oak, MI 48067
Web Site: http://www.kortx.io
Year Founded: 2014
Sales Range: $10-24.9 Million
Emp.: 20
Marketing Consulting Services
N.A.I.C.S.: 541613
Damon Henry (Founder & CEO)
Eric Lee (Mng Partner-Ops)
Chris Rowell (Mng Partner-Sls)

KORUM MOTORS INC.
100 River Rd, Puyallup, WA 98371
Tel.: (253) 841-9600
Web Site: http://www.korum.com
Rev.: $71,500,000
Emp.: 185
Automobiles, New & Used
N.A.I.C.S.: 441110
Jerome M. Korum (Pres)

KORUTRANS INTERNATIONAL INC.
2401 Morris Ave, Union, NJ 07083
Tel.: (908) 624-1880
Web Site: http://www.carotrans.com
Sales Range: $25-49.9 Million
Emp.: 40
Trucking Service
N.A.I.C.S.: 484121
Michael Forkenbrock (Pres)
Andrew Weisse (Branch Mgr)

KORVIS AUTOMATION INC.
2101 NE Jack London St, Corvallis, OR 97330
Tel.: (541) 738-4360
Web Site: http://www.korvis.com
Year Founded: 2002
Sales Range: $10-24.9 Million
Emp.: 80
Precision Machine Mfr for Semiconductor, Biotechnology & Ink Jet Printer Industries
N.A.I.C.S.: 333310
Richard Carone (CEO)
Rod W. Holmquist (VP)
Ngwan Boon Ming (Gen Mgr)
Yang Yi Qiang (Mgr-Ops)
Neal Pierce (VP-Ops-Asian)

KOSINSKI ARCHITECTURE, INC.
1401 E Broward Blvd Ste 201, Fort Lauderdale, FL 33301
Tel.: (954) 627-6988
Web Site: http://www.kosinskiarchitecture.com
Sales Range: $1-9.9 Million
Emp.: 9

Architectural Services
N.A.I.C.S.: 541310
Peter Kosinski (Principal)
Peter Kosinski Jr. (Principal)

KOSITZKA & WICKS CO.
5270 Shawnee Rd Ste 250, Alexandria, VA 22312
Tel.: (703) 642-2700
Web Site: http://www.kwccpa.com
Accounting Services
N.A.I.C.S.: 541211
Stephen G. Travis (Mng Principal-Alexandria)
Michael Wicks (Principal)
Thomas Lohr (Principal-Tax)
Jeffrey Creskoff (Principal-Alexandria)
Terri O'Brien (Principal)
Connie Hammell (Principal)
Brenda Curtis (Principal)
Howard Kramer (Principal)
Steven Biegler (Mng Principal-Richmond)

Subsidiaries:

Biegler & Associates, P.C.   (1)
5911 W Broad St, Richmond, VA 23230
Tel.: (804) 855-1200
Offices of Certified Public Accountants
N.A.I.C.S.: 541211

KOSMAS GROUP INTERNATIONAL INC.
3626 Quadrangle Blvd Ste 300, Orlando, FL 32817
Tel.: (386) 427-6892
Web Site: http://www.kgiresorts.com
Sales Range: $25-49.9 Million
Emp.: 100
Timesharer, Developer
N.A.I.C.S.: 483112
Steven Kosmas (Pres)
Trudy Duffy (VP)

KOSS-WINN BANCSHARES, INC.
101 N Main St, Buffalo Center, IA 50424
Tel.: (641) 562-2696   IA
Web Site: http://www.ftsbbank.bank
Year Founded: 1979
Bank Holding Company
N.A.I.C.S.: 551111
James Engle (Vice Chm, Pres & CEO)
Brian Vander Wilt (CEO-Farmers Trust & Savings Bank, Treas & Sec)
Douglas Leland (Pres-Farmers Trust & Savings Bank)

Subsidiaries:

Farmers Trust & Savings Bank   (1)
101 N Main St, Buffalo Center, IA 50424
Tel.: (641) 562-2696
Web Site: http://www.ftsbbank.com
Sales Range: $10-24.9 Million
Emp.: 39
Commericial Banking
N.A.I.C.S.: 522110
Alan Hagen (Sr VP-Lake Mills)
Brian Vander Wilt (CEO, Treas & Sec)
Dawn Meinders (Asst VP)
Gene Hartman (Chm)
Nancy Moklestad (VP)
James Engle (Vice Chm)
David Streuber (Sr VP-Lakota)
Douglas Leland (Pres)

KOSSMAN DEVELOPMENT COMPANY
11 Pkwy Ctr Ste 300, Pittsburgh, PA 15220-3614
Tel.: (412) 921-6100   PA
Web Site: http://www.kossman.com
Year Founded: 1949
Sales Range: $25-49.9 Million
Emp.: 150

Provider of Nonresidential Building Operator Services
N.A.I.C.S.: 531120
Curtis Kossman (Pres)
Marc Kossman (Exec VP)

KOSSMAN'S, INC.
114 N Davis Ave, Cleveland, MS 38732
Tel.: (662) 545-4098
Web Site: http://www.kossmans.com
Sales Range: $10-24.9 Million
Emp.: 35
Car Whslr
N.A.I.C.S.: 441110
Edward Kossman III (Pres)

KOSTIAL COMPANY, LLC
2001 N Lamar Blvd Ste 3, Austin, TX 78705
Tel.: (888) 241-6634
Web Site:
http://www.audienceinnovation.com
Year Founded: 2005
Sales Range: $10-24.9 Million
Emp.: 50
Advertising Agencies
N.A.I.C.S.: 541810
Paul C. Kostial (Pres)

KOSTKA ENTERPRISES INC.
3574 US 1 S, Saint Augustine, FL 32086
Tel.: (904) 797-5116
Web Site:
http://www.keidominos.com
Sales Range: $10-24.9 Million
Emp.: 450
Pizzeria Operator
N.A.I.C.S.: 722513
Greg L. Kostka (Pres)
Karl Amer (VP)
Kenny Garrido (Dir-Info Sys)

KOSTMAYER CONSTRUCTION INC.
1080 Old Spanish Trl Ste 10, Slidell, LA 70458-5002
Tel.: (504) 837-3320
Web Site: http://www.kostmayer.com
Rev.: $20,000,000
Emp.: 73
Dams, Waterways, Docks & Other Marine Construction
N.A.I.C.S.: 236210
Steve Dunn (Mgr-Construction)
James H. Kostmayer Jr. (Pres)

KOSTO FOOD PRODUCTS CO.
1325 N Old Rand Rd, Wauconda, IL 60084
Tel.: (847) 487-2600
Web Site: http://www.kostofoods.com
Desserts & Dessert Ingredients Mfr
N.A.I.C.S.: 311999

KOTIS DESIGN LLC
2101 N 34th St Ste 200, Seattle, WA 98103
Tel.: (206) 466-1800
Web Site: http://www.kotisdesign.com
Year Founded: 2003
Sales Range: $10-24.9 Million
Emp.: 57
Promotional Products
N.A.I.C.S.: 541890
Nicole Schultze (Acct Mgr)
Eric Hamlin (VP-Sls)

KOTTKE TRUCKING, INC.
211 Hwy 212 E, Buffalo Lake, MN 55314
Tel.: (320) 833-5385 MN
Web Site: http://www.kottke-trucking.com
Year Founded: 1986
Specialized Freight (except Used Goods) Trucking, Long-Distance
N.A.I.C.S.: 484230
Kory Kottke (Sr VP & Owner)
Zach Little (COO)
Subsidiaries:
FCD Enterprises, Inc. (1)
2 West Blvd N, Davenport, FL 33837
Tel.: (863) 422-8752
General Freight Trucking, Long-Distance, Truckload
N.A.I.C.S.: 484121

KOU YOU KAI, LTD.
222 S Main St Ste 500, Salt Lake City, UT 84111
Tel.: (385) 282-5041 WY
Year Founded: 2018
Emp.: 2
Holding Company
N.A.I.C.S.: 551112
Tsunenobu Arai (Pres)
Masaru Tanzawa (CEO)
Fred McLauchlin (CFO & Sec)
Sachiko Shinoda (Treas)
Doug Nosler (Pres-Liquid Dynamics)

KOURT SECURITY PARTNERS LLC
1250 N 9th St Ste 104, Stroudsburg, PA 18360-7800
Tel.: (877) 877-0345
Web Site:
http://www.selectsecurity.com
Electrical Apparatus & Equipment, Wiring Supplies & Related Equipment Merchant Whslr
N.A.I.C.S.: 423610
Dave Smalley (Mgr)

KOURY CORPORATION
400 Four Seasons Town Ctr, Greensboro, NC 27407
Tel.: (336) 299-9200
Web Site: http://www.kourycorp.com
Rev.: $60,500,000
Emp.: 50
Commercial & Industrial Building Operation
N.A.I.C.S.: 531120
Richard N. Franks (VP-Design & Plng)
Terri Greene (Asst Controller)
Ron Mack (Gen Counsel & Exec VP-Retail)
Gene Tillman (VP-Office & Indus)
Kelley Harrill (Dir-Sls & Mktg-Sheraton Greensboro)
Gordon Craig (CFO & VP)
Stephen D. Showfety (Pres)
Robin Smith (Dir-HR)
Dominic Payson (Dir-Facilities)
Christina York (Dir-Sls & Mktg-Grandover Resort)
Joel Meyer (Gen Mgr-Grandover Resort)
Jan Byrd (Mgr-Acctg Payable)
Teresa Bonnstetter (Mgr-Property)

KOVA FERTILIZER INC.
1331 N Anderson St, Greensburg, IN 47240-1011
Tel.: (812) 663-5081 IN
Web Site: http://www.ekova.com
Year Founded: 1935
Sales Range: $75-99.9 Million
Emp.: 40
Whslr of Fertilizers & Agricultural Chemicals
N.A.I.C.S.: 424910
Rob Bickel (Mgr-Credit)
Roger Dumond (Mgr-Precision Agriculture)
Chris Bierhaus (Mgr-Warehouse)
Subsidiaries:
Agri Business Finance, Inc. (1)
1330 N Anderson St, Greensburg, IN 47240
Tel.: (812) 663-5081
Agricultural Financial Services
N.A.I.C.S.: 522299
Paul Barnard (Gen Mgr)
Kova Fertilizer Inc. - Ohio Division (1)
4141 Laybourne Rd, Springfield, OH 45505
Tel.: (937) 323-1177
Web Site: http://www.ekova.com
Emp.: 10
Fertilizer Distr
N.A.I.C.S.: 424910
Michael Erwin (Mgr)
Next Generation, Inc. (1)
355 W Smith Rd, Greensburg, IN 47240
Tel.: (812) 663-5575
Web Site: http://www.nextgenerationinc.net
Fertilizer Distr
N.A.I.C.S.: 424910
Todd Reed (Pres)

KOVALCHICK SALVAGE CO.
1060 Wayne Ave, Indiana, PA 15701
Tel.: (724) 349-3300
Web Site:
http://www.kovalchickcorp.com
Sales Range: $10-24.9 Million
Emp.: 30
Railroad Equipment & Supplies
N.A.I.C.S.: 423860
Joseph Kovalchick (Pres & CEO)

KOVARUS, INC.
2000 Crow Canyon Pl Ste 250, San Ramon, CA 94583
Tel.: (650) 392-7848
Web Site: http://www.kovarus.com
Year Founded: 2003
Sales Range: $50-74.9 Million
Emp.: 49
Information Technology Consulting Services
N.A.I.C.S.: 541512
Patrick Cronin (Co-Founder & Principal)
Rich Wallace (Exec VP-Pro Svcs)
Erik Melander (Exec VP-Solutions)
Josh Howell (VP-Consulting Svcs-Pacific Northwest)
Peter Castaldi (Principal)
Lori Scott (Exec VP-Fin & Ops)

KOVEL/FULLER
9925 Jefferson Blvd, Culver City, CA 90232-3505
Tel.: (310) 841-4444 CA
Web Site: http://www.kovelfuller.com
Year Founded: 1999
Sales Range: $25-49.9 Million
Emp.: 50
Advetising Agency
N.A.I.C.S.: 541810
John Fuller (Owner)
Lee Kovel (Partner & Dir-Creative)
Len Zimmelman (Dir-Creative)
Christopher Brombach (Dir-Media)

KOWALSKI CO., INC.
2270 Holbrook Ave, Hamtramck, MI 48212
Tel.: (313) 873-8200 MI
Web Site: http://www.kowality.com
Year Founded: 1920
Sales Range: $100-124.9 Million
Emp.: 225
Sausage, Ham, Bacon & Luncheon Meat Mfr
N.A.I.C.S.: 311612
Michael Kowalski (Owner)
Linda Kowalski Jacob (Sec)

KOWALSKI COMPANIES INC.
33 Syndicate St S, Saint Paul, MN 55105
Tel.: (651) 698-4752
Web Site: http://www.kowalski.com
Sales Range: $50-74.9 Million
Emp.: 1,199
Independent Supermarket
N.A.I.C.S.: 445110
Tony Olufson (Accountant)
Subsidiaries:
Kowalski's White Bear Lake Market (1)
4391 Lake Ave S, White Bear Lake, MN 55110 (100%)
Tel.: (651) 698-4752
Web Site: http://www.kowalskis.com
Rev.: $14,800,000
Emp.: 7
Grocery Stores, Independent
N.A.I.C.S.: 445110
James Kowalski (Owner)

KOWALSKI COMPANIES INC.
2270 Holbrook St, Detroit, MI 48212
Tel.: (313) 873-8200
Web Site: http://www.kowality.com
Rev.: $32,800,000
Emp.: 182
Meat Processed from Carcasses
N.A.I.C.S.: 311612
Michael Kowalski (Pres)

KOYA LEADERSHIP PARTNERS LLC
44 Merrimac St, Newburyport, MA 01950
Web Site:
http://www.koyapartners.com
Year Founded: 2004
Sales Range: $10-24.9 Million
Emp.: 58
Business Management Services
N.A.I.C.S.: 561499
Katie Bouton (Founder & CEO)
Heather Campion (Mng Dir)
Alexandra Corvin (Mng Dir)
Molly Brennan (Partner & Exec VP)
Stephen Milbauer (VP)

KP HOLDINGS LLC
19635 US Hwy 31 N, Westfield, IN 46074
Tel.: (317) 867-0234
Rev.: $41,400,000
Emp.: 2
Motor Vehicle Parts & Accessories
N.A.I.C.S.: 336390
John Ball (Pres)
Subsidiaries:
Porter Engineered Systems Inc (1)
19635 US Hwy 31 N, Westfield, IN 46074
Tel.: (317) 867-0234
Web Site: http://www.porteres.com
Sales Range: $25-49.9 Million
Motor Vehicle Parts & Accessories
N.A.I.C.S.: 336390
Debbie Watson (Coord-Tool Crib)
Wade Shields (Dir-Quality & Mgr-Bus Unit)
Scott Hackler (Engr-Supplier Quality)
Loretta Young (Mgr-Matls)
Richard Oliver (Mgr-Ops)

KPA LLC
1380 Forest Park Cir, Lafayette, CO 80026
Tel.: (303) 228-8750
Web Site: http://www.kpaonline.com
Year Founded: 1986
Sales Range: $10-24.9 Million
Emp.: 146
Online Marketing Services
N.A.I.C.S.: 541810
Vane P. Clayton (Chm & CEO)
Gabe Orvis (CFO)
Bill Duclos (VP-Ops)
Eric Schmitz (VP-Product & Bus Dev)

KPA LLC

KPA LLC—(Continued)
Kathryn Carlson (VP-HR Mgmt Products)
Craig Creuziger (Dir-Sls Ops)
Jennifer Blake (Mgr-District)
Nick Hardesty (Mgr-District)
Peter Zaidel (Dir-Environment & Safety Product)

KPC HEALTHCARE HOLDINGS, INC.
9 KPC Pkwy Ste 301, Corona, CA 92879
Tel.: (951) 987-8100   CA
Web Site: http://www.thekpcgroup.com
Investment Holding Company; Healthcare, Education & Real Estate
N.A.I.C.S.: 551112
Kali P. Chaudhuri (Founder & Chm)

Subsidiaries:

KPC Healthcare, Inc. (1)
1301 N Tustin Ave, Santa Ana, CA 92705
Tel.: (714) 953-3652
Web Site: http://www.kpchealth.com
Office Administrative Services
N.A.I.C.S.: 561110
John A. Heydt (Chief Clinical Officer & CEO-Apex Medical Group)
Kali P. Chaudhuri (Founder & Chm)
Peter Baronoff (CEO)

Subsidiary (Domestic):

KPC Promise Healthcare, LLC (2)
900 N Federal Hwy Ste 350, Boca Raton, FL 33432
Tel.: (561) 869-6500
Web Site: http://www.kpcph.com
Holding Company; Specialty Hospital Operator
N.A.I.C.S.: 551112

Subsidiary (Domestic):

KPC Promise Hospital of Baton Rouge, LLC (3)
5130 Mancuso Ln, Baton Rouge, LA 70809
Tel.: (225) 490-9600
Web Site: http://batonrouge.kpcph.com
Specialty Care Hospital Operator
N.A.I.C.S.: 622310

KPC Promise Hospital of Dallas, LLC (3)
7955 Harry Hines Blvd, Dallas, TX 75235
Tel.: (214) 637-0000
Web Site: http://dallas.kpcph.com
Specialty Care Hospital Operator
N.A.I.C.S.: 622310

KPC Promise Hospital of Overland Park, LLC (3)
6509 W 103rd St, Overland Park, KS 66212
Tel.: (913) 649-3701
Web Site: http://overlandpark.kpcph.com
Specialty Care Hospital Operator
N.A.I.C.S.: 622310

KPC Promise Hospital of Phoenix, LLC (3)
433 E 6th St, Mesa, AZ 85203
Tel.: (480) 427-3000
Web Site: http://phoenix.kpcph.com
Specialty Care Hospital Operator
N.A.I.C.S.: 622310

KPC Promise Hospital of Salt Lake, LLC (3)
4252 Birkhill Blvd, Murray, UT 84107
Tel.: (385) 425-0050
Web Site: http://saltlake.kpcph.com
Specialty Care Hospital Operator
N.A.I.C.S.: 622310

KPC Promise Hospital of Vicksburg, LLC (3)
2100 Hwy 61 N, Vicksburg, MS 39183
Tel.: (601) 883-3265
Web Site: http://vicksburg.kpcph.com
Specialty Care Hospital Operator
N.A.I.C.S.: 622310

KPC Promise Hospital of Wichita Falls, LLC (3)
1103 Grace St, Wichita Falls, TX 76301
Tel.: (940) 720-6633
Web Site: http://wichitafalls.kpcph.com
Specialty Care Hospital Operator
N.A.I.C.S.: 622310

KPC Promise Skilled Nursing Facility of Overland Park, LLC (3)
6509 W 103rd St, Overland Park, KS 66212
Tel.: (913) 649-3701
Web Site: http://snfoverlandpark.kpcph.com
Skilled Nursing Facility Operator
N.A.I.C.S.: 623110

KPC Promise Skilled Nursing Facility of Wichita Falls, LLC (3)
1101 Grace St, Wichita Falls, TX 76301
Tel.: (940) 213-9371
Web Site: http://snfwichitafalls.kpcph.com
Skilled Nursing Facility Operator
N.A.I.C.S.: 623110

KPFF INC.
1601 5th Ave Ste 1600, Seattle, WA 98101-3038
Tel.: (206) 622-5822   WA
Web Site: http://www.kpff.com
Year Founded: 1960
Rev.: $32,000,000
Emp.: 300
Consulting Engineering Services
N.A.I.C.S.: 541330
David Seman (Principal-Seattle)
Jefferson Asher (Mng Principal)
William H. Thorpe (Principal-Structural Div-Irvine & Mgr-Engrg)
Eric Melle (Engr-Civil)
Reid Zimmerman (Dir-Technical)
Paul Schmidtke (Project Engr-Civil)
Taylor Jenkins (Mgr-Proposal)
Melissa Bayer (Engr-Structural-Portland)
Wai Kong (Engr-Structural)
Jazz Heying (Coord-Mktg)
Kallista Kidd (Coord-Mktg)

KPI 2 INCORPORATED
1250 Wood Ln, Langhorne, PA 19047
Tel.: (215) 295-6844
Web Site: http://www.kpi2inc.com
Year Founded: 1998
Sales Range: $10-24.9 Million
Emp.: 20
Roofing Installation Services
N.A.I.C.S.: 238390
Darek Falkowski (VP)
Jan Kulpinski (Pres)
Matt Samer (Dir-Field Ops)
Przemysla M. Mondrzik (Mgr-Shop)
Zibby Lupinski (Mgr-Maintenance)

KPI DIRECT LLC
22 Monument Sq 6th Fl, Portland, ME 04101
Web Site: http://www.kpidirect.com
Year Founded: 2006
Sales Range: $1-9.9 Million
Emp.: 13
Management Consulting
N.A.I.C.S.: 541618
Scott Badger (Founder & CEO)

KPI PARTNERS, INC.
39899 Balentine Dr Ste 375, Newark, CA 94560
Tel.: (510) 818-9480
Web Site: http://www.kpipartners.com
Year Founded: 2007
Sales Range: $10-24.9 Million
Emp.: 150
Information Technology Services
N.A.I.C.S.: 541512
Kusal Swarnaker (Partner)
Kumar Krishnaswamy (Gen Mgr)
Jeremiah Johnson (Sr Dir-Mktg, Bus Dev & Trng)
Rajesh Ramachandran (Sr Dir-Ops)
Sid Singh (Dir-Bus Dev)
Myles Gilsenan (Dir-Practice)
Don Hammons (VP-Cloud Strategy)

KPMG LLP
3 Chestnut Ridge Rd, Montvale, NJ 07645-0435
Tel.: (201) 307-7000   DE
Web Site: http://www.kpmg.com
Year Founded: 1897
Sales Range: $5-14.9 Billion
Emp.: 23,000
Audit, Tax & Advisory Services
N.A.I.C.S.: 541211
Ryan M. Zink (Auditor)
Stephen M. Knopik (CEO & CFO)
Conor Moore (Partner-Tech & Venture Capital Practices-Northern California)
Philip Isom (Partner & Head-M&A-Global, Corp Fin & Restructuring)
Kirke Everson (Mng Dir-Intelligent Automation Grp)
Lisa Rawls (Principal-Advisory, Governance, Risk & Compliance)
Will Williams (Mng Principal-Tax-Natl)
Peter Kinuthia (Dir-Tax & Regulatory Svcs-Kenya)
George Manu (Head-IDAS-East Africa)
Jane Mugo (Partner-Kenya)
Smita Sanghrajka (Partner-East Africa)
Andrew Jackson (Partner-Lockheed Martin-UK)
Scott Wilson (Assoc Dir-Transformation Program Mgmt-Australia)
Geoffrey Plante (Partner-State & Local Advisory)
Damian Templeton (CFO/COO-Australia)
Jenny Trimble (Assoc Dir-Audit & Advisory-Isle of Man)
Lisa Marie Pagliaro (Mgr-Guilderland)
Jeff Mabb (Mgr-Albany)
Paul Howes (Partner-Sydney)
John Teer (COO-Asia-Pacific)
Jessica Katsouris (Partner-Stockport)
Grant Ashbrook (Dir-NM Corp Tax North 1-UK)
Nicola Quayle (Head-Audit & Specialises-Isle of Man)
Chris Hearld (Chm-North Reg & Sr Partner-Leeds Office)
Helen McCourt (Dir-Capital Markets Grp-UK)
Elizabeth Meadowcroft (Dir-Deal Advisory-Manchester)
Aaron Froud (Partner-Acctg-Canberra)
Phillip Sands (Partner-Canberra)
Ryan Ballantyne (Dir-Manchester)
Adrian Wills (Dir-Property Tax-Manchester)
Andrew Stone (Dir-Manchester)
Matthew Jackson (Dir-Melbourne)
Andrew Trasler (Dir-Mgmt Consultancy)
Manny Goncalves (Exec Dir-Media Rels)
Scott Ozanus (Deputy Chm, COO & Chm-Americas Reg)
Carl Carande (Vice Chm-Advisory Svcs)
Jeff LeSage (Vice Chm-Tax Svcs)
Frank Casel (Vice Chm-Audit)
Michael J. Nolan (Vice Chm-Innovation & Enterprise Solutions)
Rosalie Collado (Mktg Dir)
Brett A. Thompson (Mng Dir)
Cathy Gonzales (Mng Partner-San Diego)
Richard Little (Head-Fin Svcs-UK)
Simon Ryder (Head-Fin Svcs-UK)
Natarajan G. (CFO/Head-Corp Svcs-India)
Angela Savin (Partner-Disputes & Investigations Team)
Kriti Velji (Dir-Transfer Pricing-New Zealand)
Nick Stevart (Dir-Transfer Pricing-UK)
Jennifer Cooper (Dir-Tax-Intl)
Alla Fokina (Dir-Transfer Pricing)
Trevor Danks (Dir-Transfer Pricing)
Maureen Davenport (Chief Comm Officer)
Elena Richards (Chief Diversity & Inclusion Officer)
Paul Knopp (Chm & CEO)

Subsidiaries:

KPMG Corporate Finance, LLC (1)
200 E Randolph St Ste 5500, Chicago, IL 60601-6436
Tel.: (312) 665-1911
Web Site: http://www.kpmgcorporatefinance.com
Investment Banking & Corporate Advisory Services
N.A.I.C.S.: 523150
Phil Isom (Head-Merger & Acq-Global)
Alex Alden (Mng Dir-Deal Advisory)
Inna Novak (Mgr-Recruiting)

KPRS CONSTRUCTION SERVICES, INC.
2850 Saturn St Ste 120, Brea, CA 92821-1701
Tel.: (714) 672-0800
Web Site: http://www.kprsinc.com
Year Founded: 1998
Sales Range: $10-24.9 Million
Emp.: 95
Civil Engineering Services
N.A.I.C.S.: 237310
Joel Stenscy (Pres)
Mike Funderberg (Mgr-Los Angeles)

KPS CAPITAL PARTNERS, LP
485 Lexington Ave 31st Fl, New York, NY 10017
Tel.: (212) 338-5100   DE
Web Site: http://www.kpsfund.com
Year Founded: 1991
Privater Equity Firm
N.A.I.C.S.: 523999
Eugene Keilin (Co-Founder)
Michael P. Psaros (Mng Partner)
David P. Shapiro (Mng Partner)
Raquel V. Palmer (Mng Partner)
Bhumika Shah (CFO)
Jay Bernstein (Partner)
Daniel Gray (Mng Dir-Bus Dev)
Ryan Baker (Partner)
Kyle Mumford (Partner)

Subsidiaries:

Autocast and Forge Pty Ltd (1)
18-24 Abbotts Rd, Seven Hills, 2147, NSW, Australia
Tel.: (61) 2 9912 8302
Web Site: http://www.autocast.net.au
Cold Forging Mfr
N.A.I.C.S.: 332111

Autokiniton Global Group, LP (1)
17757 Woodland Dr, New Boston, MI 48164
Tel.: (734) 397-6300
Investment Holding Company; Automotive Products Mfr & Whslr
N.A.I.C.S.: 551112
George Thanopoulos (CEO)

Subsidiary (Domestic):

L&W, Inc. (2)
17757 Woodland Dr, New Boston, MI 48164
Tel.: (734) 397-6300
Web Site: http://www.lw-grp.com
Automotive Stamping Mfr
N.A.I.C.S.: 336370

Tower International, Inc. (2)

COMPANIES / KPS CAPITAL PARTNERS, LP

17672 Laurel Park Dr N Ste 400E, Livonia, MI 48152
Tel.: (248) 675-6000
Web Site: http://www.towerinternational.com
Rev.: $1,571,853,000
Assets: $1,170,392,000
Liabilities: $869,478,000
Net Worth: $300,914,000
Earnings: $48,900,000
Emp.: 5,700
Fiscal Year-end: 12/31/2018
Automotive Vehicle Structural Components & Assemblies Designer & Mfr
N.A.I.C.S.: 336370
Jeffrey L. Kersten *(CFO & Exec VP)*
Mark R. Flynn *(Sr VP-HR-Global)*
Nanette Dudek *(Sec & VP-Legal Affairs & Compliance)*
Derek Fiebig *(VP-IR & Corp Comm)*
Amy Perrin *(Mgr-Treasury & IR)*
Gregory B. Guastella *(Chief Acctg Officer)*
Reid H. Southby *(Exec VP/Gen Mgr-North America)*
Doug Wagner *(Sr VP-Sls Ops)*
George Thanopoulos *(Pres)*
Scott L. Jones *(Sec)*

Subsidiary (Non-US):

Herrajes y Acabados Metalicos, S.A. de C.V. (3)
Norte 45 899 Industrial Vallejo, Azcapotzalco, Mexico, Mexico
Tel.: (52) 5553681255
Web Site: http://www.hamsa.com.mx
Motor Vehicle Body & Chass Mfr
N.A.I.C.S.: 336211
Adrian Gomez Clorio *(Head-Labor Rels)*

Seojin Industrial - Ansan (3)
13 Industrial Complex, 675-1 Seonggok-dong, Danwon-gu, Seoul, 425836, Kyounggi do, Korea (South)
Tel.: (82) 314998181
Sales Range: $10-24.9 Million
Emp.: 36
Automotive Metal Stampings & Tools Mfr
N.A.I.C.S.: 336370

Tower (Shanghai) Automotive Tech Service Co. Ltd. (3)
12/F East Hope Plaza 1777 Century Avenue, Shanghai, 200122, China (100%)
Tel.: (86) 21 6093 9060
Engineered Structural Metal Component Mfr
N.A.I.C.S.: 332312

Tower Automotive (Wuhu) Co. Ltd (3)
116 South Fengminghu Road, Wuhu, 241009, Anhui, China
Tel.: (86) 5537517816
Web Site: http://www.towerinternational.com
Engineered Structural Metal Component Mfr
N.A.I.C.S.: 332312

Tower Automotive India Pvt. Ltd. (3)
D1 Mariner Block V Plot No 17 Software Units Layout Madhapur, Beside Inorbit Mall, Hyderabad, 500081, India
Tel.: (91) 4066992513
Web Site: http://www.towerautomotive.com
Automotive Metal Stampings & Tools Mfr
N.A.I.C.S.: 336370

Tower Automotive Japan Co., Ltd. (3)
1-32-10 Nakamachidai, Tsuzuki-ku, Yokohama, 224-0041, Japan
Tel.: (81) 459434911
Web Site: http://www.towerinternational.com
Sales Range: $10-24.9 Million
Emp.: 7
Automotive Metal Stampings & Tools Mfr
N.A.I.C.S.: 336370

Tower Automotive Mexico, S.de R.L. de C.V. (3)
45 North 899 Industrial Vallejo, Azcapotzalco, Mexico, 02300, Mexico
Tel.: (52) 5543681255
Motor Vehicle Body & Chass Distr
N.A.I.C.S.: 423110

Tower Automotive do Brasil, Ltda. (3)
Av Tower Automotive 611 Rodovia Presidente Dutra Km 203 5, Bairro do Portao, 74000-000, Aruja, Sao Paulo, Brazil (100%)

Tel.: (55) 1146547501
Web Site: http://www.towerinternational.com
Engineered Structural Metal Component Mfr
N.A.I.C.S.: 332312

Subsidiary (Domestic):

Tower Defense & Aerospace, LLC (3)
20101 Hoover St, Detroit, MI 48205
Tel.: (313) 372-4131
Web Site: http://www.towertda.com
Metal Fabricating Services
N.A.I.C.S.: 332312

Subsidiary (Non-US):

Tower Golden Ring - Changchun (3)
No 3336 Zhinong St, Changchun, 130011, PRC, China
Tel.: (86) 43185774477
Web Site: http://www.towerautomotive.com
Automotive Metal Stampings & Tools Mfr; Joint Venture of Tower Automotive of USA, Fawer Automotive Parts Company & FAW SHEC of China
N.A.I.C.S.: 336370

C&D Technologies, Inc. (1)
1400 Union Meeting Rd, Blue Bell, PA 19422-0858
Tel.: (215) 619-2700
Web Site: http://www.cdtechno.com
Producer of Integrated Reserve Power Systems for Telecommunications, Electronic Information & Industrial Applications
N.A.I.C.S.: 335999
Joe Jergl *(Chief Engr)*
Jon Anderson *(COO & CTO)*
Robert F. Malley *(VP-Quality & Process Engrg)*
Vipul Chokshi *(VP-IT)*
Mara Williams *(Gen Counsel, Sec & VP)*

Division (Domestic):

C&D Technologies Dynasty Division (2)
900 E Keefe Ave, Milwaukee, WI 53212-1709
Tel.: (414) 967-6500
Web Site: http://www.cdtechno.com
UPS Batteries Mfr
N.A.I.C.S.: 335311

Subsidiary (Domestic):

Trojan Battery Company (2)
10375 Slusher Dr, Santa Fe Springs, CA 90670-3804
Tel.: (562) 236-3000
Web Site: http://www.trojanbattery.com
Battery Mfr
N.A.I.C.S.: 335910
Richard R. Godber *(Chm)*
Matthew Segal *(Sr VP-Bus Dev-Global)*
Bryan Godber *(Sr VP-Global Market Dev)*
Michael Everett *(Sr VP-Engrg)*
Will Scotson *(Mgr-Sls-West Europe)*
Michael Grundke *(Reg Gen Mgr)*
Yvonne Schroeder *(Gen Counsel, Sec & VP)*
Elke Hirschman *(Sr VP-Sls-North America & Corp Mktg)*
John Beering *(COO)*
John Getty *(Sr VP-Ops)*
Kari Garcia *(Mgr-PR)*
Phillip Taylor *(Chief HR Officer & Sr VP)*
Erguen Oezcan *(Sr Dir-Sls-Renewable Energy)*
Neil Thomas *(Pres & CEO)*

Catalyst Acoustics Group (1)
50 HP Herbert P Almgren Dr Ste A, Agawam, MA 01001
Tel.: (413) 789-1770
Web Site: http://catalystacoustics.com
Acoustic, Seismic, Vibration & Noise Control Services
N.A.I.C.S.: 238310
Jennifer Chagnon *(CMO)*
Joe Lupone *(CEO)*
Michael Shahed *(VP-Midwest Mfg Campus)*
Mark Kurtzman *(CFO)*
Laura Drummond *(Pres-Midwest)*
Neal Knueven *(Mktg Mgr-Brand)*
Chris Mazzone *(Mktg Mgr-Digital)*
Adam Hritzak *(Mktg Mgr)*

Subsidiary (Domestic):

Kinetics Noise Control, Inc. (2)

6300 Irelan Pl, Dublin, OH 43016
Tel.: (614) 889-0480
Web Site: http://www.kineticsnoise.com
Business Intelligence Services; Consulting, Surveys & Benchmarking
N.A.I.C.S.: 334519
Richard Anthony *(VP-Sls & Mktg)*
Brooke Anderson *(Gen Mgr-Canada)*
Kirk Hendricks *(CEO)*
Charles Merrimon *(Pres)*
Kelly Brown *(Mgr-Product & Mktg)*

Harsco IKG, LLC (1)
1514 S Sheldon Rd, Houston, TX 77015
Tel.: (281) 452-6637
Web Site: http://ikg.com
Sales Range: $75-99.9 Million
Emp.: 200
Industrial Grating Products
N.A.I.C.S.: 332323

International Equipment Solutions, LLC (1)
Oak Brook Point 700 Commerce Dr Ste 500, Oak Brook, IL 60523
Tel.: (630) 288-2434
Web Site: http://www.iesholdings.com
Sales Range: $300-349.9 Million
Emp.: 1,500
Holding Company; Operator-Driven Equipment Engineered Attachment Tool & Cab Enclosure Mfr
N.A.I.C.S.: 551112
Stephen Andrews *(CEO)*

Subsidiary (Non-US):

CWS Industries (Mfg) Corp. (2)
19490 92nd Avenue, Surrey, V4N 4G7, BC, Canada
Tel.: (604) 888-9008
Web Site: http://www.cwsindustries.com
Emp.: 50
Construction Machinery Mfr
N.A.I.C.S.: 333120
Derek Ritchie *(Mgr-Production)*
Steve Wright *(VP-Engrg)*

Subsidiary (Domestic):

Crenlo, LLC (2)
1600 4th Ave NW, Rochester, MN 55901-2573 (100%)
Tel.: (507) 289-3371
Web Site: http://www.crenlo.com
Sales Range: $400-449.9 Million
Emp.: 680
Mfr of Steel Frame Cab Enclosures & Rollover Structures
N.A.I.C.S.: 332999
Mark Pillers *(VP-Cab Sls & Mktg)*
David Kilburn *(Pres)*
Steve Dick *(Gen Mgr-Emcor)*

Kodiak Mfg. Inc. (2)
8849 Candies Creek Ridge Rd NW, Charleston, TN 37310
Tel.: (423) 336-8805
Web Site: http://www.kodiakmfg.com
Sales Range: $1-9.9 Million
Farm Equipment Mfr & Whslr
N.A.I.C.S.: 333111
Dennis W. Tweed *(Owner)*

Subsidiary (Non-US):

Siac do Brasil Ltda. (2)
Rodovia BR 491 Km 70, Guaranesia, 37810-000, Minas Gerais, Brazil
Tel.: (55) 3535558000
Web Site: http://www.siac.com.br
Emp.: 600
Cab Enclosure Mfr
N.A.I.C.S.: 333120
Eduardo Dubinco *(Mng Dir)*

Life Fitness, Inc. (1)
9525 Bryn Mawr Ave, Rosemont, IL 60018
Tel.: (847) 288-3300
Web Site: http://www.lifefitness.com
Fitness Equipment Mfr
N.A.I.C.S.: 339920
Judith Toland *(Chief Mktg Officer & VP)*
Alla K. Woodson *(VP-Customer Experience & Svc-Global)*

Subsidiary (Domestic):

Cybex International, Inc. (2)
10 Trotter Dr, Medway, MA 02053

Tel.: (508) 533-4300
Web Site: http://www.cybexintl.com
Exercise Equipment Marketer & Mfr
N.A.I.C.S.: 339920
Robert Cassano *(Sr Mgr-Engrg)*

Subsidiary (Non-US):

Life Fitness (Atlantic) B.V. (2)
Bijdorpplein 25 31, 2992 LB, Barendrecht, Netherlands
Tel.: (31) 180646666
Web Site: http://lifefitness.nl
Sales Range: $25-49.9 Million
Emp.: 70
Marine Parts & Accessories, Engines & Recreational Products Marketer & Mfr
N.A.I.C.S.: 423860
Frank Van Der Ven *(Gen Mgr)*
Viola Kunst *(Mgr-Mktg)*

Life Fitness (U.K.) Limited (2)
Queen Adelaide, Ely, CB7 4UB, Cambs, United Kingdom
Tel.: (44) 1353666017
Web Site: http://lifefitness.co.uk
Fitness Equipment Mfr
N.A.I.C.S.: 339920

Life Fitness Brasil (2)
Reboucas Av Pines, Sao Paulo, 05401-300, SP, Brazil
Tel.: (55) 1130955200
Web Site: http://www.lifefitness.com.br
Commercial & Home Fitness Equipment Marketer & Mfr
N.A.I.C.S.: 423910

Life Fitness Europe GmbH (2)
Neuhofweg 9, 85716, Unterschleissheim, Germany
Tel.: (49) 893177510
Web Site: http://lifefitness.de
Sales Range: $75-99.9 Million
Fitness Equipment Mfr
N.A.I.C.S.: 339920

Life Fitness Italia S.r.L. (2)
via S Pieretto, Affi, 37010, Verona, Italy
Tel.: (39) 045 723 82 04
Sales Range: $150-199.9 Million
Marine Parts & Accessories, Engines & Recreational Products Marketer & Mfr
N.A.I.C.S.: 423860

Life Fitness Japan, Ltd. (2)
4-17-33 Minami Aoyama, Minato-ku, Tokyo, 107-0062, Japan
Tel.: (81) 357705057
Fitness Equipment Distr
N.A.I.C.S.: 423910

Lufkin Industries LLC (1)
601 S Raguet St, Lufkin, TX 75904
Tel.: (936) 634-2211
Web Site: http://www.lufkin.com
Rev.: $1,281,200,000
Assets: $1,435,219,000
Liabilities: $621,248,000
Net Worth: $813,971,000
Earnings: $81,857,000
Emp.: 4,400
Fiscal Year-end: 12/31/2012
Oilfield Pumping Equipment, Industrial & Marine Propulsion Gears, Truck Trailers & Industrial Hardware Mfr
N.A.I.C.S.: 221122

Division (Domestic):

Lufkin Industries LLC - Foundry Division (2)
300 Winston, Lufkin, TX 75902-0849
Tel.: (936) 637-5813
Web Site: http://www.lufkin.com
Sales Range: $550-599.9 Million
Emp.: 2,500
Foundry Operator
N.A.I.C.S.: 331511

Lufkin Industries LLC - Oilfield Division (2)
5825 N Sam Houston Pkwy W Ste 500, Houston, TX 77086
Tel.: (281) 875-6500
Oil Field Machinery Mfr
N.A.I.C.S.: 333132

Subsidiary (Domestic):

International Lift Systems, LLC (3)

KPS CAPITAL PARTNERS, LP

KPS Capital Partners, LP—(Continued)
11050 W Little York, Houston, TX 77041
Tel.: (281) 445-7676
Web Site:
  http://www.internationalliftsystems.com
Sales Range: $1-9.9 Million
Emp.: 40
Lifting Equipment Mfr
N.A.I.C.S.: 333922

Subsidiary (Non-US):

Lufkin & Partners LLC (3)
Al Nahda Tower 2 Floor No 7 Al Nahda
Tower 2 Ghala Bowsher, Muscat, Oman
Tel.: (968) 24219418
Oilfield Pumping Equipment Mfr & Supplier
N.A.I.C.S.: 333132

Lufkin Argentina, S.A. (3)
Avda del progreso 7201 B Parque Industrial, Comodoro Rivadavia, 9000, Chubut, Argentina
Tel.: (54) 1143151641
Web Site: http://lufkin.com
Oil Well & Oil Field Pumps Mfr
N.A.I.C.S.: 333914

Lufkin Industries - Calgary (3)
808 4th Avenue Southwest 1050, Calgary, T2P 3E8, AB, Canada (100%)
Tel.: (403) 234-7692
Web Site: http://www.lufkin.com
Sales Range: $1-9.9 Million
Emp.: 6
Marketing & Sales of Pump Units
N.A.I.C.S.: 333914

Lufkin Industries SRL (3)
Willbrook Platinum Business & Convention Center, Bldg B 3rd Fl 172-176 Bucharest-Ploiesti Rd, Bucharest, 013686, Prahova, Romania
Tel.: (40) 372499110
Web Site: http://www.lufkin-romania.com
Oilfield Pumping Equipment Mfr
N.A.I.C.S.: 333914

Quinn Pumps Canada Ltd. (3)
4080-77 Street, Red Deer, T4P 3P7, AB, Canada
Tel.: (403) 347-1128
Web Site: http://www.quinnpumps.com
Reciprocating Pumps Mfr & Distr
N.A.I.C.S.: 333914

Subsidiary (US):

Quinn Pumps (California) Inc. (4)
280 W Stanley Ave, Ventura, CA 93001
Tel.: (805) 641-5534
Emp.: 8
Reciprocating Rod Pumps Mfr & Distr
N.A.I.C.S.: 333914
Wendell Mortensen (Mgr-Ops-West Coast Reg)

Quinn Pumps Inc. (4)
3611 E Hwy 158, Midland, TX 79706
Tel.: (432) 682-5945
Reciprocating Rod Pumps Mfr & Distr
N.A.I.C.S.: 333914
Mike Eddleston (Mgr-Ops)

Division (Domestic):

Lufkin Industries LLC - Power Transmission Division (2)
407 Kiln St, Lufkin, TX 75904
Tel.: (936) 634-2211
Web Site: http://www.bhge.com
Sales Range: $150-199.9 Million
Mfr of Oil Field Equipment, Pump Units, Industrial Gears & Marine Propulsion Gears
N.A.I.C.S.: 493110

Branch (Domestic):

Lufkin Industries LLC - Power Transmission Division (3)
30011 Ivy Glenn Dr 222, Laguna Niguel, CA 92677
Tel.: (949) 249-7850
Web Site: http://www.lufkin.com
Sales Range: $125-149.9 Million
Emp.: 4
Oil & Gas Machinery Mfr
N.A.I.C.S.: 333132

Oldcastle BuildingEnvelope, Inc. (1)
2745 Dallas Pkwy Ste 560, Plano, TX 75093-8724
Tel.: (469) 241-3800
Web Site: http://www.oldcastlebe.com
Tempered Glass Fabricators
N.A.I.C.S.: 327215

Subsidiary (Domestic):

C.R. Laurence Co., Inc. (2)
2503 E Vernon Ave, Los Angeles, CA 90058-1826
Tel.: (323) 588-1281
Web Site: http://www.crlaurence.com
Emp.: 600
Sale of Hardware Products
N.A.I.C.S.: 423710

Subsidiary (Non-US):

C.R. Laurence of Australia Pty Ltd. (3)
9 Shale Place, Eastern Creek, 2766, NSW, Australia
Tel.: (61) 2 9851 3444
Web Site: http://www.crlaurence.com.au
Architectural Metal Mfr & Distr
N.A.I.C.S.: 332323
Brendan Swan (Asst Mgr)
Jade Wright (Mgr-Svc Center)

C.R. Laurence of Canada (3)
65 Tigi Court, Concord, L4K 5E4, ON, Canada
Tel.: (905) 303-7966
Web Site: http://www.crlaurence.ca
Architectural Metal Mfr & Distr
N.A.I.C.S.: 332323

C.R. Laurence of Europe GmbH (3)
Boschstrasse 7, D-74360, Ilsfeld, Germany
Architectural Metal Mfr & Distr
N.A.I.C.S.: 332323
Simon Boocock (Mng Dir)
Dominik Hinzen (Mng Dir)
Lloyd Talbert (Mng Dir)

C.R. Laurence of Europe Ltd. (3)
Charles Babbage Avenue, Kingsway Business Park, Rochdale, OL16 4NW, United Kingdom
Tel.: (44) 1706863600
Web Site: https://www.crlaurence.co.uk
Architectural Metal Mfr & Distr
N.A.I.C.S.: 332323

Subsidiary (Domestic):

CRL Glass Machinery (3)
5501 W Ogden Ave, Cicero, IL 60804-3507
Tel.: (866) 583-1377
Web Site: http://www.crlaurence.com
Emp.: 38
Hardware; Glass Making Machinery
N.A.I.C.S.: 423710

CRL US Aluminum (3)
950 Solon Rd, Waxahachie, TX 75165
Tel.: (214) 634-7305
Web Site: http://www.usalum.com
Emp.: 220
Architectural Aluminum Products Mfr
N.A.I.C.S.: 332323

Unit (Domestic):

CRL US Aluminum - Carolina (4)
780 Celriver Rd, Rock Hill, SC 29730-7419
Tel.: (803) 366-8326
Web Site: http://www.usalum.com
Emp.: 30
Architectural Aluminum Products Mfr
N.A.I.C.S.: 332323

CRL US Aluminum - Illinois (4)
5501 W Ogden Ave, Cicero, IL 60804-3507
Tel.: (866) 583-1377
Web Site: http://www.crl-arch.com
Emp.: 37
Architectural Aluminum Products Mfr
N.A.I.C.S.: 332323

Subsidiary (Non-US):

CRL US Aluminum of Canada - Vancouver (4)
5377 272nd Street, Langley, V4W 1P1, BC, Canada
Tel.: (604) 857-7766
Web Site: http://www.crlaurence.ca

Aluminum Commerical Storefronts, Entrance Doors & Curtain Walls Mfr
N.A.I.C.S.: 332321
Steve Burden (Mgr-Svc Center)

Subsidiary (Domestic):

Midwest Glass Fabricators, Inc. (2)
100 Transfer Dr, Highland, MI 48357
Tel.: (248) 889-7900
Web Site: http://www.mwgf.com
Sales Range: $1-9.9 Million
Emp.: 60
Custom Fabricated Glass Glazing Services
N.A.I.C.S.: 327211
James Iaquinto (Pres)
Pat Iaquinto (Treas & Sec)

Plant (Domestic):

Oldcastle BuildingEnvelope, Inc. - Chandler (2)
50 S 56th St, Chandler, AZ 85226
Tel.: (480) 961-2000
Sales Range: $25-49.9 Million
Metal Window & Door Mfr
N.A.I.C.S.: 332321

Oldcastle BuildingEnvelope, Inc. - Dallas (2)
10453 Brockwood Rd, Dallas, TX 75238-1651
Tel.: (214) 340-7041
Sales Range: $10-24.9 Million
Curtain Wall System Mfr
N.A.I.C.S.: 332323

KQED INC.
2601 Mariposa St, San Francisco, CA 94110-1426
Tel.: (415) 864-2000 CA
Web Site: http://www.kqed.org
Year Founded: 1954
Sales Range: $200-249.9 Million
Emp.: 275
Television & Radio Broadcasting Services
N.A.I.C.S.: 516120
John L. Boland (Pres)
Jo Anne Wallace (VP-Radio, TV & Radio Programming & Gen Mgr-Radio)
Michael Isip (Chief Content Officer & Sr VP)
Tim Olson (Chief Digital Officer)
Bill Lowery (Gen Counsel & Sec)
Michael Lupetin (VP-Mktg & Brand)
DeLinda Mrowka (VP-Corp Sponsorship)
Lee Young (Dir-Engrg Facilities)
Mitzie Kelley (CFO)
Georgi Kelly (VP-Dev)
Holly Kernan (VP-News)
Dan Mansergh (CTO)

KR CAPITAL ADVISORS INC.
450 Park Ave Fl 30, New York, NY 10022
Tel.: (212) 888-6300
Web Site:
  http://www.krcapitaladvisors.com
Sales Range: $10-24.9 Million
Emp.: 8
Investment Advisory Services
N.A.I.C.S.: 523940
Martin Edward Kaplan (Pres & Portfolio Mgr)

KRA CORPORATION
11830 W Market Pl Ste M, Fulton, MD 20759
Tel.: (301) 562-2300
Web Site: http://www.kra.com
Sales Range: $10-24.9 Million
Emp.: 210
Information Retrieval Services
N.A.I.C.S.: 517810
Felicia Wessels (Program Mgr)
Nate Gordon (Program Mgr & Dir-Corp Ops)

KRACKELER SCIENTIFIC INC.
57 Broadway, Albany, NY 12202
Tel.: (518) 462-4281
Web Site: http://www.krackeler.com
Rev.: $16,000,000
Emp.: 25
Scientific & Engineering Equipment & Supplies
N.A.I.C.S.: 423490
Robert J. Krackeler (Co-Pres)
Bill Krackeler (CFO)
Anthony Krackeler (Pres)
Victor Hugo Echandy (Dir-Sls)

KRAEMER BROTHERS, LLC.
925 Park Ave, Plain, WI 53577
Tel.: (608) 546-2411
Web Site:
  http://www.kraemerbrothers.com
Rev.: $58,100,000
Emp.: 270
Commercial & Institutional Building Construction
N.A.I.C.S.: 236220
Tom Kraemer (Pres)
Paul Bartleson (Sr Dir-Safety)
Jeff Alt (VP-Productivity & Plng)
Nick Hartwig (Superintendent)

KRAEMER'S NURSERY INC.
14306 Downs Rd, Mount Angel, OR 97362
Tel.: (503) 845-2283
Web Site:
  http://www.kraemersnursery.com
Sales Range: $10-24.9 Million
Emp.: 150
Nursery Stock Whslr
N.A.I.C.S.: 424930
Barry Gregory (Mgr-Mktg & Sls)
Josh Shepherd (Mgr-Supply Chain)
Rachael Robinson (Acct Mgr)
Gil Jamison (Acct Mgr)

KRAFT & KENNEDY, INC.
630 3rd Ave 14th, New York, NY 10017
Tel.: (212) 986-4700
Web Site:
  http://www.kraftkennedy.com
Year Founded: 1988
Sales Range: $10-24.9 Million
Emp.: 50
Computer Integrated Systems Design
N.A.I.C.S.: 541512
Michael S. Kraft (Founder & Partner)
Marcus Bluestein (CTO)
Robert J. Brindell (Mng Dir)

KRAFT CHEMICAL COMPANY
1975 N Hawthorne Ave, Melrose Park, IL 60160
Tel.: (708) 345-5200
Web Site:
  http://www.kraftchemical.com
Year Founded: 1932
Sales Range: $10-24.9 Million
Emp.: 30
Chemical Coatings Supplier
N.A.I.C.S.: 424690
Rick Kraft (Pres)
Jerry Planek (Mgr-Sls)

KRAFT MOTORCAR COMPANY OF TALLAHASSEE, INC.
3277 Mahan Dr, Tallahassee, FL 32308
Tel.: (850) 576-6171
Web Site: http://www.kraftnissan.com
Sales Range: $10-24.9 Million
Emp.: 62
New Car Dealers
N.A.I.C.S.: 441110
Joseph VanLiere (Bus Mgr)
Nicholas Haggstrom (Mgr-Sls)
Mike Seay (Mgr-Parts)

Madeline Bullock *(Comptroller)*
Blaire Bussey *(Mgr-Sls)*
Bill Johnson *(Gen Mgr)*
Peter Kraft *(Co-Owner)*
Chris London *(Bus Mgr)*
Hiram Velez *(Mgr-Svcs)*
Dudley Griner *(Mgr-Customer Care)*
Gary Atkinson *(Dir-Svc & Parts)*
Jack Bennie *(Mgr-Floor)*
Chris Kraft Sr. *(Co-Owner)*
Chris Kraft Jr. *(Mgr-Inventory)*

KRAFT POWER CORP.
199 Wildwood Ave, Woburn, MA 01801
Tel.: (781) 938-9100 MA
Web Site: http://www.kraftpower.com
Year Founded: 1965
Sales Range: $25-49.9 Million
Emp.: 150
Whslr of Industrial Machinery & Equipment
N.A.I.C.S.: 423830
Owen M. Duffy *(Pres)*
Dave Barstow *(Mgr-Sls)*
Steve Andrews *(Mgr-Parts)*
Philip O'Connor *(Dir-Svc)*

KRAFT TOOL COMPANY INC.
8325 Hedge Ln Ter, Shawnee Mission, KS 66227
Tel.: (913) 422-4848
Web Site: http://www.krafttool.com
Rev.: $12,200,000
Emp.: 120
Hand & Edge Tools
N.A.I.C.S.: 332216
Ronald G. Meyer *(Pres)*

KRAGNES FARMERS ELEVATOR CO.
9749 21st St N, Moorhead, MN 56560
Tel.: (218) 233-4247
Web Site: http://www.kragnesfarmerselevator.com
Sales Range: $10-24.9 Million
Emp.: 16
Grain Elevators
N.A.I.C.S.: 722410
Terry Johnson *(Gen Mgr)*
Drav Land *(Gen Mgr)*
Todd Dravland *(Gen Mgr)*

KRAMER & LEONARD INC.
312 Roberts Rd, Chesterton, IN 46304
Tel.: (219) 926-1171
Web Site: http://www.kramerleonard.com
Year Founded: 1983
Rev.: $10,000,000
Emp.: 60
Office Supplies
N.A.I.C.S.: 424120
Gregory L. Fox *(Pres)*
Mary Fox *(Controller)*
Julie Leonard *(VP)*
Jennifer Krabbeler *(VP-Mktg)*

KRAMER BEVERAGE CO. INC.
161 S 2nd Rd, Hammonton, NJ 08037
Tel.: (609) 704-7000
Web Site: http://www.kramerbev.com
Sales Range: $50-74.9 Million
Emp.: 125
Beer & Ale
N.A.I.C.S.: 424810
Charles W. Kramer *(Chm)*
Mark Kramer *(VP & Gen Mgr)*
Susan Markert *(Controller)*

KRAMER BROS LUMBER CO. INC.
608 W Washington St, Frankfort, IN 46041
Tel.: (765) 659-3316 IN
Web Site: http://www.kramerlumber.com
Year Founded: 1872
Sales Range: $10-24.9 Million
Emp.: 25
Provider of Building Supplies
N.A.I.C.S.: 423310
Jack W. Ransom *(Pres)*

KRAMER DIRECT
100 N Central Expy Ste 300, Richardson, TX 75080
Tel.: (972) 231-3335
Web Site: http://www.kramerdirect.com
Year Founded: 1985
Sales Range: $1-9.9 Million
Emp.: 8
Qualified Leads for the Insurance & Financial Industries
N.A.I.C.S.: 524298
Allyn Kramer *(Founder)*

KRAMER LEVIN NAFTALIS & FRANKEL LLP
1177 Avenue of the Americas, New York, NY 10036
Tel.: (212) 715-9100
Web Site: http://www.kramerlevin.com
Year Founded: 1968
Sales Range: $300-349.9 Million
Emp.: 330
Law firm
N.A.I.C.S.: 541110
George M. Silfen *(Partner)*
Daniel A. Rabinowitz *(Partner)*
Tzvi Rokeach *(Partner)*
Daniel B. Goldman *(Partner)*
Andrew Charles *(Partner)*
David S. Berg *(Partner)*
Kevin P. Scanlan *(Partner)*
Zachary Jacobs *(Partner-Private Equity Practice)*
Richard Farley *(Partner-Leveraged Fin Grp)*
Eitan Tabak *(Partner)*
Darren LaVerne *(Partner)*
Jamie Kocis *(Partner)*
James Power *(Partner)*
Daniel Ross Berman *(Partner)*
Sanjay Thapar *(Partner)*
Marissa Holob *(Partner/Chm-Employee Benefits Dept)*
Harry Rubin *(Partner-Corp Dept & Head-Intellectual Property & Tech)*
Howard T. Spilko *(Co-Mng Partner)*
Paul Schoeman *(Co-Mng Partner)*
Mat Rosswood *(COO)*
Nada Llewellyn *(Chief Diversity & Inclusion Officer)*
Terry Novetsky *(Partner-Securitization & Structured Fin Practice)*
Gilbert K.S. Liu *(Chm-Securitization & Structured Fin Practice)*
Ernest S. Wechsler *(Chm)*
Yasho Lahiri *(Partner-Fund Formation Practice)*
Scott Welkis *(Partner & Chm-Special Situations Practice)*
Alexander Woolverton *(Partner-Bankruptcy & Restructuring Grp)*
Terry D. Novetsk *(Partner-Securitization & Structured Fin Practice)*

KRAMER TIRE CO. INC.
1369 Azalea Gdn Rd, Norfolk, VA 23502
Tel.: (757) 857-1234
Web Site: http://www.kramertire.com
Rev.: $36,000,000
Emp.: 40
Automobile Tires & Tubes
N.A.I.C.S.: 423130
M. Oliver *(Sec)*
Ron Kramer *(Pres)*

KRAMER-WILSON CO. INC.
12200 Sylvan St, North Hollywood, CA 91606
Tel.: (818) 760-0880
Web Site: http://www.cnico.com
Rev.: $32,582,976
Emp.: 300
Fire, Marine & Casualty Insurance Carriers
N.A.I.C.S.: 524126
Rick Remias *(Controller)*
Marie Balicki *(VP)*

KRAMME CONSOLIDATED INC.
Main St, Monroeville, NJ 08343
Tel.: (856) 358-8151
Web Site: http://www.pekramme.com
Sales Range: $10-24.9 Million
Emp.: 3
Trucking Except Local
N.A.I.C.S.: 484121
Paul E. Kramme Jr. *(Pres)*

Subsidiaries:

P.E. Kramme Inc. (1)
404 Monroeville Rd, Monroeville, NJ 08343
Tel.: (856) 358-8151
Web Site: http://www.pekramme.com
Trucking Except Local
N.A.I.C.S.: 484121

KRANICH'S JEWELERS, INC.
5580 Goods Ln Ste 1079, Altoona, PA 16602
Tel.: (814) 944-4575
Web Site: http://www.kranichs.com
Year Founded: 1903
Sales Range: $10-24.9 Million
Emp.: 50
Jewelry & Gifts Retailer
N.A.I.C.S.: 458310
Charles E. Kranich II *(Pres)*
Michael Kranich Jr. *(Co-Pres)*

KRAPF'S COACHES INC.
1060 Saunders Ln, West Chester, PA 19380
Tel.: (610) 431-1500
Web Site: http://www.krapfbus.com
Year Founded: 1940
Sales Range: $10-24.9 Million
Emp.: 1,200
Chartered Bus Transportation Services
N.A.I.C.S.: 485510
Dale N. Krapf *(Pres)*
Bob Morris *(VP & Controller)*
Karen Ferry *(Dir-Sls)*
Dallas L. Krapf *(VP & Sec)*

KRASDALE FOODS INC.
65 W Red Oak Ln, White Plains, NY 10604
Tel.: (914) 694-6400
Web Site: http://www.krasdalefoods.com
Year Founded: 1908
Sales Range: $200-249.9 Million
Emp.: 400
Grocery Whslr
N.A.I.C.S.: 424410
Charles A. Krasne *(Chm & CEO)*
Dennis Hickey *(Chief Mdsg Officer)*
Gus Lebiak *(Pres & COO)*

KRAUS CONSTRUCTION INC.
18265 Mount Baldy Cir, Fountain Valley, CA 92708
Tel.: (714) 536-1429
Web Site: http://www.krausconst.com
Sales Range: $10-24.9 Million
Emp.: 14
Commercial & Institutional Building Construction Services
N.A.I.C.S.: 236220
Greg Thien *(VP & Project Mgr)*

KRAUS-ANDERSON INCORPORATED
523 S 8th St, Minneapolis, MN 55404-1030
Tel.: (612) 332-7281 MN
Web Site: http://www.krausanderson.com
Year Founded: 1897
Sales Range: $200-249.9 Million
Emp.: 600
General Contractor, Construction Management, Real Estate Investment & Insurance Services
N.A.I.C.S.: 236220
Bruce W. Engelsma *(Chm, Pres & CEO)*
Tim Asgrimson *(CFO)*
Thomas Emison *(VP-Strategy & Innovation)*
Leslie Greves *(VP-HR)*
Philip Boelter *(COO & Exec VP)*
Alan Gerhardt *(Pres/CEO-Construction)*
Rich Jacobson *(Exec VP-Construction)*
Daniel Engelsma *(Vice Chm)*

Subsidiaries:

Kraus-Anderson Capital Inc (1)
523 S 8th St, Minneapolis, MN 55404-1030
Tel.: (612) 305-2934
Web Site: http://www.krausanderson.com
Sales Range: $10-24.9 Million
Emp.: 6
Equipment Rental & Leasing Nec
N.A.I.C.S.: 532490
Jim Jarussi *(VP)*

Kraus-Anderson Communications Group (1)
523 S 8th St, Minneapolis, MN 55404-1030
Tel.: (612) 375-1080
Web Site: http://www.krausanderson.com
Sales Range: $25-49.9 Million
Emp.: 100
Event Planning & Promotion Services
N.A.I.C.S.: 541810
Bruce W Engelsma *(CEO)*

Kraus-Anderson Construction Company, Inc. (1)
501 S 8th St, Minneapolis, MN 55404
Tel.: (612) 332-7281
Web Site: http://www.krausanderson.com
Industrial Building Construction Services
N.A.I.C.S.: 236210
Bruce Engelsma *(Chm & CEO)*
Daniel Engelsma *(Vice Chm)*
Alan Gerhardt *(Pres)*
Mark Coudron *(Sr VP)*
John Rogoz *(VP-Fin & Controller)*
Jay Vander Leest *(Dir-Safety)*
Anthony Scherber *(Mgr-Yard)*
Michael Spence *(VP-Quality Control)*
Tim Mayer *(Dir-Talent Acq)*
Nancy Martel *(Dir-Bus Dev)*
Audie Miller *(Mgr-Preconstruction Svcs)*
Jeff Ballstadt *(Superintendent-Union)*
Justin Jennrich *(Coord-Mobile Tech-Twin Cities)*
Mike Stark *(Asst Project Mgr-Twin Cities)*
Brian Hook *(Dir-Field Ops)*
Steve Sontag *(Superintendent)*
Conan Young *(Superintendent)*
David Brust *(Superintendent)*
Dave Hendel *(Dir-Project Plng & Dev)*
Tony Peleska *(CIO)*
Erik Palmer *(Project Mgr)*
Chad Savoy *(Project Mgr)*
Max Stockbridge *(Product Mgr-Technical Svcs)*

Kraus-Anderson Insurance (1)
420 Gateway Blvd, Burnsville, MN 55337-4293 (100%)
Tel.: (952) 707-8200
Web Site: http://www.kainsurance.com

KRAUS-ANDERSON INCORPORATED

Kraus-Anderson Incorporated—(Continued)
Insurance Agents
N.A.I.C.S.: 524210
Dennis G. Diessner *(COO & Exec VP)*
Jon Diessner *(Exec VP)*

Kraus-Anderson Mortgage Company (1)
523 S 8th St, Minneapolis, MN 55404-1030 (100%)
Tel.: (612) 332-7281
Web Site: http://www.kraus-anderson.com
Sales Range: $25-49.9 Million
Emp.: 6
Mortgage Bankers & Loan Correspondents
N.A.I.C.S.: 522310
Bruce W. Engelsma *(Chm, Pres & CEO)*
Daniel Engelsma *(Vice Chm)*
Bob Fitzgerald *(Dir-Ops)*
Craig Francois *(VP & Dir-Ops)*
Terry Hart *(VP & Dir-Ops)*
Jeff Iisakka *(VP & Dir-Ops)*
Mike Jankowski *(Dir-Bus Dev)*
Nick Leimer *(Dir-Ops)*
Nancy Martel *(Dir-Bus Dev)*
Tracy Pogue *(Dir-Bus Dev)*
Tom Roepke *(Dir-Ops)*
Greg Wegler *(Dir-Bus Dev)*

Kraus-Anderson Realty Company (1)
4210 W Old Shakopee Rd, Bloomington, MN 55437-2951 (100%)
Tel.: (952) 881-8166
Web Site: http://www.krausanderson.com
Sales Range: $10-24.9 Million
Emp.: 30
Real Estate Agents & Managers
N.A.I.C.S.: 531210
Daniel W. Engelsma *(Pres & COO)*
Bruce W. Engelsma *(CEO)*
Anne Jeske *(Mgr-Property)*
Jeff Hildahl *(VP & Dir-Leasing & Mktg)*
Jason Faith *(Controller)*

KRAUSE ADVERTISING
5307 E Mockingbird Ln Ste 250, Dallas, TX 75206
Tel.: (214) 823-5100 TX
Web Site:
 http://www.krauseadvertising.com
Year Founded: 1979
Sales Range: $25-49.9 Million
Emp.: 18
Education, Financial, Health Care, Real Estate, Retail, Sports Advertising Services
N.A.I.C.S.: 541810
Jim Krause *(CEO)*
Candace Krause *(VP)*

KRAUSE GENTLE CORPORATION
6400 Westown Pkwy, West Des Moines, IA 50266-7709
Tel.: (515) 226-0128 IA
Web Site: http://www.kumandgo.com
Year Founded: 1959
Sales Range: $125-149.9 Million
Emp.: 160
Gas & Grocery Distr
N.A.I.C.S.: 445131
Kyle J. Krause *(CEO)*
Randy Meyer *(Dir-Procurement)*

Subsidiaries:

Kum & Go (1)
6400 Westown Pkwy, West Des Moines, IA 50266
Tel.: (515) 226-0128
Web Site: http://www.kumandgo.com
Sales Range: Less than $1 Million
Emp.: 5,000
Convenience Store
N.A.I.C.S.: 457120
Kyle J. Krause *(Chm)*
Marty Roush *(VP-Ops-South)*
Megan Elfers *(Dir-Mktg)*
David Lemons *(VP-Ops-Western Div)*
Sara Kurovski *(Mgr-Sustainability)*
Krischelle Tennessen *(Sr VP-HR)*
Tracy Ging *(CMO)*
Carrie Clogg *(Dir-Philanthropy)*

Tanner Krause *(CEO)*
Britt Davidson *(Dir-Risk Mgmt)*
Jeff Shamburger *(VP-Foodservice)*
Reed Rainey *(COO)*
Levon Hooks *(CIO)*
Matt Spackman *(Sr VP-Grow People)*
Heather Schott *(Mgr-Diversity, Equity & Inclusion)*

KRAVCO SIMON COMPANY
234 Mall Blvd, King of Prussia, PA 19406
Tel.: (610) 768-6300
Web Site: http://www.kravco.com
Sales Range: $10-24.9 Million
Emp.: 40
Shopping Center, Property Operation Only
N.A.I.C.S.: 531120
Clinton M. Cochran *(Sr VP-Asset & Property Mgmt)*
Jon R. Powell *(Pres & CEO)*
Lisa Fair Pliskin *(COO & Gen Counsel)*
Robert C. Birkbeck *(CFO)*
Arthur L. Powell *(Chm)*

KRAVET FABRICS INC.
225 Central Ave S, Bethpage, NY 11714
Tel.: (516) 293-2000 NY
Web Site: http://www.kravet.com
Year Founded: 1918
Sales Range: $200-249.9 Million
Emp.: 450
Whslr of Decorative Fabrics, Furniture, Wallcoverings & Trimming
N.A.I.C.S.: 424310
Jerry Schwartz *(Exec VP & Gen Mgr)*
Lisa Kravet *(Gen Counsel)*
Beth Greene *(VP-Corp Mktg)*
Scott Kravet *(VP-New Products & Design)*
Ann Feldstein *(Dir-Mktg)*

Subsidiaries:

GP & J Baker (1)
6 Stinsford Road, Poole, BH17 0SW, Dorset, United Kingdom
Tel.: (44) 1202 266 700
Web Site: http://www.gpandjbaker.com
Commercial Printing & Interior Design Services
N.A.I.C.S.: 323111

Kravet Mexico (1)
Casa 280 Monte Libano 280, Col Lomas de Chapultepec, 11100, Mexico, Mexico
Tel.: (52) 55 5280 4090
Web Site: http://www.kravet.com
Emp.: 6
Home Furnishing Distr
N.A.I.C.S.: 423220
Sonia Martinez *(Mgr)*

Lee Jofa, Inc. (1)
201 Central Ave S, Bethpage, NY 11714
Tel.: (516) 752-7600
Web Site: http://www.leejofa.com
Sales Range: $10-24.9 Million
Emp.: 100
Distr of Decorative Fabrics, Furniture, Wall Coverings & Trimmings & Decorative Lighting
N.A.I.C.S.: 423210
Cary Kravet *(Owner)*
Stephen Elrod *(VP-Creative)*

KRAVET, INC.
225 Central Ave S, Bethpage, NY 11714
Tel.: (516) 293-2000 NY
Web Site: http://www.kravet.com
Year Founded: 1918
Sales Range: $25-49.9 Million
Emp.: 600
Home Furnishing Mfr
N.A.I.C.S.: 337121
Cary Kravet *(Pres)*
Lisa Kravet *(VP)*

Ann Feldstein *(Sr Dir-Mktg)*
Robert M. Duban *(Exec VP-Contract Sls)*

Subsidiaries:

Brunschwig & Fils, Inc. (1)
245 Central Ave S, Bethpage, NY 11714
Tel.: (914) 684-5800
Web Site: http://www.brunschwig.com
Sales Range: $10-24.9 Million
Emp.: 50
Piece Goods & Other Fabrics; Woven Textiles; Wallcoverings; Furniture; Lamps & Tables Mfr
N.A.I.C.S.: 424310
Dawn Carlson *(VP-Pur)*
David Toback *(Dir-Design)*

Donghia Inc. (1)
8687 Melrose Ave B624, Los Angeles, CA 90069
Tel.: (310) 657-6060
Web Site: http://www.donghia.com
Rev.: $1,520,000
Emp.: 10
Blind & Shade Mfr
N.A.I.C.S.: 337920
Glenn Ervin *(Mgr)*

Kravet Canada (1)
3600 B Laird Road Suite 6, Mississauga, L5L 6A7, ON, Canada
Tel.: (905) 607-0706
Web Site: http://www.kravetcanada.com
Emp.: 25
Home Furnishing Mfr
N.A.I.C.S.: 337121

KRB MACHINERY CO. INC.
1058 Cool Creek Rd, Wrightsville, PA 17368
Tel.: (717) 252-3667
Web Site:
 http://www.krbmachinery.com
Sales Range: $10-24.9 Million
Emp.: 60
Mfr of Rebar Bending Cutting Machines
N.A.I.C.S.: 333517
Bob Brandt *(Gen Mgr)*
John Mahala *(Mgr-IT)*

KREAGER BROTHERS EXCAVATING
PO Box 80187, Fort Wayne, IN 46808
Tel.: (260) 482-4445
Sales Range: $10-24.9 Million
Emp.: 70
Excavation Work
N.A.I.C.S.: 238910
Jerry Kreager *(Pres)*
Tony Kreager *(Sec)*
Matt Minnick *(Dir-Safety)*
Mike Aldrich *(Project Mgr)*

KREATIONS INC.
583 Grant St Ste E, Clarkesville, GA 30523
Tel.: (706) 754-1419
Web Site: http://www.erinlondon.com
Sales Range: $10-24.9 Million
Emp.: 35
Sportswear, Women's
N.A.I.C.S.: 315250
Joseph Corry *(CEO)*

KREBER GRAPHICS INC.
2580 Westbelt Dr, Columbus, OH 43228
Tel.: (614) 529-5701
Web Site: http://www.kreber.com
Year Founded: 1905
Sales Range: $10-24.9 Million
Emp.: 150
Platemaking Services
N.A.I.C.S.: 541922
Jim Kreber *(Chm)*
Arlen Stacy *(Acct Coord)*

U.S. PRIVATE

Subsidiaries:

Kreber L.L.C. (1)
221 Swathmore Ave, High Point, NC 27263-1931
Tel.: (336) 861-2700
Web Site: http://www.kreber.com
Sales Range: $10-24.9 Million
Emp.: 75
Commercial Photography Services
N.A.I.C.S.: 323120
Larry Sauer *(VP-Ops)*

KREIDER SERVICES, INC.
500 Anchor Rd, Dixon, IL 61021
Tel.: (815) 288-6691 IL
Web Site:
 http://www.kreiderservices.org
Year Founded: 1974
Sales Range: $10-24.9 Million
Emp.: 728
Developmental Disability Assistance Services
N.A.I.C.S.: 623210
Don Vock *(Treas & Sec)*
Vernon Brickley *(VP)*
Richard L. Piller *(Pres)*

KREILKAMP TRUCKING INC.
6487 Hwy 175, Allenton, WI 53002-9785
Tel.: (262) 629-5000 WI
Web Site: http://www.kreilkamp.com
Year Founded: 1934
Sales Range: $25-49.9 Million
Emp.: 350
Provider of Trucking Services
N.A.I.C.S.: 484121
Tim Kreilkamp *(VP-Ops)*
Chuck McDaniel *(Gen Mgr)*

KREISER FUEL SERVICE INC.
122 Racehorse Dr, Jonestown, PA 17038
Tel.: (717) 865-2105
Web Site:
 http://www.kreiserfuels.com
Sales Range: $10-24.9 Million
Emp.: 20
Fuel Oil Dealers
N.A.I.C.S.: 457210
Rufus R. Kreiser *(CEO)*
Ernie Spitler *(Pres)*

KREISLER BORG FLORMAN GENERAL CONSTRUCTION COMPANY INC.
97 Montgomery St, Scarsdale, NY 10583-5104
Tel.: (914) 725-4600 NY
Web Site: http://www.kbfgeneral.com
Year Founded: 1955
Sales Range: $75-99.9 Million
Emp.: 80
General Construction Contracting Services
N.A.I.C.S.: 236115
Joseph Zelazny *(Pres)*
Samuel C. Florman *(Co-Chm)*
Robert F. Borg *(Founder & Co-Chm)*

KREISS ENTERPRISES INC.
8525 Camino Santa Fe, San Diego, CA 92121
Tel.: (858) 453-6245 CA
Web Site: http://www.kreiss.com
Year Founded: 1939
Sales Range: $10-24.9 Million
Emp.: 125
Furniture, Bed Linen & Fabric Designer, Mfr & Retailer
N.A.I.C.S.: 423210
Michael Kreiss *(Pres & CEO)*

Subsidiaries:

Kreiss Collection Arizona Inc. (1)

COMPANIES

KRIPALU CENTER FOR YOGA & HEALTH

8787 N Scottsdale Rd 124, Scottsdale, AZ 85253-2334
Tel.: (480) 946-6510
Web Site: http://www.kreiss.com
Sales Range: $10-24.9 Million
Emp.: 2
Furniture
N.A.I.C.S.: 423210

Kreiss Collection Atlanta Inc. (1)
255 East Paces Ferry Rd NE Ste 100, Atlanta, GA 30305-2235 (100%)
Tel.: (404) 261-8304
Web Site: http://www.kreiss.com
Rev.: $450,000
Emp.: 3
Furniture Retailer
N.A.I.C.S.: 449110

Kreiss Collection Colorado Inc. (1)
201 Milwaukee St, Denver, CO 80206-5014 (100%)
Tel.: (303) 329-8733
Web Site: http://www.kreiss.com
Rev.: $470,000
Emp.: 2
Furniture
N.A.I.C.S.: 423210

Kreiss Collection Florida Inc. (1)
2300 Salzedo St, Coral Gables, FL 33134-5019
Tel.: (305) 441-0020
Web Site: http://www.kreiss.com
Sales Range: $10-24.9 Million
Emp.: 4
Mfr Furniture
N.A.I.C.S.: 449110

Kreiss Collection Illinois Inc. (1)
8525 Santa Fe Ste A, San Diego, CA 92121-2655 (100%)
Tel.: (312) 527-0907
Web Site: http://www.kreiss.com
Sales Range: Less than $1 Million
Emp.: 5
Retail Furniture
N.A.I.C.S.: 423210

Kreiss Collection Nevada Inc. (1)
8525 Camino Santa Fe, San Diego, CA 92121
Tel.: (852) 453-6245
Web Site: http://www.kreiss.com
Rev.: $20,000,000
Emp.: 3
Furniture
N.A.I.C.S.: 423210

KRELL ADVERTISING
179 State Route 31 Ste 10, Flemington, NJ 08822-5743
Tel.: (908) 806-7477
Web Site: http://www.krelladvertising.com
Sales Range: $10-24.9 Million
Emp.: 15
Corporate Identity, Direct Marketing, Logo & Package Design, Medical, Pharmaceutical
N.A.I.C.S.: 541810
Robert Krell (Pres)
Bill Baldwin (Sr Acct Exec)

KRELL INDUSTRIES, INC.
45 Connair Rd, Orange, CT 06477-3650
Tel.: (203) 799-9954
Web Site: http://www.krellonline.com
Year Founded: 1980
Sales Range: $10-24.9 Million
Emp.: 38
Mfr of Audio Equipment Including Amplifiers, Preamplifiers, Compact Disc Players, DVD Players, Surround Sound Processors, Digital-to-Analog Converters & Loudspeakers
N.A.I.C.S.: 334310
Nicholas Cupo (Mgr-QA)
Walter Schofield (COO)

KRELLER GROUP INC.
817 Main St, Cincinnati, OH 45202
Tel.: (513) 723-8900
Web Site: http://www.kreller.com
Year Founded: 1988
Intellectual Property Investigations/Protection & Security Risk/Site Assessment Services
N.A.I.C.S.: 541611
Harvey Rosen (VP)
Joe Davidoski (Founder & Pres)

Subsidiaries:

Smith Brandon International, Inc. (1)
1432 K St NW Ste 600, Washington, DC 20005-1749
Tel.: (202) 887-9363
Web Site: http://www.smithbrandon.com
Law firm
N.A.I.C.S.: 541199
Patricia McCormack (Office Mgr)
Gene M. Smith (Principal)
Harry B. Brandon (Principal)

KREMENTZ & COMPANY
51 Commerce St, Springfield, NJ 07081
Tel.: (973) 621-8300
Year Founded: 1866
Sales Range: $10-24.9 Million
Emp.: 50
Jewelry Mfr & Retailer
N.A.I.C.S.: 339910
Rick Krementz (Interim CEO)

KREMPP LUMBER CO.
216 Main St, Jasper, IN 47546
Tel.: (812) 482-6838
Web Site: http://www.krempp.net
Rev.: $19,500,000
Emp.: 20
Commercial & Office Building, New Construction
N.A.I.C.S.: 236220
Andrew B. Krempp (Pres)
Rita McCain (Office Mgr)

KRENZEN CADILLAC-PONTIAC INC.
2500 Mall Dr, Duluth, MN 55811
Tel.: (218) 727-2905
Web Site: http://www.krenzen.com
Sales Range: $25-49.9 Million
Emp.: 80
Automobiles, New & Used
N.A.I.C.S.: 441110
Jack Krenzen (Pres)
Scott Krenzen (VP)
Johnn Decaro (Controller)

KRESS CORPORATION
227 Illinois St, Brimfield, IL 61517
Tel.: (309) 446-3395
Web Site: http://www.kresscarrier.com
Rev.: $10,000,000
Emp.: 250
Trucks, Off-Highway
N.A.I.C.S.: 333120
Dan Boettcher (Dir-Engrg)
Mark Albright (Mgr-Publ)
Nathan Lane (Engr-Design)
Phil Slusser (Supvr-Assy)
Tudor Gradea (Engr-Hydraulic Design)

KRESS STORES OF PUERTO RICO
A St Cnr Matadero Rd, San Juan, PR 00920
Tel.: (787) 783-5374
Web Site: http://www.kressgroup.com
Rev.: $94,100,000
Emp.: 101
Purchasing Service
N.A.I.C.S.: 458110
Mark Berezdivin (Pres)
David Solomiany (Controller)

KRETZ LUMBER CO., INC.
W 11143 County Hwy G, Antigo, WI 54409
Tel.: (715) 623-5410
Web Site: http://www.kretzlumber.com
Sales Range: $10-24.9 Million
Emp.: 171
Sawmills
N.A.I.C.S.: 321113
Diane Bielen (VP & Dir-Personnel)
Troy Brown (Pres)
Daniel W. Kretz (Chm)

KRG CAPITAL MANAGEMENT, L.P.
1800 Larimer St Ste 2200, Denver, CO 80202
Tel.: (303) 390-5001 DE
Web Site: http://www.krgcapital.com
Year Founded: 1996
Sales Range: $25-49.9 Million
Emp.: 45
Equity Investment Firm
N.A.I.C.S.: 523999
Charles R. Gwirtsman (Co-Founder & Mng Dir)
Charles A. Hamilton (Mng Dir)
Bruce L. Rogers (Co-Founder & Mng Dir)
Christopher L. Lane (Mng Dir)
Stewart Fisher (Mng Dir)
Ted C. Nark (Mng Dir)
Bennett Thompson (Mng Dir)
Rick Wilhelm (VP-Fin)
Darrin DeMarch (Mgr-Fund Acctg)
Bambi Howard (Mgr-Travel)
Colton King (Mng Dir)
Piotr Biezychudek (VP)
Ben McCown (Principal)
E. Sue Cho (Principal)

Subsidiaries:

ICCNexergy, Inc. (1)
4 Westbrook Corporate Ctr Ste 900, Westchester, IL 60154
Tel.: (708) 836-3800
Web Site: http://www.iccnexergy.com
Sales Range: $150-199.9 Million
Emp.: 2,000
Designer & Mfr of Battery Packs & Chargers
N.A.I.C.S.: 335910
Stephen M. McClure (Pres & CEO)
Sophie Bielanski (Mgr-Acctg)

Unit (Domestic):

ICCNexergy, Inc. - Escondido (2)
911 South Andreasen Dr., Escondido, CA 92029
Tel.: (760) 740-6677
Sales Range: $10-24.9 Million
Emp.: 30
Designer & Mfr of Battery Packs & Chargers
N.A.I.C.S.: 335910

Inventus Power, Inc. (1)
1200 Internationale Pkwy, Woodridge, IL 60517
Tel.: (630) 410-7900
Web Site: http://www.inventuspower.com
Battery Pack Technologies Developer & Mfr
N.A.I.C.S.: 335910
Anson Martin (VP-Sls & Bus Dev)
Like Xie (VP)
Kevin O'Connor (CFO)
Chris Turner (VP-Tech)
Nick Moelders (VP-Progrms & Product Dev)
Michael Taylor (Dir-IT Ops)
Rebecca Kritzman (Dir-Strategic Plng, Mktg & Comm)
Melissa Detamble (VP-HR)
Laird Carmichael (VP-Ops)
Patrick J. Trippel (CEO)

KRIEGER AUTO GROUP
3205 N Hwy 61, Muscatine, IA 52761
Tel.: (563) 263-5324 IA
Web Site: http://www.kriegers.com
Sales Range: $10-24.9 Million
Emp.: 35
New & Used Car Dealership Owner
N.A.I.C.S.: 441110
Mark Krieger (VP)
Tom Antram (Mgr-Used Car)
Doug Krieger (Pres)

KRIEGER FORD INC.
1800 Morse Rd, Columbus, OH 43229
Tel.: (614) 888-3320
Web Site: http://www.kriegerford.com
Sales Range: $50-74.9 Million
Emp.: 150
Automobiles, New & Used
N.A.I.C.S.: 441110
Dan Kehrer (Gen Mgr-Sls)
Chris Wachtel (Mgr-Fin)
Rick Sparks (Mgr-Sls)
Mike Smith (Gen Mgr & Mgr-Customer Rels)
William Coultas (Mgr-Body Shop)
Kevin Wilush (Mgr-Svc)

KRIEGER MOTOR COMPANY INC.
501 W Bypass 61, Muscatine, IA 52761-8903
Tel.: (563) 263-5432 IA
Web Site: http://www.kriegers.com
Year Founded: 1956
Sales Range: $10-24.9 Million
Emp.: 62
Provider of Motor Services
N.A.I.C.S.: 441110
Douglas Krieger (Pres)
Jim Henderson (Gen Mgr-GM Store)
Mark Michaels (CFO)
Christine Wilder (Controller)

KRIENIK ADVERTISING, INC.
115 W Nineth St, Cincinnati, OH 45202
Tel.: (513) 421-0090
Year Founded: 1981
Rev.: $18,000,000
Emp.: 25
N.A.I.C.S.: 541810
Michael L. Krienik (Pres & CEO)
Debbie Cassidy (VP & Dir-Acctg)
Michelle Bruegee (Sr Acct Supvr)

KRIER FOODS, INC.
520 Wolf Rd, Random Lake, WI 53075
Tel.: (920) 994-2469 WI
Web Site: http://www.krierfoods.com
Year Founded: 1913
Sales Range: $75-99.9 Million
Emp.: 50
Fruit Juices & Nonalcoholic Carbonated Beverages
N.A.I.C.S.: 311421
Thomas Bretza (Treas & VP-Fin)
Steve Ihrcke (Dir-Pur)
Sue Hornacen (Mgr-DP)
John Rassel (Pres)

KRINOS FOODS INC.
4700 Northern Blvd, Long Island City, NY 11101-1028
Tel.: (718) 729-9000 NY
Web Site: http://www.krinos.com
Year Founded: 1985
Sales Range: $50-74.9 Million
Emp.: 130
Dairy Products, Except Dried or Canned; Greek Speciality Foods
N.A.I.C.S.: 424430
Eric Moscahlaidis (Owner)
Charles Vergris (Gen Mgr)
Jon Ardeljan (VP)

KRIPALU CENTER FOR YOGA & HEALTH

KRIPALU CENTER FOR YOGA & HEALTH — U.S. PRIVATE

Kripalu Center for Yoga & Health—(Continued)
57 Interlaken Rd, Stockbridge, MA 01262
Tel.: (413) 448-3152 PA
Web Site: http://www.kripalu.org
Year Founded: 1966
Sales Range: $25-49.9 Million
Emp.: 548
Yoga Instruction Services
N.A.I.C.S.: 611699
Carol O'Neil (Chm)
Barbara Vacarr (CEO)

KRISER'S
12507 Ventura Blvd, Studio City, CA 91604
Tel.: (818) 760-9550
Web Site: http://www.krisers.com
Year Founded: 2006
Sales Range: $1-9.9 Million
Emp.: 55
Pet Food & Supplies
N.A.I.C.S.: 459910
Brad Kriser (Founder)
Kirstyn Rawlings (Mgr-Plng)

KRISTAL CADILLAC, CHEVROLET, & GEO IMPORTS
5200 Kings Hwy, Brooklyn, NY 11234
Tel.: (718) 253-7575
Year Founded: 1986
Sales Range: $25-49.9 Million
Emp.: 30
Car Whslr
N.A.I.C.S.: 441110
Silovo Spallone (Pres)

KRISTEN DISTRIBUTING CO.
8301 N State Hwy 6, Bryan, TX 77807
Tel.: (979) 775-6322
Web Site: http://www.kristendistributing.com
Sales Range: $10-24.9 Million
Emp.: 120
Beer & Other Fermented Malt Liquors
N.A.I.C.S.: 424810
Mark Kristen (CEO)
Bob Gay (VP)
Macy Hannath (Mgr-HR)

KRIYA CAPITAL, LLC
17000 Dallas Pkwy, Dallas, TX 75248
Tel.: (855) 880-4791 DE
Web Site: http://www.kriya-capital.com
Year Founded: 2017
Privater Equity Firm
N.A.I.C.S.: 523999
Karan Negi (Mng Partner)
Rick Hunter (Partner)
Nafeesa Khandwala (Partner)

Subsidiaries:

Credence Resource Management, LLC (1)
4222 Trinity Mills Rd Ste 260, Dallas, TX 75287
Tel.: (855) 880-4791
Web Site: https://credencerm.com
Customer Relationship Management & Technical Support Services
N.A.I.C.S.: 541990

Subsidiary (Domestic):

Receivable Solutions Specialist, Inc. (2)
422 Main St, Natchez, MS 39120
Tel.: (601) 442-0487
Web Site: http://recspecinc.com
Account Receivable Services
N.A.I.C.S.: 561440
Jody Brice (Chm & Pres)

KRIZ-DAVIS CO., INC.
2400 W 3rd St, Grand Island, NE 68803-5324
Tel.: (308) 382-2230 NE
Web Site: http://www.krizdavis.com
Year Founded: 1974
Sales Range: $75-99.9 Million
Emp.: 185
Provider of Electrical Apparatus & Equipment Services
N.A.I.C.S.: 423610
Tracy Lukasiewicz (Controller)
Ralph Knobbe (CFO)
Tim Berry (Pres)

KROCHET KIDS INTL.
9028 E Day Rd, Mead, WA 99021
Tel.: (949) 270-6831 WA
Web Site: http://www.krochetkids.org
Year Founded: 2007
Sales Range: $1-9.9 Million
Fundraising Organization
N.A.I.C.S.: 813211
Adam Thomson (VP-Impact)
Travis Hartanov (CFO & COO)
Stewart Ramsey (VP-Sls)
Kohl Crecelius (CEO & VP-Mktg)

KROENKE SPORTS & ENTERTAINMENT, LLC
1000 Chopper Cir, Denver, CO 80204-5809
Tel.: (303) 405-1100 DE
Web Site: http://www.pepsicenter.com
Emp.: 50
Holding Company; Professional Sports Teams, Sports & Entertainment Arenas & Sports Cable Television Networks Owner & Operator
N.A.I.C.S.: 551112
E. Stanley Kroenke (Owner & Chm)
Mark Waggoner (Sr VP-Fin)
Deb Dowling-Canino (VP-Community Rels)
Doug Ackerman (Sr VP-Venues)
Dave Jolette (Sr VP-Venue Ops)
Stephen Stieneker (Gen Counsel & Exec VP)
Jim Martin (Pres & CEO)
Bruce Glazer (CFO & Exec VP)
Tom Philand (CMO & Exec VP)
Matt Hutchings (COO & Exec VP)
David Burke (Chief Ticketing Officer & Sr VP)
Tomago Collins (Exec VP-Bus Dev & Comm)

Subsidiaries:

Colorado Avalanche, LLC (1)
Pepsi Ctr 1000 Chopper Cir, Denver, CO 80204
Tel.: (303) 405-1100
Web Site: http://avalanche.nhl.com
Sales Range: $75-99.9 Million
Professional Hockey Club
N.A.I.C.S.: 711211
E. Stanley Kroenke (Owner)
Mark Waggoner (Sr VP-Fin)
Michael Benson (Treas & Sr VP-Bus Affairs)
Pierre Lacroix (Pres)
Greg Sherman (Sr VP-Bus & Team Ops)
Jean Martineau (Sr VP-Comm & Bus Ops)
Brad Smith (Dir-Player Personnel)
Craig Billington (Asst Gen Mgr)
Brendan McNicholas (Exec Dir-Media Svcs)
Charlotte Grahame (VP-Hockey Admin)
Joe Sakic (Exec VP-Hockey Ops & Gen Mgr)
Chris MacFarland (Asst Gen Mgr)
Erin DeGraff (Mgr-Team Svcs)
Wayne Flemming (Mgr-Inventory)
Cliff Halstead (Asst Mgr-Equipment)
Alan Hepple (Dir-Amateur Scouting)
Garth Joy (Asst Dir-Layer Personnel)
Brad Lewkow (Asst Mgr-Equipment)
David Oliver (Dir-Player Dev)

Kroenke Arena Company, LLC (1)
1000 Chopper Cir, Denver, CO 80204
Tel.: (303) 405-1100
Web Site: http://www.pepsicenter.com
Sports & Entertainment Arenas Operator
N.A.I.C.S.: 711310
Amy Fewox (Mgr-Venue Mktg & Publicity)
Doug Ackerman (Sr VP-Venues)

Unit (Domestic):

Dick's Sporting Goods Park (2)
6000 Victory Way, Commerce City, CO 80022
Tel.: (303) 727-3500
Web Site: http://www.dickssportinggoodspark.com
Sports & Entertainment Operator
N.A.I.C.S.: 711310
Phaidra Reed (Sr Mgr-Events)
Gene Marquez (Dir-Engrg)
Nick Miles (Dir-Youth Fields)
Phil McQuade (Dir-Turf)
Richard Clarke (Sr Dir-Comm & Digital Media)
Jerry Gerkin (VP-Fin)
Brian Theobald (Gen Mgr)

Outdoor Channel Holdings, Inc. (1)
43455 Business Park Dr, Temecula, CA 92590-6991
Tel.: (951) 699-6991
Web Site: http://www.osa.outdoorchannel.com
Rev.: $77,322,000
Assets: $149,692,000
Liabilities: $18,062,000
Net Worth: $131,630,000
Earnings: $1,894,000
Emp.: 175
Fiscal Year-end: 12/31/2012
Holding Company; Hunting, Fishing, Shooting Sports & Off-Road Motor Sports Television Network Owner & Operator
N.A.I.C.S.: 551112

Subsidiary (Domestic):

The Outdoor Channel, Inc. (2)
43455 Business Park Dr Ste 103, Temecula, CA 92590-3670 (100%)
Tel.: (951) 699-6991
Web Site: http://www.outdoorchannel.com
Sales Range: $200-249.9 Million
Television Programming, Hunting, Fishing, Shooting Sports & Off-Road Motor Sports
N.A.I.C.S.: 516210
Stacy Cerny (VP-Pricing & Plng)
Allison Hill (Mgr-Natl Acct)
Jessica Dunn (Acct Exec)
Rebecca Groth (Mgr-Integrated Sponsorship)
Viga Hall (Acct Exec)
Jessica Lamere (Acct Exec)
Bill Osborn (Sr VP-Mktg)
Mitch Petrie (VP-Programming)
Steve Smith (Exec VP-Affiliate Sls & Mktg)
Rich Walsh (Acct Exec)
Mike Williams (VP-Digital Media & Interactive)

Winnercomm, Inc. (2)
4500 S 129th E Ave Ste 200, Tulsa, OK 74136
Tel.: (918) 496-1900
Web Site: http://www.winnercomm.com
Sports Program Production Services
N.A.I.C.S.: 512110
Jim Wilburn (Pres-Sls)
Tim Cremin (Sr VP-Original Programming)

Subsidiary (Domestic):

CableCam, LLC (3)
630 N Freeway Ste 350, Fort Worth, TX 76102
Tel.: (817) 984-6840
Web Site: http://www.cablecam.com
Camera Gimbal Mfr
N.A.I.C.S.: 333310

The Denver Nuggets Limited Partnership (1)
1000 Chopper Cir, Denver, CO 80204-5809 (100%)
Tel.: (303) 405-1100
Sales Range: $75-99.9 Million
Professional Basketball Team Services
N.A.I.C.S.: 711211
E. Stanley Kroenke (Owner)
Tim Gelt (Dir-Media Rels)
Lisa Johnson (VP-Basketball Admin)
Sparky Gonzales (Mgr-Equipment)
Josh Kroenke (Pres)
Tommy Balcetis (Dir-Basketball Strategy & Analytics)
Jim Clibanoff (Dir-Scouting)
Tim Connelly (Pres-Basketball Ops)
Tim Dixon (Dir-Player Svcs & Brdcst Rels)
Amy O'Brien (Dir-Team Ops & Player Dev)
Nick O'Hayre (Dir-Basketball Ops)
Ben Tenzer (Dir-Basketball Ops)
Cody Wise (Mgr-Media Rels)
Calvin Booth (Asst Gen Mgr)

KROESCHELL, INC.
3222 N Kennicott Ave, Arlington Heights, IL 60004
Tel.: (312) 649-7980
Web Site: http://www.kroeschellinc.com
Year Founded: 1879
Sales Range: $25-49.9 Million
Emp.: 400
Provider of Plumbing, Heating & Air-Conditioning Services
N.A.I.C.S.: 238220
Edward A. Swietek (CEO)

Subsidiaries:

Kroeschell Engineering Co. Inc. (1)
3222 Kennicott Ave, Arlington Heights, IL 60004
Tel.: (312) 649-7980
Web Site: http://www.kroeschell.com
Sales Range: $10-24.9 Million
Emp.: 80
Provider of Plumbing, Heating & Air-Conditioning Services
N.A.I.C.S.: 238220
Edward Swietek (Pres & CEO)
Greg Saltzman (Controller)

Kroeschell Engineering North, Inc. (1)
3222 N Kennicott Ave, Arlington Heights, IL 60004 (100%)
Tel.: (312) 649-7980
Web Site: http://www.kroeschell.com
Sales Range: $10-24.9 Million
Emp.: 80
Provider of Plumbing, Heating & Air-Conditioning Services
N.A.I.C.S.: 238220
Edward Swietek (Exec VP)
Gary Finigan (CFO)
Rick Emery (Mgr-Quality)
Kelsey Lickiss (Mgr-Safety)
David Stavropoulos (Exec VP & Mgr-Corp Risk)

Kroeschell Engineering Service, Inc. (1)
3222 N Kennicott Ave, Arlington Heights, IL 60004
Tel.: (312) 649-7980
Web Site: http://www.kroeschel.com
Sales Range: $10-24.9 Million
Emp.: 85
Provider of Plumbing, Heating & Air-Conditioning Services
N.A.I.C.S.: 238220
Edward A. Swietek (Pres)

Kroeschell Operations Inc. (1)
3222 N Kennicott Ave, Arlington Heights, IL 60004
Tel.: (312) 649-7980
Web Site: http://www.kroeschell.com
Rev.: $2,400,000
Emp.: 300
Engineering Services, Nsk
N.A.I.C.S.: 541330
Rich Pruchniak (Pres)

KROFAM INC.
180 E Hwy 14, Philip, SD 57567
Tel.: (605) 859-2542 SD
Web Site: http://www.scotchman.com
Year Founded: 1993
Sales Range: $75-99.9 Million
Emp.: 75
Holding Company for Machine Tool Manufacturer
N.A.I.C.S.: 333517
Arthur A. Kroetch (Founder)
Jerry Kroetch (Pres)

COMPANIES

Subsidiaries:

Scotchman Credit Corp. (1)
180 E Hwy 14, Philip, SD 57567 (100%)
Tel.: (605) 859-2542
Web Site: http://www.scotchman.com
Sales Range: $50-74.9 Million
Emp.: 60
Leasing Company
N.A.I.C.S.: 522220

Scotchman Industries, Inc. (1)
180 E Hwy 14, Philip, SD 57567
Tel.: (605) 859-2542
Web Site: http://www.scotchman.com
Machine Tools Mfr
N.A.I.C.S.: 333519

KROLL DIRECT MARKETING INC.
666 Plainsboro Rd, Plainsboro, NJ 08536
Tel.: (609) 275-2900
Web Site: http://www.krolldirect.com
Sales Range: $1-9.9 Million
Emp.: 5
Direct Mail Advertising Services
N.A.I.C.S.: 541860
Leland Kroll (Pres)
Susan Dalva (VP)
Gwen Coryell (Dir-List Mgmt)

KROLL, BECKER & WING, LLC
5 Bedford Farms Dr Ste 304, Bedford, NH 03110
Tel.: (603) 792-2345
Web Site: http://www.kbwfinancial.com
Year Founded: 2005
Sales Range: $10-24.9 Million
Emp.: 30
Financial & Accounting Staffing Solutions
N.A.I.C.S.: 561311
Jason Kroll (CEO)

KRON & ASSOCIATES ADVERTISING INC.
1849 Broad Ripple Ave, Indianapolis, IN 46220-2339
Tel.: (317) 253-9050
Year Founded: 1992
Sales Range: $10-24.9 Million
Emp.: 5
Advetising Agency
N.A.I.C.S.: 541810
Randall D. Kron (Pres)

KRONOS ADVANCED TECHNOLOGIES, INC.
154 Norton Ave, Barberton, OH 44203
Tel.: (323) 680-4772
Web Site: http://www.kronosati.co
Year Founded: 1996
Air Purification Equipment Mfr
N.A.I.C.S.: 333413
Julius Toth (COO)

KROY INDUSTRIES, INC.
522 W 26th St, York, NE 68467-0309
Tel.: (402) 362-6651
Web Site: http://www.kroyind.com
Year Founded: 1998
Sales Range: $10-24.9 Million
Emp.: 120
Mfr of Aluminum Sheet, Plate & Foil
N.A.I.C.S.: 331315
Judy Gilsdorf (Mgr-Accts Payable)
Phil Seevers (Mgr-Ops)

KRUEGER ASSOCIATES INC.
105 Commerce Dr, Aston, PA 19014
Tel.: (610) 532-4700
Web Site: http://www.nfsrv.com
Sales Range: $25-49.9 Million
Emp.: 200
Direct Marketing Services
N.A.I.C.S.: 518210
Tom Krueger (VP-Mktg)
Gene Krueger (Pres)
Robert Moore (CFO)

KRUEGER FLORAL-N-GIFTS
10706 Tesch Ln, Rothschild, WI 54474
Tel.: (715) 359-7202
Web Site: http://www.kruegerfloral.com
Rev.: $12,500,000
Emp.: 200
Flower Nursery Stock & Florists Supplies Merchant Whslr
N.A.I.C.S.: 424930
Kevin Krueger (VP)
James W. Krueger (Pres & Treas)
Seth Fochs (COO)
Gary Ruplinger (CFO)

KRUEGER INTERNATIONAL, INC.
1330 Bellevue St, Green Bay, WI 54302
Tel.: (920) 468-8100   WI
Web Site: http://www.ki.com
Year Founded: 1941
Sales Range: $600-649.9 Million
Emp.: 50
Office Furniture Mfr
N.A.I.C.S.: 337211
Brian Krenke (CEO)

Subsidiaries:

KI (UK) Ltd. (1)
New Fetter Place, 8-10 New Fetter Ln, London, EC4A 1AZ, United Kingdom
Tel.: (44) 2074047441
Web Site: http://www.kieurope.com
Sales Range: $25-49.9 Million
Emp.: 35
Storage & Filing Products Manufacture & Sales
N.A.I.C.S.: 337214
Jonathan Hindle (Mng Dir)

Pallas Textiles (1)
1330 Bellevue St, Green Bay, WI 54308-8100 (100%)
Tel.: (920) 468-2660
Web Site: http://www.pallastextiles.com
Sales Range: $10-24.9 Million
Emp.: 100
Textile Designer & Mfr
N.A.I.C.S.: 313310

Sebel Furniture Ltd. (1)
92 Gow Street, Padstow, 2211, NSW, Australia
Tel.: (61) 297802222
Web Site: http://www.sebel.com.au
Sales Range: $450-499.9 Million
Emp.: 295
Institutional & Office Furniture Mfr
N.A.I.C.S.: 337127
Greg Welsh (CEO)

Subsidiary (Non-US):

Sebel Furniture Limited (NZ) (2)
4 Nikau Street Mt Eden, Auckland, 1021, New Zealand
Tel.: (64) 9373 9981
Sales Range: $10-24.9 Million
Emp.: 4
Furniture Mfr
N.A.I.C.S.: 337211

Spacesaver Corporation (1)
1450 Janesville Ave, Fort Atkinson, WI 53538
Tel.: (920) 563-6362
Web Site: http://www.spacesaver.com
Sales Range: $75-99.9 Million
Emp.: 400
Institutional Furniture Mfr
N.A.I.C.S.: 337127
Paul Olsen (Pres)
James Muth (VP)
Nick Behselich (Mgr-Off-Site Storage)
Ron Jordan (Project Mgr)

Subsidiary (Domestic):

Viking Metal Cabinet Co. (2)
420 N Main St, Montgomery, IL 60538
Tel.: (708) 594-1111
Web Site: http://www.vikingmetal.com
Rev.: $6,666,666
Metal Household Furniture Mfr
N.A.I.C.S.: 337126

KRUEGER SHEET METAL
731 N Superior St, Spokane, WA 99202
Tel.: (509) 489-0221
Web Site: http://www.kruegersheetmetal.com
Year Founded: 1948
Sales Range: $10-24.9 Million
Emp.: 75
Roofing Installation Services
N.A.I.C.S.: 238390
Thomas H. Brandt (Pres)

KRUGER BROWN HOLDINGS, LLC
N7660 Industrial Rd, Portage, WI 53901
Tel.: (608) 742-5303   OK
Web Site: http://www.trienda.com
Year Founded: 2016
Emp.: 200
Holding Company; Thermoformed Plastic Products Mfr & Whslr
N.A.I.C.S.: 551112
John Brown (Co-Owner)
David Kruger (Co-Owner)
Warren Kruger (Co-Owner)

Subsidiaries:

PendaForm Corporation (1)
200 Friendship Dr, New Concord, OH 43762
Tel.: (740) 826-5000
Web Site: http://www.pendaform.com
Holding Company; Thermoformed Plastic Products Mfr & Whslr
N.A.I.C.S.: 551112
David Kruger (Pres)
John Brown (CEO)

Subsidiary (Domestic):

Penda Corporation (2)
2344 W Wisconsin St, Portage, WI 53901
Tel.: (608) 742-5301
Web Site: http://www.pendaform.com
Thermoformed Plastic Products Mfr & Whslr
N.A.I.C.S.: 326199
Tim Williams (VP-Sls & Bus Dev)

The Fabri-Form Company (2)
200 Friendship Dr, New Concord, OH 43762
Tel.: (740) 826-5000
Web Site: http://www.pendaform.com
Thermoformed Plastic Products Mfr & Whslr
N.A.I.C.S.: 326199
Debbie Sweet (Mgr-Sls-Intl)

TriEnda Holdings, LLC (1)
N7660 Industrial Rd, Portage, WI 53901
Tel.: (608) 742-5303
Web Site: http://www.trienda.com
Thermoformed Plastic Pallet Mfr
N.A.I.C.S.: 326199
David Kruger (Pres)
John Brown (CEO)
Warren Kruger (Chm)

KRUGER FOODS INC.
PO Box 220, San Joaquin, CA 95230
Tel.: (209) 941-8518
Web Site: http://www.krugerfoods.com
Year Founded: 1930
Sales Range: $10-24.9 Million
Emp.: 100
Fruit & Vegetable Canning Services
N.A.I.C.S.: 311421
Leslie Kruger (VP & CEO)
Martin Luis (Project Mgr)

KRUMLAND CO. LLC
2211 W 2nd St, Roswell, NM 88201
Tel.: (575) 622-5860
Web Site: http://www.roswelltoyota.com
Sales Range: $25-49.9 Million
Emp.: 75
Automobiles, New & Used
N.A.I.C.S.: 441110
Thomas Krumland (Principal-Dealer)
B. J. Sills (Gen Mgr)
Joe Reiser (Mgr-Ops)
Mike Baker (Mgr-Used Cars)
Michael Moore (Dir-Fin)
Laura Barnard (Mgr-Customer Rels)
Tiffany Edwards (Mgr-Internet)
Ruben Loza (Mgr-New Car)
Jim Collins (Mgr-Svc-Columbus)

KRUPP KOMMUNICATIONS
636 Ave of the Americas 4th Fl, New York, NY 10011
Tel.: (212) 886-6700
Web Site: http://www.kruppkommunication.com
Sales Range: $1-9.9 Million
Emp.: 20
Media Buying Services
N.A.I.C.S.: 541810
Dina White (VP-Media Rels)
Heidi Krupp (CEO)
Megan Wilson (Dir-PR)

KRUPP L CONSTRUCTION INC.
415 Old State Rd, Ballwin, MO 63021
Tel.: (636) 391-8844
Year Founded: 1972
Sales Range: $25-49.9 Million
Emp.: 100
Civil Engineering Services
N.A.I.C.S.: 237310
Mark Reizer (Principal)

KRUSE WORLDWIDE COURIER, LTD.
5020 Investment Dr, Fort Wayne, IN 46808
Tel.: (260) 744-1228
Web Site: http://www.kruseworld.com
Year Founded: 2001
Rev.: $5,400,000
Emp.: 155
Freight & Courier Services
N.A.I.C.S.: 492110
Lance Adams (CEO)
Shawn Thorne (Mgr-Terminal Ops)

KRUSE-WARTHAN DUBUQUE AUTO PLAZA
600 Century Dr, Dubuque, IA 52002-3704
Tel.: (563) 583-7345
Web Site: http://www.dubuqueautoplaza.com
Year Founded: 1948
Sales Range: $10-24.9 Million
Emp.: 50
New Car Whslr
N.A.I.C.S.: 441110
Doug Warthan (Pres)
Gwyn Wilson (CFO)
Katie Schaefer (Office Mgr)
Kevin Kotz (Mgr-Svc)

KRUSKOPF COONTZ
310 4th Ave S 2nd Fl, Minneapolis, MN 55415
Tel.: (612) 338-3870   MN
Web Site: http://www.kctruth.com
Year Founded: 1988
Sales Range: $25-49.9 Million
Emp.: 20
Advertising Agencies
N.A.I.C.S.: 541810

Kruskopf Coontz—(Continued)

Susan Kruskopf (CEO)
Robb Burnham (VP & Creative Dir)
Mike Cronin (VP & Creative Dir)

KRYSTAL INFINITY LLC
2701 E Imperial Hwy, Brea, CA 92821
Tel.: (714) 986-1200
Year Founded: 1983
Sales Range: $25-49.9 Million
Emp.: 500
Limousines, Mid-Size Buses, Hearses & Specialty Automobile Mfr
N.A.I.C.S.: 336110
Ed Grech (Founder & CEO)

Subsidiaries:

Edson Financial Inc. (1)
2701 E Imperial Hwy, Brea, CA 92821
Tel.: (714) 986-3980
Web Site: http://www.g2sp.com
Rev.: $1,000,000
Emp.: 20
Provider of Automotive Financing Services
N.A.I.C.S.: 522291

KS INDUSTRIES, L.P.
6205 District Blvd, Bakersfield, CA 93384
Tel.: (661) 617-1700
Web Site:
http://www.ksindustrieslp.com
Year Founded: 1960
Sales Range: $10-24.9 Million
Emp.: 1,000
Engineering, Fabrication & Construction Services
N.A.I.C.S.: 423390
Kevin Small (Pres)
Becky Scott (CFO)
Glenda Small (Treas & Sec)

KS INTERNATIONAL INVESTMENT CORP.
1731 Industrial Pkwy N, Marinette, WI 54143-3704
Tel.: (715) 732-0181
Year Founded: 1979
Sales Range: $250-299.9 Million
Emp.: 1,003
Holding Company; Carburetors, Pistons, Rings & Valves Mfr
N.A.I.C.S.: 551112
Rick Posz (CFO)

Subsidiaries:

KS Bearings (1)
1515 West Main St, Greensburg, IN 47240-9585
Tel.: (812) 663-3401
Sales Range: $10-24.9 Million
Emp.: 125
Motor Vehicle Parts & Accessories
N.A.I.C.S.: 423840

KSA INDUSTRIES INC.
4400 Post Oak Pkwy Ste 2800, Houston, TX 77027-3421
Tel.: (713) 881-3400
Year Founded: 1949
Sales Range: $25-49.9 Million
Emp.: 587
Promoter of Sports Club; Provider of Fuel Products & Services; Holding Company
N.A.I.C.S.: 711211
Richard Abshire (VP-Exec)
Wade Taylor (VP)
W. R. Scofield (Pres & COO)

KSG DISTRIBUTING, INC.
1121 W Flint Meadow Dr, Kaysville, UT 84037
Tel.: (801) 336-1000
Web Site: http://www.ksgdist.com
Sales Range: $10-24.9 Million
Emp.: 70
Durable Goods Whslr
N.A.I.C.S.: 423990
Kevin S. Garn (Founder)

KSI TRADING COMPANY
100 A Wade Ave, South Plainfield, NJ 07080
Tel.: (908) 754-7154
Web Site:
http://www.ksiautoparts.com
Rev.: $11,020,942
Emp.: 70
Automotive Supplies & Parts
N.A.I.C.S.: 423120
Ricky Lee (Gen Mgr)
Roger Lin (Gen Mgr)

Subsidiaries:

Universal Auto Body Supply (1)
5414A W Roosevelt Rd, Chicago, IL 60644
Tel.: (773) 921-4444
Web Site: http://www.ksiautoparts.com
Rev.: $2,100,000
Emp.: 20
Motor Vehicle Supplies & New Parts
N.A.I.C.S.: 423120

KSJ & ASSOCIATES
5203 Leesburg Pike Ste 901, Falls Church, VA 22041
Tel.: (703) 824-7802
Web Site: http://www.ksj.us
Year Founded: 1996
Sales Range: $10-24.9 Million
Emp.: 90
IT Technical Support & Consulting Services
N.A.I.C.S.: 541611
Kasey S. Jarosz (Founder & CEO)
David A. Chance (Pres)
Kristine Anthony (Project Mgr)

KSL CAPITAL PARTNERS, LLC
100 Saint Paul St Ste 800, Denver, CO 80206
Tel.: (720) 284-6400
Web Site: http://www.kslcapital.com
Year Founded: 2005
Private Equity Firm
N.A.I.C.S.: 523999
Eric C. Resnick (CEO)
Steven S. Siegel (COO)
Peter R. McDermott (Partner & CIO)
Bernard N. Siegel (Partner)
Martin J. Newburger (Partner)
Coley J. Brenan (Partner & Head-Europe)
Richard Weissmann (Partner)
John A. Ege (Partner)
Craig Henrich (Partner)
Daniel Rohan (Partner)
Hal Shaw (Principal)
Jared Melnik (Principal)
Jens Blomdahl (Sr VP)
Tina Yu (Sr VP)
Martin Edsinger (Sr VP)
Matt Gaghen (Sr Dir & Head-Sls & Mktg)
Michael Mohapp (Principal)
Michael S. Shannon (Chm)

Subsidiaries:

Arapahoe Basin Ski Area (1)
28194 US 6, Keystone, CO 80435
Tel.: (970) 468-0718
Web Site: http://www.arapahoebasin.com
Skiing Facilities
N.A.I.C.S.: 713920
Alan Henceroth (COO)

Hawk Holding Company, LLC (1)
1621 18th St Ste 300, Denver, CO 80202
Tel.: (303) 749-8200
Holding Company; Skiing Resort Operator
N.A.I.C.S.: 551112
David Perry (Pres & COO)

Subsidiary (Domestic):

Alterra Mountain Company (2)
3501 Wazee St Ste 400, Denver, CO 80216
Tel.: (303) 749-8200
Web Site: http://www.alterramtnco.com
Holding Company; Resort Operator
N.A.I.C.S.: 551112
Lindsay Goszulak (Sr VP & Controller)
Rusty Gregory (CEO)
Mark Brownlie (COO-Resorts)

Subsidiary (Non-US):

Blue Mountain Resorts Limited Partnership (3)
190 Gord Canning Drive, Blue Mountains, L9Y 1C2, ON, Canada
Tel.: (705) 419-2409
Web Site: https://www.bluemountain.ca
Ski Resort Operator
N.A.I.C.S.: 713920

Subsidiary (Domestic):

Crystal Mountain, Inc. (3)
33914 Crystal Mtn Blvd, Enumclaw, WA 98022-7938
Tel.: (360) 663-2265
Web Site:
http://www.crystalmountainresorts.com
Recreation Resorts
N.A.I.C.S.: 713990
Chris MacInnes (Pres)
John Melcher (CEO)

Intrawest Hospitality Management, LLC (3)
85 Parsenn Rd, Winter Park, CO 80482
Tel.: (970) 726-1564
Web Site: http://www.winterparkresort.com
Ski Resort Lodging Manager
N.A.I.C.S.: 721199
Steve Hurlbert (Dir-PR & Comm)

Intrawest/Winter Park Operations Corporation (3)
85 Parsenn Rd, Winter Park, CO 80482
Tel.: (970) 726-5514
Web Site: http://www.winterparkresort.com
Sales Range: $1-9.9 Million
Emp.: 250
Ski Resort Operator
N.A.I.C.S.: 713920
Sky Foulkes (Pres & COO)
Gary De Frange (VP & Gen Mgr)
Molly Turk (Mgr-Sls)

Subsidiary (Non-US):

Mont Tremblant Resorts & Company, Limited Partnership (3)
1000 Chemin des Voyageurs, Mont-Tremblant, J8E 1T1, QC, Canada
Tel.: (819) 681-3000
Web Site: http://www.tremblant.ca
Ski Resort Operator
N.A.I.C.S.: 713920
Kamal Shah (Pres)

Subsidiary (Domestic):

Snowshoe Mountain, Inc. (3)
10 Snowshoe Dr, Snowshoe, WV 26209
Tel.: (304) 572-1000
Web Site:
http://www.snowshoemountain.com
Ski Resort Operator
N.A.I.C.S.: 713920
Patti Duncan (Pres & COO)
Kandy Ramos (Dir-Fin)
Sarah Guyette (VP-Mktg)

Steamboat Ski & Resort Corporation (3)
2305 Mount Werner Cir, Steamboat Springs, CO 80487-9023
Tel.: (970) 879-6111
Web Site: http://www.steamboat.com
Sales Range: $125-149.9 Million
Emp.: 250
Year-Round Resort Featuring Skiing & All Summer Activities
N.A.I.C.S.: 459110
Mike Lane (Dir-PR)
Rob Perlman (Pres & COO)
Bill Thomas (VP-HR)
Kathy Hastings (Gen Mgr-Steamboat Grand Hotel)
Blair McNamara (VP-Lodging)

The Stratton Corporation (3)
5 Village Lodge Rd, Stratton Mountain, VT 05155
Tel.: (802) 297-4100
Web Site: http://www.stratton.com
Sales Range: $100-124.9 Million
Ski Resort Operator
N.A.I.C.S.: 713920
Bill Nupp (Pres & COO)

Subsidiary (Domestic):

Deer Valley Resort Company, LLC (2)
2250 Deer Vly Dr S, Park City, UT 84060
Tel.: (435) 649-1000
Web Site: http://www.deervalley.com
Resort; Ski Facilities
N.A.I.C.S.: 713920
Karen Gibbs (Mgr-Banquet & Conference)
Emily Summers (Sr Mgr-Comm)
Cassidy Schindler (Mgr-HR Dev & Sys)
Kim Mayhew (Dir-HR)
Kim McClelland (Dir-Lodging Ops)
Lara Brucker (Sr Coord-Comm)
Todd Bennett (Pres & COO)

Subsidiary (Domestic):

Solitude Mountain Resort, LLC (3)
12000 Big Cottonwood Canyon, Salt Lake City, UT 84121
Tel.: (801) 534-1400
Web Site: http://www.solitudemountain.com
Ski Resort
N.A.I.C.S.: 713920
Sherri Harkin (Mgr-Comm)
Tim Wolfgram (Dir-Snowsports Svcs)
Philip Diana (Dir-Lodging Ops)

Subsidiary (Domestic):

Mammoth Resorts LLC (2)
10001 Minaret Rd, Mammoth Lakes, CA 93546
Tel.: (800) 626-6684
Web Site: http://www.mammothresorts.com
Holding Company; Ski Resorts Owner & Operator
N.A.I.C.S.: 551112
Mark Brownlie (Pres & COO)
Lauren Burke (Mgr-PR & Social Media)

Subsidiary (Domestic):

Big Bear Mountain Resort (3)
880 Summit Blvd, Big Bear Lake, CA 92315
Tel.: (909) 866-5766
Web Site:
http://www.bigbearmountainresort.com
Ski Resorts Operator; Recreational Facilities & Services
N.A.I.C.S.: 713920
Wade Reeser (COO)
Justin Kanton (Mgr-Media & In-Resort Mktg)

Subsidiary (Domestic):

Snow Valley LLC (4)
35100 Hwy 18, Running Springs, CA 92382
Tel.: (909) 867-2751
Web Site: http://www.snow-valley.com
Traveler Accommodation
N.A.I.C.S.: 721199
Kevin Somes (COO)

Subsidiary (Domestic):

Mammoth Mountain Ski Area, LLC (3)
10001 Minaret Rd, Mammoth Lakes, CA 93546
Tel.: (760) 934-2571
Web Site:
http://www.mammothmountain.com
Ski Resort Services
N.A.I.C.S.: 713920
Joani Lynch (VP-Mktg & Sls)
Lauren Burke (Mgr-PR & Social Media)
Mark Brownlie (Pres & COO)

Subsidiary (Domestic):

Squaw Valley Ski Holdings, LLC (2)
1960 Squaw Valley Rd, Olympic Valley, CA 96146
Tel.: (530) 583-6985
Web Site: http://www.squawalpine.com
Holding Company; Ski Resort Operator
N.A.I.C.S.: 551112

Ron Cohen *(Interim Pres & Interim COO)*

Heritage Golf Group LLC (1)
6005 Hidden Valley Rd Ste 115, Carlsbad, CA 92011
Tel.: (858) 720-0694
Web Site: http://www.heritagegolfgroup.com
Golf Courses & Country Clubs
N.A.I.C.S.: 713910
James Husband *(CEO)*

Hersha Hospitality Trust (1)
44 Hersha Dr, Harrisburg, PA 17102
Tel.: (717) 236-4400
Rev.: $405,874,000
Assets: $1,488,877,000
Liabilities: $732,416,000
Net Worth: $756,461,000
Earnings: $166,060,000
Emp.: 27
Fiscal Year-end: 12/31/2022
Hotel Real Estate Investment Trust
N.A.I.C.S.: 525990
Michael R. Gillespie *(Chief Acctg Officer)*

Unit (Domestic):

Courtyard by Marriott - Ewing Hopewell (2)
360 Scotch Rd, Ewing, NJ 08628
Tel.: (609) 771-8100
Web Site: http://www.courtyard.com
Sales Range: $10-24.9 Million
Emp.: 45
Hotel Operator
N.A.I.C.S.: 721110

Subsidiary (Domestic):

HHLP Bridgewater Associates, LLC (2)
530 Rte 22, Bridgewater, NJ 08807-2405
Tel.: (908) 725-0800
Home Management Services
N.A.I.C.S.: 721110
Howi Spellman *(Gen Mgr)*

HHLP Coconut Grove Associates, LLC (2)
44 Hersha Dr Fl 2, Harrisburg, PA 17102-2241
Tel.: (717) 651-0980
Fruit & Tree Nut Farming Services
N.A.I.C.S.: 111336

HHLP Prescott Associates, LLC (2)
48645 Van Dyke, Shelby, MI 48317
Tel.: (248) 299-9370
Restaurant Operating Services
N.A.I.C.S.: 721110

HHLP White Plains Associates, LLC (2)
101 Corporate Park Dr, White Plains, NY 10604-3301
Tel.: (914) 251-9700
Web Site: http://www.hyatthousewhitwplains.com
Sales Range: $10-24.9 Million
Emp.: 30
Home Management Services
N.A.I.C.S.: 721110

HT-315 Trumbull Street Associates, LLC (2)
315 Trumbull St, Hartford, CT 06103
Tel.: (860) 728-5151
Lodging & Restaurant Services
N.A.I.C.S.: 721110

Holiday Inn Express Boston (2)
69 Boston St Ste R, Boston, MA 02125
Tel.: (617) 288-3030
Web Site: http://www.hiexpress.com
Sales Range: $10-24.9 Million
Emp.: 40
Hotel Operations
N.A.I.C.S.: 721110

Metro 29th Street Associates, LLC (2)
232 W 29th St, New York, NY 10001
Tel.: (212) 695-7200
Emp.: 21
Restaurant Operating Services
N.A.I.C.S.: 721110

Southington Suites, LLC (2)
778 W St, Southington, CT 06489-2351
Tel.: (860) 621-4440

Emp.: 30
Home Management Services
N.A.I.C.S.: 721110

KSL Resorts (1)
50-905 Avenida Bermudas, La Quinta, CA 92253
Tel.: (760) 564-8000
Web Site: http://www.kslresorts.com
Sales Range: $10-24.9 Million
Resort Management Services
N.A.I.C.S.: 541611
Scott M. Dalecio *(Founder & CEO)*
James Struthers *(CFO & VP)*
Michael E. Erickson *(VP-Sls)*
Michael Palmeri *(Sr VP & Head-Investments & Bus Dev)*
Ed Eynon *(Chief HR Officer & Sr VP)*

Holding (Domestic):

Hotel del Coronado (2)
1500 Orange Ave, Coronado, CA 92118
Tel.: (619) 435-6611
Web Site: http://www.hoteldel.com
Luxury Hotel & Resort Operator
N.A.I.C.S.: 721110
Dane Gorup *(Dir-Events & Catering)*

Vail Mountain Lodge & Spa (2)
352 E Meadow Dr, Vail, CO 81657
Tel.: (970) 306-0361
Web Site: http://www.vailmountainlodge.com
Emp.: 20
Hotels & Spa Operator
N.A.I.C.S.: 721110
Frank Johnson *(Gen Mgr)*

Orion Expedition Cruises Pty. Ltd. (1)
2/8 West St, North Sydney, Sydney, 2060, NSW, Australia
Tel.: (61) 290338700
Web Site: http://www.orionexpeditions.com
Sales Range: $25-49.9 Million
Cruise Line Owner & Operator
N.A.I.C.S.: 483112

Outrigger Hotels Hawaii (1)
2375 Kuhio Ave, Honolulu, HI 96815
Tel.: (808) 921-6600
Web Site: http://www.outrigger.com
Hotel & Resort Operator
N.A.I.C.S.: 561109
Paul K. Richardson *(COO & Exec VP)*
Sean Dee *(CMO/Exec VP-Outrigger Enterprises Grp)*
Alan White *(CIO)*
Ed Case *(Chief Legal Officer)*
Ruthann Yamanaka *(Chief People Officer)*
Barry Wallace *(Exec VP-Hospitality Svcs)*
Tammy Uy *(VP-Creative Dev)*
Will Caraway *(Dir-Sls & Mktg-OHANA Hotels)*
Nancy Daniels *(Dir-PR)*
Laurie Hirata *(Dir-Data Mgmt)*
Raymond Scott *(Dir-Sys Integration)*
Lisa Tojo *(Dir-Interactive Commerce)*
Trina Tory *(Dir-HR Div)*
Craig Wienckowski *(Dir-Revenue, Pricing & Asset Mgmt)*
Greg Champion *(Dir-Global Mktg & Strategic Partnerships)*
Kathy Hansberry *(Mgr-PR)*
Niel Mason *(Mgr-OHANA Hotels)*
Tom Wakita *(VP-Sls & Mktg-North America)*
Bob Froio *(Dir-Sls-North America)*
Andrew Gee *(VP-Sls & Mktg-Asia Pacific)*
Jeff Wagoner *(Pres & CEO)*
Scott Dalecio *(Chm-Hospitality Brand-Global)*
Kenny Kan *(Chief Dev Officer/Sr VP-Global Beach Resort Brand)*
Angela Murphy *(VP-Sls-Americas)*

Subsidiary (Domestic):

Kaanapali Beach Properties, Inc. (2)
PO Box 10608, Lahaina, HI 96761
Tel.: (808) 667-5900
Vacation Services
N.A.I.C.S.: 721110
Nikoya Collier *(Acct Exec-Sls)*

Unit (Domestic):

Maui Eldorado Kaanapali by Outrigger (2)
2661 Kekaa Dr Kaanapali Beach, Maui, HI 96761-1933

Tel.: (808) 661-0021
Web Site: http://www.outriggermauieldoradocondo.com
Condominium Rental & Resort Operator
N.A.I.C.S.: 561599
Athena Cajudoy *(Gen Mgr)*

Royal Sea Cliff Kona by Outrigger (2)
75-6040 Alii Dr, Kailua Kona, HI 96740
Tel.: (808) 329-8021
Web Site: http://www.outriggercondominiums.com
Condominium Rental & Resort Operator
N.A.I.C.S.: 561599
Carol Hanna *(Gen Mgr)*

W.A. Holding Company (1)
1 Lombard St, San Francisco, CA 94111
Tel.: (415) 781-1874
Sales Range: $300-349.9 Million
Holding Company; Luxury Fitness & Recreational Sports Centers Owner & Operator
N.A.I.C.S.: 551112

KSL MEDIA, INC.
387 Park Ave S 4th Fl, New York, NY 10016
Tel.: (212) 352-5800
Web Site: http://www.kslmedia.com
Year Founded: 1981
Sales Range: $75-99.9 Million
Emp.: 96
N.A.I.C.S.: 541810
Kal Liebowitz *(Chm)*
David Sklaver *(Pres)*
Hank Cohen *(CEO)*
Tarun Chachra *(CTO & VP)*
Dayle Siegel *(Sr VP & Mng Dir-Direct Response)*
Mike Oddi *(CMO)*
Liz Kelly *(Exec VP & Dir-Brdcst Investment)*
Steve Kaufman *(Exec VP-Integrated Media)*
Adam Cohen *(Acct Dir)*
Mark Geller *(Mng Dir & Sr VP)*
Larry Most *(VP-Bus Dev)*
Amy DeHaen *(Sr VP & Mng Dir-Natl Brdcst)*
Danielle Cohen *(VP & Acct Dir-Digital)*
Matt Greenfield *(Exec VP & Dir-Client Svcs)*
Russell Meisels *(Exec VP & CFO)*
Jeremy Viola *(VP & Mng Dir)*

Subsidiaries:

KSL Media, Inc. (1)
15910 Ventura Blvd 9th Fl, Los Angeles, CA 91436
Tel.: (818) 461-5900
Web Site: http://www.kslmedia.com
Sales Range: $25-49.9 Million
Emp.: 62
N.A.I.C.S.: 541830
Hank Cohen *(CEO)*
Fran McCreary *(Mng Dir & Sr VP)*
Kal Liebowitz *(Chm)*
Richard Birt *(Sr VP & Dir-Customer Insight & Analytics)*
Matt Greenfield *(Sr VP & Dir-Client Svcs)*
Liz Kelly *(Exec VP & Dir-Brdcast)*
Anita Paul *(Mng Dir & Sr VP)*
Jeremy Viola *(VP & Acct Dir)*
David Sklaver *(Pres)*
Mike Oddi *(CMO)*

KSM ELECTRONICS INC.
5607 Hiatus Rd Ste 600, Fort Lauderdale, FL 33321
Tel.: (954) 971-5900
Web Site: http://www.ksmelectronics.com
Sales Range: $25-49.9 Million
Emp.: 200
Electronic Parts & Equipment Sales
N.A.I.C.S.: 423690
Sergio Santiago *(Mgr-Field Acct)*
Oscar Lopez *(CFO)*

KST DATA INC.
3699 Wilshire Blvd Ste 100, Los Angeles, CA 90010
Tel.: (213) 384-9555
Web Site: http://www.kstdata.com
Rev.: $10,500,000
Emp.: 50
Computer & Computer Peripheral Equipment & Software Merchant Whslr
N.A.I.C.S.: 423430
Armando Tan *(VP-Ops)*
Eugene Jacobowitz *(Gen Mgr)*

KT'S KITCHENS, INC.
1065 E Walnut St Ste C, Carson, CA 90746
Tel.: (310) 764-0850
Web Site: http://www.ktskitchens.com
Sales Range: $25-49.9 Million
Emp.: 250
Frozen Pizza Mfr
N.A.I.C.S.: 311412
Kathleen Taggares *(Pres)*
Cheryl Schneider *(CFO)*
Curt Ramsey *(VP-Pur & Retail Sls)*

KTH PARTS INDUSTRIES INC.
1111 SR 235 N, Saint Paris, OH 43072-9680
Tel.: (937) 663-5941
Web Site: http://www.kth.net
Year Founded: 1984
Sales Range: $400-449.9 Million
Emp.: 800
Motor Vehicle Parts & Accessories
N.A.I.C.S.: 336390
Dustin Murphy *(Engr-Quality)*
Tom Purnell *(Coord-Sls)*
Darius Collins *(Engr-Weld)*

KTI, INC.
3 Thompson Rd, East Windsor, CT 06088-9695
Tel.: (860) 623-2511
Web Site: http://www.ktiinc.com
Year Founded: 1966
Sales Range: $1-9.9 Million
Emp.: 20
Bi-Metal Strips Mfr & Electron Beam Welding Services
N.A.I.C.S.: 811490
Howard W. Orr *(Pres)*
Eric Walker *(VP & Gen Mgr)*
John Marshall *(Engr-Sls)*

KTL SOLUTIONS, INC.
4640 Wedgewood Blvd Ste 104, Frederick, MD 21703
Tel.: (301) 360-0001
Web Site: http://www.ktlsolutions.com
Year Founded: 1999
Rev.: $3,600,000
Emp.: 23
Computer Programming Services
N.A.I.C.S.: 541511
Frank Reese *(Dir-Dev)*
Kim Lally *(Controller)*
Chad Leschefsky *(Acct Mgr)*

KUBE PAK CORP.
194 Route 526, Allentown, NJ 08501
Tel.: (609) 259-3114
Web Site: http://www.kubepak.com
Sales Range: $10-24.9 Million
Emp.: 125
Nursery & Tree Production Services
N.A.I.C.S.: 111421
William Behr *(Mgr-IT)*

KUBIN-NICHOLSON CORPORATION
8440 N 87th St, Milwaukee, WI 53224
Tel.: (414) 586-4300
Web Site: http://www.kubin.com

WI

Kubin-Nicholson Corporation—(Continued)
Year Founded: 1982
Rev.: $30,000,000
Emp.: 70
Large Format Printing, Indoor Banners, Trade Show Displays, Vehicle Graphics, Wall Maps & Self-Adhesive Graphics
N.A.I.C.S.: 323111
Michael Rees *(Pres)*
Margaret Rees *(Chm & CEO)*

Subsidiaries:

Kubin-Nicholson Corp. (1)
333 N Michigan Ave Ste 404, Chicago, IL 60601
Tel.: (312) 346-3771
Web Site: http://www.kubin.com
Printing & Display Services
N.A.I.C.S.: 323111
Brian O'Brien *(VP)*

Kubin-Nicholson Corp., Chicago (1)
333 N Michigan Ave Ste 404, Chicago, IL 60601-5906
Tel.: (312) 346-3771
Web Site: http://www.kubin.com
Sales Range: $10-24.9 Million
Emp.: 1
N.A.I.C.S.: 323111

Kubin-Nicholson Corp., New York (1)
60 East 42nd St Rm 812, New York, NY 10165-0812
Tel.: (212) 986-1434
Sales Range: $10-24.9 Million
Printers of Outdoor Billboards
N.A.I.C.S.: 541820

KUCERA PROPERTIES
1 Progress Plz Ste 2100, Saint Petersburg, FL 33701
Tel.: (727) 823-8980
Web Site:
   http://www.kuceraproperties.com
Sales Range: $1-9.9 Million
Emp.: 6
Office Building Owner & Manager
N.A.I.C.S.: 531312
Austin Kucera *(Mng Partner)*
Darin Kucera *(Gen Mgr)*

KUDICK CHEVROLET-BUICK, INC.
802A N Union St, Mauston, WI 53948
Tel.: (608) 847-6324
Sales Range: $10-24.9 Million
Emp.: 20
Car Whslr
N.A.I.C.S.: 441110
Brett Kudick *(Pres)*

KUDU INVESTMENT MANAGEMENT LLC
286 Madison Ave Ste 2002 20th Fl, New York, NY 10017
Tel.: (212) 257-6422
Web Site:
   http://www.kuduinvestment.com
Year Founded: 2015
Private Equity Firm
N.A.I.C.S.: 523999
Charles A. Ruffel *(Founder & Mng Partner)*
Rob Jakacki *(CEO)*

KUDZU FABRICS INCORPORATED
2154 River Cliff Dr, Roswell, GA 30076
Tel.: (770) 641-0379
Rev.: $24,900,000
Automobile Fabrics
N.A.I.C.S.: 424990

KUEHN MOTOR COMPANY
5020 Hwy 52 N, Rochester, MN 55901
Tel.: (507) 282-7700
Web Site:
   http://www.kuehnmotors.com
Sales Range: $10-24.9 Million
Emp.: 70
Automobile Sales
N.A.I.C.S.: 441120
Michael Hewitt *(Controller)*
Charles Kuehn Jr. *(Pres)*

KUEHNE CHEMICAL COMPANY, INC.
86 N Hackensack Ave, Kearny, NJ 07032
Tel.: (973) 589-0700   NJ
Web Site:
   http://www.kuehnecompany.com
Year Founded: 1919
Sales Range: $25-49.9 Million
Emp.: 200
Industrial Inorganic Chemicals Mfr
N.A.I.C.S.: 325180
Don Nicolai *(Pres & CEO)*

KUERT CONCRETE INCORPORATED
3402 Lincolnway W, South Bend, IN 46628
Tel.: (574) 232-9911
Web Site: http://www.kuert.com
Sales Range: $10-24.9 Million
Emp.: 50
Ready Mixed Concrete
N.A.I.C.S.: 327320
Greg Towner *(VP-Ops)*
Steve Fidler *(Pres)*
Tim Miller *(VP-Sls)*
Ron Ericson *(Controller)*

KUGLER COMPANY
PO Box 1748, McCook, NE 69001-1748
Tel.: (308) 345-2280   NE
Web Site:
   http://www.kuglercompany.com
Year Founded: 1956
Sales Range: $10-24.9 Million
Emp.: 120
Farm Supplies
N.A.I.C.S.: 424910
John Kugler *(Co-Pres)*
Mike Kugler *(Co-Pres)*
Diane Kugler *(CEO)*

Subsidiaries:

Kugler Company - Culbertson Production Plant (1)
71748 Railroad Av, Culbertson, NE 69024
Tel.: (308) 278-2436
Fertilizer Mfr
N.A.I.C.S.: 325311

Kugler Company - Rapid City Production Plant (1)
1650 Culvert St, Rapid City, SD 57701
Tel.: (605) 399-2988
Fertilizer Mfr
N.A.I.C.S.: 325311

Kugler Company - Sterling Production Plant (1)
20313 Riverside Dr, Sterling, CO 80751
Tel.: (970) 522-2573
Web Site: http://www.kuglercompany.com
Emp.: 4
Fertilizer Mfr
N.A.I.C.S.: 325311
Diane Kurgler *(Pres)*

Kugler Company - Ulysses Production Plant (1)
795 S Road H, Ulysses, KS 67880
Tel.: (620) 356-4347
Fertilizer Mfr
N.A.I.C.S.: 325311

KUGLER OIL CO.
209 W 3rd St, McCook, NE 69001
Tel.: (308) 345-2280
Web Site:
   http://www.kuglercompany.com
Year Founded: 1924
Sales Range: $25-49.9 Million
Emp.: 100
Fertilizer Mfr
N.A.I.C.S.: 325314
Ron Soden *(Mgr-Specialty Mktg)*
Tom Kohmetscher *(Mgr-Sls-Grower Fertilizer)*
John Beideck *(Mgr-Mktg-K-Lawn)*

KUHIO MOTORS INC.
3033 Aukele St, Lihue, HI 96766
Tel.: (808) 245-6731
Web Site:
   http://www.kuhioautogroup.net
Rev.: $17,100,000
Emp.: 44
Automobiles, New & Used
N.A.I.C.S.: 441110
Carla Matsushima *(Mgr-Sls)*

KUHLKE CONSTRUCTION & ASSOCIATES, INC.
3704 Benchmark Dr, Augusta, GA 30909
Tel.: (706) 650-8722
Web Site: http://www.kcainc.net
Year Founded: 1953
Sales Range: $10-24.9 Million
Emp.: 42
Industrial Building Construction Services
N.A.I.C.S.: 236210
Hank Griffin *(Pres)*
Sylvia Cheek *(CFO)*

KUHLMAN CORPORATION
1845 Indian Wood Cir, Maumee, OH 43537-4072
Tel.: (419) 897-6000   OH
Web Site: http://www.kuhlman-corp.com
Year Founded: 1901
Sales Range: $50-74.9 Million
Emp.: 160
Central-Mixed Concrete Services
N.A.I.C.S.: 327320
Timothy Goligoski *(Pres)*
Ken Kuhlman *(VP)*
Pat Ferry *(Dir-Ops)*

Subsidiaries:

Kuhlman Concrete LLC (1)
2690 Rockfill Rd, Fort Myers, FL 33916
Tel.: (239) 334-3111
Readymix Concrete Mfr
N.A.I.C.S.: 327320

Kuhlman Construction Products, Inc. (1)
999 Swartz Rd, Akron, OH 44319
Tel.: (330) 724-9900
Emp.: 12
Construction Materials Whslr
N.A.I.C.S.: 423320
Jeff Johnston *(Gen Mgr)*

KUHLMAN, INC.
N 56W 16865 Ridgewood Dr Ste 100, Menomonee Falls, WI 53051
Tel.: (262) 252-9400   WI
Web Site:
   http://www.kuhlmaninc.com
Year Founded: 1957
Sales Range: $75-99.9 Million
Emp.: 55
Refrigeration Contracting Services
N.A.I.C.S.: 238220
Ronald Kuhlman *(Pres)*
Dale Kuhlman *(VP)*
Ryan Kuhlman *(Sec)*

KUHN & WITTENBORN, INC.
2405 Grand Blvd Ste 600, Kansas City, MO 64108-2519
Tel.: (816) 471-7888   MO
Web Site: http://www.kuhnwitt.com
Year Founded: 1978
Sales Range: Less than $1 Million
Emp.: 50
N.A.I.C.S.: 541810
Richard S. Kuhn *(Pres & CEO)*
Dale Wittenborn *(Chm & Founding Partner)*
Alan Doan *(Chief Creative Officer & Sr VP)*
Julie Robinson *(COO & Sr VP)*
Lisa Anderson *(Controller)*
Chelsea Purviance *(Acct Exec)*
Shelley Burrus *(Media Dir)*
Margaret Horan *(Sr Dir-Mktg Strategy)*
Randy Robinson *(Dir-Creative)*
Bill Ost *(Exec Dir-Creative)*

KUHN HONDA
3900 W Kennedy Blvd, Tampa, FL 33609
Tel.: (813) 872-4841
Web Site:
   http://www.kuhnhondavw.com
Sales Range: $75-99.9 Million
Emp.: 129
New & Used Car Dealer
N.A.I.C.S.: 441110
Derrick Fish *(Gen Mgr)*

KUHNS & HELLER CUSTOM WINDOW TREATMENTS
1110 Trexlertown Rd, Trexlertown, PA 18087
Tel.: (610) 481-9005
Web Site:
   http://www.kuhnsandheller.com
Year Founded: 1986
Sales Range: $1-9.9 Million
Emp.: 10
Custom Window Treatments
N.A.I.C.S.: 449122
Sandra Kuhns *(Pres & CEO)*

KUHNS EQUIPMENT COMPANY
Hwy 133 E Edge of Town, Arthur, IL 61911
Tel.: (217) 543-2154
Web Site:
   http://www.kuhnsequip.com
Sales Range: $10-24.9 Million
Emp.: 20
Agricultural Machinery & Equipment Mfr
N.A.I.C.S.: 423820
Leanne Wright *(Sec)*

KULBACK'S CONSTRUCTION, INC.
2 Wendling Ct, Lancaster, NY 14086
Tel.: (716) 681-1600
Web Site: http://www.kulbacks.com
Year Founded: 1962
Sales Range: $10-24.9 Million
Emp.: 70
Nonresidential Construction Services
N.A.I.C.S.: 236220
Timothy Kulbacki *(VP-Ops)*

KULESA FAUL INC.
107 S B St Ste 330, San Mateo, CA 94401
Tel.: (650) 340-1979
Web Site: http://www.kulesafaul.com
Year Founded: 2003
Sales Range: $1-9.9 Million
Emp.: 13
Communications, Public Relations, Social Media
N.A.I.C.S.: 541820

Joanna Kulesa (Pres)
Angelique Faul (Principal)
Robin Bulanti (Partner)
Cathy Wright (Mgr-Acct)
Shannon Campbell (Acct Exec)
Kelly Ferguson (Acct Exec)
Steve Eisenstadt (Dir-Content)
Scott Lechner (Dir-Media Rels)
Danielle Salvato-Earl (Supvr-Acct)

KULITE SEMICONDUCTOR PRODUCTS, INC.
1 Willow Tree Rd, Leonia, NJ 07605-2210
Tel.: (201) 461-0900   NJ
Web Site: http://www.kulite.com
Year Founded: 1959
Sales Range: $150-199.9 Million
Emp.: 900
Mfr of Pressure Transducers, Accelerometers & Solid State Strain Gages
N.A.I.C.S.: 334519
Anthony D. Kurtz (CEO)

Subsidiaries:

Kulite Italia, SRL   (1)
Centro Direzionale il Girasole Palazzo Marco Polo, 20084, Lacchiarella, Italy
Tel.: (39) 02 900 30 444
Web Site: http://www.kulite.it
Pressure Transducer Mfr
N.A.I.C.S.: 334519

Kulite Semi-Conductor, GmbH   (1)
Luxemburger Str 5, 67657, Kaiserslautern, Germany
Tel.: (49) 631 5208530 0
Web Site: http://www.kulite.de
Emp.: 750
Pressure Transducer Mfr
N.A.I.C.S.: 334519
Norah Kurtz (Gen Mgr)

Kulite Sensors China, Inc.   (1)
Room 312 Pacheer Commercial Centre 555 Nanjing West Road, Shanghai, 200041, China
Tel.: (86) 21 5213 6085
Web Site: http://www.kulitesensors.com.cn
Pressure Transducer Mfr
N.A.I.C.S.: 334519

Kulite Sensors, Ltd.   (1)
Kulite House Stroudley Road Kingsland Business Park, Basingstoke, RG 24 8UG, Hampshire, United Kingdom
Tel.: (44) 1256 461 646
Web Site: http://www.kulite.com
Emp.: 4
Pressure Transducer Mfr
N.A.I.C.S.: 334519
Alex Winterburn (Mgr-Sls)

KULLMAN BUILDINGS CORP.
1 Kullman Corporate Campus, Lebanon, NJ 08833-2163
Tel.: (908) 236-0220   NJ
Year Founded: 1927
Sales Range: $150-199.9 Million
Emp.: 250
Nonresidential Construction Services
N.A.I.C.S.: 236220
Avi Telyas (Owner & Pres)
Steve Williamson (Supvr-Rigging)

Subsidiaries:

Mark Correctional Systems   (1)
1 Kullman Corp Campus Dr, Lebanon, NJ 08833
Tel.: (908) 236-0220
Sales Range: $10-24.9 Million
Emp.: 120
Mfr of Prefabricated Modular Steel Cells for Correctional Facilities & Infectious Disease Isolation Units for the Medical Market
N.A.I.C.S.: 922140

KUNA MEAT CO, INC.
704 Kuna Industrial Dr, Dupo, IL 62239
Tel.: (618) 286-4000
Web Site: http://www.kunafoodservice.com
Year Founded: 1918
Food Products Distr
N.A.I.C.S.: 424490
Dan Bippen (Owner & Pres)

KUNAU IMPLEMENT CO. INC.
420 White St Hwy 64 W, Preston, IA 52069
Tel.: (563) 689-3311   IA
Web Site: http://www.kunauimplement.com
Year Founded: 1948
Sales Range: $10-24.9 Million
Emp.: 30
Whslr of Agricultural Machinery
N.A.I.C.S.: 423820
Dick Kunau (VP)
Todd Ganzer (Mgr-Svc)

KUNDELL COMMUNICATIONS, INC.
210 W 89 St, New York, NY 10024
Tel.: (212) 877-2798
Web Site: http://www.kundellcommunications.com
Sales Range: Less than $1 Million
Emp.: 1
Public Relations Agency
N.A.I.C.S.: 541820
Linda R. Kundell (Pres)

KUNDERT MOTORS INC.
140 State Rt 17, Hasbrouck Heights, NJ 07604
Tel.: (201) 288-8984   NJ
Web Site: http://www.kundertvolvo.com
Year Founded: 1956
Sales Range: $50-74.9 Million
Emp.: 450
Sales of New & Used Automobiles
N.A.I.C.S.: 441110
William Mark Kundert (Pres)

KUNDINGER FLUID POWER, INC.
1771 Harmon Rd, Auburn Hills, MI 48326
Tel.: (248) 391-6100   MI
Web Site: http://www.kundinger.com
Year Founded: 1961
Sales Range: $10-24.9 Million
Emp.: 25
Products & Services to the Process, Control & Instrumentation Markets
N.A.I.C.S.: 423840
John Leece (VP-Fin Ops)
Brian Kundinger (Pres)

KUNES CHEVROLET
1231 E Geneva St, Delavan, WI 53115
Tel.: (262) 728-9163
Web Site: http://www.kuneschevrolet.com
Year Founded: 1977
Sales Range: $10-24.9 Million
Emp.: 45
Car Whslr
N.A.I.C.S.: 441110
Timothy Keithley (Mgr-Collision Center)
Bill Ederer (Gen Mgr)

KUNES' COUNTRY FORD-LINCOLN-MERCURY, INC.
1234 E Geneva St, Delavan, WI 53115
Tel.: (262) 728-5544
Web Site: http://www.fordlincoln.com
Sales Range: $10-24.9 Million
Emp.: 55
Car Whslr
N.A.I.C.S.: 441110

Gregg Kunes (Pres)
Tony Wheatley (Gen Mgr)

KUNI HONDA
10750 E Arapahoe Rd, Centennial, CO 80112-3823
Tel.: (303) 708-2000
Web Site: http://www.kuni-honda.com
Year Founded: 2002
Sales Range: $10-24.9 Million
Emp.: 100
Car Whslr
N.A.I.C.S.: 441110
Chris Zimmerman (Dir-Svc)

KUNKEL MILLER & HAMENT
Orange Professional Ctr 235 N Orange Ave Ste 200, Sarasota, FL 34236
Tel.: (941) 365-6006
Web Site: http://www.kmhlaborlaw.com
Sales Range: $1-9.9 Million
Emp.: 14
Law firm
N.A.I.C.S.: 541110
John M. Hament (Pres & Atty)
Michael R. Miller (Atty)
Nikhil N. Joshi (Atty)
Jennifer Fowler-Hermes (Atty)
Torben S. Madson III (Atty)

KUNKLE REALTY, LLC
3960 Radio Rd Ste 101, Naples, FL 34104
Tel.: (239) 280-0222
Web Site: http://www.kunklerealty.com
Sales Range: $1-9.9 Million
Real Estate Broker
N.A.I.C.S.: 531210
Wes Kunkle (Pres)

KUNO OIL COMPANY INC.
5830 County Route Rd, Canton, NY 13617
Tel.: (315) 386-1000
Sales Range: $10-24.9 Million
Emp.: 10
Distr of Petroleum Products
N.A.I.C.S.: 424720
Steve Kuno (Pres)

KUNTZMAN TRUCKING INC.
13515 Oyster Rd, Alliance, OH 44601
Tel.: (330) 821-9160
Web Site: http://www.kmantrucking.com
Sales Range: $10-24.9 Million
Emp.: 43
Local Trucking without Storage
N.A.I.C.S.: 484110
Kenneth Boatright (Pres)

KUPER REALTY CORP.
6606 N New Braunfels Ave, San Antonio, TX 78209
Tel.: (210) 822-8602   TX
Web Site: http://www.kuperrealty.com
Year Founded: 1962
Sales Range: $1-9.9 Million
Emp.: 75
Offices of Real Estate Agents & Brokers
N.A.I.C.S.: 531210
Dennis Tottenham (CFO)
Brianne Alston (Controller)

Subsidiaries:

Amelia Bullock Realtors, Inc.   (1)
8008 Spicewood Ln Ste 100, Austin, TX 78759
Tel.: (512) 345-2100
Sales Range: $1-9.9 Million
Offices of Real Estate Agents & Brokers
N.A.I.C.S.: 531210

Amelia Bullock (Pres)
Marisa Phillips (Dir-Mktg)

KUPPER CHEVROLET, INC.
1500 2nd St NE, Mandan, ND 58554
Tel.: (701) 663-9851   ND
Web Site: http://www.kupper-chevrolet.com
Sales Range: $50-74.9 Million
Emp.: 125
New & Used Car Dealers
N.A.I.C.S.: 441110
Robert Kupper (Owner)

KURANI INCORPORATED
210 Ctr Ct, Anchorage, AK 99518
Tel.: (907) 562-2205
Rev.: $23,000,000
Emp.: 8
Pizzeria Operator
N.A.I.C.S.: 722513
Kurban Kurani (Pres)

KUREIJI, INC.
1945 Rosemead Blvd, South El Monte, CA 91733
Tel.: (626) 788-2657
Web Site: http://www.threadtank.com
Year Founded: 2014
Sales Range: $1-9.9 Million
Apparel Accessory Retailer
N.A.I.C.S.: 458110
Jason Mark (Dir-Fin & Ops)

KURMAN COMMUNICATIONS, INC.
345 N Canal St Ste 1404, Chicago, IL 60606-1366
Tel.: (312) 651-9000   IL
Web Site: http://www.kurman.com
Year Founded: 1983
Sales Range: Less than $1 Million
Emp.: 8
Public Relations Agency
N.A.I.C.S.: 541820
Lee A. Barrie (VP)
Cindy Kurman Barrie (Pres & CEO)
Steve Ringel (Dir-Southeast)

KURT J. LESKER COMPANY
1925 Route 51, Jefferson Hills, PA 15025
Tel.: (412) 387-9200   PA
Web Site: http://www.lesker.com
Year Founded: 1954
Vacuum Components Mfr & Distr
N.A.I.C.S.: 335999
Kurt J. Lesker (Pres)
John A. Ross (Treas)
Cynthia B. Lesker (VP)

KURT MANUFACTURING CO. INC.
5280 Main St NE, Minneapolis, MN 55421-1544
Tel.: (763) 572-1500   MN
Web Site: http://www.kurt.com
Year Founded: 1946
Sales Range: $150-199.9 Million
Emp.: 500
Precision Machine Shop; Fabricated Metal Products; Machine Tools & Accessories, Measuring Devices
N.A.I.C.S.: 332999

Subsidiaries:

Kurt Manufacturing Co. Inc. - Kurt Engineered Systems Division   (1)
9445 E River Rd NW, Minneapolis, MN 55433
Tel.: (763) 574-8309
Web Site: http://www.kurt.com
Emp.: 50
Industrial Supplies Whslr
N.A.I.C.S.: 423840
Steve Carlson (Exec VP)

KURT MANUFACTURING CO. INC.

Kurt Manufacturing Co. Inc.—(Continued)

Kurt Manufacturing Co. Inc. - Kurt Hydraulics Division (1)
302 Jeffers Ave, Lyman, NE 69352
Tel.: (308) 787-0127
Web Site: http://www.kurthydraulics.com
Emp.: 100
Hydraulic Hose Mfr
N.A.I.C.S.: 326220

Kurt Manufacturing Co. Inc. - Kurt Industrial Products Division (1)
1325 Quincy St NE, Minneapolis, MN 55413
Tel.: (763) 574-8309
Industrial Machinery Mfr
N.A.I.C.S.: 333248

Kurt Manufacturing Co. Inc. - Kurt Kinetic Division (1)
5280 Main St NE, Minneapolis, MN 55421
Web Site: http://www.kurtkinetic.com
Athletic Goods Mfr
N.A.I.C.S.: 339920

Kurt Manufacturing Co. Inc. - Kurt Machining Division (1)
32500 Excellence Ave, Pueblo, CO 81001
Tel.: (719) 948-4477
Industrial Machinery Mfr
N.A.I.C.S.: 333248

Kurt Manufacturing Co. Inc. - Kurt Manufacturing Corporate, Gear, and Machining Division (1)
5280 Main St NE, Minneapolis, MN 55421
Tel.: (763) 572-1500
Precision Gear Mfr
N.A.I.C.S.: 333517
Steve Carlsen (Pres)

Kurt Manufacturing Co. Inc. - Kurt Screw Machining and Hydraulics Divisions (1)
302 Jeffers Ave, Lyman, NE 69352
Tel.: (308) 787-1211
Industrial Supplies Whslr
N.A.I.C.S.: 423840
Steve Carlsen (Pres)

KURT ORBAN PARTNERS, LLC
111 Anza Blvd Ste 350, Burlingame, CA 94010
Tel.: (650) 579-3959 CA
Web Site: http://www.kurtorbanpartners.com
Sales Range: $10-24.9 Million
Emp.: 12
Specialty Steel Trading Services
N.A.I.C.S.: 423510
Matt Orban (Pres)
Veronica King (CFO & COO)
Mark Bordelon (Mgr-Pur & Inventory)
Yi Dong (Reg Mgr-Sls)

KURT S. ADLER, INC.
7 W 34th St Ste 100, New York, NY 10001
Tel.: (212) 924-0900 NY
Web Site: http://www.kurtadler.com
Year Founded: 1946
Sales Range: $75-99.9 Million
Emp.: 85
Nondurable Goods
N.A.I.C.S.: 424990
Ruth Petway (Project Coord-Creative)
Jim Strempel (Mgr-Mdse)
Melanie Velez (Coord-Mktg)

KURT WEISS GREENHOUSES INC.
95 Main St, Center Moriches, NY 11934-1703
Tel.: (631) 878-2500 NY
Web Site: http://www.kurtweiss.com
Year Founded: 1972
Sales Range: $10-24.9 Million
Emp.: 250
Greenhouse Operator
N.A.I.C.S.: 111422

Russell Weiss (Pres)
Kirk Weiss (VP-Production)
Wayne Weiss (VP-Ops)
Subsidiaries:

Kurt Weiss Greenhouses of Connecticut Inc. (1)
301 E Johnson Ave, Cheshire, CT 06410-1269 (100%)
Tel.: (203) 272-3061
Web Site: http://www.kurtweiss.com
Sales Range: $10-24.9 Million
Emp.: 10
Operator of Greenhouses
N.A.I.C.S.: 111422

Kurt Weiss of NJ, Inc. (1)
350 White Horse Pike, Waterford Works, NJ 08089
Tel.: (856) 767-3822
Floriculture Production Services
N.A.I.C.S.: 111422

Kurt Weiss of Pennsylvania, Inc. (1)
225 Arcos Rd, Mount Carmel, PA 17851
Tel.: (570) 339-5650
Floriculture Production Services
N.A.I.C.S.: 111422
Eric Kuijpers (Mgr)

KURTIS CHEVROLET, INC.
5369 Hwy 70 W, Morehead City, NC 28557
Tel.: (252) 726-8128
Web Site: http://www.kurtischevrolet.com
Year Founded: 1972
Sales Range: $10-24.9 Million
Emp.: 38
New Car Dealers
N.A.I.C.S.: 441110
Steve Tell (Mgr-Fin)
Carl Austin (Mgr-Sls)
Alan Carpenter (Mgr-Customer Care)
Karen Harden (Mgr-Parts)

KURTZ BROS. INC.
6415 Granger Rd, Cleveland, OH 44131
Tel.: (216) 986-7000
Web Site: http://www.kurtz-bros.com
Sales Range: $10-24.9 Million
Emp.: 167
Whslr of Lumber & Plywood, Soil & Concrete Products
N.A.I.C.S.: 423310
John T. Kurtz (Pres)
Thomas Kurtz (VP)
Faith Paulchell (Sec)

KURTZ BROS., INC.
400 Reed St, Clearfield, PA 16830-2540
Tel.: (814) 765-6561 PA
Web Site: http://www.kurtzbros.com
Year Founded: 1894
Sales Range: $100-124.9 Million
Emp.: 153
Mfr & Distributor of School Supplies, Advertising Specialties & Commercial Printing Supplies
N.A.I.C.S.: 322120
Jim Carns (Mgr-Pur & Traffic)
Dave Von Gunden (CFO)
Jeff Pistner (Mgr-Mktg)
Monty Kunes (Pres & CEO)

KURZ ELECTRIC SOLUTIONS INC.
1325 McMahon Dr, Neenah, WI 54956
Tel.: (920) 734-5644
Web Site: http://www.kurz.com
Sales Range: $10-24.9 Million
Emp.: 50
Motors & Electric Parts Distr
N.A.I.C.S.: 423610

Rick Nowak (Pres)
Bob Brost (VP)
Kenneth Gardner (Mgr)

KUSHNER COMPANIES
26 Columbia Tpke, Florham Park, NJ 07932-2213
Tel.: (973) 822-0050
Web Site: http://www.kushnercompanies.com
Sales Range: $50-74.9 Million
Emp.: 500
Real Estate Company
N.A.I.C.S.: 236115
Charles Kushner (Chm)
Sandra Hicks (Dir-HR)
Subsidiaries:

Westminster Management (1)
18 Columbia Tpke, Florham Park, NJ 07932-2213
Tel.: (973) 822-0050
Sales Range: $10-24.9 Million
Emp.: 80
Property Management
N.A.I.C.S.: 531110

KUSTOM GROUP
3 Carbon Way, Richwood, KY 41094
Tel.: (859) 485-8600
Web Site: http://www.kustomgroup.com
Year Founded: 1989
Varnishes
N.A.I.C.S.: 325998
Michael E. Gerkin (Owner)

KUSTOM US, INC.
265 Hunt Park Cv, Longwood, FL 32750
Tel.: (407) 965-1940
Web Site: http://www.kustom.us
Year Founded: 1968
Sales Range: $1-9.9 Million
Emp.: 18
Custom Sheet Metal Mfr
N.A.I.C.S.: 332322
Sarah Try (Controller)
Jeremy Howe (Dir-Project)
Andrew Zavodney Jr. (Pres & CEO)
Subsidiaries:

Abracadabra Restoration, Inc. (1)
4814 N Shamrock Pl, Tucson, AZ 85705
Tel.: (520) 323-3261
Web Site: http://www.abrarest.com
Sales Range: $1-9.9 Million
Emp.: 25
Water & Fire Damage Restoration Services
N.A.I.C.S.: 624230
Travis Christensen (Pres)

KUTAK ROCK LLP
1650 Farnam St The Omaha Bldg, Omaha, NE 68102-2186
Tel.: (402) 346-6000 NE
Web Site: http://www.kutakrock.com
Year Founded: 1965
Sales Range: $150-199.9 Million
Emp.: 501
Legal Advisory Services
N.A.I.C.S.: 541110
Jennifer L. Andrews (Co-Partner)
Michael W. Alvano (Co-Partner)
Danielle J. Amorena-Kenny (Co-Partner)
Beth M. Ascher (Co-Partner)
Steven P. Amen (Co-Partner)
Eric Bergquist (Partner)
Theresa M. Bima-Reeves (Partner)
Tory M. Bishop (Partner)
Richard K. Bonness (Partner)
Brian C. Buescher (Partner)
Patricia A. Burdyny (Partner)
Brent C. Burmood (Partner)
Kevin E. Burr (Partner)
Michael K. Bydalek (Partner)
Kasey M. Cappellano (Partner)

Whitney Arnot Kopicky (Partner)
Mark J. Maichel (Partner)
Ellen K. O'Brien (Partner)
Kristine L. Poston (Partner)
Meredith R. Riley (Partner)
Allison Swenson (Partner)
Kelley Sucher (Partner)
Leslie Powell (Partner)
Nicole Moriarty (Partner)
Hilary Jackler (Mng Partner-Washington & Richmond)
John L. Petr (Chm)
Adam Baird (Mng Partner-Spokane)
Paul S. Gerding Jr. (Mng Partner-Scottsdale)

KUTCHINS, ROBBINS & DIAMOND, LTD.
1101 Perimeter Dr Ste 760, Schaumburg, IL 60173
Tel.: (847) 240-1040
Web Site: http://www.krdcpas.com
Accounting Firm
N.A.I.C.S.: 541219
Howard P. Bakrins (Dir-Tax)
Lauren Clawson (Dir-Bus Svcs)
Robert S. Jacobson (Dir-Tax)
Subsidiaries:

Popowcer Katten Ltd. (1)
35 E Wacker Dr Ste 1550, Chicago, IL 60601
Tel.: (312) 201-6450
Accounting Services
N.A.I.C.S.: 541219

KUTIR, CORP.
37600 Central Ct Ste 280, Newark, CA 94560
Tel.: (510) 402-4526 CA
Web Site: http://www.kutirtech.com
Year Founded: 2003
Sales Range: $1-9.9 Million
Emp.: 40
Computer System Design Services
N.A.I.C.S.: 541512
Gerry Ignatius (Pres)
Prathiba Kalyan (VP-Delivery & Strategy)

KUVARE US HOLDINGS, INC.
55 W Monroe St Ste 1930, Chicago, IL 60603
Tel.: (312) 276-5200
Web Site: http://www.kuvare.com
Year Founded: 2014
Holding Company; Insurance & Annuity Products & Services
N.A.I.C.S.: 551112
Dhiren Jhaveri (CEO)
Carlos Sierra (COO)
Erik Braun (Controller)
David A Goldberg (Gen Counsel)
Brad Rosenblatt (Chief Revenue Officer)
Kevin Hovi (CFO)
Ann Mengelson-Clark (VP-Transformation & Tech)
Subsidiaries:

Guaranty Income Life Insurance Company (1)
929 Government St, Baton Rouge, LA 70802-6034
Tel.: (225) 383-0355
Web Site: http://www.gilico.com
Rev: $66,445,000
Assets: $503,700,000
Liabilities: $447,824,000
Net Worth: $55,876,000
Earnings: $5,436,000
Fiscal Year-end: 12/31/2016
Life Insurance
N.A.I.C.S.: 524113
Deborah Tatro (Sr VP-Bus Dev & Compliance)
Joy Lee (VP-Sls)
Terry Ezell (VP-Ops)

COMPANIES

Ann Mengelson-Clark (VP-Transformation & Tech)
Joe Wieser (Pres & CEO)
Steven Fry (CFO)

United Life Insurance Company (1)
118 2nd Ave SE, Cedar Rapids, IA 52401 (100%)
Tel.: (319) 399-5700
Web Site: http://www.unitedlife.com
Life Insurance Carrier
N.A.I.C.S.: 524113
Brad Rosenblatt (Pres)

KUYKENDALL & POWELL OIL CO.
1603 17th St, Tuscaloosa, AL 35401
Tel.: (205) 752-5555
Sales Range: $10-24.9 Million
Emp.: 8
Petroleum Bulk Stations
N.A.I.C.S.: 424710
Edie Evans (Sec)
Evertte C. Powell III (Owner & Pres)

KUYKENDALL GARDNER
1560 N Orange Ave Ste 750, Winter Park, FL 32789
Tel.: (407) 894-5431   FL
Web Site: http://www.kgbroker.com
Year Founded: 1953
Sales Range: $1-9.9 Million
Emp.: 40
Insurance & Risk Management Brokerage Services; Human Resource & PEO Consulting Services
N.A.I.C.S.: 524210
John Kuykendall (Pres)
Bobby Kuykendall (Exec VP)
Christopher Gardner (CEO)

KV MART CO.
522 East Vermont Ave, Anaheim, CA 92805
Tel.: (310) 816-0200
Web Site: http://www.kvmart.com
Rev.: $260,000,000
Emp.: 1,300
Supermarket Operator
N.A.I.C.S.: 445110
Darioush Khaledi (Chm & CEO)
Paul Vazin (Pres)
Greg Sproul (CFO & Sr VP)

Subsidiaries:

Valu Mart Co. (1)
522 E Vermont Ave, Anaheim, CA 92805
Tel.: (310) 816-0200
Web Site: http://www.kvmartco.com
Rev.: $11,000,000
Emp.: 20
Supermarket
N.A.I.C.S.: 445110
Paul Vezin (Pres)
Greg Spourl (CFO)

KVC DEVELOPMENT, INC.
8923 E Mission Ave 135, Spokane, WA 99212
Tel.: (509) 928-6848   WA
Web Site: http://www.kvcdevelopments.com
Year Founded: 1994
Sales Range: $10-24.9 Million
Emp.: 7
Land Subdividers & Developers, Commercial
N.A.I.C.S.: 237210
Kent Clausen (Pres)

KVIE, INC.
2030 W El Camino Ave, Sacramento, CA 95833
Tel.: (916) 929-5843   CA
Web Site: http://www.kvie.org
Year Founded: 1955
Sales Range: $10-24.9 Million
Emp.: 115
Television Broadcasting Services

N.A.I.C.S.: 516120
David Lowe (Pres & Gen Mgr)
Julia Jenness (Chm)
James Beckwith (Vice Chm)
James E. Beckwith (Vice Chm)

KVL AUDIO VISUAL SERVICES
200 Corporate Blvd S, Yonkers, NY 10701
Tel.: (914) 479-3300
Web Site: http://www.kvlav.com
Year Founded: 1976
Sales Range: $25-49.9 Million
Emp.: 200
Audio-Visual Equipment & Supply Rental
N.A.I.C.S.: 532289
Les L. Lieberman (Pres & CEO)
Bruce Katin-Borland (Exec VP)
Nick Prignano (CFO)
Bob McKiernan (VP & Mgr-Ops)

Subsidiaries:

Design & Installation Division (1)
466 Saw Mill River Rd, Ardsley, NY 10502
Tel.: (914) 479-3300
Web Site: http://www.kvlav.com
Sales Range: $10-24.9 Million
Emp.: 30
Audio Visual System Design & Installation Services
N.A.I.C.S.: 334310
Bruce Borland (Mng Dir)

Event Staging Division (1)
466 Saw Mill River Rd, Ardsley, NY 10502
Tel.: (914) 479-3300
Web Site: http://www.kvlav.com
Sales Range: $25-49.9 Million
Emp.: 30
Event Management Services
N.A.I.C.S.: 711320
Leslei Berman (Pres)

KW 1 ACQUISITION CO. LLC
13600 Brookpark Rd, Cleveland, OH 44135
Tel.: (216) 916-6000
Web Site: http://www.metrolexus.com
Sales Range: $125-149.9 Million
Emp.: 150
Automobiles, New & Used
N.A.I.C.S.: 441110
Wendy Bell (Controller)
John Spearry (Gen Mgr)

KW ASSOCIATES LLC
825 Bluff Rd, Columbia, SC 29201
Tel.: (803) 799-5490
Year Founded: 2001
Sales Range: $25-49.9 Million
Emp.: 200
Beer & Ale
N.A.I.C.S.: 424810
Gene E. Williams (CEO)
Josh Rogers (Mgr-Sls)

KW FUELS INC.
717 W Sanger St, Hobbs, NM 88240
Tel.: (575) 393-5135
Rev.: $10,000,000
Emp.: 10
Petroleum Products
N.A.I.C.S.: 424720
Mike W. Pearson (Pres)

KW LEASING INC.
1050 Skillman Dr, Cincinnati, OH 45215
Tel.: (513) 771-2345
Web Site: http://www.carpetone.com
Sales Range: $10-24.9 Million
Emp.: 60
Carpets
N.A.I.C.S.: 449121
Ken Weisbacher (Chm)
Steve Contois (VP)
Michelle Gardner (Controller)

Subsidiaries:

Carpetland Inc (1)
1050 Skillman Dr, Cincinnati, OH 45215
Tel.: (513) 771-2345
Web Site: http://www.carpetlandcincinnati.com
Sales Range: $10-24.9 Million
Carpet Installation Services
N.A.I.C.S.: 238330
Steve Contois (VP-Sls)
Winfield Baird (Chm)
Paul C. Wesch (Dir-Fin)

KW PLASTICS
1 Sanders Rd, Troy, AL 36079
Tel.: (334) 566-1563
Web Site: http://www.kwplastics.com
Rev.: $84,000,000
Emp.: 46
Polypropylene Distr
N.A.I.C.S.: 326113
Russell Liles Liles (Controller)
Brian McDaniels (Dir-Natl Sls)

KW PROPERTY MANAGEMENT, LLC
8200 NW 33rd St Ste 300, Miami, FL 33122
Tel.: (305) 476-9188
Web Site: http://www.kwpropertymanagement.com
Sales Range: $100-124.9 Million
Emp.: 650
Property Management & Consulting Services
N.A.I.C.S.: 531311
Paul Kaplan (Mng Dir)
Robert White (Mng Dir)
Andy Meyrowitz (Exec Dir)
Katalina Cruz (Mng Dir-Ops)
Kelly Vickers (Mgr-Bus Dev)
Regan Marock (Exec Dir)
Sandra Bennett (Exec Dir)
Jane Bracken (Dir-Bus Dev)
Trycia Arencibia (Mng Dir-Fin & Tech)
Kevin Ellis (Mgr-Bus Dev-Tampa)
Andy Kalikas (VP-Southwest Florida)
Paul Hemmert (VP-Tampa, Orlando & Jacksonville)
Zuly Maribona (Sr VP)

KWE PARTNERS, INC.
1581 Brickell Ave Ste 1103, Miami, FL 33129
Tel.: (305) 476-5424   NY
Web Site: http://www.kwegroup.com
Sales Range: $1-9.9 Million
Emp.: 4
Public Relations Agency
N.A.I.C.S.: 541820
Karen Weiner Escalera (Pres)

KWGC, INC. ADVERTISING & DESIGN
7616 LBJ Freeway Ste 100, Dallas, TX 75251
Tel.: (214) 987-4377   TX
Web Site: http://www.kwgc.com
Year Founded: 1985
Rev.: $15,000,000
Emp.: 12
N.A.I.C.S.: 541810
Kay Williams (Chm & Dir-Creative)
Denise Boyde (Dir-HR)

KWIAT INC.
555 Madison Ave, New York, NY 10022
Tel.: (212) 223-1111
Web Site: http://www.kwiat.com
Year Founded: 1907
Sales Range: $10-24.9 Million
Emp.: 25
Jewelry Mfr
N.A.I.C.S.: 423940

Subsidiaries:
Lowell Kwiat (Chm)
Greg Kwiat (CEO)

KWIK TRIP INC.
1626 Oak St, La Crosse, WI 54602
Tel.: (608) 781-8988   WI
Web Site: http://www.kwiktrip.com
Year Founded: 1965
Sales Range: $1-4.9 Billion
Emp.: 8,000
Convenience Store, Gas Station & Restaurant Owner & Operator
N.A.I.C.S.: 457120
Gary Gonczy (Dir-Mktg & Adv)
Mark Christianson (Mgr-Retail Efficiencies)
Bruce Bingham (Mgr-Network Svcs)
Erik Peterson (Dir-Store Engrg)
Jon Laschenski (Dir-Dairy Ops)
Carl Klemp (Engr-HVAC)
Teresa Clark (Project Mgr-Mktg)
Bradley Clarkin (Superintendent-Warehouse)
Steve Loehr (VP)
Ray Monroe (Dir-Commissary)
Randy Hanson (Mgr-Retail Acctg)

Subsidiaries:

Stop-N-Go of Madison Inc. (1)
2934 Fish Hatchery Rd, Madison, WI 53713-5015
Tel.: (608) 271-4433
Web Site: http://www.stop-n-go.com
Operate Gasoline Service Stations
N.A.I.C.S.: 457120
Andrew Bowman (VP)
Bill Ripley (Dir-Mktg)

KWIK-SET FASTENERS, INC.
1151 Commercial Dr, Lexington, KY 40505
Tel.: (859) 252-7518
Web Site: http://www.kwik-set.com
Rev.: $11,114,759
Emp.: 49
Commercial Fasteners & Power Tools Whslr & Tool Repair Services
N.A.I.C.S.: 444140
Ashley Gaines (Office Mgr)
Richard Maher (VP)

KWITTKEN & COMPANY
360 Lexington Ave 15th Fl, New York, NY 10017
Tel.: (646) 277-7111
Sales Range: $10-24.9 Million
Emp.: 22
Advetising Agency
N.A.I.C.S.: 541810
Aaron R. Kwittken (CEO & Mng Partner)
Jason Schlossberg (Pres & Partner)
Gabrielle Zucker Acevedo (Mng Dir & Partner)
Ellie Jones Rossi (Mng Dir)
Kailyn Derck (Sr Acct Exec)
Jim Gorman (Mng Dir)
Will Nikosey (Acct Supvr)
Russell Weigandt (Dir)
Elliot Schimel (Sr Acct Supvr)

KWM BEACH MANUFACTURING CO INC.
4655 Urbana Rd, Springfield, OH 45502
Tel.: (937) 399-3838
Web Site: http://www.kwmbeach.com
Sales Range: $50-74.9 Million
Emp.: 65
Motor Vehicle Parts & Accessories
N.A.I.C.S.: 336390
William R. Beach (CEO)
Bret T. Beach (Pres)

KYANA PACKAGING & INDUSTRIAL SUPPLY, INC.

KYANA PACKAGING & INDUSTRIAL SUPPLY, INC.

U.S. PRIVATE

Kyana Packaging & Industrial Supply, Inc.—(Continued)
2501 Ampere Dr, Louisville, KY 40299
Tel.: (502) 992-3333
Web Site: http://www.kyanaind.com
Sales Range: $10-24.9 Million
Emp.: 32
Industrial Supplies Whslr
N.A.I.C.S.: 423840
Kimberly A. Osborne (CFO)

KYANITE MINING CORPORATION
30 Willis Mtn Ln, Dillwyn, VA 23936
Tel.: (434) 983-2085   VA
Web Site: http://www.kyanite.com
Year Founded: 1932
Sales Range: $150-199.9 Million
Emp.: 150
Refractory Ceramic Additive Kyanite & Mullite Services
N.A.I.C.S.: 212323
Hank Jamerson (VP-Sls & Mktg)
Guy B. Dixon (Pres & Gen Mgr)
Dilip C. Jain (VP-Tech & Asia Sls)
Barry Jones (VP-Ops)
Lakshmi Bertram (Mgr-HR)

Subsidiaries:
Cavalier Hotel Corp.   (1)
42nd St Atlantic Ave, Virginia Beach, VA 23451   (100%)
Tel.: (757) 425-8555
Web Site: http://www.cavalierhotel.com
Sales Range: $25-49.9 Million
Hotel
N.A.I.C.S.: 721110
Christopher Castle (Dir-Food & Beverage)

KYBURZ-CARLSON CONSTRUCTION
729 Circle Dr, Aberdeen, SD 57401-2618
Tel.: (605) 225-6161
Web Site: http://www.kyburzcarlson.com
Sales Range: $10-24.9 Million
Emp.: 50
Nonresidential Construction Services
N.A.I.C.S.: 236220
Steve Halvorsen (Pres)
Laure Swanson (VP)
Henry Carlson III (Owner)

KYK ADVERTISING MARKETING PROMOTIONS
2600 Constant Comment Pl, Louisville, KY 40299
Tel.: (502) 636-0288
Web Site: http://www.kykmarketing.com
Year Founded: 1980
Rev: $25,000,000
Emp.: 22
Advetising Agency
N.A.I.C.S.: 541810
Jack Hagerty (Pres)
Tim Wolf (CFO)
Mark Stivers (Dir-Creative)
Kelli Simpson (Dir-Media)
Steve Coburn (Mgr-Production)
Paul Plaschke (Mgr-Sls)

KYLE CONTI CONSTRUCTION, L.L.C.
749 Clawson Ave, Hillsborough, NJ 08844
Tel.: (908) 369-5100
Web Site: http://www.kconticonstruction.com
Year Founded: 2000
Sales Range: $10-24.9 Million
Emp.: 30
Highway, Street & Bridge Construction Services
N.A.I.C.S.: 237310
Kyle Conti (Pres)
Paul Thomson (VP)

KYLE ENTERPRISES LLC
120 S Wright St, Delavan, WI 53115
Tel.: (262) 249-8705
Web Site: http://www.mymillennium.us
Year Founded: 2003
Sales Range: $25-49.9 Million
Electrical Communication Equipment Distr
N.A.I.C.S.: 423690
James Kyle (Founder & CEO)
Kyle Kulow (VP-Bus Dev)
Nate Wendt (VP-Ops-Core Bus)

KYMETA CORPORATION
12277 134th Ct NE Ste 100, Redmond, WA 98052
Tel.: (425) 896-3700
Web Site: http://www.kymetacorp.com
Year Founded: 2012
Sales Range: $10-24.9 Million
Emp.: 110
Satellite Communication System & Antennas Mfr
N.A.I.C.S.: 334290
Nathan Kundtz (Founder)
Hakan Olsson (VP-Maritime)
Bob Shuman (VP-Bus Dev)
Lisa Dreher (Dir-Mktg)
Bill Marks (Chief Comml Officer & Exec VP)
Jonas Nicholson (VP-Engrg & Product Dev)
David Geiling (VP-Sls-Asia Pacific)
Rash Jhanjee (VP-Sls-Europe, Middle East & Africa)
Steve Sybeldon (VP-Bus Dev & Sls-North & South America)
Paul Mattear (VP-Bus Dev & Sls-Govt)
Scott Glass (Dir-Sls-North America)
David Harrower (Sr VP-Global Sls)
Jon Maron (VP-Mktg & Comm)
Walter Z. Berger (Pres & COO)
Brenda Kuhns (Sr Dir-Mktg)
Stewart Douglas Hutcheson (Exec Chm & CEO)

Subsidiaries:
Lepton Global Solutions LLC   (1)
8381 Old Courthouse Rd Ste 200, Reston, VA 22182
Tel.: (571) 313-1256
Web Site: http://www.leptonglobal.com
Satellite Telecommunications
N.A.I.C.S.: 517410
James Ramsey (CEO)
Isabel LeBoutillier (Mng Partner)
Rob Weitendorf (Mng Partner)

KYNER'S AUTO SALES, INC.
2040 Lincoln Way E, Chambersburg, PA 17202
Tel.: (717) 261-1511
Web Site: http://www.kynersauto.com
Sales Range: $10-24.9 Million
Emp.: 52
New & Used Car Dealer
N.A.I.C.S.: 441110
Shawn Haupt (Gen Mgr)
Teresa Keckler (Office Mgr)
John Kyner Jr. (Pres)

KYNETIC LLC
225 Washington St, Conshohocken, PA 19428
Tel.: (610) 825-2079
Web Site: http://www.kynetic.com
Year Founded: 2011
Sales Range: $750-799.9 Million
Emp.: 1,000
Sports Merchandise Retailer
N.A.I.C.S.: 459110
Michael G. Rubin (Founder & CEO)
Michael R. Conn (CFO)
Daniel J. Winters (Gen Counsel & Sec)
Saj Cherian (VP)
Brian L. Miles (VP-Fin)
Jonathan S. Schoenfeld (Deputy Gen Counsel)
Doug Mack (CEO)
Kevin Brandis (Controller)
Steve Davis (CEO)

Subsidiaries:
Fanatics, Inc.   (1)
8100 Nations Way, Jacksonville, FL 32256
Tel.: (904) 421-1897
Web Site: https://www.footballfanatics.com
Sales Range: $450-499.9 Million
Emp.: 18,000
Clothing & Clothing Accessories Retailers
N.A.I.C.S.: 458110
Deborah Crawford (Sr VP & Head-IR)
Brian Swallow (VP-Strategy & Bus Dev)
Orlando D. Ashford (Chief People Officer)
Raphael Peck (Pres-Fanatics Branded)
Chris Orton (Chief Mktg & Revenue Officer)
Matt Madrigal (CTO)
Lonnie Phillips (VP-Ops)
Tucker Kain (Chief Strategy &Growth Officer)
Glen Giovanucci (VP-Retail Sls-Fanatics Branded-San Mateo)
Glenn H. Schiffman (CFO)
Jason White (CMO-Betting & Gaming)
Krishna Rao (CFO-Commerce)
Glenn H. Schiffman (CFO)

Subsidiary (Domestic):
Fansedge Incorporated   (2)
8100 Nations Way, Jacksonville, FL 32256
Tel.: (877) 965-3955
Web Site: http://www.fansedge.com
Sports Licensed Products Retailer
N.A.I.C.S.: 459110
Ryan Donovan (VP-Mktg)

Subsidiary (Non-US):
Kitbag Limited   (2)
Greengate, Manchester, M24 1FD, United Kingdom
Tel.: (44) 345 408 4345
Web Site: http://www.kitbag.com
Online Sports Equipment & Clothes Distr
N.A.I.C.S.: 423910

Subsidiary (Domestic):
Mounted Memories, Inc.   (2)
333 E Las Oblas Blvd Ste 300, Fort Lauderdale, FL 33301
Tel.: (866) 236-2541
Web Site: http://www.mountedmemories.com
Sports Memorabilia Mfr & Distr
N.A.I.C.S.: 423910
Mitch Adelstein (Pres)

Pro Sports Memorabilia, Inc.   (2)
725 Landwehr Rd, Northbrook, IL 60062
Tel.: (800) 689-2001
Web Site: http://www.prosportsmemorabilia.com
Licensed Sports Products Retailer
N.A.I.C.S.: 459110
Stefan Tesoriero (CEO)
Michael Gallucci (VP-Ops)
Keith Zimmerman (CTO)
Cassandra Wesch (VP-Mktg)
Jane Tesoriero (Mgr- Customer Svc & Ops)
Andres Yepez (Mgr-Mktg)

Star Struck/ProTeam, Inc.   (2)
2 Turnage Ln, Bethel, CT 06801
Tel.: (203) 794-1655
Web Site: http://www.starstruck.com
Sales Range: $50-74.9 Million
Emp.: 100
Sports Apparel & Jewelry Distr & Retailer
N.A.I.C.S.: 423910

The Comet Clothing Company, LLC   (2)
126 N 3rd St Ste 350, Minneapolis, MN 55401-1628
Tel.: (612) 332-1200

Fashion Apparel Realtor

The Greene Organization, Inc.   (2)
7027 W Broward Blvd, Fort Lauderdale, FL 33317
Tel.: (954) 370-0184
Sales Range: $10-24.9 Million
Emp.: 1
Business Consultants
N.A.I.C.S.: 611710

Wincraft Incorporated   (2)
1124 W 5th St, Winona, MN 55987
Tel.: (507) 454-5510
Web Site: http://www.wincraft.com
Sales Range: $25-49.9 Million
Emp.: 450
Novelties & Specialties, Metal
N.A.I.C.S.: 332999
John Killen (Pres & CEO)
Richard Pope (Chm)
Dave Bringe (Sr VP-Sls)
Philip Welp (VP-Bus Dev)

RueLaLa, Inc.   (1)
20 Channel Ctr, Boston, MA 02210   (70%)
Tel.: (888) 992-5252
Web Site: http://www.ruelala.com
Emp.: 600
Subscription-Based Online Shopping Services
N.A.I.C.S.: 459999
Lisa Rhodes (Pres & Chief Merchandising Officer)
Mark McWeeny (CEO)
Michael Rubin (Chm)
Mark Weinberg (CFO & COO)

KYRA SOLUTIONS INC.
4454 Florida National Dr, Lakeland, FL 33813
Tel.: (863) 686-2271   FL
Web Site: http://www.kyrasolutions.com
Year Founded: 1997
Sales Range: $1-9.9 Million
Emp.: 66
IT Consulting & Project Outsourcing
N.A.I.C.S.: 541618
Piyush Patel (Founder & CEO)
Jay Patel (VP-HR & Admin)
Devang Patel (VP-Consulting & Projects)
Rupal Patel (VP-Fin)
Katy Lee Fenton (VP-Strategic Solutions)
Louis Smith (CTO)
Apurva Desai (VP-Ops-Transportation Practice)

KYRUUS, INC.
121 High St 4th Fl, Boston, MA 02210
Tel.: (617) 419-2060
Web Site: http://www.kyruus.com
Business Support Services
N.A.I.C.S.: 561499
Christie Smith (VP-Legal & Admin)
Graham Gardner (Founder & CEO)
Paul Merrild (Pres)
Peter Boumenot (Chief Product Officer)

Subsidiaries:
Epion Health, Inc.   (1)
24 Cokesbury Rd Ste 3, Lebanon, NJ 08833
Tel.: (732) 690-1188
Web Site: http://www.epionhealth.com
Software Publisher
N.A.I.C.S.: 513210
Joe Blewitt (CEO)

KYU INVESTMENT, INC.
395 Hudson St 8th Fl, New York, NY 10014
Tel.: (646) 926-5163   DE
Web Site: http://www.kyu.com
Year Founded: 2014
Marketing Services

N.A.I.C.S.: 541613
Michael Birkin (CEO)
Tim Brown (Co-Vice Chm)
Susan Schuman (Co-Vice Chm)
AJ Hughes (CFO)
Paul Bennett (Chief Creative Officer-IDEO)
Naoto Akagi (Sr VP)

Subsidiaries:

Kepler Group LLC (1)
6 E 32nd St Fl 9, New York, NY 10016
Tel.: (646) 524-6896
Web Site: http://www.keplergrp.com
Emp.: 250
Digital Marketing Services
N.A.I.C.S.: 541613
Rick Greenberg (Exec Chm)
Remy Stiles (Founder & CEO-North America)
Joshua Lerman (CEO-Global)
Patrick McDaniel (Co-Pres-US)
Andrew Toledano (Chief Client Dev Officer)

KYYBA, INC.
28230 Orchard Lake Rd Ste 130, Farmington Hills, MI 48334
Tel.: (248) 813-9665
Web Site: http://www.kyyba.com
Year Founded: 1997
Sales Range: $10-24.9 Million
Emp.: 67
Software Development Services
N.A.I.C.S.: 541511
Tel K. Ganesan (Founder & Chm)
Thiru Ganesan (Pres & CEO)
Kevin Fitzgerald (VP)
Ken Kenjale (Chief Strategy Officer)

KYZEN CORPORATION
430 Harding Industrial Dr, Nashville, TN 37211
Tel.: (615) 831-0888   TN
Web Site: http://www.kyzen.com
Year Founded: 1990
Sales Range: $10-24.9 Million
Emp.: 30
Precision Cleaning Chemicals, Processes & Equipment for Industrial Manufacturing Operations
N.A.I.C.S.: 325612
Kyle J. Doyel (Pres & CEO)
Michael Bixenman (CTO & VP)
Thomas Forsythe (Exec VP)
R. Erik Miller (Exec VP)
Kevin Buckner (Reg Sls Mgr)
Chuck Sexton (Mgr-Product Line & Industrial-Global)

Subsidiaries:

Kyzen BVBA (1)
Vliegplein 14B, 9990, Maldegem, Belgium
Tel.: (32) 50395374
Engineering Consulting Services
N.A.I.C.S.: 541330
Kyle Doyel (CEO)

Kyzen Corporation - North American Operations Facility (1)
540 N Commercial St, Manchester, NH 03101
Tel.: (603) 622-2900
Web Site: http://www.kyzen.com
Chemical Products Mfr
N.A.I.C.S.: 325998

Kyzen Sdn. Bhd. (1)
Plot 47 Hilir Sungai Keluang 2 Phase 4 Bayan Lepas Industrial Park, Bayan Lepas, 11900, Penang, Malaysia
Tel.: (60) 4 630 3000
Web Site: http://www.kyzen.com
Engineering Consulting Services
N.A.I.C.S.: 541330

KZS ADVERTISING
811 W Jericho Tpke Ste 109E, Smithtown, NY 11787
Tel.: (631) 348-1440   NY

Year Founded: 1980
Rev.: $20,034,000
Emp.: 20
Advertising Agencies
N.A.I.C.S.: 541810
Jack Schultheis (Owner)
Richard Shepard (Supvr-Production)
Arnold Schwartz (VP & Acct Supvr)
Elaine Kerner (VP)
Michael Welch (Exec VP-Bus Dev)
Linda Rexon (Office Mgr)

L & F DISTRIBUTORS LTD.
3900 N McColl Rd, McAllen, TX 78501-9160
Tel.: (956) 687-7751
Web Site: http://www.lnfdist.com
Year Founded: 1981
Sales Range: $100-124.9 Million
Emp.: 1,000
Beer & Ale Distr
N.A.I.C.S.: 424810
Greg LaMantia (Partner & Gen Mgr)
Tony LaMantia (Partner)
Steve LaMantia (VP)
Val LaMantia Peisen (Partner)
Joe LaMantia Jr. (Chm)
Joe LaMantia III (Partner)

Subsidiaries:

L & F Distributors (1)
6949 Market Ave, El Paso, TX 79915-1111
Tel.: (915) 772-4246
Web Site: http://www.lnfdistributors.com
Sales Range: $50-74.9 Million
Emp.: 170
Beer & Ale Distr
N.A.I.C.S.: 424810

L & L ENERGY, INC.
130 Andover Park E Ste 200 2nd Fl, Seattle, WA 98188
Tel.: (206) 264-8065   NV
Web Site: http://www.llenergyinc.com
Year Founded: 1995
Sales Range: $150-199.9 Million
Emp.: 1,364
Coal Mining Services
N.A.I.C.S.: 212115
Ian Grant Robinson (CFO)
Clayton Fong (VP-Ops-US)
Norman Lee (Gen Mgr)
Yi Ping Chan (Mng Dir-Merger & Acq)
James J. Schaeffer (Exec Dir)
John Nanchiang Chang (Dir-Fin)

L & L SPECIAL FURNACE CO., INC.
20 Kent Rd, Aston, PA 19014
Tel.: (610) 459-9216
Web Site: http://www.hotfurnace.com
Emp.: 100
Industrial Process Furnace & Oven Mfr
N.A.I.C.S.: 333994
Gregory D. Lewicki (Pres)

L & N BRIDGE, LLC.
PO Box 1088, Antlers, OK 74523
Tel.: (580) 298-6974
Web Site: http://www.lnbridge.com
Year Founded: 1999
Sales Range: $10-24.9 Million
Emp.: 40
Highway, Street & Bridge Construction Services
N.A.I.C.S.: 237310
Randall Low (Co-Owner)
David Norrid (Co-Owner)

L & O POWER COOPERATIVE
1302 S Union St, Rock Rapids, IA 51246
Tel.: (712) 472-2556
Web Site: http://www.landopowercoop.com
Year Founded: 1952

Sales Range: $1-9.9 Million
Emp.: 3
Electric Power Distr
N.A.I.C.S.: 221122
Marlin D. Overman (Office Mgr)
Curt D. Dieren (Mgr)

L & S TIRE COMPANY
8119 N Regal St Bldg 5, Spokane, WA 99217-8120
Tel.: (509) 464-0976
Web Site: http://www.lstire.com
Year Founded: 1999
Sales Range: $10-24.9 Million
Emp.: 32
Tire & Tube Whslr
N.A.I.C.S.: 423130
Nicki Mayfield (Mgr-Acctg)
Scott Sander (Pres)
Mike Lavelle (VP-Sls, Research & Dev)
Dan Patterson (Treas & Sec)

L B INDUSTRIES, INC.
8770 RailRd Dr, Covington, KY 41015
Tel.: (859) 431-8300   IL
Web Site: https://lbindustriesinc.com
Year Founded: 1937
Emp.: 50
Holding Company; Metal Products Mfr, Whslr & Material Services
N.A.I.C.S.: 551112
Timothy C. Lally (Pres & CEO)
Robert J. Krems (Treas & VP)
John A. Mocker Jr. (VP)

Subsidiaries:

L B Pipe & Coupling Products, LLC (1)
21220 FM 1488, Magnolia, TX 77355
Tel.: (832) 934-1850
Web Site: http://www.lbpipeandcouplingproduct.com
Manufactures, Markets & Sells Products for Energy, Utility & Construction Markets
N.A.I.C.S.: 331210

LB Steel, LLC (1)
15700 S Lathrop Ave, Harvey, IL 60426-5118
Tel.: (708) 331-2600
Web Site: http://www.lbsteel.com
Sales Range: $150-199.9 Million
Emp.: 350
Metal Machining, Fabricating, Heat Treating & Assembly Services
N.A.I.C.S.: 332710
Pete Raketic (VP-Pur)
Richard Kovac (Sr VP-Sls)
Michael Z. Goich (Pres)
Lee Ann Trueblood (VP-Plate Products)

Unit (Domestic):

Protective Door Industries (2)
15700 S Lathrop Ave, Harvey, IL 60426
Tel.: (708) 331-2515
Web Site: http://www.protectivedoor.com
Sales Range: $1-9.9 Million
Emp.: 20
Protective Steel Door & Window Mfr
N.A.I.C.S.: 332321
Janet Cahill (Mgr-Sls)

Topeka Metal Specialties (2)
5600 S Topeka Blvd, Topeka, KS 66609
Tel.: (785) 862-1071
Web Site: http://www.topekametal.com
Sales Range: $25-49.9 Million
Emp.: 70
Metal Fabrication & Welding Services
N.A.I.C.S.: 332999
Jim Peek (Gen Mgr)
Chris Cross (Office Mgr-HR)

Lally Pipe & Tube (1)
8770 Railroad Dr, Covington, KY 41015
Tel.: (859) 431-8300
Web Site: http://www.lallypipe.com
Sales Range: $25-49.9 Million
Emp.: 60
Steel Pipe & Tubing Mfr
N.A.I.C.S.: 331210

Timothy C. Lally (Pres)
Robert J. Krems (Treas & VP)
John A. Mocker Jr. (VP)
James M. Mocker (VP)
Jamee L. Houthoofd (VP)
Jim Meier (Mgr-Sls-Southeast Reg-Structural Pipe)
Dan Siskowic (Mgr-Traffic)
Joe Kengor (Mgr-Casing & Fabrication Pipe)
Bob Mraz (Mgr-Piling & Wholesale Pipe)

L R HEIN CONSTRUCTION CORP.
1480 Industrial Dr, Itasca, IL 60143-1848
Tel.: (630) 496-2000
Web Site: http://www.lrhein.com
Year Founded: 2002
Sales Range: $10-24.9 Million
Emp.: 15
Nonresidential Construction Services
N.A.I.C.S.: 236220
Leo Hein (CEO)

L SQUARED CAPITAL MANAGEMENT LP
3434 Via Lido Ste 300, Newport Beach, CA 92663
Tel.: (949) 398-0168   DE
Web Site: http://www.lsquaredcap.com
Year Founded: 2014
Private Equity Investment Management Firm
N.A.I.C.S.: 523940
Jeff Farrero (Co-Founder & Mng Partner)
Robert P. Healy (Co-Founder & Mng Partner)
Randall Hunt (Partner)
Sean Barrette (Partner)
Adam Kimura (Partner)
Tyler Huez (Principal)
Elizabeth Hunt (CFO)
Brittany Beyer (Mgr)
Bianca Bonus (VP-Fin)
Edmund Montanari (VP)

Subsidiaries:

GWS Tool Group, LLC (1)
595 County Rd 448, Tavares, FL 32778
Tel.: (352) 343-8778
Web Site: http://www.gwstoolgroup.com
Machine Tool (Metal Cutting Types) Mfr
N.A.I.C.S.: 333517
Rick McIntyre (CEO)
Adam Lafferty (Exec VP-Sls)
Drew Strauchen (Exec VP-Bus Dev)
Kevin Zimmerman (CFO)
Tomas Roman (Dir-Inside Sls)
Jason Ford (Gen Mgr-North Carolina)
David Novak (Dir-Sys & Integration)

Subsidiary (Domestic):

CJT Koolcarb, Inc. (2)
494 Mission St, Carol Stream, IL 60188
Tel.: (630) 690-5933
Web Site: http://www.cjtkoolcarb.com
Rolled Steel Shape Mfr
N.A.I.C.S.: 331221
Terry Loveless (Pres)
Andy Piasecki (CEO)

Subsidiary (Domestic):

GenHam Diamond Tooling, Inc. (3)
11 Ponderosa Ct, Montrose, CO 81401-6201
Tel.: (970) 249-1300
Web Site: http://www.genham.com
Cutting Tool & Machine Tool Accessory Mfr
N.A.I.C.S.: 333515
Rick McBee (Mgr)

Subsidiary (Domestic):

North American Tool Corporation (2)
215 Elmwood Ave, South Beloit, IL 61080
Tel.: (815) 389-2300
Web Site: http://www.natool.com
Cutting Tools For Machine Tools

L SQUARED CAPITAL MANAGEMENT LP   U.S. PRIVATE

L Squared Capital Management LP—(Continued)
N.A.I.C.S.: 333515
Curtis Lansbery (Pres & CEO)
Phil Samuels (Dir-Sls & Mktg)

Subsidiary (Domestic):

Bitner Tooling Technologies (3)
6650 Burroughs Ave, Sterling Heights, MI 48314-2135
Tel.: (586) 977-8007
Web Site: http://www.natool.com
Rev.: $1,500,000
Emp.: 12
Cutting Tools For Machine Tools
N.A.I.C.S.: 333515

Gay Lee Corporation (3)
6501 Sims Dr, Sterling Heights, MI 48313
Tel.: (586) 803-1100
Web Site: http://www.natool.com
Rev.: $1,200,000
Emp.: 13
Saws & Sawing Machines
N.A.I.C.S.: 333517

Subsidiary (Domestic):

STF Precision Technologies & Tools, Inc. (2)
76 Old Shoals Rd, Arden, NC 28704
Tel.: (828) 687-3686
Web Site: http://www.stfprecision.com
Rev.: $3,000,000
Emp.: 24
Hand & Edge Tool Mfr
N.A.I.C.S.: 332216
David Novak (Co-Owner & VP)
Jason Ford (Co-Owner & Pres)

Taurus Tool & Engineering Inc. (2)
5101 W County Rd 400 S, Muncie, IN 47302
Tel.: (765) 282-2090
Web Site: http://www.taurustool.com
Machine Shops
N.A.I.C.S.: 332710
Jim Kantak (Pres)

Globe Scientific, Inc. (1)
610 Winters Ave, Paramus, NJ 07652
Tel.: (201) 599-1400
Web Site: http://www.globescientific.com
Sales Range: $1-9.9 Million
Emp.: 22
Medical And Hospital Equipment, Nsk
N.A.I.C.S.: 423450

Oracle Elevator Company (1)
8800 Grand Oak Cir, Tampa, FL 33637
Tel.: (844) 464-7887
Web Site: http://www.oracleelevator.com
Elevator Maintenance & Repair Services
N.A.I.C.S.: 333921
Michael West (Sr VP)
Ben Wehner (Reg VP)
Craig Hepworth (Controller-Acctg)

Subsidiary (Domestic):

Affinity Elevator Company, LLC (2)
6230 Green Acres Dr, Pensacola, FL 32526
Tel.: (850) 857-0028
Elevator Maintenance, Repair & Modernization Services
N.A.I.C.S.: 333921
Tammy Johnson (Office Mgr)

Landmark Elevator, Inc. (2)
133 S Burhans Blvd, Hagerstown, MD 21740-4747
Tel.: (301) 790-0990
Web Site: http://www.landmarkelevator.com
Building Equipment Contractors
N.A.I.C.S.: 238290
William Block (Pres)

Oracle Elevator Company - Torrington (2)
43 Daycoeton Pl, Torrington, CT 06790
Tel.: (860) 794-6051
Web Site: http://www.oracleelevator.com
Emp.: 3,500
Elevator Maintenance & Repair Services
N.A.I.C.S.: 811210
Paul Bellliveau (Pres & CEO)
Kurt Meyer (CFO)
Vong Keovongsa (VP-HR)

Raptor Scientific LLC (1)
3434 Via Lido Ste 300, New Port Beach, CA 92663
Tel.: (844) 293-2583
Web Site: https://raptor-scientific.com
Aviation & Aerospace Component Manufacturing
N.A.I.C.S.: 334511
Derek Coppinger (CEO)

Subsidiary (Domestic):

King Nutronics Corporation (2)
6421 Independence Ave, Woodland Hills, CA 91367
Tel.: (818) 887-5460
Web Site: http://www.kingnutronics.com
Sales Range: $1-9.9 Million
Emp.: 20
Instruments & Related Products Mfr for Measuring, Displaying & Controlling Industrial Process Variables
N.A.I.C.S.: 334513
Leslie King (CEO)

Space Electronics, LLC (1)
81 Fuller Way, Berlin, CT 06037
Tel.: (860) 829-0005
Web Site: http://www.space-electronics.com
Analytical Laboratory Instrument Mfr
N.A.I.C.S.: 334516

L T HAMPEL CORP.
W194 N11551 McCormick Dr, Germantown, WI 53022
Tel.: (262) 255-4540
Web Site:
 http://www.hampelcorp.com
Year Founded: 1976
Sales Range: $10-24.9 Million
Emp.: 105
Plastics Product Mfr
N.A.I.C.S.: 326199
Lance T. Hampel (Founder & CEO)

L&A CONTRACTING COMPANY INC.
100 Sims Rd, Hattiesburg, MS 39401
Tel.: (601) 264-2100   MS
Web Site:
 http://www.landacontracting.com
Year Founded: 1946
Sales Range: $25-49.9 Million
Emp.: 250
Provider of Bridge, Tunnel & Elevated Highway Services
N.A.I.C.S.: 237310
Ray Sims (Chm)
Stacie Pitts (Treas, Sec & Controller)
Lee Sims (Pres)

L&A MARKETING & ADVERTISING, INC.
3 Seadrift St, Irvine, CA 92604
Tel.: (949) 660-1180
Year Founded: 1989
Sales Range: Less than $1 Million
Emp.: 2
Advertising Agencies, Nsk
N.A.I.C.S.: 541810

L&B PAPER INC.
2275 Half Day Rd Ste 120, Bannockburn, IL 60015
Tel.: (847) 444-1450
Web Site: http://landbpaper.com
Year Founded: 1998
Sales Range: $10-24.9 Million
Emp.: 3
Personal Service Agents, Brokers & Bureaus
N.A.I.C.S.: 424130
David Culig (Gen Mgr)

L&B REALTY ADVISORS, INC.
5910 N Central Expy Swe 1200, Dallas, TX 75206
Tel.: (214) 989-0800
Web Site: http://www.lbrealty.com
Sales Range: $10-24.9 Million
Emp.: 75
Commercial Real Estate Investment
N.A.I.C.S.: 531210
G. Andrews Smith (CEO & Mng Partner)
Daniel Plumlee (Pres, Chief Investment Officer & Partner)
Mark Gerigk (Deputy Investment Officer & Exec VP-Fin)

L&B TRANSPORT INC.
708 Hwy 190 W, Port Allen, LA 70767
Tel.: (225) 387-0894
Web Site:
 http://www.landbtransport.com
Sales Range: $10-24.9 Million
Emp.: 60
Provider of Liquid Petroleum Transportation Services
N.A.I.C.S.: 484230
Louis Vielee (Owner)
Jody Guillory (VP)

Subsidiaries:

L&B Transport Inc. (1)
9561 Old Highway 43, Creola, AL 36525
Tel.: (251) 679-1535
Web Site: http://www.landbtransport.com
Sales Range: $10-24.9 Million
Emp.: 35
General Freight Trucking, Long-Distance, Truckload
N.A.I.C.S.: 484121

L&D APPLIANCES CORPORATION
11969 Telegraph Rd, Santa Fe Springs, CA 90670
Tel.: (562) 946-1105
Web Site: http://www.indappl.com
Sales Range: $10-24.9 Million
Emp.: 24
Oven Ranges
N.A.I.C.S.: 423620
Craig McGregor (Mgr)
Darrell Craig (Mgr)
Stan Fink (Mgr)

L&H AIRCO
2530 Warren Dr, Rocklin, CA 95677
Tel.: (916) 677-1000
Web Site: http://www.lhairco.net
Rev.: $11,700,000
Emp.: 45
Warm Air Heating & Air-Conditioning Equipment & Supplies Merchant Whslr
N.A.I.C.S.: 423730
Richard Racetti (Sec & VP)
Frank Wegener (Pres)
David Zierten (Engr-Control Sys)

L&H COMPANY INC.
2215 York Rd Ste 304, Oak Brook, IL 60523-4004
Tel.: (630) 571-7200
Year Founded: 1980
Sales Range: $1-9.9 Million
Emp.: 909
Provider of Electrical Work Services
N.A.I.C.S.: 238210
John Lizzadro (Chm)

Subsidiaries:

Meade Electric Company, Inc. (1)
9550 W 55th St Ste A, La Grange, IL 60525
Tel.: (708) 588-2500
Web Site: http://www.meade100.com
Providers of Electrical Services
N.A.I.C.S.: 238210
Frank J. Lizzadro (VP)

L&H INDUSTRIAL INC
913 L J Ct, Gillette, WY 82718
Tel.: (307) 682-7238
Web Site: http://www.lnh.net
Sales Range: $25-49.9 Million
Emp.: 210

Machine Shop, Jobbing & Repair
N.A.I.C.S.: 332710
Mike Wandler (Pres)
Jim Clikeman (Sr VP)
Luke Biggs (Engr-Mechanical Design)
Dustin Roush (Mgr-Canadian Acct)
Jason Percifield (Mgr-Ops)

L&H PACKING COMPANY
647 Steves Ave, San Antonio, TX 78210-3819
Tel.: (210) 532-3241   TX
Web Site: http://www.lhpacking.com
Year Founded: 1963
Sales Range: $125-149.9 Million
Emp.: 300
Wholesale Meats & Meat Packing
N.A.I.C.S.: 424470
Ken Lenord (CEO)
Gavino Ramos (Dir-Corp Comm)

Subsidiaries:

Surlean Meat Co. (1)
1545 S San Marcos, San Antonio, TX 78207-7033   (100%)
Tel.: (210) 227-4370
Web Site: http://www.surleanfoods.com
Sales Range: $25-49.9 Million
Emp.: 220
Meat Processing Plants
N.A.I.C.S.: 311612
Paul Neuenschwander (Controller)

L&H TECHNOLOGIES INC.
11529 Wilmar Blvd, Charlotte, NC 28273-6409
Tel.: (704) 588-3670   SC
Web Site: http://livhaven.com
Year Founded: 1947
Fluid Power, Mechatronic, Lubrication & Hose/Connector Mfr
N.A.I.C.S.: 423830
Anne Q. Woody (CFO)
Jerry Zimmerman (Pres)
Bob Decker (VP-Products & Tech)
Shannon Lockaby (VP-Ops)

L&J ENTERPRISES INC.
3/4 Mile W Willow, Tok, AK 99780
Tel.: (907) 883-4324
Web Site:
 http://www.threebearsalaska.com
Sales Range: $10-24.9 Million
Emp.: 350
Warehouse Club Stores; Conventional Grocery
N.A.I.C.S.: 455211
David Weitz (Pres)

L&J TECHNOLOGIES
5911 Butterfield Rd, Hillside, IL 60162
Tel.: (708) 236-6000   IL
Web Site:
 http://www.ljtechnologies.com
Year Founded: 1976
Sales Range: $75-99.9 Million
Emp.: 130
Level Controls, Liquid Level Controls, Tank Fittings, Valves, Gauges, Hydraulic Controls & Related Systems Mfr; Level Gauging Solutions
N.A.I.C.S.: 334519
Lou Jannotta (Pres & CEO)
Michael Landato (Mgr-Product Mktg)
Bob Schwaan (CFO)

L&J TRANSPORTATION COMPANIES, INC.
36 Mountainside Rd, Temple, PA 19560
Tel.: (610) 921-2063
Web Site: http://www.ljmoving.com
Year Founded: 1990
Rev.: $2,400,000
Emp.: 31
General Freight Trucking, Local
N.A.I.C.S.: 484110

James Fry *(Owner & Pres)*
Stephanie Fry *(VP-Admin)*

L&L MANUFACTURING CO.
815 N Nash St, El Segundo, CA 90245-2824
Tel.: (310) 615-0000
Sales Range: $10-24.9 Million
Emp.: 76
Women's Sportswear
N.A.I.C.S.: 424350
Mark Feldman *(Owner)*

L&L NURSERY SUPPLY, INC.
2552 Shenandoah Way, San Bernardino, CA 92407-5215
Tel.: (909) 591-0461 CA
Web Site:
 http://www.llnurserysupply.com
Year Founded: 1941
Sales Range: $125-149.9 Million
Emp.: 225
Mfr of Wooden Nursery Supplies & Soil Products; Lawn & Garden Products Except Plants, Tools, Fertilizers & Wood Products
N.A.I.C.S.: 424910
Tom Medhurst *(Pres)*
Mike Fuson *(VP-Sls)*
Daniel Folie *(VP)*

Subsidiaries:

L&L Plant Soil Division (1)
2507 Frank Albert Rd E Ste 130, Fife, WA 98424-2700
Tel.: (253) 922-7714
Web Site: http://www.nurserysupply.com
Sales Range: $25-49.9 Million
Emp.: 25
Nursery Distribution Center
N.A.I.C.S.: 424910

L&L PRODUCTS, INC.
160 McLean Dr, Romeo, MI 48065-4919
Tel.: (586) 336-1700 MI
Web Site: http://www.llproducts.com
Year Founded: 1958
Sales Range: $25-49.9 Million
Emp.: 850
Gaskets; Packing & Sealing Devices
N.A.I.C.S.: 339991
John Ligon *(CEO)*
Susan Deeb *(Controller)*
Matt Matuzak *(Controller)*
Ken Mazich *(Dir-R&D)*
Olaf Nitsche *(Program Mgr & Acct Mgr)*
Blake Synnestvedt *(Dir-Comml)*
Cheri Nowak *(Mgr-HR)*
Mohammad Motamedi *(Dir-Ops)*
Schaeffer Greene *(VP-HR)*
Tanya Vilcek *(Mgr-Fin)*
Heather Trombetta *(Dir-HR)*
Marlon Bottene *(Dir-Pur)*
Kevin Renno *(Engr-Tooling)*
Sarah Geiser *(Mgr-Employee Rels)*
Shelley Badour *(Mgr-Matls)*
Trina Yohe *(Mgr-Quality)*
Kim Rzetelny *(Sr Acct Mgr)*

Subsidiaries:

L&L Products Australia (Pty) Ltd. (1)
63-79 South Park Drive, Dandenong, 3175, VIC, Australia
Tel.: (61) 3 8710 7400
Automotive Parts & Accessory Whslr
N.A.I.C.S.: 441330

L&L Products Europe SAS (1)
1 Rue Lindberg ZA Activeum, Altorf, 67129, France
Tel.: (33) 3 88 47 95 95
Web Site: http://www.llproducts.com
Emp.: 250
Automotive Parts & Accessory Whslr
N.A.I.C.S.: 423120
Francois Rosen *(Mng Dir)*

L&L Products Otomotiv Ltd Sti (1)
kokmar 15, Nilufer, Bursa, 16140, Turkiye
Tel.: (90) 224 411 05 50
Automotive Parts & Accessory Whslr
N.A.I.C.S.: 441330

L&L Products do Brasil Ltda. (1)
Rua Dalisio Silveira Barros 370, Distrito Indaiatuba, 13347-350, Sao Paulo, Brazil
Tel.: (55) 19 3936 3748
Emp.: 20
Automotive Parts & Accessory Whslr
N.A.I.C.S.: 441330
Alessandro Fontana *(Gen Mgr)*

L&L STORES INCORPORATED
627 E Washington St, Nashville, NC 27856
Tel.: (252) 459-4475
Sales Range: $25-49.9 Million
Emp.: 130
Owner & Operator of Convenience Stores
N.A.I.C.S.: 445131
Wayne J. Land *(Pres)*

L&L WINGS INC.
666 Broadway 2 Fl, New York, NY 10012
Tel.: (212) 481-8299
Web Site:
 http://www.wingsbeachwear.com
Rev.: $38,311,584
Emp.: 10
T-Shirts; Custom Printed
N.A.I.C.S.: 458110
Shaul Levy *(Founder & Pres)*

L&M COMPANIES, INC.
2925 Huntleigh Dr Ste 204, Raleigh, NC 27604-3374
Tel.: (919) 981-8017 NC
Web Site:
 http://www.lmcompanies.com
Year Founded: 1964
Fresh Fruits & Vegetables
N.A.I.C.S.: 424480
Joseph E. McGee *(Founder & Chm)*
John Oxford *(Pres)*
Mike McGee *(Sec)*

L&M FERTILIZER INC.
28690 Las Haciendas St, Temecula, CA 92590
Tel.: (951) 676-2990
Web Site:
 http://www.landmpower.com
Rev.: $12,000,000
Emp.: 22
Fertilizer & Fertilizer Materials
N.A.I.C.S.: 424910
Leo L. McGuire Jr. *(Mgr)*

L&M FOOTWEAR INC.
5303 E Washington Blvd, Commerce, CA 90040
Tel.: (323) 948-4800
Web Site:
 http://www.robertwayne.com
Rev.: $10,793,000
Emp.: 18
Men's Shoes
N.A.I.C.S.: 458210
Meir Levin *(CEO)*
Adrian Rosas *(Dir-Online Ops)*

L&M SUPPLY INC.
1200 Hwy 169 E, Grand Rapids, MN 55744
Tel.: (218) 326-9451 IN
Web Site:
 http://www.landmsupply.com
Year Founded: 1959
Sales Range: $50-74.9 Million
Emp.: 350
Hardware Stores
N.A.I.C.S.: 444140

Terry W. Matteson *(Pres & Co-Owner)*
Don Ley *(Co-Owner & Controller)*
Paul Hanson *(Mgr-Ops)*

L&M TECHNOLOGIES, INC.
4209 Balloon Park Rd NE, Albuquerque, NM 87109-5802
Tel.: (505) 343-0200
Web Site:
 http://www.lmtechnologies.com
Sales Range: $25-49.9 Million
Emp.: 170
Business Support Services Including Logistics, Facilities Operations, Maintenance & Staff Augmentation Support
N.A.I.C.S.: 561499
Peter E. Harrod *(Pres & CEO)*
Antonette Montoya *(CFO)*
Karen Monty *(VP-HR)*
David L. Stansberry *(VP)*

L&M TRANSPORTATION SERVICES, INC.
2925 Huntleigh Dr Ste 104, Raleigh, NC 27604-3374
Tel.: (919) 825-4700 NC
Web Site: http://www.lmts.com
Year Founded: 1977
Sales Range: $25-49.9 Million
Emp.: 40
Provider of Freight Transportation Arrangements
N.A.I.C.S.: 488510
Betsy Summerlin *(VP-Acctg & IT)*
Tom Devine *(Pres)*
Jim Devine *(Dir-Bus Dev)*
Dan Giddens *(Dir-IT)*

L&R CONSTRUCTION SERVICES, INC.
16749 Dixie Hwy Ste 9, Davisburg, MI 48350
Tel.: (248) 207-5051
Web Site:
 http://www.lrconstruction.com
Year Founded: 1996
Sales Range: $1-9.9 Million
Emp.: 8
Gas Station & Convenience Store Construction
N.A.I.C.S.: 236220
Brian Lance *(Pres)*

L&R MANUFACTURING COMPANY
577 Elm St, Kearny, NJ 07032
Tel.: (201) 991-5330 DE
Web Site:
 http://www.lrultrasonics.com
Year Founded: 1930
Sales Range: $100-124.9 Million
Emp.: 200
Ultrasonic Cleaning Systems, Solutions & Accessories Mfr
N.A.I.C.S.: 325612
Robert Lazarus *(Pres)*
Bruce Letch *(Sr VP-Sls & Mktg)*

L&S ELECTRIC INC.
5101 Mesker St, Schofield, WI 54476-0740
Tel.: (715) 359-3155
Web Site: http://www.lselectric.com
Year Founded: 1933
Sales Range: $25-49.9 Million
Motors & Othe Electric Equipment Mfr
N.A.I.C.S.: 423610
Dawn Folz *(Mgr-Inside Sls)*
Shannon Rahm *(Engr-Sls)*
David Bishoff *(Engr-Mechanical)*
Dan Schultz *(Engr-Sls)*
Lynda Braun *(Mgr-Inside Sls)*

Subsidiaries:

L&S Electric Inc. - Iron Mountain (1)
619 Industrial Dr, Iron Mountain, MI 49801
Tel.: (906) 774-0468
Web Site: http://www.lselectric.com
Electrical Apparatus & Equipment, Wiring Supplies & Related Equipment Merchant Whslr
N.A.I.C.S.: 423610

L&S Electric of Canada (1)
5055 Rue Viger, Saint-Hubert, J3Y 8Y9, QC, Canada (100%)
Tel.: (450) 448-8880
Web Site: http://www.lselectric.com
Sales Range: $10-24.9 Million
Emp.: 3
Motors, Electric
N.A.I.C.S.: 423610

L&S FOOD SALES CORP.
25 W Union St, Ashland, MA 01721
Tel.: (508) 231-1426
Rev.: $40,211,013
Emp.: 30
Poultry & Poultry Products
N.A.I.C.S.: 424440
Alan Singer *(Pres)*

L&S PACKING CO., INC.
101 Central Ave, Farmingdale, NY 11735
Tel.: (631) 845-1717
Web Site: http://www.lspacking.com
Sales Range: $10-24.9 Million
Emp.: 65
Fruit & Vegetable Canning
N.A.I.C.S.: 311421
Lorraine Scaramelli *(Exec VP)*
Louis J. Scaramelli III *(Pres)*
Jacqueline Massaro *(VP)*
Louis Scaramelli IV *(VP)*

L&S TRUCK CENTER OF APPLETON
330 N Bluemound Dr, Appleton, WI 54914
Tel.: (920) 749-1700
Web Site: http://www.lstruck.com
Sales Range: $10-24.9 Million
Emp.: 28
Trucks, Tractors & Trailers: New & Used
N.A.I.C.S.: 441110
Lester Stumpf *(Chm)*

L&T MEAT CO.
3050 E 11th St, Los Angeles, CA 90023
Tel.: (323) 262-1798
Web Site: http://www.ltmeat.com
Year Founded: 1996
Sales Range: $10-24.9 Million
Emp.: 20
Whslr & Distributor of Grocery Products
N.A.I.C.S.: 424420
Scott Tea *(Gen Mgr)*

L'AMBIANCE BEACHES LTD.
3201 W Griffin Rd Ste 106, Fort Lauderdale, FL 33020-1513
Tel.: (954) 965-3636
Rev.: $43,000,000
Emp.: 2
Condominium Construction
N.A.I.C.S.: 236117
Morris Richter *(Partner)*

L-O DEL MAR HOLDING, INC.
11777 San Vicente Blvd Ste 900, Los Angeles, CA 90049
Tel.: (310) 820-6661 DE
Web Site:
 http://www.loweenterprise.com
Year Founded: 1994
Sales Range: $25-49.9 Million
Real Estate Services

L-O DEL MAR HOLDING, INC.—(Continued)
N.A.I.C.S.: 531390
Kerri A. O'Neill (Sr VP)
Christopher W. Bollinger (VP)
Jeremy J. Iaccino (Treas & VP)
Donal L. Tanaka (Sec)
Bleecker P. Seaman III (Pres)

L-SOFT INTERNATIONAL, INC.
7550 Wisconsin Ave Ste 400,
Bethesda, MD 20814
Tel.: (301) 731-0440
Web Site: http://www.lsoft.com
Year Founded: 1994
Sales Range: $10-24.9 Million
Emp.: 65
EMail List & Opt-In EMail Marketing Software & Outsourcing Services
N.A.I.C.S.: 541613
Eric Thomas (Founder & CEO)

L. & J.G. STICKLEY INC.
1 Stickley Dr, Manlius, NY 13104-2484
Tel.: (315) 682-5500 NY
Web Site: http://www.stickley.com
Year Founded: 1974
Sales Range: $75-99.9 Million
Emp.: 1,200
Furniture Mfr
N.A.I.C.S.: 337212
Blain Wrench (VP-Sls)
Aminy Audi (Co-Owner, Chm & CEO)
Edward Audi (Co-Owner & Pres)

Subsidiaries:
Nichols & Stone Co. (1)
1 Stickley Dr, Manlius, NY 13104
Tel.: (315) 682-1554
Web Site: http://www.nicholsandstone.com
Sales Range: $10-24.9 Million
Emp.: 350
Chairs, Rockers & Dining Room Furniture Mfr & Distr
N.A.I.C.S.: 337122
Carlton E. Nichols Jr. (Pres)

L. D'AGOSTINI & SONS INC.
15801 23 Mile Rd, Macomb, MI 48042
Tel.: (586) 781-5800
Sales Range: $10-24.9 Million
Emp.: 15
Provider of Sewer Line Construction Services
N.A.I.C.S.: 237110
Antonio D'agostini (Pres)

L. FERIOZZI CONCRETE COMPANY
3010 Sunset Ave, Atlantic City, NJ 08401-3737
Tel.: (609) 823-2563 NJ
Web Site: http://www.lferiozzi.com
Rev.: $11,894,118
Emp.: 2
Concrete Contractor
N.A.I.C.S.: 238140
Concetta Feriozzi (Pres)

L. FISHMAN & SON INC.
6301 E Lombard St, Baltimore, MD 21224
Tel.: (410) 633-2500
Web Site: http://www.lfishman.com
Sales Range: $25-49.9 Million
Emp.: 60
Carpet Installation Equipment
N.A.I.C.S.: 423850
Brady Sweitzer (CFO)
Bob Wagner (Pres & CEO)
Bill Mabeus (Exec VP)
Devon Clark (VP-Mktg)
Jon Karp (Dir-HR)
Rob Hoffman (Mgr-Midwest)

Jim Reisker (Mgr-Bus-West Pennsylvania & East Ohio)
Greg Paul (Mgr-Mid-Atlantic)

L. G. JORDAN OIL CO., INC.
314 N Hughes St, Apex, NC 27502
Tel.: (919) 362-8388
Web Site: http://www.lgjordanoil.com
Year Founded: 1923
Sales Range: $10-24.9 Million
Emp.: 22
Petroleum & Petroleum Product Whslr
N.A.I.C.S.: 424720
Larry M. Jordan (Pres)

L. H. HAYWARD & CO., LLC
5401 Toler St, Harahan, LA 70123
Tel.: (504) 733-8480
Web Site: http://www.camelliabrand.com
Year Founded: 1984
Sales Range: $10-24.9 Million
Emp.: 25
Bean, Pea & Lentil Preparation Services
N.A.I.C.S.: 115114
Ken Hayward (Co-Owner)
Connelly Hayward (Co-Owner)
Vince Hayward (Co-Owner)

L. J. HUGHES & SONS, INC.
320 Turnpike Rd, Summersville, WV 26651-1398
Tel.: (304) 872-1111 WV
Sales Range: $1-9.9 Million
Emp.: 58
Drilling Services for Coal Mining, Rock Quarry, Energy, Land & Engineering Companies
N.A.I.C.S.: 238990
David M. Hughes (Pres)
John M. Hughes (VP)
Fletcher G. Herold Jr. (Treas)

L. KNIFE & SON INC.
35 Elder Ave Ext, Kingston, MA 02364
Tel.: (781) 585-5165 MA
Web Site: http://www.greatbrewers.com
Year Founded: 1963
Sales Range: $10-24.9 Million
Emp.: 130
Beer & Ale Distributor
N.A.I.C.S.: 424810
Gerald Sheehan (Owner & Pres)
Charles Smith (VP-Fin)
Tim Sheehan (VP & Gen Mgr)

L. NAKAGAWA-JOHNSTON
1112 Kinau St Ph, Honolulu, HI 96814
Tel.: (808) 545-7816
Sales Range: $10-24.9 Million
Emp.: 5
Real Estate Agents & Managers
N.A.I.C.S.: 531210
Linda Y. Nakagawa (Pres)

L. POWELL COMPANY ACQUISITION CORP.
8631 Hayden Pl, Culver City, CA 90232-2901
Tel.: (310) 204-2224 CA
Web Site: http://www.powellcompany.com
Year Founded: 1968
Sales Range: $10-24.9 Million
Emp.: 99
Household Furniture Mfr & Whlsr
N.A.I.C.S.: 423210
Larry Woods (CFO & Sr VP-Fin)

L. R. WILLSON & SONS, INC.

773 Annapolis Rd, Gambrills, MD 21054
Tel.: (410) 923-6386
Web Site: http://www.lrwillsonandsons.com
Sales Range: $25-49.9 Million
Emp.: 150
Structural Steel & Precast Concrete Contracting Services
N.A.I.C.S.: 238120
Donald E. Willson (Pres)
Mary E. Sharp (CFO)
James L. Willson (VP)
L. J. Willson (Mgr-Crane Rental-Tilt Up Estimates)
Billy Ford (Mgr-Pur Shop)

L. SUZIO CONCRETE COMPANY INC.
975 Westfield Rd, Meriden, CT 06450
Tel.: (203) 237-8421
Web Site: http://www.lsuzio.com
Rev.: $17,500,000
Emp.: 37
Ready Mixed Concrete
N.A.I.C.S.: 327320
Leonardo H. Suzio (Founder & Pres)

L. THORN COMPANY INC.
6000 Grant Line Rd, New Albany, IN 47150
Tel.: (812) 246-4461
Web Site: http://www.lthorn.com
Sales Range: $10-24.9 Million
Emp.: 30
Building Materials, Interior
N.A.I.C.S.: 423310
Michael F. Ludden (Pres & CEO)
Bob Burgan (VP)
Greg Bickle (VP)

L. WOLF COMPANY
1733 Cleveland Blvd, Granite City, IL 62040
Tel.: (618) 452-8118
Sales Range: $10-24.9 Million
Emp.: 25
Commercial & Institutional Building Construction
N.A.I.C.S.: 236220
Sarah Wolf (Sec & VP)
Leo Wolf (Chm)

L.A WEB OFFSET PRINTING INC.
9639 Telstar Ave, El Monte, CA 91731
Tel.: (626) 453-8700
Web Site: http://www.chinesedaily.com
Sales Range: $10-24.9 Million
Emp.: 135
Offset Printing
N.A.I.C.S.: 323111
Steve Chiang (Exec VP)
Walter Chang (Owner & Pres)
George Para (Plant Mgr)
Shirrie Kuo (Mgr-Prepress)

L.A. BURDICK CHOCOLATE
47 Main St, Walpole, NH 03608
Tel.: (603) 756-2882
Web Site: http://www.burdickchocolate.com
Year Founded: 1987
Rev.: $2,000,000
Emp.: 120
Confectionary Mfr
N.A.I.C.S.: 311352
Cathy Watson (COO)

L.A. GAUGE CO.
7440 San Fernando Rd, Sun Valley, CA 91352-4343
Tel.: (818) 767-7193
Web Site: http://www.lagauge.com

Year Founded: 1954
Manufactures Ultra-Precision Machined Components & Assemblies to the Aviation, Defense & Commercial Industries
N.A.I.C.S.: 332999
Bob Bawa (Owner)
Jyot Bawa (COO)

L.A. GLO INTERNATIONAL, INC.
1230 Santa Anita Ave Ste H, South El Monte, CA 91733
Tel.: (626) 350-8089
Web Site: http://www.laglo.com
Year Founded: 1979
Sales Range: $10-24.9 Million
Emp.: 35
Women's, Juniors' & Misses' Dresses
N.A.I.C.S.: 315250
Joe Chang (Mgr)

L.A. HEARNE COMPANY
512 Metz Rd, King City, CA 93930
Tel.: (831) 385-5441
Web Site: http://www.hearneco.com
Sales Range: $10-24.9 Million
Emp.: 100
Fertilizers & Agricultural Chemicals
N.A.I.C.S.: 424910
Bill Crockett (Office Mgr)
Mike Hearne (Mgr-Feed)
Shuana Jones (Coord-Customer Svc)
Sandra Brunet (Mgr-Sls)

L.A. MOVERS
13812 S Figueroa St, Los Angeles, CA 90061-1026
Tel.: (310) 965-7700
Web Site: http://www.la-movers.com
Year Founded: 1983
Sales Range: $10-24.9 Million
Emp.: 120
Mfr of Women & Children's Clothing
N.A.I.C.S.: 315250
Andy Liggett (Pres)
Irene Lee (Mgr)
Lenia Sanchez (Office Mgr)
Maria Serrano (Engr-Costing)

L.A.T APPAREL, LLC
137 Leo Taylor Ln, Ball Ground, GA 30107
Tel.: (770) 479-1877
Web Site: http://www.latapparel.com
Year Founded: 1982
Imprintable Knitted Sportswear Mfr & Distr
N.A.I.C.S.: 424350
Mickie Schneider (CFO & Exec VP)
Chuck Phares (Exec VP-Sls)
Gina Watson (CEO)
Mindy Anastos (VP-Production Plng)
Barbara Teal (Mgr-Customer Svc)
Jon Hays (VP & COO)
Gerardo Castagnet (VP-Sourcing)

L.B. INDUSTRIES, INC.
465 W Main St, Boise, ID 83702
Tel.: (208) 424-2022 ID
Year Founded: 1976
Sales Range: $75-99.9 Million
Emp.: 1
Holding Company; Wholesaler & Retailer of Automobiles; Provider of Rental & Leasing; Subdivider & Developer of Nonresidential Buildings
N.A.I.C.S.: 531210
Lenora Barnes (Pres)

L.B. WHITE COMPANY INC.
411 Mason St, Onalaska, WI 54650
Tel.: (608) 783-5691
Web Site: http://www.lbwhite.com
Rev.: $14,200,000
Emp.: 102

COMPANIES

Heating Equipment Mfr
N.A.I.C.S.: 333414
Kevin Gagermeier *(CFO)*
Lou Dalrymple *(Reg Mgr-Sls-Construction & Event)*

L.C. INDUSTRIES FOR THE BLIND INC.
4500 Emperor Blvd, Durham, NC 27703-3216
Tel.: (919) 596-8277 NC
Web Site: http://www.lcibsc.com
Year Founded: 1938
Sales Range: $25-49.9 Million
Emp.: 250
Stationery Stores
N.A.I.C.S.: 459410
William L. Hudson *(Pres)*
Bill Blackton *(Dir-Stores)*
Rick Stallings *(CFO)*
Mike Brooks *(Plant Mgr)*
Tuwayna Gilbertson *(VP-New Bus Dev)*

L.C. INDUSTRIES INC.
401 N Western Ave, Chicago, IL 60612
Tel.: (312) 455-0500
Web Site: http://www.lewisnclark.com
Rev.: $10,000,000
Emp.: 23
Travel Accessory Retailer
N.A.I.C.S.: 315990
Ray Roos *(VP)*
Michael Smerling *(Pres)*

L.C. WHITFORD CO. INC.
164 N Main St, Wellsville, NY 14895-1152
Tel.: (585) 593-3601 NY
Web Site: http://www.lcwhitford.com
Year Founded: 1917
Sales Range: $10-24.9 Million
Emp.: 150
Nonresidential Construction Services
N.A.I.C.S.: 237310
L. Brad Whitford *(Pres)*
Dave Shields *(Dir-Safety)*

L.C. WILLIAMS & ASSOCIATES, LLC
150 N Michigan Ave 38th Fl, Chicago, IL 60601-7558
Tel.: (312) 565-3900
Web Site: http://www.lcwa.com
Year Founded: 1985
Public Relations Agency
N.A.I.C.S.: 541820
Kim Blazek Dahlborn *(Pres & CEO)*
Allison Kurtz *(Exec VP)*
Shannon Quinn *(Exec VP)*
Tim Young *(Sr VP)*
Hunter Hackett *(Grp Mgr)*
Matt Kasik *(Supvr-Acct)*
Jim Kokoris *(Exec VP)*
Cheryl Georgas *(Sr VP)*
Deanna Killackey *(Sr VP)*
Bill Dahlborn *(VP)*
Lindsay Lucenta *(Supvr-Acct)*
Mary Velan *(Supvr-Acct)*
Claire Vartabedian *(Supvr-Acct)*
Hannah Cheney *(Acct Exec)*
Brittni Olson *(Acct Exec)*
Brian Shutters *(Acct Exec)*

L.D. DAVIS INDUSTRIES INC.
1725 The Fairway, Jenkintown, PA 19046
Tel.: (215) 886-6001
Web Site: http://www.lddavis.com
Sales Range: $10-24.9 Million
Emp.: 50
Adhesives
N.A.I.C.S.: 325520
Stacey Kreisler *(Mgr-Sls)*
Trip Davis *(Pres)*

L.E. COPPERSMITH INC.
525 S Douglas St Ste 100, El Segundo, CA 90245-4707
Tel.: (310) 607-8000 CA
Web Site: http://www.coppersmith.com
Year Founded: 1957
Sales Range: $10-24.9 Million
Emp.: 104
Provider of Freight Transportation Arrangement Services
N.A.I.C.S.: 488510
Jeff Coppersmith *(Pres)*
Bud Coppersmith *(Exec VP)*
Douglas Walkley *(CFO)*
Lew Coppersmith *(Chm)*

L.E. JOHNSON PRODUCTS INC.
2100 Sterling Ave, Elkhart, IN 46516
Tel.: (574) 293-5664
Web Site: http://www.johnsonhardware.com
Rev.: $25,000,000
Emp.: 178
Door Opening & Closing Devices Mfr
N.A.I.C.S.: 332510
Michael Myers *(Dir-Mktg)*
Terry Gillespie *(Mgr-Credit)*
Karen Hillman *(Supvr-Assembly)*

L.E. SCHWARTZ & SON INC.
279 Reid St, Macon, GA 31206
Tel.: (478) 745-6563
Web Site: http://www.leschwartz.com
Sales Range: $10-24.9 Million
Emp.: 170
Roofing Contractors
N.A.I.C.S.: 238160
Melvin Kruger *(CEO)*
Steven Kruger *(Pres)*

L.E. SIMMONS & ASSOCIATES, INC.
600 Travis St Ste 6600, Houston, TX 77002
Tel.: (713) 227-7888 DE
Web Site: http://www.scfpartners.com
Year Founded: 1989
Sales Range: $10-24.9 Million
Emp.: 20
Privater Equity Firm
N.A.I.C.S.: 523999
L. E. Simmons *(Pres)*
Anthony F. DeLuca *(Partner)*
John W. Geddes *(Partner)*
Ann G. Fox *(Mng Dir)*
Theresa W. Eaton *(Mng Dir)*
Nicholas B. Drake *(VP)*
David C. Baldwin *(Mng Dir)*
Andrew L. Waite *(Mng Dir)*

Subsidiaries:

Westbrook Sales & Distributing Corp (1)
1111 Lockwood Dr, Houston, TX 77020
Tel.: (713) 675-6438
Web Site: http://www.westbrookmfg.com
Sales Range: $50-74.9 Million
Emp.: 150
Mfr Pipe Fittings
N.A.I.C.S.: 332919
Charles Westbrook *(Pres & CEO)*
Larry York *(VP-Sls & Customer Svc)*
Danny Westbrook *(Sr VP-Sls-North America)*
Robert McClain *(CFO)*

Subsidiary (Domestic):

Forged Components, Inc. (2)
14527 Smith Rd, Humble, TX 77396
Tel.: (281) 441-4088
Web Site: http://www.forgedcomponents.com
Sales Range: $1-9.9 Million
Emp.: 78
Iron & Steel Forging
N.A.I.C.S.: 332111

Karl Lyons *(Founder)*

L.E. SMITH CO.
1030 E Wilson St, Bryan, OH 43506
Tel.: (419) 636-4555
Web Site: http://www.lesmith.com
Sales Range: $25-49.9 Million
Emp.: 135
Builders' Hardware
N.A.I.C.S.: 423710
Amy Miller *(Dir-Bus Dev)*
Jenni Turner *(Mgr-Client Svc)*
Mari Ivan *(COO)*
Kevin Bock *(Dir-HR & Fabrication)*

L.E. WENTZ GROUP. INC.
555 Twin Dolfin Dr Ste 160, Redwood City, CA 94065
Tel.: (650) 592-3950 CA
Web Site: http://www.wentzgroup.com
Year Founded: 1975
Sales Range: $10-24.9 Million
Emp.: 75
Provider of Construction Services
N.A.I.C.S.: 236220
Brad Wentz *(Pres)*
Eric Anderson *(Controller)*

L.E.W. HOLDING CO. INC.
220 Yocumtown Rd, Etters, PA 17319
Tel.: (717) 938-1468
Web Site: http://www.lewinc.com
Rev.: $19,715,717
Emp.: 30
Holding Company
N.A.I.C.S.: 551112
Steve Tope *(Controller)*

Subsidiaries:

L.E.W. Equipment Co., Inc. (1)
220 Yocumtown Rd, Etters, PA 17319
Tel.: (717) 938-1468
Web Site: http://www.lewinc.com
Rev.: $19,715,713
Emp.: 100
Heavy Construction Equipment Rental
N.A.I.C.S.: 532412

Leon E. Wintermyer Inc. (1)
220 Yocumtown Rd, Etters, PA 17319
Tel.: (717) 938-1468
Web Site: http://www.lewinc.com
Sales Range: $10-24.9 Million
Emp.: 100
Surfacing & Paving
N.A.I.C.S.: 237310

L.F. GEORGE INC.
W 231 N 1129 HWY F, Waukesha, WI 53186
Tel.: (262) 567-6666
Web Site: http://www.lfgeorge.com
Sales Range: $10-24.9 Million
Emp.: 20
Industrial Machinery & Equipment
N.A.I.C.S.: 423830
Marshall Garcia *(Mgr-Parts)*
Charles J. Folkman Jr. *(Owner)*

L.F. MANUFACTURING INC.
Hwy 290 E CR236, Giddings, TX 78942
Tel.: (979) 542-8027
Web Site: http://www.lfm-frp.com
Sales Range: $10-24.9 Million
Emp.: 184
Plastics Pipe & Fitting Mfr
N.A.I.C.S.: 326122
David Johnston *(Gen Mgr)*

L.F. SPORTSWEAR INC.
5333 McConnelly Ave, Los Angeles, CA 90066
Tel.: (310) 437-4100 CA
Web Site: http://www.lfstores.com
Year Founded: 1980
Sales Range: $10-24.9 Million
Emp.: 60

Women's & Misses' Outerwear
N.A.I.C.S.: 315250
Phillip L. Furst *(Pres & Treas)*
Steven Katz *(VP)*

L.F.P., INC.
8484 Wilshire Blvd, Beverly Hills, CA 90211-3227
Tel.: (323) 651-5400 CA
Web Site: http://www.hustler.com
Year Founded: 1976
Sales Range: $10-24.9 Million
Emp.: 125
Periodicals Publisher & Adult-Themed Video Distr
N.A.I.C.S.: 513120
Larry Flynt *(Owner, Chm & CEO)*
Michael H. Klein *(Pres)*

Subsidiaries:

LFP Broadcasting, LLC (1)
8484 Wilshire Blvd Ste 900, Beverly Hills, CA 90211-3227
Tel.: (323) 651-5400
Web Site: http://www.hustlertv.com
Adult Entertainment Cable Broadcasting Network
N.A.I.C.S.: 516210
Michael H. Klein *(Pres)*
Jim Dettman *(Sr VP-Sls & Mktg)*

Subsidiary (Domestic):

New Frontier Media, Inc. (2)
6000 Spine Rd Ste 100, Boulder, CO 80301
Tel.: (303) 444-0900
Web Site: http://www.noof.com
Sales Range: $125-149.9 Million
Emp.: 120
Holding Company; Adult-Themed & General Motion Picture Entertainment Distr
N.A.I.C.S.: 551112
Dennis McGuire *(Dir-Technical Svcs)*
Larry Flynt *(CEO)*
Chris Woodward *(CFO)*

Subsidiary (Domestic):

Colorado Satellite Broadcasting, Inc. (3)
6000 Spine Rd Ste 100, Boulder, CO 80301
Tel.: (303) 786-8700
Web Site: http://www.tenaffiliates.com
Adult-Themed Television Broadcasting
N.A.I.C.S.: 516120
Amy Rowcliffe *(Mgr-Affiliate Sls & Mktg)*
Tim Lee *(Dir-Affiliate Sls & Mktg)*
Lillian Martin *(Sr VP-Affiliate Sls & Mktg)*
Amy Sarrazin *(Sr Mgr-Mktg)*
Jacklyn Stevenson *(Sr Mgr-Mktg)*

Lightning Entertainment Group, Inc. (3)
301 Arizona Ave 4th Fl, Santa Monica, CA 90401
Tel.: (310) 255-7999
Web Site: http://www.lightningentertainmentgroup.com
Motion Picture Production, Sales & Distribution
N.A.I.C.S.: 512120
Nancy Lanham *(Dir-Media Ops)*
James C. Walker *(Co-Pres)*

MRG Entertainment, Inc. (3)
301 Arizona Ave 4th Fl, Santa Monica, CA 90401
Tel.: (310) 255-1200
Motion Picture Distribution
N.A.I.C.S.: 512120

L.G. EVERIST INC.
350 S Main Ave Ste 400, Sioux Falls, SD 57104-6322
Tel.: (605) 334-5000 IA
Web Site: http://www.lgeverist.com
Year Founded: 1876
Sales Range: $150-199.9 Million
Emp.: 300
Producer of Aggregate Supply of Sand & Gravel for Mining & Marine Construction Services

L.G. EVERIST INC.

L.G. Everist Inc.—(Continued)
N.A.I.C.S.: 212319
Rob Everist *(Pres & CEO)*
Wayne Stoffers *(MIS Mgr)*
Tim Cheever *(Sls Mgr-Mountain)*
Mark Hoffman *(Sls Mgr-Midwest Div)*
Brian Phelps *(Gen Mgr-Cut Stone & Mgr-Mktg)*
Denny Fields *(COO)*
Steve Mousel *(CFO & VP-Resources)*
Rick Everist Jr. *(Chm)*

Subsidiaries:

D & I Railroad (1)
300 S Phillips Ave Ste 200, Sioux Falls, SD 57117
Tel.: (605) 334-5000
Web Site: http://www.dirailroad.com
Sales Range: $10-24.9 Million
Emp.: 25
Railroad Operator
N.A.I.C.S.: 482111
Jack Parliament *(Pres & Gen Mgr)*
Tim Smith *(Mgr-Ops, Safety & Trng)*

Jasper Stone Company (1)
300 S Phillips Ave Ste 200, Sioux Falls, SD 57104-6322
Tel.: (605) 330-6587
Web Site: http://www.jasperstoneco.com
Sales Range: $10-24.9 Million
Emp.: 15
Stone Product Mfr
N.A.I.C.S.: 327991

L.G. Everist Inc. - Mountain Division (1)
7321 E 88th Ave Ste 200, Henderson, CO 80640
Tel.: (303) 287-4656
Stone Product Mfr
N.A.I.C.S.: 327991

L.G. PIKE CONSTRUCTION CO.

815 W Madison Ave, Arkansas City, KS 67005
Tel.: (620) 442-9150
Web Site: http://www.lgpike.com
Year Founded: 1967
Rev.: $11,971,629
Emp.: 50
Railroad Maintenance Services
N.A.I.C.S.: 423860
Carlla Pike *(Treas & Sec)*
Darin Pike *(VP)*
Ted Biggs *(VP)*
Angela Bruce *(Treas & Sec)*

L.H. HAYWARD & CO., LLC

5401 Toler St, Harahan, LA 70123
Tel.: (504) 733-8480
Web Site:
https://www.camelliabrand.com
Year Founded: 1923
Dried Beans & Peas Whslr & Distr
N.A.I.C.S.: 424510
Vince Hayward *(Owner & CEO)*

Subsidiaries:

Gulf Coast Blenders, Inc. (1)
7801 Townsend Pl, New Orleans, LA 70126
Tel.: (504) 242-8888
Web Site: https://gulfcoastblenders.com
All Other Miscellaneous Food Mfr
N.A.I.C.S.: 311999

L.H. INDUSTRIES CORP.

4420 Clubview Dr, Fort Wayne, IN 46804
Tel.: (260) 432-5563
Web Site:
http://www.lhindustries.com
Rev.: $18,700,000
Emp.: 200
Metal Stamping
N.A.I.C.S.: 332119
Bruce Emerick *(Pres)*

Subsidiaries:

L.H. Carbide Corporation (1)
4420 Clubview Dr, Fort Wayne, IN 46804
Tel.: (260) 432-5563
Web Site: http://www.lhcarbide.com
Mfr of Stamping Dies
N.A.I.C.S.: 333514
Danny McLemore *(VP-Sls & Mktg)*

L.H. Stamping Corp. (1)
4420 Clubview Dr, Fort Wayne, IN 46804
Tel.: (260) 432-9372
Web Site: http://www.lhindustries.com
Metal Stamping Mfr
N.A.I.C.S.: 332119
Joe Siela *(COO)*

L.H. LACY COMPANY

1880 Crown, Dallas, TX 75234
Tel.: (214) 357-0146
Web Site: http://www.lhlacy.com
Rev.: $46,595,167
Emp.: 150
Concrete Construction
N.A.I.C.S.: 237310
Mike Lacy *(Chm & CEO)*
Brent Morris *(Sr VP)*
Ron Murawski *(Pres)*

L.I. CHILD & FAMILY DEVELOPMENT SERVICES, INC.

98 Austin St, Patchogue, NY 11772
Tel.: (631) 758-5200 NY
Web Site: http://www.liheadstart.org
Year Founded: 1965
Sales Range: $10-24.9 Million
Emp.: 423
Child & Family Support Services
N.A.I.C.S.: 624190
Elsa Cruciani *(Dir-Fin)*
Annette Harris *(Dir-Program Ops)*
Brenda Joyce H. Scott *(Sec)*
Kathleen Cafaro *(Treas)*
Martha A. Parry *(Co-Chm)*
Terrence D. Goode *(Co-Chm)*
Debrah Garcia *(CEO)*
Nelly Amaya *(Treas)*

L.I.S. CUSTOM DESIGNS, INC.

999 S Oyster Bay Rd Ste 407, Bethpage, NY 11714
Tel.: (516) 484-6262
Web Site: http://www.liscustom.com
Year Founded: 1929
Sales Range: $10-24.9 Million
Emp.: 80
Kitchen Cabinets
N.A.I.C.S.: 423310
Gene Spivak *(Pres)*
Ross Geylin *(Sr VP)*

L.I.S.T. INC.

84 Business Park Dr, Armonk, NY 10504
Tel.: (914) 765-0700
Web Site: http://www.l-i-s-t.com
Year Founded: 1987
Sales Range: $1-9.9 Million
Emp.: 22
Direct Mail Advertising Services
N.A.I.C.S.: 541860
Glenn Freedman *(Pres & CEO)*
Karin A. Bilich *(Dir-Mktg)*
Steve Brinley *(VP-Sls)*

Subsidiaries:

DefinitiveData, Inc. (1)
84 Business Park Dr, Armonk, NY 10504
Tel.: (914) 765-0700
Web Site: http://www.definitivedatabase.com
Marketing Database Services
N.A.I.C.S.: 518210
Chris Salvo *(Pres)*
Glenn Freedman *(CEO)*
Steve Brinley *(VP)*

L.J. STONE INC.

9100 N Wheeling Ave, Muncie, IN 47304
Tel.: (765) 288-5044
Web Site: http://www.ljstone.com
Rev.: $10,300,000
Emp.: 50
Door & Window Products
N.A.I.C.S.: 444110
Trent Stone *(Pres)*

L.J. THALMANN COMPANY

3132 Lake Ave, Wilmette, IL 60091
Tel.: (847) 256-0561
Web Site:
http://www.chaletnursery.com
Rev.: $20,811,315
Emp.: 90
Landscaping & Garden Nursery Retailer
N.A.I.C.S.: 444240
Lawrence J. Thalmann III *(Pres)*

L.L. BEAN, INC.

15 Casco St, Freeport, ME 04033
Tel.: (207) 865-4761 ME
Web Site: http://www.llbean.com
Year Founded: 1912
Sales Range: $1-4.9 Billion
Emp.: 3,900
Apparel, Housewares, Outerwear & Sports Equipment Sales
N.A.I.C.S.: 315990
Shawn Gorman *(Chm)*
L. L. Bean *(Founder)*
Stephen Smith *(Pres & CEO)*

L.L. VANN ELECTRIC INC.

833 Purser Dr, Raleigh, NC 27603
Tel.: (919) 772-2567
Web Site: http://www.llvann.net
Sales Range: $1-9.9 Million
Emp.: 100
Provider of General Electrical Contractor Services
N.A.I.C.S.: 238210
Joan Alford *(Office Mgr)*
James Sadler *(Pres)*
Roy Schmick *(Exec VP)*
Russell Richter *(VP)*

L.M. MCLAMB & SON CONSTRUCTION CO., INC.

800 McLamb Rd NW, Calabash, NC 28467
Tel.: (910) 287-6688
Web Site: http://www.lmmclamb.com
Year Founded: 1961
Sales Range: $10-24.9 Million
Emp.: 65
Sewer Line & Related Structure Construction Services
N.A.I.C.S.: 237110
Jimmy McLamb *(Pres)*

L.M. SANDLER & SONS

448 Viking Dr Ste 220, Virginia Beach, VA 23452-7331
Tel.: (757) 463-5000 VA
Sales Range: $75-99.9 Million
Emp.: 30
Real Estate Development
N.A.I.C.S.: 424460
Catherine Scarborough *(Project Mgr)*

L.M. SCOFIELD COMPANY

6533 Bandini Blvd, Los Angeles, CA 90040
Tel.: (323) 720-3000 CA
Web Site: http://www.scofield.com
Year Founded: 1915
Sales Range: $100-124.9 Million
Emp.: 140
Mfr of Colors & Texturing Systems for Concrete
N.A.I.C.S.: 325998

U.S. PRIVATE

Phillip Arnold *(Chm & CEO)*
Cam Villar *(Dir-Mktg)*

Subsidiaries:

L.M. Scofield Company (1)
4155 Scofield Rd, Douglasville, GA 30134-3985
Tel.: (323) 720-8810
Web Site: http://www.scofield.com
Sales Range: $25-49.9 Million
Emp.: 75
Mfr of Colors & Texturing Systems for Concrete
N.A.I.C.S.: 325998

L.M. Scofield Company (1)
280 Park Ave, Rutherford, NJ 07070 (100%)
Tel.: (201) 672-9050
Web Site: http://www.scofield.com
Sales Range: $25-49.9 Million
Emp.: 50
Colors & Texturing Systems for Concrete Mfr
N.A.I.C.S.: 424690
Mike DeCandia *(Mgr)*

L.M. Scofield Company (1)
1652 E Main St Ste 200, Saint Charles, IL 60174
Tel.: (630) 377-5959
Web Site: http://www.scofield.com
Sales Range: $10-24.9 Million
Emp.: 2
Sales of Colors & Texturing Systems for Concrete
N.A.I.C.S.: 325998

L.N. CURTIS & SONS

1800 Peralta St, Oakland, CA 94607-1603
Tel.: (510) 839-5111 CA
Web Site: http://www.lncurtis.com
Year Founded: 1929
Sales Range: $75-99.9 Million
Emp.: 70
Distr of Municipal & Industrial Fire Protection & Safety Equipment
N.A.I.C.S.: 423850
Paul F. Curtis *(Pres & CEO)*
Tim Henderson *(Specialist-Law Enforcement Equipment)*
Nik Taranik *(Specialist-Personal Protective Equipment-Northwest)*
John Cefalu *(Mgr-Sls-Northwest)*

Subsidiaries:

ECMS, Inc. (1)
4200 W Russell Rd Ste 113, Las Vegas, NV 89118-2365
Tel.: (702) 243-7149
Web Site: http://www.ecmsinc.biz
Sales Range: $1-9.9 Million
Emp.: 40
Protective Ensemble Cleaning Services
N.A.I.C.S.: 561990

Firefighters Bookstore, Inc. (1)
16821 Knott Ave, La Mirada, CA 90638
Tel.: (714) 375-4888
Web Site: http://www.firebooks.com
Emp.: 4
Online Book Retailer
N.A.I.C.S.: 459210
Brandon Winters *(Mgr-Store)*

L.N. Curtis & Sons - Intermountain Division (1)
1195 S 300 W, Salt Lake City, UT 84101
Tel.: (801) 486-7285
Web Site: http://www.lncurtis.com
Emp.: 15
Fire Fighting Equipment Whslr
N.A.I.C.S.: 423990
Brandon Clough *(Mgr-Sls)*

L.N. Curtis & Sons - Northwest Division (1)
6507 S 208th St, Kent, WA 98032-5230
Tel.: (206) 622-2875
Web Site: http://www.lncurtis.com
Emp.: 20
Fire Fighting Equipment Whslr
N.A.I.C.S.: 423850
Patrick Lonergan *(Mgr-Sls)*

COMPANIES

L.N. Curtis & Sons - Pacific South Division (1)
16821 Knott Ave, La Mirada, CA 90638
Tel.: (323) 780-0254
Web Site: http://www.lncurtis.com
Emp.: 20
Fire Fighting Equipment Whslr
N.A.I.C.S.: 423990
Brandon Winters (Mgr-Ops)

L.N. Curtis & Sons - Southwest Division (1)
4647 S 33rd St, Phoenix, AZ 85040
Tel.: (602) 453-3911
Emp.: 12
Fire Fighting Equipment Whslr
N.A.I.C.S.: 423990
Tim Henderson (VP-Sls)

L.P. THEBAULT COMPANY
249 Pomeroy Rd, Parsippany, NJ 07054
Tel.: (973) 884-1300
Web Site: http://www.thebault.com
Rev.: $91,614,853
Emp.: 300
Commercial Printing, Lithographic
N.A.I.C.S.: 323111

L.P.R. CONSTRUCTION CO.
1171 Des Moines Ave, Loveland, CO 80537
Tel.: (303) 665-7501
Web Site: http://www.lprconstruction.com
Year Founded: 1979
Rev.: $66,800,000
Emp.: 355
Structural Steel & Precast Concrete Contractors
N.A.I.C.S.: 238120
Mike Charley (VP)

L.R. GORRELL COMPANY INC.
544 Pylon Dr, Raleigh, NC 27606
Tel.: (919) 821-1161
Web Site: http://www.lrgorrell.com
Year Founded: 1951
Sales Range: $10-24.9 Million
Emp.: 20
Manufacturers Representative of Warm Air Heating & Air Conditioning
N.A.I.C.S.: 423730
Robbie Gorrell (Pres)
Matthew Boss (Mgr-Sls)
Jimmy Jones (Branch Mgr)
Ron Brewton (Branch Mgr)
Don Boltz (Branch Mgr)
Pat McCann (Branch Mgr)

L.W. MILLER TRANSPORTATION
1050 W 200 N, Logan, UT 84321
Tel.: (435) 753-8350
Web Site: http://www.lwmiller.com
Sales Range: $75-99.9 Million
Emp.: 450
Contract Haulers
N.A.I.C.S.: 484121
Larry W. Miller (Pres)
Chuck Webb (Mgr)
Scott Goodfellow (Mgr-Parts)
Dennis Bradshaw (Mgr)
Kent D. Stratford (CFO)

L.W. PACKARD & CO., INC.
22 Mill St, Ashland, NH 03217
Tel.: (603) 968-3351
Web Site: http://www.lwpackard.com
Year Founded: 1916
Sales Range: $10-24.9 Million
Emp.: 30
Mfr of Broadwoven Wool Fabrics
N.A.I.C.S.: 313210
John L. Glidden (Pres)

L/B WATER SERVICE INC.
540 S High St, Selinsgrove, PA 17870
Tel.: (570) 374-2355
Web Site: http://www.lbwaterservice.com
Rev.: $22,314,210
Emp.: 75
Provider of Plumbing Fittings & Supplies
N.A.I.C.S.: 423720
Colin Houser (Sec)
Jacob Jake Shadle (Mgr)
Lesley Smith (Office Mgr)
Troy Dressler (Mgr)
Ben Reichley (Mktg Mgr)

L2 CAPITAL PARTNERS
92 W Lancaster Ave Ste 210, Devon, PA 19333
Tel.: (610) 922-4030
Web Site: http://www.l2capital.net
Year Founded: 2011
Privater Equity Firm
N.A.I.C.S.: 523999
Bob Levine (Mng Partner)
Matt Klein (Partner)
Connor McMahan (Principal)

Subsidiaries:

Ecotone, Inc. (1)
2120 High Point Rd, Forest Hill, MD 21050-2206
Tel.: (410) 420-2600
Web Site: http://www.ecotoneinc.com
Environmental Consulting Services
N.A.I.C.S.: 541620
Rich Berkey (Mgr-Construction)
Gary Stokes (COO)
Scott McGill (Founder & CEO)

Orion International Consulting Group, LLC (1)
400 Regency Forest Dr Ste 310, Cary, NC 27518
Tel.: (919) 653-3720
Web Site: http://www.orioninternational.com
Sales Range: $25-49.9 Million
Emp.: 75
Former-Military Personnel Job Placement Services
N.A.I.C.S.: 561311
William H. Laughlin (Co-Founder)
Mike Starich (Pres)
Tim Isacco (COO)
Brian Henry (Officer-Recruiting & VP-Ops)
Bill Key (VP-Ops-Enlisted Recruiting)
Steve Casey (Sr Partner & VP-Sls Ops)
Vearl A. Williams (Sr Partner)
Jeffrey Evans (Chm)
Steve Bjerke (CFO)

Subsidiary (Domestic):

Novotus, LLC (2)
5508 Parkcrest Dr Ste 100, Austin, TX 78731
Tel.: (512) 733-2244
Web Site: http://www.novotus.com
Sales Range: $1-9.9 Million
Emp.: 70
Full Service Recruiting
N.A.I.C.S.: 561311
Mike Mayeux (CEO)
Cory Kruse (Pres)
Penny Lozano (CFO)
Dustin Little (Dir-Talent Solutions)

Division (Domestic):

Orion International Consulting Group, LLC - Gemini Energy Services Division (2)
2640 Financial Ct Ste G, San Diego, CA 92117
Tel.: (858) 939-1521
Web Site: http://www.geminienergyservices.com
Energy Consulting Services
N.A.I.C.S.: 541690
Jimmy Haley (Mng Dir & VP)
Kim Primerano (Dir-Bus Dev)
Rick Friesen (Dir-Field Svcs)
Crystal Friesen (Office Mgr)
Brittany Mason (Office Mgr)

Subsidiary (Domestic):

Therapy Staff, LLC (2)
705 S Main St Ste 220, Plymouth, MI 48170
Tel.: (248) 349-5050
Web Site: http://www.therapystaff.com
Sales Range: $10-24.9 Million
Emp.: 12
Healthcare Professional Recruiting & Staffing Services
N.A.I.C.S.: 561311
Joel Williams (Gen Mgr)

Division (Domestic):

Therapy Staff, LLC - Detroit Regional Division (3)
705 S Main St Ste 220, Plymouth, MI 48170
Tel.: (734) 354-8000
Therapist Recruiting & Staffing Services
N.A.I.C.S.: 561311

Therapy Staff, LLC - National Travel Division (3)
2700 Bee Caves Rd Ste 204, Austin, TX 78746
Tel.: (877) 366-2580
Therapist Recruiting & Staffing Services
N.A.I.C.S.: 561311

Robbins, Inc. (1)
4777 Eastern Ave, Cincinnati, OH 45226-2338
Tel.: (513) 871-8988
Web Site: http://www.robbinsfloor.com
Sales Range: $75-99.9 Million
Emp.: 270
Mfr of Hardwood Flooring, Portable Floors, Racquetball Courts, Squash Courts, Residential Wood Block & Parquet Flooring
N.A.I.C.S.: 321918
Todd Braun (Pres & CEO)
Ken Thomas (VP-Mktg)

Winchester Carpet & Rug, LLC (1)
116 Featherbed Ln, Winchester, VA 22601
Tel.: (540) 667-9507
Web Site: http://www.rugs-direct.com
Floor Covering Online Retailer
N.A.I.C.S.: 449121
John Kay (Controller)
Myles Felsing (CEO)
Ken Vick (Exec VP-Sls)

Subsidiary (Domestic):

Lightopia LLC (2)
2001 N Sepulveda Blvd, Manhattan Beach, CA 90266
Tel.: (949) 715-5575
Web Site: http://www.lightopiaonline.com
Lighting Equipment Designer & Mfr
N.A.I.C.S.: 335132
Holly McKenna Esslinger (Mgr-Pur)

L2T MEDIA
1840 Oak Ave Ste 315N, Evanston, IL 60201
Tel.: (847) 944-9280
Web Site: http://www.l2tmedia.com
Year Founded: 2007
Sales Range: $10-24.9 Million
Emp.: 27
Advetising Agency
N.A.I.C.S.: 541810
Tom Moorhead (Mng Partner & VP-Sls)
Brian Famiglietti (VP-Bus Dev)
Liz Prior (Mng Partner & VP-Ops)

L5E LLC
4545 Fuller Dr Ste 412, Irving, TX 75038
Tel.: (972) 445-9584
Web Site: http://www.energyby5.com
Year Founded: 2011
Energy Consulting Services
N.A.I.C.S.: 541690
Brian Hayduk (CEO)
Eric Plateis (Chief Risk Officer)
Jeff Schiefelbein (Chief Culture Officer)
Josh Coleman (COO)

Subsidiaries:

Luthin Associates, Inc. (1)
865 State Route 33 Ste 3 PMB 1077, Freehold, NJ 07728
Tel.: (732) 774-0005
Web Site: https://www.energyby5.com
Administrative Management & General Management Consulting Services
N.A.I.C.S.: 541611

LA AGENCIA DE ORCI & ASOCIADOS
11620 Wilshire Blvd Ste 600, Los Angeles, CA 90025-1706
Tel.: (310) 444-7300 CA
Year Founded: 1982
Sales Range: $10-24.9 Million
Emp.: 33
Advetising Agency
N.A.I.C.S.: 541810
Norma Orci (Co-Founder)
Hector Orci (Co-Founder)
Allen Perez (Dir-Creative Brdcst)
Roberto Santiago (Dir-Client Svcs)
Ricardo Cardenas (Exec Dir-Creative)
Valarie De La Garza (Dir-PR)
Andrew Orci (Chm)
Charles Vasquez (Dir-Media-Acct Plng)
Marina Filippelli (CEO)

LA AMAPOLA INC.
7223 Compton Ave, Los Angeles, CA 90001
Tel.: (323) 587-7118
Web Site: http://www.amapolamarket.com
Sales Range: $10-24.9 Million
Emp.: 80
Convenience Store Operator
N.A.I.C.S.: 445131
Carlos Galvan (Founder)
Bob Herrera (Controller)

LA ASSOCIATES, INC.
1953 Gallows Rd Ste 600, Vienna, VA 22182-3988
Tel.: (703) 734-5700 VA
Year Founded: 1990
Sales Range: $10-24.9 Million
Emp.: 75
Holding Company; Direct Marketing Services
N.A.I.C.S.: 551112
George G. Lizama (Pres)
Gracy K. Huff (Partner)
Greg Albright (Partner & Chief Comm Officer)
Wayne Lizama (COO & CFO)

Subsidiaries:

Production Solutions, Inc. (1)
1953 Gallows Rd Ste 600, Vienna, VA 22182-3930
Tel.: (703) 734-5700
Web Site: http://www.productionsolutions.com
Sales Range: $10-24.9 Million
Emp.: 100
Direct Marketing Services
N.A.I.C.S.: 541860
Wayne Lizama (Partner, CFO & COO)
Greg Albright (Co-Founder, Partner & Chief Comm Officer)
Benjamin Harris (Pres)
Denise Moxam (VP-HR)
Drew Wilson (Dir-Continuous Improvement)
Scott Chapman (Dir-Bus Dev)
Paul Cornetta (VP-Production)
Stephen Dougherty (Dir-Bus Dev)
Joseph Gomez (Dir-Bus Dev)
Jim Jacobs (VP-Digital Svcs)
Bill Johnson (Dir-Production)
Ella Kaszubski (Dir-Production)
Danielle Milner (Mgr-Mktg Comm)
Don Poudrier (Dir-Production)
Gigi Shanahan (Dir-Production)
Leigh Janis (VP-Sls & Client Experience)
Mark Nichols (VP-Info Tech)

LA BAGUETTE FRENCH BREAD & PASTRY SHOP

La Baguette French Bread & Pastry Shop—(Continued)

LA BAGUETTE FRENCH BREAD & PASTRY SHOP
3088 Poplar Ave, Memphis, TN 38111-3532
Tel.: (901) 458-0900
Web Site:
 http://labaguettememphis.com
Sales Range: $1-9.9 Million
Emp.: 31
Commercial Bakery Services
N.A.I.C.S.: 311812
Karen Brown *(Mgr)*
Gene Amagliani *(Gen Mgr)*

LA BELLE FASHIONS INC.
555 E Jefferson Blvd, Los Angeles, CA 90011
Tel.: (323) 235-2001
Sales Range: $25-49.9 Million
Emp.: 160
Women's, Juniors' & Misses' Dresses
N.A.I.C.S.: 315250

LA BODEGA INC.
3225 S Western Ave, Chicago, IL 60608
Tel.: (773) 847-9100
Web Site:
 http://www.labodegainc.com
Sales Range: $25-49.9 Million
Emp.: 20
Warehouse of Canned Goods
N.A.I.C.S.: 424490
Adolfo Vega *(Pres)*

LA BONITA OLE, INC.
5804 E Columbus Dr, Tampa, FL 33619
Tel.: (813) 319-2252
Year Founded: 1992
Sales Range: $25-49.9 Million
Emp.: 40
Tortilla Mfr
N.A.I.C.S.: 311830
Martha Diaz *(VP-Admin)*
Chris Meyer *(Supvr-Production)*
Tina Frizell *(Coord-Logistics)*
Greg Dingle *(CFO)*
Tammy M. Young *(Pres & CEO)*
Greg Baker-Fitzgerald *(Mgr-Maintenance)*
Dave Waters *(VP-Ops)*
Jim Kelly *(Dir-New Bus Dev)*
Gary Macri *(Dir-IT)*
Idalia Garcia *(Mgr)*

LA CADENA INVESTMENTS
301 S Tippecanoe Ave, San Bernardino, CA 92408
Tel.: (855) 782-8377   CA
Web Site: http://www.staterbros.com
Year Founded: 1936
Investment Company; Supermarkets
N.A.I.C.S.: 445110

Subsidiaries:

Stater Brothers Holdings   (1)
301 S Tippecanoe Ave, San Bernardino, CA 92408
Tel.: (909) 733-5000
Web Site: http://www.staterbros.com
Rev.: $3,859,800,000
Assets: $1,197,346,000
Liabilities: $1,083,896,000
Net Worth: $113,450,000
Earnings: $30,375,000
Emp.: 16,100
Fiscal Year-end: 09/29/2013
Holding Company; Supermarket Operator
N.A.I.C.S.: 551112
Jack H. Brown *(Chm & CEO)*
James W. Lee *(COO)*
Bruce D. Varner *(Sec)*
George A. Frahm *(Pres)*

David J. Harris *(CFO, Chief Acctg Officer & Sr VP-Fin)*
Keith Thomas *(Grp Sr VP-Retail Ops)*
Jack H. Brown *(Chm & CEO)*

Subsidiary (Domestic):

Stater Bros Development Inc   (2)
301 S Tippecanoe Ave, San Bernardino, CA 92408
Tel.: (909) 733-5000
Web Site: http://www.staterbros.com
Rev.: $210,000
Emp.: 2
Real Estate Investors, Except Property Operators
N.A.I.C.S.: 523999

Stater Bros. Markets   (2)
301 S Tippecanoe Ave, San Bernardino, CA 92408
Tel.: (909) 733-5000
Web Site: https://www.staterbros.com
Sales Range: Less than $1 Million
Emp.: 18,000
Supermarkets & Other Grocery Retailers (except Convenience Retailers)
N.A.I.C.S.: 445110
Peter Van Helden *(Chm, Chm, Chm, Pres, CEO, CEO & CEO)*
Michael Reed *(CFO & Sr VP)*
Gil Salazar *(Sr VP-IT)*
Keith Thomas *(Exec VP-Retail Ops)*
Bertha Luna *(Sr VP-Retail Ops)*
Paul Stoffel *(VP-Mktg)*
Greg McNiff *(COO)*
Rebecca Calvin *(CMO & Sr VP)*
Darold Fero *(Sr VP-Distr)*
Sean Varner *(Vice Chm)*

LA CANASTA FURNISHINGS
1235 E Quarry St Ste 101, Corona, CA 92879
Tel.: (909) 738-9636
Web Site: http://www.lacanasta.com
Rev.: $18,300,000
Emp.: 150
Furniture Retailer
N.A.I.C.S.: 449110
Javier Ramirez *(Pres)*

LA CASA DE DON PEDRO, INC.
75 Park Ave, Newark, NJ 07104
Tel.: (973) 482-8312   DE
Web Site: http://www.lacasanwk.org
Year Founded: 1972
Sales Range: $10-24.9 Million
Emp.: 242
Community Development Services
N.A.I.C.S.: 813319
Norma Sessa *(Dir-Community Improvement Div)*
Alle Ries *(Dir-Community & Economic Dev Div)*
Rosalina Melendez *(Dir-Personal Dev Div)*
Raquel D. Merlino *(CFO)*
Martha Villegas *(Dir-Early Childhood Education Div)*
Edward Hernandez *(Dir-Youth, Family, & Health Svcs)*
Raymond Ocasio *(Exec Dir)*

LA CLINICA DE LA RAZA INC.
1450 Fruitvale Ave 3rd Fl, Oakland, CA 94601
Tel.: (510) 535-4000   CA
Web Site: http://www.laclinica.org
Year Founded: 1971
Sales Range: $75-99.9 Million
Emp.: 1,062
Health Care Srvices
N.A.I.C.S.: 622110
Jane Garcia *(CEO)*
Fernando Cortez *(CIO & Officer-Information Security)*
Norma Guerrero *(Sec)*
Jill Noonan *(Pres)*
Paul Marriott Swenson *(Treas)*

Daniel Ayala *(VP)*
Alberto Diaz *(CFO)*
Paul Bayard *(Chief Medical Officer)*

LA CLIPPERS LLC
1212 S Flower 5th Fl, Los Angeles, CA 90015
Tel.: (213) 204-2813   DE
Web Site: http://www.nba.com
Year Founded: 1970
Sales Range: $900-999.9 Million
Emp.: 200
Professional Basketball Franchise & Sports Arena Owner & Operator
N.A.I.C.S.: 711211
Carl Lahr *(Sr VP-Sls & Svc)*
Denise Booth *(VP-Community Rels & Player Programs)*
Gary Sacks *(Asst Gen Mgr)*
Chuck Loth *(Dir-Ticket Ops)*
Todd Sakauye *(Controller)*
Raymond Ortegaso *(VP-HR)*
Gerald Madkins *(Asst Gen Mgr)*
Dennis Rogers *(Dir-Basketball Comm)*
Michael Winger *(Gen Mgr)*
Chris Wallace *(Chief Comm Officer)*
Scott Sonnenberg *(Chief Partnerships Officer)*
Nicole Duckett Fricke *(Gen Counsel)*
Lawrence Frank *(Pres-Basketball Ops)*
Gillian B. Zucker *(Pres-Bus Ops)*

Subsidiaries:

The Los Angeles Clippers Foundation   (1)
6951 S Centinela Ave, Playa Vista, CA 90094
Tel.: (310) 862-6000
Web Site: http://www.nba.com
Charity Organization
N.A.I.C.S.: 813219
Denise Booth *(Exec Dir)*

LA CROSSE LUMBER COMPANY
200 N Main St, Louisiana, MO 63353
Tel.: (573) 754-4533
Web Site:
 http://www.lacrosse.doitbest.com
Sales Range: $25-49.9 Million
Emp.: 25
Lumber & Other Building Materials Distr
N.A.I.C.S.: 423310
Doyle Wiskur *(VP)*

LA CROSSE PUBLIC LIBRARY
800 Main St, La Crosse, IN 54601
Tel.: (608) 789-7100
Web Site:
 https://www.lacrosselibrary.org
Year Founded: 1888
Libraries & Archives
N.A.I.C.S.: 519210
Kionna Jones *(Treas)*

LA CROSSE TRUCK CENTER INC.
205 Causeway Blvd, La Crosse, WI 54603
Tel.: (608) 785-0800
Web Site:
 http://www.lacrossetruck.com
Sales Range: $10-24.9 Million
Emp.: 75
New & Used Truck & Tractor Service & Parts
N.A.I.C.S.: 441110
Stephen Heuslein *(Pres)*
Cindy Bergum *(Sec)*
Joseph Laux *(VP)*
Mike Porter *(Controller)*

LA ESPIGA DE ORO TORTILLA FACTORY
1202 W 15th St, Houston, TX 77008
Tel.: (713) 861-4200
Web Site: http://www.laespiga.com
Rev.: $11,456,216
Emp.: 200
Producer of Tortillas
N.A.I.C.S.: 311830
Alfredo Lira *(Pres)*

LA FEMME PERFUMERY INC.
351 12th Ave S, Naples, FL 34102
Tel.: (239) 434-7444
Web Site:
 http://www.lafemmeperfumery
 naples.com
Year Founded: 1984
Sales Range: $1-9.9 Million
Emp.: 10
Perfume & Cosmetics
N.A.I.C.S.: 456120
Marie Christine *(VP)*
Michael Elden *(Pres)*

LA FOODS
5115 Clareton Dr Ste 200, Agoura Hills, CA 91301
Tel.: (818) 587-3757
Web Site: http://www.lafoods.com
Sales Range: $100-124.9 Million
Emp.: 32
Food Products Distr
N.A.I.C.S.: 424420
Michael Gold *(Dir-Food Bank Div)*
Mark Davis *(Owner)*
Kevin Wayne Campbell *(Partner & Mgr-Logistics)*
Scott Matis *(VP-Retail Sls)*

LA GRANGE GROCERY CO.
143 Busch Dr, Lagrange, GA 30241
Tel.: (706) 884-7325
Web Site:
 http://www.lagrangegrocery.com
Sales Range: $10-24.9 Million
Emp.: 50
Beer & Other Fermented Malt Liquors
N.A.I.C.S.: 424810
Al Zachry *(VP)*
James H. Zachry *(Pres)*
Randy Neighbors *(Mgr-Sls)*

LA GROU MOTOR SERVICE INCORPORATED
3514 S Kostner Ave, Chicago, IL 60632
Tel.: (773) 523-1800
Web Site: http://www.lagrou.com
Rev.: $52,000,000
Emp.: 15
Household Goods Moving & Storage, Local
N.A.I.C.S.: 484210
Donald E. Schimek *(CEO)*
Steve Schuldt *(VP-Fin)*
Timothy Kelly *(VP-Real Estate)*

LA JOLLA BEACH & TENNIS CLUB INC.
2000 Spindrift Dr, La Jolla, CA 92037-3237
Tel.: (858) 454-7126   CA
Web Site: http://www.ljbtc.com
Year Founded: 1935
Sales Range: $25-49.9 Million
Emp.: 500
Membership Sports & Recreation Clubs
N.A.I.C.S.: 713940
John Campbell *(Gen Mgr)*
Jenie Porter *(Controller)*

LA MADELEINE INC.
122201 Merit Ste 900, Dallas, TX 75251
Tel.: (214) 696-6962   TX

COMPANIES — LA TERRA FINA, INC.

Web Site:
http://www.lamadeleine.com
Year Founded: 1982
Sales Range: $150-199.9 Million
Emp.: 2,400
Eating Place
N.A.I.C.S.: 722511
Stefanie Evans *(Reg Mgr-Sls)*
Dennis Pertuit *(Mgr)*
Mike Lascola *(Dir-Ops)*
Laura Stombaugh *(Dir-Trng)*
Lindsey Fiihr *(Mgr-Pur)*
Susan Dederen *(VP-Culinary Ops)*
John Cahill *(COO)*

Subsidiaries:

La Madeleine of Maryland, Inc. (1)
6688 N Central Expy Ste 700, Dallas, TX 75206-5209 **(100%)**
Tel.: (214) 696-6962
Web Site: http://www.lamadeleine.com
Sales Range: $10-24.9 Million
Emp.: 80
Eating Place
N.A.I.C.S.: 722511

LA MANSION DEL RIO INC.
112 College St, San Antonio, TX 78205
Tel.: (210) 518-1000
Web Site: http://www.lamansion.com
Rev.: $10,200,000
Emp.: 5
Hotel
N.A.I.C.S.: 721110

LA MARCHE MANUFACTURING COMPANY
106 Bradrock Dr, Des Plaines, IL 60018
Tel.: (847) 299-1188   IL
Web Site:
http://www.lamarchemfg.com
Year Founded: 1945
Sales Range: $10-24.9 Million
Emp.: 110
Mfr of Industrial & Utility Battery Chargers, DC Power Systems, Power Supplies, DC to AC Inverters; Consta-Volt Chargers, Uninterruptible Power Systems
N.A.I.C.S.: 335999
Rick Rutkowski *(Pres)*
Raj Dhiman *(Exec VP-DP)*
Marius Hetrea *(Mgr-Field Svc)*
Mark Wong *(Engr-Mechanical)*

LA MESA RV CENTER, INC.
7430 Copley Park Pl, San Diego, CA 92111-1122
Tel.: (858) 874-8000   CA
Web Site: http://www.lamesarv.com
Year Founded: 1972
Sales Range: $125-149.9 Million
Emp.: 250
Motor Homes, Recreational Vehicles, Campers, Parts & Service
N.A.I.C.S.: 441210
James R. Kimbrell *(CEO)*
Kelly Sandstrom *(Controller)*
Bill Kendall *(Dir-Svc & Parts)*
Mike Lenoir *(Dir-Svc)*
Sharon Padley *(Mgr-Inventory-Sanford)*
Bill Miller *(Mgr-Parts-Natl)*
Paul Jackson *(Mgr-Parts-Phoenix)*
J. R. Simmons *(Mgr-Parts-Davis)*
Harry Vasilakis *(Mgr-Svc)*
Chris Pettit *(Mgr-Svc-Mesa)*
Stephanie Ross *(Mgr-Reputation)*
Jason Kimbrell *(Pres)*

LA PAZ MINING CORP.
7558 W Thunderbird Rd #1-486, Peoria, AZ 85381
Tel.: (602) 509-2822   NV
Year Founded: 2011
Uranium Mining
N.A.I.C.S.: 212290
Charles Irizarry *(Pres, CEO, CFO, Treas & Sec)*

LA PAZ REGIONAL HOSPITAL
1200 W Mohave Rd, Parker, AZ 85344
Tel.: (928) 669-9201   AZ
Web Site:
http://www.lapazhospital.org
Year Founded: 2000
Sales Range: $10-24.9 Million
Emp.: 200
Healthcare Services
N.A.I.C.S.: 622110
Juanita Phelps *(Treas & Sec)*
Carl Flanagan *(CFO)*

LA PLATA ELECTRIC ASSOCIATION
45 Stewart St, Durango, CO 81303
Tel.: (970) 247-5786
Web Site: http://www.lpea.coop
Sales Range: $75-99.9 Million
Emp.: 115
Distribution, Electric Power
N.A.I.C.S.: 221122
Linda Looman *(Dir-HR)*
Jessica Matlock *(CEO)*

LA PREFERIDA, INC.
3400 W 35th St, Chicago, IL 60632
Tel.: (773) 254-7200   IL
Web Site: http://www.lapreferida.com
Year Founded: 1898
Sales Range: $75-99.9 Million
Emp.: 60
Ethnic Food Distr
N.A.I.C.S.: 424490
David Steinbarth *(Owner)*

Subsidiaries:

Worldwide Produce, Inc. (1)
2404 S Wolcott, Chicago, IL 60608
Tel.: (312) 666-2365
Sales Range: $25-49.9 Million
Emp.: 30
Mfr & Distributor of Mexican, Cuban & Puerto Rican Foods
N.A.I.C.S.: 424490

LA PRIMA CATERING
5105 Berwyn Rd Ste 101, College Park, MD 20740
Tel.: (301) 220-1001
Web Site:
http://www.laprimacatering.com
Sales Range: $10-24.9 Million
Emp.: 200
Restaurant & Catering Services
N.A.I.C.S.: 722511
David Evans *(Pres)*
Misty Zani *(Mgr-Event)*
Dina Silnicky *(Dir-Bus Dev)*

LA RABIDA CHILDREN'S HOSPITAL
6501 S Promontory Dr, Chicago, IL 60649
Tel.: (773) 363-6700   IL
Web Site: http://www.larabida.org
Year Founded: 1896
Sales Range: $50-74.9 Million
Emp.: 400
Child Health Care Services
N.A.I.C.S.: 622110
Aden Henry *(VP-Patient Care Svcs)*
Brenda J. Wolf *(Pres & CEO)*
Mark Renfree *(CFO & VP-Admin)*

LA RANCHERA INC.
503 Berry Rd, Houston, TX 77022
Tel.: (713) 699-4400
Web Site:
http://www.larancherainc.com
Year Founded: 1994
Sales Range: $10-24.9 Million
Emp.: 20
Tortilla Mfr
N.A.I.C.S.: 311830
Caesar Zavaleta *(Pres)*

LA REGALE LLC
350 5th Ave Ste 901, New York, NY 10118
Tel.: (212) 279-8360   NY
Web Site: http://www.laregale.com
Sales Range: $10-24.9 Million
Emp.: 15
Handbags
N.A.I.C.S.: 424350
Albert Shamah *(Pres)*

LA REGINA DI SAN MARZANO USA
17 Battery Pl Ste 610, New York, NY 10004-1133
Tel.: (212) 269-4202
Sales Range: $10-24.9 Million
Emp.: 99
Food Products Mfr
N.A.I.C.S.: 311999
Felice Romano *(Principal)*

LA REINA COMPANY
316 N Ford Blvd, Los Angeles, CA 90022-1121
Tel.: (323) 268-2791   CA
Web Site: http://www.lareinainc.com
Year Founded: 1958
Sales Range: $75-99.9 Million
Emp.: 100
Mfr of Flour Tortillas, Tortilla Chips, Taco Shells, Tostado Shells, Frozen Burritos, Taquitos, Crackling Skins & other Mexican Food Related Products
N.A.I.C.S.: 311830
Mauro Robles *(Founder & Chm)*
Ricardo Robles *(Pres)*

Subsidiaries:

Anita's Mexican Foods Corp. (1)
3454 N Mike Daley Dr, San Bernardino, CA 92407
Tel.: (909) 884-8706
Web Site: http://www.lareinainc.com
Tortilla Chips Mfr
N.A.I.C.S.: 311919
Lucy Cerda *(Mgr-Pur)*

LA ROCHE CHEVROLET-OLDSMOBILE-CADILLAC, INC.
900 Highway 290 W, Brenham, TX 77833-5422
Tel.: (979) 836-6666
Web Site:
http://www.larochechevrolet.com
Sales Range: $10-24.9 Million
Emp.: 68
Car Whslr
N.A.I.C.S.: 441110
Darrell Blum *(Office Mgr-Customer Svc)*

LA ROSA DEL MONTE EXPRESS INC.
1133 35 Tiffany St, Bronx, NY 10459
Tel.: (718) 991-3300
Web Site:
http://www.larosadelmonte.com
Sales Range: $10-24.9 Million
Emp.: 200
Local Trucking with Storage
N.A.I.C.S.: 484110
Hiran Rodriguez *(Pres)*
Noel Rodriguez *(Controller)*

LA ROSA HOLDINGS CORP.
1420 Celebration Blvd Ste 200, Celebration, FL 34747
Tel.: (321) 250-1799   NV
Web Site: https://larosaholdings.com
Year Founded: 2021
Rev.: $28,797,531
Assets: $2,855,783
Liabilities: $4,169,302
Net Worth: ($1,313,519)
Earnings: $98,198
Emp.: 12
Fiscal Year-end: 12/31/21
Holding Company
N.A.I.C.S.: 551112
Joseph La Rosa *(Pres, CEO, Founder & Chm)*
Mark Gracy *(COO)*
Brad Wolfe *(CFO)*

LA ROSA'S, INC.
2334 Boudinot Ave, Cincinnati, OH 45238
Tel.: (513) 347-5660   OH
Web Site: http://www.larosas.com
Year Founded: 1954
Sales Range: $25-49.9 Million
Emp.: 1,500
Pizzeria Chain Franchisor
N.A.I.C.S.: 533110
Michael La Rosa *(CEO)*
Mark La Rosa *(Pres & Chief Culinary Officer)*
Pete Buscani *(Exec VP-Mktg)*
Michelle McMahon *(VP-Franchise Dev)*
Suzie Pfeiffer *(VP-Fin)*
Cathy Shondel *(Dir-Mktg)*
Donald S. LaRosa *(Founder)*

LA SALLE STREET SECURITIES
223 W Lk St, Chicago, IL 60606
Tel.: (312) 705-5000
Rev.: $11,000,000
Emp.: 50
Brokers Security
N.A.I.C.S.: 523150

LA SUPPLY CO.
9331 Commerce Way, Adelanto, CA 92301
Tel.: (949) 470-9900
Web Site: http://www.labelhouse.net
Sales Range: $10-24.9 Million
Emp.: 30
Label & Printing Services
N.A.I.C.S.: 323111
Randolph W. Austin *(Pres)*

LA TAPATIA - NORCAL, INC.
23423 Cabot Blvd, Hayward, CA 94545-1665
Tel.: (510) 783-4118
Sales Range: $10-24.9 Million
Emp.: 150
Tortilla Mfr
N.A.I.C.S.: 311830
Antonio Chavez *(Pres, Treas & Sec)*
Charels Hawkins *(Mgr)*
Shorn Terez *(Mgr-Maintenance)*
Ignacio Perez *(Mgr)*
Gil Hernandez *(Dir-Sls)*
Francisco Munoc *(Mgr)*
Juan Gonzalez *(Mgr)*
Guillermo Torres *(Mgr)*
Antonio Hernandez *(Dir-Sls)*

LA TERRA FINA, INC.
1300 Atlantic St, Union City, CA 94587
Tel.: (510) 404-5888
Web Site: http://www.laterrafina.com
Year Founded: 1983
Sales Range: $25-49.9 Million
Emp.: 50
Frozen Specialty Food Mfr
N.A.I.C.S.: 311412
Tim Ramsey *(COO & Gen Mgr)*
John Harrington *(Dir-Mktg)*
Sam Delucca *(Sr VP-Sls)*

LA TERRA FINA, INC.

La Terra Fina, Inc.—(Continued)
Victor Reed (VP-Sls)
Ryan Salapa (Dir-Retail Sls)
Chhaya Bhatia (Brand Mgr)
Kim Park (Mgr-Club Sls)

LA TIENDA FOODS INC.
111 N Atkinson Ave, Roswell, NM 88203
Tel.: (505) 627-5560
Rev.: $19,100,000
Emp.: 2
Supermarket
N.A.I.C.S.: 445110

LA TOURISM & CONVENTION BOARD
333 S Hope St 18th Fl, Los Angeles, CA 90071
Tel.: (213) 236-2380   CA
Web Site:
   http://www.discoverlosangeles.com
Year Founded: 1977
Sales Range: $25-49.9 Million
Emp.: 100
Convention & Visitor Bureau Services
N.A.I.C.S.: 561591
Carl Schuster (Treas & Sec)
Alan Rothenberg (Chrm)
Darren K. Green (Sr VP-Sls)
Adam Burke (Pres & CEO)

LA-CO INDUSTRIES MARKAL CO., INC.
1201 Pratt Blvd, Elk Grove Village, IL 60007
Tel.: (847) 956-7600   IL
Web Site: http://www.laco.com
Year Founded: 1934
Sales Range: $75-99.9 Million
Emp.: 112
Plumbing Chemicals & Supplies Mfr
N.A.I.C.S.: 325998
Dan Kleiman (Chm & CEO)
Benjamin Kleiman (Mgr-Mktg)

Subsidiaries:
La-Co Industries Europe S.A.S.   (1)
Allee des Combes Pl de la Plaine de l'ain, 01150, Blyes, France
Tel.: (33) 4 74 46 23 23
Sales Range: $10-24.9 Million
Emp.: 16
Marker Mfr
N.A.I.C.S.: 339999

LA-LA IMPORTS INC.
6500 Montana Ave, El Paso, TX 79925
Tel.: (915) 779-6500
Web Site: http://www.mimcoelp.com
Sales Range: $50-74.9 Million
Emp.: 125
Whslr of Gifts & Novelties
N.A.I.C.S.: 424990
Clement Marcus (Owner)
Ray Rutledge (CFO)
Richard Rotwein (CEO)

LA-Z-RECLINER SHOP INC.
9112 Le Saint Dr, Fairfield, OH 45014
Tel.: (513) 874-9110
Sales Range: $10-24.9 Million
Emp.: 15
Furniture Retailer
N.A.I.C.S.: 449110
Elliot Hilsinger (Chm)
Walt McBeath (Pres)
Jim Ballman (Controller)

LA. CARRIERS, L.L.C.
16849 E Main St, Cut Off, LA 70345
Tel.: (985) 632-5858
Web Site: http://www.lacarriers.net
Sales Range: $10-24.9 Million
Emp.: 45

Inland Water Freight Transportation Services
N.A.I.C.S.: 483211
Tommy Plaisance (Mgr-Ops)
Johnny Plaisance (Office Mgr)
Nessie Pierce (Coord-Safety & Trng)
Gary Johnston (Engr-Port)

LABADIE AUTO INC.
711 S Euclid Ave, Bay City, MI 48706
Tel.: (989) 667-2000
Web Site:
   http://www.labadieauto.com
Rev.: $27,600,000
Emp.: 140
Automobiles, New & Used
N.A.I.C.S.: 441110
Gary Labadie (Pres)
Marc Labadie (VP)

LABATT FOOD SERVICE
4500 Industry Park Dr, San Antonio, TX 78218-5405
Tel.: (210) 661-4216
Web Site: http://www.labattfood.com
Sales Range: $200-249.9 Million
Emp.: 800
Frozen Foods & Groceries Mfr
N.A.I.C.S.: 424410
Al Silva (COO & Gen Mgr)
Tony Canty (Dir-Mgmt Info Sys)
Tory Rasmussen (Mgr-Sls)
Blair P. Labatt Jr. (Pres & CEO)

LABAY-SUMMERS INTERNATIONAL INC.
23203 W Hardy Rd, Spring, TX 77373
Tel.: (281) 353-4000
Web Site:
   http://www.labaysummers.com
Rev.: $20,000,000
Emp.: 6
Brokers, Shipping
N.A.I.C.S.: 488510
Loreta Solis (Mgr-Ocean Import)
Darrell G. Summers Sr. (Pres)

LABCONCO CORPORATION
8811 Prospect Ave, Kansas City, MO 64132-2663
Tel.: (816) 333-8811   MO
Web Site: http://www.labconco.com
Year Founded: 1925
Sales Range: $25-49.9 Million
Emp.: 200
Laboratory Apparatus & Furniture Mfr
N.A.I.C.S.: 339113
Bob Applequist (Specialist-Application)
Shirley Hogenkamp (Mgr-Mktg Comm)
Adam Keithley (Mgr-Mktg)
Brad Kramer (Mgr-Project Dev)

LABCONNECT LLC
605 1st Ave Ste 300, Seattle, WA 98104
Tel.: (206) 322-4680
Web Site:
   http://www.labconnectllc.com
Year Founded: 2002
Sales Range: $10-24.9 Million
Emp.: 65
Human Sample Testing Management Services
N.A.I.C.S.: 541380
Jeff Mayhew (Chief Dev Officer)
Eudoro van der Biest (Dir-Info Svs)
Jonathan Siegel (CFO)
Trenton Harris (Sr VP-Human & Corp Dev)
Stacy Kirn-Barker (Dir-Project Mgmt)
Danuta Kuszczak (Dir-Project Initiation)

Elizabeth Koury (Assoc Dir-Scientific Ops)
Greg Forgey (Mgr-Ops)
Tim Johnson (Chm)
Dawn Sherman (CEO)

LABELLA ASSOCIATES, D.P.C.
300 State St Ste 201, Rochester, NY 14614
Tel.: (585) 454-6110   NY
Web Site: http://www.labellapc.com
Year Founded: 1978
Emp.: 1,400
Engineering, Architectural & Environmental Services
N.A.I.C.S.: 541330
Sergio Esteban (Chm & CEO)
Sal LaBella (Founder)
Aaron Schauger (Jr Engr-Energy)

Subsidiaries:
Aztech Technologies, Inc.   (1)
5 McCrea Hill Rd, Ballston Spa, NY 12020
Tel.: (518) 885-5383
Management Consulting Services
N.A.I.C.S.: 541618
Randy Hoose (Project Mgr)

Novus Engineering PC   (1)
25 Delaware Ave, Delmar, NY 12054
Tel.: (518) 439-8235
Web Site: http://www.novusengineering.com
Engineering Services
N.A.I.C.S.: 541330
Dawn Dana (Project Mgr)
Matthew Gleason (Project Mgr-Commissioning)
Ramy Girgis (Sr Engr-Mechanical-Design)

LABELTEX MILLS INCORPORATED
6100 Wilmington Ave, Los Angeles, CA 90001-1826
Tel.: (323) 582-0228
Web Site:
   http://www.labeltexusa.com
Sales Range: $25-49.9 Million
Emp.: 210
Labels, Woven
N.A.I.C.S.: 313220
Shahrokh Shamtobi (Pres)
Mishel Imani (Sr Acct Exec)

LABETTE HEALTH
1902 S US Highway 59, Parsons, KS 67357
Tel.: (620) 421-4881   KS
Web Site:
   http://www.labettehealth.com
Year Founded: 1961
Sales Range: $50-74.9 Million
Emp.: 641
Medical Care Services
N.A.I.C.S.: 622110
Perry Sorrell (VP)
Melissa Morris (Treas)
Marna George (Sec)
Dee Bohnenblust (VP)

LABOR MANAGEMENT CONCEPTS, INC.
200 Belleville Tpke, North Arlington, NJ 07031
Tel.: (201) 955-2804   NJ
Year Founded: 1989
Sales Range: $10-24.9 Million
Emp.: 500
Security Guard Services
N.A.I.C.S.: 561612
John Munro (Pres)
Gerald Munro (VP)

LABOR RELATIONS INSTITUTE, INC.
7850 S Elm Pl Ste E, Broken Arrow, OK 74011
Tel.: (918) 455-9995   OK

Web Site: http://www.lrionline.com
Year Founded: 1980
Sales Range: $1-9.9 Million
Emp.: 14
Employee Relations
N.A.I.C.S.: 334610
Phillip Wilson (Pres)
Eric Funston (VP)

LABOR STAFFING, INC.
1080 Holcomb Bridge Rd Bldg 200 Ste 140, Roswell, GA 30076
Tel.: (770) 458-7509
Web Site:
   http://www.laborstaffing.com
Year Founded: 1999
Sales Range: $1-9.9 Million
Emp.: 308
Staff Provisioning & Management
N.A.I.C.S.: 561320
Aracely Romero (Mgr-GA Branch)

LABOR-MANAGEMENT HEALTHCARE FUND
3786 Broadway St, Cheektowaga, NY 14227
Tel.: (716) 601-7980   NY
Web Site: http://www.lmhf.net
Year Founded: 2003
Sales Range: $150-199.9 Million
Emp.: 6
Employee Benefit Services
N.A.I.C.S.: 525120
Victoria Martino (Exec Dir)

LABORATORY SERVICES MSO LLC
245 Fischer Ave Ste A2, Costa Mesa, CA 92626
Tel.: (657) 267-0063   DE
Web Site:
   https://www.laboratoryservices.com
Testing Laboratory Services
N.A.I.C.S.: 541380

Subsidiaries:
Merlin Medical Supply   (1)
699 Mobil Ave, Camarillo, CA 93010
Tel.: (805) 388-7669
Web Site: http://www.merlinmed.com
Rev.: $4,186,000
Emp.: 7
Medical, Dental & Hospital Equipment & Supplies Merchant Whsl
N.A.I.C.S.: 423450

LABOTEC INC.
20900 NE 30th Ave Ste 723, Aventura, FL 33180
Web Site: http://www.labotec.com
Year Founded: 2005
Sales Range: $1-9.9 Million
Emp.: 10
Designs & Develops Mobile Apps
N.A.I.C.S.: 541519
Florian Sarousi (Founder & CEO)
Pierre-Olivier Carles (Chief Thinking Officer)
Yakov Sarousi (Founder & CEO)

LABRADA BODYBUILDING NUTRITION INC.
333 Northpark Central Dr Ste Z, Houston, TX 77073-6337
Tel.: (281) 209-2137
Web Site: http://www.labrada.com
Rev.: $15,897,774
Emp.: 30
Health Foods
N.A.I.C.S.: 456191
Lee Labrada (Founder, Pres & CEO)
Ray Raman (VP-Acctg & Controller)
Martin Shepeard (Dir-Graphics)

LABRADOR VENTURES, L.P.
535 Middlefield Ave Ste 190, Menlo Park, CA 94025

Tel.: (650) 366-6000
Web Site: http://www.labrador.com
Year Founded: 1989
Rev.: $200,000,000
Emp.: 4
Privater Equity Firm
N.A.I.C.S.: 523999
Larry Kubal *(Founder & Mng Partner)*
Stuart Davidson *(Mng Partner)*

LABRECHE
500 Washington Ave S Ste 2020, Minneapolis, MN 55415
Tel.: (612) 338-0901
Year Founded: 1990
Sales Range: $1-9.9 Million
Emp.: 20
Public Relations Agency
N.A.I.C.S.: 541820
Beth LaBreche *(Founder & CEO)*
Sara Cziok *(Dir-Comm Strategy)*
Laura Boyd *(Pres)*
Tami Kou *(Dir-PR)*
Elen Bahr *(Dir-Digital Strategy)*
Kate Rogers *(Mgr-Written Content)*
Karen Schultz *(Mgr-Bus Dev)*
Sara Blood *(Sr Mgr-Media Rels)*

LABRIOLA BAKING COMPANY
3701 W 128th Pl, Alsip, IL 60803
Tel.: (708) 377-0400
Web Site:
  http://www.labriolabaking.com
Year Founded: 1993
Sales Range: $10-24.9 Million
Emp.: 235
Bakery Products Mfr
N.A.I.C.S.: 311812
Richard Labriola *(Founder)*

LABTECH SOFTWARE, LLC
4110 George Rd Ste 200, Tampa, FL 33634
Tel.: (813) 397-4600
Web Site:
  http://www.labtechsoftware.com
Year Founded: 2004
Sales Range: $10-24.9 Million
Emp.: 150
Software Publisher
N.A.I.C.S.: 513210
Matt Nachtrab *(Co-Founder)*
Greg Buerk *(CTO)*
Drew McCallum *(Co-Founder & Sr Product Mgr)*
Brett Cheloff *(Dir-Dev)*
John Walker *(VP-Global Ops)*
Adam Slutskin *(Chief Revenue Officer & Exec VP)*
John Timko *(VP-Market Dev)*
Amy Hodge *(Dir-Community)*
Jason Magee *(Exec VP-Strategy)*
Josh Poe *(Gen Counsel)*

Subsidiaries:

LabTech Software (1)
10c Peckingham Street, Halesowen, B63 3AW, West Midlands, United Kingdom
Tel.: (44) 844 544 1690
Software Publisher
N.A.I.C.S.: 513210

LABUDDE GROUP, INC.
W63 N583 Hanover Ave, Cedarburg, WI 53012
Tel.: (262) 375-9111
Web Site: http://www.labudde.com
Rev.: $23,300,000
Emp.: 25
Farm Supplies Merchant Whslr
N.A.I.C.S.: 424910
Richard T. Erickson *(CEO)*
Lynette Kelley *(Mgr-Acctg)*
Mary Sciascia *(VP-Fin)*
Joe Pomeroy *(Mgr)*

LABVANTAGE SOLUTIONS INC.
265 Davidson Ave Ste 220, Somerset, NJ 08873
Tel.: (908) 707-4100
Web Site: http://www.labvantage.com
Rev.: $15,500,000
Emp.: 70
Computer Software Development & Applications
N.A.I.C.S.: 541511
Purnendu Chatterjee *(Chm)*
Mary Ann Cook *(Mgr-Global Sls Support)*
Ralph Goldberg *(Product Mgr)*
Sarvesh Gowda *(Product Mgr-Delivery)*
Robert T. Voelkner *(VP-Sls & Mktg)*
John Heiser *(CEO)*

LAC GROUP
10390 Santa Monica Blvd Ste 230, Los Angeles, CA 90025
Tel.: (323) 852-1083
Web Site: http://www.lac-group.com
Year Founded: 1986
Sales Range: $10-24.9 Million
Emp.: 254
Management Consulting Services
N.A.I.C.S.: 541618
Deb Schwarz *(CEO)*
Rob Corrao *(CEO)*
Len Levy *(Pres-Cost Mgmt Ops)*
Natalya Berdzeni *(Exec VP-Chase Cost Mgmt)*
Iain Dunbar *(VP-Ops-UK & EMEA)*
Eleanor Windsor *(VP-Client Engagement-UK & EMEA)*
Al Furnari *(Dir-LAC Federal Program Mgmt)*
Laura Wang *(VP-Ops)*
Tom Regal *(VP-PRO-TEK Vaults)*
John Fox *(CMO)*
Tom Miller *(Exec VP)*

Subsidiaries:

PRO-TEK Vaults (1)
10390 Santa Monica Blvd Ste 230, Los Angeles, CA 90025
Tel.: (323) 468-4450
Web Site: http://protekvaults.com
Emp.: 20
Film Library & Archive Services
N.A.I.C.S.: 519210
Jim Harwood *(Dir-Ops-Burbank)*
Tom Regal *(VP)*
Randy Gitsch *(Mgr-Still Archives)*
Donna Holbeck *(Dir-Ops-Thousand Oaks)*

LACAVA & SOWERSBY INC.
1375 Plymouth Ave, Fall River, MA 02721
Tel.: (508) 675-0512
Web Site:
  http://lacavaandsowersby.com
Rev.: $12,100,000
Emp.: 36
Automotive Supplies & Parts Distr
N.A.I.C.S.: 423120
William Sowersby *(Pres)*

LACE FOODSERVICE CORPORATION
10490 NW 26th St, Miami, FL 33172
Tel.: (305) 513-5223
Web Site:
  http://www.lacefoodservice.com
Rev.: $19,000,000
Emp.: 6
Commercial Equipment Merchant Whslr
N.A.I.C.S.: 423440
Luis C. Fernandez Jr. *(Sec & VP)*

LACE LASTIC COMPANY
610 Pine Tree Rd, Oxford, NC 27565
Tel.: (919) 693-2100

Web Site: http://www.macralace.com
Rev.: $20,000,000
Emp.: 165
Lace & Warp Knit Fabric Mills
N.A.I.C.S.: 313240
Claus Graichen *(Pres)*

LACHER & ASSOCIATES INSURANCE AGENCY, INC.
632 E Broad St, Souderton, PA 18964
Tel.: (215) 723-4378
Web Site:
  http://www.lacherinsurance.com
Year Founded: 1958
Sales Range: $1-9.9 Million
Emp.: 25
Insurance Agencies & Brokerage Services
N.A.I.C.S.: 524210
Amy Kelley *(Sr Acct Exec-Personal Insurance)*
Lois Alderfer *(Mgr-Personal Insurance Acct)*
Matt Godshall *(Acct Exec-Personal Insurance)*
Michelle Hunsberger *(Acct Exec-Personal Insurance)*
Deb Riffel *(Acct Exec-Personal Insurance)*
Sam Wonderling *(Acct Exec-Personal Insurance)*

Subsidiaries:

Brunner Insurance, Inc. (1)
19 E Union St, Richlandtown, PA 18955-0000
Tel.: (215) 529-7604
Web Site: http://www.brunnerinsurance.com
Insurance Related Activities
N.A.I.C.S.: 524298
Gus Brunner *(Founder)*

LACIMA INC.
10015 N Loop E, Houston, TX 77029
Tel.: (713) 673-1757
Web Site: http://www.trucknation.com
Sales Range: $10-24.9 Million
Emp.: 10
Sales of Pre-Owned & Used Commercial, Transportation & Class 8 Trucks
N.A.I.C.S.: 441110
Roberto A. Garcia *(Pres)*

LACK'S AARONSON, INC.
1300 San Patricia Dr, Pharr, TX 78577-2100
Tel.: (956) 702-3361   TX
Web Site: http://www.lacksvalley.com
Year Founded: 1953
Sales Range: $50-74.9 Million
Emp.: 650
Holding Company
N.A.I.C.S.: 449110

Subsidiaries:

Lack's Valley Stores Ltd. (1)
1300 San Patricia Dr, Pharr, TX 78577-2100
Tel.: (956) 702-3361
Web Site: http://www.lacksvalley.com
Sales Range: $25-49.9 Million
Emp.: 250
Furniture Retailer
N.A.I.C.S.: 449110
Randy Martin *(Controller)*
David Estes *(Gen Mgr)*

LACKAWANNA PRODUCTS CORP.
8545 Main St, Clarence, NY 14031-0660
Tel.: (716) 633-1940
Year Founded: 1982
Sales Range: $10-24.9 Million
Emp.: 100
Grain & Field Beans Distr

N.A.I.C.S.: 424510
David Alvin Olshan *(Pres & Treas)*
Scott A. Schultz *(Mgr-Trade Floor)*

LACKEY MEMORIAL HOSPITAL
330 N Broad St, Forest, MS 39074
Tel.: (601) 469-4151   MS
Web Site:
  http://www.lackeymemorialhospital.com
Year Founded: 1989
Sales Range: $10-24.9 Million
Emp.: 280
Health Care Srvices
N.A.I.C.S.: 622110
Julie Gieger *(Sec)*

LACKS ENTERPRISES, INC.
5460 Cascade Rd SE, Grand Rapids, MI 49546-6406
Tel.: (616) 949-6570   MI
Web Site:
  http://www.lacksenterprises.com
Year Founded: 1961
Sales Range: $500-549.9 Million
Emp.: 2,000
Plastic Components for the Automotive Industry Mfr
N.A.I.C.S.: 326199
Richard Lacks Jr. *(Pres & CEO)*
Nick Hrnyak *(Pres)*
Cynthia Wright *(Mgr-Laboratory)*
Tom Kline *(Dir-Quality Assurance)*
Joe Singer *(Dir-Trng)*
Kurt Lacks *(Chm & Exec VP)*
Gary Walker *(Dir-Info Sys)*
Joe Strausse *(CIO)*
Jim Green *(Dir-HR)*
Mike Clover *(CFO)*

Subsidiaries:

Lacks Trim Systems, Inc. (1)
39500 MacKenzie Dr Ste 500, Novi, MI 48377
Tel.: (248) 351-0555
Web Site: http://www.lacksenterprises.com
Sales Range: $10-24.9 Million
Emp.: 60
Interior & Exterior Plastic Products for Automotive Trim Mfr & Distr
N.A.I.C.S.: 326199
Richard Lacks Jr. *(CEO)*
Mark Montone *(Dir-Sls & Mktg)*
Mark Montond *(Dir-Sls & Mktg)*

Lacks Wheel Trim Systems, Inc. (1)
Southfield Engineering Ctr 26711 Northwestern Hwy Ste 250, Southfield, MI 48033
Tel.: (248) 351-0555
Web Site: http://www.lacksenterprises.com
Sales Range: $10-24.9 Million
Emp.: 13
Wheel Assemblies, Wheel Covers, Wheel Ornamentation & Trim Rings for Automobiles & Light Trucks Mfr
N.A.I.C.S.: 326199

Plastic Plate, Inc. (1)
3500 Raleigh Ave SE, Grand Rapids, MI 49512-2064 (100%)
Tel.: (616) 455-5055
Sales Range: $25-49.9 Million
Emp.: 150
Plastic Molding & Plating Services
N.A.I.C.S.: 326199
Richard Lacks Jr. *(CEO)*

LACLEDE ELECTRIC COOPERATIVE INC.
1400 E Rte 66, Lebanon, MO 65536
Tel.: (417) 532-3164   MO
Web Site:
  http://www.lacledeelectric.com
Year Founded: 1938
Sales Range: $25-49.9 Million
Emp.: 112
Electrical Services
N.A.I.C.S.: 221122
Kenneth Miller *(Gen Mgr)*
Douglas Kroese *(Asst Mgr)*

LACLEDE ELECTRIC COOPERATIVE INC.

Laclede Electric Cooperative Inc.—(Continued)
Carl Lowrance *(Sec)*
Gary Owsley *(Mgr-Ops)*
David Johnson *(Pres)*
Melvin Hoffman *(Treas)*
Joel Cravens *(VP)*
Joe Knapp *(Mgr-Acctg)*
Byron Dudley *(Mgr-Comm & PR)*
Terry Rosenthal *(Mgr-Engrg)*
Michael Kirkland *(Mgr-Ops)*

LACO ASSOCIATES, INC.
21 W 4th St, Eureka, CA 95501
Tel.: (707) 443-5054 CA
Web Site:
http://www.lacoassociates.us
Year Founded: 1982
Engineering Services
N.A.I.C.S.: 541330
Susan P. Clower *(Treas & Controller)*
Michael D. Nelson *(Pres & CEO)*
Bradley Thomas *(VP-Land Surveying)*
Kevin Doble *(Sr Project Mgr)*

Subsidiaries:

Doblethomas & Associates, Inc. (1)
44B Mill St, Healdsburg, CA 95448
Tel.: (707) 433-6792
Web Site: http://www.doblethomas.com
Engineeering Services
N.A.I.C.S.: 541330

LADAS & PARRY
1040 Avenue of the Americas Fl 5,
New York, NY 10018-3738
Tel.: (212) 708-1800
Web Site: http://www.ladas.com
Year Founded: 1912
Rev.: $60,000,000
Emp.: 330
Law firm
N.A.I.C.S.: 541110
Jay Bondell *(Atty)*
Pamela Beilinson *(Acct Mgr)*
Ralph H. Cathcart *(Partner)*
Dennis Prahl *(Partner)*
Michelle Dotti *(Mgr-HR)*
Scott Lebson *(Partner)*
John Richards *(Atty)*
Matthew D. Asbell *(Partner)*
Janet I. Cord *(Partner)*
Raymond A. DiPerna *(Partner)*
Burton S. Ehrlich *(Partner)*
John P. Luther *(Partner)*
Malcolm J. MacDonald *(Partner)*
Clifford J. Mass *(Partner)*
Sebastian Lovera Riso *(Partner)*

Subsidiaries:

Ladas & Parry, California (1)
5670 Wilshire Blvd Ste 2100, Los Angeles,
CA 90036-5620 **(100%)**
Tel.: (323) 934-2300
Web Site: http://www.ladasparry.com
Sales Range: $10-24.9 Million
Emp.: 40
Legal Services Concerning Patents And
Trademarks
N.A.I.C.S.: 541110
Evelyn Chang *(Sec)*
Salina Gordon *(Asst Sec)*
Bharati Bakshani *(Partner)*
Donald L. Dennison *(Partner)*
Stephen G. Janoski *(Atty)*
Taffie N. Jones *(Atty)*
John W. Kelly *(Atty)*
Young Seok Koo *(Partner)*
Adam V. Litteken *(Atty)*
Malcolm J. MacDonald *(Partner)*
Luciano Ricondo *(Atty)*

Ladas & Parry, England (1)
52 54 High Holborn, London, WC1V 6RR,
England, United Kingdom **(100%)**
Tel.: (44) 72425566
Sales Range: $10-24.9 Million
Emp.: 12
Law firm
N.A.I.C.S.: 541199

Ladas & Parry, Illinois (1)
224 S Michigan Ave Ste 1600, Chicago, IL
60604-2505
Tel.: (312) 427-1300
Web Site: http://www.ladas.com
Sales Range: $10-24.9 Million
Emp.: 40
Law firm
N.A.I.C.S.: 541110
Leta Corradino *(Office Mgr)*

Ladas & Parry, LLP, Germany (1)
Dachauerstrasse 37, D 80335, Munich,
Germany
Tel.: (49) 89269077
Web Site: http://www.ladasparry.com
Sales Range: $10-24.9 Million
Emp.: 4
Law firm
N.A.I.C.S.: 541199

Ladas Domains LLC (1)
224 S Michigan Ave Ste 1600, Chicago, IL
60604
Tel.: (312) 427-9866
Web Site: http://www.ladasdomains.com
Domain Registration Services
N.A.I.C.S.: 513199

LADD HANFORD AUTO GROUP
2247 Cumberland St, Lebanon, PA
17042
Tel.: (717) 273-4585
Web Site:
http://www.laddhanford.com
Sales Range: $10-24.9 Million
Emp.: 65
New Car Retailer
N.A.I.C.S.: 441110
Parke Hoover *(Mgr-Svc)*
Dan Albright *(Mgr-Parts)*
Gary Deibert *(Gen Mgr)*
Jason Hamer *(Mgr-Sls)*
Brian Biscotti *(Bus Mgr)*
Chris Firestine *(Bus Mgr)*
Jody Appleby *(Dir-Svc)*

LADERA RANCH MAINTENANCE CORP.
15241 Laguna Canyon Rd, Irvine, CA
92614
Tel.: (949) 218-0900 CA
Year Founded: 1998
Sales Range: $10-24.9 Million
Community Welfare Services
N.A.I.C.S.: 624190
Barton Warner *(Asst Sec)*
Ernie Medina *(Treas)*
Franco Tenerelli *(Sec)*
Abe Cook *(Pres)*
Kristin Vellandi *(VP)*

LADY ANN CRUISES INC.
9643 Kaumualii Ave, Waimea, HI
96796-0597
Tel.: (808) 338-9999
Web Site:
http://www.napaliexplorer.com
Year Founded: 1988
Sales Range: Less than $1 Million
Emp.: 15
Water Passenger Transportation
N.A.I.C.S.: 487210
Tennis Stoner *(Pres)*

LADY BURD EXCLUSIVE PRIVATE LABEL COSMETICS
44 Exec Blvd, Farmingdale, NY
11735
Tel.: (631) 454-0444
Web Site: http://www.ladyburd.com
Sales Range: $10-24.9 Million
Emp.: 50
Cosmetics
N.A.I.C.S.: 424210
Roberta Burd *(Pres & CEO)*
Allen Burd *(VP)*

LADY ESTER LINGERIE CORP.
33 E 33th St 8th Fl, New York, NY
10016-4328
Tel.: (212) 684-4446 NY
Web Site: http://www.ladyester.com
Year Founded: 1935
Sales Range: $100-124.9 Million
Emp.: 225
Lingerie Mfr
N.A.I.C.S.: 315250

Subsidiaries:

Perfectform (1)
16 E 34th St Ste 14, New York, NY
10016-5424 **(100%)**
Tel.: (212) 684-4446
Sales Range: $50-74.9 Million
Emp.: 35
Clothing Mfr
N.A.I.C.S.: 315120

LADY GRACE STORES INC.
5 Commonwealth Ave Unit 1, Woburn, MA 01801
Tel.: (781) 322-1721
Web Site: http://www.ladygrace.com
Year Founded: 1937
Sales Range: $50-74.9 Million
Emp.: 200
Women's Intimate Clothing Retailer &
Mail Order
N.A.I.C.S.: 458110
Stephen E. Berson *(Pres)*
Bruce Green *(CFO)*

LADY PRIMROSE'S, INC.
3631 W Davis Ste C, Dallas, TX
75211-3145
Tel.: (214) 747-7673
Web Site:
http://www.ladyprimrose.com
Sales Range: $10-24.9 Million
Emp.: 18
Bathing & Skin Products
N.A.I.C.S.: 325620
Carolin Rose Hunter *(Co-Founder)*
Vivian Wilcox Young *(Co-Founder)*
Shirley Pieratt *(Pres)*

LAERDAL MEDICAL CORPORATION
167 Myers Corners Rd, Wappingers
Falls, NY 12590
Tel.: (845) 297-7770
Web Site: http://www.laerdal.com
Year Founded: 1940
Rev.: $36,000,000
Emp.: 200
Mfr & Whslr of Medical & Hospital
Equipment
N.A.I.C.S.: 423450
Patricia Goodman *(Controller)*
Paul Singleton *(VP-IT)*
Clive Patrickson *(CEO)*
David Johnson *(Pres)*

LAFAIVE OIL CO.
401 W US 2, Norway, MI 49870
Tel.: (906) 563-9302
Web Site: http://www.lafaiveoil.com
Sales Range: $10-24.9 Million
Emp.: 55
Fuel Oil
N.A.I.C.S.: 424710
Dennis LaFaive *(Pres)*

LAFAYETTE COMPANY
1525 State St Ste 203, Santa Barbara, CA 93101
Tel.: (805) 965-2009
Web Site:
http://www.lafayetteinstrument.com
Sales Range: Less than $1 Million
Emp.: 1,200
Ice Cream & Frozen Deserts
N.A.I.C.S.: 311520
William J. McKinley *(Owner)*

U.S. PRIVATE

LAFAYETTE GENERAL HEALTH SYSTEM
1214 Coolidge St, Lafayette, LA
70503
Tel.: (337) 289-7991 LA
Web Site:
http://www.lafayettegeneral.com
Year Founded: 2002
Sales Range: $10-24.9 Million
Health Care Srvices
N.A.I.C.S.: 622110
Paul Molbert *(VP-Clinical Integration)*
David L. Callecod *(Pres)*
Roger Mattke *(CFO & Sr VP)*
Ziad Ashkar *(Chief Medical Officer & VP)*
Becki Benoit *(Chief Nursing Officer & VP)*
Gordon Rountree *(Chief Compliance Officer & Gen Counsel)*
Joseph Mitchell *(Co-CEO)*
Katie Hebert *(Co-CEO)*
Laurence Vincent *(Chief Nursing Officer)*
Michael Dozier *(CIO & VP-Information Sys)*
Patrick W. Gandy Jr. *(Exec VP)*

LAFAYETTE MOTOR SALES INC.
5202 Raeford Rd, Fayetteville, NC
28304
Tel.: (910) 424-0281
Web Site:
http://www.lafayetteford.com
Rev.: $67,120,964
Emp.: 150
Automobiles, New & Used
N.A.I.C.S.: 441110
Don Price *(Pres)*
James Melvin *(Mgr-Fin)*
Bill DeNicola *(Mgr-Svc)*

LAFAYETTE SQUARE USA, INC.
175 SW 7th St Unit 1911, Miami, FL
33130
Tel.: (786) 598-2348 DE
Web Site:
https://www.lafayettesquarebdc.com
Year Founded: 2020
Rev.: $3,496,000
Assets: $105,577,000
Liabilities: $33,795,000
Net Worth: $71,782,000
Earnings: ($163,000)
Emp.: 356
Fiscal Year-end: 12/31/22
Investment Management Service
N.A.I.C.S.: 523999
Damien Dwin *(Founder)*
Phil Daniele *(Chief Risk Officer)*
Renee Beaumont *(COO)*
Seren Tahiroglu *(CFO)*

LAFAYETTE VENETIAN BLIND INC.
3000 Klondike Rd 2838 W Vorsia,
West Lafayette, IN 47996
Tel.: (765) 464-2500
Web Site: http://www.lafvb.com
Rev.: $80,000,000
Emp.: 850
Drapery Hardware & Window Blinds
& Shades
N.A.I.C.S.: 337920
Christy Kerrigan *(Mgr-Natl Accts)*

LAFFERTY CHEVROLET, INC.
829 W St Rd, Warminster, PA 18974
Tel.: (215) 259-5817
Web Site:
http://www.laffertychevy.com
Sales Range: $25-49.9 Million
Emp.: 78
New Car Dealers

N.A.I.C.S.: 441110
Jack Lafferty (Owner)

LAFONTAINE AUTOMOTIVE GROUP, LLC
15123 N Rd, Fenton, MI 48430
Tel.: (833) 819-6044
Web Site: http://www.familydeal.com
Year Founded: 1980
Car Dealership
N.A.I.C.S.: 441110
Ryan LaFontaine (CEO)
Kelley LaFontaine (VP)

Subsidiaries:

Delehanty Ford Inc. (1)
1510 E Pierson Rd, Flushing, MI 48433
Web Site: http://www.delehantyford.com
Automotive Repair & Maintenance
N.A.I.C.S.: 811198
Bruce Trzil (Mgr-Svc)

Lou LaRiche Chevrolet Inc. (1)
40875 Plymouth Rd, Plymouth, MI 48170
Tel.: (734) 453-4600
Web Site: http://www.louchevy.com
Sales Range: $100-124.9 Million
Emp.: 75
New & Used Car Dealer
N.A.I.C.S.: 441110
Louis LaRiche (Pres & Principal-Dealer)
Ronald Chaudoin (Gen Mgr)

RDS Management, Inc. (1)
1111 S Commerce Rd, Walled Lake, MI 48390
Tel.: (248) 669-2010
Web Site: http://www.lafontainecdjrwalledlake.com
Sales Range: $1-9.9 Million
Emp.: 35
New Car Dealers
N.A.I.C.S.: 441110
Doris Shuman (Sec)

LAFONTAINE IMPORT MOTORS INC.
2245 S Telegraph Rd, Dearborn, MI 48124
Tel.: (313) 565-5100
Web Site: http://www.lafontainehonda.com
Sales Range: $10-24.9 Million
Emp.: 25
Sales of New & Used Cars
N.A.I.C.S.: 441110
Michael T. Lafontaine (Pres)
Tiffany Watkins (Controller)

LAFRANCE ASSOCIATES, LLC
170 Capp St Ste C, San Francisco, CA 94110
Tel.: (415) 392-2850
Web Site: http://www.lfagroup.com
Year Founded: 2000
Rev.: $2,300,000
Emp.: 25
Management Consulting Services
N.A.I.C.S.: 541618
Steven LaFrance (Founder & CEO)

LAFRANCE CORPORATION
1 LaFrance Way, Concordville, PA 19331
Tel.: (610) 361-4300   PA
Web Site: http://www.lafrancecorp.com
Year Founded: 1946
Sales Range: $150-199.9 Million
Emp.: 450
Custom Zinc Die Cast & Injection Molded Name Plates Mfr
N.A.I.C.S.: 326199
Alan Grodnitzky (Exec VP)
Brett Damadio (Mgr-Bus Dev)
Dave Grieff (Engr-Process)
Eric Cantwell (Mgr-Dev Acct)
Fran Vespa (Gen Mgr)
Jeremy Burton (Mgr-Programming)
Neil Jaross (Mgr-Bus Dev)
Sandy Rae (Mgr-Mktg)
Vince Mirarchi (Project Mgr)
Cathy McHugh (Mgr-Customer Needs)
Kin Kwong (Engr-Process)
Mike Querey (Mgr-Sls-Natl)

Subsidiaries:

LaFrance Corporation - Benmatt Industries Division (1)
1 LaFrance Way, Concordville, PA 19331
Tel.: (877) 236-6288
Web Site: http://www.benmatt.com
Automotive Dealer Identification Product Mfr
N.A.I.C.S.: 336390

LaFrance Corporation - J.A.T. Creative Products Division (1)
1 LaFrance Way, Concordville, PA 19331
Tel.: (610) 358-9137
Web Site: http://www.jatcp.com
Promotional Merchandise Mfr
N.A.I.C.S.: 339999

LaFrance Corporation - PacTec Custom Division (1)
1 LaFrance Way, Concordville, PA 19331
Tel.: (610) 361-4286
Web Site: http://www.pactecenclosures.com
Sales Range: $125-149.9 Million
Plastic Enclosure Mfr
N.A.I.C.S.: 326199

LaFrance Corporation - PacTec Standard Division (1)
1 LaFrance Way, Concordville, PA 19331
Tel.: (610) 361-4222
Web Site: http://www.pactecenclosures.com
Plastic Enclosure Mfr
N.A.I.C.S.: 326199

United States Name Plate (1)
1 Lafrance Way, Concordville, PA 19331   (100%)
Tel.: (610) 361-4300
Web Site: http://www.usnameplate.com
Sales Range: $25-49.9 Million
Emp.: 100
Signs & Advertising Specialties; Injection Molding of Plastic
N.A.I.C.S.: 326199

LAGER'S, INC.
910 Old Minnesota Ave, Saint Peter, MN 56082
Tel.: (507) 931-4070   MN
Web Site: http://www.lagersinc.com
Year Founded: 1965
Sales Range: $10-24.9 Million
Emp.: 20
New Car Dealers
N.A.I.C.S.: 441110
Franklin Lager (Gen Mgr)
Dan Wegscheid (Mgr-Sls)

LAGO BUILDERS INC.
PO Box 5740, Leander, TX 78645
Tel.: (512) 267-0702
Year Founded: 2003
Sales Range: $25-49.9 Million
Emp.: 92
Nonresidential Construction Services
N.A.I.C.S.: 236220
Tim Edwards (Owner & Sec)

LAGO MAR PROPERTIES, INC.
1700 S Ocean Ln, Fort Lauderdale, FL 33316
Tel.: (954) 523-6511
Web Site: http://www.lagomar.com
Sales Range: $25-49.9 Million
Emp.: 225
Hotel & Resort
N.A.I.C.S.: 721110
Walter Banks (Pres)

LAGOS INC.
Rittenhouse Sq 1735 Walnut St, Philadelphia, PA 19103
Tel.: (215) 567-0770
Web Site: http://www.lagos.com
Year Founded: 1917
Rev.: $10,000,000
Emp.: 50
Jewel Settings & Mountings, Precious Metal
N.A.I.C.S.: 339910
Steven Lagos (Founder, Chm & Dir-Creative)
Chris Cullen (Pres & CEO)
Isabelle Scarchilli (VP-Mktg)
Amanda Willinger (VP-PR, Digital & ECommerce)
Diana Nichols (VP-Sls)
Kathy Cope (VP-Product Dev)

LAGRAPHICO
3800 Vanowen St, Burbank, CA 91505
Tel.: (818) 295-6100
Web Site: http://www.lagraphico.com
Year Founded: 1978
Sales Range: $50-74.9 Million
Emp.: 205
Graphic Advertising
N.A.I.C.S.: 541810
Brandon Gabriel (Principal)
Warren Wong (Engr-Theatrical Structural)
Luis Flores (Mgr-Facilities)

LAGUARDIA ASSOCIATES
104 Ditmars Blvd, Elmhurst, NY 11369
Tel.: (718) 457-6300
Web Site: http://www.laguardiaplazahotel.com
Sales Range: $10-24.9 Million
Emp.: 100
Motel, Franchised
N.A.I.C.S.: 721110
John Alati (Owner)

LAGUNA TOOLS INC.
17101 Murphy Ave, Irvine, CA 92614
Tel.: (949) 474-1200
Web Site: http://www.lagunatools.com
Sales Range: $10-24.9 Million
Emp.: 29
Distr of Tools
N.A.I.C.S.: 444140
Torben Helshoj (Pres)
Catherine Helshoj (VP)

LAHEY CLINIC
41 Mall Rd, Burlington, MA 01805
Tel.: (781) 744-5100   MA
Web Site: http://www.lahey.org
Year Founded: 1923
Sales Range: $650-699.9 Million
Emp.: 4,500
Non-Profit Multi-Specialty Diagnostic Clinic & Hospital
N.A.I.C.S.: 622110
Nelson Gagnon (CIO)
Stanley B. Bello (Sr VP-Community Grp Practices)
Ron Bradley (Mgr-Clinical Nutrition)
Michael Gill (Sr VP-Revenue Fin)
Darleen Souza (VP-HR)
David Martin (Chm-Medicine)
Joanne Conroy (CEO)
Malcolm Creighton (Chm-Hospital-Based Specialties Div & Emergency Medicine Dept)
Nicole DeVita (COO-Peabody)
Patricia Roberts (Chm-Surgery)
Patrick Jordan (COO-Burlington)
Tracy Galvin (Chief Nursing Officer)
Vincent McDermott (Sr VP-Fin)

LAIBE CORPORATION
1414 Bates St, Indianapolis, IN 46201
Tel.: (317) 231-2250
Web Site: http://www.laibecorp.com
Year Founded: 1962
Sales Range: $10-24.9 Million
Emp.: 50
Monitoring Devices
N.A.I.C.S.: 423510
James R. Hopkins (Pres & CEO)
Martin E. Wright (CFO)
Jeff Calvert (Mgr-Pur & Parts)

LAIDLAW ENERGY GROUP, INC.
90 John St 4th Fl, New York, NY 10038
Tel.: (212) 480-8400   NY
Web Site: http://www.laidlawenergy.com
Sales Range: $10-24.9 Million
Emp.: 5
Oil & Gas Production
N.A.I.C.S.: 324199
Michael B. Bartoszek (Pres & CEO)
Louis T. Bravakis (Exec VP)
Theodore Alex Bravakis (VP-Project Dev & Asst Sec)
Edward Meyers (VP-IR)

LAIDLAW GLOBAL CORPORATION
575 Madison Ave, New York, NY 10022
Tel.: (212) 937-8423
Rev.: $24,067,190
Emp.: 80
Brokers Security
N.A.I.C.S.: 523150

LAIKA, INC.
1400 NW 22nd Ave, Portland, OR 97210
Tel.: (503) 225-1130
Web Site: http://www.laika.com
Year Founded: 1975
Sales Range: $25-49.9 Million
Emp.: 280
Animated Film, Commercial & Music Video Production Services
N.A.I.C.S.: 512110
Travis A. Knight (Pres & CEO)
Bradley Wald (CFO)
David Burke (CMO)
Philip H. Knight (Owner & Chm)

LAIPPLE OIL INC.
203 9th Pl NE, Hampton, IA 50441
Tel.: (641) 456-4172
Rev.: $18,200,000
Emp.: 13
Petroleum & Petroleum Products Merchant Whslr
N.A.I.C.S.: 424720
Mark J. Laipple (VP)
John Laipple (Pres & CEO)

LAIRD & COMPANY, INC.
1 Laird Rd, Scobeyville, NJ 07724-9724
Tel.: (732) 542-0312   NJ
Web Site: http://www.lairdandcompany.com
Year Founded: 1780
Sales Range: $10-24.9 Million
Emp.: 45
Liquor & Wine Importer & Mfr
N.A.I.C.S.: 424820
Larrie W. Laird (Pres)
Thomas Alberico (Sr VP-Sls & Mktg)
Janice Custer (VP-Production)
Robert Reed (Controller)
Lisa Dunn (VP)

Subsidiaries:

Laird Wine & Spirits of PA Co. (1)
22 N Railroad St, Palmyra, PA 17078-1752
Tel.: (717) 838-8872
Web Site: http://www.lairdandcompany.com
Emp.: 10

LAIRD & COMPANY, INC.

Laird & Company, Inc.—(Continued)
Wine Whslr
N.A.I.C.S.: 424820
Larrie Laird (Pres)

LAIRD CHRISTIANSON ADVERTISING, INC.
1003 Bishop St 9th Fl, Honolulu, HI 96813-6429
Tel.: (808) 531-9841
Year Founded: 1989
Sales Range: $25-49.9 Million
Emp.: 60
Advetising Agency
N.A.I.C.S.: 541810
Dennis Christianson (Pres & CEO)
Petra Herzog (VP-Acct Svcs)
Page Gaylord (VP-Media Svcs)
Kathleen M. Pahinui (VP-Acct Svcs)
David Koch (Exec VP)
Dennis Mahaffay (VP-Brdcst)
Wendi Chun (Assoc Dir-Creative)
Brad Osborn (Assoc Dir-Creative)
Melissa Alpan (Assoc Dir-Creative)
Mei Jeanne Wagner (VP-Adv-Promos)
Lauren Ruiz (Acct Exec)

LAIRD NOLLER AUTOMOTIVE INC.
935 W 23rd St, Lawrence, KS 66046
Tel.: (785) 843-3500
Web Site: http://www.lairdnoller.com
Sales Range: $50-74.9 Million
Emp.: 96
New & Used Car Dealers
N.A.I.C.S.: 441110
Gary Bennett (Pres)
Jason Schrick (Mgr-Detail & Reconditioning)

LAIRD NOLLER FORD INCORPORATED
2245 SW Topeka Blvd, Topeka, KS 66611
Tel.: (785) 235-9211
Web Site: http://www.nollerford.com
Rev.: $59,583,000
Emp.: 165
Automobiles, New & Used
N.A.I.C.S.: 441110
Jolene Piper (Controller)

LAIRD NORTON COMPANY, LLC
801 2nd Ave Ste 1700, Seattle, WA 98104
Tel.: (206) 464-5245
Web Site: http://www.lairdnorton.com
Year Founded: 1855
Rev.: $12,200,000,000
Equity Investment Firm
N.A.I.C.S.: 523999
Jefferey S. Vincent (Pres & CEO)
Sally Simpson (VP-Fin & Admin)
Anthony Cree (VP-Tax)
Brian W. McGuigan (VP-Corp Investments & Compliance)

Subsidiaries:

Laird Norton Properties (1)
801 2nd Ave Ste 1700, Seattle, WA 98104 (100%)
Tel.: (206) 464-5245
Web Site: http://lairdnortonproperties.com
Real Estate Investment Firm
N.A.I.C.S.: 531390
Jeff Vincent (Co-Pres & CEO)
Jim Reinhardsen (Co-Pres)
Audra Brown (Mgr-Asset)
Jennifer Polson (Mgr-Mktg & Comm)

Subsidiary (Domestic):

Heartland, LLC (2)
801 2nd Ave, Ste 614, Seattle, WA 98104
Tel.: (206) 682-2500
Web Site: http://www.heartlandllc.com
Real Estate Services
N.A.I.C.S.: 531390
Matt Anderson (Principal & Sr Project Dir)
Jim Reinhardsen (Sr Mng Dir)
Chris Fiori (Principal & Project Dir)
Doug Larson (Principal & Project Dir)

Laird Norton Tyee (1)
801 2nd Ave Ste 1600, Seattle, WA 98104
Tel.: (206) 464-5100
Web Site: http://www.lntyee.com
Rev.: $4,000,000,000
Emp.: 80
Financial Advisory Services
N.A.I.C.S.: 523940
Barbara A. Potter (Mng Dir-Fiduciary Svcs)
Kristi Mathisen (Mng Dir-Tax & Fin Plng)
Robert Hille (Chief Compliance Officer & Gen Counsel)
Dana Rekow (Mng Dir-Client Svcs)

Winona Capital Management, LLC (1)
980 N Michigan Ave Ste 1950, Chicago, IL 60611
Tel.: (312) 334-8800
Web Site: http://www.winonacapital.com
Rev.: $110,000,000
Emp.: 10
Equity Investment Firm
N.A.I.C.S.: 523999
Jason Sowers (Partner)
John McBlain (CFO)

LAKE AIR METAL PRODUCTS LLC
385 90th Ave NW, Minneapolis, MN 55433
Tel.: (763) 785-2429
Web Site: http://www.lakeairmetals.com
Sales Range: $10-24.9 Million
Emp.: 94
Sheet Metalwork
N.A.I.C.S.: 332322
Brad Severson (Pres)
Dan Ethen (VP)

LAKE AREA CORN PROCESSORS, LLC
46269 SD Hwy 34, Wentworth, SD 57075
Tel.: (605) 483-2676 SD
Web Site: https://www.dakotaethanol.com
Year Founded: 1999
Rev.: $280,440,962
Assets: $193,384,154
Liabilities: $57,990,725
Net Worth: $135,393,429
Earnings: $42,381,393
Emp.: 47
Fiscal Year-end: 12/31/23
Methanol Mfr
N.A.I.C.S.: 325193
Scott Mundt (Pres & CEO)

LAKE AUSTIN SPA RESORT
1705 S Quinlan Pk Rd, Austin, TX 78732
Tel.: (512) 372-7300
Web Site: http://www.lakeaustin.com
Sales Range: $1-9.9 Million
Emp.: 115
Resort & Spa
N.A.I.C.S.: 721199
Mike McAdams (Co-Owner)
Robbie Hudson (Dir-Programming)
Tracy York (Gen Mgr)
Trisha Shirey (Dir-Flora & Fauna)
Jorinda Nardone (Dir-Spa)
William W. Rucks IV (Co-Owner)

LAKE BUSINESS PRODUCTS, INC.
37200 Research Dr, Eastlake, OH 44095
Tel.: (440) 953-1199 OH
Web Site: http://www.lakebusiness.com
Year Founded: 1960
Sales Range: $125-149.9 Million
Emp.: 200
Provider of Office Products
N.A.I.C.S.: 423420
Brian Bradley (Mgr-Major Acct)
Terri Cain (Pres & CEO)
Tim Michalik (COO & VP)
Ken Opatrny (Mgr-Sls)
Rick McClain (Mgr-Building Ops)
Terri Massucci (Mgr-Acct)
Lisa Groewa (Controller)
Ed Sheehan (CFO)
MaryAnn Slattery (Sec)
Brian J. Gaughan (VP-Sls)

LAKE CABLE LLC
529 Thomas Dr, Bensenville, IL 60639
Tel.: (630) 860-5200
Web Site: http://www.lakecable.com
Sales Range: $10-24.9 Million
Emp.: 400
Nonferrous Wiredrawing & Insulating
N.A.I.C.S.: 332618
Steve Schultz (Product Mgr-OEM)
Alberto Borja (Mgr-Safety)
Brian Holland (Mgr-OEM Products)
Emile Tohme (VP-Ops)

LAKE CAPITAL MANAGEMENT LLC
875 N Michigan Ave Ste 3520, Chicago, IL 60611-2896
Tel.: (312) 640-7050 CO
Web Site: http://www.lakecapital.com
Year Founded: 1997
Rev.: $1,300,000,000
Emp.: 35
Investment Management Service
N.A.I.C.S.: 523940
Terence M. Graunke (Co-Founder & Principal)
Paul G. Yovovich (Co-Founder & Pres)
Michael J. Hayes (CFO)
Ryan Van Tiem (Mgr-Acctg)
Douglas C. Rescho (Principal)
Collin Abert (Principal)
Christopher Scales (VP)

Subsidiaries:

Opinion Research Corporation (1)
902 Carnegie Ctr Ste 220, Princeton, NJ 08540-6636
Tel.: (609) 452-5400
Web Site: http://www.orcinternational.com
Sales Range: $150-199.9 Million
Primary Market Research & Information Services
N.A.I.C.S.: 541910
Linda Shea (Mng Dir-Solutions Strategies-Global)
Brian Cruikshank (Pres-North America)
Chris Robson (Chief Innovation Officer)
Costas Pavlides (Mng Dir-Branded Products)
Craig Young (Mng Dir-Australia)
Jessica Horkan (Sr VP-Client Solutions)
Jon Harding (Sr VP-Client Solutions)
Lynne Armstrong (Sr VP-Talent Mgmt)
Oliver Rust (CEO-Global)
Richard Catrone (Exec VP-Ops)
Sally Winston (Mng Dir-Employee Res-Global)

Subsidiary (Domestic):

Guideline, Inc. (2)
625 Avenue of the Americas, New York, NY 10011-2020
Tel.: (212) 645-4500
Web Site: http://www.opinionresearch.com
Sales Range: $25-49.9 Million
Integrated Business Research & Analysis
N.A.I.C.S.: 561499
Kevin Young (Principal)
Mark Westmoreland (Founder)

Subsidiary (Non-US):

O.R.C. International Ltd. (2)

U.S. PRIVATE

186 City Road, London, EC1V 2NT, United Kingdom
Tel.: (44) 2076751000
Web Site: http://www.orcinternational.co.uk
Sales Range: $25-49.9 Million
Emp.: 80
Primary Market Research, Information Services & Marketing Services
N.A.I.C.S.: 541910
Richard Cornelius (Mng Dir)
Jeff Cox (Sr VP-Bus Dev-US)
Richard Catrone (Exec VP-Global Ops)
Brian Cruikshank (Sr VP)
Jon Harding (Exec VP-Bus Dev-US)
Patricia Hughes (VP-Client Solutions)
Christian Super (VP-Tech Solutions)
Phil Brooks (Dir-Fin Svcs Res)
Tom Markert (CEO)
Ana Mackay-Sim (CMO)
Alena Rossini (Mng Dir-Singapore)
Oliver Rust (Mng Dir-Asia Pacific)

ORC AUS Pty Ltd (2)
Level 8 171 La Trobe Street, Melbourne, 3000, VIC, Australia
Tel.: (61) 399355700
Sales Range: $25-49.9 Million
Emp.: 50
Primary Market Research, Information Services & Marketing Services
N.A.I.C.S.: 541910
Greg Wayman (Reg Mng Dir-Asia Pacific)

LAKE CITY PARTNERSHIP COUNCIL
133-B E Main St, Lake City, SC 29560
Tel.: (843) 374-0138 SC
Year Founded: 2010
Sales Range: $10-24.9 Million
Emp.: 12
City Development Services
N.A.I.C.S.: 541320
Frank Caggiano (CFO)
Sue-Ann Gerald Shannon (Gen Counsel & Asst Sec)
James P. Fields Jr. (Exec Dir)

LAKE COUNTRY CAPITAL LLC
7701 France Ave, Ste 240, Edina, MN 55435
Tel.: (612) 800-9944
Web Site: https://www.lakecountrycapital.com
Private Equity
N.A.I.C.S.: 523940

LAKE COUNTRY FOODS
132 S Concord Rd, Oconomowoc, WI 53066
Tel.: (262) 567-5521
Web Site: http://www.lcfoods.com
Rev.: $21,200,000
Emp.: 90
Dry Condensed & Evaporated Dairy Product Mfr
N.A.I.C.S.: 311514
Leon Stratman (Mgr-Quality Assurance)
Josh Waltenberry (CFO)
Phillip Kemppainen (Pres)

LAKE COUNTRY POWER
2810 Elida Dr, Grand Rapids, MN 55744
Tel.: (218) 741-8137
Web Site: http://www.lakecountrypower.com
Year Founded: 1938
Rev.: $42,000,000
Emp.: 120
Electronic Services
N.A.I.C.S.: 221122
Bill Bussey (Dir-Safety & Risk Mgmt)
Mike Birkeland (Dir-Member Svc & Community Rels)
George Harvey (Sec)
Craig D. Olson (Pres)
Sherman Liimatainen (VP)
Mark Bakk (Gen Mgr)

COMPANIES

LAKE COUNTY DODGE INC.
1001 Washington St, Jamestown, NY 14701
Tel.: (716) 484-7125
Web Site:
http://www.lakecountydodge.net
Sales Range: $1-9.9 Million
Emp.: 20
Automobiles, New & Used
N.A.I.C.S.: 441110
Gerald A. Swanson (Pres)
Ray Powell (Mgr-Parts)

LAKE COUNTY PRESS
98 Noll St, Waukegan, IL 60085
Tel.: (847) 336-4333   IL
Web Site:
http://www.lakecountypress.com
Sales Range: $200-249.9 Million
Emp.: 200
Provider of Offset & Letterpress Printing
N.A.I.C.S.: 323111
Ralph Johnson (Pres & CEO)
Robert J. Hilliard (CFO & Sr VP)
Peter J. Douglas (VP & Dir-Mktg)

LAKE ELMO BANK
11465 39th St N, Lake Elmo, MN 55042
Tel.: (651) 773-4758
Web Site:
http://www.lakeelmobank.com
Sales Range: $10-24.9 Million
Emp.: 102
State Commercial Banks
N.A.I.C.S.: 522110
Daniel D. Raleigh (Pres & CEO)
Bryan J. Kemnetz (Chief Credit Officer & Sr VP)
Christine A. Clark (VP-Mktg)
Elizabeth R. Landherr (VP-Trust & Estate Svcs)
Eric C. Graf (VP-Comml Lending)
Rebecca Billingsley (VP)
Lori V. Johnson (VP & Officer-Loan)
Anne L. Plante (VP & Mgr-Retail Banking)
Thomas Swedenburg (VP & Officer-Loan)
Dick Plummer (CFO)

LAKE ERIE ELECTRIC, INC.
25730 1st St, Westlake, OH 44145
Tel.: (440) 835-5565   OH
Web Site: http://www.leeinc.com
Year Founded: 1952
Rev.: $80,000,000
Emp.: 75
Provider of Electrical Construction Services & Contracting
N.A.I.C.S.: 238210
Peter J. Corogin (Pres & CEO)
Kenneth R. Beck (Sr VP)

Subsidiaries:

Lake Erie Electric Inc-Hirsch Division   (1)
25730 1st St, Westlake, OH 44145-1432
Tel.: (440) 835-5565
Web Site: http://www.lakeerieelectric.com
Sales Range: $25-49.9 Million
Electrical Contractor
N.A.I.C.S.: 238210
Peter Corogin (Pres)

LAKE FOREST SPORTSCARS LTD.
990 N Shore Dr, Lake Bluff, IL 60044
Tel.: (847) 295-6560
Web Site: http://www.lfsc.com
Year Founded: 1981
Sales Range: $10-24.9 Million
Emp.: 30
New Car Dealers
N.A.I.C.S.: 441110

Rick Mancuso (Owner & Pres)
Adam Mancuso (COO & VP)
Cassie Carver (Dir-Mktg)
Sean Welch (Mgr-Svc)
Nick Mancuso (Dir-Motorsports)
Greg Berner (Gen Mgr)
Dan Carver (Gen Mgr-Sls)
Scott Rothermel (Dir-Pre-Owned Sls)

LAKE GROUP MEDIA, INC.
1 Byram Brook Pl, Armonk, NY 10504
Tel.: (914) 925-2400
Web Site:
http://www.lakegroupmedia.com
Sales Range: $50-74.9 Million
Emp.: 60
Direct Mail Advertising Services
N.A.I.C.S.: 541860
Ryan Lake (CEO)
Karen Lake (COO)
Lenny Medico (Sr VP)
Lisa Dolzadelli (Dir-Client Svcs)
Mike Connolly (VP)
Joe Robinson (Sr VP)
Jennifer Cuttler (VP)
Heather Maylander (Mng Dir)
Carolyn Woodruff (Mng Dir)
Sheryl Benjamin (VP)
Danny Grubert (VP)
Belkys Reyes-Cuni (VP)
Joanne Elias (Assoc VP)
Carrie French (Assoc VP)
Mary Ellen Quirk (Assoc VP)
Kathy Stivaletti (Assoc VP)
Britt Perry (VP)
Chatty Teirstein (Acct Dir)
Jim Gallagher (Dir-Insert Media Sls)
Lenore Debellis (VP)

LAKE HOSPITAL SYSTEM, INC.
7590 Auburn Rd, Painesville, OH 44077
Tel.: (440) 354-1991   OH
Web Site: http://www.lakehealth.org
Year Founded: 1983
Sales Range: $350-399.9 Million
Emp.: 3,131
Health Care Srvices
N.A.I.C.S.: 622110
Cynthia Moore-Hardy (Pres & CEO)
Joyce Taylor (Chief Quality Officer & VP-Quality)
Mary L. Ogrinc (Chief Nursing Officer & Sr VP-Patient Care Svcs)
John Baniewicz (Chief Medical Officer & Sr VP)
Steven R. Karns (Sr VP-Admin Svcs)
Thomas P. Jubeck (Chm)
Michael E. Mayher (Vice Chm & Treas)
Paul Sirko (Sec)

LAKE JAMES LODGE
63 Lakeview Dr N, Marion, NC 28752
Tel.: (828) 652-3038
Sales Range: $10-24.9 Million
Emp.: 7
Assisted Living Facility
N.A.I.C.S.: 623312
Cathy C. Childrey (Pres)

LAKE KEOWEE CHRYSLER DODGE JEEP RAM
10815 Clemson Blvd, Seneca, SC 29678
Tel.: (864) 888-1200
Web Site:
http://www.lakekeoweechryslerdodge.com
Sales Range: $10-24.9 Million
Emp.: 47
New Car Dealers
N.A.I.C.S.: 441110
Mark Williams (Partner)

LAKE LIVINGSTON TELEPHONE COMPANY
229 Stevens Ln, Livingston, TX 77351-8905
Tel.: (936) 566-4242
Web Site:
http://www.lakelivingstontel.com
Sales Range: $50-74.9 Million
Emp.: 4
Telephone Company
N.A.I.C.S.: 517121
Terry Gentle (Gen Mgr)

LAKE LYNDON B. JOHNSON IMPROVEMENT CORPORATION
6702 Ranch Rd 2147 W, Horseshoe Bay, TX 78657
Tel.: (830) 598-2543
Web Site: http://www.hsbay.com
Year Founded: 1970
Sales Range: $10-24.9 Million
Emp.: 18
Real Estate Services
N.A.I.C.S.: 237210
Sam Tarbet (Pres)

LAKE MANAWA NISSAN INC.
920 32nd Ave, Council Bluffs, IA 51501
Tel.: (712) 366-9481
Web Site:
http://www.lakemanawanissan.com
Sales Range: $25-49.9 Million
Emp.: 100
Owner & Operator of Car Dealerships
N.A.I.C.S.: 441110
Chuck Norman (Gen Mgr)

LAKE MECHANICAL CONTRACTORS
343 N Bay St, Eustis, FL 32726
Tel.: (352) 357-3136
Web Site:
http://www.lakemechanical.net
Sales Range: $25-49.9 Million
Emp.: 100
Mechanical Contractor
N.A.I.C.S.: 238220
John B. Smith (Chm & CEO)
Evelyn H. Smith (Treas, Sec & VP)
Michele M. Alderman (VP, Asst Treas & Asst Sec)
Gary McKinley (VP)

LAKE METROPARKS
11211 Spear Rd, Painesville, OH 44077
Tel.: (440) 639-7275
Web Site:
http://www.lakemetroparks.com
Year Founded: 1958
Rev.: $13,051,325
Emp.: 151
Camping Services
N.A.I.C.S.: 441210

LAKE MICHIGAN CREDIT UNION
4027 Lake Dr SE, Grand Rapids, MI 49546
Tel.: (616) 942-3360   MI
Web Site: http://www.lmcu.org
Year Founded: 1933
Credit Union
N.A.I.C.S.: 522130
Sandy Jelinski (Pres & CEO)
Gretchen Tellman (Chm)
Ryan Todd (VP-Secondary Mktg)

Subsidiaries:

National Aircraft Finance Company   (1)
3907 Aero Pl Ste 1, Lakeland, FL 33811
Tel.: (863) 644-8463
Web Site: http://www.airloans.com
Aircraft Financing
N.A.I.C.S.: 525990
Kevin Buckland (Pres)

Pilot Bancshares, Inc.   (1)
12471 W Linebaugh Ave, Tampa, FL 33626
Tel.: (813) 496-2600
Web Site: http://www.pilotbank.com
Bank Holding Company
N.A.I.C.S.: 551111
Roy N. Hellwege (Chm & CEO)

Subsidiary (Domestic):

Pilot Bank   (2)
5140 E Fowler Ave, Tampa, FL 33617
Tel.: (813) 496-2600
Web Site: http://www.pilotbank.com
Rev.: $6,795,000
Assets: $198,831,000
Liabilities: $178,688,000
Net Worth: $20,143,000
Earnings: ($611,000)
Emp.: 49
Fiscal Year-end: 12/31/2013
Commericial Banking
N.A.I.C.S.: 522110
Roy N. Hellwege (CEO)
Shawn Hannan (Chief Lending Officer & Exec VP)
Hanisha Patel (Mgr)
Rita Lowman (Pres)
Courtenay E. Marshall (Chief Credit Officer & Sr VP)
Jen Saylor (Chief Risk Officer, Chief IT Officer & Sr VP)

LAKE PACIFIC PARTNERS, LLC
120 S LaSalle St Ste 1510, Chicago, IL 60603-3574
Tel.: (312) 578-1110
Web Site: http://www.lakepacific.com
Year Founded: 2000
Sales Range: $25-49.9 Million
Emp.: 5
Private Equity Investment Firm
N.A.I.C.S.: 523150
Wayne L. Carpenter (Mng Dir)
Susan B. Sentell (Pres & CEO)

LAKE PARK MUNICIPAL UTILITIES
217 Market St, Lake Park, IA 51347-7706
Tel.: (712) 832-3667
Web Site: http://www.lakeparkia.com
Electronic Services
N.A.I.C.S.: 221118

LAKE PRESTON COOPERATIVE ASSOCIATION
106 2nd St NW, Lake Preston, SD 57249
Tel.: (605) 847-4844
Sales Range: $25-49.9 Million
Emp.: 30
Grains
N.A.I.C.S.: 424510
James Huntemer (Pres)

LAKE REGION CO-OP OIL ASSOCIATION
4825 State Hwy 55 NW, Maple Lake, MN 55358
Tel.: (320) 963-3137
Web Site:
http://www.lakeregioncoop.com
Sales Range: $10-24.9 Million
Emp.: 10
Petroleum Bulk Stations
N.A.I.C.S.: 424710
Daniel Pribyl (Chm & Pres)
Jeff Brandl (Gen Mgr)
Michael Nix (Mgr-Facility)

LAKE REGION ELECTRIC COOP
516 S Lk Region Rd, Hulbert, OK 74441

Lake Region Electric Coop—(Continued)
Tel.: (918) 772-2526
Web Site: http://www.lrecok.coop
Rev.: $18,000,000
Emp.: 74
Distribution, Electric Power
N.A.I.C.S.: 221122
Bobby Mayfield (VP)
Jack Teague (Treas & Asst Sec)
Jim Loftin (Treas & Sec)

LAKE REGION HEALTHCARE
712 Cascade St S, Fergus Falls, MN 56537
Tel.: (218) 736-8000 MN
Web Site: http://www.lrhc.org
Year Founded: 1951
Sales Range: $100-124.9 Million
Emp.: 948
Health Care Srvices
N.A.I.C.S.: 622110
Larry Schulz (CEO)
Solveig Halbakken (Vice Chm & Sec)
Laurel Nelson (Treas)
Lucia Anderson (COO, Chief Nursing Officer & Sr VP-Ops)
Brett Longtin (CFO)
Katie Johnson (VP-Mktg & Comm)

LAKE SHORE BEHAVIORAL HEALTH, INC.
255 Delaware Ave Ste 300, Buffalo, NY 14202
Tel.: (716) 842-0440 NY
Web Site: http://www.lake-shore.org
Year Founded: 1971
Sales Range: $10-24.9 Million
Emp.: 314
Behavioral Healthcare Services
N.A.I.C.S.: 623210
Cathy Laughlan (Dir-Intensive Svcs)
Howard K. Hitzel (Pres)
Joseph C. DiStasio (CFO)
Kimberly R. Faulhaber (VP-Corp Compliance & Quality Improvement)
Elizabeth Woike-Ganga (COO)
Angela J. Benzel (Treas)
Richard J. Schechter (Co-Vice Chm)
Charles D. Syms (Co-Vice Chm)
William Gajewski (Chm)

LAKE SHORE NEWSPAPERS INC.
W 61 N 306 Washinton Ave Ul 1, Cedarburg, WI 53012
Tel.: (262) 375-5100
Web Site: http://www.gmtoday.com
Rev.: $12,500,000
Emp.: 12
Newspaper Publishers
N.A.I.C.S.: 513110
James Conley Jr. (Pres)
Mark Justesen (Office Mgr)
Heather Rogge (Mgr-Sls)
Deborah Butzmaff (Office Mgr)

LAKE SHORE RADIATOR INC.
5355 Ramona Blvd, Jacksonville, FL 32205
Tel.: (904) 389-4845
Web Site: http://www.lakeshoreautoparts.com
Sales Range: $10-24.9 Million
Emp.: 50
Automotive Supplies & Parts Distr
N.A.I.C.S.: 423120
Eric Robinson (Mgr-Accts Receivable)

LAKE SUPERIOR BREWING COMPANY
2711 W Superior St, Duluth, MN 55806
Tel.: (218) 723-4000

Web Site: http://www.lakesuperiorbrewing.com
Year Founded: 1994
Sales Range: Less than $1 Million
Emp.: 5
Beer Mfr
N.A.I.C.S.: 312120
John Perfetto (Mgr-Cellers)
Lars Kuehnow (Owner)

LAKE VIEW CHEESE CO.
1755 S Fremont Dr, Salt Lake City, UT 84104
Tel.: (801) 364-3607
Web Site: http://www.banquetcheese.com
Processed Cheese
N.A.I.C.S.: 311513
Greg Gaglio (Pres)

LAKE VILLAGE SEED & TIRE CO.
609 Lkside St, Lake Village, AR 71653
Tel.: (870) 265-3802
Web Site: http://www.lakevillageseedandtire.com
Sales Range: $10-24.9 Million
Emp.: 14
Seeds & Chemicals
N.A.I.C.S.: 424910

LAKEHEAD HOLDING CORP.
2916 Hill Ave, Superior, WI 54880-5504
Tel.: (715) 392-5181
Web Site: http://www.lakeheadconstructors.com
Year Founded: 1987
Sales Range: $50-74.9 Million
Emp.: 500
Industrial Buildings & Warehouse Mfr
N.A.I.C.S.: 236210
Brian C. Maki (Pres & CEO)

Subsidiaries:

Lakehead Constructors, Inc. (1)
2916 Hill Ave, Superior, WI 54880-5504 (100%)
Tel.: (715) 392-5181
Web Site: http://www.lakeheadconstructors.com
Sales Range: $50-74.9 Million
Industrial Buildings & Warehouses Mfr
N.A.I.C.S.: 236210
Brian Maki (Chm, Pres & CEO)

LAKELAND COOPERATIVE
Hwy 25, Ridgeland, WI 54763
Tel.: (715) 949-1165
Web Site: http://www.lakelandcoop.com
Year Founded: 1931
Sales Range: $25-49.9 Million
Emp.: 150
Farm Supply Services
N.A.I.C.S.: 424910
Karl Varnes (Gen Mgr)
Dave Score (Chm)
Charles Nelson (Vice Chm)
Chuck Solum (Treas & Sec)

LAKELAND ELECTRIC
501 E Lemon St, Lakeland, FL 33801-9881
Tel.: (863) 834-9535
Web Site: http://www.lakelandelectric.com
Sales Range: $75-99.9 Million
Emp.: 600
Electric Power Distribution & Generation Services
N.A.I.C.S.: 221122
David Kus (Asst Gen Mgr-Customer Svc)

Alan Shaffer (Deputy Gen Mgr)
Joel Ivy (Gen Mgr)
Jeff Curry (Coord-Alternative Energy)

LAKELAND PAPER CORPORATION
506 S Prairie Ave, Sturgis, MI 49091-2180
Tel.: (269) 651-5474 MI
Web Site: http://www.lakelandpaper.com
Year Founded: 1972
Sales Range: $25-49.9 Million
Emp.: 58
Converted Paper Products
N.A.I.C.S.: 322299
Graydon C. Fox (Chm)
Charles Schmidt (Pres)
Marvin Weingard (CFO)
J. R. Hark (Gen Mgr)

LAKELAND PRINTING CO INC
510 Chippewa St, Minocqua, WI 54548
Tel.: (715) 356-5236
Web Site: http://www.lakelandtimes.com
Sales Range: $10-24.9 Million
Emp.: 25
Newspaper Publishers
N.A.I.C.S.: 513110
Gregory Walker (Publr)
Heather Holmes (Gen Mgr)

Subsidiaries:

The Northwoods River News (1)
232 S Courtney St, Rhinelander, WI 54501-0778
Tel.: (715) 365-6397
Web Site: http://www.rivernewsonline.com
Sales Range: $10-24.9 Million
Emp.: 14
Community Newspaper
N.A.I.C.S.: 513110
Gregg Walker (Owner & Publr)

LAKEMARY CENTER INC.
100 Lakemary Dr, Paola, KS 66071-1855
Tel.: (913) 557-4000 KS
Year Founded: 1966
Sales Range: $10-24.9 Million
Emp.: 634
Community Welfare Services
N.A.I.C.S.: 624190
Paul Sokoloff (Chm)
William R. Craig (Pres & CEO)
Gayle Richardson (Vice Chm)
Lydia Marien (Sec)

LAKEPHARMA, INC.
520 Harbor Blvd, Belmont, CA 94002
Tel.: (650) 288-4891
Web Site: http://www.lakepharma.com
Year Founded: 2009
Sales Range: $1-9.9 Million
Emp.: 36
Biotechnology Research & Development Services
N.A.I.C.S.: 541714
Hua Tu (Founder & CEO)
Aaron K. Sato (Chief Scientific Officer)
John Lippincott (VP-Antibody Discovery)
Walter Tian (VP-Comml Ops)
David Boyle (CFO)

Subsidiaries:

Blue Sky Biotech, Inc. (1)
60 Prescott St, Worcester, MA 01605-2661
Tel.: (508) 798-5087
Web Site: http://www.blueskybioservices.com
Pharmaceutical & Biotechnology Distr
N.A.I.C.S.: 424210

Paul Wengender (Founder & CEO)
Edward Marple (Pres & CEO)
Scott Gridley (VP-Bus Dev)
Peter Glick (Chm)

LAKES AREA COOPERATIVE
459 3rd Ave SE PO Box 247, Perham, MN 56573
Tel.: (218) 346-6240
Web Site: http://lakesareacoop.com
Sales Range: $50-74.9 Million
Emp.: 15
Creamery, Farm Supply & Retail Establishments
N.A.I.C.S.: 424430
Dale Tellinghuisen (Gen Mgr)

LAKES AREA NONPROFIT SUPPORT FOUNDATION
826 Summit Ave, Detroit Lakes, MN 56501
Tel.: (218) 844-4221 MN
Year Founded: 2011
Sales Range: $1-9.9 Million
Financial Management Services
N.A.I.C.S.: 541611
Stuart Omberg (Pres)
Jan Logan (Treas)

LAKES GAS COMPANY
655 Lk St S, Forest Lake, MN 55025
Tel.: (651) 464-3345
Web Site: http://www.lakesgasco.com
Rev.: $38,000,000
Emp.: 11
Propane Gas, Bottled
N.A.I.C.S.: 457210
Howard E. Sargeant (Pres)
Steve Sargeant (VP)
Ken Downey (Plant Mgr)
Chris McGuire (Mgr-Bus Dev)

LAKES PIPE & SUPPLY CORP.
PO Box 429, Niagara Falls, NY 14305
Tel.: (716) 285-6631
Web Site: http://www.lakespipe.com
Sales Range: $10-24.9 Million
Emp.: 30
Sales of Pipes & Fittings
N.A.I.C.S.: 423720

LAKES REGION VISITING NURSE ASSOCIATION
186 Waukewan St, Meredith, NH 03253
Tel.: (603) 279-6611 NH
Web Site: http://www.lrvna.org
Year Founded: 1923
Rev.: $1,370,628
Assets: $1,215,468
Liabilities: $33,861
Net Worth: $1,181,607
Earnings: $83,292
Emp.: 28
Fiscal Year-end: 09/30/14
Nursing Care Services
N.A.I.C.S.: 623110
Cheryl Gonzalo (Exec Dir)
Edward Touhey (Sec)
Richard Goodby (Asst Treas)
Charles Thorndike (Chm)
Ray Moritz (Treas)
Robert Davis (Vice Chm)
Kevin Kelley (CEO)

Subsidiaries:

Newfound Area Nursing Association (1)
214 Lake St, Bristol, NH 03222
Tel.: (603) 744-2733
Web Site: http://www.newfoundareanursingassociation.org
Sales Range: $1-9.9 Million
Emp.: 23
Horse Association
N.A.I.C.S.: 813920

COMPANIES

Andrea Berry *(Dir-Home Care & Hospice Medical)*
Thomas McGowan *(Pres)*
John Lloyd *(Dir-Medical)*
Patricia A. Wentworth *(Exec Dir)*
Roger Lafontaine *(Treas)*
Louise Franklin *(Sec)*

LAKESHORE CAPITAL PARTNERS LLC
319 N Grant St, Hinsdale, IL 60521
Tel.: (773) 255-0301   DE
Web Site:
http://www.lakeshorecp.com
Sales Range: $10-24.9 Million
Emp.: 12
Privater Equity Firm
N.A.I.C.S.: 523999
Andrew Matricaria *(Mng Partner)*
Lee Matricaria *(Mng Partner)*
Michael J. Coyle *(Partner)*
James C. Gilstrap *(Partner)*
John R. Larson *(Partner)*
Curt Thompson *(Partner)*
Gregory T. Lucier *(Partner)*
Ronald A. Matricaria *(Partner)*

LAKESHORE ENTERTAINMENT CORP.
9268 W 3rd St, Beverly Hills, CA 90210
Tel.: (310) 867-8000
Web Site:
http://www.lakeshoreentertainment.com
Rev.: $29,100,000
Emp.: 30
Motion Picture & Video Production
N.A.I.C.S.: 512110
Thomas B. Rosenberg *(Founder)*

LAKESHORE ESTATES INC
8044 Coley Davis Rd, Nashville, TN 37221
Tel.: (615) 646-4466   TN
Web Site:
http://www.lakeshoreestates.org
Year Founded: 1949
Sales Range: $10-24.9 Million
Emp.: 362
Community Care Services
N.A.I.C.S.: 624190
David A. Sciortino *(Pres & CEO)*

LAKESHORE FOODS CORP.
100 Commerce Sq, Michigan City, IN 46360-3281
Tel.: (219) 879-3357   IN
Web Site:
http://www.alssupermarkets.com
Year Founded: 1973
Sales Range: $25-49.9 Million
Emp.: 380
Supermarkets, Chain
N.A.I.C.S.: 445110
James Ziska *(CFO & VP-Fin)*
Gil Pontius *(CEO)*
Kyle Johnson *(Dir-Adv)*
Alexis Pontius *(VP-Ops)*

LAKESHORE LEARNING MATERIALS
2695 E Dominguez St, Carson, CA 90895
Tel.: (310) 537-8600
Web Site:
http://www.lakeshorelearning.com
Sales Range: $50-74.9 Million
Emp.: 1,500
Education Aids, Devices & Supplies
N.A.I.C.S.: 459999
Bo Kaplan *(Pres)*
Adrienne Hilliard *(Mgr-Toy Mdse)*
Aaron Eskridge *(Dir-Art)*
Andy Hess *(Project Mgr)*
Angela Oliver *(Dir-Art Svcs)*
Blaine Vandyne *(VP-Sls-Intl Schools)*
Branden Summers Lakeshore *(Dir-Art)*
Brittney Castleberry *(Coord-Visual)*
Debbie Ultan *(Dir-Fin)*
Ed Sudario *(Reg Mgr)*
Eric Chyo *(Dir-Educational Software Dev)*
Erin Caldwell *(Project Coord)*
Jeffrey Campbell *(Mgr-Catalog Production)*
John Lynch *(Mgr-Web Design)*
Lisa Gonzales *(Coord-Visual Retail)*
Lou Orr *(Reg Mgr)*
Pam Kissinger *(VP-Vendor Rels)*
Rosanne Ankele *(Dir-HR & Employee Rels)*
Rose Contreras *(VP-Creative Svcs)*
Tracy Downie *(Asst Mgr-Sls & Mktg)*
Jennifer Centazzo *(COO)*
Frank Garcia *(Dir-Pur)*
David Reed *(Dir-Stores Sls)*
Gabino Banuelos *(Dir-Traffic)*
Tyler Domski *(Mgr-Bid Dept)*
Kelly Hudson *(Mgr-Retail Recruiting)*
Maribel Lopez *(Partner-Sls)*
Keshia Sih *(Project Coord)*
Shannon Wall *(Mgr-HR Ops)*
Kim Kaiser *(Mgr-Recruiting)*
Jeff Ball *(Project Mgr)*
Emily Eva Leong *(Project Mgr-Mktg Social Media)*
Sue Gaon *(VP)*
Ray Palmer *(VP-Bus Process)*

LAKESHORE MANAGEMENT GROUP
1320 W Fullerton Ave, Chicago, IL 60614
Tel.: (312) 616-9000
Web Site:
http://www.lakeshoresf.com
Rev.: $11,400,000
Emp.: 154
Health Club
N.A.I.C.S.: 713940
Heidi Volk *(Mgr-Payroll)*

LAKESHORE UTILITY TRAILER INC.
18239 Telegraph Rd, Romulus, MI 48174
Tel.: (734) 285-4560
Web Site:
http://www.lakeshoreutility.com
Sales Range: $25-49.9 Million
Emp.: 65
Trucks, Tractors & Trailers: New & Used Dealership
N.A.I.C.S.: 441110
Charles M. Pfeffer *(Pres)*
Gary Charhevillet *(Controller)*

LAKESIDE BANK
1055 W Roosevelt Rd, Chicago, IL 60608
Tel.: (312) 789-3500
Web Site:
http://www.lakesidebank.com
Sales Range: $10-24.9 Million
Emp.: 25
State Commercial Banks
N.A.I.C.S.: 522110
Eva M. Ayala *(VP & Branch Mgr)*
Ana M. Benitez *(Sr VP-Ops-BSA & Security)*
Michael L. Dollard *(VP & Controller)*
Susanna L. Fong *(VP & Branch Mgr)*
Raymond Groselak *(VP-Comml Lending)*
Connie Harris *(VP & Branch Mgr)*
Jeff W. Miller *(CIO & Sr VP)*
Carmen N. Madsen *(Asst VP & Asst Branch Mgr)*
Fanny Yuen *(VP-Personal Banking)*
Desiree D. White *(VP-Ops)*
Stan J. Bochnowski *(Chief Lending Officer & Exec VP)*
David V. Pinkerton *(Vice Chm & Pres)*
Vincent Tolve *(Officer-Trust, Gen Counsel, Sec & Exec VP)*
Philip D. Cacciatore *(Chm & CEO)*
Todd G. Monte *(CFO & Exec VP)*
Jonathan Demas *(Officer-Comml Loan)*
Lisa Formanski *(Officer-Compliance & VP)*
Alan L. Rose *(Chief Mktg Officer & Sr VP)*
Tim Savoca *(Chief Credit Officer & Sr VP)*
Jennifer Lackuzynski *(Officer-Bus Dev)*
Aniceto Ron *(Officer-Information Sys)*
Maria Baez *(Officer-Ops)*
Daniel Welz *(Sr VP & Dir-Admin)*
Jo Ann Wong *(Sr VP-Loan Ops)*
Allan Adaya *(VP & Branch Mgr)*
Angela Villegas *(VP & Branch Mgr)*
Matthew Palmisano *(VP & Dir-Treasury Mgmt)*
Daniel Van Prooyen *(VP-Comml Lending)*
Jeffrey Wisniewski *(VP-Comml Lending)*
Joshua Coburn *(VP-Comml Lending)*
Justin Newhuis *(VP-Comml Lending)*
Ken Kosin *(VP-Comml Lending)*
Michael Fogarty *(VP-Comml Lending)*
Nick Wycklendt *(VP-Comml Lending)*
Robert Matijevich *(VP-Comml Lending)*
Pat McNulty *(VP-HR)*
Olin Hill *(VP-Loan Portfolio Admin)*
Juanita Lazzerini *(VP-Retail Mortgage Loan Ops)*
Matthew Howe *(VP-Special Assets)*
Todd Probasco *(VP & Mgr-Retail Mortgage Sls)*
John H. Rogers III *(Asst VP-Bus Dev)*

LAKESIDE COUNTRY CLUB
100 Wilcrest Dr, Houston, TX 77042
Tel.: (281) 497-2222   TX
Web Site: http://www.lakesidecc.com
Year Founded: 1905
Sales Range: $10-24.9 Million
Emp.: 318
Country Club Operator
N.A.I.C.S.: 713910
Brad Greebon *(CFO)*
Craig Schaner *(Gen Mgr)*

LAKESIDE FOODS, INC.
PO Box 1327, Manitowoc, WI 54221-1327
Tel.: (920) 684-3356   WI
Web Site:
http://www.lakesidefoods.com
Year Founded: 1887
Sales Range: $400-449.9 Million
Emp.: 1,000
Canned & Frozen Vegetables, Frozen Meals, Canned Meats, Jellies & Preserves, Shelf Stable Meals, Whipped Toppings, Pasta, Salsa & Other Sauces
N.A.I.C.S.: 311421
Thomas E. Reilly *(Sr VP-HR)*
Jim Anderson *(Dir-Supply Chain)*
Dave Greenwood *(Dir-HR)*
Robert Popple *(VP-Food Svc, Indus & Chain Acct Sls)*
Dave Allen *(Sr VP-Retail Sls)*
Gwen Anschutz *(Mgr-Accts Payable)*
Joe Yanda *(VP-Retail Processed Food Sls)*
John Rusiniak *(VP-Quality Control & Product Safety)*
Erica Pezold *(Gen Mgr-Distr)*

Subsidiaries:

Cher-Make Sausage Company (1)
2915 Calumet Ave, Manitowoc, WI 54220
Tel.: (920) 683-5980
Web Site: http://www.cher-make.com
Emp.: 106
Meat Product Whslr
N.A.I.C.S.: 424470
Tom Chermak *(Pres)*

Lakeside Foods (1)
108 Main St PO Box 6, Eden, WI 53019
Tel.: (920) 477-2311
Web Site: http://www.lakesidefoods.com
Sales Range: $25-49.9 Million
Emp.: 30
Food Processing Services
N.A.I.C.S.: 311421

Lakeside Foods, Inc. - Belgium Plant (1)
705 Main St, Belgium, WI 53004
Tel.: (262) 285-3299
Web Site: http://www.lakesidefoods.com
Canned Vegetable Mfr & Distr
N.A.I.C.S.: 424480

Lakeside Foods, Inc. - Brooten Plant (1)
500 Industrial Park Rd, Brooten, MN 56316
Tel.: (320) 346-2900
Web Site: http://lakesidefoods.com
Sales Range: $25-49.9 Million
Emp.: 20
Frozen & Canned Vegetable Mfr
N.A.I.C.S.: 311421
Doug Dever *(Mgr)*

Lakeside Foods, Inc. - Manitowoc Plant (1)
510 Jay St, Manitowoc, WI 54220
Tel.: (920) 684-0151
Frozen & Canned Vegetable Mfr
N.A.I.C.S.: 311421

Lakeside Foods, Inc. - New Richmond Plant (1)
660 N 2nd St, New Richmond, WI 54017
Tel.: (715) 243-7367
Frozen Vegetable Distr
N.A.I.C.S.: 424480

Lakeside Foods, Inc. - Owatonna Plant (1)
900 N Cedar Ave, Owatonna, MN 55060
Tel.: (507) 446-7700
Web Site: http://www.lakesidefoods.com
Emp.: 240
Packaged Food Mfr & Distr
N.A.I.C.S.: 311999
Jackie Hogan *(Acct Mgr)*

Lakeside Foods, Inc. - Plainview Plant (1)
1055 W Broadway, Plainview, MN 55964
Tel.: (507) 534-3141
Web Site: http://www.lakesidefoods.com
Emp.: 110
Canned Vegetable Mfr & Distr
N.A.I.C.S.: 424480
Darryl Goss *(Gen Mgr)*

Lakeside Foods, Inc. - Random Lake Plant (1)
709 Allen St, Random Lake, WI 53075
Tel.: (920) 994-2117
Frozen & Canned Vegetable Mfr
N.A.I.C.S.: 311421

Lakeside Foods, Inc. - Reedsburg Plant (1)
200 Eagle St, Reedsburg, WI 53959
Tel.: (608) 524-2346
Sales Range: $25-49.9 Million
Emp.: 25
Frozen & Canned Vegetable Mfr
N.A.I.C.S.: 311421

Lakeside Foods, Inc. - Seymour Plant (1)
530 E Wisconsin St, Seymour, WI 54165
Tel.: (920) 833-2371
Packaged Vegetable Storage Services
N.A.I.C.S.: 493130

Peak Foods, LLC (1)
1903 W Main St, Troy, OH 45373-1016
Tel.: (937) 440-0707
Web Site: http://www.peakfoods.com

LAKESIDE FOODS, INC. U.S. PRIVATE

Lakeside Foods, Inc.—(Continued)
Sales Range: $25-49.9 Million
Emp.: 75
Joint Venture of Lakeside Foods, Inc. & Interstate Food Processing Corporation
N.A.I.C.S.: 311511
Debbie Friend *(Mgr-Production)*
Kim Mclin *(Supvr-Line)*
Bryan Adkins *(Supvr-Ops)*
Cindy Hicks *(Sr Mgr-Logistics)*
Curt Sukeena *(Sr Mgr-Logistics)*
Doug Sumpter *(Gen Mgr-Logistics)*

LAKESIDE IMPORTS INC.
3701 N Causeway Blvd, Metairie, LA 70002
Tel.: (504) 833-3311
Web Site: http://www.lakesidetoyota.com
Sales Range: $50-74.9 Million
Emp.: 200
New & Used Car Dealers
N.A.I.C.S.: 441110
Linda Reed *(Controller)*

LAKESIDE INDUSTRIES
6505 226th Pl SE Ste 200, Issaquah, WA 98027-8905
Tel.: (425) 313-2600
Web Site: http://www.lakesideindustries.com
Year Founded: 1972
Sales Range: $125-149.9 Million
Emp.: 48
Provider of Asphalt Paving Contracting Services
N.A.I.C.S.: 237310
Mike Lee *(Pres)*

Subsidiaries:

Lakeside Industries - Aberdeen Plant (1)
2400 Sargent Blvd, Aberdeen, WA 98520
Tel.: (360) 533-0610
Emp.: 15
Paving Block Mfr
N.A.I.C.S.: 327331
Tony Hammett *(Mgr)*

Lakeside Industries - Centralia Plant (1)
2001 NE Johnson Rd, Centralia, WA 98531
Tel.: (360) 736-2847
Emp.: 20
Paving Block Mfr
N.A.I.C.S.: 327331
Tony Hammeet *(Gen Mgr)*

Lakeside Industries - Foster Road Plant (1)
6400 SE 101St Ave, Portland, OR 97266
Tel.: (503) 777-7779
Paving Block Mfr
N.A.I.C.S.: 327331
Ron Green *(Gen Mgr)*

Lakeside Industries - Fremont Plant (1)
309 NW 39th St, Seattle, WA 98107
Tel.: (206) 632-2709
Paving Block Mfr
N.A.I.C.S.: 327331

Lakeside Industries - Hillsboro Plant (1)
955 Armco St, Hillsboro, OR 97124
Tel.: (503) 640-2208
Paving Block Mfr
N.A.I.C.S.: 327331

Lakeside Industries - Issaquah Plant (1)
6600 230th Ave SE, Issaquah, WA 98027
Tel.: (425) 392-6432
Emp.: 4
Paving Block Mfr
N.A.I.C.S.: 327331
Ray Craver *(Mgr)*

Lakeside Industries - Kent Plant (1)
18808 SE 256th St, Covington, WA 98042
Tel.: (253) 631-5434
Web Site: http://www.lakesideindustries.com
Emp.: 4

Paving Block Mfr
N.A.I.C.S.: 327331
Robert Dennis *(Mgr)*

Lakeside Industries - Longview Plant (1)
500 Tennant Way, Longview, WA 98632
Tel.: (360) 425-9155
Web Site: http://www.lakesideindustries.com
Paving Block Mfr
N.A.I.C.S.: 327331

Lakeside Industries - Monroe Plant (1)
14282 Galaxy Way, Monroe, WA 98272
Tel.: (360) 794-3324
Asphalt Pavement Contracting Services
N.A.I.C.S.: 238990

Lakeside Industries - Port Angeles Plant (1)
142 Eclipse West Dr, Port Angeles, WA 98363
Tel.: (360) 457-1854
Paving Block Mfr
N.A.I.C.S.: 327331

Lakeside Industries - Portland Plant (1)
4850 NW Front Ave, Portland, OR 97210
Tel.: (503) 849-7148
Paving Block Mfr
N.A.I.C.S.: 327331

Lakeside Industries - Valley Paving Plant (1)
6505 226th Pl SE Ste 150, Issaquah, WA 98027
Tel.: (425) 313-2600
Web Site: http://www.lakesideindustries.com
Paving Block Mfr
N.A.I.C.S.: 327331

LAKESIDE INTERNATIONAL TRUCKS INC.
11000 W Silver Spring Rd, Milwaukee, WI 53225
Tel.: (414) 353-4800
Web Site: http://www.lakesidetrucks.com
Sales Range: $25-49.9 Million
Emp.: 108
Trucks, Tractors & Trailers: New & Used
N.A.I.C.S.: 441110
William K. Reilley *(Pres)*
Jim Daugherty *(CFO & VP-Ops)*
Rob Durham *(Dir-HR & Mktg)*
John Litsheim *(Dir-Parts)*

Subsidiaries:

Lakeside International LLC (1)
6510 Aurora Rd Ste B, West Bend, WI 53090-9412
Tel.: (262) 629-4600
Web Site: http://www.lakesidetrucks.com
Sales Range: $10-24.9 Million
Emp.: 20
Truck Engine Repair, Except Industrial
N.A.I.C.S.: 811111
Rob Durham *(Mgr-Mktg)*

LAKESIDE MEDICAL GROUP, INC.
PO Box 371390, Reseda, CA 91337
Tel.: (818) 637-2000 CA
Web Site: http://www.lakesidemed.com
Medical Group
N.A.I.C.S.: 621491
Samuel R. La Blue *(Chief Admin Officer)*
Kermit Newman *(CFO)*

LAKESIDE METALS INC.
7000 Adams St Ste 210, Willowbrook, IL 60527
Tel.: (630) 850-3800
Web Site: http://www.lakesidemetals.com
Rev.: $20,300,000
Emp.: 15

Tin Plate
N.A.I.C.S.: 423510
Ira Nadler *(Pres)*

LAKESIDE PLASTICS, INC.
450 W 33rd Ave, Oshkosh, WI 54903
Tel.: (920) 235-3620
Web Site: http://www.lakesideplastics.net
Sales Range: $25-49.9 Million
Emp.: 60
Plastics Material & Resin Mfr
N.A.I.C.S.: 325211
Kelly Leith *(Mgr-HR)*
David Stini *(CFO)*
Mike Cuttill *(VP)*

LAKESIDE PRODUCTIONS INC.
6767 Forest Lawn Dr, Los Angeles, CA 90068-1027
Tel.: (323) 850-3032 CA
Year Founded: 1989
Sales Range: $25-49.9 Million
Motion Picture & Video Production
N.A.I.C.S.: 512110

LAKESIDE SUPPLY CO. INC.
3000 W 117th St, Cleveland, OH 44111
Tel.: (216) 941-6800
Web Site: http://www.lakesidesupply.com
Sales Range: $10-24.9 Million
Emp.: 38
Industrial Plumbing Supplies
N.A.I.C.S.: 423840
Stephen Driscoll Sr. *(CFO)*

LAKEVIEW CAPITAL, INC.
151 S Old Woodward Ave 400, Birmingham, MI 48009
Tel.: (248) 554-4900
Privater Equity Firm
N.A.I.C.S.: 523999
Jake Freeman *(Dir-Investments)*

Subsidiaries:

Mikawaya LLC (1)
800 East 4th St, Los Angeles, CA 90013
Tel.: (323) 587-5504
Web Site: http://www.mikawaya.com
Sales Range: $1-9.9 Million
Commercial Bakery
N.A.I.C.S.: 311812
Joel Friedman *(Pres & CEO)*

LAKEVIEW CONSTRUCTION INC.
10505 Corporate Dr Ste 200, Pleasant Prairie, WI 53158
Tel.: (262) 857-3336 WI
Web Site: http://www.lvconstruction.com
Year Founded: 1993
Sales Range: $75-99.9 Million
Emp.: 125
Nonresidential Construction Contractor
N.A.I.C.S.: 236220
Kent Moon *(Pres, CEO & Dir-Safety)*
Mike Anderson *(CFO)*
Marc Delsman *(VP-Ops)*

LAKEVIEW EQUITY PARTNERS, LLC
700 N Water St Ste 630, Milwaukee, WI 53202
Tel.: (414) 732-2040
Web Site: http://www.lakeviewequity.com
Privater Equity Firm
N.A.I.C.S.: 523999
W. Kent Velde *(Pres)*

LAKEVIEW FARMS LLC

PO Box 98 1600 Gressel Dr, Delphos, OH 45833-0098
Tel.: (800) 755-9925
Web Site: http://lakeviewfarms.com
Food Mfr
N.A.I.C.S.: 445298
Tom Davis *(CEO)*

Subsidiaries:

Tribe Mediterranean Foods Inc. (1)
110 Prince Henry Dr, Taunton, MA 02780
Tel.: (508) 844-5097
Web Site: http://www.tribehummus.com
Food Service Contractors
N.A.I.C.S.: 722310
Scott Webster *(CFO)*

LAKEVIEW FARMS, INC.
1600 Gressel Dr, Delphos, OH 45833-0098
Tel.: (419) 695-9925 OH
Web Site: http://www.lakeviewfarms.com
Year Founded: 1988
Rev.: $48,500,000
Emp.: 300
Sour Cream & Sour Cream-Based Dips Mfr
N.A.I.C.S.: 311511
John Kopilchack *(VP-Sls)*
Ashley Dilworth *(Coord-Labeling)*
Phil Baldauf *(Mgr)*

Subsidiaries:

Lakeview Farms, Inc. (1)
PO Box 188, Bristol, WI 53104-0188
Tel.: (262) 857-2316
Web Site: http://www.lakeviewfarms.com
Sales Range: $25-49.9 Million
Emp.: 200
Desserts & Cheese Spreads Mfr
N.A.I.C.S.: 311999

LAKEWAY MECHANICAL CONTRACTORS
341 Hamblen Ave Ste 100, Morristown, TN 37813
Tel.: (423) 587-2665
Sales Range: $10-24.9 Million
Emp.: 115
Mechanical Contractor
N.A.I.C.S.: 238220
Mark Price *(Pres)*

LAKEWAY PUBLISHERS INCORPORATED
1609 W 1st N St, Morristown, TN 37814
Tel.: (423) 581-5630
Web Site: http://www.lakewaypublishers.com
Sales Range: $10-24.9 Million
Emp.: 150
Newspapers, Publishing & Printing
N.A.I.C.S.: 513110
R. Jack Fishman *(Pres)*
Don Lovelace *(VP-Circulation)*
Sylvia Tharp *(Dir-HR)*

LAKEWAY TRUCKING INCORPORATED
444 Jones Franklin Rd, Morristown, TN 37813
Tel.: (423) 587-6880
Sales Range: $10-24.9 Million
Emp.: 3
Trucking Service
N.A.I.C.S.: 484121
Bobby L. Noe *(Pres)*

LAKEWOOD CAPITAL, LLC
7 Old Field Rd Ste 1001, Rowayton, CT 06853
Tel.: (203) 604-0863 CT
Web Site: http://www.lakewoodcap.com
Privater Equity Firm

COMPANIES

LAMBERT & CO.

N.A.I.C.S.: 523999
Roger Knight (Mng Partner)

Subsidiaries:

Orion International Consulting Group, LLC (1)
400 Regency Forest Dr Ste 310, Cary, NC 27518
Tel.: (919) 653-3720
Web Site: http://www.orioninternational.com
Sales Range: $25-49.9 Million
Emp.: 75
Former-Military Personnel Job Placement Services
N.A.I.C.S.: 561311
William H. Laughlin (Co-Founder)
Mike Starich (Pres)
Tim Isacco (COO)
Brian Henry (Officer-Recruiting & VP-Ops)
Bill Key (VP-Ops-Enlisted Recruiting)
Steve Casey (Sr Partner & VP-Sls Ops)
Vearl A. Williams (Sr Partner)
Jeffrey Evans (Chm)
Steve Bjerke (CFO)

Subsidiary (Domestic):

Novotus, LLC (2)
5508 Parkcrest Dr Ste 100, Austin, TX 78731
Tel.: (512) 733-2244
Web Site: http://www.novotus.com
Sales Range: $1-9.9 Million
Emp.: 70
Full Service Recruiting
N.A.I.C.S.: 561311
Mike Mayeux (CEO)
Cory Kruse (Pres)
Penny Lozano (CFO)
Dustin Little (Dir-Talent Solutions)

Division (Domestic):

Orion International Consulting Group, LLC - Gemini Energy Services Division (2)
2640 Financial Ct Ste G, San Diego, CA 92117
Tel.: (858) 939-1521
Web Site: http://www.geminienergyservices.com
Energy Consulting Services
N.A.I.C.S.: 541690
Jimmy Haley (Mng Dir & VP)
Kim Primerano (Dir-Bus Dev)
Rick Friesen (Dir-Field Svcs)
Crystal Friesen (Office Mgr)
Brittany Mason (Office Mgr)

Subsidiary (Domestic):

Therapy Staff, LLC (2)
705 S Main St Ste 220, Plymouth, MI 48170
Tel.: (248) 349-5050
Web Site: http://www.therapystaff.com
Sales Range: $10-24.9 Million
Emp.: 12
Healthcare Professional Recruiting & Staffing Services
N.A.I.C.S.: 561311
Joel Williams (Gen Mgr)

Division (Domestic):

Therapy Staff, LLC - Detroit Regional Division (3)
705 S Main St Ste 220, Plymouth, MI 48170
Tel.: (734) 354-8000
Therapist Recruiting & Staffing Services
N.A.I.C.S.: 561311

Therapy Staff, LLC - National Travel Division (3)
2700 Bee Caves Rd Ste 204, Austin, TX 78746
Tel.: (877) 366-2580
Therapist Recruiting & Staffing Services
N.A.I.C.S.: 561311

Vacuum Systems International, Inc. (1)
7777 Wall St, Cleveland, OH 44125
Tel.: (216) 642-8778
Web Site: http://www.vacuumhelpline.com
Sales Range: $1-9.9 Million
Emp.: 24
Commercial Vacuum Cleaner Remanufacturing Services
N.A.I.C.S.: 811412
Max Lambright (COO)

LAKEWOOD FORD
11503 Pacific Hwy SW, Lakewood, WA 98499
Tel.: (253) 474-0511
Web Site: http://www.lakewoodford.net
Year Founded: 1916
Sales Range: $25-49.9 Million
Emp.: 100
Sales of New & Used Automobiles
N.A.I.C.S.: 441110
Henry Krebs (Gen Mgr & Owner)
Jim Garner (Mgr-Svc)
Boyd Hamilton (Mgr)

LAKEWOOD RANCH GOLF & COUNTRY CLUB
7650 Legacy Blvd, Bradenton, FL 34202
Tel.: (941) 907-4700
Web Site: http://www.lakewoodranchgolf.com
Year Founded: 1985
Sales Range: $1-9.9 Million
Emp.: 175
Golf Course & Country Club
N.A.I.C.S.: 713910
Rex Jensen (CEO)
Wayne Piazza (Gen Mgr)
Bryan McMannis (Dir-Golf)
Mark Sweeny (Mgr-Food & Beverage)
Maureen Latessa (Dir-Membership)
Jennifer Caillouet (Mgr-Catering Sls)
Paul Lederman (Dir-Athletic Center Ops)

LAKEWOOD RESOURCE & REFERRAL CENTER
212 2nd St Ste 204, Lakewood, NJ 08701
Tel.: (732) 942-9292 NJ
Web Site: http://www.lrrcenter.org
Year Founded: 2004
Sales Range: $10-24.9 Million
Emp.: 236
Community Welfare Services
N.A.I.C.S.: 624190
Dovid Friedman (CEO)
Isaac Birnhack (Sr Mgr-Case)
Perl Leifer (Mgr-Case)
Leah Schnall (Coord-Vaccine Compliance Grants)

LAKEWOOD-AMEDEX INC.
7267 Delainey Ct, Sarasota, FL 34240
Tel.: (941) 225-2515
Web Site: http://www.lakewoodamedex.com
Sales Range: $1-9.9 Million
Pharmaceuticals Mfr
N.A.I.C.S.: 325412
Steve Parkinson (Chm, Pres & CEO)
Pete Ceccacci (Controller)
Paul DiTullio (VP-Product Dev)
David Carr (Dir-Corp Dev)
Stephen Miley (Chief Medical Officer)
Steven A. Kates (Chief Scientific Officer & VP-Regulatory Affairs)

LAKIN GENERAL CORPORATION
2044 N Dominick St, Chicago, IL 60614
Tel.: (773) 871-6560 IL
Web Site: http://www.lakincorp.com
Year Founded: 1917
Sales Range: $25-49.9 Million
Emp.: 49
Mfr of Rubber Products
N.A.I.C.S.: 423130
Lewis Lakin (Owner, Chm & CEO)
Ken Lakin (Pres)
Cheryl Lakin (Office Mgr)

LAMAJAK INC.
2125 Chenault Dr, Carrollton, TX 75006
Tel.: (972) 759-5000 TX
Web Site: http://www.lorishospitalgiftshops.com
Year Founded: 1981
Sales Range: $25-49.9 Million
Emp.: 1,500
Gift, Novelty & Souvenir Shop
N.A.I.C.S.: 459420
Lingling Chou (CFO)

LAMAR CONSTRUCTION COMPANY
4404 Central Pkwy, Hudsonville, MI 49426
Tel.: (616) 662-2933
Web Site: http://www.lamarconstruction.com
Sales Range: $50-74.9 Million
Emp.: 125
Nonresidential Construction Services
N.A.I.C.S.: 236220
Carl Blauwkamp (Pres)
George Holmes (Exec VP)
Doug Lenters (VP)

LAMAR PARTNERING CORPORATION
5321 Corporate Blvd, Baton Rouge, LA 70808
Tel.: (225) 926-1000 Ky
Year Founded: 2021
Investment Services
N.A.I.C.S.: 523999
Sean Reilly (Chm)
Ross Reilly (CEO)
Joe O'Brien (CFO)
Jay L. Johnson (Chief Investment Officer)

LAMAZE INTERNATIONAL
2025 M St Nw Ste 800, Washington, DC 20036-3309
Tel.: (202) 367-1128 DC
Web Site: http://www.lamazeinternational.org
Year Founded: 1960
Sales Range: $1-9.9 Million
Pregnancy Care Services
N.A.I.C.S.: 621410
John Richardson (Dir-Policy & Govt Rels)
Denis Janis (Sr Mgr-IT)
Robin Elise Weiss (Pres)
Eileen DiFrisco (Treas & Sec)
Alice Turner (Pres)
Amanda Darvill (Dir-Mktg & Comm)
Chris Peck (Program Dir-Education)
Elisabeth Bing (Co-Founder)
Andrea J. Boudreaux (CEO)

LAMB & ASSOCIATES INC.
1700 Murphy Dr, Maumelle, AR 72113
Tel.: (501) 851-0800
Web Site: http://www.lambpackaging.com
Rev.: $14,500,000
Emp.: 50
Mfr of Boxes, Paperboard & Disposable Plastic
N.A.I.C.S.: 424130
Jerry Lamb (CEO)
Kyle Lamb (Pres)

LAMB & WEBSTER INC.
601 W Main St, Springville, NY 14141
Tel.: (716) 592-4924
Web Site: http://www.lambandwebster.com
Sales Range: $10-24.9 Million
Emp.: 50
Farm Equipment & Supplies
N.A.I.C.S.: 459999
Lloyd E. Lamb (Pres)

LAMB COUNTY ELECTRIC COOPERATIVE, INC.
2415 S Phelps Ave, Littlefield, TX 79339
Tel.: (806) 385-5191 TX
Web Site: http://www.lcec.coop
Year Founded: 1938
Sales Range: $25-49.9 Million
Emp.: 52
Electric Power Distribution Services
N.A.I.C.S.: 221122
Kevin Humphreys (Treas & Sec)
Charles Ramage (Pres)
Harrell Patterson (VP)

LAMB SIGN
11979 Falling Creek Dr, Manassas, VA 20112
Tel.: (703) 791-7960
Web Site: http://www.lambsign.com
Year Founded: 1900
Sales Range: Less than $1 Million
Emp.: 3
Signs, Seals & Stencils
N.A.I.C.S.: 459410
Rosemary Schneider (Pres)

LAMB'S TIRE & AUTOMOTIVE CENTERS
2113 Wells Branch Pkwy Ste 4000, Austin, TX 78728
Tel.: (512) 257-2350
Web Site: http://www.lambstire.com
Provider of General Automotive Repair Services
N.A.I.C.S.: 811111
Jim Ramsey (Owner)

LAMBDA RESEARCH OPTICS, INC.
1695 MacArthur Blvd, Costa Mesa, CA 92626
Tel.: (714) 327-0600 CA
Web Site: http://www.lambda.cc
Year Founded: 1991
Optical Components Mfr & Sales
N.A.I.C.S.: 334516
Mike Yoon (Pres)

LAMBDA TD SOFTWARE, INC.
26132 Avenida Bonachon, Mission Viejo, CA 92691
Tel.: (702) 250-1782
Web Site: http://www.lambdatdsoftware.com
Year Founded: 2006
Software Development Services
N.A.I.C.S.: 513210
Robert M. Corcoran (Chm & CEO)
Scott H. Durham (COO)
Christopher Koning (CTO)
Michael Mayo (Creative Dir-Interactive)
Kathy M. Phillips (Chief Security Officer)
Patricia E. Herrera (Mgr-Acctg)
Joseph P. Wild (VP-Sls & Customer Svc)
Arthur De Joya (CFO)
Sheila Lynn Diaz (COO)

LAMBERT & CO.
47 Commerce Ave SW, Grand Rapids, MI 49503
Tel.: (616) 233-0500
Web Site: http://www.lambert-edwards.com
Year Founded: 1998

LAMBERT & CO.

Lambert & Co.—(Continued)
Sales Range: $10-24.9 Million
Emp.: 40
Public Relations & Investor Relations Services
N.A.I.C.S.: 541820
Jeffrey T. Lambert (CEO & Founder)
Chelsea Dubey (Dir-Bus Dev)
Salim Bourget (Dir-Digital Strategy)
Rob Dwortz (Pres)
William Nowling (Mng Dir & Partner)
Lance M. Knapp (CFO)
Donna Vandiver (Mng Dir)

Subsidiaries:

The Sterling Corporation (1)
The Hollister Bldg 106 W Allegan Ste 200, Lansing, MI 48933
Tel.: (517) 267-9012
Web Site:
  http://www.sterlingcorporation.com
Sales Range: $1-9.9 Million
Emp.: 14
Public Relations Agency
N.A.I.C.S.: 541820
Steve Linder (Partner)
Ellen Kletzka (Partner)
Heather Lombardini (Pres & Partner)
Paul Cordes (Dir-Political)

The Vandiver Group, Inc. (1)
16052 Swingley Ridge Rd Ste 210, Saint Louis, MO 63017
Tel.: (314) 991-4641
Web Site: www.vandivergroup.com
Public Relations Agency
N.A.I.C.S.: 541820
Donna Vandiver (Pres & CEO)
Amy Crump (CFO)
Andrew Likes (VP)
Patricia Olsen (Sr Acct Exec)
Shelley Lester (Sr Acct Exec)
Robert Harris (Dir-Govt & Pub Projects)
Ashley Elder (Sr Acct Exec)
Joe Bonwich (Dir-Content Strategy)
Michelle Thomas (Sr Acct Exec)
Erica Kirsch (Sr Acct Exec)
Melissa Breer (Acct Exec)
Abbey Theban (Asst Acct Exec)
Katie Miller (Asst Acct Exec)

LAMBERT OIL COMPANY INC.
701 1 2 E Henderson St, Cleburne, TX 76031
Tel.: (817) 645-2771
Rev.: $20,080,241
Emp.: 9
Petroleum Bulk Stations
N.A.I.C.S.: 424710
Kathy Lambert (CEO)

LAMBERT VET SUPPLY
714 5th St, Fairbury, NE 68352
Tel.: (402) 729-3044
Web Site:
  http://www.lambertvetsupply.com
Year Founded: 1993
Rev.: $53,500,000
Emp.: 90
Medical & Hospital Equipment
N.A.I.C.S.: 423450
Jaime Lambert (Mgr-Special Projects)
Charlotte Tietjen (Mgr-Sls)
Vicky Taylor (Mgr-Pur)

LAMBESIS, INC.
1020 Prospect St 2nd Fl, La Jolla, CA 92037
Tel.: (760) 547-2333
Web Site: http://www.lambesis.com
Year Founded: 1987
Rev.: $92,000,000
Emp.: 40
Advetising Agency
N.A.I.C.S.: 541810
Nicholas Lambesis (Chm & Founder)
Vicki Hoekstra (COO)
Brian Munce (Exec Dir-Client Svcs)

LAMBETH HOUSE, INC.
150 Broadway, New Orleans, LA 70118
Tel.: (504) 266-0282
Web Site:
  http://www.lambethhouse.com
Year Founded: 1993
Sales Range: $10-24.9 Million
Lifecare Retirement Community Operator
N.A.I.C.S.: 623311
Regan A. Forrester (Dir-Social Svcs)
Cathy Maddox (Dir-Mktg)
Tanya Becnel (Dir-Mktg)
Lynn Swetland (Treas & Sec)
Jere Hales (COO & VP)

LAMBRETTA SOUTH INCORPORATED
3671 N Dixie Hwy, Pompano Beach, FL 33064
Web Site:
  http://www.rivamotorsports.com
Year Founded: 1979
Rev.: $24,000,000
Emp.: 105
Motorized Cycles
N.A.I.C.S.: 423110
Steve Bamdas (Pres)
Leslie Ferrer (Principal)

LAMBRO INDUSTRIES INC.
115 Albany Ave, Amityville, NY 11701
Tel.: (631) 842-8088
Web Site: http://www.lambro.net
Rev.: $15,000,000
Emp.: 150
Mfr of Sheet Metal, Blowers & Fans
N.A.I.C.S.: 332322
Joe Fara (Mgr-Sls-South East Reg)
Mark Staerkel (Mgr-Sls-South West Reg)
Brian Spellmeyer (Mgr-Sls-West Coast Reg)
Denise Botterio (Mgr-Sls)

LAMBS FARM, INC.
14245 W Rockland Rd, Libertyville, IL 60048
Tel.: (847) 362-4636
Web Site: http://www.lambsfarm.org
Year Founded: 1961
Sales Range: $10-24.9 Million
Emp.: 479
Developmental Disability Assistance Services
N.A.I.C.S.: 623210
Dianne Yaconetti (Pres & CEO)
Patricia McGuire (Treas)

LAMI WOOD PRODUCTS CORPORATION
1 Lami Industrial Dr, Saint Charles, MO 63304
Tel.: (636) 441-4430
Web Site:
  http://www.signaturekb.com
Year Founded: 1976
Sales Range: $10-24.9 Million
Emp.: 95
Wood Kitchen Cabinets Distr
N.A.I.C.S.: 337110

LAMINATE TECHNOLOGIES INC.
161 Maule Rd, Tiffin, OH 44883
Tel.: (419) 448-0811
Web Site: http://www.lamtech.net
Year Founded: 1985
Sales Range: $10-24.9 Million
Emp.: 50
Structural Wood Products Mfr
N.A.I.C.S.: 321215
Allan Funkhouser (CFO)

Subsidiaries:

Laminate Technologies of Tennessee (1)
1356 Gateway Dr, Gallatin, TN 37066
Tel.: (615) 451-4554
Web Site: http://www.lamtech.net
Rev.: $979,575
Emp.: 35
Wood & Wood By-Products
N.A.I.C.S.: 423990
Fred Zoeller (Pres)

LAMINATE WORKS INC.
1200 S 5th St, Kansas City, KS 66105
Tel.: (913) 281-7474
Web Site:
  http://www.laminateworks.com
Year Founded: 1999
Sales Range: $10-24.9 Million
Emp.: 54
Laminated Panels
N.A.I.C.S.: 321219
Bert Clothier (Pres)
Shawn Foster (Mgr-Inventory)

LAMINATING SERVICES INC.
4700 Robards Ln, Louisville, KY 40218
Tel.: (502) 458-2614
Web Site: http://www.lsiwc.com
Sales Range: $10-24.9 Million
Emp.: 50
Commercial Grade Wall Covering
N.A.I.C.S.: 313320
Phillip J. Tarullo (Pres)
Steve Moad (VP-Ops)
Greg Bowling (VP-Fin)
Jim Paznokas (Mgr-Sls & Mktg)

LAMINATION DEPOT INC.
1505 E McFadden Ave, Santa Ana, CA 92705
Tel.: (714) 954-0632
Web Site:
  http://www.laminationdepot.com
Year Founded: 2002
Sales Range: $1-9.9 Million
Emp.: 8
Laminating & Binding Supplies
N.A.I.C.S.: 459410
Paul Godfrey (Pres & CEO)
Sarah Meehan (Mgr-Mktg)

LAMINATORS INC.
3255 Souderton Pike, Hatfield, PA 19440
Tel.: (215) 723-8107
Web Site: http://www.signboards.com
Year Founded: 1980
Sales Range: $10-24.9 Million
Emp.: 62
Provider of Laminating Steel
N.A.I.C.S.: 332813
Garrett Thompson (Mgr-Strategic Mktg)
Bob Crouthamel (Supvr-Shipping Receiving)
Melissa Grimes (Mgr-Mktg)
John T. Wright (VP-Engrg)
Harold Schoen (Mgr-Pur)
Paul Nelson (Mgr-IT)
Todd Oleson (Dir-QA & Process Engrg)
David Thompson (CEO)

LAMINEX, INC.
4209 Pleasant Rd, Fort Mill, SC 29708
Tel.: (704) 679-4170
Web Site: http://www.laminex.com
Year Founded: 1945
Card-based Identification Products & Wide-roll, Pouch Lamination & Related Accessories Mfr
N.A.I.C.S.: 323111

Patty Moran Lee (Sls Mgr-Global Channel)
Kim Crawford (Inside Sls Mgr)
Paul Rutter (Mgr)

LAMKIN CORPORATION
6530 Gtwy Park Dr, San Diego, CA 92154
Tel.: (619) 661-7090
Web Site:
  http://www.lamkingrips.com
Rev.: $20,600,000
Emp.: 25
Rubber Products Mfr
N.A.I.C.S.: 326299
Jason Bustamante (Mgr-Sls-Natl)
Andy Gilkison (VP-Global Sls)
Elver B. Lamkin (Founder)

LAMKONE RESTAURANTS INC.
2855 Pullman St, Santa Ana, CA 92705
Tel.: (949) 222-0670
Web Site: http://www.wahoos.com
Sales Range: $10-24.9 Million
Emp.: 600
Fast Food Restaurant Operator
N.A.I.C.S.: 722513

LAMONICA FINE FOODS
48 Gorton Rd, Millville, NJ 08332
Tel.: (856) 825-8111
Web Site:
  http://www.capemayfoods.com
Sales Range: $25-49.9 Million
Emp.: 200
Seafood Supplier & Clam Hand Shucking Plant
N.A.I.C.S.: 311710
Ron Labuda (Mgr-QA)

LAMONT DIGITAL SYSTEMS INC.
100 First Stamford Place, Stamford, CT 06902
Tel.: (203) 983-5400
Web Site: http://www.camptv.com
Year Founded: 1984
Sales Range: $10-24.9 Million
Cable Television Services
N.A.I.C.S.: 516210
Ned Lamont (Founder)
Ray York (Sr Dir-Ops)

LAMONT HANLEY & ASSOCIATES
1138 Elm St, Manchester, NH 03101-1514
Tel.: (603) 625-5547
Web Site: http://www.lhainc.com
Year Founded: 1991
Sales Range: $10-24.9 Million
Emp.: 50
Adjustment & Collection Services
N.A.I.C.S.: 561440
John Hanley (Pres)
Rhonda Sargent (Exec VP)
Karyn Makela (Acct Mgr)
Kelli Wanner (VP-Fin)

LAMORTE BURNS & CO INC.
64 Danbury Rd, Wilton, CT 06897
Tel.: (203) 761-6000
Web Site: http://www.lamorte.com
Year Founded: 1938
Sales Range: $10-24.9 Million
Emp.: 60
Insurance Adjusters
N.A.I.C.S.: 524291
Harold J. Halpin (Pres & CEO)
Robert Hanson (Mgr-Texas)
Lisa Loeber (VP-New Jersey)
Richard Weeks (Mgr-CRO)

LAMP POST FRANCHISE

COMPANIES

LAMPPOST PIZZA CORPORATION
3002 Dow Ave Ste 414, Tustin, CA 92780
Tel.: (714) 731-6171   CA
Web Site:
http://www.lamppostpizza.com
Year Founded: 1976
Sales Range: $200-249.9 Million
Emp.: 500
Restaurant Franchise
N.A.I.C.S.: 533110
Tom Barro (Pres)
Dan Barro (Treas, Sec & VP)
Marsha Lima (Controller)

LAMPERT YARDS, INC.
1850 Como Ave, Saint Paul, MN 55108
Tel.: (651) 695-3600   MN
Web Site:
http://www.lampertyards.com
Year Founded: 1887
Sales Range: $150-199.9 Million
Emp.: 633
Retailer of Lumber & Building Materials
N.A.I.C.S.: 423310
Pam R. Leier (VP-Mktg)
Brian Stoen (VP-Pur)

LAMPREY HEALTH CARE
207 S Main St, Newmarket, NH 03857
Tel.: (603) 659-3106   NH
Web Site:
http://www.ampreyhealth.org
Year Founded: 1971
Sales Range: $10-24.9 Million
Emp.: 180
Health Care Srvices
N.A.I.C.S.: 622110
Gregory White (CEO)

LAMPS PLUS INC.
20250 Plummer St, Chatsworth, CA 91311
Tel.: (818) 886-5267
Web Site: http://www.lampsplus.com
Sales Range: $125-149.9 Million
Emp.: 800
Lighting; Lamps & Accessories
N.A.I.C.S.: 449129
Dennis Swanson (Founder)
Joe Marino (Controller)
Clark Linstone (Pres & COO)
Jason Goldberger (CEO)
David Luebke (CMO)
Terre Wellington (Sr VP-Store Ops)

LAMPSON INTERNATIONAL, LLC
607 E Columbia Dr, Kennewick, WA 99336-3778
Tel.: (509) 586-0411   WA
Web Site:
http://www.lampsoncrane.com
Year Founded: 1946
Sales Range: $25-49.9 Million
Emp.: 225
Heavy Construction Equipment Rental
N.A.I.C.S.: 532412
William N. Lampson (CEO)

Subsidiaries:

Lampson Australia PTY LTD (1)
Lot 3 Awaba Road, PO Box 685, Toronto, 2283, NSW, Australia
Tel.: (61) 2 4959 6222
Web Site: http://www.lampson.com.au
Crane Rental Services
N.A.I.C.S.: 532412
John Lee (Mng Dir)

Lampson Canada, LTD (1)
20 Lampson Ave, Beiseker, T0M 0G0, AB, Canada
Tel.: (403) 947-2222

Web Site:
http://www.lampsoninternational.com
Emp.: 15
Crane Rental Services
N.A.I.C.S.: 532412

Megalift Pty Ltd (1)
8 Jackson St, Bassendean, 6054, WA, Australia
Tel.: (61) 8 9279 2988
General Freight Trucking Services
N.A.I.C.S.: 484121
Bill Quintal (Mgr)

LAMSON & GOODNOW MANUFACTURING CO.
45 Conway St, Shelburne Falls, MA 01370
Tel.: (413) 625-6331   MA
Web Site:
http://www.lamsonsharp.com
Year Founded: 1837
Sales Range: $75-99.9 Million
Emp.: 62
Mfr of Cutlery, Barbecue Tools, Kitchen Tools & Hand Tools
N.A.I.C.S.: 332215
Ross Anderson (Pres)
Brian Hayes (VP-Sls & Mktg)

LAMY
201 Allen St Unit 10104, New York, NY 10002
Tel.: (657) 315-8312   WY
Year Founded: 2022
Rev.: $11,500
Assets: $27,453
Liabilities: $82,348
Net Worth: ($54,895)
Earnings: ($25,807)
Emp.: 2
Fiscal Year-end: 05/31/24
Software Development Services
N.A.I.C.S.: 541511

LAN-CO DEVELOPMENT INC.
7330 Eastman Rd, North Syracuse, NY 13212
Tel.: (315) 452-0568
Web Site: http://www.lan-co.com
Sales Range: $10-24.9 Million
Emp.: 80
Specialty Trade Contractors
N.A.I.C.S.: 238910
Paul G. Joynt (Pres)

LANA DUKE CONSULTING
3817 Edenborn Ave, Metairie, LA 70002-1521
Tel.: (504) 888-3985
Web Site: http://www.ruthscris.ca
Year Founded: 1975
Sales Range: $10-24.9 Million
Emp.: 6
Public Relations & Brand Management
N.A.I.C.S.: 541820
Lana Duke (Owner)

LANA UNLIMITED COMPANY
736 Northwestern Ave Ste 308, Lake Forest, IL 60045
Tel.: (312) 226-5262
Web Site:
http://www.lanaunlimited.com
Year Founded: 2003
Sales Range: $50-74.9 Million
Emp.: 100
Jewelry Designer & Mfr
N.A.I.C.S.: 339910
Lana Fertelmeister (CEO)
Fallon Ryan (Mgr-Mkt)

LANCASTER AUTO GROUP
43244 Drivers Way, Lancaster, CA 93534
Tel.: (661) 949-3535

Web Site:
http://www.lancasterautomall.com
Rev.: $15,000,000
Emp.: 80
Automobile Sales
N.A.I.C.S.: 441110
Kim Dynice (CFO)

LANCASTER BINGO CO. INC.
200 Quarry Rd SE, Lancaster, OH 43130
Tel.: (740) 653-7972
Web Site:
http://www.lancasterbingo.com
Sales Range: $10-24.9 Million
Emp.: 250
Bingo Supplies
N.A.I.C.S.: 423920
Mark A. Sells (Founder & CEO)
Marc Detomaso (Mgr-E-Bingo)
Richard L. Frazier (CFO)
Doid F. McCandlish Jr. (VP-Sls & Mktg)

LANCASTER COUNTY TIMBER FRAMES, INC.
4825 E Prospect Rd, York, PA 17406
Tel.: (717) 755-2990
Web Site: http://www.lancotf.com
Year Founded: 1987
Residential & Commercial Building Construction Services
N.A.I.C.S.: 236116
Amy Good (Jr Partner)
Anthony F. Zaya (Co-Founder & Pres)
Joe M. McCarthy (Co-Founder & Partner)
Josh Coleman (Jr Partner)
Tim Diener (VP-Ops)

LANCASTER GENERAL HEALTH
555 N Duke St, Lancaster, PA 17604
Tel.: (717) 544-5511   PA
Web Site:
http://www.lancastergeneralhealth.org
Year Founded: 1983
Sales Range: $10-24.9 Million
Health Care Srvices
N.A.I.C.S.: 622110
Gary Davidson (CIO & Sr VP)
Karen Flaherty-Oxler (Pres)
Robert P. Macina (Chief Admin Officer, Chief Legal Officer, Sec & Sr VP)
Dennis R. Roemer (CFO & Exec VP)
Norma J. Ferdinand (Sr VP-Quality & Performance Improvement)
Jan L. Bergen (Pres & CEO)
Susan Wynne (Sr VP-Bus Dev)
Stacey Youcis (Sr VP-Svc Lines & Population Health)

LANCASTER HOST RESORT & CONFERENCE CENTER
2300 Lincoln Hwy E, Lancaster, PA 17602
Tel.: (717) 299-5500   MA
Web Site:
http://www.lancasterhost.com
Year Founded: 1966
Sales Range: $75-99.9 Million
Emp.: 300
Hotel & Conference Center Owner & Operator
N.A.I.C.S.: 721199
Harry Stevens (Gen Mgr)

LANCASTER NEWSPAPERS INC.
8 W King Ste, Lancaster, PA 17608-1328
Tel.: (717) 291-8681   PA
Web Site: http://www.lnpnews.com
Year Founded: 1928

Sales Range: $25-49.9 Million
Emp.: 450
Newspaper Publishing Services
N.A.I.C.S.: 513110
Robert M. Krasne (Publr)
James A. Loose (Assoc Editor)
Lori Goodlin (Editor-Print)

Subsidiaries:

Lancaster County Weeklies Inc. (1)
1 E Main St, Ephrata, PA 17522-2713
Tel.: (717) 733-6397
Web Site: http://www.lancasterfarming.com
Sales Range: $10-24.9 Million
Emp.: 50
Provider of Newspaper Publishing Services
N.A.I.C.S.: 513110
William J. Burgess (Gen Mgr)
Eric Hurlock (Editor-Digital)

Steinman Park Restaurant Inc. (1)
26 28 W King St, Lancaster, PA 17603-3809
Tel.: (717) 399-5400
Web Site:
http://www.pressroomrestaurant.com
Sales Range: $10-24.9 Million
Emp.: 32
Restaurant
N.A.I.C.S.: 722511

LANCASTER POLLARD HOLDINGS, INC.
65 E State St 16th Fl, Columbus, OH 43215
Tel.: (614) 224-8800   OH
Web Site:
http://www.lancasterpollard.com
Year Founded: 1988
Sales Range: $25-49.9 Million
Emp.: 76
Investment Management Service
N.A.I.C.S.: 523999
David Lacki (Mng Dir)
Timothy J. Dobyns (Gen Counsel & Exec VP)
Nicholas M. Gesue (CEO)
James C. Shoup (Sr VP & Dir-Asset Mgmt Div)
Michelle A. Harvey (Sr VP & Dir-Servicing)
Matthew L. Sherman (Sr VP & Dir-Comm)
Kevin J. Beerman (CFO)
Robert T. Kirkwood (COO)
Kassem K. Matt (Co-Pres)
Chad Elliott (Mng Dir-Mergers & Acquisition)
Craig S. Jones (Co-Pres & Mgr-Fund)
Kenneth A. Gould (Sr Mng Dir)
Martin Kent (Chief Credit Officer)
Doug Harper (Mng Dir-Agency Fin)
Casey Moore (Mng Dir-Agency Fin)
Joe Munhall (Dir-Syndicated Credit)
Jeffrey Banker (VP)
Chris Blanda (Sr VP-Healthcare Banker)
Adam Zeiger (Mng Dir-Merger & Acq Grp-Chicago)
Steven W. Kennedy Jr. (Sr Mng Dir)

LANCASTER REDEVELOPMENT CORP
2138 Route 522, Selinsgrove, PA 17870
Web Site:
http://www.foresthomes.com
Rev.: $10,982,228
Emp.: 60
Prefabricated Wood Building Mfr
N.A.I.C.S.: 321992
Gary Grossman (CEO)

LANCASTER TOYOTA INC.
1107 Enterprise Rd, East Petersburg, PA 17520
Tel.: (717) 569-7373

LANCASTER TOYOTA INC.

Lancaster Toyota Inc.—(Continued)
Web Site:
http://www.lancastertoyota.com
Sales Range: $75-99.9 Million
Emp.: 200
Automobiles, New & Used
N.A.I.C.S.: 441110
Rick Price *(Gen Mgr)*
Keara Dagen *(Mgr-HR)*
Robert Allen Sr. *(Pres)*

LANCE FUNK FARMS
2765 Fairgrounds Rd, American Falls, ID 83211
Tel.: (208) 226-5551
Web Site:
http://www.lancefunkfarms.net
Sales Range: $10-24.9 Million
Emp.: 60
Crop Farming
N.A.I.C.S.: 111998
C. J. Harris *(Gen Mgr)*

LANCE INDUSTRIES INC.
55 Industrial Cir, Lincoln, RI 02865
Tel.: (401) 365-6272
Web Site:
http://www.symmetryproducts.com
Year Founded: 1982
Sales Range: $10-24.9 Million
Emp.: 60
Foam Products
N.A.I.C.S.: 326150
Steven Lancia *(Pres)*
Mark Travers *(Mgr-Accts)*

LANCE INVESTIGATION SERVICE
1438 Boston Rd, Bronx, NY 10460
Tel.: (718) 893-1400
Web Site: http://www.lanceinc.net
Year Founded: 1960
Rev.: $20,300,000
Emp.: 15
Protective Services, Guard
N.A.I.C.S.: 561612
Ralph V. Johnson *(Pres)*
Mark H. Creighton *(Gen Mgr)*

LANCER DISPERSIONS INC.
1680 E Market St, Akron, OH 44305-4246
Tel.: (330) 794-9922
Year Founded: 1981
Sales Range: $25-49.9 Million
Emp.: 60
Plastics Products
N.A.I.C.S.: 326199
Linda Davis *(Acctg Mgr)*
Kevin L. Hirshfield *(Pres)*
John Wagner *(Plant Mgr-Production)*

Subsidiaries:
Cleveland Pigment & Color Inc. (1)
1732 E Market St, Akron, OH 44305-4246 (100%)
Tel.: (330) 794-9922
Web Site: http://www.clevelandpigment.com
Sales Range: $10-24.9 Million
Emp.: 10
Paints, Varnishes & Supplies
N.A.I.C.S.: 424950

LANCESOFT INC.
13454 Sunrise Vly Dr Ste 120, Herndon, VA 20171
Tel.: (703) 674-4500
Web Site: http://www.lancesoft.com
Sales Range: $10-24.9 Million
Emp.: 450
Software Installation & Integration Services
N.A.I.C.S.: 541511
Ram Karuppusamy *(Chm & CEO)*
Ruchi Jain *(Mgr-Sls)*
Ashutosh Kumar *(Mgr-Ops)*

LANCET DATA SCIENCES
11980 Portland Ave S, Burnsville, MN 55337
Tel.: (952) 230-7360
Web Site:
http://www.lancetdatasciences.com
Year Founded: 1997
Sales Range: $10-24.9 Million
Emp.: 90
Information Technology Consulting Services
N.A.I.C.S.: 541512
Tom Niccum *(Pres & CEO)*
Chris Holtan *(VP)*
Randy Mattran *(COO)*
Jaime Plante *(VP)*
Rick Thorp *(VP)*

LANCET INDEMNITY RISK RETENTION GROUP, INC.
2810 W St Isabel St Ste 100, Tampa, FL 33607
Tel.: (813) 290-8282
Web Site:
http://www.lancetindemnity.com
Sales Range: $25-49.9 Million
Emp.: 15
Professional Liability Insurance Carrier
N.A.I.C.S.: 524128
Alan J. Iezzi *(Pres)*
Anthony F. Maniscalco *(COO)*
Sam Rodriguez *(Treas & Sec)*

LANCO ASSEMBLY SYSTEMS
12 Thomas Dr, Westbrook, ME 04092
Tel.: (207) 773-2060
Web Site: http://www.lanco.net
Rev.: $15,000,000
Emp.: 80
Robots, Molding & Forming Plastics
N.A.I.C.S.: 333248
Edward J. Karabec *(Pres & CEO)*
Matthew Bresnahan *(VP-Sls & Program Mgmt)*
Bernd Klingel *(Pres)*

LANCO CORP.
2905 Veterans Memorial Hwy Ste 3, Ronkonkoma, NY 11779
Tel.: (631) 231-2300
Web Site:
http://www.lancopromo.com
Sales Range: $10-24.9 Million
Emp.: 355
Sales of Candy & Other Confectionery Products
N.A.I.C.S.: 531120
Irwin Landow *(VP)*
Michael Slade *(Chm)*
Pat Nauta *(VP-HR)*
Elizabeth McGee *(Mgr-Inventory Control)*

LANCO INTERNATIONAL INC.
3111 167th St, Hazel Crest, IL 60429
Tel.: (708) 596-5200
Web Site: http://www.mi-jack.com
Sales Range: $150-199.9 Million
Emp.: 2,000
Mfr of Construction Machinery
N.A.I.C.S.: 333120
Jack Wepfer *(Controller)*
John J. Lanigan Jr. *(Pres & CEO)*

Subsidiaries:
All Sport Couture, LLC (1)
9760 Mayflower Park Dr, Carmel, IN 46032
Tel.: (317) 672-3448
Web Site: http://www.allsportcouture.com
Women's Clothing Retailer
N.A.I.C.S.: 458110

Broderson Manufacturing Corp. (1)
14741 W 106th St, Lenexa, KS 66215
Tel.: (913) 888-0606

Web Site: http://www.bmccranes.com
Terrain Crane Mfr & Distr
N.A.I.C.S.: 333924
Nelson Morris *(Mgr-Department)*

Howell Tractor and Equipment LLC (1)
480 Blaine St, Gary, IN 46406
Web Site: http://www.howelltractor.com
Emp.: 40
Construction Equipment Sales & Rental Services
N.A.I.C.S.: 423830
Tom Dellis *(Pres)*

MJ Promotions, Inc. (1)
3011 Old Minden Rd, Bossier City, LA 71112-2426
Tel.: (318) 747-8824
Industrial Machinery Mfr & Distr
N.A.I.C.S.: 333924

Mi-Jack Products, Inc. (1)
3111 W 167th St, Hazel Crest, IL 60429-1025
Tel.: (708) 596-5200
Web Site: http://www.mi-jack.com
Sales Range: $25-49.9 Million
Emp.: 400
Material Handling Equipment Mfr
N.A.I.C.S.: 333120

Subsidiary (Non-US):

Liftking Manufacturing Corp. (2)
7135 Islington Ave, Woodbridge, L4L 1V9, ON, Canada
Tel.: (905) 851-3988
Web Site: https://www.liftking.com
Forklift Mfr & Whslr
N.A.I.C.S.: 333924
Jeff Cockerton *(VP)*

MJ EcoPower Hybrid Systems, Inc. (2)
9995 Avenue Catania Local G, Brossard, J4Z 3V7, QC, Canada
Tel.: (450) 676-7755
Web Site: http://www.ecopowerhs.com
Gantry Crane Distr
N.A.I.C.S.: 423830

Mi-Jack Canada, Inc. (2)
7609 42nd St, Leduc, T9E 0K5, AB, Canada
Tel.: (780) 986-1001
Web Site: http://www.mi-jackcanada.com
Emp.: 9
Construction Equipment Distr
N.A.I.C.S.: 423830

Q Sales, LLC (1)
16720 S Mozart Ave, Hazel Crest, IL 60429
Tel.: (708) 331-0094
Web Site: http://www.qsales.com
Foil Mfr
N.A.I.C.S.: 331315
Paul Yadron *(VP-Sls)*
Pete Mirabella *(VP-Technical Svcs)*
Robert Haberkorn *(VP-Product & Market Dev)*
Kevin Lynch *(Dir-Sls, Food & Beverage)*
Scott Borsodi *(Dir-Bus Dev)*

Western Pacific Crane & Equipment LLC (1)
8600 Calabash Ave, Fontana, CA 92335
Tel.: (562) 286-6618
Web Site: http://www.wpcrane.com
Crane Equipment Distr
N.A.I.C.S.: 423830
Mike Harma *(Coord-Svc)*
Randy Defosse *(Gen Mgr)*
Eric Knutson *(Mgr-Parts)*
Matthew Mader *(Coord-Sls)*
Dennis Piatek *(Branch Mgr)*
Elaine Piatek *(Office Mgr)*
Ken Pugh *(Branch Mgr)*
Jamie Rubalcava *(Mgr-Parts)*

LANCO MANUFACTURING CORP.
5 Urb Aponte, San Lorenzo, PR 00754
Tel.: (787) 736-4221
Web Site:
http://www.lancopaints.com
Year Founded: 1978

Sales Range: $25-49.9 Million
Emp.: 300
Adhesives & Sealants Mfr
N.A.I.C.S.: 325520
Sergio Lango *(Pres)*

LAND & BUILDINGS INVESTMENT MANAGEMENT, LLC
3 Pickwick Plz 4th Fl, Greenwich, CT 06830
Tel.: (203) 987-5830   DE
Web Site:
http://www.landandbuildings.com
Real Estate Investment Advisory & Management Services
N.A.I.C.S.: 523940
Jonathan I. Litt *(Co-Founder & CIO)*
Craig Melcher *(Co-Founder & Portfolio Mgr)*
Stephen Katchur *(CFO & COO)*

LAND & COATES, INC.
5795 Thurston Ave, Virginia Beach, VA 23455
Tel.: (757) 461-5800
Web Site:
http://www.landandcoates.com
Sales Range: $10-24.9 Million
Emp.: 41
Nursery Product Whslr
N.A.I.C.S.: 424930
CHARLES L. WINSTEAD *(CEO)*

LAND & LEGAL SOLUTIONS
300 S Hamilton Ave, Greensburg, PA 15601-4138
Tel.: (724) 853-8992   PA
Year Founded: 1997
Sales Range: $50-74.9 Million
Emp.: 3
Development & Sales of Computer Software
N.A.I.C.S.: 541110

LAND 'N SEA, INC.
1375 Broadway 2nd Fl, New York, NY 10018
Tel.: (212) 444-6000   NY
Year Founded: 1958
Sales Range: $150-199.9 Million
Emp.: 400
Mfr of Women's, Juniors', Girls', Children's & Infants' Blouses
N.A.I.C.S.: 315250
Seymour Sobel *(Chm)*
Kirk Gellin *(Co-Pres)*
Robert Sobel *(Co-Pres)*
Neil Fox *(Controller)*

LAND AIR EXPRESS INC.
6377 Cemetery Rd, Bowling Green, KY 42103-9745
Tel.: (270) 781-0655   KY
Web Site:
http://www.landairexpress.com
Year Founded: 1981
Sales Range: $50-74.9 Million
Emp.: 200
Air Courier Services
N.A.I.C.S.: 492110

LAND AIR EXPRESS OF NEW ENGLAND
59 Avenue C, Williston, VT 05495
Tel.: (802) 863-6680
Web Site: http://www.mylandair.com
Sales Range: $25-49.9 Million
Emp.: 450
Local Trucking with Storage
N.A.I.C.S.: 484110
William Spencer *(Pres)*
Cecile Provost *(Mgr-Acct Receivable)*
David Dobrowski *(VP-Sls & Mktg)*

LAND MARK ELECTRIC, INC.

COMPANIES

7876 Deering Ave, Canoga Park, CA 91304
Tel.: (818) 883-5110 CA
Web Site: http://www.lmela.com
Year Founded: 1981
Emp.: 400
Electrical Contracting & Services
N.A.I.C.S.: 238210
Lloyd Saitman *(Pres & CEO)*
Jack Mooney *(VP-Field Ops)*
John Higman *(COO)*
John Bennett *(CFO)*

LAND O'FROST, INC.
16850 Chicago Ave, Lansing, IL 60422
Tel.: (708) 474-6405 IL
Web Site: http://www.landofrost.com
Year Founded: 1958
Specialty Meat Products Mfr
N.A.I.C.S.: 311612
Donna Van Eekeren *(Chm)*
David Van Eekeren *(Pres & CEO)*

Subsidiaries:

Wellshire Farms, Inc. (1)
509 Woodstown Rd, Swedesboro, NJ 08085
Tel.: (856) 769-8933
Web Site: http://www.wellshirefarms.com
All Natural Meat Products
N.A.I.C.S.: 424470
Jessica Colameco *(VP-Sls & Mktg)*

Wimmers Meat Products Inc. (1)
126 W Grant St, West Point, NE 68788
Tel.: (402) 372-2437
Web Site: http://www.wimmersmeats.com
Sales Range: $25-49.9 Million
Emp.: 130
Meat Processing & Distribution
N.A.I.C.S.: 311612

LAND O'LAKES, INC.
4001 Lexington Ave N, Arden Hills, MN 55126-2998
Tel.: (651) 375-2222 MN
Web Site:
  http://www.landolakesinc.com
Year Founded: 1921
Rev.: $14,936,208,000
Assets: $9,124,376,000
Liabilities: $6,213,033,000
Net Worth: $2,911,343,000
Earnings: $254,485,000
Emp.: 10,000
Fiscal Year-end: 12/31/18
Dairy Products Mfr
N.A.I.C.S.: 311512
Brett W. Bruggeman *(COO, Pres-WinField United & Exec VP)*
Loren Heeringa *(Chief HR Officer & Sr VP)*
Beth E. Ford *(Pres & CEO)*
Lisa Deverell *(Pres-Purina Animal Nutrition & Exec VP)*
John Ellenberger *(Sr VP-Land)*
Bill Pieper *(CFO & Exec VP)*
Teddy Bekele *(CTO & Sr VP)*
Thea Keamy *(Sr VP-Corp Strategy & Bus Dev)*
Sheilah Stewart *(Gen Counsel & Sr VP)*
Heather L. Anfang *(Pres-Dairy Foods & Exec VP)*
Yone Dewberry *(Chief Supply Chain Officer)*

Subsidiaries:

Agriliance, LLC (1)
5500 Cenex Dr, Inver Grove Heights, MN 55077-1733
Tel.: (651) 451-5000
Sales Range: $800-899.9 Million
Emp.: 2,504
Crop Protection Products & Services; Owned by CHS Inc. & Land O'Lakes, Inc.
N.A.I.C.S.: 423820

FLM Harvest (1)
500 W Wilson Bridge Rd Ste 316, Worthington, OH 43085
Tel.: (612) 808-8400
Web Site: http://www.wideopenthinking.com
Advertising & Marketing Consulting Services
N.A.I.C.S.: 541810
Phillip Farmer *(Founder & Exec VP-Bus Dev)*
John Lumpe *(COO)*
Terry McInroy *(Sr VP)*
Lisa Smith *(Sr VP)*
David Ash *(Exec VP)*
Laurie Fleck *(CEO)*
Burke Johnson *(Sr VP)*
Joan Olson *(VP)*
Lukus Blackford *(VP)*
Cody Cheetham *(VP)*
Melissa Dykstra *(Sr VP)*
Deron Johnson *(Sr VP)*
Julie Lux *(VP)*
Laura Moser *(VP)*
David Parker *(Exec VP)*
Tom Patton *(VP)*
Alison Rauchwarter *(VP)*
Mitch Van Kampen *(Sr VP)*
Steve Zabka *(VP)*
Jim Zumwalt *(Sr VP)*
Mitch Van Kampen *(Pres & Chief Strategy Officer)*

Forage Genetics International, LLC (1)
812 1st St S, Nampa, ID 83651-3852 (100%)
Tel.: (208) 466-3568
Web Site: http://www.foragegenetics.com
Sales Range: $10-24.9 Million
Emp.: 40
Alfalfa & Grass Seed Distr
N.A.I.C.S.: 424910
Jose Arias *(Mgr-Production)*
Ken Durrant *(Mgr-Alfalfa Ops)*
Stephen Temple *(Dir-Biotech)*
Jennifer Tucher *(Controller)*
Joe Waldo *(Dir-Supply & Ops)*
Dave Whalen *(Dir-Regulatory Affairs & Quality Assurance-West Salem)*
Julie Ho *(VP-Res)*
Pete Theisen *(Pres)*
Charlie Von Feldt *(CTO & Gen Counsel)*

Kozy Shack Enterprises Inc. (1)
83 Ludy St, Hicksville, NY 11801
Tel.: (516) 870-3000
Web Site: http://www.kozyshack.com
Sales Range: $100-124.9 Million
Emp.: 330
Puddings & Desserts Mfr & Distr
N.A.I.C.S.: 311999
Vincent Gruppuso *(Chm)*

Land O'Lakes Animal Milk Products Company (1)
1080 County Rd F W, Shoreview, MN 55126
Tel.: (651) 481-2222
Web Site: http://www.lolmilkreplacer.com
Milk Replacer & Calf Care Product Mfr
N.A.I.C.S.: 112120

Plant (Domestic):

Land O'Lakes Animal Milk Products Company - Black River Falls Plant (2)
W9912 West Bauer Rd, Black River Falls, WI 54615
Tel.: (715) 284-8871
Milk Replacer & Calf Care Product Mfr
N.A.I.C.S.: 112120

Land O'Lakes Finance Co. (1)
4001 Lexington Ave, Arden Hills, MN 55126 (100%)
Tel.: (651) 375-2222
Web Site: http://www.landolakes.com
Sales Range: $10-24.9 Million
Emp.: 10
Finance & Accounting Services for Dairy Company
N.A.I.C.S.: 561110

Land O'Lakes Purina Feed LLC (1)
15840 N Simmons Rd, Portland, OR 97203-6425 (100%)
Tel.: (503) 286-6354
Web Site: http://www.landolakes.com
Sales Range: $10-24.9 Million
Emp.: 100

Prepared Foods & Food Ingredients for Animals & Fowls, Except Dogs & Cats
N.A.I.C.S.: 311119

Joint Venture (Domestic):

EPL Feed, LLC (2)
411 W Front St, Sumas, WA 98295
Tel.: (360) 988-5811
Web Site: http://www.eplfeed.com
Emp.: 55
Dairy Cattle Feed Mfr
N.A.I.C.S.: 311119
Dennis Elenbaas *(Pres)*

Plant (Domestic):

Land O'Lakes Purina Feed (2)
890 Prairie Industrial Pkwy, Mulberry, FL 33860-9588
Tel.: (863) 425-5544
Web Site: http://www.lolfeed.com
Animal Feed Mfr
N.A.I.C.S.: 311119
Fred Williams *(Mgr)*

Land O'Lakes, Inc. - Carlisle (1)
405 Park Dr, Carlisle, PA 17013-9270
Tel.: (717) 486-7000
Rev.: $90,000,000
Emp.: 120
Mfrs. of Condensed & Dry Milk Products & Butter
N.A.I.C.S.: 311511

Land O'Lakes, Inc. - Food Ingredients Division (1)
1200 W County Rd F, Saint Paul, MN 55112 (100%)
Tel.: (651) 481-2222
Web Site: http://www.landolakes.com
Sales Range: $10-24.9 Million
Emp.: 10
Food & Dairy Mfr
N.A.I.C.S.: 311512

Land O'Lakes, Inc. - International Division (1)
4001 Lexington Ave, Saint Paul, MN 55164
Tel.: (651) 481-2222
Web Site: http://www.landolakes.com
Sales Range: $25-49.9 Million
Emp.: 20
Marketing & Distribution of Dairy Products
N.A.I.C.S.: 311512

Land O'Lakes, Inc. - Kent (1)
2001 Mogadore Rd, Kent, OH 44240
Tel.: (330) 678-1578
Web Site: http://www.landolakes.com
Sales Range: $25-49.9 Million
Emp.: 280
Butter & Margarine Mfr
N.A.I.C.S.: 311512
Brad Bass *(Plant Mgr)*

Land O'Lakes, Inc. - Kiel (1)
1125 8th St, Kiel, WI 53042-4804
Tel.: (920) 894-2615
Web Site: http://www.landolakes.com
Rev.: $181,000,000
Emp.: 100
Dairy Products Mfr
N.A.I.C.S.: 311513
Kevin Schwartz *(Plant Mgr)*

Land O'Lakes, Inc. - Nashville (1)
17815 Mockingbird Rd, Nashville, IL 62263-3410
Tel.: (618) 478-5555
Web Site: http://www.landolakes.com
Animal Feed Mfr
N.A.I.C.S.: 311119
Michael Brown *(Mng Dir)*

Madison Dairy Produce Company (1)
4001 Lexington Ave N, Saint Paul, MN 55126-2934 (100%)
Tel.: (608) 256-5561
Web Site: http://www.landolakes.com
Sales Range: $10-24.9 Million
Emp.: 100
Dairy Products Butter
N.A.I.C.S.: 311512

Purina Mills, LLC (1)
100 Danforth Dr, Gray Summit, MO 63039-1128 (100%)
Tel.: (636) 742-6100

LAND PROPERTIES INC.

Web Site: http://www.purinamills.com
Rev.: $425,300,000
Emp.: 2,600
Supplier of Animal Nutrition Products
N.A.I.C.S.: 311119

Subsidiary (Domestic):

Purina Golden Sun (2)
1842 Hwy 4 S, Estherville, IA 51334-0517 (100%)
Tel.: (712) 362-3551
Sales Range: $25-49.9 Million
Emp.: 150
Mfr & Distributor of Livestock & Poultry Feeds
N.A.I.C.S.: 311119

QC, Inc. (1)
1205 Industrial Hwy, Southampton, PA 18966-4010 (100%)
Tel.: (215) 355-3900
Web Site: http://www.qclaboratories.com
Sales Range: $25-49.9 Million
Emp.: 160
Commercial Testing & Environmental Laboratory
N.A.I.C.S.: 541715
Tom Hines *(Pres)*

United Suppliers, Inc. (1)
30473 260th St, Eldora, IA 50627
Tel.: (641) 858-2341
Web Site: http://www.unitedsuppliers.com
Chemical & Agricultural Supplies Whslr
N.A.I.C.S.: 424910
Rick Reinicke *(Mgr-IT)*

LAND O'SUN MANAGEMENT CORPORATION
3715 NW 97th Blvd Ste A, Gainesville, FL 32606-5066
Tel.: (352) 333-3011 FL
Web Site:
  http://www.fasttrackstores.com
Year Founded: 1988
Sales Range: $75-99.9 Million
Emp.: 190
Retailer of Groceries
N.A.I.C.S.: 445131
Alan Fogg *(Pres)*
Steve Fogg *(VP)*

LAND OF LINCOLN CREDIT UNION
1435 N Water St, Decatur, IL 62526
Tel.: (217) 428-5232 IL
Web Site: http://www.llcu.org
Year Founded: 1947
Sales Range: $10-24.9 Million
Emp.: 121
Credit Union Operator
N.A.I.C.S.: 522130
Doug Dehority *(VP-Comml Lending)*
Chris Phillips *(VP-Mktg)*
Craig Althoff *(CFO)*
Rashanda Bond-Partee *(Asst Mgr-Consumer Loan Ops & Credit)*
Brandy Bockewitz *(Coord-Mktg)*
Toby Ragaini *(CIO)*
Andrew Young *(Chief Lending Officer)*
Corey Conroy *(Mgr-Bus Dev)*
Cayla Hittmeier *(Assoc VP-Mktg)*
Robert Ares *(Pres & CEO)*

LAND PROPERTIES INC.
255 E Cheyenne Mtn Blvd Ste 200, Colorado Springs, CO 80906
Tel.: (719) 226-7977
Web Site:
  http://www.landproperties.com
Year Founded: 1981
Sales Range: $25-49.9 Million
Emp.: 35
Real Estate Marketer
N.A.I.C.S.: 531210
David Martin *(Pres)*
Randy Lanosga Jr. *(CFO)*

LAND ROVER SAN JOSE

Land Rover San Jose—(Continued)

LAND ROVER SAN JOSE
5080 Stevens Creek Blvd, San Jose, CA 95129
Tel.: (408) 247-7600
Web Site: http://www.landroversj.com
Sales Range: $10-24.9 Million
Emp.: 32
Automobiles, New & Used
N.A.I.C.S.: 441110
Jeffrey Qvale (Pres)
Eric Swanson (Mgr-Sls)
Vinnie Torrente (Gen Mgr)

LAND SOLUTIONS, INC.
10471 6 Mile Cypress Pkwy Ste 402, Fort Myers, FL 33966
Tel.: (239) 489-4066
Web Site:
  http://www.landsolutions.net
Sales Range: $10-24.9 Million
Emp.: 15
Real Estate Brokerage Services
N.A.I.C.S.: 531210
Randy Thibaut (Owner & CEO)
Kris Denny (COO)
Jim Moore (CFO)
Doug Meschko (Dir-Market Res)
Sharail Cluck (VP-Land Svcs)
George W. Bush (Mgr-Property)
Rob Mintz (Mgr-Property Res)
Pat Whipple (Office Mgr)
Gregg Truxton (Partner)
Jason Gouw (VP-Land, Regulatory & Engagement)

LAND SOUTH CONSTRUCTION LLC
1680 The Greens Way Ste 100, Jacksonville Beach, FL 32250
Tel.: (904) 273-6004
Web Site: http://www.landsouth.com
Sales Range: $25-49.9 Million
Emp.: 15
Commercial & Office Building, New Construction
N.A.I.C.S.: 236220
James G. Pyle (Pres & CEO)

LAND SOUTH HOLDINGS, LLC
4705 Old Hwy 37, Lakeland, FL 33813
Tel.: (863) 937-8867
Web Site:
  http://www.landsouthholdings.com
Real Eastate Services
N.A.I.C.S.: 531390
Robert F. Harper IV (Founder & Owner)

Subsidiaries:

AgAmerica Lending LLC (1)
4030 S Pipkin Rd Ste 100, Lakeland, FL 33811
Tel.: (863) 607-9500
Web Site: http://www.agamerica.com
Emp.: 20
Mortgage Lending & Investing
N.A.I.C.S.: 522310
Robert Harper (Partner)
Brian Philpot (Partner)

Econ South, LLC (1)
6700 S Florida Ave Ste 4, Lakeland, FL 33813
Tel.: (863) 686-0544
Web Site: http://www.econsouth.com
Engineeering Services
N.A.I.C.S.: 541330
E. Doyle Lasseter (VP-Engrg)
John C. McVay Jr. (CEO)

Land South Realty, LLC (1)
4705 Old Hwy 37, Lakeland, FL 33813
Tel.: (863) 937-8867
Web Site: http://www.landsouthrealty.com
Emp.: 30
Real Estate Brokerage Services
N.A.I.C.S.: 531210

LAND TITLE GUARANTEE COMPANY INC.
3033 E 1st Ave Ste 600, Denver, CO 80206-5620
Tel.: (303) 321-1880 CO
Web Site: http://www.ltgc.com
Year Founded: 1966
Sales Range: $100-124.9 Million
Emp.: 600
Title Insurance
N.A.I.C.S.: 524210
Beth Costello (VP-Sls & Mktg)
Michael Heber (Gen Counsel)
Jim Renshaw (VP-Sls & Mktg)
John E. Freyer Jr. (Pres)

LAND TRUST ALLIANCE
1250 H St NW Ste 600, Washington, DC 20005
Tel.: (202) 638-4725 MA
Web Site:
  https://www.landtrustalliance.org
Year Founded: 1982
Sales Range: $10-24.9 Million
Emp.: 74
Land Conservation Services
N.A.I.C.S.: 712190
Jameson French (Vice Chm)
Laura Johnson (Chm)
Frederic C. Rich (Vice Chm)
Andrew Bowman (Pres)
Marilyn Ayres (CFO & COO)
Renee Kivikko (Dir-Education)
Todd West (Dir-Dev)
Elizabeth Ward (Dir-Comm)
Penelope Winkler (VP-Dev)
William Charles Mulligan (Treas & Sec)

LAND TRUST OF SANTA CRUZ COUNTY
617 Water St, Santa Cruz, CA 95060-4114
Tel.: (831) 429-6116 CA
Web Site:
  http://www.landtrustsantacruz.org
Year Founded: 1978
Sales Range: $10-24.9 Million
Emp.: 12
Civil & Social Organization
N.A.I.C.S.: 813410
Dan Medeiros (Project Dir)
Lisa Larson (Dir-Fin & Admin)
Lynn Overtree (Mgr-Stewardship)
Calah Pasley (Dir-Dev & Comm)
Bryan Largay (Dir-Conservation)

LAND VIEW FERTILIZER INC.
925 N Hwy 24, Rupert, ID 83350
Tel.: (208) 531-4500 ID
Web Site: http://www.lvf.com
Year Founded: 1984
Sales Range: $25-49.9 Million
Emp.: 150
Farm Supplies Mfr
N.A.I.C.S.: 424910
Roy M. Young (Pres)

LAND-RON, INC.
6753 Kingspointe Pkwy Ste 109, Orlando, FL 32819-8598
Tel.: (407) 816-7035
Web Site: http://www.landroninc.com
Sales Range: $10-24.9 Million
Emp.: 38
Nonresidential Construction Services
N.A.I.C.S.: 236220
Ronald Karpiuk (Pres)
Roy H. Karpiuk (VP)
Pablo O. Leaurre (Dir-Fin)

LANDAAL PACKAGING SYSTEMS
3256 B Iron St, Burton, MI 48529
Tel.: (989) 894-0443
Web Site: http://www.landaal.com

Year Founded: 1959
Sales Range: $25-49.9 Million
Emp.: 65
Corrugated Box Mfr
N.A.I.C.S.: 322211
Robert B. Landaal (Pres)

Subsidiaries:

Delta Containers Inc. (1)
1400 Eddy St, Bay City, MI 48708
Tel.: (810) 742-2730
Web Site: http://www.landaal.com
Rev.: $45,582,356
Emp.: 50
Corrugated Boxes
N.A.I.C.S.: 322211
Debbie McAlpine (Gen Mgr)

Flint Packaging, Inc. (1)
3256 B Iron St, Burton, MI 48529
Tel.: (810) 743-0400
Corrugated Box Mfr
N.A.I.C.S.: 322211
Steve Landaal (CEO)

LANDAIR TRANSPORT, INC.
1 Landair Way, Greeneville, TN 37743
Tel.: (423) 783-1300 TN
Web Site: http://www.landair.com
Year Founded: 1981
Medium & Short-Haul Trucking Services
N.A.I.C.S.: 484121
John A. Tweed (Pres & CEO)
Jim Massengill (VP-Supply Chain Svcs)
Matt Anderson (VP-Sls & Mktg)
Lynn Doster (Sr VP-Ops)

LANDAU BUILDING COMPANY
9855 Rinaman Rd, Wexford, PA 15090-9226
Tel.: (724) 935-8800 PA
Web Site: http://www.landau-bldg.com
Year Founded: 1890
Sales Range: $75-99.9 Million
Emp.: 100
General Contracting Services
N.A.I.C.S.: 236220
Jeffrey C. Landau (Pres)
Jason Scheible (Project Mgr)
Michael G. Nehnevajsa (VP-Ops & Dir-Safety)

Subsidiaries:

Marks-Landau Construction, LLC (1)
9855 Rinaman Rd, Wexford, PA 15090
Tel.: (724) 935-8800
Sales Range: $10-24.9 Million
Emp.: 20
Commercial Building Construction Services
N.A.I.C.S.: 236220

LANDAU DIRECT
727 N Meadow St, Allentown, PA 18102
Tel.: (610) 433-4114
Web Site:
  http://www.landaujewelry.com
Year Founded: 1987
Rev.: $13,400,000
Emp.: 219
Elegant Costume Jewelry Mfr & Retailer
N.A.I.C.S.: 339910
Nat L. Hyman (Founder & Pres)

Subsidiaries:

Nat Landau Hyman Jewels Ltd. (1)
727 N Meadow St, Allentown, PA 18102
Tel.: (610) 433-4114
Web Site: http://www.landaujewelry.com
Costume Jewelry
N.A.I.C.S.: 458110
Nat L. Hyman (Founder & Pres)

U.S. PRIVATE

LANDAU UNIFORMS INCORPORATED
8410 W Sandidge Rd, Olive Branch, MS 38654
Tel.: (662) 895-7200 TN
Web Site: http://www.landau.com
Year Founded: 1959
Sales Range: $100-124.9 Million
Emp.: 1,200
Uniform Mfr & Retailer
N.A.I.C.S.: 315250
Daryl Williams (VP-Sls & Mktg)
Jamie McClure (Supvr-Returns)
Sergio Gonzalez (Dir-Mfg & Sourcing)
Nancy E. Russell (CFO)
Leigh Worrell (Mgr-Payroll)
Jeff Donovan (Engr-Costing)
Tim Shelton (VP-IT)
Jason Panter (Dir-Logistics)

LANDAU, NASELLA & KLATSKY, LLC
81 Main St, White Plains, NY 10601
Tel.: (914) 824-5900 DE
Web Site: http://www.lnkpartners.com
Year Founded: 2005
Privater Equity Firm
N.A.I.C.S.: 523999
David Landau (Partner)
Henry J. Nasella (Partner)
Phil Mariineau (Partner)
Jeff Perlman (Partner)
Kayvan Heravi (Partner)
Patrick Boroian (Partner)
Craig Rydin (Partner-Operating)
Bob Spellman (Partner-Operating)
John Barton (Partner-Operating)
Jennifer Fox Bensimon (Principal)
Bethany Foullouis (COO & Chief Compliance Officer)
Fahad Sultan (CFO)
Eulalia Ruiz (Mgr-Admin)

LANDAVAZO BROS. INC.
29280 Pacific St, Hayward, CA 94544
Tel.: (510) 581-7104 CA
Sales Range: $10-24.9 Million
Emp.: 12
Concrete Foundation & Structure Contractor
N.A.I.C.S.: 238110
Theodore Landavazo (Co-Owner & Pres)
Derrick Landavazo (Co-Owner)

LANDCARE LANDSCAPING, INC.
6767 S Lois Ave, Tampa, FL 33616
Tel.: (813) 676-6000 FL
Web Site:
  http://www.landcaretampabay.com
Year Founded: 1972
Sales Range: $1-9.9 Million
Emp.: 60
Landscaping Services
N.A.I.C.S.: 561730
Debra Morgan (CFO)
K. C. Fisher (Founder & Owner)
Jerry Roque (VP)
Robin Rhodes (Mgr-Ops)

LANDCO CONSTRUCTION
12655 Olive Blvd Ste 325, Saint Louis, MO 63141-6362
Tel.: (314) 275-7400
Web Site: http://www.landco-construction.com
Year Founded: 2001
Sales Range: $25-49.9 Million
Emp.: 40
Nonresidential Construction Services
N.A.I.C.S.: 236220
Ron Landoit (CEO)
Nick Voght (Superintendent)
Linda Bernhard (Pres)
Michelle Yates (Dir-Bus Dev)

LANDCOAST INSULATION INC.
4017 2nd St, New Iberia, LA 70560
Tel.: (337) 367-7741
Web Site: http://www.landcoast.com
Year Founded: 1973
Sales Range: $10-24.9 Million
Emp.: 250
Industrial Insulation, Painting, Scaffolding, Fire Proofing & Heat Tracing Services
N.A.I.C.S.: 238990
Robert Michael Morton (CEO)
Michael R. Morton (Founder)
Timothy S. Morton (Exec VP)

LANDCOM INC.
4314 Pablo Oaks Ct, Jacksonville, FL 32224-9631
Tel.: (904) 992-3700
Web Site: http://www.lhmhotels.com
Year Founded: 1983
Sales Range: $10-24.9 Million
Emp.: 10
Subdividers & Developers
N.A.I.C.S.: 237210
Charles R. Johnson (Pres & COO)
Nanette P. Orlins (CFO & Sr VP)
H. Kenneth O'Steen Jr. (Chm)

LANDER VAN GUNDY AGENCY, INC.
101 S Towanda Ave, Normal, IL 61761
Tel.: (309) 452-1156
Web Site: http://www.vangundy.com
Insurance Agents
N.A.I.C.S.: 524210
Gail McNeeley (Office Mgr)

Subsidiaries:

Laiming Insurance Group (1)
314 Center St, Gridley, IL 61744-0000
Tel.: (309) 747-2133
Web Site: http://www.laiminginsurance.net
Insurance Related Activities
N.A.I.C.S.: 524298
Paul Laiming (Pres)

LANDERS & PARTNERS, INC.
13555 Automobile Blvd Ste 610, Clearwater, FL 33762
Tel.: (727) 572-5228
Web Site: http://www.landersandpartners.com
Year Founded: 1977
Sales Range: $10-24.9 Million
Emp.: 20
Advertising Agency Services
N.A.I.C.S.: 541810
Bernie Tanzi (Acct Mgmt Dir)
Jennifer Meadows (Dir-Creative)
Michelle Darr (Pres)

Subsidiaries:

Landers & Partners, Inc. (1)
3429 Farm Bank Way, Grove City, OH 43123
Tel.: (614) 991-5553
Advertising Agencies
N.A.I.C.S.: 541810
Daryl Stinemetz (VP-Ops)

LANDERS AUTO GROUP INC.
19236 Interstate 30, Benton, AR 72019
Tel.: (501) 315-2500
Web Site: http://www.landers.com
Sales Range: $10-24.9 Million
New Car Dealers
N.A.I.C.S.: 441110
James McMoran (Mgr-Fin)
Shawn Newsom (Mgr-Fin)
Chris Richmond (Mgr-Fin)
Pat Campbell (Sls Mgr)
Russ Comstock (Sls Mgr)
Terry Speer (Mgr-Fin)
Rodney Plack (Reg VP)

LANDERS-MCLARTY BENTONVILLE LLC
2609 S Walton Blvd, Bentonville, AR 72712
Tel.: (479) 273-9022
Web Site: http://www.landersmclarty.com
Sales Range: $25-49.9 Million
Emp.: 93
Automobiles, New & Used
N.A.I.C.S.: 441110
Steve Lander (Owner)
Matt McLarty (Pres)

LANDES OIL INC.
32106 State Hwy 6, Jamesport, MO 64648
Tel.: (660) 684-6611
Rev.: $13,000,000
Emp.: 30
Petroleum Bulk Stations & Terminals
N.A.I.C.S.: 424710
David Landes (VP)
Greg Landes (Pres)
Ruth Carter (Office Mgr)

LANDHOPE CORPORATION
101 E St Rd, Kennett Square, PA 19348
Tel.: (610) 444-3300
Sales Range: $10-24.9 Million
Emp.: 12
Owner & Operator of Convenience Stores
N.A.I.C.S.: 445131
W. B. Dixon Stroud Jr. (Pres)

LANDINGS CLUB INC.
71 Green Island Rd, Savannah, GA 31411
Tel.: (912) 598-8050
Web Site: http://www.landingsclub.com
Sales Range: $10-24.9 Million
Emp.: 400
Health Club Golf Tennis Clubhouse
N.A.I.C.S.: 713940
Steven Freund (Exec Dir)
Chris Kader (Dir-Court Sports)
Jacob McLendon (Dir-Fitness & Wellness)

LANDIS COMMUNICATIONS INC.
1388 Sutter St Ste 901, San Francisco, CA 94109
Tel.: (415) 561-0888
Web Site: http://www.landispr.com
Year Founded: 1990
Sales Range: $1-9.9 Million
Emp.: 15
Corporate Communications, Corporate Identity, Crisis Communications & Public Relations
N.A.I.C.S.: 541820
David Landis (Pres & CEO)
Brianne Murphy Miller (Mgr-Bus Dev & Sr PR Counselor)
Brigitta Shouppe (Sr Acct Exec)

LANDIS CONSTRUCTION CO., LLC.
8300 Earhart Blvd Ste 300, New Orleans, LA 70118
Tel.: (504) 833-6070
Web Site: http://www.landisllc.com
Sales Range: $75-99.9 Million
Emp.: 100
Nonresidential Construction
N.A.I.C.S.: 236220
James C. Landis (Chm)
George W. Voss (Sr VP-Pur)
Anne Teague Landis (CEO)
Christian Generes (Pres)
Kyle Condon (Chief Construction Officer)
Sarah Busch (VP-Ops)

LANDIS SUPER MARKET, INC.
2685 County Line Rd, Telford, PA 18969
Tel.: (215) 723-1045
Web Site: http://www.landismarket.com
Year Founded: 1938
Sales Range: $50-74.9 Million
Emp.: 520
Distr of Groceries
N.A.I.C.S.: 445110
Donald Nice (Pres)
David G. Landis (CEO)
Toni Kapes (Controller)

LANDMARK CONSTRUCTION COMPANY, INC.
3255 Industry Dr, North Charleston, SC 29418
Tel.: (843) 552-6186
Web Site: http://www.landmark-sc.com
Year Founded: 1965
Sales Range: $25-49.9 Million
Emp.: 150
Commercial & Institutional Building Construction Services
N.A.I.C.S.: 236220
Ann Mixson (Chm)
Cynthia Mixson (Pres)
Rick Mixson (VP)

LANDMARK ENGINEERING AND SURVEYING CORP.
8515 Palm River Rd, Tampa, FL 33619
Tel.: (813) 621-7841
Web Site: http://www.lesc.com
Sales Range: $1-9.9 Million
Emp.: 60
Surveying, Mapping, Planning & Civil Engineering Services
N.A.I.C.S.: 541370
David L. Hurley (Co-Founder & Pres)
E. Everett Morrow (Co-Founder & VP)

LANDMARK EQUIPMENT
1351 S Loop 12, Irving, TX 75060
Tel.: (972) 579-9999
Web Site: http://www.landmarkeq.com
Emp.: 75
Farm & Garden Machinery
N.A.I.C.S.: 423820
Mike Lyle (Pres)
Gary Lyle (Mgr-Store)
Tom Martin (Mgr-Parts)

LANDMARK GROWTH CAPITAL PARTNERS, LP
328 Market St, Warren, RI 02885
Tel.: (401) 245-1200
Investment & Management Consultancy
N.A.I.C.S.: 523940
Edward Jed DiPaolo (Partner)

Subsidiaries:

TPI Composites Inc. (1)
9200 E Pima Ctr Pkwy Ste 250, Scottsdale, AZ 85258
Tel.: (480) 305-8910
Web Site: https://www.tpicomposites.com
Rev.: $1,455,183,000
Assets: $804,080,000
Liabilities: $926,384,000
Net Worth: ($122,304,000)
Earnings: ($177,612,000)
Emp.: 12,300
Fiscal Year-end: 12/31/2023
Structural Composite Products
N.A.I.C.S.: 333611
Deane Ilukowicz (Chief People Officer)
Theo Gibson (CIO)
Thomas Adams (Sr VP-Wind)
Neil Jones (Chief Quality Officer)
Charles Stroo (COO-Wind)
William E. Siwek (Pres & CEO)
Adan Gossar (Chief Acctg Officer)
Steven G. Fishbach (Gen Counsel & Sec)
Nicholas Warchol (Sr VP-Technology & Engr)
Ryan Miller (CFO)

LANDMARK HEALTHCARE, INC.
3455 NE Loop 820, Fort Worth, TX 76137-2414
Tel.: (817) 338-0007
Web Site: http://www.landmarkhc.com
Year Founded: 1999
Sales Range: $10-24.9 Million
Emp.: 65
Medical Equipment & Supplies Distr
N.A.I.C.S.: 423450
Ron Majerus (Founder)
Lacey Karlik (Mgr-Customer Svc)
Christopher Goldsmith (Pres)
Anna Gill (Chief HR Officer)
Rod Jardine (CIO)
Nick Loporcaro (CEO)
Jessica Diaz Sr. (Dir-Brand & Mktg)

LANDMARK NURSERIES INC.
1100 E Sandy Lk Rd, Coppell, TX 75019
Tel.: (972) 471-6300
Web Site: http://www.landmarknurseries.com
Year Founded: 1985
Rev.: $12,711,394
Emp.: 50
Nursery Stock Services
N.A.I.C.S.: 424930
Jim Prewitt (CEO)
Ted R. Munselle (CFO & VP)
Kevin Norris (Pres)

LANDMARK PLASTIC CORPORATION
1331 Kelly Ave, Akron, OH 44306
Tel.: (330) 785-2200
Web Site: http://www.landmarkplastic.com
Rev.: $16,200,000
Emp.: 150
Plastics Product Mfr
N.A.I.C.S.: 326199
Robert G. Merzweiler (Chm & CEO)
Randy Gaj (CFO & VP)
Steve Beall (VP-Sls & Mktg)
Steven P. Merzweiler (Dir-Ops)

LANDMARK RETAIL CORP.
24 Newark Pompton Tpke Ste B, Little Falls, NJ 07424
Tel.: (201) 425-1411
Web Site: http://www.lrcus.com
Sales Range: $1-9.9 Million
Emp.: 8
Construction Services
N.A.I.C.S.: 236220
Jon Spencer (Pres)
Tony Pizza (Exec VP)
Carol Victoria (Coord-Facilities)

LANDMARK SCHOOL, INC.
429 Hale St, Prides Crossing, MA 01965
Tel.: (978) 236-3010
Web Site: http://www.landmarkschool.org
Year Founded: 1967
Sales Range: $25-49.9 Million
Emp.: 411
Disabled People Educational Support Services

LANDMARK SCHOOL, INC. U.S. PRIVATE

Landmark School, Inc.—(Continued)
N.A.I.C.S.: 624120
Moira M. James (Chm)
Martin P. Slark (Vice Chm)
Robert J. Broudo (Pres)
Mark R. Brislin (VP & Mgr-Bus)
Gia Meicher (Mgr-Database)

LANDMARK SERVICES COOPERATIVE
1401 Landmark Dr, Cottage Grove, WI 53527
Tel.: (608) 251-9010
Web Site: http://www.landmark.coop
Year Founded: 1933
Rev.: $373,439,184
Assets: $203,588,181
Liabilities: $77,241,435
Net Worth: $126,346,746
Earnings: $5,778,666
Emp.: 286
Fiscal Year-end: 09/30/19
Agricultural Services
N.A.I.C.S.: 493130
Jon Prochnow (Vice Chm)
Jim Lange (Chm)
Mike Elder (VP-Risk Mgmt)
Hans Pflieger (VP-Credit Ops)
Kevin Klahn (Treas & Sec-West)
Keith Arnold (CFO)
James Dell (Pres & CEO)

LANDOLL CORPORATION
1900 N St, Marysville, KS 66508-1271
Tel.: (785) 562-5381 KS
Web Site: http://www.landoll.com
Year Founded: 1963
Sales Range: $50-74.9 Million
Emp.: 850
Farm Equipment & Fork Lifts Mfr
N.A.I.C.S.: 333111
Donald Landoll (Founder, Owner & Pres)
Jim Ladner (Mgr-Trailer Sls)
Kerry Smith (Mgr-Parts Distr Center)

Subsidiaries:
Landoll Corporation - Drexel (1)
331 Maple Ave, Horsham, PA 19044
Tel.: (215) 672-2200
Web Site: http://www.drexeltrucks.com
Sales Range: $25-49.9 Million
Emp.: 150
Lift Trucks Mfr
N.A.I.C.S.: 333924

LANDON CAPITAL PARTNERS, LLC
21 Custom House St Ste 700, Boston, MA 02110
Tel.: (617) 589-3652 DE
Web Site: https://www.landoncapital.com
Year Founded: 2015
Privater Equity Firm
N.A.I.C.S.: 523999
Chris Sullivan (Mng Partner)

Subsidiaries:
919 Marketing Company (1)
102 Avent Ferry Rd, Holly Springs, NC 27540
Tel.: (919) 557-7890
Web Site: http://www.919marketing.com
Sales Range: $1-9.9 Million
Emp.: 50
Marketing Services
N.A.I.C.S.: 541613
David Chapman (Founder & CEO)
Sue Yannello (Exec VP)
Graham Chapman (VP-Acct Svcs)
Scott Curkin (VP-Acct Svcs)
Nancy Bostrom (Sr Acct Mgr)

Subsidiary (Domestic):
Fish Consulting, LLC (2)
117 NE 2nd St, Fort Lauderdale, FL 33301
Tel.: (954) 893-9150
Web Site: http://www.fish-consulting.com
Public Relations Services
N.A.I.C.S.: 541820
Jenna Kantrowitz (COO & Sr VP)
Chad Cohen (Sr VP)
Kim Ryan (VP)
Becky Peterson (Sr Acct Dir)
Lorne Fisher (CEO & Mng Partner)
Samantha Russo (Acct Mgr)
Ellie Mannix (Acct Mgr)
Tiffany Trilli (Acct Coord)
Sloane Fistel (Acct Exec)
Andie Biederman (Mgr-Acct)
Ashley Reynolds (Mgr-Social Media)
Claibourne Smith (Mgr-Acct)
Elayne Sommers (Sr Acct Mgr)
Rachel Tabacnic (Sr Acct Mgr)
Amanda Bortzfield (Sr Dir-Acct)
Lauren Simo (Sr Dir-Acct)
Julia Block (Dir-Acct)
Michelle Estevam (Sr Acct Mgr)
Courtney Whelan (Acct Exec)
Caitlin Willard (Acct Exec)
Chelsea Bear (Coord-Acct)

J.D.S. Finance Limited (1)
2 Duke Street, London, W1U 3EH, United Kingdom
Tel.: (44) 2079350992
Investment Holding Company
N.A.I.C.S.: 551112
Rupert Jocelyn Smale Edis (CEO)

LANDPARK ADVISORS, LLC
2550 Gray Falls Dr Ste 400, Houston, TX 77077
Tel.: (713) 789-2200
Web Site: https://landparkco.com
Privater Equity Firm
N.A.I.C.S.: 523940
Sam Morris (CEO)

Subsidiaries:
Reliance Property Resources Co. (1)
10565 Katy Freeway Ste 301, Houston, TX 77024-1019
Tel.: (713) 464-4618
Web Site: http://www.rprc.com
Offices of Real Estate Agents & Brokers
N.A.I.C.S.: 531210
John Anderson (Pres)

LANDPOINT INC.
5486 Airline Dr, Bossier City, LA 71111
Tel.: (318) 226-0100
Web Site: http://www.landpoint.net
Year Founded: 1984
Sales Range: $1-9.9 Million
Emp.: 100
Land Surveying
N.A.I.C.S.: 541370
James Souter (Pres)
Phillip Cordaro (Dir-HR)

LANDQWEST COMMERCIAL, LLC
1614 Colonia Blvd Ste 101, Fort Myers, FL 33907
Tel.: (239) 275-4922
Web Site: http://www.landqwestcommercial.com
Sales Range: $1-9.9 Million
Emp.: 50
Real Estate Broker
N.A.I.C.S.: 531210
Stephen A. Cunningham (Principal)
John P. Mounce (Principal)
Rokki Rogan (Principal)
Laura Juteau (Mgr-Property)
Mary Gentile (Pres-Property Mgmt)
Rich Sommerville (Dir-Land Div)
Chuck Smith (Sr Dir-Investments)
Courtney Saksefski (Sr Mgr-Mktg)
Jessica McEvoy (Dir-Bus Strategic Initiatives)
Wendy Krepak (Mng Dir-Orlando)
Heather Heinzeroth (Mgr-MKtg)
Matt Dolan (Dir-GIS & Res Svcs)
Michael Daly (Sr Dir-Retail Svcs)
Jamie Brown (Coord-Mktg)
Matt Yaniglos (Principal)
Julia Sosa (Principal-Orlando)

LANDRETH LUMBER COMPANY
511 N Washington St, Bunker Hill, IL 62014
Tel.: (618) 585-4419
Sales Range: $25-49.9 Million
Emp.: 100
Lumber & Other Building Materials Whslr
N.A.I.C.S.: 423310
Dean Landreth (Pres)

LANDROVER ORLANDO
199 S Lk Destiny Rd, Orlando, FL 32810
Tel.: (407) 695-9100
Web Site: http://www.fieldsauto.com
Sales Range: $75-99.9 Million
Emp.: 60
Automobiles, New & Used
N.A.I.C.S.: 441110
John R. Fields (Owner)
Veronica Kuchenbecker (Dir-Fin)

LANDRUM & BROWN, INCORPORATED
11279 Cornell Park Dr, Cincinnati, OH 45242-1811
Tel.: (513) 530-5333 OH
Web Site: http://www.landrum-brown.com
Year Founded: 1949
Sales Range: $50-74.9 Million
Emp.: 150
Airport & Aviation Planning & Consulting Services
N.A.I.C.S.: 541690
Jeff Thomas (CEO)
Berta Fernandez (Exec VP-Plng Svcs Div)
Mark Perryman (Pres & COO-Americas)
Doug Goldberg (Exec VP-Strategic Projects-Global)
Gary Gibb (Pres-Asia Pacific)
Rob Adams (Exec VP-Environmental Svcs Div)
Dennis E. Peters (CFO)

LANDRUM COMPANY
801 E Broadway, Columbia, MO 65201
Tel.: (573) 449-7333 MO
Web Site: http://www.landmarkbank.com
Year Founded: 1960
Sales Range: $100-124.9 Million
Bank Holding Company
N.A.I.C.S.: 551111
Kevin Gibbens (CEO)

Subsidiaries:
Landmark Bank, N.A. (1)
801 E Broadway, Columbia, MO 65201
Tel.: (573) 499-7333
Web Site: http://www.landmarkbank.com
Sales Range: $100-124.9 Million
Federal Savings Bank
N.A.I.C.S.: 522180
Kristi Story (VP & Mgr-Acctg)
Greg Reed (VP)
Jay Alexander (Sr VP-Wealth Mgmt)
Amy George (Mgr-Relationship)
Jessica Humble (Asst VP & Mgr-Relationship)
Miles James (Asst VP)
Jo Mooney (Sr VP)
Doug Moore (Exec VP & Dir-Wealth Mgmt)
DeAnn Peter (VP)
Steve Spellman (VP & Mgr-Relationship)
Nick Thurwanger (CFO & VP)
Kim Whorton (Mgr-Relationship)
Cindy Bradford (Pres-Community Bank-Mountain View & Birch Tree)

LANDRUM HUMAN RESOURCE COMPANIES, INC.
6723 Plantation Rd, Pensacola, FL 32504
Tel.: (850) 476-5100
Web Site: http://www.landrumhr.com
Sales Range: $450-499.9 Million
Emp.: 200
Human Resource Management Services
N.A.I.C.S.: 541612
Johnathan Taylor (CFO & VP)
Amie Remington (Gen Counsel)
Angela Thornton-Jones (Mgr-Ops)
Denise McLeod (COO & VP)
Holly McLeod (Mgr-HR-Landrum Consulting)
Jim Guttman (Mgr-Landrum Pro HR)
Johanna Pohlmann (Mgr-Admin & Pro Div)
Sandra Smith (Mgr-Sls)
Ted Kirchharr (COO-Landrum Pro & VP)
William Cleary (VP-Bus Dev & Client Rels)
Kara Bloomberg (VP-Ops)
J. Martin Stubblefield (Mgr-Client Rels)
Deborah Brousseau (Dir-Mktg)
David McCullough (Chief Admin Officer)
H. Britt Landrum Jr. (Founder & Pres)
Britt H. Landrum III (CEO)

Subsidiaries:
Landrum Consulting, Inc. (1)
6723 Plantation Rd, Pensacola, FL 32504
Tel.: (850) 476-5100
Web Site: http://www.landrumhr.com
Human Resource Consulting Services
N.A.I.C.S.: 541612

Landrum Professional Employer Services, Inc. (1)
6723 Plantation Rd, Pensacola, FL 32504
Tel.: (850) 476-5100
Web Site: http://www.landrumhr.com
Sales Range: $25-49.9 Million
Professional Employer Services
N.A.I.C.S.: 561330
William Cleary (Mgr-Client Rels)

Landrum Staffing Services, Inc. (1)
6723 Plantation Rd, Pensacola, FL 32504
Tel.: (850) 476-5100
Staffing Services
N.A.I.C.S.: 561320
Denis McLeod (COO & VP)
Angela Thornton-Jones (Mgr-Ops)
Sandra Smith (Mgr-Sls)
Johanna Pohlmann (Mgr-Admin-Pro Div)
H. Britt Landrum Jr. (Pres & CEO)

LANDRY HARRIS & CO. INC.
600 Jefferson St Ste 200, Lafayette, LA 70501
Tel.: (337) 266-2150 LA
Web Site: http://www.landryharris.com
Year Founded: 1950
Sales Range: $10-24.9 Million
Emp.: 210
Insurance Services
N.A.I.C.S.: 524210
Caleb Kestner (Acct Exec-Comml Lines)
Tiffany Menard (Mgr-Comml Lines Acct)
Ellen Boudreaux (Mgr-Employee Benefits Acct)
Debbie Guidry (Mgr-Personal Lines Acct)
Staci Cormier (Mgr-Personal Lines Acct)
Ashlee Boyd (Dir-Mktg)

COMPANIES

Jennifer M. Riplie *(Dir-Comm & Coord-Mktg)*
Julie M. Creswell *(Dir-Employee Benefits)*
Charon S. Harris *(Exec VP)*

LANDS END MARINA HOLDING COMPANY, INC.
1220 Apollo Beach Blvd, Apollo Beach, FL 33572
Tel.: (813) 645-5594
Web Site: http://www.landsendmarina.com
Sales Range: $1-9.9 Million
Emp.: 10
Holding Company; Marina
N.A.I.C.S.: 551112
Christie Granowicz *(Pres)*

Subsidiaries:
Lands End Marina (1)
1220 Apollo Beach Blvd, Apollo Beach, FL 33572
Tel.: (813) 645-5594
Web Site: http://www.landsendmarina.com
Marinas
N.A.I.C.S.: 713930
Kevin Howell *(Gen Mgr)*

LANDSBERG BENNETT PRIVATE WEALTH MANAGEMENT
252 W Marion Ave, Punta Gorda, FL 33950
Tel.: (941) 391-8000
Web Site: http://www.landsbergbennett.com
Rev.: $493,000,000
Emp.: 10
Financial Advisory & Investment Services
N.A.I.C.S.: 523940
Michael Landsberg *(Partner)*
Lew Bennett *(Partner)*
Anthony Dubbaneh *(Partner)*
Faiza Kedir *(Dir-Bus Dev)*

LANDSCAPE CONCEPTS MANAGEMENT, INC.
31745 Alleghany Rd, Grayslake, IL 60030
Tel.: (847) 223-3800
Web Site: http://www.landscapeconcepts.com
Year Founded: 1981
Landscape Management Services
N.A.I.C.S.: 541320
Mike Kerton *(Pres)*
John Czapla *(Acct Exec)*
Annaliza Arceo *(Mktg Mgr)*
John Blohm *(Branch Mgr-Aurora)*
Paul Bruggen *(Head-Contruction)*
Ken Carrano *(CFO & Controller)*
Fermin Gomez *(Supvr-Maintenance)*
Juan Gonzales *(Supvr-Tree & Plant Healthcare)*
Miguel Gonzales *(Ops Mgr)*
Mike Graham *(VP)*
Carrie Hancock *(Head-Seasonal Color)*
Dave Heinrich *(Sr Acct Mgr)*
Dave Galley *(Shop Mgr)*
Dominic O'Hara *(Acct Mgr)*
Kevin Stone *(Fleet Mgr)*
Tyler Martin *(Sr Coord-Project)*
Rebecca Zimmerman *(Supvr-Admin)*
Tom Thomas *(Acct Mgr)*
Amy McConnell *(Acct Mgr)*
Matt Sokolowske *(Comml Acct Mgr)*
Jesse Bozman *(VP-Sls)*

LANDSCAPE DEVELOPMENTAL INC.
28447 Witherspoon Pkwy, Valencia, CA 91355
Tel.: (661) 295-1970
Web Site: http://www.landscapedevelopment.com
Landscaping Services
N.A.I.C.S.: 561730
Gary Horton *(Pres)*

Subsidiaries:
Enhanced Landscape Management, LLC (1)
28447 Witherspoon Pkwy, Valencia, CA 91355
Tel.: (661) 295-1970
Web Site: http://www.enhancedlandscape.com
Landscaping Services
N.A.I.C.S.: 561730
Greg Epstein *(Owner)*

Subsidiary (Domestic):
Chateau Landscape, Inc. (2)
34714 Sweetwater Dr, Santa Clarita, CA 91390
Tel.: (661) 268-8866
Sales Range: $1-9.9 Million
Emp.: 30
Landscape Maintenance Services
N.A.I.C.S.: 541320
Eileen Noel Fredeking *(VP)*

Holmes Landscape Company (2)
4616 N Ave, Oceanside, CA 92056-3509
Tel.: (760) 732-3379
Web Site: http://www.holmeslandscape.com
Landscaping Services
N.A.I.C.S.: 561730
Larry Holmes *(Founder & Pres)*
Lee Frank *(VP)*

Zuke's Landscape, Inc. (2)
3373 Luyung Dr, Rancho Cordova, CA 95742
Tel.: (916) 635-6502
Web Site: http://www.zukeslandscape.com
Lawn And Garden Services
N.A.I.C.S.: 561730
Dan Zuccaro *(Pres)*
Jose Morales *(Mgr-Acct)*

LANDSCAPE FORMS, INC.
431 Lawndale Ave, Kalamazoo, MI 49048
Tel.: (269) 381-0396
Web Site: http://www.landscapeforms.com
Year Founded: 1969
Sales Range: $75-99.9 Million
Emp.: 400
Mfr of Public Site Furnishings
N.A.I.C.S.: 337127
William C. Main *(Pres & CEO)*
Richard Heriford *(VP-Mktg)*

LANDSCAPE MAINTENANCE PROFESSIONALS, INC.
13050 US 92 E, Dover, FL 33527
Tel.: (813) 757-6500
Web Site: http://www.lmppro.com
Year Founded: 1991
Sales Range: $10-24.9 Million
Emp.: 300
Landscape Architectural Services
N.A.I.C.S.: 541320
Miguel Botto *(Mgr-Orlando & Jacksonville)*
Jason Liggett *(Mgr-Pasco)*
Orlando Castillo Jr. *(Pres & CEO)*

LANDSCAPE STRUCTURES INC.
601 S 7th St, Delano, MN 55328-8605
Tel.: (763) 972-3391 MN
Web Site: http://www.playlsi.com
Year Founded: 1971
Sales Range: $75-99.9 Million
Emp.: 300
Playground Equipment Mfr
N.A.I.C.S.: 339920

Steven King *(Chm)*
Fred Caslavka *(CFO)*
Pat Faust *(Pres)*

LANDSCAPES UNLIMITED LLC
1201 Aries Dr, Lincoln, NE 68512
Tel.: (402) 423-6653
Web Site: http://www.landscapesunlimited.com
Sales Range: $100-124.9 Million
Emp.: 60
Golf Course Construction
N.A.I.C.S.: 236210
Bill Kubly *(Founder)*
Cesar Martinez *(Mgr-Programs)*
Tom Everett *(VP-Ops)*
Tim Halpine *(Gen Mgr-The Players Club)*
Brett Lacey *(Superintendent-Construction)*

LANDSHIRE, INC.
727 N 1st St, Saint Louis, MO 63102-2548
Tel.: (618) 398-8122 IL
Year Founded: 1966
Sales Range: $25-49.9 Million
Emp.: 250
Assembled & Packaged Sandwiches Mfr & Whslr
N.A.I.C.S.: 311991
Joseph Trover *(CEO)*
Dan Manning *(Dir-Food Svc)*
Kenny Landreth *(Dir-Sls-Natl)*
Bud Fuhrman *(Plant Mgr-Belleville)*
Dale Musick *(Pres)*
Kathy Brophy *(Dir-Innovation)*

LANDSTAR DEVELOPMENT CORPORATION
550 Biltmore Way Ste 1110, Coral Gables, FL 33134
Tel.: (305) 461-2440 FL
Web Site: http://www.landstardevelopment.com
Year Founded: 1978
Single-Family Housing & Commercial Buildings Construction
N.A.I.C.S.: 236115
Rodolfo Stern *(Pres)*
Bernard Eckstein *(VP)*

LANDSTAR TITLE AGENCY INC.
55 Cherry Ln Ste 200, Carle Place, NY 11514
Tel.: (516) 336-2020 NY
Web Site: http://www.landstartitle.net
Year Founded: 2002
Residential, Commercial & National Title Insurance
N.A.I.C.S.: 524210
John F. Burke *(Pres & CEO)*
Kenneth P. Warner *(Sr Counsel & VP)*
Marco A. Botarelli *(Mng Dir)*
Rich Lipman *(Gen Counsel & VP)*

Subsidiaries:
The Seaport Title Agency Ltd. (1)
106 Woodcleft Ave, Freeport, NY 11520
Tel.: (516) 867-5100
Title Abstract & Settlement Offices
N.A.I.C.S.: 541191

LANDSTED, LLC.
900 Crest View Dr Ste 220, Hudson, WI 54016
Tel.: (715) 386-1111
Web Site: http://www.landstedco.com
Sales Range: $10-24.9 Million
Emp.: 5
Housing Construction Services
N.A.I.C.S.: 236117
Mark Erickson *(Pres)*

LANDUS COOPERATIVE
2321 N Loop Dr Ste 220, Ames, IA 50010-8218
Tel.: (515) 817-2100
Web Site: http://www.landuscooperative.com
Year Founded: 2016
Emp.: 600
Agricultural Cooperative
N.A.I.C.S.: 813990
Mark Miner *(CFO)*
Milan Kucerak *(CEO)*
Brett Bell *(COO)*
Rick Vanderheiden *(Chief Strategy Officer)*
Janelle Thomas *(Dir-HR)*
Roger Fray *(Chief Commodity Mktg Officer)*
Mark Cullen *(Chief Animal Nutrition Officer)*
Dave Wagner *(CIO)*

LANDVEST INC.
10 Post Ofc Sq, Boston, MA 02109
Tel.: (617) 723-1800
Web Site: http://www.landvest.com
Year Founded: 1968
Rev.: $14,030,669
Emp.: 100
Real Estate Brokers & Agents
N.A.I.C.S.: 531210
Joseph L. Taggart *(Exec VP-Timberland)*

Subsidiaries:
Timberland Services (1)
109 N Main St, Concord, NH 03301
Tel.: (603) 228-2020
Web Site: http://www.landvest.com
Real Estate Brokers & Agents
N.A.I.C.S.: 561730

LANE AVIATION CORPORATION
4389 International Gateway, Columbus, OH 43219
Tel.: (614) 237-3747
Web Site: http://www.laneaviation.com
Rev.: $15,000,000
Emp.: 119
Aircraft Servicing & Repairing
N.A.I.C.S.: 441227
Donna Lane Earl *(CEO)*
Steve Evans *(Mgr-Ops)*

LANE COMPANY
5555 Glenridge Connector Ste 700, Atlanta, GA 30342
Tel.: (404) 459-6100
Web Site: http://www.lanecompany.com
Year Founded: 1985
Sales Range: $50-74.9 Million
Emp.: 60
Real Estate Property Management
N.A.I.C.S.: 531311
Dan Haefner *(Pres)*
Brooks Castellaw *(Exec VP)*
Jaime Miles-Rauscher *(Reg VP)*
Wendy Tucker *(Reg VP)*

LANE CONVEYORS & DRIVES, INC.
15 Industrial Plaza, Brewer, ME 04412
Tel.: (207) 989-4560
Web Site: http://www.lane.us.com
Sales Range: $10-24.9 Million
Emp.: 45
Conveyor Systems & Technical Services
N.A.I.C.S.: 333922
Bob Taylor *(Principal)*
Wes Archer *(Project Mgr)*

LANE ENTERPRISES INC.

Lane Enterprises Inc.—(Continued)

LANE ENTERPRISES INC.
3905 Hartzdale Dr Ste 514, Camp Hill, PA 17011
Tel.: (717) 761-8175
Web Site: http://www.lane-enterprises.com
Year Founded: 1934
Sales Range: $10-24.9 Million
Emp.: 250
Pipe, Sheet Metal
N.A.I.C.S.: 332322
Dan Gallagher (Controller)
Brian Chestnut (Mgr-HDPE Quality Assurance)
Jodi Glass (Office Mgr)
Patrick Collings (Pres & Gen Mgr)

LANE EQUIPMENT CO. INC.
2030 Richmond Ave, Houston, TX 77098
Tel.: (713) 529-5761
Web Site: http://www.laneequipment.com
Rev.: $12,000,000
Emp.: 40
Refrigeration Equipment & Supplies
N.A.I.C.S.: 423740
Robert C. Lane (Chm)
Dale Lane (Pres)
Mike Mangel (Natl Acct Mgr)
Lin Laney (Mgr-Sls)

LANE POWELL PC
1420 5th Ave Ste 4200, Seattle, WA 98111-9402
Tel.: (206) 223-7000
Web Site: http://www.lanepowell.com
Year Founded: 1875
Sales Range: $75-99.9 Million
Emp.: 201
Legal Advisory Services
N.A.I.C.S.: 541110
Thomas W. Sondag (VP)
Qingqing Miao (Atty)
Bret A. Finkelstein (Atty)
Genevieve G. York-Erwin (Atty)
Aaron P. Brecher (Atty)
Lauren A. McCray (Atty)
Jessica N. Yu (Atty)
Justin Hobson (Atty)
Kara A. Tredway (Atty)
Jennifer Castleberry (Chief Mktg & Client Experience Officer)
James Zack (Atty)
Vamshi Reddy (Atty)
Jamie Lanier (Atty)
Eric S. Meltzer (Dir-Strategy & Pricing)
Rachel Greenlee (Atty)
Patrick T. Murphy (Atty)
Aaron J. Fickes (Atty)
Aaron Schaer (Atty)
Meryl Hulteng (Atty)
Masa Yamaguchi (Partner)
Priya B. Vivian (Atty)
Joe Woods (COO)
Heather Hartley (Dir-HR)
Barbara J. Duffy (Pres)
Melissa M. Berry (Dir-Pro Dev & Diversity)

LANE PR
905 SW 16th Ave, Portland, OR 97205
Tel.: (503) 221-0480
Web Site: http://www.lanepr.com
Year Founded: 1990
Sales Range: $1-9.9 Million
Emp.: 30
Marketing, Digital, Public Relations
N.A.I.C.S.: 541820
Wendy Lane Stevens (Mng Partner)
Vicki Ruse (Controller)
Paula Ordway (Dir-HR)
Amber Roberts (Sr Partner)

Lisa Heathman (Partner & Mng Dir)
Megan Moran (Asst Acct Exec)
Stephanie Celenza (Assoc VP)
Shannon Brewer Riggs (Mng Dir & Partner)
Malisa Meresman (Partner)

Subsidiaries:

Lane Marketing (1)
500 5th Ave Ste 2720, New York, NY 10110
Tel.: (212) 302-5365
Web Site: http://www.lanepr.com
Emp.: 5
Public Relations & Brand Identity
N.A.I.C.S.: 541820
Amber Roberts (VP)

LANE PRESS, INC.
87 Meadowlands Dr, South Burlington, VT 05403
Tel.: (802) 863-5555   VT
Web Site: http://www.lanepress.com
Year Founded: 1904
Sales Range: $25-49.9 Million
Emp.: 200
Commercial Printing
N.A.I.C.S.: 323111
Phillip M. Dromheller (Pres)
Beth Renuad (Mgr-Mktg)

LANE SOUTHERN ORCHARDS
Hwy 96 E & 50 Ln Rd, Fort Valley, GA 31030
Tel.: (478) 825-3362
Web Site: http://www.lanesouthernorchards.com
Year Founded: 1908
Rev.: $25,800,000
Emp.: 375
Fruits Producer
N.A.I.C.S.: 115114
Mark Sanchez (CEO)
Kathy Young (Mgr-Events)
Terre Parish (Mgr-Gourmet)

LANE SUPPLY INC.
120 Fairview St, Arlington, TX 76010
Tel.: (817) 261-9116
Web Site: http://www.lanesupplyinc.com
Sales Range: $10-24.9 Million
Emp.: 100
Architectural Metalwork
N.A.I.C.S.: 332323
Ronnie Jones (CEO)
Ron Maddox (Mgr-Sls-Northwestern Reg)

LANECO CONSTRUCTION SYSTEMS INC.
6530 Exchequer Dr, Baton Rouge, LA 70809
Tel.: (225) 756-5050
Web Site: http://www.lanehart.net
Rev.: $10,600,000
Emp.: 30
Acoustical Ceiling Plastering & Drywall Contracting Services
N.A.I.C.S.: 238310
Brad Lanehart (Pres)
Mark Homburg (Gen Mgr)

LANELABS USA INC.
3 North St, Waldwick, NJ 07463
Tel.: (201) 661-6000
Web Site: http://www.lanelabs.com
Year Founded: 1994
Natural Supplements & Pharmaceuticals Mfr
N.A.I.C.S.: 424210
Andrew J. Lane (Pres)
Audrey Herget (Controller)

LANETERRALEVER
645 E Missouri Ave Ste 400, Phoenix, AZ 85012
Tel.: (602) 258-5263   AZ

Web Site: http://www.laneterralever.com
Year Founded: 1962
Emp.: 100
Advetising Agency
N.A.I.C.S.: 541810
Beau Lane (Co-Founder & CEO)
Isabelle Jazo (Sr VP-Strategic Branding)
Jody Alexander (VP-Client Satisfaction)
Chris Johnson (Co-Founder & Pres)
Andrewll Parnell (Chief Client Officer)
Scott McAndrew (Chief Digital Officer)
Gary Serviss (VP & Dir-Creative)
Jennifer Ennesser (Acct Dir)
Kim Johnson (Controller)
Raj Dubey (VP-Digital Production)
Fraser Elliott (Sr VP-Media)
Dave Foster (COO)
Gil Rodriguez (Sr VP-Media)
Ben Tsai (VP & Dir-Acct)
Ian Barry (Chief Creative Officer)

LANEY & DUKE TERMINAL WAREHOUSE CO. INC.
1560 Jessie St, Jacksonville, FL 32206-6042
Tel.: (904) 798-3500   FL
Web Site: http://www.laneyduke.com
Year Founded: 1961
Sales Range: $10-24.9 Million
Emp.: 40
General Warehousing, Storage & Logistics Services
N.A.I.C.S.: 493110
Brian Duke (Co-Pres)
Steve Duke (Co-Pres)

Subsidiaries:

Land Trucking Co. Inc. (1)
1560 Jessie St, Jacksonville, FL 32206-6042 (100%)
Tel.: (904) 798-3500
Web Site: http://www.laneyduke.com
Sales Range: $1-9.9 Million
Emp.: 5
Warehousing For Land Trucking Company
N.A.I.C.S.: 484121
Brian Duke (Co-Pres)
Steve Duke (Co-Pres)

LANEY'S INC.
55 27th St S, Fargo, ND 58103
Tel.: (701) 237-0543
Web Site: http://www.laneysinc.com
Year Founded: 1957
Sales Range: $25-49.9 Million
Emp.: 82
Electrical Wiring Services
N.A.I.C.S.: 238210
Kevin Wolf (Pres)
Matt Johnson (Mgr-Electrical Dept)
Doug Hanson (Mgr-Facilities)
Paul Hanson (Coord-Fleet & Facilities)

LANG EXTERIOR, INC.
2323 W 59th St, Chicago, IL 60636
Tel.: (773) 737-4500
Web Site: http://www.langexterior.com
Sales Range: $10-24.9 Million
Emp.: 100
New & Replacement Window & Patio Door Mfr & Distr
N.A.I.C.S.: 321911
Darb Lang (Pres)

LANG REALTY, INC.
2901 Clint Moore Rd Ste 9, Boca Raton, FL 33496
Tel.: (561) 998-0100   FL
Web Site: http://www.langrealty.com
Year Founded: 1981
Sales Range: $1-9.9 Million

Emp.: 400
Real Estate Broker
N.A.I.C.S.: 531210
Scott Agran (Pres)
Kay Steer (Gen Mgr)
Seth Caston (Dir-IT)
Renee Wilkins (Mgr-Adv)

LANGAN AUTOMOTIVE GROUP
727 New Loudon Rd, Latham, NY 12110
Tel.: (518) 783-1951
Web Site: http://www.langanauto.com
Year Founded: 1963
Sales Range: $25-49.9 Million
Emp.: 55
Automobiles, New & Used
N.A.I.C.S.: 441110
Greg Finin (VP)
Tichie Langan-Finin (Mgr-Fleet)

Subsidiaries:

Northway Motorcar Corporation (1)
727 New Loudon Rd, Latham, NY 12110-4017 (100%)
Tel.: (518) 783-5003
Web Site: http://www.langanauto.com
Sales Range: $25-49.9 Million
Retailer of New & Used Automobiles
N.A.I.C.S.: 441110
Gregory P. Finin (Gen Mgr)

LANGAN ENGINEERING & ENVIRONMENTAL SERVICES INC.
1 W Broad St Ste 200, Bethlehem, PA 18018-5717
Tel.: (610) 984-8500
Web Site: http://www.langan.com
Year Founded: 1970
Emp.: 1,500
Engineering & Environmental Consulting
N.A.I.C.S.: 541330
Gregory Elko (VP)

LANGAN ENGINEERING & ENVIRONMENTAL SERVICES, INC.
300 Kimball Dr 4th Fl, Parsippany, NJ 07054-2172
Tel.: (973) 560-4900
Web Site: http://www.langan.com
Year Founded: 1970
Sales Range: $125-149.9 Million
Emp.: 600
Engineering & Environmental Consulting
N.A.I.C.S.: 541620
David T. Gockel (Pres & CEO)
George P. Kelley (Mng Principal)
Nicholas De Rose (Mng Principal)
Andrew J. Ciancia (Chm & Mng Principal)
George E. Leventis (Mng Dir-Langan Intl & Mng Principal)
John D. Plante (Mng Principal)
Philip G. Smith (Mng Principal & Exec VP)
Rudolph P. Frizzi (Mng Principal)
Ronald A. Fuerst (Mng Principal)
Richard D. Rodgers (Mng Principal & Exec VP)
William Kraekel (CFO)
Gerald J. Zambrella (Principal)
Lori A. Simpson (Principal)
Michael A. Semeraro Jr. (Mng Principal)

Subsidiaries:

Langan Engineering & Environmental Services, Inc. (1)
21 Penn Plaza 360 W 31st St 8th Fl, New York, NY 10001-2727
Tel.: (212) 479-5400
Web Site: http://www.langan.com

Emp.: 1,100
Environmental & Engineering Consulting
N.A.I.C.S.: 541620

Langan Engineering & Environmental Services, Inc. (1)
30 Glenn St 4th Floor, White Plains, NY 10603
Tel.: (800) 952-6426
Web Site: http://www.langan.com
Environmental Consulting Services
N.A.I.C.S.: 541620
Charles Utschig Jr. *(Gen Mgr)*

Langan Engineering & Environmental Services, Inc. (1)
1818 Market St Ste 3300, Philadelphia, PA 19103-4005
Tel.: (215) 845-8900
Web Site: http://www.langan.com
Engineering & Environmental Services
N.A.I.C.S.: 541620
Christopher M. Hager *(Sr Principal)*
Gregory M. Elko *(Mng Principal)*
Alan R. Poeppel *(Mng Principal)*
Rory S. Johnston *(Officer-Corp Health & Safety & Principal)*

Langan Engineering & Environmental Services, Inc. (1)
One W Broad St Ste 200, Bethlehem, PA 18018-5717
Tel.: (610) 984-8500
Web Site: http://www.langan.com
Emp.: 18
Environmental Services
N.A.I.C.S.: 541620
Gregory M. Elko *(Sr Principal)*

Langan Engineering & Environmental Services, Inc. (1)
2700 Kelly Rd Ste 200, Warrington, PA 18976-3653
Tel.: (215) 491-6500
Web Site: http://www.langan.com
Environmental Consulting
N.A.I.C.S.: 541620
Nicholas De Rose *(Mng Principal)*

Langan Engineering & Environmental Services, Inc. (1)
Long Wharf Maritime Center 555 Long Wharf Dr, New Haven, CT 06511-6107
Tel.: (203) 562-5771
Engineering & Environmental Consulting
N.A.I.C.S.: 541620
John D. Plante *(Sr Principal)*

Langan Engineering & Environmental Services, Inc. (1)
989 Lenox Dr Ste 124, Lawrenceville, NJ 08648-2315
Tel.: (609) 282-8000
Web Site: http://www.langan.com
Emp.: 40
Engineering Consulting
N.A.I.C.S.: 541330
Daniel Disario *(Gen Mgr)*

Langan Engineering & Environmental Services, Inc. (1)
2300 Clarendon Blvd Courthouse Plz II Ste 711, Arlington, VA 22201-3367
Tel.: (571) 366-6800
Engineering Consulting
N.A.I.C.S.: 541330
Ryan Linthicum *(VP)*

Langan Engineering & Environmental Services, Inc. (1)
Parkside Corp Ctr 15150 NW 79th Ct Ste 200, Miami Lakes, FL 33016-5848
Tel.: (786) 264-7200
Environmental & Engineering Consulting Services
N.A.I.C.S.: 541620

Langan Engineering & Environmental Services, Inc. (1)
260 Peachtree St NW Suite 2200, Atlanta, GA 30303
Tel.: (404) 527-6237
Environmental Services
N.A.I.C.S.: 541620
Rudolph P. Frizzi *(Gen Mgr)*

Langan Engineering & Environmental Services, Inc. (1)
100 S Fifth St Suite 1900, Minneapolis, MN 55402
Tel.: (612) 605-6048
Web Site: http://www.langan.com
Environmental Consulting Services
N.A.I.C.S.: 541620

Langan Engineering & Environmental Services, Inc. (1)
116 N 4th St Suite 210, Bismarck, ND 58501
Tel.: (701) 250-3400
Web Site: http://www.langan.com
Environmental & Engineering Consulting
N.A.I.C.S.: 541620

Langan Engineering & Environmental Services, Inc. (1)
355 S Grand Ave Ste 2450, Los Angeles, CA 90071
Tel.: (213) 943-1310
Web Site: http://www.langan.com
Environmental Consulting
N.A.I.C.S.: 541620

Langan Engineering & Environmental Services, Inc. (1)
32 Executive Park Ste 130, Irvine, CA 92614
Tel.: (949) 255-8640
Web Site: http://www.langan.com
Engineering Consulting
N.A.I.C.S.: 541330
Rudolph P. Frizzi *(Mng Principal)*

Langan International, LLC - Abu Dhabi (1)
Corniche Road Al Hana Tower M Level Suite 109, PO Box 42794, Abu Dhabi, United Arab Emirates
Tel.: (971) 2 6359144
Web Site: http://www.langan.com
Emp.: 10
Site Development Environmental & Engineering Consulting
N.A.I.C.S.: 541330
George E. Leventis *(Mng Dir & Mng Principal)*
Alan Poeppel *(Mng Principal)*

Langan International, LLC - Greece (1)
Athens Towers 21st Floor 2-4 Messogion Avenue, 115 27, Athens, Greece
Tel.: (30) 210 74 54 307
Web Site: http://www.langan.com
Emp.: 1,100
Engineering & Environmental Services
N.A.I.C.S.: 541620
George E. Leventis *(Mng Dir & Mng Principal)*

Langan International, LLC - Qatar (1)
Al Fardan Office Tower 8th & 9th Floors, PO Box 31316, West Bay, Doha, Qatar
Tel.: (974) 441 01 815
Web Site: http://www.langan.com
Environmental Consulting
N.A.I.C.S.: 541620
Khaldoun Fahoum *(Gen Mgr)*

Langan International, LLC - Turkey (1)
Buyukdere Caddesi Kanyon Ofis Binasi No 185 K6, 34394, Istanbul, Levent, Turkiye
Tel.: (90) 212 319 7714
Web Site: http://www.langan.com
Environmental & Engineering Consulting
N.A.I.C.S.: 541620
Can Karayel *(Mng Dir)*

Langan International, LLC - United Arab Emirates (1)
22nd Floor Office No 2202B Dubai Media City, PO Box 283092, Dubai, United Arab Emirates
Tel.: (971) 4 453 9787
Web Site: http://www.langan.com
Engineering & Environmental Consulting
N.A.I.C.S.: 541620

Langan Treadwell Rollo (1)
555 Montgomery St Ste 1300, San Francisco, CA 94111
Tel.: (415) 955-5200
Web Site: http://www.langan.com
Sales Range: $25-49.9 Million
Emp.: 80
Environmental, Geotechnical & Earthquake Engineering Consulting Services
N.A.I.C.S.: 541620
Philip T. Tringale *(Mng Principal & Dir-Western Reg)*
Jeffrey F. Ludlow *(Mng Principal)*
Richard D. Rodgers *(Mng Principal)*
Dorinda C. Shipman *(Principal & VP)*
Philip G. Smith *(Mng Principal & Exec VP)*
Ramin Golesorkhi *(Principal & VP)*
Lori A. Simpson *(Principal & VP)*
Maria G. Flessas *(Principal & VP)*
John Gouchon *(Principal & VP)*
Hadi J. Yap *(VP)*
D. J. Hodson *(Principal & VP)*

Branch (Domestic):

Langan Treadwell Rollo - Oakland (2)
501 14th St 3rd Fl, Oakland, CA 94612-1420
Tel.: (510) 874-7000
Web Site: http://www.treadwellrollo.com
Emp.: 25
Environmental Consulting Services
N.A.I.C.S.: 541620
Lori A. Simpson *(Principal & VP)*

Langan Treadwell Rollo - Sacramento (2)
9608 Kiefer Blvd Suite 7, Sacramento, CA 95827-3802
Tel.: (916) 476-6790
Web Site: http://www.treadwellrollo.com
Environmental Consulting
N.A.I.C.S.: 541620

Langan Treadwell Rollo - San Jose (2)
4030 Moorpark Ave Suite 210, San Jose, CA 95117-1849
Tel.: (408) 551-6700
Web Site: http://www.treadwellrollo.com
Engineering & Environmental Consulting
N.A.I.C.S.: 541620
John Gouchon *(Gen Mgr)*

LANGE PLUMBING SUPPLY, INC.
510 E Cross Ave, Tulare, CA 93274-2858
Tel.: (559) 686-1693
Web Site: http://www.langeplumbingsupply.com
Year Founded: 1936
Sales Range: $10-24.9 Million
Emp.: 100
Plumbing & Heating Equipment Whslr
N.A.I.C.S.: 423720
Curt Lange *(Pres)*

LANGE-STEGMANN CO., INC.
1 Angelica St, Saint Louis, MO 63147-3401
Tel.: (314) 241-9531   MO
Web Site: http://www.lange-stegmann.com
Year Founded: 1964
Sales Range: $10-24.9 Million
Emp.: 60
Farm Supplies Distr
N.A.I.C.S.: 424910
Jim Schulte *(Controller)*

Subsidiaries:

Angelica Riverfront Redevelopment Inc. (1)
1 Angelica St, Saint Louis, MO 63147-3401   (100%)
Tel.: (314) 241-9531
Sales Range: $10-24.9 Million
Emp.: 3
Provider of Marine Cargo Handling
N.A.I.C.S.: 488310

LANGER ELECTRIC COMPANY
6500 NW 21th Ave, Fort Lauderdale, FL 33309
Tel.: (305) 759-5777
Web Site: http://www.langerelectric.com
Year Founded: 1957
Sales Range: $10-24.9 Million
Emp.: 130
General Contracting & Electrical Services
N.A.I.C.S.: 238210
Roger E. Langer Jr. *(VP)*

LANGER JUICE COMPANY, INC.
16195 Stephens St, City of Industry, CA 91745-1718
Tel.: (626) 336-3100   CA
Web Site: http://www.langers.com
Year Founded: 1960
Canned Fruits & Specialties; Juice Drink Products Mfr
N.A.I.C.S.: 311421
Tom Bottiaux *(Natl Sls Mgr)*
Bruce Langer *(CFO)*
David Langer *(CEO & Sec)*
Nancy Black *(Dir-Foodservice)*

LANGER TRANSPORT
420 Rte 440 N, Jersey City, NJ 07305
Tel.: (201) 434-1600
Web Site: http://www.langertransport.com
Year Founded: 1934
Rev.: $18,000,000
Emp.: 275
Contract Hauling Services
N.A.I.C.S.: 484121
Jerry Langer *(Chief Comml Officer)*
Evan Katz *(Dir-Terminal Ops)*

LANGHAM LOGISTICS INC.
5335 W 74th St, Indianapolis, IN 46268
Tel.: (317) 290-0227   IN
Web Site: http://www.elangham.com
Sales Range: $10-24.9 Million
Emp.: 85
Logistics Consulting Servies
N.A.I.C.S.: 541614
Margaret Langham *(Co-Owner & VP-Ops)*
John Langham *(Co-Owner & VP-Fin)*
Catherine A. Langham *(Owner, Pres & CEO)*
Nicholas Hoagland *(Dir-Sls & Client Success)*
Scott Swanson *(Dir-Engrg & Facilities)*
Brian Landrum *(COO)*

LANGLEY MOTOR CO., INC.
701 N Lanier Ave, Lanett, AL 36863
Tel.: (334) 644-3136   AL
Web Site: http://www.langleygm.com
Year Founded: 1959
Sales Range: $10-24.9 Million
Emp.: 17
New & Used Car Dealer
N.A.I.C.S.: 441110
Mac H. Langley *(Founder, Pres & Treas)*
Mark Langley *(Gen Mgr)*

LANGSON ENERGY, INC.
808 College Pkwy Ste 102, Carson City, NV 89706-0659
Tel.: (775) 885-0888
Web Site: http://www.langsonenergy.com
Sales Range: $25-49.9 Million
Emp.: 4
Building Equipment Installation Services
N.A.I.C.S.: 238290
Richard K. Langson *(Founder)*

LANGSTON COMPANIES, INC.
1760 S 3rd St, Memphis, TN 38109
Tel.: (901) 774-4440   TN

LANGSTON COMPANIES, INC.

Langston Companies, Inc.—(Continued)
Web Site:
http://www.langstonbag.com
Year Founded: 1946
Sales Range: $75-99.9 Million
Emp.: 600
Sacks, Bags, Wrappings, Containers & Covers Mfr & Distr
N.A.I.C.S.: 322220
George Parkey (COO)
J. R. Reese (Mgr-Ops)
Rick Hutchens (Plant Mgr)
Forrest Sexton (Mgr-Sls)

Subsidiaries:
Continental Bag Co. Inc. (1)
1900 W Blvd St, Mexico, MO 65265 (100%)
Tel.: (573) 581-3171
Web Site: http://www.continentalbag.com
Rev.: $6,100,000
Emp.: 4
Textile Bags
N.A.I.C.S.: 314910
Robert E. Langston (Pres)

Hi-Plains Bag & Bagging Co. Inc. (1)
1760 S 3rd St, Memphis, TN 38109 (100%)
Tel.: (901) 774-4440
Rev.: $170,000
Emp.: 120
Textile Bags
N.A.I.C.S.: 314910
Robert E. Langston (Pres)

LANGSTON COMPANY
2224 Exchange Ave, Oklahoma City, OK 73108
Tel.: (405) 235-9536
Web Site: http://www.langstons.com
Rev.: $11,894,456
Emp.: 42
Family Clothing Stores
N.A.I.C.S.: 458110
R. Michael Barber (Pres)

LANGUAGE SCIENTIFIC, INC.
10 Cabot Rd Ste 209, Medford, MA 02155
Tel.: (617) 621-0940
Web Site:
http://www.languagescientific.com
Year Founded: 1999
Sales Range: $1-9.9 Million
Emp.: 30
Translation & Interpretation Services
N.A.I.C.S.: 541930
Brian Kratt (Chm)
Leonid Fridman (Pres)
Sharon Blank (VP-Sls & Mktg)

LANGUAGE SERVICES ASSOCIATES, INC.
455 Business Ctr Dr, Horsham, PA 19044
Tel.: (215) 657-6571
Web Site: http://www.lsaweb.com
Year Founded: 1991
Rev.: $17,500,000
Emp.: 115
Business Services
N.A.I.C.S.: 541930
Mauricio Vicente (CIO)
Laura K. T. Schriver (Founder, Chm & CEO)
Frank Johnson (Pres)
Dennis Angeline (Mng Dir-Admin Svcs & Corp Dev)
Starla Keith (Exec VP-Sls & Mktg)

LANGUAGE TRAINING CENTER
5750 Castle Creek Pkwy Ste 487, Indianapolis, IN 46250
Tel.: (317) 578-4577
Web Site:
http://www.languagetrainingcenter.com
Year Founded: 1992
Sales Range: $1-9.9 Million
Emp.: 16
Language Training Center Operator
N.A.I.C.S.: 611430
Martin George (Pres)

LANHAM BROTHERS GENERAL CONTRACTORS
2119 W 3rd St, Owensboro, KY 42301
Tel.: (270) 683-4591
Web Site:
http://www.lanhambros.com
Sales Range: $10-24.9 Million
Emp.: 40
Commercial & Office Building; New Construction
N.A.I.C.S.: 236220
David R. Lanham (Pres)
Greg A. Carmon (Comptroller)
Earl A. Lanham (VP)
Wayne Burton (Project Mgr)

LANIER CONSTRUCTION COMPANY
4016 Hwy 321, Gaston, SC 29053
Tel.: (803) 796-9333
Web Site:
http://www.lanierconstruction.com
Sales Range: $10-24.9 Million
Emp.: 10
Grading & Paving Services
N.A.I.C.S.: 237310
Dennis Lanier (Pres)

LANIER PARKING INC.
233 Peachtree St Ne Ste 2600, Atlanta, GA 30303-1510
Tel.: (404) 881-6076
Web Site:
http://www.lanierparking.com
Year Founded: 1989
Sales Range: $25-49.9 Million
Emp.: 330
Provider of Automobile Parking Services
N.A.I.C.S.: 812930
Michael Robison (Founder)
Michael S. Brown (Exec VP)
Kathryn Dunn (VP-HR & Admin)
Richard C. Graham (COO)
Glenn M. Kurtz (Exec VP)
Jerry Skillett (CEO)
Bijan Eghtedari (Pres)
Brian Dubay (CFO)
Steven Taff (VP-Georgia & Tennessee)
Kerry Loomis (Gen Mgr-Eastern Carolinas)
Todd Griffies (Gen Mgr-Florida)
Kevin Brady (Gen Mgr-South Florida Market)
Andrew Riley (VP-Bus Dev)
Carolyn Yancey (VP-Northeast Reg)
Jimmy Heath (VP-South Central Reg)
Sam Coppage (VP-Southeast)
Justin Kinsey (Reg VP)

LANIER UPSHAW, INC.
1115 Bartow Rd, Lakeland, FL 33801
Tel.: (863) 686-2113
Web Site:
http://www.lanierupshaw.com
Year Founded: 1941
Emp.: 70
Insurance Brokerage Services
N.A.I.C.S.: 524210
Bruce Bulman (CFO & Sr VP)
C. Scott Franklin (Pres & CEO)
Bill Dorman (Principal)
H.S. Toby Turner (Sr VP)
Steve Wicorek (Sr VP)
Bill Cammann (Principal)
Tom Conger (Sr VP)
Cynthia Marcotte (VP & Dir-Employee Benefits Ops)
Tami Schloss (Sr Acct Mgr-Private Risk Mgmt Grp)
Kellie Kallhoff (VP-Property & Casualty)
Joseph Donohue (VP)
Betsy Ceneus (VP & Dir-Mktg)
Mercedes Guzman (VP & Dir-HR)
Schatzie Haines (VP)
Ronda Lewis (Asst VP)
Kathryn Koch (Principal)
Deborah A. Winters (Asst VP)
Michelle Hoffert (VP & Dir-IT)
Luke Vaughan (VP & Dir-Safety & Risk Control)
Bruce Lucas (Sr Acct Mgr-Comml Lines)

LANK OIL CO. INC.
2203 W McNab Rd, Pompano Beach, FL 33069-4304
Tel.: (954) 978-6600
Web Site: http://www.lankoil.com
Year Founded: 1965
Sales Range: $10-24.9 Million
Emp.: 30
Petroleum Products
N.A.I.C.S.: 424720
Monty A. Michel (VP)
Kristene V. Lundblad (VP-Sls & Mktg)
Terry R. Linne (VP-Transport Div)
Terrance E. Linne (Pres)

Subsidiaries:
C&K Oil Co. Inc. (1)
2203 W McNab Rd, Pompano Beach, FL 33069-4304
Tel.: (954) 978-6600
Holding Companies
N.A.I.C.S.: 551112

LANMAN & KEMP-BARCLAY CO., INC.
25 Woodland Ave, Westwood, NJ 07675
Tel.: (201) 666-4990
Web Site: http://www.lanman-and-kemp.com
Year Founded: 1808
Sales Range: $10-24.9 Million
Emp.: 15
Cologne, Soap & Hair Tonic Mfr
N.A.I.C.S.: 325611
Daisy Villegas (Gen Mgr)
George Miller (Pres)

LANMAN OIL COMPANY, INC.
10943 E County Rd 900N, Mattoon, IL 61938
Tel.: (217) 348-8020
Web Site: http://www.lanmanoil.com
Sales Range: $10-24.9 Million
Emp.: 15
Petroleum Bulk Stations
N.A.I.C.S.: 424710
Michael L. Lanman (Pres)

LANMARK TECHNOLOGY INC.
8229 Boone Blvd Ste 801A, Vienna, VA 22182
Tel.: (571) 766-2200
Web Site: http://www.lmt-inc.com
Sales Range: $10-24.9 Million
Emp.: 150
Information Technology Service Provider
N.A.I.C.S.: 519290
Lani Hay (Founder, Pres & CEO)
Juan Tanon (Project Mgr)
Anthony Cartledge (VP-Fin)
Anthony C. Artledge (Controller)

LANNAN CHEVROLET INC.
40 Winn St, Woburn, MA 01801
Tel.: (781) 935-2000
Web Site:
http://www.lannanchevy.net
Sales Range: $25-49.9 Million
Emp.: 70
Automobile Sales
N.A.I.C.S.: 441110
Peter Lannan (Pres & Gen Mgr)
Steve Alesse (Gen Mgr-Sls)
Scott Riker (Mgr-Parts)

LANO EQUIPMENT INC.
3021 133rd St W, Shakopee, MN 55379
Tel.: (952) 445-6310
Web Site: http://www.lanoequip.com
Sales Range: $1-9.9 Million
Emp.: 40
Construction & Mining Machinery
N.A.I.C.S.: 423810
Sandy Breeggemann (Controller)
Kurt Lano (VP)
Rod Lano (VP)

LANPHERE ENTERPRISES INC.
12505 SW Broadway St, Beaverton, OR 97005
Tel.: (503) 643-5577
Web Site: http://www.buybob.com
Year Founded: 1964
Sales Range: $50-74.9 Million
Emp.: 650
Owner & Operator of Car Dealerships
N.A.I.C.S.: 441110
Lorena Dryer (Controller)
Robert Walther (CFO)
Robert D. Lanphere Sr. (Chm)
Robert Lanphere Jr. (Pres)

LANSING BUILDING PRODUCTS, INC.
8501 Sanford Dr, Richmond, VA 23228-2812
Tel.: (804) 266-8893
Web Site: http://www.lansingbp.com
Year Founded: 1955
Sales Range: $25-49.9 Million
Emp.: 500
Lumber, Plywood & Millwork
N.A.I.C.S.: 423310
J. Christopher Lansing (Chm & Pres)

Subsidiaries:
Lansing Building Products, Inc. - Norfolk (1)
3644 Vlg Ave, Norfolk, VA 23502 (100%)
Tel.: (757) 857-1278
Web Site: http://www.lansingbp.com
Sales Range: $10-24.9 Million
Emp.: 30
Mfr of Lumber, Plywood & Millwork
N.A.I.C.S.: 423310
Chris Lansing (Pres)

LANSING ICE AND FUEL COMPANY
911 Center St, Lansing, MI 48906
Tel.: (517) 372-3850
Web Site:
http://www.lansingiceandfuel.com
Sales Range: $10-24.9 Million
Emp.: 20
Fuel Oil Dealers
N.A.I.C.S.: 457210
Ron Bewersdorf (Pres)

LANSINOH LABORATORIES INC.
333 N Fairfax St Ste 400, Alexandria, VA 22314
Tel.: (703) 299-1100
Web Site: http://www.lansinoh.com
Year Founded: 1984
Sales Range: $10-24.9 Million
Emp.: 120

Mfr & Sales of Breastfeeding Equipment
N.A.I.C.S.: 424350
Richard Thome (COO)
Scott Higgison (VP-Sls)
Kevin Vyse-Peacock (CEO)

LANSPEED
100 N Hope Ave Ste 20, Santa Barbara, CA 93110
Tel.: (805) 682-9981
Web Site: http://www.lanspeed.com
Year Founded: 2005
Sales Range: $1-9.9 Million
Emp.: 17
It Consulting
N.A.I.C.S.: 541690
Chris Chirgwin (Owner & CEO)
Nick Gianis (Pres)
Courtney Boudet (Mgr-Acctg)
Daniel Tuite (Acct Exec)
Jonathan Axsom (Engr-Network)
Emily Holehouse (Coord-Mktg)
Michael Lafond (Mgr-Svc Desk)
Peter Blair (CIO)
Todd Ryckman (CTO)

LANTANA COMMUNICATIONS CORP.
1700 Tech Center Pkwy Ste 100, Arlington, TX 76014
Tel.: (817) 606-3300
Web Site: http://www.lantanacom.com
Sales Range: $10-24.9 Million
Emp.: 55
Communications Equipment
N.A.I.C.S.: 459999
Jonathan Irwin (Pres)
Jim Britton (Exec VP)
Tony Jackson (VP-Ops & Acctg)

LANTEC OF LOUISIANA, LLC
11512 Lake Sherwood Ave N, Baton Rouge, LA 70816
Tel.: (225) 293-0656
Web Site: http://www.lanteccte.com
Sales Range: $1-9.9 Million
Emp.: 31
Computer Software & Professional Development Training Services
N.A.I.C.S.: 611420
Meline Lococo (Controller)
Eric Barker (CIO)
Christy Brasseaux (COO)
Rickie Comeaux (Pres & CEO)
Larry Ruth (Mgr-Sls)
Tessa Brown (Dir-HR)

LANTECH INC.
11000 Bluegrass Pkwy, Louisville, KY 40299-2316
Tel.: (502) 267-4200   KY
Web Site: http://www.lantech.com
Year Founded: 1972
Sales Range: $100-124.9 Million
Emp.: 270
Mfr & Distr of Materials Handling & Packaging Systems, Stretch Wrap Equipment, Conveyor Systems, Palletizing Systems, Case Erectors & Shrink Packaging Systems
N.A.I.C.S.: 333993
Pat Lancaster (Founder & Chm)
Jim Lancaster (Pres)
Jack Kelly (CFO)

LANTZ CONSTRUCTION COMPANY
539 S Main St, Broadway, VA 22815
Tel.: (540) 896-8911
Web Site: http://www.lantzcc.com
Rev.: $32,516,767
Emp.: 150
Commercial & Office Building, New Construction
N.A.I.C.S.: 236220
Douglas Driver (Pres)
Frankie Mauck (Superintendent)

LANZO CONSTRUCTION COMPANY INC.
28135 Groesbeck Hwy, Roseville, MI 48066-2344
Tel.: (586) 775-7566   MI
Web Site: http://www.lanzo.net
Year Founded: 1965
Sales Range: $25-49.9 Million
Emp.: 150
Provider of Water, Sewer & Utility Lines
N.A.I.C.S.: 237110
Gary D'Alessandro Jr. (Owner)

Subsidiaries:

Lanzo Construction Company Florida Inc.   (1)
125 SE 5th Ct, Deerfield Beach, FL 33441-4749
Tel.: (954) 979-0802
Web Site: http://www.lanzo.net
Sales Range: $50-74.9 Million
Emp.: 135
Construction Management, Road & Highway Construction, Wastewater Treatment Facilities & Trenchless Technology Services
N.A.I.C.S.: 237110

MRC Manufacturing, Inc.   (1)
28117 Groesbeck Hwy, Roseville, MI 48066
Tel.: (586) 777-8228
Plastics Product Mfr
N.A.I.C.S.: 326199
Norman Fortier (Program Mgr)

LAP OF LOVE, INC.
19239 N Dale Mabry Hwy #152, Lutz, FL 33548
Tel.: (813) 407-9441
Web Site: http://www.lapoflove.com
Sales Range: $10-24.9 Million
Emp.: 43
Veterinary Services
N.A.I.C.S.: 541940
Dani McVety (Co-Founder)
Mary Gardner (Co-Founder)

LAPENSEE PLUMBING INC.
401 Manatee Ave, Holmes Beach, FL 34217
Tel.: (941) 778-5622
Web Site: http://www.lapenseeplumbing.com
Year Founded: 1985
Sales Range: $1-9.9 Million
Emp.: 37
Plumbing & Pools Contractor
N.A.I.C.S.: 238220
Karen LaPensee (Pres)

LAPHAM-HICKEY STEEL CORP.
5500 W 73rd St, Chicago, IL 60638-6506
Tel.: (708) 496-6111   IL
Web Site: http://www.lapham-hickey.com
Year Founded: 1926
Sales Range: $200-249.9 Million
Emp.: 500
Specialty Steel Service Center
N.A.I.C.S.: 423510
Bill Hickey (Pres)
Brian Hickey (VP & Mgr-Info Sys)
Mike Pilarccyk (CFO)

Subsidiaries:

Clifford Metal   (1)
28 Hickey Dr, Pawcatuck, CT 06379-1349
Tel.: (860) 599-1600
Web Site: http://www.lapham-hickey.com
Sales Range: $25-49.9 Million
Emp.: 30
Metal Service Center & Office Services
N.A.I.C.S.: 423510

Lapham Hickey Steel (WI)   (1)
2585 W 20 Ave, Oshkosh, WI 54903-2483
Tel.: (920) 233-8502
Web Site: http://www.lapham-hickey-osh.com
Sales Range: $50-74.9 Million
Emp.: 150
Coil Processing & Manufacturing Services
N.A.I.C.S.: 331222
Stephen W. Ford (Exec VP)
Rick Kaminiski (Gen Mgr)

Lapham-Hickey Steel Corp   (1)
753 Marion Rd, Columbus, OH 43207   (100%)
Tel.: (614) 443-4881
Web Site: http://www.lapham-hickey.com
Sales Range: $50-74.9 Million
Emp.: 35
Steel Distr
N.A.I.C.S.: 425120
Bill Hickey (CEO)
Karen Kustich (Gen Mgr)
Mike Salmons (Mgr-Ops)
Jeff Jodi (Mgr-Pur)
Steve Ford (Chief Comml Officer)
Jeff Hobson (Chief Admin Officer-Corp Ops & Sys)
Bob Piland (CFO)

Lapham-Hickey Steel Corp.   (1)
11 Caine Dr, Madison, IL 62060
Tel.: (618) 451-1100
Web Site: http://www.lapham-hickey.com
Sales Range: $50-74.9 Million
Emp.: 50
Coil Processing & Manufacturing Services
N.A.I.C.S.: 331512
Michael Dedic (Branch Mgr)

Lapham-Hickey Steel Corp. - Fairfield Division   (1)
7001 Valley Rd, Fairfield, AL 35064
Tel.: (205) 786-7100
Web Site: http://www.lapham-hickey.com
Steel Products Mfr
N.A.I.C.S.: 331513
Bill Hickey (Pres)

Lapham-Hickey Steel Corp. - Little Canada Division   (1)
3250 Spruce St, Little Canada, MN 55117
Tel.: (651) 688-8138
Web Site: http://www.lapham-hickeysteel.com
Sales Range: $10-24.9 Million
Emp.: 60
Steel Products Mfr
N.A.I.C.S.: 331513
Pat Domeier (Gen Mgr)

LAPINE TRUCK SALES & EQUIPMENT CO. INC.
1400 Brookpark Rd, Cleveland, OH 44147-2802
Tel.: (440) 526-6363   OH
Web Site: http://www.lapinetrucks.com
Year Founded: 1973
Sales Range: $10-24.9 Million
Emp.: 20
Sales of Trucks & Related Equipment
N.A.I.C.S.: 441110
Melvin Morris (Pres & CEO)
Scott Morris (VP-Sls)

LAPLACA COHEN
43 W 24th St Tenth Fl, New York, NY 10010-3205
Tel.: (212) 675-4106
Web Site: http://www.laplacacohen.com
Year Founded: 1993
Rev.: $15,000,000
Emp.: 25
N.A.I.C.S.: 541810
Mary Davis (Dir-Client Mgmt & Media)
Tom Zetek (Exec Dir-Creative)
Wade Dansby (Sr Graphic Designer)

LAPLINK SOFTWARE, INC.
600 108th Ave Ne Ste 610, Bellevue, WA 98004-5125
Tel.: (425) 952-6000   WA
Web Site: http://www.laplink.com
Year Founded: 1983
Sales Range: $75-99.9 Million
Emp.: 85
Software Mfr
N.A.I.C.S.: 541511
Thomas Koll (Chm & CEO)
Randall L. Clark (COO & VP-Fin)
Jack Wilson (CTO & VP)

LAPP INSULATOR COMPANY, LLC
130 Gilbert St, Le Roy, NY 14482
Tel.: (585) 768-6221   DE
Web Site: http://www.lappinsulator.com
Year Founded: 1916
Sales Range: $150-199.9 Million
Emp.: 350
High Voltage Insulators Mfr
N.A.I.C.S.: 327110
Rob Johnson (Pres)

LAPPEN AUTO SUPPLY CO. INC.
421 Page St 4, Stoughton, MA 02072-1107
Tel.: (617) 471-4000   MA
Web Site: http://www.lappens.com
Year Founded: 1928
Sales Range: $25-49.9 Million
Emp.: 15
Motor Vehicle Supplies & New Parts
N.A.I.C.S.: 423120
Michael Lappen (VP-Ops)

LARAMIE ENTERPRISES, INC.
48400 West Rd, Wixom, MI 48393-3534
Tel.: (313) 273-4900
Web Site: http://www.laramiecrane.com
Year Founded: 1917
Sales Range: $25-49.9 Million
Emp.: 40
Crane Rental & Trucking Services
N.A.I.C.S.: 532412
Gordon F. Laramie III (Pres)

LARCO ENTERPRISES INC.
1525 A St NE, Miami, OK 74354-4002
Tel.: (918) 542-1679   OK
Year Founded: 1976
Sales Range: $200-249.9 Million
Emp.: 1,200
Operator of Drive-In Restaurants
N.A.I.C.S.: 523999
Larry Smith (Pres)
Kristi Radebaugh (Controller)

LARD OIL CO. INC.
914 Florida Blvd SW, Denham Springs, LA 70726
Tel.: (225) 664-3311
Web Site: http://www.lardoil.com
Sales Range: $500-549.9 Million
Emp.: 45
Petroleum & Petroleum Products Whslr
N.A.I.C.S.: 424720
Beth Murrey (CFO)

Subsidiaries:

Lard Oil Company   (1)
980 N Bierdeman Rd, Jackson, MS 39208
Tel.: (601) 939-3131
Sales Range: $50-74.9 Million
Emp.: 5
Petroleum Lubricating Oils & Specialty Products Distr
N.A.I.C.S.: 424720
Ginger Martin (Gen Mgr)

Lard Oil Company of Acadiana   (1)
701 1st St, Gueydan, LA 70542
Tel.: (337) 536-6738

LARD OIL CO. INC.

Lard Oil Co. Inc.—(Continued)
Web Site: http://www.lardoil.com
Sales Range: $25-49.9 Million
Petroleum Products
N.A.I.C.S.: 424720

LAREDO ALARM SYSTEMS INC.
1601 Jacaman Rd, Laredo, TX 78041
Tel.: (956) 723-2738
Web Site:
  http://www.laredoalarm.com
Year Founded: 1994
Sales Range: $10-24.9 Million
Emp.: 65
Electrical Apparatus, Equipment, Wiring Supplies & Related Equipment Whslr
N.A.I.C.S.: 423610
Fidel Gonzalez (Owner & CEO)

LAREDO GONZALEZ AUTO PARTS
4220 San Bernardo Ave, Laredo, TX 78041
Tel.: (956) 726-9766
Year Founded: 1964
Sales Range: $10-24.9 Million
Emp.: 35
Automotive Parts
N.A.I.C.S.: 441330
Roberto Gonzalez (Owner)
Gracie Montemayor (Sec)
Joe Gage (VP)
Javier Gonzalez (Principal)

LAREDO PAVING INC.
2701 N Hwy 350, Big Spring, TX 79720
Tel.: (432) 267-1691
Rev.: $40,000,000
Emp.: 150
Highway & Street Paving Contractor
N.A.I.C.S.: 237310
Bob Price (Gen Mgr)

LARGO CONCRETE INC.
891 W Hamilton Ave, Campbell, CA 95008
Tel.: (408) 874-2500
Web Site: http://www.largo.com
Rev.: $96,643,724
Emp.: 50
Concrete Work
N.A.I.C.S.: 238110
Marshall Bain (Mgr-Ops)
Phil Carnathan (VP-North)
Ken Long (Pres)
Fred Weaver (Mgr-Preconstruction & Bus Dev)

LARGO MEDICAL CENTER
201 14th St SW, Largo, FL 33770
Tel.: (727) 588-5200
Web Site:
  http://www.largomedical.com
Sales Range: $50-74.9 Million
Emp.: 650
Teaching Hospital & Medical Center
N.A.I.C.S.: 622310
Kathleen Smith (Coord-Program & Medical Student)
Christopher Johnson (Vice Chm)
Michael Thompson (Chm)
Adam Rudd (CEO)
Joseph Namey (Vice Chm)
Tammy Robiconti (Dir-PR & Comm)
Glenn Romig (CFO)

Subsidiaries:

Largo Medical Center-Indian Rocks Rd. Campus (1)
2025 Indian Rocks Rd, Largo, FL 33774
Tel.: (727) 581-9474
Web Site: http://www.largomedical.com
Emergency & Medical/Surgical Services

N.A.I.C.S.: 621493

LARIAT PARTNERS LP
1331 17th St Ste 1000, Denver, CO 80202
Tel.: (720) 544-6262
Web Site:
  http://www.lariatpartners.net
Private Investment Firm
N.A.I.C.S.: 523999
Jay Coughlon (Co-Founder & Mng Partner)
Kevin Mitchell (CO-Founder & Mng Partner)
Mac Hampden (VP)
Jason Urband (Partner)
Josh Sartisky (VP)

LARITECH INC.
387 Zachary St Unit 102, Moorpark, CA 93021
Tel.: (805) 529-5000
Web Site: http://www.laritech.com
Year Founded: 2001
Sales Range: $1-9.9 Million
Emp.: 50
Printed Circuit Boards Mfr & Assembler
N.A.I.C.S.: 334418
Bill Larrick (CEO)
Terry Gonzales (VP-Ops)

LARK AVE CAR WASH CORPORATION
871 E Hamilton Ave, Campbell, CA 95008
Tel.: (408) 371-2414
Web Site:
  http://www.classiccarwash.com
Sales Range: $10-24.9 Million
Emp.: 300
Owner & Operator of Carwashes
N.A.I.C.S.: 811192
Rob Miller (CFO)
Frank J. Dorsa Jr. (Pres)

LARKEN INC.
824 N St Sw, Cedar Rapids, IA 52404-2708
Tel.: (319) 366-8201
Year Founded: 1967
Sales Range: $800-899.9 Million
Emp.: 2,500
Operator of Motels & Restaurants
N.A.I.C.S.: 721110

LARKIN ENTERPRISES, INC.
317 W Broadway, Lincoln, ME 04457
Tel.: (207) 794-8700
Web Site: http://www.larkinent.com
Year Founded: 1994
Sales Range: $50-74.9 Million
Staffing Services
N.A.I.C.S.: 561311
Richard Larkin (Pres & CEO)
Scott Cram (Ops Mgr)

LARKIN INGRASSIA, PLLC
356 Meadow Ave, Newburgh, NY 12550
Tel.: (845) 237-3255
Web Site: https://www.845law.com
Year Founded: 2023
Law firm
N.A.I.C.S.: 541110
John Ingrassia (Partner)

LAROCCO ENTERPRISES INC.
601 E Edgar Ave PO Box 130, Ronceverte, WV 24970
Tel.: (304) 647-5913
Web Site:
  http://www.greenbrierww.com
Year Founded: 1969
Sales Range: $10-24.9 Million
Emp.: 40

Mfr of Millwork
N.A.I.C.S.: 321918
Claire LaRocco (Pres)
Joseph G. Stegle (Exec VP)
Patrick Driscoll (Mgr-Ops)

LAROHN INC.
1117 Vine St, Cincinnati, OH 45202
Tel.: (513) 352-0657
Rev.: $11,083,680
Emp.: 25
Retailer of Men's & Boys' Clothing
N.A.I.C.S.: 458110
Lisa Driscoll (Pres)

LAROSA BUILDING GROUP LLC
163 Research Pkwy, Meriden, CT 06450
Tel.: (203) 235-1770
Web Site: http://www.larosabg.com
Year Founded: 1979
Sales Range: $25-49.9 Million
Emp.: 40
General Contracting Design, Building & Construction
N.A.I.C.S.: 236115
Robert N. LaRosa (Owner & CEO)
James A. LaRosa (COO)
Tim Penton (Supvr-Construction)

LAROSA TORTILLA FACTORY
26 Menker, Watsonville, CA 95076
Tel.: (831) 728-5332
Web Site:
  http://www.larosatortillafactory.com
Sales Range: $10-24.9 Million
Emp.: 150
Producer of Tortillas
N.A.I.C.S.: 311830
Alfonso Solorio (Owner)

LARROC LTD.
6420 Boeing Dr, El Paso, TX 79925
Tel.: (915) 772-3733
Sales Range: $25-49.9 Million
Emp.: 150
Provider of Grocery Services
N.A.I.C.S.: 424410
Enrique Munoz (Pres)
Yvonne Bruce (Mgr)
Rebecca Sanchez (Coord-Acctg)
Maria Ibarra (Mgr-Special Projects)

LARRY BLUMBERG & ASSOCIATES
2733 Ross Clark Cir, Dothan, AL 36301
Tel.: (334) 793-6855
Web Site:
  http://www.lbaproperties.com
Year Founded: 1972
Sales Range: $10-24.9 Million
Emp.: 22
Subdividers & Developers; Hotel Management
N.A.I.C.S.: 721110
Larry Blumberg (Founder, Chm & CEO)
Sharon Powel (VP-Admin & New Dev-Hospitality)
Terrell Hodnett (VP-Sys & Fin Reporting-Hospitality)
Farrah Adams (COO-Hospitality)
Beau Benton (Pres-Hospitality)
Scott Reid (VP-Ops Support-Hospitality)

LARRY C. MCCRAE INC.
3333 W Hunting Park Ave, Philadelphia, PA 19132
Tel.: (215) 227-5060
Sales Range: $10-24.9 Million
Emp.: 150
General Electrical Contractor
N.A.I.C.S.: 238210

Larry C. McCrae (Pres)
Curtis Sedden (Superintendent)

LARRY FANNIN CHEVROLET-PONTIAC-BUICK
329 E Main St, Morehead, KY 40351
Tel.: (606) 784-6411
Web Site: http://www.larry-fannin.com
Sales Range: $10-24.9 Million
Emp.: 30
New & Used Automobiles
N.A.I.C.S.: 441110
Larry Fannin (Pres)
Ty Fannin (Pres)
Julie Garvin (Controller & Dir-HR)
Danny Purdy (CFO & Dir-Sls)

LARRY H. MILLER GROUP OF COMPANIES
9350 S 150 E Rte 1000, Sandy, UT 84070
Tel.: (801) 563-4100
Web Site: http://www.lhm.com
Year Founded: 1979
Sales Range: $1-4.9 Billion
Emp.: 5,050
Holding Company; Automobile Dealerships, Sports Franchises, Entertainment Venues, Radio & Television Media, Restaurants & Retail Stores
Owner & Operator
N.A.I.C.S.: 551112
Randy Rigby (Pres-Utah Jazz & Larry H Miller Sports & Entertainment)
Karen G. Miller (Pres)
Clark L. Whitworth (CFO)
Paul Nygard (Dir-Mktg)
Robert Tingey (Gen Counsel)
Tony Scahnurr (COO)
Roger Miller (CTO)
Sara Waldman (Dir-Comm)
Gail Miller (Owner & Chm)
Veronika Egginton (VP-Digital Dev-Dealerships)
Doug Petersen (Dir-Search Engine Mktg-Dealerships)
Taylor Christensen (Dir-Search Engine Optimization-Dealerships)
Steven E. Starks (CEO)
David Smith (Chief Strategy Officer)
Richard Hyde (Pres-Prestige Fin Svcs)

Subsidiaries:

Advanced Health Care Corporation (1)
215 N Whitley Dr Ste 1, Fruitland, ID 83619
Tel.: (208) 452-6392
Sales Range: $1-9.9 Million
Emp.: 20
Women Healthcare Services
N.A.I.C.S.: 621610
Cindy Nattress (Sec)

Larry H. Miller Group Dealerships (1)
200 W 9000 S, Sandy, UT 84070
Tel.: (385) 255-8504
Web Site: http://www.lhmauto.com
Emp.: 1,500
Car Dealership
N.A.I.C.S.: 441110

Division (Domestic):

Larry H. Miller Ford Mesa (2)
460 E Auto Center Dr, Mesa, AZ 85204
Tel.: (877) 723-5261
Web Site: http://www.lhmfordmesa.com
Sales Range: $200-249.9 Million
Emp.: 335
Car Dealership
N.A.I.C.S.: 441110
Jim Crutcher (Gen Mgr)
Steve Countryman (Gen Mgr-Sls)
Greg Okolita (Mgr-Fin)
John Hurley (Mgr-New Car Sls)
Craig Ginsberg (Mgr-Pre-Owned Sls)
Steve Davis (Mgr-Parts)
Scott Dietrich (Dir-Fleet)

June Esparza *(Mgr-Parts)*
Bob Krystofik *(Mgr-Pre-Owned Sls)*
Ed Roberts *(Mgr-Berge Quick Lane)*
Steve Roger *(Mgr-Collision Center)*

Larry H. Miller Honda (1)
5808 S State St, Murray, UT 84107
Tel.: (801) 262-3331
Web Site: http://www.lhmhonda.com
Sales Range: $25-49.9 Million
Emp.: 100
Dealer of New & Used Automobiles
N.A.I.C.S.: 441110
Scott Harding *(Pres)*

Larry H. Miller Sports & Entertainment Group of Companies (1)
301 W S Temple, Salt Lake City, UT 84101
Tel.: (801) 325-2500
Web Site: http://www.lhm.com
Sales Range: $150-199.9 Million
Emp.: 300
Holding Company; Sports Teams, Entertainment Venues, Radio & Television Broadcasting
N.A.I.C.S.: 551112
Randy Rigby *(Pres)*

Larry H. Miller Volkswagen Lakewood (1)
8303 W Colfax Ave, Lakewood, CO 80214
Tel.: (303) 237-1311
Web Site: http://www.lhmvw.com
Sales Range: $10-24.9 Million
Emp.: 100
New & Used Car Dealer
N.A.I.C.S.: 441110
Jason Villa *(Gen Mgr)*
James Zielonka *(Mgr-Svc)*

LARRY J. OVERTON & ASSOCIATES INC.
101 E College Ave Ste 302, Tallahassee, FL 32301
Tel.: (850) 224-2859
Web Site: http://www.loverton.net
Year Founded: 1985
Sales Range: $1-9.9 Million
Governmental Consulting Services
N.A.I.C.S.: 541618
Diane Gregg *(Mgr-Acctg)*

LARRY KLINE WHOLESALE MEATS, INC.
350 Goolsby Blvd, Deerfield Beach, FL 33442
Tel.: (954) 420-0071
Web Site: http://www.larryklinemeats.com
Year Founded: 1976
Sales Range: $10-24.9 Million
Emp.: 100
Whslr of Meats & Meat Products
N.A.I.C.S.: 424470
David Kline *(Pres)*
Sheri Rhodes *(Controller)*

LARRY MATHIS FINANCIAL PLANNING, LLC
7210 N 16th St,, Phoenix, AZ 85020
Tel.: (602) 393-0501
Web Site: https://mathiswealth.com
Year Founded: 2015
Investment Management
N.A.I.C.S.: 523999

Subsidiaries:

RH Wealth Advisors, Inc. (1)
5700 Ralston St Ste 102, Ventura, CA 93003
Tel.: (805) 658-1500
Web Site: http://www.rhwealth.com
Investment Advisory Services
N.A.I.C.S.: 523940

LARRY METHVIN INSTALLATION
501 Kettering Dr, Ontario, CA 91761
Tel.: (909) 605-6468
Web Site: http://www.larrymethvin.com
Rev.: $26,448,360
Emp.: 120
Doors, Glass: Made From Purchased Glass
N.A.I.C.S.: 327215
Arnie Fielding *(Mgr-Sls)*

LARRY MILLER SUNDANCE DODGE
222 Auto Dr, Boise, ID 83709
Tel.: (208) 947-6500
Web Site: http://www.sundancedodge.com
Sales Range: $25-49.9 Million
Emp.: 125
New & Used Car Dealers
N.A.I.C.S.: 441110
Penny Ivancic *(Controller)*

LARRY PEEL & CO., INC.
1006 Mo Pac Cir Ste 201, Austin, TX 78746-6806
Tel.: (512) 327-3333 TX
Web Site: http://www.larrypeel.com
Year Founded: 1977
Sales Range: $10-24.9 Million
Emp.: 50
Operator of Apartment Buildings
N.A.I.C.S.: 236117
Larry Peel *(Owner)*
David Bynum *(Controller)*

LARRY REID'S BLOOMINGTON CHRYSLER JEEP DODGE RAM
8000 Penn Ave S, Bloomington, MN 55431
Tel.: (952) 888-9541
Web Site: http://www.bloomingtonchryslerjeep.com
Sales Range: $125-149.9 Million
Emp.: 100
New & Used Car Dealer
N.A.I.C.S.: 441110
Anis Jaganjac *(Gen Mgr)*

LARRY SNYDER & CO.
PO Box 2606, Joplin, MO 64803-2606
Tel.: (417) 782-1060
Year Founded: 1978
Sales Range: $10-24.9 Million
Emp.: 50
Site Preparation Services
N.A.I.C.S.: 238910
Karen Sherar *(Coord-Customer Care)*

LARRY'S MARKET, INC.
1221 Main St, Fortuna, CA 95540
Tel.: (707) 725-7874 CA
Sales Range: $10-24.9 Million
Emp.: 10
Grocery Stores, Independent
N.A.I.C.S.: 445110
Larry Montgomery *(Pres)*
Susan Cherry *(Office Mgr)*

LARRY'S MARKETS, INC.
2400 Crooks Ave, Kaukauna, WI 54130-3914
Tel.: (920) 766-6080 WI
Year Founded: 1965
Sales Range: $50-74.9 Million
Emp.: 465
Grocery Stores
N.A.I.C.S.: 445110
Barry MacKechnie *(Pres)*
Tom Mack *(Mgr)*

LARRY'S MINING, INC.
2020 Schoonover St, Gillette, WY 82718-6904
Tel.: (307) 682-5394 WY
Year Founded: 1975
Sales Range: $10-24.9 Million
Emp.: 40
Construction & Contracting Services
N.A.I.C.S.: 236220
Lawrence F. Suchor *(Pres)*

LARS & ASSOCIATES, INC.
322 Greenpond Rd, Hibernia, NJ 07842
Tel.: (973) 625-2225
Year Founded: 1964
Sales Range: Less than $1 Million
Emp.: 5
N.A.I.C.S.: 541810
Lars Svaasand *(Chm & Acct Exec)*
Louis S. Sceusi *(Pres, Acct Exec & New Bus Contact)*
Ingrid Sceusi *(Dir-Art)*

LARSEN
7101 York Ave S Ste 120, Minneapolis, MN 55435
Tel.: (952) 835-2271
Rev.: $8,400,000
Emp.: 50
Fiscal Year-end: 12/31/06
Advertising, Brand Development & Integration, Collateral, Identity Marketing, Interactive, Internet/Web Design, Print
N.A.I.C.S.: 541810
Tim Larsen *(Founder & Pres)*
John Barta *(VP-Fin)*
Laura Bates *(Dir-Acct Svcs)*
Paul Wharton *(VP-Creative)*
Heather Olson *(Dir-Mktg)*
Jo Davison *(VP-Creative)*
Gwyneth Dwyer *(Dir-Writing Svcs)*
Jim Madson *(Dir-Bus Dev)*

Subsidiaries:

Larsen (1)
95 El Camino Real, Menlo Park, CA 94025
Tel.: (650) 233-7777
Sales Range: $10-24.9 Million
Emp.: 10
N.A.I.C.S.: 541810
Tim Larsen *(Pres & CEO)*
Jim Madson *(Dir-Bus Dev)*
Heather Olson *(Dir-Mktg)*

LARSEN MARINE SERVICE INC.
625 E Sea Horse Dr, Waukegan, IL 60085
Tel.: (847) 336-5456
Web Site: http://www.larsenmarine.com
Rev.: $12,391,335
Emp.: 50
Boat Dealers
N.A.I.C.S.: 441222
Gerald N. Larsen *(Pres)*
Ken Larsen *(VP)*
Lilly Young *(Mgr-Fin)*

LARSEN SUPPLY COMPANY INC.
12055 E Slauson Ave, Santa Fe Springs, CA 90670-2601
Tel.: (562) 698-0731
Web Site: http://www.lasco.net
Year Founded: 1930
Sales Range: $25-49.9 Million
Emp.: 175
Provider of Plumbing Fixtures, Equipment & Supplies
N.A.I.C.S.: 423720
Ric Larsen *(Pres)*
Ellen Holderness *(Controller)*
John Matthew Palumbo *(CEO)*

LARSENS CREAMERY INC.
16940 SE 130th Ave, Clackamas, OR 97015
Tel.: (503) 650-6162
Web Site: http://www.larsenscreamery.com
Rev.: $40,000,000
Emp.: 45
Creamery Butter
N.A.I.C.S.: 311512
Andy Gianopoulos *(Pres)*
Robert Armstrong *(Mgr-Ops)*

LARSON CONTRACTING CENTRAL, LLC
508 W Main St, Lake Mills, IA 50450
Tel.: (641) 592-5800
Web Site: http://www.larsoncontracting.com
Year Founded: 1977
Rev.: $16,000,000
Emp.: 100
Construction Services
N.A.I.C.S.: 236210
Milo Lien *(Mgr-Sls)*
Justin Peterson *(Owner & CEO)*
Shawn Lampman *(Pres)*

LARSON DAIRY INC.
400 NW 5th St, Okeechobee, FL 34972
Tel.: (863) 763-7330
Sales Range: $1-9.9 Million
Emp.: 76
Dairy Products Mfr
N.A.I.C.S.: 112120
Louis E. Larson Sr. *(Pres)*

LARSON DESIGN GROUP
1000 Commerce Park Dr 2nd Fl Ste 201, Williamsport, PA 17701
Tel.: (570) 323-6603
Web Site: http://www.larsondesigngroup.com
Year Founded: 1985
Sales Range: $1-9.9 Million
Emp.: 130
Architectural Design Services
N.A.I.C.S.: 541310
Brenda I. Nichols *(Chm & CFO)*
Robert J. Gehr *(VP-Retail Design)*
Mark K. Morgenfruh *(VP-HR)*
Duane R. Daniels *(Project Mgr-Construction Inspection)*
Christopher P. Iachini *(Project Mgr-Geospatial)*
Max B. Inkrote *(Program Mgr-Highway)*
Stevan C. Wilver *(VP-Transportation)*
Quentin Rissler *(Program Mgr-Bridge)*
Marshall Welch *(Vice Chm)*
Donna Jean Dragojevich *(Coord-Proposal)*
Ron Schirato *(VP-Civil Engrg)*
Nahum Sanchez *(Project Mgr-Geospatial Dept)*
David Martin *(Pres & CEO)*
Christopher Bostaph *(VP-Energy)*
Adanma Akujieze *(VP-Fin)*
Scott Kantner *(CIO)*
Terry Krezmer *(VP-HR)*

Subsidiaries:

Daniel C. Baker Associates, Inc. (1)
6056 Tuscarawas Rd, Beaver, PA 15009
Tel.: (724) 495-7020
Web Site: http://www.dcbaker.com
Civil Engineering Services
N.A.I.C.S.: 237990
Craig A. Baker *(Pres)*
Christopher P. Iachini *(Dir-Surveying)*
Karen Hicks *(Sec & Treas)*

LDG - Transportation Engineering (1)
1020 Commerce Park Dr Entrance B, Williamsport, PA 17701 **(100%)**
Tel.: (570) 323-6603
Web Site: http://www.larsondesigngroup.com
Emp.: 40
Transportation, Engineers & Surveyors
N.A.I.C.S.: 541330

LARSON DESIGN GROUP   U.S. PRIVATE

Larson Design Group—(Continued)
Douglas F. Smith (VP-Transportation)

LDG San Antonio (1)
1149 E Commerce St Suite 101, San Antonio, TX 78205
Tel.: (210) 257-8605
Web Site:
http://www.larsondesigngroup.com
Civil Engineering & Land Development
N.A.I.C.S.: 237990
Mark Kastner (Project Mgr-Energy)

Larson Design Group (1)
201 E Oregon Rd Ste 110, Lititz, PA 17543 **(100%)**
Tel.: (717) 824-4618
Web Site:
http://www.larsondesigngroup.com
Civil Engineering
N.A.I.C.S.: 237990
Steve Muller (Dir Gen)
Scott Kantner (CIO)

Larson Design Group (1)
Bethel Business Ctr 9533 Old 22, Bethel, PA 19507 **(100%)**
Tel.: (717) 933-5530
Web Site:
http://www.larsondesigngroup.com
Civil Engineering
N.A.I.C.S.: 541330
Christopher P. Iachini (Dir-Survey)

Larson Design Group (1)
2591 Wexford Bayne Rd Ste 305, Sewickley, PA 15143 **(100%)**
Tel.: (724) 591-8562
Web Site:
http://www.larsondesigngroup.com
Emp.: 30
Multidisciplinary Engineering Services
N.A.I.C.S.: 541330
Gary Sheets (Dir-Geospatial Svcs)

Larson Design Group (1)
1 W Market St Ste 301, Corning, NY 14830 **(100%)**
Tel.: (607) 936-7076
Web Site:
http://www.larsondesigngroup.com
Civil Engineering
N.A.I.C.S.: 237990
David D. Walters (Dir-Water/Wastewater Engrg)

Larson Design Group (1)
2502 Cranberry Square, Morgantown, WV 26508 **(100%)**
Tel.: (304) 777-2940
Web Site:
http://www.larsondesigngroup.com
Emp.: 16
Energy, Municipal, Civil & Transportation Engineering Services
N.A.I.C.S.: 237990

Larson Design Group (1)
1780 Route 522, Selinsgrove, PA 17870 **(100%)**
Tel.: (570) 374-5700
Web Site:
http://www.larsondesigngroup.com
Emp.: 20
Engineering & Civil Services
N.A.I.C.S.: 541330
Steven M. Beattie (Sr Project Mgr-Retail Design)

Larson Design Group - Apalachin (1)
8836 State Route 434, Apalachin, NY 13732
Tel.: (607) 258-0090
Web Site:
http://www.larsondesigngroup.com
Highway, Structural-Bridge, Site & Brand Architecture
N.A.I.C.S.: 237990

LARSON FINANCIAL HOLDINGS, LLC
14567 N Outer 40 Ste 300, Chesterfield, MO 63017
Tel.: (866) 569-2450 MO
Web Site:
http://www.larsonfinancial.com
Year Founded: 2011
Holding Company; Investment Advisory & Wealth Management Services
N.A.I.C.S.: 551112
Paul Larson (Founder & CEO)

Subsidiaries:

Larson Financial Group, LLC (1)
14567 N Outer-40 Rd Ste 300, Chesterfield, MO 63017
Web Site: http://www.larsonfinancial.com
Investment Advisory Services
N.A.I.C.S.: 523940
Paul Larson (Founder)

Larson Financial Securities, LLC (1)
14567 N Outer 40 Rd Ste 300, Chesterfield, MO 63017
Securities Brokerage & Dealing Services
N.A.I.C.S.: 523150
Scott Miller (Chief Compliance Officer)

Larson Wealth Partners, LLC (1)
14567 N Outer 40 Rd Ste 300, Chesterfield, MO 63017
Investment Advisory & Wealth Management Services
N.A.I.C.S.: 523940

Subsidiary (Domestic):

Counsel Wealth Management, Inc. (2)
6 Pine Tree Dr Ste #100, Saint Paul, MN 55112
Tel.: (651) 639-8707
Web Site: http://www.counselwealthmanagement.com
Miscellaneous Financial Investment Activities
N.A.I.C.S.: 523999
John Blaylock (Mgr-Client Svc)

LARSON FINANCIAL SERVICES, INC.
4601 College Blvd Ste 185, Leawood, KS 66211-1839
Tel.: (913) 428-2233
Web Site: http://www.larsonfs.com
Investment Advice
N.A.I.C.S.: 523940
Douglas Black (Pres)

LARSON MANAGEMENT, INC.
3502 Oakwood Mall Dr Ste A, Eau Claire, WI 54701
Tel.: (715) 834-2449 WI
Web Site:
http://www.larsoncompanies.com
Year Founded: 1990
Commercial Real Estate Development & Property Management Services
N.A.I.C.S.: 531390
Richard D. Larson (Founder & Chm)
Thomas G. Larson (Pres & Principal)

LARSON PACKAGING COMPANY, LLC
1000 Yosemite Dr, Milpitas, CA 95035
Tel.: (408) 946-4971 CA
Web Site:
http://www.larsonpallet.com
Year Founded: 1967
Sales Range: $1-9.9 Million
Emp.: 25
Wood Pallets & Skids
N.A.I.C.S.: 321920
Mark A. Hoffman (Owner & Mgr)

Subsidiaries:

First Class Packaging, Inc. (1)
280 Cypress Ln Ste B, El Cajon, CA 92020
Tel.: (619) 579-7166
Web Site: http://www.firstclasspack.com
Paperboard Mill Mfg Wood Containers Mfg Plastic Foam Prdts Whol Industrial Supplies Mfg Corrugated/Fiber Box
N.A.I.C.S.: 322130
Sandy Brock (Pres)

LARSON-DANIELSON CONSTRUCTION COMPANY, INC.
302 Tyler St, La Porte, IN 46350
Tel.: (219) 362-2127
Web Site:
http://www.ldconstruction.com
Year Founded: 1908
Sales Range: $25-49.9 Million
Emp.: 300
Commercial & Institutional Building Construction Services
N.A.I.C.S.: 236220
Terry Larson (Treas & Sec)

LARSONS APPLIANCE COMPANY
213 S 1st St, Medford, OR 97501
Tel.: (541) 779-3211
Web Site:
http://www.larsonshomefurnishings.com
Sales Range: $10-24.9 Million
Emp.: 50
All Major Electronics, Appliances, Office & Residential Furniture Sales
N.A.I.C.S.: 449210
Bruce A. Larson (Pres)

LARTOM INC.
500 8th St, San Francisco, CA 94103
Tel.: (650) 616-4968
Year Founded: 1986
Sales Range: $10-24.9 Million
Emp.: 60
Wholesale Distributor of Auto & Truck Equipment & Parts
N.A.I.C.S.: 441330
Larry Chew (Pres)

LARUE DISTRIBUTING COMPANY
2631 S 156th Cir, Omaha, NE 68130
Tel.: (402) 333-9099
Web Site: http://www.laruecoffee.com
Sales Range: $25-49.9 Million
Emp.: 35
Groceries & Related Products
N.A.I.C.S.: 424490
Tammy Garecki (Controller)
Verlyn L'Heureux (Founder & CEO)

LARUSSO CONCRETE COMPANY INC.
6101 W 11th Ave, Lakewood, CO 80214
Tel.: (303) 234-9074
Rev.: $23,761,409
Emp.: 100
Concrete Work
N.A.I.C.S.: 238110
Gerald LaRusso (Pres)
Troy LaRusso (VP)

LAS PIEDRAS CONSTRUCTION CORP.
P R 937 Kn 3, Las Piedras, PR 00771
Tel.: (787) 733-6121
Web Site: http://www.lpcdinc.com
Sales Range: $75-99.9 Million
Emp.: 540
General Contractor; Highway & Street Construction
N.A.I.C.S.: 237310
Louis Mariotoledo (Controller)

LAS VEGAS BOAT HARBOR INC.
490 Horsepower Cove Rd, Boulder City, NV 89005
Tel.: (702) 293-1191
Web Site:
http://www.boatinglakemead.com
Year Founded: 1957
Sales Range: $10-24.9 Million
Emp.: 300
Boat Dealers
N.A.I.C.S.: 441222
Bruce Nelson (Mgr-Ops)
Gail Kaiser (Treas & Mgr)
Krystal Virgin (Mgr)

LAS VEGAS POLICE PROTECTIVE ASSOCIATION CIVILIAN EMPLOYEES, INC.
9330 W Lake Mead Ste 100, Las Vegas, NV 89134
Tel.: (702) 382-9121 NV
Web Site: http://www.ppace.org
Year Founded: 1973
Sales Range: $10-24.9 Million
Emp.: 4
Employee Benefit Services
N.A.I.C.S.: 813930
Michael Edmiston (VP)
Ron Du Van (Sec)
Melissa Johanning (Pres)

LAS VEGAS VALLEY WATER DISTRICT
1001 S Vly View Blvd, Las Vegas, NV 89153
Tel.: (702) 870-2011
Web Site: http://www.lvvwd.com
Year Founded: 1947
Sales Range: $150-199.9 Million
Emp.: 2,000
Water Supply Services
N.A.I.C.S.: 221310
John J. Entsminger (Gen Mgr)
Steve Sisolak (VP)
Brian G. Thomas (CFO)
Gregory J. Walch (Gen Counsel)
Marilyn Kirkpatrick (Pres)

LAS-CAL CORPORATION
3225A S Rainbow Ste 102, Las Vegas, NV 89146
Tel.: (702) 880-5818 NV
Web Site: http://www.lascal.com
Year Founded: 1967
Sales Range: $50-74.9 Million
Emp.: 1,000
Eating Place
N.A.I.C.S.: 722513

LASALLE BANCORP, INC.
260 Bucklin St, La Salle, IL 61301
Tel.: (815) 223-7300 DE
Web Site: http://www.myhtnb.com
Sales Range: $1-9.9 Million
Emp.: 40
Bank Holding Company
N.A.I.C.S.: 551111
Jim Riley (Pres/CEO-Hometown Natl Bank)
G. F. Fitzgerald Jr. (Chm & CEO)

Subsidiaries:

Hometown National Bank (1)
260 Bucklin St, La Salle, IL 61301
Tel.: (815) 223-7300
Web Site: http://www.myhtnb.com
Sales Range: $1-9.9 Million
Commericial Banking
N.A.I.C.S.: 522110
Jim Riley (Chm)
Dave Conterio (Pres & CEO)
Chris Wren (VP-Ops & Compliance)
Darin Terry (Chief Credit Officer & Sr VP)
Lorna Ksiazkiewicz (Sr VP)

LASALLE INTERNATIONAL PARTNER
6625 N Avondale Ave, Chicago, IL 60631
Tel.: (773) 631-3200
Rev.: $43,500,000
Emp.: 9
Investment Bankers
N.A.I.C.S.: 523150
Gavriel Mairone (Partner)

COMPANIES / LAT PURSER & ASSOCIATES, INC.

Subsidiaries:

Lasalle Ventures One Ltd. (1)
501 Brickell Key Dr # 602, Miami, FL 33131
Tel.: (305) 372-7400
Hotel
N.A.I.C.S.: 721110

LASCARIS & SONS INC.
16255 E Whittier Blvd, Whittier, CA 90603
Tel.: (562) 943-1113
Web Site: http://www.lascarisdeli.com
Sales Range: $10-24.9 Million
Emp.: 75
Delicatessen Stores
N.A.I.C.S.: 445110
John B. Lascaris (Owner)

LASCO CONSTRUCTION, INC.
314 W Marland St, Hobbs, NM 88240
Tel.: (575) 393-9161
Web Site: http://www.lasco.biz
Year Founded: 1977
Sales Range: $10-24.9 Million
Emp.: 35
Commercial & Institutional Building Construction Services
N.A.I.C.S.: 236220
John D. Ragsdal (VP)
Johnie Earl Ragsdal (Owner & Pres)
Shelly Robinson (Mgr-Acctg)

LASCO ENTERPRISES
7026 Old Katy Rd Ste 250, Houston, TX 77024
Tel.: (713) 622-4003
Web Site: http://www.lascoenterprises.com
Year Founded: 2003
Sales Range: $10-24.9 Million
Emp.: 310
Wine Bars & Restaurants
N.A.I.C.S.: 722511
Jerry Lasco (Founder & CEO)
Whitney Marcantonio (Coord-Events)
Julie Godfrey (Mgr-Dev-Wine)
Lorie Cryer (Mgr-Event Sls)

LASER EXCEL, INC.
N6323 Berlin Rd, Green Lake, WI 54941
Tel.: (920) 294-6544
Web Site: http://www.laserexcel.com
Year Founded: 1982
Sales Range: $10-24.9 Million
Emp.: 80
Laser Cutting Services
N.A.I.C.S.: 339999
Lance Schumacher (Exec VP)

Subsidiaries:

Plastic Services, Inc. (1)
620 Cardinal Ln, Hartland, WI 53029
Tel.: (262) 369-5000
Sales Range: $10-24.9 Million
Emp.: 40
Plastic Profile & Shape Mfr
N.A.I.C.S.: 326199

LASER PROS INTERNATIONAL CORP.
1 International Ln, Rhinelander, WI 54501
Tel.: (715) 369-5995
Web Site: http://www.laserpros.com
Rev.: $15,511,221
Emp.: 100
Printers, Computer
N.A.I.C.S.: 423430
Steven T. Spencer (Pres)
Nelson Eisele (Acct Exec)
Steve Bishop (Acct Exec)
Eric Dombeck (Acct Exec)
Bill Donner (Acct Exec)
Todd Mackoway (Acct Exec)
Steve Vandervest (Acct Exec)

LASER SPINE INSTITUTE, LLC
5332 Avion Park Dr, Tampa, FL 33607
Tel.: (813) 289-9613
Web Site: http://www.laserspineinstitute.com
Year Founded: 2005
Sales Range: $150-199.9 Million
Emp.: 600
Spine Surgery Center
N.A.I.C.S.: 622110
Bill Horne (Chm)
Jamie Adams (Chief Strategy Officer)
Michael Perry (Co-Founder)
Ryan Fulcher (Sr VP-Ops)
Keith Fulmer (VP-Tech & Innovation)
Benjamin Hom (VP-Talent)
Sara McLear (VP-Clinic Ops)
Jose Rivera (VP-Revenue Mgmt)
Thomas Linton (Chief Patient Empowerment Officer)
Roger Cary (Pres & CEO)

LASER TECHNOLOGY, INC.
1055 W Germantown Pike, Norristown, PA 19403
Tel.: (610) 631-5043
Web Site: http://www.laserndt.com
Year Founded: 1982
Testing Equipment
N.A.I.C.S.: 334519
John Newman (Pres)
Milana Isakov (Controller)

LASERCYCLE USA, INC.
528 S Taylor Ave, Louisville, CO 80027
Tel.: (303) 666-7776
Web Site: http://www.lasercycleusa.com
Year Founded: 1991
Rev.: $2,300,000
Emp.: 15
Copiers & Printers, Document/Content Management, Toner Cartridges & Managed Print Services
N.A.I.C.S.: 333248
Kirk Peck (Founder & Pres)
Melissa Malcolm-Peck (Co-Founder)

LASERTEC, INC.
33472 Sterling Ponds Blvd, Sterling Heights, MI 48312
Tel.: (586) 274-4500
Web Site: http://www.lasertecinc.com
Year Founded: 1986
Sales Range: $1-9.9 Million
Emp.: 50
Commercial Printing
N.A.I.C.S.: 323111
Joan Kulka (Exec VP)
Tony Wilhelm (Exec VP-Bus Dev)
Jim Jones (Exec VP-Production)
Wendy Lokken (Vice Chm & Co-CEO)

LASH EXCAVATING & PAVING
412 S 1st St, Martins Ferry, OH 43935
Tel.: (740) 635-4335
Web Site: http://www.lashpaving.com
Sales Range: $10-24.9 Million
Emp.: 60
Parking Lot Construction
N.A.I.C.S.: 238990
David P. Lash Jr. (Pres)

LASITER CONSTRUCTION INC.
505 W Dixon Rd, Little Rock, AR 72206
Tel.: (501) 374-1557
Web Site: http://www.redstone-cg.com
Sales Range: $10-24.9 Million

Emp.: 300
Parking Lot Maintenance
N.A.I.C.S.: 423320
Michael Lasiter (Pres)

LASKO PRODUCTS, LLC
820 Lincoln Ave, West Chester, PA 19380-4406
Tel.: (610) 692-7400
Web Site: https://www.lasko.com
Year Founded: 1906
Electrical Household Appliance Mfr
N.A.I.C.S.: 335210
Bradford Brush (Gen Counsel)
Morris Taormina (Dir-HR)
Raafat Mikhail (CIO)
Ralph Zwakenberg (Dir-Indus Design)
Thomas Hebling (Engr-Mechanical)
Ed Vlacich (CEO)

Subsidiaries:

Air King (1)
820 Lincoln Ave, West Chester, PA 19380-4406
Tel.: (610) 692-7400
Web Site: http://www.airkinglimited.com
Sales Range: $75-99.9 Million
Emp.: 1,000
Mfr of Electric Housewares & Fans
N.A.I.C.S.: 335210

Guardian Technologies LLC (1)
26251 Bluestone Blvd 37, Euclid, OH 44132
Web Site: http://www.guardiantechnologies.com
Sales Range: $10-24.9 Million
Emp.: 17
Home & Office Health Sanitation Products Mfr
N.A.I.C.S.: 325612
Rick Farone (Mng Partner)
Dave Brickner (Mng Partner)
Chuck Thur (Dir-Engrg)

Intertex, Inc. (1)
550 S Ayon Ave, Azusa, CA 91702
Tel.: (877) 800-2247
Web Site: https://b-air.com
Site Preparation Contractor
N.A.I.C.S.: 238910
Edward Demirdjian (CEO)

LASONIC ELECTRONICS CORPORATION
15759 Tapia St, Los Angeles, CA 91706
Tel.: (626) 480-1218
Web Site: http://www.lasonicstore.com
Year Founded: 1978
Sales Range: $10-24.9 Million
Electric Appliances Mfr
N.A.I.C.S.: 423620

Subsidiaries:

Wing Tat Stereo Component Ltd. (1)
Unit B 3rd Fl Prospect Mansion, 66 68 Paterson St, Causeway Bay, China (Hong Kong) (100%)
Tel.: (852) 28906232
N.A.I.C.S.: 449210

Yung Fu Electrical Appliances Corp. (1)
39 Keji 5 Fl Technology Industrial Park, T'ainan, 709, Taiwan (100%)
N.A.I.C.S.: 449210

LASSETER TRACTOR CO., INC.
1000 Veterans Pkwy S, Moultrie, GA 31776
Tel.: (229) 985-1027
Web Site: http://www.lassetereq.com
Sales Range: $50-74.9 Million
Emp.: 35
Tractor & Farm Equipment Whslr
N.A.I.C.S.: 423820
Willard E. Lasseter (Chm)
Tony Lasseter (Pres)

Subsidiaries:

Lasseter Implement Company, LLC (1)
15795 US Hwy 41 S, Unadilla, GA 31091
Tel.: (478) 627-3291
Web Site: http://www.lassetereq.com
Sales Range: $10-24.9 Million
Farm Equipment & Supplies Whslr
N.A.I.C.S.: 459999
Judd Lasseter (Gen Mgr)

LASSITER-WARE INC.
1317 Citizens Blvd, Leesburg, FL 34748
Tel.: (352) 787-3441
Web Site: http://www.lassiterware.com
Year Founded: 1912
Sales Range: $25-49.9 Million
Emp.: 100
Insurance Brokers
N.A.I.C.S.: 524210
Don Campbell (Dir-IT)
Fernando Juarez (VP-Bus Svcs)
Ted Ostrander Jr. (CEO)

LASSUS BROS. OIL INC.
1800 Magnavox Way, Fort Wayne, IN 46804-1540
Tel.: (260) 436-1415
Web Site: http://www.lassus.com
Year Founded: 1972
Sales Range: $10-24.9 Million
Emp.: 350
Gasoline Station Services
N.A.I.C.S.: 457120
Todd Lassus (Pres)
Jessica Angel (Mgr-District)

LASTING IMPRESSIONS INC.
Rm 700 1400 Broadway, New York, NY 10018-5270
Tel.: (212) 997-1492
Year Founded: 1979
Sales Range: $10-24.9 Million
Emp.: 60
Women's & Misses' Outerwear
N.A.I.C.S.: 315250

LASTLINE INC.
203 Redwood Shores Pkwy Ste 500, Redwood City, CA 94065
Tel.: (877) 671-3239
Web Site: http://www.lastline.com
Year Founded: 2011
Sales Range: $10-24.9 Million
Emp.: 120
Cybersecurity Software Development Services
N.A.I.C.S.: 541511
Giovanni Vigna (Co-Founder & CTO)
John DiLullo (CEO)
Christopher Kruegel (Co-Founder & Chief Product Officer)
Engin Kirda (Co-Founder)
Brian Laing (Chief Revenue Officer)
Bert Rankin (Chief Mktg Officer)
George Chitouras (VP-Engrg)

LAT PURSER & ASSOCIATES, INC.
4530 Park Rd Ste 300, Charlotte, NC 28209-3716
Tel.: (704) 519-4200
Web Site: http://www.latpurser.com
Year Founded: 1961
Real Estate Services
N.A.I.C.S.: 531210
Geneva P. Henderson (Exec VP-Jacksonville-Florida)
Robert J. Otten (Pres)
Jack Levinson (Sr VP)
Lat H. Purser (Sr VP)

LAT PURSER & ASSOCIATES, INC.

Lat Purser & Associates, Inc.—(Continued)
Pete Brucia (Chief Investment Officer)
Randy Robinson (VP-Property Svcs)
Lat W. Purser III (Chm & CEO)

LATCHA+ASSOCIATES
24600 Hallwood Ct, Farmington Hills, MI 48335-1603
Tel.: (248) 482-4500
Web Site: http://www.latcha.com
Year Founded: 1998
Rev.: $18,000,000
Emp.: 105
Advetising Agency
N.A.I.C.S.: 541810
David Latcha (Owner)
Lisa Chapman (Pres)

LATE JULY SNACKS LLC
3166 Main St, Barnstable, MA 02630
Tel.: (508) 362-5859
Web Site: http://www.latejuly.com
Sales Range: $10-24.9 Million
Emp.: 20
Organic Snackfood Mfr
N.A.I.C.S.: 311821
Darby Ziruk (Co-Pres)
Nicole Dawes (Co-Founder & CEO)

LATEX CONSTRUCTION COMPANY
1353 Farmer Rd NW, Conyers, GA 30012
Tel.: (770) 760-0820
Web Site:
  http://www.latexconstruction.com
Rev.: $57,008,330
Emp.: 25
Oil & Gas Pipeline Construction
N.A.I.C.S.: 237120
Dave Stotz (Pres)
Dave Williams (VP)
T. B. Elder (Sec)
William E. Honey Jr. (Chm)

LATHAM & WATKINS LLP
355 S Grand Ave Ste 100, Los Angeles, CA 90071-1560
Tel.: (213) 485-1234
Web Site: https://www.lw.com
Year Founded: 1934
Sales Range: $1-4.9 Billion
Emp.: 4,500
Law firm
N.A.I.C.S.: 541110
Leeann Black (COO)
Despina Kartson (CMO)
Kenneth L. Heaps (CIO)
Wendy Ward (Chief Admin Officer)
Hui Xu (Partner-Corp Risk & Investigations-Shanghai)
Eli Katz (Partner-New York)
Stephen W. Ranere (Partner)
Stacey VanBelleghem (Partner)
Matthew Murchison (Partner)
Adam Greenfield (Partner)
Omar Nazif (Partner-San Diego)
Wenchi Hu (Partner-Corp Dept & Fin Institutions Grp-New York)
Michele Penzer (Mng Partner-New York)
Witold Balaban (Chm-Fin Institutions Grp-Global)
Ian Schuman (Chm-Capital Markets Practice-Global)
John T. Sheridan (Partner-Emerging Companies Practice-Silicon Valley)
Tad Freese (Mng Partner-Silicon Valley)
Patrick Pohlen (Chm-Emerging Companies Practice-Global)
Maj Vaseghi (Partner)
Nicholas McQuaid (Partner-Litigation & Trial-New York)
Michael Rubin (Partner-San Francisco)
Kevin Wheeler (Partner-Litigation & Trial Dept-Washington)
Michael Egge (Mng Partner-Washington)
Matthew Moore (Chm-Intellectual Property Litigation Practice-Global & Partner)
Bert Reiser (Partner)
Kristen Smith Grannis (Partner)
David Tolley (Partner)
J. Cory Tull (Partner)
Matthew R. Conway (Partner)
Michael E. Bern (Partner)
Andrew D. Prins (Partner)
Kristin L. Mendoza (Partner)
Lilia B. Vazova (Partner)
Peter J. Sluka (Partner)
Reza K. Mojtabaee-Zamani (Partner)
Jason C. Hegt (Partner)
Benjamin J. Cohen (Partner)
Blake T. Denton (Partner)
Todd Beauchamp (Partner-Washington)
Jeffrey E. Bjork (Partner-Restructuring, Insolvency & Workouts Practice)
Jeffrey Greenberg (Mng Partner)
Peter Gilhuly (Chm- Restructuring, Insolvency & Workouts-Global & Partner)
I. Scott Gottdiener (Chm-Fin-Global)
Jamie Underwood (Partner-Litigation & Trial Dept-Washington)
Farrell Malone (Partner)
Marc Granger (Partner)
George Davis (Chm-Restructuring & Special Situations Practice-Global)
Matthew Chase (Partner)
Yvette Valdez (Partner)
Todd Carpenter (Partner-Emerging Companies Practice-San Francisco)
Kirt Switzer (Mng Partner-San Francisco)
Ora Fisher (Chm/Partner-Silicon Valley)
Michael Haas (Partner-Fin Dept-New York & Chm-Real Estate Practice-Global)
David Callahan (Chm-Intellectual Property Litigation Practice-Global)
Tara D. Elliott (Partner-Litigation & Trial Dept-Washington)
Jane Greyf (Partner-Corp Dept & Mergers & Acq Practice)
Greg Roussel (Partner-Corp Dept & Mergers & Acq Practice-Silicon Valley)
Brad Kotler (Vice Chm & Partner-Fin-Chicago)
Sarang Damle (Partner-Intellectual Property Litigation Practice)
Jennifer Barry (Chm-Intellectual Property Litigation Practice-Global)
Andy Gass (Partner-San Francisco)
Andrew Parlen (Partner-Restructuring, Insolvency & Workouts Practice-New York)
Elizabeth Prewitt (Partner-Litigation & Trial Dept)
Amanda Reeves (Chm-Antitrust & Competition Practice-Global)
Chirag K. Dedania (Partner-New York)
Y. Bora Bozkurt (Partner-New York)
Andrew D. Baker (Partner-New York)
Nicole D. Fanjul (Partner-New York)
Adam J. Gelardi (Partner-New York)
Mark M. Bekheit (Partner-Silicon Valley)
Nathaniel Amory (Partner-Boston)
Julia A. Thompson (Partner-Washington)
Katherine G. Putnam (Partner-Washington)
Erin Brown Jones (Partner)
James Ktsanes (Partner-Chicago)
Heather A. Waller (Partner-Chicago)
Joseph Wetzel (Partner-Litigation & Trial Dept & The Intellectual Property)
Alexander Johnson (Partner-Corp Dept-New York)
Marc Jaffe (Chm-Corp Dept-Global)
Paul Sheridan (Chm-Private Equity Practice-Global)
David Beller (Partner-Corp Dept-New York)
Paul Kukish (Chm-Private Equity Practice-Global)
Pamela C. Kellet (Partner)
Nicholas J. Siciliano (Partner-Chicago)
Benjamin Berman (Partner-Washington)
Paul M. Dudek (Partner)
Brian D. Miller (Partner-Washington)
Elizabeth M. Richards (Partner-Washington)
Abhay D. Lele (Partner-New York)
Catherine H. Lee (Partner-New York)
Elizabeth Jaffe (Partner-New York)
Dennis G. Craythorn (Partner-New York)
Robert Fernandez (Partner-Corp Dept-Chicago)
Mitchell Rabinowitz (Partner-Corp Dept-Washington)
Jenny Cieplak (Partner-Corp Dept-Washington)
Ivana K. Rouse (Partner-Corp Dept-Houston)
Tim Fenn (Mng Partner-Houston)
Kathleen Walsh (Vice Chm-Corp Dept-Global)
Trevor Wommack (Partner-Houston)
Jonathan Castelan (Partner-Houston)
Edward Nelson (Partner-Corp Dept-New York)
Andrea Schwartzman (Chm-Investment Funds Practice-Global)
Suzzanne Uhland (Partner-Restructuring & Special Situations Practice-New York)
Yen Sum (Partner-London)
Jennifer Brennan (Partner-London)
George Klidonas (Partner-Restructuring & Special Situations Practice-New York)
Alexandra Bigot (Partner-Restructuring & Special Situations Practice-Paris)
Jessica Walker (Partner-Restructuring & Special Situations Practice-London)
Danielle Conley (Partner)
Alan W. Tamarelli Jr. (Partner-New York)

LATHAM HI-TECH HYBRIDS, INC.
131 180th St, Des Moines, IA 50420-8028
Tel.: (641) 692-3258
Web Site:
  http://www.lathamseeds.com
Sales Range: $10-24.9 Million
Emp.: 38
Dry Pea & Bean Farming
N.A.I.C.S.: 111130
Shannon Latham (VP)
Tom Curry (Acct Mgr-Sls)
John Latham (Pres)
Amy Rohe (Project Mgr-Sls)
Joy Bonin (Office Mgr)
Mark Grundmeier (Product Mgr-Seed)
Corey Catt (Product Mgr-Forage)
Chris Latham (CFO)
Tom Lizer (Gen Mgr)
Sharon Martin (Mgr-Acctg)
Sandie Johnson (Mgr-Sls Acct)

Craig Christians (Mgr-Territory Sls)
Myron Keltgen (Mgr-Territory Sls)

LATHAM MOTORS INC.
637 Columbia St, Latham, NY 12110
Tel.: (518) 785-4161
Web Site: http://www.lathamford.com
Rev.: $21,600,000
Emp.: 50
New Car Dealers
N.A.I.C.S.: 441110
Robert Selkis (Pres)
Margaret J. Selkis (Sec)
Thomas Selkis (VP)
John Selkis III (VP-Ops & Mfg)

LATHROP & GAGE LLP
2345 Grand Blvd Ste 2200, Kansas City, MO 64108
Tel.: (816) 292-2000
Web Site:
  http://www.lathropgage.com
Year Founded: 1873
Sales Range: $125-149.9 Million
Emp.: 290
Legal Advisory Services
N.A.I.C.S.: 541110
Joel B. Voran (Chm)
Michael J. Abrams (Partner)
William W. Beck (Partner)
Richard N. Bien (Partner)
Mark A. Bluhm (CEO)
Sherman A. Botts (Partner)
Wallace E. Brockhoff (Partner)
David V. Clark (Partner)
John T. Coghlan (Partner)
Mara H. Cohara (Partner)
Don F. Dagenais (Partner)
Peter F. Daniel (Partner)
Brian T. Fenimore (Partner)
Brian W. Fields (Partner)
William F. Ford (Partner)
Brian C. Fries (Partner)
David R. Frye (Partner)
Jon Trembath (Partner)
Robert F. Weber (Partner)
Connie Reiniger (Partner)
Bryan Minier (Partner-Banking & Creditors Rights Litigation Practice-Chicago)
Amy Brozenic (Partner)
Angela L. Ekker (Partner)
Andrew R. Ramirez (Partner)
Allan J. Sternstein (Partner)
Andrew T. Wilkins (Partner)
Bernard J. Rhodes (Partner)
A. Justin Poplin (Partner)
Alson R. Martin (Partner)
Barry L. Haith (Partner)
Bennett S. Keller (Partner)
Courtney M. Landon (CFO-Chicago)
John Terry (Partner-Environmental Practice)
Hissan Anis (Partner)
Kate O'Hara Gasper (Partner)
Brian Mack (Partner)
Mark Webster (Partner)
Stephen B. Barone (Partner)
Gary B. Chapman (Partner)

LATICRETE INTERNATIONAL, INC.
One LATICRETE Park North 91 Amity Rd, Bethany, CT 06524
Tel.: (203) 393-0010
Web Site: http://www.laticrete.com
Emp.: 1,200
Building Materials Mfr
N.A.I.C.S.: 327390
David A. Rothberg (Chm)
Brad Lesh (Mgr-Network)
Edward Metcalf (Pres-North America)
Faisal Saleem (Pres/COO-Intl Div)
Sean Boyle (VP-Mktg-North America)
Janet Brunwin (Sr VP-Fin)

Spencer Maheu *(Dir-Product Mgmt-North America)*
Ritesh Singh *(Gen Mgr-Middle East)*
Benjamin Lampi *(Product Mgr-Resinous Coatings Bus Sector)*
Dustin Prevete *(Sr Product Mgr-Membranes Business Portfolio)*
Patrick Millot *(CEO)*

Subsidiaries:

L&M Construction Chemicals, Inc. (1)
14851 Calhoun Rd, Omaha, NE 68152
Tel.: (402) 453-6600
Web Site: http://www.lmcc.com
Sales Range: $1-9.9 Million
Emp.: 35
Construction Chemicals Mfr
N.A.I.C.S.: 325998
Jeff Bonkiewicz *(Mgr-Mktg)*

LATIN AMERICAN AGRIBUSINESS DEVELOPMENT CORPORATION
2800 Ponce de Leon Blvd Ste 1200, Coral Gables, FL 33134
Tel.: (305) 445-1341
Web Site: http://www.laadsa.com
Sales Range: $25-49.9 Million
Emp.: 20
Agricultural Loan Companies
N.A.I.C.S.: 522299
Benjamin Fernandez *(Pres & CEO)*
Gustavo Martinez *(CFO & Treas)*
Daniel Araujo *(VP-Corp Strategy, HR & Compliance)*
Oscar Luzuriaga *(Reg VP)*
Rafael Cestti *(Reg VP)*
Hector Vidal *(Comptroller-Exec Mgmt)*
Juan Carlos Gamboa *(Sec & VP-Legal Affairs & Special Assets)*
Isabel Perez *(Mgr-Credit Risk)*
Javier Stacey *(Reg VP)*

LATIN AMERICAN YOUTH CENTER INC.
1419 Columbia Rd NW, Washington, DC 20009
Tel.: (202) 319-2225 DC
Web Site: http://www.layc-dc.org
Year Founded: 1974
Sales Range: $10-24.9 Million
Emp.: 218
Youth Welfare Services
N.A.I.C.S.: 624110
Lori M. Kaplan *(Pres & CEO)*
Antonio F. Marquez *(Chm)*
Lauren Eyster *(Vice Chm)*
Simon Fairclough *(Treas)*
Betsy Brand *(Sec)*
Patricia Bravo *(COO)*
Humphrey Mensah *(Chief Fin & Admin Officer)*
Barbara Myers *(Chief Dev Officer)*

LATIN PERCUSSION INC.
160 Belmont Ave, Garfield, NJ 07026
Tel.: (973) 478-6903
Web Site: http://www.lpmusic.com
Rev.: $21,435,000
Emp.: 50
Musical Instruments
N.A.I.C.S.: 423990
Martin Cohen *(Founder)*
Heidi Schaeffer *(Dir-Creative)*
Victor Filonovich *(Dir-R&D)*

LATIN WORLD ENTERTAINMENT AGENCY
3470 NW 82nd Ave Ste 860, Doral, FL 33122
Tel.: (305) 572-1515
Web Site: http://www.latinwe.com
Sales Range: $10-24.9 Million
Emp.: 30

Advertising Agencies
N.A.I.C.S.: 541810
Luis Balaguer *(Pres & CEO)*

LATINA MEDIA VENTURES, LLC
625 Madison Ave 3rd Fl, New York, NY 10022
Tel.: (212) 642-0200
Web Site: http://www.latina.com
Year Founded: 1996
Sales Range: $10-24.9 Million
Emp.: 35
Magazine Publisher
N.A.I.C.S.: 513120
Christy Haubegger *(Founder)*
Mathew Fox *(Dir-IT & Digital Media)*
Robyn Moreno *(Dir-Editorial)*

LATINA NIAGARA IMPORTING CO.
1 Scrivner Dr, Cheektowaga, NY 14227
Tel.: (716) 693-9999
Web Site: http://www.latinafoodservice.com
Sales Range: $10-24.9 Million
Emp.: 30
Bond Brokers
N.A.I.C.S.: 424410
Charles Marazzo *(Pres & CEO)*
Ann Sidoni *(CFO)*

LATITUDE 360, INC.
6022 San Jose Blvd, Jacksonville, FL 32217
Tel.: (904) 730-0011 NV
Web Site: http://www.latitude360.com
Year Founded: 2006
Sales Range: $10-24.9 Million
Emp.: 477
Restaurant & Gaming Operations
N.A.I.C.S.: 722511
Brent W. Brown *(Chm & CEO)*
Alan Jay Greenstein *(CFO & Exec VP)*

LATITUDE BEVERAGE COMPANY
1354 Commonwealth Ave 2nd Fl, Allston, MA 02134
Tel.: (617) 816-4740
Web Site: http://www.ninetypluscellars.com
Year Founded: 2006
Sales Range: $10-24.9 Million
Emp.: 18
Wine Distribution Services
N.A.I.C.S.: 424820
Kevin Mehra *(Co-Founder & Pres)*
Brett Vankoski *(Co-Founder & VP)*
Jarrod DiFranco *(Mgr-Sls-Western MA)*
Ryan Gillian *(Mgr-Sls-IL)*
Bob Lindblad *(VP-Sls)*
Alexandra Moshier *(Acct Mgr-Boston & Northern MA)*
Michael Munk *(Mgr-Sls-CT)*
Jeanine Werchniak *(Mgr-Sls-ME, NH & VT)*
Heidi Withrow *(Controller)*
Han Nguyen *(Mgr-Acct)*

LATO SUPPLY CORPORATION
3828 W Whitton Ave, Phoenix, AZ 85019
Tel.: (602) 269-8389
Web Site: http://www.latosupply.com
Sales Range: $10-24.9 Million
Emp.: 25
Hotel Equipment & Supplies
N.A.I.C.S.: 423440
Felice Jennings *(Mgr-Ops)*

LATOFF WAINER & COMPANY

1 Barleycone Ln, Rosemont, PA 19010
Tel.: (610) 525-6440
Sales Range: $25-49.9 Million
Emp.: 55
Office Equipment
N.A.I.C.S.: 423420
Thomas J. Latoff II *(Pres)*

LATORRA, PAUL & MCCANN
120 E Washington St, Syracuse, NY 13202-4000
Tel.: (315) 476-1646 NY
Web Site: http://www.lpm-adv.com
Year Founded: 1993
Sales Range: $50-74.9 Million
Emp.: 40
Advetising Agency
N.A.I.C.S.: 541810
Louis J. Latorra *(CEO)*
Darlene Latorra *(Exec VP-Fin & Admin)*
Mark Anderson *(Dir-Media)*
Barbara Straight *(Sr Mgr-Production)*
Michael Ancillotti *(Pres & CEO)*
Andy Collins *(Assoc Dir-Creative)*
Kimberly Parr *(Dir-PR)*
Bill Patrick *(VP-Ops & Fin)*
Kristi Fazio *(Media Buyer)*
Doug Potter *(Exec Dir-Creative)*

LATROBE PALLET, INC.
1284 State Route 981, Latrobe, PA 15650-4146
Tel.: (724) 537-9636
Sales Range: $10-24.9 Million
Emp.: 7
Wood Container & Pallet Mfr
N.A.I.C.S.: 321920
Scott Himler *(Pres)*
Scott Harr *(VP)*

LATSHAW DRILLING AND EXPLORATION COMPANY
4500 S 129th E Ave Ste 150, Tulsa, OK 74134
Tel.: (918) 355-4380
Web Site: http://www.latshawdrilling.com
Year Founded: 1981
Sales Range: $50-74.9 Million
Emp.: 900
Drilling Contractor
N.A.I.C.S.: 213111
Trent B. Latshaw *(Founder & Pres)*
Joey Stockton *(Mgr-Ops)*
Steve McCoy *(VP)*
Mark Cochran *(CFO & Sr VP)*
Cody Ashley *(Dir-HSE)*
Travis Hickey *(Mgr-Maintenance)*
Don Caffey *(Mgr-Trng)*
Cindy Lozano *(Dir-Risk Mgmt)*
Debbie Holloway *(Dir-Shared Svcs)*
Bill Cobb *(Exec VP-Mktg & Sls)*

Subsidiaries:

Mustang Heavy Haul LLC (1)
4905 S Perkins Rd, Stillwater, OK 74074
Tel.: (405) 743-0085
Web Site: http://www.latshawdrilling.com
Transport Services for Energy Industry
N.A.I.C.S.: 213112
Jason Burke *(Mgr-Ops)*
Richard Walborn *(Mgr-Sls-Transportation)*

LATT MAXCY CORPORATION
21299 US Hwy 27, Lake Wales, FL 33859
Tel.: (863) 679-6700
Web Site: http://www.lattmaxcy.com
Year Founded: 1963
Emp.: 7
Real Estate, Ranching, Citrus & Banking
N.A.I.C.S.: 531390
Latimer T. Wilson *(Pres)*
Clayton G. Wilson *(Chm & VP)*

Subsidiaries:

Citizen's Bank & Trust (1)
PO Box 7, Frostproof, FL 33843
Tel.: (863) 635-2244
Web Site: http://www.citizens-bank.com
Assets: $300,000,000
Emp.: 8
Banking
N.A.I.C.S.: 522110
Greg Littleton *(Pres & CEO)*
Sherry Kelley *(Sr VP & Office Mgr)*
Latimer Wilson *(Chm)*
Brian Bracey *(Officer-Credit Policy & Sr VP)*
Bonnie B. Parker *(Sr VP & Dir-Wealth Mgmt)*
Jennie Walker *(Sr VP & Dir-HR)*
Weymon Snuggs *(COO & Exec VP)*
Ed Granda *(Officer-Compliance Mgmt & Sr VP)*
Tim Brown *(CFO & Exec VP)*
Robert Loftin *(Chief Comml Officer & Sr VP)*
Steve McCullough *(Chief Residential Lending Officer & Sr VP)*

Maxcy Development Group (1)
3434 Colwell Ave Ste 120, Tampa, FL 33614
Tel.: (813) 915-3449
Real Estate
N.A.I.C.S.: 531390

LAUD COLLIER & COMPANY, LLC
466 Southern Blvd Jefferson Bldg, Chatham, NJ 07928
Tel.: (973) 822-1234
Web Site: http://www.lccap.com
Year Founded: 2002
Privater Equity Firm
N.A.I.C.S.: 523999
Paul J. Laud *(Co-Founder)*
Colby W. Collier *(Co-Founder)*

LAUFER GROUP INTERNATIONAL LTD.
20 Vesey St Ste 601, New York, NY 10007-2913
Tel.: (212) 945-6000
Web Site: http://www.laufer.com
Year Founded: 1989
Sales Range: $10-24.9 Million
Emp.: 100
Freight Transportation Arrangement Services
N.A.I.C.S.: 488510
Mark Laufer *(Pres)*
Del Dickson *(Controller)*
Martin Karczewski *(Branch Mgr)*

LAUGHERY VALLEY AG CO-OP, INC.
336 N Buckeye St, Osgood, IN 47037
Tel.: (812) 689-4401
Web Site: http://www.laugheryvalleyag.com
Farm Supplies
N.A.I.C.S.: 424910
Keith Everhart *(Gen Mgr)*

LAUGHING SAMURAI
1221-C N Orange Ave, Orlando, FL 32804
Tel.: (407) 982-4350
Web Site: http://www.laughingsamurai.com
Sales Range: $100-124.9 Million
Emp.: 25
N.A.I.C.S.: 541810
Ben Collins *(Mng Dir)*

LAUGHLIN OIL COMPANY
1920 Lafayette Ave, McMinnville, OR 97128
Tel.: (503) 472-7215
Web Site: http://www.laughlinoil.com
Year Founded: 1971
Rev.: $14,135,372
Emp.: 30

LAUGHLIN OIL COMPANY

Laughlin Oil Company—(Continued)
Petroleum Bulk Stations
N.A.I.C.S.: 424710
Ron Myhro (Owner)

LAUGHLIN/CONSTABLE, INC.
207 E Michigan St, Milwaukee, WI 53202-4998
Tel.: (414) 272-2400   WI
Web Site: http://www.laughlin.com
Year Founded: 1976
Rev.: $220,000,000
Emp.: 155
Advetising Agency
N.A.I.C.S.: 541810
Steven Laughlin (Owner & Chm)
Renee Haber (Exec VP-Acct Svcs)
Paul Brienza (CTO)
Rome Seifert (CFO)
Susan Stearns (Exec VP & Dir-Acct Svcs)
Mat Lignel (CEO)
Michael Baer (CMO)
Heather Anglim (Exec VP-HR)
Vanessa Watts (Exec VP-Media)
Kristine Naidl (Mng Dir-PR & Exec VP)
Lisa Bennett (Chief Creative Officer)
Mark Carlson (Chief Strategy Officer)
Patti Bridge (Sr VP-Acct Mgmt)
Terry Corrigan (Exec VP-Acct Svcs)

Subsidiaries:

Laughlin/Constable New York   (1)
27 Whitehall St 7th Fl, New York, NY 10004
Tel.: (212) 422-4022
Web Site: http://www.laughlin.com
Emp.: 8
Custom Publishing
N.A.I.C.S.: 541810
Michael J. Jeary (Pres)
Steve Laughlin (Partner & Exec Dir-Creative)
Chris Brignola (Dir-Creative-New York)

Laughlin/Constable, Inc.   (1)
360 N Michigan Ave 12th Fl, Chicago, IL 60601
Tel.: (414) 272-2400
Web Site: http://www.laughlin.com
Emp.: 120
Advertising Agencies, Fashion/Apparel, Financial, Food Service, Graphic Design, Interactive Agencies, Media Buying Services, Planning & Consultation, Public Relations, Retail, Travel & Tourism
N.A.I.C.S.: 541810
Renee Haber (Exec VP-Acct Svcs)
Steve Laughlin (Partner & Exec Dir-Creative)
Paul Brienza (Sr VP-Interactive Mktg)
Patrick McAuley (VP)
Joyce O'Brien (Exec VP & Dir-HR)
Kirk Ruhnke (Sr VP & Dir-Creative)
Dave Hanneken (Sr VP & Dir-Creative)
Denise Kohnke (Sr VP-Brand Strategy)
John Constable (Partner & Exec Dir-Creative)
Mat Lignel (Pres & CEO)
John Maxham (Chief Creative Officer)

LAUN-DRY SUPPLY COMPANY INC.
3800 Durazno Ave, El Paso, TX 79905
Tel.: (915) 533-8217
Web Site: http://www.laundrysupply.com
Sales Range: $10-24.9 Million
Emp.: 40
Laundry Equipment & Supplies
N.A.I.C.S.: 423850
Lynn J. Gore (Pres)
Denise Jennings (Office Mgr)

LAUNCH
351 E Kennedy St, Spartanburg, SC 29302
Tel.: (864) 580-2350

Web Site: http://www.launchsomething.com
Sales Range: Less than $1 Million
Emp.: 6
Advetising Agency
N.A.I.C.S.: 541810
Sims Hammond (Owner)
Mark Miller (Dir-Art)

LAUNCH AGENCY
4100 Midway Rd Ste 2110, Carrollton, TX 75007
Tel.: (972) 818-4100
Web Site: http://www.launchagency.com
Year Founded: 2003
Rev.: $14,000,000
Emp.: 17
N.A.I.C.S.: 541810
Michael Boone (Principal & Acct Dir)
David Wilgus (Principal & Dir-Creative)
Diane Seilmetz (Principal & Dir-Creative)

LAUNCH CREATIVE MARKETING
208 S Jefferson St 4th Fl, Chicago, IL 60661
Tel.: (312) 234-9800
Web Site: http://www.launchcreative.com
Year Founded: 1973
Sales Range: $10-24.9 Million
Emp.: 50
Graphic Design Services
N.A.I.C.S.: 541430
Jim Gelder (VP & Grp Dir-Creative)
Kevin Keating (Pres)
Tom Baer (Sr VP)

LAUNCHEQUITY PARTNERS, LLC
8585 E Bell Rd Ste 100, Scottsdale, AZ 85260
Tel.: (480) 563-3997   AZ
Privater Equity Firm
N.A.I.C.S.: 523999
Andrew C. Stephens (Mng Partner)

Subsidiaries:

MakeMusic, Inc.   (1)
7615 Golden Triangle Dr Ste M, Eden Prairie, MN 55344   (27.7%)
Tel.: (952) 937-9611
Web Site: http://www.makemusic.com
Rev.: $17,742,000
Assets: $21,358,000
Liabilities: $8,263,000
Net Worth: $13,095,000
Earnings: ($3,652,000)
Emp.: 130
Fiscal Year-end: 12/31/2012
Music Technology Products Mfr & Marketer
N.A.I.C.S.: 512230
Paul D. Carlson (CTO)

LAUNCHFAX.COM INC.
623 River Rd, Fair Haven, NJ 07704
Tel.: (732) 450-3688
Web Site: http://www.launchfax.com
Year Founded: 1996
Sales Range: $25-49.9 Million
Emp.: 10
Fax Campaign Services
N.A.I.C.S.: 517111
Ray Villa (VP)

LAUNCHPAD
100 Galen St 2nd Fl, Watertown, MA 02472
Tel.: (617) 926-8700
Web Site: http://www.launchpad.tv
Year Founded: 2002
Sales Range: $10-24.9 Million
Emp.: 8

Brand Development, Communications, Corporate Communications, Corporate Identity, E-Commerce, Internet/Web Design, Production, T.V.
N.A.I.C.S.: 541810
Alex Poulos (Co-Founder & Pres)
Jacob Eidsmoe (Co-Founder & Dir-Creative)
Todd Domke (Writer & Strategist)
Peter Mutascio (Animator)
Anthony Tattersall (Chief Sls Officer)
Andy Fang (Head)

LAUNCHPAD ADVERTISING LLC
149 5th Ave 9th Fl, New York, NY 10010
Tel.: (212) 303-7650
Web Site: http://www.lpnyc.com
Sales Range: $1-9.9 Million
Emp.: 42
Advetising Agency
N.A.I.C.S.: 541810
Scott Elser (Co-Pres)
David Low (Co-Pres)
Noah Ross (Exec Dir-Creative)

LAUNDRYLUX INC.
461 Doughty Blvd, Inwood, NY 11096
Tel.: (516) 371-4400
Web Site: http://www.laundrylux.com
Commercial Laundry Equipment Mfr & Distr
N.A.I.C.S.: 812320
Neal Milch (Exec Chm)
John Sabino (CEO)
Julia Milch (Pres)
James Fair (CFO)
Gordon Kertland (Exec VP-Sls)
Dyann Malcolm (VP-Mktg)
Wellington Lantigua (VP-IT)

Subsidiaries:

Direct Machinery Sales Corp.   (1)
50 Commerce Pl, Hicksville, NY 11801
Tel.: (516) 938-4300
Web Site: http://www.directmachinery.com
Service Establishment Equipment Whslr
N.A.I.C.S.: 423850

LAURA DAVIDSON PUBLIC RELATIONS, INC.
72 Madison Ave 11th Fl, New York, NY 10016
Tel.: (212) 696-0660   NY
Web Site: http://www.ldpr.com
Year Founded: 1991
Rev.: $1,800,000
Emp.: 17
Fiscal Year-end: 12/31/06
Consulting, Crisis Communications, Internet/Web Design, Local Marketing, Publicity/Promotions
N.A.I.C.S.: 541810
Laura Davidson (Founder & Pres)
Leslie Cohen (Exec VP)
Jennifer Sparrow Wilkes (VP)

LAURA PEARCE, LTD.
2300 Peachtree Rd NW Ste A103, Atlanta, GA 30309
Tel.: (404) 350-9207
Web Site: http://www.laurapearce.com
Year Founded: 1989
Sales Range: $25-49.9 Million
Emp.: 15
Jewelry Designer
N.A.I.C.S.: 458310
Laura Pearce (Owner)
Annie Jamison (Mgr-Ops)

LAUREL FOODSYSTEMS INC.
4590 Campbells Run Rd, Pittsburgh, PA 15205
Tel.: (412) 494-4400

U.S. PRIVATE

Web Site: http://www.laurelfoodsystems.com
Year Founded: 1974
Sales Range: $10-24.9 Million
Emp.: 250
Cigarettes Vending Machines
N.A.I.C.S.: 445132
Donald B. Diffendal (VP)
Thomas S. Diffendal Sr. (CEO)
Thomas S. Diffendal Jr. (Pres)

LAUREL FORD LINCOLN-MERCURY
2018 Hwy 15 N, Laurel, MS 39440
Tel.: (601) 649-4511
Web Site: http://www.laurelfordlm.com
Sales Range: $25-49.9 Million
Emp.: 100
New & Used Car Dealers
N.A.I.C.S.: 441110
Jimmy Walker (Pres)
Jim Swartzfager (Sec)

LAUREL GROCERY COMPANY LLC
129 Barbourville Rd, London, KY 40744-9301
Tel.: (606) 878-6601   KY
Web Site: http://www.laurelgrocery.com
Year Founded: 1922
Sales Range: $350-399.9 Million
Emp.: 450
Grocery Product Distr
N.A.I.C.S.: 424410
Doug George (CFO)
G. Winston Griffin (Vice Chm & Gen Counsel)
Bruce Chesnut (Chm)
Dennis Butler (Pres-Retail Mktg Corp)
David Pearson (Pres)

Subsidiaries:

Laurel Trucking Company Inc.   (1)
1270 Hwy 192 E, London, KY 40744
Tel.: (606) 878-6601
Sales Range: $25-49.9 Million
Emp.: 400
Trucking
N.A.I.C.S.: 484121
James K. Buchanan (Pres)

LAUREL HEALTH SYSTEMS
22 Walnut St, Wellsboro, PA 16901
Tel.: (570) 723-0500
Web Site: http://www.laurelhs.org
Year Founded: 1989
Rev.: $71,328,147
Emp.: 1,100
Medical Office Management Services
N.A.I.C.S.: 561110
Ronald J. Butler (Pres & CEO)
Joseph F. Bubacz Jr. (CIO)
Ronald M. Gilbert Jr. (CFO)

LAUREL HILL CAPITAL PARTNERS LLC
2 Robbins Ln Ste 201, Jericho, NY 11753-1849
Tel.: (516) 933-3100
Web Site: http://www.laurelhill.com
Sales Range: $25-49.9 Million
Emp.: 8
Investment Company
N.A.I.C.S.: 523940
William J. Catacosinos (Mng Partner)
James W. Catacosinos (Partner)
William W. Catacosinos (Partner)
Kathleen A. Marion (Sec)

LAUREL HOLDINGS INC.
111 Roosevelt Blvd, Johnstown, PA 15906
Tel.: (814) 533-5782

Web Site:
http://www.laurelmanagement.net
Year Founded: 1975
Sales Range: $10-24.9 Million
Emp.: 6
Plumbing Installation Services
N.A.I.C.S.: 238220
Kim W. Kunkle *(Pres & CEO)*

Subsidiaries:

Laurel Management Company (1)
111 Roosevelt Blvd, Johnstown, PA 15906
Tel.: (814) 533-5729
Web Site: http://www.laurel-management.com
Emp.: 20
Greater Johnstown Water System Operator
N.A.I.C.S.: 221310
Kim W. Kunkle *(CEO)*

LAUREL MOTORS HOLDING COMPANY
933 Eisenhower Blvd, Johnstown, PA 15904
Tel.: (814) 266-2345
Web Site:
http://www.laurelautogroup.com
Rev.: $67,554,015
Emp.: 150
Automobiles, New & Used
N.A.I.C.S.: 441110
Michael B. Smith *(Pres)*

Subsidiaries:

Laurel Imports Inc. (1)
1880 Bedford, Johnstown, PA 15902
Tel.: (814) 269-3400
Sales Range: $10-24.9 Million
Emp.: 45
Automobiles, New & Used
N.A.I.C.S.: 441110

Laurel Valley Motors Inc. (1)
3656 Rte 30, Latrobe, PA 15650
Tel.: (724) 539-5500
Web Site: http://www.laurelvalleymotors.com
Rev.: $21,000,000
Emp.: 38
Automobiles, New & Used
N.A.I.C.S.: 441110
Michael B Smith *(Pres)*

LAUREN HOLDINGS INC.
901 S 1st St, Abilene, TX 79602
Tel.: (325) 670-9660
Web Site: http://www.laurenec.com
Rev.: $32,351,953
Emp.: 1,000
Industrial Buildings & Warehouses
N.A.I.C.S.: 236220
C. Cleve Whitener *(Pres)*

Subsidiaries:

Lauren Engineers & Constructors Inc. (1)
901 S 1st St, Abilene, TX 79602
Tel.: (325) 670-9660
Web Site: http://www.laurenec.com
Sales Range: $10-24.9 Million
Emp.: 60
Engineeering Services
N.A.I.C.S.: 541330
Todd Meek *(Dir-Safety)*
Jason Burch *(Mgr-Bus Dev)*
Ronnie Ward *(Mgr-Quality Control)*
Kevin Bilger *(Supvr-Warehouse)*
John Hyland *(VP-Projects)*
Gary French *(Mgr-IT Tech Support)*
Ron Johnson *(Exec VP)*
Randy Lipps *(Pres & COO)*
Tom Modisett *(CFO)*
Clint Rosenbaum *(Exec VP)*
Jack Shoemate *(Exec VP)*
Cleve Whitener *(Chm & CEO)*

Subsidiary (Non-US):

Lauren Bharat Engineering Private Limited (2)
C401 Delphi Building Orchard Avenue Hiranandani Business Park, Powai, Mumbai, 400076, India
Tel.: (91) 22 61943500

Web Site: http://www.laurenbharat.com
Engineering Construction Services
N.A.I.C.S.: 541330
Tushar Shahane *(CEO)*

Lauren Engineers & Constructors, ULC (1)
700 736-6 Avenue SW, Calgary, T2P 3H5, AB, Canada
Tel.: (403) 237-7160
Web Site: http://www.laurenconcise.com
Emp.: 100
Engineering Construction Services
N.A.I.C.S.: 541330
Duane Shuya *(Mgr-Drafting)*
Gerry Giacomelli *(Project Mgr & Mgr-Process Engrg)*

LAUREN INTERNATIONAL INC.
2228 Reiser Ave SE, New Philadelphia, OH 44663
Tel.: (330) 339-3373
Web Site:
http://www.laureninternational.com
Sales Range: $50-74.9 Million
Emp.: 300
Molded Rubber Products Mfr
N.A.I.C.S.: 326299
Kevin Gray *(Chm, Pres & CEO)*
David J. Gingrich *(CFO & Treas)*
James Hummel *(VP-HR)*
Mike Hovan *(COO)*
Lisa Huntsman *(Pres)*

LAURENS COMMISSION OF PUBLIC WORKS
212 Church St, Laurens, SC 29360
Tel.: (864) 681-4300
Web Site: http://www.lcpw.com
Sales Range: $25-49.9 Million
Emp.: 70
Natural Gas Distr
N.A.I.C.S.: 221210
James Buchanan *(Office Mgr)*
John Young *(Gen Mgr)*
Dale Satterfield *(Gen Mgr)*

LAURENS ELECTRIC COOPERATIVE
2254 Hwy 14, Laurens, SC 29360
Tel.: (864) 682-3141
Web Site:
http://www.laurenselectric.com
Rev.: $60,343,283
Emp.: 85
Distribution, Electric Power
N.A.I.C.S.: 221122
Chad Armstrong *(Dir-HR)*
Charles Adair *(Vice Chm)*
Jim Donahoo *(Dir-Mktg)*
Chris Miers *(Dir-Member Svcs)*
J. David Wasson Jr. *(Pres & CEO)*

LAURENS RESTORATION, INC.
1870 Elmdale Ave, Glenview, IL 60026
Tel.: (847) 486-9111
Web Site:
http://www.laurensrestoration.com
Sales Range: $10-24.9 Million
Emp.: 92
Residential Remodeling Services
N.A.I.C.S.: 236118
Sherri Laurens *(VP)*
Keith A. White *(Gen Mgr-Ops)*
Steve Fuller *(Project Mgr-Mitigation)*
Jonathan A. Laurens *(Pres)*
Chris Camasta *(Project Mgr)*
Ellioc Gauze *(Mgr-Warehouse)*
Gary Jones *(Mgr-Production)*
Todd Masson *(Mgr-Construction Project)*
Susan Moore *(Mgr-Structure Mitigation Billing)*
Angelica Ramos *(Plant Mgr)*

Mary Salazar *(Mgr-Warehouse & Project Mgr)*
Cesar Sandoval *(Asst Mgr-Warehouse)*
Yaneli Arteaga *(Asst Mgr-Retail Cleaners)*
Karen Huron *(Asst Mgr-Retail Cleaners)*

LAUREY PEAT & ASSOCIATES INC.
2001 Ross Ave Ste 3170, Dallas, TX 75201
Tel.: (214) 871-8787
Web Site: http://www.lpapr.com
Year Founded: 1976
Sales Range: $1-9.9 Million
Emp.: 12
Public Relations Agency
N.A.I.C.S.: 541820
Laurey Peat *(Principal)*

LAURIDSEN GROUP INC.
2425 SE Oaktree Ct, Ankeny, IA 50021
Tel.: (515) 289-7600
Web Site:
http://www.functionalproteins.com
Sales Range: $50-74.9 Million
Emp.: 500
Protein-Based Products Mfr
N.A.I.C.S.: 311999
Louis Russell *(Pres/CEO-APC)*
Jerry Frankl *(Pres/COO-Ingredients Div)*
Joe Crenshaw *(Sr Dir-Technical Svcs)*
Javier Polo *(VP-R&D-APC)*
Jeff Wignall *(Coord-Logistics-Customer Svc-APC Inc.)*
Joy Campbell *(Sr Dir-R&D-APC Inc.)*
Lori Brown *(Dir-Customer Svc, Export & Logistics)*
Misty Coughenour *(Coord-Customer Svc & Plasma Global-APC)*
Tom Schmitt *(VP-Sls-Global)*

Subsidiaries:

American Protein Corporation Inc. (1)
2425 SE Oak Tree Ct, Ankeny, IA 50021
Tel.: (515) 289-7600
Web Site: http://www.americanprotein.com
Sales Range: $10-24.9 Million
Emp.: 90
Manufactures & Markets Animal Feed
N.A.I.C.S.: 311119
John Wheeler *(CFO & VP)*
Dennis Skou *(VP-Ops-North America)*
Louis Russell *(Exec VP)*
Jerry Frankl *(VP-Worldwide Sls)*

Subsidiary (Non-US):

APC Nutrition, Inc. (2)
41 Montee Calixa-Lavallee, Vercheres, J0L 2R0, QC, Canada
Tel.: (450) 583-2000
Emp.: 20
Animal Food Distr
N.A.I.C.S.: 424910
Eric Caputo *(Gen Mgr)*

APC Nutrition, Ltd. (2)
7115 Ogden Dale Rd SE, Calgary, T2C 2A4, AB, Canada
Tel.: (403) 236-9515
Emp.: 18
Animal Food Distr
N.A.I.C.S.: 424910
Kevin McKay *(Gen Mgr)*

APC Polska Sp. z o.o. (2)
Kijewo 53, 63-000, Sroda Wielkopolska, Poland
Tel.: (48) 61 862 18 55
Web Site: http://www.apc-polska.com.pl
Animal Food Distr
N.A.I.C.S.: 424910
Tomasz Radomyski *(Gen Dir)*

BHJ A/S (1)

Ulsnaes 33, 6300, Grasten, Denmark
Tel.: (45) 74353535
Web Site: http://www.bhj.com
Meat & Meat By-Product Mfr & Distr
N.A.I.C.S.: 311613
Torben T. Matzen *(Pres & CEO)*
Christian Mattesen *(COO)*
Thomas Bendix-Christensen *(Pres-North America)*

Subsidiary (Non-US):

ADAX S.A.S. (2)
Rte de la Bressandiere, 79200, Chatillon, Thouet, France
Tel.: (33) 549641256
Web Site: http://www.bhjadax.com
Sales Range: $10-24.9 Million
Emp.: 8
Meat & Meat By-Products Distr
N.A.I.C.S.: 424470

BHJ Baltic UAB (2)
Vytauto Didziojo g 120, 56111, Kaisiadorys, Lithuania
Tel.: (370) 37302060
Web Site: http://www.bhj.com
Sales Range: $1-9.9 Million
Emp.: 31
Meat & Meat By-Products Distr
N.A.I.C.S.: 424470

BHJ Canada Meat Products Inc. (2)
24 Nixon Road, Bolton, L7E 1K3, ON, Canada
Tel.: (905) 951-2030
Sales Range: $1-9.9 Million
Emp.: 15
Pet Food Distr
N.A.I.C.S.: 424910

BHJ Farutex Sp. Z.o.o. (2)
Ul Jesienna 4, Szczecin, 70 807, Poland
Tel.: (48) 914641240
Web Site: http://www.farutex.pl
Sales Range: $10-24.9 Million
Emp.: 40
Meat & Meat By-Products Distr
N.A.I.C.S.: 424470

BHJ Finland Oy Ab (2)
Kronvikintie 4, 65410, Sundom, Finland
Tel.: (358) 63195000
Web Site: http://www.bhj.fi.com
Sales Range: $1-9.9 Million
Emp.: 5
Meat & Meat By-Products Distr
N.A.I.C.S.: 424470
Jan Peter Nas *(Mng Dir)*
Kim Jansson *(Mgr-Sls)*

BHJ Kalino Food AB (2)
Kometvagen 2, Box 123, Staffanstorp, 24522, Sweden
Tel.: (46) 46205260
Web Site: http://www.bhj.kalino.se
Sales Range: $25-49.9 Million
Emp.: 5
Meat & Meat By-Products Distr
N.A.I.C.S.: 424470
Thomas Roriksson *(Mng Dir)*

BHJ Romania SRL (2)
Str Alexandriei nr 2A, 76950, Bragadiru, Romania
Tel.: (40) 214209596
Web Site: http://www.bhj.ro
Sales Range: $1-9.9 Million
Emp.: 7
Meat & Meat By-Products Distr
N.A.I.C.S.: 424470

BHJ UK Food Ltd. (2)
30 Neptune Street, Hull, HU3 2BP, United Kingdom
Tel.: (44) 1482585646
Web Site: http://www.bhjfood.co.uk
Sales Range: $25-49.9 Million
Emp.: 15
Meat & Meat By-Products Distr
N.A.I.C.S.: 311613

BHJ UK Protein Foods Ltd. (2)
Ramsay Rd Barnfield Ind Est, Tipton, DY4 9DU, United Kingdom
Tel.: (44) 215214300
Web Site: http://www.bhj.co.uk
Sales Range: $25-49.9 Million
Emp.: 64
Meat & Meat By-Products Distr

LAURIDSEN GROUP INC.

Lauridsen Group Inc.—(Continued)
N.A.I.C.S.: 311613

BHJ UK Seafoods Ltd. (2)
30 Neptune Street, Hull, HU3 2BP, United Kingdom
Tel.: (44) 1482585646
Web Site: http://www.bhj.us
Sales Range: $10-24.9 Million
Emp.: 30
Seafood Distr
N.A.I.C.S.: 424460
Keith Binns (Mng Dir)

Subsidiary (US):

BHJ USA, Inc. (2)
2510 Ed Babe Gomez Ave, Omaha, NE 68107
Tel.: (402) 734-8030
Web Site: http://www.bhj.us
Sales Range: $25-49.9 Million
Emp.: 40
Meat & Meat By-Products Distr
N.A.I.C.S.: 424470
Thomas Christensen (Pres)
Debbie Navarro (Office Mgr)
Steven Beam (Engr-Maintenance)

Proliant Inc. (1)
2425 SE Oak Tree Ct, Ankeny, IA 50021
Tel.: (515) 289-5100
Web Site: http://www.proliantinc.com
Sales Range: $10-24.9 Million
Emp.: 75
Develops & Manufacture Food Ingredient
N.A.I.C.S.: 311999

LAURIER ENTERPRISES INC.
1235 Market St Ste A, Kirkland, WA 98033-5440
Tel.: (425) 822-1055
Rev.: $20,000,000
Emp.: 3
Franchise Owner of Fast Food Restaurants
N.A.I.C.S.: 722511
Brian Beaulaurier (Pres)

LAURIN PUBLISHING CO., INC.
100 W St, Pittsfield, MA 01201
Tel.: (413) 499-0514
Web Site: http://www.photonics.com
Year Founded: 1954
Sales Range: $10-24.9 Million
Emp.: 70
Publisher of Trade Journals
N.A.I.C.S.: 513120

LAURITZEN CORPORATION
1620 Dodge St 525, Omaha, NE 68102
Tel.: (402) 341-2535
Rev.: $13,800,000
Emp.: 10
National Commercial Banks
N.A.I.C.S.: 522110
Bruce Lauritzen (Pres)
Kirk Winheim (Mgr-First State Agency)
Kuehl Fred (VP)
Michael Mahlendorf (Pres)
Scott Hill (VP)

LAURUS CAPITAL MANAGEMENT, LLC
875 3rd Ave 3rd Fl, New York, NY 10022-7218
Tel.: (212) 541-5800 DE
Web Site:
http://www.laurusfunds.com
Year Founded: 2001
Sales Range: $1-4.9 Billion
Investment Advisory Services
N.A.I.C.S.: 523940
Eugene Grin (Co-Founder & Mgr-Funds)
David Grin (Co-Founder & Mgr-Funds)
Phillip Levy (Mng Dir)

Subsidiaries:

North Texas Steel Company, Inc. (1)
12900 Preston Rd Ste 1230, Dallas, TX 75230
Tel.: (817) 927-5333
Web Site: http://www.ntxstl.com
Sales Range: $10-24.9 Million
Emp.: 85
Fabricated Structural Steel Products Mfr
N.A.I.C.S.: 332312

LAURUS TECHNOLOGIES, INC.
1222 Hamilton Pkwy, Itasca, IL 60143
Tel.: (630) 875-9200
Web Site: http://www.laurustech.com
Year Founded: 1999
Rev.: $64,400,000
Emp.: 57
Computer Related Services
N.A.I.C.S.: 541512
John Udelhofen (Chm, Co-Founder & CEO)
Dave Durbin (Partner-Bus Dev)
Mike Clesceri (Partner-Sys Integration & VP-Mktg)
Mike Kerrigan (VP-Bus Applications)
Tony Hotko (VP-Talent Solutions)

LAUSELL INC.
Carr 2 Km 14 10 Millwork Hato Tejas, Bayamon, PR 00959
Tel.: (787) 798-7610
Web Site: http://www.lausell.com
Year Founded: 1947
Rev.: $69,100,000
Emp.: 775
Window & Door Frames
N.A.I.C.S.: 332321
Alberto M. Recio (Pres)
Eduardo Recio (VP)

LAUTH GROUP, INC
111 Congressional Blvd Ste 300, Carmel, IN 46032
Tel.: (317) 848-6500
Web Site: http://www.lauth.net
Year Founded: 1977
Sales Range: $10-24.9 Million
Commercial & Office Building Contractors
N.A.I.C.S.: 236220
Robert L. Lauth (Chm)
Michael J. Jones (Pres & CEO)
Michael J. Garvey (Chief Investment Officer)
Jonathan L. Goodburn (CFO)
Manish B. Gandhi (Exec VP-Construction)

LAVALLEY BUILDING SUPPLY INC.
351 Sunapee St, Newport, NH 03773-1489
Tel.: (603) 863-1050 NH
Web Site: http://www.lavalleys.com
Year Founded: 1962
Sales Range: $25-49.9 Million
Emp.: 200
Lumber & Other Building Materials Mfr & Distr
N.A.I.C.S.: 423310
Harold A. Lavalley (Chm)

LAVANTURE PRODUCTS COMPANY INC.
3806 Gallatin Way, Elkhart, IN 46515
Tel.: (574) 264-0658
Web Site: http://www.lavanture.com
Rev.: $116,700,000
Emp.: 55
Electrical Apparatus & Equipment, Wiring Supplies & Related Equipment Merchant Whslr
N.A.I.C.S.: 423610

Richard E. Lavanture (CFO & Pres)
Rich Ward (VP-Sls)

LAVELLE INDUSTRIES INC.
665 McHenry St, Burlington, WI 53105
Tel.: (262) 763-2434 WI
Web Site: http://www.lavelle.com
Year Founded: 1912
Sales Range: $100-124.9 Million
Emp.: 250
Mfr Rubber & Plastic Molded Parts for the OEM & Plumbing Industries
N.A.I.C.S.: 326299
Rhonda Sullivan (Pres)
Paul Sullivan (VP)
Kathryn Turke (VP-Sls)
Chris Kurth (Mgr-Tech Sls)

LAVERDIERE CONSTRUCTION INC.
4055 W Jackson St, Macomb, IL 61455
Tel.: (309) 837-1258
Web Site:
http://www.laverdiereconstruction.com
Sales Range: $10-24.9 Million
Emp.: 40
Commercial & Office Building, New Construction
N.A.I.C.S.: 236220
Jack E. Laverdiere (Pres)
Mitch Lynn (Project Mgr)
Michelle Allaman (Office Mgr)

LAVI INDUSTRIES INC.
27810 Ave Hopkins, Valencia, CA 91355-1246
Tel.: (661) 257-7800 CA
Web Site: http://www.lavi.com
Year Founded: 1980
Sales Range: $10-24.9 Million
Emp.: 150
Suppliers of Construction Materials
N.A.I.C.S.: 332323
Gabriel Lavi (CEO)
Chrissa Harris (CFO)
Devera Bogan (Mgr-Customer Svc)
Daniel Perry (VP-Sls)
Dana Levy (Acct Exec)

Subsidiaries:

Lavi Industries Inc. - New York Facility (1)
2 Geneva Rd, Brewster, NY 10509
Tel.: (661) 257-7800
Industrial Equipment Mfr
N.A.I.C.S.: 423820

LAVIDGE & ASSOCIATES INC.
6700 Baum Dr Ste 25, Knoxville, TN 37919
Tel.: (865) 584-6121
Web Site: http://www.lavidgeinc.com
Year Founded: 1950
Rev.: $10,750,000
Emp.: 10
Public Relations Agency
N.A.I.C.S.: 541820
Arthur W. Lavidge (Pres, Treas & Acct Exec)
Hal Ernest (Exec VP & Acct Exec)
Joyce McElyea (VP & Office Mgr)
Townes Lavidge Osborn (Exec VP & Acct Exec)

LAVOIE STRATEGIC COMMUNICATIONS GROUP, INC.
12 Derby Sq S1, Salem, MA 01970
Tel.: (978) 745-4200
Web Site:
http://www.lavoiegroup.com
Sales Range: $1-9.9 Million
Emp.: 6
Public Relations Agency
N.A.I.C.S.: 541820

U.S. PRIVATE

Donna L. LaVoie (Pres & CEO)
David Connolly (VP)
Michael Webb (COO & Exec VP)
Kristina Coppola (Dir-Comm Grp)
Ella Deych (Dir-Fin & Ops)
Lisa DeScenza (Dir-HR & Talent)
Nancy Heatley (Mgr-Mktg)
Kathy Vigneault (Supvr-Acct)

LAW BULLETIN PUBLISHING COMPANY
415 N State St, Chicago, IL 60654
Tel.: (312) 644-7800
Web Site: http://www.lawbulletin.com
Sales Range: $100-124.9 Million
Emp.: 150
Legal Publishing Services
N.A.I.C.S.: 513119
Febe Santos (Acct Mgr)
David Glynn (VP-Docket Mgmt Technologies)

LAW ENFORCEMENT ASSOCIATES CORPORATION
120 Penmarc Dr Ste 113, Raleigh, NC 27603
Tel.: (919) 872-6210 NV
Web Site: http://www.leacorp.com
Year Founded: 1998
Sales Range: $1-9.9 Million
Emp.: 27
Undercover Surveillance Products Mfr & Marketer
N.A.I.C.S.: 561621
Paige Briggs (Pres)

LAW ENFORCEMENT HEALTH BENEFITS, INC.
2233 Spring Garden St, Philadelphia, PA 19130
Tel.: (215) 763-8290 PA
Web Site: http://www.lehb.org
Year Founded: 1987
Sales Range: $100-124.9 Million
Emp.: 47
Health Benefit Services
N.A.I.C.S.: 525120
Cynthia E. Garey (Mgr-Member Svc)
Kristin Maszkiewicz (Mgr-Eligibility)

LAW ENFORCEMENT OFFICERS & FIREFIGHTERS HEALTH AND WELFARE TRUST
4407 N Division St, Spokane, WA 99207
Tel.: (509) 484-5598 WA
Year Founded: 1986
Sales Range: $10-24.9 Million
Emp.: 2
Employee Medical Benefit Services
N.A.I.C.S.: 525120
Jennifer S. Wisniewski (Program Mgr)
Ted Rail (Chm)

LAWCROSSING, INC.
20 S Altadena Dr, Pasadena, CA 91107
Tel.: (626) 243-1885
Web Site:
http://www.lawcrossing.com
Year Founded: 2000
Sales Range: $10-24.9 Million
Emp.: 50
Legal Recruiting Services
N.A.I.C.S.: 561311
A. Harrison Barnes (Founder & CEO)
Mary Waldron (Coord-Editorial)

LAWLER BALLARD VAN DU-RAND
31 Inverness Center Pkwy Ste 110, Birmingham, AL 35242-4822
Tel.: (205) 995-1775 AL
Web Site: http://www.lbvd.com

Year Founded: 1991
Rev.: $26,000,000
Emp.: 25
Full Service
N.A.I.C.S.: 541810
Tinsley Van Durand (Pres)
Pam Nail (Dir-Media)
Lee Little (Dir-Art)
Danielle Harden (Graphic Designer)

Subsidiaries:

Lawler Ballard Van Durand (1)
280 Elizabeth St Ste B201, Atlanta, GA 30307
Tel.: (404) 658-0232
Web Site: http://www.lbvd.com
Emp.: 5
N.A.I.C.S.: 541810
Bob Coyle (Mng Dir)
Steve Saari (Dir-Creative)
Hillary Steifelmeyer (Sr Mgr-Mktg)
April Laws (Dir-Art)

LAWLEY AUTOMOTIVE GROUP

2900 E Fry Blvd, Sierra Vista, AZ 85635
Tel.: (520) 458-6520
Web Site: http://www.lawleycars.com
Sales Range: $10-24.9 Million
Emp.: 35
Automobiles, New & Used
N.A.I.C.S.: 441110
W. Sean Lawley (Owner & Pres)

LAWLEY MOTORS LLC

2900 E Fry Blvd, Sierra Vista, AZ 85635
Tel.: (520) 458-2141
Web Site: http://www.lawleycars.com
Rev.: $30,500,000
Emp.: 61
Automobiles, New & Used
N.A.I.C.S.: 441110

LAWLEY SERVICE INC.

361 Delaware Ave, Buffalo, NY 14202
Tel.: (716) 849-8618
Web Site: http://www.lawleyinsurance.com
Year Founded: 1945
Sales Range: $25-49.9 Million
Emp.: 370
Insurance Services
N.A.I.C.S.: 524210
Christopher D. Ross (Principal)
Michael R. Lawley (Principal)
Bill Fritts (Partner)
Brad Hall (Partner)
James Verdi (Partner)
Mark Verdi (Partner)
Phil Andolina (Partner)
Stuart Scheff (Partner)
Thomas Sachs (Partner)
Wally Gotowka (Partner)
William J. Lawley Jr. (Principal)

Subsidiaries:

Lawley Automotive (1)
361 Delaware Ave, Buffalo, NY 14202
Tel.: (716) 854-6410
Web Site: http://www.lawleyinsurance.com
Sales Range: $50-74.9 Million
Emp.: 7
Full Service Provider of Types of Auto Warranty & Aftermarket Products
N.A.I.C.S.: 524128
Todd F. Best (CEO)
Thomas R. Burke (Pres)
Carolyn Kullman (CFO & COO)

Lawley Benefits Group, LLC (1)
361 Delaware Ave, Buffalo, NY 14202
Tel.: (716) 849-8618
Web Site: http://www.lawleyinsurance.com
Sales Range: $50-74.9 Million
Emp.: 250
Provider of Employee & Financial Benefit Consultant Services
N.A.I.C.S.: 524210

T. J. Revelas (Mng Partner-Employee Benefits)
Brian Murphy (Partner)

Shoff Darby Companies Inc. (1)
401 Merritt 7 Piazza Level, Norwalk, CT 06851
Tel.: (203) 354-6200
Web Site: http://www.shoffdarby.com
Women's, Girls & Infants Cut & Sew Apparel Contractors
N.A.I.C.S.: 315210
Frank Auriemma (VP)
Matthew Roberts (Pres)

LAWMAN HEATING & COOLING, INC.

206 Ambrose St, Sackets Harbor, NY 13685
Tel.: (315) 646-2919
Web Site: http://www.lawmanhc.com
Year Founded: 1978
Sales Range: $50-74.9 Million
Emp.: 275
Plumbing, Heating & Air-Conditioning Services
N.A.I.C.S.: 238220
Neil Lawler (Gen Mgr)

LAWMEN SUPPLY COMPANY OF NEW JERSEY, INC.

7115 Airport Hwy, Pennsauken, NJ 08109
Tel.: (609) 965-7307
Web Site: http://www.lawmensupply.com
Sales Range: $10-24.9 Million
Emp.: 26
Firearms & Ammunition
N.A.I.C.S.: 459999
Linda Magolda (Pres)

LAWN AND GOLF SUPPLY CO., INC.

647 Nutt Rd, Phoenixville, PA 19460
Tel.: (610) 933-5801
Web Site: http://www.lawn-golf.com
Sales Range: $10-24.9 Million
Emp.: 28
Agricultural Equipment & Supplies Whslr
N.A.I.C.S.: 424910
Warren L. Saylor (Sec & Controller)
Robert Holman (Pres)
Dave Conver (Mgr-Credit)
Robert Miller (VP-Svc)
Ken Jeinnings (Sr VP-Sls)
Scott Holman (Dir-Mktg)

LAWN BUTLER INC.

86 S 1250 W, Bountiful, UT 84010
Tel.: (801) 298-3330
Web Site: http://www.lawnbutler.net
Year Founded: 2006
Sales Range: $1-9.9 Million
Emp.: 70
Landscape Management Services
N.A.I.C.S.: 561730
Clayton Phillipps (Mgr-Ops)

LAWN DOCTOR INC.

142 State Rte 34, Holmdel, NJ 07733
Tel.: (732) 946-0029
Web Site: http://www.lawndoctor.com
Year Founded: 1967
Sales Range: $75-99.9 Million
Emp.: 70
Lawn Care Franchisor
N.A.I.C.S.: 533110
Scott Frith (Pres & CEO)

LAWRENCE & SCHILLER, INC.

3932 S Willow Ave, Sioux Falls, SD 57105-6234
Tel.: (605) 338-8000
Web Site: http://www.l-s.com
Year Founded: 1976
Rev.: $13,500,000

Emp.: 55
Advetising Agency
N.A.I.C.S.: 541810
Scott Lawrence (Pres & CEO)
Dan Edmonds (Sr VP-Dir-Design)
John Pohlman (Exec VP)
Mark Glissendorf (Sr VP-Ops & Multimedia)
Tom Helland (VP-Bus Dev)
Dave Haan (VP-Deployment-Digital, Disruptive & PR)
John Sievert (VP-Bus Dev)
Scott Wiechmann (Sr Dir-Creative)
Sarah Pitts (Sr Dir-Art)
Laura Mitchell (Dir-Digital Mktg)
Tracy Saathoff (Dir-Consumer Insights)
Sam Gotham (Assoc Acct Exec)
Cortney Slaight (Assoc Acct Exec)

LAWRENCE A. BROOKS INC.

211 Beechwood St, Thomaston, ME 04861
Tel.: (207) 354-8763
Rev.: $10,042,093
Emp.: 27
Fishing Equipment
N.A.I.C.S.: 423910

LAWRENCE COUNTY ECONOMIC DEVELOPMENT CORPORATION

Piazza S 101 E Reynolds St, New Castle, PA 16101
Tel.: (724) 658-1488
Year Founded: 1955
Sales Range: $1-9.9 Million
Emp.: 4
Business & Economic Developmental Services
N.A.I.C.S.: 813910
Linda Nitch (Exec Dir)
Sam Biasucci (Pres)
Nicholas Paolini (Treas & Sec)

LAWRENCE COUNTY MEMORIAL HOSPITAL

2200 State St, Lawrenceville, IL 62439
Tel.: (618) 943-1000
Web Site: http://www.lcmhosp.org
Year Founded: 1950
Sales Range: $10-24.9 Million
Health Care Srvices
N.A.I.C.S.: 622110
Doug Florkowski (CEO)
Larry Spour (CFO)
Ron Waldrop (Vice Chm)
Becky Nestleroad (Sec)
Carl Aten (Chm)
Curt Benson (Treas)

LAWRENCE COUNTY NEWSPAPERS, INC.

16 S Park St, Sapulpa, OK 74066-4220
Tel.: (918) 224-5185
Web Site: http://www.sapulpaheraldonline.com
Emp.: 15
Newspaper Publishers
N.A.I.C.S.: 513110
Vickie Toothman (Office Mgr)
Teresa Cooper (Mgr-Production)
Darren Sumner (Publr)

LAWRENCE FINANCIAL CORPORATION

1400 Kasold Dr, Lawrence, KS 66049
Tel.: (785) 841-1988
Web Site: http://www.unbank.com
Year Founded: 1987
Sales Range: $1-9.9 Million
Emp.: 16
Bank Holding Company

N.A.I.C.S.: 551111
Todd Sutherland (Pres & CEO)

Subsidiaries:

The University National Bank of Lawrence (1)
1400 Kasold Dr, Lawrence, KS 66049
Tel.: (785) 841-1988
Web Site: http://www.unbank.com
Sales Range: $25-49.9 Million
Emp.: 25
Commericial Banking
N.A.I.C.S.: 522110
Todd Sutherland (Pres)
Andrea Stidham (Asst VP-Retail)
David Bennett (VP)
Jordan Riedel (Asst VP)
Sandra Studley (CFO & Sr VP)

LAWRENCE HALL CHEVROLET INC.

1385 S Danville Dr, Abilene, TX 79605
Tel.: (325) 695-8800
Web Site: http://www.lawrencehall.com
Sales Range: $10-24.9 Million
Emp.: 125
Automobiles, New & Used
N.A.I.C.S.: 441110
Larry Hall (Pres)
Kirk Kennedy (Mgr-Gen Sls)

LAWRENCE HALL CHEVROLET OLDSMOBILE BUICK INC.

2120 Comml Ave, Anson, TX 79501-5219
Tel.: (325) 823-3261
Web Site: http://www.lawrencehallchevrolet.com
Year Founded: 1973
Sales Range: $10-24.9 Million
Emp.: 50
New & Used Car Dealers
N.A.I.C.S.: 441110
John Speer (Gen Mgr)

LAWRENCE OIL CO. INC.

1610 S Broadway Ave, Othello, WA 99344
Tel.: (509) 488-9223
Rev.: $15,713,243
Emp.: 25
Petroleum Bulk Stations
N.A.I.C.S.: 424710

LAWRENCE PAPER COMPANY

2801 Lakeview Rd, Lawrence, KS 66049
Tel.: (785) 843-8111
Web Site: http://www.lpco.net
Year Founded: 1882
Sales Range: $150-199.9 Million
Emp.: 450
Corrugated Boxes & Thermoformed Packaging Mfr & Retailer
N.A.I.C.S.: 322211
Jim Mowder (Controller)
Trudy Walker (Asst Controller)
Justin Hill Jr. (Owner)

Subsidiaries:

Brad Systems, Inc. (1)
2901 Lakeview Rd, Lawrence, KS 66049
Tel.: (785) 843-2889
Web Site: http://www.lpco.net
Sales Range: $10-24.9 Million
Emp.: 50
Software Publisher
N.A.I.C.S.: 513210

The Packaging Cafe (1)
2400 Lakeview Rd, Lawrence, KS 66049
Tel.: (785) 843-8111
Web Site: http://www.thepackagingcafe.net
Sales Range: $10-24.9 Million
Emp.: 30
Packing Solutions
N.A.I.C.S.: 488991

Lawrence Paper Company—(Continued)
Dave Wiese *(Gen Mgr)*

LAWRENCE RAGAN COMMUNICATIONS, INC.
316 N Michigan Ave Suite 400, Chicago, IL 60601
Tel.: (312) 960-4100
Web Site: http://www.ragan.com
Year Founded: 1970
Sales Range: $1-9.9 Million
Emp.: 50
Social Media, Speechwriting, Events, Training, HR Communication & Public Relations
N.A.I.C.S.: 541820
Roula Amire *(VP-Editorial)*
Yolanda Maggi *(VP-Conferences & Workshops)*
Keri Gavin *(Dir-Host Rels & Custom Workshops)*
Mandy Zaransky-Hurst *(COO & CMO)*
Kristin Farmer *(Dir-Sls & Strategic Partnerships)*
Mary McMahon *(Mgr-Awards Program)*
Kirsten Beals *(Sr Mgr-Event Plng & Logistic)*
Jennifer Mazurek *(VP-Mktg Ops)*

LAWRENCE RUBEN CO.
600 Madison Ave, New York, NY 10022-1676
Tel.: (212) 293-9400
Web Site: http://www.rubenco.com
Year Founded: 1959
Sales Range: $1-4.9 Billion
Emp.: 3,000
Real Estate Management Services
N.A.I.C.S.: 531210
Perry Kamerman *(CFO)*
Susanne Lieu *(Mng Dir)*
John Schrenker *(COO)*
Joseph Zarrella *(Controller)*
Richard G. Ruben *(CEO)*

LAWRENCE TRACTOR COMPANY INC.
2530 E Main St, Visalia, CA 93292
Tel.: (559) 734-7406
Web Site: http://www.lawrencetractor.com
Sales Range: $25-49.9 Million
Emp.: 32
Dealer of Agricultural Machinery
N.A.I.C.S.: 423820
Richard Nunes *(CFO)*

LAWRENCE TRANSPORTATION SERVICES, INC.
1515 Industrial Dr NW, Rochester, MN 55901
Tel.: (507) 282-6715
Web Site: http://www.lawrencetrans.com
Year Founded: 1957
Sales Range: $50-74.9 Million
Emp.: 200
Transportation Services
N.A.I.C.S.: 488999
Stephen Lawrence *(Co-Pres)*
Eric Lawrence *(Co-Pres)*

LAWRENCE TRANSPORTATION SYSTEMS INC.
872 Lee Hwy, Roanoke, VA 24019-8516
Tel.: (540) 966-4000
Web Site: http://www.lawrencetransportation.com
Year Founded: 1932
Sales Range: $50-74.9 Million
Emp.: 350
Transportation, Moving & Storage
N.A.I.C.S.: 484210
Scott German *(Acct Mgr-Natl)*
David Snyder *(Mgr-Compliance & Safety)*
Faye Bridges *(Acct Mgr-Natl)*
Glenn Skelton *(Mgr-Freight)*
Mark Carter *(Mgr-IT)*
Shane Way *(Mgr)*
Regina Durnal *(Acct Mgr-Natl)*

LAWRENCE-LYNCH CORPORATION
396 Gifford St, Falmouth, MA 02540
Tel.: (508) 548-1800
Web Site: http://lawrencelynch.com
Year Founded: 2004
Sales Range: $10-24.9 Million
Emp.: 100
Civil Engineering Services
N.A.I.C.S.: 237310
Christopher M. Lynch *(Pres)*

LAWRENCEVILLE FORD LINCOLN MERCURY
2920 Brunswick Pike, Lawrenceville, NJ 08648
Tel.: (609) 372-5290
Web Site: http://www.lawrencevillefl.com
Sales Range: $25-49.9 Million
Emp.: 60
New Car Dealership
N.A.I.C.S.: 441110
Anthony Stewart *(Pres)*

LAWRY FREIGHT SYSTEM, INC.
1111 Southampton Rd, Westfield, MA 01085
Tel.: (413) 562-9626
Web Site: http://www.lawryusa.com
Year Founded: 1978
Supply Chain Management & Logistics Services
N.A.I.C.S.: 541614
Dan Lawry *(Owner & Pres)*

LAWRY'S RESTAURANTS, INC.
234 E Colorado Blvd Ste 500, Pasadena, CA 91101
Tel.: (626) 440-5234
Web Site: http://www.lawrysonline.com
Year Founded: 1938
Sales Range: $125-149.9 Million
Emp.: 650
Restaurant Owner & Franchise Operator
N.A.I.C.S.: 722511
Nancy Brosseit *(Mgr-Mktg & Sls)*
Ed Lepere *(Gen Mgr)*
Ellen Fremaux *(Mgr-Mktg & Sls)*
Alison Robbins *(Mgr-Sls & Mktg)*
Jim Colombo *(Gen Mgr)*
Max Maxwell *(Gen Mgr)*
Michelle Rizzo *(Mgr-Sls & Mktg)*
Shannon Tauschman *(Mgr-Sls & Mktg)*
Steven Giancotti *(Gen Mgr)*
Thea Mesina *(Gen Mgr)*

LAWSON CHEVROLET INC.
545 Hwy 515 S, Jasper, GA 30143
Tel.: (706) 692-3441
Web Site: http://www.dayschevrolet.com
Rev.: $15,000,000
Emp.: 42
Automobile Dearler
N.A.I.C.S.: 441120
Mike Cowart *(Mgr-Svc)*

LAWSON ELECTRIC COMPANY
409 Spring St, Chattanooga, TN 37405
Tel.: (423) 267-5471
Web Site: http://www.lawsonelectric.com
Sales Range: $125-149.9 Million
Emp.: 350
Electrical Contractor
N.A.I.C.S.: 238210
Ted Caldwell *(Project Mgr)*
Jeremy Eldridge *(Project Mgr)*
Bell Cranford *(Pres)*

LAWSON MECHANICAL CONTRACTORS
6090 S Watt Ave, Sacramento, CA 95829-1301
Tel.: (916) 381-5000
Web Site: http://www.lawsonmechanical.com
Year Founded: 1947
Sales Range: $100-124.9 Million
Emp.: 150
Plumbing, Heating & Air Conditioning Services
N.A.I.C.S.: 238220
Rodney Lawson *(COO)*
Rodney Barbour *(VP)*
Larry Craig *(Mgr-Acctg)*
David Lawson *(Pres & CEO)*

LAXAI PHARMA, LTD.
8905 Regents Park Dr Ste 210, Tampa, FL 33647
Tel.: (813) 428-3500
Web Site: http://www.laxai.com
Year Founded: 1988
Pharmaceutical Contract Research Services
N.A.I.C.S.: 541715
J. Ram Ajjarapu *(Chm)*
Richard J. Mycka *(Dir-Project Mgmt/Engrg)*

LAY BROTHERS INC.
775 Winterville Rd, Athens, GA 30605
Tel.: (706) 543-6571
Web Site: http://www.laybrothers.com
Rev.: $11,457,284
Emp.: 6
Petroleum Products
N.A.I.C.S.: 424720
Harriet Garrett *(Pres)*

LAYMAN CANDY COMPANY, INC.
1630 W Main St, Salem, VA 24153-4526
Tel.: (540) 389-2000
Web Site: http://www.laymandistributing.com
Year Founded: 1948
Sales Range: $75-99.9 Million
Emp.: 50
Tobacco, Tobacco Products & Confectionery Mfr & Distr
N.A.I.C.S.: 424940
Juanita L. Neely *(Pres)*
Glen Bowe *(VP)*
Judy Ross *(Treas & Sec)*

LAYTON HILLS DODGE INC.
1234 N Main St, Layton, UT 84041-4854
Tel.: (801) 546-2456
Web Site: http://www.laytonhillsdodge.com
Rev.: $37,900,000
Emp.: 50
Automobiles, New & Used
N.A.I.C.S.: 441110
Phedia Cutrubus *(Pres)*

LAZ PARKING LTD, LLC
15 Lewis St, Hartford, CT 06103
Tel.: (860) 522-7641
Web Site: http://www.lazparking.com
Year Founded: 1981
Sales Range: $1-4.9 Billion
Emp.: 10,700
Parking Management Services
N.A.I.C.S.: 812930
Alan B. Lazowski *(Co-Founder, Chm & CEO)*
Jeffrey N. Karp *(Co-Founder & Pres)*
Michael Harth *(Co-Founder & Chief Culture Officer)*
Michael J. Kuziak *(COO)*
Nathan Owen *(CFO)*
Raymond H. Skoglund *(Treas)*
Andi Campbell *(VP-HR)*

Subsidiaries:

Alpha Park (1)
1401 17th St, Denver, CO 80202-1268
Tel.: (303) 291-1111
Web Site: http://www.alphaparkco.com
Nature Parks & Other Institutions
N.A.I.C.S.: 712190
John Richmond *(Dir-Library)*

International Parking Management, Inc. (1)
505 5th Ave S Ste P1, Seattle, WA 98104
Tel.: (206) 254-0811
Web Site: http://www.ipmseattle.com
Sales Range: $1-9.9 Million
Emp.: 35
Parking Lots & Garages
N.A.I.C.S.: 812930
Stephen Sundberg *(Pres)*

LAZAR INDUSTRIES LLC
620 East Slauson Ave PO Box 11397, Los Angeles, CA 90011
Tel.: (323) 232-7170
Web Site: http://www.lazarind.com
Sales Range: $10-24.9 Million
Emp.: 250
Upholstered Household Furniture
N.A.I.C.S.: 337121

LAZARD GLOBAL TOTAL RETURN & INCOME FUND, INC.
30 Rockefeller Plz, New York, NY 10112
Tel.: (212) 632-6000
Web Site: http://www.lazardassetmanagement.com
Year Founded: 1851
Asset Management Services
N.A.I.C.S.: 523940
James M. Donald *(Mng Dir, Head-Emerging Markets & Portfolio Mgr)*
Nathan A. Paul *(Pres & CEO)*

LAZARD WORLD DIVIDEND & INCOME FUND, INC.
Lazard Funds 30 Rockefeller Plz, New York, NY 10112
Tel.: (212) 632-6000
Investment Management Service
N.A.I.C.S.: 525910
Andrew D. Lacey *(Mgr-Fund)*

LAZARE KAPLAN INTERNATIONAL, INC.
19 W 44th St, New York, NY 10036
Tel.: (212) 972-9700
Web Site: http://www.lazarediamonds.com
Year Founded: 1903
Sales Range: $350-399.9 Million
Diamond Cutter, Polisher & Distr
N.A.I.C.S.: 423940
Maurice Tempelsman *(Chm)*
Marcee M. Feinberg *(VP-Mktg)*
Danny Davis *(VP-Preferred Div)*

Subsidiaries:

Lazare Kaplan Belgium N.V. (1)
Hoveniersstraat 30 9th Fl, 2018, Antwerp, Belgium (100%)
Tel.: (32) 32138100

Web Site: http://www.lazarediamond.com
Sales Range: $25-49.9 Million
Emp.: 4
Diamond House
N.A.I.C.S.: 458310
Marc Ost (Controller)

LAZORPOINT, LLC
The Caxton Bldg 812 Huron Rd Ste 800, Cleveland, OH 44115
Tel.: (216) 325-5200
Web Site: http://www.lazorpoint.com
Year Founded: 1997
Sales Range: $1-9.9 Million
Emp.: 27
Consulting Services
N.A.I.C.S.: 541618
David M. Lazor (Mng Partner)
Tim Gregory (Mng Partner)

LAZY-BOY FURNITURE GALLERIES
20752 SW 120 Ave, Tualatin, OR 97062
Tel.: (503) 691-4444
Web Site: http://www.la-z-boy.co.uk
Sales Range: $10-24.9 Million
Emp.: 150
Furniture Retailer
N.A.I.C.S.: 449110
Brad Parker (Pres)
Jessica Walters (Office Mgr)

LAZZARA YACHT CORP.
801 Seabreeze Blvd, Fort Lauderdale, FL 33316
Tel.: (813) 839-0090
Web Site:
http://www.lazzarayachts.com
Sales Range: $25-49.9 Million
Emp.: 500
Boat Building
N.A.I.C.S.: 336612
John Murray (COO)

LB ELECTRIC SUPPLY CO. INC.
5202 New Utrecht Ave, Brooklyn, NY 11219
Tel.: (718) 438-4700
Web Site: http://www.lbelectric.com
Sales Range: $10-24.9 Million
Emp.: 50
Electrical Supplies
N.A.I.C.S.: 423610
Carol Lifton (Pres)
Jon Lifton (VP)
Lisa Lifton (VP)

LB INTERNATIONAL, INC.
150 Engineers Rd, Hauppauge, NY 11788
Tel.: (631) 236-4400
Web Site: http://www.lbimports.com
Rev.: $28,428,122
Emp.: 25
Christmas Novelties, Spring & Summer Seasonal & Furniture
N.A.I.C.S.: 424990
Chris Stanley (Mng Dir)
Michael McDermott (Mng Dir)
Lori Bliss (Mgr-Collections)
Glenn Debaere (VP)
Nick Sudano (VP-Mdsg)

LB&L CABLE INC.
1501 Southeast 4th St Ste D, Moore, OK 73160
Tel.: (405) 799-9974
Rev.: $21,069,560
Emp.: 18
Cable Television Line Construction
N.A.I.C.S.: 238210

LBA GROUP, INC.
3400 Tupper Dr, Greenville, NC 27834
Tel.: (252) 757-0279 NC
Web Site: http://www.lbagroup.com
Year Founded: 1963
Radio & Wireless Communications Equipment Mfr
N.A.I.C.S.: 334220
Lawrence V. Behr (CEO)
Juliana Price (Controller & Bus Mgr)
Jamien Durrence (Dir-HR & Admin)
Eric Martinez (Partner-Audit & Assurance Svcs)
Jonathan Lee (Mgr-Tax)
Emily Cornaire (Principal-Tax)
Becky Mincer (Principal-Tax)
Marley Harris (Dir-Bus Acctg Solutions)
Mike Britner (VP-Sls)
Ashley Johnston (Mgr-Bus & Fin)
Carolyn Linton (Mktg Dir)
Michael W. Hayden (VP-Site Svcs)
Betty Perez (Dir-Logistics & Resources)
Adam Carlson (Dir-Wireless Bus)
Ben Cobb (CFO & COO)
Bryan K. Dixon Sr. (Dir-EHS Svcs)

LBA REALTY LLC
3347 Michelson Dr Ste 200, Irvine, CA 92612
Tel.: (949) 833-0400
Web Site: http://www.lbarealty.com
Sales Range: $25-49.9 Million
Emp.: 140
Real Estate Investment & Management Services
N.A.I.C.S.: 531390
Perry Schonfeld (Principal-Ops)
Brad Neglia (Principal)
Tom Motherway (Sr VP-Dispositions)
Tom Rutherford (Sr VP-Fin)
Alice Wilson (VP-Corp Svcs)

LBF ENTERPRISES
1057 Serpentine Ln, Pleasanton, CA 94566
Tel.: (925) 461-7171
Web Site: http://www.powermatic.net
Rev.: $12,000,000
Emp.: 35
Electronic Parts
N.A.I.C.S.: 423690
Tim Willis (Mgr)

LBM CONSTRUCTION COMPANY, INC.
11421 Blankenbaker Access Dr, Louisville, KY 40299
Tel.: (502) 452-1151
Web Site:
http://www.lbmconstructionco.com
Year Founded: 1982
Sales Range: $25-49.9 Million
Emp.: 60
Commercial & Institutional Building Construction Services
N.A.I.C.S.: 236220
Jeff W. McLellan (Exec VP)

LBM CORP.
641 Cowpath Rd, Lansdale, PA 19446
Tel.: (215) 855-0400
Web Site: http://www.lizell.com
Sales Range: $10-24.9 Million
Emp.: 10
Office Furniture Distr
N.A.I.C.S.: 449110
Anthony Lizell (Pres)
Martin Kaffenderg (Controller)

LBS FINANCIAL CREDIT UNION
5505 Garden Grove Blvd, Westminster, CA 92683
Tel.: (714) 893-5111 CA
Web Site: http://www.lbsfcu.org
Year Founded: 1935
Sales Range: $25-49.9 Million
Emp.: 278
Credit Union
N.A.I.C.S.: 522130
Jeffrey A. Napper (Pres & CEO)
Eric David (Vice Chm)
Gene R. Allen (Treas & Sec)

LBU, INC.
217 Brook Ave, Passaic, NJ 07055
Tel.: (973) 773-4800
Web Site: http://www.lbuinc.com
Year Founded: 1987
Sales Range: $200-249.9 Million
Emp.: 50
Sports Bags & Gear Bags Mfr
N.A.I.C.S.: 314910
Jeff Mayer (CEO)

LC ENTERPRISES LLC
1200 E Algonquin Rd, Des Plaines, IL 60016
Tel.: (847) 827-7500
Rev.: $30,700,000
Emp.: 4
Automotive Supplies & Parts
N.A.I.C.S.: 813930
Bill Curtis (Controller)

LC GROUP LLC
708 Walnut St, Cincinnati, OH 45202
Tel.: (678) 225-3100
Emp.: 100
Scientific & Technical Consulting Services
N.A.I.C.S.: 541690
Joe Boyd (CEO & Mng Partner)
Subsidiaries:

Giant Impact, LLC (1)
3760 Peachtree Crest Dr, Duluth, GA 30097
Tel.: (678) 225-3116
Rev.: $3,000,000
Emp.: 45
Other Scientific & Technical Consulting Services
N.A.I.C.S.: 541690

LC MORTGAGE CORPORATION
4201 Wilshire Blvd Ste 501, Los Angeles, CA 90010
Tel.: (323) 954-1050
Web Site: http://www.viewtlc.com
Rev.: $50,000,000
Mortgage Services
N.A.I.C.S.: 522310

LC SUREFOOT
1500 Kearns Blvd Ste A-100, Park City, UT 84060
Tel.: (435) 655-8110
Web Site: http://www.surefoot.com
Sales Range: $10-24.9 Million
Emp.: 8
Shoe Stores
N.A.I.C.S.: 458210
Patti Polster (Controller)

LC3S INC.
11135 Folsom Blvd, Rancho Cordova, CA 95670
Tel.: (916) 638-0733
Web Site: http://www.brookrest.com
Sales Range: $10-24.9 Million
Emp.: 200
Restaurant
N.A.I.C.S.: 722511
Sam Manolakas (Pres)
Stacy Haden (VP-Ops)

LCA-VISION INC.
7840 Montgomery Rd Ste 100 1st Fl, Cincinnati, OH 45236
Tel.: (513) 792-9292 DE
Web Site: http://www.lasikplus.com
Year Founded: 1986
Sales Range: $75-99.9 Million
Laser Vision Correction Centers
N.A.I.C.S.: 621491
Rhonda S. Sebastian (Sr VP-HR)
Barb Kise (Dir-Admin)
Jenn Mullins (Sr Mgr-HR)

LCEL COLLECTIBLES INC.
132 W 36 St 2nd Fl, New York, NY 10018-4848
Tel.: (212) 944-7370
Web Site:
http://www.carmenmarcvalvo.com
Year Founded: 1993
Sales Range: $10-24.9 Million
Emp.: 50
Women's Clothing Mfr
N.A.I.C.S.: 315250
Carmen Valvo (CEO)
Joyce Bean (CFO)
Christian Knaust (Pres)

LCG TECHNOLOGIES CORPORATION
5523 Research Park Dr Ste 140, Baltimore, MD 21228
Tel.: (410) 560-0307
Web Site: http://www.lcgtech.com
Year Founded: 1994
Sales Range: $10-24.9 Million
Emp.: 60
Information & Communications Technology Solutions
N.A.I.C.S.: 541512
Tom Lang (Founder & CEO)
Nigel Knowles (Pres)
Raymond Tye (COO)

LCMC HEALTH HOLDINGS, INC.
200 Henry Clay Ave, New Orleans, LA 70118
Tel.: (504) 702-4862
Web Site: http://www.lcmchealth.org
Hospital & Healthcare Services
N.A.I.C.S.: 622110
Gregory Feirn (CEO)

LCP ACQUISITION CORP.
50 Main St Ste 1410, White Plains, NY 10606
Tel.: (914) 289-0224 Ky
Year Founded: 2020
Investment Services
N.A.I.C.S.: 523999
Steven Goldman (Chm & CEO)
E. Robert Roskind (Vice Chm)
Francis Lively (Pres & COO)
Peter Sullivan (CFO)

LCS CONSTRUCTORS, INC.
15205 Alton Pkwy, Irvine, CA 92618
Tel.: (949) 870-4500
Web Site: http://www.lcslab.com
Rev.: $18,000,000
Emp.: 65
Specialized Public Building Contractors
N.A.I.C.S.: 236220
Dominick Ranalli (Pres)
Marc Scott (VP & Mgr-Ops-Texas & Gulf Coast Reg)
Stephen A. Metzger (VP-Construction & Gen Mgr-California)
Carey Collier (Project Mgr)

LCS HOLDINGS INC.
400 Locust St Ste 820, Des Moines, IA 50309-2334
Tel.: (515) 875-4500
Web Site: http://www.lcsnet.com
Commercial & Office Building Construction
N.A.I.C.S.: 236220

LCS HOLDINGS INC.

LCS Holdings Inc.—(Continued)

Liz Bush (Sr VP-Mktg & Sls)
Ed Kenny (Chm & CEO)
Kent Larson (Dir-Dev)
Joel Nelson (Pres & COO)
Monica Friedman (Chief HR Officer & Sr VP)
Joe Weisenburger (VP & Sr Dir-Bus Dev)
Rick Exline (Exec VP)

Subsidiaries:

CRSA (1)
3350 Players Club Pkwy, Memphis, TN 38125
Tel.: (901) 685-5350
Web Site: http://www.crsaLCS.com
Emp.: 12
Elder Care Services
N.A.I.C.S.: 623312
Earl Wade (COO)
Suzanne Alford (Dir-Ops Mgmt)
Gayle Welsh (VP & Dir-Mktg & Sls)
Chrisine Weaver (Dir-Comm)
Kathy Bradshaw (Reg Dir-HR)

Chester Woods Inc. (1)
317 W Main St, Chester, CT 06412
Tel.: (860) 526-6800
Web Site: http://www.chestervillagewestlcs.com
Sales Range: $10-24.9 Million
Emp.: 40
Retirement Hotel Operation
N.A.I.C.S.: 531110
Robert Taylor (Gen Mgr)

Encore Senior Living, LLC (1)
6400 SE Lake Rd Ste 400, Milwaukie, OR 97222
Tel.: (503) 905-3300
Web Site: http://www.encoresl.com
Elder Care Services
N.A.I.C.S.: 623312

Friends Retirement Concepts, Inc. (1)
100 Monroe St, Bridgewater, NJ 08807
Tel.: (908) 595-6500
Web Site: http://www.laurelcirclelcs.com
Senior Living Services
N.A.I.C.S.: 623311
Felix Rosenwasser (CEO & CFO)

Health at Home (1)
1 10th St Ste 500, Augusta, GA 30901
Tel.: (800) 241-3368
Web Site: http://www.healthathomelcs.com
Elder Care Services
N.A.I.C.S.: 621610
Clinton Wynn (Coord-Care)

Life Care Home Health Services Corp (1)
800 NW 17th Ave Ste B, Delray Beach, FL 33445
Tel.: (561) 272-7779
Sales Range: $25-49.9 Million
Emp.: 60
Women Healthcare Services
N.A.I.C.S.: 621610
Denise Spiewak (COO & VP)
Marlene Peritzman (Coord-AR)

Life Care Services LLC (1)
400 Locust St Ste 820, Des Moines, IA 50309-2334 (100%)
Tel.: (515) 875-4500
Web Site: http://www.lcsnet.com
Retirement Communities Operator
N.A.I.C.S.: 531110
Diane C. Bridgewater (CFO, Chief Admin Officer & Exec VP)
Greg Williams (Sr VP & Sr Dir-Ops Mgmt)

Subsidiary (Domestic):

Villa at San Mateo (2)
4000 S El Camino Real, San Mateo, CA 94403-4566
Tel.: (650) 212-4400
Web Site: http://www.thevillaatsanmateo.com
Lessors of Residential Buildings & Dwellings
N.A.I.C.S.: 531110
Stephen Haws (Mgr)

LCS TECHNOLOGIES, INC.

11230 Gold Express Dr Suite 310-140, Gold River, CA 95670
Tel.: (855) 277-5527
Web Site: http://www.lcs-technologies-inc.com
Year Founded: 2006
Sales Range: $1-9.9 Million
Emp.: 16
IT Solutions, Training & Products for Oracle Software
N.A.I.C.S.: 519290
Steve Simonetto (Co-Founder & COO)
Chris Wilson (VP-Bus Dev)
Michele Johnson (Acct Mgr)

LCT GLOBAL RESOURCES, INC.

4790 Caughlin Pkwy Ste 387, Reno, NV 89519
Tel.: (775) 232-1950
Year Founded: 2011
Management Consulting Services
N.A.I.C.S.: 541618
Chee Thing Lee (Pres, CEO, CFO, Sec & Treas)

LCV CAPITAL MANAGEMENT, LLC

650 Smithfield St, Pittsburgh, PA 15222
Tel.: (412) 281-7000
Web Site: http://www.lcvcapitalmgmt.com
Investment Managment Company
N.A.I.C.S.: 523999
Lodovico de Visconti (Mng Partner)
Anthony Bonidy (CEO & Mng Dir)

Subsidiaries:

Peerless Systems Corporation (1)
1055 Washington Blvd 8th Fl, Stamford, CT 06901
Tel.: (203) 350-0040
Web Site: http://www.peerless.com
Rev.: $3,605,000
Assets: $14,066,000
Liabilities: $1,939,000
Net Worth: $12,127,000
Earnings: ($858,000)
Fiscal Year-end: 01/31/2014
Software Based Imaging Systems Mfr
N.A.I.C.S.: 334118

Subsidiary (Domestic):

Deer Valley Corporation (2)
205 Carriage St, Guin, AL 35563 (80%)
Tel.: (205) 468-8400
Web Site: https://www.deervalleyhb.com
Sales Range: $25-49.9 Million
Emp.: 200
Holding Company; Mobile Home Builder
N.A.I.C.S.: 321991

Subsidiary (Domestic):

Deer Valley Homebuilders, Inc. (3)
205 Carriage St, Guin, AL 35563
Tel.: (205) 468-8400
Web Site: http://www.deervalleyhb.com
Mobile Home Builder
N.A.I.C.S.: 321991
Steve Lawler (Co-Founder, Pres, CFO & Exec VP)
Joey Aycock (Co-Founder, Exec VP & Gen Mgr)

LDF FOOD GROUP

10610 E 26th Cir N, Wichita, KS 67226-4536
Tel.: (316) 636-6575
Web Site: http://www.ldfcompanies.com
Sales Range: $50-74.9 Million
Emp.: 1,200
Fast-Food Restaurant, Chain
N.A.I.C.S.: 722513
Larry D. Fleming (Chm)
Donald Haynes (Pres)

LDI INDUSTRIES, INC.

1864 Nagle Ave, Manitowoc, WI 54221
Tel.: (920) 682-6877
Web Site: http://www.ldi-industries.com
Rev.: $12,800,000
Emp.: 150
Lubricating Equipment & Hydraulic Components Designer & Mfr
N.A.I.C.S.: 333998
Cindy Trainor (Mgr-Production Control)

LDI LTD., LLC

54 Monument Cir Ste 800, Indianapolis, IN 46204
Tel.: (317) 237-5400
Web Site: http://www.lditld.com
Year Founded: 1912
Sales Range: $750-799.9 Million
Emp.: 2,000
Holding Company; Automotive Parts & Service
N.A.I.C.S.: 551112
Andre B. Lacy (Chm)
J. A. Lacy (Pres & CEO)
Bill Himebrook (CFO)

Subsidiaries:

Answer Products, Inc. (1)
28209 Stanford Ave, Valencia, CA 91355
Tel.: (661) 257-4411
Web Site: http://www.answerproducts.com
Sales Range: $10-24.9 Million
Emp.: 100
Mfr of Mountain Bike Components
N.A.I.C.S.: 336991

OIA Global Logistics (1)
2100 SW River Pkwy Ste 800, Portland, OR 97201
Tel.: (800) 938-3109
Web Site: http://www.oiaglobal.com
Emp.: 130
Logistics Consulting Servies
N.A.I.C.S.: 541614
Steve Akre (Founder & Exec VP-Bus Dev)
Eric Okimoto (Exec VP-Global Ops)
Dante Fornari (VP-Global Sls & Mktg)
Daniel McMorris (VP-Strategic Initiatives)
Tim Sether (CFO)
Peter Wong (Mng Dir-Asia Pacific)
Susanne Oud (Dir-Ops)
David Ower (Mng Dir-Europe)
Claus Palm Rasmussen (Dir-IT & Comm)
Terry Walpole (Mng Dir-Europe)
J. A. Lacy (Chm)
Jeffery Barrie (CEO)

Subsidiary (Domestic):

American Cargo Express, Inc. (2)
2345 Vauxhall Rd, Union, NJ 07083
Tel.: (908) 351-3400
Web Site: http://www.americancargoexpress.com
Emp.: 200
Freight Transportation Arrangement
N.A.I.C.S.: 488510

Tucker-Rocky Distributing (1)
4900 Alliance Gateway Fwy, Fort Worth, TX 76177 (100%)
Tel.: (817) 258-9000
Web Site: http://www.tuckerrocky.com
Sales Range: $25-49.9 Million
Emp.: 250
Distribution Service for Motorcycle Aftermarket Parts & Accessories
N.A.I.C.S.: 423120
Jeffrey Wood (Mgr-Warehouse)
Dan Kent (VP-Ops)
Eric Cagle (Pres)
Charlie Hadayia Jr. (VP-Pur & Mdsg)

U.S. Worldwide Logistics, Inc. (1)
2750 Earhart Ct, Hebron, KY 41048
Tel.: (859) 525-7477
Web Site: http://www.usworldwidelogistics.com
Freight Transportation Arrangement
N.A.I.C.S.: 488510

LDJ PRODUCTIONS

73 Spring St Ste 605, New York, NY 10012
Tel.: (212) 366-4789
Web Site: http://www.ldjproductions.com
Year Founded: 1999
Sales Range: $10-24.9 Million
Emp.: 10
Event Management
N.A.I.C.S.: 561920
Laurie DeJong (CEO)
David Steinberg (VP)
Ryan Griffin (Dir-Fin)
Adam Cook (CFO)
Nicole Avnet (VP-Bus Dev)
Sara Whyte (Sr Mgr-Event)
Melissa Rasmussen (Owner & Creative Dir)
Timo Sandritter (Mng Dir)

LDMI

13936 Gold Cir, Omaha, NE 68144-2359
Tel.: (402) 334-9446
Year Founded: 1982
Rev.: $12,976,970
Emp.: 21
Advetising Agency
N.A.I.C.S.: 541810
Chris Johnson (VP-Creative)
Diana Sammons (Production Mgr)
Tom Golden (Copy Chief)
Richard Stanley (Pres)
Tracy Kochenderfer (VP-Media)
Kelly Gallegos (Acct Exec)
Rod McQuinn (Controller)

LDR GROWTH PARTNERS

1401 New York Ave NW Ste 700, Washington, DC 20005
Tel.: (202) 788-8015
Web Site: https://ldrgp.com
Emp.: 100
Investment Services
N.A.I.C.S.: 523999
William Brame (Partner)

Subsidiaries:

Mustang Motorcycle Products, LLC (1)
278 Town Hill Rd, Terryville, CT 06786
Tel.: (860) 582-9633
Web Site: http://www.mustangseats.com
Emp.: 85
Motor Vehicle Parts Mfr
N.A.I.C.S.: 336390
Marilyn G. Simmons (Dir-Mktg)

LDR INDUSTRIES, INC.

600 N Kilbourn Ave, Chicago, IL 60624
Tel.: (773) 265-3000
Web Site: http://www.ldrind.com
Year Founded: 1952
Sales Range: $10-24.9 Million
Emp.: 3
Kitchen & Bathroom Appliances & Products Whslr
N.A.I.C.S.: 332913
David Pollans (VP-Fin)

LDV INC.

180 Industrial Dr, Burlington, WI 53105
Tel.: (262) 763-0147
Web Site: http://www.ldvusa.com
Year Founded: 1977
Sales Range: $10-24.9 Million
Emp.: 200
Van Conversion
N.A.I.C.S.: 811121
Nancy Strelow (CFO)
Mary Procter (Mgr-Catalog Sls)
Dan Green (Dir-Sls Ops)
Larry Guardia (Mgr-Sls Dev)

LE BLEU CORPORATION

3134 Cornatzer Rd, Advance, NC 27006
Tel.: (336) 998-2894
Web Site: http://www.lebleu.com
Rev.: $17,700,000
Emp.: 15
Bottler of Water
N.A.I.C.S.: 312112
George Andrews (CFO)

LE BOULANGER INC.
305 N Mathilda Ave, Sunnyvale, CA 94085
Tel.: (408) 774-9000
Web Site: http://www.leboulanger.com
Rev.: $20,500,000
Emp.: 65
Retail Bakeries
N.A.I.C.S.: 311811
Dan Brunello (Pres & CEO)
Jack O'Toole (VP-Fin)
Lynn Peffer (Coord-Catering & Mgr)

LE CHAPERON ROUGE
1504 Travelers Point, Avon, OH 44011
Tel.: (440) 934-0296
Web Site: http://www.lechaperonrouge.com
Year Founded: 1982
Sales Range: $1-9.9 Million
Emp.: 200
Day Care, Pre-School & Elementary School
N.A.I.C.S.: 624410
Stella Moga Kennedy (Founder & Owner)
Kelli Freed (Dir-Admin)
Veronica Liebchen (Reg Dir)
Destina Moga (Owner)

LE CLAIR INDUSTRIES INC.
2604 Sun Set Dr, Grenada, MS 38901
Tel.: (662) 226-8075
Web Site: http://www.leclairindustries.com
Rev.: $13,600,000
Emp.: 50
Insulation or Cushioning Material, Foamed Plastics
N.A.I.C.S.: 326150
Tom Leclair (Pres)

Subsidiaries:

Perma R Products Inc. (1)
2604 Sunset Dr, Grenada, MS 38901
Tel.: (662) 226-8075
Web Site: http://www.permar.com
Plastics Foam Products
N.A.I.C.S.: 326150
Tim Le Claire (CEO)

LE JEUNE INVESTMENT INC.
9393 Wayzata Blvd, Minneapolis, MN 55426
Tel.: (763) 541-9030
Web Site: http://www.liinc.net
Automobiles, New & Used
N.A.I.C.S.: 441110

LE NOBLE LUMBER CO. INC.
38-20 Review Ave, Long Island City, NY 11101
Tel.: (212) 246-0150
Web Site: http://www.lenoblelumber.com
Sales Range: $10-24.9 Million
Emp.: 100
Millwork & Lumber
N.A.I.C.S.: 444110
Matthew Dienstag (VP)
Peter Le Noble (Pres)
Marc Bernstein (Owner & VP)

LE PAFE, INC.
7547 Telegraph Rd, Montebello, CA 90640
Tel.: (323) 888-2929 CA
Web Site: http://www.lechefbakery.com
Rev.: $14,900,000
Emp.: 170
Bread, Cake & Related Products Mfr
N.A.I.C.S.: 311812
Jonathan Lau (Pres)

LE TOTE, INC.
3130 20th St, San Francisco, CA 94110
Tel.: (844) 899-8683
Web Site: http://www.letote.com
Year Founded: 2012
Departmental Store Operator
N.A.I.C.S.: 455110
Rakesh Tondon (Founder & CEO)

Subsidiaries:

Lord & Taylor LLC (1)
424 5th Ave, New York, NY 10018-2703
Tel.: (212) 391-3344
Web Site: http://www.lordandtaylor.com
Sales Range: $1-4.9 Billion
Emp.: 5,000
Clothing & Clothing Accessories Department Stores Operator
N.A.I.C.S.: 455110
J. P. Day (Mgr-Ops)
Tim Catalano (Div VP & Gen Mgr-Garden City)
Vanessa LeFebvre (Pres)

LE TRIOMPHE PROPERTY GROUP LLC
4101 Plz Tower Dr, Baton Rouge, LA 70816
Tel.: (225) 292-2882
Web Site: http://www.ltpg.us
Sales Range: $10-24.9 Million
Emp.: 5
Provider of Subdivider & Developer Services
N.A.I.C.S.: 237210
Stewart Juneau (Chm & Principal)
Mike Juneau (Vice Chm & Principal)
Neil Juneau (CEO)

LE VECKE CORP.
10810 Inland Ave, Mira Loma, CA 91752-3235
Tel.: (951) 681-8600 CA
Web Site: http://www.levecke.com
Year Founded: 1949
Sales Range: $10-24.9 Million
Emp.: 60
Provider of Beer & Ale
N.A.I.C.S.: 424810
Mark Terry (Mgr-Quality Assurance)
Emily Wei (Mgr-Acctg)
Alice Redmond (Mgr-Customer Fulfillment, Plng & Procurement)
Neil LeVecke (Pres)

LEA COUNTY ELECTRIC COOP
1300 W Ave D, Lovington, NM 88260
Tel.: (575) 396-3631
Web Site: http://www.lcecnet.com
Year Founded: 1946
Sales Range: $25-49.9 Million
Emp.: 80
Distribution of Electric Power
N.A.I.C.S.: 221122
Janette Faris (Mgr-Admin Svcs, Safety & Compliance)
Gary Hurse (Exec VP & Gen Mgr)
Mike Saris (Mgr-Acctg & Customer Svcs)
Bobby Kimbro (Mgr-Sys Ops & Plng)
John Graham (Pres)
Dan Hardin (Treas & Sec)
Robert Caudle (VP)

LEACKCO BANK HOLDING COMPANY, INC.
120 E Main St, Wessington Springs, SD 57382
Tel.: (605) 539-1222 SD
Year Founded: 1972
Sales Range: $25-49.9 Million
Emp.: 113
Bank Holding Company
N.A.I.C.S.: 551111
Jack Wareing Steele (Chm, Pres & CEO)
Lynn V. Schneider (Pres/CEO-American Bank & Trust)

Subsidiaries:

American Bank & Trust (1)
120 E Main St, Wessington Springs, SD 57382
Tel.: (605) 539-1222
Web Site: http://www.americanbanktrust.net
Sales Range: $25-49.9 Million
Commericial Banking
N.A.I.C.S.: 522110
Lynn V. Schneider (Pres & CEO)
Kevin Mebius (VP & Mgr-IT Dept)
Jack Wareing Steele (Chm)
Preston Steele (Pres-Insurance & Exec VP)

LEACO RURAL TELEPHONE COOP INC.
22 W Ave D, Lovington, NM 88260
Tel.: (575) 370-5010 MN
Web Site: http://www.leaco.net
Sales Range: $10-24.9 Million
Emp.: 30
Provider of Local & Long Distance Telephone Communications
N.A.I.C.S.: 517121
Joel Klein (Sec & Asst Treas)
Leon Hemann (Treas & Sec)

LEAD BY SALES, LLC
PO Box 1194, Tarpon Springs, FL 34688
Tel.: (727) 230-0258
Web Site: http://www.whitecloudelectroniccigarettes.com
Year Founded: 2008
Sales Range: $10-24.9 Million
Emp.: 80
Electronic Cigarette Mfr
N.A.I.C.S.: 335999
Matthew Steingraber (Co-Founder)

LEAD EDGE CAPITAL MANAGEMENT, LLC
Chrysler Bldg 405 Lexington Ave 32nd Fl, New York, NY 10174
Tel.: (212) 984-2421 DE
Web Site: http://www.leadedgecapital.com
Year Founded: 2009
Venture Capital & Private Equity Firm
N.A.I.C.S.: 523999
Avery Rosin (Principal)
Brian Neider (Partner)
Chris Pohl (CFO)
Lorrie M. Norrington (Operating Partner-Capacity)

LEAD GENERATION SOLUTIONS
1060 First Ave Ste 400, King of Prussia, PA 19406
Tel.: (610) 768-8952
Web Site: http://www.leadgenerationsolutions.com
Year Founded: 2002
Sales Range: $1-9.9 Million
Telemarketing, Trade Show & Other Lead Generation Marketing Solutions
N.A.I.C.S.: 561422
Roberta Good (Acct Exec-Inside)

LEAD IT CORPORATION
1999 Wabash Ave Ste 210, Springfield, IL 62704-1519
Tel.: (217) 726-7250
Web Site: http://www.leaditgroup.com
Year Founded: 2005
Sales Range: $10-24.9 Million
Emp.: 242
Information Technology Services
N.A.I.C.S.: 541512
Trasi Hutchens (Acct Mgr)

LEAD RESEARCH GROUP, LLC
17011 Beach Blvd Ste 822, Huntington Beach, CA 92647
Web Site: http://www.leadresearchgroup.com
Year Founded: 2005
Sales Range: $10-24.9 Million
Emp.: 17
Direct Response Marketing & Advertising Services
N.A.I.C.S.: 541860
Ryan Rasmussen (CEO)
Matthew Marsh (Founder & Pres)

LEAD5 MEDIA, LLC.
7979 Gateway Blvd Ste 110, Newark, CA 94560
Tel.: (415) 738-2400
Web Site: http://www.lead5media.com
Year Founded: 2009
Sales Range: $25-49.9 Million
Emp.: 33
Marketing Consulting Services
N.A.I.C.S.: 541613
Steve Lombardi (CEO)

LEADCREATIONS.COM LLC
12717 W Sunrise Blvd Ste 312, Fort Lauderdale, FL 33323
Tel.: (305) 831-0999
Web Site: http://www.leadcreations.com
Year Founded: 2003
Sales Range: $1-9.9 Million
Emp.: 10
Internet Marketing & Online Lead Generation
N.A.I.C.S.: 541613
Umut Vardar (Co-Founder, Mng Dir & VP-Fin & Ops)

LEADDOG MARKETING GROUP
159 W 25th St 2nd Fl, New York, NY 10001
Tel.: (212) 488-6530
Web Site: http://www.leaddogmarketing.com
Year Founded: 1999
Sales Range: $25-49.9 Million
Emp.: 110
Advertising & Marketing Agency
N.A.I.C.S.: 541810
Dan Mannix (Pres & CEO)
Donna Providenti (COO)

LEADER BANK, N.A.
141 Massachusetts Ave, Arlington, MA 02474
Tel.: (781) 646-3900
Web Site: http://www.leaderbank.com
Year Founded: 2002
Sales Range: $10-24.9 Million
Emp.: 57
Commericial Banking
N.A.I.C.S.: 522110
Sushil K. Tuli (Chm & CEO)
Jerry Amodeo (Sr VP-Comml Lending)
Howard M. Tarlow (Chief Comml Real Estate Officer-Comml Lending)
Matthew Pierce (Chief Lending Officer)

LEADER DISTRIBUTION SYSTEMS, INC. U.S. PRIVATE

Leader Distribution Systems, Inc.—(Continued)

LEADER DISTRIBUTION SYSTEMS, INC.
1566 Putney Rd, Brattleboro, VT 05301
Tel.: (802) 254-6093
Web Site: http://www.pepsibrattleboro.com
Year Founded: 1902
Sales Range: $10-24.9 Million
Emp.: 106
Beverage Bottling Services
N.A.I.C.S.: 312112
John Leader *(Chm & CEO)*
Casey Donovan *(VP & Gen Mgr)*
Roland Currier *(CFO)*
Darcy Washburn *(Controller)*
Kieth Sanderson *(Mgr-Route Dev)*
Craig Higley *(Mgr-Mdsg)*
Pam Hall *(Mgr-Food & Beverage)*
Mike Fellows *(Mgr-Ops)*
Babatunde Mustapha *(Mgr-Water Production)*

LEADER HOME CENTERS INC.
1123 Bernardston Rd, Greenfield, MA 01301
Tel.: (413) 774-6311
Web Site: http://www.leaderhome.com
Rev.: $10,800,000
Emp.: 120
Home Center Operator
N.A.I.C.S.: 444110
Geoff Harris *(Pres)*

LEADER ONE FINANCIAL CORP.
11020 King St Ste 390, Lenexa, KS 66210
Tel.: (913) 888-9545
Web Site: http://www.leader1.com
Year Founded: 1992
Sales Range: $25-49.9 Million
Emp.: 20
Real Estate Services
N.A.I.C.S.: 522292
Michael W. Lynch *(Partner)*
Adam Schwartz *(CFO)*
Brent Duhaime *(Chief Production Officer)*
A. W. Pickel III *(Founder)*

LEADER PAPER PRODUCTS INC.
901 S 5th St, Milwaukee, WI 53204
Tel.: (414) 645-5760
Web Site: http://www.leaderpaper.com
Rev.: $17,000,000
Emp.: 150
Envelopes
N.A.I.C.S.: 322230
Scott Wilke *(Pres & CEO)*

LEADER'S HOLDING COMPANY
6303 126th Ave N, Largo, FL 33773
Tel.: (727) 538-5577
Web Site: http://www.leadersfurniture.com
Year Founded: 1971
Sales Range: $10-24.9 Million
Emp.: 130
Furniture Retailer
N.A.I.C.S.: 449110
Jerry O. Newton *(Owner & Pres)*

LEADERONE FINANCIAL
1020 King St Ste 390, Overland Park, KS 66210
Tel.: (913) 747-4000
Web Site: http://www.leader1.com
Sales Range: $10-24.9 Million

Emp.: 220
Mortgage Brokerage Services
N.A.I.C.S.: 522310
Adam Schwartz *(CFO)*
Michael Brady *(CIO)*
Taryn Reuter *(Sr VP)*
Steven Light *(Chief Strategy Officer)*

LEADERS CREDIT UNION
214 Oil Well Rd, Jackson, TN 38305
Tel.: (731) 664-1784 TN
Web Site: http://www.leaderscu.com
Year Founded: 1957
Sales Range: $10-24.9 Million
Emp.: 81
Credit Union Operator
N.A.I.C.S.: 522130
Ron Hill *(Chm)*

LEADGENESYS
Pacific Stock Exchange Bldg 155 Sansome St 6th Fl, San Francisco, CA 94104
Tel.: (415) 392-0333 CA
Web Site: http://www.leadgenesys.com
Year Founded: 2002
Sales Range: $10-24.9 Million
Media Buying Services
N.A.I.C.S.: 541830
Jeff Kostermans *(Pres & CEO)*
Mike Owen *(CFO)*
Alex Litvak *(Principal-Tech Architect)*

LEADID LLC
130 Newport Center Dr Ste 200, Newport Beach, CA 92660
Tel.: (949) 706-5590
Web Site: http://www.leadid.net
Year Founded: 2007
Sales Range: $1-9.9 Million
Emp.: 11
Digital Advertising Services
N.A.I.C.S.: 541850
Rob Carroll *(CEO)*
Joey Sanchez *(CTO)*

LEADING EDGE AVIATION SOLUTIONS, LLC
35 Waterview Blvd 2nd Fl, Parsippany, NJ 07054
Tel.: (201) 891-0881 NJ
Web Site: http://www.leas.com
Year Founded: 1994
Sales Range: $25-49.9 Million
Emp.: 12
Aviation Brokerage Services
N.A.I.C.S.: 541690
Joseph L. Carfagna *(Chm & CEO)*
Craig A. Carfagna *(Exec VP-Transactions & Ops)*
Catherine J. Carfagna *(Sec)*
Frank Janik *(VP-Aircraft Transactions)*
Joe Esmerado *(VP-Tech Svcs)*
Greg Wedding *(Exec VP-Bus Dev)*
Kristen Cloud *(VP-Aircraft Sls)*
Joseph Carfagna Jr. *(Pres)*

LEADING EDGE AVIATION, INC.
63048 Powell Butte Hwy, Bend, OR 97701
Tel.: (541) 383-8825
Web Site: http://www.flyleadingedge.com
Year Founded: 2005
Sales Range: $10-24.9 Million
Emp.: 85
Flight Training Services
N.A.I.C.S.: 611512
Brad Fraley *(Founder & Pres)*
Travis Warthen *(VP & Dir-Maintenance)*

Abby Heller *(Dir-Admissions)*
Arianna Moore *(CFO)*
Marti Fraley *(Mktg Mgr)*

Subsidiaries:

Leading Edge Jet Center LLC (1)
1050 SE Sisters Ave, Redmond, OR 97756
Tel.: (541) 504-3848
Web Site: http://www.leadingedgejet.com
Business Aviation & Jet Fueling Services
N.A.I.C.S.: 324110
Steven Levesque *(CEO)*

Subsidiary (Domestic):

Exec Air Montana, Inc. (2)
2430 Airport Rd, Helena, MT 59601
Tel.: (406) 442-2190
Web Site: http://www.execairmontana.com
Petroleum & Petroleum Product Whslr
N.A.I.C.S.: 424720
John Maxness *(Pres)*

LEADING EDGE MISSISSIPPI INC.
173 Fifth Ave, Greenville, MS 38703
Tel.: (662) 334-1964
Web Site: http://www.leadingedgecorp.com
Rev.: $12,400,000
Emp.: 250
Aircraft Painting & Refurbishing
N.A.I.C.S.: 238320
Michael Manclark *(Pres)*

LEADING EDGE RECOVERY SOLUTIONS, LLC
5440 N Cumberland Ave Ste 300, Chicago, IL 60656
Tel.: (773) 380-8800
Web Site: http://www.leadingedgerecovery.com
Year Founded: 2005
Sales Range: $1-9.9 Million
Emp.: 276
Collection Agency
N.A.I.C.S.: 561440
James Nuzzo *(CFO)*

LEADING EDJE
1105 Forsyth Ln, Galena, OH 43021
Tel.: (614) 395-4477
Web Site: http://www.leadingedje.com
Year Founded: 2007
Sales Range: $1-9.9 Million
Emp.: 30
It Consulting
N.A.I.C.S.: 541690
Wendy Ivany *(Dir-Strategic Solutions)*
Chad Young *(Sr Dir-Team Engagement & Mgr-Solutions Delivery)*

LEADING LADY COMPANIES
24050 Commerce Pike, Cleveland, OH 44122
Tel.: (216) 464-5490
Web Site: http://www.leadinglady.com
Year Founded: 1939
Sales Range: $10-24.9 Million
Emp.: 50
Mfr of Lingerie
N.A.I.C.S.: 424350
Mark Corrado *(Pres)*
Haidee Johnstone *(Sr VP & Dir-Design)*
William Mahar *(Dir-Mktg & PR)*

LEADING RIDGE MANAGEMENT, LLC
1 Research Ct Ste 101, Rockville, MD 20850
Tel.: (301) 235-9020 DE
Web Site: http://www.leadingridge.com
Year Founded: 2009
Private Investment Firm

N.A.I.C.S.: 523999
Warren Coopersmith *(Partner)*
Robert Mayn *(Partner)*
Zach Coopersmith *(Partner)*

Subsidiaries:

DRS Product Returns LLC (1)
2670 Leisczs Bridge Rd ste 100, Leesport, PA 19533
Tel.: (610) 327-1133
Web Site: http://www.drsreturns.com
Consumer Product Return & Recall Services
N.A.I.C.S.: 561499
Jim Schumacher *(Chief Revenue Officer)*
Douglas N. Wurl *(Pres & CEO)*
Linda Austin *(CFO & Chief Admin Officer)*

Revertech Solutions (1)
110 Fordham Rd, Wilmington, MA 01887-2165
Tel.: (800) 274-5343
Technological Repairs
N.A.I.C.S.: 811210
Jeff Harrison *(Mgr-Customer & Bus Dev)*
Elvis de Leon *(Mgr-Mfg)*
Dan Sirois *(Sr Mgr-Matls)*

LEADING THE WAY WITH DR. MICHAEL YOUSSEF
PO Box 20100, Atlanta, GA 30325
Tel.: (404) 841-0100 GA
Web Site: http://www.leadingtheway.org
Year Founded: 1989
Sales Range: $25-49.9 Million
Emp.: 43
Community Action Services
N.A.I.C.S.: 624190
Joshua D. Youssef *(Exec VP)*

LEADJEN, INC.
1311 W 96th St Ste 250, Indianapolis, IN 46260
Tel.: (317) 844-6885
Web Site: http://www.leadjen.com
Year Founded: 2004
Sales Range: $1-9.9 Million
Emp.: 74
Marketing Consulting Services
N.A.I.C.S.: 541613
Reena Gangwani *(Mgr-Client Acct)*
Mary Jolly *(Mgr-Client Acct)*
Mary Ann Sturges *(Mgr-Client Accts)*
Jen Burdess *(Dir-Fin & Ops)*
Narinder Chaggar *(Asst Mgr-Data Svcs)*
Mary Browning *(COO)*
Nate Dagley *(Dir-Bus Dev)*
Kim Chastain *(Mgr-Client Accts)*
Rebecca Core *(Mgr-Client Accts)*
Bob Williams *(Mgr-Client Accts)*
Judy Pickett *(Mgr-Lead Dev)*
Jacob Hyten *(Mgr-Mktg)*

LEADLIFE SOLUTIONS INC.
4900 N Scottsdale Rd Scottsdale Cross, Scottsdale, AZ 85251
Tel.: (770) 670-6700
Web Site: http://www.leadlife.com
Sales Range: $1-9.9 Million
Emp.: 12
Marketing Automation Software
N.A.I.C.S.: 513210
Richard Brock *(CEO)*

LEADMAN ELECTRONICS USA, INC.
382 Laurelwood Rd, Santa Clara, CA 95054
Tel.: (408) 738-1751
Web Site: http://www.leadman.com
Rev.: $43,615,566
Emp.: 35
Computers, Peripherals & Software
N.A.I.C.S.: 423430
Frank Fu *(Gen Mgr)*
Jim Liang *(Pres)*

COMPANIES

LEADMD, INC.
9383 E Bahia Dr Ste 225, Scottsdale, AZ 85260
Tel.: (480) 278-7205
Web Site: http://www.leadmd.com
Year Founded: 2009
Sales Range: $10-24.9 Million
Emp.: 16
Marketing & Advertising Services
N.A.I.C.S.: 541613
Justin Gray *(CEO)*
Andrea Lechner-Becker *(Chief Strategy Officer & Principal)*
Shauna Bradley *(Mgr-Mktg Svcs)*
Vivi Brock *(Mgr-Mktg Svcs)*
Caleb Trecek *(Dir-Customer Success)*
Michael Davis *(Dir-Customer Success)*
Bob Blount *(VP-Sls)*

LEADNOMICS
2929 Arch St, Philadelphia, PA 19104
Tel.: (215) 987-4392
Web Site:
http://www.leadnomics.com
Sales Range: $1-9.9 Million
Emp.: 9
Search Engine Optimization Services
N.A.I.C.S.: 541511
Kimberlee Molineaux *(Controller)*
Steve Phillips *(Dir-Bus Intelligence)*
Colin Murray *(Dir-Media Acq)*
Omar Abdelhamid *(Dir-Ops)*
Julie Pacaro *(Gen Counsel)*
Claudia Stringham *(Mgr-HR & Office)*
Wendy Huffman *(Product Mgr)*
Erick Sawby *(VP-Bus Dev)*
Anthony Romano *(VP-Engrg)*
Josh Irons *(VP-Sls & Acct Mgmt)*

LEADS360 INC.
222 N Sepulveda Blvd, El Segundo, CA 90245
Tel.: (310) 765-7120   CA
Web Site: http://www.velocify.com
Year Founded: 2004
Sales Range: $1-9.9 Million
Emp.: 30
CRM Software Publishers
N.A.I.C.S.: 513210
Darian S. J. Hong *(CFO)*
Josh Evans *(Sr VP-Sls)*
Ryan McClintock *(Co-Founder & CEO)*
Manoj Goyal *(COO)*
Chandra Shekaran *(Sr VP-Engrg)*
Harry Beck *(VP-Bus Dev)*

LEADSONLINE LLC
6900 Dallas Pkwy Ste 825, Plano, TX 75024
Tel.: (972) 361-0900
Web Site:
http://www.leadsonline.com
Exterminating & Pest Control Services
N.A.I.C.S.: 561710
Lindsay Williams *(Dir-Comm)*

Subsidiaries:

Business Watch International Inc.   (1)
7351 Wiles Rd Ste 102, Coral Springs, FL 33067-4106
Web Site: http://www.bwirapid.com
All Other Support Services
N.A.I.C.S.: 561990

LEADSPACE, INC.
445 Bush Street Suite 900, San Francisco, CA 94108
Tel.: (855) 532-3772   DE
Web Site:
https://www.leadspace.com
Year Founded: 2012
Cloud-based Data Services
N.A.I.C.S.: 518210

Alex Yoder *(CEO)*
Marge Breya *(COO & CMO)*
Amnon Mishor *(Founder & CTO)*

LEADVISION MEDIA, LLC
2304 S Post Rd, Midwest City, OK 73130
Tel.: (405) 622-5046
Web Site:
http://www.leadvisionmedia.com
Emp.: 12
Online Advertising Agency
N.A.I.C.S.: 541810
Matt Stowe *(CEO)*

Subsidiaries:

RevenueAds   (1)
2304 S Post Rd, Midwest City, OK 73130
Tel.: (405) 622-5046
Web Site: http://www.revenueads.com
Emp.: 7
Affiliate Marketing Services
N.A.I.C.S.: 541890
Matt Stowe *(CEO)*
Robert Stephens *(CFO)*
Dylan Stout *(Dir-Affiliates)*
Brandon Stowe *(VP)*
Jared Thompson *(Dir-Tech & Web Dev)*

LEAF HOME, LLC
1595 Georgetown Rd, Hudson, OH 44236
Tel.: (800) 290-6106
Web Site: http://www.leafhome.com
Year Founded: 2019
Home Solutions
N.A.I.C.S.: 449129
Tom Burger *(Chm)*
Jeffrey Housenbold *(Pres & CEO)*

Subsidiaries:

Quillen Brothers, Inc.   (1)
677 N Main St, Bryan, OH 43506
Tel.: (419) 636-1303
Web Site: http://www.quillenbrosinc.com
Home Replacement Window Contractor
N.A.I.C.S.: 238130
Robert V. Quillen *(Pres)*

LEAFFILTER NORTH INC.
1595 Georgetown Rd Ste G, Hudson, OH 44236
Tel.: (330) 655-7950
Web Site: http://www.leaffilter.com
Year Founded: 2005
Sales Range: $25-49.9 Million
Emp.: 95
Gutter Protection Systems
N.A.I.C.S.: 423330
Matt Kaulig *(Owner & Pres)*
Erika Buzalka *(Mgr-Call Center Evening)*
Jesse Wilson *(Mgr-Recruiting & Dev)*
Chris Counahan *(VP)*
Joseph Roschival *(VP-Installation)*

LEAGUE OF CONSERVATION VOTERS, INC.
1920 L St NW Ste 800, Washington, DC 20036
Tel.: (202) 785-8683   MD
Web Site: http://www.lcv.org
Year Founded: 1970
Sales Range: $10-24.9 Million
Emp.: 70
Environmental Conservation Services
N.A.I.C.S.: 813312
Stacey Folsom *(Sr VP-Dev)*
Tiernan Sittenfeld *(Sr VP-Govt Affairs)*
Rich Thomas *(Gen Counsel & Sr VP-Strategic Initiatives)*
Patrick Collins *(Sr VP-Fin & Admin)*

LEAKE & WATTS SERVICES INC.
463 Hawthorne Ave, Yonkers, NY 10705-3441
Tel.: (914) 375-8700
Web Site:
http://www.leakeandwatts.org
Year Founded: 1831
Sales Range: Less than $1 Million
Emp.: 900
Residential Treatment Individual & Family Services
N.A.I.C.S.: 624110
James J. Campbell *(Exec Dir)*
Margery E. Ames *(VP)*
Anthony Hairston *(Dir-HR)*

LEAKE OIL CO. INC.
7911 United States Hwy 61, Saint Francisville, LA 70775
Tel.: (225) 635-6149
Rev.: $18,174,491
Emp.: 7
Diesel Fuel
N.A.I.C.S.: 424720
James R. Leake Jr. *(Pres)*

LEAKTITE CORPORATION
40 Francis St, Leominster, MA 01453
Tel.: (978) 537-8000
Web Site: http://www.leaktite.com
Year Founded: 1945
Plastics Product Mfr
N.A.I.C.S.: 326199
Manny Machado *(VP-Mfg)*
Jay Brooks *(VP & Dir-Sls & Mktg)*
Tom Forsberg *(VP-Sls & Mktg)*
Tobey Marchal *(VP-HR)*
Rod Sparrow *(Pres)*
Jon Hoden *(Mgr-Sls-Natl)*
Robert Gove *(Mgr-Ops)*

LEAMAN CONTAINER INC.
5701A E Rosedale St, Fort Worth, TX 76112
Tel.: (817) 429-2660
Web Site:
http://www.leamancontainer.com
Sales Range: $10-24.9 Million
Emp.: 40
Corrugated Boxes Mfr
N.A.I.C.S.: 322211
Steve Leaman *(Pres & VP-Sls)*

LEAN STAFFING SOLUTIONS, INC.
3917 NW 126th Ave, Coral Springs, FL 33065
Web Site:
http://www.leanstaffing.com
Year Founded: 2008
Sales Range: $1-9.9 Million
Emp.: 10
Human Resource Consulting Services
N.A.I.C.S.: 541612
Robert Cadena *(Founder & CEO)*

LEANDOG
1151 N Marginal Rd, Cleveland, OH 44114
Tel.: (216) 236-4705
Web Site: http://www.leandog.com
Year Founded: 2005
Sales Range: $1-9.9 Million
Emp.: 55
Software Development & Agile & Lean IT Implementation Services
N.A.I.C.S.: 519290
Jon Stahl *(Co-Founder & CEO)*
Jeff Morgan *(Co-Founder)*
James Gorjup *(COO)*

LEANIN' TREE, INC.
6055 Longbow Dr, Boulder, CO 80301
Tel.: (303) 530-1442
Web Site: http://www.leanintree.com

Year Founded: 1949
Emp.: 200
Consumer Marketing, House Agencies
N.A.I.C.S.: 541810
Tom Trumble *(Pres & CEO)*
Patrick Wallace *(Dir-Mktg)*

LEANIN' TREE, INC.
6055 Longbow Dr, Boulder, CO 80301
Tel.: (303) 530-1442   CO
Web Site: http://www.leanintree.com
Year Founded: 1949
Sales Range: $100-124.9 Million
Emp.: 250
Greeting Cards, Prints, Notes & Christmas Cards Publisher & Retailer
N.A.I.C.S.: 513191
Tom Trumble *(Pres & CEO)*
Pete Mahlstedt *(CFO & COO)*
Duff Bauer *(Controller)*
Jane Trumble *(Sr VP-Product Mgmt)*

LEAP PARTNERS
1616 W End Ave, Nashville, TN 37203
Tel.: (615) 218-5044
Web Site:
https://www.theleappartners.com
Sales Range: $1-9.9 Million
Financial Investment Services
N.A.I.C.S.: 523999
John Cerasuolo *(CEO)*
Patrick Ritter *(CFO)*

Subsidiaries:

Conditioned Air Solutions, LLC   (1)
200 Dan Tibbs Rd NW, Huntsville, AL 35806
Tel.: (256) 428-1983
Web Site:
http://www.conditionedairsolutions.com
Sales Range: $1-9.9 Million
Emp.: 20
Plumbing, Heating & Air-Conditioning Contractors
N.A.I.C.S.: 238220
Paul Snowden *(Pres)*
Karen Price *(Dir-Mktg)*
Bill Parks *(Mgr-Warehouse)*

LEAPFROG INTERACTIVE
10200 Linn Sta Rd, Louisville, KY 40223
Tel.: (502) 212-1376
Web Site:
http://www.leapfroginteractive.com
Year Founded: 1999
Sales Range: $10-24.9 Million
Emp.: 60
Computer System Design Services
N.A.I.C.S.: 541512
Daniel Knapp *(CEO)*
Alan Gilleo *(Chief Creative Officer)*
Brandon Faris *(Dir-Leap Frame)*
Bridgid Agricola *(Dir-Creative)*
Keith Adams *(Sr Dir-Art)*
Matthew Taylor *(Dir-Client Svcs)*
Michael Brown *(VP & Dir-Creative)*
Michael Wunsch *(VP-Digital Performance)*
Ryan Kolatalo *(VP-Tech)*
Sam Douglass *(VP-Acct Strategy)*
Sarah Prinsloo *(Dir-Digital Performance)*
Tyler Yarbrough *(Dir-Project Mgmt)*

LEAPFROG SOLUTIONS, INC.
3201 Jermantown Rd Ste 350, Fairfax, VA 22030
Tel.: (703) 273-7900
Web Site: http://www.leapfrogit.com
Sales Range: $1-9.9 Million
Emp.: 30
Brand Development & Integration
N.A.I.C.S.: 541810

LEAPFROG SOLUTIONS, INC.

LeapFrog Solutions, Inc.—(Continued)
Lisa Martin (Pres & CEO)
Bob Derby (VP-Strategic Comm)
Teresa Teresa Fisher (Mgr-Acctg)
Rich Gilroy (Dir-Acct Svcs)
Frank Henry (Mgr-Client Svcs)
Alix Shutello (Mgr-Program)
Jamie Spencer (Sr Dir-Art)
Sara Rassi (Sr Acct Mgr)
Brian Lennon (VP-Bus Dev)

LEARNED LUMBER

635 Pacific Coast Hwy, Hermosa Beach, CA 90254-4839
Tel.: (310) 374-3406   CA
Web Site:
   http://www.learnedlumber.com
Year Founded: 1924
Sales Range: $10-24.9 Million
Emp.: 55
Distr of Lumber, Plywood & Millwork
N.A.I.C.S.: 423310
Michael Learned (Pres & CFO)
Dave Kendall (Mgr)
Kevin McLernon (Mgr-Sls & Mgr-Lumber Sls)
Dave Kendall (Mgr)
Kevin McLernon (Mgr-Lumber Sls)
Craig Evans (Gen Mgr)
Craig Evans (Gen Mgr)
Charlene Freeman (Mgr-Credit)
Mitch Heller (Mgr-Store)

LEARNING ALLY, INC.

20 Roszel Rd, Princeton, NJ 08540
Tel.: (609) 452-0606
Web Site: http://www.learningally.org
Year Founded: 1948
Sales Range: $25-49.9 Million
Emp.: 425
Sound Recording Studios
N.A.I.C.S.: 512240
Andrew Friedman (CEO)
Jim Halliday (Exec VP)
Connie Murphy (Exec VP-Partnerships & Community Dev)
Cynthia Hamburger (COO & CIO)
Jeff Ho (VP-New Product Dev)
Tim Wilson (CFO)
Jan McDavitt (VP)
Harold J. Logan (Vice Chm)
Therese Llorente (Sec)
Cindy Cortina (VP-Sls & Mktg)
Stephen Ferranti (VP-Digital Ops)
Cheri Lin (Chief Mktg Officer)
Steven Valvano (VP-Great People-HR)
David Aycan (Chief Solutions Officer)

LEARNING ANNEX HOLDINGS, LLC

48 W 37th St 7th Fl, New York, NY 10018-7487
Tel.: (212) 371-0280
Web Site:
   http://www.learningannex.com
Year Founded: 1980
Sales Range: $100-124.9 Million
Emp.: 114
Holding Company
N.A.I.C.S.: 551112
William Zanker (Founder, Pres & CEO)

Subsidiaries:

The Learning Annex LLC   (1)
888 Charlie Ave Ste 139, New York, NY 10019
Tel.: (212) 371-0280
Web Site: http://www.learningannex.com
Sales Range: $10-24.9 Million
Emp.: 100
Specialty Learning Institution
N.A.I.C.S.: 611699

LEARNING EVOLUTION, LLC

1431 Pacific Hwy H2, San Diego, CA 92101
Tel.: (619) 342-7877
Web Site:
   http://www.learningevolution.com
Year Founded: 2003
Sales Range: $1-9.9 Million
Management Assistance & Financial Planning E-Learning Courses Developer
N.A.I.C.S.: 611710
Scott Matthews (CEO)

LEARNING RESOURCES, INC.

380 N Fairway Dr, Vernon Hills, IL 60061
Tel.: (847) 573-8400
Web Site:
   http://www.learningresources.com
Sales Range: $25-49.9 Million
Emp.: 130
Educational Material & Learning Toy Services
N.A.I.C.S.: 611710
Richard Woldenberg (Chm)
Mike Dost (CFO)

Subsidiaries:

Educational Insights, Inc.   (1)
18730 S Wilmington Ave, Rancho Dominguez, CA 90220
Tel.: (310) 884-2000
Web Site:
   http://www.educationalinsights.com
Sales Range: $1-9.9 Million
Emp.: 100
Electronic Learning Aids, Games, Activity Books, Science & Nature Products Mfr, Designer & Marketer
N.A.I.C.S.: 339999
Kelly Cole (VP-Ops)

LEARNING TRENDS, LLC

16310 Bratton Ln Ste 250, Austin, TX 78728
Tel.: (512) 231-0900   TX
Web Site: http://www.abramslearning trends.com
Year Founded: 2008
Sales Range: $1-9.9 Million
Emp.: 20
Early Childhood Educational Materials Publisher
N.A.I.C.S.: 513130
Aaron Mayers (Pres & CEO)
Lynn Keller (CFO)
Bill Thomas (Exec VP & Gen Mgr)
Bruce Warren (Sr VP-Sls)
Erin King (Exec VP-Mktg & Sls)
David Blair (Dir-IT & Web Svcs)
Zena Carter (Mgr-Customer Svc & Sls Support)

Subsidiaries:

Abrams & Company Publishers, Inc.
61 Mattatuck Hts Rd, Waterbury, CT 06705-3839
Tel.: (203) 756-6562
Web Site:
   http://www.abramslearningtrends.com
Early Childhood Educational Materials Publisher
N.A.I.C.S.: 513130

LEARNKEY INCORPORATED

35 N Main St, Saint George, UT 84770
Tel.: (435) 674-9733
Web Site: http://www.learnkey.com
Year Founded: 1987
Sales Range: $10-24.9 Million
Emp.: 70
Provider of Audio & Video Recording Services
N.A.I.C.S.: 423690
John Clemons (Founder & Chm)
Jeff Coruccini (CEO)

LEARNLIVE TECHNOLOGIES

2101 4th Ave Ste 1350, Seattle, WA 98121
Tel.: (206) 812-4700   WA
Web Site: http://www.learnlive.com
Year Founded: 2003
Sales Range: $1-9.9 Million
Emp.: 23
On-Line e-Learning Services & Webcasts
N.A.I.C.S.: 611710
Lisa Heringlake (Dir-Acct Mgmt)

LEARNOSITY LTD.

333 W 39th St Ste 1003, New York, NY 10018
Tel.: (646) 582-6162
Web Site: http://www.learnosity.com
Year Founded: 2007
Learning Services
N.A.I.C.S.: 611691
Gavin Cooney (CEO)

Subsidiaries:

Questionmark Corporation   (1)
35 Nutmeg Dr Ste 330, Trumbull, CT 06611
Tel.: (203) 425-2400
Web Site: http://www.questionmark.com
Custom Computer Programming Services
N.A.I.C.S.: 541511
Eric Shepherd (Pres)
John Kleeman (Founder)

LEASE A SALES REP

4904 Waters Edge Dr Ste 275, Raleigh, NC 27606
Tel.: (919) 827-0019
Web Site:
   http://www.leaseasalesrep.com
Sales Range: $1-9.9 Million
Emp.: 73
Strategic Analysis Solution & Service
N.A.I.C.S.: 561499
Gilbert Pagan (Founder & CEO)

LEASE CRUTCHER LEWIS

107 Spring St, Seattle, WA 98104-1005
Tel.: (206) 622-0500   WA
Web Site: http://www.lewisbuilds.com
Year Founded: 1989
Sales Range: $50-74.9 Million
Emp.: 490
Nonresidential Construction Services
N.A.I.C.S.: 236220
Jeff Cleator (Pres-Washington)
William L. Lewis (Pres & CEO)
Matt Hays (Sr Mgr-Proposals)
Geoff Anderson (Dir-Preconstruction)
Tom Dilts (Controller)
Berger Dodge (CFO)
Carey Crutcher Smith (Dir-Mktg)
Rick Workman (Gen Mgr-Holyoke & Sr Mgr-Special Projects)
Jay Sorensen (VP-Special Projects Div)
Julie Fleming (Mgr-Preconstruction)
Matthew Jackson (VP)

Subsidiaries:

Holyoke Fine Homes   (1)
107 Spring St, Seattle, WA 98104
Tel.: (206) 689-0424
Web Site: http://www.holyokefinehomes.com
Sales Range: $25-49.9 Million
Emp.: 250
Commercial & Institutional Building Construction Services
N.A.I.C.S.: 236220
Rick Workman (Project Mgr)

LEASE LINE INC.

2310 Route 130, North Brunswick, NJ 08902
Tel.: (732) 297-9200
Sales Range: $10-24.9 Million
Emp.: 120
Truck Leasing Services

N.A.I.C.S.: 532120
Glenn I. Garland (Pres)

LEASE ONE CORP.

220 Broadway Ste 102, Lynnfield, MA 01940-2352
Tel.: (781) 581-9700   MA
Web Site: http://www.leaseone.com
Year Founded: 1989
Sales Range: $10-24.9 Million
Emp.: 10
Equipment Rental & Leasing Services
N.A.I.C.S.: 532490
Joseph L. Angelo Jr. (Founder & CEO)

LEASEACCELERATOR INC.

10740 Parkridge Blvd Ste 701, Reston, VA 20191
Web Site:
   http://www.leaseaccelerator.com
Year Founded: 2003
Sales Range: $10-24.9 Million
Emp.: 180
Software Development Services
N.A.I.C.S.: 541511
Michael Keeler (Founder, Pres & CEO)
Todd Fredrick (COO)
Tracy Henriques (Chief Customer Officer)
Avo Reid (CTO)
David McCullough (CFO)

LEASEWAY OF PUERTO RICO INC.

Calle 1 G 1 Bo Palmas Ind, Catano, PR 00962
Tel.: (787) 788-7272
Web Site: http://www.leasewaypr.com
Sales Range: $10-24.9 Million
Emp.: 50
Car & Truck Rental
N.A.I.C.S.: 532120
Juan Garcia (VP)

LEASING ASSOCIATES INC.

12600 N Featherwood Ste 400, Houston, TX 77034
Tel.: (832) 300-1300   NV
Web Site:
   http://www.theleasingcompany.com
Year Founded: 1958
Sales Range: $10-24.9 Million
Emp.: 85
Commercial Vehicle Leasing Services
N.A.I.C.S.: 522220
Mark Sprague (Treas & Sr VP)

LEASING INNOVATIONS INC.

261 N Hwy 101, Solana Beach, CA 92075
Tel.: (858) 259-4794
Web Site: http://www.leasing123.com
Year Founded: 1989
Sales Range: $50-74.9 Million
Emp.: 12
Equipment Rental & Leasing
N.A.I.C.S.: 532490
Heather G. Fritz (Pres)

LEASING TECHNOLOGIES INTERNATIONAL INC.

221 Danbury Rd, Wilton, CT 06897
Tel.: (203) 563-1100
Web Site: http://www.ltileasing.com
Sales Range: $10-24.9 Million
Emp.: 23
Commercial Equipment Financing & Leasing Services
N.A.I.C.S.: 522220
F. Jared Sprole (Founder, Pres & CEO)
Arnold J. Hoegler (COO & Exec VP)
William I. MacDonald (Sr VP)

COMPANIES

LECHASE CONSTRUCTION SERVICES, LLC

Mark Theriault *(Controller)*
Hugh M. Baum *(Gen Counsel & Sec)*
George A. Parker *(CFO, CMO & Exec VP)*

Subsidiaries:

LTI Portfolio Management Corp. (1)
24 Danbury Rd, Wilton, CT 06897
Tel.: (203) 563-1100
Web Site: http://www.ltileasing.com
Rev.: $500,000
Emp.: 17
Portfolio Management Services
N.A.I.C.S.: 523940
F. Jared Sprole *(Pres & CEO)*

LEATHER CREATIONS INC.
2692 Peachtree Sq, Atlanta, GA 30360-2633
Tel.: (678) 584-1000
Web Site:
  http://www.leathercreations.net
Rev.: $13,445,633
Emp.: 60
Upholstered Household Furniture
N.A.I.C.S.: 449110
Scott Labelle *(Pres)*
Roger Miller *(CFO)*

LEATHERMAN TOOL GROUP, INC.
12106 NE Ainsworth Cir, Portland, OR 97220
Tel.: (503) 253-7826
Web Site: http://www.leatherman.com
Year Founded: 1983
Sales Range: $25-49.9 Million
Emp.: 550
Mfr of Tools
N.A.I.C.S.: 332216
Tim Leatherman *(Co-Founder & Chm)*
Benjamin Rivera *(CEO)*

LEATHERSTOCKING CORP.
1 Rockefeller Plz Fl 31, New York, NY 10020
Tel.: (607) 547-2561
Web Site:
  http://www.leatherstockingcorp.com
Rev.: $10,978,403
Emp.: 30
Hotel
N.A.I.C.S.: 721110
Kevin Moore *(Pres)*

LEAVITT GROUP ENTERPRISES, INC.
216 S 200 W, Cedar City, UT 84720
Tel.: (435) 586-6553   NV
Web Site: http://www.leavitt.com
Year Founded: 1952
Insurance Services
N.A.I.C.S.: 524210
Dane Leavitt *(Co-Chm & Co-CEO)*
Mark Leavitt *(Vice Chm & Dir-Affiliation)*
Eric Leavitt *(Co-Chm & Co-CEO)*
Rachael Woolsey *(VP-Personal Lines)*
Kelly Pareti *(Dir-Voluntary Benefits Enrollment)*
Brent Davis *(VP-Talent Dev)*
Dale Matthews *(Mgr-Talent Acquisition)*

Subsidiaries:

Grant-Hatch & Associates Inc. (1)
465 S 400 E Ste 300, Salt Lake City, UT 84111   (100%)
Tel.: (801) 308-1500
Web Site: http://www.leavitt.com
Sales Range: $25-49.9 Million
Emp.: 10
Insurance
N.A.I.C.S.: 522292
Vance Smith *(Pres)*

Harris Fowler Insurance Company, Inc. (1)
104 W Main St, Albertville, AL 35950-1626
Tel.: (256) 878-9172
Web Site: http://www.hfiains.com
Insurance Agencies & Brokerages
N.A.I.C.S.: 524210
Jonathon Allen *(Acct Mgr-Comml Insurance)*

Leavitt Group Four Corners Insurance Inc. (1)
300 W Arrington Ste 100, Farmington, NM 87401
Tel.: (505) 327-4411
Web Site: http://www.schield-leavitt.com
Rev.: $14,000,000
Emp.: 2
Provider of Insurance Services
N.A.I.C.S.: 524210
Louise Rivas *(Office Mgr)*

LEBAKKENS, INC. OF WISCONSIN
2842 Melby St, Eau Claire, WI 54703
Tel.: (715) 831-1002   WI
Web Site:
  http://www.lebakkensrto.com
Year Founded: 1975
Sales Range: $50-74.9 Million
Emp.: 59
Consumer Electronics, Appliances & Furniture Rent-to-Own Services
N.A.I.C.S.: 532210
Jeffrey Lewis Lebakken *(Owner & Pres)*
Lauri Thomas *(Reg Mgr)*

LEBAMOFF ENTERPRISES INC.
5430 Coldwater Rd, Fort Wayne, IN 46825
Tel.: (260) 483-1147   IN
Web Site: http://www.capncork.com
Year Founded: 1911
Sales Range: $10-24.9 Million
Emp.: 60
Provider of Wines, Spirits, Beer & Cigars
N.A.I.C.S.: 445320
Andy Lebamoff *(Pres)*
Joe Boust *(Owner)*
Julie Hoskins *(Controller)*

LEBANON SEABOARD CORPORATION
1600 E Cumberland St, Lebanon, PA 17042-8323
Tel.: (717) 273-1685   PA
Web Site: http://www.lebsea.com
Year Founded: 1947
Sales Range: $100-124.9 Million
Emp.: 300
Supplier of Lawn & Garden Products, Wild Bird Food, Grass Seed & Professional Turf Products
N.A.I.C.S.: 325314
Katherine Bishop *(Chm, Pres & CEO)*
Rich Newmaster *(CFO)*
Jim Kuhle *(Mgr-Ops)*
Harry Mathis *(Mgr-Supply Chain & Logistics)*
Ken Morrison *(Mgr-IT)*
Dave Heegard *(Gen Mgr-Pro Products Div)*
William Kelso *(Mgr-Consumer Products Div)*

LEBARONBROWN INDUSTRIES LLC
400 Park Ave 21st F, New York, NY 10022
Tel.: (212) 841-8500
Web Site:
  http://www.lebaronbrown.com
Privater Equity Firm
N.A.I.C.S.: 523999
Simon E. Brown *(Founder)*

Subsidiaries:

LeBaronBrown Specialties LLC (1)
32 Haviland Street, Norwalk, CT 06854
Tel.: (203) 299-3299
Web Site: http://www.lbbspecialties.com
Fragrance & Pharmaceutical Products Mfr
N.A.I.C.S.: 456110
Darren J. Birkelbach *(CEO)*

Subsidiary (Domestic):

Centerchem, Inc. (2)
20 Glover Ave, Norwalk, CT 06850
Tel.: (203) 822-9800
Web Site: http://www.centerchem.com
Specialty Ingredient Distr
N.A.I.C.S.: 424690
Jon D. Pluker *(Pres)*
Michael Boyar *(Sec)*
Jon Packer *(Pres)*

Custom Chemical Services Inc. (2)
9292 NW 101st St, Fort Lauderdale, FL 33178-1351
Tel.: (305) 687-8191
Web Site:
  http://www.customchemicalservices.com
Chemical & Allied Products Merchant Whslr
N.A.I.C.S.: 424690
Chad Hicks *(Pres)*

LEBENTHAL & CO. LLC
230 Park Ave 32 Fl, New York, NY 10169
Tel.: (212) 425-6006
Web Site: http://www.lebenthal.com
Sales Range: $10-24.9 Million
Emp.: 85
Financial Advisors
N.A.I.C.S.: 523999
Alexandra Lebenthal *(Pres & CEO)*

LEBERMUTH COMPANY
14000 McKinley Hwy, Mishawaka, IN 46545
Tel.: (574) 259-7000
Web Site: http://www.lebermuth.com
Year Founded: 1908
Sales Range: $10-24.9 Million
Emp.: 60
Essential Oils
N.A.I.C.S.: 424690
Alan S. Brown *(VP-Mktg & Admin)*
Rob Brown *(Pres)*
Carmen Wright *(Mgr-HR)*

LEBHAR-FRIEDMAN INC.
425 Park Ave, New York, NY 10022
Tel.: (212) 756-5000   NY
Web Site: http://www.lf.com
Year Founded: 1925
Sales Range: $300-349.9 Million
Emp.: 500
Advertising, Marketing & Publishing Services
N.A.I.C.S.: 541890
Bill McMahon *(Mgr-Production)*

LEBOS SHOE STORE INC.
2321 Crown Ctr Dr, Charlotte, NC 28227
Tel.: (704) 321-5000
Web Site: http://www.lebos.com
Sales Range: $10-24.9 Million
Emp.: 90
Western Apparel
N.A.I.C.S.: 458210
Jerry Levin *(CEO)*
Binyamin Levin *(VP)*
Mark Goldsmith *(Pres)*
Jennifer Glasser *(Controller)*

LEC
12 E Ohio St, Chicago, IL 60611-5311
Tel.: (312) 670-0077   IL
Web Site: http://www.lecltd.com
Year Founded: 1987
Rev.: $10,000,000
Emp.: 15
Brand Development & Integration, Broadcast, Communications, Digital/Interactive, Internet/Web Design, Print
N.A.I.C.S.: 541810
Laurie Cairns *(Pres)*
James Brophy *(Dir-Creative Svcs)*
Pamela Carmona *(Dir-Media & Campaign Mgmt)*
Karen Russell *(VP-Strategic Accts)*

LECESSE DEVELOPMENT CORPORATION
650 S Northlake Blvd Ste 450, Altamonte Springs, FL 32701
Tel.: (407) 645-5575
Web Site: http://www.lecesse.com
Year Founded: 1952
Sales Range: $125-149.9 Million
Emp.: 8
Multifamily Housing, Commercial, Industrial & Institutional Building Construction; Property Management
N.A.I.C.S.: 236117
Salvador F. LeCesse *(Pres)*
Tom Hayden *(Dir-Dev)*
John Flynn *(Dir-Acq)*
Linda Parker *(Controller)*

Subsidiaries:

Cambridge Management Services, Inc. (1)
650 S Northlake Blvd Ste 450, Altamonte Springs, FL 32701
Tel.: (407) 645-5575
Web Site: http://www.cambridgemsi.com
Sales Range: $25-49.9 Million
Residential Property Management Services
N.A.I.C.S.: 531311
Robert M. Piezon *(Pres)*
Linda Parker *(Controller)*
Debby Nichols *(Dir-HR)*
Evelyn Holland *(Reg Mgr)*

LECHASE CONSTRUCTION SERVICES, LLC
205 Indigo Creek Dr, Rochester, NY 14626-4209
Tel.: (518) 388-9200   NY
Web Site: http://www.lechase.com
Year Founded: 1997
Sales Range: $550-599.9 Million
Emp.: 400
Holding Company; Commercial, Institutional & Industrial Facility Construction, Construction Management, Facilities Management & Realty Services
N.A.I.C.S.: 551112
R. Wayne LeChase *(Chm)*
William H. Goodrich *(CEO & Mng Partner)*
William L. Mack *(Pres)*
John C. Goodrich *(VP)*
Kyle L. Sayers *(Exec VP)*
Brian J. Russo *(VP)*
Neil Schiavi *(VP)*
Richard D. Schneider *(Exec VP)*
Frederick J. Thompson *(VP)*
Lee D. Sommerman *(Mgr-Ops-Western New York)*
Christopher Havens *(Project Engr-Corning)*
Tom O'Gara *(Gen Counsel)*
Maxwell Fisher *(Coord-Mktg)*
Peter Muench *(VP)*
Russell B. Smith *(VP)*
Tony Kozlowski *(Superintendent)*
Mike Corey *(Acct Exec)*
Valerie Bono *(Sr Mgr-Mktg)*
Machelle Grospitz *(Asst Superintendent)*
Gregory Barkstrom *(Dir-Real Estate Dev)*
Stephanie Pennington *(Mgr-XBE Compliance)*
Michele Koslab *(Sr Project Mgr)*

LECHASE CONSTRUCTION SERVICES, LLC   U.S. PRIVATE

LeChase Construction Services, LLC—(Continued)
Charles L. Caranci Jr. *(CFO & Exec VP)*
A. B. Robinson Jr. *(VP-Environmental, Health & Safety)*

Subsidiaries:

C.W. Brown, Inc. (1)
1 Labriola Ct, Armonk, NY 10504
Tel.: (914) 741-1212
Web Site: http://www.cwbrown.com
General Contracting, Construction Management & Renovation Services
N.A.I.C.S.: 236220
Renee M. Brown *(VP)*
Aaron Castro *(Project Mgr)*
Fred Sciliano *(Sr VP-Client Rels)*
Peter Belmont *(Controller)*
Larry Burns *(Mgr-Field Ops)*
Chris Fredericks *(Mgr-Acctg)*
Harry Roney *(Dir-Estimating)*
Chris Strebel *(Project Mgr)*
Steve Strebel *(Sr Mgr-Project)*

Northeast Construction Services (1)
609 Erie Blvd W, Syracuse, NY 13204-2424
Tel.: (315) 423-0015
Web Site:
http://www.northeastconstruction.net
Sales Range: $25-49.9 Million
Emp.: 55
Commercial, Institutional & Industrial Construction & Construction Management Services
N.A.I.C.S.: 236220
Patrick Johnston *(Co-Founder)*
Richard Schneider *(Co-Founder & Pres)*
Robert E. Keeley *(Dir-Mktg & Bus Dev)*

LECO CORPORATION

3000 Lakeview Ave, Saint Joseph, MI 49085-2396
Tel.: (269) 983-5531   MI
Web Site: http://www.leco.com
Year Founded: 1936
Sales Range: $25-49.9 Million
Emp.: 900
Laboratory Equipment Mfr
N.A.I.C.S.: 334516
Robert J. Warren *(Owner)*
Veronica Jackson *(Head-Mktg)*
Joel Deeruyne *(CFO)*
Ryan Glaske *(Engr-Mechanical)*
Robert Phillips *(Engr-Software)*
Hutchins Maria *(Mgr-Customer Comm)*

Subsidiaries:

Japan Analyst Corporation (1)
Marawa Building 3-9-23 Nishigotanda, Shinagawa-ku, Tokyo, 141-0031, Japan   (100%)
Tel.: (81) 334937281
Sales Range: $1-9.9 Million
Emp.: 15
Laboratory Equipment Mfr
N.A.I.C.S.: 334516

LECO (Vietnam) Co., Ltd. (1)
Fosco Building 3rd Floor 06 Phung Khac Khoan St District 1, 70000, Ho Chi Minh City, Vietnam
Tel.: (84) 8 3829 8979
Emp.: 15
Analytical Laboratory Instrument Mfr
N.A.I.C.S.: 334516

LECO Africa (Pty.) Ltd. (1)
3 Vuurslag Avenue Spartan Ext 7, Box 1439, 1620, Kempton Park, South Africa
Tel.: (27) 11 974 1681
Web Site: http://www.lecoafrica.co.za
Emp.: 35
Analytical Laboratory Instrument Mfr
N.A.I.C.S.: 334516
Philip Langenhoven *(Mng Dir)*
Jackie Holder *(Dir-Fin)*

LECO Argentina S.A. (1)
Llerena 3075 Capital Federal, Buenos Aires, CP C1427DEM, Argentina
Tel.: (54) 1145238077
Web Site: http://www.lecoargentina.com.ar
Emp.: 9

LECO Australia Pty. Ltd. (1)
4 10 Salisbury Rd, Castle Hill, 2154, NSW, Australia   (100%)
Tel.: (61) 298945955
Web Site: http://www.leco.com.au
Sales Range: $10-24.9 Million
Emp.: 19
Laboratory Equipment Mfr
N.A.I.C.S.: 334516
Fabio Castro *(Gen Mgr)*

LECO Corporation Svenska AB (1)
Propellervagen 8, 18362, Taby, Sweden
Tel.: (46) 859411000
Web Site: http://www.lecoswe.se
Sales Range: $10-24.9 Million
Emp.: 14
Laboratory Equipment Mfr
N.A.I.C.S.: 334516
Lars Furueren *(Office Mgr)*

LECO Europe B.V. (1)
Vouersweg 118, Geleen, 61618 AG, Netherlands   (100%)
Tel.: (31) 464747473
Web Site: http://www.leco.com
Sales Range: $10-24.9 Million
Emp.: 16
Laboratory Equipment Mfr
N.A.I.C.S.: 334516
Al Schmidt *(Mng Dir)*

LECO France (1)
ZAC les Doucettes 22 avenue des Morilons, PO Box 74, 95144, Garges-les-Gonesse, Cedex, France
Tel.: (33) 134454600
Web Site: http://www.lecofrance.com
Sales Range: $10-24.9 Million
Emp.: 20
Laboratory Equipment Mfr
N.A.I.C.S.: 334516

LECO Instrumente GmbH (1)
Marie Bernays Ring 31, 411 99, Monchengladbach, Germany
Tel.: (49) 21666870
Web Site: http://www.leco.com
Sales Range: $10-24.9 Million
Emp.: 14
Laboratory Equipment Mfr
N.A.I.C.S.: 334516

LECO Instrumente Plzen s.r.o. (1)
Plaska 66, Plzen, 32325, Czech Republic
Tel.: (420) 377510811
Web Site: http://www.leco.cz
Sales Range: $10-24.9 Million
Emp.: 15
Laboratory Equipment Mfr
N.A.I.C.S.: 334516
Zdenek Kadlec *(Mng Dir)*

LECO Instrumentos Ltda. (1)
Pinhiero Guimaraes 70, 22281-080, Rio de Janeiro, Brazil   (100%)
Tel.: (55) 2134619006
Web Site: http://www.lecobrasil.com.br
Sales Range: $10-24.9 Million
Emp.: 15
Laboratory Equipment Mfr
N.A.I.C.S.: 334516

LECO Instrumentos S.L. (1)
Avenida De La Industria No 43, Tres Cantos, 28760, Madrid, Spain
Tel.: (34) 91 803 1250
Web Site: http://www.leco.es
Analytical Laboratory Instrument Mfr

LECO Instruments (M) Sdn. Bhd. (1)
No. 2 Lorong Tandang B Section 51, 46050, Petaling Jaya, Selangor Darul Ehsen, Malaysia
Tel.: (60) 77702100
Web Site: http://www.leco.com.my
Sales Range: $10-24.9 Million
Emp.: 8
Laboratory Equipment Mfr
N.A.I.C.S.: 334516
Dave Nightingale *(Gen Mgr)*

LECO Instruments (Thailand) Ltd. (1)
127-129 5 Sirinthorn 7, Bangkok, 10700, Thailand   (100%)
Tel.: (66) 28864350
Web Site: http://www.lecothai.com
Sales Range: $10-24.9 Million
Emp.: 20
Laboratory Equipment Mfr
N.A.I.C.S.: 334516
Suthep Kongthes *(Mng Dir)*

LECO Instruments Hong Kong Ltd. (1)
Unit 2 8th Floor Yee Kuk Industrial Centre 555 Yee Kuk Street, Kowloon, China (Hong Kong)   (100%)
Tel.: (852) 2387 7028
Web Site: http://www.leco.com
Laboratory Equipment Mfr
N.A.I.C.S.: 334516

LECO Instruments Ltd. (1)
2205 Dunwin Drive, Mississauga, L5L 1X1, ON, Canada   (100%)
Tel.: (905) 564-6577
Web Site: https://www.leco.com
Emp.: 700
Laboratory Instruments & Furniture
N.A.I.C.S.: 334516
Mark Broeden *(Controller)*

LECO Instruments S.A. (1)
Avenida de la Industria 43, Tres Cantos, 28760, Madrid, Spain
Tel.: (34) 918031250
Web Site: http://www.leco.es
Sales Range: $10-24.9 Million
Emp.: 20
Laboratory Equipment Mfr
N.A.I.C.S.: 334516

LECO Instruments Taiwan Ltd. (1)
7th Fl 117 Section 2 Minsheng East Rd, Taipei, 104, Taiwan   (100%)
Tel.: (886) 225184699
Web Site: http://www.leco.com
Sales Range: $10-24.9 Million
Emp.: 9
Laboratory Equipment Mfr
N.A.I.C.S.: 334516
Jennifer Chou *(Sec)*

LECO Instruments UK Ltd. (1)
Newby Rd Indus Est, Newby Road, Hazel Grove, Stockport, SK7 5DA, Cheshire, United Kingdom   (100%)
Tel.: (44) 614875900
Sales Range: $10-24.9 Million
Emp.: 20
Laboratory Equipment Mfr
N.A.I.C.S.: 334516

LECO Italy, S.R.L. (1)
Via N Copernico 26, Cassina de' Pecchi, 20060, Italy
Tel.: (39) 0295343391
Web Site: http://www.leco-europe.com
Sales Range: $10-24.9 Million
Emp.: 14
Laboratory Equipment Mfr
N.A.I.C.S.: 334516
Giovanni Bonanomi *(Head-Sls)*

LECO Japan Corporation (1)
Sumitomo Fudosan Shiba Building 4 13-4, Shiba 2-chome, Minato-ku, Tokyo, 105-0014, Japan
Tel.: (81) 3 6891 5800
Web Site: http://www.leco.co.jp
Analytical Laboratory Instrument Mfr
N.A.I.C.S.: 334516

LECO Korea Co. Ltd. (1)
Rm 502 Yoo Hwa B D, 995-16 Taechi-Dong, Kangnam-Gu, Seoul, 135 280, Korea (South)
Tel.: (82) 25624148
Sales Range: $10-24.9 Million
Emp.: 10
Laboratory Equipment Mfr
N.A.I.C.S.: 334516

LECO Mexico S.A. de C.V. (1)
Oficinas Generales Lazaro Cardenas #4404, Monterrey, NL, Mexico
Tel.: (52) 81 8394 4384
Web Site: http://www.lecomexico.com
Sales Range: $10-24.9 Million
Emp.: 15
Laboratory Equipment Mfr
N.A.I.C.S.: 334516
Lucio E. Perez *(Gen Mgr)*

LECO Polska Sp. z o.o. (1)
Ul Czarna 4, 43-100, Tychy, Poland
Tel.: (48) 32 200 0760
Analytical Laboratory Instrument Mfr
N.A.I.C.S.: 334516

LECO Technologies-Philippine Marketing Corporation (1)
84 Longhorn St Rancho Estate 1, Marikina, 1811, Philippines
Tel.: (63) 2 941 3159
Analytical Laboratory Instrument Mfr
N.A.I.C.S.: 334516

Z.A.O. LECO Center Moscow (1)
1 Avtozavodsky proyezd 4-1, 115280, Moscow, Russia   (100%)
Tel.: (7) 4957103818
Web Site: http://www.leco.ru
Sales Range: $10-24.9 Million
Emp.: 20
Laboratory Equipment Mfr
N.A.I.C.S.: 334516

LECORP, INC.

3503 Clinton Rd, Paducah, KY 42001
Tel.: (270) 554-9653
Web Site: http://www.lecorp.com
Year Founded: 1958
Sales Range: $10-24.9 Million
Emp.: 6
Material Processing, Handling, Control & Environmental Services
N.A.I.C.S.: 423830
Daniel E. Crane *(Pres)*

LECTORUM PUBLICATIONS, INC.

205 Chubb Ave, Lyndhurst, NJ 07071-3520
Tel.: (201) 559-2200
Web Site: http://www.lectorum.com
Book Publishers
N.A.I.C.S.: 424920
Alex Correa *(Pres & CEO)*

LECTRODRYER LLC

135 Quality Dr, Richmond, KY 40475-9621
Tel.: (859) 624-2091
Web Site: http://www.lectrodryer.com
Year Founded: 1932
Sales Range: Less than $1 Million
Emp.: 50
Equipment for Drying Air, Gases & Liquids
N.A.I.C.S.: 333998
John McPherson *(Pres)*
Stephanie Billiter *(Engr-Application)*
Kevin Boneta *(Project Mgr)*
Amelia Bell *(Product Mgr-Power Generation Div)*
Blanca Ramirez *(CMO)*

LED SOURCE, LLC

3281 Fairlane Farms Rd Ste 1, Wellington, FL 33414
Tel.: (561) 296-9599
Web Site: http://www.ledsource.com
Year Founded: 2005
Sales Range: $1-9.9 Million
Emp.: 40
LED Lighting Products Mfr
N.A.I.C.S.: 335132
Marcel Fairbairn *(Founder & CEO)*
Gavin Cooper *(Co-Founder & Pres)*
Cynthia Viteri *(Partner)*

LEDIC MANAGEMENT GROUP

2650 Thousand Oaks Blvd Ste 3100, Memphis, TN 38118
Tel.: (901) 761-9300
Web Site: http://www.ledic.com
Sales Range: $10-24.9 Million
Emp.: 500
Real Estate Managers
N.A.I.C.S.: 561499

Justin D. Towner *(Sr VP-Ops)*
Nelda Jones *(Reg VP)*
Pierce Ledbetter *(CEO)*

LEDNOVATION, INC.
13053 W Linebaugh Ave Ste 102, Tampa, FL 33626
Tel.: (813) 891-9600
Web Site:
http://www.lednovation.com
Sales Range: $1-9.9 Million
Emp.: 20
LED Lighting Mfr
N.A.I.C.S.: 335139
Israel Morejon *(Pres & CEO)*
Evan O'Sullivan *(VP-Engrg)*

LEDUC & DEXTER INC.
2833 Dowd Dr A, Santa Rosa, CA 95407
Tel.: (707) 575-1500
Web Site:
http://www.leducanddexterplumbing.com
Rev.: $10,222,792
Emp.: 65
Plumbing Contractor
N.A.I.C.S.: 238220
Art Dexter *(COO & VP)*
Tom Leduc *(Pres & CEO)*

LEDYARD COMPANY
1047 17th Ave, Santa Cruz, CA 95062
Tel.: (831) 462-4400
Web Site:
http://www.performancefoodservice.com
Sales Range: $25-49.9 Million
Emp.: 113
Restaurant Food, Equipment & Supplies Distr
N.A.I.C.S.: 424410
Remy Sablan *(Mgr-HR)*

LEE & ASSOCIATES COMMERCIAL REAL ESTATE
Tel.: (818) 812-1208
Web Site: https://www.lee-associates.com
Year Founded: 1979
Rev.: $2,400,000
Emp.: 40
Other Direct Insurance, except Life, Health & Medical, Carriers
N.A.I.C.S.: 524128
William Gosnell *(Pres)*
Kurt Saulnier *(Principal)*
Pete Batschelet *(Principal)*

LEE & ASSOCIATES LICENSING AND ADMINISTRATION CO., LP
1004 Taft Ave Ste 150, Los Angeles, CA 92865
Tel.: (714) 647-9100   NV
Web Site: http://www.lee-associates.com
Year Founded: 1979
Commercial Real Estate Brokerage Firm Franchisor
N.A.I.C.S.: 533110
Jeffrey M. Rinkov *(Chm & CEO)*

LEE & ASSOCIATES, INC.
145 S Fairfax Ave Ste 301, Los Angeles, CA 90036-2166
Tel.: (323) 938-3300
Web Site:
http://www.leeassociates.com
Year Founded: 1950
Sales Range: $1-9.9 Million
Emp.: 9
Advertising & Public Relations Agency
N.A.I.C.S.: 541820

Howard Pearlstein *(Principal & VP)*
Frank Pearlstein *(Principal & VP)*
Leo Pearlstein *(Founder)*
Caroline Dell *(Dir-Mktg-Chicago)*
Chris Huecksteadt *(Exec VP-Illinois)*
David Gronbeck *(Partner-Comml Real Estate Svcs-Idaho)*
Brian Lynch *(Chief Strategy Officer)*
Marcus Muirhead *(Principal)*
Greg Guglielmino *(Principal)*
Steven Gonzalez *(Principal)*
Robert LaCoure *(Principal-Houston)*
David Goldenberg *(CEO)*
Ron Parque *(Pres)*
Twee Pham *(VP-Mktg)*
Becky Thompson *(Principal)*
Christopher Larimore *(Founder/Pres-Pasadena)*
Chris Johnson *(Sr VP-Pasadena)*
David Violette *(Exec Dir)*

LEE & WYRSCH
212 1/2 W 5th St Ste 212, Joplin, MO 64801-2501
Tel.: (417) 623-5266   MO
Year Founded: 1977
Rev.: $1,500,000
Emp.: 9
Fiscal Year-end: 12/31/01
N.A.I.C.S.: 541810
William A. Wyrsch *(CEO & Project Coord)*
Cindy Tourtelot *(Media Buyer)*
Matthew Lee *(Pres-Sls)*
Terri Falis-Cochran *(VP-Ops)*
Tim Howard *(Dir-Art & Web Designer)*
Crystal Manning *(Graphic Designer)*
Brett Lyerla *(Graphic Designer)*

LEE A. FOLGER INC.
5701 E Independence Blvd, Charlotte, NC 28212
Tel.: (704) 536-9635
Web Site:
http://www.folgerautomotive.com
Sales Range: $25-49.9 Million
Emp.: 80
Automobiles, New & Used
N.A.I.C.S.: 441110
Jackie Robinson *(Office Mgr)*
Rick Burleson *(Mgr-Sls)*
Mike Melton *(Mgr-Parts)*
Mike Williams *(Controller)*
Clarence E. Williams Jr. *(Chm)*

LEE ADVERTISING
4381 Arrowwood Cir, Concord, CA 94521
Tel.: (925) 680-0139
Web Site:
http://www.leeadvertising.com
Sales Range: Less than $1 Million
Emp.: 5
Corporate Identity, Direct Marketing, E-Commerce, Internet/Web Design, Magazines, Newspapers & Magazines, Outdoor, Print, T.V.
N.A.I.C.S.: 541810
Ivan Lee *(Dir-Creative & Founder)*

LEE AUTOMOTIVE GROUP INC.
541 Mary Esther Cutoff, Fort Walton Beach, FL 32548
Tel.: (850) 244-7611
Web Site: http://www.leeautogrp.com
Rev.: $26,900,000
Emp.: 50
Automobiles, New & Used
N.A.I.C.S.: 441110
Steven Jarrell *(Dir-Svc & Parts)*

Subsidiaries:

Lee Pontiac-GMC, Inc.   (1)
235 Miracle Strip Pkwy SW, Fort Walton Beach, FL 32548

Tel.: (850) 243-3123
Web Site: http://www.leepontiacgmc.com
Sales Range: $25-49.9 Million
Automobiles; New & Used
N.A.I.C.S.: 441110
Gary E. Lee Jr. *(Pres)*

LEE BANK
75 Park St, Lee, MA 01238
Tel.: (413) 243-0117
Web Site: http://www.leebank.com
Rev.: $10,000,000
Emp.: 41
Federal Savings Institutions
N.A.I.C.S.: 522180
Christopher Kinne *(VP)*
Michael Norton *(Asst VP)*
Susan B. Brown *(Sr VP-HR & Admin)*
Chuck Leach *(Pres & CEO)*
Wendy Healey *(Sr VP-Community Banking)*
David Harrington *(VP-Comml Lending)*
Marianne Fresia *(Asst VP-Private Banking & Trust Svcs)*
Paula Gangell-Miller *(VP-Community Banking-Retail Ops)*
Paula Lewis *(First VP-Retail Lending)*

LEE BEVERAGE CO. INC.
2850 S Oakwood Rd, Oshkosh, WI 54904
Tel.: (920) 235-1140
Web Site:
http://www.leebeverage.com
Rev.: $21,000,000
Emp.: 104
Beer & Ale
N.A.I.C.S.: 424810
Jeff Lindemann *(Pres)*

LEE BRASS COMPANY
1800 Golden Springs Rd, Anniston, AL 36207
Tel.: (256) 831-2501
Web Site: http://www.leebrass.com
Year Founded: 1917
Sales Range: $10-24.9 Million
Emp.: 250
Brass Fitting & Related Product Mfr
N.A.I.C.S.: 332913
Reiber Heath *(CFO)*

LEE BROS FOODSERVICE INC.
660 E Gish Rd, San Jose, CA 95112
Tel.: (408) 280-1595
Web Site: http://www.leebros.com
Year Founded: 1980
Sales Range: $25-49.9 Million
Emp.: 100
Mobile Catering Services
N.A.I.C.S.: 424410
Chieu Le *(Pres)*

LEE BUILDER MART INC.
1000 N Horner Blvd, Sanford, NC 27330
Tel.: (919) 775-5555
Web Site:
http://www.leebuildermart.com
Sales Range: $10-24.9 Million
Emp.: 25
Lumber & Other Building Materials
N.A.I.C.S.: 423310
Tony G. Lett *(Pres)*
Art Coleman *(VP)*

LEE COMPANY
331 Mallory Sta Rd, Franklin, TN 37067
Tel.: (615) 567-1000
Web Site:
http://www.leecompany.com
Year Founded: 1944
Sales Range: $75-99.9 Million
Emp.: 750

Plumbing Contractors & Mechanical
N.A.I.C.S.: 238220
William B. Lee *(Chm)*
Richard C. Perko *(CEO)*
Gerald R. Vance *(Exec VP-Bus Dev)*
Lauren Painter *(Dir-Fin Ops)*
Karen Johnston *(Controller)*
Daniel Kalman *(Sr VP-Home Svcs)*
Steve Scott *(Sr VP-Facilities Solutions)*

LEE CORP HOMES INC.
20251 S Tamiami Trl, Estero, FL 33928
Tel.: (239) 498-2220
Web Site: http://www.leecorpinc.com
Rev.: $20,000,000
Emp.: 15
Manufactured Home Dealers
N.A.I.C.S.: 459930
Phillip L. Lee *(Pres)*

LEE COUNTY ELECTRIC CO-OPERATIVE, INC.
4980 Bayline Ave, North Fort Myers, FL 33917
Tel.: (239) 995-2121   FL
Web Site: http://www.lcec.net
Year Founded: 1940
Sales Range: $200-249.9 Million
Emp.: 400
Electronic Services
N.A.I.C.S.: 221118
Karen L. Ryan *(Mgr-PR)*
Cindy Neumann *(Head-Program Mgmt & Process Practices)*

LEE DRYWALL, INC.
5845 Corp Cir, Fort Myers, FL 33905
Tel.: (239) 939-9779   FL
Web Site: http://www.leedrywall.com
Year Founded: 1991
Sales Range: $1-9.9 Million
Emp.: 75
Drywall & Insulation Contractors
N.A.I.C.S.: 238310
Mitchell Lee *(Co-Founder & Co-Pres)*
Justin Lee *(VP)*
John Kucaba *(Project Mgr)*
John Hash *(Project Mgr)*
Brad Samuelson *(Mgr-Field Ops)*
Jeff Baller *(Mgr-Field Ops)*
Traci Lee *(Co-Founder & Co-Pres)*

LEE EDWARDS INC.
2218 Louisville Ave, Monroe, LA 71201-6125
Tel.: (318) 388-3540
Web Site:
http://www.leeedwardsauto.com
Year Founded: 1957
Sales Range: $10-24.9 Million
Emp.: 70
New & Used Car Dealer Services
N.A.I.C.S.: 441110
Chris Edwards *(Principal)*
Elizabeth Myers *(Exec Mgr)*
Jason Coleman *(Mgr-Sls-Internet)*
Roy Smith *(Bus Mgr)*

LEE EQUITY PARTNERS LLC
40 W 57th St Ste 1620, New York, NY 10019
Tel.: (212) 906-4900   DE
Web Site: https://www.leeequity.com
Year Founded: 2006
Privater Equity Firm
N.A.I.C.S.: 523999
Mark K. Gormley *(Partner)*
Yoo Jin Kim *(Partner)*
Joseph B. Rotberg *(CFO, Chief Compliance Officer & Partner)*
Christian Chauvet *(Partner)*
Ryan Fossella *(Principal)*
Whitney McBride *(VP-IR)*
Matthew Abramowitz *(Controller)*
Collins Ward *(Partner)*

LEE EQUITY PARTNERS LLC

Lee Equity Partners LLC—(Continued)

Subsidiaries:

Addiction & Mental Health Services, LLC (1)
2101 Magnolia Ave S Ste 518, Birmingham, AL 35205
Tel.: (205) 251-7753
Web Site: http://www.bradfordhealth.com
Outpatient Mental Health & Substance Abuse Centers
N.A.I.C.S.: 621420
Mike Rickman (CEO)

Subsidiary (Domestic):

Lakeview Health Systems, L.L.C. (2)
1900 Corporate Sq Blvd, Jacksonville, FL 32216
Tel.: (904) 513-5822
Web Site: http://www.lakeviewhealth.com
Addiction & Psychiatric Rehabilitation Services
N.A.I.C.S.: 622210
Jim Evanger (Pres & CEO)
Alan Goodstat (COO)
Jamie Stevens (VP-Ops)
Derek Gwaltney (Exec VP-Bus Dev)
Lantie Jorandby (Chief Medical Officer)
Kari Fox (Dir-Mktg)
Charlie Mercer (Dir-IT)
Sara Holt (Dir-HR)

Atria Wealth Solutions, LLC (1)
295 Madison Ave Ste 1407, New York, NY 10017
Tel.: (858) 530-4440
Web Site: https://atriawealth.com
Holding Company
N.A.I.C.S.: 551112
Doug Ketterer (Founder, CEO & Partner)
Kevin Beard (Founder, Partner & Chief Growth Officer)
Eugene Elias Jr. (Founder, Partner & COO)

Subsidiary (Domestic):

CUSO Financial Services, L.P. (2)
10150 Meanley Dr 1st Fl, San Diego, CA 92121
Tel.: (858) 530-4400
Web Site: http://www.cusonet.com
Financial Investment Services
N.A.I.C.S.: 523999
Dan Kilroy (CFO & Mng Dir)
Valorie Seyfert (Co-Founder, Pres & CEO)
Kevin Mummau (Chief Relationship Officer & Mng Dir)
Cindy Zabuska (Exec Dir-Ops & Trading)
Janine Holmes (Exec Dir-HR)
Peter Vonk (Chief Compliance Officer & Mng Dir)
Rick Dahl (Chief Compliance Officer & Exec Dir)
Karen Goldstein (VP-Practice Mgmt & Trng)

Cadaret, Grant & Co., Inc. (2)
100 Madison St, Syracuse, NY 13202
Tel.: (800) 288-8601
Web Site: http://www.cadaretgrant.com
Provider of Security Broker & Dealer Services
N.A.I.C.S.: 523150

NEXT Financial Group, Inc. (2)
2500 Wilcrest Ste 620, Houston, TX 77042
Tel.: (713) 789-7122
Web Site: http://www.nextfinancial.com
Financial Services
N.A.I.C.S.: 523940
Barry Knight (Pres & CEO)
Leslie Jallans (Chief Compliance Officer)

Western International Securities, Inc. (2)
70 S Lake Ave Ste 700, Pasadena, CA 91101
Tel.: (888) 793-7717
Web Site: http://www.wisdirect.com
Sales Range: $25-49.9 Million
Emp.: 30
Full-Service Brokerage Operations
N.A.I.C.S.: 523150
Donald Bizub (CEO)
Brad Kaiser (Sr Mng Dir & Chief Compliance Officer)
Andrew Kuo (Mng Dir-Ops, Tech, Transitions, Broker Rels & Insurance Svc)
Tom O'Conell (Assoc Dir-New Bus Dev)
Wendy Rea (Sr Mng Dir & COO)

Carisk Partners, Inc. (1)
10685 N Kendall Dr, Miami, FL 33176
Tel.: (305) 514-5300
Web Site: http://www.cariskpartners.com
Risk Transfer & Care Coordination Company
N.A.I.C.S.: 621399
Kevin Mahoney (Pres & COO)
Angel E. Garrido (Chief Medical Officer)
Allen Spokane (CTO)
Chrissy Gaul (VP-Mktg)
Alana Letourneau (Chief Clinical Strategy Officer)
Joseph Berardo Jr. (CEO)

Subsidiary (Domestic):

Carisk Specialty Services, Inc. (2)
25a Hanover Rd Ste 201, Florham Park, NJ 07932
Tel.: (973) 451-9415
Web Site: http://www.cariskpartners.com
Diagnostic Radiology & Testing Network
N.A.I.C.S.: 621512
Stephen P. Ellerman (Pres)

Cosmetic Solutions, LLC (1)
6101 Park of Commerce Blvd, Boca Raton, FL 33487
Tel.: (954) 972-7202
Web Site: http://www.naturalskincare.com
Skin Care Products Mfr & Distr
N.A.I.C.S.: 424210
Mervyn Becker (Chm)
Warren Becker (QEO)

Deb Shops, Inc. (1)
3232 E Washington Blvd, Vernon, CA 90058
Tel.: (215) 676-6000
Web Site: http://www.debshops.com
Sales Range: $300-349.9 Million
Women's Apparel Retailer
N.A.I.C.S.: 458110
Diane M. Paccione (Pres & CEO)

Pinnacle Summer Investments, Inc. (1)
4000 Legato Rd 9th Fl, Fairfax, VA 22033-4055
Tel.: (713) 224-3100
Sales Range: $150-199.9 Million
Emp.: 498
Holding Company; Wealth Management & Institutional Banking Services
N.A.I.C.S.: 551112
Fredric M. Edelman (Pres & CEO)

Affiliate (Domestic):

Global Financial Services LLC (2)
1330 Post Oak Blvd Ste 2100, Houston, TX 77056 (48.7%)
Tel.: (713) 968-0400
Web Site: http://www.globalhou.com
Sales Range: $50-74.9 Million
Emp.: 20
Investment Services
N.A.I.C.S.: 523150

Subsidiary (Domestic):

Investor Financial Solutions, LLC (2)
600 Anton Blvd Ste 1750, Huntington Beach, CA 92648 (51%)
Tel.: (714) 841-6335
Web Site: http://www.isgca.net
Sales Range: $50-74.9 Million
Emp.: 3
Investment Management Service
N.A.I.C.S.: 523940

Kissinger Financial (2)
10155 York Rd Ste 105, Hunt Valley, MD 21030 (100%)
Tel.: (410) 252-3400
Web Site: http://www.kissingernet.com
Sales Range: $1-9.9 Million
Emp.: 15
Financial Services
N.A.I.C.S.: 523940
William Kissinger (Pres)

Leonetti & Associates, LLC (2)
1130 W Lake Cook Rd Ste 300, Buffalo Grove, IL 60089 (50.1%)
Tel.: (847) 520-0999
Web Site: http://www.leonettiassoc.com
Sales Range: $50-74.9 Million
Emp.: 16
Investment Management Service

N.A.I.C.S.: 523940
Michael E. Leonetti (CEO & Mgr-Wealth)
Deborah B. Feldman (Pres, Dir-Wealth Mgmt & Mgr-Wealth)
Craig T. Johnson (Portfolio Mgr)
Matt Varner (Portfolio Mgr & Head-Trader)
David A. Jutovsky (Mgr-Wealth)
Sherwin M. Lesk (Mgr-Wealth)
Robin L. Stone (Mgr-Wealth)
Debbie Javurek (Dir-Client Svcs)
John O'Brien (Chief Compliance Officer & Dir-HR)

Miller-Green Financial Services, Inc. (2)
1330 Lake Robbins Dr Ste 360, The Woodlands, TX 77380 (100%)
Tel.: (281) 364-9100
Web Site: http://www.miller-green.com
Financial Management Services
N.A.I.C.S.: 523940
Don Gilbert (Chief Compliance Officer)

Sanders Morris Harris Inc. (2)
JP Morgan Chase Twr 600 Travis St Ste 5800, Houston, TX 77002 (100%)
Tel.: (713) 224-3100
Web Site: http://www.smhgroup.com
Sales Range: $125-149.9 Million
Emp.: 100
Wealth Management & Institutional Banking Services
N.A.I.C.S.: 523150

Subsidiary (Domestic):

SMH Capital Advisors, Inc. (3)
4800 Overton Plz Ste 300, Fort Worth, TX 76109
Tel.: (817) 569-7030
Web Site: http://www.smhca.com
Investment Advisory Services
N.A.I.C.S.: 523940
Dwayne Moyers (Pres & Chief Investment Officer)
Daniel Rudnitsky (VP & Sr Portfolio Mgr)
Jenny Don Carlos (Mgr-Platform Program)
Megan Brown (VP-Mktg & Bus Dev)
Gabriela Forster (COO)

SMH Cummer/Moyers (3)
4800 Overton Plz Ste 300, Fort Worth, TX 76109-6141 (100%)
Tel.: (817) 569-7000
Web Site: http://www.cummermoyers.com
Sales Range: $50-74.9 Million
Emp.: 13
Financial Services
N.A.I.C.S.: 523999
Ben T. Morris (Pres)
Dwayne Moyers (Chief Investment Officer & Sr Portfolio Mgr)

Subsidiary (Domestic):

The Rikoon Group, LLC (2)
2218 Old Arroyo Chamiso Rd, Santa Fe, NM 87505 (80%)
Tel.: (505) 989-3581
Web Site: http://www.rikoongroup.com
Sales Range: $50-74.9 Million
Emp.: 5
Financial Management Services
N.A.I.C.S.: 523999
Robert A. Rikoon (Pres & CEO)
Jeffrey W. Sand (Portfolio Mgr)
Kyle J. Burns (VP & Portfolio Mgr)

Summit Healthcare Management, LLC (1)
389 Nichol Mill Ln Ste 100 & 160, Franklin, TN 37067
Tel.: (615) 435-3725
Web Site: http://www.summitbhc.com
Behavioral Health Centers Management
N.A.I.C.S.: 523940
William Brent Turner (CEO)
Trey Carter (Co-Founder)
Chuck Edwards (Co-Founder & CFO)
Jeff Barnett (COO)
Karen Prince (Co-Founder)
Danny Carpenter (Exec VP-Fin Ops)
Jill Shrader (VP-Quality & Compliance)
Lisa Smith (VP-HR)
Christina Hawkins (VP-Strategic Dev & PR)
K. Anderson (VP-Admission Center Ops)
Jon O'Shaughnessy (Pres)
Brent Turner (CEO)

Subsidiary (Domestic):

Summit BHC Sevierville, LLC (2)

1096 Alpine Dr, Sevierville, TN 37876
Tel.: (877) 309-9963
Web Site: http://englishmountain.com
Drug & Alcohol Addiction Rehabilitation Services
N.A.I.C.S.: 624190
William Brent Turner (CEO)
Clay Phillips (VP-Strategy & Managed Care)
Brent Turner (CEO)
Chuck Steiner (Chief Strategy Officer)

The Ranch at Dove Tree LLC (2)
1406 Quinlan St, Lubbock, TX 79403
Tel.: (806) 746-6777
Web Site: http://www.ranchatdovetree.com
Outpatient Mental Health & Substance Abuse Centers
N.A.I.C.S.: 621420
Curt G. Maddon (CEO)
Jeanette Franks (Dir-Quality & Risk Mgmt)
Katie Trungale (Dir-Bus Dev)

TESSCO Technologies, Inc. (1)
11126 McCormick Rd, Hunt Valley, MD 21031-1494
Tel.: (410) 229-1000
Web Site: https://www.tessco.com
Rev.: $417,544,800
Assets: $202,513,300
Liabilities: $126,590,200
Net Worth: $75,923,100
Earnings: ($2,700,800)
Emp.: 530
Fiscal Year-end: 03/27/2022
Wireless Communications Products Distr
N.A.I.C.S.: 423690
Dave Eckelbarger (CEO)
David Young (CFO)
Kelly Mavias (VP-National Carrier Sls & Business Development)
Steve Schiech (VP-Commercial Sls)
Steve Marshner (VP-CFD Systems Engrg, Operations, Logistics, and QMS)
Justin Seda (VP & Controller)
Anu Gupta (VP-E & Commerce)
Andrew Sapitowicz (VP-Bus Analytics & PMO)
Thomas Callahan (VP-Infrastructure, Security, and Operations)
Ryan Smith (VP-Talent Acquisition & Human Resources)

Westfall Technik, Inc. (1)
3883 Howard Hughes Ste 590, Las Vegas, NV 89169
Tel.: (702) 659-9898
Web Site: http://www.westfall-technik.com
Holding Company; Plastic Products Mfr
N.A.I.C.S.: 551112
Rick Shaffer (Mng Dir-SW Europe)
Merritt Williams (Chief Comml Officer)
Mark Gomulka (CEO)

Subsidiary (Domestic):

10 Day Parts, Inc. (2)
235 Citation Cir, Corona, CA 92880-2523
Tel.: (951) 279-4810
Web Site: http://www.10dayparts.com
Plastics Products, Nec, Nsk
N.A.I.C.S.: 326199

AMS Plastics, Inc. (2)
1530 Hilton Head Rd Ste 205, El Cajon, CA 92019-4655
Tel.: (619) 713-2000
Web Site: http://www.amsplastics.com
Plastics Product Mfr
N.A.I.C.S.: 326199
Scott Modic (VP-Sls & Mktg)

Carolina Precision Plastics LLC (2)
111 CPP Global Dr, Mocksville, NC 27028
Tel.: (336) 283-4700
Web Site: http://www.cppglobal.com
Sales Range: $10-24.9 Million
Emp.: 135
Injection Molding Of Plastics
N.A.I.C.S.: 326199
Brian Tauber (CEO)

Delta Pacific Products, Inc. (2)
33170 Central Ave, Union City, CA 94587
Tel.: (510) 487-4411
Plastics Product Mfr
N.A.I.C.S.: 326199

Subsidiary (Domestic):

Prism Plastics Products, Inc. (3)

1544 Hwy 65, New Richmond, WI 54017
Tel.: (715) 246-7535
Web Site: http://www.prismplasticsinc.com
Sales Range: $1-9.9 Million
Emp.: 40
Custom Injection Molding Plastic Products Mfr
N.A.I.C.S.: 326199
Kevin Larson (Mgr-Quality)
Mark Fagerland (Pres)
Mike Brinkman (Gen Mgr)
Tom Schweitzer (Mgr-Engrg)

Subsidiary (Domestic):

Fairway Injection Molds, Inc. (2)
20109 Paseo Del Prado, Walnut, CA 91789
Tel.: (909) 595-2201
Web Site: http://www.fairwaymolds.com
Injection Mould Mfr
N.A.I.C.S.: 333511
Steven Bilderain (Mgr-Engrg)

Integrity Mold, Inc. (2)
905 W Alameda Dr, Tempe, AZ 85282
Tel.: (480) 829-3899
Web Site: http://www.intmold.com
Industrial Mold Mfr
N.A.I.C.S.: 333511
Mike Friend (VP & Gen Mgr)
Dan Joseph (Partner & VP)

Mold Craft, Inc. (2)
200 Stillwater Rd, Willernie, MN 55090
Tel.: (651) 426-3216
Web Site: http://www.mold-craft.com
Mfg Dies/Tools/Jigs/Fixtures
N.A.I.C.S.: 333511

LEE F. COWPER, INC.
265 Racine Dr Ste 100, Wilmington, NC 28403-8745
Tel.: (910) 392-0660
Sales Range: $10-24.9 Million
Emp.: 45
Nonresidential Construction Services
N.A.I.C.S.: 236220
Lee Cowper (Pres)

LEE HARTMAN & SONS INC.
3236 Cove Rd NW, Roanoke, VA 24017
Tel.: (540) 366-3493
Web Site: http://www.leehartman.com
Rev.: $14,861,402
Emp.: 53
Video Equipment, Electronic
N.A.I.C.S.: 423690
Quentin Mills (Mgr-Baltimore)
Larry Cox (Mgr-Hurricane)
Nick Hatgimisios (Mgr-Newport News)
Stephen Hartman (Pres)
Robert Hartman Jr. (VP)

LEE HY PAVING CORPORATION
2100 Cory Hill Rd, Rockville, VA 23146
Tel.: (804) 364-3015
Web Site: http://www.leehypaving.com
Year Founded: 1956
Sales Range: $10-24.9 Million
Emp.: 60
Highway & Street Paving Contractor
N.A.I.C.S.: 237310
Joseph B. Penick (Pres)
C. R. Langhorne (COO & Exec VP)
Claude B. Daniel (VP)
Frederick M. Luck (VP)
Stanley B. Snellings (Sec & VP)
Cynthia G. Hill (Treas)
Don Pollay (Dir-Safety)
Gordon F. Penick III (Vice Chm & CEO)

LEE HYUNDAI INC.
1960 Skibo Rd, Fayetteville, NC 28314
Tel.: (910) 864-7100
Web Site: http://www.leehyundai.com
Year Founded: 1987
Sales Range: $10-24.9 Million
Emp.: 54
Sales of New & Used Automobiles
N.A.I.C.S.: 441110
John F. Lee (Owner & Pres)
Tony Calcutt (Dir-Fin)

LEE INDUSTRIES INC.
210 4th St SW, Conover, NC 28613
Tel.: (828) 464-8318
Web Site: http://www.leeindustries.com
Year Founded: 1969
Sales Range: $25-49.9 Million
Emp.: 400
Upholstered Furniture Mfr
N.A.I.C.S.: 337121
Bill McKinney (VP)
Robert W. Montler (Chm, Pres & CEO)
Joshua T. Montler (CFO & COO)

LEE KENNEDY CO. INC.
122 Quincy Shore Dr, Quincy, MA 02171
Tel.: (617) 825-6930 MA
Web Site: http://www.leekennedy.com
Year Founded: 1978
Sales Range: $10-24.9 Million
Emp.: 75
Preconstruction Services, Construction Management & General Contracting
N.A.I.C.S.: 236220
Michael Heath (CFO)
Richard M. Robbins (VP)
Clare Costello (Dir-HR)
Eugene Kennedy (VP-Bus Dev)
Lee Michael Kennedy (Pres & CEO)
Rose Conti (Dir-Interiors & Special Projects)
Meghan Murphy (Dir-Mktg)
Chris Pennie (Sr VP)
Steve Flanagan (VP-Bus Dev)
Don Cook (VP-Construction)
Allan Fiddes (VP-Estimating & Preconstruction Svcs)
Scott Giles (VP-Interiors & Special Projects)

LEE KINSTLE CHEVROLET-OLDSMOBILE INC.
650 W Ervin Rd, Van Wert, OH 45891
Tel.: (419) 238-5902
Web Site: http://www.leekinstle.com
Year Founded: 1970
Sales Range: $10-24.9 Million
Emp.: 30
Car Dealership
N.A.I.C.S.: 441110
Eric McCracken (Owner & Gen Mgr)

LEE LEWIS CONSTRUCTION, INC.
7810 Orlando Ave, Lubbock, TX 79423
Tel.: (806) 797-8400
Web Site: http://www.leelewis.com
Year Founded: 1976
Sales Range: $25-49.9 Million
Emp.: 250
Construction Services
N.A.I.C.S.: 236220
Lee Lewis (CEO)
Tom Ferguson (Pres)
Jeanette Howell (CFO)
Liz Longer (Dir-Mktg)

LEE LUMBER & BUILDING MATERIAL CORP.
3250 N Kedzie Ave, Chicago, IL 60618
Tel.: (773) 509-6700
Web Site: http://www.leelumber.com
Sales Range: $25-49.9 Million
Emp.: 140
Lumber & Other Building Materials
N.A.I.C.S.: 423910
Lee Baumgarten (Founder)

LEE MASONRY PRODUCTS, LLC
309 Dishman Ln, Bowling Green, KY 42101
Tel.: (270) 781-9813
Web Site: http://www.leebrickandblock.com
Sales Range: $25-49.9 Million
Emp.: 220
Concrete Blocks Mfr
N.A.I.C.S.: 327331
Carol Todd Lee (Pres)
Barry Lee (Treas)

LEE MATHEWS EQUIPMENT INC.
318 Broadway St, Kansas City, MO 64105
Tel.: (816) 221-0650
Web Site: http://www.cogentcompanies.com
Sales Range: $10-24.9 Million
Emp.: 45
Industrial Machinery & Equipment
N.A.I.C.S.: 423830
Stacy Frey (CFO)
Dan Bailey (Project Mgr-Engrg)

LEE MEMORIAL HEALTH SYSTEM
PO Box 2218, Fort Myers, FL 33902
Tel.: (239) 332-1111
Web Site: http://www.leememorial.org
Sales Range: $400-449.9 Million
Emp.: 5,700
Community Healthcare System
N.A.I.C.S.: 622110
Nancy McGovern (Sec)
Scott Nygaard (Chief Medical & Clinical Integration Officer)
Sanford N. Cohen (Chm)
Therese Everly (Sec)
David F. Collins (Treas)
Donna Clarke (Vice Chm)
Ben Spence (CFO)
Elwood Leonard (Chief Foundation Officer)
Mary McGillicuddy (Chief Legal Officer & Gen Counsel)
Kevin Newingham (Chief Strategic Officer)
Michael W. Smith (CIO)
Kristine Fay (Chief Admin Officer)
David Cato (Chief Admin Officer-Outpatient Svcs)
Shelley C. Koltnow (Chief Compliance Officer)
John Chomeau (Chief Population Health Officer)
Mark A. Greenberg (VP-Medical Affairs)

Subsidiaries:

Gulf Coast Medical Center (1)
13681 Doctor's Way, Fort Myers, FL 33912
Tel.: (239) 343-1000
Web Site: http://www.leememorial.org
Sales Range: $75-99.9 Million
Emp.: 1,200
Medical Center
N.A.I.C.S.: 622110
Peter Duggan (Dir-Pharmacy)
Beverly McKee (Supvr-Microbiology Laboratory)

LEE MENTAL HEALTH CENTER, INC.
2789 Ortiz Ave, Fort Myers, FL 33905
Tel.: (239) 275-3222
Web Site: http://www.leementalhealth.org
Year Founded: 1969
Sales Range: $10-24.9 Million
Emp.: 300
Mental Health Facilities
N.A.I.C.S.: 621420
Todd Cordisco (VP-Community Rels & Dev)

LEE MICHAELS JEWELERS INC.
11314 Cloverland Ave, Baton Rouge, LA 70809
Tel.: (225) 291-9094
Web Site: http://www.lmfj.com
Sales Range: $25-49.9 Million
Emp.: 150
Jewelry, Precious Stones & Precious Metals
N.A.I.C.S.: 458310
Lee Michael Berg (Founder & Pres)
Jane Harrington (CFO)
Ryan Berg (Pres-Market-Texas)
Scott Berg (Pres-Market)

LEE NATIONAL CORPORATION
645 5th Ave, New York, NY 10022-5910
Tel.: (212) 848-0200 NY
Year Founded: 1978
Sales Range: $75-99.9 Million
Emp.: 20
Real Estate, Financial & Investment Services
N.A.I.C.S.: 237210
Alvin Dworman (Chm & Pres)
Michael Uzzi (Controller)

Subsidiaries:

Great Universal Capital Corp. (1)
645 5th Ave 8th Fl, New York, NY 10022-5910 (100%)
Tel.: (212) 848-0200
Sales Range: $10-24.9 Million
Emp.: 15
Real Estate, Financial & Investment Services
N.A.I.C.S.: 531210

LEE REEDY INC.
1480 Humboldt St, Denver, CO 80218
Tel.: (303) 333-2936
Web Site: http://www.lrxd.com
Emp.: 34
Digital Advertising Services
N.A.I.C.S.: 541810
Kelly Reedy (CEO & Partner)
John Gilbert (Partner & Chief Digital Officer)
Eric Kiker (Partner & Chief Strategy Officer)
Patrick Gill (Chm & Partner)
Jamie Reedy (Partner)
Connie Jones (CFO)

LEE SPRING COMPANY LLC
140 58th St Unit 3C, Brooklyn, NY 11220
Tel.: (888) 777-4647
Web Site: http://www.leespring.com
Mechanical Springs, Wire Forms, Stampings & Fourslide Part Mfr
N.A.I.C.S.: 332613
Steve Kempf (CEO)

LEE STEEL CORPORATION
45525 Grand River Ave, Novi, MI 48374
Tel.: (616) 538-2414 MI
Year Founded: 1947
Sales Range: $10-24.9 Million
Emp.: 43
Steel Products Mfr
N.A.I.C.S.: 423510

LEE STEEL CORPORATION

Lee Steel Corporation—(Continued)
Paul Quayhackx (Treas & Sec)

LEE SUPPLY CORP.
6610 Guion Rd, Indianapolis, IN 46268
Tel.: (317) 290-2500
Web Site:
http://www.leesupplycorp.com
Sales Range: $25-49.9 Million
Emp.: 300
Plumbing & Hydronic Heating Supplies
N.A.I.C.S.: 423720
Bob Lee (Pres)

LEE TRANSPORT INC.
228 Garden Rd, Elmer, NJ 08318
Tel.: (856) 358-7555
Sales Range: $10-24.9 Million
Emp.: 18
Petroleum Haulage
N.A.I.C.S.: 484220
Leon Sobczak Jr. (Pres)

LEE WETHERINGTON HOMES INC.
6985 Professional Pkwy E, Sarasota, FL 34240
Tel.: (941) 922-3480
Web Site: http://www.lwhomes.com
Year Founded: 1974
Sales Range: $10-24.9 Million
Emp.: 20
Residential Construction
N.A.I.C.S.: 236117
Lee Wetherington (Founder)
Jack Williams (VP-Construction)
Gregg Carlson (CEO)

LEE'S CURTAIN CO., INC.
261 5th Ave, New York, NY 10016-6515
Tel.: (212) 689-0020
Year Founded: 1973
Sales Range: $25-49.9 Million
Emp.: 300
Mfr & Sale of Curtains & Draperies
N.A.I.C.S.: 314120
Arnold Frankel (Pres)

Subsidiaries:

Table Trends Inc. (1)
36 E 31st St, New York, NY 10016 (100%)
Tel.: (212) 689-0020
Sales Range: $10-24.9 Million
Emp.: 2
Mfr of Plastic Products
N.A.I.C.S.: 326199
Joe Rancanello (Controller)

LEE'S FAMOUS RECIPES INC.
2303 E Silver Springs Blvd, Ocala, FL 34470
Tel.: (352) 732-7981
Web Site:
http://www.leesfamousrecipe.com
Year Founded: 2003
Sales Range: $10-24.9 Million
Emp.: 5
Restaurant Operators
N.A.I.C.S.: 722513
Laurie Seering (VP-Mktg)

LEE'S PET CLUB INC.
3535 Hollis St, Emeryville, CA 94608
Tel.: (510) 595-8120
Web Site: http://www.petguys.com
Rev.: $11,500,000
Emp.: 40
Pet Food
N.A.I.C.S.: 459910
Wilbur Lee (Pres)

LEE'S SUMMIT HONDA INC.
401 NE Colbern Rd, Lees Summit, MO 64086
Tel.: (816) 251-8700
Web Site:
http://www.leessummithonda.com
Rev.: $20,000,000
Emp.: 68
New Car Dealers
N.A.I.C.S.: 441110
Bob Balderston (Owner)
Jason Barrett (Mgr-Ecommerce)
Johnny Larson (Dir-Fin)
Tim Thomas (Gen Mgr)

LEE-MOORE CAPITAL COMPANY
1807 Douglas Dr, Sanford, NC 27330-9447
Tel.: (919) 775-2301
Web Site: http://www.lmoc.net
Year Founded: 1937
Sales Range: $1-9.9 Million
Emp.: 55
Gasoline & Diesel Fuel Sales
N.A.I.C.S.: 457210
Kirk J. Bradley (Chm & Pres)

LEEANN CHIN, INC.
3600 American Blvd W Ste 52, Bloomington, MN 55431-4507
Tel.: (952) 896-3606
Web Site: http://www.leeannchin.com
Year Founded: 1980
Sales Range: $25-49.9 Million
Emp.: 605
Chinese Restaurant
N.A.I.C.S.: 722511
Mike Loney (COO)
John Newstrom (Dir-Catering & Delivery)
Joseph Christenson (Asst Gen Mgr)
Todd Laramy (Dir-Ops)
Taylor Sanford (Asst Mgr)
Ashley Lohstreter (Gen Mgr)
Brad Newton (Gen Mgr)
Katrina Anderson (Supvr)

LEED SELLING TOOLS CORPORATION
9700 Hwy 57 N, Evansville, IN 47725
Tel.: (812) 867-4340
Web Site:
http://www.leedsamples.com
Sales Range: $10-24.9 Million
Emp.: 50
Sample Books
N.A.I.C.S.: 323111
Doug Edwards (Chm & Pres)
George Grace (VP)

LEEDO MANUFACTURING CO.
16856 Cabinet Rd, East Bernard, TX 77435
Tel.: (979) 335-4885
Web Site: http://www.leedo.com
Sales Range: $25-49.9 Million
Emp.: 410
Mfr of Wood Kitchen Cabinets
N.A.I.C.S.: 337110
George Hagle (Chm)
Ken Hirshman (Pres)
David Mullis (COO & Exec VP)
Michelle Baker (CFO)
Darryl Preen (CIO)
Randy Bailey (Exec VP-Sls & Installation)
Mike Katsoulis (VP-Bus Dev-Distr)
Barney Knight (VP-Bus Svcs)
Glenda Mussell (VP-HR)
John Dodrill (VP-Mfg & Environmental Health & Safety)
Rodney Robinson (VP-Multifamily Sls & Installation)
Robert Stokely (VP-Supply Chain & Installation Svc)

LEEDOM MANAGEMENT GROUP, INC.
2601 Cattlemen Rd Ste 200, Sarasota, FL 34232
Tel.: (941) 371-7999
Web Site:
http://www.leedomgroup.com
Sales Range: $10-24.9 Million
Emp.: 40
Management Consulting Services
N.A.I.C.S.: 541611
Christopher M. Leedom (Founder & Pres)
Debra Dawn (Gen Counsel)
Melissa Leedom (COO)

Subsidiaries:

Leedom & Associates, LLC (1)
2601 Cattlemen Rd Ste 200, Sarasota, FL 34232
Tel.: (941) 371-7999
Web Site: http://www.twentygroups.com
Sales Range: $1-9.9 Million
Emp.: 25
Management Consulting Services
N.A.I.C.S.: 541611
Christopher M. Leedom (Founder & Pres)
Lisa Leedom (VP-Sls & Mktg)

LEEDS EQUITY PARTNERS, LLC
590 Madison Ave 40th Fl, New York, NY 10022
Tel.: (212) 835-2000
Web Site: http://www.leedsequity.com
Year Founded: 1993
Privater Equity Firm
N.A.I.C.S.: 523999
Jeffrey T. Leeds (Co-Founder & Partner)
Robert A. Bernstein (Founder)
Peter A. Lyons (Partner & CFO)
Jacques V. Galante (Partner)
Eric Geveda (Mng Dir)
Christopher Mairs (Mng Dir)
David Neverson (Principal)
Kevin Malone (Principal)
Scott VanHoy (Partner)

Subsidiaries:

Altior Consulting & Training Limited (1)
2nd Floor Elgin House 106-107 St Mary Street, Cardiff, CF10 1DX, United Kingdom
Tel.: (44) 29 2045 1000
Web Site: http://www.altior.co.uk
Sales Range: $10-24.9 Million
Emp.: 25
Training Provider
N.A.I.C.S.: 611430
Peter Houillon (CEO)

Anthology Inc. (1)
777 Yamato Rd Ste 400, Boca Raton, FL 33431-4498
Tel.: (561) 923-2500
Web Site: https://www.anthology.com
Computer System Design Services
N.A.I.C.S.: 541512
Jim Brigadier (Sr VP-Sls & Pro Svcs)
Emiliano Diez (VP-Cloud Ops & Svcs)

Subsidiary (Domestic):

iModules Software, Inc. (2)
5101 College Blvd, Leawood, KS 66211
Tel.: (913) 888-0772
Web Site: http://www.imodules.com
Sales Range: $10-24.9 Million
Emp.: 85
Develops Web Based Software for Management of Online Communities
N.A.I.C.S.: 541512
Thomas R. Palmer (Founder & Chm)
Michael Novosel (VP-Bus Dev)
Troy Anderson (CTO)
Dan Frazier (Sr VP-Sls)
Jason Roberts (Sr VP-Customer Success)
Susan Scholes (VP-Mktg)
Craig Heldman (Pres & CEO)
Germaine Ward (VP-Product Mgmt)

Subsidiary (Domestic):

OrgSync, Inc. (3)
13140 Coit Rd Ste 405, Dallas, TX 75240
Tel.: (972) 907-0900
Web Site: http://www.orgsync.com
Sales Range: $1-9.9 Million
Emp.: 34
Software Development Services
N.A.I.C.S.: 541511
Alex Morales (VP-Sls & Mktg)
Cayce Stone (Sr VP-Enterprise Sls)
Don Fortenberry (CFO)
Eric Fortenberry (Founder, Pres & CEO)
Leanna Laskey McGrath (VP-Customer Success)
Michael Schwartz (COO)
Adam Cebulski (Sr Dir-Res & Strategic Initiatives)
J. D. Turner (Dir-Technical Support)
Brad Weltner (Sr Dir-Bus Dev)
Chris Boylan (Sr Dir-Bus Dev)
Matt Darner (Sr Dir-Bus Dev)
Kevin Wade (Dir-Product)

CeriFi LLC (1)
3625 Brookside Pkwy Ste 450, Alpharetta, GA 30022
Tel.: (877) 850-9291
Web Site: http://www.cerifi.com
Education, Training & Cerification Services
N.A.I.C.S.: 611710
Matthew Given (CEO)

Subsidiary (Domestic):

Spidell Publishing, Inc. (2)
1158 N Gilbert St, Anaheim, CA 92801
Tel.: (714) 776-7850
Web Site: http://www.spidell.com
Sales Range: $1-9.9 Million
Emp.: 20
Publisher
N.A.I.C.S.: 513199
Lynn Freer (Pres)
Dudley Goss (Gen Mgr)
Kimberley Morgan (Mgr-Customer Svc)
Kathryn Zdan (Dir-Editorial)

Exterro, Inc. (1)
4145 SW Watson Ave Ste 400, Beaverton, OR 97005
Tel.: (503) 501-5100
Web Site: http://www.exterro.com
Magnetic & Optical Recording Media Mfr
N.A.I.C.S.: 334610
Shashidhar Angadi (CTO)
Bobby Balachandran (Pres & CEO)
Richard Sheffield (Dir-Sls-Southeast)
Bill Piwonka (CMO)
Bobby Jahanbani (Sr VP-Sls)
Ajith Samuel (Chief Product Officer)
Kavitha Thangasami (Chief Dev Officer & Chief Res Officer)
Trey Tramonte (Sr VP-Sls)
Ray Pathak (VP-Data Privacy Solutions)

Subsidiary (Domestic):

AccessData Group, LLC (2)
Building H 603 East Timpanogos Cir Fl 2 Ste 2300, Orem, UT 84097
Tel.: (801) 377-5410
Web Site: http://www.accessdata.com
Sales Range: $25-49.9 Million
Emp.: 250
Electronic Discovery Collection, Processing & Analysis Software & Services
N.A.I.C.S.: 513210
Keith Lockhar (VP-Trng-Global)
Abdeslam Afras (Exec VP-Bus-Intl)
Victor Limongelli (CEO)
Samuel Maccherola (Exec VP-Worldwide Sls)
Lori Tyler (VP-Mktg-Global)
Rafik Hajem (VP-Sls-Europe, Middle East & Africa)
Christopher Johnson (VP-Sls-EMEA)
Alexander Poelma (Dir-Bus Dev-Federal Market Segments-Intl & US)
Wesley Ellis (VP-Technical & Pro Svcs-Washington)

Zapproved LLC (2)
1414 NW Northrup St Ste 700, Portland, OR 97209
Tel.: (888) 806-6750
Web Site: http://www.zapproved.com
Software Development Services

N.A.I.C.S.: 541511
Chris Bright (VP-Mktg)
Michael Keister (Chief Revenue Officer)
Aaron Laliberte (VP-Product)
Susy Dunn (Chief People Officer)
Tom Pickett (CFO)
Monica Enand (CEO)

Simplify Compliance Holdings LLC (1)
100 Winner Cir Ste, Brentwood, TN 37207
Tel.: (800) 727-5257
Bsuiness Tools Provider
N.A.I.C.S.: 519290
Dan Oswald (CEO)

Subsidiary (Domestic):

Basicsoft Inc. (2)
239 SW 3rd St, Fruitland, ID 83619-0000
Tel.: (208) 452-2296
Web Site: http://www.basicsafe.us
Software Publisher
N.A.I.C.S.: 513210
Kevin Shoemaker (Dir-Engrg Products & Svcs)

VitalSmarts LLC (1)
282 River Bend Ln Ste 100, Provo, UT 84604
Tel.: (801) 765-9600
Web Site: http://www.vitalsmarts.com
Management Consulting Training Solutions
N.A.I.C.S.: 611430
David Maxfield (VP-Res)

Subsidiary (Domestic):

Personal Strengths Publishing, Inc. (2)
1946 Kellogg Ave, Carlsbad, CA 92008-6507
Tel.: (760) 602-0086
Web Site: https://www.corestrengths.com
Professional & Management Development Training
N.A.I.C.S.: 611430
John T. Otoshi (Project Mgr)

LEEDS NOVAMARK CAPITAL
Plaza America Tower II 11710 Plaza America Dr Ste 160, Reston, VA 20190
Tel.: (703) 651-2150
Web Site: http://www.lnc-parnters.com
Emp.: 8
N.A.I.C.S.:
Matt Kelty (Mng Partner)
Robert Monk (Mng Partner)
Mark Raterman (Mng Partner)
Kevin Cunningham (Principal)

LEEDS PRECISION INSTRUMENTS
800 Boone Ave N, Minneapolis, MN 55427
Tel.: (763) 546-8575
Web Site: http://www.leedsmicro.com
Sales Range: $10-24.9 Million
Emp.: 50
Scientific & Engineering Equipment & Supplies
N.A.I.C.S.: 423490
Joann Marben (Controller)

LEEDS WELD & CO.
350 Pk Ave Fl 23, New York, NY 10021
Tel.: (212) 835-2000
Investment & Holding Services
N.A.I.C.S.: 551112
Jeffrey T. Leeds (Pres)

LEEDY MANUFACTURING CO. INC.
210 Hall St SW, Grand Rapids, MI 49507
Tel.: (616) 245-0519
Web Site: http://www.leedymfg.com
Rev.: $10,000,000
Emp.: 95
Gears, Motor Vehicle
N.A.I.C.S.: 336350
Gary King (VP)
Steve Traiynor (CFO & VP)
Harold Leedy Jr. (Pres)

LEELOWE INC.
814 A St, Galt, CA 95632
Tel.: (209) 745-1397
Sales Range: $10-24.9 Million
Emp.: 35
Owner & Operator of Grocery Stores
N.A.I.C.S.: 445110
Cynthia Lee (Pres)

LEEMAH CORPORATION
155 S Hill Dr, Brisbane, CA 94005
Tel.: (415) 394-1288
Web Site: http://www.leemah.com
Year Founded: 1971
Sales Range: $10-24.9 Million
Emp.: 150
Mfr of Electron Tubes
N.A.I.C.S.: 334419
Vivian Queirolo (Dir-HR)

Subsidiaries:

Leemah Electronics Inc. (1)
1088 Sansome St, San Francisco, CA 94111-1308
Tel.: (415) 394-1288
Web Site: http://www.leemah.com
Sales Range: $10-24.9 Million
Emp.: 100
Mfr of Electron Tubes
N.A.I.C.S.: 334419
Warren Lam (Plant Mgr)

Leemah Property Inc (1)
1088 Sansome St, San Francisco, CA 94111-1308
Tel.: (415) 394-1288
Web Site: http://www.leemah.com
Sales Range: $10-24.9 Million
Emp.: 50
Provider of Nonresidential Building Operator Services
N.A.I.C.S.: 531120

LEEPS SUPPLY CO. INC.
8001 Tyler St, Merrillville, IN 46410
Tel.: (219) 756-5337
Web Site: http://www.leeps.com
Year Founded: 1954
Sales Range: $10-24.9 Million
Emp.: 50
Heating Equipment Sales
N.A.I.C.S.: 423720
David Leep (VP)
John Hamstra (Owner & Pres)

LEES READY MIX & TRUCKING, INC.
1100 West JFK Dr, North Vernon, IN 47265
Tel.: (812) 346-9767
Web Site: http://www.leesreadymix.com
Year Founded: 1971
Sales Range: $10-24.9 Million
Emp.: 40
Ready Mixed Concrete
N.A.I.C.S.: 327320
Larry Lee (Pres)
Bob Hatfield (Dir-Sls)

LEESAR, INC.
2727 Winkler Ave, Fort Myers, FL 33901
Tel.: (239) 939-8800
Web Site: http://www.leesar.com
Year Founded: 1998
Sales Range: $150-199.9 Million
Emp.: 280
Medical Product Distr
N.A.I.C.S.: 423450
Paul McWhinnie (VP-Ops)

LEESBURG SOUTHERN ELECTRIC INC.
103 Sycolin Rd SE, Leesburg, VA 20175
Tel.: (703) 777-6200
Web Site: http://www.sescos.com
Rev.: $13,000,000
Emp.: 180
General Electrical Contractor
N.A.I.C.S.: 238210
Daniel Lee (VP)
Stephanie Loving (Office Mgr)

LEEVERS FOODS INC.
501 4th St SE, Devils Lake, ND 58301-2501
Tel.: (701) 662-8646 ND
Web Site: http://www.leeversfoods.com
Year Founded: 1997
Sales Range: $50-74.9 Million
Emp.: 950
Retailer of Grocery Services
N.A.I.C.S.: 445110
Robert Levert (Co-Pres)
James Leevers (Co-Pres)
Beth Leevers (VP)

LEEVERS SUPERMARKETS INC.
2195 N Hwy 83 Ste AA, Franktown, CO 80116-9600
Tel.: (303) 814-8646 ND
Web Site: http://www.leevers.com
Year Founded: 1938
Sales Range: $10-24.9 Million
Emp.: 300
Grocery Stores
N.A.I.C.S.: 445110
John Leevers (Pres)
Chris Leevers (VP)
Lisa Schroeder (Mgr-Acctg)

LEEWARD CONSTRUCTION, INC.
9 Collan Park, Honesdale, PA 18431
Tel.: (570) 253-4090
Web Site: http://www.leewardconstruction.com
Year Founded: 1993
Sales Range: $25-49.9 Million
Emp.: 70
Site Preparation Contracting Services
N.A.I.C.S.: 238910
Gary Linde (Pres)
Thomas Quinnan (VP-Engrg)

LEFEBVRE COMPANIES, INC.
10895 171st Ave NW, Elk River, MN 55330
Tel.: (763) 441-2681
Web Site: http://www.leftruck.com
Year Founded: 1928
Sales Range: $10-24.9 Million
Emp.: 250
Air Transportation, Scheduled
N.A.I.C.S.: 481111
Chuck LeFebvre (Pres)
John LeFebvre (Treas & VP)

Subsidiaries:

LeFebvre & Sons Inc. (1)
10895 171st Ave NW, Elk River, MN 55330
Tel.: (763) 441-0271
Rev.: $610,000
Emp.: 150
Trucking Service
N.A.I.C.S.: 484110
Paul LeFebvre (Pres)
Chuck LeFebvre (VP)
John LeFebvre (Treas)
Stuart Keppel (Mgr-Maintenance)
Mike Shefveland (Dir-Sls)
Peter Wedin (Dir-Safety)

LEFFERTS OIL TERMINAL INC.
3170 College Point Blvd, Flushing, NY 11354
Tel.: (718) 886-4500
Rev.: $67,000,000
Emp.: 6
Fuel Oil Whslr
N.A.I.C.S.: 424720
Robert Thomas (Pres)

LEFFINGWELL AG SALES CO. INC.
942 E Honolulu St, Lindsay, CA 93247
Tel.: (559) 562-4946
Web Site: http://www.cps.com
Rev.: $12,083,818
Emp.: 9
Chemicals, Agricultural
N.A.I.C.S.: 424910
Chuck Hornung (Gen Mgr)

LEFFLER AGENCY, INC.
2607 N Charles St, Baltimore, MD 21218
Tel.: (410) 235-5661
Web Site: http://www.leffleragency.com
Year Founded: 1984
Sales Range: $1-9.9 Million
Emp.: 20
Advertising Agencies
N.A.I.C.S.: 541810
Chris Raynor (COO)
Courtney Fischer (Dir-Acct Svcs)
Jim Hesch (Dir-Media Svcs)

LEFRAK ORGANIZATION INC.
40 W 57th St 23rd Fl, New York, NY 10019
Tel.: (212) 708-6600 NY
Web Site: http://www.lefrak.com
Year Founded: 1901
Sales Range: $1-4.9 Billion
Emp.: 16,200
Real Estate Owner & Manager
N.A.I.C.S.: 531110
Edward Cortese (Sr VP-Mktg & PR)
Richard Papert (CFO & Exec VP)
Camille J. Douglas (Sr Mng Dir-Acq & Dev)

LEFT BEHIND GAMES, INC.
1670 Makaloa St Ste 204, Honolulu, HI 96814
Tel.: (951) 894-6597 NV
Web Site: http://www.leftbehindgames.com
Year Founded: 2002
Sales Range: $1-9.9 Million
Emp.: 10
Video Game Publisher
N.A.I.C.S.: 513199
Craig A. Hewitt (VP-Corp Fin)

LEFTFIELD PICTURES
460 W 34th St 16th Fl, New York, NY 10001
Tel.: (212) 564-2607
Web Site: http://www.leftfieldpictures.com
Sales Range: $10-24.9 Million
Emp.: 200
Television Production Services
N.A.I.C.S.: 512110
Chris Valentini (COO)
Andrew Schechter (Sr VP-Dev)
Shawn Witt (Co-Pres)
Gretchen Palek (Co-Pres)

LEG RESOURCE INC.
350 5th Ave Ste 6408, New York, NY 10118
Tel.: (212) 736-4574
Web Site: http://www.legresource.com
Rev.: $11,500,000
Emp.: 13

Leg Resource Inc.—(Continued)
Mfr of Hosiery
N.A.I.C.S.: 315120
Wayne Lederman (Pres)

LEGACY AUDIO, INC.
3023 E Sangamon Ave, Springfield, IL 62702
Tel.: (217) 544-3178
Web Site: http://www.legacyaudio.com
Year Founded: 1983
Audio Components Mfr
N.A.I.C.S.: 334310
Bill Dudleston (Founder, Owner & Pres)

LEGACY AUTOMOTIVE GROUP
413 Industrial Blvd, McDonough, GA 30253-2635
Tel.: (770) 914-2800
Web Site: http://www.legacyford.com
Year Founded: 1997
Sales Range: $50-74.9 Million
Emp.: 75
Automobile Dealership
N.A.I.C.S.: 811111
Emanuel D. Jones (Pres)

Subsidiaries:

Legacy Ford-Mercury Inc. (1)
413 Industrial Blvd, McDonough, GA 30253
Tel.: (770) 914-2800
Web Site: http://www.legacyfordmercury.com
Sales Range: $10-24.9 Million
Emp.: 70
Automobiles; New & Used
N.A.I.C.S.: 811111
Emanuel D. Jones (Pres)

LEGACY AVIATION SERVICES INC.
1701A N Cimarron Rd, Yukon, OK 73099
Tel.: (405) 350-2100
Web Site: http://www.legacy-aviation.com
Year Founded: 2005
Rev.: $4,300,000
Emp.: 28
Air Transportation Support
N.A.I.C.S.: 488190
Raul Gomez (CEO)
Kevin Chance (CFO)
Michael Fitch (Dir-Sls & Mktg)

LEGACY BROADCASTING, LLC
805 Weightman St, Greenwood, MS 38930
Tel.: (662) 822-1655
Television Broadcasting Station
N.A.I.C.S.: 516120
Sherry Nelson (Co-Owner)
Sara Jane Ingram (Co-Owner)
Charles Harker (Co-Owner)

LEGACY COMMUNITY FEDERAL CREDIT UNION
1400 20th St S, Birmingham, AL 35255
Tel.: (205) 930-5000
Web Site: https://www.legacycreditunion.com
Loan Services
N.A.I.C.S.: 522310

Subsidiaries:

1st Resource Credit Union (1)
47 W Oxmoor Rd, Birmingham, AL 35209
Tel.: (205) 944-1192
Web Site: http://www.my1resourcecu.com
Sales Range: $1-9.9 Million
Emp.: 9
Credit Union

N.A.I.C.S.: 522130
Lindsey Jenkins (Accountant)
Rick Miller (CEO)

LEGACY COMMUNITY HEALTH
1415 California St, Houston, TX 77006
Tel.: (832) 548-5100
Web Site: https://www.legacycommunityhealth.org
Year Founded: 2005
Health Care Srvices
N.A.I.C.S.: 621610

LEGACY CONTRACTING SOLUTIONS, INC
6557 Garden Rd Ste 10, West Palm Beach, FL 33404
Tel.: (561) 844-4910
Web Site: http://www.legacycontractingsolutions.com
Sales Range: $1-9.9 Million
Emp.: 29
Metal Roofing Installation Services
N.A.I.C.S.: 238160
Bill Moore (Dir-Ops)

LEGACY FOUNDATION, INC.
1000 E 80th Pl Ste 402 N, Merrillville, IN 46410
Tel.: (219) 736-1880
Web Site: http://www.legacyfdn.org
Year Founded: 1992
Sales Range: $1-9.9 Million
Emp.: 40
Fundraising Services
N.A.I.C.S.: 813219
Carolyn Saxton (Pres)
Kelly Anoe (VP)
Robert Johnson (Chm)
Nancy L. Clifford (Chm)
Shar Miller (Sec)
Marti Rivas-Ramos (Vice Chm)
Matthew Doyle (Treas)
Marie Pittman (Program Coord-Lake County Eats Local)
Donna Catalano (Dir-Community Dev)

LEGACY GOLF MANAGEMENT LLC
850 Indian Mound Rd SE, Cartersville, GA 30120
Tel.: (770) 607-0491
Sales Range: $10-24.9 Million
Emp.: 105
Nonresidential Building Contracts
N.A.I.C.S.: 531120

LEGACY HEALTH SYSTEM
1919 NW Lovejoy, Portland, OR 97209
Tel.: (503) 415-5600
Web Site: http://www.legacyhealth.org
Year Founded: 1989
Sales Range: $1-4.9 Billion
Emp.: 9,781
Hospitals & Home Health Agencies
N.A.I.C.S.: 622110
Jeffrey D. Fullman (Chm)
Mike Newcomb (COO & Sr VP)
Maureen A. Bradley (Chief Dev Officer & Sr VP-Philanthropy)
John Kenagy (CIO & Sr VP)
Melissa Rose (Principal-Gifts & Grants)
Tamara Uppendahl (Dir-Donor Rels)
Kathryn Correia (Pres & CEO)
Alexander Gladney (Chief Legal Officer & Sr VP)

Subsidiaries:

Legacy Emanuel Children's Hospital (1)
2801 N Gantenbein Ave, Portland, OR 97227
Tel.: (503) 413-2200
Web Site: http://www.legacyhealthsystem.org
Sales Range: $10-24.9 Million
Emp.: 100
Children's Hospital
N.A.I.C.S.: 622310

Legacy Emanuel Hospital & Health Center (1)
2801 N Gantenbein Ave, Portland, OR 97227
Tel.: (503) 413-2200
Web Site: http://www.legacyhealth.org
Hospital Operations
N.A.I.C.S.: 622110
William DeLong (Dir-Spiritual Care)

Legacy Good Samaritan Hospital & Medical Center (1)
1015 NW 22nd Ave, Portland, OR 97210
Tel.: (503) 413-7711
Web Site: http://www.legacyhealth.org
Hospital Operations
N.A.I.C.S.: 622110
Tony Melaragno (Chief Admin Officer)
Jonathan Avery (Chief Admin Officer)

Legacy Meridian Park Hospital (1)
19300 SW 65th Ave, Tualatin, OR 97062
Tel.: (503) 692-1212
Hospital Operations
N.A.I.C.S.: 622110
Lisa Murphy (Coord-Surgical & Interventional Svcs)
Bob Ingber (Mgr-Facilities)
Kim Coburn (Mgr-Orthopedic Case-RN)

Legacy Mount Hood Medical Center (1)
24800 SE Stark St, Gresham, OR 97030
Tel.: (503) 674-1122
Web Site: http://www.legacyhealth.org
Hospital Operation Services
N.A.I.C.S.: 622110
George Brown (Pres)

Legacy Salmon Creek Hospital (1)
2211 NE 139th St, Vancouver, WA 98686
Tel.: (360) 487-1000
Sales Range: $10-24.9 Million
Emp.: 150
Hospital Operator
N.A.I.C.S.: 622110
Moses Fraser (Mng Dir)

LEGACY HEALTHCARE ADVISORS LLC
14251 Panama City Beach Pkwy, Panama City, FL 32413
Tel.: (850) 234-8887
Web Site: http://www.bookit.com
Year Founded: 2004
Emp.: 412
Travel Arrangement & Reservation Services
N.A.I.C.S.: 561510
Bud Finlaw (CEO)
Jesse Henson (VP-Mktg)

LEGACY INFINITI
875 Sunrise Hwy, Lynbrook, NY 11563
Tel.: (516) 536-9000
Web Site: http://www.infinitioflynbrook.com
Year Founded: 2003
Sales Range: $10-24.9 Million
Emp.: 65
New & Used Car Dealers
N.A.I.C.S.: 441110
Eduardo Martinez (Mgr-Fin)
Donnell Middleton (Mgr-Fin & Sub Prime)

LEGACY LONG DISTANCE INTERNATIONAL, INC.
10833 Valley View St Ste 150, Cypress, CA 90630
Tel.: (714) 826-0547
Web Site: http://www.golegacy.com
Year Founded: 1987
Sales Range: $10-24.9 Million
Emp.: 70
Long Distance & Operator Services
N.A.I.C.S.: 517111
Curtis Brown (Pres)

LEGACY NISSAN
939 Old Country Rd, Westbury, NY 11590
Tel.: (516) 338-5600
Web Site: http://www.legacynissanny.com
Rev.: $11,700,000
Emp.: 20
New & Used Car Dealers
N.A.I.C.S.: 441110
Mirza Kavazovic (Mgr)

LEGACY PARTNERS INC.
4000 E 3rd Ave Ste 600, Foster City, CA 94404-1132
Tel.: (650) 571-2250
Web Site: http://www.legacypartners.com
Year Founded: 1968
Sales Range: $25-49.9 Million
Emp.: 621
Subdivision & Development Services
N.A.I.C.S.: 237210
Denise Ruble (Engr-Telecom)
Douglas Woo (VP-Tax)
W. Dean Henry (CEO)
Robert A. Calleja (CFO)
Kerry L. Nicholson (Sr Mng Dir-Pacific Northwest & Midwest)
Richard Brownjohn (Sr VP)
Lane R. Cutter (VP)
David J. Eichler (Sr Mng Dir)
Michael Holt (VP)
Amelia V. Johnson (VP-HR)
Mark McKallor (VP)
Scott J. Morrison (Sr VP)

Subsidiaries:

HR Max (1)
101 Lincoln Centre Dr, Foster City, CA 94404-1132
Tel.: (650) 571-2550
Sales Range: $10-24.9 Million
Emp.: 5
Employment Agency Services
N.A.I.C.S.: 561311

LEGACY PROFESSIONALS LLP
311 S Wacker Dr Ste 4000, Chicago, IL 60606-6678
Tel.: (312) 368-0500
Web Site: http://www.legacycpas.com
Sales Range: $10-24.9 Million
Emp.: 140
Certified Public Accountants
N.A.I.C.S.: 541211
Robert Tiberi (Mng Partner)
Bob Cann (Partner & Dir-Svcs)
Paul M. Doetsch (Partner)
Eileen E. Brassil (Partner)
Adam Simaga (Partner)
Brandon Wolber (Partner)

LEGACY PUBLISHING COMPANY
10 Speirs St, Westbrook, ME 04092
Tel.: (207) 856-5600
Web Site: http://www.legacypublishingcompany.com
Year Founded: 2004
Rev.: $19,500,000
Emp.: 130
Customer Development Products & Services
N.A.I.C.S.: 513140

COMPANIES

Kevin Barney *(Mgr-Sls-Auburn)*

LEGACY RESERVES, INC.
303 W Wall St Ste 1800, Midland, TX 79701
Tel.: (432) 689-5200   DE
Web Site: http://www.legacylp.com
Year Founded: 2005
Rev.: $554,861,000
Assets: $1,474,931,000
Liabilities: $1,667,562,000
Net Worth: ($192,631,000)
Earnings: $43,833,000
Emp.: 337
Fiscal Year-end: 12/31/18
Oil & Natural Gas Exploration & Production
N.A.I.C.S.: 211120
Richard F. Betz *(CEO)*
Michael N. Stefanoudakis *(Pres & CFO)*

Subsidiaries:

Legacy Reserves Services Inc.   (1)
1211 N Price Rd, Pampa, TX 79065
Tel.: (806) 669-1417
Oil & Gas Field Services
N.A.I.C.S.: 213112

LEGACY RESOURCE CORPORATION
1936 Oak Ridge Tpke, Oak Ridge, TN 37830-6001
Tel.: (865) 483-5955
Web Site:
http://www.legacycorporation.net
Year Founded: 2002
Sales Range: $10-24.9 Million
Emp.: 213
Management Consulting Services
N.A.I.C.S.: 541618
Jeffrey L. Ginsburg *(Dir-HR)*
Laura Davis *(Founder)*

LEGACY SENIOR SERVICES
14416 Spring Lake Rd, Minnetonka, MN 55345
Tel.: (763) 537-5700   MN
Year Founded: 2001
Sales Range: $25-49.9 Million
Emp.: 1,104
Elder Care Services
N.A.I.C.S.: 623312
Roger Green *(Sec)*
Eric Lunde *(Pres & Treas)*

LEGACY SUPPLY CHAIN SERVICES
99 Bow St Ste 300W, Portsmouth, NH 03801
Tel.: (603) 422-0777
Web Site: http://www.legacyscs.com
Year Founded: 1983
Sales Range: $100-124.9 Million
Emp.: 1,500
Integrated Supply Chain Logistics Services
N.A.I.C.S.: 541614
Ken Porter *(Chief Learning Officer)*
Andy Dishner *(VP-Sls & Mktg)*
Mike Glodziak *(Pres & CEO)*
Rick Dempsey *(VP-Mktg & Strategy-Supply Chain Svcs)*
Raoul Siclait *(CFO)*
Thomas M. Rouen Jr. *(COO)*

Subsidiaries:

LEGACY Supply Chain Services - Brampton   (1)
1 Kenview Blvd Unit 210, Brampton, L6T 5E6, ON, Canada
Tel.: (416) 798-4940
Web Site: http://www.legacyscs.com
Emp.: 30
Logistics Consulting Servies
N.A.I.C.S.: 541614
Gord Kiefer *(VP)*

LEGACY Supply Chain Services - Fontana   (1)
9421 Transportation Way, Fontana, CA 92335
Tel.: (909) 829-5635
Sales Range: $25-49.9 Million
Emp.: 200
Logistics Consulting Servies
N.A.I.C.S.: 541614
Frank Rodriguez *(Sr Mgr-Transportation & Admin)*
John Munoz *(Sr Mgr-Ops-Terminal)*
Bob Bujosa *(Sr Mgr-Fleet & Compliance)*
Jody McGuire *(Mgr-Corp Office)*
Lonnie Huston *(Mgr-Facilities)*

LEGACY Supply Chain Services - Garden Grove   (1)
12465 Lewis St Ste 102, Garden Grove, CA 92840   (100%)
Tel.: (714) 748-4042
Sales Range: $50-74.9 Million
Emp.: 7
Distribution Management
N.A.I.C.S.: 488510

LEGACY Supply Chain Services - Ontario   (1)
12465 Lewis St Ste 102, Garden Grove, CA 92840
Tel.: (714) 748-4052
Web Site: http://www.legacyscs.com
Sales Range: $10-24.9 Million
Emp.: 150
Trucking Service
N.A.I.C.S.: 484121
Jim Wiesen *(CFO)*

LEGACY Supply Chain Services - Reno   (1)
5360 Capital Ct Ste 100, Reno, NV 89502
Tel.: (775) 331-8010
Web Site: http://www.logisticsgriffin.com
Sales Range: $50-74.9 Million
Emp.: 30
Integrated Supply Chain Logistics Services
N.A.I.C.S.: 541614
Lowell Moore *(Sr Dir)*
Mark Young *(Mgr-Intl)*

LEGACY TECHNOLOGIES INC.
6700 W 47th Ter, Mission, KS 66203
Tel.: (913) 432-2020
Web Site:
http://www.legacytechnologies.com
Year Founded: 1959
Electronic Glass Seal Mfr
N.A.I.C.S.: 334419
Bruce Diggett *(Pres)*

LEGACY TEXAS GROUP, INC.
5000 Legacy Dr, Plano, TX 75024
Tel.: (972) 461-1300
Web Site:
http://www.legacytexas.com
Sales Range: $25-49.9 Million
Emp.: 100
Holding Company
N.A.I.C.S.: 522110
Patrick Shelby *(Chm)*

Subsidiaries:

Legacy Bank of Texas   (1)
5000 Legacy Dr, Plano, TX 75024
Tel.: (972) 461-1300
Web Site: http://www.legacytexas.com
Rev.: $66,277,000
Emp.: 95
State Commercial Banks
N.A.I.C.S.: 522110
George A. Fisk *(Vice Chm)*

LEGACY TRANSPORTATION SERVICES
935 Mclaughlan, San Jose, CA 95122
Tel.: (408) 294-9800
Web Site: http://www.legacytsi.com
Rev.: $23,000,000
Emp.: 40
Local Trucking with Storage
N.A.I.C.S.: 484110
John Migliozzi *(Pres)*
Jim Ming *(Controller)*

John Otten *(VP-Bus Dev-Chicago)*
David O. Saucedo *(Mgr-Mobile Exhibits & Exhibits)*
Beverly Dygert *(Dir-Mobile Exhibits & Mktg)*

LEGACYXCHANGE, INC.
301 Yamato Rd Ste 1240, Boca Raton, FL 33431
Year Founded: 2010
Assets: $21,152
Liabilities: $1,489,000
Net Worth: ($1,467,848)
Earnings: ($152,336)
Fiscal Year-end: 03/31/20
Online Shopping Services
N.A.I.C.S.: 425120
William A. Bollander *(Pres, CEO, CFO, Chief Accountancy Officer, Treas & Sec)*

LEGAL ACCESS PLANS LLC
5850 San Felipe Ste 600, Houston, TX 77057
Tel.: (713) 785-7400
Web Site:
http://www.legalaccessplans.com
Year Founded: 1971
Sales Range: $1-9.9 Million
Emp.: 65
Develops & Administers Employee Legal Benefits Plans
N.A.I.C.S.: 524298
Tracy Lalasz *(COO)*
Mike Kinney *(CFO)*
Robert L. Heston Jr. *(Pres & CEO)*

LEGAL AID BUREAU, INC.
500 E Lexington St, Baltimore, MD 21202
Tel.: (410) 951-7777   MD
Web Site: http://www.mdlab.org
Year Founded: 1911
Sales Range: $25-49.9 Million
Emp.: 344
Law firm
N.A.I.C.S.: 541110
Gustava Taler *(COO)*
Denise McCain *(Dir-Program Dev & Compliance)*
Patrick Gregory *(Dir-IT)*
Wilhelm H. Joseph Jr. *(Exec Dir)*

LEGAL AID CENTER OF SOUTHERN NEVADA
725 E Charleston Blvd, Las Vegas, NV 89104
Tel.: (702) 386-1070   NV
Web Site: http://www.lacsn.org
Year Founded: 1958
Sales Range: $10-24.9 Million
Emp.: 75
Law firm
N.A.I.C.S.: 541199
Barbara E. Buckley *(Exec Dir)*
Terry Bratton *(CFO)*
J. Randall Jones *(Sec)*
Shelby Keefer *(Treas)*
Maximiliano Couvillier III *(Pres)*

LEGAL AID FOUNDATION OF LOS ANGELES
1102 Crenshaw Blvd, Los Angeles, CA 90019
Tel.: (323) 801-7991   CA
Web Site: http://www.lafla.org
Year Founded: 1929
Sales Range: $10-24.9 Million
Emp.: 172
Legal Aid Services
N.A.I.C.S.: 541110
Linda Quintana *(Dir-Fiscal Mgmt)*
Diane Talamantez *(Dir-HR & Admin Svcs)*

Silvia R. Argueta *(Exec Dir)*
Debra L. Fischer *(VP)*
Martin T. Tachiki *(Pres)*
Gia Stokes *(CFO)*

LEGAL AID OF NORTHWEST TEXAS
600 E Weatherford St, Fort Worth, TX 76102
Tel.: (817) 336-3943   TX
Web Site: http://www.lanwt.org
Year Founded: 1951
Sales Range: $10-24.9 Million
Emp.: 247
Law firm
N.A.I.C.S.: 541199
Natasha Villars *(Sec)*
Angelina LaPenotiere *(Treas)*
Richard Mitchell *(Vice Chm)*
Erika Kiser *(Sec)*
Mandy S. Price *(Vice Chm)*
Dilip Shah *(CFO)*
Maria Thomas-Jones *(CEO)*

LEGAL AID SERVICES OF OKLAHOMA, INC.
2915 N Classen Blvd Ste 500, Oklahoma City, OK 73106
Tel.: (405) 557-0020   OK
Web Site: http://www.legalaidok.org
Year Founded: 1977
Sales Range: $10-24.9 Million
Emp.: 189
Legal Aid Services
N.A.I.C.S.: 541110
Michael G. Figgins *(Exec Dir)*
Molly Aspan *(Pres)*
Earnest Ware *(VP)*
Lucille Logan *(Treas & Sec)*

LEGAL AID SOCIETY OF SUFFOLK COUNTY INC.
400 Carleton Ave 4th Fl, Central Islip, NY 11722
Tel.: (631) 853-7770   NY
Year Founded: 1956
Sales Range: $10-24.9 Million
Emp.: 154
Legal Aid Services
N.A.I.C.S.: 541199
Philip O'Reilly *(Atty)*
Edward Vitale *(Atty)*
Sabato Caponi *(Atty)*

LEGAL BRAND MARKETING, L.L.C.
22130 Clarendon St, Woodland Hills, CA 91367
Tel.: (818) 884-8075
Web Site:
http://www.legalbrandmarketing.com
Sales Range: $1-9.9 Million
Internet Marketing & Other Related Services
N.A.I.C.S.: 541613
Braden Pollock *(Founder & Owner)*
Angie Rupert *(Dir-Mktg & PR)*

LEGAL GRAPHICWORKS, INC.
2475 Mercer Ave Ste 201, West Palm Beach, FL 33401
Tel.: (561) 655-0678   FL
Web Site:
http://www.legalgraphicworks.com
Year Founded: 2010
Litigation & Trial Support Services
N.A.I.C.S.: 561492
Jim Lucas *(Pres & CEO)*
Courtney Nicholson *(COO)*

Subsidiaries:

Izamax Ventures, Inc.   (1)
1454 Prudential Dr, Jacksonville, FL 32207-8132
Web Site: http://www.legalartworks.com
Trial Support Multimedia Services

LEGAL GRAPHICWORKS, INC.

Legal Graphicworks, Inc.—(Continued)
N.A.I.C.S.: 561990

LEGAL RESEARCH CENTER, INC.
310 4th Ave S Ste 1100, Minneapolis, MN 55415-1005
Tel.: (800) 776-9377   MN
Web Site:
http://www.legalresearch.com
Year Founded: 1978
Legal Research, Knowledge Management & Compliance Support Services
N.A.I.C.S.: 541199
Mazen Haddad *(CIO)*
James R. Seidl *(Pres)*
Christopher R. Ljungkull *(CEO)*
Stacey Supina *(Dir-Res)*
Valerie Werness *(Sr Mgr-Res)*

LEGAL SERVICES NYC
40 Worth St 6th Fl, New York, NY 10013
Tel.: (646) 442-3600   NY
Web Site:
http://www.legalservicesnyc.org
Year Founded: 1967
Sales Range: $10-24.9 Million
Emp.: 136
Civil Legal Assistance Services
N.A.I.C.S.: 541199
Genia A. Wright *(COO)*

LEGAL SERVICES OF NEW JERSEY
100 Metroplex Dr Ste 402, Edison, NJ 08818-1357
Tel.: (732) 572-9100   NJ
Web Site: http://www.lsnj.org
Year Founded: 1972
Sales Range: $25-49.9 Million
Emp.: 195
Law firm
N.A.I.C.S.: 541199
Melville D. Miller Jr. *(Pres & Gen Counsel)*

LEGAL SHRED INC.
11806 S US Hwy 41, Gibsonton, FL 33534
Tel.: (813) 445-7301
Web Site: http://www.legalshred.com
Sales Range: $1-9.9 Million
Emp.: 4
Shredding Services
N.A.I.C.S.: 562998
Sean Fredricks *(Pres)*
Jason Fredricks *(VP)*
Aaron Fredricks *(Mgr-Ops)*
Karen Fredricks *(Mgr-Sls)*

LEGALL HOLDINGS, INC.
2215 N Wood Ave, Linden, NJ 07036
Tel.: (908) 448-1222   DE
Year Founded: 2016
Emp.: 3
Hotel & Restaurant Management Services
N.A.I.C.S.: 721110
Portia LeGall *(Co-CEO, Treas & Sec)*
Terrence LeGall *(Co-CEO)*
Tara P. LeGall *(VP-Mktg)*

LEGEND CLASSIC HOMES LTD.
10410 Windermere Lake Blvd, Houston, TX 77065
Tel.: (281) 671-9000
Web Site:
http://www.legendhomecorp.com
Sales Range: $50-74.9 Million
Emp.: 55
New Construction, Single-Family Houses
N.A.I.C.S.: 236115

Barbara Puskar *(Controller)*
Tom Connelly *(CFO)*
Mark Tollefsrud *(VP-Sls & Mktg)*

LEGEND CREATIVE GROUP
815-B Oakwood Rd, Lake Zurich, IL 60047
Tel.: (847) 438-3528   IL
Web Site:
http://www.legendcreative.com
Year Founded: 1992
Sales Range: $1-9.9 Million
Emp.: 12
Advetising Agency
N.A.I.C.S.: 541810
David Voitik *(Pres)*

LEGEND FINANCIAL ADVISORS, INC
5700 Corporate Dr, Pittsburgh, PA 15237-5829
Tel.: (412) 635-9210
Web Site: http://www.legend-financial.com
Sales Range: $1-9.9 Million
Emp.: 21
Portfolio Management
N.A.I.C.S.: 523940
Lou Stanasolovich *(Pres & CEO)*
Sherry Mitton *(Coord-Info Sys)*

LEGEND FOOD SERVICE LLC
29 Baer Cir Bldg 1, East Haven, CT 06512
Tel.: (475) 549-1045
Web Site: http://legendfood.com
Food Service Contractors
N.A.I.C.S.: 722310
Kyle Loughran *(Founder & CEO)*

Subsidiaries:

Jel-Cap Vending Inc.   (1)
2601 N Rolling Rd Ste 107, Baltimore, MD 21244-1988
Tel.: (410) 298-8363
Web Site: http://www.jelcapvending.com
Vending Machine Operators
N.A.I.C.S.: 445132

LEGEND HOME CORP.
10410 Windermere Lakes Blvd, Houston, TX 77065
Tel.: (281) 671-9000
Web Site:
http://www.legendhomeshouston.com
Year Founded: 1991
Sales Range: $125-149.9 Million
Emp.: 85
New Housing Operate Building Services
N.A.I.C.S.: 236117
Mark Tollefsrud *(VP-Sls & Mktg)*

LEGEND HOMES CORPORATION
12755 SW 69th Ave Ste 100, Portland, OR 97223-2513
Tel.: (503) 620-8080   OR
Web Site:
http://www.legendhomes.com
Year Founded: 1972
Sales Range: $25-49.9 Million
Emp.: 26
Real Estate Subdividers & Developers
N.A.I.C.S.: 237210
James Chapman *(Pres & Gen Mgr)*
Carol Eisenlohr *(Dir-Quality Assurance)*
Krista Boyd *(Dir-Mktg & Comm)*
Merle Dull *(Controller)*
Michelle Rosa *(Coord-Closing)*
Mike Goodrich *(Dir-Production & VP)*

Bob Brinkley *(Mgr-Quality Assurance-Portland)*
Janiegh Bettis *(Accountant-Payroll)*

LEGENDARY HOLDING, INC.
4471 Legendary Dr, Destin, FL 32541
Tel.: (850) 337-8000   FL
Web Site:
http://www.legendaryinc.com
Year Founded: 1988
Sales Range: $50-74.9 Million
Emp.: 400
Vacation Resort Operator
N.A.I.C.S.: 721110
Peter Bos *(Pres & CEO)*
Pete Knowles *(COO)*
Bryan Deane *(VP-Comml Properties)*
Tracie Blocker *(CFO)*

LEGG INC.
2551 2nd St, Livermore, CA 94550
Tel.: (925) 605-4500
Web Site: http://www.legginc.com
Year Founded: 1997
Sales Range: $1-9.9 Million
Emp.: 4
Blast-Resistant Doors & Hardware for Correctional Facilities
N.A.I.C.S.: 332321
Robert Legg *(Co-Owner, Pres & CEO)*
Tom Gallagher *(Superintendent)*

LEGGAT MCCALL PROPERTIES LLC
10 Post Ofc Sq, Boston, MA 02109
Tel.: (617) 422-7000
Web Site: http://www.lmp.com
Rev.: $49,632,000
Emp.: 25
Real Estates Developer
N.A.I.C.S.: 237210
Mamod Malihi *(Co-Pres)*
Eric Sheffels *(Pres)*
Eric Bacon *(Exec VP)*
Donald Birch *(COO & Exec VP)*
Chuck Favazzo *(Project Mgr)*
Robert Foster *(Sr VP-Dev)*
William Gause *(Exec VP)*
Paula Palombo *(Mgr-HR)*
Robert Palumbo *(VP & Sr Project Mgr)*
Chad Reynolds *(Project Mgr)*
Karl Neubauer *(Sr VP)*
Christine Stone *(Sr VP)*
Jeremiah Yankauskas *(Sr VP)*
Kim Thurber *(Sr VP)*
Bob T. Walsh *(Sr VP)*
Francis X. Jacoby III *(CFO & Exec VP)*

LEGGAT MCCALL PROPERTIES, LLC.
10 Post Office Sq, Boston, MA 02109-4603
Tel.: (617) 422-7000
Web Site: https://www.lmp.com
Year Founded: 1978
Sales Range: $10-24.9 Million
Emp.: 30
Land Subdivision Services
N.A.I.C.S.: 237210
Eric Bacon *(Exec VP)*
Donald Birch *(COO & Exec VP)*
Mark Debonis *(Sr VP)*
Robert Dickey *(Exec VP)*
Robert Foster *(Sr VP)*
Jeff Ganem *(VP)*
William Gause *(Exec VP)*
Rob Greetham *(VP)*
Tim Lombard *(Project Mgr)*
Mahmood Malihi *(Co-Pres)*
Karl Neubauer *(Sr VP)*
Chad Reynolds *(Sr VP)*
Eric Sheffels *(Co-Pres)*
Christine Stone *(Sr VP)*

Bob Walsh *(Sr VP)*
Jerry Yankauskas *(Sr VP)*
Dan Boyd *(Sr VP)*
Joy Clark *(VP)*
Chuck Favazzo *(VP)*
Michael Gerhardt *(VP)*
F. X. Jacoby *(CFO & Exec VP)*
Harry Nash *(Sr VP)*
Sam Reiche *(VP)*

LEGILITY, LLC
216 Centerview Dr Ste 250, Brentwood, TN 37027
Tel.: (615) 635-0101
Web Site: http://legility.com
Emp.: 1,000
Law firm
N.A.I.C.S.: 541199
Barry Dark *(CEO)*

LEGION ADVERTISING
1425 Greenway Dr Ste 100, Arlington, TX 75038
Tel.: (817) 784-8544
Web Site:
http://www.legionadvertising.com
Year Founded: 2000
Rev.: $15,000,000
Emp.: 22
N.A.I.C.S.: 541810
Eric Leon *(Owner)*
Isaac Lasky *(Dir-Pub Rels)*
Paola Ortega *(Acct Dir)*

LEGUM & NORMAN INC.
3130 Fairview Park Dr Ste 200, Falls Church, VA 22042
Tel.: (703) 600-6000
Web Site:
http://www.legumnorman.com
Year Founded: 1945
Rev.: $10,598,577
Emp.: 113
Real Estate Brokers & Agents
N.A.I.C.S.: 531210
Brian Kruppa *(Deputy Gen Counsel & Sr VP)*
Helen Eden Carona *(Chief Corp Officer & Exec VP)*
Lisa Meck *(Mgr-Bus Dev)*
Linda Fulkersin *(Sr VP-Resorts Div)*
John Halfhill *(VP)*
Marc McCoy *(VP)*

LEHIGH ENGINEERING ASSOCIATES, INC.
499 Riverview Dr, Walnutport, PA 18088
Tel.: (610) 767-8545
Web Site:
http://www.lehighengineering.com
Year Founded: 1984
Sales Range: $1-9.9 Million
Emp.: 29
Traffic Engineering & Residential/Commercial Design Services
N.A.I.C.S.: 541330
Larry S. Turoscy *(Dir-Engrg)*
Mark Leuthe *(Pres)*

LEHIGH VALLEY HEALTH NETWORK, INC.
1200 S Cedar Crest Blvd, Allentown, PA 18105-1556
Tel.: (610) 402-5369
Web Site: http://www.lvhn.org
Year Founded: 1899
Emp.: 18,000
Health Care Srvices
N.A.I.C.S.: 923120
William F. Hecht *(Vice Chm)*
Brian A. Nester *(Co-Pres & CEO)*
Elizabeth Wise *(Pres-Lehigh Valley Hospital-Pocono)*
Edward Dougherty *(Chief Bus Dev Officer & Sr VP)*
Terrence Purcell *(VP-Market Dev)*
John D. Stanley *(Chm)*

COMPANIES
LEIGH MARCUS, INC.

Martin K. Till *(Vice Chm)*
Jeanne Tilghman *(Co-Pres)*
Nathan Kline *(Sec)*

Subsidiaries:

Lehigh Valley Health Network
EMS (1)
119 E Holly St, Hazleton, PA 18201
Tel.: (570) 453-1445
Web Site: http://www.lvhn.org
911 Ambulance Services
N.A.I.C.S.: 621999

LEHIGH VALLEY PLASTICS INC.
187 N Commerce Way, Bethlehem, PA 18017
Tel.: (484) 893-5500
Web Site:
http://www.lehighvalleyplastics.com
Year Founded: 1971
Sales Range: $50-74.9 Million
Emp.: 100
Laminated Plastics Plate & Sheet
N.A.I.C.S.: 326130
Ian Ressler *(Mgr-Inside Sls)*
Doug Engler *(Mgr-Quality)*

LEHMAN BROTHERS HOLDINGS INC. PLAN TRUST
1271 Avenue of the Americas, New York, NY 10020
Tel.: (646) 285-9000 DE
Web Site: http://www.lehman.com
Year Founded: 1850
Holding Company; Financial Investment Services
N.A.I.C.S.: 551112
Michael Leto *(CFO & Exec VP)*
John K. Suckow *(Pres & COO)*

Subsidiaries:

Aurora Loan Services LLC (1)
10350 Park Meadows Dr, Littleton, CO 80124
Tel.: (720) 945-3000
Web Site: http://www.alservices.com
Sales Range: $1-4.9 Billion
Emp.: 550
Mortgage Banking Services
N.A.I.C.S.: 523150
James Park *(Chief Appraiser & Sr VP)*

Lehman Brothers Holdings Plc (1)
25 Bank St, London, E14 5LE, United Kingdom
Tel.: (44) 71021000
Web Site: http://www.lehmanbrothers.com
Sales Range: $250-299.9 Million
Holding Company
N.A.I.C.S.: 551112

Lehman Brothers Inc. (1)
1271 6th Ave, New York, NY 10019
Tel.: (646) 285-9000
Web Site: http://www.lehman.com
Sales Range: $1-4.9 Billion
Emp.: 300
Investment Banking Services
N.A.I.C.S.: 523150
Richard Repetto *(Founder-Internet Fin Svcs Sector)*
Michael Donahue *(Assoc)*

Lehman Commercial Paper Inc. (1)
1271 6th Ave, New York, NY 10020 (100%)
Tel.: (646) 285-9000
Web Site: http://www.lehmanholdings.com
Sales Range: $1-4.9 Billion
Buys & Sells Commercial Paper & other Money Market Instruments
N.A.I.C.S.: 523150

Moonlight Basin LLC (1)
66 Mountain Loop Rd, Big Sky, MT 59716
Tel.: (406) 682-6666
Web Site: http://www.moonlightbasin.com
Sales Range: $25-49.9 Million
Emp.: 80
Ski Resort Operator
N.A.I.C.S.: 713920
Greg Pack *(Gen Mgr)*

LEHMAN TRIKES USA, INC.
11841 Monarch St, Garden Grove, CA 92841-2110
Tel.: (800) 875-0949
Web Site:
http://www.lehmantrikes.com
Year Founded: 1985
Motorcycle Trike Conversion Mfr
N.A.I.C.S.: 336991
Craig L. Arrojo *(Pres)*
Bill Swift *(Global Sls Mgr)*
Kenny Wilson *(Sls Mgr)*

LEHMAN-ROBERTS COMPANY
1111 Wilson St, Memphis, TN 38106
Tel.: (901) 774-4000
Web Site:
http://www.lehmanroberts.com
Rev.: $31,400,000
Emp.: 400
Highway & Street Paving Contractor
N.A.I.C.S.: 237310
Gilbert Wilson *(Treas)*
Harold Edwards *(Mgr-Safety)*
Matt Cox *(Dir-Asset Mgmt)*
Richard Moore *(Dir-Bus Dev)*
Michael Ellis *(VP-South)*
Richard C. Moore Jr. *(Chm)*

LEHMANMILLET
101 Tremont St Fl 2, Boston, MA 02108
Tel.: (617) 722-0019
Web Site:
http://www.lehmanmillet.com
Year Founded: 1978
Rev.: $66,396,000
Emp.: 34
Advertising Services
N.A.I.C.S.: 541810
Deborah Lotterman *(Chief Creative Officer)*
Benjamin Beckley *(VP-Accts)*
Carolyn Morgan *(Pres)*
Chip Griffin *(Dir-Creative)*
Eric Levreault *(Sr Dir-Art)*
Danielle Stern *(Acct Supvr)*
Shannon Moore *(Acct Mgr)*
Dawn Hylton *(Sr Copy Writer)*
Kunsan Kim *(Sr VP-Plng)*
Doug Chapman *(VP & Dir-Creative)*
John Fitzpatrick *(Dir-Interactive)*
Kate Booth *(Sr VP-Strategy)*
Kristi Hansen *(Sr VP-Interactive)*
Marinella Georgino *(VP & Dir-Creative)*
Paul Balagot *(Mng Dir & Exec VP)*
Tim Boyce *(Dir-Creative Svcs)*

Subsidiaries:

LehmanMillet (1)
3 MacArthur Plc Ste 700, Santa Ana, CA 92707
Tel.: (866) 762-1507
Web Site: http://www.lehmanmillet.com
Rev.: $10,000,000
Emp.: 30
Advertising Agencies
N.A.I.C.S.: 541810
Deborah Lotterman *(Exec Dir-Creative)*
Mary Joan Chowsanitphon *(Acct Supvr)*

LehmanMillet Europe (1)
Sion Park Stansted Road Birchanger, Hertford, CM23 5PU, United Kingdom
Tel.: (44) 1279 818520
Advertising Agencies
N.A.I.C.S.: 541810

LEHR CONSTRUCTION COMPANY
2115 Frederick Ave, Saint Joseph, MO 64501
Tel.: (816) 232-4431
Web Site:
http://www.lehrconstruction.com
Sales Range: $10-24.9 Million
Emp.: 30
Nonresidential Construction Services
N.A.I.C.S.: 236220
Jon J. Lehr *(Pres)*
Bill Jackson *(VP)*

LEHRER'S FLOWERS INC.
2100 W Mississippi Ave, Denver, CO 80223-2940
Tel.: (303) 455-1234
Web Site:
http://www.thinkflowers.com
Sales Range: $10-24.9 Million
Emp.: 70
Fresh Flowers
N.A.I.C.S.: 459310
Kevin Byerly *(Exec VP)*
Michelle Medina *(Asst Mgr)*

LEHRKINDS INC.
1715 N Rouse Ave, Bozeman, MT 59715
Tel.: (406) 586-2029
Web Site:
http://www.bozemancoke.com
Rev.: $15,312,758
Emp.: 60
Soft Drink Distr
N.A.I.C.S.: 312111
Carl Lehrkind III *(Pres)*

LEIB SOLUTIONS, INC.
20 E Clementon Rd Ste 100 S, Gibbsboro, NJ 08026
Tel.: (856) 439-1179
Web Site:
http://www.leibsolutions.com
Year Founded: 1980
Sales Range: $1-9.9 Million
Emp.: 27
Collection & Insurance Agencies
N.A.I.C.S.: 561440
Carl Torban *(CFO & Exec VP)*
Robert G. Leib *(Pres & CEO)*
James P. Morris *(VP-Collections & Ops)*
Linda Locke *(Asst VP-Collections)*

LEIBLER-BRONFMAN LUBALIN
55 Fifth Ave 18th Fl, New York, NY 10003-4301
Tel.: (212) 463-9292 NY
Year Founded: 1986
Sales Range: $10-24.9 Million
Emp.: 12
Brand Development, Business-To-Business, Direct Marketing, Fashion/Apparel, Financial, Full Service, Internet/Web Design, Point of Purchase, Sales Promotion, T.V.
N.A.I.C.S.: 541810
Beth Leibler-Bronfman *(Mng Partner)*
Peter Lubalin *(Partner)*
Shannon-Megan Barreca *(Sr Art Dir)*
Albert Romano *(Dir-Media)*
Christine McArdle *(Sr Acct Exec)*

LEICHT TRANSFER & STORAGE COMPANY
1401 55 State St, Green Bay, WI 54304
Tel.: (920) 432-8632
Web Site: http://www.leichtgb.com
Rev.: $23,897,553
Emp.: 150
General Warehousing
N.A.I.C.S.: 493110
Bob Johnson *(Pres & CEO)*

LEIDEN CABINET CO.
2385 Edison Blvd, Twinsburg, OH 44087-2376
Tel.: (330) 425-8555 OH
Web Site:
http://www.leidencabinet.com
Year Founded: 1940
Sales Range: $10-24.9 Million
Emp.: 50
Store Fixtures, Wood
N.A.I.C.S.: 337212
Tom Leiden *(Pres & CEO)*
Melissa Hale *(Co-Owner)*
Mike Hopp *(Co-Owner)*

LEIF JOHNSON FORD INC.
501 E Koenig Ln, Austin, TX 78751
Tel.: (512) 454-3711
Web Site:
https://www.leifjohnsonford.com
Sales Range: $50-74.9 Million
Emp.: 270
Car Dealership
N.A.I.C.S.: 441110
Kevin Hopper *(Dir-Svc)*
Marri Stokes *(Dir-Internet)*
Jeff Buhl *(Pres)*

Subsidiaries:

Weststar Autoplex, LLC (1)
401 E Ih 20, Monahans, TX 79756
Tel.: (432) 943-4316
Sales Range: $1-9.9 Million
Emp.: 30
New Car Dealers
N.A.I.C.S.: 441110
Peggy Bryant *(Gen Mgr)*

LEIGH FIBERS, INC.
1101 Syphrit Rd, Wellford, SC 29385-9460
Tel.: (864) 439-4111 SC
Web Site: http://www.leighfibers.com
Year Founded: 1922
Rev.: $100,000,000
Emp.: 300
Recycling of Textile Waste
N.A.I.C.S.: 314999
Philip Lehner *(Chm)*
Harlow Frederick Dodge *(COO)*
Don Bockoven *(Pres)*

Subsidiaries:

Leigh Fibers, Inc., Warehouse & Distribution (1)
2935 S Vail Ave, City of Commerce, CA 90040 (100%)
Tel.: (323) 887-0824
Web Site: http://www.leighfibers.com
Sales Range: $10-24.9 Million
Emp.: 1
Processing & Sales of Textile Fibers
N.A.I.C.S.: 424310

Martex Fiber Southern Corporation (1)
6924 Orr Rd, Charlotte, NC 28213-6443
Tel.: (704) 596-2932
Web Site: http://www.martexfiber.com
Sales Range: $50-74.9 Million
Emp.: 200
Textile Recycling Services
N.A.I.C.S.: 423930
Mitchel Bollag *(Pres-Rag Div)*
Jerry Coffey *(Dir-Mfg-Rag Div)*
David Kennedy *(CFO)*
Marc Williamson *(VP-Bus & Product Dev)*
Jimmy Jarrett *(Pres-Ops)*
Jamie Jarrett *(Dir-Mfg-Fiber Div)*
Karl Kakadelis *(VP-IT)*
Chad Rothert *(VP-Fin)*
Steve Lister *(CEO)*

LEIGH MARCUS, INC.
2203 W Roscoe, Chicago, IL 60618
Tel.: (773) 299-8025
Web Site:
http://www.leighmarcus.com
Year Founded: 2004
Sales Range: $1-9.9 Million
Emp.: 8
Real Estate Services
N.A.I.C.S.: 531390

LEIGH MARCUS, INC.   **U.S. PRIVATE**

Leigh Marcus, Inc.—(Continued)
Lindsey Marcus (Bus Mgr-Real Estate)

LEIGHOW OIL COMPANY INCORPORATED
118 Eyer Rd, Danville, PA 17821
Tel.: (570) 275-3901
Web Site: http://www.leighowoil.com
Sales Range: $10-24.9 Million
Emp.: 20
Fuel Oil, Heating & Air Conditioning Services
N.A.I.C.S.: 457210
Glen Leighow (Chm)

LEIGHTON ENTERPRISES, INC.
619 W Saint Germain St, Saint Cloud, MN 56301
Tel.: (320) 251-1450   MN
Web Site:
http://www.leightonbroadcasting.com
Year Founded: 1963
Radio Broadcasting Stations
N.A.I.C.S.: 516110
Bob Leighton (CEO)
John Sowada (Pres)
Denny Niess (VP)
Stephanie Theisen (Exec Dir-Events & Dir-Mktg)
Jeff Leighton (Gen Mgr)
Heidi Lockaby (Gen Mgr-Sls)
Doug Gray (Gen Mgr)
Misty Paul (Sls Mgr)
Michael Brooks (Gen Mgr)
Subsidiaries:

Leighton Broadcasting - Fergus Falls   (1)
728 Western Ave, Fergus Falls, MN 56537
Tel.: (218) 736-7596
Web Site:
http://www.leightonbroadcasting.com
Radio Broadcasting Stations
N.A.I.C.S.: 516110

Leighton Broadcasting - Winona   (1)
752 Bluffview Cir, Winona, MN 55987
Tel.: (507) 452-4000
Web Site:
http://www.leightonbroadcasting.com
Sales Range: $1-9.9 Million
Emp.: 33
Radio Broadcasting Stations
N.A.I.C.S.: 516110

LEINBACH MACHINERY CO.
9125 NC 67 W, East Bend, NC 27018
Tel.: (336) 699-3000
Web Site: http://www.leinbachs.com
Sales Range: $10-24.9 Million
Emp.: 145
Agricultural Machinery & Equipment Mfr & Distr
N.A.I.C.S.: 423820
Janet Bates (Pres)

LEISURE BAY INDUSTRIES, INC.
3033 Mercy Dr, Orlando, FL 32808-3113
Tel.: (407) 297-0141   FL
Web Site:
http://www.recwarehouse.com
Year Founded: 1993
Sales Range: $25-49.9 Million
Emp.: 700
Sporting & Athletic Goods Mfr
N.A.I.C.S.: 339920
Michael Nimsea (Controller)
Don Check (CEO)
Subsidiaries:

Leisure Bay Distributing Co. Inc.   (1)
3033 Mercy Dr, Orlando, FL 32808-3113
Tel.: (407) 297-0141
Sales Range: $10-24.9 Million
Emp.: 25
Provider of Recreational Products Services
N.A.I.C.S.: 339920

LEISURE CARE, INC.
Ste 1900 1601 5th Ave, Seattle, WA 98101-3615
Tel.: (425) 455-5644
Web Site: http://www.leisurecare.com
Rev.: $10,000,000
Emp.: 55
Retirement Communities
N.A.I.C.S.: 531110
Dan Madsen (CEO)
Ryan Rasar (Partner & VP-Ops)
Robert Westermann (Pres-Intl)
Andy Gomes (Partner-One Eighty)
Judy Marczewski (CFO & Partner)
Traci Kuster (Dir-Mktg)
David Catherman (Dir-IT)
Clint Fowler (Dir-Resident Svcs)
Ken Robertson (VP-Dev)
Chris Lucero (Dir-Sls)
Debra Taylor (Dir-Health & Wellness)
Lisa Llewelyn (Dir-HR)
Bre Grubbs (Sr VP-New Bus)
Greg Clark (Partner & Exec VP)
Hoyt Scott (Partner & VP-Dev)
Troy Jones (VP-Ops)
Holli Korb (Dir-Ops-Communities-Washington, Idaho & Oregon)
Meg Davidson (Dir-Ops)

LEISURE HOTEL CORPORATION
4501 College Blvd Ste 275, Leawood, KS 66211
Tel.: (913) 905-1460
Web Site:
http://www.leisurehotel.com
Year Founded: 1985
Sales Range: $25-49.9 Million
Emp.: 25
Hospitality Management, Accounting, Development, Real Estate Brokerage, Investments, Construction & Renovations
N.A.I.C.S.: 551112
Steven C. Olson (CEO)
Gary Endicott (CFO & Exec VP)
Dave McNeil (VP & Controller)
Brent Jaynes (Mng Partner)
Jamie Tatge (Pres & COO)
Steve Scherer (Reg Dir-Ops)
Tess Moorehead (Reg Dir-Ops)
Subsidiaries:

Leisure Construction LLC   (1)
4501 College Blvd Ste 275, Leawood, KS 66211
Tel.: (913) 905-1460
Rev.: $2,500,000
Emp.: 20
Hotel/Motel, New Construction
N.A.I.C.S.: 236220

Leisure Hotel LLC   (1)
4501 College Blvd Ste 275, Leawood, KS 66211
Tel.: (913) 905-1460
Web Site: http://www.dodgecitysuper8.com
Sales Range: $25-49.9 Million
Emp.: 18
General Management Consultant
N.A.I.C.S.: 551112

Leisure RE Advisors LLC   (1)
5000 W 95th St Ste 100, Prairie Village, KS 66207
Tel.: (913) 905-1460
Web Site: http://www.leisurerealestate.com
Sales Range: Less than $1 Million
Emp.: 2
Venture Capital Companies
N.A.I.C.S.: 551112

LEISURE SPORTS INC.
4670 Willow Rd Ste 100, Pleasanton, CA 94588
Tel.: (925) 600-1966
Web Site:
http://www.leisuresportsinc.com
Year Founded: 1978
Sales Range: $100-124.9 Million
Emp.: 1,200
Developer & Operator of Athletic Clubs & Hotels
N.A.I.C.S.: 713940
Steven M. Gilmour (Pres & CEO)
Patrick J. O'Brien (CFO)
Cory Ferraro (VP-Sls & Mktg)
Janine L. Williams (VP-HR)
Ralph S. Rajs (Sr VP-Ops)

LEISURE TIME MARKETING INC.
18242 Enterprise Ln, Huntington Beach, CA 92648
Tel.: (714) 841-0499
Web Site:
http://www.leisuretimemarketing.com
Sales Range: $25-49.9 Million
Emp.: 25
Electronic Mobile Video
N.A.I.C.S.: 423120
Gary Chancy (Pres)

LEISURE WORLD OF MARYLAND
3701 Rossmoor Blvd, Silver Spring, MD 20906
Tel.: (301) 598-1000
Web Site: http://www.lwmc.com
Sales Range: $10-24.9 Million
Emp.: 220
Real Estate Managers
N.A.I.C.S.: 531210
Kevin Flannery (Gen Mgr)
Timothy Coursen (Asst Gen Mgr-Community Mgmt)
Barbara Stolov (Coord-Benefits)

LEISURE, WERDEN & TERRY AGENCY, INC.
200 S Los Robles Ave Ste 200, Pasadena, CA 91101
Tel.: (626) 304-1300   CA
Web Site: http://www.lwtagency.com
Year Founded: 1927
Sales Range: $10-24.9 Million
Insurance Brokerage Services
N.A.I.C.S.: 524210
Jeff Carroll (CEO)
Subsidiaries:

Colorado Brokerage Group, LLC   (1)
90 Madison St Ste 103, Denver, CO 80206-5414
Tel.: (303) 321-0565
Web Site:
http://www.coloradobrokerage.com
Sales Range: $1-9.9 Million
Emp.: 5
Insurance Brokerage Services
N.A.I.C.S.: 524210
John W. McWilliams (Owner)

LEISZLER OIL CO., INC.
635 W Crawford St, Clay Center, KS 67432-2337
Tel.: (785) 632-5648   KS
Web Site: http://www.leiszleroil.com
Year Founded: 1941
Sales Range: $25-49.9 Million
Emp.: 250
Provider of Gasoline Station Services
N.A.I.C.S.: 457120
Allison Leiszler (Owner)

LEITH HONDA ABERDEEN
11049 N US 15-501, Aberdeen, NC 28315
Tel.: (910) 692-2111

Web Site:
http://www.leithhondaaberdeen.com
Sales Range: $10-24.9 Million
Emp.: 65
Car Whslr
N.A.I.C.S.: 441110
Ted Davis (Treas)
Steve Jones (Pres)

LEJEUNE MOTOR COMPANY INC.
2215 N Marine Blvd, Jacksonville, NC 28546
Tel.: (910) 455-1551
Web Site:
http://www.lejeunemotorcompany.com
Sales Range: $10-24.9 Million
Emp.: 105
New & Used Car Dealers
N.A.I.C.S.: 441110

LEM CONSTRUCTION
10849 Kinghurst St Ste 150, Houston, TX 77099
Tel.: (281) 495-9550
Web Site: http://lemconstruction.com
Sales Range: $25-49.9 Million
Emp.: 125
Civil Engineering Services
N.A.I.C.S.: 237310
Mark Beauchamp (Coord-Site Safety)

LEM MARKETS INC.
1523 Wilborn Ave, South Boston, VA 24592
Tel.: (434) 575-7002
Sales Range: $10-24.9 Million
Emp.: 4
Grocery Stores, Chain
N.A.I.C.S.: 445110
Lloyd Bost (Pres)
Margret Bost (Treas)

LEMANS CORPORATION
3501 Kennedy Rd, Janesville, WI 53547-5222
Tel.: (608) 758-1111   WI
Web Site: http://www.parts-unlimited.com
Year Founded: 1967
Motor Vehicle Supplies & New Parts Distr
N.A.I.C.S.: 423120
Mark Scharenbroch (VP-Fin)

LEMARTEC ENGINEERING & CONSTRUCTION CORPORATION
11740 SW 80th St 3rd Fl, Miami, FL 33183
Tel.: (305) 273-8676
Web Site: http://www.lemartec.com
Rev.: $10,369,137
Emp.: 24
Industrial Buildings, New Construction
N.A.I.C.S.: 236210
Jorge Zubimendi (VP-Estimating)
Jorge Lares (Mgr-Aviation)
Felipe Aguiar (VP-Mktg & Comm)
Guillermo Garcia-Tunon Jr. (Engr-Pro)

LEMASTER STEEL ERECTORS INC.
53518 County Rd 9, Elkhart, IN 46514
Tel.: (574) 262-1531
Web Site:
http://www.lemastersteel.com
Year Founded: 1975
Sales Range: $10-24.9 Million
Emp.: 130
Structural Steel Erection Services
N.A.I.C.S.: 238120

COMPANIES

Robert Lemaster *(Owner)*
Jim Bigler *(Pres)*

LEMAY AUTO GROUP
8220 75th St, Kenosha, WI 53142
Tel.: (262) 694-2000
Web Site:
http://www.lemayautogroup.com
Sales Range: $10-24.9 Million
Emp.: 100
Automobile Sales
N.A.I.C.S.: 441110
Keith LeMay *(Owner)*

LEMCON USA CORPORATION
41 Perimeter Center E Ste 615, Atlanta, GA 30346
Tel.: (770) 392-8800 DE
Web Site: http://www.lemcon-americas.com
Year Founded: 2002
Emp.: 350
Telecommunication Infrastructure Services
N.A.I.C.S.: 517810
Alexandre Tude *(VP-Latin American Market)*
Julia Cox *(Controller)*

Subsidiaries:

Lemcon Networks Mexico S. de R.L. de C.V. (1)
Goldsmith 37 Int 202 Col Polanco Chapultepec, Del Miguel Hidalgo, Mexico, 11560, Mexico
Tel.: (52) 55 528 20512
Web Site: http://www.lemcon-americas.com
Sales Range: $25-49.9 Million
Emp.: 28
Telecommunication Networking Services
N.A.I.C.S.: 517810
Jurgen Kwass *(Country Mgr)*

LEMIEUX GROUP L.P.
1001 5th Ave, Pittsburgh, PA 15219
Tel.: (412) 642-1300 PA
Web Site:
http://www.pittsburghpenguins.com
Year Founded: 1997
Sales Range: $50-74.9 Million
Emp.: 50
Holding Company; Professional Hockey Club & Sporting Arena Owner & Operator
N.A.I.C.S.: 551112
Mario Lemieux *(Co-Owner & Chm)*
David J. Morehouse *(Pres & CEO)*
Ron Burkle *(Co-Owner)*

Subsidiaries:

Pittsburgh Penguins LLC (1)
1001 5th Ave, Pittsburgh, PA 15219
Tel.: (412) 642-1300
Web Site: http://www.nhl.com
Sales Range: $10-24.9 Million
Professional Hockey Club Operator
N.A.I.C.S.: 711211
Mario Lemieux *(Co-Owner & Chm)*
Ron Burkle *(Co-Owner)*
Ross Miller *(Sr Dir-Partnership Mktg)*
Jennifer Bullano Ridgley *(Sr Dir-Comm)*
Terry Kalna *(Sr VP-Sls & Brdcst)*
Andy O'Brien *(Dir-Sports Science)*
Devin Beahm *(Sr Mgr-Partnership Mktg)*
Travis Williams *(COO)*
Kevin Acklin *(Gen Counsel & Sr VP)*
Kevin Hart *(Sr VP-Fin)*
James Santilli *(Sr VP-Mktg)*
Sam Ventura *(Dir-Hockey Ops & Hockey Res)*
Erik Heasley *(Interim Gen Mgr-Wilkes-Barre Scranton Penguins)*
Patrik Allvin *(Asst Gen Mgr)*

LEMONLIGHT MEDIA, INC.
226 S Glasgow Ave, Inglewood, CA 90301
Tel.: (310) 402-0275
Web Site: http://www.lemonlight.com
Year Founded: 2014
Sales Range: $1-9.9 Million
Emp.: 35
Media Advertising Services
N.A.I.C.S.: 541840
Hope Horner *(Founder & CEO)*

LEMOS LABS, LLC
329 Pillow St, Buttler, PA 16001
Tel.: (724) 519-2936
Web Site: http://www.lemoslabs.com
Environmental Consulting Services
N.A.I.C.S.: 541620
Trevor Block *(Project Mgr)*
Alex Keffalas *(Dir-Ops-Northern Region)*

LEN STOLER INC.
11275 Reisterstown Rd, Owings Mills, MD 21117
Tel.: (410) 356-7000
Web Site: http://www.lenstoler.com
Year Founded: 1968
Sales Range: $150-199.9 Million
Emp.: 340
Owner & Operator of Car Dealerships
N.A.I.C.S.: 441110
Leonard Stoler *(Pres)*
Barry Stoler *(VP)*

LEN-TEX CORP.
18 Len Tex Ln, North Walpole, NH 03609
Tel.: (603) 445-2342
Web Site: http://www.lentexcorp.com
Emp.: 200
Mfr of Contract Wallcoverings
N.A.I.C.S.: 238320
Donald Lennon *(Pres)*
Phyllis Custer *(Mgr-Mktg)*

LEN-TRAN, INC.
2504 64th St Ct E, Bradenton, FL 34208
Tel.: (941) 745-2101 FL
Web Site: http://www.turnertree-landscape.com
Year Founded: 1983
Sales Range: $1-9.9 Million
Emp.: 60
Landscaping Services
N.A.I.C.S.: 561730
Darrell Turner *(Pres)*

LENAPE FORGE, INC.
1334 Lenape Rd, West Chester, PA 19382
Tel.: (610) 793-5090 PA
Web Site:
http://www.lenapeforge.com
Year Founded: 1930
Sales Range: $75-99.9 Million
Emp.: 120
Mfr of Custom Forgings
N.A.I.C.S.: 332112
Matt Troutman *(VP & Gen Mgr)*

LENAWEE FUELS INC.
4070 Allen Rd, Tecumseh, MI 49286
Tel.: (517) 423-6695
Web Site:
http://www.lenaweefuels.com
Sales Range: $25-49.9 Million
Emp.: 9
Provider of Fuel Oil
N.A.I.C.S.: 424710
Bruce Lisford *(Owner)*

LENCO MOBILE INC.
2025 1st Ave Ste 320, Seattle, WA 98121
Tel.: (800) 557-4148 DE
Sales Range: $10-24.9 Million
Emp.: 62
Mobile Phone & Internet Advertising Platforms Owner & Operator
N.A.I.C.S.: 517112
Matthew R. Harris *(CEO)*

Subsidiaries:

iLoop Mobile, Inc. (1)
111 N Market St Ste 402, San Jose, CA 95113
Tel.: (408) 907-3360
Web Site: http://www.iloopmobile.com
Sales Range: $1-9.9 Million
Mobile Technology & Services for Interactive, SMS-Based Mobile Marketing, Enterprise Solutions & Content Distribution
N.A.I.C.S.: 541512

LENDBUZZ, INC.
100 Summer St, Ste 3150, Boston, MA 02110
Tel.: (857) 999-0250
Web Site: https://lendbuzz.com
Year Founded: 2015
Emp.: 77
Financial Services & Software Publisher
N.A.I.C.S.: 522291
Amitay Kalmar *(Co-Founder & CEO)*

Subsidiaries:

Shamrock Home Loans, Inc. (1)
75 Newman Ave, Rumford, RI 02916
Tel.: (401) 434-4442
Web Site:
https://www.shamrockhomeloans.com
Rev.: $5,940,000
Emp.: 15
Consumer Lending
N.A.I.C.S.: 522291
John Lake *(Exec VP)*
Liz Letourneau *(Sr VP)*
Rod Correia *(Pres)*
Ashley Cookson *(VP-Ops)*
Bethany Nicholson *(Mgr-Compliance)*
David Bremer *(Branch Mgr)*
Greg Cambio *(VP-Underwriting)*
Jaclyn Ferri *(Coord-Loan)*
Leanne Poole *(Coord-Pur)*
Shalimar Albanese *(Dir-Mktg & Client Delight)*
Trish Harrington *(Controller)*
Suzanne Caldeira *(VP)*
Andrew Borges *(Officer-Loan)*
Bill Bento *(Officer-Loan)*
Dave Correia *(Officer-Loan)*
Don Calitri *(Mgr-Processing)*
Doug Botelho *(Mgr)*
Juan Cerda *(Officer-Loan)*
Karen Ballou *(Officer-Loan)*
Pamela Britt *(Officer-Loan)*
Shawn Hendricks *(Officer-Loan)*

LENDER'S CONSULTING GROUP, INC.
201 E Kennedy Blvd Ste 325, Tampa, FL 33602
Tel.: (813) 226-2800
Web Site: http://www.lcgadvisors.com
Year Founded: 2003
Sales Range: $1-9.9 Million
Emp.: 40
Loan, Investment Due Diligence, Corporate Finance, Mergers, Acquisitions, Financial Restructuring, Risk Mitigation & Other Advisory Services
N.A.I.C.S.: 541611
Brian M. Smith *(Co-Founder & Mng Partner)*
Paul I. Epstein *(Mng Partner)*
David Ruhlig *(Mng Dir)*
Brad Velie *(Mng Dir)*
Chris Nix *(VP)*
Scott Webb *(Mng Dir-Restructuring & Consulting Practice)*
Michael J. Reed *(Mng Dir-Bus Valuations)*

LENDING SCIENCE DM, INC.
5871 Glenridge Dr Ste 100, Atlanta, GA 30328
Tel.: (800) 769-3050
Web Site:
http://www.lendingsciencedm.com

Financial & Marketing Services
N.A.I.C.S.: 523999
Timothy Olzer *(CEO)*

LENDING SPACE INC.
107 Corporate Blvd Ste D, South Plainfield, NJ 07080
Tel.: (908) 222-8100
Sales Range: $10-24.9 Million
Emp.: 25
Mortgage Loan Software Mfr
N.A.I.C.S.: 541511
Mukesh Agarwal *(CEO)*

LENDINGONE, LLC
901 Yamato Rd Ste 150, Boca Raton, FL 33431
Web Site: http://www.lendingone.com
Year Founded: 2014
Sales Range: $10-24.9 Million
Emp.: 50
Real Estate Investment Services
N.A.I.C.S.: 531390
Bill Green *(CEO)*
Matthew Neisser *(COO)*
Jaime Arouh *(VP-Capital Markets)*
Josh Marcus *(Corp Counsel)*

LENDINGPOINT LLC
1201 Roberts Blvd NW Ste 200, Kennesaw, GA 30144
Web Site:
http://www.lendingpoint.com
Year Founded: 2014
Sales Range: $100-124.9 Million
Emp.: 190
Financial Services
N.A.I.C.S.: 522299
Tom Burnside *(Founder & CEO)*
Juan E. Tavares *(Chief Strategy Officer)*
Houman Motaharian *(Pres)*
Christy Mahon *(Sr VP-HR)*
Joe Valeo *(Gen Mgr)*
Ashish Gupta *(Chief Risk Officer)*
Ryan Scully *(CMO)*

LENDIO INC.
10235 S Jordan Gateway Ste 410, South Jordan, UT 84095
Tel.: (801) 838-9279
Web Site: http://www.lendio.com
Year Founded: 2005
Sales Range: $1-9.9 Million
Emp.: 65
Small Business Financing & Angel Investing to Qualified Entrepreneurs
N.A.I.C.S.: 525990
Brock J. Blake *(Co-Founder & CEO)*
Trent Miskin *(Founder)*
Brett Child *(Founder & Exec VP-Sls)*
Adam Michaelson *(VP-Product Strategy)*
Mark Santiago *(CFO)*
Edward Angstadt *(Sr VP-Mktg)*
David Frazier *(VP-Fin & Controller)*
Jim Granat *(COO)*
John Kuriger *(Dir-Ops)*
Lou Mazzella *(Dir-Sls & Bus Dev)*
Zach Soper *(Dir-Marketplace Lending)*
Tracy Crockett *(VP-Product Strategy)*
Ben Davis *(Chief Franchising Officer)*

LENDR, LLC
515 N State St Ste 950, Chicago, IL 60654
Web Site: http://www.lendr.online
Year Founded: 2011
Sales Range: $10-24.9 Million
Emp.: 38
Financial Services
N.A.I.C.S.: 522110
Tim Roach *(Founder & CEO)*
Karitza Hines *(Mgr-HR)*

LENFEST GROUP LLC

Lendr, LLC—(Continued)

LENFEST GROUP LLC
300 Barr Harbor Dr Ste 460, Conshohocken, PA 19428-2998
Tel.: (610) 940-0815
Sales Range: $75-99.9 Million
Emp.: 50
Insurance Agents
N.A.I.C.S.: 524298
Gerry Lenfest *(CEO)*

LENG UNIVERSAL, INC.
157B English St, Fort Lee, NJ 07024
Tel.: (210) 289-9908   DE
Year Founded: 2014
Emp.: 1
Apparel Mfr & Distr
N.A.I.C.S.: 315250
Chun Pao Leng *(Pres, CEO & Treas)*

LENNY & LARRY'S
8803 Amigo Ave, Northridge, CA 91324
Tel.: (818) 727-0191
Web Site: http://www.lennylarry.com
Year Founded: 1993
Sales Range: $1-9.9 Million
Emp.: 10
Vegan Snacks
N.A.I.C.S.: 311919
Barry Turner *(Founder)*
Jennifer Redmond *(Mgr-Ops)*

LENOIR CITY UTILITIES BOARD INC.
200 Depot St, Lenoir City, TN 37771-2917
Tel.: (865) 986-6591
Web Site: http://www.lcub.com
Year Founded: 1938
Sales Range: $25-49.9 Million
Emp.: 136
Provider of Electric Services
N.A.I.C.S.: 221122
Shannon Littleton *(Gen Mgr)*
Ron Cronan *(Mgr-Risk)*

LENSING WHOLESALE INC.
600 N 6th Ave, Evansville, IN 47710-1414
Tel.: (812) 423-6891
Web Site: http://www.lensingwholesale.com
Year Founded: 1948
Sales Range: $10-24.9 Million
Emp.: 167
Distr of Building Materials
N.A.I.C.S.: 423310
Joseph T. Theby *(Chm)*
William Theby *(Pres)*

LENTINE MANAGEMENT INC.
207 Everitts Rd Rte 31, Flemington, NJ 08822
Tel.: (908) 782-3619
Year Founded: 1976
Sales Range: $10-24.9 Million
Emp.: 15
Mfr of Concrete Block & Brick
N.A.I.C.S.: 327331

LENZ INC.
1180 Hwy 7 E, Hutchinson, MN 55350
Tel.: (320) 587-4030
Sales Range: $10-24.9 Million
Emp.: 50
Farm & Garden Machinery
N.A.I.C.S.: 423820
Craig Lenz *(Pres)*

LEO A. DALY COMPANY
8600 Indian Hills Dr, Omaha, NE 68114-4039
Tel.: (402) 391-8111   NE
Web Site: http://www.leoadaly.com
Year Founded: 1915
Sales Range: $100-124.9 Million
Emp.: 880
Architecture, Engineering Planning & Interiors Professional Services
N.A.I.C.S.: 541330
Jay Brader *(CFO & Sr VP)*
Ignacio Reyes *(VP & Corp Dir-Dev)*
Ruth Jansson *(Principal & Dir-Interiors)*
Ryan D. Martin *(Dir-Design-Hospitality Architecture)*
Rick Thompson *(Mng Principal-Washington)*
Rishi Bhasin *(Mgr-Fin)*
Sunny Onadipe *(Mgr-Specifications-Minneapolis)*
Shane Williams *(Dir-Design-Healthcare)*
Roy Follmuth *(Mng Principal & VP)*
Matthew Johnson *(Mng Principal & VP)*
Douglas Lentz *(CEO)*
Mahdi M. Mansour *(VP & Dir-Middle East & North Africa)*
Ken Martin *(Mng Principal & VP)*
Patricia Miller *(VP & Dir-Hospitality)*
Kevin Nokels *(COO & VP)*
Steven A. Lichtenberger *(Pres)*
Debra R. Crafter *(Program Mgr-Small Bus-Washington)*
Leslie Shepherd *(Principal & Dir-GSA Programs-Natl)*
Bill Kline *(Mng Principal/VP-Washington)*
Jamie E. Sobrino *(VP & Dir-Ops)*
Don Hensley *(Mng Principal-Dallas & VP)*
Leo A. Daly III *(Chm & CEO)*

Subsidiaries:
Lockwood Andrews & Newnam, Inc.   (1)
2925 Briarpark Dr Ste 400, Houston, TX 77042-3720   (100%)
Tel.: (713) 266-6900
Web Site: http://www.lan-inc.com
Sales Range: $25-49.9 Million
Emp.: 178
Engineeering Services
N.A.I.C.S.: 541330
Philip Meaders *(VP)*
Jason Maldonado *(Mgr-Storm Water Quality)*
Kerry Gregg *(VP & Dir-Mktg)*
Dev Rastogi *(VP)*
Gail Hamrick-Pigg *(Sr Project Manager)*
Luis Alday *(Mgr-Stormwater)*
Gary Bouthillier *(Dir-Aviation)*
Warren Green *(VP & Dir-Bus Grp)*
Derek St. John *(VP)*
J. P. Grom *(VP)*
Stephen Gilbreath *(VP)*
Paul Kullman *(Mgr-Program)*
Arnold Cohen *(COO & VP)*
John Montalvo *(Sr Mgr-Construction)*
Brian Broussard *(Reg Mgr-Water Resources)*
Wayne Swafford *(Exec VP)*
Kathy Caswell *(Mgr-Mktg-Orange)*
Blair Haynie *(Reg Mgr-Transportation)*
Gina M. DeLellis *(Mgr-HR)*
Donald R. Stevens *(Dir-Healthcare Facilities)*
Bob Austin *(VP)*
Jeff Thomas *(VP)*
William R. Abbott *(Dir-Ops)*
Juan Mendoza Jr. *(Mgr-Program)*
Leo A. Daly III *(Chm & CEO)*

LEO CONSTRUCTION COMPANY
24080 Lenah Rd, Aldie, VA 20105
Tel.: (703) 450-4500
Web Site: http://www.leoconstruction.us
Rev.: $12,049,436
Emp.: 50
Underground Utilities Contractor
N.A.I.C.S.: 237110
Thomas Rose *(Pres)*

LEO J. BRENNAN, INC.
2359 Livernois Rd, Troy, MI 48083-1692
Tel.: (248) 362-3131
Web Site: http://www.ljbrennan.com
Year Founded: 1969
Sales Range: Less than $1 Million
Emp.: 3
Advetising Agency
N.A.I.C.S.: 541810
Leo J. Brennan *(Pres)*
Don Boyd *(Art Dir, Mngmt Supvr & Acct Exec)*

LEO J. ROTH CORP.
841 Holt Rd, Webster, NY 14580
Tel.: (585) 872-0220
Web Site: http://www.leojroth.com
Year Founded: 1948
Sales Range: $10-24.9 Million
Emp.: 150
Roofing Installation Services
N.A.I.C.S.: 238390
Thomas Roth *(Pres)*

LEO J. SHAPIRO & ASSOCIATES, LLC
153 W Ohio St Ste 300, Chicago, IL 60654
Tel.: (312) 321-8111   DE
Web Site: http://www.ljs.com
Year Founded: 1955
Sales Range: $25-49.9 Million
Emp.: 75
Marketing Research & Analysis Services
N.A.I.C.S.: 541910
Owen Shapiro *(Pres)*
Matthew Smith *(Vice Chm)*
Zain Raj *(Chm & CEO)*
Arturo Angel *(Mng Dir)*
Sara Parikh *(Mng Dir)*
Lisa La Brooy *(Sr VP-Life Sciences Practice)*

LEO JOURNAGAN CONSTRUCTION CO.
3003 E Chestnut Expy Ste 1200, Springfield, MO 65802
Tel.: (417) 869-7222
Web Site: http://www.journagan.com
Rev.: $60,000,000
Emp.: 100
Highway & Street Construction
N.A.I.C.S.: 212312
Leo Journagan *(Chm)*
Terry Maples *(Controller)*

LEO TIDWELL EXCAVATING CORP
1890 Ramada, Paso Robles, CA 93446
Tel.: (805) 466-5832   CA
Web Site: http://www.tidwellcompanies.com
Year Founded: 1974
Sales Range: $10-24.9 Million
Telephone & Communication Line Construction Services
N.A.I.C.S.: 237130
Bert Wollerman *(VP)*
Leo W. Tidwell Jr. *(Pres)*

LEOMINSTER CREDIT UNION
20 Adams St, Leominster, MA 01453
Tel.: (978) 537-8021
Web Site: http://www.leominstercu.com
Year Founded: 1953
Rev.: $15,897,063
Emp.: 125
State Credit Union Services
N.A.I.C.S.: 522130
Richard A. Sheppard *(Treas)*
Giulio G. Greco *(Chm)*
D. Oscar O'Connor *(VP-Lending Ops)*
Barbara A. Mahoney *(Pres & CEO)*
Gary M. Abrams *(CFO & Exec VP)*
Janet Belsky *(Sr VP-Mktg)*
Tom Clancy *(VP-IT)*
Randy Harris *(Asst VP-Treasury)*
Bryon Goguen *(Asst Controller)*
John J. Diggins *(Asst VP-Contact Center)*
Joanne D. Lattanzi *(Asst VP-Mktg)*
Lydia Vazquez-Long *(Asst VP-Residential Lending & Fair Lending)*
Kim A. Cary *(Asst VP & Mgr-Holden Branch)*
Stephanie Hernandez *(Branch Mgr)*
Stephanie D. Hyles *(Chief Strategy Officer)*
Carol A. Perron *(Sr VP-Retail Banking)*
Nick Gorgoglione *(Founder)*
Lisa Perrin *(Sr VP)*
Kelli Rooney *(VP-Mktg)*
Kristen L. Gustafson I *(Mgr-North Leominster)*
Paula A. Konde II *(Mgr-Sterling)*
Tammy M. Garcia II *(Mgr-Worcester-Shrewsbury)*

LEOMINSTER NEWS INC.
6 Merriam Ave, Leominster, MA 01453
Tel.: (978) 534-8237
Sales Range: $10-24.9 Million
Emp.: 15
Newspapers
N.A.I.C.S.: 424920
Randy L. Bigelow *(Pres)*
Scott Begelow *(Treas)*

LEON D. DEMATTEIS CONSTRUCTION
820 Elmont Rd, Elmont, NY 11003
Tel.: (516) 285-5500
Web Site: http://www.dematteisorg.com
Rev.: $100,000,000
Emp.: 45
Nonresidential Construction Services
N.A.I.C.S.: 236220
Richard F. DeMatteis *(Principal)*
Alan C. Sullivan *(Exec VP)*
Raymond R. Savino *(CFO-Real Estate Dev)*
Steven V. Tartaro *(VP-Construction)*
Francisco Offemaria *(Superintendent-MEP)*
Frank X. DarConte *(VP-Plng & Dev)*
James J. Kilbride *(VP-Estimating & Procurement)*
Salvatore J. Novello *(VP-Plng & Dev)*
Andrew Borgese Jr. *(Project Mgr)*

LEON FARMER AND COMPANY INC.
100 Rail Rdg Rd, Athens, GA 30607-1337
Tel.: (706) 353-1166   GA
Web Site: http://www.leonfarmer.com
Year Founded: 1983
Sales Range: $25-49.9 Million
Emp.: 160
Supplier of Beer & Ale
N.A.I.C.S.: 424810
Tim Mackey *(CEO)*

LEON HENRY, INC.
200 N Central Ave Ste 220, Hartsdale, NY 10530
Tel.: (914) 285-3456   NY
Year Founded: 1956
Sales Range: $1-9.9 Million
Emp.: 30
Direct Mail Advertising Services
N.A.I.C.S.: 541860

COMPANIES

Leon Henry *(Chm & CEO)*
Thelma Henry *(Pres)*
Lynn Henry *(Exec VP)*
Gail Henry *(Exec VP & Gen Mgr)*
Barbara Henry *(Exec VP)*
Margaret Ginns *(Mgr-Sls)*
Jeff Angelini *(Dir-IT)*
Jackie Gizzo *(VP-Brokerage)*
Millie McFarlane *(Mgr-Acctg Dept)*

LEON JONES FEED AND GRAIN INC.
4880 Leland Dr, Cumming, GA 30041
Tel.: (770) 887-6117
Sales Range: $10-24.9 Million
Emp.: 100
Provider of Trucking Services
N.A.I.C.S.: 484121
David Hood *(Gen Mgr)*

LEON KOROL COMPANY
2050 E Devon Ave, Elk Grove Village, IL 60007
Tel.: (847) 956-1616
Web Site: http://www.leonkorol.com
Sales Range: $10-24.9 Million
Emp.: 62
Novelties, Durable
N.A.I.C.S.: 423990
Steve Korol *(Pres)*

LEON MAX INC.
3100 New York Dr, Pasadena, CA 91107
Tel.: (626) 797-6886   CA
Web Site: http://www.maxstudio.com
Year Founded: 1979
Sales Range: $50-74.9 Million
Emp.: 255
Womens & Misses Outerwear
N.A.I.C.S.: 315250
Leon Max *(Pres)*
Ching Liu *(Controller)*
Ernie Hoffer *(CFO)*

LEON MEDICAL CENTERS, INC.
101 SW 27th Ave, Miami, FL 33135
Tel.: (305) 642-5366
Web Site:
  http://www.leonmedicalcenters.com
Year Founded: 1996
Sales Range: $75-99.9 Million
Emp.: 1,800
Hospital
N.A.I.C.S.: 622110
Rafael Mas *(Chief Medical Officer & Sr VP-Medical Affairs)*
Marcus Gomez *(CIO & Sr VP)*
Maritza Pereira *(VP-HR)*
Aristides Pallin *(Dir-Ops)*
Robert McDaniel *(Dir-Ops)*
Albert Maury *(Pres)*
Benjamin Leon Jr. *(Founder)*

LEON N. WEINER & ASSOCIATES
4 Denny Rd, Wilmington, DE 19809
Tel.: (302) 764-9430
Web Site:
  http://www.arbormanagement.com
Rev.: $12,700,000
Emp.: 45
Subdividers & Developers
N.A.I.C.S.: 237210
Kevin Kelly *(Chm)*
Tom Perkins *(CFO & VP)*

LEON SPEAKERS, INC.
715 W Ellsworth Rd, Ann Arbor, MI 48108
Web Site:
  http://www.leonspeakers.com
Year Founded: 1995
Sales Range: $1-9.9 Million
Emp.: 25

Electronics Stores
N.A.I.C.S.: 449210
Noah Kaplan *(Founder & Pres)*

LEON SULLIVAN HEALTH CARE CENTER
2611 S Dearborn St, Seattle, WA 98144
Tel.: (206) 325-6700   WA
Web Site: http://www.leonsullivan.org
Year Founded: 2003
Sales Range: $10-24.9 Million
Emp.: 259
Health Care Srvices
N.A.I.C.S.: 622110
Sabine von Preyss-Friedman *(Dir-Medical)*

LEON'S FINE FOODS, INC.
2100 N Redbud Blvd, McKinney, TX 75069
Tel.: (972) 529-5050
Web Site:
  http://www.texascuisine.com
Year Founded: 1946
Sales Range: $25-49.9 Million
Emp.: 200
Snack Food Mfr & Distr
N.A.I.C.S.: 311612
Robert L. Clements *(Pres)*
Allen Dillon *(VP-Facilities)*
John Vroman *(Sr VP-Ops)*

LEONA'S PIZZERIA INC.
3931 S Leavitt St, Chicago, IL 60609
Tel.: (773) 843-0050
Web Site: http://www.leonas.com
Sales Range: $200-249.9 Million
Emp.: 2,500
Pizzeria, Independent
N.A.I.C.S.: 722513
Leon Toia *(Pres)*
Augie Monarrez *(Dir-Pur)*

LEONARD A. FEINBERG INCORPORATED
1824 Byberry Rd, Bensalem, PA 19020
Tel.: (215) 639-9300
Web Site: http://www.feathersgirl.com
Sales Range: $25-49.9 Million
Emp.: 22
Provider of Women's & Children's Clothing
N.A.I.C.S.: 424350
Bruce Feinberg *(Pres)*
Jeff Barnett *(Controller)*

LEONARD BUS SALES INC.
4 Leonard Way, Deposit, NY 13754
Tel.: (607) 467-3100
Web Site: http://www.leonardbus.com
Year Founded: 1966
Sales Range: $10-24.9 Million
Emp.: 40
Buses
N.A.I.C.S.: 423110
Michael G. Leonard *(Pres)*
Barbara R. Leonard *(VP)*
Mark Ingham *(Mgr-Svcs)*
Frank Continetti *(Gen Mgr)*

LEONARD CONSULTING LLC
370 E South Temple Ste 300, Salt Lake City, UT 84111
Tel.: (801) 359-4699
Web Site:
  http://www.leonardconsultingllc.com
Year Founded: 2005
Sales Range: $1-9.9 Million
Emp.: 15
Auditing, Accounting & Business Consulting for Department of Health & Human Services
N.A.I.C.S.: 921190

Kathleen Leonard *(CEO)*
Frank Leonard *(Founder & Pres)*
Hilary Leonard *(COO)*
John Speirs *(CFO)*

LEONARD GREEN & PARTNERS, L.P.
11111 Santa Monica Blvd Ste 2000, Los Angeles, CA 90025
Tel.: (310) 954-0444
Web Site:
  http://www.leonardgreen.com
Year Founded: 1989
Privater Equity Firm
N.A.I.C.S.: 523999
Michael Solomon *(Partner)*
Cody L. Franklin *(CFO)*
John M. Baumer *(Sr Partner)*
John Danhakl *(Mng Partner)*
Andrew Goldberg *(Gen Counsel)*
Doug Chey *(Chief Portfolio Tech Officer)*
Jeffrey Suer *(Principal)*
Reginald Holden *(Chief Procurement Officer)*
W. Christian McCollum *(Partner)*
Tai Park *(CIO)*
Usama N. Cortas *(Partner)*
J. Kristofer Galashan *(Partner)*
John G. Danhakl *(Mng Partner)*
J. Kristofer Galashan *(Partner)*
Adam T. Levyn *(Partner)*

Subsidiaries:

Advantage Sales & Marketing LLC   (1)
18100 Von Karman Ave Ste 1000, Irvine, CA 92612-1539
Tel.: (949) 797-2900
Web Site: http://www.asmnet.com
Sales Range: $750-799.9 Million
Emp.: 20,000
Grocery Sale & Marketing Services
N.A.I.C.S.: 424410
Tanya L. Domier *(CEO)*

Branch (Domestic):

Advantage Sales & Marketing - San Antonio   (2)
N Park Corp Ctr 17319 San Pedro Ave Ste 510, San Antonio, TX 78232
Tel.: (210) 494-8226
Web Site: http://www.asmnet.com
Rev.: $110,900,000
Emp.: 265
Sales & Marketing Services for the Consumer Packaged Goods Industry
N.A.I.C.S.: 541613

Advantage Sales & Marketing, LLC - Grand Rapids   (2)
56 Grandville SW, Grand Rapids, MI 49503
Tel.: (616) 831-5000
Web Site: http://www.asmnet.com
Rev.: $11,600,000
Emp.: 30
Sales & Marketing Services for the Consumer Packaged Goods Industry
N.A.I.C.S.: 541613
Kurt Johnson *(Mgr-Bus Dev)*

Advantage Sales & Marketing, LLC - Renton   (2)
841 Powell Ave SW Ste 150, Renton, WA 98057
Tel.: (425) 572-3250
Web Site: http://www.asmnet.com
Sales Range: $25-49.9 Million
Emp.: 25
Sales & Marketing Services for the Consumer Packaged Goods Industry
N.A.I.C.S.: 541613
Sonny King *(Chm & CEO)*

Advantage Sales & Marketing, LLC - Schaumburg   (2)
50 Commerce Dr Ste 170, Schaumburg, IL 60173
Tel.: (630) 339-7600
Web Site: http://www.asmnet.com
Sales Range: $25-49.9 Million
Emp.: 100
Bond Brokers

N.A.I.C.S.: 424410
Kevin Smith *(Gen Mgr)*

Advantage Sales & Marketing, LLC - Woodcliff Lake   (2)
123 Tice Blvd Ste 300, Woodcliff Lake, NJ 07677
Tel.: (201) 825-9400
Web Site: http://www.asmnet.com
Sales Range: $450-499.9 Million
Sales & Marketing Services for the Consumer Packaged Goods Industry
N.A.I.C.S.: 541613
Karen Pitts *(Mgr-Safety)*

Subsidiary (Domestic):

Sage Tree LLC   (2)
931 W 75th St Suite 137-#103, Naperville, IL 60565   (100%)
Tel.: (630) 862-9969
Web Site: http://www.sagetreellc.com
Emp.: 80
Ecommerce Services & Solutions
N.A.I.C.S.: 561499
Ian Haldimann *(Principal)*
Robb Powell *(Principal)*
John DiSanza *(VP-Sls)*

StoreBoard Media LLC   (2)
360 Lexington Ave 19th Fl, New York, NY 10017
Tel.: (212) 682-3300
Web Site: http://www.storeboards.net
Sales Range: $1-9.9 Million
Emp.: 10
Advertising Agencies
N.A.I.C.S.: 541810
Melissa Gerard Ross *(Sr Acct Dir)*
Charlie Williams *(Exec VP)*
Caroline Kelso *(Dir-Ops)*

Tri-Venture Marketing LLC   (2)
2525 Drane Field Rd Ste 1 & 2, Lakeland, FL 33811
Tel.: (863) 648-1881
Sales Range: $10-24.9 Million
Emp.: 52
Bond Brokers
N.A.I.C.S.: 424410
E. Eugene Giddens *(CEO)*
Rita Ann Sveum *(Mgr-Customer Svc)*
Matthew J. Dahl *(Mgr-Fin)*
Ken Barnes *(Sls Mgr)*
Jeff White *(Pres)*

Upshot Inc.   (2)
350 N Orleans 5th Fl, Chicago, IL 60654
Tel.: (312) 943-0900
Web Site: http://www.upshot.agency
Emp.: 170
Advertising & Public Relations Agency
N.A.I.C.S.: 541810
Brian Kristofek *(Pres & CEO)*
Brock Montgomery *(Exec VP-Creative Svcs)*
Kate May *(CFO & Sr VP-Fin & Admin)*
Scott Fujii *(Sr VP-Production)*
Ellen Slauson *(Exec VP-Acct Mgmt)*
Bill Fogarty *(VP-Creative)*
Kristie Ritchie *(VP-New Bus & Comm)*
Lionel Knight *(Sr VP-Plng)*
Brian Priest *(Sr VP-Creative)*
Kelly Gribben *(VP & Creative Dir)*

AerSale Holdings, Inc.   (1)
121 Alhambra Plz Ste 1700, Coral Gables, FL 33134
Tel.: (305) 764-3200
Web Site: http://www.aersale.com
Holding Company: Aircraft Engine Parts Mfr
N.A.I.C.S.: 551112
Nicolas Finazzo *(Chm)*
Bill Kmiotek *(VP-Global Aircraft Trading)*
Craig Wright *(VP-Aircraft Acq & Mktg)*
Tom Mcfarland *(VP-Engine Trading)*
Dwayne Adcock *(VP-Airframe Sls)*
Bill Thompson *(Sr VP-Matls)*
Iso Nezaj *(CTO)*
Ron Wolf *(VP-Ops & Quality Assurance)*
Dennis A. Zalupski *(Sr VP & Gen Mgr-Matls Grp)*
Steven Boecker *(VP-Sls)*
David Settergren *(VP-Sls-Asia Pacific)*
Charles P. McDonald *(Sr VP-MRO Svcs)*
Basil Barimo *(COO)*

Subsidiary (Domestic):

AerSale, Inc.   (2)

LEONARD GREEN & PARTNERS, L.P.

Leonard Green & Partners, L.P.—(Continued)

255 Alhambra Cir Ste 435, Coral Gables, FL 33134
Tel.: (305) 764-3200
Web Site: http://www.aersale.com
Aircraft Equipment Leasing Services
N.A.I.C.S.: 532411
Nicolas Finazzo *(Chm & CEO)*
James A. Fry *(Gen Counsel, Sec & Exec VP)*
Martin Garmendia *(CFO)*
Kevin Hill *(VP-Powerplant Ops)*
Vanessa Machado *(Sr VP-HR)*
Robert Nichols *(Vice Chm)*
Ron Wolf *(Sr VP-Ops & Quality Assurance)*
Craig Wright *(Pres-Aircraft & Engine Mgmt)*
Enrique Pizzi *(CIO)*

Subsidiary (Non-US):

AerSale Aviation, Ltd. (3)
3rd Floor Block E Iveagh Court Harcourt Road, Dublin, 2, Ireland
Tel.: (353) 1 4753000
Web Site: http://www.aersale.com
Aviation Part Mfr
N.A.I.C.S.: 336412
Aidan Harrison *(Gen Mgr)*

AerSale Singapore
883 North Bridge Road South Bank 0903, Singapore, 198785, Singapore
Tel.: (65) 6291 2064
Aircraft Equipment Mfr
N.A.I.C.S.: 336412

Subsidiary (Domestic):

Great Southwest Aviation, Inc. (3)
100 Southwest Way, Roswell, NM 88203
Tel.: (575) 347-2054
Web Site: http://www.greatsouthwestaviation.com
Sales Range: $1-9.9 Million
Emp.: 45
Aircraft Services
N.A.I.C.S.: 488119

Qwest Air Parts, Inc. (3)
4400 Delp St, Memphis, TN 38118
Tel.: (901) 797-9229
Web Site: http://www.qwestairparts.com
Aircraft Parts Distr
N.A.I.C.S.: 336413
Gary Jones *(Pres, CEO & Founder)*
Mark Penna *(VP)*

Arrow Group Industries, Inc. (1)
1680 Rte 23 N, Wayne, NJ 07474
Tel.: (973) 696-6900
Web Site: http://www.arrowsheds.com
Sales Range: $25-49.9 Million
Emp.: 40
Steel, Aluminum & Wood Outdoor Storage Buildings Mfr
N.A.I.C.S.: 332311

Authentic Brands Group LLC (1)
100 W 33rd St Ste 1007, New York, NY 10001
Tel.: (212) 760-2410
Web Site: http://www.authenticbrandsgroup.com
Emp.: 70
Brand Developement & Licensing
N.A.I.C.S.: 533110
Jamie Salter *(Founder, Chm & CEO)*
Nick Woodhouse *(Pres & CMO)*
Kevin Clarke *(CFO)*
Monica Nahum *(VP-Bus Dev-Latin America)*
Matthew Goldstein *(Sr VP-Entertainment & Special Projects)*
Marc Rosen *(Pres-Entertainment)*

Subsidiary (Domestic):

Boardriders, Inc. (2)
5600 Argosy Cir Bldg 100, Huntington Beach, CA 92649
Tel.: (714) 889-5650
Web Site: http://www.boardriders.com
Beachwear, Skiwear, Casual Sportswear, Swimwear & Snow & Skate Apparel Mfr, Designer & Distr
N.A.I.C.S.: 424350
Shannan North *(Pres-Comml Strategy & Growth)*
Mark Weber *(Gen Mgr-Billabong Men's Div-Global)*
Katie Singer *(Gen Mgr-Billabong Women's Div-Global)*
Dan Levine *(Gen Mgr-Street Div-Global)*
David Brooks *(Gen Mgr-Partnerships & Distr-Global)*
Nate Smith *(Pres-Americas)*
Nicolas Foulet *(Pres-Europe, Middle East & Africa)*
Stacy Reece *(Chief Digital Officer)*
Arne Arens *(CEO)*
Francis Roy *(CFO-Global)*
Jennifer Marques *(Chief HR Officer)*
Garry Wall *(Gen Mgr-Quiksilver-Global)*
Maryn Miller *(Gen Counsel-Global)*

Subsidiary (Non-US):

Billabong International Limited (3)
5 Billabong Place, Burleigh Heads, 4220, QLD, Australia
Tel.: (61) 755899899
Web Site: https://www.billabong.com.au
Sales Range: $750-799.9 Million
Surfwear, Accessories & Action Sports Apparel Mfr
N.A.I.C.S.: 424350
Shannan North *(Pres-Brand Billabong-Global)*

Subsidiary (US):

Element Skateboards, Inc. (4)
121 Waterworks Way Ste 100, Irvine, CA 92618
Tel.: (949) 753-7222
Web Site: http://us.elementbrand.com
Skateboards Mfr
N.A.I.C.S.: 339920
Johnny Schillereff *(Founder)*

Honolua Surf Co. International Ltd. (4)
121 Waterworks Way Ste 100, Irvine, CA 92618
Tel.: (949) 753-7222
Web Site: http://www.honoluasurf.com
Men's & Women's Casual Clothing
N.A.I.C.S.: 458110

RVCA Corporation (4)
960 W 16th St, Costa Mesa, CA 92627
Tel.: (949) 548-6223
Web Site: http://www.rvca.com
Clothing Mfr
N.A.I.C.S.: 315250
Patrick M. Tenore *(Founder)*

VeeZee, Inc (4)
121 Waterworks Way Ste 100, Irvine, CA 92618
Web Site: http://us.vonzipper.com
Sunglasses, Goggles, Accessories & Soft Goods Mfr
N.A.I.C.S.: 339920

Subsidiary (Non-US):

Boardriders Club Bratislava s.r.o. (3)
Ivanska cesta 5740/16, 82104, Bratislava, Slovakia
Tel.: (421) 243637250
Sporting Goods Retailer
N.A.I.C.S.: 459110

Boardriders Japan Co., Ltd. (3)
6-27-8 Jingumae, Shibuya-ku, Tokyo, 150-0001, Japan
Tel.: (81) 120329190
Web Site: https://www.quiksilver.co.jp
Mfr, Designer & Distr of Beachwear, Skiwear, Casual Sportswear, Swimwear & Snow & Skate Apparel for Young Men & Women
N.A.I.C.S.: 315250

Subsidiary (Domestic):

DC Shoes, Inc. (3)
5600 Argosy Cir Bldg #100, Huntington Beach, CA 92649
Tel.: (714) 889-2200
Web Site: http://www.dcshoes.com
Apparel & Footwear Products Mfr & Distr
N.A.I.C.S.: 315990

Subsidiary (Non-US):

Emerald Coast SAS (3)
162 Rue Belharra, 64500, Saint-Jean-de-Luz, France
Tel.: (33) 559515757
Web Site: http://www.dcshoes.fr

Apparel & Footwear Products Mfr & Distr
N.A.I.C.S.: 315990

Kokolo SAS (3)
Tel.: (33) 559477373
Web Site: http://www.kokolo.com
Textile & Apparel Products Printing Services
N.A.I.C.S.: 323113

Omareef Spain SL (3)
Calle Simon De Otxandetegui 99, 48640, Berango, Spain
Tel.: (34) 946681552
Web Site: http://www.omareef-spain.pymes.com
Sporting Goods Retailer
N.A.I.C.S.: 459110

PT Quiksilver Indonesia (3)
JL Raya No 362 Legian Kuta Badung Regency, Bali, 80361, Indonesia
Tel.: (62) 361751214
Mfr, Designer & Distr of Beachwear, Skiwear, Casual Sportswear, Swimwear & Snow & Skate Apparel for Young Men & Women
N.A.I.C.S.: 315250

PT Quiksilver Indonesia (3)
Jl Raya No 362 Legian Kuta Kabupaten Badung, Jakarta, 80361, Indonesia
Tel.: (62) 361751214
Mfr, Designer & Distr of Beachwear, Skiwear, Casual Sportswear, Swimwear & Snow & Skate Apparel for Young Men & Women
N.A.I.C.S.: 315990

Quiksilver Asia Sourcing Ltd. (3)
Shop UG12-15 Upper Ground Floor Kowloon City Plaza 128 Carpenter Road, Kowloon, China (Hong Kong)
Tel.: (852) 28955058
Web Site: http://www.quiksilver.hk
Textile & Apparel Products Whslr
N.A.I.C.S.: 458110

Quiksilver Australia Pty Ltd. (3)
27 Baines Cres, Torquay, 3228, VIC, Australia
Tel.: (61) 352616000
Web Site: http://www.quiksilver.com.au
Mfr, Designer & Distr of Beachwear, Skiwear, Casual Sportswear, Swimwear & Snow & Skate Apparel for Young Men & Women
N.A.I.C.S.: 315250

Quiksilver Europe (3)
162 Rue Belharra, 64500, Saint-Jean-de-Luz, France
Tel.: (33) 977556959
Web Site: http://www.quiksilver.com
Mfr, Designer & Distributor of Beachwear, Skiwear, Casual Sportswear, Swimwear & Snow & Skate Apparel for Young Men & Women
N.A.I.C.S.: 315250

Subsidiary (Domestic):

Quiksilver Eyewear, USA (3)
15202 Graham St, Huntington Beach, CA 92649
Tel.: (714) 889-2200
Mfr, Designer & Distr of Beachwear, Skiwear, Casual Sportswear, Swimwear & Snow & Skate Apparel for Young Men & Women
N.A.I.C.S.: 315250

Subsidiary (Domestic):

Eddie Bauer, Inc. (2)
10401 NE 8th St Ste 500, Bellevue, WA 98004
Tel.: (425) 755-6544
Web Site: http://www.eddiebauer.com
Sales Range: $150-199.9 Million
Emp.: 500
Men's & Women's Casual Clothing, Gear, Accessories & Footwear Mfr, Sales & Mail Order
N.A.I.C.S.: 424350
Michael Egeck *(CEO & Pres)*
Daniel E. Templin *(CFO & COO)*
Steve Venegas *(VP-Distr-North America)*

Joint Venture (Non-US):

Eddie Bauer Japan, Inc. (3)
16-9 Nihonbashi Hakozaki-cho, Chuo-Ku, Tokyo, 103-0015, Japan
Tel.: (81) 354312881
Web Site: http://www.eddiebauer.co.jp
Sales Range: $75-99.9 Million
Mail Order Catalog Services; Owned 30% by Eddie Bauer Inc. & 70% by OTTO Japan Inc.
N.A.I.C.S.: 459110

Joint Venture (Domestic):

Forever 21, Inc. (2)
2001 S Alameda St, Los Angeles, CA 90058 (37.5%)
Tel.: (213) 741-5100
Web Site: http://www.forever21.com
Sales Range: $1-4.9 Billion
Emp.: 6,000
Women's Apparel & Accessories
N.A.I.C.S.: 458110
Don W. Chang *(Founder & Pres)*
Jin Sook Chang *(Founder)*
Daniel Kulle *(CEO)*
Winnie Y. Park *(CEO)*

Subsidiary (Domestic):

Reebok International Ltd. (2)
1895 JW Foster Blvd, Canton, MA 02021-1099
Tel.: (781) 401-5000
Web Site: http://www.reebok.com
Sales Range: $1-4.9 Billion
Emp.: 9,102
Mfr, Distr & Marketer of Footwear & Athletic Apparel
N.A.I.C.S.: 316210
Sharon Bryan *(COO)*
Todd Krinsky *(Gen Mgr-Reebok Performance Bus Unit)*
Matt O'Toole *(Pres)*

Subsidiary (Domestic):

OnField Apparel Group LLC (3)
8677 Logo Athletic Ct, Indianapolis, IN 46219-1430
Tel.: (317) 895-7000
Web Site: http://www.reebok.com
Sales Range: $150-199.9 Million
Emp.: 1,000
Mfr & Distr of Licensed Sports Apparel
N.A.I.C.S.: 339920

RBK Thailand, Inc. (3)
1895 J W Foster Blvd, Canton, MA 02021-1099
Tel.: (781) 401-5000
Footwear Whslr
N.A.I.C.S.: 424340

RFC, Inc. (3)
1105 N Market St, Wilmington, DE 19801-1216
Tel.: (302) 427-2512
Sporting Goods Distr
N.A.I.C.S.: 423910

Subsidiary (Non-US):

Reebok India Company (3)
5th Floor Unitech Commercial Tower-II Block B Greenwood City Sector 45, Gurgaon, 122001, Haryana, India
Tel.: (91) 1244124100
Sporting & Athletic Goods Distr
N.A.I.C.S.: 423910
Silvia Tallon *(Sr Mng Dir)*

Reebok Jofa AB (3)
Box 66, 782 22, Malung, Sweden
Tel.: (46) 280 444 00
Web Site: http://www.jofa.se
Sporting Equipment Distr
N.A.I.C.S.: 423910
Janne Heino *(Gen Mgr)*

Reebok Jofa AS (3)
Pancoveien 26, 1624, Gressvik, Norway
Tel.: (47) 69 36 45 55
Web Site: http://www.reebokhockey.com
Sporting & Athletic Goods Whslr
N.A.I.C.S.: 423910

Reebok Produtos Esportivos Brasil Ltda.
Rua do Retiro 1371 / Bl 2 Ap 73 - Jardim Paris, Jundiai, Sao Paulo, Brazil
Tel.: (55) 1145224087
Sporting Goods Mfr

COMPANIES
LEONARD GREEN & PARTNERS, L.P.

N.A.I.C.S.: 339920

Reebok de Mexico, S.A. de C.V. (3)
Blvd Adolfo Ruiz Cortinez No 3642 Piso 11
Jardines Del Pedregal, Alvaro Obregon,
Mexico, 1900, Mexico
Tel.: (52) 5554818100
Sporting & Athletic Goods Distr
N.A.I.C.S.: 423910

Reebok-CCM Hockey GmbH (3)
Klausnerring 26, Heimstetten, 85551, Germany
Tel.: (49) 89 990 2250
Sales Range: $25-49.9 Million
Emp.: 15
Sports Equipment & Apparel Mfr & Distr
N.A.I.C.S.: 339920

Reebok-CCM Hockey Oy (3)
Bertel Jungin aukio 5, Espoo, 02600, Finland
Tel.: (358) 341421
Web Site: http://www.ccmhockey.com
Emp.: 10
Sporting Goods Distr
N.A.I.C.S.: 423910

Reebok-CCM Hockey, Inc. (3)
3400 Raymond Lasnier, Ville Saint Laurent,
H4R 3L3, QC, Canada
Tel.: (514) 461-8000
Web Site: http://www.ccmhockey.com
Sales Range: $200-249.9 Million
Emp.: 1,376
Sporting Goods & Equipment Mfr
N.A.I.C.S.: 339920

Subsidiary (Non-US):

Ted Baker Plc (2)
Ugly Brown Building 6a St Pancras Way,
London, NW1 0TB, United Kingdom
Tel.: (44) 2072554800
Web Site: http://www.tedbaker.com
Rev.: $581,430,013
Assets: $461,456,443
Liabilities: $298,003,247
Net Worth: $163,453,195
Earnings: $48,313,108
Emp.: 3,622
Fiscal Year-end: 01/29/2022
Clothing Retailer
N.A.I.C.S.: 315990
Raymond Stuart Kelvin (Founder)
Jennifer Roebuck (Chief Customer Officer)
Helena Feltham (Interim Chm)
Rachel Osborne (CEO)
David Wolffe (CFO)
Anthony Cuthbertson (Creative Dir-Global)

Subsidiary (Non-US):

Ted Baker (France) Sarl (3)
20 Rue Des Francs Bourgeois, 75003,
Paris, France
Tel.: (33) 144540298
Sales Range: $25-49.9 Million
Emp.: 7
Family Clothing Stores
N.A.I.C.S.: 458110

Subsidiary (Domestic):

Ted Baker International Ltd (3)
The Ugly Brown Building 6A Saint Pancraf
Way, London, NW1 0TB, United Kingdom
Tel.: (44) 2072554800
Web Site: http://www.tedbaker.com
Sales Range: $100-124.9 Million
Emp.: 300
Apparel & Accessory Stores
N.A.I.C.S.: 315990

Ted Baker Limited (3)
1-4 Langley Court, WC2E9JY, London,
United Kingdom
Tel.: (44) 2074978862
Clothing Stores
N.A.I.C.S.: 458110

Subsidiary (Non-US):

Ted Baker Netherlands B.V. (3)
Leidsestraat 64, 1017 PD, Amsterdam,
Netherlands
Tel.: (31) 20 235 6716
Cloth Distr
N.A.I.C.S.: 458110

Subsidiary (Non-US):

Tretorn Sweden AB (2)
Garnisonsgatan 51, PO Box 931, Helsingborg, 251 09, Sweden
Tel.: (46) 42197100
Web Site: http://www.tretorn.com
Sales Range: $25-49.9 Million
Emp.: 30
Athletic Footwear & Tennis Balls Mfr
N.A.I.C.S.: 424340
Vivica Nilsson (Dir-Mktg)
Markus Vvonko (CEO)
Fredrik Ekstrom (Mgr-Comm)

BJ's Wholesale Club, Inc. (1)
25 Research Dr, Westborough, MA 01581
Tel.: (774) 512-7400
Web Site: http://www.bjs.com
Sales Range: $5-14.9 Billion
Emp.: 24,800
Warehouse Club Merchandising; Food &
General Merchandise
N.A.I.C.S.: 455211
Michael P. Atkinson (Sr VP & Dir-Mktg & E-Commerce)
Bruce L. Graham (Sr VP & Gen Mdse Mgr)
Gina M. Iacovone (Sr VP-Field Ops)
Jessica Newman (Mgr-Community Relations)
Scott Williams (Mgr-Product Dev & Quality Assurance)
Brendan Fitzgerald (Asst VP-Asset Protection Ops)
Christopher J. Baldwin (Chm)
Dawn Albright (Gen Mgr-New Summerville Club)
Naveen Seshadri (VP-Digital Commerce & Experience-Omnichannel)
John Weisert (Dir-Risk Mgmt)
Kristy Houston (Sr Dir-Corp Comm)
Faten Freiha (VP-IR)
Monica Schwartz (Chief Digital Officer & Sr VP)
Jennie Hardin (VP-Corp Comm)
Paul Ciohocki (Exec VP-Membership, Analytics & Bus Transformation)
Christopher J. Baldwin (Chm)
Robert W. Eddy (Interim CEO, Chief Admin & Fin Officer & Exec VP)

Subsidiary (Domestic):

BJ's Charitable Foundation Inc. (2)
1 Mercer Rd, Natick, MA 01760
Tel.: (508) 651-7400
Sales Range: $250-299.9 Million
Emp.: 2,000
Grantmaking Foundations
N.A.I.C.S.: 813211

CHG Healthcare Services, Inc. (1)
7259 S Bingham Junction Blvd, Midvale, UT 84047
Tel.: (801) 930-3000
Web Site: https://www.chghealthcare.com
Sales Range: $400-449.9 Million
Temporary & Permanent Healthcare Staffing Services
N.A.I.C.S.: 561311
Scott M. Beck (CEO)
Robert B. Millard (CFO)
Rob Millard (CFO)
Kerry Norman (Exec VP)
Bill Heller (Exec VP)

Subsidiary (Domestic):

CHG Management, Inc. (2)
7259 S Bingham Jct Blvd, Midvale, UT 84047
Tel.: (801) 930-3000
Web Site: http://www.chghealthcare.com
Sales Range: $125-149.9 Million
Healthcare Employment Services
N.A.I.C.S.: 561311
Mike Weinholtz (CEO)

Subsidiary (Domestic):

CHG Medical Staffing, Inc. (3)
4700 Exchange Ct Ste 125, Boca Raton, FL 33431
Tel.: (561) 862-0011
Web Site: https://www.rnnetwork.com
Sales Range: $10-24.9 Million
Emp.: 100
Nursing Staffing Services
N.A.I.C.S.: 561311

Eric Darienzo (Pres)
Ann Smith (Mgr-Admin)

CompHealth Associates, Inc. (3)
7259 S Bingham Jct Blvd, Midvale, UT 84047
Tel.: (801) 930-3000
Web Site: http://www.comphealth.com
Sales Range: $25-49.9 Million
Emp.: 1,400
Physician Recruiters
N.A.I.C.S.: 541612
Scott Beck (CEO)

Weatherby Healthcare (3)
6451 N Federal Hwy Ste 700, Fort Lauderdale, FL 33308
Tel.: (954) 343-3050
Web Site: https://www.weatherbyhealthcare.com
Sales Range: $10-24.9 Million
Emp.: 100
Physician Staffing Services
N.A.I.C.S.: 561311
Michael DePaolis (Sr VP)
Bev Leonard (Sr VP)
Warren Wooley (Sr VP)
Luke Woodyard (Pres)

Subsidiary (Domestic):

Global Medical Staffing Limited, Inc. (2)
7259 Bingham Jct Blvd, Midvale, UT 84047
Tel.: (801) 365-0303
Web Site: https://www.gmedical.com
Emp.: 70
Medical Staffing Services
N.A.I.C.S.: 561320

Charter NEX Films, Inc. (1)
1246 E High St, Milton, WI 53563
Tel.: (608) 868-5757
Web Site: http://charternex.com
Specialty Films Mfr
N.A.I.C.S.: 325992
Kathy Bolhous (CEO)

ExamWorks Group, Inc. (1)
3280 Peachtree Rd NE Ste 2625, Atlanta, GA 30305
Tel.: (404) 952-2400
Web Site: http://www.examworks.com
Holding Company; Independent Medical Examinations, Peer & Bill Reviews & Related Services
N.A.I.C.S.: 551112
James K. Price (Co-Founder)
Wesley Campbell (Co-CEO)
Clare Y. Arguedas (Gen Counsel, Sec & Exec VP)
Robert C. Porter (Chief Medical Officer)
Miguel Fernandez de Castro (Co-CEO)
Juanita M. Biasini (Exec VP-HR)
Brian K. Kenton (CTO)
J. Miguel Fernandez de Castro (Co-CEO & CFO)
Richard E. Perlman (Co-Founder & Co-Exec Chm)
James K. Price (Co-Founder)
Jacob J. Ferro Jr. (CIO, CTO & Exec VP)

Subsidiary (Non-US):

Capital Vocational Specialists (2)
2781 Lancaster Road Suite 304, Ottawa, K1B 1A7, ON, Canada
Tel.: (613) 736-9117
Web Site: http://www.cvs.ca
Medical & Rehabilitation Services
N.A.I.C.S.: 624310
Stuart Jolliffe (Gen Mgr)

Subsidiary (Domestic):

ExamWorks Clinical Solutions, LLC (2)
2397 Huntcrest Way Ste 200, Lawrenceville, GA 30043
Tel.: (866) 270-2516
Web Site: http://www.examworks-cs.com
Medical Claim Case Management & Cost Containment Services
N.A.I.C.S.: 561499
Kevin Mahoney (COO)
Ken Loffredo (CEO)
Christie Britt (Sr VP)
Martin R. Cassavoy (VP-Medicare Secondary Payer Compliance-Woburn)

Examworks Group, Inc. (2)
4141 Southwest Fwy Ste 500, Houston, TX 77027
Tel.: (800) 761-1177
Web Site: http://www.examworks.com
Diagnostic Imaging Services
N.A.I.C.S.: 621512

Examworks Group, Inc. (2)
4 Becker Farm Rd 1st Fl, Roseland, NJ 07068-1739
Web Site: http://www.examworks.com
Medical Examination Services
N.A.I.C.S.: 541990

MES Solutions (2)
150 Presidential Way Ste 110, Woburn, MA 01801
Tel.: (781) 933-1782
Web Site: http://www.messolutions.com
Medical Examination Services
N.A.I.C.S.: 621999
Donna Walthall (Mgr-Peer Review)

MLS Group of Companies, LLC (2)
20570 Civic Ctr Dr Ste 600, Southfield, MI 48034-1097
Tel.: (888) 657-4634
Web Site: http://www.mls-ime.com
Medical Examination Services
N.A.I.C.S.: 621999
Amanda Horvath (Dir-Provider Rels)

Subsidiary (Non-US):

Matrix Health Management Corp. (2)
5025 Orbitor Drive Building #5 Suite #400, Mississauga, L4W 4Y5, ON, Canada
Tel.: (905) 624-2900
Web Site: http://matrixhealth.ca
Medical Examination Services
N.A.I.C.S.: 541990
Rafael Chow (Dir-Medical)
Carla Everts (Pres)

MedHealth Pty Limited (2)
Level 10 451 Little Bourke Street, Melbourne, 3000, VIC, Australia
Tel.: (61) 386889388
Web Site: http://www.medhealthgroup.com.au
Emp.: 1,000
Data Management Services
N.A.I.C.S.: 561410
Tim Morphy (CEO & Dir)
David Thompson (CFO)
Rob Jackson (Sec & Dir-Governance)
Sue Green (Dir-Consultant Svcs)

Subsidiary (Domestic):

Medicolegal Services, LLC (2)
20300 W 12 Mile Rd Ste 201, Southfield, MI 48076
Tel.: (248) 352-6747
Web Site: http://www.medicolegal-mi.com
Emp.: 12
Medical Examination Services
N.A.I.C.S.: 621999

Prizm LLC (2)
10 E Stow Rd Ste 100, Marlton, NJ 08053
Tel.: (856) 596-5600
Web Site: http://www.prizmllc.com
Medical & Insurance Claim Management Software & Services
N.A.I.C.S.: 513210
Linda Diekmann (Pres & CEO)

Subsidiary (Non-US):

SOMA Medical Assessments Corp. (2)
8800 Dufferin Street Suite 105, Vaughan, L4K 0C5, ON, Canada
Tel.: (905) 881-8855
Web Site: http://www.somamedical.com
Medical Examination Services
N.A.I.C.S.: 541990
Mark Wigle (Pres)
Delissa Burke (VP-Ops & Client Svcs)
George Georgiou (VP-Bus Dev)

UK Independent Medical Services Limited (2)
Brenner House Rainton Bridge Business Park, Houghton le Spring, DH4 5RA, United Kingdom
Tel.: (44) 3334141988
Web Site: http://www.ukindmed.com

LEONARD GREEN & PARTNERS, L.P. — U.S. PRIVATE

Leonard Green & Partners, L.P.—(Continued)

Medical Examination Services
N.A.I.C.S.: 541990
Paul Healey *(Chm)*
Paul Gray *(Dir-Fin)*
Lauren Scanlan *(Mgr-Ops)*
Allan Totty *(Mgr-IT)*
Jim Wood *(Head-Expert Liaison)*
Jillian Potts *(Mgr-Medical Expert Liaison)*
Chris Nairns *(Mng Dir)*

direct IME Corp. (2)
3760 14th Avenue Suite 201, Markham,
L3R 3T7, ON, Canada
Tel.: (416) 609-3211
Web Site: http://www.directime.ca
Health Care Srvices
N.A.I.C.S.: 621999

J.Crew Group, Inc. (1)
225 Liberty St, New York, NY 10281
Tel.: (203) 682-8200
Web Site: https://www.jcrew.com
Rev.: $2,483,994,000
Assets: $1,221,651,000
Liabilities: $2,493,894,000
Net Worth: ($1,272,243,000)
Earnings: ($120,079,000)
Emp.: 4,300
Fiscal Year-end: 02/02/2019
Clothing & Clothing Accessories Retailers
N.A.I.C.S.: 458110
Lynda Markoe *(Chief Admin Officer)*
Libby Wadle *(CEO)*
Michael J. Nicholson *(Pres & COO)*
Vincent Zanna *(CFO & Treas)*
Kevin Ulrich *(Chm)*
Brendon Babenzien *(Creative Dir-Men)*

Subsidiary (Domestic):

J. Crew Operating Corp. (2)
770 Broadway, New York, NY 10003
Tel.: (212) 209-2500
Web Site: http://www.jcrew.com
Clothing Retailer
N.A.I.C.S.: 458110

Subsidiary (Domestic):

Grace Holmes, Inc. (3)
770 Broadway, New York, NY 10003
Tel.: (212) 209-2500
Web Site: http://www.jcrew.com
Sales Range: $100-124.9 Million
Clothing Retailer
N.A.I.C.S.: 458110
James S. Scully *(CFO & Exec VP)*

J. Crew Virginia, Inc. (3)
770 Broadway, New York, NY 10003
Tel.: (212) 209-2500
Web Site: http://www.jcrew.com
Sales Range: $100-124.9 Million
Clothing Retailer
N.A.I.C.S.: 458110

J. Crew, Inc. (3)
770 Broadway, New York, NY 10003
Tel.: (434) 385-5775
Web Site: http://www.jcrew.com
Sales Range: $100-124.9 Million
Clothing Retailer
N.A.I.C.S.: 458110
Leigh Kohlhaas *(Mgr-Loss Prevention Ops)*

Subsidiary (Domestic):

J. Crew International, Inc. (4)
770 Broadway, New York, NY 10003
Tel.: (212) 209-2500
Web Site: http://www.jcrew.org
Sales Range: $100-124.9 Million
Emp.: 1,000
Clothing Retailer
N.A.I.C.S.: 458110
Heather Lynch McAuliffe *(Sr Dir-PR)*

Subsidiary (Domestic):

Madewell, Inc. (3)
770 Broadway, New York, NY 10003
Tel.: (212) 209-2500
Web Site: http://www.madewell1937.com
Sales Range: $100-124.9 Million
Clothing Retailer
N.A.I.C.S.: 458110
Joyce Lee *(Head-Women's Design)*

Jo-Ann Stores, Inc. (1)
5555 Darrow Rd, Hudson, OH 44236
Tel.: (330) 735-6576
Web Site: http://www.joann.com
Sales Range: $1-4.9 Billion
Emp.: 21,453
Craft & Hobby Goods Retailer
N.A.I.C.S.: 459130
Kevin Beegle *(Dir-Real Estate-Natl)*
Jeff Csuy *(Sr VP & Gen Mgr-Mdse, Fabric, and Sewing)*
Sharyn Hejcl *(Chief Mdsp Officer & Exec VP)*

Subsidiary (Domestic):

Jo-Ann Stores Supply Chain Management, Inc. (2)
5555 Darrow Rd, Hudson, OH 44236 (100%)
Tel.: (330) 650-6228
Web Site: http://www.joann.com
Sales Range: $150-199.9 Million
Emp.: 1,110
Provider of Logistics Services
N.A.I.C.S.: 541614

Team Jo-Ann Stores, Inc. (2)
5555 Darrow Rd, Hudson, OH 44236 (100%)
Tel.: (330) 656-2600
Web Site: http://www.joann.com
Sales Range: $450-499.9 Million
Emp.: 1,000
Business Services
N.A.I.C.S.: 561499
Tom Williams *(Mgr-HR)*

Leslie's Poolmart, Inc. (1)
2005 E Indian School Rd, Phoenix, AZ 85016 (75%)
Tel.: (602) 366-3999
Web Site: http://www.lesliespool.com
Sales Range: $500-549.9 Million
Emp.: 2,280
Swimming Pools, Large Fish Tanks & Related Products Retailer
N.A.I.C.S.: 459999
Michael R. Egeck *(CEO)*
Mike Africa *(Chief Digital Officer)*
Scott Bowman *(CFO)*
Dave Caspers *(Chief Stores Officer)*
Naomi Cramer *(Chief People Officer)*
Brad Gazaway *(Chief Legal Officer)*

Subsidiary (Domestic):

Cortz, Inc. (2)
320 Industrial Dr, West Chicago, IL 60185
Tel.: (630) 876-1080
Web Site: https://www.intheswim.com
Retailer of Pool & Spa Supplies
N.A.I.C.S.: 423910
Ryan Abud *(Dir-IT)*

Life Time Fitness, Inc. (1)
2902 Corporate Pl, Chanhassen, MN 55317
Tel.: (952) 947-0000
Web Site: http://www.lifetimefitness.com
Sales Range: $1-4.9 Billion
Holding Company; Fitness Centers Operator
N.A.I.C.S.: 551112
Bahram Akradi *(CEO)*
Jeffrey G. Zwiefel *(COO)*
Tom Bergman *(CFO & Exec VP)*
Jason Thunstrom *(VP-Corp Comm & PR)*
Natalie Bushaw *(Dir-PR)*
Riley McLaughlin *(Coord-PR)*

Subsidiary (Domestic):

ChronoTrack Systems Corp. (2)
111 E Diamond Ave, Evansville, IN 47711
Tel.: (812) 423-7800
Web Site: http://www.chronotrack.com
Electric Equipment Mfr
N.A.I.C.S.: 334511

Subsidiary (Non-US):

ChronoTrack Systems Europe B.V. (3)
Zuidergracht 21-21, Soest, 3763, Netherlands
Tel.: (31) 357510872
Web Site: http://www.chronotrack.com
Electric Equipment Mfr
N.A.I.C.S.: 334511
Jeroen Van Zuilen *(Dir)*

Subsidiary (Domestic):

Life Time Fitness - Bloomingdale (2)
455 Scott Dr, Bloomingdale, IL 60108
Tel.: (630) 582-4100
Web Site: http://www.lifetimefitness.com
Fitness Center Operator
N.A.I.C.S.: 713940

Life Time Fitness - Chanhassen (2)
2902 Corporate Pl, Chanhassen, MN 55317-4560
Tel.: (952) 380-0303
Web Site: http://www.lifetimefitness.com
Physical Fitness Facility Services
N.A.I.C.S.: 713940

Lucky Brand Dungarees, Inc. (1)
540 S Santa Fe Ave, Los Angeles, CA 90013
Tel.: (323) 282-4100
Web Site: http://www.luckybrandjeans.com
Sales Range: $25-49.9 Million
Emp.: 200
Apparel & Accessories Mfr & Distr
N.A.I.C.S.: 315990
Matthew A. Kaness *(Interim Chm & CEO)*

Subsidiary (Domestic):

Lucky Brand Dungarees, Inc. (2)
5233 Alcoa Ave, Vernon, CA 90058
Tel.: (323) 282-4100
Apparel & Accessories Mfr & Distr
N.A.I.C.S.: 315990

MSHC, Inc. (1)
214 N Tryon Ste 2425, Charlotte, NC 28202
Tel.: (980) 859-3660
Web Site: http://www.servicelogic.com
Energy & HVAC/Mechanical Services
N.A.I.C.S.: 238220
Craig Steinke *(CEO)*
Tim Riedel *(Pres)*

Subsidiary (Domestic):

Huckestein Mechanical Services, Inc. (2)
1505 Metropolitan St, Pittsburgh, PA 15233
Tel.: (412) 678-5900
Web Site: http://www.huckestein.com
HVAC Service Repair & Replacement & Design Build Projects
N.A.I.C.S.: 238910
Wendy P. Staso *(Pres & CEO)*

Nautica Enterprises, Inc. (1)
40 W 57th St Fl 3, New York, NY 10019-4001
Web Site: http://www.nautica.com
Active Wear & Sportswear Mfr
N.A.I.C.S.: 315250
Karen Murray *(Pres)*

Subsidiary (Domestic):

Nautica Apparel, Inc. (2)
40 W 57th St St Fl, New York, NY 10019
Tel.: (646) 264-6200
Web Site: http://www.nautica.com
Apparels Mfr
N.A.I.C.S.: 315250
Karen Murray *(Pres & CEO)*

Nautica Retail USA, Inc. (2)
40 W 57th St 8th Fl, New York, NY 10019
Tel.: (646) 264-6200
Web Site: http://www.nautica.com
Men Clothing & Accessories Whslr
N.A.I.C.S.: 458110

Pace Analytical Services, LLC (1)
1800 Elm St SE, Minneapolis, MN 55414
Tel.: (612) 607-6400
Web Site: http://www.pacelabs.com
Emp.: 3,300
Analytical Laboratory Testing Services
N.A.I.C.S.: 541380
Greg Whitman *(Pres)*
Gregory D. Kupp *(Pres-Pace Life Sciences)*
Judith Morgan *(Chief Compliance- / Trng - Officer, VP & &)*
Nicole Ott *(VP-HR)*
Eric Roman *(Pres & CEO)*
Nisheet Gupta *(CFO & Exec VP)*
Eric Roman *(CEO)*

Subsidiary (Domestic):

Aqua Protech Laboratories, Inc. (2)
1275 Bloomfield Ave Ste 6, Fairfield, NJ 07004
Tel.: (973) 227-0422
Web Site: http://www.aquaprotechlabs.com
Sales Range: $1-9.9 Million
Emp.: 48
Research & Development in the Physical, Engineering & Life Sciences
N.A.I.C.S.: 541715
Robert Barrett *(COO)*

Con-Test Analytical Laboratory (2)
39 Spruce St 2, East Longmeadow, MA 01028
Tel.: (413) 525-2332
Web Site: http://www.contestlabs.com
Testing Laboratories
N.A.I.C.S.: 541380
Stephen Beek *(Mgr-Bus Dev)*
Paul Konnik *(Mgr)*
Theresa Ferrentino *(Mgr)*
Thomas Veratti Jr. *(Pres & Gen Mgr)*

Continental Analytical Services, Inc. (2)
525 N 8th St, Salina, KS 67401
Tel.: (785) 827-1273
Web Site: http://www.cas-lab.com
Sales Range: $1-9.9 Million
Emp.: 30
Provider of Analytical Testing of Drinking Water, Waste Water, Solid & Hazardous Waste, Sludge & Soil for Government Agencies
N.A.I.C.S.: 541715
Clifford Baker *(Mgr-Technical)*
Petra Craddock *(Project Mgr)*
Greg Groene *(Mgr-Project Mgmt)*

Emerson Resources, Inc. (2)
600 Markley St, Norristown, PA 19401
Tel.: (610) 279-7450
Web Site: http://www.emersonresources.com
Rev.: $6,200,000
Emp.: 55
Testing Laboratories
N.A.I.C.S.: 541380
John Signorino *(Sr VP-Ops)*
Aaron Barkley *(Sr VP-Bus Dev)*
Joel Shea *(Dir-Bus Dev)*

Environmental Chemistry Consulting Services, Inc. (2)
2525 Advance Rd, Madison, WI 53718
Tel.: (608) 221-8700
Web Site: http://www.eccsmobilelab.com
Testing Laboratory
N.A.I.C.S.: 541380
Nick K. Nigro *(Pres)*

Environmental Science Corp. (2)
12065 Lebanon Rd, Mount Juliet, TN 37122
Tel.: (615) 758-5858
Web Site: http://www.esclabsciences.com
Testing Laboratories
N.A.I.C.S.: 541715
Peter Schulert *(CEO)*

Pace Analytical Life Sciences LLC (2)
1311 Helomo Ave N, Oakdale, MN 55128
Tel.: (651) 738-2728
Pharmaceuticals Product Mfr
N.A.I.C.S.: 325412
Gregory Kupp *(VP & CEO-Life Sciences)*

Subsidiary (Domestic):

Bio-Concept Laboratories, Inc (3)
13 Industrial Way, Salem, NH 03079
Tel.: (603) 893-7240
Web Site: http://www.bioconcept.com
Rev.: $2,300,000
Emp.: 20
Research & Development in Biotechnology
N.A.I.C.S.: 541714
Francis Smith *(Pres & CEO)*
Matthew L. Fontaine *(Controller)*

Velesco Pharmaceutical Services LLC (3)
46701 N Commerce Ctr Dr Ste A 8, Plymouth, MI 48170-2475
Tel.: (734) 527-9125
Web Site: http://www.velescopharma.com
Research & Development in Biotechnology
N.A.I.C.S.: 541714
David Barnes *(CEO)*

COMPANIES

Unit (Domestic):

Pace Analytical Services, Inc. - Asheville Environmental Laboratory (2)
2225 Riverside Dr, Asheville, NC 28804-3637
Tel.: (828) 254-7176
Web Site: http://www.pacelabs.com
Sales Range: $10-24.9 Million
Emp.: 25
Inorganic & Aquatic Toxicity Analytical Laboratory Testing
N.A.I.C.S.: 541380
Jeff Graham *(Gen Mgr)*
Barry Johnson *(Mgr-Quality)*

Pace Analytical Services, Inc. - Green Bay Environmental Laboratory (2)
1241 Bellevue St Ste 9, Green Bay, WI 54302
Tel.: (920) 469-2436
Web Site: http://www.pacelabs.com
Rev.: $15,000,000
Emp.: 80
Organic & Inorganic Analytical Laboratory Testing
N.A.I.C.S.: 541380
Nils Melberg *(Gen Mgr)*
Kate Verbeten *(Mgr-Quality-Green Bay)*

Pace Analytical Services, Inc. - Greensburg Environmental Laboratory (2)
1638 Roseytown Rd Ste 2 3 4, Greensburg, PA 15601-9302
Tel.: (724) 850-5600
Web Site: http://www.pacelabs.com
Sales Range: $10-24.9 Million
Emp.: 105
Organic & Inorganic Analytical Laboratory Testing
N.A.I.C.S.: 541380

Pace Analytical Services, Inc. - Houston LabOps/Service Center (2)
900 Gemini Ave, Houston, TX 77058-2704
Tel.: (281) 486-0534
Web Site: http://www.pacelabs.com
Organic & Inorganic Analytical Laboratory Testing
N.A.I.C.S.: 541380
Harry Klann *(Gen Mgr)*

Pace Analytical Services, Inc. - Huntersville Environmental Laboratory (2)
9800 Kincey Rd Ste 100, Huntersville, NC 28078
Tel.: (704) 875-9092
Web Site: http://www.pacelabs.com
Sales Range: $10-24.9 Million
Emp.: 40
Organic & Inorganic Analytical Laboratory Testing
N.A.I.C.S.: 541380
Felicia Grogan *(Gen Mgr)*
Cheryl Johnson *(Mgr-Quality)*

Pace Analytical Services, Inc. - Indianapolis Environmental Laboratory (2)
7726 Moller Rd, Indianapolis, IN 46268-4163
Tel.: (317) 228-3100
Web Site: http://www.pacelabs.com
Sales Range: $10-24.9 Million
Emp.: 53
Organic & Inorganic Analytical Laboratory Testing
N.A.I.C.S.: 541380
Karl Anderson *(Sr Gen Mgr)*

Pace Analytical Services, Inc. - Lenexa Environmental Laboratory (2)
9608 Loiret Blvd, Lenexa, KS 66219-2406
Tel.: (913) 599-5665
Web Site: http://www.pacelabs.com
Sales Range: $10-24.9 Million
Emp.: 50
Organic & Inorganic Analytical Laboratory Testing
N.A.I.C.S.: 541380
David Neal *(Sr Gen Mgr)*

Pace Analytical Services, Inc. - Minneapolis Environmental Laboratory (2)
1700 Elm St SE Ste 200, Minneapolis, MN 55414-2485
Tel.: (612) 607-1700
Web Site: http://www.pacelabs.com
Sales Range: $25-49.9 Million
Organic & Inorganic Analytical Laboratory Testing
N.A.I.C.S.: 541380
Tom Halverson *(Dir-Bus Dev Field Svcs)*
Stacey Larsen *(Sls Dir-Minneapolis)*
Mary Sitko *(Mgr-Sls-Minneapolis)*

Press Ganey Holdings, Inc. (1)
53 State St Ste 2101, Boston, MA 02109
Tel.: (781) 295-5000
Web Site: http://www.pressganey.com
Holding Company; Healthcare Advisory & Consulting
N.A.I.C.S.: 551112
Patrick T. Ryan *(Chm & CEO)*
Joseph Greskoviak *(Vice Chm)*
Thomas H. Lee *(Chief Medical Officer)*
Devin J. Anderson *(Gen Counsel & Sec)*
Nell Buhlman *(Chief Strategy Officer)*
Jeffrey N. Doucette *(Chief Nursing Officer)*
David Shapiro *(Sr VP/Gen Mgr-Member Experience)*
Darren Dworkin *(Pres & COO)*
Noel Hamill *(CMO)*

Subsidiary (Domestic):

Bivarus, Inc. (2)
2525 Meridian Pkwy Ste 460, Durham, NC 27713
Tel.: (919) 336-9142
Web Site: http://www.pressganey.com
Analytics & Consulting Services for Healthcare Industry
N.A.I.C.S.: 541618

Subsidiary (Domestic):

The Jackson Group Inc. (3)
219 1st Ave SW, Hickory, NC 28602
Tel.: (828) 328-8968
Analytics & Consulting Services to Healthcare Organizations
N.A.I.C.S.: 541618
Alan K. Jackson *(Dir)*

Subsidiary (Domestic):

Forsta Inc. (2)
330 7th Ave Floor 3, 10001, New York, NY
Tel.: (212) 660-1800
Web Site: https://www.forsta.com
Software Development Company
N.A.I.C.S.: 513210
Kyle Ferguson *(CEO)*
Henry Pooley *(Mng Dir-Asia Pacific)*

Subsidiary (Domestic):

Rio SEO, Inc. (3)
8080 Dagget St Ste 220, San Diego, CA 92111
Tel.: (858) 397-1500
Web Site: http://www.rioseo.com
Data Processing, Hosting & Related Services
N.A.I.C.S.: 518210
Bill Connard *(VP-Local Search)*
Mick Wilson *(VP-Customer Success)*

Subsidiary (Domestic):

Press Ganey Associates, Inc. (2)
404 Columbia Pl, South Bend, IN 46601
Tel.: (800) 232-8032
Web Site: http://www.pressganey.com
Health Care Srvices
N.A.I.C.S.: 621999
Patrick T. Ryan *(Chm & CEO)*
Nell Buhlman *(Press & COO)*

Subsidiary (Domestic):

Binary Fountain Inc. (3)
1660 International Dr Ste 225, McLean, VA 22102
Tel.: (404) 526-8301
Web Site: http://www.binaryfountain.com
Healthcare Advisory & Consulting Services
N.A.I.C.S.: 541618
Aaron Clifford *(Sr VP-Mktg)*
Ramu Potarazu *(Pres & CEO)*

Strategic Management Decisions LLC (3)
2472 Jett Ferry Rd Ste 400-107, Atlanta, GA 30338
Tel.: (404) 808-4730
Web Site: http://www.smdhr.com
Sales Range: $1-9.9 Million
Emp.: 7
Marketing Analysis Services
N.A.I.C.S.: 541910
Hannah Spell *(Dir-Res & Analytics)*
Holly Bossert *(VP-Sls)*
Natalie Ollinger *(Dir-Mktg & Project Mgmt)*
Scott Mondore *(Co-Founder & Mng Partner)*
Shane Douthitt *(Co-Founder & Mng Dir)*

Subsidiary (Domestic):

Soyring Consulting, Inc. (2)
880 21st Ave N, Saint Petersburg, FL 33704
Tel.: (727) 822-8774
Web Site: http://www.soyringconsulting.com
Healthcare Management & Consulting Services
N.A.I.C.S.: 541618
Lucas Higman *(Partner)*
Adam Higman *(Partner)*
Charles Hagood *(Partner)*
Dragan Gough *(Dir)*
Jerzy Kaczor *(Sr Mgr)*
Charles Demanche *(Project Dir & Mgr)*
Shelly Turner *(Mgr)*

Symphony Performance Health, Inc. (2)
11605 Haynes Bridge Rd Ste 400, Alpharetta, GA 30009
Tel.: (866) 460-5681
Web Site: http://www.sphanalytics.com
Health Care Data, Analytics & Consulting Services
N.A.I.C.S.: 518210
Amy Amick *(CEO)*
Matthew Fusan *(Gen Mgr-Population Health)*
Kevin Weinstein *(Pres)*

Pro Mach Group, Inc. (1)
6279 Tri-Ridge Blvd Ste 410, Loveland, OH 45140
Tel.: (513) 831-8778
Web Site: http://www.promachinc.com
Holding Company; Packaging Machinery Designer, Mfr, Distr & Maintenance Services
N.A.I.C.S.: 551112
Don Cotney *(Pres-Bottling & Capping)*
Troy Snader *(Sr VP-Flexible Pkg)*
Alan Shipman *(Pres-Labeling & Coding)*
Bud Lane *(Pres-Primary Pkg)*
Mark W. Anderson *(Pres & CEO)*
Patrick Mohan *(VP-HR)*
Thomas Scheper *(VP-IT)*
John Eklund *(VP-Mktg)*
Barry Heiser *(Pres-Global Filler & Integrated Solutions)*
Luke Barber *(VP-Corp Dev)*
Andy Moeder *(CFO)*
Doug Stambaugh *(Pres-Primary Pkg)*

Subsidiary (Domestic):

ProMach, Inc. (2)
50 E Rivercenter Blvd Ste 1800, Covington, KY 41011
Tel.: (513) 831-8778
Web Site: http://www.promachbuilt.com
Packaging Machinery Designer, Mfr, Distr & Maintenance Services
N.A.I.C.S.: 333993
Breton C. Ranc *(COO)*
Patrick Mohan *(Chief Admin Officer)*
Alan Shipman *(Pres-Labeling & Coding)*
Troy Snader *(Sr VP-Flexibles & Trays)*
Doug Stambaugh *(Pres-Primary Packaging)*
Luke Barber *(VP-Corp Dev)*
John Eklund *(VP-Mktg)*
Andy Moeder *(CFO)*
Ryan McCart *(Pres-Secondary Packaging)*
Frank Roberts *(Sr VP-Systems & Integration)*

Subsidiary (Domestic):

Allpax Products LLC (3)
13510 Seymour Meyers Blvd, Covington, LA 70033
Tel.: (985) 893-9277
Web Site: http://www.allpax.com
Food Processing & Sterilization Equipment Mfr & Distr
N.A.I.C.S.: 333993

Axon LLC (3)
3080 Business Park Dr Ste 103, Raleigh, NC 27610
Tel.: (919) 772-8383
Web Site: http://www.axoncorp.com
Heat Shrink Tunnel & Stretch Sleeve Application Machinery Designer Mfr
N.A.I.C.S.: 333994
Steve Moon *(Mgr-Aftermarket)*
Ed Farley *(Mgr-Product Line)*

Brenton, LLC. (3)
4750 County Rd 13 NE, Alexandria, MN 56308
Tel.: (320) 852-7705
Web Site: http://www.brentonengineering.com
Industrial End-of-Line Shrink-Wrapping & Packaging Machinery Mfr, Distr & Leasing Services
N.A.I.C.S.: 333993

EPI Labelers LLC (3)
1145 E Wellspring Rd, New Freedom, PA 17349
Tel.: (717) 235-8345
Web Site: http://www.epilabelers.com
Labeling Equipment Designer, Mfr & Distr
N.A.I.C.S.: 333993
Matt McLean *(VP & Gen Mgr)*

Federal Mfg. Co. (3)
N15 W23500 Stone Ridge Dr, Waukesha, WI 53188
Tel.: (414) 384-3200
Web Site: http://www.federalmfg.com
Dairy Bottle Filling, Capping Systems & Specialty Products Designer & Mfr
N.A.I.C.S.: 333111
Mark Vanzant *(VP & Gen Mgr)*

Fogg Filler Co. (3)
3455 John F Donnelly Dr, Holland, MI 49424
Tel.: (616) 786-3644
Web Site: http://www.foggfiller.com
Rev.: $9,450,000
Emp.: 50
All Other Industrial Machinery Mfr
N.A.I.C.S.: 333248
Randy Deward *(Mgr-Production)*

Fowler Products Company, LLC (3)
1965 Statham Dr, Statham, GA 30666
Tel.: (706) 549-3300
Web Site: http://www.fowlerproducts.com
Industrial Bottle & Rigid Container Capping Machinery Developer, Mfr, Whslr & Leasing Services
N.A.I.C.S.: 333993
Jackie Barrett *(Controller)*
Randy Uebler *(VP & Gen Mgr)*

Greydon, Inc. (3)
391 Greendale Rd, York, PA 17403
Tel.: (717) 848-3875
Web Site: http://www.greydon.com
Flexible Package Printing & Coding Machinery Mfr
N.A.I.C.S.: 333248
Greg Rochon *(Pres)*

ID Technology LLC (3)
2051 Franklin Dr, Fort Worth, TX 76106
Tel.: (888) 438-3242
Web Site: http://www.idtechnology.com
Labeling, Coding & Marking Equipment, Peripherals & Supplies Mfr, Distr & Maintenance Services
N.A.I.C.S.: 333993
Charles Shepherd *(Mgr-Accts-Natl)*
Joe Clear *(Sls Mgr-Natl OEM)*
Ed Sholty *(Mgr-Fort Worth)*
John Burke *(Mgr-Nashua)*
Russell Huff *(Mgr-Plant-Atlanta)*
Savio Martins *(Gen Mgr-Canada)*
Wayne Moore *(Mgr-Fresno)*
Denise Sisson *(VP-Sls)*
Kelly Harris *(VP-Corp Mktg & Partner Alliances)*
Chris Oliver *(CEO)*
Charles Osborn Jr. *(Mgr-Pewaukee)*

Branch (Domestic):

ID Technology LLC - Upper Midwest Office (4)
N26 W23323 Paul Rd, Pewaukee, WI 53072

LEONARD GREEN & PARTNERS, L.P.

Leonard Green & Partners, L.P.—(Continued)
Tel.: (262) 549-8660
Web Site: http://www.idtechnology.com
Emp.: 35
Labeling, Coding & Marking Equipment, Peripherals & Supplies Distr & Maintenance Services
N.A.I.C.S.: 423830
Charles Osborn Jr. *(Reg Mgr)*

Subsidiary (Domestic):

KLEENLine, LLC (3)
1965 Statham Dr, Statham, GA 30666
Tel.: (706) 208-0814
Web Site: http://www.kleenline.com
Conveyor & Conveying Equipment Mfr
N.A.I.C.S.: 333922
Frank Maliski *(Mgr-Electrical & Controls Engrg)*
Michael Shea *(Engr-Applications)*
Gene Shaw *(VP & Gen Mgr)*

Labeling Systems LLC (3)
48 Spruce St, Oakland, NJ 07436
Tel.: (201) 405-0767
Web Site: http://www.labelingsystems.com
Label Application Machinery Designer, Mfr, Whslr & Leasing Services
N.A.I.C.S.: 333993
Jack Roe *(VP & Gen Mgr)*

Lofton Label, Inc. (3)
6290 Claude Way, Inver Grove Heights, MN 55076
Tel.: (651) 457-8118
Web Site: http://www.loftonlabel.com
Sales Range: $1-9.9 Million
Emp.: 100
Coated & Laminated Paper Mfr
N.A.I.C.S.: 322220
Rick Gajewski *(Pres)*
William Feany *(VP & Controller)*

Matrix Packaging Machinery, LLC (3)
650 N Dekora Woods Blvd, Saukville, WI 53080
Tel.: (262) 268-8300
Web Site: http://www.matrixpm.com
Packaging Equipment Mfr
N.A.I.C.S.: 333993
Marc Wolf *(Gen Mgr)*

Modern Packaging, Inc. (3)
505 Acorn St, Deer Park, NY 11729
Tel.: (631) 595-2437
Web Site:
http://www.modernpackaginginc.com
Mfg Industrial Machinery Mfg Packaging Machinery Whol Industrial Equipment
N.A.I.C.S.: 333998
Jaroslaw Dabek *(Co-Founder & VP-Engrg)*
Syed Zaki Hossain *(Co-Founder, VP & Gen Mgr)*

Subsidiary (Non-US):

NJM Packaging (3)
5600 Kieran, Montreal, H4S 2B5, QC, Canada
Tel.: (514) 337-6990
Web Site: https://www.njmpackaging.com
Packaging Machinery & Equipment Mfr
N.A.I.C.S.: 333993
Mark Laroche *(VP-Sls)*
Tom McDaniel *(Pres)*
Steve Leduc *(VP)*

Branch (US):

NJM Packaging (4)
77 Bank St, Lebanon, NH 03766
Tel.: (603) 448-0300
Web Site: http://www.njmpackaging.com
Sales Range: $1-9.9 Million
Emp.: 28
Packaging Machinery Mfr
N.A.I.C.S.: 333993
Michel Lapierre *(Pres & CEO)*

Subsidiary (Domestic):

Ossid LLC (3)
4000 College Rd, Rocky Mount, NC 27809
Tel.: (252) 446-6177
Web Site: http://www.ossid.com
Industrial Tray, Weigh Labeling & Sealing Packaging Machinery Mfr & Leasing Services

N.A.I.C.S.: 333993
Ernie Newell *(VP & Gen Mgr)*
Jason Angel *(VP-Sls & Mktg)*
Lisa Graessle *(Mgr-Sls)*
Ty Threedy *(Sls Mgr-West)*

Pacific Packaging Machinery, Inc. (3)
200 River Rd, Corona, CA 92880
Tel.: (951) 393-2200
Web Site: http://www.pacificpak.com
Food Product Machinery Mfr
N.A.I.C.S.: 333241
Mario Bele *(Project Mgr)*

Rennco LLC (3)
300 Elm St, Homer, MI 49245
Tel.: (517) 568-4121
Web Site: http://www.rennco.com
Industrial Package Sealing Machinery Mfr, Whslr & Leasing Services
N.A.I.C.S.: 333993

Roberts PolyPro Inc. (3)
5416 Wyoming Ave, Charlotte, NC 28273
Tel.: (704) 588-1794
Web Site: http://www.robertspolypro.com
Plastic Packaging Fixtures Designer, Mfr & Application Machinery Leasing Services
N.A.I.C.S.: 326199
Roy Tetreault *(Gen Mgr)*
George Allen *(Dir-Sls)*

Sentry Equipment Erectors Inc. (3)
13150 E Lynchburg Salem Tpke, Forest, VA 24551
Tel.: (434) 525-0769
Web Site: http://www.sentryequipment.com
Rev: $21,200,000
Emp.: 120
Conveyors & Conveying Equipment
N.A.I.C.S.: 333922

Serpa Packaging Solutions, LLC (3)
7020 W Sunnyview Ave, Visalia, CA 93291
Tel.: (559) 205-9958
Web Site: http://www.serpapackaging.com
Packaging Machinery Mfr
N.A.I.C.S.: 333993
Todd Reed *(Pres)*
Fernando M. Serpa *(Pres)*
Manuela Parreira *(Sec)*

Shuttleworth, LLC (3)
10 Commercial Rd, Huntington, IN 46750-8805
Tel.: (260) 356-8500
Web Site: http://www.shuttleworth.com
Custom Conveyor Systems Mfr
N.A.I.C.S.: 333922
Bret Ranc *(Gen Mgr)*
Ken Tinnell *(VP & Gen Mgr)*
Michael Liu *(Mgr-Engrg)*
Laurie Perolio-Bullinger *(Mktg Mgr)*

Subsidiary (Non-US):

Shuttleworth Europe N.V. (4)
Karreweg 141 A, Kruishoutem, 9770, Belgium
Tel.: (32) 92211314
Web Site: http://www.shuttleworth.com
Emp.: 14
Material Handling Equipment Mfr
N.A.I.C.S.: 333922
Kurt Van Heule *(Gen Mgr)*

Subsidiary (Domestic):

Stock America, LLC (3)
101 Green Trace Ct, Garner, NC 27529
Tel.: (919) 661-1911
Web Site: http://www.stockamerica.com
In-Container Sterilization & Pasteurization Systems Mfr & Distr
N.A.I.C.S.: 333241
Timothy Schurr *(VP & Gen Mgr)*
Julio Delgado *(Sr Engr-Automation Sols)*

Weiler Labeling Systems, LLC (3)
1256 N Church St, Moorestown, NJ 08057
Tel.: (856) 273-3377
Web Site: http://www.weilerls.com
Packaging Machinery Mfr
N.A.I.C.S.: 333993
Ted S. Geiselman *(VP & Gen Mgr)*
Tom Basgil *(VP-Ops)*
Philippe Maraval *(VP-Bus Dev)*
Harry Anderson *(Mgr-Reg-Sls)*
Robert D. Moll *(Mgr-Sls-Reg)*

Subsidiary (Non-US):

Wexxar Packaging Inc. (3)
13471 Vulcan Way, Richmond, V6V 1K4, BC, Canada
Tel.: (604) 930-9300
Web Site: https://www.wexxar.com
Emp.: 180
Industrial Case-Forming, Tray-Forming & Case-Sealing Packaging Machinery Mfr
N.A.I.C.S.: 333993
William Chu *(Gen Mgr)*

Propio Language Services, LLC. (1)
10801 Mastin St. #580, Overland Park, KS 66210
Tel.: (913) 381-3143
Web Site: http://www.propio-ls.com
Sales Range: $1-9.9 Million
Emp.: 70
Language Interpretation Services
N.A.I.C.S.: 541930
Joe Fackrell *(Founder & Partner)*
Douglas Judd *(Partner-Fin & Ops)*
Brian Simkins *(Partner-IT)*
Robert Campbell *(Partner-Strategy & Bus Dev)*

Subsidiary (Domestic):

Telelanguage Inc. (2)
514 SW 6th Ave, Portland, OR 97204-1624
Tel.: (503) 535-2176
Web Site: http://www.telelanguage.com
Translation & Interpretation Services
N.A.I.C.S.: 541930

United Language Group, Inc. (2)
315 E Lake Ste #301, Wayzata, MN 55391
Tel.: (612) 916-6060
Language Service Provider
N.A.I.C.S.: 611630
Tim Kubicek *(Sr Dir-Fin & Acctg)*
Nicholas McMahon *(CEO)*

Subsidiary (Domestic):

KJ International Resources Ltd. (3)
800 Washington Ave N Ste 905, Minneapolis, MN 55401-1195
Tel.: (612) 288-9494
Web Site: http://www.kjinternational.com
Translation & Interpretation Services
N.A.I.C.S.: 541930
Kristen Giovanis *(Co-founder & CEO)*
Janna Lundberg *(Co-founder)*

Prospect Medical Holdings, Inc. (1)
3415 S Sepulveda Blvd 9th Fl, Los Angeles, CA 90034
Tel.: (310) 943-4500
Web Site: http://www.pmh.com
Sales Range: $450-499.9 Million
Emp.: 1,806
Health Care Management Services
N.A.I.C.S.: 524114
Samuel S. Lee *(Chm & CEO)*
Ellen J. Shin *(Gen Counsel & Sec)*
Steve Aleman *(CFO)*
Mitchell Lew *(Pres)*
Cindra Syverson *(Chief HR Officer & Sr VP)*
Debbie Berry *(Chief Quality & Patient Safety Officer)*
Laura Lacorte *(Chief Compliance & Privacy Officer)*

Subsidiary (Domestic):

East Orange General Hospital (2)
300 Central Ave, East Orange, NJ 07018
Tel.: (973) 672-8400
Web Site: http://www.evh.org
Health Care Srvices
N.A.I.C.S.: 622110
Paige Dworak *(Pres & CEO)*
Ronald Napiorski *(CFO)*
Robert W. Mays *(Dir-HR)*
Guy Voelbel *(COO)*
Anuj Mehta *(Chief Medical Officer)*
Rodemil Fuentes *(COO)*

Prospect Medical Group, Inc. (2)
600 City Pkwy W Ste 800, Orange, CA 92868
Tel.: (714) 796-5900
Web Site:
http://www.prospectmedicalsystems.com
Sales Range: $75-99.9 Million
Health Care Management Services
N.A.I.C.S.: 541618

Pure Gym Limited (1)
4th Floor Town Centre House Merrion Centre, Leeds, LS2 8LY, United Kingdom
Tel.: (44) 3444770005
Web Site: http://www.puregym.com
Gyms & Training Centers
N.A.I.C.S.: 713940
Peter Roberts *(Founder)*
Humphrey Cobbold *(CEO)*
Alex Wood *(CFO)*
Daniel Glyde *(CTO)*
Rebecca Passmore *(COO)*
Stephen Rowe *(CMO)*

Subsidiary (Non-US):

Fitness World A/S (2)
Gasvaerksvej 16, 1656, Copenhagen, Denmark
Tel.: (45) 50 60 61 01
Personal Services
N.A.I.C.S.: 812990
Steen Albrechtslund *(CEO)*

SRS Distribution Inc. (1)
7440 State Hwy 121, McKinney, TX 75070-2196
Tel.: (214) 491-4149
Web Site: https://srsdistribution.com
Emp.: 10,850
Roofing, Siding & Insulation Material Merchant Wholesalers
N.A.I.C.S.: 423330
Carrie David *(Chief HR Officer & Exec VP)*
Jeremy Goldschmeding *(COO-Building Products Div)*
Scott Vansant *(CFO & Exec VP)*
Dino Pappas *(Reg VP)*
Chris Arrington *(Chief Credit Officer & Sr VP)*
Rajeev Rai *(CTO & Exec VP)*
Dustin Gunderson *(Gen Counsel & Sr VP)*
Mike Hertel *(Dir-Fleet Ops)*

Subsidiary (Domestic):

A.L.L. Roofing Materials of San Jose, LLC (2)
506 Phelan Ave, San Jose, CA 95112
Tel.: (408) 293-1264
Web Site: http://www.allroofingstore.com
Sales Range: $1-9.9 Million
Emp.: 49
Roofing, Siding & Insulation Material Whslr
N.A.I.C.S.: 423330
Phil Quinet *(VP)*
Shirley Lopez *(Mgr-Credit)*
Michelle Cassady *(Gen Mgr)*

ABCO Supply, LLC (2)
46385 Continental Dr, Chesterfield, MI 48047
Tel.: (586) 949-4888
Web Site: http://www.abcosupply-mi.com
Roofing Material Distr
N.A.I.C.S.: 423330

Acorn Roofing Supply, Co. (2)
2655 W 48th St, Chicago, IL 60632-1402
Tel.: (773) 927-5851
Web Site:
http://www.acornroofingsupply.com
Rev: $2,000,000
Emp.: 8
Roofing, Siding & Insulation Material Merchant Whslr
N.A.I.C.S.: 423330
John Rociola *(Mgr)*
Bryan Sawilchik *(Gen Mgr)*
Ross Ridder *(Gen Mgr)*

Advanced Building Products, Inc. (2)
5734 Jefferson Hwy, Harahan, LA 70123
Tel.: (504) 733-8200
Web Site: http://www.advancedbldg.com
Sales Range: $10-24.9 Million
Emp.: 80
Residential Building Products Mfr & Distr
N.A.I.C.S.: 423330
Kristopher Anderson *(Pres)*

Atlanta Roofing Supply Inc (2)
900 Hwy 54 E, Fayetteville, GA 30214
Tel.: (770) 460-1817
Web Site:
http://www.atlantaroofingsupply.com
Emp.: 11

COMPANIES
LEONARD GREEN & PARTNERS, L.P.

Roofing Material Distr
N.A.I.C.S.: 423330
Chuck Betsill *(Branch Mgr)*

Cannon Supply, Inc. (2)
4955 Wrightsboro Rd, Grovetown, GA 30813
Tel.: (706) 210-3475
Web Site: http://www.cannonsupply.com
Emp.: 6
Roofing Material Distr
N.A.I.C.S.: 423330
Josh Moss *(Branch Mgr)*
Brian Mullinax *(Asst Branch Mgr)*

Crown C Supply Co., Inc. (2)
5130 Manchester Ave, Saint Louis, MO 63110-2014
Tel.: (314) 645-4640
Web Site: http://www.crowncsupply.com
Building Materials Whslr
N.A.I.C.S.: 444180
Dave Kelly *(Asst Mgr-Branch)*
George Merz *(Mgr-Customer Svc)*
Joseph A. Wiss *(Mgr-Branch)*
Mary Kay Kelly *(Mgr-Credit)*
Joe Scott *(Mgr-Facilities)*

Debel Roofing Supply, Inc. (2)
747 Petaluma Blvd S, Petaluma, CA 94952
Tel.: (707) 765-9722
Sales Range: $1-9.9 Million
Emp.: 14
Roofing, Siding & Insulation Material Merchant Whslr
N.A.I.C.S.: 423330
Andy Bel *(CEO)*

Gary-Hobart Roofing & Supply Company (2)
2520 W 37th Ave, Hobart, IN 46342-1830
Tel.: (219) 962-1173
Web Site: http://www.garyhobartroofingsupply.com
Construction Materials Whslr
N.A.I.C.S.: 423390

Heritage Landscape Supply Group, Inc. (2)
5900 S Lake Forest Dr Ste 400, McKinney, TX 75070-2196
Tel.: (214) 491-4149
Web Site: https://www.heritagelandscapesupplygroup.com
Holding Company
N.A.I.C.S.: 551112
Matt McDermott *(Pres)*

Subsidiary (Domestic):

Beehive Brick & Stone (3)
436 Universal Cir, Sandy, UT 84070-2573
Tel.: (801) 748-1818
Web Site: http://www.beehivebrick.com
Brick, Stone & Related Construction Material Merchant Whslr
N.A.I.C.S.: 423320
Brad Fairbanks *(Pres)*
Tyler Rast *(VP-Ops & Gen Mgr)*

Davis Pipe & Supply, Inc. (3)
509 Westland Dr, Edmond, OK 73013
Tel.: (405) 340-0660
Web Site: http://www.davispipe.com
Sales Range: $1-9.9 Million
Emp.: 20
Wholsale Irrigation & Turf/Landscape Lighting
N.A.I.C.S.: 423820

Florida Irrigation Supply Inc. (3)
300 Central Park Dr, Sanford, FL 32771
Tel.: (407) 323-4222
Web Site: http://www.fisoutdoor.com
Sales Range: $25-49.9 Million
Emp.: 200
Landscaping, Irrigation & Outdoor Lighting Contractor
N.A.I.C.S.: 221310
Fred Tannler *(Pres)*
Susan Macina *(CFO)*

The Urban Farmer Store, Inc. (3)
2833 Vicente St, San Francisco, CA 94116
Tel.: (415) 661-2204
Web Site: http://www.urbanfarmerstore.com
Sales Range: $1-9.9 Million
Emp.: 34
Whol Farm/Garden Machinery

N.A.I.C.S.: 423820
Tom Bressan *(Pres)*
Adrian S. *(Pres)*

Wolf Creek Company Inc. (3)
6051 Wolf Creek Pike, Trotwood, OH 45426
Tel.: (937) 854-2694
Web Site: http://www.wolfcreekcompany.com
Rev.: $7,000,000
Emp.: 30
Water Supply & Irrigation Systems
N.A.I.C.S.: 221310
Charles Knowles *(CEO)*
Brent Sainz *(Mgr-Mktg)*
Brian Ciotti *(Mgr-Territory)*
Gordon Loggins *(Mgr-Cincinnati)*
Jerry Muck *(Mgr-Svc)*

Subsidiary (Domestic):

Louis T. Ollesheimer & Son, Inc. (2)
605 E 12 Mile Rd, Madison Heights, MI 48071-2568
Tel.: (248) 544-3900
Web Site: http://www.ollesheimer.com
Emp.: 80
Roofing, Siding & Insulation
N.A.I.C.S.: 423330
Jamie Ollesheimer *(Pres)*
David Moyle *(Controller)*
Les Marinko *(Mgr-Credit)*
Lisa Hensley *(Mgr-Accts Receivable)*
Kelly Mclean *(Mgr-Accts Payable & Asst Controller)*
Jayme Parks *(Branch Mgr)*

Marsh Building Products, Inc. (2)
2700 Evans Ave Ste A, Valparaiso, IN 46383-4440
Tel.: (219) 464-0086
Web Site: http://www.marshbuild.com
Rev.: $8,400,000
Emp.: 50
Lumber, Plywood, Millwork & Wood Panel Merchant Whslr
N.A.I.C.S.: 423310

Midwest Roofing Supply Inc. (2)
460 Hoover St NE, Minneapolis, MN 55413
Tel.: (612) 378-6006
Web Site: http://www.midwestroofingsupply.com
Emp.: 17
Roofing Material Whslr
N.A.I.C.S.: 423330
Troy Baker *(Reg Mgr)*

National Building & Roofing Supplies, Inc. (2)
400 W Main St, Patchogue, NY 11772-3010
Tel.: (631) 475-5215
Web Site: http://www.nationalroofingsupplies.com
Sales Range: $1-9.9 Million
Emp.: 14
Roofing, Siding & Insulation Material Merchant Whslr
N.A.I.C.S.: 423330
Michael Capozzi *(Pres)*

Pace Roofing Supply Company (2)
414 MacDade Blvd, Collingdale, PA 19023
Tel.: (484) 496-2114
Web Site: http://www.paceroofingsupply.com
Emp.: 5
Roofing Material Distr
N.A.I.C.S.: 423330

Presta Contractors Supply, Inc. (2)
2669 W 16th St, Erie, PA 16505
Tel.: (814) 833-0655
Construction Materials Distr
N.A.I.C.S.: 444140
Tim Presta *(Pres & CEO)*

Rivercity Wholesale Inc. (2)
1110 Ulrich Ave, Louisville, KY 40219
Tel.: (502) 968-7778
Web Site: http://www.rivercitywindowsiding.com
Roofing Material Distr
N.A.I.C.S.: 423330

Roofers Supply Inc. (2)
3359 S 500 W, Salt Lake City, UT 84115
Tel.: (801) 266-1311
Web Site: http://www.roofersutah.com
Sales Range: $10-24.9 Million
Emp.: 60
Roofing Material Distributor

N.A.I.C.S.: 423330
Dino Pappas *(Pres)*

Roofline Supply & Delivery, Inc. (2)
1302 SE Armour Rd, Bend, OR 97702
Tel.: (541) 389-6790
Web Site: http://www.rooflinesupply.com
Roofing Material Distr
N.A.I.C.S.: 423330

Branch (Domestic):

Roofline Supply (3)
700 N Victory Blvd, Burbank, CA 91502
Tel.: (818) 840-8851
Sales Range: $10-24.9 Million
Emp.: 10
Roofing & Siding Materials
N.A.I.C.S.: 423330
Todd Kurten *(Mgr)*
John Lankford *(Reg Mgr-Credit)*

Subsidiary (Domestic):

Rowe Supply Co (2)
4102 Meding St, Savannah, GA 31405
Tel.: (912) 233-5737
Web Site: http://www.rowesupply.com
Emp.: 9
Roofing Material Distr
N.A.I.C.S.: 423310
Jake Arndt *(Branch Mgr)*

Division (Domestic):

SRS Distribution Inc. - Sierra Roofing Supply Division (2)
2000 E 4th St, Reno, NV 89512
Tel.: (775) 323-0747
Web Site: http://www.sierraroofingsupply.com
Emp.: 15
Roofing Material Distr
N.A.I.C.S.: 423330

Subsidiary (Domestic):

Stewart Building & Roofing Supply, Inc. (2)
6970 NW Grand Ave, Glendale, AZ 85301
Tel.: (623) 215-0370
Web Site: http://www.stewartbldg.com
Roofing Material Distr
N.A.I.C.S.: 423330

Sunniland Corp. (2)
507 N 14th St, Leesburg, FL 34748
Tel.: (352) 728-2444
Web Site: http://www.sunniland.com
Rev.: $3,354,000
Emp.: 13
Home Center Operator
N.A.I.C.S.: 444110
Chris Frank *(Mgr-Div)*
John Cahill *(Treas)*
Phil Spake *(Mgr-Credit)*
Tom Moore *(Pres & CEO)*

Superior Distribution Company (2)
2062 Generals Hwy, Annapolis, MD 21401
Tel.: (443) 837-9663
Web Site: http://www.superiordistribution.net
Roofing Material Distr
N.A.I.C.S.: 423330
Todd Holt *(Gen Mgr)*

Washoe Building Supply Company, Inc. (2)
1479 Hymer Ave, Sparks, NV 89431
Tel.: (775) 359-3622
Web Site: http://www.washoebuildingsupply.com
Lumber, Plywood, Millwork & Wood Panel Merchant Whslr
N.A.I.C.S.: 423310
Zach McGrath *(VP-Admin)*

Weatherpanel, Inc. (2)
285 Chandler St, Buffalo, NY 14207-2476
Tel.: (716) 876-5440
Web Site: http://www.weatherpanel.com
Sales Range: $1-9.9 Million
Emp.: 20
Roofing, Siding & Insulation Material Merchant Whslr
N.A.I.C.S.: 423330
Frank Vacanti *(Pres)*
Angelo Ciraolo *(Mgr-Sls-Window)*

Sagittarius Brands, Inc. (1)

1717 Elm Hill Pike Ste A1, Nashville, TN 37210
Tel.: (615) 231-2328
Sales Range: $900-999.9 Million
Holding Company; Limited Service Restaurants Franchisor & Operator
N.A.I.C.S.: 551112

TapouT LLC (1)
21800 Barton Rd #108, Grand Terrace, CA 92313
Tel.: (909) 825-1800
Web Site: http://www.Tapout.com
Sales Range: $25-49.9 Million
Emp.: 85
Mixed Martial Arts Apparel & Accessories Mfr & Distr
N.A.I.C.S.: 315990

The Container Store Group, Inc. (1)
500 Freeport Pkwy, Coppell, TX 75019
Tel.: (972) 538-6000
Web Site: https://www.containerstore.com
Rev.: $1,094,119,000
Assets: $1,197,577,000
Liabilities: $769,481,000
Net Worth: $428,096,000
Earnings: $81,718,000
Emp.: 5,200
Fiscal Year-end: 04/02/2022
Storage & Organization Products Retailer
N.A.I.C.S.: 459999
Satish Malhotra *(Pres & CEO)*
Dhritiman Saha *(COO)*
Jeffrey A. Miller *(CFO)*

Subsidiary (Domestic):

The Container Store Inc. (2)
500 Freeport Pkwy, Coppell, TX 75019
Tel.: (972) 538-6000
Web Site: http://www.containerstore.com
Sales Range: $600-649.9 Million
Emp.: 700
Storage & Organization Products
N.A.I.C.S.: 449129
Melissa Reiff *(Chm)*
Jodi L. Taylor *(CFO & Chief Admin Officer)*
Satish Malhotra *(CEO)*
Dhritiman Saha *(CIO)*
Gretchen Ganc *(Exec VP-Strategy & Analytics)*
John Gehre *(Exec VP-Mdsg & Plng)*
Eva Gordon *(Exec VP-Stores & Employee Dev)*
John Thrailkill *(Exec VP-IT & Bus Dev)*
Melissa Collins *(CMO)*
Dhritiman Saha *(CIO)*
Michelle Gill *(VP-Mdsg)*
LaTisha Brandon *(Sr Dir-Diversity, Equity & Inclusion)*
Ivet Taneva *(Sr Dir-Environmental, Social & Governance)*
Robert Higgins *(VP-Real Estate)*

WIRB-Copernicus Group, Inc. (1)
202 Carnegie Ctr Ste 107, Princeton, NJ 08540
Tel.: (609) 945-0101
Web Site: http://www.wcgclinical.com
Ethical Review Services
N.A.I.C.S.: 541715
Stephen M. McLean *(Treas & Sr VP-Corp Dev)*
Donald A. Deieso *(Chm & CEO)*
Christina Armstrong *(Sr VP-Bus Dev)*
Laurie L. Jackson *(CFO)*
Nicholas Slack *(Pres)*
Marco Capasso *(Pres-Scientific and Regulatory Review Div & Gen Counsel)*
Lindsay McNair *(Chief Medical Officer)*
Ian Neilson *(CIO)*
Stephen M. McLean *(Treas & Sr VP-Corp Dev)*
Jill Johnston *(Pres-WCG Clinical Svcs Organization)*

Subsidiary (Domestic):

Applied Clinical Intelligence, LLC (2)
3 Bala Plz W Ste 402 251 St Asaphs Rd, Bala Cynwyd, PA 19004
Tel.: (484) 429-7200
Web Site: http://www.aciclinical.com
Administrative Management & General Management Consulting Service
N.A.I.C.S.: 541611

CenterWatch (2)
100 North Washington St, Boston, MA 02114
Tel.: (617) 948-5100

LEONARD GREEN & PARTNERS, L.P.

Leonard Green & Partners, L.P.—(Continued)
Web Site: http://www.centerwatch.com
Rev.: $1,500,000
Emp.: 25
Book Publishers
N.A.I.C.S.: 513130
Christopher Pooley *(Gen Mgr)*
Brian Fernald *(Mgr-Ops)*
Joan A. Chambers *(COO)*
Kenneth A. Getz *(Founder & Owner)*
Mike Catelani *(CFO)*

Clintrax Global, Inc. (2)
5000 CentreGreen Way Ste 150, Raleigh, NC 27513
Tel.: (919) 322-2398
Web Site: http://www.clintraxglobal.com
Investigator Agreement Negotiation & Payment Services
N.A.I.C.S.: 522320
Amber Corbin *(Pres)*
Steven Jones *(Gen Counsel & Corp Sec)*
Russell John *(VP-Grants Mgmt)*
Phil Lemons *(COO)*
Jonathan Zung *(Pres)*

MedAvante-ProPhase, Inc (2)
100 American Metro Blvd 106, Hamilton, NJ 08619
Tel.: (609) 528-9400
Web Site: http://www.medavante.net
Pharmaceuticals Product Mfr
N.A.I.C.S.: 325412
Steven Downing *(CFO)*
Peter Sorantin *(Sr VP-Bus Dev & Comm)*
Angela Wilmer *(VP-Regulatory & QA)*
Jeffrey S. Litwin *(CEO)*
Christopher Randolph *(Chief Scientific Officer)*
Steven Herne *(Chief Comml Officer)*
Mark Opler *(Chief Research Officer)*
Greg Barrett *(CTO)*
Mike Ciotfi *(Sr VP-Clinical Ops)*
Sue Vallow *(VP-Patient eSolutions)*

Statistics Collaborative, Inc. (2)
1710 Rhode Is Ave NW Ste 200, Washington, DC 20036-3122
Tel.: (202) 247-9700
Web Site: http://www.statcollab.com
All Other Personal Services
N.A.I.C.S.: 812990
Janet Wittes *(Pres)*

The Avoca Group, Inc. (2)
179 Nassau St Ste 3a, Princeton, NJ 08542
Tel.: (609) 252-9020
Web Site: http://www.theavocagroup.com
Sales Range: $1-9.9 Million
Emp.: 10
Market Research Services
N.A.I.C.S.: 541613
Patricia Leuchten *(Founder & CEO)*

ThreeWire, Inc. (2)
7500 Flying Cloud Dr, Eden Prairie, MN 55344-3540
Web Site: http://www.threewire.com
Rev.: $1,300,000
Emp.: 15
Clinical Trial Recruiting & Medical Device Marketing Services
N.A.I.C.S.: 561320
Mark A. Summers *(Founder & CEO)*
Bruce K. Gould *(Sr VP-Client Dev & Mktg)*
James E, Claseman *(CFO)*

Trifecta Multimedia, LLC (2)
725 South Figueroa St, Los Angeles, CA 90035
Tel.: (310) 385-8642
Web Site: http://www.trifectamultimedia.com
Sales Range: $1-9.9 Million
Emp.: 20
Motion Picture & Video Production
N.A.I.C.S.: 512110
David Young *(CEO)*

Waife & Associates, Inc. (2)
62 Warren St, Needham, MA 02492
Tel.: (781) 449-7032
Web Site: http://www.waife.com
Biopharma Clinical Research Company; Organizational Psychology & Clinical IT Services
N.A.I.C.S.: 541715
Ronald S. Waife *(Pres)*

Washington Business Information, Inc. (2)
300 N Washington St, Falls Church, VA 22046
Tel.: (703) 538-7600
Web Site: http://www.fdanews.com
Periodical Publishers
N.A.I.C.S.: 513120
Jeff Grizzel *(Dir-Content License Deals)*
Karen Harrington *(Dir-Admin)*

WellSky Corporation (1)
11300 Switzer Rd, Overland Park, KS 66210
Tel.: (913) 307-1000
Web Site: http://wellsky.com
Clinical Management Information Solutions & Healthcare Software Services
N.A.I.C.S.: 513210
Steve Morgan *(COO)*
Joel Dolisy *(CTO)*
Shoma Sarkar Thomas *(CMO)*
Amy Shellhart *(Chief Solutions Officer)*
John Hutchinson *(Sr VP-Client Experience)*
Dana Streck *(Chief People Officer)*
Akash Raj *(CFO)*
Dale Zurbay *(Chief Growth Officer)*
Tim Ashe *(Chief Clinical Officer)*
Geoff Nudd *(Chief Strategy Officer)*
Bill Miller *(Chm & CEO)*

Subsidiary (Domestic):

Bowman Systems, L.L.C. (2)
333 Texas St Ste 300, Shreveport, LA 71101-5304
Tel.: (318) 213-8780
Web Site: http://www.mediware.com
Information Management Software Services
N.A.I.C.S.: 541519
Deborah Cox *(VP-HR)*

Fazzi Associates, Inc. (2)
11 Village Hill Rd Ste 101, Northampton, MA 01060
Tel.: (413) 584-5300
Web Site: http://www.fazzi.com
Administrative Management & General Management Consulting Services
N.A.I.C.S.: 541611
Eileen Freitag *(Partner)*
Robert A. Fazzi *(Pres)*
Peter Emmott *(VP-Bus Dev)*

Subsidiary (Non-US):

JAC Computer Services Ltd. (2)
1 Aurum Court, Sylvan Way, Basildon, SS15 6TH, Essex, United Kingdom
Tel.: (44) 1268 416348
Web Site: http://www.jac.co.uk
Medicines Management Solutions; Pharmacy Stock Control & Electronic Prescribing
N.A.I.C.S.: 513210
Robert Tysall-Blay *(CEO)*

Subsidiary (Domestic):

MEDTran Direct, Inc. (2)
105 W Sherman Way Ste 107, Nixa, MO 65714-7622
Web Site: http://www.medtrandirect.com
Electronic Billing (for Hospital & Health Care)
N.A.I.C.S.: 513210
Kalon Mitchell *(Pres)*

Mediware Consulting & Analytics (2)
9765 Randall Dr Ste D, Indianapolis, IN 46280
Tel.: (317) 575-9301
Web Site: http://www.mediware.com
Blood Management & Consulting Services
N.A.I.C.S.: 621999
Susann Nienhaus *(Dir-Client Svcs & Patient Safety)*

Mediware Reimbursement Services (2)
40 Shattuck Rd Ste 306, Andover, MA 01810
Tel.: (978) 327-6501
Web Site: http://www.mediware.com
Billing & Accounting Services
N.A.I.C.S.: 541219
Jeanne Lugli *(Gen Mgr)*

Wrench Group LLC (1)
1787 Williams Dr, Marietta, GA 30066
Tel.: (678) 784-2260
Web Site: http://www.wrenchgroup.com
Home Maintenance & Repairing Services
N.A.I.C.S.: 238220
Ken Haines *(CEO)*

Subsidiary (Domestic):

Buckeye Heating and Cooling Services, Inc. (2)
6969 Worthngtn Galena A, Worthington, OH 43085
Tel.: (614) 294-4966
Web Site: http://www.buckeyeheat.com
Sales Range: $1-9.9 Million
Emp.: 20
Plumbing, Heating & Air-Conditioning Contractors
N.A.I.C.S.: 238220
Brad Wentz *(Pres)*

Criss Enterprises, Inc. (2)
315 E Warner Rd Ste 1, Chandler, AZ 85225
Tel.: (480) 892-7556
Web Site: http://www.ecowateraz.com
Household Appliance Stores
N.A.I.C.S.: 449210
David Crissman *(Pres & VP)*
Ashley Greene *(Gen Mgr)*

Florida Cool Inc. (2)
1161 Sun Century Rd Ste 1, Naples, FL 34110
Tel.: (239) 594-9871
Web Site: http://www.floridacoolinc.com
Rev.: $1,460,000
Emp.: 10
Heating & Air-Conditioning Services
N.A.I.C.S.: 238220
Tom Caprio *(Pres)*

Ragsdale Heating & Air Conditioning, Inc. (2)
418 Butler Industrial Dr, Dallas, GA 30132
Tel.: (770) 443-1821
Web Site: http://www.ragsdaleair.com
Site Preparation Contractor
N.A.I.C.S.: 238910
Art Ragsdale *(CEO)*
John Smith *(COO)*
Meylena Gutierrez *(Corp Controller)*
Lynn Blackburn *(Mgr-HR)*
Debbie Leboff *(Mgr-Office & Mgr-Customer Svc)*

LEONARD KREUSCH, INC.
200 Legrand Ave, Northvale, NJ 07647-0910
Tel.: (201) 784-2500 NJ
Web Site: http://www.leonardkreusch wines.com
Year Founded: 1950
Sales Range: $75-99.9 Million
Emp.: 36
Wine Importer
N.A.I.C.S.: 424820
John F. Kreusch *(VP)*

Subsidiaries:

Leonard Kreusch GmbH & Co. (1)
Martinerfeld 61, 54294, Trier, Germany (100%)
Tel.: (49) 651840020
Web Site: http://www.kreuschwines.de
Sales Range: $25-49.9 Million
Emp.: 6
Importer of Estate Bottled & Regional Wines
N.A.I.C.S.: 445320

LEONARD PETERSON & CO., INC.
400 Webster Rd, Auburn, AL 36832
Tel.: (334) 821-6832 IL
Web Site: http://www.lpco.com
Year Founded: 1995
Sales Range: $10-24.9 Million
Emp.: 102
Laboratory Furniture Mfr
N.A.I.C.S.: 337127
Joyce Lethander *(Sec)*
Todd Lethander *(Pres)*
Charles McBurney *(Project Mgr)*

LEONARD S. FIORE, INC.
5506 6th Ave Rear, Altoona, PA 16602
Tel.: (814) 946-3686
Web Site: http://www.lsfiore.com
Year Founded: 1954
Sales Range: $50-74.9 Million
Emp.: 250
Commercial & Institutional Building Construction Services
N.A.I.C.S.: 236220
Michael F. Fiore *(Exec VP)*
Joseph L. Irwin *(VP-Project Estimation Dept)*
Patrick M. Irwin *(VP-Project Mgmt Dept)*
Sara L. Fiore-Gunnett *(Controller)*
Richard F. Fiore Sr. *(Pres)*
Richard F. Fiore Jr. *(VP-IT & Process Mgmt Dept)*

LEONARD'S CARPET SERVICE INC.
1121 N Red Gum St, Anaheim, CA 92806-2515
Tel.: (714) 630-1930 CA
Web Site: http://www.leonardscarpetservice.com
Year Founded: 1960
Sales Range: $25-49.9 Million
Emp.: 220
Floor Laying & Floor Work-Sales Installation
N.A.I.C.S.: 238330
Leonard Nagel *(Founder & CEO)*
Joel Nagel *(Pres)*

LEONARD'S EXPRESS INC.
8719 White Oak Ave, Munster, IN 46321
Tel.: (219) 923-1855
Web Site: http://www.leonardsexpress.com
General Freight Trucking
N.A.I.C.S.: 484110
Kyle Johnson *(Dir-IT)*

Subsidiaries:

West Coast Distributing, Inc. (1)
Commerce Pl 350 Main St, Boston, MA 02148
Tel.: (781) 665-0300
Web Site: http://www.wcd-network.com
Sales Range: $1-9.9 Million
Emp.: 50
Freight Transportation Arrangement
N.A.I.C.S.: 488510
Benjamin Foss *(Controller)*

LEONE & KEEBLE INC.
108 W Boone Ave, Spokane, WA 99220
Tel.: (509) 327-4451
Web Site: http://www.leonekeeble.com
Year Founded: 1930
Sales Range: $10-24.9 Million
Emp.: 80
Commercial & Institutional Building Construction Services
N.A.I.C.S.: 236220
Tom Mercer *(VP & Mgr-Project)*
Jeramie Keeble *(Treas, VP & Mgr-Project)*
Brendan Monroe *(Sec, VP & Mgr-Project)*

LEONETTI CELLAR
1875 Foothills Ln, Walla Walla, WA 99362
Tel.: (509) 525-1428
Web Site: http://www.leonetticellar.com
Sales Range: $10-24.9 Million
Emp.: 21
Vineyard & Wine Mfr
N.A.I.C.S.: 111332

Nancy Figgins *(Owner)*
Chris Figgins *(Pres & Dir-Winmaking)*
Amy Figgins *(Partner & Mgr)*

LEONISA USA
5240 Langford Park Dr Ste B, Norcross, GA 30071
Tel.: (770) 209-4496
Web Site: http://www.leonisa.com
Year Founded: 2007
Sales Range: $1-9.9 Million
Emp.: 15
Intimate Apparel
N.A.I.C.S.: 458110
Juan Duque *(CEO)*
Octavio Quintana *(VP)*

LEOPARDO COMPANIES INC.
5200 Prairie Stone Pkwy, Hoffman Estates, IL 60192-3709
Tel.: (847) 783-3000   IL
Web Site: http://www.leopardo.com
Year Founded: 1977
Sales Range: $10-24.9 Million
Emp.: 500
Provider of Commercial Interior Services
N.A.I.C.S.: 236220
Richard S. Mattioda *(Vice Chm)*
James A. Leopardo *(Founder & Chm)*
Michael T. Leopardo *(Pres & CEO)*
Dan Klancnik *(Dir-Project Solutions)*
Mike Behm *(Sr VP-Bus Unit)*
Pierre Cowart *(Sr VP-Community Bus Unit)*
Rick DuPraw *(Sr VP-Comml Bus Unit)*
Will Sutila *(Mgr-Strategic Accts)*
Anthony Leopardo *(Dir-Strategic Rels)*
Matt Miller *(Sr VP)*
Chris Novak *(Sr VP)*
Giancarlo Pacini *(Sr VP)*
Leigh McMillen *(Sr VP-Industrial, Retail, Municipal, Hospitality & Federal)*
Damian Eallonardo *(Sr VP-Multifamily & Strategic Accts)*

LEOPOLD KETEL & PARTNERS
112 SW 1st Ave, Portland, OR 97204
Tel.: (503) 295-1918
Year Founded: 1995
Rev.: $22,300,000
Emp.: 22
Public Relations Agency
N.A.I.C.S.: 541820
Terra Spencer *(COO & Partner)*
Olga Haley *(Mng Dir-PR)*
Stephanie Kight *(Coord-Media)*
Thomas Hollerbach *(Pres & Partner)*
Stephanie Howe *(Acct Mgr)*

LEPAGE'S CORPORATION
12900 S Huron River Dr, Romulus, MI 48174
Tel.: (734) 942-9140   PA
Web Site: http://www.lepages.com
Year Founded: 1876
Sales Range: $25-49.9 Million
Emp.: 50
Adhesives Tapes & Glue Mfr
N.A.I.C.S.: 423840

LEPERCQ, DE NEUFLIZE & CO. INC
853 Broadway, Ste 1109, New York, NY 10003
Tel.: (212) 698-0700
Web Site: https://www.lepercq.com
Year Founded: 1936
Holding Company ; Asset Management
N.A.I.C.S.: 551112

LEPIERS' INC.
320 1st St E, Fosston, MN 56542
Tel.: (218) 435-1040
Web Site: http://www.lepier.com
Sales Range: $10-24.9 Million
Emp.: 25
Petroleum Products Whslr
N.A.I.C.S.: 424720
Larry LePier *(CEO)*

LEPPINKS INC.
303 W Main St, Belding, MI 48809
Tel.: (616) 794-3660
Web Site: http://www.leppinksfoodcenters.com
Rev.: $32,300,000
Emp.: 300
Grocery Stores
N.A.I.C.S.: 445110
Robert Leppink *(Chm)*
John Leppink *(Pres)*
Carrie Daenzer *(Dir-HR)*

LEPPO INC.
176 W Ave, Tallmadge, OH 44278
Tel.: (330) 633-3999   OH
Web Site: http://www.leppos.com
Year Founded: 1945
Sales Range: $10-24.9 Million
Emp.: 100
Provider of Used Equipment
N.A.I.C.S.: 532412
Mitch Cochran *(Mgr-Parts)*
John Stride *(Pres)*

LEPRINO FOODS COMPANY
1830 W 38th Ave, Denver, CO 80211
Tel.: (303) 480-2600   CO
Web Site: https://www.leprinofoods.com
Year Founded: 1950
Sales Range: $1-4.9 Billion
Emp.: 5,000
Cheese Manufacturing
N.A.I.C.S.: 311513
Larry Jensen *(Pres)*
Paul Adams *(VP & Controller)*

LERCH BATES INC.
9780 S Meridian Blvd Ste 450, Englewood, CO 80112
Tel.: (303) 795-7956   CO
Web Site: http://www.lerchbates.com
Year Founded: 1974
Technical Consulting Services
N.A.I.C.S.: 541350
Bart Stephan *(Pres & CEO)*
John Arther *(CFO)*
Jeff Marsh *(Exec VP-Architectural Design)*
Amanda Nelson *(Mgr-HR)*
Jeffrey Schultz *(Exec VP-Strategic Accounts)*
Mike Lagana *(Mgr-Florida)*
Rajeshwar Bajaaj *(Chm)*
Alyssa McGrath *(Dir-Strategic Accts)*
Jay Popp *(Exec VP-Intl)*
Robert Baker *(Mgr-Bus Line)*
Keenan W. Potter *(Mng Dir-China)*
Eric Rupe *(VP-Great Lakes)*
Tim Isbell *(VP-Strategic Accts)*
Amit Maitra *(Mng Dir)*
Jack Tornquist Jr. *(Exec VP-Tech Support)*

Subsidiaries:

Joseph Neto & Associates Inc.   (1)
1430 Broadway Ste 908, New York, NY 10018
Tel.: (212) 596-4690
Web Site: http://www.josephneto.com
Emp.: 25
Engineeering Services
N.A.I.C.S.: 541330
Joseph Neto *(Pres)*

Pie Consulting & Engineering, Inc.   (1)
6275 Joyce Dr Ste 200, Arvada, CO 80403
Tel.: (303) 552-0177
Engineeering Services
N.A.I.C.S.: 541330
Paul Duncan *(Pres)*

LERNER CORPORATION
2000 Tower Oaks Blvd Fl 8, Rockville, MD 20852
Tel.: (301) 984-1500
Web Site: http://www.lerner.com
Rev.: $10,600,000
Emp.: 100
Real Estate Managers
N.A.I.C.S.: 531210
Mark D. Lerner *(Principal)*
Scott Mead *(Mng Dir-Comml Property Mgmt)*
Suzanne Holt *(Mng Dir)*
Valerie Kardell *(Asst Dir-Mktg)*
Cynthia Muller *(Portfolio Mgr)*
Jay Shankman *(Mng Dir-Property Mgmt)*

LERNER ENTERPRISES
2000 Tower Oaks Blvd 8th Fl, Rockville, MD 20852
Tel.: (301) 284-6000
Web Site: http://www.lernerenterprises.com
Year Founded: 1952
Rev.: $157,700,000
Emp.: 500
Real Estate Services
N.A.I.C.S.: 237210
Cindy Clipper *(Mgr-Payroll & Benefits)*
Dilip Gor *(Controller-Credit)*
Laura Koehler *(Dir-Fin)*
Stephen Patton *(Project Mgr)*
David Howell *(Sr Mgr-Property)*
Natalie Greene *(Supvr-Tax)*
Pat May *(Atty)*
Ron Charvet Jr. *(Sr VP-Asset Mgmt)*
Walter L. Jarvis Jr. *(Mgr-Security)*

LERNER ENTERPRISES, INC.
PO Box 814, Plainview, NY 11803
Tel.: (516) 752-7557
Web Site: http://www.lernersportsmarketing.com
Year Founded: 1991
Sales Range: Less than $1 Million
Emp.: 4
Promotional Sports Marketing
N.A.I.C.S.: 541820
Allan Lerner *(Pres)*

LERNER REAL ESTATE ADVISORS, INC.
5020 W Linebaugh Ave Ste 250, Tampa, FL 33624
Tel.: (813) 915-3449
Web Site: http://www.lerneradvisors.com
Sales Range: $25-49.9 Million
Emp.: 10
Real Estate Financial Consulting & Advisory Services
N.A.I.C.S.: 541611
Harry Lerner *(Pres & Mng Partner)*
Scott Campbell *(Mng Partner)*
John Blakley *(VP-Sls & Mktg)*
Michael Dady *(VP-Plng & Permitting)*
Robert Bishop *(VP-Dev)*
James Glenn Marvin *(Dir-Dev)*
Chip Jones *(Dir-Dev)*
Leah Johnson *(Dir-Fin)*
David Jae *(Mgr-Fin)*

LEROY COOPERATIVE ASSOCIATION INC.
505 6th St, Le Roy, KS 66857
Tel.: (620) 964-2225
Web Site: http://www.leroycoop.coop
Year Founded: 1960
Emp.: 45
Grain Elevators & Grain Handling, Feed Mill & Other Farm Services
N.A.I.C.S.: 424510
Steve Raaf *(Chm)*
Jim Krueger *(Vice Chm)*

LEROY HILL COFFEE COMPANY INC.
3278 Halls Mill Rd, Mobile, AL 36606-2502
Tel.: (251) 476-1234   AL
Web Site: http://www.leroyhillcoffee.com
Year Founded: 1962
Sales Range: $10-24.9 Million
Emp.: 130
Roasted Coffee Products Mfr
N.A.I.C.S.: 311920
Debbie Hill *(Pres)*

LEROY HOLDING CO., INC.
26 Main St, Albany, NY 12204
Tel.: (518) 434-0109   NY
Web Site: http://www.leroyholding.com
Year Founded: 1967
Sales Range: $10-24.9 Million
Emp.: 70
Commercial Truck Leasing & Transportation Services
N.A.I.C.S.: 532120
Josie Brooks *(Sec)*

LEROY SPRINGS & COMPANY INC.
971 Tom Hall, Fort Mill, SC 29715
Tel.: (803) 547-1000
Web Site: http://www.leroysprings.com
Sales Range: $10-24.9 Million
Emp.: 175
Golf Course Operator
N.A.I.C.S.: 713910
Debbi Kiggins *(Controller)*
Timothy Patterson *(Pres)*

LERRO CORPORATION
905 Madison Ave, Norristown, PA 19403
Tel.: (610) 650-4100
Web Site: http://www.lerro.com
Year Founded: 1949
Sales Range: $10-24.9 Million
Emp.: 18
Sales, Service, Installation & Design of Professional Television Equipment
N.A.I.C.S.: 423690
Richard J. Murphy *(Pres)*
Marion Murphy *(Treas & Sec)*
Patrick Bucher *(Sr Acct Mgr)*

LES FILE DRYWALL INCORPORATED
116 Industrial Ave NE, Albuquerque, NM 87107
Tel.: (505) 345-8283
Web Site: http://www.lesfiledw.com
Rev.: $13,879,057
Emp.: 200
Drywall
N.A.I.C.S.: 238310
Jason File *(Pres)*

LES PINKHAM LINCOLN MERCURY, INC.
1505 North Dixie, Elizabethtown, KY 42701
Tel.: (270) 737-2460
Web Site: http://www.pinkhamcars.com
Year Founded: 1978
Sales Range: $10-24.9 Million
Emp.: 37
Car Whslr
N.A.I.C.S.: 441110

LES PINKHAM LINCOLN MERCURY, INC.

Les Pinkham Lincoln Mercury, Inc.—(Continued)
Bill Pinkham *(Pres)*
Steve Pinkham *(Owner)*

LES SCHWAB TIRE CENTERS OF OREGON, INC.
PO Box 5350, Bend, OR 97708
Tel.: (541) 447-4136 OR
Web Site: http://www.lesschwab.com
Year Founded: 1952
Sales Range: $1-4.9 Billion
Emp.: 7,000
Tires, Batteries, Alignment Machinery & Wheels Distr
N.A.I.C.S.: 441340
Jerry Darnielle *(CFO & Sr Exec VP)*
Jim Goad *(Treas & VP-Fin)*
John Britton *(Pres)*
Brian Capp *(VP-Mktg)*
Richard B. Borgman *(CEO)*
Mike Broberg *(CEO)*
Jack Cuniff *(Chm)*

Subsidiaries:

Les Schwab Holding Company (1)
646 NW Madras Hwy, Prineville, OR 97754
Tel.: (541) 447-4136
Web Site: http://www.lesschwab.com
Emp.: 300
Holding Company
N.A.I.C.S.: 551112
Richard B. Borgman *(Pres)*

Les Schwab Warehouse Center, Inc. (1)
646 NW Madras Hwy, Prineville, OR 97754 (100%)
Tel.: (541) 447-4136
Web Site: http://www.lesschwab.com
Emp.: 300
Tire Distr
N.A.I.C.S.: 423130
Dick Borgman *(CEO)*

LES STANFORD CHEVROLET INC.
21730 Michigan Ave, Dearborn, MI 48124
Tel.: (313) 565-6000
Web Site: http://www.lesstanford.com
Rev.: $30,000,000
Emp.: 100
Car Dealership
N.A.I.C.S.: 441110
Paul Stanford Sr. *(Pres)*

LES STUMPF FORD
3030 W College Ave, Appleton, WI 54914
Tel.: (920) 731-5211
Web Site:
    http://www.lesstumpfford.net
Year Founded: 1921
New & Used Car Dealers
N.A.I.C.S.: 441110
Corey Stumpf *(Pres)*

LESAINT LOGISTICS LLC
868 W Crossroads Pkwy, Romeoville, IL 60446
Tel.: (630) 243-5950
Web Site: http://www.lesaint.com
Logistic Services
N.A.I.C.S.: 541614
Jeff Pennington *(Pres)*
Dino Moler *(Exec VP-Client Svcs)*
Doug Carr *(COO)*

Subsidiaries:

LeSaint Chemical Logistics (1)
13812 Dex Dr, Dallas, TX 75244
Tel.: (972) 661-5400
Web Site: http://www.chemloginc.com
Sales Range: $1-9.9 Million
Emp.: 32
Chemical Warehousing & Distribution Services
N.A.I.C.S.: 493110
Jeff Pendleton *(CEO)*

LeSaint Logistics (1)
13204 Philadelphia Ave, Fontana, CA 92337
Tel.: (630) 243-5950
Web Site: http://www.lesaint.com
Logistic Services
N.A.I.C.S.: 541614
Doug Carr *(COO)*

LeSaint Logistics Transportation, Inc. (1)
4487 Le Saint Ct, Fairfield, OH 45014
Tel.: (513) 874-3900
Web Site: http://www.lesaint.com
Sales Range: $10-24.9 Million
Emp.: 100
General Freight Trucking, Long-Distance, Truckload
N.A.I.C.S.: 484121
Daniel Harmon *(VP-Ops)*
Jeff Pennington *(Pres)*

LESCARE KITCHENS INC.
495 Orange St, New Haven, CT 06511-3809
Tel.: (203) 755-1100
Web Site: http://www.lescarepgh.com
Sales Range: $10-24.9 Million
Emp.: 170
Wood Kitchen Cabinets
N.A.I.C.S.: 337110

LESCO DISTRIBUTING
1203 E Indus Dr, Orange City, FL 32763-7106
Tel.: (386) 775-7244
Web Site:
    http://www.lescodistributing.com
Year Founded: 1996
Sales Range: $10-24.9 Million
Emp.: 65
Supplier of Electrical Appliances
N.A.I.C.S.: 334417
Steve Elmore *(Gen Mgr)*
Greg Kacarab *(Gen Mgr)*
John Sabin *(Gen Mgr)*
D. Soliz *(Gen Mgr)*

LESEA BROADCASTING CORPORATION
61300 Ironwood Rd, South Bend, IN 46614
Tel.: (574) 291-8200 IN
Web Site: http://www.lesea.com
Year Founded: 1972
Sales Range: $25-49.9 Million
Emp.: 200
Provider of Broadcasting Services
N.A.I.C.S.: 516120
Dean Korsmo *(Mgr-Production)*
Joel Taylor *(Acct Exec-Sls)*
Anna Riblet *(Mgr-Sls)*
Ron Bedward *(Acct Exec)*
Jeff Castello *(Acct Exec)*
Jennifer Eash *(Acct Exec)*
Mike Pooler *(Acct Exec)*

LESIC & CAMPER COMMUNICATIONS
172 E State St Ste 410, Columbus, OH 43215
Tel.: (614) 224-0658
Web Site:
    http://www.lesiccamper.com
Year Founded: 2002
Emp.: 9
Public Relations Agency
N.A.I.C.S.: 541820
Jenny Camper *(Principal)*
Nancy Lesic *(Principal)*
Mark Rickel *(VP)*
Steve Luttner *(VP)*
Meagan Meyer Mulloy *(Sr Acct Exec)*
Angela Snyder *(Sr Acct Exec)*

Subsidiaries:

Lesic & Camper Communications (1)

812 Huron Rd Ste 460, Cleveland, OH 44115-1123
Tel.: (216) 696-7686
Web Site: http://www.lesiccamper.com
Public Relations Agency
N.A.I.C.S.: 541820

LESLIE EQUIPMENT COMPANY
6248 Webster Rd, Cowen, WV 26206
Tel.: (304) 226-3851
Web Site: http://www.lec1.com
Sales Range: $25-49.9 Million
Emp.: 55
General Construction Machinery & Equipment
N.A.I.C.S.: 423810
Tracey Rupe *(Mgr-Acctg)*
Todd Miller *(Mgr-Parts)*
Eric Gadd *(Mgr-HR & IT)*
Brad Hayhurst *(Mgr-Sls)*
Todd Perrine *(VP & Product Mgr-Support)*

Subsidiaries:

Leslie Equipment Company (1)
2098 Lillian Ln, Fairmont, WV 26554 (100%)
Tel.: (304) 534-5454
Web Site: http://www.leslieequipment.com
Sales Range: $25-49.9 Million
Emp.: 20
Tractor Dealer
N.A.I.C.S.: 423830
John Leslie *(Pres & Owner)*

Leslie Equipment Company (1)
8331 Meade Springer Rd, Ashland, KY 41102-8907
Tel.: (606) 928-3477
Web Site: http://www.lec1.com
Sales Range: $50-74.9 Million
Emp.: 1
Heavy Vehicle Equipment Distr
N.A.I.C.S.: 425120

Leslie Equipment Company (1)
195 Industrial Park Dr, Pikeville, KY 41501-1527
Tel.: (606) 432-0321
Sales Range: $50-74.9 Million
Emp.: 25
Construction Equipment Distr
N.A.I.C.S.: 425120
David Phillips *(Mgr-Store)*

Leslie Equipment Company - Marietta (1)
105 Tennis Center Dr, Marietta, OH 45750
Tel.: (740) 373-5255
Web Site: http://www.lec1.com
Industrial Machinery & Equipment Distr
N.A.I.C.S.: 423830

LESNIK, HIMMELSBACH, WILSON, & HEARL
3005 Hwy 17 Bypass N, Myrtle Beach, SC 29577-6742
Tel.: (843) 448-1123 SC
Web Site: http://www.lhwh.com
Year Founded: 1987
Rev.: $10,000,000
Emp.: 40
Advertising Agencies, Entertainment, Financial, Health Care, Real Estate, Travel & Tourism
N.A.I.C.S.: 541810
Andrew Lesnik *(Pres-New Bus)*
Paul Himmelsbach *(Exec VP)*
Vern Hearl *(VP & Sr Copywriter)*
Lei Gainer *(Dir-PR)*
Patricia Wilkes *(Acct Exec)*
Peter Michaels *(VP-Client Svcs)*
Keith Borshak *(VP & Dir-Creative)*
Steve Ellwood *(Sr Art Dir)*
Dick Gibson *(Mgr-Production)*
Jeff Small *(VP-Creative Technologies)*

LESON CHEVROLET COMPANY, INC.

U.S. PRIVATE

1501 Westbank Expy, Harvey, LA 70058-4465
Tel.: (504) 366-4381 LA
Web Site: http://www.lesonchevy.com
Year Founded: 1931
Sales Range: $125-149.9 Million
Emp.: 200
Retailer of New & Used Automobiles
N.A.I.C.S.: 441110
Donald Trapp *(Pres)*
Adriana Tena *(Controller)*
Michele Bruner *(Gen Mgr)*

LESS ANNOYING SOFTWARE, LLC
1017 Olive St Ste 300, Saint Louis, MO 63101
Web Site:
    http://www.lessannoyingcrm.com
Year Founded: 2009
Sales Range: $1-9.9 Million
Software Development Services
N.A.I.C.S.: 541511
Tyler King *(Co-Founder)*
Bracken King *(Co-Founder)*
Alex Haimann *(Head-Bus Dev)*
Jake Joraanstad *(CEO)*
Eston Taylor *(COO)*

LESSINGS INC.
3 Consuelo Pl, Oakdale, NY 11769
Tel.: (631) 567-8200
Web Site: http://www.lessings.com
Rev.: $11,500,000
Emp.: 500
Contract Food Services
N.A.I.C.S.: 722310
Ellen Barrett *(Dir-HR)*
Jennifer Cantin *(Dir-Mktg)*
Scott McKelvey *(CFO)*

LESSITER PUBLICATIONS, INC.
16655 W Wisconsin Ave, Brookfield, WI 53005
Tel.: (262) 782-4480 WI
Web Site: http://www.lesspub.com
Year Founded: 1981
Sales Range: $10-24.9 Million
Emp.: 322
Agricultural Trade Magazine Publisher
N.A.I.C.S.: 513120
Frank Lessiter *(Chm & CEO)*
Michael Storts *(VP-Corp Fin & Admin)*
Mike Lessiter *(Pres)*
Jim Perszyk *(Mgr-Acctg)*
Patrick Sharpe *(VP-Audience Dev)*

LESTELLE COMMUNICATIONS, LLC
1 Canal Pl 365 Canal St Ste 1750, New Orleans, LA 70130
Tel.: (504) 552-2727
Web Site:
    http://www.lestellecommunications.com
Sales Range: Less than $1 Million
Emp.: 1
Communications, Consulting, Corporate Communications, Crisis Communications, Media Relations, Nonprofit/Social Marketing, Public Relations
N.A.I.C.S.: 541820
Jim Lestelle *(Pres)*

LESTER BUILDING SYSTEMS, LLC
1111 2nd Ave S, Lester Prairie, MN 55354
Tel.: (320) 395-2531 MN
Web Site:
    http://www.lesterbuildings.com
Year Founded: 1947
Sales Range: $25-49.9 Million

Emp.: 200
Pre-Engineered Wood Frame Building Mfr
N.A.I.C.S.: 236220
John Hill *(Pres)*

LESTER INC.
19 Business Park Dr, Branford, CT 06405
Tel.: (203) 488-5265
Web Site: http://www.lesterinc.com
Year Founded: 2000
Sales Range: $150-199.9 Million
Emp.: 2,000
Outsourcing, Computer Related & Marketing Services
N.A.I.C.S.: 561499
Rajiv Samant *(CEO)*
Bob Lester *(Founder-Mktg Svcs Div)*
Peter Sanford *(VP-Fin & HR)*
Joan Marcus *(Sr VP)*
Dee Galligan *(VP-Ops)*

Subsidiaries:

Lester India   (1)
C-64 TTC Indl Area Turbhe, Navi, Mumbai, 400 705, India
Tel.: (91) 22 2767 0092
Outsourcing, Computer Related & Marketing Services
N.A.I.C.S.: 561499
Kothari Kothari *(Mng Dir)*

LET FREEDOM RING, INC.
2207 Concord Pike, Wilmington, DE 19803
Tel.: (610) 793-1800   DE
Web Site:
  http://www.letfreedomringusa.com
Year Founded: 2004
Rev.: $2,391,127
Assets: $58,662
Liabilities: $17,113
Net Worth: $41,549
Earnings: $13,724
Emp.: 4
Fiscal Year-end: 12/31/14
Civic & Social Organization
N.A.I.C.S.: 813410
Colin A. Hanna *(Pres)*
Valerie K. Martin *(Treas)*
Malcolm Macdougall *(Dir-Creative)*
Curtis P. Cheyney III *(Sec)*

LET'S DO LUNCH, INC.
310 W Alondra Blvd, Gardena, CA 90248
Tel.: (310) 523-3664
Web Site:
  http://www.integratedfoodservice.com
Year Founded: 1991
Sales Range: $10-24.9 Million
Emp.: 80
Perishable Prepared Food Mfr
N.A.I.C.S.: 311991
Jon Sugimoto *(VP)*
Michelle Bass *(Dir-Sls & Mktg)*

LET'S PLAY SPORTS, INC.
8300 S County Rd, Oklahoma City, OK 73169
Tel.: (405) 261-6076
Web Site:
  http://www.letsplaysoccer.com
Indoor Sports Facilities Operator
N.A.I.C.S.: 713940
Gary Archer *(Pres & CEO)*

Subsidiaries:

SoccerZone, Inc.   (1)
7187 S Sprinkle Rd, Portage, MI 49002
Tel.: (269) 329-1212
Web Site: http://www.soccer-zone.com
Rev.: $12,100,000
Emp.: 450
Indoor Recreational Sports Facility Operator
N.A.I.C.S.: 713940

LETA ENTERPRISES INC.
500 Auto Mall Dr, O'Fallon, MO 63368
Tel.: (636) 336-5000
Web Site: http://www.letahonda.com
Sales Range: $25-49.9 Million
Emp.: 67
New & Used Automobiles Dealers
N.A.I.C.S.: 441110
Michael Brown *(CFO)*
Allen Masengill *(Gen Mgr)*
Besrat Wolday *(Mgr-Fin)*
Bill Niederwimmer *(Mgr-Parts)*
Jeff Lind *(Dir-Svc)*
Josh Williams *(Mgr-Sls)*
Kevin Dilthey *(Mgr-Sls)*
Loretta Teece *(Mgr-Fin)*
Matt Craft *(Gen Mgr-Sls)*

LETHAL PERFORMANCE INC.
3161 Fairlane Farms Rd Ste 8, Wellington, FL 33414
Tel.: (561) 753-8105
Web Site:
  http://www.lethalperformance.com
Year Founded: 2004
Sales Range: $1-9.9 Million
Emp.: 10
Specialty Automotive Aftermarket Products
N.A.I.C.S.: 441330
Jared Rosen *(Pres & CEO)*

LETNES RESTAURANT INC.
137 2nd Ave S, Waite Park, MN 56387
Tel.: (320) 259-0589
Web Site: http://www.grizzlysgrill.com
Sales Range: $10-24.9 Million
Emp.: 8
Family Restaurant Operator
N.A.I.C.S.: 722511
Steven Letnes *(Pres & CEO)*
Curtis Letnes *(CFO)*

LETSOS COMPANY
PO Box 36927, Houston, TX 77236
Tel.: (713) 783-3200
Web Site: http://www.letsos.com
Sales Range: $75-99.9 Million
Emp.: 400
Plumbing Services
N.A.I.C.S.: 238220
Mark Letsos *(CEO)*

LETTERFOLDERS.COM
159 Paris Ave, Northvale, NJ 07647
Tel.: (201) 768-1940
Year Founded: 2002
Rev.: $5,200,000
Emp.: 14
Office Equipment Merchant Whslr
N.A.I.C.S.: 459410
Chris Corday *(Owner)*

LETTERSTREAM, INC.
8541 E Anderson Dr Ste 106, Scottsdale, AZ 85255
Tel.: (480) 473-3282
Web Site:
  http://www.letterstream.com
Year Founded: 2003
Sales Range: $1-9.9 Million
Emp.: 16
Full-Service Printing & Mailing Services
N.A.I.C.S.: 561431
David Patterson *(Pres)*
Chris Coleman *(Dir-IT)*

LETTS INDUSTRIES, INC.
1111 Bellevue St, Detroit, MI 48207-3647
Tel.: (313) 579-1100   MI
Year Founded: 1909

Holding Company; Automotive Components Mfr & Whslr
N.A.I.C.S.: 551112
Charles E. Letts Jr. *(Pres & CEO)*

Subsidiaries:

Powers & Sons, LLC   (1)
44700 Helm St, Plymouth, MI 48170
Tel.: (734) 354-6575
Web Site: http://www.powersandsonsllc.com
Automotive Steering & Suspension Components Mfr & Whslr
N.A.I.C.S.: 336330
Gene Messenger *(Dir-R&D)*

Corporate Headquarters (Domestic):

Powers & Sons, LLC - Montpelier   (2)
1613 Magda Dr, Montpelier, OH 43543
Tel.: (419) 485-3151
Web Site: http://www.powersandsonsllc.com
Emp.: 230
Automotive Steering & Suspension Components Mfr
N.A.I.C.S.: 336330
Randy Priest *(Mgr-Pur)*
Chris Fink *(Mgr-Design Engrg)*

Division (Domestic):

Pioneer Forge Division   (3)
101 Industrial Ave, Pioneer, OH 43554
Tel.: (419) 737-2373
Emp.: 90
Automotive Forgings Mfr
N.A.I.C.S.: 332111

LETTUCE ENTERTAIN YOU ENTERPRISES, INC.
5419 N Sheridan Rd, Chicago, IL 60640-1964
Tel.: (773) 878-7340   DE
Web Site: http://www.leye.com
Year Founded: 1971
Sales Range: $900-999.9 Million
Emp.: 7,500
Restaurant Owner & Operator
N.A.I.C.S.: 722511
Susie Southgate-Fox *(Exec VP-HR & Corp Ops)*
Jay Stieber *(Gen Counsel & Exec VP)*
Thomas Muno *(Sr VP-Acctg & Operational Analysis)*
Kevin Brown *(CEO)*
Fred Joast *(Co-Founder & Partner)*
Gabino Sotelino *(Mng Partner)*
John Buchanan *(Sr VP)*
Howard Katz *(Pres-Wildfire & Partner)*
Joe Decker *(VP)*
Carrol Symank *(VP-Food Safety & Trng)*
Steve LaHaie *(Sr VP-Shaw's Crab)*
Mark Dorian *(VP-Pur)*
Chris Favero *(Mng Partner)*
Christopher Meers *(Partner)*
Bob Loeschorn *(VP-Wildfire)*
Jennifer Bell *(Exec VP-Mktg)*
Geoff Alexander *(Pres-Wow Bao)*
Richard J. Melman *(Co-Founder, Chm, Pres & Partner)*
R. J. Melman *(Pres)*
Steve Donahue *(Sr VP-Acctg & Operational Analysis)*
Gerard Centioli *(Sr VP)*

LETTUCE FEED YOU INC.
120 Washington St Ste 201, Watertown, NY 13601
Tel.: (315) 782-8030
Year Founded: 1971
Sales Range: $10-24.9 Million
Emp.: 4
Fast-Food Restaurant, Chain
N.A.I.C.S.: 722513
Ricky Miller *(Bus Mgr)*

LETTUCE SOUPRISE YOU, INC.
2470 Briarcliff Rd NE Ste 47A, Atlanta, GA 30329-3012
Tel.: (404) 636-8549
Web Site:
  http://www.mylettucesoupriseyou.com
Sales Range: Less than $1 Million
Emp.: 3
Restaurant Services
N.A.I.C.S.: 722511
Joseph Sok *(VP)*
Juardy Juardy *(Pres)*

LEUNER INC.
315 Sunnymead Rd, Hillsborough, NJ 08844
Tel.: (908) 359-9599   NJ
Year Founded: 1945
Rev.: $36,000,000
Emp.: 120
Retailer of Tractor Trailers
N.A.I.C.S.: 423110
Thomas Leuner *(Pres & CEO)*

Subsidiaries:

Empire Southern Tier Equipment Corp.   (1)
315 Sunnymead Rd, Hillsborough, NJ 08844
Tel.: (908) 359-9599
Sales Range: $25-49.9 Million
Emp.: 100
Trucks & Trailers
N.A.I.C.S.: 333924
Thomas Leuner *(Pres & CEO)*

Lancaster Equipment Corporation   (1)
315 Sunnymead Rd, Hillsborough, NJ 08844-4638   (100%)
Sales Range: $10-24.9 Million
Emp.: 35
Automobiles & Other Motor Vehicles
N.A.I.C.S.: 423110

LEUPOLD & STEVENS, INC.
14400 NW Greenbrier Pkwy, Beaverton, OR 97006-5790
Tel.: (503) 526-1400   OR
Web Site: http://www.leupold.com
Year Founded: 1907
Sales Range: $150-199.9 Million
Emp.: 650
Scopes, Binoculars & Mounts Mfr
N.A.I.C.S.: 333310
Bruce T. Pettet *(Pres & CEO)*
Michael Wunnicke *(Dir-Mktg)*
Lucas Burt *(Mgr-Brand Creative)*
Riza Lesser *(Mgr-Strategic Partnerships)*

LEVCOR INTERNATIONAL INC.
151 W 40th Ste 903, New York, NY 10018
Tel.: (212) 354-8500   DE
Year Founded: 1964
Sales Range: $10-24.9 Million
Emp.: 99
Apparel Accessories Whslr
N.A.I.C.S.: 424310
Pramila D. Shaheed *(CFO & Sec)*
Robert A. Levinson *(Chm, Pres & CEO)*
Robert A. Levinson *(Chm, Pres & CEO)*

LEVCOR, INC.
9660 Old Katy Rd, Houston, TX 77055
Tel.: (713) 952-0366   TX
Web Site: http://www.levcor.com
Year Founded: 1980
Sales Range: $10-24.9 Million
Emp.: 35
Nonresidential Building Operators
N.A.I.C.S.: 531120

LEVCOR, INC.

Levcor, Inc.—(Continued)
Larry Levine *(Pres)*
Dan Smith *(Sr VP)*
Bronwen Harbour *(VP-Mgmt)*

Subsidiaries:

Northwest Mall, Inc. (1)
9600 Hempstead Rd, Houston, TX 77092
Tel.: (713) 681-1303
Web Site: http://www.northwest-mall.com
Nonresidential Buildings Operator
N.A.I.C.S.: 455110
Viki Guitry *(Gen Mgr)*

LEVEE LUMBER INC.
523 Levee St, Hoquiam, WA 98550
Tel.: (360) 532-1850
Web Site: http://www.levee.com
Year Founded: 1984
Rev.: $12,755,663
Emp.: 42
Building Materials & Tools Mfr
N.A.I.C.S.: 333120
Keith German *(Gen Mgr)*

LEVEL 11
720 3rd Ave Ste 800, Seattle, WA 98104
Tel.: (855) 585-1118
Web Site: http://www.level11.com
Year Founded: 2009
Sales Range: $1-9.9 Million
Emp.: 30
Networking Products & Services to Customers Worldwide
N.A.I.C.S.: 561499
Mark Hadland *(Mng Dir, Founder & CEO)*
Ric Merrifield *(Partner)*
Todd Asher *(Mng Dir)*
Glenn Curtis *(Dir-Engrg)*

LEVEL 4 TELCOM
100 SW Albany Ave Ste 110, Stuart, FL 34994
Tel.: (772) 873-7753
Web Site:
   http://www.level4telcom.com
Telecommunications Solutions
N.A.I.C.S.: 517810
Wayne Koletzky *(Officer-Pub Rels)*

Subsidiaries:

Phoenix Telecommunications, Inc. (1)
17887 SE Federal Hwy, Tequesta, FL 33469
Tel.: (813) 737-2158
Web Site: http://www.level4telcom.com
Radio, Television & Other Electronics Stores
N.A.I.C.S.: 449210

LEVEL EQUITY MANAGEMENT, LLC
2 Grand Central Twr 140 E 45th St 42nd Fl, New York, NY 10017
Tel.: (212) 660-2470   DE
Web Site: http://www.levelequity.com
Year Founded: 1997
Holding Company
N.A.I.C.S.: 551112
Barry A. Osherow *(Partner)*
Benjamin Levin *(Founder & Co-CEO)*
Nathan Linn *(COO)*
Jake Foster *(CTO)*
Sarah Sommer *(Partner)*
George McCulloch *(Co-CEO)*
Charles Chen *(Partner)*
Gautam Gupta *(Partner)*
Michael Bauer *(VP)*
Ari Herman *(VP-Fin & Ops)*
Brad Kniejski *(VP)*
Christopher Isaac *(Principal)*
Nick Berardo *(VP)*
Arthur Tingas *(VP)*
Arin Wolfson *(Operating Partner)*
David Fleishman *(VP)*
Luis Spradley *(VP)*

Subsidiaries:

Net Health Systems, Inc. (1)
40 24th St 1st Fl, Pittsburgh, PA 15222
Web Site: http://www.nethealth.com
Custom Computer Programming Services
N.A.I.C.S.: 541511
Patrick Colletti *(Chief Innovation Officer)*
Anthony Sanzo *(Exec Chm)*
Patrick Rooney *(CFO)*
Christopher Hayes *(CTO)*
Jason Baim *(Chief Strategy Officer & Chief Corp Dev Officer)*
James J. Quagliaroli *(Chm)*
Josh Pickus *(CEO)*
Christine Jones *(Chief Client Officer)*
Jason James *(CIO)*
Aaron Brandwein *(Chief Revenue Officer)*
Linda Kricher *(Chief HR Officer)*

Subsidiary (Domestic):

Casamba, LLC (2)
5210 Lewis Rd Ste 10, Agoura Hills, CA 91301
Tel.: (818) 991-9111
Web Site: http://www.casamba.net
Sales Range: $1-9.9 Million
Emp.: 16
Software Developer for Healthcare Industry
N.A.I.C.S.: 513210
Jane Moffett *(Chief Product Officer)*
Ronnie Amrany *(Founder & Chm)*
Doron Hetz *(VP-Ops)*
Don Moore *(VP-IT Ops)*
Veronica Ornelas *(VP-Fin)*
Will Jacobus *(Sr Project Mgr)*
Brian Dwyer *(Chief Revenue Officer)*
Billie Nutter *(CEO)*

Optima Healthcare Solutions, LLC (2)
4229 SW High Meadows Ave, Palm City, FL 34990
Tel.: (772) 403-1301
Web Site: http://www.optimahcs.com
Sales Range: $1-9.9 Million
Emp.: 90
Physical Therapy Software Publisher
N.A.I.C.S.: 513210
Steve Mackie *(Co-Founder)*
Michael Katri *(Co-Founder & COO)*
Ryan Katri *(Co-Founder)*
Aaron Brandwein *(Chief Revenue Officer)*
Pat Clark *(Co-CFO)*
Josh Pickus *(CEO)*
Randy Wallin *(Chief Security Officer)*
Jason James *(CIO)*
Dinesh Senanayake *(Co-CFO & Gen Mgr-RCM)*
Christine Jones *(Chief Customer Officer)*
Jeff Browning *(Chief Product & Engrg Officer)*

Subsidiary (Domestic):

Vantage Clinical Solutions, LLC (3)
1567 SW Chandler Ave, Bend, OR 97702
Tel.: (541) 550-7291
Revenue Cycle Management, Digital Marketing & Consulting Services
N.A.I.C.S.: 541613

Subsidiary (Domestic):

PointRight, Inc. (2)
150 CambridgePark Dr Ste 301, Cambridge, MA 02140
Tel.: (781) 457-5900
Web Site: http://www.pointright.com
Software Publisher
N.A.I.C.S.: 513210
Dean Staley *(VP-Fin & Admin)*
Steven Scott *(CEO)*
Alan Dahl *(Chm)*
Steven Littlehale *(Chief Clinical Officer & Exec VP)*
Michael Laureno *(CFO)*
Cesar Goulart *(CIO)*

Planet DDS, Inc. (1)
3990 Westerly Pl Ste 200, Newport Beach, CA 92660
Tel.: (714) 486-1345
Web Site: http://www.planetdds.com
Dental Services
N.A.I.C.S.: 423450
Eric Giesecke *(CEO)*
Richard Capilla *(VP-Strategic Accts)*
Chae Kim *(Sr VP-Product)*
Angelina Hendricks *(CTO)*
Tim Tyrell-Smith *(CMO)*
Matt Walker *(Chief Customer Officer)*
Mike Huffaker *(Chief Sls Officer)*
Stephen Fong *(CFO)*
Jennifer Bigelow *(VP-People)*

Subsidiary (Non-US):

Apteryx Imaging Inc. (2)
580 Hornby Street Ste 780, Vancouver, V6C 3B6, BC, Canada
Tel.: (604) 434-4614
Web Site: http://www.leddental.com
Sales Range: $10-24.9 Million
Cancer Detection System Mfr
N.A.I.C.S.: 325412
David Gane *(CEO)*
David Gane *(CEO)*

Subsidiary (US):

LED Dental Inc (3)
2 Ravinia Dr Unit 900, Atlanta, GA 30346
Tel.: (844) 952-7327
Web Site: http://www.leddental.com
Diagnostic Imaging Services
N.A.I.C.S.: 621512
Lamar Roberts *(Pres)*

Subsidiary (Domestic):

Brands on Fire, LLC (2)
11 Spokane St Ste 200, Wenatchee, WA 98801
Web Site: http://www.legwork.com
Sales Range: $1-9.9 Million
Emp.: 43
Software Development Services
N.A.I.C.S.: 541511

LEVELFIELD FINANCIAL, INC.
1300 W 19th St Ste 7948, Houston, TX 77008-9998
Tel.: (346) 443-2311
Web Site: https://lp.levelfield.us
Financial Services Company; Traditional Banking, Securities & Digital Assets Services
N.A.I.C.S.: 522110
Gene Grant II *(CEO)*

LEVELING 8, INC.
21553 East Apache St, Catoosa, OK 74015   OK
Year Founded: 2018
Cable TV Operators
N.A.I.C.S.: 516120
David E. Chymiak *(Owner)*

Subsidiaries:

ADDvantage Technologies Group Of Missouri Inc (1)
2675 E 28th St, Sedalia, MO 65301
Tel.: (660) 826-3011
Web Site: http://www.com-tech-services.com
Provider of Cable Services
N.A.I.C.S.: 423690

ADDvantage Technologies Group of Texas (1)
216 County Rd 3004, New Boston, TX 75570-5921
Tel.: (903) 628-2791
Web Site: http://www.tulsat.com
Wired Communication Line Equipment Whslr
N.A.I.C.S.: 423690
Johnny Lopez *(Mgr-Repair)*

NCS Industries, Inc. (1)
375 Ivyland Rd, Warminster, PA 18974
Tel.: (267) 803-0781
Web Site: http://www.ncsind.com
CATV Repairs & Services
N.A.I.C.S.: 811412
Fred Baker *(Gen Mgr-Sls)*
Mike Moran *(Engr-Sls)*

Tulsat-Atlanta LLC (1)
1221 E Houston St, Broken Arrow, OK 74012-4405
Tel.: (918) 251-2887
Web Site: http://www.tulsat.com
Electrical Equipment Maintenance & Distr
N.A.I.C.S.: 335999
David E. Chymiak *(Pres)*

LEVELTWO ADVERTISING
302 N Market St Ste 300, Dallas, TX 75202
Tel.: (214) 824-9782
Web Site: http://www.ltwo.com
Year Founded: 1999
Rev.: $24,500,000
Emp.: 26
Advetising Agency
N.A.I.C.S.: 541810
Evan Meeks *(Principal)*
Steve Choppin *(Principal)*
Kelly Loter *(Principal)*
Greg Ring *(Dir-Creative)*

LEVELWING MEDIA
260 W 35th St 8th Fl, New York, NY 10001
Tel.: (646) 216-8320
Web Site: http://www.levelwing.com
Year Founded: 2002
Sales Range: $50-74.9 Million
Emp.: 40
Advetising Agency
N.A.I.C.S.: 541810
Jeff Adelson-Yan *(Co-Founder & Pres)*
Steve Parker Jr. *(Co-Founder & CEO)*

LEVENGER COMPANY
420 S Congress Ave, Delray Beach, FL 33445
Tel.: (561) 276-2436
Web Site: http://www.levenger.com
Year Founded: 1987
Sales Range: $75-99.9 Million
Emp.: 120
Retail Mail Order
N.A.I.C.S.: 424120
Lori Leveen *(Chm)*
Steven Hansen *(CEO)*
Joseph Dolac *(VP-Mdsg)*

LEVENSON & HILL, INC.
717 N Harwood Ste 2000, Dallas, TX 75201
Tel.: (214) 880-0200
Web Site:
   http://www.levensonandhill.com
Year Founded: 1984
Sales Range: $10-24.9 Million
Emp.: 70
Communications, Consumer Marketing, Entertainment, Public Relations, Retail, Sales Promotion
N.A.I.C.S.: 541810
Barbara L. Levenson *(Pres & CEO)*
Robert McEnany *(CMO & Exec VP)*
Faithe Nicholson *(Chief Acctg Officer & Sr VP)*
Cindy Evans *(Sr VP)*
Susan Clarke *(VP-Entertainment Div)*
John Simon *(VP)*
Esther Lafuente *(Controller)*
Christian Hill *(Dir-Media)*
Henry Tatum *(VP & Dir-Comm Rels)*
Katie Velez *(Acct Exec)*
Andy Harmon *(Sr VP & Dir-Acct Svcs)*
Richard Graves *(Sr VP & Dir-Creative)*
Eric Leon *(Dir-Creative)*

LEVER GLOBAL CORPORATION
Level 11 9255 W Sunset Blvd, West Hollywood, CA 90069   DE

Year Founded: 2022
Software Development Services
N.A.I.C.S.: 541511
Tanya Garcia *(Officer)*
Trent McKendrick *(Founder)*

LEVERAGE MARKETING GROUP
117-119 S Main St, Newtown, CT 06470-2380
Tel.: (203) 270-6699   CT
Web Site: http://www.leverage-marketing.com
Year Founded: 1984
Sales Range: $1-9.9 Million
Emp.: 8
Advertising Agencies, Business-To-Business, Consumer Marketing, Graphic Design, High Technology, Public Relations, Sales Promotion
N.A.I.C.S.: 541810
Michael A. Casale *(Pres)*
Richard Brzozowski *(Sr VP-Creative Svcs)*
Tom Marks *(CEO & Gen Mgr)*
Donna Sullivan *(Sr Acct Mgr)*

LEVERAGED TECHNOLOGY INC.
440 Park Ave S, New York, NY 10016
Tel.: (212) 453-1000
Web Site: http://www.lev-tech.com
Sales Range: $75-99.9 Million
Emp.: 30
Online Services Technology Consultants
N.A.I.C.S.: 541512
Jim Walker *(Exec VP)*

LEVI, RAY & SHOUP, INC.
2401 W Monroe St, Springfield, IL 62704-1439
Tel.: (217) 793-3800   IL
Web Site: http://www.lrs.com
Year Founded: 1979
Sales Range: $25-49.9 Million
Emp.: 300
Computer Integrated Systems Design Services
N.A.I.C.S.: 541511
John Runions *(Dir-Alliance Sls)*
Max Dillahunty *(VP-PensionGold Retirement Solutions)*
Dick Levi *(Pres & CEO)*
Greg Collins *(Gen Counsel & Sr VP)*
Ryan Levi *(VP)*
Pam Benad *(Sr VP-Corp Admin)*
Brian Huggins *(VP-EOM Product Dev)*
James Masters *(VP-EMEA)*
Subsidiaries:

Capella Technologies, Inc.   (1)
2099 S St Coll Ste 500, Anaheim, CA 92806
Tel.: (714) 385-4900
Web Site: http://www.capellatech.com
Sales Range: $10-24.9 Million
Emp.: 15
Software Development Data Base Management Services
N.A.I.C.S.: 541511
Christina Gilbert *(Mgr)*

LEVIATE AIR GROUP
1700 Pacific Ave 4600, Dallas, TX 75201
Tel.: (877) 407-8507
Web Site: http://www.leviateair.com
Year Founded: 2014
Aviation Services
N.A.I.C.S.: 336412
Luis Barros *(Founder & CEO)*
Rob Rosenberg *(Mng Dir)*
Randall Mize *(Pres)*

LEVIATHAN CORP.
55 Washington St Ste 457, Brooklyn, NY 11201-8323
Tel.: (718) 701-5718
Web Site: http://www.leviathancorp.com
Year Founded: 1999
Sales Range: $25-49.9 Million
Emp.: 10
Financial Services
N.A.I.C.S.: 561499
Brian Cohn *(Founder & CEO)*
Neil Galland *(Dir-Sls-Africa)*
Cody Tilson *(Creative Dir)*
Kyle Shoup *(Exec Creative Dir)*

LEVICK STRATEGIC COMMUNICATIONS, LP
1900 M St NW, Washington, DC 20036
Tel.: (202) 973-1300   DE
Web Site: http://www.levick.com
Year Founded: 1991
Sales Range: $10-24.9 Million
Emp.: 70
Public Relations & Marketing Agency
N.A.I.C.S.: 541820
Richard S. Levick *(Pres & CEO)*
Larry Smith *(Sr VP)*
Jack Deschauer *(Sr VP)*
Kathryn Devito *(Chm-Digital Practice & Sr VP)*
John Lovallo *(Chm-Fin Practice & Sr VP)*
Ian McCaleb *(Chm-Litigation Practice & Sr VP)*
Michael Rubin *(Chm-Crisis Practice & Sr VP)*
Dan Rene *(Sr VP)*
Randall Samborn *(Sr VP)*
Madison Case *(VP)*
Megan Gabriel *(VP)*
Robert Gemmill *(VP)*
Emily Kiggins *(VP)*
Andrew Ricci *(VP)*
Rachel Racoosin *(Dir-Digital)*
Lisa Santopietro *(Controller)*
Sam Huxley *(Chm-Risk & Bus Strategy Practice & Sr VP)*
Alisha Morris *(VP-Ops & Admin)*

LEVIN ENTERPRISES INC.
112 Washington Ave Ste 250, Richmond, CA 94801-3990
Tel.: (510) 215-1515
Sales Range: $10-24.9 Million
Emp.: 2
Marine Terminals
N.A.I.C.S.: 488320
Gary Levin *(Pres)*

LEVIN FINANCIAL GROUP, INC.
4830 W Kennedy Blvd Ste 800, Tampa, FL 33609
Tel.: (813) 286-2280
Web Site: http://www.levinfinancialgroup.com
Year Founded: 1996
Sales Range: $1-9.9 Million
Emp.: 60
Investment Advisory, Financial Planning & Insurance Services
N.A.I.C.S.: 525990
Michael J. Levin *(Pres & CEO)*
Joanne Smith *(Bus Mgr)*
Frank Zito Jr. *(VP)*

LEVIN PROFESSIONAL SERVICES
11242 Grandview Ave, Wheaton, MD 20902
Tel.: (301) 942-6800
Web Site: http://www.wpsworld.com
Sales Range: $25-49.9 Million
Emp.: 50
Video & Audio Equipment
N.A.I.C.S.: 423990
Robert A. Levin *(Pres)*

LEVINE COMMUNICATIONS OFFICE
1180 S Beverly Dr Ste 301, Los Angeles, CA 90035
Tel.: (310) 300-0950
Web Site: http://www.lcoonline.com
Year Founded: 1983
Sales Range: Less than $1 Million
Emp.: 15
Advetising Agency
N.A.I.C.S.: 541810
Michael Levine *(Founder & Pres)*
Liam Collopy *(Exec VP)*
Alastair Duncan *(Acct Mgr)*
Lee Runchey *(Mgr-Acct)*
Eddie Garcia *(Sr Acct Mgr)*
Shannon Donnelly *(Acct Exec)*
Gia Ghadimian *(Dir-Ops)*

LEVINE LEICHTMAN CAPITAL PARTNERS, LLC
345 N Maple Dr Ste 300, Beverly Hills, CA 90210
Tel.: (310) 275-5335   CA
Web Site: http://www.llcp.com
Year Founded: 1984
Privater Equity Firm
N.A.I.C.S.: 523999
Lauren B. Leichtman *(Co-Founder & CEO)*
Robert A. Poletti *(Partner & Head-Originations)*
Stephen J. Hogan *(Partner, CFO & Chief Admin Officer)*
John P. Romney *(Mng Dir-Dallas)*
Michael B. Weinberg *(Mng Partner)*
Andrew Schwartz *(Sr Mng Dir)*
Wouter Snoeijers *(Mng Dir)*
David Wolmer *(Chief Compliance Officer, Mng Dir & Gen Counsel)*
John O'Neill *(Mng Dir-London)*
Brooke Burlingame Adams *(Dir-Charlotte)*
Erik Nobel *(Mng Dir-Sweden)*
Arthur E. Levine *(Pres & Partner)*
Debra Sherman *(Dir-IR Grp)*
Monty Ismail *(Dir-Investment Mgmt Grp)*
Luc Sandmann *(Dir-Investment Mgmt Grp)*

Subsidiaries:

AGDATA, LP   (1)
2100 Rexford Rd Ste 300, Charlotte, NC 28211
Tel.: (704) 364-7043
Web Site: http://www.agdata.net
Emp.: 135
Crop Protection Services
N.A.I.C.S.: 111998
Garrison Smith *(Gen Counsel & VP-Corp Dev)*
Heffy Provost *(CEO)*
Helgi Bloom *(Pres & CFO)*
Keith Davies *(CTO)*

Subsidiary (Domestic):

Focus Technology Group, Inc.   (2)
4515 Harding Rd Ste 315, Nashville, TN 37205
Tel.: (615) 353-0836
Web Site: http://www.focustg.com
Emp.: 17
IT Services, Including Database Management & Data Warehousing
N.A.I.C.S.: 541511
Jimmy Haverstick *(CEO & Co-Founder)*
Chris Glaser *(Co-Founder & COO)*
Nick Streams *(VP-Ops)*
Mark Emery *(VP-Client Rels)*

BSI LLC   (1)
601 E 64th Ave Bldg A, Denver, CO 80229   (100%)
Tel.: (303) 331-8777
Web Site: https://www.bsidesigns.com
Emp.: 100
Mfr of Food Guards, Counter Systems, Stainless Fabrication & Custom Solutions
N.A.I.C.S.: 331221
Bill Reeves *(CEO)*
Stephanie Gilbert *(Exec VP-Corp Growth Strategy)*
Mike Crider *(Exec VP-Operations)*
Dave Van Otterloo *(VP-Business Development)*
Jeff Goldberg *(VP-Finance)*
Abby Green *(Mktg Dir)*

BigHand Ltd.   (1)
27 Union Street, London, SE1 1SD, United Kingdom
Tel.: (44) 20 7940 5900
Web Site: http://www.bighand.com
Software Development Services
N.A.I.C.S.: 541511
Eric Wangler *(Pres-US & Canada)*
Dan Speed *(Mng Dir)*
James Kippenberger *(Mng Dir-Product Strategy & Innovation)*
Andy Fielder *(CTO)*
Ian Churchill *(CEO)*
Sam Toulson *(CFO)*
Rob Stote *(Mng Dir-Profitability)*

Subsidiary (US):

Iridium Technology OPCO, LLC   (2)
5470 Kietzke Ln Ste 300, Reno, NV 89511
Tel.: (775) 747-2353
Web Site: http://www.iridium-technology.com
Computer System Design Services
N.A.I.C.S.: 541512
Tom Jones *(Founder & CEO)*
Jeff Suhr *(Sr VP)*

Subsidiary (Domestic):

Data Fusion Technologies Inc.   (3)
15375 Barranca Pkwy Ste A201, Irvine, CA 92618
Tel.: (480) 491-0779
Web Site: http://www.dftech.com
Rev.: $2,200,000
Emp.: 40
Data Processing, Hosting & Related Services
N.A.I.C.S.: 518210

CJ Fallon Limited   (1)
Ground Floor Block B, Liffey Valley Office Campus, Dublin, 22, Ireland
Tel.: (353) 1 6166 400
Web Site: http://www.cjfallon.ie
Educational Books & Learning Aids Publisher
N.A.I.C.S.: 513130
Brian Gilsenan *(CEO)*

Capsa Solutions LLC   (1)
4253 NE 189th Ave, Portland, OR 97230
Tel.: (503) 766-2324
Web Site: http://www.capsahealthcare.com
Sales Range: $25-49.9 Million
Healthcare Equipment & Furnishing Mfr & Whslr
N.A.I.C.S.: 337127
John Himmelstein *(Sr VP-Sls)*

Subsidiary (Domestic):

Kirby Lester, LLC   (2)
13700 W Irma Lee Ct, Lake Forest, IL 60045
Tel.: (847) 984-3377
Web Site: http://www.kirbylester.com
Sales Range: $1-9.9 Million
Automated Pharmaceutical Dispensing Devices Mfr
N.A.I.C.S.: 334519
Christopher Thomsen *(VP-Bus Dev)*
Dave Johnson *(VP-Sls & Mktg)*
Dave Schultz *(CTO)*
Garry Zage *(Pres & CEO)*
Aleks Geltser *(VP-Engrg)*

Mass Medical Storage, LLC   (2)
7848 Barton St, Lenexa, KS 66214-3403
Tel.: (913) 438-8835
Web Site: http://www.massmedicalstorage.com
Custom Architectural Woodwork & Millwork Mfr
N.A.I.C.S.: 337212
Aubrey Guezuraga *(VP-Sls & Mktg)*

LEVINE LEICHTMAN CAPITAL PARTNERS, LLC

U.S. PRIVATE

Levine Leichtman Capital Partners, LLC—(Continued)

Specialty Carts, Inc. (2)
12949 Maurer Industrial Dr, Saint Louis, MO 63127
Tel.: (314) 843-4407
Web Site: http://www.specialtycartsinc.com
Sales Range: $1-9.9 Million
Emp.: 16
Healthcare Cart Mfr
N.A.I.C.S.: 423450
Ronald Bauers (Pres)

Genova Diagnostics, Inc. (1)
63 Zillicoa St, Asheville, NC 28801
Tel.: (828) 253-0621
Web Site: http://www.gdx.net
Sales Range: $10-24.9 Million
Clinical Laboratory Services
N.A.I.C.S.: 621511
Jennifer Holmes Gillen (Dir-Mktg)
Jeffrey Ledford (CEO)
Ceco Ivanov (CIO)
Amy Peace Brewer (Sr Dir-Laboratory)
Earlene Clark (Dir-HR-Compliance)
Hugh Watson (VP-Sls)
Craig Thiel (CFO)

Subsidiary (Domestic):

Metametrix, Inc. (2)
3425 Corporate Way, Duluth, GA 30096
Tel.: (770) 446-5483
Web Site: http://www.metametrix.com
Sales Range: $10-24.9 Million
Medical Laboratories
N.A.I.C.S.: 621511
Ted Hull (CEO)

HomeVestors of America, Inc. (1)
6500 Greenville Ave Ste 400, Dallas, TX 75206
Tel.: (972) 761-0046
Web Site: http://www.homevestors.com
Real Estate Services
N.A.I.C.S.: 523999
David Hicks (CEO)
Mark Kentner (VP-Ops)

Kilwin's Chocolates Franchise, Inc. (1)
1050 Bay View Rd, Petoskey, MI 49770
Tel.: (231) 347-3800
Web Site: http://www.kilwins.com
Sales Range: $1-9.9 Million
Emp.: 20
Confectionery Merchant Whslr
N.A.I.C.S.: 424450

Milton Industries, Inc. (1)
4500 W Cortland St, Chicago, IL 60639-5105
Tel.: (773) 235-9400
Web Site: http://www.miltonindustries.com
Sales Range: $75-99.9 Million
Emp.: 150
Mfr of Industrial & Hard Rubber Pressure Valves & Regulators; Mechanics Hand Tools; Aircraft & Motor Vehicle Measurement Equipment; Battery Testers; Electrical Filters; & Lubrication Equipment
N.A.I.C.S.: 332911
Steven Gregory (CFO)

Pacific Handy Cutter, Inc. (1)
17819 Gillette Ave, Irvine, CA 92614-6501
Tel.: (714) 662-1033
Web Site: http://www.go-phc.com
Carton Cutter & Razor Blade Cutting Tools Mfr
N.A.I.C.S.: 332215
Mark Marinovich (CEO)

Pacific World Corporation (1)
100 Technology Ste 200, Irvine, CA 92618
Tel.: (949) 598-2400
Web Site: http://www.pacificworldcorp.com
Sales Range: $25-49.9 Million
Nail & Beauty Care Produrs Supply
N.A.I.C.S.: 456120
Mlou Walker (CEO)
Ken DeBaene (Exec VP-Sls)
Diego Mandelbaum (Exec VP-Mktg)
Mike Matteo (COO)
Mark Payette (CFO)

Subsidiary (Domestic):

The W.E. Bassett Company (2)
100 Trap Falls Rd, Shelton, CT 06484
Tel.: (203) 929-8483
Web Site: http://www.trim.com
Sales Range: $25-49.9 Million
Manicure Implements, Gift Sets & Personal Care Products Mfr
N.A.I.C.S.: 339999

Resolution Economics, LLC (1)
1925 Century Park E 15th Fl, Los Angeles, CA 90067
Tel.: (310) 275-9137
Web Site: http://www.resecon.com
Scientific & Technical Consulting Services
N.A.I.C.S.: 541690
Ali Saad (Owner)
Hassan Assaf (Dir)
Richard Goldberg (Dir)

Division (Domestic):

Berkshire Associates, LLC (2)
8930 State Route 108 D, Columbia, MD 21045
Tel.: (410) 995-1195
Web Site: http://www.berkshireassociates.com
Rev.: $2,210,000
Emp.: 13
Administrative Management & General Management Consulting Service
N.A.I.C.S.: 541611
Dawn Stauffer Hyde (Founder)
Beth A. Ronnenburg (Pres)
Lynn A. Clements (Dir-Regulatory Affairs)
Karl Hester (Dir-IT & Product Dev)
Lisa Roeder (Bus Mgr)
Manoj Tiwari (VP-Bus & Product Dev)
Michele Whitehead (Sr Mgr-Client Svcs)
Cheryl Boyer (VP-Client Svcs)
Carolyn K. Pittman (Sr Mgr-Mktg)

Technical Safety Services, LLC (1)
620 Hearst Ave, Berkeley, CA 94710-1922
Tel.: (510) 845-5595
Web Site: http://www.techsafety.com
Testing Laboratories
N.A.I.C.S.: 541380
Brent Hart (CEO)

Subsidiary (Domestic):

Certified Environmental Particulate Air, Inc. (2)
1140 E Locust St, Ontario, CA 91761
Tel.: (909) 923-1988
Web Site: http://www.cepatest.com
Sales Range: $1-9.9 Million
Emp.: 12
Professional, Scientific & Technical Servicesy
N.A.I.C.S.: 541990
Donald W. Copeland (Pres & Treas)

Cornerstone Commissioning, Inc. (2)
22 Shepard Ct, Winchester, MA 01890
Tel.: (978) 887-8177
Web Site: http://www.cornerstonecx.com
Biotechnology Research Services
N.A.I.C.S.: 541714
Daniel Frasier (Pres)

Therapeutic Research Center LLC (1)
3120 W March Ln, Stockton, CA 95219-2368
Tel.: (209) 472-2240
Web Site: http://www.trchealthcare.com
Medication Training & Education Services
N.A.I.C.S.: 611699
Wes Crews (CEO)

Tropical Smoothie Cafe, LLC (1)
2813 5th Ave S, Fort Dodge, IA 50501-5558
Tel.: (515) 573-1199
Web Site: http://www.tropicalsmoothie.com
Rev.: $1,900,000
Emp.: 15
Coffee & Tea Mfr
N.A.I.C.S.: 311920
Cris Dayton (Principal)
Mike Rotondo (COO)
Barry Schnur (Chief Fin & Admin Officer)
Deborah von Kutzleben (CMO)
Charles Watson (CEO)

LEVINE MANAGEMENT GROUP INC.
822 S Robertson Blvd Ste 200, Los Angeles, CA 90035
Tel.: (310) 358-3489
Web Site: http://www.levinegroups.com
Sales Range: $10-24.9 Million
Emp.: 20
Apartment Building Operator
N.A.I.C.S.: 531110
Jeffrey S. Levine (Pres)
Juanita Owens (Supvr-Property)

LEVINE PROPERTIES, INC.
8514 McAlpine Park Dr Ste 190, Charlotte, NC 28211
Tel.: (704) 366-1981
Web Site: http://www.levineproperties.com
Sales Range: $25-49.9 Million
Emp.: 25
Real Estate Development & Management Services
N.A.I.C.S.: 237210
Daniel Levine (Pres & CEO)
Steve Smith (COO)
David Smith (Dir-Construction & Dev)

LEVIS CHEVROLET-CADILLAC
316 E Howze Beach Rd, Slidell, LA 70461
Tel.: (985) 643-1300
Web Site: http://www.levischevycadillac.com
Rev.: $12,900,000
Emp.: 70
New Car Dealers
N.A.I.C.S.: 441110
Keith Williams (Gen Mgr)
Rodney Girard (Dir-Fin)
Tim Andrews (Mgr-Fin)
Kelly Weathers (Office Mgr)
Robert Levis (Sec)

LEVITON MANUFACTURING COMPANY, INC.
201 N Service Rd, Melville, NY 11747 DE
Tel.: (631) 812-6000
Web Site: http://www.leviton.com
Year Founded: 1906
Electrical Wiring Devices & Related Products
N.A.I.C.S.: 332618
William W. Marshall (Sr VP-Sls & Mktg)
Daryoush Larizadeh (Pres & COO)
Stephen J. Yunker (Acct Mgr-Natl)
Bill Cheetham (VP-Distr Sls)
Philip Warner (VP/Gen Mgr-Lighting Bus Unit)

Subsidiaries:

American Insulated Wire Corp. (1)
201 N Service Rd, Melville, NY 11747-3138 (100%)
Tel.: (401) 726-0700
Sales Range: $25-49.9 Million
Emp.: 900
Mfrof Specialty Wire & Cable for Industry & Utilities
N.A.I.C.S.: 335921

Berk-Tek LLC (1)
132 White Oak Rd, New Holland, PA 17557
Tel.: (717) 354-6200
Web Site: http://www.berktek.com
Copper & Fiber Optic Cable Mfr
N.A.I.C.S.: 335929
Paul Trunk (Pres)

Division (Domestic):

Berk-Tek Electronics Division (2)
600 South Parker Street, Elm City, NC 27822
Tel.: (252) 236-4311
Web Site: http://www.berktek.us
Sales Range: $50-74.9 Million
Emp.: 150
Cable Mfr
N.A.I.C.S.: 332618

Lionel Fomperie (Gen Mgr)

Berk-Tek Fiber Optic Division (2)
100 Technology Park Ln, Fuquay Varina, NC 27526
Tel.: (919) 552-2061
Web Site: http://www.berktek.com
Sales Range: $50-74.9 Million
Emp.: 120
Copper & Fiber Optic Cable Mfr
N.A.I.C.S.: 335921
Mike Connaughton (Mgr-Data Center Segment)

Birchwood Lighting, Inc. (1)
3340 East La Palma Ave, Anaheim, CA 92806
Tel.: (714) 550-7118
Web Site: http://www.birchwoodlighting.com
Lighting Equipment, Commercial Lighting & Residential Lighting Fixtures Mfr
N.A.I.C.S.: 335139
Robert Cone (Dir-Mktg)

Home Automation, Inc. (1)
4330 Michoud Blvd, New Orleans, LA 70129
Tel.: (504) 736-9810
Web Site: http://www.homeauto.com
Sales Range: $10-24.9 Million
Emp.: 60
Electrical Home Control Equipment & Component Mfr
N.A.I.C.S.: 335999
John R. McLellan (Pres)
Allison Read (Dir-Sls-Intl)
Thomas Morgan (Dir-Product Mgmt)
Greg Rhoades (Dir-Mktg)

Intense Lighting, LLC (1)
3340 E La Palma Ave, Anaheim, CA 92806
Tel.: (714) 630-9877
Web Site: http://www.intenselighting.com
Sales Range: $1-9.9 Million
Emp.: 88
Lighting Fixtures & Products Mfr
N.A.I.C.S.: 335132
Allan Gray (CTO)
Kenny Eidsvold (Pres)
Pat Jones (VP-Sls-West)
Tom Elam (VP-Sls-South)
Bill Kofalk (Reg Dir-Sls-Northeast)
Maryann Cassidy (Reg Dir-Sls-Northwest)
Lou Calvo (Dir-Sls-Midwest)

Leviton (1)
7800 Trade Ctr Ave, El Paso, TX 79912-8407
Tel.: (915) 877-1200
Web Site: http://www.leviton.com
Mfr of Electrical Wiring Devices
N.A.I.C.S.: 335931
Bruno Filio (VP-Sls-Intl)

Leviton Integrated Metering Systems, Inc. (1)
11701 S Belcher Rd Ste 123, Largo, FL 33773
Tel.: (727) 539-1813
Sales Range: $10-24.9 Million
Emp.: 15
Electricity Measurement Equipment Mfr
N.A.I.C.S.: 334515

Leviton Manufacturing Company, Inc. - Plant 05 (1)
113 Industrial Blvd, Morganton, NC 28655
Tel.: (828) 584-1611
Web Site: http://www.leviton.com
Sales Range: $50-74.9 Million
Emp.: 600
Electrical Wiring Device Mfr
N.A.I.C.S.: 335931
Mark Pritchard (Mgr-HR)

Leviton Manufacturing of Canada Ltd. (1)
165 Hymus Boulevard, Pointe-Claire, H9R 1E9, QC, Canada (100%)
Tel.: (514) 954-1840
Web Site: http://www.leviton.com
Sales Range: $25-49.9 Million
Emp.: 60
Mfr of Electric Wiring Devices
N.A.I.C.S.: 335931
Jean Belhumeur (Pres & COO)

Leviton Manufacturing/Southern Devices (1)
113 Industrial Blvd, Morganton, NC 28655

Tel.: (828) 584-1611
Web Site: http://www.leviton.com
Emp.: 650
Electrical Wiring Device Mfr & Whslr
N.A.I.C.S.: 335999

Leviton Middle East (1)
Jebel Ali Free Zone View 19 7th Floor Office 701, Dubai, United Arab Emirates
Tel.: (971) 4 886 4722
Web Site: http://www.leviton.com
Sales Range: $10-24.9 Million
Emp.: 12
Electrical Wiring Device Mfr & Whslr
N.A.I.C.S.: 423610
Shady Youssef (Mng Dir)

Leviton Network Solutions (1)
2222 222nd St SE, Bothell, WA 98021-4422
Tel.: (425) 486-2222
Web Site: http://www.leviton.com
Sales Range: $10-24.9 Million
Emp.: 250
Structured Cabling Services
N.A.I.C.S.: 334210
Pete Newman (Sr Dir-Intl Bus Dev)
Brad Leland (VP-Sls)

Leviton Network Solutions Pvt. Ltd. (1)
Sunriver Embassy Gold Links Business Park Off Intermediate Ring Road, Indiranagar Koramangala, Bengaluru, 560071, India
Tel.: (91) 80 4322 5671
Web Site: http://www.leviton.com
Electrical Wiring Device Mfr & Whslr
N.A.I.C.S.: 423610

Leviton Srl de C.V. (1)
Lagotana 43 Huichapan, Mexico, 11290, Mexico (100%)
Tel.: (52) 5550821040
Web Site: http://www.leviton.com
Sales Range: $25-49.9 Million
Emp.: 18
Mfr of Transformers
N.A.I.C.S.: 335311

Leviton/LES (1)
20497 SW Teton Ave, Tualatin, OR 97062
Tel.: (503) 404-5500
Web Site: http://www.leviton.com
Lighting Equipment Mfr & Whslr
N.A.I.C.S.: 335139

Visioneering Corp (1)
35 Oak Street, Toronto, M9N 1A1, ON, Canada
Tel.: (461) 245-7991
Web Site: http://www.viscor.com
Lighting & On-Lighting Products Mfr
N.A.I.C.S.: 335132
William Wiener (Pres)

LEVITT HOMES CORPORATION
B5 Calle Tabonuco Ste 207, Guaynabo, PR 00968
Tel.: (787) 781-9292
Year Founded: 1968
Sales Range: $50-74.9 Million
Emp.: 100
Single-Family Housing Construction
N.A.I.C.S.: 236115
Carmen Roman (Controller)
Jose Rodriguez (Sr VP)

LEVITTOWN FISH MARKET INC.
137 Marine St, Farmingdale, NY 11735
Tel.: (631) 420-8239
Web Site:
http://www.levittownfish.com
Sales Range: $50-74.9 Million
Emp.: 35
Fish, Fresh
N.A.I.C.S.: 424460
Robert Tuccillo (Pres)

LEVLANE ADVERTISING, PR & INTERACTIVE
100 Penn Sq E, Philadelphia, PA 19107
Tel.: (215) 825-9600
Web Site: http://www.levlane.com
Year Founded: 1984
Rev.: $40,000,000
Emp.: 35
Advetising Agency
N.A.I.C.S.: 541810
David Lane (Co-Founder & Pres)
Bruce Lev (Chief Creative Officer)
Tony Sweeney (Sr VP & Dir-Media)
Debbey Racano (Sr VP & Dir-Creative)
Drake Newkirk (VP & Dir-Creative-Interactive)
Lori Miller (VP & Strategist)
Jason Rossano (VP)
Katie Rose Thornton (Acct Mgr)
Caroline Pennartz (Acct Mgr)
Lynn Eckenrode (Mgr-Media)
Sonya Cooper (Acct Dir-Adv)
Jerry Selber (Copywriter)
Francesca Gunning (Acct Mgr)
Cortney Boothman (Acct Coord)
Myles Kellam (Dir-Client Dev)
Scott D. Tattar Sr. (Sr VP & Dir-Pub Rel)

Subsidiaries:

LevLane Advertising/PR/Interactive-Florida (1)
1326 E Fairfax Cir, Boynton Beach, FL 33436-8612
Tel.: (561) 963-0490
Web Site: http://www.levlane.com
Sales Range: $10-24.9 Million
Emp.: 1
N.A.I.C.S.: 541810
David Lane (Founder & Pres)
Bruce Lev (Chief Creative Officer)
Chris Ponzio (Acct Dir)
Scott Tattar (Sr VP)
Debbey Racano (Dir-Creative)

LEVONIAN BROTHERS INC.
27 River St, Troy, NY 12180-4449
Tel.: (518) 274-3610 NY
Year Founded: 1947
Sales Range: $75-99.9 Million
Emp.: 65
Meat Products Mfr & Distr
N.A.I.C.S.: 424470
Robert G. Nazarian (Pres)
James McCormick (Plant Mgr)

LEVY GROUP, INC.
512 7th Ave, New York, NY 10018-4603
Tel.: (212) 764-7800
Web Site:
http://www.thelevygroupinc.com
Year Founded: 1953
Sales Range: $150-199.9 Million
Emp.: 150
Women's Coats Mfr
N.A.I.C.S.: 315250
Michael Harman (CFO)

Subsidiaries:

Seabreeze Properties, Inc. (1)
204 Heaver Plz 1301 York Rd, Lutherville, MD 21093 (100%)
Tel.: (410) 321-7650
Homesite Sales
N.A.I.C.S.: 459910

LEVY JEWELERS INC.
2 E Broughton St, Savannah, GA 31401
Tel.: (912) 233-1163
Web Site:
http://www.levyjewelers.com
Sales Range: $10-24.9 Million
Emp.: 56
Jewelry Stores
N.A.I.C.S.: 458310
Lowell Kronowitz (Owner)
Brad Allman (Mgr)
Tony Boggs (COO)

LEVY MARKETING & AWARDS
2415 N Albany Ave Unit 1, Tampa, FL 33607-3019
Tel.: (813) 540-5197
Web Site: http://www.levymarketingawards.com
Sales Range: $10-24.9 Million
Emp.: 55
Trophy Whslr
N.A.I.C.S.: 423940
Michele C. Adams (Pres & CEO)
Allison Adams (VP-Ops)
Vanessa Leon (VP-Bus Dev)
Mike Adams (VP-Sls)

LEVY SECURITY CORPORATION
8750 W Bryn Mawr Ste 1000, Chicago, IL 60631
Tel.: (773) 867-9204 IL
Web Site:
http://www.levysecurity.com
Year Founded: 1976
Sales Range: $10-24.9 Million
Emp.: 900
Security & Loss Prevention Consulting Services
N.A.I.C.S.: 561612
Debbie G. Levy (Founder & CEO)
Thomas Johnson (Asst VP-Ops)
James C. Taff (Exec VP-Admin)
Abe Barkin (Pres & COO)

LEW A. CUMMINGS CO., INC.
4 Peters Brook Dr, Hooksett, NH 03106
Tel.: (603) 625-6901
Web Site:
http://www.cummingsprinting.com
Year Founded: 1914
Sales Range: $10-24.9 Million
Emp.: 100
Printing Services
N.A.I.C.S.: 323111
Jack Cummings (Owner)
Mark Hamel (COO)
John Foss (Mgr-Sls)
Chris Philippy (Plant Mgr)
Jeff Paquette (Mgr-Prepress)
Jeff Baines (Mgr-Postpress)
Sue Orr (Mgr-Customer Svc)
Karl Stone (Controller)

LEW JAN TEXTILE CORP.
366 Veterans Memorial Hwy, Commack, NY 11725
Tel.: (631) 543-0531
Web Site: http://www.lewjan.com
Rev.: $20,400,000
Emp.: 6
Textiles Mfr
N.A.I.C.S.: 424310
Lewis Janicola (Pres)
Leslie Shapiro (Acct Exec-Sls Support)
Scott Janicola (Owner)

Subsidiaries:

Comfort Care (1)
368 Veterans Memorial Hwy, Commack, NY 11725
Tel.: (631) 543-0531
Web Site: http://www.pnwt.com
Emp.: 8
Piece Goods & Other Fabrics
N.A.I.C.S.: 424310
Scott Janicola (Gen Mgr)

LEWARE CONSTRUCTION COMPANY OF FLORIDA, INC.
925 Thomas Ave, Leesburg, FL 34748
Tel.: (352) 787-1616 FL
Web Site: http://www.lewarecc.com
Sales Range: $25-49.9 Million
Emp.: 150
Highway, Street & Bridge Construction
N.A.I.C.S.: 237310
Scott M. Leware (Treas, Sec & VP)
Keith Waugh (VP)
James F. Leware Jr. (Pres)

LEWER LIFE INSURANCE COMPANY INC.
4534 Wornall Rd, Kansas City, MO 64111
Tel.: (816) 753-4390 MO
Web Site: http://www.lewer.com
Year Founded: 1956
Sales Range: $75-99.9 Million
Emp.: 50
Life Insurance Services
N.A.I.C.S.: 524130
Mike Lewer (Pres)
John Owens (VP-Special Markets)
Mike Dlugolecki (VP)
Lori Kaylor (VP-Comm)

LEWIS & CLARK CAPITAL LLC
120 S Central Ave Ste 1000, St. Louis, MN 63105
Tel.: (314) 392-5257
Web Site:
https://lewisandclarkcapital.com
Emp.: 100
Investment Services
N.A.I.C.S.: 523999
Thomas J. Hillman (Mng Partner)

Subsidiaries:

PCI, Inc. (1)
10800 Baur Blvd, Saint Louis, MO 63132-1629
Tel.: (314) 872-9333
Web Site: http://www.pcistl.com
Sales Range: $1-9.9 Million
Emp.: 25
Cleaning & Beauty Care Items
N.A.I.C.S.: 325612
Charles B. Von Doersten (Founder)
Steve McLaughlin (Pres)

LEWIS & MICHAEL, INC.
1827 Woodman Dr, Dayton, OH 45420
Tel.: (937) 252-6683
Web Site: http://www.atlaslm.com
Year Founded: 1950
Sales Range: $10-24.9 Million
Emp.: 125
Moving & Storage Services
N.A.I.C.S.: 484210
David Lewis (Pres)
Kathy Batts (VP-Sls)

LEWIS & RAULERSON, INC.
1759 State St, Waycross, GA 31501-6714
Tel.: (912) 283-2623 GA
Web Site:
http://www.lewisandraulerson.com
Year Founded: 1938
Sales Range: $50-74.9 Million
Emp.: 340
Convenience Store Services
N.A.I.C.S.: 445131
Bill Raulerson (Owner)

LEWIS & SHERON TEXTILE COMPANY
4570 Commerce Cir SW, Atlanta, GA 30336
Tel.: (404) 691-6656
Web Site: http://www.lewis-sheron-textile.com
Rev.: $11,077,435
Emp.: 32
Piece Goods & Other Fabrics
N.A.I.C.S.: 424310

LEWIS & SHERON TEXTILE COMPANY

Lewis & Sheron Textile Company—(Continued)
Anthony Rockmore *(Mgr-Custodial)*
David Pelter *(Mgr-Mdse)*
Gail Johnekins *(Mgr-Front Desk)*
Melinda Daniels *(Mgr-Shipping)*
Ricky Booth *(Mgr-Construction)*
Stacey Sheron *(CEO & Dir-Creative)*
Tommie Harber *(Mgr-Acct)*
Ward Feely *(Mgr-Customer Svc)*

LEWIS ADVERTISING, INC.
1050 Country Club Rd, Rocky Mount, NC 27804
Tel.: (252) 443-5131
Web Site:
  http://www.lewisadvertising.com
Year Founded: 1969
Sales Range: $25-49.9 Million
Emp.: 47
Advetising Agency
N.A.I.C.S.: 541810
Gene L. Lewis *(Chm)*
Donald H. Williams *(Pres)*
Fred Arnold *(VP & Assoc Dir-Creative)*
Susan Harper *(VP-Production)*
Jim Lowdermilk *(VP-Acct Svc)*
Amy Miller *(Mgr-Production)*
Phil Greer *(Sr VP & Acct Dir)*
Vicki Raper *(VP-Media)*

LEWIS BRISBOIS BISGAARD & SMITH LLP
633 West Fifth St Ste 4000, Los Angeles, CA 90071-2601
Tel.: (213) 250-1800
Web Site: http://www.lbbslaw.com
Year Founded: 1979
Sales Range: $250-299.9 Million
Emp.: 800
Business Law Services
N.A.I.C.S.: 541110
Roy M. Brisbois *(Partner)*
Christopher P. Bisgaard *(Partner)*
Nancy L. Cohen *(Partner)*
Jeffrey Spiegel *(Partner)*
Julie L. Bell *(Partner-Raleigh)*
Christopher J. Derrenbacher *(Partner)*
Phillip J. Anthony *(Mng Partner-Raleigh)*
Jessica L. Skladzien *(Partner)*
Willow Arnold *(Partner)*
Naomi J. Skura *(Partner)*
Kenneth J. Kim *(Partner)*
Kelly M. Ognibene *(Partner)*
Natasha V. Dighe *(Partner)*
Nicole Jones *(Partner)*
Jonathan Kepko *(Partner)*
Allison E. Mullings *(Partner)*
Martha L. Heiberger *(Partner)*
Michael Nathan Giacopelli *(Partner)*
Eileen T. Budd *(Partner)*
Jordan J. Ford *(Partner-Kansas City & Wichita)*
Julie Maurer *(Partner)*
Jason Hall *(Partner)*
Jeanette Cardenas *(Partner)*
Kenneth B. Walton *(Partner)*
Courtney A. Longo *(Partner)*
Chris Rodriguez *(Partner)*
Andrew Bluth *(Partner-Comml Litigation Practice)*
Leiza Dolghih *(Partner)*
Earl Touchstone *(Partner-Comml Litigation Practice)*
Cleve Glenn *(Partner-Corp Practice)*
Louis A. Huber III *(Partner)*

LEWIS BROTHERS BAKERIES, INC.
500 N Fulton Ave, Evansville, IN 47710-1571
Tel.: (812) 425-4642 IL
Web Site:
  http://www.healthylifebread.com
Year Founded: 1925
Sales Range: $200-249.9 Million
Emp.: 1,500
Mfr & Distributor of Baked Products
N.A.I.C.S.: 311812
R. Jack Lewis *(Prés & CEO)*
Peggy S. Lewis *(Exec VP)*
Jeffery Sankovitch *(CFO)*

Subsidiaries:
Hartford Bakery, Inc. (1)
500 N Fulton Ave, Evansville, IN 47710-1571
Tel.: (812) 425-4642
Web Site: http://www.lewisbakeries.net
Fresh Baked Breads & Bakery Products
N.A.I.C.S.: 311812
R. Jack Lewis Jr. *(Pres & CEO)*

Lewis Vincennes, Inc. (1)
2792 S Old Decker Rd, Vincennes, IN 47591-6109 (100%)
Tel.: (812) 886-6533
Web Site: http://www.lewisbakeries.com
Sales Range: $25-49.9 Million
Emp.: 175
Mfr of Bakery Products
N.A.I.C.S.: 424490
Dan Feyer *(Supvr-Office Svcs)*

Division (Domestic):
Lewis Bakeries (2)
800 Boyd Blvd, La Porte, IN 46350-4419 (100%)
Tel.: (219) 362-4561
Web Site: http://www.lewisbakeries.com
Sales Range: $50-74.9 Million
Bread & Buns
N.A.I.C.S.: 311812
R. Jack Lewis Jr. *(COO)*

LEWIS CHEMICAL COMPANY
PO Box 231, Rome, GA 30165
Tel.: (706) 295-7577
Web Site: http://www.lewischem.com
Year Founded: 2006
Sales Range: $10-24.9 Million
Emp.: 30
Specialty Chemical & Surfactant Mfr
N.A.I.C.S.: 325180
Gregg Lewis *(Co-Owner)*
Diane Lewis *(Co-Owner)*

LEWIS COMMODITIES, INC.
100 N Main St, Lewis, KS 67552
Tel.: (620) 324-5536
Web Site: http://www.lewiscom.org
Sales Range: $25-49.9 Million
Emp.: 50
Grain Elevators
N.A.I.C.S.: 424510
Tom Holaday *(Office Mgr)*
Bobby Martin *(Gen Mgr)*

LEWIS COMMUNICATIONS
2030 1st Ave N, Birmingham, AL 35203
Tel.: (205) 980-0774 AL
Web Site:
  http://www.lewiscommunications.com
Year Founded: 1951
Sales Range: $75-99.9 Million
Emp.: 80
Advertising Agency Services
N.A.I.C.S.: 541810
Larry Norris *(Pres & CEO)*

Subsidiaries:
Lewis Communications (1)
30 Burton Hills Blvd Ste 207, Nashville, TN 37215-6184
Tel.: (615) 661-4995
Web Site:
  http://www.lewiscommunications.com
Emp.: 15
Advertising Agencies
N.A.I.C.S.: 541810
Robert Froedge *(Dir-Creative)*
Sharon Harms *(Dir-Creative Art)*

LEWIS CORP.
15136 W Hunziker Rd, Pocatello, ID 83202
Tel.: (208) 238-1202 ID
Web Site: http://www.lcorp.com
Year Founded: 2000
Sales Range: $10-24.9 Million
Emp.: 50
Contractor of Mechanical Equipment, Heating & Air Conditioning
N.A.I.C.S.: 238220
Waylin Lewis *(Pres & CEO)*
Kenyan Lewis *(COO & VP)*
Malcolm Pope *(Controller)*

LEWIS COUNTY PRIMARY CARE CENTER
211 KY 59, Vanceburg, KY 41179
Tel.: (606) 796-3029 KY
Web Site: http://www.primaryplus.net
Year Founded: 1983
Sales Range: $10-24.9 Million
Emp.: 184
Health Care Srvices
N.A.I.C.S.: 622110
Jerry Urgin *(CEO)*

LEWIS DIRECT, INC.
400 Andrew Way, Superior, CO 80027-8300
Tel.: (303) 494-0730
Web Site: http://www.lewis-direct.com
Sales Range: $1-9.9 Million
Emp.: 8
Direct Marketing
N.A.I.C.S.: 541860
Mark Lewis *(Pres)*

LEWIS DRUG, INC.
2701 S Minnesota Ave Ste 1, Sioux Falls, SD 57105-4746
Tel.: (605) 367-2800 SD
Web Site: http://www.lewisdrug.com
Year Founded: 1946
Sales Range: $100-124.9 Million
Emp.: 1,000
Drugs & Mass Merchandising
N.A.I.C.S.: 455110
Mark E. Griffin *(Pres & CEO)*
Scott Cross *(CFO & Exec VP)*
Robert Meyer *(Sr VP-Mdsg)*
William Ladwig *(Sr VP-Professional Svcs)*

Subsidiaries:
Lewis Drug Brandon (1)
115 Splitrock Blvd, Brandon, SD 57005 (100%)
Tel.: (605) 367-2000
Web Site: http://www.lewisdrug.com
Sales Range: $10-24.9 Million
Emp.: 25
Pharmacy Distr
N.A.I.C.S.: 455110
Mark E. Griffin *(Pres & CEO)*

Lewis Drug Eastgate (1)
1301 E 10th St, Sioux Falls, SD 57103-1780
Tel.: (605) 367-2000
Web Site: http://www.lewisdrug.com
Sales Range: $25-49.9 Million
Emp.: 100
Drugs & Mass Merchandising
N.A.I.C.S.: 456110
Mark E. Griffin *(Owner, Pres & CEO)*
Scott Cross *(CFO & Exec VP)*

Lewis Drug Huron (1)
1950 Dakota Ave S, Huron, SD 57350-4026
Tel.: (605) 352-6495
Web Site: http://www.lewisdrug.com
Sales Range: $10-24.9 Million
Emp.: 35
Drugs & Mass Merchandising
N.A.I.C.S.: 455110
Matt Breems *(Mgr)*

Lewis Drug Southeast (1)
4409 E 26th St, Sioux Falls, SD 57103-4136

Tel.: (605) 367-2770
Web Site: http://www.lewisdrug.com
Sales Range: $25-49.9 Million
Emp.: 100
Drugs & Mass Merchandising
N.A.I.C.S.: 456110
Mark E. Griffin *(Pres & CEO)*

Lewis Drug Southgate (1)
5500 W 41st St, Sioux Falls, SD 57106 (100%)
Tel.: (605) 367-2000
Web Site: http://www.lewisdrug.com
Sales Range: $25-49.9 Million
Emp.: 100
Drugs & Mass Merchandising
N.A.I.C.S.: 456110

Lewis Drug Southwest (1)
5500 W 41st St, Sioux Falls, SD 57106-1009
Tel.: (605) 367-2000
Web Site: http://www.lewisdrug.com
Sales Range: $10-24.9 Million
Emp.: 100
Drugs & Mass Merchandising
N.A.I.C.S.: 455219
Bob Deaton *(Mgr-Store)*

Lewis Drug Westgate (1)
2700 W 12th St, Sioux Falls, SD 57104
Tel.: (605) 367-2000
Web Site: http://www.lewisdrug.com
Sales Range: $25-49.9 Million
Emp.: 100
Drugs & Mass Merchandising
N.A.I.C.S.: 456110
Scott Cross *(Exec VP)*

LEWIS ENERGY GROUP LTD
10101 Reunion Pl Ste 1000, San Antonio, TX 78216
Tel.: (210) 384-3200
Web Site:
  http://www.lewisenergy.com
Rev.: $150,000,000
Emp.: 275
Investment Holding Companies, Except Banks
N.A.I.C.S.: 211120
Rodney R. Lewis *(Founder & CEO)*
Michael Lacayo *(Controller-Intl)*
Jennifer Swisher *(Coord-Construction)*
Ricardo A. Torres *(Mgr-Reservoir Enrgrg)*
Randy Dill *(Chief Admin Officer)*
Stan R. Jumper *(Exec VP-Geology)*
William J. Howard Jr. *(Sr Mgr-Audit)*

LEWIS ENTERPRISES
451 Heritage Dr Ste 215, Pompano Beach, FL 33060
Tel.: (954) 782-1750
Web Site: http://www.herschellgordonlewis.com
Sales Range: $1-9.9 Million
Emp.: 19
Direct Marketing Services
N.A.I.C.S.: 541890
Herschell Gordon Lewis *(Pres)*

LEWIS FLOOR & HOME
1840 Skokie Blvd, Northbrook, IL 60062
Tel.: (847) 835-2400
Web Site:
  http://www.lewisfloorandhome.com
Rev.: $12,359,027
Emp.: 75
Home Design & Flooring Centers
N.A.I.C.S.: 449121
Susie Axelrad *(VP)*

LEWIS FOOD TOWN INC.
3316 S Shaver, South Houston, TX 77587
Tel.: (713) 947-7778 TX
Web Site:
  http://www.foodtownshopper.com
Year Founded: 1994

COMPANIES

Sales Range: $10-24.9 Million
Emp.: 25
Grocery Stores
N.A.I.C.S.: 445110
Mark Snively *(Mgr-Market)*
Robert Brown *(Mgr-Meat Dept)*

LEWIS FOODS INC.
6 Thorndal Cir, Darien, CT 06820
Tel.: (203) 656-3661
Web Site: http://www.lewisfoods.com
Sales Range: $25-49.9 Million
Emp.: 500
Fast Food Restaurant Operator
N.A.I.C.S.: 722513
Jim R. Lewis *(Pres)*

LEWIS GLASS, INC.
3085 Bellbrook Dr, Memphis, TN 38116
Tel.: (901) 332-3182
Year Founded: 1987
Sales Range: $10-24.9 Million
Emp.: 80
Automobile Glass
N.A.I.C.S.: 423120
Everett D. Lewis *(Pres)*

LEWIS HYMAN INC.
860 E Sandhill Ave, Carson, CA 90746-1221
Tel.: (310) 532-5700   NY
Web Site:
  http://www.lewishymaninc.com
Year Founded: 1930
Sales Range: $10-24.9 Million
Emp.: 60
Home Furnishing Whslr
N.A.I.C.S.: 423220
James Hyman *(Pres)*
Robert Leblanc *(COO)*

LEWIS INDUSTRIAL SERVICES, INC.
931 Grandview Ave, Muscatine, IA 52761
Tel.: (563) 263-2355
Web Site:
  http://www.lewisindustrial.com
Year Founded: 1964
Sales Range: $10-24.9 Million
Emp.: 75
Fabricated Structural Metal Mfr
N.A.I.C.S.: 332312
Steve Foster *(Co-Owner)*
Chris Benson *(Co-Owner)*

LEWIS M. CARTER MANUFACTURING CO.
US Hwy 84 W, Donalsonville, GA 39845
Tel.: (229) 524-2197
Web Site: http://www.lmcarter.com
Sales Range: $50-74.9 Million
Emp.: 160
Hulling Agricultural Machinery
N.A.I.C.S.: 333111
Stanley Brackin *(Supvr-Line)*

LEWIS MANAGEMENT INC.
3373 N College, Fayetteville, AR 72703
Tel.: (479) 442-5301
Web Site:
  http://www.lewisfordsales.com
Sales Range: $50-74.9 Million
Emp.: 250
Sales of Automobiles, New & Used
N.A.I.C.S.: 441110
Mike Baldwin *(Mgr-Inventory)*
Scott Jones *(Mgr-Fin)*
Justin Davis *(Mgr-Fin)*
Lance Drinkard *(Dir-Mktg)*
Ryan McElroy *(Mgr-Parts)*

Subsidiaries:

Lewis Brothers Leasing Co. Inc.   (1)
3373 N College Ave, Fayetteville, AR 72703
Tel.: (479) 442-5301
Web Site: http://www.lewissuperstore.com
Sales Range: $10-24.9 Million
Emp.: 3
Property & Equipment Leasing
N.A.I.C.S.: 532420

Lewis Ford   (1)
3373 N College Ave, Fayetteville, AR 72703
Tel.: (479) 442-5301
Web Site:
  http://www.northwestarkansasford.com
Rev.: $1,700,000
Emp.: 45
Automobile Dealership
N.A.I.C.S.: 441110
Tommy Lewis *(Owner)*

LEWIS MARINE SUPPLY INC.
220 SW 32nd St, Fort Lauderdale, FL 33315
Tel.: (954) 523-4371
Web Site:
  http://www.lewismarine.com
Rev.: $21,500,000
Emp.: 100
Marine Supplies
N.A.I.C.S.: 423860
John Stephens *(Gen Counsel & VP)*
Mindy Fagan *(Mgr-Traffic)*
Chelsea Beyer *(Pres)*

Subsidiaries:

Jerry's Marine Service FL, LLC   (1)
100 SW 16th St, Fort Lauderdale, FL 33315
Tel.: (954) 525-0311
Web Site: http://www.jerrysmarine.com
Rev.: $10,400,000
Emp.: 60
Marine Propulsion Machinery & Equipment
N.A.I.C.S.: 423860
Jonathan Lewis *(Pres)*

LEWIS MITTMAN INC.
979 3rd Ave Fl 9, New York, NY 10022
Tel.: (336) 841-3028
Web Site:
  http://www.lewismittman.com
Sales Range: $10-24.9 Million
Emp.: 200
Upholstered Household Furniture
N.A.I.C.S.: 337121
Ira Glazer *(Owner)*

LEWIS ONE PLAZA CENTER CORPORATION
1 Plaza Ctr, Beckley, WV 25801
Tel.: (304) 253-2755   WV
Web Site:
  http://www.lewisautomotive.com
Year Founded: 1991
Sales Range: $25-49.9 Million
Emp.: 105
Holding Company; New & Used Car Dealers
N.A.I.C.S.: 551112

Subsidiaries:

Lewis Chevrolet Company   (1)
1 Plaza Ctr PO Box 1500, Beckley, WV 25801   (100%)
Tel.: (304) 253-2755
Web Site: http://www.lewisautomotive.com
Sales Range: $10-24.9 Million
New & Used Car Dealer
N.A.I.C.S.: 441110
Chad Hopkins *(Gen Mgr)*

LEWIS OPERATING CORP.
1156 N Mountain Ave, Upland, CA 91786
Tel.: (909) 985-0971
Web Site: http://www.lewisop.com
Year Founded: 1955
Sales Range: $500-549.9 Million
Emp.: 500

Real Estate & Construction Services
N.A.I.C.S.: 531390
Richard A. Lewis *(Pres)*
John M. Goodman *(CEO & Exec VP)*
Roger G. Lewis *(Exec VP)*
Randall W. Lewis *(Exec VP-Mktg)*
Jennifer A. Lewis *(VP)*
David L. Linden *(Sr VP-Asset Mgmt)*
Bryan T. Goodman *(Sr VP/Mgr-Southern California Planned Communities)*
Robert E. Lewis *(Pres-Nevada)*

Subsidiaries:

Lewis Investment Companies, LLC   (1)
1156 N Mtn Ave, Upland, CA 91786-3633
Tel.: (909) 985-0971
Web Site: http://www.lewisop.com
Sales Range: $125-149.9 Million
Emp.: 250
Residential Developers
N.A.I.C.S.: 236220
John Goodman *(CEO)*
Richard A. Lewis *(Pres)*
Edna Montag *(Office Mgr)*

Western Land Properties   (1)
1156 N Mtn Ave, Upland, CA 91786-3633   (100%)
Tel.: (909) 985-0971
Web Site:
  http://www.westernlandproperties.com
Sales Range: $125-149.9 Million
Emp.: 141
Residential Developer
N.A.I.C.S.: 236220

LEWIS PETROLEUM PRODUCTS CO.
450 W 5th St, Salida, CO 81201
Tel.: (719) 539-6673
Rev.: $13,500,000
Emp.: 4
Petroleum Bulk Stations
N.A.I.C.S.: 424710

LEWIS PROPERTIES INC.
14772 Plz Dr Ste 200, Tustin, CA 92780
Tel.: (714) 730-9000
Rev.: $12,500,000
Emp.: 2
Operative Builders
N.A.I.C.S.: 236117
James Lewis *(Gen Counsel)*
David A. Lewis *(Pres)*
Bobby A. Bradley *(Mng Partner)*

LEWIS ROCA ROTHGERBER CHRISTIE LLP
201 E Washington St Ste 1200, Phoenix, AZ 85004
Tel.: (602) 262-5311   AZ
Web Site: http://www.lrrc.com
Year Founded: 1950
Emp.: 300
Law firm
N.A.I.C.S.: 541110
Emily A. Bayton *(Partner-Denver & Phoenix)*
Amy E. Altshuler *(Partner-Phoenix)*
Edwin A. Barkel *(Partner)*
Bryant D. Barber *(Partner)*
John E. Bragonje *(Partner-Los Angeles)*
Stephen M. Bressler *(Partner)*
Scott K. Brown *(Partner)*
Scott M. Browning *(Partner-Denver)*
Jeffrey H. Albright *(Partner-Albuquerque)*
Art Hasan *(Partner)*
Michael Phalen *(Partner-Bus Transactions Practice Grp)*
Kevin M. Posterro *(CFO)*
Marla Hudgens *(Partner)*
Jessica Fuller *(Partner)*
Tamara Goodlette *(Mng Partner-Colorado)*

LEWIS TRANSPORTATION SYSTEMS

Alfredo T. Alonso *(Principal)*
Oliver S. Bajracharya *(Partner-Los Angeles)*
Trevor G. Bartel *(Partner-Denver)*
D. Stuart Bartow *(Partner-Silicon Valley)*
Paul Michael Bielecki *(Principal-Phoenix)*
Frederick J. Baumann *(Partner-Denver)*
G. Warren Bleeker *(Partner-Los Angeles)*
Chad S. Caby *(Partner-Denver)*
Flavia Campbell *(Partner-Phoenix)*
Thomas H. Campbell *(Partner-Phoenix)*
Anderson L. Carper *(Partner-Phoenix)*
Rob Charles *(Partner-Tucson & Las Vegas)*
Joshua T. Chu *(Partner-Los Angeles & Irvine)*
Joy Allen Woller *(Partner-Denver)*
Karen L. Witt *(Partner-Denver)*
John C. West *(Partner-Phoenix)*
Jon Weiss *(Partner-Phoenix)*
Anne Wang *(Partner-Los Angeles)*
Peter R. Wand *(Partner-Phoenix)*
Dan R. Waite *(Partner-Las Vegas)*
James R. Walker *(Partner-Denver)*
Douglas B. Tumminello *(Partner-Denver)*
Kenneth Van Winkle Jr. *(Mng Partner)*

LEWIS STAGES INC.
549 W 500 S, Salt Lake City, UT 84101
Tel.: (801) 359-8677
Web Site:
  http://www.lewisstages.com
Year Founded: 1914
Sales Range: $10-24.9 Million
Emp.: 150
Bus Charters & Limousine Service
N.A.I.C.S.: 485510
Steven O. Lewis *(Vice Chm)*
Richard Bizzaro *(Pres)*

LEWIS TOYOTA INC.
2951 SW Fairlawn Rd, Topeka, KS 66614
Tel.: (785) 273-2220
Web Site: http://www.lewistoyota.com
Sales Range: $25-49.9 Million
Emp.: 65
Sell & Service New & Used Automobiles
N.A.I.C.S.: 441110
Rod Lewis *(Pres)*

LEWIS TRANSPORT INC.
116 Campbellsville St No 5, Columbia, KY 42728
Tel.: (270) 384-4132
Web Site:
  http://www.lewistransportinc.com
Sales Range: $100-124.9 Million
Emp.: 12
Liquid Petroleum Transport, Non-Local
N.A.I.C.S.: 484230
Pam Scott *(Pres)*

LEWIS TRANSPORTATION SYSTEMS
4001 12th Ave N, Fargo, ND 58102
Tel.: (701) 282-5330
Sales Range: $10-24.9 Million
Investment Holding Companies, Except Banks
N.A.I.C.S.: 551112

Subsidiaries:

Dakota Cartage Company Inc   (1)
4001 12th Ave N, Fargo, ND 58106

LEWIS TRANSPORTATION SYSTEMS

Lewis Transportation Systems—(Continued)
Tel.: (701) 282-5330
Sales Range: $10-24.9 Million
Emp.: 120
Trucking Except Local
N.A.I.C.S.: 484121

LEWIS TREE SERVICE INC.
300 Lucius Gordon Dr, West Henrietta, NY 14586-9686
Tel.: (585) 436-3208 NY
Web Site: http://www.lewistree.com
Year Founded: 1938
Sales Range: $10-24.9 Million
Emp.: 25
Ornamental Shrub & Tree Services
N.A.I.C.S.: 561730
Bernard J. Kelly *(VP-Treasury & Capital Investments & Asst Sec)*
Thomas R. Rogers *(Pres & CEO)*
Laura Ribas *(Dir-Mktg)*
James Stenger *(CFO & Sr VP)*
Dennis L. Brown Jr. *(COO & Sr VP)*

LEWIS, THOMASON, KING, KRIEG & WALDROP, P.C.
1 Center Sq 5th Fl 620 Market St, Knoxville, TN 37902
Tel.: (865) 546-4646 TN
Web Site: http://www.lewisking.com
Year Founded: 1960
Emp.: 125
Law firm
N.A.I.C.S.: 541110
Lisa Ramsay Cole *(Pres & Mng Partner)*
Rodney A. Fields *(Mng Partner-Knoxville)*
Andrew Grams *(Atty)*
R. Loy Waldrop Jr. *(Owner)*

Subsidiaries:

Lewis, Thomason, King, Krieg & Waldrop, P.C. - Memphis (1)
1 Commerce Sq 40 S Main St Ste 2900, Memphis, TN 38103
Tel.: (901) 525-8721
Web Site: http://www.lewisthomason.com
Emp.: 65
Law firm
N.A.I.C.S.: 541110
J. Kimbrough Johnson *(Partner)*
Albert C. Harvey *(Partner)*
Jerry E. Mitchell *(Partner)*
Michael M. Keeney *(Mng Partner-Memphis)*
Lucas Davidson *(Atty)*
Michael Lewis *(Atty)*
William H. Haltom Jr. *(Partner)*

LEWIS-PRICE & ASSOCIATES, INC.
8200 Greensboro Dr Ste 805, McLean, VA 22102
Tel.: (703) 727-9182
Web Site: http://www.lewisprice.com
Year Founded: 2003
Sales Range: $10-24.9 Million
Emp.: 99
Staffing & Recruitment Services
N.A.I.C.S.: 541612
Ken Coleman *(Founder, Pres & CEO)*

LEWIS-SMITH CORPORATION
1306 Columbia Hwy PO Drawer 6236, Dothan, AL 36301
Tel.: (334) 793-5088
Web Site: http://www.lewis-smithsupply.com
Year Founded: 1974
Sales Range: $10-24.9 Million
Emp.: 75
Plumbing & Hydronic Heating Supplies
N.A.I.C.S.: 423720
Benny Buchanan *(Exec VP)*
Mark Smith *(Pres)*
Dena Smith *(Controller)*

Leslie Wingate *(Mgr-Showroom)*
Tim Benton *(Gen Mgr-HVAC & Mgr-Personnel)*
Kenneth Kirkland *(Mgr-Enterprise Branch)*
Robert Mckinnon *(Branch Mgr-Marianna)*

LEWISTON DAILY SUN
104 Park St, Lewiston, ME 04240
Tel.: (207) 784-5411
Web Site: http://www.sunjournal.com
Sales Range: $10-24.9 Million
Emp.: 240
Fiscal Year-end: 12/31/14
Newspapers, Publishing & Printing
N.A.I.C.S.: 513110
Steve Costello *(VP-Mktg)*
Maureen Wedge *(VP-HR)*

LEWISTON SALES INC.
21241 Dutchmans Crossing Rd, Lewiston, MN 55952
Tel.: (507) 523-2112
Web Site: http://www.lewistonsales.com
Rev.: $12,000,000
Emp.: 12
Livestock
N.A.I.C.S.: 424520

LEX PRODUCTS CORP.
15 Progress Dr, Shelton, CT 06484
Tel.: (203) 363-3738
Web Site: http://www.lexproducts.com
Year Founded: 1989
Sales Range: $50-74.9 Million
Emp.: 212
Electrical Components Mfr & Distr
N.A.I.C.S.: 335999
Bob Luther *(Founder & CEO)*
Liz Luther *(Treas)*
Jeff deRecat *(Mgr-Sls-West)*
Donald E. Kneir *(Pres)*
Mary Luther *(Dir-Process Improvement)*

LEXA INTERNATIONAL CORPORATION
1 Landmark Sq Ste 407, Stamford, CT 06901-2601
Tel.: (203) 326-5200 DE
Year Founded: 1920
Sales Range: $100-124.9 Million
Emp.: 1,600
Investment Holding Company
N.A.I.C.S.: 551112
Antonia Johnson *(Chm)*

LEXAGENE HOLDINGS INC.
500 CUMMINGS CTR., SUITE 4550, BEVERLY, MA 01915
Tel.: (800) 215-1824 BC
N.A.I.C.S.: 339113

LEXCOM TELECOMMUNICATIONS
1803 Horseshoe Pike, Honey Brook, PA 19344
Tel.: (610) 942-7771
Web Site: http://www.4lex.com
Sales Range: $50-74.9 Million
Emp.: 15
Telephone & Telegraphic Equipment
N.A.I.C.S.: 423690
James Scott *(Pres & CEO)*
Alexis Scott *(Controller)*

LEXEL IMAGING SYSTEMS INC.
510 Henry Clay Blvd, Lexington, KY 40505-4050
Tel.: (859) 721-1600 DE
Web Site: http://www.lexelimaging.com

Year Founded: 1930
Cathode Ray Tubes Mfr
N.A.I.C.S.: 334419
Bill Frohoff *(Pres)*

LEXICON COMMUNICATIONS CORP.
520 Bellmore Way, Pasadena, CA 91103
Tel.: (626) 683-9200
Web Site: http://www.crisismanagement.com
Year Founded: 1983
Sales Range: $1-9.9 Million
Emp.: 15
Public Relations Agency
N.A.I.C.S.: 541820
Steven B. Fink *(Pres)*

LEXICON CONSULTING, INC.
124 W Main St Ste 270, El Cajon, CA 92020
Tel.: (619) 792-1530
Web Site: http://www.lexiconinc.com
Year Founded: 2005
Sales Range: $10-24.9 Million
Emp.: 50
Cultural Immersion & Language Training Services for Military Personnel; Translators & Interpreters for Overseas Military
N.A.I.C.S.: 541930
Jamie Arundell-Latshaw *(Pres & CEO)*
Terry Sharp *(COO)*
Bruce Greene *(Dir-Contracts)*

LEXICON, INC.
8900 Fourche Dam Pike, Little Rock, AR 72206
Tel.: (501) 490-4200
Web Site: http://www.lexicon-inc.com
Year Founded: 1968
Sales Range: $300-349.9 Million
Emp.: 1,400
Holding Company; Metal Fabrication & Construction Services
N.A.I.C.S.: 551112
Thomas B. Schueck *(Founder)*
Brandy Thomas *(Mgr-Benefits)*

Subsidiaries:

Heritage Links (1)
13131 Champions Dr Ste 105, Houston, TX 77069
Tel.: (281) 866-0909
Web Site: http://www.heritage-links.com
Sales Range: $1-9.9 Million
Emp.: 20
Golf Course Construction Services
N.A.I.C.S.: 541320
Jon O'Donnell *(Pres)*

L-Con Constructors Company (1)
12301 Kurland Dr Ste 200, Houston, TX 77034
Tel.: (281) 484-5266
Web Site: http://www.l-con.com
Sales Range: $1-9.9 Million
Emp.: 100
Heavy Industries Construction & Engineering Services
N.A.I.C.S.: 541330

Schueck Steel (1)
8900 Fourche Dam Pike, Little Rock, AR 72206
Tel.: (501) 490-4200
Web Site: http://www.schueck.com
Rev.: $129,000,000
Emp.: 300
Structural Steel Erection Services
N.A.I.C.S.: 238120

LEXINGTON CENTER CORPORATION
430 W Vine St, Lexington, KY 40507
Tel.: (859) 233-4567 KY
Web Site: http://www.lexingtoncenter.com

Year Founded: 1972
Sales Range: $10-24.9 Million
Emp.: 734
Meeting Space Provider
N.A.I.C.S.: 531120
Merrill Richardson *(Dir-Facilities Admin)*
Sheila Kenny *(Dir-Mktg & Comm)*
Chester Maull *(Dir-HR)*
Melissa Conley *(Mgr-Lexpo)*
Bob Stoops *(Mgr-Technical Svcs)*
William B. Owen *(Pres & CEO)*
Caroline Puterbaugh *(Mgr-Mall)*
Luanne Franklin *(Dir-Performing Arts)*
Joe Fields *(Dir-Convention Sls)*
Carl Hall *(Dir-Arena Mgmt)*
Ray Ball *(Sec)*
Holly Wiedemann *(Vice Chm)*
Craig Turner *(Chm)*
David Herald *(Mgr-Security & Guest Svcs)*
Neal Werner *(Dir-Bus Affairs)*
Robert Elliston *(Chm-Fin & Treas)*

LEXINGTON GROUP, INC.
380 Union St, West Springfield, MA 01089
Tel.: (413) 746-3064
Web Site: https://www.lexingtongroupinc.com
Year Founded: 1989
Rev.: $1,200,000
Emp.: 3
Agents & Managers for Artists, Athletes, Entertainers & Other Public Figures
N.A.I.C.S.: 711410

LEXINGTON JEWELERS EXCHANGE
57 JFK St, Cambridge, MA 02138
Tel.: (617) 864-1227
Sales Range: $10-24.9 Million
Emp.: 37
Jewelry, Precious Stones & Precious Metals
N.A.I.C.S.: 458310

LEXINGTON TROTS BREEDERS ASSOCIATION
1200 Red Mile Rd, Lexington, KY 40504
Tel.: (859) 255-0752
Web Site: http://www.theredmile.com
Rev.: $70,000,000
Emp.: 42
Harness Track
N.A.I.C.S.: 711212
Joe Costa Jr. *(CEO)*

LEXINGTON WEALTH MANAGEMENT
12 Waltham St, Lexington, MA 02421
Tel.: (781) 860-7745
Web Site: http://www.lexingtonwealth.com
Sales Range: $10-24.9 Million
Emp.: 17
Wealth Management Services
N.A.I.C.S.: 523940
Michael Tucci *(Co-Founder & CEO)*
Kristine Porcaro *(Co-Founder & Pres)*
Glenn Frank *(Dir-Investment Tax Strategy)*
Mark S. Carley *(Mng Dir)*
Frank Censullo *(Sr Mgr-Relationship)*
Scott S. Klein *(Sr Mgr-Relationship)*
Brenda VanderSluis *(VP-Ops)*
Jordi Mullor *(Mng Dir-Ops & Mktg)*
Kerry Luria *(Mng Dir-Client Advisor Svc)*

LEXUS OF NORTH MIAMI

COMPANIES

14100 Biscayne Blvd Ste 1, North Miami Beach, FL 33181-1202
Tel.: (786) 528-3747
Web Site: http://www.lexusofnorthmiami.com
Rev.: $65,000,000
Emp.: 105
New & Used Car Dealers
N.A.I.C.S.: 441110
Craig M. Zinn *(Owner, Pres & CEO)*
Chris Gonzalez *(Mgr-Fin)*
Dave Burnett *(Dir-Parts & Svc)*
Gordon Hunter *(Dir-Pre-Owned Sls)*

LEXUS OF THOUSAND OAKS
3601 Auto Mall Dr, Thousand Oaks, CA 91362
Tel.: (805) 497-7109
Web Site: http://www.lexusofthousandoaks.com
Year Founded: 1974
Sales Range: $25-49.9 Million
Emp.: 89
Car Whslr
N.A.I.C.S.: 441110
John Anderson *(Owner & Pres)*

LEXUS OF TOLEDO
7505 W Central Ave, Toledo, OH 43617
Tel.: (419) 841-3500
Web Site: http://www.lexus.com
Year Founded: 1992
Sales Range: $10-24.9 Million
Emp.: 60
New Car Whslr
N.A.I.C.S.: 441110
Chad Bolles *(CFO)*
Tim Koehrman *(Gen Mgr)*
Dave White Sr. *(Owner)*

LEXUS OF VALENCIA
24033 Creekside Rd, Valencia, CA 91355
Tel.: (661) 260-2000
Web Site: http://www.lexusofvalencia.com
Year Founded: 1968
Sales Range: $10-24.9 Million
Emp.: 55
New Car Whslr
N.A.I.C.S.: 441110
Matthew Bell *(Mgr-Sls)*

LEXYL TRAVEL TECHNOLOGIES LLC
205 Datura St 10th Fl, West Palm Beach, FL 33401
Tel.: (800) 898-1347
Web Site: http://www.hotelplanner.com
Year Founded: 2003
Travel Services & Resources Provider
N.A.I.C.S.: 561599
John Prince *(Co-Founded & Pres)*

Subsidiaries:

Room 77, Inc.   (1)
888 Villa St, Mountain View, CA 94041
Web Site: http://www.room77.com
Computer Related Services
N.A.I.C.S.: 541519
Syed Abbas *(Mgr-Production)*

LEZZER LUMBER, INC.
332 Schofield St, Curwensville, PA 16833
Tel.: (814) 236-0220
Web Site: http://www.lezzerlumber.com
Year Founded: 1927
Sales Range: $50-74.9 Million
Emp.: 400
Building Materials Mfr
N.A.I.C.S.: 444180

Michael F. Lezzer *(CEO)*
David Lezzer *(Pres)*
K. C. Lezzer *(VP)*
Josh Kroell *(Mgr)*
Chris McKeown *(Dir-Ops)*
Maurice Lezzer *(Chm)*
Mark Swatsworth *(Mgr)*

Subsidiaries:

Lezzer Lumber   (1)
194 Chad Rd, Pennsdale, PA 17756
Tel.: (570) 546-8026
Web Site: http://www.lezzerlumber.com
Emp.: 15
Lumber & Other Building Materials Whslr
N.A.I.C.S.: 423310
Jay R. Lee *(CFO, Sec & Asst Treas)*
David M. Lezzer *(Pres)*
Kenneth C. Lezzer *(Sec & Exec VP)*
John R. Lloyd *(COO)*
David Michaels *(Mgr-Comml Sls)*
Chris McKeown *(Dir-Ops)*
Jim Patterson *(Dir-Comml Sls)*
Julie A. Seighman *(Treas)*

TSI Asset Holdings, LLC   (1)
288A Corliss St, Pittsburgh, PA 15220-4814
Tel.: (412) 331-3044
Web Site: http://www.tsi.com
Other Services to Buildings & Dwellings
N.A.I.C.S.: 561790
Richard Berttotti *(Pres)*

LF GEORGE HOLDINGS, INC.
159 El Camino Real, Millbrae, CA 94030
Tel.: (650) 697-3800   DE
Web Site: http://www.lfgmanagement.com
Year Founded: 2011
Sales Range: Less than $1 Million
Holding Company; Commercial & Residential Property Management Services
N.A.I.C.S.: 551112
George Lam *(Chm & CEO)*
Henry Lam *(CFO)*
Alex Lam *(CTO)*
Suzanne Lo *(Sec)*

LFD, LLC
1500 Commerce Dr, Mission, TX 78572
Tel.: (956) 584-4500   TX
Web Site: http://www.lfdfurniture.com
Year Founded: 1952
Rev.: $33,050,254
Emp.: 260
Household Appliance & Furniture Stores
N.A.I.C.S.: 449210
Tony L. Talbott *(Chm)*
Gregg R. Thrash *(Pres)*

LFI FORT PIERCE INC.
1617 N Federal Hwy, Lake Worth, FL 33460-6638
Tel.: (561) 588-8883   FL
Year Founded: 1992
Sales Range: $10-24.9 Million
Emp.: 10
Provider of Employment Services
N.A.I.C.S.: 561311
Jeffrey Burnet *(Pres & CFO)*
Doug McCarty *(Mgr-Fin)*

LFM CAPITAL LLC
1312 3rd Ave N, Nashville, TN 37208
Tel.: (615) 983-6294
Web Site: http://www.lfmcapital.com
Year Founded: 2014
Private Investment Firm
N.A.I.C.S.: 523999
Steve Cook *(Exec Mng Dir)*
Rick Reisner *(Mng Dir)*
Dan Shockley *(Mng Dir)*
Chris Lin *(Mng Dir)*
Jessica Ginsberg *(Dir-Bus Dev)*
Richard Hanan *(Mgr-Bus Dev)*

Katie Mesha *(Mgr-Bus Dev)*
Noah Krimm *(VP)*
Myron Reising *(Operating Partner & CFO-Portfolio)*

Subsidiaries:

Heartland Steel Products, LLC   (1)
2420 Wills St, Marysville, MI 48040
Tel.: (810) 364-7421
Web Site: http://www.heartlandsteel.com
Steel Mfrs
N.A.I.C.S.: 332111

Muthig Industries, Inc.   (1)
33 E Larsen Dr, Fond Du Lac, WI 54937
Tel.: (920) 922-9814
Web Site: http://www.muthigindustries.com
Sales Range: $1-9.9 Million
Emp.: 25
Metal Stamping
N.A.I.C.S.: 332119
Ann Muthig *(VP)*
Dave Hanke *(Mgr-Quality)*

Serra Laser Precision, LLC   (1)
2400 Commerce Dr, Libertyville, IL 60048
Tel.: (847) 367-0282
Web Site: http://www.laserprecision.com
Rev.: $7,800,000
Emp.: 48
All Other Miscellaneous Fabricated Metal Product Mfr
N.A.I.C.S.: 332999
Jeff Adams *(Founder)*

Southern Tooling, Inc.   (1)
8021 Hwy 22 S, Lexington, TN 38351-7517
Tel.: (731) 249-5357
Web Site: http://www.southerntoolingonline.com
Machine Shops
N.A.I.C.S.: 332710
Jeremy Johnson *(CEO)*

Tuttle, Inc.   (1)
110 Page St, Friend, NE 68359
Tel.: (402) 947-9391
Web Site: http://www.tuttleinc.com
Sales Range: $1-9.9 Million
Emp.: 35
Conveyors And Conveying Equipment, Nsk
N.A.I.C.S.: 333922
Chere Tuttle *(Sec & VP)*
Miles McGonigle *(Project Mgr)*
Neil Formanek *(Supvr-Shop)*
John Reitz *(Mgr-Acctg)*
Andrew Derr *(Mgr-Engrg)*

LG DEVELOPMENT GROUP, LLC.
2234 W North Ave, Chicago, IL 60647-5443
Tel.: (773) 278-6983
Web Site: http://www.lgdevelopmentgroup.com
Sales Range: $10-24.9 Million
Emp.: 6
Land Subdividing Services
N.A.I.C.S.: 237210
Barry Howard *(Principal)*
Amy Lusher *(Chief Sls & Mktg Officer)*

LGAM PRIVATE CREDIT LLC
1585 Broadway, New York, NY 10036
Tel.: (212) 761-4000   DE
Year Founded: 2023
Investment Management Service
N.A.I.C.S.: 523999

LGC ASSOCIATES, LLC
8200 Haverstick Rd Ste 102, Indianapolis, IN 46240
Tel.: (317) 632-1178
Web Site: http://www.lgcassociates.com
Year Founded: 2001
Sales Range: $1-9.9 Million
Emp.: 30,000
Business Administration & Hospitality Recruiting Services
N.A.I.C.S.: 561311

Glen Greenawalt *(Exec VP)*
George Lessmeister *(Owner)*

LGCY POWER, LLC
3333 N Digital Dr Ste 600, Lehi, UT 84043
Web Site: http://www.lgcypower.com
Year Founded: 2014
Sales Range: $25-49.9 Million
Emp.: 68
Solar Panels Installation Services
N.A.I.C.S.: 238210
Doug Robinson *(Founder & CEO)*

LGE COMMUNITY CREDIT UNION
430 Commerce Park Dr, Marietta, GA 30060
Tel.: (770) 424-0060   GA
Web Site: http://www.lgeccu.org
Year Founded: 1951
Sales Range: $25-49.9 Million
Emp.: 252
Credit Union Operator
N.A.I.C.S.: 522130
S. Tillery *(VP-Lending)*
C. Leggett *(CEO)*
C. Bracewell *(CFO)*
S. Stanfield *(Chief Admin Officer)*
H. Branch III *(COO)*

LGI DEVELOPMENT
1450 Lake Robbins Dr Ste 430, Spring, TX 77380-3258
Tel.: (281) 362-8998
Web Site: http://www.lgihomes.com
Year Founded: 1995
Rev.: $95,200,000
Emp.: 300
Residential Real Estate Development
N.A.I.C.S.: 237210
Daniel Trombley *(CFO)*
Mike Snider *(CEO)*
Tom Lipar *(Chm & CEO)*
Eric Thomas Lipar *(Chm & CEO-LGI Homes)*

LGS INDUSTRIES, INC.
11550 Harter Dr, Middlebury, IN 46540
Tel.: (877) 475-5665
Web Site: http://www.looktrailers.com
Cargo Trailer Mfr
N.A.I.C.S.: 336212
Matt Arnold *(Founder & Pres)*

Subsidiaries:

Pace American Enterprises Inc.   (1)
11550 Harter Rd, Middlebury, IN 46540
Tel.: (574) 825-7223
Web Site: http://www.paceamerican.com
Sales Range: $75-99.9 Million
Emp.: 1,000
Cargo & Utility Trailers Mfr
N.A.I.C.S.: 336212
Matt Arnold *(Pres)*

Subsidiary (Domestic):

Pace American Enterprises Inc.-Fitzgerald   (2)
122 Glenn Bass Rd, Fitzgerald, GA 31750-8934
Tel.: (229) 423-7966
Web Site: http://www.paceamerican.com
Cargo & Utility Trailers Mfr
N.A.I.C.S.: 336212

Pace American Enterprises Inc.-Springville   (2)
1350 W 1650 N St, Springville, UT 84663
Tel.: (435) 628-7667
Web Site: http://www.paceamerican.com
Cargo & Utility Trailers Mfr
N.A.I.C.S.: 336212

LGS SPECIALTY SALES LTD.
1 Radisson Plz Ste 1022 10th Fl, New Rochelle, NY 10801

LGS SPECIALTY SALES LTD.

LGS Specialty Sales Ltd.—(Continued)
Tel.: (718) 542-2200
Sales Range: $25-49.9 Million
Emp.: 10
Bond Brokers
N.A.I.C.S.: 424410
Luke Sears *(Founder & Pres)*

LHB INDUSTRIES, INC.
10440 Trenton Ave, Saint Louis, MO 63132
Tel.: (314) 423-4333
Web Site:
http://www.lhbindustries.com
Year Founded: 1933
Sales Range: $25-49.9 Million
Emp.: 100
Specialty Cleaning
N.A.I.C.S.: 325612
John W. Thompson *(Pres)*
Clint Cruse *(VP-Mfg & Mgr-Berkeley Plant)*
Randi Cali *(Mgr-Warehouse)*
Mark Epstein *(Mgr-R&D)*
Clint Cruse *(VP-Mfg)*
Jennifer Coy *(Program Dir)*
Joe Kluesner *(Mgr)*

Subsidiaries:

Val-A Chicago, Inc. (1)
756 N Industrial Dr, Elmhurst, IL 60126
Tel.: (630) 279-2005
Web Site: http://www.tearmender.com
Emp.: 15
Adhesive Mfr
N.A.I.C.S.: 325520
Jerome Cismoski *(Pres)*

LHI ACQUISITION CORPORATION
332 N Henry St, Williamsburg, VA 23185
Tel.: (757) 345-3375   NV
Year Founded: 2017
Liabilities: $11,899
Net Worth: ($11,899)
Earnings: ($11,297)
Emp.: 1
Fiscal Year-end: 07/31/18
Investment Services
N.A.I.C.S.: 523999
Frank Kristan *(Pres, Treas & Sec)*

LHP SOFTWARE LLC
1888 Poshard Dr, Columbus, IN 47203
Tel.: (812) 373-0880
Web Site: http://lhpes.com
Software Publisher
N.A.I.C.S.: 513210
David Glass *(CEO)*
Ryan Hou *(Chm & Partner)*
Alex Thatcher *(COO)*
Tammy Densford *(Controller)*

LIA AUTO GROUP
1258 Central Ave, Albany, NY 12205
Tel.: (518) 641-1891
Web Site: http://www.liacars.com
Year Founded: 1977
Sales Range: $250-299.9 Million
Emp.: 758
Car Whslr
N.A.I.C.S.: 441110
Mike Castren *(Controller)*
William Lia *(Pres)*
Thomas Sinkora *(Mgr-Svc)*
Linda Karins *(Office Mgr)*

Subsidiaries:

Lia Honda Williamsville (1)
4891 Transit Rd, Williamsville, NY 14221
Tel.: (716) 632-3323
Web Site:
http://www.liahondaofwilliamsville.com

Sales Range: $10-24.9 Million
Emp.: 45
Car Dealership
N.A.I.C.S.: 441110
Kevin Cornell *(Dir-Fin)*
Steve Celano *(Bus Mgr-Customer)*
Michael Lalley *(Mgr-Sls-Used Cars)*
Tiffany Long-Rizzo *(Mgr-Fin)*
Ryan Fischer *(Mgr-Fin)*
Patrick Haman *(Mgr-Parts)*
Chris Michienzi *(Mgr-Sls)*
Christine Pashley *(Office Mgr)*
Mike Szymanski *(Mgr-Svc)*
Lincoln Walker *(Asst Mgr)*

Lia Honda of Albany (1)
1258 Central Ave, Albany, NY 12205   (100%)
Tel.: (518) 438-4555
Web Site: http://www.liacars.com
Rev.: $33,400,000
Emp.: 60
New & Used Automobiles
N.A.I.C.S.: 441110
William Lia *(Pres)*
Mike Casters *(Controller)*

Lia Nissan Ltd. (1)
2233 Central Ave, Schenectady, NY 12304
Tel.: (518) 370-7110
Web Site: http://www.liacars.com
Rev.: $15,200,000
Emp.: 36
Automobiles, New & Used
N.A.I.C.S.: 441110
Dave Tertugh *(Gen Mgr)*

Lia Toyota of Colonie (1)
2116 Central Ave, Schenectady, NY 12304
Tel.: (518) 631-5254
Web Site: http://www.liatoyotaofcolonie.com
New & Used Car Dealer
N.A.I.C.S.: 441110
William Lia *(Chm)*

Wilbraham Import Cars, Inc. (1)
2145 Boston Rd, Wilbraham, MA 01095
Tel.: (413) 596-2000
Web Site: http://www.liagroup.com
Sales Range: $1-9.9 Million
Emp.: 40
New & Used Car Dealers
N.A.I.C.S.: 441110
Michael Lia *(Pres)*

LIAISON INTERNATIONAL, INC.
311 Arsenal St, Watertown, MA 02472
Tel.: (617) 926-0504
Web Site: http://www.liaison-intl.com
Software Publisher
N.A.I.C.S.: 513210
Robert Ruiz *(VP-Client Success)*
George Haddad *(Founder & CEO)*

Subsidiaries:

TargetX.com LLC (1)
1001 E Hector St Ste 110, Philadelphia, PA 19428
Tel.: (215) 781-8796
Web Site: http://www.targetx.com
Rev.: $3,800,000
Emp.: 17
Student Recruitment Services
N.A.I.C.S.: 611710
Michael Crusi *(Co-Founder & CTO)*
Scott Parks *(Engr-Network)*
Sasha Peterson *(CEO)*

LIAISON MARKETING COMMUNICATIONS, LTD.
2354 Kemper Ln, Cincinnati, OH 45206
Tel.: (513) 281-2301   OH
Web Site:
http://www.liaisonmarketing.com
Year Founded: 1995
Sales Range: Less than $1 Million
Emp.: 7
N.A.I.C.S.: 541810
Bob Hermann *(Principal)*
Lisa Specht *(Partner)*
Kent Weber *(Owner)*

LIAM VENTURES, INC.
233 S Wacker Dr Ste 2150, Chicago, IL 60606-6370
Tel.: (312) 993-1800   DE
Year Founded: 1976
Sales Range: $350-399.9 Million
Emp.: 1,025
Railroad Parts & Automotive Body Assemblies
N.A.I.C.S.: 333994
Andrew Skroska *(Office Mgr)*
William Farley *(Owner)*

Subsidiaries:

Magnus (1)
1300 Morningside Rd, Fremont, NE 68025   (100%)
Tel.: (402) 721-9540
Web Site: http://www.magnus-farley.com
Rev.: $19,500,000
Emp.: 55
Mfr Railroad Parts
N.A.I.C.S.: 332991
John E. Macklin *(Pres)*
Dale L. Stahlecker *(Controller)*
Kate Pacner *(Mgr-Sls)*

LIBB CO. INC.
7860 N Central Dr, Lewis Center, OH 43035-9406
Tel.: (740) 549-1516   OH
Web Site: http://www.libbco.com
Year Founded: 1965
Sales Range: $10-24.9 Million
Emp.: 22
Plumbing Fixtures, Equipment & Supplies
N.A.I.C.S.: 423720
Donald Dwyer *(Owner)*
Dan Howell *(Office Mgr)*

LIBBEY, INC.
300 Madison Ave, Toledo, OH 43604
Tel.: (419) 325-2100   DE
Web Site: http://www.libbey.com
Year Founded: 1888
Rev.: $785,602,000
Assets: $706,687,000
Liabilities: $732,474,000
Net Worth: ($25,787,000)
Earnings: ($69,019,000)
Emp.: 5,872
Fiscal Year-end: 12/31/19
Mfr & Marketer of Glass Tableware, Metal Flatware & Ceramic Dinnerware
N.A.I.C.S.: 327110
James C. Burmeister *(COO & Sr VP)*
Dave Anderson *(VP-IT-Global)*
Antoine Jordans *(VP/Gen Mgr-EMEA)*
Pablo Villarreal *(VP-Mfg-Global)*
Joe Huhn *(VP/Gen Mgr-Americas)*
Chandra Mangalagiri *(VP-Global Engrg)*
Sarah Zibbel *(Chief HR Officer & Sr VP)*
Michael P. Bauer *(CEO)*
Jennifer M. Jaffee *(Gen Counsel, Sec & Sr VP)*
Juan Amezquita *(CFO, Treas & Sr VP)*

Subsidiaries:

Crisa Libbey Mexico S. de R.L. de C.V. (1)
Jose Maria Vigil 400 Col Del Norte, 64500, Monterrey, Nuevo Leon, Mexico
Tel.: (52) 8110013000
Web Site: http://www.libbey.mx
Glassware Whslr
N.A.I.C.S.: 327212

Crisal - Cristalaria Automatica, S.A. (1)
Zona Industrial, 2431-903, Marinha Grande, Portugal
Tel.: (351) 244545800
Web Site: http://crisal.pt
Emp.: 300

Glassware Mfr
N.A.I.C.S.: 327212

Libbey Europe B.V. (1)
Lingedijk 8, 4142 LD, Leerdam, Netherlands
Tel.: (31) 345671611
Web Site: http://foodservice.libbey.eu
Emp.: 350
Glassware Mfr
N.A.I.C.S.: 327212

World Tableware Inc. (1)
300 Madison Ave, Toledo, OH 43604-1567
Tel.: (419) 325-2100
Home Furnishing Products Retailer
N.A.I.C.S.: 449129

LIBCON INC.
8016 Killam Industrial Blvd, Laredo, TX 78045
Tel.: (956) 722-5126
Sales Range: $10-24.9 Million
Emp.: 100
Provider of Foundation & Footing Contractor Services
N.A.I.C.S.: 238110
Douglas B. Howland Jr. *(Pres)*

LIBERA INC.
1509 Buffalo Street Ext, Jamestown, NY 14701
Tel.: (716) 665-2800
Web Site: http://www.libera.com
Emp.: 100
Custom Computer Programming Services
N.A.I.C.S.: 541511
Albert Cecchini *(Founder)*

LIBERATION PROGRAMS INC.
4 Elmcrest Ter, Norwalk, CT 06850
Tel.: (203) 851-2077
Web Site:
http://www.liberationprograms.org
Rev.: $10,600,000
Emp.: 200
Psychiatric & Substance Abuse Hospitals
N.A.I.C.S.: 622210
Diana Washington *(Dir-Community Rels)*
George Buchanan *(Mgr-Maintenance)*

LIBERMAN BROADCASTING CORPORATION
1845 Empire Ave, Burbank, CA 91504
Tel.: (818) 729-5300
Web Site: http://www.lbimedia.com
Sales Range: $50-74.9 Million
Emp.: 300
Radio Broadcasting Services
N.A.I.C.S.: 516110
Jose Liberman *(Co-Founder)*
Lenard D. Liberman *(CEO)*
Mariano Amador *(VP-Sls)*
Jim Baral *(Sr VP-Integrated Sls-West Coast)*
Ashley Wilson *(Gen Counsel)*
Nick Valls *(Gen Mgr-WGEN-Miami)*

LIBERTO SPECIALTY COMPANY INC.
830 S Presa St, San Antonio, TX 78210
Tel.: (210) 222-1415   TX
Web Site: http://www.ricos.com
Year Founded: 1918
Sales Range: $10-24.9 Million
Emp.: 100
Provider of Concessions
N.A.I.C.S.: 424450
Frank G. Liberto *(Pres & CEO)*

Subsidiaries:

Liberto of Harlingen Inc. (1)
402 S F St, Harlingen, TX 78550-6570
Tel.: (956) 423-8770
Web Site: http://www.liberto.com

U.S. PRIVATE

COMPANIES

Sales Range: $10-24.9 Million
Emp.: 3
Service Industry Machines
N.A.I.C.S.: 333310

Rico's Products Company Inc. (1)
830 S Presa St, San Antonio, TX 78210
Tel.: (210) 222-1415
Web Site: http://www.ricos.com
Emp.: 30
Snack Food Mfr & Distr
N.A.I.C.S.: 311919
Tony Liberto *(Pres)*
Jeremy Powledge *(COO)*
Ricky Robinson *(CFO)*

LIBERTY 77 CAPITAL, L.P.
2099 Pennsylvania Ave NW, Washington, DC 20006
Tel.: (202) 984-7070
Web Site: https://libertycapitallp.com
Private Equity
N.A.I.C.S.: 523940

LIBERTY ALLIANCE
3150 A Florence Rd Ste 1, Powder Springs, GA 30127
Tel.: (770) 439-0151
Web Site:
 http://www.libertyalliance.com
Year Founded: 2007
Sales Range: $1-9.9 Million
Emp.: 14
Political News Website
N.A.I.C.S.: 513110
Brandon Vallorani *(Founder & Chm)*
Jared Vallorani *(CEO)*
Stewart Adams *(VP-Multimedia)*
Ashleigh Slater *(Acct Mgr-Website)*
Tracey Lee *(CFO)*
Kenny Rudd *(Mgr-Bus)*
James Dellinger *(VP-Adv)*
Jay Taylor *(VP-Political Strategy)*
Scott Johnston *(VP-Tobacco & Firearms Div)*

LIBERTY AUTOMOTIVE LTD.
4397 Rte 130, Burlington, NJ 08016
Tel.: (609) 386-6300
Web Site:
 http://www.libertytoyota.com
Rev.: $39,049,243
Emp.: 60
Automobiles, New & Used
N.A.I.C.S.: 441110
Chris Bennett *(Gen Mgr-Sls)*
Scott Richardson *(Gen Mgr)*

LIBERTY BANK
5801 Davis Blvd, North Richland Hills, TX 76180
Tel.: (817) 656-0038
Web Site:
 http://www.libertybankonline.com
Year Founded: 1985
Rev.: $10,658,321
Emp.: 50
State Commercial Banks
N.A.I.C.S.: 522110
Don R. Waters *(Pres & CEO)*
Laura S. Miller *(Pres-Market)*
Sheri Taylor *(Exec VP)*
Donna Moon *(Sr VP-Northeast Comml Lending)*

LIBERTY BANK
315 Main St, Middletown, CT 06457
Tel.: (888) 570-0773 CT
Web Site: http://www.liberty-bank.com
Year Founded: 1825
Rev.: $146,257,000
Assets: $5,092,876,000
Liabilities: $4,353,999,000
Net Worth: $738,877,000
Earnings: $71,566,000
Emp.: 700
Fiscal Year-end: 12/31/18

Commericial Banking
N.A.I.C.S.: 522110
Mark R. Gingras *(Chm)*
Eugene F. Shugrue *(Chief Lending Officer & Sr Exec VP)*
Paul S. Young *(CFO & Sr Exec VP)*
Barry J. Abramowitz *(CIO & Exec VP)*
Robert Parry *(Chief Admin Officer & Sr Exec VP)*
Minnie Saleh *(Chief Retail Banking Officer & Exec VP)*
David W. Glidden *(Pres & CEO)*
Audra Hamel *(CMO & Sr VP)*
Jeff Lawrence Hubbard *(Sr VP-Commercial Banking)*

Subsidiaries:

Liberty Cash-A-Check, Inc. (1)
548 Main St, Middletown, CT 06457-2810
Tel.: (860) 346-6967
Sales Range: $25-49.9 Million
Emp.: 3
Depository Banking Services
N.A.I.C.S.: 522390

LIBERTY BANK FOR SAVINGS INC.
2392 N Milwaukee Ave, Chicago, IL 60647
Tel.: (773) 384-4000 IL
Web Site: http://www.libertybank.com
Year Founded: 1960
Sales Range: $50-74.9 Million
Emp.: 148
Savings Institutions, Except Federal
N.A.I.C.S.: 522180
William J. Smigiel *(Pres & CEO)*
Jerry A. Kussy *(VP & Mgr-Sls)*

Subsidiaries:

Liberty Insurance Agency Inc. (1)
7111 W Foster Ave, Chicago, IL 60656-1967
Tel.: (773) 792-1660
Web Site: http://www.libertybank.com
Sales Range: $25-49.9 Million
Emp.: 5
Insurance Agents, Brokers & Service
N.A.I.C.S.: 524210
William J. Smigiel *(Pres)*
Jeff Dougherty *(VP & Mgr-Personal Insurance)*
Mike Mahoney *(VP & Mgr-Comml Insurance Mktg)*

LIBERTY BAY CREDIT UNION
350 Granite St Ste 1102, Braintree, MA 02184-4999
Tel.: (617) 439-6500 MA
Web Site: http://www.libertybaycu.org
Year Founded: 1917
Sales Range: $10-24.9 Million
Emp.: 78
Credit Union Operator
N.A.I.C.S.: 522130
Brian Leary *(Sr VP)*
Stephen Fulchini *(Sr VP)*
Kelly Amato *(VP-Bus Dev)*
Joel Keller *(CFO & Exec VP)*
Donna Warner *(VP-Client Implementation)*
Peter G. Dennis *(Exec VP-Affinity Banking)*
Jill Amato *(VP & Dir-Corp Comm)*
Edward Foley *(Chm)*
Robert Mitchell *(Dir-Board)*
Stephen Kelley *(Dir-Board)*
Winifred Bolter *(Sec)*
William Murphy *(Treas)*
Patrick J. Foley *(Vice Chm)*
Edward McColgan *(Vice Chm)*
James Quinn *(Exec VP-HR)*
James Carden *(VP-Consumer Lending)*
Paola Ferrara *(VP-Ops)*
Paul Gravellese *(VP-Bus Lending)*
Cindi Carlson *(VP-North Shore)*
Lyndon Matteson *(Pres & CEO)*

Joseph Bean *(Chief Lending Officer & Exec VP)*
Kathy Peila *(Sr VP-Project Admin)*
George Kelly *(Chief Strategic Officer & Sr VP)*
Fred Williams *(CFO & Sr VP)*

LIBERTY BELL WHOLESALE
217 S Main St, Liberty, IN 47353
Tel.: (765) 458-7485
Web Site:
 http://www.libertybellent.com
Sales Range: $10-24.9 Million
Emp.: 20
Whslr of General Merchandise
N.A.I.C.S.: 423840
Andy C. Pitcher *(Owner)*
Ginger Deruak *(Office Mgr)*

LIBERTY BUICK INC.
8737 W Bell Rd, Peoria, AZ 85382
Tel.: (623) 933-5000
Web Site: http://www.libertybuick.com
Sales Range: $50-74.9 Million
Emp.: 130
Automobiles, New & Used
N.A.I.C.S.: 441110
Dana Moore *(Pres)*

LIBERTY BUSINESS SYSTEMS, INC.
3431 4th Ave S, Fargo, ND 58103
Tel.: (701) 241-8504
Web Site:
 http://www.libertybusiness.com
Sales Range: $10-24.9 Million
Emp.: 20
Office Furniture & Equipment Distr
N.A.I.C.S.: 423420
Ron Fuhrman *(Owner)*
Adam Morlan *(Coord-Parts)*
Jim Wontor *(Mgr-Svc)*

LIBERTY CAPITAL INC.
2251 Rombach Ave, Wilmington, OH 45177
Tel.: (937) 382-1000 OH
Web Site:
 http://www.libertysavingsbank.com
Year Founded: 1985
Sales Range: $100-124.9 Million
Emp.: 700
Holding Company for Federal Savings Institutions
N.A.I.C.S.: 522180
James R. Powell *(Chm)*
Suzan D. Kranjc *(CFO & Exec VP)*
Stan K. Erickson *(Pres & CEO)*

Subsidiaries:

Liberty Savings Bank, F.S.B. (1)
3435 Airborne Rd Ste B, Wilmington, OH 45177-1997
Tel.: (937) 382-1000
Web Site:
 http://www.libertysavingsbank.com
Sales Range: $50-74.9 Million
Emp.: 250
Federal Savings Institutions
N.A.I.C.S.: 522180

LIBERTY COATING COMPANY LLC
21 Steel Rd S, Morrisville, PA 19067
Tel.: (215) 736-1111
Web Site:
 http://www.libertycoating.com
Rev.: $4,925,000
Emp.: 40
Metal Coating, Engraving & Allied Services to Manufacturers
N.A.I.C.S.: 332812
Don Barder *(Pres & COO)*
Bill Burke *(Chm)*

LIBERTY DATA PRODUCTS INC.

LIBERTY DIVERSIFIED INTERNATIONAL INC.

8744 Westpark Dr, Houston, TX 77063
Tel.: (713) 789-3282
Web Site: http://www.libertyoffice.com
Sales Range: $10-24.9 Million
Emp.: 31
Supplier of Office Products, Including Computer Equipment
N.A.I.C.S.: 449210
Sam Young *(Pres)*

LIBERTY DISTRIBUTORS INC.
Rt 40 E, Triadelphia, WV 26059
Tel.: (304) 547-0414
Web Site:
 http://www.libertydistributors.com
Year Founded: 1987
Sales Range: $10-24.9 Million
Emp.: 68
Industrial & Personal Service Paper Distr
N.A.I.C.S.: 424130
Mark Peluchette *(Pres)*
M. David Peluchette *(Exec VP & Co-Owner)*
Paul Peluchette *(VP-Sls & Co-Owner)*
Jim Lightner *(VP-Fin)*

LIBERTY DIVERSIFIED INTERNATIONAL INC.
5600 N Hwy 169, New Hope, MN 55428-3096
Tel.: (763) 536-6600 MN
Web Site:
 http://www.libertydiversified.com
Year Founded: 1918
Sales Range: $400-449.9 Million
Emp.: 1,500
Corrugated Packaging & Displays
N.A.I.C.S.: 322211
Michael Fiterman *(Pres & CEO)*

Subsidiaries:

Immedia, Inc. (1)
3311 Broadway St NE, Minneapolis, MN 55413
Tel.: (877) 337-4633
Web Site: http://www.immediaretail.com
Emp.: 150
Commercial Printing Services
N.A.I.C.S.: 323111

Liberty Carton Company (1)
870 Louisiana Ave S, Golden Valley, MN 55426-1672
Tel.: (763) 540-9600
Web Site: http://www.libertycarton.com
Cardboard Container Mfr
N.A.I.C.S.: 322219
Jack Fiterman *(Founder)*

Liberty Paper, Inc. (1)
13500 Liberty Ln, Becker, MN 55308-4623
Tel.: (763) 261-6100
Paper Mfr
N.A.I.C.S.: 322120
Tim Swanson *(Engr-Environmental)*

Omaha Box Company (1)
2501 N 21st St E, Omaha, NE 68110-2733
Tel.: (402) 346-8411
Web Site: http://www.omahabox.com
Emp.: 50
Corrugated Box Mfr
N.A.I.C.S.: 322211
Tyler Whitman *(Mgr-Production)*
Robert M. Knapp Jr. *(Pres)*

Presentation Packaging (1)
870 Louisiana Ave S, Minneapolis, MN 55426
Tel.: (763) 540-9544
Web Site:
 http://www.presentationpackaging.com
Packaging Services
N.A.I.C.S.: 561910

Safco Products Company (1)
9300 W Research Center Rd, New Hope, MN 55428
Tel.: (763) 536-6700
Web Site: http://www.safcoproducts.com
Emp.: 100

LIBERTY DIVERSIFIED INTERNATIONAL INC.

U.S. PRIVATE

Liberty Diversified International Inc.—(Continued)
Office Furniture Distr
N.A.I.C.S.: 423210
Carrie Eidem (Mgr-Mktg)

Subsidiary (Domestic):

Mayline Company, LLC (2)
619 N Commerce St, Sheboygan, WI 53081-3901
Tel.: (800) 822-8037
Web Site: http://www.mayline.com
Office Furniture, Filing Systems & Drafting Furniture Mfr
N.A.I.C.S.: 337214
Steve Fitzgerald (Dir-Sls)

Seeyond Architectural Solutions (1)
705 Pennsylvania Ave S, Minneapolis, MN 55426
Tel.: (800) 508-5455
Web Site: http://www.seeyond.com
Architectural Engineering Services
N.A.I.C.S.: 541330
Kirby Rea (Gen Mgr)
Kendra Dare (Mgr-Western Sls)
Lynne Webber (Mgr-Natl Sls)

Southern Diversified Industries (1)
1154 N 2nd St Gordon Industrial Pk, Baldwyn, MS 38824-0276
Tel.: (662) 365-8800
Sales Range: $10-24.9 Million
Emp.: 60
Mfr Of Plastic Containers
N.A.I.C.S.: 326199
Terry Murphy (Dir-Pur)

Takumi Machinery Co., Ltd. (1)
No 50 35th Rd, Taiching Ind Park, Taichung, 407, Taiwan
Tel.: (886) 4 23583838
Web Site: http://www.takumi.com.tw
Emp.: 70
General Purpose Machinery Mfr
N.A.I.C.S.: 333998

LIBERTY ENERGY CORP.
1400 Broadfield Blvd Ste 600, Houston, TX 77084
Tel.: (409) 422-9505   NV
Web Site: http://www.energy-liberty.com
Year Founded: 2006
Sales Range: Less than $1 Million
Oil & Gas Exploration
N.A.I.C.S.: 211120

LIBERTY FINANCIAL SERVICES, INC.
6600 Plaza Dr Ste 600, New Orleans, LA 70127
Tel.: (504) 240-5100   LA
Web Site: http://www.libertybank.net
Year Founded: 1984
Sales Range: $25-49.9 Million
Emp.: 146
Bank Holding Company
N.A.I.C.S.: 551111
Alden J. McDonald Jr. (Pres & CEO)
Norman C. Francis (Chm)
Leroy Watts (CFO & Exec VP)
Howard Brooks (Exec VP)
Rhonda M. McMillan (Chief Credit Officer & Sr VP)

Subsidiaries:

Liberty Bank & Trust Company (1)
6600 Plaza Dr Ste 600, New Orleans, LA 70127
Tel.: (504) 240-5100
Web Site: http://www.libertybank.net
Emp.: 50
Retail & Commercial Banking
N.A.I.C.S.: 522110
Alden J. McDonald Jr. (Pres & CEO)
Tammy Joseph (VP-Ops)
Norman C. Francis (Chm)
Leroy Watts (CFO & Exec VP)
Rhonda M. McMillan (Chief Credit Officer & Sr VP)
Howard Brooks (Exec VP)
Sidney King (Pres-Kansas & Missouri)
Carlton G. Stephen (VP-Mississippi)

LIBERTY FURNITURE INDUSTRIES INC.
6021 Greensboro Dr SW, Atlanta, GA 30336
Tel.: (404) 629-1003
Web Site: http://www.mylibertyfurniture.com
Sales Range: $25-49.9 Million
Emp.: 50
Manufacture & Sell Furniture
N.A.I.C.S.: 423210
Richard Brian (Founder & Pres)
Camille Youngblood (Mgr-Mktg)
Jason Wagy (VP-Fin & HR)

LIBERTY GLOVE & SAFETY, INC.
433 Cheryl Ln, City of Industry, CA 91789
Tel.: (909) 595-2992
Web Site: http://www.libertyglove.com
Rev.: $30,000,000
Emp.: 60
Safety Equipment & Supplies
N.A.I.C.S.: 423990
Michael Young (Pres)

LIBERTY GROUP OF COMPANIES
1 Tampa City Ctr, Tampa, FL 33602
Tel.: (813) 280-2000
Web Site: http://www.libertygrouphotels.com
Year Founded: 1981
Sales Range: $25-49.9 Million
Emp.: 400
Real Estate Investments, Asset Management & Commercial Property Development
N.A.I.C.S.: 531390
Raxit N. Shah (Chm)
Punit R. Shah (CEO)
Cindy Fowler (Dir-HR)
Brian Burns (Dir-Risk Mgmt)
Emily Bryan (Area Mgr-Sls & Mktg)
Margaret Lightfoot (Area Mgr-Sls & Mktg)
Jocie Rivera (Area Mgr-Sls & Mktg)
Nicholas Positano (Controller)
Richard Henrikson (COO)
Matthew Ram (Mgr-Investment)
David Marinich (Project Mgr)
Manuel Leonor (Supvr-Facilities)
Dina Lomagno (VP-Sls & Mktg)
Geoff Ballotti (Pres & CEO)
Liam Brown (Pres)
Ray Jones (Grp Mng Dir)
Charles Whitten Jr. (Mgr-Task Force Ops)

LIBERTY HALL CAPITAL PARTNERS, L.P.
350 Park Ave 27th Fl, New York, NY 10022
Tel.: (646) 291-2601
Web Site: http://www.libertyhallcapital.com
Year Founded: 2000
Privater Equity Firm
N.A.I.C.S.: 523999
Rowan G. P. Taylor (Founder & Mng Partner)
Taylor P. Catarozoli (Partner)
James C. Black (Principal)
Christopher D. Novick (VP)

Subsidiaries:

Aircraft Performance Group, Inc. (1)
4348 Woodlands Blvd, Ste 200, Castle Rock, CO 80104-2814
Tel.: (303) 539-0410
Web Site: http://www.flyapg.com
Flight Operations Software Solutions
N.A.I.C.S.: 334511

Rogers V. Hemphill (Engr-Weight & Balance Design)

Comply365, LLC (1)
655 3rd St Ste 365, Beloit, WI 53511
Tel.: (608) 313-1500
Web Site: http://www.comply365.com
Software Development Services
N.A.I.C.S.: 541512
Eric Dahlen (CTO)
Neil Thomas (VP-Customer Ops)
Tom Samuel (CEO)
Kellen Sottile (CFO)
Jeremy Sharp (VP & Head-Global Sls & Customer Success)
Shaq Mughal (VP-Product Dev)

Dunlop Aircraft Tyres Limited (1)
40 Fort Parkway, Erdington, Birmingham, B24 9HL, United Kingdom
Tel.: (44) 1213848800
Web Site: http://www.dunlopaircrafttyres.co.uk
Aircraft Tires & Tire Parts Mfr
N.A.I.C.S.: 326211
Gordon Roper (CEO)
Patrice Mougnutou (Comml Dir-Russia)
Ali R. Safari (Mng Dir-Safari)
David Olum (Comml Dir-Nigeria & West Africa)

LIBERTY HARDWOODS INC.
3900 N Kentucky, Kansas City, MO 64161
Tel.: (816) 231-0852
Web Site: http://www.libertyhardwoodsinc.com
Rev.: $21,502,001
Emp.: 40
Lumber: Rough, Dressed & Finished
N.A.I.C.S.: 423310
Larry Sumner (Pres)
Christie McGlothlin (Mgr-Credit)
Jerry Wallen (Mgr-Ops)
Michelle Blodgett (Mgr-Acctg)

LIBERTY HOME MORTGAGE CORPORATION
4401 Rockside Rd Ste 310, Independence, OH 44131
Tel.: (440) 838-5291
Web Site: http://www.libertyhomemortgage.org
Year Founded: 2014
Sales Range: $10-24.9 Million
Emp.: 86
Mortgage Lending Services
N.A.I.C.S.: 522292
Khash Saghafi (Pres)

LIBERTY HOSPITAL
2525 Glenn Hendren Dr, Liberty, MO 64068
Tel.: (816) 781-7200   MO
Web Site: http://www.libertyhospital.org
Year Founded: 1994
Sales Range: $10-24.9 Million
Emp.: 174
Health Care Srvices
N.A.I.C.S.: 622110
David Feess (Pres & CEO)
Paul Klehn (CIO)
Nancy Cattell (VP-HR)
Shirley Heintz (VP-Patient Care)
Dan Williams (VP-Fin & Support)
John Henrichs (VP-Physician Svcs)
Pat Flannery (VP-Medical Staff Dev)

LIBERTY IMPORTS INC.
1111 S Main St, Salt Lake City, UT 84111
Tel.: (801) 595-1111
Web Site: http://www.jodywilkinsonacura.com
Sales Range: $10-24.9 Million
Emp.: 50
Car Dealership Owner & Operator
N.A.I.C.S.: 441110

Joseph P. Wilkinson (Pres)
Kathy Lucas (Controller)
Jamie Daly (Dir-Sls & Fin)
Rex Gines (Mgr-Sls)

LIBERTY INSURANCE ASSOCIATES
525 Rte 33, Millstone Township, NJ 08535
Tel.: (732) 792-7000
Web Site: http://www.libertyinsurance.com
Sales Range: $25-49.9 Million
Emp.: 30
Insurance Agents, Brokers & Service
N.A.I.C.S.: 524210
Andrew Harris (Pres & CEO)
Gary Rygiel (Partner & Exec VP)
Marianne O'Connell (Mgr-Ops)
Andrea Brutzman (Mgr-Comml Lines)
Philip Zito (Exec Dir-Comml Div)
Daniel O. Barsnica (VP-Liberty Fin Svcs)

LIBERTY INVESTMENT EXCHANGE
739 E Walnut Ste 200, Pasadena, CA 91101
Tel.: (626) 405-1520
Sales Range: $10-24.9 Million
Emp.: 15
Mfr of Jewelry
N.A.I.C.S.: 423940
Art Mikaelian (Pres)
Sima Mikaelian (VP)

LIBERTY IRON & METAL, INC.
1515 E Ave, Erie, PA 16503-1570
Tel.: (814) 452-4549   PA
Web Site: http://www.libertyiron.com
Year Founded: 1932
Scrap & Waste Materials
N.A.I.C.S.: 331110
Mike Diamond (CEO)
Alexander Esser (CFO)
Worth Howard (COO)

LIBERTY LANE PARTNERS LLC
1 Liberty Ln, Hampton, NH 03842
Tel.: (603) 929-2600
Web Site: http://www.libertylp.com
Investment Services
N.A.I.C.S.: 523999
Paul M. Meister (Co-Founder & CEO)

LIBERTY MANAGEMENT GROUP, INC.
19 Spear Rd Ste 3304, Ramsey, NJ 07446
Tel.: (201) 236-8880   MA
Web Site: http://www.libertymgt.com
Year Founded: 1995
Sales Range: $50-74.9 Million
Emp.: 340
Management Services
N.A.I.C.S.: 561110
William Hartigan (Pres & CEO)

Subsidiaries:

Arms Acres Inc. (1)
75 Seminary Hill Rd, Carmel, NY 10512-1921
Tel.: (845) 225-3400
Web Site: http://www.armsacres.com
Rev.: $1,849,824
Emp.: 200
Residential Care
N.A.I.C.S.: 623990
Patrice Wallace-Moore (CEO)
Angel Duncan (Dir-Adult)

LIBERTY MEDIA FOR WOMEN, LLC
1600 Wilson Blvd Ste 801, Arlington, VA 22209
Tel.: (703) 522-4201   NY

COMPANIES

LIBERTY MUTUAL HOLDING COMPANY INC.

Web Site:
http://www.msmagazine.com
Year Founded: 1972
Sales Range: $50-74.9 Million
Emp.: 40
Magazine Publisher
N.A.I.C.S.: 513120
Gloria Steinem *(Chm)*
Katherine Spillar *(Exec Editor)*
Michel Cicero *(Mng Editor)*

Subsidiaries:

Ms. Magazine (1)
433 S Beverly Dr, Beverly Hills, CA 90212-3201
Tel.: (310) 556-2515
Web Site: http://www.msmagazine.com
Sales Range: $10-24.9 Million
Emp.: 10
Magazine Publisher
N.A.I.C.S.: 513120

LIBERTY MINISTRIES

565 Main St, Schwenksville, PA 19473
Tel.: (610) 287-5481 PA
Web Site:
http://www.libertyministries.us
Sales Range: $1-9.9 Million
Emp.: 147
Christian Ministry Services
N.A.I.C.S.: 813110
Wayne Mumbauer *(Treas)*
Daniel Emr *(Pres)*
Bob Thompson *(Exec Dir)*
Elliott Bennett *(Dir-Ops)*
Brian Jones *(Dir-Thrift)*
Jonathan Lewis *(Dir-Residential Program)*
Steve Poloway *(Dir-Prison Programs & Volunteers)*

LIBERTY MORTGAGE CO. INC.

473 E Rich St, Columbus, OH 43215
Tel.: (614) 224-4000
Web Site:
http://www.libertymortgagecompanyinc.com
Rev.: $20,000,000
Emp.: 49
Mortgage Bankers & Loan Correspondents
N.A.I.C.S.: 522310
Karen Richmond *(Pres)*

LIBERTY MUTUAL HOLDING COMPANY INC.

175 Berkeley St, Boston, MA 02116
Tel.: (617) 357-9500
Web Site:
http://www.libertymutualgroup.com
Year Founded: 1912
Rev.: $43,796,000,000
Assets: $145,377,000,000
Liabilities: $119,420,000,000
Net Worth: $25,957,000,000
Earnings: $758,000,000
Emp.: 45,000
Fiscal Year-end: 12/31/20
Insurance Holding Company
N.A.I.C.S.: 551112
David H. Long *(Chm, Pres & CEO)*
James M. McGlennon *(CIO & Exec VP)*
Timothy M. Sweeney *(Pres-Liberty Mutual)*
Christopher L. Peirce *(CFO & Exec VP)*
Melanie M. Foley *(Chief Talent & Enterprise Svcs Officer & Exec VP)*
James F. Kelleher *(Chief Legal Officer & Exec VP)*
Neeti Bhalla Johnson *(Pres-Global Risk Solutions & Exec VP)*
Mark C. Touhey *(Sec & Exec VP)*
Anthony G. Martella *(Chief Actuary & Exec VP)*
Edward J. Pena *(Treas & Exec VP)*
Dennis J. Langwell *(Vice Chm-Ops-Liberty Mutual Insurance)*
Matthew Moore *(Pres-Underwriting-Global Risk Solutions)*
Kevin Smith *(Pres-Global Risk Solutions-North America)*
Susanne Figueredo Cook *(COO-Global Risk Solutions)*
Phil Hobbs *(Pres-Liberty Specialty Markets)*
Meg Sutton *(COO-Global Risk Solutions-North America)*
Taylor Archambault *(Sr VP-Casualty Claims)*
Stephen Deane *(Chief Claims Officer-Global Risk Solutions)*
Rachel Conran *(Chief Underwriting Officer-Liberty Specialty Markets)*
Elizabeth A. Geary *(Pres-Insurance Solutions-GRS)*

Subsidiaries:

LMHC Massachusetts Holdings Inc. (1)
175 Berkeley St, Boston, MA 02116
Tel.: (617) 357-9500
Holding Company
N.A.I.C.S.: 551112
David H. Long *(Pres & CEO)*

Subsidiary (Domestic):

Liberty Mutual Group Inc. (2)
175 Berkeley St, Boston, MA 02116
Tel.: (617) 357-9500
Web Site:
http://www.libertymutualgroup.com
Sales Range: $25-49.9 Billion
Holding Company; Fire, Marine, Life & Casualty Insurance Products & Services
N.A.I.C.S.: 551112

Subsidiary (Non-US):

AmTrust Insurance Spain, S. L. (3)
Las Rozas Building 23, Las Rozas, 28290, Madrid, Spain (100%)
Tel.: (34) 91 640 37 67
Web Site: http://www.amtrust.es
Insurance Services
N.A.I.C.S.: 524298

Subsidiary (Domestic):

Employers Insurance Company of Wausau (3)
2000 Westwood Dr, Wausau, WI 54401-7802
Tel.: (715) 848-2981
Rev.: $700,000,000
Emp.: 1,400
Property, Casualty & Workers Comp Insurance
N.A.I.C.S.: 524126

Subsidiary (Domestic):

Wausau Insurance Co. (4)
2000 Westwood Dr, Wausau, WI 54401-7802
Tel.: (715) 848-2981
Property Casualty Insurance
N.A.I.C.S.: 524126

Subsidiary (Domestic):

Golden Eagle Insurance Corp. (3)
525 B St 1615 Murray Canyon Rd Ste 300, San Diego, CA 92108
Tel.: (619) 744-6000
Web Site:
http://www.liberetymutualgroup.com
Sales Range: $75-99.9 Million
Emp.: 300
Fire, Marine & Casualty Insurance
N.A.I.C.S.: 524126
Suzanne M. Cortez *(VP-HR)*
Carol Martin *(Sec)*
Peter G. McPartland *(Pres & CEO)*
Peter F. Wallick *(VP-Aliso Viejo)*
Spencer Donkoin *(Pres)*

Helmsman Management Services, LLC (3)
175 Berkeley St, Boston, MA 02116
Tel.: (617) 243-7985
Web Site: http://www.helmsmantpa.com
Sales Range: $75-99.9 Million
Emp.: 500
Claims Management Services
N.A.I.C.S.: 524292
David Dwortz *(Pres & CEO)*
Karen Reading *(Mng Dir & VP-Sls)*

Subsidiary (Domestic):

Eberle Vivian, Inc. (4)
206 Railroad Ave N, Kent, WA 98032
Tel.: (253) 854-6323
Web Site: http://www.eberlevivian.com
Sales Range: $1-9.9 Million
Emp.: 19
Insurance Agencies & Brokerages
N.A.I.C.S.: 524210
Lisa Eberle *(Pres)*

Subsidiary (Domestic):

Indiana Insurance Company (3)
350 E 96th St, Indianapolis, IN 46240-3702
Tel.: (317) 581-6400
Web Site: http://www.indiana-ins.com
Sales Range: $125-149.9 Million
Emp.: 900
Property & Casualty Insurance Services
N.A.I.C.S.: 524126
John Baird *(Reg Mgr)*

Subsidiary (Non-US):

Ironshore Inc. (3)
141 Front Street, Hamilton, HM 19, Bermuda
Tel.: (441) 2798200
Web Site: http://www.ironshore.com
Property & Casualty Insurance Services
N.A.I.C.S.: 524126
Mitchell E. Blaser *(CEO-Ironshore Insurance)*
Susan Pateras *(COO & Head-Healthcare Practice-Iron Starr)*
Kevin Kelley *(CEO)*
Rowan Bamford *(Head-Mergers & Acq & Tax-Global)*
Steve Horton *(CEO-Iron Starr)*
David Russo *(VP-Mid Atlantic-Reg)*
James R. Swan *(Head-Merger & Acq Insurance-Americas)*

Subsidiary (Non-US):

Ironshore Australia Holdings Pty Limited (4)
Level 9 1 O Connell Street, Sydney, 2000, NSW, Australia
Tel.: (61) 29583000
Web Site: http://www.ironshore.com
Holding Company; Property & Casualty Insurance Services
N.A.I.C.S.: 551112
William Lewis *(Mng Dir)*

Ironshore Canada Ltd. (4)
333 Bay Street 11th Fl Ste 1120, Toronto, M5H 2R2, ON, Canada
Tel.: (416) 216-2270
Web Site: http://www.ironshore.com
General Insurance Services
N.A.I.C.S.: 524210
Dane Hambrook *(COO)*
Daniel Lee *(VP-IronPro)*
Michael Marino *(Sr VP-Energy Property)*
Mike Wilkinson *(Asst VP)*

Subsidiary (Domestic):

Ironshore Insurance Ltd. (4)
141 Front Street, Hamilton, HM 19, Bermuda (100%)
Tel.: (441) 279 8200
Web Site: http://www.ironshore.com
Direct Property & Casualty Insurance Services
N.A.I.C.S.: 524126

Subsidiary (US):

Ironshore Holdings (U.S.) Inc. (5)
28 Liberty Street 4th Floor, New York, NY 10005
Tel.: (646) 826-6600
Web Site: http://www.ironshore.com

Holding Company; Property & Specialty Casualty Insurance Services
N.A.I.C.S.: 551112
Shaun Kelly *(CEO)*
Matthew Dolan *(Pres)*

Branch (Non-US):

Ironshore Insurance Ltd. - Singapore (5)
One Raffles Quay 40-01 North Tower, Singapore, 048583, Singapore
Tel.: (65) 66229160
Web Site: http://www.ironshore.com
General Insurance Services
N.A.I.C.S.: 524210
Hui Yun Boo *(CEO)*

Subsidiary (Non-US):

Liberty Insurance Pte. Ltd. (3)
51 Club Street 03-00 Liberty House, Singapore, 069428, Singapore
Tel.: (65) 63380990
Web Site:
http://www.libertyinsurance.com.sg
Medical, Life, Property & Casualty Insurance Services
N.A.I.C.S.: 524126

Subsidiary (Domestic):

Liberty Insurance Underwriters, Inc. (3)
55 Water St 23rd Fl, New York, NY 10041
Tel.: (212) 208-4100
Web Site: http://www.libertyiu.com
Insurance Underwriting Operations
N.A.I.C.S.: 524298
David Cohen *(Pres)*
Carl Pursiano *(Chief Underwriting Officer-Specialty Casualty & Exec VP)*
Richard Niehaus *(Sr VP-Energy & Construction)*
Richard J. Kirnbauer *(Sr VP-Product Line-Onshore Oil & Gas-North America)*
Don Harrell *(Sr VP-Marine)*
Alexander Montoya *(Mng Dir & Sr VP-Latin America)*
Valoree Celona *(Sr VP-Medical Pro Liability Insurance)*
Jessica Rogin *(Chief Claims Officer)*
Michael Finnegan *(Chief Underwriting Officer)*
Jim Hinchley *(Pres-Americas)*
Michael Carr *(Sr VP-E&S Property)*
William Bell *(Sr VP-Environmental)*
Mike Nukk *(Sr VP-Marine)*
Diana Cossetti *(Sr VP-Casualty Ops)*
Simon White *(Sr VP-Privacy, Pro & Tech Product Line)*
Robert Capicchioni *(VP-Railroad Product Line)*
Julie Ross *(VP-Global Crisis Mgmt)*
Jane McCarthy *(VP-Global Crisis Mgmt)*
Alexandre Egnell *(Sr VP-Dev & Strategy-GFR Product Line)*

Subsidiary (Non-US):

Liberty International Underwriters (4)
181 Bay St Ste 1000, Toronto, M5J 2T3, ON, Canada
Tel.: (416) 365-7587
Web Site: http://www.libertyiu.com
Sales Range: $200-249.9 Million
Emp.: 200
Insurance Services
N.A.I.C.S.: 524298
Frank O'Connor *(Exec VP)*
Gordon McBurney *(Pres & Chief Underwriting Officer)*
Daniel T.N. Forsythe *(CEO)*
Jose Luis Ruiz-Poveda *(VP & Head-Marine, Energy & Construction-Madrid)*
Mike Gosselin *(Sr VP-Marine, Energy & Construction)*

Subsidiary (Non-US):

Liberty International Insurance Ltd. (3)
13/F Berkshire House 25 Westlands Road, Quarry Bay, China (Hong Kong)
Tel.: (852) 2892 3888
Web Site:
http://www.libertyinsurance.com.hk
Medical, Property & Casualty Insurance Services

LIBERTY MUTUAL HOLDING COMPANY INC.

U.S. PRIVATE

Liberty Mutual Holding Company Inc.—(Continued)
N.A.I.C.S.: 524114

Subsidiary (Domestic):

Liberty Mutual Agency Corporation (3)
175 Berkeley St, Boston, MA 02116
Tel.: (617) 357-9500
Web Site: http://www.libertymutualgroup.com
Sales Range: $5-14.9 Billion
Emp.: 6,000
Insurance Agents
N.A.I.C.S.: 524210

Liberty Mutual Fire Insurance Co. (3)
175 Berkeley St, Boston, MA 02116-5066
Tel.: (617) 357-9500
Web Site: http://www.libertymutualgroup.com
Casualty Insurance
N.A.I.C.S.: 524126
David H. Long (Pres & CEO)

Liberty Mutual Insurance Company (3)
175 Berkeley St, Boston, MA 02116
Tel.: (617) 357-9500
Web Site: http://www.libertymutual.com
Sales Range: Less than $1 Million
Property & Casualty Insurance Products & Services
N.A.I.C.S.: 524126
David T. Perez (Chief Underwriting Officer-Global Risk Solutions)
David H. Long (Chm, Pres & CEO)
Alison B. Erbig (CFO-Global Risk Solutions)
Shelia Anderson (CIO-Corp Functions & Exec VP)
Francis Hyatt (Chief Sustainability Officer)
Tracy Ryan (Pres-Global Risk Solutions-North America)
David B. Williams (Chief Underwriting Officer & Sr VP)
Crystal Ottaviano (Chief Risk Officer-Global Risk Solutions)
Marc Orloff (Pres-Field Ops-Global Risk Solutions-North America)
Wesley Hyatt (Chief Client Officer-Global Risk Solutions)
Neal Bhatnagar (Exec VP-Major Accts Casualty-Global Risk Solutions)
Mike Fallon (Pres-Major Accts-Global Risk Solutions)
Damon Hart (Chief Legal Officer & Exec VP)
Chantal Rodriguez (Chief Underwriting Officer-Liberty Mutual Reinsurance)
Matthew Moore (Pres-Underwriting-Global Risk Solutions)
Dieter Winkel (Pres-Liberty Mutual Reinsurance)
Martin Vince (Head-Broker Mgmt-Liberty Specialty Markets)
Mark Stephenson (Head-Bus Dev & Market Relationships-Liberty Specialty Markets)
Laura Burns (Head-Client Mgmt-Liberty Specialty Markets)
Ben Johnson (Pres-Mktg-Global Risk Solutions North America)

Subsidiary (Domestic):

Liberty Mutual Mid-Atlantic Insurance Company (4)
Ste 300 275 Grandview Ave, Camp Hill, PA 17011-1742
Tel.: (717) 238-8211
Sales Range: $10-24.9 Million
Emp.: 60
Property & Casualty Insurance Products & Services
N.A.I.C.S.: 524126

Subsidiary (Domestic):

Liberty Northwest Insurance Corp. (3)
650 NE Holladay St, Portland, OR 97232-2045
Tel.: (503) 239-5800
Web Site: http://www.libertynorthwest.com
Sales Range: $125-149.9 Million
Emp.: 900
Accident & Health Insurance Carriers
N.A.I.C.S.: 524126

Julie A. Burnett (Pres & CEO)

Subsidiary (Non-US):

Liberty Seguros (3)
Av D Joao II 11 5, 1998-036, Lisbon, Portugal
Tel.: (351) 213124300
Web Site: http://www.libertyseguros.pt
Sales Range: $75-99.9 Million
Emp.: 300
Insurance Services
N.A.I.C.S.: 524298

Liberty Seguros (3)
Paseo De Las Doce Estrellas 4 4th Fl, Campo De Las Naciones, Madrid, 28042, Spain
Tel.: (34) 917229000
Web Site: http://www.libertyseguros.es
Sales Range: $75-99.9 Million
Emp.: 165
General Insurance Services
N.A.I.C.S.: 524210
Enrica Huerta (Gen Mgr)

Subsidiary (Domestic):

Seguros Genesis, S.A. (4)
Paseo de las Doce Estrellas 4, 28042, Madrid, Spain
Tel.: (34) 913422532
Web Site: http://www.genesis.es
Seller of Insurance & Pension Products
N.A.I.C.S.: 524298
Tom McIlduff (CEO)

Subsidiary (Domestic):

Ohio Casualty Corporation (3)
9450 Seward Rd, Fairfield, OH 45014-5742
Tel.: (513) 603-2400
Sales Range: $1-4.9 Billion
Emp.: 2,150
Holding Company; Property, Casualty & Life Insurance
N.A.I.C.S.: 551112

Subsidiary (Domestic):

American Fire & Casualty Co. (4)
9450 Seward Rd, Fairfield, OH 45014
Tel.: (513) 867-3000
Rev.: $73,133,856
Emp.: 1,800
Property & Casualty Insurance
N.A.I.C.S.: 524126

Avomark Insurance Co. (4)
9450 Seward Rd, Fairfield, OH 45014-5412
Tel.: (513) 867-3000
Web Site: http://www.ohiocasualty-ins.com
Rev.: $7,313,387
Emp.: 5
Property & Casualty Insurance
N.A.I.C.S.: 524126

The Ohio Casualty Insurance Company (4)
9450 Seward Rd, Fairfield, OH 45014
Tel.: (513) 603-2400
Web Site: http://www.ohiocasualty-ins.com
Property & Casualty Insurance Products & Services
N.A.I.C.S.: 524126

Subsidiary (Domestic):

Peerless Insurance Company (3)
62 Maple Ave, Keene, NH 03431
Tel.: (603) 352-3221
Web Site: http://www.peerless-ins.com
Sales Range: $125-149.9 Million
Emp.: 500
Insurance Services
N.A.I.C.S.: 524126

Risktrac Inc. (3)
230 Commerce Way, Portsmouth, NH 03801-3274
Tel.: (603) 422-0444
Web Site: http://www.libertymutual.com
Sales Range: $50-74.9 Million
Emp.: 100
Fire, Marine & Casualty Insurance
N.A.I.C.S.: 524126

Safeco Insurance Company of America (3)
1001 4th Ave, Seattle, WA 98184
Tel.: (206) 545-5000

Web Site: http://www.safeco.com
Insurance Services
N.A.I.C.S.: 524126

Division (Domestic):

SAFECO Insurance Company of America-Central Region (4)
1600 N Collins Blvd, Richardson, TX 75080-3666
Tel.: (972) 808-4000
Web Site: http://www.safeco.com
Sales Range: $200-249.9 Million
Emp.: 250
Property & Casualty Insurance Services
N.A.I.C.S.: 524126

SAFECO Insurance Company of America-Northeast Region (4)
310 E 96th St, Indianapolis, IN 46240-3702
Tel.: (603) 352-3221
Web Site: http://www.safeco.com
Property & Casualty Insurance Services
N.A.I.C.S.: 524126

SAFECO Insurance Company of America-Northwest Region (4)
1001 4th Ave, Seattle, WA 98154
Tel.: (425) 376-7700
Web Site: http://www.safeco.com
Sales Range: $1-4.9 Billion
Emp.: 6,000
Property & Casualty Insurance Services
N.A.I.C.S.: 524126
Michael Thomas (Project Mgr-IT)
Jennifer Goodhope (Mgr-Special Projects)

SAFECO Insurance Company of America-Southeast Region (4)
3011 Sutton Gate Dr, Suwanee, GA 30024
Tel.: (678) 417-3000
Web Site: http://www.safeco.com
Sales Range: $400-449.9 Million
Emp.: 350
Property & Casualty Insurance Services
N.A.I.C.S.: 524126
Erik McDowell (Branch Mgr)

SAFECO Insurance Company of America-Southwest Region (4)
120 Vantis Ste 130, Aliso Viejo, CA 92656
Tel.: (949) 860-6000
Web Site: http://www.safeco.com
Property & Casualty Insurance Services
N.A.I.C.S.: 524126

Branch (Domestic):

SAFECO Insurance Company of America (5)
330 N Brand Blvd, Glendale, CA 91203-2308
Tel.: (818) 956-4200
Emp.: 160
Property & Casualty Insurance Services
N.A.I.C.S.: 524126
Don Chambers (Gen Mgr)

Unit (Domestic):

SAFECO Surety (4)
1001 4th Ave Ste 1700, Seattle, WA 98154
Tel.: (206) 473-3799
Web Site: http://www.safeco.com
Sales Range: $200-249.9 Million
Emp.: 22
Surety Bonds Underwriter
N.A.I.C.S.: 524298

LIBERTY NATIONAL BANK
118 S Main St, Ada, OH 45810
Tel.: (419) 634-5015
Web Site: http://www.lnbbank.com
Sales Range: $10-24.9 Million
Emp.: 65
National Commercial Banks
N.A.I.C.S.: 522110
Heather Cox (Asst VP & Dir-Mktg)
Bryan Marshall (CFO & Exec VP)
Patricia A. Arnett (Officer-Cash Mgmt, Sr VP-HR & Dir-HR)
Anna Maria Brenneman (Chief Credit Officer & Exec VP)
Jana Copeland (Sr VP)
Russell Figgins (VP)
David Thrasher (VP)
Cindy Ringwald (Asst VP)

Joyce Rostorfer (Asst VP & Branch Mgr)
Sara C. Reese (Asst VP-Retail Admin)
Evan A. Smith (Officer-Compliance)
Susan Thompson (Mgr-HR)
Patrick S. Smith (Officer-Compliance)
Donald Price (VP)
Joenee D. Purcell (VP)
Angela D. Hersh (VP-Mortgage Lending)
Chase Coleman (Exec VP)
Cole Hornbuckle (VP-Johnston)
Jim Langin (Pres-Des Moines)
Courtney Wiles (Asst VP)
Carl T. Cecil (Chm)
Bill Coleman (Pres)

LIBERTY OIL CO. INC.
2 Main St, Port Carbon, PA 17965
Tel.: (570) 622-3595
Web Site: http://www.libertyoilcompany.com
Sales Range: $10-24.9 Million
Emp.: 15
Provider of Petroleum Bulk Stations
N.A.I.C.S.: 424710
Troy Ahner (Mgr)

LIBERTY ORCHARDS CO., INC.
117 Mission St, Cashmere, WA 98815
Tel.: (509) 782-2191
Web Site: http://www.libertyorchards.com
Year Founded: 1920
Sales Range: $75-99.9 Million
Emp.: 50
Candy & Confection Mfr & Retailer
N.A.I.C.S.: 311340
Gregory A. Taylor (Pres & CEO)
Kathy Paine (Coord-Sls & Mktg)

LIBERTY PAPER & PRINTING
5025 Hampton St, Los Angeles, CA 90058
Web Site: http://www.libertypp.com
Year Founded: 1986
Sales Range: $10-24.9 Million
Emp.: 20
Premium Business Papers, Quality Printing & Direct Mail Services
N.A.I.C.S.: 323111
Alex Ismail (CEO & Founder)

LIBERTY PARTNERS, L.P.
1370 Ave of the Americas 34th Fl, New York, NY 10019-4602
Tel.: (212) 541-7676
Web Site: http://www.libertypartners.com
Year Founded: 1992
Sales Range: $25-49.9 Million
Emp.: 16
Private Equity Investment Firm
N.A.I.C.S.: 551112
Michael J. Fram (Mng Dir)
G. Michael Stakias (Pres & CEO)
Ryan Chorazy (VP)

Subsidiaries:

Edison Learning, Inc. (1)
900 S Gay St Ste 1000, Knoxville, TN 37902
Tel.: (865) 329-3600
Web Site: http://www.edisonlearning.com
Educational Support Services
N.A.I.C.S.: 611710
Thom Jackson (Pres & CEO)
Gamal Brown (Dir-Student Success)
Rodd Coker (VP-Sls)
Sabrena Davis (Dir-Student Success)
Cynthia Gonzalez (VP-Strategic HR)
Romney L. Grippo (Gen Counsel)
Tara Lawrence (Dir-Student Success)
Maureen Ryan (CFO)
Christopher Wilberding (VP-Solution Ops)

Mike Williams *(CIO & VP)*
Ernest Williams *(Dir-Student Success)*
Kenneth E. Edwards Sr. *(Executives)*

Liberty Higher Education, LLC (1)
750 3rd Ave 9th Fl, New York, NY 10017
Tel.: (212) 541-7676
Web Site: http://www.libertypartners.com
Sales Range: $10-24.9 Million
All Other Miscellaneous Schools & Instruction
N.A.I.C.S.: 611699
Peter E. Bennett *(CEO)*

LIBERTY PERSONNEL SERVICES
410 Fehely Dr, King of Prussia, PA 19406
Tel.: (610) 941-6300
Web Site: http://www.libertyjobs.com
Year Founded: 2002
Sales Range: $10-24.9 Million
Emp.: 64
Professionals Recruitment Services
N.A.I.C.S.: 561311
Tony McGuire *(VP)*
Michael O'Callaghan *(Acct Mgr)*
Franco Lamesta *(Mgr)*

LIBERTY POLYGLAS, INC.
1575 Lebanon School Rd, West Mifflin, PA 15122-3464
Tel.: (412) 466-8611
Web Site: http://www.libertypultrusions.com
Fiberglass Reinforced Plastics (FRP) Pultrusion Mfr
N.A.I.C.S.: 326199

LIBERTY POWER CORP. LLC
1901 W Cypress Creek Rd Ste 600, Fort Lauderdale, FL 33309
Web Site: http://www.libertypowercorp.com
Year Founded: 2001
Sales Range: $700-749.9 Million
Emp.: 300
Electric Power Distr
N.A.I.C.S.: 221122
David Hernandez *(CEO)*
Alberto Daire *(Pres & COO)*

LIBERTY PROPERTY LIMITED PARTNERSHIP
650 E Swedesford Rd Ste 400, Wayne, PA 19087
Tel.: (610) 648-1700   PA
Year Founded: 1994
Rev.: $704,888,999
Assets: $6,934,393,999
Liabilities: $3,537,622,000
Net Worth: $3,396,771,999
Earnings: $491,021,000
Emp.: 271
Fiscal Year-end: 12/31/18
Real Estate Asset Management Services
N.A.I.C.S.: 531390
William P. Hankowsky *(Chm, Pres & CEO)*

LIBERTY PUMPS
7000 Appletree Ave, Bergen, NY 14416
Web Site: http://www.libertypumps.com
Year Founded: 1965
Rev.: $32,200,000
Emp.: 90
Pump & Pumping Equipment Mfr
N.A.I.C.S.: 333914
Jane Smith *(Acct Mgr)*
Charles Cook *(CEO)*
Ruth Vanburen *(Credit Mgr)*
Allan Davis *(VP)*
Dennis Burke *(CFO)*

LIBERTY RESOURCES, INC.
1045 James St, Syracuse, NY 13203
Tel.: (315) 425-1004   NY
Web Site: http://www.liberty-resources.org
Year Founded: 1979
Sales Range: $25-49.9 Million
Emp.: 978
Individual & Family Welfare Services
N.A.I.C.S.: 624190
Carrie Doran *(COO)*
Carl M. Coyle *(CEO)*
Marta Durkin *(VP-Behavioral Healthcare)*
Kortney R. Dale *(VP-Family Svcs)*
Joanna Viggiano *(CFO)*

LIBERTY SCIENCE CENTER, INC.
222 Jersey City Blvd, Jersey City, NJ 07305
Tel.: (201) 451-0006
Web Site: http://www.lsc.org
Year Founded: 1993
Sales Range: $10-24.9 Million
Emp.: 280
Science Exhibits, Hands-on Children's Displays & IMAX Theatre Attractions
N.A.I.C.S.: 712110
Barry Zubrow *(Chief Admin Officer)*
Elizabeth Stoner *(Sr VP-Clinical Dev)*
Paul Hoffman *(Pres & CEO)*

LIBERTY STEEL PRODUCTS INC.
11650 Mahony Ave, North Jackson, OH 44451
Tel.: (330) 538-2236   OH
Web Site: http://www.liberty-steel.com
Year Founded: 1965
Sales Range: $125-149.9 Million
Emp.: 180
Operate Metal Service Centers
N.A.I.C.S.: 423510
Jim Grasso *(VP-Fin & Admin)*
James T. Weller Sr. *(VP-Production)*
Andrew J. Weller Jr. *(VP-Ops)*

LIBERTY STREET ADVISORS, LLC
271 Riverside Ave, Riverside, CT 06878-2313
Tel.: (203) 698-9292   DE
Web Site: http://www.libertystreetadvisors.com
Sales Range: $1-9.9 Million
Corporate Consulting Services
N.A.I.C.S.: 541611
Kathleen A. O'Neil *(Pres & CEO)*

LIBERTY SUPPLY INC.
1003 N Vine, Magnolia, AR 71753-2429
Tel.: (870) 234-2031
Rev.: $10,000,000
Emp.: 22
Industrial Machinery & Equipment Merchant Whslr
N.A.I.C.S.: 423830
Bill Merritt *(VP)*
Lamar Lee *(Pres)*
David Spradlin *(Treas & Sec)*

LIBERTY SYSTEMS, INC.
475 Saw Mill River Rd, Yonkers, NY 10703
Tel.: (914) 969-6900   NY
Web Site: http://www.libertylines.com
Year Founded: 1953
Sales Range: $75-99.9 Million
Emp.: 900
Holding Company; Urban Bus Transportation Services
N.A.I.C.S.: 551112
Gerard Bernacchia *(Pres)*

Subsidiaries:

Liberty Lines Transit, Inc. (1)
475 Saw Mill River Rd, Yonkers, NY 10703
Tel.: (914) 969-6900
Web Site: http://www.libertylines.com
Emp.: 700
Urban Bus Transportation Services
N.A.I.C.S.: 485210
Thomas Murphy *(VP-Ops)*
Jerry D'Amore *(Pres)*
Neil Erickson *(VP-HR)*
Christopher Meyer *(VP-Admin)*
Perry Paulsen *(VP-Fin)*
Ray Pereira *(VP-Maintenance)*
Gerard Bernacchia *(Chm)*
Nestor Martinez *(VP-Maintenance)*

LIBERTY TRANSPORTATION, INC.
Liberty Transportation 838 Croft Rd, Greensburg, PA 15601
Tel.: (724) 668-2772
Web Site: http://www.libertytran.com
Year Founded: 1978
Local Trucking without Storage
N.A.I.C.S.: 484121
Nickie Doran *(Dir-Fin & Controller)*
Mark Palla *(Dir-Full Truck Load Ops & Logistics)*
Lori Runzo *(Mgr-Risk & Dir-Warehousing & Internet Fulfillment)*
Chuck Runzo *(Chm & Pres)*

LIBERTYVILLE BUICK, PONTIAC, GMC, INC.
PO Box 84, Barrington, IL 60011-0084
Tel.: (847) 680-5000
Year Founded: 2007
Sales Range: $10-24.9 Million
Emp.: 38
New Car Whslr
N.A.I.C.S.: 441110
Garrett Gioulos *(Owner)*

LIBERTYVILLE LINCOLN SALES INC.
941 S Milwaukee Ave, Libertyville, IL 60048
Tel.: (847) 367-1700   DE
Web Site: http://www.libertyville-lincoln.com
Year Founded: 1981
Sales Range: $100-124.9 Million
Emp.: 100
Car Dealership
N.A.I.C.S.: 441110
Daniel H. Marks *(Pres)*
Chuck Benkiel *(Gen Mgr)*

LIBLA COMMUNICATIONS INC.
7082 Hwy 67 N Ste A, Poplar Bluff, MO 63901
Tel.: (573) 785-9068
Sales Range: $10-24.9 Million
Emp.: 25
Communication Line & Transmission Tower Construction
N.A.I.C.S.: 237130
Larry W. Libla *(Owner & Pres)*

LIBLA INDUSTRIES INC.
2700 Central Ave, Poplar Bluff, MO 63901
Tel.: (800) 867-6245   MO
Web Site: http://www.magnumfasteners.com
Year Founded: 1987
Steel Nails, Brads, Staples & Collated Fasteners Mfr
N.A.I.C.S.: 332618
George Skarich *(VP-Sls & Mktg)*

LIBRA ELECTRIC COMPANY
4736 Enterprise Dr, Oklahoma City, OK 73128
Tel.: (405) 949-9371   OK
Web Site: http://www.libraelectric.net
Year Founded: 1983
Sales Range: $1-9.9 Million
Emp.: 30
Electrical Contractor
N.A.I.C.S.: 238210
Carlos Wood *(Pres)*

LIBRA INDUSTRIES, INC.
1435 N Blackstone St, Jackson, MI 49202
Tel.: (517) 787-5675
Web Site: http://www.librami.com
Year Founded: 1969
Sales Range: $10-24.9 Million
Emp.: 135
Industrial Launderers
N.A.I.C.S.: 812332
Michael Iuni *(Pres & CEO)*
Tim Lightner *(Product Mgr)*
Beth Yoxheimer *(Pres)*

LIBRA INDUSTRIES, INCORPORATED
7770 Division Dr, Mentor, OH 44060-4860
Tel.: (440) 974-7770   OH
Web Site: http://www.libraind.com
Year Founded: 1980
Sales Range: $100-124.9 Million
Emp.: 130
Printed Circuit Boards & Electronics Components Mfr
N.A.I.C.S.: 334412
Rod Howell *(CEO)*
Thomas Dykeman *(VP-Sls & Bus Dev)*
Don Kerrick *(Mgr-Pur)*
Matt Tringhese *(Dir-Mfg)*
Roy Starks *(Dir-Program Mgmt)*
Britney Huet-Scibana *(Jr Mgr-Program)*
Kim Carlson *(Mgr-HR-Dallas)*
Ryan Bodzenski *(Program Mgr)*

Subsidiaries:

Flow Thru Systems Inc. (1)
7770 Division Dr, Mentor, OH 44060-4860
Tel.: (440) 974-9770
Sales Range: $10-24.9 Million
Emp.: 20
Printed Circuit Boards
N.A.I.C.S.: 423830

LIBRARY BINDING SERVICE INC.
1801 Thompson Ave, Des Moines, IA 50316
Tel.: (515) 262-3191
Web Site: http://www.lbsbind.com
Sales Range: $10-24.9 Million
Emp.: 90
Bookbinding & Related Work
N.A.I.C.S.: 323120
Fritz James *(CEO)*
Rob Mauritz *(Pres)*
Sherri Molka *(Acct Mgr)*

LIBRARY VIDEO COMPANY
300 Barr Harbor Dr Ste 700, West Conshohocken, PA 19428
Tel.: (610) 645-4000
Web Site: http://www.libraryvideo.com
Rev.: $26,500,000
Emp.: 98
Video Cassettes, Accessories & Supplies
N.A.I.C.S.: 423990
Andrew Schlessinger *(Pres & CEO)*

LIBREMAX CAPITAL, LLC
600 Lexington Ave 19th Fl, New York, NY 10022
Tel.: (212) 612-1550

LIBREMAX CAPITAL, LLC

LibreMax Capital, LLC—(Continued)
Web Site:
http://www.libremaxcapital.com
Investment Banking & Securities Dealing
N.A.I.C.S.: 523150
John Curran *(Head-IR & Mktg)*

Subsidiaries:

Katonah Debt Advisors, L.L.C. (1)
295 Madison Ave Ste 6, New York, NY 10017-7731
Tel.: (212) 455-8303
Investment Management Service
N.A.I.C.S.: 523940
E. A. Kratzman *(Pres)*

LIBSYS, INC.
2020 Calamos Ct Ste 200, Naperville, IL 60563
Tel.: (630) 799-1556
Web Site: http://www.LibsysInc.com
Year Founded: 2002
Sales Range: $1-9.9 Million
Emp.: 100
Software Services
N.A.I.C.S.: 449210
Siva Yarramsetty *(CEO)*
Sridhar Yerramsetti *(Pres)*
Vinay Kumar *(Dir-Mktg)*

LICHTI BROTHERS OIL COMPANY
301 S Market St, Shickley, NE 68436
Tel.: (402) 627-2235
Sales Range: $10-24.9 Million
Emp.: 50
Petroleum Products
N.A.I.C.S.: 424720
Tim Lichti *(Pres)*

LICKING VALLEY OIL CO. INC.
8160 US 27 N, Butler, KY 41006
Tel.: (859) 472-7111
Web Site: http://www.lvoinc.com
Sales Range: $10-24.9 Million
Emp.: 30
Distr of Petroleum Products
N.A.I.C.S.: 424720
David Bay *(Pres)*
Kathy Banfield *(Controller)*

LIDESTRI FOODS, INC.
815 W Whitney Rd, Fairport, NY 14450-1030
Tel.: (585) 377-7700
Web Site:
http://www.lidestrifoodanddrink.com
Year Founded: 1974
Sauces & Condiments
N.A.I.C.S.: 311941
John LiDestri *(Co-Pres-Sls & Supply Chain)*
Stefani LiDestri *(Co-Pres & CMO)*
Giovanni LiDestri *(CEO)*
Jennifer Amodeo Shepker *(Dir-Fin)*
Laurie Cardillo *(VP-Product Innovation & Mmgt)*
Tony Ciulla *(VP-Contract Packing & Special Projects)*
Tom Galanti *(VP-Supply Chain)*
Judy Gosz *(VP-Food & Beverage Sls)*
John Matrachisia *(CIO)*
Joe Ragazzo *(VP-Retail & Proprietary Brands)*
Phil Viruso *(VP-Mfg)*

LIDO BEACH RESORT
700 Ben Franklin Dr, Sarasota, FL 34236
Tel.: (941) 388-2161
Web Site:
http://www.lidobeachresort.com
Sales Range: $10-24.9 Million
Emp.: 100
Hotel Operations
N.A.I.C.S.: 721110
Tom Walsh *(Pres)*
Maria Quinn *(Dir-Food & Beverage)*

LIDOCHEM, INC.
20 Village Ct, Hazlet, NJ 07730-1532
Tel.: (732) 888-8000
Web Site: http://www.lidochem.com
Year Founded: 1981
Sales Range: $10-24.9 Million
Emp.: 13
Chemicals & Fertilizers Distr
N.A.I.C.S.: 424690
Don J. Pucillo *(Pres)*
Lisa Pucillo *(CFO)*
Todd McGuire *(Mgr-Mktg & PR-Performance Nutrition)*

LIECHTY FARM EQUIPMENT INC.
1701 S Defiance St, Archbold, OH 43502
Tel.: (419) 445-1565
Web Site:
http://www.kennfeldgroup.com
Year Founded: 1939
Sales Range: $10-24.9 Million
Emp.: 30
Provider of Agricultural Machinery & Equipment
N.A.I.C.S.: 423820
Jay Beck *(Pres)*
Jody Osborn *(Mgr-Parts)*

LIEDTKA TRUCKING INCORPORATED
110 Patterson Ave, Trenton, NJ 08610
Tel.: (609) 586-6043
Web Site: http://www.liedtka.com
Year Founded: 1964
Sales Range: $10-24.9 Million
Emp.: 120
Provider of Transporting Services
N.A.I.C.S.: 484121
Holly Johnsen *(Mgr-Baltimore-MD Terminal)*
Paul Springer *(Mgr-Harrisburg-PA Terminal)*
John Mariano *(Mgr-Morrisville-PA Terminal)*
George Sexton *(Mgr-Terminal)*

LIETZ DEVELOPMENT, INC.
7904 Hopi Pl, Tampa, FL 33634
Tel.: (813) 874-5511
Web Site: http://www.datatechitp.com
Year Founded: 1996
Sales Range: $1-9.9 Million
Emp.: 16
Computer System Design Services
N.A.I.C.S.: 541512
Chris Lietz *(Pres & CEO)*
Todd Lietz *(VP)*
Lisa Dorman *(CFO)*
Mike Ponticello *(CIO)*
Kevin Kohrs *(Mgr-Data Center)*
Scott Dollar *(Dir-Bus Dev)*
Mike Puckett *(Dir-Mktg)*

LIFE ACTION MINISTRIES
2727 Niles-Buchanan Rd, Buchanan, MI 49107
Tel.: (269) 697-8600
Web Site: http://www.lifeaction.org
Year Founded: 1977
Sales Range: $10-24.9 Million
Emp.: 273
Christian Ministry
N.A.I.C.S.: 813110
Allen Mazelin *(CFO)*
Del Fehsenfeld *(Chief Pastoral Officer & Dir-Comm & Pastoral Svcs)*
Byron Paulus *(Pres & CEO)*

LIFE ALERT EMERGENCY RESPONSE INC.
16027 Ventura Blvd Ste 400, Encino, CA 91436
Tel.: (818) 700-7000
Web Site: http://www.lifealert.com
Sales Range: $10-24.9 Million
Emp.: 500
Provider of Burglary Protection Services
N.A.I.C.S.: 561612
Dawn Russo *(Office Mgr)*
Chloe Chou *(Mgr & Engr-Software)*
Lizza Mesina *(Mgr-Acctg)*
Felix Leung *(CFO)*
Barry Gates *(Mgr-Sls)*

LIFE CARE CENTER OF CARROLLTON
300 Life Care Ln, Carrollton, MO 64633
Tel.: (660) 542-0155
Web Site: https://lcca.com
Year Founded: 1985
Sales Range: $10-24.9 Million
Emp.: 85
Fiscal Year-end: 12/31/13
Nursing Care Facilities
N.A.I.C.S.: 623110
Debbie Arnold *(Principal)*
Lynn Hayes *(Exec Dir)*

LIFE CARE CENTERS OF AMERICA
3570 Keith St NW, Cleveland, TN 37312
Tel.: (423) 472-9585
Web Site: https://www.lcca.com
Year Founded: 1970
Sales Range: $1-4.9 Billion
Emp.: 40,000
Nursing Care Facilities (Skilled Nursing Facilities)
N.A.I.C.S.: 623110
Beecher Hunter *(Pres)*
Todd Fletcher *(VP-West)*
Lisa Meyer *(Reg Dir-Rehab)*
Shirley Daniels Alderman *(Dir-Volunteer Dev)*
Stacey Demps *(Dir-Nursing-East)*
Marshal Huddleston *(Exec Dir)*
Gene Chastain *(VP-IT & Cybersecurity)*
Terry Leonard *(CIO)*

LIFE CARE COMPANIES, LLC
400 Locust St Ste 820, Des Moines, IA 50309-2334
Tel.: (515) 875-4500
Web Site:
http://www.lifecareservices-seniorliving.com
Year Founded: 1971
Senior Living Management & Senior Living Marketing & Sales
N.A.I.C.S.: 623311
Joel Nelson *(Pres & CEO)*
Rick Exline *(Exec VP & Sr Mng Dir-Life Plan Communities)*
Chris Bird *(Exec VP & Dir-Rental)*
Judi Buxo *(Sr VP & Dir-Speacial Assets)*
Laura Franco *(VP-Dir-Health Care Svcs)*
Tony Galvan *(Dir-Health & Wellness)*
Earl Wade *(VP & Sr Dir-Bus Dev)*
Patrick J. Duffy *(Bd of Dirs, Executives)*

Subsidiaries:

Augusta Resource Center on Aging, Inc. (1)
4275 Owens Rd, Evans, GA 30809-3066
Tel.: (706) 868-9800
Web Site: http://www.brandonwilde.com
Continuing Care Retirement Communities

N.A.I.C.S.: 623311
Ben Guest *(Exec Dir-Interim)*
Avery Villines *(Sr Dir-Community Life Svcs)*
Arnold McGahee *(Sr Dir-Plant Ops)*
Cheryl Taylor *(Dir-Acctg)*
Stephen Pryor *(Dir-Housekeeping & Laundry Svcs)*
Jennie Phillips *(Dir-Assisted Living Svcs)*

LIFE EXCHANGE, INC.
2001 Biscayne Blvd Ste 2102, Miami, FL 33137
Tel.: (305) 572-9766
Year Founded: 2005
Sales Range: Less than $1 Million
Emp.: 4
Life Settlement Internet Services
N.A.I.C.S.: 524298

LIFE FOR RELIEF & DEVELOPMENT
17300 W 10 Mile Rd, Southfield, MI 48075
Tel.: (248) 424-7493
Web Site: http://www.lifeusa.org
Year Founded: 1992
Sales Range: $50-74.9 Million
Emp.: 24
Community Care Services
N.A.I.C.S.: 624190
Michael J. Salloum *(Treas & Sec)*
Abdulwahab Asamarai *(Chm)*
M. Yahia Abdul-Rahim *(Accountant)*
Abdallah Boumediene *(CEO)*

LIFE INSURANCE COMPANY OF ALABAMA INC.
302 Broad St, Gadsden, AL 35901-3716
Tel.: (256) 543-2022
Web Site: http://www.licoa.com
Year Founded: 1952
Sales Range: $25-49.9 Million
Emp.: 100
Life, Accident & Health Insurance
N.A.I.C.S.: 524113
Lynn Lowe *(CFO)*
L. Ashley *(VP & Dir-Agency)*
Clarence W. Daugette III *(Pres)*
Raymond R. Renfrow Jr. *(CMO & Exec VP)*

LIFE LINE EMERGENCY VEHICLES, INC.
1 Life Line Dr, Sumner, IA 50674
Tel.: (563) 578-3317
Web Site:
http://www.lifelineambulance.com
Year Founded: 1985
Sales Range: $10-24.9 Million
Emp.: 190
Mfr of Ambulance Vehicles
N.A.I.C.S.: 336211
Connie Leicher *(Pres)*

LIFE PARTNERS HOLDINGS, INC.
204 Woodhew Dr, Waco, TX 76712
Tel.: (254) 751-7797
Web Site: http://www.lphi.com
Year Founded: 1991
Life Settlement Services
N.A.I.C.S.: 524292
Mark Embry *(COO & CIO)*
Ladonna Johnson *(VP)*

Subsidiaries:

Life Partners, Inc. (1)
204 Woodhew Dr, Waco, TX 76712
Tel.: (254) 751-7797
Web Site: http://www.lifepartnersinc.com
Sales Range: $25-49.9 Million
Sale & Transfer of Life Insurance Policies for the Terminally Ill
N.A.I.C.S.: 524292

COMPANIES

R. Scott Peden (Gen Counsel)
Mark Embry (Interim Pres, COO, CIO & Sec)
Kurt D. Carr (VP-Policy Admin)

LIFE PARTNERS IRA HOLDER PARTNERSHIP, LLC
2001 Bryan St Ste 1800, Dallas, TX 75201
Tel.: (214) 560-5404   TX
Year Founded: 2016
Rev.: $44,457,156
Assets: $160,464,925
Liabilities: $443,570
Net Worth: $160,021,355
Earnings: $44,377,567
Emp.: 31
Fiscal Year-end: 12/31/21
Financial Investment Services
N.A.I.C.S.: 523940
Michael J. Quilling (Mgr)

LIFE PARTNERS POSITION HOLDER TRUST
2001 Bryan St Ste 1800, Dallas, TX 75201
Tel.: (214) 560-5404   TX
Web Site: http://www.lpi-pht.com
Year Founded: 2016
Rev.: $87,109,047
Assets: $308,928,032
Liabilities: $39,567,412
Net Worth: $269,360,620
Earnings: $76,937,048
Emp.: 2
Fiscal Year-end: 12/31/21
Portfolio Management Services
N.A.I.C.S.: 523940
Nauman Poonja (CFO)
Natalie Eilat (Chief Acctg Officer)

LIFE SAFETY COMMERCIAL FIRE & SECURITY SERVICES, INC.
60 Sonwil Dr, Buffalo, NY 14225
Tel.: (716) 656-8890   NY
Web Site:
http://www.lifesafetysecurity.com
Year Founded: 1994
Sales Range: $1-9.9 Million
Emp.: 39
Sells, Installs & Services Fire & Security Alarm Systems
N.A.I.C.S.: 561621
Robert Vezina (Pres)

LIFE SAFETY SERVICES
4720 Pinewood Rd, Louisville, KY 40218
Tel.: (502) 213-0431
Web Site:
http://www.lifesafetyservices.com
Year Founded: 2004
Sales Range: $10-24.9 Million
Emp.: 50
Business Services
N.A.I.C.S.: 541990
Amy Strecker (Mgr-Charlotte)
Andrew Brunner (Mgr-Billings)
Heidi Young (Mgr-Northern California)
Jill Evans (Mgr-Cleveland)
Jim Lightcap (Mgr-Louisville)
Michele Howard (Mgr-Los Angeles)
Scot Bergstrom (Mgr-Dallas)
Scott Riedel (Mgr-New York City)
William Mansfield (Mgr-Minneapolis)

LIFE SCIENCES RESEARCH, INC.
Mettlers Rd, East Millstone, NJ 08875
Tel.: (732) 873-2550   MD
Web Site: http://www.lsrinc.net
Year Founded: 1952
Sales Range: $200-249.9 Million
Emp.: 1,648
Provider of Clinical Research

N.A.I.C.S.: 541715
Andrew Baker (Chm & CEO)
Brian Cass (Pres & Mng Dir)
Richard A. Michaelson (CFO)
Julian T. Griffiths (VP-Ops)
Mark Bibi (Gen Counsel & Sec)
Subsidiaries:
Huntingdon Life Sciences Group plc   (1)
Woolley Rd Alconbury, Huntingdon, PE28 4HS, Cambs, United Kingdom
Tel.: (44) 1480892100
Web Site: http://www.huntingdon.com
Sales Range: $150-199.9 Million
Emp.: 950
Provider of Contract Research Services; Non-Clinical Safety & Efficacy Tests for Pharmaceutical & Chemical Industries
N.A.I.C.S.: 541715
Andrew Baker (Chm)

LIFE'S WORC
1501 Franklin Ave, Garden City, NY 11530-8165
Tel.: (516) 741-9000   NY
Web Site: http://www.lifesworc.org
Year Founded: 1972
Sales Range: $25-49.9 Million
Emp.: 1,086
Developmental Disability Assistance Services
N.A.I.C.S.: 624120
Janet Koch (CEO)
Anna-Maria Trent (Sr Dir-Community Svcs)
Laura Lovelock (Sr Dir-HR)
Donald Barrick (Co-Chm)
Lynne Koufakis (Sec)
Rick Del Mastro (Co-Chm)
Shannon Preston (Sr Dir-Dev)

LIFE-SEQ, LLC
1 Liberty Sq Fl 11, Boston, MA 02109
Tel.: (617) 226-1740
Web Site: http://www.life-seq.com
Biotechnology Research & Development Services
N.A.I.C.S.: 541714
Steve Grimaldi (CTO)
F. Nicholas Jacobs (Dir-Intl)
Timothy A. Krochuk (Co-Founder & Mng Dir)
Gregory Clair Sr. (Co-Founder)

LIFE-TECH INC.
13235 N Promenade Blvd, Stafford, TX 77477
Tel.: (281) 491-6600
Web Site: http://www.life-tech.com
Sales Range: $10-24.9 Million
Emp.: 100
Diagnostic Apparatus, Medical
N.A.I.C.S.: 339112
Alex Reyna (Mgr)
Paul Salvo (Mgr-IT)

LIFE365 PORTRAITS
23 Vreeland Rd Ste 160, Florham Park, NJ 07932-1514
Tel.: (973) 736-5600
Web Site:
http://www.life365portraits.com
Rev.: $14,300,000
Emp.: 150
Photographic Children's Studios
N.A.I.C.S.: 541921
Robert Cohen (CEO & Mng Member)
Wayne Strobel (VP-Ops)
Pauline Roding (Mgr-Photo)

LIFEBRIDGE HEALTH
2401 W Belvedere Ave, Baltimore, MD 21215
Tel.: (410) 601-9000
Web Site:
http://www.lifebridgehealth.org

Sales Range: $1-4.9 Billion
Emp.: 7,404
Medical Health Network
N.A.I.C.S.: 622110
Julie Cox (VP-Dev)
Christine DeAngelis (VP-Physician Networks & Value-Based Care Programs)
Barbara Epke (VP)
David Krajewski (CFO & Sr VP)
Tony Morris (VP-Revenue Cycle)
Martha Nathanson (VP-Govt & Community Dev)
Joel Suldan (VP)
Brian White (Pres-Northwest Hospital & Post-Acute Care Div)
Ronnie B. Footlick (Treas)
Tressa Springmann (CIO & VP-Enterprise IT & Process Improvement)
Deborah Hollenstein (VP-Strategic Mktg & Comm)
Jonathan Ringo (Chief Medical Info Officer & VP-Clinical Transformation)
Lucy Ferko (VP-Svc Lines)
James Roberge (VP-Capital Improvements & Support Svcs)
Neil Carpenter (VP-Strategic Plng & Res)
Terrence Carney (VP-Supply Chain Mgmt)
Michael D. Myers (VP-Regulatory Reporting & Reimbursement)
Joe Quinn (Chief HR Officer)
Joyce Romans (Chief Compliance Officer)
Stephen Young (VP)
Kevin Inman (Chief Nursing Officer & VP-Patient Care Svcs-Northwest Hospital)
Jason A. Blavatt (Chm)
Jeffrey A. Wothers (Sec)
Barry F. Levin (Vice Chm)
Idriz Limaj (COO-Post-Acute Svcs)
Neil Meltzer (Pres & CEO)
Stephen Witman (VP-Bus Dev, Fin & Capital Plng)
Nancy Kane (VP-Fin Reporting)

LIFECARE AMBULANCE, INC.
640 Cleveland St, Elyria, OH 44035
Tel.: (440) 323-6111   OH
Web Site:
http://www.lifecareambulance.com
Year Founded: 1987
Ambulance Service
N.A.I.C.S.: 621910
Brian Lander (Controller)
David Richards (CFO)
Richard Pozywak (Dir-IT)
David Richards (Pres & CFO)

LIFECARE MEDICAL CENTER
715 Delmore Dr, Roseau, MN 56751
Tel.: (218) 463-2500   MN
Web Site:
http://www.lifecaremedicalcenter.org
Year Founded: 1995
Sales Range: $25-49.9 Million
Emp.: 519
Health Care Srvices
N.A.I.C.S.: 622110
Cathy Huss (CFO)
Deb Haugen (Dir-Community Rels)
Shannon Carlson (VP-Support Svcs)
Milly Prachar (Dir-Health Info Mgmt)

LIFECARE MEDICAL SERVICES, INC.
3755 Boettler Oaks Dr Ste E 2, Uniontown, OH 44685
Tel.: (330) 899-0022
Web Site: http://www.lifecare-ems.com
Year Founded: 2000
Sales Range: $10-24.9 Million

LIFEDESIGNS

Emp.: 250
Emergency & Non-Emergency Medical Transportation
N.A.I.C.S.: 621910
James Caplinger (Owner)
Rick Reed (Dir-Ops)
Michele Skinner (Dir-Patient Accts)

LIFECENTER NORTHWEST
3650 131st Ave SE Ste 200, Bellevue, WA 98006
Tel.: (425) 201-6563   WA
Web Site: http://www.lcnw.org
Year Founded: 1996
Sales Range: $10-24.9 Million
Emp.: 125
Eye & Tissue Donating Services
N.A.I.C.S.: 621991
Jan Hendrix (Dir-Tissue Donation Svcs)
Megan Clark (VP-Program Dev & External Affairs)
Sean Farragher (Dir-Quality & Regulatory Affairs)
Candy Wells (Dir-Organ Donation Svcs)
Amy Wilson (Dir-HR)
Maude Blair (Sec)
Gerard Fischer (Chm)
Kevin J. O'Connor (Pres & CEO)
Jim Young (Treas)
Rachel Houck (Dir-Hospital Dev)

LIFECIRCLES
560 Seminole Rd, Muskegon, MI 49444
Tel.: (231) 733-8686   MI
Web Site: http://www.lifecircles-pace.org
Year Founded: 2007
Sales Range: $10-24.9 Million
Emp.: 65
Senior Living Services
N.A.I.C.S.: 623311
Iris Boettcher (Dir-Medical)
Daniel Caldwell (Mgr-Medical Ops)

LIFECOURSE MANAGEMENT SERVICE
2325 E 30th St, Farmington, NM 87401
Tel.: (505) 564-7958
Year Founded: 1997
Sales Range: $10-24.9 Million
Emp.: 90
Direct Health & Medical Insurance Services
N.A.I.C.S.: 524114
Gayle Cheverie (VP)

LIFECYCLE CONSTRUCTION SERVICES INC.
1315 Jefferson Davis Hwy, Fredericksburg, VA 22401
Tel.: (540) 656-2415
Web Site: http://www.lifecycle-inc.com
Year Founded: 2007
Sales Range: $25-49.9 Million
Emp.: 26
Planning, Design & Construction
N.A.I.C.S.: 237990
Sean Haynes (Pres)
Bev Desselle (Controller)

LIFEDESIGNS
200 E Winslow Rd, Bloomington, IN 47401
Tel.: (812) 332-9615   IN
Web Site:
http://www.lifedesignsinc.org
Year Founded: 1982
Sales Range: $10-24.9 Million
Emp.: 458
Disability Assistance Services
N.A.I.C.S.: 624120

LIFEDESIGNS

LifeDesigns—(Continued)
Marianne Stemm *(Dir-HR)*
Zachary Woodward *(Dir-Residential Svcs)*
Danie Norris *(Dir-Support Svcs)*
Cathy Martin *(CFO)*
Russell Bonanno *(CEO)*
Vonnie Peischl *(Chm)*

LIFEGIFT ORGAN DONATION CENTER
2510 West Rdg, Houston, TX 77054
Tel.: (713) 523-4438
Web Site: http://www.lifegift.org
Sales Range: $10-24.9 Million
Emp.: 45
Medical Help Service
N.A.I.C.S.: 561320
Patricia Rubin *(CFO & Sr Exec VP)*
Laura Frnka-Davis *(Mng Dir-Comm)*
Brian Roe *(Sr Mng Dir-Tissue Svcs & Comm Center Ops)*
R. Patrick Wood *(Chief Medical Officer & VP)*
Jessica C. Leibold *(Sr Mng Dir-Facilities & Pur)*
Jerry Dunn *(Mng Dir-Info Sys)*
Kevin A. Myer *(Pres & CEO)*
Donna Smith *(Mng Dir)*
Carolyn Olivarez *(Mng Dir-Quality Sys)*
Justin Johnson *(Mng Dir-West Reg)*

LIFEGUARD AIR AMBULANCE, INC.
4211 Jerry Maygarden Rd, Pensacola, FL 32504
Tel.: (850) 473-6776 FL
Web Site: http://www.lifeguardambulance.com
Year Founded: 1990
Sales Range: $1-9.9 Million
Emp.: 39
Ambulance Service
N.A.I.C.S.: 621910
Deborah Roche *(VP, Treas & Sec)*
John Roche *(CEO)*

LIFEGUARD TRANSPORTATION SERVICE, INC.
4211 Jerry L Maygarden Rd, Pensacola, FL 32504
Tel.: (850) 473-6776
Web Site: http://www.lifeguardambulance.com
Sales Range: $200-249.9 Million
Emp.: 800
Ambulance Service
N.A.I.C.S.: 621910
John Roche *(Pres)*

Subsidiaries:
Lifeguard Transportation Service, Inc. (1)
1933 Elm Tree Dr, Nashville, TN 37210
Tel.: (615) 724-1911
Web Site: http://www.lifeguardambulance.com
Sales Range: $50-74.9 Million
Emp.: 140
Ambulance Service
N.A.I.C.S.: 621910
David Denholm *(Mgr-Ops)*

LIFELINE YOUTH & FAMILY SERVICES, INC.
7136 Gettysburg Pike, Fort Wayne, IN 46804-5680
Tel.: (260) 745-3322 IN
Web Site: http://www.lifelineyouth.org
Year Founded: 1968
Sales Range: $10-24.9 Million
Emp.: 310
Child & Youth Care Services
N.A.I.C.S.: 624110

Mark Terrell *(CEO)*
Ruth Skeel *(Dir-Clinical & Home Based Svcs)*
Joe Gough *(Dir-Program & Svcs)*
Deb Durkes *(Mgr-HR)*

LIFELINK FOUNDATION, INC.
9661 Delaney Creek Blvd, Tampa, FL 33619
Tel.: (813) 253-2640
Web Site: http://www.lifelinkfound.org
Sales Range: $25-49.9 Million
Emp.: 400
Organ & Tissue Recovery Services
N.A.I.C.S.: 621991
Charles E. Wright *(Dir-Medical-OPO)*
Jean A. Davis *(Exec VP-Organ Recovery Svcs)*
Dennis F. Heinrichs *(Pres)*
Stephanie Hernandez *(CFO)*

LIFELONG
1002 E Seneca St, Seattle, WA 98122
Tel.: (206) 957-1600 WA
Web Site: http://www.lifelongaidsalliance.org
Year Founded: 1983
Sales Range: $25-49.9 Million
Emp.: 128
HIV Patient Wellness Services
N.A.I.C.S.: 622110
Sage Fitzpatrick *(Dir-Dev)*
Mark Baker *(Dir-Healthcare Access)*
Ace Robinson *(Dir-Health Education, Pub Policy & Comm)*
Jake Ewart *(VP)*
Michaela M. Crouch *(Treas)*

LIFELONG MEDICAL CARE
2344 6th St, Berkeley, CA 94710
Tel.: (510) 981-4100 CA
Web Site: http://www.lifelongmedical.org
Year Founded: 1996
Sales Range: $25-49.9 Million
Emp.: 746
Disability Assistance Services
N.A.I.C.S.: 624120
Marty Lynch *(CEO & Exec Dir)*
Nance Rosencranz *(Dir-Strategic Plng & Bus Dev)*
Nancy Threatt *(Sec)*

LIFEMARK SECURITIES CORP.
400 W Metro Park, Rochester, NY 14623
Tel.: (585) 424-5672
Web Site: http://www.lifemark.com
Year Founded: 1983
Sales Range: $10-24.9 Million
Emp.: 15
Security Broker & Dealer Services
N.A.I.C.S.: 523150
Vincent Micciche *(CEO & Chief Compliance Officer)*
Andy Kalinowski *(Chm & CEO)*
Ray Sickels *(Mgr-Acctg & HR)*
James J. Prisco *(Pres & COO)*
Cheri Davis *(Project Mgr)*

LIFEMATTERS
8757 Georgia Ave Ste 600, Silver Spring, MD 20910
Tel.: (301) 652-7212
Web Site: http://www.lifemattersusa.com
Year Founded: 2004
Sales Range: $1-9.9 Million
Emp.: 150
In-home Medical Health Care Assistance
N.A.I.C.S.: 621610
Scott Thompson *(Founder & CEO)*

Subsidiaries:
Lifematters (1)
7531 Leesburg Pike 202, Falls Church, VA 22046
Tel.: (703) 635-3729
In-Home Medical Care Assistance Services
N.A.I.C.S.: 621610

LIFENET HEALTH, INC.
1864 Concert Dr, Virginia Beach, VA 23453
Tel.: (757) 464-4761 VA
Web Site: http://www.lifenethealth.org
Year Founded: 1982
Sales Range: $200-249.9 Million
Emp.: 784
Health Care Srvices
N.A.I.C.S.: 622110
Gordon Berkstresser *(Sec)*
Gerald M. Bowers *(Vice Chm)*
John M. Herre *(Chm)*

Subsidiaries:
Samsara Sciences, Inc. (1)
6275 Nancy Ridge Dr Ste 110, San Diego, CA 92121
Tel.: (858) 617-0790
Web Site: http://www.samsarasciences.com
Biotechnology Research & Development Services
N.A.I.C.S.: 541714

LIFENET, INC.
6225 Saint Michael Dr, Texarkana, TX 75503
Tel.: (903) 832-8531
Web Site: http://www.lifenetems.org
Sales Range: $10-24.9 Million
Emp.: 349
Ambulance Service
N.A.I.C.S.: 621910
Danny Gray *(Chm)*
David Baumgardner *(CEO)*
Libby Vines *(Vice Chm)*
Tommy Singleton *(Dir-Ops)*
Jarrod Nall *(Mgr-Clinical)*
Netra Dutton *(Mgr-PR)*
Mandi Smith *(Dir-HR)*
Ronnie Weaver *(Dir-Ops)*
Jason Gartner *(Gen Mgr)*
Kelly McCauley *(Gen Mgr)*
Dave Dutton *(Mgr-Comm)*
David Wilder *(Mgr-Info Sys)*
Roy Morgan *(Co-Founder)*
Mary Ruggles *(Co-Founder)*

LIFEPATH
101 Munson St Ste 201, Greenfield, MA 01376-2530
Tel.: (413) 773-5555 MA
Web Site: http://www.lifepathma.org
Year Founded: 1974
Sales Range: $10-24.9 Million
Elder Care Services
N.A.I.C.S.: 624120
Regina E. Curtis *(Pres)*
Evelyn Walsh *(Pres)*
Judith Fonsh *(Sec)*
Joanie Bernstein *(VP)*
Jim Geisman *(Treas)*

LIFEPICS INC.
5777 Central Ave, Boulder, CO 80301
Tel.: (303) 413-9500
Web Site: http://www.lifepics.com
Year Founded: 2000
Sales Range: $1-9.9 Million
Emp.: 8
Online Printing & Photographic Products Retailer
N.A.I.C.S.: 323111
Vahe Christianian *(VP-Sls & Bus Dev)*
Ken McDonald *(VP-Mktg & Customer Success)*
John Volf *(Dir-Product Dev)*

LIFEPLUS INTERNATIONAL
15 Industrial Dr, Batesville, AR 72501-5512
Tel.: (870) 698-2311 AR
Web Site: http://www.lifeplus.com
Year Founded: 1992
Sales Range: $25-49.9 Million
Emp.: 150
Nutritional Supplement Distr
N.A.I.C.S.: 456191
J. Robert Lemon *(Pres)*
William T. Evans *(Co-Founder)*
Robert Christian *(Co-Founder)*
Timothy A. Nolan *(Co-Founder)*

Subsidiaries:
Lifeplus Europe Ltd. (1)
Lifeplus House Little End Road, Eaton Socon, PE19 8JH, Cambridgeshire, United Kingdom
Tel.: (44) 1480224600
Web Site: http://www.lifeplus.com
Sales Range: $25-49.9 Million
Emp.: 50
Nutritional Supplements
N.A.I.C.S.: 456191
Malcolm John Vincent *(Mng Dir)*

LIFERAY, INC.
1400 Montefino Ave, Diamond Bar, CA 91765
Tel.: (877) 543-3729 CA
Web Site: http://www.liferay.com
Year Founded: 2004
Sales Range: $25-49.9 Million
Emp.: 200
Software Publisher
N.A.I.C.S.: 513210
Bryan Cheung *(Co-Founder & CEO)*
Scott Tachiki *(CFO)*
Brian Chan *(Co-Founder)*
Brian Kim *(Co-Founder & COO)*
Michael Young *(Co-Founder & CTO)*
Paul Hinz *(CMO)*
Caris Chan *(Co-Founder & Chief Admin Officer)*
Michael MacAuley *(Gen Mgr-Liferay UK)*
Ross Kennedy *(Gen Mgr-Liferay Ireland)*
Ruud Kluivers *(Gen Mgr-Liferay Netherlands)*

Subsidiaries:
Liferay Australia Pty Ltd (1)
L21 Tower 2 Darling Park 201 Sussex Street, Sydney, 2000, NSW, Australia
Tel.: (61) 2 9006 1221
Software Publisher
N.A.I.C.S.: 513210

Liferay Brasil (1)
Rua Jaco Velosino 290 10 andar, Recife, 52061410, Brazil
Tel.: (55) 81 3033 1405
Software Publisher
N.A.I.C.S.: 513210

Liferay Dalian Software Co., Ltd. (1)
537 Hangpu Road Taide Building 1005, High-Tech Zone, Dalian, 116023, Liaoning, China
Tel.: (86) 411 8812 0855
Software Publisher
N.A.I.C.S.: 513210

Liferay GmbH (1)
Mergenthalerallee 77, 65760, Eschborn, Germany
Tel.: (49) 6196 773 0680
Web Site: http://www.liferay.com
Software Publisher
N.A.I.C.S.: 513210
Bertram Mandel *(Mng Dir)*

Subsidiary (Non-US):
Liferay France (2)
15 rue Taitbout, Paris, 75009, France
Tel.: (33) 1 73 02 08 07
Web Site: http://www.liferay.com
Software Publisher
N.A.I.C.S.: 513210

COMPANIES

Liferay Hungary Kft. (2)
Madarasz Viktor Utca 47 a-b, Budapest, 1138, Hungary
Tel.: (36) 17864575
Software Publisher
N.A.I.C.S.: 513210

Liferay Ireland (2)
2 Clanwilliam Square Grand Canal Quay, Dublin, Ireland
Tel.: (353) 1662456
Software Publisher
N.A.I.C.S.: 513210
Rof Kennedy *(Gen Mgr)*

Liferay S.L. (2)
Calle Joaquin Bau 2 Fl 1, 28036, Madrid, Spain
Tel.: (34) 91 733 63 43
Software Publisher
N.A.I.C.S.: 513210

Liferay UK (2)
45 Moorfields, London, EC2Y 9AE, United Kingdom
Tel.: (44) 20 7448 9770
Software Publisher
N.A.I.C.S.: 513210

Liferay India Pvt. Ltd. (1)
#19 1st Floor 1st Cross P&T Colony, RT Nagar, Bengaluru, 560032, India
Tel.: (91) 80 23544426
Software Publisher
N.A.I.C.S.: 513210

Liferay Japan K. K. (1)
1F Faveur Ebisu 1-26-7 Ebisu Nishi, Shibuya-ku, Tokyo, 150-0021, Japan
Tel.: (81) 3 5456 5796
Web Site: http://www.liferay.co.jp
Software Publishing Services
N.A.I.C.S.: 513210

LIFES2GOOD INC.
355 N Canal St, Chicago, IL 60606
Tel.: (888) 444-9073
Web Site: http://www.viviscal.com
Year Founded: 1997
Sales Range: $10-24.9 Million
Emp.: 15
Markets & Distributes Viviscal Hair-Growth Supplements & Hair Care Products
N.A.I.C.S.: 456191
James Murphy *(Founder & Grp CEO)*
Thomas Tierney *(CFO & Dir-Ops)*
Stuart Chidley *(Dir-Sls & Mktg)*
Mark Holland *(VP-North America)*
Giora Zucker *(Chm)*
Robert Lee *(Mgr-Ops)*
Emily Riemer *(Mgr-Content Strategy)*
Stevie Jones *(Dir-Response Mktg)*
Kelly Zahery *(Acct Mgr)*
Sandy Steiner *(Dir-Direct Mktg-US)*
Kaivan Dave *(Dir-e-Commerce)*
John Halbert *(Mgr-Viviscal Pro Sls)*
Joe Petracca *(VP-Sls & Bus Dev-US)*

LIFESAFER, INC
4290 Glendale Milford Rd, Cincinnati, OH 45242
Tel.: (513) 651-9560
Web Site: http://www.lifesafer.com
Sales Range: $25-49.9 Million
Emp.: 300
All Other Motor Vehicle Parts Mfr
N.A.I.C.S.: 336390
Richard Freund *(Founder)*
Craig Armstrong *(Pres)*

LIFESCRIPT, INC.
4000 MacArthur Blvd Ste 800, Newport Beach, CA 92660
Tel.: (949) 454-0422
Web Site: http://www.lifescript.com
Year Founded: 1999
Rev.: $22,800,000
Emp.: 52
Miscellaneous Publishing
N.A.I.C.S.: 513199

Brian J. Hogan *(COO)*
Ronald L. Caporale *(CEO)*
Edward C. Geehr *(Chief Medical Officer)*
Jack S. Hogan *(CTO)*
James L. Stock *(CFO)*
Alan Adams *(Chief Admin Officer)*
Christian Pran *(Sr VP-Sls)*
Laurie Berger *(VP)*
Terry Hartshorn *(Chm)*
Robert Cecere *(Sr VP-Pharmaceutical Adv)*
Peter Chang *(Sr VP-Sls Ops)*

LIFESERVE BLOOD CENTER
431 E Locust St, Des Moines, IA 50309
Tel.: (515) 288-0276 IA
Web Site: http://www.lifeservebloodcenter.org
Year Founded: 2010
Sales Range: $25-49.9 Million
Emp.: 420
Blood Collection & Distribution Services
N.A.I.C.S.: 621991
Stacy Sime *(CEO)*

LIFESHARE COMMUNITY BLOOD SERVICES
105 Cleveland St, Elyria, OH 44035
Tel.: (440) 322-5700 OH
Web Site: http://www.lifeshare.cc
Year Founded: 1975
Sales Range: $10-24.9 Million
Emp.: 161
Blood Bank
N.A.I.C.S.: 621991
Michael Dash *(VP-Ops)*
Vicki Finson *(Pres & CEO)*
Barbara Hallenburg *(Dir-Quality Assurance)*
Jeanne Firment *(Dir-Technical)*
Stephanie Hyster *(Dir-HR)*

LIFESPACE COMMUNITIES
100 E Grand Ave Ste 200, Des Moines, IA 50309
Tel.: (515) 288-5805
Web Site: http://www.lifespacecommunities.com
Sales Range: $150-199.9 Million
Emp.: 2,200
Continuing Care Retirement Communities
N.A.I.C.S.: 623311
Joe Chambers *(VP-Sls & Mktg)*
Jodi Bleier *(VP-Fin Ops & Strategic Growth)*
Thomas L. Brod *(Sr VP-Bus Dev)*
Kevin Knopf *(Reg Dir-Ops)*
Ann Walsh *(Sr VP-Ops)*
Jesse Jantzen *(Pres & CEO)*
Larry Smith *(CFO)*
Eddie Fenoglio *(COO)*
Tim Gorman *(Gen Counsel)*

LIFESPAN
275 Grove St Ste 2-400, Newton, MA 02466
Tel.: (781) 239-8154
Web Site: http://www.lifespantechnology.com
Year Founded: 2002
Sales Range: $1-9.9 Million
Emp.: 63
Hardware Recycling & Disposal
N.A.I.C.S.: 541519
Dag Adamson *(Pres)*
Brooks Hoffman *(VP-Fin)*

LIFESPAN CORP.
167 Point St Ste 2B, Providence, RI 02903-4771
Tel.: (401) 444-3500 RI

Web Site: http://www.lifespan.org
Year Founded: 1902
Sales Range: $800-899.9 Million
Emp.: 12,000
Data Processing & Preparation
N.A.I.C.S.: 561110
Cathy Duquette *(Exec VP-Nursing Affairs)*
John Murphy *(Exec VP-Physician Affairs)*
Peter Snyder *(Chief Res Officer & Sr VP)*
Mamie Wakefield *(CFO & Exec VP)*
Paul J. Adler *(Gen Counsel & Sr VP)*
Arthur J. Sampson *(Interim Pres & Interim CEO)*
Cedric J. Priebe III *(CIO & Sr VP)*
Lawrence A. Aubin Sr. *(Chm)*

Subsidiaries:

Lifespan Home Medical (1)
167 Point Street, Providence, RI 02865-4211
Tel.: (401) 335-2540
Web Site: http://www.lifespan.org
Rev.: $2,843,138
Emp.: 11
Miscellaneous Retail Stores
N.A.I.C.S.: 621610

LIFESPAN INCORPORATED
1511 Shopton Rd Ste A, Charlotte, NC 28217
Tel.: (704) 944-5100 NC
Web Site: https://www.lifespanservices.org
Year Founded: 1973
Rev.: $3,993,515
Assets: $2,983,810
Liabilities: $1,016,567
Net Worth: $1,967,243
Earnings: ($147,320)
Emp.: 101
Fiscal Year-end: 06/30/14
Intellectual Disabled People Assistance Services
N.A.I.C.S.: 624120
Leigh Derby *(Founder)*
Davan Cloninger *(Pres & CEO)*
Ralph Adams *(CFO & Treas)*
Christopher White *(Exec Dir)*
Lori Avery *(Sr Dir-Dev)*
Hemantkumar Patel *(CIO)*
Robert L. Mendenhall *(Vice Chm)*
John Cervantes *(Sec)*
Holly Glinski *(Asst Sec)*

LIFESPICE INGREDIENTS, LLC.
300 Cherry Ln, Palm Beach, FL 33480
Tel.: (561) 844-6334
Web Site: http://www.lifespiceingredients.com
Sales Range: $10-24.9 Million
Emp.: 8
Proprietary Spice Blend Mfr
N.A.I.C.S.: 311942
Dawn Pavela *(Controller)*

LIFESTREAM
384 W Orange Show Rd, San Bernardino, CA 92408
Tel.: (909) 885-6503 CA
Web Site: http://www.lstream.org
Year Founded: 1951
Sales Range: $50-74.9 Million
Emp.: 461
Blood Bank Operator
N.A.I.C.S.: 621991
Michael C. Jensen *(Chm)*
William T. Powers *(Treas)*
Frederick B. Axelrod *(Pres, CEO, Sec & Dir-Medical)*
Jim Peterson *(Vice Chm)*

LIFESTREAM BEHAVIORAL CENTER
PO Box 491000, Leesburg, FL 34749-1000
Tel.: (352) 315-7500 FL
Web Site: http://www.lsbc.net
Year Founded: 1971
Sales Range: $25-49.9 Million
Emp.: 629
Behavioral Healthcare Services
N.A.I.C.S.: 623220
Thomas Valente *(Dir-Medical)*
K. H. Wiener *(VP)*

LIFESTREAM COMPLETE SENIOR LIVING
11555 W Peoria Ave, Youngtown, AZ 85363
Tel.: (623) 933-3333 AZ
Web Site: http://www.lifestreamliving.com
Year Founded: 1975
Sales Range: $10-24.9 Million
Emp.: 317
Elder Care Services
N.A.I.C.S.: 623312
Donna Taylor *(Exec VP)*
Ron Estes *(Pres)*

LIFETIME ASSISTANCE INC.
425 Paul Rd, Rochester, NY 14624
Tel.: (585) 426-4120 NY
Web Site: http://www.lifetimeassistance.org
Year Founded: 1978
Sales Range: $50-74.9 Million
Emp.: 1,917
Developmental Disability Assistance Services
N.A.I.C.S.: 624120
James Branciforte *(Pres & CEO)*

LIFETIME PRODUCTS INC.
PO Box 160010, Clearfield, UT 84016
Tel.: (801) 776-1532 UT
Web Site: http://www.lifetime.com
Year Founded: 1986
Sales Range: $350-399.9 Million
Emp.: 1,600
Plastic Table Chair Picnic Table & In-Ground Basketball System Mfr
N.A.I.C.S.: 339920
Brent Allen *(VP)*
Richard Hendrickson *(Pres)*

Subsidiaries:

Emotion Kayaks, Inc. (1)
Freeport Center Bldg D-11, Clearfield, UT 84016-0010
Tel.: (800) 225-3865
Web Site: http://www.emotionkayaks.com
Boat Retailer
N.A.I.C.S.: 423910

Lifetime Metals, Inc. (1)
Freeport Center Bldg H-4, Clearfield, UT 84016-0475
Tel.: (801) 728-1729
Steel Product Mfr & Supplier
N.A.I.C.S.: 331210

LIFETIME, INC.
860 E Main Ave, Zeeland, MI 49464
Tel.: (616) 772-9131 MI
Year Founded: 1954
Sales Range: $1-9.9 Million
Emp.: 200
Lessors of Nonresidential Buildings (except Miniwarehouses)
N.A.I.C.S.: 531120
Philip Miller *(CEO)*

Subsidiaries:

Sea Otter Classic, Inc. (1)
215 W Franklin St Ste 214, Monterey, CA 93940-2715
Tel.: (831) 373-2331
Web Site: http://www.seaotterclassic.com

LIFETIME, INC.

U.S. PRIVATE

Lifetime, Inc.—(Continued)
Promoters of Performing Arts, Sports & Similar Events without Facilities
N.A.I.C.S.: 711320
Frank Yohannan (CEO)

LIFEWAVE, INC.
9775 Business Park Ave, San Diego, CA 92131
Tel.: (858) 459-9876
Web Site: http://www.lifewave.com
Year Founded: 2004
Sales Range: $25-49.9 Million
Emp.: 65
Mfr & Distr of Health Products that Stimulate Acupuncture Points Improving Energy, Sleep, Appetite Control, Pain Relief & Anti-Aging
N.A.I.C.S.: 456199
David Schmidt (Founder & CEO)
Steven Haltiwanger (Dir-Health & Science)
Jules Rudick (VP-Plng & Strategy)
Angie Morris (Dir-Customer Svc)
Joe Depanfilis (CFO)

LIFEWELL BEHAVIORAL WELLNESS
202 E Earll Ste 200, Phoenix, AZ 85012
Tel.: (602) 808-2822
Web Site: http://www.lifewell.us
Year Founded: 1974
Sales Range: $25-49.9 Million
Emp.: 433
Behavioral Healthcare Services
N.A.I.C.S.: 623220
Thomas K. McKelvey (CEO)
Doris Vaught (CFO & Exec VP)
Bryan M. Colby (CIO)
David Barnes (COO)
Thomas C. Williams (Chief Clinical Officer)
John Newton (Dir-Clinical-Residential Svcs)
Tammy Wray (Sec)
Jan Johnston (Vice Chm)
Ron Smith (Chief Dev Officer)
Alexandra Schindler (Dir-HR)
Lindsay Johnson (Dir-Quality)
Mona Amini (Chief Medical Officer)

LIFEWORKS NW
14600 NW Cornell Rd, Portland, OR 97229
Tel.: (503) 645-3581
Web Site: http://www.lifeworksnw.org
Year Founded: 1961
Sales Range: $25-49.9 Million
Emp.: 795
Community Action Services
N.A.I.C.S.: 624190
Timothy L. McMahan (Chm)

LIFEWORKS SERVICES INC.
2965 Lone Oak Dr Ste 160, Eagan, MN 55121
Tel.: (651) 454-2732
Web Site: http://www.lifeworks.org
Year Founded: 1965
Rev.: $30,977,099
Emp.: 195
Group Homes for People with Disabilities
N.A.I.C.S.: 623210
Tony Saputo (VP-Advancement)
Laura Purfeerst (VP-Fin)
Mary Lenertz (VP-Svcs)
Judy Lysne (Pres & CEO)
Kofi A. Bruce (Treas)
John Cobb (VP-HR)
Kim Mueller (VP-Employment Svcs)
Christine M. Larsen (Sec)

LIFT ATLANTA INCORPORATED
2425 Park Central Blvd, Decatur, GA 30035
Tel.: (770) 987-3200
Web Site: http://www.liftatlanta.com
Sales Range: $10-24.9 Million
Emp.: 50
Materials Handling Machinery
N.A.I.C.S.: 423830
Mitchell Milovich (Chm & CEO)
Greg Cruce (Controller)

LIFT INC.
3745 Hempland Rd, Mountville, PA 17554
Tel.: (717) 295-1800 PA
Web Site: http://www.liftincorporated.com
Year Founded: 1973
Sales Range: $25-49.9 Million
Emp.: 50
Industrial Machinery & Equipment
N.A.I.C.S.: 423830
Gayle Velky (Controller)
Scott Britcher (Mgr-Svcs)
Deborah Foreman (Owner)
Kirk Sears (VP)
Linda Weaver (Mgr-Parts)

LIFT SOLUTIONS, INC.
14616 Shepard St, Omaha, NE 68138
Tel.: (402) 330-1690
Web Site: http://www.liftsolutionsinc.net
Sales Range: $10-24.9 Million
Emp.: 80
Lift Trucks & Parts
N.A.I.C.S.: 423830
Steven Buehler (Pres)
Sheri Ladenburger (Mgr-Customer Svc)
Tim McSorley (Mgr-Fleet)
Lisa Krueger (Acct Mgr)
Mike Linton (Acct Mgr)

LIFT TRUCK SERVICE CENTER INC.
12829 Interstate 30, Little Rock, AR 72209
Tel.: (501) 568-3330
Web Site: http://www.ltsc.com
Rev.: $10,891,566
Emp.: 24
Lift Trucks & Parts
N.A.I.C.S.: 423830
Carl Morehead (Pres)
Kim Wheeler (Office Mgr)

LIFT-A-LOFT CORPORATION
9501 S Ctr Rd, Muncie, IN 47302
Tel.: (765) 288-3691
Web Site: http://www.liftaloft.com
Sales Range: $10-24.9 Million
Emp.: 50
Trucks, Tractors, Loaders, Carriers & Similar Equipment
N.A.I.C.S.: 333924
Doug Jeurissen (Mgr-Sls)
James Lee (Mgr-Customer Svc)
Todd Hunt (Pres)

LIFT-ALL CO., INC.
1909 McFarland Dr, Landisville, PA 17538-1810
Tel.: (717) 898-6615 PA
Web Site: http://www.lift-all.com
Year Founded: 1964
Sales Range: $100-124.9 Million
Emp.: 225
Material Handling Chains, Wire Ropes & Wire Mesh Mfr
N.A.I.C.S.: 331222
Jeffrey M. Klibert (Pres & CEO)
Kleinert Steve (Project Mgr)
Steven Pacilio (Gen Mgr)

LIFTOMATIC MATERIAL HANDLING INC.
700 Dartmouth Ln, Buffalo Grove, IL 60089
Tel.: (847) 325-2930
Web Site: http://www.liftomatic.com
Year Founded: 1947
Sales Range: $10-24.9 Million
Emp.: 12
Drum Handling Equipment Mfr
N.A.I.C.S.: 333924
E. Darren Berg (Pres & COO)

LIGADO NETWORKS
10802 Parkridge Blvd, Reston, VA 20191
Wireless Broadband Services
N.A.I.C.S.: 517111
Doug Smith (Pres & CEO)

LIGHT FANTASTIC REALTY, INC.
114 Boston Post Rd, West Haven, CT 06516-2043
Tel.: (203) 823-1527
Web Site: http://www.thelightingquotient.com
Commercial, Industrial & Institutional Electric Lighting Fixture Mfr
N.A.I.C.S.: 335132
Allison Schieffelin (CEO)
Andy Novotny (COO)

Subsidiaries:

Electrix, Inc. (1)
45 Spring St, New Haven, CT 06519
Tel.: (203) 776-5577
Web Site: http://www.electrix.com
Rev.: $6,666,666
Emp.: 6
Residential Electric Lighting Fixture Mfr
N.A.I.C.S.: 335131
Dan Shwisha (VP-Sls)

LIGHT IMPRESSIONS
100 Carlson Rd, Rochester, NY 14610
Web Site: http://www.lightimpressionsdirect.com
Year Founded: 1969
Distr of Archival & Presentation Supplies
N.A.I.C.S.: 326113
Bernard Findley (CEO)

LIGHT SCIENCES ONCOLOGY, INC.
12600 SE 38th St Ste 111, Bellevue, WA 98006
Tel.: (425) 957-8900 WA
Web Site: http://www.lsoncology.com
Year Founded: 2004
Sales Range: $10-24.9 Million
Emp.: 7
Developer of Light Activated Tumor Treatment
N.A.I.C.S.: 541715
Dennis H. Langer (Chm)

LIGHTBAY MANAGEMENT, LLC
11601 Wilshire Blvd Ste 2150, Los Angeles, CA 90025
Tel.: (310) 919-4300 CA
Web Site: http://www.lightbay.com
Year Founded: 2016
Privater Equity Firm
N.A.I.C.S.: 551112
Nav Rahemtulla (Founding Partner)
Adam Stein (Founding Partner)
David Burcham (Mng Dir)
Stella Ho (Mng Dir)
David Leeney (Mng Dir)
Ben Herman (Principal)
Sarah Davies (Office Mgr)

Subsidiaries:

FASTSIGNS International, Inc. (1)
2542 Highlander Way, Carrollton, TX 75006-2366
Tel.: (214) 346-5600
Web Site: http://www.fastsigns.com
Sign Production & Print Shops Franchisor
N.A.I.C.S.: 533110
Catherine Monson (CEO)
Drue Townsend (Sr VP-Mktg)
Mark Jameson (Exec VP-Franchise Support & Dev)
Chris Becraft (VP-Accts-Natl)
Jennifer Herskind (CMO)

LIGHTBEAM HEALTH SOLUTIONS LLC
222 W Las Colinas Blvd Ste 2200N, Irving, TX 75039
Tel.: (972) 831-7270
Web Site: http://www.lightbeamhealth.com
Health Management Data Hosting & Consulting Services
N.A.I.C.S.: 518210
Jerry Shultz (Pres)
Pat Cline (CEO)
Paul Bergeson (VP-Sls & Mktg)
Kirk Clove (Chief Analytics Officer)
Jeff Peterson (CFO)
Jay Orler (VP-Infrastructure & Security)
Mike Hoxter (CTO)
Bob Nary (VP-Dev)
Joseph Giroux (VP-Bus Dev)

Subsidiaries:

Browsersoft Inc. (1)
450 Navajo Ln, Shawnee Mission, KS 66217
Tel.: (913) 851-2453
Web Site: http://www.browsersoft.com
Sales Range: $1-9.9 Million
Emp.: 10
Data Processing, Hosting & Related Services
N.A.I.C.S.: 518210
Don Grodecki (Pres)

LIGHTEN THE LOAD, INC.
1395 E Irving Park Rd, Itasca, IL 60143
Tel.: (630) 350-8585
Web Site: http://www.lightentheloadinc.com
Year Founded: 2000
Rev.: $4,300,000
Emp.: 18
Freight Transportation Arrangement
N.A.I.C.S.: 488510
John W. Westermayer (Founding Partner & CEO)
Barbara A. Reynolds (Pres)

LIGHTHOUSE BANK
111 Mission St, Santa Cruz, CA 95060
Tel.: (831) 600-4000
Year Founded: 2007
Commercial Banking Services
N.A.I.C.S.: 522110
Lane S. Lawson (CEO)

LIGHTHOUSE CREDIT FOUNDATION
2300 Tall Pines Dr, Largo, FL 33771
Tel.: (727) 535-9653
Web Site: http://www.lighthousecredit.org
Rev.: $17,900,000
Emp.: 33
All Other Personal Services
N.A.I.C.S.: 812990
Mary H. Melcer (Pres & CEO)
Joe Kirane (VP)
Jason Holley (VP-Sls & Mktg)

COMPANIES

LIGHTHOUSE ELECTRONICS, INC.
86 Progress Ave Unit 1, Tyngsboro, MA 01879
Tel.: (978) 649-1220
Web Site: http://www.lhei.com
Year Founded: 1998
Sales Range: $10-24.9 Million
Emp.: 10
Electronic Components & Parts Distr
N.A.I.C.S.: 423420
Scott Williams *(CEO)*

LIGHTHOUSE GUILD INTERNATIONAL
250 W 64th, New York, NY 10023
Tel.: (212) 821-9200
Web Site: http://www.lighthouseguild.org
Year Founded: 1914
Healtcare Services
N.A.I.C.S.: 813212
Calvin W. Roberts *(Pres & CEO)*
Mark G. Ackermann *(COO & Exec VP)*
Christina Wong *(CFO)*
Karen A. Wish *(CMO)*

LIGHTHOUSE LIST COMPANY INC.
27 SE 24th Ave Ste 6, Pompano Beach, FL 33062
Tel.: (954) 489-3008
Web Site: http://www.lighthouselist.com
Year Founded: 1994
Sales Range: $1-9.9 Million
Emp.: 18
Interactive Marketing & Direct Mail Advertising
N.A.I.C.S.: 541613
Robert Orr *(Pres)*
Mark Traverso *(VP-Sls, New Bus Dev & ECommerce)*

LIGHTHOUSE LOUISIANA
123 State St, New Orleans, LA 70118
Tel.: (504) 899-4501 LA
Web Site: http://www.lighthouselouisiana.org
Year Founded: 1915
Sales Range: $1-9.9 Million
Emp.: 184
Disability Assistance Services
N.A.I.C.S.: 624120
Tabatha George *(Sec)*
Paul Masinter *(Co-Chm)*
Anne Springer *(Mgr-Comm)*
Erin McQuade Wright *(VP-Dev & Comm)*
Freida Holland *(VP-Employment Svcs)*
Jenice Heck Lotr *(VP-Vision Rehabilitation Svcs)*
Terri J. Brown *(Mgr-HR)*
Travis Smith *(Mgr-Customer Svc)*
Renee Vidrine *(Pres)*
Brian Capitelli *(Co-Chm)*
Jenice Heck *(VP-Vision Rehabilitation Svcs)*
Rick Krohn *(VP-Ops & Bus Dev)*
Stephanie Benedetti *(VP-Sls & Mktg)*
Nicky Gillies *(Dir-Deaf Svcs)*
Marlene Campos *(Mgr-Svcs)*
Alan Anderson *(Mgr-Procurement & Inventory)*
Joel Nelson *(Controller)*
Stephanie Kreller *(Coord-Community Outreach & Mktg)*

LIGHTHOUSE PROPERTY INSURANCE CORP.
500 W 2nd St Suite 1900 #203, Austin, TX 78701
Web Site: http://www.lighthouse.insurance
Year Founded: 2008
Property & Casualty Insurance Company
N.A.I.C.S.: 524298
Patrick White *(CEO & Pres)*
Scott Moore *(CFO)*
Eric Gobble *(Chief Risk Officer)*
Bruce Bessire *(Dir-Sls)*

Subsidiaries:

Prepared Insurance Company (1)
1715 N Westshore Blvd Ste 930, Tampa, FL 33607
Tel.: (813) 286-3730
Web Site: http://www.preparedins.com
Sales Range: $1-9.9 Million
Emp.: 25
Property Owners & Renters Insurance
N.A.I.C.S.: 524126
Eric Gobble *(Pres & CEO)*
Jeff E. Myers *(CFO, Treas & Sec)*
Mike Rubio *(Chief Claims Officer)*
Stephanie Siewert *(VP-Sls & Mktg)*

LIGHTHOUSE TECHNOLOGIES, INC.
1430 Oak Ct Ste 101, Dayton, OH 45430
Tel.: (937) 458-0055 OH
Web Site: http://www.lighthousetechnologies.com
Year Founded: 2000
Sales Range: $1-9.9 Million
Emp.: 49
Software Development Services
N.A.I.C.S.: 541511
Jeffrey Van Fleet *(Founder & CEO)*

LIGHTING & LAMP CORP.
2552 Pelham Pkwy, Pelham, AL 35124-1329
Tel.: (205) 271-1423
Web Site: http://www.lightingandlamp.com
Sales Range: $10-24.9 Million
Emp.: 5
Lighting Fixtures
N.A.I.C.S.: 423610
Randall W. Calhoun *(Pres)*

LIGHTING INCORPORATED
4129 Telephone Rd, Houston, TX 77087
Tel.: (713) 641-6628
Web Site: http://www.lightinginc.com
Sales Range: $10-24.9 Million
Emp.: 75
Lighting Fixtures
N.A.I.C.S.: 449129
Brad Bailey *(Owner)*
Gabriel Trinidad *(Controller)*

LIGHTING SCIENCE GROUP CORPORATION
1350 Division Rd Ste 204, West Warwick, RI 02893
Tel.: (321) 779-5520 DE
Web Site: http://www.lsgc.com
Year Founded: 1988
Sales Range: $25-49.9 Million
LED Lighting Devices & Systems Designer, Mfr & Marketer
N.A.I.C.S.: 335139
Edward D. Bednarcik *(CEO)*

LIGHTNING BUG LTD.
7400 Linder Ave, Skokie, IL 60077
Tel.: (708) 755-2100
Year Founded: 1971
Rev.: $10,000,000
Emp.: 200
Lighting Fixture Mfr
N.A.I.C.S.: 423610
Matt Vollmer *(VP-Sls)*
Jim Brewer *(Pres)*

LIGHTNING QUICK GAS-N-GO
727 Springbrook Ave, Adrian, MI 49221
Tel.: (517) 759-1314
Web Site: http://www.lightningquickgasngo.com
Year Founded: 2007
Sales Range: $10-24.9 Million
Emp.: 40
Gas Stations with Convenience Stores
N.A.I.C.S.: 457110
Rex Crist *(Owner)*

LIGHTNING ROD MUTUAL INSURANCE CO.
1685 Cleveland Rd, Wooster, OH 44691
Tel.: (330) 262-9060
Web Site: http://www.wrg-ins.com
Sales Range: $50-74.9 Million
Emp.: 265
Fire, Marine & Casualty Insurance Carriers
N.A.I.C.S.: 524126
John P. Murphy *(Pres)*
Dan Pitcher *(VP-IT)*

LIGHTNING TRANSPORTATION INC.
16820 Blake Rd Bldg C, Hagerstown, MD 21740
Tel.: (301) 582-5700
Web Site: http://www.lightningtrans.com
Sales Range: $10-24.9 Million
Emp.: 40
Transport Trucks
N.A.I.C.S.: 484121
Wayne Gaumer *(Pres)*
Mike Rankin *(VP)*
Michelle Mummert *(VP-Fin)*
Matt Hines *(Dir-Safety)*

LIGHTNING VENTURES INC.
1750 Tomah Rd, Larkspur, CO 80118-4902
Tel.: (303) 694-3340
Web Site: http://www.lightningventures.com
Sales Range: $25-49.9 Million
Emp.: 75
Commercial Excavation & Trucking Services
N.A.I.C.S.: 238190
Anthony Falcone *(Pres)*
Earl Jones *(VP)*
Donald Rainwater *(CEO)*

LIGHTS OF AMERICA, INC.
611 Reyes Dr, Walnut, CA 91789-3033
Tel.: (909) 594-7883 CA
Web Site: http://www.lightsofamerica.com
Year Founded: 1978
Sales Range: $150-199.9 Million
Emp.: 400
Mfr of Fluorescent Lighting Products & Security Motion Devices
N.A.I.C.S.: 335131
Usman U. Vakil *(Chm, Pres & Treas)*
Farooq U. Vakil *(Sec & Exec VP)*
Kameran Marza *(VP-Production)*

LIGHTSOURCES, INC.
37 Robinson Blvd, Orange, CT 06477
Tel.: (203) 799-7877
Web Site: http://www.light-sources.com
Year Founded: 1983
Sales Range: $150-199.9 Million
Emp.: 1,000
Design & Mfr of Germicidal & Specialty Fluorescent/Ultraviolet lamps
N.A.I.C.S.: 335139
Christian L. Sauska *(Founder)*
Graham Foster *(Mgr-Facilities)*
Maklad Saleh *(Mgr-Production)*

LIGHTSPEED MANAGEMENT COMPANY, LLC
2200 Sand Hill Rd Ste 100, Menlo Park, CA 94025
Tel.: (650) 234-8300 CA
Web Site: http://www.lsvp.com
Year Founded: 2000
Rev.: $2,000,000,000
Emp.: 40
Privater Equity Firm
N.A.I.C.S.: 523999
Ravi Mhatre *(Partner)*
Barry Eggers *(Partner)*
David Gussarsky *(Partner)*
Peter Nieh *(Partner)*
Bejul Somaia *(Partner)*
Yoni Cheifetz *(Partner)*
Johnna Lesch *(VP-Fin)*
Jonathan MacQuitty *(Venture Partner)*
Marian Pond *(VP-Exec Talent)*
Saqib Awan *(VP)*
Scott Young *(VP-IT)*
Dev Khare *(Partner)*
Akshay Bhushan *(Partner)*
Harsha Kumar *(Partner)*
Vaibhav Agarwal *(Partner)*
Hemant Mohapatra *(Partner)*

LIGHTSPEED SYSTEMS INC.
1800 19th St, Bakersfield, CA 93301
Tel.: (661) 716-7600
Web Site: http://www.lightspeedsystems.com
Year Founded: 2000
Rev.: $10,700,000
Emp.: 72
Computer System Design Services
N.A.I.C.S.: 541512
Brian Thomas *(CEO)*
John Genter *(COO)*
Rob Chambers *(VP-Engrg Svcs)*
Rob McCarthy *(Owner)*
Darryl LaGace *(Exec VP-Global Bus Dev)*
Greg Funk *(VP-Fin)*
Brook McShane Bock *(Chief Product Officer)*

LIGHTVIEW CAPITAL LLC
35 Beechwood Rd Ste 2B, Summit, NJ 07901
Tel.: (908) 751-1500
Web Site: http://www.lightviewcapital.com
Privater Equity Firm
N.A.I.C.S.: 523999
Rich Erickson *(Co-Founder & Mng Partner)*
Conor Mullett *(Co-Founder & Mng Dir)*
Sam Elsaadi *(VP)*

Subsidiaries:

Buchanan Technologies, Inc. (1)
1026 Texan Trl, Grapevine, TX 76051
Tel.: (972) 869-3966
Web Site: http://www.buchanan.com
Sales Range: $50-74.9 Million
Emp.: 500
Computer Facilities Management
N.A.I.C.S.: 541512
James H. Buchanan *(Founder & CEO)*
Robert Venable *(CFO)*
Deepa Flewelling *(VP-Professional Svcs-Canada)*

Subsidiary (Domestic):

Cybernoor Corp (2)
23875 Northwestern Hwy, Southfield, MI 48075
Tel.: (925) 924-0400
Web Site: http://www.cybernoor.com

LIGHTVIEW CAPITAL LLC
U.S. PRIVATE

Lightview Capital LLC—(Continued)
Sales Range: $10-24.9 Million
Emp.: 25
It Consulting
N.A.I.C.S.: 541690
Ahmed Alomari *(Pres & CEO)*
Dilip Chavan *(VP-Svc Delivery)*
Sridhar Bommareddy *(VP-India)*

Verista Inc. (1)
9100 Fall View Dr, Fishers, IN 46037
Tel.: (317) 849-0330
Web Site: https://verista.com
Business & Technology Consultancy Firm
N.A.I.C.S.: 519290

Subsidiary (Domestic):

Clarke Solutions, LLC (2)
9100 Fall View Dr, Fishers, IN 46037
Tel.: (317) 849-0330
Web Site: http://solutionsbyclarke.com
Engineering & Project Management Services
N.A.I.C.S.: 541330
John Duffin *(Pres & CEO)*

Delta Project Management, Inc. (2)
995 Market St Ste 12-103, San Francisco, CA 94103
Tel.: (415) 590-3202
Web Site: http://www.delta-pm.com
Pharmaceutical Consulting Services
N.A.I.C.S.: 541690
Feras Zubaidy *(Principal)*
Matthew Snyder *(Principal)*
Scott Kobayashi *(Principal)*
Maura Lynch *(Dir-Ops)*
Stephanie Gramata *(Mgr-Recruiting)*

LIGHTWAVE SOLAR, LLC
3026 Owen Dr Ste 104, Antioch, TN 37013-2417
Tel.: (615) 641-4050 TN
Web Site:
http://www.lightwavesolar.com
Year Founded: 2017
Solar Power Engineering & Construction Contractor
N.A.I.C.S.: 238290
Steve Johnson *(Founder)*

LIGHTWAVE TELECOMMUNICATIONS, INC.
950 Hollydell Ct, Sewell, NJ 08080
Tel.: (856) 589-9002 NJ
Web Site: http://www.lwtelecom.com
Year Founded: 1993
Sales Range: $10-24.9 Million
Emp.: 30
Telecommunication System Installation Services
N.A.I.C.S.: 238210
Catherine M. Lord *(Pres & CEO)*
Lisa Grosset *(VP-Fin & Admin)*
Earl A. Trewin *(VP-Ops)*
Matt Hehl *(Dir-Trng & Project Mgr)*
Jim Gehringer *(VP-Engrg)*

LIGHTWEDGE LLC
320 Nevada St 5th Fl, Newton, MA 02460
Tel.: (617) 969-2700
Web Site: http://www.lightwedge.com
Year Founded: 2001
Sales Range: $1-9.9 Million
Emp.: 9
Reading Lights & Accessories Mfr, Whslr & Retailer
N.A.I.C.S.: 335139

LIGHTYEAR CAPITAL LLC
9 W 57th St, New York, NY 10019
Tel.: (212) 328-0555 DE
Web Site: http://www.lycap.com
Year Founded: 2000
Privater Equity Firm
N.A.I.C.S.: 523999
Donald B. Marron *(Founder & Chm)*
Mark F. Vassallo *(Mng Partner)*
Michal Petrzela *(Mng Dir)*
Ellan Ben-Hayon *(CFO)*
George Chen *(Controller)*
Boris Rapoport *(Mng Dir)*
Doug Chiciak *(Chief Compliance Officer)*

Subsidiaries:

Allworth Financial Group LP (1)
8775 Folsom Blvd Ste 100, Sacramento, CA 95826
Tel.: (888) 242-6766
Web Site: https://allworthfinancial.com
Management Consulting Services
N.A.I.C.S.: 541611

Subsidiary (Domestic):

Allworth Financial Holdings, LLC (2)
340 Palladio Pkwy Ste 501, Folsom, CA 95630
Tel.: (916) 357-5287
Web Site: https://allworthfinancial.com
Financial Services
N.A.I.C.S.: 541611

Allworth Financial, LP (2)
8775 Folsom Blvd Ste 100, Sacramento, CA 95826
Tel.: (916) 482-2196
Web Site: http://www.allworthfinancial.com
Management Consulting Services
N.A.I.C.S.: 541611
Patrick McClain *(Co-Founder & Sr Partner)*
Scott Hanson *(Co-Founder & Sr Partner)*
Darla Sipolt *(Exec VP-Retail Growth)*

Subsidiary (Domestic):

Blueprint Financial LLC (3)
4320 44th St SW 102, Grandville, MI 49418
Tel.: (616) 988-1180
Web Site: http://www.walkaboutcamp.com
Investment Advice
N.A.I.C.S.: 523940

Houston Asset Management, Inc. (3)
1800 West Loop S Ste 1980, Houston, TX 77027
Tel.: (713) 629-5490
Web Site:
http://www.houstonassetmgmt.com
Securities Brokerage
N.A.I.C.S.: 523150
Kristian Taylor *(COO & Chief Compliance Officer)*
Emily Kerne *(Acct Coord-Svc)*
Connie Kutac *(CFO)*
Karen Lampe *(Coord-Events)*

Red Rock Wealth Management (3)
9480 S Eastern Ave Ste 251, Las Vegas, NV 89123-8037
Tel.: (702) 987-1607
Web Site: http://www.redrockwealth.com
Investment Advice
N.A.I.C.S.: 523940
Greg Phelps *(Mgr)*

Subsidiary (Domestic):

McDaniel Knutson Financial, Inc. (2)
3705 Clinton Pkwy Ste 200, Lawrence, KS 66047
Tel.: (785) 841-4664
Web Site: http://www.mcdanielknutson.com
Investment Advice
N.A.I.C.S.: 523940

Cooper Gay Swett & Crawford Limited (1)
52 Leadenhall Street, London, EC3A 2EB, United Kingdom
Tel.: (44) 20 7480 7322
Web Site: http://www.cg-sc.com
Sales Range: $1-4.9 Billion
Emp.: 1,400
Holding Company; Wholesale, Reinsurance & Specialist Retail Insurance Broker
N.A.I.C.S.: 551112
Phil Rock *(CFO)*
John Flanagan *(Chief Admin Officer)*
Shaun Hooper *(CEO-Intl)*
Carlos Reis *(Dir-Comml-CGSC Holdings Brasil)*
Thomas P. Ruggieri *(Pres/CEO-North America)*
Martin Sullivan *(Chm)*
Ulisses Soares *(CEO-Latin America)*
Alejandro Padilla *(Gen Mgr & Head-Broking-Mexico, Central America & Puerto Rico)*
Andy Wallin *(Grp Dir-Comml)*
Steve Hearn *(Grp CEO)*
Peter Hacker *(Grp Chief Innovation Officer)*
Jonathan Prinn *(Head-Global Placement)*
Wendy Kilminster *(Head-Strategy & Change)*

Subsidiary (Domestic):

Cooper Gay & Company Ltd. (2)
52 Leadenhall Street, London, EC3A 2EB, United Kingdom
Tel.: (44) 2074807322
Web Site: http://www.coopergay.com
Sales Range: $100-124.9 Million
Wholesale, Reinsurance & Specialist Retail Insurance Broker
N.A.I.C.S.: 524210
Gordon Newman *(CEO)*
Alan Main *(Dir-Reinsurance)*

Subsidiary (US):

Cooper Gay Re, Ltd. (2)
32 Old Slip 5th Fl, New York, NY 10005
Tel.: (212) 791-9745
Web Site: http://www.coopergay.com
Emp.: 40
Reinsurance Broker
N.A.I.C.S.: 524210
Peter Gorman *(CEO)*
Stephen Brewer *(Exec VP)*
Terrence Duffy *(VP)*
Carol Marquis *(Asst VP)*
Joe Vaughan *(VP)*
Mark Venturino *(Sr VP-Atlanta)*
Norman Gayle *(Mng Dir)*
Richard Stark *(Sr VP-Miami)*
Tom McGrath *(Exec VP)*
Jennifer Sadalski *(VP-Facultative-San Francisco)*

J.H. Blades & Co., Inc. (2)
520 Post Oak Blvd Ste 250, Houston, TX 77027
Tel.: (713) 780-8770
Web Site: http://www.jhblades.com
Wholesale, Reinsurance & Specialist Retail Insurance Broker
N.A.I.C.S.: 524210
Teri Krause *(Dir-Claims)*
Richard Martin *(VP)*
Bob Daniels *(Exec VP)*

Subsidiary (Non-US):

Junge & Co. Versicherungsmakler GmbH (2)
Hohe Bleichen 11, 20354, Hamburg, Germany
Tel.: (49) 40 35003 0
Web Site: http://www.junge.de
Emp.: 70
Wholesale, Reinsurance & Specialist Retail Insurance Broker
N.A.I.C.S.: 524210
Olaf Folsch *(CEO & Mng Dir)*

Subsidiary (US):

The Swett & Crawford Group, Inc. (2)
7230 McGinnis Ferry Rd Ste 300, Suwanee, GA 30024
Tel.: (770) 813-6220
Web Site: http://www.swett.com
Wholesale, Reinsurance & Specialist Retail Insurance Broker
N.A.I.C.S.: 524210
Terri T. Snell *(Chief Admin Officer & Exec VP)*
Jason White *(Exec VP)*
Mike Brennan *(CEO)*

Lendmark Financial Services, Inc. (1)
229 Village At Glynn Pl, Brunswick, GA 31525
Tel.: (912) 262-1100
Web Site: http://www.lendmarkfinancial.com
Sales Range: $25-49.9 Million
Emp.: 3
Financial & Mortgage Lending Services
N.A.I.C.S.: 522310
Robert Aiken *(Founder, Pres & CEO)*
David Neaves *(CFO)*
Steve Wheeler *(Chief Credit Officer)*
Ethan Andelman *(CMO)*
Amy Manning *(Chief Strategy Officer)*
Mark Lawrence *(CIO)*
Bret Hyler *(COO)*
Joe Burgamy *(Chief Bus Officer)*
Dennis M. Contic Jr. *(Chief Admin Officer)*

Lighthouse Technologies Holdings Corp. (1)
51 University St Ste 400, Seattle, WA 98101
Tel.: (206) 223-9690
Web Site: http://www.lighthouseglobal.com
Electronic Data Collections, Hosting & Processing Services
N.A.I.C.S.: 518210
Brian McManus *(CEO)*

Subsidiary (Domestic):

Liffey Thames Group LLC (2)
465 California St Ste 1400, San Francisco, CA 94104
Tel.: (415) 392-2900
Electronic Data Processing & Data Collection Services
N.A.I.C.S.: 518210

Lighthouse Document Technologies, Inc. (2)
51 University St Ste 400, Seattle, WA 98101
Tel.: (206) 223-9690
Web Site: http://lighthouseglobal.com
Legal Services & eDiscovery; Software Solutions
N.A.I.C.S.: 541199
Brian McManus *(CEO)*

Lighthouse eDiscovery (2)
112 Seneca St, Seattle, WA 98101-2917
Tel.: (206) 223-9690
Web Site: http://www.lhediscovery.com
Printing
N.A.I.C.S.: 323111
John Olson *(Dir-Focus Discovery)*
Quint Sabatka *(Dir-Fin)*
Paul Hiteshew *(Dir-Infrastructure Svcs)*
Paul Johnson *(Dir-Bus Dev)*
Brandon Jessup *(Dir-Technical Project Mgmt)*
Stacy Ybarra *(VP-Mktg)*
Michael Miller *(Sr VP-Sls & Mktg)*
David Binder *(CFO)*
Brian McManus *(Vice Chm)*
Michal Petrzela *(Mng Dir)*
Ron Markezich *(CEO)*

Prime Pensions, Inc. (1)
25B Vreeland Rd Ste 209, Florham Park, NJ 07932
Tel.: (973) 845-7654
Web Site: http://www.primepensionsinc.com
Retirement Plan Compliance & Administration Services
N.A.I.C.S.: 524298
Scott Feit *(CEO)*

Subsidiary (Domestic):

Associated Pension Consultants, Inc. (2)
1000 Fortress St Ste 800, Chico, CA 95973
Tel.: (530) 343-4233
Sales Range: $1-9.9 Million
Emp.: 80
Insurance Related Activities
N.A.I.C.S.: 524298
Marc Roberts *(Pres & Partner)*

Pension Benefits Unlimited, Inc. (2)
17748 Sky Park Cir, Irvine, CA 92614
Tel.: (949) 260-1880
Web Site: http://www.pbuinc.com
Sales Range: $1-9.9 Million
Emp.: 15
Insurance Related Activities
N.A.I.C.S.: 524298
Dave Kobrine *(Pres)*

eCommission Financial Services, Inc. (1)
11612 Bee Caves Rd Bldg II Ste 200, Austin, TX 78738
Tel.: (877) 882-4368
Web Site: http://www.ecommission.com
Real Estate Commission Advance Services
N.A.I.C.S.: 522299

COMPANIES

James Ciccarello *(Pres & CFO)*
Christine C. Pavelka *(Dir-Billing)*
Jonathan Vande Streek *(Dir-Ops)*
Kristen Brown *(Dir-Mktg)*
Sean Whaling *(Founder & CEO)*
Dawn Willey *(Dir-Indus Rels)*

LIGO PRODUCTS INC.
9100 W 191st St, Mokena, IL 60448
Tel.: (708) 478-1800
Web Site:
http://www.ligoproducts.com
Rev.: $22,500,000
Emp.: 83
Dining & Bedroom Furniture
N.A.I.C.S.: 337126
Shing-Shong Lee *(Founder & Pres)*
Kathy Sorensen *(Office Mgr)*

LIGON INDUSTRIES LLC
1927 1st Ave N, Birmingham, AL 35203
Tel.: (205) 322-3302
Web Site:
http://www.ligonindustries.com
Year Founded: 1998
Sales Range: $100-124.9 Million
Emp.: 100
Aluminum Foundries
N.A.I.C.S.: 331524
Leon A. Nolen *(Founder & CEO)*
Jon W. Whetsell *(CFO)*
Jan J. Ehrhardt *(VP)*
Justin A. Mayfield *(Treas & VP)*
John J. McMahon Jr. *(Chm)*
James C. Delk Jr. *(Pres)*

Subsidiaries:

Energy Manufacturing Company, Inc. (1)
204 Plastic Ln, Monticello, IA 52310-9472
Tel.: (319) 465-3537
Web Site: http://www.energymfg.com
Hydraulic Cylinder Mfr
N.A.I.C.S.: 333995
Terry Otto *(Mgr-HR)*

Fisher Hydraulics, Inc. (1)
603 Highway 10 W, Laurens, IA 50554
Tel.: (712) 845-2634
Web Site: http://www.fisherhydraulics.com
Emp.: 75
Hydraulic Cylinder Mfr
N.A.I.C.S.: 333995
Joseph S. Zakrzewski *(Gen Mgr)*

HDM Hydraulics, LLC (1)
125 Fire Tower Dr, Tonawanda, NY 14150
Tel.: (716) 694-8004
Web Site: http://www.hdmco.com
Emp.: 50
Aluminum Die-Castings Mfr
N.A.I.C.S.: 331523
William Anderson *(Pres)*

Hampton Hydraulics, LLC (1)
1483 Hwy 3, Hampton, IA 50441 **(100%)**
Tel.: (641) 456-4411
Web Site:
http://www.hamptonhydraulics.com
Sales Range: $10-24.9 Million
Emp.: 20
Holding Company for Designers & Manufacturers of Custom Hydraulic Cylinders & Components
N.A.I.C.S.: 331513

Holding (Domestic):

Great Bend Industries (2)
8701 6th St, Great Bend, KS 67530
Tel.: (620) 792-4368
Web Site:
http://www.greatbendindustries.com
Custom-designed, Welded Hydraulic Cylinders Mfr
N.A.I.C.S.: 333995

Hampton Hydraulics LLC (2)
712 1st St NW, Hampton, IA 50441
Tel.: (641) 456-4871
Web Site: http://www.hamptonhydraulics.com
Producer of Custom-sized Chromium Plated Rod & Tube Materials

N.A.I.C.S.: 336310
John Lang *(Gen Mgr)*

Seabee Corporation Cylinders (2)
712 1st St NW, Hampton, IA 50441
Tel.: (641) 456-4871
Web Site: http://www.hamptonhydraulics.com
Mfr & Provider of Hydraulic Cylinders
N.A.I.C.S.: 333995
George Winchester *(Pres)*

Seabee Corporation Foundry (2)
1483 Hwy 3, Hampton, IA 50441
Tel.: (641) 456-4411
Web Site: http://www.hamptonhydraulics.com
Emp.: 12
Producers of Steel Alloy Castings
N.A.I.C.S.: 111110
Ryan Amble *(Controller)*

Harmony Castings, LLC (1)
251 Perry Hwy, Harmony, PA 16037
Tel.: (724) 452-5811
Web Site: http://www.harmonycastings.com
Aluminum Casting Mfr
N.A.I.C.S.: 331524
Mark Fallen *(Plant Mgr)*
Rich Sellman *(Pres)*
Gary Dindinger *(Mgr-Quality Assurance)*

Hydratech, LLC (1)
1331 S West Ave, Fresno, CA 93706
Tel.: (559) 233-0876
Web Site:
http://www.hydratechcylinders.com
Sales Range: $1-9.9 Million
Hydraulic & Pneumatic Cylinder Mfr
N.A.I.C.S.: 333995
Lin Dellanina *(Dir-HR)*
Robert Morgan *(Mgr-Quality Assurance)*

Ramrod Industries LLC (1)
800 Monroe St, Spencer, WI 54479
Tel.: (715) 659-4996
Web Site: http://www.ramrodindustries.com
Rev.: $13,000,000
Emp.: 60
Mfr of Hydraulic & Pneumatic Fluid Power Cylinders
N.A.I.C.S.: 333995
Tim Brumbaugh *(Controller)*

TPi-Arcade, Inc. (1)
7888 Route 98, Arcade, NY 14009
Tel.: (585) 492-0122
Web Site: http://www.tpicast.com
Emp.: 66
Aluminum Casting Mfr
N.A.I.C.S.: 331524
Jack Pohlman *(Pres)*
Daniel Stahl *(Mgr-Matls, Health & Safety)*

Thompson Fabricating LLC (1)
1411 Commerce Pl, Tarrant, AL 35217
Tel.: (205) 841-0441
Web Site: http://www.tfco.com
Emp.: 30
Fabricated Product Distr
N.A.I.C.S.: 423390
Spencer Turner *(Gen Mgr)*
George Scott *(Mgr-Sls & Mktg)*
Don Noojin *(Mgr-Production)*
Shirley Starns *(Mgr-Admin)*
Lisa Hinds *(Mgr-Pur)*
Larry Poe *(Mgr-Shipping)*

Watry Industries LLC (1)
3312 Lakeshore Dr, Sheboygan, WI 53081
Tel.: (920) 457-4886
Web Site: http://www.watry.com
Aluminum Casting Mfr & Distr
N.A.I.C.S.: 331524
Dale Christel *(Mgr-Sls)*

LIGON OIL CO. INC.
609 Main St, Norman, AR 71960
Tel.: (870) 334-2411
Web Site: http://www.ligonoil.com
Sales Range: $25-49.9 Million
Emp.: 20
Petroleum Bulk Stations
N.A.I.C.S.: 424710
Ronnie G. Waggoner *(Pres)*
Jim Lewis *(Office Mgr)*

LIKEABLE MEDIA
240 W 37th St 7th Fl, New York, NY 10018
Tel.: (212) 660-2458
Web Site: http://www.likeable.com
Sales Range: $1-9.9 Million
Emp.: 50
Social Network Support Services
N.A.I.C.S.: 561410
Dave Kerpen *(Co-Founder & Chm)*
Carrie Kerpen *(Co-Founder & CEO)*
Honey Comer *(Dir-Acct Mgmt)*
Valerie Tirella *(VP-Creative Svcs)*

LIL' DRUG STORE PRODUCTS, INC.
9300 Earhart Ln SW, Cedar Rapids, IA 52404
Web Site: http://www.lildrugstore.com
Pharmaceuticals Distr
N.A.I.C.S.: 325412
Chris DeWolf *(Pres & CEO)*

Subsidiaries:

Mechanical Servants, LLC (1)
2755 Thomas St, Melrose Park, IL 60160
Tel.: (708) 486-1500
Web Site: http://www.cvalet.com
Consumer Products Packaging & Wholesale Services
N.A.I.C.S.: 424210
Leslie Ramirez *(Mgr-HR-Payroll)*
Steve Jungmann *(Pres & CEO)*

LILE INTERNATIONAL COMPANIES
8060 SW Pfaffoe, Tigard, OR 97223
Tel.: (503) 691-3500
Web Site: http://www.lile.net
Rev.: $24,446,730
Emp.: 325
Local Trucking with Storage
N.A.I.C.S.: 484110
Megan Rutz *(Mgr-HR)*
Barbara Lile *(VP)*
Vanessa Rimby *(CFO)*
Dan DeAutremont *(VP-Oregon)*

LILIS ENERGY, INC.
201 Main St Ste 700, Fort Worth, TX 76102
Tel.: (817) 585-9001 NV
Web Site: http://www.lilisenergy.com
Rev.: $66,063,000
Assets: $258,599,000
Liabilities: $251,226,000
Net Worth: $7,373,000
Earnings: ($297,518,000)
Emp.: 43
Fiscal Year-end: 12/31/19
Oil & Gas Exploration Services
N.A.I.C.S.: 213112
Michael G. Long *(Chm)*
Christa Garrett *(Gen Counsel & Sr VP)*
Joseph C. Daches *(Pres & CFO)*

LILIUM GROUP LLC
1811 Bering Dr. Ste 400, Houston, TX 77057
Web Site: https://lilium-holdings.com
Private Equity
N.A.I.C.S.: 523940

Subsidiaries:

Servicios de Transportacion Jaguar, S.A de C.V. (1)
Carretera a Monclova KM 5, Colonia Andres Caballero Escobedo, Nuevo León, 33635, Mexico
Tel.: (52) 8182861150
Web Site: https://stjaguar.com.mx
Truck Related Transportation Services
N.A.I.C.S.: 484122
Victor Castaneda *(Mgr-Natl Accts)*
Aldo Rosani *(Mgr-Natl Accts)*
Jorge B. Lopez Solorzano *(Mgr-New Accts)*
Hugo S. Sepulveda *(Mgr-Natl Accts)*
Enrique Favila *(Dir-Bus Dev)*

LILLARD & CLARK CONSTRUCTION COMPANY INC.

LILIUOKALANI TRUST
Alakea Corp Twr 1100 Alakea St Ste 1100, Honolulu, HI 96813
Tel.: (808) 203-6150
Web Site: http://www.onipaa.org
Year Founded: 1909
Sales Range: $10-24.9 Million
Emp.: 160
Provider of Trust Services
N.A.I.C.S.: 813211
Robert H. Ozaki *(Pres & CEO)*
LeeAnn P. Crabbe *(VP)*
Kuulani Keohokalole *(Dir-Organizational Dev)*
David Hipp *(Mgr-Sys Change)*
Nalei Akina *(Chief Program Officer & VP)*
Dawn Harflinger *(CFO & VP)*
Mahina Hugo *(Dir-Educational Innovations)*
Chiemi Terasawa Davis *(Sr Dir-Social Svcs)*
Kawika Riley *(Mgr-Community Change Initiatives)*
Mercedes Lanza *(Chief Admin Officer)*

LILJA CORP.
229 Rickenbacker Cir, Livermore, CA 94551
Tel.: (925) 455-2300
Web Site: http://www.liljacorp.com
Sales Range: $10-24.9 Million
Emp.: 6
Boiler & Furnace Contractors
N.A.I.C.S.: 236220
Vic Freeberg *(Mgr-Ops)*
Walter Bowe *(Pres & CEO)*

LILKER ASSOCIATES CONSULTING ENGINEERS, PC
1001 Ave Of The Americas 9th Fl, New York, NY 10018
Tel.: (212) 695-1000 NY
Web Site: http://www.lilker.com
Year Founded: 1985
Sales Range: $10-24.9 Million
Emp.: 80
Engineeering Services
N.A.I.C.S.: 541330
Bruce Lilker *(Pres)*
Philip Yee *(Sr VP)*
John Hassett *(Dir-Tech Solutions Grp & Assoc Principal)*
Jose Rivera *(Dir-Sanitary & Fire Protection & Assoc Principal)*
Louis Piccirillo *(VP & Dir-Long Island)*
Serge Budzyn *(Exec VP)*
Steven Hammer *(Sr VP)*

Subsidiaries:

EMO Energy Solutions, LLC. (1)
3130 Fairview Park Dr Ste 125, Falls Church, VA 22042
Tel.: (703) 205-0445
Web Site: http://www.emoenergy.com
Sales Range: $10-24.9 Million
Emp.: 34
Scientific & Technical Consulting Services
N.A.I.C.S.: 541690

LILLA P LLC
420 W 14th St Ste 3 NW, New York, NY 10014
Tel.: (212) 242-7490
Web Site: http://www.lillap.com
Year Founded: 1998
Rev.: $5,600,000
Emp.: 8
Women's Clothing & Accessories Whslr
N.A.I.C.S.: 424350
Pauline S. Nakios *(Founder)*

LILLARD & CLARK CONSTRUCTION COMPANY INC.

LILLARD & CLARK CONSTRUCTION COMPANY INC.

Lillard & Clark Construction Company Inc.—(Continued)
3775 S Knox Ct, Denver, CO 80236-6118
Tel.: (303) 761-3170
Web Site: http://www.lillardclark.com
Year Founded: 1972
Rev.: $37,788,217
Emp.: 80
Provider of Bridge, Tunnel & Elevated Highway Construction Services
N.A.I.C.S.: 237310

Subsidiaries:

Lillard & Clark-Wyoming (1)
4089 N 3rd St, Laramie, WY 82072-9547
Tel.: (307) 742-1463
Bridge, Tunnel & Elevated Highway
N.A.I.C.S.: 237310

LILLY AND ASSOCIATES INTERNATIONAL
3155 NW 82nd Ave Ste 101, Doral, FL 33122
Tel.: (305) 513-9540
Web Site: http://www.shiplilly.com
Year Founded: 1996
Sales Range: $50-74.9 Million
Emp.: 25
International Shipping & Logistics
N.A.I.C.S.: 488510
Lilly Cabrera (Founder)
Nelson R. Cabrera (Dir-Bus Dev)
Sheila Muzin (CFO)

LILYPONS WATER GARDENS INC.
6800 Lily Pons Rd, Adamstown, MD 21710
Tel.: (301) 874-5503
Web Site: http://www.lilypons.com
Year Founded: 1917
Sales Range: $10-24.9 Million
Emp.: 20
Waterlilies & Goldfish Sales
N.A.I.C.S.: 444240
Margaret Thomas Koogle (Pres)
Richard M. Koogle (Dir-Ops)

LIMA AUTO MALL INC.
2100 N Cable Rd, Lima, OH 45805
Tel.: (419) 993-6000
Web Site: http://www.limaautomall.com
Rev.: $40,500,000
Emp.: 102
New & Used Car Dealers
N.A.I.C.S.: 441110
William C. Timmermeister (Pres)
Robert Mc Clain (Gen Mgr)
Rodger McClain (VP)

LIME ROCK PARTNERS, LLC
274 Riverside Ave, Westport, CT 06880
Tel.: (203) 293-2750
Web Site: http://www.lrpartners.com
Year Founded: 1998
Privater Equity Firm
N.A.I.C.S.: 523999
Jonathan C. Farber (Co-Founder & Mng Dir)
John T. Reynolds (Co-Founder & Mng Dir)
Trevor Burgess (Mng Dir)
Will Franklin (Mng Dir)
Mark McCall (Mng Dir)
J. McLane (Chief Investment Officer & Mng Dir)
Gary Sernovitz (Mng Dir)
Greg Highberger (Mng Dir)
Allie Stone (VP-IR & Bus Dev)
Blair Barlow (Mng Dir)
Susan Oswald (CFO)
Jeffrey B. Scofield (COO & Mng Dir)

Subsidiaries:

Lime Rock Management, L.P. (1)
274 Riverside Ave, Westport, CT 06880
Tel.: (203) 293-2750
Web Site: http://www.lrpartners.com
Investment Holding Company
N.A.I.C.S.: 551112

Joint Venture (Non-US):

DHS Oil International Pty Ltd (2)
PO Box 268, Abu Dhabi, United Arab Emirates
Tel.: (971) 48153817
Web Site: http://www.vesinternational.com
Oil & Gas Surveying & Other Support Services
N.A.I.C.S.: 213112

Subsidiary (US):

Gyro Technologies, Inc. (3)
3400 CR 48, Robstown, TX 78380
Tel.: (361) 767-0602
Sales Range: $1-9.9 Million
Emp.: 20
Oil & Gas Directional Surveying Services
N.A.I.C.S.: 213112
Keith Havelka (Gen Mgr)

Joint Venture (Domestic):

Iracore International, Inc. (2)
3430 E 13h Ave, Hibbing, MN 55746
Tel.: (218) 263-8831
Web Site: http://www.irproducts.com
Sales Range: $50-74.9 Million
Pipeline & Industrial Equipment Elastomeric Protective Coatings Mfr
N.A.I.C.S.: 326299
James Skalski (CFO & Comptroller)
Christopher Liesmaki (COO & VP)

Subsidiary (Domestic):

Industrial Rubber Applicators, Inc. (3)
3804 E Beltline, Hibbing, MN 55746
Tel.: (218) 263-8831
Web Site: http://www.irproducts.com
Emp.: 100
Pipeline Elastomeric Protective Coatings Mfr
N.A.I.C.S.: 326299
James Skalski (CFO)

Irathane Systems, Inc. (3)
3516 E 13th Ave, Hibbing, MN 55746-2338
Tel.: (218) 262-5211
Web Site: http://www.iracore.com
Sales Range: $10-24.9 Million
Industrial Equipment Elastomeric Protective Coatings Mfr
N.A.I.C.S.: 326150
James Skalski (CFO)
Rick Brouwer (Pres)

Joint Venture (Domestic):

Vantage Energy Inc. (2)
116 Inverness Dr E Ste 220, Englewood, CO 80112
Tel.: (720) 458-6601
Web Site: http://www.vantageenergy.com
Emp.: 63
Holding Company; Petroleum & Natural Gas Extraction
N.A.I.C.S.: 551112
Roger J. Biemans (Chm & CEO)
W. Worth Carlin (Sr VP-Land)
Mike L. Hopkins (VP-Midstream)
Seth Urruty (VP-Dev)
Mark Brown (VP-Land & Bus Dev)
Christopher L. Valdez (VP-Mktg & Midstream Bus Dev)
Richard Starkey (VP-Subsurface Tech)
Ryan T. Gosney (Chief Acctg Officer & VP-Controller)
John J. Moran Jr. (Sr VP-Ops)
Thomas B. Tyree Jr. (Pres & CFO)

Lime Rock New Energy GP LP (1)
274 Riverside Aven Ste 3, Westport, CT 06880
Tel.: (203) 293-2750
Web Site: http://www.lrnewenergy.com
Venture Capital & Private Equity
N.A.I.C.S.: 523940
Mark Lewis (Mng Dir)

Subsidiary (Domestic):

Electric Power Engineers, LLC (2)
13001 W Hwy 71 Ste G100, Austin, TX 78738
Tel.: (512) 282-6700
Web Site: http://www.epeconsulting.com
Engineeering Services
N.A.I.C.S.: 541330
Hala N. Ballouz (Pres)
Hugo Mena (VP-Bus Dev)
Stephanie Badr (VP-Ops)
Billy F. Yancey (VP-Tech Svcs & Compliance)

LIMITLESS INTERNATIONAL INC.
8750 Exchange Dr Ste #3, Orlando, FL 32809
Tel.: (407) 852-9225
Year Founded: 2002
Sales Range: $1-9.9 Million
Emp.: 8
Transportation Warehousing & Distribution
N.A.I.C.S.: 488510
Cheryl Stockstad (Pres)
Eirik Stockstad (CEO)

LIMITLESS PROJECTS INC.
2261 Rosanna St, Las Vegas, NV 89117
Tel.: (269) 692-9418
Web Site: http://www.limitlessprojectsinc.com
Year Founded: 2020
Software Development Services
N.A.I.C.S.: 541511

LIMNES BOTTLING ACQUISITION CO.
2033 SW Jackson St, Portland, OR 97201
Tel.: (503) 224-5858
Investment Holding Company
N.A.I.C.S.: 551112
Edward Maletis (Pres)

Subsidiaries:

Portland Bottling Company (1)
1321 NE Couch St, Portland, OR 97232
Tel.: (503) 231-5035
Web Site: http://www.portlandbottling.com
Emp.: 95
Soft Drinks Mfr
N.A.I.C.S.: 312111
Tom Keenan (Pres)

LIMOLINK, INC.
701 Tama St Bldg A, Marion, IA 52302
Tel.: (319) 730-2100
Web Site: http://www.limolink.com
Year Founded: 1998
Sales Range: $25-49.9 Million
Emp.: 150
Logistics Consulting Servies
N.A.I.C.S.: 541614
Chris Wiese (VP-Sls)
Brian Jett (Acct Mgr-Client-Sls)

LIMORES LIMOS
134 W 37th St Fl 2, New York, NY 10018
Tel.: (212) 787-7777
Web Site: http://www.limores.net
Year Founded: 2004
Rev.: $22,400,000
Emp.: 118
Limousine Service
N.A.I.C.S.: 485320
Malcolm Elvey (Partner)
David E. De Leeuw (Chm)
Marko Jovanovic (Dir-Ops)
Ivan Aksentijevic (CTO)
Edward R. Burns (CFO)

Riz Husain (Exec VP-Sls & E-Commerce)
Chi Eng (Gen Counsel)

LIMOUSINE SERVICE OF WESTCHESTER
10 New King St Ste 107, White Plains, NY 10604-1211
Tel.: (914) 592-8534
Web Site: http://www.lswlimo.com
Year Founded: 1978
Sales Range: $1-9.9 Million
Emp.: 43
Transportation Services
N.A.I.C.S.: 488999
Melissa M. Thornton (CEO)

LIN R. ROGERS ELECTRICAL CONTRACTORS INC.
2050 Marconi Dr Ste 200, Alpharetta, GA 30005
Tel.: (770) 772-3400
Web Site: http://www.lrogerselectric.com
Year Founded: 1983
Sales Range: $25-49.9 Million
Emp.: 600
Electrical Contractor
N.A.I.C.S.: 238210
Lin R. Rogers (Chm)
Ken Sisson (Pres-Lighting Svcs)
Brett Amburgey (CFO)
Chris Rogers (Pres & CEO)
Lindsey Rogers Schoultz (VP-HR)

LINBECK GROUP LLC
3900 Essex Ln Ste 1200, Houston, TX 77027-5204
Tel.: (713) 621-2350
Web Site: http://www.linbeck.com
Year Founded: 1938
Sales Range: $150-199.9 Million
Emp.: 400
Commercial Buildings, Warehouses, Concrete Work & Special Purpose Facilities Construction
N.A.I.C.S.: 236220
Mel Hildebrandt (Vice Chm)
William J. Riegler (CFO & Treas)
Tony Schmitt (Controller)
Chuck Greco (Pres & CEO)
Ike Allen (VP)
Ben Johanneman (Sr VP & Gen Mgr)

Subsidiaries:

Linbeck (1)
201 Main St Ste 1801, Fort Worth, TX 76102-3121
Tel.: (650) 599-0334
Web Site: http://www.linbeck.com
General Contracting Services
N.A.I.C.S.: 236220
David Stueckler (Exec VP)

Linbeck Construction Corporation-Ft. Worth (1)
1263 W Rd Ste 202, Fort Worth, TX 76104
Tel.: (817) 332-8494
Web Site: http://www.linbeck.com
Sales Range: $25-49.9 Million
Emp.: 20
Provider of General Contracting
N.A.I.C.S.: 236115
William A. Scott (Exec VP)
John Fisher (Exec VP)
John Barnes (VP)
Mark Linenberger (Mgr-Client Dev)

Linbeck Construction Corporation-Houston (1)
3900 Essex Ln St 1200, Houston, TX 77027
Tel.: (713) 621-2350
Web Site: http://www.linbeck.com
General Contracting Services
N.A.I.C.S.: 236220
Bill Scott (Pres)

LINC SYSTEMS, INC.

COMPANIES

16540 Southpark Dr, Westfield, IN 46074
Tel.: (317) 399-3100
Web Site:
http://www.lincsystems.com
Year Founded: 1995
Fasteners, Industrial: Nuts, Bolts, Screws, Etc.
N.A.I.C.S.: 423840
Bill Dennis (*VP-Fin*)
Jeremy Hoel (*Regional Sls Mgr*)

LINCHRIS HOTEL CORP.
269 Hanover St Ste 2, Hanover, MA 02339
Tel.: (781) 826-8824　　NH
Web Site: http://www.linchris.com
Year Founded: 1985
Emp.: 100
Home Management Services
N.A.I.C.S.: 721110
Christopher Gistis (*CEO*)
Michael Sullivan (*Pres*)
Glenn Gistis (*CFO*)
Robb M. Moskowitz (*Sr VP-Ops*)
Bob Anderson (*Sr VP-Ops*)
Nick Pancoast (*VP-Ops*)
Dennis Jakubowski (*VP & Project Mgr*)
Liz Jobin (*VP-Revenue Mgmt*)
Janine Hodge (*Controller*)
Maureen Lee (*Dir-Sls & Mktg*)
Stacia Miele (*Dir-Online Mktg*)

LINCOLN BRICK AND STONE INC.
1222 Burton St SE, Grand Rapids, MI 49507
Tel.: (616) 452-6055　　MI
Year Founded: 1923
Sales Range: $10-24.9 Million
Emp.: 23
Provider of Building Materials & Services
N.A.I.C.S.: 423610
Fritz Kruer (*Pres*)

LINCOLN BUILDERS INC.
1910 Farmerville Hwy, Ruston, LA 71270
Tel.: (318) 255-3822
Web Site:
http://www.lincolnbuilders.com
Sales Range: $75-99.9 Million
Emp.: 50
Commercial & Office Building Construction
N.A.I.C.S.: 236220
Ronald Graham (*Chm*)
Danny Graham (*CEO*)
Lynn Hutchinson (*Treas*)
Andy Boniol (*Dir-Preconstruction-Baton Rouge Org*)

LINCOLN CENTER FOR THE PERFORMING ARTS, INC.
70 Lincoln Center Plz 7h Fl, New York, NY 10023
Tel.: (212) 875-5456
Web Site:
https://www.lincolncenter.org
Sales Range: $75-99.9 Million
Emp.: 511
Theatrical Producers & Services
N.A.I.C.S.: 711110
Rosemarie Garipoli (*Exec Dir-Bravo Lincoln Center Campaign*)
Jane S. Moss (*VP-Programming*)
Nigel Redden (*Dir-Lincoln Center Festival*)
Peter Duffin (*Sr VP-Brand & Mktg*)
Liza Parker (*COO*)
Scott Noppe-Brandon (*Exec Dir*)
Katherine Farley (*Chm*)
Elaine Ruiz (*Interim CFO & VP*)
David Link (*Chief Digital Officer & VP*)
Jamie Staugler (*Dir-Special Projects*)
Mary Costa (*Exec Dir-Hall-Fame*)
Ron Austin (*Exec Dir*)
Russell Granet (*Acting Pres*)
Lauren Ezrol Klein (*Gen Counsel, Sec & Exec VP*)

LINCOLN CONTRACTORS SUPPLY INC.
11111 W Hayes Ave, Milwaukee, WI 53227
Tel.: (414) 541-1327
Web Site:
http://www.lincolncontractorssupply.com
Sales Range: $25-49.9 Million
Emp.: 145
General Construction Machinery & Equipment
N.A.I.C.S.: 423810
Norman C. Knief (*Pres*)
Steve Berndt (*Controller*)
Donna Tushar (*Office Mgr & Mgr-Credit*)
Keith Turtenwald (*VP*)

LINCOLN COUNTY BANCORP., INC.
430 E Wood St, Troy, MO 63379
Tel.: (636) 528-7001　　MO
Year Founded: 1981
Bank Holding Company
N.A.I.C.S.: 551111
David Thompson (*Pres*)

Subsidiaries:

Exchange Bank of Northeast Missouri　　(1)
268 N Johnson St, Kahoka, MO 63445
Tel.: (660) 727-3344
Web Site: http://www.ebnemo.com
Rev.: $5,896,000
Assets: $143,163,000
Liabilities: $127,442,000
Net Worth: $15,721,000
Earnings: $2,141,000
Emp.: 40
Fiscal Year-end: 12/31/2012
Commericial Banking
N.A.I.C.S.: 522110
Paula Fox (*Pres & Officer-Loan*)
Jed Wilson (*Officer-Loan & Exec VP*)
C. Robert Hall (*Chm*)

Peoples Bank & Trust Co.　　(1)
430 E Wood St, Troy, MO 63379
Tel.: (636) 528-7001
Web Site: http://www.pbtc.net
Rev.: $16,055,000
Assets: $420,446,000
Liabilities: $393,785,000
Net Worth: $26,661,000
Earnings: ($1,858,000)
Emp.: 98
Fiscal Year-end: 12/31/2012
Commericial Banking
N.A.I.C.S.: 522110
David Thompson (*Pres & CEO*)
Carla Angel (*VP & Asst Gen Counsel*)
Debbie Bunfill (*Mgr-Troy Square*)
Dale Cope (*Gen Counsel & VP*)
Karen Douglas (*Dir-HR*)
Doris Kaimann (*Comptroller*)
Kris Moesch (*Asst VP & Mgr-New Accts*)
Suzette Morris (*VP-Ops*)
Margie Newsom (*Asst VP & Mgr-O'Fallon*)
Justin Pierre (*Pres & CEO*)
John Armstrong (*Officer-Loan & Exec VP*)

LINCOLN ELECTRIC SYSTEM
1040 O St, Lincoln, NE 68508-3609
Tel.: (402) 475-4211　　NE
Web Site: http://www.les.com
Year Founded: 1966
Sales Range: $150-199.9 Million
Emp.: 450
Electric Utility Services
N.A.I.C.S.: 221118
Shelley Sahling-Zart (*Gen Counsel & VP-Comm & Corp Records*)
Dan Pudenz (*VP-Energy Delivery*)
Paul Crist (*CTO & VP-Tech Svcs*)
Jason Fortik (*VP-Power Supply*)
Lisa Hale (*VP-Customer Svcs*)

LINCOLN EQUIPMENT, INC.
2051 Commerce Ave, Concord, CA 94520
Tel.: (925) 687-9500
Web Site:
http://www.lincolnaquatics.com
Year Founded: 1954
Sales Range: $10-24.9 Million
Emp.: 35
Swimming Pool Equipment & Supplies Whslr
N.A.I.C.S.: 423910
Charles Luecker (*Pres & CEO*)
Rich Eaton (*CFO*)
Kathie Luecker (*VP*)

LINCOLN FEDERAL SAVINGS BANK OF NEBRASKA
1101 North St, Lincoln, NE 68508
Tel.: (402) 474-1400
Web Site: http://www.lincolnfed.com
Year Founded: 1906
Sales Range: $25-49.9 Million
Emp.: 100
Federal Savings Bank
N.A.I.C.S.: 522180
Leo J. Schumacher (*Pres*)
Janet Anderbery (*CFO & Sr VP*)
Mike Isaacson (*VP*)
Lorna Moseman (*Asst VP & Mgr-Consumer Loan*)
Lyn Robart (*VP & Branch Mgr*)
Matthew Lyman (*VP*)
Shelly Simonson (*Asst VP-Admin*)
Billie-Leigh Marquart (*Coord-Loan Collections*)

LINCOLN HOLDINGS LLC
601 F St NW, Washington, DC 20004
Tel.: (202) 628-3200　　DE
Web Site:
http://www.monumentalsports.com
Year Founded: 1999
Sales Range: $50-74.9 Million
Emp.: 100
Holding Company; Professional Sports Franchises & Arenas Owner & Operator
N.A.I.C.S.: 551112
Mark D. Lerner (*Co-Owner*)
Richard Kay (*Co-Owner*)
Jeong Hoon Kim (*Co-Owner*)
George P. Stamas (*Co-Owner*)
Michelle DiFebo Freeman (*Co-Owner*)
Scott W. Brickman (*Co-Owner*)
Neil D. Cohen (*Co-Owner*)
Roger Mody (*Co-Owner & Mng Partner*)
Fred Schaufeld (*Partner*)
Cliff White (*Co-Owner*)
Randall Boe (*Gen Counsel & Exec VP*)
Keith Burrows (*Sr VP-Team Fin*)
Rick Moreland (*Sr VP-Exec Suites*)
Kelly Skoloda (*Sr VP-People & Culture*)
Michelle Trostle (*Sr VP-Admin*)
David Touhey (*Pres*)
Jim Van Stone (*Chief Comml Officer & Pres-Bus Ops*)
Anthony P. Nader III (*Co-Owner*)
Kate Bedingfield (*VP-Comm*)
Raul J. Fernandez (*Vice Chm*)
Richard D. Fairbank (*Partner*)
Earl W. Stafford (*Co-Owner*)

Subsidiaries:

Verizon Center　　(1)

LINCOLN INVESTMENT PLANNING INC.

601 F St NW, Washington, DC 20004
Tel.: (202) 628-3200
Web Site: http://www.verizoncenter.com
Sports & Entertainment Arena Operator
N.A.I.C.S.: 711310

Washington Capitals　　(1)
627 N Glebe Rd Ste 850, Arlington, VA 22203
Tel.: (202) 266-2200
Web Site: http://www.washingtoncaps.com
Sales Range: $10-24.9 Million
Emp.: 35
Professional Hockey Club Operator
N.A.I.C.S.: 711211
Theodore J. Leonsis (*Owner*)
Richard M. Patrick (*Vice Chm, Pres & COO*)
Brian MacLellan (*Sr VP & Gen Mgr*)
Tim Bronaugh (*Dir-Amateur Hockey Sls*)
Chris Sheap (*Sr VP-Ticket Ops*)
Don Fishman (*Asst Gen Mgr & Dir-Legal Affairs*)
Steve Richmond (*Dir-Player Dev*)
Kris Wagner (*Dir-Hockey Ops*)
Brian McPartland (*Sr Dir-IT*)
Jill Ruehle (*Sr Dir-Acctg*)
Ross Mahoney (*Asst Gen Mgr*)
Craig Leydig (*Asst Mgr-Equipment*)
Sergey Kocharov (*VP-Comm*)
Peter Robinson (*Dir-Community Rels*)
Jordan Cookler (*Dir-Ticket Ops*)
Patrick Duffy (*Sr VP-Partnerships-Global*)
Adam Heintz (*Sr VP-Bus Intelligence*)
Hunter Lochmann (*CMO*)

Washington Mystics　　(1)
601 F St NW, Washington, DC 20004
Tel.: (202) 527-7540
Web Site: http://www.wnba.com
Professional Women's Basketball Team
N.A.I.C.S.: 711211
Theodore J. Leonsis (*Owner*)
Ketsia Colimon (*Dir-Comm*)
Rebecca Winn (*VP-Mktg*)
Sashia Jones (*Sr Dir-Community Rels*)
Greg Monares (*Sr Dir-Guest Svcs*)
Chris Sheap (*Sr Dir-Ticket Ops*)
Hunter Lochmann (*Sr VP-Mktg & Brand Strategies*)
Bill Hanni (*Sr VP-Ticket,Sls & Svc*)

Washington Wizards　　(1)
601 F St NW, Washington, DC 20004
Tel.: (202) 628-3200
Professional Basketball Franchise
N.A.I.C.S.: 711211
Theodore J. Leonsis (*Owner*)
Ernie Grunfeld (*Pres*)
Cathy Smith (*Sr Dir-Basketball Admin*)
Jennifer Thomas (*Dir-Team Svcs*)
Scott Hall (*Sr Dir-Comm*)
Sashia Jones (*Sr Dir-Community Rels*)
Bill Hanni (*Sr Dir-Ticket Sls*)

LINCOLN INDUSTRIES
600 W East St, Lincoln, NE 68522
Tel.: (402) 475-3671
Web Site:
http://www.lincolnindustries.com
Year Founded: 1952
Sales Range: $75-99.9 Million
Emp.: 400
Electroplating & Plating
N.A.I.C.S.: 332813
Marc Le Baron (*Chm & CEO*)
Kaylan Maloley (*Mgr-Mktg*)
Gary Ahrens (*Mgr-Quality*)
Mark Sneed (*Dir-Quality*)
John Tiller (*Engr-Supplier Quality*)
Matt Carper (*Mgr-Quality-Motorsports Segment*)
Travis Johnson (*Mgr-Fin Plng & Analysis*)
Tanya Jackman (*Mgr-Acctg*)

LINCOLN INVESTMENT PLANNING INC.

LINCOLN INVESTMENT PLANNING INC.

Lincoln Investment Planning Inc.—(Continued)
601 Office Center Dr Ste 300, Fort Washington, PA 19034
Tel.: (215) 887-8111   DE
Web Site:
http://www.lincolninvestment.com
Year Founded: 1969
Sales Range: $10-24.9 Million
Emp.: 200
Investment Services
N.A.I.C.S.: 523999
Edward S. Forst (Pres)
Neil D. Wernick (CMO & VP)

Subsidiaries:

Capital Analysts, Inc.   (1)
303 Broadway Ste 1500, Cincinnati, OH 45202
Tel.: (513) 361-8700
Web Site: http://www.capitalanalysts.com
Investment Advice & Wealth Management Services
N.A.I.C.S.: 523940

The Legend Group   (1)
4600 E Park Dr Ste 300, Palm Beach Gardens, FL 33410
Tel.: (561) 694-0110
Web Site: http://www.legendgroup.com
Portfolio Management, Investment Advisory, Insurance & Pension Products Brokerage & Administration Services
N.A.I.C.S.: 523940
Shashi Mehrotra (COO & CIO)
Miralda Gingrich (VP-Ops)
Lee Kroening (VP-Strategic Rels)
Todd D. Stout (Reg VP)

Subsidiary (Domestic):

Legend Advisory LLC   (2)
4600 E Park Dr Ste 300, Palm Beach Gardens, FL 33410
Tel.: (866) 774-8671
Web Site:
http://www.legendadvisorycorp.com
Investment Advisory Services
N.A.I.C.S.: 523940
Shashi Mehrotra (COO & CIO)

LINCOLN LUMBER COMPANY
932 N 23rd St, Lincoln, NE 68503
Tel.: (402) 474-4488
Sales Range: $10-24.9 Million
Emp.: 16
Lumber & Other Building Materials
N.A.I.C.S.: 423310
Donald Hamill (Owner)
Bev Hamill (Treas)

LINCOLN MEDIA SERVICES, INC.
51 Sherwood Ter Ste Y, Lake Bluff, IL 60044
Tel.: (847) 229-9470
Web Site:
http://www.lincolnmedia.com
Year Founded: 1999
Sales Range: $1-9.9 Million
Emp.: 5
Media Buying Services
N.A.I.C.S.: 541830
Gary A. Jones (Pres & CEO)

LINCOLN OFFICE SUPPLY CO. INCORPORATED
205 Eastgate Dr, Washington, IL 61571-9238
Tel.: (309) 263-7777   IL
Web Site:
http://www.lincolnoffice.com
Year Founded: 1935
Sales Range: $25-49.9 Million
Emp.: 150
Furniture Dealer & Service Provider
N.A.I.C.S.: 423210
William M. Pape (Pres)

LINCOLN PARK ZOO
2001 N Clark St, Chicago, IL 60614

Tel.: (312) 742-2000
Web Site: http://www.lpzoo.com
Year Founded: 1868
Sales Range: $75-99.9 Million
Emp.: 160
Zoo Operator
N.A.I.C.S.: 712130
Kevin J. Bell (Pres & CEO)

LINCOLN PEAK CAPITAL MANAGEMENT, LLC
177 Huntington Ave 19th Fl, Boston, MA 02115
Tel.: (617) 765-4770
Web Site:
http://www.lincolnpeakcapital.com
Year Founded: 2008
Equity Investment Firm
N.A.I.C.S.: 523999
Seth W. Brennan (Co-Founder & Mng Partner)
Anthony H. Leness (Co-Founder & Mng Partner)
Austin McClintock (CFO, COO & Chief Compliance Officer)

LINCOLN PROPERTY COMPANY
2000 Mckinney Ave Ste 1000, Dallas, TX 75201-2011
Tel.: (214) 740-3300   TX
Web Site: http://www.lpc.com
Year Founded: 1965
Sales Range: $1-4.9 Billion
Emp.: 5,000
Residential & Commercial Real Estate Acquisition Development & Management Services
N.A.I.C.S.: 531210
Tom H. Kuhlmann (Sr VP)
John S. Herr (Exec VP)
Margette Hepfner (COO-Residential Mgmt Div)
Sheri Sandefur Killingsworth (VP-Mktg & Comm)
J. Elliot Prieur (Sr VP)
Mike Crockett (Sr VP)
Aleshia Lane (Mgr-Property)
Kevin Caille (VP-Indus Leasing-Southeast)
Andrew Jones (Sr VP-Property Mgmt)
James Anderson (VP-Ops-West)
Brandon Wang (Exec VP-Northern California)
David Binswanger (Co-CEO)
Scott Caldwell (Sr VP)
Robert Dozier (Exec VP)
Charlie Giammalva (Sr VP)
John Grissim (Exec VP)
Chip Mark (Sr VP)
John Walter (Exec VP)
Jinger Lane (VP-Ops-Southwest)
Sheila Carter (Reg VP)
Wade Rodgers (VP)
Brooke Caravela (Asst Mgr-Property-Houston)
Michael Kasmiersky (VP-Property Mgmt)
Omar Rawi (Exec VP-West)
Mark Kirchmeyer (Exec VP-Mid-Atlantic)
Daniel Roth (CFO & COO)
Candace Weaver (Asst VP-Client Svcs)
Christina Russo (Asst VP-Client Svcs)
Bionca Morris (Mgr-Property)
Clay Duvall (Co-CEO)
Alison Daubert (Chief Strategy & M&A Officer)
Maria Stamolis (Chief Investment Officer)

Subsidiaries:

LPC Southeast   (1)

3405 Piedmont Rd Ste 450, Atlanta, GA 30305
Tel.: (404) 266-7600
Web Site: http://www.lpcsoutheast.com
Emp.: 18
Real Estate Management Services
N.A.I.C.S.: 531390
Whitney Payne (Coord-Mktg)
Shane Froman (VP-Property Mgmt)
Michael Howell (VP-Office)
Tony Bartlett (Exec VP)
Denton Shamburger (VP)
Hunter H. Henritze (Sr VP-Atlanta Office)
Matt Davis (VP-Office Leasing)
Austin Stahley (Dir-Leasing)
Sean DuPree (Dir-Sls & Leasing)
Edward Price (VP-Property Mgmt)
Kirk Williams (VP-Retail)
Ammon Yancey (Sr Mgr-Property)

Lincoln Harris CSG   (1)
4725 Piedmont Row Dr Ste 800, Charlotte, NC 28210
Tel.: (704) 714-7600
Web Site: http://www.lincolnharriscsg.com
Real Estate Management Services
N.A.I.C.S.: 531390
John W. Harris III (Chm & CEO)
Richie Faulkenberry (Sr VP)
Brett Phillips (Sr VP & Dir-Construction Mgmt)
Ronald K. Steen (Exec VP)
Webber Beall (Exec VP)
Chris Wasko (Exec VP)
Anna Honeycutt (Exec VP & Controller)

Lincoln Harris, LLC   (1)
4725 Piedmont Row Dr Ste 800, Charlotte, NC 28210
Tel.: (704) 714-7600
Web Site: http://www.lincolnharris.com
Sales Range: $25-49.9 Million
Emp.: 45
Commercial Brokerage Services
N.A.I.C.S.: 524210
John W. Harris III (Pres)
Chris Wasko (Exec VP & Dir-Ops)
Brett Phillips (Exec VP)
Anna Honeycutt (Exec VP & Controller)
Ronald K. Steen (Exec VP)

Subsidiary (Domestic):

National Commerce Bank Services, Inc.   (2)
80 Monroe Ave Ste 250, Memphis, TN 38103
Tel.: (800) 264-2609
Web Site: http://www.ncbs.com
Financial Baking Services
N.A.I.C.S.: 541611

Subsidiary (Domestic):

Prime Performance, Inc.   (3)
12340 W Alameda Pkwy Ste 100, Lakewood, CO 80228-2806
Tel.: (303) 980-1530
Business Services
N.A.I.C.S.: 561499

Lincoln Property Company Commercial, Inc.   (1)
2000 McKinney Ave Ste 1000, Dallas, TX 75201
Tel.: (214) 740-3300
Commercial Building Construction Services
N.A.I.C.S.: 236220

Lincoln Property Company Residential   (1)
2000 McKinney Ave Ste 1000, Dallas, TX 75201-2011   (100%)
Tel.: (214) 740-3300
Web Site: http://www.lincolnapts.com
Sales Range: $25-49.9 Million
Emp.: 100
General Contractors of Residential Buildings
N.A.I.C.S.: 531210
Tim Byrne (Pres & CEO)
Dennis Streit (CFO)
Andy Atalis (Chief Acctg Officer)
Bill J. Grant (Sr VP-Construction)
Margette Hepfner (Sr VP-Client Svcs)
Jay Kenney (CIO)
Krista Washbourne (VP-Learning & Talent Dev)
Bruce Webster (Sr VP-Midwest)

U.S. PRIVATE

Kerry Braxton (Asst Gen Counsel-Legal & Corp Risk)
Chris Burns (Sr VP-Southeast)
Kim McCormick (Gen Counsel)
Allyson McKay (Sr VP-Southwest)

Lincoln Rackhouse   (1)
2000 McKinney Ave Ste 1000, Dallas, TX 75201
Tel.: (214) 740-3300
Web Site: http://www.rackhouse.com
Data Center Leasing Services
N.A.I.C.S.: 531390
Ryan Sullivan (Mng Dir)
Martin Peck (Exec VP)

Subsidiary (Domestic):

ByteGrid Holdings LLC   (2)
1800 Tysons Blvd Ste 350, McLean, VA 22102
Tel.: (703) 636-8150
Web Site: http://www.bytegrid.com
Data Center Storage
N.A.I.C.S.: 518210
Mike Clemson (VP-Critical Infrastructure)
Michael Duckett (CEO)
Carolyn Lange (Co-CFO)
Jason Silva (Pres & CTO)
William Schrader (Co-CEO)
Elyzabeth Holford (COO)
Annie Eissler (CMO)
Gaige Paulsen (CTO)

Subsidiary (Domestic):

Netriver Incorporated   (3)
4200 194th St SW, Lynnwood, WA 98036
Tel.: (425) 741-7014
Web Site: http://www.netriver.net
Sales Range: $1-9.9 Million
Emp.: 25
Internet Host Services
N.A.I.C.S.: 517810

LINCOLN PROVISION, INC.
824 W 38th Pl, Chicago, IL 60609-1415
Tel.: (773) 254-2400   IL
Web Site:
http://www.lincolnprovision.com
Year Founded: 1985
Sales Range: $75-99.9 Million
Emp.: 70
Wholesale Distributor of Meat & Meat Products
N.A.I.C.S.: 424470
Jim J. Stevens Jr. (Treas)

LINCOLN SAVINGS BANK
508 Main St, Reinbeck, IA 50669
Tel.: (319) 788-6441
Web Site: http://www.mylsb.com
Year Founded: 1902
Rev.: $31,400,000
Emp.: 167
Commericial Banking
N.A.I.C.S.: 522110
Emily Girsth (CFO & Exec VP)
Scott Jarvis (Pres-Des Moines)
Mike Schick (Chief Sales Officer/Exec VP-Reinbeck)
Mary Inbody (Exec VP & Head-Retail Banking)
Mike McCrary (First VP-ECommerce & Emerging Tech)
Brian Heying (Mgr-Fin Svcs Dept)

LINCOLN SECURITIES CORP.
155 Great Arrow Ave, Buffalo, NY 14207
Tel.: (716) 874-1380   NY
Web Site:
http://www.lincolnmovingandstorage.com
Year Founded: 1978
Sales Range: $10-24.9 Million
Emp.: 50
General Freight Trucking, Long-Distance, Truckload
N.A.I.C.S.: 484121
Tim Palisano (Owner)

COMPANIES LINDEN LLC

Subsidiaries:

Lincoln Archives Inc. (1)
155 Great Arrow Ave, Buffalo, NY 14207
Tel.: (716) 871-7040
Web Site: http://www.lincolnarchives.com
Emp.: 11
Storage & Security Products & Services
N.A.I.C.S.: 334112
William Palisano (Pres)
John Miller (Mgr-Ops)

LINCOLN STORES INC.
202 W Superior St Ste 500, Duluth, MN 55802-1967
Tel.: (218) 720-5000
Rev.: $10,283,150
Emp.: 35
Hardware Stores
N.A.I.C.S.: 444140
Terry L. Lundberg (Pres)
Scott Lundberg (VP)

LINCOLN SYMPHONY ORCHESTRA
233 S 13th St Ste 1702, Lincoln, NE 68508
Tel.: (402) 476-2211
Web Site: http://www.lincolnsymphony.org
Year Founded: 1927
Sales Range: $10-24.9 Million
Emp.: 5
Symphony Orchestra
N.A.I.C.S.: 711130
Edward Polochick (Dir-Music)
Barbara Zach (Exec Dir)

LINCOLN TECHNICAL INSTITUTE
200 Executive Dr Ste 340, West Orange, NJ 07052
Tel.: (973) 736-9340
Web Site: http://www.lincolnedu.com
Year Founded: 1946
Sales Range: $75-99.9 Million
Emp.: 165
Vocational Schools & Junior College
N.A.I.C.S.: 611210
Nella Santangelo (Dir-Career Svcs)
Kristen Kunath (Dir-Career Svcs)
Pat Tate (Supvr-Education)
Coleen Adezio (Dir-Fin Aid)

LINCOLN TEXTILE PRODUCTS CO.
900 Conroy Pl, Easton, PA 18040-6645
Tel.: (610) 438-2418
Web Site: http://www.lincolntextile.com
Rev.: $14,000,000
Emp.: 125
Bedspreads & Bed Sets Mfr
N.A.I.C.S.: 314120
Michael A. Mitch (Pres)

LINCOLN WOOD PRODUCTS, INC.
1400 W Taylor St, Merrill, WI 54452
Tel.: (715) 536-2461
Web Site: http://www.lincolnwindows.com
Rev.: $46,300,000
Emp.: 400
Wood Window & Door Mfr
N.A.I.C.S.: 321911
Lisa McRae (Controller)
Janice Oelke (Mgr-Pur)

LINCOLNSHIRE MANAGEMENT, INC.
780 3rd Ave 40th Fl, New York, NY 10017
Tel.: (212) 319-3633 DE
Web Site: http://www.lincolnshiremgmt.com
Year Founded: 1986
Sales Range: $150-199.9 Million
Emp.: 50
Privater Equity Firm
N.A.I.C.S.: 523999
Thomas J. Maloney (Chm & CEO)
Vineet Pruthi (Sr Mng Dir)
Michael J. Lyons (Pres)
Thomas R. Callahan (Mng Dir)
George J. Henry (Mng Dir)
Pieter Kodde (Mng Dir)
James McLaughlin (Mng Dir)
Kevin A. Nappi (Controller)
Philip Kim (Co-Mng Partner)
Ottavio Serena di Lapigio (Mng Dir)
Phil Jakeway (Mng Dir)
Ottavio Serena di Lapigio (Mng Dir & Mng Dir)

Subsidiaries:

Aerosim, Inc. (1)
351 Cliff Rd E, Burnsville, MN 55337
Tel.: (952) 894-4694
Web Site: http://www.aerosim.com
Pilot Training Services
N.A.I.C.S.: 611430
Phil Brown (VP-Aerosim Technologies)

Gordon Sign Co. (1)
2930 W 9th Ave, Denver, CO 80204-3713
Tel.: (303) 629-6121
Web Site: http://www.gordonsign.com
Sales Range: $25-49.9 Million
Custom Sign Mfr
N.A.I.C.S.: 339950
Harry Grass (Dir-Sls & Mktg)

Kathryn Beich Fundraising (1)
30 Greythorne Cir, Bloomington, IL 61704-2924 (100%)
Tel.: (309) 828-1311
Web Site: http://www.kathrynbeich.com
Sales Range: $25-49.9 Million
Fund Raising Candies & Products
N.A.I.C.S.: 561990

PADI (1)
30151 Tomas, Rancho Santa Margarita, CA 92688
Tel.: (949) 858-7234
Scuba Diving Training Services
N.A.I.C.S.: 611620
Drew Richardson (Pres & CEO)
Ashley Atkin (Mgr-ScubaEarth Community)
Mary Kaye Hester (Coord-Quality Mgmt & Instructor Dev)

Peripheral Computer Support, Inc. (1)
47951 Wessinghouse Dr, Fremont, CA 94539
Tel.: (510) 651-6077
Computer Peripheral Equipment
N.A.I.C.S.: 811210

Powerhouse Retail Services, LLC (1)
812 S Crowley Rd Ste A, Crowley, TX 76036
Tel.: (817) 297-8575
Web Site: https://www.powerhousenow.com
Facilities Services
N.A.I.C.S.: 561210

Subsidiary (Domestic):

Advanced Service Solutions, Inc. (2)
11 S 3rd St, Hammonton, NJ 08037-0573
Tel.: (888) 629-7569
Facility Maintenance Services
N.A.I.C.S.: 811490

Subsidiary (Domestic):

Totalfacility, Inc. (3)
500 Lapp Rd, Malvern, PA 19355
Tel.: (610) 251-9979
Janitorial Services
N.A.I.C.S.: 561720
Jahan Tavangar (CEO)

RNI-Dalbo (1)
244 West Hwy 40, Roosevelt, UT 84066
Tel.: (866) 478-6803
Web Site: http://www.dalboholdings.com
Industrial Equipment Rental Services
N.A.I.C.S.: 532490

LINCOLNVILLE TELEPHONE COMPANY
133 Back Meadow Rd, Nobleboro, ME 04555
Tel.: (207) 763-9911
Web Site: http://www.lintelco.net
Rev.: $11,000,000
Emp.: 45
Provider of Telephone Communication Services
N.A.I.C.S.: 517121
Shirley Manning (Pres & Gen Mgr)

LINCOLNWAY ENERGY, LLC
59511 W Lincoln Hwy, Nevada, IA 50201
Tel.: (515) 232-1010 IA
Web Site: http://www.lincolnwayenergy.com
Year Founded: 2004
Rev.: $171,986,079
Assets: $72,859,336
Liabilities: $33,639,747
Net Worth: $39,219,589
Earnings: $6,649,221
Emp.: 38
Fiscal Year-end: 09/30/21
Methanol Mfr
N.A.I.C.S.: 325193
Jeff Taylor (Chm)
William Couser (Vice Chm)
Richard Vaughan (Treas)
Kay Gammon (Office Mgr)
Brenda Duppong (Mgr-Lab)
Chris Cleveland (Plant Mgr)
Jeff Kistner (Interim CFO)
Catherine Rogers (Accountant-Grain)
Seth Harder (Pres & CEO)
Lisa Hedstrom (Controller)
Zach Ziesman (Mgr-Ops)
John Schmitz (Mgr-Maintenance)

LIND MARINE, INC.
300 East D St, Petaluma, CA 94952
Tel.: (707) 762-7251 CA
Web Site: http://www.lindmarine.com
Year Founded: 1909
Mfg Prepared Feeds Heavy Construction
N.A.I.C.S.: 311119
Christian Lind (Owner & VP)

Subsidiaries:

Moose Boats, Inc. (1)
1175 Nimitz Ave Ste 115, Petaluma, CA 94592
Tel.: (707) 778-9828
Web Site: http://www.mooseboats.com
Trade Contractor
N.A.I.C.S.: 238990

LINDAL CEDAR HOMES, INC.
6840 Fort Dent Way Ste 220, Seattle, WA 98188
Tel.: (206) 725-0900 DE
Web Site: http://www.lindal.com
Year Founded: 1945
Sales Range: $25-49.9 Million
Emp.: 140
Custom Cedar Home & Sunroom Mfr
N.A.I.C.S.: 321992
David Nixon (VP-Mfg & Pur)
Sig Benson (VP-Mktg)
Bob Lindal (Pres & CEO)
Christina Lindal (Exec VP)

Subsidiaries:

Lindal Building Products (1)
11596 Water Tank Rd, Burlington, WA 98233 (100%)
Tel.: (360) 757-6616
Web Site: http://www.lindal.com
Rev.: $4,900,000
Emp.: 120
Mfr & Distribution of Wood Framed Windows & Glass Products
N.A.I.C.S.: 321992
Dave Nixon (Gen Mgr)

Lindal Cedar Homes, Inc. (1)
10880 Dyke Rd, Surrey, V3V 7P4, BC, Canada (100%)
Tel.: (604) 580-1191
Web Site: http://www.lindal.com
Sales Range: $10-24.9 Million
Emp.: 2
N.A.I.C.S.: 321992

Seattle Cedar Homes (1)
4300 S 104th Pl, Seattle, WA 98178
Tel.: (206) 725-7111
Web Site: http://www.lindal.com
Emp.: 40
Real Estate Manangement Services
N.A.I.C.S.: 236115
Bob Lindal (Pres)

LINDAU CHEMICALS INC.
731 Rosewood Dr, Columbia, SC 29201
Tel.: (803) 799-6863
Web Site: http://www.lindau.net
Sales Range: $10-24.9 Million
Emp.: 50
Mfr of Industrial Organic Chemicals
N.A.I.C.S.: 325199
Myrtle Robinson (Mgr-Lab)
John Ernst (Mgr-QC & Tech Svcs)
Bill Cranford (Pres)
Bobby Wilkinson (Mgr-Sls)
Tim Robinson (VP)

LINDE CORPORATION
118 Armstrong Rd, Pittston, PA 18640
Tel.: (570) 253-2643 PA
Web Site: http://www.lindeco.com
Year Founded: 1965
Engineering & Construction Services
N.A.I.C.S.: 237990
Scott F. Linde (Pres)
Robert L. Hessling (Treas & Controller)
Christopher A. Langel (Exec VP)
Robert McGraw (VP-Civil, Mechanical & Electrical Div)
Paul Fedor (VP-Maintenance)
Pat Acker (Sr Project Mgr)
Mike Bochnovich (Sr Project Mgr-Project Dev)
Dave Remley (Mgr-Engrg)
Fred Ostroski (Mgr-Pipeline Div)

LINDELL PROPERTIES, INC.
4401 W Kennedy Blvd Ste 100, Tampa, FL 33609
Tel.: (813) 286-3800
Web Site: http://www.lindellproperties.com
Property Development & Financial Services
N.A.I.C.S.: 237210

LINDEN LLC
150 N Riverside Plz Ste 5100, Chicago, IL 60606
Tel.: (312) 506-5600 DE
Web Site: http://www.lindenllc.com
Year Founded: 2004
Equity Investment Firm
N.A.I.C.S.: 523999
Eric C. Larson (Founder, Chm & Mng Partner)
Anthony B. Davis (Co-Founder, Pres & Mng Partner)
Brian C. Miller (Co-Founder & Mng Partner)
Michael P. Watts (Partner)
Gary A. Kagan (Operating Partner)
Chris M. Kolber (Operating Partner)
Douglass W. VanDegrift (CFO & Chief Compliance Officer)
Mark T. Sullivan (Partner-Human Capital)
Ron Labrum (Operating Partner)
Ernest Waaser (Operating Partner)
Michael Farah (Partner)
Kam Shah (Partner)

LINDEN LLC

Linden LLC—(Continued)
Piyush Shukla (Partner)
Michael Bernard (VP)
Prab Crawla (VP)
Aakash Madhu (VP)
Joshua Reilly (VP)

Subsidiaries:

Aspirion Health Resources, LLC (1)
1506 6th Ave Ste 3, Columbus, GA 31901
Tel.: (706) 660-5536
Web Site: http://www.aspirionhealth.com
Reimbursement Revenue Services
N.A.I.C.S.: 524298
Jason Erdell (CEO)
Steven Filchock (CTO)
Daria Cruzen (Sr VP-Fin)

Subsidiary (Domestic):

Liberty Billing & Consulting Services,
Inc. (2)
1320 Rte 23, Wayne, NJ 07470
Tel.: (973) 872-1497
Web Site: http://www.libertybilling.com
Accounting Services
N.A.I.C.S.: 541219
Ellen Tabor (Pres)
Rosemarie Polkowski (Dir-Staff Ops)
Jeri Nardiello (Mgr-Medicare & Medicaid)
Gina Roselli (Mgr-Comml Accts)
Stephen E. Tabor (Co-Founder & Exec VP)

Hycor Biomedical, Inc. (1)
7272 Chapman Ave, Garden Grove, CA 92841
Tel.: (714) 933-3000
Web Site: http://www.hycorbiomedical.com
Sales Range: $10-24.9 Million
Medical Diagnostic Products Mfr, Developer & Marketer
N.A.I.C.S.: 325412
Richard Hockins (Sr VP-Comml Ops)
Victor Miller (CFO)
Eric Whitters (COO)

Subsidiary (Non-US):

Hycor Biomedical GmbH (2)
Otto-Hahn-Strasse 16, 34123, Kassel, Germany
Tel.: (49) 561959350
Web Site: http://www.hycorbiomedical.com
Medical Diagnostic Product Mfr
N.A.I.C.S.: 325412

Pinnacle Treatment Centers (1)
1317 Route 73 Ste 200, Mount Laurel, NJ 08054
Tel.: (856) 439-6111
Web Site: http://www.pinnacletreatment.com
Offices of Other Health Practitioners
N.A.I.C.S.: 621399
Joseph Pritchard (CEO)
Brian Thorn (COO)
Eric Mollman (CFO)
Geoffrey Wade (Chief Dev Officer)
John Henry (CMO)
Tina Adams-Salter (Chief Compliance Officer)

LINDEN STREET CAPITAL CORP.
4010 Pilot Dr Ste 103, Memphis, TN 38118
Tel.: (901) 794-8431 MS
Web Site: http://www.ffcfuelcells.com
Sales Range: $10-24.9 Million
Emp.: 50
Aircraft Maintenance & Repair Services
N.A.I.C.S.: 488190
George M. Murphree (Pres & CEO)
Fred Tavoletti (Pres & CEO)
Kevin Brewer (Dir-Sls & Mktg)
Ray Bergin (CFO & Controller)

Subsidiaries:

FFC Services Inc. (1)
4010 Pilot Dr Ste 103, Memphis, TN 38118
Tel.: (901) 794-8431
Web Site: http://www.ffcservices.aero
Rev.: $2,800,000
Emp.: 45

Aircraft Maintenance & Repair Distr
N.A.I.C.S.: 488190
Fred Tavoleti (Pres)

LINDENGROVE, INC.
13700 W National Ave, New Berlin, WI 53151
Tel.: (262) 797-4600 WI
Web Site: http://www.lindengrove.org
Year Founded: 1986
Sales Range: $25-49.9 Million
Emp.: 1,382
Health Care Srvices
N.A.I.C.S.: 621498
Mark V. Sperka (CFO & VP)
Cynthia Benson (Dir-Clinical)
Kareen Schmidtknecht (Dir-Pharmacy)
Robert J. Schaefer (Pres & CEO)

LINDER & ASSOCIATES, INC.
840 N Main St, Wichita, KS 67203-3605
Tel.: (316) 265-1616 KS
Web Site: http://www.linderandassociates.com
Year Founded: 1954
Sales Range: $75-99.9 Million
Emp.: 80
Provider of Electrical Contracting Services
N.A.I.C.S.: 238210
Bill Quaney (Pres)
Russ Wedel (Exec VP)

LINDER'S FURNITURE, INC.
12821 Knott St, Garden Grove, CA 92841
Tel.: (714) 657-7599
Year Founded: 1980
Sales Range: $75-99.9 Million
Furniture Retailer
N.A.I.C.S.: 449110
Philip Linder (Owner & CEO)
Eric Foucrier (Pres)

LINDQUIST FORD INC.
3950 Middle Rd, Bettendorf, IA 52722
Tel.: (563) 449-9001 IA
Web Site: http://www.lindquistford.com
Year Founded: 1959
Sales Range: $25-49.9 Million
Emp.: 150
New & Used Automobiles
N.A.I.C.S.: 441110
Steve Lindquist (Principal)
Glenn Seemayer (Mgr-Sls)
Gretchen Holtz (Coord-Svcs)
Lisa Honeycutt (Coord-Internet Sls)
Luke Jewell (Mgr-Bus)
Lenore Littig (Coord-Svc Appointment)
Harley Wray (Coord-Svc Appt)
Joni Lindle (Dir-Internet)
Craig Miller (Gen Mgr)
Keith Blum (Mgr-Detail)
Aaron Mielke (Mgr-Fin)
Jeremy Troutwine (Mgr-HR)

LINDQUIST MACHINE CORPORATION
610 Baeten Rd, Green Bay, WI 54304
Tel.: (920) 713-4100
Web Site: http://www.lmc-corp.com
Sales Range: $25-49.9 Million
Emp.: 100
Machine & Other Job Shop Work
N.A.I.C.S.: 332710
Janalee Wetzel (Controller)
Larry Burger (Mgr-Quality)
Terry Eiting (Coord-Throughput)
Dan De Bauche (Engr-Mfg)

LINDQUIST STEELS INCORPORATED
1050 Woodend Rd, Stratford, CT 06615
Tel.: (203) 377-2828 CT
Web Site: http://www.lindquiststeels.com
Year Founded: 1944
Sales Range: $10-24.9 Million
Emp.: 22
Provider of Steel Cutting Tools
N.A.I.C.S.: 423510
Richard M. Hoyt (Chm & CEO)
Charlene Lebo (Exec VP)

LINDSAY CADILLAC COMPANY
1525 Kenwood Ave, Alexandria, VA 22302
Tel.: (703) 998-6600
Web Site: http://www.elindsay.com
Rev.: $73,819,865
Emp.: 200
New & Used Automobiles
N.A.I.C.S.: 441110
Kim Mosley (Mgr-Fin)
Charles T. Lindsay Jr. (Pres)

LINDSAY CHEVROLET LLC
15605 Jefferson Davis Hwy, Woodbridge, VA 22191
Tel.: (703) 670-8181
Web Site: http://www.elindsaychevrolet.com
Rev.: $29,800,000
Emp.: 100
Automobiles, New & Used
N.A.I.C.S.: 441110
Chris Lindsay (Pres)
John Smallwood (Controller)
Ariel Sandy (Dir-Fin)

LINDSAY FORD, LLC
11250 Veirs Mill Rd, Wheaton, MD 20902
Tel.: (301) 949-4060
Web Site: http://www.elindsayfordofwheaton.com
Sales Range: $50-74.9 Million
Emp.: 125
Automobiles, New & Used
N.A.I.C.S.: 441110
John Smallwood (CEO)
Lora Jessee Ferguson (Office Mgr)

LINDSAY MANUFACTURING INC.
3 Darr Pk, Ponca City, OK 74601
Tel.: (800) 546-3729 OK
Web Site: http://www.lindsaymfg.com
Year Founded: 1956
Built-In Central Vacuum Systems Mfr
N.A.I.C.S.: 335210
Winston S. Lindsay III (CEO)

LINDSTROM AIR CONDITIONING & PLUMBING, INC.
3581 W McNab Rd, Pompano Beach, FL 33069
Tel.: (954) 420-5300
Web Site: http://www.lindstromair.com
Year Founded: 1975
Sales Range: $10-24.9 Million
Emp.: 101
Plumbing Services
N.A.I.C.S.: 238220
Joseph Canosa (Gen Mgr)
Jeff Lindstrom (Pres)
Andre Green (Office Mgr-Svc)
Bob Barron (Mgr-Retail Svc)
Budd Suffoletta (Mgr-Retail Svc)
Chris Adanti (Mgr-Ops)
Craig Sanscrainte (Mgr-Construction)

U.S. PRIVATE

Frank Palmero (Mgr-Plumbing)
Jeff Haines (Mgr-Construction Field)
Lisa Nelson (Mgr-Accounts Payable)

LINDY OFFICE PRODUCTS, INC.
1247 W Grove Ave, Orange, CA 92865-4135
Tel.: (714) 921-5600
Web Site: http://www.lindyop.com
Sales Range: $10-24.9 Million
Emp.: 30
Commercial Office Products Supplier
N.A.I.C.S.: 459410
Nancy Lindauer (Pres)
Norman Lindauer (Exec VP)
Jesse Kuhn (Acct Mgr)

LINDY SPRINGS
115 NW Van Buren St, Topeka, KS 66603
Tel.: (785) 234-5551
Web Site: http://www.lindyspring.com
Rev.: $10,000,000
Emp.: 50
Water Softeners
N.A.I.C.S.: 423720
John G. Levin (Pres)

LINE SYSTEMS, INC.
1645 W Chester Pike Ste 200, West Chester, PA 19382
Tel.: (610) 690-2100
Web Site: http://www.linesystems.com
Year Founded: 1999
Sales Range: $10-24.9 Million
Emp.: 100
Telecommunication & Data Products
N.A.I.C.S.: 517810
John West (VP-Fin)
Warren Reyburn (Exec VP)
Bruce Wirt (VP-Sls & Mktg)
Jace Harris (Mgr-Channel Partner-Atlanta)

LINEA PELLE, INC.
2222 Barry Ave, Los Angeles, CA 90064
Tel.: (310) 231-9950
Web Site: http://www.lineapelle.com
Sales Range: $25-49.9 Million
Emp.: 35
Mfr of Belting Leather & Sheepskin Garments
N.A.I.C.S.: 316110
Andrew Cotton (VP & Dir-Creative)

LINEAGE FINANCIAL NETWORK, INC.
188 Frnt St Ste 166-96, Franklin, TN 37064
Tel.: (615) 308-6241 TN
Financial Services
N.A.I.C.S.: 523999
Richard Herrington (Chm & CEO)
Kevin Herrington (Pres & COO)

LINEAR INDUSTRIES LTD.
1850 Enterprise Way, Monrovia, CA 91016
Tel.: (626) 303-1130
Web Site: http://www.linearindustries.com
Rev.: $10,800,000
Emp.: 57
Electronic & Mechanical Motion Control Products Whslr
N.A.I.C.S.: 423840
Anthony D. Angelica (Pres)
Christina Carrillo (Mgr-Pur)
Jean Cade (CFO)
John Cheney (Mgr-Mfg CNC Dept)

LINEAR LIGHTING CORPORATION

COMPANIES

3130 Huntersspoint Ave, Long Island City, NY 11101
Tel.: (718) 361-7552
Web Site:
 http://www.linearlighting.com
Year Founded: 1969
Sales Range: $10-24.9 Million
Emp.: 160
Mfr of Commercial Lighting Fixtures
N.A.I.C.S.: 335132
Lois Shorr *(Controller)*

LINETT & HARRISON
219 Changebridge Rd, Montville, NJ 07045
Tel.: (908) 686-0606   NJ
Web Site:
 http://www.linettandharrison.com
Year Founded: 1989
Sales Range: $1-9.9 Million
Emp.: 10
Advertising Services
N.A.I.C.S.: 541810
Sam Harrison *(Partner)*
Diane Ahle *(Dir-Recruitment Adv)*

LINGER LONGER DEVELOPMENT COMPANY
100 Linger Longer Rd, Greensboro, GA 30642
Tel.: (706) 467-3151   GA
Web Site:
 http://www.reynoldsplantation.com
Sales Range: $75-99.9 Million
Emp.: 800
Residential Housing & Golf Course Developer
N.A.I.C.S.: 237210
Jamie Reynolds *(Vice Chm)*
Mercer Reynolds *(Chm & CEO)*
Rabun Neal *(Pres/CEO-Reynolds Plantation)*

LINGLE BROS COFFEE INC.
6500 Garfield Ave, Bell, CA 90201
Tel.: (562) 927-3317
Rev.: $10,000,000
Emp.: 30
Coffee Roasting (Except By Wholesale Grocers)
N.A.I.C.S.: 311920
James Lingle *(Pres)*

LINGNER GROUP PRODUCTIONS, INC.
429 N Pennsylvania St Ste 200, Indianapolis, IN 46204
Tel.: (317) 631-2500
Web Site: http://www.lgpinc.com
Year Founded: 1989
Sales Range: $1-9.9 Million
Emp.: 20
Television Production
N.A.I.C.S.: 512110
Terry Lingner *(CEO)*

LINGO MANAGEMENT, LLC
5607 Glenridge Dr Ste 300, Atlanta, GA 30342
Tel.: (888) 445-4646   GA
Web Site: http://www.lingo.com
Year Founded: 2004
Digital Telecommunications Services
N.A.I.C.S.: 517121
Michael Nowlan *(CEO)*

Subsidiaries:

BullsEye Telecom Inc.   (1)
25925 Telegraph Rd Ste 210, Southfield, MI 48033-2527
Tel.: (248) 784-2500
Web Site: http://www.bullseyetelecom.com
Sales Range: $10-24.9 Million
Emp.: 107
Data & Voice Telephone Communication Services
N.A.I.C.S.: 517121

Tom Tisko *(Pres & CEO)*
Rosemary Albanese *(VP-Support Svcs)*
David Bailey *(VP-Corp Dev)*
Brian Babich *(VP-Channel Sls)*
Chris Otenbaker *(VP-Corp Accts)*
Kate Young *(Mgr-Channel-Texas)*
Douglas Black *(VP-Ops)*

Subsidiary (Domestic):

Bandwave Systems, LLC   (2)
438 High St, Burlington, NJ 08016
Web Site:
 http://www.bandwavesystems.com
Information Services
N.A.I.C.S.: 519290
Tom Azelby *(Mng Partner)*

LINGO STAFFING, INC.
263 Wardswoth Dr N, Chesterfield, VA 23236
Tel.: (804) 594-6667
Web Site: http://lingostaffing.com
Year Founded: 2009
Staffing & Recruitment Services
N.A.I.C.S.: 561311
Brad Gillespie *(Founder & Pres)*
Derek Pittak *(CEO)*

Subsidiaries:

Flex-Team Inc.   (1)
753 W Waterloo Rd, Akron, OH 44314
Tel.: (330) 745-3838
Web Site: http://www.flexteaminc.com
Rev.: $30,000,000
Emp.: 10
Temporary Help Service
N.A.I.C.S.: 561320
Rick Pollock *(Pres)*

LINGUALINX INC.
Hedley Park Pl, Troy, NY 12180
Tel.: (518) 388-9000
Web Site: http://www.lingualinx.com
Year Founded: 2002
Translation, Interpretation, Website Localization & Voice-Over Recording Services
N.A.I.C.S.: 541930
David Smith *(Pres)*
Jonathan Smith *(COO)*
Jim Maziejka *(Dir-Sls)*
Charlotte Knoll *(Dir-Admin)*
Bill Kelts *(Engr-Process)*

Subsidiaries:

Language Translation Inc.   (1)
4379 30th St Ste 7, San Diego, CA 92104
Tel.: (619) 400-4502
Web Site:
 http://www.languagetranslation.com
Translation & Interpretation Services
N.A.I.C.S.: 541930
Harold Nevin *(Gen Mgr)*

LINHART PUBLIC RELATIONS, LLP
3858 Walnut St, Denver, CO 80205
Tel.: (303) 620-9044
Web Site: http://www.linhartpr.com
Year Founded: 1996
Sales Range: $1-9.9 Million
Emp.: 30
Public Relations Agency
N.A.I.C.S.: 541820
Sharon Haley Linhart *(Founder)*
Kelly Janhunen *(Partner & VP)*
Paul Raab *(Mng Partner)*
Kelly Womer *(Partner & Sr VP)*
Carri Clemens *(CFO & Partner)*
Amanda Meyer *(Acct Dir)*
Ashley Campbell *(Dir-Acct)*
Danielle Davis *(Dir-Acct)*
Emma Garten *(Sr Acct Exec)*
Jake Kubie *(Sr Acct Exec)*
Geoff Renstrom *(Sr Acct Exec)*
Dani Row *(Acct Exec)*
Jennifer Tilliss *(Acct Supvr)*

Robin Zimmerman *(Sr Acct Exec)*
Kelly Nash *(Sr Acct Exec)*
Tassi Herrick *(Acct Supvr)*

LINK AMERICA INC.
3002 Century Dr, Rowlett, TX 75088
Tel.: (972) 463-0050
Web Site: http://www.linkam.com
Year Founded: 1994
Sales Range: $25-49.9 Million
Emp.: 25
Telecommunication Equipment, Warehouse Management, Engineering & Integration Services
N.A.I.C.S.: 517810
Andres Ruzo *(CEO)*
Richard D. Spence *(CFO)*

LINK COMPUTER CORPORATION
Stadium Dr PO Box 250, Bellwood, PA 16617
Tel.: (814) 742-7700
Web Site: http://www.linkcorp.com
Year Founded: 1980
Sales Range: $25-49.9 Million
Emp.: 90
Computers, Peripherals & Software
N.A.I.C.S.: 423430
Timothy Link *(Owner)*
Art Sutherland *(Controller)*
Jack Collins *(CEO)*

LINK CONSTRUCTION GROUP, INC.
5350 NW 77th Ct, Doral, FL 33166
Tel.: (305) 665-9826
Web Site:
 http://www.linkconstructiongroup.net
Year Founded: 2001
Sales Range: $50-74.9 Million
Emp.: 74
Residential Remodeler
N.A.I.C.S.: 236118
Guillermo Fernandez *(Owner & Pres)*
Mike Quesada *(VP-Construction)*

LINK ELECTRIC & SAFETY CONTROL CO.
444 McNally Dr, Nashville, TN 37211
Tel.: (615) 833-4168
Web Site: http://www.linkelectric.com
Rev.: $18,000,000
Emp.: 47
Environmental Controls
N.A.I.C.S.: 334512
Thomas W. Sellers *(VP)*
Don Denning *(VP-Ops)*
James G. Barrett III *(Pres)*

LINK ENGINEERING COMPANY
43855 Plymouth Oaks Blvd, Plymouth, MI 48170
Tel.: (734) 453-0800
Web Site: http://www.linkeng.com
Rev.: $19,700,000
Emp.: 143
Physical Property Testing Equipment
N.A.I.C.S.: 334519
Roy H. Link *(Chm & CEO)*
Jo Dillard *(Mgr-Acctg)*
Matthew Link *(Pres)*
Tim Duncan *(Exec VP)*

LINK MANUFACTURING LTD.
223 15th St NE, Sioux Center, IA 51250
Tel.: (712) 722-4874
Web Site: http://www.linkmfg.com
Sales Range: $10-24.9 Million
Emp.: 118
Motor Vehicle Parts & Accessories
N.A.I.C.S.: 336390
Jim Huls *(Pres)*
Bill Ott *(VP-Engrg)*

LINK TECHNOLOGIES

Michael Hof *(VP-Bus Dev)*
Dean Koele *(Dir-IT)*
Jeff Vierkant *(VP-Mfg)*
Mike Leakey *(VP-Sls & Mktg)*
Greg Hulstein *(Dir-Engrg)*
Joel Van Den Brink *(Mgr-Engrg)*

LINK SNACKS, INC.
1 Snack Food Ln, Minong, WI 54859
Tel.: (715) 466-2234   WI
Web Site: http://www.jacklinks.com
Year Founded: 1987
Beef Jerky & Other Meat Snacks Mfr & Distr
N.A.I.C.S.: 311612
Troy Link *(Pres & CEO)*
Jeff LeFever *(VP-Mktg)*
John Hermeier *(CFO)*
Michael McDonald *(Exec VP-Sls)*
Cherie Coenen *(Dir-HR)*
Amanda Zajac *(Mgr-HR)*
Nate Springer *(Dir-Sls-Convenience Stores Market)*
Allen McGillvrey *(Dir-IT)*
Tom Dixon *(CMO)*
Kevin McAdams *(Pres-North America)*

Subsidiaries:

Link Snacks, Inc. - Ansbach Plant   (1)
Eyber Strasse 81, 91522, Ansbach, Germany
Tel.: (49) 98118010
Sales Range: $150-199.9 Million
Emp.: 600
Beef Jerky, Sausage Products & Baked Snack Products Mfr
N.A.I.C.S.: 311612
Alfred Gehr *(Gen Mgr)*

LINK SOLUTIONS, INC.
8251 Greensboro Dr Ste 800, Reston, VA 20191
Tel.: (703) 707-6256
Web Site: http://www.linksol-inc.com
Year Founded: 2006
Sales Range: $1-9.9 Million
Emp.: 65
Information Technology & Management Consulting to the Federal Government
N.A.I.C.S.: 519290
Bhupesh Wadhawan *(Founder & CEO)*
David C. Thornton *(CFO)*
Kylene Jennings *(Mgr-Recruiting)*

LINK STAFFING SERVICES, INC.
1800 Bering Dr Ste 800, Houston, TX 77057
Tel.: (713) 784-4400
Web Site: http://www.linkstaffing.com
Year Founded: 1980
Sales Range: $75-99.9 Million
Emp.: 65
Staffing Services
N.A.I.C.S.: 561311
Bill Pitts *(Founder & CEO)*
Keith Dalhover *(Mgr-Mktg)*
Gary Valentine *(COO & VP)*
Kathryn Mujezinovic *(VP-Franchise Sls)*
Michelle Bearden *(Chief Risk Officer & VP)*
Reed Garner *(CIO)*
Marc Rosenow *(Pres)*

LINK TECHNOLOGIES
9500 Hillwood Dr Ste 112, Las Vegas, NV 89134
Tel.: (702) 233-8703   NV
Web Site:
 http://www.linktechconsulting.com
Year Founded: 2000
Sales Range: $1-9.9 Million

LINK TECHNOLOGIES

Link Technologies—(Continued)
Emp.: 65
Engineering & Information Technology Services
N.A.I.C.S.: 541330
Ted Harrison *(Dir-Fin)*
Debbie Banko *(CEO)*
Virgil Rochester *(CIO)*
Lindsay Banko-Castro *(Dir-Corp Comm)*

LINK-SYSTEMS INTERNATIONAL, INC.
4515 George Rd Ste 340, Tampa, FL 33634
Tel.: (813) 674-0660   FL
Web Site: http://www.link-systems.com
Year Founded: 1995
Sales Range: $1-9.9 Million
Emp.: 150
Education Software Developer
N.A.I.C.S.: 513210
Vincent T. Forese *(Pres & CEO)*
Emil Moskona *(COO & Sr VP)*
Yanmu Zhou *(CTO & Sr VP)*
William Barter *(Chief Product Officer & Sr VP)*
Milena Moskova *(VP-R&D)*
Chris Bergeron *(VP-Strategy & Innovation)*
Trey Bruns *(Reg Mgr-Sls-South & Central)*
Richard Meade *(VP & Gen Mgr)*
Joseph Bower *(VP-Customer Svcs)*
Douglas J. DiNardo *(VP-Sls & Mktg)*
David Littlehale *(VP-Bus Dev)*
Jeff Huettman *(VP-Product)*

LINKEDGE TECHNOLOGIES, INC.
2731 S Alameda St, Los Angeles, CA 90051
Tel.: (818) 700-2920
Web Site: http://www.linkedge.com
Year Founded: 1998
Sales Range: $1-9.9 Million
Emp.: 20
IT Services
N.A.I.C.S.: 541519
Renu Chopra *(Pres)*
Subsidiaries:
LinkEdge Technologies, Inc.   (1)
Plot No 63 Sector 18, Gurgaon, 122015, Haryana, India
Tel.: (91) 1244751920
Web Site: http://www.linkedge.com
Custom Software Development, IT Staffing, Mobile Apps & Issue Management
N.A.I.C.S.: 541519

LINKLINE COMMUNICATIONS INC.
302 S Milliken Ave Ste G1, Ontario, CA 91761
Tel.: (909) 972-7000
Web Site: http://www.linkline.com
Rev.: $10,000,000
Emp.: 30
Internet Connectivity Services
N.A.I.C.S.: 517810
Holly Ortiz *(Mgr-Sls)*

LINKMEDIA 360
2 Summit Park Dr Ste 630, Independence, OH 44131
Tel.: (216) 447-9400
Web Site:
http://www.linkmedia360.com
Year Founded: 2004
Rev.: $12,000,000
Emp.: 16
Co-op Advertising, Financial, Health Care, Internet/Web Design, Strategic Planning/Research, T.V., Telemarketing, Travel & Tourism, Yellow Pages Advertising

N.A.I.C.S.: 541810
David Wolf *(Mng Partner)*
Betty Brown *(Pres)*
Cindy Adamek *(VP-Res)*
J.K. Smith *(Mgr-Bus Dev)*
Marcie Sprosty *(Sr VP)*
Renae Dabney *(Sr VP)*
Todd Hall *(Acct Dir)*
Kurt Krejny *(VP-Mktg)*
Matt Mesenger *(Dir-Digital Mktg Strategy)*

LINKOUS CONSTRUCTION COMPANY, INC.
1661 Aaron Brenner Dr Ste 207, Memphis, TN 38120
Tel.: (901) 754-0700   TN
Web Site:
http://www.linkousconstruction.com
Year Founded: 1975
Sales Range: $75-99.9 Million
Emp.: 75
Provider of Contracting & Construction Services
N.A.I.C.S.: 236220
Rusty Linkous *(Pres)*
Mike Brewer *(Exec VP)*
Steve Haynes *(Controller & Dir-Safety)*
Terry McClure *(Mgr-Field Ops)*
Tom Harmon *(Project Mgr)*
Jamie Linkous *(Dir-Bus Dev)*
Perry Miller *(Dir-Ops)*
Kevin Scott *(Project Mgr)*
Brandon Speakman *(Project Mgr)*

LINKS FREIGHT MANAGEMENT LLC
2245 Colex Dr, Grand Junction, CO 81505-1021
Tel.: (970) 255-8100
Web Site:
http://www.linkslogistics.com
Sales Range: $10-24.9 Million
Emp.: 65
Local Trucking
N.A.I.C.S.: 484110
Janet Williams *(Co-Owner)*
Jared Williams *(Co-Owner)*

LINKSCORP LLC
500 Skokie Blvd Ste 444, Northbrook, IL 60062-2867
Tel.: (847) 405-6700   DE
Year Founded: 1991
Sales Range: $25-49.9 Million
Emp.: 1,000
Owns & Operates Golf Club
N.A.I.C.S.: 713910
Leonard Batterson *(Gen Partner)*

LINKTECH WORLDWIDE
8484 Wilshire Blvd Ste 630, Beverly Hills, CA 90211
Tel.: (310) 601-4229
Web Site:
http://www.linktechworldwide.com
Year Founded: 2004
Sales Range: $1-9.9 Million
Emp.: 150
Marketing & Fulfillment Services
N.A.I.C.S.: 541613
Jeffrey Essebag *(CEO)*
Telly Kanakis *(CFO)*
Christopher Cruz *(Mgr-Mktg)*

LINKVISUM CONSULTING GROUP
8260 Greensboro Dr Ste 120, McLean, VA 22102
Tel.: (703) 442-4575
Web Site: http://www.linkvisum.com
Year Founded: 2007
Sales Range: $10-24.9 Million
Emp.: 12

Management Consulting for Government Agencies & Private Industry
N.A.I.C.S.: 541611
Richard Paden *(Dir-Bus Dev)*

LINN AREA CREDIT UNION
3015 Blairs Ferry Rd NE, Cedar Rapids, IA 52402
Tel.: (319) 892-7300   IA
Web Site: http://www.linnareacu.org
Year Founded: 1935
Rev.: $24,012,925
Assets: $476,017,535
Liabilities: $434,807,693
Net Worth: $41,209,842
Earnings: $3,253,480
Emp.: 117
Fiscal Year-end: 12/31/18
Credit Union Operator
N.A.I.C.S.: 522130
Joan Auterman *(Vice Chm & Officer-Membership)*
Margaret Eichorn *(CFO)*
Joyce Fowler *(Chm)*

LINN COOPERATIVE OIL COMPANY
325 35th St, Marion, IA 52302
Tel.: (800) 728-4881
Web Site: http://www.linncoop.com
Year Founded: 1930
Sales Range: $1-9.9 Million
Grain & Field Beans Farming Services
N.A.I.C.S.: 111998
Rob Ball *(Gen Mgr)*
Daryl Sackett *(Mgr-Car Care Center)*
Tracy Peyton *(Branch Mgr-Springville)*
Matt Becker *(Branch Mgr-Newhall)*
Kirk Sauer *(Branch Mgr-Alburnett)*
Mike Arnold *(Mgr-Credit)*
Brad Salazar *(Mgr-Lawn Care)*
Danielle Mikkola *(Mgr-HR)*
Dale Lefebure *(Pres-Fairfax)*
Joe Meythaler *(VP-Marion)*
John N. Airy *(Treas & Sec)*

LINN COUNTY RURAL ELECTRIC COOPERATIVE ASSOCIATION
5695 Rec Dr, Marion, IA 52302
Tel.: (319) 377-1587   IA
Web Site:
http://www.linncountyrec.com
Year Founded: 1938
Sales Range: $50-74.9 Million
Emp.: 63
Electric Power Distr
N.A.I.C.S.: 221122
Roger Krug *(Asst Sec)*
Kenny Squires *(Sec)*
Ronald O'Neil *(VP)*
Gary Schropp *(Pres)*
Kirk Hiland *(Treas)*

LINN ENTERPRISES INC.
1789 Woodlane Dr Ste A, Woodbury, MN 55125
Tel.: (651) 731-0515
Web Site: http://www.thelinnco.com
Sales Range: $10-24.9 Million
Emp.: 200
Convenience Stores; Independent
N.A.I.C.S.: 445131
Stephen Linn *(CEO)*
Jeffery Linn *(VP)*
Amy Dumonceaux *(Mgr-HR)*

LINN PAPER STOCK COMPANY
10710 Otter Creek E Blvd Ste 200, Mabelvale, AR 72103
Tel.: (501) 455-5275
Web Site: http://www.linnpaper.com
Rev.: $14,414,861

Emp.: 10
Waste Paper & Plastic Brokerage & Recycling Services
N.A.I.C.S.: 423930
Quinton Linn *(Pres & CEO)*

LINN PRODUCTS, INC.
1200 Lipsey Dr, Charlotte, MI 48813-8729
Tel.: (517) 543-1820   MI
Web Site: http://www.linnproducts.net
Year Founded: 1979
Sales Range: $10-24.9 Million
Emp.: 130
Producer of Aluminum
N.A.I.C.S.: 331318
Brian Palmer *(Engr-Design)*
Joseph Kolwick *(Gen Mgr)*
Kevin McCarthy *(Controller)*
Denise A. Hummel *(Mgr-HR)*

LINOMA SOFTWARE
1409 Silver St, Ashland, NE 68003
Tel.: (402) 944-4242
Web Site:
http://www.goanywheremft.com
Year Founded: 1994
Sales Range: $1-9.9 Million
Emp.: 25
Developer of Secure File Transfer & Encryption Software Suites (GoAnywhere) for Clients
N.A.I.C.S.: 513210
Brian Pick *(VP-Sls)*
Justin Phipps *(Mgr-Mktg)*
Bob Luebbe *(Pres)*

LINON HOME DECOR PRODUCTS INC.
22 Jericho Tpke, Mineola, NY 11501
Tel.: (516) 699-1000   NY
Web Site: http://www.linon.com
Year Founded: 1991
Sales Range: $50-74.9 Million
Emp.: 35
Sales of Home Furnishings
N.A.I.C.S.: 423220
Alex Vasilakis *(VP-Fin)*
Ed Olson *(Mgr-Mdse)*
Patricia Bulerin *(Mgr-Mdse)*
Akis Voreadis *(Mgr-Shipping)*

LINPEPCO PARTNERSHIP
1901 Windhoek Dr, Lincoln, NE 68512-1269
Tel.: (402) 423-7330
Web Site: http://www.linpepco.com
Sales Range: $25-49.9 Million
Emp.: 285
Beverage Bottling Services
N.A.I.C.S.: 312112
Jen Pfeifer *(Mgr-HR)*
Tony Hulbert *(CFO)*
Steve Ford *(Mgr)*

LINQ SERVICES
6679 Santa Barbara Rd Ste D, Elkridge, MD 21075
Web Site:
http://www.linqservices.com
Year Founded: 2006
Sales Range: $25-49.9 Million
Emp.: 20
Represents Businesses in Dealing with Cellular Providers
N.A.I.C.S.: 561499
Kevin Lowe *(Pres)*

LINROC COMMUNITY SERVICE CORPORATION
Linden Blvd AT Brookdale PLZ, Brooklyn, NY 11212
Tel.: (718) 240-5200   NY
Year Founded: 1985
Sales Range: $75-99.9 Million

Business Management & Administrative Services
N.A.I.C.S.: 561110
James R. Porter (CFO)
Mark E. Toney (Pres & CEO)
Steven R. Korf (COO)
Arthur J. Fried (Asst Sec)

LINSALATA CAPITAL PARTNERS, INC.
5900 Landerbrook Dr Ste 280, Mayfield Heights, OH 44124
Tel.: (440) 684-1400
Web Site:
 http://www.linsalatacapital.com
Year Founded: 1984
Rev.: $25,000,000,000
Emp.: 25
Privater Equity Firm
N.A.I.C.S.: 523999
Frank N. Linsalata (Chm)
Stephen B. Perry (Co-Pres)
Eric V. Bacon (Co-Pres)
Daniel L. DeSantis (Mng Dir)
Timothy G. Healy (VP)
Gregory L. Taber (Sr Mng Dir)
Murad A. Beg (Mng Dir)
Kurtis P. Zabell (Chief Compliance Officer & VP-Fin)
Jeffrey S. Wahl (Mng Dir & Operating Partner)

Subsidiaries:

Eatem Corp. (1)
1829 Gallagher Dr, Vineland, NJ 08360
Tel.: (856) 692-1663
Web Site: http://www.eatemfoods.com
Food Additives Mfr
N.A.I.C.S.: 311999
Danine Freeman (Mgr-Site)
John Randazzi (CTO-Flavor Chemist)

Harden Manufacturing Corp. (1)
7155 State Hwy 13, Haleyville, AL 35565-3028
Tel.: (205) 486-7872
Web Site: http://www.hardenmfg.com
Sales Range: $200-249.9 Million
Mfr of Wood Household Furniture
N.A.I.C.S.: 337122

Manhattan Beachwear, LLC (1)
10700 Vly View St, Cypress, CA 90630
Tel.: (714) 892-7354
Web Site: http://www.mbwswim.com
Sales Range: $1-9.9 Million
Women's Swimwear & Beachwear Mfr & Retailer
N.A.I.C.S.: 315210
Brenda West (Pres)
Kevin F. Mahoney (CEO)

Paradigm Packaging, Inc. (1)
141 N 5th st, Saddle Brook, NJ 07663
Tel.: (201) 507-0900
Web Site:
 http://www.paradigmpackaging.com
Mfr Plastics Containers
N.A.I.C.S.: 326199
Robert Donnahoo (Pres)

Ring & Pinion Service Inc. (1)
10411 Airport Rd, Everett, WA 98204
Tel.: (425) 347-1199
Web Site: http://www.ringpinion.com
Automotive Repair Services
N.A.I.C.S.: 811114
Michael Naish (Sls Dir)
Andrew Delapenha (Acct Mgr-Sls-Natl)
Carson Swink (Acct Mgr-Sls)
Jeremy Little (Acct Mgr-Sls)
Jonathan Brower (Acct Dir-Natl)
Chris Anderson (Coord-Natl Accts)
Allen Booher (Mgr-Major Accts)
Blue Tipton (Mgr-Major Accts)
Brian Anderson (Mgr-Major Accts)
Joe Rankin (Mgr-Major Accts)
Tate Hudson (Mgr-Major Accts)

LINTEL INC.
196 N Forest Ave, Hartwell, GA 30643-1589
Tel.: (706) 376-4701   GA
Web Site: http://www.hartcom.net
Year Founded: 1991
Sales Range: $10-24.9 Million
Emp.: 50
Provider of Telephone Communications
N.A.I.C.S.: 517121
Randy Daniel (Pres)
Melissa Green (Controller)

Subsidiaries:

Hart Cable, Inc. (1)
196 N Forest Ave, Hartwell, GA 30643
Tel.: (706) 856-2288
Cable & Wiring Installation Services
N.A.I.C.S.: 238210
Randy Daniel (Pres)

Hart Communications Inc. (1)
196 N Forest Ave, Hartwell, GA 30643-1589
Tel.: (706) 376-5101
Internet Services
N.A.I.C.S.: 449210
Wyndee McKinnon (Mgr-Customer Svc)

Hart Telephone Company Inc. (1)
350 W Franklin St, Hartwell, GA 30643-1589
Tel.: (706) 376-4701
Web Site: http://www.htconline.net
Telephone Communication Except Radio Services
N.A.I.C.S.: 517121
J. Lee Barton (Owner)

LINTEX CO. INC.
295 5th Ave Ste 1705, New York, NY 10016
Tel.: (212) 679-8046
Web Site: http://www.estala.com
Rev.: $12,000,000
Emp.: 14
Mfr of Table Cloths
N.A.I.C.S.: 313210

LINTHICUM CORPORATION
18940 N Pima Rd Ste 150, Scottsdale, AZ 85255
Tel.: (480) 515-1700   AZ
Web Site:
 http://www.linthicumcorp.com
Year Founded: 1988
Sales Range: $10-24.9 Million
Emp.: 30
Holding Company; Commercial & Custom Residential Construction Services
N.A.I.C.S.: 551112
Eric R. Linthicum (Pres)

Subsidiaries:

Linthicum Custom Builders, LLC (1)
2222 W Pinnacle Peak Rd Ste 220, Phoenix, AZ 85027
Tel.: (623) 207-5200
Web Site: http://www.linthicumcorp.com
Custom Residential Housing Construction Services
N.A.I.C.S.: 236115

LINTON SUPPLY CO.
455 S Absaroka St, Powell, WY 82435
Tel.: (307) 754-9521
Web Site: http://www.lintonsbigr.com
Rev.: $11,676,707
Emp.: 25
Feed & Farm Supply
N.A.I.C.S.: 459999
James A. Linton (Pres & CEO)

LINUS CADILLAC BUICK GMC
1401 Us Hwy 1, Vero Beach, FL 32960
Tel.: (772) 617-4791
Web Site:
 http://www.cadillacbuickverobeach.com
Sales Range: $10-24.9 Million
Emp.: 50
New Car Dealers
N.A.I.C.S.: 441110
Casper Maier (Mgr-Sls)

LINX COMMUNICATIONS CORP.
155 E Main St 2nd Fl, Smithtown, NY 11787-2808
Tel.: (631) 361-4400   NY
Web Site: http://www.linx.com
Year Founded: 1996
Sales Range: $10-24.9 Million
Emp.: 17
N.A.I.C.S.: 541810
Michael Smith (Pres & CEO)
Andrew Jacobs (Exec VP)
Randee Smith (Treas)
Debbie Allwin (Dir-Art)
Brad Isenbek (Partner & Architect-Sys)
Lawrence Lakis (Partner & COO)
David Amatulli (VP-Interactive Svcs)

LINX LLLP
9900 East 51st Ave, Denver, CO 80238
Tel.: (303) 574-1552
Web Site: http://www.teamlinx.com
Year Founded: 1952
Sales Range: $25-49.9 Million
Emp.: 158
Power & Communication System Service
N.A.I.C.S.: 237130
Erik Isernhagen (Pres)
Troy Brumley (Partner)
Dennis Mason (Partner)
Tom Berg (Sr Project Mgr)
Kevin Emery (Mgr-Construction)
Greg Rudnicki (VP-Sls)
Shane Hague (Sls Dir-LINX Wireless)
Ron Hardy (Pres-Security Solutions)

Subsidiaries:

Teknon Corporation (1)
15443 NE 95th St, Redmond, WA 98052-2548
Tel.: (425) 895-8535
Web Site: http://www.teknon.com
Sales Range: $10-24.9 Million
Emp.: 30
CCTV Surveillance Equipment
N.A.I.C.S.: 561621
Gordon Spencer (Pres & CFO)
Neal Stobaugh (COO)
Haris Suko (Mgr-Ops)

LINX PARTNERS, LLC
100 Galleria Pkwy Ste 1150, Atlanta, GA 30339-5948
Tel.: (770) 818-0335
Web Site:
 http://www.linxpartners.com
Year Founded: 1999
Investment Firm
N.A.I.C.S.: 525990
Peter Hicks (Founder & Mng Dir)
Melissa H. Nims (CFO & Chief Compliance Officer)
Barbara M. Henagan (Founder & Mng Dir)
Giny E. Mullins (Mng Dir)
Mark R. Niznik (Mng Dir)
David J. Sawyer (VP)

LINZER PRODUCTS CORP.
248 Wyandanch Ave, West Babylon, NY 11704
Tel.: (631) 253-3333   NY
Web Site:
 http://www.linzerproducts.com
Year Founded: 1892
Sales Range: $50-74.9 Million
Emp.: 100
Retailer of Paint Brushes, Rollers & Pad Painters
N.A.I.C.S.: 339994

Brent Swenson (Pres & COO)
Tony Hazantonis (Exec VP)
Ted Robinson (VP-Sls)

LION BRAND YARN COMPANY
135 Kero Rd, Carlstadt, NJ 07072
Tel.: (212) 243-8995
Web Site: http://www.lionbrand.com
Year Founded: 1878
Hand Knitting Yarn Mfr & Whslr
N.A.I.C.S.: 424990
David Blumenthal (Chm)
Dean Blumenthal (COO & Exec VP)
Ilana Rabinowitz (VP-Mktg)
Chris Mills (Pres & CEO)

LION COPOLYMER HOLDINGS, LLC
36191 Hwy 30, Geismar, LA 70734
Tel.: (225) 673-8871   DE
Web Site:
 http://www.lioncopolymer.com
Holding Company; Polymer Products Mfr
N.A.I.C.S.: 551112
Jesse Zeringue (Pres)

Subsidiaries:

Lion Copolymer Geismar, LLC (1)
36191 Hwy 30, Geismar, LA 70734
Tel.: (225) 673-8871
Web Site: http://www.lioncopolymer.com
Polymers Mfr
N.A.I.C.S.: 325211
Jesse Zeringue (Pres)

Lion Elastomers LLC (1)
1615 Main St, Port Neches, TX 77651-3039
Tel.: (409) 721-1604
Sales Range: $250-299.9 Million
Emp.: 250
Elastomer Products Mfr & Distr
N.A.I.C.S.: 325211
Ray Smith (Mgr-Maintenance)

LION EQUITY PARTNERS, LLC
3033 East First Ave Ste 501, Denver, CO 80206
Tel.: (303) 847-4100
Web Site: http://www.lionequity.com
Privater Equity Firm
N.A.I.C.S.: 523999
Ari J. Silverman (Co-Founder)
E. James Levitas (Co-Founder)

Subsidiaries:

Avi Lion Holdings LLC (1)
3033 E 1st Ave Ste 501, Denver, CO 80206
Tel.: (303) 847-4100
Privater Equity Firm
N.A.I.C.S.: 523999

NewPoint Media Group, LLC (1)
2305 Newpoint Pkwy, Lawrenceville, GA 30043-5530
Tel.: (770) 962-7220
Web Site:
 http://www.newpointmediagroup.com
Print & Digital Media Publisher
N.A.I.C.S.: 513140
Scott Dixon (CEO)
Adam Brown (Sr VP-Real Estate Book Div)
Edward Negron (VP-Interactive)
Andrew Mintz (VP-Mktg)
Jeff Bolte (Grp CIO)
Judy Bellack (Chief Revenue Officer)

Subsidiary (Domestic):

NewPoint Franchisor, LLC (2)
1830 E Park Ave, Tallahassee, FL 32301
Tel.: (850) 575-0189
Web Site: http://www.homesandland.com
Sales Range: $10-24.9 Million
Magazine Publisher
N.A.I.C.S.: 513120
Rob Wicker (CMO)

UE Compression, LLC (1)
9461 Willow Ct, Henderson, CO 80640
Tel.: (303) 297-8100

2463

LION EQUITY PARTNERS, LLC

Lion Equity Partners, LLC—(Continued)
Sales Range: $1-9.9 Million
Emp.: 38
Air & Gas Compressor Mfr
N.A.I.C.S.: 333912
John Vevurka (Pres)
G. Keith Kern (COO)
Jeffrey Loving (Chief Engr)

LION INDUSTRIES INC.
PO Box 1301, Verdi, NV 89439-1301
Tel.: (775) 345-1331
Web Site: http://www.smartlite.net
Residential Electric Lighting Fixture Mfr
N.A.I.C.S.: 335131
Candis Bohlool (Pres)

LION LAM DIAMOND CORP.
13007 Greenway Chase Ct, Houston, TX 77072
Tel.: (713) 828-8305
Year Founded: 2010
Sales Range: Less than $1 Million
Diamonds & Jewelry Retailer & Distr
N.A.I.C.S.: 423940
Cai Yu (Pres, CEO, CFO & Chief Acctg Officer)

LIONEL HENDERSON & CO., INC.
4827 Laguna Park Dr Ste 3, Elk Grove, CA 95758
Tel.: (916) 429-8601
Web Site: http://www.lhenderson.com
Year Founded: 1986
Sales Range: $10-24.9 Million
Emp.: 13
Corporate Support Services
N.A.I.C.S.: 561499
Lionel G. Henderson (Pres & CEO)
Sophy J. Chung (Sr VP)
Jeff Withrow (Mgr-Quality Assurance)

LIONEL LLC
6301 Performance Dr, Concord, MI 28027
Tel.: (586) 949-4100
Web Site: http://www.lionestore.com
Year Founded: 1900
Sales Range: $50-74.9 Million
Emp.: 100
Model Electric Trains & Accessories Mfr
N.A.I.C.S.: 339930
Scott Turkington (CFO)
Judith Munro (Mgr-Creative Svcs)
Bill Leto (Product Mgr)
Remy Convery (Product Mgr)

LIONHEART CAPITAL
4218 NE 2nd Ave 2nd Fl, Miami, FL 33137
Tel.: (305) 573-3900
Web Site: http://www.lheartcapital.com
Real Estate Investment Services
N.A.I.C.S.: 531210
Ophir Sternberg (Founder & CEO)
Ricardo Dunin (Partner)
John Petersen (Controller-Fin)
Jessica Wasserstrom (Gen Counsel)
Ashley Spitz (Dir-Mktg & Events)
Lowry Brescia (Dir-Strategic Initiatives)
Ashley Thornburg (Dir-Retail Ops)
Carlos Bueno (Dir-Construction)
Karla Rooks (Sr Project Mgr-Architecture)
Ben Dennis (Project Mgr)
Ophir Sternberg (Founder & CEO)

Subsidiaries:

Cigarette Racing Team, LLC (1)
4355 NW 128th St, Miami, FL 33054
Tel.: (305) 931-4564
Web Site: http://www.cigaretteracing.com
Sales Range: $1-9.9 Million
Emp.: 95
Boat Building
N.A.I.C.S.: 336612
Skip Braver (Owner)

LIONHEART VENTURES
130 Keystone Dr, Montgomeryville, PA 18936
Tel.: (215) 283-8400
Web Site: http://www.lionheartventures.com
Privater Equity Firm
N.A.I.C.S.: 523999
David S. Bovenizer (CEO)
Vanessa H. Mai (Founding Partner & Dir-Mktg)
Patrick R. Laphen (Exec VP-Corp Dev)

Subsidiaries:

A-1 Machining Company (1)
235 John Downey Dr, New Britain, CT 06051
Tel.: (860) 223-6420
Web Site: http://www.a1machining.com
Sales Range: $1-9.9 Million
Emp.: 60
Aerospace Component Mfr
N.A.I.C.S.: 332721
Steve Davis (VP)
Thomas V. Daily (Pres)
Richard McMahon (Dir-Quality)

Selas Heat Technology Company LLC (1)
11012 Aurora Hudson Rd, Streetsboro, OH 44241
Tel.: (216) 662-8800
Web Site: http://www.selas.com
Sales Range: $25-49.9 Million
Emp.: 50
Combustion & Thermal Processing Equipment Mfr
N.A.I.C.S.: 333248
David S. Bovenizer (CEO)
Vanessa Mai (Exec VP & Mgr-Mktg)
Tiwari K. K. (Pres & COO)
Michael Damsell (Gen Mgr-Europe & Asia)
Jeff Malarik (VP-Sls & Mktg)

Subsidiary (Domestic):

Ensign Ribbon Burners, LLC (2)
101 Secor Ln, Pelham Manor, NY 10803
Tel.: (914) 738-0600
Web Site: http://www.erbensign.com
Sales Range: $10-24.9 Million
Emp.: 25
Combustion Equipment Mfr
N.A.I.C.S.: 333414
Mario Anelich (Dir-Sls & Tech Svcs)
John F. Cavallo (Pres)

Subsidiary (Non-US):

Maxsys Fuel Systems Ltd. (2)
3 & 4 Conwy House St Georges Court, Donnington, Telford, TF2 7BF, Shropshire, United Kingdom
Tel.: (44) 1952 619539
Web Site: http://www.maxsysltd.com
Combustion Equipment Mfr
N.A.I.C.S.: 333248
Vanessa Landreau (Mgr-Mktg)

Nippon Selas Co., Ltd. (2)
6-1 Machiya 6-chome, Arakawa-ku, Tokyo, 116 0001, Japan
Tel.: (81) 356922525
Web Site: http://www.selas.co.jp
Engineering, Designing, Manufacturing & Marketing of Industrial Furnaces, Heat Process Systems & Accessories
N.A.I.C.S.: 333994
Yasushi Kuronuma (Pres)

Selas Waermetechnik GmbH (2)
Sand Str 59 West, Ratingen, 40878, Germany
Tel.: (49) 210240720
Web Site: http://www.selas.de
Sales Range: $10-24.9 Million
Emp.: 6
Mfr of Industrial Furnaces, Burners & Parts
N.A.I.C.S.: 333994

Subsidiary (Domestic):

Webster Engineering & Manufacturing Co., L.L.C. (2)
619 Industrial Rd, Winfield, KS 67156
Tel.: (620) 221-7464
Web Site: http://www.webster-engineering.com
Sales Range: $10-24.9 Million
Commercial & Industrial Burner Mfr
N.A.I.C.S.: 332410
Kk Tiwari (Pres)

LIONMARK INC.
1620 Woodson Rd, Saint Louis, MO 63114-6129
Tel.: (314) 991-2180
Web Site: http://paceconstructionstl.com
Year Founded: 1932
Sales Range: $50-74.9 Million
Emp.: 334
Highway & Street Construction
N.A.I.C.S.: 237310
Thomas Feldman Jr. (Pres)

Subsidiaries:

Missouri Petroleum Products Co., Inc. (1)
1620 Woodson Rd, Saint Louis, MO 63114-6129
Tel.: (314) 219-7305
Web Site: http://www.missouripetroleum.com
Sales Range: $10-24.9 Million
Emp.: 34
Roofing, Siding & Insulation
N.A.I.C.S.: 423330
Greg McMurtrey (Pres)

Pace Construction Company Inc. (1)
1620 Woodson Rd, Saint Louis, MO 63114-6129
Tel.: (314) 524-7223
Web Site: http://www.paceconstructionstl.com
Sales Range: $25-49.9 Million
Emp.: 180
Highway & Street Construction
N.A.I.C.S.: 237310
Philip Hocher (Pres)

LIONS EYE INSTITUTE FOR TRANSPLANT & RESEARCH, INC.
1410 N 21st St, Tampa, FL 33605
Tel.: (813) 289-1200
Web Site: http://www.lionseyeinstitute.org
Year Founded: 1973
Eye Bank; Ocular Research & Development
N.A.I.C.S.: 541715
Jason K. Woody (Pres & CEO)
Betty Viamontes (CFO)

LIONS QUICK MARTS INC.
1307 Woodman Rd, Janesville, WI 53545
Tel.: (608) 754-1159
Web Site: http://www.citgo.com
Rev.: $20,679,143
Emp.: 40
Convenience Store
N.A.I.C.S.: 445131
Roger Leonard (Gen Mgr)
Jim Johnson (Pres)

LIONTREE LLC
660 Madison Ave 15th Fl, New York, NY 10065
Tel.: (212) 644-4200
Web Site: http://www.liontreeadvisors.com
Year Founded: 2012
Investment Banking & Brokerage Services
N.A.I.C.S.: 523150

Aryeh Bourkoff (Co-Founder & CEO)
Ehren Stenzler (Co-Founder & Mng Partner)
Jill Bright (Chief Admin Officer)

Subsidiaries:

LionTree Advisors LLC (1)
660 Madison Ave 15th Fl, New York, NY 10065
Tel.: (212) 644-4200
Web Site: http://www.liontreeadvisors.com
Investment Banking & Brokerage Services
N.A.I.C.S.: 523150
Aryeh Bourkoff (CEO)
Ehren Stenzler (Mng Partner)

Tegris LLC (1)
Seagram Bldg 400 Park Ave Ste 1510, New York, NY 10022
Tel.: (212) 488-5320
Web Site: http://www.tegrisadvisors.com
Investment Banking Services
N.A.I.C.S.: 523150
Alysa Craig (Mng Dir)
David Riessner (Sr VP)
Jason White (Sr VP)
Rene-Pierre Azria (Founder, Pres & CEO)

LIPARI ENERGY, INC.
300 Liperote Way, London, KY 40741
Tel.: (606) 577-1800
Web Site: http://www.liparienergy.com
Year Founded: 2010
Sales Range: $75-99.9 Million
Thermal Coal Mining, Production & Other Related Services
N.A.I.C.S.: 212115
Richard Liperote (Pres)
Thomas Liperote (COO)
Scott Warren (CFO)

LIPENWALD INC.
22 S Smith St, Norwalk, CT 06855
Tel.: (203) 852-0001
Web Site: http://www.lipenwald.com
Rev.: $20,000,000
Emp.: 40
General Merchandise, Mail Order
N.A.I.C.S.: 459999
Bob King (Dir-Mktg)

LIPHAM CONSTRUCTION CO. INC.
400 N Broadway St, Aspermont, TX 79502
Tel.: (940) 989-3503
Web Site: http://www.lipham.net
Sales Range: $10-24.9 Million
Emp.: 55
Highway & Street Paving Contractor
N.A.I.C.S.: 237310
Chris Lipham (Pres)

LIPHART STEEL COMPANY INC.
3308 Rosedale Ave, Richmond, VA 23230
Tel.: (804) 355-7481
Web Site: http://www.liphartsteel.com
Rev.: $21,142,632
Emp.: 80
Structural Steel Fabrication
N.A.I.C.S.: 332312
Edwin C. Jennings (Pres)

LIPMAN & LIPMAN, INC.
315 E New Market Rd, Immokalee, FL 34142-3508
Tel.: (239) 657-4421
Web Site: http://www.lipmanproduce.com
Year Founded: 1947
Sales Range: $1-4.9 Billion
Emp.: 4,000
Holding Company; Produce Farming, Packing & Distribution
N.A.I.C.S.: 551112

COMPANIES

Kent Shoemaker *(Pres & CEO)*
Toby K. Purse *(COO & Chief Farming Officer)*

Subsidiaries:

Combs Produce Co., L.P. (1)
11990 Shiloh Rd, Dallas, TX 75228
Tel.: (214) 367-6500
Web Site: http://www.combsproduce.com
Produce Distr
N.A.I.C.S.: 424480
Brett Combs *(Gen Mgr)*

Farm-Op, Inc. (1)
315 E New Market Rd, Immokalee, FL 34142-3508
Tel.: (239) 657-4421
Web Site: http://www.lipmanfamilyfarms.com
Emp.: 100
Vegetable Melon & Potato Farming Services
N.A.I.C.S.: 111219
Kent Shoemaker *(CEO)*

Kuzzen's, Inc. (1)
315 E New Market Rd, Immokalee, FL 34142-3508
Tel.: (239) 657-4421
Web Site: http://www.lipmanproduce.com
Vegetable (except Potato) & Melon Farming
N.A.I.C.S.: 111219
Kent Shoemaker *(Pres & CEO)*

Lipman-Portland, LLC (1)
2872 NE 181st Ave, Portland, OR 97230
Tel.: (503) 234-0333
Web Site: http://www.lipmanproduce.com
Sales Range: $10-24.9 Million
Emp.: 100
Vegetable Packing & Distribution
N.A.I.C.S.: 115114
Michael Basley *(Gen Mgr)*
Kent Shoemaker *(CEO)*

Six L's Packing Company, Inc. (1)
315 E New Market Rd, Immokalee, FL 34142-3508
Tel.: (239) 657-4421
Web Site: http://www.lipmanfamilyfarms.com
Vegetable Melon & Potato Farming Services
N.A.I.C.S.: 424480
Kent Shoemaker *(CEO)*

The Produce Exchange, Inc. (1)
7407 Southfront Rd, Livermore, CA 94551
Tel.: (925) 454-8700
Web Site: http://www.tpeonline.com
Sales Range: $1-9.9 Million
Emp.: 300
Fruits & Vegetables Whslr
N.A.I.C.S.: 424480
Sam Jones *(Pres & VP-Sls)*
Marty Mazzanti *(Founder)*

The Thomas Colace Company, LLC (1)
800 Grove Rd, West Deptford, NJ 08086
Tel.: (856) 384-4980
Web Site: http://www.lipmanfamilyfarms.com
Sales Range: $10-24.9 Million
Emp.: 260
Vegetable Packing & Distribution
N.A.I.C.S.: 115114
Rick Saminara *(Office Mgr)*
Thomas Colace Jr. *(Gen Mgr)*

Western Repacking, LLLP (1)
2771 French Camp Rd, Manteca, CA 95336
Tel.: (916) 688-8443
Web Site: http://www.lipmanproduce.com
Sales Range: $10-24.9 Million
Emp.: 57
Vegetable Packaging & Distribution
N.A.I.C.S.: 115114
Jerry Just *(Gen Mgr)*

World Agriculture, Inc. (1)
315 E New Market Rd, Immokalee, FL 34142-3508
Tel.: (239) 657-6205
Web Site: http://www.lipmanproduce.com
Vegetable Farming
N.A.I.C.S.: 111219
Kent Shoemaker *(Pres & CEO)*

LIPMAN HEARNE, INC.
200 S Michigan Ave 16th Fl, Chicago, IL 60604-2423
Tel.: (312) 356-8000
Web Site: http://www.lipmanhearne.com
Year Founded: 1988
Sales Range: $10-24.9 Million
Emp.: 75
Public Relations Agency
N.A.I.C.S.: 541820
Donna Van De Water *(COO)*
Arnie Fishman *(Dir-Design)*
Libby Morse *(Sr VP & Dir-Creative)*
Sara Stern *(Exec VP-Philanthropic Mktg)*
Minesh Parikh *(Sr VP-Consulting & Acct Mgmt)*
Annette Stenner *(VP & Dir-Resource & Project Mgmt)*
Jeremy Ryan *(Exec VP-Creative & Digital Svcs)*
Peter Barber *(Exec VP-Bus & Acct Dev)*
Alexia Koelling *(Exec VP-Consulting & Acct Mgmt)*
Craig Turner *(Coord-Ops)*
Kevin Lyons *(Supvr-Res)*
Kirsten Fedderke *(VP)*
Matt Mefford *(Sr Dir-Digital Art)*
Darren Norkett *(CFO)*
Lewis T. Williams *(Chief Creative Officer & Exec VP)*

Subsidiaries:

Lipman Hearne, Inc. - Washington, DC (1)
1156 15th St NW Ste 800, Washington, DC 20005
Tel.: (202) 457-8100
Web Site: http://www.lipmanhearne.com
Sales Range: $10-24.9 Million
Emp.: 30
N.A.I.C.S.: 541810
Tom Abrahamson *(Chm)*
Robert Moore *(Pres & CEO)*
Donna Van De Water *(COO)*

LIPMAN SERVICES CORP.
408 W 14th St 3rd Fl, New York, NY 10014
Tel.: (212) 684-1100   NY
Web Site: http://www.lipman-nyc.com
Year Founded: 1943
Sales Range: $10-24.9 Million
Emp.: 80
Advetising Agency
N.A.I.C.S.: 541810
David Lipman *(Chm)*
Andrew Spellman *(CEO)*

LIPPER INTERNATIONAL INC.
235 Washington St, Wallingford, CT 06492
Tel.: (203) 269-8588
Web Site: http://www.lipperinternational.com
Sales Range: $10-24.9 Million
Emp.: 50
Homefurnishings
N.A.I.C.S.: 423220
Amy Lipper *(Pres & CEO)*

LIPPERT INCORPORATED
600 W 172nd St, South Holland, IL 60473
Tel.: (708) 333-6900
Sales Range: $10-24.9 Million
Emp.: 45
Restaurant Equipment & Supplies
N.A.I.C.S.: 423440
David Wax *(Pres)*
Dave Chestnut *(VP-Sls)*

LIPPES MATHIAS WEXLER FRIEDMAN LLP
50 Fountain Plz Ste 1700, Buffalo, NY 14203
Tel.: (716) 853-5100   NY
Web Site: http://www.lippes.com
Year Founded: 1995
Sales Range: $10-24.9 Million
Emp.: 56
Law firm
N.A.I.C.S.: 541110
Gerald S. Lippes *(Co-Founder & Sr Partner)*
Brendan J. Rich *(Partner)*
Thomas J. Gaffney *(Partner)*
Christian M. Lovelace *(Partner)*
Elizabeth L. Perry *(Partner-Trusts & Estates Practice Grp)*
Martin Doster *(COO & Sr Coord-Environmental)*
Jillian E. Deck *(Partner-Banking & Fin)*
Brendan H. Little *(Partner)*
Andrea H. HusVar *(Partner)*
Scott E. Friedman *(Chm & CEO)*
Jennifer Persico *(Partner)*
Paul Mitchell *(Partner & Atty)*
Amy Habib Rittling *(Partner)*
Paul Wells *(Partner)*
Brian Bocketti *(Partner)*
Thomas J. Keable *(Partner)*
Carol E. Heckman *(Partner)*
Raymond N. Fink *(Partner)*
John Mueller *(Partner)*
Eileen M. Martin *(Partner-Immigration Practice)*
Andrew M. Wilson *(Partner)*
Brigid Maloney *(Partner)*
Ian A. Shavitz *(Partner)*
Michael G. Rossetti *(Partner)*
Nisha V. Fontaine *(Partner)*
Sarah H. Brennan *(Partner)*
Eric M. Soehnlein *(Partner)*
Stacey L. Moar *(Partner)*
Vincent M. Miranda *(Partner)*
Alessandro A. Apolito *(Partner-Trusts & Estates Practice Grp)*
Daniel D. Akel *(Partner-Jacksonville)*
Edward C. Akel *(Partner-Jacksonville)*
Kathleen Holbrook Cold *(Partner-Jacksonville)*
Shannon M. Peabody *(Dir-Mktg-Southeast)*
Ryan V. Stearns *(Partner)*
Lauren A. Suttell *(Partner)*
William E. Mathias II *(Partner)*
Richard M. Scherer Jr. *(Partner)*
Scott S. Allen Jr. *(Partner)*

Subsidiaries:

Lippes Mathias Wexler Friedman LLP - Albany (1)
54 State St Ste 1001, Albany, NY 12207
Tel.: (518) 462-0110
Web Site: http://www.lippes.com
Emp.: 20
Law firm
N.A.I.C.S.: 541110
Lawrence Schaefer *(Partner)*
Keith Jacques *(Mng Partner)*
William F. Sheehan *(Partner)*
William P. Golderman *(Partner)*
Jennifer Persico *(Partner)*
Scott Friedman *(Chm & CEO)*
Kevin Cross *(Mng Partner)*
Jennifer Greene *(Dir-Mktg & Bus Dev)*
Paul Mitchell *(Partner)*
Amy Habib Rittling *(Partner)*
Brendan Rich *(Partner)*
Paul Wells *(Partner)*
Brian Bocketti *(Partner)*
Elizabeth Perry *(Partner)*
John J. Koeppel *(Partner)*
Sean M. O'Brien *(Assoc Atty)*
Thomas Keable *(Partner)*
Mark Davis *(Partner)*

LIPPI & CO. ADVERTISING
929 W Hill St, Charlotte, NC 28208-5325
Tel.: (704) 376-2001   NC
Year Founded: 1987
Sales Range: Less than $1 Million
Emp.: 4
N.A.I.C.S.: 541810
Larry Lippi *(Pres)*
Terri Simpkins *(COO)*
Josh Orenstein *(Dir-Art)*
Lauren Kaczmarski *(Dir-Art)*

LIPSCOMB OIL CO. INC.
1010 N Broadway St, Greenville, MS 38701-2004
Tel.: (662) 332-7500   TX
Year Founded: 1978
Sales Range: $25-49.9 Million
Emp.: 250
Gasoline Service Stations
N.A.I.C.S.: 457120
James H. Lipscomb III *(Pres)*

LIPTEN COMPANY LLC
28033 Center Oaks Ct, Wixom, MI 48393
Tel.: (248) 374-8910
Web Site: http://www.lipten.com
Sales Range: $10-24.9 Million
Emp.: 13
Turn Key Powerhouse Projects
N.A.I.C.S.: 423830
Frank Hrlic *(Dir-Procurement IT & Contract Mgmt)*
Mike Huntress *(Mgr-Engrg)*
John Ingraham *(VP-EPC Bus Dev)*
Jim Marshall *(Pres)*
Jim Spencer *(CEO)*

LIQUECOLOR INKJET GROUP
2108 Research Park Blvd, Norman, OK 73069
Tel.: (405) 360-5191   OK
Web Site: http://www.liquecolor.com
Year Founded: 2004
Sales Range: $1-9.9 Million
Emp.: 14
Remanufactures Wide-Format Inkjet Cartridges
N.A.I.C.S.: 325910
Kurt Williams *(Owner)*
Martin Rizzo *(Owner)*

LIQUID CRYSTAL RESOURCES
19011 Pickwick Ln, Glenview, IL 60026
Tel.: (847) 998-8580
Web Site: http://www.hallcrest.com
Year Founded: 1960
Sales Range: $10-24.9 Million
Emp.: 40
Color Change Temperature Indicators & Microencapsulation Application Mfr
N.A.I.C.S.: 334519
Rocco Sapienza *(CEO)*

Subsidiaries:

Thermographics, Inc. (1)
1911 Pickwick Ln, Glenview, IL 60026
Tel.: (847) 998-8580
Web Site: http://www.thermographics.com
Sales Range: $1-9.9 Million
Emp.: 8
Temperature Measuring Devices Mfr
N.A.I.C.S.: 334519
Rocco Sapienza *(CEO)*

LIQUID HOLDINGS GROUP, INC.
800 3rd Ave 38th Fl, New York, NY 10022
Tel.: (212) 293-1836   DE
Web Site: http://www.liquidholdings.com
Year Founded: 2012
Sales Range: $1-9.9 Million
Emp.: 48
Brokerage & Securities Software Publisher
N.A.I.C.S.: 513210

LIQUID HOLDINGS GROUP, INC.

U.S. PRIVATE

Liquid Holdings Group, Inc.—(Continued)
Peter R. Kent (CEO & CFO)

LIQUID INVESTMENTS, INC.
3840 Via De La Valle Ste 300, Del Mar, CA 92014
Tel.: (858) 509-8510   CA
Web Site: http://www.lqdinv.com
Year Founded: 1978
Sales Range: $125-149.9 Million
Emp.: 175
Holding Company
N.A.I.C.S.: 424810
Ronald L. Fowler (Chm & CEO)

Subsidiaries:

Mesa Beverage Co., Inc.   (1)
3200 N Laughlin Rd, Santa Rosa, CA 95403
Tel.: (707) 527-3900
Web Site: http://www.mesabeverage.com
Emp.: 122
Beverage Whslr
N.A.I.C.S.: 424820
Mark Herculson (Pres)
Tony Amaral (Gen Mgr-Sls)
Shane Hilkey (Mgr-Ops)
Sharon Fierro (Office Mgr)
Lisa Burleson (Mgr-HR)

LIQUID MOTORS INC.
1755 N Collins Blvd Ste 109, Richardson, TX 75080   DE
Web Site: http://www.liquidmotors.com
Year Founded: 2005
Sales Range: $1-9.9 Million
Emp.: 50
Internet Marketing Solutions
N.A.I.C.S.: 541511
Michael Daseke (Pres & CEO)
Mark Burack (Exec VP-Sls)
Greg Lubrani (COO)
Jill Givens (Dir-Mktg)
Keith Whetter (VP-Sls)
Don R. Daseke (Chm)

LIQUID RESINS INTERNATIONAL, LTD.
4295 N Holly Rd, Olney, IL 62450
Tel.: (618) 392-3590
Web Site: http://www.liquidresins.com
Sales Range: $10-24.9 Million
Emp.: 25
Windshield Repairer
N.A.I.C.S.: 811198
James Pottor (Pres)

LIQUID TECHNOLOGY INC.
15 W 26th St, New York, NY 10010
Tel.: (212) 679-2524   NY
Web Site: http://www.liquidtechnology.net
Year Founded: 2001
Sales Range: $1-9.9 Million
Emp.: 50
Computer Liquidation Services
N.A.I.C.S.: 423430
Stephen Sidwell (VP-Tech Svcs)
Rob Ruehle (VP-Sls)
Allison Macaluso (Mgr-HR)

LIQUID WEB, INC.
4210 S Creyts Rd, Lansing, MI 48917
Tel.: (517) 322-0434   MI
Web Site: http://www.liquidweb.com
Year Founded: 1997
Sales Range: $10-24.9 Million
Emp.: 200
Web Hosting & Data Center Infrastructure
N.A.I.C.S.: 517810
Terry Flood (CFO)
Bruce Kipperman (Head-Sls)
Dominic Miraglia (Head-Strategic Partners)
Jeff Uphues (Exec VP)

Jim Geiger (CEO)
Amar Patel (Head-Global Sls & Solutions)
Chris Lema (VP-Products & Innovations)
Joe Osterling (CTO)
Colin Dowling (VP-Channel Sls & Partner Solutions)

LIQUIDAGENTS HEALTHCARE, LLC
6900 Dallas Pkwy Ste 450, Plano, TX 75024
Tel.: (972) 543-5200
Web Site: http://www.liquidagents.com
Year Founded: 2000
Sales Range: $10-24.9 Million
Emp.: 167
Healthcare Staffing Services
N.A.I.C.S.: 621999
Sheldon Arora (CEO)
Jenny Hanlon (CFO)
Oren Lavi (Dir-Client Advisory)

LIQUIDHUB, INC.
500 E Swedesford Rd, Wayne, PA 19087
Tel.: (484) 654-1400
Web Site: http://www.liquidhub.com
Sales Range: $10-24.9 Million
Emp.: 300
Systems Integration
N.A.I.C.S.: 541512
Naresh Ramdas (Partner)
Raymond Bordogna (Partner & Chief Strategy Officer)
Peter Classon (Partner)
Scott Hofmann (Partner)
Jonathan A. Brassington (Co-Founder)
Matthew Bernardini (Partner)
Kristi Rose Barron (Dir-Panel Procurement)
Rahul Sahgal (Partner)
Suzanne Lentz (Partner)
Hank Summy (Partner)
Charlton Monsanto (Partner)
Michelle Berryman (Mng Dir-Strategy & Innovation)
Paul Zaengle (Partner)
Harold Hambrose (Partner)

Subsidiaries:

Electronic Ink   (1)
1 S Broad St Fl 19, Philadelphia, PA 19107
Tel.: (215) 922-3800
Web Site: http://www.electronicink.com
Rev.: $5,400,000
Emp.: 80
Data Processing, Hosting & Related Services
N.A.I.C.S.: 518210
Harold Hambrose (Founder & CEO)
Joe Weiss (Chm)
Blair Lyon (Exec VP-Strategy & Mktg)
Johanna Hambrose (Pres)
Caryn Polin (Exec VP-Delivery Ops)

LIQUIDUS MARKETING, INC.
200 W Jackson Blvd Ste 900, Chicago, IL 60606
Tel.: (312) 270-8716
Web Site: http://www.liquidus.net
Online Video Technology Services
N.A.I.C.S.: 516210
Todd Holmes (Founder & CEO)

Subsidiaries:

ShopLocal, LLC   (1)
225 N Michigan Ave Ste 1600, Chicago, IL 60601   **(100%)**
Tel.: (312) 270-8716
Web Site: http://www.shoplocal.com
Online Shopping & Advertising Services
N.A.I.C.S.: 541890

LIQUILUX GAS CORP.
PO Box 7144, Ponce, PR 00732
Tel.: (787) 842-3320
Rev.: $12,300,000
Emp.: 40
Petroleum Bulk Stations
N.A.I.C.S.: 424710
Angel Rivera (Pres)

LISA ELIA PUBLIC RELATIONS
1285 Barry Ave Ste 302, Los Angeles, CA 90025
Tel.: (310) 479-0216
Year Founded: 1998
Sales Range: Less than $1 Million
Emp.: 7
Advetising Agency
N.A.I.C.S.: 541810
Lisa Elia (Owner)

LISCIO'S ITALIAN BAKERY
128-130 S Delsea Dr, Glassboro, NJ 08028
Tel.: (856) 881-5300
Web Site: http://www.lisciosbakery.com
Year Founded: 1994
Sales Range: $10-24.9 Million
Emp.: 120
Baked Goods Mfr
N.A.I.C.S.: 311811
Charles L. Vilotti (VP)
James Liscio (Pres)

LISK TRUCKING INC.
Hwy 742 N, Wadesboro, NC 28170
Tel.: (704) 272-7641
Web Site: http://www.lisktrucking.com
Sales Range: $10-24.9 Million
Emp.: 125
Contract Haulers
N.A.I.C.S.: 484121
Bruce Lisk (Chm)
Stacie Stoker (Mgr-Parts)
Donnie Edwards (Mgr-Safety)

LISLE CORPORATION
807 E Main St PO Box 89, Clarinda, IA 51632
Tel.: (712) 542-5101
Web Site: http://www.lislecorp.com
Year Founded: 1903
Sales Range: $100-124.9 Million
Emp.: 300
Mfr of Garage Tools, Creepers, Drill Grinders, Magnetic Plugs & Chip Detectors
N.A.I.C.S.: 332216
Marty Williams (Treas & Controller)
Jon Bielfeldt (VP-Sls & Mktg)
Jeff Anderson (Mgr-Acctg)
Chris Fasnacht (Engr-Electrical)
Ron Jackson (Mgr-Sls)
Billy Rock (Asst Mgr-Sls-OEM Div & Mgr-Freight)
Mike Streebin (Mgr-OEM Div)

LIST INDUSTRIES, INC.
401 Jim Moran Blvd, Deerfield Beach, FL 33442-1707
Tel.: (954) 429-9155   IL
Web Site: http://www.listindustries.com
Year Founded: 1936
Sales Range: $10-24.9 Million
Emp.: 285
Lockers Mfr
N.A.I.C.S.: 337215
Heather Baginski (Mgr-Order Entry & Drafting)
Diego Betancur (Mgr-IT)
Tom Casey (VP-Sls)

LIST MANAGEMENT SERVICES, INC.
5728 Major Blvd Ste 200, Orlando, FL 32819
Tel.: (407) 876-5544
Web Site: http://www.lmsonline.com
Year Founded: 1994
Sales Range: $1-9.9 Million
Emp.: 30
Marketing Consulting Services
N.A.I.C.S.: 541613
Steve Cohen (Pres & CEO)
John Craig (COO)
Felix Torres (CTO)
Kristie Cohen (CFO)
Kevin Kulikowski (Dir-HR)
Tina Martinez (Exec Dir)
Trisha Mitchell (Art Dir)
Marisa Rubinger (Dir-Mktg & Program Mgmt)
Brad Cohen (Program Dir)

LIST SERVICES CORPORATION
6 Trowbridge Dr, Bethel, CT 06801
Tel.: (203) 743-2600
Web Site: http://www.listservices.com
Year Founded: 1980
Sales Range: $10-24.9 Million
Emp.: 150
Direct Mail Advertising & Marketing Services
N.A.I.C.S.: 541860
Malcolm McCluskey (Co-Founder & Pres)
Tina MacNicholl (VP-Bus Dev)

LIST SOLUTIONS, INC.
10045 Red Run Blvd Ste 140, Owings Mills, MD 21117
Tel.: (855) 545-0251   DE
Year Founded: 2013
List Management Services
N.A.I.C.S.: 513140
David Mathias (Sec)

LISTEN UP ESPANOL INC. (LUE)
50 Monument Sq Ste 300, Portland, ME 04101
Tel.: (207) 774-1425
Web Site: http://www.listenupespanol.com
Year Founded: 2006
Sales Range: $10-24.9 Million
Emp.: 500
Full-Service Spanish-Language Call Center
N.A.I.C.S.: 561499
Craig Handley (Co-Founder & CEO)
Anthony Ricciardi (Co-Founder & Pres)
Randall Anderson (COO)

LISTEN360, INC.
11625 Rainwater Dr Ste 645, Alpharetta, GA 30009
Tel.: (678) 352-3000
Web Site: http://www.listen360.com
Year Founded: 2007
Online Feedback Information Services
N.A.I.C.S.: 519290
Mariya Babaskina (Sr Dir-Mktg)

Subsidiaries:

Qiigo, Inc.   (1)
1080 Holcomb Bridge Rd Bldg 200 Ste 210, Roswell, GA 30076
Tel.: (404) 496-6841
Web Site: http://www.qiigo.com
Sales Range: $1-9.9 Million
Emp.: 23
General Marketing Services
N.A.I.C.S.: 541613
Kirk Bogue (VP-Bus Dev)

LISTENUP.COM
685 S Pearl St, Denver, CO 80209

COMPANIES

Tel.: (303) 778-0780
Web Site: http://www.listenup.com
Year Founded: 1972
Emp.: 125
High Fidelity Stereo Equipment & Electronic Devices
N.A.I.C.S.: 449210
Steve Weiner (Co-Founder)

LISTERHILL CREDIT UNION INC.
4790 E 2nd St, Muscle Shoals, AL 35661
Tel.: (256) 383-9204
Web Site: http://www.listerhill.com
Rev.: $21,800,000
Emp.: 138
Credit Union
N.A.I.C.S.: 522130
Brad Green (Pres)

LISTO CORPORATION INC.
1925 Union St, Alameda, CA 94501
Tel.: (510) 522-2910 CA
Web Site: http://www.listo.com
Year Founded: 1921
Sales Range: $1-9.9 Million
Emp.: 5
Marking Pencils & Carton Cutters, Razor Blades & Chalk Guard Chalk Holders, Felt Tip Markers, Eraser Holders & Pocket Magnets
N.A.I.C.S.: 339940
Rick Stuart (Pres)

LISTON BRICK COMPANY OF CORONA INC.
20401 Temescal Canyon Rd, Corona, CA 92883-4973
Tel.: (951) 277-4221
Year Founded: 1974
Rev.: $25,548,121
Emp.: 60
Secondary Nonferrous Metals
N.A.I.C.S.: 331314

Subsidiaries:
Labnac Inc. (1)
23720 Sunnymead Blvd, Moreno Valley, CA 92553-3022
Tel.: (951) 924-5391
Rev.: $460,000
Emp.: 6
Refuse System
N.A.I.C.S.: 562920

LISTRAK, INC.
529 E Main St, Lititz, PA 17543
Tel.: (717) 627-4528
Web Site: http://www.listrak.com
Year Founded: 1999
Sales Range: $1-9.9 Million
Emp.: 13
Email Marketing Software & Services
N.A.I.C.S.: 513210
Howard Kramer (Co-Founder & COO)
Ross Kramer (Co-Founder & CEO)
Heather Bonura (Dir-Brand Strategy)
Keith Brown (Dir-Pro Svcs)
Brent Shroyer (Product Mgr)
Mark Kolibas (VP-Sls)
Ben Smith (Pres)

LISY CORPORATION
3400 NW 67th St, Miami, FL 33147
Tel.: (305) 836-6001
Web Site: http://www.lisycorp.com
Rev.: $14,401,948
Emp.: 100
Spices & Seasonings
N.A.I.C.S.: 424490
Henry Rosen (Gen Mgr)
Josue Alejandro Ferret (Mgr-IT)
Kathy Palmer (Mgr-Pur)

LITANIA SPORTS GROUP, INC.
601 Mercury Dr, Champaign, IL 61822
Tel.: (217) 367-8438
Web Site: http://www.litaniasports.com
Sales Range: $10-24.9 Million
Emp.: 150
Athletic Equipment Mfr
N.A.I.C.S.: 339920
David Hodge (Pres & CEO)
Steve Vogelsang (VP-Sls & Mktg)
Mike Schendel (Mgr-Mfg)
Jay Norton (CFO)

Subsidiaries:
Gill Athletics, Inc. (1)
601 Mercury Dr, Champaign, IL 61822-9648
Tel.: (217) 367-8438
Web Site: http://www.gillathletics.com
Sales Range: $10-24.9 Million
Emp.: 60
Athletic Track & Field Equipment, Volleyball, Soccer & Weights Mfr & Distr
N.A.I.C.S.: 339920
David Hodge (CEO)

Porter Athletic Equipment Company (1)
601 Mercury Dr, Champaign, IL 61822-3857
Tel.: (888) 277-7778
Web Site: http://www.porterathletic.com
Emp.: 120
Sporting & Athletic Equipment Mfr
N.A.I.C.S.: 339920
David Hodge (Pres)

LITCHNEY LAW FIRM
2260 Douglas Blvd Ste 110, Roseville, CA 95661
Tel.: (916) 235-6979
Web Site: http://www.litchneylaw.com
Year Founded: 2007
Sales Range: $1-9.9 Million
Emp.: 30
Bankruptcy, Real Estate, Litigation, Estate Planning, Business Law & Intellectual Property Services
N.A.I.C.S.: 541110
Sarah Litchney (Founder & CEO)
Laurie Alexander (Dir-Estate Plng)
Jim Salter (Gen Counsel)
Ron Holland (Dir-Bankruptcy)

LITCO PETROLEUM INC.
223 Hwy 72 W, Corinth, MS 38834-5408
Tel.: (662) 287-1471 MS
Web Site: http://www.litcopetroleum.com
Year Founded: 1988
Sales Range: $25-49.9 Million
Emp.: 295
Provider of Gasoline Service Stations
N.A.I.C.S.: 457120
Taft Little (Pres)

Subsidiaries:
Best-Wade Petroleum Inc. (1)
201 Dodge Dr, Ripley, TN 38063
Tel.: (731) 635-9661
Web Site: http://www.bestwade.com
Rev.: $30,999,596
Emp.: 20
Distr of Petroleum Products
N.A.I.C.S.: 424710
John P. Wade (Pres)
John Helton (Mgr-Acctg)
Jeff Windham (Mgr-Sls)
Robert Stone (Mgr-Pur)

Branch (Domestic):
Best-Wade (2)
4000 Interstate 55, West Memphis, AR 72301
Tel.: (870) 735-2840
Sales Range: $25-49.9 Million
Emp.: 8
Distr of Petroleum Lubricating Oils & Specialty Products
N.A.I.C.S.: 424720
Charles Hyde (Gen Mgr)

LITECONTROL CORPORATION
100 Hawks Ave, Hanson, MA 02341-1960
Tel.: (781) 294-0164 MA
Web Site: http://www.litecontrol.com
Year Founded: 1936
Sales Range: $200-249.9 Million
Emp.: 220
Architectural Fluorescent Lighting Mfr
N.A.I.C.S.: 335132
Gaylene Basa (Coord-Billing & Commissions)
Lori Humphries (Mgr-Fin & Admin)
Gregory Banks (Mgr-Project Svcs)
Chuck Moylan (Mgr-Quality Assurance)
Jim Patnaude (Mgr-Sls-Central Reg)
Chris Hogan (VP-Brand Mgmt)
Jeff Schoepf (VP-Product Dev)
Vince Santini (VP-Sls)

LITEHOUSE FOODS, INC.
1109 N Ella Ave, Sandpoint, ID 83864
Tel.: (208) 263-7569
Web Site: http://www.litehousefoods.com
Year Founded: 1958
Sales Range: $50-74.9 Million
Emp.: 5,000
Dressings Salad: Raw & Refrigerated (Except Dry Mixes)
N.A.I.C.S.: 311941
Kelly Prior (Pres & CEO)
Brent Carr (Sr VP-Sls & Mktg)
Maria Emmer-Aanes (VP-Mktg & Comm)
Daren Parsons (VP-Retail Sls)
Robert Tyrrell (VP-Mfg)
Allen Wright (Vice Chm)
Edward W. Hawkins Jr. (Co-Founder)

LITEHOUSE PRODUCTS INC.
11052 Pearl Rd, Strongsville, OH 44136-3308
Tel.: (440) 238-7300 OH
Web Site: http://www.litehouse.com
Year Founded: 1967
Sales Range: $25-49.9 Million
Emp.: 150
Pools & Spas
N.A.I.C.S.: 423910
Chris Curcio (Owner & Pres)
Rich Thompson (VP-Sls & Retail)

LITELAB CORP.
251 Elm St, Buffalo, NY 14203
Tel.: (716) 856-4491
Web Site: http://www.litelab.com
Year Founded: 1972
Sales Range: $10-24.9 Million
Emp.: 100
Commercial Lighting Fixtures
N.A.I.C.S.: 335132
Frederick A. Spaulding (Chm & Pres)
Stacie Lutsic (Mgr-Matls)

LITERARY CLASSICS OF THE UNITED STATES, INC.
14 E 60th St, New York, NY 10022-1006
Tel.: (212) 308-3360
Web Site: http://www.loa.org
Year Founded: 1979
Sales Range: $10-24.9 Million
Emp.: 18
Publisher of Books
N.A.I.C.S.: 513130
Cheryl Hurley (Pres)
Dan Baker (CFO & VP)

LITERS QUARRY INC.
5918 Haunz Ln, Louisville, KY 40241
Tel.: (502) 241-7637 KY
Web Site: http://litersinc.com
Year Founded: 1942

LITHOGRAPHIX, INC.

Sales Range: $10-24.9 Million
Emp.: 15
Supplier of Construction & Commercial Grade Aggregates
N.A.I.C.S.: 212312
Robert T. Liter (Pres)
John Liter (VP)
Kevin Woosley (CFO)
Mary Hillebrand (Mgr-HR)

LITESTREAM HOLDINGS, LLC
PO Box 74628, Atlanta, GA 30374-6268
Web Site: http://www.litestream.net
Cable Television, Internet & Digital Telephone Services
N.A.I.C.S.: 517111
Paul Rhodes (CEO)

LITHIA FORD LINCOLN OF FRESNO
3247 E Annadale Ave, Fresno, CA 93725-1902
Tel.: (559) 486-2480
Sales Range: $10-24.9 Million
Emp.: 62
Car Whslr
N.A.I.C.S.: 441110
Mark Rapin (Gen Mgr & VP)
Robert Wilson (Pres)

LITHIA SUBARU OF FRESNO
5499 N Blackstone Ave, Fresno, CA 93710-5015
Tel.: (559) 438-6200
Web Site: http://www.lithiasubarufresno.com
Sales Range: $10-24.9 Million
Emp.: 65
Car Whslr
N.A.I.C.S.: 441110
Frank Perez (Gen Mgr)

LITHIUM EXPLORATION GROUP, INC.
4635 S Lakeshore Dr Ste 200, Tempe, AZ 85282-7127
Tel.: (480) 641-4790 NV
Web Site: http://www.lithiumexploration group.com
Year Founded: 2006
Assets: $837,708
Liabilities: $6,988,728
Net Worth: ($6,151,020)
Earnings: ($6,877,124)
Emp.: 2
Fiscal Year-end: 06/30/17
Lithium Exploration & Mining Services
N.A.I.C.S.: 212290
Alexander Richard Walsh (Pres, CEO, CFO, Treas & Sec)

LITHOGRAPHICS INC.
1835 Airlane Dr, Nashville, TN 37210
Tel.: (615) 889-1200
Web Site: http://lithographicsinc.com
Year Founded: 1974
Sales Range: $25-49.9 Million
Emp.: 200
Commercial Printing
N.A.I.C.S.: 323111
Dave Lindner (VP-Ops)
Judy Davies (VP-Fin)
Chris Nash (Plant Mgr)
Cindy Tanley (Mgr-Special Projects & Mktg)

LITHOGRAPHIX, INC.
12250 Crenshaw Blvd, Hawthorne, CA 90250-3332
Tel.: (323) 770-1000 CA
Web Site: http://www.lithographix.com
Year Founded: 1954
Sales Range: $100-124.9 Million
Emp.: 300

LITHOGRAPHIX, INC.

Lithographix, Inc.—(Continued)
Lithographic Printing Services
N.A.I.C.S.: 323111
Herbert Zebrack *(Pres)*
Victor Wolfe *(CFO)*
George Wolden *(VP-Mfg)*
Randy Parkes *(VP-Mktg)*
Jeff Young *(Exec VP-Sls)*
Layne Morey *(Exec VP-Sls)*

LITHOTONE INC.
1313 W Hively Ave, Elkhart, IN 46517
Tel.: (574) 294-5521
Web Site: http://www.lithotone.com
Sales Range: $10-24.9 Million
Emp.: 59
Lithographic Commercial Printing
N.A.I.C.S.: 323111
Al Fassler *(Dir-Pre-Press)*
Terri Garlat *(Mgr-Traffic)*

LITHOTYPE COMPANY, INC.
333 Point San Bruno Blvd, South San Francisco, CA 94080-4917
Tel.: (650) 871-1750   CA
Web Site: http://www.lithotype.com
Year Founded: 1938
Sales Range: $10-24.9 Million
Emp.: 50
Flexible Packaging Mfr
N.A.I.C.S.: 323111
Linda Sartori *(CFO)*
Bob Shoreen *(Sr VP-Sls)*
Athos Ikonomou *(Pres)*

Subsidiaries:

Lithotype Company, Inc. - Midwest Facility (1)
594 Territorial Dr Unit G, Bolingbrook, IL 60440
Tel.: (630) 771-1920
Web Site: http://www.lithotype.com
Emp.: 33
Commercial Printing Services
N.A.I.C.S.: 323111
Aphos Ikonomou *(Gen Mgr)*

LITIGATION SERVICES, LLC
3960 Howard Hughes Pkwy, Ste 700, Las Vegas, NV 89169
Tel.: (702) 314-7200   NV
Web Site: http://www.litigationservices.com
Year Founded: 1999
Sales Range: $10-24.9 Million
Emp.: 50
Consulting & Court Reporting Services
N.A.I.C.S.: 561492
Seth Hertin *(COO)*
Benjamin Ross *(Sr VP)*
Ali Rizvi *(CEO)*

Subsidiaries:

Kim Thayer & Associates (1)
1326 W Herndon Ave Ste 101, Fresno, CA 93711-7178
Tel.: (559) 221-9000
Web Site: http://www.thayerreporting.com
Court Reporting & Stenotype Services
N.A.I.C.S.: 561492
Kim Thayer *(Owner)*

Verbatim Reporting Services (1)
141 Stony Cir Ste 240, Santa Rosa, CA 95401-4179
Tel.: (707) 575-1819
Web Site: http://www.verbatimreporting.com
Court Reporting & Stenotype Services
N.A.I.C.S.: 561492

LITITZ MUTUAL INSURANCE COMPANY
2 N Broad St, Lititz, PA 17543-7007
Tel.: (717) 626-4751
Web Site: http://www.lititzmutual.com
Year Founded: 1888
Sales Range: $25-49.9 Million
Emp.: 80
Insurance Services
N.A.I.C.S.: 524126
Henry H. Gibbel *(Chm & CEO)*
Lydia Stephan *(VP-IS)*

Subsidiaries:

Livingston Mutual Insurance Company (1)
2 N Broad St, Lititz, PA 17543-7007
Tel.: (585) 335-3181
Web Site: http://www.livingstonmutual.com
Sales Range: Less than $1 Million
Emp.: 6
Insurance Services
N.A.I.C.S.: 524126

LITLAMP COMMUNICATIONS GROUP
444 N Michigan Ave 12th Fl, Chicago, IL 60611   IL
Web Site: http://www.litlamp.com
Year Founded: 1995
Public Relations Agency
N.A.I.C.S.: 541820
Amy Dean *(Dir-PR)*
Donna Shultz *(Project Mgr)*
Mark Hayward *(Designer)*
Patricia Martin *(CEO)*

LITTER INDUSTRIES INC.
524 Eastern Ave, Chillicothe, OH 45601-3471
Tel.: (740) 773-2196   OH
Web Site: http://www.litterpropane.com
Year Founded: 1987
Sales Range: $10-24.9 Million
Emp.: 15
Liquefied Petroleum Gas Dealers
N.A.I.C.S.: 457210
Matt Litter *(Pres-Ops)*

Subsidiaries:

Litter Quality Propane Company (1)
524 Eastern Ave, Chillicothe, OH 45601-3471   (100%)
Tel.: (740) 773-2196
Web Site: http://www.litterpropane.com
Emp.: 20
Liquefied Petroleum Gas Dealers
N.A.I.C.S.: 457210

LITTFIN LUMBER COMPANY
555 Baker Ave W PO Box 666, Winsted, MN 55395-7816
Tel.: (320) 485-3861   MN
Web Site: http://www.littfintruss.com
Year Founded: 1962
Sales Range: $25-49.9 Million
Emp.: 340
Mfr of Wooden Roof & Floor Trusses
N.A.I.C.S.: 321215
Jack Littfin *(Pres)*
Bob Mochinski *(Mgr-Sls & Mktg)*

LITTLE & COMPANY
920 2nd Ave S Ste 1400, Minneapolis, MN 55402
Tel.: (612) 375-0077
Web Site: http://littleco.com
Year Founded: 1979
Rev.: $13,000,000
Emp.: 37
N.A.I.C.S.: 541810
Doug Franzwa *(Dir-Fin & Admin)*
Molly Schwartz *(Mktg Mgr)*
Joe Cecere *(Pres & Chief Creative Officer)*
Mary Haugh *(VP-Strategy & Acct Mgmt)*
Kris O'Malley *(Acct Supvr)*

LITTLE BIG CAT, INC.
2461 W 205th St Ste B202, Torrance, CA 90501
Tel.: (310) 782-1200

Web Site: http://www.spiritessences.com
Sales Range: $1-9.9 Million
Animal Holistic Remedies Retailer
N.A.I.C.S.: 459910
Jean Hofve *(Co-Founder)*
Jackson Galaxy *(Co-Founder & Pres)*
Siena M. Lee-Tajiri *(COO)*
Debra May *(Mgr-Ops)*

LITTLE BROWNIE PROPERTIES INC.
1350 Sheeler Rd, Apopka, FL 32703
Tel.: (407) 886-3003
Sales Range: $10-24.9 Million
Emp.: 40
Trucking Company
N.A.I.C.S.: 424410
Diane Ludwig *(Pres)*
Bobby Roche *(Gen Mgr)*
John Paul Brown *(Asst Mgr)*
Peter Wood *(CFO)*

Subsidiaries:

Transystems Inc. (1)
1350 Sheeler Rd, Apopka, FL 32703
Tel.: (407) 886-3003
Web Site: http://www.go-tpc.com
Provider of Trucking Services
N.A.I.C.S.: 484121
Philip Walker *(VP)*

LITTLE CROW FOODS
201 S Detroit St, Warsaw, IN 46580
Tel.: (574) 267-7141
Web Site: http://www.littlecrowfoods.com
Year Founded: 1903
Sales Range: $75-99.9 Million
Emp.: 57
Grain Food Products Mfr
N.A.I.C.S.: 311824
Denny Fuller *(Pres)*
Kim Fuller *(Exec VP)*
Tom Lawrence *(VP & Mgr-Sls)*
Greg Dearborn *(VP-Admin & Mgr-Pur)*
Rich Utley *(VP & Mgr-Sls)*
Ron Shipley *(VP & Mgr-Ops)*
Ellen Hoffer *(Mgr-Customer Svc)*
Tamara Knisely *(Mgr-Customer Svc)*

LITTLE DIVERSIFIED ARCHITECTURAL CONSULTING, INC.
615 S College St Ste 1600, Charlotte, NC 28202
Tel.: (704) 525-6350   NC
Web Site: https://www.littleonline.com
Year Founded: 1966
Sales Range: $25-49.9 Million
Emp.: 300
Architectural Design & Engineering Services
N.A.I.C.S.: 541310
Gavin Myers *(Office Pres-Northern Virginia Office)*
Phil Kuttner *(CEO & Partner)*
John Komisin *(Chm, Pres, Partner & COO)*
Jim Williams *(Partner & Dir-Design-Natl)*
Carol Rickard-Brideau *(Partner)*
Phil Kuttner *(CEO & Partner)*
John Komisin *(Pres, Partner & COO)*
Tom Balke *(Partner & Principal-Schools Studio)*
Bruce Barteldt *(Partner)*
Robert Bishop *(Partner & Pres-Durham Office)*
Terry Bradshaw *(CFO)*
Thomas Carlson-Reddig *(Partner)*
Ruth Cline *(Partner & Principal-Interiors Studio)*
Michael Coates *(Partner & Dir-Design)*

U.S. PRIVATE

Nancy Everhart *(Partner & Principal-Svc Retail Studio)*
Jim Hair *(Partner & Pres-Orlando Office)*
Daniel Montano *(Partner & Creative Dir)*
Tim Morrison *(Partner & Principal-Supermarkets Studio)*
Eddie Portis *(Partner & Principal-Office Studio)*
Jeff Roark *(Partner & Principal-Corp Retail Studio)*
Doug Robidoux *(Partner & Pres-LA Office)*
Jim Thompson *(Partner & Dir-Design)*
Keth Turner *(Partner)*
John Walker *(Partner)*
Jim Williams *(Partner & Dir-Design-Natl)*
Carolyn Rickard-Brideau *(CEO & Partner)*
Charles Todd *(COO)*

Subsidiaries:

Hughes Group Architects, Inc. (1)
22630 Davis Dr, Sterling, VA 20164
Tel.: (703) 437-6600
Web Site: http://hgaarch.com
Rev.: $1,000,000
Emp.: 19
Architectural Services
N.A.I.C.S.: 541310
Amado Fernandez *(Principal)*
Eliel Alfon *(Principal)*
Wayne L. Huges *(Principal)*
Lynn Reeda *(Principal)*

LITTLE DOG AGENCY INC.
3850 Bessemer Rd Ste 220, Mount Pleasant, SC 29466
Tel.: (843) 856-9201
Web Site: http://www.littledogagency.com
Year Founded: 2005
Sales Range: Less than $1 Million
Emp.: 4
Advetising Agency
N.A.I.C.S.: 541810
Brent McKay *(Pres)*
Soraya McKay *(VP)*
Bonnie Schwartz *(Office Mgr)*

LITTLE FALLS ALLOYS, INC.
171-191 Caldwell Ave, Paterson, NJ 07501
Tel.: (973) 278-1666
Web Site: http://www.lfawire.com
Year Founded: 1943
Sales Range: $50-74.9 Million
Emp.: 28
Producer of Non-Ferrous Wire
N.A.I.C.S.: 331420
Jim Dolan *(Dir-Adv)*
Tara Cullen *(Mgr-Acctg)*

LITTLE FRIENDS, INC.
140 N Wright St, Naperville, IL 60540
Tel.: (630) 355-6533   IL
Web Site: http://www.littlefriendsinc.com
Year Founded: 1970
Sales Range: $10-24.9 Million
Emp.: 735
Developmental Disability Assistance Services
N.A.I.C.S.: 623210
Michael Boone *(VP-HR)*
Dan DeBruycker *(Mgr-Facilities)*
Camille Smith *(VP-School Programs)*
Sally Allred *(Dir-Health Svcs)*
Amanda Malley *(Dir-Programs & Svcs)*
Bob Hicks *(Dir-Programs & Svcs)*
Mike Briggs *(Pres & CEO)*

LITTLE GENERAL STORE, INC.

COMPANIES

PO Box 968, Beckley, WV 25802
Tel.: (304) 253-9592   WV
Web Site: http://www.lgstoreswv.com
Year Founded: 1975
Sales Range: $10-24.9 Million
Emp.: 25
Convenience Stores Owner & Operator
N.A.I.C.S.: 445131
Cory Beasley (CEO)
Vickie Utt (Office Mgr)
Greg Darby (Pres)

LITTLE LADY FOODS, INC.
2323 Pratt Blvd, Elk Grove Village, IL 60007-5918
Tel.: (847) 631-3500   IL
Web Site:
http://www.littleladyfoods.com
Year Founded: 1961
Sales Range: $100-124.9 Million
Emp.: 180
Producer of Food & Customized Food Items
N.A.I.C.S.: 311412
John T. Geocaris (Owner)
Dan Geocaris (Vice Chm)
Patrick Shanahan (Supvr-Production)
Sam Goldberg (Supvr-Warehouse)

LITTLE OCMULGEE ELECTRIC CORPORATION
163 W RailRd Ave, Alamo, GA 30411
Tel.: (912) 568-7171
Web Site:
http://www.littleocmulgeeelc.com
Sales Range: $10-24.9 Million
Emp.: 40
Electric Power
N.A.I.C.S.: 221122
Lewis Sheffield (Gen Mgr)

LITTLE ORBIT LLC
1231 E Dyer Ste 250, Santa Ana, CA 92705
Tel.: (949) 713-5016
Web Site: http://www.littleorbit.com
Year Founded: 2010
Video Game Publisher
N.A.I.C.S.: 513210
Matt Scott (CEO)

Subsidiaries:

Little Orbit Europe Ltd.   (1)
50 Broadway, London, SW1H 0RG, United Kingdom
Tel.: (44) 20 8144 1502
Video Game Publisher
N.A.I.C.S.: 513210
Terry Malham (Mgr-Bus Dev)

Vicious Cycle Software, Inc.   (1)
1500 Perimeter Park Dr Ste 210, Morrisville, NC 27560
Tel.: (919) 370-3000
Web Site: http://www.viciouscycleinc.com
Sales Range: $1-9.9 Million
Emp.: 52
Video Game Developer
N.A.I.C.S.: 513210
Eric Peterson (Pres & CEO)

LITTLE RAPIDS CORPORATION
PO Box 19031, Green Bay, WI 54303
Tel.: (920) 496-3040   WI
Web Site: http://www.littlerapids.com
Year Founded: 1947
Sales Range: $25-49.9 Million
Emp.: 400
Paper Mills
N.A.I.C.S.: 322120
Kirk Ryan (Pres & CEO)
Corey Martell (Mgr-Maintenance)
Dan Hnilicka (Mgr-Mktg)
Gerry Paul (Mgr-Product Dev)
Heather Phillips (Mgr-Sys Dev)
Jerry Bartman (Mgr-Quality & Tech)
Joseph Celmer (Mgr-Continuous Improvement)
Mike Stumpf (Controller-Larsen Converting)
Mitch Specht (Mgr-TPM)
Patrick Hayes (Mgr-Pur)
Pete Utic (Dir-Analysis)
Peter Cyganiak (Dir-Info Sys)
Renee Jastrow (Mgr-Credit)
Scott Rusch (Mgr-Production)
Brett Buratti (Mgr-Bus Dev)

LITTLE RED SERVICES, INC.
3900 Centerpoint Dr Ste 1300, Anchorage, AK 99507-5393
Tel.: (907) 349-2931
Web Site:
http://www.littleredservices.com
Year Founded: 1983
Sales Range: $10-24.9 Million
Emp.: 200
Oil & Gas Wells Drilling Services
N.A.I.C.S.: 213111
Doug Smith (Pres & CEO)
Joe Curgus (VP-Ops)

LITTLE ROCK WASTE WATER UTILITY
11 Clearwater Dr, Little Rock, AR 72204-8009
Tel.: (501) 376-2903
Web Site: http://www.lrwu.com
Sales Range: $10-24.9 Million
Emp.: 225
Sewage Treatment Facilities
N.A.I.C.S.: 221320
Debbie Williams (Mgr-Acctg)
Charles Goss (Sec)
Greg Ramond (CEO)

LITTLE VALLEY HOMES INC.
45225 Grand River Ave, Novi, MI 48375
Tel.: (248) 349-2500
Web Site: http://www.lvhomes.net
Year Founded: 1965
Sales Range: Less than $1 Million
Emp.: 12
Mobile Home Dealers
N.A.I.C.S.: 459930

LITTLEFIELD, INC.
1350 S Boulder Ave Ste 500, Tulsa, OK 74119-3214
Tel.: (918) 295-1000   OK
Year Founded: 1980
Rev.: $29,145,000
Emp.: 30
N.A.I.C.S.: 541810
David G. Littlefield (Pres & CEO)
Laurie Tilley (VP & Brand Strategist)
Danica Bruce (Acct Dir-Plng)
Marellie Littlefield (VP-Fin & HR)
Mike Rocco (Dir-Creative)
Mike Smith (Dir-Interactive Integration)

LITTLEJOHN & CO., LLC
8 Sound Shore Dr Ste 303, Greenwich, CT 06830
Tel.: (203) 552-3500   DE
Web Site: http://www.littlejohnllc.com
Year Founded: 1996
Privater Equity Firm
N.A.I.C.S.: 523999
Michael I. Klein (CEO)
Edmund J. Feeley (Mng Dir-Private Equity)
Brian E. Ramsay (Pres)
Steven G. Raich (Mng Dir-Private Equity)
Jason D. Mosiello (Dir-Mgmt Company & Gen Partner Reporting)
Michael B. Kaplan (Mng Dir-Private Equity)
Antonio Miranda (Mng Dir-Private Equity)
Richard E. Maybaum (Mng Dir & Co-Head-Debt Strategies)
Kenneth Warren (CFO & Chief Compliance Officer)
Drew Greenwood (Mng Dir-Private Equity)
Brian W. Michaud (Mng Dir-Private Equity)
Michael E. Kassas (Dir-Fund Reporting)
Gentry S. Klein (Mng Dir-Special Situations)
Jordan N. Tongalson (Mng Dir-Bus Dev)
Courtney Hagen (Chief Talent Officer-Private Equity)
Thomas Bennet (Principal-Private Equity)
Bart Stout (Principal-Special Situations)
Charles Leung (Principal-Private Equity)
William McDavid (Principal-Private Equity)
Kaitlyn Marcinek (Controller)
Federico Persico (Head-Capital Formation)
Angus C. Littlejohn Jr. (Co-Founder, Chm & Partner)

Subsidiaries:

API Heat Transfer, Inc.   (1)
2777 Walden Ave, Buffalo, NY 14225-4748
Tel.: (716) 684-6700
Web Site: http://www.apiheattransfer.com
Sales Range: $75-99.9 Million
Emp.: 1,600
Industrial Heat Exchangers & Heat Transfer Systems
N.A.I.C.S.: 332410
Michael Sanders (Pres-Shell & Tube Grp)
Jeff Lennox (VP-Fin & Admin)
David Rice (Dir-Global Supply Chain)
Jill Kelly (VP-HR)
Arif Khan (Dir-Product Dev)
Ed Smouse (VP-Mfg)
Brett Border (Chief Mfg Officer)
John Malone (VP-Mktg)
Friedrich Schenker (Mng Dir-Plate & Thermal Sys Grp)
Guo Wei (Mng Dir-China & Asia-Pacific)
Stephen Rennie (Pres & CEO)
Steve Delaney (Chm)

Ardurra Group, LLC   (1)
4921 Memorial Hwy Ste 300, Tampa, FL 33634
Tel.: (813) 880-8881
Web Site: http://www.ardurragroup.com
Holding Company; Engineering & Disaster Management Services
N.A.I.C.S.: 551112
Scott Brasfield (COO)
Rick Cloutier (Dir-Synergy)
Ernesto Aguilar (CEO)
Cathy Cahill (CFO)
Kevin Brown (Chief HR Officer)
Kart Vaith (Chief Strategy Officer)

Subsidiary (Domestic):

AndersonPenna Partners, Inc.   (2)
3737 Birch St 250, Newport Beach, CA 92660
Tel.: (949) 428-1500
Engineeering Services
N.A.I.C.S.: 541330
Joseph Stoakley (Asst Mgr-Construction & Engr-Office)
John Wolitarsky (Sr Project Mgr)

Arredondo, Zepeda & Brunz, LLC   (2)
11355 McCree Rd, Dallas, TX 75238
Tel.: (214) 341-9900
Web Site: http://www.azb-engrs.com
Sales Range: $1-9.9 Million
Emp.: 47
Civil & Environmental Engineering & Surveying Services
N.A.I.C.S.: 541330
Victor Zepeda (Head-Mktg)

LITTLEJOHN & CO., LLC

BCG Engineering & Consulting, Inc.   (2)
3012 26th St, Metairie, LA 70002-6002
Tel.: (504) 454-3866
Web Site: http://www.bcengineers.com
Engineeering Services
N.A.I.C.S.: 541330
Kenneth L. Brown (Pres)

Constantine Engineering, Inc.   (2)
1988 Lewis Turner Blvd, Fort Walton Beach, FL 32547-0000
Tel.: (850) 244-5800
Web Site: http://www.tcgeng.com
Sewage Treatment Facilities
N.A.I.C.S.: 221320
James P. Kizer Jr. (Pres)

Design South Professionals, Inc.   (2)
3 Linwa Blvd, Anderson, SC 29621
Tel.: (864) 226-6111
Engineering Services Architectural Services Business Consulting Services
N.A.I.C.S.: 541330

E Co Consultants, Inc.   (2)
1523 8th Ave W Ste B, Palmetto, FL 34221
Tel.: (941) 722-0901
Web Site: http://www.ecoconsultants.net
Sales Range: $1-9.9 Million
Environmental Consulting Services
N.A.I.C.S.: 541620
Alec Hoffner (Principal)
Chris Bryant (Principal)

Fulghum Macindoe & Associates, Inc.   (2)
10330 Hardin Vly Rd Ste 201, Knoxville, TN 37932
Tel.: (865) 690-6419
Web Site: http://www.fulghummacindoe.com
Engineeering Services
N.A.I.C.S.: 541330
Brian Mahoney (Sr Engr-Structural)

Gunda Corporation, LLC   (2)
11750 Katy Fwy Ste 300, Houston, TX 77079
Tel.: (713) 541-3530
Web Site: http://www.gundacorp.com
Rev.: $1,100,000
Emp.: 15
Engineeering Services
N.A.I.C.S.: 541330
Ramesh Gunda (Pres)
Michael Blasdel (Dir-Client Svcs)
Reshane Dawn-Fowler (Mgr-Mktg)
Rajesh Tanwani (Sr VP)
Daniel W. Krueger (COO)
Michael Ereti (Mgr-Traffic Engrg)
Peter Smith (Dir-Transportation)

Henry Von Oesen & Associates, Inc.   (2)
3809 Peachtree Ave, Wilmington, NC 28403
Tel.: (704) 343-8973
Web Site: http://www.ardurra.com
Engineeering Services
N.A.I.C.S.: 541330

Infrastructure Engineering Corp.   (2)
14271 Danielson St, Poway, CA 92064
Tel.: (760) 529-0795
Web Site: http://www.iecorporation.com
Sales Range: $1-9.9 Million
Emp.: 50
Engineeering Services
N.A.I.C.S.: 541330
Rob Weber (Pres)

King Engineering Associates, Inc.   (2)
4921 Memorial Hwy Ste 300, Tampa, FL 33634-7520
Tel.: (813) 880-8881
Web Site: http://www.kingengineering.com
Sales Range: $10-24.9 Million
Engineering, Landscape Architecture, Surveying & Mapping Services
N.A.I.C.S.: 541330
Keith A. Appenzeller (CEO)
Richard Dutter (VP-Plng & Landscape Architecture)
Christopher F. Kuzler (Sr VP)
Michael E. Ross (Sec & Sr VP)
Jeffrey Robert Mistarz (CFO)

Ritoch-Powell & Assoc Rpa Inc.   (2)
3800 N Central Ave # 605, Phoenix, AZ 85012

LITTLEJOHN & CO., LLC

Littlejohn & Co., LLC—(Continued)
Tel.: (602) 263-1177
Web Site: http://www.ritochpowell.com
Rev.: $2,070,000
Emp.: 10
Engineeering Services
N.A.I.C.S.: 541330
Karl Obergh (Pres)

Shephard-Wesnitzer, Inc. (2)
75 Kallof Pl, Sedona, AZ 86336-5500
Tel.: (928) 282-1061
Web Site: http://www.swiaz.com
Sales Range: $1-9.9 Million
Emp.: 70
Engineering Services
N.A.I.C.S.: 541330
Art Beckwith (VP)
Nancy Wesnitzer (Mgr-Acctg)

T-O Engineers, Inc. (2)
9777 W Chinden Blvd, Boise, ID 83714
Tel.: (208) 323-2288
Web Site: http://www.to-engineers.com
Sales Range: $1-9.9 Million
Emp.: 35
Engineering Services
N.A.I.C.S.: 541330
Steven E. Holt (Sec)
William H. Russell (Pres)
Chris Mansfield (Project Mgr-Multiple Projects-Spokane)
John Carpenter (Office Mgr)
J. R. Norvell (Office Mgr)
Joe Guenther (Project Mgr-Environmental)
Bruce Harral (Project Mgr-Transportation)
Markus Green (Project Mgr)

Woodson Engineering & Surveying, Inc. (2)
124 N Elden St Ste 100, Flagstaff, AZ 86001
Tel.: (928) 774-4636
Web Site: http://www.woodsoneng.com
Engineeering Services
N.A.I.C.S.: 541330
Guadalupe Woodson (Sec)

Armorworks Enterprises, LLC (1)
305 N 54th St, Chandler, AZ 85226
Tel.: (480) 598-5711
Web Site: http://www.armorworks.com
Small Arms Ammunition Mfr
N.A.I.C.S.: 332992
Elida Voorbrood (Gen Mgr)

Subsidiary (Domestic):

Fox Valley Metal Tech, LLC (2)
1201 Parkview Rd, Green Bay, WI 54304
Tel.: (920) 337-9303
Web Site: http://www.fvmt.com
Rev.: $9,600,000
Emp.: 60
Sheet Metal Work Mfg
N.A.I.C.S.: 332322
Jo Ann Van Groll (Controller)
John West (Pres)

Brown Jordan International Inc. (1)
5 Marconi, Irvine, CA 92618
Tel.: (800) 743-4252
Web Site: http://www.brownjordan.com
Homefurnishings Store
N.A.I.C.S.: 449129
Jeff Leonard (CFO & Exec VP)
Gene J. Moriarty (Pres & CEO)
John Wojcik (CMO)
Frederick G. King (COO & Gen Counsel)

Subsidiary (Domestic):

Casual Living World Wide (2)
20 Kingbrook Pkwy, Simpsonville, KY 40067
Tel.: (866) 331-6478
Web Site: http://www.casuallivingoutdoors.com
Mfr of Outdoor Furniture
N.A.I.C.S.: 337126

Tropitone Furniture Company, Inc. (2)
5 Marconi, Irvine, CA 92618
Tel.: (949) 951-2010
Web Site: http://www.tropitone.com
Furniture Mfr
N.A.I.C.S.: 337126
Peter Homestead (VP-Design)

Cirrus Concept Consulting, Inc. (1)
1 Elizabeth Pl Bldg K W Medical Plz Ste 110, Dayton, OH 45417-3445
Tel.: (937) 228-7007
Web Site: http://www.cirrusconsulting.com
Employment Placement Agencies
N.A.I.C.S.: 561311
Charlotte Searles (Acct Mgr)
Lesli Khan (Founder & Pres)

Cornerstone Chemical Company (1)
3838 N Causeway Blvd Ste 3150, Metairie, LA 70002
Tel.: (504) 431-9511
Web Site: http://www.cornerstonechemco.com
Specialty Chemicals & Materials Developer, Marketer & Mfr
N.A.I.C.S.: 325998
Greg Zoglio (CEO)
Tom Yura (COO)
Jamie Ellen (Chief HR Officer)

Subsidiary (Non-US):

Cornerstone Chemical Company B.V. (2)
Beurs World Trade Center Office 759 Beursplein 37, 3011 AA, Rotterdam, Netherlands
Tel.: (31) 10 2053220
Web Site: http://www.cornerstonechemco.com
Intermediate Chemical Mfr
N.A.I.C.S.: 325199

GSE Holding, Inc. (1)
19103 Gundle Rd, Houston, TX 77073
Tel.: (281) 443-8564
Web Site: http://www.gseworld.com
Rev.: $417,652,000
Assets: $266,152,000
Liabilities: $246,256,000
Net Worth: $19,896,000
Earnings: ($84,526,000)
Emp.: 643
Fiscal Year-end: 12/31/2013
Holding Company; Geosynthetic Lining Products Mfr & Distr
N.A.I.C.S.: 551112
Peter R. McCourt (Pres-Intl)
Jeffery D. Nigh (Exec VP-Global Ops)
Edward Zimmel (VP-Engrg)
Daniel C. Storey (CFO & Sr VP)

Hardware Holdings (1)
324 Cranbury Half Acre Rd, Cranbury, NJ 08512
Tel.: (609) 860-9990
Hardware & Building Products Distr
N.A.I.C.S.: 423710
Donald Devine (CEO & Pres)

Subsidiary (Domestic):

Handy Hardware Wholesale Inc. (2)
8300 Tewantin Dr, Houston, TX 77061
Tel.: (713) 644-1495
Web Site: http://www.handyhardware.com
Sales Range: $200-249.9 Million
Hardware Distr
N.A.I.C.S.: 423710
Craig Cowart (Exec VP-Mdsg & CMO)
John Gearing (VP-IT & Replenishment)
James Ferguson (Dir-Warehouse Ops)

Howard Berger Co. LLC (2)
324 A Half Acre Rd, Cranbury, NJ 08512
Tel.: (609) 860-9990
Web Site: http://www.hberger.com
Sales Range: $25-49.9 Million
Hardware Distr
N.A.I.C.S.: 423710
Howard Berger (Founder)

Imperative Logistics Group (1)
Oakbrook Terrace Twr 1 Tower Ln Ste 2101, Oakbrook Terrace, IL 60181
Tel.: (630) 394-1030
Web Site: http://www.magnateworldwide.com
Logistics Assets Investment Holding Company
N.A.I.C.S.: 551112
Daniel Para (Chm & CEO)

Subsidiary (Domestic):

Cargo Logistics Group, Inc (2)
7380 Coca Cola Dr Ste 117, Hanover, MD 21076-1789

Tel.: (410) 712-4455
Web Site: http://www.cargologisticsgroup.com
Freight Transportation Arrangement
N.A.I.C.S.: 488510
David Cook (Mgr)

Jamco International Inc. (2)
8410 Tejas Loop, Laredo, TX 78045
Tel.: (956) 717-3322
Web Site: http://www.jamcointl.com
Rev.: $2,980,000
Emp.: 20
Freight Transportation Arrangement
N.A.I.C.S.: 488510
Juan Menchaca (Owner)

Holding (Domestic):

Masterpiece International Limited (2)
39 Broadway 14th Fl, New York, NY 10006
Tel.: (212) 825-4800
Web Site: http://www.masterpieceintl.com
Emp.: 200
Freight Forwarding, Customs Brokerage & Other Logistics Services
N.A.I.C.S.: 488510
Thomas Gilgen (Pres)
John O'Halloran (Pres-Fine Arts Svcs Div)
Susan Erfesoglou (VP-Ops-Houston)
Roger Huiras (Dir-Strategic Accts-Oregon)
Tony Alvarez (Dir-Strategic Accts)
Edgar Badlissi (Dir-Strategic Accts-Miami)
Nick Iosue (Exec VP-Sls)

Subsidiary (Domestic):

Somerset Marine Lines, LLC (3)
67 Walnut Ave Ste 306, Clark, NJ 07066
Tel.: (908) 431-7655
Web Site: http://www.somersetmarine.com
Freight Forwarding Services
N.A.I.C.S.: 488510
Abed Medawar (Pres)
Bill Carroll (VP-Sls)

Subsidiary (Domestic):

Quality Air Forwarding, Inc. (2)
137 W Boden St, Milwaukee, WI 53207
Tel.: (414) 281-6090
Web Site: http://www.qafi.com
Sales Range: $1-9.9 Million
Emp.: 16
Airports, Flying Fields, And Services
N.A.I.C.S.: 488119

Holding (Domestic):

Trump Card, LLC (2)
30012 Ivy Glenn Dr Ste 220, Laguna Niguel, CA 92677
Web Site: http://www.trumpcardinc.com
Freight Transportation Arrangement & Logistics Services
N.A.I.C.S.: 488510
Chris Zingrebe (VP)
Kevin Forhane (Dir-Ops)
Tiffanie Zingrebe (Assoc Dir-Back End Ops)
Joe Mills (Assoc Dir-Private Fleet)

Subsidiary (Domestic):

ASAP Expediting & Logistics, LLC (3)
100 Commerce Dr NE Ste A, Columbia, SC 29223-4562
Tel.: (803) 865-7971
Web Site: http://www.asapexpediting.net
Couriers
N.A.I.C.S.: 492110
Angela Hobgood (Mgr-Sls & Mktg)

Interior Logic Group Holdings, LLC (1)
10 Bunsen, Irvine, CA 92008
Tel.: (760) 929-6700
Web Site: http://www.interiorlogicgroup.com
Holding Company; Interior Design Services
N.A.I.C.S.: 551112
Alan K. Davenport (Pres & CEO)
Mark Fikse (Exec VP-Bus Dev & Ops)

Subsidiary (Domestic):

Coleman Floor, LLC (2)
8020 Arco Corporate Dr Ste 400, Raleigh, NC 27617
Tel.: (919) 431-1000
Web Site: http://www.colemanfloors.com
Floor Installation Services

U.S. PRIVATE

N.A.I.C.S.: 238330
Mike Hagen (Mgr-Market-NE)

Branch (Domestic):

Coleman Floor Co. (3)
400 Innovation Ave Ste 150, Morrisville, NC 27560
Tel.: (919) 936-9301
Web Site: http://www.colemanfloor.com
Drywall & Insulation Contractors
N.A.I.C.S.: 238310
Brad Ellis (Gen Mgr)

Coleman Floor Company (3)
6162 Lawyers Hill Rd, Elkridge, MD 21075-5208
Tel.: (410) 037-0441
Web Site: http://www.colemanfloors.com
Floor Covering Stores
N.A.I.C.S.: 449121
Tim Coleman (Owner)

Subsidiary (Domestic):

Interior Logic Group, Inc. (2)
2270 NW Pkwy SE, Marietta, GA 30067
Tel.: (770) 693-9668
Web Site: http://www.interiorlogicgroup.com
Interior Design Services
N.A.I.C.S.: 541410
Alan Davenport (Chm & CEO)

Subsidiary (Domestic):

L.A.R.K. Industries, Inc. (3)
4900 E Hunter Ave, Anaheim, CA 92807
Tel.: (714) 701-4200
Design Services
N.A.I.C.S.: 541490

Subsidiary (Domestic):

Intown Design, Inc. (4)
250 Villanova Dr, Atlanta, GA 30336
Tel.: (404) 812-3820
Web Site: http://www.intowndesigninc.com
Other Building Material Dealers
N.A.I.C.S.: 444180

Division (Domestic):

T.A.C. Ceramic Tile Co. (4)
11951 Tac Ct, Manassas, VA 20109
Tel.: (703) 690-2556
Flooring Contractors
N.A.I.C.S.: 238330

Subsidiary (Domestic):

Interior Specialists, Inc. (2)
1630 Faraday Ave, Carlsbad, CA 92008
Tel.: (760) 929-6700
Interior Design & Installation Services
N.A.I.C.S.: 541410
Alan K. Davenport (Pres & CEO)
Jeffrey M. Fenton (COO & Sr VP)
Robert Hess (CFO)
James J. DeGeorge (Chief Sls Officer & Sr VP)
Anne Liu (Chief Acctg Officer)
Steffani Stevens (Gen Counsel & Sr VP)
Randy Bafus (Sr VP-Comml Sls & Sr Living)
Jodi Bossak (Sr VP-Strategic Plng & Bus Dev)
Katie Prekel (VP-HR)

Kaman Industrial Technologies Corporation (1)
1 Vision Way, Bloomfield, CT 06002 (100%)
Tel.: (860) 687-5097
Web Site: http://www.ec.kamandirect.com
Sales Range: $750-799.9 Million
Emp.: 1,337
Industrial Equipment & Components Distr
N.A.I.C.S.: 423840
Steven J. Smidler (Grp Pres)
Ben Mondics (Pres & CEO)

Subsidiary (Domestic):

Catching FluidPower Inc. (2)
881 Remington Blvd, Bolingbrook, IL 60440
Tel.: (630) 771-3800
Web Site: http://www.catching.com
Sales Range: $25-49.9 Million
Emp.: 93
Hydraulic, Pneumatic & Fluid Connector Components Distr

COMPANIES
LITTLEJOHN & CO., LLC

N.A.I.C.S.: 423830
Steve Smidler *(Pres)*

Division (Domestic):

Florida Bearings (2)
10050 NW 116th Way Ste 1, Miami, FL 33178
Tel.: (305) 573-8424
Web Site: http://www.floridabearings.com
Sales Range: $10-24.9 Million
Industrial Bearings, Pumps & Drives Distr & Repair Services
N.A.I.C.S.: 423840

Subsidiary (Domestic):

KIT Zeller, Inc. (2)
14607 University Ave Ste 800, Rochester, NY 14613
Tel.: (585) 254-8840
Web Site: http://www.kamanace.com
Sales Range: $10-24.9 Million
Emp.: 240
Controls & Automation Products Distr
N.A.I.C.S.: 423610

Kaman Automation, Inc. (2)
230 S Washington Ste Ste 1, Plainville, CT 06062
Tel.: (860) 410-9904
Web Site: http://kamanautomation.com
Compact Machinery Mfr
N.A.I.C.S.: 316990

Kaman Fluid Power, LLC (2)
1 Vision Way, Bloomfield, CT 06002
Tel.: (860) 687-5000
Web Site: http://ec.kamandirect.com
Industrial Fluid Power Equipment Components Distr
N.A.I.C.S.: 423840
Patricia W. Warfield *(Sr VP & Gen Mgr)*
David Mayer *(VP & Gen Mgr)*

Subsidiary (Domestic):

Western Fluid Components, Inc. (3)
4125 Bakerview Spur, Bellingham, WA 98226
Tel.: (360) 738-1264
Web Site: http://www.westernfluidcomp.com
Industrial Equipment Merchant Whslr
N.A.I.C.S.: 423840
Dan Quam *(Branch Mgr-Sls-Outside)*

Subsidiary (Domestic):

Minarik Corporation (2)
4975 E Landon Dr, Anaheim, CA 92807
Tel.: (714) 696-3750
Web Site: http://www.minarik.com
Sales Range: $75-99.9 Million
Emp.: 250
Mfr & Distributor of Motion Control Products & Variable Frequency Drives
N.A.I.C.S.: 423610
Jodi Reynoso *(Gen Counsel & Mgr-HR)*

Maysteel Industries, LLC (1)
6199 Hwy W, Allenton, WI 53002
Tel.: (262) 251-1632
Web Site: http://www.maysteel.com
Sheet Metal Products Mfr
N.A.I.C.S.: 332322
Kevin Matkin *(CEO)*
Randy Gromowski *(CFO)*
Don Lawinger *(VP-Bus Dev)*
David Dembinski *(Plant Mgr-Allenton)*
Darci Boettcher *(Mgr-HR)*
Todd Lutz *(Dir-Engrg)*
Carlos Zozaya Torres *(Mgr-Monterrey Plant)*

Subsidiary (Domestic):

Damac Products, Inc. (2)
14489 Industry Cir, La Mirada, CA 90638
Tel.: (877) 670-0496
Web Site: http://www.damac.com
Data Center Infrastructure Equipment Mfr
N.A.I.C.S.: 334290
Amy Roberts *(Mgr-Credit)*
David Johnson *(Sr VP)*

Subsidiary (Non-US):

MSM Manufacturing de Mexico, S.A. de C.V. (2)
Av Progreso S/N Manzana 3 Lote 12, Parque Industrial La Silla, Apodaca, CP 66648, NL, Mexico

Tel.: (52) 81 8851 0100
Web Site: http://www.maysteel.com
Sheet Metal Products Mfr
N.A.I.C.S.: 332322
Carlos Zozaya Torres *(Plant Mgr)*

Subsidiary (Domestic):

Porter's Group, LLC (2)
469 Hospital Dr Ste A / Ste B2, Gastonia, NC 28054
Tel.: (704) 864-1313
Web Site: http://www.portersfab.com
Fabricated Metal Products Mfr
N.A.I.C.S.: 332999
Charles Saleh *(CEO)*
Hans Wede *(Pres)*
Clint Shuford *(CFO)*
Jim Shunkwiler *(Gen Mgr)*
Mike Taylor *(VP-Sls & Pur)*

Subsidiary (Domestic):

Karlee Co. (3)
701 S International Rd, Garland, TX 75042 (100%)
Tel.: (972) 272-0628
Web Site: http://www.karlee.com
Emp.: 250
Precision Sheet Metal Mfr & Machined Components
N.A.I.C.S.: 332322
Lee Brumit *(Founder)*

Motion Recruitment Partners, LLC (1)
131 Clarendon Street 3rd Fl, Boston, MA 02116
Tel.: (617) 585-6500
Web Site: http://www.motionrecruitment.com
IT Staffing & Recruiting Partner
N.A.I.C.S.: 561311
John Rosenbaum *(CIO)*
James Vallone *(Exec VP)*
Drew Sussberg *(VP-Ops)*
Beth Gilfeather *(CEO)*
Brad Page *(CFO)*
Matt Milano *(Pres)*

Subsidiary (Domestic):

MDI Group, Inc. (2)
780 Johnson Ferry Rd Ste 650, Atlanta, GA 30342
Tel.: (770) 416-7949
Web Site: http://www.mdigroup.com
Industrial Building Construction
N.A.I.C.S.: 236210
Ella Koscik *(Owner, Chm & CEO)*

Matrix Resources, Inc. (2)
400 Perimeter Ctr Ter Ste 300, Atlanta, GA 30346
Tel.: (770) 677-2400
Web Site: http://www.matrixresources.com
Sales Range: $125-149.9 Million
Emp.: 1,000
Employment Agency & Information Technology Staffing Firm
N.A.I.C.S.: 541611
Robert Stovall *(CFO)*
Don Palmer *(Exec VP-Accts-Natl)*
Gary Wood *(CEO)*
Jon Davis *(Exec VP-Sls-Natl)*
Elizabeth Varrenti *(VP-Pro Dev)*
Kimberly Nall *(Co-CFO)*

Northwest Hardwoods, Inc. (1)
2600 Network Blvd Ste 600, Frisco, TX 75034
Tel.: (469) 922-3778
Web Site: https://nwh.com
Lumber Product Mfr & Distr
N.A.I.C.S.: 321999
Nathan Jeppson *(CEO)*

Subsidiary (Domestic):

Post Hardwoods, Inc (2)
3544 38th St, Hamilton, MI 49419
Tel.: (269) 751-7307
Rev.: $1,300,000
Emp.: 11
Sawmills
N.A.I.C.S.: 321113
Robert Post *(Pres)*

PSC, LLC (1)
5151 San Felipe St Ste 1100, Houston, TX 77056
Tel.: (713) 623-8777

Web Site: http://www.pscnow.com
Holding Company; Industrial & Environmental Services
N.A.I.C.S.: 551112
Jeffrey Stocks *(CFO & Sr VP)*
Brad Clark *(Pres & CEO)*
Jeff Nyberg *(Sr VP-Core Svcs)*
Liz Crow *(Sr VP-Specialty Svcs)*
Joe Davis *(VP-Sls & Mktg)*
Rick Pitman *(VP-Environmental, Health, Safety & Transformation)*

Subsidiary (Domestic):

PSC Industrial Services, Inc. (2)
5151 San Felipe St Ste 1100, Houston, TX 77056
Tel.: (713) 623-8777
Web Site: http://www.pscnow.com
Industrial Remediation Services
N.A.I.C.S.: 562910
Brad Clark *(Pres & CEO)*

PlayPower, Inc. (1)
11515 Vanstory Dr Ste 100, Huntersville, NC 28078
Tel.: (704) 949-1600
Web Site: http://www.playpower.com
Commercial Playground Equipment Mfr
N.A.I.C.S.: 339920
Joseph Copeland *(Pres & CEO)*
Lynne Vandeveer *(Chief Strategy Officer & Exec VP)*
Mike Pruss *(Sr VP & CFO)*
Ashley Donde *(VP-Sls)*
Danielle Garde *(Chief HR Officer)*

Subsidiary (Domestic):

Miracle Recreation Equipment Company (2)
878 E Hwy 60, Monett, MO 65708 (100%)
Tel.: (417) 235-6917
Web Site: http://www.miracle-recreation.com
Commercial Outdoor Play Systems Mfr
N.A.I.C.S.: 339920
Mike Sutton *(VP-Sls)*

Subsidiary (Non-US):

PlayPower Canada (2)
PO Box 125, Paris, N3L 3E7, ON, Canada (100%)
Tel.: (519) 442-6331
Web Site: https://www.playpowercanada.ca
Commercial Playground Systems Mfr
N.A.I.C.S.: 339920
Brian Jenkins *(Gen Mgr)*

Subsidiary (Domestic):

PlayPower LT Farmington, Inc. (2)
878 E Highway 60, Monett, MO 65708 (100%)
Tel.: (873) 760-7325
Web Site: http://www.littletikescommercial.com
Playground Equipment Mfr
N.A.I.C.S.: 339920
Brett Kidd *(Dir-Sls)*
Ken Schober *(VP & Gen Mgr)*

Playworld Systems, Inc. (2)
1000 Buffalo Rd, Lewisburg, PA 17837-9795 (100%)
Tel.: (570) 522-9800
Web Site: http://www.playworldsystems.com
Commercial Playground Equipment Mfr & Distr
N.A.I.C.S.: 339920
Dale Miller *(Founder, Owner & Chm)*
Kevin Cook *(Chief Sls Officer)*
Julie Godfrey *(Product Mgr)*
Jenn Harry *(Mgr-Mktg Automation)*
Matt Miller *(Pres & CEO)*
Greg Harrison *(CMO)*
Victoria Cook *(Ops Mgr-Mktg)*

Soft Play, LLC (2)
11515 Vanstory Dr Ste 100, Huntersville, NC 28078 (100%)
Tel.: (704) 875-6550
Web Site: http://www.softplay.com
Outdoor Play Structures Mfr
N.A.I.C.S.: 339920
Brian Sonney *(Exec Mgr-Bus Dev-Western United States)*
Brock Hodge *(Exec Mgr-Bus Dev)*

Pritchard Industries, Inc. (1)

150 E 42 St, New York, NY 10017-6700
Tel.: (212) 382-2295
Web Site: http://www.pritchardindustries.com
Building Maintenance & Janitorial Services
N.A.I.C.S.: 561720
Peter D. Pritchard *(Chm)*
Dean Lanza *(VP & Gen Mgr)*
James Pensabene *(Controller)*
David Strupinsky *(CFO)*
Robert Sokolowski *(COO & Sr VP)*
Jay Leyden *(Pres & CEO)*

Subsidiary (Domestic):

Pritchard Industries Southwest Inc. (2)
4040 Directors Row, Houston, TX 77092-8735
Tel.: (713) 957-1387
Web Site: http://www.pritchardindustries.com
Sales Range: $75-99.9 Million
Emp.: 2,500
Provider of Building Maintenance Services
N.A.I.C.S.: 561720
Peter Sperduti *(VP)*

Branch (Domestic):

Pritchard Industries, Inc. - Vienna Office (2)
8391 Old Court House Rd, Vienna, VA 22182
Tel.: (703) 807-5100
Web Site: http://www.pritchardindustries.com
Sales Range: $50-74.9 Million
Emp.: 500
Cleaning Service
N.A.I.C.S.: 236220

Strategic Materials, Inc. (1)
17220 Katy Fwy Ste 150, Houston, TX 77094
Tel.: (281) 647-2700
Web Site: http://www.strategicmaterials.com
Glass Recycling Services
N.A.I.C.S.: 562920
Curtis Bucey *(Chief Comml Officer & Exec VP)*
Paul Faherty *(CTO)*
Matt Keresman *(Sr VP-Ops)*
Jimmy Rayford *(Sr VP-Latin America & Specialty)*
Edward May *(COO & Exec VP)*
Daniel Allinger *(Sr VP-HR)*

Subsidiary (Domestic):

American Specialty Glass, Inc. (2)
829 N 400 W, North Salt Lake, UT 84054
Tel.: (801) 294-4222
Glass Mfr
N.A.I.C.S.: 327211

Sunbelt Modular, Inc. (1)
5301 W Madison St, Phoenix, AZ 85043
Tel.: (602) 278-3355
Web Site: http://www.sunbeltmodular.com
Broom, Brush & Mop Mfr
N.A.I.C.S.: 339994
Ron Procunier *(Pres & CEO)*

The Hiller Companies, Inc. (1)
3751 Joy Springs Dr, Mobile, AL 36693
Tel.: (251) 661-1275
Web Site: https://hillerfire.com
Burglar Systems & Fire Protection Systems Design, Installation & Services
N.A.I.C.S.: 561621
Jeff Birch *(Pres)*
Santiago Perez *(CEO)*

Division (Domestic):

Advanced Safety Systems Inc. (2)
141 Summit St, Peabody, MA 01960-5198
Tel.: (978) 532-5737
Web Site: http://www.advancedsafetysystems.com
Fire Safety Products Mfr
N.A.I.C.S.: 922160
Bill Mackay *(VP & Gen Mgr)*
Bill Card *(COO)*
Charlie Hourez *(Chief Engr)*
Ralph Tenaglia *(Mgr-Warehouse)*

Subsidiary (Domestic):

American Fire Technologies, Inc (2)

LITTLEJOHN & CO., LLC

U.S. PRIVATE

Littlejohn & Co., LLC—(Continued)
2120 Capital Dr, Wilmington, NC 28405
Tel.: (910) 799-9191
Web Site: https://www.aft.net
Electrical Apparatus & Equipment, Wiring Supplies & Related Equipment Merchant Whslr
N.A.I.C.S.: 423610
Paul Hayes (Gen Mgr)

Morgan Fire & Safety Inc (2)
1025 Tate Blvd SE, Hickory, NC 28602-4024
Tel.: (813) 283-1801
Web Site: http://www.unifourfire.com
Electrical Apparatus & Equipment, Wiring Supplies & Related Equipment Merchant Whslr
N.A.I.C.S.: 423610
Morgan Anderson (Owner)

Tidel Engineering, L.P. (1)
2025 W Belt Line Rd Ste 114, Carrollton, TX 75006-6453
Tel.: (972) 484-3358
Web Site: http://www.tidel.com
Cash Handling & Security Equipment Developer & Mfr
N.A.I.C.S.: 333310
Darren Taylor (Exec VP-Global Bus Dev)
Marty Hendrickson (VP-Sls)
Steve Remis (VP-Engrng)

Total Safety U.S., Inc. (1)
3151 Briarpark Dr Ste 500, Houston, TX 77042
Tel.: (713) 353-7100
Web Site: http://www.totalsafety.com
Industrial Safety Equipment Solutions
N.A.I.C.S.: 423490
Paul Tyree (Chief Comml Officer)
Joseph Waiter (Gen Counsel & Sec)
George P. Ristevski (CEO)
Joe Sadowski (Exec VP-Bus Dev, Sls & Mktg)
Lynnelle Long (Sr VP-HR)
Steve Long (VP-Health, Safety & Environment)

Subsidiary (Domestic):

Callaway Safety Equipment Co., Inc. (2)
3229 Industrial Dr, Hobbs, NM 88240
Tel.: (505) 392-2973
Web Site: http://callawaysafety.com
Sales Range: $1-9.9 Million
Emp.: 55
Safety Equipment Distr
N.A.I.C.S.: 423490

Houston 2-Way Radio, Inc. (2)
4100 N Sam Houston Pkwy W Ste 290, Houston, TX 77086
Tel.: (713) 681-2525
Web Site: http://www.h2wr.com
Sales Range: $25-49.9 Million
Emp.: 35
Sales, Service & Rental of Radio Communications Products
N.A.I.C.S.: 423690

S&S Supplies and Solutions, Inc. (2)
501 Shell Ave, Martinez, CA 94553
Tel.: (925) 313-0360
Web Site: http://www.sns-tool.com
Sales Range: $25-49.9 Million
Emp.: 90
Equipment Rental & Leasing
N.A.I.C.S.: 532490
Steve Tomkovicz (Pres)
Tracy M. Tomkovicz (CEO)
Roy Clark (Mgr-Sls)
Barry Grace (Product Mgr)
Stephen Mayfield (Mgr-PET Lab & Ground Lab)

Sprint Safety, Inc. (2)
3880 Washington Blvd, Beaumont, TX 77705-1033
Tel.: (713) 426-4196
Sales Range: $1-9.9 Million
Emp.: 200
Industrial Machinery Whslr
N.A.I.C.S.: 423830

Webb, Murray & Associates, Inc. (2)
4210 Malone Dr, Pasadena, TX 77507
Tel.: (281) 291-4800
Web Site: http://www.webb-murray.com
Emp.: 100
Installation & Service of Safety & Fire Protection Systems; Engineering & Construction
N.A.I.C.S.: 541330
Steve Beers (Gen Mgr)

UniTek Global Services, Inc. (1)
1817 Crane Ridge Dr Ste 500, 39216, Jackson, MS
Tel.: (601) 320-0443
Web Site: http://www.unitekglobalservices.com
Wireless Telecommunication Services
N.A.I.C.S.: 517112

Subsidiary (Domestic):

FTS USA, LLC (2)
Gwynedd Hall Ste 302 1777 Sentry Pkwy W, Blue Bell, PA 19422
Tel.: (615) 515-5399
Web Site: http://www.unitekglobalservices.com
Cable Installation & Maintenance Services
N.A.I.C.S.: 335921

Southern Diversified Technologies, Inc. (2)
130 N 2nd St, Brookhaven, MS 39601
Tel.: (770) 554-4011
Web Site: http://www.sdt-1.com
Engineering Services
N.A.I.C.S.: 541330

Subsidiary (Non-US):

Wirecomm Systems, Inc. (2)
107 Corstate Ave, Concord, L4K-4Y2, ON, Canada
Tel.: (905) 405-8018
Web Site: http://www.unitekglobalservices.com
Cable Installation & Maintenance Services
N.A.I.C.S.: 517112
Domenic Sorbara (Pres)

VTL Holding, Inc. (1)
26661 Bunert Rd, Warren, MI 48089
Tel.: (586) 447-3500
Web Site: http://www.liparifoods.com
Holding Company; Food & Non-Alcoholic Beverage Distr
N.A.I.C.S.: 551112
Thom Lipari (Pres & CEO)
Brian Zilo (Dir-HR)
Spiro Liras (VP-Mfg)
Joyce Saranathan (Sr VP-Bus Dev)

Subsidiary (Domestic):

Lipari Foods Operating Company, LLC (2)
26661 Bunert Rd, Warren, MI 48089
Tel.: (586) 447-3500
Web Site: http://www.liparifoods.com
Food & Non-Alcoholic Beverage Distr
N.A.I.C.S.: 424490
Thom Lipari (Pres & CEO)
Sarvy Rostami Lipari (Mgr-HR)
Mike Koslowski (Mgr-Credit)

Subsidiary (Domestic):

Troyer Cheese, Inc. (3)
6597 County Rd 625, Millersburg, OH 44654-9274
Tel.: (330) 893-2479
Web Site: http://www.troyercheese.com
Cheese Mfr
N.A.I.C.S.: 311513

Subsidiary (Domestic):

Tuts International Export & Import Company (2)
7457 Franklin Rd Ste 200, Bloomfield Hills, MI 48301
Tel.: (313) 582-9100
Sales Range: $1-9.9 Million
Emp.: 14
General Line Grocery Merchant Whslr
N.A.I.C.S.: 424410
Ghais Shenouda (Principal)

LITTLEJOHN GRAIN INC.
8801 E US Hwy 40, Martinsville, IL 62442
Tel.: (217) 382-4158
Web Site: http://www.lttlejohngain.com
Sales Range: $25-49.9 Million
Emp.: 22
Grain Elevators
N.A.I.C.S.: 424510
Kent O. Littlejohn (Pres)

LITTLER MENDELSON P.C.
333 Bush St 34th Fl, San Francisco, CA 94104
Tel.: (415) 433-1940
Web Site: http://www.littler.com
Year Founded: 1942
Sales Range: $350-399.9 Million
Emp.: 750
Law firm
N.A.I.C.S.: 541110
Robert A. Domingues (COO)
Scott D. Rechtschaffen (Chief Knowledge Officer)
Nancy C. Reynolds (Coord-Facilities)
Jacquelyn Smith (Mgr-Event)
Natasha L. DeCourcy (Principal)
Kimberly Yates (Dir-Program & CaseSmart-Charges)
Autum Flores (Assoc Atty-Denver)
John Kloosterman (Chm-Bus & Human Rights Practice Grp)
John Cerilli (Chm-Energy Indus Practice Grp)
Cindy-Ann L. Thomas (Chm-EEO & Diversity Practice Grp)
Thomas J. Bender (Co-Pres & Mng Dir)
Jeremy A. Roth (Co-Pres & Mng Dir)
James Witz (Chm-Unfair Competition & Trade Secrets Practice Grp)
Lilanthi Ravishankar (Principal)
Thomas Burns (CFO)

Subsidiaries:

Schuster Aguilo LLC (1)
221 Ponce de Leon Ave 15th Fl, San Juan, PR 00917-1815
Tel.: (787) 765-4646
Web Site: http://www.salawpr.com
Emp.: 25
Law firm
N.A.I.C.S.: 541110
Rafael E. Aguilo-Velez (Atty)
Carl Schuster (Atty)
Anabel Rodriguez-Alonso (Atty)
Lourdes C. Hernandez-Venegas (Partner)
Magda Mariela Rexach (Partner)

LITTLETON CHEVROLET BUICK OLDS PONTIAC
851 Meadow St, Littleton, NH 03561
Tel.: (603) 444-5678
Web Site: http://www.littletonchevrolet.com
Sales Range: $10-24.9 Million
Emp.: 44
New & Used Cars
N.A.I.C.S.: 441110
Ronney Lyster (Pres & Principal)

LITTLETON COIN CO., INC.
1309 Mount Eustis Rd, Littleton, NH 03561
Tel.: (603) 444-5386 NH
Web Site: http://www.littletoncoin.com
Year Founded: 1945
Sales Range: $150-199.9 Million
Emp.: 330
Mail Order Collector Coins
N.A.I.C.S.: 459999
David M. Sundman (Pres)
Edward Hennessey (CFO)

LITTLETON REGIONAL HEALTHCARE
600 Saint Johnsbury Rd, Littleton, NH 03561
Tel.: (603) 444-9000 NH
Web Site: http://www.littletonhealthcare.org
Year Founded: 1906
Sales Range: $50-74.9 Million
Emp.: 469
Healtcare Services
N.A.I.C.S.: 622110
Nick Braccino (CFO)
Linda Gilmore (Chief Admin Officer & Chief Nursing Officer)
Georgene Novak (Dir-HR)
Gail Clark (Dir-Mktg & Community Rels)
Warren West (CEO)
Robert W. Mach (Dir-Ops)
Robert F. Nutter (Pres)
Bill Bedor (Chm)
Leslie Walker (VP-Fin Svcs)

LITURGICAL PUBLICATIONS, INC.
2875 S James Dr, New Berlin, WI 53151
Web Site: http://www.4lpi.com
Publishing Services
N.A.I.C.S.: 513199
Paul Knaapen (Pres & CEO)

Subsidiaries:

YapStone Inc. (1)
2121 N California Blvd Ste 400, Walnut Creek, CA 94596
Tel.: (925) 956-1926
Web Site: http://www.yapstone.com
Sales Range: $50-74.9 Million
Emp.: 86
Electronic Payment Processing
N.A.I.C.S.: 522320
Tom Villante (Co-Founder, Chm & CEO)
Matthew Golis (Co-Founder)
David Weiss (Pres)
Alida Rincon (VP-Legal & Compliance)
Wendy Roberts (VP-Risk)
David E. Durant (Gen Counsel, Sec & Exec VP)
Debra Tenenbaum (Chief People Officer & Exec VP)
Troy Scarlott (VP-Mktg)
Peter Rowan (Exec VP-Ops-Intl)
Arjun Thusu (Chief Security Officer & Sr VP)
Sanjay Saraf (CTO & Exec VP)
Christopher Crum (Sr VP-Sls & Customer Success)
Kurt Bilafer (Chief Revenue Officer & Exec VP)
Richard Noguera (Chief Info Security Officer)
Molly St. Louis (Sr Dir-Mktg)
Antonio Alvarez Lorenzo (Chief Compliance Officer)
Jerry Ulrich (CFO & Exec VP)
Mike Gramz (Chief Risk Officer & Exec VP)
Scott M. Honour (Co-Founder)

LIUNA MIDWEST REGION
1 N Old State Capitol Plz Ste 525, Springfield, IL 62701
Tel.: (217) 522-3381
Web Site: https://www.midwestlaborers.org
Year Founded: 1903
Professional Development Training Services
N.A.I.C.S.: 611430

LIVE MARKETING, INC.
351 W Hubbard St Ste 805, Chicago, IL 60654
Tel.: (312) 787-4800
Web Site: http://www.livemarketing.com
Sales Range: $1-9.9 Million
Emp.: 23
Trade Show & Event Marketing
N.A.I.C.S.: 541890
Mark Norby (COO)
Anne Trompeter (Principal)
Stuart Popowcer (Controller)
Matt Freitas (Mgr-Customer Rels)

COMPANIES

LIVE MEDIA GROUP, LLC
53rd St, New York, NY 10019
Tel.: (818) 287-7300
Web Site:
http://livemediagroupholdings.com
Year Founded: 2008
Television & Live Entertainment Production
N.A.I.C.S.: 516120
Brad Sexton *(Pres & CEO)*

Subsidiaries:

Coastal Satellite, Inc. (1)
26660 Agoura Rd, Calabasas, CA 91302
Tel.: (818) 880-9800
Web Site:
http://www.coastalmediagroup.com
Motion Picture & Video Production
N.A.I.C.S.: 512110

Lyon Video, Inc. (1)
1201 Olentangy River Rd, Columbus, OH 43212
Tel.: (614) 297-0001
Web Site: http://www.lyonvideo.com
Sales Range: $1-9.9 Million
Emp.: 24
Motion Picture/Video Production Motion Picture Services
N.A.I.C.S.: 512110
Robert Lyon *(Pres)*
Chad Snyder *(COO)*

LIVE OAK BANCSHARES CORPORATION
601 Guadalupe St, George West, TX 78022
Tel.: (361) 449-1571 TX
Web Site: http://www.southtrust.com
Year Founded: 1981
Sales Range: $10-24.9 Million
Emp.: 75
Bank Holding Company
N.A.I.C.S.: 551111
Ross Harris *(Chm, Pres & CEO)*

Subsidiaries:

SouthTrust Bank, N.A. (1)
601 Guadalupe St, George West, TX 78022
Tel.: (361) 449-1571
Web Site: http://www.southtrust.com
Emp.: 30
Federal Savings Bank
N.A.I.C.S.: 522180
Steve Jackson *(Pres & CEO)*

LIVE OAK GOTTESMAN, LLC.
4330 Gaines Ranch Loop Ste 100, Austin, TX 78735
Tel.: (512) 472-5000
Web Site: http://www.liveoak.com
Year Founded: 2007
Sales Range: $50-74.9 Million
Emp.: 40
Land Subdivision Services
N.A.I.C.S.: 237210
Dacia Boyce *(Sr Mgr-Property)*
Lynette Dahmer *(Dir-Internal Compliance)*
Scott Flack *(Pres)*
Sandy Gottesman *(Principal)*
Dan Herd *(Principal)*
Jennifer Hilgenberg *(Mgr-Property)*
Jim Holden *(Principal)*
Alan Peters *(Dir-Office Tenant Representation)*
Doug Thomas *(Dir-Leasing)*
Franziska Jackson *(VP-Office Property Mgmt)*
Holley Jensen *(Mgr-Property)*
Mike Joyce *(COO)*
Rhonda Jaquez *(Mng Dir-Asset Svcs)*

LIVECHAIN, INC.
50 W Liberty St, Reno, NV 89501
Tel.: (775) 322-0626
Year Founded: 1989
Oil & Gas Exploration Services
N.A.I.C.S.: 213112

Zitian Dai *(Pres, Treas & Sec)*

LIVELY GROUP, LLC
575 Lexington Ave Fl 27, New York, NY 10022
Tel.: (212) 752-3348 NY
Web Site: http://www.livelygroup.tv
Advetising Agency
N.A.I.C.S.: 541810
Ethel Rubenstein *(Owner & CEO)*
Wendy Brovetto *(Mng Dir)*
Cara Cutrone *(Mng Dir & VP)*
Jennifer Lederman *(Mng Dir & VP)*

LIVENGOOD FEEDS INC.
300 N Colorado St, Lockhart, TX 78644
Tel.: (512) 398-2351
Web Site:
http://www.livengoodfeeds.com
Sales Range: $10-24.9 Million
Emp.: 40
Feed
N.A.I.C.S.: 424910
Lee Williams *(Gen Mgr)*

LIVENGRIN FOUNDATION
4833 Hulmeville Rd, Bensalem, PA 19020
Tel.: (215) 638-5200 DE
Web Site: http://www.livengrin.org
Year Founded: 1966
Sales Range: $10-24.9 Million
Emp.: 250
Drug Addiction Rehabilitation Services
N.A.I.C.S.: 621420
Suzanne Bright *(VP-Bus Dev)*
Charles Morin *(CFO & VP)*
Scott F. Blacker *(VP-Dev)*
Haja Jabbie *(VP-HR)*
James W. Cornish *(Dir-Medical)*

LIVEOPS, INC.
101 Redwood Shores Pkwy Ste 103, Redwood City, CA 94065
Tel.: (650) 453-2700 DE
Web Site: http://www.liveops.com
Year Founded: 2003
Emp.: 120
Holding Company; Call Center Management Cloud Platform Developer & Operations Services
N.A.I.C.S.: 551112
Greg Hanover *(Pres)*
Keith Leimbach *(CEO)*
Doug DeBolt *(Sr VP-Client & Bus Dev)*
David Greenberg *(Sr VP-Mktg)*
Purnima King *(Gen Counsel & VP)*
Ron Williamson *(Sr VP-Ops)*

LIVEPROCESS CORP.
271 Grove Ave Bldg D, Verona, NJ 07044
Tel.: (973) 571-2500 NJ
Web Site: http://www.liveprocess.com
Year Founded: 2004
Sales Range: $1-9.9 Million
Emp.: 25
Develops Web-Based Emergency Health Care Management Technology
N.A.I.C.S.: 541512
Nathaniel Weiss *(Founder)*
Brian LeBlanc *(CFO)*
Kelly Flood *(VP-Client Svcs)*
George Hartz *(VP-Dev)*
Robert Seliger *(Chm)*
Terry Zysk *(CEO)*

LIVERMORE AUTO GROUP
2266 Kitty Hawk Rd, Livermore, CA 94551
Tel.: (925) 294-7700
Web Site:
http://www.livermoreautogroup.com

Sales Range: $50-74.9 Million
Emp.: 150
Automobiles, New & Used
N.A.I.C.S.: 441110
Steve Tehero *(Mgr-Fleet Sls)*
Annette Coito *(Dir-Sls)*
Chris Sims *(Mgr-Sls)*
Nick Wilson *(Mgr-Internet Sls)*
Pedram Faed *(Gen Mgr)*
Stephen Bonny *(Mgr-Internet Sls)*
Steven Lewis *(Mgr-Internet Sls)*
Talal Hayder *(Mgr-Internet Sls)*
Tommy Ryan *(Mgr-Internet Sls)*
Vern Baumbach *(Mgr-Sls)*

LIVERPOOL ENTERPRISES INC.
10924 Vance Jackson Rd, San Antonio, TX 78230-2559
Tel.: (210) 696-2216 TX
Year Founded: 1971
Rev.: $100,000,000
Emp.: 50
Electrical Appliances, Television & Radio
N.A.I.C.S.: 423620
Leonard Holzman *(Pres)*
Doug Contie *(CEO)*

LIVESTRONG FOUNDATION
2201 E 6th St, Austin, TX 78702
Tel.: (512) 236-8820 TX
Web Site: http://www.livestrong.org
Year Founded: 1997
Sales Range: $25-49.9 Million
Emp.: 65
Cancer Rehabilitation Services
N.A.I.C.S.: 622310
Blaine P. Rollins *(Sec)*
Amelie G. Ramirez *(Treas)*
Joseph C. Aragona *(Vice Chm)*
Candice Toll Aaron *(Chm)*
Lori O'Brien *(VP-Natl Dev)*
Kelly Corley *(VP-Fin)*
Greg Lee *(Pres)*
Ashley Wilson *(VP-Mktg & Comm)*
Rebecca Lundquist *(VP-People)*

LIVESTYLE, INC.
9242 Beverly Blvd Ste 350, Beverly Hills, CA 90210
Tel.: (310) 860-2800 DE
Web Site: http://www.livestyle.com
Year Founded: 2012
Live Events & Entertainment Promoter
N.A.I.C.S.: 711320
Brandon Phillips *(Pres & CEO)*
Charles Ciongoli *(Exec VP & CFO)*
Gary Richards *(Pres-North America)*
Edo van Duijn *(COO)*
Alan Walter *(Sr VP-Fin & Controller)*

Subsidiaries:

Beatport, LLC (1)
2399 Blake St Ste 170, Denver, CO 80205
Tel.: (720) 974-9500
Web Site: http://www.beatport.com
Sales Range: $10-24.9 Million
Emp.: 42
Online Digital Music Store & Music Industry Information Services
N.A.I.C.S.: 519290
Gregory Consiglio *(Pres)*
Jonas Earp Tempel *(Founder)*
Lloyd Starr *(COO)*
Gina Lux *(Dir-Mktg)*
Rachel Survil *(Mgr-Mktg)*
Zel McCarthy *(VP-Media)*
Robb McDaniels *(CEO)*
Heiko Hoffmann *(Dir-Artist & Label Rels-Berlin)*
Terry Weerasinghe *(Chief Product Officer)*

I-Motion GmbH (1)
Am Hohen Stein 8, 56218, Mulheim-Karlich, Germany **(49.9%)**
Tel.: (49) 261 921 584 0
Web Site: http://www.i-motion.ag

Emp.: 40
Live Events & Entertainment Services
N.A.I.C.S.: 711320
Sheldon Finkel *(Exec Dir)*

SFXE Netherlands Holdings B.V. (1)
Overhoeksplein 1031 KS, Amsterdam, Amsterdam, Netherlands
Tel.: (31) 208510638
Holding Company
N.A.I.C.S.: 551114
Sascha Bogerd *(Controller)*

LIVETILES LIMITED
137 W 25th St Level 6th, New York, NY 10001
Tel.: (646) 887-2730 AU
Web Site:
https://www.livetilesglobal.com
Year Founded: 2014
LVT—(ASX)
Rev.: $20,184,741
Assets: $53,719,087
Liabilities: $28,627,040
Net Worth: $25,092,046
Earnings: ($22,064,656)
Emp.: 180
Fiscal Year-end: 06/30/23
Holding Company; Digital Solutions
N.A.I.C.S.: 551112

Subsidiaries:

LiveTiles Corporation (1)
137 W 25th St 6th Fl, New York, NY 10001 **(100%)**
Tel.: (646) 887-2730
Web Site: http://www.livetilesglobal.com
Business Software & Digital Solutions
N.A.I.C.S.: 513210
Karl Redenbach *(CEO)*

LIVEWATCH SECURITY, LLC
522 W Bertrand, Saint Marys, KS 66536
Tel.: (785) 437-2534
Web Site:
http://www.livewatchsecurity.com
Year Founded: 2002
Home Security Products & Solutions
N.A.I.C.S.: 561621
Christopher Johnson *(Founder & Pres)*

LIVEWELL CLINIC, LLC
13375 University Ave Ste 100, Clive, IA 50325
Tel.: (515) 279-9900 IA
Web Site:
http://www.thelivewellclinic.com
Year Founded: 2008
Sales Range: $1-9.9 Million
Emp.: 10
Health Care Srvices
N.A.I.C.S.: 621610
Zac Watkins *(Founder)*
Christina Davis *(Mktg Dir)*
Melissa Reisinger *(Dir-Patient Education)*
Erin Webb *(Coord-Patient Experience)*

LIVEWIRE ERGOGENICS INC.
24845 Corbit Pl, Yorba Linda, CA 92887
Tel.: (714) 940-0155 NV
Web Site:
http://www.livewireenergy.com
Year Founded: 2007
Sales Range: Less than $1 Million
Chewable Energy Supplements & Other Functional Foods
N.A.I.C.S.: 325412
Bill J. Hodson *(CEO)*
William Riley *(Pres)*
Jeff Dole *(VP-Central Coast Ops)*

LIVING BREATHING

Living Breathing—(Continued)
447 Broadway Fl 2, New York, NY 10013-2562
Tel.: (978) 985-7766
Year Founded: 2008
Sales Range: Less than $1 Million
Emp.: 15
N.A.I.C.S.: 541810
Christy Liu *(Founder & Partner)*
Evan Schneyer *(Founder & Digital Producer)*

LIVING DIRECT, INC.
500 N Capital of Texas Hwy Bldg 5, Austin, TX 78746
Tel.: (512) 467-7170
Web Site: http://www.livingdirect.com
Year Founded: 1999
Sales Range: $50-74.9 Million
Emp.: 65
Electronic Shopping Services
N.A.I.C.S.: 449129
Rick Lundbom *(CEO)*

LIVING EARTH
1901 California Crossing, Dallas, TX 75220
Tel.: (972) 869-4332
Web Site: http://www.livingearth.net
Year Founded: 1985
Sales Range: $10-24.9 Million
Emp.: 200
Organic Waste Recycling Services & Mulch Mfr
N.A.I.C.S.: 562920
Scott Estes *(Gen Mgr)*

LIVING STREAM MINISTRY
2431 W La Palma Ave, Anaheim, CA 92801
Tel.: (714) 236-6001
Web Site: http://www.lsm.org
Sales Range: $25-49.9 Million
Emp.: 250
Whslr of Religious Goods
N.A.I.C.S.: 459999
Benson Phillips *(Pres)*
Elton Karr *(Controller)*

LIVING WELL DISABILITY SERVICES
680 O'Neill Dr, Eagan, MN 55121-1535
Tel.: (651) 688-8808 MN
Web Site: http://www.livingwell.org
Year Founded: 1972
Sales Range: $10-24.9 Million
Emp.: 802
Disability Assistance Services
N.A.I.C.S.: 623210
Toni Gillen *(Dir-Community Life)*
Lisa Math *(Dir-Program)*
Jaclyn Schroeder *(Chief Dev Officer)*
Ghazi Akailvi *(CFO)*
Rod Carlson *(COO)*
Kris Solz *(Dir-HR)*
Julie Manworren *(Pres & CEO)*
Vikki Krekler *(Dir-Dev)*
Jenni Zeis *(Mgr-HR)*

LIVING WELLNESS PARTNERS LLC
3305 Tyler St, Carlsbad, CA 92008
Web Site: http://www.buddhateas.com
Year Founded: 2013
Sales Range: $1-9.9 Million
Emp.: 33
Herbal Supplement Distr
N.A.I.C.S.: 456191
John Boyd *(Founder)*

LIVING WHOLE FOODS, INC.
175 W 2770 S, Salt Lake City, UT 84115
Tel.: (801) 491-8700
Web Site: http://www.wheatgrasskits.com
Year Founded: 2000
Sales Range: $1-9.9 Million
Emp.: 30
Online Retailer of Specialty Organic Indoor Gardening Kits: Wheatgrass, Sprouts, Mushrooms, Herbs & Microgreens. Also Retails Juicers & Tofu Making Kits
N.A.I.C.S.: 444240
Parker Garlitz *(VP-Web Mktg & Owner)*
Cevan Bench *(Mgr-Sls)*
Katlin Moller *(Owner & CEO)*

LIVINGSTON HOSPITAL & HEALTHCARE SERVICES, INC.
131 Hospital Dr, Salem, KY 42078
Tel.: (270) 988-2299 KY
Web Site: http://www.lhhs.org
Year Founded: 1964
Sales Range: $10-24.9 Million
Emp.: 220
Health Care Srvices
N.A.I.C.S.: 622110
Tana Myrick *(Dir-Performance Improvment)*
Joanna Stone *(Chief Nursing Officer & Dir-Nursing)*
Carla Wiggins *(Dir-HR)*
Shannan Landreth *(CIO)*
Mark Edwards *(CEO)*
Kent Giles *(CFO)*

LIVINGSTON MACHINERY CO.
5201 S Hwy 81, Chickasha, OK 73018
Tel.: (405) 224-5056
Web Site: http://www.bigbalerusa.com
Sales Range: $10-24.9 Million
Emp.: 30
Farm & Landscaping Machinery Retailer
N.A.I.C.S.: 423820
Earl Livingston *(Owner)*
Shawn Kadds *(COO & Mgr-Sls)*

LIVINGSTON PIPE AND TUBE INC.
1612 Rte 4 N, Staunton, IL 62088
Tel.: (618) 635-8700
Web Site: http://www.livingstonpipeandtube.com
Sales Range: $10-24.9 Million
Emp.: 50
Pipe & Tubing; Steel
N.A.I.C.S.: 423510
Ronald Mueller *(Pres)*

LIVINGSTON'S CONCRETE SERVICE, INC.
5416 Roseville Rd, North Highlands, CA 95660
Tel.: (916) 334-4313
Web Site: http://www.livingstonsconcrete.com
Sales Range: $10-24.9 Million
Emp.: 75
Ready-Mixed Concrete Distributors
N.A.I.C.S.: 327320
Patricia L. Henley *(Pres)*
Ted W. Henly *(VP)*

LIVINGVENTURES, INC.
9681 Gladiolus Dr, Fort Myers, FL 33908
Tel.: (239) 437-0022 FL
Web Site: http://www.livingventuresinc.com
Year Founded: 1999
Sales Range: Less than $1 Million
Emp.: 9

Senior Housing Management Services
N.A.I.C.S.: 531390
Joseph Bickley *(CFO)*

LIVONIA, AVON & LAKEVILLE RAILROAD CORP.
5769 Sweetners Blvd, Lakeville, NY 14480
Tel.: (585) 346-2090 NY
Web Site: http://www.lalrr.com
Year Founded: 1964
Sales Range: $1-9.9 Million
Emp.: 15
Line-Haul Railroads
N.A.I.C.S.: 482111
Carl Belke *(COO & VP)*
Dan Eagan *(VP-Mktg & Sls)*
Jason Witt *(Chief Mechanical Officer)*
John Magee *(CFO)*
Raymond R. Martel *(Pres & CEO)*
Vincent T. Milliken *(VP-Customer Svc)*
Eugene H. Blabey II *(Chm)*

Subsidiaries:

Ontario Midland Railroad Corp. (1)
PO Box 267, Newark, NY 14513-0267 (55%)
Tel.: (315) 483-2152
Web Site: http://www.ontariomidland.com
Line-Haul Railroads
N.A.I.C.S.: 482111
Sandi Saracen *(Mgr)*

LIZARD'S THICKET INC.
1036 Market St, Columbia, SC 29201
Tel.: (803) 799-5016
Web Site: http://www.lizardsthicket.com
Year Founded: 1978
Rev.: $21,500,000
Emp.: 657
American Restaurant
N.A.I.C.S.: 722511
Jake Meggs *(Gen Mgr)*
Clayton Tapp *(Controller)*
Serge Ratkovich *(Gen Mgr)*
Todd Walker *(Gen Mgr)*
Jim Johnson *(Mgr-Restaurant)*
Robert E. Williams Jr. *(Chm & Pres)*

LIZTON FINANCIAL CORPORATION
206 N State St, Lizton, IN 46149
Tel.: (317) 994-5115 IN
Web Site: http://www.statebankoflizton.com
Year Founded: 1981
Sales Range: $10-24.9 Million
Emp.: 90
Bank Holding Company
N.A.I.C.S.: 551111
Michael L. Baker *(Pres & CEO)*
Peter I. Moyer *(CFO, Sec & Sr VP)*

Subsidiaries:

State Bank of Lizton (1)
206 N State St, Lizton, IN 46149
Tel.: (317) 994-5115
Web Site: http://www.statebankoflizton.com
Sales Range: $10-24.9 Million
Emp.: 160
Commerical Banking
N.A.I.C.S.: 522110
Michael L. Baker *(Pres & CEO)*

LJ DISTRIBUTORS INC.
12840 Leyva St, Norwalk, CA 90650
Tel.: (562) 229-7660
Web Site: http://ljtomato.com
Rev.: $17,900,000
Emp.: 80
Fresh Fruit & Vegetable Merchant Whslr
N.A.I.C.S.: 424480
Marlene Castro *(VP)*
Lute Miyazaki *(Pres)*

LJA ENGINEERING, INC.
2929 Briar Park Dr Ste 500, Houston, TX 77042
Tel.: (713) 953-5200
Web Site: http://www.ljaengineering.com
Emp.: 100
Engineeering Services
N.A.I.C.S.: 541330
Kenneth Schrock *(Sr VP-Austin)*
David Harris *(Dir-Client Svcs)*
Brady Baggs *(Sr Project Mgr-Land Dev-San Antonio)*
Angela Batiz *(Sr Project Mgr)*
Howard Caldwell *(VP)*
Allen Sims *(VP-Water Resources)*
William H. Espey *(Dir-Water Resources-Pub Works Div)*
Noe Escobar *(VP)*
Chris LeBlanc *(VP)*
Vince Salazar *(VP)*
Eddie Rucker *(VP)*
David Rivera *(VP-Land Dev)*
Kyle Salzman *(VP-Land Dev-North Texas)*
Jim Wiegert *(Sr VP-Land Dev-North Texas)*
James Ross *(Mgr-Land Dev)*
John Grounds III *(VP)*

Subsidiaries:

Agnoli, Barber & Brundage, Inc. (1)
7400 Tamiami Trl N, Naples, FL 34108
Tel.: (239) 597-3111
Web Site: http://www.abbinc.com
Sales Range: $1-9.9 Million
Emp.: 46
Engineeering Services
N.A.I.C.S.: 541330
Daniel W. Brundage *(Pres)*
Dominick J. Amico *(VP-Ops)*
Frederick T. Barber *(Chm & CEO)*
Guy P. Adams *(VP)*
James A. Carr *(Dir-Recruitment)*
George W. Hackney *(Dir-Global Positioning Sys)*

Freeland & Kauffman, Inc. (1)
209 W Stone Ave, Greenville, SC 29609
Tel.: (864) 233-5497
Web Site: http://www.fk-inc.com
Sales Range: $1-9.9 Million
Emp.: 20
Engineering Services, Nsk
N.A.I.C.S.: 541330
Kim Kauffman *(Pres)*
John Chudoba *(Project Mgr)*
Jeff Edney *(Engr-Pro)*

LJF ASSOCIATES, INC.
26419 Oak Rdg Dr, The Woodlands, TX 77380-1964
Tel.: (281) 367-3922 TX
Web Site: http://www.ljfassoc.com
Year Founded: 1989
Sales Range: Less than $1 Million
Emp.: 7
Advetising Agency
N.A.I.C.S.: 541810
Linda Freede *(Pres)*

LJP ENTERPRISES, INC.
2160 Ringhofer Dr, North Mankato, MN 56003
Tel.: (507) 934-6029 MN
Web Site: http://www.ljpent.com
Year Founded: 1992
Sales Range: $1-9.9 Million
Emp.: 40
Solid Waste Collection
N.A.I.C.S.: 562111
Larry Biederman *(Pres)*

LKCM HEADWATER INVESTMENTS
301 Commerce St Ste 1600, Fort Worth, TX 76102
Tel.: (817) 332-3235 TX
Web Site: http://lkcmheadwater.com

Year Founded: 1979
Investment Management Service
N.A.I.C.S.: 523999
J. Bryan King *(Mng Partner)*
Kimberly A. Carter *(VP)*

Subsidiaries:

ERIKS North America, Inc. (1)
650 Washington Rd Ste 210, Pittsburgh, PA 15228-2702
Tel.: (412) 341-7100
Web Site: https://www.eriksna.com
Sales Range: $200-249.9 Million
Emp.: 1,000
Industrial Supplies Distr
N.A.I.C.S.: 423840
David R. Goetz *(Chm)*
George R. Fox *(COO)*
Jeff Crane *(CEO)*
Michael J. Kulmoski Jr. *(CFO & CTO)*

Subsidiary (Domestic):

Advanced Sealing & Supply Company, Inc. (2)
13452 Alondra Blvd, Cerritos, CA 90703
Tel.: (562) 802-7782
Web Site: http://www.advseal.com
Sales Range: $1-9.9 Million
Emp.: 24
Industrial Supplies Merchant Whslr
N.A.I.C.S.: 423840
Alan Stubblefield *(CFO & Sr VP)*
Bill Clouse *(Pres & CEO)*
Jeff Clouse *(VP-Ops)*
Rodney Navarette *(VP-Mfg)*
Terry Subia *(VP-Sls & Mktg)*

Branham Corp. (2)
207 Eiler Ave, Louisville, KY 40214
Tel.: (502) 366-0326
Web Site: http://www.branhamcorp.com
Sales Range: $10-24.9 Million
Emp.: 36
Industrial Supplies
N.A.I.C.S.: 423840
Doug Branham *(Co-Pres)*
Stephen Mingis *(Co-Pres)*
Chuck Crawford *(CFO)*

Eriks Seals & Plastics, Inc. (2)
15600 Trinity Blvd Ste 100, Fort Worth, TX 76155
Tel.: (817) 267-8837
Web Site: http://www.eriksusa.com
Sales Range: $25-49.9 Million
Emp.: 30
Machine Tool, Metal Forming Types, Mfr
N.A.I.C.S.: 333517
Shawn Courtney *(Pres)*

Subsidiary (Domestic):

ERIKS Midwest (3)
5330 S Emmer Dr, New Berlin, WI 53151
Tel.: (262) 785-1333
Sales Range: $25-49.9 Million
Emp.: 30
Carburetor, Piston, Piston Ring & Valve Mfr
N.A.I.C.S.: 336310
Kenneth Bindas *(Supvr-Pur)*

ERIKS West, Inc. (3)
2230 Lind Ave SW Bldg C Ste 110, Renton, WA 98057
Tel.: (425) 981-9900
Web Site: http://www.eriksusa.com
Sealing Products Mfr & Distr
N.A.I.C.S.: 339991

Branch (Domestic):

ERIKS West (4)
46704 Fremont Blvd, Santa Clara, CA 94538
Tel.: (408) 988-2291
Web Site: http://www.calseal.com
Sales Range: $1-9.9 Million
Emp.: 21
Sealing & Vacuum Components Mfr
N.A.I.C.S.: 339991
Ericks West *(Owner)*

Subsidiary (Domestic):

Valley Rubber & Gasket Co. Inc. (2)
10182 Croydon Way, Sacramento, CA 95827
Tel.: (916) 366-9340
Web Site: http://www.valleyrubberandgasket.com
Sales Range: $10-24.9 Million
Emp.: 35
Distr of Industrial Products, Including Hose, Belting & Packing
N.A.I.C.S.: 423840

Knack Systems, LLC (1)
1 Woodbridge Ctr Ste 335, Woodbridge, NJ 07095
Tel.: (732) 596-0110
Web Site: http://www.knacksystems.com
Sales Range: $1-9.9 Million
Emp.: 45
Computer Integrated Systems Design, Nsk
N.A.I.C.S.: 541512
Usha Musku *(Mgr)*

Subsidiary (Domestic):

Delta Business Systems, Inc. (2)
2317 Mount Olive Rd, Gardendale, AL 35071
Tel.: (205) 631-0374
Sales Range: $1-9.9 Million
Emp.: 56
Computer & Software Stores
N.A.I.C.S.: 449210
Frank Tobin *(VP)*

LKH&S
54 W Hubbard Ste 100, Chicago, IL 60610
Tel.: (312) 595-0200
Web Site: http://www.lkhs.com
Year Founded: 1991
Sales Range: $10-24.9 Million
Emp.: 50
Advetising Agency
N.A.I.C.S.: 541810
Stanton Lewin *(Principal & Mng Dir)*
Samuel Kirshenbaum *(Principal & Exec Dir-Creative)*
William Heuglin *(Assoc Dir-Creative)*
Michael Shmarak *(Dir-Pub Rels)*
Rebecca Dillon *(Dir-Print Production)*
Jennyfer Butzen Dougherty *(Media Planner & Sr AE)*
James Goldman *(Sr Acct Dir)*

Subsidiaries:

LKH&S Louisville (1)
4907 Dunbarvalley Rd, Fisherville, KY 40023
Tel.: (502) 261-9826
N.A.I.C.S.: 541810
Bill Heuglin *(Assoc Dir-Creative)*

LKL ASSOCIATES INC.
134 N 1600 W, Orem, UT 84057
Tel.: (801) 225-3830
Web Site:
http://www.lklassociates.com
Rev.: $20,000,000
Emp.: 32
Building Materials, Interior
N.A.I.C.S.: 423320
Kim L. Norris *(Pres)*
Brett Warren *(Controller)*
Joanne Martin *(Mgr-Credit)*

LL PELLING COMPANY INC.
1425 W Penn St, North Liberty, IA 52317
Tel.: (319) 626-4600
Web Site: http://www.llpelling.com
Rev.: $10,700,000
Emp.: 30
Highway & Street Paving Contractor
N.A.I.C.S.: 237310
Chuck Finnegan *(Pres)*
Brett Finnegan *(VP)*
Gary Netser *(Mgr-QC)*

LLANO UTILITY SERVICES INC.
3501 FM 2181 Ste 245, Corinth, TX 76210
Tel.: (940) 270-8700
Web Site: http://www.llanoutility.com
Rev.: $36,100,000
Emp.: 15
Underground Utilities Contractor
N.A.I.C.S.: 237110
Kathryn Rausch *(Controller)*

LLEWELLYN WORLDWIDE LIMITED
2143 Wooddale Dr, Woodbury, MN 55125-2989
Tel.: (651) 291-1970   MN
Web Site: http://www.llewellyn.com
Year Founded: 1901
Sales Range: $75-99.9 Million
Emp.: 100
Book & Magazine Publisher
N.A.I.C.S.: 513130
Carl L. Weschcke *(Owner & Chm)*

LLFLEX, LLC
1225 W Burnett St, Louisville, KY 40210
Web Site: http://www.llflex.com
Plastics Bottle Mfr
N.A.I.C.S.: 326160
Scott Lynch *(Sr Engr-Electrical)*
Kerry Cimbalo *(Dir-HR)*
Curtis Conley *(Dir-Global Supply Chain)*
John Kay *(COO)*
Thomas Bowden *(CEO)*
Tamra Koshewa *(CFO)*
Larry Posner *(Chm)*

Subsidiaries:

Hampden Papers Inc. (1)
100 Water St, Holyoke, MA 01040-6210
Tel.: (413) 536-1000
Web Site: http://www.hampdenpapers.com
Sales Range: $25-49.9 Million
Emp.: 179
Paper; Coated & Laminated Packaging
N.A.I.C.S.: 326112
Richard Wells *(Pres)*
Harold Dumas *(Mgr-IT)*
Brenda O'Connor *(Mgr-Traffic)*
Bob Adams *(VP-Sls & Mktg)*
Jim Kennedy *(Mgr-Customer Svc)*

LLI MANAGEMENT COMPANY, LLC
7000 Lanier Islands Pkwy, Buford, GA 30518-1403
Tel.: (770) 945-8787   GA
Web Site:
http://www.lakelanierislands.com
Hotel & Resort Owner & Operator
N.A.I.C.S.: 721110
Virgil R. Williams *(Principal)*

LLJ INC.
4501 Prairie Pkwy, Cedar Falls, IA 50613
Tel.: (319) 277-8000
Web Site:
http://www.lockardonline.com
Rev.: $10,000,000
Emp.: 141
Development & Real Estate
N.A.I.C.S.: 236220
Kenneth A. Lockard *(Chm)*
Robert L. Smith *(Pres)*
James M. Fettkether *(Exec VP-Construction)*
John Flint *(Dir-Asset Mgmt)*
John Brooks *(Mgr-Mktg)*

Subsidiaries:

Iowa Securities Investment Corporation (1)
3346 Kimball Ave, Waterloo, IA 50702
Tel.: (319) 236-3334
Sales Range: Less than $1 Million
Emp.: 5
Dealers, Security
N.A.I.C.S.: 523150

Lockard Development Inc. (1)
4501 Prairie Pkwy, Cedar Falls, IA 50613
Tel.: (319) 277-8000
Web Site: http://www.lockardrealty.com
Rev.: $2,360,912
Emp.: 22
Commercial & Industrial Building Operation
N.A.I.C.S.: 531120
Kenneth A. Lockard *(Chm)*
Robert Smith *(Pres)*
John Brooks *(Mgr-Comml Mktg)*
John Flint *(Exec VP-Asset Mgmt & Strategic Initiatives)*
Jack Jennings *(Dir-Sls & Leasing-South)*
Crissy Kentopp *(Accountant)*
Paul Leonardson *(Dir-Property Mgmt)*
Christopher J. Rausch *(Gen Counsel & Sr VP)*
Paul Riordan *(Mgr-Construction)*
Dustin Whitehead *(Dir-Sls & Leasing-Midwest)*

LLOG EXPLORATION OFFSHORE, INC.
1001 Ochsner Blvd Ste 200, Covington, LA 70433
Tel.: (504) 833-7700
Web Site: http://www.llog.com
Rev.: $12,600,000
Emp.: 100
Oil & Gas Exploration Services
N.A.I.C.S.: 213112
Philip Lejeune *(CFO)*
Gerald A. Boelte *(Chm)*
Scott Gutterman *(Pres & CEO)*
Michael Altobelli *(VP-Land)*
James Bassi *(Chief Risk Officer & Chief Acctg Officer)*
Kem Ducote *(Chief Admin Officer & Sec)*
Tim Lindsey *(Sr VP-Production & Ops)*

LLOYD & CO.
180 Varick St Ste 1018, New York, NY 10014
Tel.: (212) 414-3100
Web Site: http://www.lloydandco.com
Year Founded: 1994
Sales Range: $10-24.9 Million
Emp.: 25
Advertising Agencies
N.A.I.C.S.: 541810
Jodi Sweetbaum *(Pres & Mng Dir)*
Douglas Lloyd *(Pres)*

LLOYD BELT AUTOMOTIVE
2007 Business Hwy 54 S, Eldon, MO 65026
Tel.: (573) 392-3333
Web Site: http://www.lloydbelt.com
Rev.: $14,000,000
Emp.: 58
Pre-Owned Car Dealers
N.A.I.C.S.: 441120
Lloyd Belt *(Owner & Pres)*

LLOYD ELECTRIC, INC.
2615 Grant St, Wichita Falls, TX 76309
Tel.: (940) 766-3213
Web Site:
http://www.lloydelectric.com
Sales Range: $10-24.9 Million
Emp.: 10
Electrical Management & Construction Services
N.A.I.C.S.: 238210
Bobby Lloyd *(Pres)*
Paul Hix *(VP)*

LLOYD ENTERPRISES INC.
34667 Pacific Hwy S Federal Way, Federal Way, WA 98003
Tel.: (253) 874-6692
Web Site:
http://www.lloydenterprisesinc.com
Sales Range: $10-24.9 Million
Emp.: 38
Construction Sand & Gravel

LLOYD ENTERPRISES INC.

U.S. PRIVATE

Lloyd Enterprises Inc.—(Continued)
N.A.I.C.S.: 212321
Randy Lloyd (VP)

LLOYD PEST CONTROL COMPANY INCORPORATED
1202 Morena Blvd, San Diego, CA 92117
Tel.: (619) 298-9865
Web Site: http://www.lloydpest.com
Sales Range: $25-49.9 Million
Emp.: 120
Exterminating & Fumigating
N.A.I.C.S.: 561710
James A. Ogle (Pres)
Scott Crowley (COO-Gen Pest)

LLOYD STAFFING INC.
445 Broadhollow Rd Ste 119, Melville, NY 11747-3669
Tel.: (631) 777-7600
Web Site:
   http://www.lloydstaffing.com
Year Founded: 1971
Sales Range: $25-49.9 Million
Emp.: 300
Executive Search & Supplemental Staffing
N.A.I.C.S.: 561320
Merrill L. Banks (Founder & CEO)
Nancy Schuman (CMO & Chief Comm Officer)
Brian Green (VP-IT)
Donna Caputo (VP-HR)
Keith Banks (Pres)
Jason Banks (Exec VP)
William Veraszto (VP-Tech)
Gerald Angowitz (Mng Dir)
Kerry McCormick (Dir-Hospitality Mgmt)
Christine Lopez (Dir-Client Success-Creative)
Jennifer Tripodi (Dir-Client Success-Healthcare)
Jeanine Bondi Banks (Exec VP)

Subsidiaries:

Lloyd Staffing Inc. - New York City (1)
58 W 40th St, New York, NY 10018
Tel.: (212) 354-8787
Web Site: http://www.lloydstaffing.com
Emp.: 100
Human Resources & Executive Search Consulting Services
N.A.I.C.S.: 541612
Kim Unruh (Controller)
Jason Banks (Exec VP-CSP)

LLT BUILDING CORPORATION
1632 Metropolitan Cir Ste A, Tallahassee, FL 32308-3790
Tel.: (850) 222-5062
Web Site: http://www.lltbldg.com
Rev.: $25,000,000
Emp.: 30
Commercial & Institutional Building Construction
N.A.I.C.S.: 236220
Dennis Tribble (Pres & CEO)
Ron Drapeau (VP-Ops)

LM RESTAURANTS, INC.
6510 Chapel Hill Rd Ste 200, Raleigh, NC 27607
Tel.: (919) 851-0858
Web Site: http://www.lmrest.com
Year Founded: 1978
Sales Range: $50-74.9 Million
Emp.: 1,950
Restaurant Operators
N.A.I.C.S.: 722511
Tonya Towler (Controller)
Lou Moshakos (Pres)
Joy Moshakos (VP)

Subsidiaries:

Atlantic Quest Catering Company (1)
209 Englewood Dr, Wilmington, NC 28409
Tel.: (910) 313-6400
Web Site: http://www.atlanticquest.net
Catering Services
N.A.I.C.S.: 722320

LM&O ADVERTISING
2000 N 14th St 8th Fl, Arlington, VA 22201-2573
Tel.: (703) 875-2193
Web Site: http://www.lmo.com
Year Founded: 1995
Sales Range: $10-24.9 Million
Emp.: 60
Advetising Agency
N.A.I.C.S.: 541810
David Marinaccio (Chief Creative Officer)
Chris Laughlin (Pres)
Cynthia Epley (Dir-Media)
Sherri Anne Green (Dir-Bus Dev)
Karen Laughlin (Dir-Interactive Mktg)
Mike Caplanis (Dir-Creative)
Jennifer Lennon (Dir-Traffic)

LMC MARINE CENTER
14904 N Freeway, Houston, TX 77090
Tel.: (281) 443-2600
Web Site: http://www.lmcboats.com
Sales Range: $10-24.9 Million
Emp.: 9
Boat Whslr
N.A.I.C.S.: 441222
Ashley Lutz (Asst Mgr-Fin)
Susan Christine (Mgr)

LMD INTEGRATED LOGISTIC SERVICES, INC.
3136 E Victoria St, Rancho Dominguez, CA 90221-5618
Tel.: (310) 638-3862
Web Site:
   http://www.lmdlogistics.com
Sales Range: $10-24.9 Million
Emp.: 47
Trucking Except Local
N.A.I.C.S.: 484121
Bill Sampson (VP-Sls)

LMI PACKAGING SOLUTIONS, INC.
8911 102nd St, Pleasant Prairie, WI 53158
Tel.: (262) 947-3300
Web Site:
   http://www.lmipackaging.com
Sales Range: $10-24.9 Million
Emp.: 42
Commercial Flexographic Printing
N.A.I.C.S.: 323111
Jean Moran (CEO)
Vince Incandela (VP-Employee & Community Engagement)
Joe Kumpfer (VP-Fin)
Kevin Meyer (VP-Ops)

LMK AUTO GROUP LTD.
1110 Broadway Ave, Gladewater, TX 75647
Tel.: (903) 845-2132
Web Site: http://www.mckaig.net
Sales Range: $25-49.9 Million
Emp.: 17
New & Used Car Dealers
N.A.I.C.S.: 441110
Mark Abernathy (Pres)
Larry Arron (VP)
Ken Abernathy (Treas & Sec)

LMP MANAGEMENT GROUP, INC.
353 W Lancaster Ave, Wayne, PA 19087
Tel.: (610) 687-5045
Web Site:
   http://www.larsenmaccoll.com
Emp.: 9
Equity Investment Firm
N.A.I.C.S.: 523999
Jeff Larsen (Mng Partner)
Tim MacColl (Mng Partner)
Todd Marsteller (Partner)
Satya Ponnuru (Partner)
Kristen Hubbert (Dir-Ops)
Christopher J. Davis (Partner, CFO & COO)
Arielle Klinetsky (Coord-Ops & Mktg)

Subsidiaries:

S. Walter Packaging Corp. (1)
2900 Grant Ave, Philadelphia, PA 19114
Tel.: (215) 676-8888
Web Site: http://www.swalter.com
Sales Range: $100-124.9 Million
Emp.: 100
Packaging Products & Accessories Distr.
N.A.I.C.S.: 424130
Michael Jobes (Pres)
Richard L. Gettlin (CFO)
John Dowers (CEO)
Tony Patti (CIO)
Paula Wilmer (Sr VP-Sls-Natl)
Richard Alexander (Pres-Indus Pkg Div)

LMS INTELLIBOUND, INC.
6525 The Corners Pkwy Ste 520, Norcross, GA 30092
Tel.: (770) 414-1929
Web Site:
   http://www.lmsintellibound.com
Year Founded: 1986
Sales Range: $50-74.9 Million
Emp.: 2,000
Logistics & Warehouse Services
N.A.I.C.S.: 541614
Steve Taylor (CEO)
Chris Bray (Chief Partnership Officer)
David Morris (CFO)
Gene Weiland (CIO)
Matt Sedgwick (Sr VP-Fin)
Nancy Geraghty (VP-People Ops)
Rick Tomcho (Chief Comml Officer)

LNC PARTNERS
11710 Plaza America Dr Ste 160, Reston, VA 20190
Tel.: (703) 651-2150
Web Site: http://www.lnc-partners.com
Year Founded: 2011
Privater Equity Firm
N.A.I.C.S.: 523999
Matt Kelty (Mng Partner)
Robert Monk (Mng Partner)
Mark Raterman (Mng Partner)
Jon Felsher (VP)
Kevin Cunningham (Mng Dir)

LOAD DELIVERED LOGISTICS LLC
750 N Orleans Unit 100, Chicago, IL 60654
Web Site:
   http://www.loaddelivered.com
Year Founded: 2008
Sales Range: $10-24.9 Million
Emp.: 38
Logistics & Transportation
N.A.I.C.S.: 488999
Robert Nathan (Co-Founder & CEO)

LOAD ONE TRANSPORTATION & LOGISTICS
13221 Inkster, Taylor, MI 48180
Tel.: (734) 947-9440
Web Site: http://www.load1.com
Year Founded: 1977
Sales Range: $25-49.9 Million

Emp.: 170
General Freight Trucking Services
N.A.I.C.S.: 484110
Rich Gosnell (Mgr-Acct & Sls)
Erik Sturm (Mgr-Logistics)
John K. Elliott II (CEO)

LOADMATCH LOGISTICS INC.
1013 Ashes Dr Ste 200, Wilmington, NC 28405
Tel.: (910) 515-4500
Web Site:
   http://www.loadmatch123.com
Year Founded: 2006
Sales Range: $1-9.9 Million
Emp.: 11
Logistics & Transportation
N.A.I.C.S.: 488510
Gary L. Winstead (Pres)
Sarah Calson (Corp Controller)
Scott Anderson (COO)
Keith Hanson (Mgr-Ops)
Phil Alfano (CFO)

LOADSPRING SOLUTIONS, INC.
187 Ballardvale St Ste B210, Wilmington, MA 01887
Tel.: (978) 685-9715
Web Site: http://www.loadspring.com
Year Founded: 1999
Rev.: $3,700,000
Emp.: 17
Project Management Software
N.A.I.C.S.: 513210
D. Eric Leighton (Pres & CEO)
Jim Smith (Exec VP)
Al Marshall (Exec VP)
Cameron Vixie (Exec VP-Engrg & Dev)
Warren Krueger (Exec VP-Customer Experience)
Drew Senner (Exec VP-Sls)

LOADUP TECHNOLOGIES, LLC
300 Galleria Pkwy Ste 1870, Atlanta, GA 30334
Web Site: http://www.goloadup.com
Year Founded: 2014
Sales Range: $1-9.9 Million
Emp.: 15
Junk Removal & Hauling Services
N.A.I.C.S.: 562119
Greg Workman (Founder & CEO)
Jason Brown (CMO)
Riaz Virani (CTO)
Chris Getz (Dir-Ops)
Tiffany Luther (Mktg Dir)

LOAN RESOLUTION CORPORATION
7047 E Greenway Pkwy Ste 400, Scottsdale, AZ 85254
Tel.: (480) 556-0756
Web Site:
   http://www.loanresolution.com
Year Founded: 2005
Sales Range: $10-24.9 Million
Emp.: 207
Mortgage Loan Brokerage & Real Estate Management Services
N.A.I.C.S.: 522310
Doug McCabe (CEO)
Matt McCabe (Pres)
Damien Chiodo (Mng Partner)
Ty Reed (Mng Partner)

LOANATIK, LLC
4550 E Cactus Rd Ste 250, Phoenix, AZ 85032
Web Site: http://www.loanatik.com
Year Founded: 2015
Sales Range: $1-9.9 Million
Emp.: 19
Residential Brokerage Services

N.A.I.C.S.: 531210
Corey Schwartz *(Founder & Pres)*
Dan Saba *(VP)*
Marco Leone *(VP-Loan Production)*
Duchai Nguyentan *(Sls Mgr)*
Brian Cowan *(Officer-Loan)*

LOANBRIGHT.COM
27902 Meadow Dr Ste 375, Evergreen, CO 80439
Tel.: (303) 679-0552
Web Site: http://www.loanbright.com
Sales Range: $1-9.9 Million
Emp.: 17
Mortgage Comparison Shopping Services
N.A.I.C.S.: 522310
Russell Straub *(Co-Founder, Pres & CEO)*
Mark Barlow *(Co-Founder, CTO & VP)*
David Black *(Co-Founder)*
Scott Wiesenmeyer *(VP-Client Rels)*

LOANCORE REALTY TRUST, INC.
55 Railroad Ave Ste 100, Greenwich, CT 06830
Tel.: (203) 861-6000   MD
Web Site: http://www.loancore.com
Year Founded: 2013
Sales Range: $25-49.9 Million
Emp.: 50
Real Estate Investment Trust
N.A.I.C.S.: 525990
Mark Finerman *(Pres-LoanCore Capital, LLC & CEO-Jefferies LoanCore LLC)*
Jordan Bock *(Chief Investment Officer & Sec)*
Christopher McCormack *(CFO & Treas)*
Daniel Bennett *(Head-Capital Markets)*
Gary Berkman *(Chief Credit Officer)*
Perry Gershon *(Chief Investment Officer)*

LOANDEPOT.COM, LLC
26642 Towne Centre Dr, Foothill Ranch, CA 92610
Tel.: (888) 983-3240
Web Site: http://www.loandepot.com
Consumer Lending
N.A.I.C.S.: 522291
Tammy Richards *(COO)*
Rick Calle *(Chief Strategy Officer & Exec VP)*
Dan Hanson *(Chief Retail Production Officer)*
John Bianchi *(Exec VP-Natl Sls)*
John Lee *(Chief Analytics Officer)*
Kevin Tackaberry *(Exec VP-HR)*
Dean Bloxom *(Chief Strategic Partnership Officer)*
David King *(CMO)*
Jeff DerGurahian *(Exec VP-Capital Markets)*
Jeff Walsh *(COO)*

LOANSOURCE INC.
114 Mackenan Dr Ste 300, Cary, NC 27511-7903
Tel.: (919) 466-8615
Web Site: http://www.lonesource.com
Sales Range: $10-24.9 Million
Emp.: 50
Web Based Procurement Site for Office Consumables
N.A.I.C.S.: 541511
Bradley King *(Founder & CEO)*
David Ryan *(CFO & Exec VP)*
Stacey King *(COO & Exec VP)*

Subsidiaries:

Business-Supply.com, Inc.   (1)
114 Mackenan Dr Ste 300, Cary, NC 27511-7903
Tel.: (919) 465-9661
Web Site: http://www.business-supply.com
Business-Related Products Online Retailer
N.A.I.C.S.: 459410

LOAR GROUP, INC.
450 Lexington Ave, New York, NY 10017
Tel.: (212) 210-9348
Web Site: http://www.loargroup.com
Aerospace Component Mfr
N.A.I.C.S.: 336413
Dirkson Charles *(Founder & CEO)*
Glenn D'Alessandro *(CFO)*
Michael Manella *(Gen Counsel & VP)*
Jim Mullen *(VP-Engrg)*
Jonathan Fournier *(VP-Sls)*
Debra Wick *(Exec VP)*

Subsidiaries:

AGC Acquisition LLC   (1)
106 Evansville Ave, Meriden, CT 06451-0908
Tel.: (203) 639-7125
Web Site: http://www.agcincorporated.com
Sales Range: $50-74.9 Million
Precision Components Mfr for Commercial & Aerospace Industry
N.A.I.C.S.: 336413
Shelly Anderson *(Pres)*
Michael Gumprecht *(VP-Ops & Gen Mgr)*
Doris D. Harms *(Exec VP)*
Michael Doolan *(VP-Sls)*
James Dempsey *(Dir-HR)*

Aviation Manufacturing Group, LLC   (1)
719 Walnut St, Yankton, SD 57078
Tel.: (605) 665-7456
Web Site: http://www.freemanmanufacturing.com
Sales Range: $1-9.9 Million
Aircraft Parts & Auxiliary Equipment Mfr
N.A.I.C.S.: 336413
Debra Wick *(Exec VP)*
Debbie Evans *(Mng Dir-Asia Pacific)*
Adam Charles *(Exec VP-Corp Brand Experience)*

General Ecology, Inc.   (1)
151 Sheree Blvd, Exton, PA 19341
Tel.: (610) 363-7900
Web Site: http://www.generalecology.com
Rev.: $4,900,000
Emp.: 45
Drinking Water Purification Services
N.A.I.C.S.: 221310
Bonnie Williams *(Treas)*
Richard Williams *(Founder & Pres)*

Hydra-Electric Company   (1)
3151 Kenwood St, Burbank, CA 91505
Tel.: (818) 843-6211
Web Site: http://www.hydraelectric.com
Emp.: 200
Electro Mechanical Equipment Mfr
N.A.I.C.S.: 335999
Allen V.C. Davis *(Founder & Chm)*
Edwin J. Victoria *(Gen Mgr)*
David E. Schmidt *(CEO)*
Len Torres *(COO)*

Terry's Machine & Manufacturing, Inc.   (1)
12128 Cyrus Way Ste B, Mukilteo, WA 98275
Tel.: (425) 315-8866
Web Site: http://www.terrysmachine.com
Sales Range: $1-9.9 Million
Emp.: 15
Machine Shops
N.A.I.C.S.: 332710
Roger Sanford *(Owner)*

LOBSTER TRAP CO. INC.
290 Shore Rd, Bourne, MA 02532
Tel.: (508) 759-6400
Web Site: http://www.lobstertrap.com
Sales Range: $10-24.9 Million
Emp.: 50
Seafoods
N.A.I.C.S.: 424460

Logan Clarke *(Pres)*
Natalie Wagner *(Office Mgr & Coord-IT)*
Brian Murphy *(CFO)*
James Schubauer II *(COO)*

LOBUE & MAJDALANY MANAGEMENT GROUP, INC.
572 Ruger St Ste B, San Francisco, CA 94129-1795
Tel.: (415) 561-6110   CA
Web Site: http://www.lm-mgmt.com
Year Founded: 1996
Association Management Services
N.A.I.C.S.: 541611
Michael T. LoBue *(Pres & CEO)*
Michael Majdalany *(COO & VP)*
Mike Briones *(Controller)*

LOCAL LEADS HQ
2625 Townsgate Rd, Westlake Village, CA 91361
Web Site: http://www.localleadshq.com
Year Founded: 2007
Sales Range: $1-9.9 Million
Emp.: 7
Advertising & Marketing
N.A.I.C.S.: 541810
L. F. Vee *(COO)*

LOCAL MARKETING GIANT, LLC
319 N Main Ave Ste 130, Springfield, MO 65806
Tel.: (417) 315-8831
Web Site: http://www.omgcommerce.com
Year Founded: 2010
Sales Range: $1-9.9 Million
Emp.: 23
Digital Marketing Services
N.A.I.C.S.: 541810
Brett Curry *(CEO)*
Chris Brewer *(Founder)*
Sarah Edwards *(COO)*
Brandi Johnston *(Dir-Acct Mgmt)*
Allee Mixon *(Acct Mgr)*

LOCAL MARKETING SOLUTIONS GROUP, INC.
1600 Golf Rd Ste 1200 Corporate Ctr, Rolling Meadows, IL 60008-4229
Tel.: (312) 943-1600
Web Site: http://www.jgsullivan.com
Custom Computer Programming Services
N.A.I.C.S.: 541511
Al Croke *(Pres & CEO)*
Brett Knobloch *(Co-Owner)*
Lukasz Racon *(Co-Owner)*
Kevin Sullivan *(Co-Owner)*
Greg Ratliff *(Dir-Technical Engrg)*

Subsidiaries:

KMA One, Inc.   (1)
6815 Meadowridge Ct, Alpharetta, GA 30005
Tel.: (770) 886-4000
Web Site: http://www.kmaone.com
Scientific & Technical Consulting Services
N.A.I.C.S.: 541690
Keith Manning *(CEO)*
Meryl McKenna *(Pres)*

Money Mailer, LLC   (1)
6261 Katella Ave Ste 200, Cypress, CA 90630
Tel.: (714) 889-3800
Web Site: http://www.moneymailer.com
Sales Range: $25-49.9 Million
Emp.: 60
Direct Mail Advertising Services; Operator of Coupon Website
N.A.I.C.S.: 541860
John Patinella *(Sr VP-Franchise Ops)*
Dennis Jenkins *(VP-Franchise Licensing)*
Gary Mulloy *(Chm & CEO)*
Mike Hiskett *(Sr VP-Company Ops)*

LOCAL MATTERS, INC.
1221 Auraria Pkwy, Denver, CO 80204
Tel.: (303) 572-1122   DE
Web Site: http://www.localmatters.com
Sales Range: $1-9.9 Million
Emp.: 193
Software & Media Services
N.A.I.C.S.: 513210
Nancy Hamilton *(CFO)*
Nahid Giga *(Sr VP-Bus Dev)*
Eric Spencer *(VP-HR & Admin)*
David Moore *(Chm)*

LOCAL MEDIA LINK
607 N Ave Door 18, Wakefield, MA 01880
Tel.: (978) 332-8000
Web Site: http://www.localmedialink.com
Sales Range: $10-24.9 Million
Emp.: 20
Advertising Directory Publisher
N.A.I.C.S.: 513199
Richard Corbett *(Exec VP)*
Robert C. Nolan *(CFO)*
Kerri Welch *(Mgr-Sls & Ops)*

LOCAL OIL DISTRIBUTING INC.
2015 7th Ave, Anoka, MN 55303
Tel.: (763) 421-4923
Sales Range: $10-24.9 Million
Emp.: 7
Fuel Oil
N.A.I.C.S.: 424720

LOCALNET CORP.
325 Hampton Hill Dr, Williamsville, NY 14221
Tel.: (716) 632-1133
Web Site: http://www.localnet.com
Year Founded: 1994
Sales Range: $10-24.9 Million
Emp.: 120
Dial-Up Internet Access, Web Hosting & Domain Registration Services
N.A.I.C.S.: 517810
Marc P. Silvestri *(Founder & Pres)*

LOCALYTICS COMPANY
141 Tremont St 7th Fl, Boston, MA 02111
Tel.: (617) 418-4422
Web Site: http://www.localytics.com
Year Founded: 2008
Sales Range: $25-49.9 Million
Emp.: 200
Mobile Analytics Software
N.A.I.C.S.: 513210
Raj Aggarwal *(Founder)*
Henry Cipolla *(CTO)*
Nick Fasano *(VP-Sls)*
Brian Suthoff *(Chief Strategy Officer)*
Scott Bleczinski *(Chief Revenue Officer)*
Lou Orfanos *(VP-Product)*
Craig Herman *(VP-Strategic Enterprise Accts)*
Jude McColgan *(CEO)*
Paul Fitzgerald *(CFO)*

LOCATION SERVICES, LLC
11350 N Meridian St., Ste 200, Carmel, IN 46032
Tel.: (800) 588-0097
Web Site: http://www.location-services.com
Year Founded: 1995
End-to-End Location, Recovery, License Plate Recognition & Transportaiton Services
N.A.I.C.S.: 522320
Jerry Kroshus *(CEO)*
Mohit Mahajan *(CIO)*

LOCATION SERVICES, LLC

Location Services, LLC—(Continued)
Jose Delgado (COO & Chief Client Officer)
Michele Connell (VP-Client Rels)
Debbie Stokes (Dir-Remktg-Natl)
Subsidiaries:
Premier Adjusters, Inc. (1)
1229 Buschong St, Houston, TX 77039-1104
Tel.: (281) 442-0800
Web Site: http://www.premieradjusters.com
Claims Adjusting
N.A.I.C.S.: 524291

LOCHER BROS INC.
18098 365th Ave, Green Isle, MN 55338
Tel.: (507) 326-5471
Web Site: http://www.locherbros.com
Sales Range: $10-24.9 Million
Emp.: 55
Beer & Other Fermented Malt Liquors
N.A.I.C.S.: 424810
Alfred W. Locher (Chm)
Bob Utenborser (Pres)
Kim Bade (Mgr-Computer Graphics-Banner Room)
Gwen Utendorfer (Owner)

LOCHRIDGE-PRIEST INC.
2901 E Industrial, Waco, TX 76705
Tel.: (254) 772-0670
Web Site: http://www.lochridgepriest.com
Year Founded: 1997
Sales Range: $25-49.9 Million
Emp.: 340
Provider of Plumbing, Heating & Air-Conditioning Services
N.A.I.C.S.: 238220
B.J Akins (CFO)
Ridge Johnson (VP)

LOCI CONTROLS, INC.
99 S Main St Ste 310, Fall River, MA 02721-5349
Tel.: (617) 575-2716
Web Site: http://www.locicontrols.com
Year Founded: 2013
Sensor Device Mfr
N.A.I.C.S.: 334511
Peter Quigley (Chm & CEO)
Matt Taylor (Mgr-Sls & Safety)
Jack Rowbottom (Mgr-Landfill Gas Collection)

LOCK JOINT TUBE INC.
515 W Ireland Rd, South Bend, IN 46614
Tel.: (574) 299-5326
Web Site: http://www.lockjointtube.com
Rev.: $79,000,000
Emp.: 229
Welded Pipe & Tubes
N.A.I.C.S.: 331210
Wesley Davidson (Superintendent-Production & Transportation)

LOCKARD & WECHSLER
2 Bridge St Ste 200, Irvington, NY 10533
Tel.: (914) 591-6600   DE
Web Site: http://www.lwdirect.com
Year Founded: 1967
Sales Range: $75-99.9 Million
Emp.: 25
Advertising Agencies
N.A.I.C.S.: 541810
Carolyn Sura (Exec VP & Dir-Media)
Kurt Pisani (Sr VP-Client Svcs)

LOCKBOX LINK INC.
123 W Nye Ln Ste 129, Carson City, NV 89706
Tel.: (858) 353-9199   NV
Web Site: http://www.lockboxlink.com
Year Founded: 2014
Emp.: 1
Real Estate Software
N.A.I.C.S.: 513210
Natalie Moores (Pres, CEO, CFO & Sec)

LOCKE EQUIPMENT SALES CO.
1917 E Spruce St, Olathe, KS 66062
Tel.: (913) 782-8500
Web Site: http://www.lockeequipment.com
Sales Range: $10-24.9 Million
Emp.: 15
Power Plant Machinery
N.A.I.C.S.: 423830
Kim Locke (Pres)

LOCKE LORD EDWARDS LLP
2200 Ross Ave Ste 2800, Dallas, TX 75201
Tel.: (214) 740-8000   DE
Web Site: http://www.lockelord.com
Year Founded: 1891
Sales Range: $400-449.9 Million
Emp.: 1,000
Law firm
N.A.I.C.S.: 541110
Nick J. DiGiovanni (Partner)
Kimberly F. Williams (Partner)
Amy Gremminger White (Partner)
Susan M. Rainey (Partner)
Jennifer Kinney Parnell (Partner)
Julie Gilbert (CMO)
Paul E. Coggins (Partner)
Jerry K. Clements (Partner)
Alan J. Levin (Partner-Hartford & New York)
Daniel I. Schlessinger (Partner)
Bill Swanstrom (Partner)
Michael J. Gaertner (Partner)
Janis Loegering (Partner)
Heather M. Stone (Partner)
George Ticknor (Partner)
Jonathan W. Young (Partner)
Thomas G. Yoxall (Partner)
Karl P. Fryzel (Partner)
Tim Tingkang Xia (Partner)
Bryan G. Harrison (Partner)
Eric Larson (Partner)
Lauren Doughty (Partner)
Walker Clarke (Partner)
Tamer Tullgren (Partner)
Jonathan Pelayo (Partner)
John K. Arnold (Partner)
William Primps (Partner)
David F. Taylor (Partner)
Michael Blankenship (Partner)
Robert Hayes (Chm-Massachusetts Policy Grp)
Jason L. Zanetti (Chm-Federal Policy Grp)
Kathleen Swan (Partner-Private Equity & Venture Capital Practice Grp-Chicago)
John Eisel (Chm-Private Equity & Venture Capital Practice Grp-Chicago)
Mark Mansour (Partner-Washington)
Kyle Davis (Partner)
Matt Davis (Partner)
Walter J. St. Onge III (Partner-Boston)

LOCKE SUPPLY CO.
1300 SE 82nd St, Oklahoma City, OK 73149
Tel.: (405) 631-9701   OK
Web Site: http://www.lockesupply.com
Year Founded: 1955
Emp.: 140
Plumbing Fittings & Supplies

N.A.I.C.S.: 423720
Richard Haddock (Asst Mgr)
Jack Anderson (CFO)
Larry Zeller (CIO)
John Orman III (Pres & CEO)

LOCKHART CADILLAC INC.
9265 E 126th St, Fishers, IN 46038
Tel.: (317) 253-1551   IN
Web Site: http://www.lockhartcadillac.com
Year Founded: 1973
Sales Range: $100-124.9 Million
Emp.: 102
Automobile Sales
N.A.I.C.S.: 441110
Christina Trout (Dir-Customer Rels)
Subsidiaries:
Lockhart Cadillac South (1)
1287 US 31 S, Greenwood, IN 46143 (100%)
Tel.: (317) 865-1551
Web Site: http://www.lockhartcadillac.com
Sales Range: $25-49.9 Million
Emp.: 60
Retail Automotive Sales & Service
N.A.I.C.S.: 441110
Corey Lockhart (Owner)

LOCKHART COMPANIES INC.
Parcel 10-2 Remainder Estate Charlotte Amalie Unit Ste 6, Saint Thomas, VI 00802
Tel.: (340) 776-1900
Web Site: http://www.lockhart.com
Year Founded: 1936
Sales Range: $25-49.9 Million
Emp.: 19
Insurance Agents, Brokers & Service
N.A.I.C.S.: 524210
N. William Jarvis (Pres & COO)
Wesley S. Williams Jr. (Pres & COO)
Subsidiaries:
Guardian Insurance Company, Inc. (1)
Sunshine Mall 1 Estate Cane Ste 210, Frederiksted, VI 00840-9900
Tel.: (340) 692-6600
Web Site: http://www.guardianinsurance.com
Emp.: 3
Vehicle Insurance Services
N.A.I.C.S.: 524126
Petricia Simon (Mgr)

Premium Finance Co. of the Virgin Islands (1)
PO Box 4689, Kingshill, VI 00851
Tel.: (340) 778-4888
Web Site: http://www.lockhart.com
Rev.: $130,000
Emp.: 6
Provider of Automotive Financing Services
N.A.I.C.S.: 522291
Richard E. W. Grant (Pres & COO-Fin Svcs)

Premium Finance Company (E.C.) Ltd. (1)
PO Box 146, Christiansted, VI 00821-0146
Tel.: (340) 718-4888
Insurance Advisory Services
N.A.I.C.S.: 524298
Karen Bryan (Mgr)

LOCKNEY & ASSOCIATES, INC.
320 Woodridge Dr, Mineral Wells, WV 26150
Tel.: (304) 489-9405   WV
Year Founded: 1975
Sales Range: $10-24.9 Million
Emp.: 2
Business-To-Business, E-Commerce, Exhibit/Trade Shows, Financial, Health Care, Industrial, Multimedia
N.A.I.C.S.: 541810
Gary L. Lockney (Pres)

U.S. PRIVATE

LOCKPORT ICE ARENA
34 Chestnut St, Lockport, NY 14094
Tel.: (716) 628-2990   NY
Web Site: http://www.lockportice.org
Year Founded: 2008
Rev.: $4,339,250
Assets: $9,444,579
Liabilities: $5,066,063
Net Worth: $4,378,516
Earnings: $4,176,429
Fiscal Year-end: 08/31/14
Sport Promotion Services
John J. Ottaviano (Pres)
Michael E. White (Treas)
Henry W. Schmidt (Sec)
R. Charles Bell (VP)

LOCKWOOD BROADCASTING INC.
3914 Wistar Rd, Richmond, VA 23228
Tel.: (804) 672-6565   VA
Web Site: http://www.lockwoodbroadcast.com
Cable & Other Subscription Programming Services
N.A.I.C.S.: 516210
Danny Woodruff (Dir-Creative)
David A. Hanna (Pres)
Pamela B. Lawson (CFO & Exec VP)
Gerald Walsh (VP-Broadcast Ops)
Steve Wasilik (Dir-Programming & Promotion)
Tiffany Humphrey (Mgr-Bus & Traffic)
Ryan Harris (Dir-Natl Sls)
Bob Pectelidis (Dir-Corp Engrg)
Subsidiaries:
KAKE-TV (1)
1500 NW St, Wichita, KS 67203-1323
Tel.: (316) 943-4221
Web Site: http://www.kake.com
Emp.: 80
Television Broadcasting Station
N.A.I.C.S.: 516120
Neal Davis (Gen Mgr)
Neil Davis (Gen Mgr)

WFXG, LLC (1)
3933 Washington Rd, Augusta, GA 30907
Tel.: (706) 650-5400
Web Site: http://www.wfxg.com
Television Broadcasting Services
N.A.I.C.S.: 516120
David Williams (Dir-News)
J. Bryan Randall (Mgr-Digital Content)
Waylon Cawley (Sls Mgr)
Brandon Mullis (Mktg Dir)
Denise Vickers (Gen Mgr)
Taylor Barbato (Coord-Bus Office)
Marco Rivera (Dir-Engrg)
Bill Wortelboer (Mgr-IT)

WPGX, LLC (1)
700 W 23rd St Ste C-28, Panama City, FL 32405
Tel.: (850) 215-6500
Web Site: http://wpgxfox28.revrocket.us
Television Broadcasting Station
N.A.I.C.S.: 516120
Anne Dolan (Gen Mgr)
Shawna Greene (Gen Sls Mgr)
Jeff Peck (Dir-Creative Svcs)
Tim Rovere (Dir-Tech)
Donna Giancola (Bus Mgr)

LOCKWOOD BROTHERS, INC.
220 Salters Creek Rd, Hampton, VA 23661
Tel.: (757) 722-1946
Web Site: http://www.lockwoodbrothers.com
Year Founded: 1946
Sales Range: $10-24.9 Million
Emp.: 75
Long-Distance & Truckload Freight Trucking Services
N.A.I.C.S.: 484121
Garfield Boyd (Project Mgr-Heavy Lift)

Daniel K. Clark (Project Mgr-Intermodal Transportation)
William D. Koch (Project Mgr-Heavy Lift & Construction)
Will L. Phillips (Project Mgr-Heavy Lift)
Randy M. Jones (Project Mgr)
Paul Schifferli (Project Mgr-Heavy Lift & Intermodal Transportation)
James L. Lockwood Jr. (Pres)
Robert L. Phillips Sr. (VP)
John N. Schaffner Jr. (Project Mgr-Marine Div)

LOCKWOOD MCKINNON CO. INC.
45 Walpole St Ste 6, Norwood, MA 02062
Tel.: (781) 769-8900
Sales Range: $10-24.9 Million
Emp.: 400
Fast Food Restaurants
N.A.I.C.S.: 512131
Roger Lockwood (Pres)

LOCO, INC.
2249 Broadway, Grand Junction, CO 81503
Tel.: (970) 242-5857
Web Site: http://www.gjloco.com
Rev.: $52,865,523
Emp.: 75
Automobile Washing & Detailing
N.A.I.C.S.: 811198
Robert L. Lipson III (CEO)

LOCUM LEADERS
925 North Point Pkwy Ste 425, Alpharetta, GA 30005
Tel.: (877) 562-8656
Web Site: http://www.locumleaders.com
Year Founded: 2008
Sales Range: $10-24.9 Million
Emp.: 35
Recruits & Places Physicians in Contract & Part-Time Jobs
N.A.I.C.S.: 561320
Will Drescher (Pres)
Joshua Campbell (VP-Bus Dev)
John F. Smith (Mgr-Bus Dev)

LOCUST GROVE INC.
100 Cooksey St, Hazard, KY 41702
Tel.: (606) 439-5151
Rev.: $11,500,000
Emp.: 100
Strip Mining, Bituminous
N.A.I.C.S.: 212114

LODAL, INC.
620 N Hooper St, Kingsford, MI 49802
Tel.: (906) 779-1700   MI
Web Site: http://www.lodal.com
Year Founded: 1953
Sales Range: $50-74.9 Million
Emp.: 70
Provider of Refuse Collection Vehicles & Equipment
N.A.I.C.S.: 336211
Bernard Leger (Pres)
John Giuliani (Treas & Sec)
Anthony Botticello (VP)

LODESTONE ADVERTISING
318 Central Ave, Great Falls, MT 59401
Tel.: (406) 761-0288
Web Site: http://www.lodestoneadvertising.com
Year Founded: 1996
Sales Range: Less than $1 Million
Emp.: 4
Advertising, Print
N.A.I.C.S.: 541810

Chuck Fulcher (Owner & Dir-Creative)

LODGE CONSTRUCTION INC.
2161-A McGregor Blvd, Fort Myers, FL 33901
Tel.: (239) 332-4371
Web Site: http://www.lodgeconstruction.com
Year Founded: 1988
Sales Range: $25-49.9 Million
Emp.: 42
General Contractors
N.A.I.C.S.: 236220
Michael T. Dunn (Co-Owner & VP)
Debbie Packard (Controller)
Katrin Callway (Project Mgr)
Doug Masch (Project Mgr)
Bob Rousseau (Mgr-Quality Control Sys)
Russ Vought (Project Mgr)
Bill Gore (Project Mgr)
Tammy Kaminski (Project Mgr)
Bryan Shroyer (Project Mgr)
Cabot L. Dunn Jr. (Co-Owner & Pres)

LODGE OF FOUR SEASONS
315 Four Season Dr PO Box 215, Lake Ozark, MO 65049
Tel.: (573) 365-3000
Web Site: http://www.4seasonsresort.com
Year Founded: 1964
Sales Range: $1-9.9 Million
Resorts & Marinas Operator
N.A.I.C.S.: 561599
Susan Brown (Owner)
Larry McAfee (Gen Mgr)
Rob Cline (Mgr-Landscape)
Justin Pittenger (Dir-Food & Beverage)
Harold Koplar (Founder)
James Cleary (COO)

LODGECAP, INC.
190 E Stacy Rd Ste 1720, Allen, TX 75002
Tel.: (214) 618-8288   MD
Web Site: http://www.lodgecapreit.com
Year Founded: 2011
Mortgage Loans & Lending Services
N.A.I.C.S.: 525990
Billy L. Brown (Chm & CEO)
Tim Moore (Pres)

LODGING ENTERPRISES INC.
8080 E Central Ste 180, Wichita, KS 67206
Tel.: (316) 634-6100
Web Site: http://www.oaktreein.com
Year Founded: 1986
Sales Range: $50-74.9 Million
Emp.: 1,000
Provider of Hotel & Motel Services
N.A.I.C.S.: 721110
Bill Berger (Pres)

LODGING INTERACTIVE
2001 Route 46 Ste 310, Parsippany, NJ 07054
Tel.: (973) 830-1246
Web Site: http://www.lodginginteractive.com
Sales Range: $1-9.9 Million
Emp.: 50
Design, Search Engine Marketing, Online Advertising, Social Media Marketing, Copywriting, Analytics, Account Management & Technology for the Lodging Industry
N.A.I.C.S.: 541890
D. J. Vallauri (Founder & CEO)
Alicia Pavignano (Dir-Client Svcs)
Rosella Virdo (COO)

LODGING RESOURCES, INC.
98 S Fletcher Ave, Fernandina Beach, FL 32034
Tel.: (904) 277-4851   FL
Web Site: http://www.elizabethpointelodge.com
Year Founded: 1988
Sales Range: $1-9.9 Million
Emp.: 25
Inn Operations
N.A.I.C.S.: 721110
Jim Dunlop (Pres)

LODGING UNLIMITED, INC.
505 N Lake Shore Dr Ste 6309, Chicago, IL 60611
Tel.: (312) 595-1390
Web Site: http://www.lodgingunlimited.com
Year Founded: 1970
Sales Range: $10-24.9 Million
Emp.: 350
Hotel & Motel Management Services
N.A.I.C.S.: 561110
Mary Lou Koys (Exec VP)
Morris E. Lasky (Pres & CEO)

LODI MOTORS INC.
1700 S Cherokee Ln, Lodi, CA 95240
Tel.: (209) 334-6632
Web Site: http://www.lodihonda.com
Sales Range: $1-9.9 Million
Emp.: 40
Automobiles, New & Used
N.A.I.C.S.: 441110
Mark Morgan (Mgr-Svc)
Steve Cranford (Gen Mgr)
Derek Abbott (Mgr-Sls)

LODOLCE MACHINE COMPANY, INC.
196 Malden Tpke, Saugerties, NY 12477
Tel.: (845) 246-7017
Web Site: http://www.lodolce.com
Year Founded: 1960
Sales Range: $10-24.9 Million
Emp.: 30
Machine Shop Operator
N.A.I.C.S.: 332710
Michael LoDolce (Pres)

LOEB & LOEB LLP
10100 Santa Monica Blvd Ste 2200, Los Angeles, CA 90067
Tel.: (310) 282-2000
Web Site: http://www.loeb.com
Year Founded: 1909
Sales Range: $200-249.9 Million
Emp.: 295
Law firm
N.A.I.C.S.: 541110
Mickey Mayerson (Chm-Entertainment Fin)
Scott Cotie (CFO)
Patricia Anne O'Hara (CIO-New York)
Michael D. Beck (Chm)
Alan B. Cutler (COO)
Ross D. Emmerman (Partner-Chicago)
Seth Rose (Partner-Chicago)
Nathan J. Hole (Deputy Chm-Advanced Media & Tech)
David G. Mallen (Chm-Adv Disputes, Retail & Consumer Brands)
James D. Taylor (Chm-Advanced Media & Tech, Adv & Promos)
Rachel J. Harris (Chm-Intl Trusts & Estates Plng)
Tiffany A. Dunn (Partner & Office Mgr-Admin-Nashville)
Denise M. Stevens (Partner)
Marcus S. Owens (Partner-Washington)
Diara Holmes (Partner-Washington)
Tal Dickstein (Partner-New York)
Theodore Duver (Partner-New York)
Ronelle Porter (Partner-New York)
Stefan Schick (Partner-New York)
Philippe Manteau (Chm-Western Europe Corp & Partner)
Danielle Miller (Partner-Los Angeles)
Gerald Chizever (Partner)
Joseph J. Duffy (Partner-Litigation Dept-Chicago)
Corey Rubenstein (Partner-Litigation Dept-Chicago)
Mitchell Nussbaum (Vice Chm)
Laurie Ruckel (Mng Partner-New York)
Melissa R.H. Hall (Partner-Washington)
Thomas F. Hanley III (Partner-Los Angeles)

LOEB EQUIPMENT & APPRAISAL CO.
4131 S State St, Chicago, IL 60609
Tel.: (773) 548-4131
Web Site: http://www.loebequipment.com
Year Founded: 1924
Sales Range: $10-24.9 Million
Emp.: 23
Commercial Equipment
N.A.I.C.S.: 541990
Howard M. Newman (Pres)
Mary Jane Anderson (VP-Acctg & Fin)
Venice Gamble (VP-Bus Dev)

LOEB HOLDING CORPORATION
100 Wall St 19th Fl, New York, NY 10005
Tel.: (212) 483-7000
Web Site: http://www.loebpartners.com
Sales Range: $10-24.9 Million
Emp.: 50
Security Brokers & Dealers Asset Management
N.A.I.C.S.: 523150
Thomas Lenox Kempner (Chm & CEO)

Subsidiaries:

Loeb Partners Corporation   (1)
100 Wall St 19th Fl, New York, NY 10005
Tel.: (212) 483-7000
Web Site: http://www.loebpartners.com
Brokers Security
N.A.I.C.S.: 523150
Thomas Lenox Kempner (Chm & CEO)
Philip Keating (Mng Dir)
Bruce L. Lev (Mng Dir)
Peter A. Tcherepnine (Mng Dir)

Loeb Partners Realty & Development   (1)
120 E New York Ave Ste D, Deland, FL 32724-5527
Tel.: (386) 736-2402
Rev.: $400,000
Emp.: 5
Real Estate Managers
N.A.I.C.S.: 531210

PKC Inc.   (1)
521 5th Ave Rm 2300, New York, NY 10175
Tel.: (212) 883-0360
Rev.: $1,200,000
Emp.: 15
Nonresidential Building Operators
N.A.I.C.S.: 812320

LOEB INDUSTRIES INC.
1111 S 10th St, Watertown, WI 53094
Tel.: (920) 261-4920
Web Site: http://www.loeblorman.com
Sales Range: $10-24.9 Million
Emp.: 100
Scrap Metal & Waste Materials
N.A.I.C.S.: 423930

LOEB INDUSTRIES INC.

Loeb Industries Inc.—(Continued)
Bruce Loeb (Pres)
Cathy Steinbrink (Office Mgr)

LOEB PARTNERS REALTY, LLC
521 5th Ave Ste 2300, New York, NY 10175
Tel.: (212) 883-0360
Web Site: http://www.loebrealty.com
Year Founded: 1968
Sales Range: $1-9.9 Million
Emp.: 23
Asset Management, Property Management, Leasing, Financing & Construction Management Services
N.A.I.C.S.: 531210
Alan Gordon (Vice Chm & Exec VP)
Joseph S. Lesser (Chm & CEO)

LOEBER MOTORS, INC.
4255 W Touhy Ave, Lincolnwood, IL 60712-1933
Tel.: (888) 211-4485
Web Site:
 http://www.loebermotors.com
Year Founded: 1936
New & Used Automobiles
N.A.I.C.S.: 441110
George Loeber (VP)
Paul Loeber (CEO)
Michael Loeber (Pres & Gen Mgr)
Christopher Loeber (Project Mgr)
Joe Rupp (Gen Sls Mgr-Porsche)
Jeff DiSandro (Mgr-Pre-Owned)
Bill Brown (Mgr-Sprinter/Metris)
Jeff Kalinsky (Gen Mgr-Porsche)
Fred Glaeser (Mgr-Porsche Certified Service)
John David (Mgr-Porsche Pre-Owned)
Justin McCormack (Mgr-Mercedes-Benz F&)
John Larson (Mgr-Mercedes-Benz F&I)
Mario Bova (Mgr-Porsche F&I)
Amy Trudeau (Mgr-Inventory)
Ryen Smorczewski (Mgr-Customer Care)
Joe Schlauch (Dir-Mercedes-Benz Fixed Ops)
John Martin (Dir-Parts)
Bob Wendling (Mgr-)

LOEFFEL STEEL PRODUCTS INC.
27 W 951 Industrial Ave, Barrington, IL 60010
Tel.: (847) 382-6770
Web Site: http://www.loeffelsteel.com
Rev: $21,000,000
Emp.: 20
Steel Distr
N.A.I.C.S.: 423510
Tim K. Loeffel (VP & Dir-Pur)
Brian Limpus (Mgr-Traffic)
Maurice F. Loeffel Jr. (Pres)

LOEFFLER KETCHUM MOUNTJOY (LKM)
6115 Park S Dr Ste 350, Charlotte, NC 28210
Tel.: (704) 364-8969 NC
Web Site: http://www.lkmideas.com
Year Founded: 1981
Rev: $33,452,000
Emp.: 26
Advetising Agency
N.A.I.C.S.: 541810
John Ketchum (CEO)
James W. Mountjoy (Dir-Art & Creative)
Donna Forbes (Pres)
Scott Gilmore (VP & Dir-Client Svcs)
Susan Dosier (Dir-PR)

Elaine Cheedle (Media Dir)
Jennifer Jenkins (Exec VP & Dir-Client Relationship)
Stacey Pullen (Mng Dir & VP)
Sarah Peter (Exec VP-Bus Dev)
Kristin Michael (Acct Mgr-PR)

LOEKS THEATRES, INC.
2121 Celebration Dr NE, Grand Rapids, MI 49525
Tel.: (616) 447-4200 MI
Web Site:
 http://www.celebrationcinema.com
Rev: $12,500,000
Emp.: 12
Motion Picture Theaters Owner & Operator
N.A.I.C.S.: 512131
Mike Doty (Gen Mgr)
Dan Brewster (Mgr-Ops)
Kenyon Shane (VP-Ops-Revenue Dev)
Roger Lubs (VP-Facilities & Construction)
John D. Loeks Sr. (Chm)

LOEWS ANNAPOLIS HOTEL CORP.
126 West St, Annapolis, MD 21401-2802
Tel.: (410) 263-7777 MD
Web Site: http://www.loewshotel.com
Year Founded: 1990
Sales Range: $10-24.9 Million
Emp.: 180
Motel, Franchised
N.A.I.C.S.: 721110
Bonnie Finlay (Mgr-Conference Svcs)
Chera Howey (Sr Mgr-Catering Sls)
David Merklinger (Dir-Ops)
Romeo Santos III (Gen Mgr-Baroak Cookhouse & Taproom)

LOFFLER BUSINESS SYSTEMS INC.
1101 E 78th St Ste 200, Bloomington, MN 55420
Tel.: (952) 925-6800
Web Site: http://www.loffler.com
Year Founded: 1986
Sales Range: $50-74.9 Million
Emp.: 280
Distr of Office Equipment
N.A.I.C.S.: 531120
Neil Lee (CFO)

LOFFLER COMPANIES, INC.
1101 E 78th St Ste 200, Bloomington, MN 55420
Tel.: (952) 925-6800
Web Site: http://www.loffler.com
Year Founded: 1986
Sales Range: $25-49.9 Million
Emp.: 282
Office Products Distr
N.A.I.C.S.: 423420
Jim Loffler (Founder & CEO)
James Loffler (Pres)
John Hastings (Exec VP-Imaging Div)
John Turner (VP-Customer Success)

Subsidiaries:
Copier Business Solutions (1)
1715 Commerce Dr, North Mankato, MN 56003 (100%)
Tel.: (507) 625-8040
Web Site: http://www.cbsmankato.com
Stationery Products & Copiers Retailer
N.A.I.C.S.: 423420
Robert Dale (CEO & Pres)
Mark Hager (Gen Mgr)
Kathy Anderson (Controller)
Jeff Bass (Mgr-Svc)

Laser Systems, Inc. (1)
901 Westrac Dr, Fargo, ND 58103-2319
Tel.: (701) 293-6865

Computer & Office Machine Repair & Maintenance
N.A.I.C.S.: 811210

Office Systems Co. (1)
308 Iowa St, Sioux City, IA 51101
Tel.: (712) 277-7000
Office Supplies & Stationery Stores
N.A.I.C.S.: 459410

Reardon Office Equipment, Inc. (1)
1102 Main Ave, Moorhead, MN 56560-2902
Tel.: (218) 236-5435
Web Site: http://www.shopreardon.com
Office Machinery & Equipment Rental & Leasing
N.A.I.C.S.: 532420
Thomas Gourde (Treas)
Greg Reardon (Pres)

LOFFREDO FRESH PRODUCE CO., INC.
4001 SW 63rd St, Des Moines, IA 50321-1607
Tel.: (515) 285-3367 DE
Web Site: http://www.loffredo.com
Year Founded: 1892
Sales Range: $50-74.9 Million
Emp.: 300
Fresh Fruits & Vegetables
N.A.I.C.S.: 424480
John Loffredo (VP-Sls)
Mark Zimmerman (CFO & Controller)
Larry Loffredo (VP-Fin)
Mike Loffredo (VP-Pur)
Lisa Beener (Mgr-Client Svcs)
Ryan Meier (Dir-IT)
Mark Hersh (Mgr-Quality Assurance-Warehouse)
Steve Winders (COO)
Adam Babcock (Dir-Processing)
Bill Day (Mgr-Acct Sls-Natl)
Beth Schwery (Mgr-Accts Receivable)
Marcy Billings (Mgr-Quality Assurance)
Burt Clearwater (Mgr-Safety)

LOFT INC.
95 S Market St Ste 440, San Jose, CA 95113
Tel.: (408) 782-4301 DE
Web Site: http://www.rooomy.com
3-Dimensional Interior Visual Staging Platform Developer & Support Services
N.A.I.C.S.: 541511
Pieter A. J. J. Aarts (CEO)
Jan-Hein J. Pullens (COO)

Subsidiaries:
NedSense LOFT B.V. (1)
Ertskade 107, 1019 BB, Amsterdam, Netherlands (100%)
Tel.: (31) 347329696
Web Site: http://www.rooomy.com
3-Dimensional Interior Visual Staging Platform Developer & Support Services
N.A.I.C.S.: 541511
Enrico Rosa (VP-Dev & Global Ops)

LOG CABIN HOMES LTD.
410 N Pearl St, Rocky Mount, NC 27802
Tel.: (252) 454-1500
Web Site:
 http://www.logcabinhomes.com
Year Founded: 1987
Sales Range: $10-24.9 Million
Emp.: 60
Contructors of Log Cabin Homes
N.A.I.C.S.: 321992
Tom Vesce (Pres)
Barbara Muller (Branch Mgr-Sls)

LOGAN & WHALEY CO.
109 E Austin St, Marshall, TX 75670
Tel.: (903) 938-6621 TX
Web Site:
 http://www.loganwhaley.com

Year Founded: 1884
Sales Range: $25-49.9 Million
Emp.: 20
Industrial Supplies
N.A.I.C.S.: 423840
Patricia Whaley (Chm)
Tom Whaley Sr. (Pres)
Tom Whaley Jr. (Treas, Sec & VP)
John Patterson III (Mgr-Sls)

LOGAN COMMUNITY RESOURCES, INC.
2505 E Jefferson Blvd, South Bend, IN 46615
Tel.: (574) 289-4831 IN
Web Site: http://www.logancenter.org
Year Founded: 1950
Sales Range: $10-24.9 Million
Emp.: 627
Community Care Services
N.A.I.C.S.: 624190
Cheryl Schade (VP-Program Ops)

LOGAN CORPORATION
20 Mcjunkin Rd, Nitro, WV 25143
Tel.: (304) 526-4700 WV
Web Site: http://www.logancorp.com
Year Founded: 1935
Sales Range: $75-99.9 Million
Emp.: 130
Mfr & Distributor of Industrial Machine Parts
N.A.I.C.S.: 423810
John Horn (Exec VP-East Coast)
Dow Waite (Exec VP)

LOGAN COUNTY ELECTRIC COOPERATIVE
1587 County Rd 32 N, Bellefontaine, OH 43311
Tel.: (937) 592-4781 OH
Web Site:
 http://www.logancounty.coop
Year Founded: 1936
Sales Range: $10-24.9 Million
Emp.: 25
Electric Power Distr
N.A.I.C.S.: 221122
Ryan Smith (VP-Engrg & Ops)
Rick Petty (VP-Comm & Member Svcs)
Doug Miller (Pres & CEO)
Lanny Davis (Treas & Sec)
Doug Comer (Chm)

LOGAN HEALTH
310 Sunyview Ln, Kalispell, MT 59901
Tel.: (406) 752-5111 MT
Web Site: https://www.logan.org
Year Founded: 1982
Sales Range: $1-9.9 Million
Emp.: 47
Health Care Srvices
N.A.I.C.S.: 622110
James Oliverson (Exec Dir-Community Rels)
Craig Lambrecht (Pres & CEO)

LOGAN INVESTMENT CORPORATION
612 1st St PO Box 340, Bonaparte, IA 52620
Tel.: (319) 592-3372
Web Site:
 http://www.statecentralbank.com
Year Founded: 2004
Bank Holding Company
N.A.I.C.S.: 551111

LOGAN SQUARE ALUMINUM SUPPLY, INC.
2500 N Pulaski Rd, Chicago, IL 60639
Tel.: (773) 235-2500
Sales Range: $10-24.9 Million

Emp.: 120
Window & Door Frames
N.A.I.C.S.: 332321
Louis Silver *(Pres)*
Jim Liszka *(Controller)*

Subsidiaries:

Remodelers Supply Center (1)
2622 N Pulaski Rd, Chicago, IL 60639
Tel.: (773) 235-2500
Web Site:
  http://www.climateguardwindows.com
Building Supplies Distr
N.A.I.C.S.: 444110

Studio41 (1)
2500 N Pulaski Rd, Chicago, IL 60639
Tel.: (773) 235-2500
Web Site: http://www.shopstudio41.com
Home Furnishing Distr
N.A.I.C.S.: 449129

Division (Domestic):

Clark & Barlow Hardware Co. (2)
353 W Grand Ave, Chicago, IL 60654
Tel.: (312) 726-3010
Web Site: http://www.clarkandbarlow.com
Hardware Products
N.A.I.C.S.: 423710
Kevin Jackson *(Gen Mgr)*

LOGENIX INTERNATIONAL
5285 Shawnee Rd Ste 320, Alexandria, VA 22312
Tel.: (703) 256-4885
Web Site: http://www.logenix.com
Year Founded: 2001
Sales Range: $10-24.9 Million
Emp.: 18
Logistics Consulting Servies
N.A.I.C.S.: 541614
Ron Cruse *(Pres & CEO)*
Geoff Speck *(VP)*
Azam Durrani *(Dir-Middle East)*
Tariq Shalizi *(Mgr-Ops)*

LOGGHE STAMPING COMPANY
16711 E 13 Mile Rd, Fraser, MI 48026-2555
Tel.: (586) 293-2250 MI
Web Site:
  http://www.logghestamping.com
Year Founded: 1946
Sales Range: $25-49.9 Million
Emp.: 100
Mfr of Automobile Body Parts
N.A.I.C.S.: 336370
Eugene A. Logghe *(Pres)*
Dan Logghe *(VP)*
Ronald M. Logghe *(Sec & VP)*

LOGIC DEVICES INCORPORATED
1375 Geneva Dr, Sunnyvale, CA 94089
Tel.: (408) 542-5400 CA
Web Site:
  http://www.logicdevices.com
Year Founded: 1983
Sales Range: $1-9.9 Million
Emp.: 8
Developer & Marketer of Signal Processing Circuits
N.A.I.C.S.: 334413

LOGIC INTEGRATION INC.
8224 Park Meadows Dr, Lone Tree, CO 80124
Tel.: (303) 484-8237
Web Site: http://www.logicav.net
Year Founded: 2004
Sales Range: $1-9.9 Million
Emp.: 20
AV Systems, Lighting & Digital Signage
N.A.I.C.S.: 334310
Chris Bowland *(VP-Design & Sls)*

LOGIC SOLUTIONS, INC.
2929 Plymouth Rd Ste 207, Ann Arbor, MI 48105
Tel.: (734) 930-0009 MI
Web Site:
  http://www.logicsolutions.com
Year Founded: 1995
Sales Range: $10-24.9 Million
Emp.: 50
Computer System Design Services
N.A.I.C.S.: 541512
Grace Lee *(CFO)*
Samson Chu *(Dir-Offshore Svcs)*
Bruce Richardson *(Pres)*

Subsidiaries:

Quantum Compliance Systems, Inc. (1)
2929 Plymouth Rd Ste 207, Ann Arbor, MI 48105
Tel.: (734) 930-0009
Web Site: http://www.usequantum.com
Custom Computer Programing Prepackaged Software Services
N.A.I.C.S.: 513210
Patricia L. Brooks *(Founder & CTO)*

LOGICAL DESIGN SOLUTIONS INC.
100 Campus Dr Ste 205, Florham Park, NJ 07932-1026
Tel.: (973) 210-6300
Web Site: http://www.lds.com
Sales Range: $10-24.9 Million
Emp.: 65
Computer Systems Analysts & Design
N.A.I.C.S.: 541512
Mimi Brooks *(CEO)*

LOGICAL IMAGES, INC.
3445 Winton Pl Ste 240, Rochester, NY 14623
Tel.: (585) 427-2790 NY
Web Site:
  http://www.logicalimages.com
Year Founded: 1994
Sales Range: $1-9.9 Million
Emp.: 40
Developer of Visual Health Care Tools
N.A.I.C.S.: 513210
Richard S. Cohan *(CEO)*
Art Papier *(CFO)*
Bill Haake *(VP-Ops)*

LOGICAL OPERATIONS INC.
3535 Winton Pl, Rochester, NY 14623-2634
Tel.: (585) 350-7000
Web Site:
  http://www.logicaloperations.com
Year Founded: 1982
Emp.: 80
IT Training Services
N.A.I.C.S.: 611420
William Rosenthal *(CEO)*

LOGICAL SOLUTION SERVICES INC.
200 Union Ave, Lakehurst, NJ 08733
Tel.: (732) 657-7777
Web Site:
  http://www.solutionservices.us
Year Founded: 2001
Sales Range: $1-9.9 Million
Emp.: 90
Logistic Services
N.A.I.C.S.: 541614
Alicia Cruz *(Controller)*
Victor Cruz Jr. *(Pres & CEO)*
Victor Cruz Sr. *(CFO)*

LOGICAL SYSTEMS, LLC.
2756 Appling Ctr Cove, Memphis, TN 38305-2714
Tel.: (901) 377-5574

Web Site:
  http://www.logicalsysinc.com
Year Founded: 1985
Sales Range: $25-49.9 Million
Emp.: 150
Engineeering Services
N.A.I.C.S.: 541330
Larry W. Bailey *(CEO)*
Lentz Gatlin *(CFO)*
Dan Miller *(COO)*
Blane Elledge *(Mgr-Bus Dev)*
David Jackson *(Mgr-Electrical Engrg)*
Nick Riggio *(Pres-Golden)*
Gary Moore *(VP-Colorado)*
Marty Taylor *(VP-Tech-Georgia)*
Dennie Lott *(Mgr-Tennessee)*
Hansen Hu *(Mgr-Bridgeport)*
Tre Prater *(Mgr-Bridgeport)*
Ian Richardson *(Mgr-Bridgeport)*

LOGICAL VENTURES INC.
338 Clubhouse Rd, Hunt Valley, MD 21031-1305
Tel.: (410) 771-5544 MD
Web Site: http://www.syssrc.com
Year Founded: 1981
Sales Range: $25-49.9 Million
Emp.: 70
Computer Training, Sales, Rental & Consulting Services
N.A.I.C.S.: 541618
Maury Weinstein *(Co-Owner)*
Bob Roswell *(Co-Owner)*

LOGICEASE SOLUTIONS, INC.
111 Anza Blvd Ste 200, Burlingame, CA 94010-1932
Tel.: (650) 373-1111 CA
Web Site:
  http://www.complianceease.com
Year Founded: 2001
Sales Range: $1-9.9 Million
Emp.: 30
Financial Software Developer
N.A.I.C.S.: 513210
Anita Kwan *(Co-Founder)*
John Vong *(Co-Founder & Chm)*
Jason Roth *(Co-Founder & CTO)*
Dan Smith *(Sr VP)*
Steven Eakman *(Gen Counsel & Sr VP)*
Michael Jackman *(CEO)*

LOGICOM SYSTEMS INC.
800 E Hallandale Beach Blvd Ste 26, Hallandale, FL 33009
Tel.: (305) 948-4822
Web Site:
  http://www.logicomedia.com
Sales Range: $10-24.9 Million
Emp.: 35
Value-Added Resellers, Computer Systems
N.A.I.C.S.: 541512

LOGIGEAR CORPORATION
2015 Pioneer Ct, San Mateo, CA 94403
Tel.: (650) 572-1400 CA
Web Site: http://www.logigear.com
Year Founded: 1996
Sales Range: $1-9.9 Million
Emp.: 28
IT Services & Solutions
N.A.I.C.S.: 541511
Nguyen Hung *(Co-Founder & CEO)*
Hans Buwalda *(CTO)*
Michael Hackett *(Co-Founder & Sr VP)*
Joseph Hughes *(COO)*

LOGIS-TECH, INC.
9450 Innovation Dr Ste 1, Manassas, VA 20110
Tel.: (703) 393-0122
Web Site: http://www.logis-tech.com

Year Founded: 1987
Rev.: $17,611,280
Emp.: 165
Environment Stabilization Systems Mfr
N.A.I.C.S.: 423730
Robert J. Grasso *(VP-Logistics Integration)*
John Senter *(Sr VP-Bus Dev)*
James K. Bounds *(Pres)*
Roland E. Berg *(CEO)*

LOGISOLVE, LLC.
600 Inwood Ave N Ste 275, Minneapolis, MN 55128
Tel.: (763) 383-1000
Web Site: http://www.logisolve.com
Year Founded: 1999
Sales Range: $10-24.9 Million
Emp.: 120
It Consulting
N.A.I.C.S.: 541511
Ron Kimlinger *(Partner-Project Mgmt, Bus Analysis & Java Technologies)*
Rob Mohr *(Partner-Healthcare & e-Prescription)*
Kelly Wendlandt *(Partner-Sls & Mktg)*
Charlie Belisle *(Partner-Bus Intelligence & Data Mgmt)*
Tom Newman *(Partner-Sls & Mktg)*
Dave Lillquist *(Partner-Microsoft .NET Architecture & Dev)*
B. K. Sicard *(Dir-HR)*
Emily Fossey *(Dir-Recruiting)*

LOGISTIC
3200 Pk Ctr Dr Ste 500, Costa Mesa, CA 92626
Tel.: (949) 398-6454
Web Site: http://www.lojistic.com
Year Founded: 2004
Sales Range: $1-9.9 Million
Logistics Consulting Servies
N.A.I.C.S.: 541614
Luke Kupersmith *(Pres)*

LOGISTIC DYNAMICS, INC.
1140 Wehrle Dr, Amherst, NY 14221-7748
Tel.: (716) 250-3477 NY
Web Site:
  http://www.logisticdynamics.com
Year Founded: 2003
Sales Range: $10-24.9 Million
Emp.: 50
Freight & Transportation Management
N.A.I.C.S.: 484230
Dennis Brown *(Pres)*

LOGISTIC LEASING, LLC.
3303 US Hwy 70, Durham, NC 27703
Tel.: (919) 821-2925
Web Site:
  http://www.brownintegratedlogistics.com
Year Founded: 1997
Sales Range: $10-24.9 Million
Emp.: 83
Vehicle Maintenance Shop & Tractor Leasing
N.A.I.C.S.: 811111
Doug Chafin *(Mgr-HR)*
H. L. Wheeler *(Dir-Maintenance)*
Mark Johnston *(Mgr-Bus Dev)*
Spruill Mayhew *(Mgr-Bus Dev)*

LOGISTIC SERVICES INTERNATIONAL INC.
6111 Technology Ct, Jacksonville, FL 32221-8104
Tel.: (904) 771-2100 FL
Web Site: http://www.lsijax.com
Year Founded: 1978
Sales Range: $25-49.9 Million
Emp.: 460
Schools & Educational Services
N.A.I.C.S.: 611699

LOGISTIC SERVICES INTERNATIONAL INC.

U.S. PRIVATE

Logistic Services International Inc.—(Continued)
Phil D. Voss (CMO)
Jeff Bryan (Dir-Quality)
Michael S. French (COO)
Larry Sakre (Dir-Products-Intl)
Dean Leonard (VP-Courseware Programs)
Jim Martens (Dir-Publ Programs)
Warren S. Rosander (CEO & CFO)
Mike Guiry (Sr VP-Program Integration)
Jeff Tibbetts (VP-Info Sys & Facilities)
Ed Turner (VP-Intl & Trng Svcs Programs)

LOGISTIC SOLUTIONS INC.
200 Centennial Ave # 209, Piscataway, NJ 08854
Tel.: (732) 457-0015
Web Site: http://www.logistic-solutions.com
Rev.: $26,171,828
Emp.: 110
Computer Software Development
N.A.I.C.S.: 541511
Jeff Arestivo (Mgr)
Sam Abujawdeh (Exec VP-Bus Devel)
Amit Limaye (Founder & Chm)
Arthur Pereless (Exec VP-Mktg)

LOGISTICS & ENVIRONMENTAL SUPPORT SERVICES CORPORATION
4845 University Sq Ste 1, Huntsville, AL 35816
Tel.: (256) 971-7165
Web Site: http://www.lesco-logistics.com
Sales Range: $10-24.9 Million
Emp.: 300
Logistics Facilities Management
N.A.I.C.S.: 541513
Don Miller (Pres & CEO)

LOGISTICS MANAGEMENT INSTITUTE
7940 Jones Branch Dr, Tysons, VA 22102-7805
Tel.: (703) 917-9800
Web Site: http://www.lmi.org
Year Founded: 1961
Professional Organizations & Business Services
N.A.I.C.S.: 813920
Patricia Blevins (Sr VP-Logistics & Life Cycle Mgmt)
Tamara Jack (Chief Legal Officer, Sec & Sr VP)
Karren Briton (Chief Digital Officer & VP-Mktg & Comm)
Suzan Cengiz (VP-Transformation & Mgmt Office)
Donna Diederich (Sr VP & Chief Human Resources)
Sharon Hays (Chief Tech & Strategy Officer)
Doug Wagoner (Pres & CEO)
Christine Cocrane (VP-Mgmt Advisory Svcs)
Pete Pflugrath (Exec VP-Markets & Growth)
Lisa Disbrow (Chm)
Scott Recinos (VP-Homeland Security Market)
Marion Kennedy (VP-Intelligence Market)
Joe Niehaus (Sr VP-Logistics Svc)
Zaki Saleh (Sr VP-Health & Civilian Market)
Mark Eddings (Sr VP-Space Market)
Pat Tamburrino Jr. (VP-Logistics)

Subsidiaries:
Clockwork Solutions LLC (1)
6011 W Courtyard Dr Bridgepoint Sq Bldg 5 Ste 160, Austin, TX 78730
Tel.: (512) 717-5335
Web Site: http://www.clockwork-solutions.com
Scientific & Technical Consulting Services
N.A.I.C.S.: 541690
Will King (CEO)

JJR Solutions, LLC. (1)
3610 Pentagon Blvd Ste 220, Dayton, OH 45431
Tel.: (937) 912-0288
Web Site: http://www.jjrsolutions.com
Sales Range: $1-9.9 Million
Emp.: 36
Information Technology Services
N.A.I.C.S.: 541512
Linda M. Skinner (COO)
Robert W. Kinney (VP-Tech)
Carly J. Cox (VP-Ops)
Dan Marion (Chief Strategy Officer)
Paul A. Neef (VP-Capture & Solutions Delivery)
Jill Delaney-Shal (Exec VP-Customer Mission Success)
David Hart (Exec VP-Bus Dev & Strategic Relationships)
David LaBarca (VP-Veteran & Military Health)
Mandy Thompson (VP-Growth Svcs)
Eric Lundgren (VP-Fin)
David L. Judson Jr. (Pres & CEO)

LOGISTICS MANAGEMENT RESOURCES INC.
4300 Crossings Blvd, Prince George, VA 23875
Tel.: (804) 541-6193
Web Site: http://www.lmr-inc.com
Sales Range: $25-49.9 Million
Emp.: 80
Computer Related Maintenance Services
N.A.I.C.S.: 541519
Connie P. Trikoulis (Asst VP-HR)
Kenneth G. Briggs (CIO)

LOGISTICS PLANNING SERVICES, INC.
1140 Ctr Pointe Dr Ste 100 731 Bielenberg Dr Ste 108, Woodbury, MN 55125
Tel.: (651) 552-4905
Web Site: http://www.shiplps.com
Year Founded: 1987
Sales Range: $10-24.9 Million
Emp.: 36
Financial & Brokerage Services
N.A.I.C.S.: 523160
Wil Kratz (Dir-Ops)

LOGISTICS PLUS, INC.
1406 Peach St, Erie, PA 16501
Tel.: (814) 461-7600
Web Site: http://www.logisticsplus.net
Sales Range: $25-49.9 Million
Emp.: 350
Freight Transportation Management Services
N.A.I.C.S.: 488510
Adriana Zafirova (Mgr-Acctg)
Debbie Bigelow (Mgr-IT Software Svcs)
Fred Rizzuto (Pres)
Gretchen Seth (Sr VP-Intl)
Max Falkowski (Mgr-Warehouse Ops)
Dawn Fritche (Mgr-Warehouse)
Frank Wolf (Mgr-Buffalo)
Mahammad Inadullah (Coord-Customer Svc)
Suchit Sehgal (Gen Mgr)

LOGISTICS SPECIALTIES, INC.
1530 N Layton Hills Pkwy Ste 201, Layton, UT 84041-5683
Web Site: http://www.lsiwins.com
Year Founded: 1972
Sales Range: $10-24.9 Million
Emp.: 350
Marketing, Consulting & Customer Support Services
N.A.I.C.S.: 541613
Sean M. Slatter (Pres & CEO)
Kori A. Edwards (Sr VP-Ops)
Steven Myers (Chm)

LOGISTICS SUPPORT INC.
1100 New Jersey Ave SE Ste 850, Washington, DC 20003
Tel.: (202) 314-7700
Web Site: http://www.logsup.com
Year Founded: 2001
Rev.: $10,400,000
Emp.: 112
Government Services
N.A.I.C.S.: 921190
David D. Compton (Pres & CEO)
Joseph Sciacca (CFO)
Lora Adams (VP-Pro Svcs)
Paul Masters (COO)
Rosemary Travis (Dir-Navy Logistics & IT)
Jim Myers (VP-Maritime & Army Logistics Div)

LOGONATION, INC.
128 Overhill Dr Ste 102, Mooresville, NC 28117
Tel.: (704) 799-0612
Web Site: http://www.logonation.com
Year Founded: 1998
Sales Range: $1-9.9 Million
Emp.: 65
Commercial Printing Services
N.A.I.C.S.: 323111
Cindy Watson (Dir-Govt Rels)
Denny Watson (Pres)
Jennifer Watson (VP)
Mary Stewart Chatman (VP-Sls)

LOGOS LOGISTICS, INC.
8923 Inkster Rd, Taylor, MI 48180-1442
Tel.: (734) 403-1777
Web Site: http://www.logoslogisticsinc.com
Year Founded: 2008
Sales Range: $25-49.9 Million
Emp.: 22
Logistics Consulting Servies
N.A.I.C.S.: 541614
Jonguk Kim (Pres)

LOGOSPORTSWEAR.COM
12 Beaumont Rd, Wallingford, CT 06492
Tel.: (203) 272-4883
Web Site: http://www.logosportswear.com
Year Founded: 1996
Rev.: $5,000,000
Emp.: 41
Business Products & Services
N.A.I.C.S.: 323113
Jeff Martin (Dir-E-Commerce)

LOHMILLER & COMPANY
4800 Osage St, Denver, CO 80221-7816
Tel.: (303) 820-2665   CO
Web Site: http://www.lohmiller.com
Year Founded: 1990
Sales Range: $100-124.9 Million
Emp.: 85
Warm Air Heating & Air Conditioning
N.A.I.C.S.: 423730
Chuck Lohmiller (Pres)
Nick Ciccio (Controller)

LOIS GELLER MARKETING GROUP
2028 Harrison St Ste 202, Hollywood, FL 33020-7845
Tel.: (646) 723-3231   NY
Web Site: http://www.loisgellermarketinggroup.com
Year Founded: 1995
Sales Range: $10-24.9 Million
Emp.: 4
N.A.I.C.S.: 541810
Lois K. Geller (Pres)
James P. Huff (Dir-Art)
Michael McCormick (Dir-Creative)

LOJAC INC.
1401 Toshiba Dr, Lebanon, TN 37087
Tel.: (615) 449-1401
Web Site: http://www.lojac.com
Year Founded: 1983
Highway & Building Construction Services
N.A.I.C.S.: 236220
B. F. Jack Lowery (CEO)
Kellie Chambers-Mires (COO)
Glenn Chambers (Owner)

LOKEY MOTOR COMPANY
27850 US Hwy 19 N, Clearwater, FL 33761
Tel.: (727) 799-2151   FL
Web Site: http://www.lokey.com
Sales Range: $75-99.9 Million
Emp.: 200
Holding Company; New & Used Car Dealerships Owner & Operator
N.A.I.C.S.: 551112
Paul B. Lokey (Owner & Pres)
Martin Austin (Dir-Sls)

Subsidiaries:

Lokey Kia (1)
27960 US Hwy 19N, Clearwater, FL 33761
Tel.: (727) 799-4499
Web Site: http://www.lokeykia.com
Sales Range: $25-49.9 Million
Emp.: 40
Car Dealership
N.A.I.C.S.: 441110
Charlie Mohr (Gen Mgr)
Jason Polk (Mgr-Sls)
David Hampson (Mgr-Sls)
Raja Assaf (Mgr-Sls)
Ron Bigonzi (Mgr-Fin)

Lokey Nissan, Inc. (1)
27758 US Hwy 19 N, Clearwater, FL 33761
Tel.: (727) 450-7962
Web Site: http://www.lokeynissan.com
Emp.: 30
New & Used Car Dealer
N.A.I.C.S.: 441110
Bobby Louvaris (Dir-Used Cars)
Edie Senensky (Comptroller)
Glenn Jones (Gen Mgr-Sls)
Angelo Kastani (Mgr-Internet)
Brent Tansy (Gen Mgr-Sls)

Lokey Subaru of Port Richey (1)
11613 US Hwy 19 N, Port Richey, FL 34668
Tel.: (727) 862-9044
Web Site: http://www.subaruofportrichey.com
Sales Range: $25-49.9 Million
Emp.: 40
Car Dealership
N.A.I.C.S.: 441110
Chad McIntyre (Mgr-Fin Svcs)
Wes Wanamaker (Mgr-Fixed Ops)
Iain Sherk (Office Mgr)

Lokey Volkswagen (1)
27850 US Hwy 19 N, Clearwater, FL 33761
Tel.: (727) 799-2151
Web Site: http://www.lokeyvw.com
Sales Range: $25-49.9 Million
Emp.: 60
Car Dealership
N.A.I.C.S.: 441110
Eric Novak (Mgr-Parts)
Adam Chess (Mgr-VW Bus)
Spencer Hyatt (Mgr-Svc-Volkswagen)
Angel Aaron (CFO)

LOKION

88 Union Ave Fl 10, Memphis, TN 38103
Tel.: (901) 527-2220
Web Site: http://www.lokion.com
Year Founded: 2000
Rev.: $5,600,000
Emp.: 35
Data Processing, Hosting & Related Services
N.A.I.C.S.: 518210
Marcus Stafford (Founder, Pres & Partner)
Shiloh Barnat (VP-Interaction Design)
Chris Kolehmainen (VP-Fin)

LOLA TRAVEL CO., INC.
250 Summer St, Boston, MA 02210
Tel.: (617) 431-3910
Web Site: http://www.lolatravel.com
Travel Services
N.A.I.C.S.: 561599
Paul English (CTO)
Mike Volpe (CEO)
Krista Pappas (Sr VP-Bus Dev)
Dennis Doughty (Sr VP & Chief Architect)

LOLLICUP USA, INC.
6185 Kimball Ave, Chino, CA 91708
Tel.: (626) 965-8882   CA
Web Site: http://www.lollicup.com
Year Founded: 2000
Sales Range: $25-49.9 Million
Emp.: 136
Food Store Operator
N.A.I.C.S.: 445298
Alan Yu (Owner & CEO)
Marvin Cheng (VP)

LOLLIPOP CORPORATION
15500 SW Jay St 81704, Beaverton, OR 97006-6018   DE
Web Site: http://www.lollipopsports.com
Year Founded: 2011
Nutritional Supplement Distr
N.A.I.C.S.: 424210

LOLLIPROPS INC.
381 Mantoloking Rd, Brick, NJ 08723
Tel.: (732) 920-2654
Web Site: http://www.tempaper.com
Year Founded: 2008
Sales Range: $1-9.9 Million
Emp.: 13
Consumer Goods Rental Services
N.A.I.C.S.: 532289
Julia Au (Founder & CEO)

LOLLYTOGS, LTD.
100 W 33rd St Ste 1012, New York, NY 10001-2914
Tel.: (212) 502-6000   NJ
Web Site: http://www.lollytogs.com
Year Founded: 1958
Sales Range: $25-49.9 Million
Emp.: 200
Children's & Infants' Clothing
N.A.I.C.S.: 424350
Morris Sutton (Co-Owner)
Sam Gindi (Co-Owner)
Joseph Sutton (Exec VP)
Richard Sutton (CEO & Exec VP)
Charlene Alpay (Dir-Mktg)

Subsidiaries:

Lollytogs   (1)
100 W 33rd St Ste 1012, New York, NY 10001-2914
Tel.: (800) 554-7637
Web Site: http://www.healthtex.com
Sales Range: $25-49.9 Million
Emp.: 180
Children's Wear Mfr
N.A.I.C.S.: 424350
Richard Sutton (CEO)

LOLYN FINANCIAL CORPORATION
801 W Foxwood Dr, Raymore, MO 64083
Tel.: (816) 322-2100   MO
Year Founded: 1991
Sales Range: $1-9.9 Million
Bank Holding Company
N.A.I.C.S.: 551111
William R. McDaniel (Pres & CEO)

Subsidiaries:

Community Bank of Pleasant Hill   (1)
2401 N 7 Hwy, Pleasant Hill, MO 64080
Tel.: (816) 540-2525
Web Site: http://www.cbphonline.net
Commericial Banking
N.A.I.C.S.: 522110
Lisa A. Nichelson (Pres & CEO)
William R. McDaniel (Chm)
Jack D. Hopkins (Vice Chm)
Cherilyn Widhalm (Sr VP)

Division (Domestic):

First Trust of MidAmerica   (2)
2401 N 7 Hiwy, Pleasant Hill, MO 64080
Tel.: (816) 987-4012
Web Site: http://www.cbphonline.net
Investment Management Service
N.A.I.C.S.: 523991
Joe Hadel (VP-Employee Benefits)

Community Bank of Raymore   (1)
801 W Foxwood, Raymore, MO 64083-0200
Tel.: (816) 322-2100
Web Site: http://www.cbronline.net
Sales Range: $1-9.9 Million
Emp.: 27
Commericial Banking
N.A.I.C.S.: 522110
William R. McDaniel (Chm & CEO)
Tammie Farr (Officer-Ops & VP)
Shauna Stephenson (VP & Mgr-Retail)
Cindy Jobes (Officer-Consumer Loan & VP)
Andy Cooper (Sr Officer-Lending & Sr VP)
Beverley J. Brewington (CFO & Exec VP)
Brandi Torres (Asst Branch Mgr)
Carole Arnold (VP)
Donna Walsh (Officer-Trust & Sr VP)
Fallon Solscheid (VP & Mgr-Raymore)
Gina Brumbaugh (VP-Ops)
Jessica Williams (Asst Branch Mgr)
John Archer (Sr VP)
Kathy Gladden (Officer-Ops & VP)
Kevin Fallon (Officer-Loan & VP)
Sherrie L. Lindquist (VP)
Stephanie Brandes (Officer-Loan Admin)
Tina Graef (VP & Mgr-Harrisonville)
Mary Fay (Owner)
Jeremy Mansur (Officer-Trust)
Barbara A. McDaniel (Owner)
Michael Noe (Owner)
Mike Sanders (Owner)
Steve Zahn (Owner)

LOMANCO INC.
2101 W Main St, Jacksonville, AR 72076
Tel.: (501) 982-6511
Web Site: http://www.lomanco.com
Sales Range: $10-24.9 Million
Emp.: 200
Metal Ventilating Fans
N.A.I.C.S.: 332322
Scott Webb (CIO)
Mike Mitchell (Dir-Sls)
Ted Belden (Chm)
Andrew Mercer (Mgr-Sls-Natl)

LOMAR MACHINE & TOOL CO.
135 Main St, Horton, MI 49246
Tel.: (517) 563-8136
Web Site: http://www.lomar.com
Year Founded: 1976
Emp.: 100
Designer & Mfr of Standard & Custom Machine Applications
N.A.I.C.S.: 333519

Ron Geisman (Pres)
Chuck Murphy (VP-Direct Ship Program)
Mandy Hunter (Mgr-Programs)
Todd Pelton (Mgr-Engrg)
Justine Galloway (Engr-Sls)
Kelly Kohn (Mgr-Mktg)
Tim Murphy (Mgr-Machining)
John Smoyer (Mgr-Quality)
John Barnes (Engr-Sls)

LOMBARDI BROTHERS MEAT PACKERS, INC.
1926 W Elk Pl, Denver, CO 80211-1250
Tel.: (303) 458-7441   CO
Web Site: http://www.lombardibrothers.com
Year Founded: 1947
Sales Range: $75-99.9 Million
Emp.: 50
Fresh Meat Processor & Distr
N.A.I.C.S.: 424470
Jeff Harvey (Gen Mgr)
Victoria Parker-Philips (Pres)

LOMBARDI'S SEAFOOD INC.
1888 Fairbanks Ave, Winter Park, FL 32789
Tel.: (407) 628-3474
Web Site: http://www.lombardis.com
Sales Range: $10-24.9 Million
Emp.: 20
Fish & Seafoods
N.A.I.C.S.: 424460
Tony Lombardi (VP)
Anthony Lombardi Jr. (Pres)

LOMBARDO & LIPE ELECTRICAL CONTRACTORS INC.
6 Progress St, East Stroudsburg, PA 18301
Tel.: (570) 421-6525
Web Site: http://www.lombardo-lipe.com
Rev.: $28,295,741
Emp.: 20
General Electrical Contractor
N.A.I.C.S.: 238210
David Keller (Project Coord)

LOMONT MOLDING LLC
1516 E Mapleleaf Dr, Mount Pleasant, IA 52641
Tel.: (319) 385-1528   IA
Web Site: http://www.lomont.com
Year Founded: 1982
Custom Injection & Blow Molding Plastics Product Mfr
N.A.I.C.S.: 326199
Jason Bender (Pres)

Subsidiaries:

R&D Molders, Inc.   (1)
107 Park Central Blvd, Georgetown, TX 78626
Tel.: (512) 763-3600
Web Site: http://www.rdmolders.com
Custom Injection & Blow Molding Plastics Products Mfr
N.A.I.C.S.: 326199
Gregory C. Brown (Pres)

LONDEN INSURANCE GROUP, INC.
4343 E Camelback Rd, Phoenix, AZ 85018
Tel.: (602) 957-1650   AZ
Web Site: http://www.londen-insurance.com
Year Founded: 1963
Sales Range: $50-74.9 Million
Emp.: 150
Life Insurance
N.A.I.C.S.: 524113

Jack W. Londen (Chm & CEO)
Doug Turner (VP-Mktg)
Jack Roberts (Gen Partner)

Subsidiaries:

Lincoln Heritage Life Insurance Co.   (1)
4343 E Camelback Rd Ste 400, Phoenix, AZ 85018-2700   (100%)
Tel.: (602) 957-1650
Web Site: http://www.lhlic.com
Sales Range: $50-74.9 Million
Emp.: 300
Fire Insurance Services
N.A.I.C.S.: 524113
Larry Schuneman (Pres & COO)
Jack Londen III (Chm)

Londen Land Company, L.L.C.   (1)
4343 E Camelback Rd Ste 400, Phoenix, AZ 85018
Tel.: (602) 957-1650
Web Site: http://www.lhlic.com
Property Insurance Services
N.A.I.C.S.: 524126

Londen Media Group, L.L.C.   (1)
4343 E Camelback Rd Ste 130, Phoenix, AZ 85018
Tel.: (602) 977-7700
Web Site: http://www.aztv.com
Emp.: 25
General Insurance Services
N.A.I.C.S.: 524210
Rich Howe (Gen Mgr)

LONDON BAY CAPITAL LLC
15 Funston Ave, San Francisco, CA 94129
Tel.: (415) 292-1700
Privater Equity Firm
N.A.I.C.S.: 523999
Sam Humphreys (CEO)
Alton F. Irby III (Co-Founder, Chm & Partner)

Subsidiaries:

Selling Source, LLC   (1)
325 E Warm Springs Rd, Las Vegas, NV 89119
Tel.: (702) 407-0707
Web Site: http://www.sellingsource.com
Sales Range: $300-349.9 Million
Emp.: 409
Marketing Consulting Services
N.A.I.C.S.: 541613
Glenn McKay (Pres & COO)

LONDON COIN GALLERIES INCORPORATED
4525A Macarthur Blvd, Newport Beach, CA 92660
Tel.: (949) 251-0444
Web Site: http://www.londoncoin.com
Sales Range: $10-24.9 Million
Emp.: 3
Coins
N.A.I.C.S.: 423940
John Saunders (Pres)

LONDON GROUP, INC.
2210 Vanderbilt Beach Rd Ste 1300, Naples, FL 34109
Tel.: (239) 592-1400
Web Site: http://www.londonbay.com
Year Founded: 1990
Sales Range: $200-249.9 Million
Emp.: 130
Residential Property Builder
N.A.I.C.S.: 236117
Mark Wilson (Pres)
Sabra Smith (VP-HR)
Lisa Van Dien (VP)

LONE FIR CONSULTING, LLC
4810 Pt Fosdick Dr NW Ste 67, Gig Harbor, WA 98335
Tel.: (206) 486-0828
Web Site:
https://www.lonefircreative.com
Year Founded: 2015

LONE FIR CONSULTING, LLC

Lone Fir Consulting, LLC—(Continued)
Marketing, Branding & Strategy Services
N.A.I.C.S.: 541613
Subsidiaries:

MC2 Design Group, Inc. (1)
2623 Forest Ave Ste 110, Chico, CA 95928-4392
Tel.: (530) 893-4978
Web Site: http://www.morrisonco.net
Administrative Management & General Management Consulting Services
N.A.I.C.S.: 541611
Geoffrey R. Chinnock (*Principal*)

LONE STAR AG CREDIT
1612 Summit Ave Ste 300, Fort Worth, TX 76102-5916
Tel.: (254) 422-3351
Web Site:
  http://www.lonestaragcredit.com
Emp.: 100
Credit Card Issuing
N.A.I.C.S.: 522210
Bill Melton (*Interim CEO*)
David Harris (*Chm*)
Subsidiaries:

Ag New Mexico, Farm Credit Services, Pca (1)
233 Fairway Ter N, Clovis, NM 88101
Tel.: (505) 762-3828
Web Site: http://www.agnewmexico.com
Sales Range: $1-9.9 Million
Emp.: 100
International Trade Financing
N.A.I.C.S.: 522299
Bill Yoakun (*CEO*)

LONE STAR BEEF PROCESSORS, L.P.
2150 E 37th St, San Angelo, TX 76903-3415
Tel.: (325) 658-5555   TX
Web Site: http://www.lonestarbeef.net
Year Founded: 1997
Sales Range: $75-99.9 Million
Cattle Slaughtering & Processing Services
N.A.I.C.S.: 311611
John W. Cross (*Co-Founder & Pres*)
Chad Collier (*Mgr-Quality Control*)
Robert Rodriquez (*Supvr-Quality Control Tech*)
Robby Smith (*Coord-HACCP*)
Lacey Vinson (*Mgr-Lab*)
Burley Smith Jr. (*Co-Founder & VP*)

LONE STAR CAPITAL BANK, N.A.
150 N Loop 1604 E at Stone Oak Pkwy, San Antonio, TX 78232
Tel.: (210) 496-6116   TX
Web Site: http://www.lscb.com
Year Founded: 1999
Sales Range: $1-9.9 Million
Emp.: 69
Commericial Banking
N.A.I.C.S.: 522110
Danny Buck (*Pres & CEO*)
Christy McCoy (*CFO & Exec VP*)
Ralph Yzaguirre (*COO & Exec VP*)
Jesse Baza (*Chief Credit Officer & Exec VP*)
Robert Potter (*Chief Lending Officer & Exec VP*)

LONE STAR CIRCLE OF CARE
205 E University Ave Ste 200, Georgetown, TX 78626
Tel.: (512) 686-0523   TX
Web Site: http://www.lscctx.org
Year Founded: 2001
Sales Range: $50-74.9 Million
Emp.: 599
Health Care Srvices

N.A.I.C.S.: 622110
Marc Welch (*CFO*)
Denise Esper (*Chief Revenue Officer*)
Tillery Stout (*Gen Counsel*)
Jack Hunnicutt (*Chm*)
Karen Cole (*Sec*)
Steve Pena (*Treas*)
Cynthia Brien (*VP*)
Scott Alarcon (*VP*)
Denise Armstrong (*Chief Dental Officer*)
Tracy Angelocci (*Chief Medical Information Officer*)
Kathleen V. Butler (*Chief Medical Officer & Chief Quality Officer*)
Rhonda Mundhenk (*Co-CEO*)
Jon Calvin (*Co-CFO*)
Pete Perialas Jr. (*CEO*)

LONE STAR CIRCUITS INC.
901 Hensley Ln, Willis, TX 75098
Web Site: http://lscpcbs.com
Sales Range: $25-49.9 Million
Emp.: 179
Printed Circuit Board Mfr
N.A.I.C.S.: 334412
Brad Jacoby (*CEO & Sec*)
Greg Mitchell (*Dir-Tech & Military Sls*)
Jim Campbell (*Chm*)
John Freeman (*Controller*)
Scott Diacont (*Dir-Quality*)
Ed Porter (*Pres & COO*)

LONE STAR COACHES, INC.
PO Box 531668, Grand Prairie, TX 75053-1668
Tel.: (972) 623-1100
Web Site:
  http://www.lonestarcoaches.com
Charter Bus Rental Services
N.A.I.C.S.: 485510
Subsidiaries:

Tri-City Charter of Bossier, Inc. (1)
1323 Canyon Ct, Bossier City, LA 71172
Tel.: (318) 747-4754
Web Site: http://www.tricitycharter.com
Charter Bus Rental Services
N.A.I.C.S.: 485510

LONE STAR COMPANY INC.
3201 E Highland Dr, Jonesboro, AR 72401
Tel.: (870) 932-6679
Web Site:
  http://www.starcompanies.net
Rev.: $18,756,091
Emp.: 120
Gasoline
N.A.I.C.S.: 424720
Albert M. Heringer III (*Pres*)

LONE STAR CONSOLIDATED FOODS
1727 N Beckley Ave, Dallas, TX 75203
Tel.: (214) 946-2185
Web Site:
  http://www.lonestarfunfoods.com
Rev.: $37,900,000
Emp.: 130
Bakery Products, Frozen
N.A.I.C.S.: 424420
Dolores Burdine (*Owner*)
Linda Dell (*Controller*)

LONE STAR CORRUGATED CONTAINER CORPORATION
700 N Wildwood Dr, Irving, TX 75061-8832
Tel.: (972) 579-1551   TX
Web Site:
  http://www.lonestarbox.com
Year Founded: 1959
Sales Range: $50-74.9 Million
Emp.: 130

Mfr of Corrugated Shipping Containers
N.A.I.C.S.: 322211
Edward Resh (*Dir-Mktg*)
Subsidiaries:

Dixie Reel & Box Co. (1)
PO Box 7791, Charlotte, NC 28241-7791   (100%)
Tel.: (704) 588-1737
Sales Range: $10-24.9 Million
Emp.: 40
Mfr of Corrugated Shipping Containers
N.A.I.C.S.: 322211
William Harkey (*Gen Mgr*)

Lone Star Container Sales Corp. (1)
700 N Wildwood Dr, Irving, TX 75061-8832   (100%)
Tel.: (972) 579-1551
Web Site: http://www.lonestarbox.com
Sales Range: $25-49.9 Million
Emp.: 200
Box & Container Whslr
N.A.I.C.S.: 423990
Paul McLeod (*Mgr-Ops*)
John McLeod Jr. (*CEO*)
Richard Ward (*Mgr-Sls*)

LONE STAR EQUITIES, INC.
181 S Franklin Ave Ste 607, Valley Stream, NY 11581
Tel.: (516) 599-3700
Web Site:
  http://www.lonestarequitiesusa.com
Year Founded: 1950
Owner & Operator of Commercial Real Estate & Mortgages
N.A.I.C.S.: 531120
Joseph S. Soussana (*CEO*)

LONE STAR FOUNDRIES, INC.
2110 E 4th St, Austin, TX 78702
Tel.: (512) 472-1330   TX
Web Site:
  http://www.lonestarfoundries.com
Sales Range: $10-24.9 Million
Emp.: 100
Steel Foundries
N.A.I.C.S.: 331529
Andrew Edgerton (*Pres*)
Subsidiaries:

Pure Casting Company (1)
112 E MLK Jr Ind Blvd, Lockhart, TX 78644
Tel.: (512) 472-1330
Web Site: http://www.purecastingsco.com
Steel Foundries
N.A.I.C.S.: 331512

LONE STAR FUNDS
2711 N Haskell Ave, Dallas, TX 75204
Tel.: (214) 754-8300
Web Site:
  http://www.lonestarfunds.com
Year Founded: 1995
Privater Equity Firm
N.A.I.C.S.: 523940
Michael King (*Chief Compliance Officer & Mng Dir*)
Subsidiaries:

Arclin Inc. (1)
1000 Holcomb Woods Pkwy Ste 342, Roswell, GA 30076
Tel.: (678) 999-2100
Web Site: http://www.arclin.com
Adhesion & Surface Solutions
N.A.I.C.S.: 325520
Russell C. Taylor (*Pres & CEO*)
Scott Maynard (*CFO*)
Ron Huizingh (*Sr VP-Mfg*)
Mark Anderson (*Sr VP-Res & Tech*)
Bernie Cardella (*Sr VP-Supply Chain*)
Brian Adams (*Sr Dir-Bus-Intl Overlays*)
Matt Pogue (*Pres-Engineered Building Solutions*)
Subsidiary (Domestic):

Arclin USA, LLC (2)

790 Corinth Rd, Moncure, NC 27559-9345
Tel.: (919) 542-2526
Adhesion & Surface Solutions
N.A.I.C.S.: 325520
Subsidiary (Domestic):

Coveright Surfaces USA Co. (3)
1051 Jenkins Brothers Rd, Blythewood, SC 29016-7752
Tel.: (803) 754-4810
Web Site: http://www.coveright.com
Sales Range: $50-74.9 Million
Emp.: 100
Mfr of Surfacing Materials for Applications in Woodworking, Furniture & Automotive
N.A.I.C.S.: 325510

CaixaBank, S.A. (1)
Av Diagonal 621, 08028, Barcelona, Spain   (80%)
Tel.: (34) 900713325
Web Site: https://www.caixabank.com
Emp.: 45,349
Financial Investment Services
N.A.I.C.S.: 523999
Javier Pano Riera (*CFO*)
Oscar Calderon de Oya (*Sec*)
Marisa Retamosa (*Head-Internal Audit*)
Jordi Mondejar (*Chief Risks Officer*)
Jose Ignacio Goirigolzarri Tellaeche (*Exec Chm*)
Manuel Galarza (*Head-Control, Compliance, and Public Affairs*)
Eugenio Solla (*Chief Sustainability Officer*)
Inaki Badiola (*Head-CIB & Intl Banking & Corp Dir-Investment Banking*)
Tomas Muniesa Arantegui (*Deputy Chm*)
David Lopez (*Chief People Officer*)
Jaume Masana (*Head-Retail*)
Mariona Vicens (*Head-Digital Transformation & Advanced Analytics*)
Gonzalo Gortazar Rotaeche (*CEO*)
Subsidiary (Non-US):

Banco BPI, S.A. (2)
Rua Tenente Valadim 284, 4100-476, Porto, Portugal   (84.51%)
Tel.: (351) 226 073 111
Web Site: http://bpi.bancobpi.pt
Sales Range: $1-4.9 Billion
Commericial Banking
N.A.I.C.S.: 522110
Pablo Forero Calderon (*Chm*)
Alexandre Lucena e Vale (*Head-Legal & Gen Mgr*)
Ricardo Araujo (*Head-IR*)
Subsidiary (Non-US):

BPI (Suisse) S.A. (3)
1 Etienne Dumont, 1204, Geneva, Switzerland
Tel.: (41) 223183760
Web Site: http://www.bpisuisse.ch
Private Banking & Portfolio Management Services
N.A.I.C.S.: 523940
Subsidiary (Domestic):

Inter-Risco - Sociedade de Capital de Risco, S.A. (3)
Avenida da Boavista 1081, 4100-129, Porto, Norte, Portugal
Tel.: (351) 220 126 700
Web Site: http://www.inter-risco.pt
Venture Capital Fund Providers
N.A.I.C.S.: 525910
Silvia Almeida (*CFO*)
Jose Mario Leite (*Dir-Investment*)
Isabel Martins (*Dir-Investment*)
Rui Branquinho (*Partner*)
Isabel Coelho (*Partner*)
Joao Pontes Amaro (*Mng Partner*)
Subsidiary (Domestic):

Bankia, S.A. (2)
Calle del Pintor Sorolla 8, 46002, Valencia, Spain
Tel.: (34) 916024680
Web Site: http://www.bankia.com
Rev.: $3,633,979,296
Assets: $233,455,280,202
Liabilities: $218,521,838,475

COMPANIES

Net Worth: $14,933,441,726
Earnings: $607,287,760
Emp.: 16,035
Fiscal Year-end: 12/31/2019
Commercial Banking Services
N.A.I.C.S.: 522110

Subsidiary (Domestic):

Atenea Comunicacion Y Mecenazgo, S.A. (3)
Calle Santander 3 Segunda Planta, 28003, Madrid, Spain **(80%)**
Tel.: (34) 915989820
Web Site: http://www.ateneacm.es
Sales Range: $25-49.9 Million
Emp.: 20
Provider of Research Services
N.A.I.C.S.: 541910

Affiliate (Domestic):

Auseco, S.A. (3)
San Bernardo 123, Madrid, Spain **(20%)**
Provider of Debt Collection Services
N.A.I.C.S.: 561440

Subsidiary (Domestic):

Bankia Inversiones Financieras, S.A.U. (3)
Gabriel Garcia Marquez 1, 28230, Madrid, Spain **(100%)**
Tel.: (34) 902246810
Corporate Management
N.A.I.C.S.: 551114

Joint Venture (Domestic):

Bankia MAPFRE Vida, S.A. de Seguros y Reaseguros (3)
Avenida General Peron 49, ES 28020, Madrid, Spain **(49%)**
Tel.: (34) 902136524
Life Insurance
N.A.I.C.S.: 524113

Subsidiary (Domestic):

Bankia Pensiones, S.A., E.G.F.P. (3)
Paseo de la Castellana 189, 28046, Madrid, Spain
Tel.: (34) 914239494
Web Site: http://www.bankiapensiones.es
Pension Fund Management Services
N.A.I.C.S.: 524292

Branch (Domestic):

Bankia, S.A. - Madrid Operational Headquarters (3)
Paseo de la Castellana 189, 28046, Madrid, Spain
Tel.: (34) 916024680
Web Site: http://www.bankia.com
Office Administrative Services
N.A.I.C.S.: 561110
Jose Sevilla Alvarez (CEO)

Affiliate (Domestic):

Cresan, S.A. (3)
Hierro 33, 28045, Madrid, Spain **(20%)**
Tel.: (34) 915062193
Web Site: http://www.cresan.es
Data Files
N.A.I.C.S.: 518210

Registro de Prestaciones Informaticas, S.A. (3)
Capitan Haya 51, Madrid, Spain **(20%)**
Savings Institutions, Federally Chartered
N.A.I.C.S.: 522180

S.L. de Gestion Mobiliaria (3)
Avenida Diagonal 530, Barcelona, Spain **(50%)**
Portfolio Management
N.A.I.C.S.: 523940

Subsidiary (Domestic):

Sociedad de Participacion y Promocion Empresarial Caja de Madrid (3)
Eloy Gonzalo 10, Madrid, Spain **(100%)**
Web Site: http://www.cajamadrid.es
Venture Capital; Financial Company
N.A.I.C.S.: 523910

Subsidiary (Domestic):

VidaCaixa, S.A. de Seguros y Reaseguros (2)
Juan Gris 20-26, 08014, Barcelona, Spain **(100%)**
Tel.: (34) 932 278 700
Web Site: http://www.vidacaixa.com
Rev.: $9,561,753,845
Assets: $75,770,657,929
Liabilities: $71,977,360,747
Net Worth: $3,793,297,182
Earnings: $757,977,051
Emp.: 546
Fiscal Year-end: 12/31/2018
Life & Health Insurance & Pension Products & Services
N.A.I.C.S.: 524298
Tomas Muniesa Arantegui (VP)
Jorge Mercader Miro (Vice Chm)
Gonzalo Gortazar Rotaeche (Chm)
Francisco Javier Valle T-Figueras (Mng Dir)
Oscar Figueres Fortuna (Sec)

Affiliate (Domestic):

SegurCaixa Adeslas, S.A. de Seguros y Reaseguros (3)
Juan Gris 20-26, 08014, Barcelona, Spain **(49.92%)**
Tel.: (34) 902 200 200
Web Site: http://www.segurcaixaadeslas.es
Emp.: 4,037
Title, Property, Casualty & Other Non-Life Insurance Products & Services
N.A.I.C.S.: 524298
D. Juan Hormaechea Escos (Pres)

Lone Star Americas Acquisitions, LLC (1)
1441 Brickell Ave Ste 1750, Miami, FL 33131
Tel.: (786) 482-2100
Web Site: http://www.lonestarfunds.com
Private Equity
N.A.I.C.S.: 523999
John Grayken (Founder)

Holding (Domestic):

CentroMotion (2)
N19 W24200 Riverwood Dr Ste 300, Waukesha, WI 53188
Tel.: (262) 754-7300
Web Site: http://www.centromotion.com
Mechanical & Industrial Engineered Components Mfr
N.A.I.C.S.: 423830
Roger Roundhouse (CEO)
Jonathan Omer (Sr VP-Indus Segment)
Tom Vanderlaan (Sr VP)

Subsidiary (Domestic):

Carlisle Brake & Friction, Inc. (3)
920 Lk Rd, Medina, OH 44256
Tel.: (440) 528-4000
Web Site: http://www.wellmanproducts.com
Emp.: 130
Brake System Mfr
N.A.I.C.S.: 336340
Ted Messmer (Pres)

Subsidiary (Domestic):

Friction Products Co. (4)
920 Lake Rd, Medina, OH 44256
Tel.: (330) 725-4941
Motor Vehicle Transmission Mfr
N.A.I.C.S.: 336350

Wellman Products Group (4)
6180 Cochron Rd, Solon, OH 44139 **(100%)**
Tel.: (440) 528-4000
Web Site: http://www.wellmanproducts.com
Sales Range: $50-74.9 Million
Emp.: 60
Metal Clutch Plates, Facings, Brake Linings & Transmission Discs Mfr
N.A.I.C.S.: 332117

SPX FLOW, Inc. (1)
13320 Ballantyne Corporate Pl, Charlotte, NC 28277
Tel.: (704) 752-4400
Web Site: https://www.spxflow.com
Rev.: $1,529,000,000
Assets: $2,086,200,000
Liabilities: $1,049,600,000
Net Worth: $1,036,600,000
Earnings: $66,700,000
Emp.: 4,900
Fiscal Year-end: 12/31/2021
Holding Company; Flow Control Products Mfr
N.A.I.C.S.: 551112
Alvin Jeffers (VP-Supply Chain & Global Mfg)
Jaime Manson Easley (CFO, Chief Acctg Officer, Treas & VP)
Kevin J. Eamigh (CIO & VP-Bus Transformation)
Melissa Buscher (CMO & Chief Comm Officer)
Peter J. Ryan (Chief People Officer, Gen Counsel, Sec & VP)
Marc Michael (Pres & CEO)
Rudy Calderon (Pres-Nutrition & Health Waukesha Cherry-Burrell)
Wendy Malone (Pres-Mixing Solutions)
Greg Rogers (Pres-Pump Solutions)

Subsidiary (Non-US):

APV Ltd. (2)
Beehive, Beehive Ring Rd, Gatwick, RH6 0PA, W Sussex, United Kingdom
Tel.: (44) 1293527777
Web Site: http://www.apv.com
Sales Range: $25-49.9 Million
Emp.: 70
Process Equipment Manufacturing & Engineering Services
N.A.I.C.S.: 333241

Subsidiary (Non-US):

APV Benelux NV (3)
Evenbroekveld 6, 9420, Erpe-Mere, Belgium
Tel.: (32) 53602780
Web Site: http://www.apv.com
Sales Range: $10-24.9 Million
Emp.: 2
Valve Pumps Distr
N.A.I.C.S.: 332911

Subsidiary (Non-US):

Anhydro S.A.S (2)
Espace Sulzer 28 Boulevard Roger Salengro, Mantes La Ville, 78711, Mantes-la-Ville, France
Tel.: (33) 134788255
Industrial Equipment Mfr
N.A.I.C.S.: 333248

Clyde Pumps India Pvt Limited (2)
No 162 6th Floor Tower- A The Corenthum Plot No A- 41 Sector- 62, Noida, 201301, Uttar Pradesh, India
Tel.: (91) 1204640400
Web Site: http://www.spxglobe.com
Emp.: 50
Pumps Mfr
N.A.I.C.S.: 333914
Neelima Raj (Mgr-HR)

Clyde Union (France) S.A.S. (2)
39 Avenue du Pont de Tasset, 74960, Meythet, France
Tel.: (33) 4 50 05 56 00
Holding Company
N.A.I.C.S.: 551112

Clyde Union Canada Limited (2)
4151 North Service Rd, Burlington, L7L 4X6, ON, Canada
Tel.: (905) 315-3800
Emp.: 75
Pumps Mfr
N.A.I.C.S.: 333914
Shakil Ahmed (Gen Mgr)

Clyde Union DB Limited (2)
Park Gear Works Lockwood, Huddersfield, HD4 5DD, United Kingdom
Tel.: (44) 1484465500
Web Site: http://www.davidbrown.com
Emp.: 300
Industrial Machinery Distr
N.A.I.C.S.: 423830
Steve Watson (Mng Dir)

Subsidiary (Domestic):

Clyde Union Inc. (2)
4600 W Dickman Rd, Battle Creek, MI 49037
Tel.: (269) 966-4600

LONE STAR FUNDS

Centrifugal & Reciprocating Pump Mfr
N.A.I.C.S.: 333914
Jon Young (Mgr-Ops)

Subsidiary (Non-US):

Clyde Union Ltd (2)
149 Newlands Road, Cathcart, Glasgow, G44 4EX, Scotland, United Kingdom
Tel.: (44) 1416377141
Web Site: http://www.clydeunion.com
Sales Range: $300-349.9 Million
Emp.: 800
Valves & Pumping Equipment Mfr
N.A.I.C.S.: 333914
Chris Kearney (Chm, Pres & CEO)

Clyde Union Middle East LLC. (2)
Box No 74978, Dubai, United Arab Emirates
Tel.: (971) 43289011
Web Site: http://www.spxflow.com
Emp.: 1
Industrial Machinery Distr
N.A.I.C.S.: 423830

Clyde Union Pumps Middle East FZE (2)
PO Box 262785 Jebel Ali, Dubai, United Arab Emirates
Tel.: (971) 48807755
Emp.: 25
Industrial Machinery Distr
N.A.I.C.S.: 423830

Clyde Union S.A.S. (2)
Annecy Plant 39 Avenue du Pont de Tasset ZAE de Meythet, PO Box 435, 74020, Annecy, Cedex, France
Tel.: (33) 450055600
Emp.: 313
Pumps Mfr
N.A.I.C.S.: 333914
Bouvet Christopher (Gen Mgr)

Clyde Union South East Asia Pte. Ltd. (2)
9 Pioneer Walk, Singapore, 627752, Singapore
Tel.: (65) 62767117
Oil & Gas Field Operating Services
N.A.I.C.S.: 213112

Fastighets AB Kladeshandlaren (2)
Stortorget 1-3, 702 11, Orebro, Sweden
Tel.: (46) 196762230
Financial Services
N.A.I.C.S.: 541611

Subsidiary (Domestic):

Flow America, LLC (2)
5401 S Kirkman Rd Ste 475, Orlando, FL 32819
Web Site: http://www.flowamerica.com
Real Estate Development Services
N.A.I.C.S.: 531311

Philadelphia Mixing Solutions Ltd. (2)
1221 E Main St, Palmyra, PA 17078-9518
Tel.: (717) 832-2800
Web Site: http://www.philamixers.com
Industrial Mixer Mfr & Distr
N.A.I.C.S.: 333120
Jon Sasala (Dir-Supply Chain)

Subsidiary (Non-US):

Mixing Solutions Limited (3)
Venture House Bone Lane, Newbury, RG14 5SH, Berkshire, United Kingdom
Tel.: (44) 163 527 5300
Web Site: http://www.mixingsolutions.com
Industrial Mixer Distr
N.A.I.C.S.: 423840
Nick Pither (Mgr-Technical Engrg)

Subsidiary (Domestic):

S & N Pump Company (2)
8002 Breen Rd, Houston, TX 77065
Tel.: (281) 445-2243
Industrial Machinery Mfr
N.A.I.C.S.: 333924
David Draper (Owner)

Subsidiary (Non-US):

S&N Pump (Africa) Ltda (2)
Estrado do Tando Zinze Terra Nova Cabassango, PO Box 588, Terra Nova, Cabinda,

2485

LONE STAR FUNDS

Lone Star Funds—(Continued)

588, Angola
Tel.: (244) 913144413
Pumps Mfr
N.A.I.C.S.: 333120
Paul Humphrey (Mgr-Ops)

S&N Pump and Rewind Limited (2)
3 International View Aberdeen Business Park, Aberdeen, AB21 0BJ, Aberdeenshire, United Kingdom
Tel.: (44) 1224756100
Web Site: http://www.spxflow.com
Emp.: 25
Pump Distr
N.A.I.C.S.: 423120

SPX (Schweiz) AG (2)
Grabenhofstrasse 6, Kriens, 6010, Luzern, Switzerland
Tel.: (41) 417662925
Air Conditioner Mfr
N.A.I.C.S.: 333415

SPX (Shanghai) Flow Technology Co., Ltd. (2)
7F No 1568 Huashan Road, Shanghai, 200052, China
Tel.: (86) 2122085888
Industrial Machinery Distr
N.A.I.C.S.: 423830
Peilin Lu (Dir-Engrg)

Division (Domestic):

SPX Flow Technology (2)
13515 Ballantyne Corporate Pl, Charlotte, NC 28277
Tel.: (704) 752-4400
Web Site: http://www.spxflowtechnology.com
Solutions for Manufacturing Operations & Processes in the Food & Beverage, Power & Energy & Industrial Markets
N.A.I.C.S.: 423830

Unit (Domestic):

SPX Flow Control (3)
8800 W Plain Dr, Houston, TX 77041
Tel.: (281) 469-0550
Web Site: http://www.spxflowl.com
Sales Range: $50-74.9 Million
Emp.: 300
Large Fabricated Valves Mfr
N.A.I.C.S.: 332911

Subsidiary (Non-US):

SPX Flow Technology (India) Private Limited (3)
Survey No 275 Odhav Road, Odhav, Ahmedabad, 382415, Gujarat, India
Tel.: (91) 7966778811
Web Site: http://www.johnson-pump.com
Air Conditioner Mfr
N.A.I.C.S.: 333415
Amish Shah (Mgr-HR)

SPX Flow Technology (Pty) Limited (3)
Unit 12B Growthpoint Office Park Tonetti Street, Midrand, 1658, South Africa
Tel.: (27) 11 207 3700
Web Site: https://www.spxflow.com
Emp.: 50
Pumps Mfr
N.A.I.C.S.: 333914

SPX Flow Technology (Thailand) Limited (3)
Bangkok Business Center Bldg 27th Floor Unit 2702 29 Sukhumvit 63 Road, Kwaeng Klongton Nua Khet Wattana, Bangkok, 10110, Thailand
Tel.: (66) 27143838
Engineeering Services
N.A.I.C.S.: 541330

SPX Flow Technology Australia (3)
211 Atlantic Drive, Keysborough, 3170, VIC, Australia
Tel.: (61) 39 589 9222
Emp.: 150
Process Equipment Manufacturing & Engineering Services
N.A.I.C.S.: 333413

SPX Flow Technology Belgium NV (3)
Evenhoekveld 2-4, Erpe, 9420, Belgium
Tel.: (32) 53602715
Specific Pumps Mfr
N.A.I.C.S.: 333914

SPX Flow Technology Canada Inc (3)
1415 California Avenue, Brockville, K6V 7H7, ON, Canada
Tel.: (613) 345-2280
Industrial Process Furnace & Oven Mfr
N.A.I.C.S.: 333994
Richard Bays (Gen Mgr)
Jeffrey Pato (Sls Mgr-East)

SPX Flow Technology Copenhagen A/S (3)
ostmarken 7, DK 2860, Soborg, Frederiksborg, Denmark
Tel.: (45) 70278222
Web Site: http://www.gs-as.com
Emp.: 120
Food Processing Equipment Mfr
N.A.I.C.S.: 333241
Martina Grasnick (Mng Dir-Germany)

Subsidiary (Domestic):

Anhydro A/S (4)
Oestmarken 7, Soeborg, DK 2860, Copenhagen, Denmark
Tel.: (45) 70278222
Web Site: http://www.spxflowtecnology.com
Sales Range: $50-74.9 Million
Emp.: 225
Holding Company; Drying Technology
N.A.I.C.S.: 551112

Subsidiary (Non-US):

SPX Flow Technology Crawley Limited (3)
Building A Compass House Manor Royal, Crawley, RH10 9PY, West Sussex, United Kingdom
Tel.: (44) 1612491441
Web Site: http://www.spx.co.uk
Air Conditioner Mfr
N.A.I.C.S.: 333415

SPX Flow Technology Danmark A/S (3)
Pasteursvej 1, 8600, Silkeborg, Denmark
Tel.: (45) 70278278
Emp.: 170
Air Conditioner Mfr
N.A.I.C.S.: 333415

SPX Flow Technology Etten-Leur B.V (3)
Munnikenheiweg 41, 4879 NE, Etten-Leur, Netherlands
Tel.: (31) 7 650 8550
Web Site: http://www.spxflowtechnology.com
Emp.: 65
Fluid Power Pumps Mfr
N.A.I.C.S.: 333996

SPX Flow Technology Finland Oy (3)
PL119, 01601, Vantaa, Finland
Tel.: (358) 400206437
Web Site: http://www.spxflow.com
Emp.: 4
Industrial Machinery Mfr
N.A.I.C.S.: 333924
Ari Vuoriola (Mng Dir)

SPX Flow Technology Hanse GmbH (3)
Bernsteindreherweg 7, Lubeck, 23556, Germany
Tel.: (49) 45137090
Emp.: 50
Air Conditioner Mfr
N.A.I.C.S.: 333415

SPX Flow Technology Japan, Inc. (3)
Unosawa Tokyu Bldg 2F 1-19-15, Ebisu Shibuya-ku, Tokyo, 150-0013, Japan
Tel.: (81) 357935611
Web Site: http://www.spxflow.com
Pumps Mfr
N.A.I.C.S.: 333914

SPX Flow Technology Korea Co., Ltd. (3)
Yeouido-dong KT Building 11F 14 Yeouidaero, Yeongdeungpo-gu, Seoul, 07320, Korea (South)
Tel.: (82) 262974000
Web Site: http://www.spx.com
Air Conditioner Mfr
N.A.I.C.S.: 333415

SPX Flow Technology Mexico S.A. de C.V. (3)
Parque Granada 71 Piso 1 Col Parques De La Herradura, Huixquilucan, Mexico
Tel.: (52) 5552939035
Pumps Mfr
N.A.I.C.S.: 333914
Sergio Oyarvide (Dir-Fin)

SPX Flow Technology Moers GmbH (3)
Konrad-Zuse-Strasse 25, 47445, Moers, Germany
Tel.: (49) 28418190
Web Site: http://www.spx-hankison.de
Emp.: 70
Air Conditioner Mfr
N.A.I.C.S.: 333415

SPX Flow Technology New Zealand Limited (3)
2 Kaimiro Street Pukete, Hamilton, 3200, New Zealand
Tel.: (64) 78506250
Web Site: http://www.spxflow.com
Emp.: 15
Air Conditioner Mfr
N.A.I.C.S.: 333415

SPX Flow Technology Norderstedt GmbH (3)
Werkstr 4, Norderstedt, 22844, Germany
Tel.: (49) 40522020
Web Site: http://www.spxflow.com
Emp.: 200
Air Conditioner Mfr
N.A.I.C.S.: 333415
Michael Rosendahl (Mng Dir)

SPX Flow Technology Norway AS (3)
PO Box 3053 Elisenberg, Oslo, 207, Norway
Tel.: (47) 22557092
Web Site: http://www.spxflow.com
Fluid Power Pumps Mfr
N.A.I.C.S.: 333996

SPX Flow Technology Rosista GmbH (3)
Zechenstrasse 49, Unna, D-59425, Germany
Tel.: (49) 23031080
Web Site: http://www.spxflow.com
Fluid Technology Products Mfr & Distr
N.A.I.C.S.: 334514

SPX Flow Technology SAS (3)
Zone Industrielle No 2 290 rue Jacquard, 27006, Evreux, Cedex, France
Tel.: (33) 23 223 7300
Web Site: https://www.spxflow.com
Pumps Mfr
N.A.I.C.S.: 333914

SPX Flow Technology Santorso S.r.l. (3)
Via Delle Prese 14, 36014, Vicenza, Santorso, Italy
Tel.: (39) 0445540232
Pumps Mfr
N.A.I.C.S.: 333914
Andrea Vitella (Mgr-Mfg)

SPX Flow Technology Singapore Pte. Ltd. (3)
20 Pioneer Crescent 06-01 West Park Biz-Central, Singapore, 628555, Singapore
Tel.: (65) 62644366
Air Conditioner Mfr
N.A.I.C.S.: 333415

SPX Flow Technology Stockholm AB (3)
Bryggavagen 113, Ekero, 178 31, Sweden
Tel.: (46) 856034030
Web Site: http://www.spxft.com
Emp.: 20
Plumbing & Heating Products Mfr
N.A.I.C.S.: 333415
Anna-Britta Gothfeldt (Mgr-Production & Pur)

Dean Mitchell (Mgr-Global Sls-HVAC & Automotive)
Maria Andersson (Mgr-Fin)
Mattias Ifstrom (Mgr-Tech)
Michael Stralman (Mng Dir)
Sara Staffansson (Mgr-Quality)

SPX Flow Technology Sverige AB (3)
PO Box 1436, 701 14, Orebro, Sweden
Tel.: (46) 702737299
Pumps Mfr
N.A.I.C.S.: 333914
Michael Stralman (Mng Dir)

Subsidiary (Domestic):

SPX Flow Technology USA, Inc. (3)
4647 SW 40th Ave, Ocala, FL 34474-5788 (100%)
Tel.: (352) 873-5793
Web Site: http://www.spx.com
Industrial Filtration Products Mfr
N.A.I.C.S.: 333413

Subsidiary (Non-US):

SPX Flow Technology Warendorf GmbH (3)
Splieterstrasse 70 a, Warendorf, 48231, Germany
Tel.: (49) 2581636010
Web Site: http://www.spx.com
Industrial Machinery Mfr
N.A.I.C.S.: 333924

Subsidiary (Non-US):

SPX Flow Technology Germany GmbH (2)
Gottlieb-Daimler-Strasse 13, 59439, Holzwickede, Germany
Tel.: (49) 230191860
Industrial Machinery Distr
N.A.I.C.S.: 423830

Subsidiary (Non-US):

Plc Uutechnic Group Oyj (3)
Muottitie 2, FL-23500, Uusikaupunki, Finland (97.94%)
Tel.: (358) 201880511
Web Site: http://www.uutechnicgroup.fi
Rev.: $18,868,521
Assets: $19,889,833
Liabilities: $6,891,618
Net Worth: $12,998,215
Earnings: $1,169,134
Emp.: 87
Fiscal Year-end: 12/31/2019
Paper, Board & Pulp Mfr
N.A.I.C.S.: 322299
Sami-Jussi Alatalo (Chm)
Jouko Peraaho (CEO)
Martti Heikkila (Deputy CEO)
Leena Junninen (Mgr-Fin)
Zakaria Monkare (Dir-Tech)

Subsidiary (Domestic):

Japrotek Oy Ab (4)
Pohjantie 9, PO Box 12, Pietarsaari, 68601, Finland
Tel.: (358) 20 1880 511
Web Site: http://www.japrotek.fi
Emp.: 40
Paper Processing Services
N.A.I.C.S.: 322299

Subsidiary (Non-US):

Stelzer Ruhrtechnik International GmbH (4)
Speckgraben 20, Warburg, 34414, Germany
Tel.: (49) 5641 9030
Web Site: http://www.stelzerruehrtechnik.de
Emp.: 75
Paper Processing Services
N.A.I.C.S.: 322299
Christian Kessen (Mgr-Bus)
Jussi Vaarno (Mng Dir)

Subsidiary (Domestic):

Steva Oy (4)
Pohjantie 9, PO Box 12, FIN-68601, Pietarsaari, Finland
Tel.: (358) 20 1180 511
Paper Processing Services
N.A.I.C.S.: 322299

COMPANIES

Vaahto Paper Technology Ltd. (4)
Kuoppamaentie 5-7, PO Box 1000, Tampere, 33101, Finland
Tel.: (358) 20 1880 511
Emp.: 161
Paper Products & Services
N.A.I.C.S.: 322299
Vesa Alatalo (Gen Mgr)

Subsidiary (Domestic):

AP-Tela Oy (5)
Ahertajantie 18, 67800, Kokkola, Finland
Tel.: (358) 20 1880 511
Web Site: http://www.aptela.fi
Paper Products Mfr
N.A.I.C.S.: 322299

Subsidiary (Non-US):

Vaahto Pulp & Paper Machinery Distribution (Shanghai) Co. Ltd. (5)
Room 1703 Tower 1 Plaza Hyundai 369 Xian Xia Road, Changning District, Shanghai, 200336, China
Tel.: (86) 21 5155 9151
Pulp & Paper Machinery Distr
N.A.I.C.S.: 423830

ZAO Slalom (5)
Constitution Square Bldg 7 Office 626, 196247, Saint Petersburg, Russia
Tel.: (7) 812 974 8010
Paper Processing Services
N.A.I.C.S.: 322299

Subsidiary (Non-US):

SPX Flow Technology London Limited (2)
Compass House England, Crawley, RH10 9PY, United Kingdom
Tel.: (44) 1293527777
Emp.: 53
Flow Control Equipment Distr
N.A.I.C.S.: 423830

SPX Iberica S.A. (2)
C/ Livorno 60 Pol Ind del Henares, Marchamalo, Guadalajara, 19180, Spain
Tel.: (34) 949208329
Car Dealer
N.A.I.C.S.: 441110

SPX India Private Limited (2)
G-72/73 Mansarover Sanganer Ricco Industrial Area, Jaipur, 302020, Rajasthan, India
Tel.: (91) 1412396759
Air Conditioner Mfr
N.A.I.C.S.: 333415
Mayank Trivedi (Gen Mgr)

SPX International Limited (2)
Hambridge Road, Newbury, RG14 5TR, Berkshire, United Kingdom
Tel.: (44) 163542363
Metal Cap Mfr
N.A.I.C.S.: 332312

SPX Italia S.R.L (2)
Via Provinciale 12, Sala Baganza, 43038, Italy
Tel.: (39) 0521837311
Web Site: http://www.tecnotest.com
Air Conditioner Mfr
N.A.I.C.S.: 333415

SPX Middle East FZE (2)
Downtown Jebel Ali The Galleries 4, PO Box 299745, Dubai, United Arab Emirates
Tel.: (971) 4 814 3400
Sales Range: $25-49.9 Million
Air Conditioner Mfr
N.A.I.C.S.: 333415

SPX Netherlands B.V. (2)
Albert Thijsstraat 12, Kerkrade, 6471 WX, Eygelshoven, Netherlands
Tel.: (31) 455678877
Web Site: http://www.spxflow.com
Sales Range: $25-49.9 Million
Emp.: 25
Hydraulic Pumps Mfr
N.A.I.C.S.: 333914

SPX Servicos Industriais Ltda. (2)
R Joao Daprat 231 B, Jardim Dalva, Sao Bernardo do Campo, 09600-010, Sao Paulo, Brazil
Tel.: (55) 1938542520

Pumps Mfr
N.A.I.C.S.: 333914

SPX de Mexico, S.A. de C.V. (2)
Mitla No 442 Vertiz Narvarte Benito Juarez, Mexico, 3600, Mexico
Tel.: (52) 5525951630
Cooling Equipment Mfr
N.A.I.C.S.: 333415
Jean Duclaud (Gen Mgr)

UD-RD Holding Company Limited (2)
Western Drive, Bristol, BS14 0AZ, Avon, United Kingdom
Tel.: (44) 1179767776
Web Site: http://www.radiodetections.com
Emp.: 100
Cooling Equipment Mfr
N.A.I.C.S.: 333415
Kevin Lench (Gen Mgr)

LONE STAR GLOBAL ACQUISITIONS, LLC

2711 N Haskell Ave Ste 1700, Dallas, TX 75204
Tel.: (214) 754-8300 DE
Web Site:
http://www.lonestarfunds.com
Year Founded: 1995
Privater Equity Firm
N.A.I.C.S.: 523999
John P. Grayken (Chm)
Andre Collin (Pres-Comml Real Estate-North & Latin America)
William Young (Pres-Global & Chief Legal Officer)
Danick Tremblay (Sr Mng Dir-Portfolio Mgmt & Ops)
Donald Quintin (Pres-Opportunity Funds-Europe)
Michael King (Chief Compliance Officer)
Rebecca Williams Smith (Sr Mng Dir & Gen Counsel)

Subsidiaries:

Bio Clean Environmental Services (1)
398 Via El Centro, Oceanside, CA 92058 (100%)
Tel.: (760) 433-7640
Web Site:
http://www.biocleanenvironmental.com
Emp.: 50
Environmental Consulting Services & Storm Water Regulations & Installations
N.A.I.C.S.: 541620
Janet Kent (VP)
Greg Kent (Pres & CEO)

DFC Global Corp. (1)
74 E Swedesford Rd Ste 150, Malvern, PA 19355
Tel.: (610) 296-3400
Web Site: http://www.moneymartfinancialservices.com
Rev.: $1,122,300,000
Assets: $1,721,700,000
Liabilities: $1,291,000,000
Net Worth: $430,700,000
Earnings: ($900,000)
Emp.: 6,600
Fiscal Year-end: 06/30/2013
Holding Company; Loans, Check Cashing & Pawn Services
N.A.I.C.S.: 551112
Glen Wakeman (CEO)
Jim Odell (Gen Counsel)
Greg Hall (CMO)
Angela Celestin (Chief HR Officer)
Mark McNally (Sr VP-Retail Ops)

Subsidiary (Non-US):

Dollar Financial Czech Republic s.r.o. (2)
Klimentska 1216/46, Nove Mesto, Prague, Czech Republic
Tel.: (420) 228880338
Web Site: http://www.moneynow.cz
Loans, Check Cashing & Pawn Services
N.A.I.C.S.: 522390

Subsidiary (Domestic):

Dollar Financial Group, Inc. (2)
74 East Swedesford Rd Ste 150, Malvern, PA 19355 (100%)
Tel.: (610) 296-3400
Web Site: http://www.dfg.com
Sales Range: $100-124.9 Million
Emp.: 70
Financial Services
N.A.I.C.S.: 523999
Jeffrey A. Weiss (Chm & CEO)
Randall Underwood (CFO & Exec VP)

Subsidiary (Domestic):

DFG Canada, Inc. (3)
74 E Swedesford Rd Ste 150, Malvern, PA 19355
Tel.: (610) 296-3400
Holding Company; Loans, Check Cashing & Pawn Services
N.A.I.C.S.: 551112

Subsidiary (Non-US):

Money Mart Canada Inc. (4)
2680 Quadra Street, Victoria, V8T 4E4, BC, Canada
Tel.: (250) 386-0222
Web Site: http://www.moneymart.ca
Emp.: 250
Loans, Check Cashing & Pawn Services
N.A.I.C.S.: 522390
Victoria Mazza (Mgr-Mktg-North America)

Subsidiary (Domestic):

Dollar Financial U.S., Inc. (3)
2650 S Decker Lk Blvd Stea110, Salt Lake City, UT 84119
Tel.: (801) 990-2665
Web Site: http://www.dfcglobalcorp.com
Sales Range: $50-74.9 Million
Emp.: 100
Loans, Check Cashing & Pawn Services
N.A.I.C.S.: 522390
Brandon Peterson (Mgr)

Subsidiary (Domestic):

Check Mart of Louisiana, Inc. (4)
3150 Gentilly Blvd, New Orleans, LA 70122-3878
Tel.: (504) 944-2274
Loans, Check Cashing & Pawn Services
N.A.I.C.S.: 522390

Check Mart of New Mexico, Inc. (4)
4521 Central Ave NE, Albuquerque, NM 87108-1211
Tel.: (505) 262-1517
Sales Range: $25-49.9 Million
Emp.: 2
Loans, Check Cashing & Pawn Services
N.A.I.C.S.: 522390
Mike Archuleta (Mgr)

Dealers' Financial Services, LLC (4)
120 Prosperous Pl Ste 300, Lexington, KY 40509
Tel.: (866) 466-4537
Web Site: http://www.usmiles.com
Auto Loan Provider
N.A.I.C.S.: 522390
Paul del Rio (Mgr-Mktg)

Loan Mart of Oklahoma, Inc. (4)
128 N Air Depot Blvd, Oklahoma City, OK 73110
Tel.: (405) 739-8262
Loans, Check Cashing & Pawn Services
N.A.I.C.S.: 522390

Subsidiary (Non-US):

Helsingin Huutokauppakamari Oy (2)
Helsinginkatu 1, 00500, Helsinki, Finland
Tel.: (358) 927053085
Web Site: http://www.pantti.fi
Loans, Check Cashing & Pawn Services
N.A.I.C.S.: 522390

Liberis (2)
One Hammersmith Broadway, London, W6 9DL, United Kingdom
Tel.: (44) 330 017 4177
Web Site: http://www.liberis.co.uk
Unsecured Loan & Financial Services
N.A.I.C.S.: 522390

LONE STAR GLOBAL ACQUISITIONS, LLC

Paul Mildenstein (CEO)
Tim Kirk (Dir-Ops)
Tom Bason (Dir-Fin)
Deborah Mudway (Dir-Mktg)

MEM Consumer Finance Limited (2)
11-13 Talisman Road, PO Box 255, Bicester, OX26 6HR, Oxfordshire, United Kingdom
Tel.: (44) 8712716222
Web Site: http://www.mem-cf.co.uk
Sales Range: $75-99.9 Million
Emp.: 200
Loans, Check Cashing & Pawn Services
N.A.I.C.S.: 522390
Carllin Walton (Mgr-Mktg)

OK Money Poland Sp. z.o.o. (2)
Ul Grunwaldzka 82, 80-244, Gdansk, Poland
Tel.: (48) 588810102
Web Site: http://www.okmoney.pl
Loans, Check Cashing & Pawn Services
N.A.I.C.S.: 522390

Robert Biggar (ESTD. 1830) Limited (2)
312 Argyle Street, Glasgow, G2 8QW, United Kingdom
Tel.: (44) 1412215340
Web Site: http://www.robertbiggar.co.uk
Loans, Check Cashing & Pawn Services
N.A.I.C.S.: 522390

T.M. Sutton Limited (2)
127-129 Victoria Street, London, SW1E 6RD, United Kingdom
Tel.: (44) 2078340310
Web Site:
http://www.suttonsandrobertsons.com
Sales Range: $25-49.9 Million
Emp.: 8
Pawn Broking Services
N.A.I.C.S.: 522299
Philip Diaper (Dir-Ops)
Andrew Brown (Reg Mgr)

Subsidiary (Domestic):

Suttons and Robertsons Limited (3)
78 Old Brompton Road, London, SW7 3LQ, United Kingdom
Tel.: (44) 3332405808
Web Site:
http://www.suttonsandrobertsons.com
Pawn Broking Services
N.A.I.C.S.: 522299
Deborah Wynter (Mgr)

Subsidiary (Non-US):

iKassa Finland Oy (2)
Aurakatu 12 b, Turku, Finland
Tel.: (358) 204560000
Web Site: http://www.ikassa.fi
Customer Billing & Debt Collection Services
N.A.I.C.S.: 561440

Forterra plc (1)
5 Grange Park Court Roman Way, Northampton, NN4 5EA, United Kingdom
Tel.: (44) 1604707600
Web Site: https://www.forterra.co.uk
Rev.: $548,649,750
Assets: $478,909,200
Liabilities: $213,316,950
Net Worth: $265,592,250
Earnings: $70,824,600
Emp.: 1,787
Fiscal Year-end: 12/31/2022
Holding Company; Brick & Clay Building Products Mfr & Whslr
N.A.I.C.S.: 551112
Benjamin Guyatt (CFO)
Steve Jeynes (Dir-Production)
Adam Smith (Comml Dir)
Justin Atkinson (Chm)
Neil Ash (CEO)
Frances Tock (Sec)

Subsidiary (Domestic):

Forterra Building Products Limited (2)
5 Grange Park Court Roman Way, Northampton, NN4 5EA, United Kingdom
Tel.: (44) 1604 707 600
Web Site: http://www.forterra.co.uk
Sales Range: $400-449.9 Million
Emp.: 1,800
Brick & Clay Building Products Mfr & Whslr

LONE STAR GLOBAL ACQUISITIONS, LLC — U.S. PRIVATE

Lone Star Global Acquisitions, LLC—(Continued)
N.A.I.C.S.: 327331
Stephen Harrison (CEO)
Adam Smith (Comml Dir)
George Stewart (Dir-Ops)

Home Properties, L.P. (1)
850 Clinton Sq, Rochester, NY 14604-1730
Tel.: (585) 546-4900
Web Site: http://www.homeproperties.com
Sales Range: $650-699.9 Million
Emp.: 1,200
Real Estate Investment Services
N.A.I.C.S.: 531110
Marc L. Lipshy (Pres)
Dan Earle (CEO & COO)
Robert J. Luken (CFO & VP)

Subsidiary (Domestic):

Home Properties 1200 East West, LLC (2)
1200 E W Hwy, Silver Spring, MD 20910
Tel.: (301) 588-4971
Web Site: http://www.1200eastwest.homeproperties.com
Property Management Services
N.A.I.C.S.: 531390

Home Properties Cambridge Court, LLC (2)
386 Attenborough Dr, Rosedale, MD 21237
Tel.: (410) 933-3402
Web Site: http://www.cambridgecourt.homeproperties.com
Sales Range: $25-49.9 Million
Emp.: 12
Real Estate Agency & Brokerage Services
N.A.I.C.S.: 531210
Sara Strenk (Property Mgr)
Michele M. Wilson (Reg VP)
Kesha Warwick (Reg Mgr-Property)

Home Properties Cambridge Village, LLC (2)
81 Bowling Ln, Levittown, NY 11756
Tel.: (516) 579-4212
Web Site: http://www.cambridge.homeproperties.com
Emp.: 110
Residential Building Rental & Leasing Services
N.A.I.C.S.: 531110
Jen Matlach (Mgr-Property)

Home Properties Charleston, LLC (2)
3182 Normandy Woods Dr, Ellicott City, MD 21043
Tel.: (410) 465-8600
Web Site: http://www.charlestonplace.homeproperties.com
Sales Range: $25-49.9 Million
Emp.: 17
Real Estate Agency & Brokerage Services
N.A.I.C.S.: 531210
Mike Stark (Reg Mgr-Property)

Home Properties Cider Mill, LLC (2)
18205 Lost Knife Cir, Montgomery Village, MD 20886
Tel.: (301) 948-3036
Web Site: http://www.thedonaldsongroup.com
Emp.: 15
Residential Building Rental & Leasing Services
N.A.I.C.S.: 531110
Michele Fox (Gen Mgr)

Home Properties Country Village LLC (2)
201 Idlewild Rd, Bel Air, MD 21014
Tel.: (410) 879-7900
Web Site: http://www.countryvillage.homeproperties.com
Residential Building Rental & Leasing Services
N.A.I.C.S.: 531210

Home Properties Crescent Club, LLC (2)
45 Country Club Dr, Coram, NY 11727
Tel.: (631) 736-0344
Web Site: http://www.crescentclub.homeproperties.com
Emp.: 10
Real Estate Investment Services
N.A.I.C.S.: 531110
Dena Contes (Mgr-Property)

Home Properties DE Woodmont, LLC (2)
100 Ronkonkoma Ave, Lake Ronkonkoma, NY 11779
Tel.: (631) 588-5530
Real Estate Agency & Brokerage Services
N.A.I.C.S.: 531110

Home Properties Falcon Crest Townhouses, LLC (2)
25 Pittston Cir, Owings Mills, MD 21117
Tel.: (410) 356-7368
Web Site: http://www.falconcrest.homeproperties.com
Sales Range: $25-49.9 Million
Emp.: 10
Residential Buildings & Dwellings Services
N.A.I.C.S.: 531110
Mitch Mann (Reg VP)

Home Properties Falkland Chase, LLC (2)
8305 16th St, Silver Spring, MD 20910
Tel.: (301) 589-8081
Web Site: http://www.falklandchaseapartments.com
Apartments Rental & Lessors Services
N.A.I.C.S.: 531110

Home Properties Heritage Square, LLC (2)
425 Newbridge Rd, East Meadow, NY 11554
Tel.: (516) 781-9637
Web Site: http://www.heritagesquare.homeproperties.com
Residential Building Rental & Leasing Services
N.A.I.C.S.: 531110

Home Properties Holiday Square, LLC (2)
10 Muncy Ave, West Babylon, NY 11704
Tel.: (631) 422-6720
Web Site: http://www.holidaysquare.homeproperties.com
Emp.: 4
Apartments Rental & Lessors Services
N.A.I.C.S.: 531110
Brent A. Kohere (Reg VP)
Robert Fisk Jr. (Property Mgr)

Home Properties Hunters Glen, LLC (2)
1421 Key Pkwy, Frederick, MD 21702
Tel.: (301) 695-5133
Web Site: http://www.huntersglen.homeproperties.com
Emp.: 15
Real Estate Agency & Brokerage Services
N.A.I.C.S.: 531210
Melissa Ellison (Gen Mgr)

Home Properties Lake Grove, LLC (2)
9 Williams Blvd, Lake Grove, NY 11755
Tel.: (631) 981-0755
Web Site: http://www.lakegrove.homeproperties.com
Apartments Rental & Lessors Services
N.A.I.C.S.: 531110

Home Properties Mid-Island, LLC (2)
35 Penataquit Ave, Bay Shore, NY 11706
Tel.: (631) 665-6565
Web Site: http://www.homeproperties.com
Sales Range: $25-49.9 Million
Emp.: 6
Apartments Rental & Lessors Services
N.A.I.C.S.: 531110
Mary Ellen Klamm (Reg Mgr-Property)

Home Properties Morningside Heights LLC (2)
106 Pleasant Ridge Dr, Owings Mills, MD 21117
Tel.: (410) 356-4800
Web Site: http://www.morningside.homeproperties.com
Sales Range: $25-49.9 Million
Emp.: 20
Apartments Rental & Lessors Services
N.A.I.C.S.: 531110
Tammy Solomon (Mgr-Property)

Home Properties Newport Village, LLC (2)
4757 W Braddock Rd, Alexandria, VA 22311
Tel.: (703) 578-3300
Web Site: http://www.newportvillage.homeproperties.com
Apartments Rental & Lessors Services
N.A.I.C.S.: 531110

Home Properties Pleasant View, LLC (2)
258 1/2 Carlton Ave, Piscataway, NJ 08854
Tel.: (732) 968-6348
Web Site: http://www.pleasantview.homeproperties.com
Sales Range: $25-49.9 Million
Emp.: 25
Apartments Rental & Lessors Services
N.A.I.C.S.: 531110
Jeanne Bermudez (Reg Mgr-Property)

Home Properties Ridgeview at Wakefield Valley (2)
800 S Burning Tree Dr, Westminster, MD 21158
Tel.: (410) 857-9500
Web Site: http://www.ridgeview.homeproperties.com
Sales Range: $25-49.9 Million
Emp.: 5
Residential Building Rental & Leasing Services
N.A.I.C.S.: 531110
Stacey Green (Mgr-Property)
Kristing Scheihing (Asst Mgr-Property)
Micheal Steven (Mgr-Svc)

Home Properties Sayville, LLC (2)
400 Adams Way, Sayville, NY 11782
Tel.: (631) 218-2397
Web Site: http://www.sayville.homeproperties.com
Emp.: 10
Real Estate Agency & Brokerage Services
N.A.I.C.S.: 531110

Home Properties South Bay Manor, LLC (2)
333 Candee Ave, Sayville, NY 11782
Tel.: (631) 567-0800
Web Site: http://www.southbay.homeproperties.com
Apartments Rental & Lessors Services
N.A.I.C.S.: 531110
Matthew Blume (Property Mgr)

Home Properties Tamarron, LLC (2)
18101 Marksman Cir Ste 104, Olney, MD 20832
Tel.: (301) 924-1668
Web Site: http://www.tamarron.homeproperties.com
Sales Range: $25-49.9 Million
Emp.: 4
Residential Buildings & Dwellings Services
N.A.I.C.S.: 531110
Giovanna Leon (Dir-Product Mgmt)

Home Properties Topfield, LLC (2)
10701 Cardington Way Ste 104, Cockeysville, MD 21030
Tel.: (410) 667-4832
Web Site: http://www.topfield.homeproperties.com
Sales Range: $25-49.9 Million
Emp.: 4
Apartments Rental & Lessors Services
N.A.I.C.S.: 531110
Kaitlyn McClellan (Mgr-Property)

Home Properties Village Square, LLC (2)
8096 Crainmont Dr, Glen Burnie, MD 21061
Tel.: (410) 969-1523
Web Site: http://www.villagesquare.homeproperties.com
Real Estate Agency & Brokerage Services
N.A.I.C.S.: 531110
Andrea Jhonson (Mgr-Property)

Home Properties Westbrooke, LLC (2)
416 Poole Rd Ste T4, Westminster, MD 21157
Tel.: (410) 876-0701
Web Site: http://www.westbrooke.homeproperties.com
Emp.: 3
Real Estate Agency & Brokerage Services
N.A.I.C.S.: 531110
Stacey Ward (Mgr-Property)

Home Properties Westchester West, LLC (2)
3214 Hewitt Ave Ste 92, Silver Spring, MD 20906
Tel.: (301) 460-3800
Web Site: http://www.westchesterwest.homeproperties.com
Emp.: 15
Real Estate Agency & Brokerage Services
N.A.I.C.S.: 531110
Nicole Lewis (VP)

Home Properties Woodholme Manor, LLC (2)
8049 Woodgate Ct, Baltimore, MD 21244
Tel.: (410) 655-4200
Web Site: http://www.woodholmemanor.homeproperties.com
Sales Range: $25-49.9 Million
Emp.: 5
Residential Buildings & Dwellings Services
N.A.I.C.S.: 531110

Home Properties Woodmont Village, LLC (2)
100 Ronkonkoma Ave, Lake Ronkonkoma, NY 11779
Tel.: (631) 588-5530
Web Site: http://www.woodmont.homeproperties.com
Residential Building Rental & Leasing Services
N.A.I.C.S.: 531110

Jacob Ford Village, LLC (2)
1 Washington Ave Bldg 7 Apt 4A, Morristown, NJ 07960
Tel.: (973) 538-5263
Web Site: http://www.jacobfordvillage.homeproperties.com
Emp.: 3
Residential Building Rental & Leasing Services
N.A.I.C.S.: 531110
Maribel Toro (Property Mgr)

The Townhomes of Beverly (2)
201 Broughton St, Beverly, MA 01915
Tel.: (978) 712-4209
Web Site: http://www.townhomesofbeverly.com
Real Estate Agency & Brokerage Services
N.A.I.C.S.: 531210

IKB Deutsche Industriebank AG (1)
Wilhelm-Botzkes Strasse 1, 40474, Dusseldorf, Germany (100%)
Tel.: (49) 21182210
Web Site: http://www.ikb.de
International Banking Services
N.A.I.C.S.: 522299
Claus Momburg (Member-Mgmt Bd-Credit Risk Mgmt, Governance & Compliance)
Michael H. Wiedmann (Chm-Mgmt Bd)
Dirk Volz (Member-Mgmt Bd-Fin, Credit Risk Contolling, Audit & Taxation)
Jorg Oliveri Del Castillo-Schulz (Member-Mgmt Bd-Credit/Treasury Ops, IT & HR)

Subsidiary (US):

IKB Capital Corporation (2)
555 Madison Ave, New York, NY 10022-3301
Tel.: (212) 485-3600
Web Site: http://www.ikb.de
Financial Services
N.A.I.C.S.: 561499

Subsidiary (Domestic):

IKB Equity Finance GmbH (2)

Wilhelm-Botzkes-Strasse 1, PO Box 101118, 40474, Dusseldorf, Germany
Tel.: (49) 21182210
Web Site: http://www.ikb-ef.de
Emp.: 700
Financial Services
N.A.I.C.S.: 522299

IKB Immobilien Management GmbH (2)
Wilhelm-Botskes Str 1, Dusseldorf, 40470, Germany
Tel.: (49) 211822111
Web Site: http://www.ikb.de
Sales Range: $50-74.9 Million
Emp.: 50
Financial Services
N.A.I.C.S.: 522320
Heribert Wicken *(Mng Dir)*

IKB Leasing GmbH (2)
Gertrudenstrasse 2, 20095, Hamburg, Germany
Tel.: (49) 40236260
Web Site: http://www.ikb-leasing.com
Sales Range: $75-99.9 Million
Emp.: 400
Financial Services
N.A.I.C.S.: 522299
Michael Fitcher *(Gen Mgr)*

IKB Private Equity GmbH (2)
Wilhelm Botzkes Strasse 1, 40474, Dusseldorf, Germany
Tel.: (49) 21182214027
Web Site: http://www.ikb.de
Sales Range: $50-74.9 Million
Emp.: 23
Financial Services
N.A.I.C.S.: 522299

Lodgian Inc. (1)
2002 Summit Blvd Ste 300, Atlanta, GA 30319
Tel.: (404) 364-9400
Web Site: http://www.lodgian.com
Sales Range: $150-199.9 Million
Emp.: 2
Hotel Owner & Operator
N.A.I.C.S.: 721199
Amy Quinn *(VP-Fin & Acctg)*

Quintain Limited (1)
180 Great Portland Street, London, W1W 5QZ, United Kingdom
Tel.: (44) 2032192200
Web Site: http://www.quintain.co.uk
Sales Range: $75-99.9 Million
Property Investment & Development Services
N.A.I.C.S.: 531390
Kathryn McConnell *(Dir-HR)*
Tory Heazell *(Sec & Dir-Shareholder Reporting)*
James Saunders *(COO)*
Angus Dodd *(CEO)*
Olivier Brahin *(Chm)*
Catherine Webster *(Exec Dir-Strategy & Investment)*
Michael Jenkins *(Dir-Fin)*

Sino Gas & Energy Holdings Limited (1)
311-313 Hay Street, Subiaco, 6008, WA, Australia
Tel.: (61) 8 9388 8618
Web Site: http://www.sinogasenergy.com
Holding Company; Natural Gas Exploration, Development & Extraction Services
N.A.I.C.S.: 551112
Frank Fu *(COO)*
Philip Bainbridge *(Chm)*
Jim Taylor *(CEO)*

Subsidiary (Non-US):

Sino Gas & Energy Limited (2)
Suite 335 3rd Floor Office Tower A2 Lido Place 6 Jiang Tai Road, Chaoyang District, Beijing, 100004, China (100%)
Tel.: (86) 10 6530 9260
Web Site: http://www.sinogasenergy.com
Natural Gas Exploration, Development & Extraction Services
N.A.I.C.S.: 211130

Stark Danmark A/S (1)
C F Richs Vej 115, 2000, Frederiksberg, Denmark
Tel.: (45) 8252 2600

Web Site: http://www.starkgroup.dk
N.A.I.C.S.: 444180
Soren P. Olesen *(CEO)*
Lene Groth *(Chief HR Officer)*
Sisse Fjelsted Rasmussen *(CFO)*

Subsidiary (Non-US):

Stark Deutschland GmbH (2)
Hafeninsel 9, 63067, Offenbach, Germany
Tel.: (49) 69 66 81 10 0
Web Site: http://www.starkgroup.dk
Building Materials Distr
N.A.I.C.S.: 444180
Kare O. Malo *(CEO)*

Stark Suomi Oy (2)
Vanrikinkuja 2, 02600, Espoo, Finland (100%)
Tel.: (358) 93 541 3000
Web Site: http://www.stark-suomi.fi
Building Materials Distr
N.A.I.C.S.: 444180
Harri Paivaniemi *(CEO)*

Start Mortgages Limited (1)
Trimleston House Beech Hill Office Campus Clonskeagh, Dublin, 4, Ireland
Tel.: (353) 1 209 6300
Web Site: http://www.start.ie
Mortgage Lending Services
N.A.I.C.S.: 522310
Alan Casey *(CEO)*

Xella International GmbH (1)
Dusseldorfer Landstrasse 395, 47259, Duisburg, Germany
Tel.: (49) 203 60880 0
Web Site: http://www.xella.com
Construction Materials Mfr & Distr
N.A.I.C.S.: 327999
Jens Kimmig *(CFO)*
Christophe Clemente *(CEO)*

Subsidiary (Non-US):

Macon Srl (2)
Cristur Village Soseaua Hunedoarei No 1 3, 330190, Deva, Hunedoara County, Romania
Tel.: (40) 372 541 500
Web Site: http://www.macon.ro
Precast Concrete Mfr
N.A.I.C.S.: 327390

Ursa Insulation, S.A. (2)
Paseo de Recoletos, 28004, Madrid, Spain
Tel.: (34) 912758600
Web Site: http://www.ursa.es
Insulation Material Mfr
N.A.I.C.S.: 423840

Xella Kalkzandsteenfabriek Hoogdonk B.V. (2)
Hoogdonkseweg 15, 5757 PJ, Liessel, Netherlands
Tel.: (31) 493342135
Web Site: http://www.xella.nl
Calcium Silicate Blocks Mfr
N.A.I.C.S.: 327331

Xella Nederland B.V. (2)
Mildijk 141, Vuren, 4214 DR, Arnhem, Netherlands
Tel.: (31) 183671234
Web Site: http://www.xella.nl
Construction Materials Mfr
N.A.I.C.S.: 327331
Wilfred de Jong *(Mgr-ICT)*
Martin van der Hors *(Controller-Bus)*
Peter Lesage *(Coord-IT-Intl)*

LONE STAR HOLDINGS, LLC
6500 River Pl Blvd, Austin, TX 78730-1155
Tel.: (512) 873-8067   DE
Web Site: http://www.lso.com
Courier Service
N.A.I.C.S.: 492110
Richard T. Jones *(Pres & CEO)*
George Stephens *(CFO)*

LONE STAR INVESTMENT ADVISORS, LLC
13355 Noel Rd Ste 1750, Dallas, TX 75240
Tel.: (972) 702-7390   TX

Web Site: http://www.lonestarcra.com
Year Founded: 2006
Sales Range: $10-24.9 Million
Emp.: 25
Privater Equity Firm
N.A.I.C.S.: 523999
Arthur W. Hollingsworth *(Mng Partner)*
John McGuire *(Mng Dir-Ops)*
Scott Billings *(CFO)*
Carol Shine *(Office Mgr)*
Alek Blankenau *(VP)*
David Landis *(VP)*

Subsidiaries:

Continental Electronics Corporation (1)
4212 S Buckner Blvd, Dallas, TX 75227 (100%)
Tel.: (214) 381-7161
Web Site: http://www.contelec.com
Sales Range: $25-49.9 Million
Radio Broadcast Transmission Equipment Mfr
N.A.I.C.S.: 334220
Paul Utay *(Mgr-Scientific & Indus Sls)*

Subsidiary (Non-US):

Continental Lensa S.A. (2)
Ave Einstein 725, Santiagno, Chile
Tel.: (56) 24625000
Web Site: http://www.cecchile.com
Sales Range: $10-24.9 Million
Emp.: 20
Broadcast Transmitters Mfr
N.A.I.C.S.: 334220
Marcos Caballero *(Pres)*

LONE STAR LEGAL AID
1415 Fannin St, Houston, TX 77002
Tel.: (713) 652-0077   TX
Web Site: http://www.lonestarlegal.org
Year Founded: 1950
Sales Range: $10-24.9 Million
Emp.: 247
Law firm
N.A.I.C.S.: 541199
Dwayne Bilton *(COO)*
Richard Tomlinson *(Dir-Litigation)*
Debra Furrh Jr. *(Dir-Advocacy)*
Paul Furrh Jr. *(CEO)*

LONE STAR MOTORSPORTS INCORPORATED
2957 E Fairview Ave, Meridian, ID 83642
Tel.: (208) 888-6565   ID
Web Site: http://www.snakeriveryamaha.com
Year Founded: 1988
Sales Range: $10-24.9 Million
Emp.: 35
Sales of Motorcycles
N.A.I.C.S.: 441227
Barry Goff *(Pres)*

LONE STAR NATIONAL BANCSHARES-TEXAS, INC.
520 E Nolana Ave, McAllen, TX 78504
Tel.: (956) 984-2815
Web Site: http://www.lonestarnationalbank.com
Emp.: 500
Bank Holding Company; Commercial Banking
N.A.I.C.S.: 551111
A. Jabier Rodriguez *(CEO)*
George R. Carruthers *(CFO & Exec VP)*
Angie Vera-oliva *(Exec VP)*
S. David Deanda Jr. *(Pres & COO)*

LONE STAR NEW MARKETS LP

4455 LBJ Fwy Ste 300, Dallas, TX 75244
Tel.: (972) 702-7390
Web Site: http://www.lonestarnewmarkets.com
Sales Range: $25-49.9 Million
Emp.: 9
Privater Equity Firm
N.A.I.C.S.: 523999
Arthur W. Hollingsworth *(Mng Partner)*
Adrian Ocegueda *(Principal)*
John McGuire *(Mng Dir-Ops)*

Subsidiaries:

Energy Steel Products, Inc. (1)
7404 Railhead Ln, Houston, TX 77086
Tel.: (281) 760-0400
Web Site: http://www.espsteel.com
Sales Range: $10-24.9 Million
Stainless Steel Distr
N.A.I.C.S.: 423510
Marc Brod *(CFO & VP)*
Bob Dudzik *(CEO)*
Donna Tafat *(Mgr-Credit)*

Subsidiary (Domestic):

Energy Steel Products (2)
168 N Johnston St Ste 102, Dallas, GA 30132-7615
Tel.: (770) 428-3201
Web Site: http://www.energysteelproducts.com
Mill Support Center For Stainless Steel
N.A.I.C.S.: 423510

Energy Steel Products (2)
1191 W Hawthorne Ln, West Chicago, IL 60185-1913
Tel.: (630) 876-5950
Web Site: http://www.energysteelproducts.com
Sales Range: $10-24.9 Million
Emp.: 5
N.A.I.C.S.: 331513
Adam Soileau *(Mgr-Ops)*

LONESOURCE, INC.
114 MacKenan Dr Ste 300, Cary, NC 27511
Tel.: (919) 466-8615
Web Site: http://www.lonesource.com
Sales Range: $25-49.9 Million
Emp.: 200
Office Supplies Distr
N.A.I.C.S.: 424120
Bradley King *(CEO)*

LONESTAR FREIGHTLINER GROUP, LTD.
2051 Hughes Rd, Grapevine, TX 76051-7317
Tel.: (817) 428-9736
Web Site: http://www.lonestartruckgroup.com
Rev.: $20,000,000
Emp.: 500
Holding Company; Partnership
N.A.I.C.S.: 561110
Gerald Chunn *(Pres)*

Subsidiaries:

Duncan Freightliner, Inc. (1)
4800 N IH 35, Waco, TX 76705
Tel.: (254) 752-9735
Sales Range: $10-24.9 Million
Emp.: 40
Provider of Trucking Services
N.A.I.C.S.: 423110

LONESTAR MARINE SHELTERS
6800 Harborside Dr, Galveston, TX 77554
Tel.: (409) 941-1200
Web Site: http://www.lonestarmarineshelters.com
Sales Range: $10-24.9 Million
Emp.: 100
Fabricated Structural Metal Mfr

LONESTAR MARINE SHELTERS

LoneStar Marine Shelters—(Continued)
N.A.I.C.S.: 332312
Mike Kaiser (CFO)
Clayton Hazzard (Pres)
Dennis Freels (Mgr-Sls)

LONETREE CAPITAL LLC
330 Madison Ave, New York, NY 10017
Tel.: (212) 844-9589
Web Site: https://lonetreecap.com
Year Founded: 2021
Emp.: 100
Privater Equity Firm
N.A.I.C.S.: 523940
Matt Koven (Mng Partner)

Subsidiaries:

DocuPhase LLC (1)
1499 Gulf to Bay Blvd, Clearwater, FL 33755
Tel.: (727) 441-8228
Web Site: http://www.idatix.com
Sales Range: $1-9.9 Million
Emp.: 40
Workflow Automation & Document Management Software
N.A.I.C.S.: 513210
Steven Allen (Pres & CEO)
Martin Levesque (Dir-Pro Svcs)
Larry Sullivan (CMO)
Samantha McCollough (Mgr-Mktg)

Subsidiary (Domestic):

Frevvo Inc. (2)
500 E Main St, Branford, CT 06405
Tel.: (203) 208-3117
Web Site: http://www.frevvo.com
Stationery & Office Supplies Merchant Whslr
N.A.I.C.S.: 424120
Will Hitchcock (Dir-Product Dev)

Treeno Software, Inc. (2)
951 Islington St, Portsmouth, NH 03801
Tel.: (800) 528-5005
Web Site: http://www.treenosoftware.com
Sales Range: $1-9.9 Million
Emp.: 17
Computer Systems Design
N.A.I.C.S.: 541512
Steve Tentindo (Pres & CEO)
Will Thibodeau (CTO)
Fred Abrora (CIO)

iPayables, Inc. (2)
1 Spectrum Pointe Dr, Lake Forest, CA 92630
Tel.: (866) 874-7932
Web Site: http://www.ipayables.com
Prepackaged Software
N.A.I.C.S.: 513210

LONG & ASSOCIATES ARCHITECTS/ENGINEERS, INC.
4525 S Manhattan Ave, Tampa, FL 33611
Tel.: (813) 839-0506 **FL**
Web Site: http://www.longandassociates.com
Year Founded: 1974
Sales Range: $1-9.9 Million
Emp.: 26
Architectural & Engineering Services
N.A.I.C.S.: 541310
Alexander Long (VP)
Harry M. Long Jr. (Pres)

LONG BEACH AFFORDABLE HOUSING COALITION
4201 Long Beach Blvd Ste 422, Long Beach, CA 90807
Tel.: (562) 595-6111 **CA**
Web Site: http://www.lbahc.org
Year Founded: 1993
Sales Range: $1-9.9 Million
Housing & Health Care Services
N.A.I.C.S.: 623990
Patsy Howard (Sec)

LONG BEACH MEMORIAL NURSING HOME
375 E Bay Dr, Long Beach, NY 11561
Tel.: (516) 897-1000 **NY**
Year Founded: 1974
Sales Range: $10-24.9 Million
Emp.: 295
Nursing Care Services
N.A.I.C.S.: 623110
Barry Stern (CFO)

LONG BEACH PUBLIC TRANSPORTATION CO.
1963 E Anaheim, Long Beach, CA 90813
Tel.: (562) 591-8753
Web Site: http://www.lbtransit.com
Year Founded: 1963
Rev.: $47,000,000
Emp.: 775
Operator of Transportation Services
N.A.I.C.S.: 485113
Laurence W. Jackson (Pres)
Brynn Kernaghan (Exec Dir-Plng)
Lisa Patton (CFO)
Kenneth McDonald (Pres)

LONG BEACH YACHT SALES INC.
6400 E Marina Dr Ste 8, Long Beach, CA 90803
Tel.: (562) 431-3393
Web Site: http://www.lbys.com
Year Founded: 1981
Sales Range: $10-24.9 Million
Emp.: 30
Dealers & Brokers of Yachts
N.A.I.C.S.: 441222
Ray Jones (Pres)

LONG BELL VENTURES LLC.
154 Hale Rd E, Winlock, WA 98596
Tel.: (360) 785-3915
Rev.: $40,000,000
Emp.: 300
Lumber Plywood Millwork & Wood Panel Merchant Whslr
N.A.I.C.S.: 423310
Jim Woodfin (Mgr)
Charles Preston (Controller)

LONG BUILDING TECHNOLOGIES
5001 S Zuni St, Littleton, CO 80120
Tel.: (303) 975-2100
Web Site: http://www.long.com
Year Founded: 1965
Sales Range: $100-124.9 Million
Emp.: 250
Electrical Heating Equipment
N.A.I.C.S.: 423730
Mark A. Balent (Pres & CEO)
Jeff Long (Chm & Sr VP)
Valarie Daniels (Office Mgr)
Steve Hansen (VP-Fin)
Dick Johnson (Mgr-Svc-Wyoming)
Jake Gash (Dir-Warehouse Ops-Littleton)
Wayne Johnson (VP & Gen Mgr-Wyoming)
Brian Miller (VP-Sls)

LONG DISTANCE DIRECT HOLDINGS
20 Squadron Blvd Ste 210, New City, NY 10956
Tel.: (845) 639-7749
Rev.: $12,600,000
Emp.: 40
Long Distance Telephone Communications
N.A.I.C.S.: 517121

Subsidiaries:

Long Distance Direct Inc. (1)
20 Squadron Blvd Ste 210, New City, NY 10956
Tel.: (845) 639-7749
Rev.: $5,200,000
Long Distance Telephone Communications
N.A.I.C.S.: 517121

LONG ELECTRIC COMPANY INC.
1310 S Franklin Rd, Indianapolis, IN 46239-1119
Tel.: (317) 356-2455 **IN**
Web Site: http://www.longelectric.net
Year Founded: 1928
Sales Range: $25-49.9 Million
Emp.: 400
Electrical Work
N.A.I.C.S.: 238210
Jerry Chlystun (Pres)
Michael Chlystun (CFO)
John Schulz (Branch Mgr)
William Chlystun (VP)

LONG FENCE COMPANY INC.
8545 Edgeworth Dr, Capitol Heights, MD 20743-3741
Tel.: (301) 350-2400 **MD**
Web Site: http://www.longfence.com
Year Founded: 1945
Sales Range: $50-74.9 Million
Emp.: 475
Mfr of Security Doors & Window Bars
N.A.I.C.S.: 238990
Michael Ritter (Pres)
Steve Brooks (Project Mgr-Comml Div)
James Devine (Mgr-Sls)

LONG FOUNDATION DRILLING CO.
3014 Brandau Rd, Hermitage, TN 37076
Tel.: (615) 885-5664
Web Site: http://www.lfdc.com
Sales Range: $25-49.9 Million
Emp.: 17
Shaft Drilling & Pile Driving Specialty Construction Services
N.A.I.C.S.: 238990
Chris Long (VP)

LONG ISLAND CHILDREN'S MUSEUM
11 Davis Ave, Garden City, NY 11530
Tel.: (516) 224-5800
Web Site: http://www.licm.org
Sales Range: $10-24.9 Million
Emp.: 100
Children's Museum
N.A.I.C.S.: 712110
Maureen P. Mangan (Dir-Steven Cheung)
Tanya Butler Holder (Assoc Dir-Admin)
Gina Garcia (Assoc Dir-Dev)
Jeanmari Walsh Mansfield (Assoc Dir-Education)
Aimee Terzulli (Dir-Education)
Kandel Allard (Dir-Visitor & Support Svcs)
Irene Jimenez (Mgr-Early Childhood Program)
Steven Cheung (Mgr-Membership & Database)
Faun Guarino (Mgr-Rentals & Events)
James Packard (Mgr-Theater)
Philip Malakoff (Sec)
Peter Schapero (Vice Chm)

LONG ISLAND COMPOST CORP.
100 Urban Ave, Westbury, NY 11590
Tel.: (516) 334-6600
Web Site: http://www.licompost.com
Rev.: $27,200,000
Emp.: 120

U.S. PRIVATE

Fertilizer Mfr
N.A.I.C.S.: 325314
Charles Vigliotti (Founder & Pres)

LONG ISLAND FIREPROOF DOOR INC.
5 Harbor Park Dr, Port Washington, NY 11050
Tel.: (516) 390-6800
Web Site: http://www.lifd.com
Rev.: $34,000,000
Emp.: 115
Whslr of Wooden & Fireproof Doors
N.A.I.C.S.: 423310
Maria Barry (Mgr-Credit & Collections)

LONG ISLAND POWER AUTHORITY
333 Earle Ovington Blvd Ste 403, Uniondale, NY 11553
Tel.: (516) 222-7700
Web Site: http://www.lipower.org
Year Founded: 1998
Rev.: $3,576,274,000
Assets: $13,058,317,000
Liabilities: $12,043,421,000
Net Worth: $1,014,896,000
Earnings: $494,850,000
Emp.: 38
Fiscal Year-end: 12/31/18
Electricity Distribution Services
N.A.I.C.S.: 221122
Michael Deering (VP-External Affairs)
Ralph V. Suozzi (Chm)
Mark Fischl (Vice Chm)
Thomas Falcone (CEO)
Barbara Ann Dillon (Dir-HR & Admin)
Donna Mongiardo (VP & Controller)
Rick Shansky (Sr VP-Ops Oversight)
Kathleen Mitterway (VP-Audit)
Sidhartha Nathan (Dir-Comm)
Anna Chacko (Gen Counsel)
Mujib Lodhi (CIO)
Tamelo Monroe (CFO)
Justin Bell (VP-Pub Policy & Regulatory Affairs)
Jennifer Hayen (Dir-Comm)
Tom Locascio (Dir-External Affairs)

LONG JOHN SILVER'S LLC
10350 Ormsby Park Pl Ste 300, Louisville, KY 40223
Tel.: (502) 815-6100 **DE**
Web Site: http://www.ljsilvers.com
Year Founded: 1969
Sales Range: $25-49.9 Million
Emp.: 150
Quick-Service Restaurants Operator & Franchiser
N.A.I.C.S.: 722513
Marie Zhang (Chief Food Innovation Officer)
Peter Czizek (VP-Culinary Innovation)
Toni Bianco (COO-US & Intl)
Krista Foster (VP-HR)
Angela Sanders (CMO)
Blain Shortreed (COO)

LONG MEADOW RANCH WINERY & FARMSTEAD
738 Main St, Saint Helena, CA 94574
Tel.: (707) 963-4555
Web Site: http://www.longmeadowranch.com
Year Founded: 1989
Wine Mfr
N.A.I.C.S.: 312130
Kipp Ramsey (Mgr-Farm-to-Table)
Ashley Heisey (Dir-Winemaking)
Brad Groper (VP-Sls)
Stephen Barber (Dir-Culinary Ops)
Ted W. Hall (Pres & CEO)

COMPANIES

Subsidiaries:

Stony Hill Vineyard (1)
PO Box 308, Saint Helena, CA 94574
Tel.: (707) 963-2636
Web Site: http://www.stonyhillvineyard.com
Wine Mfr
N.A.I.C.S.: 312130
Eleanor McCrea *(Co-Founder)*
Fred McCrea *(Co-Founder)*
Sarah McCrea *(Pres)*

LONG MECHANICAL INC.
190 E Main St, Northville, MI 48167
Tel.: (248) 349-0373
Web Site:
http://www.longplumbing.com
Rev.: $13,000,000
Emp.: 25
Plumbing, Heating, Air-Conditioning
N.A.I.C.S.: 238220
James R. Long *(Pres)*

LONG MOTOR CORPORATION
14600 W 107th St, Lenexa, KS 66215
Tel.: (913) 541-1525   KS
Web Site: http://www.longmotor.com
Year Founded: 1984
Rev.: $106,000,000
Emp.: 140
Automotive Supply Mail Order Retailer
N.A.I.C.S.: 423120
Jon Jackson *(Mgr-Logistics)*
Mark Eversole *(Supvr-Res)*

LONG MOTORS INC.
2931 Brunswick Pike, Lawrenceville, NJ 08648
Tel.: (609) 882-0600
Web Site:
http://www.volvocountry.com
Sales Range: $50-74.9 Million
Emp.: 50
New & Used Automobiles
N.A.I.C.S.: 441110
David J. Long Sr. *(Pres)*

LONG PAINTING COMPANY
21414 68th Ave S, Kent, WA 98032
Tel.: (253) 234-8050
Web Site:
http://www.longpainting.com
Year Founded: 1967
Sales Range: $25-49.9 Million
Emp.: 250
Provider of Commercial & Industrial Painting Services
N.A.I.C.S.: 238320
Michael V. Cassidy *(Pres & Production Mgr)*
Alan Langer *(Controller)*
Denica Atwood *(CFO)*

LONG PATH PARTNERS, LP
1 Landmark Sq Unit 1920, Stamford, CT 06901
Tel.: (917) 913-6834   CT
Web Site:
http://www.longpathpartners.com
Investment Services
N.A.I.C.S.: 523999
Will Breannan *(Mng Partner & Portfolio Mgr)*
Brian Nelson *(Partner & Portfolio Mgr)*

Subsidiaries:

Basware Oyj (1)
Linnoitustie 2 Cello-rakennus, PL 97, 02601, Espoo, Finland
Tel.: (358) 9879171
Web Site: https://www.basware.com
Rev.: $188,111,097
Assets: $271,097,133
Liabilities: $181,481,058
Net Worth: $89,616,075
Earnings: ($17,481,540)
Emp.: 1,347
Fiscal Year-end: 12/31/2021
Software Publisher
N.A.I.C.S.: 513210
Jane Broberg *(Chief HR Officer)*
Lars Madsen *(CMO)*
Klaus Andersen *(CEO)*
Martti Nurminen *(CFO)*
Alwin Schauer *(Chief Revenue Officer)*
Jason Kurtz *(CEO-Basware)*
Barrett Schiwitz *(CIO)*
Sam Pathmasiri *(Gen Counsel)*

Subsidiary (Non-US):

Basware A/S (2)
Kirkebjerg Alle 84 1 Sal, 2605, Brondby, Denmark
Tel.: (45) 7 022 9955
Web Site: https://www.basware.com
Emp.: 25
Software Development Services
N.A.I.C.S.: 541511

Basware AB (2)
Gustavslundsv 151 C, 167 51, Bromma, Stockholm, Sweden
Tel.: (46) 85 057 4400
Web Site: https://www.basware.com
Sales Range: $25-49.9 Million
Emp.: 35
Software Development Services
N.A.I.C.S.: 541511
Jukka Virkkunen *(Sr VP)*

Basware AS (2)
Vollsveien 6, PO Box 241, Lilleaker, 1366, Lysaker, Norway
Tel.: (47) 2 337 0300
Web Site: http://www.basware.com
Financial Software Development Services
N.A.I.C.S.: 541511

Basware B.V. (2)
Krijn Taconiskade 436, Duivendrecht, 1087 HW, Amsterdam, Netherlands
Tel.: (31) 20 850 8020
Web Site: https://www.basware.com
Software Development Services
N.A.I.C.S.: 541511

Basware Belgium NV (2)
Clinton Park Ninovesteenweg 196, Erembodegem, 9320, Belgium
Tel.: (32) 53 60 11 11
Web Site: http://www.basware.be
Emp.: 50
Software Development Services
N.A.I.C.S.: 541511
Pieter Geeraerts *(Gen Mgr)*

Basware Corporation (2)
Ocean Financial Centre Level 40 10 Collyer, Quay, Singapore, 49315, Singapore
Tel.: (65) 6808 6494
Software Development Services
N.A.I.C.S.: 541511
Ben Selby *(Head-IR)*
Jukka Janonen *(Dir-Comm)*

Basware GmbH (2)
Rossstr 96, 40476, Dusseldorf, Germany
Tel.: (49) 211 41 55 95 50
Sales Range: $25-49.9 Million
Emp.: 70
Software Development Services
N.A.I.C.S.: 541511
Frank Wuschech *(Mng Dir)*

Basware Holdings Ltd. (2)
4th Floor 120 Old Broad Street, London, EC2N 1AR, United Kingdom
Tel.: (44) 845 603 2885
Software Services
N.A.I.C.S.: 541511

Basware India Private Limited (2)
Rajiv Gandhi IT Park DLF Building Tower A Ground Floor, Chandigarh, 160 001, India
Tel.: (91) 172 301 2020
Web Site: http://www.basware.com
Software Development Services
N.A.I.C.S.: 541511

Basware Pty Ltd (2)
Level 15 67 Albert Ave, PO Box 148, Chatswood, 2067, NSW, Australia
Tel.: (61) 2 8622 5850
Software Development Services
N.A.I.C.S.: 541511
Niclas Hill *(Dir-Consulting)*

Basware Russia (2)
Helsinki House 4 Rostovsky per 1/2, Moscow, 119121, Russia
Tel.: (7) 499 248 16 73
Web Site: http://www.basware.ru
Software Development Services
N.A.I.C.S.: 541511

Basware SAS (2)
20 Rue Caumartin, 75009, Paris, France
Tel.: (33) 14 008 1820
Web Site: https://www.basware.com
Software Development Services
N.A.I.C.S.: 541511

Basware UK Ltd. (2)
1-3 Berkeley Court Borough Road, Newcastle, ST5 1TT, Staffordshire, United Kingdom
Tel.: (44) 845 6711953
Software Development Services
N.A.I.C.S.: 541511

Subsidiary (US):

Basware, Inc. (2)
1245 Rosemont Dr Ste 200, Fort Mill, SC 29707
Tel.: (203) 487-7900
Web Site: https://www.basware.com
Sales Range: $25-49.9 Million
Emp.: 50
Software Development Services
N.A.I.C.S.: 541511
Tehseen Dahya *(Gen Mgr-North America)*

Subsidiary (Domestic):

Verian Technologies, Inc. (3)
8701 Mallard Creek Rd, Charlotte, NC 28262
Tel.: (704) 547-7301
Web Site: http://www.verian.com
Sales Range: $10-24.9 Million
Emp.: 75
Procurement Technology Solutions
N.A.I.C.S.: 513210
Tehseen Ali Dahya *(Pres & CEO)*
Lindsay Munn *(Mgr-Mktg Comm)*
Bilal Soylu *(CTO)*
Tommy Benston *(VP-Customer Svc)*
Dana Saylors *(VP-Mktg & Product Strategy)*
Jerry Ellis *(VP-SIs)*
Steve Ayala *(VP-Tech)*
Bhavin Shah *(Dir-Product Strategy)*

Subsidiary (Non-US):

Glantus Holdings Plc (2)
Marina House Block V Eastpoint Business Park, Dublin, D03 AX24, Ireland
Tel.: (353) 18895300
Rev.: $12,925,013
Assets: $32,981,867
Liabilities: $20,630,120
Net Worth: $12,351,748
Earnings: ($2,806,273)
Emp.: 124
Fiscal Year-end: 12/31/2021
Holding Company
N.A.I.C.S.: 551112

Dalet Holding SAS (1)
16 rue Rivay, 92300, Levallois-Perret, France
Tel.: (33) 1 41 2767 00
Holding Company
N.A.I.C.S.: 551112

Subsidiary (Domestic):

Dalet S.A. (2)
16 Rue Rivay, 92300, Levallois-Perret, France   (80.7%)
Tel.: (33) 1 41 27 67 00
Web Site: http://www.dalet.com
Rev.: $63,614,168
Assets: $51,287,544
Liabilities: $31,154,552
Net Worth: $20,132,992
Earnings: $2,730,227
Emp.: 450
Fiscal Year-end: 12/31/2018
Software Development Services
N.A.I.C.S.: 541511
David Lasry *(Co-Founder & CEO)*
Stephane Guez *(Co-Founder & CTO)*
Stephane Schlayen *(COO)*
Michael Elhadad *(Co-Founder & Dir-R&D)*
Salomon Elhadad *(Co-Founder & Gen Mgr-R&D)*

Subsidiary (Non-US):

Dalet Australia Pty. Ltd. (3)
7B Raymond Mall Raymond Road, Springwood, 2777, NSW, Australia
Tel.: (61) 2 4751 5033
Software Development Services
N.A.I.C.S.: 541511
Graham Martin *(Mng Dir)*

Dalet Digital Media Systems ME (3)
PO Box 31810, Dubai, United Arab Emirates
Tel.: (971) 50 624 41 72
Software Development Services
N.A.I.C.S.: 541511

Dalet Digital Media Systems Mexico (3)
Retorno 59 No 42B Col Avnante, 04460, Mexico, Mexico
Tel.: (52) 55 56784557
Software Development Services
N.A.I.C.S.: 541511
Carlos Franco-Cervantes *(Mgr-Bus Dev)*

Subsidiary (US):

Dalet Digital Media Systems USA, Inc. (3)
100 Wall St 15th Fl, New York, NY 10005
Tel.: (212) 269-6700
Software Development Services
N.A.I.C.S.: 541511
Remy Falgayrac *(Dir-US Ops)*

Subsidiary (Non-US):

Dalet GmbH (3)
Leopoldstrasse 244, 80807, Munich, Germany
Tel.: (49) 89 20 80 39 489
Software Development Services
N.A.I.C.S.: 541511

Dalet Italia SRL (3)
Via Matteotti 299, 25063, Gardone Val Trompia, Brescia, Italy
Tel.: (39) 030 8336227
Software Development Services
N.A.I.C.S.: 541511

Dalet Ltd. (3)
85-87 Bayham Street, London, NW1 0AG, United Kingdom
Tel.: (44) 207 424 7814
Software Development Services
N.A.I.C.S.: 541511
Adrian Smith *(Mgr-Bus Dev)*

Dalet Sistemas S.A. (3)
Calle Vivero 5, 28040, Madrid, Spain
Tel.: (34) 91 456 10 96
Software Development Services
N.A.I.C.S.: 541511

Dalet Systems Asia Pte Ltd. (3)
66C South Peach Road Level 4, Singapore, 58696, Singapore
Tel.: (65) 6339 3376
Software Development Services
N.A.I.C.S.: 541511

OOO DALET MEDIA SYSTEMY (3)
Prospekt Mira 119/619, Moscow, 129344, Russia
Tel.: (7) 499 301 00 75
Software Development Services
N.A.I.C.S.: 541511

LONG POINT CAPITAL LLC
437 Madison Ave 32nd Fl, New York, NY 10022-7028
Tel.: (212) 593-1800
Web Site:
http://www.longpointcapital.com
Year Founded: 1998
Rev.: $56,800,000
Emp.: 10
Privater Equity Firm
N.A.I.C.S.: 523999
Ira Starr *(Partner)*
Eric Von Stroh *(Mng Dir)*
Gerry Boylan *(Founder & Mng Dir)*
Richard Limardo *(Controller)*
Daniel Ron *(VP)*
Norman Scherr *(VP)*

LONG RIDGE EQUITY PARTNERS, LLC

Long Ridge Equity Partners, LLC—(Continued)

LONG RIDGE EQUITY PARTNERS, LLC
1120 Ave of the Americas 17th Fl,
New York, NY 10036
Tel.: (212) 951-8651
Web Site: https://long-ridge.com
Year Founded: 2007
Private Equity
N.A.I.C.S.: 523940
Jim Brown *(Founder & Mng Partner)*

Subsidiaries:

MessageGears, LLC   (1)
191 Peachtree St NE Ste 900, Atlanta, GA 30303
Web Site: http://www.messagegears.com
Sales Range: $1-9.9 Million
Emp.: 100
Software Development Services
N.A.I.C.S.: 541511
Roger Barnette *(CEO)*
Tracey Brown *(Dir-HR)*
Will Devlin *(VP-Mktg)*
Joe Gruca *(Chief Revenue Officer)*
Taylor Jones *(VP-Solutions)*

Subsidiary (Domestic):

Swrve New Media Inc.   (2)
75 Broadway, Ste 202, San Francisco, CA 94111
Tel.: (415) 830-5650
Web Site: http://www.swrve.com
Software Publisher
N.A.I.C.S.: 513210
Steven Collins *(Co-Founder & CTO)*
Christopher S. Dean *(CEO)*
Jim Mongillo *(Sr VP-Global Sls)*
Martin Doettling *(CMO)*
Ramsey Masri *(Chief Revenue Officer)*
Jon Perrin *(Head-Sls)*
Alf Saggese *(Gen Mgr-EMEA & Asia Pacific)*

LONG WAVE INCORPORATED
115 E California Ste 400, Oklahoma City, OK 73104
Tel.: (405) 235-2217
Web Site: http://www.longwaveinc.com
Year Founded: 1995
Sales Range: $10-24.9 Million
Emp.: 80
Defense Contractor; Communications, Engineering, Information Technology & Program Management Services
N.A.I.C.S.: 517810
Chris Lozano *(CMO)*
Nate Morris *(Dir-Engrg)*

LONG WHOLESALE, INC.
5173 Pioneer Rd, Meridian, MS 39301-8834
Tel.: (601) 482-3144   MS
Web Site: http://www.longwholesale.com
Year Founded: 1922
Groceries, General Line; Tobacco Products
N.A.I.C.S.: 424410
Randall Long *(Dir & VP)*
Sam E. Long III *(Dir, Treas & Sec)*
Raiford Long Jr. *(Pres)*

LONG'S ELECTRONICS, INC.
2630 5th Ave S, Irondale, AL 35210-1209
Tel.: (205) 956-6767   AL
Web Site: http://www.longselectronics.com
Year Founded: 1977
Sales Range: $25-49.9 Million
Emp.: 40
Consumer Electronics & Audio-Visual Equipment Retailer
N.A.I.C.S.: 449210

Roy Long *(Pres)*
Dennis Wood *(Mgr-Special Markets)*

LONG'S JEWELERS LTD.
60A S Ave, Burlington, MA 01803
Tel.: (781) 273-2400   MA
Web Site: http://www.longsjewelers.com
Year Founded: 1878
Sales Range: $100-124.9 Million
Emp.: 100
Jewelry Retailer
N.A.I.C.S.: 458310
Terry Drost *(Controller)*
Robert Rottenberg *(CEO)*
Pat Jusino *(Mgr)*

LONG-LEWIS INCORPORATED
2551 Hwy 150, Hoover, AL 35244
Tel.: (205) 989-3673
Web Site: http://www.longlewisford.com
Sales Range: $250-299.9 Million
Emp.: 200
New & Used Automobiles
N.A.I.C.S.: 441110
Vaughn N. Burrell *(Chm)*
Dwight Burrell *(Pres)*
Terry Poole *(Gen Mgr)*

LONG-MCARTHUR INC.
3450 S 9th St, Salina, KS 67401
Tel.: (785) 823-2237
Web Site: http://www.longmcarthur.com
Rev.: $57,707,799
Emp.: 100
New & Used Car Dealers, Service, Bodyshop, Detailing & Financing
N.A.I.C.S.: 441110
North McArthur *(CEO)*
Marty Simpson *(Bus Mgr)*
Rob Murphy *(Mgr-Sls)*

LONGDEN COMPANY INC.
446 River Rd, Hudson, MA 01749
Tel.: (978) 568-1800
Web Site: http://www.longden.com
Year Founded: 1980
Sales Range: $25-49.9 Million
Emp.: 25
Access Flooring System Installation
N.A.I.C.S.: 238330
John M. Longden *(Pres)*
Kathy A. Liptak *(CFO)*
Chris Collette *(Mgr-Warehouse)*
Joe DePasquale *(Sr Project Mgr)*
William O. Fisher *(VP)*
Kimberly Gibson *(Project Mgr-Sys)*
Michael J. Smith *(VP-Access Floor Div)*
Philip Cyr *(COO)*

LONGHORN HARLEY DAVIDSON
2830 W Interstate 20, Grand Prairie, TX 75052
Tel.: (972) 988-1903
Web Site: http://www.longhornhd.com
Year Founded: 1996
Sales Range: $50-74.9 Million
Emp.: 80
Motorcycles
N.A.I.C.S.: 441227
Alfred Keeling *(Owner & Gen Mgr)*
Maritia Keeling *(CEO & Principal)*
Mark Holcomb *(Mgr-Svc & Parts)*

LONGHORN INTERNATIONAL TRUCKS
4711 E 7th St, Austin, TX 78702
Tel.: (512) 389-1111
Web Site: http://www.longhorninternational.com
Rev.: $28,600,000

Emp.: 80
Truck Leasing
N.A.I.C.S.: 423110
Robert Sanders *(Mgr-Sls)*

LONGHORN PRODUCE COMPANY
890 E Hwy C 70 SE 1st Ln, Lamar, MO 64759-9226
Tel.: (417) 681-0200
Sales Range: $10-24.9 Million
Emp.: 55
General Freight Services
N.A.I.C.S.: 484121
Jason Bartlett *(Owner)*

LONGHORN, INC.
2640 Tarna Dr, Dallas, TX 75229-2221
Tel.: (972) 406-0222
Web Site: http://www.longhorninc.com
Year Founded: 1982
Rev.: $24,000,000
Emp.: 60
Whslr of Irrigation, Landscape & Lawn Maintenance Equipment
N.A.I.C.S.: 423820
Lynn Evans *(Exec VP)*
Tom Swor *(VP)*
Bobby Carper *(Branch Mgr)*
Nikki Carper *(Mgr-Credit)*
Brad Griffin *(Branch Mgr)*
Mike Gschwind *(Branch Mgr)*
Ben Keckler *(Branch Mgr)*
Larry Tally *(Branch Mgr)*
Larry Teague *(Branch Mgr)*
H. L. Lee Evans Jr. *(Pres)*

LONGITUDE CAPITAL MANAGEMENT CO., LLC
2740 Sand Hill Rd 2nd Fl, Menlo Park, CA 94025
Tel.: (650) 854-5700   DE
Web Site: http://www.longitudecapital.com
Year Founded: 2006
Healthcare Industry-Focused Private Equity Firm
N.A.I.C.S.: 523999
Patrick G. Enright *(Co-Founder, Mng Dir & Mng Dir)*
Marc-Henri Galletti *(Co-Founder & Mng Dir)*
Gregory Grunberg *(Mng Dir)*
David Hirsch *(Founder, Founder & Mng Dir)*
Carolyn Helms *(CFO & Chief Compliance Officer)*
Sandip Agarwala *(Mng Dir)*
Oren Isacoff *(Principal)*
Josh Richardson *(Mng Dir)*
Patrick Enright *(Co-Founder & Mng Dir)*
Andrew ElBardissi *(Principal)*
Juliet Tammenoms Bakker *(Mng Dir)*

Subsidiaries:

California Cryobank Stem Cell Services LLC   (1)
11915 La Grange Ave, Los Angeles, CA 90025
Tel.: (866) 927-9622
Reproductive & Stem Cell Products & Services
N.A.I.C.S.: 621410
Richard D. Jennings *(CEO)*

LONGLEY SUPPLY COMPANY, INC.
2018 Oleander Dr, Wilmington, NC 28403-2336
Tel.: (910) 762-7793   NC
Web Site: http://www.longleysupplycompany.com

U.S. PRIVATE

Year Founded: 1906
Sales Range: $25-49.9 Million
Emp.: 150
Plumbing Fixtures Equipment & Supplies
N.A.I.C.S.: 423720
Emily Longley *(Pres)*

Subsidiaries:

Longley Supply Company, Inc.   (1)
533 S New Hope Rd, Raleigh, NC 27610-1479   (100%)
Tel.: (919) 231-6115
Web Site: http://www.longleysupply.com
Sales Range: $10-24.9 Million
Emp.: 12
Warm Air Heating & Air Conditioning
N.A.I.C.S.: 423730

LONGMONT UNITED HOSPITAL
1950 Mountain View Ave, Longmont, CO 80501
Tel.: (303) 651-5111   CO
Web Site: http://www.luhcares.org
Year Founded: 1955
Sales Range: $150-199.9 Million
Emp.: 1,426
Community Health Care Services
N.A.I.C.S.: 622110
Neil Bertrand *(Co-CFO)*
Rebecca Herman *(VP-Clinical & Support Svcs)*
Michael Jefferies *(VP-Info Sys)*
Warren Laughlin *(VP-HR)*
Charlotte Tyson *(Treas)*
Edwina Salazar *(Asst Sec)*
Tom Chapman *(Sec)*
Clair Volk *(Chm)*
Mike Kirkland *(Vice Chm)*
Dan Frank *(Co-CFO)*
Christina Johnson *(CEO)*

LONGNECK & THUNDERFOOT LLC
199 Water St Fl 33, New York, NY 10038
Tel.: (646) 506-4421
Web Site: http://www.landt.co
Year Founded: 2013
Sales Range: $1-9.9 Million
Emp.: 30
Digital Advertising Services
N.A.I.C.S.: 541850
Jonathan Allen *(Co-Founder & Pres)*
Cooper Pickett *(Co-Founder & CEO)*
Remy Bernstein *(COO)*
Thomas Rodrigues *(Dir-Content)*
Margot Gerould *(Dir-Brand Strategy)*

LONGO ELECTRICAL-MECHANICAL INC.
1 Harry Shupe Blvd, Wharton, NJ 07885
Tel.: (973) 537-0400
Web Site: http://www.longo-ind.com
Year Founded: 1945
Sales Range: $10-24.9 Million
Emp.: 120
Electrical Equipment Repair, High Voltage
N.A.I.C.S.: 811210
Joseph M. Longo *(Pres)*
Dominic Clementi *(VP-Sls)*

LONGO-DE PUERTO RICO INC.
1018 Ashford Ste 3A9, San Juan, PR 00907
Tel.: (787) 721-5268
Sales Range: $10-24.9 Million
Emp.: 170
Sewer Line Construction
N.A.I.C.S.: 237110
Gregory Laracy *(VP)*

LONGRANGE CAPITAL LLC

100 First Stamford Place 3rd Fl, Stamford, CT 06902
Tel.: (203) 423-3935
Web Site:
https://www.longrangepartners.com
Year Founded: 2019
Investment Company
N.A.I.C.S.: 523999
Robert Berlin *(Founder & Mng Partner)*
Robert Berlin *(Founder & Mng Partner)*
Andrew Cialino *(Principal & Head-Bus Dev)*

Subsidiaries:

Batesville Casket Company, Inc. (1)
1 Batesville Blvd, Batesville, IN 47006
Tel.: (812) 934-7500
Web Site: http://www.batesville.com
Retailer of Funeral Services Products
N.A.I.C.S.: 812210

LONGREN & PARKS
14101 Brandbury Walk, Minnetonka, MN 55345
Tel.: (952) 945-0572
Web Site:
http://www.longrenparks.com
Year Founded: 1987
Sales Range: Less than $1 Million
Emp.: 6
Communications, Engineering, Industrial, Print, Public Relations
N.A.I.C.S.: 541810
Steve Longren *(Partner)*
Steve Parks *(Partner)*
Carrie Decker *(Dir-Creative)*
Chris Nelson *(Specialist-PR)*
Bonnie Snaza *(Specialist-Media Rels)*

LONGSHORE CAPITAL PARTNERS
70 W Madison St Ste 5710, Chicago, IL 60602
Tel.: (312) 237-3838
Web Site:
http://www.longshorecp.com
Year Founded: 2020
Venture Capital & Private Equity
N.A.I.C.S.: 523940
Ryan Anthony *(Co-Founder)*
Nick Christopher *(Co-Founder)*

Subsidiaries:

MetaSource, LLC (1)
67 W 13490 S Ste 200, Draper, UT 84020
Tel.: (267) 552-6379
Web Site: http://www.metasource.com
Emp.: 1,000
Business Process Outsourcing, Business Process Management & Enterprise Content Solutions Services
N.A.I.C.S.: 561499
John Nixon *(Chief Revenue Officer)*
Adam Osthed *(Pres & CEO)*
Randy Powell *(CFO & VP)*
David Carn *(CIO & VP)*
Grant Glasscock *(Sr VP-BPO Svcs)*
Mario Duckett *(Sr VP-Strategic Partnerships & Alliances)*
Mary Kladde *(Sr VP-Mortgage Svcs)*
Colin Graf *(Dir-Mktg)*
Weston Knowles *(VP-Enterprise Content Solutions)*

Subsidiary (Domestic):

Digiscribe International, LLC (2)
150 Clearbrook Rd, Elmsford, NY 10523
Tel.: (914) 586-6600
Web Site: http://www.digiscribe.info
Sales Range: $10-24.9 Million
Emp.: 20
Business Process Outsourcing Services
N.A.I.C.S.: 561499
Barbara Collins *(Co-Founder & COO)*
Mitch Taube *(Co-Founder, Pres & CEO)*

Orion Financial Group, Inc. (2)
2860 Exchange Blvd Ste 100, Southlake, TX 76092-9151
Tel.: (817) 424-1175
Web Site: http://orionfinancialgroupinc.com
Mortgage Assignment, Lien Release & Document Retrieval Services
N.A.I.C.S.: 561499
Connie Riggsby *(VP-Mortgage Svcs Div)*
Kenneth S. Green *(Co-Founder & Chm)*
Lincoln S. Ong *(Co-Founder & Vice Chm)*
Wesley Ramjeet *(CFO)*

Professional Recovery Consultants, Inc. (1)
2700 Meridian Pkwy, Durham, NC 27713
Tel.: (919) 489-7791
Web Site: http://www.prorecoveryinc.com
Collection Agencies
N.A.I.C.S.: 561440
Stephen P. Miller *(Founder & CEO)*
Jean Konzman *(Controller)*
Mike Smith *(Dir-Ops)*
Chad Jansen *(Mgr-Collections)*
Janice Sanders *(Dir-Sys & Support)*
John Cook *(Chief Client Officer)*
Mary Rogers *(Mgr-Client Svcs)*
Rene Dillard *(Officer-Compliance)*

Revco Solutions, Inc. (1)
PO Box 965, Columbus, OH 43216
Tel.: (855) 202-0113
Web Site: http://www.revcosolutions.com
Collections & Financial Services
N.A.I.C.S.: 522320
Geoff Miller *(CEO)*
Larry Ebert *(Pres)*

LONGUEVUE CAPITAL, LLC
111 Veterans Blvd Ste 1020, Metairie, LA 70005
Tel.: (504) 293-3600 LA
Web Site: http://www.lvcpartners.com
Year Founded: 2001
Financial & Investment Services
N.A.I.C.S.: 523999
Rick S. Rees *(Co-Founder & Mng Partner)*
Charles A. Cox *(VP-Investment)*
Max Z. Vorhoff *(Principal)*
Ryan Nagim *(Partner)*
Becky Toups *(CFO & Chief Compliance Officer)*
Austin Rees *(VP)*
Evan Golden *(VP)*
John C. McNamara II *(Co-Founder & Mng Partner)*

Subsidiaries:

ECA Medical Instruments (1)
2193 Anchor Ct, Thousand Oaks, CA 91320 (100%)
Tel.: (805) 376-2509
Web Site: http://www.ecamedical.com
Rev.: $4,480,000
Emp.: 105
Develops Surgical Tools for Medical Implant Installations
N.A.I.C.S.: 339112
James B. Schultz *(Exec VP)*
Rick Rees *(Chm)*
Lane Hale *(Pres & CEO)*

Summit Plastics, Inc. (1)
107 S. Laurel St, Summit, MS 39666
Tel.: (800) 790-7117
Web Site: https://summitplastics.com
Plastic Mfg.
N.A.I.C.S.: 326199
Jack Shields *(Pres)*

Subsidiary (Domestic):

Fredman Bag Company (2)
5801 W Bender Ct, Milwaukee, WI 53218
Tel.: (414) 462-9400
Web Site: http://www.fredmanbag.com
Sales Range: $1-9.9 Million
Emp.: 60
Unsupported Plastics Bag Mfr
N.A.I.C.S.: 326111
Dan Fredman *(Mgr)*

LONGUST DISTRIBUTING INC.
2432 W Birchwood Ave, Mesa, AZ 85202-1064
Tel.: (480) 820-6244 AZ
Web Site: http://www.longust.com
Year Founded: 1975
Sales Range: $10-24.9 Million
Emp.: 85
Distr of Home Furnishings
N.A.I.C.S.: 423220
Steve Wallace *(CEO)*
Drew Mittelstaedt *(Pres)*
John Laird *(COO & Sr VP)*
Bo Bobertz *(CFO)*

LONGWALL SERVICES INC.
63 Country Club Rd, Meadow Lands, PA 15347
Tel.: (724) 228-9898
Web Site:
http://www.longwallservices.com
Sales Range: $10-24.9 Million
Emp.: 40
Metal Stamping Services
N.A.I.C.S.: 332119
Ceiriog Hughes *(Pres & CEO)*

LONGWATER OPPORTUNITIES LLC
2519 Fairmount St, Dallas, TX 75201
Tel.: (469) 351-3471
Web Site:
http://www.longwateropportunities.com
Year Founded: 2009
Privater Equity Firm
N.A.I.C.S.: 523999
Timothy J. O'Keefe *(Dir-IR)*
Jordan Bastable *(Partner)*
Brooks Burgum *(Partner)*
Bern Ebersole *(Principal)*
Murphey Henk *(VP)*
Tim Mason *(Dir-Continuous Improvement)*

Subsidiaries:

Jesse Kalisher Gallery, Inc. (1)
406 E Main St, Carrboro, NC 27510-2309
Tel.: (919) 967-4300
Web Site: http://www.kalisher.com
Art Dealers
N.A.I.C.S.: 459920
Sarah Elder *(COO)*
Alex Loops *(Dir-Art Consulting)*
Amber Hunter-Love *(Dir-Bus Dev-EMEA)*
Bryn Behrenshausen *(Dir-Tech)*
Chryssha Guidry *(Dir-Pur)*
Courtney Webster *(Dir-Bus Dev)*
David Winton *(Chief Strategy Officer)*
Dennis Arreola *(Mgr-Mfg Pur)*
Erin Ellis *(Mgr-Print Production)*
Evelym Minton *(Art Dir)*
Grant Roediger *(Dir-Mfg)*
Jon Cochran *(VP-Bus Dev)*
Kat Morgan *(Studio Dir)*
Lynn Masterss *(Project Mgr-Bus Dev)*
Patrick Fennell *(Controller)*

Subsidiary (Domestic):

SOHO Myriad, LLC (2)
1250 Menlo Dr NW Ste C, Atlanta, GA 30318
Tel.: (404) 351-5656
Web Site: http://www.sohomyriad.com
All Other Miscellaneous Wood Product Mfr
N.A.I.C.S.: 321999
Tracy Chevalier *(Sr VP)*
Michael Calli *(VP)*

LONGWOOD CAPITAL GROUP, INC.
207 Jasmine Ln, Longwood, FL 32779
Tel.: (407) 475-0123 FL
Year Founded: 2014
Investment Services
N.A.I.C.S.: 523999
Roy J. Meadows *(Pres, CEO, CFO, Chief Acctg Officer, Treas & Sec)*

LONGWOOD INDUSTRIES HOLDINGS, LLC
The Summit Green Bldg 706 Green Valley Rd Ste 212, Greensboro, NC 27408
Tel.: (336) 272-3710
Web Site:
http://www.longwoodindustries.com
Holding Company
N.A.I.C.S.: 551112
Dennis DesJardin *(VP-Ops)*
Nancy Elliott *(Acct Mgr)*
Gary Smith *(CFO & Exec VP)*

Subsidiaries:

Longwood Elastomers, Inc. (1)
The Summit Green Bldg 706 Green Valley Rd Ste 212, Greensboro, NC 27408
Tel.: (336) 272-3710
Web Site: http://www.longwood-elastomers.com
Sales Range: $25-49.9 Million
Emp.: 150
Mfr of Rubber Products
N.A.I.C.S.: 326299
Nancy Elliott *(Acct Mgr)*
Kay Rudd *(Mgr-Credit)*

Scott Office Systems (1)
530 Sheppard Street, Winnipeg, R2X 2P8, MB, Canada
Tel.: (204) 697-7900
Web Site:
http://www.scottofficesystems.com
Sales Range: $10-24.9 Million
Emp.: 54
Supplier of Index Tabbing Equipment & Film, Tear Tapes & Laminate Films for the Packaging & Wire & Cable Industries
N.A.I.C.S.: 322220

LONNIE MCCURRY'S FOUR WHEEL DRIVE CENTER, INC.
212 Stevenson St, West Monroe, LA 71292
Tel.: (318) 388-0816
Web Site: http://www.skyjacker.com
Year Founded: 1973
Sales Range: $10-24.9 Million
Emp.: 48
Mfr of Motor Vehicle Parts & Supplies
N.A.I.C.S.: 423120
Nell McCurry *(Chief Admin Officer)*
Cindy Acree *(Exec Dir)*
Lonnie McCurry Sr. *(Pres & CEO)*
Lonnie McCurry Jr. *(VP)*

LOOK MEDIA USA, LLC
330 W 38th St Ste 1500, New York, NY 10018
Tel.: (305) 940-4949
Web Site:
http://www.lookmediausa.com
Sales Range: $10-24.9 Million
Emp.: 5
Public Relations Promotional Services
N.A.I.C.S.: 541820
Michael Baker *(Dir-Facility)*
Mike Alladina *(Dir)*

LOOKOUT GROUP INC.
1789 S Bagdad Road Ste 104, Leander, TX 78641
Tel.: (713) 524-5263
Web Site: http://barhbarhunting.com
Year Founded: 1994
Sales Range: $10-24.9 Million
Emp.: 12
Land Subdividers & Developers
N.A.I.C.S.: 237210
William R. Hinckley *(Pres)*
David K. Gibbs *(Treas & Sec)*

LOOKOUT, INC.
1 Frnt St Ste 2700, San Francisco, CA 94111
Tel.: (415) 281-2820
Web Site: http://www.lookout.com
Software Publisher
N.A.I.C.S.: 513210

LOOKOUT, INC.

Lookout, Inc.—(Continued)
David Helfer (VP-Worldwide Channel Dev)
Aaron Cockerill (VP-Enterprise Product)
Julie Herendeen (VP-Mktg)
Vijaya Kaza (Chief Dev Officer)
Wim van Campen (VP-Enterprise Sls-Europe)
Jim Dolce (CEO)
Pravin Kothari (Exec VP-Product & Strategy)
James A. Dolce Jr. (CEO)

Subsidiaries:
CipherCloud, Inc. (1)
333 W San Carlos St Ste 1100, San Jose, CA 95110
Web Site: http://www.ciphercloud.com
Software Publisher
N.A.I.C.S.: 513210
Varun Badhwar (VP-Product Mktg & Bus Dev)
Trevor Rodrigues-Templar (Sr VP-Sls)
Dev Ghoshal (Sr VP-Strategy)
Paige Leidig (CMO)
Bonnie Helton (Chief HR Officer)
Ajay Nigam (Chief Product Officer)
Bob West (Chief Trust Officer)
Patrick Zanoni (VP-Fin)

LOOMCRAFT TEXTILE & SUPPLY CO.
645 Lakeview Pkwy, Vernon Hills, IL 60061
Tel.: (847) 680-0000
Web Site: http://www.loomcraft.com
Sales Range: $10-24.9 Million
Emp.: 50
Woven Upholstery Fabrics
N.A.I.C.S.: 424310
Ronald Frankel (Pres)

LOOMIS COMMUNITIES, INC.
246 N Main St, South Hadley, MA 01075
Tel.: (413) 532-5325 MA
Web Site: http://www.loomiscommunities.org
Year Founded: 1983
Sales Range: $10-24.9 Million
Elderly People Assisted Living Services
N.A.I.C.S.: 623312
David W. Scruggs (Pres & CEO)
Margaret R. Mantoni (Pres & CEO)
Karen Jackson (COO)
Carol Constant (Dir-Community Engagement)

LOOMIS COMPANY
850 N Park Rd, Wyomissing, PA 19610
Tel.: (610) 374-4040
Web Site: http://www.loomisco.com
Rev.: $25,900,000
Emp.: 250
Insurance Agents
N.A.I.C.S.: 524210
Hector Medina (Sr Acct Exec)
Ed Cavanaugh (VP-Property & Casualty)
Don Saul (VP)
Dale Whitehead (VP-Employee Benefits)
Patti Walmer (Acct Mgr-Aviation)
Joe Reedy (VP-Property & Casualty)
Bill Bixler (Acct Exec)
Peter Santore (Acct Exec)
Sandi Boone (Supvr-Acct)

LOONEY ADVERTISING AND DESIGN
7 N Mountain Ave, Montclair, NJ 07042
Tel.: (973) 783-0017
Web Site: http://www.looney-advertising.com
Rev.: $35,000,000
Full Service, Graphic Design
N.A.I.C.S.: 541810
Sean Looney (Pres & Dir-Creative)
Debra Looney (Dir-Creative)
Jennifer Seaman (Dir-Media)
Michael-Paul Raspanti (Dir-Art & Graphic Designer)
Danielle Yeranian (Mgr-Production & Operation)
Chris Rich (Dir-Strategic)
Kathy Sweet (CFO)

LOOP CAPITAL MARKETS
111 W Jackson Ste 1901, Chicago, IL 60604
Tel.: (312) 913-4900
Web Site: http://www.loopcap.com
Rev.: $10,001,182
Emp.: 25
Investment Bankers
N.A.I.C.S.: 523150
James Reynolds (Co-Founder, Chm & CEO)
Rita Ho (Head-Short-Term Municipal Securities Desk)
Adrienne Banks Pitts (Mng Dir & Gen Counsel)

LOOP PAPER RECYCLING INC.
2401 S Laflin St, Chicago, IL 60608
Tel.: (312) 942-0042
Web Site: http://www.recyclingit.com
Sales Range: $10-24.9 Million
Emp.: 100
Recycling, Waste Materials
N.A.I.C.S.: 562920
George Ward (Pres)
Jeff Goffrey (CFO)

LOOP, LLC
33 N Garden Ave, Clearwater, FL 33755
Tel.: (877) 850-2010 FL
Web Site: http://www.autoloop.net
Year Founded: 2005
Emp.: 391
Auto Industry Software
N.A.I.C.S.: 513210
Steve Anderson (CEO)
Graham Annett (VP-Mktg)
Alex Eckelberry (COO)
Doug Van Sach (VP-Analytics)
Matt Rodeghero (Chief Product Officer)
Mike Kronenberg (CTO)
Patrick Kelly (VP-Client Retention-XRM)
Doug Denham (Sls Dir-Natl)

LOOP-LOC LTD.
390 Motor Pkwy, Hauppauge, NY 11788
Tel.: (631) 582-2626
Web Site: http://www.looploc.com
Year Founded: 1978
Safety Swimming Pool Covers, Removable Fencing & Vinyl Liners Mfr & Seller
N.A.I.C.S.: 326199
LeeAnn Donaton-Pesta (Pres)

LOOS & COMPANY, INC.
16 B Mashamoquet Rd, Pomfret, CT 06258
Tel.: (860) 928-7981 CT
Web Site: http://www.loosco.com
Year Founded: 1964
Sales Range: $100-124.9 Million
Emp.: 250
Mfr of Mechanical Steel Cable, Cable Assemblies, Tools & Hardware, Plastic Jacketed Cable & Stainless Steel Wire
N.A.I.C.S.: 327212
Tom Dodds (Pres-Rope & Assemblies Div)

Subsidiaries:
Loos & Company, Inc. - Cableware (1)
901 Industrial Blvd, Naples, FL 34104-3715
Tel.: (239) 643-5667
Web Site: http://www.loosnaples.com
Sales Range: $10-24.9 Million
Emp.: 100
Aircraft Fitting Mfr
N.A.I.C.S.: 336413
Anthony Naines (Pres)
Gus Loos (Founder)

LOPEZ FOODS INC.
9500 NW 4th St, Oklahoma City, OK 73127
Tel.: (405) 789-7500
Web Site: http://www.lopezfoods.com
Rev.: $173,541,948
Emp.: 500
Prepared Beef Product Mfr
N.A.I.C.S.: 311612
Bobbie Dill (Coord-Payroll)
Bruce Hall (Coord-Safety)
Cyndi Miller (Coord-Distr)
Dave Lopez (Asst VP-Sls)
Doug Konarik (CFO)
John Myers (Superintendent-Refrigeration Engrg)
Kelley Weis (Controller)
MaDonna Kenner (Dir-Corp Safety)
Michelle Wagner (Mgr-HR)
Aaron Beasecker (VP-IT)
Greg Sedlmayr (Engr-Refrigeration)
Kevin Nanke (Asst VP-Food Safety, Quality Sys & Production Innovation)

LOPEZ NEGRETE COMMUNICATIONS, INC.
3336 Richmond Ave Ste 200, Houston, TX 77098
Tel.: (713) 877-8777 TX
Web Site: http://www.lopeznegrete.com
Year Founded: 1985
Rev.: $158,580,000
Emp.: 150
Advetising Agency
N.A.I.C.S.: 541810
Alex Lopez Negrete (Pres & CEO)
Cathy Lopez Negrete (CFO, COO & Exec VP)
Howard Brown (VP & Gen Mgr)
Gustavo Foldvari (Grp Dir-Plng)
Fernando Osuna (Chief Creative Officer)
Gerry Loredo (Dir-Bus Analytics)
Julio Arrieta (Mng Dir & CMO)

Subsidiaries:
Lopez Negrete Communications West, Inc. (1)
2222 W Olive Ave, Burbank, CA 91506
Tel.: (713) 877-8777
Web Site: http://www.lopeznegrete.com
N.A.I.C.S.: 541810
Howard Brown (VP & Gen Mgr)

LOPEZ TAX SERVICE, INC.
1588 Moffett St Ste F, Salinas, CA 93905
Tel.: (831) 422-4888
Web Site: http://www.lopeztaxservice.com
Year Founded: 1999
Rev.: $2,000,000
Emp.: 17
Financial Services
N.A.I.C.S.: 541213
Carlos Lopez (Owner)

U.S. PRIVATE

LOPITO, ILEANA & HOWIE, INC.
Metro Office Park #13 First St, Guaynabo, PR 00968
Tel.: (787) 783-1160 PR
Web Site: http://www.lih.com
Year Founded: 1972
Rev.: $25,225,415
Emp.: 75
Full Service
N.A.I.C.S.: 541810
Carlos Pepe Rodriguez (Pres)
Osvaldo Ramos (VP & Dir-Media)
Noemi Diaz (CFO & Partner)
Tere Davila (VP & Dir-Creative)
Maruchi Lopez (Dir-Acct Svcs)
Daisy Rodriguez (Mgr-Print)
Jorge Sierra (Assoc Dir-Creative)
Maru Silva (Assoc Dir-Creative)
Jose Luis Alvarez (Partner & Gen Mgr)
Juliette Lanauze (Gen Mgr-DAS)

LORAIN-MEDINA RURAL ELECTRONIC COOPORATIVE, INC.
22898 W Rd, Wellington, OH 44090
Tel.: (440) 647-2133 OH
Web Site: http://www.lmre.org
Year Founded: 1936
Sales Range: $25-49.9 Million
Emp.: 44
Electric Power Distribution Services
N.A.I.C.S.: 221122
Rodney L. Eaton (Pres)
Keith E. Lowe (Treas)
James R. McConnell (Sec)
Gary L. Rowland (VP)

LORAINE'S ACADEMY, INC.
1012 58th St N, Saint Petersburg, FL 33710
Tel.: (727) 347-4247 FL
Web Site: http://www.lorainesacademy.com
Year Founded: 1966
Sales Range: $1-9.9 Million
Emp.: 15
Beauty Career Training
N.A.I.C.S.: 611511
Kathryn Alvarez (Co-Owner)
Nancy Fordham (Co-Owner)
Doris Calhaun (Dir-Admissions & Placement)

LORAM MAINTENANCE OF WAY INC.
3900 Arrowhead Dr, Hamel, MN 55340
Tel.: (763) 478-6014 MN
Web Site: http://www.loram.com
Year Founded: 1954
Sales Range: $25-49.9 Million
Emp.: 720
Provider of Railroad Maintenance & Repair Services
N.A.I.C.S.: 488210
Judy Folsom (Controller)
Phil Homan (Pres & CEO)
Joe Carlin (VP-Intl Ops & Bus Dev)
Justin Clarine (VP-Engrg)
Darwin Isdahl (VP-Safety & Quality)
Brad Willems (CFO)
Katie Hadenfeldt (VP-Sls & Mktg)
Kevin Burton (VP-Fleet Ops)
John Coulam (Engr-Sls-Friction Mgmt Div-West)
Bruce Wise (Dir-Bus Dev-Friction Mgmt Div)

LORD & SONS INC.
328 Commercial St, San Jose, CA 95112
Tel.: (408) 817-8900

Web Site:
http://www.lordandsons.com
Sales Range: $10-24.9 Million
Emp.: 100
Mfr & Wholesaler of Metal Fasteners
N.A.I.C.S.: 332510
Karin Valenzuela *(Controller)*
Alan L. Berger *(Pres)*

LORD ABBETT & CO.
90 Hudson St, Jersey City, NJ 07302-3900
Tel.: (201) 827-2000 DE
Web Site: http://www.lordabbett.com
Year Founded: 1929
Sales Range: $450-499.9 Million
Emp.: 687
Investment Advisors; Mutual Funds
N.A.I.C.S.: 523940
Douglas B. Sieg *(Mng Partner)*
Vincent J. McBride *(Partner & Portfolio Mgr)*
Daniel Solender *(Partner)*
Todd D. Jacobson *(Partner)*
Frank V. Paone *(Partner)*
Adam Backman *(Partner-Product Strategy)*
Andrew D. D'Souza *(Partner)*
Bernard M. Doucette *(Partner & CFO)*
Bernard J. Grzelak *(Partner & COO)*
Bradley Eckstein *(Partner & Sr Mgr-Reg)*
Brooke A. Fapohunda *(Partner)*
David J. Linsen *(Partner & Dir-Equities)*
Jack Baldwin *(Partner & Mgr-Rels)*
Jamey Lamanna *(Partner & Chief Digital Officer)*
Jeffrey D. Lapin *(Partner & Portfolio Mgr)*
Jennifer Karam *(Partner & Deputy Gen Counsel)*
Kevin Dunphy *(Partner)*
Kristen Maple *(Partner & Chief Admin Officer)*
Lawrence H. Kaplan *(Partner & Gen Counsel)*
Marc Furgang *(Partner & Sr Mgr-Reg)*
Mario Barbato *(Partner & Chief Transformation Officer)*
Patrick J. Browne *(Partner)*
Philip B. Herman *(Partner & Portfolio Mgr)*
Robert A. Lee *(Partner & Chief Investment Officer)*
Shane M. Magoon *(Partner & Deputy Dir-Trading)*
Stacy P. Allen *(Partner & Chief Risk Officer)*
Thomas Malone *(Partner)*
Vito Fronda *(Partner)*
Alexander I. Crawford *(Partner)*
Bruce E. Gover Jr. *(Partner)*

LORD BALTIMORE CAPITAL CORP.
6225 Smith Ave Ste B100, Baltimore, MD 21209
Tel.: (410) 415-7600
Web Site:
http://www.lordbaltimoreprop.com
Year Founded: 1921
Rev.: $48,857,000
Emp.: 25
Security Speculators For Own Account
N.A.I.C.S.: 523999
Alan E. Kerry *(Pres)*
Colleen Crews *(Controller)*
Ken FLOYD *(Dir-Taxation)*

LORD ELECTRIC COMPANY OF PUERTO RICO INC.
8 Ave Simon Madera, San Juan, PR 00924-2231
Tel.: (787) 758-4040
Web Site: http://www.lordelectric.com
Year Founded: 1989
Sales Range: $10-24.9 Million
Emp.: 397
Electrical Work
N.A.I.C.S.: 238210
Lionel Roger *(Comptroller)*
Cesar Roman *(Pres-Continental Lord Div, Treas-Admin & Fin & Exec VP)*
German Gobaira *(VP)*
Narciso Rabell *(VP-Construction)*
Manuel Rosabal *(Pres)*

LORD WEST FORMAL WEAR
140 Wharton Rd, Bristol, PA 19007-1622
Tel.: (215) 785-2300 NY
Web Site: http://www.flowformal.com
Year Founded: 1917
Sales Range: $25-49.9 Million
Mfr of Men's Formalwear & Accessories
N.A.I.C.S.: 315250
Charles Burkhalter *(VP-Creative Svcs)*

Subsidiaries:

West Mill Clothes, Tuxedo Accessories Division (DBA Lord West) (1)
257 Rittenhouse Cir Keystone Industrial Park, Bristol, PA 19007 (100%)
Tel.: (215) 785-2300
Sales Range: $25-49.9 Million
Emp.: 35
Mfr of Formal Shirts & Accessories
N.A.I.C.S.: 315250

LORD, AECK & SARGENT, INC.
1175 Peachtree St NE Ste 2400, Atlanta, GA 30361-3500
Tel.: (404) 872-0330 GA
Web Site:
http://www.lordaecksargent.com
Year Founded: 1983
Sales Range: $25-49.9 Million
Emp.: 100
Architectural Planning & Design Services
N.A.I.C.S.: 541310
Antonin Aeck *(Principal)*
Don Bush *(Principal)*
Joseph Greco *(Pres)*
Doug Glasgow *(Dir-IT Advancement)*
Stanford Harvey *(Dir-Urban Design & Planning)*
John Schneider *(Dir-Interior Design)*
John Starr *(Dir-Education, Arts & Culture)*
Jack Pyburn *(Principal)*
Jackson Kane *(Principal)*
Jim Nicolow *(Principal)*
Josh Andrews *(Principal)*
Karen M. Gravel *(Principal)*
Kent Brown *(Principal)*
Larry Lord *(Principal)*
Lauren Dunn Rockart *(Principal)*
Mark S. Lange *(Principal)*
Richard Robison *(Principal)*
Robert Begle *(Principal)*
Scott O'Brien *(Principal)*
Susan Turner *(Principal)*
Vance Stuart Cheatham *(Principal)*
Warren L. Williams *(Principal)*
John L. Kisner II *(Principal)*

LORDAE INC.
78 N State Rd, Briarcliff Manor, NY 10510
Tel.: (914) 762-8300
Web Site: http://www.lordae.com
Rev.: $10,000,000
Emp.: 12

Commercial & Industrial Building Operation
N.A.I.C.S.: 531120

LORDEN OIL CO. INC.
69 Pittsburg Rd, Ayer, MA 01432
Tel.: (978) 597-2227
Web Site: http://www.lordenoil.com
Rev.: $16,900,000
Emp.: 7
Fuel Oil Dealers
N.A.I.C.S.: 457210
Tim Lorden *(Owner)*

LOREL MARKETING GROUP LLC
590 N Gulth Rd, King of Prussia, PA 19406
Tel.: (610) 337-2343 PA
Year Founded: 1987
Sales Range: $10-24.9 Million
Emp.: 50
Advertising Agencies
N.A.I.C.S.: 541810
Lorna Rudnick *(Chm)*

LOREN AUTO GROUP
1620 Waukegan Rd, Glenview, IL 60025
Tel.: (847) 729-8900
Web Site:
http://www.lorenautogroup.com
Sales Range: $75-99.9 Million
Emp.: 36
Automobiles, New & Used
N.A.I.C.S.: 441110
Dennis Doerge *(Controller)*

LOREN BERG CHEVROLET
2700 Portland Rd, Newberg, OR 97132
Tel.: (503) 538-3161
Web Site: http://www.lorenberg.com
Sales Range: $10-24.9 Million
Emp.: 25
Automobiles, New & Used
N.A.I.C.S.: 441110
Loren Berg *(Pres)*
Angela Johnson *(Office Mgr)*

LOREN COMMUNICATIONS INTERNATIONAL LTD., INC.
155 E 55th St 4th Fl, New York, NY 10022-4038
Tel.: (212) 752-4900
Year Founded: 1975
Sales Range: $125-149.9 Million
Emp.: 500
Information Transfer Services
N.A.I.C.S.: 561499
Pamela Loren *(Chm & CEO)*
Adrianna Pell *(Dir-Medical Comm)*
Madeline S. Winters *(Pres)*

Subsidiaries:

Pamela Loren Limited, Inc. (1)
155 E 55th St 4th Fl, New York, NY 10022-4051 (100%)
Tel.: (212) 752-4900
Information Transfer Services
N.A.I.C.S.: 561499

LOREN COOK COMPANY
2015 E Dale St, Springfield, MO 65803
Tel.: (417) 869-6474
Web Site: http://www.lorencook.com
Sales Range: $50-74.9 Million
Emp.: 900
Mfr of Ventilation Systems
N.A.I.C.S.: 333413
Gerald A. Cook *(Chm & Pres)*
Steve Burney *(VP)*

LOREN INDUSTRIES INC.
14051 NW 14th St, Sunrise, FL 33323
Tel.: (954) 834-0278
Web Site: http://www.loren.com
Year Founded: 1950
Sales Range: $25-49.9 Million
Emp.: 70
Jewelers' Castings
N.A.I.C.S.: 339910
Donald Goldstein *(Pres)*

LORENZI LUMBER CO. INC.
1600 Jefferson Ave, Washington, PA 15301
Tel.: (724) 222-6100
Web Site:
http://www.lorenzilumber.com
Sales Range: $10-24.9 Million
Emp.: 50
Home Center Operator
N.A.I.C.S.: 444110
Al Lorenzi *(Pres)*
David Alderson *(Gen Mgr)*
Vincent Lorenzi *(VP)*

LORIENT CAPITAL MANAGEMENT LLC
3250 Mary St, Ste 500, Miami, FL 33133
Tel.: (248) 247-3900
Web Site: https://lorientcap.com
Year Founded: 2015
Private Equity
N.A.I.C.S.: 523940
David Berman *(Mng Partner)*

Subsidiaries:

Purposecare Homecare LLC (1)
5455 Harrison Park Lane, Indianapolis, 46216, IN, India
Tel.: (91) 3178021164
Web Site: https://purposecare.com
Women Healthcare Services
N.A.I.C.S.: 621610
Rich Keller *(CEO)*

LORING HOSPITAL
211 Highland Ave, Sac City, IA 50583
Tel.: (712) 662-7105 IA
Web Site:
http://www.loringhospital.org
Year Founded: 1993
Sales Range: $10-24.9 Million
Emp.: 144
Health Care Srvices
N.A.I.C.S.: 622110
Angie Fischer *(CFO)*
Mike Green *(Chm)*
Tancy Becker *(Sec)*
Dick Schaefer *(Vice Chm)*

LORNAMEAD, INC.
5 High Ridge Park Ste 200, Stamford, CT 06905
Tel.: (203) 517-1102 NY
Web Site:
http://www.lornameadna.com
Year Founded: 1992
Sales Range: $25-49.9 Million
Emp.: 150
Oral Care Products, Tooth Whitening Products
N.A.I.C.S.: 339114
Randy Sloan *(Pres)*

LORRAINE CAPITAL LLC
591 Delaware Ave, Buffalo, NY 14202
Tel.: (716) 816-8809
Web Site:
http://www.lorrainecapital.com
Investment Services
N.A.I.C.S.: 523999
Richard F. Gioia *(Principal)*
Justin M. Reich *(Principal)*
C. Anthony Rider *(Principal)*
William J. Maggio Jr. *(Principal)*

LORRAINE CAPITAL LLC

Lorraine Capital LLC—(Continued)

Subsidiaries:

Buffalo Hotel Supply Company, Inc. (1)
375 Commerce Dr, Amherst, NY 14228
Tel.: (716) 691-8080
Web Site:
  http://www.bhsfoodservicesolutions.com
Emp.: 70
Kitchenware; Lines; Furniture; Heavy Equipment Supplies; Designing Services
N.A.I.C.S.: 423220
Alan Krakowiak (VP-Project Mgmt)
Mark Raccuia (Project Mgr)
Kelly Appiani (CFO)
Richard F. Gioia (CEO)
Donald M. Harvey (COO)

Summit Steel & Manufacturing Inc. (1)
1005 Patriot Pkwy, Reading, PA 19605
Tel.: (610) 921-1119
Web Site: http://www.summitsteelinc.com
Sales Range: $10-24.9 Million
Emp.: 85
Steel Pipe & Tube Mfr
N.A.I.C.S.: 331210
Gary Romig (CEO)

Subsidiary (Domestic):

Laser Specialties, Inc. (2)
6611 State Hwy 66, Tulsa, OK 74131
Tel.: (918) 445-6100
Web Site: http://www.laserspecialties.com
Rev.: $6,165,000
Emp.: 45
All Other Miscellaneous Fabricated Metal Product Mfr
N.A.I.C.S.: 332999
Peter Baldauf (Gen Mgr)
Jim Clark (CEO)

LORRAINE HOME FASHIONS

295 5th Ave Ste 1013, New York, NY 10016
Tel.: (212) 684-0858
Web Site: http://www.lhf.com
Rev.: $11,200,000
Emp.: 9
Curtains
N.A.I.C.S.: 423220
Bernard Rittenberg (Pres)

LORRAINE LINENS INC.

700 W Hillsboro Blvd Bldg 4 Ste 100, Deerfield Beach, FL 33441
Tel.: (954) 425-0800
Web Site: http://lorrainelinenshq.com
Sales Range: $10-24.9 Million
Emp.: 100
Covers, Lace: Chair, Dresser, Piano & Table
N.A.I.C.S.: 313240

Subsidiaries:

Quaker Lace (1)
2844 N University Dr, Coral Springs, FL 33065-1425
Tel.: (954) 425-0800
Sales Range: $10-24.9 Million
Emp.: 4
Mfr of Decorative Lace Covers for Furniture
N.A.I.C.S.: 313240

LORRIE WALKER COMMUNICATIONS INC.

231 N Kentucky Ave Ste 209, Lakeland, FL 33801
Tel.: (863) 614-0555
Web Site:
  http://www.lorriewalkerpr.com
Sales Range: $1-9.9 Million
Public Relations
N.A.I.C.S.: 541820
Lorrie Delk Walker (Pres)
Barbara Cagle (Acct Coord)

LORUSSO CORPORATION

3 Belcher St, Plainville, MA 02762
Tel.: (508) 695-3252

Web Site:
  http://www.lorussocorp.com
Rev.: $20,000,000
Emp.: 100
Provider of Sand & Gravel Construction Services
N.A.I.C.S.: 324121
Gerard Lorusso (Pres)
Henry Grilli (CFO)
Danny Boone (VP-Ops)

LOS ALAMOS TECHNICAL ASSOCIATES, INC.

999 Central Ave Ste 300, Los Alamos, NM 87544
Tel.: (505) 662-9080   NM
Web Site: http://www.lata.com
Year Founded: 1976
Sales Range: $50-74.9 Million
Emp.: 300
Professional, Scientific & Engineering Services
N.A.I.C.S.: 541330
E. M. Cole (VP)

Subsidiaries:

LATA Environmental Services of Kentucky, LLC (1)
761 Veterans Ave, Kevil, KY 42053
Tel.: (270) 441-5000
Web Site: http://www.latakentucky.com
Environmental Remediation Services
N.A.I.C.S.: 562910

LATA-KEMRON Remediation, LLC (1)
756 Park Meadow Rd, Westerville, OH 43081-2871
Tel.: (614) 508-1200
Web Site: http://www.lata.com
Emp.: 50
Environmental Remediation Services
N.A.I.C.S.: 562910

LATA-Merrick Engineering & Environment, LLC (1)
6501 Americas Pkwy NE Ste 200, Albuquerque, NM 87110
Tel.: (505) 884-3800
Engineeering Services
N.A.I.C.S.: 541330
Bobby Templin (Dir-Defense Environmental Programs)

LATA-Sharp Remediation Services, LLC (1)
185 Lafayette Dr, Oak Ridge, TN 37830-6898
Tel.: (865) 481-3203
Environmental Remediation Services
N.A.I.C.S.: 562910
Rees Lattimer (Gen Mgr)

LOS ANGELES CHILD GUIDANCE CLINIC

3031 S Vermont Ave, Los Angeles, CA 90007
Tel.: (323) 373-2400   CA
Web Site: http://www.lachild.org
Year Founded: 1924
Sales Range: $10-24.9 Million
Emp.: 272
Mental Health Care Services
N.A.I.C.S.: 623220
Steven Talavera (VP-Fin & Admin)
Tiffany T. Rodriguez (VP-Programs)
Teresa Leingang (VP-HR & Risk Mgmt)
Elizabeth W. Pfromm (Pres & CEO)
Gail Kennard (Sec)
Shelly Holmes (Treas)
Wayne Moore (Chm)

LOS ANGELES COUNTY FAIR ASSOCIATION

1101 W McKinley Ave, Pomona, CA 91768
Tel.: (909) 623-3111
Web Site:
  http://www.lacountyfair.com

Year Founded: 1922
Sales Range: $10-24.9 Million
Emp.: 300
Convention Center
N.A.I.C.S.: 713990
Michael Ortiz (Chm & Interim CEO)

LOS ANGELES COUNTY METROPOLITAN TRANSPORTATION AUTHORITY

1 Gateway Plz, Los Angeles, CA 90012-2952
Tel.: (213) 922-6000
Web Site: http://www.metro.net
Year Founded: 1993
Emp.: 9,817
Bus & Rail Transit System Operator
N.A.I.C.S.: 485113
Michele Jackson (Sec)
Phillip A. Washington (CEO)
Eric Garcetti (Chm)
Sheila Kuehl (Vice Chm)
Elba Higueros (Chief Policy Officer)
Gregory Kildare (Chief Risk, Safety & Asset Mgmt Officer)
James T. Gallagher (COO)
Joshua Schank (Chief Innovation Officer)
Nalini Ahuja (CFO)
Pauletta Tonilas (Chief Comm Officer)
Richard F. Clarke (Chief Program Mgmt Officer)
Stephanie Wiggins (Deputy CEO)
Therese McMillan (Chief Plng Officer)
Diana Estrada (Chief Auditor)
Patrick Astredo (CIO-Interim)

LOS ANGELES COUNTY MUSEUM OF NATURAL HISTORY FOUNDATION

900 Exposition Blvd, Los Angeles, CA 90007
Tel.: (213) 763-3466   CA
Web Site: http://www.nhm.org
Year Founded: 1965
Sales Range: $25-49.9 Million
Emp.: 398
Museum Operator
N.A.I.C.S.: 712110
Thomas Jacobson (VP-Advancement)
Karen Wise (VP-Education)
James Gilson (Gen Counsel & VP)

LOS ANGELES FIREMEN'S RELIEF ASSOCIATION

7470 N Figueroa St, Los Angeles, CA 90041
Tel.: (323) 259-5200   CA
Web Site: http://www.lafra.org
Year Founded: 1906
Sales Range: $50-74.9 Million
Emp.: 28
Fireman Relief Association
N.A.I.C.S.: 813910
Liberty Unciano (Treas & Controller)
Marlene Casillas (Dir-Dev & Mktg)
Bob Dillon (Mgr-Ops)
Jeff Cawdrey (VP)
Todd Layfer (Exec Dir)
Bob Steinbacher (Pres)
Irma Mondragon (Sec)

LOS ANGELES FIREMENS CREDIT UNION

815 Colorado Blvd, Los Angeles, CA 90041
Tel.: (323) 254-1700   CA
Web Site: http://www.firecu.org
Year Founded: 1935
Sales Range: $25-49.9 Million
Emp.: 134
Credit Union Operator
N.A.I.C.S.: 522130

Cindy Iwamoto (Sr VP-Fin)
Matt Mitchell (Sr VP-Lending)
Dixie Abramian (CEO)

LOS ANGELES JEWISH HOME

7150 Tampa Ave, Reseda, CA 91335
Tel.: (818) 774-3000   CA
Web Site: http://www.jha.org
Year Founded: 1912
Sales Range: $150-199.9 Million
Emp.: 95
Elderly People Assisted Living Services
N.A.I.C.S.: 623312
Larissa Stepanians (CFO & Treas)
Sharon Z. Ginchansky (VP-HR & Corp Compliance)
Sherri B. Cunningham (Pres & CEO)
Barbara Miller-Fox Abramoff (Sec)
Molly Forrest (Pres & CEO)
Arnold Possick (CMO)
Ira Schreck (Sr VP-Jewish Home Foundation)
Noah Marco (Chief Medical Officer)
David L. Swartz (Chm)

LOS ANGELES MISSION, INC.

303 E 5th St, Los Angeles, CA 90013
Tel.: (213) 629-1227   CA
Web Site:
  http://www.losangelesmission.org
Year Founded: 1936
Rev.: $12,441,803
Assets: $31,784,426
Liabilities: $5,949,790
Net Worth: $25,834,636
Emp.: 111
Fiscal Year-end: 06/30/18
Substance Abuse Rehabilitation Services
N.A.I.C.S.: 623220
Steve Kennedy (CFO & Sr VP)
Marilyn McCoo (Vice Chm)
Randy D. Hess (Treas)
Bill Embree (Sec)
Herb Smith (Pres & CEO)
Vince Hruska (Chm)

LOS ANGELES OPERA

135 N Grand Ave, Los Angeles, CA 90012
Tel.: (213) 972-7219   CA
Web Site: http://www.laopera.org
Year Founded: 1983
Sales Range: $50-74.9 Million
Emp.: 862
Opera Organizer
N.A.I.C.S.: 711130
Christopher Koelsch (Pres & CEO)
Faith Raiguel (CFO & VP)
Marvin S. Shapiro (Sec)
Robert Ronus (Treas)
Marc I. Stern (Chm)
Warner W. Henry (Vice Chm)
Sebastian Paul Musco (Vice Chm)
Milan Panic (Vice Chm)
Marilyn Ziering (Vice Chm)
Diane Rhodes Bergman (VP-Mktg & Comm)
Stacy C. Brightman (VP-Education & Community Engagement)
Tom Bucher (Treas-Box Office)
John P. Nuckols (Exec VP)

LOS ANGELES PHILHARMONIC ASSOCIATION

151 S Grand Ave, Los Angeles, CA 90012
Tel.: (323) 850-2000
Web Site: https://www.laphil.com
Year Founded: 1919
Emp.: 195
Entertainers & Entertainment Groups
N.A.I.C.S.: 711320

COMPANIES

Alan Wayte *(Sec)*
Gustavo Dudamel *(Dir-Music & Artistic)*
Gail Samuel *(Exec Dir)*
Chad Smith *(CEO)*
Glenn Briffa *(CFO)*
James A. Rasulo *(Chm)*

LOS ANGELES PUBLIC LIBRARY DOCENTS

630 W 5th St, Los Angeles, CA 90071
Tel.: (213) 228-7000
Web Site: https://www.lapl.org
Emp.: 100
Libraries & Archives
N.A.I.C.S.: 519210

Subsidiaries:

Angel City Press (1)
2118 Wilshire Blvd Ste 880, Santa Monica, CA 90403-5704
Tel.: (310) 395-9982
Web Site: http://www.angelcitypress.com
Book Publishers
N.A.I.C.S.: 513130

LOS ANGELES RUBBER COMPANY

2915 E Washington Blvd, Los Angeles, CA 90023
Tel.: (323) 263-4131
Web Site: http://www.mrosupply.com
Sales Range: $10-24.9 Million
Emp.: 60
Manufacture Industrial Rubber
N.A.I.C.S.: 423610
Carol A. Durst *(Chm)*
Michael A. Durst *(Pres & CEO)*
Wayne Roberts *(VP-Sls)*
Richard Eckert *(Mgr-Fin)*

LOS ANGELES TIMES COMMUNICATIONS, LLC

2300 E Imperial Hwy, El Segundo, CA 90245
Tel.: (213) 237-5000   DE
Web Site: http://www.latimes.com
Year Founded: 1881
Newspaper & Magazine Publisher; News Syndication Services
N.A.I.C.S.: 513110
Ross B. Levinsohn *(Publr)*
Jim Kirk *(Editor-in-Chief)*
Norman Pearlstine *(Exec Editor)*
Angel Jennings *(Asst Mng Editor-Culture & Talent)*

Subsidiaries:

Burbank Leader (1)
221 N Brand Blvd 2nd Fl, Glendale, CA 91203
Tel.: (818) 843-8700
Web Site: http://www.burbankleader.com
Emp.: 30
Newspaper Publishers
N.A.I.C.S.: 513110

Huntington Beach Independent (1)
1375 Sunflower Ave, Costa Mesa, CA 92626
Tel.: (714) 966-4689
Web Site: http://www.hbindependent.com
Newspaper Publishers
N.A.I.C.S.: 513110

Times Community News (1)
221 N Brand Blvd 2nd Fl, Glendale, CA 91203
Tel.: (818) 637-3200
Web Site: http://www.glendalenewspress.com
Sales Range: $50-74.9 Million
Emp.: 50
Newspaper Publishers
N.A.I.C.S.: 513110

Times Community News - South (1)
10540 Talbert Ave Ste 300, Fountain Valley, CA 92708
Tel.: (714) 966-4601

Web Site: http://www.dailypilot.com
Sales Range: $50-74.9 Million
Newspaper Publishers
N.A.I.C.S.: 513110

LOS ANGELES WHOLESALE PRODUCE MARKET

1601 E Olympic Blvd, Los Angeles, CA 90021
Tel.: (213) 896-4070
Web Site: http://www.lanuthouse.com
Sales Range: $10-24.9 Million
Fresh Fruit & Vegetable Merchant Whslr
N.A.I.C.S.: 424480
Donald Presant *(Gen Mgr)*

LOS GATOS ACURA

16151 Los Gatos Blvd, Los Gatos, CA 95032
Tel.: (408) 358-8000
Web Site: http://www.losgatosacura.com
Sales Range: $10-24.9 Million
Emp.: 35
New Car Whslr
N.A.I.C.S.: 441110
Bill Kendrick *(Owner)*
Mark Maxwell *(Gen Mgr)*

LOS GATOS BREWING CO.

130 N Santa Cruz Ave, Los Gatos, CA 95030-5911
Tel.: (408) 395-9929
Web Site: http://www.lgbrewingco.com
Year Founded: 1991
Sales Range: $25-49.9 Million
Emp.: 150
Brewery Mfr
N.A.I.C.S.: 312120
Andy Pavicich *(Co-Owner)*

LOS OLIVOS PACKAGING INC.

667 S Anderson St, Los Angeles, CA 90023
Tel.: (323) 261-2218
Web Site: http://www.losolivospackaging.com
Sales Range: $25-49.9 Million
Emp.: 31
Canned Olives
N.A.I.C.S.: 311421
Louis Pavlic *(Pres)*

LOS TIOS LTD.

PO Box 395, Pattison, TX 77466-0395
Tel.: (713) 784-1900   TX
Web Site: http://www.texmexgourmet.com
Year Founded: 1970
Pickles, Sauces & Salad Dressings
N.A.I.C.S.: 311941

LOST PLANET

113 Spring St 4th Fl, New York, NY 10012
Tel.: (212) 226-5678
Web Site: http://www.lostplanet.com
Sales Range: $10-24.9 Million
Emp.: 15
Entertainment Advertising
N.A.I.C.S.: 541890
Hank Corwin *(Owner)*

Subsidiaries:

Lost Planet (1)
2515 Main St, Santa Monica, CA 90405
Tel.: (310) 396-7272
Web Site: http://www.lostplanet.com
Entertainment Advertising
N.A.I.C.S.: 541890

LOSURDO FOODS, INC.

20 Owens Rd, Hackensack, NJ 07601-3203

Tel.: (201) 343-6680   NJ
Web Site:
   http://www.losurdofoods.com
Year Founded: 1959
Sales Range: $125-149.9 Million
Emp.: 150
Mfr & Producer of Pickles, Sauces & Salad Dressings, Natural & Processed Cheeses & Prepared Pizza Dough
N.A.I.C.S.: 424410
Michael Losurdo *(Pres)*
Marc J. X. Losurdo *(Pres & CEO)*
Maria A. Losurdo *(Treas & Sec)*

LOTH MBI, INC.

3574 E Kemper Rd, Cincinnati, OH 45241-2009
Tel.: (513) 554-4900
Web Site: http://www.lothinc.com
Year Founded: 1891
Sales Range: $25-49.9 Million
Emp.: 150
Office Furniture Sales & Mfr
N.A.I.C.S.: 423210
J. B. Buse *(Chm & CEO)*
Rick Naber *(Pres)*

Subsidiaries:

Loth Inc. (1)
855 Grandview Ave, Columbus, OH 43215
Tel.: (614) 487-4000
Web Site: http://www.lothinc.com
Sales Range: $25-49.9 Million
Emp.: 80
Office Furniture Sale & Distr
N.A.I.C.S.: 423210
Lorene Elson Haimerl *(Exec VP-Sls-Columbus)*
Keith Weyler *(Pres-Cincinnati)*
Jason Lawler *(Pres & Partner-Columbus)*

OptiVia Banking Equipment & Services (1)
3574 E Kemper Rd, Cincinnati, OH 45241
Tel.: (513) 554-8860
Web Site: http://www.optiviabankequip.com
Banking Equipment Mfr
N.A.I.C.S.: 561621
Brad Athey *(Gen Mgr)*

LOTSPEICH CO.

16101 NW 54th Ave, Hialeah, FL 33014
Tel.: (305) 624-7777
Web Site: http://www.lotspeich.com
Year Founded: 1928
Sales Range: $10-24.9 Million
Emp.: 100
Residential Construction
N.A.I.C.S.: 236220
Eric Wible *(Project Mgr)*
Michael Alvarado *(Superintendent)*
Craig Gordon *(VP)*
Don Lawson *(VP-Construction Ops)*
Mike Fee *(Pres)*

LOTSPEICH CO. OF FLORIDA, INC.

6351 NW 28th Way Unit A, Fort Lauderdale, FL 33309
Tel.: (954) 978-2388
Web Site: http://www.lcfinc.com
Year Founded: 1928
Rev.: $25,000,000
Emp.: 200
Provider of Drywall Contracting Services
N.A.I.C.S.: 238310
David H. Fee *(CEO)*
Jerry Ligon *(VP)*
Michael Fee *(Pres)*

LOTT OIL COMPANY, INC.

1855 Hwy 1, Natchitoches, LA 71457-2658
Tel.: (318) 352-2055   LA
Web Site: http://www.lottoil.com
Year Founded: 1963

LOTUS INNOVATIONS LLC

Sales Range: $25-49.9 Million
Emp.: 200
Petroleum Bulk Stations & Terminals
N.A.I.C.S.: 424710
Luther W. Lott Jr. *(Pres)*

Subsidiaries:

Shop-A-Lott, Inc. (1)
1855 Hwy 1, Natchitoches, LA 71457-2658
Tel.: (318) 352-2055
Web Site: http://www.lottoil.com
Rev.: $22,900,000
Emp.: 25
Gasoline Service Stations
N.A.I.C.S.: 457120
Luther W. Lott Jr. *(Pres)*

LOTUS ADVERTISING

497 Horse Pen Ln, Vass, NC 28394
Tel.: (910) 692-3054   NC
Web Site:
   http://www.lotusadvertising.com
Year Founded: 1982
Sales Range: Less than $1 Million
Emp.: 3
Graphic Design, Health Care
N.A.I.C.S.: 541810
Jonathan D. Scott *(Owner)*

LOTUS COMMUNICATIONS CORP.

3301 Barham Blvd Ste 200, Los Angeles, CA 90068
Tel.: (323) 512-2225
Web Site: http://www.lotuscorp.com
Rev.: $31,400,000
Emp.: 500
Radio Broadcasting Stations & Low Power TV Stations
N.A.I.C.S.: 516110
Howard A. Kalmenson *(Pres & CEO)*
Bill Shriftman *(Treas & Sr VP)*
Lindy Williams *(Dir-Engrg)*
Jasmin Dorismond *(Controller)*

LOTUS INFRASTRUCTURE PARTNERS LLC

5 Greenwich Ofc Park 2nd Fl, Greenwich, CT 06831
Tel.: (203) 445-6800
Web Site:
   https://www.lotusinfrastructure.com
Privater Equity Firm
N.A.I.C.S.: 523999
Alex Daberko *(Mng Dir)*

Subsidiaries:

Allium Renewable Energy, LLC (1)
233 S Wacker Dr Ste 9450, Chicago, IL 60606
Tel.: (312) 873-0004
Renewable Energy Services
N.A.I.C.S.: 221114
Karl Dahlstrom *(CEO)*
Chris Stecklein *(VP-)*

LOTUS INNOVATIONS LLC

5151 California Ave, Irvine, CA 92617
Tel.: (949) 565-3002   DE
Web Site: http://www.lotus-innovations.com
Privater Equity Firm
N.A.I.C.S.: 523999
Christian Mack *(Mng Dir)*
Philip Jones *(Mng Dir)*
Ommid Bavarian *(CFO)*

Subsidiaries:

generationE Consulting, LLC (1)
5151 California Ave, Irvine, CA 92612
Tel.: (949) 565-3400
Web Site: http://www.gen-e.com
Cloud Data Management Support Services
N.A.I.C.S.: 541990
Christian Mack *(Founder)*
Toussaint Andry *(VP)*
Mike Henderson *(Interim CEO)*
Drew Van Pelt *(Chm)*
Rhett Williams *(Pres-EMEA)*

LOU BACHRODT CHEVROLET INC.

Lou Bachrodt Chevrolet Inc.—(Continued)

LOU BACHRODT CHEVROLET INC.
1801 W Atlantic Blvd, Pompano Beach, FL 33069-2720
Tel.: (954) 971-3000
Web Site: http://www.bachrodt.com
Year Founded: 1953
Sales Range: $10-24.9 Million
Emp.: 100
New & Used Car Dealers
N.A.I.C.S.: 441110
Mariusz Danczuk *(Mgr-Special Fin)*

LOU BACHRODT FREIGHTLINER
2840 Center Port Cir, Pompano Beach, FL 33064
Tel.: (954) 545-1000
Web Site: http://www.freightlinerfl.com
Sales Range: $25-49.9 Million
Emp.: 309
Sales New & Used Trucks & Tractors
N.A.I.C.S.: 423110
Jeffery Tolbert *(Mgr-Svc)*
Dave Counterman *(Mgr-Parts)*
Carlos Francisco *(Mgr-Warranty)*

LOU FUSZ AUTOMOTIVE NETWORK
925 N Lindbergh Blvd, Saint Louis, MO 63141
Tel.: (314) 997-3400
Web Site: http://www.fusz.com
Year Founded: 1954
Sales Range: $10-24.9 Million
Emp.: 1,200
Holding Company: Automobile Dealership
N.A.I.C.S.: 441110
Tom Biehle *(Mgr-Sls)*
Steven Kabbaz *(Mgr-Sls)*
Louis Fusz Jr. *(Chm)*

Subsidiaries:

Lou Fusz Motor Company (1)
925 N Lindbergh Blvd, Saint Louis, MO 63141 (100%)
Tel.: (314) 997-3400
Web Site: http://www.fusz.com
Automobile Dealership
N.A.I.C.S.: 441110
Lou Fusz *(Pres)*
Randy Fusz *(Pres)*

LOU HAMMOND & ASSOCIATES, INC.
900 3rd Ave, New York, NY 10022
Tel.: (212) 308-8880
Web Site: http://www.louhammond.com
Year Founded: 1984
Sales Range: $1-9.9 Million
Emp.: 40
Public Relations Agency
N.A.I.C.S.: 541820
Lou Rena Hammond *(Founder & Chm)*
Terence Gallagher *(Pres-New York)*
Stephen Hammond *(Pres)*
Melanie Mathos *(Sr VP-Charleston)*
Gina Stouffer *(Pres-Charleston)*
John O'Hearn *(VP-Digital Mktg)*
Michael Hicks *(VP-Miami)*
Rachel McAllister *(VP-New York)*

LOU LEVY & SONS FASHIONS INC.
512 Seventh Ave Fl 3, New York, NY 10018-0867
Tel.: (212) 398-2707
Web Site: http://www.thelevygroupinc.com
Year Founded: 1953
Sales Range: $25-49.9 Million
Emp.: 200
Wholesale of Womens Clothing
N.A.I.C.S.: 424350
Michael Herman *(CFO)*

LOU MADDALONI JEWELERS INC.
1870 E Jericho Tpke, Huntington, NY 11743
Tel.: (631) 499-8800
Web Site: http://www.maddaloni.net
Sales Range: $25-49.9 Million
Emp.: 18
Mfr, Designer, Repairer & Retailer of Jewelry
N.A.I.C.S.: 423940
Louis Maddaloni *(Pres)*

LOU MITCHELL'S INC.
333 S Des Plns Ste 506, Chicago, IL 60661
Tel.: (312) 382-0707
Web Site: http://www.loumitchellsrestaurant.com
Sales Range: $10-24.9 Million
Emp.: 2
Bakery Products Mfr
N.A.I.C.S.: 311812
Catherine Thanas *(Pres)*

LOUDMAC CREATIVE, INC.
11632 SW 127 Terrace, Miami, FL 33176
Tel.: (786) 693-2886
Web Site: http://www.loudmac.com
Sales Range: Less than $1 Million
Emp.: 5
Advetising Agency
N.A.I.C.S.: 541810
Brian McLeod *(Pres)*

LOUDOUN COUNTY SANITATION AUTHORITY
44865 Loudown Water Way, Ashburn, VA 20147
Tel.: (571) 291-7700
Web Site: http://www.loudounwater.org
Year Founded: 1959
Sales Range: $10-24.9 Million
Emp.: 254
Water Supply
N.A.I.C.S.: 221310
Eugene Delgadio *(Gen Mgr)*
Adam Drinko *(Head-Lifeguard)*
Bobby Burlingame *(Supvr-Pub Safety Engrg)*
Colleen McDonough *(Engr-Electrical-CCM)*
Matthew Sullivan *(Supvr-Facility)*
William Clark *(Mgr-Construction)*

LOUDOUN ELECTRIC COMPANY
22923 Quicksilver Dr Ste 117, Sterling, VA 20166
Tel.: (703) 574-5001
Web Site: http://www.loudounelectric.com
Year Founded: 1981
Rev.: $9,900,000
Emp.: 70
Electrical Contractor
N.A.I.C.S.: 238210
Leonard Piazza *(Pres)*
Annettee Hartung *(Controller)*

LOUDSPEAKER COMPONENTS, L.L.C.
7596 US Hwy 61, Lancaster, WI 53813
Tel.: (608) 723-2127
Web Site: http://www.loudspeakercomponents.com
Sales Range: $10-24.9 Million
Emp.: 50
Loudspeakers
N.A.I.C.S.: 334310
Neil Kirschbaum *(Pres)*

LOUIE'S FINER MEATS, INC.
Hwy 63 N 2025 Superior Ave, Cumberland, WI 54829
Tel.: (715) 822-4728
Web Site: http://www.louiesfinermeats.com
Year Founded: 1970
Sales Range: $25-49.9 Million
Emp.: 50
Processed Meat Mfr
N.A.I.C.S.: 311612
Louis G. Muench *(Pres)*

LOUIS A. WILLIAMS & ASSOCIATES
907 E Grand Ave, Marshall, TX 75670
Tel.: (903) 938-5191
Web Site: http://www.louisawilliams.com
Rev.: $35,992,927
Emp.: 120
Insurance Agents, Brokers & Service
N.A.I.C.S.: 524210
Sharon Broadus *(CFO)*
Billy R. Burke *(Chm)*
Christopher Allen Burke *(CEO)*
Bradford Steven Burke *(Pres)*

LOUIS F. LEEPER COMPANY
419 Friday Rd, Pittsburgh, PA 15209-2113
Tel.: (412) 821-8960
Web Site: http://www.leepercompanies.com
Year Founded: 1972
Sales Range: $25-49.9 Million
Emp.: 360
Provider of Groceries
N.A.I.C.S.: 424410
Bruno Mammone *(Mgr-Bus Dev)*
Tony Walla *(VP-Grocery & Bus Mgr-Dev)*

Subsidiaries:

Food Marketing Services (1)
418 Friday Rd, Pittsburgh, PA 15209-0091
Tel.: (412) 821-8960
Sales Range: $10-24.9 Million
Emp.: 80
Provider of Grocery Services
N.A.I.C.S.: 424410

J. Carroll & Associates, Inc. (1)
419 Friday Rd, Pittsburgh, PA 15209
Tel.: (412) 821-8960
Consumer Goods Distr
N.A.I.C.S.: 424990

LOUIS HORNICK & CO. INC.
117 E 38th St, New York, NY 10016
Tel.: (212) 679-2448
Web Site: http://www.louishornick.com
Year Founded: 1918
Sales Range: $25-49.9 Million
Curtains & Draperies Mfr
N.A.I.C.S.: 314120
Louis Hornick II *(Chm & CEO)*
Louis Hornick III *(COO)*

LOUIS J. PARADIS INC.
62 W Main St, Fort Kent, ME 04743-1213
Tel.: (207) 834-5081
Year Founded: 1946
Sales Range: $50-74.9 Million
Emp.: 500
Grocery Stores
N.A.I.C.S.: 445110
Lisa Deschene *(Sec)*
Craig Paradis *(CFO)*

LOUIS M. GERSON CO. INC.
16 Commerce Blvd, Middleboro, MA 02346
Tel.: (508) 947-4000
Web Site: http://www.gersonco.com
Sales Range: $50-74.9 Million
Emp.: 60
Mfr of Masks
N.A.I.C.S.: 314120
Ronald L. Gerson *(Chm, Pres & CEO)*

LOUIS MAULL COMPANY
219 N Market, Saint Louis, MO 63102
Tel.: (314) 241-8410
Web Site: http://www.maull.com
Year Founded: 1897
Sales Range: $10-24.9 Million
Emp.: 20
Barbecue Sauce Mfr
N.A.I.C.S.: 311421
David Ahner *(Sec & VP-Sls)*
Louis T. Maull IV *(VP)*

LOUIS PADNOS IRON & METAL COMPANY
185 W 8th St, Holland, MI 49423
Tel.: (616) 396-6521
Web Site: http://www.padnos.com
Year Founded: 1905
Sales Range: $125-149.9 Million
Emp.: 300
Process Secondary Metals & Fibres; Merchandise Mill Supplies, Machinery & Equipment
N.A.I.C.S.: 423930
Jeffrey S. Padnos *(Pres & COO)*
Mitchell W. Padnos *(VP-Sls & Mktg)*
Ben Irwin *(Controller)*

Subsidiaries:

B Clinkston & Sons Inc. (1)
1319 S 15th St, Saginaw, MI 48601
Tel.: (989) 752-3072
Web Site: http://www.clinkston.com
Rev.: $4,390,000
Emp.: 10
Recyclable Material Merchant Whslr
N.A.I.C.S.: 423930
Mark Clinkston *(Pres)*

Louis Padnos Iron & Metal Company - Cadillac Recycling Division (1)
1111 Leeson Ave, Cadillac, MI 49601
Tel.: (231) 775-7132
Web Site: http://www.cadillacrecycling.com
Metal Recycling Services
N.A.I.C.S.: 562920

Louis Padnos Iron & Metal Company - Hastings Division (1)
519 E Railroad St, Hastings, MI 49058
Tel.: (269) 945-3054
Web Site: http://www.hastingsrecycling.com
Recycling Services
N.A.I.C.S.: 562920

Louis Padnos Iron & Metal Company - Lansing Division (1)
1900 W Willow St, Lansing, MI 48917
Tel.: (517) 372-6600
Metal Recycling Services
N.A.I.C.S.: 562920

Louis Padnos Iron & Metal Company - Pere Marquette Division (1)
2601 W US 10, Ludington, MI 49431
Tel.: (231) 845-0241
Web Site: http://www.peremarquetterecycling.com
Metal Recycling Services
N.A.I.C.S.: 562920
Jeffrey Padnos *(Pres)*

Louis Padnos Iron & Metal Company - Wyoming Recycling Division (1)
500 44th St SW, Wyoming, MI 49548
Tel.: (616) 301-7900
Recyclable Material Whslr
N.A.I.C.S.: 423930

PADNOS Leitelt, Inc. (1)

2301 Turner Ave NW, Grand Rapids, MI 49544
Tel.: (616) 363-3817
Industrial Machinery & Equipment Whslr
N.A.I.C.S.: 423830

Padnos-Summit (1)
1900 W Willow St, Lansing, MI 48917
Tel.: (517) 372-6600
Web Site: http://www.padnos.com
Sales Range: $25-49.9 Million
Emp.: 100
Processed Ferrou & Non-ferrou Scrap for Remelting Purpose Primary Metal Distr
N.A.I.C.S.: 423930

LOUIS PAPPAS RESTAURANT GROUP, LLC
731 Wesley Ave, Tarpon Springs, FL 34689
Tel.: (727) 937-1770
Web Site:
  http://www.louispappas.com
Sales Range: $1-9.9 Million
Emp.: 100
Restaurant Owner & Operator
N.A.I.C.S.: 722511
Louis L. Pappas *(Owner)*

LOUIS SHANKS OF TEXAS INC.
2930 W Anderson Ln, Austin, TX 78757-1123
Tel.: (512) 451-6501   TX
Web Site:
  http://www.louisshanksfurniture.com
Year Founded: 1950
Sales Range: $25-49.9 Million
Emp.: 275
Provider of Furniture Services
N.A.I.C.S.: 449110
Mike Forewood *(Pres)*
Amor Forewood *(CEO)*
Susie Forewood *(Treas)*

LOUIS WOHL & SON INC.
11101 N 46th St, Tampa, FL 33617
Tel.: (813) 985-8870
Web Site: http://www.louiswohl.com
Sales Range: $10-24.9 Million
Emp.: 40
Hotel Equipment & Supplies
N.A.I.C.S.: 423440
Jeffrey S. Simon *(Owner)*
Steven L. Paver *(VP & Gen Mgr)*
Carol Simon *(Mgr-Mktg)*

LOUISBURG CIDER MILL, INC.
14730 Highway K-68, Louisburg, KS 66053
Tel.: (913) 837-5202
Web Site:
  http://www.louisburgcidermill.com
Rev.: $2,333,333
Emp.: 10
Mayonnaise, Dressing & Other Prepared Sauce Mfr
N.A.I.C.S.: 311941
Josh Hebert *(Mgr)*

Subsidiaries:

Pome On the Range, LLC (1)
2050 Idaho Rd, Williamsburg, KS 66095-8088
Tel.: (785) 746-5492
Web Site: http://www.pomeontherange.com
Farming
N.A.I.C.S.: 111339
Leland Gerhardt *(Owner)*

LOUISE PARIS LTD.
1407 Broadway Rm 1405, New York, NY 10018
Tel.: (212) 354-5411
Web Site: http://www.louiseparis.com
Sales Range: $600-649.9 Million
Emp.: 60
Women's & Children's Clothing
N.A.I.C.S.: 424350

Solomon Barnathan *(Pres)*
Scott Leith *(Dir-Mdsg & Design)*
Tiffany Corriente *(Coord-EDI)*
Serkan Ozgun *(Controller)*

LOUISIANA ASSOCIATION FOR THE BLIND
1750 Claiborne Ave, Shreveport, LA 71103
Tel.: (318) 635-6471
Web Site: http://www.lablind.com
Year Founded: 1927
Emp.: 100
Tablets & Pads, Book & Writing
N.A.I.C.S.: 322230
Brian Patchett *(Pres & CEO)*
Al Baca *(Exec VP)*
Audra Muslow-Hicks *(VP-Community Svcs)*
William Redcliff *(Sr Dir-Ops)*
Yolanda Lars *(Dir-HR)*
Alison Young *(Dir-Mktg)*
Shun Washington *(Sr Dir-Fin & Admin)*
John Erik Hammond *(Dir-Print Ops)*
Myrl Ray *(Dir-Base Supply Centers)*
Melinda Brown *(Dir-Client Svcs)*

LOUISIANA COMPANIES
801 North Blvd, Baton Rouge, LA 70802
Tel.: (225) 383-4761
Web Site:
  http://www.lacompanies.com
Rev.: $11,351,240
Emp.: 40
Insurance Agents
N.A.I.C.S.: 524210
Cameron Dean *(CFO)*

LOUISIANA DEALER SERVICES INSURANCE
9016 Bluebonnet Blvd, Baton Rouge, LA 70810
Tel.: (225) 769-9923
Web Site:
  http://www.theldsgroup.com
Sales Range: $10-24.9 Million
Emp.: 38
Life Insurance
N.A.I.C.S.: 524113
Dick S. Taylor *(Pres)*
Gerald Leglue *(VP)*
Ray Beatty *(Controller)*
Richard H. Barker III *(Chm)*

LOUISIANA EDUCATIONAL TELEVISION AUTHORITY
7733 Perkins Rd, Baton Rouge, LA 70810
Tel.: (225) 767-5660
Web Site: http://www.lpb.org
Year Founded: 1971
Sales Range: $10-24.9 Million
Emp.: 90
State Network of Six Non-Commercial Television Stations
N.A.I.C.S.: 516120
Jason Viso *(Dir-Programming)*
Candace Morgan *(Dir-HR)*
Kathy Hawkins Kliebert *(Sec)*
William Weldon *(Treas)*
Cynthia Rougeou *(Chief Admin Officer)*
Ed Landry *(Mgr-Production)*
Clarence Copeland *(Pres-Louisiana Pub Broadcasting & CEO-Louisiana Pub Broadcasting)*
Conrad Comeaux *(Chm)*

LOUISIANA ENERGY & POWER AUTHORITY
210 Venture Way, Lafayette, LA 70507-5319
Tel.: (337) 269-4046   LA

Web Site: http://www.lepa.com
Year Founded: 1979
Sales Range: $25-49.9 Million
Emp.: 54
Distribution of Electric Power
N.A.I.C.S.: 221122
Roy Robison *(Mgr-Acctg)*
Cordell A. Grand *(Gen Mgr)*
Kevin Bihm *(Asst Gen Mgr)*
Kevin Guidry *(Mgr-Support Svcs)*
Jerome Brunet *(Mgr-Power Supply)*
Al Levron *(Vice Chm)*
Buz Craft *(Treas & Sec)*
Charles Robichaux *(Chm)*

LOUISIANA FINE FOOD COMPANIES, INC.
4410 W 12th St, Houston, TX 77055
Tel.: (713) 957-1653
Web Site:
  http://www.louisianafoods.com
Sales Range: $10-24.9 Million
Emp.: 27
Seafood Sales
N.A.I.C.S.: 424460
Charles Coon *(Controller)*

Subsidiaries:

North Belt Restaurant, Inc. (1)
4410 W 12th St, Houston, TX 77055
Tel.: (713) 957-1653
Seafood Restaurants
N.A.I.C.S.: 722511
Margie Mohr *(Gen Mgr)*

LOUISIANA GAS DEVELOPMENT CORP.
416 Travis St Ste 700, Shreveport, LA 71101
Tel.: (318) 227-9299
Rev.: $30,000,000
Emp.: 6
Oil & Gas Exploration
N.A.I.C.S.: 213112
John Iles *(Pres)*

LOUISIANA HEALTH PLAN
PO Box 83880, Baton Rouge, LA 70884-3880
Tel.: (225) 926-6245   LA
Web Site: http://www.lahealthplan.org
Year Founded: 1992
Sales Range: $10-24.9 Million
Emp.: 10
Health & Welfare Services
N.A.I.C.S.: 525120
William Dimattia *(Treas & Sec)*
Phyllis Perron *(Vice Chm)*
Scott Westbrook *(Chm)*

LOUISIANA HEALTH SERVICE & INDEMNITY COMPANY, INC.
5525 Reitz Ave, Baton Rouge, LA 70809-3802
Tel.: (225) 295-3307
Web Site: http://www.bcbsla.com
Year Founded: 1975
Sales Range: $50-74.9 Million
Emp.: 1,700
Hospital & Medical Service Plans
N.A.I.C.S.: 524114
Dan Borne *(Chm)*
I. Steven Udvarhelyi *(Pres & CEO)*
Judy P. Miller *(Sec)*
J. Kevin McCotter *(Co-Chm)*
Michael Tipton *(Pres)*
Sheldon Faulk *(Sr VP-Govt Bus Div)*
Stephanie Mills *(Chief Medical Officer & Exec VP-Health Svcs)*

Subsidiaries:

HMO of Louisiana, Inc. (1)
5525 Reitz Ave, Baton Rouge, LA 70809-3802   (100%)
Tel.: (225) 295-3307
Web Site: http://www.bcbsla.com
Rev.: $23,197,000

Emp.: 1,500
Hospital & Medical Service Plans
N.A.I.C.S.: 524114
Lin Broussard *(Mgr-HR)*

Southern National Life Insurance Company Inc. (1)
PO Box 98044, Baton Rouge, LA 70898
Tel.: (225) 295-2525
Rev.: $5,465,063
Emp.: 1,500
Life Insurance
N.A.I.C.S.: 524113

LOUISIANA HOME BUILDERS ASSOCIATION
660 Laurel St Ste A, Baton Rouge, LA 70802
Tel.: (225) 387-2714
Web Site: http://www.lhba.org
Workers' Compensation Insurance Services
N.A.I.C.S.: 524126
Conrad Blanchard *(First VP)*
Jim Fine *(Pres)*
Nick Castjohn *(Treas & Second VP)*
April Becquet *(Assoc VP)*
Jeannie Dodd *(Exec VP)*
Monica Walker *(Co-Sec)*
Curtis M. Loftin *(Co-Sec & Third VP)*

LOUISIANA LIFT & EQUIPMENT INC.
6847 Greenwood Rd, Shreveport, LA 71119-8310
Tel.: (318) 631-5100   LA
Web Site: http://www.lalift.com
Year Founded: 1980
Sales Range: $10-24.9 Million
Emp.: 200
Repair Services Sales & Service for Lifts
N.A.I.C.S.: 811210
Larry Tate *(Pres & CEO)*
Terry McClure *(Mgr-Acctg)*

LOUISIANA MACHINERY COMPANY INC.
3799 W Airline Hwy, Reserve, LA 70084-5717
Tel.: (985) 536-1121   LA
Web Site:
  http://www.louisianacat.com
Year Founded: 1933
Sales Range: $25-49.9 Million
Emp.: 250
Agriculture & Marine; Industrial, Forestry Equipment & Engines
N.A.I.C.S.: 423810
Sarah Paola *(Mgr-Mktg)*
Clark G. Boyce Jr. *(Chm)*
Robert Webb Jr. *(Pres)*

LOUISIANA MEDIA COMPANY, LLC
5800 Airline Dr, Metairie, LA 70003
Tel.: (504) 733-0255
Year Founded: 2008
Holding Company
N.A.I.C.S.: 551102
Tom Benson *(Owner & Founder)*
Joe Cook *(Pres)*

LOUISIANA MEDICAL MUTUAL INSURANCE COMPANY
1 Galleria Blvd Ste 700, Metairie, LA 70001
Tel.: (504) 831-3756
Web Site: http://www.lammico.com
Year Founded: 1981
Sales Range: $10-24.9 Million
Emp.: 120
Liability Insurance
N.A.I.C.S.: 524126
Karen Nugent *(Div VP-Support Svcs)*
Cynthia Cox *(Dir-HR & Admin)*
Tom McCormick *(CFO)*

Louisiana Medical Mutual Insurance Company—(Continued)

Joan Winters Burmaster *(Gen Counsel)*
Shawn Paretti *(VP-Insurance Ops)*
Dawer Azizi *(Dir-Risk Mgmt & Patient Safety)*
Thomas H. Grimstad *(Pres & CEO)*
Kristi Verrette *(Co-CFO)*
Ross McBryde *(Dir-Claims)*
J. Michael Conerly *(Chm)*
William P. Coleman III *(Treas)*

Subsidiaries:

Lammico Insurance Agency Inc. (1)
1 Galleria Blvd Ste 700, Metairie, LA 70001
Tel.: (504) 837-3257
Web Site: http://www.lammico.com
Emp.: 100
Insurance Agents
N.A.I.C.S.: 524210
Karen Nugent *(Exec VP)*

LOUISIANA ORGAN PROCUREMENT AGENCY

3545 N I-10 Service Rd Ste 300, Metairie, LA 70002
Tel.: (504) 837-3355   LA
Web Site: http://www.lopa.org
Year Founded: 1987
Sales Range: $10-24.9 Million
Emp.: 154
Organ & Tissue Donation Services
N.A.I.C.S.: 621991
Kelly Ranum *(CEO)*
Joey Boudreaux *(Chief Clinical Officer)*
Chrissy Hagan *(Chief Admin Officer)*
Michelle Cavett *(Dir-Quality)*
Michelle Duvernay *(Dir-Clinical Excellence)*
Kyle Hagan *(COO)*
Cheryl D. Puckett *(Dir-Comm Center)*
Kirsten Heintz *(Dir-PR & Education)*
Michele Szegfu *(Mgr-Fin)*
Tina Madere *(Mgr-Tissue Recovery)*
Tiffany Haydel *(Dir-Clinical Ops)*
Max Prather *(Dir-IT)*
Terria Alexander *(Mgr-Family Advocate)*
Stacy Landry *(Mgr-Human Sys)*

LOUISIANA PUBLIC HEALTH INSTITUTE

1515 Poydras St Ste 1200, New Orleans, LA 70112
Tel.: (504) 301-9800   LA
Web Site: http://www.lphi.org
Year Founded: 1997
Sales Range: $10-24.9 Million
Emp.: 129
Public Health Care Services
N.A.I.C.S.: 622110
Joseph D. Kimbrell *(Co-CEO)*
Daniel Cocran *(CFO)*
Kristie Bardell *(Mgr-Comm & Outreach)*
Gordon Wadge *(Chm)*
Robert Moerland *(CIO)*
Tiffany Scuderi *(Assoc Dir-Comm)*
Sarah Gillen *(COO)*

LOUISIANA QUARTER HORSE BREEDERS ASSOCIATION

105 Carlyon Ln, Alexandria, LA 71303-7783
Tel.: (318) 487-9506   LA
Web Site: http://www.lqhba.com
Year Founded: 1966
Sales Range: $10-24.9 Million
Emp.: 6
Horse Breeding Services
N.A.I.C.S.: 112920
Leverne Perry *(Exec Dir)*
Sonya Melder *(Office Mgr-Futurity Nominations)*
Tony Patterson *(Exec Dir)*

LOUISIANA RICE MILL, LLC.

405 N Parkerson Ave, Crowley, LA 70527
Tel.: (337) 783-9777
Web Site: http://www.laricemill.com
Sales Range: $10-24.9 Million
Emp.: 100
Rice Milling Services
N.A.I.C.S.: 311212
Hanks Bobby *(Pres)*
Cart Janice *(Mgr-Safety)*
Brady Jones *(Mgr)*
Corey Robichaux *(Supvr-Maintenance)*
John Morgan *(VP)*

LOUISIANA TELEVISION BROADCASTING CORPORATION

1650 Highland Rd, Baton Rouge, LA 70802
Tel.: (225) 387-2222
Web Site: http://www.wbrz.com
Year Founded: 1955
Sales Range: $10-24.9 Million
Emp.: 150
Television Broadcasting Station
N.A.I.C.S.: 516120
Jennifer Darted *(Dir-HR)*

LOUISIANA THOROUGHBRED BREEDERS ASSOCIATION

1751 Gentilly Blvd, New Orleans, LA 70119
Tel.: (504) 947-4676   LA
Web Site: http://www.louisianabred.com
Year Founded: 1961
Sales Range: $10-24.9 Million
Emp.: 13
Horse Breeder Association
N.A.I.C.S.: 813910
Therese Arroyo *(Accountant)*
Roger Heitzmann III *(Treas & Sec)*

LOUISIANA WORKERS COMPENSATION CORP.

2237 S Acadian Trwy, Baton Rouge, LA 70808
Tel.: (225) 924-7788
Web Site: http://www.lwcc.com
Rev.: $89,248,370
Emp.: 340
Workers Compensation Insurance
N.A.I.C.S.: 524126
James N. Hall *(Chm)*
Angele Davis *(Sec)*
Byron Craig Thomson *(Vice Chm)*
Kappie Mumphrey *(CIO)*
Gary Sanders *(VP)*
Seth Irby *(Chief Mktg & Customer Experience Officer)*

LOUISVILLE & JEFFERSON COUNTY METROPOLITAN SEWER DISTRICT

700 W Liberty St, Louisville, KY 40203-1911
Tel.: (502) 540-6000   KY
Web Site: http://www.msdlouky.org
Year Founded: 1946
Sales Range: $75-99.9 Million
Emp.: 630
Storm Water & Waste Water Control
N.A.I.C.S.: 221320
Rene Thomas *(Mgr-Pur)*
Lynne Fleming *(Dir-HR)*
Daymond Talley *(Engr-Regulatory)*
Julie Blanford *(Supvr-Customer Rels)*
Rickie Jackson *(Supvr-Process-Electrical)*

LOUISVILLE BEDDING COMPANY

10400 Bunsen Way, Louisville, KY 40299
Tel.: (502) 491-3370   KY
Web Site: http://www.loubed.com
Year Founded: 1889
Sales Range: $400-449.9 Million
Emp.: 1,000
Mattress Pads, Dust Ruffles, Tablecloths, Napkins, Placemats & Bed Pillows Mfr
N.A.I.C.S.: 314120
Mike Seago *(VP-Pur)*
Steve Elias *(Pres & CEO)*
Robin Owens *(CFO)*
Teri Johnson *(Controller)*

LOUISVILLE ORCHESTRA, INC.

323 W Broadway Ste 700, Louisville, KY 40202
Tel.: (502) 587-8681
Web Site: http://www.louisvilleorchestra.org
Year Founded: 1937
Sales Range: $10-24.9 Million
Emp.: 100
Symphony Orchestra
N.A.I.C.S.: 711130
Tonya McSorley *(CFO)*
Carla Givan Motes *(Dir-Patron Svcs-Ticket Ops)*
Adrienne Hinkebein *(Mgr-Personnel)*
Bill Polk *(Mgr-Stage)*
Callie Chapman *(Mgr-Creative)*
Ed Schadt *(Dir-Planned Giving & Officer-Major gifts)*
Andrew Kipe *(Exec Dir)*
Deanna Hoying *(Dir-Education)*
Lindsay C. Vallandingham *(Gen Mgr)*
Michelle Winters *(Dir-Mktg)*
Nathaniel Koch *(Mgr-Dev)*
Leslie Antoniel *(Dir-Dev)*
Teddy Abrams *(Dir-Music)*
Robert Massey *(CEO)*
John Malloy *(Chm)*

LOUISVILLE TILE DISTRIBUTORS INC.

4520 Bishop Ln, Louisville, KY 40218-4508
Tel.: (502) 452-2037   KY
Web Site: http://www.louisville-tile.com
Year Founded: 1955
Sales Range: $10-24.9 Million
Emp.: 125
Provider of Tile Distribution Services
N.A.I.C.S.: 423320
Bob Knabel *(CFO)*
Robert De Angles *(Pres)*
Al Williams *(Mgr-Comml Sls)*
Lisa Gutting *(Coord-Mktg)*
Morgan Tiemann *(CMO)*
Matthew Saltzman *(CEO)*
Robbie Barajas *(VP-Logistics)*

Subsidiaries:

Mid-America Tile, Inc. (1)
1650 Howard St, Elk Grove Village, IL 60007-2217
Tel.: (847) 439-3110
Web Site: http://www.midamericatile.com
Sales Range: $10-24.9 Million
Emp.: 15
Flooring Whslr & Distr
N.A.I.C.S.: 423320
Thomas J. Kotel *(Pres)*

LOUISVILLE WATER CO. INC.

550 S 3rd St, Louisville, KY 40202-1839
Tel.: (502) 569-3600
Web Site: http://www.louisvillewater.com
Year Founded: 1860
Sales Range: $75-99.9 Million
Emp.: 450
Water Supply
N.A.I.C.S.: 921110

LOUNORA INDUSTRIES INC.

1402 Waterworks Rd, Columbus, MS 39701
Tel.: (662) 328-1685   DE
Web Site: http://www.jtbfurniture.com
Year Founded: 1982
Holding Company; Wooden Household & Hotel Furniture Mfr
N.A.I.C.S.: 551112
Reau Berry *(Owner)*

Subsidiaries:

Johnston-Tombigbee Furniture Mfg. Co. (1)
1402 Waterworks Rd, Columbus, MS 39701
Tel.: (662) 328-1685
Web Site: http://www.jtbfurniture.com
Wood Household Furniture
N.A.I.C.S.: 337122
Reau Berry *(Owner)*

LOUP RIVER PUBLIC POWER DISTRICT

2404 15th St, Columbus, NE 68601-5021
Tel.: (402) 564-3171
Web Site: http://www.loup.com
Year Founded: 1933
Sales Range: $25-49.9 Million
Emp.: 126
Electronic Services
N.A.I.C.S.: 221118
David Bell *(VP-Dev & Mktg)*
Ron Ziola *(VP-Engrg)*
Neal Suess *(Pres & CEO)*

LOURD CAPITAL LLC

9777 Wilshire Blvd Ste 1018, Beverly Hills, CA 90212
Tel.: (310) 300-9898
Web Site: http://www.lourdmurray.com
Investment Advisory Services
N.A.I.C.S.: 523940
Blaine Lourd *(Founder & CEO)*

Subsidiaries:

Delphi Private Advisors (1)
3611 Valley Ctr Dr Ste 125, San Diego, CA 92130
Tel.: (858) 222-8050
Web Site: http://www.delphiprivate.com
Health Management Consulting Services
N.A.I.C.S.: 541618
Marc Channick *(Co-Founder & Partner)*
Darren Reinig *(Co-Founder & Partner)*
Keith McKenzie *(Co-Founder & Partner)*
Gary Hirschfeld *(Dir-Firm Admin & Chief Compliance Officer)*

LOURDES INDUSTRIES INC.

65 Hoffman Ave, Hauppauge, NY 11788
Tel.: (631) 234-6600
Web Site: http://www.lourdesinc.com
Sales Range: $10-24.9 Million
Emp.: 50
Aircraft Parts & Equipment
N.A.I.C.S.: 332912
William Jakobsen *(Pres)*

LOURDES-NOREEN MCKEEN RESIDENCE

315 S Flagler Dr, West Palm Beach, FL 33401
Tel.: (561) 655-8544   FL
Web Site: http://www.lnmr.org
Year Founded: 1962
Sales Range: $10-24.9 Million
Emp.: 327
Lifecare Retirement Community Operator
N.A.I.C.S.: 623311
Thomas Peterson *(Dir-Fin)*

COMPANIES

LOUREIRO ENGINEERING ASSOCIATES INC.
100 Northwest Dr, Plainville, CT 06062-1559
Tel.: (860) 747-6181
Web Site: http://www.loureiro.com
Engineeering Services
N.A.I.C.S.: 541330
Jeffrey J. Loureiro *(CEO)*
Brian A. Cutler *(Pres)*
George F. Andrews Jr. *(VP)*

LOVE ADVERTISING INC.
770 S Post Oak Ln Ste 101, Houston, TX 77056-1913
Tel.: (713) 552-1055
Web Site: http://www.loveadv.com
Year Founded: 1979
Rev.: $33,000,000
Emp.: 30
N.A.I.C.S.: 541810
Brenda Love *(Pres)*
Billie Van Slyke *(Exec VP & Dir-Creative)*
Jessica Manning *(VP-PR)*
Sandi Hemmeline *(Office Mgr & Mgr-Fin)*
Shannon Moss *(Sr VP)*
Mark Miller *(VP-Media Svcs)*

LOVE BOTTLING CO.
3200 S 24th St W, Muskogee, OK 74401
Tel.: (918) 682-3434   OK
Web Site: http://www.lvbeverages.com
Year Founded: 1919
Sales Range: $10-24.9 Million
Emp.: 100
Soft Drink Bottler; Non-Alcoholic Beverage & Snack Distr
N.A.I.C.S.: 312111
Kendall Baglin *(Acct Mgr)*
Andy Sanchez *(Mgr-Vending)*

LOVE BUICK GMC, INC.
736 Saturn Pkwy, Columbia, SC 29212
Tel.: (803) 732-6500   SC
Web Site: http://www.lovebuickgmc.com
Rev.: $30,989,884
Emp.: 60
New & Used Car Dealer
N.A.I.C.S.: 441110
Michael Love *(Pres)*
Rhea Preston *(Dir-Fixed Ops)*

LOVE CHEVROLET COMPANY
100 Parkridge Dr, Columbia, SC 29212
Tel.: (803) 794-9000
Web Site: http://www.loveautoteam.com
Sales Range: $75-99.9 Million
Emp.: 200
Automobiles, New & Used
N.A.I.C.S.: 441110
Steve Hyatt *(Treas, Sec & VP)*
Michael Love *(Pres)*
Nathan J. Love *(Chm)*

LOVE REAL ESTATE COMPANY
212 S Central Ave, Saint Louis, MO 63105
Tel.: (314) 512-8711   MO
Web Site: http://www.thelovecompanies.com
Year Founded: 1905
Holding Company; Commercial Banking, Mortgage Banking, Leasing, Real Estate Development & Property Management Services
N.A.I.C.S.: 551112
Laurence A. Schiffer *(Principal)*
Andrew S. Love Jr. *(Chm)*

Subsidiaries:

Allegro Senior Living, LLC (1)
212 S Central Ave Ste 301, Saint Louis, MO 63105
Tel.: (314) 512-8511
Web Site: http://www.allegroliving.com
Continuing Care Retirement Community Services
N.A.I.C.S.: 623311
Laurence A. Schiffer *(Chm & CEO)*
Robert B. Karn *(CFO & Exec VP)*
Douglas S. Schiffer *(Pres & COO)*
Joe Ruggeri *(Pres & Dir-Ops)*
Nic Scheibel *(Exec Dir-Community)*
Peter Cowley *(Exec Dir-Fort Lauderdale)*

Love Hotel Management Company (1)
1050 Crown Pointe Pkwy Ste 960, Atlanta, GA 30338
Tel.: (770) 551-5683
Web Site: http://www.lovehotelmgmt.com
Hotel Property Management Services
N.A.I.C.S.: 531312
Laurence A. Schiffer *(CEO)*
Joseph Ruggeri *(Pres)*
Peter Schiffer *(Sr VP-Bus Dev)*
Gloria Clement *(Sr VP-Fin)*
Joseph Kenkel *(VP-Construction & Dev)*
Chris DeCosty *(Dir-Revenue)*
Kathy Meyer *(VP-HR)*

Love Management Company, LLC (1)
212 S Central Ave Ste 301, Saint Louis, MO 63105
Tel.: (314) 512-8703
Web Site: http://www.lovemgmt.com
Commercial Real Estate Leasing, Brokerage & Property Management Services
N.A.I.C.S.: 531390
Cheryl Colatruglio *(Mgr-Comml Property)*
Mike Evans *(Dir-Maintenance)*

LOVE'S TRAVEL STOPS & COUNTRY STORES, INC.
10601 N Pennsylvania Ave, Oklahoma City, OK 73120-4108
Web Site: https://www.loves.com
Year Founded: 1964
Sales Range: Less than $1 Million
Emp.: 40,000
Other Gasoline Stations
N.A.I.C.S.: 457120
Shane Wharton *(Pres)*
Jenny Love Meyer *(Chief Culture Officer & Exec VP)*

Subsidiaries:

Gemini Motor Transport, LP (1)
10601 N Pennsylvania Ave, Oklahoma City, OK 73120
Tel.: (405) 302-6718
Web Site: http://www.loves.com
Emp.: 725
Fuel, Crude & Specialty Products Transport
N.A.I.C.S.: 484230

Musket Corporation (1)
111 Bagby St, Houston, TX 77019
Tel.: (713) 332-5726
Web Site: http://www.musketcorp.com
Emp.: 120
Petroleum Commodity Supply, Trading & Logistics Services
N.A.I.C.S.: 541614
J. P. Fjeld-Hansen *(Mng Dir & VP)*
Kris Greenwood *(Sr Mgr-Trade Reporting & Logistics)*

Speedco Inc. (1)
200 4th Ave S, Nashville, TN 37201
Web Site: http://www.loves.com
Lubrication & Tire Services
N.A.I.C.S.: 811191
Mark Clark *(Co-Founder)*
Jim Dudley *(VP)*

Trillium Transportation Fuels, LLC (1)
10601 N Pennsylvania Ave, Oklahoma City, OK 73120

Tel.: (800) 920-1166
Web Site: http://www.loves.com
Petroleum Product Merchant Whslr
N.A.I.C.S.: 424710
Carson Hoyt *(Gen Mgr-Design & Build Svcs)*

LOVEBUG NUTRITION INC.
115 E 34th St Ste 1506, New York, NY 10156
Tel.: (929) 260-2893
Web Site: http://www.lovebugprobiotics.com
Year Founded: 2015
Sales Range: $1-9.9 Million
Emp.: 11
Health Supplements Distr
N.A.I.C.S.: 456191
Ashley Harris *(Co-Founder & CEO)*
Ben Harris *(Co-Founder)*

LOVECE HOLDING INC.
One Radisson Plz 9th Fl, New Rochelle, NY 10801
Tel.: (914) 235-7600
Rev.: $11,000,000
Emp.: 60
Holding Company; Provider of Bridge Construction Services
N.A.I.C.S.: 237310
David Dieter *(Treas & Sec)*
Joseph Lovece Jr. *(Pres)*

LOVEJOY INDUSTRIES INC.
194 S Main St, Versailles, KY 40383
Tel.: (859) 873-6828
Sales Range: $50-74.9 Million
Emp.: 3
Zinc & Zinc-Base Alloy Die-Castings
N.A.I.C.S.: 331523
Matthew A. Lovejoy *(Pres)*

LOVELACE RESPIRATORY RESEARCH INSTITUTE
2425 Ridgecrest Dr SE, Albuquerque, NM 87108
Tel.: (505) 348-9400
Web Site: http://www.lrri.org
Year Founded: 1947
Rev.: $71,099,115
Emp.: 664
Biomedical Research Organization
N.A.I.C.S.: 541715
David D. Griego *(Dir-Facilities)*
Penny H. Holeman *(Dir-Biosafety)*
Cheryl N. DeVaul *(Dir-HR)*
Joe L. Mauderly *(VP)*

LOVELL MINNICK PARTNERS LLC

LOVELL MINNICK PARTNERS LLC
215 Manhattan Beach Blvd 2nd Fl, Manhattan Beach, CA 90266
Tel.: (310) 414-6160   DE
Web Site: http://www.lmpartners.com
Year Founded: 1999
Privater Equity Firm
N.A.I.C.S.: 523999
Jeffrey Dale Lovell *(Co-Chm)*
Robert Myles Belke *(Mng Partner)*
Spencer P. Hoffman *(Partner)*
John D. Cochran *(Partner)*
W. Bradford Armstrong *(Partner)*
Trevor C. Rich *(Partner)*
Diane P. Satorius *(Treas)*
James Edward Minnick *(Co-Chm)*
Marji M. Hendler *(Head-Admin)*
Blaire A. Gupta *(Office Mgr)*
Jason S. Barg *(Partner)*
Irene Hong Edwards *(Partner)*
Steven Pierson *(Mng Partner)*
Roumi Zlateva *(Principal)*
Saurabh S. Desai *(Principal)*
Timothy D. Rampe *(Partner)*
Paul A. Mattson *(VP-Fin)*
Jenny Thapa *(VP)*

Jason Klein *(Principal)*
Lindsay Strait *(VP)*
Cody Isdaner *(Chief Compliance Officer)*

Subsidiaries:

Automated Payment Highway, Inc (1)
5435 Corporate Dr, Ste 300, Troy, MI 48098
Web Site: http://www.billhighway.com
Software Publisher
N.A.I.C.S.: 513210
Tom Bomberski *(CEO)*

CenterSquare Investment Management Holdings, Inc. (1)
630 W Germantown Pike Ste 300, Plymouth Meeting, PA 19462
Tel.: (610) 834-9500
Web Site: http://www.centresquare.com
Real Estate Management & Investment Services
N.A.I.C.S.: 531390
E. Todd Briddell *(CEO & Chief Investment Officer)*
Frank J. Ferro *(Gen Counsel)*
Dean Frankel *(Mng Dir & Head-Real Estate Securities)*
Joseph Law *(CFO & Chief Compliance Officer)*
Scott Maguire *(Mng Dir & Head-IR)*
David L. Rabin *(Mng Dir-Private Real Estate)*
Matthew Goulding *(Portfolio Mgr & Reg Mgr-Real Estate Securities)*
Scott Crowe *(Chief Investment Strategist)*
Debbi Flickinger *(COO)*
Tracy Steele *(Deputy Gen Counsel)*

Subsidiary (Domestic):

CenterSquare Investment Management, Inc. (2)
630 W Germantown Pike Ste 300, Plymouth Meeting, PA 19462
Tel.: (610) 834-9500
Web Site: http://www.centersquare.com
Investment Management Service
N.A.I.C.S.: 523940
E. Todd Briddell *(CEO & Chief Investment Officer)*
Scott Crowe *(Chief Investment Strategist)*
Joseph Law *(CFO & Chief Compliance Officer)*
Scott Maguire *(Mng Dir & Head-IR)*
Frank J. Ferro *(Gen Counsel)*
Debbie Flickinger *(COO)*
Kevin Maxwell *(Mng Dir & Head-Capital Markets)*
Tracey Steele *(Deputy Gen Counsel)*
Dean Frankel *(Mng Dir & Head-Real Estate Securities)*
Eric Rothman *(Portfolio Mgr-Real Estate Securities)*
David L. Rabin *(Mng Dir-Private Real Estate)*
Mark B. Greco *(Dir-Privare Real Estate)*
Jeffrey B. Reder *(Sr VP-Private Real Estate)*
Kerrisha Jenkins *(Dir-Capital Markets)*
Marcia Glass *(Dir-Capital Markets)*
Meghan Burke *(VP-IR)*

Charles Taylor Plc (1)
First Floor The Minister Building 21 Mincing Lane, London, EC3R 7AG, United Kingdom
Tel.: (44) 2033208888
Web Site: http://www.charlestaylor.com
Rev.: $4,071,833
Assets: $193,028,273
Liabilities: $1,501,844
Net Worth: $191,526,429
Earnings: $321,598
Fiscal Year-end: 12/31/2019
Insurance, Consulting & Management Services
N.A.I.C.S.: 524298
Ivan Keane *(Gen Counsel & Sec)*
Jeremy Grose *(CEO-Mgmt Svcs-UK & Intl)*
Ryan Smith *(Dir-Liability Claims-Charles Taylor Adjusting)*
Andrew Cripps *(Dir-Aviation-Charles Taylor Adjusting)*
Andrew Paton *(Dir-Marine-Charles Taylor Adjusting)*
Andrew Jackson *(Dir-Technical & Special Risks-Charles Taylor Adjusting)*

LOVELL MINNICK PARTNERS LLC

Lovell Minnick Partners LLC—(Continued)
Gordon Whyte *(Dir-RHL-Glasgow)*
Richard Cornah *(Chm-RHL)*
Edward Creasy *(Chm)*
Robert McParlin *(Mng Dir-Aviation)*
Richard Radevsky *(Dir-Charles Taylor Tech)*
Doug Jones *(CEO-Investment Mgmt)*
Jason Sahota *(CIO)*
Carlos Romeu *(Mng Dir-Insurance Tech LatAm)*
Tony Russell *(Dir-Sls & Accts Mgmt-InsureTech)*
Damian Ely *(CEO-Adjusting Svcs)*
Richard Yerbury *(Grp COO)*
Paul Trent *(CFO-Charles Taylor Svcs)*
Richard Wood *(Pres & CEO-Mgmt Svcs-Americas)*
Suzanne Deery *(Dir-HR)*
Robert Davison *(Sec)*
Alastair Hardie *(CEO-CEGA)*
Jeff Nakadate *(Mgr-Claims-Charles Claims Svcs-Long Beach-USA)*
Rob Brown *(Grp CEO)*
Alison Black *(Chief People Officer)*

Subsidiary (US):

Aasgard Summit Management Services Inc. (2)
4017 13th Ave W, Seattle, WA 98119-1350
Tel.: (206) 284-0475
Web Site: http://www.aasgardsummit.net
Administrative Management & General Management Consulting Services
N.A.I.C.S.: 541611
Steve Kennebeck *(Pres)*
Ken Madland *(VP)*
Michelle Almanza *(Dir-Ops)*

Aegis Corp. (2)
18550 W Capitol Dr, Brookfield, WI 53045
Tel.: (262) 781-7020
Web Site: http://www.aegis-corporation.com
Sales Range: $1-9.9 Million
Emp.: 40
Insurance Agencies & Brokerages
N.A.I.C.S.: 524210
John Dirkse *(Pres)*

Bowditch Marine, Inc. (2)
5350 30th Ave NW Ste A, Seattle, WA 98107
Tel.: (206) 838-7300
Web Site: http://www.bowditchmarine.net
Insurance Management Services
N.A.I.C.S.: 524292

Subsidiary (Non-US):

CTC Services (Malaysia) SDN Bhd (2)
509 5 Fl Menara Mutiara Majestic 15 Jalan Othman, 46200, Petaling Jaya, Selangor, Malaysia
Tel.: (60) 377812260
Web Site: http://www.ctplc.com
Sales Range: $25-49.9 Million
Emp.: 2
Marine Surveying Services
N.A.I.C.S.: 488390

Subsidiary (Domestic):

Charles Taylor & Co Ltd
Standard House 12-13 Essex Street, London, WC2R 3AA, United Kingdom
Tel.: (44) 2074883494
Web Site:
http://www.charlestaylorconsulting.com
Sales Range: $100-124.9 Million
Emp.: 200
Employee Benefit Services
N.A.I.C.S.: 525110

Subsidiary (Non-US):

Charles Taylor (Hamilton) Ltd (2)
PO Box HM1743, Hamilton, HMGX, Bermuda (100%)
Tel.: (441) 292.9157
Sales Range: $25-49.9 Million
Emp.: 11
Other Management Consulting Services
N.A.I.C.S.: 541618
John Rowe *(CEO)*

Charles Taylor (Japan) Limited (2)
6th Floor Takebashi Bldg 2-1-8 Kanda Nishiki-cho, Chiyoda-ku, Tokyo, 101-0054, Japan
Tel.: (81) 335189601
Insurance Management Services
N.A.I.C.S.: 524292

Charles Taylor Adjusting (Australia) Pty Ltd (2)
Ground Fl 1 Havelock St, Perth, 6005, WA, Australia
Tel.: (61) 893212022
Web Site:
http://www.charlestayloradj.com.au
Insurance Claims Adjusting Services
N.A.I.C.S.: 524291

Subsidiary (Domestic):

Charles Taylor Adjusting Limited (2)
88 Leadenhall Street, London, EC3A 3BA, United Kingdom
Tel.: (44) 2076231819
Web Site: http://www.charlestayloradj.com
Sales Range: $100-124.9 Million
Emp.: 200
General Insurance Services
N.A.I.C.S.: 524210
Mike McMahon *(Deputy Mng Dir-Natural Resources)*
Damian Ely *(CEO)*
Vince Cole *(CEO/Head-US)*
Oliver Hutchings *(Mng Dir-Marine-Europe & Singapore)*

Subsidiary (Domestic):

Charles Taylor Aviation (Asset Management) Limited. (3)
Second Floor Office Suite New House Market Place, Ringwood, PH24 1EN, Hampshire, United Kingdom
Tel.: (44) 1725 511144
Web Site: http://www.ctaam.com
Sales Range: $25-49.9 Million
Emp.: 8
Aviation Consulting Services
N.A.I.C.S.: 541618

Subsidiary (Non-US):

Charles Taylor Adjusting SARL (2)
142 Rue de Rivoli, 75001, Paris, France
Tel.: (33) 153430030
Insurance Management Services
N.A.I.C.S.: 524292

Subsidiary (Domestic):

Charles Taylor Administration Services Limited (2)
5th Floor Cathedral Buildings Dean Street, Newcastle upon Tyne, NE1 1PG, Tyne and Wear, United Kingdom
Tel.: (44) 1912322745
Emp.: 5
Secretarial Services
N.A.I.C.S.: 561410
Susan Green *(Mng Dir)*

Subsidiary (Non-US):

Charles Taylor Consulting (Australia) Pty Ltd (2)
1 Havelock St, Perth, 6005, WA, Australia
Tel.: (61) 893212022
Web Site: http://www.cttlc.com
Emp.: 10
General Insurance Services
N.A.I.C.S.: 524210

Charles Taylor Consulting (Canada) Inc (2)
Ste 1010 250 6th Ave SW, Calgary, T2P 3H7, AB, Canada
Tel.: (403) 266-3336
Web Site:
http://www.charlestaylorconsulting.com
Sales Range: $50-74.9 Million
Emp.: 25
Insurance Management Consulting Services
N.A.I.C.S.: 524298

Charles Taylor Consulting (Japan) Limited (2)
2-10-12 Kandatsukasamachi Park Side 7 Building 3f, Chiyoda-Ku, Tokyo, 101-0048, Japan
Tel.: (81) 332558640
Web Site: http://www.rhlg.com
General Insurance Services
N.A.I.C.S.: 524210
Subsidiary (Domestic):

Charles Taylor Insurance Services Limited (2)
Lloyds Chambers 1 Portsoken Street, London, E1 8BT, United Kingdom
Tel.: (44) 2077672700
Web Site:
http://www.ctinsuranceservices.co.uk
General Insurance Services
N.A.I.C.S.: 524210
Luisa Barile *(CEO)*

Charles Taylor Investment Management Company Limited (2)
Standard House 12-13 Essex St, London, WC2R 3AA, United Kingdom
Tel.: (44) 20 7488 3494
Web Site:
http://www.charlestaylorconsulting.com
Sales Range: $100-124.9 Million
Emp.: 200
Investment Management Service
N.A.I.C.S.: 523999

Subsidiary (US):

Charles Taylor P&I Management (Americas) Inc. (2)
75 Broad St Ste 2505, New York, NY 10004
Tel.: (212) 809-8085
Insurance Management Services
N.A.I.C.S.: 524292

Subsidiary (Non-US):

Charles Taylor RSLAC Inc. (2)
Twist Tower- Oficina 22B Calle 54 Este Y Samuel Lewis Obarrio, Panama, Panama
Tel.: (507) 3887037
Insurance Management Services
N.A.I.C.S.: 524292

Subsidiary (Domestic):

Criterion Adjusters Limited (2)
River House Broadford Business Park, Shalford, Guildford, GU4 8EP, Surrey, United Kingdom
Tel.: (44) 1483891999
Web Site: http://www.criterionadjusters.com
Insurance Management Services
N.A.I.C.S.: 524292

Criterion Surveyors Limited (2)
Suite 3 River House Broadford Business Park, Shalford, Guildford, GU4 8EP, Surrey, United Kingdom
Tel.: (44) 1483891999
Web Site: http://www.criterionsurveyors.com
Insurance Management Services
N.A.I.C.S.: 524292

Subsidiary (Non-US):

FGR Hanna Limitada (2)
Hendaya 60 office 302, Santiago, Chile
Tel.: (56) 27903100
Web Site: http://www.fgrhanna.cl
Insurance Management Services
N.A.I.C.S.: 524292

Subsidiary (Domestic):

LCL Acquisitions Limited (2)
Lloyds Chambers 1 Portsoken Street, London, E1 8BT, United Kingdom
Tel.: (44) 20 7767 2700
Web Site: http://www.lcl-group.com
Reinsurance Services
N.A.I.C.S.: 524130
Anson Game *(Dir-Claims)*

Subsidiary (Non-US):

LCL Group Limited (2)
Lloyds Chambers 1 Portsoken St, E1 8BT, London, United Kingdom - England (100%)
Tel.: (44) 2077672700
Web Site: http://www.lcl-group.com
Sales Range: $50-74.9 Million
Emp.: 8
Reinsurance Carriers
N.A.I.C.S.: 524130
Anson Game *(Gen Mgr)*

LCL Services (IOM) Limited (2)
St Georges Court Upper Church Street, Douglas, IM1 1EE, Isle of Man
Tel.: (44) 1624683699
Web Site: http://www.lcl.co.im
Sales Range: $50-74.9 Million
Emp.: 35
General Insurance Services
N.A.I.C.S.: 524210
Jeffrey More *(CEO)*

LCL Services (Ireland) Limited (2)
10 Herbert Street, Dublin, 2, Ireland
Tel.: (353) 1 6766620
Web Site: http://www.lcl-group.ie
Sales Range: $50-74.9 Million
Emp.: 2
General Insurance Services
N.A.I.C.S.: 524210

Overseas Adjusters and Surveyors Co (2)
1205-7 12 F 237 Fu Hsing South Road Section 2, Taipei, 106, Taiwan
Tel.: (886) 2 2706 6509
Marine Consulting Services
N.A.I.C.S.: 541618

PT Radita Hutama Internusa (2)
Kawasan Niaga dan Hunian Terpadu Sudirman JL Jend Sudirman Kav 52-53, Jakarta, 12190, Indonesia
Tel.: (62) 215152084
Sales Range: $50-74.9 Million
Emp.: 40
General Insurance Services
N.A.I.C.S.: 524210
Guntur Tampubolon *(Mng Dir)*

Richard Hoggs Lindley (Hellas) Greece Limited (2)
85 Akti Miaouli, Piraeus, 18538, Greece
Tel.: (30) 2104291870
Insurance Management Services
N.A.I.C.S.: 524292

Richard Hoggs Lindley (India) Limited (2)
1007 10th Floor Maker Chambers V 221 Nariman Point, Mumbai, 400 021, India
Tel.: (91) 2222835851
Insurance Management Services
N.A.I.C.S.: 524292

Richards Hogg Lindley (Hellas) Ltd. (2)
85 Akti Miaouli, 185 38, Piraeus, Greece
Tel.: (30) 210 4291 300
Web Site: http://www.rhlg.com
Sales Range: $50-74.9 Million
Emp.: 5
Marine Insurance Services
N.A.I.C.S.: 524298

Richards Hogg Lindley (India) Ltd (2)
319 Maker Chambers V 221 Nariman Point, Mumbai, 400021, Maharashtra, India
Tel.: (91) 22 2283 5851
Web Site: http://www.rhlg.com
Sales Range: $50-74.9 Million
Emp.: 2
General Insurance Services
N.A.I.C.S.: 524210
Alex Pinto *(Mgr)*

Subsidiary (US):

SBSA, Inc. (2)
5926 McIntyre St, Golden, CO 80403-7445
Web Site: http://www.callsbsa.com
Engineeering Services
N.A.I.C.S.: 541330
Edward Fronpfel *(Owner)*

Subsidiary (Domestic):

The Richards Hogg Lindley Group Limited (2)
88 Leadenhall Stewwt, London, EC3A 3BA, United Kingdom (100%)
Tel.: (44) 2076231819
Web Site: http://www.ctplc.com
Sales Range: $100-124.9 Million
Emp.: 150
Claims Adjusting
N.A.I.C.S.: 524291

Consolidated Information Services Solutions, LLC (1)
370 Reed Rd Ste 100, Broomall, PA 19008
Tel.: (888) 212-4200

COMPANIES / LOVEMAN STEEL CORPORATION

Web Site: http://universalcis.com
Financial Services
N.A.I.C.S.: 522320
Perry Steiner *(Chm)*
Jerry Haftmann *(CEO)*
Robert Dumont *(CFO)*
Jayne Kelly *(Chief Integrations Officer)*
Michael Delaporta *(CTO)*
Bill Merryman *(Pres)*
Andrew Gladston Andrew Gladston *(Exec VP-Corp Dev & Strategy)*
Julie Davis Wink *(Exec VP)*

Subsidiary (Domestic):

Credit Plus Inc. (2)
3810 E Pikes Peak Ave, Colorado Springs, CO 80909-6717
Web Site: http://www.creditplus.com
Credit Bureaus
N.A.I.C.S.: 561450
Debbie Atencio *(Mgr)*

Global Financial & Credit, LLC (1)
100 1st Ave N, Great Falls, MT 59401
Tel.: (406) 761-7743
Web Site: http://www.globalmontana.com
Rev.: $1,200,000
Emp.: 13
Real Estate Credit
N.A.I.C.S.: 522292

Subsidiary (Domestic):

Omni Healthcare Inc. (2)
1344 S Apollo Blvd Ste 303, Melbourne, FL 32901
Tel.: (321) 777-7888
Web Site: http://www.omnihealthcare.com
Sales Range: $300-349.9 Million
Emp.: 100
Office Of Physician
N.A.I.C.S.: 621111
Craig Deligdish *(VP)*
Salina Vanderpool *(Mgr)*
Mark Bobango *(Dir-Fin)*

Held Enloe & Associates, LLC (1)
1140 Connecticut Ave NW Ste 609, Washington, DC 20036-4012
Tel.: (202) 822-4620
Web Site: http://www.heldenloe.com
Construction Consulting Services
N.A.I.C.S.: 237990
Lisa Enloe *(Principal)*

London & Capital Group Ltd. (1)
Two Fitzroy Place 8 Mortimer Street London,, London, W1T 3JJ, United Kingdom
Tel.: (44) 2073963200
Web Site: https://www.londonandcapital.com
Wealth Management Services
N.A.I.C.S.: 541618

National Auto Care Corporation (1)
208 Ponte Vedra Park Dr, Ponte Vedra Beach, FL 32082
Web Site: http://www.nationalautocare.com
Automotive Care Services
N.A.I.C.S.: 811198
Tony Wanderon *(CEO)*
Christina Schrank *(COO)*
Courtney Wanderon *(VP-Sls & Client Rels)*
Deby Burgi *(Gen Counsel & VP-Legal & Compliance)*

Subsidiary (Domestic):

Pritchard Insurance Inc. (2)
8701 271st St NW, Stanwood, WA 98292
Tel.: (360) 629-4852
Web Site: http://www.pritchardinsurance.com
Insurance Agencies & Brokerages
N.A.I.C.S.: 524210
David Pritchard *(VP)*
Greg Welch *(Pres)*

Pathstone Family Office, LLC
10 Sterling Blvd Ste 402, Englewood, NJ 07631
Tel.: (201) 944-7284
Web Site: http://www.pathstone.com
Investment Consulting & Wealth Management Services
N.A.I.C.S.: 523940
Steve Braverman *(Co-CEO)*
Allan Zachariah *(Co-CEO)*
Matthew Fleissig *(Pres & Partner)*
Matthew Sher *(CTO & Chief Procurement Officer)*

Amy Blitzer *(Dir-Acctg & Fin Reporting)*
Joe Balducci *(Partner)*
Stacy Rush *(Dir Gen)*
Allison Kaplan *(Mng Dir)*
Charles M. A. Winn *(Mng Dir)*
Dan Gross *(Mng Dir)*
David Kahn *(Mng Dir)*
Gabriel Decker *(Mng Dir)*
Janet Mertz *(Mng Dir)*
John Elmes *(Mng Dir)*
John Workman *(Mng Dir)*
Kelly Maregni *(Mng Dir)*
Mark Peters *(Mng Dir)*
Mike Slud *(Mng Dir)*
Paul Gloth *(Mng Dir)*
Sheila Stinson *(Mng Dir)*
John R. LaPann Jr. *(Chm)*
Charles A. Walsh III *(Mng Dir)*

Subsidiary (Domestic):

Cornerstone Advisors, Inc. (2)
10885 NE 4th St Ste 1400, Bellevue, WA 98004
Tel.: (425) 646-7600
Web Site: http://www.buildbeyond.com
Management Consulting Services
N.A.I.C.S.: 541611
Ken Hart *(CEO)*

Co-Headquarters (Domestic):

Federal Street Advisors, Inc. (2)
24 Federal St, Boston, MA 02110
Tel.: (617) 350-8999
Web Site: http://www.federalstreet.com
Investment Consulting & Wealth Management Services
N.A.I.C.S.: 523940
Kristin Slusser Fafard *(Chief Investment Officer)*
Richard M. Tardiff *(Gen Counsel)*
Eric Godes *(Co-COO)*
Jennifer Christian Murtie *(Co-COO & CMO)*
Kelly Maregni *(Mng Dir)*
John R. LaPann Jr. *(Founder & Chm)*

Subsidiary (Domestic):

Hall Capital Partners LLC (2)
1 Maritime Plz, San Francisco, CA 94111
Tel.: (415) 288-0544
Web Site: http://www.hallcapital.com
Rev.: $7,700,000
Emp.: 55
Portfolio Management
N.A.I.C.S.: 523940
Craig Summers *(Controller)*
David Schofield *(Mng Dir)*

Tortoise Investments, LLC (1)
5100 W 115th Pl, Leawood, KS 66211
Tel.: (913) 981-1020
Web Site: http://www.tortoiseadvisors.com
Rev.: $21,300,000,000
Emp.: 207
Holding Company; Investment Fund Management & Advisory Services
N.A.I.C.S.: 551112
P. Bradley Adams *(Mng Dir-Fin Ops)*
H. Kevin Birzer *(CEO)*
Gary Henson *(Pres)*
Michelle Kelly Johnston *(CFO & Sr Mng Dir)*
Matthew Sallee *(Sr Mng Dir & Head-Listed Energy)*
Brent Newcomb *(Sr Mng Dir & Chief Dev Officer)*
Mary Meacham *(Mng Dir & Chief People Officer)*
Kayla White *(VP)*
Edward Russell *(Sr Mng Dir)*
Connie Savage *(COO & Sr Mng Dir)*
P. Bradley Adams *(Mng Dir-Fin Ops)*
Vincent Barnouin *(Mng Dir-Strategic Investment)*
Brad Beman *(Mng Dir)*
Dan Bentzinger *(CIO & Mng Dir)*
Jeremy GOff *(Mng Dir-Social Infrastructure)*
Kyle Krueger *(Mng Dir-Trading & Performance)*

Subsidiary (Domestic):

Tortoise Capital Advisors, LLC (2)
5100 W 115th Pl, Leawood, KS 66211
Tel.: (913) 981-1020
Web Site: http://www.tortoiseadvisors.com
Investment Fund Management Services
N.A.I.C.S.: 523940

H. Kevin Birzer *(CEO)*
P. Bradley Adams *(Mng Dir-Fin Ops)*
David John Schulte *(Co-Founder)*
Matthew Sallee *(Sr Mng Dir & Head-Listed Energy)*
Diane M. Bono *(Mng Dir & Chief Compliance Officer)*
Michelle Kelly Johnston *(CFO & Sr Mng Dir)*
James Mick *(Mng Dir & Sr Portfolio Mgr-Energy)*
Robert Thummel *(Mng Dir & Sr Portfolio Mgr-Energy)*
Dan Bentzinger *(Mng Dir & CIO)*
Mary Meacham *(Mng Dir & Chief People Officer)*
Brent Newcomb *(Sr Mng Dir & Chief Dev Officer)*

Affiliate (Domestic):

Tortoise Energy Independence Fund, Inc. (3)
5100 W 115th Pl, Leawood, KS 66211
Tel.: (913) 981-1020
Web Site: http://www.tortoiseadvisors.com
Rev.: $1,648,702
Assets: $88,683,765
Liabilities: $27,133,430
Net Worth: $61,550,335
Earnings: ($1,490,748)
Fiscal Year-end: 11/30/2019
Closed-End Investment Fund
N.A.I.C.S.: 525990
H. Kevin Birzer *(CEO)*
Courtney Gengler *(CEO)*
Matthew G. P. Sallee *(Exec Officer & Principal)*

Tortoise Energy Infrastructure Corporation (3)
6363 College Blvd Ste 100A, Overland Park, KS 66211
Tel.: (913) 981-1020
Closed-End Investment Fund
N.A.I.C.S.: 525990
H. Kevin Birzer *(Chm)*
David John Schulte *(Sr VP)*
Matthew Sallee *(Portfolio Mgr)*

Tortoise Midstream Energy Fund, Inc. (3)
6363 College Blvd Ste 100A, Leawood, KS 66211
Tel.: (913) 981-1020
Closed-End Investment Fund
N.A.I.C.S.: 525990
Matthew Sallee *(Pres & CEO)*

Tortoise Pipeline & Energy Fund, Inc. (3)
5100 W 115th Pl, Leawood, KS 66211
Tel.: (913) 981-1020
Web Site: http://www.tortoiseadvisors.com
Rev.: $4,278,169
Assets: $192,751,218
Liabilities: $62,864,657
Net Worth: $129,886,561
Earnings: ($1,235,742)
Fiscal Year-end: 11/30/2019
Closed-End Investment Fund
N.A.I.C.S.: 525990
Matthew Sallee *(CEO)*
Robert Thummel *(Mng Dir & Sr Portfolio Mgr-Energy)*
Gary P. Henson *(Pres)*
Michelle Kelly Johnston *(Sr Mng Dir & CFO)*
Edward Russell *(Sr Mng Dir & Head-Private Infrastructure)*
Jennifer Ashlock *(Mng Dir & CMO)*
Vincent Barnouin *(Mng Dir-Strategic Investment)*
Dan Bentzinger *(Mng Dir & CIO)*
Diane M. Bono *(Mng Dir & Chief Compliance Officer)*
Michael S. McKeigue *(Mng Dir & Head-Distr)*
Larry Pokora *(Dir-Institutional Sls & Consultant Rels)*
Daniel Olson *(Dir-Institutional Sls & Consultant Rels)*
Justin Moulder *(VP-Institutional Sls & Consultant Rels)*
Laura Fray *(VP & Asst Controller)*
Julie Pace *(VP & Mgr-Acctg)*
Jason Benson *(Dir-Corp Fin)*
Ryan Channell *(Fin Dir-Ops)*
Shobana Gopal *(Dir-Tax)*

Jennifer Black *(VP-Tax)*
Mary Meacham *(Mng Dir & Chief People Officer)*
Sara Oberlin *(Office Mgr)*
Eva Jenny Lipner *(Mktg Dir)*
Jon Svensson *(Dir-Digital Mktg)*
Tammie Griffin *(VP & Mgr-Creative)*
Jessica Jones *(Dir-Ops)*

Tortoise Power & Energy Infrastructure Fund, Inc. (3)
6363 College Blvd Ste 100A, Overland Park, KS 66211
Tel.: (913) 981-1020
Closed-End Investment Fund
N.A.I.C.S.: 525990
Courtney Gengler *(CEO)*

Subsidiary (Domestic):

Tortoise Credit Strategies, LLC (2)
5100 W 115th Pl, Leawood, KS 66211
Tel.: (913) 981-1020
Web Site: http://www.tortoiseadvisors.com
Investment Advisory & Portfolio Management Services
N.A.I.C.S.: 523940
P. Bradley Adams *(Mng Dir-Fin Ops)*
H. Kevin Birzer *(CEO)*
P. Bradley Adams *(Mng Dir-Fin Ops)*
Jennifer Ashlock *(Mng Dir & CMO)*
Vincent Barnouin *(Mng Dir-Strategic Investment)*
Diane M. Bono *(Mng Dir & Chief Compliance Officer)*
Gary P. Henson *(Pres)*
Michelle Johnston *(CFO & Sr Mng Dir)*
Kyle Krueger *(Mng Dir-Trading & Performance)*
Jason McElwee *(Mng Dir-Distr)*
Michael S. McKeigue *(Mng Dir-Strategic Client Grp)*
Brent Newcomb *(Sr Mng Dir & Chief Dev Officer)*
Matthew S. Ordway *(Mng Dir-Private Clean Energy & Infrastructure)*
Edward Russell *(Sr Mng Dir)*
Connie Savage *(Sr Mng Dir & COO)*
David Sifford *(Mng Dir-Social Infrastructure)*

Venio LLC (1)
1001 Ave of the Americas 14th Fl, New York, NY 10018
Tel.: (212) 764-6800
Web Site: http://www.keaneunclaimedproperty.com
Emp.: 200
Unclaimed Property Communications, Compliance & Consulting Services
N.A.I.C.S.: 541690
Michael O'Donnell *(CEO)*
Nick Nichols *(COO)*
Richard Goggin *(Sr Mgr-Natl Consulting & Advisory Svcs)*

LOVELL PUBLIC RELATIONS, INC.

10455 N Central Expwy Ste 109-355, Dallas, TX 75231
Tel.: (972) 788-4511
Web Site: http://www.lovellpr.com
Emp.: 4
Marketing & Public Relations
N.A.I.C.S.: 541820
Betty Lovell *(Pres)*
Tresa Hardt *(Sr VP)*
Colleen Pierson *(Acct Dir)*

LOVEMAN STEEL CORPORATION

5455 Perkins Rd, Cleveland, OH 44146
Tel.: (440) 232-6200
Web Site: http://www.lovemansteel.com
Sales Range: $10-24.9 Million
Emp.: 50
Plates, Metal
N.A.I.C.S.: 423510
Ralph E. Loveman *(Owner)*
Milica Kolar *(Coord-AP)*
John Steagall *(VP & Product Mgr-Annealing Div)*

LOVER'S LANE & CO.

Lover's Lane & Co.—(Continued)

LOVER'S LANE & CO.
46750 Port St, Plymouth, MI 48170
Tel.: (734) 414-0010
Web Site: http://www.loverslane.com
Sales Range: $10-24.9 Million
Emp.: 150
Clothing Accessories Stores
N.A.I.C.S.: 458110
Michael D. Allmond *(VP)*
Marie Leirstein *(Mgr-HR)*

LOVETT INC.
6920 NE 42nd Ave, Portland, OR 97218-1106
Tel.: (503) 737-8423
Web Site:
http://www.lovettservices.com
Site Preparation Contractor
N.A.I.C.S.: 238910
Dale R. Lovett *(Pres)*

Subsidiaries:

C H Kruse Plumbing, Inc. (1)
5802 NE 88th St, Vancouver, WA 98665
Tel.: (360) 573-4337
Web Site: http://www.chkruseplumbing.com
Sales Range: $1-9.9 Million
Emp.: 20
Plumbing, Heating & Air-Conditioning Contractors
N.A.I.C.S.: 238220
Carl Kruse *(Founder & CEO)*

Mike Patterson Plumbing Inc. (1)
17845 SE 82nd Dr., Gladstone, OR 97027
Tel.: (503) 632-7374
Web Site:
http://www.mikepattersonplumbing.com
Plumbing, Heating & Air-Conditioning Contractors
N.A.I.C.S.: 238220

LOVETT MILLER & CO.
1700 S MacDill Ave Ste 300, Tampa, FL 33629
Tel.: (813) 222-1477
Web Site: http://www.lovettmiller.com
Year Founded: 1997
Sales Range: $1-9.9 Million
Emp.: 5
Investment & Portfolio Management
N.A.I.C.S.: 523940
W. Scott Miller *(Co-Founder & Mng Partner)*
William Radford Lovett II *(Chm & CEO)*

LOVGREN MARKETING GROUP
809 N 96th St Ste 2, Omaha, NE 68114
Tel.: (402) 397-7158
Web Site: http://www.lovgren.com
Sales Range: $10-24.9 Million
Emp.: 5
N.A.I.C.S.: 541810
Linda Lovgren *(Pres & CEO)*
Tom Nemitz *(Dir-Art & Mgr-Production)*

LOVIN CONSTRUCTION, INC.
6204 33rd St E, Bradenton, FL 34203
Tel.: (941) 755-4312 FL
Year Founded: 1997
Sales Range: $1-9.9 Million
Emp.: 45
Bridge, Tunnel & Elevated Highway Construction
N.A.I.C.S.: 237310
Tonie Lovin *(Pres)*

LOVING HANDS LTD.
676 Winters Ave, Paramus, NJ 07652
Tel.: (201) 265-3523
Web Site:
http://www.lovinghandshealthservices.com
Sales Range: $10-24.9 Million
Emp.: 300
Medical Help Service
N.A.I.C.S.: 561320
Paul Provost *(Pres)*

LOVING PETS CORP.
110 Melrich Rd Ste 1, Cranbury, NJ 08512
Tel.: (609) 655-3700
Web Site:
http://www.lovingpetsproducts.com
Year Founded: 2005
Sales Range: $10-24.9 Million
Emp.: 25
All Natural Pet Treats & Feeding Bowls
N.A.I.C.S.: 459910
Eric Abbey *(Founder & Pres)*

LOVIO GEORGE INC.
681 W Forest Ave, Detroit, MI 48201-1113
Tel.: (313) 832-2210 MI
Web Site:
http://www.loviogeorge.com
Year Founded: 1979
Sales Range: $1-9.9 Million
Emp.: 15
Advertising Agency & Public Relations Agency
N.A.I.C.S.: 541820
Christina Lovio-George *(Founder, Pres & CEO)*
Jim Boyle *(VP-Integrated Mktg)*

LOW COUNTRY MACHINERY, INC.
1008 E Hwy 80, Pooler, GA 31322
Tel.: (912) 330-0130
Web Site:
http://www.jcbofgeorgia.com
Sales Range: $10-24.9 Million
Emp.: 20
Construction & Mining Equipment Whslr
N.A.I.C.S.: 423810
Doug Ramsey *(Mgr-Svc)*

LOW VOLTAGE CONTRACTORS, INC.
4200 W 76th St, Minneapolis, MN 55435
Tel.: (952) 835-4600
Web Site: http://www.lvcinc.com
Year Founded: 1982
Sales Range: $10-24.9 Million
Emp.: 71
Construction Engineering Services
N.A.I.C.S.: 541330
Dan Westberg *(VP)*
Dave Bieniek *(Project Mgr)*
Jeff Nelson *(CFO)*
Bert Bongard *(VP-Sls & Mktg)*

LOWCOUNTRY FOOD BANK INC.
2864 Azalea Dr, Charleston, SC 29405
Tel.: (843) 747-8146 SC
Year Founded: 1983
Sales Range: $25-49.9 Million
Emp.: 62
Hunger Relief Services
N.A.I.C.S.: 624210
Patricia Walker *(CEO)*

LOWE ELECTRIC SUPPLY COMPANY
1525 Forsyth St, Macon, GA 31201
Tel.: (478) 743-8661
Web Site:
http://www.loweelectric.com
Sales Range: $10-24.9 Million
Emp.: 69
Electrical Supplies
N.A.I.C.S.: 423610
Jim Kinman *(Owner & CEO)*
Bo Southers *(Branch Mgr)*

LOWE ENTERPRISES, INC.
11777 San Vicente Blvd Ste 900, Los Angeles, CA 90049
Tel.: (310) 820-6661 LA
Web Site: http://www.lowe-re.com
Year Founded: 1972
Sales Range: $50-74.9 Million
Emp.: 150
Holding Company; Commercial, Hospitality & Residential Real Estate Investment, Management & Development
N.A.I.C.S.: 551112
Robert J. Lowe Jr. *(Co-CEO)*
Michael H. Lowe *(Co-CEO)*
John M. DeMarco *(Gen Counsel & Sr VP)*
Suzi Morris *(Sr VP)*
Alan Chamorro *(Sr VP)*
Mara Fabian *(Sr VP)*
K. Mark Muller *(Sr VP)*
Robert Reitenour *(Sr VP)*
David Sonderegger *(Sr VP)*
Thomas W. Wulf *(Exec VP)*
Edward Baird *(VP)*
Erik Clore *(VP)*
Tom Clyman *(VP)*
Andrew Arthurs *(Sr VP)*
Dan Battista *(Sr VP)*
Martin Caverly *(Exec VP)*
Tom Cullinan *(Sr VP)*
Chris Currie *(CFO & Sr VP)*
Ted Lennon *(Sr VP)*
Peter Loedding *(Sr VP)*
Mike McNerney *(Exec VP)*
Robert Mellwig *(Sr VP)*
Mark Rivers *(Exec VP)*
Andy Segal *(Sr VP)*
Matt Walker *(Exec VP)*

Subsidiaries:

Lowe Commercial Services LLC (1)
11777 San Vicente Blvd Ste 900, Los Angeles, CA 90049
Tel.: (320) 820-6661
Commercial Property Management Services
N.A.I.C.S.: 531390
Marty Caverly *(Exec VP)*

Subsidiary (Domestic):

Keys Commercial Real Estate LLC (2)
1919 14th St Ste 800, Boulder, CO 80302-5327
Tel.: (303) 447-2700
Web Site: http://www.keys-commercial.com
Offices of Real Estate Agents & Brokers
N.A.I.C.S.: 531210

Lowe Enterprises Texas Inc. (1)
11777 San Vicente Blvd Ste 900, Los Angeles, CA 90049-5011
Tel.: (310) 820-6661
Web Site: http://www.loweenterprises.com
Emp.: 99
Subdividers & Developers
N.A.I.C.S.: 531210
Bob Lowe *(Dir-Board)*

Lowe Hospitality Group (1)
11777 San Vicente Blvd Ste 900, Los Angeles, CA 90049
Tel.: (310) 820-6661
Web Site: http://www.loweenterprises.com
Sales Range: $25-49.9 Million
Emp.: 100
Hotel & Resort & Resort Community Acquisition, Development & Management Services
N.A.I.C.S.: 721110
William T. Wethe *(CFO & Sr VP)*

Subsidiary (Domestic):

Lowe Destination Development, Inc. (2)
11777 San Vicente Blvd Ste 900, Los Angeles, CA 90049
Tel.: (310) 820-6661
Web Site: http://www.lowedestinations.com
Sales Range: $25-49.9 Million
Emp.: 100
Hotel & Resort Real Estate Developer
N.A.I.C.S.: 237210
Robert J. Lowe Jr. *(Chm, Pres & CEO)*
Matthew H. Walker *(Sr VP-Bus Dev & Project Mgmt-Hotels & Resorts)*
Theodore R. Lennon *(Sr VP)*
Jeffrey L. Allen *(Exec VP)*
William T. Wethe *(CFO & Sr VP)*

Division (Domestic):

Lowe Destination Development Desert (3)
74-001 Reserve Dr, Indian Wells, CA 92210-7041
Tel.: (760) 837-4800
Web Site: http://www.lowedestinations.com
Hotel & Resort Real Estate Developer
N.A.I.C.S.: 237210
Thomas R. Cullinan *(COO & Sr VP)*
Jeffrey L. Allen *(Exec VP)*
Thomas P. Luersen *(Reg Mng Dir)*
Matthew H. Walker *(Sr VP)*
William T. Wethe *(CFO & Sr VP)*

Lowe Destination Development Southeast (3)
4 Old Kings Rd N, Palm Coast, FL 32137
Tel.: (386) 447-1900
Web Site: http://www.lowedestinations.com
Sales Range: $25-49.9 Million
Emp.: 12
Subdividers & Developers
N.A.I.C.S.: 237210
Robert D. DeVore *(Pres)*

Lowe Real Estate Group (1)
233 Lowe Dr, Shepherdstown, WV 25443
Tel.: (304) 876-8000
Sales Range: $50-74.9 Million
Emp.: 100
Commercial & Residential Real Estate Acquisition, Development & Management
N.A.I.C.S.: 531390
Michael H. Lowe *(Co-CEO)*
David Sonderegger *(Sr VP)*
Jeff Allen *(Exec VP)*
Andrew Arthurs *(CIO & Sr VP)*
Dan Battista *(Sr VP)*
Martin Caverly *(Exec VP)*
Bill Cockrum *(Sr VP)*
Tom Cullinan *(Sr VP)*
Chris Currie *(CFO & Sr VP)*
Jim Defrancia *(Pres-Community Dev)*
Leonard Iseri *(Treas & Sr VP)*
Ted Lennon *(Sr VP)*
Peter Loedding *(Sr VP)*
Mike McNerney *(Exec VP)*
Robert Mellwig *(Sr VP)*
Mark Rivers *(Exec VP)*
Andy Segal *(Sr VP)*
Matt Walker *(Exec VP)*
Tom Wulf *(Exec VP)*

Branch (Domestic):

Lowe Enterprises Real Estate Group (2)
1515 Arapahoe St Ste 900 Twr 3, Denver, CO 80202-2110
Tel.: (303) 628-0800
Web Site: http://www.loweenterprises.com
Rev.: $770,000
Emp.: 25
Real Estate Agents & Managers
N.A.I.C.S.: 531210

Lowe Enterprises Real Estate Group (2)
1300 Connecticut Ave NW Ste 250, Washington, DC 20036
Tel.: (202) 496-2900
Web Site: http://www.loweenterprises.com
Rev.: $4,400,000
Emp.: 12
Subdividers & Developers
N.A.I.C.S.: 531210
Larry Welsh *(Sr VP)*
Marcey Zaborski *(VP)*
Mark Rivers *(Mng Dir)*

LOWE TRACTOR & EQUIPMENT, INC.

2213 State Hwy 64 W, Henderson, TX 75652
Tel.: (903) 657-3538
Web Site: http://lowetractor.com
Year Founded: 1976
Sales Range: $10-24.9 Million
Emp.: 15
Farm & Garden Machinery Whslr
N.A.I.C.S.: 423820
John Lowe *(Co-Owner)*
Steve Lowe *(Co-Owner)*
Steve Hudson *(Mgr-Svc)*
Gyce Butler *(Gen Mgr-Sls)*

LOWE WILD DUNES INVESTORS LP
5757 Palm Blvd, Isle of Palms, SC 29451-2734
Tel.: (843) 886-6000
Web Site: http://www.wilddunes.com
Year Founded: 1992
Rev.: $31,167,279
Emp.: 250
Property Management Services
N.A.I.C.S.: 722511

LOWE'S COMMERCIAL PAINTING
6655 68th Ave, Pinellas Park, FL 33781
Tel.: (727) 742-1492
Web Site:
http://www.lowespainting.com
Sales Range: $1-9.9 Million
Emp.: 35
Painting Contractor
N.A.I.C.S.: 238320
Mike Lowe *(Pres)*
Jim Tenderholt *(VP)*

LOWE'S PAY AND SAVE INC.
1804 Hall Rd, Littlefield, TX 79339
Tel.: (806) 385-3366
Year Founded: 1964
Sales Range: $250-299.9 Million
Emp.: 5,000
Owner & Operator of Grocery Stores
N.A.I.C.S.: 445110
Roger C. Lowe *(Pres)*
Mike Murphy *(Dir-Adv & Pricing)*
Roger Lowe Jr. *(VP)*

LOWE'S PELLETS & GRAIN, INC.
2372 W State Rd 46, Greensburg, IN 47240
Tel.: (812) 663-7863
Web Site:
http://www.lowespellets.com
Year Founded: 1963
Sales Range: $25-49.9 Million
Emp.: 30
Mfr of Animal Seeds
N.A.I.C.S.: 424510
Alan Lowe *(VP)*
Don Lowe *(Chm & CEO)*

LOWE-NORTH CONSTRUCTION INC.
800 S A-Line Dr, Spring Hill, KS 66083
Tel.: (913) 686-3080
Web Site: http://www.lowe-north.com
Sales Range: $10-24.9 Million
Emp.: 30
Transmitting Tower Construction
N.A.I.C.S.: 237130

LOWELL COMMUNITY HEALTH CENTER, INC.
175 Cabot St Ste 420, Lowell, MA 01854
Tel.: (978) 322-8592
Web Site: http://www.lchealth.org
Year Founded: 1986
Sales Range: $25-49.9 Million
Emp.: 351
Community Health Care Services
N.A.I.C.S.: 624190
Henry Och *(COO & CIO)*
Kumble Rajesh *(Chief Medical Officer)*
Susan West Levine *(CEO)*
Bruce Robinson *(Chm)*
Robert Ebersole *(CFO)*
Rubin Williams *(Chief HR Officer)*

LOWELL FIVE CENT SAVINGS BANK
34 John St, Lowell, MA 01852
Tel.: (978) 452-1300
Web Site: http://www.lowellfive.com
Sales Range: $25-49.9 Million
Emp.: 100
State Savings Bank
N.A.I.C.S.: 522180
Robert A. Caruso *(Chm)*
Robert C. Dolan *(VP-Comml Lending)*
Glenn B. Goldman *(Sr VP-Risk & Compliance)*
Helen R. Hamel *(VP)*
Kevin A. Kouble *(CIO & Sr VP)*
Belinda M. Morang *(Branch Mgr)*
Rachel A. Tierney *(VP & Mgr-Customer Svcs Center)*
David E. Wallace *(Pres & CEO)*
Alison E. Kalman *(Exec VP)*
Gary Croft *(VP-Comml Lending)*
Thomas M. Boucher *(VP-Comml Lending)*
David J. Karpinsky *(VP-Fin)*
Steven Martin Rochette *(VP-Electronic Banking)*
David J. Clapp *(Sr VP)*
John S. Pratt Jr. *(Sr VP-Credit & Collections)*

LOWELL PACKING COMPANY
125 Harper Ct, Fitzgerald, GA 31750-8692
Tel.: (229) 423-2051
Year Founded: 1942
Sales Range: $10-24.9 Million
Emp.: 95
Meat Packing Plants
N.A.I.C.S.: 311611
Dorothy Fuller *(Treas & Sec)*
Scott Lowell Downing *(Pres)*

LOWELL WOLF INDUSTRIES INC.
612 N Sawyer Rd, Oconomowoc, WI 53066
Tel.: (262) 965-2121
Web Site: http://www.wolfpaving.com
Year Founded: 1941
Sales Range: $10-24.9 Million
Emp.: 15
General Contractor, Highway & Street Construction
N.A.I.C.S.: 237310
Lowell Wolf *(Pres & Treas)*

Subsidiaries:

Wolf Paving & Excavating of Madison (1)
5423 Reiner Rd, Sun Prairie, WI 53590
Tel.: (608) 249-7931
Web Site: http://www.wolfpaving.com
Asphalt & Asphaltic Paving Mixtures (Not From Refineries)
N.A.I.C.S.: 324121
Lowell Wolf *(Pres)*
Sean Wolf *(VP)*

Wolf Paving Co. Inc. (1)
612 N Sawyer Rd, Oconomowoc, WI 53066
Tel.: (262) 965-2121
Web Site: http://www.wolfpaving.com
Blacktop (Asphalt) Work
N.A.I.C.S.: 237310
Devin Wolf *(Pres)*
Kyle Bode *(Mgr-Project)*

Tim Hansen *(Mgr-Project)*
Julie Messmer *(Mgr-Sls)*
Riley Stendel *(Mgr-Project)*
Sean Wolf *(VP)*

LOWEN CORPORATION
1111 Airport Rd, Hutchinson, KS 67501
Tel.: (620) 663-2161
Web Site: http://www.lowen.com
Rev.: $22,100,000
Emp.: 300
Provider of Commercial Printing Services
N.A.I.C.S.: 424990
Matt Lowen *(Pres & CEO)*
Linda Daniels *(CFO)*
Jeryl Hendricks *(VP-HR)*
Dean M. Bowers *(Mgr-Creative & Prepress)*

Subsidiaries:

Lowen Corporation - Lowen Certified Division (1)
1121 N Halstead St, Hutchinson, KS 67501
Web Site: http://www.lowencertified.com
Emp.: 4
Certification Testing Services
N.A.I.C.S.: 541380
Dennis Shea *(Dir-Ops)*

Lowen Corporation - Lowen IT Division (1)
1330 E 4th Ave, Hutchinson, KS 67504-1528
Tel.: (620) 665-2854
Web Site: http://www.lowenit.com
Information Technology Consulting Services
N.A.I.C.S.: 541512
Joel Keller *(VP)*

Lowen Visual Imaging (1)
1152 SE Gateway Dr, Grimes, IA 50111
Tel.: (515) 288-0000
Web Site: http://www.imagetransform.com
Digital Printing Services
N.A.I.C.S.: 323111

LOWENSTEIN SANDLER PC
65 Livingston Ave, Roseland, NJ 07068
Tel.: (973) 597-2500
Web Site: http://www.lowenstein.com
Year Founded: 1961
Sales Range: $200-249.9 Million
Emp.: 583
Law firm
N.A.I.C.S.: 541110
Gary M. Wingens *(Chm & Mng Partner)*
Michael A. Brosse *(Corp Partner)*
Shavar D. Jeffries *(Partner)*
Ethan L. Silver *(Partner-Investment Mgmt Practice)*
Scott McBride *(Partner-White Collar Criminal Defense Practice)*
James Shehan *(Head-FDA Regulatory Practice)*
Michael J. Lerner *(Chm-Life Sciences Practice)*
Donatella Verrico *(Chief HR Officer)*
Jeffrey Cohen *(Partner-Bankruptcy Practice)*
Kenneth A. Rosen *(Chm-Bankruptcy, Fin Reorganization & Creditors Rights Dept)*
A. Faith English *(Mgr-Diversity & Inclusion)*

Subsidiaries:

Lowenstein Sandler PC (1)
1251 Avenue of the Americas, New York, NY 10020
Tel.: (212) 262-6700
Web Site: http://www.lowenstein.com
Legal Firm
N.A.I.C.S.: 922130
Steven M. Skolnick *(Partner)*
Lowell A. Citron *(Partner & Chm-Debt Fin)*
Peter H. Ehrenberg *(Partner & Chm-Governance & Compliance)*

James E. Gregory *(Partner)*
Marita A. Makinen *(Partner & Chm-Mergers & Acq Practice)*
Benjamin Kozinn *(Partner-Investment Mgmt)*
Robert G. Minion *(Partner & Chm-Investment Mgmt)*
Peter D. Greene *(Vice Chm-Investment Mgmt)*
Victor Barkalov *(Chief Innovation & Info Officer)*
William B. Farrell *(CFO)*
Kevin Iredell *(Chief Mktg Officer)*
Joseph J. Palermo *(COO)*

Lowenstein Sandler PC (1)
390 Lytton Ave, Palo Alto, CA 94301 (100%)
Tel.: (650) 433-5800
Web Site: http://www.lowenstein.com
Emp.: 40
Law firm
N.A.I.C.S.: 922130
Kathi A. Rawnsley *(Partner)*
Anthony W. Raymundo *(Partner)*
John L. Berger *(Partner-New Jersey)*
Jeffrey Blumenfeld *(Partner-Washington)*
Lynda A. Bennett *(Partner-New York)*
Matthew Boxer *(Partner-New York)*
Mary J. Hildebrand *(Founder, Chm-Privacy & Cybersecurity & Partner-New Jersey)*
Richard Bernstein *(Partner-New York)*

LOWER BUCKS HOSPITAL
501 Bath Rd, Bristol, PA 19007
Tel.: (215) 785-9200
Web Site:
http://www.lowerbuckshosp.com
Year Founded: 1956
Sales Range: $75-99.9 Million
Emp.: 1,061
Health Care Srvices
N.A.I.C.S.: 622110
Courtney Coffman *(CFO)*
Patricia Bain *(Chief Nursing Officer)*
Prem Reddy *(Chm)*
Sonia Mehta *(Reg CEO)*

LOWER COLORADO RIVER AUTHORITY
3700 Lake Austin Blvd, Austin, TX 78703
Tel.: (512) 578-3200
Web Site: http://www.lcra.org
Year Founded: 1934
Sales Range: $650-699.9 Million
Emp.: 2,000
Electric Power Distribution Services
N.A.I.C.S.: 221122
Thomas Michael Martine *(Vice Chm)*
Timothy Timmerman *(Chm)*
Phil Wilson *(Gen Mgr)*
Stephen F. Cooper *(Sec)*
John Hofmann *(Exec VP-Water)*
Bill Lauderback *(Exec VP-Pub Affairs)*
John Miri *(Chief Admin Officer)*
Thomas E. Oney *(Gen Counsel)*
Ken Price *(Chief Comml Officer)*
Kristen Senechal *(Exec VP-Transmission)*
Jim Travis *(CFO)*

Subsidiaries:

GenTex (1)
PO Box 1605, Austin, TX 78767-1605 (100%)
Tel.: (512) 473-4084
Web Site: http://www.lcra.org
Sales Range: $25-49.9 Million
Emp.: 100
Generating Units For Electricity
N.A.I.C.S.: 237990

LOWER EASTSIDE SERVICE CENTER, INC.
80 Maiden Ln 2nd Fl, New York, NY 10038
Tel.: (212) 566-5372
Web Site: http://www.lesc.org
Year Founded: 1959
Sales Range: $10-24.9 Million

LOWER EASTSIDE SERVICE CENTER, INC.   U.S. PRIVATE

Lower Eastside Service Center, Inc.—(Continued)
Emp.: 209
Substance Abuse Services
N.A.I.C.S.: 621420
Jackie DeCarlo (VP)
Lee H. Pavis (CFO, CIO & VP)
Joseph Krasnansky (Chief Program Officer & VP)
Jacqueline Vargas (VP-HR)
Lolita Silva-Vazquez (VP-Quality Improvement)

LOWER GREAT LAKES KENWORTH INC
4625 W Western Ave, South Bend, IN 46619
Tel.: (574) 234-9007
Web Site:
http://www.lowergreatlakesken worth.com
Sales Range: $25-49.9 Million
Emp.: 80
Trucks, Commercial
N.A.I.C.S.: 441110
Ronald Whiteford II (Pres)

LOWER HOLDING COMPANY
8621 Robert Fulton Dr Ste 150, Columbia, MD 21046
Tel.: (571) 277-2120
Web Site: https://www.lower.company
Real Estate Services
N.A.I.C.S.: 531390

LOWER NECHES VALLEY AUTHORITY
7850 Eastex Fwy, Beaumont, TX 77708-2815
Tel.: (409) 892-4011
Web Site: http://www.lnva.org
Year Founded: 1933
Sales Range: $10-24.9 Million
Emp.: 98
Sewer Construction Services
N.A.I.C.S.: 237110
L. M. Daws (CFO)
Scott Hall (Owner & Sec)
Annette Purington (Principal)

LOWER VALLEY ENERGY INC.
236 N Washington, Afton, WY 83110
Tel.: (307) 885-3175
Web Site: http://www.lvenergy.com
Year Founded: 1937
Rev.: $31,152,158
Emp.: 46
Distribution of Electric Power
N.A.I.C.S.: 221122
Jim Webb (Pres & CEO)
Anna Helm (Mgr-Acctg)

LOWER VALLEY HOSPITAL ASSOCIATION
228 N Cherry, Fruita, CO 81521
Tel.: (970) 858-9871 CO
Web Site:
http://www.familyhealthwest.org
Year Founded: 1949
Sales Range: $25-49.9 Million
Emp.: 608
Community Health Care Services
N.A.I.C.S.: 621498
JoAnn Cline-Lucas (Dir-Billing & Patient Svcs)
Mark Francis (Pres, CEO & Sec)
Britney Guccini (Dir-Emergency)
Karen Hatch (Dir-Health Records)
Lennie Ecker (Dir-Inpatient)
Nicholas J. Saller (Dir-Rehabilitation Svcs)
Lynn Finley (Dir-Quality Improvement)
Angelina Salazar (VP-Bus Dev)
Kay Garcia (Dir-Dietary Svcs)
Kelly Murphy (VP-HR)

Meghan Bustamante (Mgr-Social Svcs)
Michelle Angelo (Dir-X-Ray & Imaging)

LOWERY CORPORATION
5282 E Paris Ave SE, Grand Rapids, MI 49512
Tel.: (616) 554-5200 MI
Web Site:
http://www.appliedimaging.com
Year Founded: 1986
Sales Range: $10-24.9 Million
Emp.: 200
Office Equipment
N.A.I.C.S.: 423420
John Lowery (Pres)
John Konynenbelt (VP)

LOWRY HOLDING COMPANY INC.
9420 Maltby Rd, Brighton, MI 48116
Tel.: (810) 229-7200 MI
Web Site:
http://www.lowrycomputer.com
Year Founded: 1995
Sales Range: $25-49.9 Million
Emp.: 225
Computers Peripherals & Software
N.A.I.C.S.: 423430
Michael Lowry (Pres & CEO)

Subsidiaries:

Lowry Computer Products, Inc.   (1)
9420 Maltby Rd, Brighton, MI 48116
Tel.: (810) 229-7200
Web Site: http://www.lowrycomputer.com
Sales Range: $25-49.9 Million
Emp.: 220
Mfr of Bar Code Solutions & Wireless Networking Software
N.A.I.C.S.: 423430
Michael Lowry (Pres & CEO)
Steve Lowry (Exec VP)

LOWRY OIL COMPANY INCORPORATED
313 Old Salem Rd, Seneca, SC 29672
Tel.: (864) 882-2441
Sales Range: $1-9.9 Million
Emp.: 6
Petroleum Bulk Stations
N.A.I.C.S.: 424710
Roy E. Adams (Pres)

LOWRY PARK ZOOLOGICAL SOCIETY OF TAMPA INC.
1101 W Sligh Ave, Tampa, FL 33604
Tel.: (813) 935-8552
Web Site:
http://www.lowryparkzoo.com
Sales Range: $10-24.9 Million
Emp.: 300
Zoo
N.A.I.C.S.: 712130
Rachel Nelson (Dir-PR)
Emma Dortch (Grp Mgr-Event)
Robert C. Rasmussen (Chm)
Debbie Brown (Dir-HR)
Elizabeth Hennig (CFO)
Joseph A. Couceiro (CEO)
Justin Wyatt (Dir-IT)
Mark Abel (Dir-Fin)
Mark Haney (Chief Advancement Officer)
Marylou Bailey (Treas)
Ray L. Ball (Dir-Medical Sciences)
Tony Moore (COO)

LOY CLARK PIPELINE CO. INC.
19020 A SW Cipole Rd, Tualatin, OR 97062-6937
Tel.: (503) 644-2137
Web Site: http://www.loyclark.com
Year Founded: 1957

Sales Range: $25-49.9 Million
Emp.: 5,000
Provider of Water, Sewer & Utility Line Services
N.A.I.C.S.: 237110
Steve Klepak (VP)

LOY-LANGE BOX COMPANY
222 Russell Blvd, Saint Louis, MO 63104
Tel.: (314) 776-4712
Web Site:
http://www.loylangebox.com
Year Founded: 1897
Rev.: $12,099,757
Emp.: 65
Corrugated Boxes
N.A.I.C.S.: 322211
Jim Cochran (Controller)
Marian Smith (Office Mgr-Shipping)

LOYAL CHRISTIAN BENEFIT ASSOCIATION
8811 Peach St, Erie, PA 16509
Tel.: (814) 453-4331
Web Site: http://www.lcbalife.org
Sales Range: $10-24.9 Million
Emp.: 35
Life Insurance
N.A.I.C.S.: 524113
Doug Tuttle (Pres & CEO)
Michele M. King (VP-Membership & Mktg)
Walter H. Losee (VP-Sls)
Ross Aresco (Treas & VP-Fin)
Rebecca Black (Sec & VP-Admin)
Alex Miller (VP-Ops)

LOYAL SOURCE GOVERNMENT SERVICES, LLC
12612 Challenger Pkwy Ste 365, Orlando, FL 32826
Tel.: (407) 306-8441 FL
Web Site:
http://www.loyalsource.com
Year Founded: 2009
Sales Range: $10-24.9 Million
Workforce Solutions Provider
N.A.I.C.S.: 561311
Jerry MacLellan (VP-Bus Dev)
Steve Lockwood (Pres-Travel Nursing)
Leigh Pace (COO)

LOYD'S ELECTRIC SUPPLY INC.
838 Stonetree Dr, Branson, MO 65616
Tel.: (417) 334-2171
Web Site:
http://www.loydselectric.com
Sales Range: $25-49.9 Million
Emp.: 50
Electrical Supplies
N.A.I.C.S.: 423610
Phillip D. Loyd (Pres)

LOYOLA RECOVERY FOUNDATION
1159 Pittsford Victor Rd, Pittsford, NY 14534
Tel.: (585) 203-1005 NY
Web Site:
http://www.loyolarecovery.org
Year Founded: 1927
Sales Range: $1-9.9 Million
Emp.: 150
Alcoholism Rehabilitation Services
N.A.I.C.S.: 622210
George Basher (Pres & CEO)
Jane Fyffe (VP-Inpatient Svcs)
Deborah L. Partridge (VP-Admin Svcs)
Mark Brewer (CFO & VP-Fin)
Kim Anger (Program Dir-Bath Unit)

Richard Bifulco (Treas)
Glenn Currier (Chm)
Donald Ballard (Sec)

LOZANO ENTERPRISES, LP
700 S Flowers St Ste 3000, Los Angeles, CA 90017
Tel.: (213) 622-8332 CA
Web Site: http://www.laopinion.com
Year Founded: 1926
Sales Range: $10-24.9 Million
Emp.: 250
Newspapers
N.A.I.C.S.: 561499
Jose I. Lozano (Principal)
Mary Zerafa (VP-Strategic Plng)
Jim Pellegrino (Dir-Circulation)
Maria Reyes (CEO & Gen Mgr)

LOZIER CORPORATION
6336 John J Pershing Dr, Omaha, NE 68110
Tel.: (402) 457-8000 NE
Web Site: http://www.lozier.com
Year Founded: 1956
Sales Range: $350-399.9 Million
Emp.: 2,100
Mfr & Retailer of Retail Store Fixtures & Storage Systems
N.A.I.C.S.: 337126
Jan Muller (Treas & VP)
Steve Franz (CFO)
Bob Schoby (Mgr-Grp Product Line)
David Hale (Mgr-Corp Logistics)
Henri Schiphorst (Mgr-Budgeting & Leasing)
Jay Daily (VP-Engrg)
Jeff Zadina (Acct Mgr)
Jim Nelson (Coord-Safety & Environmental)
Larry Schmitz (Plant Mgr)
Megan Mahal (Engr-Indus)
Ralph Kleinsmith (Plant Mgr)
Rick Kohler (Dir-Corp Pur)
Robert Braun (VP)
Shara Swapp (Mgr-Corp Benefits)
Sherri Gunderson (Mgr-Tax)
Tony Brown (Dir-Info Sys)
Travis Backlund (Area Mgr)
Gina Bliss (Mgr)
Jason Nocita (Mgr-Database)
Brad Browne (Mgr-Distr Center)
Dave Halen (Mgr-Engrg)
John Philo (Portfolio Mgr)
Peter Maier (Reg Mgr-Sls)
Kaiser Jess (Coord-Mechanic & Trng)

Subsidiaries:

Lozier Corporation - Scottsboro Plant 1   (1)
401 Taylor St, Scottsboro, AL 35768
Tel.: (256) 259-6100
Web Site: http://www.lozier.com
Store Fixture Mfr
N.A.I.C.S.: 337215

Lozier Corporation - Scottsboro Plant 2   (1)
401 Taylor St, Scottsboro, AL 35768
Tel.: (256) 259-5141
Store Fixture Mfr
N.A.I.C.S.: 337215

LOZINAK PROFESSIONAL BASEBALL LLC
1000 Park Ave, Altoona, PA 16602
Tel.: (814) 943-5400
Web Site:
http://www.altoonacurve.com
Sales Range: $25-49.9 Million
Emp.: 24
Holding Company; Professional Baseball Club Owner & Operator
N.A.I.C.S.: 551112
Bob Lozinak (Owner)

COMPANIES / LRG MARKETING COMMUNICATIONS, INC.

Subsidiaries:

Altoona Curve Baseball Club (1)
1000 Park Ave, Altoona, PA 16602
Tel.: (814) 943-5400
Web Site: http://www.altoonacurve.com
Sales Range: $10-24.9 Million
Emp.: 20
Professional Baseball Club
N.A.I.C.S.: 711211
Bob Lozinak (Mng Partner)
Joan Lozinak (Mng Partner)
David Lozinak (COO)
Mike Lozinak (CFO)
Steve Lozinak (Chief Admin Officer)
Rob Egan (Gen Mgr)
Mary Lamb (Dir-Fin)

LP FIRST CAPITAL
7500 Rialto Boulevard Bldg.2, Suite 230, Austin, TX 78735
Tel.: (737) 237-2760
Web Site:
 https://www.lpfirstcapital.com
Year Founded: 2018
Emp.: 100
Private Equity
N.A.I.C.S.: 523940
Joseph Denham (Mng Dir)

Subsidiaries:

Flow Service Partners (1)
725 Cool Springs Blvd., Suite 600, Franklin, TN 37067
Tel.: (502) 558-1264
Web Site: https://www.flowservice.com
HVAC Plumbing & Refrigeration Services
N.A.I.C.S.: 238220
Michael Epperson (CEO)

Subsidiary (Domestic):

R. Brooks Mechanical, Inc. (2)
PO Box 1090, Rising Sun, MD 21911
Tel.: (410) 658-0822
Web Site:
 http://www.rbrooksmechanical.com
Plumbing, Heating & Air-Conditioning Contractors
N.A.I.C.S.: 238220

United Land Services, Inc. (1)
12276 San Jose Blvd Ste 747, Jacksonville, FL 32223
Tel.: (904) 829-9255
Web Site:
 https://www.unitedlandservices.com
Landscape Installation & Design Services
N.A.I.C.S.: 561730
Bob Blandford (CEO)

Subsidiary (Domestic):

Georgia Scapes, Inc. (2)
1285 Turner Rd SW, Lilburn, GA 30047-6728
Tel.: (770) 921-7938
Web Site: http://www.georgiascapes.com
Landscape Architectural Services
N.A.I.C.S.: 541320
Duane Carter (Pres)

Landscape Service Professionals, Inc. (2)
11820 NW 37th St, Coral Springs, FL 33065
Tel.: (954) 721-6920
Web Site:
 http://www.landscapeservicepros.com
Landscape Design Services
N.A.I.C.S.: 541320
Sandra Benton (Pres)
Tom Benton (VP)
Karmen Burn (COO & VP)
Steve Burn (VP-Irrigation Div)
Mark Christofori (Gen Mgr)
Ed Barry (Mgr-Landscape Property Maintenance)
Jennifer Benton (Coord-Bus Dev)

LPCIMINELLI INC.
2421 Main St, Buffalo, NY 14214
Tel.: (716) 855-1200 NY
Web Site: http://www.lpciminelli.com
Year Founded: 1961
Sales Range: $200-249.9 Million
Emp.: 350
General Contractors
N.A.I.C.S.: 238910
Louis P. Ciminelli (Chm & CEO)
Bob Overhoff (Dir-Safety)
Jim Fenton (VP-Strategy)
Amy L. Clifton (CFO)
Eugene T. Partridge (Exec VP)
Gail Ettaro (Sr Dir-Mktg)
Joseph A. Mannarino (Exec VP)
Kevin C. Schuler (Sr VP-Corp Comm)
Kirsti A. Hunt (VP)
Kyle W. Tuttle (Sr VP)
Patrick Smally (VP-Risk Mgmt)
Steven Giordano (VP)
Mark Caspers (Exec VP)
Frank L. Ciminelli II (Pres)

Subsidiaries:

L P Ciminelli Construction Company Inc. (1)
2421 Main St, Buffalo, NY 14214-1725 (100%)
Tel.: (716) 855-1200
Web Site: http://www.lpciminelli.com
Rev.: $11,800,000
Emp.: 150
Nonresidential Construction
N.A.I.C.S.: 238910
Jack Depasquale (Controller)

Louis P. Ciminelli Construction Co. Inc. (1)
2421 Main St, Buffalo, NY 14214 (100%)
Tel.: (716) 855-1200
Web Site: http://www.lpciminelli.com
Sales Range: $25-49.9 Million
Emp.: 150
Management Consulting Services
N.A.I.C.S.: 541618

LPI, INC.
304 Hudson St, New York, NY 10013
Tel.: (212) 233-2737 NY
Web Site: http://www.lpiny.com
Year Founded: 1885
Engineering & Technical Consulting Services
N.A.I.C.S.: 541330
Robert Vecchio (CEO)
Joseph Crosson (Principal)
Thomas Esselman (Principal)

LPI, INC.
506 Twin Oaks Dr, Johnson City, TN 37601
Tel.: (423) 349-2900
Web Site: http://lpiinc.com
Hot Tub & Tanning Bed Mfr
N.A.I.C.S.: 333414
David Hatley (CEO)

Subsidiaries:

Golf Cart World, Inc. (1)
27 Pine Bluff Rd, Eastman, GA 31023-7946
Tel.: (478) 837-7200
Web Site: http://www.ezgodealer.com
Automobile & Other Motor Vehicle Merchant Whslr
N.A.I.C.S.: 423110
Tim Moore (Owner)

LPK
19 Garfield Pl, Cincinnati, OH 45202
Tel.: (513) 241-6401
Web Site: http://www.lpk.com
Sales Range: $25-49.9 Million
Emp.: 400
Brand Development & Integration, Corporate Identity, Identity Marketing
N.A.I.C.S.: 541810
Jerry Kathman (Chm)

Subsidiaries:

LPK GMbH Frankfurt (1)
Hamburger Allee 45, 60486, Frankfurt am Main, Germany
Tel.: (49) 69 713 7660
Emp.: 20
N.A.I.C.S.: 541810
Marek Bareta (Mgr-New Clients)

LPK Sarl Geneva (1)
Avenue des Morgines 12, Petit-Lancy, CH-1213, Geneva, Switzerland
Tel.: (41) 22 300 3300
Emp.: 20
N.A.I.C.S.: 541810
Cathy Lowe (Dir-Bus Dev)

LPM FORKLIFT SALES & SERVICE, INC.
7700 NW 39th Expy, Bethany, OK 73008
Tel.: (405) 235-3635
Web Site: http://www.lpmok.com
Rev.: $12,939,466
Emp.: 100
Truck Rental Services
N.A.I.C.S.: 532490
Lisa Garza (Mgr-Ops)

LPS INDUSTRIES INC.
10 Caesar Pl, Moonachie, NJ 07074-1701
Tel.: (201) 438-3515
Web Site: http://www.lpsind.com
Year Founded: 1959
Sales Range: $25-49.9 Million
Emp.: 250
Mfr of Flexible Packaging Materials
N.A.I.C.S.: 322120
Madeleine D. Robinson (CEO)
Philip Pasqualone (VP)

LPX, INC.
1801 Payne St, Louisville, KY 40206
Tel.: (502) 583-1726
Web Site: http://www.loupavine.com
Year Founded: 1949
Sales Range: $25-49.9 Million
Emp.: 200
Holding Company; Site Construction & Asphalt Paving Contractor Services
N.A.I.C.S.: 551112
William B. Dougherty (Chm, Pres & CEO)
Joseph W. Dougherty (Pres-Louisville Paving)
John T. Dougherty (CEO-Louisville Paving)

Subsidiaries:

Louisville Paving Company, Inc. (1)
1801 Payne St, Louisville, KY 40206
Tel.: (502) 583-1726
Web Site: http://www.loupaving.com
Site Construction & Asphalt Paving Contractor Services
N.A.I.C.S.: 238990
John T. Dougherty (Chm)
Joseph W. Dougherty (CEO)
Larry Hobson (Dir-Bus Dev)
Kevin Klain (VP-Paving Div)
Corey Brown (Dir-Fixed Asset Mgmt)
Jason Grace (Mgr-Ops-Site Div)
Aaron Johnson (Mgr-Project-Site Div)
Brian McDonald (CFO & Treas)
Lisa Neal (Dir-Safety)
Jason Schmidt (Mgr-Ops-Site Div)
Kristi Travelstead (Dir-HR)
Chris Wilson (Mgr-Asphalt Plants)
F. Hunter Strickler (Pres)

Material Transfer, Inc. (1)
7811 W 101st Ave, Crown Point, IN 46307
Tel.: (219) 865-9575
General Freight Trucking Services
N.A.I.C.S.: 484110

Pace Contracting, LLC (1)
200 Willinger Ln, Jeffersonville, IN 47130
Tel.: (812) 283-5784
Construction Engineering Services
N.A.I.C.S.: 541330

LR3 ENTERPRISES INC.
1535 N Maitland Ave, Maitland, FL 32751-3383
Tel.: (407) 260-2220 FL
Year Founded: 1980
Art Insurance Services
N.A.I.C.S.: 524298

LRE GROUND SERVICES, INC.
1115 S Main St, Brooksville, FL 34601
Tel.: (352) 796-0229 FL
Web Site: http://www.lregsi.com
Year Founded: 1989
Sales Range: $1-9.9 Million
Emp.: 130
Specialty Trade Contractors
N.A.I.C.S.: 238990
Jesse Miller (Dir-Field Ops)
Susan Larke Woolever (Pres)
Christopher Coburn (Mgr-Production)
Brandon Best (Mgr-Production)
Paul Grey (Mgr-Sls)
Gina Varn (Coord-Mktg)
Rachel Vitale (Pres & Treas)
Jesse Hill (Project Coord)
Jim Flynn (VP & Gen Mgr)

LRES CORP.
765 The City Dr S Ste 300, Orange, CA 92868
Tel.: (714) 520-5737
Web Site: http://www.lres.com
Year Founded: 2001
Sales Range: $1-9.9 Million
Emp.: 60
Real Estate Appraisal Services
N.A.I.C.S.: 531320
Paul Abbamonto (COO)
Selene Nunez (VP-Valuations)
Roger Beane (Founder & CEO)
Ann Song (Sr VP-Ops)
Susheel Mantha (CFO)
Joseph Hendren (VP-Bus Dev)
Yvonne Thompson (VP-HR)
Audrey Clearwater (VP-Ops)
Paul Bush (VP-Tech)
Mark R. Johnson (Pres)
Jill Haro (VP-Corp Admin)
Scott Spencer (CTO)
Todd Taylor (CFO)

Subsidiaries:

InsideValuation Partners, LLC (1)
241 Ridge St Fourth Floor, Reno, NV 89501
Tel.: (775) 828-4044
Web Site: http://www.insidevaluation.com
Offices of Real Estate Appraisers
N.A.I.C.S.: 531320
Audrey Clearwater (VP-Ops)
Cassie Vega (Acct Mgr-Client)
Ryan Clearwater (Dir-Client Relations)
Colleen Nelson (Accountant)
Roger Beane (CEO)
Paul Abbamonto (COO)
Mark Johnson (Chief Strategy Officer)
Susheel Mantha (CFO)

Keystone Asset Management, Inc. (1)
3015 Advance Ln, Colmar, PA 18915-8915
Tel.: (215) 855-3350
Web Site: http://www.keystonebest.com
Real Estate Services
N.A.I.C.S.: 531210
Jane Hennessy (Founder)
Ryan Hennessy (CEO)

Lender's Choice Inc. (1)
3460 Marron Rd Ste 103, Oceanside, CA 92056
Tel.: (760) 730-9565
Web Site: http://www.lci-network.com
Real Estate Appraiser
N.A.I.C.S.: 531320
Rodney Squires (CEO)

LRG MARKETING COMMUNICATIONS, INC.
48 Burd St, Nyack, NY 10960
Tel.: (845) 358-1801 NY
Web Site:
 http://www.lrgmarketing.com
Year Founded: 2003
Sales Range: $10-24.9 Million
Emp.: 30
Advertising & Marketing Services
N.A.I.C.S.: 541613

LRG MARKETING COMMUNICATIONS, INC.   U.S. PRIVATE

LRG Marketing Communications, Inc.—(Continued)
Diana Wolff (Pres)

LRN CORPORATION
745 5th Ave 8th Fl, New York, NY 10151
Tel.: (646) 862-2040 DE
Web Site: http://www.lrn.com
Year Founded: 1994
Corporate Sustainability & Ethical Advisory Services
N.A.I.C.S.: 541618
Dov Seidman (Founder & Chm)
Ron Charow (CFO)
Sunil Bheda (Head-Tech & Product Dev)
Amy Hanan (CMO)
Marie Burke (Chief Content Officer)
Ty Francis (Chief Advisory Officer)
Matt Plass (Head-Segments-Global)
Margaret Sweeney (Chief HR Officer)
Kevin Michielsen (CEO)

LRP PUBLICATIONS
360 Hiatt Dr, Palm Beach Gardens, FL 33418
Tel.: (561) 622-6520 PA
Web Site: http://www.lrp.com
Year Founded: 1977
Sales Range: $100-124.9 Million
Emp.: 300
Publisher of Business-to-Business Newsletters, Magazines, Books, Software & On-line Services
N.A.I.C.S.: 513120
Kenneth Kahn (Founder & Pres)
Stephen Bevilacqua (Dir-Editorial-Special Education Grp)

Subsidiaries:

LRP Publications - Pennsylvania (1)
747 Dresher Rd, Horsham, PA 19044-0980 (100%)
Tel.: (215) 784-0941
Web Site: http://www.lrp.com
Books, Pamphlets, Newsletters, Videos & Online Resources Publisher
N.A.I.C.S.: 513130

LRX GROUP, INC.
2600 Dogals Rd Ste 1111, Coral Gables, FL 33134
Tel.: (305) 507-1200 IL
Web Site: http://www.lrxgroup.com
Sales Range: $10-24.9 Million
Emp.: 10
Real Estate Consultant
N.A.I.C.S.: 531320
Alan Marcus (Gen Counsel)
Bruce Horwich (Pres)

LS & COMPANY
11201 Corporate Cir N Ste 120, Saint Petersburg, FL 33716
Tel.: (727) 579-0383 FL
Web Site: http://www.lsandco.com
Year Founded: 1991
Sales Range: $1-9.9 Million
Accounting Firm
N.A.I.C.S.: 541211
Lisa Smithson (Founder & Mng Partner)
Kristen Beverage (Dir-Assurance & Acctg Svcs)
Marnie Hardie (Mgr-Tax)

LS POWER DEVELOPMENT, LLC
1700 Broadway 35th Fl, New York, NY 10019
Tel.: (212) 615-3456 DE
Web Site: http://www.lspower.com
Year Founded: 1990

Holding Company; Power Generation & Electricity Transmission Infrastructure Investment, Development & Operation Services
N.A.I.C.S.: 551112
Edward J. Sondey (Sr Mng Dir)
Michael Segal (Founder & Chm)
Paul Segal (CEO)
Joseph Esteves (Head-Private Equity)
Ron Fischer (Gen Counsel & Exec VP)
James Bartlett (Vice Chm)
Darpan Kapadia (COO)
Mark Brennan (Treas & Exec VP-Admin)
John Staikos (Gen Counsel-Private Equity & Sr VP)
Paul Thessen (Pres)
Shimon Edelstein (Exec VP & Head-Tax)
John King (Exec VP-Renewables)
Carolyne Murff (Sr VP & Head-Asset Mgmt)
Ernest Kim (Sr VP-Private Equity)
Jeff Wade (Chief Compliance Officer)
Joe Myers (Sr VP-Acctg & Fin)
John Burke (Mng Dir-Private Equity & Fin)
Kevin R. Johnson (Sr VP-Project Dev)
Lawrence Willick (Sr VP-Project Dev)
Mark Strength (Sr VP-Project Dev)
Matthew Mitchell (Sr VP-Private Equity)
Nathan Hanson (Sr VP-Energy & Comml Mgmt)
Richard Roloff (Sr VP-Private Equity & Fin)
Robert Colozza (Sr VP-Project Dev)
Scott Carver (Sr VP)
Suzanne Pepe (Sr VP-Tax Counsel)

Subsidiaries:

LS Power Equity Advisors, LLC (1)
1700 Broadway 35th Fl, New York, NY 10019
Tel.: (212) 615-3456
Web Site: http://www.lspower.com
Power Generation & Electricity Transmission Infrastructure Investment Advisory & Asset Management Services
N.A.I.C.S.: 523940
Edward J. Sondey (Sr Mng Dir)
James Bartlett (Vice Chm)
David Nanus (Co Head-Private Equity)
Mike Segal (Chm)
Paul Segal (CEO)
Darpan Kapadia (COO)
Joseph Esteves (CFO & Co Head-Private Equity)
Ron Fischer (Exec VP & Gen Counsel)

Subsidiary (Domestic):

EVgo Services LLC (2)
11390 W Olympic Blvd Ste 250, Los Angeles, CA 90064
Tel.: (877) 494-3833
Web Site: http://www.evgo.com
Tidal Electric Power Generation Services
N.A.I.C.S.: 221118
Cathy Zoi (CEO)
Julie Blunden (Chief Comml Officer)
Ivo Steklac (COO & CTO)
Olga Shevorenkova (Interim CFO)
Jonathan Levy (VP-Strategic Initiatives)

Enerwise Global Technologies, Inc. (2)
1001 Fleet St Ste 400, Baltimore, MD 21202
Tel.: (844) 276-9371
Web Site: http://www.cpowerenergymanagement.com
Energy Management Services
N.A.I.C.S.: 541618
Carl Almeter (VP & Gen Mgr-NY)
Jason Babik (Sr VP-Strategic Plng & Bus Dev)
Glenn Bogarde (Sr VP-Sls)
Raymond Berkebile (Sr Dir-Engrg Ops)

Peter Bergeron (Sr Dir-Customer Fulfillment)
Joe Stickney (Sr Dir-Mktg)
Shelley Schopp (Sr VP-Ops)
Constantine Damaskos (Sr VP-Market Dev)
Yana Fayer (Controller-Fin)
Joe Gatto (VP & Gen Mgr-Sls-Northeast & Natl)
John Horton (Pres & CEO)
Kyle Harbaugh (Sr VP-IT & Product Mgmt)
Kyle Wiggins (CFO)
Dailey Tipton (VP & Gen Mgr-PJM)
Rob Windle (Exec Dir-Strategic Alliances)
Mike Abramson (Sr VP-Fin & Operational Analytics)
Tony Alvarado-Rivero (Dir-Infrastructure & Product Mgmt)
Jobin Arthungal (Mgr-Marker Dev)

Unit (Domestic):

Ocean State Power (2)
1575 Sherman Farm Rd, Harrisville, RI 02830
Tel.: (401) 568-9550
Electric Power Plant Operator
N.A.I.C.S.: 221118
Harold Kvisle (Pres & CEO)

Safe Harbor Water Power Corporation (1)
1 Powerhouse Rd, Conestoga, PA 17516
Tel.: (717) 872-5441
Web Site: http://www.shwpc.com
Hydroelectric Power Plant
N.A.I.C.S.: 221111
Wyatt F. Morrison (Treas & Sec)

Santa Rosa Energy Center, LLC (1)
5001 Sterling Way, Milton, FL 32571-2758
Tel.: (850) 995-2100
Web Site: http://www.calpine.com
Power Generation Services
N.A.I.C.S.: 221118

LS SYSTEMS, LLC
1417 Knecht Ave Ste 2A, Arbutus, MD 21227
Tel.: (410) 552-1777
Web Site: http://www.lssmd.com
Year Founded: 1996
Sales Range: $10-24.9 Million
Emp.: 66
Construction Services
N.A.I.C.S.: 236220
Amy Smolenski (Mgr-HR)

LS3P ASSOCIATES LTD.
205 1/2 King St, Charleston, SC 29401-3129
Tel.: (843) 577-4444
Web Site: http://www.ls3p.com
Emp.: 100
Architectural Services
N.A.I.C.S.: 541310
Mary Beth Branham (VP)
Melanie Rose (Coord-Mktg-Raleigh)
Brian Tressler (Project Mgr)
Dana Speight Reed (Principal)
Mari-Ann Williams (Assoc Principal)
Tom Norman (Principal)
Scott Brady (Principal & Sr Project Mgr)

Subsidiaries:

Ebert Norman Brady Architects PA (1)
1361 13th Ave S, Jacksonville Beach, FL 32250
Tel.: (904) 241-9997
Web Site: http://www.enbarchitects.com
Rev.: $1,510,000
Emp.: 10
Architectural Services
N.A.I.C.S.: 541310
William Ebert (Founder)

LSC ACQUISITION CORPORATION
Ste 1900 400 N Ashley Dr, Tampa, FL 33602-4311
Tel.: (313) 894-2808
Sales Range: $10-24.9 Million

Emp.: 25
Funeral Home
N.A.I.C.S.: 523999
C. H. Chen (Vice Chm)
Raymond Soong (Chm)

Subsidiaries:

LSC Michigan Corp. (1)
Ste 1900 400 N Ashley Dr, Tampa, FL 33602-4311
Tel.: (313) 894-2808
Sales Range: $1-9.9 Million
Emp.: 20
Funeral Home
N.A.I.C.S.: 812210

LSCG MANAGEMENT, INC.
70 W Madison St Ste 5710, Chicago, IL 60602
Tel.: (312) 236-7041 DE
Web Site: http://www.lasallecapital.com
Year Founded: 2004
Private Equity Investment Management Firm
N.A.I.C.S.: 523940
Rocco J. Martino (Co-Founder & Partner)
Jeffrey M. Walters (Co-Founder & Mng Partner)
David R. Murav (VP)
Dustin R. Bishop (VP-Fin)
Lindsey C. Kremer (Office Mgr)
Nicholas S. Christopher (Partner)
Kelly A. Cornelis (Partner)

Subsidiaries:

Delorio Foods, Inc. (1)
2200 Bleecker St, Utica, NY 13501
Tel.: (315) 732-7612
Web Site: http://www.deiorios.com
Frozen Dough Products Mfr
N.A.I.C.S.: 311813
Rob Ragusa (CEO)

Eclipse Advantage, LLC (1)
6905 N Wickham Rd Ste 405, Melbourne, FL 32940
Tel.: (321) 250-6380
Web Site: http://www.eclipseadvantage.com
Outsourced Warehouse Fulfillment & Logistics Services
N.A.I.C.S.: 561499
Bob Miggins (CFO)
Matt Smith (Pres & Chief Corp Officer)
Pete Westermann (CEO)
Cody McSwain (VP-Ops)
Nichole Winch (VP-HR)

Impex Global, LLC (1)
8708 W Little York Rd Ste 170, Houston, TX 77040
Tel.: (281) 416-4449
Web Site: http://www.impexfilms.com
Sales Range: $10-24.9 Million
Flexible Films Distr
N.A.I.C.S.: 424610
John Maxwell (Pres & CEO)

LaSalle Capital Group Partners, LLC (1)
70 W Madison St Ste 5710, Chicago, IL 60602-4370
Tel.: (312) 236-7041
Web Site: http://www.lasallecapitalgroup.com
Privater Equity Firm
N.A.I.C.S.: 523999
Andrew Shackelford (VP & CFO)

National Gift Card Corporation (1)
300 Millennium Dr, Crystal Lake, IL 60012
Tel.: (847) 792-2273
Web Site: http://www.ngc-group.com
Sales Range: $125-149.9 Million
Emp.: 45
Gift Card Supplier
N.A.I.C.S.: 459420
Adam Van Witzenburg (CEO)
Rick Rubin (Exec VP-Sls)
Joan Travelstead (CTO)
Nancy Knutsen (Dir-Bus Dev)
Eric Thiegs (Sr VP)
Bill St. Clair (Sr VP-Ops)
Steve Van Witzenburg (Sr VP-Ops)
Brian Dreger (CIO)

COMPANIES

Westminster Foods, LLC (1)
1 Scale Ave Ste 81 Bldg 14, Rutland, VT 05701
Tel.: (802) 773-8888
Web Site: http://www.wstfoods.com
Holding Company; Seasonings, Syrups & Crackers Mfr
N.A.I.C.S.: 551112
Bob Abramowitz (CEO)
Sally Pancheri (CFO)

Subsidiary (Domestic):

Gold's Pure Foods, LLC (2)
1 Brooklyn Rd, Hempstead, NY 11550-6619
Tel.: (516) 483-5600
Web Site: http://www.goldshorseradish.com
Sales Range: $10-24.9 Million
Emp.: 70
Condiments, Sauces, Soups & Syrups Mfr
N.A.I.C.S.: 311941
Bob Abramowitz (CEO)

Westminster Cracker Company, Inc. (2)
1 Scale Ave Ste 81 Bldg 14, Rutland, VT 05701
Tel.: (802) 773-8888
Web Site:
  http://www.westminstercrackers.com
Cracker Mfr
N.A.I.C.S.: 311821
Bob Abramowitz (CEO)
Mark Dooley (VP-Ops)
Sally Pancheri (CFO)
Stephanie Audinot (Fin Mgr)

LSI INC.
39210 221st St, Alpena, SD 57312
Tel.: (605) 849-3367
Web Site: http://www.lsijax.com
Sales Range: $25-49.9 Million
Emp.: 1,200
Sausages & Other Prepared Meats
N.A.I.C.S.: 311612
Jack Link (CEO)
Doug Walz (Controller-Fin)
Rick Tebay (Plant Mgr)
Kathy Watson (Dir-HR)
Michael S. French (COO)
Corkey Harvey (VP-Fin)
Mike Pakovic (CTO & VP-Simulation)
Warren S. Rosander (CEO & CFO)
Ed Turner (VP-Intl & Trng Svcs Programs)

LSP TECHNOLOGIES, INC.
6161 Shamrock Ct, Dublin, OH 43016-1284
Tel.: (614) 718-3000
Web Site:
  http://www.lsptechnologies.com
Year Founded: 1995
Sales Range: $1-9.9 Million
Emp.: 200
Laser Peening Production Services
N.A.I.C.S.: 333517
Jeff Dulaney (Founder, Co-Pres & CEO)
Eric Collet (Co-Pres & COO)
Suzanne Dulaney (Chief Compliance Officer & Gen Counsel)
David Lahrman (VP-Bus Dev)
Mark Bloomberg (VP-Engrg)

LSQ FUNDING GROUP, L.C.
2600 Lucien Way Ste 100, Maitland, FL 32751
Tel.: (407) 206-0022
Web Site: http://www.lsq.com
Year Founded: 1996
Emp.: 130
Commercial Specialized Financing Services
N.A.I.C.S.: 522220
Maxwell Eliscu (Founder, Pres & CEO)
Bill Kirth (VP-Intermountain Reg)
Renee Jackson (Sls Dir-Natl)

LST MARKETING, LLC
7950 N Georgetown Rd, Indianapolis, IN 46268
Tel.: (317) 383-0256   IN
Web Site:
  http://www.lstmarketing.com
Year Founded: 2015
Advertising & Public Relations Agency
N.A.I.C.S.: 541810
John Lopes (CEO)
Starke Taylor (Pres)
Gregory J. Smith (Chief Creative Officer)

Subsidiaries:

GRand Solutions LLC (1)
1140 W Main St, Speedway, IN 46224
Tel.: (317) 731-6394
Web Site: http://www.grand-solutions.net
Public Relations Agency
N.A.I.C.S.: 541820
Gene Cottingham (Co-Founder & Partner)
Ruthie Forbes (Co-Founder & Partner)

LT ACQUISITION CORP.
15335 Morrison St Ste 240, Sherman Oaks, CA 91403
Tel.: (818) 788-0500
Web Site: http://www.louises.com
Rev.: $18,900,000
Emp.: 300
Italian Restaurant
N.A.I.C.S.: 722511

LT APPAREL GROUP
100 W 33rd St Ste 1012, New York, NY 10001
Tel.: (212) 502-6000
Web Site: http://www.frenchtoast.com
Rev.: $31,500,000
Emp.: 200
Infants Cut & Sew Apparel Mfr
N.A.I.C.S.: 315250
Richard A. Sutton (CEO)
Donna Amatucci (Mgr-HR)
Albert Setyon (Mgr-Production)
Brandi Occean (Coord-Show Room)
Erica Parks (Coord-Sls)
Larissa Montrose (Dir-Creative)
Leo Chan (Dir-IT)
Rita Poloncsak (Mgr-Credit & Collections)
Deena Amin (Mgr-Customer Compliance & Logistics)
Jing Chen (Mgr-Tech Design)
David Queen (VP-Supply Chain)

LT TRUST COMPANY
1675 Broadway, Denver, CO 80202-3331
Tel.: (303) 658-3500   CO
Web Site: http://www.ltretire.com
Year Founded: 2009
Emp.: 130
Holding Company; Retirement Plan Administration Services
N.A.I.C.S.: 551112
Bob Beriault (Chm & CEO)

Subsidiaries:

LT Plan Services, Inc. (1)
1675 Broadway Ste 500, Denver, CO 80202
Tel.: (303) 658-3500
Web Site: http://www.ltretire.com
Retirement Plan Administration Services
N.A.I.C.S.: 524292
Bob Beriault (Chm & CEO)

LTC GLOBAL, INC.
6201 Presidential Ct, Fort Myers, FL 33919   NV
Web Site: http://www.ltcglobal.com
Year Founded: 2002
Emp.: 100
Insurance Agencies & Brokerages
N.A.I.C.S.: 524210

Nickie Cheney (Gen Counsel)
Steven A. Hensley (Chief Admin Officer)
Sukhjit Bassi (COO)
David A. Yost (CFO)
Mark S. Dinsmore (Co-Founder, CMO & Dir)
Eric W. Anderson (Co-Founder, Chief res Officer & Dir)
Daniel G. Schmedlen Jr. (CEO)

Subsidiaries:

Acsia Partners LLC (1)
16932 Woodinville Redmond Rd NE Ste A204, Woodinville, WA 98072
Tel.: (425) 284-2148
Web Site: https://www.acsiapartners.com
Emp.: 100
Insurance Services
N.A.I.C.S.: 524210
Denise Gott (CEO)

Subsidiary (Domestic):

LTC Financial Partners, LLC. (2)
6201 Presidential Ct, Fort Myers, FL 33919
Long-Term Care Insurance Services
N.A.I.C.S.: 524298

American Insurance Marketing Services, Inc. (1)
4240 Carmichael Rd, Montgomery, AL 36106-2804
Tel.: (800) 325-9876
Web Site: http://www.aimsbenefits.com
Insurance Agencies & Brokerages
N.A.I.C.S.: 524210
Carlton Center (Pres)

Glenn G Geiger Company Inc (1)
3 Parklands Dr, Darien, CT 06820
Tel.: (203) 662-4620
Web Site:
  http://www.thegeigercompany.com
Rev.: $1,300,000
Emp.: 12
Administrative Management & General Management Consulting Service
N.A.I.C.S.: 541611
Susan A. Fitzpatrick (VP)
Scott A. Geiger (Pres & CEO)
Daniel W. Geiger (VP)

The Blair Agency, Inc. (1)
1401 S Brentwd Blvd, Saint Louis, MO 63144
Tel.: (314) 961-0013
Web Site: http://www.capitalfinancial.com
Sales Range: $1-9.9 Million
Emp.: 16
Insurance Agencies & Brokerages
N.A.I.C.S.: 524210
Michael Blair (Pres)

LTD COMMODITIES LLC
2800 Lakeside Dr, Bannockburn, IL 60015
Tel.: (847) 295-5501
Web Site:
  http://www.ltdcommodities.com
Sales Range: $200-249.9 Million
Emp.: 1,500
Mail Order Services
N.A.I.C.S.: 449129
Aimee Day (Supvr-Production)
Burt Greene (Mgr-Facilities)
Rick Luciani (Dir-DC Ops)
Sherry Alvarez (Mgr-Accts Processing Center)
Tom Baron (Mgr-Distr Ops)
Harri Broman (Sr Mgr-Logistics)
Cheryl A. Bulka (Supvr-Order & Payment Processing Center)
Christine Eckheart (Mgr-Mdse Div)
Louie Gomez (Mgr-Database Svcs)
Michael Hara (Pres & CEO)
Mike Hori (VP-Mdsg)
Sandy McCarty (Dir-Accts Processing Center & Order Processing)
Lori Roedl (Mgr-Telecom)
Rebecca Ullrich (Dir-Adv)
Susan Wallace (VP-Info Svcs)
Jack Voigt (VP-Ops)

LTN GLOBAL COMMUNICATIONS, INC.

LTI DEVELOPMENT CO. INC.
10800 N Military Trl, Palm Beach Gardens, FL 33410
Tel.: (561) 296-1193
Sales Range: $10-24.9 Million
Emp.: 3
Concrete Work
N.A.I.C.S.: 238110
Ross Person (Pres)

LTI POWER SYSTEMS, INC.
10800 Middle Ave Bldg B, Elyria, OH 44035-7890
Tel.: (440) 327-5050   OH
Web Site:
  http://www.ltipowersystems.com
Year Founded: 1977
Sales Range: $1-9.9 Million
Emp.: 15
Mfr of Uninterrupted Power Inverters & Static Switching Power Converters
N.A.I.C.S.: 335311
Bob Morog (Pres)
Chris Desimone (CFO)

LTL HOLDINGS, INC.
2728 Agnes St, Corpus Christi, TX 78405-2208
Tel.: (361) 882-3311
Year Founded: 1995
Sales Range: $25-49.9 Million
Emp.: 200
Petroleum Products
N.A.I.C.S.: 424720
Garnett T. Brooks (Pres)

Subsidiaries:

Difco, Inc. (1)
2728 Agnes St, Corpus Christi, TX 78405-2208
Tel.: (361) 882-3625
Web Site: http://www.txstar.com
Sales Range: $10-24.9 Million
Emp.: 9
Petroleum Products
N.A.I.C.S.: 424720

LTL HOME PRODUCTS, INC.
125 Rt 61 S, Schuylkill Haven, PA 17972
Tel.: (570) 385-5470
Web Site:
  http://www.ltlhomeproducts.com
Year Founded: 1989
Rev.: $24,000,000
Emp.: 65
Home Products Mfr & Distr
N.A.I.C.S.: 423310
Malcolm Groff (Pres)

LTM INC.
925 E Main St Ste 66, Havelock, NC 28532
Tel.: (252) 444-6881
Web Site: http://www.ltminc.net
Year Founded: 1994
Sales Range: $10-24.9 Million
Emp.: 235
Engineering, Logistics, Acquisition & Information Technology Services
N.A.I.C.S.: 541511
David W. Baldwin (Founder & Pres)

LTN GLOBAL COMMUNICATIONS, INC.
8600 Foundry St, Savage, MD 20763
Tel.: (240) 855-0004
Web Site: http://www.ltnglobal.com
Software Publisher
N.A.I.C.S.: 513210
Yousef Javadi (Pres & CEO)
Malik Khan (Founder & Chm)
Alan Young (CTO & Head-Strategy)

Subsidiaries:

Crystal Computer Corporation (1)

LTN GLOBAL COMMUNICATIONS, INC.

LTN Global Communications, Inc.—(Continued)
4550 River Green Pkwy Ste 220, Duluth, GA 30096
Tel.: (770) 932-0970
Software Publisher
N.A.I.C.S.: 513210
Roger Franklin *(Pres & CEO)*

Subsidiary (Domestic):

Video Design Software (USA), Inc. (2)
2 Melville Rd Huntington Station, Melville, NY 11746
Tel.: (631) 249-4399
Custom Computer Programming Services
N.A.I.C.S.: 541511

LTP MANAGEMENT GROUP, INC.
4411 Cleveland Ave, Fort Myers, FL 33901
Tel.: (239) 275-4666   FL
Web Site:
http://www.hootersflorida.com
Year Founded: 1987
Emp.: 75
Holding Company; Franchise Restaurant & Sports Bar Operator
N.A.I.C.S.: 551112
David Lageschulte *(CEO)*
Terry K. Brawner *(Pres)*

Subsidiaries:

Hooters of Cape Coral, Inc. (1)
3120 Del Prado Blvd S, Cape Coral, FL 33904
Tel.: (239) 945-4700
Web Site: http://www.hootersflorida.com
Sales Range: $1-9.9 Million
Emp.: 51
Restaurant & Sports Bar Operator
N.A.I.C.S.: 722511

Hooters of Crystal Lake, Inc. (1)
107 Hampton Rd Ste 200, Clearwater, FL 33759
Tel.: (727) 725-2551
Web Site: http://www.hootersflorida.com
Sales Range: $1-9.9 Million
Restaurant & Sports Bar Operator
N.A.I.C.S.: 722511

Hooters of Cypress Creek, Inc. (1)
6345 N Andrews Ave, Fort Lauderdale, FL 33309
Tel.: (954) 928-0026
Web Site: http://www.hootersflorida.com
Rev.: $1,100,000
Emp.: 46
Fiscal Year-end: 12/31/2006
Restaurant & Sports Bar Operator
N.A.I.C.S.: 722511

Hooters of Doral, Inc. (1)
8695 NW 13th Ter, Miami, FL 33126
Tel.: (305) 593-5088
Web Site: http://www.hootersflorida.com
Sales Range: $1-9.9 Million
Emp.: 60
Restaurant & Sports Bar Operator
N.A.I.C.S.: 722511

LUBA MUTUAL HOLDING COMPANY
2351 Energy Dr Ste 2000, Baton Rouge, LA 70808-2600
Tel.: (225) 389-5822
Web Site: http://www.lubasif.com
Insurance Related Activities
N.A.I.C.S.: 524298
David Bondy *(Founder & CEO)*
Russell Michiels *(Mgr-Claims Dept)*

Subsidiaries:

FHM Insurance Company (1)
4601 Touchton Rd E Ste 3150, Jacksonville, FL 32246-4485
Tel.: (904) 724-9890
Web Site: http://www.fhmic.com
General Management Consulting Services
N.A.I.C.S.: 541611

Mary Ann Richardson *(Sec)*
Matthew Lupino *(VP-Bus Dev)*

LUBAR & CO., INC.
833 E Michigan St Ste 1500, Milwaukee, WI 53202
Tel.: (414) 291-9000
Web Site: http://www.lubar.com
Sales Range: $10-24.9 Million
Emp.: 11
Private Investment Firm
N.A.I.C.S.: 523999
David Bauer *(Chief Investment Officer)*
David Kuehl *(Gen Counsel)*
Jamie Ward *(Controller)*
Vince Shiely *(Partner)*
Sheldon Bernard Lubar *(Founder & Chm)*
Jean Ellen Trubshaw *(Mng Dir-Family Office)*
Gary R. Sarner *(Partner-Operating)*
Wendy Cartwright *(Asst Controller)*
David John Lubar *(Pres & CEO)*

Subsidiaries:

ChemDesign Products, Inc. (1)
2 Stanton St, Marinette, WI 54143
Tel.: (715) 735-9033
Web Site:
http://www.chemdesignproducts.com
Sales Range: $25-49.9 Million
Custom Chemicals Mfr
N.A.I.C.S.: 325998
David Mielke *(Pres & CEO)*
Rae Johnson *(VP-Sls & Mktg)*
Tim Swavely *(Dir-Health Environment & Safety)*
Randy Christl *(CFO & Controller)*
Brian Bourgeois *(Mgr-HR & Employee Dev)*
Bela T. Lanczy *(Mgr-Comml Dev)*
Paul Zizelman *(Dir-Tech)*

LUBBOCK SYMPHONY ORCHESTRA
601 Avenue K, Lubbock, TX 79401
Tel.: (806) 762-1688
Web Site:
http://www.lubbocksymphony.org
Year Founded: 1946
Sales Range: Less than $1 Million
Emp.: 10
Symphony Orchestra Services
N.A.I.C.S.: 711130
Briana Thompson *(Dir-Patron Svcs)*
Galen Wixson *(Pres & CEO)*
Harry Zimmerman *(Chm)*

LUBERSKI INC.
310 N Harbor Blvd Ste 205, Fullerton, CA 92832
Tel.: (714) 680-3447   CA
Web Site: http://www.hiddenvilla.com
Year Founded: 1953
Emp.: 325
Poultry & Poultry Products Distr & Whslr
N.A.I.C.S.: 424440
Tim Luberski *(Founder & Pres)*
Don Lawson *(CFO)*
Michael Sencer *(Exec VP)*
Robert J. Kelly *(Exec VP)*
Greg Schneider *(COO)*

LUBICOM MARKETING CONSULTING
1428 36th St Ste 207, Brooklyn, NY 11218
Tel.: (718) 854-4460   NY
Web Site: http://www.lubicom.com
Year Founded: 1984
Sales Range: $10-24.9 Million
Emp.: 12
Advertising Agencies
N.A.I.C.S.: 541810
Menachem Lubinsky *(CEO)*
Eda Kram *(Dir-Mktg & Sls)*

LUBNER GROUP, LLC
14560 Global Pkwy, Fort Myers, FL 33913
Tel.: (239) 561-1806
Web Site:
http://www.lubnergroup.com
Sales Range: $10-24.9 Million
Emp.: 80
Home Furnishings Stores
N.A.I.C.S.: 449129
Dan Lubner *(Principal)*

LUBRICATION ENGINEERS, INC.
300 Bailey Ave, Fort Worth, TX 76107-5906
Tel.: (817) 834-6321   TX
Web Site: http://www.le-inc.com
Year Founded: 1951
Sales Range: $75-99.9 Million
Emp.: 100
Mfr of Lubricating Oils & Greases
N.A.I.C.S.: 324191
Scott Schwindaman *(Pres)*
Aaron Murphree *(Mgr-Eastern Div)*
Jeff Turner *(Exec VP)*
Vincent M. Tofani *(VP-Sls)*

LUBRICATION TECHNOLOGIES, INC.
900 Mendelssohn Ave N, Golden Valley, MN 55427
Tel.: (763) 545-0707   MN
Web Site: http://www.lubetech.com
Year Founded: 1993
Lubricating Oils & Greases Developer & Mfr
N.A.I.C.S.: 424720
Dan Hennen *(Mgr-Fuels Bus)*
Mark Kuglin *(Mgr-Ops)*
Ray Baker *(Mgr-Ops)*
Matt Olund *(Acct Mgr)*

Subsidiaries:

Lube-Tech & Partners, LLC (1)
858 Transfer Rd, Saint Paul, MN 55114
Tel.: (651) 636-7990
Web Site: http://www.lubetech.com
Petroleum Product Distr
N.A.I.C.S.: 424720
David Boyer *(Dir-Ops & Sls-Iowa)*
Andrew Haag *(VP-Sls & Mktg)*
Chris Bame *(Chm)*

Lube-Tech Liquid Recycling, Inc. (1)
2420 County Rd C W, Roseville, MN 55113
Tel.: (763) 417-1370
Web Site: http://www.lubetech.com
Sales Range: $1-9.9 Million
Emp.: 30
Recycling Solutions for Oils, Used Filters & Coolants
N.A.I.C.S.: 562211
Christian Bame *(CEO)*

LUBRICORP, LLC
2648 Byington Solway Rd, Knoxville, TN 37931
Tel.: (865) 525-7125   TN
Web Site: http://www.lubricorp.net
Year Founded: 1958
Mfr & Retailer of Motor Oil & Fuel
N.A.I.C.S.: 424720
Mike Foltz *(CEO)*
Chadd Landress *(Engr-Tech Sls)*
Steve Owens *(Mgr-Facility)*

LUBY'S FUDDRUCKERS RESTAURANTS, LLC
13111 Northwest Fwy Ste 600, Houston, TX 77040
Tel.: (713) 462-4508   TX
Web Site:
http://www.fuddruckers.com
Year Founded: 1980
Hamburger Restaurant Owner, Operator & Franchisor
N.A.I.C.S.: 722511

LUBY'S RESTAURANTS LP
13111 NW Fwy Ste 600, Houston, TX 77040
Tel.: (713) 329-6800   TX
Web Site: http://www.lubys.com
Restaurant Services
N.A.I.C.S.: 722511

LUCA TECHNOLOGIES INC.
500 Corporate Cir Ste C, Golden, CO 80401
Tel.: (303) 534-4344   DE
Web Site:
http://www.lucatechnologies.com
Year Founded: 2003
Sales Range: $1-9.9 Million
Emp.: 50
Biotechnology Natural Gas Producer & Distr
N.A.I.C.S.: 213112
Brian J. Cree *(CFO & COO)*
William R. Mahaffey *(CTO)*
Michael Sabol *(Chief Acctg Officer)*
Matthew J. Micheli *(Sec)*
Jeffrey L. Weber *(VP-Geosciences)*
Roland P. DeBruyn *(VP-Engrg)*
R. Verlin Dannar *(VP-Field Ops)*
Lisa Rice *(VP-Admin & HR)*
Eric Szaloczi *(Chm)*

LUCAS OIL PRODUCTS INC.
302 N Sheridan St, Corona, CA 92880
Tel.: (951) 270-0154
Web Site: http://www.lucasoil.com
Rev.: $11,300,000
Emp.: 39
Lubricating Oils & Greases
N.A.I.C.S.: 324191
Forrest Lucas *(Founder, Pres & CEO)*
Tom Fredrickson *(COO)*
Manny Gutierrez *(Dir-Mktg)*
Alex Striler *(Dir-Sls-Lucas Team)*
Mark Negast *(Dir-Tech)*
Jay M. Kim *(Dir-Sls)*

LUCE SCHWAB & KASE INC.
9 Gloria Ln, Fairfield, NJ 07004
Tel.: (973) 227-4840
Web Site: http://www.lskair.com
Sales Range: $10-24.9 Million
Emp.: 31
Air Conditioning Equipment
N.A.I.C.S.: 423740
Jim Luce *(Owner)*

LUCENT POLYMERS, INC.
1700 Lynch Rd, Evansville, IN 47711
Tel.: (812) 421-2216
Web Site:
http://www.lucentpolymers.com
Year Founded: 1997
Sales Range: $25-49.9 Million
Emp.: 100
Plastic Film & Sheet Mfr
N.A.I.C.S.: 326113
Don Todd *(Pres)*

LUCERNE CAPITAL MANAGEMENT, LP
73 Arch St, Greenwich, CT 06830
Tel.: (203) 983-4400
Web Site:
https://www.lucernecap.com
Year Founded: 2000
Investment Management
N.A.I.C.S.: 523999

LUCID AGENCY, LLC
51 W 3rd St Ste E101, Tempe, AZ 85281
Tel.: (480) 219-7257
Web Site:
http://www.lucidagency.com
Sales Range: $1-9.9 Million
Emp.: 20

Interactive Advertising
N.A.I.C.S.: 541810
Ken Bonham (Partner)
Scott Kaufmann (Partner)
Lilly Babakitis (Acct Coord)
Holly Haro (Mgr-Bus Dev)
Ben Stone (Acct Mgr)
Megan Owens (Acct Mgr)
Stephanie Ranson (Acct Mgr)

LUCID TECHNOLOGY
1754 N Wilmot, Chicago, IL 60647
Tel.: (312) 238-8976
Web Site: http://www.lucidtec.com
Year Founded: 1998
Sales Range: $1-9.9 Million
Emp.: 25
Information Technology Services
N.A.I.C.S.: 541512
Eva J. Pan (Pres & CEO)
Pablo E. Aguirre (Dir-Program Svcs)

LUCIDWORKS INC.
3800 Bridge Pkwy Ste 101, Redwood City, CA 94065
Tel.: (650) 353-4057
Web Site: http://www.lucidworks.com
Sales Range: $1-9.9 Million
Emp.: 30
Big Data Analytics Software
N.A.I.C.S.: 513210
Sarath Jarugula (VP-Customer Success)
Stephen Tsuchiyama (Sr VP-Worldwide Sls & Svcs)
Will Hayes (CEO)
Gerald Kanapathy (VP-Products)
Keith Messick (CMO)
Ravi Krishnamurthy (VP-Technical Svcs)
Reade Frank (CFO)
Jeff Depa (Sr VP-Worldwide Field Ops)
Trey Grainger (Sr VP-Engrg)
Robert Lau (COO-Global Emerging Markets & Asia Pacific)

LUCILLE MAUD CORPORATION
513 N Olden Ave, Trenton, NJ 08638
Tel.: (609) 393-7555
Web Site: http://www.lucillemaud.com
Year Founded: 1985
Sales Range: $10-24.9 Million
Emp.: 11
Mfr of Information Processing Systems
N.A.I.C.S.: 334111
Louis Muirhead (Pres & CEO)

LUCK BROTHERS INC.
73 Trade Rd, Plattsburgh, NY 12901
Tel.: (518) 561-4321
Sales Range: $10-24.9 Million
Emp.: 100
Construction Engineering Services
N.A.I.C.S.: 237310
Chris Luck (VP)

LUCK STONE CORPORATION
PO Box 29682, Richmond, VA 23242-0682
Tel.: (804) 784-6300 DE
Web Site: http://www.luckstonecompany.com
Year Founded: 1923
Sales Range: $50-74.9 Million
Emp.: 560
Provider of Crushed & Broken Stone
N.A.I.C.S.: 212313
Mark S. Fernandes (VP)
John Pullen (VP)
Joe Carnahan (VP-Southeast)
Charles S. Luck III (Chm)
Charles S. Luck IV (Pres & CEO)

LUCKETT & FARLEY ARCHITECTS, ENGINEERS AND CONSTRUCTION MANAGERS, INC.
737 S 3rd St, Louisville, KY 40202
Tel.: (502) 585-4181
Web Site: http://www.luckett-farley.com
Architectural Services
N.A.I.C.S.: 541310
Michelle Smith (Mgr-HR)
Aric Andrew (Pres & CEO)

LUCKETT TOBACCOS INC.
3 2000 Warrington Way, Louisville, KY 40222-6467
Tel.: (502) 561-0070 AR
Year Founded: 1906
Sales Range: $50-74.9 Million
Emp.: 400
Retailer of Raw Materials
N.A.I.C.S.: 424590

Subsidiaries:

Hail & Cotton (1)
815 Bill Jones Industrial Dr, Springfield, TN 37172-5014 (100%)
Tel.: (615) 384-2421
Web Site: http://www.hailcotton.com
Sales Range: $10-24.9 Million
Emp.: 100
Farm-Product Raw Materials
N.A.I.C.S.: 424590

Hail & Cotton Inc. (1)
2500 S Main St, Springfield, TN 37172-4528
Tel.: (615) 384-9576
Web Site: http://www.hailcotton.com
Sales Range: $10-24.9 Million
Emp.: 125
Farm-Product Raw Materials
N.A.I.C.S.: 424590
Andy Spies (Pres-Intl Ops)
Patricia Rietveld (VP-Intl Fin & Admin)
Roderick Roe (CFO & Exec VP-Fin & Admin)
Chris Cooksey (Pres-Ops-North America)
Eric van Der Linden (Pres-DAC Ops)

LUCKEY FARMERS INC.
PO Box 217, Woodville, OH 43469
Tel.: (419) 849-2711
Web Site: http://www.luckeyfarmers.com
Sales Range: $50-74.9 Million
Emp.: 121
Grain Elevators
N.A.I.C.S.: 424510
Andy Swerlin (Gen Mgr)
Andy Swerlein (Pres & CEO)
John Bratton (Mgr-Agronomy Ops)

LUCKIE & CO. LTD.
600 Luckie Dr Ste 150, Birmingham, AL 35223-2429
Tel.: (205) 879-2121
Web Site: http://www.luckie.com
Year Founded: 1953
Rev.: $115,000,000
Emp.: 110
N.A.I.C.S.: 541810
Tom Luckie (Chm & CEO)
Ed Mizzell (Mng Dir)
Jane Mantooth (CFO & Sr VP)
Brad White (Chief Creative Officer)
Bob Harrison (Assoc Dir-Creative)
Suzanne Wright (Assoc Dir-Media)
John Cobbs (Mgr-Dev Team)
Bill Abel (VP & Dir-Digital Dev)
John Heenan (CMO)
Giannina Stephens (VP & Dir-Production)
Melissa Wheeler (Sr VP-HR)
John Gardner (Pres)
Chris Statt (COO)
Laura Long (Sr VP-Strategic Engagement)
R. L. Bhagyalakshmi (Coord-Database)
Bryn Gardner (Acct Exec)
Chip Bailey (Program Dir)
Erin Smith (Project Mgr)
Jason Martin (Assoc Dir-Creative)
Karen Kizzire (Mgr-Brdcst Production)
Sylvia Adamson (Sr Mgr-Field Mktg)
Tripp Durant (VP & Acct Dir)
Eunice Carter (VP & Dir-Media)
Mark Unrein (VP-Delivery)
Stephanie Naman (CTO)
Andy Odum (Dir-Creative)
Mary Winslow (VP & Grp Acct Dir)
Ginger Williford (Acct Dir)
Amy Wilson (Coord-Digital Content)
Dannielle Boozer (Coord-HR)
Chris Benson (CTO)
Mary Reynolds Porter (Coord-Traffic)
Gavin Johnston (VP-Brand Plng)
Susan Brown (Coord-Traffic)
Brandon Doty (Chief Creative Officer)
Brian Conley (Acct Dir)
Nick Utley (Mgr-Fin)
Nicole Redeker (Dir-Insights)
Tifanie Noblin (Mgr-Creative Project)
Monique Bosier (Sr Mgr-Engagement)
Jeaneen Benson (Dir-Integrated Art)
Lindsay Sexton (Mgr-Engagement)
Sean Vibert (Mgr-Engagement)
Cesar Jauregui (Coord-Engagement-Reg Acct)
Caley Goins (Mgr-Engagement)
Kristin Layman (Dir-Strategic Engagement)
Dan Atkinson Sr. (Dir-IT)

Subsidiaries:

Integrative Logic LLC (1)
2397 Huntcrest Way Ste 200, Lawrenceville, GA 30043
Tel.: (678) 638-2600
Emp.: 65
Advetising Agency
N.A.I.C.S.: 541810
Delia Cyra (Dir-Media Strategy)
Lane Andrews (Dir-Creative)

LUCKINBILL INC.
304 E Broadway Ave, Enid, OK 73701
Tel.: (580) 233-2026
Web Site: http://www.luckinbill.com
Sales Range: $10-24.9 Million
Emp.: 128
Plumbing Contractor
N.A.I.C.S.: 238220
Dennis Luckinbill (Pres)
Cindy Cooley (Dir-Legal & Risk Mgmt)
Jacob Bailey (Project Mgr)

LUCKS FOOD DECORATING COMPANY
3003 S Pine St, Tacoma, WA 98409-4713
Tel.: (253) 383-4815 WA
Web Site: http://www.lucks.com
Year Founded: 1903
Sales Range: $25-49.9 Million
Emp.: 225
Pastry Decoration Mfr
N.A.I.C.S.: 424490
Rick Ellison (Pres)
Carl Lucks (CFO)
Dan Elliott (Sr VP-Ops)

LUCKWEL PHARMACEUTICALS INC.
125 Cambridge Park Dr Ste 301, Cambridge, MA 02140
Tel.: (617) 430-5222 NV
Web Site: https://www.luckwel.com
Year Founded: 2013
LWEL—(OTCBB)
Assets: $46,681
Liabilities: $490,949
Net Worth: ($444,268)
Earnings: ($436,013)
Emp.: 1
Fiscal Year-end: 03/31/21
Pharmaceuticals Distr
N.A.I.C.S.: 424210
Kingrich Lee (Founder, Chm, Pres, CEO, Treas & Sec)
Mark Carrao (CFO)

LUCKY BUMS LLC
4663 Enterprise St, Boise, ID 83705
Web Site: http://www.luckybums.com
Year Founded: 2004
Sales Range: $1-9.9 Million
Emp.: 12
Outdoor Recreation Products
N.A.I.C.S.: 423910
Jeff Streeter (Chm, Co-Founder & CEO)
Julie Streeter (Co-Founder)

LUCKY DOLLAR STORES INC.
1404 River St, Wilkesboro, NC 28697
Tel.: (336) 667-3487
Web Site: http://www.lucky-dollar.com
Sales Range: $10-24.9 Million
Emp.: 6
General Merchandise
N.A.I.C.S.: 424990
Earl Parsons (Pres)

LUCKY INTERNATIONAL TRADING, INC.
4925 Stilwell St, Kansas City, MO 64120-1133
Tel.: (816) 231-3168
Sales Range: $10-24.9 Million
Emp.: 20
Frozen Specialty Food Mfr
N.A.I.C.S.: 311412
George King (Owner)

LUCKY START LTD.
8785 SW 165th Ave Ste 301, Miami, FL 33193
Tel.: (305) 382-6688
Sales Range: $10-24.9 Million
Emp.: 7
Land Subdividers & Developers, Commercial & Residential
N.A.I.C.S.: 237210
Antonio Balestena (Pres)

LUCKY'S TRAILER SALES, INC.
402 Vermont Rte 107, South Royalton, VT 05068
Web Site: http://www.luckystrailers.com
Sales Range: $1-9.9 Million
Trailer Sales & Rental
N.A.I.C.S.: 441227
Sharon Dimmick (Treas & Sec)
Russell Dimmick Jr. (Pres)

Subsidiaries:

Lucky's Lease, Inc. (1)
402 Vermont Rte 107, South Royalton, VT 05068
Tel.: (802) 763-3400
Web Site: http://www.luckyslease.com
Trailer Leasing Services
N.A.I.C.S.: 532120
Alexis Dimmick (Mgr)

LUCOR, INC.
790 Pershing Rd, Raleigh, NC 27608
Tel.: (919) 828-9511 FL
Sales Range: $75-99.9 Million
Emp.: 2,117

LUCOR, INC.

Lucor, Inc.—(Continued)
Operates Chain of Automotive Fast Oil Change, Fluid Maintenance, Lubrication & General Preventive Maintenance Service Centers Under the Name Jiffy Lube
N.A.I.C.S.: 811191
David Barnett (Mgr-Mktg)
Jerry B. Conway (Pres & COO)
Michael D. Davis (VP-Admin)
Reba Whiwer (Controller)

Subsidiaries:

Carolina Lubes Inc. (1)
790 Pershing Rd, Raleigh, NC 27608-2712
Tel.: (919) 828-9511
Web Site: http://www.jiffylube.com
Rev.: $17,400,000
Emp.: 40
Provider of Automotive Services
N.A.I.C.S.: 811191

LUDGATE ENGINEERING CORP.
10 Vanguard Dr Ste 90, Reading, PA 19606
Tel.: (610) 404-7290
Web Site: http://www.ludgate-eng.com
Year Founded: 1974
Sales Range: $1-9.9 Million
Emp.: 25
Surveying & Civil Engineering Services
N.A.I.C.S.: 541330
Thomas B. Ludgate (COO & VP)
Robert B. Ludgate Sr. (Pres)

LUDLOW CO-OPERATIVE ELEVATOR COMPANY INC.
North Rte 45, Ludlow, IL 60949
Tel.: (217) 396-4111
Web Site: http://www.ludlowcoop.com
Year Founded: 1904
Sales Range: $25-49.9 Million
Emp.: 28
Grain & Field Beans Distr
N.A.I.C.S.: 424510
Steve Myer (Mgr-Ops)
Paul Seaman (Gen Mgr)
Rick Nelson (Pres)

LUDLOW COMPOSITES CORPORATION
2100 Commerce Dr, Fremont, OH 43420
Tel.: (419) 332-5531
Web Site: http://www.ludlow-comp.com
Carpet-Topped Vinyl-Backed Floor Mats, Latex & Sponge Vinyl Anti-Fatigue Products Mfr
N.A.I.C.S.: 326299
Joshua Dusseau (VP-Ops)

Subsidiaries:

Crown Matting Technologies (1)
2100 Commerce Dr, Fremont, OH 43420
Tel.: (419) 332-5531
Web Site: http://www.crown-mats.com
Carpet-Topped Vinyl-Backed Floor Mats Mfr
N.A.I.C.S.: 314110

LUDLOW TEXTILES COMPANY, INC.
PO Box 507, Mount Holly, NC 28120
Tel.: (704) 827-4311
Year Founded: 1868
Sales Range: $75-99.9 Million
Emp.: 100
Mfr of Synthetic & Natural Threads & Twines
N.A.I.C.S.: 313110

LUDLUM MEASUREMENTS INC.
501 Oak St, Sweetwater, TX 79556
Tel.: (325) 235-4947
Web Site: http://www.ludlums.com
Rev.: $10,000,000
Emp.: 400
Nuclear Radiation & Testing Apparatus
N.A.I.C.S.: 334519
Mick Truitt (VP-Sls & Mktg & Bus Dev)
Martin Baker (Mgr-Production)
Richard Smola (Dir-Engrg)

LUDVIK ELECTRIC CO., INC.
3900 S Teller St, Lakewood, CO 80235-2213
Tel.: (303) 781-9601
Web Site: http://www.ludvik.com
Year Founded: 1980
Sales Range: $25-49.9 Million
Emp.: 500
Electrical Work
N.A.I.C.S.: 238210
Richard B. Giles (CFO & Treas)
Nick Herrera (Project Mgr)
Ken Danielson (Dir-IT)

LUDVIK HOLDINGS, INC.
1521 Concord Pike Ste 301, Wilmington, DE 19803
Tel.: (206) 984-3470
Web Site: http://www.ludvikholdings.com
Private Investment Firm
N.A.I.C.S.: 523999
Frank Kristan (Pres & CEO)

Subsidiaries:

Unitiv, Inc. (1)
925 Sanders Rd Ste A, Cumming, GA 30041
Tel.: (678) 455-9445
Web Site: http://www.unitiv.com
Enterprise IT Solutions
N.A.I.C.S.: 541512
Frank Kristan (Principal)

LUDWIG DISTRIBUTING CO., INC.
503 E 13th St, Stuttgart, AR 72160-5419
Tel.: (870) 673-4481
Year Founded: 1968
Sales Range: $1-9.9 Million
Emp.: 20
Beer & Ale Distr
N.A.I.C.S.: 424810
William Ludwig (Pres)

LUEDER CONSTRUCTION COMPANY
9999 J St, Omaha, NE 68127
Tel.: (402) 339-1000
Web Site: http://www.lueder.com
Sales Range: $25-49.9 Million
Emp.: 95
Commercial & Office Building
N.A.I.C.S.: 236220
Carmie Egger (Sec)
Brad von Gillern (Pres)
Jim Romano (Superintendent)
Jeff Sawyer (Superintendent)
Josh Shearer (Superintendent)

LUEDERS ENVIRONMENTAL, INC.
PO Box 920279, Needham, MA 02492-0279
Web Site: http://www.luedersco.com
Appliance Repair & Maintenance
N.A.I.C.S.: 811412
Michael Lueders (Pres)

LUEKEN'S FOOD STORE INC.
1171 Paul Bunyan Dr NW, Bemidji, MN 56601
Tel.: (218) 444-3663
Web Site: http://luekens.com
Sales Range: $50-74.9 Million
Emp.: 200
Independent Supermarket
N.A.I.C.S.: 445110
Brent Sicard (Pres)

LUGGAGE AMERICA INCORPORATED
19600 S Vermont Ave, Torrance, CA 90502
Tel.: (310) 233-2950
Web Site: http://www.olympiausa.com
Rev.: $27,081,655
Emp.: 34
Luggage
N.A.I.C.S.: 423990
Chris S. Yu (CEO)

LUGGAGE FORWARD, INC.
50 Congress St Ste 340, Boston, MA 02109
Tel.: (617) 482-1100
Web Site: http://www.luggageforward.com
Sales Range: $1-9.9 Million
Emp.: 13
Freight Transportation Services
N.A.I.C.S.: 488510
Keith Kirley (Pres)
Zeke Adkins (Co-Founder)
Aaron Kirley (Co-Founder)

LUHR BROS., INC.
250 W Sand Bank Rd, Columbia, IL 62236-1044
Tel.: (618) 281-4106
Web Site: http://www.luhr.com
Year Founded: 1938
Sales Range: $75-99.9 Million
Emp.: 385
Delivery, Unloading & Stone Placement Operations
N.A.I.C.S.: 212311
Sheryl Metzger (Treas & Sec)
Michael Luhr (Pres)
Jay Luhr (Exec VP)
William Gardner (VP)

LUHRSEN LAW GROUP, P.L.
7430 N Tamiami Trl, Sarasota, FL 34243
Tel.: (941) 957-4878
Web Site: http://www.luhrsen.com
Sales Range: $1-9.9 Million
Emp.: 10
Law firm
N.A.I.C.S.: 541110
Jeffrey A. Luhrsen (Pres)

LUIDIA, INC.
125 Shoreway Rd Ste D, San Carlos, CA 94070
Tel.: (650) 413-7500
Web Site: http://www.luidia.com
Sales Range: $10-24.9 Million
Emp.: 25
Idea-Capturing Systems Mfr, Sales & Services
N.A.I.C.S.: 541512
Ralf Holtzman (CEO)
Daniel Manian (VP-Product)
Brad Richter (Sr Dir-Design)
Jacob Harel (VP-Engrg)

Subsidiaries:

Luidia UK Ltd. (1)
Symes News 37 Camden High Street, London, NW1 7JE, United Kingdom
Tel.: (44) 01525377345
Sales Range: $10-24.9 Million
Emp.: 20
Idea-Capturing Systems Sales
N.A.I.C.S.: 423430

LUIHN FOOD SYSTEMS INC.
2950 Getway Ct Blvd, Morrisville, NC 27560
Tel.: (919) 850-0558
Web Site: http://www.luihnfood.com
Year Founded: 1966
Sales Range: $50-74.9 Million
Emp.: 1,200
Eating Place
N.A.I.C.S.: 722513
Bret Hooppaw (Dir-Ops-Taco Bell)
Teresa Eberwein (Dir-Mktg)
Jody Luihn (Pres)

LUIS A. AYALA COLON SUCRS. INC.
3091 Avenida Santiago de Los Caballeros, Ponce, PR 00716
Tel.: (787) 848-9000
Web Site: http://www.ayacol.com
Sales Range: $25-49.9 Million
Emp.: 88
Stevedoring
N.A.I.C.S.: 488320
Luis A. Ayala-Parsi (Chm)
Nelson Riollano (Sr VP)

LUIS PALAU ASSOCIATION
1500 NW 167th Pl, Beaverton, OR 97006
Tel.: (503) 614-1500
Web Site: http://www.palau.org
Year Founded: 1978
Sales Range: $10-24.9 Million
Emp.: 60
Christian Ministry Services
N.A.I.C.S.: 813110
Kevin Palau (Pres)
Simon Berry (Chm)
David E. Hall (Vice Chm)

LUK CRISIS CENTER, INC.
545 Westminster St, Fitchburg, MA 01420
Tel.: (978) 345-0685
Year Founded: 1970
Sales Range: $10-24.9 Million
Emp.: 232
Youth & Family Support Services
N.A.I.C.S.: 624190
David Hamolsky (Dir-Clinical)

LUK, INC.
545 Westminster St, Fitchburg, MA 01420
Tel.: (978) 345-0685
Web Site: http://www.luk.org
Year Founded: 1970
Sales Range: $10-24.9 Million
Emp.: 232
Community Care Services
N.A.I.C.S.: 624190
Sona Klimowicz (Dir-Residential Svcs)
Michele M. Morrissey (Dir-Community Placement)
Richard Hooks Wayman (CEO)
Thomas A. Hall (COO)
Beth Barto (Dir-Quality Assurance)
David Hamolsky (Dir-Clinical)
James Cassidy (Dir-HR)
Joe Sova (Treas)
Michael J. Roberts (CFO)
Ryan McGuane (Pres)

LUKE & ASSOCIATES, INC.
775 E Merritt Isle Causeqay Ste 230, Merritt Island, FL 32952
Tel.: (321) 452-4601
Web Site: http://www.lukeassoc.com
Year Founded: 2004
Sales Range: $100-124.9 Million
Emp.: 950
Medical Care, Advisory, Consulting & Engineering Services to U.S. Military
N.A.I.C.S.: 541690

COMPANIES

Jim Barfield *(Pres & CEO)*
Rich Hall *(CFO & CIO)*

LUKE BROTHERS, INC.
5532 Auld Ln, Holiday, FL 34690
Tel.: (727) 937-6448   FL
Web Site:
   http://www.lukebrothers.com
Year Founded: 2002
Sales Range: $10-24.9 Million
Emp.: 270
Landscaping Services
N.A.I.C.S.: 561730
Scott Brantley *(Branch Mgr)*
Patrick Miles *(Branch Mgr)*

LUKIE GAMES INC.
1337 NW 155th Dr, Miami Gardens, FL 33169
Tel.: (305) 624-0540
Web Site:
   http://www.lukiegames.com
Year Founded: 2005
Sales Range: $1-9.9 Million
Emp.: 20
Video Games & Systems
N.A.I.C.S.: 459120
Jesse Cover *(Owner & Pres)*
Sara Cover *(VP)*

LULA-WESTFIELD LLC
451 Hwy 1005, Paincourtville, LA 70391
Tel.: (985) 369-6450
Web Site: http://www.luwest.com
Sales Range: $25-49.9 Million
Emp.: 150
Producers of Raw Cane Sugar
N.A.I.C.S.: 311314
Michael Daigle *(CEO)*
E. Savoie *(Plant Mgr)*
Rex Charlet *(Supvr-Electrical)*

LULU INC.
3101 Hillsborough St, Raleigh, NC 27607-5436
Tel.: (919) 459-5858
Web Site: http://www.lulu.com
Year Founded: 2002
Publishing Services
N.A.I.C.S.: 513199
Harish Abbott *(Chief Product Officer)*

LULU'S
195 Humboldt Ave, Chico, CA 95928
Tel.: (530) 343-3545
Web Site: http://www.lulus.com
Year Founded: 1996
Sales Range: $10-24.9 Million
Emp.: 70
Women's Clothing Store
N.A.I.C.S.: 424350
Debra Cannon *(Co-Founder)*
Colleen Winter *(Co-Founder)*

LUM'S AUTO CENTER INC.
1605 SE Ensign Ln, Warrenton, OR 97146
Tel.: (503) 325-3421
Web Site:
   http://www.lumsautocenter.com
Sales Range: $1-9.9 Million
Emp.: 50
Automobiles, New & Used
N.A.I.C.S.: 441110
David Lum *(Pres)*
Laurie Lum *(Gen Mgr)*
Julie Lum *(Mgr-Parts)*

LUMAS REALTY, INC.
10805 SW 95th St, Miami, FL 33176-3264
Tel.: (305) 596-2626   FL
Web Site: http://lumasrealty.com
Year Founded: 1972
Sales Range: $75-99.9 Million

Emp.: 9
Provider of Real Estate Services
N.A.I.C.S.: 531210
Antonio A. Sarmiento *(Chm, Pres & Sec)*

LUMASTREAM, INC.
2201 1st Ave S, Saint Petersburg, FL 33712
Tel.: (727) 827-2805
Web Site:
   http://www.lumastream.com
Sales Range: $1-9.9 Million
Emp.: 50
LED Lighting Fixtures
N.A.I.C.S.: 335132
Eric Higgs *(Pres & CEO)*
Michael Gaydos *(VP-Market Dev)*
Chris Booth *(VP-Design)*
Minesh Patel *(Chm)*

LUMBEE RIVER ELECTRIC MEMBERSHIP CORP.
605 E 4th Ave, Red Springs, NC 28377-1668
Tel.: (910) 843-4131
Web Site:
   http://www.lumbeeriver.com
Year Founded: 1940
Sales Range: $25-49.9 Million
Emp.: 105
Electronic Services
N.A.I.C.S.: 221122
Walter White *(Dir-Mktg & Economic Dev)*
Carmen E. Dietrich *(Interim CEO)*
Jeff Jackson *(Dir-IT)*
Roger Oxendine *(Chm)*
Hampton Oxendine *(VP-Fin Svcs)*
James Hardin *(Treas)*

LUMBER GROUP INC.
819 Cowarts Rd, Dothan, AL 36303-6323
Tel.: (334) 793-6028   AL
Web Site:
   http://www.wholesalewoodonline.com
Year Founded: 1979
Sales Range: $75-99.9 Million
Emp.: 130
Mfr, Wholesaler & Retailer of Lumber
N.A.I.C.S.: 423310
George C. Harris *(Chm & Pres)*
Charles M. Andre *(Controller)*
James C. Stuckey Jr. *(Exec VP)*

Subsidiaries:

Cole Hall Lumber Co.   (1)
2500 Oak St, Pelham, AL 35124
Tel.: (205) 663-2900
Rev.: $3,254,574
Emp.: 11
Retails Building Materials
N.A.I.C.S.: 423310

Custom Lumber Mfg. Co.   (1)
819 Cowarts Rd, Dothan, AL 36303   (100%)
Tel.: (334) 793-1527
Web Site: http://www.plantationcypress.com
Sales Range: $25-49.9 Million
Emp.: 50
Timber Product Mfr
N.A.I.C.S.: 321113
George C. Harris *(Founder)*

Wholesale Wood Products   (1)
819 Cowarts Rd, Dothan, AL 36303
Tel.: (334) 793-6028
Web Site:
   http://www.wholesalewoodonline.com
Sales Range: $25-49.9 Million
Emp.: 45
Mfr & Wholesaler of Lumber & Related Products
N.A.I.C.S.: 423310
James C. Stuckey *(VP)*
Chuck Harris *(CEO & Gen Mgr)*

Charles Andre *(CFO)*
Georgia Harmon *(Mgr-Engineered Wood)*
Warren Reeves *(VP-Sls & Mktg)*

LUMBER INSURANCE CO.
1661 Worcester Rd Ste 300, Framingham, MA 01701
Tel.: (508) 872-8111   MA
Year Founded: 1895
Rev.: $127,823,561
Emp.: 5
Fire, Marine & Casualty Insurance
N.A.I.C.S.: 524126
Sean Carmody *(Pres & CEO)*

LUMBER INVESTORS LLC
3401 Eddie Williams Ave, Alexandria, LA 71302-4758
Tel.: (318) 448-0945   LA
Year Founded: 1986
Sales Range: $25-49.9 Million
Emp.: 70
Lumber, Plywood & Millwork & Building Materials
N.A.I.C.S.: 423310
Ken Cox *(CFO)*
H. Allen Wiggens *(Pres)*
Walter C. Melter *(VP)*
Floyd T. Andres *(Exec VP)*

Subsidiaries:

Martin Building Materials, LLC   (1)
1170 Expressway Dr, Pineville, LA 71360
Tel.: (318) 487-8586
Web Site:
   http://www.martinbuildingmaterials.com
Sales Range: $1-9.9 Million
Emp.: 34
Home Center Operator
N.A.I.C.S.: 444110
Beau Edwards *(Mgr-Sls)*

LUMBER KING INC.
S Fork Shopping Ctr, Whitley City, KY 42653
Tel.: (606) 376-5097
Web Site: http://www.lumberking.com
Rev.: $17,800,000
Emp.: 15
Lumber & Other Building Materials
N.A.I.C.S.: 423310
Wille Boyatt *(Mgr)*
Della Jones *(Sec)*
Marlene Kidd *(CFO & VP)*
Ronnie Kidd *(VP-Commodities)*

LUMBER MART INC.
Bus Hwy 2 E, East Grand Forks, MN 56721
Tel.: (218) 773-1151
Web Site:
   http://www.lumbermarteast.com
Sales Range: $10-24.9 Million
Emp.: 50
Lumber Products
N.A.I.C.S.: 444110
Robert E. Peabody *(Pres)*

LUMBER SPECIALTIES LTD.
1700 Beltline Rd E, Dyersville, IA 52040
Tel.: (563) 875-2858
Web Site: http://www.lbrspec.com
Sales Range: $10-24.9 Million
Emp.: 100
Trusses, Wooden Roof
N.A.I.C.S.: 321215
Wendy Hawkins *(Controller)*

LUMBER TECHNOLOGY CORPORATION
500 Morrris Ave, Springfield, NJ 07081-0614
Tel.: (973) 467-1766
Web Site:
   http://www.lumbertechnology.com
Year Founded: 1971

LUMBERMEN'S UNDERWRITING ALLIANCE

Sales Range: $10-24.9 Million
Emp.: 100
Provider of Lumber, Plywood & Millwork
N.A.I.C.S.: 423310
Monroe Satsky *(Pres)*
Darren Stasky *(CEO)*

LUMBERJACK'S, INC.
723 E Tallmadge Ave, Akron, OH 44310
Tel.: (330) 762-2401   OH
Web Site:
   http://www.lumberjacksbest.com
Year Founded: 1978
Sales Range: $10-24.9 Million
Emp.: 21
Kitchen Cabinets
N.A.I.C.S.: 444180
Jack Allen *(Pres)*

LUMBERMEN'S BRICK & SUPPLY CO.
13709 Industrial Rd, Omaha, NE 68137
Tel.: (402) 894-2222
Web Site: http://www.lumbermens.biz
Sales Range: $10-24.9 Million
Emp.: 60
Provider of Bricks, Except Refractory
N.A.I.C.S.: 423320
Jeff Funk *(Pres)*

LUMBERMEN'S CREDIT ASSOCIATION OF BROWARD COUNTY, INC.
701 E Commercial Blvd 4th Fl, Fort Lauderdale, FL 33334
Tel.: (954) 771-2100
Web Site: http://www.golca.com
Year Founded: 1958
Sales Range: $10-24.9 Million
Emp.: 115
Commercial (Mercantile) Credit Reporting Bureau
N.A.I.C.S.: 561450
Van Saliba *(Chm)*

LUMBERMEN'S INC.
4433 Stafford Ave SW, Grand Rapids, MI 49548
Tel.: (616) 538-5180
Web Site: http://www.lumbermens-inc.com
Sales Range: $25-49.9 Million
Emp.: 20
Roofing, Asphalt & Sheet Metal
N.A.I.C.S.: 423330
Roger Vanverheide *(Pres)*
John David *(Mgr-Sls)*
Bob Prins *(Gen Mgr-LPI Div)*
Rick Woltjer *(VP-Sls)*
Gordon DeYoung *(Mgr)*
Randy Martin *(VP-Entry Door Div)*
Henry Bouma Jr. *(Chm)*

LUMBERMEN'S UNDERWRITING ALLIANCE
1905 NW Corporate Blvd, Boca Raton, FL 33431
Tel.: (561) 994-1900
Web Site:
   http://www.lumbermensunderwriting.com
Year Founded: 1905
Sales Range: $125-149.9 Million
Emp.: 300
Fire, Marine & Casualty Insurance Carriers
N.A.I.C.S.: 524126
Christine Lynn *(Chm & CEO)*
James W. Osterman *(VP)*
Michael E. North *(Pres & COO)*
Mindy P. Appel *(Gen Counsel, Sec & VP)*
Maurice R. Piche *(VP)*

LUMBERMEN'S UNDERWRITING ALLIANCE

Lumbermen's Underwriting Alliance—(Continued)
Carol A. Salamida *(VP)*
James T. Trenter *(VP)*
Edward H. Mosher Jr. *(Treas & Sr VP)*

LUMBERMENS MERCHANDISING CORPORATION
137 W Wayne Ave, Wayne, PA 19087-4018
Tel.: (610) 293-7000   PA
Web Site: http://www.lmc.net
Year Founded: 1935
Sales Range: $1-4.9 Billion
Emp.: 200
Whslr of Building Materials & Lumber
N.A.I.C.S.: 423310
Fran Monk *(Mgr-Mktg)*
Jim Muthersbaugh *(Mgr-Mid Atlantic Reg)*

LUMBERMENS MUTUAL GROUP
1 Corporate Dr Ste 200, Lake Zurich, IL 60047
Tel.: (847) 320-2711   IL
Web Site: http://www.lmcco.com
Year Founded: 1912
Sales Range: $500-549.9 Million
Emp.: 300
Insurance Services
N.A.I.C.S.: 524210
Douglas S. Andrews *(Pres & CEO)*
Tami Distel *(Mgr-Accts Payable & Procurement)*
Chris Freund *(Dir-Data Mgmt)*

Subsidiaries:

American Manufacturers Mutual Insurance Company   (1)
1 Corporate Dr Ste 200, Lake Zurich, IL 60047   **(100%)**
Tel.: (847) 320-2000
Web Site: http://www.lmcco.com
Property & Casualty
N.A.I.C.S.: 524126

Lumbermen's Mutual Casualty Company   (1)
1 Corporate Dr Ste 200, Lake Zurich, IL 60047-8945   **(100%)**
Tel.: (847) 320-2000
Web Site: http://www.lmcco.com
Property & Casualty Insurance
N.A.I.C.S.: 524126
William D. Smith *(Pres & COO)*

Subsidiary (Domestic):

American Motorists Insurance Co.   (2)
1 Corporate Dr Ste 200, Lake Zurich, IL 60047-8945   **(100%)**
Tel.: (847) 320-2000
Sales Range: $500-549.9 Million
Emp.: 299
Automobile Insurance
N.A.I.C.S.: 524126

LUMBERYARD SUPPLIERS INC.
3405 N Main St, East Peoria, IL 61611
Tel.: (309) 694-4356
Web Site: http://www.ls-usa.com
Rev.: $19,220,984
Emp.: 30
Roofing, Siding & Insulation
N.A.I.C.S.: 423330
Troy Reed *(Pres)*

LUMENAD INC.
111 N Higgins Ave, Missoula, MT 59802
Tel.: (406) 552-1022   MT
Web Site: http://www.lumenad.com
Year Founded: 2014
Sales Range: $10-24.9 Million
Emp.: 60

Digital Marketing Services
N.A.I.C.S.: 541850
Ryan Hansen *(Founder & CEO)*
Kyle Kienitz *(VP-R&D)*
Daniel Bennion *(Sr VP-Product Dev & Mktg)*
Shane Dowaliby *(VP-Client Svcs)*
Jeannine Widmann *(VP-People & Ops)*

LUMENATE.COM
16633 Dallas Pkwy Ste 450, Addison, TX 75001-6811
Tel.: (972) 248-8999
Web Site: http://www.lumenate.com
Year Founded: 2002
Rev.: $36,200,000
Emp.: 60
Computer System Design Services
N.A.I.C.S.: 541512
Reagan Dixon *(Pres)*
Mike Voneper *(Reg Dir-Sls)*
Collin Miles *(Principal)*

LUMENDATA, INC.
5201 Great America Pkwy Suite 350, Santa Clara, CA 95054
Tel.: (855) 695-8636
Web Site: http://www.lumendata.com
Year Founded: 2007
Sales Range: $10-24.9 Million
Emp.: 45
Planning, Implementation, Integration, Maintenance & Training Services for Enterprise Information Management Solutions
N.A.I.C.S.: 541618
Nimish Mehta *(Co-Founder & Chm)*
Tarun Batra *(Co-Founder & CEO)*
Lin Chan *(CFO)*
Ken Readus *(Sr VP-Sls)*
Kiran Naik *(Chief Revenue Officer & Mng Principal)*

Subsidiaries:

LumenData, Inc.   (1)
2nd Floor D-Block RMZ Centennial ITPL Road Whitefield, Bengaluru, 560048, India   **(100%)**
Tel.: (91) 80 4135 3200
Web Site: http://www.lumendata.com
Enterprise Information Management Solutions & Data Strategy
N.A.I.C.S.: 513210
Amar Doshi *(Mgr)*

LUMETRICS, INC.
1565 Jefferson Rd Ste 420, Rochester, NY 14623-3190
Tel.: (585) 214-2455
Web Site: http://www.lumetrics.com
Optical Instrument & Lens Mfr
N.A.I.C.S.: 333310
John Hart *(Pres & CEO)*

LUMIERE CHILDREN'S THERAPY, INC.
1500 N Clybourn Ste C-105, Chicago, IL 60610
Tel.: (312) 242-1665
Web Site: http://www.lumierechild.com
Year Founded: 2009
Sales Range: $1-9.9 Million
Emp.: 45
Health Care Srvices
N.A.I.C.S.: 621610
Kitsa Antonopoulos *(Founder)*

LUMINA FOUNDATION FOR EDUCATION
30 S Meridian St Ste 700, Indianapolis, IN 46204
Tel.: (317) 951-5300
Web Site: http://www.luminafoundation.org
Sales Range: $25-49.9 Million

Emp.: 40
Student Loan Marketing Association
N.A.I.C.S.: 522299
Samuel D. Cargile *(VP)*
Shelley Lloyd *(Dir-HR & Admin)*
Kevin Corcoran *(Dir-Strategy)*
Holiday Hart McKiernan *(COO, Gen Counsel & Exec VP)*
Jamie P. Merisotis *(Pres & CEO)*
Danette Howard *(Chief Strategy Officer & Sr VP)*
Scott Jenkins *(Dir-Strategy)*
Debra Humphreys *(VP-Strategic Engagement)*
Courtney Brown *(VP-Strategic Impact)*
Chad Ahren *(Officer-Strategy)*
Lori B. Drzal *(Officer-Rels)*
John Duong *(Mng Dir-Lumina Impact Ventures)*
Dakota Pawlicki *(Officer-Strategy Community Mobilization)*
Candace Brandt *(Officer-Grants Mgmt)*
Monique Crowell *(Officer-Sr Acctg)*
Cody Coppotelli *(Officer-Investing)*
Amia Foston *(Officer-Strategic Impact & Res)*
Beverly W. Hudson *(Officer-Acctg)*
Linh C. Nguyen *(VP-Equity, Culture & Talent)*
Frank Swanzy Essien Jr. *(Officer-Strategy)*
Thomas Major Jr. *(Gen Counsel)*

LUMINATE CAPITAL MANAGEMENT, INC.
1 Letterman Dr Ste CM 500, San Francisco, CA 94129
Tel.: (914) 834-4334
Web Site: http://luminatecapital.com
Privater Equity Firm
N.A.I.C.S.: 523999
Hollie Haynes *(Founder & Mng Partner)*
Kate Scott *(CFO)*
Dave Ulrich *(Partner)*
Scott Kingsfield *(Operating Partner)*
Mark Pierce *(Operating Partner)*

Subsidiaries:

Ease Inc.   (1)
27405 Puerta Real Ste 380, Mission Viejo, CA 92691-6399
Tel.: (949) 266-9851
Web Site: http://www.easeinc.com
Computer Related Services
N.A.I.C.S.: 541519
John Smith *(VP)*
Eric Stoop *(CEO)*

LUMINUS MANAGEMENT, LLC
1811 Bering Dri Ste 400, Houston, TX 77057
Tel.: (713) 263-3300
Web Site: http://www.luminusmgmt.com
Year Founded: 2002
Investment Management
N.A.I.C.S.: 523999

Subsidiaries:

Servicios de Transportacion Jaguar, S.A de C.V.   (1)
Carretera a Monclova KM 5, Colonia Andres Caballero Escobedo, Nuevo Leon, 33635, Mexico
Tel.: (52) 8182861150
Web Site: https://stjaguar.mx
Truck Related Transportation Services
N.A.I.C.S.: 484122
Victor Castaneda *(Mgr-Natl Accts)*
Aldo Rosani *(Mgr-Natl Accts)*
Jorge B. Lopez Solorzano *(Mgr-New Accts)*
Hugo S. Sepulveda *(Mgr-Natl Accts)*
Enrique Favila *(Dir-Bus Dev)*

LUMITEX INC.
8443 Dow Cir, Cleveland, OH 44136
Tel.: (440) 243-8401
Web Site: http://www.lumitex.com
Sales Range: $10-24.9 Million
Emp.: 100
Manufactures Lighting Systems
N.A.I.C.S.: 335132
Peter W. Broer *(Pres & CEO)*
Bill Voit *(Controller)*
Mike Andrich *(VP)*
Scott Shanahan *(Mgr-Ops)*
Tara Mapson *(Engr-Design)*
Ron Bate *(VP-HR)*
Peggy Grospitch *(VP-HR)*

LUMITHERA, INC.
19578 10th Ave NE Ste 200, Poulsbo, WA
Tel.: (844) 342-3333
Web Site: https://www.lumithera.com
Year Founded: 2013
Optical Treatment & Solutions Developer
N.A.I.C.S.: 333310

Subsidiaries:

Diopsys, Inc.   (1)
16 Chapin Rd, Pine Brook, NJ 07058
Tel.: (973) 244-0622
Web Site: http://www.diopsys.com
Rev.: $4,000,000
Emp.: 100
Surgical & Medical Instrument Mfr
N.A.I.C.S.: 339112
Scott Kahn *(CFO, VP-Fin & HR & Controller)*
Joseph Fontanetta *(Pres & CEO)*
Alberto Gonzalez Garcia *(Chief Medical Officer)*
Donald Lepone *(COO & Exec VP)*
Matthew Emmer *(VP-Bus Dev & Clinical Affairs)*
Laurie Cox *(VP-Engrg)*
Alan Rich *(VP-Sls)*
Bill Shields *(VP-Sls-Intl)*
Peter Derr *(VP-Clinical Documentation & Regulatory Affairs)*

LUMMUS CORPORATION
1 Lummus Dr, Savannah, GA 31422
Tel.: (912) 447-9000
Web Site: http://www.lummus.com
Sales Range: $10-24.9 Million
Emp.: 210
Cotton Ginning Machinery
N.A.I.C.S.: 333248
Phil Dilorio *(Chm)*
Ben Hinnen *(CEO)*

Subsidiaries:

Belt-Wide Industries, Inc.   (1)
1116 50th St, Lubbock, TX 79404
Tel.: (806) 747-2633
Cotton Ginning Machinery Distr
N.A.I.C.S.: 423830

Carver Inc.   (1)
1 Lummus Dr, Savannah, GA 31422
Tel.: (912) 447-9000
Sales Range: $10-24.9 Million
Emp.: 100
Oil Seed Processing Machinery & Screening & Separating Equipment Mfr
N.A.I.C.S.: 333241

Lummus Australia Pty. Ltd.   (1)
55 Tycannah Street, PO Box 210, Moree, 2400, NSW, Australia
Tel.: (61) 267 511 088
Cotton Ginning Machinery Distr
N.A.I.C.S.: 423830

Lummus Do Brasil Ltda.   (1)
Avenida Beira Rio 1055, Box 03, 78070-200, Cuiaba, Brazil
Tel.: (55) 65 634 8452
Cotton Ginning Machinery Distr
N.A.I.C.S.: 423830

LUMMUS SUPPLY COMPANY INC.
1554 Bolton Rd, Atlanta, GA 30331

U.S. PRIVATE

Tel.: (404) 794-1501 GA
Web Site: http://www.lummus-supply.com
Year Founded: 1925
Sales Range: $25-49.9 Million
Emp.: 135
Provider of Lumber & Other Building Materials
N.A.I.C.S.: 423310
William Lummus (Pres)
Jackie Barber (Treas & Sec)
Robert H. Lummus Jr. (Chm)

LUNA CARPET & BLINDS CO., INC.
10 Davis Dr, Bellwood, IL 60104-1047
Tel.: (773) 202-5862
Web Site: http://www.luna.com
Sales Range: $10-24.9 Million
Emp.: 55
Carpet & Rug Distr
N.A.I.C.S.: 423220
Steve DeZara (CEO)

LUNA DATA SOLUTIONS, INC.
1408 W Koenig Ln Unit D, Austin, TX 78756
Tel.: (512) 828-7906
Web Site: http://www.lunadatasolutions.com
Sales Range: $1-9.9 Million
Emp.: 26
Human Resource Consulting Services
N.A.I.C.S.: 541612
Dana Jones (Pres)

LUNAN CORPORATION
414 N Orleans St Ste 402, Chicago, IL 60645
Tel.: (312) 645-9898
Web Site: http://www.lasvegasarbys.com
Sales Range: $10-24.9 Million
Emp.: 20
Franchise Owner of Fast-Food Restaurants
N.A.I.C.S.: 722513
Michael Schulson (Pres)
Steve Ganek (Controller)

LUNARDI'S SUPER MARKET INC.
432 N Canal St Ste 22, South San Francisco, CA 94080
Tel.: (650) 588-7507
Web Site: http://www.lunardis.com
Sales Range: $75-99.9 Million
Emp.: 700
Supermarket
N.A.I.C.S.: 445110
Alfred Lunardi (Pres)
Tom Uhrinak (Controller)

LUNARLINE, INC.
3300 N Fairfax Dr Ste 308, Arlington, VA 22201
Tel.: (571) 481-9300
Web Site: http://www.lunarline.com
Year Founded: 2004
Sales Range: $10-24.9 Million
Emp.: 72
Data Processing & Related Services
N.A.I.C.S.: 518210
Waylon Krush (Founder & CEO)
Keith Mortier (Pres & COO)
Ashley Roan (Engr-Security)
Narayani Siva (Assoc Dir-Privacy)

LUNARPAGES INTERNET SOLUTIONS
1908 N Enterprise St, Orange, CA 92865
Tel.: (714) 521-8150
Web Site: http://www.lunarpages.com
Year Founded: 1998
IT Solutions & Global Web Hosting Services
N.A.I.C.S.: 518210
Andrew DeLira (Mgr-Mktg)

LUND & FRANGIE MOTORS INC.
12350 Los Osos Vly, San Luis Obispo, CA 93405
Tel.: (805) 543-7001
Sales Range: $25-49.9 Million
Emp.: 50
New & Used Car Sales
N.A.I.C.S.: 441110
John Frangie (Pres & CEO)

LUND FOOD HOLDINGS, INC.
4100 W 50th St Ste 2100, Edina, MN 55424-1200
Tel.: (952) 548-1400 MN
Web Site: http://www.lfhi.com
Year Founded: 1939
Sales Range: $25-49.9 Million
Emp.: 5,500
Holding Company; Grocery, Bakery & Liquor Stores
N.A.I.C.S.: 445110
Phil Lombardo (Chief Mktg & Mdsg Officer)
Betty Johnson (Mgr-Pharmacy)
Brigitte Reuther (Project Mgr)
Carrie Wnuk (Mgr-Wines & Spirits Dept)
Chet Cooper (Mgr-Center Store)
Chris Gindorff (Sr Mgr-Quality Assurance)
Chuck Dahlmeir (Gen Mgr)
Dave Mickelberg (Mgr-Produce Category)
John C. Johansen (Mgr-Store)
Patty Horton (Gen Mgr)
Rick Steigerwald (Dir-Produce & Bakery)
Stephen Sorensen (Sr Mgr-Category)
Theresa Bentz (Mgr-Safety & Sanitation)
Blake Elgren (Mgr-Ops)
Julie Griffin (Dir-Private Brands)
Laura Miller (Coord-Food Svc Sys)
Jonathan Castillo (Supvr-Production)
Joseph Klimek (Mgr-Grocery)
Molly Mample (Mgr-Events & Promos)
Robert Muehl (Supvr-Store)
Tom Henderson (Mgr-Network Ops)
Bresser Scott (Mgr-Center Store)
Dan O'Rourke (Mgr-Mktg)
Jeff Kramm (Mgr-Store)
Jessie Seamans (Mgr-Ops)
Subsidiaries:
Byerly's Inc. (1)
4100 W 50th St Ste 2100, Edina, MN 55424-1200
Tel.: (952) 548-1400
Web Site: http://www.lundsandbyerlys.com
Sales Range: $25-49.9 Million
Emp.: 100
Grocery, Bakeries & Liquor Stores
N.A.I.C.S.: 445110
Fred Miller (VP-Fin)
Lund's Inc. (1)
4100 W 50th St Ste 2100, Edina, MN 55424-1266 (100%)
Tel.: (952) 927-3663
Web Site: http://www.lundsandbyerlys.com
Sales Range: $25-49.9 Million
Emp.: 100
Grocery Stores, Chain
N.A.I.C.S.: 445110

LUND'S FISHERIES, INC.
997 Ocean Dr, Cape May, NJ 08204
Tel.: (609) 884-7600 NJ
Web Site: http://www.lundsfish.com
Year Founded: 1954
Sales Range: $10-24.9 Million
Emp.: 130
Seafood Products Producer & Distr
N.A.I.C.S.: 424460
Wayne Reichle (Co-Owner & Pres)
Joe David (VP-Ops)
David Gray (VP-Value Added)
Randy Spencer (Dir-Sls)
Jeff Reichle (Co-Owner & Chm)
Matt Viall (CFO)

LUNDAHL BUILDING SYSTEMS, INC.
2005 N 600 W Ste C, Logan, UT 84321
Tel.: (435) 753-0888
Web Site: http://www.lundahlbuilding.com
Year Founded: 1983
Sales Range: $25-49.9 Million
Emp.: 56
Commercial & Institutional Building Construction
N.A.I.C.S.: 236220
Justin Robinson (CFO & Controller)
Todd Lundahl (Pres)
Jeff Lundahl (VP)

LUNDE AUTO CENTER
140 40th St SW, Fargo, ND 58103
Tel.: (888) 696-1553
Web Site: http://www.lundeautos.com
New & Used Car Dealers
N.A.I.C.S.: 441110
Andrew Boen (Owner)
Alex Boen (Gen Mgr)
Adams Berg (Sls Mgr-Kia)
Beth Olson (Mgr-Internet)
Jeff Laney (Mgr-Sls-Used Car)
Jeremy Thomson (Bus Mgr)
Joe Tweed (Gen Mgr-Kia)
Todd Potulny (Bus Mgr)
Todd Vetsch (Mgr-Lincoln)

LUNDMARK ADVERTISING + DESIGN INC.
104 W 9th St Ste 104, Kansas City, MO 64105
Tel.: (816) 842-5236
Web Site: http://www.lundmarkadvertising.com
Year Founded: 1947
Sales Range: Less than $1 Million
Emp.: 6
N.A.I.C.S.: 541810
Kia Hunt (Partner-Creative Svcs)
Brandon Myers (Mng Partner)

LUNDY CONSTRUCTION CO., INC.
200 Arch St, Williamsport, PA 17701
Tel.: (570) 323-8451 PA
Web Site: http://www.lundyconstruction.com
Year Founded: 1932
Sales Range: $10-24.9 Million
Emp.: 45
Provider of Contracting & Construction Services
N.A.I.C.S.: 236220
John Houser (Pres)
Stephen Thaler (Project Mgr)
Sean Hartranft (Mgr-Energy Svcs)
Frank Lundy II (Treas & Chief Engr)

LUNDY SERVICES INC.
4050 Black Gold Dr, Dallas, TX 75247
Tel.: (214) 951-8181
Web Site: http://www.lundy-services.com
Sales Range: $10-24.9 Million
Emp.: 500
Provider of Home/Office Interiors Finishing, Furnishing & Remodeling Services
N.A.I.C.S.: 238990
Ken Phillips (Co-Owner)

LUNEXA, LLC
301 Howard St Ste 1410, San Francisco, CA 94105
Tel.: (415) 325-5902
Web Site: http://www.lunexa.com
Year Founded: 2004
Sales Range: $1-9.9 Million
Emp.: 60
Data-Related Services, Including Business Intelligence, Data Warehousing & Enterprise Data Integration
N.A.I.C.S.: 513210
Alex Macievich (Partner)
David Cole (Partner)
Jagrit Malhotra (Partner)

LUNSETH PLUMBING AND HEATING CO.
1710 N Washington St, Grand Forks, ND 58203
Tel.: (701) 772-6631
Web Site: http://www.lunseth.com
Rev.: $22,427,820
Emp.: 111
Plumbing Contractor
N.A.I.C.S.: 238220
William O'Connell (Pres)
David Kvidt (VP)
Denny Coulter (Project Mgr)
Marty Becker (Mgr-Safety)
Philip Kraemer (VP)

LUNZ PREBOR FOWLER ARCHITECTS
58 Lake Morton Dr, Lakeland, FL 33801
Tel.: (863) 682-1882
Web Site: http://www.lunz.com
Year Founded: 1987
Sales Range: $1-9.9 Million
Emp.: 21
Architectural Services
N.A.I.C.S.: 541310
Edward Lunz (Pres & Principal)
Dan Fowler (Principal)
Bradley Lunz (Principal)

LUPIENT AUTOMOTIVE GROUP, INC.
7100 Wayzata Blvd Ste 200, Minneapolis, MN 55426
Tel.: (763) 544-6666
Web Site: http://www.lupient.com
Year Founded: 1969
Automobile Dealership
N.A.I.C.S.: 441110

LUPIENT CHEVROLET INC.
1601 Southtown Dr, Bloomington, MN 55431
Tel.: (952) 884-3333
Web Site: http://www.lupientchev.com
Sales Range: $50-74.9 Million
Emp.: 123
New & Used Car Sales
N.A.I.C.S.: 441110
Leslie Johnson (Mgr-HR)

LUPUS FOUNDATION OF AMERICA, INC.
2000 L St NW Ste 410, Washington, DC 20036
Tel.: (202) 349-1155 DC
Web Site: http://www.lupus.org
Year Founded: 1977
Sales Range: $10-24.9 Million
Emp.: 49
Medical Research Services
N.A.I.C.S.: 541715
Seung-Ae Chung (CFO)
Kimberly Cantor (VP-Advocacy & Govt Rels)

LUPUS FOUNDATION OF AMERICA, INC.

Lupus Foundation of America, Inc.—(Continued)
Mary T. Crimmings *(VP-Mktg & Comm)*
Sandra C. Raymond *(CEO)*
Susan Manzi *(Dir-Medical)*
Leslie Hanrahan *(VP-Education & Res)*
Diana Gray *(VP-Network Dev)*
Duane Peters *(Sr Dir-Comm)*
Donna Grogan *(VP-Dev & Fundraising)*
Lynn Blandford *(Treas)*
Stevan W. Gibson *(Pres)*
Joseph Arnold *(Sec)*

LUQUIRE GEORGE ANDREWS, INC.
4201 Congress St Ste 400, Charlotte, NC 28209
Tel.: (704) 552-6565
Web Site: http://www.lgaadv.com
Year Founded: 1984
Rev.: $50,000,000
Emp.: 45
Advetising Agency
N.A.I.C.S.: 541810
Steve Luquire *(Founder & CEO)*
Peggy Brookhouse *(Pres & Partner)*
David Coburn *(Sr VP-PR)*
Todd Aldridge *(Sr VP & Dir-Creative)*
Judi Wax *(Exec VP & Dir-Pub Rels)*
Philip Tate *(Sr VP)*
Bobbi Adderton *(Sr Mgr-Production)*
Jennifer Jones *(VP & Grp Dir-Creative)*
Jon Cain *(Dir-Art & Assoc Dir-Creative)*
Jane Duncan *(VP & Supvr-Mgmt)*
Liz Chandler *(VP-PR)*
Chuck Griffiths *(VP & Controller)*
Gretchen Voth *(VP & Dir-Content Strategy)*
Brooks Luquire *(Sr VP & Dir-Client Svc)*
Scott Gilmore *(Sr. VP & Dir-Travel & Recreation Brands)*
Shawn Gordon *(VP & Dir-Media)*
Stacey McCray *(VP-PR)*
Jeremy Selan *(Mgr-Acctg & Ops)*
Michelle Reino *(Partner & Program Mgr)*
Courtney Ottelin *(Sr Mgr-Digital Project)*
Ryan Coleman *(Dir-Creative Grp)*
Jarvis Holliday *(Sr Mgr-Digital Content)*
Mateo Wellman *(Dir-Digital)*
Stephanie Spicer *(VP & Dir-Brand Strategy)*
Barry Finkelstein *(Sr VP & Dir-PR)*
Ellen Huffman *(Sr Dir-Art)*
Sarah Helms *(Acct Supvr)*
Taryn Huson *(Acct Exec)*
Bridgette Smith *(Acct Coord)*
Ashley Kelley *(Sr Acct Exec)*
Amanda Gurkin *(Acct Exec)*
Chelsea Zipperer *(Dir-Art)*
Glen Hilzinger *(Chief Creative Officer)*

LURIE INVESTMENTS, INC
5501 Charles St, Bethesda, MD 20814
Tel.: (855) 569-7373
Financial Services
N.A.I.C.S.: 523999
Subsidiaries:

Knexus Research Corp. (1)
174 Waterfront St Ste 310, National Harbor, MD 20745
Web Site: http://www.knexusresearch.com
Intelligent Systems Research & Development Services
N.A.I.C.S.: 541715
Justin Karneeb *(Engr-Software)*
Adam Lurie *(CEO)*
Kalyan Gupta *(VP-R&D)*

LURN INC.
100 Lakeforest Blvd Ste 610, Gaithersburg, MD 20877
Tel.: (240) 252-4228
Web Site: http://www.lurn.com
Year Founded: 2004
Sales Range: $1-9.9 Million
Emp.: 72
Online Training Courses
N.A.I.C.S.: 611420
Anik Singal *(Founder & CEO)*
Richard Ruggiero *(COO)*

LUSARDI CONSTRUCTION CO.
1570 Linda Vista Dr, San Marcos, CA 92078
Tel.: (760) 744-3133
Web Site: http://www.lusardi.com
Sales Range: $150-199.9 Million
Emp.: 177
Commercial & Office Building, New Construction
N.A.I.C.S.: 236220
Scott Free *(CEO)*
Larry Letts *(VP-Field Ops)*
Jeff R. Jenco *(VP)*
Stanley P. Prigmore *(CFO)*
John A. Bailey *(Chm)*
Kurt Evans *(Pres)*
John A. Bailey *(Chm)*
Scott Free *(CEO)*
Stanley P. Prigmore *(CFO)*
Chris A. Hess *(VP-Ops)*
Larry L. Letts *(VP-Field Ops)*
Boyd A. Suemnick *(VP)*
Jeff R. Jenco *(VP)*
Nick Novak *(VP)*
Colton Hoge *(VP)*

LUSCOMBE ENGINEERING COMPONENTS CO. INC.
4682 Calle Bolero Ste D, Camarillo, CA 93012-8593
Tel.: (805) 987-4880
Web Site: http://www.lecc.com
Year Founded: 1993
Sales Range: $10-24.9 Million
Emp.: 43
Distr of Electro-Mechanical Passive & Active Products
N.A.I.C.S.: 423690
Doug Canterbury *(Pres)*

LUSE HOLDINGS, INC.
3990 Enterprise Ct, Aurora, IL 60504
Tel.: (630) 862-2600 IL
Web Site: http://www.luse.com
Year Founded: 1923
Emp.: 50
Holding Company
N.A.I.C.S.: 551112
Steven T. Luse *(Pres & CEO)*
Mike Strahler *(VP-Corp Sls & Mktg)*
Jessica Tooley *(Project Mgr-Thermal Technologies)*
Zach Krugler *(Project Mgr-Environmental Svcs)*
John Lorenz *(CFO & Exec VP)*
Subsidiaries:

Luse Companies, Inc. (1)
3990 Entepise Ct, Aurora, IL 60504-1405 (100%)
Tel.: (630) 862-2600
Web Site: http://www.luse.com
Rev.: $7,845,034
Emp.: 40
Specialty Trade Contractors
N.A.I.C.S.: 562910
Steven T. Luse *(Pres)*
John A. Lorenz *(CFO)*

Luse Thermal Technologies LLC (1)
3990 Enterprise Ct, Aurora, IL 60504
Tel.: (630) 862-2600
Insulation Contractor
N.A.I.C.S.: 238310

Steven T. Luse *(Pres)*
Luse-Stevenson Co. Inc. (1)
3990 Enterprise Ct, Aurora, IL 60504
Tel.: (630) 862-2600
Web Site: http://www.luse.com
Sales Range: $10-24.9 Million
Emp.: 55
Specialty Trade Contractors
N.A.I.C.S.: 238990
Steven T. Luse *(Pres & Sec)*
John A. Lorenz *(CFO)*

LUSIVE DECOR
3400 Medford St, Los Angeles, CA 90063
Tel.: (323) 227-9207
Web Site: http://www.lusivedecor.com
Year Founded: 2003
Sales Range: $1-9.9 Million
Emp.: 41
Mfr of High End Lighting & Accessories
N.A.I.C.S.: 335132
Jason Cooper *(Pres)*
Sally Thomas Cooper *(Pres-Sls & Mktg)*
Jason Miranda *(CEO)*
Octavio Cornejo *(Mgr-Shipping & Production)*

LUSTER PRODUCTS INC.
1104 W 43rd St, Chicago, IL 60609
Tel.: (773) 579-1800
Web Site: http://www.lusterproducts.com
Year Founded: 1957
Sales Range: $150-199.9 Million
Emp.: 400
Beauty Aids Mfr
N.A.I.C.S.: 325620
Jory Luster *(Pres)*
Reginald Maynor *(Dir-Sls-Intl)*
Fred Luster II *(VP-Res & Dev)*

LUSTER-ON PRODUCTS, INC.
54 Waltham Ave, Springfield, MA 01109-3335
Tel.: (413) 739-2541
Web Site: http://www.luster-on.com
Year Founded: 1969
Sales Range: $1-9.9 Million
Emp.: 20
Metal Finishing Products Mfr & Distr
N.A.I.C.S.: 325998
Alexander J. Price *(Pres)*
Stephen Gilbert *(VP-Sls)*

LUSTROS, INC.
9025 Carlton Hills Blvd, Santee, CA 92071
Tel.: (619) 449-4800 UT
Web Site: http://www.lustros.com
Year Founded: 2005
Sales Range: Less than $1 Million
Emp.: 42
Copper Mining
N.A.I.C.S.: 212230
Zirk Engelbrecht *(Vice Chm)*
William F. Farley *(CEO)*

LUTCO, INC.
677 Cambridge St, Worcester, MA 01610
Tel.: (508) 756-6296
Web Site: http://www.lutco.com
Year Founded: 1945
Sales Range: $10-24.9 Million
Emp.: 125
Precision Turned Product Mfr
N.A.I.C.S.: 332721
John C. Stowe *(Pres)*

LUTE PLUMBING SUPPLY INC.
3920 US Hwy 23, Portsmouth, OH 45662
Tel.: (740) 353-1447 OH
Web Site: http://www.lutesupply.com

Year Founded: 1952
Sales Range: $25-49.9 Million
Emp.: 85
Plumbing Supplies Whslr
N.A.I.C.S.: 423720
Christopher H. Lute *(Chm & CEO)*
Jason Lute *(Pres & COO)*
Brian Hancock *(Sr VP)*

LUTGEN & ASSOCIATES, INC.
3520 Pan American Fwy Ste A2, Albuquerque, NM 87107
Tel.: (505) 888-3005 NM
Web Site: http://www.doctech.com
Year Founded: 1991
Sales Range: $1-9.9 Million
Office Equipment Dealer
N.A.I.C.S.: 423420
Michael Lutgen *(Owner & Chm)*
Isaiah Thompson *(Pres)*

LUTH RESEARCH, LLC
1365 4th Ave, San Diego, CA 92101
Tel.: (619) 234-5884
Web Site: http://www.luthresearch.com
Year Founded: 1977
Sales Range: $75-99.9 Million
Emp.: 212
Marketing Research & Public Opinion Polling
N.A.I.C.S.: 541910
Becky Wu *(Sr Exec VP)*
Roseanne Luth *(CEO)*

LUTH-AR, LLC
3312 12th St SE, Saint Cloud, MN 56304
Tel.: (763) 263-0166
Web Site: http://www.luth-ar.com
Year Founded: 2013
Firearm Component Mfr
N.A.I.C.S.: 332994
Randy E. Luth *(Pres & Founder)*
Randy Luth *(Founder, Owner & Pres)*

LUTHER BROOKDALE TOYOTA
6700 Brooklyn Blvd, Brooklyn Center, MN 55429-1714
Tel.: (763) 566-0060
Web Site: http://www.lutherbrookdaletoyota.com
Sales Range: $25-49.9 Million
Emp.: 93
Car Whslr
N.A.I.C.S.: 441110
David Luther *(Owner & Pres)*
Ron Murray *(Gen Mgr)*
Matthew Rossetter *(Bus Mgr)*

LUTHER BURBANK MEMORIAL FOUNDATION
50 Mark W Springs Rd, Santa Rosa, CA 95403
Tel.: (707) 527-7006 CA
Year Founded: 1978
Sales Range: $1-9.9 Million
Emp.: 190
Arts Promotion Services
N.A.I.C.S.: 711310
Rick Nowlin *(Pres & Exec Dir)*
Katherine Leader *(CFO)*
Bruce Decrona *(Treas)*
Kevin McCullough *(Sec)*
Sherry Swayne *(Chm)*

LUTHER HOLDING COMPANY
3701 Alabama S, Saint Louis Park, MN 55416
Tel.: (763) 593-5755
Web Site: http://www.lutherauto.com
Rev.: $232,200,000
Emp.: 40
New & Used Automobiles
N.A.I.C.S.: 441110

COMPANIES

David Luther *(Pres)*
Barbara Hilbert *(CFO)*

Subsidiaries:

Brookdale Motor Sales Inc (1)
4301 68th Ave N, Brooklyn Center, MN 55429
Tel.: (763) 561-8161
Web Site: http://www.lutherauto.com
New & Used Automobiles
N.A.I.C.S.: 441110

Hansord Agency Inc. (1)
3701 Alabama Ave S, Saint Louis Park, MN 55416
Tel.: (763) 593-5755
Web Site: http://www.lutherauto.com
Sales Range: Less than $1 Million
Emp.: 2
Commercial & Industrial Building Operation
N.A.I.C.S.: 531120
David Luther *(Pres)*

Infiniti of Bloomington Inc. (1)
1500 W 81st St, Bloomington, MN 55431
Tel.: (952) 888-5555
Web Site: http://www.lutherauto.com
Rev: $5,900,000
Emp.: 35
New & Used Automobiles
N.A.I.C.S.: 441110
Scott Hanebeck *(Mgr-Used Car)*

Jaguar Land Rover Minneapolis (1)
8905 Wayzata Blvd, Golden Valley, MN 55426
Tel.: (763) 222-2200
Web Site: http://www.lutherauto.com
New & Used Automobiles
N.A.I.C.S.: 441110
Ted Terp *(Gen Mgr)*

Luthers Rudy White Bear Motors (1)
3525 Hwy 61 N, Saint Paul, MN 55110
Tel.: (651) 481-7000
Web Site: http://www.lutherauto.com
New & Used Automobiles
N.A.I.C.S.: 441110
Dan Movan *(Gen Mgr)*

R.L. Brookdale Motors Inc. (1)
6800 Brooklyn Blvd, Brooklyn Center, MN 55429
Tel.: (763) 331-6800
Web Site: http://www.lutherbrookdalehonda.com
New & Used Car Retailer
N.A.I.C.S.: 441110
Jim Haertzen *(Gen Mgr)*

R.L. Imports Inc. (1)
7801 Lyndale Ave S, Bloomington, MN 55420
Tel.: (952) 881-6200
Sales Range: $25-49.9 Million
New & Used Automobiles
N.A.I.C.S.: 441110
Mark Rosenthal *(Gen Mgr)*

Republic Leasing Corporation (1)
3701 Alabama Ave S, Saint Louis Park, MN 55416
Tel.: (952) 258-8800
Web Site: http://www.lutherauto.com
Sales Range: $25-49.9 Million
Truck Leasing
N.A.I.C.S.: 532120

Rudy Luther Toyota Scion (1)
8805 Wayzata Blvd, Golden Valley, MN 55426
Tel.: (763) 222-2020
Web Site: http://www.rudyluthertoyota.com
New & Used Automobiles
N.A.I.C.S.: 441110
R. Daniel Luther *(Owner)*

Rudy Luthers Hopkins Honda (1)
250 5th Ave S, Hopkins, MN 55343-7766
Tel.: (952) 938-1717
Web Site: http://lutherhopkinshonda.com
Body Shop, Automotive
N.A.I.C.S.: 811121
R. Daniel Luther *(Co-Owner)*
David Luther *(Owner & Pres)*

LUTHER KING CAPITAL MANAGEMENT CORPORATION

301 Commerce St Ste 1600, Fort Worth, TX 76102
Tel.: (817) 332-3235   DE
Web Site: http://www.lkcm.com
Year Founded: 1979
Emp.: 86
Investment Advisory & Management Services
N.A.I.C.S.: 523940
Paul W. Greenwell *(Principal, VP & Portfolio Mgr)*
Scot C. Hollmann *(Principal, VP & Portfolio Mgr)*
David L. Dowler *(Principal, VP & Portfolio Mgr)*
Joan M. Maynard *(Principal, VP & Portfolio Mgr)*
Gary G. Walsh *(Principal, VP & Portfolio Mgr)*
James J. Kerrigan *(VP)*
Michael C. Yeager *(VP & Dir-Res)*
Mark L. Johnson *(Principal, VP & Portfolio Mgr)*
Alan D. Marshall *(VP-Equity Trader)*
Jacob D. Smith *(Chief Compliance Officer, Principal, Gen Counsel & VP)*
Steven R. Purvis *(Principal, VP & Portfolio Mgr)*
Frederick B. Labatt *(Mgr-Portfolio)*
M. Bradley Wallace *(Mgr-Private Equity)*
Andrew D. Zacharias *(Mgr-Private Equity)*
Jonathan B. Deweese *(Principal, VP & Portfolio Mgr)*
Jeremy A. Blackman *(VP & Portfolio Mgr)*
David M. Lehmann *(VP & Portfolio Mgr)*
Scott A. Neuendorf *(VP & Portfolio Mgr)*
Gregory L. McCoy *(Officer-Tax & VP)*
Richard W. Lenart *(Treas & Sec)*
Elisabeth J. Schrimpshere *(VP)*
Trisha Kroutil *(Chief Client Admin Officer & VP)*
Lisa L. Rettew *(Principal, Treas, VP & Asst Sec)*
John Bryan King *(Principal, VP & Portfolio Mgr)*
Tracey Ezelle *(Sec)*
John E. Gunthorp *(VP & Portfolio Mgr)*
Craig I. Hester *(Principal, VP & Portfolio Mgr)*
Mason D. King *(Principal)*
Mason D. King *(Principal, Principal, VP & Portfolio Mgr)*

LUTHER P. MILLER, INC.

S Edgewood Ave Cannel St, Somerset, PA 15501
Tel.: (814) 445-6569   DE
Web Site: http://www.lpminc.net
Year Founded: 1954
Sales Range: $10-24.9 Million
Emp.: 100
Petroleum Bulk Stations & Terminals
N.A.I.C.S.: 424710
Janet Thierry *(Mgr-Credit)*

LUTHERAN CHURCH MISSOURI SYNOD

1333 S Kirkwood Rd, Saint Louis, MO 63122-7295
Tel.: (314) 965-9000
Web Site: https://www.lcms.org
Year Founded: 1847
Social Organization Services
N.A.I.C.S.: 813920

LUTHERAN COMMUNITY SERVICES NORTHWEST

4040 S 188th St Ste 300, Seatac, WA 98188
Tel.: (206) 901-1685   OR
Web Site: http://www.lcsnw.org
Year Founded: 1926
Sales Range: $25-49.9 Million
Emp.: 738
Social Welfare Services
N.A.I.C.S.: 813410
Rick Hutchins *(VP-HR)*
Kay Reed *(VP-Fin)*
Daina Vitolins *(Vice Chm)*
Roberta Nestaas *(Pres & CEO)*
Bill Brueggemann *(Chm)*

LUTHERAN FAMILY SERVICES IN THE CAROLINAS

616 Hutton St, Raleigh, NC 27606
Tel.: (919) 832-2620
Web Site: http://www.lfscarolinas.org
Sales Range: $125-149.9 Million
Emp.: 350
Homes for Children & Aged
N.A.I.C.S.: 623110
Eric Hoyle *(Chm)*
Elizabeth Kuhn *(Chief Dev Officer)*
Kesha Smith *(Co-COO)*

LUTHERAN FAMILY SERVICES OF VIRGINIA, INC.

2609 McVitty Rd, Roanoke, VA 24018-3513
Tel.: (540) 774-7100   VA
Web Site: http://www.lfsva.org
Year Founded: 1982
Sales Range: $25-49.9 Million
Emp.: 549
Individual & Family Support Services
N.A.I.C.S.: 624190
Ellen Bushman *(VP-Dev)*
Ray Ratke *(COO)*
Doris Cook *(VP-HR)*
Julie Swanson *(CEO)*
David Pruett *(CFO)*
Carole Todd *(VP-Comm & Mktg)*
Robin Crowder *(Chm)*
Robert Burger *(Vice Chm)*
Diane Exner *(Dir-Developmental Svcs)*
Terri L. Webber *(Dir-Education Svcs)*
Evelyn Jones *(VP-IT)*
Lisa Morgan *(VP-Program Ops)*
Tresha Lafon *(VP-Program Ops)*
Judith N. Green *(Sec)*
Frederick Kraegel *(Treas)*

LUTHERAN HOME FOR THE AGED

149 W 22nd St, Erie, PA 16502-2899
Tel.: (814) 452-3271   PA
Web Site: http://www.vals.org
Year Founded: 1906
Sales Range: $10-24.9 Million
Emp.: 297
Nursing Care Services
N.A.I.C.S.: 623110
Mark Gusek *(CEO)*

LUTHERAN HOMES OF OCONOMOWOC

1305 W Wisconsin Ave, Oconomowoc, WI 53066
Tel.: (262) 567-8341   WI
Web Site: http://www.shorehavenliving.org
Year Founded: 1939
Sales Range: $10-24.9 Million
Emp.: 422
Lifecare Retirement Community Operator
N.A.I.C.S.: 623311
Ed Somers *(CEO)*
Joan Birr *(CFO)*
Barbara Dehnert *(Dir-Dining)*
Carolyn Clauter *(Dir-HR)*
Dale Dahlke *(COO)*
Holly Tunak *(Dir-Dev)*
Sarah Williams-Berg *(Dir-Community Rels)*

LUTHERAN IMMIGRATION AND REFUGEE SERVICE

700 Light St, Baltimore, MD 21230
Tel.: (410) 230-2700   MD
Web Site: http://www.lirs.org
Year Founded: 1966
Sales Range: $50-74.9 Million
Emp.: 120
Refugee & Immigrant Care Services
N.A.I.C.S.: 624230
Annie Wilson *(Chief Strategy Officer)*
Jane Anthon *(VP-Fin & Admin)*
Michael Mitchell *(VP-Programs)*
Staci Coomer *(VP-Dev, Outreach & Comm)*
Gary Gold-Moritz *(COO)*
William Bisbee *(CIO)*
William Swanson *(Treas)*
Evan Moilan *(Sec)*
Linda Stoterau *(Vice Chm)*
Bishop Michael Rinehart *(Chm)*
Kay Bellor *(VP-Programs)*
Krish OMara Vignarajah *(CEO)*

LUTHERAN SERVICES FLORIDA INC.

3627A W Waters Ave, Tampa, FL 33614
Tel.: (813) 875-1408   FL
Web Site: http://www.lsfnet.org
Year Founded: 1982
Sales Range: $125-149.9 Million
Emp.: 822
Human Service Organization
N.A.I.C.S.: 813410
George Wallace *(Exec VP-Fin & Admin)*
Christopher J. Card *(Pres & COO)*
Samuel M. Sipes *(CEO)*
Bob Wydra *(CFO & VP)*
Amelia Fox *(Chief Strategy Officer)*
Phil Hubbell *(Exec VP-HR)*
Stacy Martin *(Chief Comm & Dev Officer)*

LUTHERAN SOCIAL SERVICES OF NORTHEAST FLORIDA

4615 Philips Hwy, Jacksonville, FL 32207
Tel.: (904) 448-5995   FL
Web Site: http://www.lssjax.org
Year Founded: 1979
Sales Range: $25-49.9 Million
Emp.: 139
Social Advocacy Services
N.A.I.C.S.: 813319
Heather Vaughan *(Dir-Human Svcs)*
Richard Mochowski *(Controller)*
Dwane D. Tyson *(Chm)*
Jeanne Maszy *(Vice Chm)*
Jerome Crawford *(VP-Ops & Dir-Representative Payee Svcs)*
Bill Brim *(Dir-Bus Dev)*

LUTHERAN SOCIAL SERVICES OF THE SOUTH, INC.

8305 Cross Park Dr, Austin, TX 78754
Tel.: (512) 459-1000   TX
Web Site: http://www.lsss.org
Year Founded: 1926
Sales Range: $50-74.9 Million
Emp.: 1,142
Christian Ministry Services
N.A.I.C.S.: 813110
Michael Loo *(Pres & COO)*
Kurt Senske *(CEO)*
Glynn Bloomquist *(Vice Chm)*
Sigmund Cornelius *(Chm)*
Janet Kearney *(Dir-Victoria)*
Mike Nevergall *(VP-Agency Advancement)*
Donna Palmer *(Chief External Rels Officer)*
Sharon Smith *(Treas)*

LUTHERCARE

Lutheran Social Services of the South, Inc.—(Continued)

LUTHERCARE
600 E Main St, Lititz, PA 17543
Tel.: (717) 626-1171   PA
Web Site: http://www.luthercare.org
Year Founded: 1949
Sales Range: $25-49.9 Million
Emp.: 980
Elder Care Services
N.A.I.C.S.: 623312
Carl R. McAloose (Pres & CEO)
Elizabeth Brennan (CFO & Treas)
William C. Snyder (VP-Philanthropy & Community Engagement)
Gregory T. Holsinger (Chm)
Bernard J. LaPine (Sec)
Blake S. Daub (Sr VP-HR & Admin Svcs)
Eleonore I. Shay (Dir-Quality Assurance & Compliance)
Jeffrey S. High (Controller)
Kristen M. Loose (Dir-Clinical Sys Integration)
Mark H. Diffenderfer (Dir-Info Svcs)
Sally D. Groome (VP-Mktg & Comm)
William Perham (Gen Mgr-Dining Svcs)
Matthew C. Oathout (Sr VP-Ops)

LUV 'N CARE LTD.
3030 Aurora Ave Fl 2, Monroe, LA 71201
Tel.: (318) 388-4916
Web Site: http://www.nuby.com
Rev.: $64,000,000
Emp.: 499
Plastics Bottles
N.A.I.C.S.: 326160
Brad Wilson (Engr-Design)
Lisa Bandy (Coord-Export)

LUVEL DAIRY PRODUCTS, INC.
926 Veterans Memorial Dr, Kosciusko, MS 39090
Tel.: (662) 289-2511   MS
Year Founded: 1919
Sales Range: $25-49.9 Million
Emp.: 225
Fluid Milk & Ice Cream Mfr
N.A.I.C.S.: 424430
James H. Briscoe (Gen Mgr)
Richard Briscoe (VP)
Sam Dodd (Mgr-Maintenance)

LUX AIR JET CENTERS
1658 S Litchfield Rd, Goodyear, AZ 85338
Tel.: (623) 932-1200
Web Site: http://www.luxairjetcenters.com
Sales Range: $150-199.9 Million
Emp.: 20
Aircraft Services
N.A.I.C.S.: 488119
Ryan Reeves (Gen Mgr)

LUX BOND & GREEN INCORPORATED
46 Lasalle Rd, West Hartford, CT 06107
Tel.: (860) 521-3015   CT
Web Site: http://www.lbgreen.com
Year Founded: 1898
Sales Range: $25-49.9 Million
Emp.: 210
Provider of Jewelry, Precious Stones & Precious Metals
N.A.I.C.S.: 458310
John A. Green (Pres)

LUX CAPITAL, LLC
920 Broadway 11th Fl, New York, NY 10010
Tel.: (646) 475-4385
Web Site: http://www.luxcapital.com
Year Founded: 2005
Emp.: 20
Venture Capital Firm
N.A.I.C.S.: 523999
R. James Woolsey (Partner-Venture)
Bibi Masara (Office Mgr)
Josh Wolfe (Co-Founder & Mng Partner)
Adam Kalish (Gen Partner)
Zack Schildhorn (Partner)
Shahin Farshchi (Partner)
John Raymont (Pres)
Robert Paull (Co-Founder & Venture Partner)
Adam Goulburn (Partner)
Renata Quintini (Partner)
Brandon Reeves (Partner)
Steven Brody (COO)
Segolene Scarborough (CFO)
Shahin Farshchi (Partner)
Bilal Zuberi (Partner)
Zavain Dar (Partner)
Peter Hebert (Mng Partner)

LUX CONSULTING GROUP INC
8403 Colesville Rd Ste 1100, Silver Spring, MD 20910
Tel.: (301) 585-1261
Web Site: http://www.luxcg.com
Year Founded: 1999
Sales Range: $10-24.9 Million
Emp.: 55
It Consulting
N.A.I.C.S.: 541690
Leonard Boyd (Pres & CEO)
Johnny Erickson (CIO)

LUX HEALTH TECH ACQUISITION CORP.
920 Broadway 11th Fl, New York, NY 10010
Tel.: (646) 475-4385   DE
Web Site: http://www.luxhealth.tech
Year Founded: 2020
Investment Services
N.A.I.C.S.: 523999
Peter Hebert (Chm)
Josh DeFonzo (CEO)
Segolene Scarborough (CFO & Treas)

LUXE BRANDS, INC.
6825 W Sunrise Blvd, Plantation, FL 33313
Tel.: (954) 791-6050
Fragrances & Beauty Products Sales & Distr
N.A.I.C.S.: 456120
Tony Bajaj (Founder)
Lee Davis (VP-Sls)
Joel B. Ronkin (CEO)
Amy Sachs (Chief Comml Officer)

Subsidiaries:

Fekkai Brands, LLC (1)
712 5th Ave Henri Bendel 4 Fl, New York, NY 10019
Tel.: (212) 753-9500
Web Site: http://www.fekkai.com
Beauty Salons Owner & Operator
N.A.I.C.S.: 812112
Frederic Fekkai (Founder)

Subsidiary (Domestic):

Frederic Fekkai (Mark NY), LLC (2)
25 E 77th St, New York, NY 10075
Tel.: (212) 396-4600
Web Site: http://www.fekkai.com
Beauty Salons
N.A.I.C.S.: 812112
Tammy Sherman (Creative Dir)

Frederic Fekkai Dallas, LLC (2)
30-B Highland Park Vlg, Dallas, TX 75205
Tel.: (214) 219-3600

Web Site: http://www.fekkai.com
Emp.: 17
Beauty Salons
N.A.I.C.S.: 812112
Jamie Moreland (Gen Mgr)

Frederic Fekkai Greenwich, LLC (2)
2 Lewis Ct, Greenwich, CT 06830
Tel.: (203) 861-6700
Web Site: http://www.fekkai.com
Beauty Salons
N.A.I.C.S.: 812112
Alexandre Chouery (Creative Dir)

Frederic Fekkai New York, LLC (2)
712 5th Ave 4th Fl, New York, NY 10019
Tel.: (212) 753-9500
Web Site: http://www.fekkai.com
Beauty & Hairstyling Salons
N.A.I.C.S.: 812112
Stephane Andre (Creative Dir)
Reyad Fritas (Creative Dir)
Elie Camoro (Creative Dir)

LUXE RV, INC.
356 Canon Dr, Beverly Hills, CA 90210   CA
Web Site: http://www.luxervrental.com
Year Founded: 2014
Sales Range: $1-9.9 Million
Emp.: 26
Travel Agency Services
N.A.I.C.S.: 561510
Adrian Ghila (CEO)

LUXMOBILE GROUP
274 N Goodman St Ste B265, Rochester, NY 14607
Tel.: (585) 672-5083
Web Site: http://www.luxmobilegroup.com
Year Founded: 2005
Sales Range: $1-9.9 Million
Emp.: 20
High End Accessories for Mobile Devices
N.A.I.C.S.: 334210
Wasim Khaled (Co-Founder)

LUXON FINANCIAL LLC
901 E Byrd St Ste 1001, Richmond, VA 23219
Tel.: (804) 340-8100   VA
Web Site: http://www.luxonfinancial.com
Year Founded: 2002
Wealth Management Services
N.A.I.C.S.: 523999
Joseph R. Schmuckler (CEO & Mng Dir)

Subsidiaries:

Cary Street Partners Investment Advisory LLC (1)
901 E Byrd St Ste 1001, Richmond, VA 23219
Tel.: (804) 340-8100
Web Site: https://carystreetpartners.com
Investment Services
N.A.I.C.S.: 523999
Joseph R. R. Schmuckler (CEO)

LUXOR CAPITAL GROUP, LP
1114 Avenue of the Americas 29th Fl, New York, NY 10036-7703
Tel.: (212) 763-8000
Web Site: http://www.luxorcap.com
Financial Services
N.A.I.C.S.: 523999
Adam Miller (COO)

LUXURY BRAND HOLDINGS
9 Ross Simons Dr, Cranston, RI 02920
Tel.: (401) 463-3100
Web Site: http://www.luxurybrandholdings.com
Jewellery Distr
N.A.I.C.S.: 458310

U.S. PRIVATE

David Pawlak (CFO)

LUXURY BRANDS, LLC
205 Longshore Way, Fayetteville, GA 30215
Tel.: (770) 881-7131
Emp.: 100
Beauty Product Mfr
N.A.I.C.S.: 456120
Michael Dodo (Pres & CEO)

Subsidiaries:

Youngblood Skin Care Products, LLC (1)
4583 Ish Dr, Simi Valley, CA 93063
Tel.: (805) 577-0102
Web Site: https://www.ybskin.com
Sales Range: $1-9.9 Million
Emp.: 25
Beauty Product Mfr
N.A.I.C.S.: 456120
Lori Dejarnett (Principal)

LUZERNE COUNTY HEAD START, INC.
23 Beekman St, Wilkes Barre, PA 18702
Tel.: (570) 829-6231   PA
Web Site: http://www.lchs.hsweb.org
Year Founded: 1977
Sales Range: $10-24.9 Million
Emp.: 288
Day Care Services
N.A.I.C.S.: 624410
Lisa Malarkey (Mgr-HR)
Lynn Watters (Asst Mgr-HR)
Fran Langan (VP)
David Kowalek (Treas)
Robert Schaub (Pres)

LUZIER PERSONALIZED COSMETICS, INC.
7910-7912 Troost Ave, Kansas City, MO 64131-1920
Tel.: (816) 531-8338   MO
Web Site: http://www.luzier.com
Year Founded: 1923
Sales Range: $50-74.9 Million
Emp.: 20
Skin Care & Cosmetics Mfr & Whslr
N.A.I.C.S.: 325620
Kathy Grissom (Chm & CEO)
Grant Grissom (COO)

LUZO FOODSERVICE CORPORATION
115 Church St, New Bedford, MA 02746
Tel.: (508) 999-1771   MA
Web Site: http://www.luzo.com
Year Founded: 1928
Sales Range: $10-24.9 Million
Emp.: 15
Grocery Stores
N.A.I.C.S.: 424410
Carl Ribiero (Pres)
Mark Shampage (Controller)

LWCBANCORP, INC.
1000 E. Lincoln Hwy, New Lenox, IL 60451
Tel.: (815) 462-4300
Web Site: https://lwcbank.com
Year Founded: 2008
Sales Range: $1-9.9 Million
Emp.: 100
Bank Holding Company
N.A.I.C.S.: 551111

Subsidiaries:

Lincoln Way Community Bank (1)
1000 E Lincoln Hwy, New Lenox, IL 60451
Tel.: (815) 462-4300
Web Site: http://www.lwcbank.com
Rev.: $2,600,000
Emp.: 20
Banking Services

N.A.I.C.S.: 522110
Dave Gabrielse (VP)
Frank Toland (Mgr-Loan Production)

LWD INC.
1101 Fort St Mall, Honolulu, HI 96813
Tel.: (808) 532-1596
Sales Range: $10-24.9 Million
Emp.: 100
Fast-Food Restaurant, Chain
N.A.I.C.S.: 722513
Victor Lim (Pres)

LWP CLAIMS SOLUTIONS, INC.
PO Box 349016, Sacramento, CA 95834-9016
Tel.: (800) 565-5694   CA
Web Site: http://www.lwpclaims.com
Year Founded: 1990
Third Party Workers' Compensation Administrator
N.A.I.C.S.: 524292
Judy Adlam (Pres & CEO)
Erica Igoe (Owner)

LWT COMMUNICATIONS
8140 Old Federal Rd, Montgomery, AL 36117
Tel.: (334) 244-9933   AL
Year Founded: 1959
Rev.: $3,500,000
Emp.: 26
Fiscal Year-end: 12/31/01
N.A.I.C.S.: 541810
David Allred (Principal)
Jim Leonard (Principal)
Camille Leonard (VP & Creative Dir)
Pamela Perkins (Mgr-Bus)
Lani Asher (Sr Acct Exec)
Roberta Pinkston (Media Buyer)
Vicki Dickson (Media Buyer)
Mary Catherine Phillips (Acct Exec)
Megan Singleton (Mgr-Traffic)
Ben Shoults (Graphic Designer)
Brittney Roland (Graphic Designer)
Kathleen McCullough (Acct Coord)
Laura Hicks (Acct Exec)
Shannon Havranek (Graphic Designer)
Shawn Tritz (Graphic Designer)

LY BROTHERS CORPORATION
1963 Sabre St, Hayward, CA 94545
Tel.: (510) 782-2118
Web Site:
   http://www.sugarpowrbakery.com
Year Founded: 1993
Sales Range: $25-49.9 Million
Emp.: 250
Bakery Products Mfr
N.A.I.C.S.: 311812
Andrew Ly (Pres & CEO)
John Ying (Interim CFO)
Sam Ly (Exec VP)

LYBARGER OIL INC.
704 Maple St, Garnett, KS 66032
Tel.: (785) 448-5512
Web Site: http://www.lybargeroil.com
Sales Range: $10-24.9 Million
Emp.: 22
Petroleum Bulk Stations
N.A.I.C.S.: 424710
David Lybarger (Pres)

LYCOMING COMMUNITY CARE INC
2140 Warrensville Rd, Montoursville, PA 17754
Tel.: (570) 433-3161   PA
Web Site: http://www.valleyview.org
Year Founded: 1990
Sales Range: $10-24.9 Million
Emp.: 314
Nursing Care Services

N.A.I.C.S.: 623110
Louise Eakin (Exec Dir)
Stephen Fry (CFO)
Louann Simpson (Dir-Nursing)
Stephen E. Schopfer (Pres)
Sue E. Stackhouse (Sec)
Joseph Cipriani (Treas)
Nicholas Catino (VP)

LYCOMING-CLINTON JOINDER BOARD
200 East St, Williamsport, PA 17701
Tel.: (570) 326-0924   PA
Year Founded: 1982
Sales Range: $25-49.9 Million
Emp.: 208
Disability Assistance Services
N.A.I.C.S.: 624120
Adam Coleman (VP)
Ernest P. Larson (Treas)
Tony R. Mussare (Pres)

LYCON, INC.
1110 Harding St, Janesville, WI 53545
Tel.: (608) 754-7701
Web Site: http://www.lyconinc.com
Sales Range: $10-24.9 Million
Concrete & Building Products Mfr
N.A.I.C.S.: 327320
Goodwin R. Lyons (Owner)

Subsidiaries:

M&M Concrete   (1)
700 Teller Rd, Neenah, WI 54956   (100%)
Tel.: (920) 727-1400
Web Site: http://www.michels.com
Rev.: $64,000
Emp.: 20
Concrete Work
N.A.I.C.S.: 238110

LYDA SWINERTON BUILDERS, INC.
5707 SW Pkwy Bldg 1 Ste 200, Austin, TX 78735
Tel.: (512) 327-5599   TX
Web Site: http://www.swinerton.com
Year Founded: 1888
Nonresidential Construction
N.A.I.C.S.: 236220
Bret Hall (Mgr-Div)

LYDEN OIL COMPANY
2649 Tracey Rd, Northwood, OH 43619
Tel.: (419) 666-1948
Web Site:
   http://www.lydenoilcompany.com
Year Founded: 1919
Sales Range: $50-74.9 Million
Emp.: 160
Bulk Oil & Lubricant Distr
N.A.I.C.S.: 424720
Breen Lyden (Pres & CEO)
Paul Lyden (VP)
Gene McMillin (Mgr-Sls & Ops)

Subsidiaries:

Lyden Oil Company-Lansing Division   (1)
16275 National Pkwy, Lansing, MI 48906
Tel.: (517) 485-2285
Web Site: http://www.lydenoil.com
Sales Range: $25-49.9 Million
Emp.: 70
Bulk Oil & Lubricant Distr
N.A.I.C.S.: 424710
Laura Lyden (Mgr-Sls & Ops)
Gene McMillin (Mgr-Sls & Ops)
Jerry Rose (Mgr-Western Michigan Div)

Lyden Oil Company-Youngstown Division   (1)
3711 LeHarps Dr, Youngstown, OH 44515
Tel.: (330) 792-1100
Web Site: http://www.lydenoilcompany.com
Bulk Oil & Lubricant Distr
N.A.I.C.S.: 424710

Laura Lyden (Mgr-Sls & Ops)

LYDIG CONSTRUCTION INC.
11001 E Montgomery Dr, Spokane, WA 99206
Tel.: (509) 534-0451   WA
Web Site: http://www.lydig.com
Year Founded: 1956
Sales Range: $50-74.9 Million
Emp.: 80
Provider of New Construction; Commercial & Office Building
N.A.I.C.S.: 236220
Larry Swartz (Pres)
Mark Bray (CFO)

LYERLY AGENCY INC.
126 N Main St, Belmont, NC 28012
Tel.: (704) 525-3937
Web Site: http://www.lyerly.com
Year Founded: 1977
Sales Range: $10-24.9 Million
Emp.: 9
Advertising Agencies
N.A.I.C.S.: 541810
Elaine M. Lyerly (Pres & CEO)
Melia L. Lyerly (COO & Exec VP)
Kelly Peace (VP-Client Svcs)
Melinda Skutnick (Dir-PR)

LYFE MARKETING LLC
50 Hurt Plz SE, Atlanta, GA 30303
Tel.: (404) 596-7925   GA
Web Site:
   http://www.lyfemarketing.com
Year Founded: 2011
Sales Range: $1-9.9 Million
Emp.: 35
Digital Marketing Services
N.A.I.C.S.: 541810
Sherman Standberry (Founder & Partner)

LYKES BROTHERS INC.
400 N Tampa St Ste 1900, Tampa, FL 33602-4719
Tel.: (813) 470-5000   FL
Web Site: http://www.lykes.com
Year Founded: 1900
Sales Range: $450-499.9 Million
Emp.: 300
Cattle Ranching & Citrus & Sugarcane Production Services
N.A.I.C.S.: 112111
Michael L. Carrere (Exec VP-Citrus)
Joseph L. Carrere (Chm)
Carl J. Bauman (CFO & VP)
Charles P. Lykes Jr. (Pres & COO)

Subsidiaries:

EcoAsset Solutions, LLC   (1)
400 N Tampa St Ste 1900, Tampa, FL 33602
Tel.: (813) 470-5000
Web Site: http://www.lykes.com
Sustainability Management Consulting Services
N.A.I.C.S.: 541990

Lykes Bros. Inc. - Ranch Division   (1)
106 SW CR 721, Okeechobee, FL 34974-8613
Tel.: (863) 763-3041
Web Site: http://www.lykesranch.com
Sales Range: $10-24.9 Million
Emp.: 33
Forest Management Services
N.A.I.C.S.: 115310
Chris Shoemaker (Office Mgr)

Lykes Brothers Inc. - Lykes Citrus Division   (1)
7 Lykes Rd, Lake Placid, FL 33852
Tel.: (863) 465-4127
Web Site: http://www.lykes.com
Orange Farming Services
N.A.I.C.S.: 111310
Charles Lykes (CEO)

Lykes Insurance, Inc.   (1)
400 N Tampa St Ste 1900, Tampa, FL 33602-4716   (100%)
Tel.: (813) 223-3911
Web Site: http://www.lykesinsurance.com
Emp.: 25
Full Line Insurance Agency
N.A.I.C.S.: 524210
Bob Pariseau (VP-Employee Benefits)
Bill Taulbee (Pres & CEO)
Christopher Tritt (VP-Fort Myers)
Cindy Sineriz (Mgr-Ops-Fort Myers Office)
Debra J. Coad (Sr Acct Exec-Tampa)
Diane Cocking (Sr Acct Exec-Tampa)
Janice Lowe (Sr Acct Exec-Fort Myers)
Linda K. Johnson (Sr Acct Exec-Fort Myers)
R. Mark Webb (Sr VP-Fort Myers)
Tanya Russo (Sr Acct Exec-Tampa)
Wendy Johnson (Sr Acct Exec-Fort Myers)
Yaritza Guzman (Mgr-Acct)
Yenitza Guzman (Mgr-Acct)
Alefa S. Kerry (Mgr-Acct)
Jennifer Zibilich (Sr Acct Exec-Tampa)
Jeremy Miller (Dir-Ops)
Ricka Zimmerman (Mgr-Acctg)
Sarah Green (Acct Mgr-Comml)
Jennifer Hannen (Acct Mgr-Employee Benefits)
Lana Liniger (Acct Mgr-Employee Benefits)
Stephanie Douglas (Acct Exec-Benefits)
April Buber (Acct Exec-Personal Lines)
Richard Russo Jr. (Sr VP-Tampa)

Lykes Land Investments, Inc.   (1)
3200 Bailey Ln Ste 120, Naples, FL 34105
Tel.: (239) 434-8911
Web Site:
   http://www.lykeslandinvestments.com
Natural Resources Conserving Services
N.A.I.C.S.: 813312
Terrey Dolan (Dir-Bus Dev & Plng)
John Bertram (Dir-Fin Mgmt)
John Wakefield (Dir-Bus Dev)
Howell L. Ferguson (Chm)
John A. Brabson Jr. (Co-Pres & Co-CEO)
Charles P. Lykes Jr. (Co-Pres & Co-CEO)

LYKES CARTAGE COMPANY, INC.
590 Greenhill Dr, Round Rock, TX 78665
Tel.: (512) 933-9060
Web Site:
   http://www.lykescartage.com
Year Founded: 1978
Rev.: $10,278,291
Emp.: 200
Pickup & Delivery for Air Freight Industry
N.A.I.C.S.: 492210
Joe Lykes (Owner)
Lisa Lykes (Treas & Sec)
Derrick Page (Gen Mgr)

LYKINS COMPANIES, INC.
5163 Wolfpen Pleasant Hill Rd, Milford, OH 45150
Tel.: (513) 831-8820   OH
Web Site:
   http://www.lykinsenergy.com
Year Founded: 1948
Petroleum Product Distr
N.A.I.C.S.: 424720
D. Jeffery Lykins (Pres & CEO)
Robert J. Manning (CFO & VP)
Ronald Lykins (VP-Transportation)

Subsidiaries:

Campbell Oil, Inc.   (1)
7977 Hills & Dales Rd NE, Massillon, OH 44646
Tel.: (330) 833-8555
Web Site: http://www.campbelloil.com
Full-Service Heating Oil & Commercial Fuels Dealer
N.A.I.C.S.: 457210

Subsidiary (Domestic):

BellStores Inc.   (2)
611 Erie St S, Massillon, OH 44646-6711   (100%)
Tel.: (330) 833-8555
Web Site: http://www.bellstores.com
Convenience Store Operator

LYKINS COMPANIES, INC.

Lykins Companies, Inc.—(Continued)
N.A.I.C.S.: 445131
Brian D. Burrow (Pres & CEO)

D & L Leasing, Inc. (1)
10381 Evendale Dr, Cincinnati, OH 45241
Tel.: (513) 554-2906
Web Site: http://www.dandlleasing.com
Automobile Leasing Services
N.A.I.C.S.: 532112

Lykins Oil Company (1)
5163 Wolfpen Present Hill Rd, Milford, OH
45150 **(100%)**
Tel.: (513) 831-8820
Web Site: http://www.lykinsoil.com
Sales Range: $25-49.9 Million
Emp.: 75
Commercial & Residential Oil Whslr & Distr
N.A.I.C.S.: 424720
D. Jeffery Lykins (Pres)
Joyce Spizzirri (Mgr-Branded Sls)

Subsidiary (Domestic):

Petron, LLC (2)
1600 Harris St, Alexandria, LA 71301-6217
Tel.: (318) 445-5685
Web Site: http://www.petron-us.com
Sales Range: $10-24.9 Million
Emp.: 15
Retail & Wholesale Petroleum Products &
Gasoline Equipment; Real Estate Developers
N.A.I.C.S.: 484230
John R. Ayres (Gen Mgr)

Lykins Transportation (1)
5163 Wolfpen Pleasant Hill Rd, Milford, OH
45150
Tel.: (513) 831-8820
Web Site: http://www.lykinsenergy.com
Petroleum Transportation Services
N.A.I.C.S.: 424720
Ronald Lykins (VP-Transportation)

LYLE MACHINERY CO.
650 US Hwy 49 S, Richland, MS
39218
Tel.: (601) 939-4000 MS
Web Site:
  http://www.lylemachinery.com
Year Founded: 1995
Sales Range: $10-24.9 Million
Emp.: 90
Construction & Mining Machinery
Distr
N.A.I.C.S.: 423810
Dan Lyle (Pres)
Jim Luther (VP-Sls)
Eddie White (Mgr-Svc)
Chris Shelton (Mgr-Ops, Parts & Svc)
Bobby Scott (Mgr-Store-Retail)
Barry Franklin (Bus Mgr)
Jim King (VP-Product Support)
Jim Kin (VP-Product Support)
Rick Rigsby (Mgr-Parts)
Nathan Bagwell (Mgr-Rental)
Chuck Mohler (Mgr-Sls)
Ernest Thomas (Mgr-Used Equipment)
Raymy Johnson (Mgr-Used Parts)
John Lyle Jr. (Chm)

LYLE SIGNS INC.
6294 Bury Dr, Eden Prairie, MN
55346
Tel.: (952) 934-7653
Web Site: http://www.lylesigns.com
Sales Range: $10-24.9 Million
Emp.: 75
Signs & Advertising Specialties
N.A.I.C.S.: 339950
Peter Pears (CEO)

LYLES DIVERSIFIED INC.
1210 W Olive Ave, Fresno, CA
93728-2816
Tel.: (559) 441-1900 CA
Web Site: http://www.lylesgroup.com
Year Founded: 1946
Rev.: $130,000,000

Emp.: 1,000
Water, Sewer & Utility Lines, Heavy
Concrete Construction & Paving
N.A.I.C.S.: 237110
William M. Lyles III (VP)
Todd Sheller (Asst VP & Mgr-Investment)

Subsidiaries:

American Paving Co. Inc. (1)
315 N Thorne Ave, Fresno, CA
93706-1444 **(100%)**
Tel.: (559) 268-9886
Web Site:
  http://www.americanpavingco.com
Sales Range: $10-24.9 Million
Emp.: 50
Highway & Street Construction Services
N.A.I.C.S.: 237310
John Sloan (Pres)

Kaweah Construction Co. Inc. (1)
335 N Thorn Ave, Fresno, CA
93706 **(100%)**
Tel.: (559) 268-1540
Web Site:
  http://www.kaweahconstruction.com
Sales Range: $10-24.9 Million
Emp.: 50
Heavy Construction
N.A.I.C.S.: 237990

Lyles Mechanical Co. (1)
5014 E University Ave, Fresno, CA 93727
Tel.: (559) 237-2200
Web Site: http://www.lylesmech.com
Emp.: 40
Plumbing & Boiler Installation Services
N.A.I.C.S.: 238220
John Sloan (Pres & CEO)

Lyles Utility Construction, LLC (1)
1200 N Plaza Dr, Visalia, CA 93291
Tel.: (559) 487-7999
Web Site: http://www.lylesutility.com
Emp.: 70
Utility Construction Services
N.A.I.C.S.: 237990
Tamara Lyles (Pres & CEO)
Brad E. Zeimet (Sr VP)

W.M. Lyles Co. (1)
1210 W Olive Ave Ste B, Fresno, CA
93728-2816 **(100%)**
Tel.: (559) 441-1900
Web Site: http://www.wmlylesco.com
Sales Range: $10-24.9 Million
Emp.: 40
Water, Sewer & Utility Lines
N.A.I.C.S.: 237110
Richard Amigh (Sr VP & Mgr-Bus Dev)

LYMAN BROS.
10288 S Jordan Gateway Ste K,
South Jordan, UT 84095
Tel.: (801) 501-9090
Web Site: http://lbisat.com
Sales Range: $10-24.9 Million
Emp.: 26
Satellites; Communications
N.A.I.C.S.: 334220
Roger Lyman (Pres)
Bob Griffith (Dir-Sls)

LYMAN DAVIDSON DOOLEY, INC.
1640 Powers Ferry Rd SE Ste 100,
Marietta, GA 30067
Tel.: (770) 850-8494
Web Site: http://www.lddi-architects.com
Year Founded: 1988
Sales Range: $1-9.9 Million
Emp.: 62
Architectural & Interior Design Services
N.A.I.C.S.: 541310
Rowland Davidson (Sr Principal)
Steven G. Lyman (Sr Principal)
Steven D. Barthlow (Principal & Dir-Corp, Healthcare & Mixed-Use Studios)

Phillip B. Laney (Principal & Dir-Church Studio)
David L. McBrayer (Principal & Dir-Education Studio)
Dave McCauley (Principal & Dir-Recreation Studio)
Benjamin K. Starks (Dir-Govt Studio)

Subsidiaries:

Lyman Davidson Dooley Inc. (1)
1640 Powers Ferry Rd Bldg 1 Ste 100,
Marietta, GA 30067
Tel.: (770) 850-8494
Web Site: http://www.lddi-architects.com
Sales Range: $1-9.9 Million
Emp.: 10
Architectural Services
N.A.I.C.S.: 541310

LYMAN PRODUCTS CORPORATION
475 Smith St, Middletown, CT 06457
Tel.: (860) 632-2020 CT
Web Site:
  http://www.lymanproducts.com
Year Founded: 1878
Sales Range: $75-99.9 Million
Emp.: 100
Hunting Accessories
N.A.I.C.S.: 333248
Rick Ranzinger (VP-Sls & Mktg)
Denis LeBlanc (Controller)

Subsidiaries:

Pachmayr (1)
5459 2nd St, Irwindale, CA
91706-2072 **(100%)**
Tel.: (626) 960-2622
Web Site: http://www.pachmayr.com
Sales Range: $10-24.9 Million
Emp.: 10
Recoil Pads, Pistol Grips & Other Gunfire
Accessories Mfr
N.A.I.C.S.: 459110

Raytech Industries Division (1)
475 Smith St, Middletown, CT
06457-1529 **(100%)**
Tel.: (860) 632-2020
Web Site: http://www.raytech-ing.com
Sales Range: $10-24.9 Million
Emp.: 5
Mfr of Vibratory Tumblers & Lapidary Equipment
N.A.I.C.S.: 333248
Rick Ranzinger (Pres)

Trius Traps, LLC (1)
475 Smith St, Middletown, CT 06457
Tel.: (860) 362-2020
Shotgun Component Mfr
N.A.I.C.S.: 332994

LYMAN-RICHEY CORPORATION
2625 S 158th Plz, Omaha, NE 68130
Tel.: (402) 558-2727
Web Site:
  http://www.lymanrichey.com
Sales Range: $1-9.9 Million
Emp.: 30
Concrete, Sand & Gavel, Block &
Brick Mfr
N.A.I.C.S.: 212321
John Dickerson (Mgr-Equipment & Pur)
Jarod Hendricks (VP-Concrete Companies)

Subsidiaries:

Shamrock Concrete Company (1)
9305 S 97th St, La Vista, NE 68128
Tel.: (402) 339-5676
Readymix Concrete Mfr
N.A.I.C.S.: 327320

Standard Ready Mix Concrete Co. (1)
1221 Steuben St, Sioux City, IA 51105
Tel.: (712) 252-1807
Ready Mixed Concrete

N.A.I.C.S.: 327320

LYMTAL INTERNATIONAL, INC.
4150 S Lapeer Rd, Lake Orion, MI
48359
Tel.: (248) 373-8100
Web Site: http://www.lymtal.com
Year Founded: 1929
Sales Range: $10-24.9 Million
Emp.: 30
Mfr of Polyurethane Waterproofing
Products
N.A.I.C.S.: 325510
Frank M. Lymburner (Co-Founder)
Magdy M. Talaat (Co-Founder)

LYN-LAD GROUP LTD.
220 S Common St, Lynn, MA 01905
Tel.: (781) 598-6010
Web Site: http://www.lynnladder.com
Sales Range: $25-49.9 Million
Emp.: 400
Mfr & Distributor of Ladders, Scaffolding, Truck Equipment & Specialty
Items
N.A.I.C.S.: 321999
Amy Burt (Mgr-Credit)

LYNAY HEALTHCARE INC.
Ste 300 342 W Woodlawn Ave, San
Antonio, TX 78212-3314
Tel.: (210) 651-4940
Web Site: http://www.lynay.org
Rev.: $18,471,432
Emp.: 9
Medical Equipment Rental
N.A.I.C.S.: 532283

LYNC LOGISTICS, LLC
2407 8th Ave, Chattanooga, TN
37407
Tel.: (423) 305-7600
Web Site:
  http://www.lynclogistics.com
Year Founded: 2014
Sales Range: $25-49.9 Million
Emp.: 36
Freight Transportation Services
N.A.I.C.S.: 488510
Cindy Lee (Founder, Pres & CEO)
Taylor Vinson (Exec VP)
Keith Gray (VP-Ops)
Mathew Soloff (VP-Sls)

LYNCH FORD MOUNT VERNON INC.
410 Hwy 30 W, Mount Vernon, IA
52314
Tel.: (319) 895-8500 IA
Web Site:
  http://www.lynchfordchevy.com
Year Founded: 1982
Sales Range: $10-24.9 Million
Emp.: 85
Sales of New & Used Automobiles
N.A.I.C.S.: 441110
Dan Lynch (Pres)

LYNCH HOLDINGS, LLC
4550 Travis St Ste 560, Dallas, TX
75205
Tel.: (954) 599-9653 TX
Web Site: https://lynchholdings.com
Investment Services
N.A.I.C.S.: 523999

Subsidiaries:

Atlantis Fire Protection (1)
4550 Travis St Ste 560, Dallas, TX 75205
Tel.: (954) 599-9653
Web Site: https://atlantisfire.com
Fire Protection Services
N.A.I.C.S.: 922160
Patrick Lynch (CEO)

COMPANIES / LYNN ECONOMIC OPPORTUNITY, INC.

Subsidiary (Domestic):

Keller's, Inc. (2)
6750 Gordon Rd, Wilmington, NC 28411-8464
Tel.: (910) 392-7011
Web Site: http://www.kellersinc.com
Fire Protection Products Mfr
N.A.I.C.S.: 922160
Stella Black *(Pres)*

McCoy Fire & Safety, Inc. (2)
537 Temple St, Auburn, AL 36830-4019
Tel.: (334) 501-2228
Web Site: http://www.mccoyfire.com
Electrical Apparatus & Equipment, Wiring Supplies & Related Equipment Merchant Whslr
N.A.I.C.S.: 423610
Vince McCoy *(Pres)*

LYNCH LIVESTOCK INC.
331 3rd St NW, Waucoma, IA 52171-9448
Tel.: (563) 776-6861 IA
Web Site:
  http://www.lynchlivestock.com
Year Founded: 1975
Sales Range: $100-124.9 Million
Emp.: 150
Provider of Livestock Services
N.A.I.C.S.: 424520
Kenneth Hemesath *(Mgr)*
Erin Golly *(Mgr)*
Paulette Dagit *(Controller)*

LYNCH MATERIAL HANDLING CO.
2810 Industrial Ln, Broomfield, CO 80020-1612
Tel.: (303) 466-2317
Web Site: http://www.lmhco.com
Sales Range: $10-24.9 Million
Emp.: 15
Shelving, Commercial & Industrial
N.A.I.C.S.: 423440
Erma Mantey *(Chm)*
Norman Ooms *(Pres)*
Donald Rutkowski *(VP)*

LYNCHBURG HYUNDAI MITSUBISHI INC
3400 Old Forest Rd, Lynchburg, VA 24501
Tel.: (434) 846-0667
Sales Range: $10-24.9 Million
Emp.: 20
New & Used Car Dealers
N.A.I.C.S.: 441110
Chris Mabry *(Pres)*
Larry Nicholes *(Treas)*

LYNCO FLANGE & FITTING, INC.
5114 Steadmont Dr, Houston, TX 77040
Tel.: (713) 690-0040
Web Site:
  http://www.lyncoflange.com
Rev: $13,000,000
Emp.: 20
Provider of Industrial Supplies Products & Services
N.A.I.C.S.: 423840
Lynn Vanover *(Pres)*

LYNDALE ENTERPRISES INC.
Ste N 3333 Wrightsville Ave, Wilmington, NC 28403-4183
Tel.: (910) 794-8669 NC
Year Founded: 1975
Sales Range: $10-24.9 Million
Emp.: 31
Drugs, Proprietaries & Sundries Mfr
N.A.I.C.S.: 424210
W. Keith Elmore *(Pres & CEO)*
Jane M. Elmore *(Sec)*

Subsidiaries:

King Drug Company of Florence Inc. (1)
605 W Lucas St, Florence, SC 29501-2823
Tel.: (843) 662-0411
Sales Range: $10-24.9 Million
Emp.: 20
Distr of Drugs, Proprietaries & Sundries
N.A.I.C.S.: 424210

LYNDAN, INC.
5402 E Hanna Ave, Tampa, FL 33610
Tel.: (813) 977-6683 FL
Web Site: http://www.lyndan.com
Year Founded: 1981
Sales Range: $1-9.9 Million
Emp.: 25
Custom Architectural Woodwork & Millwork Mfr
N.A.I.C.S.: 337212
Dana L. Guy *(Pres)*

LYNDEN INCORPORATED
18000 Intl Blvd Ste 800, Seattle, WA 98188-4263
Tel.: (206) 241-8778 WA
Web Site: http://www.lynden.com
Year Founded: 1906
Sales Range: $400-449.9 Million
Emp.: 1,200
Multi-Mode Freight Transportation & Construction Distr
N.A.I.C.S.: 484121
Jon Burdick *(Pres & CEO)*

Subsidiaries:

Alaska Marine Lines, Inc. (1)
5615 W Marginal Way SW, Seattle, WA 98106-1521 (100%)
Tel.: (206) 763-4244
Web Site: http://www.shipaml.com
Sales Range: $10-24.9 Million
Emp.: 52
Marine Transportation
N.A.I.C.S.: 483113

Alaska West Express, Inc. (1)
1048 Whitney Rd, Anchorage, AK 99501-1185 (100%)
Tel.: (907) 339-5100
Web Site: http://www.lynden.com
Sales Range: $10-24.9 Million
Emp.: 38
Intercity Hauling General Freight
N.A.I.C.S.: 484122
Scott Hicks *(Pres)*

Alaskan Marine Lines, Inc. (1)
5615 W Marginal Way SW, Seattle, WA 98106-1521
Tel.: (206) 763-4244
Web Site: http://www.shipaml.com
Sales Range: $10-24.9 Million
Emp.: 100
Equipment Rental & Leasing
N.A.I.C.S.: 483113
Don Reid *(VP-Ops)*
Kevin Anderson *(Pres)*

Bering Marine Corporation (1)
6400 S Airpark Pl Ste 1, Anchorage, AK 99502 (100%)
Tel.: (907) 248-7646
Web Site: http://www.bmc.lynden.com
Sales Range: $55-99.9 Million
Towing & Tugboat Service
N.A.I.C.S.: 336612
David Rosenzweig *(Dir-Mktg)*

Knik Construction Co., Inc. (1)
PO Box 3757, Seattle, WA 98124-3757 (100%)
Tel.: (206) 439-5525
Web Site: http://www.knik.lynden.com
Sales Range: $10-24.9 Million
Emp.: 2
General Construction Contracting
N.A.I.C.S.: 237310
Parry Rekers *(VP)*

LTI, Inc. (1)
8631 Depot Rd, Lynden, WA 98264-0433 (100%)
Tel.: (360) 354-2101
Web Site: http://www.lynden.com
Sales Range: $10-24.9 Million
Emp.: 80
Trucking Except Local
N.A.I.C.S.: 484121
Jason Jansen *(Pres)*

Division (Domestic):

LTI, Inc. (2)
9414 Ne Vancouver Way, Portland, OR 97211-1242 (100%)
Tel.: (360) 256-2577
Web Site: http://www.ltii.lynden.com
Trucking Except Local
N.A.I.C.S.: 484220

Milky Way (2)
8631 Depot Rd, Lynden, WA 98944-9739 (100%)
Tel.: (509) 839-5844
Web Site: http://www.ltii.lynden.com
Bulk Milk Hauling
N.A.I.C.S.: 484122
Jason Jansen *(Pres)*

Lynden Air Cargo, LLC (1)
6441 S Airpark Dr, Anchorage, AK 99502-1809
Tel.: (907) 243-7248
Web Site: http://www.lac.lynden.com
Sales Range: $10-24.9 Million
Emp.: 175
Air Transportation, Nonscheduled
N.A.I.C.S.: 481212
Richard Zerkel *(Pres)*
Christopher Diltz *(Mgr-Aircraft Maintenance-Anchorage Station)*

Lynden Air Freight, Inc. (1)
18000 International Blvd Ste 700, Seattle, WA 98188-4202 (100%)
Tel.: (206) 777-5300
Web Site: http://www.laf.lynden.com
Sales Range: $10-24.9 Million
Emp.: 70
Air Freight Forwarding
N.A.I.C.S.: 488510
Laura Sanders *(VP-Ops)*
David Richardson *(Pres)*

Lynden International (1)
18000 International Blvd, Seattle, WA 98124
Tel.: (800) 926-5703
Freight Transportation Services
N.A.I.C.S.: 488510
Dennis Mitchell *(VP)*
Charlie Ogle *(Sr Dir-Global Sls)*
Megan Parmer *(Mgr-Houston)*
Dorene Kolb *(Dir-Sls & Mktg Support)*
Gregg Bergstrom *(Mgr-Quality, Health, Safety & Environmental)*
John Kaloper *(Pres)*
Jeff Bell *(VP-Sls & Mktg)*
David Rosenzweig *(VP-Mktg & Media)*

Subsidiary (Domestic):

Haas Industries, Inc. (2)
26554 Danti Ct, Hayward, CA 94545
Tel.: (510) 785-5222
Web Site: http://www.lynden.com
Sales Range: $1-9.9 Million
Emp.: 29
Freight Transportation Arrangement
N.A.I.C.S.: 488510
Keith Haas *(Pres)*
Carmen Holster *(COO)*

Lynden International Logistics Co. (1)
4441 - 76th Avenue S E West Building, Calgary, T2C 2G8, AB, Canada
Tel.: (403) 279-2700
Web Site: http://www.lynden.com
Emp.: 40
Logistics Consulting Servies
N.A.I.C.S.: 541614
Gordon Hendrickson *(Branch Mgr)*

Lynden Logistics, Inc. (1)
PO Box 3757, Seattle, WA 98124-3757 (100%)
Tel.: (206) 241-8778
Web Site: http://www.llog.lynden.com
Sales Range: $100-124.9 Million
Project Management
N.A.I.C.S.: 484110
David Rosenzweig *(Dir-Mktg)*

Lynden Transport, Inc. (1)
18000 International Blvd Ste 600, Seatac, WA 98188-4263 (100%)
Tel.: (206) 575-9575
Web Site: http://www.ltia.lynden.com
Sales Range: $10-24.9 Million
Emp.: 30
Interstate Hauling, General Freight
N.A.I.C.S.: 484121
Howard Hales *(Mgr)*
Colleen Fort *(Mgr-Intl)*

Northland Services, Inc. (1)
PO Box 24527, Seattle, WA 98124
Tel.: (206) 763-3000
Web Site: http://www.northlandservices.com
Cargo Transportation Services
N.A.I.C.S.: 483113
Kevin Anderson *(Pres)*

LYNDON STEEL COMPANY LLC
1947 Union Cross Rd, Winston Salem, NC 27107
Tel.: (336) 785-0848
Web Site:
  http://www.lyndonsteel.com
Year Founded: 1977
Fabricated Structural Metal
N.A.I.C.S.: 332312
Sam Winters *(Pres)*
George Sells *(VP-Sls)*

LYNEER STAFFING SOLUTIONS, LLC
1011 Whitehead Rd Ext, Ewing, NJ 08638
Tel.: (609) 882-8400
Web Site: https://lyneer.com
Year Founded: 2010
Employment Placement Agencies
N.A.I.C.S.: 561311
Todd McNulty *(CEO)*
Jim Radvany *(CFO)*

Subsidiaries:

Anchor Staffing, Inc. (1)
7550 Teague Rd Ste 103, Hanover, MD 21076
Tel.: (410) 761-9640
Temporary Help Service
N.A.I.C.S.: 561320

LYNGSO GARDEN MATERIALS, INC.
19 Seaport Blvd, Redwood City, CA 94063
Tel.: (650) 364-1730
Web Site:
  http://www.lyngsogarden.com
Year Founded: 1953
Sales Range: $10-24.9 Million
Emp.: 45
Farm Supplies Whslr
N.A.I.C.S.: 424910
Vic Thomas *(VP-Sls & Mktg)*
James Kolter *(VP-Ops)*
Daniel Garcia *(Mgr-Sls)*
Paul Truyts *(Mgr-Outside Sls)*

LYNN ASSOCIATES INC.
8175 Sheridan Dr Bldg 1 Ste 1 1st Fl, Buffalo, NY 14221-5968
Tel.: (716) 631-0054 NY
Web Site: http://www.lynninc.com
Year Founded: 1984
Sales Range: $10-24.9 Million
Emp.: 17
Mfr of Electronic Parts & Equipment
N.A.I.C.S.: 423690
Richard Lynn *(Pres & Principal)*

LYNN ECONOMIC OPPORTUNITY, INC.
156 Broad St, Lynn, MA 01901
Tel.: (781) 581-7220 MA
Web Site: http://www.leoinc.org
Year Founded: 1964

LYNN ECONOMIC OPPORTUNITY, INC.

Lynn Economic Opportunity, Inc.—(Continued)
Sales Range: $10-24.9 Million
Emp.: 229
Community Action Services
N.A.I.C.S.: 624190
Ken Weeks *(Dir-IT)*
Jennifer Mauche *(Dir-HR)*
Darlene Gallant *(Dir-Community Svcs)*
Marilyn Perry *(Dir-Nutrition & Health)*
Birgitta Damon *(CEO)*
Kristina Tecce *(CFO)*
Lilian Romero *(Chief Program Officer)*

LYNN LAYTON FORD
3300 Highway 31 S, Decatur, AL 35603-1410
Tel.: (256) 350-2120
Web Site:
 http://www.lynnlaytonford.com
Year Founded: 1983
Sales Range: $10-24.9 Million
Emp.: 65
New Car Whslr
N.A.I.C.S.: 441110
Lynn Layton *(Pres)*
Randy Brown *(Mgr-Pre-Owned)*

LYNN ROBERTS INTERNATIONAL
9100 F St, Omaha, NE 68127
Tel.: (402) 331-5400
Web Site:
 http://www.golynnroberts.com
Sales Range: $10-24.9 Million
Emp.: 65
Sunglasses
N.A.I.C.S.: 423990
Keith Josephson *(CEO)*
Judy Wozny *(Pres)*
Jeff Cooper *(VP)*

LYNN-ETTE & SONS, INC.
1512 Kent Rd, Kent, NY 14477-9703
Tel.: (585) 682-4435
Web Site: http://lynnettefarms.com
Sales Range: $10-24.9 Million
Emp.: 130
Vegetable & Melon Farming Services
N.A.I.C.S.: 111219

LYNNHAVEN MARINE BOATEL INC.
2150 W Great Neck Rd, Virginia Beach, VA 23451
Tel.: (757) 481-0700
Web Site:
 http://www.lynnhavenmarine.com
Sales Range: $10-24.9 Million
Emp.: 32
Boat Dealers
N.A.I.C.S.: 441222
Charles Guthrie *(Pres)*

LYNNS MARKET INC.
5660 York Rd, New Oxford, PA 17350
Tel.: (717) 624-4674
Sales Range: $10-24.9 Million
Emp.: 50
Independent Supermarket
N.A.I.C.S.: 445110
Lorijoe Baker *(Office Mgr)*
Deb Redding *(Dir-HR & Mgr-Store)*

LYNTEGAR ELECTRIC COOPERATIVE INC.
1807 Main St, Tahoka, TX 79373
Tel.: (806) 561-4588 TX
Web Site: http://www.lyntegar.coop
Year Founded: 1938
Sales Range: $10-24.9 Million
Emp.: 80
Electrical
N.A.I.C.S.: 517211

Greg Henley *(CEO)*
Barry Pittman *(Mgr-Member Svcs)*
Jana Bishop *(Mgr-HR)*
Jerry Reno *(Supvr-IT)*
Richard Lopez *(Coord-Inside Engrg Svcs)*
Ray Bo *(CFO)*

LYNWOOD BUILDING MATERIALS, INC.
1146 W Laurel, San Antonio, TX 78201
Tel.: (210) 477-3000
Web Site: http://www.lynwoodsa.com
Sales Range: $10-24.9 Million
Emp.: 30
Construction Materials Whslr
N.A.I.C.S.: 423320
Chris Christians *(Pres)*

LYNX OPERATING COMPANY INCORPORATED
2100 Ross Ave Ste 860 LB 52, Dallas, TX 75201
Tel.: (214) 969-5555
Web Site:
 http://www.lynxproduction.net
Rev.: $10,000,000
Emp.: 15
Provider of Oil & Gas Exploration Services
N.A.I.C.S.: 213112
Robert S. Craine *(Pres)*

LYNXS HOLDING LLC
106 E 6th St Ste 550, Austin, TX 78701
Tel.: (512) 530-2190
Web Site: http://www.lynxs.com
Rev.: $20,000,000
Emp.: 5
Air Cargo Carrier, Scheduled
N.A.I.C.S.: 481112
Alice Zinni *(Controller)*
Robert Althuis *(Chief Investment Officer)*
Raymond Brimble *(Founder & CEO)*
Teresa Ledbetter *(Dir-Ops)*

LYON & DITTRICH HOLDING COMPANY
420 N Main St, Montgomery, IL 60538
Tel.: (630) 892-8941 IL
Web Site:
 http://www.lyonworkspace.com
Year Founded: 1901
Sales Range: $700-749.9 Million
Emp.: 1,600
Holding Company
N.A.I.C.S.: 551112
Douglas M. Harrison *(COO)*
Tammi Pfister *(Controller)*
Peter Washington *(Chm & Pres)*

Subsidiaries:

Durand Products, LLC (1)
524 B Impereal Ct, Bensalem, PA 19020 (100%)
Tel.: (215) 638-8240
Web Site: http://www.durandproducts.com
Sales Range: $25-49.9 Million
Emp.: 2
Workbench, Utility Cart & Storage System Distr
N.A.I.C.S.: 423440

RiverPoint Kansas, L.L.C. (1)
8700 Indian Creek Pkwy Ste 100, Overland Park, KS 66210-2620
Tel.: (913) 663-2002
Web Site: http://www.riverpoint.com
Sales Range: $25-49.9 Million
Emp.: 8
Information Technology Consulting Firm Services
N.A.I.C.S.: 541512
Dominic Schilt *(Owner)*

Sycamore Systems, Inc. (1)
449 N California St, Sycamore, IL 60178-1297 (100%)
Tel.: (815) 895-8322
Web Site: http://www.sycamoresystems.com
Sales Range: $25-49.9 Million
Emp.: 120
Mfr of Steel Lockers & Storage Cabinets
N.A.I.C.S.: 337126

LYON ROOFING & SUPPLY
485 Industrial Park Rd, Piney Flats, TN 37686
Tel.: (423) 538-5169
Web Site:
 http://www.wesellmetalroofing.com
Sales Range: $10-24.9 Million
Emp.: 54
Metal Roofing Services
N.A.I.C.S.: 238160
John Lyon *(Mgr)*

LYON-COFFEY ELECTRIC COOPERATIVE, INC.
1013 N 4th St, Burlington, KS 66839
Tel.: (620) 364-2116 KS
Web Site: http://www.lyon-coffey.coop
Year Founded: 1989
Sales Range: $10-24.9 Million
Emp.: 35
Electric Power Distribution Services
N.A.I.C.S.: 221122
Eugene Huston *(Treas)*
Donna Williams *(Sec)*
David Kunkel *(VP)*
Robert Converse *(Pres)*

LYONS INDUSTRIES, INC.
30000 M-62 W, Dowagiac, MI 49047
Tel.: (269) 782-3404
Web Site:
 http://www.lyonsindustries.com
Year Founded: 1968
Sales Range: $10-24.9 Million
Emp.: 91
Plastics Plumbing Fixture Mfr
N.A.I.C.S.: 326191
Lance Lyons *(Pres)*

LYRASIS INC.
1438 W Peachtree St NW Ste 200, Atlanta, GA 30309
Tel.: (404) 892-0943 PA
Web Site: http://www.lyrasis.org
Year Founded: 1936
Rev.: $74,917,841
Assets: $27,237,932
Liabilities: $21,556,232
Net Worth: $5,681,700
Earnings: ($84,379)
Emp.: 66
Fiscal Year-end: 06/30/14
Library Management Software Publisher
N.A.I.C.S.: 513210
Paquita Wright *(Dir-HR)*
Kate Nevins *(Exec Dir)*
Vern Ritter *(CFO)*
M. J. Tooey *(Vice Chm)*
Jay Schafer *(Treas)*
Siobhan Reardon *(Chm)*
John Arnold *(Sec)*
Laurie Gemmill Arp *(Dir-Digital & Preservation Svcs)*
Jennifer Bielewski *(Mgr-Mktg Content)*
Steve Eberhardt *(Project Mgr-HBCU Photographic)*
John Herbert *(Dir-Digital Programs)*
Alicia Johnson *(Coord-Admin)*
Raili Throndson *(Dir-Bus Sys & Processes)*
Brad Westbrook *(Mgr-ArchivesSpace Program)*
Robert Miller *(CEO)*

Subsidiaries:

BiblioLabs, LLC (1)
100 Calhoun St Ste 220, Charleston, SC 29401
Tel.: (843) 475-1225
Web Site: http://www.biblioboard.com
Sales Range: $10-24.9 Million
Emp.: 25
Hybrid Media-Software Curates & Publishes Historical Materials in Digital Formats
N.A.I.C.S.: 513210
Mitchell Davis *(CEO)*
Carolyn Morris *(VP-Digital Products)*
Nitin Arora *(Dir-Digital Svcs)*

LYTTON GARDENS INC.
656 Lytton Ave, Palo Alto, CA 94301
Tel.: (650) 617-7373 CA
Web Site:
 http://www.lyttongardens.org
Year Founded: 1980
Retirement Community Operator
N.A.I.C.S.: 623311
Rosanna Cook *(Coord-Resident Svc)*
Bonnie Chang *(Coord-Resident Svc)*

M & A ELECTRIC POWER COOPERATIVE
4169 Highway PP, Poplar Bluff, MO 63902-0670
Tel.: (573) 785-9651 MO
Web Site: http://www.maelectric.com
Year Founded: 1948
Sales Range: $10-24.9 Million
Emp.: 46
Electric Power Distr
N.A.I.C.S.: 221122
Daryl Sorrell *(Gen Mgr)*
Mona Johnson *(Sec)*
Stephen Pogue *(Mgr-Risk & Compliance)*
Gregory Ponder *(Mgr-Fin)*

M & D MASONRY, INC.
PO Box 6133, Americus, GA 31709
Tel.: (229) 928-6087
Sales Range: $10-24.9 Million
Emp.: 150
Masonry Contracting Services
N.A.I.C.S.: 238140
David Weldon *(CFO)*
Michael Weldon *(CEO)*
Maria Howell *(Sec)*

M & E PAINTING, LLC.
540 W 66th St B1, Loveland, CO 80538
Tel.: (970) 207-1005
Web Site:
 http://www.mandepainting.com
Year Founded: 2005
Sales Range: $10-24.9 Million
Emp.: 15
Painting
N.A.I.C.S.: 238320
Matt Shoup *(Founder)*

M & J ENGINEERING, P.C.
2003 Jericho Tpke New Hyde Park, Rosedale, NY 11040
Tel.: (718) 525-5500
Web Site:
 http://www.mjengineers.com
Year Founded: 2004
Sales Range: $1-9.9 Million
Emp.: 50
Building Construction Services
N.A.I.C.S.: 236220
Maqsood Malik *(Founder, Pres & CEO)*
Daniel McLoughlin *(Sr VP & Office Mgr-East Coast)*
Albert Pozotrigo *(Exec VP & Dir-Construction Mgmt)*
Arnold Rubenstein *(VP & Dir-Tech Grp)*
Alexandros Constantinides *(VP)*

COMPANIES

Shawn Kelly *(VP & Dir-Construction Svcs)*
Charles Leute *(Sr VP)*
Robert Moarkech *(Sr VP)*
John Pfisterer *(Sr VP)*
Manuel J. Silva *(VP & Dir-Construction Svcs)*

M & K TRUCK & TRAILER, LLC
8800 Byron Commerce Dr, Byron Center, MI 49315
Tel.: (616) 583-2100
Web Site:
http://www.mktruckcenters.com
Year Founded: 1989
Sales Range: $50-74.9 Million
Emp.: 50
New & Used Trucks, Tractors & Trailers Whslr & Distr
N.A.I.C.S.: 423110
Ronald J. Meyering *(Owner-M&K Truck Centers)*
Tracy Schnitzler *(Dir-Svc Ops)*
Tim Schimmel *(Mgr-Sls-New Trucks)*
Ted Pilecki *(COO)*
Steve Waters *(Reg VP-Ops)*

Subsidiaries:

M&K Trailer Centers (1)
2655 Burlingame Ave SW, Grand Rapids, MI 49509
Tel.: (616) 534-1300
Web Site: http://www.lvtrailer.com
Sales Range: $1-9.9 Million
Emp.: 25
New & Used Trailers Whslr & Distr
N.A.I.C.S.: 423110
Josh Wolf *(Mgr-Ops)*
Robert Velthouse *(Pres)*
Heidi Vanos *(Office Mgr)*

M & M DODGE HYUNDAI, INC
3220 S Macarthur Dr, Alexandria, LA 71301
Tel.: (318) 445-6504
Web Site:
http://www.mmhyundai.com
Rev.: $11,300,000
Emp.: 45
New Car Dealers
N.A.I.C.S.: 441110
Oliver L. McMickens *(Pres)*

M & M MILLING, INC.
33 Globe Ave, Texarkana, AR 71854
Tel.: (870) 772-3906
Web Site:
http://www.mandmmilling.com
Sales Range: $10-24.9 Million
Emp.: 60
Nut Shell, Corn & Allied Product Milling Services
N.A.I.C.S.: 311221
Holmes Morel *(Pres)*
John Morel *(Sr VP)*
Robert L. Long *(Plant Mgr)*

M & N FOODS LLC.
1355 Grand Ave Ste 101, San Marcos, CA 92078-3973
Tel.: (760) 471-2494
Sales Range: $50-74.9 Million
Emp.: 550
Breakfast Cereal Mfr
N.A.I.C.S.: 311230
Michael D. Borchard *(Pres)*

M & W HOT OIL INC
2902 Balmorhea Hwy, Pecos, TX 79772
Tel.: (432) 447-2108
Web Site: http://www.mwhotoil.com
Year Founded: 1954
Sales Range: $10-24.9 Million
Emp.: 60
Trucking Service

N.A.I.C.S.: 484121
Bruce McKee *(Founder)*

M A T PARCEL EXPRESS, INC.
2719 Kurtz St Ste C, San Diego, CA 92110
Tel.: (619) 849-9600 CA
Web Site: http://www.matexpress.net
Year Founded: 1985
Sales Range: $1-9.9 Million
Emp.: 60
Local Trucking, Without Storage, Nsk
N.A.I.C.S.: 484110
Diane Eggert *(Treas & Sec)*

M C BANCSHARES, INC.
1201 Brashear Ave, Morgan City, LA 70380
Tel.: (985) 384-2100
Web Site: https://www.mcbt.com
Bank Holding Company
N.A.I.C.S.: 551111
Christopher P. LeBato *(CEO)*

Subsidiaries:

M C Bank & Trust Company (1)
6413 Highway 182 E, Morgan City, LA 70380
Tel.: (985) 385-4988
Web Site: http://www.mcbt.com
Rev.: $3,010,000
Emp.: 10
Banking Services
N.A.I.C.S.: 522110
Larry J. Callais *(Pres & CEO)*

M CORP
947 Enterprise Dr Loft C, Sacramento, CA 95825
Tel.: (916) 254-0355
Web Site: http://www.the-mcorp.com
Year Founded: 2004
Sales Range: $10-24.9 Million
Emp.: 40
Business Management Consulting Services
N.A.I.C.S.: 541611
Alex Castro *(Partner)*
Chuck Czajkowski *(Partner)*
Hung Lee *(Partner)*
Mike Reed *(Head-Cloud Analytics Software-Austin)*

M FINANCIAL GROUP
1125 NW Couch St Ste 900, Portland, OR 97209
Tel.: (503) 232-6960
Web Site: https://www.mfin.com
Year Founded: 1978
Financial Services
N.A.I.C.S.: 522310
Russell Bundschuh *(Pres & CEO)*
Jason Christian *(Chief Legal Officer)*
Jenn Congdon *(Chief HR Officer)*
Jeff Currie *(VP & Head-Corp Solutions)*
Andy Graves *(VP & Head-Member Firm Dev)*
Tamara Kravec *(CFO & Chief Risk Officer)*
T. V. Kumaresh *(Chief Strategy Officer)*
Michael Schoonmaker *(VP & Head-Wealth Solutions)*
Jesse Whitethorn *(Sr Dir-Information Sys & Architecture)*
Kim Williams *(VP-Partner Rels)*

M FINANCIAL HOLDINGS INCORPORATED
1125 NW Couch St Ste 900, Portland, OR 97209
Tel.: (503) 232-6960 DE
Web Site: http://www.mfin.com
Year Founded: 1978
Sales Range: $400-449.9 Million
Emp.: 150

Holding Company; Insurance, Investment & Executive Benefits
N.A.I.C.S.: 551112
Randall M. O'Connor *(CFO & Sr VP)*
Dave Watros *(VP-Bus Dev & Relationship Mgmt)*
Westley V. Thompson *(Pres & CEO)*

M FORCE STAFFING
1626 Downtown W Blvd, Knoxville, TN 37919
Tel.: (865) 862-3900
Web Site:
http://www.mforcestaffing.com
Year Founded: 2007
Sales Range: $1-9.9 Million
Emp.: 15
Technical Recruiting Staffing
N.A.I.C.S.: 561320
Andy Moss *(Pres)*
Joe Conger *(VP)*
Krista Jones *(Mgr-Acct-Professional Svcs)*

M HIDARY & COMPANY INC.
10 W 33rd St Rm 900, New York, NY 10001
Tel.: (212) 736-6540
Web Site: http://www.mhidary.com
Sales Range: $200-249.9 Million
Emp.: 100
Women's & Children's Clothing
N.A.I.C.S.: 424350
Abraham Hidary *(Pres)*

M INTERNATIONAL INC.
1301 Dolley Madison Blvd, McLean, VA 22101
Tel.: (703) 448-4400
Web Site: http://www.mintex.net
Year Founded: 1979
Sales Range: $10-24.9 Million
Emp.: 15
Aircraft & Parts
N.A.I.C.S.: 423860
Richard McConn *(CEO)*
Mehdi Protzuk *(Sec)*
Wanda Richardson *(Project Mgr)*
Chuck Hurdleston *(VP-Sls & Mktg)*
Rob Ruck *(Pres & COO)*

Subsidiaries:

Airborne Engines Ltd. (1)
7762 Progress Way, Delta, V4G 1A4, BC, Canada
Tel.: (604) 244-1668
Web Site: http://www.airborneengines.com
Compressor Mfr & Distr
N.A.I.C.S.: 336390
Rob Ruck *(Pres)*
Darcy McAlpine *(Dir-Bus Dev)*
Steve Walford *(VP)*
Shahbaz Ahmed *(CFO)*

Keystone Turbine Services LLC (1)
885 Fox Chase Ste 111, Coatesville, PA 19320
Tel.: (610) 268-6200
Web Site: http://www.kts-aero.com
Automotive Engine Repair Services
N.A.I.C.S.: 811111
Wes Kimata *(Gen Mgr)*
John Fraser *(VP-Ops)*
Gayle Walker *(Controller)*
Tom Raichle *(Mgr-Production)*
Tim Kline *(Mgr-Accessories)*
Tom Hall *(Mgr-Sls & Support)*
Perry Siler *(Mgr-Sls & Support)*
Chuck Hurdleston *(Mgr-Sls & Support)*
Tim Walsh *(Mgr-Quality Assurance)*

Mint Turbines LLC (1)
2915 N State Hwy 99, Stroud, OK 74079-0460 (100%)
Tel.: (918) 968-9561
Web Site: http://www.mintturbines.com
Sales Range: $10-24.9 Million
Emp.: 43
Overhaul & Repair of Aircraft Engines
N.A.I.C.S.: 811210

M STRATEGIES, INC.

Richard McConn *(Pres)*
Wayne Bond *(Reg Mgr)*
Skip Cross *(Mgr-IT)*
Gilbert Palacios *(Mgr-Field Svc)*

Southwest Fuel Systems LLC (1)
975 W Grant Rd Ste 105, Tucson, AZ 85705-5359
Tel.: (520) 623-2918
Web Site: http://www.southwestfuelsys.com
Fuel System Repair Services
N.A.I.C.S.: 811198
Holly Griffin *(Controller)*

M ROGERS DESIGN, INC.
3400 W Lake Ave, Glenview, IL 60026-1213
Tel.: (847) 564-5033 IL
Web Site:
http://www.dimensiondesign.com
Year Founded: 2002
Rev.: $4,000,000
Emp.: 35
Convention & Trade Show Organizers
N.A.I.C.S.: 561920
Michael Rogers *(Pres)*

Subsidiaries:

Media Works, Ltd. (1)
1425 Clarkview Rd Ste 500, Baltimore, MD 21209
Tel.: (443) 470-4400
Web Site: http://www.medialtd.com
Sales Range: $50-74.9 Million
Emp.: 30
Marketing & Advertising Agencies
N.A.I.C.S.: 541810
Jody S. Berg *(CEO)*
Amy Wisner *(Exec VP)*
Jennifer Pupshis *(Media Buyer)*
Michele Selby *(Exec VP)*
Mandy Remeto *(Supvr-Acct)*
Betsy Clark *(VP)*
Gail Corbett *(Office Mgr)*
Megan Olson *(VP)*
Jason Pool *(Acct Mgr)*
Julie Block Padden *(Acct Mgr)*
Ashlea Wolcott *(VP)*
Allison Shields *(Mgr-Acct)*

Branch (Domestic):

Media Works Charlotte (2)
9401 Standenvick Ln, Huntersville, NC 28078
Tel.: (704) 947-2000
Web Site: http://medialtd.com
Emp.: 20
Media Buying Services
N.A.I.C.S.: 541830
Tami Frey *(VP)*

M SS NG P ECES
836 Manhattan Ave, Brooklyn, NY 11222
Tel.: (646) 290-7931
Web Site:
http://www.mssngpeces.com
Year Founded: 2005
Sales Range: $1-9.9 Million
Emp.: 7
Video Production & Advertising Agency Services
N.A.I.C.S.: 512110
Ari Kuschnir *(Founder & CEO)*
Kate Oppenheim *(Mng Partner)*
Dave Saltzman *(Head-Production)*
Brian Latt *(Mng Partner)*

M STRATEGIES, INC.
208 N Market St Ste 375, Dallas, TX 75202
Tel.: (214) 741-2100
Web Site:
http://www.mstrategiesinc.com
Sales Range: $10-24.9 Million
Emp.: 12
Public Relations Agency
N.A.I.C.S.: 541820
L. Michelle Smith *(Pres & CEO)*
James E. Smith *(COO & Exec VP-Fin)*

M Strategies, Inc.—(Continued)
Neil Foote *(VP-Strategy & Dev)*
John W. Humphress *(CTO)*
Heather Woodard *(Acct Supvr)*

M&A SUPPLY COMPANY INC.
194 River Hills Dr, Nashville, TN 37210
Tel.: (615) 889-8820 TN
Web Site:
http://www.masupplycompany.com
Year Founded: 1969
Sales Range: $10-24.9 Million
Emp.: 70
Provider of Roofing, Siding, Insulation, Heat & Air Conditioning
N.A.I.C.S.: 423730
Charles E. Anderson *(Chm & CEO)*
Brian Smith *(Mgr-Pur)*

M&A TECHNOLOGY, INC.
2045 Chenault Dr, Carrollton, TX 75006-5021
Tel.: (972) 387-6783 TX
Web Site: http://www.macomp.com
Year Founded: 1984
Sales Range: $50-74.9 Million
Emp.: 120
Whslr of Computer Peripherals & Software
N.A.I.C.S.: 423430
Magdy S. Elwany *(Founder, Pres & CEO)*
Val Overbey *(CTO)*
Donna Shepard *(Exec VP)*
Tom Garrett *(VP-Mgmt Info Sys & Acctg)*

M&B CORPORATION
3112 S 67th St, Omaha, NE 68106
Tel.: (402) 393-8200
Web Site: http://www.okelectric.net
Sales Range: $1-9.9 Million
Emp.: 30
Investment Holding Companies, Except Banks
N.A.I.C.S.: 551112
Richard Bowen *(Pres)*
William McMahon *(VP)*

Subsidiaries:

Kure Associates LLC (1)
3112 S 67th St, Omaha, NE 68106
Tel.: (402) 453-2255
Web Site: http://www.kureassociates.com
Sales Range: $1-9.9 Million
Emp.: 20
Computerized Controls Installation
N.A.I.C.S.: 238210
John McMahon *(Pres)*

M&B METAL PRODUCTS CO. INC.
8575 Pkwy Dr SW, Leeds, AL 35094
Tel.: (205) 699-2171
Web Site: http://www.mbhangers.com
Sales Range: $10-24.9 Million
Emp.: 130
Garment Hangers, Made From Purchased Wire
N.A.I.C.S.: 332618
Milton M. Magnus III *(Pres)*

M&B PRODUCTS INC.
8601 Harney Rd, Tampa, FL 33637
Tel.: (813) 988-2211
Web Site:
http://www.mbproducts.com
Year Founded: 1987
Sales Range: $25-49.9 Million
Emp.: 160
Fruit Juices, Milk, Water & Desserts Production & Canning
N.A.I.C.S.: 311411
Dale McClellan *(Pres & CEO)*
Tom Hammerschmidt *(Gen Mgr)*
Andrea McClellan *(Office Mgr-HR & Asst Controller)*
Daniel McClellan *(Mgr-Shipping)*
Quentin Roman *(Mgr-Distr)*

Subsidiaries:

M&B of Tampa Inc. (1)
8601 Harney Rd, Tampa, FL 33637
Tel.: (813) 988-2211
Web Site: http://www.mbproducts.com
Rev.: $990,000
Emp.: 100
Dairy Farm
N.A.I.C.S.: 112120
Dale McClellan *(Pres & CEO)*

M&F BANCORP, INC.
650 Hwy 7 S, Holly Springs, MS 38635
Tel.: (662) 252-1341 MS
Web Site:
http://www.mandfbankhs.com
Year Founded: 1991
Sales Range: $1-9.9 Million
Emp.: 37
Bank Holding Company
N.A.I.C.S.: 551111
H. Gregory Taylor *(Pres & CEO)*

Subsidiaries:

Merchants & Farmers Bank (1)
650 Hwy 7 S, Holly Springs, MS 38635
Tel.: (662) 252-1341
Web Site: http://www.mandfbankhs.com
Retail & Commercial Banking
N.A.I.C.S.: 522110
Ken Hughes *(Pres & CEO)*
Janell Allbritton *(VP-HR)*
Lea Ann Purtiman *(VP)*
Megan Fox *(Asst VP)*
Trevor Cooley *(Asst VP-Lending-Vernon Parish & Southwest Louisiana)*
Melody Carter *(Mgr-Bank-New Llano)*
Alesia Lewis *(Asst VP & Mgr-Bank-Rosepine)*
JoLynn Snapp *(Asst VP-Leesville)*

M&F WESTERN PRODUCTS INC.
1303 Holiday Dr, Sulphur Springs, TX 75482
Tel.: (903) 885-8646
Web Site: http://www.mfwestern.com
Year Founded: 1969
Rev.: $14,869,386
Emp.: 70
Caps, Men's & Boys'
N.A.I.C.S.: 424350
Mickey F. Eddins *(Owner)*
Paul Eddins *(CFO)*

M&G ELECTRONICS CORP.
889 Seahawk Cir, Virginia Beach, VA 23452
Tel.: (757) 468-6000
Web Site:
http://www.mgelectronic.com
Sales Range: $100-124.9 Million
Emp.: 300
The Company Produces Harness Wiring
N.A.I.C.S.: 335313
Mark F. Garcea *(Pres)*
Larry Holleman *(Gen Mgr)*
Joan Hoffman *(Pur Mgr)*
Mark Showich *(QA Mgr)*
Gary Bunch *(Controller)*
Susan Ferguson *(Mgr-HR)*

M&J GENERAL CONTRACTORS INC.
860 Summit St Ste 232, Elgin, IL 60120
Tel.: (847) 741-9611
Web Site: http://www.mjgcinc.net
Year Founded: 1998
Sales Range: $10-24.9 Million
Industrial Constructors
N.A.I.C.S.: 236210
Max Dobson *(Pres)*

M&J MANAGEMENT CORPORATION
147 Delta Dr, Pittsburgh, PA 15238
Tel.: (412) 963-6550
Sales Range: $10-24.9 Million
Emp.: 20
Fast-Food Restaurant, Chain
N.A.I.C.S.: 722513
Michael J. Delligatti *(Pres)*
Dan Hubert *(Controller)*

M&J MATERIALS INC.
7561 Gadsden Hwy, Trussville, AL 35173-1629
Tel.: (205) 655-7451 AL
Year Founded: 1976
Sales Range: $10-24.9 Million
Emp.: 50
Provider of Roofing, Siding & Sheet Metal Work
N.A.I.C.S.: 238390
Joyce Kell *(Controller)*
Frank C. Hopson III *(Pres)*

M&J MOTORS INC.
3590 S Western Blvd, Orchard Park, NY 14127
Tel.: (716) 826-4200
Web Site: http://www.raylaks.com
Rev.: $16,850,197
Emp.: 100
New & Used Car Dealers
N.A.I.C.S.: 441110
Raymond Laks *(Pres)*

M&J TRIMMING COMPANY INC.
1008 Avenue of the Americas, New York, NY 10018
Tel.: (212) 391-9072
Web Site: http://www.mjtrimm.com
Sales Range: $10-24.9 Million
Emp.: 30
Apparel Trimmings
N.A.I.C.S.: 424310
Joel Cohen *(CEO)*

M&K ENTERPRISE LLC
1950 E Maule Ave, Las Vegas, NV 89119
Tel.: (702) 876-1517
Sales Range: $10-24.9 Million
Emp.: 100
Gift Shop
N.A.I.C.S.: 459420
Cheryl Wiggins *(Office Mgr)*
V. Paglia *(Pres)*

M&L INDUSTRIES INC.
1210 Charles St, Houma, LA 70360
Tel.: (985) 876-2280
Web Site: http://www.mlind.net
Sales Range: $25-49.9 Million
Emp.: 30
Materials Handling Machinery
N.A.I.C.S.: 423830
Steve Marmande *(Pres)*

M&L PETROLEUM INC.
205 N Kinney Ave, Mount Pleasant, MI 48858
Tel.: (989) 772-6068
Web Site:
http://www.mlpetroleum.com
Sales Range: $10-24.9 Million
Emp.: 7
Petroleum
N.A.I.C.S.: 424720
Mark Beard *(Pres)*

M&L ROSE ENTERPRISES INC.
737 Regal Row, Dallas, TX 75257
Tel.: (214) 637-6900 TX
Web Site: http://www.rose-tree.com
Year Founded: 1979
Sales Range: $25-49.9 Million
Emp.: 150
Mfr of Linen Fabrics
N.A.I.C.S.: 314999
Lydia Rose *(Founder & Pres)*

M&L SUPPLY COMPANY INCORPORATED
4114 E Ferry Ave, Spokane, WA 99202
Tel.: (509) 535-4774
Web Site: http://www.mlsupply.com
Sales Range: $10-24.9 Million
Emp.: 28
Plumbing & Hydronic Heating Supplies
N.A.I.C.S.: 423720
Ron Wesselman *(Controller)*

M&M BEVERAGES LLC
5337 W 78th St, Indianapolis, IN 46268
Tel.: (317) 876-1188
Rev.: $104,900,000
Emp.: 300
Liquor
N.A.I.C.S.: 424820
Chris Moore *(Dir-Natl Accts)*

M&M CARTAGE CO. INC.
4106 Eastmoor Rd, Louisville, KY 40218
Tel.: (502) 456-4586
Web Site: http://www.mmcartage.com
Rev.: $11,480,525
Emp.: 250
Light Haulage & Cartage, Local
N.A.I.C.S.: 484110
Don Hayden *(Pres)*
Arthur Potter *(Dir-Sls & Mktg)*
Billy Bowyer *(Mgr-Fleet Svcs)*
Rob Birk *(VP-Ops)*
Tracy Stephens *(Mgr-Safety)*
Ron Hildenbrand *(Controller)*
Stacey Murphy *(Mgr-HR)*
Marty Mullaney *(Mgr-Ops)*
John Roos *(VP-Fin)*

M&M INTERNATIONAL TRADING
14 Self Blvd, Carteret, NJ 07008
Tel.: (732) 855-1600
Web Site:
http://www.goldenbrazil.com
Rev.: $10,973,082
Emp.: 3
Roasted Coffee
N.A.I.C.S.: 311920

M&M LIGHTING LP
5620 S Rice Ave, Houston, TX 77081
Tel.: (713) 667-5611
Web Site: http://www.mmlighting.com
Sales Range: $25-49.9 Million
Emp.: 55
Lighting Fixtures, Commercial & Industrial
N.A.I.C.S.: 423610
Alan Margolin *(Owner)*
Scott Shore *(Mgr-Sls-Multi Family Div)*

M&M PUMP & SUPPLY CO. INC.
1125 Olivepte Exec Pkwy Ste 110, Saint Louis, IL 63132
Tel.: (618) 676-1915
Web Site:
http://www.mandmpump.com
Sales Range: $10-24.9 Million
Emp.: 75
Distr of Oil Well Machinery, Equipment & Supplies
N.A.I.C.S.: 423830

Debra Buerster *(Sec)*

M&M SALES INCORPORATED
817 S 24th St, Easton, PA 18042
Tel.: (610) 330-0395
Year Founded: 1982
Sales Range: $10-24.9 Million
Emp.: 4
Hardware
N.A.I.C.S.: 423710
Robert A. Mease *(Pres)*

M&M SERVICE CO. INC.
130 N Chiles St, Carlinville, IL 62626
Tel.: (217) 854-4516
Web Site: http://www.mmservice.com
Sales Range: $50-74.9 Million
Emp.: 200
Grain Elevators
N.A.I.C.S.: 424510
Brad Klaus *(Gen Mgr)*

M&M SUPPLY CO.
901 W Peach Ave, Duncan, OK 73533
Tel.: (580) 252-7879
Web Site: http://www.mmsupply.com
Sales Range: $10-24.9 Million
Emp.: 60
Oil Well Machinery, Equipment & Supplies
N.A.I.C.S.: 423830
Ed Foreman *(Exec VP)*
Michael Mullica *(Reg Mgr-Sls)*

M&O INSULATION COMPANY
17217 Ashland Ave, Hazel Crest, IL 60429
Tel.: (708) 799-3850
Web Site:
 http://www.moinsulation.com
Year Founded: 1975
Sales Range: $10-24.9 Million
Emp.: 35
Building Insulation
N.A.I.C.S.: 238310
Kevin Doherty *(Pres)*
Andrea Sims *(Coord-Logistics)*
Stephen Castellarin *(Mgr-Comml Div)*

M&Q PLASTIC PRODUCTS, INC.
542 N Lewis Rd Ste 206, Royersford, PA 19468
Tel.: (267) 498-4000
Web Site:
 http://www.mqplasticproducts.com
Year Founded: 1956
Sales Range: $25-49.9 Million
Emp.: 203
Mfr of Plastic Products
N.A.I.C.S.: 326199
Mike Schmal *(Pres)*
Joe Mallozzi *(CFO)*

Subsidiaries:

M&Q Packaging Corporation (1)
3 Earl St, Schuylkill Haven, PA 17972
Tel.: (570) 385-4991
Web Site: http://www.mqplastics.com
Sales Range: $10-24.9 Million
Emp.: 87
Plastics Products
N.A.I.C.S.: 326199
Michael Schmal *(Pres)*

M&R HOLDINGS INC.
1 N 372 Main St, Glen Ellyn, IL 60137
Tel.: (630) 858-6101
Web Site: http://www.mrprint.com
Year Founded: 1993
Rev.: $60,000,000
Emp.: 400
Printing Trades Machinery
N.A.I.C.S.: 333248

Rich Hoffman *(Pres & CEO)*
Howard Bloom *(CFO)*
Dave Zimmer *(Product Mgr)*

Subsidiaries:

M&R Printing Equipment Inc. (1)
1 N 372 Main St, Glen Ellyn, IL 60137
Tel.: (630) 858-6101
Web Site: http://www.mrprint.com
Rev.: $55,000,000
Printing Equipment Mfr
N.A.I.C.S.: 333248
Richard Hossman *(Pres & CEO)*

Subsidiary (Domestic):

Amscomatic, Inc. (2)
6200 Howard St, Niles, IL 60714
Tel.: (847) 967-4400
Web Site: http://www.mrprint.com
Rev.: $3,000,000
Emp.: 50
Packaging Machinery Mfr
N.A.I.C.S.: 333310
Rich Hoffmann *(Pres)*
John Murray *(Mgr-Product)*

NuArc Company, Inc. (2)
6200 W Howard St, Niles, IL 60714
Tel.: (847) 967-4400
Web Site: http://www.nuarc.com
Sales Range: $25-49.9 Million
Emp.: 300
Mfr of Graphic Arts Equipment
N.A.I.C.S.: 333310

Division (Domestic):

NuArc Western Div. (3)
3162 E La Palma Ave Ste C, Anaheim, CA 92806-2810
Tel.: (714) 630-5567
Sales Range: $10-24.9 Million
Emp.: 6
Mfr of Graphic Arts Equipment
N.A.I.C.S.: 333310

M&R Sales & Service Inc. (1)
6200 W Howard St, Niles, IL 60714
Tel.: (847) 967-4400
Web Site: http://www.mrprint.com
Rev.: $1,300,000
Emp.: 16
Textile Machinery Mfr
N.A.I.C.S.: 333248

M&R Sales & Service Inc. (1)
440 Medinah Rd, Roselle, IL 60172
Tel.: (630) 858-6101
Web Site: http://www.mrprint.com
Sales Range: $10-24.9 Million
Emp.: 40
Mfr of Screen Printing Equipment, Dryers & Cure Units & Ancillary Equipment
N.A.I.C.S.: 541820

M&S BARGAIN HUNTER INC.
2455 McDonald Ave Ste 202, Brooklyn, NY 11223-5232
Tel.: (718) 346-3774
Rev.: $12,019,755
Emp.: 15
Variety Stores
N.A.I.C.S.: 455219
Solomon Cohen *(Pres)*
Maurice Kassin *(Comptroller)*

M&S ENGINEERING, LLC
6477 FM 311, Spring Branch, TX 78070
Tel.: (844) 267-3647
Web Site: http://www.msengr.com
Engineeering Services
N.A.I.C.S.: 541330
Brian Meuth *(Owner & Pres)*
Jason Moseley *(Partner-Electrical Engrg)*
Bill Newcomer *(Mgr-Distr)*
Cory Kadlacek *(Mgr-Substation)*
Paul Elkins *(Mgr-Georgetown Electrical)*
Jeremy Duncan *(Mgr-Woodlands Electrical)*

Subsidiaries:

San Antonio Design Group Inc. (1)
6609 Blanco Rd Ste 165, San Antonio, TX 78216
Tel.: (210) 260-8140
Web Site: http://www.sadesigngroup.com
Engineering Services
N.A.I.C.S.: 541330

M&S FAB INC.
13720 Cimarron Ave, Gardena, CA 90249-2462
Tel.: (310) 808-0008
Sales Range: $10-24.9 Million
Emp.: 7
Import Yarn
N.A.I.C.S.: 424310
Sang Yeul Lee *(Pres)*

M&V PROVISIONS CO. INC.
1827 Flushing Ave, Ridgewood, NY 11385-1040
Tel.: (718) 456-7070
Web Site:
 http://www.mnvprovisions.com
Sales Range: $25-49.9 Million
Emp.: 25
Meat Producer
N.A.I.C.S.: 424470
Joseph Guitian *(Asst VP & Mgr-IT)*
Mike Ciuffo *(VP & Dir-Pur)*
Joseph Vallario *(Exec VP & Gen Mgr)*
Pat Lasker *(Office Mgr)*
Tony Ciuffo *(Pres)*
Joseph Castrogiovanni *(VP & Plant Mgr)*

M-B COMPANIES, INC.
1615 Wisconsin Ave, New Holstein, WI 53061
Tel.: (920) 898-1560
Web Site: http://www.m-bco.com
Year Founded: 1907
Sales Range: $75-99.9 Million
Emp.: 90
Pavement Sweeping & Marking Equipment Mfr
N.A.I.C.S.: 561110
Susan Torrison *(Mgr-Admin)*
Aaron Schulz *(Mgr-Product Support & Parts)*
Scott Scharinger *(Mgr-Sls-Western)*
Steve Karlin *(Sr VP & Gen Mgr-Airport Maintenance Products)*

Subsidiaries:

M-B Companies, Inc. - Airport Snow Removal Division (1)
1200 Park St, Chilton, WI 53014
Web Site: http://www.m-bco.com
Snow Removal Equipment Mfr
N.A.I.C.S.: 333112
Aaron Schulz *(Mgr-Product Support & Parts)*
Scott Scharinger *(Mgr-Sls-Western Reg)*
Alan Luke *(Sls Mgr-Federal Govt-Eastern)*
Steve Karlin *(Sr VP & Gen Mgr)*

M-B Companies, Inc. - Pavement Marking Equipment Division (1)
79 Montgomery St, Montgomery, PA 17752
Tel.: (570) 547-1621
Pavement Marking Equipment Mfr
N.A.I.C.S.: 333120
Robert Bowman *(Mgr-North Eastern Reg)*

M-B-W INC.
250 Hartford Rd, Slinger, WI 53086
Tel.: (262) 644-5234
Web Site: http://www.mbw.com
Sales Range: $10-24.9 Million
Emp.: 50
Tampers, Powered
N.A.I.C.S.: 551112
Bert Multerer *(COO)*
Andy Multerer *(Pres & CEO)*

M-C INDUSTRIES INC.
3601 SW 29th St Ste 250, Topeka, KS 66614
Tel.: (785) 273-3990
Web Site: http://www.mcind.com
Year Founded: 1957
Sales Range: $25-49.9 Million
Emp.: 45
Plastics Hardware & Building Products
N.A.I.C.S.: 326199
Rob Ward *(VP-IT)*
Kent Garlinghouse *(Chm)*

Subsidiaries:

Polo Custom Products (1)
3601 SW 29th St, Topeka, KS 66614
Tel.: (785) 273-3990
Web Site:
 http://www.polocustomproducts.com
Plastics Product Mfr
N.A.I.C.S.: 326199
Anna Bolan *(Dir-Sls & Mktg)*
Kent Lammers *(Pres & CEO)*
Rob Ward *(VP-IT)*
Brian Weber *(Sr VP-Mfg-Global)*

Subsidiary (Domestic):

Foarm Following Function, Inc. (2)
501 E Gutierrez St, Santa Barbara, CA 93103
Tel.: (805) 962-5553
Web Site: http://www.foarm.com
Sales Range: $1-9.9 Million
Plastics Foam Products
N.A.I.C.S.: 326150

Sunflower Marketing (1)
3601 SW 29th St, Topeka, KS 66614
Tel.: (800) 337-1097
Web Site:
 http://www.sunflowermarketing.com
Marketing Services
N.A.I.C.S.: 541870
Karla Klem *(Pres & CEO)*
William Kampsen *(Dir-Art)*

M-D BUILDING PRODUCTS, INC.
4041 N Santa Fe Ave, Oklahoma City, OK 73118
Tel.: (800) 654-8454
Web Site: http://www.mdteam.com
Year Founded: 1920
Building Product Mfr
N.A.I.C.S.: 444180
Jim Robertson *(VP-Mktg Flooring Products)*
Loren Plotkin *(Chm & CEO)*
Larry Sanford *(Exec VP)*
Fredrik Olsson *(VP-Sls-Pro)*
Joe Comitale *(Pres-PRO & Canada)*
Ryan Plotkin *(Pres)*

M-E COMPANIES, INC.
635 Brooksedge Blvd, Westerville, OH 43081
Tel.: (614) 818-4900
Sales Range: $25-49.9 Million
Emp.: 135
Highway, Street & Bridge Construction Services
N.A.I.C.S.: 237310
Timothy R. Foley *(Pres)*
Tim Foley *(Pres & CEO)*

M-E ENGINEERS, INC.
10055 W 43rd Ave, Wheat Ridge, CO 80033
Tel.: (303) 421-6655
Web Site: http://www.me-engineers.com
Year Founded: 1981
Rev.: $15,100,000
Emp.: 240
Engineeering Services
N.A.I.C.S.: 541330
Art Smith *(Principal)*
Brian Unekis *(Principal)*
George Reiher *(Principal)*

M-E ENGINEERS, INC.

M-E Engineers, Inc.—(Continued)
Mike Day (Principal)
Scott Gerard (Principal & VP)
Charlie Lengal (Principal)
Chris Jones (Principal)
Darrell Lackey (Principal)
Jeff Sawarynski (Principal)
Austin Simmons (Principal)
Dave Groulx (Principal)
Leonard Gurule (Principal)
Paul Hillier (Principal)
Roger Loomis (Principal)
Sean Hira (Principal)
Shane Lazaroff (Principal)
Ted Prythero (Principal)
Jeremy O. Brien (Principal)
Kevin Devore (Principal)
Lyle Hays (Principal)
Brian Kannady (Principal)
George Lui (Principal)
Bob McCoy (Principal)
Mohit Mehta (Principal & Dir-Sustainable Design)
Jey Nageswaran (Principal)
Andrew Shivley (Principal)
Charles Warner (Principal)

M-E-C COMPANY
1402 W Main St, Neodesha, KS 66757
Tel.: (620) 325-2673
Web Site: http://www.m-e-c.com
Sales Range: $10-24.9 Million
Emp.: 123
Dehydrating Equipment, Food Processing
N.A.I.C.S.: 333241
Brent Kingston (Controller)

M-G INC.
1201 County Rd, Weimar, TX 78962
Tel.: (979) 725-8581
Web Site: http://www.m-ginc.com
Sales Range: $10-24.9 Million
Emp.: 80
Feed Farm Service Center, Frozen Food Selling, Chainsaw, Agriculture
N.A.I.C.S.: 424440
Mark Kloesel (Pres)

M-PAK, INC.
11255 Camp Bowie W Ste 1011, Aledo, TX 76008
Tel.: (817) 696-0004
Web Site: http://www.mpakpackaging.com
Year Founded: 1999
Sales Range: $1-9.9 Million
Emp.: 6
Distributes Industrial Packaging Materials
N.A.I.C.S.: 423840
Debbie Miliara (Pres)
Anna Boulware (VP)

M-S CASH DRAWER CORPORATION
2085 E Foothill Blvd, Pasadena, CA 91107
Tel.: (626) 792-2111 CA
Web Site: http://www.mscashdrawer.com
Year Founded: 1946
Sales Range: $10-24.9 Million
Emp.: 30
N.A.I.C.S.: 423420
Paul Masson (Owner & Pres)
Andrew Lamb (Dir)

M. & O. INSULATION COMPANY
17217 Ashland Ave, Homewood, IL 60430
Tel.: (708) 799-3850
Web Site: http://www.mocompany.com
Year Founded: 1972
Sales Range: $25-49.9 Million
Emp.: 35
Drywall & Insulation Contracting Services
N.A.I.C.S.: 238310
Michael Consorti (Controller)

M. ALFIERI CO. INC.
399 Thornall St, Edison, NJ 08837
Tel.: (732) 548-2200
Rev.: $22,000,000
Emp.: 100
Commercial & Office Building, New Construction
N.A.I.C.S.: 236220
Dominick Alfieri (Chm)
Shannon Moore (Mgr-Tenant Rels)

M. ALJANICH ASSOCIATES INC.
1805 W Chanute Rd, Peoria, IL 61615
Tel.: (309) 691-5550
Sales Range: $10-24.9 Million
Emp.: 2
Machine Tools & Accessories
N.A.I.C.S.: 423830
Dennis Nash (Pres)

M. ARTHUR GENSLER JR. & ASSOCIATES INC.
2 Harrison St Ste 400, San Francisco, CA 94105-2704
Tel.: (415) 433-3700 CA
Web Site: http://www.gensler.com
Year Founded: 1965
Sales Range: $750-799.9 Million
Emp.: 5,412
Architectural Services
N.A.I.C.S.: 541310
Andy Cohen (Chm & Co-CEO)
Joseph Brancato (Mng Principal-Northeast & Latin America)
Scott Dunlap (Mng Principal-Northwest Reg)
Robert Jernigan (Mng Principal-Southwest Reg)
Robin Klehr Avia (Mng Principal-Northeast & Latin America)
Julia Simet (Mng Dir & Principal)
Jon Gambrill (Mng Dir & Principal)
Ty Osbaugh (Principal)
Edward Muth (Principal)
Kimberly Hickson (Principal)
Sumita Arora (Principal)
Francisco Gonzalez (Principal)
Laura DeBonis (Principal & Dir-Technical)
Tom Shen (Principal)
Aleksandar Zeljic (Principal & Dir-Design)
Gerald Gehm (Mng Dir & Principal)
Kirsten Ritchie (Principal & Dir-Consulting Project)
Paul Manno (Principal)
Jacob Simons (Dir-Studio)
Carlos Valera (Mng Dir & Principal)
Meena Krenek (Dir-Design)
Bill Baxley (Mng Dir-Minneapolis)
Jared Krieger (Principal & Dir-Co-Studio)
Kimberly Sullivan (Principal & Dir-Co-Studio)
John McKinney (Principal & Dir-Design)
Carrie Renegar (Dir-Design)
Xiaomei Lee (Mng Dir & Principal)
Tory Winn (Dir-Co-Studio-Atlanta)
Ayeesha Jahi (Coord-Studio-Charlotte)
Sergio Bakas (Sr Mgr-Design-Miami)
Vaki Mawema (Mgr-Design)
Luigi Franceschina (Mgr-Design-Chcago)
Grant Uhlir (Mng Principal-North Central)
Nila R. Leiserowitz (Reg Mng Principal)
Rory Carder (Dir-Workplace-Phoenix)
Kristen Conry (Mng Dir-Chicago)
Brian Vitale (Mng Dir-Chicago)
Todd Heiser (Mng Dir-Chicago)
Lisa Morgenroth (Dir-Studio)
Alex Burkholder (Dir-Studio)
Denise Korn (Creative Dir-Brand Strategy & Design Studio-Real Estate)
Javier Cortes (Dir-Studio-Brand Strategy, Brand Design & Digital Experience)
David Lynch (Principal & Dir-Studio)
David Kramer (Principal & Dir-Digital)
Tim Hudson (Principal)
Simona Furini (Sr Mgr-Design)
Sharon Steinberg (Project Dir-Houston)
Diane J. Hoskins (Co-Chm & Co-CEO)
Agus Rusli (Dir-Design-Dallas)
Jenny West (Dir-Strategy-Denver)

M. BLOCK & SONS, INC.
5020 W 73rd St, Bedford Park, IL 60638-2131
Tel.: (708) 728-8400 IL
Web Site: http://www.mblock.com
Year Founded: 1945
Sales Range: $200-249.9 Million
Emp.: 300
Distr & Importer of Housewares, Small Appliances & Giftware
N.A.I.C.S.: 423620
Bruce Levy (Pres & CEO)
Debbie Johnson (Comptroller)
Ed Roels (CFO)
Paul Nowak (VP)

M. COHEN & SONS INC.
400 Reed Rd, Broomall, PA 19008
Tel.: (610) 544-7100 PA
Web Site: http://www.theironshop.com
Year Founded: 1931
Emp.: 100
Stairs, Staircases, Stair Treads: Prefabricated Metal Mfr & Designer
N.A.I.C.S.: 332323
Allen Cohen (Pres)

M. DAVID PAUL & ASSOCIATES
100 Wilshire Blvd Ste 1600, Santa Monica, CA 90401
Tel.: (310) 393-9653
Web Site: http://www.worthe.com
Sales Range: $50-74.9 Million
Emp.: 20
Commercial & Office Building Contractors
N.A.I.C.S.: 236220
David Paul (Owner)
Kimberly Hefner (Mgr-Property)

M. DAVIS & SONS INC.
19 Germay Dr, Wilmington, DE 19804-1074
Tel.: (302) 998-3385 DE
Web Site: http://www.mdavisinc.com
Year Founded: 1870
Sales Range: $10-24.9 Million
Emp.: 325
Provider of Plumbing, Heating & Air-Conditioning Services
N.A.I.C.S.: 288220
John Gooden (Pres)
Peggy Del Fabbro (CEO)
Todd P. Moran (VP-Risk Mgmt)
Scott N. Cudmore (Dir-Safety)
Mike Gilmartin (CFO)
Judy Pieper (Sec)
Scott Dolor (Mgr-Ops)
Christina MacMillan (VP-Strategic Dev)

M. FABRIKANT & SONS, INC.
999 Central Ave Ste 208, Woodmere, NY 11598-1205
Tel.: (212) 757-0790 NY
Web Site: http://www.fabrikant.com
Year Founded: 1895
Sales Range: $900-999.9 Million
Emp.: 1,000
Wholesale Distr of Diamonds & Jewelry
N.A.I.C.S.: 339910
Charles Fabrikant Fortgang (Chm)

M. FREDRIC
28024 Dorothy Dr, Agoura Hills, CA 91301
Tel.: (818) 597-0212
Web Site: http://www.mfredric.com
Year Founded: 1979
Sales Range: $10-24.9 Million
Emp.: 200
Women, Men & Kids Clothing Stores
N.A.I.C.S.: 458110
Fredric Levine (Pres)

M. GLOSSER & SONS INC.
72 Messenger St, Johnstown, PA 15902
Tel.: (814) 533-2800
Web Site: http://www.glossernet.com
Sales Range: $10-24.9 Million
Emp.: 70
Bars, Metal
N.A.I.C.S.: 423510
Daniel S. Glosser (Pres-Glosser Mfg)

M. HOLLAND COMPANY
400 Skokie Blvd Ste 600, Northbrook, IL 60062
Tel.: (847) 272-7370
Web Site: http://www.mholland.com
Year Founded: 1950
Plastics Resins Distributors
N.A.I.C.S.: 424610
Edward Holland (Pres & CEO)
Pat McKune (CFO)
Julian Wiles (VP-Ops)
Eugenio Calderon (VP-Intl)
Dwight Morgan (Exec VP-Corp Dev)
Michael Foldvary (Dir-Distr Sourcing)
Neil Goodrich (Chief innovation Officer)

M. KINGSBURY CONCRETE INC.
6301 Hitt Ln, Louisville, KY 40241
Tel.: (502) 243-0070
Web Site: http://www.kingsburyconcrete.com
Rev.: $16,900,000
Emp.: 140
Ready Mixed Concrete
N.A.I.C.S.: 327320
Ken Sims (Gen Mgr)
Alan Kingsbury (Pres)

M. L. SMITH, JR., INC.
2338 Farmerville Hwy, Ruston, LA 71270
Tel.: (318) 255-4474
Web Site: http://www.mlsji.com
Year Founded: 1976
Sales Range: $10-24.9 Million
Emp.: 80
Masonry Construction Services
N.A.I.C.S.: 238140
Stephanie Smith (Co-Owner)

M. LAVINE DESIGN WORKSHOP

2330 County Road 137, Waite Park, MN 56387
Tel.: (320) 230-6650
Web Site: http://www.mlavine.com
Year Founded: 1976
Rev.: $2,900,000
Emp.: 15
Showcase, Partition, Shelving & Locker Mfr
N.A.I.C.S.: 337215
Jackie Bach (CEO)
Paul Bach (CFO)
Gary Huls (Exec VP)
Chris Thomas (Pres)

M. LEVIN & COMPANY HOLDINGS, INC.
6700 Essington Ave Unit H2-H5, Philadelphia, PA 19153-5612
Tel.: (215) 336-2900
Web Site: http://www.mlevinco.com
Year Founded: 1906
Sales Range: $25-49.9 Million
Emp.: 55
Holding Company; Fresh Fruit & Vegetable Whslr
N.A.I.C.S.: 551112
Michael Levin (Pres & CEO)

Subsidiaries:

M. Levin & Company, Inc. (1)
326 Pattison Ave, Philadelphia, PA 19148 (100%)
Tel.: (215) 336-2900
Web Site: http://www.mlevinco.com
Fresh Fruit & Vegetable Whslr
N.A.I.C.S.: 424480
Michael Levin (Pres & CEO)

M. LIPSITZ & CO., LTD.
100 Elm St, Waco, TX 76703-2507
Tel.: (254) 756-6661
Web Site: http://www.mlipsitzco.com
Year Founded: 1895
Sales Range: $25-49.9 Million
Emp.: 134
Metal Scrap & Waste Materials
N.A.I.C.S.: 423930
Thomas G. Salome (Co-Owner & Pres)
Tim Nemec (CFO)
Charles Johnson (COO-Ferrous Mktg)
Melvin Lipsitz Jr. (Co-Owner & VP)

Subsidiaries:

Brownwood Iron & Metal Co (1)
1500 Melwood Ave, Brownwood, TX 76804
Tel.: (325) 646-7058
Emp.: 6
Recyclable Material Whslr
N.A.I.C.S.: 423930
Chris Goodrich (Gen Mgr)

Bryan Iron & Metal, Ltd. (1)
2011 Hwy 21 W, Bryan, TX 77803
Tel.: (979) 775-7190
Recyclable Material Whslr
N.A.I.C.S.: 423930

Market Street Recycling LLC (1)
8700 Market St, Houston, TX 77029
Tel.: (713) 676-2621
Web Site: http://www.marketstreetrecycling.com
Emp.: 20
Recyclable Material Whslr
N.A.I.C.S.: 423930

National Steel Compressing (1)
726 El Paso St, San Antonio, TX 78207
Tel.: (210) 227-4687
Recyclable Material Whslr
N.A.I.C.S.: 423930
Wacy Biersehwale (Gen Mgr)

OK Iron & Metal Co (1)
700 P NE, Ardmore, OK 73402
Tel.: (580) 223-2283
Recyclable Material Whslr
N.A.I.C.S.: 423930

Recycle Midland (1)
3601 Industrial Ave, Midland, TX 79703
Tel.: (432) 520-2700
Web Site: http://www.keepmidlandbeautiful.org
Recyclable Material Whslr
N.A.I.C.S.: 423930

Terrell Iron & Metal Inc. (1)
1031 S Delphine, Terrell, TX 75160-4500
Tel.: (972) 563-5386
Web Site: http://www.cityofterrell.org
Sales Range: $10-24.9 Million
Emp.: 8
Metal Scrap & Waste Materials
N.A.I.C.S.: 423930

Texas Commercial Waste (1)
1820 N Harvey Mitchell Pkwy, Bryan, TX 77807
Tel.: (979) 314-3238
Web Site: http://www.texascommercialwaste.com
Industrial Waste Collection Services
N.A.I.C.S.: 562119
Ron Schmidt (Gen Mgr)

Tyler Iron & Metal Company (1)
1630 WNW Loop 323, Tyler, TX 75702
Tel.: (903) 592-8144
Web Site: http://www.tylerironandmetal.com
Recyclable Material Whslr
N.A.I.C.S.: 423930

M. LUIS CONSTRUCTION CO., INC.
326 Saint Paul Pl Ste 200, Baltimore, MD 21202
Tel.: (410) 545-0641
Web Site: http://www.mluisconstruction.com
Year Founded: 1985
Sales Range: $50-74.9 Million
Emp.: 143
Construction Services
N.A.I.C.S.: 236115
Cidalia Luis-Adkbar (Owner)
Natalia Luis (Owner)

M. MISTI CIGAR CO.
7770 US Hwy 1 S Ste F, Bunnell, FL 32110
Tel.: (386) 585-9800
Web Site: http://www.crownjewelcigars.com
Sales Range: $1-9.9 Million
Cigar Mfr & Distr
N.A.I.C.S.: 312230
Kimberly Rotunno (CFO)
Peter Moreno (Dir-Mfg)
Maria A. Beovides (Dir-Product Dev)
Mark Mistie Jr. (Founder)

M. RUBIN & SONS INC.
34-01 38th Ave, Long Island City, NY 11101
Tel.: (718) 361-2800
Web Site: http://www.bluegeneration.com
Year Founded: 1944
Apparel Importer & Mfr
N.A.I.C.S.: 315120
Eric Rubin (Pres)
Phil Rubin (CEO)

M. SIMON ZOOK CO. INC.
4960 Horseshoe Pike, Honey Brook, PA 19344
Tel.: (610) 273-3776
Web Site: http://www.goldenbarrel.com
Year Founded: 1934
Sales Range: $1-9.9 Million
Emp.: 100
Provider of Wholesale Baking
N.A.I.C.S.: 424490
Larry E. Martin (Pres)

M. SLAVIN & SONS LTD.
800 Food Center Dr Hunts Point Unit 66, Bronx, NY 10474
Tel.: (718) 495-2800
Web Site: http://www.mslavin.com
Rev.: $38,300,000
Emp.: 30
Fresh Fish Sales
N.A.I.C.S.: 424460
Edward Polania (Acct Mgr)

M. T. LANEY COMPANY, INC.
5400 Enterprise St, Eldersburg, MD 21784-9322
Tel.: (410) 795-1761
Web Site: http://www.mtlaney.com
Year Founded: 1990
Sales Range: $10-24.9 Million
Emp.: 300
Concrete Finishing Services
N.A.I.C.S.: 238140
Melvin T. Laney (Owner)

M.A. ANGELIADES INC.
544 47th Ave, Long Island City, NY 11101
Tel.: (718) 786-5555
Web Site: http://www.angeliades.com
Sales Range: $50-74.9 Million
Emp.: 20
Specialized Public Building Contractors
N.A.I.C.S.: 236220
Mike Angeliades (Founder & Pres)

M.A. BONGIOVANNI INC.
1400 Jamesville Ave, Syracuse, NY 13210-4226
Tel.: (315) 475-9937
Web Site: http://www.mabinc.net
Year Founded: 1948
Sales Range: $200-249.9 Million
Emp.: 120
Construction Contractor
N.A.I.C.S.: 237110
Michael A. Bongiovanni (Pres & Treas)
Joseph J. Bongiovanni Jr. (Sec & VP)
Mitch Carmody (Project Mgr)

Subsidiaries:

JMJ Environmental Inc. (1)
1400 Jamesville Ave, Syracuse, NY 13210-4226
Tel.: (315) 475-7928
Web Site: http://www.mabinc.net
Sales Range: $10-24.9 Million
Emp.: 10
Heavy Construction
N.A.I.C.S.: 236210

M.A. DEATLEY CONSTRUCTION INC.
829 Evans Rd, Clarkston, WA 99403
Tel.: (509) 751-1580
Web Site: http://www.madcon.net
Rev.: $39,100,000
Emp.: 100
Construction & Mining Machinery & Equipment Merchant Whslr
N.A.I.C.S.: 423810
Scott Palmer (VP)
Mark Deatley (Pres)
Jack Paluso (Treas)

M.A. FORD MANUFACTURING CO.
7737 NW Blvd, Davenport, IA 52806
Tel.: (563) 391-6220
Web Site: http://www.maford.com
Sales Range: $25-49.9 Million
Emp.: 215
Drills (Machine Tool Accessories)
N.A.I.C.S.: 333515

M.A. INDUSTRIES, INC.
303 Dividend Dr, Peachtree City, GA 30269
Tel.: (770) 487-1411
Web Site: http://www.maind.com
Year Founded: 1969
Sales Range: $10-24.9 Million
Emp.: 110
Molding Primary Plastics
N.A.I.C.S.: 326199
Nancy Bullington (Mgr-HR)
Scott Peacock (Mgr)
Greg Peacock (Supvr-Customer Svc)
Jose Rivera (VP)

M.A. MORTENSON COMPANY
700 Meadow Ln N, Minneapolis, MN 55422-4817
Tel.: (763) 522-2100
Web Site: http://www.mortenson.com
Year Founded: 1954
Sales Range: $1-4.9 Billion
Emp.: 1,800
Building Construction; Contracting Services
N.A.I.C.S.: 236220
David Mortenson (Chm)
Tom Wacker (COO)
Craig Southorn (VP-Preconstruction)
Daniel L. Johnson (CEO)
Brent Webb (Mgr-Dev)
Lois M. Martin (CFO)
Rick Clevette (Sr VP-HR)
Derek Cunz (Sr VP)
Dwight Larson (Gen Counsel & Sr VP)
John Nowoj (Sr VP)
John Ohman (Sr VP)
Maja Rosenquist (Sr VP)
Mark Sherry (Sr VP)
Bob Solfelt (Sr VP)
Krista Twesme (Sr VP)
Greg Werner (Sr VP)
Jim Yowan (Sr VP)
Brian Fitzpatrick (VP-Ops)
Stephanie Abla (Mgr-Community Affairs)

Subsidiaries:

Federal Contracting Group (1)
700 Meadow Ln N, Minneapolis, MN 55422
Tel.: (763) 522-2100
Construction Management Services
N.A.I.C.S.: 541611
Mark Ruffino (VP & Gen Mgr)
Bob Leonard (VP-Grp Ops)
Mark Schmidt (VP & Dir-Preconstruction)
Nathan Lingard (Dir-Bus Dev)

Full Service Facility Solutions (1)
700 Meadow Ln N, Minneapolis, MN 55422
Tel.: (763) 287-5497
Web Site: http://www.mortenson.com
Emp.: 2
Construction Engineering Services
N.A.I.C.S.: 541330
Scott West (Dir-Quality)

Mortenson Development, Inc. (1)
700 Meadow Ln N, Minneapolis, MN 55422
Tel.: (763) 522-2100
Web Site: http://www.mortenson.com
Real Estate Development Services
N.A.I.C.S.: 531390
Bob Solfelt (Sr VP)
Nate Gundrum (VP-Real Estate Dev)
Dan Lessor (Dir-Real Estate Dev)
Nathan Podratz (VP & Head-Capital Markets)

M.A. NORDEN COMPANY INC.
6955 Cary Hamilton Rd, Theodore, AL 36582
Tel.: (251) 653-0003
Web Site: http://www.manorden.com
Sales Range: $25-49.9 Million
Emp.: 71
Scrap & Waste Materials
N.A.I.C.S.: 423930
Martin A. Norden III (Pres)

M.A. PATOUT & SON LIMITED
3512 J Patout Burns Rd, Jeanerette, LA 70394

M.A. Patout & Son Limited—(Continued)
Tel.: (337) 276-4592
Web Site: http://www.mapatout.com
Year Founded: 1825
Sales Range: $100-124.9 Million
Emp.: 245
Producer & Processor of Sugar Cane
N.A.I.C.S.: 311314
Franklin William Patout *(Chm)*
Randall K. Romero *(CEO)*
Jacques H. Hebert *(Pres)*
Lance Weber *(Gen Mgr)*
Gerald Guiberteau *(Mgr-Agricultural Ops)*
Jerome W. Fitch *(Treas)*
Wilson A. Leblanc Sr. *(VP-Engrg)*

Subsidiaries:

Raceland Raw Sugar Corp. (1)
PO Box 159, Raceland, LA 70394-0159 (100%)
Tel.: (985) 537-3533
Sales Range: $25-49.9 Million
Emp.: 150
Mfr of Raw Sugar
N.A.I.C.S.: 311314

Sterling Sugars Inc. (1)
609 Irish Bend Rd, Franklin, LA 70538-3345
Tel.: (337) 828-0620
Sales Range: $25-49.9 Million
Emp.: 95
Manufactures Raw Cane Sugar
N.A.I.C.S.: 311314

M.A.P. INTERNATIONAL INC.
4700 Glynco Pkwy, Brunswick, GA 31525-6800
Tel.: (912) 265-6010 IL
Web Site: http://www.map.org
Year Founded: 1954
Sales Range: $550-599.9 Million
Emp.: 190
Health & Relief Services
N.A.I.C.S.: 813319
Immanuel Thangaraj *(Chm)*
Steve Stirling *(Pres & CEO)*
Jill Richardson *(CFO & VP)*

M.B. JONES OIL COMPANY INC.
US Hwy 1 S 556, Wrens, GA 30833
Tel.: (706) 547-2585
Web Site: http://www.mbjonesoil.com
Sales Range: $10-24.9 Million
Emp.: 20
Petroleum Products
N.A.I.C.S.: 424720

M.B. KAHN CONSTRUCTION CO., INC.
101 Flintlake Rd, Columbia, SC 29223-7851
Tel.: (803) 736-2950 SC
Web Site: http://www.mbkahn.com
Year Founded: 1927
Sales Range: $250-299.9 Million
Emp.: 600
Provider of General Contracting & Construction Management Services
N.A.I.C.S.: 236220
Alan Kahn *(Chm)*
William H. Neely *(Pres)*
Robert Chisholm *(CFO)*
Rick Ott *(Sr. Exec VP)*
H.A. Pleming *(Sr VP)*
Tim Cullum *(VP)*
Bill Cram *(VP)*

M.B.A. HOLDINGS, INC.
9419 E San Salvador Ste 105, Scottsdale, AZ 85258
Tel.: (480) 860-2288
Web Site: http://www.mbadirect.com
Year Founded: 1996
Sales Range: $10-24.9 Million
Emp.: 21

Direct Property & Casualty Insurance Carriers
N.A.I.C.S.: 524126
Gaylen M. Brotherson *(Chm & CEO)*
Judy K. Brotherson *(Pres)*

M.B.R. INDUSTRIES, INC.
3201 NW 116th St, Miami, FL 33167-2917
Tel.: (305) 769-1000
Web Site: http://www.mbrind.com
Year Founded: 1972
Rev.: $52,000,000
Emp.: 100
Electronic Parts & Equipment
N.A.I.C.S.: 423690
Bernard Pomeranc *(Pres)*
Brian Pomeranc *(Dir-Sls)*

Subsidiaries:

Econoquality Freight Forwarders, Inc. (1)
3201 NW 116th St Ste B, Miami, FL 33167-2917
Tel.: (305) 769-0114
Web Site: http://www.econoquality.com
Sales Range: $10-24.9 Million
Emp.: 5
Freight Transportation Arrangement
N.A.I.C.S.: 488510

M.C. COMMUNICATION, INC.
8131 Lyndon B Johnson Fwy Ste 275, Dallas, TX 75251-1352
Tel.: (972) 480-8383
Web Site: http://www.mccom.com
Year Founded: 1986
Sales Range: $10-24.9 Million
Emp.: 30
Advertising Agencies
N.A.I.C.S.: 541810
Mike Crawford *(Pres)*
Pam Watkins *(Sr VP-Bus & Media Strategy)*
Jim Terry *(Sr VP-Acct Svcs)*
Kathy Andrews *(Dir-Ops)*
Shannon Sullivan *(VP & Acct Dir)*
Todd Brashear *(VP-Creative)*

M.C. DEAN, INC.
1765 Greensboro Sta Pl, Tysons, VA 22102
Tel.: (703) 802-6231 VA
Web Site: http://www.mcdean.com
Year Founded: 1949
Electrical, Electronic & Telecommunication Engineering Services
N.A.I.C.S.: 238210
William H. Dean *(CEO)*
Douglas N. Cummins *(CFO)*
Misty Mirran *(Mgr-HR)*
Jalal Rahim *(VP-Mgmt Info Sys)*

M.C. GILL CORPORATION
4056 Easy St, El Monte, CA 91731-1087
Tel.: (626) 443-4022 CA
Web Site: http://www.thegillcorp.com
Year Founded: 1945
Sales Range: $75-99.9 Million
Emp.: 700
Mfr of Specialty Laminators of Flat & Contoured Fiberglass Cloth, Reinforced Plastics, Composites & Sandwich Panels
N.A.I.C.S.: 326199
M. C. Gill *(Founder)*
Stephen E. Gill *(Chm, Pres & CEO)*
Robert Cumberledge *(Reg Mgr-Sls)*

Subsidiaries:

Alcore, Inc. (1)
Lakeside Business Park 1502 Quarry Dr, Edgewood, MD 21040 (100%)
Tel.: (410) 676-7100
Web Site: http://www.alcore.com

Sales Range: $10-24.9 Million
Emp.: 130
Aerospace Composites Mfr
N.A.I.C.S.: 326130

Subsidiary (Non-US):

Alcore Brigantine SA (2)
Route de l'Aviation, 7 allee Etchecopar, 64600, Anglet, France
Tel.: (33) 559412525
Web Site: http://www.mcgillcorp.com
Sales Range: $10-24.9 Million
Emp.: 100
Structural Core Materials Technology & Technical Bonding
N.A.I.C.S.: 339999

Castle Industries (1)
601 S Dupont Ave, Ontario, CA 91761-1506 (100%)
Tel.: (909) 390-0899
Web Site: http://www.castleindustries.com
Sales Range: $10-24.9 Million
Emp.: 70
Fabricates Aluminum Parts for the Commercial Aviation Industry & Manufactures Seating for Commercial
N.A.I.C.S.: 332322
Steve Gill *(CEO)*

M.C. Gill Europe, Ltd. (1)
23 Enterprise Rd, Balloo S Industrial Estate, Bangor, BT19 7TA, United Kingdom (100%)
Tel.: (44) 2891470073
Rev.: $3,000,000
Emp.: 16
Thermal & Sound Dampening Insulation for Commercial Aircraft; Fabricates Flooring & Other Interior Panels for Commercial Aircrafts
N.A.I.C.S.: 336413
Margaret Wright *(Mgr-Customer Svc)*
Gary Morrison *(Mng Dir)*

M.C.M. TECHNOLOGIES, INC.
175 Dupont Dr, Providence, RI 02907
Tel.: (401) 785-9204
Web Site: http://www.mcmtech.com
Year Founded: 1997
Sales Range: $10-24.9 Million
Emp.: 80
Rolled Steel Shape Mfr
N.A.I.C.S.: 331221
Chris D'Angelo *(VP)*
Ray Bert *(VP-Product Dev)*
Marilyn Fernandes *(Project Mgr)*
Danny Rodriguez *(Mgr-Production)*
Maria Kenny *(Office Mgr)*
Bob Grenon *(Mgr-Shipping & Receiving)*

M.C.S. INDUSTRIES INC.
2280 Newlins Mill Rd, Easton, PA 18045-7813
Tel.: (610) 253-6268 PA
Web Site: http://www.mcsframes.com
Year Founded: 1980
Picture Frame Mfr
N.A.I.C.S.: 339999
Richard L. Master *(Chm & CEO)*
Greg Yocco *(CFO)*
Bob Goldfarb *(VP-Wall Decor)*
Josh MacNeel *(Pres)*

M.D. DESCANT, INC.
206 Evergreen St, Bunkie, LA 71322
Tel.: (318) 346-6657
Web Site: http://www.mddescantconstruction.com
Rev.: $36,364,678
Emp.: 30
Industrial Buildings, New Construction,
N.A.I.C.S.: 236210
Cindy Craig *(Office Mgr)*
Chuck Descant *(VP-Fin)*
Trent Descant *(VP)*

M.D. SASS HOLDINGS, INC.
1185 Avenue of the Americas 18th Fl, New York, NY 10036-2699
Tel.: (212) 730-2000 NY
Web Site: http://www.mdsass.com
Year Founded: 1972
Emp.: 70
Investment Management Service
N.A.I.C.S.: 523999
Martin D. Sass *(Founder & CEO)*
Bobby Liu *(COO & Gen Counsel)*
Philip M. Sivin *(CFO & Sr Mng Dir)*
Ingrid Eppich *(Sr VP & Head-Client Svcs)*
Ari D. Sass *(Pres)*
Donna Langan *(Mgr-Client Svcs)*
Brian Duhn *(Sr Mng Dir-Institutional Sls)*

Subsidiaries:

M.D. Sass Associates, Inc. (1)
55 West 46th St 28th Fl, New York, NY 10036
Tel.: (212) 730-2000
Web Site: http://www.mdsass.com
Sales Range: $1-9.9 Million
Emp.: 80
Investment Advice
N.A.I.C.S.: 523940
Martin D. Sass *(Founder, Chm & CEO)*
Ari D. Sass *(Pres)*
Bobby Liu *(Sr VP & Gen Counsel)*
Sam Friedman *(Sr VP & CFO)*

M.D. Sass Investors Services, Inc. (1)
1185 Avenue of the Americas 18th Fl, New York, NY 10036-2699
Tel.: (212) 730-2000
Web Site: http://www.mdsass.com
Investment Management Service
N.A.I.C.S.: 523940
Martin D. Sass *(Chm & CEO)*
Ingrid Eppich *(Sr VP & Head-Client Svcs)*
Bobby Liu *(COO & Gen Counsel)*
Ari Sass *(Exec VP & Mgr-Portfolio)*
Donna Langan *(Mgr-Client Svcs)*

M.E. FIELDS INC.
2100 Frontage Rd, Glencoe, IL 60022
Tel.: (847) 998-5200
Web Site: http://www.fieldsauto.com
Sales Range: $10-24.9 Million
Emp.: 2,000
New & Used Automobiles
N.A.I.C.S.: 441110
John R. Fields *(CEO)*
Dan Fields *(VP)*

Subsidiaries:

Fields Imports Inc. (1)
700 W Frontage Rd, Northfield, IL 60093
Tel.: (847) 441-5300
Web Site: http://www.fieldsbmw.com
Rev.: $28,500,000
Emp.: 65
New & Used Automobiles
N.A.I.C.S.: 441110
John R. Fields *(Pres)*

Fields Jeep, Inc. (1)
2800 Patriot Blvd, Glenview, IL 60026
Tel.: (847) 446-5100
Web Site: http://www.fieldsjeep.com
Rev.: $15,700,000
Emp.: 54
New & Used Car Dealer
N.A.I.C.S.: 441110

Fields of Lake County Inc. (1)
1121 S Milwaukee Ave, Libertyville, IL 60048
Tel.: (847) 362-9200
Web Site: http://www.gregoryinfiniti.com
Rev.: $2,400,000
Emp.: 75
New & Used Automobiles
N.A.I.C.S.: 441110
Gregory Mauro *(Owner)*

M.F. FOLEY COMPANY
24 W Howell St, Boston, MA 02125
Tel.: (617) 288-1300

Web Site: http://www.foleyfish.com
Sales Range: $10-24.9 Million
Emp.: 25
Sales of Fish & Fish Products
N.A.I.C.S.: 424460
Michael F. Foley *(Pres)*
Linda Foley *(CFO)*
Peter Ramsden *(CEO)*

M.G. ABBOTT, INC.
5207 Ebright Rd, Canal Winchester, OH 43110
Tel.: (614) 837-3614
Web Site: http://www.mgabbott.com
Sales Range: $10-24.9 Million
Emp.: 15
Electrical Wiring Services
N.A.I.C.S.: 238210
Martin Gene Abbott *(Pres)*
Joseph Abbott *(VP)*

M.G. NEWELL CORPORATION
301 Citation Ct, Greensboro, NC 27409
Tel.: (336) 393-0100
Web Site: http://www.mgnewell.com
Rev.: $10,500,000
Emp.: 42
Industrial Machinery & Equipment
N.A.I.C.S.: 423830
Wic Dunlap *(Mgr-Territory)*

M.G.T. INDUSTRIES INC.
13889 S Figueroa St, Los Angeles, CA 90061-1025
Tel.: (310) 516-5900
Year Founded: 1983
Sales Range: $25-49.9 Million
Emp.: 100
Women's & Children's Underwear
N.A.I.C.S.: 315250
Sandy Strahl *(Dir-Mdsg)*
Tom Stevenson *(VP-Ops)*
Jeffrey P. Mirvis *(CEO)*

M.H. EBY INC.
1194 Main St, Blue Ball, PA 17506
Tel.: (717) 354-4971
Web Site: http://www.mheby.com
Year Founded: 1938
Sales Range: $25-49.9 Million
Emp.: 180
Truck Bodies Mfr
N.A.I.C.S.: 336211
Loren Benner *(Controller)*
Leon Martin *(Mgr-Dealer Sls)*
Gary Musselman *(Plant Mgr)*
Russell Redding *(Sec)*
Doug Bryant *(Mgr-Dealer-Southwest)*
Menno H. Eby Jr. *(Pres)*

M.H. KING COMPANY INC.
1032 Idaho Ave, Burley, ID 83318
Tel.: (208) 678-7181
Web Site:
  http://www.kingsdiscount.com
Sales Range: $10-24.9 Million
Emp.: 300
Department Stores
N.A.I.C.S.: 455110
Thomas King *(Pres & CEO)*
Jennifer Dayley *(Controller)*

M.H. PODELL COMPANY
1201 Howard Ave Fl 3, Burlingame, CA 94010
Tel.: (650) 579-7900
Web Site: http://www.mhpodell.com
Year Founded: 1963
Sales Range: $10-24.9 Million
Emp.: 55
Subdividers & Developers
N.A.I.C.S.: 237210
Michael Podell *(Pres)*
Robin Lee *(Asst Mgr)*
Rita Chaffee *(VP)*

M.J. HARRIS INC.
1 Riverchase Rdg Ste 300, Birmingham, AL 35244
Tel.: (205) 380-6800
Web Site: http://www.mjharris.com
Rev.: $32,000,000
Emp.: 120
Commercial & Office Building Contractors
N.A.I.C.S.: 236220
Michael Harris *(Pres & CEO)*
Bobby Harris *(Chm)*
Lyle Dubois *(Sr VP-Employee Rels)*

M.L. ALBRIGHT & SONS, INC.
6182 Lapwai Rd, Lewiston, ID 83501
Tel.: (208) 743-2100
Sales Range: $10-24.9 Million
Emp.: 30
Excavation Services
N.A.I.C.S.: 238910
Marvin Albright *(Owner)*

M.L. BALL CO. INC.
6255 Atlantic Blvd, Norcross, GA 30071
Tel.: (770) 447-5660
Web Site: http://www.mlball.com
Sales Range: $10-24.9 Million
Emp.: 15
Industrial Fittings
N.A.I.C.S.: 423830
James Marcus Ball *(Pres)*

M.L. MCDONALD SALES CO., INC.
50 Oakland St, Watertown, MA 02472-2202
Tel.: (617) 923-0900
Web Site:
  http://www.mlmcdonald.com
Year Founded: 1980
Sales Range: $25-49.9 Million
Emp.: 300
Subcontractors For Painting & Paper Hanging
N.A.I.C.S.: 238320
Kevin O'Donald *(Chm)*
Charles Mossali *(VP)*
Steve O'Donald *(CFO)*
Joseph Mayne *(Head-Painting)*

M.L.B. CONSTRUCTION SERVICES, LLC
1 Stone Break Rd, Malta, NY 12020
Tel.: (518) 289-1371
Web Site: http://www.mlbind.com
Year Founded: 1947
Sales Range: $10-24.9 Million
Emp.: 60
Nonresidential Construction
N.A.I.C.S.: 236220
James Dawsey *(Pres)*
Scott Shephard *(VP-Ops)*

M.L.F. & ASSOCIATES, INC.
1220 Collins Ave, Miami Beach, FL 33139
Tel.: (305) 673-5548
Web Site:
  http://www.thewebstermiami.com
Year Founded: 2009
Sales Range: $1-9.9 Million
Women's & Men's Clothing Retailer
N.A.I.C.S.: 458110
Laure Heriard Dubreuil *(Founding Partner & CEO)*
Milan Vukmirovic *(Founding Partner & Dir-Creative)*

M.M. FOWLER INC.
4220 Neal Rd, Durham, NC 27705-2322
Tel.: (919) 309-2925

Web Site:
  http://www.familyfareconveniencestores.com
Year Founded: 1974
Sales Range: $10-24.9 Million
Emp.: 20
Gasoline Service Stations
N.A.I.C.S.: 457120
Marvin L. Barnes *(Owner)*
Jessie Daughtride *(CFO)*
Lee Barnes *(Pres)*

M.M.C., INC.
Tel.: (513) 381-3550
Web Site:
  http://www.modernmachinerycompany.com
Year Founded: 1959
Emp.: 24
Sell Industrial Machinery & Equipment
N.A.I.C.S.: 425120
Brian Mohr *(Co-Owner)*
Brett Wittner *(Engr-Forming Applications)*
Ryan Wasik *(Engr-Robotics Applications)*
Carlos Alicea *(Mgr-Svc)*
Amy Mulvihill *(Coord-Svc)*
Barb Laramore *(CFO)*
Barrington Von Kendrick *(Chief Morale Officer)*
Mike Sargent *(Accountant)*

M.R. DANIELSON ADVERTISING LLC
1464 Summit Ave, Saint Paul, MN 55105-2241
Tel.: (651) 698-1512
Web Site: http://www.mrdan.com
Year Founded: 1988
Sales Range: $10-24.9 Million
Emp.: 8
N.A.I.C.S.: 541810
Michael Danielson *(Pres)*
Janna Strange *(VP & Dir-Creative)*

M.R. TANNER DEVELOPMENT & CONSTRUCTION
1327 W San Pedro St, Gilbert, AZ 85233
Tel.: (480) 633-8500
Web Site: http://www.mrtanner.com
Sales Range: $10-24.9 Million
Emp.: 85
Grading & Paving
N.A.I.C.S.: 236115
Maurice R. Tanner Jr. *(CEO)*

M.S. JACOBS & ASSOCIATES
810 Noblestown Rd, Pittsburgh, PA 15205
Tel.: (412) 923-2090
Web Site: http://www.msjacobs.com
Year Founded: 1950
Sales Range: $10-24.9 Million
Emp.: 18
Provider of Controlling Instruments & Accessories
N.A.I.C.S.: 423830
Elmer J. Sigety *(Pres)*

M.S. WALKER, INC.
20 3rd Ave, Somerville, MA 02143-4450
Tel.: (617) 776-6700
Web Site: http://www.mswalker.com
Year Founded: 1931
Sales Range: $100-124.9 Million
Emp.: 275
Marketer Wine Spirit & Cigar Spirit Mfr
N.A.I.C.S.: 312140

Subsidiaries:

M.S. Walker, Inc. - MSW New Hampshire Facility (1)
157 River Rd, Bow, NH 03304
Tel.: (603) 410-6231
Web Site: http://www.mswalker.com
Emp.: 14
Alcoholic Beverage Mfr & Whslr
N.A.I.C.S.: 312130
Maria Taylor *(Office Mgr)*

M.S. Walker, Inc. - MSW Rhode Island Facility (1)
16 Commercial Way, Warren, RI 02885
Tel.: (401) 247-0646
Web Site: http://www.mswalker.com
Sales Range: $25-49.9 Million
Emp.: 20
Wine & Spirit Whslr
N.A.I.C.S.: 424820
Brett Allen *(Gen Mgr)*

M.S.G. ASSOCIATES INC.
545 E West St, Wind Gap, PA 18091-1255
Tel.: (610) 863-2000
Year Founded: 1984
Sales Range: $25-49.9 Million
Emp.: 50
Commercial Business Construction
N.A.I.C.S.: 236117
Michael Goffredo *(Pres)*
Mark Goffredo *(VP)*
Mike Seagreaves *(Controller)*
John Goffredo *(Treas & Sec)*

M.S.T. STEEL CORPORATION
24417 Groesbeck Hwy, Warren, MI 48089-4723
Tel.: (586) 773-5460
Web Site: http://www.mststeel.com
Year Founded: 1977
Sales Range: $50-74.9 Million
Emp.: 70
Metals Service Centers & Offices
N.A.I.C.S.: 423510
Richard Thompson *(Pres)*

M.Z. BERGER & CO., INC.
29 76 Northern Blvd 4th Fl, Long Island City, NY 11101
Tel.: (718) 472-7500
Web Site: http://www.mzb.com
Year Founded: 1950
Sales Range: $75-99.9 Million
Emp.: 100
Watches, Clocks & HBA Designer & Distr
N.A.I.C.S.: 423940
Joseph Mermelstein *(Pres)*
Bernard Mermelstein *(CEO)*
Marci Gordon *(CMO)*

M/E ENGINEERING, P.C.
150 N Chestnut St, Rochester, NY 14604
Tel.: (585) 288-5590
Web Site:
  http://www.meengineering.com
Year Founded: 1991
Rev.: $25,700,000
Emp.: 190
Value-Driven Engineering Services
N.A.I.C.S.: 541330
Calvin J. Puffer *(Principal)*
James P. Chatelle *(Principal)*
John A. Dredger *(Principal)*
W. Bruce Knapp *(Principal)*
Anthony V. Thomas *(Principal)*
F. Joseph Straub *(VP)*
William P. Liberto *(VP)*
Ronald C. Mead *(VP)*
Michelle Stark *(Sr Engineer-Electrical)*
Barbara McAdams *(Office Mgr)*

M/K ADVERTISING PARTNERS, LTD.

U.S. PRIVATE

M/K Advertising Partners, Ltd.—(Continued)

M/K ADVERTISING PARTNERS, LTD.
28 W 25th St 9th Fl, New York, NY 10010
Tel.: (212) 367-9225   DE
Year Founded: 1997
Rev.: $15,000,000
Emp.: 12
Fiscal Year-end: 06/30/00
N.A.I.C.S.: 541810
Karin Henderson-Gorant *(Principal & Exec Creative Dir)*
Ingrid Laub *(Partner & Exec Acct Dir)*
Michael Yuen *(Principal & Exec Creative Dir)*
Michael Thomas *(Office Mgr)*

M2 MEDIA GROUP, LLC
1127 High Ridge Rd Ste 335, Stamford, CT 06905-1332
Tel.: (203) 276-0330
Web Site:
  http://www.m2mediagroup.com
Sales Range: $1-9.9 Million
Magazine Subscription Services
N.A.I.C.S.: 511199
Michael Borchetta *(CEO)*
Michael Frank *(Pres)*
Dave Rock *(Sr VP)*
Michael Donnarumma *(VP-Sls)*
Karen Phillips *(VP-Mktg)*

Subsidiaries:

American Publishers LLC   (1)
2401 Sawmill Pkwy Ste 10, Huron, OH 44839
Tel.: (419) 626-0623
Web Site: http://www.american-publishers.com
Institutional Fundraising Services
N.A.I.C.S.: 561499

M2 TECHNOLOGY, INC.
21702 Hardy Oak Ste 100, San Antonio, TX 78258
Tel.: (210) 566-3773
Web Site: http://www.m2ti.com
Year Founded: 2000
Sales Range: $25-49.9 Million
Emp.: 25
Computer Products & Services
N.A.I.C.S.: 541512
Mark Martinez *(Pres)*
Sue McElyea *(CFO)*
Mike Tollinger *(Dir-Contracts)*
Jay Hart *(Mgr-Sls Support)*
Lisa Hayes *(Sr Acct Mgr)*

M2E LLC
5815 SW 68 St, Miami, FL 33143
Tel.: (305) 665-1700
Web Site: http://www.m2e.com
Year Founded: 2005
Sales Range: $10-24.9 Million
Emp.: 65
Engineeering Services
N.A.I.C.S.: 541330
Miroslav Misha Mladenovic *(Pres)*
Dejan Tepavac *(CTO)*
Vladimir Markoski *(Sr VP)*
Scott Harvey-Lewis *(VP)*
Brandy Massie *(Office Mgr)*

M2L INC.
135 Madison Ave Fl 2, New York, NY 10016-6712
Tel.: (212) 832-8222
Web Site: http://www.m2l.com
Sales Range: $10-24.9 Million
Emp.: 10
Furniture
N.A.I.C.S.: 423210
Michael Manes *(Founder)*
Miriam Hersh *(Dir-Contract Sls)*

M2L2 COMMUNICATIONS
121 Loring Ave Enterprise Ctr Ste 550, Salem, MA 01970
Tel.: (617) 834-3146
Sales Range: Less than $1 Million
Emp.: 5
N.A.I.C.S.: 541810
Matt Lloyd *(Owner)*
Melanie Lloyd *(Chief Creative & Designer)*

M2M COMMUNICATIONS
5771 N Discovery Way, Boise, ID 83713
Tel.: (208) 947-9500
Web Site: http://www.m2mcomm.com
Year Founded: 2002
Rev.: $4,600,000
Emp.: 30
Miscellaneous Electrical Equipment & Component Mfr
N.A.I.C.S.: 335999
Steve L. Hodges *(Pres & CEO)*
Rick Anderson *(VP)*

M3 ACCOUNTING SERVICES INC.
340 Jesse Jewel Pkwy SE Ste 600, Gainesville, GA 30501
Tel.: (770) 297-1925
Web Site: http://www.m3as.com
Year Founded: 1998
Sales Range: $1-9.9 Million
Hospitality Accounting Software
N.A.I.C.S.: 513210
John McKibbon *(CEO)*
Allen Read *(Pres & COO)*
Casi Johnson *(VP-Ops)*
Scott Watson *(VP-Sls)*
Dennis Jackson *(Exec VP-Fin)*
Carolyn Hollum *(Sr VP-Professional Svcs)*

M3 CAPITAL PARTNERS LLC
150 S Wacker Dr 31st Fl, Chicago, IL 60606
Tel.: (312) 499-8500
Web Site: http://www.m3cp.com
Year Founded: 1991
Sales Range: $25-49.9 Million
Emp.: 250
Provider of Venture Capital Services
N.A.I.C.S.: 522310
Donald E. Suter *(CEO)*
Garret C. House *(VP)*

M3 GLASS TECHNOLOGIES
2924 Rock Island Rd, Irving, TX 75060
Tel.: (972) 399-2112
Web Site: http://www.m3glass.com
Year Founded: 1956
Sales Range: $10-24.9 Million
Emp.: 91
Custom Glass Products
N.A.I.C.S.: 327215
Scott Lee *(Mgr-HR)*

M3 INSURANCE SOLUTIONS, INC.
828 John Nolen Dr, Madison, WI 53713-2830
Tel.: (608) 273-0655
Web Site: http://www.m3ins.com
Sales Range: $25-49.9 Million
Emp.: 150
Insurance Agents
N.A.I.C.S.: 524210
Michael E. Victorson *(Pres & CEO)*
Chris Halverson *(Dir-Risk Mgmt, Property & Casualty)*
Richard Kekula *(Exec VP-Sls)*
Dale E. Dam *(Exec VP-Sls, Property & Casualty)*
James Yeager *(VP)*
Tom Golden *(Exec VP-Corp Svcs)*

Rich Twietmeyer *(Exec VP-Sls & Employee Benefits)*
Phil Procter *(Acct Exec)*
Nezih Hasanoglu *(VP-Bus Dev)*
Rebecca Menefee *(Mgr-Employee Benefits Sls)*
Ryan Barbieri *(VP-Employee Benefits)*
Kim Kolesari *(Acct Exec)*
Nicole Dahl *(Acct Exec)*
Michelle McLane *(VP-Sls, Property & Casualty)*

M3 MIDSTREAM LLC
600 Travis St Ste 5600, Houston, TX 77002
Tel.: (713) 783-3000   DE
Web Site:
  http://www.m3midstream.com
Year Founded: 2004
Oil & Gas Pipeline Transportation Operations
N.A.I.C.S.: 486110
Joe Giles *(Sr VP-Ops)*
George Passela *(Vice Chm)*
George C. Francisco *(CFO & Exec VP)*
Brant Baird *(COO & Exec VP)*
John Taylor *(Exec VP-Engrg & Construction)*
Laranne Breagy *(Gen Counsel & Exec VP)*
Frank D. Tsuru *(Pres & CEO)*
William E. Pritchard III *(Chm)*

M45 MARKETING SERVICES
524 W Stephenson St Ste 100, Freeport, IL 61032
Tel.: (815) 232-2121
Web Site: http://www.m45.com
Emp.: 18
Public Relations
N.A.I.C.S.: 541820
Marilyn Smit *(Co-Owner)*
Joe Vaske *(Co-Owner)*
Sarah Rogers *(Mgr-PR, Employee Comm & Promos)*

M7 SERVICES, LLC
654 N Sam Houston Pkwy E Ste 110, Houston, TX 77060   TX
Web Site:
  http://www.m7services.com
Year Founded: 2014
Sales Range: $1-9.9 Million
Emp.: 30
Information Technology Services
N.A.I.C.S.: 541512
Jessie McMahon *(Founder & CEO)*
Finn Pinson *(COO)*
John Blackmon *(CFO)*
Charif Zahrane *(VP-Tech)*
Christine Morgan *(VP-Client Rels)*

M9 SOLUTIONS
3 Ravinia Dr Ste 1800, Atlanta, GA 30346
Tel.: (770) 396-9990
Web Site:
  http://www.m9solutions.com
Year Founded: 2007
Sales Range: $10-24.9 Million
Emp.: 40
It Consulting
N.A.I.C.S.: 541690
Sean DuGuay *(Pres & CEO)*
David Callner *(Chief Growth Officer)*

MA FEDERAL INC.
12030 Sunrise Valley Ste 300, Reston, VA 20191
Tel.: (703) 356-1160
Web Site: http://www.igov.com
Sales Range: $50-74.9 Million
Emp.: 100
Computers, Peripherals & Software

N.A.I.C.S.: 541511
Patrick Neven *(Chm & CEO)*
Michael Tyrrell *(Pres & COO)*
Mark Valentine *(CFO)*
Deborah Sutton *(VP-HR)*

MA LABORATORIES, INC.
2075 N Capitol Ave, San Jose, CA 95132
Tel.: (408) 941-0808   CA
Web Site: https://www.malabs.com
Year Founded: 1983
Sales Range: Less than $1 Million
Emp.: 3,000
Computer & Computer Peripheral Equipment Distr
N.A.I.C.S.: 423430
Christine Pan *(Mgr)*
Mark Musto *(Gen Counsel)*
Angela Chorng *(VP-Product Mgmt)*

MA MANAGED FUTURES FUND, LP
4440 PGA Blvde Ste 600, Palm Beach Gardens, FL 33410
Tel.: (561) 623-5310   DE
Year Founded: 2011
Investment Services
N.A.I.C.S.: 523999
Monty Agarwal *(Mng Partner & CEO)*

MAALI ENTERPRISES INC.
7932 W Sunlake Rd Ste 300, Orlando, FL 32819
Tel.: (407) 352-9205
Web Site:
  http://ponderosasteakhouses.com
Rev.: $11,586,179
Emp.: 5
Steak Restaurant
N.A.I.C.S.: 561499
Basse Maali *(Pres)*

Subsidiaries:

Maali Restaurant Inc.   (1)
7932 W Sand Lake Rd Ste 300, Orlando, FL 32819-7230
Tel.: (407) 345-9200
Sales Range: $10-24.9 Million
Provider of Family Restaurant Services
N.A.I.C.S.: 722511

MAAS-HANSEN STEEL CORPORATION
2435 E 37th St, Vernon, CA 90058-1704
Tel.: (323) 583-6321   CA
Web Site:
  http://www.maashansen.com
Year Founded: 1929
Sales Range: $10-24.9 Million
Emp.: 98
Metals Service Centers & Offices
N.A.I.C.S.: 423510
Carlin Warner *(Reg Controller)*
Allen Trent *(Gen Mgr)*
John Simon *(VP-Sls)*

MAASS CORPORATION
1721 Ditty Ave, Santa Rosa, CA 95403
Tel.: (707) 285-2550   CA
Web Site:
  http://www.oliversmarket.com
Year Founded: 1988
Emp.: 1,100
Independent Supermarket
N.A.I.C.S.: 445110
Steve Maass *(Founder & Pres)*
Jill Olsen *(CFO)*
Scott Gross *(Gen Mgr)*
Eric Meuse *(Gen Mgr-Ops)*
Susan Walling *(Dir-HR)*
Patty Butler *(Office Mgr)*
Paula Biancalana *(Mgr-Bookkeeping)*
Todd Davis *(Coord-Meat & Seafood)*
Kirsty Leach *(Mgr-Graphics)*

Michael Johnston *(Mgr-Sys Maintenance)*
Jeff Spackman *(Dir-Store-Cotati)*
Frank Camilleri *(Dir-Store-Montecito)*
Roger Guttridge *(Dir-Store-Stony Point)*
Laurie Tuxhorn *(Dir-Store-Windsor)*
Mike Peterson *(Coord-Produce)*

MAB LTD.
265 Eastchester Dr Ste 13, High Point, NC 27262
Tel.: (336) 889-4691
Rev.: $22,000,000
Emp.: 2
Furniture
N.A.I.C.S.: 423210

MABBETT & ASSOCIATES, INC.
5 Alfred Cir, Bedford, MA 01730-2318
Tel.: (781) 275-6050
Web Site: http://www.mabbett.com
Year Founded: 1980
Sales Range: Less than $1 Million
Emp.: 35
Engineeering Services
N.A.I.C.S.: 541330
Arthur N. Mabbett *(Chm & CEO)*
Paul D. Steinberg *(Pres)*
Susan S. Smits *(Sr VP)*
Christopher L. Mabbett *(VP-Ops)*
Sharon T. Morgan *(VP-Fin & Admin)*
Nicole K. Burnett *(Mgr-Bus Dev)*
Freddie J. Ferreira *(Mgr-Tri-State Reg)*
Nicole C. White *(Mgr-Bus Dev)*

MABREY BANCORPORATION INC.
101 E 6th St, Okmulgee, OK 74447
Tel.: (918) 756-7910
Sales Range: $25-49.9 Million
Emp.: 45
Bank Holding Company
N.A.I.C.S.: 551111
W. Carlisle Mabrey III *(CEO)*

Subsidiaries:

Mabrey Bank (1)
14821 S Memorial Dr, Bixby, OK 74008
Tel.: (918) 366-4000
Web Site: http://www.mabreybank.com
Sales Range: $25-49.9 Million
Commericial Banking
N.A.I.C.S.: 522110
John Fidler *(Pres-East Central Oklahoma Reg & Exec VP)*
John Pixley *(Pres-Market)*
Bruce Mabrey *(Exec VP-Facilities Mgmt)*
Marilyn Sulivant *(Chm)*
John Mabrey *(Chief Admin Officer & Sr Exec VP)*
Scott Mabrey *(Pres)*
Katie Mabrey *(VP & Dir-Mktg)*
Mark Mabrey *(VP-Lending)*
W. Carlisle Mabrey III *(CEO)*
Carlisle Mabrey IV *(COO, CTO & Exec VP)*

MABUS BROTHERS CONSTRUCTION COMPANY INC.
920 Molly Pond Rd, Augusta, GA 30901-3718
Tel.: (706) 722-8941
Sales Range: $10-24.9 Million
Emp.: 70
Civil Engineering Services
N.A.I.C.S.: 237110
Larry Goolsby *(VP)*
Tommy Mabus *(Pres)*

MAC CONSTRUCTION & EXCAVATING, INC.
1908 Unruh Ct, New Albany, IN 47150
Tel.: (812) 941-7895
Web Site:
http://www.macconstruction.com

Year Founded: 1980
Sales Range: $25-49.9 Million
Emp.: 150
Provider of Water Main & Sewer Construction Services
N.A.I.C.S.: 237110
Jean M. Unruh *(Pres, CEO & Co-Owner)*
Victor Unruh *(Co-Owner & VP)*
Norman Kruer *(CFO)*

MAC CORPORATION
4717 Massachusetts Ave, Indianapolis, IN 46218
Tel.: (317) 545-3341 IN
Web Site: http://www.maccorp.us
Year Founded: 1973
Commercial & Industrial Waste Handling Equipment Mfr
N.A.I.C.S.: 332420
A. K. Hobbs *(Treas)*
Roger Hobbs *(Pres)*

MAC ELECTRIC INC.
2499 S Virginia Dr, Yuma, AZ 85364
Tel.: (928) 314-1208
Web Site: http://www.meisw.com
Year Founded: 2005
Sales Range: $10-24.9 Million
Emp.: 90
Electrical & Solar Systems
N.A.I.C.S.: 335999
Ari Harrington *(Pres)*
John Navarro *(Project Mgr)*

MAC GROUP INCORPORATED
17385 Ryan Rd, Detroit, MI 48212-1115
Tel.: (313) 366-4443 MI
Web Site:
http://www.metroalloys.com
Year Founded: 1941
Sales Range: $10-24.9 Million
Emp.: 60
Metals Service Centers & Offices
N.A.I.C.S.: 423510
Jan Lederman *(Pres)*
Bob Higgins *(Sr VP-Sls)*
Fred Windholz *(Mgr-Lighting Technical Sls)*
Victor Ha *(Dir-ECommerce & Mktg Channels)*
Alan Shapiro *(CMO)*
Gil Spilman *(CEO)*

Subsidiaries:

Mac Castings Inc. (1)
13600 Girardin St, Detroit, MI 48212-2000 **(100%)**
Tel.: (313) 365-4455
Sales Range: $10-24.9 Million
Emp.: 20
Nonferrous Die-Castings, Except Aluminum
N.A.I.C.S.: 331523

Metropolitan Alloys Corporation (1)
17385 Ryan Rd, Detroit, MI 48212-1115 **(100%)**
Tel.: (313) 366-4443
Web Site: http://www.metroalloys.com
Mfr of High Quality Caster Of Zinc & Aluminum Alloys
N.A.I.C.S.: 423510
Barry Spilman *(Mgr-Sls)*
Mark Weiss *(VP)*

MAC HAIK CHEVEROLET
11711 Katy Fwy, Houston, TX 77079
Tel.: (281) 497-6600
Web Site:
http://www.machaikchevy.com
Rev.: $145,873,900
Emp.: 250
Dealer of New & Used Automobiles
N.A.I.C.S.: 441110
Mac Haik *(Pres)*

MAC LEAN PRECISION MACHINE CO.
Route 113, Madison, NH 03849
Tel.: (603) 367-9011
Web Site:
http://www.macleanprecision.com
Rev.: $4,305,000
Emp.: 100
All Other Miscellaneous Fabricated Metal Product Mfr
N.A.I.C.S.: 332999
Allan MacLean *(Pres)*
Steve Holland *(Mgr-Ops)*

MAC VALVES, INC.
30569 Beck Rd, Wixom, MI 48393-7011
Tel.: (248) 624-7700 MI
Web Site: http://www.macvalves.com
Year Founded: 1948
Sales Range: $250-299.9 Million
Emp.: 3,500
Mechanical Air Fittings
N.A.I.C.S.: 332912
Robert Neff *(Pres)*
Doug McClifton *(VP-Sls)*
Martha Welsh *(CFO)*

Subsidiaries:

Great Lakes Rubber Co. Inc. (1)
30573 Beck Rd, Wixom, MI 48393-2817
Tel.: (248) 624-5710
Web Site:
http://www.greatlakesrubberco.com
Sales Range: $1-9.9 Million
Emp.: 60
Fabricated Rubber Products
N.A.I.C.S.: 326299
Don DeMallie *(Pres)*

MAC Valves Asia, Inc. (1)
Room 1006 No 798 Zhaojiabang Rd, Shanghai, 200030, China
Tel.: (86) 21 54651733
Industrial Valve Mfr
N.A.I.C.S.: 332911

MAC Valves Europe, Inc. (1)
Rua Marie Curie 12, Loncin, 4431, Loncin, Belgium **(100%)**
Tel.: (32) 42396868
Web Site: http://www.macvalves.com
Sales Range: $10-24.9 Million
Emp.: 50
Mfr of Power Valves & Hose Fittings
N.A.I.C.S.: 332912
Delvaux Thierry *(Mng Dir)*

MAC Valves Pacific (1)
20 Alfred St, PO Box 12221, Penrose, Auckland, 1642, New Zealand **(100%)**
Tel.: (64) 96349400
Web Site: http://www.macvalves.co.nz
Sales Range: $10-24.9 Million
Emp.: 8
Mfr of Power Valves & Hose Fittings
N.A.I.C.S.: 332912
Rex Nightingale *(Gen Mgr)*

MAC Valves, Inc.-Dundee (1)
5555 N Ann Arbor Rd, Dundee, MI 48131-9759
Tel.: (734) 529-5099
Sales Range: $10-24.9 Million
Emp.: 100
Mfr of Power Valves & Hose Fittings
N.A.I.C.S.: 332510

MACADAM FLOOR & DESIGN
6655 SW Macadam Ave, Portland, OR 97239
Tel.: (503) 246-9800
Web Site:
http://www.macadamflooranddesign.com
Rev.: $10,000,000
Emp.: 30
Floor Covering Stores
N.A.I.C.S.: 449121
Timothy Aldinger *(Pres)*
Anthony Ivelia *(Gen Mgr)*

MACADOS INC.
120 W Church Ave Ste B, Roanoke, VA 24011
Tel.: (540) 345-8034
Web Site: http://www.macados.net
Sales Range: $10-24.9 Million
Emp.: 18
Delicatessen (Eating Places)
N.A.I.C.S.: 722513
Richard H. Macher *(Pres)*

MACALLISTER MACHINERY CO. INC.
6300 Southeastern Ave, Indianapolis, IN 46203
Tel.: (317) 545-2151
Web Site: http://www.macallister.com
Year Founded: 1945
Sales Range: $10-24.9 Million
Emp.: 550
Supplier of Construction & Mining Services
N.A.I.C.S.: 423810
Dave Baldwin *(CFO)*
Chris MacAllister *(Pres)*
Betty Blunk *(Dir-HR)*
Jay Swearingen *(Mgr-Rental Div)*

MACANDREWS & FORBES INCORPORATED
35 E 62nd St, New York, NY 10065
Tel.: (212) 572-8600 DE
Web Site:
http://www.macandrewsandforbes.com
Holding Company
N.A.I.C.S.: 551112
Ronald O. Perelman *(Chm & CEO)*
Steven M. Cohen *(Chief Admin Officer, Gen Counsel & Exec VP)*
James Chin *(Chief Capital Markets Officer & Exec VP)*
George Davis *(Exec VP-Talent)*
Mark Dowley *(Chief Strategy Officer & Exec VP)*
Adam Ingber *(Chief Tax Officer & Sr VP)*
Evan Knisely *(Sr VP-Govt Affairs)*
Mendel Pinson *(Sr VP)*
Edward P. Taibi *(Exec VP)*
Richard S. Nelson *(Exec VP-Corp Dev)*
Paul G. Savas *(Exec VP)*

Subsidiaries:

AM General LLC (1)
105 N Niles Ave, South Bend, IN 46617
Tel.: (574) 237-6222
Web Site: http://www.amgeneral.com
Sales Range: $25-49.9 Million
Emp.: 1,500
High-Mobility Vehicles Mfr; Owned 70% by MacAndrews & Forbes Holding Inc. & 30% by Renco Group Inc.
N.A.I.C.S.: 336992
James J. Cannon *(Pres)*
R. Andrew Hove *(CEO)*
Christopher P. Vanslager *(Exec VP-US Defense)*
Claudia Gast *(Sr VP-Strategy & Corp Dev)*
John P. Chadbourne *(Sr VP-DC Ops)*
Kevin A. Rahrig *(Exec VP-Comml)*
Mark Minne *(Chief Admin Officer & VP)*
Nguyen Trinh *(Exec VP-Defense-Intl)*
Robert Gold *(CFO & Exec VP)*
Stephen Zink *(COO & Exec VP)*
Tricia Sherick *(Gen Counsel & Exec VP)*

Subsidiary (Domestic):

AM General Aftermarket Fulfillment and Training Center (2)
5448 Dylan Dr, South Bend, IN 46628
Tel.: (574) 237-6222
Specialized Vehicle Mfr
N.A.I.C.S.: 336211

AM General Technology and Engineering Center (2)
1399 Pacific Dr, Auburn Hills, MI 48326
Tel.: (574) 237-6222

MACANDREWS & FORBES INCORPORATED — U.S. PRIVATE

MacAndrews & Forbes Incorporated—(Continued)
Specialized Vehicles Designer & Mfr
N.A.I.C.S.: 336211

General Engine Products LLC (2)
2000 Watkins Glen Dr, Franklin, OH 45005
Tel.: (937) 704-1800
Engine Products Mfr
N.A.I.C.S.: 333618

Plant (Domestic):

Mishawaka Manufacturing Campus (2)
13200 McKinley Hwy, Mishawaka, IN 46545
Tel.: (574) 237-6222
Specialized Vehicle Mfr
N.A.I.C.S.: 336211

Deluxe Laboratories, Inc. (1)
5433 Fernwood Ave, Hollywood, CA 90027
Tel.: (323) 960-3600
Web Site: http://www.bydeluxe.com
Motion Picture Film Processing, Production & Distribution Services
N.A.I.C.S.: 512191

Subsidiary (Non-US):

Deluxe Laboratories, Ltd. (2)
Denham Media Park North Orbital Road, Denham, UB9 5HQ, Uxbridge, United Kingdom
Tel.: (44) 1895832323
Web Site: http://www.bydeluxe.com
Sales Range: $75-99.9 Million
Emp.: 140
Motion Picture Film Processing, Production & Distribution Services
N.A.I.C.S.: 512191
Oliver Ronicle (Dir-Sls)

M & F Worldwide Corp. (1)
35 E 62nd St, New York, NY 10021-8032
Tel.: (212) 572-8600
Web Site: http://www.mandfworldwide.com
Sales Range: $1-4.9 Billion
Emp.: 337
Holding Company; Direct Marketing, Technology Consulting, Licorice Products Mfr & Educational Consulting
N.A.I.C.S.: 551112
Paul G. Savas (CFO & Exec VP)

Subsidiary (Domestic):

Mafco Worldwide Corporation (2)
3rd St & Jefferson Ave, Camden, NJ 08104
Tel.: (856) 964-8840
Web Site: http://www.mafcolicorice.com
Rev.: $24,200,000
Emp.: 275
Licorice Products & Flavor Additive Mfr
N.A.I.C.S.: 311340

Vericast (2)
15955 La Cantera Parkway, San Antonio, TX 78256
Tel.: (210) 694-8888
Web Site: http://www.harlandclarkeholdings.com
Sales Range: $1-4.9 Billion
Printed Forms & Software Mfr for Financial Institutions
N.A.I.C.S.: 323111
Richard S. Nelson (Exec VP-Corp Dev)
Charles Dawson (Chm)
Susan Yun Lee (Grp Pres-Digital Marketing & Technology Solutions)
Judy Norris (Gen Counsel & Sr VP)
Peter A. Fera Jr. (CFO & Exec VP)
Joe Bilman (Chief Digital Officer)
Scott Hansen (CMO)
Debbie Serot (Sr VP-Corp Comm)
Joe Filer (Chief Info Security Officer & Chief Privacy Officer)
John O'Malley (CEO)
Andrew R. Bland III (Sr VP-Corp Security Grp)

Subsidiary (Domestic):

Harland Clarke Corp. (3)
10931 Laureate Dr, San Antonio, TX 78249
Tel.: (210) 697-8888
Web Site: http://www.harlandclarke.com
Sales Range: $10-24.9 Million
Emp.: 45

Integrated Payment, Marketing Services, Security Services & Retail Products
N.A.I.C.S.: 561499
Rick Ebrey (Pres-Payment Div)
Don Dolan (Pres-Retail Channels Div)
Mike Fay (Pres-Mktg Svcs Div)
Geoff Thomas (Sr VP-Product Dev)
Carrie Stapp (Sr VP-Product Mgmt)

Subsidiary (Domestic):

Checks In The Mail, Inc. (4)
2435 Goodwin Ln, New Braunfels, TX 78135-0001
Tel.: (830) 609-5500
Web Site: http://www.checksinthemail.com
Check Printing Services
N.A.I.C.S.: 323111
Cindi Champion (Mgr-Mktg)

John H. Harland Co. of Puerto Rico (4)
Rd 189 KM 189 O'Reilly Industrial Park, Gurabo, PR 00778
Tel.: (787) 737-8406
Web Site: http://www.harlandclarke.com
Printing
N.A.I.C.S.: 323111
Ralph Crane (Pres)

Subsidiary (Domestic):

QuickPivot Corporation (3)
2400 District Ave Ste 410, Burlington, MA 01803
Tel.: (617) 880-4000
Web Site: http://www.quickpivot.com
Sales Range: $25-49.9 Million
Emp.: 75
System Integration Services
N.A.I.C.S.: 541512
Kenneth E. Marshall (Chm)
Christine Dostal (Treas, VP & Controller)
Jennifer Allison (Dir-HR)
Chris Baribeau (VP-Acct Svcs)
Ann Liotta (VP-HR)
Paul Mandeville (VP-Strategy)
Chris Malone (Dir-Tech Svcs)

RetailMeNot, Inc. (3)
301 Congress Ave Ste 700, Austin, TX 78701
Tel.: (512) 777-2970
Web Site: https://www.retailmenot.com
Online Coupons & Deals Website Operator
N.A.I.C.S.: 541890

Subsidiary (Non-US):

RetailMeNot UK Ltd. (4)
6th Floor 200 Grays Inn Road, London, WC1X 8XZ, United Kingdom
Tel.: (44) 203 540 6700
Web Site: http://www.retailmenot.com
Online Coupons & Deals Website Operator
N.A.I.C.S.: 541890

RetailMeNot, France, SAS (4)
11 rue Paul Lelong, 75002, Paris, France
Tel.: (33) 1 4261 1580
Web Site: http://www.retailmenot.com
Online Coupons & Deals Website Operator
N.A.I.C.S.: 541890
Sophie Cazaux (Sr Mgr-PR-Consumer)

Subsidiary (Domestic):

RxSaver, Inc. (4)
301 Congress Ave, Austin, TX 78701
Tel.: (855) 569-6337
Web Site: http://www.rxsaver.retailmenot.com
Physical Prescription Discount Cards/Coupons Services
N.A.I.C.S.: 541870
Shaun Dubuque (VP-Engrg)

Subsidiary (Domestic):

SubscriberMail, LLC (3)
3333 Warrenville Rd Ste 530, Lisle, IL 60532 (100%)
Tel.: (630) 303-5000
Web Site: http://www.subscribermail.com
Sales Range: $1-9.9 Million
Emp.: 32
Email Marketing Services
N.A.I.C.S.: 541890
Mike Ferguson (CEO)

Valassis Communications, Inc. (3)

19975 Victor Pkwy, Livonia, MI 48152
Tel.: (734) 591-3000
Web Site: http://www.valassis.com
Sales Range: $1-4.9 Billion
Emp.: 6,400
Media & Marketing Services; Direct Mail Advertising Services
N.A.I.C.S.: 323111
Rex Boatright (Dir-Creative Svcs)
Rajat Shroff (VP-Product Dev-Brand.net)
Steve Carrington (CIO & Sr VP)
Wayne Powers (COO)
Mark Ellis (Chief Revenue Officer)
Bonnie Bisson (VP-Sls Enablement)

Subsidiary (Domestic):

House 2 Home Showcase (4)
13405 Folsom Blvd Ste 450, Folsom, CA 95630-4773
Tel.: (916) 608-0874
Web Site: http://www.house2homeshowcase.com
Publisher
N.A.I.C.S.: 513199
Paul Corsaro (Owner)

MaxPoint Interactive Inc. (4)
3020 Carrington Mill Blvd Ste 300, Morrisville, NC 27560
Tel.: (800) 916-9960
Web Site: http://www.valassisdigital.com
Sales Range: $150-199.9 Million
Business Intelligence & Marketing Automation Software Publisher
N.A.I.C.S.: 513210

NCH Marketing Services, Inc. (4)
155 N Pfingsten Rd Ste 200, Deerfield, IL 60015
Tel.: (847) 317-5500
Web Site: http://www.nchmarketing.com
Sales Range: $25-49.9 Million
Emp.: 150
Promotional Marketing Services
N.A.I.C.S.: 541613
Charles K. Brown (VP-Mktg)
Mark W. Dennis (Sr VP & Gen Mgr-US)
David G. Johnson (Sr VP-Acct Mgmt & Sls)
Laura Czekala (VP-Product Mgmt)
Angelo Tosoni (Mng Dir-Italy)
Maureen Greene (VP-HR)
Michelle Carey Jones (Gen Counsel & VP)
Neil McManus (VP-IT)

Spotzot, Inc. (4)
564 Market St #616, San Francisco, CA 94104
Tel.: (415) 363-6520
Web Site: http://www.spotzot.com
Software Developer
N.A.I.C.S.: 513210
Jim Schreitmueller (VP-Sls & Bus Dev)
Pehr Luedtke (CEO)
Bobby Jadhav (Co-Founder & Chief Product Officer)
Sanjay Mittal (Co-Founder & CTO)
Sergeja Elam (Head-Ops & Acct Mgmt)

Valassis Direct Mail, Inc. (4)
1 Targeting Ctr 235 Great Pond Dr, Windsor, CT 06095
Tel.: (860) 285-6100
Direct Mail Marketing Services
N.A.I.C.S.: 541860
Steven M. Mitzel (Pres)

Mafco Consolidated Group Inc. (1)
300 Jefferson St, Camden, NJ 08104
Tel.: (856) 968-4011
Web Site: http://www.macandrewsandforbes.com
Sales Range: $10-24.9 Million
Emp.: 75
Flavoring Syrup & Concentrate Mfr
N.A.I.C.S.: 311930
Edna Napoleon (Mgr-Product Dev)

Unit (Domestic):

Mafco Natural Products (2)
4400 Williamsburg Ave, Richmond, VA 23231-1210
Tel.: (804) 222-1600
Sales Range: $10-24.9 Million
Emp.: 12
Spices & Flavorings Mfr
N.A.I.C.S.: 311942

Merisant Company (1)

125 S Wacker Dr Ste 3150, Chicago, IL 60606
Tel.: (312) 840-6000
Web Site: http://www.merisant.com
Sales Range: $200-249.9 Million
Emp.: 430
Synthetic Sweeteners Mfr & Marketer
N.A.I.C.S.: 424690
Brian Alsvig (VP-Fin, Plng & Analysis)
George Manor (Treas & Controller)
Lori Schwartz (Sr Mgr-Brand, Mktg & Strategy)
Rich Mewborn (Pres & CEO)
Doug Cherry (VP, Gen Counsel & Sec)

Subsidiary (Non-US):

Merisant Australia Pty Ltd (2)
Level 1/ 115 Alexander Street, Crows Nest, 2065, NSW, Australia
Tel.: (61) 94384892
Web Site: http://www.merisant.com
Natural & Artifical Sweetener Mfr
N.A.I.C.S.: 311314

Subsidiary (Domestic):

Merisant Corp. (2)
33 N Dearborn St, Chicago, IL 60602
Tel.: (312) 840-6000
Web Site: http://www.merisant.com
Rev.: $20,300,000
Emp.: 100
Synthetic Sweeteners
N.A.I.C.S.: 325199

Subsidiary (Non-US):

Merisant France SAS (2)
12 Avenue de l'arche, Courbevoie, France
Tel.: (33) 1 41 45 45 00
Natural & Synthetic Sweeteners Mfr
N.A.I.C.S.: 325998

Merisant India Private Limited (2)
202 The Chambers 1865 Rajdanga Main Rd, Kolkata, 700107, West Bengal, India
Tel.: (91) 33 2442 8051
Natural & Artificial Sweetener Mfr
N.A.I.C.S.: 311314

Merisant UK, Ltd. (2)
St Johns Court Easton Street, High Wycombe, HP11 1JX, United Kingdom
Tel.: (44) 1494 855301
Web Site: http://www.merisant.com
Artificial & Natural Zero & Reduced-calorie Sweeteners Mfr
N.A.I.C.S.: 325199

Subsidiary (Domestic):

Merisant US, Inc. (2)
33 N Dearborn St Ste 200, Chicago, IL 60602
Tel.: (312) 840-6000
Web Site: http://www.merisant.com
Natural & Artificial Sweetener
N.A.I.C.S.: 311314

Whole Earth Sweetener Company, LLC (2)
33 North Dearborn Suite 200, Chicago, IL 60602
Tel.: (800) 824-2334
Natural & Artificial Sweetener Mfr
N.A.I.C.S.: 311314

Revlon, Inc. (1) (77.4%)
Tel.: (212) 527-4000
Web Site: https://www.revlon.com
Rev.: $2,078,700,000
Assets: $2,432,500,000
Liabilities: $4,446,600,000
Net Worth: ($2,014,100,000)
Earnings: ($206,900,000)
Emp.: 5,800
Fiscal Year-end: 12/31/2021
Holding Company; Cosmetics, Beauty Products & Fragrances Mfr & Distr
N.A.I.C.S.: 551112
Ronald O. Perelman (Chm)
Christine Chen (Interim Chief Acctg Officer & Controller)
E. Scott Beattie (Vice Chm)
Geralyn R. Breig (Pres-North America)
Keyla Lazardi (Chief Scientific Officer)
Ely Bar-Ness (Chief HR Officer)
Jose Urquijo (CIO)

MACANDREWS & FORBES INCORPORATED

Martine Williamson *(CMO)*
Thomas Cho *(Chief Supply Chain Officer)*
Matt Kvarda *(Interim CFO)*

Subsidiary (Non-US):

Beautyge Beauty Group, S.L. (2)
Calle Tirso De Molina 40, Cornella De Llobregat, Barcelona, 08940, Spain
Tel.: (34) 934009300
Cosmetics Products Mfr
N.A.I.C.S.: 325620

Beautyge Denmark A/S (2)
Vesterbrogade 18, Copenhagen, 1620, Denmark
Tel.: (45) 70222298
Cosmetic Product Whslr
N.A.I.C.S.: 424210

Beautyge France SAS (2)
29 Rue du Colisee, Paris, 75008, France
Tel.: (33) 156437100
Cosmetics Products Mfr
N.A.I.C.S.: 325620

Beautyge Germany GmbH (2)
Abraham-Lincoln-Strasse 22, 65189, Wiesbaden, Germany
Tel.: (49) 61126237800
Web Site: http://www.revlon-pro.de
Cosmetics Products Mfr
N.A.I.C.S.: 325620
Maria Marchueta *(Mgr-Mktg-Revlon Professional & American Crew)*

Beautyge Logistics Services, S.L. (2)
Lugar Wtc-Almeda Park Tirso De Molina Numero 40, Cornella De Llobregat, 08940, Barcelona, Spain
Tel.: (34) 934009300
Cosmetics Products Mfr
N.A.I.C.S.: 325620

Beautyge Participations, S.L. (2)
Calle Tirso De Molina World Trade C Almeda 40, Cornella De Llobregat, Barcelona, 08940, Spain
Tel.: (34) 934009300
Holding Company
N.A.I.C.S.: 551112

Beautyge Portugal - Produtos Cosmeticos e Profissionais Lda. (2)
Avenida Da Liberdade 245 7 Lisboa, Lisbon, 1250-143, Portugal
Tel.: (351) 217944000
Cosmetics Products Mfr
N.A.I.C.S.: 325620

Beautyge Professional Limited (2)
Unit 5, Dublin, Ireland
Tel.: (353) 18869300
Cosmetics Products Mfr
N.A.I.C.S.: 325620

CBBeauty Ltd (2)
2-6 Boundary Row, London, SE1 8HP, United Kingdom
Tel.: (44) 2037144300
Web Site: http://www.cbbeauty.com
Cosmetic Product Distr
N.A.I.C.S.: 424210
Lisa Ricci *(Sr VP-Brands)*
Jean-Philippe Verdet *(VP-EMEA)*

Subsidiary (Domestic):

Elizabeth Arden, Inc. (2)
888 SW 145th Ave Ste 200, Pembroke Pines, FL 33027
Tel.: (800) 326-7337
Web Site: http://www.elizabetharden.com
Sales Range: $900-999.9 Million
Fragrances & Cosmetics Mfr
N.A.I.C.S.: 325620
Oscar E. Marina *(Gen Counsel, Sec & Exec VP)*
Lita Cunningham *(Sr VP-Global HR)*
George Cleary *(Pres-Global Fragrances)*

Subsidiary (Non-US):

Elizabeth Arden (Australia) PTY Ltd. (3)
12 Julius Avenue, North Ryde, 2113, NSW, Australia
Tel.: (61) 180002488
Web Site: http://www.elizabetharden.com.au
Cosmetics Mfr
N.A.I.C.S.: 456120

Elizabeth Arden (Canada) Limited (3)
1590 South Gate Way Rd, Mississauga, L4W 0A8, ON, Canada
Tel.: (905) 276-4500
Web Site: https://www.elizabetharden.ca
Cosmetics Mfr
N.A.I.C.S.: 456120

Elizabeth Arden (Denmark) ApS (3)
Kirkebjerg Parkvej 9-11 C, Brondby, 2605, Denmark
Tel.: (45) 43284800
Web Site: http://www.elizabetharden.dk
Cosmetics Products Mfr
N.A.I.C.S.: 325620
Palle Petersen *(Mng Dir)*

Elizabeth Arden (New Zealand) Limited (3)
Level 2 19 Great South Road, Newmarket, New Zealand
Tel.: (64) 95293200
Web Site: http://www.elizabetharden.co.nz
Cosmetic Product Distr
N.A.I.C.S.: 424210
Valerie Riley *(Gen Mgr)*

Elizabeth Arden (South Africa) (Pty) Ltd. (3)
Plattekloof House Tygerberg Park 163 Uys Krige Drive, Plattekloof, Cape Town, 7500, South Africa
Tel.: (27) 2129365900
Web Site: http://www.elizabetharden.co.za
Cosmetics Mfr
N.A.I.C.S.: 325620
Cornelius Nel *(Head-Bus)*

Elizabeth Arden (UK) Ltd. (3)
87-91 Newman St, London, W1T 3EY, United Kingdom
Tel.: (44) 2075742700
Web Site: http://www.elizabetharden.co.uk
Cosmetics Mfr
N.A.I.C.S.: 325620
Michael T. Sheehan *(Dir)*

Subsidiary (Domestic):

Elizabeth Arden International Holding, Inc. (3)
2400 SW 145th Ave, Miramar, FL 33027-4145
Tel.: (954) 364-6900
Web Site: http://corporate.elizabetharden.com
Holding Company;Business Services
N.A.I.C.S.: 325620

Subsidiary (Non-US):

Elizabeth Arden International S.a.r.l. (3)
26-28 Chemin de Joinville, PO Box 43, Cointrin, 1216, Geneva, Switzerland
Tel.: (41) 227918711
Web Site: http://www.elizabetharden.com
Cosmetics Mfr
N.A.I.C.S.: 325620
Sharon Harrison *(Dir-Intl Systems Dev)*

Elizabeth Arden Korea Yuhan Hoesa (3)
Shinwha Building 6 Fl 17 Hannamdaero-21gil, Yongsan-gu, Seoul, 140 887, Korea (South)
Tel.: (82) 220711800
Web Site: http://www.corporate.elizabetharden.com
Cosmetics Mfr
N.A.I.C.S.: 325620

Subsidiary (Non-US):

Europeenne de Produits de Beaute S.A.S. (2)
64 rue Ranelagh, 75016, Paris, France
Tel.: (33) 155743333
Cosmetics Products Mfr
N.A.I.C.S.: 325620

Revlon (Suisse) S.A. (2)
Badenerstrasse 116, Schlieren, 8952, Switzerland
Tel.: (41) 447118820
Web Site: http://www.teucrous.com
Cosmetics Products Mfr
N.A.I.C.S.: 325620
Roland Redmond *(Gen Mgr)*

Revlon Australia Pty Limited (2)
12 Julius Ave, North Ryde, 2113, NSW, Australia
Tel.: (61) 288759700
Web Site: http://www.revlon.com.au
Emp.: 60
Cosmetics Products Mfr
N.A.I.C.S.: 325620

Subsidiary (Domestic):

Revlon Consumer Products Corporation (2)
55 Water St, New York, NY 10041 (100%)
Tel.: (212) 527-4000
Web Site: https://www.revloninc.com
Rev.: $1,980,399,999
Assets: $2,701,600,000
Liabilities: $5,209,300,000
Net Worth: ($2,507,700,000)
Earnings: ($679,100,000)
Emp.: 5,599
Fiscal Year-end: 12/31/2022
Perfumes, Cosmetics & Other Toilet Preparations
N.A.I.C.S.: 325620
Ronald O. Perelman *(Chm)*
Debra G. Perelman *(Pres & CEO)*
Victoria L. Dolan *(COO)*
Christine Chen *(Interim Chief Acctg Officer & Controller)*
Victoria L. Dolan *(CFO)*

Subsidiary (Domestic):

Revlon (Puerto Rico), Inc. (3)
Calle Escorial 920 Mario Julia Industrial Pk, San Juan, PR 00920-2029
Tel.: (787) 781-2323
Sales Range: $25-49.9 Million
Emp.: 20
Mfr & Distributor of Beauty Products
N.A.I.C.S.: 424210

Revlon Development Corp. (3)
2121 State Rte 27, Edison, NJ 08817-3329 (100%)
Tel.: (732) 287-1400
Web Site: http://www.revlon.com
Sales Range: $25-49.9 Million
Emp.: 150
Beauty Care Research & Development
N.A.I.C.S.: 541715

Revlon Government Sales, Inc. (3)
237 Park Ave, New York, NY 10017 (100%)
Tel.: (212) 527-4000
Web Site: http://www.revlon.com
Sales Range: $25-49.9 Million
Emp.: 300
Retailer of Beauty Products
N.A.I.C.S.: 325620

Revlon International Corporation (3)
237 Park Ave, New York, NY 10017-1801 (100%)
Tel.: (212) 527-4000
Web Site: http://www.revlon.com
Sales Range: $50-74.9 Million
Emp.: 300
Holding Company; Beauty Products, Cosmetics & Fragrances Mfr & Distr
N.A.I.C.S.: 551112

Subsidiary (Non-US):

Revlon Canada Inc. (4)
1590 South Gateway Road, Mississauga, L4Y 1R9, ON, Canada
Tel.: (905) 276-4500
Web Site: http://www.revlon.com
Sales Range: $75-99.9 Million
Emp.: 150
Perfumes Cosmetics & Other Toilet Preparations
N.A.I.C.S.: 325620

Revlon Group Limited (4)
Greater London House Hampstead Rd, London, NW1 7QX, United Kingdom (100%)
Tel.: (44) 2073917400
Web Site: http://www.revloninc.com
Sales Range: $50-74.9 Million
Emp.: 100
Mfr of Cosmetics & Fragrances

Revlon, S.A. (4)
Tirso de Molina 40, Cornella de Llobregat, 08940, Barcelona, Spain
Tel.: (34) 934009300
Sales Range: $50-74.9 Million
Emp.: 11
Cosmetic Product Distr
N.A.I.C.S.: 456120
Ronald O. Perelman *(Chm)*

Subsidiary (Non-US):

Revlon Manufacturing Ltd. (2)
1 Scotts Road No 24-01 Shaw Centre Newton, Singapore, 228208, Singapore
Tel.: (65) 68340123
Cosmetics Products Mfr
N.A.I.C.S.: 325620

Revlon New Zealand Limited (2)
Level 2/32 34 Mahuhu Cresent, Auckland, New Zealand
Tel.: (64) 94889800
Web Site: http://www.revlon.co.nz
Emp.: 5
Cosmetics Products Mfr
N.A.I.C.S.: 325620

Subsidiary (Domestic):

Revlon Real Estate Corporation (2)
466 Lexington Ave Fl 13, New York, NY 10017-3140
Tel.: (212) 527-4000
Cosmetics Products Mfr
N.A.I.C.S.: 325620

Subsidiary (Non-US):

Revlon S.p.A. (2)
Piazzale dell'Industria 46, 00144, Rome, Italy
Tel.: (39) 06549391
Web Site: http://www.revlonitaly.com
Cosmetics Products Mfr
N.A.I.C.S.: 325620

Revlon South Africa (Proprietary) Limited (2)
1 Tungsten Road, Isando, 1600, Gauteng, South Africa
Tel.: (27) 119710812
Web Site: http://www.revlon.co.za
Cosmetics Products Mfr
N.A.I.C.S.: 325620

Revlon, S.A. de C.V. (2)
Av Insurgentes SUR 2453 Floor 1 Ofic 101, Colonia Tizapan Alvaro Obregon, Mexico, Mexico
Tel.: (52) 2591408000
Cosmetics Products Mfr
N.A.I.C.S.: 325620
Jaime Vazquez *(Gen Mgr)*

Subsidiary (Domestic):

Roux Laboratories, Inc. (2)
2210 Melson Ave, Jacksonville, FL 32254
Tel.: (904) 693-1200
Cosmetics Products Mfr
N.A.I.C.S.: 325620

Subsidiary (Non-US):

SAS and Company Limited (2)
SAS House 1 Chertsey Road, Woking, GU21 5AB, Surrey, United Kingdom
Tel.: (44) 1483755772
Web Site: http://www.sasandcompany.com
Cosmetic Product Distr
N.A.I.C.S.: 424210
Shelley Smyth *(CEO)*
Paul Saayman *(Dir-Commi)*
Tracy Beer *(Dir-Sls)*
Elin Kikano *(Mgr-Mktg-Morris Brands)*
Kirsty Hayward *(Mgr-Mktg-Parlux Brand)*

The Colomer Group (2)
WTC Almeda Park C/ Tirso de Molina 40, 08940, Cornella de Llobregat, Spain
Tel.: (34) 93 400 93 00
Web Site: http://www.thecolomergroup.com
Sales Range: $500-549.9 Million
Emp.: 1,500
Professional Hair Care & Beauty Products Mfr & Distr
N.A.I.C.S.: 325620

MACANDREWS & FORBES INCORPORATED

U.S. PRIVATE

MacAndrews & Forbes Incorporated—(Continued)

Subsidiary (Domestic):

Colomer Beauty and Professional Products, S.L. (3)
C/ Tirso de Molina 40 ed 4, Cornella del Llobregat, 8940, Barcelona, Spain
Tel.: (34) 93 400 93 00
Professional Beauty Products Mfr & Whsr
N.A.I.C.S.: 456120

Subsidiary (Non-US):

Colomer Denmark A/S (3)
Vesterbrograde 18 3 sal, DK-1620, Copenhagen, Denmark
Tel.: (45) 70 22 2298
Professional Beauty Supply Mfr
N.A.I.C.S.: 339999

Colomer France SAS (3)
29 rue du Colisee, Paris, 75008, France
Tel.: (33) 156437100
Web Site: http://www.thecolomergroup.com
Sales Range: $10-24.9 Million
Emp.: 85
Professional Hair Care Products Distr
N.A.I.C.S.: 424210
Francoise Keller *(Dir-Mktg)*

Colomer Germany GmbH (3)
Prinzenallee 5, North Rhine-Westphalia, D-40549, Dusseldorf, Germany
Tel.: (49) 211 50 73 55 0
Emp.: 30
Professional Beauty Supply Mfr
N.A.I.C.S.: 339999
Thomas Kruager *(Mng Dir)*

Colomer Italy SpA (3)
Via Zaccarelli 5-7, Padulle di Sala, 40010, Bologna, Italy
Tel.: (39) 051 682 3111
Professional Beauty Supply Mfr
N.A.I.C.S.: 339999

Colomer Netherlands BV (3)
Giraffeweg 2, 1338 EG, Almere, Netherlands
Tel.: (31) 365467506
Emp.: 5
Professional Beauty Supply Mfr
N.A.I.C.S.: 339999
Karine Croese *(Gen Mgr)*

Colomer Professional Ltd. (3)
Unit 5 St johns Court, Santry, Dublin, 9, Ireland
Tel.: (353) 886 9300
Beauty Supply Mfr
N.A.I.C.S.: 339999

Subsidiary (Non-US):

Colomer Professional Ltd.-London (4)
Claremont House 22-24, Claremont Road, Surbiton, KT6 4QU, Surrey, United Kingdom
Tel.: (44) 20 8339 9080
Professional Beauty Supply Mfr
N.A.I.C.S.: 339999

Subsidiary (Non-US):

Colomer Rus CJSC (3)
2 Kabelnaya Ulitsa 2/4, 11024, Moscow, Russia
Tel.: (7) 495 777 81 06
Professional Beauty Supply Mfr
N.A.I.C.S.: 339999

Division (US):

Colomer USA, Inc.
5344 Overmyer Dr, Jacksonville, FL 32254
Tel.: (904) 693-1200
Web Site: http://www.thecolomergroup.com
Sales Range: $450-499.9 Million
Professional Cosmetic & Hair Care Products Mfr & Distr
N.A.I.C.S.: 325620
Angela Littleton *(Supvr-Labor Rels)*

Subsidiary (Domestic):

American Crew, Inc. (4)
1515 Wazee St Suite 200, Denver, CO 80202-2705
Tel.: (303) 292-4850
Web Site: http://www.americancrew.com
Sales Range: $25-49.9 Million
Emp.: 30
Men's Professional Hair & Personal Care Products Mfr
N.A.I.C.S.: 325620

Creative Nail Design, Inc. (4)
2755 Dos Aarons Way Ste B, Vista, CA 92081
Tel.: (760) 599-2900
Web Site: http://www.cnd.com
Sales Range: $25-49.9 Million
Emp.: 100
Nail Care & Beauty Products Mfr
N.A.I.C.S.: 325620
Jan Arnold *(Co-Founder)*
Tony Nemer *(VP-Intl Sls)*

Subsidiary (Non-US):

Colomer-Portugal Produtos Cosmet. e Profesionais, Ltda (3)
Av Liberdade 245 7 A, 1250-143, Lisbon, Portugal
Tel.: (351) 21 794 4000
Beauty Supply Mfr
N.A.I.C.S.: 339999

SIGA Technologies, Inc. (1)
31 E 62nd St, New York, NY 10065
Tel.: (212) 672-9100
Web Site: https://www.siga.com
Rev.: $110,775,610
Assets: $195,035,923
Liabilities: $24,875,881
Net Worth: $170,160,042
Earnings: $33,904,806
Emp.: 39
Fiscal Year-end: 12/31/2022
Infectious Disease Prevention & Treatment Pharmaceutical Developer & Mfr
N.A.I.C.S.: 325412
Eric A. Rose *(Chm)*
Diem Nguyen *(CEO)*
Tove' C. Bolken *(Chief Supply Chain Officer & Sr VP-Operations)*
Larry Miller *(Gen Counsel)*
Daniel J. Luckshire *(CFO & Exec VP)*

Unit (Domestic):

SIGA Development Operations (2)
4575 SW Research Way Ste 110, Corvallis, OR 97333
Tel.: (541) 753-2000
Biotechnology
N.A.I.C.S.: 541714

vTv Therapeutics Inc. (1)
3980 Premier Dr Ste 310, High Point, NC 27265
Tel.: (336) 841-0300
Web Site: https://www.vtvtherapeutics.com
Rev.: $2,018,000
Assets: $33,238,000
Liabilities: $43,978,000
Net Worth: ($10,740,000)
Earnings: ($19,164,000)
Emp.: 13
Fiscal Year-end: 12/31/2022
Holding Company; Biopharmaceutical Developer
N.A.I.C.S.: 551112
Richard S. Nelson *(Exec VP-Corp Dev)*
Carmen Valcarce *(Chief Scientific Officer & Exec VP)*
Paul Sekhri *(CEO)*
Steven Tuch *(CFO & Exec VP)*
Thomas Strack *(Chief Medical Officer)*
Paul J. Sekhri *(Chm, Pres & CEO)*

Subsidiary (Domestic):

vTv Therapeutics LLC (2)
4170 Mendenhall Oaks Pkwy, High Point, NC 27265
Tel.: (336) 841-0300
Web Site: http://www.vtvtherapeutics.com
Biopharmaceutical Developer
N.A.I.C.S.: 325412
Imogene Dunn *(Sr VP-BioMetrics & Regulatory Affairs)*
Carmen Valcarce *(Chief Scientific Officer & Sr VP)*
Robert C. Andrews *(Sr VP-Chemistry)*
Aaron H. Burstein *(Sr VP-Clinical Dev)*
Samuel B. Rollins *(VP-Intellectual Property)*
Stephen L. Holcombe *(Pres & CEO)*
Rudy Howard *(CFO)*

MACARI-HEALEY PUBLISHING COMPANY, LLC
110 N Rubey Dr Ste 120, Golden, CO 80403
Tel.: (303) 279-5541 **CO**
Web Site:
    http://coloradocommunitymedia.com
Emp.: 60
Holding Company; Newspaper Publisher
N.A.I.C.S.: 551112
Jerry Healey *(Pres & Publr)*

Subsidiaries:

Colorado Community Media (1)
9137 S Ridgeline Blvd Ste 210, Highlands Ranch, CO 80129
Tel.: (303) 566-4100
Web Site:
    http://www.coloradocommunitymedia.com
Emp.: 25
Newspaper Publishers
N.A.I.C.S.: 513110
Jerry Healey *(Publr & Owner)*
Erin Addenbrooke *(Dir-Adv)*
Chris Rotar *(Editor)*

Jackalope Publishing, Inc. (1)
110 N Rubey Dr Ste 120, Golden, CO 80403
Tel.: (303) 279-5541
Web Site: http://www.ourcoloradonews.com
Rev.: $2,700,000
Emp.: 40
Newspaper Publishers
N.A.I.C.S.: 513110

MACARTHUR CO.
2400 Wycliff St, Saint Paul, MN 55114-1220
Tel.: (651) 646-2773 **MN**
Web Site:
    http://www.macarthurco.com
Year Founded: 1911
Sales Range: $50-74.9 Million
Emp.: 168
Provider of Commercial Roofing, Mechanical Insulation & HVAC Products
N.A.I.C.S.: 423330
Clyde Rhodes *(CEO)*

Subsidiaries:

American Metal Supply Co., Inc. (1)
2335 E Chestnut Expy, Springfield, MO 65802
Tel.: (417) 447-3763
Web Site:
    http://www.americanmetalssupply.com
Sales Range: $1-9.9 Million
Emp.: 10
Industrial Machinery & Equipment Merchant Whslr
N.A.I.C.S.: 423830
Chrissy Nardini *(Pres)*
Jim Morton *(Exec VP)*
Steve Hassebrock *(CEO)*
Eric Cameron *(Mgr-Indianapolis)*
Jeremy Jett *(Mgr-Oklahoma City)*
John Klint *(Mgr-Springfield)*
Mike Bowersock *(Mgr-Springfield & Lenexa)*

BBL Buildings & Components, Ltd. (1)
232 Semo Ln, Perryville, MO 63775-8892
Tel.: (573) 547-8363
Sales Range: $1-9.9 Million
Construction Engineering Services
N.A.I.C.S.: 541330
Dale Schemel *(Gen Mgr)*

Energy Panel Structures, Inc. (1)
603 N Van Gordon Ave, Graettinger, IA 51342
Tel.: (712) 859-3219
Web Site: http://www.epsbuildings.com
Sales Range: $10-24.9 Million
Emp.: 150
Prefabricated Metal Buildings
N.A.I.C.S.: 332311
Chris Spaeth *(Dir-Sls & Mktg-EPS Buildings)*

Insulation Distributors, Inc. (1)
1869 Research Way, West Valley City, UT 84119-2348
Tel.: (801) 972-2874
Web Site: http://www.macarthurco.com
Emp.: 8
Insulation Material Distr
N.A.I.C.S.: 423330
Jeff Davie *(Gen Mgr)*

Insulation Plus, LLC (1)
1300 Kirk St, Elk Grove Village, IL 60007-6741
Tel.: (630) 948-4830
Emp.: 25
Construction Engineering Services
N.A.I.C.S.: 541330
Dominick Marino *(Gen Mgr)*

MacArthur Co. (1)
202 N 47th Ave, Phoenix, AZ 85043-3801
Tel.: (602) 272-6806
Web Site: http://www.macarthurco.com
Rev.: $10,500,000
Emp.: 12
Building Materials Distr
N.A.I.C.S.: 423330
Chuck Crim *(Gen Mgr)*

Milwaukee Insulation Co., Inc. (1)
2126B Angie Ave Bldg 7, Green Bay, WI 54302-1271
Tel.: (920) 406-6090
Insulation Material Whslr
N.A.I.C.S.: 423330

Snavely Forest Products, Inc. (1)
600 Delwar Rd, Pittsburgh, PA 15236-1351 **(100%)**
Tel.: (412) 885-4000
Web Site: http://www.snavelyforest.com
Sales Range: $10-24.9 Million
Emp.: 180
Provider of Lumber & Plywood Distr
N.A.I.C.S.: 423310
Stephen V. Snavely *(Chm & CEO)*
John Stockhausen *(Pres)*
Susan Fitzsimmons *(VP)*
Alexis Joseph *(Dir-Mktg)*
Clark Spitzer *(Pres)*

Sunroom Concepts (1)
2540 YH Hanson Ave, Albert Lea, MN 56007-3419
Tel.: (507) 377-8100
Web Site: http://www.sunroomconcepts.com
Sales Range: $10-24.9 Million
Emp.: 20
Mfr of Sun Rooms
N.A.I.C.S.: 332311

MACAYO RESTAURANTS LLC
1480 E Bethny Home Rd Ste 130, Phoenix, AZ 85014
Tel.: (602) 264-1831
Web Site: http://www.macayo.com
Rev.: $31,000,000
Emp.: 110
Mexican Restaurant
N.A.I.C.S.: 722511
Randall Ling *(Dir-Catering)*

MACBEATH HARDWOOD COMPANY INC.
2150 Oakdale Ave, San Francisco, CA 94124
Tel.: (415) 647-0782 **CA**
Web Site: http://www.macbeath.com
Year Founded: 1954
Sales Range: $10-24.9 Million
Emp.: 112
Suppliers of Lumber Plywood & Millwork
N.A.I.C.S.: 423310
Joseph Cortese *(Chm)*
Carter Rothrock *(Pres & CEO)*

MACBER INC.
401 N E St, Anaheim, CA 92805-3338
Tel.: (714) 778-2461 **CA**
Year Founded: 1977
Rev.: $30,100,000
Emp.: 280
Grocery Stores
N.A.I.C.S.: 445110

William R. MacAloney (Pres)
Tammy Wilson (CFO)

Subsidiaries:

Jax Markets (1)
401 NE St, Anaheim, CA 92805-3338
Tel.: (714) 778-2461
Web Site: http://www.jaxmarkets.com
Sales Range: $10-24.9 Million
Emp.: 45
Grocery Stores
N.A.I.C.S.: 445110

MACC OF ILLINOIS INC.
2906 N Oak St, Urbana, IL 61802-7203
Tel.: (217) 355-9115
Year Founded: 1995
Sales Range: $25-49.9 Million
Emp.: 200
Provider of Heavy Highway & Street Construction Services
N.A.I.C.S.: 237310
Hugh Gallivan (Pres & CEO)
Scott Stromberg (CFO)

MACDONALD & OWEN VENEER & LUMBER CO., INC.
1900 Riley Rd, Sparta, WI 54656
Tel.: (608) 269-4417
Web Site:
http://www.hardwoodlumber.net
Year Founded: 1968
Sales Range: $25-49.9 Million
Emp.: 52
Lumber Product Whslr
N.A.I.C.S.: 423310
David Twite (Owner)

MACDONALD MEDIA
141 W 36th St 16th fl, New York, NY 10018
Tel.: (212) 578-8735
Web Site:
http://www.macdonaldmedia.com
Year Founded: 1997
Sales Range: $50-74.9 Million
Emp.: 25
Media Buying Services
N.A.I.C.S.: 541830
Andrea MacDonald (Pres & CEO)

Subsidiaries:

MacDonald Media/Los Angeles (1)
701 E 3rd St Ste 320, Los Angeles, CA 90013
Tel.: (213) 680-3094
Web Site: http://www.macdonaldmedia.com
Emp.: 5
Media Buying Services
N.A.I.C.S.: 541810

MACDONALD-MILLER FACILITY SOLUTIONS INC.
7717 Detroit Ave SW, Seattle, WA 98106
Tel.: (206) 763-9400
Web Site: http://www.macmiller.com
Rev.: $22,200,000
Emp.: 1,100
Electrical Contractor
N.A.I.C.S.: 238210
Mark Webster (VP-Construction)
Gus Simonds (Pres)
Stephanie Gebhardt (Treas & Sec)
Bradd Busick (CIO)

MACDOUGALL BIOMEDICAL COMMUNICATIONS, INC.
888 Worcester St Ste 370, Wellesley, MA 02482
Tel.: (781) 235-3060
Web Site:
http://www.macbiocom.com
Sales Range: $10-24.9 Million
Emp.: 12
Advetising Agency

N.A.I.C.S.: 541810
Douglas MacDougall (Pres)
Kari M.L. Watson (Sr VP)
Chris Erdman (Sr VP)
Sarah Cavanaugh (VP)
Jennifer Conrad (Sr Acct Exec)

MACELROYS INC.
3209 S Topeka Blvd, Topeka, KS 66611
Tel.: (785) 266-4870
Web Site: http://www.mcelroys.com
Sales Range: $10-24.9 Million
Emp.: 75
Mechanical Contractor
N.A.I.C.S.: 238210
Dan Bial (Pres)
Brad Hutton (VP)

MACEY'S, INC.
7850 S 1300 E, Sandy, UT 84094
Tel.: (801) 255-4888
Web Site: http://www.maceys.com
Year Founded: 1967
Sales Range: $125-149.9 Million
Emp.: 2,000
Grocery Stores
N.A.I.C.S.: 445110

MACFADDEN COMMUNICATIONS GROUP, LLC
333 7th Ave, New York, NY 10001
Tel.: (212) 979-4800
Web Site: http://www.macfad.com
Year Founded: 1900
Sales Range: $75-99.9 Million
Emp.: 50
Magazine & Website Publisher
N.A.I.C.S.: 513120
Peter J. Callahan (CEO)
Anna Blanco (Sr VP)
Michelle David (Chief Digital Officer)
Jerald J. Cerza Jr. (CFO)

Subsidiaries:

Dance Magazine (1)
333 7th Ave 11th Fl, New York, NY 10001
Tel.: (212) 979-4800
Web Site: http://www.dancemagazine.com
Sales Range: $10-24.9 Million
Emp.: 10
Magazine
N.A.I.C.S.: 513120
Brian McTigue (Dir-Circulation)
Raymond Mingst (Dir-Creative)
Madeline Schrock (Mng Editor)
Karen Hildebrand (Chief Content Officer)
Joanna Harp (Chief Revenue Officer & Publr)

MACFARLAND PICK & SAVE
5709 US Hwy 51, McFarland, WI 53558
Tel.: (608) 838-3604
Web Site:
http://www.pickandsave.com
Sales Range: $10-24.9 Million
Emp.: 700
Grocery Stores
N.A.I.C.S.: 445110

MACH1 GLOBAL SERVICES, INC.
1530 W Broadway Rd, Tempe, AZ 85282
Tel.: (480) 921-3900
Web Site:
http://www.mach1global.com
Year Founded: 1988
Sales Range: $75-99.9 Million
Emp.: 230
Logistics Consulting Servies
N.A.I.C.S.: 541614
Jamie Fletcher (CEO)
Rob Lively (COO)
Debbie Wilcox (VP-Fin)
Heriberto Salinas (Mgr-Mexico)

Austin Fisher (VP-Western Div)
Jared Licata (VP-Central Div)
Jennifer Fischer (VP-HR)
Joshua Klopatek (VP-Southern Region)
Justin M. Panasewicz (VP-Intl Ops)
Marva Washburn (VP-Trade Svcs)
Mike Harris (VP-Corp Ops)
Rick Batia (VP-Sls)

MACHADO/GARCIA-SERRA PUBLICIDAD, INC.
1790 Coral Way, Miami, FL 33145
Tel.: (305) 444-4647
Web Site: http://www.mgscomm.com
Year Founded: 2003
Rev.: $100,000,000
Emp.: 100
N.A.I.C.S.: 541810
Al Garcia-Serra (COO & Co-Chm)
Jorge Manach (Sr VP-Client Svcs)
Christina Alvarez (VP-Mktg & Res)
Yvonne Lorie (Sr VP)
Tony Suarez (Sr VP-Ops)
Jorge E. Reynardus (Chief Revenue Officer & Chief Strategy Officer)
Jorge R. Moya (Chief Creative Officer)
Manuel E. Machado (Co-Chm & CEO)
Keric Smotrilla (Chief Interactive Officer)
Brenda Novo (VP & Dir-Ops)
Harry Redlich (Exec Dir-Creative)
Fernando E. Bonet (Exec VP)
Andreea Redis-Coste (VP & Dir-Media)
Ashley Rowe (Assoc Dir-Buying)
Federico Mejer (Mng Dir)
Gisela Fabelo (VP-Fin)
Henry Alvarez (Dir-Creative)
Jorge Espinosa (Sr VP & Acct Grp Dir-Svcs)
Luis Mallo (Dir-Creative)
Manolo Zota (Dir-Creative)
Maria Romero (VP & Dir-Plng)
Maritere Llorente (VP & Dir-Acct Svcs Grp)
Michel Rivero (Dir-Creative)
Yocasta Shames (VP & Dir-Acct Svcs Grp)

Subsidiaries:

MGSCOMM - Mexico City (1)
Calle Mario Pani Lote 10 Piso 9, Col Santa Fe Del Cuajimalpa, CP 05348, Mexico, DF, Mexico
Tel.: (52) 55 5292 7133
Web Site: http://www.mgscomm.com
Emp.: 2
N.A.I.C.S.: 541810
Lorena Delgado (Mgr)

MGSCOMM - New York City (1)
817 Broadway 2nd Fl, New York, NY 10003
Tel.: (212) 204-8340
Emp.: 22
Advertising Specialties, Direct Marketing, Event Marketing, Hispanic Marketing, Media Buying Services, Public Relations, Strategic Planning
N.A.I.C.S.: 541810
Jorge E. Reynardus (Chief Strategy Officer & CRO)
Jorge R. Moya (Grp Chief Creative Officer)
Sofia Aguilar (VP & Exec Dir-Creative)
Federico Mejer (Mng Dir)

MACHIAS SAVINGS BANK
4 Center St, Machias, ME 04654
Tel.: (207) 255-3347
Web Site:
http://www.machiassavings.bank
Year Founded: 1869
Sales Range: $10-24.9 Million
Emp.: 200
Savings Bank
N.A.I.C.S.: 522180

Chris Fitzpatrick (Exec VP-Bus Banking)
Ronald Gardiner (Mgr-Calais)
Jill Golding (Branch Mgr)
Jessica Cloukey-Lincoln (Mgr-Bridgeport)
Ken White (VP & Branch Mgr)

MACHINE & WELDING SUPPLY COMPANY
1660 Hwy 301 S, Dunn, NC 28334
Tel.: (910) 892-4016
Web Site: http://www.mwsc.com
Year Founded: 1972
Sales Range: $25-49.9 Million
Emp.: 200
Sales & Distr of Industrial Machinery & Safety Equipment
N.A.I.C.S.: 423830
Jeff Johnson (VP-Sls & Mktg)
Tommy Stewart (VP-Ops)
Emmett C. Aldredge Jr. (Pres)

MACHINE MAINTENANCE, INC.
2300 Cassens Dr, Fenton, MO 63026
Tel.: (636) 343-9970
Web Site:
http://www.lubyequipment.com
Sales Range: $10-24.9 Million
Emp.: 45
General Construction Machinery & Equipment
N.A.I.C.S.: 423810
Tom Bognar (Mgr-Svc)
Brian Burwinkel (Mgr-Svc)
Bob Luby (Pres & CEO)
Tim Luby (Mgr-Mktg)
Tom Samuelson (Asst Controller)

Subsidiaries:

Potter Equipment Co (1)
302 Industrial Park Rd, Harrison, AR 72601
Tel.: (870) 741-8900
Web Site: http://www.potterequipment.com
Rev.: $5,705,000
Emp.: 7
Construction & Mining, except Oil Well, Machinery & Equipment Merchant Whslr
N.A.I.C.S.: 423810
Larry Rogers (Mgr-Svc)
Dave Crigler (Mgr-Parts)
Marvin Estes (Mgr-Parts)
Frank Jerome (Mgr-Store)
Joe Sisco (Mgr-Svc)
Clint Harmon (Mgr-Svc)

MACHINE SERVICE INC.
1000 Ashwaubenon St, Green Bay, WI 54304
Tel.: (920) 339-3000
Web Site:
http://www.machineservice.com
Rev.: $19,863,528
Emp.: 100
Truck Parts & Accessories
N.A.I.C.S.: 423120
Michael Anderson (Controller)
Jillane Exton (Supvr-Accts Payable)
Edward L. Fowles Jr. (Pres)

MACHINE TOOL TECHNOLOGIES INC.
3073 S Chase Ave, Milwaukee, WI 53207
Tel.: (847) 301-9555
Web Site: http://www.mac-tech.com
Year Founded: 2006
Rev.: $13,200,000
Emp.: 30
Industrial Machinery & Equipment Merchant Whslr
N.A.I.C.S.: 423830
Mike Ryan (Pres)
Michael C. Ryan (Pres & Treas)
Alan R. Gildemeister (Chm & CEO)

MACHINERY SALES CO.

Machinery Sales Co.—(Continued)
MACHINERY SALES CO.
17253 Chestnut St, City of Industry, CA 91748-2314
Tel.: (626) 581-9211
Web Site: http://www.mchysales.com
Year Founded: 1938
Sales Range: $10-24.9 Million
Emp.: 20
Provider of Metal Cutting Machinery
N.A.I.C.S.: 423830
Gary Smith (Chm)
Robert Medical (Controller)
Garry Frost (Pres)

MACHINERY SYSTEMS INC.
614 E State Pkwy, Schaumburg, IL 60173-4533
Tel.: (847) 882-8085
Web Site: http://www.machsys.com
Year Founded: 1977
Sales Range: $10-24.9 Million
Emp.: 50
Industrial Machinery & Equipment
N.A.I.C.S.: 423830
Mike Cekanor (Sr VP)
Tim Cirone (Engr-Sls)
Eric Hilliard (Pres)
Gary Dickinson (Engr-Sls)

Subsidiaries:

Machinery Tooling & Supply LLC (1)
614 E State Pkwy, Schaumburg, IL 60173
Tel.: (847) 310-8665
Web Site: http://www.mt-s.com
Sales Range: $10-24.9 Million
Industrial Machinery & Equipment
N.A.I.C.S.: 423830
Robert Cuthbertson (Pres)

MACHINETOOLS.COM
5720 W Maple Rd, West Bloomfield, MI 48322
Tel.: (630) 405-5934
Web Site: http://www.machinetools.com
Year Founded: 1999
Rev.: $2,500,000
Emp.: 15
Business Products & Mfr
N.A.I.C.S.: 561439
Stuart Carlin (Founder & CEO)

MACHINING TIME SAVERS INC.
1338 S State College Pkwy, Anaheim, CA 92806
Tel.: (714) 635-7373
Web Site: http://www.mtscnc.com
Year Founded: 1988
Sales Range: $25-49.9 Million
Emp.: 50
Mfr & Service of Tools
N.A.I.C.S.: 423830
Don Martin (Pres)
Gary Sladek (VP)
Arjen Sakes (Mgr-Mktg)
Maria Magallon (Office Mgr)

MACHINISTS INCORPORATED
PO Box 80505, Seattle, WA 98108-0505
Tel.: (206) 763-0990
Web Site: http://www.machinistsinc.com
Sales Range: $10-24.9 Million
Emp.: 250
Machine & Other Job Shop Work
N.A.I.C.S.: 332710
Hugh Labossier (Pres)
Webb Tougan (CFO)
Jeff Thompson (Mgr-Sls & Mktg)

MACINTOSH LINEN & UNIFORM RENTAL
2255 City Line Rd, Bethlehem, PA 18017
Tel.: (610) 867-6773
Web Site: http://www.macintosh-services.com
Year Founded: 1919
Sales Range: $10-24.9 Million
Emp.: 220
Uniform Suppliers
N.A.I.C.S.: 812331
Jody Waller (Mgr-Territory)
James J. Rodgers Sr. (Pres & CEO)

MACK BORING & PARTS CO.
2365 Rte 22 W, Union, NJ 07083
Tel.: (908) 964-0700
Web Site: http://www.mackboring.com
Rev.: $43,000,000
Emp.: 80
Engines & Parts, Diesel
N.A.I.C.S.: 423830
Steve McGovern (Pres)
Al Young (Mgr-Bus Dev)

MACK ENERGY CORPORATION
11344 Lovington Hwy, Artesia, NM 88210
Tel.: (575) 748-1288
Web Site: http://www.mec.com
Sales Range: $25-49.9 Million
Emp.: 900
Crude Petroleum & Natural Gas
N.A.I.C.S.: 211120
Brad Bartek (CFO)
Mack Chase (Pres)
Robert Chase (Exec VP)
Tom H. McCasland III (Pres)

Subsidiaries:

Arrowhead Pipe & Supply Co (1)
11352 Lovington Hwy, Artesia, NM 88210
Tel.: (505) 748-1288
Rev.: $10,000,000
Emp.: 5
Crude Petroleum & Natural Gas
N.A.I.C.S.: 211120

MACK GROUP INC.
608 Warm Brook Rd, Arlington, VT 05250
Tel.: (802) 375-2511
Web Site: http://www.mack.com
Year Founded: 1920
Sales Range: $50-74.9 Million
Emp.: 1,400
Plastics Product Mfr
N.A.I.C.S.: 326199
Donald S. Kendall (Co-Pres & CEO)
Jeff Somple (Pres-Northern Ops)

MACK HARVEY SALES & SERVICE
29 E Commons Blvd Ste 300, New Castle, DE 19720
Tel.: (302) 324-8340
Web Site: http://www.harveytruckcenter.com
Rev.: $10,900,000
Emp.: 60
Trailers For Trucks
N.A.I.C.S.: 423110
Edgar Thomas Harvey III (Pres)

MACK HILS, INC.
544 North Ave, Moberly, MO 65270
Tel.: (660) 263-7444
Web Site: http://www.mackhils.com
Year Founded: 1973
Sales Range: $10-24.9 Million
Emp.: 105
Custom Metal Product Fabrication & Machining Services
N.A.I.C.S.: 332999
Mike Bowlby (COO)
Roger L. Payne (Pres)

MACK INDUSTRIES INC.
201 Columbia Rd, Valley City, OH 44280
Tel.: (330) 483-3111
Web Site: http://www.mackconcrete.com
Year Founded: 1932
Rev.: $15,700,000
Emp.: 70
Burial Vaults Mfr
N.A.I.C.S.: 327390
Betsy Mack Nespeca (Pres)

MACK MCBRIDE SALES INC.
Hwy 13 E, Carbondale, IL 62901
Tel.: (618) 457-4642
Web Site: http://www.mcbridemack.com
Sales Range: $10-24.9 Million
Emp.: 19
Commercial Trucks
N.A.I.C.S.: 423110
Kelly Sanders (Mgr-Mktg)

MACK MOLDING COMPANY INC.
608 Warm Brook Rd, Arlington, VT 05250
Tel.: (802) 375-2511
Web Site: http://www.mack.com
Year Founded: 1920
Sales Range: $150-199.9 Million
Emp.: 900
Custom Molded Plastics Mfr
N.A.I.C.S.: 326199
Will Kendall (Pres & CEO)
Denis Poirier (CFO)
Mat Degan (Treas & Sec)

Subsidiaries:

Synectic Engineering, Inc. (1)
60 Commerce Park, Milford, CT 06460
Tel.: (203) 877-8488
Web Site: http://www.synectic.net
Sales Range: $10-24.9 Million
Emp.: 10
Medical Device Product Mfr
N.A.I.C.S.: 339112
Adam Lehman (Pres)

MACK OIL CO. INC.
45 Branch Ave PO Box 557, Berwyn, PA 19312
Tel.: (610) 644-0562
Web Site: http://www.mackservicesgroup.com
Year Founded: 1931
Sales Range: $10-24.9 Million
Emp.: 25
Dealers of Fuel Oil
N.A.I.C.S.: 457210
Dave McCorry (Pres)
Scott McCorry (VP)

MACK OPERATIONS LLC
1616 S 31st Ave, Phoenix, AZ 85009
Tel.: (602) 237-0292
Industrial Services
N.A.I.C.S.: 238990
Chris Mihaletos (Pres)

Subsidiaries:

Arizona Industrial & Municipal Services LLC (1)
1616 S 31st Ave, Phoenix, AZ 85009
Tel.: (602) 237-0292
Web Site: http://www.azindustrialcleaning.com
Sales Range: $1-9.9 Million
Emp.: 30
Industrial Cleaning Services
N.A.I.C.S.: 238990
James Quinn (VP)
Chris Mihaletos (Pres)

CleanServe, Inc. (1)
3808 Knapp Rd, Pearland, TX 77581
Tel.: (281) 485-8816
Web Site: http://www.cleanserveinc.com

U.S. PRIVATE

Sales Range: $1-9.9 Million
Emp.: 50
Pipe Cleaning & Inspection Services
N.A.I.C.S.: 238990

Pipeline Video Inspections & Cleaning LLC (1)
1616 S 31st Ave, Phoenix, AZ 85009
Tel.: (602) 237-0292
Web Site: http://www.pvicaz.com
Sales Range: $1-9.9 Million
Emp.: 10
Pipe Inspection & Maintenance Services
N.A.I.C.S.: 238990
Maria Mihaletos (CEO)

MACKAY & SPOSITO, INC.
1325 SE Tech Ctr Dr Ste 140, Vancouver, WA 98683
Tel.: (360) 695-3411
Web Site: http://www.mackaysposito.com
Year Founded: 1974
Sales Range: $10-24.9 Million
Emp.: 98
Civil Engineering Services
N.A.I.C.S.: 541330
Tim Schauer (Pres & CEO)
Derrick Smith (Sr VP)
Lisa Schauer (COO & Sr VP)
Damon Webster (Principal)
Rob Palena (VP-Construction Mgmt)

MACKAY COMMUNICATIONS, INC.
3691 Trust Dr, Raleigh, NC 27616-2955
Tel.: (919) 850-3000
Web Site: http://www.mackaycomm.com
Year Founded: 1987
Sales Range: $25-49.9 Million
Emp.: 110
Marine Telecommunication Services
N.A.I.C.S.: 423860
Ben Pratt (Co-Pres)
Jeff Schlacks (Co-Pres)
David Eckstein (Controller)
Sue Ellen Rosen (Mgr-Mktg)

MACKAYMITCHELL ENVELOPE COMPANY
2100 Elm St SE, Minneapolis, MN 55414-2597
Tel.: (612) 331-9311
Web Site: http://www.mackaymitchell.com
Year Founded: 1959
Sales Range: $25-49.9 Million
Emp.: 400
Envelope Mfr
N.A.I.C.S.: 322230
Harvey B. Mackay (Chm)
Scott Mitchell (CEO)

Subsidiaries:

MackayMitchell Envelope Company - Iowa Manufacturing Facility (1)
1500 Mackay Ave, Mount Pleasant, IA 52641
Tel.: (319) 385-9061
Envelope Mfr
N.A.I.C.S.: 322230

MACKENZIE CAPITAL MANAGEMENT, LP
89 Davis Rd Ste 100, Orinda, CA 94563
Tel.: (925) 631-9100
Web Site: http://www.mackenziecapital.com
Year Founded: 1982
Real Estate Investment Management Services
N.A.I.C.S.: 531390
Berniece Patterson (Co-Founder)
Glen W. Fuller (Mng Dir & COO)

Robert E. Dixon *(Mng Dir & Chief Investment Officer)*
Paul F. Koslosky *(CFO)*
Brooke Buckley *(Sr VP-Capital Markets)*
Charles Patterson *(Owner, Mng Dir & Gen Counsel)*

Subsidiaries:

MCM Advisers, LP (1)
1640 School St, Moraga, CA 94556
Tel.: (925) 631-9100
Emp.: 30
Real Estate Investment Advisory Services
N.A.I.C.S.: 523940
C. E. Patterson *(Chm)*

MACKENZIE GROUP INC.
72 Reade St, New York, NY 10007
Tel.: (212) 227-1630
Web Site: http://www.mackenzie-group.com
Sales Range: $75-99.9 Million
Emp.: 125
Window & Door Installation
N.A.I.C.S.: 238130
Scott MacKenzie *(VP)*
Roger Soucek *(Pres)*

MACKENZIE MOTOR CO.
4151 SE Tualatin Vly Hwy, Hillsboro, OR 97123
Tel.: (503) 640-6500   OR
Web Site: http://www.mackenzieford.com
New & Used Car Dealers
N.A.I.C.S.: 441110
John Gillis *(Mgr-Parts)*
Ryan Lawson *(Gen Sls Mgr)*
Ron Trask *(Sls Mgr)*
Pat Hampson *(Sls Mgr)*
Darwin Vietzke *(Bus Mgr)*
Eric Owens *(Bus Mgr)*
Mandi DeHaven *(Mgr-Internet)*
Josh Wojahn *(Dir-Svc)*

MACKEY BANCO, INC.
624 Main St, Ansley, NE 68814
Tel.: (308) 935-1700   NE
Year Founded: 1995
Sales Range: $1-9.9 Million
Bank Holding Company
N.A.I.C.S.: 551111
William E. Brush *(Pres & CEO)*

Subsidiaries:

Security State Bank (1)
624 Main St, Ansley, NE 68814
Tel.: (308) 935-1700
Web Site: http://www.ssbnebraska.com
Sales Range: $1-9.9 Million
Commericial Banking
N.A.I.C.S.: 522110
William E. Brush *(Pres & CEO)*

Branch (Domestic):

Dundee Bank (2)
5015 Underwood Ave, Omaha, NE 68132-2206
Tel.: (402) 250-4000
Web Site: http://www.dundeebanking.com
Commericial Banking
N.A.I.C.S.: 522110
Jeffrey C. Royal *(Pres)*

MACKIN EDUCATIONAL RESOURCES
3505 County Rd 42 W, Burnsville, MN 55306
Tel.: (952) 895-9540
Web Site: http://www.mackin.com
Year Founded: 1983
Sales Range: $25-49.9 Million
Emp.: 400
School & Library Media Products Mfr
N.A.I.C.S.: 611710
Kitty Heise *(Co-Owner)*
Randal Heise *(Co-Owner)*

MACKIN TECHNOLOGIES
1 Centerpointe Dr Ste 430, La Palma, CA 90623-1077
Tel.: (714) 523-4998
Web Site: http://www.mackinusa.com
Sales Range: $10-24.9 Million
Emp.: 5
Fiber Optic Cable Mfr
N.A.I.C.S.: 335921
Hiroshi Kobayashi *(Chm)*

MACKINAC ISLAND REALTY, INC.
Historic Market St, Mackinac Island, MI 49757
Tel.: (906) 847-6483
Web Site: http://www.mackinacislandrealty.com
Year Founded: 1985
Sales Range: $10-24.9 Million
Emp.: 9
Real Estate Agent & Brokerage Services
N.A.I.C.S.: 531210
Bill Borst *(Owner)*

MACKLOWE PROPERTIES, L.L.C.
GM Bldg 767 5th Ave, New York, NY 10153
Tel.: (212) 265-5900   NY
Web Site: https://macklowproperties.com
Year Founded: 1996
Sales Range: $1-9.9 Million
Emp.: 51
Commercial & Residential Building Acquirer, Developer, Owner & Property Manager
N.A.I.C.S.: 531390
Harry Macklowe *(CEO)*
Richard Wallgren *(Exec VP-Sls & Mktg)*
Mary Leprohon *(CFO)*

Subsidiaries:

Macklowe Management Co., Inc. (1)
767 5th Ave 21st Fl, New York, NY 10153
Tel.: (212) 265-5900
Holding Company; Commercial & Residential Property Management Services
N.A.I.C.S.: 551112

Subsidiary (Domestic):

Macklowe Management, LLC (2)
767 5th Ave 21st Fl, New York, NY 10153
Tel.: (212) 207-0200
Commercial & Residential Property Management Services
N.A.I.C.S.: 531312

MACKOUL DISTRIBUTORS INC.
3425 N Main St, Jacksonville, FL 32206-2130
Tel.: (904) 355-2721   FL
Web Site: http://www.mackoulfoods.com
Year Founded: 1957
Sales Range: $10-24.9 Million
Emp.: 40
Tobacco & Tobacco Products Mfr & Distr
N.A.I.C.S.: 424940
Jerome R. MacKoul *(Pres)*
Ron MacKoul *(Pres)*

MACLEAN-FOGG CO.
5600 Wilson Rd, Richmond, IL 60071
Tel.: (847) 566-0010
Web Site: http://www.macleanfoggcs.com
Year Founded: 1925
Emp.: 2,000
Bolt, Nut, Screw, Rivet & Washer Mfr
N.A.I.C.S.: 332722

Subsidiaries:

Mallard Manufacturing Corp. (1)
101 Mallard Road, Sterling, IL 61081
Tel.: (815) 625-9491
Web Site: http://www.mallardmfg.com
Rev.: $2,333,333
Emp.: 20
Conveyor & Conveying Equipment Mfr
N.A.I.C.S.: 333922
Diane Kennington *(Mgr-Accts-Natl)*
Michael Gunderson *(VP)*
Scott Garriott *(Mgr-Engrg)*
Kevin Risch *(Pres)*

MACLEAN-FOGG COMPANY
1000 Allanson Rd, Mundelein, IL 60060-3890
Tel.: (847) 566-0010   DE
Web Site: http://www.macleanfoggcs.com
Year Founded: 1925
Sales Range: $1-4.9 Billion
Emp.: 4,000
Holding Company; Automotive, Aerospace & Industrial Component Mfr & Whslr
N.A.I.C.S.: 551112
Barry L. MacLean *(Chm)*
Michael Isaacs *(CFO & Exec VP)*

Subsidiaries:

MacLean-Fogg Component Solutions, LLC (1)
1000 Allanson Rd, Mundelein, IL 60060-3890
Tel.: (847) 566-0010
Web Site: http://www.macleanfoggcs.com
Emp.: 200
Holding Company; Fasteners, Engineered Components, Linkage & Suspension Components Mfr & Whslr
N.A.I.C.S.: 551112
Duncan MacLean *(Pres)*
Christopher Martens *(Gen Mgr)*

Subsidiary (Domestic):

Engineered Plastics Company, LLC (2)
W142 N9078 Fountain Blvd, Menomonee Falls, WI 53051
Tel.: (262) 251-9500
Web Site: http://www.macleanfoggcs.com
Engineered Plastic Components Mfr & Whslr
N.A.I.C.S.: 326199
Robert Whitney *(Pres)*

MacLean Curtis, LLC (2)
50 Thielman Dr, Buffalo, NY 14206
Tel.: (716) 898-7800
Web Site: http://www.macleanfoggcs.com
Automotive Steering System & Transmission Components Mfr & Whslr
N.A.I.C.S.: 332721
James R. Frost *(Gen Mgr-Ops-Buffalo)*
Michelle Barber *(Mgr-HR)*
Marty J. Nuara *(Mgr-Supply Chain)*
Greg J. Blaszak *(Mgr-Quality)*

Plant (Domestic):

MacLean Curtis, LLC - Cornelius Plant (3)
20401 N Zion St, Cornelius, NC 28031-8549
Tel.: (704) 892-5503
Web Site: http://www.macleanfoggcs.com
Automotive Steering System & Transmission Components Mfr & Whslr
N.A.I.C.S.: 332721
John O'Neill *(Gen Mgr)*

Subsidiary (Domestic):

MacLean Maynard LLC (2)
50855 E Russell Schmidt Blvd, Chesterfield, MI 48051
Tel.: (248) 853-2525
Fastener Mfr
N.A.I.C.S.: 339993

Maclean Fasteners, LLC (2)
1000 Allanson Rd, Mundelein, IL 60060
Tel.: (847) 566-0010
Web Site: http://www.macleanfoggcs.com
Emp.: 250
Fastener Whslr
N.A.I.C.S.: 423710

Master Automatic Machine Company, Inc. (2)
40485 Schoolcraft Rd, Plymouth, MI 48170
Tel.: (734) 414-0500
Web Site: http://www.masterautomatic.com
Screw Machine Products
N.A.I.C.S.: 332721
James Ward *(VP)*
Mark Evasic *(Pres)*
John D. Evasic Jr. *(Chm)*

Metform, LLC (2)
7034 Rte 84 S, Savanna, IL 61074
Tel.: (815) 273-2201
Web Site: http://www.macleanfoggcs.com
Sales Range: $50-74.9 Million
Emp.: 300
Iron & Steel Forgings
N.A.I.C.S.: 332111
Dan Cavanagh *(Pres)*

Maclean Investment Partners, LLC (1)
1000 Allanson Rd, Mundelein, IL 60060
Tel.: (847) 566-0010
Web Site: http://www.macleanfogg.com
Investment Holding Company
N.A.I.C.S.: 551112
Barry MacLean *(Pres & CEO)*

Holding (Domestic):

Janco Engineered Products, LLC (2)
1217 E 7 St, Mishawaka, IN 46544-4883
Tel.: (574) 255-3169
Web Site: http://www.jancoengineeredproducts.com
Emp.: 100
Filament Mfr
N.A.I.C.S.: 325220
Peter Giczewski *(Pres)*
Sandra Wright *(Mgr-Pur)*

Reynolds Cycling, LLC (2)
9091 Sandy Pkwy, Sandy, UT 84070
Tel.: (801) 565-8003
Web Site: http://www.reynoldscycling.com
Emp.: 20
Bicycle Parts Mfr
N.A.I.C.S.: 336991
Heather Elliott *(Mgr-Customer Svc)*
Wayne Bradshaw *(Mgr-Matls)*
Tom Gosselin *(Mgr-Domestic Sls)*
Alexander Mai *(Mgr-Sls & Mktg-EMEA)*
Mike Dufner *(CFO)*
Travis Erwin *(Dir-Global Sls-Maastricht)*
Scott Montgomery *(CEO)*

Tramec LLC (2)
30 Davis St, Iola, KS 66749
Web Site: http://www.tramec.com
Truck Trailer Mfr
N.A.I.C.S.: 336212

Subsidiary (Domestic):

Tramec Continental-Aero, LLC (3)
5619 W 115th St, Alsip, IL 60803
Tel.: (708) 377-0360
Web Site: http://www.continental-aero.com
Emp.: 40
Paper Distribution
N.A.I.C.S.: 322211
Bill Giddens *(VP)*
Marty Schneider *(Pres)*

Tramec Hill Fastener, LLC (3)
1602 Mcneil Rd, Rock Falls, IL 61071
Tel.: (815) 625-6600
Web Site: http://www.hillfastener.com
Screw Mfr
N.A.I.C.S.: 332722

Tramec Sloan, LLC (3)
534 E 48th St, Holland, MI 49423
Web Site: http://www.tramecsloan.com
Emp.: 70
Electrical & Air Brake Component Mfr
N.A.I.C.S.: 336340
Mark Holm *(Pres)*

Unit (Domestic):

Kansas Plastics Company Inc. (4)
32 Clark Ave, Wellington, KS 67152   (100%)
Tel.: (620) 326-5007

MACLEAN-FOGG COMPANY — U.S. PRIVATE

MacLean-Fogg Company—(Continued)
Web Site: http://www.kansasplastics.com
Injection Molded Component Mfr & Supplier
N.A.I.C.S.: 333511
Richard Bloomer (VP-Ops)

MACLELLAN INTEGRATED SERVICES
3120 Wall St Ste 100, Lexington, KY 40513-1833
Tel.: (859) 219-5400
Web Site:
  http://www.maclellanlive.com
Rev.: $19,500,000
Emp.: 13
Critical Industrial Process & Facility Cleaning, Process Equipment & Robotics Maintenance, Plant & Building Facilities Management, Line Side Production Support
N.A.I.C.S.: 561720
Jeffrey K. Betzoldt (Pres)
David Bacon (Dir-Ops)
Kim Christner (Mgr-Sls & Mktg)
Alan Lyndon (Mgr-Bus Dev & Proposals)

MACLEOD CONSTRUCTION INC.
4879 N Hwy 16, Denver, NC 28037
Tel.: (704) 483-3580
Web Site:
  http://www.macleodconstruction.com
Sales Range: $1-9.9 Million
Emp.: 19
Concrete Grading
N.A.I.C.S.: 237310
Robert Macleod (Pres)
Lorne Macleod (Exec VP)
Steve Weisbecker (Project Mgr)
Sue Werth (Office Mgr)

MACMILLAN COMPANY INC.
17 Elm St, Keene, NH 03431
Tel.: (603) 352-3070
Web Site: http://www.macmillin.com
Year Founded: 1946
Sales Range: $50-74.9 Million
Emp.: 35
Provider of Commercial & Office Building, New Construction
N.A.I.C.S.: 236220
Gregory L. Domingue (Dir-Safety)

MACNEILL GROUP, INC.
1300 Sawgrass Corporate Ctr Ste 300, Sunrise, FL 33323-2804
Tel.: (954) 331-4800
Web Site:
  http://www.macneillgroup.com
Year Founded: 1946
Sales Range: $100-124.9 Million
Emp.: 250
Insurance Broker Services
N.A.I.C.S.: 541611
Kevin M. Tromer (Pres & CEO)
Laura Decespedes (Sr VP-HR)

MACOMB PIPE & SUPPLY CO. INC.
6600 15 Mile Rd, Sterling Heights, MI 48312
Tel.: (586) 274-4100
Web Site:
  http://www.macombgroup.com
Sales Range: $10-24.9 Million
Emp.: 500
Valves & Fittings
N.A.I.C.S.: 423830
Keith Schatko (VP-Sls)
William McGivern Jr. (Pres)

MACOMB-OAKLAND REGIONAL CENTER
16200 19 Mile Rd, Clinton Township, MI 48038-0070
Tel.: (586) 263-8700
Web Site: http://www.morcinc.org
Year Founded: 1996
Sales Range: $150-199.9 Million
Emp.: 302
Disability Assistance Services
N.A.I.C.S.: 624120
Dennis Bott (COO)
Peter Lynch (Chief HR Officer)
Dan Manzardo (CIO)
Robert Lechy (Dir-Medical)

MACON BIBB COUNTY ECONOMIC OPPORTUNITY COUNCIL, INC.
1680 Broadway Ste B, Macon, GA 31201
Tel.: (478) 738-3240
Web Site:
  http://www.maconbibbeoc.com
Year Founded: 1965
Sales Range: $10-24.9 Million
Emp.: 325
Economic Development Services
N.A.I.C.S.: 541720
Miller Fluellen (Dir-Special Projects)
Karen Collier (Fin Dir)
Sarita R. Hill (Exec Dir)

MACON CIGAR & TOBACCO CO.
575 12th St, Macon, GA 31201
Tel.: (478) 743-2236
Web Site: http://www.mctweb.com
Sales Range: $75-99.9 Million
Emp.: 55
Tobacco & Tobacco Products
N.A.I.C.S.: 424940
Thomas Alfred Sams Jr. (Pres)

MACON WATER AUTHORITY
790 2nd St, Macon, GA 31202-0108
Tel.: (478) 464-5600
Web Site: http://www.maconwater.org
Year Founded: 1976
Sales Range: $25-49.9 Million
Emp.: 184
Water Supply
N.A.I.C.S.: 221310
Frank Amerson (Chm)
Tony Rojas (Pres)
Gary McCoy (Dir-Water Ops)
Arleen Samuels (Mgr-Acctg & Pur)
Mark Wyzalek (Dir-Laboratory)
Kirk Nylund (Dir-Customer Care & Field Svc)
Ray Shell (Dir-Ops)
Frank Patterson (Vice Chm)
Sam Hart (Chm)

MACPHERSON WESTERN TOOL & SUPPLY CO. INC.
203 D Lawrence Dr, Livermore, CA 94551-0251
Tel.: (925) 443-8665
Web Site: http://www.westtool.com
Year Founded: 1986
Sales Range: $25-49.9 Million
Emp.: 100
Machine Shop for Cutting Tools
N.A.I.C.S.: 444140
Jerry L. Gerardot (Pres)
Ken Schuman (Dir-Mktg)

Subsidiaries:

Macpherson Western Tool & Supply Co. Inc. - Tool & Gage Associates Division (1)
4252 SE International Way Ste B, Portland, OR 97222-8822
Tel.: (503) 257-3321
Web Site:
  http://www.toolandgageassoc.com
Emp.: 4

Industrial Supplies Whslr
N.A.I.C.S.: 423840
Jerry Geredot (Pres)

MACQUARIUM INTELLIGENT COMMUNICATIONS
1800 Peachtree St NW Ste 250, Atlanta, GA 30309
Tel.: (404) 554-4000
Web Site:
  http://www.macquarium.com
Year Founded: 1992
Emp.: 120
Marketing Consulting Services
N.A.I.C.S.: 541810
Marc F. Adler (Founder & Chm)
Peter Forsstrom (COO)
Art Hopkins (Pres)
Marc Adler (Chm)
John Cataldi (Dir-Bus Dev-Americas & Europe)

MACRO ENERGY
The Peterman Bldg 105 Montgomery Ave, Montgomeryville, PA 18936
Tel.: (215) 997-0531
Web Site: http://www.macro-energy.com
Year Founded: 2008
Sales Range: $1-9.9 Million
Emp.: 8
Lighting Design Services
N.A.I.C.S.: 541490
Steve Herchenrider (Dir-Ops)

MACRO OIL COMPANY INC.
101 Millstone Rd, Broussard, LA 70518
Tel.: (337) 839-5000
Web Site: http://www.macrooil.com
Year Founded: 1929
Sales Range: $25-49.9 Million
Emp.: 200
Petroleum Products Supplier
N.A.I.C.S.: 424720
Mildred R. McElligott (Pres)
Bill McElligott (VP)
Richard McElligott (CEO)

MACRO-Z-TECHNOLOGY COMPANY
841 E Washington Ave, Santa Ana, CA 92701
Tel.: (714) 564-1130
Web Site: http://www.mztco.com
Rev.: $19,900,000
Emp.: 97
Concrete Construction: Roads, Highways & Sidewalks
N.A.I.C.S.: 237310
Simon Hallsworth (Mgr-Construction)

MACROBRIGHT LLC
2818 Cypress Ridge Blvd Ste 110, Wesley Chapel, FL 33544
Tel.: (813) 333-7026
Web Site: http://www.mb2x.com
Sales Range: $1-9.9 Million
Software Developer
N.A.I.C.S.: 513210
Ana Abraham (Co-Founder & CEO)
Steve Abraham (Co-Founder)

MACROMARKETS LLC
14 Main St, Madison, NJ 07940
Tel.: (973) 889-1973
Sales Range: $25-49.9 Million
Emp.: 10
Investment Services
N.A.I.C.S.: 523150
Samuel Masucci III (Co-Founder, Pres & CEO)
John Flanagan (CFO)
Larry Larkin (Mng Dir)
Terry Loebs (Mng Dir)

Robert Shiller (Co-Founder & Chief Economist)
Robert Tull (Mng Dir)

Subsidiaries:

MacroShares Housing Depositor, LLC (1)
14 Main St, Madison, NJ 07940
Tel.: (973) 889-1973
Sales Range: $75-99.9 Million
Emp.: 6
Investment Services
N.A.I.C.S.: 523999

MACS MINIT MART
Hwy 17 S, Vernon, AL 35592
Tel.: (205) 695-9765
Rev.: $10,265,054
Emp.: 15
Convenience Store
N.A.I.C.S.: 445131
Lanita Mayers (Pres)
Daphne Barnes (Mgr)

MACTUS GROUP
4034 148th Ave NE Ste K1C1, Redmond, WA 98052
Tel.: (425) 883-3640
Web Site:
  http://www.mactusgroup.com
Year Founded: 2007
Sales Range: $1-9.9 Million
Emp.: 50
Business Management Consulting Services
N.A.I.C.S.: 541611
Carol Spires (Office Mgr)
Gigi Burton (Acct Dir)

MAD ANTHONY'S INCORPORATED
10502 NE 37th Cir Bldg 8, Kirkland, WA 98033-3732
Tel.: (425) 455-0732
Web Site: http://www.anthonys.com
Year Founded: 1969
Sales Range: $50-74.9 Million
Emp.: 1,500
Provider of Restaurant Services
N.A.I.C.S.: 722511
Lane Hoss (VP-Mktg)
Ray Caldwell (CFO)
Herbert M. Gould III (Pres)

MAD BY DESIGN LLC
1754 W Division St, Chicago, IL 60622
Tel.: (301) 895-4792
Web Site: http://www.mad-bags.com
Year Founded: 2004
Sales Range: $1-9.9 Million
Emp.: 12
Women's Handbags
N.A.I.C.S.: 316990
Marta Stein (Co-Owner)
Doug Stein (Co-Owner)

MAD CATZ INTERACTIVE INC.
10680 Treena St Ste 500, San Diego, CA 92131
Tel.: (858) 790-5008
Web Site: http://www.madcatz.com
Year Founded: 1989
Sales Range: $125-149.9 Million
Emp.: 151
Controllers & Accessories for Video Game Consoles & Personal Computers Mfr, Distr & Marketer
N.A.I.C.S.: 334118
Brian Andersen (COO)
Andrew Brian Young (CTO)
David McKeon (CFO)
Tyson Marshall (Gen Counsel & Sec)

Subsidiaries:

Mad Catz Europe Limited (1)
Wales 1 Business Park Building 102, New-

port Road Magor, Cardiff, NP26 3DG, United Kingdom
Tel.: (44) 1633883110
Web Site: http://www.saitek.com
Sales Range: $25-49.9 Million
Emp.: 30
Computer Keyboard, Game Controller & Other Peripheral Mfr
N.A.I.C.S.: 334118
Andreas Young (Gen Mgr)

Subsidiary (Non-US):

Mad Catz GmbH (2)
Landsberger Strasse 400, 81241, Munich, Germany
Tel.: (49) 895467570
Sales Range: $125-149.9 Million
Emp.: 20
Computer Keyboard, Game Controller & Other Peripheral Mfr
N.A.I.C.S.: 334118
Martin Eberle (Mng Dir)
Michael Alber (Dir-Sls)

Mad Catz SAS (2)
21 Rue d'Hauteville Bte B, 75010, Paris, France
Tel.: (33) 155331360
Computer Keyboard, Game Controller & Other Peripheral Mfr
N.A.I.C.S.: 334118

Mad Catz Interactive Asia Limited (1)
Unit 05-08 20F Miramar Tower 132 Nathan Road, Tsim Sha Tsui, Kowloon, China (Hong Kong)
Tel.: (852) 27289988
Web Site: http://www.madcatz.com
Emp.: 34
Video Game Controllers & Accessory Mfr
N.A.I.C.S.: 334118
Arto Makela (Gen Mgr)

Mad Catz, Inc. (1)
7480 Mission Vly Rd Ste 101, San Diego, CA 92108
Tel.: (619) 683-9830
Web Site: http://www.madcatz.com
Sales Range: $10-24.9 Million
Emp.: 60
Software Producer
N.A.I.C.S.: 334610
Brian Andersen (COO)

MAD DOG DESIGN & CONSTRUCTION CO., INC.
1203 Miccosukee Rd, Tallahassee, FL 32308
Tel.: (850) 878-8272 FL
Web Site: http://www.maddogweb.com
Year Founded: 1973
Sales Range: $1-9.9 Million
Emp.: 14
Nonresidential Construction
N.A.I.C.S.: 236220
Kelly Dozier (Chief Community Officer & Sr VP)
Laurie Dozier (Pres)
Curtis Whigham (VP & Sr Project Mgr)
Shawn Roberts (COO)
Mike Daughtry (VP-Field Ops)
Scott Rowse (Project Mgr)

MAD MOBILE, INC.
2701 N Rocky Point Dr Ste 500, Tampa, FL 33607
Tel.: (813) 400-2000
Web Site: http://www.madmobile.com
Sales Range: $1-9.9 Million
Emp.: 45
Mobile Developer & Marketing Services
N.A.I.C.S.: 541519
Bruce Bennett (CEO)
Steven Grant (CFO)
Thomas Lichtwerch (VP-Sls)
Emily Laux (VP-Client Svcs)
Doug Iverson (Chief Revenue Officer)

Kim Porter (VP-Digital Innovation & User Experience)
Jason Carney (VP-Tech Ops)
Patrick Walsh (Sr VP-Sls & Ops)

MADA MEDICAL PRODUCTS INC.
625 Washington Ave, Carlstadt, NJ 07072
Tel.: (201) 460-0454 NJ
Web Site: http://www.madamedical.com
Year Founded: 1969
Sales Range: $10-24.9 Million
Emp.: 25
Distr of Medical & Dental Equipment & Supplies
N.A.I.C.S.: 423450
Jeffrey Adam (Pres)
Robert Chasmar (CFO)
Rob Sorbello (VP-Sls & Mktg)

MADDEN COMMUNICATIONS, INC.
901 Mittel Dr, Wood Dale, IL 60191
Tel.: (630) 787-2200
Web Site: http://www.madden.com
Year Founded: 1957
Sales Range: $150-199.9 Million
Store Fixtures & Display Equipment Mfr
N.A.I.C.S.: 423440
James Donahugh (CEO)

MADDEN CONTRACTING COMPANY INC.
11288 Hwy 371, Minden, LA 71055
Tel.: (318) 377-0928 LA
Web Site: http://www.maddencontracting.com
Year Founded: 1955
Sales Range: $25-49.9 Million
Emp.: 140
Provider of Highway & Street Construction Services
N.A.I.C.S.: 237310
Doug Madden (VP)
James C. Madden (Pres)

Subsidiaries:

Longview Asphalt Inc. (1)
20 Robert Wilson Rd, Longview, TX 75602-4886
Tel.: (903) 758-0065
Sales Range: $10-24.9 Million
Emp.: 35
Provider of Asphalt Paving Mixture Services
N.A.I.C.S.: 324121
Rodney Price (Mgr-Site)

MADDEN LINCOLN MERCURY INC.
1444 River Ro Dr, Tuscaloosa, AL 35406-2390
Tel.: (205) 562-1800
Rev.: $15,700,000
Emp.: 22
New & Used Automobiles
N.A.I.C.S.: 441110

MADDOCK DOUGLAS, INC.
111 Adell Pl, Elmhurst, IL 60126
Tel.: (630) 279-3939
Web Site: http://www.maddockdouglas.com
Year Founded: 1991
Sales Range: $10-24.9 Million
Emp.: 65
Advertising Agencies
N.A.I.C.S.: 541810
G. Michael Maddock (CEO & Founding Partner)
Diana Kander (Dir-Innovation, Culture & Habits)
Maria Ferrante-Schepis (Pres)

MADDOX INDUSTRIAL TRANSFORMER, LLC
303B Greer Dr, Simpsonville, SC 29681
Web Site: http://www.maddoxtransformer.com
Year Founded: 2015
Sales Range: $10-24.9 Million
Emp.: 23
Transformer Mfr
N.A.I.C.S.: 335311
Camden Spiller (CEO)
Tracey Clakley (CFO)
Heath Blundell (Dir-Ops)
Mac Spiller (Dir-Sls)
Randall Maddox (Mgr-Inventory)

MADDOX METAL WORKS INC.
4116 Bronze Way, Dallas, TX 75237
Tel.: (214) 333-2311
Web Site: http://www.maddoxmetalworks.com
Sales Range: $10-24.9 Million
Emp.: 62
Metalworks Manufacturing
N.A.I.C.S.: 333241
Samuel Louis Maddox (Pres)
James Carlin (VP)
Steve McAfee (Mgr-Snack Food Machinery)

MADE YA SMILE DENTAL
1415 Hwy 6 S Ste C 200, Sugar Land, TX 77478
Tel.: (281) 265-1111
Web Site: http://www.madeyasmile.com
Year Founded: 2004
Sales Range: $1-9.9 Million
Emp.: 125
Dental Practice
N.A.I.C.S.: 621210
Michael L. Kesner (Founder & Owner)

MADEIRA USA LTD.
30 Bayside Ct, Laconia, NH 03246
Tel.: (603) 528-2944
Web Site: http://www.madeirausa.com
Sales Range: $10-24.9 Million
Emp.: 50
Thread Distributor
Shirley Clark (Pres)
Stephen Sacco (Dir-Fin)

MADELAINE CHOCOLATE NOVELTIES, INC.
9603 Beach Channel Dr, New York, NY 11693
Tel.: (718) 945-1500
Web Site: http://www.madelainechocolate.com
Year Founded: 1949
Sales Range: $25-49.9 Million
Emp.: 300
Chocolate Candy Mfr
N.A.I.C.S.: 311351
Jorge Farber (Pres)
Sam Farber (VP-Production)

MADEN TECH CONSULTING INC.
4601 N Fairfax Dr Ste 1030, Arlington, VA 22203
Tel.: (703) 769-4440 DE
Web Site: http://www.madentech.com
Year Founded: 1986
Sales Range: $25-49.9 Million
Emp.: 340
Provider of Computer Related Services
N.A.I.C.S.: 541512
Omar Maden (CEO)
Tommy T. Osborne (CTO)

MADER CONSTRUCTION CORP
970 Bullis Rd, Elma, NY 14059-9638
Tel.: (716) 655-3400 NY
Web Site: http://www.maderconstruct.com
Year Founded: 1975
Sales Range: $25-49.9 Million
Emp.: 200
Provider of Commercial Interior Construction
N.A.I.C.S.: 561110
Kevin Biddle (Pres)
Harold Keller (VP)
James E. Biddle Jr. (Chm & Treas)
Joe Knarr (VP)

MADERA AUTO CENTER
1300 Country Club Dr, Madera, CA 93638
Tel.: (559) 674-9000
Web Site: http://www.maderaauto.com
Rev.: $16,400,000
Emp.: 45
Automobiles, New & Used
N.A.I.C.S.: 441110
Roxann Stebbins (Mgr-Parts)
Gary Fontanilla (Mgr-Parts)
Henry M. Mayfohrt Jr. (Pres)
Lloyd G. Wright Jr. (Dir-Fixed Ops)

MADETOORDER
1244-A Quarry Ln, Pleasanton, CA 94566-4756
Tel.: (925) 484-0600 DE
Web Site: http://www.madetoorder.com
Year Founded: 2002
Sales Range: $10-24.9 Million
Emp.: 30
Sales Promotion
N.A.I.C.S.: 541810
Barbara Brown (CEO)
Rod Brown (CFO)
Rex Shoemake (Sr Partner-Sls)
Sandy Gonzalez (Sr Partner-Sls)
Cris Aldridge (Partner-Sls)
Tony Brennan (Partner-Sls)
Rick Ventimiglia (Partner-Sls)
Matt Poel (Sr Partner-Sls)
Kevin Spawn (Partner-Sls)
Kevin Cassidy (Sr Partner-Sls)
Nancy Hakkinen (Sr Partner-Sls)
Robin Garb (Partner)

MADEWELL GROUP, INC.
30-30 47th Ave, Long Island City, NY 11101
Tel.: (718) 340-5701 DE
Year Founded: 2010
Rev.: $2,483,994,000
Assets: $1,223,937,000
Liabilities: $2,793,686,000
Net Worth: ($1,569,749,000)
Earnings: ($67,778,000)
Emp.: 3,040
Fiscal Year-end: 02/28/19
Holding Company
N.A.I.C.S.: 551112

MADISON APPROACH STAFFING, INC.
45 Knollwood Rd Ste 101, Elmsford, NY 10523
Tel.: (914) 428-4800
Web Site: http://www.madisonapproach.com
Year Founded: 1988
Employee Staffing Solutions
N.A.I.C.S.: 561311
Allison Madison (Pres & CEO)

MADISON AVENUE HOLDINGS, INC.

MADISON AVENUE HOLDINGS, INC.   U.S. PRIVATE

Madison Avenue Holdings, Inc.—(Continued)

3505 Hart Ave Ste 201, Rosemead, CA 91770
Tel.: (626) 576-4333   DE
Year Founded: 2004
Liabilities: $2,000
Net Worth: ($2,000)
Earnings: ($20,810)
Emp.: 2
Fiscal Year-end: 12/31/20
Holding Company
N.A.I.C.S.: 551112
Alex Kam *(Pres, CEO & Sec)*
Pan-Rong Liu *(CFO)*

MADISON COMMUNITY HOSPITAL INC.

30781 Stephenson Hwy, Madison Heights, MI 48071
Tel.: (248) 619-9771   MI
Year Founded: 1969
Sales Range: $10-24.9 Million
Emp.: 4
Health Care Srvices
N.A.I.C.S.: 622110
Ralph P. Binggeser *(Pres)*

MADISON COMPONENTS LLC

2 Marin Way Unit 3, Stratham, NH 03885
Tel.: (603) 758-1780
Web Site: http://www.madisoncomponentsllc.com
Year Founded: 2006
Sales Range: $1-9.9 Million
Emp.: 26
Aviation & Aerospace Component Distr
N.A.I.C.S.: 423860
Eric O'Brien *(CFO)*
Timothy W. Kratt *(Dir-Pur)*

MADISON COUNTY WOOD PRODUCTS, INC.

3311 Chouteau Ave, Saint Louis, MO 63103
Tel.: (314) 772-1722   MO
Web Site: http://www.mcwp.com
Year Founded: 1981
Sales Range: $10-24.9 Million
Emp.: 90
Pallets, Wood
N.A.I.C.S.: 321920
James Kesting *(Pres)*

MADISON DEARBORN PARTNERS, LLC

70 W Madison Ave Ste 4600, Chicago, IL 60602
Tel.: (312) 895-1000   DE
Web Site: http://www.mdcp.com
Year Founded: 1992
Privater Equity Firm
N.A.I.C.S.: 523999
Harry M. Jansen Kraemer Jr. *(Exec Partner)*
Samuel M. Mencoff *(Co-CEO)*
Thomas S. Souleles *(Co-Pres & Mng Dir)*
Zaid F. Alsikafi *(Mng Dir & Co-Head-Telecom, Media & Tech Svcs)*
Karla J. Bullard *(Mng Dir & CFO)*
Jason Shideler *(Mng Dir)*
Annie Terry *(Mng Dir, Chief Compliance Officer & Gen Counsel)*
Scott G. Pasquini *(Mng Dir & Co-Head-Telecom, Media & Tech Svcs)*
David E. Pequet *(Mng Dir)*
Douglas C. Grissom *(Mng Dir)*
Vahe A. Dombalagian *(Mng Dir)*
Mike Dolce *(Mng Dir & Head-Capital Markets)*
Joshua M. Damon *(Mng Dir & Head-Portfolio Resources Function)*
Elizabeth Q. Betten *(Mng Dir)*
John Anthony Canning Jr. *(Chm)*
Timothy P. Sullivan *(Mng Dir)*
Thomas S. Souleles *(Co-Pres & Mng Dir)*
Paul J. Finnegan *(Co-Founder & Co-CEO)*
Robin P. Selati *(Mng Dir)*

Subsidiaries:

APM Human Services International Limited   (1)
58 Ord Street, West Perth, 6005, WA, Australia   (100%)
Tel.: (61) 894631300
Web Site: https://www.apm.net.au
Rev.: $1,236,515,616
Assets: $2,051,780,009
Liabilities: $1,075,355,676
Net Worth: $976,424,333
Earnings: $70,874,356
Emp.: 14,750
Fiscal Year-end: 06/30/2023
Management Consulting Services
N.A.I.C.S.: 541618
Megan Wynne *(Founder)*
Peter Magill *(Chief Dev Officer)*

Subsidiary (Domestic):

Biosymm Pty Ltd.   (2)
5-7 Belmont Avenue, Belmont, 6104, WA, Australia
Tel.: (61) 1300424679
Web Site: https://www.biosymm.com
Health Care Srvices
N.A.I.C.S.: 621498

Subsidiary (Non-US):

CNLR Horizons Limited   (2)
5th Floor 18 Mansell Street, London, E1 8AA, United Kingdom
Tel.: (44) 2079376224
Web Site: https://www.cicwellbeing.com
Mental Health Support Services
N.A.I.C.S.: 621330

Subsidiary (Domestic):

Clinpsych Psychology Services Pty. Ltd.   (2)
29 Dequetteville Terrace, Kent Town, 5067, SA, Australia
Tel.: (61) 1300277924
Web Site: https://www.humanpsychology.com.au
Mental Health Care Services
N.A.I.C.S.: 621610

Subsidiary (US):

DB Grant Associates Inc.   (2)
39 Broadway Fl 31, New York, NY 10006
Tel.: (212) 684-2700
Web Site: https://www.grantassociatesinc.com
Recruitment Consulting Services
N.A.I.C.S.: 541612

Dynamic Workforce Solutions - Texas, LLC   (2)
237 S St, Waukesha, WI 53186
Tel.: (262) 544-4971
Web Site: https://dwfs.us
Business Management Consulting Services
N.A.I.C.S.: 541611

Dynamic Workforce Solutions, LLC   (2)
237 S St, Waukesha, WI 53186
Tel.: (262) 544-4971
Web Site: https://www.dwfs.us
Business Consulting Services
N.A.I.C.S.: 541611

Subsidiary (Domestic):

Early Start Australia Pty Ltd.   (2)
169 Broadway, Nedlands, 6009, Australia
Tel.: (61) 1300372439
Web Site: https://www.earlystartaustralia.com.au
Therapy Services
N.A.I.C.S.: 621610

FBG Group Pty Ltd.   (2)
Level 3 350 Collins St, Melbourne, 3000, VIC, Australia
Tel.: (61) 396000067
Web Site: https://www.fbggroup.com.au
Business Consulting Services
N.A.I.C.S.: 541611

Innovative Training & Recruitment Pty Ltd.   (2)
490 Regency Road, Greenfields, 5085, SA, Australia
Tel.: (61) 1300006347
Vocational Rehabilitation Services
N.A.I.C.S.: 624310

Integrated Care Pty Ltd.   (2)
169 Broadway, Nedlands, 6009, WA, Australia
Tel.: (61) 1300769894
Web Site: https://www.myintegra.com.au
Disability People Plan Management & Support Coordination Services
N.A.I.C.S.: 624120

MCI Institute Pty Ltd.   (2)
Level 13 201 Miller Street, North Sydney, 2060, NSW, Australia
Tel.: (61) 1300658388
Web Site: https://www.mciinstitute.edu.au
Education Training & Support Services
N.A.I.C.S.: 611710

Management Consultancy International Pty Ltd.   (2)
Level 13 201 Miller Street, North Sydney, 2060, NSW, Australia
Tel.: (61) 1300768550
Web Site: https://mci.edu.au
Education Services
N.A.I.C.S.: 611430

Mobility Australia Pty Ltd.   (2)
Unit 8 12 Railway Road, Subiaco, 6008, WA, Australia
Tel.: (61) 1300438227
Web Site: https://www.mobility.com.au
Home Care Services
N.A.I.C.S.: 621610

Springday Pty. Ltd.   (2)
58 Ord Street, West Perth, 6005, WA, Australia
Tel.: (61) 894631300
Web Site: https://myspringday.com.au
Fitness & Wellbeing Improving Services
N.A.I.C.S.: 812990

American Broadband Holding Company   (1)
153 W Dave Dugas Rd, Sulpher, LA 70665
Tel.: (337) 583-2111
Web Site: https://fastwyre.com
Broadband & Internet Services
N.A.I.C.S.: 517810
Chris Eldredge *(CEO)*

Subsidiary (Domestic):

Cameron Communication LLC   (2)
153 W Dave Dugas Rd, Sulpher, LA 70665
Tel.: (337) 583-2111
Web Site: https://www.camtel.com
Sales Range: $25-49.9 Million
Emp.: 200
Telephone Communication, Except Radio
N.A.I.C.S.: 517121
William L. Henning Sr. *(Chm)*

Subsidiary (Domestic):

Cameron Telephone Company Inc   (3)
153 W Dave Dugas Rd, Sulphur, LA 70665
Tel.: (337) 583-2111
Web Site: http://www.camtel.com
Rev.: $16,994,988
Emp.: 100
Telephone Communication, Except Radio
N.A.I.C.S.: 517121
Bruce Petry *(Pres)*

Elizabeth Telephone Company   (3)
153 W Dave Dugas Rd, Sulphur, LA 70665
Tel.: (337) 583-2111
Web Site: http://www.camtel.net
Sales Range: $25-49.9 Million
Emp.: 165
Telephone Communication, Except Radio
N.A.I.C.S.: 517121

Arch Precision Components Corp.   (1)
730 W 22nd St, Tempe, AZ 85282
Tel.: (480) 968-1178
Advanced Precision-machining Components Mfr
N.A.I.C.S.: 332721
Andy Spiering *(CEO)*

Subsidiary (Domestic):

Metalcraft Technologies, Inc.   (2)
526 N Aviation Way, Cedar City, UT 84721
Tel.: (435) 586-3871
Web Site: http://www.metalcraft.net
Other Guided Missile, Space Vehicle Parts & Auxiliary Equipment Mfr
N.A.I.C.S.: 336419
Cameron Avery *(Engr-Methods)*
Corey Judd *(Pres)*

Benefytt Technologies, Inc.   (1)
3450 Buschwood Park Dr Ste 201, Tampa, FL 33618
Tel.: (813) 397-1187
Web Site: http://www.hiiquote.com
Rev.: $381,808,000
Assets: $651,858,000
Liabilities: $511,884,000
Net Worth: $139,974,000
Earnings: $29,614,000
Emp.: 342
Fiscal Year-end: 12/31/2019
Health Insurance Plans & Ancillary Products
N.A.I.C.S.: 524210
Todd Baxter *(CEO)*
Erik H. Helding *(CFO, Treas & Sec)*
Domenick DiCicco *(Gen Counsel)*

Subsidiary (Domestic):

Insurance Center for Excellence, LLC   (2)
123 NW 13th St 101, Boca Raton, FL 33432
Tel.: (561) 404-0251
Insurance Agency & Brokerage Services
N.A.I.C.S.: 524210

RxHelpline, LLC   (2)
7551 Wiles Rd 106, Coral Springs, FL 33067
Web Site: http://www.therxhelpline.com
Health Insurance Services
N.A.I.C.S.: 524114

Total Insurance Brokers, LLC   (2)
3109 W Dr Martin Luther King Jr Blvd Ste 400, Tampa, FL 33607
Web Site: http://www.tibhealth.com
Health Insurance Services
N.A.I.C.S.: 524114
Jennifer Dadzie *(VP)*

BlueCat Networks, Inc.   (1)
4100 Yonge St 3rd Floor, Toronto, M2P 2B5, ON, Canada
Tel.: (416) 646-8400
Web Site: http://www.bluecatnetworks.com
IP Address Management Services
N.A.I.C.S.: 513210
Michael Hyatt *(Founder)*
Michael Harris *(Chm & CEO)*
Andrew Wertkin *(Chief Product & Tech Officer)*
David Duncan *(CMO)*
Sujeet Kini *(CFO)*
Martin McNealis *(Chief Product Officer)*

Subsidiary (Non-US):

BlueCat Japan Co., Ltd.   (2)
1-6-16 7F Ginza 1616 Building, Ginza Chuo-ku, Tokyo, 104-0061, Japan
Tel.: (81) 3 6264 4201
Web Site: http://www.bluecatnetworks.co.jp
Information Technology Consulting Services
N.A.I.C.S.: 541512
David Jones *(Sr VP-Asia Pacific/Japan)*

CoVant Management, Inc.   (1)
1650 Tysons Blvd Ste 850, McLean, VA 22102
Tel.: (703) 917-0360
Web Site: http://www.covant.com
Governmental Technology Solutions Investment Holding Company
N.A.I.C.S.: 551112
Joseph M. Kampf *(Co-Founder, Chm & CEO)*
James K. Heilman *(Exec VP)*
Roger A. Gurner *(Exec VP)*
Jason S. Kampf *(VP & Dir-Res)*

COMPANIES

MADISON DEARBORN PARTNERS, LLC

Fitness International, LLC (1)
2600 Michelson Dr Ste 600, Irvine, CA 92612-4406
Tel.: (949) 255-7330
Web Site: http://www.lafitness.com
Sales Range: $1-4.9 Billion
Health & Fitness Club Operator
N.A.I.C.S.: 713940
Louis Welch (CEO)

Hobbs and Associates Inc. (1)
4830 Brookside Ct Ste 100, Norfolk, VA 23502
Tel.: (757) 468-8800
Web Site: http://www.hobbsassociates.com
Sales Range: $10-24.9 Million
Emp.: 40
Supplier of Warm Air Heating Equipment & Supplies: HVASC-R
N.A.I.C.S.: 423730
William Jacoby (VP-Ops-Tennessee)
William Hobbs Jr. (VP-Ops-Virginia)

Subsidiary (Domestic):

C.G. Wood Company, Inc. (2)
1 Virginia Manor Rd Ste 360, Beltsville, MD 20705-4203
Tel.: (240) 241-5242
Web Site: http://www.cgwoodco.com
Industrial, Commercial Fan, Blower & Air Purification Equipment Mfr
N.A.I.C.S.: 333413
Kyle McCullough (Engr-Sls)

Energy Transfer Solutions, LLC (2)
1220 Ward Ave Ste 300, West Chester, PA 19380
Tel.: (610) 444-0333
Web Site: https://www.etshvac.com
Engineeering Services
N.A.I.C.S.: 541330

The Kirkman Oliver Company (2)
41 Harrison Dr, Newtown Square, PA 19073
Tel.: (610) 960-1074
Web Site: http://www.tko-co.com
Engineeering Services
N.A.I.C.S.: 541330
Chris Miller (VP-Ops & Tech Svcs)

IPL Plastics Inc (1)
Huguenot House 35-38 St Stephens Green, Dublin, D02 NY63, Ireland
Tel.: (353) 16121151
Web Site: https://www.iplglobal.com
Rev.: $605,068,000
Assets: $901,050,000
Liabilities: $528,913,000
Net Worth: $372,137,000
Earnings: $13,857,000
Emp.: 2,065
Fiscal Year-end: 12/31/2019
Holding Company; Packaging Products
N.A.I.C.S.: 551112
Alan Walsh (Pres & CEO)
P. J. Browne (Chief Risk Officer & Sec)
Conor Wall (Chief Sustainability Officer & Head-Environment, Health, Safety, and Sustainability)
Aileen Joyce (CFO)
Ida Murphy (Chief People Officer)

Subsidiary (Non-US):

ClearCircle Environmental (NI) Ltd (2)
110 Trewmount Road Killyman, Dungannon, BT71 7EF, Tyrone, United Kingdom
Tel.: (44) 2887789315
Web Site: http://www.clearcircle.com
Metal Recycling Services
N.A.I.C.S.: 562920

Subsidiary (Domestic):

ClearCircle Environmental Limited (2)
Block 402 Grants Drive Greenogue Business Park, Dublin, 24 AP04, Ireland
Tel.: (353) 14018000
Web Site: http://www.clearcircle.com
Emp.: 1,000
Holding Company; Recycling & Hazardous Waste Management Services
N.A.I.C.S.: 551112
Alan Walsh (CEO)

Subsidiary (Non-US):

Ampthill Metal Company Ltd. (3)
Station Road Industrial Estate, Ampthill, MK45 2QY, Beds, United Kingdom
Tel.: (44) 1525403388
Web Site: http://www.ampthillmetal.co.uk
Emp.: 30
Metal Recycling Services
N.A.I.C.S.: 562920
Roger Daniel (Gen Mgr)

Subsidiary (Domestic):

ClearCircle Metals Ireland Limited (3)
151 Thomas Street, Dublin, 8, Ireland
Tel.: (353) 16121100
Web Site: http://www.clearcirclemetals.com
Metal Recycling Facilities Operator
N.A.I.C.S.: 562920
Liam O'Shea (Head-Ferrous Sls)

Subsidiary (Domestic):

A1 Metal Recycling Ltd. (4)
Acragar, Mountmellick, Laois, Ireland
Tel.: (353) 578624119
Web Site: http://www.clearcircle.com
Emp.: 25
Metal Recycling Services
N.A.I.C.S.: 562920
Sinbarr Bride (Gen Mgr)

ClearCircle Metals (Limerick) Ltd. (4)
Ballysimon Road, Limerick, Ireland
Tel.: (353) 61418153
Web Site: http://www.clearcircle.com
Metal Recycling Services
N.A.I.C.S.: 562920

Cork Metal Company Ltd. (4)
Dublin Hill, Cork, Ireland
Tel.: (353) 214309910
Web Site: http://www.clearcircle.com
Metal Recycling Services
N.A.I.C.S.: 562920

Galway Metal Company Ltd. (4)
Galway Business Park, Oranmore, Galway, Ireland
Tel.: (353) 91794358
Web Site: http://www.clearcircle.com
Metal Recycling Services
N.A.I.C.S.: 562920

Subsidiary (Non-US):

One51 ES Metals (North) Ltd (2)
Darbishire Street Off Waterloo Street, Bolton, BL1 2TN, Lancashire, United Kingdom
Tel.: (44) 1204533662
Metal Recycling Services
N.A.I.C.S.: 562920

Subsidiary (Domestic):

One51 Plastics Holdings Limited (2)
151 Thomas Street, Dublin, 11T0TY5E, Ireland (100%)
Tel.: (353) 16121151
Web Site: http://www.one51.com
Holding Company; Plastic Products Mfr
N.A.I.C.S.: 551112
Alan Walsh (CEO)

Subsidiary (Non-US):

AAC Structural Foam Ltd. (3)
Denis House Mariner, Lichfield Road Industrial Estate, Tamworth, B79 7UL, Staffs, United Kingdom
Tel.: (44) 1484710611
Web Site: http://www.aacplastics.co.uk
Injection Molding & Foam Molding Plastic Products Mfr
N.A.I.C.S.: 326199
Ray Waspe (Mng Dir)

MGB Plastics Ltd. (3)
Barbot Hall Industrial Estate Mangham Road, Rotherham, S61 4RJ, S Yorkshire, United Kingdom
Tel.: (44) 1709362448
Web Site: http://www.mgbplastics.com
Wheeled Plastic Bins Mfr
N.A.I.C.S.: 326199

Straight Ltd (3)
Somerden Road, Hull, HU9 5PE, United Kingdom
Tel.: (44) 1482785200
Web Site: http://www.straight.co.uk
Plastic Container Mfr
N.A.I.C.S.: 326199

Subsidiary (Domestic):

Thormac Engineering Ltd. (3)
Bay 128/129 Shannon Industrial Estate, Shannon, Clare, Ireland
Tel.: (353) 61472030
Web Site: http://www.thormac.ie
Injection Molding Plastic Products Mfr
N.A.I.C.S.: 326199
Sean Ryan (Mng Dir)

Subsidiary (Non-US):

Protech Performance Plastics Ltd (2)
1688 ZhuanXing Rd, Shanghai, China
Tel.: (86) 2164425528
Web Site: http://www.protechplastics.net
Plastics Product Mfr
N.A.I.C.S.: 325991

InMoment, Inc. (1)
10355 S Jordan Gateway #600, Salt Lake City, UT 84095
Web Site: http://www.inmoment.com
Software Development Services
N.A.I.C.S.: 541511
Kristi Knight (CMO)
Bryan Rellinger (COO)
Richard Barber (CFO)
John Lewis (Chm & CEO)
Wendy Rand (Chief HR Officer)
David Joiner (CTO & VP-Engrg)
Gary Challburg (Gen Counsel & VP)
Sandeep Garg (Chief Product Officer)

Subsidiary (Domestic):

Lexalytics, Inc. (2)
48 N Pleasant St Unit 301, Amherst, MA 01002
Tel.: (617) 249-1049
Web Site: http://www.lexalytics.com
Software Development Services
N.A.I.C.S.: 541511
Jeff Catlin (CEO)

Intermedia.net, Inc. (1)
825 E Middlefield Rd, Mountain View, CA 94043
Web Site: http://www.intermedia.net
Cloud Data Services
N.A.I.C.S.: 518210
Michael Gold (CEO)
Jonathan McCormick (COO)
Andrew Gachechiladze (Sr VP-Product Dev & Engrg)
Irina Shamkova (Sr VP-Product Mgmt)
Jonathan Levine (CTO)
Jeff Eisenberg (Chief Admin Officer & Gen Counsel)
Scott Anderson (CMO)
Jason Veldhuis (CFO)

Subsidiary (Domestic):

Cosnet, Inc. (2)
7777 Center Ave Ste 520, Huntington Beach, CA 92647-3099
Tel.: (714) 890-3008
Web Site: http://www.cosnet.com
Web Conferencing Solutions
N.A.I.C.S.: 518210
Costin Tuculescu (Founder & Pres)

MoneyGram International, Inc. (1)
2828 N Harwood St, Dallas, TX 75201
Tel.: (214) 999-7552
Web Site: https://www.moneygram.com
Rev.: $1,283,600,000
Assets: $4,476,500,000
Liabilities: $4,661,500,000
Net Worth: ($185,000,000)
Earnings: ($37,900,000)
Emp.: 3,072
Fiscal Year-end: 12/31/2021
Holding Company; Payment & Money Order Processing Services
N.A.I.C.S.: 551112
W. Alexander Holmes (Chm & CEO)
Lawrence Angelilli (Vice Chm)
Andres Villareal (Chief Compliance Officer)
Robert L. Villasenor (Chief Admin Officer, Gen Counsel & Sec)
Brian Johnson (CFO)
Anna Greenwald (COO)
Greg Hall (CMO)
Joe Vaughan (CTO)
Sara Vassar (Chief Product Officer)
Veronica Larson (CIO)
Cory Feinberg (Sec)
Christopher H. Russell Jr. (Chief Acctg Officer)

Subsidiary (Domestic):

MoneyGram Foundation, Inc. (2)
2828 N Harwood Fl 15, Dallas, TX 75201
Tel.: (214) 303-9923
Web Site: http://www.moneygramfoundation.com
Electronic Payment Services
N.A.I.C.S.: 522320

MoneyGram Payment Systems Worldwide, Inc. (2)
1550 Utica Ave S Ste 100, Minneapolis, MN 55416
Tel.: (952) 591-3000
Web Site: http://www.moneygram.com
Electronic Payment Services
N.A.I.C.S.: 522320

Subsidiary (Non-US):

MoneyGram International Holdings Ltd. (3)
Third Floor 30 Churchill Place Canary Wharf, London, E14 5RE, United Kingdom
Tel.: (44) 2030363999
Sales Range: $25-49.9 Million
Emp.: 77
Holding Company
N.A.I.C.S.: 551112

Subsidiary (Domestic):

MoneyGram International Ltd. (4)
1 Bevington Path, London, SE1 3PW, United Kingdom
Tel.: (44) 2070895400
Web Site: http://www.moneygram.com
Payment & Money Order Processing Services
N.A.I.C.S.: 522320

Subsidiary (Non-US):

MoneyGram Overseas (Pty) Limited South Africa (4)
The Woodlands, 2191, Sandton, Gauteng, South Africa
Tel.: (27) 113049900
Web Site: http://moneygram.co.za
Electronic Payment Services
N.A.I.C.S.: 522320

MoneyGram Payment Systems Belgium N.V. (4)
Carnotstraat 41, 2060, Antwerp, Belgium
Tel.: (32) 606730
Emp.: 5
Electronic Payment Services
N.A.I.C.S.: 522320
Benjamin Kouassi (Country Mgr)

MoneyGram Payment Systems Italy, S.r.l. (4)
Via Laurentina 449/451, 00184, Rome, Italy
Tel.: (39) 0664232111
Sales Range: $50-74.9 Million
Emp.: 5
Payment & Money Order Processing Services
N.A.I.C.S.: 522320

MoneyGram Payment Systems Spain, S.A. (4)
Plaza Manuel Gomez Moreno 2, 28020, Madrid, Spain
Tel.: (34) 900101488
Electronic Payment Services
N.A.I.C.S.: 522320

Subsidiary (Domestic):

MoneyGram Payment Systems, Inc. (2)
1550 Utica Ave S Ste 100, Minneapolis, MN 55416
Tel.: (952) 591-3000
Web Site: http://www.moneygram.com
Payment & Money Order Processing Services
N.A.I.C.S.: 522320

MADISON DEARBORN PARTNERS, LLC

U.S. PRIVATE

Madison Dearborn Partners, LLC—(Continued)

Subsidiary (Domestic):

FSMC, Inc. (3)
431 Lakeview St, Lake Lillian, MN 56253-9525
Tel.: (320) 664-4161
Sales Range: $10-24.9 Million
Emp.: 150
Financial Services; High Volume Check Processing
N.A.I.C.S.: 522320

Option Care Enterprises, Inc. (1)
10924 John Galt Blvd, Omaha, NE 68137-2309
Tel.: (402) 331-0980
Web Site: http://www.optioncare.com
Nursing & Home Health Care Services
N.A.I.C.S.: 623110
Cliff Berman *(Gen Counsel, Corp Sec & Sr VP)*
Matthew Deans *(VP-Bus Dev)*
Brett Michalak *(CIO)*
John C. Rademacher *(CEO)*
Cari Reed *(Chief Compliance Officer)*
Mike Rude *(Chief HR Officer & Sr VP)*
Mike Shapiro *(CFO)*
Brenda Wright *(VP-Clinical Svcs)*
Harry Kraemer *(Chm)*

Performance Health Holdings, Inc. (1)
28100 Torch Pkwy, Warrenville, IL 60555
Tel.: (630) 393-6000
Web Site:
   http://www.performancehealth.com
Holding Company; Medical Dental & Hospital Equipment Whslr
N.A.I.C.S.: 551112
Harry Kraemer *(Chm)*
Francis Dirksmeier *(CEO)*
Greg Nulty *(CFO)*
Isabel Afonso *(Chief Comml Officer)*
Laurie Byrne *(Chief HR Officer)*
Jameson Eisenmenger *(Gen Counsel)*
Joy Gallo *(Chief Procurement Officer)*
Paul Hanneman *(VP-Regulatory Affairs & Quality Assurance)*
Adam Shapiro *(CIO)*
John Toney *(VP-Mfg Ops-Global)*
Sean Muniz *(Chief Supply Chain Officer)*

Subsidiary (Non-US):

Ausmedic Australia Pty Limited (2)
PO Box 1006, North Ryde, 2113, NSW, Australia
Tel.: (61) 1300473422
Medical Dental & Hospital Equipment & Supplies Whslr
N.A.I.C.S.: 423450

Patterson Medical Canada, Inc. (2)
6675 Milcreek Dr Unit 3, Mississauga, L5N 5M4, ON, Canada
Tel.: (905) 858-6000
Splinting & Rehabilitation Products for Occupational & Physical Therapists
N.A.I.C.S.: 423450

Performance Health International Limited (2)
Nunn Brook Road, Huthwaite, Sutton in Ashfield, NG17 2HU, Nottinghamshire, United Kingdom
Tel.: (44) 1623448706
Medical & Hospital Equipment Supplier
N.A.I.C.S.: 423450
Andrew Booker *(Sec)*

Subsidiary (Domestic):

Days Healthcare U.K. Limited (3)
5 North Rd Bridgend Industrial Estate, Bridgend, CF3 13TP, United Kingdom
Tel.: (44) 1656664700
Mobility Aid Equipment Mfr
N.A.I.C.S.: 339112
Karen Leay *(Sec)*

Subsidiary (Domestic):

Performance Health Supply, Inc. (2)
28100 Torch Pkwy Ste 700, Warrenville, IL 60555
Tel.: (630) 393-6000
Web Site:
   http://www.performancehealth.com

Rehabilitation Supplies & Non-Wheelchair Assistive Patient Products Distr
N.A.I.C.S.: 423450
Francis Dirksmeier *(Pres)*

The Hygenic Corporation (2)
1245 Home Ave, Akron, OH 44310
Tel.: (330) 633-8460
Web Site: http://www.hygeniccorp.com
Latex Product Mfr
N.A.I.C.S.: 326299
Greg Dalton *(Dir-IT)*

SIRVA, Inc. (1)
1 Parkview Plz, Oakbrook Terrace, IL 60181
Tel.: (216) 606-7912
Web Site: https://www.sirva.com
Sales Range: $1-4.9 Billion
Emp.: 4,200
Corporate & Consumer Relocation Services
N.A.I.C.S.: 484230
John Kirk *(Chief Info & Tech Officer & Exec VP)*
Linda Smith *(Chief Strategy Officer & Chief Comml Officer)*
Margaret E. Pais *(Chief HR Officer & Exec VP-HR)*
Jeffrey Margolis *(Gen Counsel & Exec VP)*
Bob Olmsted *(Pres & COO)*
Joe Genautis *(CTO)*
Thomas W. Oberdorf *(Chm & CFO)*

Subsidiary (Non-US):

Allied Pickfords (2)
202-228 Greens Road, Dandenong, 3175, VIC, Australia
Tel.: (61) 3 9797 1500
Web Site: http://www.alliedpickfords.com
Emp.: 25
Goods Moving Services
N.A.I.C.S.: 484210

Subsidiary (Domestic):

Allied Van Lines, Inc. (2)
700 Oakmont Ln, Westmont, IL 60559
Tel.: (630) 570-3686
Web Site: http://www.alliedvan.com
Sales Range: $100-124.9 Million
Emp.: 1,000
Moving Services
N.A.I.C.S.: 484210
Jodie Galassi *(VP)*

Affiliate (Domestic):

Central Van & Storage, Inc. (3)
595 Meadowlands Blvd, Washington, PA 15301
Tel.: (724) 225-7510
Web Site: http://www.centralvan.com
Full Service Worldwide Relocation Provider
N.A.I.C.S.: 484210

Division (Domestic):

DJK Residential (2)
101 Fifth Ave 7th Fl, New York, NY 10003 (100%)
Tel.: (212) 964-4300
Web Site: http://www.djkresidential.com
Sales Range: $25-49.9 Million
Emp.: 100
New York City Real Estate & Relocation Services
N.A.I.C.S.: 531390
Phyllis J. Pezenik *(Mng Dir-Brokerage Svcs & VP)*
Michelle Couperthwaite *(Dir-Relocation & Property Mgmt)*
Sau Chee Lok *(Dir-IT)*

Subsidiary (Domestic):

Executive Relocation Corporation (2)
1 Metropolitan Sq 211 N Bdwy Ste 2130, Saint Louis, MO 63102
Tel.: (314) 244-6000
Web Site: http://www.sirva.com
Sales Range: $10-24.9 Million
Emp.: 60
Relocation Services
N.A.I.C.S.: 484210
Stephen Casssel *(CFO)*

North American Van Lines (2)
5001 US Hwy 30 W, Fort Wayne, IN 46818-9701
Tel.: (260) 429-2511

Web Site: http://www.northamerican.com
Sales Range: $1-4.9 Billion
Emp.: 500
Transportation Moving Services
N.A.I.C.S.: 484121
Dan Robertson *(VP & Gen Mgr)*
Kevin Murphy *(VP-Acct Mgmt-Natl)*
Steve Yahn *(Reg VP)*

Subsidiary (Non-US):

Pickfords Limited (2)
Unit 10 Laxcon Close, London, NW10 0TG, United Kingdom
Tel.: (44) 2031882655
Web Site: http://www.pickfords.co.uk
Railroad Transportation Services
N.A.I.C.S.: 488210
Russell Start *(Mng Dir)*

SIRVA Canada LP (2)
310 10403 172nd Street, Edmonton, T5S 1K9, AB, Canada
Tel.: (780) 443-6800
Web Site: http://www.ca.sirva.com
Emp.: 30
Office Goods Moving Services
N.A.I.C.S.: 484210
Norman Struges *(Mgr)*

Subsidiary (Domestic):

North American Van Lines, Inc. (3)
Suite 350 10403-172 Street Station Main, PO Box 639, Edmonton, T5J 2L3, AB, Canada
Web Site:
   http://www.northamericanvanlines.ca
Household Goods Moving Services
N.A.I.C.S.: 484210
Dan Robertson *(VP & Gen Mgr)*

Subsidiary (US):

NAVL LLC (4)
700 Oakmont Ln, Westmont, IL 60559
Tel.: (630) 570-3009
Emp.: 400
Food Transportation Services
N.A.I.C.S.: 484210

North American International Holding Corporation (4)
5001 US Highway 30 W, Fort Wayne, IN 46818
Tel.: (260) 429-2511
Holding Company
N.A.I.C.S.: 551112

Subsidiary (Domestic):

SIRVA Mortgage, Inc. (2)
6200 Oak Tree Blvd Ste 300, Independence, OH 44131
Tel.: (216) 606-4000
Web Site: http://www.sirvamortgage.com
Commercial Mortgage Services
N.A.I.C.S.: 522310
Bryan Griffin *(VP & Controller)*
Lizz Bontos *(Mgr-Legal Transactional)*
Matt Spicuzza *(Mgr-Mortgage Trading)*
Rita Collins *(Mgr-Re-Location Svcs)*
Rosa Di Gennaro *(Coord-Re-Location Acctg)*

Subsidiary (Non-US):

SIRVA Pty. Ltd (2)
202-228 Greens Rd, Dandenong, 3175, VIC, Australia
Tel.: (61) 397971500
Food Transportation Services
N.A.I.C.S.: 484210

Subsidiary (Domestic):

SIRVA Relocation LLC (2)
One Park View Plz, Oakbrook Terrace, IL 60181
Tel.: (630) 570-3047
Emp.: 300
Office Goods Moving Services
N.A.I.C.S.: 484210

SIRVA Worldwide, Inc. (2)
1 Parkview Plz, Oakbrook Terrace, IL 60181
Tel.: (630) 570-3047
Railroad Transportation Services
N.A.I.C.S.: 488210

Shaw Development, LLC (1)
25190 Bernwood Dr, Bonita Springs, FL 34135
Tel.: (239) 405-6100
Web Site: http://www.shawdev.com
Sales Range: $25-49.9 Million
Emp.: 150
Fuel, Oil & Diesel Exhaust Fluid Systems Mfr
N.A.I.C.S.: 333995
Thomas Goettel *(Controller)*
Kevin Hawkesworth *(Pres & CEO)*

Subsidiary (Domestic):

Dixon Pumps, Inc. (2)
1110 Maggie Ln, Billings, MT 59101
Tel.: (406) 259-8282
Web Site: http://www.dixonpumps.com
Sales Range: $1-9.9 Million
Emp.: 12
Pump & Pumping Equipment Mfr
N.A.I.C.S.: 333914
Randy Dixon *(Pres & CEO)*

The Topps Company, Inc. (1)
1 Whitehall St, New York, NY 10004-2109
Tel.: (212) 376-0300
Web Site: http://www.topps.com
Sales Range: $300-349.9 Million
International Marketer of Collectible Trading Cards, Confections, Sticker Collections, Collectible Strategy Games & Comic Books
N.A.I.C.S.: 323111
Christopher Rodman *(Grp Mng Dir & VP)*
John Mueller *(CFO)*
Michael Brandstaedter *(CEO)*
David Leiner *(Gen Mgr)*
Jason Thaler *(Gen Counsel)*
Deniz Gezgin *(VP & Gen Mgr-Digital)*

Subsidiary (Non-US):

Topps Argentina SRL (2)
Pedro I Rivera No 26 2A V Adelina, B1607CFB, Buenos Aires, San Isidro, Argentina
Tel.: (54) 11 4717 2626
Web Site: http://www.topps.com.ar
Sales Range: $25-49.9 Million
Emp.: 100
Retail & Collectible Services
N.A.I.C.S.: 459999

Topps Canada, Inc. (2)
PO Box 31011, Oshawa, L1H 8N9, ON, Canada
Tel.: (416) 622-3425
Sales Range: $25-49.9 Million
Emp.: 3
Trading Card & Confectionery Mfr
N.A.I.C.S.: 311352

Topps Europe Limited (2)
18 Vincent Ave, Crownhill, Milton Keynes, MK8 0AW, United Kingdom
Tel.: (44) 1908800100
Web Site: http://www.toppsdirect.com
Sales Range: $25-49.9 Million
Emp.: 50
Trading Cards & Confectionery Mfr
N.A.I.C.S.: 311352
William Hiller *(Dir-Fin)*

Topps Ireland Ltd. (2)
Ballincollig Innishmore, Ballincollig, County Cork, Ireland
Tel.: (353) 214289200
Web Site: http://www.topps.ie
Sales Range: $25-49.9 Million
Emp.: 21
Trading Cards & Confectionery Mfr
N.A.I.C.S.: 311352

Topps Italia SRL (2)
Via Villoresi 13, 20143, Milan, Italy
Tel.: (39) 0283116125
Sales Range: $25-49.9 Million
Emp.: 10
Trading Cards & Confectionery Mfr
N.A.I.C.S.: 311352

MADISON ELECTRIC COMPANY

31855 Van Dyke Ave, Warren, MI 48093-1047
Tel.: (586) 825-0200   MI
Web Site:
   http://www.madisonelectric.com
Year Founded: 1914

Sales Range: $75-99.9 Million
Emp.: 200
Electrical Supplies Wholesale Distr
N.A.I.C.S.: 423610
Scott Leemaster (VP & Gen Mgr)
Richard Sonenklar (CIO & VP)
Bennett Rosenthal (CFO)

MADISON FARMERS ELEVATOR CO.
222 N Farmer Ave, Madison, SD 57042
Tel.: (605) 256-4584
Web Site:
http://www.madisonfarmerselevator.com
Sales Range: $25-49.9 Million
Emp.: 20
Grain Elevators
N.A.I.C.S.: 424510
Mark Stoller (Gen Mgr)

MADISON HOSPITALITY GROUP, LLC
1914 S 7th St, Brainerd, MN 56401
Tel.: (218) 829-8730
Web Site:
http://www.madisonhospitalitygroup.com
Real Estate Services
N.A.I.C.S.: 531390
Steve Madison (Pres)

MADISON HUNTSVILLE COUNTY AIRPORT AUTHORITY
1000 Glenn Hearn Blvd, Huntsville, AL 35824
Tel.: (256) 772-9395
Web Site: http://www.hsvairport.org
Sales Range: $10-24.9 Million
Emp.: 110
N.A.I.C.S.: 488119
Betty D. Fletcher (Chm)
Mark McDaniel (Treas & Sec)
Carl J. Gessler Jr. (Vice Chm)

MADISON INDUSTRIES HOLDINGS LLC
444 West Lake Ste 4400, Chicago, IL 60606
Tel.: (312) 277-0156 IL
Web Site:
http://www.madisoncapitalpartners.net
Year Founded: 1994
Privater Equity Firm
N.A.I.C.S.: 523999
Larry W. Gies (Founder & CEO)
Matt Huser (CMO)
David J. Ball (Mng Dir)
John E. Udelhofen (Exec VP-Owner Relations)
Christian Bernert (Sr Mng Dir & Head-Europe)
George C. Nolen (Vice Chm)
Frank S. Ptak (Sr Mng Dir)
Michael Ellis (Chief People Officer)
Andrew V. Masterman (Sr Mng Dir)
Christopher Domke (CFO)
C. Kenneth Holmes (CIO)

Subsidiaries:

CAE Healthcare Inc. (1)
6300 Edgelake Dr, Sarasota, FL 34240
Tel.: (941) 377-5562
Web Site: http://www.caehealthcare.com
Healtcare Services
N.A.I.C.S.: 621999
David Wildermuth (CMO & VP-Mktg)
Stefan Monk (Chief Medical Officer)
Amar Patel (Chief Learning Officer)
Jeff Evans (Pres)
Randee Stapleton (VP-Strategic Bus)
Giovanni Tuck (VP-Sls-Military & Govt Area-Global)

Delta-T Corp. (1)
2348 Innovation Dr, Lexington, KY 40511
Tel.: (859) 233-1271
Web Site: http://www.bigassfans.com
Sales Range: $25-49.9 Million
Warehouse & Commercial Fan Mfr & Distr
N.A.I.C.S.: 333415
Carey Smith (Pres)

Filtran LLC (1)
875 Seegers Rd, Des Plaines, IL 60016-3045
Tel.: (847) 635-6670
Web Site: http://www.filtranllc.com
Sales Range: $25-49.9 Million
Emp.: 200
Transmission Filters & Automotive Components
N.A.I.C.S.: 336350

Unit (Domestic):

Fluid Technologies, Inc. (2)
1016 E Airport Rd, Stillwater, OK 74075 (100%)
Tel.: (405) 624-0400
Web Site: http://www.fluidtechnologies.com
Sales Range: $10-24.9 Million
Emp.: 20
Filtration Testing Technology
N.A.I.C.S.: 541380

Subsidiary (Non-US):

IBS Filtran Kunstoff-/Metallerzeugnisse GmbH (2)
Industriestrasse 19, 51597, Morsbach, Germany (100%)
Tel.: (49) 2294 98124
Web Site: http://www.filtranllc.com
Sales Range: $25-49.9 Million
Emp.: 120
Filtration Testing Technology
N.A.I.C.S.: 541380

Filtration Group Corporation (1)
600 W 22nd St, Oak Brook, IL 60523
Tel.: (630) 968-1730
Web Site: http://www.filtrationgroup.com
Filtration Equipment Mfr
N.A.I.C.S.: 333413
George Nolen (Chm)
Tim McCarty (CEO)
Hang Gek Low (Pres-Filtration Grp Asia)
John Lavorato (Gen Counsel & VP)
Jon Peacock (Pres-Life Sciences Div)
Kristofer Howard (Pres-Indor Air Quality)
Robert Carpio (Pres-Porex)
Matt Huser (CMO)
Mike Ellis (Chief HR Officer)
Dave Janicek (CFO)

Subsidiary (Domestic):

Kaydon Custom Filtration Corporation (2)
1571 Lukken Industries Dr W, Lagrange, GA 30240
Tel.: (706) 884-3041
Web Site: http://www.kaydonfiltration.com
Fuel & Oil Filtering & Conditioning Solutions Mfr & Whslr
N.A.I.C.S.: 333248
James Mash (Pres & CEO)

Medtek Devices, Inc. (2)
595 Commerce Dr, Buffalo, NY 14228
Tel.: (716) 835-7000
Web Site: http://www.buffalofilter.com
Sales Range: $10-24.9 Million
Emp.: 50
Holding Company: Medical Equipment
N.A.I.C.S.: 551112
Christopher Palmerton (Pres)
Daniel Palmerton (VP-Sls & Mktg)
Nicole Kane (Dir-Fin)
Joseph Lynch (Exec Dir-Mktg)

Subsidiary (Non-US):

Molecular Products Group Limited (2)
Pkwy Harlow Business Park, Harlow, CM19 5FR, Essex, United Kingdom
Tel.: (44) 1279445111
Web Site:
http://www.molecularproducts.com
Molecular Products Design & Mfr
N.A.I.C.S.: 325120
Kelly Reinke (Pres)

Subsidiary (US):

The OC Lugo Co., Inc. (3)
633 CTC Blvd, Louisville, CO 80027
Tel.: (303) 666-4400
Web Site: http://www.oclugo.com
Chemical & Allied Products Merchant Whslr
N.A.I.C.S.: 424690
Susan Farber (Mgr-Customer Svc)
Richard Lugo (Pres)

Subsidiary (Domestic):

Porex Corporation (2)
500 Bohannon Rd, Fairburn, GA 30213 (100%)
Tel.: (770) 964-1421
Web Site: http://www.porex.com
Porous Plastic Product Mfr
N.A.I.C.S.: 326199
Rob Carpio (Pres)
Nils Gustavsson (Chief Comml Officer)
Angie Scott (VP-Global Ops)
Dan Gutierrez (Sr VP-Fin & IT)
Avi Robbins (VP-Global Product Dev R & D)
Ashley Barefoot (VP-Stategic Mktg)

Purafil, Inc. (2)
2654 Weaver Way, Doraville, GA 30340-1554
Tel.: (770) 662-8545
Web Site: http://www.purafil.com
Air & Odor Purification Systems Mfr
N.A.I.C.S.: 333413
Alan Block (Ops Mgr)
Greg Langston (VP-Sls)
John Michael McCracken (Controller)
Rob Carpio (Pres)

Holmatro N.V. (1)
Lissenvelt 30, PO Box 66, 4940 AA, Raamsdonksveer, Netherlands
Tel.: (31) 162589200
Web Site: http://www.holmatro.com
Sales Range: $75-99.9 Million
Emp.: 350
Hydraulic Industrial & Rescue Equipment, Rescue Assist Tools & Shoring Systems Mfr
N.A.I.C.S.: 333991
Bert Willems (Dir-Rescue Equipment)
Harm Hermans (Pres & CEO)

Subsidiary (US):

Holmatro, Inc. (2)
505 McCormick Dr, Glen Burnie, MD 21061-3254 (100%)
Tel.: (410) 768-9662
Web Site: http://www.holmatro-usa.com
Sales Range: $25-49.9 Million
Emp.: 60
Mfr & Sales of Rescue Equipment
N.A.I.C.S.: 333998
Fran Dunigan (Mgr-Product)
Tony Barboza (Mgr-Sls-Natl)
Daniel Reese (Pres)

Specified Air Solutions LLC (1)
1250 William St, Buffalo, NY 14240
Tel.: (716) 852-4400
Web Site: http://www.specifiedair.com
Sales Range: $75-99.9 Million
HVAC Equipment Mfr
N.A.I.C.S.: 333414
Stephan Richter (VP-Engrg)
Madonna Courtney (VP-Corp Mktg)
Charley Brown (CEO)

Subsidiary (Non-US):

Combat HVAC Limited (2)
Unit A Kings Hill Business Park, Darlaston Road, Wednesbury, WS10 7SH, West Midlands, United Kingdom
Tel.: (44) 121 506 7700
Web Site: http://www.robertsgordon.co.uk
Heating Equipment Mfr
N.A.I.C.S.: 333415

SAS Dectron Company (2)
5685 Rue Cypihot, Saint Laurent, H4S 1R3, QC, Canada
Tel.: (514) 336-3330
Web Site: http://www.dectron.com
Emp.: 500
Dehumidification, Refrigeration, Air Conditioning & Indoor Air Quality Products Mfr & Supplier
N.A.I.C.S.: 333415

Dalia Garabetian (Mgr-HR)

Subsidiary (Domestic):

Circul-Aire Inc. (3)
1840 Transcanada Hwy, Dorval, H9P 1h7, QC, Canada
Tel.: (514) 337-3331
Web Site: http://www.circul-aire.com
Emp.: 20
Chemical Filtration & Air Purification Products Mfr
N.A.I.C.S.: 333413
Ness Lakdawala (Pres)

Refplus Inc. (3)
2777 Grande Allee, Saint-Hubert, J4T 2R4, QC, Canada
Tel.: (450) 641-2665
Web Site: http://www.refplus.com
Emp.: 500
Air-Conditioning, Warm Air Heating & Industrial Refrigeration Equipment Mfr
N.A.I.C.S.: 333415

Subsidiary (US):

SAS Dectron Company (3)
419 E Crossville Rd Ste 105-106, Roswell, GA 30075
Tel.: (770) 649-0102
Web Site: http://www.dectron.com
Air Conditioning & Warm Air Heating Products Distr
N.A.I.C.S.: 423730

MADISON INDUSTRIES INC.
295 5th Ave Ste 512, New York, NY 10016
Tel.: (212) 679-5110 DE
Year Founded: 1967
Sales Range: $25-49.9 Million
Emp.: 600
Household Furnishings Mfr
N.A.I.C.S.: 314120

MADISON INDUSTRIES, INC.
Old Water Works Rd, Old Bridge, NJ 08857
Tel.: (732) 727-2225 NJ
Year Founded: 1963
Sales Range: $1-9.9 Million
Emp.: 35
Basic Inorganic Chemical Mfr
N.A.I.C.S.: 325180
Bruce Bzura (Pres)

Subsidiaries:

Reelcraft Industries Inc. (1)
2842 E Business 30, Columbia City, IN 46725
Tel.: (855) 634-9109
Web Site: http://www.reelcraft.com
Fabricated Metal Products Mfr
N.A.I.C.S.: 332999
Todd Bredice (Dir-Quality)
Bill Martin (Mgr-Sls-Natl)

MADISON INTERNATIONAL REALTY, LLC
410 Park Ave 10th Fl, New York, NY 10022
Tel.: (212) 688-8777
Web Site: http://www.madisonint.com
Year Founded: 2002
Privater Equity Firm
N.A.I.C.S.: 523999
Nausheen Hussain (Dir-HR)
Ronald M. Dickerman (Founder & Pres)
Carey Flaherty (Co-Chief Investment Officer)
Derek Jacobson (Co-Chief Investment Officer)
Matthias Cordier (Mng Dir)

Subsidiaries:

Capital Park S.A. (1)
Grupa Capital Park 1 Franciszka Klimczaka Street, 02-797, Warsaw, Poland (65.99%)
Tel.: (48) 223188888
Web Site: https://www.capitalpark.pl
Rev.: $15,535,198
Assets: $544,566,366
Liabilities: $277,766,511

MADISON INTERNATIONAL REALTY, LLC

Madison International Realty, LLC—(Continued)
Net Worth: $266,799,855
Earnings: ($6,400,272)
Fiscal Year-end: 12/31/2020
Real Estate Development Services
N.A.I.C.S.: 531390
Jan Motz *(Chm-Mgmt Bd & CEO)*
Marcin Juszczyk *(CFO, CIO & Member-Mgmt Bd)*
Kinga Nowakowska *(COO & Member-Mgmt Bd)*

MADISON INVESTMENT ADVISORS, INC.
550 Science Dr, Madison, WI 53711 — WI
Web Site: https://madisoninvestments.com
Year Founded: 1974
Emp.: 100
Portfolio Management
N.A.I.C.S.: 523940
Frank Edward Burgess *(Chm)*

MADISON LIQUIDITY INVESTORS LLC
619 DTC Parkway Ste 800, Greenwood Village, CO 80111
Tel.: (212) 687-0518
Web Site: http://www.madisoncap.com
Year Founded: 1996
Rev.: $10,500,000
Emp.: 7
Investment Advice
N.A.I.C.S.: 523940
Bryan E. Gordon *(Chm & Mng Dir)*
Barbara A. O'Hare *(Pres & Mng Dir)*

MADISON LUTHERAN HOME
900 2nd Ave, Madison, MN 56356
Tel.: (320) 598-7536 — MN
Web Site: http://www.mlhmn.org
Year Founded: 1945
Sales Range: $10-24.9 Million
Emp.: 328
Health Care Srvices
N.A.I.C.S.: 622110
Scott Larson *(Pres & CEO)*

MADISON MAIDEN
135 Madison Ave 12th Fl, New York, NY 10016
Tel.: (212) 686-2410
Web Site: http://jny.com
Sales Range: $10-24.9 Million
Emp.: 25
Lingerie
N.A.I.C.S.: 424350
Steven Kattan *(Pres)*

MADISON MARQUETTE DEVELOPMENT CORPORATION
670 Water St SW, Washington, DC 20024
Tel.: (202) 741-3800 — DE
Web Site: http://www.madisonmarquette.com
Year Founded: 1992
Sales Range: $10-24.9 Million
Emp.: 550
Holding Company; Specialty Retail Property Investor & Developer
N.A.I.C.S.: 551112
Amer Hammour *(Chm)*
Gary Mottola *(Pres-Property Investments)*
David Brainerd *(Chief Investment Officer)*
Thomas W. Gilmore *(Sr Mng Dir-Real Estate Svcs)*
Whitney Livingston *(Sr VP-Mgmt Svcs)*
Chuck Taylor *(Sr VP-Leasing)*
John Elliott *(CFO & Chief Admin Officer)*
Natasha Stancill *(VP-Mktg)*
Peter Tomai *(Mng Dir-Investments)*
Daniel Meyers *(Sr VP-Project Mgmt)*
Vince Costantini *(CEO)*
John Fleury *(Pres)*

Subsidiaries:

Madison Marquette Realty Services LLC (1)
1000 Maine Ave SW, Washington, DC 20024
Tel.: (202) 741-3800
Web Site: http://www.madisonmarquette.com
Emp.: 60
Specialty Retail Property Investor & Developer
N.A.I.C.S.: 237210
Amer Hammour *(Chm)*
Peter Jun *(COO)*
David Brainerd *(Chief Investment Officer)*
John Elliott *(CFO)*
Martin Kamm *(Mng Dir-Capital Markets)*
Brad Muth *(Sr Mng Dir-Portfolio Mgmt)*
Charlotte Stoller *(Mng Dir-Property Svcs)*
Vince Costantini *(CEO)*
John Fleury *(Pres)*

Subsidiary (Domestic):

The Roseview Group LLC (2)
100 High St Ste 410, Boston, MA 02110
Tel.: (617) 951-3900
Web Site: http://www.roseview.com
Emp.: 20
Investment Management & Advisory Services
N.A.I.C.S.: 523999

Subsidiary (Domestic):

Roseview Capital Partners LLC (3)
75 Federal St Ste 610, Boston, MA 02110
Tel.: (215) 240-1177
Web Site: http://www.roseview.com
Secondary Market Financing
N.A.I.C.S.: 522299
Vincent J. Costantini *(CEO & Partner)*

MADISON ONE HOLDINGS
1919 S Stoughton Rd, Madison, WI 53716
Tel.: (608) 222-3484
Web Site: http://www.boumatic.com
Sales Range: $25-49.9 Million
Emp.: 250
Holding Company
N.A.I.C.S.: 551112
Jerry Thain *(CFO)*

Subsidiaries:

BouMatic LLC (1)
2001 S Stoughton Rd, Madison, WI 53716
Tel.: (608) 222-3484
Web Site: http://www.boumatic.com
Dairy Equipment Mfr
N.A.I.C.S.: 333111
John Kopps *(Owner)*

MADISON PARKER CAPITAL
715 Boylston St, Boston, MA 02116
Tel.: (617) 910-0081 — MA
Web Site: http://www.madisonparkercapital.com
Year Founded: 2006
Privater Equity Firm
N.A.I.C.S.: 523999
Brent Brown *(Mng Partner)*

Subsidiaries:

Klone Lab, LLC (1)
9 Water St 3rd Fl, Amesbury, MA 01913
Tel.: (978) 378-3434
Web Site: http://www.klonelab.com
Sales Range: $25-49.9 Million
Emp.: 15
Licensing & Marketing of Sports & Lifestyle Accessory Products
N.A.I.C.S.: 423910

Subsidiary (Domestic):

IPATH LLC (2)
200 Domain Dr, Stratham, NH 03885-2575
Tel.: (310) 787-6600
Web Site: http://www.ipath.com
Sales Range: $10-24.9 Million
Emp.: 5
Footwear Mfr
N.A.I.C.S.: 316210

MADISON WOOD PRESERVERS INC.
216 Oak Pk Rd, Madison, VA 22727
Tel.: (540) 948-6801
Web Site: http://www.madwood.com
Sales Range: $75-99.9 Million
Emp.: 103
Wood Preserving
N.A.I.C.S.: 423310
Bobby Berrey *(Treas & Sec)*
Cindy Miller *(Mgr-Credit)*
Steve Lillard *(Pres)*
J. William Price III *(CEO)*

MADISON-KIPP CORPORATION
201 Waubesa St, Madison, WI 53704
Tel.: (608) 244-3511 — DE
Web Site: http://www.madison-kipp.com
Year Founded: 1898
Sales Range: $150-199.9 Million
Emp.: 600
Mfr of Aluminum & Zinc Castings
N.A.I.C.S.: 331523
Doug Buechel *(Mgr-Tool Procurement)*
Thomas Harrington *(Engr-Mfg)*
Terry Schrader *(Mgr-Maintenance)*
Lesley Sefcik *(Engr-Quality)*
Brian Strohmenger *(Mgr-Production)*
Matthew Mullen *(Mgr-Production)*
Ryan Hennessy *(Engr-Quality)*
Kim Eggers *(Dir-OS EHS)*
Mari Fuller *(Mgr-Logistics)*
David Grebe *(Plant Mgr)*
Dan McLean *(VP-Sls & Mktg)*
Tony Koblinski *(Pres & CEO)*

MADIX INC.
PO Box 729, Terrell, TX 75160-9001
Tel.: (972) 563-5744 — TX
Web Site: http://www.madixinc.com
Year Founded: 1962
Sales Range: $25-49.9 Million
Emp.: 1,400
Provider of Partitions & Store Fixtures
N.A.I.C.S.: 337126
Alan H. Sharaway *(CEO)*
T. A. Satterfield *(Pres)*
Sherif Sharawi *(Exec VP)*
Shawn Kahler *(VP-Sls & Mktg)*
Robert Hilton *(Dir-Sls)*

MADONNA ENTERPRISES
284 Higuera St, San Luis Obispo, CA 93401
Tel.: (805) 543-0300
Web Site: http://www.madonnainn.com
Sales Range: $25-49.9 Million
Emp.: 160
Highway & Street Construction
N.A.I.C.S.: 459420
Phyllis Madonna *(Pres)*
Michael Hardy *(Mgr-Steakhouse)*

MADRID ENGINEERING GROUP, INC.
2030 State Rd 60 E, Bartow, FL 33830
Tel.: (863) 533-9007
Web Site: http://www.madridengineering.com
Year Founded: 1992
Sales Range: $1-9.9 Million
Emp.: 45
Geotechnical Engineering & Environmental Consulting Services
N.A.I.C.S.: 541620
Larry D. Madrid *(Pres)*
Brian Murphy *(Sr Project Mgr)*
John Delashaw *(Chief Engr-Geotechnical)*
Lennon Jordan *(Chief Engr-Structural)*

MADRID HOME COMMUNITIES
613 W N St, Madrid, IA 50156
Tel.: (515) 795-3007 — IA
Web Site: http://www.madridhome.com
Year Founded: 1906
Sales Range: $10-24.9 Million
Emp.: 353
Community Housing Services
N.A.I.C.S.: 624229
Keith Kudej *(Pres & CEO)*
Carol Mallory *(Coord-Admissions)*
Diane Fredrick *(Coord-Mktg & Admissions)*
Kevin Houlette *(Chm)*
Don Catus *(Vice Chm)*
Marita Rouse *(Treas)*
Debi D. Weddll-Schutt *(Sec)*
Stephanie Webb *(Dir-Nursing)*
Brittany Crouse *(Dir-Social Svc)*

MADRONA SOLUTIONS GROUP
119 1st Ave S Ste 400, Seattle, WA 98104
Tel.: (206) 686-8701
Web Site: http://www.madronasg.com
Year Founded: 2005
Sales Range: $1-9.9 Million
Emp.: 21
Computer Design System Service
N.A.I.C.S.: 541512
Brian Paulen *(Principal)*
Jeff Finken *(Principal)*
Wei Gao *(Venture Partner)*
Anna Baird *(Operating Partner)*
Vivek Ramaswami *(Partner)*
Karan Mehandru *(Mng Dir)*
Scott Jacobson *(Mng Dir)*

MAESTRO FILMWORKS LLC
1021 N 3rd St Ste 301, Philadelphia, PA 19123
Tel.: (267) 908-4336
Web Site: http://www.maestrofilmworks.com
Year Founded: 2005
Sales Range: $1-9.9 Million
Emp.: 10
Video Production Services
N.A.I.C.S.: 512120
Kris Mendoza *(Founder)*
Geoff Nichols *(VP-Production)*
Joanna Shen *(Production Mgr)*
Kate Feher *(Mgr-Studio)*

MAESTRO LLC
401 E Michigan Ste 202, Kalamazoo, MI 49007 — MI
Web Site: http://www.meetmaestro.com
Year Founded: 2007
Sales Range: $1-9.9 Million
Emp.: 21
Business Software Developer
N.A.I.C.S.: 513210
Jessy Jex *(Project Mgr)*
Nate Norman *(Exec VP-Sls & Strategy)*
John Pinkster *(VP-Engrg)*

MAESTRO PRINT MANAGEMENT LLC
44 E Long Lake Rd, Bloomfield Hills, MI 48304
Tel.: (248) 430-5742
Web Site: http://www.maestromps.com
Print Management Solutions

N.A.I.C.S.: 323120
Shiva Palaniswami *(Pres & CEO)*

Subsidiaries:

International Business Systems, Inc. (1)
431 Yerkes Rd, King of Prussia, PA 19406
Tel.: (610) 265-8210
Web Site: http://www.ibsdm.com
Direct Response Printing & Marketing Services
N.A.I.C.S.: 541860
George H. Schnyder *(CEO)*
Ted Sherwin *(Pres)*
Shaun Buss *(CFO)*
Jaime Capacete *(VP-Sls)*
June Busch *(VP-Client Svcs)*

MAESTRO TECHNOLOGIES, INC.
707 Alexander Rd Ste 204, Princeton, NJ 08540
Tel.: (609) 520-9800
Web Site: http://www.maestro.com
Year Founded: 2003
Sales Range: $1-9.9 Million
Emp.: 59
Information Technology Services
N.A.I.C.S.: 541618
Daniele Loffreda *(Dir-IT)*
Kamal Bathla *(Mng Dir)*

MAETEC POWER, INC.
388 Mason Rd, Fairport, NY 14450
Tel.: (585) 425-1954
Web Site:
  http://www.maetecpower.com
Sales Range: $1-9.9 Million
Emp.: 17
DC Power & Battery Installation Services
N.A.I.C.S.: 238990
Mark Miller *(Pres)*
James Allen *(VP)*

MAFCOTE INDUSTRIES INC.
108 Main St, Norwalk, CT 06851-4640
Tel.: (203) 847-8500   DE
Web Site: http://www.mafcote.com
Year Founded: 1975
Sales Range: $25-49.9 Million
Emp.: 300
Paperboard Mills
N.A.I.C.S.: 322130
Steven A. Schulman *(Pres)*

MAG DS CORP.
12730 Fair Lakes Cir Ste 600, Fairfax, VA 22033
Tel.: (703) 376-8993   DE
Web Site: http://www.magaero.com
Year Founded: 2004
Aerial Surveillance; Intelligence & Surveillance Services
N.A.I.C.S.: 519290
Joe Fluet *(Chm)*
Joseph B. Paull *(Vice Chm & COO)*
Matt Bartlett *(Pres & Chief Growth Officer)*
Joseph Reale *(CEO)*
Robert Heller *(Exec VP-Surveillance, Engrg & Comm (SEC) Bus Unit)*
Justin Janaskie *(CTO & Dir-C5ISR Programs)*
Nicholas Veasey *(CFO)*
Lorna Derosa *(Gen Counsel & Sr VP)*
Jerry Rippon *(Exec VP-Advanced Engrg & Tech (AET) Bus Unit)*

Subsidiaries:

Ausley Associates Inc. (1)
46611 Corporate Dr St101, Lexington Park, MD 20653
Tel.: (301) 863-2800
Web Site: http://ausley.us

Sales Range: $1-9.9 Million
Engineeering Services
N.A.I.C.S.: 541330
Paul Ausley *(Founder & CEO)*
Scott Sanders *(Pres)*
Stephen Cassetta *(Mgr-Div)*
Wendy Lee *(VP-Strategic Plng & Dev)*
Doug Leepa *(Dir-Corp Ops)*
Jay Pearsall *(Mgr-Air Combat Demand-Div)*
Patrick Smith *(Mgr-Advanced Programs-Div)*

BOSH Global Services, Inc. (1)
1 Compass Way Ste 250, Newport News, VA 23606
Tel.: (757) 271-3428
Web Site: http://www.boshgs.com
Sales Range: $10-24.9 Million
Emp.: 133
Surveillance System Installation Services
N.A.I.C.S.: 238210
Buzz Kleemann *(CFO)*
Michael Archuleta *(COO)*
Shelly Fitzgerald *(Exec VP)*

MAG IAS HOLDINGS, INC.
444 Madison Ave 27th Fl, New York, NY 10022
Tel.: (212) 400-2655   NY
Web Site: http://www.mag-ias.com
Holding Company
N.A.I.C.S.: 551112
Moshe I. Meidar *(Chm)*
Rainer Schmueckle *(CEO)*

Subsidiaries:

MAG India Industrial Automation Systems Pvt. Ltd. (1)
67 1st Main Industrial Suburb, 2nd Stage Yeshwantpur, Bengaluru, 560 022, India
Tel.: (91) 80 4067 7000
Emp.: 54
Machine Tools Sales, Marketing & Customer Service
N.A.I.C.S.: 423830
Manoj Kumar *(Mgr-Indus Equipment-Aerospace Projects)*
Riyaz Nune *(Project Mgr)*
William Bernard *(Mgr-Customer Svc)*
Shashank M P *(Pres)*

MAG Maintenance UK Limited (1)
Unit 6 Maybrook Road Maybrook Business Park, Minworth, Birmingham, B76 1AL, United Kingdom
Tel.: (44) 1213135300
Web Site: http://www.mag-ias.com
Sales Range: $150-199.9 Million
Emp.: 50
Metal Working Machinery & Machine Tools Mfr
N.A.I.C.S.: 333517
John Boyd *(Mng Dir)*

MAG INSTRUMENT INC.
1635 S Sacramento Ave PO Box 50600, Ontario, CA 91761
Tel.: (909) 947-1006
Web Site: http://www.maglite.com
Year Founded: 1955
Sales Range: $25-49.9 Million
Emp.: 800
Mfr of Lighting Equipment
N.A.I.C.S.: 423610
Anthony Maglica *(Founder, Pres & CEO)*
Mike Mayhugh *(Supvr-Injection Molding)*
Malissa Peace *(CMO)*

MAG MUTUAL INSURANCE COMPANY
3535 Piedmont Rd NE 14 Bldg 1000, Atlanta, GA 30305-1556
Tel.: (404) 842-5500   GA
Web Site: http://www.magmutual.com
Year Founded: 1982
Sales Range: $150-199.9 Million
Disability Insurance Services
N.A.I.C.S.: 524126

Ed Lynch *(Chief Bus Ops Officer)*
Karen Civali *(Mgr-Risk & Patient Safety)*
Rebecca Summer-Lowman *(Mgr-Risk & Patient Safety)*

MAG-NIF INC.
8820 E Ave, Mentor, OH 44060-4306
Tel.: (440) 255-9366   OH
Web Site: http://www.magnif.com
Year Founded: 1963
Sales Range: $10-24.9 Million
Emp.: 200
Mfr of Games Toys Puzzles & Childrens Banks
N.A.I.C.S.: 339930
Vill Knox *(Pres)*
Bill Reed *(Mgr-Shipping Traffic)*
Terri Gernentz *(Mgr-Quality Assurance)*
Dennis Delaat *(VP-Ops)*

MAG-TEK INC.
1710 Apollo Ct, Seal Beach, CA 90740
Tel.: (562) 546-6400   CA
Web Site: http://www.magtek.com
Year Founded: 1972
Sales Range: $10-24.9 Million
Emp.: 225
Mfr of Computer Peripheral Equipment
N.A.I.C.S.: 334118
Mimi Heart *(Pres)*
Andrew Deignan *(Chm, Pres & CEO)*
John Arato *(VP & Product Mgr)*
Steve Harvey *(COO)*
Nedal Almomani *(CTO)*
Satish Govindarajan *(Chief Sls & Strategy Officer)*

MAGA DESIGN GROUP
1838 Columbia Rd NW, Washington, DC 20009
Tel.: (202) 234-8685
Web Site:
  http://www.magadesign.com
Year Founded: 2005
Rev.: $2,100,000
Emp.: 13
Commercial Research
N.A.I.C.S.: 541910
Scott Williams *(Owner)*
Brooke Smith *(Chief Growth Officer)*

MAGAZINES.COM INC.
325 Seaboard Ln Ste 150, Franklin, TN 37067-6431
Tel.: (615) 778-2100   DE
Web Site: http://www.magazines.com
Year Founded: 1991
Sales Range: $10-24.9 Million
Emp.: 75
Online Magazine Subscription Agency
N.A.I.C.S.: 459210
Jay Clarke *(Pres & CEO)*
Andy Sperry *(VP-Mktg & Bus Dev)*

MAGBEE CONTRACTORS SUPPLY
1065 Bankhead Hwy, Winder, GA 30680-8415
Tel.: (678) 425-2600   GA
Web Site: http://www.magbee.com
Year Founded: 1954
Sales Range: $25-49.9 Million
Emp.: 100
Millwork
N.A.I.C.S.: 321918
Robert Magbee *(Pres & Sec)*
Blase Grady *(COO)*

MAGEE GENERAL HOSPITAL
300 3rd Ave SE, Magee, MS 39111
Tel.: (601) 849-5070   MS
Web Site: http://www.mghosp.org

Year Founded: 1942
Sales Range: $10-24.9 Million
Emp.: 358
Health Care Srvices
N.A.I.C.S.: 622110
Melissa Cooper *(Dir-Nursing)*
Chanda Roberts *(Controller)*
Serina Blackwell *(Dir-Revenue Cycle)*
Kirby Craft *(CIO)*
Charles Pruitt III *(Chm)*

MAGELLAN JETS LLC.
1250 Hancock St Ste 802 N Twr, Quincy, MA 02169
Tel.: (617) 328-5387
Web Site:
  http://www.magellanjets.com
Year Founded: 2008
Sales Range: $10-24.9 Million
Emp.: 15
Jet Charter Services
N.A.I.C.S.: 481211
Joshua Hebert *(Co-Founder & CEO)*
Anthony Tivnan *(Co-Founder & Pres)*
Gregory Belezerian *(VP)*
Kirby Shimko *(Chief Strategy Officer)*
Patricia Reed *(Dir-Flight Support)*

MAGELLAN SEARCH GROUP, INC.
1275 Drummers Ln, Wayne, PA 19087
Tel.: (610) 941-0100
Web Site:
  http://www.magellangroup.com
Year Founded: 2002
Sales Range: $1-9.9 Million
Emp.: 7
Human Resource Consulting Services
N.A.I.C.S.: 541612
Joseph Nicolas *(CEO)*

MAGEX CORPORATION
520 Madison Ave, New York, NY 10022-4213
Tel.: (917) 639-7600
Web Site: http://www.magex.com
Rev.: $12,100,000
Emp.: 150
Data Processing Consultant
N.A.I.C.S.: 541512
David F. Kvederis *(Pres & CEO)*
Mary Ellen Putnam *(VP & Gen Mgr)*
Don Suva *(CFO)*

MAGGARD ENTERPRISES INC.
10370 Hemet St Ste 240, Riverside, CA 92503
Tel.: (909) 343-1010
Rev.: $15,000,000
Emp.: 12
Seafood Restaurants
N.A.I.C.S.: 722511

MAGGIES ENTERPRISES INC.
5393 Wesleyan Dr Ste 104, Virginia Beach, VA 23455-6900
Tel.: (757) 498-0008
Web Site:
  http://www.mattressdiscountersva.com
Sales Range: $10-24.9 Million
Emp.: 4
Beds & Accessories
N.A.I.C.S.: 337910
Roger E. Magowitz *(Pres)*

MAGGY LONDON INTERNATIONAL LTD. INC.
530 7th Ave Fl 16, New York, NY 10018-4856
Tel.: (212) 944-7199   NY
Web Site:
  http://www.maagylondon.com
Year Founded: 1979

Maggy London International Ltd. Inc.—(Continued)
Sales Range: $10-24.9 Million
Emp.: 100
Provider of Womens, Juniors & Misses Dresses
N.A.I.C.S.: 315250
Larry Lefkowitz (Pres)

MAGIC HAT CONSULTING
455 Pennsylvania Ave Ste 125, Fort Washington, PA 19034
Tel.: (215) 540-1200
Web Site: http://www.magichatconsulting.com
Sales Range: $1-9.9 Million
Emp.: 27
Business Research & Development Services
N.A.I.C.S.: 541720
Jim Lyons (Pres & CEO)

MAGIC JOHNSON ENTERPRISES
9100 Wilshire Blvd Ste 700 E Tower, Beverly Hills, CA 90212
Tel.: (310) 246-6149
Web Site: http://www.magicjohnson.com
Year Founded: 1987
Sales Range: $75-99.9 Million
Emp.: 25
Corporate Endorsement, Venture Capital & Real Estate Investment Firm
N.A.I.C.S.: 523999
Earvin Johnson (Chm & CEO)
Kawanna Brown (COO)
Sheila Ewing (CFO)
Christina M. Francis (Pres)

Subsidiaries:

EquiTrust Life Insurance Company (1)
7100 Westown Pkwy Ste 200, West Des Moines, IA 50266-2521
Tel.: (888) 400-5759
Web Site: http://www.equitrust.com
Fire Insurance Services
N.A.I.C.S.: 524113
Kevin Klocke (Mgr-Sys Application)
Jeanne Taylor (VP-Annuity & Life Sls)
Ana Bumgardner (VP-Product Mgmt)
Heather Kane (Sr Mgr-Sls-Life & Annuity)
Carol Woodruff (Dir-Info Sys)
Rosemary Parson (Sr VP-Community Rels & Policy Admin & VP)

MAGIC LOGIX INC.
3234 Commander Dr, Carrollton, TX 75006
Tel.: (214) 694-2162
Web Site: http://www.magiclogix.com
Sales Range: $1-9.9 Million
Emp.: 15
Digital Marketing Services
N.A.I.C.S.: 541613
Hassan Bawab (CEO & Mgr-Bus Dev)
Cristin Padgett (Mgr-Bus Dev)
Farid Kiblawi (VP-Sls & Bus Dev)

MAGIC MOMENTS, INC.
2112 11th Ave S Ste 219, Birmingham, AL 35205
Tel.: (205) 638-9372 AL
Web Site: http://www.magicmoments.org
Year Founded: 1984
Rev.: $1,031,754
Assets: $937,691
Liabilities: $296,506
Net Worth: $641,185
Earnings: $89,982
Emp.: 8
Fiscal Year-end: 12/31/14
Grantmaking Services
N.A.I.C.S.: 813219

Kamala Quintana (Mgr-Production)
Ruby Hershberger (Second VP)
Ted Kuenz (Pres)
Kelly Morrison (Chm)

MAGIC STEEL CORPORATION
4242 Clay Ave SW, Grand Rapids, MI 49548
Tel.: (616) 532-4071
Web Site: http://www.magicsteelsales.com
Rev.: $93,000,000
Emp.: 120
Iron & Steel (Ferrous) Products
N.A.I.C.S.: 423510
Joseph L. Maggini (Chm & Pres)
Brian Williams (Plant Mgr)

MAGIC TILT TRAILERS, INC.
2161 Lions Club Rd, Clearwater, FL 33764
Tel.: (727) 535-5561
Web Site: http://www.magictilt.com
Year Founded: 1953
Sales Range: $10-24.9 Million
Emp.: 63
Aluminum Extruded Product Mfr
N.A.I.C.S.: 331315
Elizabeth Coccia (Mgr-HR)
Joe Rubino (CFO)
Jeff Dobbs (Mgr-Shipping)
Craig Clawson (Pres & CEO)

MAGIC VALLEY ELECTRIC COOPERATIVE
2910 Monte Cristo, Edinburg, TX 78539
Web Site: http://www.magval.com
Year Founded: 1937
Rev.: $85,354,626
Emp.: 90
Electronic Services
N.A.I.C.S.: 221118
John W. Herrera (Gen Mgr)

MAGIC VALLEY FRESH FROZEN, INC.
3701 W Military Hwy, McAllen, TX 78503-4403
Tel.: (956) 994-8947
Sales Range: $10-24.9 Million
Emp.: 300
Malt Mfr
N.A.I.C.S.: 311213

MAGID GLOVE SAFETY MANUFACTURING CO. LLC
1300 Naperville Dr, Romeoville, IL 60446
Tel.: (773) 384-2070
Web Site: http://www.magidglove.com
Sales Range: $25-49.9 Million
Emp.: 400
Mfr, Importer & Distr of Work Gloves, Leather Gloves, Disposable Gloves & Industrial Safety Equipment
N.A.I.C.S.: 315990
Abe Cohen (Co-Founder)
Pete Baltes (VP-Accts)

MAGILL CONSTRUCTION COMPANY, INC.
977 Koopman Ln, Elkhorn, WI 53121
Tel.: (262) 723-2283
Web Site: http://www.magillconstruction.com
Rev.: $12,000,000
Emp.: 55
Commercial & Institutional Building Construction
N.A.I.C.S.: 236220
Robert K. Magill (Pres)
Matt Magill (VP)
Steven Knudson (VP)

MAGLINE, INC.
1205 W Cedar St, Standish, MI 48658-9535
Tel.: (989) 879-2411 MI
Web Site: http://www.magliner.com
Year Founded: 1947
Sales Range: $75-99.9 Million
Emp.: 130
Hand Trucks & Accessories Mfr
N.A.I.C.S.: 333924
D. Brian Law (Chm & CEO)
Kari Michalski (Mgr-Channel)
Alan Martin (Controller)
Terry Perkins (Mgr-Quality)
Andrea Horner (VP-Mktg)
Jennifer Lovett (Mgr-HR)
Karen Perry (Mgr-Customer Svc)
John Baird (CFO)

Subsidiaries:

Magline Sano GmbH (1)
PO Box 902130, 21055, Hamburg, Germany
Tel.: (49) 76795291
Web Site: http://www.magliner.com
Hand Trucks & Accessories Whslr
N.A.I.C.S.: 333924

Magliner Do Brasil (1)
Rodovia Br 277 1315 A - Km 205, Campo Largo, 83605-420, Parana, Brazil
Tel.: (55) 4132929192
Hand Truck Whslr
N.A.I.C.S.: 333924

Magliner International LLC (1)
PO Box 2948, Stert Devises, Swindon, SN109AD, Wiltshire, United Kingdom
Tel.: (44) 380725070
Sales Range: $25-49.9 Million
Hand Truck Whslr
N.A.I.C.S.: 333924

MAGLIO BROS INC.
3632 S 3rd St, Philadelphia, PA 19148
Tel.: (215) 465-3902
Web Site: http://www.maglios.com
Rev.: $13,700,000
Emp.: 40
Mfr Of Sausages, From Purchased Meat
N.A.I.C.S.: 311612
Anthony L. Maglio (VP)
Anthony J. Maglio Jr. (Pres)

MAGNA CARTA COMPANIES
1 Park Ave 15th Fl, New York, NY 10016-5807
Tel.: (212) 591-9500
Web Site: http://www.mcarta.com
Sales Range: $100-124.9 Million
Emp.: 300
Fire, Marine & Casualty Insurance
N.A.I.C.S.: 524126
Theodore Smyk (VP)
Mark Battistelli (VP)
Lon Cagley (VP)
Louis Masucci (VP-Underwriting)
Grace Yang (VP-Actuarial)
Kevin Leong (VP-Claims)

MAGNA IV
2401 Commercial Ln, Little Rock, AR 72206
Tel.: (501) 376-2397
Web Site: http://www.magna4.com
Year Founded: 1975
Sales Range: $10-24.9 Million
Emp.: 65
High-Resolution Scanning & Lithography Services
N.A.I.C.S.: 323111
Gary Middleton (Co-Founder)
Pat Middleton (Co-Founder)
Kent Middleton (CEO)
Kristi Dannelley (COO)
Barbara Bosshardt (Mgr-Customer Svc)

Jonathan Martin (Mgr-Asst Plant)
Anne Eden (Mgr-Estimating)
Jon Davis (Dir-Sls Northwest Arkansas)
Megan Miller (Coord-mktg)

MAGNA MACHINE CO. INC.
11180 Southland Rd, Cincinnati, OH 45240
Tel.: (513) 851-6900
Web Site: http://www.magna-machine.com
Sales Range: $10-24.9 Million
Emp.: 130
Machine Shop, Jobbing & Repair
N.A.I.C.S.: 332710
Scott Kramer (Pres)
Todd Broxterman (Engr-Design)

MAGNADRIVE CORPORATION
14660 NE North Woodinville Way, Woodinville, WA 98072
Tel.: (425) 463-4700
Web Site: http://www.magnadrive.com
Sales Range: $1-9.9 Million
Emp.: 24
Magnetic Couplings for Connecting Large Industrial Motors to Drive Shafts
N.A.I.C.S.: 333248
Geoff Harmon (Sr Engr-Applications)

MAGNADYNE CORPORATION
1111 W Victoria St, Compton, CA 90220
Tel.: (310) 884-7777
Web Site: http://www.magnadyne.com
Rev.: $14,400,000
Emp.: 50
Automotive Electronics
N.A.I.C.S.: 423620
Barry Caren (Founder & Pres)
Pat Reardon (VP)
Ben Yeh (Mgr-QA)

MAGNANI CARUSO DUTTON
138 W 25th St 5th Fl, New York, NY 10001
Tel.: (212) 500-4500
Web Site: http://www.mcdpartners.com
Sales Range: $10-24.9 Million
Emp.: 92
Advetising Agency
N.A.I.C.S.: 541810
John Caruso (Partner & Dir-Creative)
John Dutton (Owner)
Wasim Choudhury (Partner)
James Warren (Dir-Tech & QA)

MAGNAPLAN CORPORATION
1320 Rte 9, Champlain, NY 12919-5007
Tel.: (518) 298-8404
Web Site: http://www.visualplanning.com
Sales Range: $1-9.9 Million
Emp.: 40
Display & Graphic Arts Products Mfr
N.A.I.C.S.: 541430
Joseph P. Josephson (Mng Dir)
Carl Maurice (Mgr-Graphic Arts)

Subsidiaries:

Magnaplan Corporation Visual Planning Division (1)
1320 Rte 9, Champlain, NY 12919
Tel.: (518) 298-8404
Web Site: http://www.visualplanning.com
Graphic Visual Controls, Layout Boards & Stationery Supplies Whslr
N.A.I.C.S.: 332999
Boris Polanski (Mgr-Adv)

MAGNATE CAPITAL PARTNERS, LLC
Oakbrook Terrace Twr 1 Tower Ln, Ste 2101, Oakbrook Terrace, IL 60181
Tel.: (312) 725-6603 DE
Web Site: http://www.magnatecp.com
Year Founded: 2012
Privater Equity Firm
N.A.I.C.S.: 523999
Daniel Para *(Founder & CEO)*
John Musolino *(Partner)*
Bob Para *(Partner)*
Frank Shinnick *(Partner)*
Mike Welch *(Partner)*

MAGNECO/METREL, INC.
223 W Interstate Rd, Addison, IL 60101-4513
Tel.: (630) 543-6660 OH
Web Site: http://www.magneco-metrel.com
Year Founded: 1979
Sales Range: $100-124.9 Million
Emp.: 175
Mfr Refractory Clay Products & Ceramics for Steel Industry
N.A.I.C.S.: 327120
Colleen Connors *(Gen Counsel & VP)*
Madjid Soofi *(Exec VP-Mktg, Tech & Engrg)*
Thomas Fisher *(VP-Sls-Eastern Reg)*
Jerry Moore *(District Mgr)*
Michael Anderson *(VP-Res)*
Susan C. Malloy *(CFO & VP)*
Thomas E. Wank *(VP-Field Technical Svcs)*
Albert J. Dzermejko *(VP-Engrg)*
Scott Knarr *(Mgr-Mfg)*
James Colander *(Plant Mgr)*
Mark Taylor *(VP-Europe)*
Morgan Meng *(VP-Asia)*
Thomas J. Colander *(VP-Sls-Central)*
Timothy Maruk *(VP-Sls-Northern Reg)*
Mauro Gonzalez *(Mgr-District)*
Charles W. Connors Jr. *(Pres & COO)*

Subsidiaries:

Magneco/Metrel UK Ltd. (1)
Hackworth Industrial Park, Shildon, DL4 1HG, Durham, United Kingdom
Tel.: (44) 138 877 7484
Emp.: 8
Ferro Alloy Whslr
N.A.I.C.S.: 423510
Mark Caylor *(Gen Mgr)*

MAGNECORP, INC.
1400 Eddy Ave, Rockford, IL 61103
Tel.: (763) 383-1400
Web Site: http://www.magnecorp.com
Year Founded: 1977
Sales Range: $25-49.9 Million
Emp.: 5
Ladderless Systems for Hanging Signs Mfr
N.A.I.C.S.: 337126

MAGNER SANBORN
111 N Post Ste 400, Spokane, WA 99201
Tel.: (509) 688-2200
Web Site: http://www.magnersanborn.com
Year Founded: 2003
Sales Range: $10-24.9 Million
Emp.: 35
Advertising Agencies, Brand Development, Point of Sale
N.A.I.C.S.: 541810
Jeff Sanborn *(VP & Dir-Creative)*
Dennis Magner *(Owner)*
Chelsea Newman *(Acct Coord)*
Teresa Ide *(Acct Coord)*

MAGNESS OIL COMPANY INC.
167 Tucker Cemetery Rd, Gassville, AR 72635
Tel.: (870) 425-4353
Web Site: http://www.magnessoil.com
Sales Range: $25-49.9 Million
Emp.: 700
Petroleum Bulk Stations
N.A.I.C.S.: 424710
Benny Magness *(Pres)*
Jannie Magness *(Treas & Sec)*

MAGNET INC.
1768 E 25th St, Cleveland, OH 44114
Tel.: (216) 432-5300 OH
Web Site: http://www.magnetwork.org
Year Founded: 1984
Sales Range: $10-24.9 Million
Emp.: 50
Business Associations
N.A.I.C.S.: 813910
Christopher L. Mapes *(Vice Chm)*
David Crain *(Dir-Entrepreneurial Svcs)*
Ethan Karp *(Pres & CEO)*

MAGNET LLC
7 Chamber Dr, Washington, MO 63090-5258
Tel.: (636) 239-5661
Web Site: http://www.themagnetgroup.com
Year Founded: 1984
Sales Range: $25-49.9 Million
Emp.: 400
Mfr of Fabricated Metal Products
N.A.I.C.S.: 332999
Bill Korowitz *(CEO)*
Doug Reinecke *(Mgr-Maintenance & Facility)*

Subsidiaries:

Phonecard Express, LLC (1)
7 Chamber Dr, Washington, MO 63090-5258
Tel.: (636) 239-5661
Web Site: http://www.magnetgroup.com
Sales Range: $25-49.9 Million
Emp.: 200
Provider of Commercial Printing & Lithographic Services
N.A.I.C.S.: 323111

MAGNETAR CAPITAL, LLC
1603 Orrington Ave 13th Fl, Evanston, IL 60201
Tel.: (847) 905-4400
Web Site: http://www.magnetar.com
School & Employee Bus Transportation
N.A.I.C.S.: 485410
David Snyderman *(Principal)*
Alec Litowitz *(Founder & CEO)*
Brian Portnoy *(Dir-Education)*
Neil Tiwari *(Partner-Private Healthcare Ventures)*

MAGNETIC ANALYSIS CORPORATION
103 Fairview Park Dr Ste 2, Elmsford, NY 10523-1544
Tel.: (914) 699-9450 NY
Web Site: http://www.mac-ndt.com
Year Founded: 1928
Sales Range: $25-49.9 Million
Emp.: 130
Mfr of Electro-Magnetic Testing Equipment & Ultrasonic Instrumentation
N.A.I.C.S.: 334519
Greg Gionta *(Plant Mgr)*

Subsidiaries:

Magnetic Analysis Australia, Pty. Ltd. (1)
Unit A9 16A Amax Avenue, Girraween, 2145, NSW, Australia
Tel.: (61) 296 316 580
Web Site: http://www.mac-ndt.com.au
Laboratory Testing Services
N.A.I.C.S.: 541380

Magnetic Analysis Italia, S.r.l. (1)
MBE via Montebello 20, 27058, Voghera, Italy
Tel.: (39) 0348 4458 584
Web Site: http://www.mac-ndt.it
Laboratory Testing Services
N.A.I.C.S.: 541380

Magnetic Analysis Ltd (1)
Unit 1 The Old Mill, Ilkeston, DE7 8ZG, Derbyshire, United Kingdom
Tel.: (44) 1159303690
Web Site: http://www.mac-ndt.co.uk
Laboratory Testing Services
N.A.I.C.S.: 541380

Magnetic Analysis Nordic AB (1)
Arena Vagen 4, 83132, Ostersund, Sweden
Tel.: (46) 63 51 77 20
Web Site: http://www.manordic.com
Laboratory Testing Services
N.A.I.C.S.: 541380

MAGNETIC COMPONENT ENGINEERING INC.
2830 Lomita Blvd, Torrance, CA 90505
Tel.: (310) 784-3100
Web Site: http://www.mceproducts.com
Rev.: $18,500,000
Emp.: 67
Mfr of High Performance Magnets, Magnet Assemblies & Magnetic Components for Aerospace/Defense, Medical, Industrial, Semiconductor, Research Laboratories & Telecommunications
N.A.I.C.S.: 332999

MAGNETIC MEDIA ONLINE, INC.
5 9 Union Sq W 3rd Fl, New York, NY 10003
Tel.: (212) 757-3189
Web Site: http://www.magnetic.com
Online Advertising Services
N.A.I.C.S.: 541810
James Green *(CEO)*
Hugh McGoran *(Chief Revenue Officer)*
Paul McCarthy *(VP-People Ops)*
Lauren Dubick *(Chief Privacy Officer & Gen Counsel)*
Jason Shriver *(Sr VP-Client Success)*
Dave Villano *(CTO)*

MAGNETIC PRODUCTS & SERVICES, INC.
7500 Boone Ave N Ste 104, Minneapolis, MN 55428
Tel.: (763) 424-2700
Web Site: http://www.mpsinc.org
Year Founded: 1989
Sales Range: $10-24.9 Million
Emp.: 30
Computer Magnetic Tap
N.A.I.C.S.: 811210
Michelle Morey *(Co-Owner & VP-Sls & Mktg)*
Kristine Hunter *(Co-Owner & VP-Ops)*

MAGNETIC SPRINGS WATER COMPANY
1917 Joyce Ave, Columbus, OH 43219
Tel.: (614) 421-1780
Web Site: http://www.magneticsprings.com
Rev.: $11,900,000
Emp.: 70
Mineral or Spring Water Bottling
N.A.I.C.S.: 424490

James E. Allison *(Pres)*

MAGNETIC TICKET & LABEL CORP.
8719 Diplomacy Row, Dallas, TX 75247
Tel.: (214) 634-8600
Web Site: http://www.magticket.com
Rev.: $70,000,000
Emp.: 180
Ticket & Label Mfr
N.A.I.C.S.: 322299
Kaylynne Phillips *(Mgr-HR)*
Jimmy Woods *(Supvr-Production)*

Subsidiaries:

HFS Holding CORPORATION (1)
8900 Ambassador Row, Dallas, TX 75247-4510
Tel.: (214) 634-8900
Web Site: http://www.hforms.com
Sales Range: $1-9.9 Million
Emp.: 30
Paper Products Mfr
N.A.I.C.S.: 322299
Peter A. Pyhrr *(Pres)*
Tom Hellenbrook *(VP-Mfg)*
Rick Vullo *(Mgr-Customer Svc & Sls)*

MAGNETIKA, INC.
2041 W 139th St, Gardena, CA 90249
Tel.: (310) 527-8100
Web Site: http://www.magnetika.com
Emp.: 100
Designer & Mfr of Transformers, Inductors & Custom Magnetic Components
N.A.I.C.S.: 334416
Sheryl Furst-Heier *(Controller)*
Nick Defalco *(Gen Mgr)*
Nagui Guirgis *(Mgr-Ops & Eng)*
Basil P. Caloyeras *(Chm & Pres-Gen Partner)*

Subsidiaries:

Magnetika, Inc. (1)
300 Red School Ln, Phillipsburg, NJ 08865
Tel.: (908) 454-2600
Web Site: http://www.magnetika.com
Sales Range: $10-24.9 Million
Emp.: 50
Magnetic Components Mfr
N.A.I.C.S.: 335311
Meggie Guirgis *(Gen Mgr)*

Magnetika, Inc.-Gardena (1)
2041 W 139th St, Gardena, CA 90249
Tel.: (310) 527-8100
Web Site: http://00879ca.netsolhost.com
Transformers, Inductors & Custom Magnetic Components Designer & Mfr
N.A.I.C.S.: 334419
Basil Caloyeras *(Chm)*

MAGNI GROUP INC.
390 Park St Ste 300, Birmingham, MI 48009
Tel.: (248) 647-4500
Web Site: http://www.themagnigroup.com
Year Founded: 1978
Rev.: $40,000,000
Emp.: 14
Mfr of Protective Coating Systems: Rust Resisting Compounds
N.A.I.C.S.: 325998
David E. Berry *(Founder & Chm)*
Doug Paul *(VP-Magni Asia Sls & Mktg)*

Subsidiaries:

Anti-Friction Enterprises 1985 (1)
150 Summerlea Road, Brampton, L6T 4X3, ON, Canada
Tel.: (905) 793-4493
Web Site: https://www.anti-friction.ca
Coating, Rust Preventive
N.A.I.C.S.: 332812

Depor Industries Inc. (1)

MAGNI GROUP INC.

Magni Group Inc.—(Continued)

1902 NW, Troy, MI 48084
Tel.: (248) 362-3900
Web Site: http://www.deporindustries.net
Coating, Rust Preventive
N.A.I.C.S.: 332812
Ted Howard *(Gen Mgr)*
Dave Steiner *(Mgr-Sls)*

Magni America do Sul (1)
Av Pierre Simon de Laplace 901 BL 08
Techno Park, Campinas, 13069320, Brazil
Tel.: (55) 1937839548
Web Site: http://www.magnibrasil.com.br
Emp.: 10
Metal Plating Services
N.A.I.C.S.: 332812
Francisco Carlos Benite *(Gen Dir)*

Magni Europe GmbH & Co. KG (1)
Heinkelstr 21-23, 73614, Schorndorf, Germany
Tel.: (49) 7181 97776 0
Web Site: http://www.lack-schmid.de
Metal Plating Services
N.A.I.C.S.: 332812
Gunter Hieber *(Mng Dir & Gen Mgr-Sls Mgmt)*
Stefan Weber *(CFO-Purchase, Employees, Acctg, Fin & IT)*

Magni-Industries Inc. (1)
2771 Hammond St, Detroit, MI 48209
Tel.: (313) 843-7855
Web Site: http://www.magnigroup.com
Sales Range: $10-24.9 Million
Rust Resisting Compounds
N.A.I.C.S.: 325998
Warren Knape *(Supvr-Analytical Lab)*

SprayTek, Inc. (1)
2535 Wolcott, Ferndale, MI 48220
Tel.: (248) 399-5580
Web Site: http://www.spraytekinc.com
Metal Plating Services
N.A.I.C.S.: 332812
Marvin Hairston *(Gen Mgr)*

MAGNI-POWER COMPANY INC.

5511 E Lincoln Way, Wooster, OH 44691-8607
Tel.: (330) 264-3637
Web Site: http://www.magnipower.com
Year Founded: 1948
Sales Range: $10-24.9 Million
Emp.: 300
Fabricated Structural Metal; Thermoforming & Custom Magnetic Assemblies
N.A.I.C.S.: 332312
Bala Venkataraman *(Pres & CEO)*
Dean Yoder *(Gen Mgr)*
Ken Troxel *(VP-Ops)*

Subsidiaries:

Magni-Fab Southwest Co. Inc. (1)
5511 E Lincoln Way, Wooster, OH 44691-8607
Tel.: (330) 264-3637
Web Site: http://www.magnipower.com
Rev.: $14,376,148
Emp.: 90
Fabricated Structural Metal
N.A.I.C.S.: 332312
Greg Morgan *(Mgr-Sls)*

Plasto-Tech Corporation (1)
708 Lowell St, Elyria, OH 44035-4843 (100%)
Tel.: (440) 323-6300
Web Site: http://www.plasto-tech.com
Sales Range: $1-9.9 Million
Emp.: 11
Mfr of Custom Thermo Forming
N.A.I.C.S.: 326121
Dean Yoder *(Gen Mgr)*
Laks Venkataraman *(VP)*
Greg Morgan *(Mgr-Sls)*

MAGNIFI FINANCIAL CREDIT UNION

20 4th Ave SE, Melrose, MN 56352
Tel.: (320) 208-2729
Web Site: https://mymagnifi.org
Credit Union
N.A.I.C.S.: 522130
Charles Freiderichs *(CEO)*
Mark Meyer *(Chm)*
Steve Danzl *(Vice Chm)*
Jim Gondringer *(Treas)*
Marty Mahowald *(Sec)*

Subsidiaries:

Financial One Credit Union (1)
843 40th Ave NE, Columbia Heights, MN 55421
Tel.: (763) 404-7600
Web Site: http://www.financialonecu.com
Sales Range: $1-9.9 Million
Emp.: 36
Credit Union Operator
N.A.I.C.S.: 522130
Joann Cirks *(Chm)*
Ross Bloomquist *(Pres & CEO)*

MAGNO SOUND INC.

729 7th Ave Fl 2, New York, NY 10019
Tel.: (212) 302-2505
Web Site: http://www.magnosound.com
Sales Range: $50-74.9 Million
Emp.: 150
Sound Effects & Music Production, Motion Picture
N.A.I.C.S.: 512191
Robert Friedman *(Pres)*
David Friedman *(Exec VP)*

MAGNODE CORPORATION

400 E State St, Trenton, OH 45067-1549
Tel.: (513) 988-6351   OH
Web Site: http://www.magnode.com
Year Founded: 1947
Sales Range: $25-49.9 Million
Emp.: 200
Mfr & Extruder of Aluminum Products
N.A.I.C.S.: 331318
Arthur W. Bidwell *(Chm & CEO)*
Martin J. Bidwell *(Pres & COO)*
Joseph M. Bidwell *(VP-Extrusion)*
Kathleen B. Gramke *(Dir-HR)*
Richard A. Hinkle *(VP-Sls & Mktg)*
Gregory M. Hinsey *(Dir-Quality)*
Mark L. Butterfield *(VP)*

MAGNOLIA BAKERY INC.

401 Bleecker St, New York, NY 10014
Tel.: (212) 462-2572
Web Site: http://www.magnoliabakery.com
Year Founded: 1996
Sales Range: $10-24.9 Million
Emp.: 250
Bakery Products Mfr
N.A.I.C.S.: 311812
Simone Wilson *(Gen Mgr)*
Grace Na *(Mgr-Call Center)*
Albert Hasse *(Project Mgr-Franchise Rels)*

MAGNOLIA BANKING CORPORATION

200 E Main St, Magnolia, AR 71753
Tel.: (870) 235-7000
Web Site: http://www.myfarmers.bank
Year Founded: 1906
Sales Range: $75-99.9 Million
Emp.: 268
Bank Holding Company
N.A.I.C.S.: 551111
Robert L. Burns *(Chm, Pres & CEO)*
Bruce Maloch *(COO)*
Becky Palmer *(VP-Ops)*
Jeff White *(VP)*
April Marrison *(CFO & Sr VP)*
Laura Long *(Dir-HR)*
Fred Vining *(Sr VP-Admin)*

Subsidiaries:

Farmers Bank & Trust Company (1)
200 E Main St, Magnolia, AR 71753
Tel.: (870) 235-7000
Web Site: http://www.myfarmers.bank
Sales Range: $75-99.9 Million
Commericial Banking
N.A.I.C.S.: 522110
Robert L. Burns *(Chm)*
Chris Gosnell *(Pres & CEO)*
Monty Harrington *(Pres-Market)*
Phyllis Skinner *(Acct Supvr)*

MAGNOLIA ENTERTAINMENT LLC

900 N Broadway, Oklahoma City, OK 73102
Tel.: (405) 236-8742
Sales Range: $10-24.9 Million
Emp.: 4
Holding Company
N.A.I.C.S.: 711320

Subsidiaries:

CD Warehouse, Inc. (1)
722 N Broadway Ave Ste Mezz, Oklahoma City, OK 73102-6007
Tel.: (405) 236-8742
Web Site: http://www.cdwarehouse.com
Owner & Franchiser of New & Used CD Stores
N.A.I.C.S.: 449210
Christopher Salyer *(Chm, Pres & CEO)*

MAGNOLIA FOREST PRODUCTS INC.

13252 Interstate 55 SE, Terry, MS 39170
Tel.: (601) 878-2581
Web Site: http://www.magnoliaforest.com
Sales Range: $25-49.9 Million
Emp.: 60
Dress & Finish Rough Lumber
N.A.I.C.S.: 423310
Steve Brent *(VP)*
Dennis Berry *(Pres)*

Subsidiaries:

Carrollton Wood Products Inc (1)
855 Cedar St, Carrollton, GA 30117
Tel.: (770) 830-7348
Rev.: $700,000
Emp.: 15
Lumber, Rough, Dressed & Finished
N.A.I.C.S.: 423310

Lewisville Wood Products Inc. (1)
808 Industrial Park Dr, Lewisville, AR 71845
Tel.: (870) 921-5877
Sales Range: $10-24.9 Million
Emp.: 15
Lumber, Rough, Dressed & Finished
N.A.I.C.S.: 423310
Dennis Berry *(Controller)*

MAGNOLIA HOTELS

818 17th St, Denver, CO 80202-3101
Tel.: (303) 607-0707
Web Site: http://www.stoutstreethospitality.com
Year Founded: 1993
Sales Range: $10-24.9 Million
Emp.: 20
Hotel Operator
N.A.I.C.S.: 721110
Eric Holtze *(Co-CEO)*
Sarah Treadway *(Pres & Co-CEO)*

Subsidiaries:

Omaha Magnolia Hotel (1)
1615 Howard St, Omaha, NE 68102
Tel.: (402) 342-2222
Web Site: http://www.magnoliahotels.com
Sales Range: $1-9.9 Million
Hotel Operations
N.A.I.C.S.: 721110
Tim Darby *(Gen Mgr)*

MAGNOLIA METAL CORPORATION

10675 Bedford Ave Ste 200, Omaha, NE 68134
Tel.: (402) 455-8760
Web Site: http://www.magnoliabronze.com
Sales Range: $10-24.9 Million
Emp.: 15
Copper Foundries
N.A.I.C.S.: 331529
Michael Koslosky *(Pres)*

MAGNOLIA PETROLEUM PLC

18452 E 111th St, Broken Arrow, OK 74011
Tel.: (918) 449-8750
Web Site: http://www.magnoliapetroleum.com
Sales Range: $1-9.9 Million
Oil & Gas Exploration & Production
N.A.I.C.S.: 211120
Rita Fern Whittington *(Pres & CEO)*
Derec Norman *(CFO)*
Leonard Wallace *(Interim Chm)*

MAGNOLIA PROPERTIES & INVESTMENTS INC.

3370 Capital Cir NE, Tallahassee, FL 32308
Tel.: (850) 386-8660   FL
Web Site: http://www.magnoliaproperties.com
Year Founded: 1981
Real Estate Manangement Services
N.A.I.C.S.: 531390
V. S. Brown *(Pres)*

MAGNUM BUILDERS OF SARASOTA, INC.

4545 Northgate Ct, Sarasota, FL 34234
Tel.: (941) 351-5560
Web Site: http://www.magnumbuilders.com
Year Founded: 1983
Sales Range: $1-9.9 Million
Emp.: 5
General Contractors
N.A.I.C.S.: 236220
Douglas W. Baltzer *(Mgr)*

MAGNUM CONSTRUCTION MANAGEMENT

6201 SW 70th St Fl 2, Miami, FL 33143
Tel.: (305) 541-6869
Web Site: http://www.mcmcorp.com
Rev.: $45,358,529
Emp.: 220
Commercial & Office Building, New Construction
N.A.I.C.S.: 236220
Alexis Leal *(Dir-Corp Ops)*
Greg Alexander *(Reg VP)*
Gustavo Fernandez *(Dir-Ops-Panama)*
Robert T. Murphy *(Dir-Civil Ops-Florida)*

MAGNUM CORPORATION

910 Gladstone Ave, Columbus, IN 47201
Tel.: (812) 372-0281
Web Site: http://www.caltherm.com
Motor Vehicle & Machinery Thermostats Mfr
N.A.I.C.S.: 336320
Martin L. Abel *(Pres)*

COMPANIES

Subsidiaries:

Caltherm Corporation (1)
910 S Gladstone Ave, Columbus, IN 47201
Tel.: (812) 372-0281
Web Site: http://www.caltherm.com
Thermostatic & Pressure Control Devices Mfr
N.A.I.C.S.: 333248

MAGNUM ENTERPRISES INC.
2515 W Woodland Dr, Anaheim, CA 92801
Tel.: (714) 828-1191   CA
Web Site: http://www.meigc.com
Year Founded: 1983
Sales Range: $10-24.9 Million
Emp.: 98
Nonresidential Construction
N.A.I.C.S.: 236220
Chrystal Gonzalez (Mgr-Ops)
Craig Galloway (Project Mgr)
Mark Ebert (Project Mgr)
Dan Dingman (Project Mgr)

MAGNUM FEEDYARD, LLC.
11665 Morgan County Rd 1, Wiggins, CO 80654
Tel.: (970) 483-7339
Web Site: http://www.magnumfeedyard.com
Year Founded: 1994
Sales Range: $10-24.9 Million
Emp.: 17
Animal Food Distr
N.A.I.C.S.: 424910
Steve Gabel (Owner)

MAGNUM LOGISTICS, INC.
6312 SEern Ave, Indianapolis, IN 46203
Tel.: (317) 396-1655   IN
Web Site: http://www.gomagnum.com
Year Founded: 1999
Sales Range: $25-49.9 Million
Emp.: 30
Logistics Management Services
N.A.I.C.S.: 488510
James Sharp (Founder & Principal)

MAGNUM MACHINING INCORPORATED
20959 State Hwy 6, Deerwood, MN 56444
Tel.: (218) 534-3552
Web Site: http://www.magnummachining.com
Sales Range: $10-24.9 Million
Emp.: 100
Machine & Other Job Shop Work
N.A.I.C.S.: 332710
Jerry Bowman (Pres, CEO & CFO)
Kevin Hall (Mgr-Quality)

MAGNUM MAGNETICS CORPORATION
801 Masonic Pk Rd, Marietta, OH 45750
Tel.: (740) 373-7770   OH
Web Site: http://www.magnummagnetics.com
Year Founded: 1991
Magnetic Products Mfr
N.A.I.C.S.: 332999
Mark F. Bradley (Pres)
Ryan Watters (Dir-Ops)
Greg Buckley (Dir-IT)
Kyle O'Keefe (Mgr-Maintenance)
Allen Love (CEO)
Neil Hawkins (Mgr-Mktg)
Joe Stout (Dir-Product Dev)

MAGNUM PRINT SOLUTIONS, INC.
1535 S Albro Pl, 98108, Seattle, WA
Tel.: (206) 624-7715
Web Site: http://magnumlaser.com
Year Founded: 1993
Toner Cartridge Remanufacturer; Office & Printing Supplies Whslr & Repair Center
N.A.I.C.S.: 424110
Stephen Seavecki (Co-Owner, Pres & CEO)
Ryan Van Quill (Co-Owner)

Subsidiaries:

Laser Image Plus Imaging Products, Inc. (1)
14751 Franklin Ave Ste B, 92780, Tustin, CA
Tel.: (714) 556-5277
Web Site: https://www.laserimageplus.com
Carbon Paper & Inked Ribbon Mfr
N.A.I.C.S.: 339940

MAGNUM STAFFING SERVICES INC.
2900 Smith St Ste 250, Houston, TX 77006
Tel.: (713) 658-0068
Web Site: http://www.magnumstaffing.com
Sales Range: $25-49.9 Million
Emp.: 35
Providers of Temporary Staffing
N.A.I.C.S.: 561320
Caroline Brown (Pres & CEO)
Diana Cantu (Branch Mgr)
Maria Carcamo (Coord-Sls)
Mireille Zakaria (Mgr-Acctg)
Tracie Laws (Branch Mgr)

MAGNUM VENUS PRODUCTS
11692 56th Ct, Clearwater, FL 33760
Tel.: (727) 573-2955   FL
Web Site: http://www.mvpind.com
Year Founded: 2000
Sales Range: $10-24.9 Million
Emp.: 150
Mfr & Sales of Spray Equipment
N.A.I.C.S.: 333912
Joan Tracy (VP-Sls & Mktg)

Subsidiaries:

MVP Manufacturing (1)
1862 Ives Ave, Kent, WA 98032-7502
Tel.: (253) 854-2660
Sales Range: $10-24.9 Million
Emp.: 50
Reinforced Thermoset Plastics Mfr
N.A.I.C.S.: 333912
Joan Tracy (VP-Sls & Mktg-Intl)
Bob Clay (Gen Mgr)

MAGNUM, LTD.
3000 7th Ave N, Fargo, ND 58102
Tel.: (701) 293-8082   ND
Web Site: http://www.magnumlog.com
Year Founded: 1978
Sales Range: $75-99.9 Million
Emp.: 640
Freight Trucking, Warehousing & Logistics Services
N.A.I.C.S.: 484121
Joe Lusty (Mgr-Warehouse)

Subsidiaries:

Magnum LTL, Inc. (1)
3000 7th Ave N, Fargo, ND 58102
Tel.: (701) 293-8082
Web Site: http://www.magnumlog.com
Less Than Truckload Freight Trucking Services
N.A.I.C.S.: 484122
Wayne Gadberry (Pres & CEO)
James Johannesson (VP)
Stan Wiens (Mgr-Bus Dev)
David Gadberry (VP-Logistics)
Randy Gilbertson (Dir-Equipment & Maintenance)
Don Jemtrud (CFO)

Magnum Logistics, Inc. (1)
3000 7th Ave N, Fargo, ND 58107-2023
Tel.: (701) 293-8082
Web Site: http://www.magnumlog.com
Freight Logistics Services
N.A.I.C.S.: 541614
Wayne Gadberry (Pres & CEO)
David Gadberry (VP)

Magnum Warehousing, Inc. (1)
3000 7th Ave N, Fargo, ND 58107-2023
Tel.: (701) 293-8082
Web Site: http://www.magnumlog.com
Freight Warehousing Services
N.A.I.C.S.: 493110

MAGNUSON HOTELS
525 E Mission Ave, Spokane, WA 99202
Tel.: (509) 747-8713
Web Site: http://www.magnusonhotels.com
Year Founded: 2002
Rev.: $3,100,000
Emp.: 26
Hotel Services
N.A.I.C.S.: 721110
Thomas Magnuson (Co-CEO & Principal)
Melissa Magnuson (Co-CEO & Principal)
Jason Beasley (CFO)
Adnan Malik (Dir-Distr & Revenue)
Jeremie Dardard (COO)

MAGNUSON SOD/HAAG SERVICES
5901 Nicollet Ave, Minneapolis, MN 55419
Tel.: (612) 869-6992   MN
Web Site: http://www.magnuson-sod.com
Year Founded: 1988
Rev.: $8,000,000
Emp.: 35
Fiscal Year-end: 12/31/10
Farm Supplies Merchant Whslr
N.A.I.C.S.: 424910
Glynn Haag (Pres)

Subsidiaries:

S Klier' Nursery, Inc. (1)
5901 Nicollet Ave, Minneapolis, MN 55419
Tel.: (612) 866-8771
Web Site: http://www.kliersnursery.com
Landscaping Supplies & Equipment, Gardening Tools Repair, Maintenance & Sharpening Requirements
N.A.I.C.S.: 333112
Glynn Haag (Pres)

MAGNUSSEN'S AUBURN IMPORTS
800 Nevada St, Auburn, CA 95603
Tel.: (530) 885-8484
Web Site: http://www.auburntoyota.com
Rev.: $36,900,000
Emp.: 100
Automobiles, New & Used
N.A.I.C.S.: 441110
Bernard Magnussen (Pres)

MAGNUSSEN'S AUBURN TOYOTA
800 Nevada St, Auburn, CA 95603-3709
Tel.: (530) 885-8484
Web Site: http://www.auburntoyota.com
Year Founded: 1984
Sales Range: $25-49.9 Million
Emp.: 100
Car Whslr
N.A.I.C.S.: 441110
David Harrison (Gen Mgr-Sls)
Tony Toohey (Pres)

MAGNUSSEN'S CAR WEST AUTO BODY
6077 Dublin Blvd, Dublin, CA 94568
Tel.: (925) 648-7100
Web Site: http://www.carwestautobody.com
Rev.: $17,000,000
Emp.: 150
Automotive Body Paint & Interior Repair & Maintenance
N.A.I.C.S.: 811121
Bernard Magnussen (Pres)
Craig Moe (CEO)

MAGRUDER HOLDINGS INC.
11820 Park Ln Dr Ste 200, Rockville, MD 20852-5615
Tel.: (301) 230-3000   MD
Year Founded: 1985
Sales Range: $25-49.9 Million
Emp.: 200
Operator of Grocery & Liquor Stores
N.A.I.C.S.: 445110
Mike Isip (Controller)
Steven L. Fanaroff (CFO & VP)

Subsidiaries:

Magruders (1)
981 Rollins Ave, Rockville, MD 20852-5615
Tel.: (301) 230-3000
Web Site: http://www.magruder.com
Sales Range: $50-74.9 Million
Operator of Grocery Stores
N.A.I.C.S.: 445110

MAGRUDER HOSPITAL
615 Fulton St, Port Clinton, OH 43452
Tel.: (419) 734-3131   OH
Web Site: http://www.magruderhospital.com
Year Founded: 1940
Sales Range: $50-74.9 Million
Emp.: 441
Health Care Srvices
N.A.I.C.S.: 622110
Nickolas Marsico (VP-Ancillary Svcs)
Julie Georgoff (CFO & VP-Fin)

MAGUIRE AUTOMOTIVE GROUP
840 Route 206, Bordentown, NJ 08505
Tel.: (609) 298-0234
Web Site: http://www.maguireautomotivegroup.com
Rev.: $35,300,000
Emp.: 46
Automobiles
N.A.I.C.S.: 441110
Robert J. Maguire (CEO)

MAGUIRE AUTOMOTIVE, LLC
370 Elmira Rd, Ithaca, NY 14850
Tel.: (607) 257-1515
Web Site: http://www.maguirecars.com
Sales Range: $100-124.9 Million
Emp.: 200
Automobile Dealership Operator
N.A.I.C.S.: 441110
Timothy J. Maguire (Owner)
Francis Loiacono (CFO)

Subsidiaries:

Maguire Chevrolet-Cadillac (1)
35 Cinema Dr, Ithaca, NY 14850
Tel.: (607) 216-9040
Web Site: http://www.maguirechevroletcadillac.com
Sales Range: $10-24.9 Million
Emp.: 26
Automotive Distr
N.A.I.C.S.: 441110
Phil Maguire (Owner & Pres)

Maguire Imports (1)
370 Elmira Rd, Ithaca, NY 14850-1631
Tel.: (607) 257-1515
Web Site: http://www.maguirecars.com

MAGUIRE AUTOMOTIVE, LLC

Maguire Automotive, LLC—(Continued)
Sales Range: $25-49.9 Million
Emp.: 90
Automobile Dealership
N.A.I.C.S.: 441110
Austin Foote *(Gen Mgr)*
Gene Beavers *(Dir-Collision Center & Mgr Grounds)*
Bill Hamelin *(Mgr-Fixed Ops)*
Mary Spicer *(VP-Insurance)*

MAGUIRE OIL COMPANY INC.
5950 Berkshire Ln Ste 1500, Dallas, TX 75225-5843
Tel.: (214) 741-5137   NV
Year Founded: 1969
Sales Range: $100-124.9 Million
Emp.: 12
Provider of Oil Exploration & Development
N.A.I.C.S.: 211120
Cary M. Maguire *(Pres & CEO)*
Blainey McGuire Hess *(VP)*
Pamela M. Coffelt Mounts *(Treas & Sec)*

MAGUIRE RESOURCES COMPANY INC.
500 N Rainbow Blvd Ste 300, Las Vegas, NV 89107-1061
Tel.: (702) 221-1928   NV
Year Founded: 1990
Sales Range: $25-49.9 Million
Emp.: 285
Provider of Crude Petroleum & Natural Gas Services
N.A.I.C.S.: 211120

MAGUIRE'S FORD OF HERSHEY, PA. INC.
100 N Thistledown Dr, Palmyra, PA 17078
Tel.: (717) 838-8300
Web Site: http://www.maguiresford.com
Year Founded: 1998
Sales Range: $10-24.9 Million
Emp.: 75
Car Whslr
N.A.I.C.S.: 441110
Keith A. Rohrer *(Pres)*
K. Robert Rohrer *(VP)*

MAGYAR & ASSOCIATES
PO Box 327, Hellertown, PA 18055
Tel.: (610) 838-5149
Web Site: http://www.magyarinc.com
Year Founded: 1958
Sales Range: $1-9.9 Million
Emp.: 10
Product Design, Process/HVAC Instrumentation, SCADA/HMI & Wireless Communications
N.A.I.C.S.: 334513
Alice Karpa *(Pres)*

MAGYAR BANCORP, MHC
400 Somerset St, New Brunswick, NJ 08903
Tel.: (732) 342-7600   DE
Web Site: http://www.magbank.com
Sales Range: $25-49.9 Million
Emp.: 20
Mutual Holding Company
N.A.I.C.S.: 551111
Joseph J. Lukacs Jr. *(Chm)*

Subsidiaries:

Magyar Bancorp, Inc.   (1)
400 Somerset St, New Brunswick, NJ 08901   (54.03%)
Tel.: (732) 342-7600
Web Site: https://www.magbank.com
Rev.: $48,571,000
Assets: $951,918,000
Liabilities: $841,370,000
Net Worth: $110,548,000

Earnings: $7,783,000
Emp.: 91
Fiscal Year-end: 09/30/2024
Bank Holding Company
N.A.I.C.S.: 551111
Andrew G. Hodulik *(Vice Chm)*
Thomas Lankey *(Chm)*
Jon R. Ansari *(CFO & Exec VP)*
John S. Fitzgerald *(Pres & CEO)*
Peter Brown *(Chief Lending Officer)*

Subsidiary (Domestic):

Magyar Bank   (2)
400 Somerset St, New Brunswick, NJ 08901
Tel.: (732) 342-7600
Web Site: http://www.magbank.com
Sales Range: $200-249.9 Million
Emp.: 89
Savings, Loans & Commercial Banking Services
N.A.I.C.S.: 522180
Thomas Lankey *(Chm)*
Jon R. Ansari *(CFO, Exec VP, VP-Fin, Controller & Asst Controller)*
John S. Fitzgerald *(Pres & CEO)*
Edward C. Stokes III *(Gen Counsel)*
Victoria Gorman *(Mgr)*
Lillian Lund *(VP)*
Jean McDonnell *(VP)*
Peter M. Brown *(Chief Lending Officer)*

MAHAFFEY FABRIC STRUCTURES.
4161 Delp St, Memphis, TN 38118
Tel.: (901) 363-6511
Web Site: http://www.fabricstructures.com
Year Founded: 1924
Rev.: $20,200,000
Emp.: 55
Consumer Goods Rental
N.A.I.C.S.: 532289
William J. Pretsch *(Pres)*
George Smith *(VP)*

MAHAR TOOL SUPPLY COMPANY INC.
112 Williams St, Saginaw, MI 48602
Tel.: (989) 799-5530   MI
Web Site: http://www.mahartool.com
Year Founded: 1947
Sales Range: $10-24.9 Million
Emp.: 150
Distr of Cutting Tools
N.A.I.C.S.: 423840
Barbara Mahar Lincoln *(CEO)*

MAHARD FEED MILL INC.
410 E 1st St, Prosper, TX 75078
Tel.: (972) 347-2421
Web Site: http://www.mahard.com
Year Founded: 1960
Sales Range: $10-24.9 Million
Emp.: 17
Animal Feed Producer
N.A.I.C.S.: 311119

MAHASKA BOTTLING COMPANY INC.
1407 17th Ave E, Oskaloosa, IA 52577-3559
Tel.: (641) 673-3481   IA
Web Site: http://www.mahaska.com
Year Founded: 1947
Rev.: $40,000,000
Emp.: 100
Bottled & Canned Soft Drinks
N.A.I.C.S.: 312111
Chad Irving *(CMO)*
Peyton Berkeley *(Chief Investment Officer)*
Aaron Goodman *(CFO)*

Subsidiaries:

Pepsi-Cola Bottling Co. of Salina Inc.   (1)
604 N 9th St, Salina, KS 67401-1944
Tel.: (785) 827-7297

Sales Range: $10-24.9 Million
Emp.: 60
Soft Drink Mfr & Bottler
N.A.I.C.S.: 312111
Bradley G. Muhl *(Owner)*

MAHER CHEVROLET INC.
2901 34th St N, Saint Petersburg, FL 33713
Tel.: (727) 323-5000
Web Site: http://www.maherchevrolet.com
Rev.: $69,000,000
Emp.: 250
Automobiles
N.A.I.C.S.: 441110
Fritz Bickell *(Mgr-Body Shop)*

MAHER OIL COMPANY INC.
401 N Prospect Ave, Kansas City, MO 64120-1532
Tel.: (816) 241-2400   MO
Year Founded: 1977
Sales Range: $10-24.9 Million
Emp.: 25
Sales of Petroleum Products
N.A.I.C.S.: 424720
Janice Patterson *(Pres)*

MAHONEY'S ROCKY LEDGE FARM GARDEN
242 Cambridge St, Winchester, MA 01890
Tel.: (781) 729-5900
Rev.: $17,000,000
Emp.: 210
Garden Store Operator
N.A.I.C.S.: 444240
Paul J. Mahoney *(Owner)*

MAHONEY'S SILVER NUGGET INC.
2140 Las Vegas Blvd N, North Las Vegas, NV 89030
Tel.: (702) 399-1111
Rev.: $15,524,726
Emp.: 274
Casino Hotels
N.A.I.C.S.: 721120
Raoh Marino *(Gen Mgr)*
Robert Wright *(Mgr)*

MAHONING & TRUMBULL BUILDING TRADES INSURANCE FUND
33 Fitch Blvd, Youngstown, OH 44515
Tel.: (330) 270-0453
Sales Range: $10-24.9 Million
Emp.: 2
Lumber & Building Material Whslr
N.A.I.C.S.: 444110
Thomas E. Arida *(Pres)*

MAHWAH BERGEN RETAIL GROUP, INC.
933 MacArthur Blvd, Mahwah, NJ 07430
Tel.: (551) 777-6700   DE
Web Site: http://www.ascenaretail.com
Rev.: $5,493,400,000
Assets: $2,699,800,000
Liabilities: $2,548,800,000
Net Worth: $151,000,000
Earnings: ($661,400,000)
Emp.: 53,000
Fiscal Year-end: 08/03/19
Holding Company; Women's Clothing Stores Owner & Operator
N.A.I.C.S.: 551112
Kevin Michael Trolaro *(Chief Acctg Officer & VP)*
Gary P. Muto *(CEO)*
Carrie W. Teffner *(Interim Chm & Pres)*
Daniel Lamadrid *(CFO & Exec VP)*

Subsidiaries:

Charming Shoppes, Inc.   (1)
450 Winks Ln, Bensalem, PA 19020
Tel.: (215) 245-9100
Web Site: http://www.ascenaretail.com
Women's & Plus-Sized Women's Sportswear, Dresses, Coats, Lingerie, Accessories & Footwear Retail Stores
N.A.I.C.S.: 458110

Subsidiary (Domestic):

Catherines Stores Corporation   (2)
3750 State Road Suite 7B, Bensalem, PA 19020
Tel.: (215) 245-9100
Web Site: http://www.catherines.com
Sales Range: $200-249.9 Million
Emp.: 200
Womens Large Size Clothing & Accessories Retail Stores
N.A.I.C.S.: 458110

FB Distro, Inc.   (2)
1901 E State Rd 240, Greencastle, IN 46135
Tel.: (765) 653-7500
Women's Clothing & Accessories Retailer
N.A.I.C.S.: 458110

Subsidiary (Non-US):

Kirkstone Ltd.   (2)
Rm 1103 7 11th Fl S Wing Tower 1 Harbour Ctr 1 Hok Cheung St, Kowloon, China (Hong Kong)   (100%)
Tel.: (852) 23339033
Sales Range: $25-49.9 Million
Emp.: 150
Procures Clothing Products
N.A.I.C.S.: 425120
Visa Vei *(Pres)*

Subsidiary (Domestic):

Modern Woman, Inc.
215 E Orangethorpe Ave, Fullerton, CA 92832
Tel.: (714) 267-6080
Women Apparel Distr
N.A.I.C.S.: 458110

DBI Holdings, Inc.   (1)
30 Dunnigan Dr, Suffern, NY 10901-4101
Tel.: (845) 369-4500
Web Site: http://www.dressbarn.com
Women's Clothing & Accessories Retailer
N.A.I.C.S.: 458110

Subsidiary (Domestic):

DBX, Inc.   (2)
30 Dunnigan Dr, Suffern, NY 10901
Tel.: (865) 369-4500
Ladies' Apparel
N.A.I.C.S.: 561110

Tween Brands, Inc.   (1)
8323 Walton Pkwy, New Albany, OH 43054
Tel.: (614) 775-3500
Web Site: http://www.justiceretail.com
Sales Range: $900-999.9 Million
Emp.: 500
Fashion Retailer
N.A.I.C.S.: 458110

Subsidiary (Non-US):

Ascena Global Sourcing Hong Kong Limited   (2)
Rm 2508 25/F Metro Loft, Kwai Chung, New Territories, China (Hong Kong)
Tel.: (852) 23339033
Apparel Distr
N.A.I.C.S.: 424350

Subsidiary (Domestic):

FSHC, LLC   (2)
1175 Peachtree St NE 10th Fl Ste 1000, Atlanta, GA 30361
Tel.: (678) 973-2750
Web Site: http://www.fshcglobal.com
Health Care Srvices
N.A.I.C.S.: 622110
Betty R. Smith *(CEO)*

MAID OF THE MIST CORPORATION

COMPANIES

151 Buffalo Ave Ste 204, Niagara Falls, NY 14303
Tel.: (716) 284-8897 NY
Web Site:
http://www.maidofthemist.com
Year Founded: 1971
Rev.: $1,100,000
Emp.: 200
Sightseeing Boat
N.A.I.C.S.: 487210
Christopher Glynn (Pres)

MAID-RITE STEAK COMPANY INC.
105 Keystone Indus Pk, Dunmore, PA 18512-1518
Tel.: (570) 343-4748 PA
Web Site:
http://www.maidritesteak.com
Year Founded: 1960
Sales Range: $25-49.9 Million
Emp.: 170
Sausages, Other Prepared Meats & Sandwich Steaks
N.A.I.C.S.: 311612
Donald Bernstein (Pres & Treas)
Elaine Herzog (Dir-Mktg)
Nathaniel Taylor (Engr-Maintenance)

MAIDEN LANE JEWELRY, LTD.
80 Wall St Ste 815, New York, NY 10005
Tel.: (212) 840-8477 NY
Year Founded: 2012
Jewelry Retailer
N.A.I.C.S.: 458310

MAIDSTONE CLUB INC
50 Old Beach Ln, East Hampton, NY 11937-6141
Tel.: (631) 324-0510 NY
Web Site:
http://www.maidstoneclub.org
Year Founded: 1891
Sales Range: $10-24.9 Million
Recreation Club Operator
N.A.I.C.S.: 713910
Kenneth J. Koch (Gen Mgr)

MAIER ADVERTISING, INC.
1789 New Britain Ave, Farmington, CT 06032-3317
Tel.: (860) 677-4581 CT
Web Site: http://www.maier.com
Year Founded: 1971
Sales Range: $1-9.9 Million
Emp.: 16
Advertising Agencies
N.A.I.C.S.: 541810
Todd Russell (Chief Mktg Officer)

MAIL SHARK
4125 New Holland Rd, Mohnton, PA 19540
Web Site:
http://www.themailshark.com
Year Founded: 2008
Sales Range: $1-9.9 Million
Emp.: 25
Advertising & Marketing Consulting
N.A.I.C.S.: 541860
Brian Johnson (Pres)
Josh Davis (VP-Sls)
Tyndra Sterner (VP-Production)
Bryan Mull (Mgr-Digital Mktg)
Jess Plunket (Mgr-Bus Ops)
Jordan Baylor (Mgr-Prepress)
MaryBeth Lemon (Mgr-Fin & HR)
Steve Burns (Mgr-Production Ops)

MAILING LIST SYSTEMS CORP.
6115 Camp Bowie Blvd Ste 200, Fort Worth, TX 76116
Tel.: (817) 989-3800 TX
Web Site: http://www.mlsc.com
Year Founded: 1982
Sales Range: $1-9.9 Million
Emp.: 60
Data Management Solutions
N.A.I.C.S.: 518210
Robert M. McDaniels (Pres & CEO)

Subsidiaries:

MLS Data Management Solutions Inc. (1)
1920 Yonge Street Second Floor, Toronto, M4S 3E2, ON, Canada
Tel.: (416) 572-7717
Web Site: http://www.mlsc.com
Data Management Solutions
N.A.I.C.S.: 518210
Robert Daniel (Pres)

MAILING SYSTEMS, INC.
2431 Mercantile Dr Ste A, Rancho Cordova, CA 95742
Tel.: (916) 674-2035 CA
Web Site: http://www.msimail.net
Year Founded: 1991
Sales Range: $10-24.9 Million
Emp.: 42
Direct Mail & Internet Advertising & Marketing Services
N.A.I.C.S.: 541860
Mike Lebeck (Pres)
Gentry Jones (Mgr)

MAILINGS UNLIMITED
116 Riverside Industrial Pkwy, Portland, ME 04103
Tel.: (207) 347-5000
Web Site:
http://www.growwithmail.com
Year Founded: 2002
Sales Range: $10-24.9 Million
Emp.: 31
Direct Mail Advertising
N.A.I.C.S.: 541860
John Webel (CFO)
Matt Berry (Dir-IT Internet Support)
Paul Rogers (Pres)

MAILSOUTH, INC.
5901 Hwy 52 E, Helena, AL 35080
Tel.: (205) 620-6200
Web Site: http://www.mspark.com
Year Founded: 1988
Emp.: 100
Direct Mail Marketing Services
N.A.I.C.S.: 541860
Albert B. Braunfisch (Chm)
Lori Sigler (CFO & COO)
Susan R. Knight (Dir-Corp Admin & Comm)
John D. Faure (Dir-HR)
Steven R. Laney (VP-Ops)
Darrell W. Edwards (CMO)
Thomas W. Caprio (VP-Local Sls)
Gregori D. Bogich (CEO)
Anna Marie Chapman (VP-HR)
Whit Cox (Dir-Acctg & Fin Reporting)
Glenn Kawasaki (Sr Dir-Consumer Analytics)
Ron Sereika (Dir-Credit & Client Payment Solutions)
Stacey Sedbrook (VP-Brand Sls)
Sherri Finley (Dir-Talent Dev & Virtual Sls)
Laura Dickinson (Mgr-Talent Dev Team)
Rusty Martin (Sls Mgr-Alabama)
Tim Falvey (VP-Natl Sls)
Nicole Swiney (Dir-Sls Ops)
Vickie McMullen (Dir-Education Partnerships)
Kevin Zall (VP-Bus Dev)
Tiffany Kearley (Dir-Virtual Sls)
Chad Graves (Dir-Fin Plng & Analysis)
Antionette Bird (Dir-Local Sls-South & East Teams)

Brian Blackman (Chief Customer Officer)
Ritu Parr (Sr Dir-Mktg)
Sheila Storch (VP-HR)
Michele Rygiel (Dir-HR)
Steve Templeton (VP-Mktg)

MAIN BROTHERS OIL COMPANY, INC.
1 Booth Ln, Albany, NY 12205-1403
Tel.: (518) 438-7856
Web Site:
http://www.maincareenergy.com
Year Founded: 1937
Sales Range: $100-124.9 Million
Emp.: 150
Provider of Petroleum Products
N.A.I.C.S.: 457210
Marcia Booth (VP)
David Tarsa (Pres)

MAIN EVENT CATERERS
3870 S 4 Mile Run Dr, Arlington, VA 22206
Tel.: (703) 820-2028
Web Site:
http://www.maineventcaterers.com
Year Founded: 1995
Sales Range: $1-9.9 Million
Emp.: 49
Occasional Catering Services
N.A.I.C.S.: 722320
Roberto Zuleta (Mgr-Warehouse)
Hamza Shaikh (Dir-Staffing)
Taylor Hutchison (Dir-Sls)

MAIN IDEAS
26485 482nd Ave, Brandon, SD 57005
Tel.: (605) 582-7800
Web Site: http://www.mainideas.com
Year Founded: 1992
Sales Range: Less than $1 Million
Emp.: 3
Advertising Agencies, Brand Development, Business-To-Business, Consumer Marketing
N.A.I.C.S.: 541810
Lisa Peterson (Partner)
Steve Peterson (Owner)

MAIN LINE EQUITY PARTNERS, LLC
Plz 16 Ste 202 16 E Lancaster Ave, Ardmore, PA 19003
Tel.: (215) 620-6993
Web Site:
http://www.mainlineequity.com
Emp.: 6
Privater Equity Firm
N.A.I.C.S.: 523999
Chris Randazzo (Founder & Mng Partner)
Mark Gorman (Mng Dir)
Douglas B. Hart (Operating Partner)
James Mayhall (Mng Dir)

Subsidiaries:

Cianflone Scientific LLC (1)
135 Industry Dr, Pittsburgh, PA 15275
Tel.: (412) 787-3600
Web Site: http://www.cianflone.com
Emp.: 10
X-Ray Spectrographic Instruments Mfr
N.A.I.C.S.: 334516
Douglas B. Hart (Pres)
Brian Diamond (Mgr-Quality Assurance)
Ann Seibel (Controller)

Subsidiary (Domestic):

Tensitron, Inc. (2)
733 S Bowen St, Longmont, CO 80501
Tel.: (303) 702-1980
Web Site: http://www.tensitron.com
Tension Measuring Instrumentation Design & Mfr
N.A.I.C.S.: 334519

Douglas B. Hart (Pres)

MAIN LINE SUPPLY CO. INC.
300 N Findlay St, Dayton, OH 45403
Tel.: (937) 254-6910
Web Site:
http://www.mainlinesupply.com
Sales Range: $10-24.9 Million
Emp.: 33
Valves & Fittings Industrial
N.A.I.C.S.: 423830
Tim Kroger (Pres)
Jeff Poast (Controller)
Mike O'Brien (Pres)

MAIN POST PARTNERS, L.P.
1 Embarcadero Ctr Ste 3500, San Francisco, CA 94111-4226
Tel.: (415) 398-0770 DE
Web Site:
http://www.mainpostpartners.com
Privater Equity Firm
N.A.I.C.S.: 523999
Scott M. Bell (Partner)
Jeffrey S. Mills (Mng Partner)
Sean Honey (Mng Partner)
Denise Davis (Chief Compliance Officer & VP-Fin)
Megan DeGennaro Maxson (Dir-Bus Dev)

MAIN PULZE, INC.
9267 Haven Ave Ste 225, Rancho Cucamonga, CA 91730 DE
Web Site: http://www.mainpulze.com
Community-Based Continuous Care Facilities Operator
N.A.I.C.S.: 623110
Daniel N. Rastein (CEO)
Darryl W. Monteilh (COO)
Lori Serafino (Chief Compliance Officer)

MAIN STREET CAPITAL HOLDINGS, LLC
1 Oxford Ctr 301 Grant St 14th Fl, Pittsburgh, PA 15219
Tel.: (412) 904-4020 PA
Web Site: http://www.mainstcap.com
Year Founded: 1994
Emp.: 5
Privater Equity Firm
N.A.I.C.S.: 523999
Gerald M. Prado (Principal)
Donald J. Jenkins (Principal)
W. Ryan Davis (Principal)
Dennis G. Prado (Principal)

Subsidiaries:

Conelec of Florida, LLC (1)
3045 Technology Pkwy, Deland, FL 32724 (100%)
Tel.: (386) 873-3800
Web Site: http://www.conelec.net
Sales Range: $10-24.9 Million
Emp.: 100
Electronic Components Mfr
N.A.I.C.S.: 334419
Ty Eggemeyer (Chm & CEO)
Joe Benz (VP-Ops)
Natalie Cockayne (CFO)

LTS Scale Company, LLC (1)
1500 Enterprise Pkwy, Twinsburg, OH 44087
Tel.: (330) 425-3092
Web Site: http://www.ltsscale.com
Sales Range: $1-9.9 Million
Mobile Scale & Weighing Systems Designer & Mfr
N.A.I.C.S.: 333998
John A. Pangrazio (Pres)

MAIN STREET INGREDIENTS LLC
2340 Enterprise Ave, La Crosse, WI 54603
Tel.: (608) 781-2345

MAIN STREET INGREDIENTS LLC

Main Street Ingredients LLC—(Continued)
Web Site: http://www.mainstreetingredients.com
Rev.: $41,983,000
Emp.: 250
Dry, Dairy Products
N.A.I.C.S.: 311514
Shawn Wegner (Mgr-Ops)

MAIN STREET MARKET SQUARE REDEVELOPMENT AUTHORITY
909 Fannin Ste 1650, Houston, TX 77010
Tel.: (713) 752-0827 TX
Web Site: http://www.mainstreettirz.com
Year Founded: 1999
Sales Range: $10-24.9 Million
City Redevelopment Services
N.A.I.C.S.: 541320
Robert Eury (Exec Dir)

MAINCO INVESTMENTS INC.
1861 VanDerhorn Dr, Memphis, TN 38134-6328
Tel.: (901) 377-5010 TN
Year Founded: 1980
Sales Range: $10-24.9 Million
Emp.: 300
Supplier of Electrical Equipment & Supplies
N.A.I.C.S.: 335999
John Phebus (VP)

Subsidiaries:

ESI Companies Inc. (1)
1861 Vanderhorn Dr, Memphis, TN 38134-6328
Tel.: (901) 386-7340
Web Site: http://www.esicompanies.com
Security Systems & Products
N.A.I.C.S.: 332321

L & H Supply Co. Inc. (1)
1906 Vanhorn Dr, Memphis, TN 38131-0403
Tel.: (901) 332-3400
Web Site: http://www.lhcorp.com
Sales Range: $10-24.9 Million
Emp.: 11
Supplier of Electrical Apparatus & Equipment
N.A.I.C.S.: 423610

Saba Inc. (1)
1861 VanDerhorn Dr, Memphis, TN 38134-6328
Tel.: (901) 377-5010
Web Site: http://www.sabainc.com
Sales Range: $10-24.9 Million
Emp.: 5
Supplier of Electrical Apparatus & Equipment
N.A.I.C.S.: 561621

MAINE COAST REGIONAL HEALTH FACILITIES INC.
50 Union St, Ellsworth, ME 04605
Tel.: (207) 667-5311 ME
Web Site: http://www.mainehospital.org
Year Founded: 1947
Sales Range: $25-49.9 Million
Emp.: 600
Operator of General Medical & Surgical Hospital
N.A.I.C.S.: 622110
Karen W. Stanley (Chm)
Peter J. Ossanna (Pres-Medical Staff)

MAINE COMMUNITY BANCORP, MHC
100 Larrabee Rd Bldg 400, Westbrook, ME 04098
Tel.: (207) 786-5705
Web Site: https://www.mainecb.com
Emp.: 100
Bank Holding Company
N.A.I.C.S.: 551111

Subsidiaries:

Maine Community Bank (1)
254 Main St, Biddeford, ME 04005-2400
Tel.: (207) 571-5603
Web Site: https://www.mainecb.com
Credit Card Issuing
N.A.I.C.S.: 522210
Wayne A. Sherman (Pres)

MAINE COMMUNITY FOUNDATION
245 Main St, Ellsworth, ME 04605
Tel.: (207) 667-9735 ME
Web Site: http://www.mainecf.org
Year Founded: 1983
Sales Range: $25-49.9 Million
Emp.: 36
Grantmaking Services
N.A.I.C.S.: 813211
Amy Pollien (Mgr-Grants)
Carl Little (Dir-Comm & Mktg)
Jennifer Southard (VP-Donor Svcs & Gift Planning)
Cherie Galyean (Dir-Education Initiatives Programs & Grantmaking Svcs)
Lelia De Andrade (Dir-Grantmaking Svcs)
Bryan Clontz (Founder & Pres)
Jim Geary (CFO, VP & Dir-Investments)
Peter Rothschild (Chief Investment Officer)
Steven Rowe (Pres & CEO)
Laura Young (VP-Philanthropy)

MAINE DRILLING & BLASTING INC.
542 Brunswick Ave, Gardiner, ME 04345
Tel.: (207) 582-2338 ME
Web Site: http://www.mdandb.com
Year Founded: 1966
Sales Range: $50-74.9 Million
Emp.: 300
Heavy Construction & Drilling & Blasting Services
N.A.I.C.S.: 236210
Dan Werner (Pres & CEO)
Tim Maynard (CFO)
Mitch Green (Sr VP)
Todd Barrett (Sr VP)

Subsidiaries:

Maine Drilling & Blasting Inc. - Central Division (1)
88 Gold Ledge Ave, Auburn, NH 03032
Tel.: (603) 647-9770
Rock Blasting Quarry & Drilling Services
N.A.I.C.S.: 212319
Jason Riley (Mgr)

Maine Drilling & Blasting Inc. - Eastern Division (1)
423 Brunswick Ave, Gardiner, ME 04345
Tel.: (207) 582-8794
Rock Blasting Quarry & Drilling Services
N.A.I.C.S.: 212319
Will Purington (Asst Mgr)

Maine Drilling & Blasting Inc. - Mid-Atlantic Division (1)
61 Brown Rd, Bethel, PA 19507
Tel.: (800) 422-4927
Web Site: http://www.mvnd.com
Emp.: 40
Rock Blasting Quarry & Drilling Services
N.A.I.C.S.: 212319
Travis Martzall (Mgr)

Maine Drilling & Blasting Inc. - North Division (1)
296 West St, Milford, MA 01757
Tel.: (508) 478-9239
Rock Blasting Quarry & Drilling Services
N.A.I.C.S.: 212319
Dan Werner (Mgr)

Maine Drilling & Blasting Inc. - South Division (1)
103 Old Windsor Rd, Bloomfield, CT 06002
Tel.: (860) 242-9375
Rock Blasting Quarry & Drilling Services
N.A.I.C.S.: 212319
Todd Barrett (Mgr)

Maine Drilling & Blasting Inc. - Western Division (1)
7190 State Route 40, Argyle, NY 12838
Tel.: (518) 632-9170
Rock Blasting Quarry & Drilling Services
N.A.I.C.S.: 212319
Guy Keefe (Mgr)

MAINE EMPLOYERS MUTUAL INSURANCE CO.
261 Commercial St, Portland, ME 04101
Tel.: (207) 791-3300
Web Site: http://www.memic.com
Year Founded: 1993
Sales Range: $150-199.9 Million
Emp.: 243
Workers Compensation Insurance
N.A.I.C.S.: 524126
David M. Labbe (Chm)
Daniel McGarvey (CFO, Treas & Sr VP)
Donald Hale (COO & Sr VP-Underwriting)
Catherine Lamson (Chief Admin Officer & Sr VP)
Michael Bourque (Pres & CEO)
Jeff Funk (Pres-Atlantic Reg)
Matt Harmon (Sr VP-Claims)
Greg Jamison (Sr VP-Underwriting)
Jack Yao (CIO & Sr VP)
Ruchir Jaipuriyar (VP-IT)
Bryan Kotlyar (Dir-Software Engrg)

MAINE OXY-ACETYLENE SUPPLY CO.
22 Albiston Way, Auburn, ME 04287
Tel.: (207) 784-5788
Web Site: http://www.maineoxy.com
Sales Range: $10-24.9 Million
Emp.: 100
Welding Machinery & Equipment
N.A.I.C.S.: 423830
Dan Guerin (Pres)
Brian Painchaud (Mgr-Inventory Control)
Carl Paine (Mgr-Bus Dev)
Ray Cusson (Mgr-IT & Customer Svc)
Larry Bates (Mgr-DOT)
Jason Goldrup (Mgr)
Butch Hannan (Mgr)
Brent Lovett (Mgr)
Allison Brothers (Mgr-Corp Acctg)
Arthur Smith (Mgr-Rentals & Repair)
Diana Picavet (Mgr-Mktg)
John St.Pierre (Mgr-Auburn Store)
Lisa Erskine (Dir-HR)
Rob Piccirilli (Mgr-Sls-North)
Ted Suess (CFO)
Tim Mann (Mgr-Retail Store-North)
Tom Cyr (Mgr-Ops)

MAINE POTATO GROWERS, INC.
261 Main St, Presque Isle, ME 04769-2157
Tel.: (207) 764-3131 ME
Web Site: http://www.mpgco-op.com
Year Founded: 1932
Sales Range: $50-74.9 Million
Emp.: 150
Provider of Agricultural Supplies & Services
N.A.I.C.S.: 424480
Pierre Patenaude (Pres & CEO)

Subsidiaries:

MPG Crop Services, LLC. (1)
261 Main St, Presque Isle, ME 04769
Tel.: (207) 764-8517
Emp.: 50
Potato Farming Services
N.A.I.C.S.: 111211

MPG Truck & Tractor, Inc. (1)
261 Main St, Presque Isle, ME 04769
Tel.: (207) 768-5211
Emp.: 35
Truck & Tractor Rental Services
N.A.I.C.S.: 532120
Bob Hoffses (Mgr-Parts)
Lynwood Winslow (Mgr-Dept)

MAINE SECURITIES CORPORATION
15 Monument Sq, Portland, ME 04101
Tel.: (207) 775-0800
Web Site: http://www.mainesec.com
Rev.: $12,000,000
Emp.: 5
Investment Broker & Dealer Services
N.A.I.C.S.: 523150
Bradley C. McCurtain (Pres)

MAINE STATE CREDIT UNION
200 Capitol St, Augusta, ME 04330
Tel.: (207) 623-1851 ME
Web Site: http://www.mainestatecu.org
Sales Range: $10-24.9 Million
Emp.: 83
Credit Union
N.A.I.C.S.: 522130
Leonard Cabana (Chm)
Betty Norton (Vice Chm)
Rose Breton (Sec)
Joseph Suga (Treas)
Tucker Cole (Pres & CEO)

MAINE TURNPIKE AUTHORITY
2360 Congress St, Portland, ME 04102
Tel.: (207) 871-7771
Web Site: http://www.maineturnpike.com
Year Founded: 1941
Sales Range: $50-74.9 Million
Emp.: 500
Toll Road Operation
N.A.I.C.S.: 488490
Douglas D. Davidson (CFO)
Peter S. Merfeld (COO)
Stephen R. Tartre (Dir-Engrg & Building Maintenance)
Gerard P. Conley (Chm)
Peter Mills (Exec Dir)
Dan Morin (Mgr-Pub Affairs)

MAINEGENERAL HEALTH INC.
Ballard Ctr 6 E Chestnut St, Augusta, ME 04330-5717
Tel.: (207) 623-2977 GA
Web Site: http://www.mainegeneral.org
Year Founded: 1997
Sales Range: $250-299.9 Million
Emp.: 3,000
Health Care Management Services
N.A.I.C.S.: 622110
Chelsea Moeller (Dir-Philanthropy)
Gary Peachey (Chm)

Subsidiaries:

MaineGeneral Medical Center (1)
6 E Chestnut St, Augusta, ME 04330
Tel.: (207) 626-1000
Web Site: http://www.mainegeneral.org
Hospital & Surgical Facilities
N.A.I.C.S.: 622110
Paul Stein (COO)

MAINEHEALTH
110 Free St, Portland, ME 04101
Tel.: (207) 661-7001
Web Site: http://www.mainehealth.org
Year Founded: 1996

COMPANIES

Sales Range: $400-449.9 Million
Emp.: 33
Integrated Healthcare Delivery System
N.A.I.C.S.: 541611
Gregory A. Dufour *(Vice Chm)*
Mark A. Harris *(Chief Plng Officer)*
Jon Kevin Griffin *(Chief Strategy Officer)*
Andrea Dodge Patstone *(Sr VP-Sys Dev)*
Colin T. McHugh *(Sr VP-Payor Rels)*
Robert Frank *(Gen Counsel, Sec & Sr VP)*
Terri Cannan *(CMO & Chief Comm Officer)*
Susannah Swihart *(Chm)*
Joan Boomsma *(Chief Medical Officer)*
Katie Fullam Harris *(Sr VP-Govt Rels & Accountable Care Strategy)*
Richard W. Petersen *(Pres)*
William L. Caron Jr. *(CEO)*
Albert G. Swallow III *(CFO & Treas)*

Subsidiaries:

Maine Medical Partners (1)
301 Us Route 1, Scarborough, ME 04074-4400
Tel.: (207) 761-0650
Web Site: http://www.mmc.org
Healthcare & Medical Practice Management Services
N.A.I.C.S.: 531210
Peter Wood *(Exec Dir)*
Steve Kasabian *(Pres)*
Daniel Spratt *(Partner)*
William Caron *(Pres)*
James C. M. Chan *(Dir-Res)*
Sean Dugan *(Dir-Special Projects)*
Cindy Richards *(Dir-Program)*
Jeff Aalberg *(Dir-Quality)*
David Bachman *(Sr Dir-Medical)*
Vance Brown *(Chief Medical Officer)*
Jackie Cawley *(Sr Dir-Medical)*
Mark Fourre *(Sr Dir-Medical)*
Neil Korsen *(Dir-Medical)*
Julie Osgood *(Sr Dir-Ops)*
Marjorie Wiggins *(VP-Nursing)*

Mid Coast Hospital (1)
123 Medical Ctr Dr, Brunswick, ME 04011-2652
Tel.: (207) 319-7956
Web Site: http://www.midcoasthealth.com
General Medical & Surgical Hospitals
N.A.I.C.S.: 622110
Herbert Paris *(Mgr)*

MAINES PAPER & FOOD SERVICE, INC.
101 Broome Corporate Pkwy, Conklin, NY 13748
Tel.: (607) 779-1200 NY
Web Site: http://www.maines.net
Year Founded: 1919
Sales Range: $1-4.9 Billion
Emp.: 2,000
Canned, Packaged & Frozen Foods Distr
N.A.I.C.S.: 424420
Christopher Mellon *(CEO)*

MAINETODAY MEDIA, INC.
1 City Ctr, Portland, ME 04101
Tel.: (207) 791-6080 DE
Web Site: http://www.mainetodaymedia.com
Emp.: 400
Newspaper Publishers
N.A.I.C.S.: 513110
Lisa DeSisto *(CEO)*
Cliff Schechtman *(Exec Editor)*
Stewart B. Wright *(CIO)*
Matt Fulton *(VP-Digital Dev)*
Barbara Bock *(VP-Adv)*
Stefanie Manning *(VP-Mktg)*
Maryann Kelly *(VP-Labor & Employee Rels)*
Steve Greenlee *(Mng Editor-Portland Press Herald & Maine Sunday Telegram)*
Ole Amundsen *(Dir-Maine Audubon)*
Jody Marra *(VP-HR)*

Subsidiaries:

Kennebec Journal (1)
36 Anthony Ave, Augusta, ME 04330
Tel.: (207) 623-3811
Web Site: http://www.kjonline.com
Sales Range: $25-49.9 Million
Emp.: 40
Newspaper Publishers
N.A.I.C.S.: 513110
Scott Monroe *(Mng Editor)*
Maureen Milliken *(Editor-News)*

Morning Sentinel (1)
31 Front St, Waterville, ME 04901
Tel.: (207) 873-3341
Web Site: http://www.onlinesentinel.com
Newspaper Publishers
N.A.I.C.S.: 513110
Scott Monroe *(Mng Editor)*
Maureen Milliken *(Editor-News)*
Bill Stewart *(Editor-Sports)*
Evan Crawley *(Asst Editor-Sports)*
Denise Vear *(Mgr-Creative Innovations)*

Portland Press Herald (1)
1 City Ctr 5th Fl, Portland, ME 04101-3514
Tel.: (207) 791-6650
Web Site: http://www.pressherald.com
Sales Range: $50-74.9 Million
Newspaper Publishers
N.A.I.C.S.: 513110
Cliff Schechtman *(Exec Editor)*
Steve Greenlee *(Mng Editor)*
Barbara Bock *(VP-Adv)*
Dieter Bradbury *(Deputy Mng Editor)*
Julia McCue *(Editor-Database)*
Maryann Kelly *(VP-Labor & Employee Rels)*
Stefanie Manning *(VP-Circulation & Mktg)*

The Coastal Journal (1)
PO Box 2221, Murrells Inlet, SC 29576
Tel.: (843) 421-2363
Web Site: http://www.thecoastaljournal.com
Emp.: 6
Newspaper Publishers
N.A.I.C.S.: 513110

MAINGEAR INC.
206 Market St, Kenilworth, NJ 07033
Tel.: (908) 620-9050
Web Site: http://www.maingear.com
Year Founded: 2002
Sales Range: $1-9.9 Million
Emp.: 15
Computer Systems
N.A.I.C.S.: 541512
Wallace Santos *(Co-Founder)*
Jonathan Magalhaes *(Co-Founder)*

MAINLINE FIRE PROTECTION, LLC
505 Empire Dr, Jefferson City, MO 65109-6315
Tel.: (573) 635-6238
Web Site: http://www.wsfp.com
Sales Range: $10-24.9 Million
Emp.: 7
Plumbing Services
N.A.I.C.S.: 238220
Lori Newton *(Office Mgr)*

MAINLINE PRINTING INC.
3500 S Topeka Blvd, Topeka, KS 66611
Tel.: (785) 233-2338
Web Site: http://www.mainlineprinting.com
Sales Range: $10-24.9 Million
Emp.: 85
Offset Printing
N.A.I.C.S.: 323111
John Parker *(Pres)*
Cindy Calderwood *(Mgr-Acctg)*
Paul Kuestersteffen *(Project Coord)*

MAINLINING SERVICE INC.
555 Pound Rd, Elma, NY 14059
Tel.: (716) 652-3700
Web Site: http://www.mainlining.com
Sales Range: $10-24.9 Million
Emp.: 45
Water Main Construction
N.A.I.C.S.: 237110
Craig Perkins *(Pres)*
Laurie Sisti *(Sec)*

MAINSAIL LODGING & DEVELOPMENT, LLC
4602 Eisenhower Blvd, Tampa, FL 33634
Tel.: (813) 243-2613
Web Site: http://www.mainsailhotels.com
Year Founded: 1998
Sales Range: $50-74.9 Million
Emp.: 280
Hotel, Apartments & Other Real Estate Developer, Owner & Manager
N.A.I.C.S.: 237210
Joe C. Collier *(Founder & Pres)*
Julianne V. Corlew *(Mng Partner & VP)*
Maura Palmer *(Controller)*
Dale O'Neil *(Dir-Procurement)*
Norwood Smith *(VP-Sls & Mktg)*
Nan Feng *(Reg Dir-Fin)*
Tom Haines *(VP-Ops & Transitions)*
Brandon Marshall *(Corp Dir-Sls)*
Brad Hayden *(VP-Fin)*
Taylor Grey *(VP-Bus Dev & Projects)*
Charlie Albanos *(VP-Ops)*
Becky Hayes *(Gen Mgr-Residence Inn Wesley Chapel & Dir-Sls-Residence Inn Wesley Chapel)*

Subsidiaries:

Mainsail Suites Hotel & Conference Center Tampa (1)
5108 Eisenhower Blvd, Tampa, FL 33634
Tel.: (813) 243-2600
Web Site: http://www.mainsailtampa.com
Sales Range: $10-24.9 Million
Emp.: 220
Hotel
N.A.I.C.S.: 721110
Neisja Jones *(Gen Mgr)*

MAINSAIL MANAGEMENT COMPANY, LLC
One Front St Ste 3000, San Francisco, CA 94111
Tel.: (415) 391-3150
Web Site: http://mainsailpartners.com
Privater Equity Firm
N.A.I.C.S.: 523999
Lynn Atkinson *(COO)*
Gavin Turner *(Mng Partner)*
Emily Azevedo *(Operating Partner)*
Jason Frankel *(Principal)*
Rebecca Glatt *(Dir-Talent)*
Cleo Nguyen *(Dir-Compliance)*

Subsidiaries:

ServiceCore, LLC (1)
405 Urban St Ste 120, Lakewood, CO 80228
Tel.: (844) 336-0611
Web Site: https://servicecore.com
Septic & Portable Software Services
N.A.I.C.S.: 513210

MAINSPRING, INC.
20010 Fisher Ave Ste E, Poolesville, MD 20837-2034
Tel.: (301) 948-8077
Web Site: http://www.gomainspring.com
Year Founded: 1993
Computer System Design Services
N.A.I.C.S.: 541512
Jeremy Kaikko *(Chief Info Officer-Virtual)*
Tom Keller *(Pres)*

MAINSTREAM TECHNOLOGIES, INC

Marshall Micheals *(Founder & CEO)*
Brenda Sneed *(CFO)*
Ray Steen *(Chief Strategy Officer)*
Chuck Melton *(Mgr-Application Dev)*
Tony Blevins *(Mgr-Professional Svcs & Support Center)*
Ryan Swartz *(Mgr-Info Sys Security)*

MAINSTAY BUSINESS SOLUTIONS
605 Coolidge Dr, Folsom, CA 95630
Tel.: (916) 294-6700
Year Founded: 2003
Sales Range: $50-74.9 Million
Emp.: 100
Temporary & Permanent Employment Services
N.A.I.C.S.: 561320
Eric Ramos *(CEO)*
Robert J. Vitamante *(CFO)*
Sally Fandrich *(Mgr-Central California)*

MAINSTAY TECHNOLOGIES
201 Daniel Webster Hwy, Belmont, NH 03220
Tel.: (603) 524-4774
Web Site: http://www.mstech.com
Sales Range: $1-9.9 Million
Emp.: 19
Information Technology Services
N.A.I.C.S.: 541512
Ryan Barton *(Pres)*
Ryan Robinson *(Dir-Bus Dev)*
Melissa Abbott *(Dir-Admin & Fin)*
Jason Golden *(Chief Info Security Officer)*

MAINSTREAM DATA, INC.
375 Chipeta Way Ste B, Salt Lake City, UT 84108-1261
Tel.: (801) 584-2800
Web Site: http://www.mainstreamdata.com
Year Founded: 1985
Sales Range: $10-24.9 Million
Emp.: 40
Provider of Computer Information Networking Services
N.A.I.C.S.: 541512
Scott Calder *(Pres & CEO)*
Mitch Rasmussen *(CFO & Sr VP-Fin)*
Scott Smith *(CTO & VP-Tech)*
Greg Weeks *(VP-Sls)*

MAINSTREAM ENERGY CORPORATION
775 Fiero Ln Ste 200, San Luis Obispo, CA 93401
Tel.: (805) 528-9705 DE
Web Site: http://www.mainstreamenergy.com
Year Founded: 2005
Emp.: 700
Holding Company; Solar Panel Mfr, Whslr & Installation Services
N.A.I.C.S.: 551112
Ken Ambur *(Gen Counsel)*
Ethan Miller *(VP & Gen Mgr-Reg)*
David Morosoli *(VP & Gen Mgr-Comml)*
Gregg Fisher *(VP & Gen Mgr-Distr)*
Michelle Berlin *(Dir-HR)*
Jesse Elliott *(Dir-Safety, Quality & Cost)*

MAINSTREAM TECHNOLOGIES, INC
325 W Capitol Ave 2nd Fl, Little Rock, AR 72201
Tel.: (501) 801-6700 AR
Web Site: http://www.mainstreamtech.com
Year Founded: 1996
Sales Range: $1-9.9 Million
Emp.: 34

MAINSTREAM TECHNOLOGIES, INC

Mainstream Technologies, Inc—(Continued)
Software Development Services
N.A.I.C.S.: 541511
Jeffrey Byers *(VP-Software Solutions)*
John Burgess *(Founder, Pres & Chief Security Officer)*
Daniel Weatherly *(Dir-Managed Svc)*
Jeff Pracht *(Dir-Security Svcs)*
Justin Leavell *(Dir-IT)*
Paul Watson *(Engr-Sys)*
Sara Christie *(Mgr-Security Customer Relationship)*
Amanda Legate *(Dir-HR)*
Park Kelley *(Sr Engr-Managed Svcs)*

MAINSTREET CREDIT UNION
13001 W 95th St, Lenexa, KS 66215
Tel.: (913) 599-1010   KS
Web Site:
  http://www.mainstreetcu.org
Year Founded: 1953
Rev.: $22,089,665
Assets: $444,258,634
Liabilities: $405,184,543
Net Worth: $39,074,091
Earnings: $3,266,588
Fiscal Year-end: 12/31/18
Credit Union
N.A.I.C.S.: 522130
John D. Beverlin *(Pres & CEO)*
Gerald Baird *(Chm)*
Paul Alvarado *(Vice Chm)*
Gary Ulmer *(Treas)*
Bill Frick *(Sec)*

MAINSTREET INVESTMENT COMPANY, LLC
14390 Clay Ter Blvd Ste 205, Carmel, IN 46032
Tel.: (317) 582-6200   IN
Web Site:
  http://www.mainstreetinvestment.com
Holding Company; Real Estate Investment & Development
N.A.I.C.S.: 551112
Paul Ezekiel Turner *(Founder & CEO)*
Nicole Bickett *(Chief Admin Officer)*
Scott Fankhauser *(Chief Investment Officer)*

Subsidiaries:

Mainstreet Property Group, LLC   (1)
14390 Clay Terrace Blvd Ste 205, Carmel, IN 46032
Tel.: (317) 582-6200
Web Site:
  http://www.mainstreetinvestment.com
Real Estate Investment & Development Services
N.A.I.C.S.: 531390
Paul Ezekiel Turner *(Founder & CEO)*
Christopher J. Lukaart *(Exec VP-Production)*

MAINSTREET PROPERTY GROUP
14390 Clay Tarrace Blvd Ste160, Carmel, IN 46032
Tel.: (317) 420-0205
Web Site:
  http://www.mainstreetcap.net
Year Founded: 2002
Sales Range: $1-9.9 Million
Emp.: 145
Real Estate Investment
N.A.I.C.S.: 525990
Zeke Turner *(Founder, Chm & CEO)*
V. Edward Grogg *(Pres)*
Adlai Chester *(CFO)*
Rob Bassler *(VP-Production Ops)*

MAINTAINCO INC.
65 E Leuning St, South Hackensack, NJ 07606
Tel.: (201) 487-2565

Web Site: http://www.maintainco.com
Rev.: $14,000,000
Emp.: 50
Material Handling Equipment Whslr & Rentals
N.A.I.C.S.: 423830
James G. Picarillo *(Chm & Pres)*
Drew Bartsch *(Mgr-Planned Maintenance)*
Felicia Steele *(Mgr-Sls)*

MAINTENANCE ENGINEERING
3001 S University Dr, Fargo, ND 58103
Tel.: (701) 293-7383
Web Site: http://www.me-dtc.com
Rev.: $13,500,000
Emp.: 12
Lighting Fixtures, Commercial & Industrial
N.A.I.C.S.: 423610
Curtis H. Kesselring *(Pres)*
Dennis Leno *(VP)*
Eric Brown *(Mgr-Sls-Veteran)*

MAINTENANCE SOLUTIONS INC.
8812 Jericho City Dr, Landover, MD 20785
Tel.: (301) 350-5401
Rev.: $2,800,000
Emp.: 5
Service Establishment Equipment & Supplies Merchant Whslr
N.A.I.C.S.: 423850
Craig White *(Pres)*

MAINTENANCE SUPPLY COMPANY INC.
1837 S Meridan St, Wichita, KS 67213
Tel.: (316) 264-7929   KS
Web Site: http://www.massco.com
Year Founded: 1982
Sales Range: $10-24.9 Million
Emp.: 80
Provider of Janitors' Supplies
N.A.I.C.S.: 423850
Anthony Savaiano *(Owner & CEO)*
Bob Coates *(CFO)*

MAINTHIA TECHNOLOGIES, INC.
7055 Engle Rd Ste 502, Cleveland, OH 44130
Tel.: (440) 816-0202
Web Site: http://www.mainthia.com
Year Founded: 1996
Sales Range: $10-24.9 Million
Emp.: 250
Systems Operations & Engineering, Safety & Risk Management, Quality Assurance & Configuration Management & Other IT Services
N.A.I.C.S.: 541519
Hemant Mainthia *(Owner & Pres)*
Craig Dunn *(Engr-Control Sys)*
Thomas Jones *(Mgr-Work Control)*

MAISTO INTERNATIONAL, INC.
7751 Cherry Ave, Fontana, CA 92336-4002
Tel.: (909) 357-7988   CA
Web Site: http://www.maisto.com
Year Founded: 1992
Sales Range: $10-24.9 Million
Emp.: 40
Toys & Hobby Goods
N.A.I.C.S.: 423920
Pui Y. Ngan *(Pres)*
Charlie Liu *(Gen Mgr)*
Rick Berman *(Dir-Sls)*

MAITA ENTERPRISES INC.
2500 Auburn Blvd, Sacramento, CA 95821

Tel.: (916) 481-0855
Web Site:
  http://www.maitatoyota.com
Emp.: 300
New & Used Automobile Retailer
N.A.I.C.S.: 441110
Vincent Maita *(Owner)*
Eric Wilson *(Gen Mgr-Sls)*

MAITA'S NISSAN OF SACRAMENTO
2820 Auburn Blvd, Sacramento, CA 95821
Tel.: (916) 488-5400
Web Site:
  http://www.maitasnissanofsacramento.com
Rev.: $53,786,000
Emp.: 84
Automobiles, New & Used
N.A.I.C.S.: 441110
Matt Bassett *(Gen Mgr)*

MAITLAND PRIMROSE GROUP
7220 N 16th St Ste C, Phoenix, AZ 85020
Tel.: (602) 944-0046
Web Site:
  http://www.maitlandprimrose.com
Sales Range: $10-24.9 Million
Emp.: 3
Publisher
N.A.I.C.S.: 513130
Margaret Tritch *(Pres)*

MAJEK FIRE PROTECTION INC.
1707 Imperial Way, Thorofare, NJ 08086
Tel.: (856) 845-4800
Web Site:
  http://www.majekfireprotection.com
Sales Range: $25-49.9 Million
Emp.: 115
Sprinkler Contractors
N.A.I.C.S.: 238220
Jim Mc Kay *(Controller)*
James J. McKay *(CFO & VP-Fin)*

MAJESTIC CONSTRUCTION LLC
275 N Franklin Tpke, Ramsey, NJ 07446
Tel.: (201) 327-1919
Sales Range: $10-24.9 Million
Emp.: 25
Apartment Building Construction
N.A.I.C.S.: 236117

Subsidiaries:

HRW LLC   (1)
275 N Franklin Tpke, Ramsey, NJ 07446
Tel.: (201) 327-1919
Sales Range: $10-24.9 Million
Emp.: 15
Commercial & Office Building, New Construction
N.A.I.C.S.: 236220

MAJESTIC LIQUOR STORES INC.
1111 Jacksboro Hwy, Fort Worth, TX 76107
Tel.: (817) 335-5252
Sales Range: $25-49.9 Million
Emp.: 160
Liquor Stores
N.A.I.C.S.: 445320
Ben Lanford *(Pres)*

MAJESTIC MARBLE AND GLASS CO.
8411 Glenwood Ave Ste 107, Raleigh, NC 27612

Tel.: (919) 256-9225
Rev.: $12,486,411
Emp.: 65
Bathroom Fixtures, Cut Stone
N.A.I.C.S.: 327991
Danny Cox *(Pres)*

MAJESTIC MOTORS INC.
509 Quaker Ln, West Warwick, RI 02893
Tel.: (401) 822-2000   RI
Web Site:
  http://www.majestichonda.com
Year Founded: 1960
Sales Range: $50-74.9 Million
Emp.: 65
Sales of New & Used Automobiles
N.A.I.C.S.: 441110
Burton L. Charren *(Pres)*
Mark Charren *(CEO)*

MAJESTIC OIL CO. INC.
2104 Fairfax Ave, Cherry Hill, NJ 08003
Tel.: (856) 751-8801
Rev.: $12,048,616
Emp.: 8
Fuel Oil
N.A.I.C.S.: 424720
Eugene Raymond III *(CEO)*

MAJESTIC STAR CASINO & HOTEL
1 Buffington Harbor Dr, Gary, IN 46406-3000
Tel.: (219) 977-7100   IN
Web Site:
  http://www.majesticstarcasino.com
Year Founded: 1993
Sales Range: $350-399.9 Million
Emp.: 2,700
Holding Company Casino Hotel
Owner & Operator
N.A.I.C.S.: 551112
Peter Liguori *(Pres)*

Subsidiaries:

Barden Mississippi Gaming, LLC   (1)
711 Lucky Ln, Robinsonville, MS 38664-9141
Tel.: (662) 363-5825
Web Site: http://www.fitzgeraldstunica.com
Sales Range: $200-249.9 Million
Casino Hotel Operator
N.A.I.C.S.: 721120
Steve Disakus *(VP & Gen Mgr)*

The Majestic Star Casino II, Inc.   (1)
1 Buffington Harbor Dr, Gary, IN 46406-1023
Tel.: (219) 977-9999
Web Site: http://www.majesticstar.com
Sales Range: $75-99.9 Million
Emp.: 1,500
Hotel & Casino
N.A.I.C.S.: 713290

MAJESTIC STEEL SERVICE, INC.
5300 Majestic Pkwy, Bedford, OH 44146-1744
Tel.: (440) 786-2666   OH
Web Site:
  http://www.majesticsteel.com
Year Founded: 1979
Sales Range: $25-49.9 Million
Emp.: 250
Metals, Service Centers & Offices
N.A.I.C.S.: 423510
Susan Suvak *(CFO)*
Todd Leebow *(Pres)*

MAJESTIC TRANSPORTATION
283 Lockhaven Ste 100, Houston, TX 77073
Tel.: (281) 869-8031
Web Site:
  http://www.majestictransportation.com
Year Founded: 2001
Sales Range: $10-24.9 Million

Emp.: 10
Transportation Services
N.A.I.C.S.: 541614
Steve Rutledge *(Founder, Owner & Pres)*
Jason Hughes *(Co-Owner)*
Clay Brown *(Mgr-Ops)*

MAJIC WHEELS, INC.
1950 Custom Dr, Fort Myers, FL 33907
Tel.: (239) 313-5672
Year Founded: 2007
Emp.: 2
Waste Management Services
N.A.I.C.S.: 562998
Denise S. Houghtaling *(Pres & CEO)*

MAJOR AFFILIATES INC.
150 W Washington St, Shelbyville, IN 46176
Tel.: (317) 398-5271   IN
Year Founded: 1988
Sales Range: $10-24.9 Million
Hospital Facility Support Services
N.A.I.C.S.: 561210
Douglas Carter *(Chm)*
Jeff Beaty *(Treas & Sec)*
Gene Jones *(Vice Chm)*

MAJOR BRANDS, INC.
6701 Southwest Ave, Saint Louis, MO 63143
Tel.: (314) 645-1843   MO
Web Site:
    http://www.majorbrands.com
Year Founded: 1934
Beer, Wine & Distilled Alcoholic Beverages Distr
N.A.I.C.S.: 424820
Susan B. McCollum *(Chm & CEO)*

MAJOR LEAGUE BASEBALL
245 Park Ave, New York, NY 10167
Tel.: (212) 931-7800
Web Site: http://www.mlb.com
Year Founded: 1903
Professional Basketball Organization
N.A.I.C.S.: 813990
Thomas C. Brasuell *(VP-Community Affairs)*
Peter Woodfork *(Sr VP-Baseball Ops)*
Pat Courtney *(Chief Comm Officer)*
Tony Reagins *(Sr VP-Youth Programs)*
Bob Starkey *(Co-CFO)*
Josh Alkin *(VP-Govt Rels-Washington)*
Dan Halem *(Chief Legal Officer)*
John Blake *(Exec VP-Comm)*
Mike Bullock *(VP-IT)*
Jim Cochrane *(Sr VP-Partnerships & Client Svcs)*
Jon Daniels *(Pres-Ops & Gen Mgr)*
Ray C. Davis *(Co-Chm)*
Sean Decker *(Sr VP-Ops & Events)*
Paige Farragut *(Sr VP-Ticket Sls & Svcs)*
Kellie Fischer *(Co-CFO & Exec VP)*
Starr Gulledge *(VP & Controller)*
Jack Hill *(Sr VP-Project Dev)*
Becky Kimbro *(VP-Mktg)*
Rob Matwick *(Exec VP-Bus Ops)*
Blake Miller *(VP-Security & Parking)*
Chuck Morgan *(Exec VP-Ballpark Entertainment & Productions)*
Karin Morris *(VP-Community Outreach & Exec Dir-Foundation)*
Mark Neifeld *(VP-Special Events)*
Katie Pothier *(Gen Counsel & Exec VP)*
Bob R. Simpson *(Co-Chm)*
Terry Turner *(Sr VP-HR & Risk Mgmt)*
Sami Kawakami *(Mng Dir-Japan)*
Rodrigo Fernandez *(Mng Dir-Latin America)*
Charlie Hill *(VP-Intl Strategic Dev)*
Jim Small *(Sr VP-Intl)*
Michele Meyer-Shipp *(Chief People & Culture Officer)*
Karin Timpone *(CMO & Exec VP)*
Chris Marinak *(Chief Ops & Strategy Officer)*

Subsidiaries:

MLB Advanced Media, L.P.   (1)
75 9th Ave 5th Fl, New York, NY 10011
Tel.: (646) 495-4091
Internet & Interactive Media Services
N.A.I.C.S.: 513199
Matthew Gould *(VP-Corp Comm)*
David Glass *(Owner)*
Justin Klemm *(Dir-Instant Replay)*
Pat Courtney *(Chief Comm Officer)*
Dan Halem *(Chief Legal Officer)*
Tony Petitti *(COO)*
Bob Starkey *(CFO)*

Joint Venture (Domestic):

Rawlings Sporting Goods Co., Inc.   (2)
510 Maryville University Dr Ste 110, Saint Louis, MO 63141
Tel.: (314) 819-2800
Web Site: http://www.rawlings.com
Athletic Equipment, Apparel & Sporting Goods Mfr
N.A.I.C.S.: 339920
Michael Zlaket *(Pres)*

Subsidiary (Non-US):

Rawlings Canada Inc.   (3)
131 Savanah Oak Dr, Brantford, N3V 1E8, ON, Canada
Tel.: (519) 750-1380
Web Site: http://www.rawlings.com
Sporting Goods Whslr
N.A.I.C.S.: 423910
Randy Beatty *(Gen Mgr)*

Subsidiary (Domestic):

Worth Inc.   (3)
510 Maryville University Dr Ste 110, Saint Louis, MO 63141
Tel.: (314) 819-2800
Web Site: http://www.worthsports.com
Baseball & Softball Equipment Mfr
N.A.I.C.S.: 339920

Subsidiary (Domestic):

Tickets.com, Inc.   (2)
555 Anton Blvd Fl 11, Costa Mesa, CA 92626
Tel.: (714) 327-5400
Web Site: http://www.tickets.com
Sales Range: $50-74.9 Million
Emp.: 610
Online Tickets Seller
N.A.I.C.S.: 561599
Derek Argobright *(CTO)*
Joe Choti *(Pres & CEO)*
Curt Clausen *(Gen Counsel)*
Cristine Hurley *(CFO)*
Derek Palmer *(Mng Dir & Exec VP-Intl)*

Major League Baseball Properties, Inc.   (1)
245 Park Ave, New York, NY 10167
Tel.: (212) 931-7800
Intellectual Property Holding Company
N.A.I.C.S.: 551112
Ethan G. Orlinsky *(Gen Counsel)*

MAJOR LEAGUE SOCCER LLC
420 5th Ave, New York, NY 10018
Tel.: (212) 450-1200   DE
Web Site: http://www.mlssoccer.com
Year Founded: 1995
Sales Range: $50-74.9 Million
Emp.: 300
Professional Soccer League
N.A.I.C.S.: 713990
Sean Prendergast *(CFO)*
Dan Courtemanche *(Exec VP-Comm)*
Joshua Neier *(Sr Dir-Fin)*
Kathy Carter *(Pres-Mktg-Soccer United)*
Howard Handler *(CMO-MLS & Soccer United)*
Gary R. Stevenson *(Pres, Pres, Mng Dir & Mng Dir)*
Julian Woll *(Mgr-Bus Dev)*
JoAnn Neale *(Chief Admin Officer)*
J. Todd Durbin *(Exec VP-Player Rels & Competition)*
Bill Ordower *(Gen Counsel & Sr VP)*
Gary Stevenson *(Pres & Mng Dir)*
Maribeth Towers *(Sr VP-Consumer Products)*
Seth Bacon *(Sr VP-Media)*
Al Dagostino *(Dir-Comm)*
Jurgen Mainka *(Chief Bus Officer)*

MAJOR MARKET, INC.
504 E Alvarado St Ste 207, Fallbrook, CA 92028-2365
Tel.: (760) 723-7305
Web Site:
    http://www.majormarketgrocery.com
Year Founded: 1994
Sales Range: $10-24.9 Million
Emp.: 250
Grocery Stores
N.A.I.C.S.: 445110
Ray Nicol *(Controller)*
Sam Logan *(Pres & CEO)*
John Kuper *(Mgr-Front End)*

MAJOR PETROLEUM INDUSTRIES INC.
PO Box 377, Rosenhayn, NJ 08352
Tel.: (856) 451-3700
Sales Range: $10-24.9 Million
Emp.: 30
Distr of Petroleum Products
N.A.I.C.S.: 424710
Nate Pizzo *(Pres)*

MAJOR SUPPLY INC.
5400 NW 35th Ter Ste 104, Fort Lauderdale, FL 33309
Tel.: (954) 739-2852
Rev.: $15,185,309
Emp.: 20
Light Bulbs & Related Supplies
N.A.I.C.S.: 423610
Howard Kleier *(Pres)*

MAJOR TOOL & MACHINE, INC.
1458 E 19th St, Indianapolis, IN 46218-4228
Tel.: (317) 636-6433   IN
Web Site: http://www.majortool.com
Year Founded: 1946
Sales Range: $25-49.9 Million
Emp.: 335
Machining & Fabrication Services
N.A.I.C.S.: 332710
Stephen J. Weyreter *(Pres & CEO)*

MAJORPOWER CORPORATION
7011 Indus Blvd, Mebane, NC 27302
Tel.: (919) 563-6610   NY
Web Site:
    http://www.majorpower.com
Year Founded: 1990
Sales Range: $10-24.9 Million
Emp.: 25
Power Supply Components & Parts Mfr, Distr & Supplier
N.A.I.C.S.: 335999
Samuel Norman *(COO)*

MAJORS MANAGEMENT, LLC
305 A Equipment Court, Lawrenceville, GA 30046-6739
Tel.: (770) 338-2620
Web Site:
    http://www.majorsmanagement.com
Year Founded: 1970
Office Administrative Services
N.A.I.C.S.: 561110
Jennifer Bolas *(Mgr-Real Estate & Mktg)*

Subsidiaries:

Bowden Oil Company, Inc.   (1)
40865 US Hwy 280, Sylacauga, AL 35150
Tel.: (256) 245-5611
Web Site: http://www.bowdenoil.com
Gas Stations with Convenience Stores Owner & Operator
N.A.I.C.S.: 457110
Donna Jones *(VP)*

K & H Truck Plaza Inc.   (1)
PO Box 247, Gilman, IL 60938-0247
Tel.: (815) 265-7625
Web Site: http://www.khtruckplaza.com
Gasoline Engine & Engine Parts Mfr
N.A.I.C.S.: 336310
Tony Lyons *(Mgr-Parts)*

MAPCO Express, Inc.   (1)
801 Crescent Ctr Dr Ste 300, Franklin, TN 37067
Tel.: (877) 722-4664
Web Site: http://www.mapcoexpress.com
Convenience Stores & Gasoline Pumping Stations Operator
N.A.I.C.S.: 457110

MAJORS PLASTICS INC.
10117 I St, Omaha, NE 68127
Tel.: (402) 331-1660
Web Site:
    http://www.majorsplastics.com
Rev.: $17,230,104
Emp.: 130
Plastic Kitchenware, Tableware & Housewares Mfr
N.A.I.C.S.: 326199
James Abbott *(Mgr-Assembly Plant)*
Dave Schiemann *(Program Mgr & Engr-Tooling)*
John May *(Engr-Molding)*
Micheal Herzog *(CFO)*

MAJORS SCIENTIFIC BOOKS, INC.
2137 Butler St, Dallas, TX 75235
Tel.: (972) 353-1100   TX
Web Site: http://www.majors.com
Year Founded: 1966
Sales Range: $10-24.9 Million
Emp.: 100
Book Stores, Sell to Libraries & Corporations
N.A.I.C.S.: 459210
Albert Majors McClendon *(Pres)*

MAJULAH INVESTMENT, INC.
1180 Avenue Of The Americas 8th Fl, New York, NY 10036
Tel.: (347) 305-2121   DE
Year Founded: 2016
Liabilities: $69,813
Net Worth: ($69,813)
Earnings: ($19,816)
Emp.: 1
Fiscal Year-end: 02/28/18
Real Estate Asset Management Services
N.A.I.C.S.: 531390
Ding Jie Lin *(Pres, CEO, CFO & Chief Acctg Officer)*

MAK MEDIA INC.
1720 Ne 199th St, Miami, FL 33179-3119
Tel.: (305) 956-9563
Year Founded: 1990
Rev.: $10,000,000
Emp.: 4
Full Service
N.A.I.C.S.: 541810
Marc Plotkin *(Pres)*
Debra A. Fimiani *(Office Mgr & Dir-Media)*

MAKAI CAPITAL PARTNERS LLC

Makai Capital Partners LLC—(Continued)

MAKAI CAPITAL PARTNERS LLC
17615 River Ford Dr, Davidson, NC 28036-8844
Tel.: (704) 491-9292 NC
Web Site: https://www.makaicapitalpartners.com
Year Founded: 2023
Privater Equity Firm
N.A.I.C.S.: 523999
Andrew Fulford (Mng Partner)

Subsidiaries:

New Life Chemical & Equipment, Inc. (1)
15 N Kings Rd, Greenville, SC 29605
Tel.: (864) 277-5516
Web Site: http://www.newlife-chem.com
Sales Range: $1-9.9 Million
Emp.: 12
Chemical & Allied Products Merchant Whslr
N.A.I.C.S.: 424690
Tim Northcutt (Pres)

MAKAR PROPERTIES, LLC
4100 MacArthur Blvd Ste 200, Newport Beach, CA 92660
Tel.: (949) 255-1100
Web Site: http://www.makarproperties.com
Real Estate Services
N.A.I.C.S.: 531390
Paul P. Makarechian (Founder & CEO)
Peter Ciaccia (Pres)

Subsidiaries:

The Lone Mountain Ranch, Inc. (1)
750 Lone Mountain Ranch A, Big Sky, MT 59716
Tel.: (406) 995-4644
Web Site: http://www.lonemountainranch.com
Sales Range: $1-9.9 Million
Emp.: 15
Recreational & Vacation Camps
N.A.I.C.S.: 721214
Paul Robertson (Gen Mgr)

MAKE THE ROAD NEW YORK
301 Grove St, Brooklyn, NY 11237
Tel.: (718) 418-7690 NY
Web Site: http://www.maketheroadny.org
Year Founded: 1992
Sales Range: $10-24.9 Million
Emp.: 197
Immigrant Support Services
N.A.I.C.S.: 624230
Sarah Landes (Dir-Youth & School Partnerships)
Sierra Stoneman-Bell (Dir-Adult Education & Career Pathways)
Julie Quinton (Dir-Adult Literacy)
Julie Miles (Dir-Dev)

MAKE-A-WISH FOUNDATION OF AMERICA
1702 E Highland Ave Ste 400, Phoenix, AZ 85016
Tel.: (602) 279-9474 AZ
Web Site: http://www.wish.org
Year Founded: 1983
Sales Range: $100-124.9 Million
Emp.: 228
Child Support Services
N.A.I.C.S.: 624110
David Mulvihill (VP)
Deborah Thompson (VP-Chapter Support)
Kathy Forshey (VP-Corp Alliances)
Leslie Motter (Chief HR Officer)
Paul Mehlhorn (CFO)
Bill Baumbach (CIO & VP)
Richard K. Davis (Pres & CEO)

MAKE-A-WISH FOUNDATION OF GREATER LOS ANGELES
11390 W Olympic Blvd Ste 300, Los Angeles, CA 90064
Tel.: (310) 788-9474
Web Site: https://wish.org
Year Founded: 1983
Sales Range: $1-9.9 Million
Emp.: 20
Non-Profit Organization That Grants Wishes to Children with Life Threatening Illnesses
N.A.I.C.S.: 813410
Suzanne Kolb (Chm)
Alejandra Rivera (Coord-Wish)
Cindi Berns (VP)
Eric Happe (Dir-Fin & IT)
Felisha Baquera (Sr Dir-Volunteer Svcs)
Iris Gelt-Warner (VP-Mktg & Comm)
Kelly Schumann (Mgr-Medical Outreach)
Kristen Blanc (Coord-Wish)
Kristin Tomlinson (Mgr-Wish Assists)
Maria Ayala (Mgr-Wishes)
Melanie Underhill (Mgr)
Michelle Becker (Mgr-Dev)
Monica Del Real (Program Coord)
Ramin Baschshi (CEO & COO)
Sarina Aguirre (Dir-Wishes)
Stephanie Bediee (Dir-Corp Alliances)
Taylor Kalman (Coord-External Events)
Vanessa Petersen (Dir-Special Events)
Wendy Wood (VP-Mission Delivery)

MAKERS NUTRITION, LLC
71 Mall Dr, Commack, NY 11725
Web Site: http://www.makersnutrition.com
Year Founded: 2014
Sales Range: $25-49.9 Million
Emp.: 30
Dietary Supplement & Tablet Mfr
N.A.I.C.S.: 325412
Jason Provenzano (Pres & CEO)

MAKI CORPORATION
160 Mass Ave Rt 2A, Lunenburg, MA 01462
Tel.: (978) 343-7422 MA
Web Site: http://www.makicorp.com
Year Founded: 1975
Sales Range: $75-99.9 Million
Emp.: 100
Lumber & Other Building Material
Lumber Plywood & Millwork Paint
Glass & Wallpaper Metal Screen
Door Aluminum Extruded Product Mfr
N.A.I.C.S.: 423310
Glenn Maki (Pres)

Subsidiaries:

Maki Home Center, Inc. (1)
160 Mass Ave, Lunenburg, MA 01462 (100%)
Tel.: (978) 343-7422
Web Site: http://www.makicorp.com
Sales Range: $10-24.9 Million
Emp.: 25
Lumber & Other Building Materials; Plywood & Millwork; Paint, Glass & Wallpaper; Metal Screen Doors; Aluminum Extended Products
N.A.I.C.S.: 423310
Glen Maki (Pres)

MAKKE LLC
92 N Main St, Windsor, NJ 08561
Tel.: (609) 443-5522
Web Site: http://www.pyrometer.com
Sales Range: $10-24.9 Million
Emp.: 30
Holding Company
N.A.I.C.S.: 551112
David Crozier (CEO)

Subsidiaries:

American Teratec, Inc. (1)
92 N Main St Bldg 18D, Windsor, NJ 08561
Tel.: (609) 443-5551
Shipping Vessel Engine Management & Electronic System Control
N.A.I.C.S.: 334513

Automated Measurement & Control Corporation (1)
92 N Main St 18-D, Windsor, NJ 08561
Tel.: (609) 443-5050
Web Site: http://www.amccusa.com
Marine & Industrial Safety Monitoring Systems
N.A.I.C.S.: 334513

Pyrometer Instrument Co., Inc. (1)
92 N Main St Bldg 18-D, Windsor, NJ 08561-0479
Tel.: (609) 443-5522
Web Site: http://www.pyrometer.com
Rev.: $5,000,000
Emp.: 25
Precision Temperature Measurement Instruments for Space, Defense, Science & Industry
N.A.I.C.S.: 334513

MAKO MEDICAL LABORATORIES, LLC
8461 Garvey Dr, Raleigh, NC 27616
Web Site: http://www.makomedical.com
Year Founded: 2014
Sales Range: $75-99.9 Million
Emp.: 502
Medical Laboratory Testing Services
N.A.I.C.S.: 621511
Joshua Arant (Founder & COO)

MAKOVSKY & COMPANY, INC.
16 E 34th St 15th Fl, New York, NY 10016
Tel.: (212) 508-9600
Web Site: http://www.makovsky.com
Year Founded: 1979
Sales Range: $25-49.9 Million
Emp.: 50
Public Relations Agency
N.A.I.C.S.: 541820
Kenneth D. Makovsky (Founder)

MAKOVSKY RINGEL GREENBERG, LLC.
1010 June Rd Ste 200, Memphis, TN 38119-3722
Tel.: (901) 683-2220
Web Site: http://www.mrgmemphis.com
Year Founded: 1967
Sales Range: $10-24.9 Million
Emp.: 220
Real Estate Brokerage Services
N.A.I.C.S.: 531210
James M. Ringel (COO)
Michael Greenberg (CEO)
Gary Lubin (VP-Comml Leasing & Mgmt)
Justin Lubin (VP-Comml Leasing & Mgmt)
Gary Makowsky (Chief Dev Officer)
Roger McLemore (VP-Comml Property Svcs)

MAKRO TECHNOLGIES, INC.
1 Washington Park Ste 1502, Newark, NJ 07102
Tel.: (973) 481-0100
Web Site: http://makrotech.com
Year Founded: 1996
Sales Range: $25-49.9 Million
Global Consulting & IT Services
N.A.I.C.S.: 541618
Mahesh Malneedi (CEO)

MAL ENTERPRISES, INC.
300 Hailey, Sweetwater, TX 79556-4719
Tel.: (325) 236-6351 TX
Year Founded: 1972
Sales Range: $10-24.9 Million
Emp.: 20
Grocery Stores
N.A.I.C.S.: 445110
Neil Hoover (Sec)

MALARKEY ROOFING PRODUCTS
3131 N Columbia Blvd, Portland, OR 97217-7472
Tel.: (503) 283-1191 OR
Web Site: http://www.malarkeyroofing.com
Year Founded: 1956
Sales Range: $25-49.9 Million
Emp.: 120
Mfr of Commercial & Residential Asphalt Roofing Products
N.A.I.C.S.: 324122
Shannon Yagi (Mgr-Pur)
John R. Kouba (Dir-Tech Svcs)
Jennifer Kettlestrings (Controller)

MALCO ENTERPRISES NEVADA INC.
7135 Gilespie St, Las Vegas, NV 89119-1217
Tel.: (702) 736-1212 NV
Web Site: http://www.budgetvegas.com
Year Founded: 1989
Sales Range: $25-49.9 Million
Emp.: 185
Budget Rent-a-Car Franchise
N.A.I.C.S.: 532111
John Mallo (Pres)

MALCO PRODUCTS, INC.
361 Fairview Ave, Barberton, OH 44203
Tel.: (330) 753-0361 OH
Web Site: http://www.malcopro.com
Year Founded: 1953
Sales Range: $100-124.9 Million
Emp.: 300
Chemical Specialty Product Mfr, Packager & Marketer
N.A.I.C.S.: 325612
Timothy White (VP-Ops)

Subsidiaries:

Whiz Automotive Chemicals Div (1)
361 Fairview Ave, Barberton, OH 44203-2774 (100%)
Tel.: (330) 753-0361
Web Site: http://www.malcoproducts.com
Sales Range: $25-49.9 Million
Emp.: 150
Malco Automotive Chemical Specialties; Industrial & Household Chemicals
N.A.I.C.S.: 325612
Stuart Glauberman (Pres)

MALCO PRODUCTS, INC.
14080 State Hwy 55 NW, Annandale, MN 55302
Tel.: (320) 274-8246
Web Site: http://www.malcotools.com
Year Founded: 1950
Rev.: $13,000,000
Emp.: 172
Hand & Edge Tools
N.A.I.C.S.: 332216
Michael Hemmesch (Dir-Bus Intelligence)
Rich Benninghoff (Pres & CEO)

Subsidiaries:

Malco International (1)
14080 State Hwy 55 NW, Annandale, MN 55302
Tel.: (320) 274-2376
Sales Range: $25-49.9 Million
Emp.: 3
Exports Hand & Edge Tools
N.A.I.C.S.: 423710

Malco Products (1)
14080 State Hwy 55 NW, Annandale, MN 55302-3457
Tel.: (320) 274-8246
Web Site: http://www.marcoproducts.com
Hand & Edge Tools Mfr
N.A.I.C.S.: 332216
Jeannette Rieger-Borer (CFO)
Karla Braun (Coord-Mktg Svcs)
Jon Navratil (Engr-New Products)
Mike Janey (Mgr-Mktg Svcs)
Paul Hansen (Pres)
Nancy Gunnerson (Portfolio Mgr-Plng)
Lucas Runke (Engr-Mfg & Mechanical-II)

MALCO THEATRES INC.
5851 Ridgeway Center Pkwy, Memphis, TN 38120
Tel.: (901) 761-3480
Web Site: http://www.malco.com
Year Founded: 1915
Sales Range: $25-49.9 Million
Emp.: 700
Motion Picture Theater Operator
N.A.I.C.S.: 512131
Steve Lightman (Pres)

MALCOLM DRILLING COMPANY INC.
92 Natoma St Ste 400, San Francisco, CA 94105
Tel.: (415) 901-4400
Web Site:
http://www.malcolmdrilling.com
Year Founded: 1962
Sales Range: $50-74.9 Million
Emp.: 400
Provider of Building Contracting Services
N.A.I.C.S.: 238990
John M. Malcolm (Pres & CEO)
Barry Kannon (Chm)
Roy Fukumura (Controller)

MALCOLM GROUP INC.
415 E N Water St Unit 1605, Chicago, IL 60611
Tel.: (312) 467-1400
Web Site:
http://www.malcolmgroup.com
Sales Range: $25-49.9 Million
Emp.: 175
Metal Badges; Government Occupations
N.A.I.C.S.: 541890
Malcolm Roebuck (Pres)

Subsidiaries:

Badge-A-Minit Ltd (1)
345 N Lewis Ave, Oglesby, IL 61348
Tel.: (815) 883-8822
Web Site: http://www.badgeaminit.com
Sales Range: $10-24.9 Million
Emp.: 30
Advertising Specialties
N.A.I.C.S.: 541890
Cindy Kurkowski (Pres)

Best Impressions Catalog Company (1)
345 N Lewis Ave, Oglesby, IL 61348
Tel.: (815) 883-3532
Web Site: http://www.bestimpressions.com
Rev.: $16,459,224
Emp.: 30
Promotional Products Mail Order Catalog Sales
N.A.I.C.S.: 455219
Cindy Kurkowski (Pres & CEO)

MALEK MANAGEMENT CORPORATION
1491 Coney Island Ave, Brooklyn, NY 11230
Tel.: (718) 692-0003
Rev.: $12,000,000
Emp.: 5
Apartment Building Operator
N.A.I.C.S.: 531110
David Malek (Owner)

MALEY & WERTZ, INC.
900 E Columbia St, Evansville, IN 47724
Tel.: (812) 425-3358
Web Site:
http://www.maleyandwertz.com
Year Founded: 1968
Sales Range: $1-9.9 Million
Emp.: 45
Hardwoods Supplier
N.A.I.C.S.: 321211
Arthur W. Klipsch (Owner, Pres & Mgr-Pur)
Michael F. Powers (Gen Mgr)

Subsidiaries:

Kirkham Hardwoods, Inc. (1)
3956 S State Rd 63, Terre Haute, IN 47802-8747
Tel.: (812) 232-0624
Sales Range: $1-9.9 Million
Emp.: 50
Hardwoods Supplier
N.A.I.C.S.: 321211
Percy Mossbarger (Pres)

MALGOR & CO. INC.
Carr 5 Km 3.5 Barrio Palmas, Catano, PR 00962
Tel.: (787) 788-0303
Web Site: http://www.malgorco.com
Sales Range: $50-74.9 Million
Emp.: 100
Groceries, General Line
N.A.I.C.S.: 424410
Conrado Garcia Guerra (Pres)
Antonio Garcia Mendez (VP)

MALIBU TEXTILES INC.
39 W 37th St, New York, NY 10018
Tel.: (212) 354-6707
Web Site:
http://www.malibutextiles.com
Sales Range: $10-24.9 Million
Emp.: 14
Lace Fabrics
N.A.I.C.S.: 424310
Dinora Espinal (Controller)
Valerie James (Mgr-Import)
John Irwin (Owner)

MALIN INTEGRATED HANDLING SOLUTIONS & DESIGN
15870 Midway Rd, Addison, TX 75001
Tel.: (972) 458-2680
Web Site: http://www.malinusa.com
Sales Range: $200-249.9 Million
Emp.: 430
Industrial Machinery & Equipment Merchant Whslr
N.A.I.C.S.: 423830
John Creme (Pres)
Gavin Rick (Dir-IT)
Kathleen Flores (Coord-Sls)
Brian Ford (Mgr-Sls)
Adela Gonzales (Coord-Svcs)
David Goyette (VP)
Jeff Grossman (Mgr-Parts)
Jill Jackson (Mgr-Transportation)
Joni Mashburn (Mgr-Rental)
Linda Montague (Coord-Sls)
Richard McCarter (Sr Acct Mgr-Sls)
Erik Boranian (Coord-Rental)
Christine Clark (Supvr-Sls)
Jack Cain (VP-Fin)
Jack Baker (Engr-Sys)
John O'Donnell (Mgr-Inventory Control)
Scott Chontos (CEO)

MALKIN PROPERTIES, L.L.C.
60 E 42nd St Fl 26, New York, NY 10165
Tel.: (212) 953-0888 NY
Web Site:
http://www.malkinproperties.com
Year Founded: 1965
Sales Range: $10-24.9 Million
Emp.: 200
Real Estate Investment
N.A.I.C.S.: 523999
Anthony E. Malkin (Pres)

Subsidiaries:

Malkin Securities Corp. (1)
60 E 42nd St 48th Fl, New York, NY 10165-0006
Tel.: (212) 687-8700
Web Site: http://www.malkinsecurities.com
Sales Range: $10-24.9 Million
Emp.: 200
Real Estate Development & Management Services
N.A.I.C.S.: 531120
Peter L. Malkin (Chm)

Subsidiary (Domestic):

Empire State Building Company LLC (2)
60 E 42nd St 48th Fl, New York, NY 10165-0006
Tel.: (212) 736-3100
Web Site: http://www.esbnyc.com
Sales Range: $125-149.9 Million
Nonresidential Building Operators
N.A.I.C.S.: 531120
Pia Silvestri (Dir-Ops)

MALKO ELECTRIC COMPANY
6200 Lincoln Ave, Morton Grove, IL 60053
Tel.: (847) 967-9500
Web Site:
http://www.malkoelectric.com
Sales Range: $10-24.9 Million
Emp.: 90
Electronic Services
N.A.I.C.S.: 238210
Dennis Chmielewski (Exec VP)

MALL CHEVROLET
75 Haddonfield Rd, Cherry Hill, NJ 08002
Tel.: (856) 662-7000
Web Site: http://www.mallchevy.com
Year Founded: 1986
Sales Range: $10-24.9 Million
Emp.: 65
Car Whslr
N.A.I.C.S.: 441110
Charles Foulke III (Principal)

MALL CHRYSLER-SUZUKI
75 Haddonfield Rd, Cherry Hill, NJ 08002-1453
Tel.: (856) 722-8900
Sales Range: $25-49.9 Million
Emp.: 66
Automobiles
N.A.I.C.S.: 441110
Charles Falkenstien (Pres)
Craig Liss (Controller)

MALL CRAFT INC.
2225 N Windsor Ave, Altadena, CA 91001
Tel.: (626) 398-3598
Web Site: http://www.mallcraft.com
Rev.: $20,131,780
Emp.: 35
Commercial & Office Building Contractors
N.A.I.C.S.: 236220
Gerald L. Fishbein (Chm)
J. M. Garber (Sec)
S. E. Pappas (VP)

MALLARD HOLDING COMPANY LLC
201 Lafayette Cir Ste 205, Lafayette, CA 94549
Tel.: (805) 489-6944
Sales Range: $10-24.9 Million
Emp.: 600
Fast-Food Restaurant, Chain
N.A.I.C.S.: 722513

MALLARD OIL COMPANY INC.
1502 Greenville Hwy, Kinston, NC 28501
Tel.: (252) 527-7191
Web Site: http://www.mallardoil.com
Sales Range: $25-49.9 Million
Emp.: 250
Petroleum Products Distr
N.A.I.C.S.: 424710
Felix Harvey (Chm)
Frank Famularo (Pres)

MALLOF, ABRUZINO & NASH MARKETING
765 Kimberly Dr, Carol Stream, IL 60188-9407
Tel.: (630) 929-5200 IL
Web Site:
http://www.manmarketing.com
Year Founded: 1980
Sales Range: $10-24.9 Million
Emp.: 28
Advertising Agencies
N.A.I.C.S.: 541810
Edward G. Mallof (Pres)
Lucy Ferrari (Acct Exec)
Kelley Stiles (Sr Acct Exec)
Jamie Golden (Acct Coord)
Lee Zuika (Controller-Fin)
Christina Vasta (Acct Coord)
Guy Lieberman (Dir-Digital Mktg)
Jane Wiedmeyer (Acct Coord)
Jon Malone (Dir-Art)
Kathleen Knox (Acct Coord)
Lori Thornton (Acct Coord)
Renata Serpico (Acct Coord)
Toni Mallof (VP & Dir-Creative)
Tony Locke (Dir-Art)

MALLORY & EVANS INC.
625 Kentucky St Bldg A, Scottdale, GA 30079
Tel.: (404) 297-1000
Web Site:
http://www.malloryandevans.com
Rev.: $36,000,000
Emp.: 50
Mechanical Contractor
N.A.I.C.S.: 238220
John G. Dixon (Chm)
Pam Swain (Mgr-Payroll)

MALLORY ALEXANDER INTERNATIONAL LOGISTICS, LLC
4294 Swinnea Rd, Memphis, TN 38118
Tel.: (901) 367-9400
Web Site:
http://www.mallorygroup.com
Year Founded: 1925
Sales Range: $75-99.9 Million
Freight Forwarding Services
N.A.I.C.S.: 488510
Claudio Onofrio (VP-Global Bus Dev-Dallas)
Tinamarie Newman (COO)
Robert Mallory (Chief Admin Officer)
W. Neely Mallory III (Pres)

MALLORY SAFETY & SUPPLY LLC
1040 Industrial Way, Longview, WA 98632
Tel.: (360) 636-5750
Web Site: http://www.malloryco.com
Sales Range: $10-24.9 Million
Emp.: 60
Safety Equipment & Supplies
N.A.I.C.S.: 423990

MALLORY SAFETY & SUPPLY LLC

Mallory Safety & Supply LLC—(Continued)
Tim Loy *(Pres)*
Shawn Murray *(COO)*
Brian Loy *(CIO)*
Subsidiaries:

B.E.E. Industrial Supply, Inc. (1)
25634 Nickel Pl, Hayward, CA 94545
Tel.: (510) 293-3180
Web Site: http://www.beeind.com
Sales Range: $1-9.9 Million
Emp.: 10
Industrial Supply Distr
N.A.I.C.S.: 423840

California Safety & Supply Co. (1)
44380 Osgood Rd, Fremont, CA 94539
Tel.: (510) 770-8610
Sales Range: $1-9.9 Million
Emp.: 20
Safety Equipment & Supply Distr
N.A.I.C.S.: 423990
Michael Carmassi *(VP-Sls)*

Mallory Safety & Supply LLC - San Bernardino (1)
236 W Orange Show Rd, San Bernardino, CA 92408
Tel.: (909) 383-0147
Web Site: http://www.malloryco.com
Sales Range: $10-24.9 Million
Emp.: 40
Safety Equipment
N.A.I.C.S.: 423830
Tim Loy *(Pres)*

Portland Contractors Supply, Inc. (1)
120 NE 9th Ave, Portland, OR 97232
Tel.: (503) 232-5173
Web Site:
http://www.portlandcontractorssupply.com
Sales Range: $1-9.9 Million
Emp.: 12
Construction & Industrial Supplier
N.A.I.C.S.: 423390

R J Safety Supply Co, Inc. (1)
7320 Convoy Ct, San Diego, CA 92111
Tel.: (858) 541-2880
Web Site: http://www.rjsafety.com
Sales Range: $1-9.9 Million
Emp.: 20
Industrial Machinery & Equipment Merchant Whslr
N.A.I.C.S.: 423830
Tifani Swink *(Pres)*

Rocky Mountain Industrial Supply, Inc (1)
1711 W English Ave, Casper, WY 82601-1600
Tel.: (307) 382-3720
Web Site: http://www.rmiwyoming.com
Industrial Machinery & Equipment Merchant Whslr
N.A.I.C.S.: 423830
Jim Golay *(Owner)*

Safety & Supply Company (1)
5510 E Marginal Way S, Seattle, WA 98134
Tel.: (206) 762-8500
Web Site: http://www.safetyandsupply.com
Sales Range: $10-24.9 Million
Emp.: 45
Safety Equipment & Supplies
N.A.I.C.S.: 423990
Shawn Murray *(Pres)*

MALLOY AUTOMOTIVE OF WINCHESTER LLC
6510 Little River Turnpike, Alexandria, VA 22312-0000
Tel.: (866) 788-9507
Web Site: https://www.malloy.com
Motor Vehicle Dealers
N.A.I.C.S.: 441227
Subsidiaries:

Price Chevrolet Co. (1)
2150 Seminole Trl, Charlottesville, VA 22901
Tel.: (434) 817-1881
Web Site: https://www.jimpricechevy.net
Sales Range: $25-49.9 Million
Emp.: 109
Car Whslr

N.A.I.C.S.: 441110
Sandy Fewell *(Pres)*

MALLOY INC.
5411 Jackson Rd, Ann Arbor, MI 48103-1861
Tel.: (734) 665-6113   MI
Web Site:
http://www.edwardsbrothersmalloy.com
Year Founded: 1960
Sales Range: $25-49.9 Million
Emp.: 600
Provider of Printing Services
N.A.I.C.S.: 323117
John Edwards *(Pres & CEO)*
Bill Upton *(CFO & VP)*
Laura Conlin *(Project Mgr)*
Cheri Dunn *(Mgr-Mktg)*
Bob Durgy *(VP-Sls & Mktg)*

MALNOVE INCORPORATED
13434 F St, Omaha, NE 68137-1118
Tel.: (402) 330-1100   NE
Web Site: http://www.malnove.com
Year Founded: 1991
Rev.: $100,000,000
Emp.: 750
Folding Paperboard Boxes
N.A.I.C.S.: 322212
Paul Malnove *(Founder & CEO)*
Subsidiaries:

Malnove Incorporated of Florida (1)
10500 Canada Dr, Jacksonville, FL 32218-4968   (100%)
Tel.: (904) 757-5030
Web Site: http://www.malnove.com
Sales Range: $25-49.9 Million
Emp.: 200
Paperboard Mills
N.A.I.C.S.: 322130
Paul Malnove *(Founder & CEO)*

Malnove Incorporated of Nebraska (1)
13434 F St, Omaha, NE 68137-1118   (100%)
Tel.: (402) 330-1100
Web Site: http://www.malnove.com
Sales Range: $25-49.9 Million
Emp.: 250
Folding Paperboard Boxes
N.A.I.C.S.: 322212
Paul Malnove *(Founder & CEO)*
Dale Houck *(Pres)*
Shannon Doll *(CFO)*
Peter Hofmann *(Exec VP-Sls)*
Kari Narduzzo *(Exec VP-HR)*

Malnove Incorporated of Utah (1)
Freeport Ctr Bldg A 16F, Clearfield, UT 84016-0128
Tel.: (801) 773-7400
Web Site: http://www.malnove.com
Rev.: $25,000,000
Emp.: 100
Paperboard Mills
N.A.I.C.S.: 322130
Paul Malnove *(Chm)*

Malnove Packaging Systems Inc. (1)
13434 F St, Omaha, NE 68137-1118
Tel.: (402) 330-1100
Rev.: $600,000
Emp.: 225
Industrial Machinery & Equipment
N.A.I.C.S.: 423830

MALONE WORKFORCE SOLUTIONS
1868 Campus Pl, Louisville, KY 40299
Tel.: (502) 456-2380
Web Site:
http://www.malonesolutions.com
Year Founded: 1969
Emp.: 200
Employment Placement Services
N.A.I.C.S.: 561311
Joseph C. Malone *(Founder)*
Terrance Malone *(Co-Owner)*

Tim Malone *(Co-Owner)*
Beth Delano *(CEO)*
Dawn Meyers *(COO)*
Ed Coleman *(Sr VP-Sls & Mktg)*
Subsidiaries:

J.C. Malone Associates (1)
1868 Campus Pl, Louisville, KY 40299
Tel.: (502) 456-2380
Web Site: http://www.malonesolutions.com
Sales Range: $10-24.9 Million
Emp.: 35
Executive Recruiting & Temporary Staffing Services
N.A.I.C.S.: 561320

Nextaff, LLC (1)
6842 W 121st Ct, Overland Park, KS 66209
Tel.: (913) 562-5610
Web Site: http://www.nextaff.com
Staffing & Employment Services
N.A.I.C.S.: 561311
James Windmiller *(Co-Founder & Dir-Ops)*
Cary T. Daniel *(Co-Founder & Dir)*

MALONE'S FOOD STORES, LLC
7730 Forney Rd, Dallas, TX 75227
Tel.: (214) 388-4756   TX
Web Site:
http://www.malonesfoods.com
Year Founded: 1976
Grocery Stores Owner & Operator
N.A.I.C.S.: 445110
Ronnie Malone *(CEO)*

MALONEY & BELL GENERAL CONTRACTORS, INC. OF CALIFORNIA
2620 Mercantile Dr, Rancho Cordova, CA 95742
Tel.: (916) 635-7600   CA
Web Site:
http://www.maloneyandbell.com
Year Founded: 1981
Sales Range: $10-24.9 Million
Emp.: 50
Provider of Construction Services
N.A.I.C.S.: 236220
Steven C. Kuhs *(VP & Project Mgr)*

MALOUF BUICK-GMC
US Rt 1 & Adams Ln, North Brunswick, NJ 08902
Tel.: (732) 821-5400
Web Site: http://www.maloufbpg.com
Year Founded: 1980
Sales Range: $10-24.9 Million
Emp.: 50
Car Whslr
N.A.I.C.S.: 441110
Richard Malouf *(Pres)*

MALOUF CONSTRUCTION CORP.
602 Crescent Pl Ste 200, Ridgeland, MS 39157-8676
Tel.: (601) 856-1044   MS
Web Site:
http://www.maloufconstruction.com
Year Founded: 1987
Sales Range: $25-49.9 Million
Emp.: 150
Nonresidential Construction
N.A.I.C.S.: 236220
George F. Malouf *(Co-Founder)*
Andy Holliday *(VP)*

MALT PRODUCTS CORP. OF N.J.
88 Market St, Saddle Brook, NJ 07663-4830
Tel.: (201) 845-4420   NJ
Web Site:
http://www.maltproducts.com
Year Founded: 1962
Sales Range: $25-49.9 Million
Emp.: 200

Mfr of Malt
N.A.I.C.S.: 311213
Ronald G. Targen *(Pres)*
Joseph W. Hickenbottom *(VP-Sls-Mktg)*
Evan Lushing *(Gen Counsel)*
Michele Straub *(Coord-Sls)*

MALT REALTY & DEVELOPMENT INC.
1614 Colonial Blvd Ste 102, Fort Myers, FL 33907
Tel.: (239) 936-1320
Web Site: http://www.maltrealty.com
Sales Range: $10-24.9 Million
Real Estate Developer, Manager & Sales
N.A.I.C.S.: 531210
David G. Malt *(Owner & Pres)*
Judith M. Palumbo *(Mgr-Property)*

MALTBIE, INC.
7000 Commerce Pkwy Ste C, Mount Laurel, NJ 08054-2288
Tel.: (856) 234-0052
Web Site: http://www.maltbie.com
Rev.: $20,000,000
Emp.: 85
Displays, Paint Process
N.A.I.C.S.: 339950
Curt Cederquist *(VP-Museum Sls)*
Charles M. Maltbie Jr. *(Pres)*

MALTBY ELECTRIC SUPPLY COMPANY
336 7th St, San Francisco, CA 94103
Tel.: (415) 863-5000
Web Site: http://www.maltbyelec.com
Sales Range: $25-49.9 Million
Emp.: 70
Electrical Apparatus & Equipment
N.A.I.C.S.: 423610
John A. Maltby *(Pres & Treas)*
Marivic P. Go *(Controller)*
Andy Kawamura *(VP)*
Lily Maltby *(Sec)*
Rodney Jason *(COO & VP)*
Justin Phelan *(Mgr-Bridgeport)*
Jim Saltzman *(Mgr-IT)*
Joseph Larsen *(Mgr-Warehouse)*

MALTON ELECTRIC CO.
1505 Chestnut St W, Virginia, MN 55792
Tel.: (218) 741-8252
Rev.: $13,452,328
Emp.: 30
Switchgear & Switchgear Accessories
N.A.I.C.S.: 335313

MAMAC SYSTEMS INC.
8189 Centre Blvd, Chanhassen, MN 55317-3720
Tel.: (952) 556-4900
Web Site: http://www.mamacsys.com
Sales Range: $75-99.9 Million
Emp.: 100
Process Control Instruments
N.A.I.C.S.: 334513
S. Asim Gul *(Pres)*
Renee Paul *(Controller)*
Subsidiaries:

Mamac Systems (Asia) Pte Limited (1)
22 Lorong 21E Geylang #11-02, Prosper Industrial Building, Singapore, 388431, Singapore
Tel.: (65) 63927273
Web Site: http://www.mamacsys.com
Sales Range: $10-24.9 Million
Emp.: 10
Process Control Instruments
N.A.I.C.S.: 334513

Mamac Systems (Canada) Limited (1)
675 Cochrane Drive East Tower 6th Floor, Toronto, L3R 0B8, ON, Canada

COMPANIES

Tel.: (905) 474-9215
Sales Range: $10-24.9 Million
Process Control Instruments Mfr
N.A.I.C.S.: 334513

Mamac Systems (UK) Limited (1)
4200 Waterside Centre, Solihull Parkway, Birmingham, B37 7YN, W Midlands, United Kingdom (100%)
Tel.: (44) 1384271113
Web Site: http://www.mamacsys.com
Sales Range: $1-9.9 Million
Emp.: 5
Process Control Instruments
N.A.I.C.S.: 334513

Mamac Systems Pty Limited (1)
4 Armiger Court Unit 2, Adelaide, 5088, SA, Australia
Tel.: (61) 883954333
Sales Range: $10-24.9 Million
Emp.: 3
Process Control Instruments
N.A.I.C.S.: 334513
Asim Gul *(Mng Dir)*

MAMCO CORPORATION
8630 Industrial Dr, Franksville, WI 53126
Tel.: (262) 886-9069
Web Site: http://www.mamcomotors.com
Rev.: $22,200,000
Emp.: 100
Motors, Electric
N.A.I.C.S.: 335312
William H. Meltzer *(Pres)*
Jeff Behnke *(VP-Ops)*

MAMIYE SALES, INC.
1385 Broadway, New York, NY 10018
Tel.: (212) 279-4150   DE
Web Site: http://www.mamiye.com
Year Founded: 1946
Sales Range: $25-49.9 Million
Emp.: 140
Womens, Childrens & Infants Clothing
N.A.I.C.S.: 424350
Charlie D. Mamiye *(Chm & Pres)*
Heidi Mamiye *(VP)*
Brian Martin *(CFO)*

MAMMA ILARDO'S CORP.
110 W Rd Ste 201, Towson, MD 21204
Tel.: (410) 296-9104   MD
Web Site: http://www.mammailardos.com
Year Founded: 1976
Pizzeria Franchisor & Operator
N.A.I.C.S.: 722511
Harry Ilardo *(Pres & CEO)*

MAMMOTH INVESTMENTS INC.
10545 E Apache Trl, Apache Junction, AZ 85120-3305
Tel.: (480) 984-0074
Sales Range: $10-24.9 Million
Emp.: 2
Sales of Mobile Homes
N.A.I.C.S.: 459930

MAMMOTH PROPERTIES, INC.
3310 Main St, Mammoth Lakes, CA 93546
Tel.: (760) 934-6881   CA
Web Site: http://www.mammoth-properties.com
Year Founded: 1964
Sales Range: $1-9.9 Million
Emp.: 28
Subdividers & Developers
N.A.I.C.S.: 237210
David L. Buckman *(Pres)*

Subsidiaries:

Mammoth Property Reservations (1)
3310 Main St, Mammoth Lakes, CA 93546

Tel.: (760) 934-4242
Web Site: http://www.1888mammoth.com
Sales Range: $1-9.9 Million
Emp.: 10
Vacation Rentals
N.A.I.C.S.: 531390

MAMOLO'S CONTINENTAL & BAILEY BAKERIES INC.
703 S Main St, Burbank, CA 91506-2528
Tel.: (818) 841-9347
Sales Range: $10-24.9 Million
Emp.: 327
Baked Goods Mfr
N.A.I.C.S.: 311811
Ugo Mamolo *(Pres)*
Roger Terzuolo *(VP, Treas & Sec)*

MAN MARKETING, INC.
765 Kimberly Dr, Carol Stream, IL 60188
Tel.: (630) 929-5200
Web Site: http://www.manmarketing.com
Year Founded: 1979
Emp.: 50
Marketing Solutions
N.A.I.C.S.: 541613
Ed Mallof *(Pres)*
Toni Mallof *(VP & Creative Dir)*
Frank DiMatteo *(Reg Dir-Acct)*
Doug Pieper *(Creative Dir-Brdcst)*
Lee Zuika *(Controller & Dir-Fin)*
Guy Lieberman *(Dir-Digital Mktg)*

MAN-CON INCORPORATED
3460 SW 11th St, Deerfield Beach, FL 33442
Tel.: (954) 427-0230
Web Site: http://www.mancon.ws
Year Founded: 1985
Sales Range: $10-24.9 Million
Emp.: 19
Water & Sewer Line Construction
N.A.I.C.S.: 237110
Guy A. Mancini *(Pres)*

MAN-DELL FOOD STORES, INC.
24110 Hillside Ave, Bellerose, NY 11426-1334
Tel.: (718) 470-1930
Year Founded: 1936
Sales Range: $50-74.9 Million
Emp.: 600
Owns & Operates Supermarkets
N.A.I.C.S.: 445110
Ronald Schubert *(Pres)*
Lawrence Mandel *(CEO)*
Joel Mandel *(Treas & Sec)*

MAN-MACHINES SYSTEMS ASSESSMENT, INC.
1101 14th St NW Ste 1020, Washington, DC 20005
Tel.: (202) 408-0042   TX
Web Site: http://www.msaincorp.com
Year Founded: 1990
Sales Range: $10-24.9 Million
Emp.: 60
Test & Evaluation, Administrative & Management Support, Transportation Safety Analysis & Emergency Planning Services
N.A.I.C.S.: 561499
Lillian Harris *(CEO)*

MANAFORT BROTHERS INCORPORATED
414 New Britain Ave, Plainville, CT 06062
Tel.: (860) 229-4853
Web Site: http://www.manafort.com
Rev.: $188,000,000
Emp.: 800

Site Development
N.A.I.C.S.: 238910
Brian Barrett *(CFO)*
Michelle Lester *(Project Mgr)*
Mick Tarsi *(VP-Engrg)*
Karen Barracliff *(Supvr-Payroll)*
Joseph Czapiga *(Project Mgr)*
Ken Sedlak *(Dir-HR)*
Vince Mando *(Project Mgr)*
James Manafort Jr. *(Pres)*

MANAGE INC.
47 Veterans Dr, Chicopee, MA 01022
Tel.: (413) 593-9128
Web Site: http://www.manage-inc.com
Rev.: $12,000,000
Emp.: 100
Harness Assemblies, For Electronic Use: Wire Or Cable
N.A.I.C.S.: 334419

MANAGED BUSINESS SOLUTIONS LLC
12325 Oracle Blvd Ste 200, Colorado Springs, CO 80921
Tel.: (719) 314-3400
Web Site: http://www.mbshome.com
Year Founded: 1993
Rev.: $24,000,000
Emp.: 200
Information Technology Services
N.A.I.C.S.: 541512
Dennise Lumberg *(Controller)*

MANAGED CARE NETWORK INC.
1625 Buffalo Ave Ste 1v, Niagara Falls, NY 14303-1545
Tel.: (716) 285-5710
Web Site: http://www.managedcarenetwork.com
Sales Range: $1-9.9 Million
Emp.: 60
Workers' Compensation & Disability Case Third Party Negotiator
N.A.I.C.S.: 524292
Jeanne Battaglia-Dillon *(Pres)*
Gina Mayo-Hawk *(Mgr-Mktg & Sls)*
Mary Ann Moran *(Mgr-Medical & Vocational Dept)*

MANAGED CARE OF AMERICA INC.
1910 Cochran Rd Manoroak Bldg 2 Ste 605, Pittsburgh, PA 15220
Tel.: (412) 922-2803
Web Site: http://www.mcoa.com
Sales Range: $50-74.9 Million
Emp.: 70
Insurance Agents, Brokers & Service
N.A.I.C.S.: 524210
Charles Davidson *(COO)*
Phyllis Shehab *(Treas & Sec)*
Patrick Howard *(Dir-IT)*

Subsidiaries:

Benefit Planners & Associates Inc. (1)
Manor Oak 2 Ste 605 1910 Cochran Rd, Pittsburgh, PA 15220
Tel.: (412) 922-2803
Web Site: http://www.mcoa.com
Sales Range: Less than $1 Million
Emp.: 20
Benefit Plan Management Services
N.A.I.C.S.: 524210
Charles E. Davidson *(Pres)*

CARE Network (1)
820 Parish St, Pittsburgh, PA 15220
Tel.: (412) 922-4616
Emp.: 48
Health Care Srvices
N.A.I.C.S.: 621999
Phyllis Shehab *(Owner)*

Enterprise Underwriting Svcs (1)

Nanor Oak Two Ste 605 1910 Cochran Rd, Pittsburgh, PA 15220
Tel.: (412) 928-8980
Rev.: $13,500,000
Emp.: 12
Insurance Agents, Brokers & Service
N.A.I.C.S.: 524210

MANAGED CARE OF NORTH AMERICA, INC.
200 W Cypress Creek Rd Ste #500, Fort Lauderdale, FL 33309
Tel.: (800) 494-6262
Web Site: http://www.mcna.net
Medicare & Commercial Dental Plans & Insurance Services
N.A.I.C.S.: 524114

Subsidiaries:

MCNA Health Care Holdings, LLC (1)
200 W Cypress Creek Rd Ste #500, Fort Lauderdale, FL 33309
Tel.: (800) 494-6262
Medicare & Commercial Dental Plans & Insurance Services
N.A.I.C.S.: 524114
Jeffrey Feingold *(Chm & CEO)*

Subsidiary (Domestic):

MCNA Insurance Company (2)
200 W Cypress Creek Rd Ste #500, Fort Lauderdale, FL 33309
Tel.: (800) 494-6262
Web Site: http://www.mcna.net
Medicare & Commercial Dental Plans & Insurance Services
N.A.I.C.S.: 524114
Philip Hunke *(Pres-Plan)*
Shannon Boggs-Turner *(Exec VP)*
Carlos Garcia *(Chief Dental Officer)*

Subsidiary (Domestic):

Healthplex, Inc. (3)
The Omni Bldg 333 Earle Ovington Blvd Ste 300, Uniondale, NY 11553
Tel.: (516) 542-2200
Web Site: http://www.healthplex.com
Sales Range: $1-9.9 Million
Emp.: 267
Dental Insurance & Discount Dental Plans
N.A.I.C.S.: 524114
Christopher Schmidt *(Pres & CEO)*

MANAGED ENERGY SYSTEMS LLC
11301 Nall Ave Ste 210, Leawood, KS 66211
Tel.: (913) 565-2505
Web Site: http://www.energymes.com
Year Founded: 2013
Sales Range: $50-74.9 Million
Emp.: 8
Energy Management Services
N.A.I.C.S.: 237130
Vlad Kaufman *(Pres)*
Bruce Johnson *(Mgr-Energy Acct)*
Collin Farrow *(Office Mgr)*
Denise Martin *(Mgr-Client Svcs)*
Farryl Prater *(Mgr-Field-Lighting Solutions)*

MANAGED FUTURES PREMIER WARRINGTON L.P.
200 Crescent Ct Ste 520, Dallas, TX 75201
Tel.: (214) 230-2100   NY
Rev.: $61,191
Assets: $14,510,429
Liabilities: $198,060
Net Worth: $14,312,369
Earnings: ($1,164,558)
Emp.: 33
Fiscal Year-end: 12/31/22
Investment Services
N.A.I.C.S.: 523999
Scott C. Kimple *(Mgr-Sole)*

MANAGEDSTORAGE INTER-

MANAGEDSTORAGE INTER—(CONTINUED)

NATIONAL, INC.
12647 Alcosta Blvd, San Ramon, CA 94583
Tel.: (925) 217-5930
Web Site: http://www.managedstorage.com
Rev.: $12,800,000
Emp.: 65
Data Management Services
N.A.I.C.S.: 518210
Kevin Thomas *(Mktg Commun Dir)*
Suzanne Becker-Gallagher *(Sr VP-Mktg)*

MANAGEMENT & TRAINING CORPORATION
500 N Market Pl Dr, Centerville, UT 84014-1708
Tel.: (801) 693-2600
Web Site: http://www.mtctrains.com
Year Founded: 1981
Sales Range: $450-499.9 Million
Emp.: 9,300
Job Training & Management Services for Correctional Facilities
N.A.I.C.S.: 611710
Scott Marquardt *(Chm, Pres & CEO)*
Lyle J. Parry *(CFO, Treas, Sec & Sr VP)*
Mike Murphy *(VP-Corrections Mktg)*
Celeste McDonald *(VP-Corp Comm)*
Sergio Molina *(Sr VP-Bus Dev & Admin)*
Teresa N. Aramaki *(VP-HR)*
Marjorie Brown *(VP-Reg Ops-Corrections)*
Rich Skeen *(VP-Info Sys)*
Greg Niblett *(VP-Economic & Social Dev)*
Dean Hoffman *(VP-Western Reg-Job Corps)*
Tom Fitzwater *(VP-North Central Reg-Job Corps)*
Virleen Ferre *(VP-Contract Admin)*
Dawn M. Call *(Gen Counsel & VP)*
Jane Marquardt *(Vice Chm)*
Lynn Intrepidi *(VP-Northeast Reg)*
Michael Bell *(VP-Reg Ops Corrections)*
Connie Cruz *(VP-Dev)*
Dave Doty *(VP-Education & Trng)*
Dan Joslin *(VP-Reg Ops Corrections)*
John Pedersen *(Sr VP-Education & Trng)*
Leann Bertsch *(Sr VP-Corrections)*

Subsidiaries:

Billy Moore Correctional Center (1)
8500 Fm 3053 N, Overton, TX 75684-6008
Tel.: (903) 834-6186
Web Site: http://www.mtctrains.com
Sales Range: $10-24.9 Million
Emp.: 123
Correctional Center
N.A.I.C.S.: 561210
Debbie Ruthven *(Warden)*

West Texas ISF (1)
2002 Lamesa Hwy, Brownfield, TX 79316-9595
Tel.: (806) 637-4032
Web Site: http://www.mtctrains.com
Sales Range: $10-24.9 Million
Emp.: 50
Management of Prisons, Correctional & Detention Facilities
N.A.I.C.S.: 922140
Issa Arnita *(Dir-Corp Comm)*
Celeste McDonald *(VP-Corp Comm)*

MANAGEMENT ALLIANCE PROGRAMS, INC.
N 92 W 1742 Appleton Ave Ste 200, Menomonee Falls, WI 53051
Tel.: (262) 345-6699
Web Site: http://www.map-sg.com
Sales Range: $10-24.9 Million
Emp.: 75
Workforce Recruitment & Management Services, Professional Payroll Services & Business Consulting Services
N.A.I.C.S.: 541611
Dave Aragon *(Pres)*

MANAGEMENT ANALYSIS & UTILIZATION, INC.
501 Greene St, Augusta, GA 30901
Tel.: (706) 722-6806
Web Site: http://www.mau.com
Sales Range: $25-49.9 Million
Emp.: 115
Employment Agencies
N.A.I.C.S.: 561311
Randy Hatcher *(Pres)*
Carl Henson *(VP-Mktg & Bus Dev)*
David Brown *(VP-HR)*
Doug Duncan *(VP-Pro Svcs)*
Ed O'Neal *(VP-Fin Svcs)*
Rod Hutcheson *(VP-Comml Staffing)*

Subsidiaries:

Doozer Software, Inc. (1)
4 Riverchase Rdg, Birmingham, AL 35244
Tel.: (205) 413-8302
Web Site: http://www.doozer.com
Emp.: 50
Software Development Services
N.A.I.C.S.: 513210
Sandy Syx *(Pres)*
Ron Perkins *(VP)*
Heath Wade *(Dir-Bus Dev)*
Barry Sykes *(Founder)*

MANAGEMENT ANALYTICS GROUP, LLC
8236 Linden Dr, Prairie Village, KS 66208
Tel.: (913) 381-0256
Year Founded: 1999
Sales Range: Less than $1 Million
Emp.: 1
Advertising, Business-To-Business, Consulting, Consumer Marketing, Direct Response Marketing, Information Technology, Planning & Consultation, Strategic Planning/Research
N.A.I.C.S.: 541810
John Trewolla *(Principal Analyst)*

MANAGEMENT AND ENGINEERING TECHNOLOGIES INTERNATIONAL, INC.
8600 Boeing Dr, El Paso, TX 79925
Tel.: (915) 772-4975
Web Site: http://www.meticorp.com
Year Founded: 1994
Sales Range: $50-74.9 Million
Emp.: 475
Supplies Information Technology & Engineering Support Services to the Federal Sector & Private Industry
N.A.I.C.S.: 334610
Renard U. Johnson *(CEO)*
Carolina Palacios *(Coord-Intl Programs)*

MANAGEMENT APPLIED PROGRAMMING INC.
13191 Crossroads Pkwy N Ste 205, City of Industry, CA 91746-3434
Tel.: (562) 908-4567
Web Site: http://www.bpabenefits.com
Sales Range: $10-24.9 Million
Emp.: 90
Data Processing Services
N.A.I.C.S.: 518210
Zane P. Dalal *(Exec VP)*
Hormazd P. Dalal *(CFO)*

MANAGEMENT CAPITAL, LLC
10 Dorrance St Ste 500, Providence, RI 02903
Tel.: (401) 246-0050
Web Site: http://www.mgtcapital.com
Privater Equity Firm
N.A.I.C.S.: 523999
Humphreys D. Ernest *(Co-Founder & Principal)*
Robert D. Manchester *(Co-Founder & Principal)*

MANAGEMENT CONSULTING, INC.
1961 Diamond Springs Rd, Virginia Beach, VA 2345-53009
Tel.: (757) 460-6308
Web Site: http://www.manconinc.com
Year Founded: 1983
Sales Range: $100-124.9 Million
Emp.: 1,500
Government Logistics & Certified Hazardous Material Shipping Services
N.A.I.C.S.: 488991
Rick Clark *(Co-Pres)*
Richard Clarke *(Co-Pres)*
David Meadows *(VP)*
Bart Consford *(Dir-Bus Dev)*

MANAGEMENT DATA SYSTEMS INTERNATIONAL
1265 Oak Industrial Ln, Cumming, GA 30041
Tel.: (678) 947-1629
Web Site: http://www.mdsiinc.com
Sales Range: $75-99.9 Million
Emp.: 40
Computers; Peripherals & Software
N.A.I.C.S.: 423690
Lisa Jillson *(Owner)*
Bob Pike *(Pres)*
Shannon Payne *(VP-Ops)*

MANAGEMENT PARTNERS, INC.
875 Grandview Dr, Roscoe, IL 61073
Year Founded: 1991
Sales Range: $1-9.9 Million
Holding Company
N.A.I.C.S.: 551112
J. Robert Clarke *(Co-Founder & CEO)*
Sherrie Barch *(Pres)*
Jim Schmidt *(VP)*
Rod Gould *(VP-Mgmt-West Coast)*
Janet Carlson *(Sec)*

Subsidiaries:

Furst Group (1)
2902 McFarland Rd, Rockford, IL 61107
Web Site: http://www.furstgroup.com
Health Industry Executive Search Services
N.A.I.C.S.: 541612
J. Robert Clarke *(CEO)*
Sherrie Barch *(Pres)*
Dave Appino *(VP)*
Deanna Banks *(Principal)*
Jessica Homann *(VP)*
Joe Mazzenga *(VP)*
Kevin Reddy *(VP)*
Pete Eisenbarth *(VP)*
Tim Frischmon *(Principal)*

MANAGEMENT RECRUITERS INC. BOSTON
607 Boylston St Ste 700, Boston, MA 02116
Tel.: (617) 262-5050
Web Site: http://www.mri-boston.com
Sales Range: $10-24.9 Million
Emp.: 100
Executive Placement
N.A.I.C.S.: 541612
Jack Mohan *(CEO)*
Michael Bacon *(Sr VP)*
Monique Kenney *(Sr VP-Tech & Admin)*
Gail Pezzi *(VP)*
Jane Pollock *(Sr VP)*
Margaret Pratico *(VP)*
Stephen Morse *(Mgr-Store-Retail)*
John Kroehler *(VP)*
Judi Wennerberg *(Sr VP)*
David Leshowitz *(VP)*
Kristen McCart *(Sr VP-Tech & Admin)*

MANAGEMENT RECRUITERS INTERNATIONAL, INC.
1735 Market St Ste 200, Philadelphia, PA 19103
Tel.: (215) 569-2200
Web Site: http://www.mrinetwork.com
Year Founded: 1965
Executive Search & Recruitment Services
N.A.I.C.S.: 561311
Ann Santomas *(VP)*
Ronni Nuzzi *(Dir-Field Svc)*
Nancy Halverson *(Gen Mgr)*
Scott Bass *(Dir-Mktg)*
Mark Cosens *(Gen Mgr)*
Vince Webb *(VP-Mktg)*
Sherry Engel *(VP-Learning & Talent Dev)*
Alfred W. D'Iorio *(CFO)*
Marquis Parker *(VP-Bus Svcs)*
Bert Miller *(Pres & CEO)*

Subsidiaries:

Access Point LLC (1)
28800 Orchard Lk Rd, Farmington Hills, MI 48334
Tel.: (248) 504-6539
Web Site: http://www.accesspointhr.com
Sales Range: $100-124.9 Million
Emp.: 1,000
Professional Employer Services
N.A.I.C.S.: 561330
Jim Mack *(Pres)*
Spencer Packer *(Dir-Mktg & Comm)*
Gregory Packer *(CEO-Washington)*

Division (Domestic):

AP Veritas (2)
9990 Coconut Rd Ste 101, Bonita Springs, FL 34135
Tel.: (800) 397-1566
Web Site: http://www.myaphr.com
Sales Range: $25-49.9 Million
Professional Employer Services
N.A.I.C.S.: 561330
Greg Packer *(CEO)*

CDI-Infrastructure, LLC (1)
415 Moon Clinton Rd, Coraopolis, PA 15108-3886
Tel.: (412) 262-5400
Web Site: http://www.cdicorp.com
Sales Range: $75-99.9 Million
Emp.: 300
Architectural Services
N.A.I.C.S.: 541310

MANAGEMENT RECRUITERS OF TAMPA-NORTH, INC.
8517 Gunn Hwy, Odessa, FL 33556
Tel.: (813) 264-7165
Web Site: http://www.mrtampanorth.com
Year Founded: 1989
Sales Range: $1-9.9 Million
Emp.: 6
Human Resources & Executive Search Consulting Services
N.A.I.C.S.: 541612
Jackie Rademaker *(VP-Sls)*
Gary King *(Pres & Mng Partner)*
Carol Taylor *(Dir-Ops)*

MANAGEMENT SCIENCE & INNOVATION LLC
14340 Sullyfield Cir Ste 200, Chantilly, VA 20151-1621
Tel.: (703) 437-5236
Web Site: https://www.msiconsulting.com

COMPANIES

Year Founded: 2002
General Management Consulting Services
N.A.I.C.S.: 541611
Cynthia Sieber (Sec)

Subsidiaries:

Ascolta, LLC (1)
1100 Exploration Wy Ste 316J, Hampton, VA 23666
Tel.: (571) 485-4633
Web Site: http://www.ascolta.com
Sales Range: $1-9.9 Million
Emp.: 40
Management Consulting Services
N.A.I.C.S.: 541611

MANAGEMENT SCIENCES FOR HEALTH, INC.
784 Memorial Dr, Cambridge, MA 02139-4613
Tel.: (617) 250-9312 MA
Web Site: http://www.msh.org
Year Founded: 1971
Sales Range: $75-99.9 Million
Emp.: 550
Educational & Scientific Management Consulting Services
N.A.I.C.S.: 541618
Marian W. Wentworth (Pres & CEO)
Dana Sandstrom Keating (Head-Bus Dev & Partnerships)

MANAGEMENT SERVICES NORTHWEST
2257 Northgate Spur, Ferndale, WA 98248
Tel.: (360) 366-4600
Web Site: http://www.managementservicesnorthwest.com
Year Founded: 1995
Rev.: $5,000,000
Emp.: 183
Business Support Services
N.A.I.C.S.: 561499
Janelle Bruland (Pres & CEO)
Wayne K. Galloway (Dir-Ops)
Terell Weg (Dir-Dev & Culture)

MANAGEMENT SEVEN, LLC
145 N Highland Dr, Many, LA 71449
Tel.: (318) 590-0007 LA
Web Site: http://www.managementseven.com
Nursing Care & Continuing Care Facilities Owner & Operator
N.A.I.C.S.: 623110
Jack H. Sanders (CEO)
Kassie Martinez (Officer-Compliance)
Denise Billodeaux (Mgr-HR)
Russell Suire Jr. (COO)

Subsidiaries:

Azalea Gardens of Mobile (1)
1758 Spring Hill Ave, Mobile, AL 36607-3508
Tel.: (251) 479-0551
Sales Range: $50-74.9 Million
Emp.: 100
Nursing Care & Rehabilitation Facility
N.A.I.C.S.: 623110
David Grimes (Exec Dir)

MANAGEMENT SOLUTIONS, LLC
2202 Award Winning Way Ste 201, Knoxville, TN 37932
Tel.: (865) 963-0400
Web Site: http://www.managementsolutionsllc.com
Year Founded: 2002
Sales Range: $1-9.9 Million
Emp.: 34
Management Consulting Services
N.A.I.C.S.: 541611

Misty Mayes (Founder & CEO)
Sam Mayes (VP-Client Svcs)
Sherry Browder (Pres-Govt Svcs)

MANAGEMENT TECHNOLOGY, INC.
7700 Old Branch Ave, Clinton, MD 20735
Tel.: (301) 265-8900 MD
Web Site: http://www.mtiinc.com
Year Founded: 1985
Sales Range: $10-24.9 Million
Emp.: 83
Computer Facilities Management
N.A.I.C.S.: 541513
Pauline C. Brooks (Pres & CEO)

MANAGEMENT TRAINING & CONSULTING INC.
9720 Capital Ct Ste 400, Manassas, VA 20110-2052
Tel.: (254) 213-5328 TX
Web Site: http://www.mtci.us
Year Founded: 1999
Sales Range: $10-24.9 Million
Emp.: 150
Staffing, Training, Base Operations, Remanufacturing, Logistics, Maintenance & Information Technology
N.A.I.C.S.: 561311
Sam Kanouse (CEO)
Dalena Kanouse (Pres & CEO)
Domonique Basler (VP-Corp Support Svcs)

Subsidiaries:

Logistics & Information Technology (LOGIT) Division (1)
One Killeen Center Ste 204 1711 E Central Texas Expy, Killeen, TX 76541 (100%)
Tel.: (254) 616-6900
Staffing, Training & Logistics Services
N.A.I.C.S.: 611430

MTCI-Northeast (1)
9817 Godwin Dr, Manassas, VA 20110 (100%)
Tel.: (254) 213-5328
Sales Range: $10-24.9 Million
Emp.: 40
Staffing, Training, Maintenance & Information Technology
N.A.I.C.S.: 561311

MTCI-South Central (1)
1 Killeen Ctr Ste 204 1711 E Central Texas Expy, Killeen, TX 76541 (100%)
Tel.: (254) 213-5328
Staffing, Training, Base Operation, Maintenance & Information Technology
N.A.I.C.S.: 561311

MANAR, INC.
906 S Walnut St, Edinburgh, IN 46124-2002
Tel.: (812) 526-6859 IN
Web Site: http://www.manarinc.com
Year Founded: 1974
Sales Range: $25-49.9 Million
Emp.: 400
Mfr of Plastic Products
N.A.I.C.S.: 326199
Gene Nolen (Owner)
Doug Kamman (Engr-Sls)

Subsidiaries:

Key Manufacturing Inc (1)
915 Industrial Dr, Madison, IN 47250
Tel.: (812) 265-5073
Emp.: 60
Injection Molding Machine Mfr
N.A.I.C.S.: 333248
Scott Hartwell (Gen Mgr)

Manar, Inc. - CEW Enterprise Division (1)
1050 W JKF Dr, North Vernon, IN 47265
Tel.: (812) 346-2858
Web Site: http://www.cewenterprises.com
Emp.: 45
Injection Molding Machine Mfr

N.A.I.C.S.: 333248
Greg Nolen (Gen Mgr)

Manar, Inc. - GTR Division (1)
905 S Walnut St, Edinburgh, IN 46124
Tel.: (812) 526-2891
Emp.: 100
Injection Molding Machine Mfr
N.A.I.C.S.: 333248

Manar, Inc. - Plasfinco Division (1)
1060 W JFK Industrial Park, North Vernon, IN 47265
Tel.: (812) 346-3900
Web Site: http://www.plasfinco.com
Metal Plating Services
N.A.I.C.S.: 332812

Manar, Inc. - Tennplasco - Lafayette Division (1)
30 Industrial Dr, Lafayette, TN 37803
Tel.: (615) 666-5580
Web Site: http://www.tennplasco.com
Emp.: 110
Metal Plating Services
N.A.I.C.S.: 332812

MANASIAN INC.
560 Harrison Ave Ste 503, Boston, MA 02118-2592
Tel.: (617) 338-4441
Web Site: http://www.manasian.com
Year Founded: 2004
Sales Range: Less than $1 Million
Emp.: 8
Advetising Agency
N.A.I.C.S.: 541810
Jean Manasian (Pres)

MANASOTA COMMERCIAL CONSTRUCTION CO., INC.
5515 21st Ave W Ste D, Bradenton, FL 34209
Tel.: (941) 795-2732 FL
Web Site: http://www.manasotaconstruction.com
Year Founded: 1987
Sales Range: $1-9.9 Million
Emp.: 17
Commercial & Institutional Building Construction
N.A.I.C.S.: 236220
Clayton D. Johnson (Sec & VP)
Stanley E. Stephens (Pres & Treas)
Mark Unger (Project Mgr)

MANASOTA FLOORING INC.
4551 N Washington Blvd, Sarasota, FL 34234
Tel.: (941) 355-8437
Web Site: http://www.manasotaonline.com
Rev.: $21,301,204
Emp.: 35
Distribute Carpets
N.A.I.C.S.: 449121
Robert Tiffany (CEO)
Barbara Tiffany (Pres)

MANASOTA GROUP, INC.
PO Box 14302, Bradenton, FL 34280
Tel.: (941) 462-1640
Sales Range: Less than $1 Million
Property Management Services
N.A.I.C.S.: 531312
Charles S. Conoley (Pres & CEO)
Kathleen M. Jepson (CFO & Sr VP)

MANASQUAN RIVER REGIONAL SEWERAGE AUTHORITY
89 Havens Br Rd, Howell, NJ 07727
Tel.: (732) 431-8185
Web Site: http://www.manasquanriverregionalsa.com
Rev.: $10,000,000
Emp.: 13
Sewerage Systems

N.A.I.C.S.: 221320
Brian Brach (Gen Mgr)

MANASSAS ICE & FUEL CO. INC.
9009 Ctr St, Manassas, VA 20110
Tel.: (703) 368-3121
Rev.: $24,477,710
Emp.: 25
Fuel Oil Dealers
N.A.I.C.S.: 457210

MANATEE COUNTY PORT AUTHORITY
300 Tampa Bay, Palmetto, FL 34221
Tel.: (941) 722-6621
Port Operations
N.A.I.C.S.: 488310
Carlos Buqueras (CEO & Exec Dir)
George F. Isiminger (Sr Dir-Plng, Engrg & Environmental Affairs)
Denise Stufflebeam (Sr Dir-Bus Admin & Fin)
Dave Sanford (COO & Deputy Exec Dir)

MANATT'S, INC.
1775 Old 6 Rd, Brooklyn, IA 52211
Tel.: (641) 522-9206 IA
Web Site: http://www.manatts.com
Year Founded: 1947
Sales Range: $50-74.9 Million
Emp.: 125
Highway & Street Paving Contractor
N.A.I.C.S.: 237310
Adam Grier (Dir-Safety)
Jeff Upah (Mgr)
Larry Ford (Mgr)
Brian Peterson (Mgr-Shop)
Robert Arthur (Mgr-Shop)
Sandy Durr (Office Mgr)
Kyle Lint (Plant Mgr)
Jeff Steinkamp (Project Mgr)
Tim Tometich (Project Mgr)
Joann Manatt (VP-Board)
Tim Douglas (CFO)

MANATT, PHELPS & PHILLIPS LLP
2049 Century Park E Ste 1700, Los Angeles, CA 90067
Tel.: (310) 312-4000
Web Site: https://www.manatt.com
Year Founded: 1965
Sales Range: $250-299.9 Million
Emp.: 325
Law firm
N.A.I.C.S.: 541110
James J. Bonham (Chm)
Donna L. Wilson (CEO & Mng Partner)
Andrew Zimmitti (Partner)
David Gershon (Partner-Fin Svcs & Banking)
Jesse M. Brody (Partner-Adv, Mktg & Media)
Arunabha Bhoumik (Partner-Litigation-New York)
Thomas J. Poletti (Partner-Corp, Fin, Capital Markets, M&A & Private Equity)
Katherine J. Blair (Partner-Capital Markets)
John Gatti (Partner)
Mandana Massoumi (Partner)
Gordon M. Bava (Partner-Corp & Fin)
John M. LeBlanc (Partner-Litigation)
Nigel Wilkinson (Partner)
Benjamin G. Chew (Partner-Litigation)
Lisl J. Dunlop (Partner-Litigation)
Andrew E. Schultz (Partner-Real Estate & Land Use)
Brian S. Korn (Partner-Fin Svcs Grp)
Doug Boggs (Partner)
Alan Noskow (Partner)
Joseph Passaic (Partner-Corp Fin & Fin Svcs & Banking)

MANATT, PHELPS & PHILLIPS LLP

Manatt, Phelps & Phillips LLP—(Continued)
Yuri Mikulka (Partner-Intellectual Property Practice-Orange County)
Brian Ashin (Partner)
Jill DeGraff Thorpe (Partner-Healthcare Practice-Washington)
Chiquita Brooks-LaSure (Mng Dir-Manatt Health Solution)
Adrianne E. Marshack (Partner-Litigation Practice-Orange County)
Beth A. Fox (Partner)
Robert Duran (Partner-Tax, Employee Benefits & Exec Compensation Practice)
Richard P. Lawson (Partner-Consumer Protection Practice Grp)
Richard E. Gottlieb (Partner-Litigation & Govt Enforcement-Multidisciplinary Fin Svcs)
Irah H. Donner (Partner-Intellectual Property Practice Grp-New York)
Yasser M. El-Gamal (Partner & Intellectual Property)
Jeffrey S. Edelstein (Partner)
Sandy W. Robinson (Mng Dir-Manatt Health-Washington)
Deborah P. Kelly (Partner-Employment & Labor Practice-Washington)
Christopher Broderick (Partner-Intellectual Property Practice)
Michael Merritt (Mng Dir-Manatt Health-New York)
William S. Bernstein (Chm-Manatt Health)
Jack Quinn (Chm-Federal Regulatory Govt Practice & Partner-Litigation Grp-Was)
Robert Garretson (Mng Dir-Govt & Regulatory Grp-Washington)
Christopher Lisy (Partner-Disputes-Boston)
Yarmela Pavlovic (Partner-San Francisco)
Meghan McNamara (Partner-Regulatory-New York)
Susan K. Hori (Executives)
Monte M. Lemann II (Gen Counsel-Corp & Fin)
Kathleen L. Brown (Partner)

MANCAN INC.
48 1st St NE, Massillon, OH 44646
Tel.: (330) 832-4595
Web Site: http://www.mancan.com
Sales Range: $100-124.9 Million
Emp.: 5
Industrial Help Service
N.A.I.C.S.: 561320
Amy King (VP-Admin)

MANCARI CHRYSLER JEEP INC.
4630 W 95th St, Oak Lawn, IL 60453
Tel.: (708) 423-0910
Web Site: http://www.mancari.com
Rev.: $40,500,000
Emp.: 100
Automobiles, New & Used
N.A.I.C.S.: 441110
Allen Siegel (Gen Mgr)
Frank Mancari Sr. (Owner & Pres)

MANCARI'S CHRYSLER JEEP INC.
4630 W 95th St, Oak Lawn, IL 60453-2514
Tel.: (708) 423-0910
Web Site: http://www.mancari.com
Year Founded: 1981
Sales Range: $10-24.9 Million
Emp.: 90
Car Whslr
N.A.I.C.S.: 441110

Gary Fast (Mgr-Svc)
Frank Mancari (Pres)
Alan Siegel (Gen Mgr)

MANCHAUG POND FOUNDATION
PO Box 154, Sutton, MA 01526-0154
Tel.: (508) 865-3915 MA
Web Site: http://www.manchaugpond.net
Year Founded: 2009
Sales Range: $1-9.9 Million
Reservoir Maintenance Services
N.A.I.C.S.: 221310
Phyllis Charpentier (Sec)
David Schmidt (Pres)
Marty Jo Henry (First VP)
William Wence (Second VP)
Andrew Mosher (Treas)
Alice Smith (Sec-Recording)

MANCHESTER HONDA
24 Adams St, Manchester, CT 06042-1802
Tel.: (860) 645-3100
Web Site: http://www.manchesterhonda.com
Year Founded: 1964
Sales Range: $75-99.9 Million
Emp.: 104
New Car Retailer
N.A.I.C.S.: 441110
Joe Marconi (Mgr-Sls)
James Larabee (Dir-Ops)
Brian Fitzpatrick (Bus Mgr)

MANCHESTER MARKETING, INC.
1040 Old Bon Air Rd, Richmond, VA 23235-4835
Tel.: (804) 276-3728 VA
Web Site: http://www.seibertcos.com
Year Founded: 1976
Sales Range: $50-74.9 Million
Emp.: 115
Holding Company; Gasoline Station, Towing Services, Body Shop & Auto Auction
N.A.I.C.S.: 551112
Randy Seibert (Pres)

MANCHESTER SUBARU
764 2nd St, Manchester, NH 03102
Tel.: (603) 668-2411
Web Site: http://www.manchestersubaru.com
Year Founded: 2003
Sales Range: $10-24.9 Million
Emp.: 35
New Car Whslr
N.A.I.C.S.: 441110
Todd Berkowitz (Pres & Treas)

MANCHESTER WHOLESALE DISTRIBUTORS, INC.
64 Old Granite St, Manchester, NH 03101-2328
Tel.: (603) 625-5461 NH
Year Founded: 1939
Sales Range: $10-24.9 Million
Emp.: 65
Tobacco & Tobacco Products
N.A.I.C.S.: 424940
Emile J. Tetu (Treas & Sec)

MANCINI FOODS
PO Box 157, Zolfo Springs, FL 33890
Tel.: (863) 735-2000
Web Site: http://www.mancinifoods.com
Year Founded: 1922
Sales Range: $10-24.9 Million
Emp.: 100
Pepper Product Mfr
N.A.I.C.S.: 311942

Mark Swisher (Plant Mgr)
Richard Mancini (CEO & Dir)

MANCINI'S SLEEPWORLD INC.
599 Hawthone Pl, Livermore, CA 94550
Tel.: (925) 456-6400
Web Site: http://www.sleepworld.com
Sales Range: $10-24.9 Million
Emp.: 104
Owner & Operator of Furniture Stores
N.A.I.C.S.: 449110
Randy Mancini (Pres)
Marc Sey (VP)
Chris Berry (Mgr)
John Hoffman (Mgr-Store)
Marie Higgins (Mgr-Acctg)
Marc Fey (COO & VP)
Micah Burke (Dir-Art)
Scott Serface (Mgr-Sls)

MANCINO HOLDINGS INC.
3111 Grand Ave, Pittsburgh, PA 15225
Tel.: (412) 747-7777
Web Site: http://www.tristatetrailer.com
Sales Range: $25-49.9 Million
Emp.: 12
Truck Trailer Sales
N.A.I.C.S.: 423110
Frank Mancini (Pres)

MANDA PACKING CO. INC.
2445 Sorrel Ave, Baton Rouge, LA 70802
Tel.: (225) 344-7636
Web Site: http://www.mandafinemeats.com
Sales Range: $25-49.9 Million
Emp.: 250
Sausages & Other Prepared Meats
N.A.I.C.S.: 311612
Robert Yarborough (CEO)

MANDAL'S, INC.
4002 Hewes Ave, Gulfport, MS 39507
Tel.: (228) 864-1474
Web Site: http://mandalsroofing.com
Sales Range: $10-24.9 Million
Emp.: 60
Roofing Installation Services
N.A.I.C.S.: 238390
Chris Cooper (Pres)

MANDALA COMMUNICATIONS, INC.
2855 NW Crossing Dr Ste 201, Bend, OR 97701-2744
Tel.: (541) 389-6344 OR
Web Site: http://www.mandala.agency
Year Founded: 1980
Advetising Agency
N.A.I.C.S.: 541810
Paul Grignon (Creative Dir)
Matthew Bowler (Partner)
Laury Benson (CFO & COO)
Laura Bryant (Dir-Media & Digital Strategy)
Lori Hell (Dir-Awesome)

MANDALAY ENTERTAINMENT GROUP
4751 Wilshire Blvd 3rd Fl, Los Angeles, CA 90010
Tel.: (323) 549-4300
Web Site: http://www.mandalay.com
Year Founded: 1995
Multimedia Holding Company
N.A.I.C.S.: 551112
Paul M. Schaeffer (Vice Chm & COO)
Peter Gruber (Chm & CEO)

Diane Sabourin (Controller)
Nicole Young (VP-Bus Dev)
Shelly Riney (Sec & Exec VP-Corp Ops)

Subsidiaries:

Mandalay Pictures, LLC (1)
4751 Wilshire Blvd 3rd Fl, Los Angeles, CA 90010
Tel.: (323) 549-4300
Web Site: http://www.mandalay.com
Motion Picture Production & Distr
N.A.I.C.S.: 512110
Peter Gruber (Chm & CEO)
Paul Schaeffer (Vice Chm & COO)
David Zelon (Head-Production)
Michelle Hastings (Sr VP-Motion Picture Admin)
Adam Stone (VP-Production & Dev)
Nicole Young (Dir-Bus Dev)
Carmody Herzberg (Mgr-Bus Affairs Admin)

Mandalay Sports Entertainment LLC (1)
4751 Wilshire Blvd 3rd Fl, Los Angeles, CA 90010
Tel.: (323) 549-4300
Web Site: http://www.mandalay.com
Emp.: 50
Holding Company; Professional Sports Teams & Sports Marketing Services
N.A.I.C.S.: 551112
Peter Guber (Chm)
Paul M. Schaeffer (Vice Chm & COO)

Joint Venture (Domestic):

Mandalay Baseball Properties, LLC (2)
4751 Wilshire Blvd 3rd Fl, Los Angeles, CA 90010
Tel.: (323) 549-4300
Web Site: http://www.mandalay.com
Holding Company; Professional Baseball Clubs
N.A.I.C.S.: 551112
Robert Murphy (COO)
Larry Freedman (Pres-Mandalay Baseball)
James Bailey (CFO)
Eric Deutsch (Exec VP-Admin)
Gary Mayse (Exec VP-Facility Ops)
Rich Neumann (Pres-Baseball Dev)
John Deeter (VP-Fin)

Joint Venture (Domestic):

SWB Yankees, LLC (3)
235 Montage Mountain Rd, Moosic, PA 18507
Tel.: (570) 969-2255 (50%)
Web Site: http://www.swbrailriders.com
Sales Range: $10-24.9 Million
Professional Baseball Club
N.A.I.C.S.: 711211
Kristina Knight (Dir-Corp Svcs & Special Events)
Karen Luciano (Mgr-Corp Svcs)
Rob Galdieri (Ops Mgr)
Curt Camoni (VP-Stadium Ops)
William Steiner (Dir-Gameday Ops)
Steve Horne (Dir-Field Ops)
Seth Atkinson (Dir-Ticket Ops)
Jeremy Ruby (Exec VP-Ops)
Joe Villano (Dir-Ballpark Ops)
Paul Chilek (Exec VP-Bus Ops)
Katie Beekman (VP-Mktg & Corp Svcs)
Mike Trudnak (VP-Sls)
Rob Crain (Pres & Gen Mgr)
John Sadak (Dir-Media Rels & Brdcst)

MANDEL METALS INC.
11400 Addison Ave, Franklin Park, IL 60131
Tel.: (847) 455-6606
Web Site: http://www.mandelmetals.com
Rev.: $25,000,000
Emp.: 70
Aluminum Bars, Rods, Ingots, Sheets, Pipes, Plates, Etc.
N.A.I.C.S.: 423510
Rick Mandel (Pres)
Roger Miro (Mgr-Traffic)
Tom Cunniff (VP)

COMPANIES

MANET COMMUNITY HEALTH CENTER, INC.
110 W Squantum St, North Quincy, MA 02171
Tel.: (617) 376-3000   MA
Web Site: http://www.manetchc.org
Year Founded: 1978
Sales Range: $10-24.9 Million
Emp.: 183
Healtcare Services
N.A.I.C.S.: 622110
Jennifer Sabir *(Interim Chief Medical Officer)*
Ivette Arias *(Dir-HR)*
Jean Giagrande *(Dir-Clinical Ops)*

MANEVAL CONSTRUCTION CO. INC.
1015 N Corp Cir Ste D, Grayslake, IL 60030
Tel.: (847) 548-2244
Web Site: http://www.manevalconstruction.com
Rev.: $12,000,000
Emp.: 70
Asphalt & Underground Work
N.A.I.C.S.: 238110
Mike Maneval *(Owner)*

MANEY INTERNATIONAL INC.
375 33rd Ave S, Saint Cloud, MN 56301
Tel.: (320) 251-9511
Web Site: http://www.maneyinternational.com
Sales Range: $10-24.9 Million
Emp.: 50
Retailer & Repair of Trucks
N.A.I.C.S.: 423110
William P. Maney *(Pres)*
Ed Meyer *(Controller)*

MANFREDI OF GREENWICH, LTD.
121 Greenwich Ave, Greenwich, CT 06830
Tel.: (203) 622-1414
Web Site: http://www.manfredijewels.com
Year Founded: 1988
Rev.: $19,600,000
Emp.: 11
Jewelry Stores
N.A.I.C.S.: 458310
Roberto Chiappelloni *(Pres)*
Silvena Chiappelloni *(VP)*
Robert Weintraub *(Mgr)*

MANGAN HOLCOMB PARTNERS
2300 Cottondale Ln Ste 300, Little Rock, AR 72202
Tel.: (501) 376-0321   AR
Web Site: http://www.manganholcomb.com
Year Founded: 1972
Rev.: $10,000,000
Emp.: 30
Fiscal Year-end: 12/31/04
Agriculture, Financial, Full Service, Health Care, Transportation
N.A.I.C.S.: 541810
Steve Holcomb *(Chm)*
Chip Culpepper *(Chief Creative Officer)*
David Rainwater *(CEO)*
Sharon Tallach Vogelpohl *(Pres)*
Barbara King Dozier *(Dir-Media)*
Caroline Tyler *(Mgr-Acct Svc)*

MANGAN, INC.
3901 Via Oro Ave, Long Beach, CA 90810
Tel.: (310) 835-8080   CA
Web Site: http://manganinc.com
Year Founded: 1990
Control, Instrument, Electrical, Analytical & Process Safety Engineering Services
N.A.I.C.S.: 423490
Amin Solehjou *(Pres & CEO)*
Subsidiaries:
Horizon Consultants, Inc. (1)
2230 S Commerce Ave, Gonzales, LA 70737
Tel.: (225) 755-6330
Web Site: https://manganinc.com
Process Technology Expertise & Risk Assessment Services
N.A.I.C.S.: 541611

MANGANARO MIDATLANTIC, LLC
6405 D Ammendale Rd, Beltsville, MD 20705
Tel.: (301) 937-0580
Web Site: http://www.manganaro.com
Year Founded: 1958
Sales Range: $50-74.9 Million
Emp.: 45
Masonry & Other Stonework Service
N.A.I.C.S.: 238140
Brian Loveless *(VP-Richmond Virginia)*
Tom Vagrin *(CEO)*
Westley Douglas *(Pres)*
John Livingston *(Dir-Bus Dev)*
Charlene Bryant *(Mgr-Bus Dev)*
Dan Dinger *(CFO)*
Subsidiaries:
Manganaro Northeast, LLC (1)
52 Cummings Park, Woburn, MA 01801
Tel.: (781) 937-8880
Web Site: http://www.manganaro.com
Sales Range: $10-24.9 Million
Emp.: 20
Masonry, Drywall & Acoustical Ceilings Subcontracting Services
N.A.I.C.S.: 238310
Peter Iverson *(Mgr-Ops)*
David Manganaro *(Pres)*

MANGAR INDUSTRIES INC.
97 Britain Dr, New Britain, PA 18901
Tel.: (215) 230-0300
Web Site: http://www.mangar.com
Year Founded: 1986
Sales Range: $10-24.9 Million
Emp.: 125
Converter of Packaging Materials for Disposable Medical Devices
N.A.I.C.S.: 339112
Tom Jeziorski *(Dir-Global Sls)*
Robert Haines *(Acct Dir-Natl)*
Norie Shelley *(Reg Dir-Sls)*
Joyce Grow *(Coord-Customer Svc)*
Jill Adair *(Coord-Sls)*
Karen Barr *(Coord-Sls)*
Laura Boyd *(Coord-Sls)*
Kirstin Francis *(Coord-Sls)*
Diane Gartner *(Coord-Sls)*
Pam Gelone *(Coord-Sls)*
Georgianna Le *(Coord-Sls)*
James Dwyer *(Dir-Technical & Customer Svcs)*
Anna Vakhilt *(Project Mgr)*

MANGINO HOLDING CORP.
299 Market St, Saddle Brook, NJ 07663
Tel.: (973) 742-3000   NJ
Year Founded: 1987
Sales Range: $50-74.9 Million
Emp.: 25
Holding Company
N.A.I.C.S.: 551112
Joseph Mangino Jr. *(Chm)*
Subsidiaries:
Metropolitan Logistic Services Inc. (1)
299 Market St Ste 300, Saddle Brook, NJ 07663-5312
Tel.: (973) 742-3000
Web Site: http://www.metlog.com
Sales Range: $25-49.9 Million
Emp.: 300
Freight Transportation Arrangement
N.A.I.C.S.: 488510

MANGO LANGUAGES
30445 Northwestern Hwy Ste 300, Farmington Hills, MI 48334
Tel.: (248) 254-7450
Web Site: http://www.mangolanguages.com
Year Founded: 2008
Sales Range: $1-9.9 Million
Emp.: 55
Language Learning Software
N.A.I.C.S.: 611630
Jason Teshuba *(CEO)*
Ryan Whalen *(Co-Founder & Dir-Creative)*
Amanda Kmetz *(Coord-HR)*
Iryna Kulchytska *(Mgr-Special Projects)*
Andres Bedon *(Mgr-IT Infrastructure)*
Gulshen Karahann *(Accountant)*
Julian Fiander *(Project Mgr)*
Lorenzo Malene *(Project Mgr)*
Mallory Lapanowski *(Mgr-Creative)*
Mike Goulas *(Co-Founder)*
Milica Petranovic *(Mgr-Product Mktg)*
Nicole Choinski *(Coord-Events)*
Sam Borin *(Project Mgr)*
Steve Perakis *(CFO)*

MANGOSPRING INC
4122 Factoria Blvd SE Ste 405, Bellevue, WA 98006
Tel.: (425) 274-9950
Web Site: http://www.mangoapps.com
Year Founded: 2007
Sales Range: $1-9.9 Million
Emp.: 70
Social Networking Services
N.A.I.C.S.: 516210
Anup Kejriwal *(Founder & CEO)*
Vishwa Malhotra *(Co-Founder & CTO)*
Patrick Allman *(Exec VP-Sls)*
Ashish Agarwal *(VP-Product)*
Anjali Ghadge *(VP-HR)*
Russ Wolfe *(VP-Engrg)*

MANGROVE EQUITY PARTNERS, LP
101 S Franklin St Ste 205, Tampa, FL 33602
Tel.: (813) 868-4500
Web Site: http://www.mangroveequity.com
Depository Credit Intermediation
N.A.I.C.S.: 522180
Glenn Oken *(Mng Dir)*

MANHATTAN BEER DISTRIBUTORS LLC
955 E 149th St, Bronx, NY 10455
Tel.: (718) 292-9300   NY
Web Site: http://www.manhattanbeer.com
Year Founded: 1978
Sales Range: $50-74.9 Million
Emp.: 900
Beer & Ale Distr
N.A.I.C.S.: 424810
Simon Bergson *(Pres & CEO)*
Bill Bessette *(COO)*
George Wertheimer *(CFO)*
Al Greco *(VP-Mktg)*

MANHATTAN MARKETING ENSEMBLE
443 Park Ave S 4th Fl, New York, NY 10016-7322
Tel.: (212) 779-2233
Web Site: http://www.mme.net
Year Founded: 1989
Sales Range: $50-74.9 Million
Emp.: 35
Advetising Agency
N.A.I.C.S.: 541810
Maury R. Maniff *(Sr Partner)*
Don Raskin *(Sr Partner)*
James T. Rowe *(Sr Partner)*

MANHATTAN MOTORCARS, INC.
270 11th Ave, New York, NY 10001
Tel.: (212) 594-6200
Web Site: http://www.manhattanmotorcars.com
Year Founded: 1995
Sales Range: $10-24.9 Million
Emp.: 60
New Car Dealers
N.A.I.C.S.: 441110
Brian Miller *(CEO)*
Manny Quinones *(Mgr-Sls)*
Paul Dumont *(Mgr-Bentley Sls)*

MANHATTAN PARKING SYSTEMS GARAGE
545 5th Ave Rm 310, New York, NY 10017
Tel.: (212) 490-3460
Web Site: http://www.mpsparking.com
Rev.: $12,700,000
Emp.: 10
Parking Garage
N.A.I.C.S.: 812930
Claudia Santana *(Office Mgr)*

MANHATTAN PARKING SYSTEMS-PARK AVE
277 Park Ave, New York, NY 10172
Tel.: (212) 753-6116
Sales Range: $10-24.9 Million
Emp.: 4
Parking Garage
N.A.I.C.S.: 812930
Martin Meyer *(Pres)*

MANHATTAN PARTNERS
2711 N Sepulveda Blvd Ste 147, Manhattan Beach, CA 90266
Web Site: http://www.manhattan-partners.com
Year Founded: 2010
Privater Equity Firm
N.A.I.C.S.: 523999
Dean Bosacki *(Co-Founder & Mng Partner)*
Patrick McBride *(Co-Founder & Mng Partner)*

MANHATTAN REVIEW INC.
2 Park Ave Ste 2010, New York, NY 10016
Tel.: (212) 316-2000
Web Site: http://www.manhattanreview.com
Year Founded: 1999
Professional & Management Development Training
N.A.I.C.S.: 611430
Joern Missner *(Founder)*
Subsidiaries:
Get Prepped LLC (1)
603 W 115th St No 284, New York, NY 80501-5341
Tel.: (800) 321-7214
Web Site: http://www.getprepped.com
All Other Support Services
N.A.I.C.S.: 561990
Patrick O'Malley *(Founder & Pres)*

MANHATTAN SPECIAL BOTTLING CORP.

Manhattan Special Bottling Corp.—(Continued)

MANHATTAN SPECIAL BOTTLING CORP.
342 Manhattan Ave, Brooklyn, NY 11211-2404
Tel.: (718) 388-4144 NY
Web Site:
http://www.manhattanspecial.com
Year Founded: 1895
Sales Range: $75-99.9 Million
Emp.: 28
Espresso & Iced Coffee Drinks & Sodas Distr
N.A.I.C.S.: 312111
Aurora Passaro (Pres)
Louis Passaro (Exec VP)

MANHATTAN THEATRE CLUB, INC.
311 W 43rd St 8th Fl, New York, NY 10036
Tel.: (212) 399-3000 NY
Web Site:
http://www.manhattantheatreclub.com
Year Founded: 1970
Sales Range: $10-24.9 Million
Emp.: 90
Theater Club
N.A.I.C.S.: 711110
Florie Seery (Gen Mgr)
Amy Gilkes Loe (Dir-Artistic Ops)
Nancy Piccione (Dir-Casting)
Lynne Randall (Dir-Dev)
W. Gregg Slager (Treas)
Barbara J. Fife (Sec)
Lynne Meadow (Dir-Artistic)
Thomas F. Secunda (Pres)
Debra Waxman-Pilla (Dir-Mktg)
Emily Fleisher (Assoc Dir-Dev)
Jessica Adler (Dir-Fin)
Joshua Helman (Dir-Production)
Katy Higgins (Dir-Institutional Giving)
Kelly Gillespie (Dir-Casting)
Mendy Sudranski (Mgr-IT)
David C. Hodgson (Chm)

MANIFEST DIGITAL
35 E Wacker Ste 1000, Chicago, IL 60601
Tel.: (312) 563-1945
Web Site:
http://www.manifestdigital.com
Year Founded: 2001
Rev.: $9,200,000
Emp.: 54
Marketing Consulting Services
N.A.I.C.S.: 541613
Jason Benedict (CEO)
Beth Tomkiw (Chief Content Officer)
Jamie Anderson (Chief Strategy Officer)
Jill Geimer (Sr VP-HR)
John Conmy (Exec VP-Client Svcs)
Ryan Brown (Dir-Creative)
Shelby Mangum (Dir-Recruiting)
Simon Goodship (Chief Experience Officer)
Liz Koman (Chief Mktg Officer)
Melissa Bouma (Pres)
Eric Rivera (Acct Dir)
Jessica Becker (Mng Partner-US & Canada)

MANIFEST DISCS & TAPES INCORPORATED
1563 Bush River Rd, Columbia, SC 29202
Tel.: (803) 798-2606
Web Site:
http://www.manifestdisc.com
Rev.: $16,752,559
Emp.: 30
Record & Prerecorded Tape Stores
N.A.I.C.S.: 449210

MANIFOLD CAPITAL CORP.
140 Broadway 47th Fl, New York, NY 10005
Tel.: (212) 375-2000 DE
Sales Range: $10-24.9 Million
Emp.: 115
Holding Company; Financial Guaranty Insurance Policies Management Services
N.A.I.C.S.: 551112
Ellan Ben-Hayon (CEO)

Subsidiaries:

ACA Financial Guaranty Corporation (1)
600 5th Ave 2nd Fl, New York, NY 10020-2335
Tel.: (212) 375-2000
Web Site: http://www.aca.com
Rev.: $42,830,397
Assets: $404,720,809
Liabilities: $303,963,343
Net Worth: $100,757,466
Earnings: ($14,272,705)
Fiscal Year-end: 12/31/2014
High Yield Municipal Bond Insurance Management Services
N.A.I.C.S.: 524292
Steven Joseph Berkowitz (Pres & CEO)
Carl Benedict McCarthy (Chief Compliance Officer, Gen Counsel & Sec)
Brendan Malone (Asst Gen Counsel)
Arnold Barry Jay Brousell (CFO & Treas)

MANIFOLD SERVICES INC.
6101 Newport Rd, Portage, MI 49002
Tel.: (269) 323-9484
Web Site:
http://www.edwardrose.com
Rev.: $31,500,000
Emp.: 94
Land Subdividers & Developers, Commercial
N.A.I.C.S.: 237210
Karen Gorman (Asst Mgr)
Jeff Barnum (Dir-Property)

MANIILAQ ASSOCIATION
2nd Ave Ste 733, Kotzebue, AK 99752
Tel.: (907) 442-3311 AK
Web Site: http://www.maniilaq.org
Year Founded: 1971
Sales Range: $75-99.9 Million
Emp.: 835
Community Action Services
N.A.I.C.S.: 624190
Nate Kotch (VP)
Timothy Schuerch (Pres & CEO)

MANITOBA CORPORATION
122-130 Central Ave, Lancaster, NY 14086
Tel.: (716) 685-7000 NY
Web Site:
http://www.manitobacorp.com
Year Founded: 1916
Sales Range: $10-24.9 Million
Emp.: 50
Provider of Scrap & Waste Material Services
N.A.I.C.S.: 423930
Brian K. Shine (Pres)
Richard Shine (CEO)
Leonard Post (Mgr-Facilities)
Derrick Pearce (Supvr-Production)

MANITOU EQUIPMENT CORP.
PO Box 637, La Mirada, CA 90637
Tel.: (213) 941-8771
Rev.: $9,000,000
Emp.: 32
Heavy Construction Equip.
N.A.I.C.S.: 425120

MANITOWOC PUBLIC UTILITIES
1303 S 8th St PO Box 1090, Manitowoc, WI 54221
Tel.: (920) 683-4600
Web Site: http://www.mpu.org
Year Founded: 1889
Sales Range: $10-24.9 Million
Emp.: 85
Power Utilities
N.A.I.C.S.: 221118
Nilaksh Kothari (Gen Mgr)
Daniel W. Salm (Mgr-Customer Rels)
Tom Reed (Engr-Environmental)
Robert Michaelson (Mgr-Water Systems & Pur)
Steve Bacalzo (Mgr-Distr Ops)
Phil Platteter (Sr Electric Engr)

MANKATO FORD ACQUISITION CORP.
PO Box 3009, Mankato, MN 56002-3009
Tel.: (507) 387-3454
Web Site:
http://www.mankatoford.com
Sales Range: $10-24.9 Million
Emp.: 54
Car Whslr
N.A.I.C.S.: 441110
Gary Nelson (Mgr-Detail)
Mike Rstom (Owner & Pres)

MANKATO MOTOR CO.
1815 E Madison Ave, Mankato, MN 56001
Tel.: (507) 625-5641
Web Site:
http://www.mankatomotors.com
Rev.: $52,500,000
Emp.: 70
New & Used Car Dealers
N.A.I.C.S.: 441110
Dale Schmitt (Owner)
Dustin Elkins (Bus Mgr)

MANKATO REHABILITATION CENTER, INC.
15 Map Dr, Mankato, MN 56002-0328
Tel.: (507) 386-5600 MN
Web Site:
http://www.mrciworksource.org
Year Founded: 1953
Sales Range: $50-74.9 Million
Emp.: 4,883
Disability Assistance Services
N.A.I.C.S.: 624120
Jeff Call (CFO)
Brian Benshoof (CEO)
Bill Lehner (CIO)
Laura Bealey (COO)
Georg Marti (Mgr-New Ulm Branch)
Nancy Abel (Supvr-Case Mgmt)
Margaret Remiger (Mgr-Ops)
Vickie Apel (Dir-Foundation)
Bill Groskreutz (VP)
Steven Rohlfing (Pres)
Charles Guggisberg (Treas & Sec)

MANKE LUMBER COMPANY, INC.
1717 Marine View Dr, Tacoma, WA 98422-4104
Tel.: (253) 572-6252 WA
Web Site:
http://www.mankelumber.com
Sales Range: $150-199.9 Million
Emp.: 500
Producer & Retailer of Logs & Lumber
N.A.I.C.S.: 321113
Charles Manke (Pres)
J. Randal Jordan (Controller)
James Manke (Mgr-Sls)

Subsidiaries:

Superior Wood Treating (1)

13702 Stewart Rd, Sumner, WA 98390
Tel.: (253) 863-4495
Web Site: http://www.superiorwoodtreating.com
Wood Products Mfr
N.A.I.C.S.: 321999

MANKIN MEDIA SYSTEMS, INC.
129 Confederate Dr, Franklin, TN 37064
Tel.: (615) 324-8350
Web Site:
http://www.mankinmedia.com
Year Founded: 2001
Media Production Services
N.A.I.C.S.: 512110
Ben Mankin (Founder & Pres)
Shane Skaggs (Dir-Design)
Kendall Barrett (Dir-Ops)
Chris Flood (Deploy Mgr)
Dan Shivener (Project Mgr)
Michael Wells (CTO)
Jonathan Frazier (Dir-Comm)
Justin Neill (Dir-Engrg)
John O'Leary (Video Engr)
Travis Brigman (Design Engr)
Mike Gold (CIO)

MANKO WINDOW SYSTEMS INC.
800 Hayes Dr, Manhattan, KS 66502
Tel.: (785) 776-9643
Web Site:
http://www.mankowindows.com
Rev.: $15,000,000
Emp.: 200
Metal Doors, Sash & Trim
N.A.I.C.S.: 332321
Gary Jones (Pres)
Bill Ulrich (Controller)
Joe Jones (VP)
Steve Jones (VP)

MANLY GMC BUICK HYUNDAI MITSUBISHI
2755 Corby Ave, Santa Rosa, CA 95407-7845
Tel.: (707) 545-8220
Year Founded: 1899
Sales Range: $10-24.9 Million
Emp.: 60
New Car Whslr
N.A.I.C.S.: 441110
Brian Manly (Owner & Pres)

MANN CHRYSLER-PLYMOUTH-DODGE-JEEP
806 Alexa Dr, Mount Sterling, KY 40353
Tel.: (859) 498-0232
Web Site:
http://www.mann.fivestardealer.com
Sales Range: $25-49.9 Million
Emp.: 20
Automobiles, New & Used
N.A.I.C.S.: 441110
James R. Mann (Pres)

MANN REALTY COMPANY
8653 Bash St, Indianapolis, IN 46250
Tel.: (317) 849-0452
Year Founded: 1970
Sales Range: $10-24.9 Million
Emp.: 30
Land Subdividing Services
N.A.I.C.S.: 237210
Gerald D. Ma (Principal)

MANN THEATERS INC.
900 E 80th St, Bloomington, MN 55420
Tel.: (952) 767-0102
Web Site:
http://www.manntheatresmn.com
Sales Range: $10-24.9 Million

COMPANIES

Emp.: 600
Motion Picture Theater, Except Drive-In
N.A.I.C.S.: 512131
Steve Mann (Pres)
Benji Mann (Owner)

MANN'S INTERNATIONAL MEAT SPECIALTIES INC.
9097 F St, Omaha, NE 68127
Tel.: (402) 339-7000
Web Site:
http://www.tastetraditions.com
Sales Range: $10-24.9 Million
Emp.: 125
Processed Meat Mfr
N.A.I.C.S.: 311612
Jeff Souba (Pres & Gen Mgr)
Dee Felici (Dir-Sls-Northern Plains Reg)
Lewis Marshall (Mgr-Sls-South Eastern Reg)
Bill Shimek (Mgr-Pur)
Dennis Smith (Mgr-Sls-South Central Reg)
Joan Suter (Mgr-Customer Svc)
Kim Brummett (Controller)

MANNA DISTRIBUTION
2440 Enterprise Dr, Saint Paul, MN 55120
Tel.: (651) 686-0103
Web Site: http://www.manna.com
Rev.: $15,000,000
Emp.: 55
Domestic Freight Forwarding International
N.A.I.C.S.: 488510

MANNEY'S SHOPPER, INC.
380 Jackson St Ste 700, Saint Paul, MN 55101
Tel.: (218) 263-8357
Sales Range: $10-24.9 Million
Emp.: 150
Newspaper Publisher & Distr
N.A.I.C.S.: 513110
Randy Cope (CEO)

MANNHEIM, LLC
712 5th Ave 32nd Fl, New York, NY 10019
Tel.: (212) 664-8600　　DE
Emp.: 15
Equity Investment Firm
N.A.I.C.S.: 523999
Martin Bussmann (Mng Dir)

Subsidiaries:

Mannheim Holdings, LLC　　(1)
712 5th Ave 32nd Fl, New York, NY 10019　　(100%)
Tel.: (212) 664-8600
Holding Company
N.A.I.C.S.: 551112
Martin Bussmann (Mng Dir)

Holding (Domestic):

Demos Medical Publishing, LLC　　(2)
11 W 42nd St 15th Fl, New York, NY 10036
Tel.: (212) 683-0072
Web Site: http://www.demosmedpub.com
Sales Range: $1-9.9 Million
Emp.: 7
Medical Book Publisher
N.A.I.C.S.: 513130
Richard Winters (Exec Editor-Medical)
Reina Santana (Dir-Sls)
Beth Kaufman Barry (Publr)

Springer Publishing Company, LLC　　(2)
11 W 42nd St 15th Fl, New York, NY 10036
Tel.: (212) 431-4370
Web Site: http://www.springerpub.com
Sales Range: $1-9.9 Million
Healthcare & Social Work Professional Book & Periodical Publisher
N.A.I.C.S.: 513130

Mary E. Gatsch (CEO & Publr)
Gary Darlington (Sr Dir-Sls-Higher Education)
Jill Ferguson (Sr Mgr-Sls-Higher Education)
Annette Imperati (Dir-Sls-Corp, Govt & Associations)
Mark Wenger (Sr Mgr-Sls-Higher Education)
Kathy Wiess (Sr Dir-Sls-Trade, Corp & Govt Sls)
Nancy Hale (Dir-Editorial-Social Sciences)

MANNING & LEWIS ENGINEERING COMPANY
675 Rahway Ave, Union, NJ 07083
Tel.: (908) 687-2400
Web Site:
http://www.manninglewis.com
Year Founded: 1937
Sales Range: $1-9.9 Million
Emp.: 60
Shell & Tube Heat Exchangers Mfr
N.A.I.C.S.: 332410
Kurt Nelson (Pres & CEO)
Kevin Elwood (Mgr-Adv & Sls)

MANNING ENTERPRISES INC.
12000 Westport Rd, Louisville, KY 40245
Tel.: (502) 426-5210　　KY
Web Site: http://www.truckequip.com
Year Founded: 1954
Sales Range: $25-49.9 Million
Emp.: 100
Installer of Trucking Equipment
N.A.I.C.S.: 423110
Michael Stich (Pres)

Subsidiaries:

Manning Equipment, LLC　　(1)
12000 Westport Rd, Louisville, KY 40245-1767　　(100%)
Tel.: (502) 426-5210
Web Site: http://www.truckequip.com
Sales Range: $25-49.9 Million
Mfr, Distr & Whslr of Truck Related Equipment
N.A.I.C.S.: 423110
Mark Payton (VP-Sls)

Subsidiary (Domestic):

Dealers Truck Equipment, Inc.　　(2)
12000 Westport Rd, Louisville, KY 40245-1767
Tel.: (502) 426-6623
Web Site: http://www.truckequip.com
Sales Range: $25-49.9 Million
Emp.: 70
Installer of Trucking Equipment
N.A.I.C.S.: 441330

Manning Light Truck Equipment, LLC　　(2)
12000 Westport Rd, Louisville, KY 40245
Tel.: (502) 426-5210
Sales Range: $25-49.9 Million
Emp.: 60
Light Truck Equipment & Parts
N.A.I.C.S.: 441330
Larry Westhousing (Chief Engr)

Manning Truck Modification　　(2)
12000 Westport Rd, Louisville, KY 40245-1767
Tel.: (502) 426-5210
Web Site: http://www.truckequip.com
Modification of Trucks
N.A.I.C.S.: 423110

MANNING FINANCIAL GROUP, INC.
9412 United States Hwy 1, Sebastian, FL 32958
Tel.: (772) 589-0097
Web Site:
http://www.manningfinancial.com
Sales Range: $10-24.9 Million
Emp.: 10
Mortgage Banker
N.A.I.C.S.: 522292

Donald Manning (Pres & CEO)
Melody Manning (VP)

MANNING GROSS + MASSENBURG LLP
125 High St Oliver St Tower 6th Fl, Boston, MA 02110
Tel.: (617) 670-8800
Web Site: http://www.mgmlaw.com
Law firm
N.A.I.C.S.: 541110
Silvio J. Talarico (Exec Dir)
Christopher P McDevitt (CFO)
Danielle V. Carr (Dir-HR)

MANNING MANAGEMENT CORPORATION
680 Ben Franklin Hwy, Birdsboro, PA 19508
Tel.: (610) 385-6797
Web Site:
http://www.manningmaterials.com
Rev.: $20,000,000
Emp.: 40
Structural Assemblies, Prefabricated: Non-Wood
N.A.I.C.S.: 423390
Drew Seibert (Pres)

MANNING REGIONAL HEALTHCARE CENTER
410 Main St, Manning, IA 51455
Tel.: (712) 655-2072　　IA
Web Site: http://www.mrhcia.com
Year Founded: 1997
Sales Range: $10-24.9 Million
Emp.: 223
Health Care Srvices
N.A.I.C.S.: 622110
John O'Brien (CEO)

MANNING'S BEEF LLC.
9531 E Beverly Rd, Pico Rivera, CA 90661-6545
Tel.: (562) 699-6884
Web Site:
http://www.manningsnatural beef.com
Year Founded: 1990
Sales Range: $10-24.9 Million
Emp.: 79
Beef Product Production & Distribution Services
N.A.I.C.S.: 311611
Claudia Tamayo (Mgr-HR)

MANNING, INC.
4720 Moffett Rd, Mobile, AL 36618
Tel.: (251) 343-1485　　AL
Web Site:
http://www.manningsmarket.com
Year Founded: 1974
Sales Range: $10-24.9 Million
Emp.: 35
Grocery Store Owner & Operator
N.A.I.C.S.: 445110
Danny Manning (Owner)
K. C. Constantine (Gen Mgr)

MANNING-SQUIRES-HENNIG CO. INC.
8426 7 Springs Rd, Batavia, NY 14020
Tel.: (585) 343-5365　　NY
Web Site: http://www.mshco.com
Year Founded: 1958
Sales Range: $25-49.9 Million
Emp.: 26
Provider of New Construction For Commercial & Industrial Buildings
N.A.I.C.S.: 236220
Gary Squires (Pres)
Ralph Taccone (Controller)
James J. Whelehan (Asst Controller)
Peter Mietus (Dir-Safety & Mgr-Risk)

MANNINGTON MILLS, INC.

MANNINGTON MILLS, INC.
75 Mannington Mills Rd, Salem, NJ 08079
Tel.: (856) 935-3000　　NJ
Web Site:
http://www.mannington.com
Year Founded: 1915
Sales Range: $400-449.9 Million
Emp.: 2,200
Flooring Mfr
N.A.I.C.S.: 326199
Keith S. Campbell (Chm)
Russell Grizzle (Pres & CEO)
David Sheehan (VP-Strategic Dev)

Subsidiaries:

Amtico International Ltd.　　(1)
Kingfield Road, Coventry, CV6 5AA, Warcs, United Kingdom
Tel.: (44) 2476 487 149
Web Site: http://www.amtico.com
Vinyl Floor Tile & Carpet Mfr & Whslr
N.A.I.C.S.: 326199
Jonathan Duck (CEO)

Subsidiary (US):

Amtico USA, LLC　　(2)
1844 US Hwy 41 SE, Calhoun, GA 30701
Tel.: (404) 267-1900
Web Site: http://www.amtico.com
Flooring Product Whlsr
N.A.I.C.S.: 423220

Burke Industries, Inc.　　(1)
2250 S 10th St, San Jose, CA 95112-4114
Tel.: (408) 297-3500
Web Site: http://www.burkeind.com
Rev.: $50,000,000
Emp.: 250
Rubber Floor Tile, Stair Treads & Custom Molded Rubber Products; Flexible Membranes for Liners & Covers; Single-Ply Roofing Systems Mfr
N.A.I.C.S.: 326199
Robert Pitman (Pres & CEO)
Joe Walker (Dir-Sls)

Division (Domestic):

Burke Flooring Products Division　　(2)
2250 S 10th St, San Jose, CA 95112-4114
Tel.: (408) 297-3500
Web Site: http://www.burkeindustries.com
Sales Range: $25-49.9 Million
Emp.: 50
Mfr of Rubber Floor Tile, Stair Treads & Custom Molded Rubber Products; Flexible Membranes for Liners & Covers; Single-Ply Roofing Systems
N.A.I.C.S.: 326199
Roger Castillo (Product Mgr)

Plant (Domestic):

Burke Flooring Products　　(3)
37235 State Rd 19, Umatilla, FL 32784-8070
Tel.: (352) 357-4119
Web Site: http://www.burkeindustries.com
Sales Range: $25-49.9 Million
Emp.: 100
Mfr of Extruded Plastic Flooring, Baseboards
N.A.I.C.S.: 326199
Jerry Glatz (VP)

Division (Domestic):

Burke Industries, Inc. - Burkeline Roofing Systems Division　　(2)
2250 S 10th St, San Jose, CA 95112-4114
Tel.: (408) 297-3500
Roofing System Installation Services
N.A.I.C.S.: 238160

Burke Industries, Inc. - Custom Process　　(2)
2250 S 10th St, San Jose, CA 95112-4114
Tel.: (408) 297-3500
Web Site: http://www.burkeindustries.com
Sales Range: $150-199.9 Million
Rubber Floor Tile, Stair Treads & Custom Molded Rubber Products Mfr; Flexible Membranes for Liners & Covers; Single-Ply Roofing Systems
N.A.I.C.S.: 326291

MANNINGTON MILLS, INC. — U.S. PRIVATE

Mannington Mills, Inc.—(Continued)

Burke Rubber Co. (2)
2250 S Tenth St, San Jose, CA 95112
Tel.: (408) 297-3500
Web Site: http://www.burkeindustries.com
Sales Range: $25-49.9 Million
Emp.: 150
Mfr of Rubber Floor Tile, Stair Treads & Custom Molded Rubber Products; Flexible Membranes for Liners & Covers; Single-Ply Roofing Systems
N.A.I.C.S.: 326199

Mannington Carpets (1)
1844 US Hwy 41 SE, Calhoun, GA 30701-7004
Tel.: (706) 629-7301
Web Site: http://www.manningtoncommercial.com
Sales Range: $50-74.9 Million
Emp.: 600
Carpet Mfr
N.A.I.C.S.: 314110

Mannington Resilient Floors (1)
75 Mannington Mills Rd, Salem, NJ 08079
Tel.: (856) 935-3000
Web Site: http://www.mannington.com
Sales Range: $50-74.9 Million
Emp.: 700
Flooring Mfr
N.A.I.C.S.: 326199
Edward Duncan (VP-Mktg)

Mannington Wood Floors (1)
1327 Lincoln Dr, High Point, NC 27260
Tel.: (336) 884-5600
Web Site: http://www.mannington.com
Sales Range: $25-49.9 Million
Emp.: 250
Wood Floor Mfr
N.A.I.C.S.: 321918

MANNIX MARKETING, INC.
11 Broad St 3rd Fl, Glens Falls, NY 12801
Tel.: (518) 743-9424   NY
Web Site: http://www.mannixmarketing.com
Sales Range: $1-9.9 Million
Emp.: 28
Search Engine Optimization Services
N.A.I.C.S.: 541511
Sara Mannix (Founder & CEO)
Destiny Malone (Mng Editor)
Pam Holt (CFO)
Jennifer Manz (Dir-Digital Mktg)
Mark Mannix (CTO)

MANNY'S TV AND APPLIANCES
1872 Boston Rd, Wilbraham, MA 01095
Tel.: (413) 543-2467
Web Site: http://www.mannystv.com
Year Founded: 1977
Sales Range: $10-24.9 Million
Emp.: 80
Electric Household Appliances, Major
N.A.I.C.S.: 449210
Emanuel Rovithis (Pres)

MANOR HOUSE KITCHENS INC.
589 Rugh St, Greensburg, PA 15601
Tel.: (724) 837-3800
Web Site: http://www.manorhousekitchens.com
Sales Range: $10-24.9 Million
Emp.: 70
Cabinets, Kitchen
N.A.I.C.S.: 444180
Michael Backus (CEO)
Jeffrey Backus (Pres)

MANOR HOUSE PUBLISHING CO, INC.
880 Louis Dr, Warminster, PA 18974
Tel.: (215) 259-1700
Periodical Publishers
N.A.I.C.S.: 513120

MANPOWER HOLDING CORP.
231 S 3rd St Ste 285, Las Vegas, NV 89101
Tel.: (702) 363-2626   NV
Web Site: http://www.manpowerlv.com
Sales Range: $25-49.9 Million
Emp.: 100
Holding Company; Temporary Staffing & Employment Placement Services
N.A.I.C.S.: 551112
Andrew Katz (Pres)

Subsidiaries:

Manpower, Incorporated of Southern Nevada (1)
8170 W Sahara Ave Ste 207, Las Vegas, NV 89117
Tel.: (702) 363-2626
Web Site: http://www.manpowerlv.com
Rev.: $22,503,050
Emp.: 35
Temporary Staffing & Employment Placement Services
N.A.I.C.S.: 561320
Andrew Katz (Pres)

MANSA CAPITAL MANAGEMENT, LLC
500 Boylston St 5th Fl, Boston, MA 02116
Tel.: (617) 424-4940   DE
Web Site: http://www.mansaequity.com
Year Founded: 2003
Privater Equity Firm
N.A.I.C.S.: 523999
Jason P. Torres (COO & Partner)
Stephen Agular (Partner-Venture)
Caleb DesRosiers (Partner-Venture)

MANSFIELD COOPERATIVE BANK
80 N Main St, Mansfield, MA 02048
Tel.: (508) 851-3600
Web Site: http://www.mansfieldbank.bank
Year Founded: 1883
Federal Savings & Loan Associations
N.A.I.C.S.: 522180
Daniel Conrad (First Sr VP)
Carie Ann Bailey (VP)
Jeaune Borden (Asst VP & Branch Mgr-Norton)
Debbie Cote (VP & Branch Mgr-Plainville & North Attleboro)
Susan Cunniff (VP & Branch Mgr-West Bridgewater)
Deborah Brackett (Asst VP & Branch Mgr-Easton)
Kenneth A. Larsen (Chm)
John R. Korona (Pres & CEO)
Russell J. Anderson (Dir)
F. Andrew Beise (Dir)
Debra M. Crowell (Dir)
Kimberly A. Thomas (Dir)
Gilbert J. Campos Jr. (Dir)

MANSFIELD ENERGY CORP.
1025 Airport Pkwy SW, Gainesville, GA 30501
Tel.: (678) 450-2000   GA
Web Site: https://www.mansfield.energy
Year Founded: 1957
Sales Range: Less than $1 Million
Emp.: 550
Offices of Other Holding Companies
N.A.I.C.S.: 551112
John Byrd (CFO)
Michael F. Mansfield Sr. (CEO)
Blake Young (Pres)
Greg Allarding (CIO)
Andy Austin (Sr VP-Specialty Products)
Andy Milton (Sr VP-Supply & Distr)
Kevin O'Brien (Sr VP-Sls Ops-Canadian Acquisitions & Valuations)
Brad Puryear (Gen Counsel)

Subsidiaries:

Mansfield Oil Company of Gainesville, Inc. (1)
1025 Airport Pkwy SW, Gainesville, GA 30501-6813
Tel.: (678) 450-2000
Web Site: http://www.mansfieldoil.com
Emp.: 440
Petroleum Products, Ethanol & Diesel Distr
N.A.I.C.S.: 424720
John Byrd (COO)
Michael F. Mansfield Sr. (Chm & CEO)
Ted Roccagli (Mktg Mgr-Retail)
James Bo Bearden (Dir-Retail Ops)
Mark Helms (VP-Sls & Mktg)
Joe Campbell (Sr VP-Ops)
Tony Yocum (Dir-Bus Dev)
Kristin Kimzey (Mktg Mgr)
Blake Young (Pres)

Western Fleet Services, Inc. (1)
15600 E 19th Ave, Aurora, CO 80011
Tel.: (303) 361-0096
Web Site: http://www.westernfleetservices.com
Sales Range: $1-9.9 Million
Emp.: 21
Petroleum Bulk Stations & Terminals
N.A.I.C.S.: 424710
Chris Downs (Pres)
James Dante (Office Mgr)

MANSFIELD MOTOR GROUP
1493 Park Ave W, Mansfield, OH 44906
Tel.: (419) 529-4000
Web Site: http://www.mansfieldmotorgroup.com
Year Founded: 1967
Sales Range: $10-24.9 Million
Emp.: 65
Car Whslr
N.A.I.C.S.: 441110
Dirk Schluter (Pres)

MANSFIELD PAPER CO. INC.
380 Union St Ste 117, West Springfield, MA 01089
Tel.: (413) 781-2000   MA
Web Site: http://www.mansfieldpaper.com
Year Founded: 1945
Sales Range: $10-24.9 Million
Emp.: 75
Mfr of Bags, Paper & Disposable Plastics
N.A.I.C.S.: 424130
Michael Shapiro (Pres)

MANSFIELD PLUMBING PRODUCTS LLC
150 E First St, Perrysville, OH 44864
Tel.: (419) 938-5211
Web Site: http://www.mansfieldplumbing.com
Sales Range: $125-149.9 Million
Emp.: 750
Vitreous Plumbing Fixtures
N.A.I.C.S.: 327110
Candace Bishop (Mgr-Talent Dev)

MANSFIELD-MARTIN EXPLORATION MINING, INC.
1137 Hwy 80 E, Tombstone, AZ 86638
Tel.: (520) 457-8404   NV
Web Site: http://www.mansfieldmartin.com
Year Founded: 2011
Exploration & Mining Services
N.A.I.C.S.: 213115
John T. Bauska (Pres, CEO, CFO, Treas & Sec)

MANSI GLOBIZ INC.

401 N Parsons Ave Ste 107B, Brandon, FL 33510
Tel.: (813) 661-7048
Web Site: http://www.mgingredients.com
Sales Range: $50-74.9 Million
Emp.: 5
Chemical Products Distr
N.A.I.C.S.: 424690
Vimal Agarwal (Pres & CEO)

MANSI MEDIA
3899 N Front St, Harrisburg, PA 17110-1535
Tel.: (717) 703-3030   PA
Web Site: http://www.mansimedia.com
Year Founded: 1954
Sales Range: $200-249.9 Million
Emp.: 32
Media Buying Services
N.A.I.C.S.: 541810
Lisa Knight (VP-Adv)
Chris Kazlauskas (Dir-Media)
Wes Snider (Dir-Client Solutions)
Matt Caylor (Dir-Interactive)
Ken Sanford (Mgr-Acct)
Carin Hoover (Mgr-Acct)
Louella Reynolds (Mgr-Statewide Network)
Lindsey Artz (Mgr-Acct)

MANSON CONSTRUCTION CO., INC.
5209 E Marginal Way S, Seattle, WA 98134-2409
Tel.: (206) 762-0850
Web Site: http://www.mansonconstruction.com
Year Founded: 1930
Sales Range: $25-49.9 Million
Emp.: 250
Heavy Construction
N.A.I.C.S.: 236210

Subsidiaries:

Manson Gulf LLC (1)
392 Old Bayou Dularge Rd, Houma, LA 70363
Tel.: (985) 580-1900
Web Site: http://www.mansonconstruction.com
Offshore Consulting Services
N.A.I.C.S.: 541611
Brandt Stagni (Mgr-Construction)

MANSUETO VENTURES LLC
7 World Trade Ctr, New York, NY 10007-2195
Tel.: (212) 389-5300   DE
Web Site: http://www.mansueto.com
Year Founded: 2005
Sales Range: $25-49.9 Million
Emp.: 200
Print & Online Business Magazine Publisher
N.A.I.C.S.: 513120
Joe Mansueto (Owner)
Chareyl Ramos (Mgr-Payroll)
Jackie Nurse (Mgr-Acctg)

Subsidiaries:

Fast Company Magazine (1)
7 World Trade Ctr Fl 29, New York, NY 10007
Tel.: (212) 389-5300
Web Site: http://www.fastcompany.com
Sales Range: $25-49.9 Million
Emp.: 75
Print & Online Business Magazine Publisher
N.A.I.C.S.: 513120
Noah Robischon (Exec Editor)
Wesley Diphoko (Editor-in-Chief)
Morgan Clendaniel (Deputy Editor-Digital)

Inc. Magazine (1)
7 World Trade Ctr Fl 29, New York, NY 10007-2195
Tel.: (212) 389-5360

COMPANIES

Web Site: http://www.inc.com
Emp.: 175
Business Magazine Publisher
N.A.I.C.S.: 513120
Jon Fine *(Exec Editor)*

Subsidiary (Domestic):

Inc.com LLC (2)
7 World Trade Ctr, New York, NY 10007-2195
Tel.: (212) 389-5300
Web Site: http://www.inc.com
Sales Range: $1-9.9 Million
Emp.: 170
Online Business Magazine Publisher
N.A.I.C.S.: 513120
Blake Taylor *(Dir-Creative)*

MANTA MEDIA, INC.
8760 Orion Pl Ste 200, Columbus, OH 43240
Tel.: (614) 807-5103
Web Site: http://www.manta.com
Year Founded: 2005
Sales Range: $1-9.9 Million
Emp.: 50
Business Solutions for Small Businesses
N.A.I.C.S.: 513140
George Troutman *(CFO)*
Brad Warnick *(VP-Platform & Tech)*
John Swanciger *(CEO)*
Dario Ambrosini *(COO)*
Joey Glowacki *(VP-Sls)*

MANTECA FORD MERCURY, INC.
PO Box 2185, Manteca, CA 95336-1160
Tel.: (209) 239-3561
Web Site: http://www.mantecaford.com
Sales Range: $10-24.9 Million
Emp.: 45
Car Whslr
N.A.I.C.S.: 441110
Valerie Wallace *(Office Mgr)*
Phil Waterford *(Owner & Pres)*

MANTHEI INC.
3996 US 31 S, Petoskey, MI 49770-9744
Tel.: (231) 347-4675 MI
Web Site: http://www.mantheiinc.com
Year Founded: 1967
Sales Range: $25-49.9 Million
Emp.: 110
Hardwood Veneer & Plywood
N.A.I.C.S.: 321211
Jim Manthei *(Mng Partner)*
Mark Manthei *(Mng Partner)*
Tim Manthei *(Mng Partner)*
Ben Manthei *(Mng Partner)*

MANTI RESOURCES, INC.
800 N Shoreline Blvd Ste 900 S, Corpus Christi, TX 78401
Tel.: (361) 888-7708
Web Site: http://www.mantires.com
Year Founded: 1989
Sales Range: $25-49.9 Million
Emp.: 38
Entertainer Managing Services
N.A.I.C.S.: 711410
Lee Barberito *(Chm & CEO)*
Gani Sagingaliyev *(VP-Reservoir)*
Tim Boyle *(Sr VP-Land)*
Chris Douglas *(Sr VP-Exploration)*

MANTLE WHITE PARTNERSHIP
4400 N Scottsdale Rd, Scottsdale, AZ 85251-3331
Tel.: (480) 946-8008
Year Founded: 1983
Sales Range: $25-49.9 Million
Emp.: 402

Mfr of Wood Kitchen Cabinets
N.A.I.C.S.: 337110

Subsidiaries:

Mantle White Cabinet Group, Inc. (1)
4400 N Scottsdale Rd Ste 9-399, Scottsdale, AZ 85251-3331
Tel.: (480) 946-8008
Sales Range: $10-24.9 Million
Emp.: 1
Wood Kitchen Cabinets
N.A.I.C.S.: 337110

MANTRA PUBLIC RELATIONS, INC.
110 W 26th St 3rd Fl, New York, NY 10001
Tel.: (212) 645-1600
Web Site: http://www.mantrapublicrelation.com
Year Founded: 1987
Sales Range: $1-9.9 Million
Emp.: 4
Business-To-Business, Communications, Entertainment, Health Care, Public Relations, Publicity/Promotions, Restaurant, Transportation, Travel & Tourism
N.A.I.C.S.: 541820
Gaye Carleton *(Founder & CEO)*

MANTUA MANUFACTURING CO. INC.
7900 Northfield Rd, Walton Hills, OH 44146
Tel.: (440) 232-8865 OH
Web Site: http://www.bedframes.com
Year Founded: 1952
Sales Range: $25-49.9 Million
Emp.: 100
Mfr of Metal Household Furniture
N.A.I.C.S.: 337126
Edward Weintraub *(Chm & CEO)*
Jeff Weekley *(Controller)*
Neil Dwyer *(Mgr-Sls & Mktg)*
David Jaffe *(Pres)*

MANTZ AUTOMATION, INC.
1630 Innovation Way, Hartford, WI 53027
Tel.: (262) 673-7560
Web Site: http://www.mantzautomation.com
Year Founded: 1989
Rev.: $16,000,000
Emp.: 88
Tool, Die Set, Jig, Special Die & Fixture Mfr
N.A.I.C.S.: 333514
Denise Mantz *(Pres)*

MANUAL WOODWORKERS & WEAVERS, INC.
3737 Howardgap Rd, Hendersonville, NC 28792-8928
Tel.: (828) 692-4865 NC
Web Site: http://www.manualww.com
Year Founded: 1932
Sales Range: $25-49.9 Million
Emp.: 200
Woven Products, Rugs, Afghans & Accessories Mfr
N.A.I.C.S.: 314120
C. Lemuel Oates *(Co-Owner)*
Jim Clarke *(VP)*
Scott Sargent *(Plant Mgr)*
Vicky Grant *(Dir-Creative)*
Molly Sherrill *(Owner)*
Amanda Ivey *(Mgr-Pur)*

MANUEL HUERTA TRUCKING INC.
21 Kipper St, Rio Rico, AZ 85648
Tel.: (520) 281-2058
Web Site: http://www.mht-jcv.com

Sales Range: $75-99.9 Million
Emp.: 144
Provider of Trucking Services
N.A.I.C.S.: 484121
Manuel Huerta *(Pres)*

MANUEL LUJAN INSURANCE, INC.
7770 Jefferson NE, Albuquerque, NM 87109
Tel.: (505) 266-7771 NM
Web Site: http://www.hubinternational.com
Year Founded: 1997
Sales Range: $100-124.9 Million
Emp.: 160
Insurance Agents
N.A.I.C.S.: 524210
Randall Perkins *(Pres)*
Barry Cordeiro *(CIO & VP)*
Deborah Deters *(Chief HR Officer)*
John Albright *(Chief Legal Officer)*
Joseph C. Hyde *(CFO)*
W. Kirk James *(Chief Strategy Officer)*

MANUEL VILLA ENTERPRISES INC.
710 Lander Ave, Turlock, CA 95380
Tel.: (209) 669-2500
Web Site: http://www.lptmarkets.com
Sales Range: $10-24.9 Million
Emp.: 300
Supermarket
N.A.I.C.S.: 311830
Manuel Villa *(Pres)*
Lilia Bacon *(Mgr-Admin)*
Bertha Villa *(VP)*

MANUFACTURED ASSEMBLIES CORPORATION
1625 Field Stone Way, Vandalia, OH 45377
Tel.: (937) 454-0722
Web Site: http://www.mac-cable.com
Year Founded: 1976
Sales Range: $25-49.9 Million
Harness Wiring Sets & Cable Assemblies Mfr
N.A.I.C.S.: 335929
Brad Nimer *(Pres)*
Daniel Nimer *(VP)*
E. Randall Woody *(Gen Mgr)*
Tyler Nimer *(Gen Mgr)*
Ken Haupt *(Mgr-Quality)*
Steve Williams *(Mgr-Ops)*
Ken Difranco *(Reg Mgr-Sls)*
James Harrelson *(Program Mgr)*

MANUFACTURED STRUCTURES CORP.
3089 E Ft Wayne Rd, Rochester, IN 46975
Tel.: (574) 223-4794
Web Site: http://www.mscoffice.com
Sales Range: $10-24.9 Million
Emp.: 10
Mobile Buildings: For Commercial Use
N.A.I.C.S.: 321991
Austin Gulick *(Pres)*
Todd Hopkins *(Dir-Sls & Engrg)*

MANUFACTURERS DISCOUNT FURNITURE & BEDDING, INC.
2301 E 7th St, Los Angeles, CA 90023-1035
Tel.: (323) 589-5471
Year Founded: 1970
Sales Range: $10-24.9 Million
Emp.: 100
Distr of Bedding, Decorative Pillows & Bath Accessories Sold To Mass Merchants
N.A.I.C.S.: 314120

MAOLA MILK & ICE CREAM COMPANY

MANUFACTURERS PRODUCTS COMPANY
26020 Sherwood Ave, Warren, MI 48091-1252
Tel.: (586) 755-0097 MI
Year Founded: 1949
Sales Range: $25-49.9 Million
Emp.: 175
Mfr of Automotive Stampings & Assemblies
N.A.I.C.S.: 336370

MANUFACTURERS' NEWS, INC.
1633 Central St, Evanston, IL 60201-1569
Tel.: (847) 864-7000 IL
Web Site: http://www.mni.net
Year Founded: 1912
Directories & Databases Mfr
N.A.I.C.S.: 513140
Thomas G. Dubin *(Pres & CEO)*
Scott Kartsounes *(CTO)*

MANUFACTURING TECHNICAL SOLUTIONS INC.
7047 Old Madison Pike Ste 302, Huntsville, AL 35806
Tel.: (256) 890-9090 TN
Web Site: http://www.mts-usa.com
Year Founded: 2001
Sales Range: $10-24.9 Million
Emp.: 122
Technical & Business Management Solutions
N.A.I.C.S.: 541690
Paul M. Curd *(Pres)*
Doug Robley *(Mgr-Acctg)*

MANZI INSURANCE
215 Main St S, Woodbury, CT 06798
Tel.: (203) 263-8881
Web Site: http://www.manziins.com
Insurance Related Activities
N.A.I.C.S.: 524298
Ray Manzi *(Owner)*

Subsidiaries:

Newtown Insurance Service, LLC (1)
34 Church Hill Rd, Newtown, CT 06470-2783
Tel.: (203) 426-2273
Web Site: http://www.manziins.com
Insurance Agencies & Brokerages
N.A.I.C.S.: 524210

MANZI METALS, INC.
15293 Flight Path Dr, Brooksville, FL 34604
Tel.: (352) 799-8211 FL
Web Site: http://www.manzimetals.com
Year Founded: 1993
Sales Range: $1-9.9 Million
Emp.: 10
Metals Service Center
N.A.I.C.S.: 423510
Barbara Manzi *(Owner)*

MANZO PHARMACEUTICALS, INC.
PO Box 107, Milford, PA 18337
Tel.: (570) 249-6000
Web Site: http://www.manzopharma.com
Pharmaceuticals Mfr
N.A.I.C.S.: 325412
Kenneth Manzo *(Founder)*

MAOLA MILK & ICE CREAM COMPANY
305 Ave C, New Bern, NC 28560-3113
Tel.: (844) 287-1970 NC
Web Site: http://www.maolamilk.com

MAOLA MILK & ICE CREAM COMPANY — U.S. PRIVATE

Maola Milk & Ice Cream Company—(Continued)
Year Founded: 1945
Dairy Products Supplier
N.A.I.C.S.: 311511
John Bjorklund (Mgr-Quality Assurance)
Harold Suber (Branch Mgr)

MAP CARGO INTERNATIONAL INC.
2501 Santa Fe Ave, Redondo Beach, CA 90278
Tel.: (310) 297-8300
Web Site: http://www.mapcargo.com
Rev.: $20,000,000
Emp.: 63
Domestic Freight Forwarding
N.A.I.C.S.: 488510
Marek A. Panasewicz (Founder, Chm & CEO)
John Tiseo (COO)

MAP COMMUNICATIONS INC.
840 Greenbrier Cir Ste 202, Chesapeake, VA 23320
Tel.: (757) 424-1191
Web Site: http://www.mapcommunications.com
Year Founded: 1990
Sales Range: $25-49.9 Million
Emp.: 225
Radio Pager (Beeper) Communication Services
N.A.I.C.S.: 561421
David Jones (Engr-Network)
LeAnne Jordan (Controller)
Brian Dailey (Sr VP-IT)

MAP OF EASTON, INC.
3 Danforth Dr, Easton, PA 18045-7898
Tel.: (610) 253-7135
Web Site: http://www.mapeaston.com
Year Founded: 1973
Sales Range: $10-24.9 Million
Emp.: 250
Acoustical Products Mfr
N.A.I.C.S.: 238310
Jakub Daniszewski (Engr-R&D)
Sean Fisher (Dir-Sls)
Michael Wanish (Mgr-Pur)
John A. D'Amico Sr. (CEO)

MAPES 5 & 10 STORES LTD.
224 Haverford Ave 228, Narberth, PA 19072
Tel.: (610) 664-0447
Sales Range: $10-24.9 Million
Emp.: 50
Variety Stores
N.A.I.C.S.: 444140
Joseph Raymond Benner (CEO)

MAPLE CITY RUBBER COMPANY
55 Newton St, Norwalk, OH 44857
Tel.: (419) 668-8261
Web Site: http://www.maplecityrubber.com
Sales Range: $75-99.9 Million
Emp.: 85
Toy Balloons Mfr
N.A.I.C.S.: 326299
Paul Bennett (VP-Production)
Michael Bick (VP)

MAPLE CITY SAVINGS, MHC
145 Main St, Hornell, NY 14843
Tel.: (607) 324-1822
Web Site: http://www.maplecitysavings.com
Year Founded: 2002
Savings & Loan Mutual Holding Company
N.A.I.C.S.: 551111

Thomas Beers (Pres/CEO-Maple City Savings Bank, FSB)

Subsidiaries:
Maple City Savings Bank, FSB (1)
145 Main St, Hornell, NY 14843
Tel.: (607) 324-1822
Web Site: http://www.maplecitysavings.com
Federal Savings Bank
N.A.I.C.S.: 522180
Thomas Beers (Pres & CEO)

MAPLE GROVE HOSPITAL
9875 Hospital Dr, Maple Grove, MN 55369
Tel.: (763) 581-1000   MN
Web Site: http://www.maplegrovehospital.org
Year Founded: 2007
Sales Range: $125-149.9 Million
Health Care Srvices
N.A.I.C.S.: 622110
Andrew S. Cochrane (CEO)
Wade Larson (Chm-Pediatrics)
Kevin Croston (Chm)
Ahmed Omar (Chm-Medicine)
Tommy Cho (Vice Chm-Medicine)
Matthew Kissner (Chm-Surgery Dept)
Kathryn Flory (Chm-OB Dept)
Mary Martinie (Vice Chm-OB)
Christina Russell (Vice Chm-Peds)

MAPLE HILL AUTO GROUP
5622 W Main St, Kalamazoo, MI 49009
Tel.: (269) 342-6600
Web Site: http://www.maplehillauto.com
Sales Range: $25-49.9 Million
Emp.: 71
New & Used Automobile Dealership
N.A.I.C.S.: 441110
James Vandenberg (Owner & Gen Mgr)
Monie VandenBerg (Mgr-HR)
Joyce Nutt (Office Mgr)

MAPLE ISLAND ESTATES, INC.
15704 48th Ave, Coopersville, MI 49404
Tel.: (616) 837-9793
Sales Range: $10-24.9 Million
Emp.: 60
Sales of Mobile & Modular Homes
N.A.I.C.S.: 459930
Josh L. Rebeduu (Gen Mgr)

MAPLE ISLAND INC.
2497 Seventh Ave E Ste 105, Saint Paul, MN 55109-2907
Tel.: (651) 773-1000   MN
Web Site: http://www.maple-island.com
Year Founded: 1935
Sales Range: $10-24.9 Million
Emp.: 100
Supplier of Dry, Condensed, Evaporated Products
N.A.I.C.S.: 311514
Greg A. Johnson (Pres)
Dave Froehle (Office Mgr)
Scott Larson (Plant Mgr)
Dave Doebler (Mgr-Sls)

MAPLE LEAF FARMS INC.
101 E Church St, Leesburg, IN 46538
Tel.: (574) 453-4500   IN
Web Site: http://www.mapleleaffarms.com
Year Founded: 1958
Sales Range: $25-49.9 Million
Emp.: 750
Duck & Duck Products Production
N.A.I.C.S.: 112390

Terry L. Tucker (Chm & CEO)
Scott M. Tucker (Co-Pres)
Janelle Deatsman (Mgr-Comm)
John Tucker (Co-Pres)

MAPLE LIFE FINANCIAL, INC.
4350 E W Hwy Ste 900, Bethesda, MD 20814
Tel.: (240) 333-7388
Web Site: http://www.maplelifefinancial.com
Financial Investment Activities
N.A.I.C.S.: 523999
Sharmaine Miller (VP-Ops)

MAPLE RIDGE MOBILE HOMES OF CALIFORNIA, INC.
2313 E Philadelphia St Ste K, Ontario, CA 91761
Tel.: (909) 923-6566
Web Site: http://www.maple-ridgehomes.com
Rev.: $49,000,000
Emp.: 15
Mobile Home Dealers
N.A.I.C.S.: 459930
Sam Silverman (Pres)

MAPLE RIVER GRAIN & AGRONOMY, LLC.
1630 1st Ave S, Casselton, ND 58012
Tel.: (701) 347-4465
Web Site: http://www.maplerivergrain.com
Year Founded: 2004
Rev.: $11,900,000
Emp.: 35
Grain & Field Beans Whslr
N.A.I.C.S.: 424510
McClaine Johnson (Mgr-Fertilizer Plant)
Terry Johnson (Gen Mgr)
Jon Watt (Sec)
Laurie Krone (VP)
Mike Nelson (Pres)

Subsidiaries:
Chaffee Lynchburg Farmers Elevator (1)
4406 153rd Ave SE, Fargo, ND 58012
Tel.: (701) 347-5487
Sales Range: $25-49.9 Million
Emp.: 30
Grain & Field Beans Whslr
N.A.I.C.S.: 424510

MAPLE SHADE MOTOR CORP.
2921 Bridge 73 S, Maple Shade, NJ 08052
Tel.: (856) 667-8004
Web Site: http://www.msmazda.com
Year Founded: 1972
Sales Range: $25-49.9 Million
Emp.: 160
New & Used Car Dealers
N.A.I.C.S.: 441110
Robert Dimmerman (Owner & Pres)

MAPLE SYSTEMS, INC.
808 134th St SW Ste 120, Everett, WA 98204
Tel.: (425) 745-3229   WA
Web Site: http://www.maplesystems.com
Year Founded: 1983
Sales Range: $1-9.9 Million
Emp.: 22
Mfr of Operator Interface Terminals for Industrial Control Applications
N.A.I.C.S.: 335314
Larry St. Peter (Pres & CEO)
Sam Schuy (Mgr-Engrg)
Andre Zins (Mgr-Mfg)

MAPLE-LEAF CONSTRUCTION CO, INC.
5 Congress St, Nashua, NH 03062
Tel.: (603) 882-7498
Web Site: http://www.maple-leafnh.com
Sales Range: $10-24.9 Million
Emp.: 19
Commercial & Institutional Building Construction Services
N.A.I.C.S.: 236220
Loren Dubois (Pres)

MAPLEHURST FARMS INC.
936 S Moore Rd, Rochelle, IL 61068
Tel.: (815) 562-8723
Web Site: http://www.maplehurstfarms.com
Sales Range: $50-74.9 Million
Emp.: 70
Agricultural Services
N.A.I.C.S.: 493130
Bob Rogers (Mgr-Agronomy)
Mark McCartney (Superintendent-Grain)

MAPLES INDUSTRIES INC.
2210 Moody Rdg Rd, Scottsboro, AL 35768
Tel.: (256) 259-1327
Sales Range: $125-149.9 Million
Emp.: 2,000
Rug Mfr
N.A.I.C.S.: 314110
Larry Barley (Pres)
Robert Allen (Mgr-Warehouse)
Tiffany Watts (Dir-Safety)

MAPLETON COMMUNICATIONS, LLC
10900 Wilshire Blvd 15th Fl, Los Angeles, CA 90024
Tel.: (310) 209-7221   DE
Holding Company; Radio Broadcasting Stations Owner & Operator
N.A.I.C.S.: 551112
Adam Nathanson (Pres & CEO)

Subsidiaries:
Mapleton Communications, LLC - Radio Merced (1)
514 W 19 St, Merced, CA 95340
Tel.: (209) 723-2191
Sales Range: $10-24.9 Million
Emp.: 20
Radio Broadcasting Stations
N.A.I.C.S.: 516110
Jan Brawley (Bus Mgr)
Diane Garcia (Gen Mgr-Sls)
Damien Galarza (Gen Mgr)

Mapleton Communications, LLC - Radio Monterey Bay (1)
60 Garden Ct Ste 300, Monterey, CA 93940
Tel.: (831) 658-5200
Sales Range: $10-24.9 Million
Emp.: 50
Radio Broadcasting Stations
N.A.I.C.S.: 516110
Rachel Ybarra (Bus Mgr)
Jodi Morgan (Gen Mgr)
Tommy Del Rio (Program Dir)

Mapleton Communications, LLC - Radio Spokane (1)
1601 E 57th Ave, Spokane, WA 99223
Tel.: (509) 448-1000
Sales Range: $10-24.9 Million
Emp.: 50
Radio Broadcasting Stations
N.A.I.C.S.: 516110
Sharon Bonds (Program Dir-KDRK)
Merlee Williams (Bus Mgr)

MAPLEWOOD BEVERAGE PACKERS, LLC.
45 Camptown Rd, Maplewood, NJ 07040
Tel.: (973) 416-4582

Web Site:
http://www.drinkarizona.com
Sales Range: $10-24.9 Million
Emp.: 165
Beverage Bottling Services
N.A.I.C.S.: 312112
Dimirio Nick *(Mng Dir)*
Roseann Semler *(Office Mgr)*

MAPLEWOOD BUILDING SPECIALTIES
100 Main St Ste 2, Allenhurst, NJ 07711-1142
Tel.: (973) 761-5700
Web Site:
http://www.maplewood.com
Sales Range: $10-24.9 Million
Emp.: 123
Provider of Brass, Bronze & Iron Door & Cabinet Hardware
N.A.I.C.S.: 423310
Lawrence Rosenthal *(Pres)*
Paul Chin *(Controller)*

MAPP CONSTRUCTION, LLC
344 3rd St, Baton Rouge, LA 70801
Tel.: (225) 757-0111 LA
Web Site:
http://www.mappconstruction.com
Year Founded: 1991
Sales Range: $10-24.9 Million
Emp.: 125
Nonresidential Construction
N.A.I.C.S.: 236220
Michael Polito *(Pres)*
Richard Setliff *(Exec VP)*
Mark LaHaye *(VP)*
Grif McKowen *(CFO)*

MAPR.AGENCY, INC.
1919 14th St., Ste 700, Boulder, CO 80302
Tel.: (303) 786-7000
Web Site: https://comprise.agency
Year Founded: 1992
Public Relations & Communications Services
N.A.I.C.S.: 541820

MAPS CREDIT UNION
PO Box 12398, Salem, OR 97309
Tel.: (503) 588-0181 OR
Web Site: http://www.mapscu.com
Year Founded: 1935
Sales Range: $10-24.9 Million
Emp.: 187
Credit Union Operator
N.A.I.C.S.: 522130
Toni Silbernagel *(VP-Consumer Lending & Gen Mgr)*
Patricia A. Walker *(VP-Bus & Real Estate Lending)*
Traci Kendall *(VP-Branch Ops)*
C. J. Daiker *(VP-IT)*
David Deckelmann *(VP-Operational Subsidiaries)*
Gordon Sawser *(Vice Chm)*
Mark Zook *(Pres & CEO)*
Joe Phillippay *(Chm)*

MAPSYS INC.
920 Michigan Ave, Columbus, OH 43215
Tel.: (614) 224-5193
Web Site: http://www.mapsysinc.com
Rev.: $14,427,896
Emp.: 30
Sales of Business Oriented Computer Software
N.A.I.C.S.: 513210
Steve Bernard *(Pres)*
Jim Heiberger *(VP)*
Terry Payne *(Mgr-Software & Svcs)*

MAQ SOFTWARE
15446 Bel Red Rd Ste 201, Redmond, WA 98052
Tel.: (425) 526-5399
Web Site:
http://www.maqsoftware.com
Sales Range: $10-24.9 Million
Emp.: 200
Business Application Software
N.A.I.C.S.: 513210
Rajeev Agerwal *(Founder)*
Dilip Naik *(CTO)*
Chris McDougall *(Project Mgr-Tech & Engr-Software)*
Kevin Ong *(Engr-Software Test)*
Siddhartha Joshi *(Engr-Software Test)*
Srikumar Iyer *(Coord-On-Site-PM)*

MAQUOKETA VALLEY ELECTRIC COOP
109 N Huber St, Anamosa, IA 52205
Tel.: (319) 462-3541
Web Site: http://www.mvec.com
Sales Range: $10-24.9 Million
Emp.: 51
Electronic Services
N.A.I.C.S.: 221118
James M. Lauzon *(CEO)*
Charles McCullough *(Sec)*
Eldon R. Busch *(Sec)*
Judy A. Gotto *(Treas)*

MAR-BAL INC.
16930 Munn Rd, Chagrin Falls, OH 44023
Tel.: (440) 543-7526
Web Site: http://www.mar-bal.com
Year Founded: 1971
Sales Range: $25-49.9 Million
Emp.: 120
Provider of Thermalset Plastic Molding Services
N.A.I.C.S.: 326199
Scott Balogh *(Pres & CEO)*
Ron Poff *(Mgr-Mktg)*
Vince Profeta *(Dir-Ops)*
Marc Imbrogno *(Dir-Matls Engrg)*

MAR-CONE APPLIANCE PARTS CO.
1 City Pl Ste 400, Saint Louis, MO 63141
Tel.: (314) 993-9196 MO
Web Site: http://www.marcone.com
Year Founded: 1932
Sales Range: $50-74.9 Million
Emp.: 540
Electrical Appliance Services
N.A.I.C.S.: 811412
Avichal Jain *(COO)*

Subsidiaries:

Mar-Cone Appliance Parts Center Inc. (1)
527 S US Hwy 301, Tampa, FL 33619
Tel.: (314) 993-9196
Web Site: http://www.marcone.com
Rev.: $25,210,738
Emp.: 105
Electrical Appliances, Television & Radio
N.A.I.C.S.: 423620
Mitchell Markow *(CEO)*

MAR-JAC HOLDINGS INC.
1020 Aviation Blvd, Gainesville, GA 30501-6839
Tel.: (770) 531-5000 GA
Web Site:
http://www.marjacpoultry.com
Year Founded: 1954
Sales Range: $150-199.9 Million
Emp.: 1,000
Holding Company; Poultry Slaughtering & Processing
N.A.I.C.S.: 551112
Jamal Al-Baranzinji *(Pres)*

Subsidiaries:

Mar-Jac Poultry, Inc. (1)
1020 Aviation Blvd, Gainesville, GA 30501-6839
Tel.: (770) 531-5000
Web Site: http://www.marjacpoultry.com
Sales Range: $150-199.9 Million
Emp.: 100
Poultry Processing
N.A.I.C.S.: 112340
Pete Martin *(VP-Sls)*
Randy Bruce *(Controller)*

MAR-MAC MANUFACTURING COMPANY, INC.
884 S 7th S, McBee, SC 29101
Tel.: (843) 335-8211 SC
Year Founded: 1953
Sales Range: $100-124.9 Million
Emp.: 300
Mfr of Protective & Disposable Garments & Accessories
N.A.I.C.S.: 315250
John S. McLeod *(Chm)*
Rex Blackwell *(VP)*
John S. McLeod Jr. *(Pres)*

MAR-VAL FOOD STORE 1 INC.
429 W Lockeford St, Lodi, CA 95240
Tel.: (209) 369-3611
Web Site:
http://www.marvalfoodstores.com
Rev.: $14,994,326
Emp.: 10
Independent Supermarket
N.A.I.C.S.: 445110
Ray Seghefio *(Controller)*
Steve Rodacker *(VP)*

MARAKANA INC.
301 Howard St Ste 550, San Francisco, CA 94105
Tel.: (415) 647-7000
Web Site: http://www.marakana.com
Year Founded: 2001
Sales Range: $1-9.9 Million
Emp.: 12
It Consulting
N.A.I.C.S.: 541690
Marko Gargenta *(Founder)*

MARAN INC.
1400 Broadway # 28, New York, NY 10018-5300
Tel.: (201) 867-8833
Year Founded: 1977
Sales Range: $100-124.9 Million
Emp.: 60
Women's & Children's Clothing Whslr
N.A.I.C.S.: 424350
David Greenberg *(Pres)*
Richard Huang *(Exec VP)*

Subsidiaries:

Amica Apparel Corp (1)
4301 Tonnelle Ave, North Bergen, NJ 07047
Tel.: (201) 867-8833
Rev.: $50,787,808
Emp.: 40
Women's & Children's Clothing
N.A.I.C.S.: 424350

Chiori Apparel Inc. (1)
1385 Broadway Rm 808, New York, NY 10018
Tel.: (212) 398-6868
Rev.: $1,553,897
Emp.: 3
Men's & Boy's Clothing
N.A.I.C.S.: 424350

MARANA AEROSPACE SOLUTIONS, INC.
24641 E Pinal Air Park Rd, Marana, AZ 85653
Tel.: (520) 682-4181
Web Site:
http://www.maranaaerospace.com

Aircraft Maintenance, Repair, Overhaul & Storage Services
N.A.I.C.S.: 488190
Deanna Hackney *(Sr Dir-Contracts & Proposals)*
Mike Michels *(Sr Dir-Quality)*
Jeff Johnson *(Sr Dir-HR)*
Lou Moore *(Sr Dir-Maintenance)*
Steve Coffaro *(Sr Dir-Sls)*
Greg Mitchell *(Sr VP-MRO Svcs)*
Jim Martin *(Pres & CEO)*
Annette Feasel *(Mgr-Customer Svcs)*
Betsy Shaw *(Mgr-Customer Svcs)*
Greg Emerson *(Sr VP-Ops)*
Mike Scott *(Sr Dir-Sls)*
Richard Fleming *(Dir-Sls)*
Sue Acuna *(Sr Dir-IT & Internal Controls)*
Terry Payne *(VP-Fin & Admin)*

Subsidiaries:

Ascent Aviation Services Corp. (1)
24641 Pinal Air Park Rd, Marana, AZ 85653
Tel.: (520) 682-4181
Web Site: http://www.ascentmro.com
Aircraft Maintenance, Repair, Overhaul & Modification Services
N.A.I.C.S.: 488190
David T. Querio *(Pres)*
Dave Querio *(Pres)*
Matt Rey *(CEO)*
Bart Burdman *(CFO)*
Alexander Kocksch *(Dir-Pur & Matls)*

MARANATHA VOLUNTEERS INTERNATIONAL, INC.
990 Reserve Dr Ste 100, Roseville, CA 95678
Tel.: (916) 774-7700 MI
Web Site: http://www.maranatha.org
Year Founded: 1969
Sales Range: $10-24.9 Million
Emp.: 35
Institutional Building Construction Services
N.A.I.C.S.: 236220
Kyle Fiess *(VP-Mktg & Projects)*
Susan Bushnell *(VP-Fin)*
Don Noble *(Chm & Pres)*

MARANDA ENTERPRISES, LLC
6350 W Donges Bay Rd, Mequon, WI 53092
Tel.: (262) 236-3970
Web Site:
http://www.marandaenterprises.com
Year Founded: 1996
Rev.: $4,200,000
Emp.: 6
Marketing Consulting Services
N.A.I.C.S.: 541613
Mark Fuchs *(Owner)*

MARANON & ASSOCIATES ADVERTISING
300 Sevilla Ave Ste 311, Coral Gables, FL 33134
Tel.: (305) 476-5050
Web Site:
http://www.maranonad.com
Year Founded: 1985
Sales Range: $10-24.9 Million
Emp.: 15
N.A.I.C.S.: 541810
Richard Maranon *(CEO)*
Legia Maranon *(Pres)*
Ariel Martinez *(CFO)*
Lazaro Gonzalez *(Dir-Graphic Arts)*
Teresa Gutierrez *(VP & Dir-Media)*
Clara Hernandez *(Dir-Creative)*

MARATHON ASSET MANAGEMENT LP
1 Bryant Park 38th Fl, New York, NY 10036
Tel.: (212) 500-3000

MARATHON ASSET MANAGEMENT LP

Marathon Asset Management LP—(Continued)
Web Site:
http://www.marathonfund.com
Year Founded: 1998
Sales Range: $25-49.9 Million
Emp.: 125
Alternative Investment & Asset Management Services
N.A.I.C.S.: 523999
Bruce Richards (Co-Founder, Chm & CEO)
Louis Hanover (Chief Investment Officer & Mng Partner)
Gabriel Szpigiel (Partner & Head-Emerging Markets)
Jamie Raboy (Chief Risk Officer & Partner)
Stuart Goldberg (Partner & Sr Mgr-Portfolio)
Andrew Springer (Partner & Sr Mgr-Portfolio)
Curt Lueker (Mng Dir)
Michael Schlembach (Mng Dir & Sr Portfolio Mgr)
Louis Hanover (Co-Founder & CIO)
Ed Cong (Partner)
Alex Howell (Sr Mng Dir & Head-European Alternative Credit Bus)

Subsidiaries:

Marathon Automotive Group LLC (1)
1 Bryant Park 38th Fl, New York, NY 10036
Tel.: (212) 500-3000
Holding Company
N.A.I.C.S.: 551112

Division (Domestic):

CONTECH LLC (2)
21177 Hilltop St, Southfield, MI 48033
Tel.: (248) 351-1051
Sales Range: $25-49.9 Million
Emp.: 35
Precision Die-Cast Components Mfr
N.A.I.C.S.: 332999

MARATHON CHEESE CORP.
304 E St, Marathon, WI 54448-9643
Tel.: (715) 443-2211 WI
Web Site:
http://www.marathoncheese.com
Year Founded: 1952
Sales Range: $500-549.9 Million
Emp.: 1,500
Provider of Cheese & Cheese Packaging Services
N.A.I.C.S.: 561910
Dan Zastoupil (Pres)
Carol Auner (Coord-Benefit)
Amy Janke (Controller)
John Wanish (Plant Mgr)
Kevin Dunn (Mgr-Network)
Mike Mathias (VP-Sls & Mktg)
Paul Kannenberg (Dir-Pur)
Scott Stieber (Dir-Quality Control & Assurance)

MARATHON COACH, INC.
91333 Coburg Industrial Way, Coburg, OR 97408-9492
Tel.: (541) 343-9991 OR
Web Site:
http://www.marathoncoach.com
Year Founded: 1993
Sales Range: $10-24.9 Million
Emp.: 150
Supplier of Luxury Motor Homes
N.A.I.C.S.: 336213
Robert Schoellhorn (Chm & CEO)
Bob Phebus (Dir-Sls & Mktg-East)
Steve Schoellhorn (Pres & COO)

MARATHON CONSTRUCTION CORP.
10108 Riverford Rd, Lakeside, CA 92040
Tel.: (619) 276-4401 CA
Web Site:
http://www.marathonconstruction.biz
Year Founded: 1983
Sales Range: $10-24.9 Million
Emp.: 30
Marine Construction
N.A.I.C.S.: 236210
Michael V. Furby (Pres & Project Mgr)
Claire Kennedy (Office Mgr)
Charles F. Cunningham (VP & Project Mgr)
John David Cunningham (VP & Project Mgr)
Jon Ruth (COO & Project Mgr)
Timothy G. Meyer (Project Mgr)
Joseph P. Ellis (Project Mgr)
Michael Mickey (Mgr-Safety)

MARATHON CONSULTING
4525 Columbus St Ste 200, Virginia Beach, VA 23462
Tel.: (757) 427-6999
Web Site:
http://www.marathonus.com
Year Founded: 2006
Sales Range: $1-9.9 Million
Emp.: 70
IT Consulting Services
N.A.I.C.S.: 541618
Al Moore (Co-Founder & Pres)
Harris Pezzella (Co-Founder & VP)
Ben Ricks (Co-Founder & Partner)
Tony Cortinas (Co-Founder & Partner)

MARATHON ELECTRICAL CONTRACTORS, INC.
614 S 38th St, Birmingham, AL 35222
Tel.: (205) 323-8500
Web Site:
http://www.marathonelectrical.com
Sales Range: $25-49.9 Million
Emp.: 235
Electronic Services
N.A.I.C.S.: 238210
Larry Argo (Pres)
Bruce Taylor (CEO)
Mark Harry (Treas & Sec)
Chris McGregor (VP)

MARATHON ENTERPRISES, INC.
9 Smith St, Englewood, NJ 07631-4607
Tel.: (201) 935-3330 NJ
Web Site: http://www.sabrett.com
Year Founded: 1964
Sales Range: $25-49.9 Million
Emp.: 150
Sales of Sausages & Other Prepared Meats
N.A.I.C.S.: 311612
Mark Rosen (VP-Sls)
Jerry Melissaratos (Controller)
Boyd Adelman (Pres)
Kari Venturini (Asst VP-Social Media, Internet Sls & Web Promotions)

MARATHON FLINT OIL COMPANY
1919 S Dort Hwy, Flint, MI 48503
Tel.: (810) 234-6678
Web Site:
http://www.marathonflint.com
Rev.: $13,250,536
Emp.: 15
Petroleum Bulk Stations
N.A.I.C.S.: 424710

MARATHON HVAC SERVICES, LLC
9826 Painter Ave Unit E, Whittier, CA 90695
Tel.: (626) 565-4146
Web Site:
https://www.marathonhvac.com
Emp.: 100
Plumbing, Heating & Air-Conditioning Contractors
N.A.I.C.S.: 238220

Subsidiaries:

Ak Hvac, Inc. (1)
8523 Canoga Ave, Canoga Park, CA 91304-2662
Tel.: (818) 772-6215
Web Site: http://www.kapplhvac.com
Plumbing, Heating & Air-Conditioning Contractors
N.A.I.C.S.: 238220

Aloha Air Conditioning, Inc. (1)
9826 Painter Ave E, Whittier, CA 90605
Tel.: (562) 693-2553
Web Site: http://www.alohaair.net
Rev.: $1,022,000
Emp.: 7
Site Preparation Contractor
N.A.I.C.S.: 238910

MARATHON MEDIA LLC
737 N Michigan Ave Ste 2350, Chicago, IL 60611-2680
Tel.: (312) 204-9900
Sales Range: $10-24.9 Million
Emp.: 10
Radio Broadcasting Stations
N.A.I.C.S.: 516110
Christopher Deviene (Pres)
Bruce Buzil (VP)

MARATHON STRATEGIES, LLC
6 Grand Central at 666 3rd Ave Ste 1702, New York, NY 10017
Tel.: (212) 960-8120
Web Site:
https://www.marathonstrategies.com
Year Founded: 2008
Sales Range: $10-24.9 Million
Emp.: 41
Business Communications Services
N.A.I.C.S.: 517810
Phil Singer (Founder & Mng Dr)
Jane Hardey (Mng Dir & COO)
Matthew West (Chief Talent Officer)
Jim Scott Polsinelli (Chief Creative Officer)
Michael Harinstein (CMO)

MARATHON TS, INC.
132 Irvington Rd, Kilmarnock, VA 22482-0000
Tel.: (703) 230-4200
Web Site: http://www.marathonts.com
Information Services
N.A.I.C.S.: 519290
Mark T. Krial (Pres)

Subsidiaries:

The Proven Method Inc. (1)
470 E Paces Ferry Rd NE, Atlanta, GA 30305
Tel.: (404) 480-9918
Web Site: http://www.provenmethod.com
Sales Range: $10-24.9 Million
Emp.: 150
Business & Technical Consulting
N.A.I.C.S.: 561330
Jack Nale (Pres)
Jim Biles (VP-Recruiting)
David Brunke (VP-Cloud Collaboration Network & Security)
Andy Nale (VP-Project Staffing)
Lloyd Wilkinson (CTO & VP-Professional Svcs)

MARAVAI LIFESCIENCES, INC.
10770 Wateridge Cir Ste 200, San Diego, CA 92121
Tel.: (312) 953-3305
Web Site: http://www.maravai.com
Year Founded: 2014

U.S. PRIVATE

Scientific Research & Development Services
N.A.I.C.S.: 541715
Eric Tardif (Co-Founder, Pres & Partner)
Carl Hull (Co-Founder, CEO & Partner)
Kevin Herde (CFO & VP)
David Weber (Chief Compliance Officer & VP)
Peter Leddy (Chief Admin Officer & Exec VP)

Subsidiaries:

Glen Research Corp. (1)
22825 Davis Dr, Sterling, VA 20164
Tel.: (703) 437-6191
Web Site: http://www.glenresearch.com
Spice & Extract Mfr
N.A.I.C.S.: 311942
Andrew Murphy (Dir-Ops)

MARAWOOD CONSTRUCTION SERVICES
2025 W Veterans Pkwy, Marshfield, WI 54449
Tel.: (715) 387-1256
Web Site: http://www.marawood.com
Sales Range: $10-24.9 Million
Emp.: 35
Provider of Construction Services
N.A.I.C.S.: 236220
Scott Hoover (Mgr-Admin & Fin)
John Lobner (Mgr-Svcs Dept)
Benjamin Vance (Co-Owner & Mgr-Sls)

MARBLE CRAFT DESIGN, INC.
425 Industrial St, Lake Worth, FL 33461
Tel.: (561) 547-2779
Web Site:
http://www.marblecraftdesign.com
Year Founded: 1998
Sales Range: $10-24.9 Million
Emp.: 89
Brick & Related Construction Material Whslr
N.A.I.C.S.: 423320
Raphael Gonzalez (Pres)
Oscar Giraldo (CEO)
Julio Giraldo (Chm)
Christina Hamilton (Office Mgr)

MARBLEHEAD BANK
21 Atlantic Ave, Marblehead, MA 01945
Tel.: (781) 631-5500
Web Site:
http://www.marblebank.com
Year Founded: 1871
Sales Range: $1-9.9 Million
Emp.: 44
Banking Services
N.A.I.C.S.: 522110
Julie Livingston (Pres & CEO)
Amy Hart (Mgr-Loan Originations & Collections)
Merrill Belmer (Exec VP)
Peter Schwager (VP)

MARBORG INDUSTRIES INC.
728 E Yanonali St, Santa Barbara, CA 93103
Tel.: (805) 963-1852
Web Site: http://www.marborg.com
Sales Range: $10-24.9 Million
Emp.: 150
Rubbish Collection & Disposal
N.A.I.C.S.: 562111
Derek Carlson (Bus Mgr)

MARBURG TECHNOLOGY INC.
304 Turquoise St, Milpitas, CA 95035
Tel.: (408) 262-8400

Web Site: http://www.glidewright.com
Sales Range: $25-49.9 Million
Emp.: 60
Disk & Diskette Equipment, Except Drives
N.A.I.C.S.: 334118
Francis Burga (Pres)
B. G. Ebrahimi (CFO & VP-Fin)

MARBURN STORES INC.
13-A Division St, Fairview, NJ 07022
Tel.: (201) 943-0222
Web Site: http://www.marburn.com
Sales Range: $25-49.9 Million
Emp.: 65
Provider of Draperies
N.A.I.C.S.: 449122
Mildred Sanchez (Mgr-Retail)

MARC GLASSMAN, INC.
5841 W 130th St, Cleveland, OH 44130-1039
Tel.: (216) 265-7700   OH
Web Site: http://www.marcs.com
Year Founded: 1979
Sales Range: $750-799.9 Million
Emp.: 6,500
Owner & Operator of Pharmacies & Closeout Merchandise Stores
N.A.I.C.S.: 455219
Marc Glassman (Chm)
Kevin Yaugher (COO)
Beth Weiner (CFO)

MARC MILLER BUICK GMC, INC.
4700 S Memorial Dr, Tulsa, OK 74145-6988
Tel.: (918) 663-4700
Web Site:
    http://www.marcmillerbuickgmc.com
Year Founded: 1969
Sales Range: $150-199.9 Million
Emp.: 175
New Car Dealers
N.A.I.C.S.: 441110
Steve Lahmeyer (Asst Mgr-Svc)

MARC MOTORS INC.
1357 Main St, Sanford, ME 04073
Tel.: (207) 324-3454
Web Site:
    http://www.marcmotors.com
Sales Range: $25-49.9 Million
Emp.: 60
Automobiles, New & Used
N.A.I.C.S.: 441110
Norman Greenberg (Pres)
Suzanne Lontine (Office Mgr)

Subsidiaries:

Marc Motors Nissan   (1)
1357 Main St, Sanford, ME 04073
Tel.: (207) 324-3454
Web Site: http://www.marcmotors.com
Sales Range: $10-24.9 Million
Emp.: 30
New Car Dealers
N.A.I.C.S.: 441110
Marc Greenberg (Owner)
Shaugn McCormack (Gen Mgr)
Kevin Mannette (Mgr-Sls)
Matt Webb (Mgr-Fin)
Aimee Lontine-Harris (Mgr-Internet)
Ethan Hyde (Mgr-Parts)
Susan Lontine (Comptroller)
Lori Perron (Office Mgr)
Phil Royer (Mgr-Svc)
Jade St Laurent (Coord-Svc)
Paul Anderson (Mgr-Sls)

MARC RUTENBERG HOMES INC.
2895 Grey Oaks Blvd, Tarpon Springs, FL 34688
Tel.: (727) 945-0077

Web Site: http://www.marcrutenberghomes.com
Rev.: $21,933,023
Emp.: 30
Single-Family Housing Construction
N.A.I.C.S.: 236115
George Nuebling (VP)

MARC TRUANT & ASSOCIATES, INC.
32 Warren St, Cambridge, MA 02141
Tel.: (617) 868-8630
Web Site: http://www.mtruant.com
Year Founded: 1983
Sales Range: $10-24.9 Million
Emp.: 13
Preconstruction Planning & Construction Management Services
N.A.I.C.S.: 541310
Marc Truant (Pres & COO)
Glen Sullivan (Superintendent)
Chelsea Cohen (Project Mgr)

MARC USA, LLC
225 W Station Square Dr Ste 500, Pittsburgh, PA 15219-1119
Tel.: (412) 562-2000   PA
Web Site: http://www.marcusa.com
Year Founded: 1955
Sales Range: $250-299.9 Million
Emp.: 300
Advetising Agency
N.A.I.C.S.: 541810
Karen Leitze (Dir-Res & Strategy)
Jerry Thompson (Dir-PR)
Cari Bucci (Pres)
Chris Heitmann (Chief Innovation Officer)
Joe Burke (Chief Creative Officer & Exec VP)
Stu Zolot (CFO)

Subsidiaries:

MARC USA, LLC - Chicago   (1)
325 N LaSalle St Ste 750, Chicago, IL 60654
Tel.: (312) 321-9000
Web Site: http://www.marcusa.com
Emp.: 25
Advetising Agency
N.A.I.C.S.: 541810
Jean McLaren (CMO & Pres-Chicago)
Tony L. Bucci (Chm)
Karen Leitze (Dir-Res & Strategic)
Cari Bucci Hulings (Pres)
Joe Burke (Chief Creative Officer)
Chris Heitmann (Chief Innovation Officer)
Jerry Thompson (Dir-PR)

MARCA Hispanic LLC   (1)
3390 Mary St Ste 254, Miami, FL 33133
Tel.: (305) 423-8300
Emp.: 13
Advetising Agency
N.A.I.C.S.: 541810
Tony Nieves (Pres & Partner)
Armando Hernandez (Chief Creative Officer & Partner)
Alejandro Berbari (Sr VP & Exec Dir-Creative)
Annie Berenson (Mgr-HR)
Alan Campbell (COO)

Starmark Global, Inc.   (1)
210 S Andrews Ave, Fort Lauderdale, FL 33301
Tel.: (954) 874-9000
Web Site: http://www.starmark.com
Emp.: 17
Advetising Agency
N.A.I.C.S.: 541810
Jacqueline Hartnett (Pres)
Peggy Nordeen Estes (CEO)

MARCALI YACHT BROKERAGE & CONSULTING, LLC
1401 Lee St Ste B, Fort Myers, FL 33901
Tel.: (239) 275-3600
Web Site:
    http://www.marcaliyacht.com

Sales Range: $1-9.9 Million
Yacht Brokerage & Consulting
N.A.I.C.S.: 441222
Marc Harris (CEO)

MARCATO CAPITAL MANAGEMENT, LP
1 Montgomery St Ste 3250, San Francisco, CA 94104
Tel.: (415) 796-6352   DE
Web Site:
    http://www.marcatocapitalmanagement.com
Equity Investment Firm
N.A.I.C.S.: 523999
Richard Trainor McGuire III (CEO, Mng Partner & Portfolio Mgr)

MARCEL & HENRI SELECT MEATS, INC.
415 Browning Way, South San Francisco, CA 94080
Tel.: (650) 871-4230
Web Site:
    http://www.marcelethenri.com
Sales Range: $10-24.9 Million
Emp.: 20
Frozen Specialty Food Mfr
N.A.I.C.S.: 311412
Ivette Ishper (Office Mgr)

MARCH MANUFACTURING INC.
1819 Pickwick Ave, Glenview, IL 60026
Tel.: (847) 729-5300   DE
Web Site:
    http://www.marchpump.com
Year Founded: 1954
Sales Range: $75-99.9 Million
Emp.: 65
Centrifugal Pump Mfr
N.A.I.C.S.: 333914
Fred N. Zimmermann (CEO)

MARCHANT CHEVROLET, INC.
5700 Savannah Hwy, Ravenel, SC 29470
Tel.: (843) 722-8208
Web Site:
    http://www.marchantchevy.net
Sales Range: $10-24.9 Million
Emp.: 45
Car Whslr
N.A.I.C.S.: 441110
A. S. Marchant (Mgr-Mktg)
Robert L. Marchant III (Principal)

MARCHETTI CONSTRUCTION INC.
184 Harbor Way, South San Francisco, CA 94080
Tel.: (650) 588-3893
Web Site:
    http://www.marchetticonstruction.com
Sales Range: $10-24.9 Million
Emp.: 40
Provider of General Contracting Services
N.A.I.C.S.: 236220
John Barrett (Project Mgr)
Nelson Hiraga (Sr VP-Ops)

MARCK & ASSOCIATES, INC.
300 Phillips Ave, Toledo, OH 43612
Tel.: (419) 478-0900
Web Site: http://www.m-ware.com
Year Founded: 1986
Emp.: 40
Dishware & Decor Items Distr & Mfr
N.A.I.C.S.: 339999
Gary Marck (Founder)

Subsidiaries:

Cactus Coatings, Inc.   (1)

463 28 1/2 Rd Ste A, Grand Junction, CO 81501
Tel.: (970) 241-3011
Web Site: http://www.cactusmugs.com
Emp.: 25
Metal Coating, Engraving (except Jewelry & Silverware) & Allied Services to Mfr
N.A.I.C.S.: 332812

MARCO BEACH OCEAN RESORT MANAGEMENT INC.
480 S Collier Blvd, Marco Island, FL 34145
Tel.: (239) 393-1400
Web Site:
    http://www.marcoresort.com
Sales Range: $1-9.9 Million
Emp.: 100
Resort Hotel
N.A.I.C.S.: 721110
Aubrey Ferrao (Owner)
Joseph Fisher (Gen Mgr)

MARCO COLOR LABORATORY, INC.
1970 W 139th St, Gardena, CA 90249-2408
Tel.: (310) 527-4333   CA
Year Founded: 1973
Sales Range: $50-74.9 Million
Emp.: 45
Custom Colorants Mfr
N.A.I.C.S.: 812921
Linda Snyder (Controller & Mgr-Pur)

MARCO CRANE & RIGGING CO.
221 S 35th Ave, Phoenix, AZ 85009
Tel.: (602) 272-2671
Web Site:
    http://www.marcocrane.com
Rev.: $21,275,940
Emp.: 62
Heavy Construction Equipment Rental
N.A.I.C.S.: 532412
Daniel Mardian Jr. (Pres)

MARCO DESTIN INC.
10800 NW 106th St Ste 6, Medley, FL 33178
Tel.: (305) 471-9394
Web Site:
    http://www.alvinsisland.com
Rev.: $24,000,000
Emp.: 350
Owner & Operator of Family Clothing Stores
N.A.I.C.S.: 458110
Eliezer Tabib (Pres)
Dror Levy (CFO & VP)
Malki Shabtai (Mgr)
Heather Dennison (Mgr-Pur)

MARCO ENTERPRISES, INC.
3504 Watkins Ave, Landover, MD 20785
Tel.: (301) 773-5656
Web Site:
    http://www.marcoenterprises.com
Year Founded: 1998
Rev.: $24,800,000
Emp.: 15
Construction Services
N.A.I.C.S.: 236220
Donna P. Seaton-Fagon (Pres & CEO)
Daniel F. Wodiska (VP)

MARCO GLOBAL INC.
4259 22nd Ave W, Seattle, WA 98199-1206
Tel.: (206) 285-3200   WA
Web Site:
    http://www.marcoglobal.com
Year Founded: 1953
Sales Range: $10-24.9 Million
Emp.: 25

MARCO GLOBAL INC.

MARCO Global Inc.—(Continued)
Mfr of Marine Machinery & Pollution Control Equipment
N.A.I.C.S.: 336611
Peter G. Schmidt (Owner)
Dick Boehm (Gen Mgr)
Jan Fisk (Mgr-HR)

Subsidiaries:

Commodore Financial Corp. (1)
4259 22nd Ave W, Seattle, WA 98199-1206 (100%)
Tel.: (206) 285-3200
Web Site: http://www.marcoglobal.com
Sales Range: $10-24.9 Million
Emp.: 10
N.A.I.C.S.: 336611
Peter Schmidt (Pres)
Bobbi Miles (Sec)

Marco Seattle, Inc. (1)
4259 22nd Ave W, Seattle, WA 98199-1206 (100%)
Tel.: (206) 285-3200
Sales Range: $10-24.9 Million
Emp.: 20
Mfr & Designer of Commercial & Fishing Vessels, Marine Machinery & Oil Skimming Vessels; Export Supplier of Marine Materials & Equipment
N.A.I.C.S.: 336611
John Hedelend (Controller)

MARCO POLO INTERNATIONAL, INC.
532 Broadhollow Rd Ste 135/136, Melville, NY 11747
Tel.: (631) 629-4520 NY
Web Site: http://www.mar-pol.com
Year Founded: 1985
Sales Range: $25-49.9 Million
Emp.: 40
Plastics Distr
N.A.I.C.S.: 424610
Marco Liuzzo (Pres & CEO)
David Guimond (COO)
Tony Masso (VP-Latin America)
Troy Mercado (Mgr-Sls)

MARCOA PUBLISHING INC.
9955 Black Mtn Rd, San Diego, CA 92126
Tel.: (858) 695-9600
Web Site: http://www.marcoa.com
Sales Range: $10-24.9 Million
Emp.: 140
Producer of Specialized Publications for Organizations, Associations & Military Installations
N.A.I.C.S.: 513199
Michael Martella (Founder)
Joe Stoekl (Mgr-Press Room)
Scott Ogan (VP-Ops)
Mike Shows (VP-Sls Admin)
Matt Benedict (Pres)
Forrest Smith (Dir-IT)
Jason Keene (Controller)
Kevin Brewer (VP-Sls)
Susan Purcell (Dir-HR)

MARCOM GROUP
3975 Fair Ridge Dr 175N, Fairfax, VA 22033
Tel.: (703) 218-1600
Web Site: http://www.marcomgroup.com
Year Founded: 1996
Sales Range: $1-9.9 Million
Emp.: 20
Research & Strategy Services, Brand Development, Marketing Communications & Digital Services to Government, Commercial & Nonprofit Clients
N.A.I.C.S.: 541613
Robert Rainford (CEO & Chief Creative Officer)

MARCON & BOYER INC.
3400 High Point Blvd, Bethlehem, PA 18017-2270
Tel.: (610) 866-5959 PA
Year Founded: 1959
Rev.: $69,181,076
Emp.: 700
Plastering, Drywall & Insulation
N.A.I.C.S.: 238310
Frank Boyer (Pres)

Subsidiaries:

Duggan & Marcon Inc. (1)
645 W Hamilton St, Allentown, PA 18101-2270
Tel.: (610) 866-5959
Web Site: http://www.dugganandmarcon.com
Sales Range: $10-24.9 Million
Emp.: 50
Plastering, Drywall & Insulation
N.A.I.C.S.: 238310

Eastern Exterior Wall Systems Inc. (1)
3400 Highpoint Blvd, Bethlehem, PA 18017-2102
Tel.: (610) 868-5522
Web Site: http://www.eews.com
Rev.: $16,274,031
Emp.: 100
Prefabricated Wood Buildings
N.A.I.C.S.: 321992
L. Charles Marcon (Pres)

MARCONE SUPPLY COMPANY
1 City Pl Ste 400, Saint Louis, MO 63141
Tel.: (314) 993-9196
Web Site: http://www.marcone.com
Sales Range: $150-199.9 Million
Emp.: 500
Electrical Apparatus Equipment Wiring Supplies & Related Equipment Merchant Whslr
N.A.I.C.S.: 423610
Dave Cook (Sr VP)
Joe Mendoza (Gen Mgr-Property Maintenance)
Keri Llewellyn (Pres-Comml Kitchen Grp)
E. J. Morrow (Chief Comml Officer-Comml Kitchen Grp)
Steve Otto (VP-Manufacturer Partnerships-Comml Kitchen Div)

MARCOU TRANSPORTATION GROUP LLC
224 Calvary St, Waltham, MA 02453
Year Founded: 2012
Sales Range: $250-299.9 Million
Emp.: 3,000
Holding Company; Passenger Transportation Services
N.A.I.C.S.: 551112
Derek Marcou (Co-Owner)
David H. Marcou Jr. (Co-Owner)

Subsidiaries:

BostonCoach (1)
69 Norman St, Everett, MA 02149
Tel.: (617) 545-6648
Web Site: http://www.bostoncoach.com
Limousine Service
N.A.I.C.S.: 485320
David Marcou (Mng Partner)
Scott Solombrino (Pres)

Dav-El Transportation, Inc. (1)
200 2nd St, Chelsea, MA 02150-1802
Tel.: (617) 884-2600
Web Site: http://www.davel.com
Sales Range: $350-399.9 Million
Emp.: 1,000
Limousine Service
N.A.I.C.S.: 485320
Scott A. Solombrino (Pres)
Steve Pitel (VP-Sls-Worldwide)
David H. Marcou Jr. (CEO)

Subsidiary (Domestic):

Dav-El Los Angeles, Inc. (2)
500 S Douglas, El Segundo, CA 90245
Tel.: (310) 643-1200
Sales Range: $25-49.9 Million
Emp.: 150
Limousine Service
N.A.I.C.S.: 485320
Kyle Davidson (Gen Mgr)

Dav-El Services, Inc. (2)
2157 Borden Ave, Long Island City, NY 11101
Tel.: (718) 729-2400
Sales Range: $10-24.9 Million
Emp.: 50
Limousine Service
N.A.I.C.S.: 485320

Harrison Transportation Services, Inc. (1)
621 Main St Ste 9, Waltham, MA 02452-5571
Tel.: (919) 439-2024
Web Site: http://www.smartertransportation.com
Transportation Services, Including Dispatch Services for Taxis, Limousines & School Buses
N.A.I.C.S.: 485320
Derek R. Marcou (Sec)
David H. Marcou Jr. (Pres & Treas)

Metropolitan Limousine, Inc. (1)
1836 S Wabash Ave, Chicago, IL 60616
Tel.: (312) 808-8000
Web Site: http://www.metropolitanlimo.com
Emp.: 250
Limousine Service
N.A.I.C.S.: 485320
Thomas Mulligan (Mng Dir)
Chris Thomsen (Dir-Ops)
Mike Mulligan (Gen Mgr)
Craig Gehrke (Acct Exec)

Torrey Pines Transportation (1)
8929 Aero Dr Ste E, San Diego, CA 92123
Tel.: (858) 587-1184
Web Site: http://www.torreypinestrans.com
Emp.: 30
Chauffeured Transportation Services
N.A.I.C.S.: 485320
Anne Daniel (Gen Mgr)

MARCRAFT APPAREL GROUP
6 Ram Rdg Rd, Chestnut Ridge, NY 10977-6713
Tel.: (845) 371-1600
Year Founded: 1972
Sales Range: $10-24.9 Million
Emp.: 54
Mfr of Mens Suits
N.A.I.C.S.: 424350
Sheldon Brody (Chm & CEO)
Joseph Messina (CFO)
Angel Morralis (VP-Ops)

MARCUM WEALTH LLC
6685 Beta Dr, Cleveland, oh 44143
Tel.: (866) 605-1901
Web Site: https://www.marcumwealth.com
Emp.: 100
Investment Services
N.A.I.C.S.: 523999

MARCUS BROTHERS TEXTILES, INC.
980 Ave of the Americas, New York, NY 10018-5443
Tel.: (212) 354-8700 NY
Web Site: http://www.marcusbrothers.com
Year Founded: 1906
Sales Range: $75-99.9 Million
Emp.: 100
Mfr & Producer of Cotton, Cotton Blends & Woven & Knit Textiles
N.A.I.C.S.: 314999
Martin Marcus (CEO)
Regina Storms (Mgr-Export Sls)
Lisa Shepard Stewart (Mgr-Mktg)
Pati Violick (Dir-Mktg & Adv)

Indra Rampersaud (Mgr-Customer Svc)
Laura Berringer (Dir-Design)
Stephanie Dell Olio (Pres-Retail Div)

MARCUS CENTER FOR THE PERFORMING ARTS
123 E State St, Milwaukee, WI 53202
Tel.: (414) 273-7121 WI
Web Site: http://www.marcuscenter.org
Year Founded: 2004
Sales Range: $10-24.9 Million
Emp.: 385
Arts Promotion Services
N.A.I.C.S.: 711310
Mark Barnes (Dir-Event Svcs)
George Batayias (Dir-Technical)
Heidi Lofy (VP-Sls & Mktg)
Dick Hecht (COO & VP)
Paul F. Mathews (Pres & CEO)
Jerome M. Janzer (Chm)
Laura Lenhart (VP-Fin & Admin)
Ray Wilson (Treas)
Anthony D. Smith (Dir-Community Engagement & Diversity)

MARCUS DAIRY, INC.
4 Eagle Rd, Danbury, CT 06810-7401
Tel.: (203) 748-5611 CT
Web Site: http://www.marcusdairy.com
Year Founded: 1923
Sales Range: $25-49.9 Million
Emp.: 140
Home Delivery Dairy & Grocery Products
N.A.I.C.S.: 311511
Neil Marcus (Pres)
Heather Reed (Sec)
William Fitchett (VP & Gen Mgr)
Jeffrey A. Marcus (VP)

MARCUS DALY MEMORIAL HOSPITAL
1200 Westwood Dr, Hamilton, MT 59840
Tel.: (406) 363-2211 MT
Web Site: http://www.mdmh.org
Year Founded: 1938
Sales Range: $50-74.9 Million
Emp.: 546
Healtcare Services
N.A.I.C.S.: 622110
Susan Hill (Dir-Nursing)
Jane Hron (Dir-Home Care & Hospice)
Amy James-Linton (Dir-Mktg)
Debbie Morris (Dir-HR)
John M. Bartos (CEO, Treas & Sec)
Donja Erdman (CFO)
Don Lodmell (Chm)

MARCUS FOOD COMPANY, INC.
240 N Rock Rd Ste 246, Wichita, KS 67206-2245
Tel.: (316) 686-7649
Web Site: http://www.marcusfoodco.com
Year Founded: 1980
Sales Range: $10-24.9 Million
Emp.: 45
Distr of Meats Meat Products & Packaged Frozen Foods
N.A.I.C.S.: 424470
Rick Finney (Dir-HR)

MARCUS INVESTMENTS, LLC
301 N Broadway Ste 300, Milwaukee, WI 53202
Tel.: (414) 585-8840
Web Site: http://www.marcusinvestments.com
Year Founded: 1935

Professional, Scientific & Technical Services
N.A.I.C.S.: 541990
Christopher Nolte (Pres)
David Marcus (CEO)
Chris Meinecke (CFO)

MARCUS PARTNERS, INC.
260 Franklin St, Boston, MA 02110
Tel.: (617) 556-5200
Web Site:
http://www.marcuspartners.com
Sales Range: $25-49.9 Million
Emp.: 18
Real Estate Investment Services
N.A.I.C.S.: 523999
Paul Marcus (Founder & CEO)
David Fiore (Principal)
David Hooke (Principal)
Jan Machnik (Principal)
William McAvoy (Principal)
Kyle O'Connor (Principal)
Peter Scoba (Principal)
J. Mark Stroud (Principal)
Peter Cameron (Principal)
John Busby (Principal & Dir-Property Mgmt)
Steve Wassersug (Sr VP-Construction & Dev)
Ryan McDonough (Principal)
Shawn Hurley (Pres)

MARCUS THOMAS LLC
4781 Richmond Rd, Cleveland, OH 44128
Tel.: (216) 292-4700   OH
Web Site:
http://www.marcusthomasllc.com
Year Founded: 1937
Sales Range: $100-124.9 Million
Emp.: 200
Advertising Agency Services
N.A.I.C.S.: 541810
Mark E. Bachmann (Partner)
Joseph J. Blaha (CFO & Partner)
Jennifer Hirt-Marchand (Partner)
Todd Morgano (Partner & Dir-PR)
King Hill (Sr VP)

Subsidiaries:

DigiKnow, Inc.   (1)
3615 Superior Ave E Bldg 44 4th Fl, Cleveland, OH 44114
Tel.: (216) 325-1800
Web Site: http://www.digiknow.com
Sales Range: $10-24.9 Million
Emp.: 70
Internet Service Provider
N.A.I.C.S.: 541810

Marcus Thomas LLC-Public Relations   (1)
4781 Richmond Rd, Cleveland, OH 44128
Tel.: (216) 292-4700
Web Site: http://www.marcusthomasllc.com
Sales Range: $25-49.9 Million
Emp.: 125
Communications, Event Marketing, Public Relations
N.A.I.C.S.: 541810
Mark Bachmann (Partner & Chief Client Officer)
King Hill (Sr VP)

MARDECK LIMITED
1700 Rockville Pike Ste 560, Rockville, MD 20852-5601
Tel.: (301) 468-0707   DC
Year Founded: 1965
Sales Range: $150-199.9 Million
Emp.: 1,000
Holding Company; Hotels Owner & Operator
N.A.I.C.S.: 551112
Ralph Deckelbaum (Pres)
Mo Bernstein (Controller)
Allan Margolius (Sr VP)

MARDEL INC.
7727 SW 44th St, Oklahoma City, OK 73179
Tel.: (405) 745-1300
Web Site: http://www.mardel.com
Sales Range: $50-74.9 Million
Emp.: 700
Religious Goods
N.A.I.C.S.: 459999
Kevin McDonell (Mgr-Mdse)
Liz Gellenbeck (Sec)
Craig Stoll (Mgr-Mdsg)
Joe Warfield (Dir-Tech)
Shannon Brown (Mgr-Online Mktg)

MARDEN'S, INC.
184 College Ave, Waterville, ME 04901-6220
Tel.: (207) 873-6111   ME
Web Site:
http://www.mardensinc.com
Year Founded: 1963
Sales Range: $100-124.9 Million
Emp.: 850
Department Stores
N.A.I.C.S.: 455110
Harold A. Marden (Pres)
John Marden (Co-Owner & VP)

MARDEN-KANE, INC.
195 Frochilinch Form Blvd, Woodbury, NY 11797
Tel.: (516) 365-3999   NY
Web Site:
http://www.mardenkane.com
Year Founded: 1957
Sales Range: $25-49.9 Million
Emp.: 30
Sales Promotion
N.A.I.C.S.: 541810
Alan Richter (CFO)
Barbara Chien (Asst Controller)
Fae Savignano (Sr VP)
Josephine Angiuli (VP & Acct Mgr)
Martin Glovin (Sr VP-Digital Innovations)
Peggy Seeloff (VP)
Rosemary Stein (VP & Gen Mgr)
Jennifer Hibbs (Acct Dir-Interactive)

Subsidiaries:

Marden-Kane, Inc.   (1)
611 Rockland Rd Ste 204, Lake Bluff, IL 60044-2000
Tel.: (847) 283-0441
Web Site: http://www.mardenkane.com
Sales Range: Less than $1 Million
Emp.: 5
Sales Promotion
N.A.I.C.S.: 541810
Rosemary Stein (VP-Chicago)
Adam Kramer (Sr Mgr-Acct)
Martin Glovin (Chief Product Officer)
Jennifer Hibbs (VP & Dir-Interactive Acct)
Alan Richter (CFO & Gen Mgr)
Fae Savignano (Sr VP)

MARDER TRAWLING, INC.
22 S Water St, New Bedford, MA 02740-7235
Tel.: (508) 991-3200   MA
Web Site:
http://www.scallopguys.com
Year Founded: 1986
Sales Range: $25-49.9 Million
Emp.: 40
Sales of Fish & Seafoods
N.A.I.C.S.: 424460
Brian Marder (Pres)
David Cournoyer (Mgr-Sls)

MAREK BROTHERS SYSTEMS, INC.
3539 Oak Forest Dr, Houston, TX 77018-6121
Tel.: (512) 312-2756   TX
Web Site: http://www.marekbros.com

Year Founded: 1938
Sales Range: $50-74.9 Million
Emp.: 700
Drywall & Insulation
N.A.I.C.S.: 238310
Mike Holland (COO)
Sabra Phillips (Dir-Talent Dev)
Ralph Stan Marek Jr. (CEO)

MARESCO INTERNATIONAL CORP.
7 Edge Rd, Alpha, NJ 08865
Tel.: (908) 454-4770
Web Site:
http://www.taylormachineworks.com
Sales Range: $10-24.9 Million
Emp.: 8
Industrial Machinery & Equipment Supplier
N.A.I.C.S.: 423830
Dudley Hulse (Pres)

MARGARET MARY COMMUNITY HOSPITAL
321 Mitchell Ave, Batesville, IN 47006
Tel.: (812) 934-6624   IN
Web Site: http://www.mmhealth.org
Year Founded: 1967
Sales Range: $50-74.9 Million
Emp.: 500
Community Health Care Services
N.A.I.C.S.: 621498
Julie Keene (VP-Physician Svcs)
Brian Daeger (CFO & VP-Fin Svcs)
Kim Inscho (VP-Community Rels & HR)
John Dickey (Vice Chm)
George Junker (Chm)
Timothy Putnam (Pres & CEO)

MARGARET O'LEARY INC.
50 Dornan Ave, San Francisco, CA 94124
Tel.: (415) 864-5547
Web Site:
http://www.margaretoleary.com
Sales Range: $10-24.9 Million
Emp.: 50
Womens & Girls Cut & Sew Other Outerwear Mfr
N.A.I.C.S.: 315250
Margaret O'Leary (Pres)
Rena Chavezderas (CFO)
Stacie Funston (Reg Mgr-Sls)
Diana Lee (Controller-Inventory)
Vesselina Nedeva (Project Mgr)

MARGIE KORSHAK INC.
875 N Michigan Ave Ste 3700, Chicago, IL 60611
Tel.: (312) 751-2121
Web Site: http://www.korshak.com
Year Founded: 1969
Sales Range: $1-9.9 Million
Emp.: 30
Advertising & Public Relations Agency
N.A.I.C.S.: 541820
Margie Korshak (Chm)
Janie Goldberg-Dicks (Pres)

MARGIE WOOD TRUCKING INC.
10272 SE 58th Ave, Belleview, FL 34420
Tel.: (352) 748-3482   FL
Sales Range: $10-24.9 Million
Emp.: 90
Truck Freight Services
N.A.I.C.S.: 484220
Donna McLaughlin (Pres)

MARGOLIN, WINER & EVENS LLP
400 Garden City Plz Ste 500, Garden City, NY 11530
Tel.: (516) 747-2000
Web Site: http://www.mwellp.com
Year Founded: 1946
Sales Range: $10-24.9 Million
Emp.: 185
Certified Public Accountants
N.A.I.C.S.: 541211
Teddy Selinger (Mng Partner)
Mike Rosenberg (Partner)
Howard Fielstein (Chm & Partner)

MARIA REGINA RESIDENCE
1725 Brentwood Rd Bldg 1, Brentwood, NY 11717
Tel.: (631) 299-3000   NY
Web Site:
http://www.mariareginaresidence.org
Year Founded: 2001
Sales Range: $10-24.9 Million
Emp.: 396
Nursing Care Services
N.A.I.C.S.: 623110
Craig W. Best (Mgr-Admissions & Mktg)
Janeen Bush (Dir-Therapeutic Recreation)
Ryan Cahill (Dir-Medical)
Elizabeth Looney (Dir-Nutritional Svcs)
Ann Moyette (Dir-Nursing Svcs)
Maribeth Baldwin (Dir-Rehabilitation Therapies)
Joan Hackett (Dir-Pastoral Care)
Marlene McDowell (Coord-Admissions)
Lucille Johnson (Dir-Adult Day Health Svcs)
Theresa Mintern (Dir-HR)
Basil Wattley Jr. (Dir-Building Svcs)

MARIAH MEDIA INC.
Outside Plz 400 Market St, Santa Fe, NM 87501
Tel.: (505) 989-7100
Web Site:
http://www.outsideonline.com
Rev.: $10,100,000
Emp.: 60
Magazine Publisher
N.A.I.C.S.: 513120
Scott Parmeley (Dir-Publ)
Paul Rolnick (Dir-Consumer Mktg)
Lawrence J. Burke II (CEO & Editor-in-Chief)

MARIAN HEATH GREETING CARDS LLC
9 Kendrick Rd, Wareham, MA 02571
Tel.: (508) 291-0766
Web Site:
http://www.marianheath.com
Year Founded: 1941
Sales Range: $10-24.9 Million
Emp.: 50
Greeting Card Mfr
N.A.I.C.S.: 513191
Diane Reposa (Coord-Licensing)
Teri Desautels (Dir-Line)
Kevin Corrigan (VP-Product Procurement)
Shawna O'Brien (Coord-AP)
Marc Salkovitz (Owner & Pres)
Leta Areski (Dir-Mktg)
Dana Ashworth (CFO)

Subsidiaries:

Marian Heath Greeting Cards   (1)
40 Main St Ste 254, Biddeford, ME 04005
Tel.: (207) 324-4153
Web Site: http://www.viabella.com
Sales Range: $10-24.9 Million
Greeting Cards Publisher
N.A.I.C.S.: 513191

MARIAN INC.

Marian Heath Greeting Cards LLC—(Continued)

MARIAN INC.
1011 E Saint Clair St, Indianapolis, IN 46202
Tel.: (317) 638-6525   IN
Web Site: http://www.marianinc.com
Year Founded: 1954
Industrial Supplies
N.A.I.C.S.: 423840
William Witchger (Pres)

MARIAN SHIPPING LTD.
25660 Crenshaw Blvd Ste 101, Torrance, CA 90505-7171
Tel.: (562) 590-8610
Sales Range: $10-24.9 Million
Emp.: 5
Transportation Logistics
N.A.I.C.S.: 488510
Thomas Solomon (Pres & Gen Mgr)
Butch Grass (Mgr)

MARIANI NUT COMPANY
709 Dutton St, Winters, CA 95694
Tel.: (530) 795-3311
Web Site: http://www.marianinut.com
Sales Range: $10-24.9 Million
Emp.: 100
Nuts: Dried, Dehydrated, Salted Or Roasted
N.A.I.C.S.: 111335
Gary Sutton (Dir-Fin & Acctg)
Lloyd Ramsey (Mgr-Facility & Plant Engr)

MARIANI PACKING COMPANY
500 Crocker Dr, Vacaville, CA 95688-8706
Tel.: (707) 452-2800
Web Site: http://www.mariani.com
Year Founded: 1906
Sales Range: $10-24.9 Million
Emp.: 350
Dried Fruit Production & Sales
N.A.I.C.S.: 311423
Mark A. Mariani (Chm & CEO)
George Sousa Jr. (Pres)

MARIANNA IMPORTS INC.
11222 I St, Omaha, NE 68137
Tel.: (402) 593-0211   NE
Web Site:
http://www.mariannaind.com
Year Founded: 1964
Sales Range: $10-24.9 Million
Emp.: 220
Beauty Products Mfr & Distr
N.A.I.C.S.: 424210
Robert Bagley (Pres)
Subsidiaries:

Marianna Memphis Inc.   (1)
1178 Pope St, Memphis, TN 38108   **(100%)**
Tel.: (901) 273-2222
Web Site: http://www.mariannaind.com
Sales Range: $10-24.9 Million
Emp.: 26
Aerosol Products Mfr
N.A.I.C.S.: 456120

MARIE CALLENDER'S, INC.
27101 Puerta Real Ste 260, Mission Viejo, CA 92691
Tel.: (949) 448-5300   WY
Web Site:
http://www.mariecallenders.com
Year Founded: 2019
Holding Company; Restaurant Franchisor & Operator
N.A.I.C.S.: 551112
Michael Nakhleh (Pres & CEO)
Subsidiaries:

Marie Callender Pie Shops, LLC   (1)
27101 Puerta Real Ste 260, Mission Viejo, CA 92691

Tel.: (949) 448-5300
Web Site: http://www.mariecallenders.com
Casual Dining Restaurant & Bakery Operator & Franchisor
N.A.I.C.S.: 722511

MARIETTA AREA HEALTH CARE, INC.
401 Matthew St, Marietta, OH 45750
Tel.: (740) 374-1400
Web Site: http://www.mhsystem.org
General Medical & Surgical Hospitals
N.A.I.C.S.: 622110
Colleen Cook (Chm)
Michael Archer (Vice Chm)

MARIETTA COAL CO.
67705 Friends Church Rd, Saint Clairsville, OH 43950
Tel.: (740) 695-2197
Sales Range: $10-24.9 Million
Emp.: 15
Bituminous Coal Surface Mining
N.A.I.C.S.: 212114

MARIETTA DRAPERY & WINDOW COVERINGS CO., INC.
22 Trammell St SW, Marietta, GA 30064-3225
Tel.: (770) 428-3337   GA
Web Site:
http://www.mariettadrapery.com
Year Founded: 1946
Sales Range: $25-49.9 Million
Emp.: 150
Bedspread, Drapery, Window Covering & Other Home Furnishing Mfr
N.A.I.C.S.: 423220
Andrew F. Bentley (Pres)
Dan Wicker (Dir-Pur)
Brandon Reynolds (Project Mgr)
Casey Williamson (Plant Mgr)
Chris Martin (Mgr-Sls-Atlanta)

MARIETTA INDUSTRIAL ENTERPRISES
17943 State Rte 7, Marietta, OH 45750
Tel.: (740) 373-2252
Web Site: http://www.miecorp.com
Sales Range: $10-24.9 Million
Emp.: 96
Marine Cargo Handling
N.A.I.C.S.: 488320
W. Scott Elliott (Pres)

MARIETTA SILOS LLC
2417 Waterford Rd, Marietta, OH 45750
Tel.: (740) 373-2822
Web Site:
http://www.mariettasilos.com
Specialty Trade Contractors
N.A.I.C.S.: 238990
Dennis Blauser (CEO)
Subsidiaries:

San-Con Industries, Inc.   (1)
320 Maple St Ste A, Upper Sandusky, OH 43351
Tel.: (419) 294-5609
Web Site: http://www.san-con.com
Sales Range: $1-9.9 Million
Emp.: 40
Concrete Products Construction & Repair
N.A.I.C.S.: 327390

MARIETTA WRECKER SERVICE LLC
950 Allgood Rd NE, Marietta, GA 30062
Tel.: (770) 765-1933
Web Site:
http://www.mariettawrecker.com
Commercial Towing Services
N.A.I.C.S.: 488410
Terri Wechel (Co-Founder)

Subsidiaries:

New Image Towing & Recovery, LLC   (1)
4780 Old Dixie Hwy, Forest Park, GA 30297
Tel.: (404) 684-0121
Rev.: $3,500,000
Emp.: 12
Motor Vehicle Towing
N.A.I.C.S.: 488410
Lawton Howard (Pres)

MARILLAC ST. VINCENT FAMILY SERVICES
2145 N Halsted St, Chicago, IL 60614
Tel.: (773) 722-7440
Web Site:
https://www.marillacstvincent.org
Year Founded: 1914
Youth Organization Services
N.A.I.C.S.: 813410

MARILYN MIGLIN, L.P.
1230 W Washington Blvd Ste 100, Chicago, IL 60607
Tel.: (312) 266-4600   IL
Web Site:
http://www.marilynmiglin.com
Year Founded: 1963
Sales Range: $50-74.9 Million
Emp.: 20
Cosmetics, Fragrances & Skin Care Products Mfr
N.A.I.C.S.: 456120
Marilyn Miglin (Partner)
Marlena Miglin (Owner)

MARIN HEALTHCARE DISTRICT
100-B Drake's Landing Rd Ste 250, Greenbrae, CA 94904
Tel.: (415) 464-2090
Web Site:
http://www.marinhealthcare.org
Health Care Services Organization
N.A.I.C.S.: 813920
Lee Domanico (CEO)
James P. McManus (CFO)
Jon Friedenberg (COO)
Ann Sparkman (Chm)
Harris Simmonds (Vice Chm)
Jennifer Hershon (Sec)
Subsidiaries:

Marin General Hospital   (1)
250 Bon Air Rd, Greenbrae, CA 94904
Tel.: (415) 925-7000
Web Site: http://www.maringeneral.org
Emp.: 1,800
Hospital Operator
N.A.I.C.S.: 622110
Joel Sklar (Chief Medical Officer)
Mark Zielazinski (CIO & Chief Tech Integration Officer)
Jon Friedenberg (COO)
James P. McManus (CFO)
Linda Lang (Chief HR Officer)
Andrea Schultz (Sec)
David Hill (Vice Chm)
Lee Domanico (CEO)
Paul Kirincic (Chm)
Robert Peirce (Treas)
Liz Kolcun (Chief Dev Officer & Pres-MGH Foundation)
Karin Reese (Chief Nursing Officer)

MARIN LUXURY CARS, LLC.
195 Casa Buena Dr, Corte Madera, CA 94925-1709
Tel.: (415) 460-4600
Web Site:
http://www.marinluxurycars.com
Sales Range: $75-99.9 Million
Emp.: 123
Car Whslr
N.A.I.C.S.: 441110
Bryan Anton (Mgr-Customer Svcs)
Fred Cziska (Gen Mgr)

U.S. PRIVATE

MARIN MUNICIPAL WATER DISTRICT
220 Nellen Ave, Corte Madera, CA 94925-1102
Tel.: (415) 945-1455
Web Site: http://www.marinwater.org
Year Founded: 1912
Sales Range: $25-49.9 Million
Emp.: 235
Water Supply Services
N.A.I.C.S.: 221310
Larry Russell (Pres)
Armando Quintero (VP)
Krishna Kumar (Gen Mgr)

MARIN SANITARY SERVICE INC.
1050 Andersen Dr, San Rafael, CA 94901
Tel.: (415) 456-2601
Web Site:
http://www.marinsanitary.com
Sales Range: $10-24.9 Million
Emp.: 140
Provider of Waste Management Services
N.A.I.C.S.: 562111

MARINA ICE CREAM CO., INC.
13314 Jamaica Ave, Richmond Hill, NY 11418-2617
Tel.: (718) 297-9090   NY
Web Site:
http://www.marinaicecream.com
Year Founded: 1979
Sales Range: $100-124.9 Million
Emp.: 2,000
Production & Sales of Ice Cream & Ices
N.A.I.C.S.: 424430
Frank Barone (Pres)
Mike Barone (Mgr-Long Island)

MARINA INVESTMENT MANAGEMENT INC.
8610 Bay Pines Blvd, Saint Petersburg, FL 33709
Tel.: (727) 384-3625
Emp.: 5
Holding Company; Marinas
N.A.I.C.S.: 551112
Larry Saglio (Pres)
Subsidiaries:

Lighthouse Point Marina   (1)
8610 Bay Pines Blvd, Saint Petersburg, FL 33709
Tel.: (727) 384-3625
Web Site:
http://www.lighthousepointmarina.net
Marinas
N.A.I.C.S.: 713930
Butch Cataldo (Gen Mgr)

MARINE & INDUSTRIAL SUPPLY COMPANY, INC.
150 Virginia St, Mobile, AL 36603-2032
Tel.: (251) 438-4617
Web Site:
http://www.marineandindustrial.com
Year Founded: 1976
Sales Range: $10-24.9 Million
Emp.: 14
Industrial Machinery & Equipment Whslr
N.A.I.C.S.: 423830
Thomas Benton (Pres)

MARINE BANCORP, INC.
3050 Wabash Ave, Springfield, IL 62704
Tel.: (217) 726-0600
Web Site:
http://www.ibankmarine.com
Year Founded: 1993

COMPANIES

Sales Range: $25-49.9 Million
Emp.: 180
Bank Holding Company
N.A.I.C.S.: 551111
Roger Chandler *(Pres)*

Subsidiaries:

Marine Bank (1)
3050 Wabash Ave, Springfield, IL 62704
Tel.: (217) 726-0600
Web Site: http://www.ibankmarine.com
Sales Range: $50-74.9 Million
Emp.: 200
Commercial Banking Services
N.A.I.C.S.: 522110
Roger Chandler *(Pres)*
Chris R. Zettek *(CEO)*
Susan Raaum *(VP)*
Mark Richardson *(Chm)*

MARINE CHEVROLET COMPANY, INC.
1408 Western Blvd, Jacksonville, NC 28546-6661
Tel.: (910) 455-2121 NC
Web Site:
 http://www.marinechevy.com
Year Founded: 1946
Sales Range: $10-24.9 Million
Emp.: 100
Car Whslr
N.A.I.C.S.: 441110
Michael K. Alford *(Pres)*
Michael Hoopes *(Gen Mgr)*
Heather Taylor *(Asst Controller)*

MARINE ELECTRIC SYSTEMS, INC.
80 Wesley St, South Hackensack, NJ 07606-1510
Tel.: (201) 531-8600
Web Site:
 http://www.marineelectricsystems.com
Marine Monitoring & Control Systems Mfr
N.A.I.C.S.: 334513
Caroline Coniglio *(VP-Sls)*

MARINE HOME CENTER
134 Orange St, Nantucket, MA 02554
Tel.: (508) 228-0900
Web Site:
 http://www.marinehomecenter.com
Year Founded: 1945
Sales Range: $10-24.9 Million
Emp.: 90
Lumber & Other Building Materials Retailer
N.A.I.C.S.: 444110
Greg Marsh *(Mgr-Yard)*

MARINE OIL CO. INC.
608 N Center St, Warsaw, NC 28398
Tel.: (910) 293-4328
Sales Range: $10-24.9 Million
Emp.: 25
Petroleum Bulk Stations
N.A.I.C.S.: 424710
Audrey McCullen *(Pres)*

MARINE PARK COMPUTERS
3126 Avenue U, Brooklyn, NY 11229
Tel.: (718) 891-1878
Web Site:
 http://www.marineparkpc.com
Year Founded: 1992
Rev.: $50,000,000
Emp.: 30
Computer, Camera & Video Equipment Retailer
N.A.I.C.S.: 449210

MARINE SPILL RESPONSE CORPORATION
220 Spring St Ste 500, Herndon, VA 20170-5255
Tel.: (703) 326-5600 TN
Web Site: http://www.msrc.org
Year Founded: 1990
Sales Range: $10-24.9 Million
Emp.: 190
Oil Spill Response Company
N.A.I.C.S.: 562910
Judith Roos *(VP-Mktg, Customer Svcs & Corp Rels)*

MARINE SPORTS LLC
2330 Twin View Blvd, Redding, CA 96003
Tel.: (530) 243-0175
Web Site:
 http://www.harrisonsmarine.com
Sales Range: $25-49.9 Million
Emp.: 14
Boat Dealers
N.A.I.C.S.: 441222
Rod Dole *(Pres & CEO)*

MARINE TOWING OF TAMPA, LLC
908 S 20th St, Tampa, FL 33605
Tel.: (813) 242-6500
Web Site:
 http://www.marinetowingtampa.com
Sales Range: $1-9.9 Million
Emp.: 25
Navigational Services to Shipping
N.A.I.C.S.: 488330
Jim Kimbrell *(Pres)*
Stephen Swindal *(Chm)*
Norman Atkins *(Dir-Ops)*
Dwayne Keith *(Mgr-Ops)*
James C. Brantner *(Partner)*
Lori Palmer *(Controller)*

MARINE TRANSPORT INC.
200 Central Ave, Mountainside, NJ 07092
Tel.: (908) 686-0086
Web Site: http://www.marine-trans.com
Sales Range: $10-24.9 Million
Emp.: 8
Freight Transportation Arrangement
N.A.I.C.S.: 488510
Robert Castelo *(Pres)*
Sammy Santomo *(Mgr)*
George Fuller *(Gen Mgr)*

MARINE TRANSPORTATION SERVICES, INC.
3830 Frankford Ave, Panama City, FL 32405
Tel.: (850) 769-1459
Web Site:
 http://www.marinetransportationservices.com
Rev.: $16,900,000
Emp.: 45
Coastal & Great Lakes Freight Transportation
N.A.I.C.S.: 483113
Judy Davis *(VP)*
Grover Davis *(Pres)*
Kerrie Beasley *(Treas)*
Kimberly Davis Whitfield *(Gen Counsel, Sec & Dir-HSE)*

MARINE TRAVELIFT, INC.
49 E Yew St, Sturgeon Bay, WI 54235
Tel.: (920) 743-6202 WI
Web Site:
 http://www.marinetravelift.com
Year Founded: 1975
Sales Range: $25-49.9 Million
Emp.: 140
Marine Hoists, Boat Lifts & Marine ForkLifts
N.A.I.C.S.: 333120
Erich Pfeifer *(Pres & CEO)*

Subsidiaries:

ExacTech, Inc. (1)
107 E Walnut St, Sturgeon Bay, WI 54235-1962 (100%)
Tel.: (920) 746-0082
Web Site: http://www.exactechinc.com
Sales Range: $10-24.9 Million
Emp.: 50
Steel Fabrication
N.A.I.C.S.: 332312

Shuttlelift, Inc. (1)
49 E Yew St, Sturgeon Bay, WI 54235 (100%)
Tel.: (920) 743-8650
Web Site: http://www.shuttlelift.com
Sales Range: $10-24.9 Million
Emp.: 8
Industrial Mobile Gantry Cranes Mfr
N.A.I.C.S.: 333923
Steve Pfeifer *(Pres & CEO)*

MARINER INTERNATIONAL TRAVEL INC.
93 Park Place Blvd, Clearwater, FL 33759
Tel.: (727) 530-5424 DE
Web Site: http://www.moorings.com
Year Founded: 1998
Sales Range: $50-74.9 Million
Emp.: 650
Amusement & Recreation
N.A.I.C.S.: 561520
Matthew Prior *(CEO)*

MARINER INVESTMENT GROUP LLC
485 Lexington Ave 28th Fl, New York, NY 10017
Tel.: (914) 670-4300
Web Site:
 http://www.marinerinvestment.com
Year Founded: 1992
Investment Advisory Services
N.A.I.C.S.: 523940
William J. Michaelcheck *(Founder, Partner, Co-Chief Investment Officer & Mgr-Portfolio)*
Russell A. Thompson *(Chief Compliance Officer & Deputy Gen Counsel)*
John C. Kelty *(COO)*
Peter J. O'Rourke *(Partner & Gen Counsel)*
Dmitry Green *(Chief Risk Officer)*
Curtis Arledge *(Chm & CEO)*
Jamie Silver *(Mng Dir)*
Charles R. Howe II *(Pres, Partner & CFO)*
Edward G. Fisher III *(Co-Chief Investment Officer & Head-Liquid Markets)*

MARINER WEALTH ADVISORS, LLC
5700 W 112th St Ste 200, Overland Park, KS 66211
Tel.: (913) 382-2791 KS
Web Site:
 https://www.marinerwealthadvisors.com
Emp.: 435
Holding Company; Financial Services
N.A.I.C.S.: 551112
Martin C. Bicknell *(CEO)*

Subsidiaries:

Ascent Investment Partners, LLC (1)
1401 S Brentwood Blvd Ste 390, Saint Louis, MO 63144
Tel.: (314) 227-3275
Web Site:
 http://www.ascentinvestmentpartners.com
Fixed-Income Investment & Portfolio Management Services
N.A.I.C.S.: 523940
Sandra Pourcillie *(Principal)*
Brian Tournier *(Dir-Res)*
Ross Maynard *(Dir-Client Portfolio Mgmt)*

Convergence Investment Partners, LLC (1)
1245 Cheyenne Ave Ste 102, Grafton, WI 53024
Tel.: (262) 240-0117
Web Site: http://www.investcip.com
Portfolio Management Services
N.A.I.C.S.: 523940
David J. Abitz *(Pres & Chief Investment Officer)*
Justin Neuberg *(Portfolio Mgr)*
Todd Hanson *(Mng Partner & Dir-Tech)*
Jonathan Franklin *(Mng Partner & Head-Res)*
Jim Dwyer *(Dir-Client Rels & Portfolio Mgr-Client)*

Enterprise Risk Strategies, LLC (1)
4215 E McDowell Rd Ste 115, Mesa, AZ 85215
Tel.: (913) 981-0515
Web Site: http://www.eriskstrategies.com
Insurance Risk Mitigation Services
N.A.I.C.S.: 524292
Robert Nizzi *(Pres)*
Bruce Slapper *(Exec VP)*
Luis Filipe *(VP & Dir-Captive Ops)*

Flyover Capital Partners, LLC (1)
5700 W 112th St Ste 500, Overland Park, KS 66211
Tel.: (913) 904-5700
Web Site: http://www.flyovercapital.com
Technology-Focused Venture Capital Firm
N.A.I.C.S.: 523999
Martin C. Bicknell *(Gen Partner)*
Thomas A. DeBacco *(Gen Partner)*
Keith Molzer *(Gen Partner)*
Thad Langford *(Gen Partner)*
Michael Peck *(Gen Partner)*

Mariner Wealth Advisors LLC (1)
5700 W 112th St Ste 200, Overland Park, KS 66211
Tel.: (913) 382-2791
Web Site:
 http://www.marinerwealthadvisors.com
Privater Equity Firm
N.A.I.C.S.: 523999
Martin C. Bicknell *(Pres & CEO)*
Kevin Corbett *(Mng Dir-Corp Dev)*
Debra Light *(Dir)*
Todd Block *(Dir-Tax)*
Cheryl Bicknell *(COO & Chief Strategy Officer)*
Jeff Poe *(CFO)*
Katrina Radenberg *(Chief Investment Officer)*

Subsidiary (Domestic):

Allied Business Group, Inc. (2)
7007 College Blvd Ste 400, Overland Park, KS 66211
Tel.: (913) 897-3599
Web Site: http://www.alliedbizgroup.com
Sales Range: $1-9.9 Million
Emp.: 6
Investment Banking, Valuation Advisory & Forensic Accounting Services
N.A.I.C.S.: 523150
Tim Skarda *(Founder & Mng Dir)*
David Holzman *(Pres)*
Robbie VanTrump *(Mgr-Mktg)*
Todd Middleton *(Mng Dir)*
Tom Tilley *(Mng Dir)*
Jeff Johnson *(Dir-Valuation)*
David Hill *(Mng Dir)*

Klevens Capital Management, Inc. (2)
500 108th Ave NE Ste 765, Bellevue, WA 98004-5593
Tel.: (425) 453-6353
Web Site: http://www.klevenscapitalmanagement.com
Financial Investment Activities
N.A.I.C.S.: 523999
John Klevens *(Pres)*

Riverpoint Capital Management, Inc. (2)
312 Walnut St Ste 3120, Cincinnati, OH 45202
Tel.: (513) 421-3100
Web Site: http://www.riverpointcm.com
Sales Range: $1-9.9 Million
Emp.: 20
Investment Advice

MARINER WEALTH ADVISORS, LLC

Mariner Wealth Advisors, LLC—(Continued)
N.A.I.C.S.: 523940
Jonathon A. Bresnen (Portfolio Mgr)
Jeff Krumpelman (Mng Dir & Sr Portfolio Mgr)
Mindy McLaughlin (Mng Dir)
Nolan K. Kamerer (Portfolio Mgr)
Mary Sawyer (Dir-Trading)
Ryan Brown (Mng Dir)
Anthony Roberts (Mng Dir)
Kristin Fishbaugh (Portfolio Mgr)
Lauren Michalos (Portfolio Mgr)
Kyle Moore (Portfolio Mgr)
Bradley I. Morgan (Portfolio Mgr)
Michael J. Murphy (Portfolio Mgr)
Mary C. Rawe (Office Mgr)
Raymond D. Smego (Portfolio Mgr)

Singer & Xenos, Inc. (2)
800 S Douglas Rd Ste 750, Coral Gables, FL 33134
Tel.: (305) 443-0060
Web Site: http://www.singerxenos.com
Investment Advice
N.A.I.C.S.: 523940
Faith Read Xenos (Founder, CIO, COO & Partner)
Jay Schechter (Partner)
Lindsey Hemphill (Dir-Singer Xenos Events)
Marc Singer (Founder & Partner)
Michelle Grillone (Dir-Ops)
Neil Sosler (Partner)
Sam Sudame (Dir-Res)

Patriot Wealth Management, Inc. (1)
5847 San Felipe Ste 200, Houston, TX 77057
Tel.: (713) 344-9303
Web Site: http://www.patriotwealth.com
Depository Credit Intermediation
N.A.I.C.S.: 522180
Todd Hanslik (Pres)

Woodbridge International LLC (1)
1764 Litchfield Tpke Ste 250, New Haven, CT 06525
Tel.: (203) 389-8400
Web Site: http://www.woodbridgegrp.com
Corporate Merger Consulting Services
N.A.I.C.S.: 541618
Robert M. Koenig (Founder, Pres & CEO)
Don Krier (Partner & Mng Dir)
Larry Reinharz (Mng Dir)
Robert F. Murphy (Mng Partner)
Marni K. Connelly (Mng Dir-Ops)
Andrew Buchholtz (Head-Investment Banking)
Lori Green (Sr VP-Strategic Mktg)
Greg Michaels (VP-Bus Dev)
Simon Wibberley (VP-Ops)
Mitch Wein (Creative Dir)
Elias B. Klaich (Mng Dir)
Matt Mahan (Mgr-Info Sys)
Jonathan Wesner (Dir-Sell Side Merger & Acq)
Kyle Richard (Partner & Mng Dir)

MARINEX INC.
735 Challenger St, Brea, CA 92821-2948
Tel.: (714) 578-1600
Web Site: http://www.marinexusa.com
Sales Range: $10-24.9 Million
Emp.: 6
Automotive Supplies & Parts Whslr
N.A.I.C.S.: 423120
Sang W. Hyun (Pres)
Henry Park (Mng Dir)

MARINI MANUFACTURING, INC.
5100 21st St, Racine, WI 53406
Tel.: (262) 554-6811
Web Site: http://www.marinimfg.com
Rev.: $3,075,000
Emp.: 25
All Other Miscellaneous Fabricated Metal Product Mfr
N.A.I.C.S.: 332999
Tom Marini (Pres & CEO)

Subsidiaries:

Accu-Turn Inc. (1)
1375 Industrial Park Dr, Union Grove, WI 53182
Tel.: (262) 878-4432
Web Site: http://www.accu-turn.net
Sales Range: $1-9.9 Million
Emp.: 10
Commercial & Service Industry Machinery Mfr
N.A.I.C.S.: 333310
David Hubeler (Gen Mgr)

MARINO CHRYSLER JEEP DODGE
5133 W Irving Park Rd, Chicago, IL 60641
Tel.: (773) 777-2000
Web Site: http://www.marinocjd.com
Rev.: $19,000,000
Emp.: 65
New & Used Motor Vehicles
N.A.I.C.S.: 441110
Greg Marino (Owner)
Julie Lindahl (Mgr-Sls)

MARIO CAMACHO FOODS, LLC
2502 Walden Woods Dr, Plant City, FL 33566
Tel.: (813) 305-4534
Web Site: http://www.mariocamachofoods.com
Sales Range: $75-99.9 Million
Emp.: 35
Fruits & Vegetable Mfr & Distr
N.A.I.C.S.: 311411
Jeffrey Compas (Mgr-Import & Logistics)
Shawn Kaddoura (Pres)
Jon Nordquist (VP-Foodservice Sls)

MARIO INDUSTRIES OF VIRGINIA
2490 Patterson Ave SW, Roanoke, VA 24016
Tel.: (540) 342-1111
Web Site: http://www.marioindustries.com
Rev.: $10,500,000
Emp.: 56
Residential Lighting Fixtures
N.A.I.C.S.: 335131
Louis Scutellaro (Pres)

MARION DAILY REPUBLICAN
18 E Main St, Du Quoin, IL 62832
Tel.: (618) 993-2626
Web Site: http://www.dailyrepublicannews.com
Prepress Services
N.A.I.C.S.: 323120
Holly Kee (Mng Editor)

MARION GENERAL HOSPITAL, INC
441 N Wabash Ave, Marion, IN 46952
Tel.: (765) 660-6000
Web Site: http://www.mgh.net
Year Founded: 1910
Sales Range: $150-199.9 Million
Emp.: 1,149
Health Care Srvices
N.A.I.C.S.: 622110
Joe Martin (Chm)
Paul L. Usher (Co-Pres & CEO)
Jerome T. Holderead (Vice Chm)
Sally Jenks (Sec)

MARION PLYWOOD CORPORATION
222 S Parkview Ave, Marion, WI 54950-9698
Tel.: (715) 754-5231
Web Site: http://www.marionplywood.com
Sales Range: $10-24.9 Million
Emp.: 250

Mfr of Hardwood Plywood & Veneer
N.A.I.C.S.: 321211
Peter T. Rogers (Pres)
David Williams (VP)
Mike Burkart (Product Mgr-Dev)

Subsidiaries:

Great Lakes Veneer Inc. (1)
222 S Parkview Ave, Marion, WI 54950-9698 (100%)
Tel.: (715) 754-2501
Web Site: http://www.greatlakesveneer.com
Emp.: 200
Lumber, Plywood & Millwork Distr
N.A.I.C.S.: 423310
Peter T. Rogers (CEO)
Kelly Rottier (CFO & VP)

MARION TOYOTA
3300 W Deyoung St, Marion, IL 62959-5885
Tel.: (618) 997-5692
Web Site: http://www.mariontoyota.com
Year Founded: 1986
Sales Range: $10-24.9 Million
Emp.: 44
New Car Whslr
N.A.I.C.S.: 441110
Lana Rizzo (Asst Mgr-Parts)
Jeff Mayer (Principal)

MARION-POLK FOOD SHARE
1660 Salem Industrial Dr NE, Salem, OR 97301-0374
Tel.: (503) 581-3855
Web Site: http://www.marionpolkfoodshare.org
Year Founded: 1987
Sales Range: $10-24.9 Million
Emp.: 47
Hunger Relief Services
N.A.I.C.S.: 624210
Rick Gaupo (Pres & CEO)
Phil McCorkle (VP-Dev)
Holly Larson (CFO)
Abisha Dunivin (Dir-Ops)

MARIOS INC.
805 SW Broadway Ste 400, Portland, OR 97205
Tel.: (503) 241-5034
Web Site: http://www.marios.com
Sales Range: $10-24.9 Million
Emp.: 75
Men's & Boy's Clothing Stores
N.A.I.C.S.: 458110
Mario K. Bisio (Pres)

MARIPOSA MEDSPA
4214 N Classen Bvld, Oklahoma City, OK 73118
Tel.: (405) 759-7546
Web Site: http://www.mariposamedspaokc.com
Year Founded: 2007
Sales Range: $1-9.9 Million
Emp.: 10
Health Care Spa & Weight Treatment Services
N.A.I.C.S.: 721110
J. Arden Blough (Dir-Medical)
Kristy Murrow (Mng Partner)
Tobi Reubell (Mgr-Patient Svcs)

MARIS DISTRIBUTING CO. INC.
4060 NE 49th Ave, Gainesville, FL 32609
Tel.: (352) 378-2431
Rev.: $20,000,000
Emp.: 10
Distr of Beer & Ale
N.A.I.C.S.: 424810
Rudolph M. Maris (Pres)

MARIS, WEST & BAKER, INC.
18 Northtown Dr, Jackson, MS 39211-3016
Tel.: (601) 977-9200
Web Site: http://www.mwb.com
Year Founded: 1970
Sales Range: $10-24.9 Million
Emp.: 21
Automotive, Financial, Government/Political/Public Affairs, Health Care, Restaurant
N.A.I.C.S.: 541810
Mike Booth (CFO)
Peter Marks (CEO)
Donna Sims (VP & Dir-Media)
Marc Leffler (Dir-Creative)
Randy Lynn (VP & Dir-Creative)
Tammy Smith (VP-Production)
Austin Cannon (VP-Interactive Svcs)
Jonathan Pettus (Sr Acct Exec)
Tim Mask (Pres)

MARISCO LTD.
91 607 Malakole Rd, Kapolei, HI 96707
Tel.: (808) 682-1333
Web Site: http://www.marisco.net
Year Founded: 1972
Sales Range: $10-24.9 Million
Emp.: 120
Shipbuilding & Repairing
N.A.I.C.S.: 336611
Alfred Anawati (Pres)
John Stewart (VP & Gen Mgr)
Judd See (Mgr-Production)
Darlene Martin (Dir-Support-Plng)
Stephen Hinton (Mgr-Environmental Compliance)
Jui Dutt-Spiller (CFO)

MARISTAFF INC.
560 W Crossville Rd 201, Roswell, GA 30075
Tel.: (678) 739-0009
Web Site: http://www.maristaff.com
Sales Range: $10-24.9 Million
Emp.: 300
Temporary Help Service
N.A.I.C.S.: 561320
Kelly Pelletier (Branch Mgr)
Bryn Daniel (Dir-Ops)

MARITIME ENERGY, INC.
234 Pk St, Rockland, ME 04841-2126
Tel.: (207) 594-4487
Web Site: http://www.maritimeenergy.com
Year Founded: 1939
Sales Range: $25-49.9 Million
Emp.: 220
Dealers of Fuel & Oil
N.A.I.C.S.: 457210
John Ware (Pres-Sr Mgmt)
Becky Stearns (Mgr-Fin)
Charon Curtis (VP-Maritime Farms)
Chris Seavey (VP-Sls)

MARITIME EXCHANGE FOR THE DELAWARE RIVER AND BAY
240 Cherry St, Philadelphia, PA 19106-1906
Tel.: (215) 925-2615
Web Site: http://www.maritimedelriv.com
Year Founded: 1882
Sales Range: $10-24.9 Million
Emp.: 14
Trade Assocation
N.A.I.C.S.: 813910
Michael Fink (Dir-IT)
Lisa B. Himber (VP)
Uwe Schulz (Vice Chm)
A. Robert Degen (Sec)
Dennis Rochford (Pres)
John T. Reynolds (Chm)
Robert A. Herb (Treas)

COMPANIES

Beverly Ford (Coord-Govt Affairs)
Darleen Michalak (Coord-IT & Ops)
Ed Fern (Dir-Fin & Admin)
Paul Myhre (Dir-Ops)

MARITZ HOLDINGS INC.
1375 N Hwy Dr, Fenton, MO 63099
Tel.: (636) 827-4000   MO
Web Site: http://www.maritz.com
Year Founded: 1894
Sales Range: $1-4.9 Billion
Emp.: 3,665
Consulting Services
N.A.I.C.S.: 519290
W. Stephen Maritz Jr. (Chm)
Jennifer Larsen (Sr Dir-Brand & Reputation)
Richard T. Ramos (CFO & Exec VP)
Charlotte Blank (Chief Behavioral Officer)
David Peckinpaugh (Pres, CEO & Pres-Maritz Global Events)
Steve Gallant (Co-Pres & Gen Counsel-Maritz Motivation)
Jeff Kellstrom (Pres-Maritz Automotive)

Subsidiaries:

Maritz Dealer Solutions   (1)
1375 N Highway Dr, Fenton, MO 63099
Tel.: (636) 827-4000
Web Site: http://www.maritz.com
Emp.: 250
Marketing Consulting Services
N.A.I.C.S.: 541613
Steve Maritz (CEO)

Maritz Marketing Research, Inc.   (1)
1355 N Hwy Dr, Fenton, MO 63099-0001   (100%)
Tel.: (636) 827-4000
Web Site: http://www.maritzresearch.com
Sales Range: $25-49.9 Million
Emp.: 700
Marketing Research
N.A.I.C.S.: 541910
W. Stephen Maritz Jr. (CEO)
Keith Chrzan (Chief Res Officer)
Gina Wiseman (VP-Virtual Customers Res Div)
Chris Cottle (CMO)
Adam Edmunds (Chief Strategy Officer)
Mark Magee (VP-Product Mgmt)
Todd Miceli (CFO)
Troy Monney (COO)
Ed Reilly (Exec VP-Worldwide Sls)
Jason Taylor (CTO)
Justin Thompson (VP-Strategy)

Division (Non-US):

Maritz Research   (2)
5900 Maritz Dr, Mississauga, L5W 1L8, ON, Canada   (100%)
Tel.: (416) 922-1140
Sales Range: $75-99.9 Million
Emp.: 350
Management Consulting Services
N.A.I.C.S.: 541611

Maritz Motivation Solutions Inc.   (1)
1375 N Hwy Dr, Fenton, MO 63099
Tel.: (636) 827-4000
Web Site: http://www.maritzmotivation.com
Employee Recognition Program Provider
N.A.I.C.S.: 923130
Drew Carter (Pres)
Steve Maritz (Chm & CEO)
Chris Dornfeld (VP & Head-Employee Engagement Solution)
Cameron Conway (VP-Sls Performance & Chanel Loyalty Practice)

Maritz Performance Improvement Company   (1)
1400 S Highway Dr, Fenton, MO 63099-0001   (100%)
Tel.: (636) 827-4000
Web Site: http://www.maritz.org
Sales Range: $500-549.9 Million
Sales Motivation Programs, Training Services & Sales & Business Meetings
N.A.I.C.S.: 611710
Vienna Bergholtz (Project Coord)

Maritz Research GmbH   (1)
Borselstrasse 18, 22765, Hamburg, Germany
Tel.: (49) 403698330
Web Site: http://www.maritzresearch.de
Sales Range: $10-24.9 Million
Emp.: 50
Marketing Consulting Services
N.A.I.C.S.: 541910
Stephan Thun (Gen Mgr)
Michael Allenson (Sr Dir-Strategic Consulting)

Maritz Research Ltd.   (1)
Artisan Hillbottom Road, High Wycombe, HP12 4HJ, Bucks, United Kingdom
Tel.: (44) 1494590600
Web Site: http://www.maritzresearch.co.uk
Sales Range: $10-24.9 Million
Emp.: 200
Marketing Consulting Services
N.A.I.C.S.: 541613
Nigel Cover (VP-Bus Svcs)
Stephan Thun (Mng Dir)

Maritz Travel Co.   (1)
1395 N Hwy Dr, Fenton, MO 63099-0001   (100%)
Tel.: (636) 827-4000
Web Site: http://www.maritztravel.com
Sales Range: $500-549.9 Million
Emp.: 400
Incentive & Business Travel
N.A.I.C.S.: 561510
W. Stephen Maritz Jr. (Chm & CEO)
Eduardo Chaillo (Gen Mgr-Latin America & Mexico-Global)
Ben Goedegebuure (Gen Mgr-Europe, Middle East & Africa-Global)
Ping He (Gen Mgr-Asia Pacific-Global)
Pat Schaumann (Sr Dir-Compliance)
Steve O'Malley (Div Pres)
Steve Gallant (Gen Counsel)
John Wahle (VP-Tech)

Stratejic Solutions S.A. de C.V.   (1)
Gobernador J G Covarrubias 78 2 Pisa, San Miguel, Mexico, 11850, Chapultepec, Mexico
Tel.: (52) 5550892130
Web Site: http://www.strategix.com.mx
Sales Range: $10-24.9 Million
Emp.: 40
Motivation & Training Programs, Group & Business Travel, Marketing Research, Sales & Business Meetings, Database Marketing, Teleservices, Management Information
N.A.I.C.S.: 561599

The Maritz Institute   (1)
1375 N Highway Dr, Fenton, MO 63099
Tel.: (636) 827-2170
Web Site: http://www.themaritzinstitute.com
Marketing Consulting Services
N.A.I.C.S.: 541613
Derek Mays (Chief Privacy Officer)
Charlotte Blank (Exec Dir)

MARJON SPECIALTY FOODS, INC.
3508 Sydney Rd, Plant City, FL 33566
Tel.: (813) 752-3482
Web Site: http://www.marjonspecialtyfoods.com
Year Founded: 1972
Sales Range: $10-24.9 Million
Emp.: 80
Salad Dressing & Vegetable Mfr
N.A.I.C.S.: 311941
John J. Miller (Co-Owner)
Marcia Miller (Co-Owner)

MARK 3 SYSTEMS, INC.
3600 S Gessner Rd Ste 170, Houston, TX 77063-5149
Tel.: (713) 664-9850
Web Site: http://www.markiiisys.com
Sales Range: $10-24.9 Million
Emp.: 16
Server, Storage & Networking Product Distr
N.A.I.C.S.: 423430
Leslie T. Powell (Co-Founder & Pres)
Ann Wilkerson (VP-Fin)

Stan Wysocki (VP-Sls)
Stephen Rodriguez (VP-Technical Resources)
Leslie Hattig (Acct Exec)
Noelle Kuehn (Acct Exec)
Lisa Stone (Acct Exec)

MARK ANDY, INC.
18081 Chesterfield Airport Rd, Chesterfield, MO 63005
Tel.: (636) 532-4433   MO
Web Site: http://www.markandy.com
Year Founded: 1946
Emp.: 450
Narrow Web Printing Equipment Mfr
N.A.I.C.S.: 333248
Steve Schulte (VP-Sls & Mktg)
P. J. Desai (Partner)
Lukasz Chruslinski (Mgr-Sls)
Dave Telken (Dir-Aftermarket Ops-Global)
Chris Yanko (Dir-Digital Sls)

Subsidiaries:

Presstek LLC   (1)
55 Executive Dr, Hudson, NH 03051
Tel.: (603) 595-7000
Web Site: http://www.presstek.com
Digital Offset Printing Solutions Mfr & Distr
N.A.I.C.S.: 333248
Cathleen V. Cavanna (VP-HR)
Geoffrey Loftus (Chief Comml Officer)
Ralph Jenkins (Dir-Worldwide Sls & Mktg)
Sean Downey (CFO)
Jerry Aucoin (Dir-Worldwide Svcs)
Kevin Ray (Dir-R&D Printing Plates)
Avigdor Beiber (CTO)
Donn Goldstick (Reg Sls Mgr-Digital Printing Sys-North America)
Harry Manzi (Acct Mgr-Thermal Printing Plates-North America)
Scott Porter (Mgr-Sls-DIÂ® Sys-Orange County)
Sean McGovern (Mgr-Sls-CTP Systems & Printing Plates-Central)
Yuval Dubois (CEO)

Subsidiary (Non-US):

Presstek Europe Ltd.   (2)
Unit 30 Riverside Way, Uxbridge, UB8 2YF, Mddx, United Kingdom
Tel.: (44) 20 8745 8000
Web Site: http://www.presstek.com
Emp.: 15
Printing Machinery & Equipment Mfr
N.A.I.C.S.: 333248
Becky Blackstone (Mgr-HR)

MARK C. POPE ASSOCIATES INC.
4910 Martin Ct SE, Smyrna, GA 30082
Tel.: (770) 435-2471
Web Site: http://www.markcpope.com
Sales Range: $10-24.9 Million
Emp.: 63
Whslr of Electrical Apparatus & Equipment
N.A.I.C.S.: 423610
Stephen L. Josey (Pres & CEO)
Walter Acton (Asst Mgr-Parts)
Philip Harper (Mgr-Svc)

MARK CHEVROLET INC.
33200 Michigan Ave, Wayne, MI 48184-1876
Tel.: (734) 722-9100   MI
Web Site: http://www.markchevrolet.com
Sales Range: $25-49.9 Million
Emp.: 85
Sales of Automobiles
N.A.I.C.S.: 441110
Charles Cabana (Pres)

MARK CHRISTOPHER AUTO CENTER
2131 E Convention Center Way, Ontario, CA 91764-4495

Tel.: (909) 390-2900
Web Site: http://www.markchristopher.com
Year Founded: 1975
Sales Range: $75-99.9 Million
Emp.: 275
New Car Whslr
N.A.I.C.S.: 441110
Greg Heath (COO)
Dawn Strickland (Mgr-BDC)
Robert Montes (Mgr-Parts)
Sharon Borgo (Dir-Fin)

MARK CONSTRUCTION CO. INC.
421 Gold Medal Ct, Longwood, FL 32750
Tel.: (407) 831-6275
Web Site: http://www.markconstruction.com
Sales Range: $10-24.9 Million
Emp.: 15
Commercial & Office Building, New Construction
N.A.I.C.S.: 236220
Don Randall (VP-Sls & Mktg)
Jackie Chambers (Treas & Sec)
Todd Jorgensen (Pres)
Phil Jorgensen (CEO)

MARK DUNNING INDUSTRIES, INC.
100 Race Track Rd, Dothan, AL 36303
Tel.: (334) 983-1506
Web Site: http://www.markdunning.com
Year Founded: 1980
Sales Range: $10-24.9 Million
Emp.: 250
Residential Waste Management Services
N.A.I.C.S.: 562998
Mark Dunning (Pres)
Scott G. Smith (Reg Mgr-Sls)

MARK FACEY & COMPANY
225 N Main St, Bristol, CT 06010
Tel.: (860) 589-0221
Web Site: http://www.markfacey.com
Year Founded: 1986
Sales Range: $75-99.9 Million
Emp.: 2,000
Telemarketing Services
N.A.I.C.S.: 561422
Mark Facey (Pres)
Jeff Neistat (CFO & VP)
Jeanette Hopson (Dir-Customer Svc)

MARK HERSHEY FARMS INC.
479 Horseshoe Pike, Lebanon, PA 17042
Tel.: (717) 867-4624
Web Site: http://www.markhersheyfarms.com
Year Founded: 1936
Sales Range: $10-24.9 Million
Emp.: 30
Grain Mill Product Mfr
N.A.I.C.S.: 311119
Daryl Alger (Pres)
David Stanilla (Treas)

MARK JACOBSON & ASSOCIATES
32400 Telegraph Rd Ste 200, Bingham Farms, MI 48025
Tel.: (248) 642-8080
Web Site: http://www.markmanagementco.com
Rev.: $10,800,000
Emp.: 12
Apartment Building Construction
N.A.I.C.S.: 236117

MARK LINE INDUSTRIES

MARK LINE INDUSTRIES

Mark Line Industries—(Continued)
51687 County Rd 133, Bristol, IN 46507
Tel.: (574) 825-5851
Web Site: http://www.marklinein.com
Sales Range: $10-24.9 Million
Emp.: 100
Commercial Modular Offices
N.A.I.C.S.: 321991
George Kijak (Project Mgr)

MARK MITSUBISHI
1901 Eastbell Rd, Phoenix, AZ 85022
Tel.: (623) 934-1111
Web Site:
   http://www.markmitsuphoenix.com
Year Founded: 1995
Sales Range: $10-24.9 Million
Emp.: 50
New Car Retailer
N.A.I.C.S.: 441110
Dylan Mougel (Gen Mgr)
Patrick Lockwood (Gen Mgr-Sls)
Adam Struse (Mgr-Sls, Customer Svc, Fin, Mktg & Internet)
Nicholas Redondo (Dir-Fin)
Chet Stens (Mgr-Svc)
John Chernick (Mgr-Parts)

MARK MITSUBISHI SCOTTSDALE
6910 E Mcdowell Rd, Scottsdale, AZ 85257
Tel.: (480) 425-5300
Year Founded: 1996
Sales Range: $25-49.9 Million
Emp.: 80
Car Whslr
N.A.I.C.S.: 441110
Josh Spencer (Gen Mgr-Sls)

MARK MOTORS INC.
1765 Park Ave, Plover, WI 54467
Tel.: (715) 421-5000
Web Site:
   http://www.markmotors.com
Sales Range: $50-74.9 Million
Emp.: 45
Automobiles, New & Used
N.A.I.C.S.: 441110
Mark Olinyk (Pres)
Tim Durigan (Gen Mgr)
Dave Graczkowski (Mgr-Parts)
Dave Newsom (Mgr-Svcs)

MARK RICHEY WOODWORKING & DESIGN, INC.
40 Parker St, Newburyport, MA 01950
Tel.: (978) 499-3800
Web Site: http://www.markrichey.com
Sales Range: $10-24.9 Million
Emp.: 80
Millwork Services
N.A.I.C.S.: 321918
Mark Richey (Pres)
Teresa Richey (Treas)
Greg Porfido (COO)

MARK SCOTT CONSTRUCTION, INC.
PO Box 4658, Walnut Creek, CA 94596-0658
Tel.: (925) 944-0502
Web Site:
   http://www.mscommercialinc.com
Year Founded: 1989
Sales Range: $10-24.9 Million
Emp.: 80
Housing Construction Services
N.A.I.C.S.: 236117
Mark Scott (Owner)
Chris Trent (Project Mgr)

MARK SHALE
10441 Beaudin Blvd Ste 100, Woodridge, IL 60517-4987
Tel.: (630) 427-1100
Web Site: http://www.markshale.com
Year Founded: 1929
Sales Range: $200-249.9 Million
Emp.: 450
Retailer of Men's & Women's Upscale Traditional Clothing
N.A.I.C.S.: 458110
Brian Lewandowski (Mgr-Mens Div)

Subsidiaries:

Mark Shale Direct (1)
10441 Beaudin Blvd Ste 100, Woodridge, IL 60517 (100%)
Tel.: (630) 427-1100
Web Site: http://www.markshale.com
Sales Range: $25-49.9 Million
Emp.: 35
Retail Mens & Womens Upscale Traditional Clothing
N.A.I.C.S.: 458110

MARK STEEL CORPORATION
1230 W 200 S, Salt Lake City, UT 84104-1808
Tel.: (801) 521-0670   UT
Web Site: http://www.marksteel.net
Year Founded: 1968
Sales Range: $10-24.9 Million
Emp.: 125
Fabricated Plate Work
N.A.I.C.S.: 332313
Chad Spencer (COO)

MARK STEVENS INDUSTRIES INC.
4340 Will Rodgers Pkwy, Oklahoma City, OK 73108
Tel.: (405) 948-1077
Web Site:
   http://www.christianworldinc.com
Sales Range: $10-24.9 Million
Emp.: 20
Christian Music Soundtracks
N.A.I.C.S.: 334610
Mark Stevens (Pres & CEO)

MARK THOMAS MOTORS INC.
2315 Santiam Hwy SE, Albany, OR 97322
Tel.: (541) 967-9105
Web Site:
   http://www.markthomasmotors.com
Rev.: $12,900,000
Emp.: 40
Automobiles, New & Used
N.A.I.C.S.: 441110
Jason Tharp (Dir-Svcs)
Mark Patrzik (Gen Mgr)
Danielle Schippmann (Controller)

MARK WESTBY & ASSOCIATES, INC.
5335 S Sheridan, Tulsa, OK 74145
Tel.: (918) 632-0010
Web Site: http://www.mwestby.com
Year Founded: 2003
Rev.: $5,400,000
Emp.: 9
Logistics & Transportation
N.A.I.C.S.: 488510
Mark Westby (Pres)
Lance Thresher (Mgr)

MARK WRIGHT CONSTRUCTION INC.
3326 N Winstel Blvd, Tucson, AZ 85716
Tel.: (520) 323-7071
Web Site: http://mwci1.com
Rev.: $17,700,000
Emp.: 124
New Construction of Single-Family Houses
N.A.I.C.S.: 236220

MARK'S CARD SHOPS INC.
1430 SE Water Ave, Portland, OR 97204
Tel.: (503) 234-4331   OR
Web Site:
   http://www.markshallmark.com
Year Founded: 1990
Sales Range: $25-49.9 Million
Emp.: 600
Gift, Novelty & Souvenir Shop
N.A.I.C.S.: 459420
Jim Cox (Pres)

Subsidiaries:

Marks Inc. (1)
1097 Andover Pk E, Tukwila, WA 98188-7615
Tel.: (206) 575-8028
Rev.: $1,100,000
Emp.: 9
Nondurable Goods
N.A.I.C.S.: 424990

MARK-IT SMART INC.
128 E Dyer Rd Unit A, Santa Ana, CA 92707
Tel.: (714) 673-6400
Web Site:
   http://www.markitsmart.com
Year Founded: 1999
Sales Range: $1-9.9 Million
Emp.: 15
Promotional Items & Gifts
N.A.I.C.S.: 459420
Mark Ditteaux (Owner & Pres)
Ryan Paradee (VP-Sls-Casino)

MARK/TRECE INC.
2001 Stockton Rd, Joppa, MD 21085
Tel.: (410) 879-0060
Web Site: http://www.marktrece.com
Sales Range: $10-24.9 Million
Emp.: 200
Printing Plates
N.A.I.C.S.: 333248
Richard Godfrey (CEO)
Lee Grantham (VP)

MARKEL CORPORATION
4521 Highwoods Pkwy, Glen Allen, VA 23060-6148
Insurance Services
N.A.I.C.S.: 524298

MARKER SEVEN, INC.
300 Beale St # A, San Francisco, CA 94105-2090
Tel.: (415) 447-2841
Web Site:
   http://www.markerseven.com
Year Founded: 2001
Rev.: $1,600,000
Emp.: 26
Fiscal Year-end: 12/31/06
Data Processing And Preparation
N.A.I.C.S.: 518210
John Clauss (CEO)
Nicole Reber (Dir-Digital Mktg)
Scott Abbott (Dir-Creative)
Sallie Nelson (Dir-Client Svcs)

MARKET & JOHNSON, INC.
2350 Galloway St, Eau Claire, WI 54703-3472
Tel.: (715) 834-1213   WI
Web Site: http://www.market-johnson.com
Year Founded: 1948
Sales Range: $75-99.9 Million
Emp.: 200
General Building Contractors
N.A.I.C.S.: 236220
Jason Plante (Dir-Mktg)
Kevin Monson (Controller)
Gerry Sheak (Pres & CEO)

MARKET AMERICA REALTY

U.S. PRIVATE

AND INVESTMENTS, INC.
2147 First St, Fort Myers, FL 33901
Web Site:
   http://www.todaysbetterhomes.com
Sales Range: $25-49.9 Million
Emp.: 50
Real Estate Broker & Investment Services
N.A.I.C.S.: 531210
Gregg Fous (Founder & Pres)
Nils Richter (Mgr-Comml)
Julia Schultz (Mgr-Property)

MARKET AMERICA WORLDWIDE, INC.
1302 Pleasant Ridge Rd, Greensboro, NC 27409
Tel.: (336) 605-0040
Web Site:
   http://www.marketamerica.com
Year Founded: 1992
Sales Range: $150-199.9 Million
Product Brokerage & Internet Marketing Services
N.A.I.C.S.: 541519
James R. Ridinger (Pres & CEO)
Loren Ridinger (Sr Exec VP-Internet Retailing)
Dennis Franks (Exec VP)
Marty Weissman (Exec VP)
Marc Ashley (COO)
Joe Bolyard (Exec VP-Intl Dev)
Anthony Akers (VP-Comm)
Eddie Alberty (VP-Strategic Partnerships)
Michael Brady (CIO)
Clement D. Erhardt (Gen Counsel)
Chris Peddycord (VP-Bus Analysts)
Brandi Quinn (VP-Ops)
Sam Ritchie (VP-Res & Dev)
Eugene Wallace (CTO)
Andrew Weissman (VP)
Jim Winkler (VP-Sls)
Mark Lange (Dir-Quality Control)

MARKET BASKET
813 Franklin Lks Rd, Franklin Lakes, NJ 07417
Tel.: (201) 891-1329
Web Site:
   http://www.marketbasket.com
Sales Range: $25-49.9 Million
Emp.: 150
Provider of Meat & Fish Markets
N.A.I.C.S.: 445240
Travis Campbell (Mgr-Sushi)

MARKET BASKET FOOD STORE, INC.
1337 NC Hwy 16 S, Taylorsville, NC 28681-4180
Tel.: (828) 632-9230   NC
Year Founded: 1983
Sales Range: $25-49.9 Million
Emp.: 250
Grocery Stores
N.A.I.C.S.: 445131
Ronald Hunt (Pres)
Steve Hunt (VP)

MARKET CONTRACTORS LTD.
10250 NE Marx St, Portland, OR 97220
Tel.: (503) 255-0977
Web Site:
   http://www.marketcontractors.com
Sales Range: $10-24.9 Million
Emp.: 70
Commercial & Office Building, New Construction
N.A.I.C.S.: 236220
David Kay (Superintendent-Comml Construction)
Rick Rogers (COO & VP)
Thinh Tran (CTO)

Troy Gallagher *(Pres)*
Dana Free *(Acct Exec)*
James Gjesdal *(Superintendent-Field)*

Subsidiaries:

Financial Supermarkets, Inc. (1)
383 Clarkesville St, Cornelia, GA 30531
Tel.: (706) 778-1199
Web Site: http://www.supermarketbank.com
Rev.: $1,200,000
Emp.: 10
Supermarket Banking Branch Developer
N.A.I.C.S.: 561499
Roy E. Bell *(Pres & CEO)*
Judy M. Moreland *(Sr VP & Dir-Client Support & Trng)*
Gail M. Breedlove *(VP-Admin, Project & Sls Support)*
Tina H. Coleman *(Sr VP & Dir-Mktg)*
Kelly S. Franklin *(Controller)*
Lisa S. Harper *(CFO)*
C. Scott Johnson *(Sr VP & Dir-Retail)*
Linda K. Monnin *(Officer-Bus Dev)*
Randall J. Phillips *(VP & Sr Project Mgr)*
Kathleen B. Tench *(Sr VP-Admin & Retail)*
Patrick J. Flaherty *(Exec VP & Dir-Sls)*
Patricia A. Clemens *(Sr VP)*
Don A. Dixon *(Sr VP)*

MARKET DAY CORPORATION
555 W Pierce Rd Ste 200, Itasca, IL 60143
Tel.: (630) 285-1470
Web Site: http://www.marketday.com
Rev.: $235,000,000
Emp.: 100
Food Brokers; A Fundraising Food Cooperative, Providing Opportunities to Raise Money for Schools by Selling Food Products
N.A.I.C.S.: 424410
John Loftus *(Mgr-IT)*

MARKET DEVELOPMENT GROUP, INC.
5151 Wisconsin Ave NW 4th Fl, Washington, DC 20016
Tel.: (202) 298-8030
Web Site: http://www.mdginc.org
Year Founded: 1978
Rev.: $50,000,000
Emp.: 33
N.A.I.C.S.: 541810
W. Michael Gretschel *(Pres & CEO)*
John Alahouzos *(Exec VP)*
Ann Papp *(Sr VP)*
Mark Stancik *(Grp VP)*

Subsidiaries:

List America (1)
5151 Wisconsin Ave NW 4th Fl, Washington, DC 20016
Tel.: (202) 298-9206
Management Consulting Services
N.A.I.C.S.: 541611

National Outdoor Sports Advertising, Inc. (1)
5151 Wisconsin Ave NW, Washington, DC 20016
Tel.: (202) 965-9850
Emp.: 30
Advertising Services
N.A.I.C.S.: 541810
Mike Gretschel *(Pres)*

MARKET ENHANCEMENT GROUP, INC.
12463 Rancho Bernardo Rd Ste 108, San Diego, CA 92128-2143
Tel.: (800) 549-9327
Web Site: http://www.meg-research.com
Year Founded: 1977
Sales Range: $10-24.9 Million
Emp.: 192
Market Research
N.A.I.C.S.: 541910
Barry Quarles *(Pres)*
Rick Hoffman *(Sr Dir)*

MARKET FINDERS INSURANCE CORP.
9117 Leesgate Rd Ste 201, Louisville, KY 40222
Tel.: (502) 423-1800
Web Site: http://www.mfic.com
Sales Range: $10-24.9 Million
Emp.: 40
Insurance Services
N.A.I.C.S.: 524210
Joseph Miller *(CEO)*
Marcia Vires *(Mgr-Claims)*

MARKET FIRST, INC.
975 Cobb Place Blvd, Kennesaw, GA 30144
Tel.: (770) 425-9911
Web Site: http://www.redrhinomg.com
Year Founded: 1995
Rev.: $10,000,000
Emp.: 10
Provider of Marketing Programs
N.A.I.C.S.: 541860
Julie Henry *(CEO)*
Bernie Evans *(VP-Sls)*
Robert Henry *(Pres)*

MARKET FORCE INFORMATION, INC.
371 Centennial Pkwy Ste 210, Louisville, CO 80027
Tel.: (303) 536-1924
Web Site: http://www.marketforce.com
Year Founded: 2005
Sales Range: $50-74.9 Million
Emp.: 390
Business Consulting Services
N.A.I.C.S.: 541618
Jim Radcliff *(Pres-Theatrical Svcs)*
Madeleine Earl-Gray *(Dir-Ops)*
Ray Walsh *(CEO)*
Dan Weil *(VP-Strategic Relationships-North America)*
Emily Kehrberg *(VP-Ops-North America)*
Gail Funderburk *(VP-Strategic Relationships-North America)*
Matt Nydell *(Chief Legal & Dev Officer)*
Randy Law *(VP-Analytics & Insights-North America)*
Ryan Stewart *(VP-Ops-North America)*
Scott Griffith *(Chief Mktg & Sls Officer)*
Jeff DePiazza *(CTO)*

MARKET GROCERY COMPANY, INC.
16 Forest Pkwy Bldg K State Farmers Market, Forest Park, GA 30297
Tel.: (404) 361-8620
Web Site: http://www.marketgrocery.com
Year Founded: 1988
Sales Range: $10-24.9 Million
Emp.: 100
General Line Groceries
N.A.I.C.S.: 424410
Don A. Barnette *(Pres)*

MARKET LOGISTICS INC.
496 Garlington Rd Ste B, Greenville, SC 29615
Tel.: (864) 676-0309
Web Site: http://www.utilitypartners.com
Sales Range: $25-49.9 Million
Emp.: 25
Groceries, General Line
N.A.I.C.S.: 423110

MARKET MATCH MEDIA, INC.
1112 Mount Vernon St, Orlando, FL 32803
Tel.: (407) 641-0152
Web Site: http://www.digitalbrew.com
Year Founded: 2011
Sales Range: $1-9.9 Million
Emp.: 10
Advertising & Marketing Services
N.A.I.C.S.: 541810
Michael Cardwell *(Founder & Creative Dir)*
Teresa Huff *(Project Mgr)*
Beau Benson *(Dir-Animation)*
Amiet Gill *(Mgr-Bus Dev)*
Ryan Jarman *(Art Dir)*

MARKET PLACE INC.
521 W Diversey Pkwy, Chicago, IL 60614
Tel.: (773) 348-5721
Web Site: http://themarketplacechicago.com
Sales Range: $10-24.9 Million
Emp.: 75
Grocery Stores, Independent
N.A.I.C.S.: 445110
Peter Stellas *(Pres & Owner)*
George Stellas Jr. *(VP)*

MARKET PROBE INC.
2655 N Mayfair Rd, Milwaukee, WI 53226
Tel.: (414) 778-6000
Web Site: http://www.marketprobe.com
Sales Range: $25-49.9 Million
Emp.: 300
Market Research & Consulting Services
N.A.I.C.S.: 541910
Anne Wagner *(Sr VP)*
Joseph Retzer *(Chief Res Officer)*
Andrea Corrado *(VP)*
Dennis Syrkowski *(Exec VP)*

MARKET RESEARCH FOUNDATION
4153 Chain Bridge Rd, Fairfax, VA 22030
Tel.: (703) 865-7490
Web Site: http://www.marketresearchfoundation.org
Year Founded: 2006
Sales Range: $1-9.9 Million
Emp.: 4
Market Research Services
N.A.I.C.S.: 541715

MARKET SHARE DEVELOPMENT
516 N Blakely St, Dunmore, PA 18512
Tel.: (570) 961-3762
Web Site: http://www.market-shareinc.com
Sales Range: $10-24.9 Million
Emp.: 4
Graphic Design & Custom Printing Services
N.A.I.C.S.: 323111
Bethany Staples *(Sr Acct Mgr & Dir-Interactive Media)*

MARKET STAFF INC.
29 N Wacker Dr Ste 250, Chicago, IL 60606
Tel.: (312) 346-4971
Web Site: http://www.marketstaff.com
Year Founded: 1977
Rev.: $12,750,000
Emp.: 10
Provider of Human Resources Services
N.A.I.C.S.: 561330
Karen Felix *(Founder & Pres)*

MARKET TRANSPORT LTD.
110 N Marine Dr, Portland, OR 97217
Tel.: (503) 283-2405
Web Site: http://www.markettransport.com
Sales Range: $100-124.9 Million
Emp.: 500
Contract Haulers
N.A.I.C.S.: 484121
Cindy Miller *(Controller)*

MARKET VANTAGE, LLC
274 Main St Ste 5, Groton, MA 01450
Tel.: (978) 482-0130
Web Site: http://www.market-vantage.com
Sales Range: $1-9.9 Million
Internet Marketing
N.A.I.C.S.: 541613
Hans Riemer *(Pres & CEO)*
Darryl DeLong *(Dir-Client Svcs)*
Cindy Wilson *(Dir-Project Mgmt)*
Fred Bell *(Exec VP)*

MARKETCOM PUBLIC RELATIONS, LLC
36 E 23rd St Suite 602, New York, NY 10010
Tel.: (212) 537-5177
Web Site: http://www.marketcompr.com
Sales Range: Less than $1 Million
Emp.: 8
Marketing & Public Relations
N.A.I.C.S.: 541820
Greg Miller *(Pres)*
Rosalia Scampoli *(Sr Dir-Media)*
Laura Brophy *(Dir-Client Svcs)*

MARKETCOUNSEL
61 W Palisade Ave, Englewood, NJ 07631
Tel.: (201) 705-1200
Web Site: http://www.marketcounsel.com
Year Founded: 2000
Rev.: $3,100,000
Emp.: 28
Engineeering Services
N.A.I.C.S.: 541330
Daniel A. Bernstein *(Dir-Pro Svcs)*
Brian Hamburger *(Founder)*
Dan Bernstein *(Dir-R&D)*
Loren Morris *(Dir-Strategic Dev)*

MARKETEX COMPUTER CORP.
1601 Civic Center Dr Ste 206, Santa Clara, CA 95050-4109
Tel.: (408) 241-3677
Web Site: http://www.marketex.com
Year Founded: 1997
Sales Range: $10-24.9 Million
Emp.: 5
Computer Peripheral Equipment Rental & Leasing
N.A.I.C.S.: 532420
Nancy Fabrick *(VP-Ops)*
Russell Schneider *(Pres)*

MARKETFISH INC.
524 2nd Ave Ste 200, Seattle, WA 98104
Tel.: (206) 905-1090
Web Site: http://www.marketfish.com
Sales Range: $1-9.9 Million
Lead Generation Services
N.A.I.C.S.: 513140
Dave Scott *(Founder)*

MARKETING & CREATIVE SERVICES, INC.
2695 Inke Rd, Richmond, IN 47374-3707
Tel.: (765) 935-1127
Year Founded: 1982

MARKETING & CREATIVE SERVICES, INC.   U.S. PRIVATE

Marketing & Creative Services, Inc.—(Continued)
Sales Range: Less than $1 Million
Emp.: 2
N.A.I.C.S.: 541810

MARKETING & ENGINEERING SOLUTIONS INC.
625 Bear Run, Lewis Center, OH 43035
Tel.: (740) 201-8112
Web Site: http://www.mesinc.net
Year Founded: 2000
Sales Range: Less than $1 Million
Emp.: 88
Transportation
N.A.I.C.S.: 488999
Hiten Shah (Founder)

MARKETING ALTERNATIVES, INC.
300 Exchange Dr, Crystal Lake, IL 60014-7208
Tel.: (847) 719-2299
Web Site: http://www.mktalt.com
Year Founded: 1983
Emp.: 250
Advertising Agency
N.A.I.C.S.: 541810
Gary Jon Stanko (Pres)
Geraldine Costello (Sr VP-Strategic Bus Dev)
Ram Patibandla (CIO & Exec VP)
Anissa Fox (Dir-Fulfillment)
Kari Milinkovich (Mgr-Client Svcs)
Danielle Shelton (Acct Mgr)

MARKETING CONCEPTS GROUP
6 Old Field Rd, Weston, CT 06883
Tel.: (203) 454-0800
Web Site: http://www.mcgtec.com
Year Founded: 1981
Sales Range: Less than $1 Million
Emp.: 5
Advertising Agencies, Automotive, Brand Development, Collateral, Consumer Marketing, E-Commerce, High Technology, Internet/Web Design, Print, Sales Promotion, Sweepstakes
N.A.I.C.S.: 541810
David Weaver (Dir-Creative)
Paul D. Weaver (Pres)
Tomas Jablonski (CTO)
Lawrence Kilfoy (Mgr-Bus Dev)

MARKETING CONCEPTS OF MINNESOTA, INC.
130 Lake Ave, Spicer, MN 56288
Tel.: (320) 796-6245
Web Site: http://www.marketingconcepts.com
Rev.: $17,200,000
Emp.: 101
Mail Order Services
N.A.I.C.S.: 541430
Diane Buzzeo (CEO)
Michael Liebelt (Mgr-Web Adv)

MARKETING DOCTOR, INC.
55 Damon Rd Ste 1, Northampton, MA 01060
Tel.: (413) 341-5513   MA
Web Site: http://www.mymarketingdoctor.com
Year Founded: 2003
Sales Range: $1-9.9 Million
Emp.: 14
Online Advertising Services
N.A.I.C.S.: 541810
Janet Casey (Founder & CEO)
Carol Lucardi (Dir-Digital & Traditional Media Buying)
Beth Coushaine-Goddeau (Bus Mgr)
Kate Popp (Sls Dir)
Kiki Castiglione (Specialist-Comm)

MARKETING EVOLUTION, INC.
4364 Town Ctr Blvd Ste 320, El Dorado Hills, CA 95762
Tel.: (916) 933-7536
Web Site: http://www.marketingevolution.com
Sales Range: $10-24.9 Million
Emp.: 55
Software Development Services
N.A.I.C.S.: 541511
Rex Briggs (Founder & CEO)
Christine Grammier (Head-Partners & Alliances)
Shane Desrochers (Chief Revenue Officer)
Kristin Hambelton (CMO)
Michael Cohen (Chief Data Science & Analytics Officer & Sr VP)

MARKETING GROUP
880 Louis Dr, Warminster, PA 18974
Tel.: (215) 259-1500
Web Site: http://www.mgadvertising.com
Year Founded: 1975
Sales Range: $10-24.9 Million
Emp.: 37
Advertising Agencies
N.A.I.C.S.: 541810
Tom Gilmore (Sr Acct Exec)

MARKETING IN COLOR INC.
3414 W Bay to Bay Blvd, Tampa, FL 33629
Tel.: (813) 258-3771
Web Site: http://www.marketingincolor.com
Sales Range: $1-9.9 Million
Emp.: 10
Marketing Services
N.A.I.C.S.: 541613
Cheryl Parrish (Pres & CEO)
John Parrish (VP-Creative Svcs)
Herb Young (VP-Strategic Dev)
Jen Straw (Dir-PR & Social Media)
Bobbi Royak (Dir-Media-Print & Outdoor)
Tyler Freriks (Acct Exec)
MaryKay Scott (Acct Exec)
Angela Mitchell (Assoc Dir-Creative)
Diego Aguirre (Assoc Dir-Creative)
Lindsey Howe (Project Mgr)
Stephanie Lucas (Acct Exec)
Christopher Hayes (Editor-Video)

MARKETING INFORMATICS, INC.
5629 Professional Cir, Indianapolis, IN 46241
Tel.: (317) 788-4440
Web Site: http://www.marketinginformatics.com
Year Founded: 1987
Sales Range: $10-24.9 Million
Emp.: 15
National Direct Marketing Services
N.A.I.C.S.: 541860
Robert D. Massie (Owner)
Derrick L. Smith (Pres)
Marc Becher (Dir-Client Svcs)

MARKETING INNOVATORS INTERNATIONAL, INC.
9701 W Higgins Rd, Rosemont, IL 60018
Tel.: (847) 696-1111
Web Site: http://www.marketinginnovators.com
Year Founded: 1978
Sales Range: $75-99.9 Million
Emp.: 50
Management Incentive Products & Services
N.A.I.C.S.: 541612

Lois M. LeMenager (Founder, Chm & CEO)
Richard A. Blabolil (Pres)
Jig Sanani (VP-Tech Products)

MARKETING MANAGEMENT, INC.
4717 Fletcher Ave, Fort Worth, TX 76107-6826
Tel.: (817) 731-4176   TX
Web Site: http://www.mmibrands.com
Year Founded: 1966
Sales Range: $1-9.9 Million
Emp.: 250
Private Label Marketing Company
N.A.I.C.S.: 424410
Donna Smith (CFO & VP)
Randy Hurr (Pres)
Ed Mieskoski (VP)
Chandi Gmuer (VP-Consumer Sciences)
Lindsey Hurr (VP-Immotion Studios)
Tim Hauser (VP-Strategic Bus Alliances)
Pat Abbey (VP-HR)
Paul Nichols (VP-IT)

MARKETING MANIACS, INC.
25 Post St, San Jose, CA 95113
Tel.: (408) 280-0435
Web Site: http://www.maniacidea.com
Year Founded: 1998
Sales Range: Less than $1 Million
Emp.: 10
Marketing, Creative Services, Events & Promotions & Public Relations
N.A.I.C.S.: 541820
Darlene Tenes (Pres & CEO)

MARKETING MATTERS
2700 N 29th Ave Ste 103, Hollywood, FL 33020-1513
Tel.: (954) 925-1511
Web Site: http://www.marketingmatters.net
Year Founded: 1997
Sales Range: $10-24.9 Million
Emp.: 5
Advertising, Collateral, Entertainment, Event Planning & Marketing, Luxury, Newspaper, Product Placement, Public Relations, Publishing, Strategic Planning/Research
N.A.I.C.S.: 541810
Coleen Stern Leith (Founder & Pres)
Scott Moody (Dir)
Kyle E. Glass (Mgr-PR & Mktg)
Marie Holloway (Dir-Creative)
Morgan Roush (Dir-PR)

MARKETING OPTIONS, LLC
7986 Clyo Rd Ste B, Dayton, OH 45459-5010
Tel.: (937) 436-2648
Web Site: http://www.moptions.com
Year Founded: 1987
Sales Range: $25-49.9 Million
Emp.: 3
Advertising, E-Commerce, Internet/Web Design
N.A.I.C.S.: 541810
Barbara Weber Castilano (Owner & Pres)
Michael Krumm (Dir-Multimedia, Web & Tech)
Noah Medlen (Dir-Art)

MARKETING PARTNERS INC.
6583 Ruch Rd, Bethlehem, PA 18017
Tel.: (610) 443-2220
Web Site: http://www.marketingpartners.com
Year Founded: 1997
Sales Range: $1-9.9 Million
Emp.: 13

Direct Mail Programs, Website Development, Graphic Design, Social Media & In-House Printing
N.A.I.C.S.: 541430
Tina Green (Pres)

MARKETING PERFORMANCE GROUP, INC.
4755 Technology Way Ste 103, Boca Raton, FL 33431
Tel.: (561) 988-2181   FL
Web Site: http://www.marketingperformancegroup.com
Year Founded: 1986
Sales Range: $25-49.9 Million
Emp.: 10
Media Buying Services
N.A.I.C.S.: 541810
Cindy Kurtz (Principal)
Brad Kurtz (Principal)

MARKETING SOLUTIONS UNLIMITED, LLC
109 Talcott Rd, West Hartford, CT 06110
Tel.: (860) 523-0670
Web Site: http://www.msuprint.com
Direct Mail Advertising
N.A.I.C.S.: 541860
Heidi Buckley (Founder & CEO)
Eric Pritchard (Pres)

Subsidiaries:

Paladin Commercial Printers, LLC   (1)
300 Hartford Ave, Newington, CT 06111
Tel.: (860) 953-4900
Web Site: http://www.paladinp.com
Commercial Printing
N.A.I.C.S.: 323111
Jeff Long (Acct Exec)

MARKETING SUPPORT, INC.
200 E Randolph Dr Ste 5000, Chicago, IL 60601
Tel.: (312) 565-0044   IL
Web Site: http://www.msinet.com
Year Founded: 1962
Rev.: $101,750,000
Emp.: 90
N.A.I.C.S.: 541810
Stacy Gelman (Exec VP)
Molly Dineen (Dir-Media)
Jerry Barone (Dir-Creative)

MARKETING TECHNOLOGY CONCEPTS, INC.
1827 Walden Office Sq Ste 200, Schaumburg, IL 60173
Tel.: (847) 303-0022
Web Site: http://www.mtcperformance.com
Sales Range: $25-49.9 Million
Emp.: 30
Incentives Fulfillment & Management Services
N.A.I.C.S.: 541611
George A. Kriza (Pres & CEO)

MARKETING VISIONS, INC.
520 White Plains Rd Ste 500, Tarrytown, NY 10591-5118
Tel.: (914) 631-3900
Web Site: http://www.marketingvisions.com
Year Founded: 1986
Sales Range: $1-9.9 Million
Emp.: 8
Advetising Agency
N.A.I.C.S.: 541810
H. Jay Sloofman (Pres)

MARKETING WORKS, INC.
740 Lakeview Plz Blvd Ste 100, Worthington, OH 43085
Tel.: (614) 540-5520

Web Site: http://www.marketing-works.net
Sales Range: Less than $1 Million
Emp.: 10
Advetising Agency
N.A.I.C.S.: 541810
Stacy Wood *(Dir-Client Svc)*
Tom Matthews *(VP)*
Alexandra Can *(Acct Mgr)*
Lauren Hartman *(Dir-Acct Svcs)*

MARKETING WORKSHOP INC.
3725 Da Vinci Ct Ste 200, Norcross, GA 30092
Tel.: (770) 449-6767
Web Site: http://www.mwshop.com
Sales Range: $10-24.9 Million
Emp.: 30
Market Analysis Research
N.A.I.C.S.: 541910
James H. Nelems *(CEO)*
Randy Kosloski *(VP-Client Svcs)*
Alec Schendzelos *(VP-Client Svcs)*
Cari Pirello *(Pres)*
Cristina Flores *(Mgr-Mktg)*
David Nelems *(Dir-Innovation)*
Eddie King *(Mgr-IT)*
Felicia Seabolt *(Sr Mgr-Data)*
Marvin Collins *(Sr Mgr-Data)*
Steve Pugh *(Sr Mgr-Data)*
Rohan Ullal *(Dir-Mktg Sciences)*

MARKETINGPROFS, LLC
160 Greentree Dr Ste 101, Dover, DE 19904
Tel.: (866) 557-9625
Web Site: http://www.marketingprofs.com
Year Founded: 2000
Sales Range: $1-9.9 Million
Marketing Consulting Services
N.A.I.C.S.: 541613
Allen Weis *(Founder & CEO)*
Ann Handley *(Chief Content Officer)*
Aaron Lorentz *(CTO & Exec VP)*
Sharon Hudson *(VP-Mktg & Svcs)*
Valerie Witt *(VP-Pro Dev Solutions)*

MARKETLAB, INC.
6850 Southbelt Dr, Caledonia, MI 49316
Tel.: (616) 656-2484 MI
Web Site: http://www.marketlabinc.com
Year Founded: 1994
Emp.: 100
Medical & Healthcare Products Distr
N.A.I.C.S.: 423450
Heather Shank-Elmer *(Mgr-HR)*
Phil Lloyd *(Dir-IT)*
Steven Bosio *(Pres)*
Linda Hurley *(Exec VP-Mdsg & Product Dev)*

Subsidiaries:

Medi-Tech International Corporation (1)
26 Ct St Ste 1301, Brooklyn, NY 11242-1113
Web Site: http://www.medi-techintl.com
Surgical Appliance & Supplies Mfr
N.A.I.C.S.: 339113
Jacqueline Fortunato *(CEO)*

MARKETNET SERVICES, LLC
14998 Cleveland St Ste S, Spring Lake, MI 49456
Tel.: (616) 847-7992
Web Site: http://www.marketnetservices.com
Year Founded: 1996
Sales Range: $1-9.9 Million
Emp.: 20
Lead Management Software
N.A.I.C.S.: 513210
Steve Rajkovich *(Dir-Database Dev)*
J. Troke *(Pres)*

MARKETOPIA, LLC
3600 75th Ter N, Pinellas Park, FL 33781
Web Site: http://www.marketopia.com
Year Founded: 2014
Sales Range: $1-9.9 Million
Emp.: 85
Digital Marketing Services
N.A.I.C.S.: 541810
Terry Hedden *(CEO)*
Andra Hedden *(CMO)*
Arnie Perez *(Dir-Global Channel Programs)*
Heather Hurd *(Dir-Content Mktg)*
Jennifer Layton *(Dir-Traffic & Production)*

MARKETPATH, INC.
3850 Priority Way South Dr Ste 100, Indianapolis, IN 46240
Tel.: (317) 660-0209
Web Site: http://www.marketpath.com
Year Founded: 2001
Sales Range: $1-9.9 Million
Emp.: 6
Content Management Software
N.A.I.C.S.: 513210
Matt Zentz *(Founder & CEO)*
Kevin Kennedy *(CMO)*
Adam Brand *(VP-Creative & Client Svcs)*

MARKETPLACE HOMES
17197 N Laurel Park Dr Ste 340, Livonia, MI 48152
Tel.: (734) 862-4750
Web Site: http://www.marketplacehomes.com
Year Founded: 2002
Sales Range: $1-9.9 Million
Emp.: 52
Real Estate
N.A.I.C.S.: 531210
Shawn Dawson *(Coord-Property Mgmt)*
Steven Ubelhor *(Mgr-Solutions)*
Mike Kalis *(CEO)*
Mark Shaftner *(COO)*
Leslie Owens *(Dir-Comm)*
Jon Wilson *(VP-Customer Svc)*
Chintan Pathak *(VP-Ops)*

MARKETRESEARCH.COM
11200 Rockville Pike Ste 504, Rockville, MD 20852
Tel.: (240) 747-3093
Web Site: http://www.marketresearch.com
Year Founded: 1998
Rev.: $32,200,000
Emp.: 105
Information Retrieval Services
N.A.I.C.S.: 519290
Robert Granader *(Chm & CEO)*
Kelly Carlson *(VP-Global Ops)*
Rocco DiStefano *(VP-Sls)*

Subsidiaries:

The Freedonia Group, Inc. (1)
767 Beta Dr, Cleveland, OH 44143
Tel.: (440) 684-9600
Web Site: http://www.freedoniagroup.com
Sales Range: $1-9.9 Million
Emp.: 100
Industry Market Research & Analysis
N.A.I.C.S.: 541910
Jennifer Neumore *(Mgr-Agent Rels)*
Corinne Gangloff *(Dir-Media Rels)*
Paul Goehrke *(Mgr-Subscription Sls)*

MARKETSHARE PLUS, INC.
12730 Coldwater Rd Ste 102, Fort Wayne, IN 46845
Tel.: (260) 497-9988
Web Site: http://www.marketshareplus.com
Year Founded: 1992
Sales Range: Less than $1 Million
Emp.: 5
N.A.I.C.S.: 541810
Thomas D. Mattern *(Pres)*

MARKETSHARE PUBLICATIONS, INC.
7171 W 95th St Ste 600, Overland Park, KS 66212
Tel.: (913) 338-3360
Web Site: http://www.marketsharepubs.com
Sales Range: $10-24.9 Million
Emp.: 40
Publisher of Consumer Card Packs
N.A.I.C.S.: 541860
Rod Chapin *(Sr Acct Mgr)*
Susie Benson *(Sr Acct Mgr)*

Subsidiaries:

Direct Response Decks Inc. (1)
4347 S 90th St, Omaha, NE 68127-1309
Tel.: (402) 339-9900
Web Site: http://www.directresponselists.com
Rev.: $2,500,000
Emp.: 32
Miscellaneous Publishing
N.A.I.C.S.: 513199

MARKETSMITH, INC.
2 Wing Dr, Cedar Knolls, NJ 07927
Tel.: (973) 889-0006
Web Site: http://www.marketsmithinc.com
Year Founded: 1999
Sales Range: $25-49.9 Million
Emp.: 23
Marketing Consulting Services
N.A.I.C.S.: 541613
Monica C. Smith *(Founder & CEO)*
Michael Waksbaum *(Sr VP-Plng)*
Nasir Michael *(CFO)*
Carina Pologruto *(Chief Innovation Officer)*
Davey Rosenbaum *(Sr VP-Res)*
Steve Mickolajczyk *(VP-Client Svcs)*
Nicole Malino *(Sr VP-Client Svcs)*
Laura Buoncuore *(VP & Creative Dir)*
Rob Bochicchio *(Pres)*
Norman Lane *(Exec VP-Media Investment)*
Jon Renner *(Exec VP-Creative Svcs)*
Gina Callan *(Sr VP & Media Dir)*
Larry Durst *(Sr VP & Exec Creative Dir)*

Subsidiaries:

Brushfire, Inc. (1)
2 Wing Dr, Cedar Knolls, NJ 07927
Tel.: (973) 871-1700
Web Site: http://www.brushfireinc.com
Advertising Agency Services
N.A.I.C.S.: 541810
Jon Renner *(Exec VP-Client Svcs)*
Lois P. Marks *(Exec VP-Client Svcs)*
Gina Callan *(Dir-Media Svcs)*
Jill B. Draper *(Pres)*

MARKETSPHERE CONSULTING, LLC
14301 First National Bank Pkwy Ste 1011, Omaha, NE 68154
Tel.: (402) 392-4000
Web Site: http://www.marketsphere.com
Year Founded: 2002
Sales Range: $50-74.9 Million
Emp.: 15
Professional Services Consulting Firm
N.A.I.C.S.: 541618
Lonnie Janecek *(VP)*
Steve Sestak *(CEO)*

MARKETVISION
8647 Wurzbach Rd Ste J100, San Antonio, TX 78240
Tel.: (210) 222-1933
Web Site: http://www.mvculture.com
Year Founded: 1998
Sales Range: $10-24.9 Million
Emp.: 37
Advetising Agency
N.A.I.C.S.: 541810
Yvonne Garcia *(Founder & CEO)*
Norma Casillas *(VP-HR & Bus Ops)*
Frenchie Guajardo *(Exec VP-Shopper & Digital Mktg)*
Alexis Baldwin-Scarcliff *(VP & Dir-Production Svcs)*
Susan Evangelista *(VP-Ops, Promos & Client Svcs)*
Colleen Love *(VP-Fin)*
Pam Salazar *(Dir-Content, Comm Strategy & Community Outreach)*
Luis A. Garcia *(Pres)*

MARKEY MACHINE LLC
7266 8th Ave S, Seattle, WA 98108
Tel.: (206) 622-4697 WA
Web Site: https://markeymachine.com
Year Founded: 2022
Marine Deck Equipment & Winch Manufacturing
N.A.I.C.S.: 488390
Blaine Dempke *(Owner & CEO)*

Subsidiaries:

JonRie InterTech LLC (1)
30 Bolton Ln, West Creek, NJ 08092
Tel.: (609) 978-3523
Web Site: http://www.marinewinch.com
Marine Winch Systems Design & Manufacturing
N.A.I.C.S.: 488390
Brandon Durar *(Founder)*

MARKEYS AUDIO VISUAL INC.
2365 Enterprise Park Pl, Indianapolis, IN 46218
Tel.: (317) 783-1155
Web Site: http://www.markeys.com
Year Founded: 1959
Sales Range: $10-24.9 Million
Emp.: 160
Audio-Visual Equipment & Supply Rental
N.A.I.C.S.: 532289
Mark Miller *(CEO)*

Subsidiaries:

Ironman Sound Industries, LLC (1)
290 Hanley Industrial Dr, Brentwood, MO 63144-1907
Tel.: (314) 494-7349
Web Site: http://www.ironmansound.com
Amusement & Recreation Industries
N.A.I.C.S.: 713990
Bob Horner *(Pres)*
Kevin Beabout *(Mgr-Production)*

MARKFEST INC.
1613 N Central Ave, Marshfield, WI 54449
Tel.: (715) 384-8866
Rev.: $30,000,000
Emp.: 310
Supermarkets & Other Grocery Stores
N.A.I.C.S.: 445110
Mark Skogen *(Pres)*
David Skogen *(Chm)*
Kirk Stoa *(CFO & Exec VP)*
Jeff Main *(VP-IT)*

MARKHAM NORTON MOSTELLER WRIGHT & COMPANY, P.A.
8961 Conference Dr Ste 1, Fort Myers, FL 33919
Tel.: (239) 433-5554
Web Site: http://www.markham-norton.com
Year Founded: 1988

MARKHAM NORTON MOSTELLER WRIGHT & COMPANY, P.A. U.S. PRIVATE

Markham Norton Mosteller Wright & Company, P.A.—(Continued)
Sales Range: $1-9.9 Million
Emp.: 30
Accounting Services
N.A.I.C.S.: 541211
L. Gail Markham (Founder & Partner-Litigation Support & Forensic Acctg)
Joni L. Norton (Partner-Consulting)
Randy L. Wright (Partner-Tax)

MARKHAM WOODS PRESS PUBLISHING CO., INC.
1756 Saddleback Ridge Rd, Apopka, FL 32703
Tel.: (407) 462-3177   FL
Web Site:
http://www.opportunistmagazine.com
Year Founded: 2006
Online Magazine Publisher
N.A.I.C.S.: 513120
Donna Rayburn (Pres, Treas, Sec & Publr)
Leslie Stone (Mng Editor)

MARKIN TUBING, INC.
1 Markin Ln, Wyoming, NY 14591
Tel.: (585) 495-6211   DE
Web Site:
http://www.markintubing.com
Year Founded: 1958
Sales Range: $75-99.9 Million
Emp.: 160
Mfr of Cold Rolled Electrical Welded Mechanical Steel Tubing
N.A.I.C.S.: 331210
Arthur Smith (VP-Sls)
Jim Coates (Mgr-Quality Sys)

MARKLAND INDUSTRIES INC.
1111 E McFadden Ave, Santa Ana, CA 92705
Tel.: (714) 245-4923
Web Site:
http://www.marklandindustries.com
Rev.: $30,000,000
Emp.: 170
Mfr of Motorcycle Accessories
N.A.I.C.S.: 336991
Donald R. Markland (Pres)
Miguel Armenta (Mgr-Environmental & Laboratory)

MARKLEY MOTORS INC.
3401 S College Ave, Fort Collins, CO 80525
Tel.: (970) 226-2213
Web Site:
http://www.markleymotors.com
Sales Range: $75-99.9 Million
Emp.: 150
Automobiles, New & Used
N.A.I.C.S.: 441110
Doug Markley (Pres)
Roger Belisle (Gen Mgr)
Steve Roper (Mgr-Sls)

MARKLUND CHILDREN'S HOME
1 S 450 Wyatt Dr, Geneva, IL 60134
Tel.: (630) 593-5500   IL
Web Site: http://www.marklund.org
Year Founded: 1957
Rev.: $25,620,607
Assets: $41,870,715
Liabilities: $3,017,743
Net Worth: $38,852,972
Emp.: 393
Fiscal Year-end: 06/30/18
Disabled People Health Care Services
N.A.I.C.S.: 624120

Gunjan Patel (Dir-Children's Svcs)
Gilbert Fonger (Pres & CEO)
Diana Book (Dir-Facility Svcs)
Heather Graves (Chief Dev Officer)

MARKMANS DIAMOND BROKERS INC.
6932 Kingston Pike, Knoxville, TN 37919
Tel.: (865) 584-0247
Web Site:
http://www.markmansdiamonds.com
Sales Range: $10-24.9 Million
Emp.: 40
Jewelry; Precious Stones & Precious Metals
N.A.I.C.S.: 458310
Roy Mullinax (Mgr-Stores)

MARKMASTER, INC.
11111N 46th St, Tampa, FL 33617
Tel.: (813) 988-6000
Web Site:
http://www.markmasterinc.com
Year Founded: 1933
Sales Range: $1-9.9 Million
Emp.: 80
Sign Mfr
N.A.I.C.S.: 339950
Ron Govin (Chm)
Kevin Govin (CEO)

MARKO FOAM PRODUCTS, INC.
2500 White Rd Ste A, Irvine, CA 92614
Tel.: (951) 272-4700   DE
Web Site: http://www.markofoam.com
Year Founded: 1961
Sales Range: $10-24.9 Million
Emp.: 15
Plastics Foam Products
N.A.I.C.S.: 326150
Donald J. Peterson (Chm)
Ty Peterson (Pres)

MARKQUART INC.
2191 S Prairie View Rd, Chippewa Falls, WI 54729
Tel.: (715) 833-0450
Web Site: https://www.markquart.com
Year Founded: 1981
Car Dealer
N.A.I.C.S.: 441110

Subsidiaries:

Markquart Toyota   (1)
1844 Commercial Blvd, Chippewa Falls, WI 54729
Tel.: (715) 834-4440
Web Site: http://www.markquarttoyota.com
Sales Range: $25-49.9 Million
Emp.: 200
Car Dealer
N.A.I.C.S.: 441120
Steven Stensen (Mgr-Sls)
Terry Huppert (Mgr-Sls)
Josh Zuleger (Mgr-Sls)
Brian Brunner (Mgr-Internet)
Pete Taylor (Mgr-Inventory)
Matt Murray (Dir-F&I)
Cindy Halberg (Bus Mgr)
Joel Henchel (Bus Mgr)
Justin Babel (Asst Mgr-Svc)
Chad Larson (Asst Mgr-Svc)

R V World, Inc.   (1)
7405 Highway 10 NW, Anoka, MN 55303
Tel.: (763) 712-1393
Web Site: http://www.rvworldmn.com
Sales Range: $1-9.9 Million
Emp.: 20
Recreational Vehicle Dealers
N.A.I.C.S.: 441210
Darren Mann (Gen Mgr)
Kevin Strusz (Mgr-Bus)
Justin Kehner (Office Dir)
Matt D. Ciaciura (Mgr-Svc)

MARKS BROTHERS, INC.
9455 NW 104th St, Medley, FL 33178
Tel.: (305) 805-6900
Web Site:
http://www.marksbrothersinc.com
Rev.: $14,700,000
Emp.: 115
Highway Street & Bridge Construction
N.A.I.C.S.: 237310
Martin Marks (Pres)

MARKS CRANE & RIGGING CO. LTD.
6501 E I H 20, Odessa, TX 79762
Tel.: (432) 337-1538
Web Site:
http://www.markscrane.com
Equipment Rental & Leasing Services
N.A.I.C.S.: 532412
David Landreth (Branch Mgr)
Gus Chavarria (Filed Supvr-Sls)
Henry Enriquez (Field Supvr-Sls)
Karl Ballantine (Mgr-Ops)
Kurt Ballantine (Branch Mgr)

MARKS PANETH LLP
685 3rd Ave 5th Fl, New York, NY 10017
Tel.: (212) 503-8800   NY
Web Site:
http://www.markspaneth.com
Year Founded: 1907
Accounting, Auditing, Tax & Consulting Services
N.A.I.C.S.: 541211
Steven Eliach (Principal & Head-Tax Svcs)
Harry Moehringer (Mng Partner)
Diane Paoletta (CMO)
Debbie Davidman (CIO)
Brian L. Fox (CFO & COO)
Steven D. Sacks (Chief Human Resource Officer)
Lisa Minniti-Soska (Partner-Real Estate Grp)
Anya L. Naschak (Dir-Advisory Svcs Grp)

MARKSNELSON LLC
1310 E 104th St Ste 300, Kansas City, MO 64131-4504
Tel.: (816) 743-7700   KS
Web Site:
http://www.marksnelsoncpa.com
Sales Range: $1-9.9 Million
Emp.: 160
Accounting & Consulting Services
N.A.I.C.S.: 541211
Mark Radetic (Mng Partner)
Jeff Marks (Partner)
Dennis Nelson (Partner)
Mary Lou Hamlin (Mgr-Tax)
Brett Hedberg (Mgr-Acctg Svcs & Bus Advisory)
Adam Collyer (Partner)
Alana Neale (Mgr-Consulting)
Sarah Schiltz (Partner)
Tammy Siegrist (Partner)
Shannon Wolcott (Mgr-Tax)
Beth Van Leeuwen (Mgr-Tax)
Rachel Bertelsmeier (Mgr-Specialty Svcs Dept)
Jack Maier (Mgr-Assurance & Bus Advisory Dept)
Shari Fox (Partner-Tax)

MARKSTEIN BEVERAGE CO. UNION CITY
65 Oak CT, Danville, CA 94526
Tel.: (925) 755-5739
Sales Range: $10-24.9 Million
Emp.: 100
Beer & Other Fermented Malt Liquors Distributors
N.A.I.C.S.: 424810

Cynthia Hardin (Mgr-Community Outreach)

MARKWEST PINNACLE LP
2500 City West Blvd Ste 740, Houston, TX 77042
Tel.: (713) 965-9151
Web Site: http://www.markwest.com
Sales Range: $25-49.9 Million
Emp.: 8
Natural Gas Transmission
N.A.I.C.S.: 211130
Ted Smith (Sr VP & Controller)

MARKWINS INTERNATIONAL CORPORATION
22067 Ferrero Pkwy, City of Industry, CA 91789
Tel.: (909) 595-8898   CA
Web Site: http://www.markwins.com
Year Founded: 1984
Cosmetic Preparations
N.A.I.C.S.: 325620
Eric Chen (Founder & CEO)
Jane Gosal (Mgr-Mdsg)
David Tsai (Mgr-Mgmt Info Sys)
Leslie Hernandez (CFO)
Eric Weeks (Pres-Sls & Revenue-North America, Canada & Mexico)

Subsidiaries:

Physicians Formula Holdings, Inc.   (1)
22067 Fearro, City of Industry, CA 91789
Tel.: (626) 334-3395
Sales Range: $75-99.9 Million
Emp.: 146
Holding Company; Cosmetics Mfr & Whslr
N.A.I.C.S.: 551112

Subsidiary (Domestic):

Physicians Formula Cosmetics, Inc.   (2)
22067 Serrero Pkwy, City of Industry, CA 91789
Tel.: (626) 334-3395
Web Site: http://www.physiciansformula.com
Sales Range: $75-99.9 Million
Emp.: 146
Cosmetics Mfr
N.A.I.C.S.: 325620
Bill George (CEO)

MARLABS, INC.
1 Corporate Pl S, Piscataway, NJ 08854
Tel.: (732) 287-7800
Web Site: http://www.marlabs.com
Year Founded: 1996
Sales Range: $50-74.9 Million
Emp.: 1,200
Information Technology Services & Consultants
N.A.I.C.S.: 519290
Siby Vadakekkara (CEO)
Henrik De Gyor (Dir-Digital Asset Mgmt Svcs)
Sanjay Vidyadharan (CIO & Chief Legal Officer)
Krishnan Ramachandran (CFO)
Anil Raghavan (Chief Delivery Officer)
Jay Nair (COO & Sr VP)
Srinivasan Balram (Co-Founder & CTO)
Manish Singhvi (CFO)
Venu Nambiar (VP-Brand & Mktg)
Vikas Kumar (Chief Comml Officer & Exec VP)

Subsidiaries:

Marlabs Software Private Ltd.   (1)
Koramangala Industrial Estate, Bengaluru, 560 034, India
Tel.: (91) 80 51217421
Web Site: http://www.marlabs.com
IT Services
N.A.I.C.S.: 541511

COMPANIES

Marlabs, Inc. (1)
2299 Brodhead Rd Suite L&M, Bethlehem, PA 18020
Tel.: (610) 691-6744
Web Site: http://www.marlabs.com
IT Services
N.A.I.C.S.: 611420

MARLBORO MANUFACTURING, INC.
11750 Marlboro Ave NE, Alliance, OH 44601
Tel.: (330) 935-2445
Web Site:
http://www.marlborohinge.com
Year Founded: 1960
Sales Range: $10-24.9 Million
Emp.: 50
Hardware Mfr
N.A.I.C.S.: 332510
James F. Cain (Founder)

MARLBOROUGH SAVINGS BANK
81 Granger Blvd, Marlborough, MA 01752
Tel.: (508) 481-8300
Web Site: http://www.agreatbank.com
Rev.: $13,000,000
Emp.: 190
Savings & Loan Associations, Not Federally Chartered
N.A.I.C.S.: 522180
Inna Voloshina (Branch Mgr)
Linda Maguire (Branch Mgr)
Ellen W. Dorian (Exec VP-Retail Banking)
Christopher DiBenedetto (Sr VP-Enterprise Risk Mgmt)
Donna Briscoll (Branch Mgr)
Donna Driscoll (Mgr-Sudbury)
Judy Bell (Mgr-Marlborough Post Road)
Nicole Ostergren (Mgr-Northborough)
Sean Coyle (Mgr-Westborough)
Sue Mankaruos (Mgr-Southborough)

MARLETTE REGIONAL HOSPITAL
2770 Main St, Marlette, MI 48453
Tel.: (989) 635-4000 MI
Web Site:
http://www.marletteregionalhospital.org
Year Founded: 1951
Sales Range: $25-49.9 Million
Emp.: 445
Community Health Care Services
N.A.I.C.S.: 621498
Dan Babcock (CEO)

MARLEX PHARMACEUTICALS, INC.
50 Mccullough Dr, New Castle, DE 19720
Tel.: (302) 328-3355
Web Site:
http://www.marlexpharm.com
Sales Range: $10-24.9 Million
Emp.: 35
Third Party Over-the-Counter Pharmaceutical, Vitamin & Nutritional Supplement Mfr & Distr
N.A.I.C.S.: 325412
Sarav Patel (Pres)

MARLIN & ASSOCIATES NEW YORK LLC
600 Lexington Ave 36th Fl, New York, NY 10022
Tel.: (212) 257-6300
Web Site: http://www.marlinllc.com
Year Founded: 2002
Sales Range: $1-9.9 Million
Emp.: 25
Administrative Management & General Management Consulting Services
N.A.I.C.S.: 541611
Ken Marlin (Founder & Mng Partner)
Michael Maxworthy (Founder & Partner)
Jason Panzer (COO & Chief Compliance Officer)
Afsaneh Naimollah (Founder)

MARLIN COMPANY
10 Research Pkwy, Wallingford, CT 06492
Tel.: (203) 249-9800
Web Site:
http://www.themarlincompany.com
Sales Range: $10-24.9 Million
Emp.: 100
Pamphlets: Publishing & Printing
N.A.I.C.S.: 513130
David W. Thibault (VP-Fin)
Carolyn Voelkening (Dir-Content)
Frank Kenna III (Pres & CEO)

MARLIN EQUITY PARTNERS, LLC
338 Pier Ave, Hermosa Beach, CA 90254
Tel.: (310) 364-0100 DE
Web Site:
http://www.marlinequity.com
Year Founded: 2005
Privater Equity Firm
N.A.I.C.S.: 523999
David McGovern (Co-Founder, Chm & CEO)
Nick Kaiser (Co-Founder & Sr Mng Dir)
Peter Spasov (Sr Mng Dir)
Peter Chung (Mng Dir)
Ryan Wald (Mng Dir)
Nicholas Lukens (Mng Dir)
Evan Smith (Mng Dir & Principal)
Alex Beregovsky (Mng Dir)

Subsidiaries:

AVI-SPL, Inc. (1)
6301 Benjamin Rd Ste 101, Tampa, FL 33634
Tel.: (813) 884-7168
Web Site: http://www.avispl.com
Holding Company; Audio Video Communications Technology Products & Services
N.A.I.C.S.: 551112
John Zettel (CEO)
Steve Benjamin (Exec VP)
Steve Palmer (CFO)
John Murphy (COO)

Branch (Domestic):

AVI-SPL, Inc. - Chicago (2)
2266 Palmer Dr, Schaumburg, IL 60173
Tel.: (847) 437-7712
Web Site: http://www.avispl.com
Audio Visual Equipment Support Services & Whslr
N.A.I.C.S.: 423620

AVI-SPL, Inc. - Dallas (2)
13859 Diplomat Dr Ste 180, Dallas, TX 75234
Tel.: (972) 243-4422
Web Site: http://www.avispl.com
Emp.: 50
Audio Visual Equipment Support Services
N.A.I.C.S.: 811210
Cory Vankleeck (Gen Mgr)

AVI-SPL, Inc. - Fort Lauderdale (2)
772 S Military Trail, Deerfield Beach, FL 33442
Tel.: (954) 938-9382
Web Site: http://www.avispl.com
Audio Visual Equipment Support Services & Whslr
N.A.I.C.S.: 423620
Michael Arencibia (Gen Mgr)

AVI-SPL, Inc. - Jacksonville (2)
9143 Phillips Hwy Ste 450, Jacksonville, FL 32256
Tel.: (904) 281-2714
Web Site: http://www.avispl.com
Audio Visual Equipment Support Services & Whslr
N.A.I.C.S.: 423620

AVI-SPL, Inc. - Orlando (2)
337 Northlake Blvd Ste 1004, Orlando, FL 32701
Tel.: (407) 786-5000
Web Site: http://www.avispl.com
Audio Visual Equipment Support Services & Whslr
N.A.I.C.S.: 423620

AVI-SPL, Inc. - Tallahassee (2)
6753 Thomasville Rd, Tallahassee, FL 32312-3966
Tel.: (850) 894-3030
Web Site: http://www.avispl.com
Audio Visual Equipment Support Services & Whslr
N.A.I.C.S.: 423620

AVI-SPL, Inc. - Washington, D.C. (2)
540 B Huntmar Park Dr Ste B, Herndon, VA 20170
Tel.: (703) 796-9011
Web Site: http://www.avispl.com
Emp.: 60
Audio Visual Equipment Support Services & Whslr
N.A.I.C.S.: 423620

Subsidiary (Domestic):

Digital Video Networks LLC (2)
9105 E Del Camino Ste 100, Scottsdale, AZ 85258
Tel.: (480) 588-3511
Web Site:
http://www.digitalvideonetworks.com
System Integration Services
N.A.I.C.S.: 541512
Bill Blair (Founder & Mng Partner)
Tom Kertesz (CFO)
Dan Frantz (Sr Project Mgr)
Lee Toone (Reg Mgr)

Signal Perfection Ltd. (2)
9180 Rumsey Rd Ste B-12, Columbia, MD 21045
Tel.: (410) 964-8100
Web Site: http://www.avispl.com
Audio Visual Equipment Support Services & Whslr
N.A.I.C.S.: 423620

VideoLink LLC (2)
1230 Washington St, West Newton, MA 02465
Tel.: (617) 340-4100
Web Site: http://www.videolinktv.com
Emp.: 200
Television & Video Productions Services
N.A.I.C.S.: 516120
Douglas M. Weisman (Founder & Chm)
Gina Chudnow (Principal)
Richard G. Silton (Pres & CEO)
Lloyd Bunting (Sr VP-Sls & Mktg)
Gregg Bevan (VP-Production)
Leigh Willis (Dir-Engrg)
Kristen Mobilia (Dir-Fin & Admin)
Mark Pantridge (Gen Mgr-ReadyCam)

Aldon Computer Group (1)
6001 Shellmound St Ste 600, Emeryville, CA 94608
Tel.: (510) 839-3535
Web Site: http://www.aldon.com
Sales Range: $25-49.9 Million
Application Lifecycle Management Software Developer
N.A.I.C.S.: 513210
Ronald Oliveira (CTO)
Matt Scholl (Pres & COO)
David Lefkowich (VP-Global Sls)
Craig Tobey (VP-Sls-US)
Alison Ishimaru (VP-Mktg & Product Mgmt)

Arcserve (USA) LLC (1)
8855 Columbine Rd Ste 150, Eden Prairie, MN 55347
Tel.: (844) 639-6792
Web Site: http://www.arcserve.com
Data Protection & Recovery Software Publisher
N.A.I.C.S.: 513210
Erica Antony (VP-Product Mgmt)
Darin McAreavey (CFO)
Oussama El-Hilali (VP-Products)
Scott Petersen (VP-Global Channel & Alliances)
Nikhil Korgaonkar (Dir-Reg Sls-India)
Dave Hansen (Chm)
Alex Becker (VP & Gen Mgr)
Sue Fossnes (Dir-Channel-North America)
Brannon Lacey (CEO)
Christian van den Branden (CTO)
Vitali Edrenkine (CMO)

Subsidiary (Domestic):

StorageCraft Technology Corporation (2)
380 Data Dr Ste 300, Draper, UT 84020
Tel.: (801) 545-4700
Web Site: http://www.storagecraft.com
Software Publisher
N.A.I.C.S.: 513210
Mike Kunz (VP-Sls)
Matt Medeiros (Chm & CEO)
Andy Zollo (Head-Global Sls)
Marvin Blough (VP-Worldwide Sls)
Ellen Marie Hickey (Dir-Mktg-Europe)
Brad Thomas (Mgr-PR & Social Media)
Douglas Brockett (Pres)

Zetta, Inc. (2)
1362 Borregas Ave, Sunnyvale, CA 94089-1004
Tel.: (650) 590-0950
Web Site: http://www.zetta.net
Archiving Technology Services
N.A.I.C.S.: 513210
Ali Jenab (CEO)
Mark Seaman (VP-Sls)

Asentinel, LLC (1)
International Pl Tower 2 Ste 200 6410 Poplar Ave, Memphis, TN 38119
Tel.: (901) 752-6201
Web Site: http://www.asentinel.com
Computer & Computer Peripheral Equipment & Software Merchant Whslr
N.A.I.C.S.: 423430
Debbie Putnam (Co-CFO)
Richard Janis (Sr VP-Sls & Mktg)
Tim Whitehorn (CEO)
Mike Hobday (VP-Acct Mgmt)
Moe Arnaiz (Sr VP-Mobility)
Laurentiu Herbei (VP-Tech)
Paul Phillips (VP-Svc Excellence)
Chris Taylor (Co-CFO)
Philippe Lignac (Chief Sls Officer)

Subsidiary (Domestic):

Tangoe, Inc. (2)
169 Lackawanna Ave Ste 2B, Parsippany, NJ 07054
Tel.: (973) 257-0300
Web Site: http://www.tangoe.com
Communications Software & Services
N.A.I.C.S.: 513210
Chris Ortbals (Chief Product Officer)
Mark Desautelle (Chief Revenue Officer)
Ivan Latanision (Exec VP-Product)
Dave Hansen (Chm)
James Parker (CEO)
Craig Librett (Dir-Comm)
Becky Carr (CMO)
Yaakov Shapiro (CTO)
Gay Beach (VP-MarCom, Digital & Demand)
Gay Beach (VP-MarCom, Digital & Demand)

Subsidiary (Domestic):

MOBI Wireless Management, LLC (3)
6100 W 96th St Ste 175, Indianapolis, IN 46278-6008
Web Site: http://www.mobiwm.com
Management Consulting Services
N.A.I.C.S.: 541618
Josh Garrett (Pres & Co-Founder)

Subsidiary (Non-US):

Tangoe (China) Co., Ltd. (3)
6F Science & Technology Mansion Tsinghua Science Park, 1666 Zuchongzhi South Road, Kunshan, 215347, Jiangsu, China
Tel.: (86) 51257019068
Web Site: http://www.tangoe.com

MARLIN EQUITY PARTNERS, LLC
U.S. PRIVATE

Marlin Equity Partners, LLC—(Continued)
IT Expense Management Software & Services
N.A.I.C.S.: 513210
Kyle Borner *(Gen Mgr & Dir-Ops)*

Tangoe Europe Limited (3)
9-10 Park Square Milton Park, Abingdon,
OX14 4RR, Oxon, United Kingdom
Tel.: (44) 1235829444
Web Site: http://www.tangoe.com
Telecommunication Management Consulting Services
N.A.I.C.S.: 541618

Tangoe India Softek Services Private Limited (3)
Global Technology Park Tower-B 2nd & 3rd Floor, Marathahalli Outer Ring Road Devarabesenahalli Village Varthur Hobli, Bengaluru, 560 103, India
Tel.: (91) 80 6693 9000
Web Site: http://www.tangoe.com
IT Expense Management Software & Services
N.A.I.C.S.: 513210
Vikas Vyas *(Acct Mgr-Ops)*

Bazaarvoice, Inc. (1)
10901 Stonelake Blvd, Austin, TX 78759
Tel.: (512) 551-6000
Web Site: http://www.bazaarvoice.com
Software Publisher
N.A.I.C.S.: 513210
Keith Nealon *(CEO)*
Gracie Renbarger *(Chief Compliance Officer, Gen Counsel & Sr VP)*
Ken Hashman *(CFO)*
Fritz Hesse *(Exec VP-Engrg & Chief Tech Officer)*
Tom Addis *(Pres)*

Subsidiary (Domestic):

Curalate, Inc. (2)
1500 Walnut S Ste 501, Philadelphia, PA 19102
Tel.: (855) 223-1459
Web Site: http://www.curalate.com
Software Publisher
N.A.I.C.S.: 513210
Laurie Weisberg *(Chief Revenue Officer)*
Olivia Saeger *(VP-Brand Strategy)*
Scott Casey *(CFO)*
Laurie Weisberg *(Chief Revenue Officer)*
Apu Gupta *(Co-Founder & CEO)*
Nick Shifta *(Co-founder)*

Voxpop Communities, Inc. (2)
10901 Stonelake Blvd, Austin, TX 78759
Tel.: (512) 551-6000
Web Site: http://www.influenster.com
Online Shopping Services
N.A.I.C.S.: 455110

Burroughs, Inc. (1)
41100 Plymouth Rd, Plymouth, MI 48170-1892
Tel.: (734) 737-4000
Web Site: http://www.burroughs.com
Sales Range: $10-24.9 Million
Emp.: 200
Financial Transaction Imaging & Processing Technologies Developer, Mfr, Whslr & Support Services
N.A.I.C.S.: 333310
Larry McCarter *(Pres)*
Ed Boyd *(COO)*
Steve Collins *(VP-Shared Svcs)*
Adam Hobelmann *(VP-Sls & Mktg)*
Anson Martin *(CEO)*
John Gatti *(Chm)*

Subsidiary (Domestic):

Pendum LLC (2)
41100 Plymouth Rd, Plymouth, MI 48170-1892
Tel.: (800) 422-6835
Web Site: http://www.pendum.com
ATM Equipment Sales & Maintenance
N.A.I.C.S.: 423490

TRM Copy Centers, LLC (2)
12441 NE Marx St, Portland, OR 97230
Tel.: (503) 943-3800
Web Site: http://www.trmcopycenters.com
Self-Service Photocopying Machine Distr
N.A.I.C.S.: 561439

Gary Cosmer *(Pres & CEO)*

Clarus Commerce LLC (1)
500 Enterprise Dr 2nd Fl, Rocky Hill, CT 06067
Tel.: (860) 358-9198
Web Site: http://www.claruscommerce.com
Custom Loyalty Programs, Marketing, E-Commerce & Subscription-based Solutions
N.A.I.C.S.: 541613
Tom Caporaso *(CEO)*

Subsidiary (Domestic):

PrizeLogic, LLC (2)
25200 Telegraph Rd Ste 405, Southfield, MI 48033
Tel.: (847) 742-2937
Web Site: http://www.prizelogic.com
Promotional Contests & Sweepstakes
N.A.I.C.S.: 541890
Aaron Lobliner *(Sr VP & Mng Dir)*
Chris Cubba *(VP & Mng Dir)*
Grant Kravitz *(VP & Mng Dir)*
Matthew Kates *(CMO)*
Keith Simmons *(Founder & Chm)*
Ryan LaMirand *(CEO)*

Coriant America, Inc. (1)
220 Mill Rd, Chelmsford, MA 01824
Tel.: (978) 250-2900
Web Site: http://www.coriantamerica.com
Multiservice Switching & Digital Cross-Connect Services
N.A.I.C.S.: 334210
Anthony Petrillo *(CFO & Treas)*
David Guerrera *(Pres, Gen Counsel & Sec)*
Vikram V. Shanbhag *(Mng Dir-Asia Pacific South)*
Homayoun Razavi *(Chief Customer Officer)*
Pat DiPietro *(Vice Chm & CEO)*
Cass Traub *(Chm)*
Reza Ghaffari *(COO)*

Subsidiary (Domestic):

Coriant America, Inc. (2)
100 Century Pkwy Ste 120, Mount Laurel, NJ 08054-1149
Tel.: (978) 250-2900
Sales Range: $25-49.9 Million
Emp.: 263
Data Communications Equipment Mfr
N.A.I.C.S.: 334210
Carole McCarthy *(Mgr-Mktg Comm)*

Subsidiary (Non-US):

Coriant Japan K.K. (2)
Otemachi 1rst Sq E 4F, 1-5-1 Otemachi Chiyoda-Ku, Tokyo, 100 0004, Japan
Tel.: (81) 352191260
Sales Range: $100-124.9 Million
Computer Systems Mfr
N.A.I.C.S.: 541511
Grant Soh *(VP-Sls-Asia Pacific)*

Coriant Networks (Shanghai) Co., Ltd. (2)
Building No 19 Floor 5 No 1515 Gumei Road Caohejing Hi-Tech Park, Shanghai, 200233, China
Tel.: (86) 21 2405 0888
Bandwidth Management Solutions
N.A.I.C.S.: 541511

Exegy, Inc. (1)
349 Marshall Ave Ste 100, Saint Louis, MO 63119
Tel.: (314) 218-3600
Web Site: http://www.exegy.com
Computer & Computer Peripheral Equipment & Software Merchant Whslr
N.A.I.C.S.: 423430
James V. O'Donnell *(Chm & CEO)*
Rod Arbaugh *(Co-Pres & COO)*
Scott Parsons *(CIO)*
David Taylor *(Co-Pres & CTO)*
Krista Steward *(CFO & Sec)*
Craig Schachter *(Chief Revenue Officer)*

Subsidiary (Domestic):

Vela Trading Systems LLC (2)
211 E 43rd St 5th Fl, New York, NY 10017
Tel.: (646) 713-2773
Web Site: http://www.tradevela.com
Electronic-trading Solutions Provider
N.A.I.C.S.: 425120

Jennifer Nayar *(CEO)*
Keith Cacciola *(Chief Customer Officer)*
Stephen Mathey *(CFO)*
Ollie Cadman *(Chief Product Officer)*

Subsidiary (Domestic):

OptionsCity Software, Inc. (3)
150 S Wacker Dr Ste 2300, Chicago, IL 60606
Tel.: (312) 605-4500
Software Publisher
N.A.I.C.S.: 513210

Fourth Ltd. (1)
90 Long Acre Covent Garden, London, WC2E 9RA, United Kingdom
Tel.: (44) 2075343700
Web Site: http://www.fourth.com
Hospitality Industry Software Developer
N.A.I.C.S.: 513210
Ben Hood *(Co-Founder & CEO)*
Christian Berthelsen *(CTO)*
Simon Bocca *(COO)*
James England *(Sr VP-Strategic Partnerships)*
Stuart Goldblatt *(CFO)*
Jeff Horing *(Chm)*
Adam Sternberg *(VP-Sls-North America)*
Saverio Ferraro *(Dir-Sls-US)*
Clint Dabelgott *(Dir-Sls-US)*

Hospedia Holdings Limited (1)
Landmark Pl 1-5 Windsor Rd, Slough, SL1 2EJ, United Kingdom
Tel.: (44) 8454146000
Web Site: http://www.hospedia.co.uk
Sales Range: $75-99.9 Million
Emp.: 340
Holding Company; Health Communication & Information Services
N.A.I.C.S.: 551112
David Stronach *(CEO)*

Subsidiary (Domestic):

Hospedia Limited (2)
Landmark Pl 1-5 Windsor Rd, Slough, S012EJ, United Kingdom **(100%)**
Tel.: (44) 8454146000
Web Site: http://www.hospedia.com
Sales Range: $25-49.9 Million
Emp.: 50
Patient Bedside Console Telecommunications
N.A.I.C.S.: 517810
David Stroach *(CEO)*

Subsidiary (Non-US):

Patientline Exploitatie BV (2)
De Boedingen 39, Postbus 177, 4900, Oosterhout, Netherlands **(100%)**
Tel.: (31) 162480100
Web Site: http://www.patientline.nl
Sales Range: $25-49.9 Million
Emp.: 180
Other Commercial & Industrial Machinery & Equipment Rental & Leasing
N.A.I.C.S.: 532490

IBS AB (1)
Hemvarnsgatan 8, PO Box 1350, 171 26, Solna, Sweden
Tel.: (46) 8 627 23 00
Web Site: http://www.ibs.net
Distribution Software Publisher
N.A.I.C.S.: 513210
Mohit Paul *(VP-Sls-EMEA)*
Laura L. Fese *(Gen Counsel)*
Jayne Archbold *(CEO)*
Michael Wohlwend *(Gen Mgr-Americas)*
Anders Tang Christensen *(CFO)*
Graham Newland *(Chief Customer Officer)*
Renee Truttmann *(CMO)*
Bill Tomasi *(Sr VP-Product Mgmt)*
Sharon Plested *(Sr VP-Professional Svcs)*
Paul Nobbs *(Gen Mgr-APAC)*

Inkling Systems, Inc. (1)
343 Sansome St Ste 800, San Francisco, CA 94104
Tel.: (415) 975-4420
Web Site: http://www.inkling.com
Computer Software Product Mfr
N.A.I.C.S.: 513210
Jeff Carr *(CEO)*
Eileen Treanor *(CFO)*
John Crowther *(VP-Product)*
Tami Mandeville *(VP-Mktg)*

Jeff Bieller *(VP-Sls)*
Scott Dunnewind *(VP-Customer Success)*
Ariel Zach *(VP-Engrg)*
Ben Willis *(VP-Strategy)*
Malyssa Caharian *(Dir-HR)*

Learning Pool Limited (1)
Old City Factory, 100 Patrick St, Derry, BT48 7EL, United Kingdom
Tel.: (44) 207 101 9383
Web Site: https://learningpool.com
Emp.: 350
Educational Software
N.A.I.C.S.: 611710
Ben Betts *(CEO)*

Subsidiary (US):

Remote-Learner.net, Inc (2)
1550 Larimer St Ste 785, Denver, CO 80202
Tel.: (877) 299-1293
Web Site: http://www.remote-learner.com
Integrated E-Learning Solutions
N.A.I.C.S.: 611710

MDeverywhere, Inc. (1)
120 Commerce Dr Ste 100, Hauppauge, NY 11788
Tel.: (631) 232-4260
Web Site: http://www.mdeverywhere.com
Sales Range: $75-99.9 Million
Emp.: 510
Medical, Dental & Hospital Equipment & Supplies Merchant Whslr
N.A.I.C.S.: 423450
Ann Bilyew *(Co-CEO)*
Doug Salas *(VP-Dev)*
Allison Jones *(Dir-Mktg)*
Michael Liter *(Sr VP-Ops)*
Ramesh Rao *(Sr VP-Client Svcs)*
Monica Gillespey *(VP-HR)*
Patrick Hall *(Exec VP-Bus Dev)*
Christine Morgan *(Exec VP-Client Svcs)*
Sean Murtagh *(VP-Sls)*
Alan Ortego *(CTO)*
Ted Pakes *(CFO)*
Derek A. Pickell *(Co-CEO)*

Mapp Digital US, LLC (1)
9276 Scranton Rd Ste 500, San Diego, CA 92121
Tel.: (619) 295-1856
Web Site: http://www.mapp.com
Emp.: 60
Email Marketing Solutions & Consulting Services
N.A.I.C.S.: 541613
Claire Long *(CFO)*
Chris Frasier *(Sr VP-Client Success)*
Ulf Poelke *(Sr VP-Product)*
Claudia Uchima *(Sr VP-HR)*
Juhan Lee *(CTO)*
Matthew Langie *(CMO)*
Steve Warren *(CEO)*
Eric Lubow *(Chief Product & Tech Officer)*

Phoenix Technologies Ltd. (1)
915 Murphy Ranch Rd, Milpitas, CA 95035
Tel.: (408) 570-1000
Web Site: http://www.phoenix.com
Sales Range: $50-74.9 Million
Emp.: 400
Systems Software for Personal Computers & Peripherals
N.A.I.C.S.: 513210
Larry Gill *(VP-Sls)*
J. J. Schoch *(VP-Corp Mktg)*
Gerard Moore *(Pres & CEO)*
Jonathan O'Connell *(CFO)*

Subsidiary (Non-US):

Phoenix Technologies (Korea) Ltd. (2)
2 FL Cheongwn B 33 Teheranhro 8 Gangnam-gu, Gangnam-gu, Seoul, 135935, Korea (South) **(100%)**
Tel.: (82) 230144700
Web Site: http://www.phoenix.com
Sales Range: $1-9.9 Million
Emp.: 3
Software Production & Sales
N.A.I.C.S.: 334610

Phoenix Technologies (Taiwan) Ltd. (2)
7F No 88 Rueihu St, Neihu District, Taipei, 114, Taiwan **(100%)**
Tel.: (886) 277455600

COMPANIES

Web Site: http://www.phoenix.com
Sales Range: $25-49.9 Million
Software Production & Sales
N.A.I.C.S.: 334610
Michelle Luke *(Gen Mgr)*

Phoenix Technologies KK (2)
Gotanda NN Building 8th Floor 2-12-19
Nishi-Gotanda, Shinagawa-ku, Tokyo, 141
0031, Japan **(100%)**
Tel.: (81) 354356700
Web Site: http://www.phoenix.com
Sales Range: $10-24.9 Million
Emp.: 80
Software Sales
N.A.I.C.S.: 334610

Red Book Connect, LLC (1)
344 Preston Ridge Rd Ste 650, Alpharetta,
GA 30005
Tel.: (877) 741-9610
Web Site: http://www.redbookconnect.com
Software Development Services
N.A.I.C.S.: 541511
John W. Chidsey *(Chm)*
Odair Ferro *(Gen Mgr)*
Titus Striplin *(Dir-Hospitality Ops)*
Erin Beil *(Controller)*
David Cantu *(Chief Revenue Officer)*
Brian Gaffney *(VP-Engrg)*
Granya Gormley *(Dir-HR)*
Matthew Helgren *(VP-Product Dev)*
Anthony Lye *(Pres & CEO)*
Jay Prange *(Sr Dir-Budgeting & Fin)*

Revenue Well Systems, LLC (1)
2275 Half Day Rd Ste 337, Bannockburn,
IL 60015
Tel.: (847) 597-1745
Web Site: http://www.revenuewell.com
Sales Range: $10-24.9 Million
Emp.: 104
Cloud Based Dental Software Provider
N.A.I.C.S.: 541511
Max Longin *(Founder)*
Matt Carroll *(VP-Sls)*
Sue Fuller *(Dir-HR)*
Ron Madsen *(Fin Dir)*
Joe Keehnast *(Dir-Product Mgmt)*
Serge Longin *(CEO)*
Jay Levine *(VP)*

Subsidiary (Domestic):

Protective Business & Health Systems, Inc. (2)
978 Route 45 Ste 200, Pomona, NY 10970
Tel.: (845) 362-5405
Web Site: http://www.pbhs.com
Sales Range: $1-9.9 Million
Emp.: 5
Cloud-Based Dental Software Provider
N.A.I.C.S.: 513210
Jay Levine *(Gen Mgr)*

Serenova, LLC (1)
7300 Ranch Rd 2222 Bldg III Ste 200, Austin, TX 78730
Web Site: http://www.serenova.com
Web-Based & Cloud Platform Solutions
N.A.I.C.S.: 518210
Julian Critchfield *(COO)*
Matt Despain *(Chief Product Officer)*
John Lynch *(CEO)*
Meg Marsh *(VP-People)*
Michelle Burrows *(Chief Mktg Officer)*
David Nelson *(CFO)*

Subsidiary (Domestic):

TelStrat, Inc. (2)
1101 Central Expwy S Ste 150, Allen, TX
75013-8062
Tel.: (972) 543-3500
Web Site: http://www.telstrat.com
Software Publisher
N.A.I.C.S.: 513210
Bob Carroll *(Pres & CEO)*

Tellabs, Inc. (1)
1 Tellabs Ctr 1415 W Diehl Rd, Naperville,
IL 60563
Tel.: (630) 798-8800
Web Site: http://www.tellabs.com
Rev.: $1,052,600,000
Assets: $1,638,100,000
Liabilities: $536,800,000
Net Worth: $1,101,300,000
Earnings: ($171,700,000)
Emp.: 2,525

Fiscal Year-end: 12/28/2012
Holding Company; Telecommunications
Equipment Designer & Marketer
N.A.I.C.S.: 551112
Rizwan Khan *(Exec VP-Global Mktg)*
Gerry Pagano *(VP-Sls)*
Rich Schroder *(Pres & CEO)*
Karen Leos *(VP-Global Sls & Pro Svcs)*

Subsidiary (Domestic):

Tellabs Operations, Inc. (2)
1 Tellabs Ctr 1415 W Diehl Rd, Naperville,
IL 60563 **(100%)**
Tel.: (630) 798-8800
Web Site: http://www.tellabs.com
Sales Range: $900-999.9 Million
Telecommunications Equipment Designer &
Marketer
N.A.I.C.S.: 334210

Subsidiary (Non-US):

Tellabs AB (3)
Svardvagen 13, Danderyd, 182 33, Sweden
Tel.: (46) 850314840
Sales Range: $10-24.9 Million
Emp.: 9
Telecommunications Equipment Designer &
Marketer
N.A.I.C.S.: 334220
Petri Markkanen *(CEO)*

**Tellabs Communications (Malaysia)
Sdn. Bhd.** (3)
Suite 13 03 Level 13 Menara IGB No 1 The
Boulevard, Mid Valley City Lingkaran Syed,
59200, Kuala Lumpur, Malaysia
Tel.: (60) 322878807
Telecommunications Equipment Designer &
Marketer
N.A.I.C.S.: 334220

**Tellabs Communications International
Limited** (3)
Unit 1805-1807 Bright China Chang An
Bldg, No 7 Jianguomen Neidajie Dong,
100005, Beijing, China
Tel.: (86) 1065101871
Telecommunications Equipment Designer &
Marketer
N.A.I.C.S.: 334220

Tellabs Deutschland GmbH (3)
Landshuter Allee 12, 80637, Munich, Germany
Tel.: (49) 8920703900
Sales Range: $10-24.9 Million
Emp.: 7
Telecommunications Equipment Designer &
Marketer
N.A.I.C.S.: 334220

Tellabs India Private Limited (3)
53 I Floor Empire Tower Railway Parallel
Road, Kumarapark West, Bengaluru, 560
020, Karnataka, India
Tel.: (91) 8023464188
Sales Range: $10-24.9 Million
Emp.: 6
Telecommunications Equipment Designer &
Marketer
N.A.I.C.S.: 334220

Tellabs Oy (3)
Sinikalliontie 7, Espoo, 2630,
Finland **(100%)**
Tel.: (358) 9413121
Sales Range: $150-199.9 Million
Emp.: 500
Mfr, Designer & Marketer of Products Used
by Independent Telephone Operating Companies, Regional Bell Operating Companies, Specialized & Common Carriers & Private Businesses Worldwide
N.A.I.C.S.: 334418

Tellabs Pty Limited (3)
Level 30 80 Collins Street, Melbourne,
3000, VIC, Australia
Tel.: (61) 386483000
Telecommunications Equipment Designer &
Marketer
N.A.I.C.S.: 334220

**Tellabs South Africa (Proprietary)
Limited** (3)
Building 12 2nd Floor 13 Akkerboom Street,
Centurion Gate Business Park, Centurion,
0157, Gauteng, South Africa

Tel.: (27) 126410680
Telecommunications Equipment Designer &
Marketer
N.A.I.C.S.: 334220

Tellabs do Brasil, Ltda. (3)
Rua James Joule No 92 Edificio Plaza I,
Suites 31 & 32 3rd Floor, Sao Paulo,
04576-080, Brazil
Tel.: (55) 1135726200
Telecommunications Equipment Designer &
Marketer
N.A.I.C.S.: 334220

Unit (Domestic):

Tellabs Santa Clara (2)
4555 Great America Pkwy Ste 601, Santa
Clara, CA 95054
Tel.: (408) 970-2400
Web Site: http://www.tellabs.com
Network Management Application Developer
N.A.I.C.S.: 513210

Virgin Pulse, Inc. (1)
75 Fountain St, Providence, RI 02902
Tel.: (401) 537-6300
Web Site: http://www.virginpulse.com
Employee Health & Engagement Software
Platform Developer
N.A.I.C.S.: 541511
Richard Boylan *(COO)*
Wendy Werve *(CMO)*
Ron Hildebrandt *(Chief Product Officer)*
Rajiv Kumar *(Chief Medical Officer & Pres-Virgin Pulse Institute)*
Kim Stephan *(Gen Counsel)*
Andrew Reeves *(Chief Revenue Officer)*
Diane Holman *(Chief People Officer-Global)*
Kristen Larson *(Sr VP-Client Success)*
Chris Michalak *(CEO)*
Rik Thorbecke *(CFO)*
Amit Jain *(CTO)*

Subsidiary (Domestic):

Preventure, LLC (2)
2000 Nooseneck Hill Rd, Coventry, RI
02816
Tel.: (401) 385-9312
Web Site: http://www.preventure.com
Health Care Management Services
N.A.I.C.S.: 713940
Mark D. Correia *(CEO)*
Kathy O'Neel-Webster *(VP-Security & Compliance)*
Laura Walmsley *(Chief Client Officer)*
Michael G. Cooley *(VP-Sls Ops)*
Barry Pailet *(VP-Product Dev)*
Barry Silver *(VP-Tech Ops)*

Unit (Domestic):

Shape Up (2)
111 Chestnut St Ste 1, Providence, RI
02903-4169
Tel.: (401) 274-1577
Web Site: http://www.shapeup.com
Emp.: 134
Social Networking & Incentive-based Employee Wellness Programs
N.A.I.C.S.: 923120
Rajiv Kumar *(Pres)*

Subsidiary (Domestic):

Simplywell Inc. (2)
10670 N Central Expy Ste 110, Dallas, TX
75231
Tel.: (214) 827-4400
Web Site: http://www.viverae.com
Sales Range: $1-9.9 Million
Emp.: 156
Health Assessment Software
N.A.I.C.S.: 541618
Michael Nadeau *(Founder & CEO)*
Dave Smith *(CTO)*
Jim Trimarco *(Chief Sls Officer)*
Kirsten Lester *(VP-Product)*
Michelle Brown *(Sr VP-Client Svcs)*
Ramarao Desaraju *(Asst VP-Architecture & Core Svcs)*
Erika Turnbull *(Asst VP-Bus Ops)*
Kristi Manning *(Asst VP-Content & Creative Dev)*
Mahesh Salem *(Asst VP-Info Mgmt & Analytics)*
Patricia Dixon *(Asst VP-Screening Svcs)*
Candyce Bailey *(Asst VP-Software Dev)*

MARLO MARKETING COMMUNICATIONS

Depu Abraham *(Asst VP-Technical Ops)*
Robyne Gaudreau *(CFO & COO)*
Jeff Brizzolara *(Chief Clinical Officer)*

WorkSoft, Inc. (1)
15851 Dallas Pkwy Ste 855, Addison, TX
75001
Tel.: (214) 239-0400
Web Site: http://www.worksoft.com
Software Publisher
N.A.I.C.S.: 513210
Joseph Loria *(VP-Customer Experience)*
Tony Sumpster *(CEO)*
Joel Carabello *(VP-Sls-North America)*
Elizabeth Blackman *(VP-Mktg)*
Brian Smith *(VP-Engrg)*
Lawrence Rankin *(Head-Product)*

MARLIN STEEL WIRE PRODUCTS LLC
2640 Merchant Dr, Baltimore, MD
21230-3307
Tel.: (410) 644-7456
Web Site: http://www.marlinwire.com
Year Founded: 1968
Sales Range: $1-9.9 Million
Emp.: 28
Steel Wire Basket & Hook Mfr
N.A.I.C.S.: 331222
Drew Greenblatt *(Pres)*
Alex Levin *(CFO)*

MARLING LUMBER CO., INC.
1801 E Washington Ave, Madison, WI
53707-7668
Tel.: (608) 244-4777 WI
Web Site: http://www.marling.com
Year Founded: 1904
Sales Range: $50-74.9 Million
Emp.: 120
Lumber & Other Building Materials
N.A.I.C.S.: 423310
Tom Marling *(Pres)*

MARLITE, INC.
1 Marlite Dr, Dover, OH 44622
Tel.: (330) 343-6621 IL
Web Site: http://www.marlite.com
Year Founded: 1930
Sales Range: $75-99.9 Million
Emp.: 250
Specialty Wall Systems & Interior
Building Products Mfr
N.A.I.C.S.: 321911
Greg Triplett *(VP-Sls & Mktg)*
Kevin Krieger *(Mgr-Product Dev)*

MARLO FURNITURE CO., INC.
3300 Marlo Ln, Forestville, MD 20747
Tel.: (301) 735-2000 MD
Web Site:
  http://www.marlofurniture.com
Year Founded: 1955
Sales Range: $200-249.9 Million
Emp.: 600
Furniture Retailer
N.A.I.C.S.: 449110
Aquilla Ross *(Dir-HR)*

MARLO MARKETING COMMUNICATIONS
38 Chauncy St Fl 3, Boston, MA
02111
Tel.: (617) 375-9700
Web Site:
  http://www.marlomarketing.com
Sales Range: $10-24.9 Million
Emp.: 35
Full-Service Strategic, Integrated
Public Relations & Marketing
N.A.I.C.S.: 541820
Marlo Fogelman *(Principal)*
Christina Berlinguet *(Office Mgr)*
Karen Wong *(VP-Consumer Products)*
Meghan McCarrick *(Acct Mgr)*
Robbin Watson *(Acct Mgr)*
Ann Peterson *(Exec VP)*

MARLO MARKETING COMMUNICATIONS

Marlo Marketing Communications—(Continued)
Ariel Sasso Gardner (VP)
Brianne Johanson (VP)
Lisa LaMontagne MacGillivray (Exec VP)
Travis Talbot (VP)

MARMALADE LLC
1731 Broadway, Santa Monica, CA 90404
Tel.: (310) 829-0093
Web Site:
http://www.marmaladecafe.com
Year Founded: 1990
Sales Range: $25-49.9 Million
Emp.: 700
Cafe
N.A.I.C.S.: 722511
Selwyn Yosslowitz (Pres)

MARMIE MOTORS INC.
1724 10th St, Great Bend, KS 67530
Tel.: (620) 792-2571
Web Site: http://www.marmies.net
Rev.: $26,200,000
Emp.: 48
New & Used Car Dealers
N.A.I.C.S.: 441110
Jerry Marmie (Gen Mgr)
Karla Siefers (Mgr-F&I)

MARMION INDUSTRIES CORP.
9103 Emmott Rd Bldg 6, Houston, TX 77040
Tel.: (713) 466-6585
Year Founded: 2004
Sales Range: $1-9.9 Million
Emp.: 15
Plumbing, Heating & Air-Conditioning Contractors
N.A.I.C.S.: 238220
Ellen Raidl (Treas & Sec)
Bill Marmion (Pres)

MARNELL CORRAO ASSOCIATES, INC.
222 Via Marnell Way, Las Vegas, NV 89119
Tel.: (702) 739-2999
Web Site:
http://www.marnellcorrao.com
Year Founded: 1974
Sales Range: $200-249.9 Million
Emp.: 1,200
Commercial Building Contractor
N.A.I.C.S.: 236220
Anthony A. Marnell III (Owner, Chm & CEO)
Brad Schnepf (Pres-Marnell Properties)
James A. Barrett (CFO & Treas)
Cary Rehm (COO)

Subsidiaries:

Marnell Sher Gaming LLC (1)
222 Via Marnell Way, Las Vegas, NV 89119
Tel.: (702) 739-2000
Web Site:
http://www.marnellcompanies.com
Emp.: 85
Holding Company
N.A.I.C.S.: 551112
Anthony A. Marnell III (Chm & CEO)

Subsidiary (Domestic):

Colorado Belle Hotel & Casino (2)
2100 S Casino Dr, Laughlin, NV 89029
Tel.: (702) 298-4000
Web Site: http://www.coloradobelle.com
Hotel & Casino
N.A.I.C.S.: 721120

Edgewater Hotel & Casino (2)
2020 S Casino Dr, Laughlin, NV 89029-1518
Tel.: (702) 298-2453
Web Site: http://www.edgewater-casino.com

Sales Range: $10-24.9 Million
Hotel & Casino
N.A.I.C.S.: 721120
Jeff Pfeiffer (Sr VP & Gen Mgr)
Diana Kagley (Mgr-Hotel)

MARNOY INTERESTS LTD.
10030 Bent Oak Dr, Houston, TX 77040
Tel.: (713) 803-0000
Web Site: http://www.ophouston.com
Sales Range: $25-49.9 Million
Emp.: 80
Office Furniture Sales
N.A.I.C.S.: 423210
Steve Marnoy (Owner)

MARODYNE MEDICAL, LLC
2000 E Edgewood Dr Ste 211, Lakeland, FL 33803
Tel.: (863) 667-1628
Web Site: http://www.marodyne.com
Sales Range: $1-9.9 Million
Medical Researcher & Developer
N.A.I.C.S.: 541715
Clinton T. Rubin (Chief Scientific Officer)
Patrick Foote (COO)

MAROIS BROTHERS, INC.
115 Blackstone River Rd, Worcester, MA 01607-1491
Tel.: (508) 791-8134
Web Site:
http://www.maroisbrothers.com
Year Founded: 1918
Sales Range: $10-24.9 Million
Emp.: 65
Site Preparation Services
N.A.I.C.S.: 238910
John Brown (Exec VP-Mktg)

MARON ELECTRIC COMPANY
328 S Jefferson St Ste 920, Chicago, IL 60661
Tel.: (847) 626-6500
Web Site:
http://www.maronelectric.com
Year Founded: 1926
Electronic Services
N.A.I.C.S.: 238210
Mchael Lee (Controller)
Eric Nixon (Pres)
Luke Fenner (COO)

MARONDA INC.
202 Parkwest Dr, Pittsburgh, PA 15275
Tel.: (412) 788-7400
Year Founded: 1972
Sales Range: $300-349.9 Million
Emp.: 1,700
Residential Construction
N.A.I.C.S.: 237210
William J. Wolf (Chm)
Ron Wolf (Pres)
Jeff Gagat (Controller)

MAROTTA CONTROLS, INC.
78 Boonton Ave, Montville, NJ 07045
Tel.: (973) 334-7800
Web Site: http://www.marotta.com
Year Founded: 1943
Sales Range: $75-99.9 Million
Emp.: 150
Mfr of Solenoid Valves & Regulators, Relief & Check Valves, Electronic Control Devices & Flow Control Devices
N.A.I.C.S.: 332919
Michael J. Leahan (Chief Sls Officer & Sr VP)
Patrick Marotta (Pres & COO)
Steven Fox (VP-Eng)
Mike Bohanan (Sr Dir-Bus Dev-Weapons Sys)

Yoshi Genchi (Gen Mgr)
Chris Williams (Mgr-East Australia)
Rick Vacheresse (Mgr-Logistics & Military Program)

Subsidiaries:

Custom Engineering and Designs, Inc. (1)
78 Boonton Ave, Montville, NJ 07045
Tel.: (973) 334-7800
Design Engineering Services
N.A.I.C.S.: 541330

MARPAN INC.
222 E Pershing St, Tallahassee, FL 32301
Tel.: (850) 224-9353
Web Site: http://www.marpan.com
Year Founded: 1966
Sales Range: $10-24.9 Million
Emp.: 74
Lightning & Safety Equipment Distr; Recycling Services
N.A.I.C.S.: 423830
Kim Williams (Pres)
Larry Lassiter (VP)

MARQUAM GROUP
811 SW Naito Pkwy Ste 600, Portland, OR 97204
Tel.: (503) 276-1590
Web Site: http://www.marquam.com
Year Founded: 1998
Sales Range: $10-24.9 Million
Emp.: 33
Computer System Design Services
N.A.I.C.S.: 541512
Chad Layman (Pres)
John Pontefract (Founder, Partner & Exec VP)
Martin Wells (VP-Delivery)
Brad Paris (VP-Bus Dev)
Bob Hestand (Sr Dir-Cloud Svcs)
Jake Rahner (Mgr-Mktg)
Mark Wernet (Dir-Bus Dev)
Erin Moore (Mgr-Client Svcs)

MARQUARDT & ROCHE AND PARTNERS
5 High Ridge Pk, Stamford, CT 06905
Tel.: (203) 327-0890
Year Founded: 1970
Sales Range: $10-24.9 Million
Emp.: 15
Advertising Agencies
N.A.I.C.S.: 541810
Howard Meditz (Pres)

MARQUARDT BUICK, INC.
1421 S Barrington Rd, Barrington, IL 60010-5205
Tel.: (847) 381-2100
Web Site:
http://www.marquardtbuick.com
Sales Range: $10-24.9 Million
Emp.: 45
Car Whslr
N.A.I.C.S.: 441110
Daniel J. Marquardt (Gen Mgr)
Kurt Marquardt (Pres)

MARQUEE BRANDS LLC
50 W 57th St, New York, NY 10019
Tel.: (212) 203-8135
Web Site:
http://www.marqueebrands.com
Year Founded: 2024
Brand Acquisition & Development
N.A.I.C.S.: 525990
Michael DeVirgilio (Pres)
Cory M. Baker (COO)
Mia Rothstein (Sr VP-Brand Mgmt)
Neil Fiske (CEO)

U.S. PRIVATE

Subsidiaries:

Americas Test Kitchen Limited Partnership (1)
17 Station St, Brookline, MA 02445
Tel.: (617) 232-1000
Web Site:
http://www.americastestkitchen.com
Publisher of Cooking Related Materials
N.A.I.C.S.: 513120
Colleen Zelina (Sr VP-HR & Organizational Dev)
Dan Suratt (CEO)

Body Glove International, LLC (1)
504 N Broadway, Redondo Beach, CA 90277
Tel.: (310) 374-3441
Web Site: http://www.bodyglove.com
Wetsuits, Sporting Goods & Swimming Apparel Mfr & Online Retailer
N.A.I.C.S.: 339920
Russell Lesser (Pres)
Kenna Meistrell (Dir-Admin & Mgr-Brand & Mktg)

Martha Stewart Living Omnimedia, Inc. (1)
601 W 26th St, New York, NY 10001
Tel.: (212) 827-8000
Web Site: http://www.marthastewart.com
Emp.: 260
How-To Publishing, Television Broadcasting, Internet Production & Merchandising Services
N.A.I.C.S.: 334220
Kevin Sharkey (Exec Dir-Editorial)

MARQUEE BROADCASTING, INC.
4400 Brookeville Rd, Brookeville, MD 20833-1608
Tel.: (301) 661-9610
Web Site:
http://www.marqueebroadcasting.com
Sales Range: $25-49.9 Million
Emp.: 120
Television Broadcasting Stations & Other Media Owner & Operator
N.A.I.C.S.: 516120
Patricia R. Lane (Owner, Pres & CEO)

Subsidiaries:

WMDT-TV (1)
202 Downtown Plz, Salisbury, MD 21801
Tel.: (410) 742-4747
Web Site: http://www.wmdt.com
Television Broadcasting Station
N.A.I.C.S.: 516120
Kathleen McLain (Gen Mgr)
Gregory W. LaFrance (Dir-Digital Media)
Sarah Truitt (Dir-News)
Lindsy Adkins (Bus Mgr)
Phil Bankert (Sls Mgr)
John Ebert (Mgr-Creative Svcs)

MARQUETTE ASSOCIATES, INC.
180 N La Salle St, Chicago, IL 60601
Tel.: (312) 527-5500
Web Site:
http://www.marquetteassociates.com
Portfolio Management
N.A.I.C.S.: 523940
Tim Fallon (Mng Dir)
Miguel Zarate (Owner & Mng Partner)
Brian Wrubel (Pres & CEO)
David H. Smith (Mng Dir)
Doug Oest (Mng Partner)
James Wesner (Mng Partner)
Kweku Obed (Mng Partner)
Mike Piotrowski (Mng Partner)
Neil S. Capps (VP)
Sarah E. R. Wilson (VP)
Tim Hamann (Chief Compliance Officer & Mng Partner)
Tom Salemy (Mng Partner)
Amy Miller (Sr VP)

COMPANIES / MARQUIS WEALTH MANAGEMENT GROUP

Subsidiaries:

Peirce Park Group, Inc. (1)
600 Willowbrook Ln Ste 610, West Chester, PA 19382
Tel.: (610) 719-0300
Web Site:
http://www.marquetteassociates.com
Portfolio Management
N.A.I.C.S.: 523940
Lee Martin *(Principal)*

MARQUETTE COPPERSMITH-ING CO., INC.
960 E Chicago Ave # 209, Naperville, IL 60540-5510
Tel.: (561) 784-9927 PA
Year Founded: 1888
Sales Range: $75-99.9 Million
Emp.: 150
Packless Corrugated Expansion Joints For Power & Process Pipe Lines, Related Pipe Fittings, Bellows Assemblies & Flexible Metal Tubing
N.A.I.C.S.: 928110
Jay Huttner *(CFO)*
Andrew T. Heller *(Exec VP)*
Edward L. Barrett *(Sr VP & Dir-Sls)*
Chester M. Heller Sr. *(Chm-Pres & CEO, Chief Engr)*
Chester M. Heller Jr. *(Vice Chm & Treas)*

Subsidiaries:

Marquette Coppersmithing-Manufacturing Division (1)
960 E Chicago Ave # 209, Naperville, IL 60540-5510 (100%)
Tel.: (561) 784-9927
Sales Range: $10-24.9 Million
Mfr of Pipe Fittings
N.A.I.C.S.: 332710

Marquette Coppersmithing-Piping Design Division (1)
960 E Chicago Ave # 209, Naperville, IL 60540-5510
Tel.: (561) 784-9927
Web Site: http://www.pipingdesign.com
Sales Range: $50-74.9 Million
Piping Design Services
N.A.I.C.S.: 331410

MARQUETTE LUMBER CO. INC.
3201 Cardinal Dr, Vero Beach, FL 32963
Tel.: (772) 231-5252
Web Site:
http://www.marquettelumber.com
Rev.: $13,000,000
Emp.: 14
Lumber: Rough, Dressed & Finished
N.A.I.C.S.: 423310

MARQUETTE SAVINGS BANK
920 Peach St, Erie, PA 16501
Tel.: (814) 455-4481
Web Site:
http://www.marquettesavings.bank
Year Founded: 1908
Rev.: $32,268,142
Assets: $861,086,422
Liabilities: $705,610,827
Net Worth: $155,475,595
Earnings: $7,780,716
Emp.: 126
Fiscal Year-end: 12/31/18
Federal Savings Bank
N.A.I.C.S.: 522180
Michael B. Edwards *(CEO, Sec & Sr Exec VP)*
Julie M. Wilson *(CFO, Treas & Exec VP)*
David L. Carll *(Chief Retail Banking Officer, Exec VP & Asst Sec)*
Kelly A. Montefiori *(COO & Exec VP)*
Stephen M. Danch *(Chm & Pres)*
John C. Dill *(Exec VP & Dir-Bus Banking)*
Pete Sitter *(Sr VP)*
Steve Kightlinger *(Sr VP)*
Lisa N. Lopez *(Sr VP)*
Edmund A. Drexler *(Sr VP)*
Stella LaPaglia *(Sr VP)*
Richele D. Herman *(VP)*
Grace Ewanick *(VP)*
Eugene Cirka *(VP)*
Anita Hans *(VP)*
Blaine Fellows *(VP)*
Jon Patsy *(VP)*
Meredith Johnson *(VP)*
Thomas Hesch *(Asst VP & Asst Sec)*
Nancy Enterline *(Asst VP)*
Debra Mealy *(Asst VP)*
Jennifer Bond *(Asst VP)*
Sherry Waller *(Asst VP)*
Cora Mozina *(Asst VP)*
Terry Danko *(Asst VP)*
Trisha Snook *(Asst VP)*
Kelly Pratt *(Asst VP)*
Debra Schwenk *(Asst VP)*
Scott Shaffer *(Asst VP)*

MARQUETTE TOOL & DIE COMPANY
3185 S Kings Hwy Blvd, Saint Louis, MO 63139
Tel.: (314) 771-8509
Web Site:
http://www.marquettetool.com
Sales Range: $10-24.9 Million
Emp.: 8
Metal Stamping
N.A.I.C.S.: 332119
Tom Houska *(Controller)*
Don E. Freber *(Pres)*
Jenifer Spiroff *(Mgr-Pur)*

MARQUETTE TRANSPORTATION CO.
150 Ballard Cir, Paducah, KY 42001
Tel.: (270) 443-9404
Web Site:
http://www.marquettetrans.com
Rev.: $33,400,000
River Transportation
N.A.I.C.S.: 483211
Blake Denton *(Sr VP-Sls & Logistics)*
Jeff Bishop *(Engr-Port)*
Paul Dutton *(Mgr-Human Capital)*
Whitney Overstreet *(Mgr-Sls & Logistics)*
James Adams *(Mgr-Logistics)*
Josh Eschete *(Mgr-Logistics)*
Ricky Martin *(Mgr-Sls & Logistics)*
Corey Robertson *(Mgr-Sls & Logistics)*
Lance Wrinkle *(Mgr-Sls & Logistics)*
Ken Schule *(Sr Mgr-Sls & Logistics)*
Kieffer Bailey *(Sr VP-Sls & Logistics)*
Kelley Cromwell *(VP-Sls & Logistics)*
Tom Fisher *(VP-Sls & Logistics)*

MARQUEZ BROTHERS INTERNATIONAL, INC.
5801 Rue Ferrari, San Jose, CA 95138-1857
Tel.: (408) 960-2700
Web Site:
http://www.marquezbrothers.com
Year Founded: 1981
Sales Range: $50-74.9 Million
Emp.: 380
Mexican Style Dairy Products & Meats & Canned Goods & Imports Grocery Items from Mexico & Central America Mfr & Distr
N.A.I.C.S.: 424410
Danny Amaro *(Supvr-Sls)*
Demetrio Nanez *(Coord-Pricing & Promos)*

Subsidiaries:

MARQUEZ BROTHERS ENTERPRISES, INC. (1)
15480 Vly Blvd, City of Industry, CA 91746-3325
Tel.: (626) 330-3310
Sales Range: $1-9.9 Million
Emp.: 200
Dairy Product Mfr & Distr
N.A.I.C.S.: 311514

MARQUEZ BROTHERS FOODS, INC. (1)
3805 N Freeway Blvd, Sacramento, CA 95834-1928
Tel.: (916) 929-2800
Dairy Product Mfr & Distr
N.A.I.C.S.: 311514

MARQUEZ BROTHERS INTERNATIONAL S.A. DE C.V. (1)
Camino a San Clemente Km 1, 36200, Romita, Mexico
Tel.: (52) 4327453001
Web Site:
http://www.conservaselmexicano.com
Emp.: 179
Food Product Mfr & Distr
N.A.I.C.S.: 311514

MARQUEZ BROTHERS NEVADA, INC. (1)
3650 E Post Rd Ste E, Las Vegas, NV 89120-3205
Tel.: (702) 456-9400
Sales Range: $1-9.9 Million
Emp.: 25
Dairy Products Distr
N.A.I.C.S.: 424490

MARQUEZ BROTHERS RENO, INC. (1)
1550 Hymer Ave, Sparks, NV 89431-5614
Tel.: (775) 359-0300
Dairy Product Mfr & Distr
N.A.I.C.S.: 311514

MARQUEZ BROTHERS SOUTHERN CALIFORNIA, INC. (1)
2133 Britannia Blvd, San Diego, CA 92154-1397
Tel.: (619) 661-5700
Emp.: 15
Fiscal Year-end: 12/31/2006
Dairy Product Mfr & Distr
N.A.I.C.S.: 311514
Juan Lotez *(Mgr)*
Alex Magallon *(Gen Mgr)*

MARQUEZ BROTHERS SOUTHWEST, INC. (1)
7310 W Roosevelt St Bldg 3 Ste 38, Phoenix, AZ 85043-2215
Tel.: (623) 478-9900
Dairy Products Distr
N.A.I.C.S.: 424490

MARQUEZ BROTHERS TEXAS, LP (1)
1405 N Interstate 35 E, Carrollton, TX 75006
Tel.: (972) 402-8750
Dairy Product Mfr & Distr
N.A.I.C.S.: 311514
Alejandro Aramburu Mejia *(Mgr-Acctg)*
Melinda Llanos *(Mgr-Acctg)*

MARQUIS BANCORP, INC.
355 Alhambra Cir Ste 125, Coral Gables, FL 33134
Tel.: (305) 443-2922 FL
Web Site:
http://www.marquisbank.com
Sales Range: $25-49.9 Million
Bank Holding Company
N.A.I.C.S.: 551111
Javier Holtz *(Chm & CEO)*
Filip G. Feller *(CFO & Exec VP)*
Miriam Lopez *(Pres/Chief Lending Officer-Bank)*

Subsidiaries:

Marquis Bank (1)
355 Alhambra Cir Ste 125, Coral Gables, FL 33134
Tel.: (305) 443-2922
Web Site: http://www.marquisbank.com
Sales Range: $25-49.9 Million
Emp.: 68
Commericial Banking
N.A.I.C.S.: 522110
Javier Holtz *(Chm & CEO)*
Wayne Miller *(Chief Credit Officer & Sr VP)*
Frank Casal *(Sr VP & Dir-Ops)*
Monica Garbati *(VP & Branch Mgr-Coral Gables)*
David E. DiMuro *(Exec VP-Lending)*
Amy Reyes *(VP & Branch Mgr-Aventura)*
Elsa C. Soler *(Sr VP & Controller)*
Filip G. Feller *(CFO & Exec VP)*
Miriam Lopez *(Pres & Chief Lending Officer)*

MARQUIS GRAIN, INC.
11953 ESK Rd, Hennepin, IL 61327
Tel.: (815) 925-7300 IL
Web Site:
http://www.marquisgrain.com
Year Founded: 1976
Sales Range: $10-24.9 Million
Emp.: 30
Grain & Field Beans Whslr
N.A.I.C.S.: 424510
Darrell L. Marquis *(Pres)*

Subsidiaries:

Marquis Energy LLC - NECEDAH WI PLANT (1)
N 9585 State Rd 80, Necedah, WI 54646
Tel.: (608) 565-3912
Ethanol Product Mfr
N.A.I.C.S.: 325193

MARQUIS INDUSTRIES, INC.
17310 Teunis Dr, Spring Lake, MI 49456
Tel.: (616) 842-2810 MI
Web Site:
http://www.michiganbrass.com
Year Founded: 1969
Sales Range: $10-24.9 Million
Contract Metal Product Fabrication Services
N.A.I.C.S.: 332999
John H. Pimm Jr. *(VP-Sls)*

MARQUIS INDUSTRIES, INC.
5597 US Hwy 98 W, Santa Rosa Beach, FL 32459-3282
Tel.: (850) 267-2290 FL
Web Site:
http://www.marquisindustries.com
Year Founded: 1995
Sales Range: $1-9.9 Million
Emp.: 15
Kitchen & Bath Products Design Services, Customization & Retailer
N.A.I.C.S.: 444110
Nick M. Zargari *(Pres)*

MARQUIS PROPERTIES REALTY
933 Fleming St, Key West, FL 33040
Tel.: (305) 240-1090
Web Site:
http://www.rudymolinet.com
Sales Range: $25-49.9 Million
Real Estate Broker
N.A.I.C.S.: 531210
Rudy Molinet *(Owner)*

MARQUIS WEALTH MANAGEMENT GROUP
6216 Whiskey Creek Dr Ste A, Fort Myers, FL 33919
Tel.: (239) 454-1117
Web Site:
http://www.marquiswealthgroup.com
Sales Range: $1-9.9 Million
Emp.: 6
Investment Advisory Services
N.A.I.C.S.: 523940

MARQUIS WEALTH MANAGEMENT GROUP

Marquis Wealth Management Group—(Continued)
Richard E. Krichbaum (Pres)
Kim Sands (Partner & Mgr-Client Svcs)
Trevor Whitley (Partner)
Brian P. O'Connell (Partner)

MARQUIS WHO'S WHO, LLC
100 Connell Dr Ste 2300, Berkeley Heights, NJ 07922
Tel.: (908) 673-1000
Web Site: http://www.marquiswhoswho.com
Year Founded: 1898
Sales Range: $75-99.9 Million
Emp.: 70
Publisher of Biographical Reference Materials
N.A.I.C.S.: 513199
Fred Marks (Editor in Chief)
Kelli MacKinnon (Dir-Sls)

MARQUIS-LARSON BOAT GROUP
790 Markham Dr, Pulaski, WI 54162
Tel.: (920) 822-3214
Web Site: http://www.marquis-larson.com
Boat Mfr
N.A.I.C.S.: 336612
Rob Parmentier (CEO)
Steve Christensen (CFO & COO)
Matthew Vetzner (VP-Mktg)
Josh Delforge (VP-Design & Engrg)

MARR COMPANIES
1 D St, Boston, MA 02127
Tel.: (617) 269-7200
Web Site: http://www.marrcos.com
Sales Range: $10-24.9 Million
Emp.: 120
Heavy Construction Equipment Rental
N.A.I.C.S.: 532412
Robert L. Marr (Chm)
David E. Hughes (VP-Equipment & Properties)
Paul S. Tilley (VP & Controller)
Paula M. Wiles (VP-HR)
Danny D. Young (Mgr-Sys)
Matthew Botto (CFO)
Rick DeAmelio (Dir-Equipment Maintenance)
Kathy Fyfe (Dir-Mktg)
Bob Dembitzki (VP-Scaffold & Shoring)
Don Cartwright (Mgr-Contractor Supply Warehouse)
Frank Medina (Mgr-Providence Ops)
Renee Bird (Mgr-Springfield Office)
Susan Clark (Project Coord)
Eric Stalmon (VP-Safety & Trng)

MARRAZZO'S THRIFTWAY
1400 Pkwy Ave, Ewing, NJ 08628
Tel.: (609) 434-0020
Web Site: http://www.thriftwayshopnbag.com
Sales Range: $10-24.9 Million
Emp.: 163
Grocery Stores
N.A.I.C.S.: 445110
Samuel D. Marrazzo (Owner)

MARRICK MEDICAL
PO Box 173704, Denver, CO 80217-3704
Tel.: (303) 221-9299
Web Site: http://www.marrickmedical.com
Year Founded: 2007
Sales Range: $1-9.9 Million
Emp.: 45

Medical Provider Network Accessing All Areas of Medical Care for Accident Victims
N.A.I.C.S.: 524114
Perry Rickel (CEO)

MARRINER MARKETING COMMUNICATIONS, INC.
6731 Columbia Gateway Dr Ste 250, Columbia, MD 21046
Tel.: (410) 715-1500 MD
Web Site: http://www.marriner.com
Year Founded: 1989
Rev.: $60,000,000
Emp.: 40
Advetising Agency
N.A.I.C.S.: 541810
Tighe Merkert (Pres)
Wendy Simms (Dir-Media)
Rob Levine (Partner & VP-Acct Strategy)
Susan Gunther (Partner & VP-Client Svcs)
Linda Henley (VP-Pkg & Mgr-Production)
Jessica Painter (Assoc Dir-Art)
Josie Griffin (Controller)
Trey Buckingham (Dir-Digital Art & Tech)
Bill Coveney (Dir-Digital Content & Insights)
Dawn Widener (Mgr-Acctg)
Mike Sidlowski (Sr Dir-Art)
Chris Just (VP & Exec Dir-Creative)

MARRS ELECTRIC INC.
1141 S 120th E Ave, Tulsa, OK 74128
Tel.: (918) 437-5802
Web Site: http://www.marrselectric.com
Year Founded: 1978
Sales Range: $10-24.9 Million
Emp.: 50
General Electrical Contractor
N.A.I.C.S.: 238210
Gene Marrs (CEO)
Mick Marrs (VP-Oklahoma)
Terry Penix (Pres)

MARS & CO.
124 Mason St, Greenwich, CT 06830
Tel.: (203) 629-9292
Web Site: http://www.marsandco.com
Year Founded: 1979
Sales Range: $25-49.9 Million
Emp.: 250
Consulting Services
N.A.I.C.S.: 541618
Dominique Mars (Founder)
Jeffrey Alpert (Project Mgr)
Lei Cui (Project Mgr)

MARS ADVERTISING GROUP
25200 Telegraph Rd, Southfield, MI 48033
Tel.: (248) 936-2200 MI
Web Site: http://www.themarsagency.com
Year Founded: 1973
Sales Range: $200-249.9 Million
Emp.: 200
Advetising Agency
N.A.I.C.S.: 541810
Ken Barnett (CEO-Global)
Jeff Stocker (Chief Creative Officer)
Fern Grant (Exec VP)
Jake Berry (Exec VP & Gen Mgr)
Rob Rivenburgh (CEO-North America)
Theresa Lyons (Sr VP-Strategic Plng)
Darren Keen (CEO-Europe)
Greg Iszler (Exec VP-Strategy & Insights)
Jason Jakubiak (VP)
David Wysocki (Dir-Creative Grp)

Jim Feltz (Dir-Creative)
Jason Parzuchowski (Dir-Creative)
Suzanna Bierwirth (Chief Creative Officer)
Ethan Goodman (Sr VP-Innovation)
Jason Hittleman (Chief Admin Officer)
Derek Joynt (Exec VP & Gen Mgr-Toronto)

MARS ELECTRIC CO., INC.
38868 Mentor Ave, Willoughby, OH 44094-7931
Tel.: (440) 946-2250 OH
Web Site: http://www.mars-electric.com
Year Founded: 1952
Sales Range: $25-49.9 Million
Emp.: 65
Electrical Apparatus & Equipment
N.A.I.C.S.: 423610
Mark Doris (Pres)
Abbey Lauer (Mgr-Credit)
Chris Arnold (Branch Mgr)

MARS STEEL CORPORATION
2401 N 25th Ave, Franklin Park, IL 60131
Tel.: (847) 455-6277
Web Site: http://www.marssteel.com
Year Founded: 1974
Sales Range: $10-24.9 Million
Emp.: 25
Metals Service Centers & Offices
N.A.I.C.S.: 423510
Robert Perkaus (Pres)
Lynn Pikrone (Office Mgr)
Jim Mayer (CFO)

MARS SUPER MARKETS, INC.
9627 Philadelphia Rd Ste 100, Baltimore, MD 21237
Tel.: (410) 590-0500 MD
Web Site: http://www.marsfood.com
Year Founded: 1943
Sales Range: $250-299.9 Million
Emp.: 1,700
Supermarket
N.A.I.C.S.: 445110
Christopher D'Anna (Sec & VP)
Theodore D'Anna (VP)
Philip Hanlon (CFO & VP)
Carmen V. D'Anna Jr. (Pres)

MARS, INCORPORATED
6885 Elm St, McLean, VA 22101
Tel.: (703) 821-4900 DE
Web Site: https://www.mars.com
Year Founded: 1911
Sales Range: Less than $1 Million
Emp.: 140,000
Confectionery Manufacturing from Purchased Chocolate
N.A.I.C.S.: 311352
Claus Aagaard (CFO)
Eric Minvielle (VP-People & Org)
Fiona Dawson (Pres-Mars Food, Multisales & Customers-Global)
Jean-Christophe Flatin (Pres-Innovation, Science, Tech & Mars Edge)
Poul Weihrauch (Pres-Global Pet-care)
Andy Pharoah (VP-Corp Affairs & Strategic Initiatives & Sustainability)
Stefanie Straub (Gen Counsel & VP)
Maria Velissariou (Chief Science Officer & VP-Corp R&D-Global)
Anton V. Vincent (Pres-Mars Wrigley-North America)
Andrew Clarke (Pres-Snacking-Global)

Subsidiaries:

Heska Corporation (1)
3760 Rocky Mtn Ave, Loveland, CO 80538
Tel.: (970) 493-7272

Web Site: https://www.heska.com
Rev.: $257,307,000
Assets: $585,816,000
Liabilities: $163,608,000
Net Worth: $422,208,000
Earnings: ($19,889,000)
Emp.: 808
Fiscal Year-end: 12/31/2022
Holding Company; Veterinary Equipment & Animal Health Products Developer, Mfr & Whslr
N.A.I.C.S.: 551112

Subsidiary (Non-US):

CVM Diagnostico Veterinario, S.L. (2)
Imperial Channel of Aragon S/N, La Barrena Industrial Estate Tudela, 31500, Navarra, Spain
Tel.: (34) 948821713
Web Site: http://www.cvm.es
Veterinary Medical Equipment Mfr
N.A.I.C.S.: 339112

Subsidiary (Domestic):

Diamond Animal Health, Inc. (2)
400 E Ct Ave, Des Moines, IA 50309
Tel.: (515) 263-8600
Web Site: http://www.heska.com
Pharmaceutical & Biological Manufacturing Facility
N.A.I.C.S.: 325414

Subsidiary (Non-US):

Heska AG (2)
16 Grands-Places, 1700, Fribourg, Switzerland (100%)
Tel.: (41) 263472140
Web Site: http://www.heska.com
Sales Range: $10-24.9 Million
Emp.: 10
Mfr & Marketer of Allergy Diagnostic Products for Use in Veterinary & Human Medicine
N.A.I.C.S.: 325412
Aldere Carre (Mng Dir)

Subsidiary (Domestic):

Heska Imaging International, LLC (2)
3760 Rocky Mountain Ave, Loveland, CO 80538 (100%)
Tel.: (970) 493-7272
Web Site: http://www.heska.com
Veterinary Digital Imaging Equipment Distr
N.A.I.C.S.: 423450
Kevin S. Wilson (Founder & CEO)

Heska Imaging US, LLC (2)
3760 Rocky Mountain Ave, Loveland, CO 80538-7084
Tel.: (970) 775-2261
Web Site: http://www.heska.com
Veterinary Digital imaging Equipment Designer & Mfr
N.A.I.C.S.: 334517
Kevin S. Wilson (Founder & CEO)

Subsidiary (Non-US):

Optomed SAS (2)
6 Avenue des Andes, 91940, Les Ulis, France
Tel.: (33) 169290198
Web Site: http://www.optomed.fr
Veterinary Medical Equipment Mfr
N.A.I.C.S.: 339112

Scil Animal Care Company France Sarl (2)
3 rue Jacqueline Auriol, 67120, Altorf, France
Tel.: (33) 390201640
Web Site: https://www.scilvet.fr
Veterinary Diagnostic Services
N.A.I.C.S.: 541940

Scil Animal Care Company SL (2)
La Barrena industrial estate Imperial Channel of Aragon, Alcobendas, 31500, Tudela, Spain
Tel.: (34) 948821713
Web Site: https://www.scilvet.es
Veterinary Diagnostic Services
N.A.I.C.S.: 541940

Scil Animal Care Company Srl (2)

Via Rossaro 11, 24047, Treviglio, BG, Italy
Tel.: (39) 0363360656
Web Site: https://www.scilvet.it
Veterinary Diagnostic Services
N.A.I.C.S.: 541940

Scil Diagnostics Sdn. Bhd. (2)
15 Jalan Othman Section 3 Menara Mutiara Majestic 506 Level 5, 46000, Petaling Jaya, Selangor, Malaysia
Tel.: (60) 379562643
Veterinary Diagnostic Services
N.A.I.C.S.: 541940

scil animal care company GmbH (2)
Dina-Weissmann-Allee 6, 68519, Viernheim, Germany
Tel.: (49) 620478900
Web Site: https://www.scilvet.com
Animal Health Laboratory Services & Imaging Diagnostic Products Distr
N.A.I.C.S.: 621511
Eleanor F. Baker (Mng Dir, COO & Exec VP)
Christopher D. Sveen (Pres-Diamond Animal Health)
Steven M. Eyl (Pres)

Subsidiary (US):

Scil Animal Care Company (3)
151 N Greenleaf St, Gurnee, IL 60031
Web Site: http://www.scilvet.com
Animal Health Laboratory Services & Imaging Diagnostic Products Distr
N.A.I.C.S.: 621512

Hotel Chocolat Group Limited (1)
Mint House Newark Close, Royston, SG8 5HL, United Kingdom
Tel.: (44) 3444932323
Rev.: $307,025,297
Assets: $277,057,701
Liabilities: $143,481,134
Net Worth: $133,576,567
Earnings: ($12,815,519)
Emp.: 2,431
Fiscal Year-end: 06/26/2022
Chocolate Product Mfr & Distr
N.A.I.C.S.: 311351
Lisa Maree Mather (Dir)
Ross Anthony Plagman (Dir)

Mars AS (1)
Hovfaret 13, PO Box 274, Oslo, 0213, Norway
Tel.: (47) 22514300
Web Site: http://www.mars.no
Emp.: 15
Food & Pet Products
N.A.I.C.S.: 311999
Atle Farmen (Mng Dir)

Mars Australia (1)
Wodonga Petcare Place, Victoria, 3690, Australia
Tel.: (61) 2 6055 5200
Emp.: 700
Confectionery, Food & Pet Food Mfr
N.A.I.C.S.: 311999

Mars Austria (1)
Eisenstaedterstrasse 80, Breitenbrunn, A-7091, Austria
Tel.: (43) 21626010
Confectionery & Pet Food Mfr
N.A.I.C.S.: 311999
Christer Gavelstad (Mng Dir)

Mars Belgium (1)
Kleine Kloosterstraat 8 Brussels, 1932, Saint-Stevens-Woluwe, Belgium
Tel.: (32) 27127222
Web Site: http://www.masterfoods.be
Sales Range: $300-349.9 Million
Emp.: 308
Confectionery Mfr
N.A.I.C.S.: 311352
Pierre Laubies (Pres)

Mars Brazil (1)
Rua Dr Rafael de Barros 209 - 8o Andar Paraiso, Sao Paulo, 04003-041, Brazil
Tel.: (55) 1135728500
Confectionery, Food & Pet Food Mfr
N.A.I.C.S.: 311999

Mars Bulgaria (1)
161 Iztochna Tangenta St, 1592, Sofia, Bulgaria
Tel.: (359) 24024993

Sales Range: $10-24.9 Million
Emp.: 6
Confectionery, Food & Pet Food Mfr
N.A.I.C.S.: 311999

Mars Canada Inc. (1)
37 Holland Dr, Bolton, L7E 5S4, ON, Canada (100%)
Tel.: (905) 857-5780
Web Site: http://www.marscanada.ca
Sales Range: $700-749.9 Million
Emp.: 600
Dog & Cat Food Mfr
N.A.I.C.S.: 311111
Christine Parent-Inch (Brand Dir)

Mars Caribbean & Central America (1)
Metro Office Park No 2 St 1 Ste 300, Guaynabo, PR 00968
Tel.: (787) 620-1430
Web Site: http://www.nns.com
Confectionery & Pet Food Mfr
N.A.I.C.S.: 311999

Mars Chocolat France (1)
3 Chemin de la Sandlach, BP 10036, Haguenau, 67500, France
Tel.: (33) 388051600
Emp.: 800
Confectionery Mfr
N.A.I.C.S.: 311352

Mars Croatia (1)
Bile I 1, 10000, Zagreb, Croatia
Tel.: (385) 16593160
Confectionery, Food & Pet Food Mfr
N.A.I.C.S.: 311999
Ales Zavrsnik (Mng Dir)

Mars Czech Republic (1)
Michelska 1552/58 1400, Prague, Czech Republic
Tel.: (420) 227024500
Emp.: 100
Confectionery, Food & Pet Food Mfr
N.A.I.C.S.: 311999

Mars Denmark A/S (1)
Orestads Boulevard 67, 2300, Copenhagen, Denmark
Tel.: (45) 43245100
Web Site: http://www.mars.dk
Sales Range: $10-24.9 Million
Emp.: 75
Food & Pet Food Mfr
N.A.I.C.S.: 311999

Mars Drinks France (1)
Roissytech 2 Rue Du Cercle, BP 11484, 95708, Charles de Gaulle, Cedex, France
Tel.: (33) 141845100
Sales Range: $10-24.9 Million
Emp.: 40
Soft Drinks Mfr
N.A.I.C.S.: 312111
Slochel Gazig (Pres)

Mars Espana (1)
Parque Empresarial Alvia Edificio 3, C/JoseEchegaray 8, Las Rozas, 28230, Spain
Tel.: (34) 915908700
Web Site: http://www.mars.es
Sales Range: $10-24.9 Million
Emp.: 40
Confectionery, Food & Pet Food Mfr
N.A.I.C.S.: 311999
Jorg Oostdam (Gen Mgr)
Aly Meyers (Sls Dir)
Julia Manchon (Dir-Mktg & Category)
Manuel Rey (Dir-People & Org)
Carlos Collado (Fin Dir)
Jose Antonio Gallego (Head-Logistics)
Jose Maria Jimenez (Mgr-Ops)
Nuria Merino (Head-R&D)
Ramiro Pastor (Head-Maintenance)
Enrique de Miguel (Mgr-Factory)

Mars Finland Oy (1)
Tyopajankatu 5 5 krs, 00580, Helsinki, 00580, Finland
Tel.: (358) 9773941
Web Site: http://www.mars.fi
Sales Range: $10-24.9 Million
Emp.: 50
Confectionery Product Mfr
N.A.I.C.S.: 311352

Mars Food (China) Co., Ltd. (1)

Yanqi Economic Development Zone, Huairou, Beijing, 101407, China
Tel.: (86) 1061667410
Web Site: http://www.mars.com
Confectioner & Pet Food Mfr
N.A.I.C.S.: 311999
Alberto Mora (Gen Counsel, Sec & VP)
Richard Ware (VP-R&D & Procurement)
Aileen Richards (VP-Personnel & Org)

Mars Food Europe C.V. (1)
Benjamin Franklinstraat 19, 3261 LW, Oud-Beijerland, Netherlands
Tel.: (31) 186645333
Sales Range: $25-49.9 Million
Emp.: 250
Confectionery, Food & Pet Food Mfr
N.A.I.C.S.: 311999

Mars Global Services (1)
100 International Dr, Mount Olive, NJ 07828-1383
Tel.: (973) 691-3500
Emp.: 50
Data Processing Services
N.A.I.C.S.: 518210
Lynn Robinson (Sr Mgr-Bus Transformation)
Eloise Backer (Mgr-Infrastructure & Global Comml)

Mars Greece (1)
19-3 Marcopolo Ave, 11741, Peania, Greece
Tel.: (30) 2108196200
Sales Range: $10-24.9 Million
Emp.: 60
Confectionery, Food & Pet Food Mfr
N.A.I.C.S.: 311999
Thomas Harambopoulos (Gen Mgr)

Mars Hong Kong (1)
Suite 2001 20/f The Gateway Tower 6 9 Canton Road, Kowloon, China (Hong Kong)
Tel.: (852) 27217477
Sales Range: $10-24.9 Million
Emp.: 50
Confectionery, Food & Pet Food Mfr
N.A.I.C.S.: 311999

Mars Indonesia (1)
Jl Kima 10 Kav 46, Kawasan Industri Makassar, Sulawesi, 90241, Indonesia
Tel.: (62) 411515702
Web Site: http://www.mars.com
Sales Range: $10-24.9 Million
Emp.: 125
Confectionery, Food & Pet Food Mfr
N.A.I.C.S.: 311999

Mars Ireland Ltd. (1)
Burton Ct Burton Hall Rd, Dublin, 18, Ireland
Tel.: (353) 14353200
Sales Range: $25-49.9 Million
Emp.: 120
Confectionary Product Mfr
N.A.I.C.S.: 445292
Rosanna Yick Ming Wong (Exec VP-Federation of Youth Grps-Hong Kong)
Pierre Laubies (Pres-Petcare)

Mars Italia S.p.A. (1)
Centro Direzionale Milanofiori Viale Milanofiori, Assago, Milan, 20090, Italy
Tel.: (39) 025776111
Web Site: http://www.mars.it
Emp.: 200
Confectionery, Food & Pet Food Mfr
N.A.I.C.S.: 311999

Mars Japan (1)
Arco Tower 9F 1-8-1 Shimomeguru, Tokyo, 153-0064, Japan
Tel.: (81) 54343434
Web Site: http://www.marsjapan.co.jp
Confectionery, Food & Pet Food Mfr
N.A.I.C.S.: 311999

Mars Korea (1)
Samyoung Building, 637 Shinsa-Dong Kangnam-Gu, Seoul, 6017, Korea (South)
Tel.: (82) 232189898
Web Site: http://www.mars.co.kr
Confectionery & Pet Food Mfr
N.A.I.C.S.: 311999

Mars Latvia (1)
Gertrudes Street 10/12 4th Floor, LV 1010, Riga, Latvia
Tel.: (371) 7797000
Web Site: http://www.mars.com

Confectionery, Food & Pet Food Mfr
N.A.I.C.S.: 311999

Mars Lietuva (1)
Statybininkug 2, LT-96002, Gargzdai, Lithuania
Tel.: (370) 46394901
Sales Range: $50-74.9 Million
Emp.: 800
Confectionery, Food & Pet Food Mfr
N.A.I.C.S.: 311999

Mars Magyarorszag Ertekesito Bt. (1)
Bocskai ut 134-146, 1113, Budapest, Hungary
Tel.: (36) 1 469 2100
Web Site: http://www.mars.com
Snack Food Mfr
N.A.I.C.S.: 311919
Zsolt Mayer (Dir-Corp Affairs)

Mars Malaysia (1)
T1-13 Level 13 Tower 1 Jaya 33, No 3 Jalan Semangat, Petaling Jaya, 46000, Malaysia
Tel.: (60) 378443300
Web Site: http://www.mars.com
Confectionery, Food & Pet Food Mfr
N.A.I.C.S.: 311999

Mars Nederland B.V. (1)
Taylorweg 5, 5466 AE, Veghel, Netherlands
Tel.: (31) 413383333
Emp.: 1,200
Confectionery, Food & Pet Food Mfr
N.A.I.C.S.: 311999

Mars New Zealand Limited (1)
19 Lambie Drive, Manukau City, Auckland, 2155, New Zealand
Tel.: (64) 92610900
Web Site: http://www.mars.com
Sales Range: $25-49.9 Million
Emp.: 200
Confectionery, Food & Pet Food Mfr
N.A.I.C.S.: 311999

Mars North America (1)
800 High St, Hackettstown, NJ 07840-1552
Tel.: (908) 852-1000
Web Site: http://www.mars.com
Food, Snack & Petcare Products Mfr
N.A.I.C.S.: 311351
Claus Aagaard (CFO)

Subsidiary (Domestic):

Ethel M. Chocolates, Inc. (2)
2 Cactus Garden Dr, Henderson, NV 89014-2309 (100%)
Tel.: (702) 458-8864
Web Site: http://www.ethelschocolate.com
Sales Range: $10-24.9 Million
Emp.: 90
Chocolate Mfr & Whlsr
N.A.I.C.S.: 311351

Mars Fishcare, Inc. (2)
50 E Hamilton St, Chalfont, PA 18914
Tel.: (215) 822-8181
Web Site: http://www.aquariumpharm.com
Sales Range: $50-74.9 Million
Aquariums, Aquarium Equipment, Water Treatment & Fish Food Products Mfr & Supplier
N.A.I.C.S.: 112519

Subsidiary (Non-US):

Rena (3)
BP 90003, 74373, Pringy, France (100%)
Tel.: (33) 450572050
Web Site: http://www.rena.fr
Sales Range: $10-24.9 Million
Emp.: 40
Aquariums & Electrical Aquarium Products Mfr, Designs & Distr
N.A.I.C.S.: 332999

Subsidiary (Domestic):

Mars Horsecare US, Inc. (2)
330 E Schultz Ave, Dalton, OH 44618
Tel.: (330) 828-2251
Web Site: http://www.buckeyenutrition.com
Sales Range: $10-24.9 Million
Emp.: 50
Horse & Other Animal Feed Products Mfr
N.A.I.C.S.: 311119
Ed Yuhas (Gen Mgr)

MARS, INCORPORATED

Mars, Incorporated—(Continued)

Unit (Domestic):

Mars Petcare (2)
315 Cool Springs Blvd, Franklin, TN 37067
Tel.: (615) 807-4626
Web Site: http://www.marspetcare.com
Pet Food Mfr
N.A.I.C.S.: 311111
David Kamenetzky (VP-Corp Affairs & Strategic Initiatives)
Srinivasa Rao P. V. V. (Head-Pet Foods)
Ikdeep Singh (Pres-Pet Nutrition-North America)
Chris Sackree (Interim VP-Supply Chain-Pet Nutrition-North America)
Ruben Cejudo (VP-Supply Chain-North America)
Lonnie Shoff (Executives)

Mars Snackfoods U.S. (2)
295 Brown St, Elizabethtown, PA 17022-2127
Tel.: (717) 367-1500
Web Site: http://www.mars.com
Sales Range: $25-49.9 Million
Emp.: 100
Solid Chocolate Bars Mfr
N.A.I.C.S.: 311352
Michele Kessler (VP-Mktg)
William Clements (Dir-Sponsorships & Sports Mktg)
Frank Debrincat (Sr Mgr-Package Dev)
Paul Lieberman (Dir-Mdse)

Subsidiary (Domestic):

Nutro Products Inc. (2)
315 Cool Springs Blvd, Franklin, TN 37067
Tel.: (615) 628-5500
Web Site: http://www.nutroproducts.com
Sales Range: $10-24.9 Million
Pet Food Mfr
N.A.I.C.S.: 311111

Preferred Brands International, Inc. (2)
3 Landmark Sq, Stamford, CT 06901
Tel.: (203) 348-0030
Web Site: http://www.tastybite.com
Specialty Foods Mfr
N.A.I.C.S.: 311412

Subsidiary (Non-US):

Tasty Bite Eatables Ltd. (3)
201-202 Mayfair Towers Wakdewadi Shivajinagar, Pune, 411 005, Maharashtra, India (74.2%)
Tel.: (91) 2030216000
Web Site: https://www.tastybite.co.in
Rev.: $58,681,014
Assets: $55,273,785
Liabilities: $26,079,851
Net Worth: $29,193,933
Earnings: $3,622,085
Emp.: 247
Fiscal Year-end: 03/31/2023
Food Products Mfr & Distr
N.A.I.C.S.: 311999
Bikram K. Barai (Head-Quality Assurance & Food Safety)
Ankit Singhal (Deputy Gen Mgr-Supply Chain)
Pradeep Poddar (Chm)
Dilen Gandhi (Mng Dir)
Abhash Nigam (Assoc Dir-Bus)
Sandhya Khorate (Assoc Dir-Res Center)
Sharad Nawani (Head-Plant & Dir-Site)
Vimal Tank (Officer-Compliance & Sec)

Mars Norway (1)
Hovfaret 13, Skoyen, N-0213, Oslo, Norway
Tel.: (47) 22514300
Web Site: http://www.mars.no
Confectionery, Food & Pet Food Mfr
N.A.I.C.S.: 311999

Mars PF France (1)
Boulevard des Chenats, 45550, Saint-Denis-de-l'Hotel, France
Tel.: (33) 238596161
Web Site: http://www.mars.com
Sales Range: $25-49.9 Million
Emp.: 250
Snack Food & Pet Food Mfr
N.A.I.C.S.: 311919

Mars Petcare (1)

Eitzer Strasse 215, PO Box 1280, 27283, Verden, Germany
Tel.: (49) 4231940
Web Site: http://www.mars.com.de
Sales Range: $100-124.9 Million
Emp.: 1,000
Pet Food Mfr
N.A.I.C.S.: 311111
David Kamenetzky (VP-Corp Affairs & Strategic Initiatives)
Damian Guha (Mng Dir-UK)

Mars Philippines (1)
11/F Tower 1 The Enterprise Centre, 6766 Ayala Avenue, Makati, 1226, Philippines
Tel.: (63) 28877000
Web Site: http://www.mars.com
Sales Range: $10-24.9 Million
Emp.: 20
Confectionery & Pet Food Mfr
N.A.I.C.S.: 311999
Henry Azcarraga (Gen Mgr)

Mars Polska sp. z.o.o. (1)
Kozuszki Parcel 42, 96-500, Sochaczew, Poland
Tel.: (48) 225955000
Web Site: http://www.mars.pl
Emp.: 1,400
Confectionery, Food & Pet Food Mfr
N.A.I.C.S.: 311999

Mars Singapore (1)
47 Scotts Road, 07-01/02 Goldbell Towers, Singapore, 228223, Singapore
Tel.: (65) 67333991
Sales Range: $10-24.9 Million
Emp.: 20
Confectionery & Pet Food Mfr
N.A.I.C.S.: 311999

Mars Snackfood (1)
Industriering 17, Viersen, 41751, Germany
Tel.: (49) 21625000
Web Site: http://www.mars.com
Sales Range: $50-74.9 Million
Emp.: 615
Snack Food Mfr
N.A.I.C.S.: 445298
Richard Ware (VP-Supply, Res, Dev & Procurement)
Alberto Mora (Gen Counsel, Sec & VP)

Mars Southern Core (1)
Calle 505 Nro 538, Buenos Aires, 6608, Gowland, Argentina
Tel.: (54) 2324439000
Confectionery & Pet Food Mfr
N.A.I.C.S.: 311999

Mars Switzerland (1)
Baarermattstrasse 6, 6302, Zug, Switzerland
Tel.: (41) 417691414
Web Site: http://www.mars.com
Sales Range: $10-24.9 Million
Emp.: 100
Confectionery, Food & Pet Food Mfr
N.A.I.C.S.: 311351

Mars Taiwan (1)
7F 2 #19-2 San Chung Road, Taipei, 11501, Nan Kang District, Taiwan
Tel.: (886) 266166666
Web Site: http://www.mars.com
Sales Range: $10-24.9 Million
Emp.: 65
Confectionery & Pet Food Mfr
N.A.I.C.S.: 311999
Scott Mien (Gen Mgr)

Mars Thailand, Inc. (1)
19th Floor Suntower Building A, 123 Vibhawadi-Rangsit Road, Bangkok, 10900, Chompol Sub-District, Thailand
Tel.: (66) 26546799
Web Site: http://www.mars.com
Confectionery & Pet Food Mfr
N.A.I.C.S.: 311999

Mars UK Ltd. (1)
Dundee Road, Slough, SL1 4LG, Berkshire, United Kingdom
Tel.: (44) 1753550055
Web Site: http://www.mars.co.uk
Sales Range: $125-149.9 Million
Emp.: 2,000
Confectionery Mfr & Distr
N.A.I.C.S.: 311352

Division (Domestic):

Mars Drinks (2)

Armstrong Road, Basingstoke, RG24 8NU, United Kingdom
Tel.: (44) 1256471500
Web Site: http://www.marsdrinks.co.uk
Sales Range: $75-99.9 Million
Emp.: 400
Soft Drinks Mfr
N.A.I.C.S.: 312111
Bobby Chacko (Pres & Gen Mgr-North America)

Mars Vietnam (1)
Fosco Building 2nd Floor Room 207 35 Bis Phung Khac Khoan Street, District 1, Ho Chi Minh City, Vietnam
Tel.: (84) 838 273 773
Confectionery & Pet Food Distr
N.A.I.C.S.: 424450

Medical Management International Inc. (1)
18101 SE 6th Way, Vancouver, WA 98683
Web Site: http://www.banfield.com
Veterinary Services
N.A.I.C.S.: 541940
Daniel Aja (Chief Medical Officer & Sr VP)
Karen K. Faunt (VP-Veterinary Quality Ops)
Brian Garish (Pres)
Stephanie Neuvirth (Sr VP-People & Org)
Jim Ashby (COO)
Ludek Janousek (CFO)
Thiruvallur Srikanth (Sr VP-IT)
Anthony Guerrieri (Sr VP-Corp Affairs)
Megan Croce (Sr VP-Legal)

Royal Canin S.A. (1)
RN 113 650 avenue de la Petite Camargue, 30470, Aimargues, France
Tel.: (33) 4 6673 6400
High-Nutrition Dry Pet Food Mfr
N.A.I.C.S.: 311111
Charlotte Young (Mgr-Ecommerce Key Acct-Castle Cary)
John O'Connor (Mktg Mgr)
Gemma Sainsbury (Acct Mgr-Natl)
James Mills (Acct Mgr-Natl)

Subsidiary (US):

Royal Canin USA Inc. (2)
500 Fountain Lakes Blvd Ste 100, Saint Charles, MO 63301-4354
Tel.: (636) 926-0003
Web Site: http://www.royalcanin.us
Sales Range: $25-49.9 Million
Emp.: 150
Dog & Cat Food Mfr
N.A.I.C.S.: 311111
Kamie Eckert (Pres)
Daryn Brown (Pres-North America)
Kira Best (VP-Sls-Chewy)

VCA Inc. (1)
12401 W Olympic Blvd, Los Angeles, CA 90064
Tel.: (310) 571-6500
Web Site: http://www.vca.com
Sales Range: $1-4.9 Billion
Emp.: 25,000
Animal Health Care Services
N.A.I.C.S.: 541940
Robert L. Antin (Founder)
Tomas W. Fuller (CFO & VP)
Joyce Wagner (Dir-Medical)
Lesa Cash (Mgr-Katonah Bedford Veterinary Center)
Diana Nguyen (Sr Dir-Knowledge & Learning)

Subsidiary (Non-US):

Antech Diagnostics Canada Ltd. (2)
6625 Kitimat, Mississauga, L5N 6J1, ON, Canada
Tel.: (905) 567-0597
Web Site: http://www.antechdiagnostics.com
Animal Health Care Services
N.A.I.C.S.: 541940

Subsidiary (Domestic):

Sound Technologies, Inc. (2)
5810 Van Allen Way, Carlsbad, CA 92008
Tel.: (760) 918-9626
Web Site: http://www.soundvet.com
Animal Health Care Medical Products
N.A.I.C.S.: 541940
Tom Jacobi (Pres)
John Jacobs (Dir-Strategic Intl Accts)

U.S. PRIVATE

VCA Animal Hospitals, Inc. (2)
2723 W Olive Ave, Burbank, CA 91505
Tel.: (818) 845-7246
Web Site: http://www.vcahospitals.com
Animal Health Care Services
N.A.I.C.S.: 541940
Marie Kerl (Chief Medical Officer)
Todd Lavender (Pres)
Garrett Lewis (COO)

Vicar Operating, Inc. (2)
12401 W Olympic Blvd, Los Angeles, CA 90064
Tel.: (310) 571-6500
Animal Health Care Services
N.A.I.C.S.: 541940
Tomas W. Fuller (Sec)

Wm. Wrigley Jr. Company (1)
930 W Evergreen Ave, Chicago, IL 60642
Tel.: (312) 794-6200
Web Site: http://www.wrigley.com
Sales Range: $1-4.9 Billion
Emp.: 350
Confectionery Food Products Mfr
N.A.I.C.S.: 445298
Florance Naviner (CFO)

Subsidiary (Domestic):

Northwestern Flavors, LLC (2)
120 N Aurora St, West Chicago, IL 60185
Tel.: (630) 231-0489
Web Site: http://www.wrigley.com
Sales Range: $25-49.9 Million
Emp.: 40
Flavoring Mfr
N.A.I.C.S.: 311942

Subsidiary (Non-US):

The Wrigley Company (E.A.) Ltd. (2)
PO Box 30767, Nairobi, 00100, Kenya
Tel.: (254) 20532033
Web Site: http://www.wrigley.com
Sales Range: $25-49.9 Million
Emp.: 90
Chewing Gum Mfr
N.A.I.C.S.: 311340

The Wrigley Company (H.K.) Limited (2)
23 Fl Dorset House Taikoo Place, Shek Tong Tsui, Hong Kong, China (Hong Kong)
Tel.: (852) 28589202
Web Site: http://www.wrigley.com
Sales Range: $25-49.9 Million
Emp.: 10
Chewing Gum Distr
N.A.I.C.S.: 424450
Peter Tsang (Mng Dir)

The Wrigley Company (Malaysia) Sdn. Bhd. (2)
Glenmarie Hicom Indus Pk 2 Jalan Peguam Satu Sec U1 25A, 40150, Shah Alam, Selangor, Malaysia
Tel.: (60) 355692807
Web Site: http://www.wrigley.com
Sales Range: $25-49.9 Million
Emp.: 70
Chewing Gum Mfr
N.A.I.C.S.: 311340

The Wrigley Company (N.Z.) Limited (2)
45 Banks Rd Mount Wellington, Auckland, 1134, New Zealand
Tel.: (64) 95799063
Web Site: http://www.wrigley.com
Sales Range: $25-49.9 Million
Emp.: 12
Chewing Gum Mfr
N.A.I.C.S.: 311340

The Wrigley Company Ltd. (2)
Estover, Plymouth, PL6 7PR, Devon, United Kingdom
Tel.: (44) 1752 701107
Sales Range: $50-74.9 Million
Emp.: 490
Chewing Gum Mfr
N.A.I.C.S.: 311340
Andy Turner (Dir-Factory)

COMPANIES

Subsidiary (Non-US):

Wrigley Scandinavia AB (3)
Jan Stenbecks torg 17, 164 40, Kista, Ruotsi, Sweden
Tel.: (46) 854476000
Web Site: http://www.wrigley.se
Sales Range: $25-49.9 Million
Emp.: 200
Chewing Gum Mfr
N.A.I.C.S.: 311340

Wrigley Scandinavia AS (3)
Ryensvingen 15, 0680, Oslo, Norway
Tel.: (47) 22083210
Web Site: http://www.wrigley.no
Sales Range: $10-24.9 Million
Emp.: 10
Chewing Gum Mfr
N.A.I.C.S.: 311340

Subsidiary (Non-US):

The Wrigley Company Pty. Ltd. (2)
PO Box 754, Epping, 1710, NSW, Australia
Tel.: (61) 298150300
Web Site: http://www.wrigley.com.au
Sales Range: $50-74.9 Million
Chewing Gum Mfr
N.A.I.C.S.: 311340

Wrigley & Company Ltd., Japan (2)
1 2 3 Kita Aoyama, Minato-ku, Tokyo, 107-0061, Japan
Tel.: (81) 334 035 281
Web Site: http://www.wrigley.com
Chewing Gum Mfr
N.A.I.C.S.: 311340

Wrigley Austria Ges.m.b.H. (2)
Werner Von Siemens Platz 1, Salzburg, 5101, Austria
Tel.: (43) 662657000
Web Site: http://www.wrigley.ag
Sales Range: $25-49.9 Million
Emp.: 30
Chewing Gum Mfr
N.A.I.C.S.: 311340
Dominik Thiele (Gen Mgr)

Wrigley Bulgaria EOOD (2)
5 L Sanchez street 10th floor, Sofia, 1756, Bulgaria
Tel.: (359) 29714847
Web Site: http://www.wrigley.com
Emp.: 50
Chewing Gum & Candy Sales & Distr
N.A.I.C.S.: 424450
Alexandr Sharshakov (Gen Mgr)

Wrigley Chewing Gum Company Ltd. (2)
111 Youyi Road, Guangzhou, 510730, China
Tel.: (86) 2082218816
Web Site: http://www.wrigley.com.cn
Chewing Gum Mfr
N.A.I.C.S.: 311340
Sabrina Denji (Mgr)

Wrigley Co., S.A.U. (2)
Via Augusta 2, Barcelona, 08006, Spain
Tel.: (34) 932287900
Web Site: http://www.wrigley.com
Sales Range: $25-49.9 Million
Emp.: 100
Chewing Gum Mfr
N.A.I.C.S.: 311340

Wrigley France SNC (2)
Zn Indus Rue 52, Biesheim, 68600, France
Tel.: (33) 389721919
Web Site: http://www.wrigley.com
Sales Range: $50-74.9 Million
Chewing Gum Mfr
N.A.I.C.S.: 311340
Stefaan Dumez (Gen Mgr)

Wrigley GmbH (2)
Biberger Strasse 18, Unterhaching, 82008, Germany
Tel.: (49) 89665100
Web Site: http://www.wrigley.de
Sales Range: $25-49.9 Million
Emp.: 250
Chewing Gum Mfr
N.A.I.C.S.: 311340

Wrigley Hungaria, Kft. (2)
Bocskaiut 134, Budapest, 1025, Hungary
Tel.: (36) 13457900

Web Site: http://www.wrigley.com
Sales Range: $25-49.9 Million
Emp.: 80
Chewing Gum Mfr
N.A.I.C.S.: 311423
Gabor Dosa (Gen Mgr)

Wrigley India Private Limited (2)
Bldg 9B 10th Fl Dlf Cyber City Phase 3, Gurgaon, 122 002, Haryana, India
Tel.: (91) 124 3041901
Web Site: http://www.wrigley.com
Sales Range: $25-49.9 Million
Emp.: 60
Chewing Gum & Candy Mfr
N.A.I.C.S.: 311351

Wrigley Philippines, Inc. (2)
Marcos Highway Sitio Putting Bato, Barangay Inarawan, Antipolo City, Rizal, 1870, Philippines
Tel.: (63) 26311749
Web Site: http://www.wrigley.com
Sales Range: $25-49.9 Million
Emp.: 300
Chewing Gum Mfr
N.A.I.C.S.: 311340

Wrigley Poland Sp. zo.o. (2)
Ul Skrytka Poctowa 69, PL 61 249, Poznan, Poland
Tel.: (48) 618744400
Web Site: http://www.wrigley.com
Sales Range: $75-99.9 Million
Chewing Gum Mfr
N.A.I.C.S.: 311423

Wrigley Romania SRL (2)
Strada Tipografilor Nr 11-15, 13714, Bucharest, Romania
Tel.: (40) 214082820
Web Site: http://www.wrigley.com
Sales Range: $450-499.9 Million
Chewing Gum & Candy Mfr
N.A.I.C.S.: 311340
Ceabuca Narcis (Reg Mgr-Modern Trade)

Wrigley Taiwan Ltd. (2)
112 Chung Hsiao East Road, Section 1 Floor 9, Taipei, 10046, Taiwan
Tel.: (886) 223223123
Web Site: http://www.wrigley.com
Sales Range: $25-49.9 Million
Emp.: 200
Chewing Gum Mfr
N.A.I.C.S.: 311340

Wrigley d.o.o. (2)
Letaliska 29 A, Trzin, 1000, Slovenia
Tel.: (386) 15800350
Web Site: http://www.wrigley.com
Sales Range: $25-49.9 Million
Emp.: 45
Chewing Gum Mfr
N.A.I.C.S.: 311340
Darja Sustersic (Head-Mktg)

Wrigley s.r.o. (2)
Michelska 1552/58, Prague, 14000, Czech Republic
Tel.: (420) 227024111
Web Site: http://www.wrigley.cz
Sales Range: $25-49.9 Million
Emp.: 55
Chewing Gum Mfr
N.A.I.C.S.: 311340

Subsidiary (Domestic):

Wrigley Confections CR, kom. spol. (3)
Prazska 320, Porici nad Sazavou, 25721, Czech Republic
Tel.: (420) 317 760 111
Sales Range: $25-49.9 Million
Snack Food Mfr
N.A.I.C.S.: 311919
Artur Nowak (Mng Dir)

MARSALA BEVERAGE LLC
825 Stone Ave, Monroe, LA 71201
Tel.: (318) 323-8871
Web Site: http://www.abwholesaler.com
Sales Range: $10-24.9 Million
Emp.: 60
Beer & Other Fermented Malt Liquors
N.A.I.C.S.: 424810

Damon Marsala (VP)
Charles Marsala (Pres)
Mike Lee (VP-Sls & Mktg)
Terry Hilton (Branch Mgr)
Tyler Flemister (VP-Mktg)
Trey Green (Mgr-Sls)

MARSDEN HOLDING, L.L.C.
380 St Peter St Ste 760 Ste 603, Saint Paul, MN 55102
Tel.: (651) 523-6611
Web Site: http://www.marsdenholdingllc.com
Sales Range: $200-249.9 Million
Emp.: 8,000
Holding Company
N.A.I.C.S.: 551112
Guy Mingo (CEO)
Skip Marsden (Founder)
Dave Nowacki (VP-Ops)
Troy Marcotte (Reg Mgr-Ops)

Subsidiaries:

Marsden Building Maintenance Company, L.L.C. (1)
1717 University Ave W, Saint Paul, MN 55104
Tel.: (651) 641-1717
Web Site: http://www.marsden.com
Sales Range: $300-349.9 Million
Emp.: 5,500
Janitorial Services
N.A.I.C.S.: 561720
David Ketcham (VP-Bus Dev)

Subsidiary (Domestic):

Cleanpower LLC (2)
124 N 121st St, Milwaukee, WI 53226
Tel.: (414) 302-3000
Web Site: http://www.cleanpower1.com
Sales Range: $50-74.9 Million
Emp.: 1,200
Janitorial Services
N.A.I.C.S.: 561720
Barbara Whitstone (Sr VP-Bus Ops-Racine)
Bill Reinhard (Sr VP-Ops-Eastern Wisconsin)
Mike Stollenwerk (VP-Ops-South East Wisconsin & Illinois)
David Gollata (VP-Green Bay)
Ariel Gallardo (Mgr-Madison)
Jason Herheim (Mgr-Stevens Point)

MARSH CONSTRUCTION SERVICES, INC.
191 Pattonwood Dr, Rochester, NY 14617
Tel.: (585) 342-1150
Web Site: http://www.marshconstructionservices.com
Sales Range: $1-9.9 Million
Emp.: 4
General Construction Mainly for Airport Tenants
N.A.I.C.S.: 236220
Philip Marsh (Principal)
David Marsh (Principal)

MARSH ELECTRONICS, INC.
1563 S 101st St, Milwaukee, WI 53214
Tel.: (414) 475-6000
Web Site: http://www.marshelectronics.com
Year Founded: 1937
Sales Range: $10-24.9 Million
Emp.: 50
Electronic Parts & Equipment
N.A.I.C.S.: 423690
Gary Stika (Mgr-Ops)
Jim Banovich (Owner)
Dan Birch (Sr Acct Mgr)
Rod Boeldt (Mgr-Product Mktg)
Carolyn Kastern (Mgr-Product Mktg)
Steve Spaeth (Branch Mgr)
Judy Strelka (Supvr-Acctg)
Tom Theisen (Mgr-Milwaukee)

Celia Reinke (Product Mgr)
Sarah Mullins (Product Mgr)
William Hanson (Product Mgr)

MARSH FURNITURE COMPANY
1001 S Centennial St, High Point, NC 27261
Tel.: (336) 884-7363 NC
Web Site: http://www.marshfurniture.com
Year Founded: 1906
Sales Range: $50-74.9 Million
Emp.: 600
Wood Kitchen Cabinets Mfr
N.A.I.C.S.: 337110
Kevin Smith (CFO)

MARSH LANDING MANAGEMENT COMPANY, INC.
4200 Marsh Landing Blvd Ste 200, Jacksonville Beach, FL 32250-2471
Tel.: (904) 273-3033
Web Site: http://www.marshlanding.org
Emp.: 100
Office Administrative Services
N.A.I.C.S.: 561110
Tripp Richland (Pres)
Kristy Richland (VP)

MARSH VENTURES INC.
10642 Pioneer Trl, Truckee, CA 96161
Tel.: (530) 550-2350
Web Site: http://www.tnt-materials.com
Rev.: $13,503,910
Emp.: 20
Batching Plants for Aggregate Concrete & Bulk Cement
N.A.I.C.S.: 333120
Brian Marsh (Pres)
Mike Rodart (VP)
Kelly Hackley (Mgr-Accts)

MARSH, BERRY & COMPANY, INC.
28601 Chagrin Blvd, Woodmere, OH 44142
Tel.: (440) 354-3230 OH
Web Site: http://www.marshberry.com
Year Founded: 1981
Sales Range: $25-49.9 Million
Corporate Consulting Services
N.A.I.C.S.: 541611
John M. Wepler (Chm & CEO)
Valerie DeMell (Exec VP)
Dan Skowronski (Sr VP)
Megan Bosma (Sr VP)
Tom Linn (Exec VP)
Albert Lloyd (Exec VP)
Wayne Walkotten (Exec VP)
Chris Darst (Sr VP)
Tommy McDonald (VP)
Phil Trem (Sr VP)
Jessica Stogran (VP)
Curt Vondrasek (VP)
Dale A. Myer (Mgr-Insurance Svcs)
Chad Morgan (VP-Insurance Svcs Div)
Christina Moran (Mgr-Bus Unit)
Sarah Lucas (VP)
Stephanie Hanayik (Chief Compliance Officer & VP)
Steven K. Bolland (Mng Dir)
Brad Unger (VP)
Eric Hallinan (VP)
George Bucur (VP)
Nick Kormos (VP)
Rob Hamilton (VP)
Ben Swann (VP & Dir-Sls)
David Soforenko (Exec VP)
Gerard Vecchio (Sr VP)
Mike Metz (CFO)
Mike Haselden (Sr VP-Connect Platform)

MARSH, BERRY & COMPANY, INC.

U.S. PRIVATE

Marsh, Berry & Company, Inc.—(Continued)

Subsidiaries:

Marsh, Berry & Company, Inc. - New York (1)
535 5th Ave 34th Fl, New York, NY 10017
Tel.: (212) 972-4880
Web Site: http://www.marshberry.com
Sales Range: $1-9.9 Million
Emp.: 5
Corporate Consulting Services
N.A.I.C.S.: 541611
Steven K. Bolland (Exec VP)
Dale A. Myer (Exec VP)

MarshBerry Capital, Inc. (1)
28601 Chagrin Blvd, Woodmere, OH 44122
Tel.: (440) 354-3230
Web Site: http://www.marshberry.com
Emp.: 85
Corporate Financial Advisory, Securities Brokerage & Securities Dealing Services
N.A.I.C.S.: 523150
John M. Wepler (Chm & CEO)
Valerie DeMell (Exec VP)
Tom Linn (Exec VP)
Wayne Walkotten (Exec VP)

MARSHA LYNN BUILDING CORP.
468 S Independence Blvd Ste B122, Virginia Beach, VA 23452
Tel.: (757) 490-5900
Year Founded: 1970
Sales Range: $10-24.9 Million
Emp.: 5
Speculative Builder of Single-Family Houses
N.A.I.C.S.: 236115
Donald Moore (Pres)

MARSHA SALDANA INC
City View Plaza Ste 700 48 Rd 165 Km 1.2, Guaynabo, PR 00949
Tel.: (787) 721-2600
Web Site: http://www.marshsaldana.com
Rev.: $21,283,968
Emp.: 180
Insurance Brokers
N.A.I.C.S.: 524210
Manuel Roman (VP-Fin)
Francisco Tirado (Pres)

MARSHAL MIZE FORD, INC.
5348 Hwy 153, Chattanooga, TN 37343
Tel.: (423) 875-2023
Web Site: http://www.marshalmizeford.com
Year Founded: 1977
Sales Range: $25-49.9 Million
Emp.: 115
Car Dealer
N.A.I.C.S.: 441110
Lewis J. Dyer (Pres)

MARSHALL & STERLING ENTERPRISES, INC.
110 Main St, Poughkeepsie, NY 12601
Tel.: (845) 454-0800   NY
Web Site: http://www.marshallsterling.com
Year Founded: 1994
Emp.: 400
Holding Company; Risk Management, Insurance & Financial Services
N.A.I.C.S.: 551112
Timothy E. Dean (CEO)
Eric Diamond (Pres-Employee Benefits)
Jeanne M. Maloy (Pres-Upstate Property & Casualty Ops)

Subsidiaries:

Marshall & Sterling, Inc. (1)
110 Main St, Poughkeepsie, NY 12601
Tel.: (845) 454-0800
Web Site: http://www.marshallsterling.com
Emp.: 325
Risk Management, Insurance & Financial Services
N.A.I.C.S.: 524210
John O'Shea (Chm)

Subsidiary (Domestic):

Master Risk, Inc. (2)
110 Main St, Poughkeepsie, NY 12601
Tel.: (845) 452-3857
Web Site: http://www.marshallsterling.com
Rev.: $150,000
Emp.: 2
Financial Services
N.A.I.C.S.: 522291
Tim Rychcik (Pres)

MARSHALL & STEVENS INC.
355 South Grand Ave, Los Angeles, CA 90071
Tel.: (323) 612-8000
Web Site: http://www.marshall-stevens.com
Rev.: $5,000,000
Emp.: 35
Other Management Consulting Services
N.A.I.C.S.: 541618
Alfred King (Vice Chm)
Barry Hacker (Sr Mng Dir)
Craig Tompkins (Chm)
John Oates (Mng Dir)
Kendall Raine (Exec Mng Dir)
Ralph Consola (Principal & Mng Dir)
Mark W. Santarsiero (Pres & CEO)

Subsidiaries:

Rocky Mountain Advisory, LLC (1)
215 S State St Ste 550, Salt Lake City, UT 84111-2319
Tel.: (801) 428-1600
Web Site: http://www.rockymountainadvisory.com
Offices of Certified Public Accountants
N.A.I.C.S.: 541211
Dan Johnson (Mgr)

MARSHALL & WINSTON INC.
6 Desta Dr Ste 3100, Midland, TX 79705
Tel.: (432) 684-6373
Sales Range: $10-24.9 Million
Emp.: 15
Crude Petroleum Production
N.A.I.C.S.: 211120
William S. Marshall (Chm)

MARSHALL ADVERTISING, INC.
1501 S Dale Mabry Hwy Ste A-8, Tampa, FL 33629
Tel.: (813) 254-8300
Web Site: http://www.marshalladvertising.com
Year Founded: 1994
Sales Range: $1-9.9 Million
Emp.: 10
Media Buying Agency
N.A.I.C.S.: 541830
Kevin Marshall (Co-Owner & Pres)
Jennifer Marshall (Co-Owner)

MARSHALL ASSOCIATES, INC.
1131 W Blackhawk 2 Fl, Chicago, IL 60642
Tel.: (312) 266-8500   DE
Web Site: http://www.marshassoc.com
Year Founded: 1973
Sales Range: $200-249.9 Million
Emp.: 135
Home & Garden, Sporting Goods & Toy Distr
N.A.I.C.S.: 423820
John R. Kazmer (Pres)
Jack Eisinger (CFO)

Dan DeVito (VP & Mgr-Sls)
Sam Evans (Acct Mgr)
Maris Formas (Mgr-E-Commerce)

MARSHALL BROTHERS INC.
2737 Erie Dr, Weedsport, NY 13166
Tel.: (315) 834-6687
Year Founded: 1983
Sales Range: $10-24.9 Million
Emp.: 200
Distr of Convenience Stores
N.A.I.C.S.: 445131
James Marshall (VP)
Case Marshall (VP)

MARSHALL COMPANY
1001 2nd St, Corpus Christi, TX 78404
Tel.: (361) 883-4369
Web Site: http://www.marshallcompanyinc.com
Sales Range: $25-49.9 Million
Emp.: 29
Commercial & Office Building, New Construction
N.A.I.C.S.: 236220
Michael Dodson (Pres)
Karla Wilburn (Sec & Gen Mgr)
Richard Dodson (VP)
Fidel Mendoza (Project Mgr)

MARSHALL COUNTY HOSPITAL
615 Old Symsonia Rd, Benton, KY 42025
Tel.: (270) 527-4800   KY
Web Site: http://www.marshallcountyhospital.org
Year Founded: 1978
Sales Range: $10-24.9 Million
Emp.: 284
Health Care Srvices
N.A.I.C.S.: 622110
Jennie Russell (Dir-Cardiopulmonary)
Janice Kelley (CFO)
Phyllis Blackwell (Chief Clinical Officer)
Stacy Poe (Dir-Quality & Resource Mgmt)
David Fuqua (CEO)
Jeannie Lee (Dir-HR & Business Office)
Patrick Waters (Dir-IT)
Everett Bloodworth (Dir-Laboratory)
Marica White (Dir-Public Rels & Foundation)
Sonia Morehead (Coord-Medical Staff)
Paul Schaper (Chm)

MARSHALL DENNEHEY WARNER COLEMAN & GOGGIN, P.C.
2000 Market St Ste 2300, Philadelphia, PA 19103
Tel.: (215) 575-2600
Web Site: http://www.marshalldennehey.com
Year Founded: 1962
Emp.: 467
Law firm
N.A.I.C.S.: 541110
Colleen M. Bannon (Dir-Legal Info Resources)
Ronda K. O'Donnell (Chm-Employment Law Practice Grp)
Howard P. Dwoskin (Dir-Casualty Dept)
Michael L. Turner (Partner)
Niki T. Ingram (Dir-Workers Compensation Dept)
Christopher E. Dougherty (Chm & Dir-Pro Liability Dept)
Liz L. Brown (COO)

Roger L. Bonine (Dir-IT)
Pattie A. Day (Dir-Billing & Acctg)
Joseph S. Goldshear (Dir-Mktg & Bus Dev)
Karen Rudderow (Dir-HR)
Ernie J. DiFilippo (Dir-Fin)
Marianne C. Boyne (Dir-Admin Svcs)
Linda F. Barron (Dir-Paralegal Svcs)
Lawrence J. Schempp (Dir-Pro Dev)
Frank Stransky (Dir-Fin)
T. Kevin FitzPatrick (Dir-Health Care)
Steven J. Forry (Atty-Supervising-Health Care Dept-Pittsburgh)
G. Mark Thompson (Pres & CEO)
Craig S. Hudson (Mng Atty-Florida)

MARSHALL ELECTRIC CORPORATION
425 N State Rd 25 N, Rochester, IN 46975
Tel.: (574) 223-4367
Web Site: http://www.marshall-electric.com
Rev.: $17,200,000
Emp.: 150
Electronic Coil, Transformer & Other Inductor Mfr
N.A.I.C.S.: 334416
Thomas C. Marrs (CEO)

MARSHALL ENGINES, INC.
404 W 8th St, Kearney, NE 68845
Tel.: (308) 234-6788
Web Site: http://www.marshallengines.com
Year Founded: 1982
Sales Range: $10-24.9 Million
Automotive Engine Mfr
N.A.I.C.S.: 333618
Norris Marshall (Pres & Dir)
Eric Trettle (COO)
Lori Marshall (Sec & Dir)

MARSHALL INDUSTRIES, INC.
3800 W 2100 S, Salt Lake City, UT 84120-1206
Tel.: (801) 266-2428
Web Site: http://www.marshallind.com
Year Founded: 1975
Sales Range: $10-24.9 Million
Emp.: 60
Electronic Equipment & Supplies Distr
N.A.I.C.S.: 423690
Dennis Savage (Mgr-Sls)
Adam Handy (Engr)
Randy McCleve (Bus Mgr)
Terry Seguin (Mgr-Warehouse)

MARSHALL JUNCTION PARTNERS, LLC
290 W Mt Pleasant Ave, Livingston, NJ 07039
Tel.: (212) 403-7017
Web Site: http://www.marshalljunction.com
Year Founded: 2001
Privater Equity Firm
N.A.I.C.S.: 523999
Gregg Alwine (Mng Partner)
David Barnett (Mng Partner)

MARSHALL MEDICAL CENTER
1100 Marshall Way, Placerville, CA 95667
Tel.: (530) 622-1441   CA
Web Site: http://www.marshallmedical.org
Year Founded: 1959
Sales Range: $200-249.9 Million
Emp.: 1,563
Health Care Srvices
N.A.I.C.S.: 622110
James Whipple (CEO)
Laurie Eldridge (CFO)

Kathy Krejci (Chief Nursing Officer)
Shannon Truesdell (COO)
Gabrielle Marchini (Treas & Sec)
John Driscoll (Chm)

Subsidiaries:

Marshall Medical Center North (1)
8000 Al Hwy 69, Guntersville, AL 35976
Tel.: (256) 571-8000
Health Care Srvices
N.A.I.C.S.: 622110
Gary Gore (CEO)

MARSHALL MUSIC CO.

3240 E Saginaw St, Lansing, MI 48912
Tel.: (517) 337-9700
Web Site:
http://www.marshallmusic.com
Rev.: $17,201,007
Emp.: 165
Band Instruments
N.A.I.C.S.: 459140
David McBride (Coord-Lansing)
Aaron Fram (Coord-Grand Rapids)
Bobbi Lukowski (Coord-Kalamazoo)
Elaine Althouse (Coord-Allen Park)
Lisa Clement (Coord-Traverse)
Patty Cantwell (Coord-Troy)
Todd Murphy (Coord-West Bloomfield)

MARSHALL RESOURCES INC.

2435 S Alston Ave, Durham, NC 27713
Tel.: (919) 598-0292
Web Site:
http://www.marshallresources.com
Sales Range: $1-9.9 Million
Emp.: 5
Computer Related Consulting Services
N.A.I.C.S.: 541512
Christopher Marshall (Owner)

MARSHALL SCIENTIFIC LLC

102 Tide Mill Rd Units 3 & 4, Hampton, NH 03842
Tel.: (603) 601-8511
Web Site:
http://www.marshallscientific.com
Year Founded: 2012
Sales Range: $1-9.9 Million
Emp.: 10
Laboratory Equipment Refurbished Services
N.A.I.C.S.: 811210
S. Steve (Bus Dir)
S. Max (Mktg Dir)
M. Garrett (Mgr-Technical)
M. John (Mgr-Logistics)
S. Rebecca (Mgr-Content)

MARSHALL STREET CAPITAL, INC.

330 E Kilbourn Ave Ste 1400, Milwaukee, WI 53202
Tel.: (414) 223-1560 WI
Web Site: http://www.mscap.com
Year Founded: 2014
Investment Management Service
N.A.I.C.S.: 523940
J. Douglas Gray (Pres, CEO & Chief Investment Officer)
Bruce J. Betters (CFO & Treas)
Todd J. Flunker (VP, Controller & Asst Treas)
Lori A. Schantz (Dir-Tax)
Thomas J. Hauske Jr. (Chm)

MARSHALL SUPPLY CO.

629 Palmyra Rd, Dixon, IL 61021
Tel.: (815) 288-3353
Rev.: $27,242,957
Emp.: 60
Beauty & Barber Shop Equipment & Supplies
N.A.I.C.S.: 423850
Mark Clevenger (Dir-Ops & Mktg)

MARSHALL TOOL & SUPPLY CORP.

9000 Lurline Ave, Chatsworth, CA 91311
Tel.: (818) 717-1965
Web Site:
http://www.marshalltool.com
Sales Range: $10-24.9 Million
Emp.: 45
Precision Tools
N.A.I.C.S.: 423490
James Dewitt (Pres)

MARSHALL UNIVERSITY RESEARCH CORP.

1 John Marshall Dr, Huntington, WV 25755-8100
Tel.: (304) 696-6793
Web Site: http://www.marshall.edu
Commercial, Technical Training & Workforce Development Services
N.A.I.C.S.: 541715
Brian Brown (Mgr-Site & Sr Engr-Mfg)
Charlotte Weber (Pres-Federal Programs)
John Maher (VP-Res-Marshall University & Exec Dir)
Amanda Plumley (Exec Office Mgr)
Joe Ciccarello (Dir-Grants & Contracts & Assoc Exec Dir)
Amanda Arbaugh (Officer-Grants)
Lisa Daniel (Officer-Grants-School of Medicine)
Martha Spalding Mozingo (Coord-Sponsored Programs)
Chris Schlenker (Officer-Grants-College of Science)
Jennifer Wood (Interim CFO)
Kelly Stump (Coord-HR)
Bruce Day (Dir-Res Integrity)
Amy Melton (Asst Dir-Tech Transfer Office & Coord-Conflict of Interest)
Trula Stanley (Coord-Medical)

MARSHALLS HOLDING CO.

20220 International Blvd S, Seattle, WA 98198
Tel.: (206) 433-5911
Web Site:
http://www.kenworthnorthwest.com
Sales Range: $75-99.9 Million
Emp.: 150
Trucks, Commercial
N.A.I.C.S.: 423110
Marshall Cymbaluk (Pres)

MARSHALLTOWN MEDICAL & SURGICAL CENTER

3 S 4th Ave, Marshalltown, IA 50158
Tel.: (641) 754-5151
Web Site:
http://www.everydaychampions.org
Rev.: $53,100,000
Emp.: 690
General Medical & Surgical Hospitals
N.A.I.C.S.: 622110
Liz Zurrcher (Dir-PR)
Hilary Dolbee (CFO)
John Hughes (Pres & CEO)

MARSHALLTOWN TROWEL COMPANY

104 S 8th Ave, Marshalltown, IA 50158
Tel.: (641) 753-5999 IA
Web Site:
http://www.marshalltown.com
Year Founded: 1905
Sales Range: $10-24.9 Million
Emp.: 300
Hand & Edge Tools
N.A.I.C.S.: 332216

Joe Carteer (VP)

MARSHFIELD CLINIC

1000 N Oak Ave, Marshfield, WI 54449
Tel.: (715) 387-5511 WI
Web Site:
http://www.marshfieldclinic.org
Year Founded: 1916
Sales Range: $1-4.9 Billion
Emp.: 6,700
Medical Clinic, Research Foundation
N.A.I.C.S.: 621111
Mark D. Bugher (Chm-Health System)
Susan Turney (CEO)

Subsidiaries:

Marshfield Clinic-Medical Research Foundation (1)
1000 N Oak Ave, Marshfield, WI 54449 (100%)
Tel.: (715) 387-5511
Web Site: http://www.marshfieldclinic.org
Sales Range: $350-399.9 Million
Emp.: 2,000
N.A.I.C.S.: 541720
Susan Turney (CEO)

MARSPRING CORPORATION

4920 Boyle Ave, Vernon, CA 90058
Tel.: (323) 589-5637
Web Site: http://www.lafiber.com
Sales Range: $10-24.9 Million
Emp.: 50
Spring Cushions
N.A.I.C.S.: 337910
Ronald J. Greitzer (Pres)

MARSTALLER MOTORS, INC.

1601 S Vly Mills Dr, Waco, TX 76711
Tel.: (254) 756-5511
Web Site:
http://www.marstallermotors.com
Year Founded: 1955
Sales Range: $10-24.9 Million
Emp.: 60
New Car Dealers
N.A.I.C.S.: 441110
Ronnie Marstaller (VP)
Tim Harner (Mgr-Svc)
Charles Marstaller (Pres)

MARSTEL-DAY, LLC

417 Wolfe St, Fredericksburg, VA 22401
Tel.: (540) 371-3338
Web Site: http://www.marstel-day.com
Year Founded: 2002
Sales Range: $10-24.9 Million
Emp.: 120
Scientific & Technical Consulting Services
N.A.I.C.S.: 541690
Rebecca Rubin (Pres & CEO)
H. Lee Halterman (Partner)
James Huber (Partner)
Sean B. Donahoe (Partner)
Jennifer Graham (Partner)
Diego Negron (Coord-GIS)

MARSTON IMPORT AGENCIES, INC.

PO Box 12656, Dallas, TX 75225
Tel.: (214) 373-0051
Sales Range: $10-24.9 Million
Emp.: 5
Frozen Fruit, Juice & Vegetable Production Services
N.A.I.C.S.: 311411
Ortiz Martha (Mgr-HR)

MARSTON WEBB INTERNATIONAL

60 Madison Ave Ste 1212, New York, NY 10010

Tel.: (212) 684-6601
Web Site:
http://www.marstonwebb.com
Year Founded: 1982
Sales Range: $25-49.9 Million
Emp.: 11
N.A.I.C.S.: 541810
Madlene Olson (VP & Gen Mgr)
Robert Schantz (Treas)
MaryAnn Huisman (Acct Asst)
George Haddad (Dir-Creative Svcs)
Bill Fitzgerald (Acct Exec)
Victor G. Webb (Pres)

MART FINANCIAL GROUP INCORPORATED

1410 N Meacham Rd, Schaumburg, IL 60173
Tel.: (847) 882-2800
Rev.: $10,000,000
Emp.: 5
Photographic Equipment Rental
N.A.I.C.S.: 532289
Matthew S. Martorano (Pres)
Linda Martorano (VP)

MARTAM CONSTRUCTION, INC.

1200 Gasket Dr, Elgin, IL 60120-7305
Tel.: (847) 608-6800
Web Site: http://www.martam.com
Year Founded: 1973
Sales Range: $25-49.9 Million
Emp.: 40
Civil Engineering Services
N.A.I.C.S.: 237310
Robert Kutrovatz (VP)

MARTCO INC.

1720 Watterson Trl, Louisville, KY 40209
Tel.: (502) 635-1600
Web Site: http://www.martcoinc.com
Year Founded: 1961
Sales Range: $25-49.9 Million
Emp.: 80
Provider of Closed Circuit TV, Access Control & Electronic Security Equipment
N.A.I.C.S.: 423690
Beau Hicks (Product Mgr)

MARTEL CONSTRUCTION, INC.

1203 S Church Ave, Bozeman, MT 59715-5801
Tel.: (406) 586-8585 MT
Web Site:
http://www.martelconst.com
Year Founded: 1960
Sales Range: $25-49.9 Million
Emp.: 200
Commercial, Industrial, Institutional & Residential Construction Licensed in MT, ID, CA, NV, WA & AZ
N.A.I.C.S.: 236210
Tony Martel (Pres)

Subsidiaries:

Bigfork Custom Woodworks (1)
305 Hwy 83, Bigfork, MT 59911
Tel.: (406) 837-1063
Web Site:
http://www.bigforkcustomwoodworks.com
Custom Architectural Woodwork Mfr
N.A.I.C.S.: 337212

MARTELL ELECTRIC, LLC

4601 Cleveland Rd Ext, South Bend, IN 46628-9742
Tel.: (574) 245-4640
Web Site:
http://www.martellelectric.com
Year Founded: 2001
Emp.: 120

MARTELL ELECTRIC, LLC

Martell Electric, LLC—(Continued)
Electrical Contractor & Engineering Services
N.A.I.C.S.: 238210
Matt Gayer *(Project Mgr)*
Tom Rowell *(Project Mgr)*
Tony Cave *(Coord-Svc)*

MARTENS CARS OF WASHINGTON, INC.
4800 Wisconsin Ave NW, Washington, DC 20016
Tel.: (202) 537-3000
Web Site:
http://www.martenscars.com
Year Founded: 1954
Sales Range: $10-24.9 Million
Emp.: 100
Car Whslr
N.A.I.C.S.: 441110
Steuart Martens *(Pres)*
Harry Martens III *(CEO)*

MARTENS VOLVO
4800 Wisconsin Ave NW, Washington, DC 20016
Tel.: (202) 537-3000
Web Site:
http://www.martensvolvo.com
Rev.: $36,000,000
Emp.: 90
New & Used Car Dealers
N.A.I.C.S.: 441110

MARTHA & MARY LUTHERAN SERVICES
19160 Front St NE, Poulsbo, WA 98370
Tel.: (360) 779-7500
Web Site:
http://www.marthaandmary.org
Year Founded: 1995
Sales Range: $10-24.9 Million
Emp.: 477
Child Care Services
N.A.I.C.S.: 624110
Mary Berglind *(Dir-Comm & Outreach)*
Anna Winney *(Dir-HR & Organizational Design)*
Leah Meadows *(CFO)*
Lynette Ladenburg *(CEO)*

MARTHA'S TABLE
2114 14th St NW, Washington, DC 20009
Tel.: (202) 328-6608
Web Site:
http://www.marthastable.org
Year Founded: 1979
Sales Range: $10-24.9 Million
Emp.: 88
Community Support Services
N.A.I.C.S.: 624190
Amy Kurz *(COO)*
Timothy Jones *(Dir-Healthy Connections & Project Lead-Community Engagement)*
Joan Woods *(Dir-Dev)*
Ryan Palmer *(Dir-Community Outreach)*
Tiffany Williams *(Pres & CEO)*
Ken Bacon *(Chm)*
Parag Sachdeva *(COO)*

MARTHA'S VINEYARD SAVINGS BANK
78 Main St, Edgartown, MA 02539
Tel.: (508) 627-4266
Web Site: http://www.mvbank.com
Year Founded: 1955
Sales Range: $50-74.9 Million
Emp.: 100
Commercial Banking Services
N.A.I.C.S.: 522110

Thomas J. Sharkey *(Interim Pres & Interim CEO)*
Charles Kroll *(CFO)*
Frank Fenner *(Chm)*
James Anthony *(Pres & CEO)*

Subsidiaries:

Martha's Vineyard Financial Group (1)
496 State Rd, West Tisbury, MA 02575
Tel.: (508) 693-8850
Web Site: http://www.mvbank.com
Sales Range: $25-49.9 Million
Emp.: 6
Investment Management, Estate Planning & Brokerage Services
N.A.I.C.S.: 523940
Luke Murphy *(Mng Dir)*

MARTIGNETTI COMPANIES
975 University Ave, Norwood, MA 02062-2643
Tel.: (781) 278-2000
Web Site: http://www.martignetti.com
Year Founded: 1986
Sales Range: $25-49.9 Million
Emp.: 150
Wholesale Distributor of Wine & Distilled Beverages & Operator of Liquor Stores
N.A.I.C.S.: 424820
Anthony Bruneau *(Mgr-Sls-Metro Boston)*
Maureen Candito *(Mgr-Pur & Inventory)*
Matthew Chivian *(Portfolio Mgr)*
Steven Coval *(Mgr-Fine Wine Inventory)*
Jessica Cyr *(Portfolio Mgr)*
Linda Davis *(Supvr-Payroll)*
John Downey *(Mgr-Receiving)*
David Fasulo *(Portfolio Mgr-Wine)*
Dennis Gilligan *(Portfolio Mgr)*
Mike Gorman *(Mgr-Sls)*
Gary Keimach *(Sr VP)*
Kathie Mansfield *(VP-HR)*
Al Mendes *(Sr VP-IT)*
Brian Mundy *(Mgr-Sls)*
Ken Ochs *(Mgr-Sls)*
Mary Lou Segreve *(Sr VP-Admin Ops)*
Dwight Walker *(VP)*
Jim Young *(Mgr-Sls)*
Arthur Zikos *(Dir-Pur & Logistics)*
Tricia Murphy *(Mgr-Mktg)*
Beth Ethier *(Mgr-Credit)*
Justin Wolff *(Mgr-Fin)*
Neal Fisher *(VP)*
D. Dean Williams *(Exec VP)*
Carl Martignetti *(Principal)*
Carmine Martignetti *(Principal)*

Subsidiaries:

Classic Wine Imports, Inc. (1)
975 Universe Ave, Norwood, MA 02062
Tel.: (781) 352-1100
Web Site:
http://www.classicwineimports.com
Distr of Fine Wine
N.A.I.C.S.: 424820

Martignetti Companies - United Liquors Division (1)
175 Campanelli Dr, Braintree, MA 02185-9219
Tel.: (781) 348-8000
Wine & Spirit Whslr
N.A.I.C.S.: 424820

Martignetti Companies of NH (1)
540 North Commercial St Ste 311, Manchester, NH 03101
Tel.: (603) 669-5884
Web Site: http://www.nhwines.com
Wine & Spirit Whslr
N.A.I.C.S.: 424820
D. Dean Williams *(Exec VP & Gen Mgr)*
Chris Conrad *(VP-Sls)*
Laurie Baines *(Dir-Graphics)*
Jim Fadden *(Mgr-NHSLC & Retail Stores)*
Ed Parker *(Controller)*

MARTIN & BAYLEY, INC.
1311 A W Main St, Carmi, IL 62821-4930
Tel.: (618) 382-2334
Web Site:
http://www.martinandbayley.com
Year Founded: 1960
Sales Range: $500-549.9 Million
Emp.: 1,500
Convenience Stores Owner & Operator
N.A.I.C.S.: 445131
Charles Martin *(Vice Chm)*
Mark Bayley *(Chm)*
Todd Jenney *(Pres & CEO)*

MARTIN BROS./MARCOWALL, INC.
17104 S Figueroa St, Gardena, CA 90248
Tel.: (310) 532-5335
Web Site: http://www.martinbros.net
Year Founded: 1956
Sales Range: $25-49.9 Million
Emp.: 150
Plastering Drywall & Insulation Services
N.A.I.C.S.: 238310
Ana Tinajero *(Sec)*
Bob Jones *(CEO)*
Michael Eastman *(Project Mgr)*
Raffi Ounanian *(Partner & VP)*

MARTIN BROTHERS CONSTRUCTION, INC.
8801 Folsom Blvd Ste 260, Sacramento, CA 95826
Tel.: (916) 381-0911
Web Site:
http://www.martinbrothers.net
Year Founded: 1996
Sales Range: $1-9.9 Million
Emp.: 50
Highway & Street Construction
N.A.I.C.S.: 237310
Felipe Martin *(Co-Founder)*

MARTIN BROTHERS DISTRIBUTING COMPANY, INC.
6623 Chancellor Dr, Cedar Falls, IA 50613
Tel.: (319) 266-1775
Web Site: http://www.martinsnet.com
Year Founded: 1941
Sales Range: $50-74.9 Million
Emp.: 500
Groceries, General Line
N.A.I.C.S.: 424410
Brooks J. Martin *(CEO)*
John R. Martin *(Pres)*

MARTIN CADILLAC COMPANY, INC.
12101 W Olympic Blvd, Los Angeles, CA 90064
Tel.: (310) 622-9334
Web Site:
http://www.martinautogroup.com
Year Founded: 1950
Sales Range: $150-199.9 Million
Emp.: 250
New Car Dealers
N.A.I.C.S.: 441110
Scott Allen *(Mgr-Preowned)*
Reggie Shelton *(Mgr-Svc)*

MARTIN CAR FINANCING INC.
3150 Milton Martin Toyota Way, Gainesville, GA 30507
Tel.: (770) 532-4355
Web Site:
http://www.miltonmartintoyota.com
Sales Range: $25-49.9 Million
Emp.: 88
New & Used Automobiles
N.A.I.C.S.: 441110

U.S. PRIVATE

Mike Martin *(Co-Owner)*
Ricky Martin *(Co-Owner)*
Jimmy Hernandez *(Dir-Ops-Fixed)*
Tommy Martin *(Co-Owner & Gen Mgr)*
Tony Powell *(Mgr-Svcs)*
Chad Smith *(Mgr-VIP Loyalty)*

MARTIN CHEVROLET SALES, INC.
8800 Gratiot Rd, Saginaw, MI 48609
Tel.: (989) 781-4590
Year Founded: 1912
Sales Range: $50-74.9 Million
Emp.: 75
Car Whslr
N.A.I.C.S.: 441110
Bill Martin *(Owner)*
Tad Veremis *(Mgr-Sls)*

MARTIN CHEVROLET-BUICK, INC.
420 W Southline, Cleveland, TX 77327-4858
Tel.: (281) 592-2644
Web Site:
http://www.martinchevroletbuickgmc.com
Sales Range: $25-49.9 Million
Emp.: 65
Car Whslr
N.A.I.C.S.: 441110
Tom Broadway *(Gen Mgr)*

MARTIN COUNTY PETROLEUM & PROPANE
3586 SW Martin Hwy, Palm City, FL 34990-8140
Tel.: (772) 287-1900
Web Site:
http://www.comoflorida.com
Petroleum Products
N.A.I.C.S.: 424720

MARTIN DOOR MANUFACTURING, INC.
2828 S 900 West, Salt Lake City, UT 84119-2420
Tel.: (801) 973-9310
Web Site: http://www.martindoor.com
Year Founded: 1936
Sales Range: $10-24.9 Million
Emp.: 115
Steel, Sectional Overhead Garage Doors Mfr
N.A.I.C.S.: 332321
Dean Clark *(CFO)*
Virginia H. Martin *(Treas & Sec)*
David Haslam *(Dir-Sls-North America)*
Carey Peterson *(Dir-Adv)*
Mark Stromberg *(CEO)*

MARTIN EAGLE OIL COMPANY, INC.
2700 James St, Denton, TX 76205-7662
Tel.: (940) 383-2351
Web Site:
http://www.martineagle.com
Year Founded: 1962
Sales Range: $10-24.9 Million
Emp.: 35
Distribution of Petroleum Products
N.A.I.C.S.: 424720
Steve Martin *(Pres)*
Gary Martin *(VP)*
Bill Meek *(Controller)*

MARTIN EMPLOYEES, INC.
19014 E Admiral Pl, Catoosa, OK 74015
Tel.: (918) 258-8321
Web Site: http://www.infinitepkg.com
Year Founded: 1996
Flexible Packaging Products & Labels Mfr

COMPANIES   MARTIN RESOURCE MANAGEMENT CORPORATION

N.A.I.C.S.: 326112
Lynn Higgs *(CEO)*

MARTIN ENGINEERING
1 Martin Pl, Neponset, IL 61345-9766
Tel.: (309) 852-2384   IL
Web Site: http://www.martin-eng.com
Year Founded: 1944
Rev.: $55,352,064
Emp.: 250
Mining Machinery Mfr
N.A.I.C.S.: 333131
Edwin H. Peterson *(Chm)*
Robert J. Nogaj *(Pres & CEO)*
Adam Pallai *(VP)*
Steve Walker *(Exec VP)*
Kevin McKinley *(CFO & Head-IT-Global)*
Paul Harrison *(CTO & Dir-Conveyor Products Bus Grp-Global)*

Subsidiaries:

Cougar Industries, Inc.   (1)
3600 Cougar Dr, Peru, IL 61354-9336
Tel.: (815) 224-1200
Web Site: http://www.cougarindustries.com
Rev.: $3,000,000
Emp.: 25
Industrial Vibrating Equipment Mfr
N.A.I.C.S.: 333120

Martin Bulk Handling Solutions (Pty) Limited   (1)
Corner Antwerpen Street and Arnhemsingel, Die Heuwel, Witbank, 1042, Mpumalanga, South Africa
Tel.: (27) 13 656 5135
Web Site: http://www.martin-eng.co.za
Industrial Equipment Whsr
N.A.I.C.S.: 423830

Martin Engineering Company India Private Limited   (1)
Gat No 301 Kharabwadi Chakan Tal-Khed, Pune, 410501, India
Tel.: (91) 2135 674000
Web Site: http://www.martin-eng.in
Industrial Equipment Whsr
N.A.I.C.S.: 423830
Bill Shukla *(Mng Dir)*

Martin Engineering GmbH   (1)
In der Rehbach 14, 65396, Walluf, Germany
Tel.: (49) 6123 97820
Web Site: http://www.martin-eng.de
Industrial Equipment Whsr
N.A.I.C.S.: 423830

Martin Engineering Italy SRL   (1)
Via Buonarroti 43/A, 20064, Gorgonzola, Italy
Tel.: (39) 02 95383851
Web Site: http://www.martin-eng.it
Industrial Equipment Whsr
N.A.I.C.S.: 423830

Martin Engineering Limited   (1)
8 Experian Way ng2 Business Park, Nottingham, NG2 1EP, United Kingdom
Tel.: (44) 11 59 464 746
Web Site: http://www.martin-eng.co.uk
Industrial Equipment Whsr
N.A.I.C.S.: 423830

Martin Engineering Ltda.   (1)
Rua Estacio de Sa 2104, Jd Sta Genebra, Campinas, 13080-010, Brazil
Tel.: (55) 19 3709 7200
Web Site: http://www.martin-eng.com.br
Industrial Equipment Whsr
N.A.I.C.S.: 423830

Martin Engineering Peru SRL   (1)
Calle 2 Lote 7 Mz C Urb Industrial La Merced Ate Vitarte, Lima, Peru
Tel.: (51) 1 660 4315
Web Site: http://www.martin-eng.pe
Industrial Equipment Whsr
N.A.I.C.S.: 423830

Martin Engineering S. de R.L. de C.V.   (1)
Av Tecnologico No 6500-B3 Col Parral, 31150, Chihuahua, Chih, Mexico
Tel.: (52) 614 419 17 19
Web Site: http://www.martin-eng-mx.com
Emp.: 53
Industrial Equipment Whsr
N.A.I.C.S.: 423830
Julieta Gomez *(Mgr)*

Martin Engineering SARL   (1)
Eurocentre 50 50 Avenue d'Alsace, Colmar, 68025, France
Tel.: (33) 3 89 206 324
Web Site: http://www.martin-eng.fr
Emp.: 4
Industrial Equipment Whsr
N.A.I.C.S.: 423830
Sam Chenoweth *(Gen Mgr)*

MARTIN EQUIPMENT OF ILLINOIS
400 W Martin Dr, Goodfield, IL 61742
Tel.: (309) 965-2502
Web Site: http://www.meoi.com
Year Founded: 1981
Sales Range: $75-99.9 Million
Emp.: 150
General Construction Machinery & Equipment
N.A.I.C.S.: 423810
Tony Gurdian *(Controller)*
Jeff Deboeuf *(Mgr-Parts)*
Ryan Ehlers *(Mgr-Svc)*
Robert S. Martin Sr. *(Chm)*
Robert S. Martin Jr. *(Pres)*

MARTIN FINANCIAL GROUP
3030 Lyndon B Johnson Freeway Ste 1450, Dallas, TX 75234
Tel.: (214) 522-4245
Web Site:
  http://www.martinfinancialgroup.com
Emp.: 100
Insurance Agencies & Brokerages
N.A.I.C.S.: 524210
Richard Martin *(Owner)*

MARTIN FLUID POWER COMPANY, INC.
84 Minnesota Dr, Troy, MI 48083
Tel.: (248) 585-8170
Web Site: http://www.mfpseals.com
Year Founded: 1977
Sales Range: $10-24.9 Million
Emp.: 100
Seals, Industrial
N.A.I.C.S.: 423840
Wayne M. King *(Pres)*

MARTIN FLYER INC.
70 W 36th St 6th Fl, New York, NY 10018
Tel.: (212) 840-8899
Web Site: http://www.martinflyer.com
Sales Range: $10-24.9 Million
Emp.: 25
Jewelry Mfr
N.A.I.C.S.: 339910
Gary Flyer *(Pres)*

MARTIN HEALTH SYSTEM
200 SE Hospital Ave, Stuart, FL 34994
Tel.: (772) 287-5200
Web Site:
  http://www.martinhealth.org
Sales Range: $10-24.9 Million
Emp.: 2,700
Medical Health Network
N.A.I.C.S.: 622110
Miguel Coty *(Chief Mktg, Comm & Patient Experience Officer & VP)*
Angie Metcalf *(Chief HR Officer & VP)*
Jessica McLain *(Chief Philanthropic Officer & VP)*
John Loewenberg *(Chm)*
Cheryl Jordan *(Chm-Family Practice)*
Tiffany Weakley *(Pres-Medical Staff)*
H. William Lichtenberger *(Sec)*
Theora Webb *(Treas)*
Chuck Cleaver *(CFO & Sr VP)*
Marian Wossum *(Chief Legal Officer & VP)*
Fernando Petry *(Chief Medical Officer & Sr VP)*
Libby Flippo *(Chief Nursing Officer & Sr VP)*
Laurence Rothstein *(Chief Physician Grp Officer & Sr VP)*
Edmund Collins *(CIO & VP)*
Robert L. Lord Jr. *(Pres & CEO)*
James Orr III *(Vice Chm)*

MARTIN L WEINER & ASSOCIATES
43585 Monterre Ave, Palm Desert, CA 92260
Tel.: (760) 770-7777
Sales Range: $10-24.9 Million
Emp.: 10
Bond Brokers
N.A.I.C.S.: 424410
Martin L. Weiner *(Pres)*

MARTIN LIBRARY ASSOCIATION
159 E Market St, York, PA 17401
Tel.: (714) 846-5300   PA
Year Founded: 1916
Sales Range: $1-9.9 Million
Library Association
N.A.I.C.S.: 519210
William Schell *(Pres)*
Robert Bowen *(Treas)*
Tim Tate *(Chm)*
John Senft *(Sec)*

MARTIN LITHOGRAPH, INC.
505 N Rome Ave, Tampa, FL 33606
Tel.: (813) 254-1553   FL
Web Site: http://www.mlicorp.com
Year Founded: 1970
Sales Range: $1-9.9 Million
Emp.: 30
Commercial Lithographic Printing
N.A.I.C.S.: 323111
Martin Saavedra *(Pres)*

MARTIN LUTHER KING, JR. COMMUNITY HEALTH FOUNDATION
1680 E 120th St, Los Angeles, CA 90059
Tel.: (213) 622-2344   CA
Web Site: http://www.mlk-chf.org
Year Founded: 2011
Sales Range: $1-9.9 Million
Emp.: 3
Community Health Care Services
N.A.I.C.S.: 621498
Dyan Sublett *(Pres)*
Zulma Vitalich *(Mgr-Philanthropy)*
Linda Griego *(Chm)*
Paul King *(Treas)*
Robert Margolis *(Sec)*
Manuel A. Abascal *(Chm)*

MARTIN NEWARK DEALERSHIP, INC.
298 E Cleveland Ave, Newark, DE 19711
Tel.: (302) 738-5200
Web Site:
  http://www.martindelivers.com
Year Founded: 1985
Sales Range: $50-74.9 Million
Emp.: 225
Car Whslr
N.A.I.C.S.: 441110
Homayoun Poursaied *(Gen Mgr)*

MARTIN OIL COMPANY
528 N 1st St, Bellwood, PA 16617
Tel.: (814) 742-8438   PA
Web Site: http://www.martinoilco.com
Year Founded: 1962
Sales Range: $25-49.9 Million
Emp.: 140
Fuel Oil Dealers
N.A.I.C.S.: 457210
Janice Martin *(Gen Mgr)*
Dan Martin *(Controller)*

MARTIN PETERSEN COMPANY, INC.
9800 55th St, Kenosha, WI 53144
Tel.: (262) 658-1326
Web Site: http://www.mpcmech.com
Sales Range: $25-49.9 Million
Emp.: 280
Plumbing Heating & Air-Conditioning Contractors
N.A.I.C.S.: 238220
John Donnell *(Pres)*
Rob Jossart *(CFO & VP)*
Dan Ashburn *(VP)*
Kevin Louis *(VP)*

MARTIN PREFERRED FOODS LP
2011 Silver St, Houston, TX 77007
Tel.: (713) 869-6191
Web Site:
  http://www.martinpreferredfood.com
Rev.: $99,000,000
Emp.: 300
Poultry Production Services
N.A.I.C.S.: 424440
Bob Leslie *(Mgr-Retail Sls)*
James Daniels *(Project Mgr)*
Jarrett Hudek *(VP-Meat Ops)*

MARTIN RESOURCE MANAGEMENT CORPORATION
4200 B Stone Rd, Kilgore, TX 75662-6935
Tel.: (903) 983-6200   TX
Web Site: http://www.martin-gas.com
Year Founded: 1951
Sales Range: $450-499.9 Million
Emp.: 1,800
Transportation, Terminalling, Marketing & Logistics Management Services
N.A.I.C.S.: 424720
Ruben S. Martin III *(Chm, Pres & CEO)*
Robert D. Bondurant *(CFO & Exec VP)*
Chris Booth *(Chief Legal Officer, Gen Counsel, Sec & Exec VP)*
Terry D. King *(Sr VP)*
Randall L. Tauscher *(COO & Exec VP)*
Scot A. Shoup *(Sr VP-Ops)*
Johnnie Murry *(Sr VP-Surface Transportation)*
Mike Ginzel *(Sr VP-Fuel Oil & Asphalt)*
Michael Newton *(Sr VP-Roddey Enrgy Svcs)*

Subsidiaries:

ALTEC Environmental Consulting, LLC   (1)
10100 Woolworth Rd, Keithville, LA 71047
Tel.: (318) 687-3771
Web Site: http://www.altecenv.com
Environmental Consulting Services
N.A.I.C.S.: 541620
Robert B. Raines III *(VP)*

Martin Asphalt Company   (1)
Three Riverway Ste 1250, Houston, TX 77056
Tel.: (713) 350-6800
Web Site: http://www.martinasphalt.com
Sales Range: $10-24.9 Million
Emp.: 40
Asphalt Products
N.A.I.C.S.: 324121

Branch (Domestic):

Martin Asphalt Company   (2)

MARTIN RESOURCE MANAGEMENT CORPORATION

U.S. PRIVATE

Martin Resource Management Corporation—(Continued)

300 Christy Pl, South Houston, TX 77587-5165
Tel.: (713) 941-4410
Paving & Roofing Products, Asphalt & Petroleum Products Mfr
N.A.I.C.S.: 324121

Martin Energy Services LLC (1)
3 Riverway Ste 400, Houston, TX 77056
Tel.: (713) 350-6800
Fuel Distr
N.A.I.C.S.: 424720
Jennifer Kirby (Mgr-Customer Logistics)

Martin LP Gas Inc. (1)
2606 N Longview St, Kilgore, TX 75662 (100%)
Tel.: (903) 984-0781
Web Site: http://www.martin-gas.com
Sales Range: $10-24.9 Million
Emp.: 10
Propane Gas Distr
N.A.I.C.S.: 457210
Jerry Sullivan (Gen Mgr)

Martin Product Sales LLC (1)
3 Riverway Ste 1250, Houston, TX 77056
Tel.: (713) 350-5350
Emp.: 21
Petroleum Product Whslr
N.A.I.C.S.: 424720

Martin Resource Management Corp. - Pax Division (1)
580 West 1300 South, Salt Lake City, UT 84115-5134
Tel.: (801) 973-2800
Web Site: http://www.martinresources.com
Sales Range: $10-24.9 Million
Emp.: 9
Lawn & Garden Fertilizer Mfr
N.A.I.C.S.: 325311

Martin Resources, Inc. (1)
HCR 2 Box 17, Plainview, TX 79072 (100%)
Tel.: (806) 293-2501
Web Site: http://www.martinresources.com
Sales Range: $10-24.9 Million
Emp.: 70
Mfr, Distr & Packager of Fertilizer
N.A.I.C.S.: 325311
Billy Wood (Gen Mgr)

Martin Resources, Inc. (1)
4200 Stone Rd, Kilgore, TX 75662-6935
Tel.: (903) 983-6200
Web Site: http://www.martin-gas.com
Sales Range: $25-49.9 Million
Emp.: 147
Mfr of Petroleum, Sulter Products & Fertilizers
N.A.I.C.S.: 424720
Robert D. Bondurant (CFO & Exec VP)
Johnnie Murry (Sr VP-Surface Transportation)
Scot A. Shoup (Sr VP-Ops)
Scott Southard (VP-Comml Dev)
Randall L. Tauscher (COO & Exec VP)
Ralph Hernandez (Mgr-Logistics & Sls)
Katie Tiegs (Mgr-Logistics & Sls)
Mark Bohn (Mgr-Contracts & Sls)
Ken Griffin (Supvr-Crude Ops)
John Scott (VP-Ops)

Martin Transport, Inc. (1)
4200 B Stone Rd, Kilgore, TX 75662 (100%)
Tel.: (800) 256-6644
Web Site: http://www.dmartincompany.com
Emp.: 200
General Freight Trucking Services
N.A.I.C.S.: 484121
Jhonny Maurry (Gen Mgr)

Roddey Engineering Services, Inc.
10100 Woolworth Rd, Keithville, LA 71047
Tel.: (318) 221-1996
Web Site: http://www.roddey-engr.com
Sales Range: $1-9.9 Million
Emp.: 20
Chemical Engineering Services
N.A.I.C.S.: 541330
Michael Newton (Sr VP)
Clay Marbry (Project Mgr)

MARTIN SPROCKET & GEAR, INC.

3100 Sprocket Dr, Arlington, TX 76015-2828
Tel.: (817) 258-3000   TX
Web Site:
    http://www.martinsprocket.com
Year Founded: 1951
Sales Range: $350-399.9 Million
Emp.: 1,500
Roller Chain Sprockets & Gears, Screw Conveyors & Bucket Elevators; V-belt Sheaves & Hand Tool Mfr
N.A.I.C.S.: 333612
Joe R. Martin (Chm)
Paul Taylor (VP-Sls & Mktg)
Gretchen Rudd (Dir-Creative)
Chris Junkin (Mgr-Inside Sls)

Subsidiaries:

Martin Sprocket & Gear (Shanghai) Co., Ltd. (1)
No 81 Tang Yao Road Hua Ting Town, Jiading, Shanghai, 201816, China
Tel.: (86) 67084888
Web Site: http://www.martin-asia.com
Sprocket & Gear Mfr
N.A.I.C.S.: 333613

Martin Sprocket & Gear de Mexico, S.A. de C.V.
Km 52 Carretera Naucalpan-Toluca, Toluca 2000 Calle 3 Lote 11, Toluca, 50233, Mexico
Tel.: (52) 7222760800
Web Site: http://www.martinsprocket.com
Sales Range: $50-74.9 Million
Emp.: 800
Power Transmission Equipment Mfr
N.A.I.C.S.: 333613
Carlos Tello (Mgr-Sls)

Martin Sprocket & Gear, Inc. - Martin Tools Division (1)
3600 McCart Ave, Fort Worth, TX 76101
Tel.: (817) 258-3000
Web Site:
    http://www.martintoolandforge.com
Industrial Hand Tool Mfr & Distr
N.A.I.C.S.: 332216

Martin Sprocket & Gear, Inc. - Mississauga (1)
896 Meyerside Drive, Mississauga, L5T 1R9, ON, Canada
Tel.: (905) 670-1991
Web Site: http://www.martinsprocket.com
Machine Tools Mfr & Services
N.A.I.C.S.: 333517
Shawn Grant (VP)

MARTIN SUPPLY COMPANY INC.

200 E Appleton Ave, Sheffield, AL 35660-3458
Tel.: (256) 383-3131   AL
Web Site:
    http://www.martinsupply.com
Year Founded: 1934
Sales Range: $25-49.9 Million
Emp.: 220
Industrial Supplies
N.A.I.C.S.: 423840
Edith Martin Ruggles (Chm)
David Langford (Mgr-Pur)
Gordon Ruggles (CFO)
Ann Richey (Mgr-HR)

Subsidiaries:

Gordon Street Corporation (1)
120 Johnson St 120, Jackson, TN 38301-5917
Sales Range: $10-24.9 Million
Emp.: 1
Nonresidential Building Operators
N.A.I.C.S.: 531120

Martin Supply Company Inc. (1)
120 Johnson St, Jackson, TN 38301-5917 (100%)
Tel.: (731) 935-8700
Sales Range: $25-49.9 Million
Emp.: 45
Electrical Apparatus & Equipment
N.A.I.C.S.: 332321

MARTIN THOMAS, INC.

42 Riverside Dr, Barrington, RI 02806
Tel.: (401) 245-8500
Web Site:
    http://www.martinthomas.com
Year Founded: 1987
Sales Range: Less than $1 Million
Emp.: 9
Advertising Services
N.A.I.C.S.: 541810
Martin K. Pottle (Founder)

Subsidiaries:

Martin Thomas International, Public Relations Division (1)
20367 Clover Field Ter, Sterling, VA 20165
Tel.: (401) 245-8500
Web Site: http://www.martinthomas.com
Advetising Agency
N.A.I.C.S.: 541810
Martin K. Pottle (Founder)

MARTIN TIRE CO.

1341 N Lee Trevino Dr, El Paso, TX 79936
Tel.: (915) 592-6496
Web Site: http://www.martintire.com
Rev.: $13,678,760
Emp.: 70
Automotive Tires
N.A.I.C.S.: 441340
Ronald L. Martin (Pres)
Daivd Martin (VP)

MARTIN UNIVERSAL DESIGN, INC.

4444 Lawton St, Detroit, MI 48208
Tel.: (313) 895-0700   MI
Web Site:
    http://www.martinuniversaldesign.com
Year Founded: 1946
Sales Range: $50-74.9 Million
Emp.: 25
Artist Furniture, Drawing Tables & Drafting Supplies Importer & Distr
N.A.I.C.S.: 337211
Dennis Kapp (CEO)
Elizabeth Clark (Pres)
Duane Parker (VP-Sls & Mktg)

Subsidiaries:

Martin/F. Weber Company (1)
2727 Southampton Rd, Philadelphia, PA 19154-1293
Tel.: (215) 677-5600
Web Site: http://www.weberart.com
Sales Range: $25-49.9 Million
Mfr Art Materials
N.A.I.C.S.: 339940
Michael Gorak (Pres)

MARTIN WELLS INDUSTRIES

5886 Compton Ave, Los Angeles, CA 90001
Tel.: (323) 581-6266
Web Site:
    http://www.martinwellsco.com
Rev.: $25,000,000
Emp.: 6
Engine Parts Mfr
N.A.I.C.S.: 336390
Joseph J. Keon Jr. (Pres)

MARTIN WHALEN OFFICE SOLUTIONS INC.

148 N Kinzie Ave, Bradley, IL 60915
Tel.: (815) 933-3358
Web Site: http://www.mwos.com
Year Founded: 1936
Sales Range: $10-24.9 Million
Emp.: 51
Office Equipment Whslr
N.A.I.C.S.: 423420
Marty Whalen (Pres)
Dan Whalen (VP)

MARTIN'S FAMOUS PASTRY SHOPPES

1000 Potato Roll Ln, Chambersburg, PA 17201
Tel.: (717) 263-9580   DE
Web Site: http://www.potatoroll.com
Sales Range: $200-249.9 Million
Emp.: 500
Snack Foods, Pastries & Cookies Mfr
N.A.I.C.S.: 311812
Jeff Joyce (Mgr-Sls)

Subsidiaries:

Martin's Famous Pastry Shoppes - Snack Division (1)
1000 Potato Roll Ln, Chambersburg, PA 17202-8897
Tel.: (717) 263-9580
Web Site: http://www.potatoroll.com
Sales Range: $25-49.9 Million
Emp.: 195
Mfr of Potato Chips & Snacks
N.A.I.C.S.: 311812

MARTIN-SCHAFFER, INC.

6601 Old Stage Rd, Rockville, MD 20852-4327
Tel.: (301) 951-3388
Web Site:
    http://www.martinschaffer.com
Year Founded: 1983
Advetising Agency
N.A.I.C.S.: 541810
Mita M. Schaffer (Co-Owner)

MARTINEZ & TUREK, INC.

300 S Cedar Ave, Rialto, CA 92376
Tel.: (909) 820-6800
Web Site:
    http://www.martinezandturek.com
Rev.: $18,300,000
Emp.: 115
Machine Shops
N.A.I.C.S.: 332710
Donald A. Turek (VP & Gen Mgr)
Laurence Martinez (VP)
John Romero (VP-Sls)
Larry Tribe (Pres & Bus Mgr)

MARTINI MEDIA INC.

415 Brannan St, San Francisco, CA 94107
Tel.: (415) 913-7445
Web Site:
    http://www.martinimedianetwork.com
Sales Range: $10-24.9 Million
Emp.: 50
Advertising Services
N.A.I.C.S.: 541810
Skip Brand (CEO)
Erik Pavelka (COO)
Pavelka O'Regan (Pres & CRO)
Gagan Saksena (CTO)
Bill Rowley (Sr VP-Bus Dev & Publ)
Matt Gower (Mng Dir-Europe)
Vincent Krsulich (Sr VP-Sls)

MARTINO FLYNN LLC

175 Sully's Trl Ste 100, Pittsford, NY 14534
Tel.: (585) 421-0100
Web Site:
    http://www.martinoflynn.com
Year Founded: 1967
Rev.: $33,000,000
Emp.: 52
Fiscal Year-end: 12/31/15
Advertising Services
N.A.I.C.S.: 541810
Ray Martino (Partner)
Chris Flynn (Partner)
Robbie Magee (Exec Dir)
Jill Wegman (Dir-Bus Dev)
Colleen Bogart (Exec Dir-Media Sls)
Tim Downs (Exec Dir-Creative)
Bethx Van-Vliet (Acct Dir)

Beth VanVliet *(Dir-Client Svcs)*
Alex Chernyak *(Dir-Bus Dev)*
Evan Thorpe *(Art Dir-Digital)*

MARTINS COUNTRY MARKET
1717 W Main St, Ephrata, PA 17522-1129
Tel.: (717) 738-3754 PA
Web Site:
http://www.familyownedmarkets.com
Year Founded: 1983
Sales Range: $25-49.9 Million
Emp.: 170
Grocery Stores
N.A.I.C.S.: 445110

MARTINS INC.
6821 Dogwood Rd, Baltimore, MD 21244
Tel.: (410) 265-1300 MD
Web Site:
http://www.martincaterers.com
Year Founded: 1991
Sales Range: $25-49.9 Million
Emp.: 500
Catering Services
N.A.I.C.S.: 722320
Wayne Resnick *(Pres)*

MARTINS PETERBILT INC.
174 Old Whitley Rd, London, KY 40744
Tel.: (606) 878-6410
Web Site:
http://www.martinspeterbilt.com
Rev.: $30,000,000
Emp.: 55
Service, Sell Parts & Sales Of Truck Tractors
N.A.I.C.S.: 423110

MARTINS POTATO CHIPS INC.
5847 Lincoln Hwy W, Thomasville, PA 17364
Tel.: (717) 792-3565
Web Site:
http://www.martinschips.com
Year Founded: 1941
Sales Range: $10-24.9 Million
Emp.: 145
Potato Chips & Other Potato-Based Snacks
N.A.I.C.S.: 311919
C. Fitz *(CFO)*
Kenneth A. Potter Jr. *(Pres & CEO)*

MARTINS RESTAURANT SYSTEMS INC.
5222 Floyd Rd SW, Mableton, GA 30126-0689
Tel.: (770) 948-3922
Web Site:
http://www.martinsrestaurants.com
Sales Range: $10-24.9 Million
Emp.: 370
Fast-Food Restaurant, Chain
N.A.I.C.S.: 722513
Jerry D. Thompson *(Pres)*
Tina Christopher *(Dir-Mktg)*
Mike Jacobs *(VP-Admin)*
Milan Savick *(Exec VP)*

MARTINSBURG FARMERS ELEVATORS CO
102 S 2nd St, Martinsburg, MO 65264
Tel.: (573) 492-6218
Web Site:
http://www.martinsburgfarmerselevators.com
Sales Range: $10-24.9 Million
Emp.: 9
Grain & Feed Distr
N.A.I.C.S.: 424510
Phil Gastler *(Pres)*

MARTIS CAPITAL MANAGEMENT LLC
101 California St Ste 3260, San Francisco, CA 94111
Tel.: (415) 592-5908
Web Site:
http://www.martiscapital.com
Privater Equity Firm
N.A.I.C.S.: 523999
Barry Uphoff *(Founder & Mng Partner)*
David Zhang *(VP)*

MARTS & LUNDY, INC.
1200 Wall St W Fl 5A, Lyndhurst, NJ 07071
Tel.: (201) 460-1660 NJ
Web Site:
http://www.martsandlundy.com
Year Founded: 1926
Emp.: 200
Philanthropic & Consulting Services
N.A.I.C.S.: 541611
Donald M. Fellows *(Pres & CEO)*
Katherine McStowe *(Asst Sec & Asst Treas)*
Robert Miskura *(CFO & VP)*
Daniel R. Boyer *(Dir-Client Rels)*
John M. Cash *(Chm)*

MARTY FELDMAN CHEVROLET, INC.
42355 Grand River Ave, Novi, MI 48375
Tel.: (248) 348-7000
Web Site:
http://www.martyfeldmanchevy.com
Year Founded: 1981
Sales Range: $10-24.9 Million
Emp.: 70
New Car Dealers
N.A.I.C.S.: 441110
Marla Feldman *(VP)*
Jason Curie *(Gen Mgr)*

MARTY FRANICH FORD LINCOLN MERCURY INC
550 Auto Center Dr, Watsonville, CA 95076-3728
Tel.: (831) 722-4181 CA
Web Site: http://www.franichford.com
Year Founded: 1950
Sales Range: $100-124.9 Million
Emp.: 70
Auto Dealership
N.A.I.C.S.: 441110
Ken Hobbs *(Mgr-Parts)*
Leyton Felix *(Gen Mgr-Sls)*

MARTY SHOES, INC.
121 Carver Ave, Westwood, NJ 07675
Tel.: (201) 497-6637 NJ
Web Site:
http://www.martyshoes.com
Year Founded: 1974
Sales Range: $25-49.9 Million
Emp.: 150
Shoe Stores
N.A.I.C.S.: 458210
John Adams *(Pres & CEO)*
Gary Kennedy *(CIO)*

MARTY SUSSMAN ORGANIZATION
1940 Jenkintown Rd, Jenkintown, PA 19046
Tel.: (215) 887-1800
Web Site:
http://www.sussmanauto.com
Sales Range: $125-149.9 Million
Emp.: 200
Automobiles, New & Used
N.A.I.C.S.: 441110
Martin E. Sussman *(Chm)*
Eric Sussman *(Pres)*

Subsidiaries:

Marty Sussman Motors Inc (1)
1543 Easton Rd, Abington, PA 19001
Tel.: (215) 657-7050
Web Site: http://www.sussmanhonda.com
Rev.: $36,273,394
Emp.: 65
Automobiles, New & Used
N.A.I.C.S.: 441110
M. Eric Sussman *(Pres & CEO)*
Joe Wilcox *(VP)*
Jim Jackson *(Gen Mgr)*

MARTZ COMMUNICATIONS GROUP INC.
86 Porter Rd, Malone, NY 12953
Tel.: (518) 483-1100
Web Site:
http://www.radioworksbest.com
Year Founded: 1995
Sales Range: $1-9.9 Million
Emp.: 25
Radio Stations
N.A.I.C.S.: 516110
Michael Boldt *(Gen Mgr)*

Subsidiaries:

WAMO 100.1 FM (1)
2100 Yost Blvd Ste 505, Pittsburgh, PA 15221
Tel.: (412) 829-0100
Web Site: http://www.wamo100.com
Radio Stations
N.A.I.C.S.: 516110
Jamal Woodson *(Gen Mgr)*
Stephanie Baker *(Dir-Sls)*

MARUCCI AND GAFFNEY EXCAVATING CO.
18 Hogue St, Youngstown, OH 44502
Tel.: (330) 743-8170
Web Site:
http://www.maruccigaffney.com
Sales Range: $10-24.9 Million
Emp.: 15
Excavation Work
N.A.I.C.S.: 238910
William Gaffney *(Pres)*
Scott Marucci *(VP)*

MARUDAS GRAPHICS, INC.
20 Yorkton Ct, Saint Paul, MN 55117
Tel.: (651) 697-7820 MN
Web Site: http://www.marudas.com
Year Founded: 1983
Sales Range: $50-74.9 Million
Emp.: 25
Custom Business Forms, Office Supplies & Promotional Products Mfr & Distr
N.A.I.C.S.: 424120
Philip P. Marudas *(Pres)*

MARUZ CORPORATION
2253 Loiza St Cnr Soldado Cruz, San Juan, PR 00913
Tel.: (787) 726-8150
Rev.: $23,923,099
Emp.: 55
Independent Supermarket
N.A.I.C.S.: 445110

MARVAC ELECTRONICS
2001 Harbor Blvd, Costa Mesa, CA 92627
Tel.: (949) 650-2001
Web Site: http://www.marvac.com
Sales Range: $10-24.9 Million
Electronic Parts & Equipment Distr
N.A.I.C.S.: 423690
Deno Vaccher *(VP-Ops)*
Vince Vaccher *(Owner, Pres & CEO)*

MARVAL INDUSTRIES, INC.
315 Hoyt Ave, Mamaroneck, NY 10543
Tel.: (914) 381-2400 NY

Web Site:
http://www.marvalindustries.com
Year Founded: 1956
Sales Range: $75-99.9 Million
Emp.: 75
Mfr of Plastic Materials, Synthetic Resins, Color Concentrates & Dry Color
N.A.I.C.S.: 326199
Thomas Vimmerman *(Pres)*

MARVEL ENGINEERING COMPANY
2085 N Hawthorne Ave, Melrose Park, IL 60160
Tel.: (708) 343-4090 DE
Web Site:
http://www.marvelengineering.com
Sales Range: $10-24.9 Million
Emp.: 30
Filters, General Line: Industrial
N.A.I.C.S.: 333998
Forest Niccum *(Founder)*

MARVEL TECHNOLOGIES, INC.
42400 Grand River Ave Ste 207, Novi, MI 48375
Tel.: (248) 946-4023
Web Site:
http://www.marveltechus.com
Year Founded: 2006
Sales Range: $1-9.9 Million
Emp.: 55
Information Technology Services
N.A.I.C.S.: 541512
Bala Rajaraman *(Pres & CEO)*
Imthiaz Shabeer Ahmed *(VP-SAP Solutions & Products)*

MARVELL TOWER INSURANCE AGENCIES
3517 N Spaulding Ave, Chicago, IL 60618
Tel.: (312) 467-1200
Web Site:
http://www.marveltowers.net
Rev.: $12,000,000
Emp.: 15
Insurance Agents
N.A.I.C.S.: 524210
Jerry Allen *(Pres)*

MARVIL PACKAGE COMPANY
PO Box 210, Wilmington, NC 28401
Tel.: (910) 763-9991
Sales Range: $10-24.9 Million
Emp.: 110
Mfr of Veneer
N.A.I.C.S.: 327331
Edward M. Corbett *(VP)*
Jeff Sewell *(Controller)*

MARVIN DEVELOPMENT CORP.
12670 New Brittany Blvd Ste 202, Fort Myers, FL 33907
Tel.: (239) 433-1112
Web Site: http://www.marvin-homes.com
Year Founded: 1972
Sales Range: $10-24.9 Million
Emp.: 20
Residential Construction
N.A.I.C.S.: 236115
Richard F. Durling *(Pres)*
Joe Gavitt *(Dir-Sls & Mktg)*
Michael Reitmann *(Dir-Mktg-Intl)*

MARVIN ENGINEERING COMPANY, INC.
261 W Beach Ave, Inglewood, CA 90302-2903
Tel.: (310) 674-5030 CA
Web Site: http://www.marvineng.com

MARVIN ENGINEERING COMPANY, INC.

U.S. PRIVATE

Marvin Engineering Company, Inc.—(Continued)
Year Founded: 1963
Rev.: $50,000,000
Emp.: 300
Machine Shop; Jobbing & Repair
N.A.I.C.S.: 336413
David Gussman (Pres & COO)

Subsidiaries:

Flyer Defense, LLC (1)
151 W 135th St, Los Angeles, CA 90061
Tel.: (310) 324-5650
Web Site: http://www.marvingroup.com
Emp.: 30
Military & Defence Vehicle Component Mfr
N.A.I.C.S.: 336992
Oded Nechustan (Pres)

Marvin Land Systems (1)
261 W Beach Ave, Inglewood, CA 90302
Tel.: (310) 674-5030
Web Site: http://www.marvinland.com
Machine Shop, Jobbing & Repair
N.A.I.C.S.: 336413
Jerry Friedman (Chm, Pres & CEO)

Marvin Test Solutions, Inc. (1)
1770 Kettering, Irvine, CA 92614-5616
Tel.: (949) 263-2222
Web Site: http://www.marvintest.com
Sales Range: $10-24.9 Million
Emp.: 100
Global Producer of PXI & PC-Based Test Equipment & Test Solution Mfr
N.A.I.C.S.: 334515
Loofie Gutterman (Pres)
Stephen T. Sargeant (CEO)

MARVIN F. POER & COMPANY

12700 Hillcrest Rd Ste 125, Dallas, TX 75230-2009
Tel.: (972) 770-1100   TX
Web Site: http://www.mfpoer.com
Year Founded: 1964
Sales Range: $10-24.9 Million
Emp.: 72
Provide State & Local Tax Consulting Services
N.A.I.C.S.: 541618
Marvin F. Poer (Founder, Chm & CEO)
William L. DuBois (Pres & COO)
Nicholas J. Muros (Sr VP-West Reg)
Miles Friend (Sr VP-East Reg)
Tom Rawlston (Sr VP-IT)
Kathryn McBride (VP-Fin)
W. Ken Parsons (Sr VP)
Paul Miller (VP)

MARVIN K. BROWN AUTO CENTER, INC.

1441 Camino Del Rio S, San Diego, CA 92108
Tel.: (619) 291-2040
Web Site: http://www.mkb.com
Year Founded: 1964
Sales Range: $50-74.9 Million
Emp.: 140
New Car Dealers
N.A.I.C.S.: 441110
James E. Brown (Pres)

MARVIN TRAUB ASSOCIATES, INC.

885 3rd Ave Ste 2620, New York, NY 10022
Tel.: (646) 723-2990
Web Site: http://www.traub.io
Year Founded: 1992
Sales Range: $1-9.9 Million
Emp.: 12
Business Development Services
N.A.I.C.S.: 926110
Mortimer Singer (CEO)
Geoffrey D. Lurie (Pres & COO)
Amy Hafkin (Gen Mgr)
Brian Crosby (Mng Dir-Traub Capital)
Kelsey Groome (Mng Dir)
James Mun (Mng Dir-Luxury Home & Lifestyle)

Subsidiaries:

Traub Capital (1)
885 3rd Ave Ste 2620, New York, NY 10022
Tel.: (646) 723-2990
Investment Services
N.A.I.C.S.: 523999
Brian Crosby (Mng Dir)

Subsidiary (Domestic):

Mana Products, Inc. (2)
3202 Queens Blvd, Long Island City, NY 11101
Tel.: (718) 361-2550
Web Site: http://www.manaproducts.com
Toilet Preparation Mfr
N.A.I.C.S.: 325620
Nikos Mouyiaris (CEO)

Signature Brands, LLC (2)
808 SW 12 th St, Ocala, FL 34471
Tel.: (352) 622-3134
Web Site: http://www.signaturebrands.com
Sales Range: $150-199.9 Million
Emp.: 307
Seasonal Gifts
N.A.I.C.S.: 424450
Jennifer Kalkowski (Brand Mgr)
Donna Dodson (Dir-IT)
Tim Hudgens (Engr-Maintenance)
Gary Stenzel (Sr VP)

Subsidiary (Domestic):

Houston Harvest Gift Products LLC (3)
3501 Mount Prospect Rd, Franklin Park, IL 60131-1312
Tel.: (847) 957-9191
Sales Range: $25-49.9 Million
Emp.: 150
Popcorn Products Mfr & Distr
N.A.I.C.S.: 311919

MARVIN WINDOWS & DOORS INC.

2020 Silver Bell Rd Ste 15, Eagan, MN 55122
Tel.: (218) 386-1430   MN
Web Site: http://www.marvin.com
Year Founded: 1912
Sales Range: $1-4.9 Billion
Emp.: 2,700
Custom Window & Door Mfr
N.A.I.C.S.: 321911
Susan I. Marvin (Vice Chm)
Jim Macaulay (CFO & Sr VP-Corp Strategy)

Subsidiaries:

TruStile Doors LLC (1)
1780 E 66th Ave, Denver, CO 80229
Tel.: (303) 286-3931
Web Site: http://www.trustile.com
Door Mfr
N.A.I.C.S.: 321911
Chuck Tamblyn (Sr VP-Mktg & Customer Support)
Scott A. Schmid (Pres & CEO)
Jeff Elkin (CFO & COO)
Robert Stuart (VP-Engrg)
Steve Jara (VP-Ops)
Phil Foy (Dir-Customer Dev)

MARVIN'S FOOD WAREHOUSE, INC.

600 E Cherokee Ave, Sallisaw, OK 74955-4800
Tel.: (918) 775-4418   OK
Year Founded: 1974
Sales Range: $50-74.9 Million
Emp.: 400
Grocery Stores
N.A.I.C.S.: 445110
Rick Whitworth (Mgr)
James L. Marvin Jr. (Pres)

MARVIN'S FOODS

2614 W 6th St, Fayetteville, AR 72701-7698
Tel.: (479) 442-4323
Year Founded: 1988

Sales Range: $25-49.9 Million
Emp.: 250
Grocery Stores
N.A.I.C.S.: 445110
C.V. Combs (Owner)
Philip Huff (Dir-Produce Ops & District Mgr)

MARWELL CORPORATION

PO Box 139, Mentone, CA 92359
Tel.: (909) 794-4192   DE
Web Site: http://www.marwellcorp.com
Year Founded: 1979
Mfr of Angle Meter Socket Adapter
N.A.I.C.S.: 335313
Kathy K. Powell (Pres)
Robert Ashford (VP)
Kyle Farmer (Mktg & Sls Mgr)

MARWIT CAPITAL

100 Bayview Cir Ste 550, Newport Beach, CA 92660
Tel.: (949) 861-3636
Web Site: http://www.marwit.com
Sales Range: $25-49.9 Million
Emp.: 5
Privater Equity Firm
N.A.I.C.S.: 523999
Chris Britt (Mng Partner)
Matthew L. Witte (Mng Partner)
David M. Browne (Principal)
Laurie Seymour (Controller)

MARX COMPANIES, LLC

PO Box 540, Atlantic Highlands, NJ 07716
Tel.: (732) 936-1211
Web Site: http://www.marxcompanies.com
Meat Brokers
N.A.I.C.S.: 424470
Sarah Mickey (Project Mgr)

MARX MCCLELLAN THRUN

207 E Buffalo St Ste 643, Milwaukee, WI 53202
Tel.: (414) 277-7743
Sales Range: Less than $1 Million
Emp.: 15
Advertising Agencies
N.A.I.C.S.: 541810
Rick Thrun (Founding Partner & Dir-Creative)
Laura Marx (Partner)
Jim Utech (Assoc Dir-Creative)
Tim Panicucci (Dir-New Media)

MARX/OKUBO ASSOCIATES, INC.

455 Sherman St Ste 200, Denver, CO 80203
Tel.: (303) 861-0300
Web Site: http://www.marxokubo.com
Year Founded: 1982
Rev.: $20,470,690
Emp.: 86
Business Consulting Services
N.A.I.C.S.: 541330
Catherine L. Walker (Asst VP)
Leo James Marx (CEO)
Christian Stover (Project Coord)

MARY ANN MORSE HEALTHCARE CENTER

45 Union St, Natick, MA 01760
Tel.: (508) 433-4400   MA
Web Site: http://www.maryannmorse.org
Year Founded: 1990
Sales Range: $10-24.9 Million
Emp.: 372
Rehabilitation & Senior Nursing Care Services
N.A.I.C.S.: 623110

Mary Poirier (Dir-Social Svcs)
Kathleen Donaldson (Dir-Nursing Svcs)
Sandra Scott (Dir-Admissions)
Lisa Kubiak (Exec Dir)
Ferdinand Rondan (Dir-Environmental Svcs)
Catherine Ellen Didriksen (Dir-Activities)

MARY BIRD PERKINS CANCER CENTER

4950 Essen Ln, Baton Rouge, LA 70809
Tel.: (225) 767-0847   LA
Web Site: http://www.marybird.com
Year Founded: 1968
Sales Range: $25-49.9 Million
Emp.: 371
Cancer Treatment Services
N.A.I.C.S.: 622310
Thomas J. Adamek (Treas & Sec)
Todd D. Stevens (Pres & CEO)
Bill O'Quin (Chm)
Art E. Favre (Vice Chm)

MARY FEED & SUPPLIES, INC.

12905 W Okeechobee Rd 3, Hialeah Gardens, FL 33108
Tel.: (305) 556-7620   FL
Year Founded: 2008
Sales Range: $1-9.9 Million
Emp.: 3
Horse Feed, Poultry Feed, Dog Food, Cat Food, Bird Food & Oother Pet & Animal Products & Accessories
N.A.I.C.S.: 459910
Lazaro Roig (Pres & CEO)

MARY FRANCES ACCESSORIES, INC.

3732 Mt Diablo Blvd Ste 260, Lafayette, CA 94549
Tel.: (925) 962-2111
Web Site: http://www.maryfrances.com
Sales Range: $10-24.9 Million
Emp.: 26
Handbag & Purse Mfr
N.A.I.C.S.: 316990
Mary Francis (CEO)

MARY JANE'S CBD DISPENSARY, INC.

302 W Victory Dr, Savannah, GA 31405
Tel.: (912) 349-7666   NV
Web Site: http://www.mjcbdd.com
Year Founded: 2016
Rev.: $509,832
Assets: $385,683
Liabilities: $187,264
Net Worth: $198,419
Earnings: ($217,457)
Emp.: 8
Fiscal Year-end: 12/31/18
Tobacco Product Distr
N.A.I.C.S.: 424940
Moses Campbell (Pres, CEO & Sec)
Jorge Verar (CFO)

MARY KAY HOLDING CORPORATION

16251 Dallas Pkwy, Addison, TX 75001-6801
Tel.: (972) 687-6300   DE
Web Site: https://www.marykay.com
Year Founded: 1963
Sales Range: $1-4.9 Billion
Emp.: 5,000
Offices of Other Holding Companies
N.A.I.C.S.: 551112
David B. Hall (Chm & CEO)
Ryan Rogers (Chief Investment Officer)
Deborah Gibbins (COO)

Julia A. Simon *(Chief Legal Officer & Sec)*
Kregg Jodie *(CIO)*
Melinda Foster Sellers *(Chief People Officer)*
Nathan Moore *(Co-Pres)*
Sheryl Adkins-Green *(CMO)*
Wendy Wang *(Pres-Asia Pacific)*

Subsidiaries:

Hangzhou Mary Kay Cosmetics Co. Ltd. (1)
Fl 11 Juishi Renaissance Mansion 918 Middle Huaihai Road, Shanghai, 200020, China **(100%)**
Tel.: (86) 2164159398
Sales Range: $25-49.9 Million
Emp.: 200
Cosmetics & Toiletries Mfr & Sales
N.A.I.C.S.: 325620

LLC "Mary Kay (Moldova) Limited" (1)
62 A Sciusev Street, MD-2012, Chisinau, Moldova
Tel.: (373) 22 259 800
Web Site: http://www.marykay.md
Beauty Product Whslr & Distr
N.A.I.C.S.: 456120

Mary Kay (China) Cosmetics Co., Ltd. (1)
20th Floor Plaza 66 Tower II No 1366 Nan Jing Road W, Shanghai, 200040, China
Tel.: (86) 21 2208 8888
Beauty Supply Store Operator
N.A.I.C.S.: 456120
Katherine Weng *(Gen Mgr)*

Mary Kay (Hong Kong) Limited (1)
Manulife Provident Funds Bldg Rm 02-03 12th Floor 345 Nathan Rd, Kowloon, China (Hong Kong) **(100%)**
Tel.: (852) 29228133
Web Site: http://www.marykay.com.hk
Sales Range: $10-24.9 Million
Emp.: 15
Cosmetics Mfr & Distr
N.A.I.C.S.: 325620

Mary Kay (Kazakhstan) LLP (1)
140 Dostyk Av, Almaty, 050051, Kazakhstan
Tel.: (7) 327 2 60 72 30
Web Site: http://www.marykay.kz
Cosmetics Distr
N.A.I.C.S.: 456120

Mary Kay (Malaysia) Sdn Bhd (1)
T1-8-1 8th Floor Jaya 33 No 3 Jalan Semangat, Seksyen 13, Petaling Jaya, 46100, Selangor, Malaysia
Tel.: (60) 3 7711 7555
Web Site: http://www.marykay.com.my
Cosmetics Distr
N.A.I.C.S.: 456120

Mary Kay (Singapore) Private Limited (1)
10 Anson Road, No 13-08 International Plaza, Singapore, 079903, Singapore
Tel.: (65) 6226 6888
Web Site: http://www.marykay.com.sg
Sales Range: $10-24.9 Million
Emp.: 3
Beauty Product Retailer
N.A.I.C.S.: 456120

Mary Kay Asia Services Limited (1)
Suites 4308-11 Tower One Times Square 1 Matheson Street, Causeway Bay, Hong Kong, China (Hong Kong)
Tel.: (852) 2 922 8133
Web Site: http://www.marykay.com.hk
Beauty Product Retailer
N.A.I.C.S.: 456120

Mary Kay Cosmeticos de Mexico, S.A. de C.V. (1)
Antonio L Rodriguez 1882 Plaza Sur, Colonia Santa Maria, 64650, Monterrey, Nuevo Leon, Mexico **(100%)**
Tel.: (52) 8183807222
Web Site: http://www.marykay.com.mx
Sales Range: $25-49.9 Million
Emp.: 230
Cosmetics Distr
N.A.I.C.S.: 456120

Jose Smeke *(Pres-Latin America)*

Mary Kay Cosmeticos do Brazil Ltda. (1)
Rua Do Rocio No 267, Sao Paulo, 04552-000, Brazil **(100%)**
Tel.: (55) 11 3040 0757
Web Site: http://www.marykay.com.br
Sales Range: $10-24.9 Million
Emp.: 30
Cosmetics & Toiletries Distr
N.A.I.C.S.: 456120

Mary Kay Cosmeticos, S.A. (1)
Av Corrientes 316 Piso 1 Office 150, 1314, Buenos Aires, Argentina **(100%)**
Tel.: (54) 11 4321 5600
Web Site: http://www.marykay.com.ar
Sales Range: $10-24.9 Million
Emp.: 55
Cosmetics Distr
N.A.I.C.S.: 456120
Jose Smeke *(Pres)*
Mestor Fernandez *(Pres)*

Mary Kay Cosmetics (New Zealand) Inc. (1)
Unit 5 66 Hobill Avenue, PO Box 97211, Manukau City, Auckland, 2241, New Zealand
Tel.: (64) 9 262 0254
Web Site: http://www.marykay.com.au
Cosmetics Distr
N.A.I.C.S.: 456120

Mary Kay Cosmetics (Taiwan) Inc. (1)
13F 319 Sec 2 Tun Hwa, South Road, Taipei, 106, Taiwan
Tel.: (886) 2 2735 8066
Cosmetics Sales & Distr
N.A.I.C.S.: 424210
K. K. Chua *(Pres)*

Mary Kay Cosmetics (U.K.) Ltd. (1)
163 Eversholt Street, London, NW1 1BU, United Kingdom
Tel.: (44) 207 380 8200
Web Site: http://www.marykay.co.uk
Emp.: 32
Cosmetics Distr & Whslr
N.A.I.C.S.: 424210
Tara Eustace *(Pres-European)*

Mary Kay Cosmetics GmbH (1)
Baierbrunner Strasse 15, 81379, Munich, Germany **(100%)**
Tel.: (49) 898009000
Web Site: http://www.marykay.de
Sales Range: $10-24.9 Million
Emp.: 50
Cosmetics Distr
N.A.I.C.S.: 456120
Elke Kopp *(Exec Dir)*
Tara Eustace *(Pres)*
Gorg Lindertal *(Mgr-Fin)*

Mary Kay Cosmetics Ltd. (1)
2020 Meadowvale Blvd, Mississauga, L5N 6Y2, ON, Canada **(100%)**
Tel.: (905) 858-0020
Web Site: http://www.marykay.ca
Sales Range: $10-24.9 Million
Emp.: 100
Cosmetics Sales & Distr
N.A.I.C.S.: 424210
Lynda Rose *(Gen Mgr)*

Mary Kay Cosmetics Poland Sp. z. o.o. (1)
ul Zaryna 2B bud C, 02 593, Warsaw, Poland
Tel.: (48) 22 211 00 00
Web Site: http://www.marykay.com.pl
Cosmetics Distr & Sales
N.A.I.C.S.: 424210
Tara Eustace *(Pres)*

Mary Kay Cosmetics Pty. Ltd. (1)
Level 1 1 Lakeside Drive, Burwood East, 3151, VIC, Australia **(100%)**
Tel.: (61) 3 9881 4244
Web Site: http://www.marykay.com.au
Sales Range: $10-24.9 Million
Emp.: 30
Cosmetics Distr
N.A.I.C.S.: 424210
K. K. Chua *(Pres)*

Mary Kay Cosmetics de Espana, S.A. (1)
Edificio Portico Calle Mahonia 2-3a planta, 28043, Madrid, Spain
Tel.: (34) 91 781 81 30
Web Site: http://www.marykay.es
Cosmetics Sales & Distr
N.A.I.C.S.: 424210

Mary Kay Czech Republic S.R.O. (1)
Andel Media Centrum Karla Englise 519/11, 150 00, Prague, Czech Republic **(100%)**
Tel.: (420) 296114111
Web Site: http://www.marykay.cz
Sales Range: $10-24.9 Million
Emp.: 35
Cosmetic & toiletry Distr
N.A.I.C.S.: 456120
Barbora Chuecos *(CEO)*
Tara Eustace *(Pres-Europe)*

Mary Kay Inc. (1)
16251 Dallas Pkwy, Addison, TX 75001
Tel.: (972) 687-6300
Web Site: http://www.marykay.com
Sales Range: $100-124.9 Million
Emp.: 1,250
Cosmetics & Toiletries Retailer Mfr
N.A.I.C.S.: 325620
David B. Holl *(Chm)*
Richard R. Rogers *(Founder)*
Nathan Moore *(Pres-Global Sls & Mktg)*
Melinda Foster Sellers *(Chief People Officer)*
Sheryl Adkins-Green *(Chief Customer Relationship Officer)*
Tara Eustace *(Pres-European Reg)*
Jose Smeke *(Pres-Latin American Reg)*
Laura Beitler *(VP-Sls)*
Deborah Gibbins *(COO)*
Julia A. Simon *(Chief Legal Officer & Sec)*
Lucy Gildea *(Chief Scientific Officer & Sr VP)*
Chaun Harper *(Chief Mfg Officer & Sr VP)*
Paula K. Garrett *(VP-Fin, Ops & Info Sys Tech-Latin America)*
Wendy Wang *(Pres-Asia Pacific)*
Ryan Rogers *(CEO)*
James Whatley *(CIO)*

Mary Kay Korea, Ltd. (1)
12 F Air Tower 159-9 Samsung-dong, Kangnam-gu, Seoul, 135-973, Korea (South)
Tel.: (82) 2 2016 7770
Web Site: http://www.marykay.co.kr
Cosmetics Distr
N.A.I.C.S.: 456120

Mary Kay Lithuania (1)
Kalvariju G 140, 08209, Vilnius, Lithuania
Tel.: (370) 5 2072222
Web Site: http://www.marykay.lt
Beauty Supply Store Operator
N.A.I.C.S.: 456120

Mary Kay Philippines, Inc. (1)
2nd Floor Allegro Center 2284 Pasong Tamo Extension, Makati, Philippines
Tel.: (63) 28596222
Web Site: http://www.marykay.com.ph
Cosmetics Sales & Distr
N.A.I.C.S.: 424210
K. K. Chua *(Pres)*
Sobee Duenas Choa *(Gen Mgr)*

Tov Mary Kay (Ukraine) Ltd (1)
2 Novovokzalna St, 03038, Kiev, Ukraine
Tel.: (380) 44 490 6850
Web Site: http://www.marykay.ua
Cosmetics Sales & Distr
N.A.I.C.S.: 424210

ZAO Mary Kay (1)
16-th floor Ulitsa Smolnaya 24d, 125445, Moscow, Russia
Tel.: (7) 4957059311
Web Site: http://www.marykay.ru
Cosmetics Sales & Distr
N.A.I.C.S.: 424210

MARY MAXIM, INC.
2001 Holland Ave, Port Huron, MI 48060
Tel.: (810) 987-2000 MI
Web Site:
http://www.marymaxim.com
Year Founded: 1952
Sales Range: $100-124.9 Million
Emp.: 150
Mail Order Retailer of Needlework & Craft Kits
N.A.I.C.S.: 459130
Brian Harris *(VP)*
Paul William *(VP-Ops)*
Mike Schommer *(Dir-E-Commerce & IT)*

Subsidiaries:

Mary Maxim, Ltd. (1)
75 Scott Ave, Paris, N3L 3G5, ON, Canada **(100%)**
Tel.: (519) 442-6342
Web Site: https://www.marymaxim.ca
Sales Range: $10-24.9 Million
Emp.: 60
Mail Order & Retail Needlework & Crafts
N.A.I.C.S.: 459130
Carol Steed *(Exec VP)*

MARY RUTAN HOSPITAL
205 Palmer Ave, Bellefontaine, OH 43311
Tel.: (937) 592-4015 OH
Web Site:
http://www.maryrutanhospital.org
Year Founded: 1919
Sales Range: $75-99.9 Million
Emp.: 630
Health Care Srvces
N.A.I.C.S.: 622110
Grant Varian *(Dir-Medical Staff)*
Mandy Goble *(Pres & CEO)*
Tammy Allison *(COO)*
Kelli Zimmerly *(Sec)*
Steve Brown *(VP-Fin Svcs)*
Frank Gilham *(VP)*

MARY'S GONE CRACKERS
PO Box 965, Gridley, CA 95948
Tel.: (530) 846-5100 CA
Web Site:
http://www.marysgonecrackers.com
Year Founded: 2001
Sales Range: $1-9.9 Million
Emp.: 60
Mfr & Distr of Gluten-Free Cookies & Crackers
N.A.I.C.S.: 311821
Mary Waldner *(Co-Founder & Chm)*
Dale Rodrigues *(Co-Founder & Pres)*
John C. Sheptor *(CEO)*

MARY'S RIVER LUMBER CO., INC.
4515 NE Elliott Cir, Corvallis, OR 97330-9402
Tel.: (541) 752-0218 OR
Web Site:
http://www.marysriverlumber.com
Year Founded: 1974
Sales Range: $10-24.9 Million
Emp.: 200
Operating of General Sawmills & Planing Mills
N.A.I.C.S.: 321912
Robert Avery *(Chm)*
Brad Kirkbride *(Pres)*

MARYFIELD, INC.
109 Penny Rd, High Point, NC 27260
Tel.: (336) 821-4050 NC
Web Site:
http://www.pennybyrnatmaryfield.org
Year Founded: 1950
Sales Range: $10-24.9 Million
Emp.: 454
Lifecare Retirement Community Operator
N.A.I.C.S.: 623311
Scott Toth *(CFO)*

MARYHAVEN, INC.
1791 Alum Creek Dr, Columbus, OH 43207
Tel.: (614) 445-8131 OH

MARYHAVEN, INC.

Maryhaven, Inc.—(Continued)
Web Site: http://www.maryhaven.com
Year Founded: 1967
Sales Range: $25-49.9 Million
Emp.: 439
Behavioral Healthcare Services
N.A.I.C.S.: 623220
Sara A. McIntosh *(Dir-Medical)*
Angela Stewart *(Dir-HR & Diversity Dev)*
Charles Williams *(Dir-Adult Svcs & Coord-Student Placement)*
John Littlejohn *(Vice Chm)*
Rich Mueller *(Treas & Sec)*
Greg Ritter *(Dir-Adolescent Svcs)*
Nanon Morrison *(Dir-Dev)*
Robert S. Davis *(CFO)*
Paul Warrick Schkolnik *(Chief Res Officer)*
Charles A. Schneider *(Treas & Sec)*
Krisanna Deppen *(Dir-Medical-Addiction Stabilization Center)*
Adam Rowan *(COO)*
Kevin Brady *(Chm)*
Oyauma Garrison *(CEO)*

MARYL GROUP, INC.
75 1000 Henry St Ste 203, Kailua Kona, HI 96740-1691
Tel.: (808) 331-8100
Web Site: http://www.maryl.com
Year Founded: 1986
Sales Range: $25-49.9 Million
Emp.: 20
Commercial Property Management, Construction, Architecture & Planning, Landscaping, Commercial Sales & Leasing
N.A.I.C.S.: 237210
Mark S. Richards *(Co-Founder)*
Cheryl Richards *(Co-Founder)*

Subsidiaries:

Coldwell Banker Maryl Realty, Inc. (1)
75-1000 Henry St Ste 203, Kailua Kona, HI 96740
Tel.: (808) 331-8200
Construction Engineering Services
N.A.I.C.S.: 236220

Maryl Construction, Inc. (1)
55 Merchant St Ste 2900, Honolulu, HI 96813
Tel.: (808) 545-2920
Construction Engineering Services
N.A.I.C.S.: 236220

MARYLAND & VIRGINIA MILK PRODUCERS COOP ASSOCIATION INC
1985 Isaac Newton Sq W, Reston, VA 20190
Tel.: (703) 742-6800
Web Site: http://www.mdvamilk.com
Sales Range: $600-649.9 Million
Emp.: 300
Milk
N.A.I.C.S.: 424430
Jay Bryant *(Gen Mgr)*

MARYLAND AUTOMOBILE INSURANCE FUND
1750 Forest Dr, Annapolis, MD 21401-4211
Tel.: (410) 269-1680   MD
Web Site: http://www.emaif.com
Year Founded: 1972
Sales Range: $100-124.9 Million
Emp.: 575
Automobile Insurance Services
N.A.I.C.S.: 524210
Kent M. Krabbe *(Exec Dir)*
Alex Fernandez *(Dir-Actuarial Svcs)*
Anita Wyatt Anita *(Mgr)*
Cheryl Kehoe *(Dir-Underwriting)*
Jacqueline Wright *(Mgr-Claims)*
Joanne Daum *(Dir-Auditing)*
John Richards *(Supvr-Matl Damage)*
Karen Powers *(Mgr-Customer Svc)*
Liz Gruendl *(Mgr-Casualty Claims)*
Michael Vukovan *(Mgr-Matl Damage)*
Nicole Weigman *(Mgr-Casualty Claims)*
Matt Ailstock *(Mgr-IT Sys)*
Sue Evans *(Mgr-HR)*
Cindy Warkentin *(CIO)*
Nancy Dodd *(Dir-HR)*
Feyella Toney *(Supvr-Claims)*

MARYLAND CHEMICAL COMPANY, INC.
3310 Childs St, Baltimore, MD 21226
Tel.: (410) 752-1800
Web Site: http://www.mdchem.com
Rev.: $9,000,000
Emp.: 18
Chemical & Allied Products Merchant Whslr
N.A.I.C.S.: 424690
Fred J. Glose Sr. *(Chm)*
Jeanette Partlow *(Pres)*
Ashley Huber *(Mgr-Customer Solutions-South)*
Brian Menifee *(Engr-Field Svc-South & Curtis Bay)*

MARYLAND ECONOMIC DEVELOPMENT CORPORATION
300 E Lombard St Ste 1000, Baltimore, MD 21202
Tel.: (410) 625-0051   MD
Web Site: http://www.medco-corp.com
Year Founded: 1984
Sales Range: $125-149.9 Million
Emp.: 10
Economic Development Program Administration Services
N.A.I.C.S.: 926110
Scott Dorsey *(Treas)*
John Genakos *(Assoc Dir-Dev & IT)*
L. Jay Nocar *(Asst Controller)*
Jeff Wilke *(Asst Dir-Bond Fin)*
James Miller *(Controller)*
Susan Zimmerman Whitman *(Asst Dir)*
Thomas Kingston *(Vice Chm)*
Tom Sadowski *(Exec Dir)*

MARYLAND STATE EDUCATION ASSOCIATION
140 Main St, Annapolis, MD 21401
Tel.: (410) 263-6600   MD
Web Site: http://www.marylandeducators.org
Year Founded: 1947
Sales Range: $10-24.9 Million
Emp.: 104
Teaching Professional Development Services
N.A.I.C.S.: 611430
Kristy Anderson *(Gen Counsel)*
Adam Mendelson *(Mng Dir-Comm & Program Svcs)*
Jacqueline Blue *(Accountant)*
Paula Voelker *(Mng Dir)*
Cathy Perry *(Mng Dir)*

MARYLAND ZOOLOGICAL SOCIETY, INC.
Druid Hill Park, Baltimore, MD 21217
Tel.: (443) 552-5250
Web Site: http://www.marylandzoo.org
Year Founded: 1876
Sales Range: $10-24.9 Million
Emp.: 250
Zoo & Animal Research & Conservation Operator
N.A.I.C.S.: 712130
Jane Ballentine *(Dir-Mktg & PR)*

MARYS PIZZA SHACK
19327 Sonoma Hwy, Sonoma, CA 95476
Tel.: (707) 938-3602
Web Site: http://www.maryspizzashack.com
Rev.: $20,100,000
Emp.: 800
Italian Restaurant
N.A.I.C.S.: 722511
Cullen Williamson *(CEO)*
Andy Laden *(Gen Mgr)*
Sam Borquez *(Dir-Ops)*
Robin Carlson *(Dir-HR)*
Bruce Lane *(Dir-IT)*
Jake Pewitt *(Mgr-Facilities)*
Mike Sevilla *(Mgr-Safety)*
Brittany Alderson *(Mgr)*
Cameron Budd *(Mgr)*
Jennifer Lennen *(Mgr-Svcs)*
John Carter *(Mgr-Svcs)*
Bruce Wilson *(CFO)*
Stefanie Bagala *(Dir-Mktg)*
Mike Sheppard *(Mgr-Pur)*

MARYSVILLE MARINE DISTRIBUTORS
1551 Michigan Ave, Marysville, MI 48040
Tel.: (810) 364-7653
Web Site: http://www.marysvillemarine.com
Sales Range: $10-24.9 Million
Emp.: 30
Marine Propulsion Machinery & Equipment
N.A.I.C.S.: 423860
Mark Knust *(Pres)*

MARYVALE
7600 Graves Ave, Rosemead, CA 91770
Tel.: (626) 280-6510   CA
Web Site: http://www.maryvale-ca.org
Year Founded: 1983
Sales Range: $10-24.9 Million
Emp.: 308
Child Day Care Services
N.A.I.C.S.: 624410
Steve Gunther *(Pres & CEO)*
Martha Garcia *(VP-Mission Integration)*
Rachela Silvestri *(Chm)*
Marsha Chan *(Treas & Sec)*
Jacquie Dolan *(Vice Chm)*
Juliann Curabba *(Exec VP-Programs)*
Carole D. Tremblay *(VP-Dev & Comm)*
David Carter *(VP-Fin)*

MARYVILLE DATA SYSTEMS INC.
540 Maryville Ctr Dr, Saint Louis, MO 63141
Tel.: (636) 519-4100
Web Site: http://www.maryville.com
Year Founded: 1994
Sales Range: $75-99.9 Million
Emp.: 52
Computer Integrated Systems Design
N.A.I.C.S.: 541512
David Taylor *(Dir-Product Mgmt)*

MAS ADVISORS, LLC
501 Brickell Key Dr, Ste 509, Miami, FL 33131
Tel.: (786) 364-3101   FL
Web Site: http://masadvisorsllc.com
Year Founded: 2012
Asset Management Services
N.A.I.C.S.: 541618

Subsidiaries:

Wealth Strategies Group Inc. (1)
8001 Centerview Pkwy Ste 201, Cordova, TN 38018
Tel.: (901) 473-9000
Portfolio Management
N.A.I.C.S.: 523940

MAS GLOBAL CONSULTING, LLC
3450 E Lake Rd, Palm Harbor, FL 34685
Tel.: (727) 474-3212
Web Site: http://www.masglobalconsulting.com
Year Founded: 2013
Sales Range: $1-9.9 Million
Emp.: 90
Information Technology Consulting Services
N.A.I.C.S.: 541690
Monica Hernandez *(CEO)*
Walter Morales *(Dir-International Ops)*
Alejandro Castano *(Dir-Nearshore Dev)*
Sterling Engelhard *(VP-Sls & Mktg)*
Jhirleny M. Hernandez *(Dir-Ops)*

MAS MEDICAL STAFFING
156 Harvey Rd, Londonderry, NH 03103
Tel.: (603) 296-0953
Web Site: http://www.masmedicalstaffing.com
Year Founded: 2002
Rev.: $9,100,000
Emp.: 175
Health Services
N.A.I.C.S.: 561320
Kenneth Johnson *(Pres)*
Michael O. Keefe *(Treas)*

MAS, INC.
2718 Brecksville Rd, Richfield, OH 44286-9735
Tel.: (330) 659-3333   OH
Web Site: http://www.maspremium.com
Year Founded: 1971
Sales Range: $10-24.9 Million
Emp.: 70
Distr of Electrical Appliances Television & Radio Custom Embroidery & Corporate Logos
N.A.I.C.S.: 423620
C. Edwin Howard *(Owner)*

MASCAL ELECTRIC, INC.
1888 State St, Dekalb, IL 60115
Tel.: (815) 758-8164
Web Site: http://www.mascal.com
Year Founded: 1963
Sales Range: $10-24.9 Million
Emp.: 100
Provider of Electrical Contracting Services
N.A.I.C.S.: 238210
Anthony W. Marzano *(Treas & Sec)*
George Schofield *(Chm)*
Bill Wines *(Controller)*

MASCARO CONSTRUCTION CO. LP
1720 Metropolitan St, Pittsburgh, PA 15233
Tel.: (412) 321-4901
Web Site: http://www.mascaroconstruction.com
Sales Range: $75-99.9 Million
Emp.: 175
Commercial & Office Building, New Construction
N.A.I.C.S.: 236220
Bill Rost *(Dir-Electrical Svcs)*
Ron Nestico *(Project Mgr)*
Tony Rolin *(Dir-Heavy & Highway Estimating)*

MASCHHOFF FAMILY FOODS, LLC

7475 State Rte 127, Carlyle, IL 62231
Tel.: (618) 594-2125   IL
Web Site: https://themaschhoffs.com
Holding Company; Pig & Poultry Production, Processing & Meat Whslr
N.A.I.C.S.: 551112
Kenneth D. Maschhoff *(Chm)*
Julie A. Maschhoff *(VP-Pub Policy & PR)*
Greg Billhartz *(CFO, Gen Counsel & Exec VP)*
Troy Van Hauen *(Exec VP-HR)*
Tim Schellpeper *(CEO)*

Subsidiaries:

JFC LLC   (1)
4150 2nd St S, Saint Cloud, MN 56301-7314
Tel.: (320) 251-3570
Sales Range: $400-449.9 Million
Emp.: 2,000
Holding Company; Poultry Hatcheries, Chicken Production, Processing & Product Whslr
N.A.I.C.S.: 112340
Stephen Jurek *(Pres-Gold'n Plump)*
Jason Logsdon *(CEO)*

The Maschhoffs, LLC   (1)
7475 State Rte 127, Carlyle, IL 62231
Tel.: (618) 594-2125
Web Site: http://www.themaschhoffs.com
Sales Range: $700-749.9 Million
Emp.: 160
Holding Company; Pig Production
N.A.I.C.S.: 551112
Jason Logsdon *(CEO)*
Kenneth D. Maschhoff *(Chm)*
Bradley Wolter *(Pres)*
Aaron Gaines *(VP-Nutrition & Housing)*
Troy Van Hauen *(Exec VP-HR)*
Jeff Diesen *(Strategy & Commodity Risk Mgmt)*
Greg Billhartz *(CFO, Gen Counsel & Exec VP)*
Tim Schellpeper *(CEO)*
Justin Fix *(Dir-Genetics)*
Rich Hollis *(VP-People Strategy & Resources)*

MASCOLA ADVERTISING
434 Forbes Ave, New Haven, CT 06512-1932
Tel.: (203) 469-6900
Web Site: http://www.mascola.com
Year Founded: 1987
Rev.: $30,000,000
Emp.: 30
Advetising Agency
N.A.I.C.S.: 541810
Charles J. Mascola *(Strategist)*
Caryl Behmoiras *(Dir-Media)*
Nick Healey *(Dir-Creative)*

Subsidiaries:

Caffeine   (1)
438 Forbes Ave, New Haven, CT 06512-1932
Tel.: (203) 468-6396
Web Site: http://www.getcaffeinated.com
Sales Range: $10-24.9 Million
Emp.: 10
Internet/Web Design
N.A.I.C.S.: 541810
William Mulligan *(Founder & Pres)*
Donovan Young *(Web Designer)*

MASCOMA CORPORATION
67 Etna Rd Ste 300, Lebanon, NH 03766
Tel.: (603) 676-3320
Web Site: http://www.mascoma.com
Emp.: 110
Biotechnology Research & Development
N.A.I.C.S.: 541714
Timothy P. Linkkila *(Gen Counsel)*
Kevin S. Wenger *(Sr VP-Res & Dev)*
Justin Van Rooyen *(VP-Corp Dev)*
William J. Brady Jr. *(Pres & CEO)*

MASCOMA MUTUAL FINANCIAL SERVICES CORPORATION
67 N Park St, Lebanon, NH 03766
Tel.: (603) 448-3650
Web Site: http://www.mascomabank.com
Year Founded: 1899
Sales Range: $75-99.9 Million
Emp.: 317
Mutual Bank Holding Company
N.A.I.C.S.: 551111
Stephen F. Christy *(Pres & CEO)*
Barry E. McCabe *(COO & Exec VP)*
Donald N. Thompson *(CFO, Treas & Sr VP)*
Gretchen E. Cherington *(Chm)*
Edward T. Kerrigan *(Sec)*
Philip S. Latvis *(Pres/CEO-Centurion Insurance Grp)*
Christine E. Morlin *(Chief Risk Officer & Sr VP)*
Frank J. Leibly III *(Vice Chm)*

Subsidiaries:

Mascoma Savings Bank   (1)
On The Common 67 N Park St, Lebanon, NH 03766-1317
Tel.: (603) 448-3650
Web Site: http://www.mascomabank.com
Sales Range: $25-49.9 Million
Federal Savings Bank
N.A.I.C.S.: 522180
Barry E. McCabe *(COO & Exec VP)*
Donald N. Thompson *(CFO, Treas & Sr VP)*
Debra L. Carter *(Sr VP-Retail Svcs)*
W. Grant MacEwan *(Sr VP-Comml Lending)*
Christine E. Morin *(Chief Risk Officer & Sr VP-Ops)*
Kevin P. Beauregard *(Sr VP & Mgr-Program-Mascoma Fin Advisors)*
Samantha L. Pause *(Sr VP-Mktg, Sls & Svc)*
Kenneth D. Wells *(Sr VP-Retail Lending)*
Robert T. Boon *(Sr VP-Wealth Mgmt)*
Kevin J. Raleigh *(Officer-Comml Loan & Sr VP)*
Beverly A. Widger *(VP-HR)*
Catherine A. Ells *(VP & Controller)*
Gerald Grimo *(Officer-Compliance & Asst VP)*
Kathie J. Nolet *(Officer-HR Ops & Asst VP)*
Lauren B. Schumacher *(Asst VP & Mgr-Consumer Lending)*
Chad R. Stearns *(Branch Mgr)*
Michael Tolaro *(Branch Mgr)*
Linda M. Wright *(Asst Controller)*
Sheila Jacobs *(VP-Bus & Municipal Svcs)*
James E. Larrick *(VP-Comml Lending)*
Cheryl A. Lindberg *(Officer-Bus Dev)*

MASCON INCORPORATED
8550 Tiogawoods Dr, Sacramento, CA 95828
Tel.: (916) 689-7400
Web Site: http://www.mascon-inc.com
Year Founded: 1992
Sales Range: $10-24.9 Million
Emp.: 15
Commercial & Institutional Building Construction Services
N.A.I.C.S.: 236220
Michael A. Schneider *(Founder & Pres)*
Paul R. Brooks *(Mgr-Ops)*

MASCOT CORPORATION
620 Ramsey Ave, Hillside, NJ 07205
Tel.: (908) 436-1800   NJ
Web Site: http://www.mascott.co
Year Founded: 1989
Sales Range: $10-24.9 Million
Emp.: 15
American Restaurant
N.A.I.C.S.: 722511
Scott Gillman *(CEO)*
Marc Gillman *(Pres)*
Guy Stanton *(Sr Controller)*
John White *(Dir-HR)*
Andrea Brody Gillman *(Principal & VP-Real Estate)*
Marybeth De La Cruz *(Mgr-Mktg & Admin)*

MASDA CORPORATION
22 Troy Rd, Whippany, NJ 07981
Tel.: (973) 386-1100   NJ
Web Site: http://www.masdacorp.biz
Year Founded: 1932
Sales Range: $10-24.9 Million
Emp.: 15
Grills, Barbecue
N.A.I.C.S.: 423220
Daniel Darche *(Pres)*

MASELLE & ASSOCIATES, INC.
4001 Lakeland Dr, Jackson, MS 39232
Tel.: (800) 700-2121   MS
Web Site: http://www.century21.com
Year Founded: 1983
Real Estate Agency
N.A.I.C.S.: 531210
Michael Miedler *(Pres & CEO)*
Cara Whitley *(CMO)*

MASHANTUCKET PEQUOT GAMING ENTERPRISE INC.
350 Trolley Line Blvd, Mashantucket, CT 06338
Tel.: (860) 312-3000
Web Site: http://www.foxwoods.com
Year Founded: 1991
Gambling Resort & Hotels Owner & Operator
N.A.I.C.S.: 721120
Rodney Butler *(Chm)*

Subsidiaries:

Foxwoods Resort Casino   (1)
350 Trolley Line Boulevard, Mashantucket, CT 06338
Tel.: (800) 369-9663
Web Site: http://www.foxwoods.com
Casino
N.A.I.C.S.: 721120
Jason Guyot *(Pres & CEO)*
Augie Renna *(VP-Natl Mktg)*
Jennifer Johnson *(VP-Loyalty Mktg)*
Jesse Luis *(VP-Resort Dev)*

Grand Pequot Tower   (1)
Rr 2, Ledyard, CT 06339-9802
Hotel & Resort.
N.A.I.C.S.: 561499

Great Cedar Hotel   (1)
Rr 2, Ledyard, CT 06339-9802
Hotel & Resort
N.A.I.C.S.: 721199

Pequot Pharmaceutical Network Management Services   (1)
1 Annie George Dr Bldg 3, Mashantucket, CT 06338
Tel.: (860) 396-6483
Web Site: http://www.prxn.com
Mail-Order Prescription Service
N.A.I.C.S.: 561110
Joanne Burgess *(Gen Mgr)*

Two Trees Inn   (1)
240 Indiantown Rd, Ledyard, CT 06339-1137
Tel.: (860) 312-4013
Web Site: http://www.foxwoods.com
Emp.: 50
Hotel & Recreation Services
N.A.I.C.S.: 721199

MASHBURN CONSTRUCTION COMPANY
1820 Sumter St, Columbia, SC 29201-2502
Tel.: (803) 400-1000   SC
Web Site: http://www.mashburnconstruction.com
Year Founded: 1976
Sales Range: $25-49.9 Million
Emp.: 100
Provider of Contracting & Construction Services
N.A.I.C.S.: 236220
Harry L. Mashburn *(Chm)*
Paul Mashburn *(COO)*
Brian Johnston *(VP-Ops)*
Jordan Smith *(Asst Superintendent)*
Richard Kinard *(VP-Coastal)*
James Hudson *(Dir-Bus Dev)*
Berry Ponder *(VP-Upstate)*
H. Lee Mashburn Jr. *(Pres)*

MASLOW LUMIA BARTORILLO ADVERTISING
182 N Franklin St, Wilkes Barre, PA 18701-1404
Tel.: (570) 824-1500
Web Site: http://www.mlbadvertising.com
Year Founded: 1979
Sales Range: Less than $1 Million
Emp.: 7
Advetising Agency
N.A.I.C.S.: 541810
Melanie Maslow Lumia *(Chm)*
John C. Bartorillo *(Pres)*
Morrell Devlin *(Dir-Media)*
Michael Scholl *(Art Dir)*
A. J. Zambetti *(Art Dir)*
John Nackley Jr. *(Dir-Mktg & Bus Dev)*

MASON BANCSHARES, INC.
111 Westmoreland St, Mason, TX 76856
Tel.: (325) 347-5911   TX
Web Site: http://www.masonbank.com
Year Founded: 2000
Bank Holding Company
N.A.I.C.S.: 551111
George Brannies *(Chm & CEO)*
Thomas Canfield Jr. *(Pres)*

Subsidiaries:

Mason Bank   (1)
111 Westmorland, Mason, TX 76856
Tel.: (325) 347-5911
Web Site: http://www.masonnational.com
Sales Range: $1-9.9 Million
Emp.: 16
Commericial Banking
N.A.I.C.S.: 522110
Amanda McMillian *(Sr VP-Investments)*
George Brannies *(Chm)*
Thomas Canfield Jr. *(Pres)*

MASON CITY FORD
215 15th St SW, Mason City, IA 50401
Tel.: (641) 424-8550
Web Site: http://www.masoncityford.com
Sales Range: $10-24.9 Million
Emp.: 35
Owner & Operator of Car Dealerships
N.A.I.C.S.: 441110
Don O'Connor *(Gen Mgr)*
Ron Lafrenz *(Sec & Controller)*

MASON CLAIM SERVICES, INC.
121 Pecan St, Boerne, TX 78006
Tel.: (830) 816-2929
Web Site: http://www.masonclaims.com
Year Founded: 1995
Sales Range: $10-24.9 Million
Emp.: 20
Claim Adjusting Services
N.A.I.C.S.: 524291
Phil Mason *(Principal)*
Cody House *(Pres)*

MASON CLAIM SERVICES, INC.

Mason Claim Services, Inc.—(Continued)
Zane Mason (COO)
Randy Niemeier (CFO)
Forrest Marlin (Dir-IT)

MASON COMPANIES, INC.
1251 1st Ave, Chippewa Falls, WI 54729-1408
Tel.: (715) 723-1871 WI
Web Site: http://www.masoncompaniesinc.com
Year Founded: 1904
Sales Range: $150-199.9 Million
Emp.: 400
Mail Order Catalog Men's & Women's Shoes
N.A.I.C.S.: 316210
Dan Hunt (CEO)
Darin Schemenauer (VP-Mktg)
Greg Wallace (Mgr-Graphics)
Aaron Zwiefelhofer (Mgr-Catalog)
Jodi Bresina (Mgr-Internet)

Subsidiaries:

B.A. Mason (1)
1251 1st Ave, Chippewa Falls, WI 54729-1408 (100%)
Tel.: (715) 723-1871
Web Site: http://www.bamasoncompaniesinc.com
Sales Range: $10-24.9 Million
Emp.: 25
Retailer & Mail Order of Men's & Women's Footwear
N.A.I.C.S.: 458210

Duncan Creek Inc. (1)
522 N Grove St, Chippewa Falls, WI 54729-2642 (100%)
Tel.: (715) 720-9797
Web Site: http://duncancreekwood.com
Sales Range: $10-24.9 Million
Emp.: 10
Investment
N.A.I.C.S.: 337110

Figi's, Inc. (1)
3200 S Central Ave, Marshfield, WI 54449
Tel.: (866) 855-0203
Web Site: http://www.figis.com
Sales Range: $100-124.9 Million
Direct-to-Consumer Mail Order Food Gifts
N.A.I.C.S.: 424450
Rick Boudreau (Dir-IS)
Craig Warosh (Engr-Pkg)
Roni Stargardt (Sr Mgr-Ops-Call Center)
Jeff Ellis (Sr Mgr-Warehousing)

Subsidiary (Domestic):

Figi's Business Services, Inc. (2)
3200 S Central Ave, Marshfield, WI 54449
Tel.: (866) 752-2450
Web Site: http://www.fbsgifts.com
Mail Order & Online Food Gifts for Retail Market
N.A.I.C.S.: 424450
Melissa Larson (VP-Sls)
Marlene Gerrits (Sr Mgr-Sls-Retail-Natl)
Barb Boyer (Sr Mgr-E-Commerce)

MASON CORPORATION
123 W Oxmoor Rd, Birmingham, AL 35209
Tel.: (205) 942-4100
Web Site: http://www.masoncorp.com
Year Founded: 1948
Sales Range: $10-24.9 Million
Emp.: 162
Fabricated Structural Metal Mfr
N.A.I.C.S.: 332312
Gordon Scott (Mgr-Territory & District)

MASON COUNTY PUBLIC UTILITY DISTRICT 3
2621 E Johns Prairie Rd, Shelton, WA 98584
Tel.: (360) 426-8255
Web Site: http://www.masonpud3.org
Sales Range: $25-49.9 Million
Emp.: 115
Generation, Electric Power
N.A.I.C.S.: 221118
John Bennett (Dir-Bus Svcs)
Annette Creekpaum (Mgr-Admin)
Dale Knutson (Mgr-Telecom)
Joel Myer (Mgr-Pub Info & Govt Rels)
Terry Peterson (Dir-Engrg)
Michelle Wicks (Mgr-HR & Labor Rels)
Linda R. Gott (Pres)
Bob Smith (Mgr-Admin Svcs)
Nancy Bolender (Mgr-Contracts & Pur)
Justin Holzgrove (Mgr-Telecom & Community Rels)
Diane Archer (Mgr-Customer Svc)
Sherry Speaks (Treas)

MASON DISTRIBUTORS, INC.
15750 NW 59 Ave, Miami Lakes, FL 33014-6336
Tel.: (800) 327-6005 FL
Web Site: http://www.masonvitamins.com
Year Founded: 1967
Sales Range: $75-99.9 Million
Emp.: 100
Whslr of Vitamins
N.A.I.C.S.: 424210
Gilbert Duarte (Gen Mgr-Mgmt Info Sys)
Ofelia Perez (Pres & COO)
Gary Pigott (VP-Sls)
Kazuhiro Hoshi (COO)
Yosuke Honjo (CEO)
Mauricio Perez (Mgr-Adv)

Subsidiaries:

Mason Vitamins, Inc. (1)
15750 NW 59 Ave, Miami Lakes, FL 33014
Tel.: (305) 428-6800
Vitamins & Supplement Distr
N.A.I.C.S.: 424210
Delmy P. Talavera (Mgr-HR & Gen Affairs)
Manny Albelo (Sr Mgr-Pur)
Doris Puente (Sr Mgr-Sls)
Kazuhiro Hoshi (Pres & COO)

MASON FOREST PRODUCTS INC.
6975 United States Hwy 49 N, Hattiesburg, MS 39402
Tel.: (601) 268-2990
Web Site: http://www.masonforestproduct.com
Sales Range: $10-24.9 Million
Emp.: 25
Whslr of Lumber
N.A.I.C.S.: 423310
Danny Mason (Pres)
Bob Mcdonald (Controller)

MASON INDUSTRIES
350 Rabro Dr, Hauppauge, NY 11788
Tel.: (631) 348-0282 NY
Web Site: http://www.mason-ind.com
Year Founded: 1958
Sales Range: $10-24.9 Million
Emp.: 200
Noise & Vibration Control Products & Rubber Products Mfr
N.A.I.C.S.: 335314
Henry Smith (Plant Mgr)
Doug Valerio (VP)
Dawn Nevins (Asst Mgr-Sls)
James Tauby (Chief Engr)
Mike Leuck (CIO)

Subsidiaries:

The Mercer Rubber Company (1)
350 Rabro Dr, Hauppauge, NY 11788-4257
Tel.: (631) 582-1524
Web Site: http://www.mercer-rubber.com
Sales Range: $1-9.9 Million
Emp.: 100
Mechanical Rubber Product Mfr
N.A.I.C.S.: 326299

Norman J. Mason (Pres)
Mae Ryan (Controller)

MASON SELKOWITZ MARKETING, INC
400 Whitney Rd, Penfield, NY 14526
Tel.: (585) 249-1100 NY
Web Site: http://masonmarketing.com
Year Founded: 1986
Advertising Agencies
N.A.I.C.S.: 541810
Timothy J. Mason (Pres & CEO)
Brad Schultz (Dir-Creative)
Terri Cubiotti (COO-Mason Marketing LLC)
Jim Dennis (COO-Mason Digital LLC)

MASON STRUCTURAL STEEL, INC.
7500 Northfield Rd, Walton Hills, OH 44146
Tel.: (440) 439-1040
Web Site: http://www.masonsteel.com
Year Founded: 1958
Sales Range: $10-24.9 Million
Emp.: 100
Fabricated Structural Metal Mfr
N.A.I.C.S.: 332312
Keith Polster (Pres)
Scott Polster (VP-Residential Sls)
Harry Tepper (VP & Controller)
Daryl Rothenfeld (VP-Building Products)

MASON WELLS, INC.
411 E Wisconsin Ave Ste 1280, Milwaukee, WI 53202
Tel.: (414) 727-6400 WI
Web Site: http://www.masonwells.com
Year Founded: 1982
Sales Range: $25-49.9 Million
Emp.: 25
Private Equity Firm Services
N.A.I.C.S.: 523999
Jim Domach (CFO)
Jay Radtke (Sr Mng Dir)
Kevin Kenealey (Sr Mng Dir)
Greg Myers (Sr Mng Dir)
Tom Smith (Chm & Exec Mng Dir)
Ben Holbrook (Mng Dir)
Christopher Pummill (Dir)

Subsidiaries:

Buffalo Games, LLC (1)
220 James E Casey Dr, Buffalo, NY 14206
Tel.: (716) 827-8393
Web Site: http://www.buffalogames.com
Sales Range: $10-24.9 Million
Emp.: 50
Board Games & Jigsaw Puzzles Mfr
N.A.I.C.S.: 339930
Eden Scott Dedrick (VP)
Laurie Shaw (Mgr-Sls)
Mark Predko (Dir-Sls & Mktg)
Carl Dedrick (Mgr-Production Process)

Nex Performance Films (1)
18 Industrial Blvd, Turners Falls, MA 01376
Tel.: (413) 863-3171
Web Site: http://www.nex-films.com
Sales Range: $25-49.9 Million
Polyethylene Film Mfr
N.A.I.C.S.: 326113

Structural Concepts Corporation (1)
888 E Porter Rd, Muskegon, MI 49441-5848
Tel.: (231) 798-8888
Web Site: http://www.structuralconcepts.com
Sales Range: $10-24.9 Million
Emp.: 250
Wood Partitions & Fixtures
N.A.I.C.S.: 337212
Bob Matych (Mgr-Natl Sls)
Jeff Schneider (VP-Sls & Mktg)
Brad Gates (Pres & CEO)

U.S. PRIVATE

MASON'S MILL & LUMBER CO., INC.
9885 Tanner Rd, Houston, TX 77041
Tel.: (713) 462-6975
Web Site: http://www.masonsmillandlumber.com
Sales Range: $10-24.9 Million
Emp.: 57
Lumber, Plywood, Millwork & Wood Panel Whslr
N.A.I.C.S.: 423310
Michael Spellings (Owner & Pres)

MASON, INC.
23 Amity Rd, Bethany, CT 06524-3417
Tel.: (203) 393-1101 CT
Web Site: http://www.mason23.com
Year Founded: 1951
Sales Range: $25-49.9 Million
Emp.: 50
Advertising Services
N.A.I.C.S.: 541810
Elmer Grubbs (Dir-Creative)
Richard Gamer (VP & Dir-Creative)
Neil Johnson (Dir-Creative-Digital)
Derek Beere (Dir-Brand & Engagement)
Melissa Augeri (Dir-Brand)
Nick Koutsopoulos (Dir-Media Plng & Buying)
Brenda Zamberllo (VP-Media Svcs)
Mark Scheethf (Dir-Digital Strategies & Analytics)
Michael Field (Exec Creative Dir)
Charles T. Mason Jr. (CEO)

MASON-MCDUFFIE MORTGAGE CORP.
2010 Crow Canyon Pl Ste 400, San Ramon, CA 94583
Tel.: (925) 242-4400
Web Site: http://www.masonmcduffiemortgage.com
Year Founded: 2005
Emp.: 200
Mortgage Lending Services
N.A.I.C.S.: 522310
Herb Tasker (Chm)
Marilyn Richardson (Pres & CEO)
Jack Radin (CFO)
Bill Godfrey (Exec VP-Capital Markets)
Kevin Conlon (Exec VP-Ops)
Jason C. Frazier (CIO)
Bill Simpson (Exec VP-Production)
Mark Lynch (Sr VP-Production)
Joseph Sprecher (Sr VP-Production Ops)
Denis Roden (Officer-Loan)
George Fagundes (Sr VP-Mktg)
Renee Rovai (Dir-Mktg)
Blair Bell (Branch Mgr)
Matthew MontsDeOca (Mgr-Portland)

MASONIC HOME OF VIRGINIA
500 Masonic Ln, Henrico, VA 23223
Tel.: (804) 222-1694 VA
Web Site: http://www.mahova.com
Year Founded: 1890
Sales Range: $10-24.9 Million
Emp.: 281
Community Care Services
N.A.I.C.S.: 621610
Anne B. Hagen (CFO)

MASONIC HOMES OF CALIFORNIA, INC.
34400 Mission Blvd, Union City, CA 94587
Tel.: (510) 471-3434
Web Site: http://www.masonichome.org
Year Founded: 1890
Sales Range: $25-49.9 Million

Emp.: 450
Nursing Home
N.A.I.C.S.: 623312
Gary G. Charland (Pres & CEO)
Michael J. Cornell (Vice Chm)
Arthur L. Salazar Jr. (Treas)

MASONRY BUILDERS, INC.
5012 W Cypress St, Tampa, FL 33607
Tel.: (813) 286-4707   FL
Web Site:
http://www.masonrybuilders.com
Year Founded: 1988
Sales Range: $10-24.9 Million
Emp.: 110
Masonry/Stone Contractor
N.A.I.C.S.: 238140
Thomas B. Bradley (Pres)
Todd Bradley (VP)

MASONRY REINFORCING CORPORATION AMERICA
400 Rountree Rd, Charlotte, NC 28217
Tel.: (704) 525-5554
Web Site: http://www.wirebond.com
Sales Range: $25-49.9 Million
Emp.: 200
Masonry Reinforcing Mesh & Wire
N.A.I.C.S.: 332618
John Morgan (Controller)
Mike Ripley (Mgr-Sls)
Ralph O. Johnson Jr. (Pres)

MASONRYARTS, INC.
2105 3rd Ave N, Bessemer, AL 35020
Tel.: (205) 428-0780   DE
Web Site:
http://www.masonryarts.com
Year Founded: 1979
Sales Range: $10-24.9 Million
Emp.: 124
Specialty Sub Contractor, Provides Commercial & Industrial Masonry, Stone & Glass Work
N.A.I.C.S.: 238150
Roy V. Swindal (Pres)
Shane Campbell (Dir-Safety)
Tom Olive (Project Mgr-Masonry)

MASPETH FEDERAL SAVINGS & LOAN ASSOCIATION
5618 69th St, Maspeth, NY 11378
Tel.: (718) 335-1300
Web Site:
http://www.maspethfederal.com
Rev.: $44,700,000
Emp.: 250
Federal Savings & Loan Associations
N.A.I.C.S.: 522180
Rosalie Betz (Dir-HR)
Kennith Rudzewick (Pres)
Eugene Kapica (Exec VP)

MASQUE SOUND & RECORDING CORP.
21 E Union, East Rutherford, NJ 07073
Tel.: (201) 939-8666
Web Site:
http://www.masquesound.com
Year Founded: 1936
Sales Range: $10-24.9 Million
Emp.: 55
Audio-Visual Equipment & Supply Rental
N.A.I.C.S.: 532289
Geoff Shearing (VP)
Gary M. Stocker (Dir-Technical)
George Hahn (Dir-Production)
Scott Kalata (Dir-Sls)
Rich Rizzio (Dir-Facilities)
Todd Neilsen (Mgr-Pur)
Mike Siersma (Project Mgr)
Casandra Michels (Controller)

Matthew Dale (Coord-Production)
Doug Cross (Coord-Technical)
Brian Fox (Mgr-HR)
Shawn Mooney (Mgr-Info Sys)
Gabriel Bennett (Mgr-Installations Project)
Mike Letrick (Mgr-Inventory)
Leslie Stong (Sr Project Mgr)

MASS AUDUBON
208 S Great Rd, Lincoln, MA 01773
Tel.: (781) 259-9500   MA
Web Site:
http://www.massaudubon.org
Year Founded: 1896
Rev.: $28,496,989
Earnings: $1,456
Emp.: 77
Fiscal Year-end: 06/30/19
Natural Resource Preservation Services
N.A.I.C.S.: 813312
Christopher Klem (Vice Chm)
Anne Snyder (Vice Chm)
Bancroft R. Poor (VP-Ops & Asst Treas)
Beth Kressley Goldstein (Chm)
Jan O'Neil (Dir-Membership & Annual Fund & Asst Treas)
Stu Weinreb (Dir-Capital Assets & Plng)
Kris Scopinich (Dir-Education & Engagement)
Bob Wilber (Dir-Land Conservation)
Nora Frank (Asst Treas)
Gail Yeo (VP-Wildlife Sanctuaries & Programs)
Jeff Collins (Dir-Conservation Science)
David J. O'Neill (Pres)
Ellen McBride (Sec)
Robert P. Ball (Treas)
Hillary Truslow (VP-Mktg & Comm)
Donna Minnis (Dir-Foundation & Govt Support)
Henrietta Yelle (Dir-Major Gifts)
Jan Adams (Dir-Planned Giving)
Liz Albert (Dir-Dev & Statewide Initiatives)
Rick Arnaud (Dir-Leadership Giving)
Amy Garfield (Controller)
Greg Berry (Dir-IT)
Melanie Prusinoski (Dir-HR)

MASS CONNECTIONS, INC.
11838 Western Ave, Stanton, CA 90680-3438
Tel.: (562) 365-0200   CA
Year Founded: 1991
Emp.: 75
Advertising Agencies
N.A.I.C.S.: 541810
Caroline Cotten-Nakken (Pres & CEO)
Robert Dickson (Gen Counsel)

Subsidiaries:
MC2 Marketing Inc.   (1)
13131 E 166th St, Cerritos, CA 90703-2202
Tel.: (562) 365-0200
Emp.: 10
Advertising Agencies
N.A.I.C.S.: 541810

MASS DESIGN, INC.
41 Simon St, Nashua, NH 03060
Tel.: (603) 886-6460   NH
Web Site:
http://www.massdesign.com
Year Founded: 1986
Sales Range: $10-24.9 Million
Emp.: 100
Printed Circuit Board Mfr
N.A.I.C.S.: 334412
Neil Chulada (Dir-Ops)
Paul Boduch (VP)
Tony Bourassa (Pres)
Bill Gately (Mgr-Sls)

Subsidiaries:
Electropac Co., Inc.   (1)
252 Willow St, Manchester, NH 03103
Tel.: (603) 622-3711
Web Site: http://www.electropac.com
Sales Range: $1-9.9 Million
Emp.: 40
Printed Circuit Board Mfr
N.A.I.C.S.: 334412

MASS GENERAL BRIGHAM INCORPORATED
Prudential Center 800 Boylston St 11th Fl, Boston, MA 02199
Tel.: (617) 278-1000
Web Site:
https://www.massgeneralbrigham.org
Year Founded: 1994
Health Care Services
N.A.I.C.S.: 621610

MASS HISPANIC
2301 NW 87th Ave Ste 600, Doral, FL 33172
Tel.: (305) 351-3600   DE
Web Site: http://www.eventuslive.com
Year Founded: 1986
Sales Range: $10-24.9 Million
Emp.: 30
Advertising Agencies
N.A.I.C.S.: 541810
Margarita Godoy (Controller)

MASS HYSTERIA ENTERTAINMENT COMPANY, INC.
2920 W Olive Ave Ste 208, Burbank, CA 91505
Tel.: (310) 285-7800   NV
Web Site:
http://www.masshysteriafilms.com
Year Founded: 2005
Sales Range: Less than $1 Million
Emp.: 1
Motion Picture Production & Distribution Services
N.A.I.C.S.: 512110
Daniel Grodnik (Chm, Pres & CEO)
Sam Teplitsky (Sr VP-Mobile)
Brent V. Friedman (Sr VP-Product Dev & Mktg)

MASS INTEGRATED SYSTEMS
18 Henry Graf Junior Rd Ste 1, Newburyport, MA 01950
Tel.: (978) 465-6190
Web Site:
http://www.massintegrated.com
Year Founded: 2002
Rev.: $7,500,000
Emp.: 12
Computer Peripheral Equipment & Software Merchant Whlslr
N.A.I.C.S.: 423430
Eric Primack (Founder & CEO)
Steve Cavanaugh (VP-Sls & Gen Mgr)
Sue Zappala (VP-Fin, Controller & Admin)

MASS MEDIA MARKETING
229 Fury's Ferry Rd Ste 123, Augusta, GA 30907
Tel.: (706) 651-0053
Web Site:
http://www.massmediamktg.com
Year Founded: 2000
Sales Range: $10-24.9 Million
Emp.: 23
Advertising Agencies
N.A.I.C.S.: 541810
Rick Donaldson (Owner, Acct Exec-Grunt & Craft Svcs)
Amy Paggett (Bus Mgr)
Ashley Drummond (Acct Exec)

MASS PRECISION SHEETMETAL
2010 Oakland Rd, San Jose, CA 95131
Tel.: (408) 954-0280
Web Site:
http://www.massprecision.com
Sales Range: $25-49.9 Million
Emp.: 400
Sheet Metalwork
N.A.I.C.S.: 332322
Jim Shelton (Exec VP)
Mike Subocz (Program Mgr)
Len Bushnell (Mgr-Quality Assurance)
Al Stucky Jr. (Pres)

MASSACHUSETTS BAY BREWING CO.
306 Northern Ave, Boston, MA 02210
Tel.: (617) 574-9551
Web Site:
http://www.harpoonbrewery.com
Year Founded: 1986
Rev.: $12,500,000
Emp.: 85
Brewers of Malt Beverages Mfr
N.A.I.C.S.: 312120
Richard A. Doyle (Co-Founder)
Dan Kenary (Co-Founder)

Subsidiaries:
Long Trail Brewing Company   (1)
5520 Route 4, Bridgewater, VT 05035
Tel.: (802) 672-5011
Web Site: http://www.longtrail.com
Sales Range: $1-9.9 Million
Emp.: 60
Beverages Mfr
N.A.I.C.S.: 312120
Andy Pherson (Founder & Pres)
Dave Hartmann (Head-Brewer)

MASSACHUSETTS BAY HEALTH CARE TRUST FUND
758 Marrett Rd, Lexington, MA 02421
Tel.: (781) 861-6500   MA
Year Founded: 1993
Sales Range: $10-24.9 Million
Health Care Awareness Services
N.A.I.C.S.: 813212
Kathy Tierney (Co-Chm)
Leanne Lyons (Co-Chm)

MASSACHUSETTS CAPITAL RESOURCE COMPANY
420 Boylston St, Boston, MA 02116
Tel.: (617) 536-3900   MA
Web Site:
http://www.masscapital.com
Year Founded: 1977
Emp.: 10
Equity Investment Firm
N.A.I.C.S.: 523999
Suzanne L. Dwyer (VP)

MASSACHUSETTS CONVENTION CENTER AUTHORITY
415 Summer St, Boston, MA 02210-1719
Tel.: (617) 954-2000
Web Site:
http://www.massconvention.com
Year Founded: 1982
Rev.: $79,057,183
Assets: $769,057,382
Liabilities: $89,598,233
Net Worth: $679,459,149
Earnings: ($13,913,320)
Emp.: 91
Fiscal Year-end: 06/30/19
Auditorium & Hall Operation
N.A.I.C.S.: 531120
Susan Byrnes (Office Mgr)
Dennis Callahan (Deputy Dir)

MASSACHUSETTS GREEN

MASSACHUSETTS GREEN — (CONTINUED)

HIGH PERFORMANCE COMPUTING CENTER INC.
100 Bigelow St, Holyoke, MA 01040
Tel.: (413) 552-4900   MA
Web Site: http://www.mghpcc.org
Year Founded: 2010
Sales Range: $10-24.9 Million
Scientific Research Services
N.A.I.C.S.: 541715
Robert Brown (Chm)
Thomas Nedell (Treas)
John Goodhue (Exec Dir)

MASSACHUSETTS HOSPITAL ASSOCIATION, INC.
5 New England Executive Park, Burlington, MA 01803
Tel.: (781) 262-6000   MA
Web Site: http://www.mhalink.org
Year Founded: 1936
Sales Range: $10-24.9 Million
Emp.: 50
Hospital Association
N.A.I.C.S.: 813910
Patricia Crowley (VP-Governance & Member Rels)
Timothy F. Gens (Gen Counsel & Exec VP)
Christine A. Baratta (VP-Mktg & Comm)
Anuj K. Goel (VP-Legal & Regulatory Affairs)
Patricia Noga (VP-Clinical Affairs)
Kate E. Walsh (Chm)
Michael E. Sroczynski (VP-Govt Advocacy)
Steven Walsh (Pres & CEO)

MASSACHUSETTS INSTITUTE OF TECHNOLOGY
77 Massachusetts Ave, Cambridge, MA 02139
Tel.: (617) 253-1000
Web Site: http://www.mit.edu
Emp.: 12,852
College & Universities
N.A.I.C.S.: 611310
David C. Page (Professor-biology)
Dustin Koehl (Partner-FreightLab)
L. Rafael Reif (Pres)
Andrew W. Lo (Dir-Laboratory for Fin Engrg)
Robert S. Langer (Professor)
Robert S. Langer Jr. (Professor)

MASSACHUSETTS INSTITUTE OF TECHNOLOGY
77 Massachusetts Ave, Cambridge, MA 02139
Tel.: (617) 253-1000
Web Site: https://www.mit.edu
Educational Support Services
N.A.I.C.S.: 611710

MASSACHUSETTS LABORERS BENEFIT FUNDS
1400 District Ave Ste 200, Burlington, MA 01803
Tel.: (781) 272-1000   MA
Web Site: http://www.mlbf.org
Year Founded: 1952
Sales Range: $100-124.9 Million
Emp.: 36
Employee Benefit Services
N.A.I.C.S.: 525120
Barry McAnarney (Exec Dir)
Joseph Bonfiglio (Co-Chm)
Thomas J. Gunning (Treas & Sec)
Louis Mandarini Jr. (Co-Chm)

MASSACHUSETTS LEAGUE OF COMMUNITY HEALTH CENTERS
40 Court St 10th Fl, Boston, MA 02108
Tel.: (617) 426-2225   MA
Web Site: http://www.massleague.org
Year Founded: 1972
Sales Range: $10-24.9 Million
Emp.: 73
Healthcare Services
N.A.I.C.S.: 622110
Kerin O'Toole (Dir-Pub Affairs)
Robert Spellane (Dir-Community & Bus Dev)
Cheryl Shaughnessy (Dir-Membership Svcs)
Ellen Hafer (COO & Exec VP)
James W. Hunt Jr. (Pres & CEO)

MASSACHUSETTS MEDICAL SOCIETY
860 Winter St Waltham Woods Corp Ctr, Waltham, MA 02451-1411
Tel.: (781) 893-4610
Web Site: http://www.massmed.org
Sales Range: $75-99.9 Million
Emp.: 420
Publisher of Medical Journals; Medical Association
N.A.I.C.S.: 813920
Susan Webb (Dir-Pub Health & Education)
Kathy Bellisle (Mgr-Distance Learning)
Catherine Salas (Mgr-Reg Outreach)
Patricia Newton (Sec)
Shelia Kozlowski (Mgr-Reg Outreach)
Maryanne C. Bombaugh (VP)
Joseph Bergeron (Treas & Sec)
Lois Dehls Cornell (Exec VP)
Lynda G. Kabbash (Treas & Sec)

Subsidiaries:

The New England Journal of Medicine   (1)
10 Shattuck St, Boston, MA 02115-6094
Tel.: (617) 734-9800
Web Site: http://www.nejm.org
Sales Range: $10-24.9 Million
Emp.: 200
Medical Journal Published by the Massachusetts Medical Society
N.A.I.C.S.: 513120
Jeffrey M. Drazen (Editor)
Christopher R. Lynch (VP-Publ)
Karen Daly (Mgr-Editorial Office Svcs)
Andrea Graham (Mgr-Online Editorial Production)
Lauren Lindenfelser (Mgr-Editorial Admin)
David Lyons (Specialist-Electronic Content)
Deborah Moskowitz (Mgr-Manuscript Editing)
Elizabeth Quilty (Mgr-Editorial Scheduling & Tracking)
Deborah Stone (Mgr-Quality Assurance)
Timothy Vining (Mgr-Medical & Scientific Illustration)
Maryanne C. Bombaugh (Pres)
Lois Dehls Cornell (Exec VP)

MASSACHUSETTS MUNICIPAL WHOLESALE ELECTRIC CO.
327 Moody St, Ludlow, MA 01056-0426
Tel.: (413) 547-6400   MA
Web Site: http://www.mmwec.org
Sales Range: $25-49.9 Million
Emp.: 79
Power Supply Services
N.A.I.C.S.: 221118
Ronald C. DeCurzio (CEO & Sec)
Nancy Brown (Asst Sec)
Michael J. Flynn (Chm)
Carol A. Martucci (Dir-Fin Reporting & Corp Tech)
Stephen J. Smith (Asst Treas)
Jonathan V. Fitch (Mgr-West Boylston Municipal Light)
Peter Dion (Pres & Mgr-Wakefield Municipal Gas & Light Dept)
Matthew J. Ide (Treas & Exec Dir-Energy & Fin Markets)
Edward Kaczenski (Dir-Engrg & Generation Assets)
Daniel Suppin (Dir-IT)
Michael J. Lynch (Dir-Market Mgmt & Plng)

MASSACHUSETTS MUTUAL LIFE INSURANCE COMPANY
1295 State St, Springfield, MA 01111
Tel.: (413) 788-8411   MA
Web Site: http://www.massmutual.com
Year Founded: 1851
Sales Range: $25-49.9 Billion
Emp.: 27,000
Life Insurance & Pension Products Sales
N.A.I.C.S.: 524292
Roger W. Crandall (Chm, Pres & CEO)
Elizabeth A. Ward (CFO)
Mark D. Roellig (Gen Counsel & Exec VP)
Michael R. Fanning (Exec VP-Mass Mutual US)
Hugh O'Toole (Head-Workplace Distr)
Sears Merritt (Head-Enterprise Tech & Experience)
Michael Timothy Corbett (Chief Investment Officer & Exec VP)
Susan M. Cicco (Sr VP)
Gareth Ross (Chief Customer Officer & Sr VP)
Eddie Ahmed (Chm/CEO-MassMutual Intl)
David J. Brennan (Chm/CEO-Baring Asset Management Limited)
Arthur Steinmetz (Chm/CEO-OppenheimerFunds)
Dennis Duquette (Head-Community Responsibility)
Jennifer Halloran (Head-Brand & Adv)
Aaron Miller (Head-Strategy & Corp Dev)
David Ely (Mgr-Sls-Pittsburgh)
Jesse Goodall (Mgr-Sls-Pittsburgh)
Nabil Hachem (Head-Data Engrg)
Geoffrey J. Craddock (Chief Risk Officer)
Morgan Ferrarotti (Sr Dir-Integrated Mktg)
Bob Carroll (Head-Workplace Distr)
Arthur Wallace (Chief Actuary)
John Rugel (Head-Ops)
Regina Heyward (Head-Supplier Diversity)
William Porter (Head-Procurement)
Ying Yu (Head-Sustainability)
Greta Hager (Head-Fin Plng & Analysis)
Julieta Sinisgalli (Treas)
Paul LaPiana (Head-Product-US)
Andrea Anastasio (Head-Investment Mgmt Solutions)
Jackson Lee Davis (Head-Diversity, Equity & Inclusion)
Anis Baig (Head-Talent Equity, Attraction & Insights)
Morris Taylor (CIO)
Jessica Lozano Williams (Head-Supplier Diversity)

Subsidiaries:

Barings LLC   (1)
300 S Tryon St Ste 2500, Charlotte, NC 28202
Tel.: (704) 805-7200
Web Site: http://www.barings.com
Rev.: $284,000,000,000
Emp.: 2,000
Asset Management & Private Equity Investment Services
N.A.I.C.S.: 523940
Christopher A. DeFrancis (Chief Compliance Officer & Head-Compliance-Global)
David M. Mihalick (Head-Private Assets)
Scott D. Brown (Head-Real Estate-Global)
Eric J. Lloyd (Pres)
Russell D. Morrison (Mng Dir)
Anthony Sciacca (Head-Barings Alternative Investments)
Paul Thompson (CFO, COO & Head-Investment Svcs-Global)
Christopher DeFrancis (Chief Compliance Officer & Head-Compliance-Global)
Sheldon Francis (Chief Legal Officer & Head-Legal-Global)
Susan Moore (Chief Admin Officer & Head-HR & Corp Comm-Global)
Mike Freno (Chm, Pres & CEO)
Chasity Boyce (Chief Diversity, Equity & Inclusion Officer)
Caroline Mandeville (Chief HR Officer)
Benjamin Tecmire (Asst Gen Counsel)

Subsidiary (Non-US):

Baring Asset Management Ltd.   (2)
155 Bishopsgate, London, EC2M 3XY, United Kingdom
Tel.: (44) 2076286000
Web Site: http://www.barings.com
Rev.: $57,400,000,000
Emp.: 800
Asset Management
N.A.I.C.S.: 523999

Subsidiary (Non-US):

Baring Asset Management (Asia) Limited   (3)
35/F Gloucester Tower 15 Queens Road, Central, China (Hong Kong)
Tel.: (852) 2841 1411
Web Site: http://www.barings.com
Asset Management
N.A.I.C.S.: 523940

Baring Asset Management (Japan) Limited   (3)
7F Kyobashi Edogrand 2-2-1 Kyobashi, Chuo-ku, Tokyo, 104-0031, Japan
Tel.: (81) 345651000
Web Site: http://www.barings.com
Asset Management
N.A.I.C.S.: 523940

Baring Asset Management GmbH   (3)
Ulmenstrasse 37-39, 60325, Frankfurt, Germany
Tel.: (49) 69 7169 1888
Web Site: http://www.barings.com
Sales Range: $75-99.9 Million
Emp.: 12
Asset Management Services
N.A.I.C.S.: 523150

Baring Asset Management Korea Limited   (3)
7th Floor Samsung Fire & Marine Insurance Building 87 Euljirol-ga, Jung-gu, Seoul, 100 782, Korea (South)
Tel.: (82) 2 3788 0500
Web Site: http://www.barings.com
Emp.: 52
Asset Management Services
N.A.I.C.S.: 523940
Thae Surn Khwarg (CEO)

Baring France SAS   (3)
35 Avenue Franklin Roosevelt, 75008, Paris, France
Tel.: (33) 1 53 93 60 00
Web Site: http://www.barings.com
Sales Range: $75-99.9 Million
Emp.: 4
Asset Management Services
N.A.I.C.S.: 523150
Benoit du Mesnil du Buisson (Pres)

Baring SICE (Taiwan) Ltd   (3)
TWTC International Trade Building Room 2112 21st Floor, 333 Keeling Road Sec 1, Taipei, 11012, Taiwan
Tel.: (886) 2 6638 8188
Web Site: http://www.barings.com
Asset Management
N.A.I.C.S.: 523940
Barry Lin (Gen Mgr)

Affiliate (Domestic):

Barings Emerging EMEA Opportunities PLC   (3)

COMPANIES
MASSACHUSETTS MUTUAL LIFE INSURANCE COMPANY

6th Floor 65 Gresham Street, London,
EC2V 7NQ, United Kingdom
Tel.: (44) 3716640300
Sales Range: $1-9.9 Million
Closed-End Investment Fund
N.A.I.C.S.: 525990
Christopher A. DeFrancis (Chief Compliance Officer & Head-Compliance)
Christopher DeFrancis (Chief Compliance Officer & Head-Compliance)
Matthias Siller (Head)
Adnan El-Araby (Mgr-Investment)
Mike Freno (Head-Financial Services)

Subsidiary (Domestic):

Baring North America LLC (2)
Independence Wharf 470 Atlantic Ave, Boston, MA 02110-2208
Tel.: (617) 946-5200
Web Site: http://www.barings.com
Asset Management Services
N.A.I.C.S.: 523940
Michael T. Brown (Pres)
Michael Siciliano (Sr VP & Head-Sls & Bus Dev-North America)
Barbara Cassidy (VP-Client Svc)
Kieran Stover (VP-Sls & Bus Dev)
Eric Lareau (Dir-Sls & Bus Dev)
Michael Annis (Head-Sls & Bus Dev)
Susan Marshall (Sr VP-Client Svc)

Branch (Domestic):

Baring North America LLC - San Francisco Office (3)
1 Embarcadero Ctr Ste 555, San Francisco, CA 94111
Tel.: (415) 834-1500
Web Site: http://www.barings.com
Emp.: 2
Asset Management Services
N.A.I.C.S.: 523940
Susan Marshall (Sr VP-Client Svc)

Affiliate (Domestic):

Barings Corporate Investors (2)
300 S Tryon St Ste 2500, Charlotte, NC 28202
Tel.: (704) 805-7200
Rev.: $28,414,469
Assets: $346,773,968
Liabilities: $38,524,548
Net Worth: $308,249,420
Earnings: $22,580,877
Fiscal Year-end: 12/31/2019
Closed-End Investment Fund
N.A.I.C.S.: 525990
Sean M. Feeley (VP)
Janice M. Bishop (Chief Legal Officer, Sec & VP)
Christopher D. Hanscom (Treas)

Barings Global Short Duration High Yield Fund (2)
550 S Tryon St Ste 3300, Charlotte, NC 28202
Tel.: (704) 805-7200
Rev.: $48,941,163
Assets: $519,631,330
Liabilities: $149,213,029
Net Worth: $370,418,301
Earnings: $39,220,735
Fiscal Year-end: 12/31/2015
Closed-End Investment Fund
N.A.I.C.S.: 525990

Barings Participation Investors (2)
c/o Barings LLC 300 S Tryon St Ste 2500, Charlotte, NC 28202
Tel.: (413) 226-1516
Sales Range: $10-24.9 Million
Closed-End Investment Fund
N.A.I.C.S.: 525990
Melissa M. LaGrant (Chief Compliance Officer)
Michael Cowart (Chief Compliance Officer)

Subsidiary (Domestic):

Barings Real Estate Advisers LLC (2)
1 Financial Plz, Hartford, CT 06103-2604
Tel.: (860) 509-2200
Web Site: http://www.barings.com
Emp.: 2,000
Real Estate Investment & Equity Management Services
N.A.I.C.S.: 531390

Victor Woolridge (Mng Dir)
Gunther Deutsch (Head-Real Estate Transactions-Europe)
James Alan Henderson (Chief Investment Officer-Alternative Investments)
Jere Fredriksson (Head-Real Estate Transactions-Helsinki)

Joint Venture (Domestic):

CTI Foods, LLC (2)
22303 Hwy 95, Wilder, ID 83676
Tel.: (208) 482-7844
Web Site: http://www.ctifoods.com
Sales Range: $700-749.9 Million
Emp.: 2,000
Processed Food Mfr & Supplier
N.A.I.C.S.: 311999
Bobby Horowitz (CEO)
Ben Badiola (VP-Ops)
Sam Rovit (Pres & CEO)

Plant (Domestic):

CTI Foods, LLC - Carson Plant (3)
20644 S Fordyce Ave, Carson, CA 90810
Tel.: (310) 637-0900
Sales Range: $50-74.9 Million
Emp.: 300
Prepared Food Mfr
N.A.I.C.S.: 311991
Jeff Golangco (VP-Supply Chain)

Subsidiary (Domestic):

Liguria Foods, Inc. (3)
1515 15th St N, Humboldt, IA 50548
Tel.: (515) 332-4121
Web Site: http://www.liguriafood.com
Emp.: 200
Processed Meat Mfr
N.A.I.C.S.: 311612
Mark Majewski (Sr VP & Gen Mgr)
Joe Christopherson (VP-Ops)

Subsidiary (Domestic):

Midatech Pharma US Inc. (2)
8601 6 Forks Rd Ste 160, Raleigh, NC 27615
Tel.: (919) 872-5578
Web Site: http://www.darabio.com
Metabolic Disease Treatment Developer
N.A.I.C.S.: 325412
David Benharris (Pres)
Mary Kay Delmedico (VP-Scientific & Regulatory Affairs)
Tim Cochran (VP-Sls & Mktg)

Wood Creek Capital Management, LLC (2)
157 Church St 20th Fl, New Haven, CT 06510
Tel.: (203) 401-3220
Web Site: http://www.woodcreekcap.com
Emp.: 21
Investment Advisory & Management Services
N.A.I.C.S.: 523940
Glenn H. Pease (Mng Dir)
Alex Thomson (Mng Dir)
Brett D. Hellerman (Co-Founder & Chm)
Doug Terry (Mng Dir)
Matt Sandoval (Mng Dir)
Thomas Juterbock (Mng Dir)
Jonathan Rotolo (Co-Founder, CEO & Chief Investment Officer)
Bob Saul (Mng Dir)
Gregory Smith (Chief Compliance Officer)
Ethan Tyminski (Controller)

Holding (Domestic):

Concord Bicycle Music (3)
8447 Wilshire Blvd Ste 400, Beverly Hills, CA 90211
Tel.: (310) 286-6600
Sales Range: $125-149.9 Million
Music Recording, Publishing & Rights Management Services
N.A.I.C.S.: 512250
Scott Pascucci (CEO)
Ruth Martinez (Chief People Officer)

Subsidiary (Domestic):

Concord Music Group, Inc. (4)
100 N Crescent Dr Garden Level, Beverly Hills, CA 90210
Tel.: (310) 385-4455

Web Site: http://www.concordmusicgroup.com
Sales Range: $10-24.9 Million
Emp.: 160
Music Production Services
N.A.I.C.S.: 512250
Sig Sigworth (Pres-Label)
Tina Funk (Mng Dir-Publ-Germany)
John Minch (Pres-Publ-Europe)
Rebecca Berman (Sr VP & Co-Head-Intl)
Michael Nance (Co-Head-Intl)
Tom Whalley (Chief Label Officer)

Subsidiary (Domestic):

Rounder Records Corporation (5)
1209 Pine St, Nashville, TN 37203
Web Site: http://www.rounder.com
Emp.: 110
Record Production Services
N.A.I.C.S.: 512250
John Strohm (Pres)

Samuel French Inc. (5)
235 Park Ave S 5th Fl, New York, NY 10003
Tel.: (212) 206-8990
Web Site: http://www.samuelfrench.com
Rev.: $16,600,000
Emp.: 46
Book Publishing & Printing
N.A.I.C.S.: 513130
Abbie Van Nostrand (Dir-Corp Comm)
Ryan Pointer (Mgr-Mktg)
Amy Rose Marsh (Dir-Literary)
David Geer (Mgr-Publ)
Bruce Lazarus (Exec Dir)
Alfred Contreras (Mgr-Shipping)
Caitlin Bartow (Supvr-Bus Affairs)
Lori Thimsen (Dir-Licensing Compliance)
Nate Collins (Pres)

Sugar Hill Records, Inc. (5)
501 Washington St, Durham, NC 27701
Tel.: (919) 489-4349
Web Site: http://www.sugarhillrecords.com
Sales Range: $1-9.9 Million
Emp.: 16
Record Production
N.A.I.C.S.: 512250
Kevin Welk (Chief Creative Officer)
Cliff O'Sullivan (COO)

Vanguard Records (5)
2700 Penn Ave Ste 1100, Santa Monica, CA 90404
Tel.: (310) 829-9355
Web Site: http://www.vanguardrecords.com
Sales Range: $1-9.9 Million
Emp.: 45
Record Production
N.A.I.C.S.: 512250
Bill Bentley (Sr Dir-A&R)
Seymour Solomon (Founder)

Subsidiary (Domestic):

The Bicycle Music Company (4)
8447 Wilshire Blvd Ste 400, Beverly Hills, CA 90211
Tel.: (310) 286-6600
Web Site: http://www.bicyclemusic.com
Music Publishing & Rights Management Services
N.A.I.C.S.: 512230
Jake Wisely (CEO)

Holding (Domestic):

Milestone Equipment Holdings, LLC (3)
591 Redwood Hwy Ste 5280, Mill Valley, CA 94941
Tel.: (415) 888-8830
Web Site: http://www.milecorp.com
Equipment Rental Services
N.A.I.C.S.: 532412
Robert Thull (Chm)
Sarah Johnson (Exec VP-Branch Ops)
Carolyn Mueller (VP-Acctg)
Amy Genobles (Pres-Intermodal)
Jeff Alpert (Pres-Trailer Leasing)
Doug Hoehn (Exec VP-Chassis & Managed Assets)
Marc Meunier (Exec VP-Trailer Leasing & Bus Dev)
Annette Kaptur (VP-Contracts & Admin)
Lisa Asher (Mgr-Pricing & Fin Reporting)
Shelley Shannon (Dir-Credit & Risk Mgmt)
Dan Keating (Dir-IT)

Tim Schumer (Mgr-HR)
Don Clayton (Pres & CEO)
Phil Shook (Exec VP-Domestic Intermodal)

C.M. Life Insurance Company (1)
100 Bright Meadow Blvd, Enfield, CT 06082
Tel.: (413) 788-8411
Fire Insurance Services
N.A.I.C.S.: 524113

Financial Design Associates (1)
200 W Forsyth St Ste 600, Jacksonville, FL 32202
Tel.: (904) 998-7300
Web Site: http://www.fn-design.com
Sales Range: $1-9.9 Million
Emp.: 50
Insurance Agencies & Brokerages
N.A.I.C.S.: 524210
S. Roger Dominey (Mng Partner)
Everette Seay (Mgr-Sls)

Fortis Lux Financial, Inc. (1)
277 Park Ave 44th Fl, New York, NY 10172
Tel.: (212) 578-0300
Web Site: http://www.ortislux.com
Financial Consulting Services
N.A.I.C.S.: 522320
Felix Malitsky (Foudner & Pres)
Thomas j. Picone (CEO)
Roman Moldavsky (COO)
Jo Ann Burns (CFO)
Tony Wong (CIO)
Sunita Bajaj (Mng Dir)
Jamie McGrory (Mng Dir)

Great American Life Insurance Company (1)
301 E 4th St, Cincinnati, OH 45202 (100%)
Tel.: (513) 333-5300
Life Insurance; Retirement Annuities
N.A.I.C.S.: 524113
Chad Stewart (CIO & Sr VP)
Mark Muething (Pres & COO)

Subsidiary (Domestic):

Annuity Investors Life Insurance Company (2)
PO Box 5423, Cincinnati, OH 45201-5420 (100%)
Tel.: (513) 333-5300
Web Site: http://www.gafri.com
Sales Range: $150-199.9 Million
Annuity Products
N.A.I.C.S.: 524113

Great American Lloyds Inc. (2)
2435 N Central Expy Ste 1400, Richardson, TX 75080
Tel.: (972) 437-7100
Web Site: http://www.greatamericaninsurance.com
Sales Range: $1-9.9 Million
Emp.: 40
Insurance
N.A.I.C.S.: 524210

Manhattan National Life Insurance Company (2)
PO Box 5420, Cincinnati, OH 45201-5420
Fire Insurance Services
N.A.I.C.S.: 524210

MML Bay State Life Insurance Company (1)
100 Bright Meadow Blvd, Enfield, CT 06082
Tel.: (860) 562-1000
Fire Insurance Services
N.A.I.C.S.: 524113

MML Distributors, LLC (1)
1295 State St, Springfield, MA 01111-0001
Tel.: (413) 737-8400
Security Brokers & Dealers
N.A.I.C.S.: 523150

MML Investors Services, Inc. (1)
1295 State St, Springfield, MA 01111-0001 (100%)
Tel.: (413) 737-8400
Web Site: http://www.mmlisi.com
Sales Range: $50-74.9 Million
Emp.: 100
Investment Management for Large & Mid-Sized Institutional Marketplace
N.A.I.C.S.: 523150

MassMutual International LLC (1)

MASSACHUSETTS MUTUAL LIFE INSURANCE COMPANY U.S. PRIVATE

Massachusetts Mutual Life Insurance Company—(Continued)
1295 State St, Springfield, MA 01111
Tel.: (413) 788-8411
Health & Life Insurance Services
N.A.I.C.S.: 524114
Shan Nie *(Dir-Bus Ops)*
Alethea O'Donnell *(Asst VP-Strategic Solutions & Shared Svcs-US)*
David DaSilva *(Mgr-Relationship)*
Scott Palmer *(Sr VP-Retirement Svcs Sys)*

The MassMutual Trust Company, FSB (1)
100 Bright Meadow Blvd, Enfield, CT 06082-1981 (100%)
Tel.: (860) 562-2720
Web Site: http://www.massmutualtrust.com
Rev.: $100,000,000
Emp.: 15
Fire Insurance Services
N.A.I.C.S.: 522180

MASSACHUSETTS PORT AUTHORITY
1 Harborside Dr Ste 200 S, East Boston, MA 02128-2905
Tel.: (617) 428-2800
Web Site: http://www.massport.com
Year Founded: 1956
Sales Range: $75-99.9 Million
Emp.: 1,300
Owns & Operates Logan International Airport, Public Terminals in the Port of Boston, the Tobin Memorial Bridge & Hanscom Airfield
N.A.I.C.S.: 488119
Kevin Laffey *(Dir-Freight Mktg)*
Edward C. Freni *(Dir-Aviation)*
David M. Gambone *(Dir-HR)*
Danny Theodat Levy *(Dir-Strategic Mktg & Comm)*
Jim Doolin *(Chief Dev Officer)*
George Nacca *(Chief Security Officer)*
Lauren Gleason *(Deputy Dir-Port-Bus Dev)*
Derek Tavares *(Mgr-Fleet)*
John Pranckevicius *(Acting CEO)*
Sheriff Lew G. Evangelidis *(Chm)*
Jose C. Masso III *(Dir-Community Rels)*

MASSACHUSETTS SOCIETY FOR THE PREVENTION OF CRUELTY TO CHILDREN
99 Summer St 6th Fl, Boston, MA 02110
Tel.: (617) 587-1500 MA
Web Site: http://www.mspcc.org
Year Founded: 1878
Sales Range: $10-24.9 Million
Emp.: 525
Child Care Development Services
N.A.I.C.S.: 624110
Nancy Allen Scannell *(Dir-Policy & Plng)*
Karen Litchfield *(VP-HR)*
Monica Roizner *(Dir-Clinical Svcs)*

MASSAGE ENVY FRANCHISING, LLC
14350 N 87th St Ste 200, Scottsdale, AZ 85260
Tel.: (602) 889-1090
Web Site: http://www.massageenvy.com
Sales Range: $25-49.9 Million
Emp.: 62
Massage & Spa Services
N.A.I.C.S.: 812199
Dawn Weiss *(Dir-Brand Continuity)*
George Hines *(CIO)*
Derek Detenber *(Sr VP-Mktg)*
Lee Knowlton *(Sr VP-Global Franchise Sls & Intl Div)*
Beth Stiller *(CEO)*
Julie M. Cary *(Chief Mktg & Innovation Officer)*

MASSAGE HEIGHTS
13750 US Hwy 281 N Ste 230, San Antonio, TX 78232-8232
Web Site: http://www.massageheights.com
Personal Care Services
N.A.I.C.S.: 812199
Susan Boresow *(Pres & CEO)*
Shane Evans *(Founder & Vice Chm)*
C. G. Funk *(Sr VP-Culture & Industry Rels)*

Subsidiaries:

Gents Place Men's Fine Groom (1)
6975 Lebanon Rd, Frisco, TX 75034-6752
Tel.: (469) 579-4417
Web Site: http://www.thegentsplace.com
Emp.: 55
Barber Shops
N.A.I.C.S.: 812111
Ben Davis *(Owner)*

MASSAGE THERAPY CONNECTIONS LLC
9020 58th Dr E Ste 101, Lakewood Ranch, FL 34202
Tel.: (941) 755-0406
Web Site: http://www.massagetherapyconnections.com
Sales Range: $10-24.9 Million
Emp.: 10
Massage Therapy Services
N.A.I.C.S.: 812112
Shea Daignault *(Co-Owner & Partner)*
Nancy Strand *(Co-Owner & Partner)*

MASSENGILL TIRE CO. INC.
Hwy 411, Benton, TN 37307
Tel.: (423) 338-2027
Web Site: http://www.massengilltire.com
Rev.: $10,215,532
Emp.: 11
Tires & Tubes
N.A.I.C.S.: 423130
Richard M. Massengill Jr. *(Pres)*

MASSEY
1706 Massey Blvd, Hagerstown, MD 21740
Tel.: (301) 739-6756
Web Site: http://www.masseyauto.com
Sales Range: $10-24.9 Million
Emp.: 40
New Car Retailer
N.A.I.C.S.: 441110
Jerry Massey *(Owner & Pres)*
Faith Massey *(Gen Mgr)*
Trevor Widmyer *(Mgr-Fin)*
Matt Whetzel *(Dir-Svcs)*

MASSEY CONSTRUCTION INC.
3204 Regal Dr, Alcoa, TN 37701
Tel.: (865) 573-4200
Web Site: http://www.masseyelectric.com
Rev.: $12,000,000
Emp.: 113
General Electrical Contractor
N.A.I.C.S.: 238210
Charity Thompson *(Mgr-HR)*

MASSEY MOTORS INC.
2434 Atlantic Blvd, Jacksonville, FL 32207
Tel.: (904) 398-6877
Web Site: http://www.masseyjax.com
Sales Range: $25-49.9 Million
Emp.: 100
Automobiles, New & Used
N.A.I.C.S.: 441110
Robert B. Massey Sr. *(Chm)*

MASSEY QUICK SIMON & CO., LLC
360 Mt Kemble Ave, Morristown, NJ 07960
Tel.: (973) 525-1000
Web Site: http://www.mqsadvisors.com
Year Founded: 2004
Alternate Investment Manager
N.A.I.C.S.: 523999
Stewart Massey *(Mng Partner)*
Les Quick *(Founding Partner & Mng Partner)*
J. Peter Simon *(Mng Partner)*
Joe Belfatto *(Mng Partner)*
Christopher Moore *(Cheif Investment Officer & Mng Partner)*
Mark DeLotto *(COO, Chief Compliance Officer & Mng Partner)*
William E. Simon Jr. *(Partner)*

MASSEY SERVICES, INC.
315 Groveland St, Orlando, FL 32804
Tel.: (407) 645-2500 FL
Web Site: http://www.masseyservices.com
Year Founded: 1985
Sales Range: $125-149.9 Million
Emp.: 1,250
Residential & Commercial Pest Prevention, Termite Protection, Lawn Tree & Shrub Care Services
N.A.I.C.S.: 561710
Harvey L. Massey *(Chm)*
Gwyn Elias *(CIO & Exec VP)*
Ed Dougherty *(COO & Exec VP)*
Jean Nowry *(CFO & Exec VP)*
Jeff Buhler *(Sr VP-Customer Svc)*
Barbara Corino *(Sec & VP)*
Lynne Frederick *(Sr VP-Mktg)*
Adam Jones *(VP & Dir-Quality Assurance)*
Ian Robinson *(VP-Bus Org Dev)*
Eric Hernandez *(VP-Fleets & Assets)*
Adam Scheinberg *(VP-IT)*
Marcellene Baugh *(VP-Fin & Acctg)*
Tony Massey *(Pres & CEO)*
Bill Cohn *(Dir-Irrigation Technical & Trng)*
Perry Brown *(Mgr-Southwest Florida)*
Barry Neveras *(Sr Dir-Pur)*

Subsidiaries:

Insight Pest Solutions, LLC (1)
1214 Copeland Oaks Dr, Morrisville, NC 27560-6614
Tel.: (888) 234-2847
Web Site: http://www.insightpest.com
Pest Control Services
N.A.I.C.S.: 561710
Adam Villareal *(Owner & Pres)*

Island Pest Control Inc. (1)
142 Island Dr, Hilton Head Island, SC 29926
Tel.: (843) 681-5188
Web Site: http://www.islandpestcontrol.com
Rev.: $1,700,000
Emp.: 22
Exterminating & Pest Control Services
N.A.I.C.S.: 561710
John Kaiser *(Pres)*

Massey Communications, Inc. (1)
1201 S Orlando Ave, Winter Park, FL 32789
Tel.: (407) 581-4222
Web Site: http://www.masseycommunications.com
Emp.: 11
Advetising Agency
N.A.I.C.S.: 541810
Kim Sachse *(VP-Creative Svcs)*
Sam Stark *(Pres & CEO)*
Katherine Coulthart *(Sr Dir-PR & Mktg)*
Matt Masterson *(Dir-Brand Dev)*
D'Anne Mica *(VP)*

Massey Services Inc. (1)
433 SW Thornhill Dr, Port Saint Lucie, FL 34984

Tel.: (772) 873-1386
Web Site: http://www.masseyservices.com
Sales Range: $1-9.9 Million
Emp.: 30
Pet Control & Landscaping Services
N.A.I.C.S.: 561710
Andrea Massey-Farrell *(Sr VP-Community Rels)*

Massey Services, Inc. - Port Charlotte (1)
17303 Abbott Ave, Port Charlotte, FL 33954
Tel.: (941) 629-6669
Web Site: http://www.masseyservices.com
Pest Prevention & Termite Protection Services
N.A.I.C.S.: 561710

MASSEY WOOD & WEST INC.
11707 Westwood Ave, Richmond, VA 23230-0105
Tel.: (804) 355-1721
Web Site: http://www.masseywoodandwest.com
Rev.: $33,241,481
Emp.: 48
Fuel Oil Dealers
N.A.I.C.S.: 457210
Gerard W. Bradley *(Chm, Pres & CEO)*
Patricia Wolf *(Treas & Sec)*
Kirk Clausen *(VP)*

MASSEY'S PLATE GLASS & ALUMINUM, INC.
734 E Main St, Branford, CT 06405
Tel.: (203) 488-2377
Web Site: http://www.masseysglass.com
Sales Range: $25-49.9 Million
Emp.: 135
Glass & Glazing Work Services
N.A.I.C.S.: 238150
Philip Delise *(Pres)*

MASSILLON CABLE TV, INC.
814 Cable CT NW, Massillon, OH 44647
Tel.: (330) 833-4134
Web Site: http://www.massilloncabletv.com
Sales Range: $10-24.9 Million
Emp.: 125
Provider of Cable Television Services
N.A.I.C.S.: 516210
Richard W. Gessner *(Pres)*
Robert Gessner *(VP)*
Susan Gessner *(VP)*

MASSIVE DYNAMICS, INC.
1057 E Henrietta Rd, Rochester, NY 14623
Tel.: (408) 973-7857 NV
Year Founded: 2011
Emp.: 1
Communication Towers Engineering & Compliance Services
N.A.I.C.S.: 541330
Jonathan J. Howard *(CEO & Sec)*

MASSMAN CONSTRUCTION CO.
8901 State Line Rd, Kansas City, MO 64114-3245
Tel.: (816) 523-1000 MO
Web Site: http://www.massman.net
Year Founded: 1908
Sales Range: $75-99.9 Million
Emp.: 250
Provider of Contracting & Construction Services
N.A.I.C.S.: 237310
Henry J. Massman IV *(Pres)*
Mark H. Schnoebelen *(VP)*
Joseph T. Kopp *(Treas, Sec & VP)*
Jeff Ryan *(Controller)*

MASSMEDIA CORPORATE COMMUNICATIONS

2230 Corporate Cir Ste 210, Henderson, NV 89074
Tel.: (702) 433-4331 NV
Web Site:
http://www.massmediacc.com
Year Founded: 1997
Sales Range: Less than $1 Million
Emp.: 25
Public Relations Services
N.A.I.C.S.: 541820
Paula Yakubik (Mng Partner)
Georgeann Pizzi (Pres)
Casey Floyd (VP-Integrated Mktg)

MASSO ENTERPRISES
1 Rafael Cordero St, Caguas, PR 00726
Tel.: (787) 746-1251
Web Site: http://www.masso.net
Year Founded: 1961
Rev.: $60,500,000
Emp.: 800
Lumber Yard
N.A.I.C.S.: 423310
Juan Carlos Gonzalez (Controller)
Hildo Masso Jr. (Pres)

Subsidiaries:

Fabrica De Bloques Masso Inc. (1)
1 Calle Rafael Cordero, Caguas, PR 00725-2541 (100%)
Tel.: (787) 746-1251
Web Site: http://www.masso.com
Sales Range: $10-24.9 Million
Emp.: 3
Concrete Block & Brick
N.A.I.C.S.: 327331
Sergio Gonzalez (Mgr)

MAST GENERAL STORE INCORPORATED
Hwy 194 S, Valle Crucis, NC 28691
Tel.: (828) 963-6511
Web Site:
http://www.mastgeneralstore.com
Sales Range: $10-24.9 Million
Emp.: 45
Department Stores, Non-Discount
N.A.I.C.S.: 455110
Mark Gould (CFO)
Faye B. Cooper (Owner)
Lisa Cooper (Pres)
John E. Cooper Jr. (Founder)

MAST UTILITY BARNS
10483 Hwy 70 N, Crossville, TN 38571-2394
Tel.: (931) 277-3312
Sales Range: $1-9.9 Million
Emp.: 4
Prefabricated Wood Building Mfr
N.A.I.C.S.: 321992
Daniel Mast (Partner)
Elians Mast (Partner)
Ruth Mast (Partner)
Micah Mast (Partner)

MASTEN ENTERPRISES LLC
420 Bernas Rd, Cochecton, NY 12726
Tel.: (845) 932-8206
Sales Range: $10-24.9 Million
Emp.: 75
Grits Mining (Crushed Stone)
N.A.I.C.S.: 212319
John Bernas (Pres)

MASTEN-WRIGHT, INC.
280 State St, North Haven, CT 06473-2132
Tel.: (203) 230-4130 CT
Web Site: http://www.exportdept.com
Year Founded: 1944
Sales Range: $10-24.9 Million
Emp.: 12
Exporters of Sporting & Recreation Goods & Electric Insulating Materials

N.A.I.C.S.: 423910
Gregory Wright (Pres)
Cheryl LaClair (Mgr-Export Admin)

MASTER APPLIANCE CORP.
2420 18th St, Racine, WI 53403
Tel.: (262) 633-7791 WI
Web Site:
http://www.masterappliance.com
Year Founded: 1958
Sales Range: $1-9.9 Million
Emp.: 30
Heat Tools & Soldering Irons Mfr
N.A.I.C.S.: 335999
Scott Radwill (Pres & CEO)
Linda Radwill (Sec & VP)
John Brott (Dir-Sls)

MASTER BOND INC.
154 Hobart St, Hackensack, NJ 07601
Tel.: (201) 343-8983
Web Site:
http://www.masterbond.com
Year Founded: 1976
Sales Range: $10-24.9 Million
Emp.: 25
Adhesives, Sealants & Coatings Mfr & Retailer
N.A.I.C.S.: 325520
Walter Brenner (Dir-Technical)
Robert Michaels (VP)

MASTER CHEMICAL CORPORATION
501 W Boundary St, Perrysburg, OH 43551-3001
Tel.: (419) 874-7902 OH
Web Site:
http://www.masterchemical.com
Year Founded: 1951
Sales Range: $50-74.9 Million
Emp.: 100
Lubricating Oils & Greases
N.A.I.C.S.: 324191
Xinfang Lu (Exec VP-Asia Ops)
Steven H. Sigmon (Gen Mgr)
David A. Barned (VP-Ops & Supply Chain-Global & Gen Mgr)
Paul Madden (Mgr-Sls)
Cary Glay (CFO)
Michael A. McHenry (CEO)

Subsidiaries:

Master Chemical (Shanghai) Co., Ltd. (1)
1234 Kangqiao East Road Kangqiao Industrial District, Pudong, Shanghai, 201319, China
Tel.: (86) 21 5813 3527
Web Site: http://www.masterchemical.com
Chemical Products Distr
N.A.I.C.S.: 424690

Master Chemical (Tianjin) Co., Ltd. (1)
No 66 No 9 Xin Ye Street TEDA West Area, Tianjin, 300462, China
Tel.: (86) 22 6632 0088
Web Site: http://www.masterchemical.com
Chemical Products Distr
N.A.I.C.S.: 424690

Master Chemical Europe Ltd. (1)
33 Maitland Road Lion Barn Business Park, Needham Market, IP6 8NZ, Suffolk, United Kingdom
Tel.: (44) 1449 726800
Web Site: http://www.masterchemical.com
Emp.: 50
Chemical Products Distr
N.A.I.C.S.: 424690
Petr Sturva (Mng Dir)

Master Chemical Siam Co., Ltd. (1)
128/889 Moo1 Tambol Bangsaothong, Amphur Bangsaothong, Samut Prakan, 10540, Thailand
Tel.: (66) 2 763 8606
Chemical Products Distr
N.A.I.C.S.: 424690

Adman Lateh (Gen Mgr)

Master Chemical Vietnam Co., Ltd. (1)
Unit 101, 25 Dinh Bo Linh Street Ward 24, Binh Thanh District, Ho Chi Minh City, Vietnam
Tel.: (84) 8 5 4453496
Chemical Products Distr
N.A.I.C.S.: 424690

Master Fluid Solutions (India) Private Limited (1)
B-41 Chakan Industrial Area Phase - 2 Bhambuli, Vasuli Khed, Pune, 410501, Maharashtra, India
Tel.: (91) 2135 678360
Chemical Products Distr
N.A.I.C.S.: 424690
Mahesh Deshpande (Controller-Fin)

MASTER DESIGN LLC
163 13th St, Brooklyn, NY 11215
Tel.: (718) 499-9717
Rev.: $18,500,000
Emp.: 100
Vacuum Cleaner Bags: Made From Purchased Materials
N.A.I.C.S.: 322220
Joseph Terzuoli (Chm)

MASTER ELECTRIC CO. INC.
8555 W 123rd St, Savage, MN 55378
Tel.: (952) 890-3555 MN
Web Site:
http://www.masterelectric.com
Year Founded: 1979
Sales Range: $10-24.9 Million
Emp.: 120
Providers of Electrical Services
N.A.I.C.S.: 238210
Jeff Loftsgaarden (Owner & Pres)
Dan Schmitz (Controller)
Kim Loftsgaarden (Owner)
Anthony Loftsgaarden (Pres)

MASTER FIBERS INCORPORATED
1710 E Paisano Dr, El Paso, TX 79901
Tel.: (915) 544-2299
Web Site:
http://www.masterfibers.com
Sales Range: $25-49.9 Million
Emp.: 30
Waste Paper
N.A.I.C.S.: 423930
Jose Pinon (Supvr-Slant)

MASTER FLEET, LLC
3360 Spirit Way, Green Bay, WI 54304
Tel.: (920) 347-1800
Web Site: http://www.masterfleet.com
Rev.: $30,000,000
Emp.: 90
Trailers For Trucks & Tractors
N.A.I.C.S.: 441110
Larry Chaplin (Pres)
Roger Kvitek (Mgr-Svcs-Tractor Dept)
Tom Anderson (VP-Ops & Fin)
Gerri Krueger (Dir-Comml Fleet Mgmt)
David T. Haessly (Dir-Bus Dev)
Kimm DeWitt (Gen Mgr)
Dennis Vondrachek (Mgr-Parts)
Marty Rusch (Controller)
Matt Luenenburg (VP-Master Fleet)

MASTER INTERNATIONAL CORP.
1220 Olympic Blvd, Santa Monica, CA 90404-3722
Tel.: (310) 452-1229 CA
Web Site:
http://www.masterinternational.com
Year Founded: 1965
Sales Range: $25-49.9 Million
Emp.: 137

Component Distribution
N.A.I.C.S.: 423690
Ike Nizam (Chm)
Jamil Nizam (Pres)

Subsidiaries:

Master Electronics (1)
1301 Olympic Blvd, Santa Monica, CA 90404-3725 (100%)
Tel.: (310) 452-1229
Web Site: http://www.masterelectronics.com
Sales Range: $25-49.9 Million
Electronic Components Distr
N.A.I.C.S.: 423690
Jamil Nizam (Pres)

MASTER KEY RESOURCES LLC
4915 Saint Elmo Ave Ste 500, Bethesda, MD 20814
Tel.: (301) 907-8789
Web Site:
http://www.masterkeyconsulting.com
Year Founded: 2000
Sales Range: $10-24.9 Million
Emp.: 100
Management & IT Consulting Services
N.A.I.C.S.: 541690
Jonathan Wilber (CEO)
Torrance L. Lawery (Project Mgr)
Rosalind Miller (CFO)
David H. Wilber (CIO)

MASTER LINE SHIPPING CO.
1330 NW 84th Ave, Doral, FL 33126
Tel.: (305) 599-9935
Web Site: http://www.masterline.us
Year Founded: 1997
Sales Range: $10-24.9 Million
Emp.: 20
Cargo Transportation
N.A.I.C.S.: 483111
Nancy Esquivel (Owner)

MASTER MOLDED PRODUCTS CORPORATION
1000 Davis Rd, Elgin, IL 60123
Tel.: (847) 695-9700 IL
Web Site:
http://www.mastermolded.com
Year Founded: 1946
Sales Range: $10-24.9 Million
Emp.: 120
Mfr of Custom Thermoplastic Molders
N.A.I.C.S.: 326199

MASTER PROTECTION CORPORATION
13050 Metro Pkwy Ste 1, Fort Myers, FL 33966
Tel.: (239) 896-1680
Web Site:
http://www.masterprotection.com
Fire Protection Services
N.A.I.C.S.: 561990

MASTER PUMPS & EQUIPMENT CORPORATION
PO Box 1778, Grapevine, TX 76099
Tel.: (817) 251-6745
Web Site:
http://www.masterpumps.com
Sales Range: $10-24.9 Million
Emp.: 85
Whslr of Pumps & Pumping Equipment
N.A.I.C.S.: 423830
Kevin Figge (Treas & Sec)
Don W. Moilan Jr. (Chm, Pres & CEO)

MASTER SPORTS
PO Box 1625, Havre, MT 59501
Tel.: (406) 265-4712
Sales Range: $10-24.9 Million

MASTER SPORTS / U.S. PRIVATE

Master Sports—(Continued)
Emp.: 20
Miscellaneous Textile Product Mfr
N.A.I.C.S.: 314999
Robert A. Evans (Pres)

MASTER'S SUPPLY, INC.
4505 Bishop Ln, Louisville, KY 40218-4507
Tel.: (502) 459-2900 DE
Web Site: http://www.masterssupply.net
Year Founded: 1939
Sales Range: $10-24.9 Million
Emp.: 80
Whslr of Plumbing Fixtures & Heating Equipment
N.A.I.C.S.: 423840
John Burke (CFO)
David Wachtel (Pres)
Dale Steinke (Dir-MIS)
Kenneth Rue (Branch Mgr)
John Bowling (VP-Pur)
Jack Bell (VP-Ops)

MASTERANK INC.
2 Corporate Plaza Dr Ste 125, Newport Beach, CA 92660
Tel.: (949) 719-9668
Web Site: http://www.masterank.com
Sales Range: $75-99.9 Million
Emp.: 9
Chemicals, Industrial & Heavy
N.A.I.C.S.: 424690
Janet Jordan (VP-Ops)

MASTERCONTROL, INC.
6330 S 3000 E Ste 200, Salt Lake City, UT 84121
Tel.: (801) 942-4000
Web Site: http://www.mastercontrol.com
Year Founded: 1993
Sales Range: $10-24.9 Million
Emp.: 103
Management Software & Services
N.A.I.C.S.: 541513
Jonathan Beckstrand (CEO)
Jeff Peck (CFO)
Randall Autry (Sr VP-Engrg)
Brian Curran (Sr VP-Strategic Mktg & Product Mgmt)
Matthew M. Lowe (Exec VP-Global Sls & Mktg)
Kevin Ash (Sr VP-Svcs)
Curt Porritt (Sr VP-Mktg)
Chad Fox (Mng Dir-Asia Ops)
Michael Bothe (Partner-Ops & Sr VP-Sls)
Kiran Dhanuka (Chief Customer Officer)

MASTERCORP INC.
3505 N Main St, Crossville, TN 38555
Tel.: (931) 484-1752
Web Site: http://www.mastercorpinc.com
Sales Range: $10-24.9 Million
Emp.: 3,500
Building Cleaning Services
N.A.I.C.S.: 561720
D. Alan Grindstaff (Pres & CEO)
David Goff (COO)
Kevin Swafford (CFO)

MASTERCRAFT INDUSTRIES, INC.
120 W Allen St, Rice Lake, WI 54868
Tel.: (715) 234-8111
Web Site: http://www.holidaykitchens.com
Rev.: $17,400,000
Emp.: 268
Wood Kitchen Cabinet & Countertop Mfr
N.A.I.C.S.: 337110

MASTERCUT TOOL CORP.
965 F Harbor Lake Dr, Safety Harbor, FL 34695-2309
Tel.: (727) 726-5336
Web Site: http://www.mastercuttool.com
Sales Range: $1-9.9 Million
Emp.: 100
Cutting Tool Mfr
N.A.I.C.S.: 333515
Michael Shaluly (Pres)

MASTERFLIGHT FOUNDATION INC.
6000 IL Route 173, Richmond, IL 60071
Tel.: (202) 360-7603 IL
Web Site: http://www.master-flight-training.org
Year Founded: 2006
Sales Range: $10-24.9 Million
Aviation Training Services
N.A.I.C.S.: 611512
Linda Garding (Sec)
Guadalupe Lopez (Treas)
Mark Levin (Founder & Exec Dir)
Mordechai Levin (Founder, Chm & Exec Dir)

MASTERMIND MARKETING
1450 W Peachtree St NW, Atlanta, GA 30309-2955
Tel.: (678) 420-4000 GA
Web Site: http://www.mastermindmarketing.com
Year Founded: 1983
Sales Range: $50-74.9 Million
Emp.: 41
Advertising Agencies
N.A.I.C.S.: 541810
Maria Akridge (Sr VP)
Joe Schab (Pres & COO)
Daniel Dodson Jr. (Founder & CEO)

MASTERMINDS
6727 Delilah Rd, Egg Harbor Township, NJ 08234
Tel.: (609) 484-0009
Web Site: http://www.masterminds1.com
Year Founded: 1985
Rev.: $35,000,000
Emp.: 42
Advetising Agency
N.A.I.C.S.: 541810
Nancy Smith (CEO)
Joseph McIntire (Pres)
Shawna Hurley (Acct Exec)
Dan Cooper (Administrator-Sys)
Jennifer Fink (Acct Supvr)
James Garrison (Sr Dir-Art)
Erika White (Media Buyer)
Laura Formica (Mgr-Acctg)
Joe McDonough (VP & Exec Dir-Creative)
Jean Pierre Blanchet (Sr Dir-Art)
Matt Krohmer (Graphic Designer)
Chris Holland (Dir-Art)
Pragati Mulani (Copywriter)
Subsidiaries:

Factor 3 Media (1)
6727 Delilah Rd 2nd Fl, Egg Harbor Township, NJ 08234
Tel.: (609) 484-9517
Sales Range: Less than $1 Million
Emp.: 5
Media Buying Services
N.A.I.C.S.: 541830
Bill Porter (Mng Dir)
Cristy Hoffman (Media Planner & Media Buyer)

MASTERS CRAFT CORPORATION
1383 S Hwy 63, West Plains, MO 65775
Tel.: (417) 256-6559
Web Site: http://www.themasterscraft.com
Sales Range: $10-24.9 Million
Emp.: 100
Wood Flooring
N.A.I.C.S.: 423220
Pat Elbrecht (Pres)
Mike Kettle (Controller)

MASTERS GALLERY FOODS, INC.
328 County Rd PP, Plymouth, WI 53073-4143
Tel.: (920) 893-8431 WI
Web Site: http://www.mastersgalleryfoods.com
Year Founded: 1974
Sales Range: $10-24.9 Million
Emp.: 260
Packing of Dairy Products
N.A.I.C.S.: 424430
Jim Jirschele (VP-Food Svc Sls)
Dan Macphee (VP-Retail Sls)
Jeff Giffin (Chm)
Jeff Gentine (Pres & CEO)

MASTERS MANNA INC.
46 N Plains Industrial Rd, Wallingford, CT 06492
Tel.: (203) 678-3042 CT
Web Site: http://www.mastersmanna.org
Year Founded: 2007
Sales Range: $1-9.9 Million
Emp.: 3
Community Action Services
N.A.I.C.S.: 624190
Dan Trzcinski (Project Mgr)
Sean Marshall (Mgr-Warehouse)
Susan Heald (Mgr)
Cheryl Trzcinski Trzcinski (Co-Founder & CEO)

MASTERWORK ELECTRONICS INC.
630 Martin Ave, Rohnert Park, CA 94928
Tel.: (707) 588-9906
Web Site: http://www.masterworkelectronics.com
Year Founded: 1994
Rev.: $22,000,000
Emp.: 200
Printed Circuit Boards
N.A.I.C.S.: 334412
Robert E. Weed (Pres)
Joseph Poslosky (Mgr-Quote)

MASTORAN RESTAURANT INC.
822 Lexington St Fl 2, Waltham, MA 02452
Tel.: (781) 893-0990
Sales Range: $25-49.9 Million
Emp.: 700
Fast-Food Restaurant, Chain
N.A.I.C.S.: 722513
Larry W. Kohler (Pres)

MASTRIA BUICK-PONTIAC-GMC TRUCK
1525 New State Hwy, Raynham, MA 02767
Tel.: (508) 880-7000
Web Site: http://www.mastria.com
Rev.: $25,000,000
Emp.: 58
New & Used Car Dealers
N.A.I.C.S.: 441110
Richard Mastria Jr. (Owner)

MASTRO PROPERTIES
510 Rainier Ave S, Seattle, WA 98144
Tel.: (206) 323-5393
Web Site: http://www.mrmastro.com
Rev.: $25,000,000
Emp.: 200
Residential Buildings & Dwellings
N.A.I.C.S.: 531110
Susan Chang (Gen Counsel)

MASTRY MANAGEMENT LLC
4363 Montgomery St, Oakland, CA 94611
Tel.: (800) 483-1140 DE
Web Site: https://mastry.vc
Year Founded: 2021
Investment Services
N.A.I.C.S.: 523999
Rudy Cline-Thomas (Founder & Mng Partner)
Subsidiaries:

Athletes First, LLC (1)
23091 Mill Creek Dr, Laguna Hills, CA 92653-1258
Tel.: (949) 475-1006
Web Site: http://www.athletesfirst.net
Business Associations
N.A.I.C.S.: 813910
Rudy Cline-Thomas (Chm)
Brian Murphy (CEO)
Jene Elzie (Chief Growth Officer)

MASY BIOSERVICES, INC.
27 Lomar Pk, Pepperell, MA 01463
Tel.: (888) 433-6279 MA
Web Site: http://masy.com
Year Founded: 1984
Investment Services
N.A.I.C.S.: 523999
Jeb Evans (COO)
Keith Kelly (VP-Quality)
Steve Masiello (Dir-Pur)
John Orange (Sr Dir-Biorepository Ops)
Matt Thompson (Sr Dir-Pharma Svcs)
Sylvan Poeckh (Dir-Validation)
Scott McKittrick (Dir-IT)
Deb Sarbacker (Dir-HR)
Chris Masiello (Dir-Facilities)
Dave Ramirez (Dir-Engrg)
Catherine Newman (Controller)

MAT-SU SERVICES FOR CHILDREN AND ADULTS INC.
1225 W Spruce Ave, Wasilla, AK 99654
Tel.: (907) 352-1200 AK
Year Founded: 1985
Sales Range: $10-24.9 Million
Emp.: 354
Developmental Disability Assistance Services
N.A.I.C.S.: 623210
Jean Kincaid (Exec Dir)
Susan Garner (Dir-Fin)
Michael Honner (VP)
Stephen McComb (Treas)
Bonnie Burgan-Kelly (Sec)
Delenna Levan (Pres)

MATAGA OF STOCKTON
3261 Auto Center Cir, Stockton, CA 95212-2838
Tel.: (209) 951-2600
Web Site: http://www.mataga.com
Year Founded: 1996
Sales Range: $10-24.9 Million
Emp.: 50
New Car Whslr
N.A.I.C.S.: 441110
Yosh Mataga (Pres)

MATANUSKA ELECTRIC ASSOCIATION, INC.
163 E Industrial Way, Palmer, AK 99645

Tel.: (907) 745-3231
Web Site: http://www.mea.coop
Year Founded: 1941
Sales Range: $50-74.9 Million
Emp.: 165
Transmission, Electric Power
N.A.I.C.S.: 221121
Heidi Kelley (Dir-HR)
Tony Izzo (Gen Mgr)
Julie Estey (Dir-PR)
Matt Reisterer (CFO)

MATASSA CONSTRUCTION INC.
130 Commercial St, Plainview, NY 11803
Tel.: (516) 485-7343   NY
Web Site:
  http://www.matassaconstruction.com
Year Founded: 1981
Sales Range: $25-49.9 Million
Emp.: 29
Commercial & Office Building Contracts Services
N.A.I.C.S.: 236220
Vincent Matassa (Pres)

MATCHPOINT
2300 Bernadette Dr, Columbia, MO 65203
Tel.: (573) 445-4073
Sales Range: $1-9.9 Million
Emp.: 10
Women's, Children's & Infants' Clothing & Accessories Merchant Whslr
N.A.I.C.S.: 424350
Daniel Allen (Principal)

MATCO ELECTRIC CORPORATION
3913 Gates Rd, Vestal, NY 13850
Tel.: (607) 729-4921   DE
Web Site:
  http://www.matcoelectric.com
Sales Range: $25-49.9 Million
Emp.: 350
Electrical Contractor
N.A.I.C.S.: 238210
Mark Freije (Pres)
Kenneth Elliott (CEO)
Kathy Towery (Treas)
Devin Ashman (Sr Project Mgr)
Lenny Gilbert (Project Mgr)
Marty Lewis (Project Mgr)
Joe Tomazin (Project Mgr)
Greg Smyder (Project Mgr)
Tony Salvatore (Project Mgr)
Phil Randall (Mgr-Svc)

MATCON CONSTRUCTION SERVICES, INC.
1717 E Busch Blvd Ste 601, Tampa, FL 33612
Tel.: (813) 600-5555
Web Site:
  http://www.matconconstruction.com
Sales Range: $1-9.9 Million
Emp.: 13
Commercial & Industrial Construction
N.A.I.C.S.: 236220
Derek Mateos (Pres)

MATE PRECISION TOOLING INC.
1295 Lund Blvd, Anoka, MN 55303-1092
Tel.: (763) 421-0230   MN
Web Site: http://www.mate.com
Year Founded: 1962
Sales Range: $50-74.9 Million
Emp.: 350
Mfr of Sheet Metal Fabrication Tooling
N.A.I.C.S.: 333517
Dean A. Sundquist (Chm & CEO)
Kevin Nicholson (Pres)

Michael Brown (VP-Intl Sls)
Josh Capilinger (Mgr-Sls-East)
Patrick Vandeputte (Mgr-Sls-Western Europe)

MATEC INSTRUMENT COMPANIES, INC.
56 Hudson St, Northborough, MA 01532-1922
Tel.: (508) 393-0155   MA
Web Site: http://www.matec.com
Year Founded: 1968
Sales Range: $10-24.9 Million
Emp.: 45
Holding Company; Ultrasonic Quality Control Inspection & Production Testing Equipment Mfr
N.A.I.C.S.: 551112
Kenneth C. Bishop (Pres, CEO & Owner)
Jose Gabriel Dos Ramos (VP)

Subsidiaries:

Crystal Biotech   (1)
56 Hudson St, Northborough, MA 01532-1922   (100%)
Tel.: (508) 393-0155
Web Site: http://www.matec.com
Medical Hemodynamic Equipment Mfr
N.A.I.C.S.: 339112
Kenneth C. Bishop (Pres)

Matec Applied Sciences   (1)
56 Hudson St, Northborough, MA 01532-1922   (100%)
Tel.: (508) 393-0155
Web Site:
  http://www.matecappliedsciences.com
Particle Measurement Instruments Mfr
N.A.I.C.S.: 334519

Matec Instruments NDT   (1)
56 Hudson St, Northborough, MA 01532-1922   (100%)
Tel.: (508) 393-0155
Web Site: http://www.matec.com
Ultrasonic Network Diagnostic Testing Equipment Mfr
N.A.I.C.S.: 334519
Kenneth C. Bishop (Pres)

MATECH, INC.
510 Naylor Mill Rd, Salisbury, MD 21801
Tel.: (410) 548-1627
Web Site: http://www.matech.net
Rev.: $22,000,000
Emp.: 252
Machine Shops
N.A.I.C.S.: 332710
Pedro Lorenzen (Mgr-Mfg)
Rodrigo Ramos (Dir-Engrg)

MATENAER CORPORATION
810 Schoenhaar Dr, West Bend, WI 53090
Tel.: (262) 338-0700
Web Site: http://www.matenaer.com
Year Founded: 1972
Sales Range: $10-24.9 Million
Emp.: 55
Washers & Metal Stampings
N.A.I.C.S.: 332722
Tim Wiedmeyer (VP-Sls)
Rick Lathers (Mgr-Accts & Sls)
Warren Stringer Jr. (Pres)

MATERIA, INC.
2674 E Walnut St, Pasadena, CA 91107-3748
Tel.: (626) 584-8400   CA
Web Site: http://www.materia-inc.com
Year Founded: 1998
Catalysts & Specialty Resins Mfr
N.A.I.C.S.: 325199
Ray Roberge (Chm)
Mark S. Trimmer (CTO & Exec VP)
Scott Krog (CFO)
Christopher J. Cruce (VP-Comml Tech)

Cliff Post (Pres & CEO)
Richard L. Pederson (VP-R&D)
Neal Gilmore (VP-Ops)
Jay Dupre (Dir-Corp Dev & Legal Affairs)

MATERIAL CONTROL SYSTEMS INC.
15509 Route 84 N, Cordova, IL 61242
Tel.: (309) 654-9031
Web Site: http://www.matconusa.com
Sales Range: $10-24.9 Million
Emp.: 50
Mfr of Containers
N.A.I.C.S.: 423990
Donn Larson (Pres)
Todd Simmer (Engr-Sls-South & East)
Brandon Johnson (Engr-Sls-Midwest & West)
Jeff Stringham (Mgr-Sls)

MATERIAL HANDLING INC
631 N Glenwood Ave, Dalton, GA 30721
Tel.: (706) 278-1104
Web Site: http://www.mhiusa.net
Sales Range: $25-49.9 Million
Emp.: 100
Lift Trucks & Parts
N.A.I.C.S.: 423830
Amar V. Sain (Chm)
Patrick Sain (Pres)
William Gleaton (Mgr-Fin)

MATERIAL HANDLING INDUSTRY
8720 Red Oak Blvd Ste 201, Charlotte, NC 28217
Tel.: (704) 676-1190   PA
Web Site: http://www.mhi.org
Year Founded: 1945
Sales Range: $10-24.9 Million
Emp.: 27
Material Handling & Logistic Trade Association
N.A.I.C.S.: 813910
Amy Shelton (Mgr-Creative)
Carol Miller (VP-Mktg & Comm Svcs)
Daniel Stanton (VP-Education & Pro Dev)
Gary Forger (Mng Dir-Pro Dev)
Tom Carbott (Sr VP-Exhibitions)
David Schwebel (Mgr-Solution & Product Grps)
George Prest (CEO)
Angela Jenkins (Coord-Education)
Devon Birch (Dir-Membership)
Jay Traylor (Coord-Inventory Svcs)
Greg Baer (Dir-Sls)
Joey Holt (Mgr-IT)
Brian Reaves (Exec VP)
John Paxton (COO)
Michael Mikitka (Exec VP-Knowledge Value Center)

Subsidiaries:

Warehousing Education and Research Council   (1)
1100 Jorie Blvd Ste 170, Oak Brook, IL 60523-4413
Tel.: (630) 990-0001
Web Site: http://www.werc.org
Sales Range: $1-9.9 Million
Emp.: 6
Logistics Association
N.A.I.C.S.: 813920
Rita M. Coleman (Exec VP)
Roseanna Nania (Office Mgr)
Angie Silberhorn (Dir-Conference)
Fred Rake (Dir-Indus Rels)
Michael J. Mikitka (CEO)
Sheila Benny (Pres)
Sylvia Spore (Dir-Web Svcs)
Tony Ward (Dir-Mktg Membership)
Dave Pardo (Mgr-Mktg)

MATERIAL HANDLING PRODUCTS CORP
6601 Joy Rd, East Syracuse, NY 13057
Tel.: (315) 437-2891
Web Site: http://www.mhpcorp.com
Sales Range: $1-9.9 Million
Emp.: 40
Materials Handling Machinery
N.A.I.C.S.: 423830
Scott Minich (Pres)
John Nelson (VP)

MATERIAL HANDLING SERVICES, LLC
3235 Levis Commons Blvd, Perrysburg, OH 43551
Tel.: (567) 336-9764
Web Site:
  http://www.onpointgroup.com
Year Founded: 2002
Material Handling Equipment Whslr
N.A.I.C.S.: 423830
Thomas J. Cox (CEO)

Subsidiaries:

GSG Financial   (1)
45 Main St Ste 537, Brooklyn, NY 11201-0027
Tel.: (718) 243-2243
Web Site: http://www.graphicsavings.com
Investment Advice
N.A.I.C.S.: 523940
Andrew A. Bender (CEO)

MATERIAL HANDLING SUPPLY, INC.
100 Old Salem Rd, Brooklawn, NJ 08030
Tel.: (856) 541-1290
Web Site: http://www.mhslift.com
Sales Range: $10-24.9 Million
Emp.: 115
Supplier of Material Handling Machinery
N.A.I.C.S.: 423830
Robert J. Levin (Founder)
David J. Brown (CFO)

MATERIAL HANDLING TECHNOLOGIES
113 International Dr, Morrisville, NC 27560
Tel.: (919) 388-0050
Web Site:
  http://www.materialhandlingtech.com
Sales Range: $10-24.9 Million
Emp.: 60
Materials Handling
N.A.I.C.S.: 423830
John Englert (Pres)
Scott Englert (VP)
Sherry Bunce (Controller)

MATERIAL TECHNOLOGY & LOGISTICS, INC.
1325 Mellow Dr, Jessup, PA 18434
Tel.: (570) 487-6162
Web Site: http://www.mtlpa.com
Sales Range: $10-24.9 Million
Emp.: 70
Fabric Product Mfr
N.A.I.C.S.: 313210
Michael J. Hillebrand (Pres)

MATERIALS HANDLING EQUIPMENT CORP.
7433 US Hwy 30 E, Fort Wayne, IN 46803
Tel.: (260) 749-0475   IN
Web Site: http://www.mhec.com
Year Founded: 1949
Sales Range: $10-24.9 Million
Emp.: 35
Provider of Materials Handling Machinery

MATERIALS HANDLING EQUIPMENT CORP. — U.S. PRIVATE

Materials Handling Equipment Corp.—(Continued)
N.A.I.C.S.: 423830
Helen E. Fisher (Chm)
Kellen Watkins (Pres)

MATERIALS MARKETING CORP.
120 W Josephine St, San Antonio, TX 78212
Tel.: (210) 731-8453
Web Site:
http://www.mstoneandtile.com
Year Founded: 1975
Sales Range: $10-24.9 Million
Emp.: 75
Whslr of Brick & Stone
N.A.I.C.S.: 423320
Tim Roberts (Office Mgr)
Michael Mortensen (Office Mgr)

MATERIALS PROCESSING INC.
17423 Jefferson, Riverview, MI 48192
Tel.: (734) 282-1888
Web Site: http://www.mpi-usa.com
Year Founded: 1978
Sales Range: $10-24.9 Million
Emp.: 50
Provider of Packaging & Labeling Services
N.A.I.C.S.: 561910
Maureen Tanner (Dir-HR)
Emmett Windisch (Pres)
Mike Mitchell (Plant Mgr)

MATERIALS RESEARCH SOCIETY
506 Keystone Dr, Warrendale, PA 15086-7537
Tel.: (724) 779-3003
Web Site: http://www.mrs.org
Year Founded: 1973
Sales Range: $10-24.9 Million
Emp.: 50
Material Researcher Association
N.A.I.C.S.: 813920
J. Ardie Dillen (Dir-Fin & Admin)
Bob Braughler (Mgr-Virtual Engagement)
Patricia A. Hastings (Dir-Meetings Activities)
Michele L. Feder (Mgr-Volunteer Affairs)

MATERIALS SCIENCE INTERNATIONAL, INC.
1660 Georgesville Rd, Columbus, OH 43228-3620
Tel.: (614) 870-0400
Web Site: http://www.msitarget.com
Year Founded: 1981
Emp.: 100
Metals Mfr
N.A.I.C.S.: 332999

MATERIALS TRANSPORTATION CO.
1408 Commerce Dr, Temple, TX 76504
Tel.: (254) 298-2900
Web Site:
http://www.mtcworldwide.com
Sales Range: $10-24.9 Million
Emp.: 150
Steel Fabrication
N.A.I.C.S.: 333248
William A. Jones (CEO)
Bob Neill (Pres)

MATERRA, LLC.
1340 W Valley Pkwy Ste 208, Escondido, CA 92029
Tel.: (760) 755-7500
Year Founded: 2011
Sales Range: $25-49.9 Million
Commercial Farming Services
N.A.I.C.S.: 111998
Brent Grizzle (CEO)

MATH FOR AMERICA
915 Broadway, 16th Fl, New York, NY 10010
Tel.: (646) 437-0904
Web Site:
http://www.mathforamerica.org
Year Founded: 2004
Sales Range: $10-24.9 Million
Emp.: 29
Mathematics & Science Educational Support Services
N.A.I.C.S.: 611710
Sarah Rooney (Dir-Comm & Mktg)
John Ewing (Pres)
Michael Driskill (Dir-Advocacy)
Deborah Hoffman (Dir-Fin)
James H. Simons (Chm)

MATHAND, INC.
103 Smoke Hill Ln Ste 130, Woodstock, GA 30188
Tel.: (770) 926-4110
Web Site: http://www.mathand.net
Year Founded: 1979
Rev.: $5,200,000
Emp.: 8
Industrial Machinery & Equipment Merchant Whslr
N.A.I.C.S.: 423830
Damon Costner (Sec)
Connie Costner (Pres)

MATHEMATICA INC.
600 Alexander Park Ste 100, Princeton, NJ 08540-6346
Tel.: (609) 799-3535
Web Site: http://www.mathematica-mpr.com
Year Founded: 1986
Sales Range: $25-49.9 Million
Emp.: 1,000
Public Policy Research & Data Collection Services
N.A.I.C.S.: 541910
Paul T. Decker (Pres & CEO)
Pamela L. Tapscott (VP-Contract Ops)

Subsidiaries:
Mathematica Policy Research Inc. (1)
600 Alexander Park Ste 100, Princeton, NJ 08540-6346
Tel.: (609) 799-3535
Web Site: http://www.mathematica-mpr.com
Emp.: 1,145
Evidence-Based Research & Data Collection Services
N.A.I.C.S.: 541720
Adam Coyne (Chief Admin Officer & Sr VP)
Paul T. Decker (Pres & CEO)
Larry G. Massanari (Chm)
Pamela Tapscott (VP & Dir-Contract Ops)
Allison Logie (VP & Dir-Strategic Bus Dev)

Mathematica Policy Research Inc. (1)
111 E Wacker Dr Suite 920, Chicago, IL 60601
Tel.: (312) 994-1002
Web Site: http://www.mathematica-mpr.com
Medical Research
N.A.I.C.S.: 541720
Myles Maxfield (Sr VP)
Tamara Barnes (Gen Counsel & VP)
Diane Herz (Dir-Survey Res)
Lisa Schwartz (VP-Bus Practice)

Mathematica Policy Research Inc. (1)
220 E Huron St Ste 300, Ann Arbor, MI 48104-1912
Tel.: (734) 794-1120
Web Site: http://www.mathematica-mpr.com
Emp.: 50
Research Services
N.A.I.C.S.: 541720

Mary Harrington (VP & Dir-Res Svcs)
Mathematica Policy Research Inc. (1)
955 Massachusetts Ave Ste 801, Cambridge, MA 02139 (100%)
Tel.: (617) 491-7900
Web Site: http://www.mathematica-mpr.com
Research Services
N.A.I.C.S.: 541720

Mathematica Policy Research Inc. (1)
1100 1st St NE 12th Fl, Washington, DC 20002-4221 (100%)
Tel.: (202) 484-9220
Web Site: http://www.mathematica-mpr.com
Policy & Human Research Services
N.A.I.C.S.: 541720
Allison Logie (VP & Dir-Strategic Bus Dev)
Greg Farah (VP & Dir-Data Analytics Tech)
Tim Lake (VP & Dir-Health Res)

Mathematica Policy Research Inc. (1)
505 14th StSte800, Oakland, CA 94612-1475 (100%)
Tel.: (510) 830-3700
Web Site: http://www.mathematica-mpr.com
Policy & Human Research Services
N.A.I.C.S.: 541720

The Center for Studying Health System Change Inc. (1)
1100 First St NE 12th Fl, Washington, DC 20002-4221
Tel.: (202) 484-5261
Web Site: http://www.hschange.org
Rev.: $7,500,000
Emp.: 200
Health Policy Research & Analysis Services
N.A.I.C.S.: 541910
Paul B. Ginsburg (Founder & Pres)

MATHEMATICAL ASSOCIATION OF AMERICA, INCORPORATED
1529 18th St NW, Washington, DC 20036-1358
Tel.: (202) 387-5200
Web Site: http://www.maa.org
Year Founded: 1920
Sales Range: $10-24.9 Million
Emp.: 40
Educational Support Services
N.A.I.C.S.: 611710
Michael Pearson (Exec Dir)
William M. K. Rannels (Mgr-Facilities)
Steve Dunbar (Dir-Competitions)
Angelique Wilkins (Dir-Meetings & Facilities)
Lyn Soudien (Dir-Dev)
Ben Spaisman (Chief Bus Officer)

MATHENY MEDICAL AND EDUCATIONAL CENTER
65 Highland Ave, Peapack, NJ 07977
Tel.: (908) 234-0011
Web Site: http://www.matheny.org
Year Founded: 1950
Sales Range: $25-49.9 Million
Emp.: 658
Disability Assistance Services
N.A.I.C.S.: 624120
Kenneth Robey (Dir-Res)
Nancy Petrillo (VP-HR)

MATHER & CO., CPAS, LLC
9100 Shelbyville Rd, Louisville, KY 40222
Tel.: (502) 429-0800
Web Site:
http://www.matherandcompany.com
Accounting & Business Advisory Services
N.A.I.C.S.: 541211
Bruce Smith (Co-Founder & Partner)
Arthur Wissing (Partner)
Innes Mather (Co-Founder)
Jack Schaefer (Partner)
Michael B. Jones (Mng Partner)

Vince Hill (Co-Founder)
Brandon Hardy (Partner)
Frank X. Clements (Partner)
Nichole Powell (Partner)
Sally M. Mudd (Partner)

MATHER LIFEWAYS
1603 Orrington Ave Ste 1800, Evanston, IL 60201
Tel.: (847) 492-7500
Web Site:
http://www.matherlifeways.com
Year Founded: 2006
Sales Range: $10-24.9 Million
Elder Care Services
N.A.I.C.S.: 624120
Christopher Manella (Treas & VP-Fin)
David Kane (Sr VP-Senior Living & Strategic Initiatives)
Gale Morgan (VP-Sls)
Carol Sussenbach (CFO)

MATHES MANAGEMENT ENTERPRISES
5517 Hansel Ave, Orlando, FL 32809
Tel.: (407) 240-2345
Year Founded: 1973
Sales Range: $10-24.9 Million
Emp.: 80
General & Industrial Loan Institutions
N.A.I.C.S.: 522299
P. C. Mathes (CEO)

Subsidiaries:
Sterling Finance Company (1)
100 Lee Ave, Waycross, GA 31501
Tel.: (912) 283-4788
Web Site:
http://www.sterlingfinancecompany.com
Rev.: $170,000
Emp.: 2
Personal Loan Lender
N.A.I.C.S.: 522291

MATHESON TRUCKING, INC.
9785 Goethe Rd, Sacramento, CA 95827
Tel.: (916) 685-2330
Web Site:
http://www.mathesoninc.com
Sales Range: $10-24.9 Million
Emp.: 2,000
Trucking Service
N.A.I.C.S.: 484121
Mark Matheson (Pres & CEO)
Debra White (VP-IT)
Michael Wilbourn (VP-HR)
Patty Kepner (Dir-Fin)
Brock M. Vann (Dir-Ops)
Charles J. Mellor (COO & Gen Counsel)
Dave Harman (Mgr-Fleet Ops)
Josh Matheson (VP-Corporate Ops)
Kaylath Harper (Mgr-Terminal)
Lauren Matheson (VP-Ops)
Shirley Curran (Chief HR Officer)
Tamrya Ford (CFO)
Mark Olszewski (Dir-Postal Ops)

MATHEW HALL LUMBER CO
127 6th Ave N, Saint Cloud, MN 56303
Tel.: (320) 252-1920
Web Site:
http://www.mathewhall.com
Rev.: $16,900,000
Emp.: 55
Millwork & Lumber
N.A.I.C.S.: 444110
Loren T. Hall (Pres)

MATHEW ZAHERI CORPORATION
25115 Mission Blvd, Hayward, CA 94544
Tel.: (510) 885-1000

Web Site: http://www.vwhayward.com
Rev.: $11,700,000
Emp.: 28
New & Used Automobiles
N.A.I.C.S.: 441110

MATHEW'S DODGE CHRYSLER JEEP, INC.
1866 Marion Waldo Rd, Marion, OH 43302
Tel.: (740) 389-2341
Web Site:
http://www.mathewsdodgechryslerjeep.com
Sales Range: $10-24.9 Million
Emp.: 30
Car Whslr
N.A.I.C.S.: 441110
Tom Westin *(Gen Mgr)*

MATHEWS ASSOCIATES, INC.
220 Power Ct, Sanford, FL 32771
Tel.: (407) 323-3390
Web Site: http://www.maifl.com
Rev.: $16,400,000
Emp.: 60
Storage Battery Mfr
N.A.I.C.S.: 335910
Linda Horton *(VP-HR)*
Judy Perreualt *(Treas & Sec)*
Barbara Jordan *(Mgr-Sls)*

MATHEWS FORD SANDUSKY, INC.
610 E Perkins, Sandusky, OH 44870
Tel.: (419) 626-4721
Web Site:
http://www.mathewsford.com
Sales Range: $10-24.9 Million
Emp.: 60
Car Whslr
N.A.I.C.S.: 441110
Thurman Mathews *(Pres)*
Tom Ripley *(Gen Mgr)*

MATHEWS INC.
919 River Rd, Sparta, WI 54656
Tel.: (608) 269-2728
Web Site:
http://www.mathewsinc.com
Rev.: $32,000,000
Emp.: 130
Sporting & Athletic Goods Mfr
N.A.I.C.S.: 339920
Marty Byrd *(CFO)*
Steve McPherson *(Pres)*
Matt McPherson *(CEO)*

MATHEWS KENNEDY FORD LINCOLN-MERCURY INC.
1155 Delaware Ave, Marion, OH 43302
Tel.: (740) 387-3673
Web Site:
http://www.mathewsautogroup.com
Sales Range: $25-49.9 Million
Emp.: 100
Sales of New & Used Automobiles
N.A.I.C.S.: 441110
Thurman Mathews *(Pres)*

MATHIAS BANCSHARES, INC.
432 Madison 1650, Huntsville, AR 72740
Tel.: (479) 738-2147   AR
Web Site:
http://www.todaysbank.com
Year Founded: 1991
Sales Range: $1-9.9 Million
Bank Holding Company
N.A.I.C.S.: 551111

Subsidiaries:

Today's Bank   (1)
432 Madison 1650, Huntsville, AR 72740
Tel.: (479) 738-2147
Web Site: http://www.todaysbank.com

Sales Range: $1-9.9 Million
Commericial Banking
N.A.I.C.S.: 522110
Sam Mathias *(Chm)*
Larry Olson *(Pres & CEO)*
Arthur Thurman *(Vice Chm)*
Marivel Radcliffe *(COO & Exec VP)*
Mark Marks *(Chief Lending Officer & Sr VP)*

MATHIOWETZ CONSTRUCTION COMPANY
30676 County Rd 24, Sleepy Eye, MN 56085-4359
Tel.: (507) 794-6953
Web Site:
http://www.mathiowetzconst.com
Sales Range: $25-49.9 Million
Emp.: 145
Civil Engineering Services
N.A.I.C.S.: 237310
Brian Mathiowetz *(Owner)*

MATHIS BROS. FURNITURE CO. INC.
3434 W Reno Ave, Oklahoma City, OK 73107-6134
Tel.: (405) 943-3434   OK
Web Site:
http://www.mathisbrothers.com
Year Founded: 1959
Sales Range: $75-99.9 Million
Emp.: 500
Furniture Retailer
N.A.I.C.S.: 449110
Bill Mathis *(Pres)*
Steve Russell *(VP-Ops)*

Subsidiaries:

Factory Direct Inc.   (1)
219 S Portland, Oklahoma City, OK 73108-1018
Tel.: (405) 947-1919
Web Site: http://www.factorydirect-usa.com
Rev.: $4,300,000
Emp.: 75
Mfr of Mattresses & Bedsprings
N.A.I.C.S.: 337910

MATHIS EXTERMINATING
3890 E State Route 302, Belfair, WA 98528-9374
Tel.: (206) 264-1100
Web Site:
http://www.propestcontroller.com
Year Founded: 1992
Exterminating & Pest Control Services
N.A.I.C.S.: 561710
Damon Martin *(Founder)*

MATHIS-KELLEY CONSTRUCTION SUPPLY CO.
1046 W Jefferson St, Morton, IL 61550
Tel.: (309) 266-9733
Web Site: http://www.mathis-kelley.com
Year Founded: 1972
Sales Range: $10-24.9 Million
Emp.: 30
Fabricated Structural Metal
N.A.I.C.S.: 332312
Mike Baynard *(Pres)*
Mark Mingus *(Treas)*

MATHY CONSTRUCTION CO
920 10th Ave N, Onalaska, WI 54650
Tel.: (608) 783-6411
Web Site: http://mathy.com
Sales Range: $50-74.9 Million
Emp.: 70
General Contractor, Highway & Street Construction
N.A.I.C.S.: 237310
Erv Dukatz *(VP-Matls & Res)*
Dan Staebell *(Dir-Pavement Svcs)*
Marty Hohl *(VP-Fin)*
Roger Overson *(Mgr-Compliance)*

Tim Snider *(Dir-Maintenance)*
David Eitland *(Mgr)*
Tony Tomashek *(VP)*

MATICH CORPORATION
1596 Harry Sheppard Blvd, San Bernardino, CA 92408
Tel.: (909) 382-7400   CA
Web Site: http://www.matichcorp.com
Year Founded: 1918
Sales Range: $25-49.9 Million
Emp.: 300
Highway & Street Construction
N.A.I.C.S.: 237310
Steven Matich *(Pres)*
Randall Valadez *(CFO)*

Subsidiaries:

Matich Corporation - Cabazon Asphalt Plant   (1)
13984 Apache Trl, Cabazon, CA 92230
Tel.: (951) 849-8280
Asphalt Product Mfr
N.A.I.C.S.: 324122

Matich Corporation - Redlands Asphalt Plant   (1)
8397 Alabama St, Redlands, CA 92373
Tel.: (909) 792-3650
Asphalt Product Mfr
N.A.I.C.S.: 324122

Matich Corporation - Rialto Asphalt Plant   (1)
3221 N Riverside Ave, Rialto, CA 92376
Tel.: (909) 356-0537
Asphalt Product Mfr
N.A.I.C.S.: 324122

MATLINPATTERSON GLOBAL ADVISERS LLC
70 E 55th St 9th Fl, New York, NY 10022
Tel.: (212) 651-9500   DE
Web Site:
http://www.matlinpatterson.com
Year Founded: 1994
Privater Equity Firm
N.A.I.C.S.: 523999
Peter H. Schoels *(Mng Partner & Portfolio Mgr-Control & Illiquid Investments)*
Robert Weiss *(Partner & Gen Counsel)*
Sherry Gao *(CFO)*
Marc Rosenthal *(Co-CEO & Mgr-Portfolio)*
Noelle Savarese *(Co-CEO & Mgr-Portfolio)*
Josh Nester *(Principal)*
Daniel McNamara *(Principal)*
Jesse Liu *(Principal)*
Graham Albert *(Sr VP)*

Subsidiaries:

Global Aviation Holdings, Inc.   (1)
101 World Dr, Peachtree City, GA 30269-6965
Tel.: (770) 632-8000
Web Site: http://www.glah.com
Sales Range: $1-4.9 Billion
Holding Company; Airline & Management Operations
N.A.I.C.S.: 551112
James LaChance *(Chm)*

Matussiere & Forest S.A.   (1)
27 avenue Du Granier, PO Box 18, 38241, Meylan, Cedex, France
Tel.: (33) 476614200
Web Site: http://www.matussiere-forest.com
Sales Range: $150-199.9 Million
Paper Mfr & Whslr
N.A.I.C.S.: 322120

MATLOCK ADVERTISING & PUBLIC RELATIONS
107 Luckie St, Atlanta, GA 30303
Tel.: (404) 872-3200

Web Site: http://www.matlock-adpr.com
Year Founded: 1986
Rev.: $25,000,000
Emp.: 15
N.A.I.C.S.: 541810
Kent Matlock *(Chm & CEO)*
Lilla Jean Matlock *(Vice Chm & Treas)*
S. Edward Rutland *(Mng Partner & Exec VP)*
Tobi Carvana-Moore *(Assoc Dir-Creative)*
Kirstin Popper *(Sr VP & Gen Mgr)*
Donald Webster *(Sr VP & Controller)*
George Matlock *(Dir-Ops)*
Jennifer Price *(Sr Acct Exec)*

Subsidiaries:

Matlock Advertising & Public Relations-NY   (1)
230 Park Ave 10 Fl Ste 25, New York, NY 10169
Tel.: (212) 532-3800
Web Site: http://www.matlock-adpr.com
Sales Range: $50-74.9 Million
Emp.: 5
N.A.I.C.S.: 541820
S. Edward Rutland *(Mng Partner & Exec VP)*
Kent Matlock *(Chm & CEO)*
Kelly Graham *(Sr VP, Dir-Creative)*
Donald Webster *(Sr VP & Controller)*
Nathalie Simon *(Gen Counsel)*

MATOT INC.
2501 Van Buren, Bellwood, IL 60104-2459
Tel.: (708) 263-4088
Web Site: http://www.matot.com
Year Founded: 1888
Material Lift Equipment Mfr
N.A.I.C.S.: 333921
Anne B. Matot *(Co-Owner & Co-Pres)*
Cathryn M. Matot *(Co-Owner & Co-Pres)*

Subsidiaries:

Kelair Products Inc.   (1)
2501 Van Buren, Bellwood, IL 60104
Tel.: (708) 547-1888
Web Site: http://www.kelairdampers.com
Dampers Custom Design & Fabrication
N.A.I.C.S.: 332312

MATRIX COMMUNICATIONS INC.
171 Cheshire Ln N Ste 700, Minneapolis, MN 55441
Tel.: (763) 475-5500
Web Site:
http://www.matrixcomm.com
Year Founded: 1985
Sales Range: $10-24.9 Million
Emp.: 120
Integrator of Telecommunications Interconnect Communications
N.A.I.C.S.: 811210
Mike Ellis *(Owner & CEO)*
Lynn Harris *(Mgr-HR)*
Chris Reitan *(Engr-Telecom Network)*

MATRIX DEVELOPMENT GROUP INC.
Forsgate Dr CN 4000, Cranbury, NJ 08512
Tel.: (732) 521-2900
Web Site:
http://www.matrixcompanies.com
Year Founded: 1979
Sales Range: $10-24.9 Million
Emp.: 60
Real Estate Investor & Developer
N.A.I.C.S.: 237210
Joseph S. Taylor *(Pres & CEO)*
Richard Johnson *(Sr VP)*

MATRIX DEVELOPMENT GROUP INC.

U.S. PRIVATE

Matrix Development Group Inc.—(Continued)

Subsidiaries:

CNGC Matrix Inc. (1)
300 Tournament Dr, Horsham, PA 19044
Tel.: (215) 672-4141
Web Site:
http://www.commonwealthgolfclub.com
Sales Range: $1-9.9 Million
Emp.: 50
Golf Club, Membership
N.A.I.C.S.: 713910
Joseph Taylor *(Pres)*

Commonwealth Matrix LP (1)
Forsgate Dr, Cranbury, NJ 08512
Tel.: (732) 521-2900
Web Site: http://www.matrixcompany.com
Rev.: $1,700,000
Emp.: 40
Country Club Membership
N.A.I.C.S.: 713910

Matrix Golf & Hospitality (1)
Forsgate Dr CN 4000, Cranbury, NJ 08512
Tel.: (732) 521-2900
Web Site: http://www.matrixcompanies.com
Owner & Manager of Golf & Country Clubs
N.A.I.C.S.: 713910
Robert Twomey *(Sr VP)*
Charles Taylor *(VP)*

Subsidiary (Domestic):

Echo Farms Golf & Country Club, Inc. (2)
4114 Echo Farms Blvd, Wilmington, NC 28412
Tel.: (910) 791-9318
Web Site: http://www.echofarmsgc.com
Sales Range: $10-24.9 Million
Emp.: 25
Land Subdividers & Developers
N.A.I.C.S.: 541519
Daniel Fountain *(Head-Golf Pro-PGA)*
Brian Stachowtc *(Gen Mgr)*

MATRIX ENERGY SERVICES INC.
3239 Ramos Cir, Sacramento, CA 95827
Tel.: (916) 363-9283
Web Site:
http://www.matrixescorp.com
Year Founded: 2006
Sales Range: $10-24.9 Million
Emp.: 150
Energy Consulting
N.A.I.C.S.: 541690
Lillie Mozaffari *(Pres)*

MATRIX HUMAN SERVICES
120 Parsons St, Detroit, MI 48201
Tel.: (313) 831-1000
Web Site:
http://www.matrixhumanservices.org
Year Founded: 1915
Sales Range: $25-49.9 Million
Emp.: 743
Social Advocacy Services
N.A.I.C.S.: 813319
Daryl Hurley *(CFO)*
Terry Berry *(Sec)*
Mike Blotkamp *(Chm & Mng Dir)*
Karen Bisdorf *(COO)*
Deborah Snyder *(VP)*

MATRIX INFORMATION CONSULTING, INC.
266 Harristown Rd 202, Glen Rock, NJ 07452
Tel.: (201) 587-0777
Web Site:
http://www.hiredbymatrix.com
Sales Range: $25-49.9 Million
Emp.: 250
IT Consulting & Permanent Employee Placement Services
N.A.I.C.S.: 541519
Sharon Olzerowicz *(Founder, Pres & CEO)*

MATRIX INTEGRATION LLC
417 Main St, Jasper, IN 47546
Tel.: (812) 634-1550
Web Site:
http://www.matrixintegration.com
Year Founded: 1971
Sales Range: $25-49.9 Million
Emp.: 85
IT Infrastructure, Personal Computing & Access Devices, Networking Services, Structured Cabling, Telephony, Printing, Imaging & After-Sale Services
N.A.I.C.S.: 541512
Brenda Stallings *(Founder & CEO)*
Dan Fritch *(Exec VP)*
Amy Williams *(Mgr-Sls Ops)*
Abby Stallings *(VP-People & Culture)*
Nathan Stallings *(VP-Sls)*
Steve Hauser *(Acct Mgr)*
James Aldridge *(VP-Tech)*
Mike Childs *(Dir-Bus Dev)*
Reggie Gresham *(VP-Sls & Mktg)*
Rob Wildman *(VP-Pro Svcs)*

Subsidiaries:

Cornwell Communications, Inc. (1)
1225 S Walnut St, Bloomington, IN 47401-5825
Tel.: (812) 331-7575
Web Site:
http://www.cornwellcommunications.com
All Other Miscellaneous Store Retailers (except Tobacco Stores)
N.A.I.C.S.: 459999
Tom Cornwell *(Owner)*

MATRIX INTERNATIONAL LTD.
449 Gardner St, South Beloit, IL 61080
Tel.: (815) 389-3771
Web Site: http://www.matrix-international.com
Sales Range: $50-74.9 Million
Emp.: 400
Engineering Systems
N.A.I.C.S.: 423840

Subsidiaries:

Inertia Dynamics, Inc. (1)
31 Industrial Park Rd, New Hartford, CT 06057
Tel.: (860) 379-1252
Web Site: http://www.idicb.com
Sales Range: $10-24.9 Million
Emp.: 115
Electric Brake Mfr
N.A.I.C.S.: 333613

MATRIX IV INC.
610 E Judd St, Woodstock, IL 60098
Tel.: (815) 338-4500
Web Site: http://www.matrixiv.com
Sales Range: $10-24.9 Million
Emp.: 50
Molding Primary Plastics
N.A.I.C.S.: 326199
Raymond C. Wenk Sr. *(Founder & Pres)*

MATRIX MEDIA SERVICES, INC.
463 E Town St, Columbus, OH 43215-4757
Tel.: (614) 228-2200
Web Site:
http://www.matrixmediaservice.com
Year Founded: 1988
Sales Range: $25-49.9 Million
Emp.: 25
Media Buying Services
N.A.I.C.S.: 541830
Charles E. McCrimmon *(Mng Gen Partner)*
Ashley Shipley *(Dir-Social Media Mktg)*
Marty Blanton *(Mgr-Production Sls)*
Bryan Baxendale *(Asst Dir-Media)*

MATRIX PARTNERS
101 M St 17th Fl, Cambridge, MA 02142
Tel.: (617) 494-1223
Web Site:
http://www.matrixpartners.com
Year Founded: 1977
Sales Range: $25-49.9 Million
Emp.: 30
Venture Capital Firm
N.A.I.C.S.: 523999
Paul J. Ferri II *(Founder & Gen Partner)*
Timothy A. Barrows *(Gen Partner)*
Stan J. Reiss *(Gen Partner)*
Andrew W. Verhalen *(Gen Partner)*
Dana C. Stalder *(Gen Partner)*
David Skok *(Gen Partner)*
Lisa Donahue *(VP-Fin Ops)*
Paul Sherer *(Partner-Venture)*
Phyllis Doherty *(Partner-Admin)*
Hardi Meybaum *(Gen Partner)*
Ilya Sukhar *(Gen Partner)*
Alexa McLain *(Partner)*
Jake Jolis *(Partner)*
Jared Sleeper *(Partner)*
Allen Miller *(Partner)*
Antonio Rodriguez *(Partner)*

MATRIX SYSTEMS, INC.
1041 Byers Rd, Miamisburg, OH 45342-5487
Tel.: (937) 438-9033
Web Site: http://www.matrixsys.com
Year Founded: 1979
Sales Range: $10-24.9 Million
Emp.: 93
Controlled Access & Timing Attendence Computer Integrated Systems Design
N.A.I.C.S.: 541512
Holly Tsourides *(CEO)*
Kelly Cain *(CFO)*
Bruce Rogoff *(Chm)*

MATRIX TECHNOLOGIES INCORPORATED
1760 Indian Wood Cir, Maumee, OH 43537-4006
Tel.: (419) 897-7200
Web Site: http://www.matrixti.com
Year Founded: 1980
Sales Range: $25-49.9 Million
Emp.: 350
Control System Integration & Multi-Disciplined Engineering Firm Engaged In Process, Mechanical, Electrical, Architectural, Structural & Civil Engineering
N.A.I.C.S.: 541330
David J. Blaida *(Pres & CEO)*
Kevin Grohnke *(Sr VP-Reg Ops)*
Dan Pruss *(CFO)*

Subsidiaries:

Matrix Technologies, Inc. (1)
6625 Network Way st 160, Indianapolis, IN 46278-1928 (100%)
Tel.: (317) 347-7700
Web Site: http://www.matrixti.com
Sales Range: $10-24.9 Million
Emp.: 44
Control System Integration & Multi-Disciplined Engineering Firm Engaged in Process, Mechanical, Electrical, Architectural, Structural & Civil Engineering
N.A.I.C.S.: 541330
Perry Tobin *(Project Mgr)*
Kevin Grohnke *(Reg VP-Ops)*
Dave Bishop *(Pres & CEO)*
Dave Blaida *(Exec VP)*
Tim Lemoine *(Assoc Dir-Engrg)*
Bill Schuller *(Dir-Engrg)*
Charlie Sheets *(Dir-Indus Sys)*

Matrix Technologies, Inc. (1)
1760 Indian Wood Cir, Maumee, OH 43537 (100%)
Tel.: (419) 897-7200
Web Site: http://www.matrixti.com
Sales Range: $10-24.9 Million
Emp.: 7
Control System Integration & Multi-Disciplined Engineering Firm Engaged in Process, Mechanical, Electrical, Architectural, Structural & Civil Engineering
N.A.I.C.S.: 541611
Lisa Behrendt *(Dir-HR)*
Dave Blaida *(Pres & CEO)*
Kevin Grohnke *(Sr VP-Reg Ops)*
Dan Pruss *(CFO)*

MATRIX WIRE, INC.
1955 McMillan St, Auburn, AL 36832
Tel.: (334) 887-6200
Web Site: http://www.matrixwire.net
Sales Range: $10-24.9 Million
Emp.: 125
Fabricated Wire Product Mfr
N.A.I.C.S.: 332618
Sonia Seay *(Mgr-Customer Svc)*

MATSCHEL OF FLAGLER INC.
71 Hargrove Grade, Palm Coast, FL 32137
Tel.: (386) 446-4595
Web Site:
http://www.sunbeltchemicals.com
Sales Range: $10-24.9 Million
Emp.: 55
Swimming Pool & Spa Chemicals
N.A.I.C.S.: 424690
Mike Carey *(Exec VP)*

MATSON DISTRIBUTING, INC.
1221 1st Ave N, Moorhead, MN 56560
Tel.: (218) 236-6248
Year Founded: 1945
Sales Range: $10-24.9 Million
Emp.: 1
Petroleum Product Whslr
N.A.I.C.S.: 424720
Terri Sloan *(CEO)*

MATSON, DRISCOLL & DAMICO
1411 Opus Pl Ste 240, Downers Grove, IL 60515
Tel.: (630) 725-9220
Web Site: http://www.mdd.com
Year Founded: 1933
Sales Range: $300-349.9 Million
Emp.: 250
Forensic & Investigative Accounting Services
N.A.I.C.S.: 541219
Neal S. Cason *(Partner)*
Dayne Grey *(Partner)*
William J. Bradshaw *(Mng Partner)*
Shannon Rusnak *(Partner)*
Peter J. Karutz *(Partner)*
Matthew W. Woodcock *(Partner)*
Jeffrey P. Belack *(Partner)*
Brad R. Ryden *(Partner)*
George D. Uhl *(Partner)*
Jack Flaherty *(Partner)*
Kevin M. Flaherty *(Partner)*
Glenn Ricciardelli *(Partner)*
Dusty L. Bredeson *(Partner)*
Daniel G. Markowicz *(Partner)*
Chris Ehlers *(Partner)*
David R. Elmore Jr. *(Partner)*
Paul A. McGowan Jr. *(Partner)*

MATT BLATT INC.
501 N Delsea Dr, Glassboro, NJ 08028
Tel.: (856) 881-0444
Web Site: http://www.mattblatt.com
Sales Range: $25-49.9 Million
Emp.: 50
New & Used Car Dealers
N.A.I.C.S.: 441110
Roy Blatt *(Pres & CEO)*

MATT CASTRUCCI, LLC
3013 Mall Park Dr, Dayton, OH 45459
Tel.: (937) 434-4723   OH
Web Site: http://www.mattcastrucciautomall.com
Sales Range: $10-24.9 Million
Emp.: 140
New & Used Car Dealer
N.A.I.C.S.: 441110
Matt Castrucci *(Pres)*
Rosemary Walton *(Comptroller)*

MATT CONSTRUCTION CORPORATION
9814 Norwalk Blvd Ste 100, Santa Fe Springs, CA 90670-2936
Tel.: (562) 903-2277   CA
Web Site: http://www.mattconstruction.com
Year Founded: 1991
Sales Range: $25-49.9 Million
Emp.: 150
Construction Consulting & General Contractors
N.A.I.C.S.: 541618
Steven F. Matt *(Founder, Chm & CEO)*
Alan B. Matt *(Exec VP)*
Michael Fedorchek *(VP)*
James A. Muenzer *(Sr VP)*
Robert L. Welch *(VP)*
Marvin Wheat *(Pres & Chief Comml Officer)*
Daniel A. Stafford *(Sr VP-Ops)*
Laurie Sowd *(VP-Ops)*
Dafna Zilafro *(VP-Mktg)*
Ken Blakeley *(CFO)*
Jennifer Halstead *(COO & Exec VP)*
Holly Wilde *(Dir-Mktg)*

MATT INDUSTRIES INC.
1 Dupli Park Dr, Syracuse, NY 13204
Tel.: (315) 472-1316
Web Site: http://www.duplionline.com
Sales Range: $10-24.9 Million
Emp.: 130
Envelope Printing Services
N.A.I.C.S.: 323111
A. Thomas Booth *(Dir-Sls)*
J. Kemper Matt Sr. *(Pres)*

Subsidiaries:

Dupli Envelopes & Graphics - Malvern   (1)
2533 Yellow Springs Rd, Malvern, PA 19355
Tel.: (610) 644-4188
Web Site: http://www.duplionline.com
Emp.: 25
Commercial Flexographic Printing
N.A.I.C.S.: 323111
Robert Haraschak *(Mgr-Customer Svc)*

PCI, Paper Conversion Inc.   (1)
6761 Thompson Rd N, Syracuse, NY 13211
Tel.: (315) 437-1641
Web Site: http://www.stikwithit.com
Envelope Printing Services
N.A.I.C.S.: 322230
Kemper Matt *(Pres)*

MATT MANAGEMENT INC.
5320 Departure Dr, Raleigh, NC 27616
Tel.: (919) 872-0539
Rev.: $10,600,000
Emp.: 4
Truck Parts & Accessories
N.A.I.C.S.: 423120
Fred Matt *(Pres)*

Subsidiaries:

Aftermarket Parts Inc   (1)
150 Market St, New Bern, NC 28560-2644
Tel.: (252) 633-2155
Web Site: http://www.rightparts.com

Sales Range: $10-24.9 Million
Emp.: 20
Logging & Forestry Machinery & Equipment
N.A.I.C.S.: 423810
Timothy Matt *(Pres)*
Jean Hardtle *(Mgr-Mktg)*

Triple T Parts & Equipment Co   (1)
2715 Hwy 421 N, Wilmington, NC 28401
Tel.: (910) 763-6281
New & Used Trucks, Tractors & Trailers
N.A.I.C.S.: 441110
Tim Matt *(Chm & CEO)*

MATT MARTIN REAL ESTATE MANAGEMENT LLC
8521 Leesburg Pike Ste 300, Tysons Corner, VA 22182
Tel.: (703) 766-5777
Web Site: http://www.mmrem.com
Year Founded: 2004
Sales Range: $25-49.9 Million
Emp.: 110
Real Estate Development Services
N.A.I.C.S.: 531390
Matt Martin *(Co-Founder & CEO)*

MATT SLAP SUBARU
255 E Cleveland Ave, Newark, DE 19711
Tel.: (302) 453-9900
Web Site: http://www.mattslap.com
Year Founded: 1980
Sales Range: $10-24.9 Million
Emp.: 35
New Car Dealers
N.A.I.C.S.: 441110
Eve Slap *(Owner & Gen Mgr)*

MATTEI COMPRESSORS INC.
9635 Liberty Rd Ste E, Randallstown, MD 21133-2436
Tel.: (410) 521-7020
Web Site: http://www.matteicomp.com
Air & Gas Compressor Mfr
N.A.I.C.S.: 333912
Peggy Hogan *(Mgr)*

Subsidiaries:

Transit Engineering Services, Inc.   (1)
10082-A Tyler Pl, Ijamsville, MD 21754
Tel.: (301) 874-3773
Web Site: http://www.matteicomp.com
Custom-engineered Electro-pneumatic Test equipment Mfr
N.A.I.C.S.: 238290

MATTEO ALUMINUM, INC.
1261 E 289th St, Wickliffe, OH 44092
Tel.: (440) 585-5213
Web Site: http://www.matteoaluminum.com
Year Founded: 1995
Sales Range: $10-24.9 Million
Emp.: 15
Sheet Metal Work Mfg
N.A.I.C.S.: 332322
Steven Matteo *(Pres)*

MATTER
7005 Oxford St, Saint Louis Park, MN 55426
Tel.: (952) 500-8652   MN
Web Site: http://www.mattermore.org
Year Founded: 2002
Sales Range: $25-49.9 Million
Emp.: 28
Community Care Services
N.A.I.C.S.: 624190
Laura Fixsen *(VP-Dev)*
Angie Dammeier *(Dir-Exec Projects & Talent)*
Mike Muelken *(VP-Procurement & Intl Programs)*
Derrick Johnson *(Dir-Comml Banking)*
Julie Flaherty *(Atty)*

Dennis Doyle *(Founder)*
Megan Doyle *(Founder)*
Quenton Marty *(Pres)*
Jeremy Newhouse *(Sr VP-Ops)*
Joe Newhouse *(VP-Strategy & Innovation)*
Victor Salamone *(VP-Bus Ops)*
James A. Robinson Jr. *(Founder)*

MATTER COMMUNICATIONS INC.
50 Water St, Mill #3, The Tannery, Newburyport, MA 01950
Tel.: (978) 499-9250
Web Site: http://www.matternow.com
N.A.I.C.S.: 541810
Scott Signore *(Founder & CEO)*
Patty Barry *(Principal)*
Colleen Sheehan *(Sr VP)*
Matt Landry *(VP)*
Jesse Ciccone *(Mng Dir & VP)*
Andy Meltzer *(VP & Gen Mgr-Providence)*
Ariane Doud *(Acct Mgr)*
Tobi Young *(Acct Dir)*
John McElhenny *(VP)*
Elise Ouellette *(Acct Dir)*
Anne Lines *(Acct Dir)*
Parry Headrick *(VP-Mktg & Comm)*
Nicole Brooks *(Acct Mgr)*
Owen Mack *(Dir-Creative Svcs)*
Amanda King *(VP-Boulder)*
Meghan Gardner *(VP-Portland)*
Maria Brown *(Gen Mgr-West)*
Brittany Gould *(Acct Exec)*

Subsidiaries:

Calypso Communications LLC   (1)
20 Ladd St #200, Portsmouth, NH 03801
Tel.: (603) 431-0816
Web Site: http://www.calypsocom.com
Public Relations & Communications
N.A.I.C.S.: 541810
Kevin Stickney *(Founder & Pres)*
Sarah Grazier *(VP-Strategic Comm)*
Devan Meserve *(Mgr-Content & Social Media)*
Tiffany Nelson *(Mgr-PR)*

Branch (Domestic):

Calypso Communications   (2)
121 Bow St Bldg 6, Portsmouth, NH 03801
Tel.: (603) 431-0816
Web Site: http://www.calypsocom.com
Sales Range: $10-24.9 Million
N.A.I.C.S.: 541810
Tory Mazzola *(Dir-Strategic Comm)*
Lauren Smith *(Sr Mgr-PR)*
Houssam Aboukhater *(Mng Partner)*
Carter Foster *(Coord-Social Media)*

MATTHEW 25 MINISTRIES, INC
11060 Kenwood Rd, Blue Ash, OH 45242
Tel.: (513) 793-6256   OH
Web Site: http://www.m25m.org
Year Founded: 1992
Sales Range: $100-124.9 Million
Emp.: 60
Residential Care Services
N.A.I.C.S.: 623990
Tim Mettey *(CEO)*
Karen Otto *(VP-Mktg & HR)*
Don Olson *(CFO & CIO)*
Patty Dilg *(Dir-Ops)*
Wendell Mettey *(Founder & Pres)*
Joodi Archer *(Dir-Dev & Media & PR)*
Sally Phelps *(Mgr-HR)*
Douglas W. Thomson *(Sec)*
Linda Gill *(Treas)*
Michael Brandy Jr. *(Chm)*

MATTHEWS AUTO GROUP
3721 Old Vestal Rd, Vestal, NY 13850
Tel.: (607) 798-8000
Web Site: http://www.mathewsautogroup.com

Sales Range: $10-24.9 Million
Emp.: 200
Owner & Operator of Car Dealerships
N.A.I.C.S.: 441110
Megan Kosar *(Office Mgr)*

MATTHEWS CONSTRUCTION CO., INC.
210 1st Ave S, Conover, NC 28613
Tel.: (828) 464-7325
Web Site: http://www.matthewsconstruction.com
Sales Range: $50-74.9 Million
Emp.: 75
Industrial Building Construction
N.A.I.C.S.: 236210
Bobby E. Matthews *(CEO)*
Nathan Andy Matthews *(Exec VP)*
Ken Deloach *(Dir-HR)*
Gary E. Matthews *(Pres)*
Kevin Tolbert *(Controller)*
Ed Vegter *(Dir-Construction Conover Div)*
Steven Sigmon *(Dir-Construction Charlotte Div)*

MATTHEWS HARGREAVES CHEVROLET
2000 E 12 Mile Rd, Royal Oak, MI 48067
Tel.: (248) 398-8800
Web Site: http://www.mhchevy.com
Year Founded: 1950
Sales Range: $25-49.9 Million
Emp.: 80
Car Whslr
N.A.I.C.S.: 441110
Lisa Burr *(Mgr)*
Rob Eret *(Mgr-New Car)*

MATTHEWS INTERNATIONAL CAPITAL MANAGEMENT, LLC
4 Embarcadero Ctr Ste 550, San Francisco, CA 94111
Tel.: (415) 955-8122   DE
Web Site: http://www.matthewsasia.com
Year Founded: 1991
Investment Advisory & Fund Management Services
N.A.I.C.S.: 523940
William J. Hackett *(CEO)*
David A. Hartley *(CFO)*
Robert J. Horrocks *(Chief Investment Officer & Portfolio Mgr)*
Jonathan D. Schuman *(Head-Bus Dev-Global)*
Mark Lidstone *(Head-Mktg-Global)*
Manoj K. Pombra *(Chief Compliance Officer)*
Timothy B. Parker *(Dir-Intl Strategy, Product & Ops)*
James E. Walter *(Head-Investment Ops)*
John P. McGowan *(Head-Fund Admin)*
Cheryl Fung *(Head-HR & Office Admin-Global)*
Mark W. Headley *(Chm)*

MATTHEWS REAL ESTATE INVESTMENT SERVICES
1600 W End Ave Ste 1500, Nashville, TN 37203
Web Site: https://www.matthews.com
Year Founded: 2015
Real Estate Investment Services
N.A.I.C.S.: 531190

MATTHEWS STUDIO EQUIPMENT, INC.
4520 W Valerio St, Burbank, CA 91505
Tel.: (818) 843-6715
Web Site: http://www.msegrip.com

MATTHEWS STUDIO EQUIPMENT, INC. U.S. PRIVATE

Matthews Studio Equipment, Inc.—(Continued)
Year Founded: 1970
Sales Range: $10-24.9 Million
Emp.: 80
Motion Picture Equipment Mfr
N.A.I.C.S.: 333310
Ed Phillips (Pres & CEO)
Robert Kulesh (VP-Sls & Mktg)
Linda Swope (Mgr-Sls)

MATTHEWS, EVANS & ALBERTAZZI
1111 6th Ave Fl 6, San Diego, CA 92101
Tel.: (619) 238-8500 CA
Web Site: http://www.measd.com
Year Founded: 1982
Sales Range: $10-24.9 Million
Emp.: 35
Advertising Agency
N.A.I.C.S.: 541810
James Matthews (CEO)
Mark Albertazzi (Dir-Creative)
Fernando Campos (Dir-Digital Creative)

MATTHIAS PAPER CORPORATION
301 Arlington Blvd, Swedesboro, NJ 08085
Tel.: (856) 467-6970
Web Site: http://www.matthiaspaper.com
Sales Range: $10-24.9 Million
Emp.: 30
Paper, Wrapping Or Coarse & Products
N.A.I.C.S.: 424130
Warren Storck (Sec & VP)
Neal Dagenhart (Gen Mgr)
Mark Sekel (Controller)

MATTRESS DEPOT USA
14603 NE 20th St, Bellevue, WA 98007
Tel.: (425) 644-0056
Web Site: http://www.mattressdepotusa.com
Year Founded: 2003
Sales Range: $10-24.9 Million
Emp.: 45
Bedding Product Retailer
N.A.I.C.S.: 449110
David Smith (Owner)
Daniel Martinez (District Mgr)
Ryan Leaf (Owner-Franchise)

MATTRESS DIRECT, INC.
3105 Riverport Tech Ctr Dr Maryland Heights, Maryland Heights, MO 63043
Tel.: (314) 434-7328 MO
Web Site: http://www.stlmattressdirect.com
Year Founded: 2010
Direct Showroom Mfr
N.A.I.C.S.: 337910
Pat McCurren (Pres & CEO)

Subsidiaries:
Campbell Sleep, LLC (1)
100 S Minnesota St, Cape Girardeau, MO 63703
Tel.: (573) 334-7148
Web Site: http://www.campbellsleep.com
Mattress Mfr
N.A.I.C.S.: 337910
Pat McCurren (Pres)

MATTRESS DISCOUNTERS CORP
8200 Stayton Dr, Jessup, MD 20794
Tel.: (703) 962-1651
Web Site: http://www.mattressdiscounters.com
Rev.: $244,212,000
Emp.: 500
Bedding & Bedsprings
N.A.I.C.S.: 449110
Andrew A. Giordano (Chm)
Gregg R. Moore (Reg Mgr)
Jeffery Huffman (Mgr-Inventory & Pur)
William Burr (Mgr-Sls)

MATTRESS LAND SLEEPFIT
4626 N Bendel Ave, Fresno, CA 93722
Tel.: (559) 277-9459
Web Site: http://www.mattressland.com
Emp.: 100
Beds & Accessories
N.A.I.C.S.: 449110
James Smith (Pres)

MATTS CASH & CARRY BUILDING MATERIALS
401 East Expy 83, Pharr, TX 78577
Tel.: (956) 787-5513
Web Site: http://www.mattsbuildingmaterials.com
Sales Range: $10-24.9 Million
Emp.: 160
Lumber & Other Building Materials
N.A.I.C.S.: 449121
Diana Smith (VP)
Danny Smith (Pres & CEO)

MATTSCO SUPPLY CO.
1111 N 161st E Ave, Tulsa, OK 74116
Tel.: (918) 836-0451 OK
Web Site: http://mattsco.com
Oilfield Pipe, Fittings & Valves Mfr & Distr
N.A.I.C.S.: 332919
Eric Clower (Pres)

Subsidiaries:
Tool Center, Inc. (1)
1447 N Yale Ave, Tulsa, OK 74115
Tel.: (918) 838-7411
Web Site: http://toolcenterinc.com
Sales Range: $1-9.9 Million
Emp.: 10
Industrial Machinery And Equipment
N.A.I.C.S.: 423830
Bill Bowles (Chm)

MATULAITIS NURSING HOME
10 Thurber Rd, Putnam, CT 06260
Tel.: (860) 928-7976 CT
Web Site: http://www.matulaitisnh.org
Year Founded: 1978
Sales Range: $10-24.9 Million
Emp.: 207
Nursing Care Services
N.A.I.C.S.: 623110
Onile Sestokas (Pres)
Edwin Higgins (Sec)
Gintaras Cepas (Treas)
Robert Fournier (VP)

MATVEST INC.
37244 Groesbeck Hwy, Clinton Township, MI 48036
Tel.: (586) 461-2051
Web Site: http://www.bermexinc.com
Rev.: $13,500,000
Emp.: 236
Contract Services
N.A.I.C.S.: 333515
Henry Mello (Pres)

MAU WORKFORCE SOLUTIONS
501 Greene St, Augusta, GA 30901
Tel.: (706) 724-5367
Web Site: http://www.mau.com
Year Founded: 1973
Sales Range: $200-249.9 Million
Emp.: 4,765
Temporary Staffing Services
N.A.I.C.S.: 561320
William Hatcher (CEO)
Randy Hatcher (Pres)
Rod Hutcheson (VP-Comml Staffing)
Carl Henson (VP-Mktg & Bus Dev)
Doug Duncan (VP-Pro Svc)
Adam Hatcher (Gen Counsel & VP-Human Capital)
Ed O'Neal (VP-Fin Svcs)

MAU-SHERWOOD SUPPLY CO
8400 Barrow Rd 1, Twinsburg, OH 44087
Tel.: (330) 405-1200
Web Site: http://www.mausherwood.com
Sales Range: $10-24.9 Million
Emp.: 20
Industrial Supplies
N.A.I.C.S.: 423840
Howard Busse (Pres)

MAUCH CHUNK TRUST COMPANY
1111 North St, Jim Thorpe, PA 18229
Tel.: (570) 325-2265
Web Site: http://www.mauchchunktrust.com
Year Founded: 1902
Sales Range: $10-24.9 Million
Emp.: 80
Commericial Banking
N.A.I.C.S.: 522110
Patrick H. Reilly (Pres & CEO)
Richard A. Minnick (Mgr-Ops Div)
Denise M. Rautzhan (CFO)
Kathleen A. Schwick (Mgr-Customer Svc Div)
Deborah A. Price (Chief Lending Officer)
Michael F. Klapac (Mgr-Ops Div)
Charles E. Wildoner (Chm)
Carla Green (Dir-Comml Loan)
Richard M. Kistner (Officer-Loan)
Shannon L. Gogal (Officer-Trust)
William R. Reabold Jr. (Treas & Sec)

MAUDLIN INTERNATIONAL TRUCKS, INC.
2300 S Division Ave, Orlando, FL 32805
Tel.: (407) 849-6440
Web Site: http://www.maudlininternational.com
Sales Range: $25-49.9 Million
Emp.: 160
Car Whslr
N.A.I.C.S.: 441110
Kirk Morse (Dir-Parts)
Mike Maudlin (Gen Mgr)
Don DaVanzo (Mgr-Used Truck)

MAUGEL ARCHITECTS INC
200 Ayer Rd Ste 200, Harvard, MA 01451
Tel.: (978) 456-2800 MD
Web Site: http://www.maugel.com
Architectural Services
N.A.I.C.S.: 541310
Brent Maugel (Founder & Pres)
Daniel Barton (Principal)
Mark Pelletier (Principal)
Sarah Cormier (Project Mgr)
John Lawlor (COO)
John Almy (Dir-Client Rels)
Jennifer Ferreira (Dir-Interiors)

Subsidiaries:
Legacy Structures, LLC (1)
23 High St, Portsmouth, NH 03801-4009
Tel.: (603) 431-8701
Architectural Services
N.A.I.C.S.: 541310

MAUGER & COMPANY, INC.
300C Lawrence Dr, West Chester, PA 19380-4263
Tel.: (610) 429-8200 PA
Web Site: http://www.maugerco.com
Year Founded: 1963
Sales Range: $10-24.9 Million
Emp.: 126
Petroleum Products, Heating & Oil Distr
N.A.I.C.S.: 424720
Thomas Walter (Controller)

MAUI CHEMICAL & PAPER PRODUCTS, INC.
875 Alua St, Wailuku, HI 96793
Tel.: (808) 244-7311
Web Site: http://www.mauichem.com
Year Founded: 1969
Sales Range: $10-24.9 Million
Emp.: 50
Whslr of Industrial & Personal Paper Products
N.A.I.C.S.: 424130
Miles Kawasaki (Pres)
Harry Nakagawa (Gen Mgr)
Warren Ohta (Controller)
Henry Domingo (Mgr-Ops)
Todd Kawasaki (VP)
Sam Tabieros (Mgr-Sls)

MAUI CLOTHING CO. INC.
878 Front St, Lahaina, HI 96761
Tel.: (808) 667-6090
Web Site: http://www.mauiclothingcompany.com
Rev.: $15,797,457
Emp.: 40
Women's Apparel
N.A.I.C.S.: 458110
Edward D. Wayne (Pres)

MAUI DIVERS OF HAWAII, LTD.
1520 Liona St, Honolulu, HI 96814-2441
Tel.: (808) 946-7979 HI
Web Site: http://www.mauidivers.com
Year Founded: 1958
Sales Range: $200-249.9 Million
Emp.: 400
Designer of Jewelry
N.A.I.C.S.: 458310
Jan Iwai (Dir-Sls & Mktg)

MAUI LEONES LLC
94 Kupuohi St A5, Lahaina, HI 96761
Tel.: (808) 419-1000
Web Site: http://www.coconutcondos.com
Year Founded: 2011
Sales Range: $1-9.9 Million
Emp.: 9
Real Property Management Services
N.A.I.C.S.: 561599
Angela Leone (Owner & CEO)
Lisa Meadows (COO)
Caitlin Mishler (Mgr-Reservations)
Mark Haley (Mgr-Housekeeping & Inspections)
Joel Steinberg (Mgr-Property)

MAUI MAGNETS INC.
332 2nd Street, Oakland, CA 94607
Tel.: (510) 286-2280
Rev.: $10,500,000
Emp.: 10
Novelties
N.A.I.C.S.: 459420
Jamie Fung (Mgr)

MAUI RESORT RENTALS INC.
30 Halawai St Ste B4-5, Lahaina, HI 96761
Tel.: (808) 662-6284

COMPANIES

Web Site:
http://www.mauiresortrentals.com
Year Founded: 2010
Sales Range: $1-9.9 Million
Emp.: 35
Resort Rental Services
N.A.I.C.S.: 561599
Chris Geng (Founder & CEO)
Richard Bourland (Mng Dir)
Tony Carstens (Dir-Tech)
Marc Fair (Dir-Ops)
Keith Hertz (Dir-Sls & Experience)

MAUI VARIETIES, LTD.
2810 Paa St, Honolulu, HI 96819-4429
Tel.: (808) 838-7773
Web Site: http://www.mvlhawaii.com
Year Founded: 1972
Sales Range: $25-49.9 Million
Emp.: 100
Holding Company for Variety Stores & Real Estate Investments
N.A.I.C.S.: 444140
Guy Kamitaki (Co-Owner & Pres)
Wayne K. Kamitaki (CEO)

MAUI WOWI FRANCHISING, INC.
5445 DTC Pkwy Ste 1050, Greenwood Village, CO 80111
Tel.: (877) 849-6992
Web Site: http://www.mauiwowi.com
Beverage Retailer
N.A.I.C.S.: 722513
Mike Weinberger (CEO)

MAUL ELECTRIC INC.
10 Griggs Dr, Dayton, NJ 08810
Tel.: (732) 329-4656
Web Site:
http://www.maulelectric.com
Year Founded: 1984
Sales Range: $10-24.9 Million
Emp.: 43
Electrical Wiring Services
N.A.I.C.S.: 238210
Craig Coffey (VP)

MAULDIN & JENKINS, LLC
2303 Dawson Rd, Albany, GA 31707
Tel.: (229) 446-3600
Web Site: http://www.mjcpa.com
Rev.: $16,220,691
Emp.: 55
Certified Public Accountants
N.A.I.C.S.: 541211
John McDuffie (Partner)
David Clayton (Partner)
Ryan Inlow (Partner)
Joanna Hancock (Partner)
Christy Tinsley (Partner)
Ron Mitchell (Partner)
Aleisa Howell (Partner-Atlanta)
Bill Curtis (Partner-Birmingham)
Brannon Medley (Mgr-Macon)
Cliff Williams (Partner-Atlanta)
Donny Luker (Mng Partner)
D. Greg Morgan (Partner-Atlanta)
Joel Black (Partner-Atlanta)
Steve Parent (Partner-Bradenton)
Steven Reagan (Dir-Compliance Svcs)
Hanson Borders (Mng Partner)
Heather Batson (Partner)
Nicole Cunningham (Partner)
Derrick Cowart (Partner)
Michael Gordon (Partner)
Tim Lyons (Partner)

MAULDIN CORPORATION
3300 S Shoshone St, Sheridan, CO 80110
Tel.: (303) 788-1890
Web Site: http://www.lazyboy.com
Sales Range: $10-24.9 Million
Emp.: 14
Furniture Retailer
N.A.I.C.S.: 449110
Arthur Mauldin (Pres)

MAULDIN-DORFMEIER CONSTRUCTION
3240 N Millbrook Ave, Fresno, CA 93726
Tel.: (559) 252-4600
Web Site: http://www.mdc-inc.com
Rev.: $100,000,000
Emp.: 190
Specialized Public Building Contractors
N.A.I.C.S.: 236220
Patrick Mauldin (Pres)
Alan Dorfmeier (VP)

MAUPINTOUR INC.
2893 Executive Pk Dr Ste 201, Weston, FL 33331-3608
Tel.: (800) 255-4266
Web Site: http://www.maupintour.com
Year Founded: 1951
Tour Operator
N.A.I.C.S.: 561520

MAURER SUPPLY INC.
220 S Mead St, Seattle, WA 98108
Tel.: (206) 323-8640
Web Site:
http://www.maurersales.com
Sales Range: $10-24.9 Million
Emp.: 3
Food Industry Machinery
N.A.I.C.S.: 423830
Michael Maurer (Pres)

MAUREY MANUFACTURING CORPORATION
410 S Indus Park Rd, Holly Springs, MS 38635-3400
Tel.: (662) 252-1898
Web Site: http://www.maurey.com
Year Founded: 1917
Sales Range: $75-99.9 Million
Emp.: 75
Mfr of V-Belt Pulleys
N.A.I.C.S.: 333613
Chuck Lloyd (VP-Sls)
Joe Maurey (Pres)

MAURICE ELECTRICAL SUPPLY COMPANY
3355 V St NE, Washington, DC 20018
Tel.: (202) 675-9400
Web Site:
http://www.mauriceelectric.com
Year Founded: 1922
Rev.: $90,000,000
Emp.: 150
Electrical Supplies; Hardware Stores
N.A.I.C.S.: 423610
Jim Facciolo (Pres)
Janelle Larsen (Mgr-Credit)
Ericka Porter (Office Mgr)

Subsidiaries:

Maurexco International (1)
14504 Greenview Dr Ste 106, Laurel, MD 20708 (100%)
Tel.: (410) 792-8030
Web Site: http://www.maurexco.com
Sales Range: $25-49.9 Million
Emp.: 4
Mfr of Mechanical & Electrical Architectural Supplies
N.A.I.C.S.: 424990

MAURICE J. MARKELL SHOE CO., INC.
PO Box 246, Yonkers, NY 10702-0246
Tel.: (914) 963-2258
Web Site:
http://www.markellshoe.com
Year Founded: 1914
Sales Range: $10-24.9 Million
Emp.: 10
Comfort & Orthopedic Shoes & Shoe Correction Products Mfr
N.A.I.C.S.: 316210
Richard Markell (Co-Pres)
Jonathan J. Markell (Co-Pres)

MAURICE PINCOFF COMPANY INC.
1235 North Loop W Ste 510, Houston, TX 77008-4702
Tel.: (713) 681-5461
Web Site: http://www.pincoffs.com
Year Founded: 1978
Sales Range: $10-24.9 Million
Emp.: 18
Marketing & Distribution of Steel Products
N.A.I.C.S.: 423510
John I. Griffin (Pres & CEO)
Debra Wilder (Dir-Corp Affairs)

MAURIN-OGDEN PROPERTIES
109 Northpark Blvd Ste 300, Covington, LA 70433
Tel.: (985) 898-2022
Web Site: http://www.stirlingprop.com
Year Founded: 1975
Sales Range: $125-149.9 Million
Emp.: 245
Real Estate Developer, Management & Brokerage
N.A.I.C.S.: 237210
Grady K. Brame (Partner & Exec VP)
Marty A. Mayer (Pres & CEO)
Donna L. Derokey (VP-Mktg & Adv-Stirling Properties)
Judy McKee (VP-HR)
Peter Aamodt (VP-Dev)
Townsend Underhill (Dir-Dev)
Chris Abadie (VP & Dir-Comml Div)

Subsidiaries:

Stirling Properties, Inc. (1)
601 Poydras St Ste 2755, New Orleans, LA 70130
Tel.: (504) 523-4481
Web Site: http://www.stirlingproperties.com
Real Estate Operations
N.A.I.C.S.: 531210
Martin A. Mayer (Pres & CEO)
Elizabeth G. Schmelling (Controller)
Lewis Stirling (Exec VP)
Nancy Rome (Gen Mgr)
Christopher Abadie (VP & Mgr-Comml Brokerage)
Michael Bucher (Dir-Dev)

MAURY, DONNELLY & PARR, INC.
24 Commerce St., Baltimore, MD 21202
Tel.: (410) 685-4625
Web Site: https://www.mdpins.com
Year Founded: 1875
Emp.: 117
Insurance Services
N.A.I.C.S.: 524210
Leigh Brent (Pres)

Subsidiaries:

Campion Insurance Inc. (1)
900 S Main St Ste 106, Bel Air, MD 21014-5473
Tel.: (410) 838-5480
Web Site:
http://www.campioninsurance.com
Insurance Agencies & Brokerages
N.A.I.C.S.: 524210

Wetzel & Lanzi Inc. (1)
1301 York Rd Ste 702, Lutherville, MD 21093-6065
Tel.: (410) 339-7400
Web Site: http://www.wetzelandlanzi.com

Insurance Agencies & Brokerages
N.A.I.C.S.: 524210
David Wetzel (Mgr)

MAUS & HOFFMAN, INC.
800 E Las Olas Blvd, Fort Lauderdale, FL 33301
Tel.: (954) 463-1472
Web Site:
http://www.mausandhoffman.com
Year Founded: 1940
Sales Range: $10-24.9 Million
Emp.: 35
Retailer of Clothing
N.A.I.C.S.: 458110
John G. Maus (Pres)

MAUST CORPORATION
2200 140th Ave E Ste 200, Sumner, WA 98390
Tel.: (253) 321-3200
Web Site: http://www.maustcorp.com
Sales Range: $10-24.9 Million
Emp.: 15
Local Trucking without Storage
N.A.I.C.S.: 484121
Edward A. DeVito (Pres)

MAVENHILL CAPITAL
100 N Main St Ste 430, Chagrin Falls, OH 44022
Tel.: (440) 490-6170
Web Site:
http://www.mavenhillcapital.com
Privater Equity Firm
N.A.I.C.S.: 523999
Jay Studdard (Mng Partner)
Rhodes McKee (Mng Partner)
Nathan Schuster (Principal)
Alex Trouten (Principal)

Subsidiaries:

Connecticut Coining, Inc. (1)
10 Trowbridge Dr, Bethel, CT 06801-2858
Tel.: (203) 743-3861
Web Site: http://www.ctcoining.com
Sales Range: $1-9.9 Million
Emp.: 50
Deep-Drawn Metal Parts Mfr
N.A.I.C.S.: 332710
Lisa Pittman (Mgr-Pur)

MAVERIC MINI MARTS INC.
106 1/2 N Harrison Ave, Cushing, OK 74023
Tel.: (918) 225-3641
Sales Range: $10-24.9 Million
Emp.: 10
Convience Stores
N.A.I.C.S.: 444110
Glenn McCauley (Pres)
Sandy McCauley (CEO)

MAVERICK BOAT CO. INC.
3207 Industrial 29th St, Fort Pierce, FL 34946
Tel.: (772) 465-0631
Web Site:
http://www.maverickboats.com
Sales Range: $25-49.9 Million
Emp.: 200
Small Fishing Boats Mfr
N.A.I.C.S.: 336612
Stephen Farinacci (VP-Fin)
Jim Leffew (VP)

Subsidiaries:

Hewes Manufacturing Co. (1)
3027 Industrial 29th St, Fort Pierce, FL 34946
Tel.: (772) 465-0631
Web Site: http://www.hewes.com
Rev.: $490,000
Boatbuilding & Repairing
N.A.I.C.S.: 336612

MAVERICK CONSTRUCTION CORPORATION

MAVERICK CONSTRUCTION CORPORATION   U.S. PRIVATE

Maverick Construction Corporation—(Continued)

1 W House Plz Bldg D, Boston, MA 02136
Tel.: (617) 361-6700
Web Site:
 http://www.maverickcorporation.com
Year Founded: 1997
Rev.: $11,000,000
Emp.: 85
Provider of Communications Construction Services
N.A.I.C.S.: 237130
Michael McNally (Pres)
Christopher Sage (Sr VP)

MAVERICK DENTAL, LLC

1615 Golden Mile Hwy, Monroeville, PA 15146
Tel.: (724) 733-7444
Web Site:
 http://www.maverickdental.com
Year Founded: 2003
Rev.: $5,800,000
Emp.: 40
Dental Laboratories
N.A.I.C.S.: 339116
Joseph P. Fey (Pres & CEO)
Lawrence Albensi (Owner)

MAVERICK FRAMING, INC.

808 Hensley Ln, Wylie, TX 75098-4906
Tel.: (972) 442-7801
Web Site:
 http://www.maverickframing.com
Sales Range: $10-24.9 Million
Emp.: 15
Housing Construction Services
N.A.I.C.S.: 236117
Charles Cheshire (Pres)

MAVERICK GOLD LLC

2626 Montessouri St, Las Vegas, NV 89117
Tel.: (800) 848-7300   NV
Web Site:
 http://www.maverickgaming.com
Gambling & Casino
N.A.I.C.S.: 713290
Eric Persson (CEO)
Justin L. Beltram (COO)
Thomas Granite (CFO)
Brett C. Kline (CMO)
Freddy Kim (CIO)
Dennis Dougherty (Sr VP-Analytics)

Subsidiaries:

Evergreen Gaming Corporation (1)
8200 Tacoma Mall Blvd, Lakewood, WA 98499
Tel.: (425) 282-4172
Web Site: http://www.evergreengaming.com
Rev.: $21,761,870
Assets: $39,449,977
Liabilities: $17,009,682
Net Worth: $22,440,295
Earnings: ($2,751,810)
Fiscal Year-end: 12/31/2020
Casino Hotel Operator
N.A.I.C.S.: 721120
Leonard Libin (Sec & VP)

Great American Gaming Corporation (1)
18300 Cascade Ave S, Seattle, WA 98188
Tel.: (253) 480-3000
Web Site:
 http://www.greatamericancasino.com
Casino Operator
N.A.I.C.S.: 721120

Subsidiary (Domestic):

Evergreen Entertainment Corporation (2)
14040 Interurban Ave S, Tukwila, WA 98168
Tel.: (206) 244-5200
Casino Operation Services
N.A.I.C.S.: 713210

Nevada Gold & Casinos, Inc. (1)
133 E Warm Springs Rd Ste 102, Las Vegas, NV 89119
Tel.: (702) 685-1000
Web Site: http://www.nevadagold.com
Rev.: $74,552,526
Assets: $49,123,096
Liabilities: $14,869,711
Net Worth: $34,253,385
Earnings: $1,323,425
Emp.: 1,260
Fiscal Year-end: 04/30/2018
Gaming Facilities & Hotel Owner & Operator
N.A.I.C.S.: 721120
Eric Persson (Pres)

Subsidiary (Domestic):

A.G. Trucano, Son & Grandsons, Inc. (2)
155 Sherman St, Deadwood, SD 57732-1563
Tel.: (605) 578-2111
Casino Operator
N.A.I.C.S.: 713210

CGE Assets, Inc. (2)
300 E Bennett Ave, Cripple Creek, CO 80813
Tel.: (719) 689-3517
Web Site: http://www.coloradogrande.com
Casino & Hotel
N.A.I.C.S.: 721120

Colorado Grande Enterprises, Inc. (2)
300 E Bennett Ave, Cripple Creek, CO 80813
Tel.: (719) 689-3517
Web Site: http://www.coloradogrande.com
Sales Range: $10-24.9 Million
Emp.: 70
Casino Operator
N.A.I.C.S.: 713210

Gaming Ventures of Las Vegas, Inc. (2)
725 S Racetrack Rd, Henderson, NV 89015
Tel.: (702) 566-5555
Web Site: http://www.clubfortunecasino.com
Sales Range: $10-24.9 Million
Emp.: 175
Casino Hotels
N.A.I.C.S.: 721120
Michael Shaughnessy (Owner)

Nevada Gold BVR, L.L.C. (2)
50 Briar Hollow Ln Ste 500W, Houston, TX 77027-9304
Tel.: (713) 621-2245
Web Site: http://www.nevadagold.com
Sales Range: $25-49.9 Million
Emp.: 11
Casino Operator
N.A.I.C.S.: 713210
Michael Shaughnessy (CEO)

Washington Gold Casinos LLC (2)
711 Powell Ave SW, Renton, WA 98057
Tel.: (425) 264-1050
Web Site: http://www.wagoldcasinos.com
Casino Operator
N.A.I.C.S.: 713210
Keisha Roland (Controller)

MAVERICK INTERACTIVE, INC.

2802 N Howard Ave, Tampa, FL 33607
Tel.: (813) 514-1806
Web Site: http://www.mav-inc.com
Sales Range: $1-9.9 Million
Interactive Advertising & Marketing Services
N.A.I.C.S.: 541810
Mark Marchetta (CEO)

MAVERICK MOTORS, LLC

10320 Pendleton Pike, Indianapolis, IN 46236
Tel.: (317) 545-8551   IN
Web Site:
 http://www.sharpcarsofindy.com
Sales Range: $10-24.9 Million
Emp.: 55
New & Used Car Dealer

N.A.I.C.S.: 441110
Bob Thomas (Owner)
Matt Beeler (Gen Mgr)
Heather Bay (Office Mgr)

MAVERICK NATURAL RESOURCES, LLC

1111 Bagby St Ste 1600, Houston, TX 77002
Tel.: (713) 437-8000
Web Site:
 http://www.mavresources.com
Year Founded: 1988
Sales Range: $500-549.9 Million
Crude Petroleum & Natural Gas Production
N.A.I.C.S.: 211120
Larry Johnson (Dir-HR)
Chris Canon (Dir-Bus Dev)

Subsidiaries:

BreitBurn Florida LLC (1)
909 County Rd 846, Immokalee, FL 34142-9724
Tel.: (239) 657-2171
Web Site: http://www.breitburn.com
Sales Range: $50-74.9 Million
Emp.: 14
Crude Petroleum & Natural Gas Extraction Services
N.A.I.C.S.: 211120
Vicky Pass (Office Mgr)

BreitBurn Management Company, LLC (1)
8400 E Prentice Ave Ph 1500, Greenwood Village, CO 80111-2927
Tel.: (303) 409-7636
Emp.: 2
Crude Petroleum & Natural Gas Extraction Services
N.A.I.C.S.: 211120

BreitBurn Operating L.P. (1)
515 S Flower St Ste 4800, Los Angeles, CA 90017-2241
Tel.: (213) 225-5900
Emp.: 80
Crude Petroleum & Natural Gas Extraction Services
N.A.I.C.S.: 211120
Hal Washdurn (Pres)

Breitburn Transpetco LP LLC (1)
707 Wilshire Blvd Ste 4600, Los Angeles, CA 90017
Tel.: (213) 225-5900
Web Site: http://www.breitburn.com
Emp.: 50
Natural Gas Distr
N.A.I.C.S.: 221210
Halbert S. Washburn (CEO)

MAVERICK NETWORKS, INC.

7060 Koll Center Pkwy Ste 306, Pleasanton, CA 94566
Tel.: (925) 931-1900
Web Site:
 http://www.mavericknetworks.net
Sales Range: $1-9.9 Million
Emp.: 11
Telecommunications Specializing in VoIP & Video Conferencing
N.A.I.C.S.: 517810
Aaron Lee (CEO)

MAVERICK USA, INC.

13301 Valentine Rd, North Little Rock, AR 72117
Tel.: (501) 945-6130   AR
Web Site:
 http://www.maverickusa.com
Year Founded: 1980
Sales Range: $75-99.9 Million
Emp.: 1,000
Long Distance Local Logistics & Transportation Services
N.A.I.C.S.: 484230
Steve R. Williams (Chm & CEO)
Debbie Mitchell (CFO & Exec VP)
John A. Culp (Pres)

Letha Haymes (VP-HR)
John Coppens (VP-Ops)
Craig Brown (VP-Glass)
Steve Swain (VP-Sls)
Mike Jeffress (VP-Maintenance)
Drew Allbritton (VP)
Justin Brown (VP-Dedicated Ops)
Wayne Brown (VP-Info Tech)
Kim Williams Gary (Exec VP)
Eric Grant (VP-Fin)
Doug Richey (COO & Exec VP)
Brad Vaughn (VP-Recruiting)

Subsidiaries:

Maverick Leasing, LLC (1)
5404 Planters Rd, Fort Smith, AR 72916
Tel.: (479) 648-1027
Truck & Trailer Leasing Services
N.A.I.C.S.: 532120

Maverick USA, Inc. - NC Facility (1)
12801 S Rocky Ford Rd, Laurinburg, NC 28352
Tel.: (910) 276-7253
Truckload Transportation & Logistic Services
N.A.I.C.S.: 484121
Steve Williams (CEO)

MAVERIK COUNTRY STORES, INC.

880 W Ctr St, North Salt Lake, UT 84054-2913
Tel.: (801) 936-5557
Year Founded: 1928
Convenience Store & Gas Station Operator
N.A.I.C.S.: 457120
Ashley Ray (Dir-HR)

MAVIK CAPITAL MANAGEMENT, LP

205 W 28th St 12th Fl, New York, NY 10001
Tel.: (212) 753-5100
Web Site:
 https://www.mavikcapital.com
Financial Investment Services
N.A.I.C.S.: 523999
Vic Uppal (CEO & Chief Investment Officer)

Subsidiaries:

XS Financial, Inc. (1)
1901 Avenue of the Stars Ste 120, Los Angeles, CA 90067
Tel.: (310) 683-2336
Web Site: https://www.xsfinancial.com
Rev.: $11,675,203
Assets: $84,091,723
Liabilities: $80,631,138
Net Worth: $3,460,585
Earnings: ($6,507,019)
Fiscal Year-end: 12/31/2023
Financial Investment Services
N.A.I.C.S.: 523999
David Kivitz (CEO)
Antony Radbod (COO)
Joel Fazzini (CFO)
Alex Karol (VP-Tech)
Jim Bates (Dir-Credit)

MAWSON & MAWSON INC.

1800 E Old Lincoln Hwy, Langhorne, PA 19047
Tel.: (215) 750-1100
Web Site:
 http://www.mawsonandmawson.com
Sales Range: $25-49.9 Million
Emp.: 400
Heavy Hauling
N.A.I.C.S.: 484121
Timothy G. Durbin (Owner)
Sean Durbin (VP-Ops)
Michael Harkins (Exec VP-Ops & Safety)
Jeff Sacks (VP-Logistics)

MAX ADVERTISING

3190 NE Expy Ste 120, Atlanta, GA 30341
Tel.: (770) 454-7100
Web Site: http://www.maxadv.com
Year Founded: 1992
Sales Range: $10-24.9 Million
Emp.: 12
N.A.I.C.S.: 541810
Tom Matte *(Pres & CEO)*
Christie Matte *(VP-Opers)*
Nathan Phaneuf *(Acct Exec)*
Gregg Bauer *(Dir-Creative)*
Jim Benson *(Dir-Art)*
Julie Polstra *(Mgr-Ops)*
Katie Visscher *(Graphic Designer)*
Ken Maudsley *(VP)*
Meghan Carfang *(Acct Coord)*
Cara Wilmer *(Acct Coord)*
Beth Isikoff *(Dir-New Bus Dev)*

MAX ARNOLD & SONS, INC.
702 N Main St, Hopkinsville, KY 42240
Tel.: (270) 885-8488
Web Site: http://www.maxfuel.net
Rev.: $45,000,000
Emp.: 200
Petroleum Products Whslr & Distr; Operator of Convenience Stores
N.A.I.C.S.: 424710
Bob Arnold *(Pres, CEO & COO)*
Gary Logan *(CFO)*
Karen McGregor *(Dir-Ops)*

MAX AUTO SUPPLY CO.
1101 Monroe St, Toledo, OH 43604
Tel.: (419) 243-7281
Web Site: http://www.katzmidas.com
Sales Range: $50-74.9 Million
Emp.: 45
Provider of Automotive Parts & Services
N.A.I.C.S.: 811114
Ted Banken *(Controller)*

MAX BORGES AGENCY
80 SW 8th St Suite 1900, Miami, FL 33130
Tel.: (305) 374-4404
Web Site: http://www.maxborgesagency.com
Year Founded: 2002
Sales Range: Less than $1 Million
Emp.: 25
Technology Public Relations & Social Media
N.A.I.C.S.: 541820
Matt Shumate *(Acct Supvr)*
Max Borges *(Founder & CEO)*

MAX CREDIT UNION
400 Eastdale Cir, Montgomery, AL 36117
Tel.: (334) 260-2600   AL
Web Site: http://www.mymax.com
Year Founded: 1955
Sales Range: $25-49.9 Million
Emp.: 331
Credit Union Operator
N.A.I.C.S.: 522130
Scott Lindley *(CIO)*
H. Greg McClellan *(Pres & CEO)*
K. Sue Jackson *(Sec)*

MAX FINKELSTEIN INC.
2840 31st St, Long Island City, NY 11102-1745
Tel.: (718) 274-8900
Web Site: http://www.maxfinkelstein.com
Year Founded: 1919
Sales Range: $25-49.9 Million
Emp.: 150
Sales of Tires & Tubes
N.A.I.C.S.: 531120

Harold Finkelstein *(Pres)*
Scott Paticoff *(Controller)*

MAX FOOTE CONSTRUCTION COMPANY, INC.
225 Antibes St W Ste 3, Mandeville, LA 70448-5125
Tel.: (985) 624-8569   LA
Web Site: http://www.maxfoote.com
Year Founded: 1977
Sales Range: $75-99.9 Million
Emp.: 140
Heavy Construction
N.A.I.C.S.: 237110
Max E. Foote Jr. *(Pres)*

MAX GRIGSBY CO. INC.
6800 Sands Point Dr, Houston, TX 77074
Tel.: (713) 800-7300
Web Site: http://www.mgcinc.net
Rev.: $20,946,067
Emp.: 100
Prefabricated Structures
N.A.I.C.S.: 423390
David Mahood *(CEO)*
Bill Jones *(Reg Mgr-Sls)*
Tommy Vickers *(Acct Mgr)*
Judson Wolfe *(Exec VP)*
Jeff Rea *(Mgr-Sls-Arizona & New Mexico)*
Jeremy Sanders *(Mgr-Sls-Colorado)*
Aaron Martinez *(Mgr-Louisiana & Southern Mississippi)*
Tom Bredenberg *(Project Mgr)*
Allan Judice *(Dir-Bus Dev-Oklahoma & Western Arkansas)*

MAX GROUP CORPORATION
17011 Green Dr, City of Industry, CA 91745
Tel.: (626) 935-0050   CA
Web Site: http://www.maxgroup.com
Year Founded: 1985
Sales Range: $50-74.9 Million
Emp.: 165
Computers, Peripherals & Software Distr
N.A.I.C.S.: 423430
Thierry Lim *(Product Mgr & Coord-Mktg)*
Cecilia Liang *(Product Mgr)*

MAX J. KUNEY CONSTRUCTION COMPANY
120 N Ralph St, Spokane, WA 99220
Tel.: (509) 535-0651
Web Site: http://www.maxkuney.com
Sales Range: $25-49.9 Million
Emp.: 115
Highway Street & Bridge Construction
N.A.I.C.S.: 237310
Daniel Kuney *(VP)*
Max J. Kuney IV *(Founder & Pres)*
Greg Waugh *(VP)*

MAX JANTZ EXCAVATING, LLC.
26503 11 Rd, Montezuma, KS 67867-9065
Tel.: (620) 846-2634
Web Site: http://www.maxjantzexcavating.com
Sales Range: $10-24.9 Million
Emp.: 160
Excavation Services
N.A.I.C.S.: 238910
Aaron Jantz *(Co-Owner)*
Heather Jantz *(Co-Owner)*
Max Jantz *(Co-Owner)*

MAX KAHAN INC.
20 W 47th St, New York, NY 10036-3303
Tel.: (212) 575-4646   DE
Sales Range: $50-74.9 Million

Emp.: 10
Precious Metals
N.A.I.C.S.: 339910
Max Kahan *(Pres)*
David Glock *(VP)*

MAX MADSEN IMPORTS INC.
2424 Ogden Ave, Downers Grove, IL 60515
Tel.: (630) 960-5040
Web Site: http://www.maxmadsen.com
Sales Range: $50-74.9 Million
Emp.: 50
Sales & Service For New & Used Automobiles
N.A.I.C.S.: 441110
Max A. Madsen *(Pres)*
Scott Grove *(Pres)*

MAX OIL COMPANY INC.
939 Fort Dale Rd, Greenville, AL 36037
Tel.: (334) 382-5471
Sales Range: $10-24.9 Million
Emp.: 55
Convenience Store
N.A.I.C.S.: 445131
James McGowen *(Pres)*
Mints McGowen *(VP)*

MAX PLANCK FLORIDA CORPORATION
1 Max Planck Way, Jupiter, FL 33458
Tel.: (561) 972-9000
Web Site: http://www.maxplanckflorida.org
Sales Range: $25-49.9 Million
Research Services
N.A.I.C.S.: 541715
David Fitzpatrick *(CEO & Dir-Scientific)*
Peter Gruss *(Chm)*

MAX SOLUTIONS INC.
2558 Pearl Buck Rd, Bristol, PA 19007
Tel.: (910) 833-2709
Web Site: https://www.biggerthanpackaging.com
Year Founded: 2021
Specialty Packaging Services
N.A.I.C.S.: 561910
Marc Shore *(CEO)*
Dennis Kaltman *(Pres & COO)*

Subsidiaries:

LTi Printing, Inc.   (1)
518 N Centerville Rd, Sturgis, MI 49091-9601
Tel.: (269) 651-7574
Web Site: http://www.ltiprinting.com
Printing Services
N.A.I.C.S.: 323120
Cheryl Jordan *(Dir-First Impressions)*
Mike Frost *(CEO)*
Mike Frost *(CEO)*

MAX TECHNICAL TRAINING
4900 Pkwy Dr Ste 160, Mason, OH 45040
Tel.: (513) 322-8888   OH
Web Site: http://www.maxtrain.com
Year Founded: 1998
Sales Range: $1-9.9 Million
Emp.: 20
Information Technology Training Services
N.A.I.C.S.: 611420
Denise Bartick *(Pres & CEO)*
Patricia Miller *(Dir-Initiative)*

MAX TRANS LOGISTICS OF CHATTANOOGA, LLC
1848 Rossville Ave, Chattanooga, TN 37408

Tel.: (423) 362-7210   TN
Web Site: http://www.maxtranslogistics.com
Year Founded: 2014
Sales Range: $25-49.9 Million
Emp.: 28
Freight Forwarding & Transportation Services
N.A.I.C.S.: 488510
Mike McCallie *(Mng Partner)*

MAX YIELD COOPERATIVE
313 3rd Ave NE, West Bend, IA 50597
Tel.: (515) 887-7211   IA
Web Site: http://www.maxyieldcooperative.com
Year Founded: 1915
Sales Range: $10-24.9 Million
Emp.: 104
Grain & Field Beans
N.A.I.C.S.: 424510
Harry Bormann *(Mgr-Grain)*
Diane Streit *(Dir-HR)*
Keith Heim *(CEO)*

MAXCO SUPPLY INC.
605 S Zediker Ave, Parlier, CA 93648
Tel.: (559) 646-6700
Web Site: http://www.maxcopackaging.com
Year Founded: 1972
Rev.: $28,005,095
Emp.: 400
Shipping Supplies
N.A.I.C.S.: 424130
Max Flaming *(Founder & CEO)*

Subsidiaries:

Maxco Supply Inc., Box Division   (1)
605 S Zediker Ave, Parlier, CA 93648
Tel.: (559) 646-6700
Web Site: http://www.mx2co.com
Sales Range: $25-49.9 Million
Emp.: 175
Shipping Supplies
N.A.I.C.S.: 424130
David Bryant *(Treas & Sec)*

Maxco Supply Inc., Machinery Division   (1)
605 S Zediker Ave, Parlier, CA 93648
Tel.: (559) 646-6700
Web Site: http://www.maxcopackaging.com
Packaging Film Mfr
N.A.I.C.S.: 326112
Tracy Arakaki *(Sls Admin)*
Max Flaming *(Founder & CEO)*

MAXEY ENERGY CO.
447 West Main St, Uvalde, TX 78801
Tel.: (830) 278-3711
Web Site: http://www.maxeyenergy.com
Sales Range: $10-24.9 Million
Emp.: 20
Petroleum Bulk Stations
N.A.I.C.S.: 424710
Merlin Maxey *(Pres)*
Terry Maxey *(VP)*

MAXEY LOGISTICS, INC
400 Isaac Shelby Dr, Shelbyville, KY 40065-9130
Tel.: (502) 647-0430
Web Site: http://www.maxeylogistics.com
Automotive Repair & Maintenance
N.A.I.C.S.: 811198
Jeff Allred *(Mgr)*

Subsidiaries:

Hartlage Manufacturing, Inc.   (1)
Two Quality Pl, Buckner, KY 40010
Tel.: (502) 222-0488
Web Site: http://www.hartlagemanufacturing.com
Rev.: $3,500,000
Emp.: 15

MAXEY LOGISTICS, INC   U.S. PRIVATE

Maxey Logistics, Inc—(Continued)
All Other Plastics Product Mfr
N.A.I.C.S.: 326199

MAXEY TRAILERS MFG., INC.
7075 FM 38, Brookston, TX 75421
Tel.: (903) 306-2910
Web Site:
http://www.maxxdtrailers.com
Year Founded: 1999
Sales Range: $25-49.9 Million
Emp.: 150
Trailer Parts Mfr & Distr
N.A.I.C.S.: 336390
Kendall Kornelsen (CEO & Mktg Dir)

MAXFIELD ENTERPRISES INC.
8825 Melrose Ave, Los Angeles, CA 90069
Tel.: (310) 274-8800
Web Site: http://www.maxfieldla.com
Year Founded: 1969
Sales Range: $10-24.9 Million
Emp.: 50
Retailer of Clothing
N.A.I.C.S.: 458110
Cerrdre Wheaton (Gen Mgr)
Geirge Wheaton (Gen Mgr)
Miguel Lopez (CFO)

MAXI FOODS LLC
8616 California Ave, Riverside, CA 92504
Tel.: (951) 688-0538
Year Founded: 1993
Sales Range: $10-24.9 Million
Emp.: 50
Operator of Grocery Stores
N.A.I.C.S.: 445110
Finn Mathew (Mgr)

MAXIFY SOLUTIONS INC.
4835 Sinora Dr Ste 400, Charlotte, NC 28273
Web Site: http://www.maxify-solutions.com
E-Commerce & Warehousing
N.A.I.C.S.: 561499
Ofir Baharav (CEO)

Subsidiaries:

SimiGon Ltd.   (1)
1 Sapir St, PO Box 12050, Herzliyya, 4685205, Israel
Tel.: (972) 9 956 1777
Web Site: http://www.simigon.com
Rev.: $3,221,000
Assets: $7,400,000
Liabilities: $2,505,000
Net Worth: $4,895,000
Earnings: $2,180,000)
Fiscal Year-end: 12/31/2020
Software Development Services
N.A.I.C.S.: 541511
Ary Nussbaum (VP-Bus Dev-Americas)
Richard Clem (Sr VP)
Hagai Piechowicz (VP)

Subsidiary (US):

SimiGon, Inc.   (2)
111 S Maitland Ave Ste 210, Maitland, FL 32751
Tel.: (407) 951-5548
Web Site: http://www.simigon.com
Sales Range: $1-9.9 Million
Software Development Services
N.A.I.C.S.: 513210

MAXIL TECHNOLOGY SOLUTIONS, INC.
2625 Butterfield Rd Ste 316W, Oak Brook, IL 60523
Tel.: (630) 472-7335
Web Site:
http://www.maxiltechnology.com
Year Founded: 1999
Sales Range: $1-9.9 Million
Emp.: 75

Information Technology Solutions & Services
N.A.I.C.S.: 541511
Abdul Baig (VP)

MAXIM AUTOMOTIVE PRODUCTS LLC
950 W Valley Rd Ste 2802, Wayne, PA 19087
Tel.: (610) 265-6600
Web Site:
http://www.maximautomotive.com
Sales Range: $10-24.9 Million
Emp.: 22
Mobile Telephone Equipment
N.A.I.C.S.: 449210
James Maxim Sr. (Chm)

MAXIM ENTERPRISES, INC
6726 Wales Ave NW, Massillon, OH 44646
Tel.: (330) 499-9289
Year Founded: 1998
Sales Range: $10-24.9 Million
Emp.: 11
Property Preservation & Contractor Consulting
N.A.I.C.S.: 531190
Jim Overcash (Mgr)

MAXIM HEALTHCARE SERVICES, INC.
7227 Lee Deforest Dr, Columbia, MD 21046
Tel.: (410) 910-1500
Web Site:
http://www.maximhealthcare.com
Sales Range: $25-49.9 Million
Emp.: 900
Medical & Government Staffing Services
N.A.I.C.S.: 561320
W. John Langley (Chief Medical Officer, Chief Quality Officer & Sr VP)
Toni-Jean Lisa (Gen Counsel & Sr VP)
William Butz (CEO)
Kevin Apperson (CIO)
Raymond Carbone (CFO & Sr VP)
Julie Judge (Chief Experience Officer)
Kellie Lanier (Sr VP-Clinical Ops)

Subsidiaries:

Care Focus, Inc.   (1)
555 N Pleasantburg Dr Ste 100A, Greenville, SC 29607
Tel.: (864) 877-1069
Web Site: http://www.carefocus.com
Developmental Disability Assistance Services
N.A.I.C.S.: 623210

Centrus Premier Homecare, Inc.   (1)
225 Water St Ste A150, Plymouth, MA 02360
Tel.: (508) 747-3521
Web Site: http://www.centrushomecare.com
Health Care Srvices
N.A.I.C.S.: 621999
Pat Gauthier (Mgr-HR)

Logix Healthcare Search Partners, LLC   (1)
40 York Rd Ste 502, Towson, MD 21204
Tel.: (410) 769-9166
Web Site: http://www.logixhsp.com
Medical Staff Recruitment Services
N.A.I.C.S.: 561311
Scott Ketchen (Exec Dir-Search)

Maxim Health Information Services   (1)
1515 190th St Ste 165, Gardena, CA 90248
Tel.: (866) 316-8773
Web Site:
http://www.maximhealthinformationservices.com
Emp.: 4
Document Preparation Services
N.A.I.C.S.: 561410

Kyle Pragnell (Office Mgr)
Maxim Healthcare Services Inc.   (1)
800 Corporate Cir Ste 100, Harrisburg, PA 17110
Tel.: (717) 526-4555
Web Site: http://www.maximhealthcare.com
Sales Range: $10-24.9 Million
Emp.: 5
Homecare & Clinical Staffing Services
N.A.I.C.S.: 561320
Toni-Jean Lisa (Gen Counsel & VP)
W. Bradley Bennett (CEO)
W. John Langley (Chief Medical Officer, Chief Quality Officer & VP)
Timothy Kuhn (Chief Culture Officer & VP)
Sharon Smith (VP-HR)
Kevin Apperson (CIO)
Andy Friedell (VP-Govt Affairs)
Bart Kelly (VP-HR)
Cheryl Ann Nelson (Sr VP-Clinical Affairs)

Maxim Home Health Resources, Inc.   (1)
4100 Holiday St NW, Canton, OH 44718
Tel.: (330) 493-7866
Web Site: http://www.maximhomehealthresources.com
Health Care Services
N.A.I.C.S.: 621999
Brad Bennett (Pres)

Maxim Physician Resources, LLC   (1)
5001 LBJ Fwy Ste 900, Dallas, TX 75244
Tel.: (888) 800-1853
Web Site: http://www.maximphysicians.com
Medical Staff Recruitment Services
N.A.I.C.S.: 561311
Megan Blanco (Mgr-Ops)

Maxim Staffing Solutions - TravelMax Division (1)
600 N W Shore Blvd 6th Fl, Tampa, FL 33609-1137
Tel.: (888) 800-1855
Web Site: http://www.travmax.com
Medical Staff Recruitment Services
N.A.I.C.S.: 561311
Joanna Skibko (Mgr-Natl Recruitment)

Reflectx Services   (1)
600 NW Shore Blvd Suite 600, Tampa, FL 33609
Tel.: (407) 833-8815
Web Site: http://www.reflectxstaffing.com
Rehabilitation Therapy Staffing Services
N.A.I.C.S.: 561311
Christopher Hunter (Mgr)
Brent Healy (Mgr-Mktg)
Carla Wright (VP-Sls & Trng)
Carolee Bavaro (Gen Mgr & Mgr-Ops)

Timeline Recruiting, LLC   (1)
601 Business Loop 70 W Ste 124, Columbia, MO 65203
Tel.: (573) 214-2763
Web Site: http://www.tlrec.com
Medical Staff Recruitment Services
N.A.I.C.S.: 561311

MAXIM INSURANCE AGENCY INC.
18050 Saturn Ln, Houston, TX 77058
Tel.: (281) 337-2516
Web Site: http://www.maximblue.com
Rev.: $15,000,000
Emp.: 30
Insurance Agents
N.A.I.C.S.: 524210
Charles Hall (Chm)
Ron Masters (Pres)
Marie Baker (Mgr-Acctg)

MAXIMO MARINA
4801 37th St S, Saint Petersburg, FL 33711
Tel.: (727) 867-1102
Web Site:
http://www.maximomarina.com
Sales Range: $1-9.9 Million
Marinas
N.A.I.C.S.: 713930
Lee Hicks (Gen Mgr)

MAXIMUM CORPORATION
2185 N Glenville Dr, Richardson, TX 75082
Tel.: (972) 699-2700
Web Site: http://www.cslic.com
Sales Range: $25-49.9 Million
Emp.: 56
Life Insurance
N.A.I.C.S.: 524113
William H. Lewis Jr. (Chief Investment Officer)
Jim Lewis (Chm, Pres & COO)
Donis Balfour (COO, Sec & Exec VP)

Subsidiaries:

Insmark Company   (1)
2175 N Glenville Dr, Richardson, TX 75083-3879
Tel.: (972) 699-2770
Web Site: http://www.insmark.com
Rev.: $295,000
Emp.: 22
Provider of Life Insurance Services
N.A.I.C.S.: 524113
Jim Lewis (Pres)

Subsidiary (Domestic):

Champions Life Insurance Co.   (2)
2175 N Glenville Dr, Richardson, TX 75082
Tel.: (972) 699-2770
Web Site: http://www.championslife.com
Life Insurance Carrier
N.A.I.C.S.: 524113

Subsidiary (Domestic):

Central Security Life Insurance Co.   (3)
2175 N Glenville Dr, Richardson, TX 75082
Tel.: (972) 699-2770
Web Site: http://www.cslic.com
Life Reinsurance Carriers
N.A.I.C.S.: 524130

Subsidiary (Domestic):

Western American Life Insurance Co.   (4)
2175 N Glenville Dr, Richardson, TX 75082
Tel.: (972) 699-2770
Web Site: http://www.cslic.com
Sales Range: $125-149.9 Million
Emp.: 32
Mutual Association Life Insurance
N.A.I.C.S.: 524113
James Lewis (Pres)

MAXIMUM DESIGN & ADVERTISING
7032 Wrightsville Ave Ste 201, Wilmington, NC 28403
Tel.: (910) 256-2320
Web Site:
http://www.maximumdesign.com
Year Founded: 1998
Sales Range: Less than $1 Million
Emp.: 8
Brand Development & Integration, Exhibit/Trade Shows, Internet/Web Design, Media Buying Services, Media Planning, Outdoor, Real Estate, Strategic Planning/Research
N.A.I.C.S.: 541810
Amy Tharrington (Principal)
Kelly Burnette (Owner)
Paula Knorr (Dir-Creative)
Benson Wills (Mgr-Internet Dev)
Elizabeth Galloway (Mgr-Client Acct)

MAXIMUM IMPACT INC.
1410 Broadway Ste 1001, New York, NY 10018
Tel.: (212) 447-7857
Web Site:
http://www.maximumimpact.net
Year Founded: 1994
Sales Range: $10-24.9 Million
Emp.: 8
Sales Promotion
N.A.I.C.S.: 541810
Valerie Haskell (Pres & CEO)
David Herman (Mgr-Production)

MAXIMUM MEDIA ENTERPRISES, INC.
100 Corporate Pl Ste 102, Peabody, MA 01960
Tel.: (978) 536-9600
Year Founded: 2003
Sales Range: $10-24.9 Million
Emp.: 7
Advertising, Email, Event Planning & Marketing, Graphic Design, Internet/Web Design, Local Marketing, Media Buying Services, Print, Production, Radio, T.V.
N.A.I.C.S.: 541810
Nick DeAngelo (CEO)
Cheryl DeAngelo (Pres)
Lisa Morello (Office Mgr-HR & Fin)

MAXIMUM ONE REALTY
5041 Dallas Hwy Ste 700, Powder Springs, GA 30127
Tel.: (770) 919-8825
Web Site: http://www.maximumonerealty.com
Year Founded: 2007
Sales Range: $1-9.9 Million
Emp.: 450
Real Estate Agency
N.A.I.C.S.: 531210
Ronniese House (Principal)
Dave Kubat (Owner)

MAXIMUM QUALITY FOODS
3351 Tremley Point Rd Ste 2, Linden, NJ 07036
Tel.: (908) 474-0003
Web Site: http://www.maximumqualityfoods.com
Year Founded: 1973
Sales Range: $75-99.9 Million
Emp.: 100
Dried & Dehydrated Food Mfr
N.A.I.C.S.: 311423
Adolfo Velez (Mgr-Warehouse)
Larry Taner (Gen Mgr)

MAXIMUS COFFEE GROUP, LLC.
3900 Harrisburg, Houston, TX 77003
Tel.: (713) 228-9501
Web Site: http://www.maximuscoffee.com
Year Founded: 1985
Sales Range: $25-49.9 Million
Emp.: 350
Roasted Coffee Mfr & Distr
N.A.I.C.S.: 311920
Shyann Batiste (Coord-Employee Rels)

MAXINE OF HOLLYWOOD, INC.
6600 Katella Ave, Cypress, CA 90630-5104
Tel.: (332) 358-8922 CA
Year Founded: 1954
Sales Range: $10-24.9 Million
Emp.: 500
Provider of Women's, Misses' & Juniors' Bathing Suits
N.A.I.C.S.: 315250

MAXISAVER GROUP, INC.
555 US Hwy 1 S Ste 220, Iselin, NJ 08830
Tel.: (212) 391-0002
Web Site: http://www.maxisavergroup.com
Sales Range: $1-9.9 Million
Emp.: 10
Coupons & Savings Information
N.A.I.C.S.: 323111
Doris Barros (Mgr-Mktg)

MAXITROL COMPANY
23555 Telegraph Rd, Southfield, MI 48033
Tel.: (248) 356-1400 MI
Web Site: http://www.maxitrol.com
Year Founded: 1946
Sales Range: $100-124.9 Million
Emp.: 275
Mfr of Emergency Safety Valves & Pressure & Temperature Controls for the Gas Appliances & Equipment
N.A.I.C.S.: 334512
John Schlachter (VP-R&D)
Richard Bargert (VP-Mktg & Comm)
David Holcomb (VP-Sls)
Jeff Rainer (Engr-Test)

Subsidiaries:

Maxitrol Company - Blissfield Division (1)
235 Sugar St, Blissfield, MI 49228
Tel.: (517) 486-2820
Electric Equipment Mfr
N.A.I.C.S.: 335999

Maxitrol Company - Colon Division (1)
1000 E State St, Colon, MI 49040
Tel.: (269) 432-3291
Heating Equipment Whslr
N.A.I.C.S.: 423730

Maxitrol Company - Maxitrol Electronics Division (1)
23600 Telegraph Rd, Southfield, MI 48033
Tel.: (248) 356-1400
Electric Equipment Mfr
N.A.I.C.S.: 334419

Mertik Maxitrol Gmbh & Co., KG (1)
3 Warnstedter St, Thale, 6502, Germany (100%)
Tel.: (49) 39474000
Web Site: http://www.mertikmaxitrol.com
Sales Range: $25-49.9 Million
Emp.: 160
Mfr of Industrial Controls, Gas Controls, Radiator Controls & Specialty Valves
N.A.I.C.S.: 335314
Larry Koskela (Mng Dir)

Mertik Maxitrol Gmbh & Co., KG (1)
Industrie Strasse 1, 48308, Senden, Germany
Tel.: (49) 259796320
Web Site: http://www.mertikmaxitrol.com
Temperature Controls Mfr
N.A.I.C.S.: 334512

MAXON LIFT CORP.
11921 Slauson Ave, Santa Fe Springs, CA 90670-2221
Tel.: (562) 464-0099 CA
Web Site: http://www.maxonlift.com
Year Founded: 1957
Sales Range: $200-249.9 Million
Emp.: 422
Mfr of Hydraulic Lift Gates
N.A.I.C.S.: 423830
Howard Smith (VP-Sls)
Brian Hufnagl (Dir-Central Reg)
Troy Overfelt (VP-Natl Accounts)
Dan Callison (Mgr-Natl Customer Retention)
Hugo Carbajal (Mgr-Sls-Mexico & Latin America)
Hakan Peterson (VP-Strategic Growth)

Subsidiaries:

Maxon Industries, S.A. de C.V. (1)
Calle Centenario, No 1010 La Presa, Tijuana, 22680, BC, Mexico (100%)
Tel.: (52) 6646894124
Web Site: http://www.maxonlift.com
Sales Range: $10-24.9 Million
Emp.: 120
Mfr of Metal Refuse Containers
N.A.I.C.S.: 332439

MAXOR NATIONAL PHARMACY SERVICES CORPORATION
320 S Polk St Ste 100, Amarillo, TX 79101-1426
Tel.: (800) 658-6146 TX
Web Site: http://www.maxor.com
Year Founded: 1926
National Provider of Pharmacy & Healthcare Services
N.A.I.C.S.: 456110
Mike Ellis (CEO)
Leah Bailey (Gen Counsel)
Joe Ellison (Sr VP-HR)
Eric Wan (Chief Comml Officer)
David Wheeler (CFO)
Jennifer Gallego (COO)
Michael T. Einodshofer (Chief Pharmacy Officer)
Suzanne Hansen (Exec VP-Pharmacy Ops)
Karin Humphrey (Pres-MaxorPlus)

Subsidiaries:

Pharmaceutical Specialties LLC (1)
150 Cleveland Rd Ste A, Bogart, GA 30622
Tel.: (800) 818-6486
Web Site: http://www.psipharmacy.com
Pharmacy Services
N.A.I.C.S.: 456110

MAXPAX LLC
401 E Morrissey Dr, Elkhorn, WI 53121
Tel.: (262) 275-3484
Web Site: http://maxpaxllc.com
N.A.I.C.S.:
Rick Geiger (CEO)

MAXS OF SAN FRANCISCO INC.
120 E Grand Ave, South San Francisco, CA 94080
Tel.: (650) 873-6297
Web Site: http://www.maxsworld.com
Sales Range: $1-9.9 Million
Emp.: 500
Investment Holding Companies, Except Banks
N.A.I.C.S.: 551112
Dennis Berkowitz (Pres)

MAXTON MOTORS INC.
114 West Main St, Butler, IN 46721
Tel.: (260) 868-2195
Web Site: http://www.maxtonmotors.com
Rev.: $16,562,000
Emp.: 6
Dealership of New & Used Automobiles
N.A.I.C.S.: 441110

MAXUM ENERGY LOGISTICS PARTNERS, LP
20 Horseneck Ln, Greenwich, CT 06830
Tel.: (203) 861-1200 DE
Sales Range: $1-4.9 Billion
Refined Petroleum Distr
N.A.I.C.S.: 424720
Michel P. Salbaing (CFO & Sr VP)
William W. Huffman Jr. (Chief Acctg Officer)

MAXWELL & MILLER MARKETING COMMUNICATIONS
141 E Michigan Ste 500, Kalamazoo, MI 49007-3943
Tel.: (269) 382-4060 MI
Web Site: http://www.maxwellandmiller.com
Year Founded: 1981
Sales Range: Less than $1 Million
Emp.: 10
N.A.I.C.S.: 541810

Gregory A. Miller (Pres & Dir-Creative)
Ruth Nurrie (Dir-Media)
Dan Willoughby (Assoc Dir-Creative)

MAXWELL FOODS, LLC
938 Millers Chapel Rd, Goldsboro, NC 27534-7772
Tel.: (919) 778-3130 NC
Year Founded: 1989
Sales Range: $100-124.9 Million
Emp.: 1,000
Hog, Pig & Turkey Farming
N.A.I.C.S.: 112210
Thomas Howell (CFO)
Walter Pelletier (Vp)
J.L. Maxwell III (Pres)

Subsidiaries:

Butterball, LLC (1)
1 Butterball Ln, Garner, NC 27529 (50%)
Tel.: (919) 255-7900
Web Site: https://www.butterballcorp.com
Sales Range: $1-4.9 Billion
Turkey Processing
N.A.I.C.S.: 112330
Ron Tomaszewski (VP-HR)
Brett Worlow (Gen Counsel & Sec)

Subsidiary (Domestic):

Butterball, LLC (2)
411 N Main St, Carthage, MO 64836-1327
Tel.: (417) 423-8801
Web Site: http://www.butterballcorp.com
Sales Range: $50-74.9 Million
Emp.: 800
Turkey Processing
N.A.I.C.S.: 112330
Shawnda Doerr (Mgr-Logistics)

Butterball, LLC (2)
1240 E Diehl Rd, Naperville, IL 60563
Tel.: (630) 955-3000
Web Site: https://www.butterball.com
Sales Range: $10-24.9 Million
Emp.: 70
Turkey Processing
N.A.I.C.S.: 112330

Gusto Packing Co., Inc. (2)
2125 Rochester Dr, Montgomery, IL 60538
Tel.: (630) 896-8608
Web Site: http://www.gustopack.com
Sales Range: $10-24.9 Million
Emp.: 500
Packaged Meats Distr
N.A.I.C.S.: 311611
Ryan Ruettiger (Mgr-Territory Sls)
Dennis Keene (VP-Sls & Mktg)

MAXWELL PRODUCTS, INC.
6707 N 54th St, Tampa, FL 33610
Tel.: (813) 514-1328 FL
Web Site: http://www.baycityplywood.com
Year Founded: 1979
Sales Range: $25-49.9 Million
Emp.: 40
Home Center Operator
N.A.I.C.S.: 444110
Carl Dunbar (Pres)

MAXWELL RESOURCES, INC.
848 N Rainbow Blvd 2741, Las Vegas, NV 89107
Tel.: (702) 706-5576 NV
Web Site: http://www.maxwellre.com
Year Founded: 2010
Sales Range: Less than $1 Million
Emp.: 1
Metal Mining Services
N.A.I.C.S.: 212290
Mike Edwards (Pres & CEO)

MAXX HD SUNGLASSES
738 Synthes Ave, Monument, CO 80132
Tel.: (719) 550-8116
Web Site: http://www.maxxsunglasses.com

MAXX HD SUNGLASSES

Maxx HD Sunglasses—(Continued)
Year Founded: 2005
Sales Range: $1-9.9 Million
Emp.: 46
Sunglasses
N.A.I.C.S.: 456180
Nancy Milner *(Co-Owner)*
Rick Milner *(Co-Owner)*
Billy Witter *(Dir-Licensed Sls)*
Travis Howell *(Dir-Comm)*

MAXXAM, INC.
1330 Post Oak Blvd Ste 2000, Houston, TX 77056-3058
Tel.: (713) 975-7600   DE
Web Site: http://charleshurwitz.com
Year Founded: 1955
Sales Range: $75-99.9 Million
Emp.: 1,080
Holding Company; Operations in the Aluminum, Forest Products, Real Estate & Racing Industries
N.A.I.C.S.: 551112
Charles E. Hurwitz *(Pres & CEO)*

Subsidiaries:

MAXXAM Property Company   (1)
1330 Post Oak Blvd Ste 2000, Houston, TX 77056   **(100%)**
Tel.: (713) 975-7600
Sales Range: $75-99.9 Million
Emp.: 17
Land Development
N.A.I.C.S.: 113110

Subsidiary (Domestic):

MCO Properties Inc.   (2)
13620 N Sagaro Blvd Ste 200, Fountain Hills, AZ 85268   **(100%)**
Tel.: (480) 837-9660
Web Site: http://www.mcoproperties.com
Sales Range: $10-24.9 Million
Emp.: 10
Land Development Services
N.A.I.C.S.: 531210

MAXXESS SYSTEMS, INC.
22661 Old Canal Rd, Yorba Linda, CA 92887
Tel.: (714) 772-1000   DE
Web Site: http://www.maxxess-systems.com
Year Founded: 1975
Sales Range: $10-24.9 Million
Emp.: 20
Access Technology Services
N.A.I.C.S.: 335999
Lee Copland *(Mng Dir)*
Joel Slutzky *(Chm)*

Subsidiaries:

MAXxess Systems Europe, Ltd.   (1)
Atrium Court The Ring, Doncastle Road, Bracknell, RG12 1BW, Berkshire, United Kingdom
Tel.: (44) 1344 440083
Web Site: http://www.maxxess-systems.com
Emp.: 8
Access Technology Services
N.A.I.C.S.: 335999

MAXYMILLIAN TECHNOLOGIES INC.
1801 E St, Pittsfield, MA 01201
Tel.: (413) 499-3050
Web Site: http://www.maxymillian.com
Rev.: $29,766,936
Emp.: 100
Environmental Cleanup Services
N.A.I.C.S.: 562910
John B. Anthony *(Project Mgr)*
Rick Desano *(CFO)*
Chester Trzcinski *(Project Mgr)*

MAXYMISER INC.
532 Broadway 10th Fl, New York, NY 10012
Tel.: (212) 201-2359
Web Site: http://www.maxymiser.com
Sales Range: $1-9.9 Million
Software Publisher
N.A.I.C.S.: 513210
Kathleen Rohrecker *(VP-Mktg)*

Subsidiaries:

Maxymiser GmbH   (1)
Neuer Zollhof 3, 40221, Dusseldorf, Germany
Tel.: (49) 211 220 59 355
Software Publisher
N.A.I.C.S.: 513210

Maxymiser Technical Center   (1)
Barykkadna str 1a, Dnepropetrovsk, 40221, Ukraine
Tel.: (380) 56 377 44 09
Emp.: 50
Software Publisher
N.A.I.C.S.: 513210
Volk Elena *(Mgr-HR)*

MAXZONE VEHICLE LIGHTING INC.
15889 Soover Ave, Fontana, CA 92337
Tel.: (909) 822-3288
Web Site: http://www.maxzone.com
Sales Range: $10-24.9 Million
Emp.: 19
Mfr of Automotive Lamps
N.A.I.C.S.: 336320
Polo Hsu *(Pres)*

MAY CONSTRUCTION CO.
2226 Cottondale Ln No 100 A, Little Rock, AR 72202
Tel.: (501) 663-5524
Sales Range: Less than $1 Million
Emp.: 10
Industrial Buildings, General Construction
N.A.I.C.S.: 236210
Lewis W. May *(CEO)*
Bob Butler *(Sr VP-Mktg)*
Patrick McLain *(Dir-Bus Unit)*

MAY INSTITUTE, INC.
41 Pacella Park Dr, Randolph, MA 02368
Tel.: (781) 440-0400   MA
Web Site: http://www.mayinstitute.org
Year Founded: 1955
Sales Range: $75-99.9 Million
Emp.: 2,696
Developmental Disability Assistance Services
N.A.I.C.S.: 623210
Deidre L. Donaldson *(Chief Clinical Officer)*
Ralph B. Sperry *(COO)*
Debra Blair *(Chief Fin & Admin Officer & Treas)*
Kevin M. More *(CIO)*
Stephen S. Young *(Chm)*
Mary Lou Maloney *(Vice Chm & Asst Treas)*
Lauren C. Solotar *(Pres & CEO)*
Robert F. Putnam *(Exec VP-Positive Behavior Interventions & Supports)*
Neal Todrys *(Sec)*
Erica Kearney *(Exec Dir-BCBA)*
Serra R. Langone *(Dir-Clinical-BCBA)*
Mary Tiernan *(Sr VP-Philanthropy)*

MAY RIVER CAPITAL, LLC
1 N Wacker Dr Ste 1920, Chicago, IL 60606
Tel.: (312) 750-1772   IL
Web Site: http://www.mayrivercapital.com
Year Founded: 2012
Privater Equity Firm
N.A.I.C.S.: 523999
Charles B. Grace *(Co-Founder & Partner)*
Daniel N. Barlow *(Co-Founder & Partner-Portfolio Mgmt)*
Stephen M. Griesemer *(Partner)*
Pat St. John *(Principal)*

Subsidiaries:

Cashco, Inc.   (1)
607 W 15th St, Ellsworth, KS 67439
Tel.: (785) 472-4461
Web Site: https://www.cashco.com
Sales Range: $75-99.9 Million
Emp.: 155
Self-Contained Regulators & Control Valves; Spare Parts for Coal Pulverizing Systems Used in Power Plant Mfr
N.A.I.C.S.: 332911
Clint Rogers *(Mgr-Mktg)*
Jerry Soukup *(Controller)*
Randy Helus *(Asst Controller)*

Subsidiary (Domestic):

Valve Concepts, Inc.   (2)
PO Box 6, Ellsworth, KS 67439-0006   **(100%)**
Tel.: (713) 271-7171
Web Site: http://www.valveconcepts.com
Sales Range: $25-49.9 Million
Emp.: 150
Pilot Operated Tank Blanketing Valves & Vent Valves & Tank Blanketing Systems
N.A.I.C.S.: 332911

Dickson/Unigage, Inc.   (1)
930 S Westwood Ave, Addison, IL 60101
Tel.: (630) 543-3747
Web Site: http://www.dicksondata.com
Sales Range: $1-9.9 Million
Emp.: 70
Test & Measurement Instrument Mfr
N.A.I.C.S.: 334513
Michael Unger *(Pres)*
Mark Kohlmeier *(CFO)*
Chris Sorensen *(VP-Mktg & Sls)*
Fred Kirsch *(VP-Mfg & Engrg)*
Sue Webb *(Mgr-HR)*
Jeff Renoe *(Mktg Mgr)*
Antoine Nguyen *(Dir-Svcs)*

Subsidiary (Non-US):

Oceasoft SAS   (2)
126 Rue Emile Baudot, 34000, Montpellier, France   **(100%)**
Tel.: (33) 499136730
Web Site: http://www.oceasoft.com
Sales Range: $1-9.9 Million
Surveillance Systems Mfr
N.A.I.C.S.: 561621
Laurent Rousseau *(CEO)*
Pierre Schwich *(CFO)*

Kason Corp.   (1)
67-71 E Willow St, Millburn, NJ 07041-1416
Tel.: (973) 467-8140
Web Site: http://www.kason.com
Industrial Filtration & Separation Equipment Mfr
N.A.I.C.S.: 333248
Becky Alderman *(Dir-Ops)*
Henry Alamzad *(Pres)*
Jonathan Weiner *(CEO)*
James Schak *(Mgr-Product-Fluid Bed Processing Equipment)*

MECA & Technology Machine, Inc.   (1)
1281 Parkview Rd, Green Bay, WI 54304
Tel.: (920) 336-7382
Web Site: http://www.mecagb.com
Sales Range: $10-24.9 Million
Printing Industry Machinery Mfr
N.A.I.C.S.: 333248
Mick Karchinski *(VP-Sls)*
Dean J. Re *(Pres & CEO)*

Pressed Paperboard Technologies, LLC   (1)
30400 Telg Rd Ste 386, Franklin, MI 48025
Tel.: (248) 646-6500
Sales Range: $1-9.9 Million
Emp.: 52
Paperboard Mills
N.A.I.C.S.: 322130
Al Fotheringham *(Chief Dev Officer)*
Jim Morgan *(CEO)*

Raymond & Lae Engineering, Inc.   (1)
208 Commerce Dr Ste 3C, Fort Collins, CO 80524
Tel.: (970) 484-6510
Web Site: http://www.rletech.com
Sales Range: $1-9.9 Million
Emp.: 15
Measuring & Controlling Device Mfr
N.A.I.C.S.: 334519
Donald Raymond *(CEO)*
Anna Stodghill *(Mgr-Acctg)*
Cam Rogers *(Dir-Sls)*
Don Garrison *(Dir-Ops)*
Jeremy Swanner *(Exec VP-Sls & Mktg)*
Katie Scherer *(Mgr-Project)*
Kendra Kelly *(Mgr-HR)*
Nick Bettis *(VP-Mktg)*

Unibloc-Pump, Inc.   (1)
1650 Airport Rd Ste 110, Kennesaw, GA 30144
Tel.: (770) 218-8900
Web Site: http://www.unibtocpump.com
Rev.: $1,500,000
Emp.: 12
Industrial Mold Mfr
N.A.I.C.S.: 333511
Chris Stevens *(CEO)*

Subsidiary (Domestic):

Standard Pump, Inc.   (2)
1610 Satellite Blvd Ste D, Duluth, GA 30097
Tel.: (770) 307-1003
Web Site: http://www.standardpump.com
Pump & Pumping Equipment Mfr.
N.A.I.C.S.: 333914
Christopher Murphy *(Dir-Ops)*
James Murphy *(Dir-Sales)*
Don Murphy *(Co-Founder)*

MAY TRUCKING COMPANY INC.
4185 Brooklake Rd, Salem, OR 97303
Tel.: (503) 393-7030   ID
Web Site: http://www.maytrucking.com
Year Founded: 1945
Sales Range: $75-99.9 Million
Emp.: 1,000
Trucking Service
N.A.I.C.S.: 484121
C. Marvin May *(CEO)*
Dave Temple *(CFO)*
David M. Daniels *(Pres)*

Subsidiaries:

Trendsetters Inc.   (1)
2141 Bonnie Dr, Payette, ID 83661-3064
Tel.: (541) 889-7291
Rev.: $700,000
Emp.: 10
Book Stores
N.A.I.C.S.: 459420

MAYA STEELS FABRICATION, INC.
301 E Compton Blvd, Gardena, CA 90248
Tel.: (310) 532-8830
Web Site: http://www.mayasteel.com
Year Founded: 1982
Sales Range: $10-24.9 Million
Emp.: 64
Structural Metal Mfr
N.A.I.C.S.: 332312
Meir Amsalam *(VP)*
Darren Madden *(Sr Project Mgr)*
Yechiel Yogev *(Treas & VP)*

MAYCO INDUSTRIES, LLC
18 W Oxmoor Rd, Birmingham, AL 35209
Tel.: (205) 942-4242   DE
Web Site: http://www.maycoindustries.com
Lead Recycling, Smelting & Lead Products Mfr & Reclamation Shot
N.A.I.C.S.: 331492
Greg Lasonde *(CEO)*
Rhonda Bower *(Mgr-Purchasing)*

COMPANIES

Tammy Manns *(Sls Mgr-Roofing & Plumbing Products)*
Jennifer Banbury *(Sls Mgr-Specialty Products & Ballast)*
Paul Medvec *(Engr-Tech Sls)*
Robyn Richardson *(Mgr-Ammunition Products)*

MAYER BROS. APPLE PRODUCTS, INC.
3300 Transit Rd, West Seneca, NY 14224
Tel.: (716) 668-1787
Web Site: http://www.mayerbrothers.com
Year Founded: 1852
Sales Range: $10-24.9 Million
Emp.: 150
Provider of Apple Cider, Juices & Spring Water
N.A.I.C.S.: 311421
John Mayer *(Owner, Pres & CEO)*
Linda Tryka *(Controller)*
Alan Zak *(Controller)*
Deborah Schasel *(Mgr-HR)*

MAYER BROTHERS CONSTRUCTION CO.
1902 Cherry St, Erie, PA 16502
Tel.: (814) 452-3748
Sales Range: $10-24.9 Million
Emp.: 60
Highway & Street Paving Contractor
N.A.I.C.S.: 237310
John H. Laver *(Pres)*
Richard T. Wischler *(VP)*
Debbie Snyder *(Office Mgr)*

MAYER BROWN LLP
71 S Wacker Dr, Chicago, IL 60606
Tel.: (312) 782-0600   IL
Web Site: http://www.mayerbrown.com
Year Founded: 1881
Sales Range: $1-4.9 Billion
Emp.: 1,001
Legal Advisory Services
N.A.I.C.S.: 541110
Heather W. Adkerson *(Co-Partner)*
Lee N. Abrams *(Co-Partner)*
Richard M. Assmus *(Co-Partner)*
Paul J. Astolfi *(Co-Partner)*
Michael D. Adams *(Co-Partner)*
Paul W. Theiss *(Chm)*
Kenneth S. Geller *(Mng Partner)*
Timothy W. Bishop *(Partner)*
Christian F. Binnig *(Partner)*
Edward S. Best *(Partner)*
James R. Barry *(Partner)*
Zachary K. Barnett *(Partner)*
Robert C. Baptista *(Partner)*
Melissa A. Anyetei *(Partner)*
Matthew Rossi *(Partner)*
Laurence Urgenson *(Partner)*
Julie Myers Wood *(CEO)*
Gabriela Sakamoto *(Partner)*
Nancy G. Ross *(Partner)*
Jessica Crutcher *(Partner)*
D. Nathan McMichael *(Partner)*
Clinton Brannon *(Partner)*
Francisco Mendez *(Partner)*
Andrew Young *(Partner)*
David Harrison *(Partner)*
Mark Mansour *(Partner)*
Christopher Mikson *(Partner-Litigation & Dispute Resolution Practice-Washington)*
Alexander Behrens *(Partner-Banking & Fin Practice-Frankfurt)*
William Stallings *(Partner)*
Brian Winterfeldt *(Partner)*
Paul Hughes *(Partner-Litigation & Dispute Resolution-Washington)*
Donald Waack *(Partner-Fin Svcs Regulatory & Enforcement Practice-Washington)*
Kfir Levy *(Partner-Washington)*
Timothy Hicks *(Partner)*
Kiel Bowen *(Partner)*
John Cise *(Partner)*
Steven Garden *(Partner)*
Laura Hammargren *(Partner)*
Andres Romay *(Partner)*
Tahan Thraya *(Partner & Head-Middle East Corp & Comml Team-Washington)*
Adam Wolk *(Partner-Banking & Fin-New York)*
Terry Schiff *(Partner-Banking & Fin Practice-New York)*
Richard McCormick *(Partner-Intellectual Property Practice-New York)*
David Wang *(Partner)*
Perry Yam *(Partner & Head-Private Equity-London)*
Kieron Dwyer *(Partner-Fin-London)*
Steven Kaplan *(Partner-Washington)*
Laurence Platt *(Partner-Washington)*
Phillip Schulman *(Partner-Washington)*
Melanie Brody *(Partner-Washington)*
Frank Monaco *(Partner-Global Corp, Securities Practice & Insurance Indus Grp)*
Jonathan Jaffe *(Partner-Palo Alto)*
David Tallman *(Partner)*
Douglas Donahue *(Partner)*
David Burton *(Partner-Tax Transactions & Consulting Practice & Renewable Energy)*
Barry N. Machlin *(Partner)*
Brian Aronson *(Partner)*
Christopher J. Brady *(Partner)*
Christopher P. B. Erckert *(Partner)*
Debora de Hoyos *(Partner)*
George K. Miller *(Partner)*
Jill D. Block *(Partner)*
Los Angeles *(Partner)*
Scott T. Buser *(Partner)*
Doo-Soon Choi *(Partner-Banking & Fin-Hong Kong)*
Marjorie Harris Loeb *(Partner-Corp & Securities Practice)*
David Simon *(Partner)*
Robert Woll *(Partner-Hong Kong)*
Mitchell Holzrichter *(Partner-Govt Practice & Global Infrastructure Grp)*
Robert I. Bressman *(Partner-Global Real Estate Practice)*
Mae Rogers *(Partner-Banking & Fin Practice-New York)*
Gary Wilcox *(Partner-Tax Controversy & Transfer Pricing Practice-Washington)*
Leah Robinson *(Partner)*
Nicolette Kost De Sevres *(Partner-Litigation & Dispute Resolution Practice-Washington)*
Ameer Ahmad *(Partner-Corp & Securities Practice)*
James John Antonopoulos *(Partner-Banking, Fin Practice & Structured Fin Grp)*
Matthew D. O'Meara *(Partner-Banking & Fin Practice & Head-Private Credit Grp-Global)*
Audrey Harris *(Partner-Washington)*
Ashley McDermott *(Partner-Banking & Fin Practice-London)*
Phyllis Korff *(Partner-Capital Markets-New York)*
Daniel Jones *(Partner-Washington)*
Justin Ilhwan Park *(Partner-Washington)*
Oral Pottinger *(Partner-Washington)*
Tori Shinohara *(Partner-Washington)*
Jad Taha *(Partner-Washington)*
Paul P. Chen *(Partner-Corp & Securities Practice-Northern California)*
Steven Tran *(Partner-Corp & Securities Practice-Hong Kong)*
Philip Brandes *(Partner-New York)*
Marlon Paz *(Partner-Washington)*
L. Kevin Sheridan Jr. *(Partner)*
James Fussell III *(Partner-Washington)*

MAYER ELECTRIC SUPPLY COMPANY INC.
3405 4th Ave S, Birmingham, AL 35222-2305
Tel.: (205) 583-3500   DE
Web Site: http://www.mayerelectric.com
Year Founded: 1930
Sales Range: $500-549.9 Million
Emp.: 850
Electrical Apparatus & Equipment Whslr & Distr
N.A.I.C.S.: 423610
Wes Smith *(Pres)*
Nancy Goedecke *(Chm & CEO)*
Glenn Goedecke *(Exec VP-Bus Dev)*

Subsidiaries:

Mayer Electric Financial Corporation (1)
3405 Fourth Ave S, Birmingham, AL 35222-2305
Tel.: (205) 583-3500
Web Site: http://www.mayerelectric.com
Sales Range: $25-49.9 Million
Emp.: 200
Electrical Apparatus & Equipment
N.A.I.C.S.: 423610

Mayer Electric Supply Company, Inc. (1)
2510 Greengate Dr, Greensboro, NC 27406 (100%)
Tel.: (336) 275-9603
Web Site: http://www.mayerelectric.com
Electrical Supply Distr
N.A.I.C.S.: 423610
Eddie Jones *(Branch Mgr)*

Mayer Electric Supply Service Co. Inc. (1)
3405 4th Ave S, Birmingham, AL 35222-2305
Tel.: (205) 583-3500
Web Site: http://www.mayerelectric.com
Rev.: $1,200,000
Emp.: 500
Accounting, Auditing & Bookkeeping
N.A.I.C.S.: 541219
Glenn Goedecke *(VP-Sls & Mktg)*
Nancy Collat Goedecke *(Chm & CEO)*
Wes Smith *(Pres)*

MAYER HOFFMAN MCCANN, P.C.
700 W 47th St Ste 1100, Kansas City, MO 64112
Tel.: (913) 234-1900
Web Site: http://www.mhmcpa.com
Year Founded: 1954
Sales Range: $650-699.9 Million
Emp.: 4,010
Accounting Services
N.A.I.C.S.: 541211
Bill Hancock *(Pres)*

MAYER/BERKSHIRE CORPORATION
Po Box 244, Wayne, NJ 07474
Tel.: (973) 696-6200   NJ
Web Site: http://www.eberkshire.com
Year Founded: 1945
Sales Range: $75-99.9 Million
Emp.: 80
Hosiery; Panty Hose; Underwear & Related Apparel; Retail Apparel
N.A.I.C.S.: 424350
Joseph Weinstein *(VP)*

MAYESH WHOLESALE FLORIST, INC.
5401 W 104th St, Los Angeles, CA 90045-6011
Tel.: (310) 348-4921   CA
Web Site: http://www.mayesh.com
Year Founded: 1938
Fresh Flowers Whslr
N.A.I.C.S.: 424930
Patrick Dahlson *(Owner & CEO)*
Isabelle Buckley *(Gen Mgr-Shipping)*

MAYFAIR CONSTRUCTION GROUP, LLC.
170 Mason St, Greenwich, CT 06830
Tel.: (203) 622-1070
Web Site: http://mayfairconstruction.com
Sales Range: $10-24.9 Million
Emp.: 6
Housing Construction Services
N.A.I.C.S.: 236117
Timothy Ryan *(Owner)*

MAYFIELD EQUIPMENT CO.
235 E Perkins St, Ukiah, CA 95482
Tel.: (707) 462-2404
Web Site: http://www.rainbowag.com
Year Founded: 1977
Sales Range: $10-24.9 Million
Emp.: 45
Retailer & Servicer of Irrigation Equipment & Heavy Agricultural Equipment; Animal Feeds
N.A.I.C.S.: 423820
Jim Mayfield *(Pres)*

MAYFIELD FUND
2484 Sand Hill Rd Ste 250, Menlo Park, CA 94025
Tel.: (650) 854-5560
Web Site: http://www.mayfield.com
Year Founded: 2001
Sales Range: $1-4.9 Billion
Emp.: 60
Privater Equity Firm
N.A.I.C.S.: 523999
James Beck *(COO)*
Navin Chaddha *(Mng Dir)*

MAYFIELD GRAIN COMPANY INC.
622 Allen St, Mayfield, KY 42066
Tel.: (270) 247-1661
Web Site: http://www.mayfieldgrain.com
Sales Range: $10-24.9 Million
Emp.: 5
Grain
N.A.I.C.S.: 424510
Donald Wray *(Pres)*
Bobby Whitford *(Gen Mgr)*

MAYFIELD PAPER CO. INC.
1115 S Hill St, San Angelo, TX 76903
Tel.: (325) 653-1444
Web Site: http://www.mayfieldpaper.com
Sales Range: $25-49.9 Million
Emp.: 50
Sanitary & Food Containers
N.A.I.C.S.: 424130
J. Stanley Mayfield *(Co-Pres)*
Deanna Mayfield *(Co-Pres)*

MAYFIELD TRANSFER COMPANY INCORPORATED
3200 W Lake St, Melrose Park, IL 60160
Tel.: (708) 681-4440
Web Site: http://www.mfld.net
Rev.: $18,595,315
Emp.: 70
Local Trucking
N.A.I.C.S.: 484110
R. J. Emerick *(Pres)*
Colleen Palesch *(Controller)*
Raymond J. Emerick Jr. *(CEO)*

MAYFLOWER FOOD STORES INC.

U.S. PRIVATE

Mayfield Transfer Company Incorporated—(Continued)

MAYFLOWER FOOD STORES INC.
102 E 22nd St, Stuttgart, AR 72160
Tel.: (870) 673-4640
Sales Range: $10-24.9 Million
Emp.: 75
Provider of Independent Supermarket Services
N.A.I.C.S.: 445110
David Leech (Pres)

MAYFLOWER INN & SPA
118 Woodbury Rd Route 47, Washington, CT 06793
Tel.: (860) 868-9466
Web Site: http://www.mayflowerinn.com
Sales Range: $1-9.9 Million
Emp.: 110
Inn & Spa Owner & Operator
N.A.I.C.S.: 721110
John Trevenen (Owner)

MAYFRAN INTERNATIONAL, INC.
6650 Beta Dr, Cleveland, OH 44143-2321
Tel.: (440) 461-4100
Web Site: http://www.mayfran.com
Year Founded: 1933
Sales Range: $75-99.9 Million
Emp.: 7,500
Conveyor & Scrap Handling Systems Mfr
N.A.I.C.S.: 333922
Andy Tiltins (VP & Gen Mgr)

Subsidiaries:

Mayfran International, B.V. (1)
Edisonstraat 14, 6370 AA, Landgraaf, Netherlands (100%)
Tel.: (31) 455329292
Web Site: http://www.mayfran.nl
Sales Range: $25-49.9 Million
Emp.: 300
Conveyor Mfr
N.A.I.C.S.: 333922
Wilhelmus Kroonen (Mng Dir)

MAYHEW STEEL PRODUCTS INC.
199 Industrial Blvd, Turners Falls, MA 01376
Tel.: (413) 863-4860
Web Site: http://www.mayhew.com
Sales Range: $10-24.9 Million
Emp.: 44
Provider of Steel Tools
N.A.I.C.S.: 332216
John C. Lawless (Pres)
Eric Mills (VP-Sls & Mktg)
Wayne Smith (Sls Mgr-West)

MAYHUGH REALTY, INC.
13690 Eagle Ridge Dr, Fort Myers, FL 33912
Tel.: (239) 278-4945
Web Site: http://www.mayhughrealty.com
Sales Range: $1-9.9 Million
Emp.: 9
Real Estate Broker
N.A.I.C.S.: 531210
Charles Mayhugh (Pres)

MAYMONT FOUNDATION
1700 Hampton St, Richmond, VA 23220
Tel.: (804) 358-7166
Web Site: http://www.maymont.org
Year Founded: 1947
Sales Range: $1-9.9 Million
Emp.: 126
Museum Operator
N.A.I.C.S.: 712110

Clint M. Bowes (Pres)
Eric Nedell (Treas)
Janet Dibbs (Sec)

MAYNARD STEEL CASTING COMPANY
2856 S 27th St, Milwaukee, WI 53215-3603
Tel.: (414) 645-0440
Web Site: http://www.maynardsteel.com
Year Founded: 1913
Sales Range: $25-49.9 Million
Emp.: 300
Mfr of Steel Castings
N.A.I.C.S.: 331513
Eugene O'Kelly (VP-HR)
Edmund D. Wabiszewski (Owner)
Robert Thill (Pres & CEO)
Mike Wabiszewski (Pres & CEO)

MAYNARD, COOPER & GALE, P.C.
2400 Regions Harbert Plz 1901 6th Ave N, Birmingham, AL 35203-2618
Tel.: (205) 254-1000
Web Site: http://www.maynardcooper.com
Year Founded: 1984
Emp.: 300
Law firm
N.A.I.C.S.: 541110
Janell M. Ahnert (Atty)
Julia G. Bernstein (Atty)
Elizabeth G. Beaube (Atty)
Scott A. Abney (Atty)
Jim Pool (Atty)
John Lanier (Atty)
Katherine A. Collier (Atty)
Matthew W. Grill (Atty)
Olivia Woodard (Atty-Contract)
Jessica Stetler Grover (Atty)
Stuart Roberts (Atty-Labor & Employment)
Ragan Barker (Mgr-Acctg)
Lucas B. Gambino (Atty)
Michael D. Mulvaney (Atty)
Sasha Rao (Partner)
Brandon Stroy (Partner)
Leanne Bains (Dir-Litigation Support)
Vitale Buford (Dir-Mktg & Bus Dev)
Ray Bullock (COO)
Jason Dover (Dir-IT)
Susan Tucker (Controller)
Brian Chapuran (Atty-Huntsville)
Lindsay Whitworth (Atty-Real Estate Practice)
Gregory S. Curran (Chm)
Lee E. Bains Jr. (Atty)

Subsidiaries:

McKenzie Laird Ottinger Leach, PLLC (1)
3835 Cleghorn Ave Ste 250, Nashville, TN 37215
Tel.: (615) 916-3220
Web Site: http://www.mckenzielaird.com
Law firm
N.A.I.C.S.: 541199

MAYNARDS ELECTRIC SUPPLY, INC.
3445 Winton Pl, Rochester, NY 14623
Tel.: (585) 272-0860
Web Site: http://www.maynardselectric.com
Rev.: $23,500,000
Emp.: 106
Electrical Apparatus & Equipment Wiring Supplies & Related Equipment Merchant Whslr
N.A.I.C.S.: 423610
Glenn Hellman (VP)
Bruce Hellman (Pres & CEO)
Steven Grammatica (Mgr-Shipping & Receiving)

MAYO CLINIC
200 1st St SW, Rochester, MN 55905
Tel.: (507) 284-2511
Web Site: http://www.mayoclinic.org
Year Founded: 1819
Sales Range: $1-4.9 Billion
Emp.: 63,134
Hospital Operator
N.A.I.C.S.: 622110
Wyatt W. Decker (VP)
Gianrico Farrugia (Pres & CEO)
Karl Nath (Editor-in-Chief-Mayo Clinic Proceedings)
Dennis Dahlen (CFO)
G. Anton Decker (Pres-Intl)
Robert Albright (VP-Mayo Clinic Health Sys-Southeast Minnesota)

Subsidiaries:

Mayo Clinic Arizona (1)
13400 E Shea Blvd, Scottsdale, AZ 85259
Tel.: (480) 301-8000
Web Site: http://www.mayoclinic.org
Health Care Srvices
N.A.I.C.S.: 622110
Wyatt W. Decker (CEO)

Mayo Clinic Florida (1)
4205 Belfort Rd Ste 1100, Jacksonville, FL 32216
Tel.: (904) 296-5876
Web Site: http://www.mayoclinic.org
Hospital Operator
N.A.I.C.S.: 622110
Christina Zorn (Chief Admin Officer)

MAYO FOUNDATION FOR MEDICAL EDUCATION & RESEARCH
13400 E Shea Blvd, Scottsdale, AZ 85259
Tel.: (480) 301-8000
Web Site: https://www.mayo.edu
Educational Support Services
N.A.I.C.S.: 611710

MAYO KNITTING MILL INC.
2204 W Austin St, Tarboro, NC 27886
Tel.: (252) 823-3101
Web Site: http://www.mayoknitting.com
Year Founded: 1932
Sales Range: $10-24.9 Million
Emp.: 100
Mfr & Retailer of Socks
N.A.I.C.S.: 315120
Bryan Mayo (VP-Production & Sls)
Columbus W. Mayo III (Gen Mgr)
Ben C. Mayo Jr. (Pres)

MAYO PERFORMING ARTS CENTER
100 South St, Morristown, NJ 07960
Tel.: (973) 539-0345
Web Site: http://www.mayoarts.org
Year Founded: 1995
Theater Operator
N.A.I.C.S.: 711110
Ed Kirchdoerffer (Gen Mgr)
Allison Larena (Pres & CEO)
Anita J. Siegel (Sec)
Joseph Goryeb (Chm)
Matthew Finlay (Treas)
Robert Mulholland (Vice Chm)
Cathy Roy (Dir-Education)
Sasha Pensado (Fin Dir)
Jean Leonard (Mktg Dir)
Marysue DePaola (Dir-Dev)
Anthony Scareon (Mgr-Admin & Board Rels)
Julie Dwoskin (Office Mgr)
Michael Dundon (Mgr-Audience Dev)
Lana Missaggia (Mgr-Membership & Special Events)
Justin Wynn (Asst Dir-Dev)
Chris Ball (Dir-Production)
Adrienne Beck (Mgr-Programming)
Lauren Soule (Mgr-Digital Content)

Lindsey Fu (Mktg Mgr)
Jenny Boeckel (Mgr-Education)
David A. Brown (Mgr-Production)
Karen Kogut (Mgr-Hospitality)
Jim Sargent (Dir-Lighting)
Cheryl Yosh (Mgr-Box & Audience Svcs)
Lee Kaloidis (Dir-Ops)
Mark Mattera (Mgr-Ops & Starlight Room)
Erin Pach (Sr Mgr-House & Volunteer Program)

MAYORGA COFFEE INC.
15151 Southlawn Ln, Rockville, MD 20850
Tel.: (301) 315-8093
Web Site: http://www.mayorgacoffee.com
Year Founded: 1996
Sales Range: $1-9.9 Million
Emp.: 89
Coffee Roasters
N.A.I.C.S.: 311920
Martin Mayorga (Pres)

MAYOSEITZ MEDIA
Hillcrest 1 751 Arbor Way Ste 130, Blue Bell, PA 19422
Tel.: (215) 641-8700
Web Site: http://www.mayoseitzmedia.com
Year Founded: 1997
Sales Range: $10-24.9 Million
Emp.: 37
Media Buying Services
N.A.I.C.S.: 541830
Jon Seitz (Co-Founder & Mng Dir)
Ray Mayo (Co-Founder & Mng Dir)
Adam Yansick (VP & Dir-Media Strategy & Analytics)
Mary Tyrrell (Chief Media & Ops Officer & Exec VP)
Kate Golmulka (Mgr-Campaign Analytics)
Lisa Volpe (Mgr-HR)

MAYPOLE CHEVROLET INC.
1223 S Big A Rd, Toccoa, GA 30577
Tel.: (706) 886-7481
Web Site: http://www.maypolechevrolet.com
Rev.: $16,354,412
Emp.: 25
New & Used Automobiles
N.A.I.C.S.: 441110
Charles Maypole (Pres)
Judson Moorely (VP)
Mary Ann Kirk (Controller)
David Philip (Mgr-Parts)

MAYPORT C&C FISHERIES INC.
36 W 6th St, Atlantic Beach, FL 32233
Tel.: (904) 246-1138
Web Site: http://www.candcfisheries.com
Year Founded: 1987
Sales Range: $1-9.9 Million
Emp.: 25
Fish & Seafood Distr
N.A.I.C.S.: 424460
Atillio Cerqueira (Pres)
Graeme Thomson (Gen Mgr)

MAYPORT FARMERS CO-OP
945 3rd St SE, Mayville, ND 58257
Tel.: (701) 786-4263
Web Site: http://www.mayportfarmers.com
Year Founded: 1994
Sales Range: $10-24.9 Million
Emp.: 25
Farmers Cooperative Society
N.A.I.C.S.: 424510

COMPANIES

Jason Strand *(Pres)*

MAYS CHEMICAL COMPANY
5611 E 71st St, Indianapolis, IN 46220-3920
Tel.: (317) 842-8722 IN
Web Site: http://www.mayschem.com
Year Founded: 1980
Sales Range: $200-249.9 Million
Emp.: 70
Distr of Industrial Chemicals
N.A.I.C.S.: 424690
Kristin Mays-Corbitt *(Co-Pres)*

Subsidiaries:

Mays Captree (1)
134 Clinton Rd, Fairfield, NJ 07004
Tel.: (973) 808-7081
Sales Range: $10-24.9 Million
Emp.: 30
Distr of Industrial & Specialty Chemicals
N.A.I.C.S.: 424690
Bob Albert *(Mgr-Sls)*

Mays Chemical Company (1)
400 Commerce Pkwy W Dr, Greenwood, IN 46143-6043
Tel.: (317) 638-4112
Industrial Chemical Distr
N.A.I.C.S.: 424690

Mays Chemical Company - Mays Life Sciences Divison (1)
5611 E 71st St, Indianapolis, IN 46220
Tel.: (317) 842-8722
Web Site: http://www.mayslifesciences.com
Medical Equipment Distr
N.A.I.C.S.: 339112
Korbin Mays *(Mgr-Bus Dev)*

MAYS DISTRIBUTING COMPANY
102 N Martin Luther King Blvd, Union Springs, AL 36089
Tel.: (334) 738-5469
Sales Range: $10-24.9 Million
Emp.: 18
Sales of Automotive Supplies & Parts
N.A.I.C.S.: 423120
Charles May *(Pres)*

MAYSE AUTOMOTIVE GROUP
2032 S Elliot, Aurora, MO 65605
Tel.: (417) 678-7606
Web Site:
  http://www.mayseautomotive.com
Car Dealer
N.A.I.C.S.: 441110
Matthew Mayse *(Gen Mgr)*
Sherri Williams *(Comptroller)*
Greg Poe *(Mgr-New Car)*
Doug Crisp *(Mgr-Pre-Owned Vehicles)*
Bill Baremore *(Mgr-Svc)*
Stan Davidson *(Mgr-Pre-Owned Vehicles)*
Steve Shiveley *(Mgr-Internet Sls)*
Mike Warnow *(Mgr-Quick Lube)*
Larry Carriger *(Mgr-Detail)*
Ken Grozinger *(Mgr-Parts)*
Jeff Silvey *(Mgr-Fin)*
Rob Bieber *(Mgr-Fin)*
Tripp Cook *(Mgr-Fin)*
Matt Molica *(Mgr-Fin)*
Anna Klem *(Mgr-Digital Media)*

MAYWOOD PARK TROTTING ASSOCIATION, INC.
8600 W North Ave, Melrose Park, IL 60160
Tel.: (708) 343-4800
Web Site:
  http://www.maywoodpark.com
Year Founded: 1946
Sales Range: $100-124.9 Million
Emp.: 250
Horse Racetrack Operator
N.A.I.C.S.: 711212

Duke Johnston *(Pres)*
Paul Svendsen *(VP-Fin)*
Jim Hannon *(Dir-Simulcast Ops)*
John Johnston *(VP)*

MAYZO, INC.
3935 Lakefield Ct, Suwanee, GA 30024
Tel.: (770) 449-9066
Web Site: http://www.mayzo.com
Year Founded: 1986
Sales Range: $25-49.9 Million
Emp.: 25
Specialty Chemical Product Mfr & Distr
N.A.I.C.S.: 424690
Ben Milazzo *(Founder)*
Mark Youorski *(Mgr-Warehouse)*
Keith Bernard *(VP-Sls & Mktg)*
Doug Hartman *(Dir-Sls & Customer Care)*
Eduardo Padilla *(Pres)*

MAZDA COMPUTING
2526 Qume Dr Ste 22, San Jose, CA 95131
Tel.: (510) 440-8988
Web Site:
  http://www.mazdacomputing.com
Emp.: 15
Hardware & Software IT Solutions
N.A.I.C.S.: 513210
John Dang *(Mgr-Contract)*

MAZDA KNOXVILLE
8814 Kingston Pike, Knoxville, TN 37923
Tel.: (865) 690-9395
Web Site:
  http://www.mazdaknoxville.com
Rev.: $30,000,000
Emp.: 60
New & Used Automobiles
N.A.I.C.S.: 441110
Lenita Kidd *(Controller & Office Mgr)*
Karl Ackermann *(Gen Mgr)*
Chris Heath *(Mgr-Bus)*
Michael Pogue *(Mgr-Bus)*
Jeff Nissen *(Mgr-Internet Sls)*
Robbie Rule *(Mgr-Parts)*

MAZDA OF MESQUITE
15900 Lbj Fwy, Mesquite, TX 75150-7209
Tel.: (972) 686-6200
Web Site:
  http://www.mazdaofmesquite.com
Year Founded: 2010
Sales Range: $50-74.9 Million
Emp.: 55
New Car Whslr
N.A.I.C.S.: 441110
David Gomez *(Gen Mgr)*

MAZEL & COMPANY INCORPORATED
4300 W Ferdinand St, Chicago, IL 60624
Tel.: (773) 533-1600
Web Site:
  http://www.mazelandco.com
Rev.: $12,500,000
Emp.: 30
Nails
N.A.I.C.S.: 423510
Joel Handelman *(Pres)*

MAZER'S DISCOUNT HOME CENTERS
816 Green Spring Hwy, Homewood, AL 35209
Tel.: (205) 591-6565
Web Site: http://www.mazers.com
Sales Range: $25-49.9 Million
Emp.: 131
Home Center Operator

N.A.I.C.S.: 444110
Mike Mazer *(Pres-Mazer Discount Superstore & VP)*

MAZZARO'S ITALIAN MARKET, LLC
2909 22nd Ave N, Saint Petersburg, FL 33713
Tel.: (727) 321-2400
Web Site:
  http://www.mazzarosmarket.com
Sales Range: $1-9.9 Million
Restaurant
N.A.I.C.S.: 722511
Sam J. Cuccaro *(Partner)*
Patricia A. Cuccaro *(Partner)*
Kurt A. Cuccaro *(Partner)*

MAZZELLA LIFTING TECHNOLOGIES
21000 Aerospace Pkwy, Cleveland, OH 44142
Tel.: (440) 239-7000 OH
Web Site:
  http://www.mazzellalifting.com
Year Founded: 1954
Sales Range: $50-74.9 Million
Emp.: 350
Miscellaneous Fabricated Wire Products
N.A.I.C.S.: 332618
Jim Humphries *(Mgr-Ops, Progressive Crane & Engineered Products)*

Subsidiaries:

New Tech Machinery Corp. (1)
1300 40th St Ste B, Denver, CO 80205
Tel.: (303) 294-0538
Web Site:
  http://www.newtechmachinery.com
Sales Range: $1-9.9 Million
Emp.: 50
Construction Machinery Mfr
N.A.I.C.S.: 333120
Tom Laird *(Mgr-Sls)*

Rouster Wire Rope & Rigging Inc. (1)
102 Ridge St, Mabscott, WV 25871
Tel.: (304) 252-6031
Web Site: http://www.rousterwrr.com
Synthetic Rope, Wire Rope, Chain Slings, Nylon & Polyester Web Slings Supplier
N.A.I.C.S.: 423510
Chuck Farmer *(Pres)*
Justin Yoke *(Mgr-Ops)*

MAZZIO'S CORPORATION
4441 S 72nd E Ave, Tulsa, OK 74145-4692
Tel.: (918) 663-8880
Web Site: http://www.mazzios.com
Year Founded: 1961
Sales Range: $200-249.9 Million
Emp.: 4,100
Pizzeria & Italian Restaurant Owner, Operator & Franchiser
N.A.I.C.S.: 533110
Ken Selby *(VP-Brand Dev)*
Lori Carver *(Pres & CEO)*

Subsidiaries:

Mazzio's Pizza (1)
4441 S 72nd E Ave, Tulsa, OK 74145-4610
Tel.: (918) 663-8880
Web Site: http://www.mazzios.com
Sales Range: $10-24.9 Million
Emp.: 60
Pizza & Restaurant
N.A.I.C.S.: 722511

MAZZOLA FINANCIAL SERVICES
543 N Main St Ste 213, Rochester, MI 48307-1485
Tel.: (248) 652-6300 MI
Year Founded: 1985
Sales Range: $50-74.9 Million
Emp.: 2

MB INVESTMENTS, INC.

Provider of Insurance Services
N.A.I.C.S.: 524210
John Mazzola *(Pres)*

Subsidiaries:

Security Builders Ltd. Inc. (1)
543 N Main St Ste 213, Rochester Hills, MI 48307-1485
Tel.: (248) 652-6300
Insurance Agents Brokers & Service
N.A.I.C.S.: 524210

MAZZONE MANAGEMENT GROUP LTD, INC.
1 Glen Ave, Scotia, NY 12302
Tel.: (518) 374-7262 NY
Web Site:
  http://www.onereputation.com
Year Founded: 1988
Sales Range: $10-24.9 Million
Emp.: 347
Banquet Hall Facilities, Restaurant, Off-Premises Caterers & Contract Food Services
N.A.I.C.S.: 722320
Angelo Mazzone *(Owner & Pres)*

MB CONSULTANTS LTD.
5190 Main St, South Fallsburg, NY 12779
Tel.: (800) 588-5051
Web Site:
  http://www.murrayschicken.com
Year Founded: 1992
Poultry Slaughtering & Processing
N.A.I.C.S.: 311615
Murray Bresky *(Founder)*
Dean Koplik *(COO)*

MB FOOD SERVICE INC.
1877 East 4800 South, Salt Lake City, UT 84117
Tel.: (801) 272-9233
Rev.: $12,000,000
Emp.: 220
Owner of Fast-Food Restaurants
N.A.I.C.S.: 722513
Mark McKay *(Pres)*

MB GLOBAL ADVISERS, LLC
1325 6th Ave, New York, NY 10019
Tel.: (212) 887-1192
Web Site:
  https://mbglobalpartners.com
Emp.: 100
Investment Services
N.A.I.C.S.: 522320

Subsidiaries:

MD Helicopters, Inc. (1)
4555 E McDowell Rd, Mesa, AZ 85215
Tel.: (480) 346-6344
Web Site: http://www.mdhelicopters.com
Sales Range: $25-49.9 Million
Helicopter Mfr
N.A.I.C.S.: 336411
Lynn Tilton *(CEO)*
Edward P. Dolanski *(Chm)*

MB HAYNES CORPORATION
187 Deaverview Rd, Asheville, NC 28806
Tel.: (828) 254-6141
Web Site: http://www.mbhaynes.com
Year Founded: 1921
Rev.: $87,800,000
Emp.: 500
Construction Services
N.A.I.C.S.: 236115
Carolyn Adkins *(Office Mgr)*
Faison Hester *(CFO)*
Nat E. Cannady III *(Pres)*
Bill Toms *(Dir-Safety)*
Ellis Cannady Jr. *(Chm)*

MB INVESTMENTS, INC.
2322 W Oak St, Milwaukee, WI 53206

MB INVESTMENTS, INC.

MB Investments, Inc.—(Continued)
Tel.: (474) 962-3214 WI
Web Site: http://www.lenasfoods.com
Year Founded: 1965
Sales Range: $25-49.9 Million
Holding Company; Supermarkets Owner & Operator
N.A.I.C.S.: 551112
Greg Martin (Co-Owner & VP)

MB REAL ESTATE
181 W Madison St Ste 3900, Chicago, IL 60602
Tel.: (312) 726-1700
Web Site: http://www.mbres.com
Rev.: $20,400,000
Emp.: 236
Commercial & Industrial Building Operation
N.A.I.C.S.: 531120
Mark A. Buth (Mng Dir-Leasing Svcs & Exec VP)
Gary A. Denenberg (Exec VP & Co-Mng Dir-Leasing Svcs)
Peter E. Ricker (Chm & CEO)
Andrew J. Davidson (Exec VP & Mng Dir-Corp Svcs & Tenant Advisory)
Kevin M. Purcell (COO & Exec VP)
John T. Murphy (Vice Chm)
Sara Spicklemire (VP-Leasing Svcs)
Tamara Jensen (Chief Mktg Officer & Sr VP-Mktg)
Caitlin Ritter (Mgr-Market Res & Analysis)
David R. Graff (Mng Dir-Project Svcs & Sr VP)
Gere G. Ricker (Mng Dir-Corp Svcs & Tenant Advisory-New York & Exec VP)
Patricia Aluisi (Chief Admin Officer, Gen Counsel & Exec VP)
Ellen Trager (VP-Leasing Svcs)
Eileen Flynn (CFO)
Karoline Eigel (Chief Mktg Officer & Sr VP)
Michael A. Hull (Sr VP-Corp Svcs & Tenant Advisory)
Pamela Rose (Sr VP-Corp Svcs & Tenant Advisory)
Konstantine T. Sepsis (VP-Corp Svcs & Tenant Advisory)
Boris G. Yelyashov (VP-Corp Svcs & Tenant Advisory)

MB TECHNOLOGY HOLDINGS, LLC
240 S Pineapple Ave Ste 701, Sarasota, FL 34236
Tel.: (941) 954-8701 DE
Web Site: http://www.mbtechnologyholdings.com
Year Founded: 2010
Technology Investment Holding Company
N.A.I.C.S.: 551112
Richard Lee Mooers (Chm & CEO)

MB2 DENTAL SOLUTIONS LLC
2403 Lacy Ln, Carrollton, TX 75006
Tel.: (972) 869-3789
Web Site: http://www.mb2dental.com
Year Founded: 2007
Sales Range: $1-9.9 Million
Health Care Srvices
N.A.I.C.S.: 621610
Chris Steven Villanueva (Founder & CEO)
Jake Berry (Chief Dev Officer)

Subsidiaries:

Simon Dentistry LLC (1)
625 3 Springs Rd, Bowling Green, KY 42104-7528
Tel.: (270) 782-5115
Web Site: http://www.smilesbysimon.com
Offices of Dentists
N.A.I.C.S.: 621210
Tara Alford (Office Mgr)

MBA HEALTHGROUP
55 Community Dr Ste 201, South Burlington, VT 05403
Tel.: (800) 300-8782
Web Site: http://www.mbahealthgroup.com
Year Founded: 1990
Sales Range: $1-9.9 Million
Emp.: 60
Health Care Consulting Services
N.A.I.C.S.: 541611
Lauren Parker (VP)
Ethan Bechtel (COO)
Nicholas Junjulas (Exec Dir-Consulting)

MBA TULSA BEVERAGE COMPANY
510 W Skelly Dr, Tulsa, OK 74107-9453
Tel.: (918) 445-8012
Year Founded: 1986
Sales Range: $50-74.9 Million
Emp.: 1,000
Nonalcoholic, Carbonated Beverages Packaged In Cans & Bottles
N.A.I.C.S.: 312111
Mark Johnson (Gen Mgr)

MBC HOLDINGS, INC.
1613 S Defiance St, Archbold, OH 43502-9488
Tel.: (419) 445-1015 OH
Web Site: http://www.mbcholdings.com
Year Founded: 1994
Sales Range: $25-49.9 Million
Emp.: 341
Holding Company; Highway & Street Construction Services
N.A.I.C.S.: 237310
Brad Miller (Pres)

Subsidiaries:

Miller Bros. Construction (1)
1613 S Defiance St, Archbold, OH 43502-9488
Tel.: (419) 445-8110
Web Site: http://www.millerbrosconst.com
Sales Range: $10-24.9 Million
Emp.: 18
Provider Of Bridge, Tunnel & Elevated Highway Services
N.A.I.C.S.: 237310
Brad Miller (Pres)

MBD CONSTRUCTION COMPANY, INC.
8305 Tom Dr, Baton Rouge, LA 70815-8051
Tel.: (225) 928-5569
Web Site: http://mbdmaintenance.com
Year Founded: 1989
Sales Range: $10-24.9 Million
Emp.: 100
Civil Engineering Services
N.A.I.C.S.: 237310
Andrew McLendon (Pres)

MBE CPAS LLP
E10890 Penny Ln, Baraboo, WI 53913-8120
Tel.: (608) 356-7733
Web Site: https://mbe.cpa
Year Founded: 1982
Emp.: 156
Accounting Services
N.A.I.C.S.: 541219

Subsidiaries:

E&H Certified Public Accountants & Management Consultants P.C. (1)
2021 Broadway, Scottsbluff, NE 69361
Tel.: (308) 632-6570
Web Site: https://www.ehcpaspc.com
Accounting Services
N.A.I.C.S.: 541211

MBF HEALTHCARE PARTNERS, L.P.
121 Alhambra Plz Ste 1100, Coral Gables, FL 33134
Tel.: (305) 461-1162
Web Site: http://www.mbfhp.com
Sales Range: $1-9.9 Million
Emp.: 10
Healthcare-Focused Private Equity Firm
N.A.I.C.S.: 523999
Marcio C. Cabrera (Mng Dir)
Jorge L. Rico (Mng Dir)
Michael B. Fernandez (Chm)
Isabel Pena (CFO)
Michael J. Vaughan (Operating Partner)
Preston Brice (Mng Dir)
Josh M. Weber (Mng Dir)

MBF INDUSTRIES, INC.
210 Tech Dr, Sanford, FL 32771
Tel.: (407) 323-9414 FL
Web Site: http://www.mbfindustries.com
Year Founded: 1992
Sales Range: $10-24.9 Million
Emp.: 40
Specialty Vehicle Mfr
N.A.I.C.S.: 336110
Jim Saboff (CFO)
John Baker (Founder & Pres)
Jim Saboff (CFO)
Glen Johnston (Project Mgr-Engrg)
John Baker (Pres)

MBI, INC.
47 Richards Ave, Norwalk, CT 06857
Tel.: (203) 853-2000 DE
Web Site: http://www.mbi-inc.com
Year Founded: 1969
Sales Range: $100-124.9 Million
Emp.: 600
Direct Marketer Collectibles
N.A.I.C.S.: 459420
Monica Ogrodowski (Sr Mgr-Product Dev)

Subsidiaries:

Danbury Mint (1)
47 Richards Ave, Norwalk, CT 06857 (100%)
Tel.: (203) 838-3800
Web Site: http://www.danburymint.com
Sales Range: $25-49.9 Million
Emp.: 250
Sports Collectibles Direct Mailer
N.A.I.C.S.: 459420

Easton Press (1)
78 Technology Park Dr, Torrington, CT 06790 (100%)
Tel.: (203) 855-8717
Web Site: http://www.eastonpress.com
Leatherbound Book Publisher
N.A.I.C.S.: 513130

Postal Commemorative Society Collection (1)
47 Richards Ave, Norwalk, CT 06857 (100%)
Tel.: (203) 853-2000
Web Site: http://www.mbi-inc.com
Retail-by-Mail Postal Commemorative Stamps
N.A.I.C.S.: 459420
Tom Reese (Mgr-Personnel)

MBK REAL ESTATE LTD.
4 Park Plz Ste 1000, Irvine, CA 92614
Tel.: (949) 789-8300
Web Site: http://www.mbk.com
Rev.: $180,000,000

Emp.: 51
Land Subdividers & Developers
N.A.I.C.S.: 541191
Katsuo Yamanaka (Chm)
Edward Stokx (CFO & Chief Admin Officer)

MBL TECHNOLOGIES
1 Research Ct Ste 450, Rockville, MD 20850
Tel.: (703) 732-6419
Web Site: http://www.mbltechnologies.com
Year Founded: 2007
Sales Range: $10-24.9 Million
Emp.: 28
Information Technology Consulting Services
N.A.I.C.S.: 541512
Bryan Laird (Pres)
Matt Buchert (CEO)
Rob Roemer (Sr Mgr)

MBM CORPORATION
2641 Meadowbrook Rd, Rocky Mount, NC 27801
Tel.: (252) 985-7200 NC
Year Founded: 1947
Sales Range: $1-4.9 Billion
Emp.: 3,000
Food & Related Products Services to National Restaurant Chains
N.A.I.C.S.: 722310
Jerry L. Wordsworth (CEO)
Jeffrey M. Kowalk (CFO)
Tim Ozment (Dir-HR)

MBO PARTNERS
13454 Sunrise Valley Dr Ste 300, Herndon, VA 20171
Tel.: (703) 793-6004
Web Site: http://www.mbopartners.com
Year Founded: 1986
Sales Range: $1-9.9 Million
Emp.: 450
Employment & Financial Services for Independent Professionals & Clients
N.A.I.C.S.: 518210
Gene Zaino (Founder)
Bob Lucas (Sr VP-Bus Dev)
Julian Richards (VP-Product Mgmt)
John Piazza (VP-Solutions Design)
John Dahlberg (Dir-Prod Dev)
Kris Stevens (VP-Mktg)
Chris Mack (CFO)
Linda Mann (Sr VP)
Dawnette Cooke (Chief Client Officer & Sr VP)
Miles Everson (CEO)

MBR CONSTRUCTION SERVICES INC.
307 June Ave, Reading, PA 19510
Tel.: (610) 926-1490
Web Site: http://www.mbrcsi.com
Year Founded: 1934
Sales Range: $50-74.9 Million
Emp.: 170
Electrical, Heating, Ventilation, Air Conditioning & Mechanical Construction
N.A.I.C.S.: 238210
Kenneth R. Field (CEO)
Brendon R. Field (Pres)
Lynn Field (Mgr-HR)
Vic Pajan (Mgr-Sls & Mktg)

Subsidiaries:

MBR Construction Services Inc. (1)
Suite J 8839 Kelso Dr, Baltimore, MD 21221 (100%)
Tel.: (410) 687-3529
Web Site: http://www.mbrcsi.com
Electrical, Heating & Mechanical Construction
N.A.I.C.S.: 237990
Tom Loughry (Gen Mgr)

COMPANIES

MBS INSURANCE SERVICES INC.
215 Myrtle Ave, Boonton, NJ 07005
Tel.: (973) 939-3171
Web Site: http://www.mbsinsure.com
Rev.: $15,000,000
Emp.: 13
Insurance Agents, Brokers & Service
N.A.I.C.S.: 524210
Michael Bernal-Silva *(Pres & CEO)*
Maria DeNotaris *(VP-Ops & Fin)*
Nicole Bahr *(Supvr-Pro Liability Dept)*

MBS VALUE PARTNERS, LLC
501 Madison Ave, New York, NY 10022-5602
Tel.: (212) 223-4147 NY
Web Site: http://www.mbsvalue.com
Year Founded: 2006
Corporate Financial Advisors
N.A.I.C.S.: 541219
Katja Buhrer *(Mng Dir)*

MBT MARKETING
5331 SW Macadam Ave Ste 370, Portland, OR 97239-3848
Tel.: (503) 232-7202
Web Site: http://www.mbtmarketing.com
Sales Range: $10-24.9 Million
Emp.: 15
Advertising Agencies
N.A.I.C.S.: 541810
Jen Burke *(Dir-Media Svcs)*

MC COMMUNICATIONS INC.
3111 Valley Vw Ste T101, Las Vegas, NV 89102-8390
Tel.: (702) 367-1103
Rev.: $11,953,002
Emp.: 110
Cable Television Installation
N.A.I.C.S.: 238210
Michael Boatright *(Pres)*
Rob Heiss *(VP)*
John Wehrman *(CFO)*
Rob Haight *(CEO)*

MC CURRY-DECK MOTORS, INC.
1740 US Highway 74A, Forest City, NC 28043
Tel.: (828) 286-2381
Web Site: http://www.mccurry-deck.com
Sales Range: $10-24.9 Million
Emp.: 34
New Car Retailer
N.A.I.C.S.: 441110
David Rogers *(Mgr-Internet)*
Paul Deck *(Pres)*

MC GOWAN BUILDERS, INC.
160 E Union Ave, East Rutherford, NJ 07073
Tel.: (201) 865-4666 NY
Web Site: http://www.mcgowanbuilders.com
Year Founded: 2001
Rev.: $26,000,000
Emp.: 25
Nonresidential Building Construction Services
N.A.I.C.S.: 236220
A. Forte Maldonado *(CFO)*
Martin C. McGowan *(Pres & Principal)*
Patrick J. McGowan *(CEO & Principal)*

MC GROUP
8959 Tyler Blvd, Mentor, OH 44060
Tel.: (440) 209-6200
Web Site: http://www.themcgroup.com
Year Founded: 1953
Signage, Lighting & Electrical Solutions Services
N.A.I.C.S.: 541870
Tim Eippert *(CEO)*
Subsidiaries:
Icon Identity Solutions, Inc. (1)
1418 Elmhurst Rd, Elk Grove Village, IL 60007-6417 (100%)
Tel.: (847) 364-2250
Web Site: http://www.iconid.com
Sales Range: $25-49.9 Million
Advertising Display Services
N.A.I.C.S.: 339950
Kurt Ripkey *(Pres & CEO)*
Thomas Hunt *(Exec VP-Ops)*
John Callan *(CFO)*
Melanee Jech *(Exec VP & Gen Mgr-Maintenance Ops)*
Evan Wollak *(Exec VP-Program Mgmt & Tech)*
Kevin Hughes *(Exec VP-Sls & Mktg)*

MC PARTNERS INC.
75 State St Ste 2500, Boston, MA 02109
Tel.: (617) 345-7200 BC
Web Site: http://www.mcpartners.com
Year Founded: 2011
Investment Services
N.A.I.C.S.: 523999
Edward J. Keefe *(CFO & Chief Compliance Officer)*
Gillis S. Cashman *(Mng Partner)*
Brian M. Clark *(Mng Partner)*
David D. Croll *(Mng Partner)*
James F. Wade *(Mng Partner)*
John W. Watkins *(Mng Partner)*
Travis Keller *(Mng Partner)*
Arvind Viswanathan *(VP)*

MC SQUARED ENERGY SERVICES, LLC
2 N Riverside Plz Ste 1350, Chicago, IL 60606 IL
Web Site: http://www.mc2energyservices.com
Year Founded: 2008
Electric Power Distr
N.A.I.C.S.: 221122
Charles C. Sutton *(Pres)*
John Clark *(CFO)*
Mark J. McGuire *(Gen Counsel & Exec VP)*
Sharon Hillman *(Exec VP-Regulatory Affairs & Bus Dev)*

MC&A INC.
615 Piikoi St Fl 10, Honolulu, HI 96814-3116
Tel.: (808) 589-5500 HI
Web Site: http://www.mcahawaii.com
Year Founded: 1983
Sales Range: $25-49.9 Million
Emp.: 125
Provider of Travel Services
N.A.I.C.S.: 561520
Chris Resich *(Pres & CEO)*
Mike Fukumoto *(CIO & Sr VP)*
Michelle Ramos *(CFO)*
Mike Dolan *(Sr VP & Gen Mgr)*
Jamie Lambert *(Dir-Sls)*
Heather Bailey *(Dir-Program Dev)*
Mary Beth Kahn *(Chief Sls Officer)*

MC2 SECURITY INC.
615 Jackson Ave, Bronx, NY 10455
Tel.: (718) 401-4006
Year Founded: 1988
Sales Range: $25-49.9 Million
Emp.: 1,200
Security Services
N.A.I.C.S.: 561612

MCA COMMUNICATIONS INC.
483 W 38th St, Houston, TX 77018
Tel.: (281) 591-2434
Web Site: http://www.mcacom.com
Year Founded: 1983
Sales Range: $25-49.9 Million
Emp.: 145
Telephone & Telephone Equipment Installation
N.A.I.C.S.: 811210
Kelly Sarvis *(Project Coord)*

MCA COMMUNICATIONS, LLC
420 S Palm Canyon Dr 2nd Fl, Palm Springs, CA 92262
Tel.: (760) 318-7000
Holding Company
N.A.I.C.S.: 551112

MCABEE CONSTRUCTION, INC.
5724 21st St, Tuscaloosa, AL 35403
Tel.: (205) 349-2212 AL
Web Site: http://www.mcabeeconstruction.com
Year Founded: 1963
Sales Range: $50-74.9 Million
Emp.: 900
Mechanical & Industrial Construction & Fabrication
N.A.I.C.S.: 237990
Leroy McAbee *(Founder & CEO)*
Gary Nichols *(Pres & COO)*
Wendell McAbee *(VP & Gen Mgr)*
Herald Parker *(Dir-Bus Dev)*

MCAD DESIGN, INC.
2075 Bryant St, Denver, CO 80211
Tel.: (303) 969-8844
Web Site: http://www.mcad.com
Year Founded: 1994
Sales Range: $1-9.9 Million
Emp.: 27
Engineering Software Training, Support & Sales
N.A.I.C.S.: 611420
Joel Quizon *(VP)*
Mike Pelock *(Gen Mgr-Mexico)*

MCAFEE INSTITUTE, INC.
73 W Monroe, Chicago, IL 60603
Tel.: (888) 263-1650
Web Site: http://www.mcafeeinstitute.com
Year Founded: 2007
Sales Range: $10-24.9 Million
Emp.: 15
Education, Training & Certification for Anti-Fraud Professionals
N.A.I.C.S.: 611430
Nicole McAfee *(Corp Counsel & VP-Legal)*
Roderick Bailey *(COO)*
Bill Wooters *(Chief Experience Officer)*

MCANINCH CORPORATION
4001 Delaware Ave, Des Moines, IA 50313
Tel.: (515) 267-2500
Web Site: http://www.mcaninchcorp.com
Year Founded: 1959
Sales Range: $50-74.9 Million
Emp.: 275
Earthmoving, Excavating, Water, Sewer & Utility Lines
N.A.I.C.S.: 237110
Dave Manning *(CFO & Treas)*
Dave Stitz *(VP-Fin)*
Doug McAninch *(Pres & COO)*

MCARDLE LTD.
1600 E Main St Ste B, Saint Charles, IL 60174
Tel.: (630) 584-6580
Web Site: http://www.oakbrookcompanies.com
Year Founded: 1983
Sales Range: $50-74.9 Million
Emp.: 150
Provider of Resort Hotel
N.A.I.C.S.: 721110
David A. McArdle *(Chm & COO)*
Philip J. Held *(CFO)*

MCARTHUR FARMS, INC.
1550 NE 208th St, Okeechobee, FL 34972-7229
Tel.: (863) 763-4719 FL
Year Founded: 1927
Sales Range: $10-24.9 Million
Emp.: 160
Dairy Farms & Citrus Fruit Production
N.A.I.C.S.: 112120
Nancy J. Davis *(Pres & CEO)*
Bob Moore *(Controller)*
Bob Rydzewski *(VP)*

MCBARSCOT COMPANY
211 S Main St, Poland, OH 44514
Tel.: (330) 757-3761
Sales Range: $25-49.9 Million
Emp.: 2
Commercial & Industrial Building Operation
N.A.I.C.S.: 531120
John P. Scotford Jr. *(Pres)*

MCBEE OPERATING COMPANY LLC
4301 W Side Dr Ste 200, Dallas, TX 75209
Tel.: (214) 526-1500
Sales Range: $10-24.9 Million
Emp.: 11
Crude Petroleum Production
N.A.I.C.S.: 211120
Kelley Henderson *(Controller)*
Michael McBee Jr. *(VP)*

MCBRIDE & SON ENTERPRISES INC.
16091 Swingley Ridge Rd Ste 300, Chesterfield, MO 63017
Tel.: (636) 537-2000
Web Site: http://www.mcbridehomes.com
Year Founded: 1946
Sales Range: $10-24.9 Million
Emp.: 70
Provider of Home Construction Services
N.A.I.C.S.: 531210
John Eilermann *(Chm & CEO)*

MCBRIDE CONSTRUCTION RESOURCES, INC.
224 Nickerson St, Seattle, WA 98109
Tel.: (206) 283-7121
Web Site: http://www.mcbrideconstruction.com
Sales Range: $150-199.9 Million
Emp.: 100
Commercial & Institutional Building Construction Services
N.A.I.C.S.: 236220
Ken McBride *(Founder)*
Rick Witte *(CEO)*
Dennis Edwards *(Partner)*
Connor McBride *(Founder)*
Bob Gross *(Project Mgr)*
Chad Heitlauf *(Gen Mgr-Ops-Portland & Project Mgr)*
Brad Kelln *(Project Mgr)*
Steve Leigh *(Dir-Safety)*
Scott McClellan *(Project Mgr)*
John Niederegger *(Project Mgr)*
James Serres *(Project Mgr)*
Anthony Young *(Project Mgr)*
Jeff Leer *(Project Mgr)*
Jim Wheelock *(Project Mgr)*

MCBRIDE ELECTRIC INC.

MCBRIDE ELECTRIC INC.

U.S. PRIVATE

McBride Electric Inc.—(Continued)
6480 Weathers Pl Ste 340, San Diego, CA 92121
Tel.: (858) 450-1414
Web Site:
http://www.mcbrideelectric.com
Sales Range: $50-74.9 Million
Emp.: 500
Electrical Work
N.A.I.C.S.: 238210
Marc McBride *(CEO)*
Debbie Tonello *(Controller)*

MCC INCORPORATED
2600 N Roemer Rd, Appleton, WI 54911
Tel.: (920) 749-3360 WI
Web Site: http://www.mcc-inc.bz
Year Founded: 1946
Sales Range: $25-49.9 Million
Emp.: 250
Central-Mixed Concrete, Highway & Street Construction
N.A.I.C.S.: 327320
Joseph Murphy *(Pres)*
Rick Kranzusch *(Treas)*
Nichole Fassbender *(Mgr-HR Safety)*

MCC INTERNATIONAL, INC.
110 Centrifugal Ct, McDonald, PA 15057
Tel.: (724) 745-0300 PA
Web Site:
http://www.millercentrifugal.com
Year Founded: 1957
Ferrous & Non-ferrous Products Mfr (Bearing Parts, Gear Blanks, Valve Bodies, etc.) & Centrifugal Casting
N.A.I.C.S.: 331529
Rodney Francis *(Sec)*

MCCAFFERTY FORD SALES INC.
1939 E Lincoln Hwy, Langhorne, PA 19047
Tel.: (215) 945-8000 PA
Web Site: http://www.mccafferty.com
Year Founded: 1954
Sales Range: $75-99.9 Million
Emp.: 680
Sales of New & Used Automobiles
N.A.I.C.S.: 441110
Todd V. Buch *(CEO)*
Chris Scott *(Gen Mgr)*

MCCALL HANDLING CO.
8801 Wise Ave 200Dundalk, Baltimore, MD 21222
Tel.: (410) 244-1700
Web Site:
http://www.mccallhandling.com
Year Founded: 1948
Sales Range: $10-24.9 Million
Machinery Rental Services
N.A.I.C.S.: 423830
James Kenny *(Owner)*
Paul Geiman *(Mgr-Warehouse)*
Joe Karasek *(Mgr-Ops)*

MCCALL OIL & CHEMICAL CORP.
5480 NW Front Ave, Portland, OR 97210-1114
Tel.: (503) 221-6400 WA
Web Site: http://www.mccalloil.com
Year Founded: 1939
Sales Range: $200-249.9 Million
Emp.: 25
Storage & Distribution of Asphalt & Fuel Oils; Real Estate Activities
N.A.I.C.S.: 424720
Ted McCall *(Co-Pres)*
Mike Walsh *(CFO)*
Kevin Jones *(Co-Pres & CEO)*

MCCALL-THOMAS ENGINEERING COMPANY, INC.
845 Stonewall Jackson Blvd, Orangeburg, SC 29115
Tel.: (803) 534-1040 SC
Web Site:
http://www.mccallthomas.com
Year Founded: 1945
Engineeering Services
N.A.I.C.S.: 532420
Russell Bozard *(Dir-Comm Engrg Div)*
Shawn Higbe *(VP & Dir-Engrg)*
Ryan Snoak *(Pres)*

MCCALLION STAFFING
601 Bethlehem Pike A, Montgomeryville, PA 18936
Tel.: (215) 855-8000
Web Site:
http://www.mccallionstaffing.com
Rev.: $12,000,000
Emp.: 12
Temporary Help Service
N.A.I.C.S.: 561320
Lisa McCallion *(VP-Sls & Mktg)*
Kathy Karthauser *(Acct Mgr)*
James Mccallion III *(CEO)*

MCCALLS INC.
394 Lakecity Hwy, Johnsonville, SC 29555-0039
Tel.: (843) 386-3323 SC
Web Site: http://www.mccallsinc.com
Year Founded: 1960
Sales Range: $10-24.9 Million
Emp.: 130
Warm Air Heating & Air Conditioning
N.A.I.C.S.: 423730
Kevin Davis *(CFO)*
Constance McCall-Baxley *(Pres & CEO)*

MCCANN INDUSTRIES INC.
543 S Rohlwing Rd, Addison, IL 60101
Tel.: (630) 627-8700
Web Site:
http://www.mccannonline.com
Rev.: $57,000,000
Emp.: 104
General Construction Machinery & Equipment
N.A.I.C.S.: 423810
Jim McCann *(CEO)*
Mike Sexton *(Branch Mgr)*
Tom Killion *(Mgr-Parts)*
Brian Pieczynski *(Mgr-Rental)*

MCCARTER & ENGLISH LLP
4 Gateway Ctr 100 Mulberry St, Newark, NJ 07102
Tel.: (973) 622-4444
Web Site: http://www.mccarter.com
Year Founded: 1844
Sales Range: $200-249.9 Million
Emp.: 409
Law firm
N.A.I.C.S.: 541110
David L. Woronov *(Partner)*
Michael A. Leonardi *(CFO)*
Kenneth R. Levonaitis *(CIO)*
Michael Schetlick *(Dir-Office Svcs)*
Michael A. Guariglia *(Partner)*
Michael P. Kelly *(Chm)*
James H. Donoian *(Partner)*
Keith Toms *(Partner)*
Matthew R. Van Eman *(Partner)*
Makenzie Windfelder *(Partner)*
Jonathan R. Harris *(Partner-Boston)*
John A. Zurawski *(Partner)*
Catherine A. Mohan *(Partner)*
Christine A. Lydon *(Dir-HR)*
Edward T. McDermott *(Partner)*
Howard M. Berkower *(Partner)*
Jeffrey S. Muller *(Partner)*
Joel E. Horowitz *(Partner)*
Joseph R. Scholz *(Partner)*
Joseph Boccassini *(Mng Partner)*

MCCARTHY AUTO GROUP
675 N Rawhide Rd, Olathe, KS 66061
Tel.: (913) 782-5600
Web Site:
http://www.mccarthyautogroup.com
Rev.: $14,000,000
Emp.: 14
New & Used Car Dealers
N.A.I.C.S.: 441120
Brian Schaffer *(COO & Partner)*
Bryan Sams *(Mgr-Body Shop)*

MCCARTHY BUSH CORPORATION
5401 Victoria Ave, Davenport, IA 52807-2991
Tel.: (563) 359-0500 IA
Web Site:
http://www.mccarthybushcorp.com
Year Founded: 1995
Rev.: $50,300,000
Emp.: 400
Highway & Street Construction
N.A.I.C.S.: 237310
Greg Bush *(CEO)*
Mike Daniel *(CFO)*

Subsidiaries:

Bush Construction Company, Inc. (1)
5401 Victoria Ave Ste 400, Davenport, IA 52807
Tel.: (563) 344-3791
Web Site: http://www.bushconstruct.com
Sales Range: $10-24.9 Million
Emp.: 25
Building Construction
N.A.I.C.S.: 236220
A. J. Loss *(Pres)*
Rob Davis *(VP-Ops)*
Jerod Engler *(VP-Construction)*

Clinton Engineering Co., Inc. (1)
2101 Lincoln Way, Clinton, IA 52732
Tel.: (563) 242-5732
Emp.: 45
Construction Engineering Services
N.A.I.C.S.: 541330
Brian Johnson *(Project Mgr)*

Linwood Mining & Minerals Corp. (1)
5401 Victoria Ave, Davenport, IA 52807-2991
Tel.: (563) 359-8251
Web Site: http://www.linwoodmining.com
Sales Range: $25-49.9 Million
Emp.: 12
Crushed & Broken Limestone
N.A.I.C.S.: 212312
Gregory J. Bush *(CEO)*
Joseph D. Bush *(Pres)*

McCarthy Improvement Company (1)
5401 Victoria Ave, Davenport, IA 52807-2991
Tel.: (563) 359-0321
Web Site:
http://www.mccarthyimprovement.com
Rev.: $30,000,000
Emp.: 175
Highway & Street Construction
N.A.I.C.S.: 237310
Annette Snyder *(Dir-HR)*

Midwest Metals, Inc. (1)
2060 W River Dr, Davenport, IA 52808
Tel.: (563) 324-5244
Web Site: http://www.midwestmetalsinc.net
Industrial Equipment Whsr
N.A.I.C.S.: 423830

Oertel Sheet Metal, Inc. (1)
9104 N Zenith Ave, Davenport, IA 52806
Tel.: (563) 322-4930
Web Site: http://www.oertelsheetmetal.com
Emp.: 45
Sheet Metal Work Mfg
N.A.I.C.S.: 332322

Tom Bush *(VP)*

Premier Partners, LLC (1)
5401 Victoria Ave Ste 500, Davenport, IA 52807
Tel.: (563) 324-7000
Web Site:
http://www.premiercommercial.com
Real Estate Management Services
N.A.I.C.S.: 531390

MCCARTHY GROUP, LLC
1601 Dodge St Ste 3800, Omaha, NE 68102
Tel.: (402) 932-8600 NE
Web Site:
http://www.mccarthycapital.com
Year Founded: 1986
Rev.: $500,000,000
Emp.: 45
Investment Advisory Service & Private Equity Firm
N.A.I.C.S.: 523940
Michael Robert McCarthy *(Chm & Partner)*
Patrick J. Duffy *(Pres & Mng Dir)*
Rober Y. Emmert *(Mng Partner)*
Phillip N. Dudley *(VP)*
Chase M. Meyer *(VP)*
Brian P. Zaversnik *(VP)*
Teri L. Mercer *(CFO)*

Subsidiaries:

Election Systems & Software Inc. (1)
11208 John Galt Blvd, Omaha, NE 68137-2320
Tel.: (402) 593-0101
Web Site: http://www.essvote.com
Sales Range: $75-99.9 Million
Computer Peripheral Equipment Mfr
N.A.I.C.S.: 334118

Subsidiary (Domestic):

Premier Election Solutions, Inc. (2)
1611 Wilmeth Rd, McKinney, TX 75069-8250
Tel.: (972) 542-6000
Web Site: http://www.premierelections.com
Sales Range: $200-249.9 Million
Electronic Voting Systems Mfr
N.A.I.C.S.: 541512

Guild Holdings Company (1)
5887 Copley Dr, San Diego, CA 92111
Tel.: (858) 560-6330
Rev.: $1,164,821,000
Assets: $3,239,591,000
Liabilities: $1,990,304,000
Net Worth: $1,249,287,000
Earnings: $328,598,000
Emp.: 4,000
Fiscal Year-end: 12/31/2022
Holding Company
N.A.I.C.S.: 551112
Terry L. Schmidt *(CEO)*
Desiree A. Elwell *(CFO)*

Subsidiary (Domestic):

Cherry Creek Mortgage LLC (2)
6841 S Yosemite St Ste 3c, Centennial, CO 80112-1410
Tel.: (720) 468-5626
Web Site: http://www.720gotloan.com
Other Activities Related to Credit Intermediation
N.A.I.C.S.: 522390
Dan Connor *(Mgr)*

First Centennial Mortgage Corporation (2)
11 N Edgelawn Dr, Aurora, IL 60506-4362
Tel.: (773) 248-4300
Web Site: http://www.gofcm.com
Mortgage & Nonmortgage Loan Services
N.A.I.C.S.: 522310
Steven McCormick *(Pres)*

Guild Mortgage Company, LLC (2)
5898 Copley Dr Ste 4, San Diego, CA 92111-7916
Tel.: (858) 560-6330
Web Site: http://www.guildmortgage.com

Sales Range: $25-49.9 Million
Emp.: 2,000
Mortgage Banker
N.A.I.C.S.: 522292
Mary Ann McGarry (Supvr-Internal Audit)
Terry L. Schmidt (CEO, Partner & Exec VP)
Theresa Cherry (Mgr-California Coastal)
Terry Schmidt (CFO, Partner & Exec VP)
Mary Ann McGarry (CEO)
Catherine Blocker (Partner & Exec VP-Production Ops)
Mike Rish (Partner & Sr VP-Secondary Mktg)
Barry Horn (Exec VP & Production Mgr-Natl)
Linda Scott (Partner & Sr VP-Tech & Software Dev)
Rhona Kaninau (Partner & Sr VP-Loan Admin)
Lisa Klika (Sr VP-Compliance & Quality Assurance)
David Battany (Exec VP-Capital Markets)
Cindy Flynn (Reg Mgr-Ops)
Gina Durosko (Mgr-Western Washington)
Casey Oiness (Mgr-Sls-Kirkland)
James Madsen (Exec VP-Loan Admin)
David M. Neylan (Pres & COO)
Amber Elwell (Sr VP-Fin)
Kat Foster (Sr VP & Dir-Credit Risk)
Bob Engelke (Mgr-Oregon)
Rob Allphin (Reg Mgr-Mountain)
Matt MacGillivray (Reg Mgr-Southeast)
Charles Nay (Reg Mgr-Northwest)
Arthur Ochoa (Reg Mgr-Texas)
William Rizzo (Reg Mgr-Hawaii)
Andy Stewart (Reg Mgr-Southwest)
Jeff Tarbell (Reg Mgr-California Inland)
Wendy Wong (CMO & Sr VP)
Drew Gillett (Mgr-Mktg Program)
Minde Harper (Mgr-Grand Junction)
Russ Fowlie (Exec VP-Loan Servicing)
Victoria Garcia DeLuca (VP-Marketplace Diversity Strategy)

Division (Domestic):

Guild Mortgage (3)
150 120th Ave NE Ste 300, Bellevue, WA 98005
Tel.: (425) 945-8000
Mortgage & Nonmortgage Loan Brokers
N.A.I.C.S.: 522310
Peter E. Nordstrom (Founder & Loan Officer)
Barry Horn (Exec VP-Natl Production)
Gemma Currier (VP-Retail Sls Ops-Natl)
Rob Dawson (Mgr-Builder Div-Natl)

Subsidiary (Domestic):

Inlanta Mortgage, Inc. (3)
W239 N3490 Pewaukee Rd Ste 200, Pewaukee, WI 53072
Web Site: http://www.inlanta.com
Offices of Real Estate Agents & Brokers
N.A.I.C.S.: 531210
John Watry (CFO)
Gary Grocholski (Mgr-Third-Party Origination)
Dan Werner (Mgr-Elgin)
Mark Schulenburg (Mng Partner-Oak Brook)
Nicholas DelTorto (CEO)
Chad Gomoll (Sr VP)
David Williams (Reg VP-Bus Dev)
Kevin Laffey (Reg Mgr-Production)
John Knowlton (Chm)
Paul Buege (Pres & COO)

McCarthy Capital Corporation (1)
1601 Dodge St Ste 3800, Omaha, NE 68102
Tel.: (402) 932-8600
Web Site: http://www.mccarthycapital.com
Investment Advisor
N.A.I.C.S.: 523940
Patrick J. Duffy (Pres & Mng Partner)
Michael Robert McCarthy (Chm)
Patrick J. Duffy (Pres & Mng Partner)
Robert Y. Emmert (Mng Partner)
Teri L. Mercer (CFO)

MCCARTHY HOLDINGS, INC.
12851 Manchester Rd, Saint Louis, MO 63131
Tel.: (314) 968-3300   DE
Web Site: https://www.mccarthy.com
Year Founded: 1996
Sales Range: $1-4.9 Billion
Emp.: 7,359
Offices of Other Holding Companies
N.A.I.C.S.: 551112
Michael D. Bolen (Chm)
Scott Wittkop (Pres & COO)
Mike Schulte (Sr VP-Southern Reg)
Kristine Newman (Sr VP-Fin)
Shaun Sleeth (Sr VP-Northern Pacific Reg)
Jonathan Schmaltz (Dir-Bus Dev-Heavy Civil Marine Indus Grp)
Ray Sedey (CEO & CEO)
Kamecia Mason (VP-Diversity, Equity & Inclusion)
Amanda Skillern (VP-Quality)
Jim Stevenson (Pres-Houston)

Subsidiaries:

McCarthy Building Companies, Inc. (1)
1341 N Rock Hill Rd, Saint Louis, MO 63124
Tel.: (314) 968-3300
Web Site: http://www.mccarthy.com
Sales Range: $1-4.9 Billion
Commercial, Institutional, Civil & Industrial Construction Services
N.A.I.C.S.: 236220
Michael D. Bolen (Chm & CEO)
J. Douglas Audiffred (CFO)
Robert Betz (Exec VP-Ops)
Lisa Hunt (Coord-Mktg)
Nayan Bhakta (Mgr-Preconstruction)
Julian Halkett (Dir-Preconstruction)
Mike Corso (VP-Ops)
David Clarkson (Project Dir-Healthcare Construction)
Dhruv Patel (VP-Engrg, Procurement & Construction)
Sean Fitzgerald (Project Mgr-Colorado)
Kevin Williams (Sr VP-Colorado)
Chad Dorgan (VP-Quality & Sustainability)
Paul Erb (VP-Ops)
Matt Lawson (Gen Counsel & Sr VP)
James Madrid (VP-Bus Dev)
Kyle Masters (Dir-Bus Dev)
Antonya Williams (Dir-Design Integration)
Scott Wittkop (Pres & COO)
Joe Brotherton (VP-Bus Dev)
Guy Voss (Dir-Bus Dev-McCarthy Water-Southwest)
Steve Meuschke (VP-Ops)
Christine Mostaert (VP-Fin)
Shaun Sleeth (Pres-Northern Pacific Reg)
Stefanie Becker (VP-Integrated Design Delivery)
Ann Poppen (Sr VP-Ops-Northern Pacific Reg)
Nikki Marongiu (Dir-Bus Dev-San Francisco)
Adrienne Williams (Dir-Diversity & Community Outreach-Southern Reg)
Mark Mohning (VP-Integrated Design Delivery-Las Vegas)
Ross Edwards (Sr VP)

Subsidiary (Domestic):

Castle Contracting, LLC (2)
345 Marshall Ave, Saint Louis, MO 63119
Tel.: (314) 421-0042
Web Site: http://www.digcastle.com
Sales Range: $10-24.9 Million
Emp.: 135
Civil Engineering Services
N.A.I.C.S.: 237990
Mike Myers (Owner & VP)
Scott Beutel (Mgr-Field)
Sherri Cavaletti (Controller)
Ashley Faraar (Coord-Acctg)
Jake Goss (Project Mgr)
A. J. Johnson (Mgr-Field)
Julie C. Ledbetter (Founder, Owner & CEO)
Rich Ledbetter (Pres)
Joshua Lehde (Owner & VP)
Rich Mueller (Mgr-Project-Sewer & Utility)
Michael Pranger (Principal & VP-Ops)
Christie Brinkman (Dir-Design-Build)
Amy Huller (Mgr-Design)
James Parks (Sr Mgr-Design)

MC Industrial, Inc. (2)
3117 Big Bend Blvd, Saint Louis, MO 63143
Tel.: (314) 646-4100
Web Site: http://www.mc-industrial.com
Sales Range: $25-49.9 Million
Emp.: 100
Industrial Plant Construction Services
N.A.I.C.S.: 236210
Thomas S. Felton (Pres)
Robert L. Kohlburn (VP)
Tim McDougal (Dir-Bus Dev)
Jared Ragsdale (Dir-Safety)
Brian Boeglin (Dir-Quality)
Chad Cotter (VP-Ops)
Marcus Hoover (Mgr-Staffing)
Tom Kreher (Sr VP-Indus Process & Mfg)
Troy Larson (VP-Estimating)
Steve Miller (Dir-Safety)
Mike Mooney (VP-Field Ops)
Brian Timmer (Mgr-Bus Dev)
Rowena Amelung (Mgr-Bus Dev)

Division (Domestic):

McCarthy Building Companies, Inc. - Central Division (2)
1341 N Rock Hill Rd, Saint Louis, MO 63124-1498
Tel.: (314) 968-3300
Web Site: http://www.mccarthy.com
Sales Range: $75-99.9 Million
Emp.: 100
Commercial, Institutional & Civil Construction Services
N.A.I.C.S.: 236220
Jim Contratto (VP-Bus Dev, Advanced Tech & Mfg)
Ryan Freeman (VP-Comml)
Jennifer Abbott (Dir-Bus Dev-Education)
Steve Miller (Dir-Safety)
Jennifer Bradshaw (Dir-Bus Dev-Healthcare)
John Buescher (Pres)
Josh Gaghen (Dir-Bus Dev-Federal Programs)
Chris Campbell (Engr-Virtual Design & Construction)
Ryan Denisi (Dir-Bus Dev)

McCarthy Building Companies, Inc. - Nevada/Utah Division (2)
2340 Corporate Cir Ste 125, Henderson, NV 89074
Tel.: (702) 990-6707
Web Site: http://www.mccarthy.com
Commercial, Institutional & Civil Construction Services
N.A.I.C.S.: 236220

McCarthy Building Companies, Inc. - Northern Pacific Division (2)
1265 Bettery St, San Francisco, CA 94111
Tel.: (415) 397-5151
Web Site: http://www.mccarthy.com
Emp.: 50
Commercial, Institutional & Civil Construction Services
N.A.I.C.S.: 236220
Richard Henry (Pres)
Frances Choun (VP-Bus Dev-Northern Pacific Div)
Alice Nguyen (Dir-Estimating)
Julian Halkett (Dir-Preconstruction)
Eric Dickey (VP-Ops)

Branch (Domestic):

McCarthy Building Companies, Inc. - Northern Pacific Division-Sacramento (3)
2241 Douglas Blvd Ste 200, Roseville, CA 95661-3831
Tel.: (916) 786-3833
Web Site: http://www.mccarthy.com
Commercial, Institutional & Civil Construction Services
N.A.I.C.S.: 236220

Division (Domestic):

McCarthy Building Companies, Inc. - Southeast Division (2)
2727 Paces Ferry Rd SE Bldg 2 Ste 1600, Atlanta, GA 30339
Tel.: (770) 980-8183
Web Site: http://www.mccarthy.com
Sales Range: $75-99.9 Million
Emp.: 75
Commercial, Institutional & Civil Construction Services
N.A.I.C.S.: 236220
Kevin Kuntz (Pres)
Mark Allnutt (VP)

Benjamin Watkins (VP-Ops)
Bobby Campbell (Sr VP)
Stephanie Lee (Sr Coord-Diversity & Community Outreach)

McCarthy Building Companies, Inc. - Southern California Division (2)
20401 SW Birch St, Newport Beach, CA 92660-1798
Tel.: (949) 851-8383
Web Site: http://www.mccarthy.com
Commercial, Institutional & Civil Construction Services
N.A.I.C.S.: 236220
Jamie Shrader (Controller)
James Madrid (Dir-Bus Dev)
Scott Lawrence (Dir-Bus Dev-Healthcare)
Paul King (Dir-Bus Dev-San Diego)
Randy Highland (Pres)

McCarthy Building Companies, Inc. - Southwest Division (2)
6225 N 24th St Ste 200, Phoenix, AZ 85016
Tel.: (480) 449-4700
Web Site: http://www.mccarthy.com
Commercial, Institutional & Civil Construction Services
N.A.I.C.S.: 236220
Robert Calbert (Pres-Southwest)
Tara Malloy (Dir-Client Svcs)
Antonya Williams (Dir-Design Integration)
Doug Audiffred (CFO)
Robert Betz (Exec VP-Ops)
Crystal Carter (Dir-Bus Dev)
Katy Corrigan (Dir-Bus Dev)
Paul King (Dir-Bus Dev)
Kyle Masters (Dir-Bus Dev)
Nick Sandersfeld (Dir-Bus Dev)
Barry Sutherland (Dir-Bus Dev)
Josh Molitor (Mgr-VDC)
Lloyd Hiser (Superintendent)
Tom Walker (Superintendent)
Joe Kilgallen (Mgr-Preconstruction)
Carlos Rodriguez (Superintendent)
Bryan Kuster (VP-Ops)
Ashley Codispoti (Mgr-Bus Dev-Education Team)
Brenda Byers (Dir-Solar Preconstruction Svcs)
Chris Nickle (Exec VP)
Jeremy Melvin (Dir-HR)
Michaela Rempkowski (Dir-Integrated Design)

McCarthy Building Companies, Inc. - Texas Division (2)
12001 N Central Expwy Ste 400, Dallas, TX 75243
Tel.: (972) 991-5500
Web Site: http://www.mccarthy.com
Emp.: 50
Commercial, Institutional & Civil Construction Services
N.A.I.C.S.: 236220
Kyle Masters (Dir-Bus Dev)
Kurt Knebel (VP-Civil Ops)
Blanca Rodriguez (Mgr-Mktg)
Doug Audiffred (CFO)
Robert Betz (Exec VP-Ops)
Mike Bolen (Chm & CEO)
Crystal Carter (Dir-Bus Dev)
Frances Choun (VP-Bus Dev)
Paul Erb (VP-Ops)
Ryan Freeman (VP-Comml)
James Madrid (VP-Bus Dev)
Barry Sutherland (Dir-Bus Dev)
Nathan Kowallis (VP-Ops-Bus Unit)
Mike Benford (Dir-Bus Dev-South)
Charles Buescher III (VP-Bus Dev)

MCCARTHY HYUNDAI
3030 S Outer Rd, Blue Springs, MO 64015
Tel.: (816) 229-7070
Web Site: http://www.bluespringsnissan.com
Year Founded: 1978
Sales Range: $10-24.9 Million
Emp.: 60
New Car Retailer
N.A.I.C.S.: 441110
Doug Miller (Gen Mgr)

MCCARTHY TIRE SERVICE COMPANY

MCCARTHY TIRE SERVICE COMPANY

McCarthy Tire Service Company—(Continued)
340 Kidder St, Wilkes Barre, PA 18702
Tel.: (570) 822-3151 PA
Web Site:
  http://www.mccarthytire.com
Year Founded: 1926
Sales Range: $25-49.9 Million
Emp.: 900
Tire Dealers
N.A.I.C.S.: 441340
Joseph Patrick Doyle (COO)
Kathleen McCarthy Lambert (CFO)
John D. McCarthy Sr. (Chm & CEO)
John D. McCarthy Jr. (Pres)

Subsidiaries:

McCarthy Tire and Automotive Center (1)
980 Broadway, Albany, NY 12204
Tel.: (518) 449-5185
Web Site: http://www.mccarthytire.com
General Auto Repair Supplies Mfr
N.A.I.C.S.: 423130
Doug Nadeau (Mgr)

Piedmont Truck Tires Inc. (1)
312 S Regional Rd, Greensboro, NC 27409
Tel.: (336) 668-0091
Web Site:
  http://www.piedmonttrucktires.com
Sales Range: $25-49.9 Million
Emp.: 160
Truck Tires & Tubes
N.A.I.C.S.: 423130
Dan Rice (Pres)
Brian Hunter (Gen Mgr)
Monty Mills (Mgr-Svc)

MCCARTY CONSTRUCTION INC.
4995 Avalon Ridge Pkwy Ste 250, Norcross, GA 30071
Tel.: (770) 447-4332
Web Site:
  http://www.mccartyconstruction.com
Year Founded: 1980
Sales Range: $1-9.9 Million
Emp.: 15
Restaurant Construction
N.A.I.C.S.: 236220
David M. McCarty (Co-Founder & Co-Owner)
Don Conway (Project Mgr)
Don Davidson (Pres)
Tom Yeager (Project Mgr)
Denise Wegesin (Controller & Office Mgr)
Celia McCarty (Co-Founder & Co-Owner)

MCCARTY CORPORATION
13496 Pond Springs Rd, Austin, TX 78729
Tel.: (512) 258-6611
Sales Range: $10-24.9 Million
Emp.: 50
General Remodeling Services
N.A.I.C.S.: 236118
Mike McCarty (Pres)
Pat Morris (Office Mgr)
Linda Jackson (Controller)

Subsidiaries:

Tex-Cap Electric Inc. (1)
13494 Pond Springs Rd, Austin, TX 78729
Tel.: (512) 250-1742
Rev.: $12,000,000
Emp.: 4
General Electrical Contractor
N.A.I.C.S.: 238210
Mike McCarty (CEO)
Linda Jackson (Controller)

Truform Metalservice Inc (1)
13496 Pond Springs Rd, Austin, TX 78729
Tel.: (512) 258-1675
Warm Air Heating & Air Conditioning Contractor
N.A.I.C.S.: 238220

MCCARTY-HULL INC.
4714 NE 24th AVE, Amarillo, TX 79107
Tel.: (806) 383-8383 TX
Web Site: http://www.mccarty-hull.com
Year Founded: 1961
Sales Range: $10-24.9 Million
Emp.: 120
Tobacco & Tobacco Products, Confectioneries & Groceries Whslr
N.A.I.C.S.: 424940
Terry Cato (VP-Mktg)
Chuck Cota (VP-Pur)
Gordon Atkins (Pres)
Frank Hill (Mgr-Wholesale Ops)
Robin Ortega (Coord-Mktg)
Joe Bob Blackburn (VP-Sls)
David Carter (Mgr-DP)

MCCAULEY LUMBER COMPANY INCORPORATED
626 Aldine Bender Rd, Houston, TX 77060
Tel.: (281) 448-1374
Web Site:
  http://mccauleyslumber.com
Sales Range: $25-49.9 Million
Emp.: 100
Lumber & Other Building Materials
N.A.I.C.S.: 423310
Curtis A. McCauley (Pres)
Karen McCauley (Controller)
Francis Deeton (Mgr-Ops)

MCCAULOU'S, INC.
3512 Mt Diablo Blvd, Lafayette, CA 94549-3814
Tel.: (925) 283-3380
Web Site: http://www.mccaulous.com
Year Founded: 1963
Sales Range: $50-74.9 Million
Emp.: 500
Family Clothing Stores
N.A.I.C.S.: 458110
Michelle Ball (Asst Mgr)
Ken Stoddard (Dir-Fin)
David R. McCaulou (Owner)

MCCLAINS RV INC.
5601 S Interstate 35 E, Denton, TX 76210
Tel.: (940) 498-4330
Web Site: http://www.mcclainsrv.com
Sales Range: $10-24.9 Million
Emp.: 195
Recreational Vehicle Dealers
N.A.I.C.S.: 441210
Larry McClain (CEO)
Nate McClain (Pres)
Tod McClain (VP)

MCCLANCY SEASONING CO.
1 Spice Rd, Fort Mill, SC 29707
Tel.: (803) 548-2366
Web Site: http://www.mcclancy.com
Sales Range: $10-24.9 Million
Emp.: 120
Frozen Specialty Food Mfr
N.A.I.C.S.: 311412
Reid Wilkerson (Pres)

MCCLARIN PLASTICS, LLC
15 Industrial Dr PO Box 486, Hanover, PA 17331
Tel.: (800) 233-3189 PA
Web Site:
  http://www.mcclarinplastics.com
Year Founded: 1953
Plastics Product Mfr
N.A.I.C.S.: 326199
Jeffrey A. Geiman (VP-Ops)
Jerry Armstrong (CEO)
Charles Bennett (Chm)

MCCLASKEY ENTERPRISES

Ste 120 1498 SE Tech Center Pl, Vancouver, WA 98683-5508
Tel.: (360) 699-4013
Sales Range: $75-99.9 Million
Emp.: 800
Owner & Operator of Hotels
N.A.I.C.S.: 481111

MCCLEARY INC.
239 Oak Grove Ave, South Beloit, IL 61080
Tel.: (815) 389-3053
Sales Range: $10-24.9 Million
Emp.: 135
Corn Chips & Other Corn-Based Snacks
N.A.I.C.S.: 311919
Charles Patrick McCleary (Co-Pres)
Nick McCleary (VP)

MCCLELLAND HEALTH SYSTEMS
85 Interstate Dr, West Springfield, MA 01089
Tel.: (413) 733-8600
Web Site:
  http://www.mcclellands.com
Year Founded: 1860
Sales Range: $10-24.9 Million
Emp.: 75
Medical Equipment Rental
N.A.I.C.S.: 532283

MCCLENAHAN BRUER COMMUNICATIONS
5331 SW Macadam Ave Ste 220, Portland, OR 97239
Tel.: (503) 546-1000
Web Site: http://www.mcbru.com
Year Founded: 1993
Sales Range: $1-9.9 Million
Emp.: 18
Advetising Agency
N.A.I.C.S.: 541810
Kerry McClenahan (Founder & CEO)
James McIntyre (Partner & VP-Client Svcs)
Sam Templeman (Designer)
Jonathan Adam (Dir-Creative)
Sarah MacKenzie (Coord-Acct)
Anna Reinhard (Coord-Acct)
Betsy Reed (Dir-Bus Dev)
Sharon Burk (Mgr-Acctg)
Janel Pettit (Mgr-Social Media)
Dana Bacharach (Project Mgr)

MCCLENDON RESOURCES INC.
404 N Gabbert St, Monticello, AR 71655
Tel.: (870) 367-9755
Sales Range: $75-99.9 Million
Emp.: 130
Boat Building & Repairing Services
N.A.I.C.S.: 336612
Robin McClendon (Pres)

Subsidiaries:

SeaArk Marine Inc. (1)
404 N Gabbert St, Monticello, AR 71655
Tel.: (870) 367-9755
Web Site: http://www.seaark.com
Sales Range: $10-24.9 Million
Emp.: 2
Aluminum Boat Builders
N.A.I.C.S.: 336612
John McClendon (Pres & CEO)

MCCLINTOCK ELECTRIC, INC.
402 E Henry St, Wooster, OH 44691
Tel.: (330) 264-6380 OH
Web Site:
  http://www.mcclintockelectric.com
Year Founded: 1963
Sales Range: $10-24.9 Million
Emp.: 44
Electrical Contractor

U.S. PRIVATE

N.A.I.C.S.: 238210
Michael McClintock (Pres)
Aaron Shields (Project Mgr)
Kimberley Simmons (Controller)
Scott Zacharias (Mgr-Tech Ops)
Rick Westfall (Mgr-Electrical Ops)
Shaun Riggenbaugh (Mgr-Tech Project)
Steve Boydston (Project Mgr)

MCCLONE CONSTRUCTION COMPANY, INC.
4340 Product Dr, Shingle Springs, CA 95682-8492
Tel.: (530) 677-1022 CA
Web Site: http://www.mcclone.net
Year Founded: 1993
Sales Range: $25-49.9 Million
Emp.: 150
Concrete Contracting Services
N.A.I.C.S.: 238110
Brett Steed (CEO)
Chris Foster (VP)
Grant Orr (COO)
Ken Ridens (VP)
Roy Cloud (VP)
Tim Eble (VP)
Ted Hoffman (CFO)

Subsidiaries:

McClone Construction Company-Northwest Regional Office (1)
28610 Maple Vly Hwy Ste 200, Maple Valley, WA 98038-7420 (100%)
Tel.: (425) 413-1440
Web Site: http://www.mcclone.net
Sales Range: $10-24.9 Million
Emp.: 16
Concrete Contracting Services
N.A.I.C.S.: 238110
Tim Eble (Pres)
Roy Cloud (VP)
Mark McClone (Chief Safety Officer & VP)
Grant Orr (COO)
Ted Hoffman (CFO)
Brett Steed (CEO)

McClone Construction Company-Southwest Regional Office (1)
7471 North Remington Ste 102, Fresno, CA 93711-6227
Tel.: (559) 431-9411
Web Site: http://www.mcclone-formwork.com
Sales Range: $10-24.9 Million
Emp.: 10
Provider of Concrete Contracting Services
N.A.I.C.S.: 238110
Mike Sherfield (Reg Mgr)

MCCLOSKEY MOTORS INC.
6710 N Academy Blvd, Colorado Springs, CO 80918
Tel.: (719) 594-9400
Web Site: http://www.bigjoeauto.com
Rev.: $14,000,000
Emp.: 100
New & Used Car Dealers
N.A.I.C.S.: 441110
Joseph Mccloskey (Pres)
Pam Fuller (CFO)

MCCLUNG-LOGAN EQUIPMENT COMPANY, INC.
4601 Washington Blvd, Baltimore, MD 21227
Tel.: (410) 242-6500
Web Site: http://www.mcclung-logan.com
Year Founded: 1939
Sales Range: $25-49.9 Million
General Construction Machinery & Equipment Mfr
N.A.I.C.S.: 333120
Darrin Brown (Pres)
Mike Smith (VP-Sls)
Dave Beehner (Mgr-Municipal & Fin)
Guy Logan (Mgr-Div)
Jamie Reid (Mgr-Territory)

COMPANIES

John Chartier *(Mgr-Territory)*
Nick Lepore *(Mgr-Territory)*
Chad Sidow *(Mgr-Territory)*
Bob Kaase *(Mgr-Territory)*
David Welch *(Mgr-Territory)*
Phil Parrish *(Mgr-Territory)*
Tom Cunningham *(Mgr-Territory)*
Paul Brockman *(Mgr-Territory)*
Tad Lynch *(Mgr-Territory)*
Ralph Murphy *(Mgr-Territory)*
Austin Frederick *(VP-Product Support)*
Tom Ficklin *(Gen Mgr-Compact Equipment Div)*

Subsidiaries:

White Oak Equipment Inc. (1)
9115 Industry Dr, Manassas, VA 20111
Tel.: (757) 538-1870
Web Site:
http://www.whiteoakequipment.com
Provider of Construction & Mining Machinery
N.A.I.C.S.: 423810
Janice Graves *(Controller)*
Mark McCarty *(Sls Mgr-Compact Equipment Div)*

MCCLURE ASSOCIATES INC.
475 Capital Dr, Lake Zurich, IL 60047
Tel.: (847) 550-9570
Web Site: http://www.fairchildind.com
Year Founded: 1956
Rev.: $15,000,000
Emp.: 25
Industrial Supplies
N.A.I.C.S.: 423840
Robert Schauer *(Pres)*

MCCLURE ENGINEERING CO.
1360 NW 121st St, Clive, IA 50325
Tel.: (515) 964-1229   IA
Web Site: http://www.mecresults.com
Year Founded: 1956
Engineering & Surveying Services
N.A.I.C.S.: 541330
Dennis Folden *(Pres)*
Terry J. Lutz *(CEO)*
Derick Anderson *(VP-Water)*
Kristi Gaskill *(Partner-HR Bus)*
Troy Jerman *(VP-Transportation)*

MCCLURE OIL CORPORATION
1212 W County Rd 500 S, Marion, IN 46953-9320
Tel.: (765) 674-9771   IN
Web Site:
http://www.in.mclureoil.net
Year Founded: 1906
Sales Range: $50-74.9 Million
Emp.: 350
Gasoline Service Stations
N.A.I.C.S.: 457120
Tom Smith *(CFO)*
David Cain *(VP-Sls)*
Lori Rigsbee *(Asst Mgr-Sls)*
Kelly McClure *(Pres)*

MCCLURE PROPERTIES LTD.
PO Box 936, Palmetto, FL 34221-5154
Tel.: (941) 722-4545
Web Site:
http://www.westcoasttomato.com
Year Founded: 1987
Sales Range: $50-74.9 Million
Emp.: 12
Supplier of Vegetables & Melons
N.A.I.C.S.: 111219

Subsidiaries:

West Coast Tomato LLC (1)
502 6th Ave W, Palmetto, FL 34221-5154
Tel.: (941) 722-4545
Web Site: http://www.westcoasttomato.com
Sales Range: $25-49.9 Million
Fresh Fruits & Vegetables Supplier
N.A.I.C.S.: 424480

MCCLUSKEY CHEVROLET INC.
8525 Reading Rd, Cincinnati, OH 45215
Tel.: (513) 761-1111
Web Site:
http://www.mccluskeychevrolet.com
Rev.: $100,593,344
Emp.: 200
New & Used Automobiles
N.A.I.C.S.: 441110
Keith P. McCluskey *(Pres)*
Keith McCluskey *(CEO)*
Mark Meyers *(Mgr-Fleet Sls)*
Jeffrey Reiss *(Mgr-Parts Dept)*
David Anderson *(Mgr-Sls & Fin)*

MCCLYMONDS SUPPLY & TRANSIT CO. INC.
296 Currie Rd, Portersville, PA 16051
Tel.: (724) 368-8040
Web Site:
http://www.mcclymonds.com
Rev.: $35,200,000
Emp.: 210
Sand, Construction
N.A.I.C.S.: 484110
Mark McClymonds *(Pres & CEO)*
Marc Carneghi *(COO)*
Pat McGinnis *(CFO)*

MCCOLLA ENTERPRISES LTD.
2945 SW Wanamaker Dr, Topeka, KS 66614
Tel.: (785) 272-8529
Web Site:
http://www.streetcorner.com
Year Founded: 1988
Sales Range: $10-24.9 Million
Emp.: 8
Mini-Convenience Store Franchiser
N.A.I.C.S.: 459210
Peter La Colla *(CEO)*

MCCOLLISTER'S TRANSPORTATION GROUP INC.
8 Terri Ln, Burlington, NJ 08016
Tel.: (609) 386-0600   DE
Web Site:
http://www.mccollisters.com
Year Founded: 1945
Sales Range: $50-74.9 Million
Emp.: 1,000
Trucking Service
N.A.I.C.S.: 551112
H. Daniel McCollister *(Pres)*
Ed Stryker *(Supvr-Trng)*
George Davenport *(Sr VP)*
George Sanders *(Acct Mgr-Comml)*
Frank Musmeci *(Dir-Billing)*

Subsidiaries:

Horseless Carriage Carriers, Inc. (1)
61 Iowa Ave, Paterson, NJ 07503
Tel.: (973) 742-1525
Web Site: http://www.horselesscarriage.com
Sales Range: $1-9.9 Million
Emp.: 40
Used Household & Office Goods Moving
N.A.I.C.S.: 484210

Logistics Management Services Ltd. (1)
24031 Reasearch Dr, Farmington Hills, MI 48335
Tel.: (866) 797-9567
Web Site: http://www.selectlms.com
Logistics Consulting Servies
N.A.I.C.S.: 541614

McCollister Moving & Storage of New York (1)
7 Tucker Dr, Poughkeepsie, NY 12603
Tel.: (845) 905-5000
Rev.: $10,546,158
Emp.: 120
Contract Haulers
N.A.I.C.S.: 484121

H. Daniel Mccollister *(Pres)*
Tom Weight *(Gen Mgr)*

MCCOMBIE GROUP, LLC
901 Ponce de Leon Blvd Ste 402, Coral Gables, FL 33134
Tel.: (786) 664-8340
Web Site:
http://www.mccombiegroup.com
Privater Equity Firm
N.A.I.C.S.: 551112
David W. McCombie III *(Founder & CEO)*

Subsidiaries:

Atlantic Tractor (1)
150 Whiteside Dr, Oxford, PA 19363
Tel.: (610) 998-9680
Web Site: http://www.atlantictractor.net
Rev.: $2,490,000
Emp.: 5
Farm & Garden Machinery & Equipment Merchant Whslr
N.A.I.C.S.: 423820
Jay S. Lipsey *(Partner)*

MCCOMBS ENTERPRISES
755 E Mulberry Ave Ste 600, San Antonio, TX 78212
Tel.: (210) 821-6523   TX
Web Site: http://www.redmac.com
Year Founded: 1944
Sales Range: $150-199.9 Million
Emp.: 33
Holding Company
N.A.I.C.S.: 523999
Gary V. Woods *(Pres)*
B. J. McCombs *(Chm & COO)*
Steve Cummings *(CFO)*

Subsidiaries:

McCombs Partners (1)
755 E Mulberry Ave Ste 600, San Antonio, TX 78212
Tel.: (210) 821-6523
Web Site: http://www.mccombspartners.com
Investment Management Service
N.A.I.C.S.: 523940

Red McCombs Superior Hyundai (1)
4800 NW Loop 410, San Antonio, TX 78229   (100%)
Tel.: (210) 684-7440
Web Site:
http://www.mccombssuperiorhyundai.com
Sales Range: $150-199.9 Million
Car Dealership
N.A.I.C.S.: 441110
Red McCombs *(Partner)*

MCCOMBS WEST FORD
7111 NW Loop 410, San Antonio, TX 78238
Tel.: (210) 509-1000
Year Founded: 1960
Sales Range: $25-49.9 Million
Emp.: 160
Car Whslr
N.A.I.C.S.: 441110
Tim Cliver *(COO)*

MCCONNELL AUTOMOTIVE
3150 Dauphin St, Mobile, AL 36606-4039
Tel.: (251) 476-4141   DE
Web Site:
http://www.mcconnellautomotive.com
Year Founded: 1955
Sales Range: $100-124.9 Million
Emp.: 274
Retail Sales of New & Used Automobiles
N.A.I.C.S.: 441110
Julia Hatton *(Controller)*
Edy McConnell *(Owner)*

MCCONNELL CABINETS, INC.
13110 Louden Ln, La Puente, CA 91746
Tel.: (626) 937-2200   CA
Year Founded: 1944
Sales Range: $200-249.9 Million
Emp.: 400
Mfr of Wood & Plastic Built-in Cabinets
N.A.I.C.S.: 238350
William S. McConnell *(Pres)*
Maryanne Sarrail *(CFO)*

Subsidiaries:

Coastal Wood Products, Inc. (1)
13110 Louden Ln, City of Industry, CA 91744   (100%)
Tel.: (626) 333-1104
Rev.: $12,800,000
Emp.: 10
Laminated Panels
N.A.I.C.S.: 322299

MCCONNELL GOLF LLC
400 Donald Ross Dr, Raleigh, NC 27610
Tel.: (919) 231-5501
Web Site:
http://www.mcconnellgolf.com
Year Founded: 2003
Private Country Club & Golf Courses
N.A.I.C.S.: 713910
John McConnell *(Owner & Pres)*
Christian Anastasiadis *(COO)*
Michael Shoun *(Dir-Agronomy & VP)*
Brian Kittler *(VP-Golf Ops)*

Subsidiaries:

Country Club of Asheville (1)
170 Windsor Rd, Asheville, NC 28804
Tel.: (828) 258-9183
Web Site: http://www.ccofasheville.com
Emp.: 80
Country Club Operator
N.A.I.C.S.: 713910

MCCORD BROS INC.
990 Tennant Way, Longview, WA 98632
Tel.: (360) 425-3900
Web Site:
http://www.mccorddodge.com
Sales Range: $10-24.9 Million
Emp.: 24
New & Used Automobiles
N.A.I.C.S.: 441110
Marion C. McCord *(Pres)*
Rob Bordonski *(VP)*
Tera Trekas *(Office Mgr)*

MCCORMACK BARON SALAZAR, INC.
720 Olive St Ste 2500, Saint Louis, MO 63101-2313
Tel.: (314) 621-3400
Web Site:
http://www.mccormackbaron.com
Rev.: $14,400,000
Emp.: 435
Real Estate Management Services
N.A.I.C.S.: 237210
Richard D. Baron *(Founder & Chm)*
Claudia Brodie *(Sr VP)*
Michael Saunders *(Sr VP & Dir-Design & Construction)*
Vincent R. Bennett *(Pres)*
Lisa Beffa *(Sr VP)*
Thomas C. Cella *(VP)*
Aaron N. Swain *(Sr VP-Property Mgmt Svcs)*
Hillary B. Zimmerman *(Pres-McCormack Asset Mgmt & Gen Counsel)*
Julie DeGraaf Velazquez *(Sr VP-Project Mgmt)*
John P. Hambene *(Sr VP-Project Mgmt)*
Michael Duffy *(COO)*
Tony Salazar *(Pres-West Coast Ops)*
Yusef Freeman *(Mng Dir-New Bus)*

MCCORMACK BARON SALAZAR, INC.

U.S. PRIVATE

McCormack Baron Salazar, Inc.—(Continued)
Meg Manley *(Sr VP-Project Mgmt)*
Daniela Greville *(VP)*
Gary Schwartz *(VP)*
Kelly Kinnaman *(VP)*
Lashona McGrew *(Reg VP)*
Liane Laughlin *(Reg VP)*
Randy Rhoads *(VP)*
Susan Tempesta *(VP)*
Antonio Garate *(VP & Dir-Dev-Puerto Rico)*

Subsidiaries:

Baron Salazar & Associates (1)
720 Olive St Ste 25th Fl, Saint Louis, MO 63101
Tel.: (314) 621-3400
Sales Range: $1-9.9 Million
Emp.: 100
Subdividers & Developers
N.A.I.C.S.: 237210
Richard D. Baron *(Chm & CEO)*

McCormack Baron Management Services (1)
720 Olive St Ste 2500, Saint Louis, MO 63101-2313
Tel.: (314) 621-3400
Web Site: http://www.cupplesstation.com
Rev.: $3,514,154
Emp.: 100
Real Estate Managers
N.A.I.C.S.: 531210
David Nargang *(Pres)*

MCCORMICK ARMSTRONG CO. INC.
1501 E Douglas Ave, Wichita, KS 67211
Tel.: (316) 264-1363
Web Site: http://www.mcaprint.com
Sales Range: $10-24.9 Million
Emp.: 75
Offset Printing
N.A.I.C.S.: 323111
Jacob W. Shaffer *(Chm & CEO)*
John Bobbitt *(Pres)*

MCCORMICK COMPANY
701 S Taylor St Ste 400, Amarillo, TX 79101
Tel.: (806) 374-5333 TX
Year Founded: 1926
Rev.: $82,000,000
Emp.: 100
Advetising Agency
N.A.I.C.S.: 541810
Mark Perrin *(Pres)*
Tiffany Obrecht *(Acct Exec-Indianapolis)*

Subsidiaries:

McCormick Company (1)
9245 Northpark Dr, Johnston, IA 50131
Tel.: (515) 251-8805
Sales Range: $10-24.9 Million
Emp.: 20
Full Service
N.A.I.C.S.: 541810
Melissa Sudman *(Mgr-Traffic)*
Dana Scheidegger *(Sr Dir-Art & Mgr-Creative)*

McCormick Company (1)
1201 NW Briarcliff Pkwy Ste 200, Kansas City, MO 64116-1774
Tel.: (816) 584-8444
Emp.: 52
N.A.I.C.S.: 541810
Marla Jannings *(Dir-Art)*
Jeff Modean *(Dir-Creative)*
Stephen Nottingham *(Sr Dir-Art)*
Laura Mayfield *(VP-Contact Strategy)*
Nina Holdren *(Acct Exec)*

MCCORMICK DISTILLING CO., INC.
1 McCormick Ln, Weston, MO 64098-9558
Tel.: (816) 640-2276 MO

Web Site: http://www.mccormickdistilling.com
Year Founded: 1856
Sales Range: $100-124.9 Million
Emp.: 185
Mfr & Importer Distilled Spirits
N.A.I.C.S.: 312140
Chris Fernandez *(CFO)*
Ed Pechar *(Owner & Chm)*
Jim Zargo *(Pres)*
Mick Harris *(Vice Chm & Mgr-Natl Sls)*

MCCORMICK INCORPORATED
4000 12th Ave N, Fargo, ND 58108-2846
Tel.: (701) 277-1225
Web Site: http://www.northernimprovement.com
Year Founded: 1981
Rev.: $80,000,000
Emp.: 150
Provider of Construction Services
N.A.I.C.S.: 237310
Steve McCormick *(Pres-McCormick)*
Thomas McCormick *(Pres-Northern Reg)*

Subsidiaries:

Asphalt Paving & Supply Inc. (1)
2425 N Glassford Hill Rd, Prescott Valley, AZ 86314-2236
Tel.: (928) 772-6363
Web Site: http://www.asphaltpavingsupply.com
Asphalt & Concrete Product Distr
N.A.I.C.S.: 423320
Christopher Mathern *(Mgr-Matls)*

Roberts Construction Company Inc. (1)
137 Bear River Dr, Evanston, WY 82930-2815
Tel.: (307) 789-5792
Sales Range: $10-24.9 Million
Emp.: 5
Provider of Construction Services
N.A.I.C.S.: 237310

MCCORMICK INSULATION SUPPLY
11424 Cronhill Dr, Owings Mills, MD 21117
Tel.: (410) 581-0040
Web Site: http://www.mccormickinsulation.com
Sales Range: $10-24.9 Million
Emp.: 50
Distr of Insulation
N.A.I.C.S.: 423330
Robert H. McCormick *(Pres)*
Aimee Turrall *(VP)*
Dan Ullmann *(Asst Mgr-Warehouse)*

MCCORMICK MARKETING INC.
2401 Avenue Q, Snyder, TX 79549
Tel.: (325) 573-6365
Rev.: $14,000,000
Emp.: 9
Provider of Petroleum Products
N.A.I.C.S.: 424720
Michael B. Dennis *(Owner & Pres)*

MCCORMICK PAINT WORKS COMPANY
2355 Lewis Ave, Rockville, MD 20851-2335
Tel.: (301) 770-3235 MD
Web Site: http://www.mccormickpaints.com
Year Founded: 1960
Sales Range: $100-124.9 Million
Emp.: 150
Mfr of Paint & Architectural Coatings
N.A.I.C.S.: 325510

T.P. McCormick *(CEO)*
J Casey McCormick *(Pres)*
Casey McCormick *(Pres)*

MCCORMICK STEVENSON CORP.
25400 US Hwy 19 N Ste 162, Clearwater, FL 33763
Tel.: (727) 735-9633 FL
Web Site: http://www.mccst.com
Year Founded: 1999
Sales Range: $1-9.9 Million
Emp.: 10
Engineeering Services
N.A.I.C.S.: 541330
Melissa McCormick *(CFO)*
Noel McCormick *(Founder & Pres)*
Paul Stevenson *(VP)*

MCCORMICK TAYLOR
2001 Market St Fl 10, Philadelphia, PA 19103
Tel.: (215) 592-4200
Web Site: http://www.mccormicktaylor.com
Year Founded: 1946
Rev.: $52,000,000
Emp.: 400
Construction Design & Engineering Consulting Services
N.A.I.C.S.: 237310
Patrick J. Guise *(Chief Visionary Officer)*
Gary J. Bellotti *(VP)*
Paul G. Archibald *(VP)*

MCCORMIX CORP.
22 N Calle Cesar Chavez, Santa Barbara, CA 93103-3639
Tel.: (805) 963-9366
Web Site: http://www.mccormix.com
Year Founded: 1997
Sales Range: $1-9.9 Million
Emp.: 9
Petroleum Bulk Stations & Terminals
N.A.I.C.S.: 424710
Kenneth Olsen *(Pres)*
Steven Oslen *(Gen Mgr)*

MCCOURT CONSTRUCTION CO. INC.
60 K St Ste 2, Boston, MA 02127
Tel.: (617) 269-2330
Web Site: http://www.mccourtconstruction.com
Rev.: $73,000,000
Emp.: 40
Highway & Street Construction
N.A.I.C.S.: 237310
Joshua Palen *(Engr-Safety)*

MCCOURT LABEL COMPANY
20 Egbert Ln, Lewis Run, PA 16738
Tel.: (814) 362-3851 PA
Web Site: http://www.mccourtlabel.com
Year Founded: 1896
Sales Range: $75-99.9 Million
Emp.: 68
Custom Pressure-Sensitive Labels Mfr
N.A.I.C.S.: 322299
David Ferguson *(Pres)*

MCCOY GROUP, INC.
2099 S Park Ct, Dubuque, IA 52003
Tel.: (563) 584-2670
Year Founded: 1958
Trucking Service
N.A.I.C.S.: 484121
Jim Kane *(VP-Procurement, Facilities & Audit)*

Subsidiaries:

Mccoy Nationalease, Inc. (1)
2401 Progress Way, Kaukauna, WI 54130

Tel.: (920) 380-9910
Sales Range: $1-9.9 Million
Emp.: 25
Truck, Utility Trailer & Recreational Vehicle Rental & Leasing Services
N.A.I.C.S.: 532120

MCCOY MOTORS INC.
361 N Switzer Canyon Dr, Flagstaff, AZ 86001
Tel.: (928) 774-1472 AZ
Year Founded: 1968
Sales Range: $50-74.9 Million
Emp.: 50
Car Dealership
N.A.I.C.S.: 441110
Lewis McCoy *(Founder & Dir)*
Dorothy Lively *(Pres)*

MCCOY'S BUILDING SUPPLY CENTERS
1350 N Interstate 35, San Marcos, TX 78666-7118
Tel.: (512) 353-5400 TX
Web Site: http://www.mccoys.com
Year Founded: 1966
Sales Range: $25-49.9 Million
Emp.: 2,250
Retail of Lumber & Other Building Materials
N.A.I.C.S.: 423310
Brian McCoy *(Chm & CEO)*
G. Richard Neal *(CFO & Sr VP)*
Dan Stauffer *(VP-Mktg)*
Meagan McCoy Jones *(Pres & COO)*
Joshua Whitley *(Controller)*
Adam Weatherly *(Mgr-Store-Cleburne)*
Joanne Corum *(VP-Info Svcs)*
Bane Phillippi *(VP & Gen Counsel)*
Horacio Castillo *(Mgr-Store)*
Will Fritzlan *(Mgr-Store-Alvin)*
Raul Avalos *(Mgr-Store-Roswell)*
Holton Walker *(Mgr-Store-Beeville)*
Robert Aranda *(Mgr-South Gen McMullen Drive)*
Stan Nelson *(Mgr-Laurel)*
Jason Harrison *(Mgr-Store-Southeast San Antonio)*
Moses Sambrano *(Mgr-Store-Hobbs)*
Mike Wauson *(Mgr-Store-Corpus Christi)*
Jessica Walshak *(Dir-Mktg & Adv)*
Chuck Churchwell III *(Exec VP)*

MCCRACKEN FINANCIAL SOLUTIONS CORP.
8 Suburban Park Dr, Billerica, MA 01821-3903
Tel.: (978) 439-9000 DE
Web Site: http://www.mccrackenfs.com
Year Founded: 1991
Sales Range: $10-24.9 Million
Emp.: 75
Commercial Mortgage Servicing Solutions
N.A.I.C.S.: 541512
Kim Cooper *(Mgr-Corp Comm)*

MCCRANEY PROPERTY COMPANY
2257 Vista Pkwy Ste 17, West Palm Beach, FL 33411
Tel.: (561) 478-4300
Web Site: http://www.mccraneyproperty.com
Sales Range: $1-9.9 Million
Emp.: 12
Commercial Leasing, Construction, Property Management & Asset Management
N.A.I.C.S.: 531390
Steven McCraney *(Pres & CEO)*
James Marvel *(CFO & Sr VP)*
Andrew Jacobson *(VP-Legal Affairs)*

COMPANIES

Michael Lanford (Mgr-Property)
Valerie Sanders (Mgr-Asset)
David Williams (Mng Dir/Principal-Charlotte)

MCCRAW OIL CO. INC.
2207 N Center St, Bonham, TX 75418
Tel.: (903) 583-7481   TX
Web Site: http://www.mccrawoil.com
Year Founded: 1948
Petroleum Bulk Stations & Terminals
N.A.I.C.S.: 424710
Doyce Taylor (Pres)

MCCRAY LUMBER COMPANY
10741 El Monte Ln, Overland Park, KS 66211-1406
Tel.: (913) 341-6900   MO
Web Site: http://www.mccraylumber.com
Year Founded: 1947
Sales Range: $25-49.9 Million
Emp.: 250
Lumber & Other Building Materials Sales
N.A.I.C.S.: 423310
Brian Hall (CFO)

Subsidiaries:

McCray Lumber Company - McCray Lumber & Millwork Division   (1)
207 S 9th St, Edwardsville, KS 66111
Tel.: (913) 422-1300
Emp.: 200
Lumber Product Distr
N.A.I.C.S.: 423310
Gene Bosley (Gen Mgr-Edwardsville)

MCCREA HEATING AND AIR CONDITIONING
4463 Beech Rd, Temple Hills, MD 20748
Tel.: (301) 423-6623
Web Site: http://www.mccreaway.com
Year Founded: 1935
Rev.: $32,640,000
Emp.: 350
Heating & Air Conditioning Services
N.A.I.C.S.: 238220
Wayne Lanhardt (Pres)

MCCREADY FOUNDATION, INC.
201 Hall Hwy, Crisfield, MD 21817
Tel.: (410) 968-1200   MD
Web Site: http://www.mccreadyfoundation.org
Year Founded: 1923
Sales Range: $10-24.9 Million
Emp.: 243
Community Health Care Services
N.A.I.C.S.: 623312
Joy A. Strand (CEO)
Michael Hall (Chm)
Percy Purnell (Vice Chm)

MCCREARY MODERN INC.
2564 US Hwy 321 S, Newton, NC 28658
Tel.: (828) 464-6465
Rev.: $67,682,992
Emp.: 600
Upholstered Household Furniture
N.A.I.C.S.: 337121
Rick Coffee (Pres)
Bob J. Mccreary (CEO)
Mark Shull (Mgr)
Steven Snyder (Plant Mgr)
Mike Ridenhour (Dir-Engrg)
Alan Fisher (Dir-IT)

MCCREE GENERAL CONTRACTORS & ARCHITECTS
500 E Princeton St, Orlando, FL 32803
Tel.: (407) 898-4821
Web Site: http://www.mccree.com
Emp.: 50
General Construction & Architectural Services
N.A.I.C.S.: 236220
Joe O. Robertson (VP)
Tom Griffin (VP)
Cindy McCree-Bodine (VP-Mktg & HR)
Eric Dodson (VP-Educational Construction)
Richard Gaines (VP-Architecture)
Helen Donnell (Controller)
Richard T. McCree Sr. (Chm)
Richard McCree Jr. (Pres & CEO)

MCCRORY CONSTRUCTION CO., LLC
522 Lady St, Columbia, SC 29201-3122
Tel.: (803) 799-8100   SC
Web Site: http://www.mccroryconstruction.com
Year Founded: 1918
Sales Range: $25-49.9 Million
Emp.: 80
Provider of Contracting & Construction Services
N.A.I.C.S.: 236220
Dennis G. Shealy (VP-Bus Dev)
Randy Morrison (VP-HR)
Allen B. Amsler (Pres & CEO)
Gail Chapman (VP-Preconstruction Svcs)

MCCUE CORPORATION
13 Centennial Dr, Peabody, MA 01960
Tel.: (978) 741-8500
Web Site: http://www.mccuecorp.com
Rev.: $29,207,672
Emp.: 60
Store Fixtures & Display Equipment
N.A.I.C.S.: 423440
David McCue (Founder)
Alicia Parslow (Coord-Accts Payable)
David DiAntonio (CEO)
Ricky Chen (Dir-Ops)
Emma Panter (Mng Dir-UK)

MCCULLOUGH COMMUNICATIONS & MARKETING
4590 MacArthur Blvd Ste 500, Newport Beach, CA 92660-2028
Tel.: (949) 833-1135
Web Site: http://www.mcculloughmarcom.com
Year Founded: 1981
Sales Range: Less than $1 Million
Emp.: 7
N.A.I.C.S.: 541810
Jack McCullough (CEO)
Alvin Morrison (Pres)
Allan Wash (Creative Dir-Concept Copy)
Brian Miller (Copy Chief)
Catharine Cooper (Creative Dir-Design)
Melissa Adams (PR Dir)
Anita Price (VP)

MCCULLOUGH PUBLIC RELATIONS, INC.
3570 Executive Dr Ste 104, Uniontown, OH 44685
Tel.: (330) 244-9980
Web Site: http://www.mcculloughpr.com
Sales Range: Less than $1 Million
Emp.: 4
Video Production, Public Relations
N.A.I.C.S.: 541820
Shari McCullough-Arfons (Pres)

MCCUNE TECHNOLOGY
4801 Research Dr, Fayetteville, NC 28306
Tel.: (910) 424-2978
Web Site: http://www.mccune1.com
Fabricated Structural Metal Mfr
N.A.I.C.S.: 332312
David M. McCune Sr. (Pres)

MCCURDY & COMPANY INC
275-291 Main St, Rochester, NY 14604
Tel.: (585) 473-6030
Sales Range: $10-24.9 Million
Emp.: 10
Operator of Shopping Centers
N.A.I.C.S.: 531120
Gilbert K. McCurdy (CEO)

MCCURTAIN MEMORIAL MEDICAL MANAGEMENT, INC.
1301 E Lincoln Rd, Idabel, OK 74745
Tel.: (580) 286-7623   OK
Web Site: http://www.mmhok.com
Year Founded: 1975
Sales Range: $10-24.9 Million
Emp.: 350
Health Care Srvices
N.A.I.C.S.: 622110
Ray B. Whitmore Jr. (CFO)

MCCUTCHEON ENTERPRISES, INC.
250 Park Rd, Apollo, PA 15613
Tel.: (724) 568-3623
Web Site: http://www.completewastemgmt.com
Year Founded: 1947
Rev.: $11,200,000
Emp.: 130
Waste Management Services
N.A.I.C.S.: 562998
Calvin S. McCutcheon (Pres & Treas)
Craig Kinley (Mgr-Ops)
Debra Williams (Mgr-IT & Acctg)
Matthew Hawk (Dir-Safety)

MCDANIEL FOOD MANAGEMENT INC.
404 Wall St, Columbia, LA 71418
Tel.: (318) 649-5964
Web Site: http://www.macsfreshmarket.com
Sales Range: $10-24.9 Million
Emp.: 30
Provider of Grocery Store Services
N.A.I.C.S.: 445110
Cleavon McDaniel (Pres)
Jackie Lawrence (Co-Owner)

MCDANIEL MACHINERY, INC.
187 Cahaba Vly Pkwy, Pelham, AL 35124
Tel.: (205) 403-9900
Web Site: http://www.mcdanielmachinery.com
Sales Range: $10-24.9 Million
Emp.: 10
Machine Tools & Accessories
N.A.I.C.S.: 423830
James McDaniel (VP-Fin)
George Wroclawski (Mgr-Svcs-Computer Numerical Control)
Richard McDaniel Jr. (Pres)

MCDANIEL MOTOR CO.
1111 Mount Vernon Ave, Marion, OH 43302
Tel.: (740) 389-2355
Year Founded: 1916
Sales Range: $50-74.9 Million
Emp.: 70
New Car Retailer
N.A.I.C.S.: 441110
Jeffrey Cerny (Gen Mgr)
Michael J. McDaniel (Pres)

MCDERMOTT WILL & EMERY LLP

MCDERMOTT AUTO GROUP
655 Main St, East Haven, CT 06512
Tel.: (203) 466-1000
Web Site: http://www.mcdermottauto.com
Rev.: $25,900,000
Emp.: 65
New & Used Automobiles
N.A.I.C.S.: 441110
David McDermott (Pres)
Michael Silvestri (Dir-Parts & Svc)

Subsidiaries:

David McDermott Chevrolet   (1)
655 Main St, East Haven, CT 06512
Tel.: (203) 466-1000
Web Site: http://www.davemcdermottchevrolet.com
Automobiles, New & Used
N.A.I.C.S.: 441110
David McDermott (Pres)
David McDermott (Pres)

David McDermott of New Haven   (1)
655 Main St, East Haven, CT 06512
Tel.: (203) 466-9999
Web Site: http://www.mcdermottlexus.com
Rev.: $3,600,000
Emp.: 13
Automobiles, New & Used
N.A.I.C.S.: 441110
David McDermott (Owner & Pres)

MCDERMOTT CENTER
932 W Washington, Chicago, IL 60607
Tel.: (312) 226-7984   IL
Web Site: http://www.hcenter.org
Year Founded: 1975
Sales Range: $10-24.9 Million
Emp.: 582
Detoxification Center Operator
N.A.I.C.S.: 621420
Dan Lustig (Pres & CEO)
Anna Kuzak (Controller)
Jeffrey Collord (VP-Ops)

MCDERMOTT WILL & EMERY LLP
340 Madison Ave, New York, NY 10173-1922
Tel.: (212) 547-5400   IL
Web Site: http://www.mwe.com
Year Founded: 1934
Sales Range: $800-899.9 Million
Emp.: 1,001
Legal Advisory Services
N.A.I.C.S.: 541110
Timothy J. Alvino (Partner-New York)
Bronwyn Andreas (Partner-New York)
Banks Brown (Partner-New York)
John J. Calandra (Partner-New York)
Bari Cariello (Partner-New York)
Joan-Elisse Carpentier (Partner-New York & Silicon Valley)
Madeline Chiampou Tully (Partner-New York)
Robert H. Cohen (Partner-New York)
Harold C. Davidson (Partner-New York)
Andrew J. Genz (Partner-Washington)
Joel C. Rush (Partner-Washington)
Michael W. Ryan (Partner-Washington)
Takashi Saito (Partner)
Sally A. Rosenberg (Partner-Washington)
Toni Ann Kruse (Partner)
Joel Hugenberger (Partner)
Jay Reiziss (Partner)
Veleka Peeples-Dyer (Partner-Washington)
Kristin E. Michaels (Partner-Chicago)
Alexander Clavero (Partner)
Ibrahim Barakat (Partner)
Barrington Dyer (Partner)

MCDERMOTT WILL & EMERY LLP

McDermott Will & Emery LLP—(Continued)
Nitin Gambhir (*Partner*)
Vernessa Pollard (*Head-Food Drug Admin Practice-Washington*)
Erin Kartheiser (*Partner-Chicago*)
Roy McDonald (*Partner-Litigation Practice-San Francisco*)
Henrik Holzapfel (*Partner-Intellectual Property-Dusseldorf*)
Sarah Chapin Columbia (*Head-Intellectual Property Practice-Global*)
Rebecca C. Martin (*Partner-Litigation Practice Grp*)
David Lipkin (*Partner-Menlo Park*)
Martha Pugh (*Partner*)
Alexander Ott (*Partner*)
Kate McDonald (*Partner*)
Justin Jesse (*Partner*)
Dawn Helak (*Partner*)
Britt Haxton (*Partner*)
Heather Cooper (*Partner*)
Eliot Burriss (*Partner-Litigation Practice Grp-Dallas*)
Erin Turley (*Partner-Dallas*)
Allison Wilkerson (*Partner-Dallas*)
Gregory Metz (*Partner-Chicago*)
Michael Austin (*Partner*)
Sarah E. Walters (*Partner-Boston*)
Roy Larson (*Partner*)
Anh Lee (*Partner-Fin & Private Equity Practices-Chicago*)
Lee Schneider (*Partner-Fin Institutions Advisory Practice Grp*)
Lilya Tessler (*Partner*)
Ira J. Coleman (*Chm*)
David L. Taub (*Head-Fin Institutions Advisory Practice Grp*)
Stephen W. Bernstein (*Partner & Head--Intl*)
Henry Christensen III (*Partner-New York*)
James A. Cannatti III (*Partner-Health Indus Advisory Practice-Washington*)

MCDERMOTT-COSTA CO., INC.
1045 MacArthur Blvd, San Leandro, CA 94577
Tel.: (510) 351-7460   CA
Web Site:
   http://www.mcdermottcosta.com
Year Founded: 1938
Insurance & Brokerages Services
N.A.I.C.S.: 524210
Mike McDermott (*Partner & VP*)

MCDEVITT TRUCKS INC
1 Mack Ave, Manchester, NH 03103-5916
Tel.: (603) 668-1700   NH
Web Site: http://www.mctrucks.com
Year Founded: 1974
Sales Range: $100-124.9 Million
Emp.: 200
Automobiles & Heavy Trucks
N.A.I.C.S.: 423710
Jim Lagana (*Gen Mgr*)
Fred Smith (*Mgr-Sls*)
David Pittarelli (*Controller*)
John J. Mcdevitt Jr. (*Pres*)

MCDONALD AUTOMOTIVE GROUP
6060 S Broadway, Littleton, CO 80121
Tel.: (303) 795-1100
Web Site:
   http://www.mcdonaldag.com
Sales Range: $50-74.9 Million
Emp.: 650
New Car Retailer
N.A.I.C.S.: 441110
Douglas McDonald (*Owner & CEO*)
Micheal McDonald (*Pres*)

MCDONALD EQUIPMENT COMPANY
37200 Vine St, Willoughby, OH 44094-6346
Tel.: (440) 951-8222   OH
Web Site:
   http://www.mcdonaldequipment.com
Year Founded: 1968
Sales Range: $25-49.9 Million
Emp.: 22
Distr of Engines & Generators
N.A.I.C.S.: 423830
Scott McDonald (*Pres & CEO*)
Tami Weisbarth (*Mgr-Acctg*)

MCDONALD FORD INC.
6790 Midland Rd, Freeland, MI 48623
Tel.: (989) 695-5566
Web Site:
   http://mcdonaldford.dealerconnection.com
Sales Range: $10-24.9 Million
Emp.: 49
New & Used Car Dealers
N.A.I.C.S.: 441110
Thomas McDonald Jr. (*Pres*)

MCDONALD LUMBER CO. INC.
126 Cedar Creek Rd PO Box 2185, Fayetteville, NC 28312
Tel.: (910) 483-0381
Web Site:
   http://www.mcdonaldlumber.doitbest.com
Sales Range: $25-49.9 Million
Emp.: 78
Lumber & Other Building Materials
N.A.I.C.S.: 423310
Greg McDonald (*VP*)
Robert McDonald (*Treas*)
Frances Jackson (*Controller & Mgr-DP*)

MCDONALD PONTIAC-CADILLAC-GMC-OLDS INC.
5155 State St, Saginaw, MI 48603
Tel.: (989) 790-5155
Web Site:
   http://www.mcdonaldauto.com
Sales Range: $25-49.9 Million
Emp.: 101
Owner & Operator of Car Dealerships
N.A.I.C.S.: 441110
Mark Trokopenko (*CFO*)
T. William McDonald Jr. (*Pres*)

MCDONALD STEEL CORPORATION
100 Ohio Ave, McDonald, OH 44437-1900
Tel.: (330) 530-9118
Web Site:
   http://www.mcdonaldsteel.com
Year Founded: 1980
Sales Range: $10-24.9 Million
Emp.: 160
Blast Furnaces & Steel Mill Services
N.A.I.C.S.: 331110
Subsidiaries:
McDonald Industrial Land Co.   (1)
100 Ohio Ave, McDonald, OH 44437-1900
Tel.: (330) 530-9118
Provider of Building Operation Services
N.A.I.C.S.: 531120

MCDONALD TECHNOLOGIES INTERNATIONAL INC.
2310 Mcdaniel Dr, Carrollton, TX 75006-6843
Tel.: (972) 243-6767   TX
Web Site: http://www.mcdonaldtech.com
Year Founded: 1988
Sales Range: $10-24.9 Million
Emp.: 300
Mfr of Printed Circuit Boards
N.A.I.C.S.: 334412
Pip Sivakumar (*Pres & CEO*)

MCDONALD WHOLESALE CO.
2350 W Broadway, Eugene, OR 97402-2704
Tel.: (541) 345-8421   OR
Web Site:
   http://www.mcdonaldwhsl.com
Year Founded: 1926
Sales Range: $10-24.9 Million
Emp.: 114
Whslr of Groceries, Candy, Beer & Ale
N.A.I.C.S.: 424810
Gary Thomsen (*Controller*)

MCDONALD YORK BUILDING COMPANY
801 Oberlin Rd Ste 235, Raleigh, NC 27605-3313
Tel.: (919) 832-3770   NC
Web Site:
   http://www.mcdonaldyork.com
Year Founded: 1989
Sales Range: $10-24.9 Million
Emp.: 30
Construction & Contracting Services
N.A.I.C.S.: 236220
John M. McDonald (*Co-Owner & Chm*)
Tanner Holland (*Pres*)
Kellie Renzi (*Dir-Preconstruction & Estimating*)
Emily Massey (*CFO & VP*)
Cary Lail (*VP*)
Edward Schofield (*Superintendent*)
Mike Kriston (*Sr VP*)

MCDONALD'S AMUSEMENTS INC.
1965 Great Falls Hwy, Lancaster, SC 29720
Tel.: (803) 286-5676
Rev.: $17,000,000
Emp.: 22
Provider of Amusement Equipment
N.A.I.C.S.: 713120
Jimmy Mcdonald (*Pres*)

MCDONALDS OF CALHOUN INC.
806 Columbia Ave W, Battle Creek, MI 49015
Tel.: (269) 965-1402
Sales Range: $25-49.9 Million
Emp.: 1,448
Provider of Fast-Food Services
N.A.I.C.S.: 722513
H. Jim Brasseur (*Pres*)

MCDONALDS OF SCOTTSDALE
16097 N 82nd St Ste 300, Scottsdale, AZ 85260
Tel.: (480) 367-9500
Web Site: http://www.mcstate.com
Rev.: $16,000,000
Emp.: 15
Provider of Fast-Food Services
N.A.I.C.S.: 722513
Mark E. Kramer (*Pres*)
Jerry Wernau (*VP*)

MCDONALDS OF SIOUX CITY
3253 Floyd Blvd, Sioux City, IA 51108
Tel.: (712) 239-1747
Sales Range: $1-9.9 Million
Emp.: 600
Provider of Fast-Food Services
N.A.I.C.S.: 722513
Keith Petrie (*Owner*)

U.S. PRIVATE

MCDONOUGH BOLYARD PECK, INC.
Williams Plz 1 3040 Williams Dr Ste 300, Fairfax, VA 22031
Tel.: (703) 641-9088
Web Site: http://www.mbpce.com
Year Founded: 1989
Sales Range: $25-49.9 Million
Emp.: 302
Engineeering Services
N.A.I.C.S.: 541330
Blake V. Peck (*Pres & COO*)
Jim Mascaro (*VP & Dir-Commissioning Svcs*)
Robert Hixon (*Dir-Govt Svcs*)
James T. V. L. Peck (*Sr VP-Strategic Markets & Svcs*)
Mairav R. Mintz (*VP & Mgr-Maryland*)
Bob Fraga (*VP & Reg Mgr*)
Christopher J. Payne (*Exec VP*)
Duncan Stewart (*Mgr-Virginia*)
Don C. Young (*Sr VP & Reg Mgr*)
Charles E. Bolyard Jr. (*Chm & CEO*)
John L. MacKay Jr. (*Sr VP & Reg Mgr*)

MCDONOUGH CORPORATION
21050 N Pima Rd Ste 100, Scottsdale, AZ 85255
Tel.: (602) 544-5900
Web Site:
   http://www.mcdonoughcorp.com
Year Founded: 1998
Sales Range: $125-149.9 Million
Emp.: 100
Millwork Services
N.A.I.C.S.: 321918
Matt Beverage (*Treas & Dir-Bus Information Sys*)
Brendan Riccobene (*Pres & CEO*)
Shannon Overcash (*Chief Admin Officer & Gen Counsel*)

Subsidiaries:

Arizona Stairs, Inc.   (1)
625 E Baseline Rd Ste 104, Gilbert, AZ 85233
Tel.: (480) 507-5433
Web Site: http://www.arizonastairs.com
Stair Railing Mfr
N.A.I.C.S.: 332323

Colonial Millworks Ltd. Inc.   (1)
US Rte 250 S, Beverly, WV 26253
Tel.: (304) 636-9338
Web Site: http://www.colonialmillwork.com
Sales Range: $10-24.9 Million
Emp.: 130
Provider of Millwork Services
N.A.I.C.S.: 321918
Andy Kidd (*Co-Founder*)
Jeff Simmons (*Co-Founder*)

McDonough Elevator Sales & Rentals Inc   (1)
8411 Villa Dr, Houston, TX 77061
Tel.: (888) 525-1375
Web Site: http://www.mcdelevators.com
Emp.: 30
Elevator Whslr
N.A.I.C.S.: 423830
Kevin Harrison (*Mgr-Ops*)

McDonough Marine Service, Inc.   (1)
1750 Clearview Pkwy Ste 201, Metairie, LA 70001
Tel.: (504) 780-8100
Web Site:
   http://www.mcdonoughmarine.com
Marine Transportation Services
N.A.I.C.S.: 488390
Eric Anderson (*Mgr-Sls*)
Pat Stant (*Pres*)
Shannon Badeaux (*Mgr-Ops*)

Preferred Millwork Enterprises Inc.   (1)
1331 Davis Rd, Elgin, IL 60123
Tel.: (847) 531-5600
Sales Range: $10-24.9 Million
Provider of Lumber, Plywood & Millwork Services

N.A.I.C.S.: 423310

Titan Stairs Inc. (1)
5550 Cameron St Ste H, Las Vegas, NV 89118
Tel.: (702) 221-9980
Web Site: http://www.titanstairs.com
Sales Range: $1-9.9 Million
Stair Railing Mfr
N.A.I.C.S.: 332323
Mike Dilnot-Smith (Mgr-Trng & Safety)

MCDONOUGH MANUFACTURING COMPANY
2320 Melby St, Eau Claire, WI 54702
Tel.: (715) 834-7755
Web Site: http://www.mcdonough-mfg.com
Year Founded: 1888
Sales Range: $10-24.9 Million
Emp.: 30
Sawmill Products Mfr
N.A.I.C.S.: 333248
Susan K. Tietz (Pres & CEO)
Jason Meyer (Engr-Design)
Matt Tietz (VP)

MCDOUGAL COMPANIES
5001 W Loop 289, Lubbock, TX 79414
Tel.: (806) 797-3162
Web Site: http://www.mcdougal.com
Year Founded: 1984
Real Estate Investment Trust
N.A.I.C.S.: 525990
Delbert McDougal (*)
Marc McDougal McDougal (CEO)
Julie Berger (CFO)
Mont McClendon (COO & Gen Counsel)
David Miller (Pres-Construction)
Gina Milford (VP-HR)
Steve Colella (Sr VP-Ops)
Carl Tepper (VP-Special Projects)
Doug Duncan (VP-Realtors)
Andy Clayton (VP-Multifamily Housing)
Bree Walker Uline (Dlr-Mktg)

MCDOWALL COMPANY
1431 Prosper Dr PO Box 606, Waite Park, MN 56387
Tel.: (320) 251-8640
Web Site: http://www.mcdowallco.com
Year Founded: 1895
Sales Range: $25-49.9 Million
Emp.: 130
Heating, Air Conditioning & Architectural Sheet Metal Contractors
N.A.I.C.S.: 238220
John W. McDowall (Pres & CEO)
Karen Athmann (Gen Mgr)
Arnie Dingmann (Asst Gen Mgr)
Jay Mumm (Mgr-Roofing)
Mathew McDowall (Sec & Mgr-Ops)

MCDOWELL & WALKER INC.
4 Depot St, Delhi, NY 13753
Tel.: (607) 746-2314
Web Site: http://www.mcdowellwalker.com
Sales Range: $10-24.9 Million
Emp.: 18
Feed & Farm Supply
N.A.I.C.S.: 459999
Barry James (Pres)

MCDOWELL SUPPLY COMPANY
3266 Robert C Byrd Dr, Beckley, WV 25801
Tel.: (304) 253-4262
Sales Range: $10-24.9 Million
Emp.: 17
Provider of Cigarettes & Cigars
N.A.I.C.S.: 424940

Dennis Ramella (Pres)

MCE CORPORATION
6515 Trinity Ct, Dublin, CA 94568
Tel.: (925) 803-4111
Web Site: http://www.mce-corp.com
Sales Range: $10-24.9 Million
Emp.: 120
Curb & Sidewalk Contractors
N.A.I.C.S.: 238110
Dean McDonald (Mgr-Projects)
Jeff Core (Pres)

MCE DISTRIBUTING AND SUPPLY
2886 NW 79th Ave, Miami, FL 33122
Tel.: (305) 598-9465
Rev.: $14,500,000
Emp.: 1
Industrial Supplies
N.A.I.C.S.: 423840
Edward Wahn (Partner)

MCELENEY MOTORS INC.
2421 Lincolnway, Clinton, IA 52733
Tel.: (563) 243-7000 IA
Web Site: http://www.mceleney.com
Year Founded: 1914
Sales Range: $25-49.9 Million
Emp.: 90
Sales & Service of New & Used Automobiles
N.A.I.C.S.: 441110
W.J. McEleney (Chm)
John J. McEleney (Pres)

MCELROY MANUFACTURING, INC.
833 N Fulton Ave, Tulsa, OK 74115-6408
Tel.: (918) 836-8611 OK
Web Site: http://www.mcelroy.com
Year Founded: 1954
Sales Range: $200-249.9 Million
Emp.: 400
Mfr & Design of Special Industry Machinery
N.A.I.C.S.: 333248
Donna Dutton (Exec VP)
Arthur H. McElroy II (Chm, Pres & CEO)
Peggy Tanner (Exec VP)
Mike Vaughn (Gen Mgr-Acctg)
Scott Reeder (Mgr-Facilities)

MCELROY METAL MILL, INC.
1500 Hamilton Rd, Bossier City, LA 71111-3812
Tel.: (318) 747-8000 LA
Web Site: http://www.mcelroymetal.com
Year Founded: 1963
Sales Range: $1-4.9 Billion
Emp.: 535
Prefabricated Metal Buildings
N.A.I.C.S.: 332311
Amy Malone (Supvr-Tax)
Thomas E. McElroy Jr. (CEO)

MCELROY TRUCK LINES INC.
111 80 Spur, Cuba, AL 36907-9633
Tel.: (205) 392-5579 AL
Web Site: http://www.mcelroytrucklines.com
Year Founded: 1963
Sales Range: $25-49.9 Million
Emp.: 425
Trucking Service
N.A.I.C.S.: 484121
Jay McElroy (Pres)
Billy Rawson (CFO)
Sean McElroy (VP)

Subsidiaries:
Sumter Timber Company, LLC (1)

25000 Al Hwy 28, Demopolis, AL 36732-5622
Tel.: (334) 289-3100
Web Site: http://www.sumtertimber.com
Sales Range: $10-24.9 Million
Emp.: 85
Timber Supplier
N.A.I.C.S.: 113310
Roy Geiger (Owner)

MCELROY'S, INC.
3209 SW Topeka Blvd, Topeka, KS 66611-2234
Tel.: (785) 266-4870
Web Site: http://www.mcelroys.com
Year Founded: 1951
Sales Range: $10-24.9 Million
Emp.: 75
Plumbing Services
N.A.I.C.S.: 238220
Charlie Campbell (Mgr-Plumbing)
Martin Decker (Mgr-Sheet Metal)
Janet McElroy (Sec)
Keith Watkins (Mgr-HVAC Svc)

MCELROY, DEUTSCH, MULVANEY & CARPENTER, LLP
1300 Mount Kemble Ave, Morristown, NJ 07962-2075
Tel.: (973) 993-8100
Web Site: http://www.mdmc-law.com
Year Founded: 1983
Sales Range: $100-124.9 Million
Emp.: 306
Law firm
N.A.I.C.S.: 541110
H. George Avery (Partner)
Robert J. Alter (Partner)
John P. Beyel (Partner)
Jeffrey Bernstein (Partner)
John P. Belardo (Partner)

MCELVAIN OIL & GAS PROPERTIES INC
1050 17th St Ste 2500, Denver, CO 80265-2080
Tel.: (303) 893-0933
Web Site: http://www.mcelvain.com
Year Founded: 1992
Sales Range: $75-99.9 Million
Emp.: 40
Production of Oil & Gas Wells
N.A.I.C.S.: 211120

MCELWAIN CHEVROLET & OLDSMOBILE
911 Lawrence Ave, Ellwood City, PA 16117
Tel.: (724) 758-4588
Web Site: http://www.mcelwains.com
Year Founded: 1930
Sales Range: $10-24.9 Million
Emp.: 50
Car Whslr
N.A.I.C.S.: 441110
Debra R. McElwain (Controller)

MCENANY ROOFING & CONTRACTING INC.
8803 Industrial Dr, Tampa, FL 33637
Tel.: (813) 988-1669
Web Site: http://www.mcenanyroofing.com
Year Founded: 1985
Sales Range: $10-24.9 Million
Emp.: 125
Roofing Contractors
N.A.I.C.S.: 238160
Mike McEnany (Founder & Pres)
Bruce Goodin (Sr VP & Gen Mgr)
Mark Sloat (VP)
Dan Noderer (Branch Mgr)

MCENEARNEY ASSOCIATES INC.
109 S Pitt St, Alexandria, VA 22314

Tel.: (703) 549-9292 VA
Web Site: http://www.mcenearney.com
Year Founded: 1980
Sales Range: $10-24.9 Million
Emp.: 315
Provider of Real Estate Services
N.A.I.C.S.: 531210
Maureen Dunn (Pres)
Glenn Lewis (Exec VP)

MCESSY INVESTMENTS CO.
1025 W Everett Rd, Lake Forest, IL 60045
Tel.: (847) 234-3427
Rev.: $15,200,000
Emp.: 900
Provider of Fast-Food Services
N.A.I.C.S.: 722513
William H. McEssy (Owner)
Ernie Massucci (Pres)

MCFA LLC
101 Kings Hwy E, Haddonfield, NJ 08033
Tel.: (856) 795-6111
Web Site: http://www.mcfaplanning.com
Year Founded: 2003
Rev.: $3,700,000
Emp.: 40
Scientific & Technical Consulting Services
N.A.I.C.S.: 541690
B. J. Kraemer (Dir-Client Strategy & Dev)
Jeffrey Weissman (VP & Gen Mgr)

MCFADDEN & MILLER CONSTRUCTION
11350 Luna Rd, Dallas, TX 75229
Tel.: (972) 401-2356
Web Site: http://www.mcfaddenandmiller.com
Sales Range: $10-24.9 Million
Emp.: 80
Civil Engineering Services
N.A.I.C.S.: 237310
Rose Zrubek (Office Mgr)

MCFARLAND & COMPANY, INC.
960 Hwy 88 W, Jefferson, NC 28640
Tel.: (336) 246-4460
Web Site: http://www.mcfarlandpub.com
Year Founded: 1979
Sales Range: $10-24.9 Million
Emp.: 32
Reference Book Publisher
N.A.I.C.S.: 513130
Robert Franklin (CEO)
Rhonda Herman (VP)
Steve Wilson (Assoc VP)
Kim M. Hadley (Gen Mgr)

MCFARLAND JOHNSON INC.
Metrocenter 49 Ct St, Binghamton, NY 13902-1980
Tel.: (607) 723-9421
Web Site: http://www.mjinc.com
Year Founded: 1946
Emp.: 50
Engineeering Services
N.A.I.C.S.: 541330
Richard J. Brauer (Pres & CEO)
James M. Festa (COO & Sr VP)
Frederick Mock (VP)
Chad Nixon (Officer-Bus Dev & Sr VP)
Ruthanne Bulman (Mgr-HR)

MCFARLANE MANUFACTURING COMPANY INC.
1259 Water St, Sauk City, WI 53583-1617

MCFARLANE MANUFACTURING COMPANY INC.

McFarlane Manufacturing Company Inc.—(Continued)
Tel.: (608) 643-3321 WI
Web Site: http://www.flexharrow.com
Year Founded: 1919
Sales Range: $10-24.9 Million
Emp.: 195
Farm Equipment & Machinery
N.A.I.C.S.: 332312
John McFarlane (Pres)
Dick McFarlen (VP)
Rauel Labreche (Controller)

MCFARLING FOODS, INC.
333 W 14th St, Indianapolis, IN 46202-2204
Tel.: (317) 635-2633 IN
Web Site: http://www.mcfarling.com
Year Founded: 1948
Sales Range: $125-149.9 Million
Emp.: 155
Provider of Wholesale Groceries for Restaurants & Institutional Markets
N.A.I.C.S.: 424470
Greg Clay (VP-Sls & Mktg)
Frank Chandler (Controller)
Hortense White (Dir-HR)
Scott Stroud (Dir-Pur)

MCFRANK & WILLIAMS ADVERTISING AGENCY, INC.
266 W 37th St, New York, NY 10018
Tel.: (212) 531-5700
Web Site: http://www.mcfrank.com
Year Founded: 1968
Sales Range: $25-49.9 Million
Emp.: 35
Advertising Agencies, Interactive Agencies, Recruitment
N.A.I.C.S.: 541810
Michael Bruce (Founder & Pres)

MCG GLOBAL, LLC
300 Long Beach Blvd Ste 13, Stratford, CT 06615
Tel.: (203) 386-0615 DE
Year Founded: 1995
Privater Equity Firm
N.A.I.C.S.: 523999
Vincent A. Wasik (Co-Founder & Principal)
Jeffrey T. Hendrickson (Principal)
S. Garrett Stonehouse Jr. (Co-Founder & Principal)

MCGARD INC.
3875 California Rd, Orchard Park, NY 14127
Tel.: (716) 662-8980
Web Site: http://www.mcgard.com
Sales Range: $25-49.9 Million
Emp.: 315
Provider of Security Products
N.A.I.C.S.: 423710
Lewis D. McCauley (Chm)
Durham McCauley (Pres)
Peter McCauley (Pres)
Mike Reilly (Mgr-Sls-Natl)

MCGARRAH JESSEE
121 W 6th St, Austin, TX 78701-2913
Tel.: (512) 225-2000
Web Site: http://www.mc-j.com
Year Founded: 1996
Rev.: $72,000,000
Emp.: 70
N.A.I.C.S.: 541810
James Mikus (Exec Dir-Creative)
Britton Upham (CEO)
Michael Anderson (Dir-Art)
Klaire Hensley (Head-Growth)
Subsidiaries:
Chaos Concept Manufacturing (1)
205 Brazos St, Austin, TX 78701
Tel.: (512) 225-2000

N.A.I.C.S.: 541810
Craig Crutchfield (Designer)
WebberMcJ (1)
205 Brazos St, Austin, TX 78701
Tel.: (512) 225-2000
Emp.: 65
Communications, Public Relations, Strategic Planning/Research
N.A.I.C.S.: 541820
Mark McGarrah (Partner)
Bryan Jessee (Mng Partner)

MCGARVEY DEVELOPMENT COMPANY
9260 Estero Park Commons Blvd Ste 101, Estero, FL 33928
Tel.: (239) 738-7800
Web Site: http://www.mcgarveycustomhomes.com
Year Founded: 1985
Sales Range: $25-49.9 Million
Emp.: 50
Real Estate Development, Management & Leasing Services
N.A.I.C.S.: 237210
John S. McGarvey (Pres & CEO)
John Berry (VP-Comml Construction)
Jay Schwarzer (VP)
William Price Jr. (Exec VP-Asset Mgmt)

MCGEAN-ROHCO, INC.
2910 Harvard Ave, Cleveland, OH 44105
Tel.: (216) 441-4900 OH
Web Site: http://www.mcgean.com
Year Founded: 1929
Sales Range: $75-99.9 Million
Emp.: 50
Chemicals Mfr
N.A.I.C.S.: 325998
Dickson L. Whitney (Chm & Pres)
Subsidiaries:
McGean Rohco (UK) Ltd. (1)
Qualcast Road Lower Horseley Fields, Wolverhampton, WV1 2QP, West Midlands, United Kingdom
Tel.: (44) 1902 456563
Web Site: http://www.mcgean-rohco.co.uk
Emp.: 25
Specialty Chemicals Mfr
N.A.I.C.S.: 325199

McGean-Rohco Singapore Pte Ltd (1)
No 6 Gul Link, Singapore, 629376, Singapore
Tel.: (65) 6 863 2296
Specialty Chemicals Mfr
N.A.I.C.S.: 325199

MCGEARY ORGANICS, INC.
941 Wheatland Ave Ste 401, Lancaster, PA 17603
Tel.: (717) 394-6843
Web Site: http://www.mcgearyorganics.com
Year Founded: 1952
Sales Range: $10-24.9 Million
Emp.: 18
Organic Grains, Organic Feeds, Organic Flours & Organic Fertilizers
N.A.I.C.S.: 424510
David R. Poorbaugh (Pres)

MCGEE & THIELEN INSURANCE BROKERS
3840 Rosin Ct Ste 245, Sacramento, CA 95834
Tel.: (916) 646-1919
Web Site: http://www.mcgeethieles.com
Sales Range: $25-49.9 Million
Emp.: 20
Provider of Insurance Services
N.A.I.C.S.: 524210

Dave Wood (VP)

MCGEE BROTHERS CO. INC.
4608 Carriker Rd, Monroe, NC 28110-7490
Tel.: (704) 753-4582
Web Site: http://www.mcgeebrick.com
Year Founded: 1971
Sales Range: $50-74.9 Million
Emp.: 600
Provider of Masonry Services
N.A.I.C.S.: 238140
Subsidiaries:
McGee Brothers Co. Inc. - Concrete Plant (1)
13800 Bill McGee Rd, Midland, NC 28107
Tel.: (704) 888-6466
Readymix Concrete Mfr
N.A.I.C.S.: 327320

McGee-Huntley Construction Co. Inc. (1)
4608 Carriker Rd, Monroe, NC 28110-7490
Tel.: (704) 753-4582
Web Site: http://www.mcgeebrick.com
Sales Range: $25-49.9 Million
Emp.: 300
Provider of Construction Services
N.A.I.C.S.: 236115

MCGEE CO.
10513 Hathaway Dr, Santa Fe Springs, CA 90670
Tel.: (562) 789-1777 CA
Web Site: http://www.mcgeeco.com
Year Founded: 1984
Sales Range: $10-24.9 Million
Emp.: 100
Mfr of Electrical Apparatus & Equipment
N.A.I.C.S.: 423610
Tracey Miller (CFO)
Subsidiaries:
Desert States Electrical Sales (1)
2920 E Elwood St, Phoenix, AZ 85040
Tel.: (602) 268-7008
Web Site: http://www.desertstates.com
Mfr of Electrical Equipment
N.A.I.C.S.: 335999
Steve Smith (Pres)

MCGEE COMPANY
1140 S Jason St, Denver, CO 80223
Tel.: (303) 777-2615
Web Site: http://www.mcgeecompany.com
Sales Range: $10-24.9 Million
Emp.: 100
Automotive Supplies
N.A.I.C.S.: 423830
John Lebresch (Gen Mgr)
Rick Arnold (Controller)
Charles J. McGee Jr. (Pres)

MCGEE GROUP
510 Commerce Park Dr, Marietta, GA 30060
Web Site: http://www.mcgeegroup.com
Year Founded: 1976
Sales Range: $25-49.9 Million
Emp.: 58
Eyeware
N.A.I.C.S.: 456130
Wayne McGee (Pres & CEO)

MCGEE TIRE STORES INC.
3939 US 98 S, Lakeland, FL 33812
Tel.: (863) 667-3702
Web Site: http://www.mcgeetire.com
Sales Range: $10-24.9 Million
Emp.: 190
General Automotive Repair Shops
N.A.I.C.S.: 531120

Bob Lanpher (COO)
Terry Borglund (CFO)

MCGEORGE CONTRACTING CO., INC.
1501 Heartwood St, White Hall, AR 71602
Tel.: (870) 534-7120 AR
Web Site: http://www.mcgeorgecontracting.com
Year Founded: 1933
Sales Range: $25-49.9 Million
Emp.: 252
Heavy Construction, Mining & Grading
N.A.I.C.S.: 212313
W. Scott McGeorge (Chm)
Subsidiaries:
Cranford Construction Co. (1)
1350 Eureka Garden Rd, North Little Rock, AR 72117
Tel.: (501) 945-7176
Sales Range: $25-49.9 Million
Emp.: 40
Producer & Paver of Hot Mix Asphalt Paving Materials
N.A.I.C.S.: 237310

MCGEORGES ROLLING HILLS RV
11525 Sunshade Ln, Ashland, VA 23005
Tel.: (804) 550-7323
Web Site: http://www.mcgeorgerv.com
Year Founded: 1969
Sales Range: $10-24.9 Million
Emp.: 130
Recreational Vehicle Retailer
N.A.I.C.S.: 441210
Edward L. McGeorge (Owner)
Ed McNamara (Pres)
Nat Ambrose (Mgr-Sls)

MCGEOUGH LAMACCHIA REALTY INC.
411 Waverley Oaks Rd Bldg 3 Ste 311, Waltham, MA 02452
Tel.: (781) 899-4901
Web Site: http://www.mlrealtyne.com
Year Founded: 2005
Sales Range: $1-9.9 Million
Emp.: 25
Real Estate Energy
N.A.I.C.S.: 531210
Anthony Lamacchia (Owner)
Nicole Pirnie (Mgr-Agent Dev)
Angela Walker (Mgr-Listing)
Michael McGrory (Sls Mgr)
Sarah Chaisson (Dir-Ops)

MCGHEE RISK CAPITAL LLC
1453 3rd St Ste 305, Santa Monica, CA 90401
Tel.: (310) 499-5097
Web Site: http://www.mcgheeriskcapital.com
Emp.: 1
Merchant Banking & Strategic Advisory Services for Insurance Industry
N.A.I.C.S.: 523150
Christopher M. McGhee (Mng Dir)

MCGILL MAINTENANCE LLP
6402 E Hwy 332, Freeport, TX 77541
Tel.: (979) 233-5438
Web Site: http://www.mcgillmaintenance.com
Rev.: $11,400,000
Emp.: 200
Machine Shop, Jobbing & Repair
N.A.I.C.S.: 332710
John K. McGill (Pres)
John Woods (VP)
Clifford Louis Guidry (Treas & Sec)

MCGINNIS & MARX MUSIC PUBLISHERS

236 W 26th St Ste 11 S, New York, NY 10001-6736
Tel.: (212) 243-5233
Sales Range: Less than $1 Million
Emp.: 8
Provider of Publishing Services
N.A.I.C.S.: 512230
Paul Sadowski (Pres)

MCGINNIS SISTERS SPECIAL FOOD STORES
3825 Saw Mill Run Blvd, Pittsburgh, PA 15227
Tel.: (412) 884-2323 PA
Web Site: http://www.mcginnis-sisters.com
Year Founded: 1946
Sales Range: $10-24.9 Million
Grocery Services
N.A.I.C.S.: 445110
Bonnie Mcginnis (Pres)

MCGINTY-GORDON & ASSOCIATES
225 Marina Dr, Saint Simons Island, GA 31522-2243
Tel.: (912) 638-8600 GA
Web Site: http://www.mgassi.com
Year Founded: 1948
Sales Range: $150-199.9 Million
Emp.: 32
Insurance Services
N.A.I.C.S.: 524210
Frederick W. McGinty (CEO)
Terri Mikowski (VP & Acct Mgr)
Greg Gordon (Pres)
Richard Russell (VP)
Patrick Newton (VP)
Mike Maloy (VP-Benefits Dept)
Kim Kennedy (Mgr-Personal Lines)
Katie Lewis (Acct Mgr)
Lesa Canas (Mgr-Claims)
Tina Rogers (Acct Mgr)
Terry Waller (Acct Mgr)
Dianne Cramer (Acct Mgr)
Debra Wilson (Acct Mgr)
Montie Anderson (Acct Mgr)

MCGOLDRICK CONSTRUCTION SERVICES CORPORATION
8627 Cinnamon Creek Dr Ste 301, San Antonio, TX 78240
Tel.: (210) 690-4585
Sales Range: $1-9.9 Million
Emp.: 7
Commercial & Institutional Building Construction Services
N.A.I.C.S.: 236220
Patrick McGoldrick (Pres)

MCGOUGH CONSTRUCTION CO. INC.
2737 Fairview Ave N, Saint Paul, MN 55113
Tel.: (651) 633-5050
Web Site: http://www.mcgough.com
Rev.: $176,500,000
Emp.: 855
Nonresidential Construction
N.A.I.C.S.: 236220
Tom McGough (Pres)
Bob Eno (Sr VP)
Bryan Butterfield (Project Mgr)
Jim Murphy (Sr Mgr-Facility)
Rick Valli (Superintendent)
Ty Pope (Project Mgr)
Brad Wood (COO)
Kenneth Norful (Project Mgr)
Kristen Howard (Dir-Bus Dev & Mktg)
Scott North (Exec VP-Natl Health Care Grp)
Keith Schuler (Exec VP-Fin)
Tim Reimann (Exec VP-Lean Ops)

Bake Baker (Exec VP-Preconstruction Svcs)
John Pfeifer (Exec VP-Project Mgmt)
Dave Pothen (VP)

MCGOVERN AUTO GROUP CORP SERVICES, INC.
777 Washigton St, Newton, MA 02460
Tel.: (617) 762-5710
Web Site: https://www.mcgovernauto.com
Year Founded: 2006
Motor Vehicles Mfr
N.A.I.C.S.: 336390
Matt McGovern (Owner)

Subsidiaries:
York Ford Inc. (1)
1481 Broadway, Saugus, MA 01906
Tel.: (781) 231-1945
Web Site: http://www.yorkford.com
Rev.: $28,400,000
Emp.: 60
Sales of New & Used Automobiles
N.A.I.C.S.: 441110
Brad York (Pres)
Elaine Christman (Comptroller)
Cheryl Perreira (Asst Bus Mgr)
David O'Shea (Mgr-Sls)

MCGOWAN INSURANCE GROUP INC.
355 Indiana Ave Ste 200, Indianapolis, IN 46204
Tel.: (317) 464-5000
Web Site: http://www.mcgowaninc.com
Insurance Related Activities
N.A.I.C.S.: 524298
Angela Whitaker (Mgr-Acctg)

Subsidiaries:
J.M. Thompson Insurance, Inc. (1)
121 S Washington St, Crawfordsville, IN 47933-2443
Tel.: (765) 362-8858
Web Site: http://www.jmthompsonins.com
Rev.: $1,900,000
Emp.: 100
Insurance Agencies & Brokerages
N.A.I.C.S.: 524210
Stan Wethington (Acct Exec)

MCGOWAN WORKING PARTNERS INC.
1837 Crane Ridge Dr, Jackson, MS 39216
Tel.: (601) 982-3444
Sales Range: $25-49.9 Million
Emp.: 22
Crude Petroleum Production
N.A.I.C.S.: 211120
David Russell (Pres)
Glenn Hepner (Mgr-Regulatory)
Jim Email (VP)

MCGRATH AUTOMOTIVE GROUP INC.
4610 Center Point Rd NE, Cedar Rapids, IA 52402
Tel.: (319) 393-4610 IA
Web Site: http://www.mcgrathauto.com
Year Founded: 1953
Sales Range: $125-149.9 Million
Emp.: 350
New & Used Automobiles Sales
N.A.I.C.S.: 441110
Pat McGrath (Pres)
Cory Hosch (Dir-Internet Sls)
Matt Byers (Mgr-Sls)
Rick Sayre (VP)

MCGRATH AUTOMOTIVE, INC.
500 E Ogden Ave, Westmont, IL 60559
Tel.: (630) 323-5600 IL

Web Site: http://www.mcgrathlex.com
Sales Range: $50-74.9 Million
Emp.: 70
Provider of Automobile Sales & Service
N.A.I.C.S.: 441110
Michael J. McGrath (Pres)
Mike Agnello (Dir-Bus)
Mike Connery (Sr Mgr-Bus)
Tom O'Connor (Mgr-New Car Sls)
Jim Tran (Gen Mgr)

Subsidiaries:

McGrath City Hyundai (1)
6750 W Grand Ave, Chicago, IL 60707-2212
Tel.: (773) 889-3030
Sales Range: $10-24.9 Million
New Car Whslr
N.A.I.C.S.: 441110

McGrath Honda (1)
2020 N Randall Rd, Elgin, IL 60123-7801
Tel.: (847) 695-8000
Web Site: http://www.mcgrathhonda.com
Sales Range: $10-24.9 Million
Emp.: 40
Car Whslr
N.A.I.C.S.: 441110
Mike McGrath (Owner)
Gary McGrath (Owner)

McGrath Lexus of Westmont (1)
500 E Ogden Ave, Westmont, IL 60559-1228
Tel.: (630) 323-5600
Web Site: http://www.mcgrathlexusofwestmont.com
Sales Range: $25-49.9 Million
Car Whslr
N.A.I.C.S.: 441110
Ronald Colosimo (Sec)
Kay Pollock (Bus Mgr)
Louise Rudd (Bus Mgr)
Michael McGrath Jr. (Pres)

MCGRATH NISSAN
945 E Chicago St, Elgin, IL 60120-6820
Tel.: (847) 695-6700
Web Site: http://www.mcgrathnissan.com
Year Founded: 1990
Sales Range: $10-24.9 Million
Emp.: 100
Car Whslr
N.A.I.C.S.: 441110
Scott McGrath (Pres)
Keith Kowalczyk (Gen Mgr-Sls)

MCGRATH SYSTEMS
1787 Sentry Pkwy W Bldg 16 Ste 215, Blue Bell, PA 19422
Tel.: (610) 238-5306
Web Site: http://www.mcgrathsystems.com
Sales Range: $10-24.9 Million
Emp.: 444
Human Resources & Executive Search Consulting Services
N.A.I.C.S.: 541612
Michael Wiley (CEO)

MCGRATH'S PUBLICK FISH HOUSE
1935 Davcor St SE, Salem, OR 97302
Tel.: (503) 399-8456
Web Site: http://www.mcgrathsfishhouse.com
Rev.: $24,000,000
Emp.: 600
Seafood Restaurant Services
N.A.I.C.S.: 722511
John P. McGrath (Pres)

MCGRAW COMMUNICATIONS, INC.
521 Fifth Ave 14th Fl, New York, NY 10175

Tel.: (212) 849-2300 NY
Web Site: http://www.mcgrawcom.net
Year Founded: 1996
Sales Range: $25-49.9 Million
Emp.: 47
Telecommunication Servicesb
N.A.I.C.S.: 517810
Francis X. Ahearn (CEO)
John Cunningham (Pres)
Jay Monaghan (COO)

MCGRAW WENTWORTH, INC.
3331 W Big Beaver Rd Ste 200, Troy, MI 48084
Tel.: (248) 822-8000 MI
Web Site: http://www.mma-mi.com
Year Founded: 1997
Sales Range: $10-24.9 Million
Emp.: 95
Employee Group Benefit Consulting Services
N.A.I.C.S.: 541611
Thomas McGraw (Pres)
Christi Soussan (Dir-IT)

MCGREGOR & ASSOCIATES, INC.
365 Carr Dr, Brookville, OH 45309
Tel.: (937) 833-6768 OH
Web Site: http://www.mcgregor-surmount.com
Year Founded: 1975
Emp.: 150
Electronic Components Mfr
N.A.I.C.S.: 334419
Beverly McGregor (Sec)

MCGREGOR & ASSOCIATES, INC.
997 Governors Ln Ste 175, Lexington, KY 40513
Tel.: (859) 233-4377
Web Site: http://www.mcgregoreba.com
Sales Range: $1-9.9 Million
Employee Benefits Administration & Consulting Services
N.A.I.C.S.: 524292
Lauren Johnson (Partner)
Todd Wetzel (Partner)

MCGREGOR COMPANY
111 W Main St, Marshalltown, IA 50158
Tel.: (641) 753-3381
Web Site: http://www.mcgregorsfurniture.com
Sales Range: $25-49.9 Million
Emp.: 200
Furniture Retail Stores
N.A.I.C.S.: 449110
Robert S. McGregor (VP)

MCGREGOR INDUSTRIES INC.
46 Line St, Dunmore, PA 18512
Tel.: (215) 386-1342
Web Site: http://www.mcgregorindustries.com
Sales Range: $10-24.9 Million
Emp.: 85
Architectural Metalwork
N.A.I.C.S.: 332323
Robert R. McGregor (Owner)
Fred Mooseberger Jr. (CFO)

MCGRIFF INDUSTRIES INC.
86 Walnut St NE, Cullman, AL 35055
Tel.: (256) 739-0710
Web Site: http://www.mcgrifftire.com
Year Founded: 1948
Sales Range: $25-49.9 Million
Emp.: 300
Provider of Tire Rebuilding & Retreading Services
N.A.I.C.S.: 326212

MCGRIFF INDUSTRIES INC.

U.S. PRIVATE

McGriff Industries Inc.—(Continued)
Bertis McGriff (Chm)
Barry McGriff (Pres)
Bill Ricketts (Mgr-Ops)
Randy Drake (Exec VP)
Mike Johnson (Mgr-Svc)

MCGUFFEY'S RESTAURANTS, INC.
Ste H2 370 N Louisiana Ave, Asheville, NC 28806-3659
Tel.: (828) 252-3300
Year Founded: 1983
Sales Range: $125-149.9 Million
Emp.: 500
Theme Restaurant Operator
N.A.I.C.S.: 722511
George M. Hill (Pres)

MCGUIRE & ASSOCIATES
1450 Madruga Ave Ste 405, Coral Gables, FL 33146
Tel.: (305) 665-5743
Year Founded: 1972
Rev.: $20,000,000
Emp.: 4
N.A.I.C.S.: 541810
Geoffrey D. McGuire (Owner)
Jason McGuire (Partner)

MCGUIRE BEARING COMPANY, INC.
947 SW Market St, Portland, OR 97214-3556
Tel.: (503) 581-2000
Web Site:
http://www.mcguirebearing.com
Year Founded: 1954
Sales Range: $25-49.9 Million
Emp.: 153
Bearings & Power Transmission Products
N.A.I.C.S.: 423840
Timothy D. McGuire (Pres)
Steve McGuire (VP-Mktg)
Mike McGuire (VP)
Dave McGuire (VP-Sls)

MCGUIRE CADILLAC
910 US Hwy 1 N, Woodbridge, NJ 07095
Tel.: (732) 326-0300
Web Site:
http://www.mcguirecadillac.com
Sales Range: $25-49.9 Million
Emp.: 43
Sales of New & Used Automobiles
N.A.I.C.S.: 441110
Regan P. McGuire (Owner)

MCGUIRE DEVELOPMENT COMPANY, LLC
455 Cayuga Rd Ste 100, Buffalo, NY 14225
Tel.: (716) 829-1900
Web Site: http://www.mcguiredevelopment.com
Sales Range: $1-9.9 Million
Emp.: 23
Real Estate Developers
N.A.I.C.S.: 237210
F. James McGuire (CEO)
Jeffrey P. Lehrbach (CFO & VP)
Danielle Eisen Shainbrown (Chief Legal Officer & Exec VP)
Vito J. Picone (Sr Dir-Bus Dev)
James Geiger (Dir-Bus Dev)
Sean Doyle (Asst VP-Property Mgmt)
Jennifer Teach (Controller)
James F. Dentinger (Pres)
Dave Carswell (Asst VP-Dev & Acq)
Marty Houck (Sr Mgr-Property)
Heather Roberts (Mgr-Property)
Megan Tafelski (Dir-Mktg)
Lisa Hicks (Assoc Dir-Dev & Fin)

Aleece Burgio (Asst Gen Counsel)
G. David Von Derau Jr. (VP)
Robert Pyszczynski III (VP-Construction)

Subsidiaries:

McGuire Real Estate Services Group (1)
560 Delaware Ave Ste 300, Buffalo, NY 14202
Tel.: (716) 829-1900
Real Estate Brokerage Services
N.A.I.C.S.: 531210
F. James McGuire (CEO)

MCGUIRE FAMILY FURNITURE MAKERS
239 Main St, Isle La Motte, VT 05463
Tel.: (802) 928-4190
Web Site:
http://www.mcguirefamilyfurnituremakers.com
Sales Range: Less than $1 Million
Emp.: 3
Antique Reproduction Furniture Mfr
N.A.I.C.S.: 337122
Jack McGuire (Pres)

MCGUIRE HARLEY-DAVIDSON LLC
93 1st Ave N, Walnut Creek, CA 94553
Tel.: (925) 945-6500
Web Site: http://www.mcguire-hd.com
Rev.: $15,000,000
Emp.: 40
Motorcycle Dealers
N.A.I.C.S.: 441227
Michael McGuire (Chm)
Dave Lowery (Parts Mgr)
Owen Barry (Mgr-Sls)

MCGUIREWOODS LLP
1 James Ctr 901 E Cary St, Richmond, VA 23219
Tel.: (804) 775-1000
Web Site:
http://www.mcguirewoods.com
Year Founded: 1834
Sales Range: $500-549.9 Million
Emp.: 900
Law firm
N.A.I.C.S.: 541110
George K. Martin (Sr Partner & Partner)
Amy B. Manning (Chm-Antitrust & Trade Regulation Dept & Partner)
Dale G. Mullen (Partner)
Diane Flannery (Partner)
Suzanne S. Long (Partner)
Rosemary Becchi (Partner)
Joseph Calve (Chief Mktg & Bus Dev Officer)
Peter N. Farley (Partner)
Brad R. Newberg (Partner)
Sara F. Holladay-Tobias (Partner)
William I. Sanderson (Partner)
Kenneth W. Wire (Partner)
Penny E. Zacharias (Partner)
Andrea C. Chomakos (Partner)
Angela M. Spivey (Partner)
Jodie Herrmann Lawson (Partner)
Charles B. Hampton (Partner)
Peter C. Butcher (Partner)
David S. Reidy (Partner)
Charles D. Case (Partner)
Jean Gordon Carter (Partner)
Mary Nash K. Rusher (Partner)
K. Issac deVyver (Partner)
Marc A. Lackner (Partner)
Carolee Anne Hoover (Partner)
Joel S. Allen (Partner)
John D. Adams (Partner)
Vassilis Akritidis (Partner)
Jonathan L. Lewis (Partner)
Todd Mullins (Partner)

Michael J. Adams (Partner-Data Privacy & Security-Charlotte)
Andrew Konia (Chm-Data Privacy & Security Indus)
Tyler VanHoutan (Partner-IP Litigation & Patents-Houston)
Brian Riopelle (Chm-IP Litigation & Patents)
John Henderson (Partner-Product & Consumer Litigation Dept-Dallas)
Sam Tarry (Chm-Product & Consumer Litigation Dept)
Akash Sethi (Mng Partner-Dallas)
Richard Deutsch (Partner)
Jeffrey P. Connor (CFO)
J. D. Neary (Chief Legal Talent Officer)
Stacy I. Reyan (Chief HR Officer)
Sharon B. Ross (Chief Admin Ops Officer)
Samira G. Serbanescu (Deputy Mng Dir-Emerging European Markets)
Gregg R. Sutfin (CIO)
Jonathan P. Harmon (Chm)
J. Tracy Walker (Mng Partner)
Emily Gordy (Partner-Washington)
Amy Morrissey Turk (Partner-Labor & Employment Dept)
Bruce Steen (Chm-Labor & Employment Practice)
John Padgett (Mng Partner-Norfolk)
Stuart Rasley (Partner-Private Equity Team-Dallas)
Michael Woodard (Chm-Merger & Acq & Corp Transactions Dept)
Chris Molen (Partner-Debt Fin Dept-Atlanta)
Chad Werner (Partner-Debt Fin Dept-Atlanta)
Ava E. Lias-Booker (Partner)
Dayan Rosen (Partner-Debt Fin Practice-Los Angeles)
Richard W. Viola (Deputy Mng Partner-Corp Practice)
Jon Mooney (Partner-Debt Fin Practice-Pittsburgh)
Alan Holliday (Partner-Debt Fin Practice-London)
Jeff Goldfarb (Partner-Debt Fin Practice-New York)
Kevin McGinnis (Chm-Debt Fin)
Kevin McGinnis (Chm-Debt Fin)
Hamid Namazie (Mng Partner-Los Angeles)
Joseph K. Reid III (Partner)
Gerald V. Thomas II (Partner)
George J. Terwilliger III (Partner)
Arthur E. Anderson II (Partner)
David D. Addison Jr. (Atty)
James M. Anderson III (Partner)
John Huske Anderson Jr. (Partner)
Cecil E. Martin III (Partner)
L. F. Payne Jr. (Pres)

MCGUYER HOMEBUILDERS INC.
7676 Woodway Dr Ste 104, Houston, TX 77063
Tel.: (713) 952-6767
Web Site: http://www.mhinc.com
Sales Range: $350-399.9 Million
Emp.: 280
Single-Family Housing Construction
N.A.I.C.S.: 236115
Frank B. McGuyer (Chm & CEO)
David Bruning (CFO)
Keith Faseler (Pres-Land Div)
Scott Taylor (Project Mgr)
William McKinnie (Gen Counsel)

MCH CORP.
995 Purple Heart Trl Hwy 11 S, Sweetwater, TN 37874
Tel.: (423) 836-9600
Web Site: http://www.mchcorp.com

Year Founded: 1998
Sales Range: $1-9.9 Million
Emp.: 30
IT & Security Consulting
N.A.I.C.S.: 541690
Michael P. Hamilton (Founder)

MCH, INC.
601 E Marshall St, Sweet Springs, MO 65351
Tel.: (660) 335-6373
Web Site: http://www.mchdata.com
Year Founded: 1928
Sales Range: $1-9.9 Million
Emp.: 90
Direct Mail Advertising Services
N.A.I.C.S.: 541860
Peter E. Long (CEO)
Jerry Reisberg (VP)
Kirk Chritton (Exec Dir-Infinite Access)
Amy Rambo (Pres)
Lynn Schear (Dir-Res)
Joan Whitney (Dir-Sls)

MCHUGH ENTERPRISES INC.
1737 S Michigan Ave, Chicago, IL 60616
Tel.: (312) 986-8000
Web Site:
http://www.mchughconstruction.com
Sales Range: $200-249.9 Million
Emp.: 115
Holding Company
N.A.I.C.S.: 236220
John E. Sheridan (Sr VP)
David Alexander (Sr VP)
Patrick Seery (CFO)
Robert Soldan (Sr VP)

Subsidiaries:

James McHugh Construction Co. (1)
1737 S Michigan Ave, Chicago, IL 60616-1211
Tel.: (312) 986-8000
Web Site:
http://www.mchughconstruction.com
Sales Range: $50-74.9 Million
Emp.: 500
General Contracting Services
N.A.I.C.S.: 236220
Patrick Seery (CFO)
David Alexander (Pres)
John Sheridan (Sr VP)
Robert Soldan (Sr VP)
Karl Bechtoldt (Mgr-Rail Road Ops)
Andy Totten (VP)
Tom Stuit (VP)
Dave Bartolai (VP-Preconstruction)
Carlos del Val Cura (VP)
Zachary Renk (Superintendent-Nashville)
Sean Mullen (Sr Project Mgr-Nashville)

MCI INC.
26 1st Ave N, Waite Park, MN 56387
Tel.: (320) 253-5078
Web Site:
http://www.mcicarpetone.com
Sales Range: $10-24.9 Million
Emp.: 60
Floor Covering Stores
N.A.I.C.S.: 449121
Ryan Corrigan (Controller)
Nicole Olesen (Project Mgr)

MCI, LC
2937 Sierra Ct Sw, Iowa , IA 52240
Tel.: (877) 542-8625
Web Site: https://www.mci.world
Year Founded: 2002
Emp.: 2,000
Holding Company : Outsourcing & Offshoring Consulting
N.A.I.C.S.: 551112
Anthony Marlowe (CEO)

MCILHENNY COMPANY
Hwy 329, Avery Island, LA 70513

Tel.: (337) 365-8173 ME
Web Site: http://www.tabasco.com
Year Founded: 1868
Sales Range: $100-124.9 Million
Emp.: 200
Mfr of Pepper Sauces & Condiments
N.A.I.C.S.: 311941
Anthony Simmons (Pres & CEO)
Harold Osborn (Exec VP-Sls & Mktg-Intl)

MCILVAINE TRUCKING INC.
7556 Cleveland Rd, Wooster, OH 44691
Tel.: (330) 345-7033
Web Site: http://www.sterlingtransport.com
Sales Range: $10-24.9 Million
Emp.: 133
Long Haul Trucking
N.A.I.C.S.: 484121
Hugh Hinton (Pres)

MCINERNEY & ASSOCIATES, INC.
2515 Winford Ave, Nashville, TN 37211-2147
Tel.: (615) 726-0076
Web Site: http://www.mcinerney-and-associates.com
Sales Range: $10-24.9 Million
Emp.: 15
Fence Installation Services
N.A.I.C.S.: 238990
Sandra Wallace (Principal)

MCINERNEY INC.
14100 W Eight Mile Rd, Oak Park, MI 48237-3045
Tel.: (248) 398-8200 DE
Web Site: http://www.northlandchryslerjeepdodge.com
Year Founded: 1963
Sales Range: $150-199.9 Million
Emp.: 250
Sales of Automobiles
N.A.I.C.S.: 441110
Joe Marino (Gen Mgr)

MCINERNEY'S WOODHAVEN CHRYSLER JEEP
23940 Allen Rd, Woodhaven, MI 48183
Tel.: (734) 362-3100
Web Site: http://www.woodhavencjd.com
Sales Range: $10-24.9 Million
Emp.: 50
Car Whslr
N.A.I.C.S.: 441110
Thomas McInerney Sr. (Pres)

MCINNIS BUILDERS, LLC.
17320 Panama City Beach Pkwy Ste 107, Panama City Beach, FL 32413
Tel.: (850) 249-9840
Web Site: http://www.mcinnisbuilders.com
Sales Range: $10-24.9 Million
Emp.: 7
Commercial & Institutional Building Construction Services
N.A.I.C.S.: 236220
Procter McInnis (Pres)
George McInnis (Chm)

MCINTOSH BOX & PALLET CO. INC.
5864 Pyle Dr, East Syracuse, NY 13057
Tel.: (315) 446-9350
Web Site: http://www.mcintoshbox.com
Sales Range: $10-24.9 Million
Emp.: 170
Mfr of Boxes
N.A.I.C.S.: 321920
Rich Huftalen (CFO)
Will Wester (Pres)
Brian Cole (Dir-Sls)

MCINTYRE & ASSOCIATES INC.
205 E Reynolds Dr., Ruston, LA 71270
Tel.: (318) 251-9003
Web Site: http://www.mcintyreassoc.com
Insurance Agencies & Brokerages
N.A.I.C.S.: 524210
William McIntyre (Owner)

MCINTYRE ELWELL & STRAMMER GENERAL CONTRACTORS, INC.
1645 Barber Rd, Sarasota, FL 34240
Tel.: (941) 377-6800
Web Site: http://www.mesgc.com
Year Founded: 1987
Sales Range: $25-49.9 Million
Emp.: 80
Commercial & Residential Construction
N.A.I.C.S.: 236220
John A. McIntyre (Sr Project Mgr)
Ryan McIntyre (Project Mgr)
Greg C. Elwell (Sr Project Mgr)
Eric Clayton (Project Mgr)

MCINTYRE, PANZARELLA, THANASIDES, BRINGGOLD & TODD, P.A.
6943 E Fowler Ave, Temple Terrace, FL 33617
Tel.: (813) 990-0662
Web Site: http://www.mcintyrefirm.com
Year Founded: 2006
Sales Range: $1-9.9 Million
Emp.: 45
Law firm
N.A.I.C.S.: 541110
Richard J. McIntyre (Atty-Litigation & Bankruptcy)
Dan Herrejon (Mgr-Collections)
Katie Brinson Hinton (Atty)
Margaret Kramer (Atty)
Dustin D. Deese (Atty-Several Litigation Fields)
Stephen A. Leal (Atty-Criminal Defense)
Zala Forizs (Atty-Comml, Litigation, Bankruptcy & Creditors)

MCIVER CLINIC
710 Lomax St, Jacksonville, FL 32204
Tel.: (904) 355-6583 FL
Web Site: http://www.mciverclinic.com
Year Founded: 1921
Urology Services; Diagnostic & Treatment
N.A.I.C.S.: 621111
Apoorva Vashi (Mng Partner & Dir-Robotic Prostate Surgery)

MCK BUILDING ASSOCIATES INC.
221 W Division St, Syracuse, NY 13204
Tel.: (315) 475-7499
Web Site: http://www.mckbuildingassociates.com
Rev.: $12,400,000
Emp.: 25
Commercial & Office Building, New Construction
N.A.I.C.S.: 236220
Robert Medina (Pres)
Thomas Osborne (Project Mgr)

MCKAFKA DEVELOPMENT GROUP, LLC
1 Aventura Executive Ctr 20900 30th Ave Ste 603, Aventura, FL 33180
Tel.: (305) 917-7673
Web Site: http://www.mckafka.com
Sales Range: $1-9.9 Million
Real Estate Investment & Development Services
N.A.I.C.S.: 523999
Fernando Levy Hara (CEO & Mng Partner)
Stephan Gietl (CFO, COO & Mng Partner)

MCKAMISH CHESAPEAKE INC.
50 55th St, Pittsburgh, PA 15201
Tel.: (412) 781-6262
Web Site: http://www.mckamish.com
Rev.: $28,000,000
Emp.: 180
Mechanical Contractor
N.A.I.C.S.: 238220
David McKamish (Pres & CEO)
David L. Casciani (VP-Bus Dev & Estimating)
John Jordan (VP-Svc)
David Lyon (VP-Comml Construction)
Dennis McKamish (CFO)

MCKAY AUTO PARTS INCORPORATED
414 N Old Rte 66, Litchfield, IL 62056
Tel.: (217) 324-3971
Web Site: http://www.mckayauto.net
Rev.: $13,000,000
Emp.: 30
Automotive Supplies & Parts
N.A.I.C.S.: 423120
Ed Hammann (VP)
Ryan Ocepek (Reg Mgr)

MCKAY'S CHRYSLER JEEP DODGE
2020 Frontage rd S, Waite Park, MN 56387-1806
Tel.: (320) 252-7170
Web Site: http://www.mckaysdodge.com
Sales Range: $10-24.9 Million
Emp.: 55
Car Whslr
N.A.I.C.S.: 441110
Travis Benoit (Principal)

MCKEAN DEFENSE GROUP LLC
3 Crescent Dr Ste 410, Philadelphia, PA 19112
Tel.: (215) 271-6108
Web Site: http://www.mckean-defense.com
Year Founded: 2006
Sales Range: $25-49.9 Million
Emp.: 243
Engineering, Consulting & IT Services
N.A.I.C.S.: 541330
Larry D. Burrill (Co-Founder & Pres-Fleet Programs)
Joseph L. Carlini (Chm & CEO)
Roderick F. Smith (CTO)
Robert Pennoyer (VP-Bus Dev)
Michael Denny (Chief Strategy & Growth Officer)
Theodore Zobel (VP & Mgr-Naval Sea Sys Command Acct)
Leonard F. DeStefano Jr. (Co-Founder & Pres-Naval Engrg)

Subsidiaries:

Mikros Systems Corporation (1)
707 Alexander Rd Ste 208, Princeton, NJ 08540
Tel.: (609) 987-1513
Web Site: http://www.mikrossystems.com
Rev: $6,366,226
Assets: $3,177,907
Liabilities: $756,833
Net Worth: $2,421,074
Earnings: $30,532
Emp.: 26
Fiscal Year-end: 12/31/2019
Electronic Systems for Military Applications
N.A.I.C.S.: 334419
Henry Silcock (CTO)
Walter T. Bristow III (Pres & COO)

MCKEE ASSET MANAGEMENT
1001 B Ave Ste 203, Coronado, CA 92118
Tel.: (619) 435-7780
Web Site: http://www.mckeecompany.com
Year Founded: 1985
Sales Range: $1-9.9 Million
Emp.: 25
Property Management Services
N.A.I.C.S.: 531311
Russell B. McKee (Pres)

MCKEE AUTO CENTER INC.
400 1st St Hwy 141 & 58, Perry, IA 50220
Tel.: (515) 465-3564
Web Site: http://www.mckeeauto.com
Year Founded: 1985
Rev.: $17,000,000
Emp.: 15
Dealer of New & Used Automobiles
N.A.I.C.S.: 441110
Anthony McKee (Pres)

MCKEE FOODS CORPORATION
10260 McKee Rd, Collegedale, TN 37315
Tel.: (423) 238-7111 TN
Web Site: http://www.mckeefoods.com
Year Founded: 1934
Cake & Cookie Baker
N.A.I.C.S.: 311812
Mike McKee (Pres)

Subsidiaries:

Blue Planet Foods, Inc. (1)
PO Box 2178, Collegedale, TN 37315-2178 (100%)
Tel.: (423) 396-3145
Web Site: http://www.blueplanetfoods.com
Sales Range: $25-49.9 Million
Emp.: 160
Retail Natural Foods & Cereals
N.A.I.C.S.: 311230
Deris Bagli (Gen Mgr)

McKee Foods Transportation, LLC (1)
10260 McKee Rd, Collegedale, TN 37315
Tel.: (423) 238-7111
Web Site: http://www.mckeefoods.com
Snack Cake Distr
N.A.I.C.S.: 484220
Richard Mendoza (Project Mgr-Supply Chain)
Darren Bledsoe (Supvr-Mfg)

Prairie City Bakery, Co. (1)
100 N Fairway Dr Ste 138, Vernon Hills, IL 60061-1859
Tel.: (800) 338-5122
Web Site: http://www.pcbakery.com
Bakery Products Mfr & Distr
N.A.I.C.S.: 311812
William Skeens (Co-Founder)
Robert Rosean (Co-Founder)
Anna Masur (VP-Sls)
John Plescia (CFO)
John Williams (Pres)
Andy Lang (CEO)

McKee Foods Corporation—(Continued)

MCKEE GROUP REALTY, LLC
940 W Sproul Rd, Springfield, PA 19064
Tel.: (610) 604-9580
Web Site: http://www.mckeegroup.net
Year Founded: 1948
Sales Range: $25-49.9 Million
Apartment Building Operator
N.A.I.C.S.: 531110
Frank J. McKee (Chm & CEO)
Joe Santangelo (CFO)

MCKEE WALLWORK & COMPANY
1030 18th St NW, Albuquerque, NM 87104
Tel.: (505) 821-2999 NM
Web Site: http://www.mckeewallwork.com
Year Founded: 1997
Advertising Agencies
N.A.I.C.S.: 541810
Steve McKee (Pres & Partner)
Pat Wallwork (Partner & Dir-Media)
Jonathan David Lewis (Partner, VP & Dir-Strategy)
David Ortega (Partner & Creative Dir)

MCKEEVER ENTERPRISES INC.
4216 S Hocker Dr Ste 100, Independence, MO 64055
Tel.: (816) 478-3095 MO
Year Founded: 1985
Sales Range: $50-74.9 Million
Emp.: 1,050
Grocery Stores
N.A.I.C.S.: 445110
Allan McKeever (Pres)
Jeff Blobaum (CFO)

MCKELVEY HOMES, LLC.
218 Chesterfield Towne Ctr, Chesterfield, MO 63005
Tel.: (636) 530-6900
Web Site: http://www.mckelveyhomes.com
Year Founded: 1898
Sales Range: $25-49.9 Million
Emp.: 25
New Single Family Housing Construction Services
N.A.I.C.S.: 236115
James Brennan (Pres)
Clyde Oliver (Mgr-Sls)
Tim Knoche (Mgr-Sls)
Tracy K. Geraghty (Mgr-Sls)
Sheri Luster (Mgr-Sls)
Bev Sharamitaro (Mgr-Sls)
Bob Hanson (Dir-Ops)

MCKENNA HAWAII INC.
725 Kailua Rd, Kailua, HI 96734
Tel.: (808) 266-7000
Web Site: http://www.windwardfordhawaii.com
Year Founded: 1986
Sales Range: $10-24.9 Million
Emp.: 75
Car Dealer
N.A.I.C.S.: 531120
Mike McKenna (Owner)

MCKENNA MOTOR COMPANY INC.
10900 Firestone Blvd, Norwalk, CA 90650
Tel.: (562) 868-3233
Web Site: http://www.mckennacars.com
Sales Range: $25-49.9 Million
Emp.: 230
Sales of New & Used Automobiles
N.A.I.C.S.: 441110
Janet Connor (COO)
John Hall (Gen Mgr)
Daniel J. Mckenna III (Pres)

MCKENNA MOTORS INC.
5325 NE 14th St, Des Moines, IA 50313
Tel.: (515) 263-3600
Web Site: http://www.mckennatrucks.com
Sales Range: $10-24.9 Million
Emp.: 50
Sales of New & Used Trucks
N.A.I.C.S.: 441110
William McKenna (Pres)
Steve Kellerhals (Controller)

MCKENNEY CHEVROLET, INC.
831 S Main St, Lowell, NC 28098
Tel.: (704) 825-3306
Web Site: http://www.mckenneychevrolet.com
Sales Range: $25-49.9 Million
Emp.: 62
Car Whslr
N.A.I.C.S.: 441110
H. Ray McKenney (Owner & Pres)
Jeannette Stabler (Principal)
Jace Stowe (VP & Gen Mgr)
Matt Surbeck (Gen Mgr-Sls)

MCKENNEY'S INC.
1056 Moreland Industrial Blvd, Atlanta, GA 30316
Tel.: (404) 622-5000
Web Site: http://www.mckenneys.com
Year Founded: 1948
Sales Range: $25-49.9 Million
Mechanical Construction & Engineering Services
N.A.I.C.S.: 541330
David M. Mckenney (Chm)
Jay Mann (Mgr-Safety)

MCKENZIE ELECTRIC COOPERATIVE, INC.
908 4th Ave NE, Watford City, ND 58854-0649
Tel.: (701) 444-9288 ND
Web Site: http://www.mckenzieelectric.com
Year Founded: 1945
Sales Range: $50-74.9 Million
Emp.: 54
Electric Power Distr
N.A.I.C.S.: 221122
John Skurupey (CEO)
Jamie Cross (Bus Mgr)

MCKENZIE MEMORIAL HOSPITAL
120 N Delaware St, Sandusky, MI 48471
Tel.: (810) 648-3770 MI
Web Site: http://www.mckenziehealth.org
Sales Range: $10-24.9 Million
Emp.: 234
Health Care Srvices
N.A.I.C.S.: 622110
Roger Loding (Chm)
Joan Nagelkirk (Sec)
Judy Ferguson (Vice Chm)
Steve Barnett (Pres & CEO)
Al Stoutenburg (Chm)
Chris Clark (Vice Chm)

MCKENZIE OIL CO. INC.
222 N Eufaula Ave, Eufaula, AL 36027
Tel.: (334) 687-3531
Sales Range: $10-24.9 Million
Emp.: 90
Gasoline Distr
N.A.I.C.S.: 424720

Dan B. McKenzie (Pres)
Martha McKenzie (VP)

MCKENZIE SUPPLY COMPANY
726 E 16th St, Lumberton, NC 28358
Tel.: (910) 738-4801
Web Site: http://www.mckenziesupplyco.com
Year Founded: 1959
Sales Range: $10-24.9 Million
Emp.: 17
Provider of Plumbing Supplies
N.A.I.C.S.: 423720
John Larry Pope (Pres)
Bobby Britt (Mgr-Credit)

MCKEON ROLLING STEEL DOOR COMPANY, INC.
44 Sawgrass Dr, Bellport, NY 11713
Tel.: (631) 803-3000 NY
Web Site: http://www.mckeondoor.com
Year Founded: 1946
Sales Range: $50-74.9 Million
Emp.: 50
Mfr of Coiling Grilles, Doors, Fire Doors & Custom Engineered Closures
N.A.I.C.S.: 332321
Joseph J. McKeon (Pres)
Andrew C. Lambridis (Sr VP)

Subsidiaries:

McKeon Door West, Inc. (1)
44 Sawgrass Dr, Bellport, NY 11713
Tel.: (631) 803-3000
Web Site: http://www.mckeondoor.com
Sales Range: $50-74.9 Million
Door Mfr
N.A.I.C.S.: 332321

McKeon Door of Nevada, Inc. (1)
3074 W Post Rd, Las Vegas, NV 89118
Tel.: (702) 636-9338
Web Site: http://www.mckeondoor.com
Sales Range: $10-24.9 Million
Emp.: 5
Door Mfr
N.A.I.C.S.: 332321
Kevin Sweeney (Gen Mgr)

McKeon Door of Washington DC (1)
8904 Oak Ln, Fort Washington, MD 20744
Tel.: (301) 807-1006
Web Site: http://www.mckeondoor.com
Door Mfr
N.A.I.C.S.: 332321
Bernie Rosser (Mgr)

MCKIBBON HOTEL MANAGEMENT, INC.
5315 Avion Park Dr Ste 170, Tampa, FL 33607
Tel.: (813) 241-2399
Web Site: http://www.mckibbon.com
Sales Range: $350-399.9 Million
Emp.: 3,000
Hotel Management
N.A.I.C.S.: 721110
Vann Herring (CEO)
Bruce Baerwalde (Exec VP)
Randy Hassen (Pres-McKibbon Hospitalitys)
Erik Rowen (VP-Dev)
Wes Townson (VP-Acq)
James Coyle (Gen Counsel-McKibbon Hospitality Org-Gainesville)
Courtney Semler (Mgr-Benefits)
Jess Hayden (VP-Operational Excellence-McKibbon Hospitalitys)
John McKibbon III (Chm)

MCKIE FORD INC.
2010 East Mall Dr, Rapid City, SD 57701
Tel.: (605) 348-1400
Web Site: http://www.mckieford.com
Sales Range: $50-74.9 Million
Emp.: 200

New & Used Automobiles
N.A.I.C.S.: 441110
Mark McKie (Pres)

MCKIE FORD LINCOLN MERCURY
2010 East Mall Dr, Rapid City, SD 57701
Tel.: (605) 348-1400
Web Site: http://www.mckieford.com
Sales Range: $25-49.9 Million
Emp.: 134
Car Whslr
N.A.I.C.S.: 441110
Ross McKie (Owner)

MCKIM & CREED, INC.
1730 Varsity Dr Venture IV Bldg Ste 500, Raleigh, NC 27606-2689
Tel.: (919) 233-8091 NC
Web Site: http://www.mckimcreed.com
Year Founded: 1978
Engineering & Surveying Services
N.A.I.C.S.: 541330
Kristin Beamer (Corp Dir-Mktg)
Chris Nelson (CFO)
David Jones (Sr VP-Geomatics)
Street Lee (CEO)
Edward Pollard (Gen Counsel)
Charles Douglass (Dir-IT)
Barbara Johnson (Chief HR Officer)

Subsidiaries:

Texas Engineering & Mapping Co. (1)
12810 Century Dr, Stafford, TX 77477
Tel.: (281) 491-2525
Web Site: http://www.team-civil.com
Sales Range: $1-9.9 Million
Emp.: 25
Engineering Services
N.A.I.C.S.: 541330
Carlos Barillas (Pres)

MCKINLEY ASSOCIATES INC.
320 N Main St Ste 200, Ann Arbor, MI 48104
Tel.: (734) 769-8520
Web Site: http://www.mckinley.com
Sales Range: $250-299.9 Million
Emp.: 1,458
Real Estate Managers
N.A.I.C.S.: 531110
Albert M. Berriz (CEO)
Cheryl Rabbit (Sr VP-Tax, Acctg, Treasury & Entity Mgmt)
Albert L. Berriz (Mng Dir & Sr VP-Owned Residential Real Estate)
Dave A. Peabody (VP-HR)
Nate Lewis (VP & Mng Dir)
Royal E. Caswell III (Mng Dir & Sr VP-Institutional Real Estate)

MCKINLEY CAPITAL MANAGEMENT
3301 C St Ste 500, Anchorage, AK 99503
Tel.: (907) 563-4488
Web Site: http://www.mckinleycapital.com
Rev: $12,900,000
Emp.: 110
Investment Advisory Services
N.A.I.C.S.: 523940
Robert Gillam (Pres & CEO)
Robert Rob (VP)
Diane Wilke (VP)
Jeffrey B. Patterson (Dir-Mktg)

MCKINLEY EQUIPMENT CORP.
17611 Armstrong Ave, Irvine, CA 92614
Tel.: (949) 261-9222
Web Site: http://www.mckinleyequipment.com
Rev: $11,700,000

Emp.: 50
Materials Handling Machinery
N.A.I.C.S.: 423830
Kevin Rusin (CFO)
Marc Crockett (VP-Sls)

MCKINLEY FINANCIAL SERVICES, INC.
545 N Andrews Ave, Fort Lauderdale, FL 33301
Tel.: (954) 938-2685
Web Site: http://www.mckinleyinsurance.com
Year Founded: 1987
Sales Range: $100-124.9 Million
Emp.: 30
Life, Health, Property & Other Insurance Services
N.A.I.C.S.: 524128
Ralph W. Campbell (Pres & CEO)

MCKINLEY GROUP, INC.
6465 Wayzata Blvd Ste 970, Minneapolis, MN 55426
Tel.: (952) 767-1130   MN
Web Site: http://www.mckinleygroupinc.com
Year Founded: 2001
Holding Company; Specialty Employment Placement, Executive Search & Consulting Services
N.A.I.C.S.: 551112
Tony Sorensen (Partner)
Kurt Rakos (Partner)

Subsidiaries:

McKinley Consulting, Inc. (1)
6465 Wayzata Blvd Ste 970, Minneapolis, MN 55426
Tel.: (952) 767-1120
Web Site: http://www.versique.com
Emp.: 42
Information Technology Consulting Services
N.A.I.C.S.: 541690
Tony Sorensen (CEO)

McKinley Finance, Inc. (1)
6465 Wayzata Blvd Ste 970, Minneapolis, MN 55426
Tel.: (952) 767-1130
Accounting & Financial Executive Recruiting Services
N.A.I.C.S.: 561311

MCKINNEY CHICAGO
55 W Wacker Dr, Chicago, IL 60601-1609
Tel.: (312) 944-6784
Web Site: http://www.mckinneychicago.com
Year Founded: 1936
Sales Range: $10-24.9 Million
Emp.: 20
Business-To-Business
N.A.I.C.S.: 541810
Daniel E. Hoexter (Pres & Exec Creative Dir)
Alan Zachary (Dir-Pub Rel & Bus Dev)
Seth Schwartz (Dir-Digital Solutions)
Greg Kokes (Sr Dir-Art)
Katie Jeter (Dir-Media Plng)

MCKINNEY TRAILERS & CONTAINERS
8400 Slauson Ave, Pico Rivera, CA 90660-4325
Tel.: (562) 949-7961
Web Site: http://www.mckinneytrailers.com
Year Founded: 1988
Rev.: $26,492,798
Emp.: 25
Utility Trailer Rental
N.A.I.C.S.: 532120
Les Dobson (Pres & CEO)
Mark Bedard (CFO)
Sam Gambino (Mgr-Ops)

Subsidiaries:

Mckinney Trailers & Containers (1)
4450 B St NW, Auburn, WA 98001-1716
Tel.: (253) 859-0900
Web Site: http://www.mckinneytrailers.com
Provider of Semi Trailer Rental Services
N.A.I.C.S.: 812199
Les Dobson (Co-CEO)
Dave Tavares (Pres)
David Tyler (VP-Sls-Western Reg)
Lori Kincannon (VP-Mktg & Bus Dev)
Mark Bedard (CFO)
Rich Loughran (Sr Exec VP)
Rob Dobson (Co-CEO)
Richard Swenson (VP-Ops)
T. K. Gardner (CIO)

MCKINSEY & COMPANY, INC.
3 World Trade Ctr 175 Greenwich St, New York, NY 10007
Tel.: (212) 446-7000   NY
Web Site: https://www.mckinsey.com
Year Founded: 1926
Sales Range: $1-4.9 Billion
Emp.: 45,000
Administrative Management & General Management Consulting Services
N.A.I.C.S.: 541611
Vikram Malhotra (Sr Partner)
Gerard Cunningham (Co-Founder-Green Bus Building)
Florian Budde (Sr Partner-Frankfurt)
Michael Della Rocca (Partner-Philadelphia)
Nicolas Denis (Partner-Brussels)
Lutz Goedde (Sr Partner-Denver)
Matteo Mancini (Partner-Singapore)
Azam Mohammad (Sr Partner-Singapore)
Rohit Razdan (Sr Partner-Singapore)
Katsuhiro Sato (Partner-Tokyo)
Roberto Uchoa (Sr Partner-Chicago)
Ulrich Weihe (Sr Partner-Frankfurt)
Gautam Kumra (Mng Dir-India & Sr Partner-Gurugram)
Gadi BenMark (Pres/Gen Mgr-Social)
Satty Bhens (Partner-Digital)
Philip E. Bruno (Partner)
Kevin Buehler (Sr Partner)
Manish Chopra (Sr Partner)
Laura Corb (Sr Partner)
Kevin Dehoff (Sr Partner)
Vijay D'Silva (Sr Partner)
Andre Dua (Sr Partner)
Alexander Edlich (Sr Partner)
Andrew Goodman (Partner-London)
Julie Goran (Partner)
Jonathan Gordon (Partner)
Jason Heller (Partner)
Tania Holt (Partner-London)
Aly S. Jeddy (Sr Partner)
James Kaplan (Partner)
Karl Kellner (Sr Partner)
Somesh Khanna (Sr Partner)
David G. Knott (Sr Partner)
Tim Koller (Partner)
Krish Krishnakanthan (Partner)
Hugues Lavandier (Partner)
Jonathan K. Law (Partner)
Ari Libarikian (Sr Partner)
Daniel Pacthod (Sr Partner)
Michael Park (Sr Partner)
David Quigley (Sr Partner)
Charlotte Relyea (Partner)
Kayvaun Rowshankish (Partner)
Roger Rudisuli (Sr Partner-Toronto)
Liz Hilton Segel (Sr Partner)
Ishaan Seth (Sr Partner)
Prasoon Sharma (Partner-Digital)
Michael Silber (Sr Partner)
Dan Singer (Partner)
Ramesh Srinivasan (Sr Partner)
Kurt Strovink (Sr Partner)
Humayun Tai (Sr Partner)
Yael Taqqu (Sr Partner)
Jannick Thomsen (Partner)
Hyo Yeon (Partner-Digital)
Navjot Singh (Sr Partner-Boston)
Jonathan Silver (Partner)
Carla Arellano (Partner)
Michael Barriere (Partner)
Ramiro Prudencio (Dir-Comm-Global)
Adrian V. Mitchell (Co-Founder-NA Lean Ops Retail Practice-North American)
Dale LeFebvre (Analyst)
Andre Andonian (Senior Partner Emeritus)
Dev Vardhan (Sr Partner)
David G. Fubini (Founder-Merger Integration Practice-Worldwide)
Michael S. Della Rocca (Partner-Philadelphia)
Pratik Shah (Co-Founder)

Subsidiaries:

Candid Partners, LLC (1)
817 W Peachtree St Ste M-100, Atlanta, GA 30308
Tel.: (404) 815-4599
Web Site: http://www.candidpartners.com
Sales Range: $1-9.9 Million
Emp.: 49
Management Consulting Services
N.A.I.C.S.: 541611
Merrick Olives (Co-Founder & Mng Partner)
Liana Anheier (Dir-Cloud Mktg)
Rick Spair (Mgr-Bus Dev)
John Peak (Co-Founder & Mng Partner)

McKinsey & Company, Inc. - Midwest (1)
300 E Randolph St Ste 3100, Chicago, IL 60601
Tel.: (312) 551-3500
Web Site: http://www.mckinsey.com
Sales Range: $50-74.9 Million
Emp.: 600
Management Consulting Services
N.A.I.C.S.: 541611
Praveen Adhi (Partner)
Jim Banaszak (Partner)
Matt Banholzer (Partner)
Dilip Bhattacharjee (Partner)
Kimberly Borden (Partner)
Anusha Dhasarathy (Partner)
Sumit Dutta (Partner)
Mark Dzierzc (Sr Dir-Design)
Dave Elzinga (Partner)
Tony Gambell (Partner)
Neha Gargi (Partner)
Trish Gyorey (Partner)
Kimberly Henderson (Partner)
Steve Hoffman (Partner)
Jeff Jacobs (Partner)
Dan Jamieson (Partner)
Akshay Kapur (Partner)
Jesse Klempner (Partner)
Katherine Linzer (Partner)
Siddarth Madhav (Partner)
Evgeniya Makarova (Partner)
Inga Maurer (Partner)
Chris McShea (Partner)
Christopher Paquette (Partner)
Parag Patel (Partner)

MCKINSEY MOTOR FORD
1415 S Hwy 183, Clinton, OK 73601
Tel.: (580) 323-0258
Web Site: http://www.mckinseymotors.com
Sales Range: $10-24.9 Million
Emp.: 15
New Car Whslr
N.A.I.C.S.: 441110
Max McKinsey (Pres)

MCKINSTRY CO., LLC
5005 3rd Ave S, Seattle, WA 98134
Tel.: (206) 762-3311   WA
Web Site: http://www.mckinstry.com
Year Founded: 1960
Sales Range: $500-549.9 Million
Emp.: 2,000
Mechanical Construction, Engineering, Architectural Metal, Maintenance & Facility Management
N.A.I.C.S.: 238220
David Allen (Exec VP)
Bill Teplicky (Exec VP)
Ron Johnson (COO)
Mike Locke (VP-Specialty Grps)
Jamie Pedersen (Gen Counsel & VP)
Ash Awad (Chief Market Officer)
Thomas Tellefson (Dir-Mechanical Construction-Western Washington)
Joan Smith (Dir-Bus Dev-Mechanical Construction)
James Miller (Dir-Risk Mgmt)
Lee Riback (Mgr-Commissioning)
Marco Hunt (Acct Exec)
Greg Zaleski (Acct Exec)
Joseph Hagar (CFO)
Brent Guinn (Exec VP-Design & Construction)
Doug Moore (Pres)
Ned Gebert (VP-Ops)
Dale Silha (VP-Energy & Technical Svcs-Pacific Northwest)
Dan Ronco (Dir-Electrical Construction-West)
Lisa Loupe (Project Dir-Sls-South)
Allen Range (CTO)
Alli Burton (Dir-Talent Acq)
Brad Liljequist (Sr Program Mgr-Zero Energy)
Jim Grimm (Mgr-Mechanical Engrg-Portland)
Matt Nelson (Dir-Preconstruction-Mechanical Construction)
Hendrik Van Hemert (Dir-Technical Svcs-Pacific Northwest)
Geremy Wolff (Dir-Technical Svcs Bus Dev)
Julie Milner (Dir-Talent Dev)
Karen Vogel (Dir-HR Ops)
Doug Ekstrom (Mgr-Technical Svcs Bus Dev-South)
Rick Becker (Project Dir-Technical Svcs-Oregon & Southern Washington)
Jennifer Koch (Dir-Ops-Svc)

Subsidiaries:

McKinstry Essention, Inc. (1)
5005 3rd Ave S, Seattle, WA 98134
Tel.: (206) 768-7730
Web Site: http://www.mckinstry.com
Facilities Management Services
N.A.I.C.S.: 561210
Bill Teplicky (CFO)

MCL COMPANIES
505 Illinois St Ste 1, Chicago, IL 60611-3540
Tel.: (312) 321-8900   IL
Web Site: http://www.mclcompanies.com
Year Founded: 1991
Sales Range: $10-24.9 Million
Emp.: 100
New Residential & Commercial Construction
N.A.I.C.S.: 236220
Daniel Mclean (Pres & CEO)

MCL RESTAURANT & BAKERY
2730 E 62nd St, Indianapolis, IN 46220-2958
Tel.: (317) 257-5425   IN
Web Site: http://www.mymclmeal.com
Year Founded: 1950
Sales Range: $50-74.9 Million
Emp.: 1,600
Restaurant & Bakery
N.A.I.C.S.: 722511
Craig Mc Gaughey (Chm & Pres)
Jesse Feil (COO)
Casey McGaughey (VP)
Jason Golden (Mgr-Chef)

MCLAIN PLUMBING & ELECTRIC SERVICE

MCLAIN PLUMBING & ELECTRIC SERVICE

McLain Plumbing & Electric Service—(Continued)
107 Magnolia St, Philadelphia, MS 39350
Tel.: (601) 656-6333
Web Site: http://www.mclaininc.com
Year Founded: 1979
Sales Range: $10-24.9 Million
Emp.: 148
Plumbing Contractor
N.A.I.C.S.: 238220
John F. McLain (Pres)

MCLANAHAN CORPORATION
200 Wall St, Hollidaysburg, PA 16648
Tel.: (814) 695-9807
Web Site: http://www.mclanahan.com
Year Founded: 1835
Sales Range: $10-24.9 Million
Emp.: 225
Custom Engineer Process Solutions for Mineral, Paper & Agriculture
N.A.I.C.S.: 333131
George Sidney (Pres & COO)
Scott O'Brien (Dir-Process Engrg)
Sean K. McLanahan (CEO)
Cory Jenson (VP-Global Product Mgmt & Dev)
Mark Krause (Mng Dir-North America)
John Rabel (Exec VP-Mfg & Supply)

Subsidiaries:

Eagle Iron Works, LLC (1)
129 E Holcomb Ave, Des Moines, IA 50313-4936
Tel.: (515) 243-1123
Web Site: http://www.eiwllc.com
Ore Processing Equipment; Castings, Special Aggregate Equipment, Water Clarifiers, Dredge Ladders, Mixers, Pattern Shop Special Fabrications, Coal Plants & Clay Crushers Mfr
N.A.I.C.S.: 333131
John Ware (Gen Mgr)
Tim Denehy (Mgr-Sls)

MCLANE ADVANCED TECHNOLOGIES, LLC
4001 Central Pointe Pkwy, Temple, TX 76504
Web Site: http://www.mclaneat.com
Year Founded: 2004
Sales Range: $50-74.9 Million
Emp.: 306
Software & IT Support Services
N.A.I.C.S.: 513210
James Chambers (COO)

MCLANE GROUP LP
4001 Central Pointe Pkwy, Temple, TX 76504
Tel.: (254) 770-6100
Web Site: http://www.mclanegrp.com
Rev.: $40,000,000
Emp.: 10
Provider of Investment Services
N.A.I.C.S.: 541611
Lesley Foster (Controller)
Robert Drayton McLane Jr. (Owner, Chm & Co-CEO)

Subsidiaries:

M-C McLane Group International (1)
16607 Central Green Blvd Ste 400, Houston, TX 77302
Tel.: (281) 210-3295
Web Site: http://www.mclaneglobal.com
Sales Range: $25-49.9 Million
International Trade Management, Global Sourcing & Logistics
N.A.I.C.S.: 238990
Mike Julian (Chm)
Shaundrea Fortson (Coord-Logistics)
Tim Frey (Mgr-Supply Chain-Intl)
Yujing Huang (Mgr-Bus-Intl)
Michael Lin (Mgr-Bus-Intl)
Michael D. Martin (Mgr-Distr)
Hank Morton (Mgr-IT)

Nam Nguyen (Controller)
Stacey Walker (Mgr-Logistics)
Michelle Weisberg (Sr VP-Brand Dev)

MCLANE LIVESTOCK TRANSPORT
US Hwy 67, Poplar Bluff, MO 63901
Tel.: (573) 785-0177
Web Site: http://www.mclanetransport.com
Rev.: $12,000,000
Emp.: 75
Refrigerated Products Transport
N.A.I.C.S.: 484230
J.P. McLane (Pres)

MCLAREN HEALTH CARE CORPORATION
3235 Beecher Rd Ste B, Flint, MI 48532
Tel.: (810) 342-1100 MI
Web Site: http://www.mclaren.org
Sales Range: $1-4.9 Billion
Emp.: 15,000
Holding Company; Hospitals & Healthcare Centers Operator
N.A.I.C.S.: 551112
Derek Morkel (CIO)
Dave Mazurkiewicz (CFO & Exec VP)
Gregory Lane (Chief Admin Officer & Sr VP)
William Peterson (VP-HR)
Kevin Tompkins (VP-Mktg)
Michael McKenna (Exec VP)
Ron Strachan (CIO)
Clarence Sevillian (Pres-Bay Reg)
Chad M. Grant (COO & Exec VP)
Robert F. Flora (Dir-Medical Education-McLaren Bay Reg)
Michael P. Lacusta (VP-Bus Dev)
Cheryl Ellegood (Dir-Svc Lines)
Mujahed Abbas (Mng Dir)
Leah Searcy (VP-Ops)
Timothy Kasprzak (Chief Medical Officer)
Justin F. Klamerus (Chief Medical Officer-Grand Blanc & Exec VP-Grand Blanc)
Phillip A. Incarnati (Pres & CEO)

MCLARENS, INC.
5555 Triangle Pkwy Ste 200, Norcross, GA 30092-3330
Tel.: (770) 448-4680 DE
Web Site: http://www.mclarens.com
Year Founded: 1987
Sales Range: $500-549.9 Million
Emp.: 1,200
Loss Adjustment Third-Party Administrator & Other Claim Services
N.A.I.C.S.: 524298
Vernon F. Chalfant (Chm, Pres & CEO)
Gary K. Gabriel (CFO)
Laura Miller (Mgr-IT)
Steve Whitmarsh (COO-US & Canada)
Gary Brown (CEO)
Chris Panes (COO-Europe, Middle East & Asia-Pacific)
Kristen Early (Head-Third-Party Admin-Global)

Subsidiaries:

American Environmental Group, Inc. (1)
5655 Lindero Canyon Rd Ste 120, Westlake Village, CA 91362
Tel.: (818) 865-7901
Web Site: http://www.americanenv.com
Scientific & Technical Consulting Services
N.A.I.C.S.: 541690
Jay Barkley (Pres & CEO)

McLarens Young International (1)
Ibex House 42-47 Minories, London, EC3N 1DY, United Kingdom
Tel.: (44) 2074813399

Web Site: http://www.mclarens.com
Rev.: $15,956,077
Emp.: 20
Claims Management, Loss Adjusting, Pre-Risk & Damage Surveying Services
N.A.I.C.S.: 524291
Nigel Minett (Dir-Ops)

MCLARTY CAPITAL PARTNERS UK LLP
50 Rockefeller Plz Fl 2 Ste 201, New York, NY 10020
Tel.: (212) 956-1061 UK
Web Site: https://firmament.com
Year Founded: 2013
Investment Holding Company
N.A.I.C.S.: 551112
Mack McLarty (Chm)

Subsidiaries:

PRN Health Services, Inc. (1)
1101 E South River St, Appleton, WI 54915
Tel.: (920) 997-8800
Web Site: http://www.prnhealthservices.com
Sales Range: $10-24.9 Million
Emp.: 1,000
Employment Placement Agencies
N.A.I.C.S.: 561311
Angie Berghuis (CFO)

Subsidiary (Domestic):

Alliant Staffing, LLC (2)
7700 Old Georgetown Rd, Bethesda, MD 20814
Tel.: (301) 654-1002
Web Site: http://www.alliantstaffing.com
Administrative Management & General Management Consulting Service
N.A.I.C.S.: 541611
Marvin Rabovsky (Pres)

e4 Services, LLC (1)
139 W Market St Ste C, West Chester, PA 19382
Tel.: (770) 448-4680
Web Site: http://www.e4-services.com
Sales Range: $100-124.9 Million
Emp.: 59
Healtcare Services
N.A.I.C.S.: 621999
Niall Doherty (Co-Founder)
Mike Brensinger (Co-Founder)
Jim Hennessy (CEO)

MCLAUGHLIN BODY CO.
2430 River Dr, Moline, IL 61265
Tel.: (309) 762-7755
Web Site: http://www.mclbody.com
Sales Range: $75-99.9 Million
Emp.: 300
Truck & Combine Bodies
N.A.I.C.S.: 336211
Raymond L. McLaughlin (Chm)
Nick Spencer (Engr-Indus)

Subsidiaries:

Bee Line Company (1)
2700 62nd St Ct, Bettendorf, IA 52722-5575
Tel.: (563) 332-4066
Web Site: http://www.beeline-co.com
Sales Range: $10-24.9 Million
Emp.: 45
Mfr of Truck Wheel Alignment & Wheel Correction Equipment for Autos & Heavy Duty Trucks
N.A.I.C.S.: 333248
Kerry Dobereiner (Controller)
Tricia Kane (Mgr-Mktg & Sls Comm)

MCLAUGHLIN MOTORS
4101 41st St, Moline, IL 61265
Tel.: (309) 797-5654
Web Site: http://www.mcmotors.com
Sales Range: $10-24.9 Million
Emp.: 50
New & Used Car Dealers
N.A.I.C.S.: 441110
Peter J. McLaughlin (Pres)

MCLAUGHLIN PAPER CO. INC.
61 Progress Ave, West Springfield, MA 01089

Tel.: (413) 732-7485
Web Site: http://www.mclaughlinpaper.com
Year Founded: 1968
Rev.: $12,000,000
Emp.: 12
Supplier of Industrial & Personal Service Paper
N.A.I.C.S.: 424130
Denis Bauke (VP)

MCLAUGHLIN RESEARCH CORPORATION
130 Eugene O'Neill Dr Ste 200, New London, CT 06320
Tel.: (860) 447-2298
Web Site: http://www.mrcds.com
Sales Range: $10-24.9 Million
Emp.: 200
Engineering & Technical Support Services
N.A.I.C.S.: 541330
Conn L. Kelly (CEO)
Andra McLaughlin Kelly (Owner)

MCLAUGHLIN, DELVECCHIO & CASEY, INC.
1 Church St, New Haven, CT 06510-3330
Tel.: (203) 624-4151
Web Site: http://www.mdcads.com
Year Founded: 1972
Rev.: $15,225,000
Emp.: 6
Advetising Agency
N.A.I.C.S.: 541810
David B. Casey (Principal & Exec Creative Dir)
Pasquale DelVecchio (Mng Principal & Exec Dir-Art)
JoAnn Scillia (Dir-Creative Svcs)
Dave DelVecchio (Acct Exec)
Meg Barone (Dir-Pub Rel)
Laura Whinfield (Mktg Dir-Svc)

MCLAURIN PARKING COMPANY INC.
421 Fayetteville St, Raleigh, NC 27601
Tel.: (919) 833-7522
Web Site: http://www.mclaurinparking.com
Year Founded: 1946
Sales Range: $10-24.9 Million
Emp.: 300
Parking Lots
N.A.I.C.S.: 812930
Jeff Wolfe (Pres & CEO)

MCLEA'S TIRE & AUTOMOTIVE CENTERS
800 Piner Rd, Santa Rosa, CA 95403
Tel.: (707) 542-0363
Web Site: http://www.mcleastire.com
Sales Range: $10-24.9 Million
Emp.: 50
Tire & Related Product Whslr
N.A.I.C.S.: 441340
Les McLea (Owner)

MCLEAN CAPITAL MANAGEMENT
4975 Ringwood Meadow, Sarasota, FL 34235
Tel.: (941) 371-7600
Web Site: http://www.mcleancapital.com
Rev.: $50,000,000
Investment Services
N.A.I.C.S.: 523999
Richard McLean (Founder & CEO)

MCLEAN COMPANY

6681 Chittenden Rd, Hudson, OH 44236
Tel.: (330) 655-5900
Web Site:
http://www.themcleancompany.com
Sales Range: $10-24.9 Million
Emp.: 40
Highway Construction Equipment
N.A.I.C.S.: 423810
Donald S. McLean (Pres)
F. Scott McLean (VP & Mgr-Field Sls)
Scott Riffle (Gen Mgr-Parts)

MCLEAN CONSTRUCTION LTD.
4101 Trimmier Rd, Killeen, TX 76542
Tel.: (254) 634-4514
Web Site: http://www.mcleanlc.com
Year Founded: 1972
Rev.: $12,800,000
Emp.: 75
Telephone & Communication Line Construction
N.A.I.C.S.: 237130
Gary Richardson (Controller)
James Mclean (Pres & CEO)

MCLEAN CONTRACTING COMPANY INC.
6700 McLean Way, Glen Burnie, MD 21060-6418
Tel.: (410) 553-6700
Web Site:
http://www.mcleancontracting.com
Year Founded: 1903
Construction Services; Dredging & Bridge Construction; Timber Work & Fender System; Steel Erection
N.A.I.C.S.: 237310
Cory M. Heisey (VP-Ops)
Julie Bechtel (Mgr-Benefits)
Bryan Ellis (Mgr-Bus Dev)
Ben Frank (Project Mgr)
Ryan Turner (Project Mgr)
Jay Musser (Area Mgr-North)
David Kimberly (Mgr-Bus Dev)
Joe Hoffman (Asst VP)
Joe Wallenfelsz (Project Mgr)
Keith Aschenbach (Dir-Equipment-Interim)
Paula Sidlowski (CFO)
Sam Belvins (Dir-Bus Dev)
Tracy Lowther (Mgr-HR)
Chad Scott (Project Mgr)
Michael Filipczak (Pres & CEO)
Ned Fitter (Dir-Safety)
Kevin Mullen (Dir-Pre-Construction Svcs)
Keith Christiansen Jr. (Area Mgr-South)

MCLEAN COUNTY ASPHALT & CONCRETE COMPANY, INC.
1100 W Market St, Bloomington, IL 61701
Tel.: (309) 827-4811
Web Site: http://www.mc-asphalt.com
Year Founded: 1964
Sales Range: $10-24.9 Million
Emp.: 80
Provider of Highway & Street Paving Contracting Services
N.A.I.C.S.: 327320
Forrest G. Kaufman (Co-Owner)
Randy G. Kaufman (Co-Owner & VP)
Linda Lay (Controller)
John Edwards (Mgr-Matl Yard)
Scott Duvall (Coord-Asphalt Sls Dept)

MCLEAN FAULCONER INC.
503 Faulconer Dr Ste 5, Charlottesville, VA 22903
Tel.: (434) 295-1131
Web Site:
http://www.mcleanfaulconer.com
Year Founded: 1980
Rev.: $486,000,000
Emp.: 14
Real Estate Services
N.A.I.C.S.: 531210
Stephen T. McLean (Pres)
Teresa Campbell (Office Mgr)
James W. Faulconer Jr. (Owner)

MCLEAN IMPLEMENT INCORPORATED
Hwy 130 S Railroad 4, Albion, IL 62806
Tel.: (618) 445-3676
Web Site: http://www.mcleanimp.com
Year Founded: 1964
Sales Range: $10-24.9 Million
Emp.: 40
Farm & Garden Machinery Parts & Service
N.A.I.C.S.: 423820
Robert L. Mason (Owner)
Diane Buza (Office Mgr)

MCLEAN INCORPORATED
3409 E Miraloma Ave, Anaheim, CA 92806-2102
Tel.: (714) 996-5451
Web Site: http://mcleaninc.com
Year Founded: 1964
Sales Range: $1-9.9 Million
Emp.: 20
Mfr of Machine Tools, Lathes & Dovetail Slides
N.A.I.C.S.: 333517
Mike McLean (Pres)

MCLEAN PACKAGING CORPORATION
1504 Glen Ave, Morristown, NJ 08057
Tel.: (856) 359-2600
Web Site:
http://www.mcleanpackaging.com
Year Founded: 1961
Rev.: $50,000,000
Emp.: 350
Design Rigid Paper Box Mfr
N.A.I.C.S.: 322211
Joseph Fenkel (Founder, Chm & CEO)
Stuart Fenkel (Pres)
Jeff Besnick (Gen Mgr-Folding Carton Div)

Subsidiaries:

McLean Packaging Corporation - Corrugated Division (1)
1000 Thomas Busch Memorial Hwy, Pennsauken, NJ 08110
Tel.: (856) 359-2600
Packaging Products Mfr
N.A.I.C.S.: 322220
Stuart Fenkel (Pres)

McLean Packaging Corporation - Rigid Paper Box Division (1)
Broad & Easton St, Nazareth, PA 18064
Tel.: (610) 759-3550
Packaging Products Mfr
N.A.I.C.S.: 322220
David Seidenberg (VP & Gen Mgr)

PhilCorr LLC (1)
2317 Almond Rd, Vineland, NJ 08360
Tel.: (856) 205-0557
Web Site: http://www.philcorr.com
Corrugated Sheet Mfr
N.A.I.C.S.: 322211
Philip Johnson (Coord-Maintenance)

MCLEMORE BUILDING MAINTENANCE INC.
110 Fargo St, Houston, TX 77006
Tel.: (713) 528-7775
Web Site: http://www.mbminc.com
Sales Range: $10-24.9 Million
Emp.: 500
Janitorial Service, Contract Basis
N.A.I.C.S.: 561720
Curtis McLemore (CEO)
Richard Rodriguez (VP-Ops)
Dave Prewitt (VP-Sls & Mktg)

MCLEMORE MARKETS
10505 Highway 64, Arlington, TN 38002-5768
Tel.: (901) 372-0956
Sales Range: $1-9.9 Million
Emp.: 5
Owner & Operator of Convenience Stores
N.A.I.C.S.: 445110
Billy M. Mclemore (Pres)

MCLEOD ADDICTIVE DISEASE CENTER, INC.
515 Clanton Rd, Charlotte, NC 28217
Tel.: (704) 332-9001
Web Site:
http://www.mcleodcenter.com
Year Founded: 1970
Sales Range: $10-24.9 Million
Emp.: 373
Behavioral Healthcare Services
N.A.I.C.S.: 623220
Tonda Wilde (VP-Criminal Justice Svcs)
Bob Schurmeier (Sec)
Bill Stetzer (Chm)

MCLEOD BANCSHARES, INC.
4625 County Rd 101, Minnetonka, MN 55345
Tel.: (952) 933-9550
Web Site:
http://www.firstmnbank.com
Year Founded: 1982
Sales Range: $10-24.9 Million
Emp.: 80
Bank Holding Company
N.A.I.C.S.: 551111
Lowell G. Wakefield (CEO)
Dean Perry (Pres-Mktg & Exec VP)

Subsidiaries:

First Minnesota Bank (1)
4625 County Rd 101, Minnetonka, MN 55345
Tel.: (952) 933-9550
Web Site: http://www.firstmnbank.com
Emp.: 15
Commericial Banking
N.A.I.C.S.: 522110
Lowell G. Wakefield (CEO)
Cliff Simon (Pres)

MCLEOD COOPERATIVE POWER ASSOCIATION
1231 Ford Ave, Glencoe, MN 55336
Tel.: (320) 864-3148
Web Site:
http://www.mcleodcoop.com
Year Founded: 1935
Sales Range: $10-24.9 Million
Emp.: 37
Electric Power Administration Cooperative
N.A.I.C.S.: 926130
Keith Peterson (Pres)
Gerald Roepke (Asst Sec & Asst Treas)
Doug Kirtz (Treas & Sec)
Joe Griebie (VP)
Carrie Buckley (Gen Mgr)

Subsidiaries:

McLeod Cooperative Power Trust (1)
1231 Ford Ave, Glencoe, MN 55336
Tel.: (320) 864-3148
Web Site: http://www.mcleodcoop.com
Charity Organization
N.A.I.C.S.: 813211
Virgil Stender (Pres)

MCLEOD HEALTH
555 E Cheves St, Florence, SC 29506-2606
Tel.: (843) 777-2000
Web Site:
http://www.mcleodhealth.org
Year Founded: 1906
Healthcare Services Organization
N.A.I.C.S.: 813920
Deborah D. Locklair (Chief HR Officer)

Subsidiaries:

Chesterfield General Hospital (1)
711 Chesterfield Hwy, Cheraw, SC 29520
Tel.: (843) 537-7881
Web Site:
http://www.chesterfieldgeneral.com
Health Care Srvices
N.A.I.C.S.: 622110

Marlboro Park Hospital (1)
1138 Cheraw St, Bennettsville, SC 29512
Tel.: (843) 479-2881
Web Site:
http://www.marlboroparkhospital.com
Hospital Operator
N.A.I.C.S.: 622110
Jeff Reece (CEO)

MCLEOD OIL COMPANY INC.
933 W Ctr St, Mebane, NC 27302
Tel.: (919) 563-3172
Sales Range: $10-24.9 Million
Emp.: 50
Distr of Petroleum Products
N.A.I.C.S.: 424720
Mike Tompkins (Pres & CEO)

MCLOUGHLIN ENTERPRISES INC.
20745 M 60 E, Cassopolis, MI 49031-9431
Tel.: (269) 445-2495
Web Site: http://www.mrc.com
Year Founded: 1984
Sales Range: $10-24.9 Million
Emp.: 160
Supplier of Industrial Machinery
N.A.I.C.S.: 332710

Subsidiaries:

K&M Machine-Fabricating Inc. (1)
20745 M 60 E, Cassopolis, MI 49031-9431
Tel.: (269) 445-2495
Web Site: http://www.k-mm.com
Supplier of Industrial Machinery Services
N.A.I.C.S.: 332710
Michael McLoughlin (CEO)

MCM CAPITAL GROUP INCORPORATED
2365 N Side Dr 3rd Fl, San Diego, CA 92108
Tel.: (858) 560-2600
Web Site: http://www.mcmcg.com
Rev.: $36,560,000
Emp.: 200
Financial Services
N.A.I.C.S.: 522299
Brandon Black (Pres & CEO)

MCM CAPITAL PARTNERS, LP
25101 Chagrin Blvd # 310, Cleveland, OH 44122
Tel.: (216) 514-1840
Web Site:
http://www.mcmcapital.com
Year Founded: 1992
Sales Range: $1-9.9 Million
Emp.: 118
Securities Brokerage
N.A.I.C.S.: 523150
Kevin F. Hayes (CFO)
Mark E. Mansour (Mng Partner)
Robert R. Kingsbury (Principal)

MCM CAPITAL PARTNERS, LP

Mcm Capital Partners, LP—(Continued)

Subsidiaries:

Aim Processing, Inc. (1)
1650 Skyway Dr, Longmont, CO 80504
Tel.: (303) 684-0931
Web Site: http://www.aimprocessing.com
Sales Range: $1-9.9 Million
Emp.: 18
Plastics Products, Nec, Nsk
N.A.I.C.S.: 326199
Jon Gelston *(Pres & Owner)*

MCM CONSTRUCTION, INC.
6413 32nd St, North Highlands, CA 95660-3001
Tel.: (916) 334-1221 CA
Web Site:
http://www.mcmconstructioninc.com
Year Founded: 1973
Sales Range: $10-24.9 Million
Emp.: 370
Bridge, Tunnel Elevated Highway
N.A.I.C.S.: 237310
James A. Carter *(Pres & Partner)*
Manny Martinez *(Supvr)*

MCM CORP.
6201 SW 70th St 2nd Fl, Miami, FL 33143
Tel.: (305) 541-0000
Web Site: http://www.mcmcorp.com
Year Founded: 1983
Sales Range: $75-99.9 Million
Emp.: 560
Construction Services
N.A.I.C.S.: 236210
Jorge Munilla *(Pres)*
Juan Munilla *(VP)*
Fernando Munilla *(VP)*
Pedro Munilla *(VP)*
Raul Munilla *(VP)*
Jorge Munilla *(Pres)*
Alexis Leal *(Dir-Corp Ops)*
Gustavo Fernandez *(Dir-Ops-Panama)*
Joe Fernandez *(Dir-Building Construction Ops)*
Luis Munilla *(Dir-Ops-Texas)*
Robert T. Murphy *(Dir-Civil Ops-Florida)*
Greg Alexander *(Reg VP)*

MCM CORPORATION
702 Oberlin Rd, Raleigh, NC 27605-1102
Tel.: (919) 833-1600
Year Founded: 1977
Sales Range: $100-124.9 Million
Emp.: 800
Provider of Insurance Services
N.A.I.C.S.: 524126
George E. King *(Chm & CEO)*
Stephen Stephano *(CEO)*

Subsidiaries:

Occidental Fire & Casualty Company of North Carolina Inc. (1)
702 Oberlin Rd Ste 300, Raleigh, NC 27605-1129
Tel.: (919) 833-1600
Sales Range: $50-74.9 Million
Emp.: 150
Provider of Insurance Services
N.A.I.C.S.: 524126
C. Stefano *(CEO)*

Wilshire Insurance Co. Inc. (1)
702 Oberlin Rd Ste 300, Raleigh, NC 27605-1102
Tel.: (919) 833-1600
Sales Range: $50-74.9 Million
Emp.: 150
Provider of Insurance Services
N.A.I.C.S.: 524126

MCM PAVING & CONSTUCTION
9518 Grant Rd, Houston, TX 77040
Tel.: (713) 466-7670
Sales Range: $50-74.9 Million
Emp.: 275
Nonresidential Construction Services
N.A.I.C.S.: 236220
Matt C. Mabry *(Pres)*

MCMAHON CONTRACTING, L.P.
PO Box 153086, Irving, TX 75015-3086
Tel.: (972) 263-6907
Web Site: http://www.mcmahoncontracting.com
Sales Range: $25-49.9 Million
Emp.: 106
Highway & Street Construction Services
N.A.I.C.S.: 237310
Jayce McMahon *(Mgr)*

MCMAHON FORD
3300 S Kingshighway Blvd, Saint Louis, MO 63139
Tel.: (314) 664-4100
Web Site: http://www.mcmahonlm.com
Sales Range: $50-74.9 Million
Emp.: 91
New & Used Car Dealers
N.A.I.C.S.: 441110
William J. Schicker *(Pres & CEO)*
John Schicker *(Gen Mgr)*
Michelle Clemens *(Controller)*
Ike Bibas *(Mgr-Sls)*

MCMAHON FORD, LLC
1 Main St, Norwalk, CT 06851
Tel.: (203) 838-4801
Web Site: http://www.mcmahonfordllc.com
Year Founded: 2000
Sales Range: $10-24.9 Million
Emp.: 38
New Car Dealers
N.A.I.C.S.: 441110
Christopher O. McMahon *(Principal)*

MCMAHON INSURANCE INC.
901 Simpson Ave, Ocean City, NJ 08226
Tel.: (609) 399-0060
Web Site: http://mcmahonagency.com
Insurance Services
N.A.I.C.S.: 524210
Bill McMahon III *(Pres)*

MCMAHON PUBLISHING COMPANY
83 Peaceable St, Redding, CT 06896-3108
Tel.: (203) 544-8389
Web Site: http://www.mcmahonmed.com
Rev.: $11,500,000
Emp.: 96
Periodical Publishers
N.A.I.C.S.: 513120
Rose Anne McMahon *(Treas & VP)*
Van N. Velle *(Pres)*

MCMAHON TIRE, INC.
4201 Coldwater Rd, Fort Wayne, IN 46805
Tel.: (260) 483-9594
Web Site: http://www.mcmahontires.com
Year Founded: 1975
Sales Range: $10-24.9 Million
Emp.: 60
Retailer & Wholesaler of Automotive Tires
N.A.I.C.S.: 441340

Paul Zurcher *(Owner)*
Kim Mc Mahon *(Controller)*

MCMANGA FOODS, INC.
8605 Indiana Ave, Riverside, CA 92504
Tel.: (951) 689-8400
Web Site: http://www.hanasports.com
Rev.: $8,700,000
Emp.: 500
Fast Food Restaurants
N.A.I.C.S.: 722513
Thomas Mangione *(CEO)*
Terry Bromley *(COO)*

MCMASTER-CARR SUPPLY COMPANY
600 N County Line Rd, Elmhurst, IL 60126-2034
Tel.: (630) 834-9600 IL
Web Site: http://www.mcmaster.com
Sales Range: $1-9.9 Million
Emp.: 900
Retail & Mail Order Supplier of Industrial Machines & Equipment
N.A.I.C.S.: 423840
Dave Mack *(Mgr-Source)*
Justin Aschenbener *(Coord-Sys On-Boarding)*
Al Franjoine *(Gen Mgr)*
Allison Dale *(Supvr-Ops-McMaster-Carr Supply)*
Bob Kovats *(Mgr-E-Learning)*
C. Brody *(Mgr-Employee Rels)*
Gary Austin *(Mgr-Source)*
Gerald Schaefer *(Mgr-Sourcing)*
Marty Earley *(Mgr-Sourcing)*
Erica Levinsky *(Mgr-Warehouse)*
Deric Bertrand *(Project Mgr)*
Jeremy Bourne *(Supvr-Warehouse)*

MCMASTERS-KOSS CO.
4224 Normandy Ct, Royal Oak, MI 48073
Tel.: (248) 549-1414
Web Site: http://www.mcmasterskoss.com
Sales Range: $10-24.9 Million
Emp.: 25
Industrial Supplies Whslr
N.A.I.C.S.: 423840
Gary Gibbs *(Pres)*
Ed Koss *(VP)*
Bill Jackovich *(Office Mgr)*
Paul Pirtle *(Mgr-Special Projects)*
Robert Reifert *(Mgr-Quality)*
Chris Butzu *(Mgr-Fin)*

MCMC LLC
300 Crown Colony Dr Ste 203, Quincy, MA 02169
Tel.: (617) 375-7700 DE
Web Site: http://www.mcmcllc.com
Medical Care Management Services
N.A.I.C.S.: 621999
Brenda Calia *(Sr VP-Integrated Svcs)*
B. J. Dougherty *(Sr VP-Medical Bill Review)*
Mark Laffey *(Sr VP-Medical Bill Review)*
Steve Mazefsky *(Sr VP-Litigation Solutions)*
Stephen Junker *(VP-Customer Svc & Implementations)*
Paul J. Lanning *(Sr VP-Peer Review)*
Paul Gilleece *(VP-Independent Peer Review)*
Brian Roberts *(VP-IT)*
Bob Watters *(VP-Mktg)*
Larry Brinton Jr. *(Sr VP-Medical Bill Review)*

Subsidiaries:

Litigation Solutions, LLC (1)
Brentwood Town Ctr 101 Towne Sq Way Ste 251, Pittsburgh, PA 15227
Tel.: (412) 263-5656
Web Site: http://www.litsol.com
Sales Range: $25-49.9 Million
Emp.: 250
Investigative & Litigation Support Services
N.A.I.C.S.: 541199
Steve Mazefsky *(Pres)*
Christie Grisetti *(VP-Ops-Litigation Support Dept)*
John Tomasic *(VP-Ops-Investigative Dept)*

OccHealth Systems, LLC (1)
3100 S Gessner Rd Ste 225, Houston, TX 77063
Tel.: (713) 520-0358
Web Site: http://www.ohstexas.com
Workers' Compensation & Disability Management Services
N.A.I.C.S.: 519290

MCMENAMINS INC.
430 N Killingsworth, Portland, OR 97217
Tel.: (503) 223-0109 OR
Web Site: http://www.mcmenamins.com
Year Founded: 1983
Sales Range: $100-124.9 Million
Emp.: 2,000
Restaurant, Hotel & Brewery Operator
N.A.I.C.S.: 722511
Mike McMenamin *(Co-Owner)*
Renee Rank Ignacio *(Dir-Mktg)*
Brian McMenamin *(Co-Owner)*
D. J. Simcoe *(COO-Hotels)*
Clark McCool *(Mgr-Distillery)*
Rich Smith *(COO-Pubs)*
Rob Vallance *(Gen Mgr-Brewery)*

MCMILLAN BROTHERS ELECTRIC SERVICE
1515 S Van Ness Ave, San Francisco, CA 94110-4608
Tel.: (415) 826-5100
Web Site: http://www.mcmillanco.com
Year Founded: 1965
Sales Range: $25-49.9 Million
Emp.: 190
Electrical Wiring Services
N.A.I.C.S.: 238210
Patric McMillan *(Pres)*

MCMILLAN ELECTRIC COMPANY
400 Best Rd, Woodville, WI 54028
Tel.: (715) 698-2488
Web Site: http://www.mcmillanelectric.com
Rev.: $54,000,000
Emp.: 650
Mfr of Electric Motors
N.A.I.C.S.: 335312
Ron Wolfgram *(Pres)*
Evan Anderson *(VP-Mfg)*
Dewain Wasson *(VP-Tech & New Bus Dev)*
Greg Luecke *(VP-Quality Assurance)*
Tom Rundle *(VP-Sls & Mktg)*

MCMILLION RESEARCH
1012 Kanawha Blvd E Ste 301, Charleston, WV 25301
Tel.: (304) 343-9650
Web Site: http://www.mcmillionresearch.com
Sales Range: $100-124.9 Million
Emp.: 150
National Data Collection & Market Research Services
N.A.I.C.S.: 513140
Gary McMillion *(Pres)*
Jay Mace *(VP)*
Andrew Steele *(Project Mgr)*
Jerry McMillion *(Dir-Programming & Data Svcs)*

MCMULLAN EQUIPMENT COMPANY, INC.

401 Broadway Dr, Hattiesburg, MS 39401
Tel.: (601) 544-2430
Web Site:
http://www.mcmullanequipment.com
Rev.: $10,600,000
Emp.: 45
Auto & Truck Sales Parts Retailer
N.A.I.C.S.: 441110
Wyche L. McMullan *(Pres)*

MCMULLEN OIL CO. INC.
11965 49th St N, Clearwater, FL 33762
Tel.: (727) 573-0016
Web Site:
http://www.mcmullenoil.com
Sales Range: $10-24.9 Million
Emp.: 15
Fuel Oil Dealers
N.A.I.C.S.: 457210
Paul McMullen *(Pres)*

MCMURRAY FABRICS INC.
105 Vann Pl, Aberdeen, NC 28315
Tel.: (910) 944-2128
Web Site:
http://www.mcmurrayfabrics.com
Rev.: $13,300,000
Emp.: 200
Mfr of Fabrics
N.A.I.C.S.: 313240
Brian L. McMurray *(Pres)*
David McCarter *(Mgr-Dyehouse)*
Glenda Graham *(Asst Mgr-HR)*
Kevin Pace *(Engr-Advanced)*
Marcia Heath *(Mgr-Production Control)*
Michael Clark *(Dir-Mfg)*

MCN DISTRIBUTORS INC.
300 N Connecting Rd, Islandia, NY 11749
Tel.: (631) 234-0389
Web Site:
http://www.mcndistributors.com
Rev.: $30,000,000
Emp.: 25
Air Conditioning Equipment
N.A.I.C.S.: 423730
Jason Kwasna *(Branch Mgr)*

MCNABB CHEVROLET, OLDS, CADILLAC
2000 N Jackson St, Tullahoma, TN 37388
Tel.: (931) 455-3451
Web Site:
http://www.stanmcnabb.com
Sales Range: $25-49.9 Million
Emp.: 48
Automobiles, New & Used
N.A.I.C.S.: 441110
Stan McNabb *(Pres)*
Trey McNabb *(Gen Mgr-Chrysler and Ford)*
Dolly McNabb *(Dir-Mktg & Communications)*
Paul Jernigan *(Mgr-Sls Chevrolet)*
Ryan Ruff *(Mgr-Sls Chevy)*
Mike Wingerter *(Dir-Svc Chevy)*
Terry Johnson *(Mgr-Parts Chrysler)*
Coty Hall *(Mgr-Collision Center)*

MCNALLY CAPITAL, LLC
190 S LaSalle St Ste 3250, Chicago, IL 60603
Tel.: (312) 357-3710
Web Site:
http://www.mcnallycapital.com
Investment Services
N.A.I.C.S.: 523999
Ward McNally *(Mng Partner)*
Adam Lerner *(Principal)*
Brett Mitchell *(Principal)*
Beth Rahn *(VP)*
Anna Quinlan *(Office Mgr)*
Ravi P. Shah *(Principal)*
Nicole M. Henderson *(Head-Fundraising & IR)*
Frank A. McGrew IV *(Mng Partner)*
Subsidiaries:

Dedicated Computing, LLC (1)
N26 W23880 Commerce Cir, Waukesha, WI 53188-1018
Tel.: (262) 951-7200
Web Site:
http://www.dedicatedcomputing.com
Electronic Computer Mfr
N.A.I.C.S.: 334111
Eric Lien *(VP-Mktg)*
Dave Guzzi *(Sr VP-Sls & Mktg)*
Don Schlidt *(Pres & CEO)*
Jane Menheer *(CFO)*
David Gervasio *(VP-Ops & Supply Chain)*
Jeff Durst *(Dir-Product Mgmt)*
Richard Ross *(VP-Tech & Product Dev)*

Orbis Operations, LLC (1)
6849 Old Dominion Dr Ste 370, McLean, VA 22101-3729
Tel.: (703) 639-0911
Web Site: http://www.orbisops.com
Professional & Management Development Training
N.A.I.C.S.: 611430
Josh Mayne *(CEO)*

MCNALLY INDUSTRIES, LLC
340 W Benson Ave, Grantsburg, WI 54840
Tel.: (715) 463-8300 MN
Web Site: http://www.mcnally-industries.com
Year Founded: 1942
Sales Range: $75-99.9 Million
Emp.: 207
Mfr of Precision Components, Mechanical Systems & Hydraulic Equipment
N.A.I.C.S.: 333914
Lori Lien *(VP-Fin)*
Troy Goetz *(VP-Ops)*
Jim Segelstrom *(Pres & CEO)*
Dewey Klaphake *(VP-Bus Dev)*
Subsidiaries:

Sun Country Industries LLC (1)
6801 Gruber Ave NE, Albuquerque, NM 87109
Tel.: (505) 344-1611
Web Site:
http://www.suncountryindustries.com
Sales Range: $25-49.9 Million
Emp.: 100
Aerospace Components & Assemblies Mfr
N.A.I.C.S.: 336413
Ruben Aragon *(Mgr-Production)*
Dan Schroeder *(VP-Quality Assurance)*
Tim Hollingsworth *(Gen Mgr)*

MCNALLY OPERATIONS LLC
435 W Norfolk Ave, Norfolk, NE 68701
Tel.: (402) 371-2108
Office Supplies Whslr
N.A.I.C.S.: 459410
Steve McNally *(Co-Owner)*
Heidi McNally *(Co-Owner)*
Subsidiaries:

Davis Typewriter Company, Inc. (1)
1158 Oxford St, Worthington, MN 56187
Tel.: (507) 343-2001
Web Site:
http://www.westernofficetechnologies.com
Sales Range: $1-9.9 Million
Emp.: 55
Office Equipment Merchant Whslr
N.A.I.C.S.: 423420
Michele Carlson *(Mgr)*

MCNAUGHTON & GUNN, INC.
960 Woodland Dr, Saline, MI 48176-1634
Tel.: (734) 429-5411 MI
Web Site:
http://www.bookprinters.com
Year Founded: 1975
Sales Range: $10-24.9 Million
Emp.: 150
Provider of Book Printing Services
N.A.I.C.S.: 323117
Robert L. McNaughton *(Chm)*
Julie McFarland *(Pres)*
David Stress *(Mgr-Info Svcs)*
Jonnie A. Bryant *(Exec Dir-Sls & Mktg)*
Carlene Rogers *(Mgr-Fin Svc)*
Jim Clark *(Dir-Ops)*
Jeff Briegel *(Mgr-Print Ops)*
Ron Kokelaar *(Mgr-Bindery)*
Del Dunn *(Mgr-Shipping & Receiving)*
Butch Clark *(Mgr-Maintenance)*
Jennifer E. Thompson *(Mgr-Estimating & Pricing)*
K. Page Boyer *(Dir-Social Media Mktg)*
Marc Moore *(Mgr-Sls-IA, IL, IN, MN, MO & WI)*
Frank Gaynor *(Mgr-Sls-West Coast)*
Chris Shore *(Mgr-Sls-CT, DE, MA, NJ & NY)*

MCNAUGHTON-MCKAY ELECTRIC COMPANY
1357 E Lincoln Ave, Madison Heights, MI 48071-4134
Tel.: (248) 399-7500 MI
Web Site: http://www.mc-mc.com
Year Founded: 1910
Sales Range: $500-549.9 Million
Emp.: 800
Whslr of Industrial Electrical Supplies & Equipment
N.A.I.C.S.: 423610
Walt Reynolds *(COO)*
Gregory H. Chun *(VP-Mktg)*
John D. Kuczmanski *(CFO & Exec VP)*
R. Scott Sellers *(Exec VP-Ops)*
Laura Del Pup *(Gen Counsel)*
Donald D. Slominski Jr. *(CEO)*
Subsidiaries:

S&D Service & Distribution GmbH (1)
Bischofstrasse 113, 47809, Krefeld, Germany (100%)
Tel.: (49) 21 51 45 76 600
Web Site: http://www.sud-gmbh.de
Electrical Equipment Distr
N.A.I.C.S.: 423610
Matthias Kistler *(Mng Dir)*

The Reynolds Company (1)
2680 Sylvania Cross Dr, Fort Worth, TX 76137
Tel.: (817) 626-3636
Web Site: http://www.reynoldsonline.com
Electrical Apparatus & Equipment Distr
N.A.I.C.S.: 423610
Walt Reynolds *(Pres)*
Donald Reynolds Jr. *(COO)*
Douglas Deitz *(Pres & CEO)*

MCNEECE BROTHERS OIL CO. INC.
691 E Heil Ave, El Centro, CA 92243-4603
Tel.: (760) 352-4721 CA
Web Site:
http://www.mcneecebros.com
Year Founded: 1959
Sales Range: $10-24.9 Million
Emp.: 25
Distr of Shell Lubricants & Other Petroleum Products
N.A.I.C.S.: 424720

MCNEEL INTERNATIONAL CORPORATION
5401 W Kennedy Blvd Ste 751, Tampa, FL 33609-2447
Tel.: (813) 286-8680 FL
Year Founded: 1963
Sales Range: $50-74.9 Million
Emp.: 500
Holding Company; Polyethylene Bag Mfr & Whslr
N.A.I.C.S.: 551112
Clayton W. McNeel *(Pres)*
David Ramos *(CFO)*
Subsidiaries:

Chemplast International Corp. (1)
5401 W Kennedy Blvd Ste 751, Tampa, FL 33609
Tel.: (813) 286-3027
Web Site: http://www.chemplastintl.com
Sales Range: $10-24.9 Million
Emp.: 12
Masterbatch Mfr
N.A.I.C.S.: 326111
Charles Dawson *(Gen Mgr)*

MCNEELY, PIGOTT & FOX
611 Commerce St Ste 2800, Nashville, TN 37203
Tel.: (615) 259-4000
Web Site: http://www.mpf.com
Year Founded: 1987
Sales Range: $1-9.9 Million
Emp.: 65
Public Relations Agency
N.A.I.C.S.: 541820
Mark McNeely *(Sr Partner)*
David Fox *(Mng Partner)*
Katy Varney *(Partner)*
Keith Miles *(Partner)*
Jennifer Brantley *(Mng Partner)*
Alice Pearson Chapman *(Partner)*
Roger Shirley *(Dir-Editorial)*
Deborah Armour *(Dir-Info Svcs)*
Brooks Harper *(Dir-Art)*
Javier Solano *(VP)*
Chad Raphael *(CFO)*
Courtenay Rossi *(VP)*
Mary Ruth Raphael *(VP)*
Jennifer Hinkle *(Dir-Paid Media)*

MCNEIL & NRM INC.
96 E Crosier St, Akron, OH 44311-2392
Tel.: (330) 253-2525 OH
Web Site: http://www.mcneilnrm.com
Year Founded: 1904
Sales Range: $50-74.9 Million
Emp.: 100
Tire Cutting Presses & Equipment Mfr
N.A.I.C.S.: 333248
Robert Nelson *(CFO & VP-Fin)*
A.M. Melek *(Exec VP)*
John McCormick *(Exec VP-Sls)*
A. P. Singh *(Exec VP)*

MCNEIL COMPANY, INC.
4666 S 132nd St, Omaha, NE 68137
Tel.: (402) 333-1462 NE
Web Site:
http://www.mcneilcompany.com
Year Founded: 1979
Sales Range: $1-9.9 Million
Emp.: 28
New Single-Family Housing Construction (except Operative Builders)
N.A.I.C.S.: 236115
Joe Pogge *(Pres)*

MCNEIL, GRAY & RICE
1 Washington Mall, Boston, MA 02108-2603
Tel.: (617) 367-0100
Web Site: http://www.mgr1.com
Year Founded: 1989
Sales Range: $10-24.9 Million
Emp.: 35
Public Relations Agency
N.A.I.C.S.: 541820

McNeil, Gray & Rice—(Continued)

Susan Rice McNeil (Principal-Agency)
Bob McNeil (Mng Partner & Principal)

MCNEILUS STEEL INC.
702 2nd Ave S, Dodge Center, MN 55927
Tel.: (507) 374-6336 MN
Web Site: http://www.mcneilus.com
Year Founded: 1948
Sales Range: $200-249.9 Million
Emp.: 500
Distr of Metals & Steel
N.A.I.C.S.: 423510
Brandon Vermilyea (Mgr-Database)
Chad Gossard (Mgr-Sls)
Mark Packard (Mgr-Inventory)
Tim Johnston (Mgr-Quality)

MCNICHOLS COMPANY
2502 N Rocky Point Dr Ste 750, Tampa, FL 33607-1042
Tel.: (813) 282-3828 OH
Web Site: http://www.mcnichols.com
Year Founded: 1952
Perforated & Expanded Metals, Wire Mesh & Designer Metals Supplier
N.A.I.C.S.: 332313
Eugene H. McNichols (Chm & CEO)
Scott McNichols (Pres)

MCO TRANSPORT, INC.
3301 Hwy 421 N, Wilmington, NC 28401
Tel.: (910) 763-4531
Web Site: http://www.mcotransport.com
Year Founded: 1970
Sales Range: $10-24.9 Million
Emp.: 100
Provider of Trucking Services
N.A.I.C.S.: 484110
Danny McComas (Pres)
Jim Prince (VP-Fin)
Ryan Andresen (VP-Ops)

MCP INDUSTRIES INC.
708 S Temescal St Ste 101, Corona, CA 92878-1839
Tel.: (951) 736-1881 CA
Web Site: http://www.mcpind.com
Year Founded: 1950
Sales Range: $25-49.9 Million
Emp.: 350
Supplier of Rubber, Plastic & Clay Products
N.A.I.C.S.: 326299

MCPC INC.
9277 Centre Pointe Dr Ste 400, West Chester, OH 45069
Tel.: (513) 826-3247
Web Site: http://www.mcpc.com
Technology Products Mfr
N.A.I.C.S.: 513210
Michael Trebilcock (Founder & Chm)
Rob Young (CFO & Treas)
Charlene Barth (VP-Contracts, Compliance & Audit)
Jason Taylor (Pres-Asset Disposition)
Beth Stec (Dir-HR)
Andy Jones (CEO)
Dale Phillips (VP-Bus Ops)
Ira Grossman (CTO)
Peter Anagnostos (Sr VP-Sls Ops)
Teresa Hooper (VP-Ops & Applications)
Tom Reddy (Sr VP-Sls)
David Hildebrandt (Gen Counsel)
Robert Eckman (Chief Information Security Officer)
Ronnie Munn (Chief Information Security Officer)
Geoff Green (Co-CTO)

Subsidiaries:

Forquer Group, Inc. (1)
100 State St Ste 310, Erie, PA 16507
Tel.: (814) 453-3366
Emp.: 25
Computer & Software Whslr
N.A.I.C.S.: 423430
Russell J. Forquer (Pres)

MCQUADE & BANNIGAN, INC.
1300 Stark St, Utica, NY 13502
Tel.: (315) 724-7119 NY
Web Site: http://www.mqb.com
Year Founded: 1907
Rev.: $15,689,777
Emp.: 50
General Construction Machinery & Equipment
N.A.I.C.S.: 423810
Thomas F. Sebastian (Pres & CEO)

MCQUAID & COMPANY
464 Bayfront Pl, Naples, FL 34102
Tel.: (239) 300-4880
Web Site: http://www.mcquaidco.com
Sales Range: $10-24.9 Million
Emp.: 15
Real Estate Broker
N.A.I.C.S.: 531210
Tiffany McQuaid (Owner)

MCR DEVELOPMENT LLC
1 World Trade Ctr Fl 86, New York, NY 10007
Tel.: (212) 277-5602
Web Site: http://www.mcrhotels.com
Home Management Services
N.A.I.C.S.: 721110
Tyler Morse (CEO)

Subsidiaries:

Royalton, LLC (1)
44 W 44th St, New York, NY 10036
Tel.: (212) 869-4400
Web Site: http://www.royaltonhotel.com
Sales Range: $1-9.9 Million
Emp.: 125
Hotel Operator
N.A.I.C.S.: 721110
Ian Schrager (Pres)

MCREL INTERNATIONAL
4601 DTC Blvd Ste 500, Denver, CO 80237-2596
Tel.: (303) 337-0990 MO
Web Site: http://www.mcrel.org
Year Founded: 1966
Sales Range: $10-24.9 Million
Emp.: 139
Educational Support Services
N.A.I.C.S.: 611710
Bryan Goodwin (COO)

MCS GROUP INC.
1601 Market St Ste 800, Philadelphia, PA 19103
Tel.: (215) 246-0900
Web Site: http://www.themcsgroup.com
Year Founded: 1979
Sales Range: $10-24.9 Million
Emp.: 300
Legal & Tax Services
N.A.I.C.S.: 541199
David J. Bean Sr. (Co-Founder & COO)
Rosemary Gould Esposito (Co-Founder & CEO)
Loren LaQuintano (Exec VP-Mgmt Svcs)
Gerri Finnegan (Exec VP & Mgr-Northeast Reg)
Stephen Ehrlich (CIO & Exec VP-Tech Solutions)
Russell T. Pickus (CFO)
Matthew DeMarco (Exec VP-Bus Dev)
Frank Altamuro III (Pres)

MCS HEALTHCARE PUBLIC RELATIONS
1420 US Hwy 206 N Ste 100, Bedminster, NJ 07921-2652
Tel.: (908) 234-9900
Web Site: http://www.mcspr.com
Year Founded: 1985
Sales Range: $1-9.9 Million
Emp.: 30
Public Relations Agency
N.A.I.C.S.: 541820
Joe Boyd (CEO)
Karen Dombek (VP)
Eliot Harrison (Pres)
Laura De Zutter (VP)
Amanda Merced (Sr Acct Suprv)
Marianne Altadonna (Supvr-Acct)
Meredith Mandato (Supvr-Acct)
Chad Hyett (Exec VP)
Emily Dell (Sr Acct Suprv)

MCS OF TAMPA, INC.
8510 Sunstate St, Tampa, FL 33634
Tel.: (813) 872-0217
Web Site: http://www.missioncriticalsolutions.com
Year Founded: 1989
Technology Solutions & Telecommunications Products & Services
N.A.I.C.S.: 541512
Gilbert T. Gonzalez (Founder & Pres)
Brian Calka (CFO)
Scott Sikes (VP-Ops)
John Varney (VP-UC Ops)
Kevin J. Runia (Pres-Building & Electrical Tech Div)
James V. Slagle Jr. (COO)

MCSAM HOTEL GROUP LLC
13 Mayflower Pl, Floral Park, NY 11001
Tel.: (516) 773-9300
Year Founded: 2001
Rev.: $10,000,000
Emp.: 11
Fiscal Year-end: 12/31/06
Law Firm
N.A.I.C.S.: 541199

Subsidiaries:

Paradise Stream Resort (1)
6208 Paradise Vly Rd, Cresco, PA 18326
Tel.: (800) 987-2050
Web Site: https://www.covepoconoresorts.com
Honeymoon & Vacation Resort
N.A.I.C.S.: 721110

Subsidiary (Domestic):

Cove Haven Entertainment Resorts (2)
194 Lakeview Dr, Lakeville, PA 18438
Tel.: (866) 500-0488
Web Site: http://www.covepoconoresorts.com
Vacation Resort
N.A.I.C.S.: 721110

Pocono Palace, Inc. (2)
206 Fantasy Rd, East Stroudsburg, PA 18302 (100%)
Tel.: (866) 500-0488
Web Site: http://www.covepoconoresorts.com
Vacation Resort
N.A.I.C.S.: 721110

MCSHARES, INC.
1835 E N St, Salina, KS 67401
Tel.: (785) 825-2181 KS
Web Site: http://repcoworld.com
Year Founded: 1946

Flour Oxidation & Maturing Services; Vitamin & Mineral Concentrates Mfr & Distr
N.A.I.C.S.: 311211
Monte White (Pres & CEO)
Doris Chase (VP-Admin Affairs)
Tom Reed (VP-North American Sls-Flour Milling Div)
Dan Lee (CFO)
Lynn Elder (VP-Engrg)

Subsidiaries:

Research Products Company (1)
PO Box 1460, Salina, KS 67402-1460
Tel.: (785) 825-2181
Web Site: http://www.repcoworld.com
Processed Food Additive Products Mfr
N.A.I.C.S.: 311211
Monte White (Pres)

MCSTAIN ENTERPRISES
400 Centennial Pkwy Ste 200, Denver, CO 80027
Tel.: (303) 494-5900
Web Site: http://www.mcstain.com
Rev.: $13,200,000
Emp.: 35
New Construction, Single-Family Houses
N.A.I.C.S.: 236115
Thomas Hoyt (Founder & Principal)
Caroline Hoyt (Principal)

MCSWAIN CARPETS INC.
2430 E Kemper Rd, Cincinnati, OH 45241-1812
Tel.: (513) 771-1400 OH
Web Site: http://www.mcswaincarpets.com
Year Founded: 1968
Sales Range: $50-74.9 Million
Emp.: 155
Retailer of Carpeting & Flooring
N.A.I.C.S.: 449121
Kevin Carnes (VP)

MCSWEENEY RICCI INSURANCE AGENCY INC.
420 Washington St Ste 200, Braintree, MA 02184
Tel.: (781) 848-8600
Web Site: http://www.mcsweeneyricci.com
Sales Range: $10-24.9 Million
Emp.: 70
Insurance Agents
N.A.I.C.S.: 524210
Mary Lou Leary (Pres & CEO)
Susan M. Riggins (Dir-Ops)
MaryEllen Sullivan (Exec VP)
Timothy Hall (Exec VP)

MCT CREDIT UNION
2736 Nall St, Port Neches, TX 77651
Tel.: (409) 727-1446 TX
Web Site: http://www.mctcu.org
Year Founded: 1953
Sales Range: $10-24.9 Million
Emp.: 95
Credit Union Operator
N.A.I.C.S.: 522130
Thad Angelle (Pres & CEO)

MCT INDUSTRIES INCORPORATED
7451 Pan American Fwy NE, Albuquerque, NM 87109
Tel.: (505) 345-8651 NM
Web Site: http://www.mct-ind.com
Year Founded: 1972
Sales Range: $10-24.9 Million
Emp.: 200
Truck Trailer Designer & Mfr
N.A.I.C.S.: 336212
Ted R. Martinez (Pres)
Bennie Martinez (VP)

COMPANIES

MCT TRADING, INC
350 10th Ave Ste 850, San Diego, CA 92101
Tel.: (619) 543-5111
Web Site: http://www.mct-trading.com
Sales Range: $1-9.9 Million
Emp.: 25
Training & Secondary Marketing Services
N.A.I.C.S.: 522299
Curtis Richins *(Pres)*
Philip Rasori *(COO)*
Thomas P. Farmer *(Mng Dir)*
Bill Wooten *(Mng Dir)*
Bill Petersohn *(Mng Dir)*
Steve Pawlowski *(Mng Dir & HeadTech Solutions)*

MCV COMPANIES INC.
305 Enterprise St Ste 2, Escondido, CA 92029
Tel.: (760) 294-9858
Web Site: http://www.mcvcompanies.com
Sales Range: $1-9.9 Million
Commercial & Institutional Building Construction
N.A.I.C.S.: 236220
Virgil P. Enriquez *(Founder & Treas)*
Maricris Enriquez *(Founder & Pres)*

MCWANE, INC.
2900 Hwy 280 Ste 300, Birmingham, AL 35223
Tel.: (205) 414-3100   DE
Web Site: https://www.mcwane.com
Year Founded: 1921
Sales Range: Less than $1 Million
Emp.: 6,000
Iron Foundries
N.A.I.C.S.: 331511
Phillip McWane *(Chm)*
Charles F. Nowlin *(CFO & Sr VP)*
Michael C. Keel *(Sr VP-Compliance & Corp Affairs)*
Francesca Dunbar *(VP-Grp Mktg-Plumbing Grp)*
Kurt Winter *(Exec VP-Plumbing Grp)*
Jeff Otterstedt *(Sr VP-Pipe Div)*
Jitendra Radia *(Sr VP-Environmental, Safety & HR)*
Key Foster *(Sr VP)*
James M. Proctor II *(Gen Counsel & Sr VP)*

Subsidiaries:

AMI Investments, LLC   (1)
100 Decker Ct Ste 215, Irving, TX 75062
Tel.: (972) 717-5555
Web Site: http://www.nighthawkcontrol.com
Sales Range: $10-24.9 Million
Emp.: 16
Technical Management Services
N.A.I.C.S.: 541990

Atlantic States Cast Iron Pipe Company   (1)
183 Sitgreaves St, Phillipsburg, NJ 08865
Tel.: (908) 454-1161
Web Site: http://www.atlanticstates.com
Iron Pipe Mfr
N.A.I.C.S.: 331210
Danny L. Fittro *(Plant Mgr)*
Patrick Hennessy *(Dir-Environmental Engrg)*
Brendon LaPort *(Dir-Safety)*
Dale Schmelzle *(VP & Gen Mgr)*
Craig Spitzer *(Gen Mgr-Sls)*
Hal Eddings *(Dir-Technical)*

Canada Pipe Co. Ltd.   (1)
55 Frid St Unit 1, Hamilton, L8P 4M3, ON, Canada   (100%)
Tel.: (905) 547-3251
Web Site: https://www.canadapipe.com
Sales Range: $10-24.9 Million
Emp.: 20
Supplier of Ductile Pipe
N.A.I.C.S.: 423510

Subsidiary (Domestic):

Canada Pipe Co. Ltd.   (2)
400 Saint Martin Ouest Blvd Ste 200, Laval, H7M3Y8, QC, Canada   (100%)
Tel.: (450) 668-5600
Web Site: http://www.canadapipe.com
Emp.: 3
Supplier of Ductile Pipe
N.A.I.C.S.: 423510
Phillip McWane *(Owner)*

Canada Pipe Co. Ltd.   (2)
1200 W 73rd Ave Ste 1100, Vancouver, V6P 6G5, BC, Canada   (100%)
Tel.: (604) 737-1279
Web Site: http://www.canadapipe.com
Retail Supplier of Ductile Pipes
N.A.I.C.S.: 423510
John Braun *(Mgr-Sls)*

Clow Canada Inc.   (1)
55 Frid St Unit 1, PO Box 2849, Hamilton, L8P 4M3, ON, Canada
Tel.: (905) 548-9604
Web Site: http://www.clowcanada.com
Valve & Fire Hydrant Mfr
N.A.I.C.S.: 332911

Clow Valve Division   (1)
902 S 2nd St, Oskaloosa, IA 52577
Tel.: (641) 673-8611
Web Site: http://www.clowvalve.com
Sales Range: $25-49.9 Million
Emp.: 300
Mfr of Waterworks Valves & Fire Hydrants
N.A.I.C.S.: 332919
Leon McCullough *(VP & Gen Mgr)*
Mike Vore *(Gen Mgr-Sls)*
Mark Willett *(Gen Mgr)*

Clow Water Systems Co.   (1)
PO Box 6001, Coshocton, OH 43812-6001
Tel.: (740) 622-6651
Web Site: http://www.clowwatersystems.com
Sales Range: $50-74.9 Million
Emp.: 400
Mfr of Metallic Pipes
N.A.I.C.S.: 331511

ComTech Korea Co., Ltd.   (1)
Woolim-Biz center 1-907 Guro-Dong, Guro-Gu, Seoul, 152-769, Korea (South)
Tel.: (82) 2-2108 1920
Web Site: http://www.comtechkorea.com
Sales Range: $10-24.9 Million
Emp.: 25
Broadband Internet Service Provider
N.A.I.C.S.: 517112
Eric Oh *(CEO)*

Kennedy Valve   (1)
1021 E Water St, Elmira, NY 14901
Tel.: (607) 734-2211
Web Site: http://www.kennedyvalve.com
Sales Range: $50-74.9 Million
Emp.: 250
Mfr of Valves & Fire Hydrants
N.A.I.C.S.: 332911
Arne Feyling *(Asst Gen Mgr)*
Brad Bidlack *(Engr-Mfg)*
Daniel Burczynski *(Mgr-Engrg)*
Greg Clarke *(Mgr-Kennedy Valve Plant)*
Paul Gardner *(Mgr-HR)*
Matthew Hicks *(Mgr-Health & Safety)*
Leon G. McCullough *(Exec VP-Waterworks Fittings Grp)*
Jack McPike *(Asst Gen Mgr)*
Mike Vore *(Mgr-Sls & Mktg)*

M&H Valve Co.   (1)
605 W 23rd St, Anniston, AL 36201
Tel.: (256) 237-3521
Web Site: http://www.mh-valve.com
Valve & Hydrant Mfr
N.A.I.C.S.: 332911
Greg Davis *(Mgr-Sls-Natl)*
Sue Thornburg *(Mgr-Inside Sls)*
Danny Lewis *(Mgr-Environmental)*
Ray McClay *(Mgr-HR)*
Leon G. McCullough *(Exec VP)*
Tony Orlowski *(Gen Mgr)*
Terry Sledge *(Controller)*

Manchester Tank & Equipment Company   (1)
1000 Corporate Center Dr Ste 300, Franklin, TN 37067
Tel.: (615) 370-3833
Web Site: http://www.mantank.com
Sales Range: $10-24.9 Million
Emp.: 25
ASME Tank, DOT Cylinder, Propane Fuel Cylinders & Air Receivers Mfr
N.A.I.C.S.: 332313
Robert M. Graumann *(Pres)*
Tom Schilson *(VP-Ops-North America)*
Brendan Dillmann *(Sr VP-Sls & Mktg)*
Alessandro Bottino *(Mng Dir-Latin America)*

Subsidiary (Non-US):

Manchester Tank & Equipment   (2)
21 McMillan Rd, Echuca, 3564, VIC, Australia
Tel.: (61) 3 5482 0500
Web Site: http://www.mantank.com
Metal Tank Mfr
N.A.I.C.S.: 332420
Ken Woods *(Gen Mgr)*

Plant (Non-US):

Manchester Tank & Equipment Company - Chile Plant   (2)
Way Melipilla 11000, Maipu, Santiago, Chile
Tel.: (56) 2 351 0272
Emp.: 5
Pressure Vessel Mfr
N.A.I.C.S.: 332420
Alexandra Bottino *(Gen Mgr)*

McWane Services Private Ltd   (1)
17 New No18 Dhamotharaswamy Naidu Nagar Sowripalayam, Coimbatore, Tamil Nadu, India
Tel.: (91) 9865003979
Industrial Valve Mfr
N.A.I.C.S.: 332911

McWane, Inc. - AB&I Foundry Division   (1)
7825 San Leandro St, Oakland, CA 94621
Tel.: (510) 632-3467
Web Site: http://www.abifoundry.com
Iron Product Mfr
N.A.I.C.S.: 331511
Michael Lowe *(Gen Mgr)*

McWane, Inc. - American R/D Division   (1)
1800 Greenbrier Dear Rd, Anniston, AL 36207
Tel.: (256) 831-2236
Web Site: http://www.american-rd.com
Valve Mfr
N.A.I.C.S.: 332911

McWane, Inc. - Anaco Division   (1)
1001 El Camino Real, Corona, CA 92879
Tel.: (951) 372-2732
Web Site: http://www.anaco-husky.com
Sales Range: $25-49.9 Million
Emp.: 134
Gasket & Coupling Mfr
N.A.I.C.S.: 333613
Jack Dunaway *(Mgr-Technical Sls)*
Angelina Halverson *(Mgr-Inside Sls)*
Jonathan Kenney *(Mgr-Natl Sls)*

McWane, Inc. - McWane Poles Division   (1)
1143 Vanderbilt Rd, Birmingham, AL 35234
Tel.: (205) 323-2400
Web Site: http://www.mcwanepoles.com
Iron Pipe Mfr
N.A.I.C.S.: 331210

McWane, Inc. - Tyler Pipe & Coupling Division   (1)
11910 County Rd 492, Tyler, TX 75706
Tel.: (800) 527-8478
Web Site: http://www.tylerpipe.com
Emp.: 200
Iron Pipe Mfr
N.A.I.C.S.: 331210
Victor Hatcher *(Mgr)*
Sterlink Bowman *(Mgr-Natl Sls)*
Jay Helms *(Mgr-Sls-South Central Reg)*

McWane, Inc. - Tyler Union Company Division   (1)
11910 CR 492, Tyler, TX 75706
Tel.: (800) 527-8478
Web Site: http://www.tylerunion.com
Iron Product Mfr
N.A.I.C.S.: 331511
Malcolm Morriss *(Mgr-Quality)*
Jerry Jansen *(Mgr-Natl Sls)*
Sundra Welch *(Mgr-Inside Sls-Natl)*
Steve Johnson *(Gen Mgr)*

Leon G. McCullough *(Exec VP)*
Jon Pollard *(Mgr-Plant)*
Richard Tatman *(VP & Gen Mgr)*

Pacific States Cast Iron Pipe Company   (1)
1401 E 2000 S, Provo, UT 84603
Tel.: (801) 373-6910
Web Site: http://www.pscipco.com
Iron Product Mfr
N.A.I.C.S.: 331110
Jeff Otterstedt *(Sr VP-Pipe Division)*
Kent Brown *(VP & Gen Mgr)*
Joseph Hall *(Controller)*
Scott Jarvis *(Plant Mgr)*

Synapse Wireless Inc.   (1)
6723 Odyssey Dr NW, Huntsville, AL 35806
Tel.: (256) 852-7888
Web Site: http://www.synapse-wireless.com
Emp.: 70
Wireless Control & Monitoring Services
N.A.I.C.S.: 517112
Brent Dix *(VP-Engrg)*
Jim Doyle *(VP-Sls)*
John White *(Dir-Bus Dev & Strategic Acct)*
Key Foster *(Vice Chm)*

Tyler (Xianxian) Foundry Co., Ltd.   (1)
Guozhuang Bei Xian, Cangzhou, Hebei, China
Tel.: (86) 317 4419828
Ductile Iron Fitting Mfr
N.A.I.C.S.: 331511

MCWHORTER CAPITAL PARTNERS, LLC
162 W Main St Ste 303, Cartersville, GA 30120
Tel.: (770) 386-0022   GA
Web Site: http://www.mcwhortercp.com
Year Founded: 1990
Privater Equity Firm
N.A.I.C.S.: 523999
Harvey McWhorter *(Pres)*
Bob Hamilton *(CFO)*
Josh McWhorter *(Founder & CEO)*
Deanna Berry *(COO)*
Kathryn Gazaway *(Chief Sls Officer & Chief Bus Dev Officer)*

Subsidiaries:

Pennant Construction Management, Inc.   (1)
102 N Bartow St, Cartersville, GA 30120-3106
Tel.: (770) 382-7200
Web Site: http://www.pennantom.com
Real Estate Services
N.A.I.C.S.: 531210
Ron Goss *(Mgr)*

MCWILLIAMS ELECTRIC CO. INC.
1401 Rodenburg Rd, Schaumburg, IL 60193
Tel.: (847) 301-2600
Web Site: http://www.mcwilliamselectric.com
Sales Range: $10-24.9 Million
Emp.: 155
Electrical Work
N.A.I.C.S.: 238210
James J. McGlynn *(Pres & CEO)*
Maureen Lucenti *(CFO)*
Scott Swayze *(VP)*
Norm Spiegel *(Project Mgr)*
Sam Santiemmo *(Sr VP)*
Joe Ramello *(Project Mgr)*
Bill Siemek *(Mgr-Pur)*
Frank Laesure *(Project Mgr)*
Fred Mahler *(Project Mgr)*
James Raymond *(Project Mgr)*
Paul Karwoski *(Superintendent-Electrical)*

MCWILLIAMS FORGE CO.
387 Franklin Ave, Rockaway, NJ 07866

MCWILLIAMS FORGE CO.

McWilliams Forge Co.—(Continued)
Tel.: (973) 627-0200 NJ
Web Site:
http://www.mcwilliamsforge.com
Year Founded: 1880
Sales Range: $25-49.9 Million
Emp.: 100
Provider of Open & Closed Die Forgings for Aircraft
N.A.I.C.S.: 332111
Steven Strauss (CFO)
Peter V. McWilliams (VP & Gen Mgr)
Scott G. McWilliams (VP-Mktg)
Jamie Chesman (Sls Mgr)
Joseph Pascoe (Mgr-Quality)

MD CARLISLE CONSTRUCTION CORP
5847 Francis Lewis Blvd, Oakland Gardens, NY 11364
Tel.: (718) 631-0606
Web Site: http://www.emporis.com
Rev.: $100,000,000
Emp.: 20
Apartment Building Construction
N.A.I.C.S.: 236117
Richard Lewis (VP)

MD ENTERPRISES INC.
1720 E Locust St, Ontario, CA 91761
Tel.: (909) 947-2276
Sales Range: $10-24.9 Million
Emp.: 15
Buildings Mfr
N.A.I.C.S.: 332311
Bruce Thomas (Pres)

MD ESTHETICS, LLC
29 Indian Rock Rd Fl 2, Windham, NH 03087
Tel.: (833) 407-7865
Web Site:
https://www.mdestheticsus.com
Emp.: 100
Massage Wellness Spa & Other Skin Care Services
N.A.I.C.S.: 812199

Subsidiaries:

Skin, A Medical Spa (1)
332 Granby St, Norfolk, VA 23451
Tel.: (757) 228-5100
Web Site: http://www.skinamedicalspa.com
Outpatient Care Centers
N.A.I.C.S.: 621498
Annabelle Walsh (Office Mgr)

MD ON-LINE INC.
4 Campus Dr, Parsippany, NJ 07054
Tel.: (888) 499-5465
Web Site: http://www.mdon-line.com
Electronic Data Interchange Solutions
N.A.I.C.S.: 513210
Bill Bartzak (CEO)
Jeff Meehan (Chief Comml Officer)
Eleftheriades George (COO & CTO)
Paul Dobrowsky (CFO)
Ashish Vachhani (Exec VP)

Subsidiaries:

Healthware Solutions, LLC (1)
23 Eugene Dr, Mountville, NJ 07045
Tel.: (973) 316-0180
Web Site:
http://www.healthwaresolutions.net
Sales Range: $10-24.9 Million
Emp.: 5
Custom Computer Programming Services
N.A.I.C.S.: 541511
P. Berkley (Mgr)

Strategic Edge Communciations, Inc. (1)
6 Century Dr Ste 2, Parsippany, NJ 07960
Tel.: (973) 292-2503
Web Site: http://www.strategicedge.com
Sales Range: $10-24.9 Million
Emp.: 25
Marketing Consulting Services
N.A.I.C.S.: 541613

MD ORTHOPAEDICS, INC.
604 N Pkwy St, Wayland, IA 52654
Tel.: (319) 256-5656
Web Site:
http://www.mdorthopaedics.com
Sales Range: $1-9.9 Million
Emp.: 26
Environmental Consulting Services
N.A.I.C.S.: 541620
John Mitchell (Founder)

MD&E CLARITY
3201 Peachtree Corners Cir, Norcross, GA 30092
Tel.: (678) 291-9690
Web Site: http://www.mdeclarity.com
Year Founded: 1992
Sales Range: $10-24.9 Million
Emp.: 93
Human Resource Consulting Services
N.A.I.C.S.: 541612
Eleanor Morgan (Co-Founder, Pres & CEO)
Reno Borgognoni (CFO)

MD-DE-DC AD PLACEMENT SERVICE
2191 Defense Hwy Ste 300, Crofton, MD 21114-2487
Tel.: (410) 721-5115 MD
Web Site: http://www.mddcpress.com
Year Founded: 1996
Sales Range: $10-24.9 Million
Emp.: 8
Media Buying Services
N.A.I.C.S.: 541830
Gay Fraustro (Coord-Print Media)
Jack Murphy (Exec Dir)
Jen Thornberry (Coord-Member Svcs)
Stephanie Wilder (Mgr-Commun)
Stacey Riley (Coord-HR)

MDC VACUUM PRODUCTS, LLC
23842 Cabot Blvd, Hayward, CA 94545-1661
Tel.: (510) 265-3500 CA
Web Site:
http://www.mdcvacuum.com
Year Founded: 1976
Sales Range: $10-24.9 Million
Emp.: 220
Provider of Industrial Valves
N.A.I.C.S.: 332911
Tom Bogdan (Dir-Tech Sls)
Arthur Carlson (VP)
Robles Johnny (Supvr-Production)

MDG CONNECTED SOLUTIONS, INC.
220 Exchange Dr Ste A, Crystal Lake, IL 60014
Web Site: http://www.mdgcs.com
Year Founded: 1988
Sales Range: $10-24.9 Million
Emp.: 25
Telecommunication Servicesb
N.A.I.C.S.: 517810
Michael Ginsberg (Founder & CEO)
Maureen Wachter (Partner & Mgr-E-Commerce)
Kevin Pfeifer (Mgr-Sls & Support)
Melanie Niemann (Office Mgr)
Matt Bauman (Mgr-Bus Dev)

MDI ACCESS
12300 South Keeler Ave, Alsip, IL 60803
Tel.: (708) 597-0111
Web Site: http://www.mdielectric.com
Year Founded: 2002
Sales Range: $1-9.9 Million
Emp.: 30
Voice & Data System Infrastructure Design & Installation Services
N.A.I.C.S.: 517810
Robert Heiderscheidt (Pres)
Mark Untiedt (Project Mgr)
John M. Rea (VP & Partner)

MDI WORLDWIDE
38271 W 12 Mile Rd, Farmington Hills, MI 48331-3041
Tel.: (248) 553-1900 MI
Web Site:
http://www.mdiworldwide.com
Year Founded: 1965
Emp.: 200
Point of Purchase Displays, Lightboxes, Poster Frames, Floorstands, Menu Boards, Curb Displays & Traffic Control Products Design & Mfr
N.A.I.C.S.: 339950

Subsidiaries:

MDI France SA (1)
11 rue de Villeneuve Icade Park, PO Box 90130, 94523, Rungis, Cedex, France
Tel.: (33) 1 55 53 16 30
Web Site: http://www.mdiworldwide.com
Emp.: 4
Digital Sign Board Mfr
N.A.I.C.S.: 339950
Michel Granger (Mng Dir)

MDI Worldwide UK Ltd (1)
Mill Studio Crane Mead, Ware, SG12 9PY, Hertfordshire, United Kingdom
Tel.: (44) 1920 444351
Web Site: http://www.mdiworldwide.co.uk
Sign Distr
N.A.I.C.S.: 423990
Rob Clarke (Gen Mgr)

MDJ INCORPORATED
595 Orange Show Rd, San Bernardino, CA 92408
Tel.: (909) 381-1771
Sales Range: $25-49.9 Million
Emp.: 75
Lumber, Plywood & Millwork
N.A.I.C.S.: 423310
Milton Johnson (Dir-HR)

MDM COMMERCIAL ENTERPRISES, INC.
1102 A1A N Ste 205, Ponte Vedra Beach, FL 32082
Tel.: (904) 241-2340 FL
Web Site:
http://www.mdmcommercial.com
Year Founded: 1990
Sales Range: $10-24.9 Million
Emp.: 9
Television Sets
N.A.I.C.S.: 423620
Steve Austin (Owner & CEO)
Dave Lingor (Exec VP)
Jeff Miller (VP)
David Stroly (Reg VP)
John O'Reilly (Reg VP)
Lee Whittaker (Pres)
Susan Slappey (CFO)
Rob Weber (Dir-Mktg)
Chase Natoli (Project Mgr)
Themis Koumoutseas (VP-Bus Dev)
Heather Townsend (VP-Patient Engagement)

MDM SUPPLY INCORPORATED
2609 Bozeman Ave, Helena, MT 59604
Tel.: (406) 443-4012
Web Site:
http://www.mdmsupply.com
Sales Range: $10-24.9 Million
Emp.: 60
Plumbing Fittings & Supplies
N.A.I.C.S.: 423720

Craig Skinn (VP)

MDS MEDICAL SOFTWARE
19820 N 7th St Ste 100, Phoenix, AZ 85024
Tel.: (602) 493-3570
Web Site:
http://www.mdsmedicalsoftware.com
Year Founded: 2002
Rev.: $2,700,000
Emp.: 12
Medical & Hospital Equipment Whslr
N.A.I.C.S.: 423450
William J. Schoeder (Pres)

MDSCRIPTS, INC.
4735 Walnut St, Boulder, CO 80301
Web Site: http://www.mdscripts.com
Year Founded: 2009
Sales Range: $1-9.9 Million
Emp.: 13
Pharmaceutical Billing Services
N.A.I.C.S.: 541219
Gary Mounce (Pres)

ME SALVE ISABELA INC.
Rd No 5 KM 4 0 Catano, Toa Baja, PR 00962
Tel.: (787) 622-9400
Web Site: http://www.salve.com
Rev.: $42,003,902
Emp.: 3
Provider of Children's Wear
N.A.I.C.S.: 458110
Sender Shub (Pres)

ME TOO MARK TUCKER INC.
1370 Avenue Of The Americas, New York, NY 10019
Tel.: (212) 246-3939
Web Site:
http://www.metooshoes.com
Rev.: $12,600,000
Emp.: 20
Shoe Retailer
N.A.I.C.S.: 424340
Mark Tucker (CEO)
Adam Tucker (Pres)

MEAD & HUNT, INC.
6501 Watts Rd, Madison, WI 53719
Tel.: (608) 273-6380
Web Site: http://www.meadhunt.com
Sales Range: $50-74.9 Million
Emp.: 482
Architectural Services
N.A.I.C.S.: 541310
Andrew Platz (Pres)
Rajan I. Sheth (Chm & CEO)

MEAD CLARK LUMBER COMPANY INCORPORATED
2667 Dowd Dr, Santa Rosa, CA 95407
Tel.: (707) 576-3333
Web Site: http://www.meadclark.com
Sales Range: $25-49.9 Million
Lumber & Other Building Materials
N.A.I.C.S.: 423310
John Sousa (Controller)
Glenn Suyeyasu (Mgr-Engrg Wood Products)

MEADE COUNTY RURAL ELECTRIC COOP
1351 Hwy 79, Brandenburg, KY 40108
Tel.: (270) 422-2162
Web Site: http://www.mcrecc.com
Sales Range: $10-24.9 Million
Emp.: 59
Electronic Services
N.A.I.C.S.: 221118
Anna Swanson (VP-Acctg & Fin)
David Poe (VP-Ops)
David Pace (VP-Member Svc & Mktg)

COMPANIES

Erica Whelan (Mgr-Membership Accts)
Marty Littrel (Pres & CEO)

MEADE GROUP INC.
45001 N Pke Blvd, Utica, MI 48315
Tel.: (586) 726-7900
Web Site:
http://www.meadelexus.com
Sales Range: $200-249.9 Million
Emp.: 53
Automobiles, New & Used
N.A.I.C.S.: 441110
Kenneth G. Meade (Chm)

Subsidiaries:

Meade Lexus of Lakeside (1)
45001 Northpointe Blvd, Utica, MI 48315-5852
Tel.: (586) 726-7900
Web Site: http://www.lexusoflakeside.com
Sales Range: $25-49.9 Million
Retailer of New & Used Automobile
N.A.I.C.S.: 441110
Kenneth Meade (Pres)
Keith Baer (Bus Mgr)

MEADE TRACTOR
840 State St Ste 200, Bristol, TN 37620
Tel.: (276) 628-5126
Web Site:
http://www.meadetractor.com
Sales Range: $25-49.9 Million
Agriculture & Lawn Equipment Dealer
N.A.I.C.S.: 423820
Charles D. Meade III (Pres)

Subsidiaries:

Meade Tractor - Louisville (1)
13090 Aiken Rd, Louisville, KY 40223
Tel.: (502) 253-3721
General Construction Machinery & Equipment Dealership
N.A.I.C.S.: 423810
Kent Able (Reg Mgr)
Don Miller (Mgr-Svc)
Randy Rhodes (Mgr-Sls)

MEADEN SCREW PRODUCTS COMPANY
16 West 210 83rd St, Hinsdale, IL 60527
Tel.: (630) 655-0888
Web Site: http://www.meaden.com
Rev.: $11,500,000
Emp.: 85
Screw Machine Products
N.A.I.C.S.: 332721
Thomas Meaden (Pres)
Craig Busch (Mgr-Engrg)

MEADOR CHRYSLER JEEP
2351 S East Loop 820, Fort Worth, TX 76119
Tel.: (817) 535-0535
Web Site:
http://www.meadorauto.com
Sales Range: $10-24.9 Million
Emp.: 86
Car Whslr
N.A.I.C.S.: 441110
Kyle Hunter (Principal)

MEADOR STAFFING SERVICES INC.
722 Fairmont Pkwy Ste A, Pasadena, TX 77504-2804
Tel.: (713) 941-0616
Web Site: http://www.meador.com
Year Founded: 1968
Sales Range: $10-24.9 Million
Emp.: 180
Provider of Help Supply Services
N.A.I.C.S.: 561320
Ben Meador (Vice Chm)
Janice Meador (VP)
Brian Critelli (VP)

Linda Fields (VP)
Tamara Stucky (Branch Mgr)
Valerie Smith (Branch Mgr)
Darla Haygood (Dir-Community Rels & Volunteer Svcs)
Kathy Cowart (Mgr-Risk)
Melinda Torrison (Pres & COO)
Morgan Sheen (VP-Brand Mgmt)
Pam Bratton (VP-Contract Admin)
Ruby Lovelace (Controller)
Ryan Meador (Dir-Wellness)

Subsidiaries:

Temporary Systems Inc. (1)
722 Fairmont Pkwy Ste A, Pasadena, TX 77504-2804 **(100%)**
Tel.: (713) 941-0616
Sales Range: $10-24.9 Million
Emp.: 50
Staffing Services
N.A.I.C.S.: 561320
Linda Field (VP)

MEADOW RIVER HARDWOOD, LLC.
Snake Island Rd, Rainelle, WV 25962
Tel.: (304) 438-8060
Sales Range: $10-24.9 Million
Emp.: 25
Wood Products Mfr
N.A.I.C.S.: 321999
Leonard Waid (Plant Mgr)

MEADOWCRAFT, INC.
PO Box 1357, Birmingham, AL 35201-1357
Tel.: (205) 853-2220   DE
Web Site:
http://www.meadowcraft.com
Year Founded: 1946
Sales Range: $1-4.9 Billion
Emp.: 2,500
Wrought-Iron Outdoor Furniture & Accessories
N.A.I.C.S.: 337126
Larry York (VP-HR)
Pat Soileau (Mgr-HR)
Todd Wingrove (VP-Sls)
Wendell Richardson (Engr-Indus)

MEADOWKIRK RETREAT DELTA FARM
38012 Delta Farm Ln, Middleburg, VA 20117
Tel.: (540) 687-5565   VA
Web Site: http://www.meadowkirk.org
Year Founded: 2008
Sales Range: $1-9.9 Million
Emp.: 24
Recreational Facility Provider
N.A.I.C.S.: 721214
Rachel Mercer (Treas)
Andy Haith (Sec)

MEADOWLAND FARMERS CO-OP INC.
101 1st Ave E, Lamberton, MN 56152-1169
Tel.: (507) 752-7352   DE
Year Founded: 1905
Sales Range: $10-24.9 Million
Emp.: 92
Grain & Field Beans
N.A.I.C.S.: 424510
Jack Reiner (Chm)
John Valentine (Gen Mgr)

MEADOWLANDS NISSAN
45 Rte 17 S, Hasbrouck Heights, NJ 07604
Tel.: (201) 796-5050
Web Site:
http://www.meadowlandsnissan.com
Sales Range: $25-49.9 Million
Emp.: 37

Automobiles New & Used Service & Parts
N.A.I.C.S.: 441110
Parminder Singh (Dir-Fin)
Xavier Salazar (Mgr-Sls & Bus)
Bernardo Wohlermann (Pres)

MEADOWS FARMS INC.
43054 John Mosby Hwy, Chantilly, VA 20152
Tel.: (703) 327-3940
Web Site:
http://www.meadowsfarms.com
Sales Range: $10-24.9 Million
Emp.: 25
Retail Nurseries & Garden Stores
N.A.I.C.S.: 444240
William J. Meadows (Owner & CEO)
Jay Meadows (Pres)
Karen Shores (VP-Fin)

MEADOWS HOMES INC
124 S Dixie Ave, Cookeville, TN 38501
Tel.: (931) 528-2800
Web Site:
http://www.meadowshomes.com
Sales Range: $25-49.9 Million
Emp.: 30
Mobile Home Dealers
N.A.I.C.S.: 459930
Donny Meadows (Pres)

MEADOWS OFFICE FURNITURE COMPANY INC.
71 W 23rd St, New York, NY 10010-4102
Tel.: (212) 741-0333
Web Site:
http://www.meadowsoffice.com
Year Founded: 1989
Sales Range: $10-24.9 Million
Emp.: 53
Provider of Office Furniture
N.A.I.C.S.: 423210
Mary Connelly (Acct Mgr)
David Eppinger (Acct Mgr-Global)
Dina Radoncic (Gen Mgr)
Rick Lynch (Global Acct Mgr-New Bus)
Leonardo Betancourt (Mgr-Design)
Sabrina G. Cervantes (Project Coord)
Mike O'Brien (Sr Acct Exec)

MEADOWS URQUHART ACREE & COOK, LLP
1802 Bayberry Ct Ste 102, Richmond, VA 23226
Tel.: (804) 249-5786
Web Site: http://www.muacllp.com
Year Founded: 2004
Sales Range: $1-9.9 Million
Emp.: 18
Tax & Auditing Services
N.A.I.C.S.: 541213
Kelli Meadows (Partner)
Doug Urquhart (Partner)
David Acree (Partner)
Shannon Cook (Partner)
Karl A. Headley (Dir-Audit)

MEADVILLE MEDICAL CENTER
1034 Grove St, Meadville, PA 16335
Tel.: (814) 333-5000   PA
Web Site: http://www.mmchs.org
Year Founded: 1986
Sales Range: $150-199.9 Million
Emp.: 1,358
Health Care Srvices
N.A.I.C.S.: 622110
Philip Pandolph (CEO)
Valerie B. Waid (VP-Clinical Ops)
Michael C. Downing (CEO-Community Health Svcs)

MEARTHANE PRODUCTS CORPORATION

Denise Johnson (Chief Medical Officer)
Lee Clinton (VP-Sys Integration)
Greg Maras (VP-HR)
Rosalind Staskiewicz (Pres)

MEAL MART INCORPORATED
56-20 59th St, Maspeth, NY 11378
Tel.: (718) 894-2000
Web Site: http://www.mealmart.com
Rev.: $13,200,000
Emp.: 25
Meats, Cured Or Smoked
N.A.I.C.S.: 424470
Mendel Weinstock (Pres)

MEAL TICKET
1020 W Main St Ste 270, Boise, ID 83702
Tel.: (208) 352-6240
Web Site: http://www.mealticket.com
Year Founded: 2011
Technology Solutions & Software (for Food Service Businesses)
N.A.I.C.S.: 541511
Wink Jones (CEO)

Subsidiaries:

Distributor Resource Management, Inc. (1)
627 Cape Coral Pkwy W #202, Cape Coral, FL 33914
Tel.: (239) 540-9200
Web Site: http://www.trackmax.com
Direct Selling Establishments
N.A.I.C.S.: 541614
Tom Rawson (Co-Founder)
Tim Rawson (Co-Founder)

MEALSUITE, INC.
3330 Keller Springs Ste 205, Carrollton, TX 75006
Tel.: (972) 238-7200   NV
Web Site: http://www.surequest.com
Year Founded: 1984
Sales Range: $1-9.9 Million
Emp.: 20
Dietary & Food Service Management Software, Menu Services & Dietary Consulting
N.A.I.C.S.: 541511
Alma Sudderth (VP-Product Design & Solutions Architect)
Holly Wainscott (Mgr-Implementation & Trng)
Melinda Safir (Mgr-Data Svcs)
Sean Rowe (Pres & CEO)
Victoria Thrash (Mgr-Technical Support)

MEANS NURSERY INC.
33668 Johnson's Landing Rd, Scappoose, OR 97056
Tel.: (503) 543-7405
Web Site:
http://www.meansnursery.com
Sales Range: $10-24.9 Million
Emp.: 75
Nursery Stock
N.A.I.C.S.: 424930
Steven Greisen (Engr-Logistics)

MEARS MOTOR LIVERY CORPORATION
3905 El Rey Rd, Orlando, FL 32808
Tel.: (407) 298-2982
Web Site:
http://www.mearsleasing.com
Sales Range: $25-49.9 Million
Emp.: 25
Truck Leasing
N.A.I.C.S.: 532120
James C. Hartman (Pres)

MEARTHANE PRODUCTS CORPORATION

MEARTHANE PRODUCTS CORPORATION — U.S. PRIVATE

Mearthane Products Corporation—(Continued)
16 Western Industrial Dr, Cranston, RI 02921
Tel.: (401) 946-4400
Web Site: http://www.mearthane.com
Rev.: $5,000,000
Emp.: 54
All Other Plastics Product Mfr
N.A.I.C.S.: 326199
Carol Teixeira (Controller)
Kevin C. Redmond (Pres)
Pete Kaczmarek (CEO)

Subsidiaries:

Whitfield Plastics Corporation (1)
2300 WW Thorne Dr, Houston, TX 77073-3316
Tel.: (281) 214-8514
Web Site: http://www.whitfieldplastics.com
Sales Range: $1-9.9 Million
Emp.: 20
Polyurethane Molding Mfr
N.A.I.C.S.: 333511
Bill Whitefield (Pres)
Robert Navarrete (Gen Mgr)

MEASURABL, INC.
707 Broadway Suite 1000, San Diego, CA 92101
Tel.: (619) 719-1716
Web Site: https://www.measurabl.com
Year Founded: 2013
Emp.: 200
Software Devolpement
N.A.I.C.S.: 513210
Matt Ellis (Founder & CEO)

Subsidiaries:

WegoWise, Inc. (1)
50 Castilian Drive, Santa Barbara, CA 93117
Tel.: (617) 367-9346
Web Site: http://www.wegowise.com
Software & Technology Development Services
N.A.I.C.S.: 513210
Barun Singh (Founder & CTO)
Dan Teague (Chief Strategy Officer)
Sarah Allen (Client Services)
Kristina DiSanto (Client Services)

MEASURED PROGRESS INC.
100 Education Way, Dover, NH 03820
Tel.: (603) 749-9102
Web Site: http://www.measuredprogress.org
Rev.: $32,031,562
Emp.: 400
Educational Research
N.A.I.C.S.: 541720
Martin Borg (Chief Solutions Officer)
Mark Elgart (Sec)
Shelly Craig (CFO)
Audra Ahumada (Dir-Alternate Assessment)
Richard Swartz (Sr VP-Strategy, Products & Portfolio)
Candace McCloy (VP-HR)
Dan Caton (Chm)
Eugene White (Vice Chm)
Albert Mayo (CTO)
Annette Bohling (Chief Accreditation Officer)
Heather Kinsey (COO)
Justine Hargreaves (CMO)
Kenneth Bergman (Chief Legal Officer)
Rosario Rodriguez (CFO)
Stephen Murphy (Chief Assessment Officer)

Subsidiaries:

New Horizons In Child Development (1)
171 Watson Rd, Dover, NH 03820
Tel.: (603) 749-1094
Rev.: $84,000
Emp.: 6
Child Day Care Services
N.A.I.C.S.: 624410

MEASUREMENT ANALYSIS CORP.
23850 Madison St, Torrance, CA 90505
Tel.: (310) 378-5261
Web Site: http://www.macorp.net
Sales Range: $10-24.9 Million
Emp.: 50
Commercial Physical Research
N.A.I.C.S.: 541715
Michael D. Lamers (Pres)
Joseph Wainauskas (CFO)
Robert Coppolino (CTO)

MEASUREMENT INNOVATIONS CORP.
34 Dutch Mill Rd, Ithaca, NY 14850   DE
Tel.: (607) 257-5300
Emp.: 100
Biomedical Measurement Instrumentation Products Mfr
N.A.I.C.S.: 334519
Cornelis Drost (Pres & CEO)

Subsidiaries:

Transonic Systems Inc. (1)
34 Dutch Mill Rd, Ithaca, NY 14850
Tel.: (607) 257-5300
Web Site: http://www.transonic.com
Measuring & Controlling Devices
N.A.I.C.S.: 334519
Cornelis J. Drost (Founder & Engr-R&D)

Subsidiary (Non-US):

Transonic Asia Inc. (2)
6 F-3 No 5 Hangsiang Road, Dayuan, 33747, Taoyuan, Taiwan
Tel.: (886) 3 399 5806
Measuring & Controlling Device Mfr
N.A.I.C.S.: 334519
Papricia Chen (Mng Dir)

Transonic Europe B.V. (2)
Business Park Stein 205, 6181 MB, Elsloo, Netherlands
Tel.: (31) 43 407 7200
Measuring & Controlling Device Mfr
N.A.I.C.S.: 334519

Transonic Japan Inc. (2)
Maruha Building 11-1 Matsuba-cho, Tokorozawa, 359-0044, Saitama, Japan
Tel.: (81) 4 2946 8541
Web Site: http://www.transonic.com
Emp.: 84
Measuring & Controlling Device Mfr
N.A.I.C.S.: 334519
Susumu Kobayashi (Pres)

Transonic Scisense Inc (2)
3397 White Oak Rd Unit 3, London, N6E 3A1, ON, Canada
Tel.: (519) 680-7677
Web Site: http://www.scisense.com
Emp.: 12
Micro Sensing Device Mfr
N.A.I.C.S.: 339112
Mandy Conlon (Mng Dir)

MEATHEAD MOVERS
3600 S Higuera, San Luis Obispo, CA 93401
Tel.: (805) 544-6328
Web Site: http://www.meatheadmovers.com
Year Founded: 1997
Sales Range: $1-9.9 Million
Emp.: 148
Professional Moving Services
N.A.I.C.S.: 484210
Evan Steed (VP)
Angela Allen (Gen Mgr)
Jeremy Scriven (Mgr-Quality Assurance)
Aaron Steed (Pres & CEO)
Erin Steed (Controller)

MEATHEADS
305 N Veterans Pkwy Ste 107, Bloomington, IL 61704
Tel.: (309) 661-8866
Web Site: http://www.meatheadsburgers.com
Year Founded: 2007
Sales Range: $10-24.9 Million
Emp.: 210
Restaurant Offering Made-to-Order Burgers
N.A.I.C.S.: 722511
Nancy Geden (Mgr-HR & Trng)
Brian Landstrom (CFO & Partner)

MECA INC.
401 N Carroll St, Madison, WI 53703
Tel.: (608) 257-0681   WI
Web Site: http://www.mullinsgroup.com
Sales Range: $10-24.9 Million
Emp.: 120
Whslr of Household Furniture
N.A.I.C.S.: 423210
Carol M. Mullins (Treas & Sec)
Bradley C. Mullins (VP)

MECA SPORTSWEAR INC.
1120 Townline Rd, Tomah, WI 54660
Tel.: (608) 374-6450
Web Site: http://www.mecasportswear.com
Year Founded: 1969
Rev.: $14,000,000
Emp.: 175
Mfr of Athletic Apparel & Accessories
N.A.I.C.S.: 458110
Thomas A. Bramwell (Pres)
Richard Schuster (CFO & VP)

MECCON, INC.
529 Grant St Ste 100, Akron, OH 44311
Tel.: (330) 253-6188
Year Founded: 1967
Sales Range: $10-24.9 Million
Emp.: 2
Plumbing Services
N.A.I.C.S.: 238220
Ronald R. Bassak (Pres)

MECCOR INDUSTRIES, LTD.
3933 Oakton St, Skokie, IL 60076
Tel.: (847) 676-0202
Web Site: http://www.meccor.com
Year Founded: 1984
Sales Range: $10-24.9 Million
Emp.: 50
Highway, Street & Bridge Construction Services
N.A.I.C.S.: 237310
Jonathan Eng (Pres)

MECHANICAL CONSTRUCTION SERVICES
PO Box 335, Newark, AR 72562
Tel.: (870) 799-3113   AR
Web Site: http://www.mcspower.com
Year Founded: 1984
Sales Range: $10-24.9 Million
Emp.: 60
Boiler Maintenance Contractor Services
N.A.I.C.S.: 238220
Richard Greg (CEO & Pres)

MECHANICAL CONTRACTING SERVICES INC.
3670 Underwood Rd, La Porte, TX 77571
Tel.: (281) 479-6200
Web Site: http://www.mcsistaffing.com
Sales Range: $10-24.9 Million
Emp.: 100
Employment Agencies
N.A.I.C.S.: 561311
Doree Kieborz (Mgr)

MECHANICAL CONTRACTORS, INC.
1733 University Commercial Pl, Charlotte, NC 28213
Tel.: (704) 372-2460
Web Site: http://www.mcihvac.com
Year Founded: 1948
Sales Range: $25-49.9 Million
Emp.:
Contracting Services
N.A.I.C.S.: 238990
Donald O. Kay (Treas)
William H. Champion (VP-Construction)
Dane E. Osburn (Branch Mgr)
Geoffrey K. Cutler (VP-Integrated Building Svcs)
Ralph L. Burt Jr. (Pres)

MECHANICAL EQUIPMENT COMPANY INC.
68375 Compass Way E, Mandeville, LA 70471
Tel.: (985) 249-5500   LA
Web Site: http://www.meco.com
Year Founded: 1928
Sales Range: $75-99.9 Million
Emp.: 180
Special Industry Machinery
N.A.I.C.S.: 333248
George Gsell (Pres)

Subsidiaries:

MECO U.K. (1)
Wellsbourne House, 5 Savoy Park, Ayr, KA7 2XA, Scotland, United Kingdom (100%)
Tel.: (44) 1292618239
Web Site: http://www.meco.com
Sales Range: $10-24.9 Million
Emp.: 2
Special Industry Machinery
N.A.I.C.S.: 333310

United Technical Services (1)
Plot No 3E Sector MN-3 Musaffah, PO Box 277, Abu Dhabi, United Arab Emirates (100%)
Tel.: (971) 26774400
Web Site: http://www.uts.ae
Sales Range: $10-24.9 Million
Emp.: 60
Provider of Industrial Machinery Services
N.A.I.C.S.: 811310
John Dsouza (CFO)

MECHANICAL INDUSTRIES, LLC
8900 N 51st St, Milwaukee, WI 53223
Tel.: (414) 354-8070   WI
Web Site: http://www.mechanicalindustries.com
Year Founded: 1948
Sales Range: $25-49.9 Million
Emp.: 110
Boat, Motorcycle & Outdoor Power Equipment Mfr
N.A.I.C.S.: 336612
Charles J. Norris (Pres & CEO)

MECHANICAL MAINTENANCE INCORPORATED
1850 E Riverview Dr, Phoenix, AZ 85034
Tel.: (480) 497-1100   AZ
Web Site: http://www.midstatemechanical.com
Year Founded: 1985
Rev.: $14,800,000
Emp.: 200
Heating, Air Conditioning & Ventilation Systems & Services
N.A.I.C.S.: 238220
Kevin Carrol (Treas & Sec)

MECHANICAL PRODUCTS INC.
1112 N Garfield St, Lombard, IL 60148
Tel.: (517) 782-0391   MI
Web Site: http://www.mechprod.com
Year Founded: 1940
Sales Range: $10-24.9 Million
Emp.: 25
Circuit Breaker Mfr
N.A.I.C.S.: 335313
Larry Bajorek (Owner)
Mark Baker (CFO)
Jim Allison (VP-Engrg)
Jan Bailey (Mgr-Sls-Worldwide)
Rich Regole (Pres & CEO)

MECHANICAL REPS INC.
3901 Woodbury Dr, Austin, TX 78704-7320
Tel.: (512) 444-1835
Web Site: http://www.mechreps.com
Year Founded: 1974
Sales Range: $25-49.9 Million
Emp.: 45
HVAC Equipment Sales & Services
N.A.I.C.S.: 551112
Larry Bloomquist (CEO)
Lauren Beverly (VP-HR & Accts Payable)
Stephen Greco (Mgr-Engrg & Owner Sls)

Subsidiaries:
Mechanical Reps Inc.   (1)
4710 Perrin Creek Ste 300, San Antonio, TX 78217   **(100%)**
Tel.: (210) 650-9005
Web Site: http://www.mechreps.com
Emp.: 20
HVAC Product & Services
N.A.I.C.S.: 423730
Ken Graham (Pres)

MECHANICAL SERVICES INC.
400 Presumpscot St, Portland, ME 04103
Tel.: (207) 774-1531   ME
Web Site: http://www.mechanicalservices.com
Year Founded: 1963
Sales Range: $10-24.9 Million
Emp.: 100
Heating, Air Conditioning & Ventilation Services
N.A.I.C.S.: 238220
Christopher Green (Pres & Controller)

MECHANICAL SYSTEMS INC.
625 E 13th St N, Wichita, KS 67214
Tel.: (316) 262-2021
Web Site: http://www.msi-group.com
Year Founded: 1976
Rev.: $18,000,000
Emp.: 65
Mechanical Contractor
N.A.I.C.S.: 238220
Mark Johnson (Pres)

MECHANICAL TOOL & ENGINEERING CO.
4701 Kishwaukee St, Rockford, IL 61109
Tel.: (815) 397-4701
Web Site: http://www.mtehydraulics.com
Rev.: $34,075,946
Emp.: 210
Pumps, Hydraulic Power Transfer
N.A.I.C.S.: 333996
Richard D. Nordlof (Pres)

MECHANICS BANC HOLDING COMPANY
319 Main St, Water Valley, MS 38965
Tel.: (662) 473-2261   MS
Web Site: http://www.mechanicsbankms.com
Sales Range: $10-24.9 Million
Bank Holding Company
N.A.I.C.S.: 551111
Cam Tyler (Pres & CEO)
Robert T. Rosson Jr. (Sec)

Subsidiaries:
Mechanics Bank   (1)
319 Main St, Water Valley, MS 38965
Tel.: (662) 473-2261
Web Site: http://www.mechanicsbankms.com
Sales Range: $10-24.9 Million
Emp.: 66
Commericial Banking
N.A.I.C.S.: 522110
Cam Tyler (Pres & CEO)
Jon Gunter (COO & Sr VP)
Nell Jobe (Sr VP & Controller)
Debbie Rogers (VP-Ops)
Tyler Hill (Chief Credit Officer & VP)

MECHANICS BUILDING MATERIAL CO.
51-15 35th St, Long Island City, NY 11101
Tel.: (718) 381-6600
Sales Range: $10-24.9 Million
Emp.: 50
Supplier of Interior Building Materials
N.A.I.C.S.: 423310
Kevin Brady (Pres)

MECHANICS SAVINGS BANK NA
2 S Main St, Mansfield, OH 44902
Tel.: (419) 524-0831
Web Site: http://www.mymechanics.com
Sales Range: $10-24.9 Million
Emp.: 90
Banking Services
N.A.I.C.S.: 522180
Deb Schenk (Pres)

MECHANICSBURG FARMERS GRAIN CO.
305 N 1st St, Mechanicsburg, IL 62545
Tel.: (217) 364-4438
Sales Range: $10-24.9 Million
Emp.: 7
Provider Of Agricultural Services
N.A.I.C.S.: 424510

MECHATRONICS INC.
8152 304th Ave SE, Preston, WA 98050
Tel.: (425) 222-5900   WA
Web Site: http://www.mechatronicsinc.com
Year Founded: 1979
Sales Range: $25-49.9 Million
Emp.: 114
Industrial Supplies Bearings
N.A.I.C.S.: 423840
Tasha Alex (Mgr-Database)

MECHDYNE CORP.
11 E Church St 4th Fl, Marshalltown, IA 50158-5011
Tel.: (641) 754-4649
Web Site: http://www.mechdyne.com
Sales Range: $10-24.9 Million
Emp.: 150
3D Audio Video Systems Developer
N.A.I.C.S.: 334310
Christopher Clover (Pres & CEO)
James W. Gruening (Sr VP)
Kurt Hoffmeister (Co-Founder & VP-Res & Dev)

Subsidiaries:
Mechdyne Canada   (1)
1580 King Street North Unit B2, Saint Jacobs, N0B 2N0, ON, Canada   **(100%)**
Tel.: (519) 664-0036
Sales Range: $10-24.9 Million
Emp.: 18
3D Audio Video Systems Developer
N.A.I.C.S.: 334310

MECHEL BLUESTONE INC.
100 Cranberry Creek Dr, Beckley, WV 25801
Tel.: (304) 252-8528   DE
Holding Company; Bituminous Coal-Underground Mining
N.A.I.C.S.: 551112
James C. Justice III (Pres)

Subsidiaries:
Bluestone Industries, Inc.   (1)
100 Craig Berry Creek Dr, Beckley, WV 25801
Tel.: (304) 252-8528
Coal Mining Services
N.A.I.C.S.: 213113
James C. Justice III (Pres)

MECHTRONICS CORPORATION
1 New King St, White Plains, NY 10604
Tel.: (914) 989-2700
Web Site: http://www.mechtron.com
Rev.: $13,300,000
Emp.: 145
Provider of Displays & Signs
N.A.I.C.S.: 339950
Keith Arndt (VP-Creative)

MECKLENBURG ELECTRIC COOPERATIVE
11633 Hwy 92 W, Chase City, VA 23924
Tel.: (434) 372-6100   VA
Web Site: http://www.meckelec.org
Year Founded: 1938
Rev.: $38,861,000
Emp.: 100
Electric Services Provider
N.A.I.C.S.: 221118
David H. Lipscomb (VP-Member & Energy Svcs)
Leilani L. Todd (VP-HR)
Brian Woods (Dir-Engrg)
David J. Jones (Chm)
D. Stanley Duffer (Treas & Sec)
Donald L. Moore (Treas & Asst Sec)
Franklin B. Myers (Vice Chm)
John C. Lee Jr. (Pres & CEO)

Subsidiaries:
Mecklenburg Communications Services, Inc.   (1)
11633 Hwy 92, Chase City, VA 23924-4009
Tel.: (434) 372-6169
Web Site: http://www.meckcom.net
Internet Access & Long Distance Telephone Services Provider
N.A.I.C.S.: 221118

MECKLERMEDIA CORPORATION
50 Washington St Ste 912, Norwalk, CT 06854
Tel.: (203) 662-2800   DE
Web Site: http://www.mecklermedia.com
Year Founded: 1998
Sales Range: $1-9.9 Million
Emp.: 16
Global Trade Shows & Online Publications
N.A.I.C.S.: 519290
Alan M. Meckler (Chm & CEO)

Subsidiaries:
Comstock Images   (1)
601 34 St Unit Main, Seattle, WA 98103-8603
Tel.: (908) 518-6200
Web Site: http://www.comstock.com
Sales Range: $150-199.9 Million
Commercial Photography
N.A.I.C.S.: 541922

Jupiter Events   (1)
23 Old Kings Hwy S, Darien, CT 06820
Tel.: (203) 662-2800
Web Site: http://www.jupiterevents.com
Organizer of Trade Shows & Conferences
N.A.I.C.S.: 518210
Michael Gartenberg (VP)

MECKLEYS LIMESTONE PRODUCTS
1543 State Rte 225, Herndon, PA 17830
Tel.: (570) 758-3011
Web Site: http://www.meckleys.com
Sales Range: $10-24.9 Million
Emp.: 82
Limestones, Ground
N.A.I.C.S.: 212312
Matthew G. Markunis (Pres)
Lori Myers (Controller)
Michael Bowman (Gen Mgr)

MECO CORPORATION
1500 Industrial Rd, Greeneville, TN 37745
Tel.: (423) 639-1171   TN
Web Site: http://www.meco.net
Year Founded: 1959
Sales Range: $100-124.9 Million
Emp.: 263
Mfr & Marketer Residential Folding Furniture & Outdoor Barbecue Grills & Accessories
N.A.I.C.S.: 332119
Robert Austin (Owner)
Dexter Blakeley (Dir-Compliance)
Denise Williams (Mgr-Customer Svc & Info Analysis)
Mark Proffitt (Pres & Dir-Bus Unit)

MECO INC.
3711 Clinton Dr, Houston, TX 77020
Tel.: (713) 222-2351
Web Site: http://www.mecoonline.com
Sales Range: $10-24.9 Million
Emp.: 30
Water Treatment Chemicals & Services
N.A.I.C.S.: 221310
Brad Hance (Pres)

MECO OF ATLANTA INCORPORATED
4471 Amwiler Rd NW, Doraville, GA 30360
Tel.: (770) 448-6933
Web Site: http://www.mecoatlanta.com
Year Founded: 1952
Sales Range: $10-24.9 Million
Emp.: 65
Whslr of Service Station Equipment: Engines & Gasoline
N.A.I.C.S.: 423830
F. R. Scudder (Pres)

Subsidiaries:
Meco North Florida Inc.   (1)
3626 Phoenix Ave, Jacksonville, FL 32206
Tel.: (904) 354-6981
Rev.: $260,000
Emp.: 20
Service Station Equipment Whslr
N.A.I.C.S.: 423830
Mark Scudder (Pres)
Lamar Scott (Gen Mgr)

Meco of Savannah Inc.   (1)
311 Stiles Ave, Savannah, GA 31415
Tel.: (912) 233-4523
Web Site: http://www.meco.com
Sales Range: $1-9.9 Million
Emp.: 13
Gas Equipment, Parts & Supplies
N.A.I.C.S.: 423840

MECO OF ATLANTA INCORPORATED U.S. PRIVATE

Meco of Atlanta Incorporated—(Continued)
William Campbell *(Gen Mgr)*

MECOM LTD.
500 E 96th St Ste 360, Indianapolis, IN 46240-3774
Tel.: (317) 571-3898
Web Site: http://www.mecomltd.com
Sales Range: $10-24.9 Million
Emp.: 40
Carrying Cases
N.A.I.C.S.: 423990
J. Cory Moyars *(Gen Mgr)*
David Bilby *(Mng Dir)*
Cathy McAtee *(Mgr-Acctg)*
Rusty Michael *(COO)*
Susan Michael *(CEO)*
Lisa Yohler *(Mgr-Billing)*
Carol Saunders *(Pres)*
Jeff Saunders *(CFO)*

MECUM AUCTION, INC.
445 S Main St, Walworth, WI 53184-8261
Tel.: (815) 568-8888
Web Site: http://www.mecum.com
Automobile Auction
N.A.I.C.S.: 441227
Dana Mecum *(Pres)*

MED ONE CAPITAL INCORPORATED
10712 S 1300 E, Sandy, UT 84094-5094
Tel.: (801) 566-6433
Web Site: http://www.medonecapital.com
Rev.: $22,846,000
Emp.: 50
Medical Equipment Rentals & Leasing
N.A.I.C.S.: 532283
Larry R. Stevens *(Pres & CEO)*
Brent H. Allen *(Owner & Sr Exec VP)*
Jeff Easton *(CFO)*
Andrew D'Ascenzo *(Sec)*

MED STAR SURGICAL & BREATHING EQUIPMENT, INC.
127-17 20th Ave, College Point, NY 11356
Tel.: (718) 460-2900
Sales Range: $10-24.9 Million
Emp.: 150
Miscellaneous Product Whslr
N.A.I.C.S.: 456120
Oasier F. Pirzada *(Pres)*

MED SYSTEMS ASSOCIATES LP
3241 Western Branch Blvd, Chesapeake, VA 23321
Tel.: (757) 686-3508
Web Site: http://www.msaphy.com
Rev.: $11,700,000
Emp.: 150
Billing & Bookkeeping Service
N.A.I.C.S.: 541219
James T. Hartz *(Pres)*

MED TECH SOLUTIONS
25060 Ave Stanford Ste 250, Valencia, CA 91355
Tel.: (626) 486-9330
Web Site: http://www.medtechsolutions.com
Year Founded: 2006
Healthcare Technology Development Services
N.A.I.C.S.: 541511
Mona Abutaleb Stephenson *(CEO)*
James Deck *(CEO)*

Subsidiaries:
Emedapps Inc. (1)
1325 Remington Rd, Schaumburg, IL 60173
Tel.: (847) 490-6869
Web Site: http://www.emedapps.com
Rev.: $1,570,000
Emp.: 10
Custom Computer Programming Services
N.A.I.C.S.: 541511
Vik Sheshadri *(Pres)*

MED TRENDS, INC.
1700 Rockville Pike Ste 400, Rockville, MD 20852
Tel.: (240) 235-2609
Web Site: http://www.medtrends.net
Year Founded: 2005
Rev.: $2,700,000
Emp.: 18
Computer System Design Services
N.A.I.C.S.: 541512
Jeffrey Gilchrist *(Dir-Ops)*

MED, INC.
9200 Arboretum Pkwy Ste 120, Richmond, VA 23236
Tel.: (804) 674-6688
Sales Range: $1-9.9 Million
Emp.: 20
Medical Equipment & Respiratory Products & Services
N.A.I.C.S.: 423450
Dennis Afling *(Principal)*

MED-LAB SUPPLY COMPANY, INC.
923 NW 27th Ave, Miami, FL 33125-3016
Tel.: (305) 642-5144 FL
Web Site: http://www.medlab.com
Year Founded: 1965
Sales Range: $10-24.9 Million
Emp.: 60
Sales & Servicer of Electromedical Equipment
N.A.I.C.S.: 423450
Gonzalo E. Diaz *(Pres)*
Saul Diaz *(Sec & VP)*
Gonzalo A. Diaz Jr. *(Treas & VP)*

MED-LOZ LEASE SERVICE INC.
1 Mile N Hwy 83, Zapata, TX 78076
Tel.: (956) 765-6029
Rev.: $15,100,741
Emp.: 145
Provider of Excavation Services
N.A.I.C.S.: 238910
Juan A. Medina *(Pres)*

MED-STAT USA LLC
2606 South 162nd St, New Berlin, WI 53151
Tel.: (262) 754-3919
Web Site: http://www.medstatusa.com
Medical Logistics & Delivery Services
N.A.I.C.S.: 541614
Ken DeMuth *(CEO)*

Subsidiaries:
E-Freight Courier, LLC (1)
3540 N 126 St Unit A, Brookfield, WI 53005-3005
Tel.: (262) 439-9111
Web Site: http://www.efreightcourier.com
Local Messengers & Local Delivery
N.A.I.C.S.: 492210
Patrick Engeleiter *(Owner & Pres)*

MED-TEL.COM INC
79 Pine St Ste 200, New York, NY 10005
Web Site: http://www.medtel.com
Year Founded: 1994
Sales Range: $10-24.9 Million
Emp.: 52
Medical Device & Pharmaceutical Finder
N.A.I.C.S.: 517810
Ronald D. Coleman *(Chm)*

MED-X, INC.
8236 Remmet Ave, Canoga Park, CA 91304
Tel.: (818) 349-2870 NV
Web Site: https://www.medx-rx.com
Year Founded: 2014
Rev.: $1,010,431
Assets: $3,816,184
Liabilities: $1,662,174
Net Worth: $2,154,010
Earnings: ($4,907,432)
Emp.: 16
Fiscal Year-end: 12/31/21
Holding Company
N.A.I.C.S.: 551112
Matthew A. Mills *(CEO)*
Ronald J. Tchorzewski *(CFO)*
Nick Phillips *(CMO)*

Subsidiaries:
Pacific Shore Holdings, Inc. (1)
9736 Eton Ave, Chatsworth, CA 91311-4305
Tel.: (818) 998-0996
Web Site: http://www.pac-sh.com
Marketing Consulting Services
N.A.I.C.S.: 541613

MEDAIRE INC.
4722 N 24th St Ste 450, Phoenix, AZ 85016
Tel.: (480) 333-3700
Web Site: http://www.medaire.com
Year Founded: 1985
Sales Range: $25-49.9 Million
Emp.: 75
Medical Emergency Management Services
N.A.I.C.S.: 488999
Joan Sullivan Garrett *(Founder & Chm)*
Grant Jeffery *(CEO)*
Jeffrey Gregorec *(Exec Dir)*
Hany Bakr *(Dir-Security-Europe, Middle East & Africa)*
John Cauthen *(Dir-Security-Global)*

Subsidiaries:
MedAire Ltd. (1)
Farnborough Airport, London, GU14 6XA, Hampshire, United Kingdom
Tel.: (44) 1252517951
Sales Range: $10-24.9 Million
Emp.: 25
Medical Emergency Management Services
N.A.I.C.S.: 488999
Grant Jefferly *(CEO)*

MEDALIST PARTNERS, LP
777 3rd Ave Ste 1402, New York, NY 10017
Tel.: (212) 493-4477
Web Site: http://www.medalistpartners.com
Year Founded: 2018
Investment Management Firm
N.A.I.C.S.: 523999
Greg Richter *(CEO & Co-Head-Structured Credit & Asset Fin)*
Brian Herr *(CIO & Co-Head-Structured Credit & Asset Fin)*
Bryan Hamm *(Pres & CEO-Medalist Partners Corp Fin)*

Subsidiaries:
JMP Credit Advisors LLC (1)
3440 Preston Ridge Rd Ste 350, Alpharetta, GA 30005 (50.1%)
Tel.: (678) 368-4150
Web Site: http://www.jmpg.com
Specialty Lending Services
N.A.I.C.S.: 523999

MEDALLIC ART COMPANY, LTD.
80 Airpark Vista Blvd, Dayton, NV 89403
Tel.: (775) 246-6000
Web Site: http://www.medallic.com
Year Founded: 1903
Sales Range: $50-74.9 Million
Emp.: 40
Mfr of Medallions, Plaques, Jewelry & Belt Buckles
N.A.I.C.S.: 339910
Ross Henson *(Pres)*

MEDALLION HOMES GULF COAST, INC.
2212 58th Ave E, Bradenton, FL 34203
Tel.: (941) 359-9000
Web Site: http://www.medallionhome.com
Year Founded: 1984
Sales Range: $50-74.9 Million
Emp.: 45
New Home Construction
N.A.I.C.S.: 236115
Carlos Beruff *(CEO)*
Pete Logan *(VP)*

MEDALLION INDUSTRIES INC.
3221 NW Yeon Ave, Portland, OR 97210-1537
Tel.: (503) 221-0170
Web Site: http://www.medallionindustries.com
Sales Range: $10-24.9 Million
Emp.: 50
Provider of Doors & Wood Products
N.A.I.C.S.: 321911
Tim Mahassy *(Pres)*
Heidi Hegge *(Mgr-Shipping)*
Julie Nix *(Sr VP)*
Mike Mahaffy *(VP-Sls)*

MEDALLION INSTRUMENTATION SYSTEMS LLC.
17150 Hickory St, Spring Lake, MI 49456
Tel.: (616) 847-3700
Web Site: http://www.medallionis.com
Rev.: $29,000,000
Emp.: 146
All Other Motor Vehicle Parts Mfr
N.A.I.C.S.: 336390
Steven Vasko *(Supvr-Acctg)*
Jacob Vanderwall *(Engr-Software)*

MEDART INC.
124 Manufacturers Dr, Arnold, MO 63010
Tel.: (636) 282-2300 MO
Web Site: http://www.medartinc.com
Year Founded: 1912
Sales Range: $10-24.9 Million
Emp.: 130
Wholesale Distributor of Industrial Machinery & Equipment
N.A.I.C.S.: 423830
J. Michael Medart *(Owner)*
David Strubberg *(CFO & Exec VP)*
Peggy A. Hartupee *(Mgr-Credit)*

MEDBIO, INC
5346 36th St, Grand Rapids, MI 49512
Tel.: (616) 245-0214
Web Site: http://www.medbioinc.com
Year Founded: 2004
Sales Range: $1-9.9 Million
Emp.: 61
Medical Device & Supplies Mfr
N.A.I.C.S.: 339112
Ronald A. Williams *(Chm)*
Christopher R. Williams *(Pres)*
Sean Callaghan *(VP-Ops)*
Joe Szyperski *(VP-Quality & Regulatory Affairs)*

MEDCARE EQUIPMENT COMPANY, LLC
115 Equity Dr, Greensburg, PA 15601
Tel.: (800) 503-5554

Web Site:
http://www.medcareequipment.com
Offices of Physicians (except Mental Health Specialists)
N.A.I.C.S.: 621111
Patricia Mastandrea *(CEO)*

Subsidiaries:

Somerset Med Services, Inc. (1)
4309 Glades Pike, Somerset, PA 15501
Tel.: (814) 443-1496
Medical, Dental & Hospital Equipment & Supplies Merchant Whslr
N.A.I.C.S.: 423450
Jeffrey Curry *(Sec)*

MEDCERTS LLC
13955 Farmington Rd, Livonia, MI 48154
Tel.: (734) 274-2993
Web Site: http://www.medcerts.com
Year Founded: 2008
Sales Range: $10-24.9 Million
Emp.: 58
Online Career Training Services
N.A.I.C.S.: 611519
Jason Aubrey *(CEO)*
Kelly Hover *(Exec VP-Ops & Student Engagement)*

MEDCO RESPIRATORY INSTRUMENTS INC
10305 Round Up Ln, Houston, TX 77064-4855
Tel.: (713) 956-5288
Web Site: http://www.e-medco.com
Sales Range: $10-24.9 Million
Emp.: 75
Medical Equipment & Supplies
N.A.I.C.S.: 423450
Alma Gomez *(Pres)*
John C. Calhoun IV *(Pres)*

MEDELITA, LLC
23456 S Point Dr, San Clemente, CA 92653
Tel.: (949) 542-4100
Web Site: http://www.medelita.com
Sales Range: $1-9.9 Million
Emp.: 12
Healthcare Uniforms & Lab Coats Mfr & Sales
N.A.I.C.S.: 315250
Joe Francisco *(Pres)*
Lara Manchik *(Founder)*
Dan Stepchew *(Dir-e-Commerce)*

MEDEM, INC.
649 Mission St 2nd Fl, San Francisco, CA 94105
Tel.: (415) 644-3800 CA
Year Founded: 1999
Sales Range: $10-24.9 Million
Emp.: 40
Physician Patient Communications & Secure Online Personal Health Records
N.A.I.C.S.: 517810
Edward J. Fotsch *(CEO)*
Debra A. Del Guidice *(Pres & COO)*
Nancy Dickey *(Editor-in-Chief)*
Nick Krym *(VP-Engrng)*
Mark M. Simonian *(Dir-Medical)*
David W. Parke II *(Chm)*

MEDEXPRESS PHARMACY, LTD
1431 W Innes St, Salisbury, NC 28144
Tel.: (704) 633-3113
Web Site:
http://www.1800medexpress.com
Year Founded: 1995
Sales Range: $1-9.9 Million
Emp.: 25
Mail Order Pharmacy Service
N.A.I.C.S.: 456110

Jerry Purcell *(CEO)*

MEDFORD CO-OPERATIVE INC.
160 Medford Plz, Medford, WI 54451
Tel.: (715) 748-2056
Web Site:
http://www.medfordcoop.com
Sales Range: $100-124.9 Million
Emp.: 200
Independent Grocery Store
N.A.I.C.S.: 445110
Lisa Olson *(Mgr-IT)*
Cathy Smith *(Mgr-Credit)*
Graham Courtney Jr. *(Gen Mgr)*

MEDFORD FABRICATION, CSC INC.
1109 Court St, Medford, OR 97501
Tel.: (541) 779-1970
Web Site: http://www.medfab.com
Sales Range: $10-24.9 Million
Emp.: 50
Metal Fabrication, Assembly & Installation
N.A.I.C.S.: 332322
Bill Thorndike *(Pres)*
Kirby Renfro *(Exec VP & Gen Mgr)*
Daniel C. Thorndike *(Treas & Sec)*
David Thorndike *(VP-Mktg)*
Rob Kornstad *(Mgr-Ops)*
Ric Walch *(Sr Project Engr & Coord-Continuing Education)*
Ron Buckingham *(Mgr-Engrg & Engr-Mechanical)*
Tony Vargas *(Mgr-Custom Sls)*
Jim Lloyd *(Mgr-MIS Sys)*

MEDGLUV INC
4720 NW 15th Ave Ste B4, Fort Lauderdale, FL 33309
Tel.: (954) 202-7880
Web Site: http://www.medgluv.com
Year Founded: 2001
Rev.: $10,200,000
Emp.: 6
Hospital Equipment & Supplies Merchant Whslr
N.A.I.C.S.: 423450
Jerry Leong *(CEO)*
Stephen G. Webb *(CFO)*

MEDHOK HEALTHCARE SOLUTIONS, LLC
5550 W Idlewild Ave Ste 150, Tampa, FL 33634
Web Site: http://www.medhok.com
Sales Range: $1-9.9 Million
Emp.: 75
Healthcare Software Developer
N.A.I.C.S.: 513210
Anil Kottoor *(CEO)*
Vig Ponnusamy *(CTO)*
Marc S. Ryan *(Chief Strategy & Compliance Officer)*
David Bricker *(Chief Pharmacy Officer)*
Michelle Frank *(Chief Growth Officer)*
Gary D. Stuart *(Pres)*
Rayn Smith *(Chief Revenue Officer)*

Subsidiaries:

Continuum Performance Systems Inc. (1)
634 Boston Post Rd, Madison, CT 06443
Tel.: (203) 245-5000
Web Site:
http://www.continuumperformance.com
Software Development Services
N.A.I.C.S.: 513210
Brad Turley *(Owner)*

MEDI IP, LLC
509 S Hyde Park Ave, Tampa, FL 33606-2266
Tel.: (813) 228-6534

Web Site:
http://www.mediweightloss.com
Year Founded: 2005
Sales Range: $10-24.9 Million
Emp.: 50
Weight Loss Services
N.A.I.C.S.: 812191
John Kaloust *(Sr VP-Ops)*
Edward Kaloust *(Founder & CEO)*
Ilka A. Fahey *(Dir-Medical-Orlando)*
Andrew Cox *(Sr VP-Bus Dev)*

MEDI-DYNE HEALTHCARE PRODUCTS LTD.
1812 Industrial Blvd, Colleyville, TX 76034
Tel.: (817) 251-8660
Web Site: http://www.medi-dyne.com
Sales Range: $10-24.9 Million
Emp.: 16
Health Care Products Mfr
N.A.I.C.S.: 339920
Craig DiGiovanni *(VP-Sls & Mktg)*

Subsidiaries:

Cho-Pat (1)
Unit 6 Lippincott Ln Mt Holly Indus Commons, Mount Holly, NJ 08060
Tel.: (609) 261-1336
Web Site: http://www.cho-pat.com
Sales Range: $10-24.9 Million
Sports Medical Devices Mfr
N.A.I.C.S.: 334510
Craig DiGiovanni *(VP-Sls & Mktg)*

MEDI-NUCLEAR CORP.
6850 Southbelt Dr SE, Caledonia, MI 49316
Tel.: (248) 926-9500
Web Site: http://www.medinuc.com
Rev.: $11,300,000
Emp.: 16
Medical, Dental & Hospital Equipment & Supplies Merchant Whslr
N.A.I.C.S.: 423450
Steve Bosio *(Pres)*

MEDIA & MORE, INC.
17 New England Exec Park, Burlington, MA 01803
Tel.: (781) 272-0440 MA
Year Founded: 1999
Sales Range: $10-24.9 Million
Emp.: 5
Advertising Agencies
N.A.I.C.S.: 541810
Gloria Langham *(Dir-Media)*
Deborah Ring *(Mgr-Fin)*

MEDIA ATLANTIC
33247 Westwood Dr, Dade City, FL 33523
Tel.: (877) 510-1007
Year Founded: 2001
Sales Range: $10-24.9 Million
Emp.: 3
N.A.I.C.S.: 541810
Will Crawford *(Pres)*

MEDIA BREAKAWAY, LLC
1490 W 121st Ave Ste 201, Westminster, CO 80234
Tel.: (303) 464-8164 NV
Web Site:
http://www.mediabreakaway.com
Year Founded: 2001
Customer Relationship Management, Direct Response Marketing, Email, Search Engine Optimization, Web (Banner Ads, Pop-ups, etc.)
N.A.I.C.S.: 541810
Kacy Manning *(Mgr-Special Projects)*
Scott Richter *(CEO)*
Karen Vidick *(Dir-Acctg)*
Laura Molinaro *(Dir-Affiliate Rels)*

Brian Chase *(Mgr-The Parking Place & Redirect)*
Dani Hayes *(Mgr-HR)*

MEDIA BROKERS INTERNATIONAL, INC.
555 N Point Ctr E Ste 700, Alpharetta, GA 30022
Tel.: (678) 514-6200
Web Site: http://www.media-brokers.com
Sales Range: $10-24.9 Million
Emp.: 59
Media Buying Services
N.A.I.C.S.: 541830
Howard Steuer *(Exec VP)*

MEDIA BUYING DECISIONS
5665 Arapaho Rd, Dallas, TX 75248
Tel.: (214) 485-2494 TX
Web Site:
http://www.mediabuyingdecisions.com
Year Founded: 1986
Sales Range: $1-9.9 Million
Emp.: 3
Media Buying Services
N.A.I.C.S.: 541830
Todd Brewster *(Founder)*

MEDIA BUYING SERVICES, INC.
4545 E Shea Blvd Ste 162, Phoenix, AZ 85028-6008
Tel.: (602) 996-2232
Year Founded: 1986
Sales Range: $10-24.9 Million
Emp.: 11
Media Buying Services
N.A.I.C.S.: 541810
Kathy Munson *(CEO)*
Chuck Munson *(CFO & COO)*
Laura Gastelum *(Sr Media Buyer & Planner)*
Cheri Moreno *(Sr Media Buyer & Planner)*

Subsidiaries:

MBS West (1)
1523 1st St R 110, Coronado, CA 92118
Tel.: (619) 435-5952
Emp.: 2
Media Buying Services
N.A.I.C.S.: 541830
Chuck Munson *(CFO & COO)*
Kathy Munson *(CEO)*

MEDIA CAMPING CENTER INC.
1233 W Baltimore Pike, Media, PA 19063-5501
Tel.: (610) 566-1833 PA
Web Site:
http://www.mediacampingcenter.com
Year Founded: 1965
Sales Range: $50-74.9 Million
Emp.: 5
Dealers of Recreational Vehicles
N.A.I.C.S.: 441210
E. Hadden Smith *(Pres)*
Kevin Smith *(Mgr-Sls)*

MEDIA CANDO LLC
5901 Wisconsin Cir, Minneapolis, MN 55428
Tel.: (612) 208-3477
Web Site:
http://www.mediacando.com
Year Founded: 2001
Sales Range: $1-9.9 Million
Emp.: 6
Media Buying Services
N.A.I.C.S.: 541830
Henk Berkheij *(Pres)*

MEDIA COMMUNICATIONS GROUP

MEDIA COMMUNICATIONS GROUP   U.S. PRIVATE

Media Communications Group—(Continued)
130 Church St #12, New York, NY 10007
Tel.: (416) 879-9230
Web Site: http://www.mediacom.com
Sales Range: $1-9.9 Million
Emp.: 6
Digital Publishing Solutions
N.A.I.C.S.: 541810
Jan Moore *(Mgr-Admin)*
Alan Arthur *(Exec VP-Sls & Mktg)*

MEDIA DEPARTMENT II, INC.
12000 Biscayne Blvd Ste 706, North Miami Beach, FL 33181-2727
Tel.: (305) 892-5272 FL
Year Founded: 1977
Sales Range: $1-9.9 Million
Media Planning, Buying & Marketing
N.A.I.C.S.: 541830
Stephanie Garland Ruiz *(Pres)*

MEDIA DESIGN
5569 Bowden Rd Ste 5, Jacksonville, FL 32216-8034
Tel.: (904) 636-5131 FL
Web Site: http://www.mediadesignjax.com
Year Founded: 1999
Sales Range: $10-24.9 Million
Emp.: 5
N.A.I.C.S.: 541810
Keith Ferguson *(CEO & Dir)*
Karen Favorite *(Sr Dir-Art)*
Lindsay Carpenter *(Dir-Mktg)*
Kristyn Patterson *(Dir-Art)*

MEDIA DIRECT, INC.
1000 E Hillsboro Blvd Ste 105, Deerfield Beach, FL 33441
Tel.: (954) 949-9500
Web Site: http://www.mediadirect.co
Year Founded: 2008
Sales Range: $1-9.9 Million
Emp.: 200
Advertising Services
N.A.I.C.S.: 541810
Scott Hirsch *(Founder & CEO)*

MEDIA DIRECTIONS ADVERTISING, INC.
9724 Kingston Pike Ste 301, Knoxville, TN 37922-6910
Tel.: (865) 691-9482
Web Site: http://www.mdadv.com
Year Founded: 1982
Sales Range: $1-9.9 Million
Emp.: 5
Media Buying Services
N.A.I.C.S.: 541810
Debbie Conner *(Bus Mgr)*
Carey Merz *(COO & Exec VP)*
Maureen Patteson *(Pres & Dir-Media)*

MEDIA DREAM
PO Box 3610, Seal Beach, CA 90740
Tel.: (714) 310-4342 CA
Year Founded: 2004
Sales Range: $1-9.9 Million
Community Support Services
N.A.I.C.S.: 813210
Shady A. Toma *(Treas)*
Samuel Estefanos *(Co-Founder & Pres)*
Mona Estefanos *(Co-Founder & VP)*

MEDIA EDGE, INC.
531 Hadley Dr, Palm Harbor, FL 34683
Tel.: (727) 641-6800
Web Site: http://www.mediaedgeinc.com
Year Founded: 1986
Sales Range: $10-24.9 Million
Emp.: 6

Media Buying Services
N.A.I.C.S.: 541830
James Kelley *(Pres)*

MEDIA ETC.
2222 Kalakaua Ave Ste 701, Honolulu, HI 96815-2516
Tel.: (808) 922-8974
Web Site: http://www.mediaetc.net
Year Founded: 1992
Sales Range: Less than $1 Million
Emp.: 5
Advetising Agency
N.A.I.C.S.: 541810
Yuko Porter *(Mgr-Production)*
Chihiro Lykes *(Pres)*
Hiroyo Klink *(VP & Coord-Admin & Acctg)*
Mutsumi Matsunobu *(Coord & Writer)*

MEDIA FIRST PUBLIC RELATIONS
23611 Chagrin Blvd, Cleveland, OH 44122
Tel.: (212) 920-1470
Year Founded: 1991
Sales Range: $10-24.9 Million
Emp.: 50
Communications, Digital/Interactive, Financial, Government/Political/Public Affairs, Health Care, Information Technology, Local Marketing, Media Relations, Public Relations
N.A.I.C.S.: 541810
Rob Wyse *(CEO)*
Aaron Berger *(Exec VP)*

MEDIA FUSION, INC.
4951 Century St, Huntsville, AL 35816
Tel.: (256) 532-3874
Web Site: http://www.fusiononline.com
Year Founded: 1995
Sales Range: $1-9.9 Million
Emp.: 100
Advertising Agency Services
N.A.I.C.S.: 541810
Tim McElyea *(CEO)*
Richard Williams *(Pres)*
Betty Roberts *(Mgr-Facility Security)*
Toby Hall *(Dir-Creative)*

MEDIA GRAPHICS INC.
7300 32nd Ave N, Minneapolis, MN 55427
Tel.: (763) 537-5533
Web Site: http://www.featherlite.com
Year Founded: 1964
Trade Show Displays
N.A.I.C.S.: 339950
Graeme E. Nelson *(CEO)*

MEDIA INSIGHT
1101 Westchester Ave, White Plains, NY 10604
Tel.: (914) 694-5454
Web Site: http://www.combe.com
Year Founded: 1973
Sales Range: $10-24.9 Million
Emp.: 10
House Agencies, Media Buying Services
N.A.I.C.S.: 541810
Gail R. Perlow *(Pres)*
Patrice M. Massaro *(Sr VP & Dir-Natl Brdcst)*
Joy J. Ovadek *(VP & Dir-Media Ops)*
Steve Berger *(Sr VP & Dir-Media Plng)*
Joanne Albrecht *(Assoc Dir-Media)*
Megan Haggerty *(VP & Dir-Natl Brdcst)*
Dawn Peddie *(Assoc Dir-Natl Brdcst)*
Michele Tierney *(Natl Brdcst Buyer)*

MEDIA LOGIC USA, LLC
1 Park Pl, Albany, NY 12205
Tel.: (518) 456-3015
Web Site: http://www.mlinc.com
Year Founded: 1984
Sales Range: $1-9.9 Million
Emp.: 44
Fiscal Year-end: 01/27/14
Advertising Agencies
N.A.I.C.S.: 541810
David M. Schultz *(Pres)*
Christina Smith *(Sr VP)*
Jim Sciancalepore *(VP & Sr Dir-Creative)*
Carol Ainsburg *(Dir-Studio Svcs)*
Greg Johnson *(Dir-Design)*
Emily Conner *(Sr Mgr-Social Content)*
Jim McDonald *(Dir-Bus Dev)*
Scott Rodgers *(Sr Dir-Creative)*
Shana Cooper *(Acct Exec)*

MEDIA MATTERS FOR AMERICA
455 Massachusetts Ave NW 6th Fl, Washington, DC 20001
Tel.: (202) 756-4100 DC
Web Site: http://www.mediamatters.org
Year Founded: 2003
Sales Range: $10-24.9 Million
Emp.: 103
Progressive Research & Information Center Operator
N.A.I.C.S.: 519290
Angelo Carusone *(VP)*
Jeremy Holden *(Dir-Res)*
Scott Derome *(Dir-IT)*
Bradley Beychok *(Pres)*

MEDIA POWER ADVERTISING
18047 W Catawba Ave Ste 200, Cornelius, NC 28031
Tel.: (704) 567-1000 NC
Web Site: http://www.mediapoweradvertising.com
Year Founded: 1985
Sales Range: $10-24.9 Million
Emp.: 4
Media Buying Services
N.A.I.C.S.: 541810
Barbara Goldstein *(Pres)*

MEDIA PRINTING CORPORATION
4300 N Powerline Rd, Pompano Beach, FL 33073-3071
Tel.: (954) 984-7300 FL
Web Site: http://www.earthcolor.com
Year Founded: 1972
Sales Range: $100-124.9 Million
Emp.: 138
Provider of Lithographic Commercial Printing Services
N.A.I.C.S.: 323111
James Grubman *(Pres & CEO)*
Clay H. Grubman *(Sec & VP)*

MEDIA RAIN LLC
3333 Digital Dr Ste 700, Lehi, UT 84043
Tel.: (801) 802-6464
Web Site: http://www.mediarain.com
Year Founded: 2000
Sales Range: $1-9.9 Million
Emp.: 50
Advetising Agency
N.A.I.C.S.: 541810
Andrew Howlett *(Owner)*

MEDIA RELATIONS, INC.
350 W Burnsville Pkwy Ste 350, Burnsville, MN 55337
Tel.: (612) 798-7200 MN
Web Site: http://www.publicity.com
Year Founded: 1988

Sales Range: $1-9.9 Million
Emp.: 45
Public Relations
N.A.I.C.S.: 541820
Heather Champine *(VP-Media Production & Partner)*
Lonny Kocina *(CEO)*
Mike Danielson *(Partner & Dir-Health & Nutrition Div)*
Robin Miller *(Editor-in-Chief)*
Cynde Bock *(Mgr-Mktg)*

MEDIA RESOURCES, LTD.
4450 Belden Vlg Ave NW Ste 502, Canton, OH 44718
Tel.: (330) 492-1111
Web Site: http://www.mediaresourcesonline.com
Year Founded: 1996
Sales Range: $25-49.9 Million
Emp.: 40
Media Buying Services
N.A.I.C.S.: 541810
Gloria Cuerbo-Caley *(Pres & CEO)*
Augustine Cuerbo *(VP-Ops)*

Subsidiaries:

Media Resources, Ltd. (1)
6 Parkview Rd, Reading, MA 01867
Tel.: (781) 944-2521
Web Site: http://www.mediaresourcesonline.com
Emp.: 1
Media Buying Services
N.A.I.C.S.: 541810
Gloria Cuerbo-Caley *(Pres & CEO)*

MEDIA RESPONSE, INC.
3201 Griffin Rd 3rd Fl, Fort Lauderdale, FL 33312
Tel.: (954) 967-9899
Year Founded: 1989
Sales Range: $25-49.9 Million
Emp.: 6
N.A.I.C.S.: 541810
Ellis Kahn *(Pres)*
Bruce Halkin *(Dir-Media)*
Brooke Kahn *(Dir-Creative)*

MEDIA SOLUTIONS, INC.
707 Commons Dr Ste 201, Sacramento, CA 95825
Tel.: (916) 648-9999 CA
Web Site: http://www.mediasol.com
Year Founded: 1991
Sales Range: $10-24.9 Million
Emp.: 10
Media Buying Services
N.A.I.C.S.: 541810
Carol Michael *(Co-Founder & Partner)*
Cynthia Metler *(Co-Founder & Partner)*
Debi Giorchino *(Sr Media Buyer)*

MEDIA SOURCE, INC.
7858 Industrial Pkwy, Plain City, OH 43064
Tel.: (614) 873-7635
Web Site: http://mediasourceinc.net
Sales Range: $10-24.9 Million
Emp.: 89
Books Publishing Services
N.A.I.C.S.: 513130
Andrew Thorne *(VP-Mktg)*
Steve Zales *(CEO)*
Judy Goldstein *(Sr VP-Mktg)*
Dave Myers *(CFO)*

MEDIA SPADE, INC.
130 Prominence Pt Pkwy Ste 130-165, Canton, GA 30114
Tel.: (678) 999-8511
Web Site: http://www.mediaspade.com
Year Founded: 2004
Sales Range: $10-24.9 Million
Media Buying Services

N.A.I.C.S.: 541830
Mollisa DiStefano *(Owner & Pres)*

MEDIA STORM LLC
99 Washington St, South Norwalk, CT 06854
Tel.: (203) 852-8001
Web Site: http://www.mediastorm.biz
Year Founded: 2001
Sales Range: $150-199.9 Million
Emp.: 65
Media Buying Services
N.A.I.C.S.: 541830
Lourdes Marquez *(Dir-Local Brdcst)*
Michelle Guglielmelli *(Chief Talent Officer)*
Steve Piluso *(Head-Media & Integration)*
Julie Berger *(Exec Dir-Audience Networks)*

MEDIA STRATEGIES & RESEARCH
1580 Lincoln St 510, Denver, CO 80203
Tel.: (303) 989-4700
Web Site: http://www.mediastrategies.com
Sales Range: $10-24.9 Million
Emp.: 10
Media Buying Services
N.A.I.C.S.: 541830
Jon Hutchens *(Pres)*
Kyle Osterhout *(Partner)*
Colleen Madden *(Mng Dir)*
Racheal Beale *(Dir-Media)*

MEDIA VISTA GROUP, LLC
26101 S Tamiami Trl, Bonita Springs, FL 34134
Tel.: (239) 254-9995
Web Site: http://www.mediavista.tv
Sales Range: $1-9.9 Million
Emp.: 12
Magazine Publisher; Television Broadcasting
N.A.I.C.S.: 513120
Orlando Rosales *(CEO)*

MEDIA WHIZ HOLDINGS, LLC
77 Water St Fl 12, New York, NY 10005-4408
Tel.: (646) 442-0074
Year Founded: 2001
Emp.: 140
Media Buying Services, Media Planning, Search Engine Optimization, Sweepstakes, Web (Banner Ads, Pop-ups, etc.)
N.A.I.C.S.: 541830
Jason Cohen *(Co-Pres)*
Yannick Tessier *(Founder)*
Thomas Lanzetta *(CFO & COO)*
Eduard Kats *(Exec VP-Performance Mktg)*
Peter Klein *(Gen Mgr)*
Adam Scott Riff *(Gen Mgr-Search)*
Donney Dye *(VP-Sls)*

MEDIA3, INC.
PO Box 1448, Englewood Cliffs, NJ 07632
Tel.: (201) 941-9491   NJ
Year Founded: 2003
Sales Range: $50-74.9 Million
Emp.: 7
Brand Development, Entertainment, Logo & Package Design, Magazines, Media Buying Services, Newspaper, Publicity/Promotions, Restaurant, Travel & Tourism
N.A.I.C.S.: 541810

MEDIABRAINS, INC.
720 Goodlette Rd N Ste 400, Naples, FL 34102
Tel.: (239) 594-3200
Web Site: http://www.mediabrains.com
Year Founded: 1997
Sales Range: $25-49.9 Million
Emp.: 22
Business-to-Business Online Directory Advertising
N.A.I.C.S.: 425120
Joe Buckheit *(Founder & CEO)*
Jim Murchison *(VP-Tech)*
Michele Goguen *(Dir-Fin)*
Christina Hardy *(Dir-Mktg)*
Sadie Ludwig *(Pres)*
Rae Krivohlavek *(VP-Sls)*
Jacob Buckheit *(Dir-Product)*

MEDIACOM COMMUNICATIONS CORPORATION
1 Mediacom Way, Mediacom Park, NY 10918
Tel.: (845) 695-2600   DE
Web Site: https://www.mediacomcc.com
Year Founded: 1995
Sales Range: $1-4.9 Billion
Emp.: 4,600
Media Streaming Distribution Services, Social Networks & Other Media Networks & Content Providers
N.A.I.C.S.: 516210
Mark E. Stephan *(CFO & Exec VP)*
Tapan Dandnaik *(Sr VP-Ops, Product Strategy & Consumer Experience)*
Suzanne Sosiewicz-Leggio *(Grp VP-Fin Svcs)*
William Jensen *(Grp Vp-Lakes)*
Dean Throm *(Grp VP-Acctg)*
Danny Williams *(VP-IT)*
Rod Cundy *(Sr Dir-Ops)*
Cynthia Pawliske *(VP-Bus Ops)*
Kim Stacklum *(VP-Fin & Programming)*
Jack Griffin *(Grp VP-Corp Fin)*
Julien Dancona *(Sr VP & Controller-Corp)*
Ken Kohrs *(Grp VP-Fin Reporting)*
Thomas Larsen *(Sr VP-Govt & PR)*
John Pascarelli *(Exec VP-Ops)*
Subsidiaries:

Mediacom LLC   (1)
1 Mediacom Way, Chester, NY 10918   (100%)
Tel.: (845) 443-2600
Web Site: http://www.mediacomcc.com
Rev.: $738,710,000
Assets: $1,561,336,000
Liabilities: $1,328,620,000
Net Worth: $232,716,000
Earnings: $123,009,000
Emp.: 1,879
Fiscal Year-end: 12/31/2015
Interactive Fiber Networks Operations; Cable Television Services
N.A.I.C.S.: 516210
Rocco B. Commisso *(CEO)*
Mark E. Stephan *(CFO & Exec VP)*
John G. Pascarelli *(Exec VP-Ops)*
Italia Commisso Weinand *(Exec VP-Programming & HR)*
Joseph E. Young *(Gen Counsel, Sr VP & Sec)*
Brian M. Walsh *(Sr VP & Controller)*
Subsidiary (Domestic):

Mediacom Broadband LLC   (2)
1 Mediacom Way, Chester, NY 10918   (100%)
Tel.: (845) 443-2600
Web Site: http://www.mediacomcc.com
Rev.: $1,059,086,000
Assets: $2,316,683,000
Liabilities: $1,918,855,000
Net Worth: $397,828,000
Earnings: $159,256,000
Emp.: 2,394
Fiscal Year-end: 12/31/2017
Interactive Fiber Networks Operations
N.A.I.C.S.: 516210
Rocco B. Commisso *(CEO)*
Mark E. Stephan *(CFO & Exec VP)*
John G. Pascarelli *(Exec VP-Ops)*
Italia Commisso Weinand *(Exec VP-Programming & HR)*
Joseph E. Young *(Gen Counsel, Sec & Sr VP)*
Brian M. Walsh *(Sr VP & Controller)*
Subsidiary (Domestic):

Mediacom Broadband Corporation   (3)
1 Mediacom Way Mediacom Park, New York, NY 10918
Tel.: (845) 443-2600
Rev.: $1,100,675,999
Assets: $2,331,731,999
Liabilities: $1,557,822,999
Net Worth: $773,908,999
Earnings: $197,685,999
Emp.: 2,325
Fiscal Year-end: 12/31/2018
Cable Broadcasting & Telecommunication Services
N.A.I.C.S.: 516210
Rocco B. Commisso *(Chm & CEO)*
Mark E. Stephan *(CFO & Exec VP)*
John G. Pascarelli *(Exec VP-Ops)*
Joseph E. Young *(Gen Counsel, Sec & Sr VP)*
Subsidiary (Domestic):

Mediacom Iowa LLC   (2)
2205 Ingersoll Ave, Des Moines, IA 50312-5229
Tel.: (515) 246-1890
Web Site: http://www.mediacomcable.com
Sales Range: $50-74.9 Million
Emp.: 200
Operates Cable Television Systems
N.A.I.C.S.: 516210
Steve Purcell *(VP-Reg)*

MEDIACOMP, INC.
13810 Champion Forest Dr Suite 210, Houston, TX 77069
Tel.: (713) 621-1071   TX
Web Site: http://www.mediacomp.com
Year Founded: 1973
Media Buying Services
N.A.I.C.S.: 541830
Tami Weitkunat *(Pres & Owner)*
Brandy Bellamy Castille *(Dir-Media)*
Angela Bolton *(Dir-IT)*
Kathy Wantulla *(Asst Acct)*

MEDIACROSSING, INC.
9W Broad St Ste 250, Stamford, CT 06902
Tel.: (203) 652-1600
Web Site: http://www.mediacrossing.com
Year Founded: 2012
Sales Range: $10-24.9 Million
Emp.: 21
Digital Marketing Services
N.A.I.C.S.: 541810
Michael K. Kalman *(Founder & CEO)*
Rob Henrikson *(Sr VP-Ops)*

MEDIAFORGE
6985 S Union Pk Ctr Ste 300, Salt Lake City, UT 84047
Tel.: (801) 993-2281
Web Site: http://www.mediaforge.com
Year Founded: 2005
Sales Range: $1-9.9 Million
Emp.: 100
Online Re-Branding Specialist & Marketing Consultant
N.A.I.C.S.: 541613
Anthony Zito *(CEO)*
Rhett Frandsen *(VP-Sls & Bus Dev)*
Adam Grow *(VP-Fin & Yield Optimization)*
Danny Kourianos *(VP-Product Dev)*

MEDIALIVE INTERNATIONAL INC.
795 Folsom St 6th Fl, San Francisco, CA 94107
Tel.: (415) 905-2300   DE
Web Site: http://www.medialiveinternational.com
Sales Range: $150-199.9 Million
Emp.: 350
Organizer of Information Technology Trade Shows
N.A.I.C.S.: 561990

MEDIAMORPHOSIS INC.
39-15 29 St 2 Fl, Long Island City, NY 11101
Tel.: (718) 472-3700
Web Site: http://www.mediamorphosisinc.com
Sales Range: $10-24.9 Million
Emp.: 10
Advetising Agency
N.A.I.C.S.: 541810
Daniel Ocner *(Dir-Strategic Plng & Dev)*
Shahid Khan *(Strategist)*
Subsidiaries:

MediaMorphosis   (1)
57A Southern Avenue Module House 1st Floor, Kolkata, 700 029, India
Tel.: (91) 9830867536
N.A.I.C.S.: 541810
Adris Chakraborty *(Mng Dir)*

MEDIAONE OF UTAH
4770 S 5600 W, West Valley City, UT 84118
Tel.: (801) 237-2800
Web Site: http://www.mediaoneutah.com
Sales Range: $10-24.9 Million
Emp.: 600
Newspaper Publishers
N.A.I.C.S.: 513110
Kelly Roberts *(Sr VP-Circulation)*
Brent J. Low *(Pres & CEO)*
Scott Porter *(Sr VP-Ops)*

MEDIASHIFT, INC.
20062 SW Birch St #220, Newport Beach, CA 92660
Tel.: (949) 407-8488   NV
Web Site: http://www.mediashift.com
Year Founded: 2004
Sales Range: $1-9.9 Million
Emp.: 60
Advertising Technology Platform
N.A.I.C.S.: 541890
David Lazar *(Chm, Pres, CEO, CFO & Sec)*

MEDIASMITH INC.
115 Sansome St Ste 300, San Francisco, CA 94104
Tel.: (415) 252-9339
Web Site: http://www.mediasmith.com
Year Founded: 1989
Media Buying Services
N.A.I.C.S.: 541830
David L. Smith *(Chm)*
Karen T. McFee *(Sec)*
John Cate *(CEO)*
Marcus Pratt *(VP-Insights & Tech)*
Greg Pomaro *(Exec VP-Media)*
Ryan Buensuceso *(Dir-Fin)*

MEDIASPACE SOLUTIONS
904 Mainstreet, Hopkins, MN 55343
Tel.: (612) 253-3900
Web Site: http://www.mediaspacesolution.com
Year Founded: 1999
Sales Range: $100-124.9 Million
Emp.: 55
Print & Digital Media Buying Services
N.A.I.C.S.: 541830

MEDIASPACE SOLUTIONS

Mediaspace Solutions—(Continued)
Bama Salonek (Chief Mktg Officer)
Mike Koosa (VP-Tech)

MEDIASPOT, INC.
1550 Bayside Dr, Corona Del Mar, CA 92625-1711
Tel.: (949) 721-0500
Web Site: http://www.mediaspot.com
Year Founded: 1991
Sales Range: $200-249.9 Million
Emp.: 25
Media Buying Services
N.A.I.C.S.: 541810
Arthur R. Yelsey (Pres)
Kathy J. McLaughlin (Exec VP)
Tamiko Fujimoto (Sr VP-Client Svcs)
Jennifer Connell (Dir-Out-of-Home & Acct Supvr)
Quinn Truong (Controller)
Erin Hopkins (Dir-Local Brdcst)
Deborah Hohman (Dir-Local Brdcst)
Gail Israel (Dir-Local Brdcst)
Miko Hoshino (Mgr-Digital Media)

MEDIASSOCIATES, INC.
75 Glen Rd, Sandy Hook, CT 06482
Tel.: (203) 797-9500
Web Site: http://www.mediassociates.com
Year Founded: 1994
Sales Range: $10-24.9 Million
Emp.: 40
Media Buying Services
N.A.I.C.S.: 541810
Scott Brunjes (Pres & CEO)
Charlie Menduni (VP-Client Svcs)
Ben Kunz (VP-Strategic Plng)

MEDIASTREET, INC.
44 W Jefryn Blvd Unit Y, Deer Park, NY 11729
Tel.: (631) 242-5505
Web Site: http://mediastreetgroup.com
Sales Range: $10-24.9 Million
Emp.: 110
Inkjet Printer Ink & Paper Mfr & Distr
N.A.I.C.S.: 325130
Norm Levy (Pres)

MEDIATRUST
404 Park Ave S 2nd Fl, New York, NY 10016-8404
Tel.: (212) 802-1160
Web Site: http://www.mediatrust.com
Year Founded: 2004
Sales Range: $50-74.9 Million
Emp.: 60
Marketing & Advertising
N.A.I.C.S.: 541613
Joe Hopkins (VP-Engrg)
Peter A. Bordes Jr. (Co-Founder)

MEDIAWHIZ
75 Broad St, New York, NY 10004
Tel.: (646) 442-0074
Year Founded: 2001
Rev.: $9,300,000
Emp.: 17
Fiscal Year-end: 12/31/06
Advertising, Affiliate Marketing, Email, Search Engine Optimization
N.A.I.C.S.: 541810
Yannick Tessier (Co-Pres & Pres-Global Resource Systems)
Eduard Kats (Exec VP)
Tom Lanzetta (COO)
Sal Guido (CIO)
Patrick Gavin (Pres-MediaWhiz Display)
Peter Klein (Gen Mgr-Monetizeit)
Daryl Colwell (VP-Monetizeit)
Avishan Hodjat (VP-Advertiser Svcs)
Mitch Tuch (Gen Mgr-Data Acq)
Jeff Zelaya (Acct Exec)

Adam Riff (Sr VP-Digital Strategy)
John Kuendig (CEO)
Steve La Peruta (Sr VP-IT)

MEDICA, INC.
401 Carlson Pkwy, Minnetonka, MN 55305
Tel.: (952) 992-2900
Web Site: http://www.medica.com
Year Founded: 1994
Sales Range: $1-4.9 Billion
Emp.: 900
Insurance Services
N.A.I.C.S.: 524114
Rob Longendyke (Chief Mktg Officer & Sr VP)
Jim Jacobson (Gen Counsel & Sr VP)
Mark Baird (CFO & Sr VP)
Greg Bury (Sr Mgr-PR)
Nichole White (VP-Health Svcs)
John Naylor (Pres & CEO)
Brian A. Bonner (Chief Experience Officer-CaringBridge & Sr VP)
Tom Lindquist (Sr VP/Gen Mgr-Govt Programs)
Tim Thull (CIO & Sr VP)
Paul Crowley (Sr VP & Gen Mgr-Comml Markets)
John R. Mach (Chief Medical Officer & Sr VP)
Lori Nelson (Sr VP-Provider Strategy & Network Mgmt)

MEDICAL ACADEMIC & SCIENTIFIC COMMUNITY ORGANIZATION, INC.
375 Longwood Ave, Boston, MA 02215
Tel.: (617) 632-2788
Web Site: http://www.masco.org
Year Founded: 1972
Sales Range: $25-49.9 Million
Emp.: 100
Subdividers & Developers
N.A.I.C.S.: 237210
Maria T. Curtin (Controller)
Gary J. DuPont (Dir-Telecomm)
Sarah J. Hamilton (VP-Area Plng & Dev)
Norva H. Kennard (Gen Counsel)
Holli G. Roth (CFO & VP-Admin & Fin)
Susan Chase (Dir-Collaborative Svcs)
Chuck Badeau (Dir-IT)
Christine Fennelly (Dir-Strategic Comm)
P. J. Cappadona (VP-Ops)
Glen Davis (Dir-HR)

MEDICAL BENEFITS MUTUAL LIFE INSURANCE CO. INC.
1975 Tamarack Rd, Newark, OH 43058
Tel.: (740) 522-8425
Web Site: http://www.medben.com
Year Founded: 1938
Sales Range: $25-49.9 Million
Emp.: 168
Provider of Insurance Services
N.A.I.C.S.: 524114
Douglas J. Freeman (Pres & CEO)
Diana Vlachos (Dir-HR)
Brian Fargus (VP-Sls & Mktg)

Subsidiaries:

Medical Benefits Administrators Inc (1)
1975 Tamarack Rd, Newark, OH 43055-1300
Tel.: (740) 522-8425
Sales Range: $50-74.9 Million
Emp.: 100
Health Benefit Management Services
N.A.I.C.S.: 525120
Douglas Freeman (Chm)

Vision Plus of America Inc. (1)
1975 Tamarack Rd, Newark, OH 43055
Tel.: (740) 522-8425
Sales Range: $50-74.9 Million
Emp.: 165
Provider of Insurance Services
N.A.I.C.S.: 524114

MEDICAL BILLING MANAGEMENT EAST
44 Magaletta Dr, Westwood, MA 02090
Tel.: (781) 320-9680
Web Site: http://www.mbme.net
Year Founded: 1990
Sales Range: $10-24.9 Million
Emp.: 5
Provider of Financial & Business Services
N.A.I.C.S.: 541219
Betsy V. Spear (Owner & Pres)

MEDICAL BUSINESS SERVICE INC.
2555 Ponce De Leon Blvd 4th Fl, Coral Gables, FL 33134
Tel.: (305) 446-4681
Web Site: http://www.mbs-net.com
Rev.: $10,000,000
Emp.: 100
Billing Services For Doctors
N.A.I.C.S.: 541219
Tom Herald (Founder)
William Herald (Founder)

MEDICAL CARE DEVELOPMENT INC.
11 Parkwood Dr, Augusta, ME 04330
Tel.: (207) 622-7566
Web Site: http://www.mcd.org
Sales Range: $10-24.9 Million
Emp.: 625
Retirement Hotel Operation
N.A.I.C.S.: 531110
Edward W. Miles (Asst Treas)
Mark Battista (Gen Mgr)
Heather Metten (Mgr-Acctg)
Alphonsine Allen Laney (Project Co-ord)

MEDICAL COACHES INCORPORATED
399 County Hwy 58, Oneonta, NY 13820
Tel.: (607) 432-1333
Web Site: http://www.medcoach.com
Sales Range: $25-49.9 Million
Emp.: 30
Bus & Other Large Specialty Vehicle Assembly
N.A.I.C.S.: 336120
Leonard Marsh (COO & Exec VP)
Jim Bazan (Controller)
Geoffrey A. Smith (Pres)

MEDICAL COST MANAGEMENT CORP.
200 W Monroe St Ste 200, Chicago, IL 60606
Tel.: (312) 236-2694
Web Site: http://www.medicalcost.com
Health Care Srvices
N.A.I.C.S.: 621610
Michael J. O'Connor (Founder & CEO)
Roger B. Perry (Dir-Medical & Clinical Ops)
Amy Gasbarro (Pres)
Alana Warren (Dir-Case & Disease Mgmt)
Lawrence J. Kerns (Assoc Dir-Medical)

U.S. PRIVATE

Bob Kellam (VP-Health & Welfare Svcs)
Connie J. Wolf (Sr VP-Sls & Mktg)
Tom O'Connor (COO)

Subsidiaries:

Med-Care Management, Inc. (1)
2459 S Congress Ave, West Palm Beach, FL 33406
Tel.: (561) 966-9901
Sales Range: $1-9.9 Million
Emp.: 50
Health Care Srvices
N.A.I.C.S.: 621610
Margaret Lemkin (Pres & Owner)

MEDICAL DATA SYSTEMS INC.
2001 9th Ave Ste 312, Vero Beach, FL 32960
Tel.: (772) 770-2255
Web Site: http://www.meddatsys.com
Rev.: $10,000,000
Emp.: 180
Billing & Bookkeeping Service
N.A.I.C.S.: 541219
Giles Miller (Pres & CEO)
Tammy Ortiz (Mgr-Ops)
Shaina Justice (Mgr-Insurance)

MEDICAL DEPOT, INC.
99 Seaview Blvd, Port Washington, NY 11050
Tel.: (516) 998-4600
Web Site: http://www.drivemedical.com
Year Founded: 2000
Wheelchairs, Mobile Beds & Other Medical Equipment Mfr & Distr
N.A.I.C.S.: 339113
Harvey P. Diamond (Co-Founder, Chm & CEO)
Richard S. Kolodny (Pres)
Jeffrey Schwartz (Co-Founder & Exec VP-Sls)
Douglas Francis (Co-Founder & Exec VP)
Michael Serhan (Exec VP-Product Dev)
William Cerniglia (CIO)
Mitchell Yoel (Exec VP-Bus Dev)
Craig Zumbo (Controller)
Edward J. Link (CMO)
Mark LaVacca (VP-Ops)
Seth Diamond (VP-e-Commerce Div)
Jim McGuiness (VP-Retail Sls)
Evan Epstein (Dir-Technical Svcs)
Barry Fink (VP-Pur)
Will Fraser (VP-Corp Accts)
Jason Moskowitz (Reg VP)
Jordan Marsh (Reg VP-Respiratory Sls)
Marie Auguste (Dir-Matls Plng)
Stephen Mora (Dir-Northeast Ops)
Amy O'Keefe (CFO & Exec VP)

Subsidiaries:

DeVilbiss Healthcare LLC (1)
100 DeVilbiss Dr, Somerset, PA 15501-2125
Tel.: (814) 443-4881
Web Site: http://www.devilbisshc.com
Respiratory Medical Products Design, Mfr & Marketer
N.A.I.C.S.: 423450
Bob Wolk (Mgr-Facilities)
Allan Jones (Dir-Engrg)
George Illar (Mgr-Quality)

Subsidiary (Non-US):

DeVilbiss Healthcare GmbH (2)
Kamenzer Strasse 3, 68309, Mannheim, Germany
Tel.: (49) 621 178 98 0
Web Site: http://www.devilbisshc.de
Medical Equipment Mfr & Distr
N.A.I.C.S.: 423450

DeVilbiss Healthcare Ltd (2)

COMPANIES

Unit 3 Bloomfield Park Bloomfield Road, Tipton, DY4 9AP, W Midlands, United Kingdom
Tel.: (44) 121 521 3140
Web Site: http://www.devilbisshc.com
Medical Equipment Mfr & Distr
N.A.I.C.S.: 423450
David Haines (Gen Mgr)

DeVilbiss Healthcare PTY Ltd (2)
Unit 8 15 Carrington Road, Castle Hill, 2154, NSW, Australia
Tel.: (61) 2 9899 3144
Web Site: http://www.devilbisshc.com.au
Emp.: 15
Medical Equipment Mfr & Distr
N.A.I.C.S.: 423450
John Zunic (Gen Mgr)

DeVilbiss Healthcare S.A.S. (2)
13 Rue Joseph Priestley, 37100, Tours, France
Tel.: (33) 2 47 42 99 42
Web Site: http://www.devilbisshc.fr
Medical Equipment Mfr & Distr
N.A.I.C.S.: 423450
Oliver Niemann (Head-Intl Ops)

Inovo, Inc. (1)
2975 Horseshoe Dr S Ste 600, Naples, FL 34104
Tel.: (239) 643-6577
Web Site: http://www.inovoinc.com
Sales Range: $1-9.9 Million
Emp.: 100
Mfg Surgical/Medical Instruments
N.A.I.C.S.: 339112
Kiran Shetty (Mgr-Mktg)

MEDICAL DIRECT CLUB LLC
2026 Lindell Ave, Nashville, TN 37203
Tel.: (615) 371-2996
Web Site: http://www.medicaldirectclub.com
Year Founded: 2009
Sales Range: $10-24.9 Million
Emp.: 46
Mail Order Urological Supplies
N.A.I.C.S.: 423450
Bradford Gulmi (CEO)

MEDICAL DOCTOR ASSOCIATES INC.
4775 Peachtree Industrial Blvd Ste 300, Norcross, GA 30092
Tel.: (770) 246-9191
Web Site: http://www.mdainc.com
Year Founded: 1987
Sales Range: $25-49.9 Million
Emp.: 200
Provider of Placement Agency Services
N.A.I.C.S.: 561311
Anne B. Anderson (Exec VP-MDA Holdings)
Timothy Fischer (Pres)

MEDICAL EDUCATION BROADCAST NETWORK
9157 Whistable Walk, Tamarac, FL 33321-4173
Tel.: (603) 432-7099
Year Founded: 1999
Sales Range: $25-49.9 Million
Emp.: 25
Healthcare Long Distance Learning & Educational Programs
N.A.I.C.S.: 923110
Sharyn Lee (Pres & CEO)
Ronald Minerd (COO & VP-Product Dev)
Pamela Kleinman (Dir-Accreditation & Outcomes Analysis)
Robin Hendricks (Dir-Mng Editors)

MEDICAL EMERGENCY PROFESSIONALS
12410 Milestone Ctr Dr Ste 225, Germantown, MD 20876
Tel.: (301) 944-0034
Web Site: http://www.emergencydocs.com
Sales Range: $50-74.9 Million
Emp.: 136
Medical Care Professional Services
N.A.I.C.S.: 813920
Angelo L. Falcone (CEO)
David N. Klein (Pres & COO)
Aaron M. Snyder (CFO)

MEDICAL IMAGING TECHNOLOGIES, INC.
875 Vly St, Colorado Springs, CO 80915
Tel.: (719) 520-1511 CO
Web Site: http://www.medicalimagingtech.com
Year Founded: 1983
Sales Range: $10-24.9 Million
Emp.: 15
Medical Imaging Equipment Whslr & Services
N.A.I.C.S.: 423450
Charlie Kleeberg (Pres)
Curtis Malfeld (COO & VP)
Karol Whitlow (Dir-Sls)

MEDICAL INDUSTRIAL PLASTICS
75683 Duval Ct, Palm Desert, CA 92211
Tel.: (760) 779-9401
Sales Range: $10-24.9 Million
Emp.: 1
Provider of Plastic Materials
N.A.I.C.S.: 424610
Henry Monahan (Partner)

MEDICAL INFORMATION TECHNOLOGY, INC.
Meditech Cir, Westwood, MA 02090
Tel.: (781) 821-3000 MA
Web Site: http://www.meditech.com
Year Founded: 1969
Rev.: $493,844,632
Assets: $669,475,349
Liabilities: $111,724,941
Net Worth: $557,750,408
Earnings: $180,157,193
Emp.: 3,531
Fiscal Year-end: 12/31/19
Information System Software for Medical Industry
N.A.I.C.S.: 423430
A. Neil Pappalardo (Co-Founder & Chm)
Lawrence A. Polimeno (Vice Chm)
Howard Messing (CEO)
Steven B. Koretz (Sr VP-Client Svcs)
Hoda Sayed-Friel (Exec VP)
Michelle O'Connor (Pres & COO)
Helen M. Waters (Exec VP)
Leah L. Farina (VP-Client Svcs)
Scott Radner (VP-Advanced Tech)
James W. Merlin (Chief Acctg Officer & Controller)
Geoff Smith (VP-Product Dev)
Barbara A. Manzolillo (CFO & Treas)

MEDICAL MANAGEMENT SYSTEMS INC.
5420 Hill 23 Dr, Flint, MI 48507
Tel.: (810) 238-1666
Web Site: http://www.cbiz.com
Rev.: $10,400,000
Emp.: 155
Other Accounting Services
N.A.I.C.S.: 541219
Randal J. Roat (Sec & VP)

MEDICAL MARKETING SERVICE INC.
935 National Pkwy Ste 93510, Schaumburg, IL 60173
Tel.: (630) 350-1717
Web Site: http://www.mmslists.com

Year Founded: 1929
Sales Range: $1-9.9 Million
Emp.: 30
List Management & Email Marketing
N.A.I.C.S.: 518210
Richard Elliott (Chm & CEO)
Garth Elliott (Pres & COO)
Kirk Elliott (CIO)
Damon Schultz (VP-Strategic Dev)
Kristy Vanderplow (Dir-Acct Svcs)
Cindy Morrison (Dir-Email Svcs)

MEDICAL MEDIA TELEVISION, INC.
321 N Kentucky Av Ste 1, Lakeland, FL 33801
Tel.: (863) 686-4205
Digital Advertising Services
N.A.I.C.S.: 541810
Philip M. Cohen (Pres & CEO)

MEDICAL MUTUAL LIABILITY INSURANCE SOCIETY OF MARYLAND
225 International Cir, Hunt Valley, MD 21030
Tel.: (410) 785-0050
Web Site: http://www.medicalmutualofmd.com
Sales Range: $75-99.9 Million
Emp.: 100
Liability Insurance
N.A.I.C.S.: 524126
John R. Franklin (Asst VP-Comm)
Mary Lura Duvall (CFO)
Keith Allen (Sr VP)
Gittel Fooksman (Mgr-Claims Ops)

MEDICAL MUTUAL OF OHIO
2060 E 9th St, Cleveland, OH 44115
Tel.: (216) 687-7000 OH
Web Site: http://www.medmutual.com
Year Founded: 1934
Sales Range: $1-4.9 Billion
Emp.: 2,500
Health Insurance Services
N.A.I.C.S.: 524114
Don Olson (Dir-Corp Comm)
Susan Tyler (Chief Experience Officer & Exec VP)
Jared Chaney (Chief Comm Officer & Exec VP)
Rick Chiricosta (Chm, Pres & CEO)
Mary Novak (VP-Sls & Svc)
Ann Vickers (Sr Dir-Mktg)
Ezell Underdown (Dir-Legal Affairs)
Karen Williams (Dir-Fin Reporting)
Kathy Golovan (CIO & Exec VP-Care Mgmt)
Steffany Larkins (Chief Diversity Officer, Exec VP & Head-Staff)
Ray Mueller (CFO & Exec VP)
Andrea Hogben (Sr VP-Strategic Comm)
Chad Francis (Reg VP-Cincinnati & Dayton)

Subsidiaries:

Bravo Wellness, LLC (1)
1 International Pl 20445 Emerald Pkwy Dr SW Ste 400, Cleveland, OH 44135
Tel.: (216) 658-9500
Web Site: http://www.bravowell.com
Sales Range: $10-24.9 Million
Emp.: 105
Wellness & Health Care Services
N.A.I.C.S.: 621610
Jim Pshock (Founder & CEO)
Dave Campbell (Pres)
Cheryl Tidwell (Exec VP-Bus Dev)
Samantha Veeck (VP-Product & Project Mgmt)
Jeff Moore (VP-Sls)
Anthony Vance (Chief Growth Officer)

Medical Mutual Services, LLC (1)
17800 Royalton Rd, Strongsville, OH 44136
Tel.: (440) 878-4800

Web Site: http://www.medmutual.com
Administrative Management Services
N.A.I.C.S.: 541611
Richard Thiricosta (Pres)

Mutual Health Services (1)
PO Box 5700, Cleveland, OH 44101
Tel.: (330) 666-0337
Web Site: http://www.mutualhealthservices.com
Health Care Srvices
N.A.I.C.S.: 621999
Peter Voitko (Dir-Specialty TPA Ops)
Sean Phillips (Dir-Fin)
Terry McPeters (Mgr-Ops)

Reserve National Insurance Company (1)
601 E Britton Rd, Oklahoma City, OK 73114
Tel.: (405) 848-7931
Web Site: https://www.reservenational.com
Sales Range: $125-149.9 Million
Emp.: 170
Life & Medical Insurance Services
N.A.I.C.S.: 524113
Matt Fairchild (VP-Southeast)
John Schuster (VP-Great Lakes)
Roger Schuster (VP-Mid-South)

MEDICAL PRODUCTS INC.
127 Kingsley Rd, Ripley, MS 38663
Tel.: (662) 837-8522
Web Site: http://www.med-pro.com
Rev.: $10,400,000
Emp.: 10
Medical Equipment & Supplies
N.A.I.C.S.: 423450
Eddie McCafferty (Pres)

MEDICAL RESEARCH CONSULTANTS, INC.
10114 W Sam Houston Pkwy S Ste 200, Houston, TX 77099
Tel.: (713) 528-6326
Web Site: http://www.mrchouston.com
Year Founded: 1983
Sales Range: $25-49.9 Million
Emp.: 268
Medical Record Management Services
N.A.I.C.S.: 541611
Gretchen Watson (Pres & CEO)
Janette Nguyen (Dir-Records Mgmt)
Charles Houseworth (Dir-Nursing)
Duane Geyer (Dir-Fin)
Eric Bjork (Dir-Dev)

MEDICAL RESOURCE ASSOCIATION, INC.
PO Box 2859, Sarasota, FL 34230-2859
Web Site: http://www.mrasrq.com
Year Founded: 1998
Sales Range: $10-24.9 Million
Emp.: 60
Medical Consulting Services
N.A.I.C.S.: 541611
Kristen Beury (Pres & CEO)

MEDICAL SERVICES OF AMERICA, INC.
PO Box-1928 171 Monroe Ln, Lexington, SC 29072
Tel.: (803) 957-0500
Web Site: http://www.msa-corp.com
Sales Range: $200-249.9 Million
Emp.: 3,000
N.A.I.C.S.: 621610
Ronnie L. Young (Pres & CEO)
Wayne Jeffcoat (COO & Exec VP)
Christy Jeffcoat (VP)
Kenny Boggs (CFO)
Deborah Jordon-Ruff (Dir-HR)
Timothy W. Stewart (Gen Counsel)
Sharon Clouner-Wienand (CIO)

MEDICAL SPECIALISTS OF THE PALM BEACHES, INC.

MEDICAL SPECIALISTS OF THE PALM BEACHES, INC.   U.S. PRIVATE

Medical Specialists of The Palm Beaches, Inc.—(Continued)
7593 W Boynton Beach Blvd Ste 220, Boynton Beach, FL 33437
Tel.: (561) 649-7000
Web Site:
https://www.mspbhealth.com
Year Founded: 1995
Medical Devices
N.A.I.C.S.: 622110
Casey Waters (CEO)
Carlos Lira (Chief Medical Officer)

Subsidiaries:

Cohen Medical Associates LLC (1)
15300 Jog Rd, Delray Beach, FL 33446-0000
Tel.: (561) 496-7200
Web Site: http://www.cohenmedical.com
Health Practitioners
N.A.I.C.S.: 621399
Robert Cohen (Founder)

MEDICAL TEAMS INTERNATIONAL
14150 SW Milton Ct, Tigard, OR 97224
Tel.: (503) 624-1000   OR
Web Site:
http://www.medicalteams.org
Year Founded: 1979
Sales Range: $50-74.9 Million
Emp.: 116
Medical Care Services
N.A.I.C.S.: 621498
Pamela Blikstad (VP-Fin)
Jon Beighle (VP-Mktg & Dev)
Joe Dicarlo (VP-Programs)
Doug Fountain (VP-Ops Support)
Ann Klein (Vice Chm)
Phil Lane (Sec)
Mark S. Dodson (Chm)
Debra Hirsh (Dir-Corp Philanthropy)
Jeffrey A. Rideout (Treas)

MEDICAL TECHNOLOGY ASSOCIATES, LLC
12445 62nd St Unit 305, Largo, FL 33773
Tel.: (727) 535-3007   FL
Web Site: http://www.mtaius.com
Year Founded: 1979
Sales Range: $1-9.9 Million
Emp.: 20
Medical, Dental & Hospital Equipment & Supplies Merchant Whslr
N.A.I.C.S.: 423450
Valeri Marks (Pres & CEO)

Subsidiaries:

Air Filtration Management Inc. (1)
1505 W Broad St, Bethlehem, PA 18018
Tel.: (610) 867-3869
Web Site: http://www.airfiltrationmgmt.com
Rev.: $3,584,000
Emp.: 16
Surgical & Medical Instrument Mfr
N.A.I.C.S.: 339112

Cal Tec Labs, Inc. (1)
501 Mansfield Ave, Pittsburgh, PA 15205
Tel.: (412) 919-1377
Web Site: http://www.cal-tec.com
Rev.: $1,200,000
Emp.: 10
Testing Laboratories
N.A.I.C.S.: 541380
George Urban (VP-Ops)
Mark Palmer (Mgr-Sls)
Jon Urban (VP-Admin)

MEDICAL UNIVERSITY OF SOUTH CAROLINA
171 Ashley Ave, Charleston, SC 29425
Tel.: (843) 792-1414
Web Site: http://muschealth.org
Year Founded: 1824
Colleges & Universities
N.A.I.C.S.: 611310
Morris Kalinsky (Dir-Cardiology Board)
David J. Cole (Pres)
Mark S. Sothmann (VP-Academic Affairs & Provost)
Etta Pisano (VP-Medical Affairs)
Lisa P. Montgomery (Exec VP-Fin & Ops)
Frank C. Clark (CIO & VP-IT)
Bob Branson (Project Mgr)
Susan Carullo (Dir-Admin)
Alex Chung (Project Mgr)
Dee Crawford (Mgr-Benefits & Records)
Wade Gatlin (Project Mgr)
Patricia A. Kelly (Mgr-Info Sys Mgmt)
Rhonda Richardson (Asst Dir-Employment Svcs)
Debra Battjes-Siler (Dir-Res Admin)
Kelly Long (Dir-Student Svcs)
Hazel Rider (Mgr-Multimedia Comm)
Dana Tumbleston (Mgr-Employee Rels)
Pat Cawley (CEO-Medical Center & VP-Clinical Ops)
Wallace Bonaparte (Dir-EEO/AA)
Sarah King (Dir-PR Office)
Michael Rusnak (Exec Dir-Res Dev Foundation)
Jim Fisher (VP-Dev)
Wayne L. Brannan (Dir-Risk Mgmt)
Jennifer Taylor (Mgr-Bus Admin & Insurance Programs)
Amanda Ritsema (Mgr-Emergency)
Cheryl Brian (Mgr-Employee Health & Workers Compensation)
Kenny Murray (Mgr-Environmental Health)
John Walden (Mgr-Environmental Health)
Donald R. Johnson II (Chm)
William H. Bingham Sr. (Vice Chm)

Subsidiaries:

Carolinas Medical Alliance, Inc. (1)
805 Pamplico Hwy, Florence, SC 29505
Tel.: (843) 674-5000
Web Site: http://muschealth.org
Billing & Accounting Services
N.A.I.C.S.: 541219

Chester HMA, Inc. (1)
1 Medical Park Dr, Chester, SC 29706
Tel.: (803) 581-3151
Web Site: http://muschealth.org
Sales Range: $25-49.9 Million
Emp.: 320
Hospital Services
N.A.I.C.S.: 622110
Page Vaughan (Mgr)

MEDICCOMM CONSULTANTS, INC.
40 Blacksmith Rd, Dracut, MA 01826
Tel.: (978) 937-1316
Web Site:
http://www.medicomminc.com
Year Founded: 1992
Sales Range: Less than $1 Million
Emp.: 2
Advertising, Health Care, Medical, Pharmaceutical
N.A.I.C.S.: 541810
Robert DeSimone (Pres)

MEDICINES 360
353 Sacramento St Ste 900, San Francisco, CA 94111-3615
Tel.: (415) 951-8700   CA
Web Site:
http://www.medicines360.org
Year Founded: 2009
Sales Range: $1-9.9 Million
Emp.: 41
Women Legal Support Services
N.A.I.C.S.: 541199

Andrea Olariu (Chief Medical Officer, VP-Clinical & Regulatory Affairs & Gen Mgr)
Brad Luke (CFO & VP-Fin & IT)
Sally Stephens (Chief Bus Officer & Sr VP-Corp Dev)
Brad Luke (VP-Fin & IT)
Sally Stephens (Sr VP-Corp Dev)
Athena Cross (Head-Access)
Peter Schell (VP-Strategy & Comml)
Leslie Benet (Chm)
Victoria Hale (Founder)
Andrea Olariu (VP-Clinical & Regulatory Affairs & Gen Mgr)
Leslie Benet (Chm)
Victoria Hale (Founder)
Mark Busch (VP-Quality)
Tina Raine-Bennett (CEO)

MEDICO INDUSTRIES, INC.
1500 Hwy 315, Wilkes Barre, PA 18702
Tel.: (570) 825-7711   PA
Web Site: http://www.medicoind.com
Year Founded: 1937
Sales Range: $25-49.9 Million
Emp.: 300
Heavy Machinery Retailer
N.A.I.C.S.: 532412
Thomas Medico (Pres)
Mark Casper (Mgr-Svc)
Phillip Medico (Gen Mgr)
Rich Yanalis (Mgr-Parts)

Subsidiaries:

Louis Cohen & Sons, Inc. (1)
9 Fellows Ave, Hanover, PA 18706 (79%)
Tel.: (570) 823-0113
Web Site:
http://www.louiscohenrecycling.com
Sales Range: $10-24.9 Million
Emp.: 25
Metal Recycling Services
N.A.I.C.S.: 423930
Charles S. Medico Jr. (VP)

MEDICO INTERNATIONAL INC.
PO Box 3092, Palmer, PA 18043
Tel.: (610) 253-7009   NV
Web Site:
https://medicointernational.com
Year Founded: 2015
Liabilities: $493,306
Net Worth: ($493,306)
Earnings: ($33,612)
Fiscal Year-end: 12/31/18
Dental Clinic Operator
N.A.I.C.S.: 339116

MEDICS ENTERPIRSES
1609 Atlantic Ave, Virginia Beach, VA 23451-3422
Tel.: (757) 422-9342
Sales Range: $10-24.9 Million
Emp.: 20
Ice Cream & Frozen Dessert Mfr
N.A.I.C.S.: 311520
Richard Medic (Owner)

MEDICUS SOLUTIONS, LLC
3780 Mansell Rd Ste 250, Alpharetta, GA 30022
Tel.: (678) 495-5900
Web Site: http://medicusit.com
Year Founded: 2004
Sales Range: $1-9.9 Million
Emp.: 18
Computer Facility Management Services
N.A.I.C.S.: 541513
Chris Jann (Pres & CEO)
Mike Jann (Dir-IT)
Emily Sorrick (Chief People Officer)

Subsidiaries:

Clear Choice Telephones Inc (1)
1165 Hembree Rd, Roswell, GA 30076
Tel.: (770) 255-3333
Web Site: http://www.clearchoiceinc.com
Rev.: $1,400,000
Emp.: 9
Radio, Television & Other Electronics Stores
N.A.I.C.S.: 449210
Michael Higgins (Pres)

SPDJ Holdings, LLC (1)
256 Rangeline Rd, Longwood, FL 32750
Tel.: (407) 745-1848
Web Site: http://medicusit.com
IT Solutions Services
N.A.I.C.S.: 519290

MEDIEVAL DINNER & TOURNAMENT, INC.
7662 Beach Blvd, Buena Park, CA 90620-1838
Tel.: (714) 562-0221   CA
Web Site:
http://www.medievaltimes.com
Year Founded: 1986
Sales Range: $125-149.9 Million
Emp.: 500
Restaurants & Entertainment with a Medieval Theme
N.A.I.C.S.: 711110
David Manuel (Mgr-Mktg & Sls)
Ricko Montaner (Sr VP)

Subsidiaries:

Medieval Times Management Inc. (1)
7662 Beach Blvd, Buena Park, CA 90620
Tel.: (714) 521-4740
Rev.: $5,400,000
Emp.: 250
Dinner Theatre
N.A.I.C.S.: 711110

Schaumburg Castle Inc. (1)
2001 N Roselle Rd, Schaumburg, IL 60195
Tel.: (847) 843-3900
Web Site: http://www.medievaltimes.com
Rev.: $4,100,000
Emp.: 200
Dinner Theatre
N.A.I.C.S.: 711110

MEDIGOLD
6150 E Broad St Ste EE320, Columbus, OH 43213-1574
Tel.: (614) 546-4000   OH
Web Site: http://www.medigold.com
Year Founded: 1996
Sales Range: $400-449.9 Million
Elder Care Services
N.A.I.C.S.: 624120
Douglas E. Alfred (CMO)
Karen Allenbach (Dir-Utilization Mgmt)
Timothy J. Kern (Controller)
Jennifer L. Calder (Dir-Compliance Quality)
Juan Fraiz (CFO)

MEDIKE, INC.
145 Fritz Mar Ln, Athens, GA 30607
Tel.: (706) 543-9744
Web Site: http://www.medike.com
Rev.: $4,500,000
Emp.: 40
Textile & Fabric Finishing, except Broadwoven Fabric, Mills
N.A.I.C.S.: 313310
Jonathan Harris (Pres)

Subsidiaries:

Landes Lederwarenfabrik GmbH (1)
Arist-Dethleffs-Strasse 7, 88316, Isny im Allgau, Germany
Tel.: (49) 75627060
Web Site: http://www.landes-global.com
Leather Belt Mfr
N.A.I.C.S.: 316990

Subsidiary (Non-US):

Landes Canada Inc. (2)
400 Rue Saint-Vallier, Granby, J2G 7Y4,

QC, Canada
Tel.: (450) 378-9853
Web Site: http://www.landes-global.com
Leather Label & Handbag Mfr
N.A.I.C.S.: 316990
Subsidiary (Non-US):

Landes Hong Kong Limited (3)
3/F Kras Asia Industrial Building No 79
Hung To Road, Kwun Tong, Kowloon, China (Hong Kong)
Tel.: (852) 31022727
Leather Label & Handbag Mfr
N.A.I.C.S.: 316990
Mandy Lo (Dir)

MEDIMPACT HEALTHCARE SYSTEMS, INC.
10181 Scripps Gateway Ct, San Diego, CA 92131
Tel.: (858) 566-2727　　　　　CA
Web Site: http://www.medimpact.com
Year Founded: 1989
Sales Range: $25-49.9 Million
Pharmacy Benefit Management Product & Services
N.A.I.C.S.: 524292
Carine Scherlippens (Dir-Medicare Part D Programs)
Jonathan McDooling (Dir-Sls Ops)
Greg Watanabe (Co-Pres & COO)
Frederick Howe (Founder, Chm & CEO)
Dale Brown (Co-Pres)
Thomas E. Hutton (Chief HR Officer & Sr VP-HR-Global)
Dave Halter (Sr VP-Strategic Fin Ops)
Virginia Howe (Sr VP-Health Svcs)
Lisa A. Varrato (Sr VP-Acct Mgmt)
Paul Chan (Sr VP-Ops)
Vasu Bobba (CTO)
Asokan Selvaraj (CIO)

Subsidiaries:

Medical Security Card Company, LLC (1)
4911 E Broadway Blvd Ste 200, Tucson, AZ 85711
Tel.: (520) 888-8070
Web Site: http://www.scriptsave.com
Emp.: 55
Pharmacy Prescription Benefit Plan Services
N.A.I.C.S.: 525120
Mark Chamness (VP-Pharmacy Networks)
Marcus Sredzinski (Exec VP-PBM Svcs & Health Informatics)
Scott Paul (Exec VP-Corp Dev & Sls)
Paige Berger (Sr VP-Bus Rels)
Jerry Parker (VP-IT & Client Ops)
Jennifer Kimbrough (VP-Fin)

MEDINA CAPITAL PARTNERS, INC
2333 Ponce De Leon Blvd Ste 900, Coral Gables, FL 33134
Tel.: (305) 375-6000　　　　　FL
Web Site: http://www.medinacapital.com
Investment Services
N.A.I.C.S.: 523999
Manuel Medina (Founder & Mng Partner)
Nelson Fonseca (Partner)
Barry Field (Partner)
Randy Rowland (Partner)
Rene A. Rodriguez (Partner)
Tony Jimenez (Mng Dir)

MEDINA ELECTRIC CO-OPERATIVE
2308 18th St, Hondo, TX 78861
Tel.: (866) 632-3532
Web Site: http://www.medinaec.org
Sales Range: $25-49.9 Million
Emp.: 34
Generation, Electric Power
N.A.I.C.S.: 221118

Annette Sorrells (Treas & Sec)
Kenneth White (VP)

MEDINA MANAGEMENT COMPANY, LLC
3205 Medina Rd, Medina, OH 44256
Tel.: (330) 555-5555　　　　　OH
Web Site:
　http://www.medinaautomall.net
Year Founded: 2007
New & Used Car Dealer
N.A.I.C.S.: 441110
Gary Panteck (Owner, Pres & CEO)

MEDIQUANT, INC.
6900 S Edgerton Rd Ste 100, Brecksville, OH 44141-3193
Tel.: (440) 746-2300
Web Site: http://www.mediquant.com
Year Founded: 1999
Hospital Data Archiving & Interoperability Services
N.A.I.C.S.: 518210
Adrian Sands (Dir-Bus Dev)
Jim Jacobs (CEO)

MEDIREVV INC.
2600 University Pkwy, Coralville, IA 52241
Tel.: (678) 947-1801
Web Site: http://www.medirevv.com
Year Founded: 2007
Sales Range: $1-9.9 Million
Emp.: 68
Healthcare Revenue Cycle Management
N.A.I.C.S.: 541618
Kent Smith (VP-Sls)
Chris Klitgaard (CEO)
Brad Baldwin (Pres)
Dee Rountree (Dir-Sls Support)

MEDISOUTH, INC.
6229 Theall Rd, Houston, TX 77066
Tel.: (832) 533-2646
Web Site: http://www.medisouth.com
Year Founded: 2009
Sales Range: $25-49.9 Million
Business Management Services
N.A.I.C.S.: 561499
Greg Stadler (VP)

MEDISTAR, INC.
12 Cambridge Dr, Trumbull, CT 06611
Tel.: (203) 372-1900
Web Site:
　http://www.medistarbilling.com
Year Founded: 1997
Sales Range: $1-9.9 Million
Emp.: 45
Health Care Account Management
N.A.I.C.S.: 541618
Sali Borres (Dir-Ops & Quality Control)

MEDISYS HEALTH COMMUNICATIONS, LLC
65 Main St, High Bridge, NJ 08829
Tel.: (908) 638-5885
Web Site: http://www.medevoke.com
Year Founded: 2004
Sales Range: $1-9.9 Million
Emp.: 17
Biopharmaceutical Research & Development Services
N.A.I.C.S.: 541715
Marc Sirockman (Pres)
Anna Walz (CEO)
David Segarnick (Chief Medical Officer)
Shauna Aherne (Sr VP-Strategic Accts)
Fred Short (VP-Strategic Accts)

MEDIUM BLUE MULTIMEDIA GROUP LLC
670 Eleventh St NW, Atlanta, GA 30318
Tel.: (404) 525-4420
Web Site: http://www.mediumblue.com
Year Founded: 2000
Sales Range: $1-9.9 Million
Emp.: 15
Search Engine Optimization & Internet Marketing
N.A.I.C.S.: 541890
Scott Buresh (CEO)
Lauren Chadwell (Dir-Mktg)

MEDIUSA, LP.
6481 Franz Warner Pkwy, Whitsett, NC 27377-3000
Tel.: (336) 449-4440
Web Site: http://www.mediusa.com
Year Founded: 1984
Sales Range: $1-9.9 Million
Emp.: 75
Compression Hosiery Product Mfr & Distr
N.A.I.C.S.: 424350
Markus Frischholz (Mgr-IT)

MEDIVO, INC.
55 Broad St 16th Fl, New York, NY 10004
Web Site: http://www.medivo.com
Sales Range: $1-9.9 Million
Health Monitoring Services
N.A.I.C.S.: 513210
Sundeep Bhan (Co-Founder & CEO)
Steve Chase (CFO)
John Alfano (VP-Ops)
Brett Shamosh (VP-Product Dev)
Dan Berlinger (VP-Engrg)
Allison Keeley (Dir-Mktg)
Louisy Raymond (Dir-Mktg)
Donna Salerno (Gen Counsel)
Mark Grove (Sr VP-Clinical Data & Analytics Sls)
J. C. Muyl (Sr VP-Ops)
Wayne Caldwell (VP-Bus Dev)
Sanjiv Lall (VP-Bus Dev)
Cathy Wong (VP-Consultative Svcs)
Anne Bentley (VP-Ops)
Rohit Nambisan (VP-Product)

MEDIX STAFFING SOLUTIONS INC.
477 E Butterfield Rd Ste 400, Lombard, IL 60148
Tel.: (630) 725-9041
Web Site: http://www.medixteam.com
Year Founded: 2001
Sales Range: $50-74.9 Million
Emp.: 182
Recruitment & Staffing
N.A.I.C.S.: 561311
Alex Johnson (Acct Exec-Medix Scientific)
Brian Anstiss (CFO)
Kristin Danesi (Coord-Hr)
Chris Sioukas (Gen Counsel)
Adam Wenig (Mgr-IT)

MEDLER ELECTRIC COMPANY INC.
2155 Redmond Dr, Alma, MI 48801-1335
Tel.: (989) 463-1108　　　　　MI
Web Site:
　http://www.medlerelectric.com
Year Founded: 1918
Sales Range: $50-74.9 Million
Emp.: 125
Electrical Apparatus & Equipment
N.A.I.C.S.: 423610
Kelly Vliet (Mgr-Sls)
Doug Dietlein (Controller)

MEDLEY MATERIAL HANDLING CO.
4201 Will Rogers Pkwy, Oklahoma City, OK 73108
Tel.: (405) 946-3453
Web Site:
　http://www.medleycompany.com
Rev.: $16,308,622
Emp.: 60
Industrial Machinery & Equipment
N.A.I.C.S.: 423830
Mark J. Medley (Owner)
Nita Jones (Controller)
Scott Davis (Pres)
Brendan Russell (VP-Ops)
Jimmy Walker (VP-Sls & Mktg)

MEDLINE INDUSTRIES, LP
3 Lakes Dr, Northfield, IL 60093
Tel.: (847) 949-5500　　　　　IL
Web Site: https://www.medline.com
Year Founded: 1966
Sales Range: Less than $1 Million
Emp.: 36,000
Surgical Appliance & Supplies Manufacturing
N.A.I.C.S.: 339113
Andrew Mills (Pres)
Jim Abrams (COO)
Jim Boyle (CEO)

Subsidiaries:

Centurion Medical Products Corporation (1)
100 Centurion Way, Williamston, MI 48895
Tel.: (517) 546-5400
Web Site: http://www.medline.com
Emp.: 1,100
Mfr & Designer of Medical Products
N.A.I.C.S.: 339112
Thomas A. Archipley II (Pres)

MedCal Sales LLC (1)
388 E Court St Ste 202, Kankakee, IL 60901-3987
Tel.: (815) 936-3021
Pharmaceutical Product Mfr & Whslr
N.A.I.C.S.: 325412

Medical Mart Supplies Limited (1)
6200 Cantay Road, Mississauga, L5R 3Y9, ON, Canada
Tel.: (905) 624-6200
Web Site: http://www.medimart.com
Sales Range: $10-24.9 Million
Emp.: 200
Health Care Products Supplier
N.A.I.C.S.: 424210
Adeeb Matrouk (VP-Inventory Mgmt)
Erin Foster (Sr Dir-HR)
Dave Forte (Sr VP-Sls-LTC & PC)
Ernie Philip (Pres)
Roger Bourbonnais (Sr VP-Sls-Acute Care)
Kaveh Razzaghi (Sr VP-Comml Excellence)

Medline Accucare Division (1)
1 Medline Pl, Mundelein, IL 60060-4485
Tel.: (847) 949-5500
Web Site: http://www.medline.com
Mfr of Medical Supplies
N.A.I.C.S.: 339113

Medline Dermal Management Systems (1)
1 Medline Pl, Mundelein, IL 60060-4485　　　　　(100%)
Tel.: (847) 949-5500
Web Site: http://www.medline.com
Sales Range: $250-299.9 Million
Emp.: 1,000
Mfr of Medical Supplies
N.A.I.C.S.: 339999

Medline Dynacor Division (1)
1 Medline Pl, Mundelein, IL 60060-4485
Tel.: (847) 949-5500
Web Site: http://www.medline.com
Sales Range: $50-74.9 Million
Emp.: 35
Mfr of Medical Supplies
N.A.I.C.S.: 524113

Medline Industries Holdings, L.P. (1)
4800 E Valley Hwy E, Sumner, WA 98390
Tel.: (253) 891-3779

MEDLINE INDUSTRIES, LP
U.S. PRIVATE

Medline Industries, LP—(Continued)
Web Site: http://www.medline.com
Investment Management Service
N.A.I.C.S.: 523999

Medline Industries Ltd. (1)
3rd Floor Quayside Wilderspool Business Park Greenalls Avenue, Chelford Road, Warrington, WA4 6HL, Cheshire, United Kingdom (100%)
Tel.: (44) 844 334 5237
Web Site: http://www.medline.eu
Sales Range: $50-74.9 Million
Emp.: 200
Surgical Product Mfr & Distr
N.A.I.C.S.: 339113

Medline International Belgium BVBA (1)
Pegasuslaan 5 B, 1831, Diegem, Belgium
Tel.: (32) 28087493
Web Site: http://www.medline.eu
Medical & Surgical Equipment Mfr
N.A.I.C.S.: 339112

Medline International Denmark ApS (1)
c/o Moalem Weitemeyer Bendtsen Amaliegade 3-5, 1256, Copenhagen, Denmark
Tel.: (45) 89882737
Medical & Surgical Equipment Mfr
N.A.I.C.S.: 339112

Medline International France SAS (1)
Le Val Saint Quentin 2 Rue Rene Caudron Building 13 F, Voisins-le-Bretonneux, 78960, France
Tel.: (33) 1 30 05 34 00
Sales Range: $10-24.9 Million
Emp.: 85
Medical & Surgical Equipment Whslr
N.A.I.C.S.: 423450

Medline International Germany GmbH (1)
Wilhelm-Sinsteden-Strasse 5-7, 47533, Kleve, Germany
Tel.: (49) 2821 7510 0
Web Site: http://www.medline.com
Pharmaceutical Product Mfr & Whslr
N.A.I.C.S.: 325412

Medline International Iberia S.L.U (1)
Parque Empresarial San Fernando Edificio Munich Planta Baja local B, Avenida de Castilla 2 San Fernando de Henares, 28830, Madrid, Spain
Tel.: (34) 900 600 602
Web Site: http://www.medline.eu
Medical & Surgical Product Mfr & Whslr
N.A.I.C.S.: 339112
Jorge Saguar (Mgr-Sls)

Medline International Italy S.R.L. (1)
Piazzale della Resistenza 3, Scandicci, 50018, Florence, Italy
Tel.: (39) 0 55 776 6511
Web Site: http://www.medline.com
Sales Range: $10-24.9 Million
Emp.: 30
Pharmaceutical Product Mfr & Whslr
N.A.I.C.S.: 325412

Medline International Netherlands BV (1)
Wilhelm Sinsteden Strasse 5-7, 47533, Kleve, Netherlands
Tel.: (31) 88 00 11 900
Web Site: http://www.medline.com
Emp.: 40
Medical & Surgical Product Mfr
N.A.I.C.S.: 339112
Gerald Derickson (Mng Dir)

Medline International Switzerland Sarl (1)
A-One Business Centre Z A Verse la Piece 1-A5, Zone dactivites Vers la piece No 10, 1180, Rolle, Switzerland (100%)
Tel.: (41) 848244433
Sales Range: $50-74.9 Million
Emp.: 80
Mfr of Health Care Products & Management Services
N.A.I.C.S.: 339112

Medline International Two Australia Pty Ltd (1)
2 Fairview Place, Kings Park, 2765, NSW, Australia
Tel.: (61) 2 9830 0111
Web Site: http://www.medline.com
Emp.: 150
Medical & Surgical Equipment Whslr
N.A.I.C.S.: 339112
Young Lee Lan (Pres)

Medline Medcrest Division (1)
1 Medline Pl, Mundelein, IL 60060-4485
Tel.: (847) 949-5500
Web Site: http://www.medline.com
Sales Range: $50-74.9 Million
Emp.: 800
Mfr of Medical Supplies
N.A.I.C.S.: 339113
Andy Mills (Pres)

Professional Hospital Supply, Inc. (1)
42500 Winchester Rd, Temecula, CA 92590
Tel.: (951) 296-2600
Web Site: http://www.phsyes.com
Sales Range: $75-99.9 Million
Emp.: 1,500
Medical & Hospital Supplies Distr; Custom Packaging Solutions
N.A.I.C.S.: 423450
Shawn Huber (Dir-Q&A & Regulatory Affairs)

United Medco, LLC (1)
3952 Coral Ridge Dr, Coral Springs, FL 33065
Web Site: http://www.unitedmedco.com
Sales Range: $10-24.9 Million
Emp.: 12
Pharmaceuticals Product Mfr
N.A.I.C.S.: 325412
William Cuervo (CFO)

MEDMARK SERVICES, INC.
401 E Corporate Dr Ste 220, Lewisville, TX 75057
Tel.: (214) 379-3300 DE
Web Site: http://www.medmark.com
Addiction Treatment Centers Operator
N.A.I.C.S.: 621420
David K. White (Pres & CEO)
Daniel Gutschenritter (CFO)
Frank Baumann (Sr VP-Ops & Dev)
Robin A. Johnson (VP-Sls & Mktg)

MEDNET SOLUTIONS, INC.
110 Cheshire Ln Ste 300, Minnetonka, MN 55305
Tel.: (763) 258-2735 MN
Web Site: http://www.mednetstudy.com
Year Founded: 2000
Sales Range: $10-24.9 Million
Emp.: 78
Clinical Trial Management Solutions
N.A.I.C.S.: 541990
Rob Robertson (Pres & CEO)
Brian E. Sweeney (VP-Bus Dev)
Alan D. Sherwood (Sr VP-R&D)
Dennis Thalhuber (CFO)
Richard Murg (Chief Revenue Officer)

MEDOPTIONS, INC.
55 Hatchetts Hill Rd, Old Lyme, CT 06371
Tel.: (800) 370-3651
Web Site: http://www.medoptionsinc.com
Behavioral Health Services
N.A.I.C.S.: 923130
Ed Mercadante (Chm)
Thomas McInerney (CEO)
Bernadette Greatorex (Dir-Bus Dev)
Nicholas J. Mercadante (Pres & COO)
Richard Nankee (CFO)
Mark Cooke (Chief Compliance Officer)
Tim Lary (Chief Talent Officer)
Laura Etre (Chief Psychology Officer)
Amy Rader (Exec VP-Natl Field Ops)

MEDOSWEET FARMS INC.
915 1st Ave S, Kent, WA 98035
Tel.: (253) 852-4110
Web Site: http://www.medosweet.com
Sales Range: $10-24.9 Million
Emp.: 75
Distr of Dairy Products
N.A.I.C.S.: 424430
Craig Flintoff (VP-Ops)
Eric Flintoff (Pres)
Bryan Flintoff (VP-Exec Accts)
Victor Mejia (Gen Mgr)

MEDOVATIONS, INC.
102 E Keefe Ave, Milwaukee, WI 53212
Tel.: (414) 265-7620 WI
Web Site: http://www.medovations.com
Year Founded: 1986
Sales Range: $1-9.9 Million
Emp.: 50
Medical Device Mfr
N.A.I.C.S.: 339112
Brant Stanford (Pres & CEO)
Ryan Ford (Engr-Mfg)
Jason Larcheid (Mgr-Bus & Mfg Svcs)
Alyssa Roelli (Engr-Quality & Supply Chain)
Meg Vierling (Pres & COO)

Subsidiaries:

Sandhill Scientific, Inc. (1)
9150 Commerce Center Cir # 500, Littleton, CO 80129
Tel.: (303) 470-7020
Web Site: http://www.sandhillsci.com
Sales Range: $1-9.9 Million
Emp.: 35
Surgical & Medical Instrument Mfr
N.A.I.C.S.: 339112
Frederick Jory (Pres & CEO)
Stu Wildhorn (VP & Gen Mgr)
Laura Boll (VP-Quality & Regulatory Affairs)
Patti Leaf (Mgr-Customer & Technical Svcs)
Amanda Lecher (Dir-Talent Acq & Leader Dev)
Charles Lindsay (Dir-Engrg)
Dennis Meyer (Controller)
Margaret W. Vierling (Pres & CEO)

MEDPROPERTIES HOLDINGS, LLC
2100 McKinney Ave Ste 1450, Dallas, TX 75201
Tel.: (214) 661-1000
Web Site: http://www.medpropertieslp.com
Year Founded: 2007
Sales Range: $25-49.9 Million
Emp.: 10
Private Equity Real Estate Firm
N.A.I.C.S.: 523999
Darryl E. Freling (Mng Principal)
Michael R. Horowitz (Mng Principal)
Eric Minor (Mng Dir)
Roman J. Kupchynsky II (Mng Principal)

MEDSCRIBE INFORMATION SYSTEMS, INC.
800 Sea Gate Dr Ste 101, Naples, FL 34103
Tel.: (239) 430-0068 FL
Web Site: http://www.med-scribe.com
Year Founded: 1992
Sales Range: $1-9.9 Million
Emp.: 160
Medical Transcription
N.A.I.C.S.: 561492
John Langley (Pres & CEO)
Lori Eytel Langley (VP-HIM Svcs)
Bill Langley (VP-Ops)
Mike Irwin (VP-Sls & Mktg)

MEDSIGN INTERNATIONAL CORPORATION
651 Okeechobee Blvd Ste 1112, West Palm Beach, FL 33401
Tel.: (561) 304-8438 DE
Year Founded: 2009
Personal Emergency Response Systems Mfr & Marketer
N.A.I.C.S.: 339112
Thomas Conroy (CTO & Sec)
Michael Varrasse (COO)
Philip A. Verruto (CEO & CFO)

MEDSOURCE
16902 El Camino Real, Houston, TX 77058
Tel.: (281) 286-2003
Web Site: http://www.medsource.com
Year Founded: 1997
Rev.: $8,000,000
Emp.: 45
Management Consulting Services
N.A.I.C.S.: 541618
Eric Lund (Pres)
Matthew Wagener (Dir-Ops)
Jenny Ingram (Coord-Lab Svcs)

MEDSPHERE SYSTEMS CORP.
1220 E. 7800 S., Fl 3, Sandy, UT 84094
Tel.: (760) 692-3700 CA
Web Site: http://www.medsphere.com
Year Founded: 2002
Healthcare Information Technology Platform Solutions & Services
N.A.I.C.S.: 513210
Irv H. Lichtenwald (CEO)
Richard K. Sullivan (Chief Revenue Officer & Chief Government Officer)
Lily S. Chang (CTO)
Paul Corbett (VP-Sls-Comml)
Rita Schaefer (CFO)

Subsidiaries:

ChartLogic, Inc. (1)
3995 S 700 East Ste 200, Salt Lake City, UT 84107
Tel.: (801) 365-1800
Web Site: http://www.chartlogic.com
Emp.: 10
Health Care Srvices
N.A.I.C.S.: 621999
Zubin Emsley (CEO)
Rita Schaefer (CFO)
Brad Melis (Founder)
Chris Langehaug (Sr VP-Ops)

MBS/Net, Inc. (1)
735 Beta Dr Ste C, Cleveland, OH 44143
Tel.: (440) 461-7650
Web Site: http://www.mbsnetinc.com
Sales Range: $1-9.9 Million
Emp.: 30
Electronic Health Record Software Solutions
N.A.I.C.S.: 513210
Thomas Tucker (VP-Product Dev)
Jim Zeroff (Mgr-IT)
David Pelleg (CFO)

Micro Office Systems, Inc. (1)
1463 Warrensville Ctr Dr Ste 1, South Euclid, OH 44121
Tel.: (216) 297-0160
Web Site: http://www.micro-officesystems.com
Industrial Machinery & Equipment Merchant Whslr
N.A.I.C.S.: 423830
Oscar Quezada (Owner)
Norman Efroymson (CEO)

Wellsoft Corp. (1)
27 Worlds Fair Dr, Somerset, NJ 08873
Tel.: (800) 597-9909
Web Site: https://www.medsphere.com
Sales Range: $1-9.9 Million
Emp.: 4
Custom Computer Programing
N.A.I.C.S.: 541511
John Santmann (Pres)

MEDSTAFF, INC.

3805 W Chester Pike Ste 200, Newtown Square, PA 19073
Tel.: (610) 356-6337
Sales Range: $10-24.9 Million
Emp.: 130
Nurses' Registry
N.A.I.C.S.: 561311
Tim Rodden (COO)

MEDSTAR HEALTH
5565 Sterrett Pl 5th Fl, Columbia, MD 21044
Tel.: (410) 772-6719   MD
Web Site:
  http://www.medstarhealth.org
Year Founded: 1998
Sales Range: $25-49.9 Million
Emp.: 283
Healthcare Services
N.A.I.C.S.: 622110
Michael J. Curran (CFO, Chief Admin Officer & Exec VP)
Stephen R. T. Evans (Chief Medical Officer & Exec VP-Medical Affairs)
Maureen P. McCausland (Chief Nursing Officer & Sr VP)
Bruce A. Bartoo (Chief Philanthropy Officer & Sr VP)
Eric R. Wagner (Exec VP-Insurance & Diversified Ops)
Kenneth A. Samet (Pres & CEO)
Kevin Kowalski (Sr VP-Mktg & Strategy)
Joel N. Bryan (Treas & VP)
Larry L. Smith (VP-Risk Mgmt)
Loretta Walker (Chief HR Officer & Sr VP)
M. Joy Drass (COO & Exec VP)
Stuart M. Levine (Sr VP)
William R. Roberts (Chm)
Neil Weissman (Chief Scientific Officer)
Oliver M. Johnson II (Gen Counsel & Exec VP)
William J. Oetgen Jr. (Vice Chm)

MEDSTREAMING, LLC
9840 Willows Rd Ste 200, Redmond, WA 98052
Tel.: (425) 629-6388
Web Site:
  http://www.medstreaming.com
Healthcare IT Solutions
N.A.I.C.S.: 513210
Michael Thompson (COO)
Wael Elseaidy (Founder & CEO)
Jack L. Cronenwett (Chief Medical Officer)

Subsidiaries:

Physician Billing Partners LLC (1)
Jefferson Sq 4700 42nd Ave SW Ste 465, Seattle, WA 98116-4589
Tel.: (206) 932-9025
Web Site:
  http://www.physicianbillingpartners.com
Revenue Cycle Management Services
N.A.I.C.S.: 522180
Rachel Couwenberg (Founder)

MEDSURGE HOLDINGS, INC.
3330 Earhart Dr Ste 200, Carrollton, TX 75006
Tel.: (972) 720-0425
Year Founded: 2002
Sales Range: $25-49.9 Million
Emp.: 120
Medical Equipment Marketer & Distr for Aesthetic Medicine
N.A.I.C.S.: 423450
John D. Eubank (VP-Sls & Mktg-US)
Gabe Lewis (VP-Mktg)

Subsidiaries:

MedSurge Advances (1)
3330 Earhart Dr Ste 200, Carrollton, TX 75006
Tel.: (972) 720-0425
Web Site: http://www.osyrismedicalusa.com
Sales Range: $10-24.9 Million
Emp.: 50
Medical Equipment Marketer & Distr for Aesthetic Medicine
N.A.I.C.S.: 423450

MEDSYS GROUP CONSULTING
5465 Legacy Dr Ste 550, Plano, TX 75024
Tel.: (972) 464-0020
Web Site:
  http://www.medsysgroup.com
Year Founded: 2008
Sales Range: $10-24.9 Million
Emp.: 140
Health Care Srvices
N.A.I.C.S.: 621999
Alan Kravitz (Founder, Pres & CEO)
Dick Taylor (Chief Medical Officer & Exec VP)
Nancy Ellefson (CFO)
Luther Nussbaum (Chm)
Mark Embry (Co-Founder & Sr VP-Client Dev)
Ann Bartnik (Dir-Ops)
Gretchen Hydo (Dir-PR)
Romona Rivere (Mgr-Recruiting Trng)
Georgia Dittmeier (Principal)
Carl Ferguson (Sr VP)
Meg Grimes (Principal)
Jennifer Bula (Principal)
Nancy Miracle (Chief Nursing Officer & Exec VP)

MEDTEL SERVICES, LLC
2511 Corporate Way, Palmetto, FL 34221
Tel.: (941) 753-5000   DE
Web Site:
  http://www.medtelservices.com
Sales Range: $1-9.9 Million
Emp.: 40
Equipment & Application Software Developer, Mfr & Marketer for the Telecommunications Industry
N.A.I.C.S.: 334418
Richard W. Begando (Sr VP-Intl Sls)

Subsidiaries:

MEDTELL Ltd (1)
36-40 Yardley Rd, Olney, MK46 5ED, Buckinghamshire, United Kingdom (100%)
Tel.: (44) 8456800724
Equipment & Application Software Developer, Mfr & Marketer for the Telecommunications Industry
N.A.I.C.S.: 334210

MEDTEST DX, INC.
510 Furnace Dock Rd, Cortlandt Manor, NY 10567
Tel.: (914) 930-3110   DE
Web Site: http://www.medtestdx.com
Clinical Diagnostic Testing Services
N.A.I.C.S.: 541380
Randy Daniel (Chm)
Hanjoon Ryu (CEO)
Len Stigliano (CFO)

Subsidiaries:

Pointe Scientific, Inc. (1)
5449 Research Dr, Canton, MI 48188
Tel.: (734) 487-8300
Web Site: http://www.pointescientific.com
Sales Range: $1-9.9 Million
Emp.: 50
Clinical Diagnostic Product Developer Mfr
N.A.I.C.S.: 334516
Randy Daniel (Chm)
Wayne Brinster (CEO)

MEDTHINK COMMUNICATIONS
3301 Benson Dr Ste 400, Raleigh, NC 27609
Tel.: (919) 786-4918
Web Site: http://www.medthink.com
Year Founded: 2004
Sales Range: Less than $1 Million
Emp.: 12
Advetising Agency
N.A.I.C.S.: 541810
Scott Goudy (Partner)
Walt Clarke (Partner)
Steven Palmisano (VP-Medical Comm)
Syed Moinuddin (Acct Dir)
Jon Hudson (VP-Digital & Media Svcs)
Todd A. Parker (Dir-Scientific)
Joseph R. Conwell (Sr VP & Exec Creative Dir)
Bridget Dean (Acct Exec)
Laura Dutterer (Acct Exec)
Greg O'Donnell (Acct Dir-Promotional Acct Svcs)
Alejandro Arciniegas (Acct Supvr)
Edward Leon (Acct Dir)
Brian Peters (VP & Dir-Promotional Svcs)
Jeff Hill (Dir-Digital Strategy & Tech)

MEDVANTX, INC.
5626 Oberlin Drive, San Diego, CA 92121
Tel.: (858) 625-2990
Web Site: http://www.medvantx.com
Year Founded: 2000
Sales Range: $25-49.9 Million
Emp.: 118
Medication Management & Delivery Sevices
N.A.I.C.S.: 561320
Robert Feeney (Founder & CEO)
Scott Peterson (CFO)
Peter J. Kounelis (VP-Employer Solutions & Workplace Health Programs)
Dan Kloiber (VP-Bus Dev)
Bobbie Montgomery (VP-Sls & Mktg)

MEDVED AUTOPLEX
11001 W I 70 Frontage Rd, Wheat Ridge, CO 80033
Tel.: (303) 421-0100
Web Site: http://www.medved.com
Sales Range: $25-49.9 Million
Emp.: 500
New & Used Car Dealers
N.A.I.C.S.: 441110
John Medved (Owner, Pres & CEO)
Diana Blanch (Gen Mgr)

MEDWING.COM INC.
815 Brazos St 9th Fl, Austin, TX 78701
Tel.: (512) 687-1600
Year Founded: 2002
Sales Range: $1-9.9 Million
Emp.: 20
Retail Websites Specializing in Personal Care Products
N.A.I.C.S.: 541519
Matthew Rettig (Dir-Sls & Mktg)
Mark Winger (Founder & CEO)

MEDWISH INTERNATIONAL
17325 Euclid Ave, Cleveland, OH 44112
Tel.: (216) 692-1685   OH
Web Site: http://www.medwish.org
Year Founded: 1994
Sales Range: $10-24.9 Million
Emp.: 12
Medical Care Support Services
N.A.I.C.S.: 622110
Chance DeWerth (Dir-Ops)
Britta Harman (Dir-Bus Ops)
Carolina Masri (Exec Dir)
Jamie Lebovitz (Sec)
Lee Ponsky (Founder & Pres)
Michael Smith (Treas)
Michael Zweig (VP)
Ban Senter (Mgr-Volunteer Program)

MEDX PUBLISHING INC.
215 Centerview Dr Ste 350, Brentwood, TN 37027
Tel.: (615) 349-9933
Web Site: http://www.medicare.com
Year Founded: 2004
Sales Range: $1-9.9 Million
Emp.: 6
Online Guide to Medicare Covered Products & Services
N.A.I.C.S.: 513199
Bill Kimberlin (CEO)

MEE ENTERPRISES INC.
11721 W Carmen Ave, Milwaukee, WI 53225
Tel.: (414) 353-3300
Web Site: http://www.meelift.com
Rev.: $29,000,000
Emp.: 75
Materials Handling Machinery
N.A.I.C.S.: 423830
Pamela Borgue (Pres)

MEEDER EQUIPMENT COMPANY
3495 S Maple Ave, Fresno, CA 93725
Tel.: (559) 485-0979
Web Site: http://www.meeder.com
Sales Range: $10-24.9 Million
Emp.: 27
Industrial Machinery & Equipment
N.A.I.C.S.: 423830
Jeffrey D. Vertz (Pres)

MEEHAN AUTOMOBILES INC.
18 Uxbridge Rd, Mendon, MA 01756
Tel.: (508) 473-3100
Web Site:
  http://www.imperialcars.com
Sales Range: $450-499.9 Million
Emp.: 350
New & Used Automobiles
N.A.I.C.S.: 441110
Ika Nika (Owner & Pres)

MEERS ADVERTISING
1811 Walnut St, Kansas City, MO 64108
Tel.: (816) 474-2920   MO
Year Founded: 1993
Rev.: $10,000,000
Emp.: 16
Fiscal Year-end: 12/31/01
Advetising Agency
N.A.I.C.S.: 541810
Sam Meers (Founder & CEO)
Kathy Luetkenhoelter (Controller)
Sheree Johnson (Dir-Bus Intelligence)
David Thornhil (Dir-Creative)
Jeff Mott (COO)
Dave Altis (Exec Dir-Creative)
Allisyn Wheeler (Pres)

MEES DISTRIBUTORS INC.
1541 W Fork Rd, Cincinnati, OH 45223
Tel.: (513) 541-2311
Web Site:
  http://www.meesdistributors.com
Sales Range: $10-24.9 Million
Emp.: 20
Brick, Stone & Related Material
N.A.I.C.S.: 423320
Howard L. Mees (Owner)

MEESHAA INC.
1115 Inman Ave Ste 333, Edison, NJ 08820
Tel.: (908) 279-7986   NJ

MEESHAA INC.

Meeshaa Inc.—(Continued)
Web Site: http://www.meeshaa.com
Year Founded: 2009
Imitation Diamond Jewelry Mfr & Online Retailer
N.A.I.C.S.: 339910
Raja Shah (Founder & CEO)

MEETING ALLIANCE, LLC.
Bank Plaza 14 Main St, Robbinsville, NJ 08691
Tel.: (609) 208-1908
Web Site: http://www.meetingalliance.com
Year Founded: 1999
Rev.: $29,800,000
Emp.: 19
Convention & Trade Show Organizers
N.A.I.C.S.: 561920
Michael Franks (Co-Founder & Partner)
David P. D'Eletto (Co-Founder & Partner)
Dorisann Elcenko (Office Mgr)

MEETING PROFESSIONALS INTERNATIONAL (MPI)
3030 LBJ Freeway Ste 1700, Dallas, TX 75234-2759
Tel.: (972) 702-3000
Web Site: http://www.mpiweb.org
Year Founded: 1972
Emp.: 81
Membership Organization Addressing the Meetings Profession
N.A.I.C.S.: 541611
Paul Van Deventer (Pres & CEO)
Matthew Marcial (VP-Education & Events)
Bernie Schraer (Sr VP-Bus Dev-Global)
Diane Hawkins (VP-People, Performance & Admin Svcs)
Jodi Ann LaFreniere Ray (VP-Membership & Volunteer Experience)
Gerrit Jessen (Vice Chm-Fin)
Darren Temple (COO)
Michael Crumrine (VP-IT)
Nicole Edmund (VP-Community)
Melissa Majors (Dir-MPI Academy)
Julie Holmen (Dir-Bus Dev-Canada, Europe & Asia)
Drew Holmgreen (Sr Dir-Mktg & Comm)
Annette Gregg (Sr VP-Experience)

Subsidiaries:

Meeting Professionals International (MPI) (1)
6700 Century Ave Ste 100, Mississauga, L5N 6A4, ON, Canada (100%)
Tel.: (905) 567-9591
Web Site: https://www.mpi.org
Professional Meeting & Event Planners
N.A.I.C.S.: 541611
Leslie Wright (Exec Dir)

MEETING TOMORROW, INC.
1802 W Berteau Ave, Chicago, IL 60613
Tel.: (773) 907-0114
Web Site: http://www.meetingtomorrow.com
Sales Range: $1-9.9 Million
Emp.: 80
Consumer Electronics & Appliances Rental
N.A.I.C.S.: 532210
Mark Aistrope (Founder & CFO)
Lauren Reeves (Dir-Acct Svcs)
Phil Hamstra (Dir-Ops)

MEETINGS & EVENTS INTERNATIONAL INC.
1314 Burch Dr, Evansville, IN 47725
Tel.: (812) 868-2500
Web Site: http://www.meintl.com
Rev.: $22,300,000
Emp.: 75
Administrative Management & General Management Consulting Services
N.A.I.C.S.: 541611
Teresa Hall (CEO)
Jason McDowell (Controller)
Angie Moffett (Asst VP-Client Svcs)

MEETINGS & INCENTIVES
10520 7 Mile Rd, Caledonia, WI 53108
Tel.: (262) 835-3553
Web Site: http://www.meetings-incentives.com
Sales Range: $10-24.9 Million
Emp.: 110
Group Travel & Meeting Related Services
N.A.I.C.S.: 561599
Tina Madden (CFO)
Jean Johnson (Pres)

MEGA CONSTRUCTION CORP. OF NJ
1 American Way, Spotswood, NJ 08884-1254
Tel.: (732) 251-1740
Web Site: http://www.megaconst.com
Rev.: $16,000,000
Emp.: 8
Plaster & Drywall Work
N.A.I.C.S.: 238310
Steve Bodeker (VP)
Ramiro Quintans (Partner)

MEGA MANUFACTURING INC.
650 Race St, Rockford, IL 61105
Tel.: (815) 964-6771
Web Site: http://www.piranhafab.com
Year Founded: 1989
Sales Range: $1-9.9 Million
Emp.: 370
Machine Tools, Metal Forming Type
N.A.I.C.S.: 333517
Tom Scott (Gen Mgr)

Subsidiaries:

Mega Manufacturing Inc. - Bertsch Division (1)
3310 E 4th Ave, Hutchinson, KS 67504-0457
Tel.: (620) 663-1127
Industrial Machinery Mfr
N.A.I.C.S.: 333248

Mega Manufacturing Inc. - Whitney Division (1)
650 Race St, Rockford, IL 61105
Tel.: (815) 964-6771
Web Site: http://www.wawhitney.com
Fabricated Structural Metal Mfr
N.A.I.C.S.: 332312

Whitney/Piranha/Bertsch (1)
650 Race St, Rockford, IL 61105
Tel.: (815) 964-6771
Web Site: http://www.piranhafab.com
Heavy Plate Fabricating Machinery
N.A.I.C.S.: 423830
Martin Trent (Gen Mgr)

Division (Domestic):

W.A. Whitney Co. (2)
650 Race St, Rockford, IL 61101-1434
Tel.: (815) 964-6771
Web Site: http://www.wawhitney.com
Machine Builder & Punches & Dies Mfr
N.A.I.C.S.: 333517

MEGA MEX, L.P.
1823 Roughneck Dr, Humble, TX 77338-5228
Tel.: (281) 548-1544
Web Site: http://www.megamex.com
Year Founded: 1990
Sales Range: $10-24.9 Million
Emp.: 10
Specialty Metal Supplier
N.A.I.C.S.: 423510
Alan G. Lever (Mng Partner)

MEGAN DRISCOLL, LLC
49 W 24th St 7th Fl, New York, NY 10010
Tel.: (646) 517-4220
Web Site: http://www.evolvemkd.com
Year Founded: 2014
Sales Range: $1-9.9 Million
Emp.: 20
Media Advertising Services
N.A.I.C.S.: 541840
Megan Driscoll (CEO)
Adeena Fried (Sr VP)
Katherine Greene (VP)

MEGAS, INC.
9313 Canyon Classic, Las Vegas, NV 89147
Tel.: (702) 900-5550
Web Site: http://www.megasglobal.com
Year Founded: 2009
Emp.: 7
Entertainment & Wellness Products
N.A.I.C.S.: 561499
Charles Mui (Pres, Sec & Treas)
Don Hunter (Chm & CEO)

MEGATRAX PRODUCTION MUSIC, INC.
7629 Fulton Ave, North Hollywood, CA 91605
Tel.: (818) 255-7100
Web Site: http://www.megatrax.com
Year Founded: 1992
Rev.: $5,000,000
Emp.: 30
Music Production
N.A.I.C.S.: 512290
J. C. Dwyer (Co-Owner & Chief Compliance Officer)
Ron Mendelsohn (Co-Owner, Pres & CEO)
Leisa Korn (VP-Bus Affairs & Global Rels)
Philip Macko (Sr VP-Sls)
Scott Linn (Office Mgr-Acctg, Fin & Admin)
Steven Naugle (CFO)
Marcia Kellogg (Mgr-Mktg, Adv & Publicity)

MEHADRIN DAIRY CORP.
100 Trumbull St, Elizabeth, NJ 07206
Tel.: (718) 456-9494
Web Site: http://www.mehadrin.com
Sales Range: $10-24.9 Million
Emp.: 42
Provider of Dairy Products
N.A.I.C.S.: 424430
Sam Leifer (Pres)

MEHAFFY & WEBER, A PROFESSIONAL CORPORATION
2615 Calder Ave Ste 800, Beaumont, TX 77702
Tel.: (409) 835-5011
Web Site: http://www.mehaffyweber.com
Year Founded: 1946
Law Firm
N.A.I.C.S.: 541110
Sandra F. Clark (Atty)
Louis M. Scofield (Atty)
Robert A. Black (Mng Partner)
Roger S. McCabe (Atty)
Patricia D. Chamblin (Atty)

MEHERRIN AGRICULTURE & CHEMICAL CO.
413 Main St, Severn, NC 27877
Tel.: (252) 585-1744
Web Site: http://www.hamptonfarms.com
Year Founded: 1946
Sales Range: $75-99.9 Million
Emp.: 150
Farm Chemicals, Seed & Fertilizer Distr
N.A.I.C.S.: 424910
Dallas Barnes (Pres)
Jim Davis (Dir-Sls & Mktg)

MEHRAVISTA HEALTH
32196 US Hwy 19 N Ste A, Palm Harbor, FL 34684
Tel.: (727) 781-2007
Web Site: http://www.mehravistahealth.com
Sales Range: $1-9.9 Million
Mental Health Services
N.A.I.C.S.: 621112
Rahul N. Mehra (CEO & Chief Medical Officer)
Vicki B. Davis (COO)

MEI TECHNOLOGIES, INC.
18050 Saturn Ln Ste 300, Houston, TX 77058
Tel.: (281) 283-6200
Web Site: http://www.meitechinc.com
Year Founded: 1992
Sales Range: $150-199.9 Million
Emp.: 781
Engineeering Services
N.A.I.C.S.: 541330
Edelmiro Muniz (Chm)
Stephanie Murphy (Vice Chm)
Karen Todd (CFO)
David Cazes (CEO)
Richard Larson (Exec Dir-Bus Dev)

MEIER
907 Broadway 4th Fl, New York, NY 10010
Tel.: (212) 460-5655
Year Founded: 1979
Rev.: $1,500,000
Emp.: 6
Fiscal Year-end: 09/30/04
N.A.I.C.S.: 541810
Diane Meier (Creative Dir)

MEIJER, INC.
2929 Walker NW, Grand Rapids, MI 49544-9424
Web Site: https://www.meijer.com
Year Founded: 1934
Sales Range: $5-14.9 Billion
Emp.: 70,000
Supermarkets & Other Grocery Retailers (except Convenience Retailers)
N.A.I.C.S.: 445110
Hendrik G. Meijer (Chm)
Rick Keyes (Pres & CEO)
Roger Harkrider (Dir-Produce)

MEINECKE-JOHNSON COMPANY, INC.
5 14th St N, Fargo, ND 58102-4216
Tel.: (701) 293-1040
Web Site: http://www.meineckejohnsoncompany.com
Sales Range: $75-99.9 Million
Emp.: 60
Nonresidential Construction Services
N.A.I.C.S.: 236220
Eric Johnson (Mgr)

MEIRXRS
100 N Brand Blvd Ste 306-309, Glendale, CA 91203
Tel.: (800) 507-5277
Web Site: http://www.meirxrs.com
Year Founded: 1992
Sales Range: $1-9.9 Million
Emp.: 10
Medical Recruitment Specialists
N.A.I.C.S.: 561320

COMPANIES

Rosemarie Christopher *(Pres & CEO)*
Jan Clements *(Mgr-Clinical Res, Medical Affairs & Talent)*
Lewie Casey *(Mgr-Talent, Quality & Regulatory Affairs)*

MEISINGER CONSTRUCTION COMPANY
121 Bridgepoint Way, South Saint Paul, MN 55075-2475
Tel.: (651) 452-4778
Web Site: http://www.meisingerconstruction.com
Sales Range: $10-24.9 Million
Emp.: 10
Commercial & Office Buildings, Renovation & Repair
N.A.I.C.S.: 236220

MEISNER ELECTRIC, INC.
220 NE 1st St, Delray Beach, FL 33444
Tel.: (561) 278-8362
Web Site: http://www.mei.cc
Year Founded: 1953
Rev.: $35,845,000
Emp.: 300
Contractor of General Electrical Services
N.A.I.C.S.: 238210
Janet I. Onnen *(CEO)*

MEISNER GALLERY, INC.
215 Central Ave, Farmingdale, NY 11735-1403
Tel.: (631) 777-1711
Web Site: http://www.meisnerart.com
Sales Range: $10-24.9 Million
Emp.: 16
Non-Durable Goods Whslr
N.A.I.C.S.: 424990
Mitchell Meisner *(Owner)*

MEISTER MEDIA WORLDWIDE INC.
37733 Euclid Ave, Willoughby, OH 44094
Tel.: (440) 942-2000
Web Site: http://www.meistermedia.com
Year Founded: 1932
Sales Range: $10-24.9 Million
Emp.: 110
Magazine Publisher
N.A.I.C.S.: 513120
Gary T. Fitzgerald *(Chm & CEO)*
James C. Sulecki *(Chief Content Officer & Head-Precision Initiative-Global)*
William A. Rigo *(Dir-Mktg)*
Cynthia L. Gorman *(VP & Dir-HR)*
Joe W. Monahan *(Dir-Media Bus)*
Michael L. DeLuca *(Pres)*
Nick Mlachak *(Dir-Media Svcs)*
Donald Hohmeier *(CFO & VP)*
Katie Smith *(Dir-Corp Events)*
Charlie Craine *(CTO & Dir-Data Products)*
Susan Chiancone *(Co-CFO & VP)*
William J. Miller II *(Vice Chm)*

MEITEC INC.
2800 Veterans Memorial Blvd Ste 260, Metairie, LA 70002-6178
Tel.: (504) 455-2600
Web Site: http://www.meitec.net
Sales Range: $10-24.9 Million
Emp.: 185
Electrical Work
N.A.I.C.S.: 238210
Tom Isbell *(Exec VP)*
Gary Williams *(VP-Safety)*

MEKANISM, INC.
640 Second St 3rd Fl, San Francisco, CA 94107
Tel.: (415) 908-4000   CA
Web Site: http://www.mekanism.com
Year Founded: 2000
Sales Range: $10-24.9 Million
Emp.: 65
Advetising Agency
N.A.I.C.S.: 541810
Tommy Means *(Founder, Partner & Exec Creative Dir)*
Pete Caban *(Partner-Strategic Dev)*
Jason Harris *(Pres & CEO)*
Jason Lonsdale *(Chief Strategy Officer)*
Tom Lyons *(Exec VP & Dir-Creative)*
Stephanie Warne *(Dir-Talent/Recruiting)*
Hilary Lee *(Dir-Brand Mgmt)*
Mike Zlatoper *(COO)*
Lisa Townsend Zakroff *(Mng Dir-Seattle)*
Adama Sall *(head-Plng-East)*
Jillian Goger *(Dir-Creative-New York)*
Matt Fischvogt *(Dir-Creative-MillerCoors Acct-Chicago)*
Melissa Hill *(Head-Brand Mgmt-East)*
Anna Boyarsky *(Head-Brand Mgmt-West)*
David Horowitz *(Exec Dir-Creative-New York)*
Rick Thornhill *(Mng Dir-Chicago)*
Caroline Moncure *(Dir-Brand Dev-Chicago)*

MEKETA INVESTMENT GROUP, INC.
80 University Ave, 02090, Westwood, MA
Tel.: (781) 471-3500
Web Site: http://www.meketagroup.com
Year Founded: 1978
Investment Advice
N.A.I.C.S.: 523940
James Edward Meketa *(Founder)*
Molly LeStage *(Sr VP)*
Stephen McCourt *(Co-CEO & Mng Principal)*
Peter Woolley *(Co-CEO)*
Ted L. Disabato *(Mng Principal)*
Frank Benham *(Mng Principal & Dir-Research)*
David Eisenberg *(Principal)*
LaRoy Brantley *(Principal)*
Amy Hauke *(Exec VP-Chicago)*
John Haggerty *(Dir-Private Market Investments)*
Sandra Ackermann-Schaufler *(Principal)*
Amy Hsiang *(Dir-Public Markets Mgr Res)*
Josh Brough *(Head-Equity Res)*
Mark McKeown *(Head-Fixed Income Res)*
Judy Chambers *(Mng Principal)*
Hannah Webber *(Dir-Consulting Svcs)*

MEL BERNIE & COMPANY INC.
3000 W Empire Ave, Burbank, CA 91504
Tel.: (818) 841-1928   CA
Web Site: http://www.1928.com
Year Founded: 1968
Costume Jewelry Mfr
N.A.I.C.S.: 339910
Melvyn Bernie *(Founder)*

MEL FOSTER CO. INC.
7566 Market Pl Dr, Eden Prairie, MN 55344-3636
Tel.: (952) 941-9790
Web Site: http://www.melfoster.com
Electronic Parts
N.A.I.C.S.: 423690
Michael Gorman *(VP)*
Ed Thurmes *(Mgr-Distr)*

MEL FOSTER CO. INC.
3211 E 35th St Ct, Davenport, IA 52807
Tel.: (563) 359-4663
Web Site: http://www.melfosterco.com
Rev.: $28,100,000
Emp.: 350
Mortgage Banker
N.A.I.C.S.: 522292
Rob Sidk *(Pres & CEO)*
Ray Cassady *(CFO)*
Fred Dasso *(Mgr)*

MEL HAMBELTON FORD INC.
11771 W Kellogg St, Wichita, KS 67209
Tel.: (316) 462-3673
Web Site: http://www.melhambeltonford.com
Rev.: $58,300,000
Emp.: 148
Automobiles, New & Used
N.A.I.C.S.: 441110
Mel Hambelton *(Pres)*

MEL RAPTON HONDA
3630 Fulton Ave, Sacramento, CA 95821-5104
Tel.: (916) 482-5400   CA
Web Site: http://www.melraptonhonda.com
Year Founded: 1961
Sales Range: $125-149.9 Million
Emp.: 160
Provider of Sales & Service of New & Used Automobiles
N.A.I.C.S.: 441110
Katina Rapton *(Owner)*
Charlie Moulton *(Controller)*

MEL STEVENSON & ASSOCIATES, INC.
2840 Roe Ln, Kansas City, KS 66103-1104
Tel.: (913) 384-0804   MO
Web Site: http://www.speccorp.com
Year Founded: 1973
Roofing, Siding & Insulation
N.A.I.C.S.: 423330
Melvin Stevenson *(Chm & CEO)*
Doug Stevenson *(Pres)*
John Ruhlman *(CFO)*
Brook Benge *(COO)*
Shawn Gastner *(VP-Fin)*
Dan Hollabaugh *(VP-Pur)*
Tim Stickney *(VP-Specialty Products)*
Pat Breshears *(VP-North Regional)*
Judson Pelt *(Mgr-Central Region District)*
Don Reed *(VP-Southwest Regional)*
Charles Clark *(VP-South Texas Regional)*
Jim Coston *(VP-Florida Regional)*

MEL WHEELER, INC.
5001 S Hulen St Ste 107, Fort Worth, TX 76132-1936
Tel.: (817) 294-7644   TX
Rev.: $29,400,000
Emp.: 200
Television Broadcasting Station
N.A.I.C.S.: 516120
Gretchen Cummings *(Controller)*
Leonard Wheeler *(Owner & Pres)*
Steve Wheeler *(VP)*
Clark Wheeler *(VP)*
Brett Sharp *(Gen Mgr)*
Nadra Scott *(VP-Sls)*

MEL-JEN

MELANOMA RESEARCH ALLIANCE

2107 Westwood Blvd, Los Angeles, CA 90025
Tel.: (310) 475-0606   CA
Web Site: http://www.wallywine.com
Year Founded: 1968
Sales Range: $10-24.9 Million
Wine & Liquor Store Owner & Operator
N.A.I.C.S.: 445320
Maurice Marciano *(Co-Owner)*
Paul Marciano *(Co-Owner)*
Christian Navarro *(Co-Owner & Pres)*
Armand Marciano *(Co-Owner & CEO)*

MEL-O-CREAM DONUTS INTERNATIONAL, INC.
5456 International Pkwy, Springfield, IL 62711
Tel.: (217) 483-7272
Web Site: http://www.mel-o-cream.com
Year Founded: 1932
Sales Range: $10-24.9 Million
Emp.: 80
Frozen Cake, Pie & Pastries Mfr
N.A.I.C.S.: 311813
Dan Alewelt *(Dir-Ops)*
Jeremey McClure *(Mgr-Sanitation)*
David Waltrip *(Pres & CEO)*
Jeffrey Alexander *(Dir-Logistics & Procurement)*
John Armstrong *(Dir-Tech & Engrg)*

MELALEUCA INC.
4609 W 65th S, Idaho Falls, ID 83402-4342
Tel.: (208) 522-0700   ID
Web Site: http://www.melaleuca.com
Year Founded: 1985
Sales Range: $75-99.9 Million
Emp.: 1,200
Provider of Personal Care Items
N.A.I.C.S.: 325411
Frank Vandersloot *(Founder & Chm)*
Kevin Cook *(Mgr-Facilities)*
Noel Jenkins *(VP-Plant Ops)*
Troy Peterson *(Assoc Gen Counsel)*
John Burden *(Treas)*
Dean Johnson *(Mgr-Fin Analyst)*
Debi Hunter Croft *(Mgr-Production)*
McKay Christensen *(Mgr)*
Jerry Felton *(CEO)*

MELAMEDRILEY ADVERTISING, LLC
1468 W Ninth St Ste 440, Cleveland, OH 44113
Tel.: (216) 241-2141   OH
Web Site: http://www.mradvertising.com
Year Founded: 1930
Sales Range: $10-24.9 Million
Emp.: 25
Advetising Agency
N.A.I.C.S.: 541810
Sarah Melamed *(Pres)*
Rick Riley *(Exec Creative Dir)*

MELANOMA RESEARCH ALLIANCE
730 15th St NW, Washington, DC 20005
Tel.: (202) 336-8935   DE
Web Site: http://www.curemelanoma.org
Year Founded: 2007
Rev.: $5,562,604
Assets: $37,272,765
Liabilities: $17,748,650
Net Worth: $19,524,115
Earnings: ($10,842,368)
Emp.: 11
Fiscal Year-end: 12/31/18
Disease Research Organization
N.A.I.C.S.: 813212
Debra Black *(Co-Founder & Chm)*
Margaret Anderson *(Sec)*

Melanoma Research Alliance—(Continued)
Michael Kaplan (Pres & CEO)
Marc Hurlbert (Chief Science Officer)
Kristen Mueller (Sr Dir-Scientific Program)

MELCHER & PRESCOTT INSURANCE
426 Main St, Laconia, NH 03246
Tel.: (603) 524-4535
Web Site: http://www.melcher-prescott.com
Year Founded: 1862
Insurance Agents & Broker
N.A.I.C.S.: 524210
Tom Volpe (VP)
William Bald (VP-Life Health & Employee Benefits)
Chris Volpe (Pres & CEO)
Holly Marston (Bus Mgr-Admin)
Jill Martineau (Mgr-Comml Lines)
Nancy Perron (Mgr-Personal Lines)
Lisa Graham (Mgr-IT)
Vincent Schuck (Chief Revenue Officer)
Waneta Forbes (Asst Mgr-Comml Lines)

MELCO INTERNATIONAL LLC
1575 W 124th Ave, Denver, CO 80234-1707
Tel.: (303) 457-1234
Web Site: http://www.melco.com
Year Founded: 1972
Textile Machinery & Software Mfr
N.A.I.C.S.: 333248
Dale Sanders (Pres & CEO)
Geoffrey Stuart Davis (CFO)

MELE COMPANIES, INC.
2007 Beechgrove Pl, Utica, NY 13501
Tel.: (315) 733-4600 NY
Web Site: http://www.melejewelrybox.com
Year Founded: 1912
Sales Range: $75-99.9 Million
Emp.: 30
Mfr of Musical & Non-Musical Jewelry Boxes
N.A.I.C.S.: 322130
Thomas J. Kinney (Controller)
Mike Volza (VP)
Gerard Morrissey (Asst Controller)
Joanne Archer (Mgr-Internet Mktg)

MELETIO ELECTRICAL SUPPLY CO.
10930 Harry Hines Blvd, Dallas, TX 75220
Tel.: (214) 352-3900
Web Site: http://www.meletio.com
Rev.: $14,858,752
Emp.: 50
Electrical Supplies
N.A.I.C.S.: 423610
Ken Reiser (Pres)

MELILLO CONSULTING INC.
285 Davidson Ave Ste 202, Somerset, NJ 08873-4153
Tel.: (732) 563-8400 NJ
Web Site: http://www.mjm.com
Year Founded: 1988
Sales Range: $10-24.9 Million
Emp.: 80
Provider of Custom Computer Programming Services
N.A.I.C.S.: 541511
Sean McDonald (Dir-Bus Dev)
Mike McDonnell (Dir-Bus Dev)
Don Scobell (Dir-Bus Dev)
Mike Armbrust (VP-Sls)
Joe Staiber (Chief Revenue Officer)
Scott Dunsire (CEO)

MELINK CORPORATION
5140 River Valley Rd, Milford, OH 45150
Tel.: (513) 965-7300 OH
Web Site: http://www.melinkcorp.com
Year Founded: 1987
Sales Range: $10-24.9 Million
Emp.: 85
Energy Efficiency & Renewable Energy Products Whslr & Services
N.A.I.C.S.: 221118
Stephen K. Melink (Founder & CEO)
Craig Bishop (Mgr-Production)
Donna Jones (CFO)
Jason Jimison (Coord-Acct)
Phyllis Kramer (Dir-First Impressions)
Craig Davis (Dir-Project Mgmt)
David Smith (Mgr-Bus Dev-Central)

MELISSA CORPORATION
22382 Avenida Empresa, Rancho Santa Margarita, CA 92688-2112
Tel.: (800) 635-4772
Web Site: http://www.melissa.com
Year Founded: 1985
Emp.: 200
Data Quality & Address Management Services
N.A.I.C.S.: 541511
Raymond F. Melissa (Founder & Pres)
Bud Walker (VP-Enterprise Sls & Strategy)
Greg Brown (VP-Mktg)
Rick Brusca (Sls Dir-Data Quality Solutions)
Admound Chou (VP-Product Dev)
Bette Hagerty (Mgr-HR)
Chris Rowe (VP-Data Svcs)
Dennis Bedford (Chief Compliance Officer & Gen Counsel)
Phil Maitino (CTO)
John Melissa (CFO)
Charles Gaddy (Dir-Global Sls & Alliances)

MELISSA DEVOLENTINE PUBLIC RELATIONS
6538 Collins Ave Ste 186, Miami Beach, FL 33141
Tel.: (305) 864-4200
Web Site: http://www.mdevolentinepr.com
Year Founded: 1999
Sales Range: Less than $1 Million
Emp.: 1
Full-Service Public Relations, Marketing & Advertising
N.A.I.C.S.: 541820
Melissa DeVolentine (Founder)

MELLACE FAMILY BRANDS, INC.
6195 El Camino Real, Carlsbad, CA 92009
Tel.: (760) 448-1940
Web Site: http://www.mamamellace.com
Year Founded: 2001
Rev.: $19,600,000
Emp.: 75
Roasted Nuts & Peanut Butter Mfr
N.A.I.C.S.: 311911
Mike Mellace (Pres)
Shanae Johnson (Controller)

MELLANO & COMPANY
766 S Wall St, Los Angeles, CA 90014
Tel.: (213) 622-0796
Web Site: http://www.mellano.com
Rev.: $20,000,000
Emp.: 50
Flowers & Florists Supplies
N.A.I.C.S.: 424930

John Mellano (Founder)
Phil Kenney (Mgr-Sls)
Ryan Neumann (Gen Mgr)

MELLING TOOL COMPANY INC.
2620 Saradan Dr, Jackson, MI 49202-1214
Tel.: (517) 787-8172 MI
Web Site: http://www.melling.com
Year Founded: 1944
Sales Range: $25-49.9 Million
Emp.: 400
Mfr of Motor Vehicle Parts & Accessories
N.A.I.C.S.: 336310
Mark Melling (CEO)

Subsidiaries:

Dura-Bond Bearing Co. (1)
3200 Arrowhead Dr, Carson City, NV 89706
Tel.: (775) 883-8998
Web Site: http://www.mellingdurabond.com
Sales Range: $1-9.9 Million
Machine Tools Mfr
N.A.I.C.S.: 333517
Charles Barnett (Owner)
Andre Moser (Gen Mgr-Sls)

Melling Industries Inc. (1)
2720 Saradan Dr, Jackson, MI 49202-1216
Tel.: (517) 787-5484
Web Site: http://www.mellingindustries.com
Sales Range: $10-24.9 Million
Emp.: 50
Mfg Of Screw Machine Products
N.A.I.C.S.: 332721

Melling Products Corporation (1)
333 Grace St, Farwell, MI 48622-9702
Tel.: (989) 588-6147
Web Site: http://www.mellingproducts.com
Rev.: $5,100,000
Emp.: 70
Automotive Stampings
N.A.I.C.S.: 336370
Jennifer Struble (Office Mgr)

Melling Tool Company Inc (1)
2620 Saradan Dr, Jackson, MI 49202-1214
Tel.: (517) 787-8172
Web Site: http://www.melling.com
Rev.: $13,000,000
Emp.: 1,100
Automotive Equipment Mfr & Distr
N.A.I.C.S.: 336310

Melling Tool Company Inc. - AC Foundry Division (1)
1146 N Raymond Rd, Battle Creek, MI 49014
Tel.: (269) 963-8539
Web Site: http://www.acfoundry.com
Aluminum Casting Services
N.A.I.C.S.: 331524
Brian Shaughnessy (Gen Mgr)

Melling Tool Company Inc. - Melling Cylinder Sleeves Division (1)
140 Jacobson Dr, Maquoketa, IA 52060
Tel.: (563) 652-6806
Web Site: http://www.melling.com
Machine Tools Mfr
N.A.I.C.S.: 333517
Dan McDonell (Plant Mgr)
Kedric Moore (Mgr-Quality)

Melling Tool Company Inc. - Melling Engine Parts Division (1)
2620 Saradan Dr, Jackson, MI 49204
Tel.: (517) 787-8172
Web Site: http://www.mellingengine.com
Automotive Engine Parts Mfr
N.A.I.C.S.: 336310
Steve Arent (Mgr-Sls-Reg)

Melling Tool Company Inc. - Melling Select Performance Division (1)
2620 Saradan Dr, Jackson, MI 49204
Tel.: (517) 787-8172
Web Site: http://www.melling.com
Emp.: 250
Automotive Engine Parts Mfr
N.A.I.C.S.: 336310
Mark Melling (CEO)

Melling Tool Company Inc. - Melling Sintered Metals Division (1)
Hwy 15 E, Billings, OK 74630
Tel.: (580) 725-3293
Web Site: http://www.mellingsinteredmetals.com
Emp.: 66
Machine Tools Mfr
N.A.I.C.S.: 333517

Prescott Products Inc. (1)
5250 Henderson Lake Rd, Prescott, MI 48756
Tel.: (989) 873-4294
Web Site: http://www.prescottproducts.com
Rev.: $1,000,000
Emp.: 9
Screw Machine Products
N.A.I.C.S.: 332721

REXITE, S.A. de C.V. (1)
Calle 2A 1 Col Fraccionamiento Industrial San Pablo Xalpa, Tlalnepantla, 54090, Mexico
Tel.: (52) 55 5369 5547
Web Site: http://www.rexite.net
Automotive Part Whslr
N.A.I.C.S.: 423120

Save Time Convenience Stores Inc. (1)
2700 Airport Rd, Jackson, MI 49202-1240
Tel.: (517) 782-3038
Web Site: http://www.savetimepizza.com
Rev.: $170,000
Emp.: 3
Convenience Store Operator
N.A.I.C.S.: 445131

MELLOY BROTHERS ENTERPRISES
7707 Lomas Blvd NE, Albuquerque, NM 87110-7413
Tel.: (505) 265-8721 NM
Web Site: http://www.melloynissan.com
Year Founded: 1958
Sales Range: $100-124.9 Million
Emp.: 115
Investment Holding Company; New & Used Automobiles & Pickups
N.A.I.C.S.: 441110
Robert E. Melloy (Dir-Social Media)
Alan Selimovic (Mgr-Sls-Used Car)
Isaac Cordova (Asst Mgr-Sls)
John Herbrand (Mgr-Internet)
Ken Engle (Mgr-Fin)
Matt Kneip (Mgr-Sls-Used Car)
Mike Lee (Mgr-Internet & Fleet Sls)
Mike Turri (Dir-Fin)
Roy Benson (Gen Mgr)
Shawn Silva (Mgr-New Car Sls)
Vince DeFazio (Asst Mgr-Sls)

MELO CONTRACTORS, INC.
159 W Westfield Ave, Roselle Park, NJ 07204
Tel.: (908) 245-5280 NJ
Web Site: http://www.melocontractors.com
Year Founded: 1964
Sales Range: $1-9.9 Million
Emp.: 11
Commercial & Residential Building Construction & Remodeling
N.A.I.C.S.: 236220
Michael Melango (CEO)

MELODY INVESTMENT ADVISORS LP
600 5th Ave 27F, New York, NY 10020
Web Site: http://www.melodyinvestmentadvisors.com
Year Founded: 2019
Alternative Asset Manager & Financial Services
N.A.I.C.S.: 525990
Omar Jaffrey (Founder & Mng Partner)

John Apostolides *(Partner-Investment)*
Joshua Oboler *(Partner-Investment)*
Spencer Zakarin *(VP)*
David Bacino *(Operating Partner)*
Jorge Pedraza *(Partner-Ops)*
Chester R. Dawes *(CFO & COO)*
Jonathan Cole *(Chief Compliance Officer)*
Robert Bueti *(Controller)*
Anna Tovbin *(Dir-HR & ESG)*

Subsidiaries:

CTI Towers, Inc. (1)
5000 CentreGreen Wy Ste 325, Cary, NC 27513
Tel.: (919) 893-2841
Web Site: http://www.ctitowers.com
Commercial & Industrial Machinery & Equipment Rental & Leasing
N.A.I.C.S.: 532490
Mikala Mann *(Coord-Sls & Mktg)*
Tony Peduto *(CEO)*
Scott Crisler *(COO)*

MELROSE BANCORP, INC.
638 Main St, Melrose, MA 02176
Tel.: (781) 665-2500   MD
Web Site:
http://www.melrosebank.com
Rev.: $10,802,000
Assets: $323,954,000
Liabilities: $278,739,000
Net Worth: $45,215,000
Earnings: $1,770,000
Emp.: 28
Fiscal Year-end: 12/31/18
Bank Holding Company
N.A.I.C.S.: 551111
Jeffrey D. Jones *(Pres & CEO)*
James E. Oosterman *(VP-Lending & Mktg)*
Diane Indorato *(CFO & Sr VP)*
Darren Bisso *(VP-Fin-Melrose Bank)*
Mark Zink *(VP-Comml Lending-Melrose Bank)*
Susan Doherty *(Officer-IT/Asst VP-Melrose Bank)*
Frank Giso III *(Chm)*

Subsidiaries:

Melrose Cooperative Bank (1)
638 Main St, Melrose, MA 02176
Tel.: (781) 665-2500
Web Site: http://www.melrosecoop.com
Commericial Banking
N.A.I.C.S.: 522110

MELROSE DAIRY PROTEINS, LLC.
1000 E Kraft Dr, Melrose, MN 56352
Tel.: (320) 256-7461
Year Founded: 1968
Sales Range: $25-49.9 Million
Emp.: 150
Cheese Mfr
N.A.I.C.S.: 311513
Hank Braegelmann *(Plant Mgr)*

MELROSEMAC, INC.
2400 W Olive Ave, Burbank, CA 91506
Tel.: (818) 840-8466   CA
Web Site:
http://www.melrosemac.com
Year Founded: 2003
Sales Range: $25-49.9 Million
Emp.: 59
Information Technology Support Services
N.A.I.C.S.: 541512
Sandy Nasseri *(Co-Founder & Pres)*
Sean Nasseri *(Co-Founder)*
Reza Safai *(VP-Retail)*
Laura Thommen *(VP-Sls Strategy-MeltoseTEC Enterprise Storage)*

MELTMEDIA
1255 W Rio Salado Pkwy Ste 209, Tempe, AZ 85281
Tel.: (602) 340-9440
Web Site: http://www.meltmedia.com
Sales Range: $10-24.9 Million
Emp.: 60
Web Application Software Development Services
N.A.I.C.S.: 541511
Mike Moulton *(CTO & Partner)*
Justin Grossman *(CEO & Partner)*
Robin Fossen *(Dir-PM)*
Liam Sherman *(Mgr-Analysis & Strategy)*
Matthew Rausch *(Dir-HR)*
Jason Kwolek *(Dir-PM)*
Will Mejia *(Dir-Design)*
David Knutson *(Coord-Project)*
Amy Grant *(Project Mgr)*
Tisha Bachechi *(Project Mgr)*
Destiny Bira *(Mgr-Release)*
Ron Barry *(Founder & Dir-Bus Dev)*

MELTON MANAGEMENT INC.
6778 Lantana Rd Ste 8, Lake Worth, FL 33467
Tel.: (561) 721-2927
Sales Range: $25-49.9 Million
Emp.: 10
Fast-Food Restaurant Chain Operator
N.A.I.C.S.: 722513
Keith Melton *(Pres)*
Mark Watson *(Owner)*

MELTON SALES, INC.
200 N Lynn Riggs Blvd, Claremore, OK 74017-6816
Tel.: (918) 341-1512
Web Site:
http://www.meltonsales.com
Sales Range: $10-24.9 Million
Emp.: 100
Car Whslr
N.A.I.C.S.: 441110
Amy Gordon *(Mgr-Ops)*
Rob Melton *(Mgr)*
Larry Melton *(VP)*

MELTON TRUCK LINES INC.
808 N 161 St E Ave, Tulsa, OK 74116
Tel.: (918) 234-1000
Web Site:
http://www.meltontruck.com
Sales Range: $25-49.9 Million
Emp.: 700
Trucking Except Local
N.A.I.C.S.: 484121
Robert A. Peterson *(Pres)*
Angie Buchannon *(VP-Safety)*
Mike Dargel *(VP-Risk Mgmt & Claims)*
Brice Peters *(VP-Sls & Mktg)*

MELTWATER NEWS US INC.
225 Bush St Ste 1000, San Francisco, CA 94104
Tel.: (415) 236-3144   DE
Web Site: http://www.meltwater.com
Year Founded: 2007
Software Company
N.A.I.C.S.: 513210
Jorn Lyseggen *(Founder)*
Aditya Jami *(CTO)*
Scott Gibbs *(Sr VP-Global Enterprise)*
John Box *(CEO)*
David Hickey *(Exec Dir-Asia Pacific)*
Anthony Herman *(Head-Legal)*
Alissa Sargeant *(Head-Talent Acq)*
Upali Dasgupta *(Mktg Dir)*

Subsidiaries:

Sysomos Inc. (1)
25 York Street Suite 900, Toronto, M5J 2V5, ON, Canada

Tel.: (647) 933-8744
Web Site: http://www.sysomos.com
Social Analytics & Monitoring Software
N.A.I.C.S.: 513210
Lance Concannon *(Dir-Mktg-EMEA)*

MELVIN CAPITAL MANAGEMENT LP
535 Madison Ave, New York, NY 10022
Tel.: (212) 373-1270   DE
Web Site:
http://www.melvincapital.com
Year Founded: 2014
Investment Services
N.A.I.C.S.: 523999
David F. Kurd *(COO)*
Gabriel Plotkin *(Founder & Chief Investment Officer)*
Robert R. Rasamny *(Head-Legal)*

MELVIN L. DAVIS OIL CO. INC.
11042 Blue Star Hwy, Stony Creek, VA 23882
Tel.: (434) 246-2600
Web Site: http://www.dtc33.com
Sales Range: $10-24.9 Million
Emp.: 115
Independent Convenience Store
N.A.I.C.S.: 445131
J. Rex Davis *(Pres)*
John Hile *(Controller)*

MEM PROPERTY MANAGEMENT CORPORATION
35 Journal Sq Ste 1025, Jersey City, NJ 07306
Tel.: (201) 798-1080
Web Site:
http://www.memproperty.com
Year Founded: 1989
Sales Range: $1-9.9 Million
Emp.: 21
Property Management Services
N.A.I.C.S.: 531311
Martin H. Laderman *(Founder & CEO)*
Matthew K. Laderman *(VP-Ops)*
Salvatore Sanft *(VP)*

MEMBERS 1ST CREDIT UNION
4710 Mountain Lakes Blvd, Redding, CA 96003
Tel.: (530) 222-6060   CA
Web Site:
http://www.membersonline.org
Year Founded: 1936
Credit Union
N.A.I.C.S.: 522130
Ricki Miller *(Chm)*
Ken Reed *(Sec)*
Ed Niederberger *(Co-Vice Chm)*
Jim Breslin *(Co-Vice Chm)*

MEMBERS COOPERATIVE CREDIT UNION
101 14th St, Cloquet, MN 55720
Tel.: (218) 625-8500   MN
Web Site:
http://www.membersccu.org
Year Founded: 1936
Sales Range: $10-24.9 Million
Emp.: 149
Credit Union Operator
N.A.I.C.S.: 522130
Russ Salgy *(Chm)*
Tammy Heikkinen *(Pres & CEO)*

MEMBERS TRUST COMPANY
14025 Riveredge Dr Ste 280, Tampa, FL 33637
Tel.: (813) 631-9191
Web Site:
http://www.memberstrust.com
Year Founded: 1987

Sales Range: $1-9.9 Million
Emp.: 20
Financial & Investment Services
N.A.I.C.S.: 525990
Jonathan D. Rich *(Chm)*
Kevin Thompson *(Sr VP-Asset Mgmt Products)*
Neil P. Archibald *(Chief Compliance Officer & Gen Counsel)*
Kate Braddock *(Co-Chief Investment Officer)*
Sheldon Reynolds *(VP-Trust & Investments)*
Jason Ritzenthaler *(Co-Chief Investment Officer)*
Kenneth E. Lako *(Pres & CEO)*

MEMCO INC.
296 Carlton Rd, Hollister, MO 65672
Tel.: (417) 334-6681
Web Site:
http://www.themiddletongroup.com
Rev.: $18,700,000
Emp.: 50
Industrial Machinery & Equipment
N.A.I.C.S.: 423830
Drew Horst *(Exec VP)*

MEMORIAL COMMUNITY HEALTH, INC.
1423 7th St, Aurora, NE 68818
Tel.: (402) 694-3171   NE
Web Site:
http://www.memorialcommunityhealth.org
Year Founded: 1964
Sales Range: $10-24.9 Million
Emp.: 350
Health Care Srvices
N.A.I.C.S.: 622110
John Ferguson *(Treas)*
Roger Levering *(Sec)*
Dennis Ferguson *(Pres)*
Jason Schneider *(VP)*

MEMORIAL HEALTH CARE SYSTEMS
300 N Columbia Ave, Seward, NE 68434
Tel.: (402) 643-2971   NE
Web Site: http://www.mhcs-seward.org
Year Founded: 1956
Sales Range: $25-49.9 Million
Emp.: 287
Health Care Srvices
N.A.I.C.S.: 622110
Roger Reamer *(CEO)*
Judy Bors *(Dir-Nursing)*
Greg Jerger *(CFO)*

MEMORIAL HEALTH SERVICES
17360 Brookhurst St, Fountain Valley, CA 92708
Tel.: (714) 377-2900   CA
Web Site:
http://www.memorialcare.org
Year Founded: 1937
Sales Range: $1-4.9 Billion
Emp.: 11,192
Non-Profit Hospital Administration Organization
N.A.I.C.S.: 813920
Barry Arbuckle *(Pres & CEO)*

Subsidiaries:

Earl & Loraine Miller Children's Hospital (1)
2801 Atlantic Ave, Long Beach, CA 90806
Tel.: (562) 933-2000
Web Site: http://www.memorialcare.org
Sales Range: $10-24.9 Million
Emp.: 7
Hospital Services
N.A.I.C.S.: 622110

MEMORIAL HEALTH SERVICES

Memorial Health Services—(Continued)

Long Beach Memorial Medical Center (1)
2801 Atlantic Ave, Long Beach, CA 90806-1737
Tel.: (562) 933-2000 (100%)
Web Site: http://www.memorialcare.org
Sales Range: $650-699.9 Million
Emp.: 3,500
Medical Facility
N.A.I.C.S.: 524114
Stanley W. Arnold (Pres-Edinger Medical Grp)

MemorialCare Surgical Center at Orange Coast, LLC (1)
9920 Talbert Ave, Fountain Valley, CA 92708-5153
Tel.: (714) 378-7000
Web Site: http://www.memorialcare.org
Sales Range: $250-299.9 Million
Emp.: 1,100
Medical Devices
N.A.I.C.S.: 524114
Marcia Manker (CEO)

MemorialCare Surgical Center at Saddleback, LLC (1)
24451 Health Center Dr, Laguna Hills, CA 92653-3689
Tel.: (949) 837-4500
Web Site: http://www.memorialcare.org
Sales Range: $250-299.9 Million
Emp.: 1,400
Medical Insurance Services
N.A.I.C.S.: 524114

Unit (Domestic):

Saddleback Memorial at San Clemente (2)
654 Camino De Los Mares, San Clemente, CA 92673-2827
Tel.: (949) 496-1122
Web Site: http://www.sanclementehospital.com
Sales Range: $25-49.9 Million
Emp.: 250
Hospital
N.A.I.C.S.: 622110
Tony Strother (Mgr-Admin)

Seaside Health Plan (1)
17360 Brookhurst St, Fountain Valley, CA 92708
Web Site: http://www.seasidehealthplan.org
Health Care Srvices
N.A.I.C.S.: 621999
Maribel Ferrer (CEO)

MEMORIAL HERMANN FOUNDATION
929 Gessner Ste 2650, Houston, TX 77024
Tel.: (713) 242-4400 TX
Web Site: https://www.memorialhermann.org
Year Founded: 1969
Rev.: $1,000,000
Emp.: 35
Fiscal Year-end: 12/31/06
Social Services, Nec, Nsk
N.A.I.C.S.: 813319

MEMORIAL HERMANN HEALTHCARE SYSTEM
929 Gessner Dr Ste 2600, Houston, TX 77024
Tel.: (713) 448-5555 TX
Web Site: http://www.memorialhermann.org
Sales Range: $350-399.9 Million
Emp.: 19,500
Health Care System
N.A.I.C.S.: 622110
James R. Montague (Chm)
Chuck Stokes (Pres, CEO & COO)
Brian Dean (CFO-Systemwide & Exec VP)
Greg Haralson (CEO-Texas Medical Center & Sr VP)
Malisha Patel (CEO-Sugar Land & Southwest Hospitals & Sr VP)

MEMORIAL HOSPITAL, INC.
91 Hospital Dr, Towanda, PA 18848
Tel.: (570) 265-2191 PA
Web Site: http://www.memorialhospital.org
Year Founded: 1946
Sales Range: $25-49.9 Million
Emp.: 587
Health Care Srvices
N.A.I.C.S.: 622110
Staci Tovey (Pres & CEO)
Myron S. McCoo (VP-HR)

MEMORIAL SLOAN-KETTERING CANCER CENTER INC.
1275 York Ave, New York, NY 10065
Tel.: (212) 639-2000
Web Site: http://www.mskcc.org
Year Founded: 1884
Sales Range: $450-499.9 Million
Emp.: 8,768
Hospital
N.A.I.C.S.: 622310
Michael P. Gutnick (CFO & Exec VP)
Kathryn Martin (COO)
Philip Kantoff (Chm-Medicine)
Clifford A. Hudis (Chief Advocacy Officer & VP-Govt Rels)
Luis F. Parada (Dir-Brain Tumor Center)
Robert Sidlow (Head-Survivorship & Supportive Care)
Ed Taliaferro (Chief Compliance Officer & VP-Internal Audit & Compliance)
Jason Klein (Chief Investment Officer & Sr VP)
Kerry Bessey (Chief HR Officer & Sr VP)
Ned Groves (Exec VP)
Patricia Skarulis (CIO & Sr VP-Info Sys)
Richard Naum (Sr VP-Dev)
Roger Parker (Gen Counsel & Exec VP)
Jeffrey A. Drebin (Chm-Surgery Dept)
Craig B. Thompson (Pres & CEO)
Roxanne Taylor (Chief Mktg & Comm Officer)
Remy Evard (Chief Digital Officer & Head-Tech)

MEMORIAL SPECIALTY HOSPITAL
PO Box 1447, Lufkin, TX 75902
Tel.: (936) 639-7016 TX
Year Founded: 1992
Sales Range: $10-24.9 Million
Emp.: 85
Health Care Srvices
N.A.I.C.S.: 622110
Leeann Haygood (Chief Network Officer)
Brenda Broadway (Chief Network Officer)

MEMORY 4 LESS
1504 W Commonwealth Ave, Fullerton, CA 92833
Tel.: (714) 821-3354
Web Site: http://www.memory4less.com
Year Founded: 1985
Sales Range: $25-49.9 Million
Emp.: 17
Computer Memory Upgrade Services
N.A.I.C.S.: 423430
Faisal Ismael (Co-Owner)
Fahim Abbas Khemji (Mgr-Software Dev)

MEMORY GARDENS MANAGEMENT CORPORATION
3733 N Meridian St PO Box 88269, Indianapolis, IN 46208
Tel.: (317) 923-5474
Year Founded: 1953
Sales Range: $10-24.9 Million
Emp.: 200
Funeral Homes, Cemeteries, Burial Vaults & Burial Insurance
N.A.I.C.S.: 812220
Robert Nelms (Pres & CEO)
Ron Downey (VP-Ops)
Steve Wheeler (Mgr-Funeral Home)
Barry Bedford (Controller)

MEMOSUN, INC.
17665A Newhope St, Fountain Valley, CA 92708
Tel.: (714) 424-3900
Web Site: http://www.memosun.com
Sales Range: $10-24.9 Million
Emp.: 5
Computer & Computer Peripheral Equipment & Software Merchant Whslr
N.A.I.C.S.: 423430
Diana Kong (Pres)

MEMPHIS AREA TRANSIT AUTHORITY
1370 Levee Rd, Memphis, TN 38108-1011
Tel.: (901) 722-7100
Web Site: http://www.matatransit.com
Year Founded: 1974
Sales Range: $10-24.9 Million
Emp.: 632
Software Publishing Services
N.A.I.C.S.: 513210
Lavelle Fitch (Dir-HR)
Phyllis Dodson (Coord-Events)
Tom Fox (Deputy Gen Mgr)
Nicole Lacey (Chief Comm Officer)
Gary Rosenfeld (CEO)
William Hudson Jr. (Pres & Gen Mgr)

MEMPHIS BASKETBALL, LLC
191 Beale St, Memphis, TN 38103-3715
Tel.: (901) 205-1234 NV
Web Site: http://www.nba.com
Year Founded: 1995
Professional Basketball Team; Sports & Entertainment Arena Operator
N.A.I.C.S.: 711211
Dennis O'Connor (VP-Ticket Sls & Svc)
Lamont Nelson (Dir-Dev)
David Thompson (Sr Dir-Brand Mktg)
Chris Wallace (Gen Mgr)
John Hollinger (Exec VP-Basketball Ops)
Chantal Hassard (VP-Team Ops & Player Programs)
Robert J. Pera (Owner)
Arnetria Knowles (VP-HR)
Ed Stefanski (Exec VP-Player Personnel)
Allen L. Gruver (Dir-Medical)
Eric Oetter (Dir-Sports Medicine)
Zachary Kleiman (Exec VP-Basketball Ops)
Chris Pongrass (Dir-Basketball Ops)
Chris Makris (Dir-Player Personnel)

MEMPHIS BUSINESS INTERIORS, LLC
4539 W Distriplex Dr, Memphis, TN 38118
Tel.: (901) 360-8899
Web Site: http://www.gombi.com
Year Founded: 1995
Sales Range: $25-49.9 Million
Emp.: 50
Office Furniture Whslr
N.A.I.C.S.: 423210

U.S. PRIVATE

MEMPHIS CITY EMPLOYEES CREDIT UNION
2608 Avery Ave, Memphis, TN 38112
Tel.: (901) 321-1200 TN
Web Site: http://www.memphiscu.org
Year Founded: 1969
Sales Range: $10-24.9 Million
Emp.: 101
Credit Union Operator
N.A.I.C.S.: 522130
John Michael Rhea (VP-Acctg & Audit)
William Oldham (Treas)
Wanda Corcoran (Sec)
Charles Chumley (Chm)

MEMPHIS DEVELOPMENT FOUNDATION
PO Box 3370, Memphis, TN 38173-0370
Tel.: (901) 525-7800 TN
Web Site: http://www.orpheum-memphis.com
Year Founded: 1976
Sales Range: $10-24.9 Million
Emp.: 288
Educational Support Services
N.A.I.C.S.: 611710
Teresa Ward (VP-Sls)
Paulette Luker (VP-Fin)
Brett Batterson (Pres & CEO)
Andy Taylor (Chm)

MEMPHIS EQUIPMENT COMPANY
766 S 3rd St, Memphis, TN 38106
Tel.: (901) 774-0600
Web Site: http://www.memphisequipment.com
Rev.: $11,300,000
Emp.: 38
Commercial Trucks
N.A.I.C.S.: 423110
Hasbury Jones (Pres)

MEMPHIS INVEST GP
130 Timber Creek, Cordova, TN 38018
Tel.: (901) 751-7191
Web Site: http://www.memphisinvest.com
Year Founded: 2004
Sales Range: $25-49.9 Million
Emp.: 30
Rental Real Estate Investment
N.A.I.C.S.: 531390
Brett Clothier (Partner)
Chris Clothier (Partner & Dir-Sls & Mktg)
Kent Clothier Sr. (Founder & Partner)

MEMPHIS LIGHT, GAS & WATER
220 S Main St, Memphis, TN 38103-3917
Tel.: (901) 544-6549 TN
Web Site: http://www.mlgw.com
Year Founded: 1939
Sales Range: $1-4.9 Billion
Emp.: 5,100
Municipal Utility Services
N.A.I.C.S.: 221118
Christopher Bieber (VP-Customer Care)
Alonzo Weaver (VP-Ops & Engrg)
Dana Jeanes (CFO, Treas, Sec & VP)
Gale Jones Carson (Dir-Corp Comm)
Nick Newman (VP-Construction & Maintenance)
Cliff DeBerry (Dir-Analysis & Strategy & Performance)
Jerry Collins (Pres & CEO)
Cheryl W. Patterson (Gen Counsel & VP)
LaShell Vaughn (CTO & VP)

Lesa Walton (Dir-Internal Audit)
Roland McElrath (Controller)
Von Goodloe (VP-HR)

MEMPHIS SCALE WORKS INC.
3418 Cazassa Rd, Memphis, TN 38116
Tel.: (901) 332-5070
Web Site: http://www.mtaweighing.com
Sales Range: $10-24.9 Million
Emp.: 65
Scales
N.A.I.C.S.: 423440
Jerry Michie (Pres)

MEMPHIS SHELBY COUNTY AIRPORT AUTHORITY, INC.
2491 Winchester Rd Ste 113, Memphis, TN 38116-3851
Tel.: (901) 922-8000
Web Site: http://www.mscaa.com
Year Founded: 1969
Sales Range: $75-99.9 Million
Emp.: 300
Provider of Airports & Flying Fields Services
N.A.I.C.S.: 488119
Scott A. Brocknan (Pres & CEO)
Will Livsey (Sr Mgr-Air Svc R&D)
Rob Robertson (Mgr-Mktg & PR)
Christy Kinard (Gen Counsel)
Glen Thomas (Dir-Strategic Mktg & Comm)

MENARD ELECTRIC COOPERATIVE
14300 State Hwy 97, Petersburg, IL 62675
Tel.: (217) 632-7746
Web Site: http://www.menard.com
Year Founded: 1936
Sales Range: $125-149.9 Million
Emp.: 35
Distr of Electric Energy
N.A.I.C.S.: 221122
Lynn A. Frasco (Gen Mgr)
Trish Michels (Mgr-HR)

MENARD OIL CO. INC.
519 Jacqulyn St, Abbeville, LA 70510
Tel.: (337) 893-2428
Web Site: http://www.menardoil.com
Sales Range: $10-24.9 Million
Emp.: 17
Gasoline
N.A.I.C.S.: 424720
Mona D. Menard (Pres)
Brenda Harman (VP)
Carl Menard (Gen Mgr)

MENARD, INC.
3210 N Clairemont Ave, Eau Claire, WI 54703
Tel.: (715) 830-0011
Web Site: https://www.menards.com
Year Founded: 1958
Sales Range: $5-14.9 Billion
Emp.: 45,000
Lumber, Plywood, Millwork & Wood Panel Merchant Wholesalers
N.A.I.C.S.: 423310
Dave Wagner (CIO)
John Leonauskas (Mgr-Mktg)
Terri Jain (Mgr-Payroll)
Elizabeth Menard (VP)

MENASHA CORPORATION
1645 Bergstrom Rd, Neenah, WI 54956-9701
Tel.: (920) 751-1000
Web Site: http://www.menasha.com
Year Founded: 1849
Sales Range: $800-899.9 Million
Emp.: 3,750
Corrugated Containers, Paperboard, Plastics & Product Identification Items Mfr
N.A.I.C.S.: 322130
Mark P. Fogarty (Gen Counsel, Sec & VP)
Lee Ann Hammen (Treas & VP)
James M. Kotek (Pres & CEO)
Evan S. Pritz (Vp-Corp Dev)
Shannon Van Dyke (VP & Controller)

Subsidiaries:

Menasha Corp., POLY Hi Solidur (1)
200 Industrial Dr, Delmont, PA 15626-1015 (100%)
Tel.: (724) 468-6868
Web Site: http://www.menasha.com
Sales Range: $25-49.9 Million
Emp.: 70
N.A.I.C.S.: 325211

Menasha Corp., Traex Division (1)
101 Traex Plz, Dane, WI 53529-9501
Tel.: (608) 241-7856
Web Site: http://www.libbey.com
Sales Range: $25-49.9 Million
Emp.: 90
Mfr of Plastic Items
N.A.I.C.S.: 326199

Menasha Packaging Company, LLC (1)
1645 Bergstrom Rd, Neenah, WI 54956
Tel.: (920) 751-1000
Web Site: http://www.menashapackaging.com
Sales Range: $25-49.9 Million
Emp.: 150
Printing & Packaging Services
N.A.I.C.S.: 323111
Michael D. Riegsecker (Pres)

Plant (Domestic):

Menasha Packaging Company, LLC - Aurora Facility (2)
1700 Edgelawn Dr, Aurora, IL 60506
Tel.: (630) 236-4033
Logistics Consulting Servies
N.A.I.C.S.: 541614
Mark Bonzalski (Gen Mgr)

Menasha Packaging Company, LLC - Bethlehem Facility (2)
2600 Brodhead Rd, Bethlehem, PA 18020
Tel.: (630) 236-5051
Logistics Consulting Servies
N.A.I.C.S.: 541614

Menasha Packaging Company, LLC - Brooklyn Park Plant (2)
7301 Northland Dr, Brooklyn Park, MN 55428
Tel.: (763) 424-6606
Sales Range: $50-74.9 Million
Emp.: 70
Corrugated Box Mfr
N.A.I.C.S.: 322211
Lee Benson (Mgr-Ops)

Menasha Packaging Company, LLC - Cincinnati Facility (2)
310 Culvert St Ste 300, Cincinnati, OH 45202
Tel.: (513) 381-3400
Sales Range: $25-49.9 Million
Emp.: 10
Paperboard Mfr
N.A.I.C.S.: 322130

Menasha Packaging Company, LLC - Coloma (2)
238 N West St, Coloma, MI 49038
Tel.: (269) 468-3153
Web Site: http://www.menasha.com
Sales Range: $1-9.9 Million
Emp.: 24
Corrugated & Solid Fiber Box Mfr
N.A.I.C.S.: 322211

Menasha Packaging Company, LLC - Edwardsville Facility (2)
3101 Westway Dr, Edwardsville, IL 62025
Tel.: (618) 931-1900
Sales Range: $100-124.9 Million
Logistics Consulting Servies
N.A.I.C.S.: 541614

Menasha Packaging Company, LLC - Erie (2)
5800 Bundy Dr, Erie, PA 16509
Tel.: (814) 825-1055
Sales Range: $1-9.9 Million
Emp.: 25
Corrugated & Solid Fiber Box Mfr
N.A.I.C.S.: 322211
Rick Srnka (Project Mgr)

Menasha Packaging Company, LLC - Fanfold Plant (2)
238 N W St, Coloma, MI 49038
Tel.: (800) 253-1526
Web Site: http://www.menasha.com
Packaging Paperboard Mfr
N.A.I.C.S.: 322130

Menasha Packaging Company, LLC - Hartford Plant (2)
621 Wacker Dr, Hartford, WI 53027
Tel.: (262) 673-5880
Web Site: http://www.menasha.com
Sales Range: $50-74.9 Million
Emp.: 250
Logistics Consulting Services
N.A.I.C.S.: 541614
Bill Berg (Mgr-Ops)
Mike Otto (Mgr-Ops)

Menasha Packaging Company, LLC - Hodgkins Facility (2)
7435 Santa Fe Dr, Hodgkins, IL 60525
Tel.: (708) 482-7619
Logistics Consulting Servies
N.A.I.C.S.: 541614

Menasha Packaging Company, LLC - Lakeville Plant (2)
8085 220th St W, Lakeville, MN 55044
Tel.: (952) 469-4451
Web Site: http://www.menashapackaging.com
Emp.: 175
Logistics Consulting Services
N.A.I.C.S.: 541614

Menasha Packaging Company, LLC - Minooka Facility (2)
456 Internationale Pkwy N, Minooka, IL 60447
Tel.: (815) 290-6120
Sales Range: $25-49.9 Million
Emp.: 120
Repackaging Services
N.A.I.C.S.: 541614

Menasha Packaging Company, LLC - Muscatine Plant (2)
3206 Hershey Ave Bldg 2, Muscatine, IA 52761
Tel.: (563) 264-1201
Web Site: http://www.menashapackaging.com
Emp.: 40
Logistics Consulting Services
N.A.I.C.S.: 541614
Larry Luce (Plant Mgr)

Menasha Packaging Company, LLC - Ontario Facility (2)
3971 Airport Dr 102 Wanamaker Ave, Ontario, CA 91761
Tel.: (909) 390-6238
Logistics Consulting Services
N.A.I.C.S.: 541614

Menasha Packaging Company, LLC - Philadelphia Plant (2)
601 E Erie Ave, Philadelphia, PA 19134
Tel.: (215) 426-7110
Web Site: http://www.menashapackaging.com
Sales Range: $25-49.9 Million
Emp.: 135
Corrugated & Solid Fiber Boxes
N.A.I.C.S.: 322211
Dart Edgarton (Gen Mgr)

Menasha Packaging Company, LLC - Rock Island Facility (2)
7800 14th St W, Rock Island, IL 61201
Tel.: (309) 787-1747
Web Site: http://www.menashapakaging.com
Emp.: 25
Logistics Consulting Servies
N.A.I.C.S.: 541614
Pammy Johnson (Mgr-Ops)

Menasha Packaging Company, LLC - Santa Fe Springs Plant (2)
8110 Sorensen Ave, Santa Fe Springs, CA 90670-2122
Tel.: (562) 698-3705
Web Site: http://www.menasha.com
Sales Range: $25-49.9 Million
Emp.: 130
Mfr of Corrugated & Solid Fiber Boxes
N.A.I.C.S.: 322211

Menasha Packaging Company, LLC - St. Cloud Plant (2)
640 60th St S, Saint Cloud, MN 56301
Tel.: (320) 252-0522
Logistics Consulting Servies
N.A.I.C.S.: 541614

Menasha Packaging Company, LLC - Yukon Plant (2)
567 Waltz Mill Rd, Ruffs Dale, PA 15679
Tel.: (800) 245-2486
Paperboard Mfr
N.A.I.C.S.: 322130
Greg Clawson (Gen Mgr)

Subsidiary (Domestic):

Strine Printing Company Inc. (2)
30 Grumbacher Rd, York, PA 17406
Tel.: (717) 767-6602
Web Site: http://www.strine.com
Sales Range: $50-74.9 Million
Emp.: 300
Offset Printing
N.A.I.C.S.: 323111
Michael A. Strine (CEO)
William Kirk (Pres)

The Strive Group LLC (2)
350 N Clark St Ste 300, Chicago, IL 60654
Tel.: (312) 880-4620
Web Site: http://www.strivegroup.com
Sales Range: $10-24.9 Million
Emp.: 50
Promotional Display Mfr
N.A.I.C.S.: 322219
Randy Thrasher (VP & Gen Mgr)
Pat Morrissey (Controller)
Pam Horine (Dir-Quality & Continuous Improvement)

Division (Domestic):

Chicago Converting (3)
4545 W Palmer St, Chicago, IL 60639
Tel.: (773) 227-6000
Corrugated Product Mfr
N.A.I.C.S.: 322211
Ed Bright (Mgr-Production)

ORBIS Corporation (1)
1055 Corporate Center Dr, Oconomowoc, WI 53066-4829
Tel.: (262) 560-5000
Web Site: http://www.orbiscorporation.com
Sales Range: $50-74.9 Million
Emp.: 250
Plastics Product Mfr
N.A.I.C.S.: 326199

Subsidiary (Domestic):

CORBI Plastics, LLC (2)
1055 Corporate Center Dr, Oconomowoc, WI 53066
Tel.: (608) 852-8840
Web Site: http://www.corbiplastics.com
Sales Range: $25-49.9 Million
Emp.: 85
Unlaminated Plastics Film & Sheet Mfr
N.A.I.C.S.: 326113
Jack E. Graham (Pres)

National Consolidation Services, LLC (2)
465 W Crossroads Pkwy, Bolingbrook, IL 60440
Tel.: (630) 679-8000
Web Site: http://www.ncs-logistics.com
Sales Range: $10-24.9 Million
Emp.: 100
Freight Transportation Services
N.A.I.C.S.: 488510
Rim Gulbinas (Pres)
Steve VanLear (VP-Ops)
Larry McIntyre (Dir-Pricing)
Chuck Mackin (Dir-Transportation)

Subsidiary (Non-US):

ORBIS (Shanghai) Material Handling Co., Ltd. (2)

MENASHA CORPORATION

Menasha Corporation—(Continued)
ADD Building 2 No 1350 Chunhe Road, Baoshan District, Shanghai, 200941, China
Tel.: (86) 21 67681433
Web Site:
http://www.orbiscorporation.com.cn
Plastics Product Mfr
N.A.I.C.S.: 326199

Division (Domestic):

ORBIS Corporation - LEWISBins+ Division (2)
1055 Corporate Center Dr, Oconomowoc, WI 53066
Tel.: (262) 560-5700
Web Site: http://www.lewisbins.com
Sales Range: $25-49.9 Million
Emp.: 200
Storage Container Mfr
N.A.I.C.S.: 326199
Bill Ash *(Mng Dir)*

MENASHA ELECTRIC & WATER UTILITIES
321 Milwaukee St, Menasha, WI 54952-2704
Tel.: (920) 967-5180
Web Site:
http://www.menashautilities.com
Year Founded: 1905
Sales Range: $50-74.9 Million
Emp.: 60
Electric & Other Services Combined
N.A.I.C.S.: 221118
Mark L. Allwardt *(Pres)*
Melanie Krause *(Gen Mgr-Bus Ops)*
Joseph P. Guidote *(Sec)*
Paula Maurer *(Mgr-Customer Svcs)*

MENDEL PLUMBING & HEATING, INC.
3 N 640 N 17th St, Saint Charles, IL 60174
Tel.: (630) 377-3608
Web Site: http://www.callmendel.com
Year Founded: 1985
Sales Range: $10-24.9 Million
Emp.: 50
Air Conditioning System Installation Services
N.A.I.C.S.: 238220
Michael L. Mendel *(Pres)*

MENDEZ & CO. INC.
Km 2.4 Rd 20 Expreso Martinez Nadal, Guaynabo, PR 00969
Tel.: (787) 793-8888
Web Site:
http://www.mendezcopr.com
Rev.: $113,200,000
Emp.: 500
Liquor Distributors
N.A.I.C.S.: 424820
Jose Alvarec *(Pres)*

MENDO MILL & LUMBER CO.
1870 N State St, Ukiah, CA 95482
Tel.: (707) 462-4244
Web Site: http://www.mendomill.com
Rev.: $16,770,768
Emp.: 65
Lumber & Other Building Materials
N.A.I.C.S.: 423310
Bob Hildebrand *(CFO)*
Ken Smith *(Mgr-Mdse)*
David Land *(Dir-Fleet)*
Jeff Ward *(VP)*

MENDOCINO REDWOOD COMPANY, LLC
PO Box 996, Ukiah, CA 95482
Tel.: (707) 463-5110
Web Site: http://www.mrc.com
Year Founded: 1998
Sales Range: $25-49.9 Million
Emp.: 750
Provider of Millwork Services

N.A.I.C.S.: 113110
Bob Mertz *(CEO)*

MENEMSHA
4950 W 145th St, Hawthorne, CA 90250
Tel.: (310) 343-3430
Web Site:
http://www.menemshasolutions.com
Year Founded: 1992
Sales Range: $10-24.9 Million
Emp.: 130
Commercial & Institutional Building Construction Services
N.A.I.C.S.: 236220
John Daigle *(Pres & CEO)*
Tom Speroni *(Exec VP)*
Laurie Collins *(COO)*
Melani Dannenberg *(Dir-Retail Architecture)*
Jason Tropp *(VP-Architecture & Facility Svcs)*
Ashley Carter *(VP-Dev)*

MENIN HOTELS, INC.
1801 Collins Ave, Miami Beach, FL 33139
Tel.: (305) 531-1271
Web Site:
http://www.meninhospitality.com
Hotel
N.A.I.C.S.: 721110
Keith Menin *(Principal)*
Jared Galbut *(Mng Principal)*
Marisa Marcus *(Dir-Mktg)*
Stacy Bernstein *(Dir-Style)*

Subsidiaries:

Gale South Beach & Regent Hotel (1)
1690 Collins Ave, Miami Beach, FL 33139
Tel.: (305) 673-0199
Web Site: http://www.galehotel.com
Hotel
N.A.I.C.S.: 721110
Kevin Waldstein *(Gen Mgr)*

Raffaello Chicago Hotel (1)
201 E Delaware Pl, Chicago, IL 60611
Tel.: (312) 943-5000
Web Site: http://www.chicagoraffaello.com
Hotel
N.A.I.C.S.: 721110
Joseph Natale *(Gen Mgr)*

Sanctuary Hotel and Spa (1)
1745 James Ave, Miami Beach, FL 33139
Tel.: (305) 673-5455
Web Site: http://www.sanctuarysobe.com
Hotel & Spa
N.A.I.C.S.: 721110

The Bentley Hotel & Beach Club (1)
510 Ocean Dr, Miami Beach, FL 33139
Tel.: (305) 538-1700
Web Site: http://www.thebentleyhotel.com
Emp.: 25
Hotel
N.A.I.C.S.: 721110
Russell Yost *(Gen Mgr)*

MENLO EQUITIES LLC
490 S California Ave Fl 4, Palo Alto, CA 94306
Tel.: (650) 326-9300
Web Site:
http://www.menloequities.com
Sales Range: $25-49.9 Million
Emp.: 15
Real Estate Agents & Managers
N.A.I.C.S.: 531210
Richard J. Holmstrom *(Vice Chm)*
Henry D. Bullock *(Founder & Chm)*
Chad Iverson *(Sr VP)*
Lyn Barshay *(VP-Property Mgmt)*
Kevin Kujawski *(CFO, COO & Partner)*

MENLO INNOVATIONS LLC

410 N 4th Ave 3rd Fl, Ann Arbor, MI 48104
Tel.: (734) 665-1847
Web Site:
http://www.menloinnovations.com
Year Founded: 2001
Sales Range: $1-9.9 Million
Emp.: 15
Software Developer
N.A.I.C.S.: 513210
Richard Sheridan *(Co-Founder & CEO)*

MENNA DEVELOPMENT & MANAGEMENT, INC.
PO Box 4189, Clearwater, FL 33758
Tel.: (727) 796-0021
Web Site: http://www.mdmhotels.com
Sales Range: $25-49.9 Million
Emp.: 120
Hotel Development & Management
N.A.I.C.S.: 721110
Anthony Menna *(Founder & Pres)*

MENNEL MILLING LOGAN
1 W Front St, Logan, OH 43138
Tel.: (740) 385-6824
Web Site:
http://www.keynesbros.com
Sales Range: $10-24.9 Million
Emp.: 50
Flour Mills, Cereal (Except Rice)
N.A.I.C.S.: 311211
Charlie Keynes *(Pres)*
William Keynes Jr. *(Sec)*

MENNELLA'S POULTRY CO. INC.
100 George St, Paterson, NJ 07503-2319
Tel.: (973) 345-1300
Web Site: http://www.mennella.com
Year Founded: 1944
Sales Range: $10-24.9 Million
Emp.: 55
Poultry & Poultry Products
N.A.I.C.S.: 424440
Keith Mennella *(Pres)*

MENNO TRAVEL SERVICE, INC.
116 Lake St, Ephrata, PA 17522-2707
Tel.: (717) 733-4131
Web Site: http://www.mtstravel.com
Year Founded: 1947
Sales Range: $50-74.9 Million
Emp.: 160
Travel Agency & Special Arrangement Services
N.A.I.C.S.: 561510

Subsidiaries:

MTS Travel - Colorado Springs (1)
620 Southpointe Ct Ste 130, Colorado Springs, CO 80906
Tel.: (719) 471-8080
Web Site: http://www.mtstravel.com
Sales Range: $10-24.9 Million
Emp.: 8
Travel Agency & Special Arrangement Services
N.A.I.C.S.: 561510
Janet Batchelder *(Mgr-Client Dev)*

MENNOMEDIA, INC.
1251 Virginia Ave, Harrisonburg, VA 22802
Tel.: (724) 887-8500
Web Site:
http://www.mennomedia.org
Sales Range: $10-24.9 Million
Emp.: 30
Religious Book Retail & Publishing
N.A.I.C.S.: 459210
Phillip Bontrager *(Pres)*
Russ Eanes *(Exec Dir)*
Barbara Finnegan *(Dir-Fin & Ops)*

MENNONITE FRIENDSHIP COMMUNITIES
600 W Blanchard Rd, South Hutchinson, KS 67505
Tel.: (620) 663-7175
Web Site:
http://www.mennofriend.com
Year Founded: 1972
Sales Range: $10-24.9 Million
Emp.: 334
Lifecare Retirement Community Operator
N.A.I.C.S.: 623311
Lowell Peachey *(Pres & CEO)*
Pauline Buller *(VP-Advancement)*
Allan Bartel *(VP-Community Dev)*

MENNONITE GENERAL HOSPITAL, INC.
PO Box 1379, Aibonito, PR 00705
Tel.: (787) 735-8001
Web Site:
http://www.hospitalmenonita.com
Year Founded: 1976
Sales Range: $150-199.9 Million
Emp.: 1,778
Health Care Srvices
N.A.I.C.S.: 622110
Marta Mercado Surd *(COO)*
Jose E. Solivan Rivera *(CFO)*
Pedro L. Melendez Rosario *(CEO)*

MENONO, INC.
17836 Homer St, Roseville, MI 48066
Tel.: (586) 907-7222
Year Founded: 2014
Emp.: 1
Home Improvement & Construction Consulting & Management Services
N.A.I.C.S.: 541611
William Foster *(Pres, CEO, CFO, Principal Acctg Officer, Treas & Sec)*

MENORAH CAMPUS, INC.
2700 N Forest Rd, Getzville, NY 14068
Tel.: (716) 639-3311
Web Site:
http://www.weinbergcampus.org
Year Founded: 1990
Sales Range: $25-49.9 Million
Emp.: 575
Elder Care Services
N.A.I.C.S.: 624120
Samuel Shapiro *(Vice Chm)*
Richard H. Gordon *(Sec)*
Robert Mayer *(Pres & CEO)*

MENORAH MANOR
255 59th St N, Saint Petersburg, FL 33710
Tel.: (727) 345-2775
Web Site:
http://www.menorahmanor.org
Year Founded: 1981
Sales Range: $10-24.9 Million
Emp.: 324
Elder Care Services
N.A.I.C.S.: 623312
Donna Perryman *(CFO)*
Judy Ludin *(Chief Dev & Community Rels Officer)*
David A. LeVine *(Chief Medical Officer)*
Robert Goldstein *(CEO)*
Cheryl Wagner *(Dir-Admissions)*
Greg Yann *(Controller)*
Heidi Celichowski *(Dir-Health Info Svcs)*
Kim McFadden *(Dir-Social Svcs)*
Melissa D. DiGiacomo *(Dir-HR)*
Ray Teasdale *(Dir-Therapeutic Recreation)*
Ted Jacobsen *(Dir-Maintenance)*
Irwin Miller *(Pres)*
Melissa Purvis *(Chief Nursing Officer)*

COMPANIES

MENORAH PARK CENTER FOR SENIOR LIVING
27100 Cedar Rd, Beachwood, OH 44122
Tel.: (216) 831-6500   OH
Web Site: http://www.menorahpark.org
Year Founded: 1906
Sales Range: $50-74.9 Million
Emp.: 1,200
Elder Care Services
N.A.I.C.S.: 624120
Michael Knight *(Chief Medical Officer & VP-Medical Dept)*
Robert S. Matitia *(CFO)*
Beth Silver *(Dir-PR & Mktg)*
Jamie Herbst *(VP-HR)*
Peter Meisel *(Chm)*
Joel Fox *(VP-Menorah Park Foundation)*
Ross Wilkoff *(VP-Residential Svcs)*
James P. Newbrough Jr. *(CEO)*

MENTAL HEALTH ASSOCIATION OF CONNECTICUT INC.
61 S Main St Ste 100, West Hartford, CT 06107
Tel.: (860) 529-1970   CT
Web Site: http://www.mhact.org
Year Founded: 1908
Sales Range: $10-24.9 Million
Emp.: 344
Mental Health Care Services
N.A.I.C.S.: 621420
Robert Mercado *(CFO)*
Jill Currier *(Chief HR Officer)*
Lesa Laraia *(Dir-Mktg & Dev)*
Remi Kyek *(COO)*
Luis B. Perez *(Pres & CEO)*
Steven H. Madonick *(Vice Chm)*
Sharad Saxena *(Treas)*
Donald Neel *(Sec)*
Edwin M. Norse *(Chm)*
Christina Fisher *(Mgr-Organizational Performance)*
Amanda Truppi-Eckert *(Dir-Statewide Programs)*
Carleen Zambetti *(Dir-Residential Svcs)*
Domenique S. Thornton *(Gen Counsel)*

MENTAL HEALTH ASSOCIATION OF NEW YORK CITY
50 Broadway 19th Fl, New York, NY 10004
Tel.: (212) 254-0333   NY
Web Site: http://www.mhaofnyc.org
Year Founded: 1964
Sales Range: $10-24.9 Million
Emp.: 265
Mental Health Care Services
N.A.I.C.S.: 621420
Kathryn Salisbury *(Exec VP-Strategy & Bus Dev)*
Kimberly Williams *(Pres)*
Jennifer Ashley *(Chm)*
Kevin J. Danehy *(Chm)*
Lynn D. Sherman *(Treas)*
Robert P. Borsody *(Sec)*
David Koosis *(CIO)*
Alen Meltzer *(Dir-Fin)*
Michael Nissan *(Vice Chm)*
John Draper *(Chief Clinical Officer)*
Joseph F. Peyronnin III *(Vice Chm)*

MENTAL HEALTH CARE, INC.
5707 N 22nd St, Tampa, FL 33610
Tel.: (813) 272-2244
Web Site: http://www.mhcinc.org
Sales Range: $25-49.9 Million
Emp.: 750
Mental Health Services
N.A.I.C.S.: 923120
Julian I. Rice *(CEO)*
Joseph Rutherford *(Exec Dir)*
Lenny Moore *(CIO)*

MENTAL HEALTH CONNECTICUT, INC.
61 S Main St Ste 100, West Hartford, CT 06107
Tel.: (860) 529-1970   CT
Web Site: http://www.mhconn.org
Year Founded: 1908
Sales Range: $10-24.9 Million
Emp.: 344
Health Care Srvices
N.A.I.C.S.: 622110
Jill M. Currier *(Chief HR Officer)*
Remi G. Kyek *(VP-Ops)*
Suzi K. Craig *(Sr Dir-Advocacy & Dev)*

MENTAL HEALTH PARTNERS
1333 Iris Ave, Boulder, CO 80304
Tel.: (303) 443-8500   CO
Web Site: http://www.mhpcolorado.org
Year Founded: 1964
Sales Range: $25-49.9 Million
Emp.: 600
Behavioral Healthcare Services
N.A.I.C.S.: 621420
Beth Lonergan *(Chief Clinical Officer)*
Bill Myers *(Chief Dev Officer)*
Jeff Almony *(Chief Medical Officer)*
Kelly E. Phillips-Henry *(CEO)*

MENTAL HEALTH SERVICES FOR CLARK AND MADISON COUNTIES, INC.
474 N Yellow Springs St, Springfield, OH 45504
Tel.: (937) 399-9500   OH
Web Site: http://www.mhscc.org
Year Founded: 1969
Sales Range: $25-49.9 Million
Emp.: 198
Behavioral Healthcare Services
N.A.I.C.S.: 623220
Marry Beth Taylor *(VP-Fin)*
Shawn Taylor *(Vice Chm)*
Mark A. Smith *(Chief Clinical Officer)*
James Perry *(CEO)*

MENTOR MITSUBISHI
8505 Mentor Ave, Mentor, OH 44060
Tel.: (440) 534-5000
Web Site: http://www.mentormitsubishi.com
Year Founded: 1990
Sales Range: $25-49.9 Million
Emp.: 35
Car Whslr
N.A.I.C.S.: 441110
Al Zarzour *(Gen Mgr)*
Jeffrey Soukup *(Gen Mgr)*

MENTOR PARTNERS LLC
20 Park Plz 4th Fl, Boston, MA 02116
Tel.: (617) 395-7465
Web Site: http://www.mentorllc.com
Sales Range: $10-24.9 Million
Emp.: 16
Mentoring Consultants & Partnering Services
N.A.I.C.S.: 541611
Stephen LeGraw *(Founder & Pres)*

Subsidiaries:
Adco, Inc.   (1)
900 W Main St, Sedalia, MO 65301-3709
Tel.: (660) 826-3300
Web Site: http://www.adco-inc.com
Sales Range: $10-24.9 Million
Dry Cleaning & Laundry Products Researcher, Developer, Mfr & Marketer
N.A.I.C.S.: 325612

MENTORCLIQ, INC.
595 S 3rd St 2nd Fl, Columbus, OH 43215
Web Site: http://www.mentorcliq.com
Mentoring Software Services
N.A.I.C.S.: 611430
Phil George *(CEO)*

Subsidiaries:
Triple Creek Associates, Inc.   (1)
7955 E Arapahoe Ct Ste 1100, Centennial, CO 80112
Tel.: (303) 707-0800
Web Site: http://www.riversoftware.com
Sales Range: $1-9.9 Million
Emp.: 31
Human Resources & Executive Search Consulting Services
N.A.I.C.S.: 541612
Randy Emelo *(Founder)*
Chris Browning *(Pres)*
Rob Meidal *(CTO)*
Laura Francis *(VP-Mktg)*

MENTORING MINDS LP
4862 Hightech Dr, Tyler, TX 75703
Tel.: (903) 509-4002   TX
Web Site: http://www.mentoringminds.com
Year Founded: 2002
Sales Range: $10-24.9 Million
Emp.: 75
Develops & Publishes Affordable Learning Tools for Children
N.A.I.C.S.: 513199
Lisa Lujan *(Co-Founder)*
Michael L. Lujan *(Co-Founder)*
Robert L. Bush *(CEO)*
Theresa Avirett *(COO)*

MENU MAKER FOODS INC.
913 Big Horn Dr, Jefferson City, MO 65109-0336
Tel.: (573) 893-3000   MO
Web Site: http://www.menumakerfoods.com
Year Founded: 1968
Sales Range: $10-24.9 Million
Emp.: 90
Provider of Grocery Services
N.A.I.C.S.: 424410
John Richard Graves *(Pres)*

Subsidiaries:
John Graves Food Service Inc.   (1)
725 Industrial Rd, Chillicothe, MO 64601-3216
Tel.: (660) 646-6918
Sales Range: $10-24.9 Million
Emp.: 27
Provider of Meat Packing Services
N.A.I.C.S.: 311611

MENZEL INC.
951 Simuel Rd, Spartanburg, SC 29301
Tel.: (864) 576-5690
Web Site: http://www.menzelus.com
Rev.: $10,000,000
Emp.: 50
Textile Machinery
N.A.I.C.S.: 333248

MENZNER LUMBER AND SUPPLY CO.
105 Main St, Marathon, WI 54448
Tel.: (715) 443-2354
Web Site: http://www.menznerhardwoods.com
Sales Range: $25-49.9 Million
Emp.: 250
Provider of Unfinished & Prefinished Wood Moldings
N.A.I.C.S.: 321918
Philip J. Menzner *(Pres)*
Phil Jensen *(Controller)*

MEPLUSYOU
12404 Park Central Ste 420, Dallas, TX 75251
Tel.: (214) 224-1200
Web Site: http://www.meplusyou.com
Year Founded: 1995
Sales Range: $25-49.9 Million
Emp.: 500
Advetising Agency
N.A.I.C.S.: 541810
Doug Levy *(CEO)*
Bryan Bradley *(Sr VP-Partners & Alliances)*
Michael J. Davis *(Chief Creative Officer)*
Colin Turney *(Pres & Chief Client Officer)*
Evelyn Henry Miller *(CFO)*

Subsidiaries:
MEplusYou   (1)
622 3rd Ave 11th Fl, New York, NY 10017
Tel.: (212) 430-3200
Web Site: http://www.meplusyou.com
Sales Range: $10-24.9 Million
Emp.: 37
Advetising Agency
N.A.I.C.S.: 541810

MEPT 501, INC.
7315 Wisconsin Ave Ste 350 W, Bethesda, MD 20814
Tel.: (240) 235-9976   DE
Year Founded: 1998
Sales Range: $10-24.9 Million
Property Management Services
N.A.I.C.S.: 813990
Robert S. Edwards *(Pres)*
Ian Butler *(Treas, Sec & VP)*

MERA PHARMACEUTICALS, INC.
73-4460 Queen Ka'ahumanu Hwy Ste 110, Kailua Kona, HI 96740
Tel.: (808) 326-9301   DE
Web Site: http://www.merapharma.com
Year Founded: 1998
Sales Range: Less than $1 Million
Emp.: 4
Marine Biotechnology Company with Focus on Biofuel & Nutriceutical Products Manufacturing & Distribution
N.A.I.C.S.: 541713
Kenneth I. Crowder *(COO)*
Melanie Kelekolio *(VP & Gen Mgr-Ops & Production Facility)*
Charles G. Spaniak Sr. *(Pres & CFO)*

MERAGE INVESTMENT GROUP
660 Newport Center Dr Ste 1300, Newport Beach, CA 92660
Tel.: (949) 474-5800
Web Site: http://www.migcap.com
Year Founded: 2002
Emp.: 70
Investment Services
N.A.I.C.S.: 523999
Paul Merage *(Chm)*

Subsidiaries:
MIG Absolute Return   (1)
660 Newport Beach Center Dr Ste 1300, Newport Beach, CA 92660
Tel.: (949) 474-5800
Investment Services
N.A.I.C.S.: 523999
Richard P. Merage *(CEO)*
Paul Merage *(Chm)*

MIG Private Equity   (1)
660 Newport Center Dr Ste 1300, Newport Beach, CA 92660
Tel.: (949) 474-5800
Private Equity Services
N.A.I.C.S.: 523999
Doug Wolter *(Mng Dir)*
Paul Merage *(Chm)*

Merage Investment Group—(Continued)

MIG Real Estate (1)
660 Newport Center Dr Ste 1300, Newport Beach, CA 92660
Tel.: (949) 474-5800
Web Site: http://www.migcap.com
Rev.: $650,000,000
Emp.: 50
Real Estate Owner, Manager & Investor
N.A.I.C.S.: 531390
Paul Merge (Chm)
Greg Merage (CEO)

MERAGE JEWISH COMMUNITY CENTER OF ORANGE COUNTY
1 Federation Way Ste 200, Irvine, CA 92603
Tel.: (949) 435-3400   CA
Web Site: http://www.jccoc.org
Year Founded: 1983
Sales Range: $10-24.9 Million
Emp.: 343
Jewish Community Services
N.A.I.C.S.: 624190
Samantha Cohen (VP-Program Svcs & Assoc Exec Dir)
Heather Rosenblatt (Dir-Membership Svcs)
Sheila Dalva-Hornback (Dir-Admissions)
Dan Bernstein (Pres & CEO)

MERAS ENGINEERING, INC.
4213 Technology Dr, Modesto, CA 95356
Tel.: (415) 240-4918
Web Site: http://www.meras.com
Year Founded: 2004
Rev.: $4,100,000
Emp.: 40
Engineeering Services
N.A.I.C.S.: 541330
Daniel B. O'Connell (Pres)
Dupre Danelle (Office Mgr)
Tony Delgado (Acct Mgr)

MERCADO LATINO INC.
245 Baldwin Pike Blvd, City of Industry, CA 91746-1404
Tel.: (626) 333-6862
Web Site: http://www.mercadolatinoinc.com
Year Founded: 1967
Rev.: $1,500,000
Emp.: 206
Provider of General Line Groceries
N.A.I.C.S.: 424410
Graciliano Rodriguez (Founder)

MERCED IRRIGATION DISTRICT
744 W 20th St, Merced, CA 95340
Tel.: (209) 722-5761
Web Site: http://www.mercedid.org
Sales Range: $25-49.9 Million
Emp.: 31
Provider of Irrigation Services
N.A.I.C.S.: 221118
Dave Long (Pres-Div 3)
Scott Koehn (VP-Div 2)

MERCEDES BENZ OF HAGERSTOWN
1955 Dual Hwy, Hagerstown, MD 21740-6603
Tel.: (301) 733-2301
Web Site: http://www.drivemb.com
Year Founded: 2001
Sales Range: $10-24.9 Million
Emp.: 50
New Car Whslr
N.A.I.C.S.: 441110
J. Harbert (Gen Mgr)
Brandon Younger (Owner)

MERCEDES BENZ OF NOVI
39500 Grand River Ave, Novi, MI 48375
Tel.: (248) 426-9600
Web Site: http://www.mercedesbenzofnovi.com
Sales Range: $10-24.9 Million
Emp.: 43
Car Whslr
N.A.I.C.S.: 441110
Lee Ghesquire (Principal)

MERCEDES ELECTRIC SUPPLY, INC.
8550 NW S River Dr, Miami, FL 33166
Tel.: (305) 887-5550
Web Site: http://www.mercedeselectric.com
Sales Range: $10-24.9 Million
Emp.: 30
Electrical Supplies Whslr
N.A.I.C.S.: 423610
Mercedes C. LaPorta (Owner & Pres)

MERCEDES HOMES INC.
6905 N Wickham Rd Ste 501, Melbourne, FL 32940
Tel.: (321) 259-6972
Year Founded: 1984
Sales Range: $10-24.9 Million
Emp.: 15
Provider of New Construction Services
N.A.I.C.S.: 236115

Subsidiaries:

BDR Title Corporation (1)
6905 N Wickham Rd Ste 503, Melbourne, FL 32940
Tel.: (321) 751-2673
Rev.: $520,000
Emp.: 8
Title Insurance
N.A.I.C.S.: 524127

Cornerstone Home Mortgage (1)
12001 Science Dr, Orlando, FL 32826-2915
Tel.: (407) 381-1702
Web Site: http://www.merhomes.com
Mortgage Services
N.A.I.C.S.: 522310

Mercedes Homes of Texas Ltd. (1)
4100 Alpha Rd Ste 915, Farmers Branch, TX 75244
Tel.: (469) 718-7200
Web Site: http://www.mercedeshomes.com
Construction Services
N.A.I.C.S.: 236115

Space Coast Holding Corp. (1)
201 Paint St, Rockledge, FL 32955
Tel.: (321) 632-7511
Web Site: http://www.merhomes.com
Rev.: $1,600,000
Provider of Business Services
N.A.I.C.S.: 321215

MERCEDES MEDICAL INC.
7590 Commerce Ct, Sarasota, FL 34240
Tel.: (941) 355-3333
Web Site: http://www.mercedesmedical.com
Year Founded: 1991
Sales Range: $25-49.9 Million
Emp.: 60
Medical Dental & Hospital Equipment & Supplies Merchant Whslr
N.A.I.C.S.: 423450
Troy Barnett (COO)
Dave Johnson (Exec VP)
Andy Wright (Pres)
Alexandra Miller (CEO)
Robert S. Haft (Vice Chm)
Noelle A. Haft (Chm)
Carole Anzioano (Exec Dir-HR & Customer Care)

Myles Rivera (Mgr-Warehouse)
Michael Jenkins (Mgr-Mktg)
Shaina McClaugherty (Supvr-Customer Svc)

MERCEDES PORSCHE AUDI OF MELBOURNE
509 E Nasa Blvd, Melbourne, FL 32901
Tel.: (321) 956-0600
Web Site: http://www.mbmelbourne.com
Rev.: $18,300,000
Emp.: 120
Automobiles, New & Used
N.A.I.C.S.: 441110
Maria Moises (Mgr-HR)
Charles Kleinschnitz (Mgr-Sls)

MERCEDES-BENZ OF BROOKLYN
1810 Shore Pkwy, Brooklyn, NY 11214
Tel.: (718) 258-5100
Web Site: http://www.mbofbrooklyn.com
Sales Range: $25-49.9 Million
Emp.: 270
New & Used Car Dealership
N.A.I.C.S.: 441110
Douglas Wells (Pres)
Lou Romano (Mgr-Pre-Owned Sls)
Tanya Pamornsut (Mgr-Inventory Control)
Antoinette Gordon-Hessing (Mgr-Bus Dev)
Steve Bylis (Mgr-Svc)
Sharon Incarnato (Controller)
Roger Pittman (COO)
Robert Ramellini (Dir-IT)
Domenico Gramuglia (Mgr-Body Shop)
Phil Katz (Mgr-Fin)
Georgi Natalichvilli (Mgr-Fin)
Eddie Atehortua (Mgr-Parts-Columbus)
Barry Martins (Mgr-Sls)
Patrick Muhler (Mgr-Svc-Columbus)
Devin Prediger (Mgr-Svc-Columbus)

MERCEDES-BENZ OF CALDWELL
1230 Bloomfield Ave, Fairfield, NJ 07004
Tel.: (973) 225-4443
Web Site: http://www.mbofcaldwell.com
Year Founded: 1967
Owner & Operator of Car Dealerships
N.A.I.C.S.: 441110
Steve Reedy (Gen Mgr)
George Ikonomakos (Sls Mgr)
Al Reci (Bus Mgr)
Jonathan Polera (Mgr-Svc)
Michael Hoehman (Asst Mgr-Svc)
Anthony Leary (Mgr-Loaner Car)
Eric Ehrhart (Mgr-Parts)
Steve Zabriskie (Asst Mgr-Parts)

MERCEDES-BENZ OF CORAL GABLES
300 Almeria Ave, Coral Gables, FL 33134-5812
Tel.: (305) 445-8593   FL
Web Site: http://www.ussery.mercedesdealer.com
Year Founded: 1970
Sales Range: $75-99.9 Million
Emp.: 250
Retailer of New & Used Car Dealers
N.A.I.C.S.: 441110
Ronit Canet (Treas, Sec & CFO-Bill Ussery Motors Grp)
Paula Brockway (VP)
Andy Llanes (Mgr-Parts)

Angel Rabassa (Dir-Fin Svcs)
Juan Gonzalez (Mgr-Sls)
Nicole Waters (Dir-Mktg)
Richard Santalla (Dir-Svc)
Miles Charlton (Mgr-Smart Brand)
Scott Cooper (Dir-Fin)
Luis Gutierrez (Dir-Svc Ops)
Ann Popplewell (Dir-HR)
Monique Ramirez (Mgr-HR)
Rene Aldana (Mgr-Sls)
Hector Brito (Mgr-Sls)
Tommy Juan (Mgr-Svc)

Subsidiaries:

MB Leasing Corp. (1)
300 Almeria Ave, Coral Gables, FL 33134-5812 (100%)
Tel.: (305) 445-8593
Web Site: http://www.mercedes-benzofcoralgables.com
Sales Range: $25-49.9 Million
Passenger Car Leasing
N.A.I.C.S.: 532112
Zulema Pericich (Office Mgr)

MERCEDES-BENZ OF NANUET
99 Rte 304, Nanuet, NY 10954
Tel.: (845) 624-1500   NY
Web Site: http://www.mbofnanuet.com
Year Founded: 1974
New & Used Car Dealers
N.A.I.C.S.: 441110
Rich Hesse (Owner)
Alex Wander (Mgr-Parts)

MERCEDES-BENZ OF NAPLES
501 Airport Rd S, Naples, FL 34104
Tel.: (239) 643-5006
Web Site: http://www.mercedesbenznaples.com
Sales Range: $10-24.9 Million
Emp.: 90
Car Dealership Owner & Operator
N.A.I.C.S.: 441110
Terry Taylor (Pres)
Tom Neglio (Dir-Fin & Lease)
Mike Cozza (Dir-Svc & Parts)
David Wachs (Mng Partner & Gen mgr)
Brian Lambert (Dir-Pre-Owned)
Rich Grimes (Mgr-Sls)
Dean Smith (Mgr-Pre-Owned Sls)
Joe Jalbert (Mgr-Fin & Lease)
Berry Allen (Mgr-Parts)
Joe Pitt (Asst Mgr-Svc)

MERCEDES-BENZ OF SEATTLE
2025 Airport Way S, Seattle, WA 98134
Tel.: (206) 467-9999
Web Site: http://www.mbseattle.com
Sales Range: $25-49.9 Million
Emp.: 125
New Car Dealers
N.A.I.C.S.: 441110
John Ramstetter (Gen Mgr-Sls)
Troy Coachman (Dir-Fin)
Ed Wagor (Mgr-Svc)
John Shepard (Mgr-Svc)
Jason Graham (Gen Mgr)
Paul West (Mgr-Sls)
Sergey Makhanov (Mgr-Sls-Pre-Owned)
Kristifer Capps (Mgr-Fin)
Amy Topping (Mgr-Fin)
Chris Reade (Mgr-Internet)
Francisco Leal (Mgr-Parts)
Al Monjazeb (Owner)
John McMillen (Gen Mgr)
Kathryn Walton (Mgr-Ops)
Sunil Chandwani (Mgr-Pre-Owned)
Andrew Plata (Mgr-Sls)
Peter Williams (Mgr-Svc-Columbus)

COMPANIES

MERCEDES-BENZ OF SPOKANE
21802 E George Gee Ave I, Liberty Lake, WA 99019
Tel.: (509) 455-9100
Web Site: http://www.spokanemercedes.com
Sales Range: $50-74.9 Million
Emp.: 40
Automobiles, New & Used
N.A.I.C.S.: 441110
Dan Crowley *(Gen Mgr)*

MERCER COUNTY STATE BANCORP
3279 S Main St, Sandy Lake, PA 16145-0038
Tel.: (724) 376-2100 PA
Web Site: http://www.mcsbank.bank
Year Founded: 1911
Sales Range: $10-24.9 Million
Emp.: 104
Provider of Financial Services
N.A.I.C.S.: 551111

Subsidiaries:

Mercer County State Bank (1)
3279 S Main, Sandy Lake, PA 16145
Tel.: (724) 376-7015
Web Site: http://www.mercercountystatebank.com
Sales Range: $25-49.9 Million
Emp.: 24
Provider of Financial Services
N.A.I.C.S.: 551111
Suzanne Rosenfelder *(Mgr-Svc Ctr)*
Patty Adamson *(Branch Mgr)*
Scott Patton *(Pres/COO-Hermitage)*
Ray Kaltenbaugh *(CEO)*

MERCER FORGE CORPORATION
200 Brown St, Mercer, PA 16137
Tel.: (724) 662-2750
Rev.: $24,300,000
Emp.: 150
Iron & Steel Forgings
N.A.I.C.S.: 332111
Sharon Altman *(Controller)*
Jim Ackerman *(Pres)*
Ron Bromley *(Mgr-HR)*

MERCER FRASER COMPANY
200 Dinsmore Dr, Fortuna, CA 95540
Tel.: (707) 443-6371
Rev.: $13,118,457
Emp.: 35
General Remodeling, Single-Family Houses
N.A.I.C.S.: 236118
Cassie Coppini *(Office Mgr)*

MERCER LANDMARK INC.
426 W Market St, Celina, OH 45822
Tel.: (419) 586-2303
Web Site: http://www.mercerlandmark.com
Year Founded: 1933
Sales Range: $100-124.9 Million
Emp.: 250
Agricultural Support Services
N.A.I.C.S.: 424510
Tom Belt *(Mgr-Agronomy)*
Ken Puthoff *(Branch Mgr)*
Ken Stammen *(Chm)*
John Morris *(Sec)*
Robert Todd Matthews *(Vice Chm)*

Subsidiaries:

CW Service (1)
5215 State Rd Rte 118, Coldwater, OH 45828
Tel.: (419) 678-4811
Rev.: $25,000,000
Emp.: 15
Gasoline Sales
N.A.I.C.S.: 457120

MERCER TRANSPORTATION COMPANY
1128 W Main St, Louisville, KY 40203-1432
Tel.: (502) 584-2301 IN
Web Site: http://www.mercer-trans.com
Year Founded: 1977
Sales Range: $200-249.9 Million
Emp.: 250
Provider of Long-Haul Trucking Operations
N.A.I.C.S.: 484121
James L. Stone *(Pres & COO)*
Jeff Howard *(Treas & Sec)*
John Sallot *(Gen Mgr)*
William G. Howard Jr. *(Chm & CFO)*

MERCHANDISE PARTNERS, LLC
11111 N 46th St, Tampa, FL 33617
Tel.: (813) 899-6955
Web Site: http://www.merchandisepartners.com
Year Founded: 2008
Sales Range: $25-49.9 Million
Emp.: 5
Promotional Products Distr & Online Retailer
N.A.I.C.S.: 425120
Mark Govin *(Co-Founder)*
Kevin Govin *(Co-Founder)*

MERCHANDISE, INC.
5929 State Rte 128, Miamitown, OH 45041
Tel.: (513) 353-2200
Web Site: http://www.merchandiseinc.com
Year Founded: 1964
General Merchandise Distr
N.A.I.C.S.: 424210
Donald J. Karches *(Pres)*
Beth Schwarb *(Dir-Cosmetics & Mgr-HR)*
Brian Longbottom *(Mgr-Acctg Dept)*
Greg Christopfel *(Mgr-Natl Sls)*
Jim Powell *(Gen Dir-Mdse)*
Terry Potts *(Mgr-Retail Svc)*
Nick Bachus *(Dir-Ops)*
Matt Denney *(Supvr-Warehouse)*

MERCHANDISING WORKSHOP, INC.
119 E 38th St, New York, NY 10016
Tel.: (212) 246-2121 NY
Web Site: http://www.mwny.com
Year Founded: 1975
Sales Range: $25-49.9 Million
Emp.: 25
Sales Promotion
N.A.I.C.S.: 541870
Norman Alshooler *(Pres)*
Jeanine Millman *(Controller)*
Angel Toledo *(Color Lab Opers Dir)*
Jay Gross *(Acct Dir)*

MERCHANDIZE LIQUIDATORS, LLC
7815 W 20th Ave, Hialeah, FL 33014
Tel.: (954) 454-7100
Web Site: http://www.merchandizeliquidators.com
Year Founded: 2003
Sales Range: $10-24.9 Million
Emp.: 15
Reseller of Surplus Wholesale Overstock Products, General Merchandise & Clothing
N.A.I.C.S.: 424350
Joseph Martin *(Founder & Pres)*
Pierina Pena *(Mgr-Sls)*

MERCHANT & EVANS, INC.
308 Connecticut Dr, Burlington, NJ 08016-4104
Tel.: (609) 387-3033
Web Site: http://www.ziprib.com
Year Founded: 1866
Rev.: $4,000,000
Emp.: 30
Roofing System Services
N.A.I.C.S.: 332323
Steve Buck *(Pres)*
Joseph Depaulo *(Project Coord)*
Ron Jaconelli *(VP-Ops)*
Tony Thompson *(Mgr-Engrg)*

Subsidiaries:

Zip-Rib, Inc. (1)
308 Connecticut Dr, Burlington, NJ 08016
Tel.: (800) 257-6215
Web Site: http://www.ziprib.com
Architectural & Structural Roofing Products Mfr
N.A.I.C.S.: 444110

MERCHANT EQUIPMENT STORE
5316 W Hwy 290 Ste 130, Austin, TX 78735
Web Site: http://www.merchantequip.com
Year Founded: 2005
Sales Range: $1-9.9 Million
Emp.: 9
Electronic Payment Processing
N.A.I.C.S.: 522320
Peter Estep *(Pres)*

MERCHANT FACTORS CORP.
1441 Broadway 22nd Fl, New York, NY 10018
Tel.: (212) 840-7575
Web Site: http://www.merchantfactors.com
Year Founded: 1985
Rev.: $40,600,000
Emp.: 60
Provider of Credit Services
N.A.I.C.S.: 522299
Joshua Goodhart *(Sr VP & Mgr-Sls-Natl)*
Scott Adler *(Chief Credit Officer & Exec VP)*
Adam Winters *(Pres & CEO)*
Craig Miller *(Sr VP-Mktg & New Bus Dev)*
Neville Grusd *(Exec VP)*

MERCHANT INDUSTRY LLC
36-36 33rd St Ste 306, Long Island City, NY 11106
Web Site: http://www.merchantindustry.com
Year Founded: 2007
Sales Range: $10-24.9 Million
Emp.: 100
Sells & Services Credit Card Processing Products
N.A.I.C.S.: 522320
Leo Vartanov *(Co-Founder & CEO)*
Jennifer Vartanov *(Co-Founder & CFO)*

MERCHANT INVESTMENT MANAGEMENT, LLC
600 Madison Ave 17th Fl, New York, NY 10022
Tel.: (646) 979-4070
Web Site: http://www.merchantim.com
Year Founded: 2017
Financial Services
N.A.I.C.S.: 523999
Matt Brinker *(Mng Dir)*
Tim Bello *(Founder & Mng Partner)*
Scott Steven Prince *(Exec Chm)*

MERCHANT ONE
524 Arthur Godfrey Rd 3rd Fl, Miami Beach, FL 33140
Web Site: http://www.merchantone.com
Year Founded: 2001
Sales Range: $10-24.9 Million
Emp.: 72
Short-Term Business Credit Institution
N.A.I.C.S.: 522299
Sandy Saka *(Pres)*

MERCHANT PROCESSING SERVICES, INC.
132 W 36th St 3rd Fl, New York, NY 10018
Tel.: (212) 931-5180
Year Founded: 2003
Sales Range: $25-49.9 Million
Emp.: 56
Credit Card Payment Processing
N.A.I.C.S.: 522320

MERCHANT SERVICES DIRECT LLC
9212 E Montgomery Ave Ste 400, Spokane, WA 99206
Tel.: (509) 928-3099
Web Site: http://www.msdmerchants.com
Year Founded: 2007
Sales Range: $1-9.9 Million
Emp.: 45
Credit Card Equipment Planning Equipment Suppliers & Services
N.A.I.C.S.: 522210
Shane Hurley *(CEO)*
Arthur Ryan *(Acct Exec)*

MERCHANT SERVICES LTD.
675 NW 97th St, Miami, FL 33150
Tel.: (305) 673-3334
Web Site: http://www.merchantservicesltd.com
Year Founded: 2001
Sales Range: $1-9.9 Million
Emp.: 30
Credit Card Processing Services
N.A.I.C.S.: 522320
Lisbeth Durand *(Dir-Pricing & Underwriting)*

MERCHANTS BANK
1901 College Ave, Jackson, AL 36545
Tel.: (251) 246-4425
Web Site: http://www.merchantsbk.com
Sales Range: $10-24.9 Million
Emp.: 75
State Commercial Banks
N.A.I.C.S.: 522110
Craig L. Scrugs *(Pres)*
Kathy Autry *(VP)*
Andrew Guzzo *(Pres & Chief Banking Officer)*
Michael J. Dunlap *(Pres, CEO & Co-COO)*
Scott A. Evans *(COO)*

MERCHANTS BONDING COMPANY
2100 Fleur Dr, Des Moines, IA 50321
Tel.: (515) 243-8171
Web Site: http://www.merchantsbonding.com
Sales Range: $10-24.9 Million
Emp.: 100
Fidelity Or Surety Bonding
N.A.I.C.S.: 524126
Larry Taylor *(Chm & Pres)*
Josh Penwell *(VP-Contract Underwriting)*
Don Blum *(CFO & Treas)*
Brad Rasmussen *(CIO)*
Therese Wielage *(VP-Mktg)*

MERCHANTS BUILDING MAINTENANCE CO.

Merchants Building Maintenance Co.—(Continued)

MERCHANTS BUILDING MAINTENANCE CO.
1190 Monterey Pass Rd, Monterey Park, CA 91754
Tel.: (323) 881-6700
Web Site: http://www.mbmonline.com
Rev.: $34,847,609
Emp.: 20
Security Guard Services
N.A.I.C.S.: 561612
Theodore Haas (Chm)
David Haas (Pres)
Anita Bay (Controller)

MERCHANTS EXPORT INC.
200 Martin Luther King Jr Blvd, Riviera Beach, FL 33404-7506
Tel.: (561) 844-7000   FL
Web Site:
   http://www.merchantsmarket.com
Year Founded: 1975
Sales Range: $10-24.9 Million
Emp.: 70
Provider of Grocery Services
N.A.I.C.S.: 424420
Isabel Amengual Galindo (CEO)
Steve Shoupp (Dir-Sls)
Kevin Rodriguez (Mgr-Non-Foods Category Pur)
Jeff Ullian (VP)

MERCHANTS METALS RECYCLING II CD, LLC
6775 Bingle Rd, Houston, TX 77092
Tel.: (713) 862-5588
Holding Company; Metal Recycling Services
N.A.I.C.S.: 551112
Beau Landry (CEO)

Subsidiaries:

C & D Scrap Metal Recyclers Co, Inc.   (1)
815 W 25th St, Houston, TX 77008
Tel.: (713) 862-5588
Web Site: http://www.cdscrapmetal.com
Sales Range: $1-9.9 Million
Emp.: 19
Whol Scrap/Waste Material
N.A.I.C.S.: 423930
Cynthia Laviage (VP)
Dennis Laviage (Founder)

MERCHANTS OFFICE FURNITURE COMPANY
2261 Broadway, Denver, CO 80205-2535
Tel.: (303) 297-1100
Web Site:
   http://www.merchantsofficefurniture.com
Office Furniture Mfr
N.A.I.C.S.: 337214
Lexi Sanders (Mgr)

Subsidiaries:

Pear, LLC   (1)
1515 Arapahoe St Ste 100, Denver, CO 80202-2139
Tel.: (303) 382-2000
Web Site: http://www.pearwork.com
Office Furniture Mfr
N.A.I.C.S.: 337214
John Robbins (Pres & CEO)

MERCHANTS' CREDIT GUIDE CO.
223 W Jackson Blvd Ste 700, Chicago, IL 60606
Tel.: (312) 360-3000
Web Site: http://www.merchantscreditguide.com
Year Founded: 1896
Sales Range: $10-24.9 Million
Emp.: 53

Accounts Receivable Management Services
N.A.I.C.S.: 561440
Dan Burtis (Chm & Pres)
Edwin Burtis (Treas)

MERCOM CORPORATION
313 Commerce Dr, Pawleys Island, SC 29585
Tel.: (843) 979-9957
Web Site:
   http://www.mercomcorp.com
Year Founded: 2000
Sales Range: $25-49.9 Million
Emp.: 90
Data Network Infrastructure Management, Sales & Installation Services
N.A.I.C.S.: 541511
Stella Mercado Colwell (Pres)
Meagan Leventis (Mgr-Sls)
Diane Veverka (Project Coord)
Tara Flowe (Acct Exec-Sls)

MERCURY ADVISORS LLC
511 W Bay St Ste 350, Tampa, FL 33606
Tel.: (813) 321-1984
Web Site: http://www.mercury-advisors.com
Sales Range: $1-9.9 Million
Real Estate Investment Services
N.A.I.C.S.: 523999
Ken K. Stoltenberg (Principal)
Frank H. Bombeeck (Principal)

MERCURY AIR GROUP INC.
2780 Skypark Dr, Torrance, CA 90505
Tel.: (310) 827-2737   NY
Web Site:
   http://www.mercuryairgroup.com
Year Founded: 1956
Sales Range: $600-649.9 Million
Emp.: 800
Aviation Fuel & Related Services, Air Cargo Services & Forwarders
N.A.I.C.S.: 488190
Joseph A. Czyzyk (Chm & CEO)
John Peery (COO & Exec VP)
Homan Asiri (VP-Fuel Sls)
Lawrence R. Samuels (CFO)
Robert Lovejoy (CIO)
Kathryn M. Schwertfeger (Gen Counsel)
Carolina Gutierrez (Sec & VP-Admin)

Subsidiaries:

Final Mile Logistics, Inc.   (1)
165 CW Grant Pkwy, Atlanta, GA 30354
Tel.: (404) 608-9021
Web Site: http://www.finalmilelogistics.com
Sales Range: $10-24.9 Million
Emp.: 15
Logistics Consulting Servies
N.A.I.C.S.: 541614
Robert Gentzke (COO)

Hermes Aviation, Inc.   (1)
6040 Avion Dr 3nd Fl, Los Angeles, CA 90045
Tel.: (310) 258-6100
Web Site: http://www.mercuryaircargo.com
Air Cargo Services
N.A.I.C.S.: 492110

Maytag Aircraft Corp.   (1)
6145 Lehman Dr Ste 300, Colorado Springs, CO 80918-3440   (100%)
Tel.: (719) 593-1600
Web Site: http://www.maytagaircraft.com
Sales Range: $10-24.9 Million
Emp.: 10
Provider of Aircraft Fueling Services
N.A.I.C.S.: 488190
David D. Nelson (Pres & COO)

MercFuel, Inc.   (1)
2780 Skypark Dr, Torrance, CA 90505
Tel.: (310) 827-2737

Sales Range: $10-24.9 Million
Emp.: 40
Fuel Sales & Service
N.A.I.C.S.: 424720
Christopher Cooper (Exec VP-Corp Fuels)

Mercury Air Cargo, Inc.   (1)
6040 Avion Dr Ste 200, Los Angeles, CA 90045
Tel.: (310) 641-5667
Web Site: http://www.mercuryair.com
Sales Range: $25-49.9 Million
Emp.: 700
Aircraft Services
N.A.I.C.S.: 481212
Joseph A. Czyzyk (Chm & CEO)

Mercury Refueling, Inc.   (1)
6851 W Imperial Hwy, Los Angeles, CA 90045-6322   (100%)
Tel.: (310) 646-2994
Sales Range: $10-24.9 Million
Emp.: 2
Provider of Aircraft Fueling Services
N.A.I.C.S.: 424720

MERCURY AIRCRAFT INC.
15 17 Wheeler Ave, Hammondsport, NY 14840-9566
Tel.: (607) 569-4200
Web Site:
   http://www.mercuryaircraftinc.com
Year Founded: 1920
Sales Range: $50-74.9 Million
Emp.: 900
Provider of Sheet Metalwork Services
N.A.I.C.S.: 332322
Greg Hintz (CFO)
Peter Hannan (VP)
Mark Hammond (Dir-Tech)
Rich Bussmann (Mgr-Engrg)
John Fairbanks (Engr-Mfg)

Subsidiaries:

Airspeed, LLC   (1)
980 Corporate Dr Ste 200, Hillsborough, NC 27278
Tel.: (919) 644-1222
Web Site: http://www.airspeedllc.com
Electronic Components Mfr
N.A.I.C.S.: 334419

Atlas Metal Industries Inc.   (1)
1135 NW 159th Dr, Miami, FL 33169-5807
Tel.: (305) 625-2451
Web Site: http://www.atlasfoodserv.com
Sales Range: $25-49.9 Million
Emp.: 150
Food Service Equipment
N.A.I.C.S.: 333310
David C. Meade (Pres & Treas)

Mercury Aircraft, Mexico S. de R.L. de C.V.   (1)
Barre De Navidad, Acatlan de Juarez, Jalisco, Mexico
Tel.: (52) 3 87 772 1103
Fabricated Metal Product Distr
N.A.I.C.S.: 423510

Mercury Minnesota Inc.   (1)
901 Hulett Ave, Faribault, MN 55021-3613
Tel.: (507) 334-5513
Web Site: http://www.medichem.com
Rev.: $19,900,000
Emp.: 200
Provider of Sheet Metalwork Services
N.A.I.C.S.: 332322
Judy Cross (Mgr-Engrg)

MERCURY CAPITAL CORP.
100 Merrick Rd Ste 504 E, Rockville Centre, NY 11570
Tel.: (212) 661-8700   NY
Web Site:
   http://www.mercurycap.com
Year Founded: 1988
Sales Range: $25-49.9 Million
Emp.: 5
Provider of Mortgage Services
N.A.I.C.S.: 523999
Marc Gleitman (Co-Founder & Pres)
Meir Krengel (Principal)

MERCURY CAPITAL PARTNERS, L.P.
726 Exchange St Ste 410, Buffalo, NY 14210
Tel.: (716) 332-9575
Web Site:
   http://www.mercurycapitalpartners.com
Year Founded: 1994
Sales Range: $25-49.9 Million
Emp.: 6
Private Equity Services
N.A.I.C.S.: 523999
Charles W. Banta (Pres)
Sandy A. Miller (Principal & Controller)

MERCURY ENTERPRISES, INC.
11300 49th St N, Clearwater, FL 33762-4807
Tel.: (727) 573-0088   FL
Web Site:
   http://www.mercurymed.com
Year Founded: 1963
Sales Range: $25-49.9 Million
Emp.: 170
Hospital Equipment & Biomedical Distr
N.A.I.C.S.: 423450
Stanley G. Tangalakis (Chm & CEO)
Mark Maynard (Mgr-Customer Svc)
John Gargaro (CEO)
Douglas Smith (VP-Sls & Mktg)

MERCURY EQUIPMENT FINANCE GROUP
27702 Crown Vly Pkwy Ste D4-205, Ladera Ranch, CA 92694
Tel.: (949) 218-8700
Web Site: http://www.mer-cap.com
Year Founded: 2001
Sales Range: $1-9.9 Million
Emp.: 5
Equipment Lease Financing Services to Small Businesses
N.A.I.C.S.: 522220
Barry Lyon (Founder)

MERCURY FUEL SERVICE INC.
43 Lafayette St, Waterbury, CT 06708-3801
Tel.: (203) 756-7284   CT
Web Site:
   http://www.mercuryenergy.com
Year Founded: 1946
Sales Range: $10-24.9 Million
Emp.: 110
Provider of Petroleum Products
N.A.I.C.S.: 424720
Michael Devino (Pres)

MERCURY INTERNATIONAL TRADING CORP.
20 Alice Agnew Dr, North Attleboro, MA 02763
Tel.: (508) 699-9000
Web Site:
   http://www.mercuryfootwear.com
Sales Range: $75-99.9 Million
Emp.: 100
Mfr of Men's Casual Branded Shoes & Boots
N.A.I.C.S.: 424340
Irving Wiseman (Chm)
Howard Wiseman (Pres & CEO)
Judy Foley (VP-Sourcing)

Subsidiaries:

Madison Footwear Co. Ltd.   (1)
No 7 Shihuan Road Qianjin Cun, Dongpu Zhen Tianhe District, 510660, Guangzhou, China
Tel.: (86) 2082568888
Footwear Mfr
N.A.I.C.S.: 316210

MERCURY

COMPANIES

LUGGAGE/SEWARD TRUNK
4843 Victor St, Jacksonville, FL 32207-7963
Tel.: (904) 733-9595 FL
Web Site:
http://www.mercuryluggage.com
Year Founded: 1946
Sales Range: $75-99.9 Million
Emp.: 100
Luggage Mfr
N.A.I.C.S.: 316990
Andrew Pradella (Owner)

Subsidiaries:

Mercury Luggage/Seward Trunk (1)
1818 Dock St, Petersburg, VA 23803-2847 (100%)
Tel.: (804) 733-5222
Web Site: http://www.mercuryluggage.com
Sales Range: $25-49.9 Million
Emp.: 50
Mfr of Trunks, Footlockers & Other Storage Products
N.A.I.C.S.: 316990
Andrew Pradella (Owner)

Mercury Luggage/Seward Trunk (1)
1190 Orange Ave, Corcoran, CA 93212-9609 (100%)
Tel.: (559) 992-5925
Web Site: http://www.mercuryluggage.com
Sales Range: $10-24.9 Million
Emp.: 17
Mfr of Luggage
N.A.I.C.S.: 321920

MERCURY MEDIA HOLDING CORP.
520 Broadway Ste 400, Santa Monica, CA 90401-2462
Tel.: (310) 451-2900 CA
Year Founded: 1989
Sales Range: $150-199.9 Million
Emp.: 120
Advertising Agencies, Direct Marketing, E-Commerce, Infomercials, Media Buying Services, Strategic Planning
N.A.I.C.S.: 541830
John Barnes (Pres)
Olga Ackad (VP & Dir-Client Svcs)
Beth Vendice (Pres-Performance Div)
Kristi Tropp (VP & Dir-Client Svcs)
Kristofer Johnson (VP-Sls)
Nicholas Nocca (CEO)
Ari S. Milstein (CFO)

Subsidiaries:

Mercury Media - Boston (1)
225 Cedar Hill St, Marlborough, MA 01752
Tel.: (508) 449-3253
N.A.I.C.S.: 541810
Kristi Tropp (VP & Dir-Client Svcs)
Justin Henderson (VP-Digital Svcs)
Keith Kochberg (Pres-Digital)
Ari Milstein (CFO)
Nick Nocca (CEO)
Alex Sapoznikov (Sr VP-Analytics & Data Strategy)
Liz Woodhouse (VP-HR)

Mercury Media - Princeton (1)
100 Canal Pointe Blvd Ste 216, Princeton, NJ 08540-7063
Tel.: (609) 921-0400
Sales Range: $25-49.9 Million
Emp.: 15
Digital Advertising Services
N.A.I.C.S.: 541810

Mercury Media -Santa Monica (1)
520 Broadway Ste 400, Santa Monica, CA 90401-2462
Tel.: (310) 451-2900
Web Site: http://www.mercuryglobal.com
Sales Range: $10-24.9 Million
Emp.: 6
Advertising Agencies, Infomercials, Media Buying Services, Strategic Planning
N.A.I.C.S.: 541810

MERCURY MOSAICS & TILE, INC.
1620 Central Ave NE Ste 125, Minneapolis, MN 55413
Tel.: (612) 236-1646
Web Site:
http://www.mercurymosaics.com
Year Founded: 2002
Sales Range: $1-9.9 Million
Tiles Mfr
N.A.I.C.S.: 327120
Mercedes Austin (Founder & Owner)

MERCURY NEW MEDIA, INC.
4350 W Cypress St Ste 701, Tampa, FL 33607
Tel.: (813) 933-9800
Web Site:
http://www.mercurynewmedia.com
Year Founded: 1998
Sales Range: $10-24.9 Million
Emp.: 20
Website & Custom Web-Based Application Developer & Marketer
N.A.I.C.S.: 513210
Christopher Karlo (Partner)
Donald Bickel (Partner)

MERCURY PAINT CORP.
4808 Farragut Rd, Brooklyn, NY 11203
Tel.: (718) 469-8787
Web Site:
http://www.mercurypaintcorp.com
Rev.: $15,600,000
Emp.: 75
Paints & Paint Additives
N.A.I.C.S.: 325510

MERCURY PARTNERS 90 BI INC.
1200 Greenleaf Ave, Elk Grove Village, IL 60007
Tel.: (847) 437-9690
Web Site: http://www.bruckerco.com
Sales Range: $10-24.9 Million
Emp.: 50
Heating Equipment (Hydronic)
N.A.I.C.S.: 423720
Russ Martinek (CFO)
Vince Radosta (CEO)
Larry Kasza (Pres)

MERCURY PLASTICS INC.
14825 Salt Lk Ave, City of Industry, CA 91746
Tel.: (626) 961-0165
Web Site:
http://www.sigmaplasticsgroup.com
Sales Range: $50-74.9 Million
Emp.: 600
Mfr of Plastic Bags
N.A.I.C.S.: 326111
Benjamin Deutsch (CEO)
Ademar Quiros (Plant Mgr)
Stanley Tzenkov (VP-Mktg & Customer Rels)

MERCURY PLASTICS, INC.
15760 Madison Rd, Middlefield, OH 44062
Tel.: (440) 632-5281
Web Site: http://www.mercury-plastics.com
Year Founded: 1965
Sales Range: $10-24.9 Million
Emp.: 600
Plastic Pipe & Pipe Fitting Mfr
N.A.I.C.S.: 326122
William W. Rowley (Pres)
Scott Gardner (Mgr-Sls & Mktg)
Paul Sharron (Mgr-HR)

MERCURY PRODUCTS CORP.
1201 Mercury Dr, Schaumburg, IL 60193-3513
Tel.: (847) 524-4400
Web Site: http://www.mercprod.com
Sales Range: $25-49.9 Million
Emp.: 20
Automotive Stampings
N.A.I.C.S.: 336370
Marcy Aranda (Mgr-HR)
Maria Jimenez (Mgr-Pur)
Bruce Havel (Pres)
Ronald Anderson (Mgr-Quality Assurance)

MERCURY PROMOTIONS & FULFILLMENT, INC.
35610 Mound Rd, Sterling Heights, MI 48310-4725
Tel.: (248) 936-2600
Web Site: http://www.mercuryfs.com
Year Founded: 1996
Sales Range: $10-24.9 Million
Emp.: 75
Advertising Services
N.A.I.C.S.: 541810
Jon Sloan (CEO)

MERCURY TECHNOLOGIES, INC.
32 Old Slip, New York, NY 10005
Tel.: (212) 483-0300
Web Site: http://www.mercury.com
Year Founded: 1990
Sales Range: $10-24.9 Million
Emp.: 20
Custom Computer Software Systems Analysis & Design
N.A.I.C.S.: 541511
Philip Meese (Pres)

MERCURYCSC
22 S Grand Ave, Bozeman, MT 59715
Tel.: (406) 586-2280
Web Site:
http://www.mercurycsc.com
Year Founded: 1998
Sales Range: $10-24.9 Million
Emp.: 22
Advertising Agency Services
N.A.I.C.S.: 541810
Jeff Welch (Exec Dir-Creative)
Tanya White (COO)
Jaclyn Moos (Acct Mgr)
Seth Neilson (Assoc Dir-Creative)
Mike Cook (Dir-Art)
Donnie Clapp (Dir-Emerging Media)
Mike Geraci (Chief Creative Officer)
Stacie Wunsch (Pres)

MERCY FLIGHTS INC.
2020 Milligan Way, Medford, OR 97504
Tel.: (541) 858-2600 OR
Web Site:
http://www.mercyflights.com
Year Founded: 1949
Sales Range: $10-24.9 Million
Emp.: 137
Air & Ground Ambulance Services
N.A.I.C.S.: 621910
Doug Stewart (CEO)
Amy Hall (CFO)
Tim James (COO)
April Sevcik (Vice Chm)
Greg Yechout (Sec)
Richard Brewster (Treas)
Debbie Adair (Mgr-Billing)
Steve Deaton (Dir-Flight Ops)
Chad Keever (Mgr-Fleet)
Damon May (Dir-Flight Maintenance)
Matt Philbrick (Mgr-Medical Ops)
Leslie Terrell (Mgr-Comm)
Amy Szefel Starck (VP-Mktg & Dev)
Ashley Coder (Dir-Dev & Events)
Kate Glaser (Dir-Mktg & Pub Affairs)
Mike Burrill Jr. (Chm)

MERCY HEALTH SERVICES
301 St Paul Pl, Baltimore, MD 21202-2102
Tel.: (410) 332-9000 MD
Web Site: http://www.mdmercy.com
Year Founded: 1874
Sales Range: $200-249.9 Million
Emp.: 4,000
Provider of Healthcare Services
N.A.I.C.S.: 622110
M. Karen McNally (Chief Admin Officer-Stella Maris & Sr VP)
Scott A. Spier (Sr VP-Medical Affairs)
John E. Topper (Chief Risk Officer & Exec VP)
Helen Amos (Chm)
Maria Jacobs (Dir-Radio Oncology)
Neil B. Friedman (Dir-The Hoffberger Breast Center-Mercy Medical Center)
Judith A. Weiland (Sr VP-Strategic, Capital Plng & Facilities)
Nicholas J. Koas (Sr VP-Institutional Advancement)
David N. Maine (Pres & CEO)

MERCY MARICOPA INTEGRATED CARE
4350 E Cotton Center Blvd Bldg D, Phoenix, AZ 85040
Tel.: (602) 586-1841 AZ
Web Site:
http://www.mercymaricopa.org
Rev.: $1,424,568,435
Assets: $221,023,864
Liabilities: $85,175,371
Net Worth: $135,848,493
Earnings: ($13,150,796)
Fiscal Year-end: 08/30/18
Physical & Mental Health Care Services
N.A.I.C.S.: 624190
Eddy Broadway (CEO)
Kathy Benaquista (CFO-Interim)
Gene Cavallo (VP-Behavioral Health Svcs)

MERCY MEMORIAL HOSPITAL SYSTEM
718 N Macomb St, Monroe, MI 48162
Tel.: (734) 240-8400 MI
Web Site:
http://www.mercymemorial.org
Year Founded: 1971
Sales Range: $150-199.9 Million
Emp.: 1,882
Health Care Srvices
N.A.I.C.S.: 622110
John Kibble (VP-Bus Dev)

MEREDITH DIGITAL
119 East Alton Ave Ste A & B, Santa Ana, CA 92707
Web Site:
http://www.meredithdigital.com
Year Founded: 1996
Sales Range: $1-9.9 Million
Emp.: 17
Reseller of IT Supplies
N.A.I.C.S.: 423430
David Sarthou (Exec Dir-Campaign Strategy & Insights)
Selena LoRusso (Dir-Sls Dev & Strategy)
Kristen LoGrasso (Mgr-Sls)
Anastasia Cohen (Mgr-Sls)
Marla Newman (VP-Sls)
Marc Rothschild (Sr VP)

MEREDITH LODGING LLC
2015 NW 39th St, Lincoln City, OR 97367
Web Site:
http://www.meredithlodging.com
Year Founded: 2005
Sales Range: $10-24.9 Million
Emp.: 152
Real Estate Manangement Services

MEREDITH LODGING LLC

Meredith Lodging LLC—(Continued)
N.A.I.C.S.: 531390
Meredith Oksenholt (Co-Founder & Co-Owner)
Jon Oksenholt (Co-Founder & Co-Owner)

MEREDITH VILLAGE SAVINGS BANK
24 State Rte 25, Meredith, NH 03253
Tel.: (603) 279-7986
Web Site: http://www.mvsb.com
Year Founded: 1869
Sales Range: $25-49.9 Million
Emp.: 201
Federal Savings Bank
N.A.I.C.S.: 522180
Brian J. Chalmers (VP-Comml Loan)
Charleen Hughes (Asst VP-Branch & Mgr-Bus Dev)
Gracie E. Cilley (VP-Comml Loan)
Charles G. Hanson (Vice Chm & Sec)
Michelle L. McEwen (Chm)
Rick Burgess (Officer-Comml Loan & VP)
Dan Dolan (Officer-Comml Loan & VP)
Arthur Letendre (Officer-Consumer Loan & Sr VP)
Cindy Motta (VP)
Dan Osetek (Officer-Comml Loan & VP)
Angela Strozewski (Officer-Ops & Sr VP)

MEREDITH-WEBB PRINTING CO. INC.
334 N Main St, Burlington, NC 27217
Tel.: (336) 228-8378
Web Site: http://www.meredithwebb.com
Sales Range: $10-24.9 Million
Emp.: 110
Provider of Commercial Lithographic Printing
N.A.I.C.S.: 323111
Kelley Webb (Exec VP)
Mark Chapmon (Supvr-Pre-Press)
George Travers Webb III (Pres & CEO)

MEREX HOLDING CORPORATION
1283 FLynn Rd, Camarillo, CA 93012
Tel.: (805) 446-2700 DE
Web Site: http://www.merexinc.com
Holding Company; Military Aircraft Components Mfr, Distr, Maintenance, Overhaul & Repair Services
N.A.I.C.S.: 551112
Nathan Skop (Exec VP-Contracts & Compliance)
Anthony Grant (VP-Bus Transformation)
Sonja Roberts (VP-HR)
Carl Vickers (VP-Ops)

Subsidiaries:

Merex Aircraft Company, Incorporated (1)
1283 Flynn Rd, Camarillo, CA 93012-8046
Tel.: (805) 446-2700
Web Site: http://www.merexinc.com
Aircraft Components Mfr
N.A.I.C.S.: 336413
David Faulkner (Pres-Engrg & Mfg)
Dean Brady (Pres-Distr & Supply Chain-Global)
Stuart Reid (Interim VP-Sls & Mktg)

MERICAL LLC
2995 E Miraloma Ave, Anaheim, CA 92806
Tel.: (714) 238-7225
Web Site: http://www.merical.com
Year Founded: 1965
Nutritional Supplements Mfr
N.A.I.C.S.: 325412
Brian P. Smith (CEO)
Jeff Stallings (Pres)
Dean Baltzell (Founder & Dir)
Brent Moore (Exec VP-Ops Team)

Subsidiaries:

Pro Pac Labs, Inc. (1)
3804 Airport Rd, Ogden, UT 84405-1533
Tel.: (801) 621-0900
Web Site: http://www.propaclabs.com
Nutritional Supplements Mfr
N.A.I.C.S.: 325412
Kyle Griffiths (VP-Mktg & Sls)

MERICHEM COMPANY
5455 Old Spanish Trl, Houston, TX 77023
Tel.: (713) 428-5000 DE
Web Site: http://www.merichem.com
Year Founded: 1945
Sales Range: $25-49.9 Million
Emp.: 450
Industrial Chemical & Licensing & Fabricating of Proprietary Technology Mfr
N.A.I.C.S.: 325199
Kendra Lee (Chm & CEO)

Subsidiaries:

Merichem Chemicals & Refining Services LLC (1)
5455 Old Spanish Trl, Houston, TX 77023-5013 (100%)
Tel.: (713) 428-5100
Web Site: http://www.merichem.com
Sales Range: $10-24.9 Million
Emp.: 105
Mfr of Industrial Chemicals
N.A.I.C.S.: 325180

Subsidiary (Domestic):

Gas Technology Products LLC (2)
846 E Algonquin Rd Ste A100, Schaumburg, IL 60173
Tel.: (847) 285-3850
Web Site: http://www.gtp-merichem.com
Chemical Products Mfr
N.A.I.C.S.: 325998

Merichem Company - Merichem Catalyst Plant (1)
2701 Warrior Rd, Tuscaloosa, AL 35404
Tel.: (205) 462-2300
Chemical Products Mfr
N.A.I.C.S.: 325998

Merichem Hong Kong Ltd. (1)
F7I World Plaza No 855 PuDong South Rd, PuDong, Shanghai, 200120, China
Tel.: (86) 21 58779901
Emp.: 10
Chemical Products Mfr
N.A.I.C.S.: 325998
Dayong Dong (Gen Mgr)

Merisol Antioxidants LLC (1)
292 State Route 8, Oil City, PA 16301
Tel.: (814) 677-2028
Web Site: http://www.merisol.com
Sales Range: $10-24.9 Million
Emp.: 37
Mfr of Fine Chemicals
N.A.I.C.S.: 325199

MERICKEL LUMBER MILLS INC.
630 Ash Ave, Wadena, MN 56482
Tel.: (218) 631-3570
Web Site: http://www.merickellumber.com
Rev.: $10,000,000
Emp.: 30
Lumber & Other Building Materials
N.A.I.C.S.: 423310
James R. Merickel (Pres)

MERICLE COMMERCIAL REAL ESTATE SERVICES
100 Baltimore Dr, Wilkes Barre, PA 18702
Tel.: (570) 823-5500
Web Site: http://www.mericle.com
Year Founded: 1986
Sales Range: $10-24.9 Million
Emp.: 40
Provider of Commercial & Office Building Construction
N.A.I.C.S.: 531210
Robert Mericle (Pres)
Fred Lohman (VP)
Kenneth Carroll (Project Mgr-Mechanical Div)
Steve Barrouk (VP-Bus Dev)
Jim Cummings (VP-Mktg)

MERICO ABATEMENT CONTRACTORS, INC.
201 Estes Dr, Longview, TX 75602
Tel.: (903) 757-2656
Web Site: http://www.merico.com
Sales Range: $10-24.9 Million
Emp.: 60
Provider of Asbestos Removal & Encapsulation Services
N.A.I.C.S.: 562910
Dozier Lonnie (Mgr-Site)
Mark Neas (Pres)

MERIDIAN BEHAVIORAL HEALTHCARE, INC.
4300 SW 13th St, Gainesville, FL 32608
Tel.: (352) 374-5600 FL
Web Site: http://www.mbhci.org
Year Founded: 1978
Sales Range: $25-49.9 Million
Emp.: 754
Behavioral Healthcare Services
N.A.I.C.S.: 623220
Patricia Yates (Chm)
Sharon Gay (Vice Chm)
Sharon Longworth (Sec)
Jackie Knabel (Chief HR Officer & Sr VP)
Donald Savoie (COO & Exec VP)
John Corneilson (CFO & Sr VP)
Tonia Werner (Chief Medical Officer & VP-Medical Svcs)
Mindy Chambers (Chief Performance Officer & Sr VP)
Carali McLean (Sr VP-Clinical Svcs)
Karen Savoie (VP-Billing & Collections)
Tom Rossow (VP-Facilities)
Morelle Sinclair (VP-Fin & Acctg & Comptroller)
Leah Vail (VP-Forensic Svcs)
Melisa Urrutia (VP-Health Information Svcs)
Karen Brown (VP-Housing Svcs)
Heather Akpan (VP-HR)
Shantel Jones (VP-Medical Practice Mgmt)
Laurie Michaelson (VP-Mktg, Comm & Advancement)
Myriah Brady (VP-Outpatient & Recovery Svcs-North)
Terri Crawford (VP-Outpatient & Recovery Svcs-South)
Joe Munson (VP-Prevention & Community Education)
Alan Paulin (VP-Residential Svcs)
Logan Anglin (VP-Staffing & Recruitment)

MERIDIAN CAPITAL, LLC
1809 7th Ave Ste 1330, Seattle, WA 98101
Tel.: (206) 623-4000
Web Site: http://www.meridianllc.com
Year Founded: 1995
Sales Range: $1-9.9 Million
Emp.: 12

Investment Banking & Securities Dealing
N.A.I.C.S.: 523150
Chuck Wilke (Principal)
Brian Murphy (Pres & Mng Dir)
John O'Dore (Mng Dir)
Bruce Pym (Mng Dir)
Patrick Ringland (Mng Dir)
Kristin Brandtner (VP)
James Rothenberger (Mng Dir)

Subsidiaries:

Moss Adams Capital LLC (1)
999 Third Ave Ste 2800, Seattle, WA 98104
Tel.: (206) 302-6500
Investment Banking
N.A.I.C.S.: 523150
Harman Wales (Mng Dir)
Wiley P. Kitchell (Mng Dir)

MERIDIAN COCA-COLA BOTTLING CO.
2016 Hwy 45 N, Meridian, MS 39301
Tel.: (601) 483-5272
Rev.: $21,100,000
Emp.: 170
Provider of Soft Drink Canning & Bottling Services
N.A.I.C.S.: 312111
Hardy P. Graham (Chm)
John Summers (Gen Mgr)

MERIDIAN CREATIVE ALLIANCE LLC
113 E Church St, Ozark, MO 65721-8313
Tel.: (417) 581-2884 MO
Year Founded: 1997
Sales Range: $1-9.9 Million
Advetising Agency
N.A.I.C.S.: 541810
Bob Bryant (Partner)
John Dillon (Partner)
Jim Lewis (Partner)
Chuck Branch (Dir-Print Media)

MERIDIAN ENTERPRISES CORPORATION
951 Hornet Dr, Hazelwood, MO 63042-2309
Tel.: (314) 592-3000 MO
Web Site: http://www.meridinet.com
Year Founded: 1978
Sales Range: $100-124.9 Million
Emp.: 230
Provider of Management Consulting Services
N.A.I.C.S.: 541613
Samuel G. Toumayan (Founder & CEO)
Steve Puchalsky (Exec VP-Sls)
John E. Ebann (Exec VP-Sls)
James J. Costello (Exec VP-Sls)
Deb Hill-Jablonski (Mng Dir-Ops & Exec VP)
Brian Bell (Exec VP-Sls)
Kevin Higgins (CFO)

MERIDIAN GENERAL, LLC
46 E Peninsula Ctr, Rolling Hills Estates, CA 90274
Tel.: (310) 818-4500
Web Site: http://www.meridiangeneral.com
Holding & Investment Company
N.A.I.C.S.: 551112
Ravi Rao (Founder & Gen Partner)
Doug Jacobson (Principal & Chief Fin Analyst)

Subsidiaries:

Powdercoat Services, Inc. (1)
1747 W Lincoln Ave Ste K, Anaheim, CA 92801
Tel.: (714) 533-2251
Web Site: http://www.powdercoatservices.com

COMPANIES

Sales Range: $1-9.9 Million
Emp.: 75
Metal Coating And Allied Services, Nsk
N.A.I.C.S.: 332812
Kay Monteleone (Mgr-Prod)

MERIDIAN GROUP INC.
2249 Pinehurst Dr, Middleton, WI 53562-0800
Tel.: (608) 836-1152 WI
Web Site:
http://www.meridiangroupinc.net
Year Founded: 1975
Sales Range: $10-24.9 Million
Residential Building Rental Services
N.A.I.C.S.: 531110
Doug Strub (CEO)
Kurt Wolff (CFO & Treas)
Rodney Tapp (Pres)

MERIDIAN GROUP INTERNATIONAL, INC.
9 Pkwy N Ste 500, Deerfield, IL 60015-5274
Tel.: (847) 964-2664 IL
Web Site:
http://www.onlinemeridian.com
Year Founded: 1979
Sales Range: $75-99.9 Million
Emp.: 115
IT & Financial Business Solutions
N.A.I.C.S.: 561499
Mike Sell (Sr VP-Sls)
Nick King (COO-IT & Sr VP-Ops)
Tim Patronik (Sr VP-Ops)
Tim McDermott (Exec VP & Gen Mgr)
Jeff Murray (CEO)
Juan Pablo Reyes (CFO)
Scott Schrader (VP-Mktg & Comm)
Charulata Shah (Gen Counsel, Sec & Exec VP)

Subsidiaries:

Concat AG IT Solutions (1)
Berliner Ring 127-129, Bensheim, 64625, Germany
Tel.: (49) 6251 7026 0
Web Site: http://www.concat.de
Sales Range: $25-49.9 Million
Information Technology Consulting Services
N.A.I.C.S.: 541990
Dexter McGinnis (Founder)

Meridian IT Limited (1)
17 High Street, Henley-in-Arden, B95 5AA, Warwickshire, United Kingdom
Tel.: (44) 1564 330650
Web Site: http://www.meridianitlimited.co.uk
Sales Range: $10-24.9 Million
Emp.: 15
Information Technology Consulting Services
N.A.I.C.S.: 541512
Stephen Young (Mng Dir)
Phil Hyams (Dir-Sls)
Anthony Hughes (Dir-Fin)

Meridian IT Pty Ltd. (1)
Suite 602 Building C 11 Talavera Road, Macquarie Park, 2113, NSW, Australia
Tel.: (61) 2 8870 9000
Web Site: http://www.meridianit.com.au
Information Technology Consulting Services
N.A.I.C.S.: 541512
Steve White (Mng Dir)

Meridian IT Singapore (1)
12 Tannery Road HB Centre 1 09-04, Singapore, 347722, Singapore
Tel.: (65) 6686 3307
Web Site:
http://www.meridianitsingapore.com
Sales Range: $10-24.9 Million
Emp.: 5
Information Technology Consulting Services
N.A.I.C.S.: 541512
Colin Robertson (Gen Dir)

Meridian IT, Inc. (1)
Ian Pye 9 Pkwy N Ste 500, Deerfield, IL 60015-2547
Tel.: (847) 964-2700
Web Site: http://www.onlinemeridian.com

Sales Range: $50-74.9 Million
Computers, Peripherals & Software
N.A.I.C.S.: 423430
Lisa Pettay (Pres)
Greg Ciesla (Acct Mgr)

Meridian Leasing (1)
5775 Wayzata Blvd Ste 850, Minneapolis, MN 55416
Tel.: (952) 544-7952
Management Consulting Services
N.A.I.C.S.: 541611

MERIDIAN HEALTH SERVICES
240 N Tillotson Ave, Muncie, IN 47304
Tel.: (765) 288-1928 IN
Web Site: http://www.meridianhs.org
Year Founded: 1971
Sales Range: $25-49.9 Million
Emp.: 687
Health Care Srvices
N.A.I.C.S.: 622110
Hank Milius (Pres & CEO)
Brent Webster (Acct Exec-USI Insurance Grp)
Mark Hardwick (CFO & COO)
Jennifer Henderson (VP-Primary Care)

MERIDIAN HOME MORTGAGE CORP.
1363 N Main St, Hampstead, MD 21074
Tel.: (410) 374-3000
Web Site:
http://www.meridianhm.com
Year Founded: 2002
Sales Range: $10-24.9 Million
Emp.: 60
Mortgage Banking
N.A.I.C.S.: 522292
Mike Zgorski (Sec)
Glenn Belt (Pres)

MERIDIAN INDUSTRIES, INC.
735 N Water St Ste 630, Milwaukee, WI 53202-4104
Tel.: (414) 224-0610 WI
Web Site:
http://www.meridiancompanies.com
Year Founded: 1944
Sales Range: $10-24.9 Million
Emp.: 10
Holding Company; Producers of Textiles, Rubber Products & Pharmaceutical Preparations
N.A.I.C.S.: 326299
Bruce E. Pindyck (Chm & CEO)
Douglas C. Miller (VP)
Frank DeGuire (Gen Counsel)
Deb Falk (Mgr-Benefits)
Robert P. Matz (Pres)

Subsidiaries:

Aurora Specialty Textiles Group, Inc. (1)
911 N Lake St, Aurora, IL 60506
Tel.: (800) 864-0303
Web Site: http://www.auroratextile.com
Emp.: 100
Textile Products Mfr
N.A.I.C.S.: 314999
John Schuster (Dir-Plant Ops)
Erik Nees (Acct Mgr-Sls)
Dan LaTurno (Pres)

Kent Elastomer Products, Inc. (1)
1500 Saint Clair Ave, Kent, OH 44240-0668
Tel.: (330) 673-1011
Web Site: http://www.kentelastomer.com
Sales Range: $10-24.9 Million
Elastomer & Latex Product Mfr
N.A.I.C.S.: 325212
Tom Harrington (Dir-Technical-Rubber & Plastics)
Mary Wills (Dir-HR)
Don Leeper (Sr VP-Fin & Admin)
Beverly Kiglics (Dir-Quality Assurance)

Bob Oborn (Pres)
Lee Ann Pringle (Sec)
Keith Wengerd (Dir-Ops)

Kleen Test Products Division Mequon Plant (1)
5600 W County Line Rd, Mequon, WI 53092
Tel.: (262) 284-6600
Web Site: http://www.kleentest.com
Manufacture Fabric Cleaner Mfr
N.A.I.C.S.: 325620
Angie Radl (Mgr-HR)
Foga Zellermayer (Mgr-IT)
Bill Ahlborn (Pres)
Brandon Silvani (Supvr-Production)
Kelly Arnold (Supvr-Quality Sys)

Majilite Corporation (1)
1530 Broadway Rd, Dracut, MA 01826
Tel.: (978) 441-6800
Web Site: http://www.majilite.com
Emp.: 130
Leather Product Mfr
N.A.I.C.S.: 316110
Muriel Parseghian (VP-Mktg & Customer Svc)
Cindy Kennedy (Controller)

Meridian Specialty Yarn Group, Inc. (1)
312 Colombo St SW, Valdese, NC 28690
Tel.: (828) 874-2151
Web Site: http://www.msyg.com
Dyed Yarn Mfr
N.A.I.C.S.: 313110
Ed Carroll (VP-Fin)
Amy Isenhour (Mgr-Sls & Mktg)
Tim Manson (Pres)

MERIDIAN INSURANCE SERVICE, INC.
4501 E La Palma Ave # 150, Anaheim, CA 92807
Tel.: (714) 693-9100 CA
Rev.: $11,231,000
Emp.: 4
Provider of Insurance Services
N.A.I.C.S.: 524210
Jerrard French (Pres)

MERIDIAN INTERNATIONAL GROUP, INC.
4703 W Electric Ave, Milwaukee, WI 53219
Tel.: (414) 649-9230
Web Site:
http://www.meridiangrp.com
Sales Range: $10-24.9 Million
Emp.: 10
Metal Cleaning, Polishing & Finishing Services
N.A.I.C.S.: 332813
Zbigniew Kulig (Pres)

Subsidiaries:

American Metalcast Technologies (1)
4703 W Electric Ave, Milwaukee, WI 53219
Tel.: (414) 649-9230
Web Site: http://www.meridiangrp.com
Sales Range: $1-9.9 Million
Low Pressure, Permanent Mold, Brass Casting Technology Services
N.A.I.C.S.: 331529

GRAFF (1)
3701 W Burnham St, Milwaukee, WI 53215
Tel.: (414) 649-9850
Web Site: http://www.graff-faucets.com
Bathroom & Kitchen Fixture Mfr
N.A.I.C.S.: 327110
Ziggy Kulig (Pres)
Chris Kulig (Dir-Bus Strategy & Dev)

Polco Metal Finishing Inc. (1)
4703 W Electric Ave, Milwaukee, WI 53219
Tel.: (414) 649-9230
Plating & Polishing; Non-Captive Finishing Services
N.A.I.C.S.: 332813
Zbigniew Kulig (Pres)
Troy Merkl (Dir-Ops)

VALVEX S.A. (1)

MERIDIAN VENTURE PARTNERS

ul Nad Skawa 2, 34-240, Jordanow, Poland
Tel.: (48) 182693220
Web Site: http://www.valvex.com
Bathroom & Kitchen Fixture Mfr
N.A.I.C.S.: 327110

MERIDIAN PACIFIC PROPERTIES INC.
910 W San Marcos Blvd Ste 210, San Marcos, CA 92078
Web Site:
http://www.meridianpacificproperties.com
Year Founded: 2006
Sales Range: $1-9.9 Million
Emp.: 10
Real Estate
N.A.I.C.S.: 531390
Kevin Conlon (Founder & Principal)
Jeffrey King (Founder & Principal)

MERIDIAN TECHNOLOGIES, INC.
5210 Belfort Rd Ste 400, Jacksonville, FL 32256
Tel.: (904) 332-7000 FL
Web Site:
http://www.meridiantechnologies.net
Year Founded: 1997
Sales Range: $10-24.9 Million
Emp.: 100
Computer Technology
N.A.I.C.S.: 423430
Christopher Pillay (Pres & CEO)
Diane Fangman (Controller)
Heide Odom (Mgr-Acctg)
Marc Carlson (CFO)

MERIDIAN TECHNOLOGY GROUP
12909 SW 68th Pkwy Ste 100, Portland, OR 97223
Tel.: (503) 697-1600
Web Site:
http://www.meridiangroup.com
Sales Range: $10-24.9 Million
Emp.: 100
Computer Related Consulting Services
N.A.I.C.S.: 541512
D. Richard Creson (Pres)
Rick Skogmo (VP-Bus Dev)

MERIDIAN TRANSPORTATION RESOURCES, LLC
720 S Forest St, Seattle, WA 98134
Tel.: (206) 838-8148
Web Site: http://www.mtrwestern.com
Year Founded: 2003
Sales Range: $10-24.9 Million
Emp.: 175
Charter Motorcoach Services
N.A.I.C.S.: 485510
Alicia Reinhard (VP-Bus Dev)
Keith Jeffries (VP-Ops)
H. S. Wright III (Founder & Chm)

MERIDIAN VENTURE PARTNERS
259 N Radnor-Chester Rd Ste 130, Radnor, PA 19087
Tel.: (610) 254-2999 PA
Web Site: http://www.mvpcap.com
Emp.: 8
Privater Equity Firm
N.A.I.C.S.: 523999
Robert Ellis Brown (Mng Partner)
Thomas A. Penn (Sr Partner)

Subsidiaries:

SupplyOne Holdings Company, Inc. (1)
11 Campus Blvd Ste 150, Newtown Square, PA 19073
Tel.: (484) 582-5005
Web Site: http://www.supplyone.com
Holding Company; Packaging Products Mfr

MERIDIAN VENTURE PARTNERS

Meridian Venture Partners—(Continued)
N.A.I.C.S.: 551112
William T. Leith (Founder, Pres & CEO)

The Praxis Companies, LLC (1)
435 Industrial Rd, Savannah, TN 38372
Tel.: (731) 925-7656
Web Site: http://www.praxiscompanies.com
Sales Range: $25-49.9 Million
Emp.: 250
Molded Plastic Bathware Products Mfr & Distr
N.A.I.C.S.: 326191
Rick Stonecipher (Pres)
Will Rice (Reg Mgr)
Sandy L. Moore (Mgr-HR)
Ginger Young (Mgr-Warranty)

MERIDIAN WORLDWIDE TRANSPORTATION GROUP
1710 Little Orchard St, San Jose, CA 94125
Tel.: (408) 271-0700
Web Site: http://www.meridianww.com
Sales Range: $10-24.9 Million
Emp.: 45
Trucking Service
N.A.I.C.S.: 488510
George C. Schmidt (CEO)

MERIDIEN RESEARCH
4751 66th St N, Saint Petersburg, FL 33709
Tel.: (727) 347-8839
Web Site: http://www.meridienresearch.net
Sales Range: $10-24.9 Million
Emp.: 50
Medical Research Laboratories
N.A.I.C.S.: 621511
Beth DeLuca (Coord-Clinical Res)
Jenn McCaffrey (Dir-Site)

MERIDIENNE CORPORATION
1958 W 59th St, Chicago, IL 60636-1650
Tel.: (773) 918-1900
Sales Range: $10-24.9 Million
Emp.: 85
Nonresidential Construction Services
N.A.I.C.S.: 236220
Arturo Chavez (Owner)

MERIEUX NUTRISCIENCES CORP.
111 East Wacker Dr Ste 2300, Chicago, IL 60601
Tel.: (312) 938-5151
Web Site: http://www.merieuxnutriscience.com
Nutrition, Analytical & Safety Services
N.A.I.C.S.: 541690
Samim Saner (Dir-Corp Scientific)

Subsidiaries:

Acumen Scientific Sdn. Bhd. (1)
Plot No 256 Tingkat Perusahaan 5 Kawasan Perindustrian Perai 2, 13600, Perai, Pulau Pinang, Malaysia
Tel.: (60) 43981609
Web Site: http://www.acumen.com.my
Analytical Testing & Consulting Services
N.A.I.C.S.: 541690

MERING & ASSOCIATES
1700 I St Ste 210, Sacramento, CA 95811
Tel.: (916) 441-0571
Web Site: http://www.mering.com
Sales Range: $10-24.9 Million
Emp.: 50
N.A.I.C.S.: 541810
Dave Mering (CEO & Dir-Creative)
Chris Pagano (Media Dir)
Debi Houston (Office Mgr)
Dennis Millett (Dir-Art)
Lori Bartel (Acct Supvr)
Tammy Haughey (Acct Exec)

Subsidiaries:

MeringCarson (1)
1010 S Coast Hwy 101 Ste 105, Encinitas, CA 92024
Tel.: (760) 635-2100
N.A.I.C.S.: 541810
Paul Whitbeck (Gen Mgr)
Kristen Haro (Mgr-Social & Digital Project)
Emily Bonsignore (Coord-Social Media)
Jeff DePew (Coord-Connections)
Matthew Falkenthal (Editor-Sacramento)
Sarah Tjoa (Mgr-Brand)
Scott Conway (Dir-Creative-San Diego)
Sharon Wicks (Mgr-Broadcast Media)
Mark Taylor (Chief Creative Officer)

MERIT BRASS COMPANY INC.
1 Merit Dr, Cleveland, OH 44143-1457
Tel.: (216) 261-9800 OH
Web Site: http://www.meritbrass.com
Year Founded: 1937
Sales Range: $10-24.9 Million
Emp.: 225
Mfr of Plumbing Fixture Fittings & Trim
N.A.I.C.S.: 332913
Michael Charna (VP-Sls)
Kimberly Wallingford (Mgr-Mktg)

MERIT CAPITAL PARTNERS
303 W Madison St Ste 2100, Chicago, IL 60606
Tel.: (312) 592-6111
Web Site: http://www.meritcapital.com
Year Founded: 1993
Privater Equity Firm
N.A.I.C.S.: 523999
Marc J. Walfish (Mng Dir)
Thomas F. Campion (Mng Dir)
Evan R. Gallinson (Mng Dir)
David M. Jones (Mng Dir)
Timothy J. MacKenzie (Mng Dir)
Daniel E. Pansing (Mng Dir)
Terrance M. Shipp (Mng Dir)
Anne E. Boland (Controller)
Van T. Lam (CFO)
Lauren M. Hamlin (Principal)

Subsidiaries:

Circuit Check Inc. (1)
6550 Wedgwood Rd, Maple Grove, MN 55311
Tel.: (763) 694-4100
Web Site: http://www.circuitcheck.com
Sales Range: $25-49.9 Million
Mfr of Test Equipment for Electronics & Electro-Mechanical Devices
N.A.I.C.S.: 334515
Greg Michalko (Pres)
Chris Scorse (CEO)

Crown Products & Services, Inc. (1)
319 S Gillette Ave Ste 303, Gillette, WY 82716
Tel.: (307) 696-8175
Web Site: http://www.crownps.us
Specialty Chemical Products & Services
N.A.I.C.S.: 325199
S. Douglas Simmons (Pres & CEO)
John Opseth (COO)
Gregg Simmons (Exec VP-Western Div)
Robin Baker (VP-Fin & Admin)
Michael Lucy (Dir-Safety & Compliance)
Carlyn Vigil (Mgr-Mktg & Contract Admin)

Identity Group Holdings Corp. (1)
51 Century Blvdd Ste 100, Nashville, TN 37214
Tel.: (931) 432-4000
Web Site: http://www.identitygroup.com
Sales Range: $25-49.9 Million
Emp.: 250
Signs, Stamps & Stationery Mfr
N.A.I.C.S.: 339940
Lee Brantley (Exec VP-HR)
Paul Morgan (Mgr-Mfg Engrg)
Brad Wolf (Pres & CEO)
Brian Mogensen (CFO & Exec VP)
David Durfee (Exec VP-Ops)
Warren Soltis (Exec VP-Info Svcs)

Reliant Home Health, Inc. (1)
1101 Raintree Cir Ste 180, Allen, TX 75013
Tel.: (972) 390-7733
Web Site: http://reliant.care
Hospital & Health Care Services
N.A.I.C.S.: 622110
Jerry Copeland Jerry has a account (CFO)

Subsidiary (Domestic):

Bridgeway Health Services, LLC (2)
3880 Hulen St Ste 670, Fort Worth, TX 76107
Tel.: (817) 878-4277
Web Site: http://www.bridgemyhealth.com
Women Healthcare Services
N.A.I.C.S.: 621610
Donna Rawdon (Mgr)

Revision Military Ltd. (1)
7 Corporate Dr, Essex Junction, VT 05452
Tel.: (802) 879-7002
Web Site: http://www.revisionmilitary.com
Protective Soldier Equipment Mfr & Distr
N.A.I.C.S.: 423990
Amy Coyne (CEO)

Storage Solutions Inc. (1)
910 E 169th St, Westfield, IN 46074
Tel.: (317) 867-2001
Web Site: http://www.storage-solutions.com
Shelving, Commercial & Industrial
N.A.I.C.S.: 423440
Craig R. McElheny (CEO)
Kevin Rowles (Pres)

MERIT CHEVROLET COMPANY
I-94 & Century Ave, Maplewood, MN 55119-4748
Tel.: (651) 739-4400
Web Site: http://www.meritchev.com
Sales Range: $25-49.9 Million
Emp.: 105
Car Whslr
N.A.I.C.S.: 441110
Bruce Rinkel (Pres)

MERIT ELECTRIC COMPANY, INC.
6520 125th Ave N, Largo, FL 33773
Tel.: (727) 536-5945
Web Site: http://www.meritelectricco.com
Year Founded: 1974
Sales Range: $1-9.9 Million
Emp.: 60
Electrical Contractor
N.A.I.C.S.: 238210
G.H. Wooten (Pres)
Timothy Wooten (VP)

MERIT ELECTRIC INC.
2643 Midpoint Dr Ste F, Fort Collins, CO 80525
Tel.: (970) 266-8100
Web Site: http://www.meritelec.com
Sales Range: $25-49.9 Million
Emp.: 100
General Electrical Contractor
N.A.I.C.S.: 238210
Royce Glader (Founder & Pres)
Joel Bagley (Mgr-Denver)
Todd Rogers (VP)

MERIT ELECTRIC OF SPOKANE
815 N Helena St, Spokane, WA 99202
Tel.: (509) 535-3930
Web Site: http://www.meritelectric.net
Year Founded: 1982
Sales Range: $10-24.9 Million
Emp.: 80
General Electrical Contractor
N.A.I.C.S.: 238210
Frank Baker (Pres)

U.S. PRIVATE

MERIT ENERGY COMPANY INC.
13727 Noel Rd Ste 1200 Tower 2, Dallas, TX 75240
Tel.: (972) 628-1511 DE
Web Site: http://www.meritenergy.com
Year Founded: 1989
Sales Range: $1-4.9 Billion
Emp.: 700
Oil & Gas Asset Investment Services
N.A.I.C.S.: 523999
Melanie Lane (VP-HR)
Meghan Cuddihy (VP)
Jason Lindmark (VP-Bus Dev)

MERIT FINANCIAL GROUP, LLC
2400 Lakeview Pkwy Ste 550, Alpharetta, GA 30009
Tel.: (678) 867-7050 GA
Web Site: http://www.meritfinancialadvisors.com
Investment Advisory Services; Financial Planning & Wealth Management
N.A.I.C.S.: 523940
Rick L. Kent (Founder & CEO)
D. Tyler Vernon (Reg Dir)
Timothy Ralph (Mng Partner)
Kay Lynn Mayhue (Pres)
Chrissy Lee (COO)

Subsidiaries:

Biltmore Capital Advisors LLC (1)
33 Witherspoon St Ste E, Princeton, NJ 08542-3212
Tel.: (609) 688-8701
Web Site: http://www.biltmorecap.com
Investment Advice
N.A.I.C.S.: 523940

Clearbridge Wealth Management, LLC (1)
7000 Central Pkwy, Atlanta, GA 30328
Tel.: (770) 350-9605
Web Site: http://www.clearbridgewealth.com
Intermediation
N.A.I.C.S.: 523910
Preston Byers (Pres)

MERIT PHARMACEUTICALS
2611 N San Fernando Rd, Los Angeles, CA 90065-1316
Tel.: (323) 227-4831 CA
Web Site: http://www.meritpharm.com
Mfr of Pharmaceuticals
N.A.I.C.S.: 424210

MERITDIRECT, LLC
2 International Dr, Rye Brook, NY 10573
Tel.: (914) 368-1000
Web Site: http://www.meritdirect.com
Year Founded: 1999
Sales Range: $1-9.9 Million
Emp.: 140
Direct Mail Advertising & Marketing Services
N.A.I.C.S.: 541860
Rob Sanchez (CEO)
Christopher Pickering (Exec VP & Mgr)
Todd Love (Chief Comml Officer)
Deirdre Blohm (Sr VP-Mktg)

Subsidiaries:

MeritDirect UK (1)
3 More London Riverside, London, SE1 2RE, United Kingdom
Tel.: (44) 203 283 4264
Web Site: http://www.meritdirect.com
Emp.: 11
Direct Mail Advertising & Marketing Services
N.A.I.C.S.: 541860
Karie Burt (VP-Intl)

MERITECH INC.
4577 Hanckyel Industrial Pkwy, Cleveland, OH 44190
Tel.: (216) 459-8333
Web Site: http://www.meritechinc.com
Sales Range: $10-24.9 Million
Emp.: 80
Provider of Electric Business Machine Repair Services
N.A.I.C.S.: 449210
Dennis Bednar (Founder, Pres & CEO)
Anthony Panlilio (Sr Mgr-MSP Project)
Mary Flynn (Mgr-Sls-West Side)
Andy Furda (Dir-Svc)
Brian Bednar (Mgr-Support)
Frank S. Vigliucci (Dir-Major Accts)
Irene Panlilio (Controller)
Jared Miller (Sr Mgr-MSP Ops)
Ken Vanden Haute (VP-Sls)
Mary Ann Bednar (VP-Ops)
Richard Rieck (Mgr-Sls-East Side)
Terry Goostree (Gen Mgr-Akron)

MERITRUST CREDIT UNION
8710 E 32nd St N, Wichita, KS 67226
Tel.: (316) 683-1199 KS
Web Site: http://www.meritrustcu.org
Year Founded: 1936
Sales Range: $50-74.9 Million
Emp.: 272
Credit Union Operator
N.A.I.C.S.: 522130
Duane Van Camp (Vice Chm)
Marci Johnson (Treas & Sec)
Rick Dodds (Chm)
Karen Callaway (Chief Risk Officer)
Cliff Shoff (CTO)
Jamie Taulbee (Chief Retail Officer & VP-Retail Banking)
Evan Wilson (Chief Experience Officer)
Angie Meuten (Dir-Special Accts)
Mitch Crouch (Mgr-Real Estate Sls)
Cole Wilkins (Mgr-Bus Relationship)

MERITUM ENERGY HOLDINGS, LP
1826 N Loop 1604 W Ste 325, San Antonio, TX 78248
Tel.: (210) 876-3560 DE
Web Site: http://www.meritumenergy.com
Year Founded: 2015
Holding Company; Propane & Natural Gas Distr
N.A.I.C.S.: 551112
Christopher P. Hill (Co-Founder, Pres & CEO)
Robert W. Chalmers (Co-Founder, CFO & Exec VP)
Anthony Kusenberger (VP-Ops)
Brent Grider (Controller)

Subsidiaries:

Pico Petroleum Products Ltd. (1)
307 E 10th St, Del Rio, TX 78840
Tel.: (830) 775-7761
Web Site: http://www.picopropane.com
Petroleum Product Distr
N.A.I.C.S.: 424720
Randall Baum (Mgr)
Anthony Kusenberger (COO)

MERITURN PARTNERS, LLC
234 Fayetteville St 6th Fl, Raleigh, NC 27601
Tel.: (919) 821-1550 DE
Web Site: http://www.meriturn.com
Equity Investment Firm
N.A.I.C.S.: 523999
Michela O'Connor Abrams (Partner-Operating)
Vito Russo (Partner-Operating)
Andrew S. Whitman (Partner-Operating)
Lee C. Hansen (Partner)
T. Ronan Kennedy (Principal)

Subsidiaries:

Johnston Textiles, Inc. (1)
300 General Colin Powell Pkwy, Phenix City, AL 36869
Tel.: (334) 664-3298
Web Site: http://www.johnstontextiles.com
Rev.: $100,000,000
Emp.: 850
Polyester Broadwoven Fabrics
N.A.I.C.S.: 313210

Meriturn Partners, LLC - San Francisco (1)
3030 Bridge Way Ste 111, Sausalito, CA 94965
Tel.: (415) 616-9800
Web Site: http://www.meriturn.com
Equity Investment Firm
N.A.I.C.S.: 523999
Lee C. Hansen (Partner)
Hank L. Holzapfel (Partner-Operating)
Mark G. Miller (Partner-Operating)
Kurt C. Thomas (Partner-Operating)
Vito Russo (Partner-Operating)
Mark W. Kehaya (Partner)

MERIWETHER LEWIS ELECTRIC COOPERATIVE
1625 Hwy 100, Centerville, TN 37033-1426
Tel.: (931) 729-3558 TN
Web Site: http://www.mlec.com
Year Founded: 1939
Sales Range: $25-49.9 Million
Emp.: 87
Providers of Electrical Services
N.A.I.C.S.: 221122
Hal Womble (CEO)
Randy James (CFO)
Brent Warf (Engr-Electrical)
Ed Greenwell (VP-Ops)

MERKEL BROTHERS INC.
205 S Main St, Chelsea, MI 48118
Tel.: (734) 475-8621
Web Site: http://www.merkelcarpetone.com
Sales Range: $10-24.9 Million
Emp.: 30
Distr of Carpets
N.A.I.C.S.: 449121
James T. Merkel (Pres)

MERLE BOES INC.
11372 E Lakewood Blvd, Holland, MI 49424
Tel.: (616) 392-7036
Web Site: http://www.merleboes.com
Rev.: $27,859,607
Emp.: 35
Petroleum Brokers
N.A.I.C.S.: 424720
Todd Vanderboegh (Supvr-Maintenance)

MERLE NORMAN COSMETICS, INC.
9130 Bellanca Ave, Los Angeles, CA 90045-4710
Tel.: (310) 641-3000 CA
Web Site: http://www.merlenorman.com
Year Founded: 1931
Sales Range: $75-99.9 Million
Emp.: 510
Cosmetics Mfr
N.A.I.C.S.: 325620
Arthur O. Armstrong (CEO)
Mark Grimmet (CFO)
Carmen Ginter (VP-Personnel)

MERLE STONE CHEVROLET CADILLAC
800 W Henderson Ave, Porterville, CA 93257-1743
Tel.: (559) 781-8355
Web Site: http://www.stonechevyporterville.com
Year Founded: 1957
Sales Range: $10-24.9 Million
Emp.: 29
New Car Whslr
N.A.I.C.S.: 441110
Dave Stone (Mgr-Sls)

MERLIN TECHNICAL SOLUTIONS, INC.
4 B Inverness Ct E, Englewood, CO 80111
Tel.: (303) 221-0797
Year Founded: 1997
Sales Range: $75-99.9 Million
Emp.: 58
Information Technology Solutions & Services
N.A.I.C.S.: 541519
David Phelps (Chm & CEO)
Jim Regele (Pres & COO)
John Trauth (Pres-Tech Sys Div)

MEROLLIS CHEVROLET SALES & SERVICE INC.
21800 Gratiot Ave, Eastpointe, MI 48021
Tel.: (586) 775-8300
Web Site: http://www.merollischevy.com
Sales Range: $10-24.9 Million
Emp.: 85
Sales of Automobiles
N.A.I.C.S.: 441110
Bill Perkins (Pres)
Monte Perkins (Gen Mgr)

MERRELL-BENCO AGENCY LLC
67 E Broadway, Monticello, NY 12701
Tel.: (845) 796-1500
Web Site: http://www.mbagency.com
Sales Range: $10-24.9 Million
Emp.: 15
Insurance Agents & Brokers
N.A.I.C.S.: 524210

MERRICK & COMPANY INC.
5970 Greenwood Plaza Blvd, Greenwood Village, CO 80111
Tel.: (303) 751-0741 CO
Web Site: http://www.merrick.com
Year Founded: 1959
Sales Range: $50-74.9 Million
Emp.: 500
Engineering, Architecture, Design-Build, Surveying, Planning & Geospatial Services
N.A.I.C.S.: 541330
Sandy Turnbull (VP)
Scott North (Mgr-Geomatics-SE)
Jennifer Harms (Dir-Bus Dev)
Christopher Sherry (Pres & CEO)
Robert A. Berglund (Sr VP-Corp Bus Dev)
Mark Henline (VP)
Gilles Tremblay (Dir-Commissioning Svcs)
Paul Langevin (Dir-Laboratory Design)
Ross Graham (Dir-Laboratory Ops)
Sandy Ellis (Dir-Laboratory Plng & Programming)
Chris Kiley (Dir-Life Sciences Engrg)
Tamara Johnson (VP)
Steve Betts (CFO)

Subsidiaries:

Merrick & Company Inc. - Decatur (1)
160 Clairemont Ave Ste 600, Decatur, GA 30030
Tel.: (404) 789-2700
Web Site: http://www.merrick.com
Engineering, Architecture, Design-Build, Surveying, Planning & Geospatial Services
N.A.I.C.S.: 541330

Merrick Advanced Photogrammetry of the Americas, S. de R.L. de C.V. (1)
Rio Volga No 3 Bis 7o Piso Col, Cuauhtemoc, 06500, Mexico
Tel.: (52) 55 55 25 81 23
Web Site: http://www.mapamerrick.com.mx
Satellite Imagery & Software Reselling Services
N.A.I.C.S.: 449210

MERRICK ANIMAL NUTRITION, INC.
2415 Parview Rd, Middleton, WI 53562-0307
Tel.: (608) 831-3440
Web Site: http://www.merricks.com
Animal Feed Mfr
N.A.I.C.S.: 115210
Johanna Kuehn (CEO & Pres)

MERRICK ENGINEERING, INC.
1275 Quarry St, Corona, CA 92879
Tel.: (951) 737-6040
Web Site: http://www.merrickintl.com
Year Founded: 1973
Sales Range: $50-74.9 Million
Emp.: 750
Mfr of Injection Molded Plastic Products
N.A.I.C.S.: 326199
Abraham M. Abdi (Pres)
Mina Abdi (Treas)

MERRICK INDUSTRIES INCORPORATED
808 E Liberty St, Louisville, KY 40204-1025
Tel.: (502) 584-6258 KY
Web Site: http://www.merrickind.com
Year Founded: 1971
Sales Range: $25-49.9 Million
Emp.: 150
Provider of Commercial Printing & Lithographic Services
N.A.I.C.S.: 323111
David Merrick (Pres)
William P. Merrick (Exec VP)
Ken Everhart (VP)
Fred J. Merrick Sr. (Owner)

Subsidiaries:

Digital Print Impressions, Inc. (1)
2604 River Green Cir, Louisville, KY 40206
Tel.: (502) 899-1717
Commercial Printing Services
N.A.I.C.S.: 323111

Merrick - Kemper (1)
3808 Ralph Ave, Louisville, KY 40201-0185
Tel.: (502) 449-1234
Web Site: http://www.merrick-kemper.com
Roofing Contractors
N.A.I.C.S.: 238160
Gary Hudson (Project Mgr & Mgr-Sls)
Jeremy Merrick (Project Mgr)
John Thompson (Project Mgr)

Merrick Construction Companies, Inc. (1)
3808 Ralph Ave, Louisville, KY 40211-2037 (100%)
Tel.: (502) 449-1234
Web Site: http://www.merrickind.com
Sales Range: $10-24.9 Million
Emp.: 50
Provider of Roofing, Siding & Sheetmetal Work Services
N.A.I.C.S.: 238390

The Merrick Printing Company Inc. (1)
808 E Liberty St, Louisville, KY 40204-1025
Tel.: (502) 584-6258

MERRICK INDUSTRIES INCORPORATED U.S. PRIVATE

Merrick Industries Incorporated—(Continued)
Web Site: http://www.merrickind.com
Sales Range: $10-24.9 Million
Emp.: 110
Provider of Commercial Printing & Lithographic Services
N.A.I.C.S.: 323111
David Merrick (Pres)

MERRICK TOWLE COMMUNICATIONS
5801-F Ammendale Rd, Beltsville, MD 20705-1264
Tel.: (301) 974-6000
Web Site: http://www.merricktowle.com
Year Founded: 1985
Sales Range: $10-24.9 Million
Emp.: 70
Real Estate
N.A.I.C.S.: 541810
Glenn Towle (Partner & COO)
Roger Everhart (Assoc Dir-Creative)
Donna Hodge (Dir-Engagement)
Harry Merrick IV (Partner & CEO)

MERRIFIELD GARDEN CENTER CORP.
8132 Lee Hwy, Merrifield, VA 22116
Tel.: (703) 560-6222   VA
Web Site: http://www.merrifieldgardencenter.com
Year Founded: 1971
Sales Range: $300-349.9 Million
Emp.: 500
Retail Nurseries & Garden Stores
N.A.I.C.S.: 444240
Robert P. Warhurst (Pres)
David Watkins (Gen Mgr)
Lynn Warhurst (Controller)

MERRILL & RING
506 2nd Ave Ste 2300, Seattle, WA 98104
Tel.: (425) 778-7900
Web Site: http://www.merrillring.com
Sales Range: $10-24.9 Million
Emp.: 5
Provider of Forestry & Land Management Services
N.A.I.C.S.: 423310
Richard Strobel (CEO)
Ron Hurn (Mgr-Ops)
Norm Schaaf (VP)
Paul Whyatt (CFO)

Subsidiaries:

Welco-Skookum Lumber USA   (1)
813 E 8th St, Port Angeles, WA 98362
Tel.: (360) 452-2367
Web Site: http://www.welcolumberusa.com
Western Red Cedar Lumber
N.A.I.C.S.: 321113

MERRILL COMPANY
601 1st Ave SW, Spencer, IA 51301
Tel.: (712) 262-1141
Web Site: http://www.arnoldmotorsupply.com
Sales Range: $10-24.9 Million
Emp.: 51
Automotive Supplies & Parts
N.A.I.C.S.: 423120
Dennis Spooner (Gen Mgr)

MERRILL DISTRIBUTING INC.
1301 N Memorial Dr, Merrill, WI 54452
Tel.: (715) 536-4551
Web Site: http://www.merrilldistributing.com
Rev.: $19,600,000
Emp.: 50
Tobacco & Tobacco Product Merchant Whslr
N.A.I.C.S.: 424940

John Tyler (Pres)

MERRILL TOOL & MACHINE INC.
1023 S Wheeler St, Saginaw, MI 48602
Tel.: (989) 791-6676
Web Site: http://www.merrilltg.com
Year Founded: 1968
Sales Range: $10-24.9 Million
Emp.: 225
Provider of Machine Welded Products
N.A.I.C.S.: 332313
Gary Yackel (Pres)
Thomas Rider (Controller)
Mike Beyer (CFO)

MERRIMAC INDUSTRIAL SALES INC.
111 Neck Rd, Haverhill, MA 01835
Tel.: (978) 372-6006
Web Site: http://www.merrimacindustrial.com
Sales Range: $10-24.9 Million
Emp.: 40
Industrial Equipment & Supplies
N.A.I.C.S.: 423830
Paul Kelly (Engr-Design)
Raymond Rynkowski (Engr-EM Application)
David Meurillon (Mgr-Panel Shop)
Philip G. Aberizk Jr. (Pres)

MERRIMACK STREET GARAGE INC.
4056 Merrimack St, Manchester, NH 03108-5708
Tel.: (603) 623-8015
Web Site: http://www.merrimackstvolvo.com
Sales Range: $10-24.9 Million
Emp.: 23
Sales of New & Used Automobiles
N.A.I.C.S.: 441110
Roger Jackson (Gen Mgr)
Marc Saidel (Mgr-New Car Sls)
Alex Saidel (Pres)

MERRIMAN HOLDINGS, INC.
250 Montgomery St 16th Fl, San Francisco, CA 94104
Tel.: (415) 248-5600   DE
Web Site: http://www.merrimanco.com
Year Founded: 1987
Sales Range: $10-24.9 Million
Holding Company; Investment Banking & Securities Brokerage Services
N.A.I.C.S.: 551112
Ronald L. Chez (Co-Chm)
Michael C. Doran (Gen Counsel)
Sumit Mahay (Dir-Brokerage Ops)
Becky Borden Popoff (Mng Dir-Capital Markets & Ops)
Adriana Piltz (Pres)

Subsidiaries:

Merriman Capital, Inc.   (1)
600 California St 9th Fl, San Francisco, CA 94108
Tel.: (415) 248-5600
Web Site: http://www.merrimanco.com
Investment Banking & Securities Brokerage Services
N.A.I.C.S.: 523150
D. Jonathan Merriman (CEO)
Kim Tu (VP-Fin & Controller)
Drew Finnegan (Mng Dir-Digital Capital Network)

MERRITT ESTATE WINERY
2264 King Rd, Forestville, NY 14062
Tel.: (716) 965-4800
Web Site: http://www.merrittestatewinery.com
Year Founded: 1976
Sales Range: $10-24.9 Million

Emp.: 50
Vineyard & Wine Mfr
N.A.I.C.S.: 111332
Jason C. Merritt (Gen Mgr)
William T. Merritt (Pres)
Sandra Penharlow (Office Mgr)

MERRITT GROUP
11600 Sunrise Valley Dr Ste 320, Reston, VA 20191-1416
Tel.: (703) 390-1500
Web Site: http://www.merrittgrp.com
Year Founded: 1996
Sales Range: $10-24.9 Million
Emp.: 30
Public Relations Agency
N.A.I.C.S.: 541820
Ben Merritt (Founder)
Alisa Valudes Whyte (CEO & Sr Partner)
Thomas Rice (Partner & Sr VP)
John Conrad (Partner & Sr VP)
Jayson Schkloven (Partner & Sr VP)
Paul Miller (VP-Fin & Acctg)
Michelle Schafer (VP-Security)
Melissa Chadwick (Dir-Networking & Mobility)

MERRITT ISLAND RHF HOUSING INC
911 N Studebaker Rd, Long Beach, CA 90815
Tel.: (562) 257-5100   FL
Web Site: http://www.rhf.org
Year Founded: 1986
Sales Range: $10-24.9 Million
Emp.: 166
Lifecare Retirement Community Operator
N.A.I.C.S.: 623311
Stuart Hartman (VP-Ops)
Peter Peabody (VP-Healthcare Ops)
Nada Battaglia (VP-HR)
Laverne R. Joseph (Pres)
Robert Amberg (Gen Counsel & Sr VP)

MERRITT MANAGEMENT CORPORATION
2066 Lord Baltimore Dr, Baltimore, MD 21244
Tel.: (410) 298-2600   MD
Web Site: http://www.merrittproperties.com
Year Founded: 1967
Sales Range: $25-49.9 Million
Emp.: 120
Holding Company; Commercial & Industrial Property Management Services
N.A.I.C.S.: 551112

Subsidiaries:

Merritt Properties, LLC   (1)
2066 Lord Baltimore Dr, Baltimore, MD 21244
Tel.: (410) 298-2600
Web Site: http://www.merrittproperties.com
Emp.: 100
Commercial & Industrial Property Management Services
N.A.I.C.S.: 531312
Robb Merritt (Pres)
Scott E. Dorsey (Chm & CEO)

Division (Domestic):

Merritt Construction Services   (2)
2066 Lord Baltimore Dr, Baltimore, MD 21244
Tel.: (410) 298-2600
Web Site: http://www.merrittconstructionservice.com
Site Development, General Construction & Redevelopment Services
N.A.I.C.S.: 238910
Daniel Pallace (Dir-Construction)
Gary Swatko (Dir-Land Dev & Construction)
Pat Myers (Dir-Field Ops)
Scott E. Dorsey (Chm & CEO)
Robb L. Merritt (Pres)

MERRITT OIL CO. INC.
952 S Conception St, Mobile, AL 36603-2027
Tel.: (251) 432-6711   AL
Web Site: http://www.merrittoil.com
Year Founded: 1945
Sales Range: $25-49.9 Million
Emp.: 125
Convenience Store
N.A.I.C.S.: 424710
Fred R. Walding (Pres)
Jeff Walding (Mgr-HR)

MERROW MACHINE COMPANY
502 Bedford St, Fall River, MA 02720
Tel.: (508) 689-4095   DE
Web Site: http://www.merrow.com
Year Founded: 1838
Sales Range: $10-24.9 Million
Emp.: 150
Industrial Sewing Machine Mfr
N.A.I.C.S.: 333248
Charles Merrow (Pres)

MERRY X-RAY CORPORATION
4444 Viewridge Ave Ste A, San Diego, CA 92123-1622
Tel.: (858) 565-4472
Web Site: http://www.merryxray.com
Year Founded: 1958
Sales Range: $100-124.9 Million
Emp.: 1,500
X-Ray & Imaging Equipment Mfr
N.A.I.C.S.: 423450
Ted Sloan (VP)

Subsidiaries:

Sywest Medical Technologies Inc.   (1)
18 Corporate Circle Ste 5, East Syracuse, NY 13057-1081   (100%)
Tel.: (315) 414-0313
Web Site: http://www.sywestmed.com
Imaging Equipment & Services
N.A.I.C.S.: 621512
Betty Peters (Bus Mgr)
Tom Snyder (Pres)

Universal Medical Systems, Inc.   (1)
29500 Aurora Rd Ste 16, Solon, OH 44139-7214
Tel.: (440) 349-3210
Web Site: http://www.veterinary-imaging.com
Medical, Dental & Hospital Equipment & Supplies Merchant Whslr
N.A.I.C.S.: 423450

MERRYMANN-FARR, LLC.
305 Hill Ave, Nashville, TN 37210-4711
Tel.: (615) 254-8050
Web Site: http://merryman-farr.com
Year Founded: 2000
Sales Range: $10-24.9 Million
Emp.: 125
Plumbing Services
N.A.I.C.S.: 238220
Mark Farr (VP)
Steve Merryman (Pres)

MERRYMEETING, INC.
4745 N 7th St Ste 320 PO Box 7610 85011, Phoenix, AZ 85014
Web Site: http://www.merrymtg.com
Sales Range: $25-49.9 Million
Emp.: 40
Investment Company
N.A.I.C.S.: 523999
John Davies (CEO)
Jeff Harcourt (COO)
Bill Bishilany (Dir-Franchisee Coaching)
Greg Coffey (Dir-Bus Dev)
Shari Kosec (Dir-Onboarding & Trng)
Tyson Ware (VP & Brand Mgr-Frontier Adjusters)

COMPANIES
MESA OIL INC.

Ashley Gooding *(Dir-Mktg)*
Diane Hewlett *(Controller)*
John Elson *(Dir-Field Ops, Support & Education for Inspect)*
Kim Weinberger *(Dir-Ops)*

Subsidiaries:

Frontier Adjusters of America, Inc. (1)
PO Box 7610, Phoenix, AZ 85011
Tel.: (602) 264-1061
Web Site: http://www.frontieradjusters.com
Sales Range: $10-24.9 Million
Emp.: 20
Provider of Claims Adjusting Services to Insurance Companies, Self-Insureds, Municipalities, General Agents, Brokers & Others
N.A.I.C.S.: 531110

Sunbelt Business Advisors Network, LLC (1)
7100 E Pleasant Vly Rd Ste 300, Independence, OH 44131
Tel.: (216) 674-0645
Web Site: http://www.sunbeltnetwork.com
Rev.: $16,000,000
Emp.: 50
Franchised Business Brokerage Services
N.A.I.C.S.: 541990
John Davies *(CEO)*
Matt Ottaway *(Pres)*
Jeff Harcourt *(COO)*

MERRYWEATHER FOAM INC.
11 Brown St, Barberton, OH 44203
Tel.: (330) 753-0353
Web Site: http://www.merryweather.com
Year Founded: 1985
Sales Range: $10-24.9 Million
Emp.: 94
Mfr & Distributing of Plastics Foam Products
N.A.I.C.S.: 326150
Robert G. McCune *(Pres)*

MERS/MISSOURI GOODWILL INDUSTRIES
1727 Locust St, Saint Louis, MO 63103
Tel.: (314) 241-3464   MO
Web Site: http://www.mersgoodwill.org
Year Founded: 1917
Sales Range: $1-9.9 Million
Emp.: 1,246
Job Training/Related Services
N.A.I.C.S.: 624310
Lewis C. Chartock *(CEO)*
Mark Arens *(Exec VP)*
Mark Kahrs *(Exec VP-Retail Svcs)*
Deann Briggs *(VP)*
Hilary Wagner *(VP)*
Barry Ginsburg *(Asst Treas)*
Michael Iskiwitch *(Treas)*
Louis Loebner *(Sec)*
James Mosqueda *(Asst Sec)*
Christopher Tabourne *(Chm)*
Dawayne Barnett *(CFO)*
Beth Brown *(Asst VP-Program Svcs)*
Jeff Cartnal *(VP-Program Dev)*
Elizabeth Drennan *(Asst VP-Program Svcs)*
Colin Kricensky *(VP-Contracts)*
David Kutchback *(COO)*
Kristy Lance *(Sr VP-Retail)*
Rebecca Polwort *(VP-Retail)*
Kevin Shaw *(VP-Retail)*
Marvin Washington *(VP-Contracts)*

MERSCHMAN SEEDS INC.
103 Ave D, West Point, IA 52656
Tel.: (319) 837-6111   IA
Web Site: http://www.merschmanseeds.com
Year Founded: 1954
Sales Range: $10-24.9 Million
Emp.: 30
Field, Garden & Flower Seeds Mfr & Distr
N.A.I.C.S.: 111422
Skip Long *(Product Mgr)*
Turk Regennitter *(Gen Sls Mgr)*

MERTES CONTRACTING CORPORATION
2665 S 25th Ave, Broadview, IL 60155
Tel.: (708) 343-4600
Web Site: http://www.mertes.com
Sales Range: $100-124.9 Million
Emp.: 50
Commercial & Institutional Building Construction
N.A.I.C.S.: 236220
James Mertes *(VP)*
Allen M. Mertes *(Pres)*

MERUELO GROUP LLC
9550 Firestone Blvd Ste 105, Downey, CA 90241
Tel.: (562) 745-2300   CA
Web Site: http://www.meruelogroup.com
Investment Holding Company
N.A.I.C.S.: 551112
Alex Meruelo *(Chm & CEO)*
Al Stoller *(CFO)*
Steve Delavan *(CIO)*
Mario Tapanes *(Gen Counsel)*
Armando Delgado *(VP-Real Estate Acq & Dev)*
Mark Ernst *(VP-HR)*

Subsidiaries:

KLOS Radio, LLC (1)
3321 S La Cienega Blvd, Los Angeles, CA 90016-3114
Tel.: (310) 840-4800
Web Site: http://www.955klos.com
Emp.: 75
Radio Broadcasting Stations
N.A.I.C.S.: 516110

KPWR-FM (1)
2600 W Olive Ave 8th Fl, Burbank, CA 91505
Tel.: (818) 953-4200
Web Site: http://www.power106.com
Sales Range: $25-49.9 Million
Emp.: 100
Radio Broadcasting Services
N.A.I.C.S.: 515110
Val Maki *(VP-Radio Div)*
Dianna Jason *(Sr Dir-Mktg & Promos)*
Rick Cummings *(Pres-Radio Div)*
Aimee Bittourna *(Dir-Emmis Mktg Grp)*
Edwin Bizarro *(Coord-Promos & Flava Unit Mgmt)*
Janet Brainin *(Dir-Sls)*
Terry McGovern *(Dir-Digital Dev)*

Meruelo Capital Investments, Inc. (1)
9550 Firestone Blvd Ste 105, Downey, CA 90241
Tel.: (562) 745-2300
Web Site: http://www.meruelogroup.com
Privater Equity Firm
N.A.I.C.S.: 523999
Xavier A. Gutierrez *(Pres & Chief Investment Officer)*

Meruelo Enterprises, Inc. (1)
9550 Firestone Blvd Ste 105, Downey, CA 90241
Tel.: (562) 745-2300
Web Site: http://www.meruelenterprises.com
Holding Company; Utilities Engineering, Construction & Maintenance Services
N.A.I.C.S.: 551112
Joe Marchica *(Exec VP)*
Alex Meruelo *(Chm & CEO)*
Luis Armona *(VP)*
Al Stoller *(CFO)*
Mario Tapanes *(Gen Counsel)*
Todd Maxwell *(VP-Tech)*

Division (Domestic):

Meruelo Construction (2)
9550 Firestone Blvd Ste 105, Downey, CA 90241
Tel.: (562) 745-2300
Web Site: http://www.merueloconstruction.com
Holding Company; Utilities Engineering, Construction & Maintenance Services
N.A.I.C.S.: 551112

Meruelo Foods, Inc. (1)
9550 Firestone Blvd, Downey, CA 90241
Tel.: (562) 745-2300
Web Site: http://meruelogroup.com
Holding Company; Restaurant Franchisor, Operator & Food Products Mfr
N.A.I.C.S.: 551112
Alex Meruelo *(Chm, Pres & CEO)*

Holding (Domestic):

Fuji Food Products, Inc. (2)
14420 Bloomfield Ave, Santa Fe Springs, CA 90670-5410
Tel.: (562) 404-2590
Web Site: http://www.fujifood.com
Sushi & Other Asian Prepared Food Products Mfr & Distr
N.A.I.C.S.: 311991

Subsidiary (Domestic):

Okami, Inc. (3)
11037 Penrose St, Sun Valley, CA 91352
Tel.: (818) 252-6833
Web Site: http://www.okamifoods.com
Sushi & Other Fresh Food Mfr & Distr
N.A.I.C.S.: 311991

Plant (Domestic):

Okami, Inc. - Denver Plant (4)
6211 E 42nd Ave, Denver, CO 90216
Tel.: (303) 322-5524
Sushi & Other Fresh Food Mfr & Distr
N.A.I.C.S.: 311991

Holding (Domestic):

La Pizza Loca, Inc. (2)
9550 Firestone Blvd Ste 105, Downey, CA 90241
Tel.: (562) 862-4470
Web Site: http://www.lapizzaloca.com
Pizzeria Restaurant Franchisor & Operator
N.A.I.C.S.: 722513
Alex Meruelo *(Founder, Pres & CEO)*

Meruelo Properties, Inc. (1)
9550 Firestone Blvd Ste 105, Downey, CA 90241
Tel.: (562) 745-2300
Holding Company; Real Estate Investment & Property Management Services
N.A.I.C.S.: 551112

Holding (Domestic):

Cantamar Property Management, Inc. (2)
9550 Firestone Blvd Ste 105, Downey, CA 90241
Tel.: (562) 745-2300
Sales Range: $50-74.9 Million
Emp.: 50
Property Management Services
N.A.I.C.S.: 531312
Armando Delgado *(Head-Real Estate, Admin & Acctg)*

MERVIS INDUSTRIES INC.
3295 E Main St, Danville, IL 61834
Tel.: (217) 442-5300
Web Site: http://www.mervis.com
Sales Range: $75-99.9 Million
Emp.: 325
Metal Scrap & Waste Materials
N.A.I.C.S.: 423930
Tim Geary *(Dir-Comml Sls)*
Jennifer Kline *(CFO & Treas)*
Carl Meece *(Mgr-Non-Ferrous)*
Jim Picillo *(COO & VP)*
Marty Wells *(Gen Mgr)*

MERX TRUCK & TRAILER, INC.
5200 Proviso Dr Hwy 290-294, Melrose Park, IL 60163
Tel.: (847) 558-7823
Web Site: https://www.merxtt.com
Truck & Trailer Repair Services
N.A.I.C.S.: 811198
Christian Peneff *(CEO)*

Subsidiaries:

North Texas Fleet Services LLC (1)
2938 Oakland Ave, Garland, TX 75041-3912
Tel.: (972) 278-2400
Web Site: http://www.ntxfleet.com
General Automotive Repair
N.A.I.C.S.: 811111
Mike Karkhoff *(Partner)*

MERYX, INC.
510 Meadowmont Village Cir Ste 359, Chapel Hill, NC 27517
Tel.: (919) 260-3118
Web Site: http://www.meryxpharma.com
Biotechnology Research & Development Services
N.A.I.C.S.: 541714
Seth Rudnick *(Chm)*
Doug Graham *(Founder)*
Sailash Patel *(CEO)*

MESA EQUIPMENT & SUPPLY COMPANY
7100 2nd St NW, Albuquerque, NM 87107
Tel.: (505) 345-0284
Web Site: http://www.mesaequipment.com
Sales Range: $10-24.9 Million
Emp.: 35
Supplier of Industrial Machinery & Equipment
N.A.I.C.S.: 423830
Richard Moya *(Pres)*

MESA FULLY FORMED INC.
1111 S Sirrine, Mesa, AZ 85210
Tel.: (480) 834-9331
Web Site: http://www.valleywidecountertops.com
Sales Range: $10-24.9 Million
Emp.: 120
Mfr of Plastic Products
N.A.I.C.S.: 326130
Larry A. Cassaday *(Pres)*
Brad Mitchell *(Supvr-Granite)*
Mark Witte *(Gen Mgr)*
Tony Knudsen *(Supvr-Laminate)*
Mia King *(Mgr-Environmental Health & Safety)*
Crystal Brown *(Mgr-HR)*

MESA INDUSTRIES INC.
1726 S Magnolia Ave, Monrovia, CA 91016
Tel.: (626) 359-9361
Web Site: http://www.mesarubber.com
Sales Range: $10-24.9 Million
Emp.: 30
Mfr of Hoses
N.A.I.C.S.: 423840
Terry Segeberg *(Chm)*
Daniel Wheeler *(Controller)*
Craig Longe *(Coord-Quality Control)*
Daniel Adams *(Mgr-Engrg)*
Carlos Carrion *(Mgr-Ops)*
Brian Karns *(Pres & COO)*

MESA OIL INC.
6395 E 80th Ave, Commerce City, CO 80022
Tel.: (303) 426-4777
Web Site: http://www.mesaoil.com
Rev.: $11,600,000
Emp.: 65
Re-Refiner of Lubricating Oils & Greases
N.A.I.C.S.: 324191

MESA OIL INC.

Mesa Oil Inc.—(Continued)
Lawrence Meers (Pres)

MESA SAFE COMPANY, INC.
337 W Freedom Ave, Orange, CA 92865
Tel.: (800) 490-5624
Web Site: http://www.mesasafe.com
Year Founded: 1981
Sales Range: $10-24.9 Million
Emp.: 30
Safes & Vaults Mfr
N.A.I.C.S.: 332999
George L. Vicente (Founder)

MESA SYSTEMS, INC.
681 Railroad Blvd, Grand Junction, CO 81505
Tel.: (970) 341-1774
Web Site: http://www.mesa-moving.com
Year Founded: 1981
Household Goods Transport
N.A.I.C.S.: 484210
Steven Elliott (CFO)
Jerome Lange (Pres)
Kevin Head (Pres & CEO)

Subsidiaries:

Mergenthaler Transfer & Storage Co. (1)
1414 North Montana Ave, Helena, MT 59601
Tel.: (406) 442-9470
Rev.: $30,636,791
Emp.: 130
Trucking Transfer Storage
N.A.I.C.S.: 484121
Dave Gardner (VP)

MESA VINEYARD MANAGEMENT, INC.
110 Gibson Rd, Templeton, CA 93465
Tel.: (805) 434-4100
Web Site: http://www.mesavineyard.com
Year Founded: 1989
Sales Range: $10-24.9 Million
Emp.: 150
Farm Management Services
N.A.I.C.S.: 115116
Dana M. Merrill (Pres)
Gregg Hibbits (Gen Mgr)
Kevin Merill (Mgr-Vineyard)
Bill Erickson (Controller)
Bob Thomas (Mgr-Vineyard)

MESA/BOOGIE LIMITED
1317 Ross St, Petaluma, CA 94954
Tel.: (707) 778-6565
Web Site: http://www.mesaboogie.com
Rev.: $10,000,000
Emp.: 100
Provider of Amplifiers
N.A.I.C.S.: 334310
Jim Aschow (Pres)
John Chumley (Supvr-Production)

MESASIX, LLC
2430 Victory Park Ln Ste 1809, Dallas, TX 75219
Tel.: (443) 637-2749
Web Site: http://www.mesasix.com
Sales Range: $1-9.9 Million
Online Marketing Services
N.A.I.C.S.: 541613
Robert Hoddenbagh (Founder)

MESCA FREIGHT SERVICES
47 Water St, Hallowell, ME 04347
Tel.: (207) 622-9029
Web Site: http://www.mesca.com
Sales Range: $10-24.9 Million
Emp.: 50
Freight Transportation Arrangement
N.A.I.C.S.: 488510

John Heckman (CEO)
Noah Wilmot (Pres)

MESH ARCHITECTURE + FABRICATION
2900 44th Ave N, Saint Petersburg, FL 33714
Tel.: (727) 823-3760
Web Site: http://www.mesh.ws
Sales Range: $25-49.9 Million
Emp.: 35
Architectural & Metal Fabrication Services
N.A.I.C.S.: 332323
Jovica Milic (Founder & Pres)
Tim Clemmons (Principal)
Gary Grooms (CEO)

MESILLA VALLEY TRANSPORTATION SERVICES INC.
3590 W Picacho Ave, Las Cruces, NM 88005
Tel.: (505) 524-2835
Web Site: http://www.m-v-t.com
Rev.: $43,586,210
Emp.: 60
Provider of Trucking Services
N.A.I.C.S.: 484121
Royal Jones (Pres & CEO)
Dean Rigg (CFO)
Jimmy Ray (VP)

MESIROW FINANCIAL HOLDINGS, INC.
353 N Clark St, Chicago, IL 60654-3452
Tel.: (312) 595-6000
Web Site: http://www.mesirowfinancial.com
Year Founded: 1937
Sales Range: $650-699.9 Million
Emp.: 1,100
Holding Company; Diversified Financial Services
N.A.I.C.S.: 551112
Bruce J. Young (CEO-Capital Markets)
Kristie P. Paskvan (CFO & COO)
Marc E. Sacks (CEO-Private Equity)
Thomas E. Galuhn (Pres-Private Equity)
Lavanya Batchu (VP-Investment Strategies)
Adam Goldman (Sr Mng Dir)
David S. Israel (Sr Mng Dir)
Dennis B. Black (Sr Mng Dir)
Michael E. Annin (Sr Mng Dir)
Hrach Alexanian (Sr VP)
Wenli Tan (VP)
Michael DuCharme (Dir-Currency Solutions)
Joe Hoffman (CEO-Currency Mgmt)
Brian D. Price (Mng Dir)
Francois Teissonniere (Sr Mng Dir)
Kathryn A. Vorisek (Sr Mng Dir-Equity Mgmt)
Michael Zehfuss (Sr Mng Dir-Currency Mgmt)
Robert Sydow (Sr Mng Dir-Fixed Income Mgmt)
Stephen D. Jacobson (Sr Mng Dir-CTL & Structured Debt Products)
Thomas F. Hynes (Sr Mng Dir-Institutional Sls & Mktg)
Todd E. Waldrop (Sr Mng Dir-Pub Fin)
Brian Lorber (Mng Dir)
Shane McDaniel (Mng Dir)
Christopher Langs (Mng Dir/Portfolio Mgr-Core Fixed Income Mgmt Grp)
Zach Fox (VP-Sale Leaseback Capital Grp)
James Logan (Sr VP-Retirement Plng & Advisory Grp)
Amy Middleton (Sr VP)
Barbara Arquilla (Sr VP)

Bethany Neckvatal (Sr VP)
David Fishler (Sr VP)
Edward Baker (Sr Mng Dir)
Jeffrey M. Levine (Sr Mng Dir & Gen Counsel)
Jennifer E. Rosenblum (Sr Mng Dir-Wealth Advisor)
Jessica Platko (Sr VP)
Martin Podorsky (Sr VP)
Matthew Olsen (Sr VP)
Matt Roberts (Sr VP)
Natalie Brown (CEO)
Nathaniel Sager (Sr Mng Dir)
Paul Meier (Sr VP)
Peter Henricks (Sr Mng Dir)
Steve Swierczewski (Sr Mng Dir-Investment Mgmt Distr-Global)
William Chapman (Sr VP)
Jeffrey A. Golman (Vice Chm/Vice Chm-Mesirow Financial Investment Banking)
Bradley Karelitz (Sr VP)

Subsidiaries:

Benefits & Incentives Group, Inc. (1)
1777 S Harrison St Ste 700, Denver, CO 80210-3932
Tel.: (303) 375-6200
Web Site: http://www.bigroupinc.com
Human Resource Consulting Services
N.A.I.C.S.: 541612
Rich Johnson (Owner)

Front Barnett Associates LLC (1)
70 W Madison St, Chicago, IL 60602
Tel.: (312) 641-9000
Web Site: http://www.front-barnett.com
Rev.: $8,300,000
Emp.: 20
Portfolio Management
N.A.I.C.S.: 523940
Marshall B. Front (Sr Mng Dir & Portfolio Mgr)
Mickey MacMillan (Sr Mng Dir & Portfolio Mgr)
Peter Wahlstrom (Mng Dir-Investment Res)

Mesirow Financial Administrative Corporation (1)
350 N Clark St, Chicago, IL 60654-4712
Tel.: (312) 595-6000
Web Site: http://www.mesirowfinancial.com
Financial Management Services
N.A.I.C.S.: 541611
Richard Price (CEO)

Mesirow Financial Agriculture Management, LLC (1)
353 N Clark St, Chicago, IL 60654
Tel.: (312) 595-7157
Web Site: http://www.mesirowfinancial.com
Sales Range: $10-24.9 Million
Emp.: 5
Agricultural Property Management Services
N.A.I.C.S.: 531312
Jon Brorson (Mng Dir)
Van Bitner (Sr VP)
Geoffrey Lutz (Sr VP)
Debbie Krieps (Mng Dir & Head-Corp Comm)

Mesirow Financial Commodities Management, LLC (1)
353 N Clark St, Chicago, IL 60654
Tel.: (312) 595-6000
Investment Management Service
N.A.I.C.S.: 523940

Mesirow Financial Consulting, LLC (1)
666 3rd Ave FL 21, New York, NY 10017
Tel.: (212) 808-8330
Financial Consulting Services
N.A.I.C.S.: 541611

Mesirow Financial Hong Kong, Limited (1)
Suite 2002 20/F 100 Queens Road Central, Central, China (Hong Kong)
Tel.: (852) 35193000
Web Site: http://www.mesirowfinancial.com
Sales Range: $25-49 Million
Emp.: 7
Investment Management Service
N.A.I.C.S.: 523940

U.S. PRIVATE

Muj Ali (Gen Mgr)

Mesirow Financial Interim Management, LLC (1)
353 N Clark St, Chicago, IL 60654
Tel.: (312) 595-6000
Financial Management Services
N.A.I.C.S.: 541611
Richard Price (Pres)

Mesirow Financial International UK, Limited (1)
Sackville House 40 Piccadilly, London, W1J 0DR, United Kingdom
Tel.: (44) 2078511700
Sales Range: $10-24.9 Million
Emp.: 10
Financial Consulting Services
N.A.I.C.S.: 541611

Mesirow Financial Investment Management, Inc. (1)
353 N Clark St, Chicago, IL 60654
Tel.: (312) 595-6000
Web Site: http://www.mesirowfinancial.com
Emp.: 600
Financial Consulting Services
N.A.I.C.S.: 541611

Mesirow Financial Private Equity Advisors, Inc. (1)
353 N Clark St, Chicago, IL 60654
Tel.: (312) 595-6000
Investment Management Service
N.A.I.C.S.: 523940

Mesirow Financial Private Equity, Inc. (1)
353 N Clark St, Chicago, IL 60654
Tel.: (312) 595-6000
Investment Management Service
N.A.I.C.S.: 523940
Thomas E. Galuhn (Pres)
Marc E. Sacks (CEO)
Daniel P. Howell (Mng Dir)
Robert M. DeBolt (Mng Dir)
Courtney Wilson Haynes (Sr VP)

Mesirow Financial Real Estate Brokerage, Inc. (1)
353 N Clark St, Chicago, IL 60654
Tel.: (312) 595-7205
Web Site: http://www.mesirowfinancial.com
Real Estate Brokerage Services
N.A.I.C.S.: 531210

Mesirow Financial Services, Inc. (1)
610 Central Ave Ste 200, Highland Park, IL 60035-5636
Tel.: (847) 681-2300
Web Site: http://www.mesirowfinancial.com
Investment Management Service
N.A.I.C.S.: 523940

Mesirow Financial Structured Settlements, LLC (1)
353 N Clark St, Chicago, IL 60654
Tel.: (312) 595-6000
Web Site: http://www.mesirowfinancial.com
General Insurance Services
N.A.I.C.S.: 524298
Maureen Flood (Mng Dir)
Daniel J. Goodmann (Mng Dir)
Neil P. Herald (VP)

Mesirow Financial, Inc. (1)
353 N Clark St Ste 400, Chicago, IL 60654
Tel.: (312) 595-6000
Web Site: http://www.mesirowfinancial.com
Emp.: 800
Diversified Financial Services
N.A.I.C.S.: 523999
Richard Scott Price (Chm & CEO)
Bruce J. Young (Vice Chm & Pres-Institutional Sls & Trading)
Kristie P. Paskvan (CFO)

Branch (Domestic):

Mesirow Financial, Inc. - Detroit (2)
220 Park Ave Ste 350, Birmingham, MI 48009-3477
Tel.: (248) 642-6580
Web Site: http://www.mesirow.com
Sales Range: $75-99.9 Million
Emp.: 3
Financial Services
N.A.I.C.S.: 523150

Mesirow Financial, Inc. - Fort Lauderdale (2)

225 NE Ste 600 Mizner Blvd, Boca Raton, FL 33432
Tel.: (954) 356-0330
Web Site: http://www.mesirowfinancial.com
Sales Range: $75-99.9 Million
Emp.: 30
Provider of Financial Services
N.A.I.C.S.: 523940

Mesirow Financial, Inc. - Highland Park (2)
610 Central Ave Ste 200, Highland Park, IL 60035-3216
Tel.: (847) 681-2300
Web Site: http://www.mesirowfinancial.com
Sales Range: $100-124.9 Million
Emp.: 80
Provider of Financial Services
N.A.I.C.S.: 523150

Mesirow Financial, Inc. - New York City (2)
666 3rd Ave, New York, NY 10017
Tel.: (212) 425-3200
Web Site: http://www.mesirowfinancial.com
Sales Range: $75-99.9 Million
Emp.: 30
Provider of Financial Services
N.A.I.C.S.: 523160
Richard S. Price *(Chm & CEO)*

Mesirow Financial, Inc. - Oakbrook (2)
1 Oakbrook Ter Ste 500, Oakbrook Terrace, IL 60181-4468
Tel.: (630) 705-2000
Web Site: http://www.mesirowfinancial.com
Sales Range: $75-99.9 Million
Emp.: 25
Provider of Financial Services
N.A.I.C.S.: 524210

Mesirow Financial, Inc. - Pittsburgh (2)
650 Smithfield St Ste 230, Pittsburgh, PA 15222-3907
Tel.: (412) 281-2005
Web Site: http://www.mesirowfinancial.com
Sales Range: $25-49.9 Million
Emp.: 2
Provider Of Business Financial Services
N.A.I.C.S.: 561499

Mesirow Financial, Inc. - Tampa (2)
400 N Ashley Dr Ste 2175, Tampa, FL 33602-4300
Tel.: (813) 221-4424
Web Site: http://www.mesirow.com
Sales Range: $75-99.9 Million
Emp.: 4
Provider of Financial Services
N.A.I.C.S.: 523150
Kevin Murname *(Mng Dir)*

Mesirow Real Estate Investments, Inc. (1)
353 N Clark St, Chicago, IL 60654
Tel.: (312) 595-6000
Real Estate Investment Services
N.A.I.C.S.: 531390

Mesirow Realty Services, Inc. (1)
353 N Clark St, Chicago, IL 60654
Tel.: (312) 595-6000
Real Estate Investment Services
N.A.I.C.S.: 531110

MESKO GLASS AND MIRROR CO.
801 Wyoming Ave, Scranton, PA 18509
Tel.: (570) 346-0777
Web Site: http://www.mesko.com
Rev.: $13,994,296
Emp.: 40
Glass & Glazing Work
N.A.I.C.S.: 238150
Joseph N. Mesko *(Pres)*

MESQUITE GAMING, LLC
950 W Mesquite Blvd, Mesquite, NV 89027
Tel.: (702) 346-7529   NV
Web Site: http://www.mesquitegaming.com
Sales Range: $150-199.9 Million
Emp.: 1,700
Holding Company; Casino Hotels & Resorts Owner & Operator
N.A.I.C.S.: 551112
Anthony Toti *(CEO)*
Chris Lazzara *(VP-Mktg & Adv)*
Tom Jannarone *(Gen Mgr)*

Subsidiaries:

Virgin River Casino Corporation (1)
100 N Pioneer Blvd, Mesquite, NV 89027
Tel.: (702) 346-6800
Web Site: http://www.virginriver.com
Sales Range: $10-24.9 Million
Emp.: 100
Hotel Casinos Ownership & Operation
N.A.I.C.S.: 721120
Antony Toti *(CEO)*

Subsidiary (Domestic):

Casablanca Resorts, LLC (2)
950 W Mesquite Blvd, Mesquite, NV 89027
Tel.: (702) 346-7529
Web Site: http://www.casablancaresorts.com
Casino Hotels Ownership & Operation
N.A.I.C.S.: 721120
Robert R. Black Sr. *(CEO)*

MESSER CONSTRUCTION CO.
643 W Ct St, Cincinnati, OH 45203
Tel.: (513) 242-1541   OH
Web Site: http://www.messer.com
Year Founded: 1932
Sales Range: $75-99.9 Million
Emp.: 900
Provider of Contracting & Construction Services
N.A.I.C.S.: 236220
Thomas M. Keckeis *(Chm)*
C. Allen Begley *(Sr VP)*
Tom Lampe *(VP)*
Nick Apanius *(VP-Health Care)*
Karen B. Pawsat *(VP-HR)*
John Megibben *(VP)*
Andrew J. Burg *(VP)*
Matthew Verst *(VP)*
Bernard P. Suer *(Sr VP)*
Kevin M. Cozart *(VP)*
Kristin M. Wainscott *(VP)*
Robert L. Williams *(VP)*
Steven M. Bestard *(VP)*
John Jeffries *(Mgr-Environmental Health & Safety-Knoxville)*
Brian Walker *(Project Engr-Knoxville)*
John Blum *(VP)*
Mike Mosko *(Project Mgr-Charlotte)*
Deressa Prater *(Project Engr-Charlotte)*
Gabriel Slivka *(Project Engr-Charlotte)*
Tyler Cavin *(Project Engr-Charlotte)*
Mark R. Gillming *(Sec & Sr VP)*
Mark S. Luegering *(Sr VP-Ops)*
Tim Steigerwald *(Sr VP-Bus Dev)*
Alex Munoz *(VP-Safety & Risk Mgmt)*
Brian A. Doyle *(VP-Fin)*
Brooks A. Parker *(VP-Craftforce Dev)*
Greg L. Herrin *(VP)*
J. Steve Eder *(VP)*
John F. Carder *(CIO & VP-IT)*
Mark A. Hill *(VP-Ops-Lexington)*
Matt Monnin *(VP-Bus Dev)*
Robert J. Inkrot *(VP-Ops)*
Stephen L. Keckeis *(VP-Charlotte)*
Steve A. Jones *(VP-Ops-Nashville)*
Thomas A. Hart *(VP-Ops-Indianapolis)*
Timothy O. Gusler *(VP-Ops-Columbus)*
Ashley Bielefeld *(Mgr-Bus Dev)*
Tom Belanich *(Dir-Indus Market-Dayton)*
Erin Thompson *(VP)*
Stanford T. Williams Jr. *(Chief Inclusion & Diversity Officer & VP)*
E. Paul Hitter Jr. *(CFO, Treas & Sr VP)*
Robert E. Verst Jr. *(Sr VP-Ops Svcs-Columbus)*

MESSICK FARM EQUIPMENT INC.
187 Merts Dr, Elizabethtown, PA 17022
Tel.: (717) 367-1319
Web Site: http://www.messicks.com
Sales Range: $50-74.9 Million
Emp.: 180
Agricultural Machinery
N.A.I.C.S.: 423820
Ken Messick *(VP)*
Doug Breneman *(Mgr-Svc)*

MESSINA WILDLIFE MANAGEMENT
55 Willow St Ste 1, Washington, NJ 07882
Tel.: (908) 320-7009
Web Site: http://www.messinawildlife.com
Year Founded: 1998
Sales Range: $1-9.9 Million
Emp.: 9
Animal Protection Services
N.A.I.C.S.: 813312
James Messina *(VP)*

MET LABORATORIES INC.
914 W Patapsco Ave, Baltimore, MD 21230
Tel.: (410) 354-3300
Web Site: http://www.metlabs.com
Rev.: $13,875,394
Emp.: 83
Testing Laboratories
N.A.I.C.S.: 541715
Robert Frier *(Pres)*
Troy Franklin *(VP-Ops)*
Kevin Harbarger *(VP-Bus Dev)*
Rick Cooper *(Dir-Safety Laboratory)*
Cedric Valiente *(Mgr-Technical)*
Jerry Frey *(Reg Mgr-Sls)*
Asad Bajwa *(Dir-EMC Laboratory)*
Jordan Yeng *(Gen Mgr-Ops-Asia)*

MET-CON CONSTRUCTION INC.
15760 Acorn Trl, Faribault, MN 55021
Tel.: (507) 332-2266
Web Site: http://www.met-con.com
Sales Range: $300-349.9 Million
Emp.: 175
Industrial Buildings & Warehouses
N.A.I.C.S.: 236220
Thomas McDonough *(Founder & Pres)*
Troy Zabinski *(VP-Dev)*
Jim Roush *(Gen Mgr-Met & Con Kato)*

MET/HODDER INC.
1201 Harmon Pl Ste 300, Minneapolis, MN 55403
Tel.: (612) 333-1025
Web Site: http://www.methodder.tv
Sales Range: $10-24.9 Million
Emp.: 20
Provider of Television Film Production Services
N.A.I.C.S.: 512110
Kent Hodder *(Pres & CEO)*
Nancy Bordson *(VP & Dir-Ops)*

META DATA SOFTWARE, INC.
11111 Santa Monica Blvd Ste 2250, Los Angeles, CA 90025
Tel.: (323) 922-4985
Web Site: https://www.fabricdata.com
Emp.: 100
Software Publisher
N.A.I.C.S.: 513210
Rob Delf *(CEO)*

Subsidiaries:

Internet Video Archive LLC (1)
207 White Horse Pike, Haddon Heights, NJ 08035
Tel.: (856) 310-1981
Web Site: http://www.internetvideoarchive.com
Rev.: $1,000,000
Emp.: 15
Wired Telecommunications Carriers
N.A.I.C.S.: 517111
Michele Devery *(Dir-Ops)*
Jed Horovitz *(CEO)*
Boo Kolo *(VP-Tech)*
Jason Schneid *(Mgr-Client Svcs)*
Robert Kelly *(Mgr-Mktg)*

METABO CORPORATION
1231 Wilson Dr, West Chester, PA 19380-4243
Tel.: (610) 436-5900   DE
Web Site: http://www.metabo.us
Sales Range: $10-24.9 Million
Emp.: 50
Mfr of Industrial Hand Tools
N.A.I.C.S.: 423710
Martin Cross *(Pres)*
Jens Knudsen *(VP-Fin & Ops)*
Mark Linn *(Dir-Natl Accts)*
Larry Pecht *(Mgr-Natl Key Acct)*
Christopher Berg *(Pres/CEO-US & Canada)*
Jere L. Geib Jr. *(Mgr-Mktg)*

METABOLON, INC
617 Davis Dr Ste 400, Durham, NC 27713
Tel.: (919) 572-1711
Web Site: http://www.metabolon.com
Year Founded: 2000
Sales Range: $10-24.9 Million
Emp.: 100
Research & Development in Biotechnology
N.A.I.C.S.: 541714
Michael Milburn *(Chief Scientific Officer)*
Eric Button *(Sr VP)*
Lisa Miller *(VP & Gen Mgr-Precision Medicine)*
David Memel *(Chief Medical Officer)*
R. John Fletcher *(Chm)*
Rohan Hastie *(Pres & CEO)*
Tom Houseman *(VP-Ops)*
Frank Fee III *(CFO)*

METACOM INC.
Ste 5 6055 Nathan Ln N, Minneapolis, MN 55442-1675
Tel.: (763) 391-0300   MN
Year Founded: 1983
Rev.: $30,000,000
Emp.: 100
Producer of Prerecorded Records & Tapes
N.A.I.C.S.: 334610

METAIRIE PHYSICIAN SERVICES, INC.
2801 Via Fortuna Ste 500, Austin, TX 78746-7573
Tel.: (512) 899-3995   LA
Year Founded: 2012
Sales Range: $10-24.9 Million
Emp.: 24
Healthcare & Social Welfare Services
N.A.I.C.S.: 525120
Scott Posecai *(Treas)*
Dionne Viator *(Pres)*
M. L. Lagarde III *(Sec)*

METAL ART OF CALIFORNIA, INC.
640 N Cypress St, Orange, CA 92867
Tel.: (714) 532-7100   CA

METAL ART OF CALIFORNIA, INC.

Metal Art of California, Inc.—(Continued)
Web Site: http://www.sign-mart.com
Year Founded: 1974
Rev.: $13,000,000
Emp.: 91
Signs & Advertising Specialties
N.A.I.C.S.: 339950
Gene S. Sobel (Pres)

METAL COMPONENTS LLC.
3281 Roger B Chaffee Memorial, Grand Rapids, MI 49548
Tel.: (616) 252-1900
Web Site:
http://www.metalcompinc.com
Sales Range: $10-24.9 Million
Emp.: 100
Metal Fabricating
N.A.I.C.S.: 332322
Bert Brown (Plant Mgr)
Craig Balow (Gen Mgr)
John Grygiel (Mgr-Matls)

METAL EXCHANGE CORPORATION
111 Westport Plz Ste 350, Saint Louis, MO 63146
Tel.: (314) 434-3500
Web Site:
http://www.metalexchangecorp.com
Aluminum & Other Non-ferrous Metal Trading, Processing & Transportation Services
N.A.I.C.S.: 423510
Scott Bichel (Dir-Engrg Svcs-Trading Div)
Ben Evans (Pres-Trading Div)
Rick Merluzzi (COO)
Mike Lefton (Exec Chm)
Tom Marklin (VP-IT)
Matt Rohm (Pres & CEO)
Mark Butterfield (Pres-Mfg)

Subsidiaries:

Continental Aluminum Company (1)
29201 Milford Rd, New Hudson, MI 48165
Tel.: (248) 437-1001
Web Site:
http://www.continentalaluminum.com
Sales Range: $1-9.9 Million
Emp.: 60
Miscellaneous Chemical Product & Preparation Mfr
N.A.I.C.S.: 325998
Mark Buchner (Gen Mgr)

METAL MARKETPLACE INTERNATIONAL
718 Sansom St, Philadelphia, PA 19106
Tel.: (215) 592-8777
Web Site:
http://www.metalmarketplace.com
Sales Range: $10-24.9 Million
Emp.: 15
Jewelry Mfr
N.A.I.C.S.: 339910
Anthony Acquaviva (Pres)
Barry Hochman (VP-Sls)
Joe Evich (Exec VP)
Veronica Felmey (Project Mgr)

METAL MASTER SALES CORPORATION
1159 N Main St, Glendale Heights, IL 60139
Tel.: (630) 858-4750
Web Site:
http://www.metalmaster.com
Year Founded: 1989
Emp.: 15
Specialists in Custom Slit Flat Rolled Steel Products
N.A.I.C.S.: 331221
James C. Jensen (Founder & Pres)
Jeff Keiner (VP-Sls & Pur)
Dan Macek (CFO)

METAL PRODUCTS COMPANY
300 Garfield St, McMinnville, TN 37110
Tel.: (931) 473-5513
Web Site:
http://www.mpcmidsouth.com
Sales Range: $10-24.9 Million
Emp.: 70
Sheet Metalwork
N.A.I.C.S.: 332322
Arthur J. Dyer III (CEO)

METAL RESOURCE SOLUTIONS
7770 W Chester Rd Ste 120, West Chester, OH 45069
Tel.: (513) 874-7630
Web Site:
http://www.metalresourcesolutions.net
Year Founded: 2002
Sales Range: $1-9.9 Million
Emp.: 8
Stainless Steel & Brass Wire Distr for Fasteners, Screws & Rivets
N.A.I.C.S.: 423510
Rich Tereba (Pres)

METAL SEAL & PRODUCTS, INC.
4323 Hamann Pkwy, Willoughby, OH 44094-5625
Tel.: (440) 946-8500
Web Site: http://www.metalseal.com
Year Founded: 1949
Sales Range: $100-124.9 Million
Emp.: 200
Mfg Of Screw Machine Products
N.A.I.C.S.: 332721

METAL SPINNERS INC.
914 Wohlert St, Angola, IN 46703
Tel.: (260) 665-2158
Web Site:
http://www.metalspinners.com
Sales Range: $10-24.9 Million
Emp.: 130
Provider of Metal Spinning Services
N.A.I.C.S.: 332119
Olin M. Wiland (Pres & CEO)
Jessica Reinig (Controller)
Jamie Burger (VP-Mfg)

METAL SURFACES INC.
6060 Shull St, Bell Gardens, CA 90201
Tel.: (562) 927-1331
Web Site:
http://www.metalsurfaces.com
Sales Range: $10-24.9 Million
Emp.: 170
Provider of Metals Services
N.A.I.C.S.: 332813
Craig Snyder (Controller)
Charles Bell (Pres)
Nell Wallace (Mgr-HR & Payroll)
Julia Anderson (Mgr-Shipping & Receiving)
Armando Celis (Mgr-Quality Assurance)
Bill Serrano (Mgr-Main Shop)
Chris Boltz (Mgr-Sls & Mktg)

METAL TECHNOLOGIES, INC.
1401 S Grandstaff Dr, Auburn, IN 46706-2664
Tel.: (260) 925-4717
Web Site: http://www.metal-technologies.com
Sales Range: $50-74.9 Million
Emp.: 50
Gray Iron Foundry
N.A.I.C.S.: 541330
Rick James (Chm)
Matthew J. Fetter (CEO)

Subsidiaries:

Metal Technologies Three Rivers (1)
429 W 5th St, Three Rivers, MI 49093-1601
Tel.: (269) 278-1765
Web Site: http://www.metal-technologies.com
Sales Range: $25-49.9 Million
Gray Iron Castings
N.A.I.C.S.: 331511
Douglas Monroe (Pres)

Metal Technologies West Allis Ductile Iron (1)
1706 S 68th St, West Allis, WI 53214 (100%)
Tel.: (414) 302-4444
Sales Range: $25-49.9 Million
Ductile Iron Mfr
N.A.I.C.S.: 331511

Metal Technologies Woodstock (1)
303 Tecumseh St, PO Box 35, Woodstock, N4S 7W5, ON, Canada (100%)
Tel.: (519) 421-1967
Sales Range: $10-24.9 Million
Provider of Metal Casting Services
N.A.I.C.S.: 331523

Ravenna Casting Center, Inc. (1)
3800 Adams Rd, Ravenna, MI 49451
Tel.: (231) 853-0300
Web Site: http://www.metal-technologies.com
Sales Range: $25-49.9 Million
Provider of Metal Casting Services
N.A.I.C.S.: 331511
Dean Lynn (Gen Mgr)

METAL TRADING CORPORATION
111 Center St Ste 2150, Little Rock, AR 72201
Tel.: (501) 374-9017
Year Founded: 1995
Sales Range: $10-24.9 Million
Emp.: 3
Scrap & Waste Materials
N.A.I.C.S.: 423930
Linda Peotter (Pres)

METAL WORKS INC.
24 Industrial Dr, Londonderry, NH 03053
Tel.: (603) 669-6180
Web Site: http://www.metalworks-inc.com
Year Founded: 1985
Sales Range: $10-24.9 Million
Emp.: 72
Mfr of Sheet Metalwork
N.A.I.C.S.: 332322
Thomas Masiero (COO)
Fred Pierce (CEO)
David Staffiere (VP)
Bob Swift (Dir-Sls & Mktg)

METAL-MATIC, INC.
629 2nd St SE, Minneapolis, MN 55414-2106
Tel.: (612) 378-0411
Web Site: http://www.metal-matic.com
Year Founded: 1951
Sales Range: $50-74.9 Million
Emp.: 500
Mfr & Sales of Steel Tubing
N.A.I.C.S.: 331210
Robert Van Krevelen (Exec VP)
Thomas Bliss (Pres)
Thomas Jackson (CFO)
Gerald Bliss Jr. (VP)

Subsidiaries:

Metal-Matic, Inc. - Bedford Park Plant (1)
7200 S Narragansett Ave, Bedford Park, IL 60638
Tel.: (708) 594-7553
Steel Pipe & Tube Mfr
N.A.I.C.S.: 331210

Metal-Matic, Inc. - Ohio Plant (1)
1701 Made Industrial Dr, Middletown, OH 45044
Tel.: (513) 261-6729
Steel Pipe & Tube Mfr
N.A.I.C.S.: 331210

METALADE N.Y., INC.
2025 Brighton Henrietta Town Line Rd T, Rochester, NY 14623
Tel.: (585) 424-3260
Web Site: http://www.metalade.com
Sales Range: $10-24.9 Million
Emp.: 57
Sheet Metalwork
N.A.I.C.S.: 332322
Richard F. Groth (Pres)
Tony Delvecchio (Mgr-Ops)
Greg Zink (Plant Mgr)
Dan Olson (Controller)

METALCOAT INC. OF FLORIDA
1910 State Rd 37 S, Mulberry, FL 33860
Tel.: (863) 425-1185
Sales Range: $10-24.9 Million
Emp.: 50
Provider of Metal Coating Services
N.A.I.C.S.: 238990
Cleo Hall (Owner & Pres)

METALCRAFT INDUSTRIES, INC.
1250 W 124th Ave, Westminster, CO 80234
Tel.: (303) 280-2700
Web Site:
http://www.metalcraftind.com
Year Founded: 2001
Sales Range: $10-24.9 Million
Emp.: 35
Metal Stamping
N.A.I.C.S.: 332119
Larry Caschette (Pres)

Subsidiaries:

Northwest Metalcraft, Inc. (1)
13305 41st Ave NE, Marysville, WA 98271-7848
Tel.: (360) 657-2759
Aerospace Component Mfr
N.A.I.C.S.: 336413

METALCRAFT OF MAYVILLE, INC.
1000 Metalcraft Dr, Mayville, WI 53050-0151
Tel.: (920) 387-3150
Web Site: http://www.mtlcraft.com
Year Founded: 1922
Sales Range: $25-49.9 Million
Emp.: 550
Metal Fabrication & Precision Machining Services
N.A.I.C.S.: 332999
Randy Gloede (Pres & COO)
Martin Gallun (CEO)

METALEX MANUFACTURING INC.
5750 Cornell Rd, Cincinnati, OH 45242-2010
Tel.: (513) 489-0507
Web Site:
http://www.metalexmfg.com
Year Founded: 1974
Sales Range: $10-24.9 Million
Emp.: 120
Provider of Industrial Machinery
N.A.I.C.S.: 383998
Werner Kummerle (Co-Owner & CEO)
Sue Kummerle (Co-Owner)
Dan Rorick (Engr-Mfg)
Leslie Schneider (Coord-Accts Receivable & Shipping)

COMPANIES

Philip Palko (Coord-ISO)
Ward Tom (Controller)
Chris Gentry (Mgr-Shipping)
Fred Fenner Jr. (Mgr-IT Sys)

METALFAB, INC.
Prices Switch Rd, Vernon, NJ 07462
Tel.: (973) 764-2000
Web Site:
http://www.metalfabinc.com
Year Founded: 1977
Sales Range: $10-24.9 Million
Emp.: 30
Dry Solids Processing Equipment Mfr
N.A.I.C.S.: 332322
Mike Randazzo (COO)

METALICO INC.
135 Dermody St, Cranford, NJ 07016
Tel.: (908) 497-9610
Web Site: http://www.metalico.com
Year Founded: 1997
Sales Range: $450-499.9 Million
Metal Services
N.A.I.C.S.: 331492
Eric W. Finlayson (Treas, Sr VP & Dir-Risk Mgmt)
Michael J. Drury (Pres & CEO)
Kevin R. Whalen (CFO & Sr VP)
David J. DelBianco (VP-Bus Dev)
Pete Meyers (VP-Ferrous Sls & Mktg)
K. K. Wong (VP-Non-Ferrous Sls & Mktg)

Subsidiaries:

American CatCon, Inc. (1)
17401 US Route 35, Buda, TX 78610
Tel.: (512) 295-4659
Web Site: http://www.metalico.com
Sales Range: $25-49.9 Million
Emp.: 50
Catalytic Converters & Metal Recycling Services
N.A.I.C.S.: 331492
George Ostendorf (CEO)

Federal Autocat Recycling, LLC (1)
502 York St, Elizabeth, NJ 07201
Tel.: (973) 273-0866
Web Site: http://www.federalautocat.com
Business to Business Electronic Markets
N.A.I.C.S.: 425120
Kurt Ellis (Gen Mgr-Natl)
Rich Arronenzi (Mgr-Comml-Natl)
Andy Cohen (Mgr-Pur-Midwest)

Mayco Industries (1)
1200 16th St, Granite City, IL 62040-4444
Tel.: (618) 451-4400
Web Site: http://www.maycoindustries.com
Sales Range: $25-49.9 Million
Emp.: 50
Metal Services
N.A.I.C.S.: 331491

Metalico Akron, Inc. (1)
943 Hazel St, Akron, OH 44305
Tel.: (330) 376-1400
Web Site: http://www.metalico.com
Emp.: 50
Scrap Metal Recycling Services
N.A.I.C.S.: 423930
Kevin Robinson (Mgr-Market)

Metalico Aluminum Recovery, Inc. (1)
6223 Thompson Rd, Syracuse, NY 13206
Tel.: (315) 463-9500
Web Site: http://www.metalico.com
Emp.: 20
Scrap Metal Recycling Services
N.A.I.C.S.: 331492
Andy Clements (Gen Mgr)

Metalico Annaco (1)
943 Hazel St, Akron, OH 44305-1609
Tel.: (330) 376-1400
Web Site: http://www.annaco.com
Sales Range: $25-49.9 Million
Emp.: 30
Scrap & Waste Metal Processing Services
N.A.I.C.S.: 423930
Kavin Robinson (Mgr-Non-Ferrous)

Metalico Buffalo, Inc. (1)
127 Fillmore Ave, Buffalo, NY 14210
Tel.: (716) 823-3788
Web Site: http://www.metalicobuffalo.com
Scrap Metal Processing & Recycling Services
N.A.I.C.S.: 331492

Metalico Niagara, Inc. (1)
2133 Maple Ave, Niagara Falls, NY 14305
Tel.: (716) 284-8729
Scrap Metal Recycling Services
N.A.I.C.S.: 423930

Metalico Rochester, Inc. (1)
1515 Scottsville Rd, Rochester, NY 14623
Tel.: (585) 436-0713
Web Site: http://www.metalicorochester.com
Emp.: 60
Metal Recycling Services
N.A.I.C.S.: 331492
Patti Schlien (Controller)

Metalico Youngstown, Inc. (1)
100 Division St Ext, Youngstown, OH 44510
Tel.: (330) 743-9000
Web Site: http://www.youngstowniron.com
Metal Recycling Services
N.A.I.C.S.: 423930

Santa Rosa Lead Products Inc. (1)
33 S University St, Healdsburg, CA 95448-4021
Tel.: (707) 431-1638
Web Site: http://www.santarosalead.com
Rev.: $3,600,000
Emp.: 27
Provider of Steel Services
N.A.I.C.S.: 339113

Skyway Auto Parts, Inc. (1)
637 Tifft St, Buffalo, NY 14220-1863
Tel.: (716) 824-4348
Web Site: http://www.skywayauto.com
Sales Range: $25-49.9 Million
Emp.: 6
Automobile Parts Used & Rebuilt Whslr
N.A.I.C.S.: 459510
Frank Dragone (Mgr)

Tranzact Corporation (1)
1185 Lancaster Pike, Quarryville, PA 17566
Tel.: (717) 284-0843
Web Site: http://www.tranzactinc.com
Metal Recycling Services
N.A.I.C.S.: 423930

West Coast Shot, Inc. (1)
18 W Oxmoor Rd, Birmingham, AL 35209-6410 (100%)
Tel.: (775) 246-5588
Sales Range: $25-49.9 Million
Emp.: 9
Ammunition Mfr
N.A.I.C.S.: 332992

METALKRAFT INDUSTRIES, INC.
1944 Shumway Hill Rd, Wellsboro, PA 16901
Tel.: (570) 724-6800   PA
Web Site:
http://www.metalkraftpm.com
Year Founded: 1983
Computerized Manufacturing Systems
N.A.I.C.S.: 541512
Aaron K. Singer (Pres & CEO)

Subsidiaries:

Keystone Automatic Technology, Inc. (1)
1 S Maple St, Emporium, PA 15834
Tel.: (814) 486-0513
Web Site:
http://www.keystoneautomatic.com
Sales Range: $1-9.9 Million
Emp.: 30
Metal Precision Parts Mfr
N.A.I.C.S.: 332999
Aaron K. Singer (Pres, CEO & Dir-Admin)
George Salter (Plant Mgr)

METALLIC BUILDING SYSTEMS, LLC
7301 Fairview St, Houston, TX 77041

Web Site: http://www.metallic.com
Building Engineering Services
N.A.I.C.S.: 541330
William Boutwell (Owner)

METALLICS, INC.
W7274 Cty Hwy Z, Onalaska, WI 54650
Tel.: (608) 781-5200
Web Site: http://www.metallics.net
Rev.: $10,300,000
Emp.: 250
Metal Coating Engraving & Allied Services Mfr
N.A.I.C.S.: 332812
Doug Dale (Pres)
Todd Dale (Pres)
Tim Strey (Mgr-Quality)

METALLIX INC.
59 Avenue at the Commons Ste 201, Shrewsbury, NJ 07702
Tel.: (732) 936-0050
Web Site:
http://www.metallixrefining.com
Rev.: $36,800,000
Emp.: 20
Provider of Metals Services
N.A.I.C.S.: 331410
Eric Leiner (CEO)

METALLOY INDUSTRIES INC.
13101 Rachel Blvd, Alachua, FL 32615-6690
Tel.: (386) 418-1088   FL
Web Site: http://www.metalloy.com
Year Founded: 1980
Sales Range: $10-24.9 Million
Emp.: 40
Metals Service Centers & Offices, Plumber Fittings, Brass Nipples, Computers, Computer Peripheral Equipment & Software Wholesale
N.A.I.C.S.: 423510
Glenn Blumberg (Pres)

METALMARK CAPITAL HOLDINGS LLC
1177 Avenue of the Americas 40th Fl, New York, NY 10036
Tel.: (212) 823-1900   DE
Web Site:
http://www.metalmarkcapital.com
Year Founded: 2004
Private Equity Firm
N.A.I.C.S.: 523999
Howard I. Hoffen (Chm & CEO)
Michael C. Hoffman (Partner)
Leigh J. Abramson (Partner & Mng Dir)
Jeffrey M. Siegal (Partner)
Vanessa L. Adler (Principal)
M. Glen Itwaru (Principal)
Kumar Valliappan (Mng Dir)
John R. Richardson (VP)
Jeremy Xia (VP)
Jordan M. Roker (Mng Dir)

Subsidiaries:

Camin Cargo Control Inc. (1)
218 Centaurus St, Corpus Christi, TX 78405
Tel.: (361) 884-3922
Web Site: http://www.camincargo.com
Rev.: $5,000,000
Emp.: 15
Inspection & Laboratory Services
N.A.I.C.S.: 541380
Bret Morrison (COO)
Kim Holloway (Mgr)
John Hodson (CEO)

HDT Engineered Technologies, Inc. (1)
30525 Aurora Rd, Solon, OH 44139
Tel.: (440) 248-6111
Web Site: http://www.hdtglobal.com

METALS AND ADDITIVES

Sales Range: $1-4.9 Billion
Aerospace, Robotics, Military, Environmental Control, Expeditionary Shelter & Power Systems Engineering
N.A.I.C.S.: 541330
Greg Miller (Sr VP-Bus-US)
John Gilligan (Chm)
Anthony DiLucente (CFO & Exec VP)
Prabha Gopinath (Sr VP-Intl Bus)
Mike Kinney (VP-Ops)
Todd Nelson (CIO & VP)
Carl Pates (CTO & Sr VP)
Rita Thomas (Gen Counsel & Sr VP)
Scott Thompson (VP-Global Mktg & Strategy)

Subsidiary (Domestic):

HDT Expeditionary Systems, Inc. (2)
6051 N Lee Hwy, Fairfield, VA 24435
Tel.: (540) 377-5001
Web Site: http://www.base-x.com
Sales Range: $25-49.9 Million
Temporary Shelter & Building Mfr
N.A.I.C.S.: 624221
Kevin Almarode (Product Dir-Mgmt)

Subsidiary (Non-US):

HDT Global Europe Ltd (2)
20-22 Bedford Row, London, WC1R 4JS, United Kingdom
Tel.: (44) 7538 059472
Web Site: http://www.hdtglobal.com
Emp.: 7
Aerospace, Robotics, Military, Environmental Control, Expeditionary Shelter & Power Systems Engineering
N.A.I.C.S.: 541330
David Morgan (Mgr-Bus Dev)

Subsidiary (Domestic):

Hunter Manufacturing Company (2)
30525 Aurora Rd, Solon, OH 44139
Tel.: (440) 248-6111
Web Site: http://www.huntermfgco.com
Sales Range: $50-74.9 Million
Military Heating System & Chemical Filtration Products Mfr
N.A.I.C.S.: 335999

Metalmark Management LLC (1)
1177 Avenue of the Americas 40th Fl, New York, NY 10036
Tel.: (212) 823-1930
Emp.: 29
Investment Management Service
N.A.I.C.S.: 523940

Premier Research International LLC (1)
1st Floor Rubra 2 Mulberry Business Park, Fishponds Road, Wokingham, RG41 2GY, United Kingdom
Tel.: (44) 1189364000
Web Site: http://www.premier-research.com
Pharmaceutical & Medical Device Clinical Research Services
N.A.I.C.S.: 541380
Krista Armstrong (VP-Global Clinical Trial Mgmt)
Ludo Reynders (CEO)
Joanne Emmett (VP-Medical Devices)
Colin Hayward (Chief Medical Officer)

Subsidiary (US):

Premier Research Group International Ltd. (2)
234 Copeland St 4th Fl, Quincy, MA 02169
Tel.: (617) 237-1100
Web Site: http://www.premier-research.com
Sales Range: $25-49.9 Million
Pharmaceutical & Medical Device Clinical Testing Services
N.A.I.C.S.: 541380
Ludo Reynders (CEO)
Mike Wilkinson (COO)

Subsidiary (Domestic):

Pivotal Research Centers LLC (3)
13128 N 94th Dr Ste 200, Peoria, AZ 85381
Tel.: (623) 815-9714
Sales Range: $1-9.9 Million
Clinical Research Services
N.A.I.C.S.: 541715

METALS AND ADDITIVES

METALS AND ADDITIVES

METALS AND ADDITIVES —(CONTINUED)

CORPORATION, INC.
5929 Lakeside Blvd, Indianapolis, IN 46278
Tel.: (317) 290-5000
Sales Range: $10-24.9 Million
Emp.: 80
Chemicals Mfr
N.A.I.C.S.: 325180
Mark M. Caughey (VP)
Greg B. Stevens (Pres & CEO)
Gregg R. Bennett (CFO & Sec)

Subsidiaries:

Addenda Corporation (1)
5929 Lakeside Blvd, Indianapolis, IN 46278
Tel.: (317) 290-5007
Web Site:
http://www.addendacorporation.com
Chemical Additive Mfr
N.A.I.C.S.: 325998

Subsidiary (Non-US):

Addenda Chemical Corporation Limited (2)
Room 1011 Metro Plaza No 183 Tianhe North Road, Tianhe District, Guangzhou, 510620, China
Tel.: (86) 20 8756 2371
Web Site: http://www.addenda-china.com
Chemical Additives
N.A.I.C.S.: 325998

PAG Holdings, Inc. (1)
5929 Lakeside Blvd, Indianapolis, IN 46278
Tel.: (317) 290-5006
Web Site: http://www.pagholdings.com
Chemical Additive Mfr
N.A.I.C.S.: 325998

METALS ENGINEERING, INC.
1800 S Broadway, Green Bay, WI 54304-4904
Tel.: (920) 437-7686
Web Site:
http://www.metalsengineering.net
Year Founded: 1968
Metal Heat Treating
N.A.I.C.S.: 332811
Ted Kemen (CEO)
Paul Knoll (Pres)

METALS INC.
6701 Distribution Dr, Beltsville, MD 20705-1402
Tel.: (301) 931-1000
Web Site:
http://www.strombergmetals.com
Year Founded: 1988
Sales Range: $50-74.9 Million
Emp.: 475
Provider of Plumbing, Heating & Air-Conditioning Services
N.A.I.C.S.: 238220

Subsidiaries:

Comfort Control Inc. (1)
6711 Distribution Dr, Beltsville, MD 20705-1402
Tel.: (301) 931-9300
Web Site:
http://www.comfortcontrolbalance.com
Sales Range: $10-24.9 Million
Emp.: 40
Plumbing, Heating & Air-Conditioning Services
N.A.I.C.S.: 238220
Kathleen Bigelow (VP)

Stromberg Sheet Metal Works Inc. (1)
6701 Distribution Dr, Beltsville, MD 20705-1402
Tel.: (301) 931-1000
Web Site: http://www.strombergmetals.com
Sales Range: $25-49.9 Million
Emp.: 300
Plumbing, Heating & Air-Conditioning Services
N.A.I.C.S.: 238220

Mary Patricia Suhr (CFO)
William Gawne (COO)

METALS SERVICE CENTER INSTITUTE
4201 Euclid Ave, Rolling Meadows, IL 60008
Tel.: (847) 485-3000   IL
Web Site: http://www.msci.org
Year Founded: 1909
Sales Range: $10-24.9 Million
Emp.: 18
Retail Trade Association
N.A.I.C.S.: 813910
Kathy Spellman (VP-Bus Dev)
Rose Manfredini (VP-Membership & Events)
Monique Kaiserauer (VP-Pro Dev, Non-Dues Revenue & Tubular Products Div)
Chris Marti (VP-Data Analytics, Demand Forecasting & Exec Education)
Marc A. Schupan (Vice Chm)
Todd Fogel (Treas)
Brian R. Hedges (Vice Chm)
M. Robert Weidner III (Pres,CEO & sec)

METALTEK INTERNATIONAL
905 E St Paul Ave, Waukesha, WI 53188-3804
Tel.: (262) 544-7777   DE
Web Site: http://www.metaltek.com
Year Founded: 1980
Sales Range: $100-124.9 Million
Emp.: 1,400
Metalworking Technologies & Alloys
N.A.I.C.S.: 331511
Andrew Cope (Chm)
Robert Smickley (CEO)
Rick Danning (CFO)
Larry Blanton (VP & Gen Mgr)
E. J. Kubick (COO)
Rod Anderson (VP-Sls & Mktg)

Subsidiaries:

Bearium Metals Corporation (1)
905 E St Paul Ave, Waukesha, WI 53188
Tel.: (262) 544-7777
Web Site: http://www.metaltek.com
Fabricated Structural Metal Mfr
N.A.I.C.S.: 332312
Teresa Lisa Smith (Controller)

Carondelet Corporation (1)
8600 Commercial Blvd, Pevely, MO 63070 (100%)
Tel.: (636) 479-4499
Web Site: http://www.metaltek.com
Sales Range: $25-49.9 Million
Emp.: 200
Produces Custom Cast Products
N.A.I.C.S.: 331513

Mackson, Inc. (1)
2346 Southway Dr, Rock Hill, SC 29730
Tel.: (803) 329-6545
Web Site: http://www.macksoninc.com
Sales Range: $10-24.9 Million
Emp.: 15
Nuclear Fasteners, Tubing & Components Mfr
N.A.I.C.S.: 333248
Eric Giavobino (Pres)

Meighs Castings Ltd (1)
Campbell Road, Stoke-on-Trent, ST4 4ER, United Kingdom
Tel.: (44) 1782 418421
Sand Casting Mfr
N.A.I.C.S.: 331529

MetalTek International - MetalTek - Europe Division (1)
Campbell Rd, Stoke-on-Trent, ST4 4ER, United Kingdom
Tel.: (44) 1782 844055
Fabricated Structural Metal Mfr
N.A.I.C.S.: 332312

MetalTek International - MetalTek Energy Products Division (1)

4180 S Creek Rd, Chattanooga, TN 37406
Tel.: (855) 633-3086
Industrial Supplies Whslr
N.A.I.C.S.: 423840

MetalTek International - MetalTek Energy Solutions Division (1)
4180 S Creek Rd, Chattanooga, TN 37406
Tel.: (855) 633-3086
Industrial Supplies Whslr
N.A.I.C.S.: 423840

Oil Systems, Inc. (1)
14135 W Kostner Ln, Waukesha, WI 53151
Tel.: (262) 544-7982
Industrial Supplies Whslr
N.A.I.C.S.: 423840

SMCI Inc. (1)
4015 Drane Field Rd, Lakeland, FL 33811
Tel.: (863) 644-8432
Web Site: http://www.smci-inc.com
Sales Range: $10-24.9 Million
Emp.: 97
Fabricated Structural Metal Component Mfr
N.A.I.C.S.: 332312

Sandusky International Inc. (1)
615 W Market St, Sandusky, OH 44871
Tel.: (419) 626-5340
Web Site: http://www.sanduskyintl.com
Sales Range: $50-74.9 Million
Emp.: 150
Paper Mill Suction Rols & Industrial Centrifugal Casting Mfr
N.A.I.C.S.: 333243

Holding (Non-US):

Sandusky Limited (2)
Viewfield Estate, Glenrothes, KY6 2RQ, United Kingdom (100%)
Tel.: (44) 1592773030
Web Site: http://www.metaltek.com
Sales Range: $25-49.9 Million
Emp.: 60
Paper Mill Suction Roll & Industrial Centrifugal Casting Mfr
N.A.I.C.S.: 333243
Bob Smitka (CEO)

Southern Centrifugal, Inc. (1)
4180 S Creek Rd, Chattanooga, TN 37406
Tel.: (423) 622-4131
Industrial Supplies Whslr
N.A.I.C.S.: 423840

Wisconsin Centrifugal, Inc. (1)
905 E St Paul Ave, Waukesha, WI 53188
Tel.: (262) 544-7777
Web Site: http://www.metaltek.com
Emp.: 500
Industrial Supplies Whslr
N.A.I.C.S.: 423840
Robert Smickley (CEO)

Wisconsin Investcast Inc. (1)
661 S 12th St, Watertown, WI 53094
Tel.: (920) 261-2114
Emp.: 80
Fabricated Structural Metal Mfr
N.A.I.C.S.: 332312
Randy Altmann (Gen Mgr)

METALWORKING GROUP HOLDINGS, INC.
9070 Pippin Rd, Cincinnati, OH 45251-3174
Tel.: (513) 521-4119
Web Site:
http://www.metalworkinggroup.com
Metal Stampings & Services Provider
N.A.I.C.S.: 332322
Michael Schmitt (Pres)
Doug Watts (CFO)

METALWORKING LUBRICANTS COMPANY, INC.
25 W Silverdome Industrial Park, Pontiac, MI 48342-2994
Tel.: (248) 332-3500   MI
Web Site:
http://www.metalworkinglubricants.com
Year Founded: 1952
Sales Range: $50-74.9 Million

Emp.: 75
Lubricating Oils & Greases Mfr
N.A.I.C.S.: 424720
Robert F. Tomlinson (CEO)
James Tomlinson (VP)
Nilda Grenier (VP-Engrg)
Robert Tomlinson Jr. (Owner)

METAMORPHIC VENTURES
257 Park Ave S 6 Fl, New York, NY 10010
Tel.: (646) 794-1330
Web Site: http://www.metamorphic.vc
Emp.: 115
Venture Capital Investment Firm
N.A.I.C.S.: 523999
David Hirsch (Mng Partner)
Tara Eckert (VP-Fin)

METAPOINT PARTNERS LP
3 Centennial Dr, Peabody, MA 01960-7906
Tel.: (978) 531-4444   DE
Web Site: http://www.metapoint.com
Year Founded: 1988
Sales Range: $1-9.9 Million
Emp.: 4
Holding Company; Investment Partnership
N.A.I.C.S.: 523999
Keith C. Shaughnessy (Chm & CEO)
Stuart I. Mathews (Pres)

Subsidiaries:

Northeastern Nonwovens, Inc. (1)
7 Amarosa Dr Unit 3, Rochester, NH 03868
Tel.: (603) 332-5900
Web Site: http://www.nenonwovens.com
Sales Range: $10-24.9 Million
Emp.: 25
Industrial Non-woven Fabric & Composite Material Mfr
N.A.I.C.S.: 313230
Michael Roche (Pres & CEO)

METARESPONSE GROUP, INC.
700 W Hillsboro Blvd Ste 4-107, Deerfield Beach, FL 33441
Tel.: (954) 360-0644
Web Site:
http://www.metaresponse.com
Sales Range: $1-9.9 Million
Emp.: 12
Direct Mail Advertising & Marketing Services
N.A.I.C.S.: 541860
Jerry Whiteway (Pres)
Ali DiBlasi (VP-Mktg)

METASTAT, INC.
27 Drydock Ave 2nd Fl, Boston, MA 02210
Tel.: (617) 531-6500   NV
Web Site: http://www.metastat.com
Year Founded: 2009
Rev.: $23,300
Assets: $729,634
Liabilities: $2,278,576
Net Worth: ($1,548,942)
Earnings: ($3,181,024)
Emp.: 6
Fiscal Year-end: 02/28/18
Biotechnology Research & Development
N.A.I.C.S.: 541714
Jerome Bernard Zeldis (Chm)
Douglas A. Hamilton (Pres & CEO)

METASYS TECHNOLOGIES, INC.
3460 Summit Rdg Pkwy Ste 401, Duluth, GA 30096
Tel.: (678) 218-1600
Web Site: http://www.metasysinc.net
Sales Range: $10-24.9 Million
Emp.: 259

Professional Staffing & Information Technology Services
N.A.I.C.S.: 561311
Sandeep Gauba (Pres & CEO)

METAVERSE CORPORATION
295 Madison Ave 12th Fl, New York, NY 10017
Tel.: (917) 289-0288 DE
Year Founded: 2020
Assets: $8,181
Liabilities: $2,000
Net Worth: $6,181
Earnings: ($144)
Emp.: 4
Fiscal Year-end: 12/31/21
Investment Services
N.A.I.C.S.: 523999
Aaron McDonald (Co-CEO)
Chris Ensey (Co-CEO)
Khadija Mustafa (Vice Chm)
Weixuan Luo (CFO)
John Joyce (Chm)

METCALFE INC.
726 N Midvale Blvd, Madison, WI 53705
Tel.: (608) 238-7612
Web Site:
http://www.shopmetcalfes.com
Rev.: $13,800,000
Emp.: 125
Provider of Grocery Services
N.A.I.C.S.: 531210
Tim Metcalfe (Pres)

METCON INC.
7400 Deep Branch Rd, Pembroke, NC 28372-7707
Tel.: (910) 521-8013
Web Site: http://www.metconnc.com
Sales Range: $10-24.9 Million
Emp.: 75
Civil Engineering Services
N.A.I.C.S.: 237310
Deborah Alrad (Mgr)

METCRAFT INC.
903 E 104th St, Kansas City, MO 64131
Tel.: (816) 761-3250
Rev.: $13,000,000
Emp.: 50
Commercial & Service Industry Machinery Mfr
N.A.I.C.S.: 333310
John Cantrell (Pres & Treas)

METEC ASSET MANAGEMENT, LC
2600 Douglas Ste 800, Miami, FL 33134
Tel.: (305) 854-1711
Web Site:
http://www.themetecgroup.com
Rev.: $600,000
Emp.: 7
Administrative Management & General Management Consulting Services
N.A.I.C.S.: 541611
Eric J. Torano (Chm, CEO & Principal)

METEOR EXPRESS, INC.
875 Harbor Dr, Scottsboro, AL 35769
Tel.: (256) 218-3000
Web Site: http://www.meteorx.com
Year Founded: 2000
Rev.: $22,000,000
Emp.: 115
General Freight Trucking, Long-Distance & Truckload
N.A.I.C.S.: 484121

Lynn Buckley (Pres)
Keith Letson (Controller)
John Jeffery (Dir-Safety)
Roxanne Dawe (Mgr-Ops)

METEORA CAPITAL LLC
1200 N Federal Hwy Ste 200, Boca Raton, FL 33432
Tel.: (917) 887-5990
Emp.: 100
Investment Services
N.A.I.C.S.: 523999

METHENY CONCRETE PRODUCTS INC.
1617 S Lowery Ave, Oklahoma City, OK 73129
Tel.: (405) 947-5566
Web Site:
http://www.methenyconcrete.com
Sales Range: $10-24.9 Million
Emp.: 120
Provider of Ready-Mixed Concrete Services
N.A.I.C.S.: 327320
Richard Metheny (Pres)
Randy Dunn (VP)

METHOD ARCHITECTURE, PLLC
2118 Lamar St #200, Houston, TX 77003
Tel.: (713) 842-7500
Web Site:
http://www.methodarchitecture.com
Year Founded: 2016
Architecture, Design & Planning Services
N.A.I.C.S.: 541310
Keith Holley (Principal)
Eric Hudson (Principal)
Jake Donaldson (Mng Principal)
Vanessa Ortega (Principal)
Danny Gaitan (Mgr-Studio-Buildings)
Angel Gonzales (Mgr-Studio-Buildings)
Betzy Infante (Mgr-Studio-Landlord Svcs Interiors)
Jonathan Leon (Mgr-Studio-Buildings)
Katherine Rorie (Mgr-Studio-Architectural Interiors)
Jacqueline Rye (Mgr-Studio-Buildings)
Megan De Los Santos (Coord-Proposal)
Catrice Mays (Coord-Acctg)
Jessica McDonald (Mgr-HR)
Melissa Pasche (Mgr-Acctg)
Halie Reisinger (Coord-Mktg)
Corryn Williams (Mgr-Comm & Mktg)
Sonia Zarazua (Coord-Acctg)

METHOD3, INC.
415 St Johns Church Rd Ste 205, Camp Hill, PA 17011
Tel.: (717) 221-0825
Web Site: http://www.method3.com
Year Founded: 1998
Administrative Management & General Management Consulting Services
N.A.I.C.S.: 541611
John Laporta (Mng Partner)

METHODFACTORY, INC.
1005 N Orange Ave, Sarasota, FL 34236
Tel.: (941) 364-8161
Web Site:
http://www.methodfactory.com
Year Founded: 2000
Sales Range: $1-9.9 Million
Emp.: 40
Software Developer
N.A.I.C.S.: 513210
Steve Walter (Partner)

METHODICAL INC.
3773 Cherry Creek N Dr Ste 778, Denver, CO 80209
Tel.: (303) 720-7906
Web Site:
http://www.methodicalinc.com
Year Founded: 2002
Sales Range: $1-9.9 Million
Emp.: 14
Information Technology Service for Clinics
N.A.I.C.S.: 541512
Shem Isukh (Pres)
Sreedhar Madanapalli (VP)

METHODIST HEALTH SYSTEM
1441 N Beckley Ave, Dallas, TX 75203
Tel.: (214) 947-8181
Web Site:
http://www.methodisthealthsystem.org
Year Founded: 1927
Emp.: 5,000
Health Clinic & Hospital Operator
N.A.I.C.S.: 622110
Stephen L. Mansfield (Pres & CEO)
Pamela Stoyanoff (COO & Exec VP)
Michael O. Price (Chief Legal Officer & Exec VP)
Cheryl Flynn (Chief HR Officer & Sr VP)
Pamela G. McNutt (CIO & Sr VP)
Martin L. Koonsman (Chief Medical Officer)
Craig Bjerke (CFO & Exec VP)

Subsidiaries:

Methodist Southlake Hospital, LLC (1)
421 E State Hwy 114 Frontage Rd, Southlake, TX 76092
Tel.: (817) 865-4400
Web Site:
http://www.methodistsouthlake.com
General Medical & Surgical Hospital
N.A.I.C.S.: 622110
Bob Medlin (Chief Restructuring Officer)
June A. Lawrence (Mgr-Medical Staff Svcs)
Michael Putman (Dir-Imaging & Laboratory Svcs)

METHODIST HEALTHCARE
1211 Union Ave Ste 700, Memphis, TN 38104
Tel.: (901) 516-0791
Web Site:
http://www.methodisthealth.org
Year Founded: 1982
Sales Range: $900-999.9 Million
Emp.: 10,000
Hospital Services
N.A.I.C.S.: 622110
Cato Johnson (Sr VP-Pub Policy & Regulatory Affairs)
Chris McLean (Exec VP-Fin)
Gail Thurmond (Sr VP-Clinical Effectiveness)
Harry Durbin (Sr VP-Faith & Health)
Mark McMath (CIO & Sr VP)
Hugh Jones (Sr VP-Strategic Plng & Mktg)
Gene Fernandez (CTO)
Monica Wharton (Chief Legal Officer)
Tabrina Davis (VP-Mktg & Comm)
Naren Balasubramaniam (Chief HR Officer & Sr VP)

METHODIST HEALTHCARE MINISTRIES OF SOUTH TEXAS, INC.
4507 Medical Dr, San Antonio, TX 78229
Tel.: (210) 692-0234 TX
Web Site: http://www.mhm.org
Year Founded: 1984
Health Care Services Organization

N.A.I.C.S.: 813910
Kevin C. Moriarty (Founder)
Anthony LoBasso (CFO)
George Thomas (COO)
Marc C. Raney (Interim CEO)
Philip Brown (Sr VP-Dental Svcs)
Edward Dick (Sr VP-Integrated Health Svcs-Medical Svcs)
Brian Skop (Sr VP-Beghavioral Health Svcs)
Cindy McCloy (VP-Acctg & Controller)
Jennifer Knoulton (VP-Reg Ops)
Oanh H. Maroney-Omitade (VP-Clinical Ops)
DeAnna Bokinsky (VP-Strategic Plng & Growth)

Subsidiaries:

Methodist Healthcare System of San Antonio, Ltd. (1)
15727 Anthem Pkwy Ste 600, San Antonio, TX 78249
Tel.: (210) 575-0355
Web Site: http://www.sahealth.com
Sales Range: $800-899.9 Million
Emp.: 5,400
Hospital Operator
N.A.I.C.S.: 622110
Jaime Wesolowski (Pres & CEO)

Subsidiary (Domestic):

MHS Surgery Centers, L.P. (2)
8109 Fredericksburg Rd Ste 2, San Antonio, TX 78229
Tel.: (210) 242-7169
Emp.: 3
Healthcare Training Services
N.A.I.C.S.: 621111

Methodist Ambulatory Surgery Hospital - Northwest (2)
15727 Anthem Pkwy Ste 600, San Antonio, TX 78249
Tel.: (210) 575-0355
Web Site:
http://www.methodisthealthcare.com
Surgical Care Services
N.A.I.C.S.: 621493

Methodist Hospital Hill Country (2)
1020 S State Hwy 16, Fredericksburg, TX 78624
Tel.: (830) 997-4353
Web Site: https://sahealth.com
Sales Range: $50-74.9 Million
Emp.: 797
Health Care Srvices
N.A.I.C.S.: 622110
Clinton Kotal (CEO)

Methodist Hospital South (2)
1905 Hwy 97 E, Jourdanton, TX 78026
Tel.: (830) 769-3515
Web Site: https://www.sahealth.com
Hospital Operator
N.A.I.C.S.: 622110

Methodist Inpatient Management Group (2)
8109 Fredericksburg Rd, San Antonio, TX 78229-3311
Tel.: (210) 575-8505
Health Care Srvices
N.A.I.C.S.: 621610

Methodist Medical Center ASC, L.P. (2)
4411 Medical Dr, San Antonio, TX 78229
Tel.: (210) 575-4521
Health Care Srvices
N.A.I.C.S.: 621399

Methodist Physician Alliance (2)
8109 Fredericksburg Rd, San Antonio, TX 78229
Tel.: (210) 575-0252
Web Site:
http://www.methodistphysicianalliance.com
Health Care Srvices
N.A.I.C.S.: 621399

Methodist Stone Oak Hospital (2)
1139 E Sonterra Blvd, San Antonio, TX 78258
Tel.: (210) 638-2000
Web Site: https://sahealth.com

METHODIST HEALTHCARE MINISTRIES OF SOUTH TEXAS, INC. — U.S. PRIVATE

Methodist Healthcare Ministries of South Texas, Inc.—(Continued)
Health Care Srvices
N.A.I.C.S.: 621399
Marc Strode (CEO)

Metropolitan Methodist Hospital (2)
1310 McCullough Ave, San Antonio, TX 78212
Tel.: (210) 757-2200
Web Site: https://www.joinmethodist.com
Health Care Srvices
N.A.I.C.S.: 621399

Metropolitan Methodist Hospital, a Methodist Hospital facility (2)
1310 McCullough Ave, San Antonio, TX 78212
Tel.: (210) 757-2200
Web Site: https://sahealth.com
Health Care Srvices
N.A.I.C.S.: 621610
Tamara Peavy (Chief Nursing Officer)

Northeast Methodist Hospital (2)
12412 Judson Rd, Live Oak, TX 78233
Tel.: (210) 757-7000
Web Site: https://www.joinmethodist.com
Health Care Srvices
N.A.I.C.S.: 621399

METHODIST HOME OF THE DISTRICT OF COLUMBIA
4901 Connecticut Ave NW, Washington, DC 20008
Tel.: (202) 966-7623   DC
Web Site: http://www.methodisthomeofdc.org
Year Founded: 1889
Sales Range: $10-24.9 Million
Emp.: 167
Senior Living Services
N.A.I.C.S.: 623311
Sandy Douglass (CEO)
Diana Lowe (CFO)
Jennifer Marie Brown (Dir-Admissions & Mktg)
Mary Savoy (Dir-Health Svcs)
Jennifer Howell (Dir-Health Svcs)
Linda Moreno (Dir-Therapeutic Recreation)
Diane Heyde (Mgr-Admissions & Mktg)
Cheryl Shreiner (Program Dir)
Karen Fryer (Dir-Resident Svcs)
Karen Ross (Mgr-Assisted Living Nurse)

METHODIST HOMES OF ALABAMA & NORTHWEST FLORIDA
1520 Cooper Hill Rd, Birmingham, AL 35210
Tel.: (205) 951-2442   AL
Web Site: http://www.methodisthomes.org
Year Founded: 1956
Sales Range: $25-49.9 Million
Emp.: 923
Elder Care Services
N.A.I.C.S.: 623312
Christopher W. Tomlin (Pres & CEO)
Michael D. Giles (COO, Gen Counsel & Sr VP)
Regina T. Lawler (VP & Dir-IT)
Vicki H. Jackson (VP & Dir-HR)
Sherri Easdon (Dir-PR)
Julie Marcus (Dir-Mktg & Admissions)
Liz Prosch (VP-Quality & Mission Integration)
Bruce W. Akins (CFO)

METHODIST HOSPITAL
1205 N Elm St, Henderson, KY 42420
Tel.: (270) 827-7700
Web Site: http://www.methodisthospital.net
Year Founded: 1944
Health Care Srvices
N.A.I.C.S.: 622110
Dane Shields (Chm)
Linda White (Vice Chm)
Garland Certain (Treas)
Steve Austin (Sec)
Benny Nolen (Pres & CEO)
Jack Hogan (VP-Ancillary Svcs)
Stephanie Jenkins (VP-Ops & Strategy)
Ty Kahle (VP-HR)
David Massengale (CFO & VP)
Kristi Melton (VP-Nursing)

Subsidiaries:

Methodist Hospital Union County (1)
4604 US Hwy 60 W, Morganfield, KY 42437
Tel.: (270) 389-5000
Emp.: 170
Health Care Srvices
N.A.I.C.S.: 622110
Benny Nolen (Pres & CEO)

METHODIST HOSPITAL FOUNDATION
8701 W Dodge Rd Ste 450, Omaha, NE 68114
Tel.: (402) 354-4825
Web Site: https://www.methodisthospitalfoundation.org
Year Founded: 1977
Health Care Srvices
N.A.I.C.S.: 621610

METHODIST HOSPITAL OF SOUTHERN CALIFORNIA
300 W Huntington Dr, Arcadia, CA 91007
Tel.: (626) 898-8000   CA
Web Site: http://www.methodisthospital.org
Year Founded: 1937
Sales Range: $250-299.9 Million
Emp.: 2,176
Health Care Srvices
N.A.I.C.S.: 621610
B. S. Chandrasekhar (Chief Medical Officer)
Clifford R. Daniels (Chief Strategy Officer & Sr VP)
Steven A. Sisto (COO & Sr VP)
William Lewis (Chm)
Dan F. Ausman (Pres & CEO)
James Romo (Vice Chm)
E. DeWayne McMullin (Sec)

METHODIST REHABILITATION CENTER
1350 E Woodrow Wilson Ave, Jackson, MS 39216
Tel.: (601) 981-2611   MS
Web Site: http://www.methodistonline.org
Year Founded: 1969
Sales Range: $50-74.9 Million
Physical Rehabilitation Services
N.A.I.C.S.: 622310
Walter S. Weems (Chm)
David L. McMillin (Vice Chm)
Michael A. Reddix (Sec)
Mark A. Adams (Pres & CEO)
Mike P. Sturdivant Jr. (Treas)

METHODIST SERVICES INC.
221 NE Glen Oak Ave, Peoria, IL 61636
Tel.: (309) 672-5914   IL
Year Founded: 1981
Sales Range: $10-24.9 Million
Property Rental Services
N.A.I.C.S.: 531390
Robert Quin (CFO & Treas)
Peter Johnsen (Chm)
Deborah Simon (Pres & CEO)

METHODS MACHINE TOOLS INC.
65 Union Ave, Sudbury, MA 01776-2245
Tel.: (978) 443-5388
Web Site: http://www.methodsmachine.com
Year Founded: 1970
Sales Range: $25-49.9 Million
Emp.: 300
Machine Tools Sales & Service
N.A.I.C.S.: 423830
Scott McIver (Chm)
Stephen L. Bond (Mgr-Natl Sls)
Dale Hedberg (VP-Ops)
James Previti (Product Mgr-YASDA)
James Hanson (COO-Methods 3D, Inc.)
Matthew Sheehan (Dir-Fin Svcs)
Kevin Sarro (Dir-Fin)
Sergio Tondato (Product Mgr-Nakamura-Tome)
Jon Dobosenski (Gen Mgr-State of the Art Memphis Tech Center)
Mark Wright (Pres & CEO)

METIER, LTD.
2611 Jefferson Davis Hwy Ste 9050, Arlington, VA 22202
Tel.: (703) 412-0120
Web Site: http://www.metier.com
Sales Range: $1-9.9 Million
Emp.: 50
Technology Project Analysis & Management Software Mfr
N.A.I.C.S.: 513210
Douglas D. Clark (CEO)
Sandra K. Richardson (CMO)
Amy E. Vaccari (COO)
Anthony Comfort (Dir-Pro Svcs)

METISENTRY LLC
17 S Main St Ste 201, Akron, OH 44308
Tel.: (303) 294-4910
Web Site: http://metisentry.com
Year Founded: 2006
Software Developer
N.A.I.C.S.: 513210
Marling Engle (Pres)
Jeff Schafer (Chief Revenue Officer)
Mike Fisher (CEO)

Subsidiaries:

WillCo Technologies, Inc. (1)
4033 Central St, Kansas City, MO 64111
Tel.: (816) 842-6262
Web Site: http://www.willcotech.com
Software Publisher
N.A.I.C.S.: 513210

METOVA, INC.
3301 Aspen Grove Dr Ste 301, Franklin, TN 37067
Tel.: (615) 771-0975
Web Site: http://www.metova.com
Sales Range: $1-9.9 Million
Emp.: 21
Mobile Phone Application Developer
N.A.I.C.S.: 513210
Dave Lane (Dir-Dev)
Dave McAllister (Pres)
Kevin Lind (Dir-Bus Dev)
Nick Sinas (Dir-Tech)
Stephanie Funk (VP-Creative Svcs-Fayetteville)
Tim Mushen (Exec VP-Sls & Mktg)

METPAR CORP.
95 State St, Westbury, NY 11590
Tel.: (516) 333-2600   NY
Web Site: http://www.metpar.com
Year Founded: 1952
Sales Range: $125-149.9 Million
Emp.: 75
Toilet Partitions, Shower Stalls & Dressing Compartments Mfr
N.A.I.C.S.: 332999
David Bonade (CFO & Dir-Fin)
Vincent Salierno (VP-Ops)
Brian Pechar (Mgr-Sls-Natl)
Matthew Russell (Dir-Engrg & IT)

METRA ELECTRONICS CORPORATION
460 Walker St, Holly Hill, FL 32117
Tel.: (386) 257-1186
Web Site: http://www.metraonline.com
Year Founded: 1982
Sales Range: $25-49.9 Million
Emp.: 532
Mfr of Motor Vehicle Parts & Accessories
N.A.I.C.S.: 336390
Jake Bates (Mgr-Sls)
Carlos Muniz (Reg Mgr-Sls)
Colin Ehrhardt (Dir-Res & Tech)
Mauricio Soto (Mgr-Sls-Intl)

METRALITE INDUSTRIES INC.
13270 34th Ave, Flushing, NY 11354
Tel.: (718) 961-1770
Sales Range: $10-24.9 Million
Emp.: 150
Glass & Glazing Work
N.A.I.C.S.: 238150
Jeff Silverstein (Pres)
Goran Stojanovic (Mgr-Ops)

METRIC & MULTISTANDARD COMPONENTS CORPORATION
120 Old Saw Mill River Rd, Hawthorne, NY 10532-1515
Tel.: (914) 769-5020   NY
Web Site: http://www.metricmcc.com
Year Founded: 1963
Sales Range: $10-24.9 Million
Emp.: 125
Wholesale Distributor of Fasteners, Industrial Nuts, Bolts, Screws & Hand Tools; Machinists Precision Measuring Tools & Cutting Tools
N.A.I.C.S.: 423840
Rosemary Hacaj (Exec VP)
Ivo Peske (Gen Mgr)
Mary Marello (Asst Mgr-Sls)
William Gwynn (Acct Mgr)
John Hayes (CFO)

Subsidiaries:

MCG Metric Components GmbH (1)
Halstenbeker Weg 96, 25462, Rellingen, Germany
Tel.: (49) 4101 400815
Fastener & Industrial Component Distr
N.A.I.C.S.: 423710

METRIC ENGINEERING INC.
13940 SW 136th St Ste 200, Miami, FL 33186
Tel.: (305) 235-5098
Web Site: http://www.metriceng.com
Rev.: $16,400,000
Emp.: 260
Engineeering Services
N.A.I.C.S.: 541330
Silvia Benitez (Mgr-HR)
Raul Driggs (Dir-Tech & Sr Project Mgr)

METRIC MACHINING
1425 S Vineyard Ave, Ontario, CA 91761
Tel.: (909) 947-9222
Web Site: http://www.metricorp.com
Sales Range: $25-49.9 Million
Emp.: 150
Machine Tools, Metal Cutting Type
N.A.I.C.S.: 333517

COMPANIES

David Parker *(Pres)*

METRIC TEST EQUIPMENT, INC.
25841 Industrial Blvd Ste 200, Hayward, CA 94545
Tel.: (510) 264-0887
Web Site: http://www.metrictest.com
Year Founded: 1992
Sales Range: $25-49.9 Million
Emp.: 70
Electronic Test Equipment Whslr
N.A.I.C.S.: 423690
Mike Clarke *(CEO)*

METRICA INC.
100 NE Loop 410 Ste 520, San Antonio, TX 78216
Tel.: (210) 822-2310
Web Site: http://www.metricanet.com
Sales Range: $10-24.9 Million
Emp.: 100
Computer Related Consulting Services
N.A.I.C.S.: 541512
Jonathan Fast *(VP)*
Mark Beckerman *(Mgr-IT)*
Gary Whitney *(CFO)*

METRICSTREAM, INC.
2479 E Bayshore Rd Ste 260, Palo Alto, CA 94303
Tel.: (650) 620-2900
Web Site:
   http://www.metricstream.com
Year Founded: 1999
Sales Range: $10-24.9 Million
Emp.: 70,000
Business Software Developer
N.A.I.C.S.: 513210
Gunjan Sinha *(Exec Chm)*
Gaurav Kapoor *(Founder & Co-CEO)*
Vidya Phalke *(Chief Innovation & Cloud Officer)*
Brenda L. Boultwood *(Sr VP-Industry Solutions)*
Steven R. Springsteel *(CFO)*
Mikael Hagstroem *(Pres)*
Anindo Banerjea *(Sr VP-Engrg)*
Margaret Costella *(VP & Deputy Gen Counsel)*
Mark Johnston *(VP-Internal Audit)*
Peter Brooks *(VP-Risk Mgmt & Corp Audit)*
Venky Yerrapotu *(Exec VP-Professional Svcs & Engrg)*
Wayne Whittingham *(VP-Corp Quality)*
Jessica Zhou *(Chief Legal Officer)*
Rohit Bedi *(Exec VP-Partnerships & Alliances)*
Vasant Balasubramanian *(Sr VP-Product Mgmt)*
Susan Palm *(Sr VP-Industry Solutions)*
Prasad Sabbineni *(Co-CEO)*

Subsidiaries:

MetricStream-Asia Regional Office (1)
Amr tech park 4b, 23 & 24 hongasandra village ho, Bengaluru, 560 068, Karnataka, India
Tel.: (91) 8040496363
Web Site: http://www.metricstream.com
Emp.: 1,200
Software Devolepment
N.A.I.C.S.: 513210
Shankar Baskaran *(Mng Dir)*

MetricStream-Atlanta Regional Office (1)
3901 Roswell Rd NE Ste 337, Marietta, GA 30062
Tel.: (770) 578-7580
Web Site: http://www.metricstream.com
Software Developer
N.A.I.C.S.: 513210

TBD Networks, Inc. (1)
2 N 1st St Fl 2, San Jose, CA 95113
Tel.: (408) 278-1590
Web Site: http://www.tbdnetworks.com
Custom Computer Programming Services
N.A.I.C.S.: 541511

METRIX INC.
20975 Swenson Dr # 400, Waukesha, WI 53186
Tel.: (262) 798-8560   WI
Year Founded: 1980
Sales Range: $10-24.9 Million
Emp.: 50
Provider of Business Oriented Computer Software Services
N.A.I.C.S.: 513210
Larry Laux *(CEO)*

METRO APPLIANCES & MORE
5313 S Mingo Rd, Tulsa, OK 74146-5736
Tel.: (918) 622-7692
Web Site:
   http://www.metroappliancesandmore.com
Year Founded: 1975
Sales Range: $25-49.9 Million
Emp.: 146
Supplier of Electrical Appliances
N.A.I.C.S.: 423620

Subsidiaries:

Metro Appliances & More (1)
5571 N Main St, Joplin, MO 64801
Tel.: (417) 782-1008
Web Site:
   http://www.metroappliancesandmore.com
Sales Range: $25-49.9 Million
Emp.: 14
Supplier of Electrical Appliances
N.A.I.C.S.: 423620
R. John Anderson *(Gen Mgr)*

METRO AVIATION, INC.
1214 Hawn Ave, Shreveport, LA 71107
Tel.: (318) 698-5200
Web Site:
   http://www.metroaviation.com
Year Founded: 1982
Sales Range: $10-24.9 Million
Emp.: 500
Helicopter Chartering & Flight Training Services; Air Ambulance Services; Helicopter Maintenance & Completion Services
N.A.I.C.S.: 621999
Thomas Michael Stanberry *(Pres & CEO)*
Kenny Morrow *(COO)*
Milton Geltz *(Mng Dir)*
Becky Ross *(Dir-Transport Bus Svcs)*
Ed Stockhausen *(Dir-Safety)*
Ann Lowell *(Mgr-OCC Field Trng)*
Jim Arthur *(Dir-Ops)*
Stewart Corbin *(Mgr-Customer Comm Center Trng)*

Subsidiaries:

Paradigm Aerospace Corporation (1)
226 Airport Rd, Mount Pleasant, PA 15666
Tel.: (724) 887-4413
Web Site: http://www.paradigm-aero.com
Sales Range: $10-24.9 Million
Emp.: 50
Helicopter Completion & Customizing Services
N.A.I.C.S.: 336413
Ed Wahl *(Dir-Maintenance)*
Dayna Cortazzo *(Dir-Admin)*

METRO CREDIT UNION
200 Revere Beach Pkwy, Chelsea, MA 02150
Tel.: (617) 889-7727   MA
Web Site: http://www.metrocu.org
Year Founded: 1926

Sales Range: $50-74.9 Million
Emp.: 380
Credit Union
N.A.I.C.S.: 522130
Thomas Nadeau *(COO-Lending, Retail Svcs & HR)*
Eileen Danahey *(CFO & COO)*
Michael McGovern *(CTO & Sr VP)*
Betsy Mulvey *(Sr VP-HR)*
Keith Pequeno *(CMO & Sr VP)*
Kevin Gannon *(Mgr-Mortgage Originations)*
Dawn Dawson *(VP-Mortgage Originations & Ops)*

METRO CYCLES OF ATLANTA INC.
631 Thornton Rd, Lithia Springs, GA 30122
Tel.: (770) 941-9050
Web Site:
   http://www.metrocycles.com
Rev.: $11,000,000
Emp.: 25
Motorcycles
N.A.I.C.S.: 441227
Bob Haehn *(Pres)*
Angie Wheeler *(Office Mgr)*

METRO DEVELOPMENT GROUP, LLC
2502 N Rocky Point Dr Ste 1050, Tampa, FL 33607
Tel.: (813) 288-8078
Web Site: http://www.mdgflorida.com
Year Founded: 2004
Sales Range: $1-9.9 Million
Emp.: 20
Land Subdivision, Development, Investment, Management & Advisory Services
N.A.I.C.S.: 237210
John M. Ryan *(Founder & CEO)*
Greg Singleton *(Pres)*
Rob Ahrens *(Mng Dir-Land Acq & Sls)*
Mike Lawson *(Mng Dir-Land Dev)*

METRO ELECTRIC INC.
1901 Industrial Dr, McAllen, TX 78504
Tel.: (956) 686-2323
Web Site: http://www.metroelectric-rgv.com
Sales Range: $10-24.9 Million
Emp.: 200
General Electrical Contractor
N.A.I.C.S.: 238210
Jack L. Gerdes *(Pres)*
Michael Gerdes *(VP)*

METRO FILM EXPRESS INC.
875 Fee Fee Rd, Maryland Heights, MO 63043
Tel.: (314) 993-8888
Sales Range: $10-24.9 Million
Emp.: 20
General Freight Trucking, Local
N.A.I.C.S.: 484110
Pats Heartwig *(Mgr)*
Karen Rugg *(VP)*
John Whaley *(VP)*
Tom Whaley *(Pres)*

METRO FORD SALES, INC.
3601 State St, Schenectady, NY 12304
Tel.: (518) 382-1010   DE
Web Site:
   http://www.metrofordsales.com
Year Founded: 1980
Sales Range: $100-124.9 Million
Emp.: 130
Retailer of New & Used Automobiles
N.A.I.C.S.: 441110

David Dariano *(Gen Mgr)*
William Rickard *(Mgr-Concern Resolution)*
Dave Carach *(Gen Mgr-Sls)*
Howard Bisner *(Mgr-Truck Sls)*
Nick Saccone *(Mgr-Svc)*
James Rosamino *(Mgr-Used Car Sls)*
James A. McHale *(Mgr-Parts)*
James Tibbetts *(Mgr-Sls)*
William A. Thorp Jr. *(Dir-Parts & Svc)*

METRO FORD, INC.
9000 NW 7th Ave, Miami, FL 33150-2308
Tel.: (305) 751-9711   DE
Web Site: http://www.metroford.com
Year Founded: 1983
Sales Range: $100-124.9 Million
Emp.: 100
Retailer of New & Used Automobiles
N.A.I.C.S.: 441110
Lombardo Perez *(VP)*
Barby Terzian *(Controller)*
Lino Castro *(Mgr-Fin)*

METRO FORD-LINCOLN-MERCURY
1000 Barnes Crossing Rd, Tupelo, MS 38804
Tel.: (662) 841-1000
Web Site:
   http://www.metrofordautosales.com
Sales Range: $10-24.9 Million
Emp.: 42
Car Whslr
N.A.I.C.S.: 441110
Beyrone Erby *(Gen Mgr)*

METRO FUEL INC.
807 Rainbow Dr, Waterloo, IA 50701
Tel.: (319) 236-0997
Sales Range: $25-49.9 Million
Emp.: 30
Provider of Convenience Store & Gasoline Services
N.A.I.C.S.: 457210
Jessie Sorensen *(Office Mgr)*
Norris S. Annis II *(Pres)*

METRO IMPORTS, INC.
13775 Brookpark Rd, Brook Park, OH 44142
Tel.: (216) 267-7000
Web Site:
   http://www.metrotoyato.com
Year Founded: 1969
Sales Range: $10-24.9 Million
Emp.: 90
Car Whslr
N.A.I.C.S.: 441110
Jerald Schneider *(Pres)*

METRO LABEL CORP.
3366 Miller Park Dr S, Garland, TX 75042-7771
Tel.: (972) 272-8689
Year Founded: 1998
Sales Range: $10-24.9 Million
Emp.: 75
Custom Label Mfr
N.A.I.C.S.: 322220
Scott Metico *(Mgr-IT)*
Leonard J. Suazo *(CFO)*

METRO LUMBER WHOLESALE CO. INC.
3717 Miller Park Dr, Garland, TX 75042
Tel.: (972) 494-2516
Sales Range: $10-24.9 Million
Emp.: 20
Lumber, Plywood & Millwork
N.A.I.C.S.: 423310
Lou Mills *(Pres)*
Ronna Vojnovich *(Mgr-Acctg)*

METRO MEDICAL SUPPLY INC.

Metro Medical Supply Inc.—(Continued)

METRO MEDICAL SUPPLY INC.
200 Cumberland Bend, Nashville, TN 37228-1804
Tel.: (615) 312-9800 TN
Web Site:
http://www.metromedical.com
Year Founded: 1984
Sales Range: $25-49.9 Million
Emp.: 150
Supplier of Drugs, Proprietaries & Sundries
N.A.I.C.S.: 456199

METRO METALS NORTHWEST INC.
5611 NE Columbia Blvd, Portland, OR 97218
Tel.: (503) 287-8861
Web Site:
http://www.metrometalsnw.com
Year Founded: 1997
Rev.: $22,300,000
Emp.: 150
Metal Scrap & Waste Materials Services
N.A.I.C.S.: 423930
Victor Winkler (Pres)
Dan Jacobson (CFO)
Steve Zusman (Exec VP)

Subsidiaries:

All Recycling, Inc. (1)
1775 W Wesley Ave, Englewood, CO 80110
Tel.: (303) 922-7722
Web Site: http://www.allrecyclinginc.com
Sales Range: $10-24.9 Million
Emp.: 50
Refuse System
N.A.I.C.S.: 562920
Craig Urhig (Pres)

METRO MOLD & DESIGN, INC.
20600 County Rd 81, Rogers, MN 55374-9567
Tel.: (763) 428-4690
Web Site: http://www.metromold.com
Sales Range: $10-24.9 Million
Emp.: 200
Plastic Injection Molds, Injection Molded Parts & Precision Machining Services
N.A.I.C.S.: 333511
Greg Heinemann (Pres)

Subsidiaries:

Metro Mold & Design - ICM Plastics (1)
20600 County Rd 81, Rogers, MN 55374
Tel.: (763) 428-8310
Web Site: http://www.metomold.com
Emp.: 250
Injection Molding Of Plastics
N.A.I.C.S.: 326199
Donna Luehring (Supvr-Quality Assurance)
Travis Rosenbaum (Mgr-Pur)

METRO MOTOR GROUP
1667 Hartford Ave, Johnston, RI 02919
Tel.: (401) 351-6600
Web Site:
http://www.metromotorgroup.com
Rev.: $10,192,000
Emp.: 65
New & Used Car Dealers
N.A.I.C.S.: 441110
Andrea Hochstrasser (Controller)
Neil Rowey (Mgr-Corp Fixed Ops)
Keith Kramer (Asst Mgr)
Michael Doyle (Gen Mgr)

METRO NEWS SERVICE INC.
150 Dalton Dr, Desoto, TX 75115
Tel.: (972) 227-6170

Web Site: http://www.metro-news.com
Year Founded: 1975
Rev.: $14,000,000
Emp.: 10
Provider of News Services
N.A.I.C.S.: 516210
Horace W. Southward (Pres)
Eric Southward (VP-Mktg)
Chris Southward (VP-Ops)

METRO PAVIA HEALTH SYSTEM, INC.
101 San Patricio Ave, Guaynabo, PR 00968
Tel.: (787) 620-9770
Web Site: http://www.metropavia.com
Specialty Hospitals
N.A.I.C.S.: 622310
Miguel Salva (Mgr-Matls)

Subsidiaries:

Grupo HIMA-San Pablo, Inc. (1)
100 Avenida Luis Munoz Marin, Caguas, PR 00726
Tel.: (787) 653-3434
Web Site: http://www.himapr.com
Rev.: $394,800,000
Emp.: 4,500
General Medical & Surgical Hospitals
N.A.I.C.S.: 622110
Joaquin Rodriguez Sr. (Pres)
Miguel Rivera (VP-Fin)

METRO PAVING CORPORATION
5470 Lafayette Pl, Hyattsville, MD 20781
Tel.: (301) 454-8111
Web Site: http://www.metropaving.net
Rev.: $14,000,000
Emp.: 105
Highway Street & Bridge Construction
N.A.I.C.S.: 237310
Mitchell Otero (Pres)
Anitra Robinson (Controller)
Addie Rodrigues (Mgr-Acctg)

METRO PRINTED PRODUCTS, INC.
1001 Commerce Pkwy S Dr H, Greenwood, IN 46143
Tel.: (317) 885-0077
Web Site:
http://www.metroprintedproduct.com
Sales Range: $1-9.9 Million
Emp.: 5
Printed Products Distr
N.A.I.C.S.: 323111
Tim Burk (Pres)

Subsidiaries:

Promote For Less (1)
5555 W Linebaugh Ave Ste 300, Tampa, FL 33624-5090
Tel.: (813) 962-8882
Web Site: http://www.promoteforless.com
Printing & Promotional Marketing Services
N.A.I.C.S.: 541613
Paul Beatty (Founder & Pres)

METRO PUBLIC ADJUSTMENT, INC.
3551 Bristol Pike, Bensalem, PA 19020
Tel.: (215) 633-8000
Web Site: http://www.metropa.com
Rev.: $3,800,000
Emp.: 23
Claims Adjusting
N.A.I.C.S.: 524291
Steven J. McCaffrey (Pres)

Subsidiaries:

Dimont & Associates, LLC (1)
18451 Dallas Pkwy Ste 200, Dallas, TX 75287
Tel.: (972) 428-6900

Web Site: http://www.dimont.com
Hazard Insurance Claims Management Services
N.A.I.C.S.: 524291
Albert Strausser (CFO)
Dick Volentine (Gen Counsel)
Fran Weischel (Dir-Client Rels)
Darcy Stennes (Sr Mgr-Client Relationship)
Collin Harbour (Dir-Bus Dev)
Rick Lewellen (Dir-Natl Sls)
Teresa Epperson (Dir-HR)
Judi Ray (Mgr-Client Rels)
Mark Siratt (Mgr-Client Rels)
Mark Lehner (Mgr-Client Rels)
Anne Foltz (Mgr-Mktg)
Lyne' Donovan (Controller)
Tom Bradham (COO)
Tom Stover (Chief Solutions Officer)
Rick Hart (Sr VP)
Scott Arnold (Sr VP-Fin & Admin)
Nancy Mellon (Sr Dir-Client Dev)
Laura MacIntyre (Pres)

METRO PUBLISHING, INC.
550 S 1st St, San Jose, CA 95113
Tel.: (408) 200-1300 CA
Web Site: http://www.metronews.com
Year Founded: 1978
Rev.: $22,500,000
Emp.: 75
Publisher of Newspapers
N.A.I.C.S.: 513110
Chris Janz (Mng Dir)
Mark Hawthorne (Publr-Victoria)

Subsidiaries:

Metro Newspapers (1)
550 S 1st St, San Jose, CA 95113
Tel.: (408) 298-8000
Web Site: http://www.metroactive.com
Sales Range: Less than $1 Million
Emp.: 80
Online Service Providers
N.A.I.C.S.: 513110
Dan Pulcrano (CEO & Editor)
Petra Sherey (Controller)
Harry Allison (Mgr-Pro)
Kara Brown (Dir-Design)
John Haugh (Mgr-Adv Sls)
Jorge Lopez (Mgr-Circulation)
Gary Sunbury (Mgr-Circulation)
Maree Thurston (Coord-Promos)

Unit (Domestic):

Gilroy Dispatch (2)
PO Box 22365, Gilroy, CA 95021-2365
Tel.: (408) 842-6400
Web Site: http://www.gilroydispatch.com
Daily Newspaper
N.A.I.C.S.: 513110

Good Times (2)
1101 Pacific Ave 320, Santa Cruz, CA 95060
Tel.: (831) 458-1100
Web Site: http://www.gtweekly.com
Rev.: $4,050,000
Emp.: 30
Newspaper Publishers
N.A.I.C.S.: 513110
Ron Slack (Publr)
Jeanne Howard (Publr)

Hollister Free Lance (2)
356th St PO Box 1417, Hollister, CA 95024-1417
Tel.: (831) 637-5566
Web Site:
http://www.sanbenitocountytoday.com
Daily Newspaper
N.A.I.C.S.: 513110

Morgan Hill Times (2)
17500 Depot Street Ste, Morgan Hill, CA 95037-3669
Tel.: (408) 842-6400
Web Site: http://www.morganhilltimes.com
Publishing Newspapers
N.A.I.C.S.: 513110
Cindy Courter (Mgr-Ad Svcs)
Chuck Gibbs (Mgr-Production & IT)

METRO REALTY
2121 E Coast Hwy Ste 100, Corona Del Mar, CA 92625

Tel.: (949) 720-9422
Web Site:
http://www.metroestates.com
Sales Range: $50-74.9 Million
Emp.: 50
Real Estate Agents & Managers
N.A.I.C.S.: 531210
Darrell Pash (Owner & Pres)
Jonie Smith (Office Mgr)
Brad Coleman (Owner & VP)

METRO SALES, INC.
1620 E 78th St, Minneapolis, MN 55423-4645
Tel.: (612) 861-4000 MN
Web Site: http://www.metrosales.com
Year Founded: 1969
Sales Range: $25-49.9 Million
Emp.: 240
Office Equipment Distr
N.A.I.C.S.: 423420
Jerry Mathwig (Founder & Pres)

METRO SIGN & AWNING
170 Lorum St, Tewksbury, MA 01876
Tel.: (978) 851-2424
Web Site: http://www.metrosign.net
Year Founded: 2004
Sales Range: $10-24.9 Million
Emp.: 25
Plastics Product Mfr
N.A.I.C.S.: 326199
Brian A. Chipman (Pres)
Susan Koren (Office Mgr)
Thomas E. Dunn (VP)

METRO TRAILER LEASING INC.
100 Metro Pkwy, Pelham, AL 35124
Tel.: (205) 985-8701
Web Site:
http://www.metroministorage.com
Rev.: $12,000,000
Emp.: 15
Industrial Truck Rental
N.A.I.C.S.: 532490
Edwin B. Lumpkin (Founder & Pres)

METRO USA INC.
120 Broadway Ste 220, New York, NY 10271
Tel.: (212) 256-9268
Web Site: http://www.metro.us
Sales Range: $10-24.9 Million
Emp.: 70
Newspaper Publisher Services
N.A.I.C.S.: 511110
Yggers Mortensen (CEO)

Subsidiaries:

Metro Philadelphia (1)
Graham Bldg 30 S 15th St 14th Fl, Philadelphia, PA 19102
Tel.: (215) 717-2600
Web Site: http://www.metro.us
Sales Range: $10-24.9 Million
Emp.: 25
Newspaper Publishers
N.A.I.C.S.: 513110
Yggers Mortinson (CEO & Publr)

METRO VALLEY PAINTING CORP.
659 E Main St, Mesa, AZ 85203
Tel.: (480) 461-8181
Web Site:
http://www.metrovalley.com
Sales Range: $1-4.9 Billion
Emp.: 40
Painting & Paper Hanging
N.A.I.C.S.: 238320
Michael Dudley (Pres)

METRO WASTE AUTHORITY
300 E Locust St, Des Moines, IA 50309
Tel.: (515) 244-0021

COMPANIES

Web Site: http://www.mwatoday.com
Year Founded: 1969
Sales Range: $10-24.9 Million
Emp.: 70
Sanitary Landfill Operator
N.A.I.C.S.: 562212
Jeff Dworek *(Dir-Ops)*
Mike Fairchild *(Mgr-Ops)*

METRO WASTEWATER RECLAMATION DISTRICT
6450 York St, Denver, CO 80229
Tel.: (303) 286-3000
Web Site:
http://www.metrowastewater.com
Year Founded: 1961
Sales Range: $75-99.9 Million
Emp.: 400
Sewage Treatment Services
N.A.I.C.S.: 221320
Margaret R. Medellin *(Dir)*
Gerald Schulte *(Treas)*
Peter Baertlein *(Sec)*

METRO WELLNESS AND COMMUNITY CENTERS
3251 3rd Ave N Ste 125, Saint Petersburg, FL 33713
Tel.: (727) 321-3854
Web Site:
http://www.metrotampabay.org
Sales Range: $25-49.9 Million
Emp.: 87
Wellness & Community Centers
N.A.I.C.S.: 621498
Lorraine Langlois *(CEO)*
Priya Rajkumar *(VP)*
Kathleen Farrell *(Sec)*
Michelle Joseph *(CFO)*
Julia Delmerico *(Dir-Case Mgmt)*
Chris Rudisill *(Dir-LGBT Community Center Svcs)*
Kirsty Gutierrez *(Dir-Re-Entry & Health Svcs)*

METRO WIRE & CABLE CO
6636 Metropolitan Pkwy, Sterling Heights, MI 48312-1030
Tel.: (586) 264-3050
Web Site: http://www.metrowire.net
Rev.: $14,000,000
Emp.: 26
Wire & Cable
N.A.I.C.S.: 423610
Donald D. Ezop *(Pres)*
Al Martins *(Acct Mgr)*
Nathan Tallman *(Dir-Dev & Mktg)*

METRO-GOLDWYN-MAYER INC.
245 N Beverly Dr, Beverly Hills, CA 90210
Tel.: (310) 449-3000 DE
Web Site: http://www.mgm.com
Year Founded: 1924
Sales Range: $1-4.9 Billion
Emp.: 280
Holding Company; Motion Picture, Television, Home Video & Theatrical Production & Distribution Services
N.A.I.C.S.: 551112
Kenneth J. Kay *(CFO)*
Chris Ottinger *(Pres-Worldwide Television Distr & Acq)*
Steve Stark *(Pres-Television Production & Dev)*
Nancy Tellem *(Exec Dir)*
Kevin C. Conroy *(Pres-New Platforms & Digital)*
Kenneth J. Kay *(CFO)*
Mark Burnett *(Chm-Worldwide Television Grp)*
Mina Patel *(VP-TV Distr-Worldwide)*
Todd Parkin *(Sr VP & Gen Mgr-Domestic Networks)*
Simon Graty *(Exec VP-Worldwide Branded Svcs)*
Annie Khostegyan *(Sr VP-Domestic Television Distr)*
Kristin Cotich *(Exec VP-Comm-Worldwide)*
Chris Brearton *(COO)*
Katie Martin Kelley *(Chief Comm Officer)*
David Luner *(Exec VP-Worldwide Television Mktg)*
Michael Fisk *(Exec VP-Film Mktg)*
Val Aveni *(VP-Social Media & Brand Strategy)*
Stephen Bruno *(CMO)*
Rola Bauer *(Pres-Television Productions-Intl)*
Klaudia Bermudez-Key *(Sr VP-Intl TV Distr-Latin America & US Hispanic)*
Matt Vassallo *(Exec VP-Intl TV Distr-Asia Pacific & Latin America)*

Subsidiaries:

Evolution Film & Tape, Inc. (1)
3310 W Vanowen St, Burbank, CA 91505
Tel.: (818) 260-0300
Web Site: http://www.evolutionusa.com
Motion Picture & Video Production
N.A.I.C.S.: 512110
Douglas Ross *(Founder & Pres)*

METROCORP HOLDINGS INC.
601 Walnut St Ste 200, Philadelphia, PA 19106
Tel.: (215) 564-7700
Web Site: http://www.phillymag.com
Year Founded: 1991
Sales Range: $10-24.9 Million
Emp.: 105
Provider of Periodical Services
N.A.I.C.S.: 541330
Herbert D. Lipson *(Chm & Pres)*
Deborah Cassell *(Dir-Product)*
Ashley Patterson *(Publr)*

Subsidiaries:

Metrocorp Corporation (1)
1818 Maket St 36th Fl, Philadelphia, PA 19103-3638
Tel.: (215) 564-7700
Web Site: http://www.metrocorp.com
Provider of Periodical Services
N.A.I.C.S.: 541330

METROFUSER LLC
475 Division St, Elizabeth, NJ 07201
Tel.: (908) 245-2100
Web Site: http://www.metrofuser.com
Year Founded: 2003
Rev.: $4,600,000
Emp.: 38
Repair & Maintenance Services
N.A.I.C.S.: 811210
Eric Katz *(Co-Pres)*
Ken Lang *(Dir-Sls)*
Mark Makuch *(Mgr-Ops)*
Will DeMuth *(Co-Pres)*

METROLINA STEEL INC.
2601 Westinghouse Blvd, Charlotte, NC 28273
Tel.: (704) 598-7007
Web Site:
http://www.metrolinasteel.com
Year Founded: 1977
Rev.: $12,711,682
Emp.: 60
Provider of Steel Products
N.A.I.C.S.: 423510
Thomas Hurt *(Pres)*
Terry Ginger *(Mgr-QA)*

METROLINE INC.
2250 Meijer Dr, Troy, MI 48084
Tel.: (248) 288-7000
Web Site:
http://www.metrolinedirect.com
Sales Range: $10-24.9 Million
Emp.: 60
Electronic Parts & Equipment Whslr
N.A.I.C.S.: 423690
Irina Mac *(Controller)*

METROMEDIA COMPANY
810 7th Ave Fl 29, New York, NY 10019
Tel.: (212) 606-4400 NJ
Year Founded: 1986
Sales Range: $1-4.9 Billion
Emp.: 29,500
Holding Company
N.A.I.C.S.: 551112
Silvia Kessel *(Sr VP)*
Robert A. Maresca *(Treas & Sr VP-Fin)*
Vincent Sasso *(VP-Fin Reporting)*
David Persing *(Gen Counsel, Sr VP & Sec)*
Stuart Subotnick *(Pres & CEO)*

METROMONT CORPORATION
2802 White Horse Rd, Greenville, SC 29611
Web Site: http://www.metromont.com
Year Founded: 1925
Precast/Prestressed Concrete Building Mfr
N.A.I.C.S.: 327390
Richard H. Pennell *(Pres & CEO)*
Chris Pastorius *(VP & Gen Mgr-VA)*
Tony Smith *(VP & Asst Gen Mgr-GA)*
Harry Gleich *(VP-Engrg)*
Steve Babcock *(Dir-Engrg & Drafting)*
Chris Rogers *(Dir-Sls-NC & SC)*
Jason Woodard *(VP-Corp Svcs)*
Russell Rumley *(CFO & VP)*
Mike Ward *(Dir-Estimating)*
Terri Ward *(Mgr-Mktg)*

Subsidiaries:

The Shockey Precast Group (1)
219 Stine Ln, Winchester, VA 22603-5409
Tel.: (540) 401-0101
Web Site: http://www.shockeyprecast.com
Mfr of Concrete Products
N.A.I.C.S.: 327390
Marshal Sorrenson *(VP-Bus Dev, Sls & Estimating)*
David Orndorff *(VP-Engrg)*
Rick Pennell *(Pres & CEO)*

METRON CONSTRUCTION CO. INC.
1825 Sunset Pt Rd, Clearwater, FL 33795
Tel.: (727) 736-5400
Sales Range: $10-24.9 Million
Emp.: 6
Commercial & Office Building Contractors
N.A.I.C.S.: 236220
Frank E. Touloumis *(Pres)*
Jane Long *(Office Mgr)*

METRONATIONAL CORPORATION
945 Bunker Hill Ste 400, Houston, TX 77024
Tel.: (713) 973-6400
Web Site:
http://www.metronational.com
Year Founded: 1955
Sales Range: $1-9.9 Million
Emp.: 300
Management Services
N.A.I.C.S.: 531120
Roy Johnson *(Chm)*
Steve Goss *(Controller)*
Jason Johnson *(Vice Chm & Pres)*
William P. Hicks *(COO)*
Warren Alexander *(Dir-Office Leasing)*
Lance Pace *(Gen Counsel & Exec VP)*

METROPOLITAN AREA AGENCY ON AGING, INC.

METROPARK USA, INC.
5750 Grace Pl, Los Angeles, CA 90022
Tel.: (323) 622-3600 DE
Year Founded: 2003
Sales Range: $50-74.9 Million
Emp.: 764
Young Adult Clothing, Apparel Retailer
N.A.I.C.S.: 458110
Lance Hutchison *(COO, Sec & Exec VP-Store Ops)*
Karen Green *(VP)*
Orval Madden *(Chm)*
Cynthia Hariss *(CFO)*

METROPLEX ECONOMIC DEVELOPMENT CORP.
6777 W Kiest Blvd, Dallas, TX 75236
Tel.: (214) 333-6468 TX
Year Founded: 1998
Sales Range: $10-24.9 Million
Emp.: 9
Economic Development Services
N.A.I.C.S.: 541720
Darwin Bruce *(Chm)*
Consuela Holmes *(Treas)*

METROPLEX HOLDINGS INC.
15 Commerce Dr S, Harriman, NY 10926-3101
Tel.: (845) 781-5000
Year Founded: 1988
Sales Range: $25-49.9 Million
Emp.: 230
Providers of Grocery Related Services
N.A.I.C.S.: 531120
Peter R. Grimm *(CEO)*
Phillip Bain *(Pres)*

Subsidiaries:

Metroplex Harriman Corp. (1)
Six Commerce Dr S, Harriman, NY 10926-3101
Tel.: (732) 549-5000
Sales Range: $10-24.9 Million
Emp.: 55
Provider of Grocery Services
N.A.I.C.S.: 424490
Steve Klock *(Dir-Info Svcs)*

Metroplex Long Island Corporation (1)
6 Commerce Dr S, Harriman, NY 10926-3101
Tel.: (631) 234-4501
Sales Range: $10-24.9 Million
Emp.: 85
Provider of Grocery Services
N.A.I.C.S.: 424490

METROPOLITAN COMMITTEE ON ANTI-POVERTY OF SAN DIEGO COUNTY, INC.
1355 3rd Ave, Chula Vista, CA 91911
Tel.: (619) 426-3595 CA
Web Site: http://www.maacproject.org
Year Founded: 1965
Sales Range: $25-49.9 Million
Emp.: 631
Community Welfare Services
N.A.I.C.S.: 624190
Arnulfo Manrique *(Pres & CEO)*
Austin Foye *(CFO & VP)*
Arlene Gibbs *(Chief HR Officer)*
Terri Lapinsky *(COO)*
Alethea Arguilez *(Dir-Child Dev)*
Michelle Soltero *(Sec)*
Tony Valladolid *(VP)*
Jesse Allen *(Chm)*
Viviana Ochoa *(Treas)*

METROPOLITAN AREA AGENCY ON AGING, INC.
2365 N. McKnight Rd Ste 3, North Saint Paul, MN 55109

METROPOLITAN AREA AGENCY ON AGING, INC.

U.S. PRIVATE

Metropolitan Area Agency on Aging, Inc.—(Continued)
Tel.: (651) 641-8612 MN
Web Site: http://www.metroaging.org
Year Founded: 1994
Sales Range: $10-24.9 Million
Emp.: 116
Elderly People Assistance Services
N.A.I.C.S.: 624120
Bob Roepke (Pres)
Jess Luce (Sec)
Jim McDonough (Vice Chm)
Mike Slavik (Treas)

METROPOLITAN ASSOCIATION FOR RETARDED CITIZENS, INC.
12345 W Alameda Pkwy, Lakewood, CO 80228
Tel.: (303) 231-9222
Web Site: http://www.arcthrift.com
Year Founded: 1963
Sales Range: $25-49.9 Million
Emp.: 600
Sales of Used Clothing
N.A.I.C.S.: 459510
Loyd Lewis (Pres & CEO)
Frances Owens (Dir-Community Rels)

METROPOLITAN ATLANTA RAPID TRANSIT AUTHORITY
2424 Piedmont Rd NE, Atlanta, GA 30324-3311
Tel.: (404) 848-5000 GA
Web Site: http://www.itsmarta.com
Year Founded: 1971
Sales Range: $100-124.9 Million
Emp.: 4,500
Provider of Transit Services
N.A.I.C.S.: 485113
Ryland McClendon (Asst Gen Mgr-Comm External Affairs)
Arthur Troup (Deputy Gen Mgr)
Robbie Ashe (Chm)
Gordon L. Hutchinson (CFO)
Luz Borrero (Chief Admin Officer)
Virgil Fludd (Asst Gen Mgr-External Affairs)
Colleen Kiernan (Sr Dir-Govt & Community Affairs)
Jacob Vallo (Sr Dir-Transit Oriented Dev & Real Estate)

METROPOLITAN BAKING COMPANY
8579 Lumpkin St, Hamtramck, MI 48212-3622
Tel.: (313) 875-7246
Web Site: http://www.metropolitanbaking.com
Year Founded: 1945
Sales Range: $10-24.9 Million
Emp.: 65
Commercial Bakery Services
N.A.I.C.S.: 311812
Michael Zrimeck (Gen Mgr)

METROPOLITAN CABINET DISTRIBUTORS
505 Univ Ave, Norwood, MA 02062
Tel.: (781) 949-8900
Web Site: http://www.metcabinet.com
Sales Range: $10-24.9 Million
Emp.: 100
Kitchen Cabinets
N.A.I.C.S.: 423310
Stuart Elfland (Pres)

METROPOLITAN CLUB
1 E 60th St, New York, NY 10022
Tel.: (212) 838-7400 NY
Web Site: http://www.metropolitanclubnyc.org
Year Founded: 1891
Sales Range: $10-24.9 Million
Emp.: 137
Clubhouse
N.A.I.C.S.: 713910
Charles Hudak (Controller)
Anthony Nuttall (Gen Mgr)

METROPOLITAN CONTRACT CARPETS
625 E Chapel Ave, Cherry Hill, NJ 08034
Tel.: (856) 795-1177
Sales Range: $25-49.9 Million
Emp.: 140
Carpet Laying
N.A.I.C.S.: 238330
Bill Hickey (Mgr-Contract)
Frank Pelosi Jr. (Pres)

METROPOLITAN CORPORATION
4350 Baker Rd Ste 230, Minnetonka, MN 55343
Tel.: (952) 893-1277
Sales Range: $150-199.9 Million
Emp.: 500
Holding Company; New & Used Car Dealerships
N.A.I.C.S.: 551112
Thomas Grossman (Chm)
Dave Norton (CFO)

METROPOLITAN EMPLOYEES BENEFITS ASSOCIATION
4371 Latham St Ste 101, Riverside, CA 92501
Tel.: (951) 779-8521 CA
Web Site: http://www.mymeba.org
Year Founded: 1994
Sales Range: $75-99.9 Million
Employee Benefit Services
N.A.I.C.S.: 525120
Christine Balentine (Chm)
Patrick Prezioso (Chm)
Ed Atkinson (Chm)

METROPOLITAN ENTERTAINMENT & CONVENTION AUTHORITY
455 N 10th St, Omaha, NE 68102
Tel.: (402) 341-1500 NE
Web Site: http://www.omahameca.com
Year Founded: 1997
Sales Range: $25-49.9 Million
Emp.: 754
Public Venue Building & Management Services
N.A.I.C.S.: 236220
Lea French (CFO)
Tom O'Gorman (VP-Corp Sls & Mktg)
Claire Alt (VP-HR)
Kevin Raymond (Sr VP-Ops)

METROPOLITAN FOODS INC.
3300 Brown St, Little Rock, AR 72204
Tel.: (501) 280-9999
Web Site: http://www.metrofoodsarkansas.com
Rev.: $16,057,158
Emp.: 150
Supplier of Groceries
N.A.I.C.S.: 424410
Kevin Womack (CEO)
Carl Sullivan (Pres & Dir-Pur)
Stephen Dean (Mgr-Opers)

METROPOLITAN FOODS, INC.
174 Delawanna Ave, Clifton, NJ 07014
Tel.: (973) 672-9400
Web Site: http://www.driscollfoods.com
Year Founded: 1971
Emp.: 700

Food Service Distr
N.A.I.C.S.: 424410
Subsidiaries:

Metropolitan Foods (1)
105 Quist Rd, Amsterdam, NY 12010
Tel.: (518) 770-1900
Web Site: http://www.driscollfoods.com
Emp.: 85
Food Service Distr
N.A.I.C.S.: 424410
Steven Donnelly (Pres-Amsterdam Div)

METROPOLITAN HEALTH CARE, INC.
1340 John A Papalas Dr, Lincoln Park, MI 48146
Tel.: (734) 947-9400
Web Site: http://www.concordems.com
Year Founded: 1997
Sales Range: $1-9.9 Million
Emp.: 100
Ambulance Service
N.A.I.C.S.: 621910
Thomas Buckles (Principal)

METROPOLITAN INDUSTRIES, INC.
37 Forestwood Dr, Romeoville, IL 60446
Tel.: (815) 886-9200
Web Site: http://www.metropolitanind.com
Year Founded: 1957
Water Pumps & Control Systems Manufacturer
N.A.I.C.S.: 333914
Subsidiaries:

Emecole Metro LLC (1)
50 E Montrose Dr, Romeoville, IL 60446
Tel.: (815) 372-2493
Web Site: http://www.emecole.com
Emp.: 50
Waterproofing & Concrete Crack Repair Contractor
N.A.I.C.S.: 238390
Louis F. Cole (Founder)
Samme Cuthbertson (Dir-Design Dept)

METROPOLITAN INTERACTIVE, LTD.
100 Willenbrock Rd, Oxford, CT 06478 CT
Web Site: http://www.metropolitaninteractive.com
Year Founded: 2013
Sales Range: $10-24.9 Million
Emp.: 24
Software Development Services
N.A.I.C.S.: 541511
Rachel Mele (Pres)
Jeff Mele (CEO)
Karen Stevenson (VP-Product Dev)
Deborah Patten (Dir-Ops)
Gregory J. Downing (Dir-Engrg)

METROPOLITAN JEWISH HEALTH SYSTEM
6323 7th Ave, Brooklyn, NY 11220
Tel.: (718) 921-7601
Web Site: http://www.mjhs.org
Sales Range: $75-99.9 Million
Emp.: 1,400
Health Care Srvcs
N.A.I.C.S.: 621610
Robert E. Leamer (Gen Counsel & Sr VP)
Alexander S. Balko (Pres & CEO)
Elliot M. Brooks (Sr VP-HR)
Jeff Davis (CFO)
David Wagner (CFO & COO-Health Plans)
Jay Gormley (Chief Strategy & Plng Officer)
Tim Higgins (COO-Provider Svcs)
Ronald M. Chaffin (Pres-Health Plans)
Lydia Galeon (Sr VP-Bus Dev & Initiatives)
Carol Altieri (VP-Corp Svcs)
Jeannie H. Cross (VP-Govt Affairs)

METROPOLITAN KNOXVILLE AIRPORT AUTHORITY
2055 Alcoa Hwy, Knoxville, TN 37701
Tel.: (865) 342-3000
Web Site: http://www.tys.org
Year Founded: 1978
Sales Range: $25-49.9 Million
Emp.: 155
Airport
N.A.I.C.S.: 488119
William F. Marrison (Pres)
Michael R. Bachman (VP-Fin & Admin)
Trevis D. Gardner (VP-Ops)
Bryan White (VP-Engrg & Plng)
Becky Huckaby (VP-Pub Rels)
Henrietta Grant (Sec)
Michael G. Long (Controller)
James H. Evans Jr. (VP-Mktg & Air Svc Dev)

METROPOLITAN LUMBER & HARDWARE
617 11th Ave, New York, NY 10036-2001
Tel.: (212) 246-9090 NY
Web Site: http://www.themetlumber.com
Year Founded: 1979
Sales Range: $10-24.9 Million
Emp.: 150
Lumber Plywood & Millwork
N.A.I.C.S.: 444140
Mike King (Mgr-Paint Dept)
Stephen DiPietro (Mgr)

METROPOLITAN MARKET LLC
4025 Delridge Way SW Ste 100, Seattle, WA 98106
Tel.: (206) 923-0740
Web Site: http://www.metropolitan-market.com
Sales Range: $50-74.9 Million
Emp.: 750
Grocery Stores
N.A.I.C.S.: 445110
Terry R. Halverson (CEO)

METROPOLITAN MEDICAL PRACTICE PLAN PC
234 E 149th St Ste 8D200, Bronx, NY 10451
Tel.: (718) 579-6200 NY
Year Founded: 2011
Sales Range: $10-24.9 Million
Health Care Srvices
N.A.I.C.S.: 622110
Sari Kaminsky (Pres)
Marc Wallack (Sec)
Gregory Almond (VP)
Ronnie Swift (Treas)

METROPOLITAN MOVING & STORAGE
1230 Walnut St Midatlantic Blvd, Laurel, MD 20708
Tel.: (301) 279-0090
Web Site: http://www.dcmetropolitanmoving.com
Year Founded: 2005
Sales Range: $1-9.9 Million
Emp.: 45
Residential & Commercial, Local & Long-Distance Moving Services
N.A.I.C.S.: 484210
Jonathan Neal (Co-Founder)
Robert Bistle (Co-Founder)

COMPANIES

METROPOLITAN OPERA ASSOCIATION, INC.
30 Lincoln Ctr, New York, NY 10023
Tel.: (212) 362-6000   NY
Web Site: https://www.metopera.org
Year Founded: 1883
Opera Performer Association
N.A.I.C.S.: 813910
James Levine *(Dir-Music)*
Peter Gelb *(Gen Mgr)*

METROPOLITAN PAPER RECYCLING INC.
847 Shepherd Ave, Brooklyn, NY 11208
Tel.: (718) 257-8584
Web Site: http://www.metropaperrecycling.com
Year Founded: 1999
Sales Range: $10-24.9 Million
Emp.: 110
Waste Paper Recycling Services
N.A.I.C.S.: 562920
Gregory Bianco *(CEO)*

METROPOLITAN PIER & EXPOSITION AUTHORITY
301 E Cermak Rd, Chicago, IL 60616
Tel.: (312) 791-7500
Web Site: http://www.mpea.com
Sales Range: $150-199.9 Million
Emp.: 500
Convention & Show Services
N.A.I.C.S.: 561920
Jon Pounds *(Exec Dir)*
Julie Chavez *(Treas & Sec)*
Larita Clark *(Acting CEO)*
Brett J. Hart *(Chm)*
Robert G. Reiter Jr. *(Vice Chm)*

METROPOLITAN PROPERTIES AMERICA INCORPORATED
101 Federal St 22nd Fl, Boston, MA 02110
Tel.: (617) 603-7000
Web Site: http://www.metprop.com
Sales Range: $50-74.9 Million
Emp.: 140
Commercial & Industrial Building Operation
N.A.I.C.S.: 531120
Jeffrey J. Cohen *(CEO)*
Norbert F. Callahan *(CTO)*
Mark Consoli *(CFO)*

METROPOLITAN PROPERTIES SYSTEMS
1370 W 6th St Ste 206, Cleveland, OH 44114-1902
Tel.: (216) 696-6311   OH
Web Site: http://www.metroparkingsystem.com
Year Founded: 1972
Sales Range: $50-74.9 Million
Emp.: 30
Acquisitions & Operations of Parking Facilities; Commercial Real Estate Development & Investment
N.A.I.C.S.: 812930
James Kassouf *(Pres, CEO & Treas)*

Subsidiaries:

Metro Parking Systems Inc   (1)
Ste 206 1370 W 6th St, Cleveland, OH 44113-1315
Tel.: (216) 696-6311
Web Site: http://www.metroparkingsystems.com
Sales Range: $10-24.9 Million
Emp.: 2
Owner & Operator of Parking Facilities
N.A.I.C.S.: 812930
Fatmir Saliolari *(Mgr)*

METROPOLITAN SALES DISTRIBUTORS INCORPORATED
238 Atlantic Ave, Lynbrook, NY 11563
Tel.: (516) 599-7900
Web Site: http://www.metsales.com
Rev.: $25,129,342
Emp.: 20
Computer Peripheral Equipment
N.A.I.C.S.: 423430

METROPOLITAN SIDING & WINDOWS
11701 Central Ave Ste 104, Waldorf, MD 20601
Tel.: (301) 870-4500
Web Site: http://www.metropolitanexterior.com
Rev.: $14,300,000
Emp.: 10
Supplier of Siding, Windows & Roofing
N.A.I.C.S.: 238130
Jeff Thomas *(Pres)*

METROPOLITAN STEEL INDUSTRIES INC.
601 Fritztown Rd, Reading, PA 19608-1511
Tel.: (610) 678-6411   PA
Year Founded: 1972
Sales Range: $10-24.9 Million
Emp.: 10
Mfr of Fabricated Structural Metal
N.A.I.C.S.: 332312
Steven Hynes *(Pres)*
Nathan Bedford *(Project Mgr)*
Michael Endler *(Treas)*

METROPOLITAN TELECOMMUNICATIONS, INC.
55 Water St 32st Fl, New York, NY 10041-3299
Tel.: (212) 607-2000
Web Site: http://www.mettel.net
Year Founded: 1996
Sales Range: $600-649.9 Million
Emp.: 370
Telecommunication Servicesb
N.A.I.C.S.: 517111
Marshall Aronow *(CEO)*
Andoni Economou *(COO & Exec VP)*
Sam Vogel *(Exec VP-Product Mgmt & Regulatory Affairs)*
Max Silber *(VP-Mobility)*
Donald Keane *(VP-Mktg)*
Mark Timothy Marshall *(Exec Dir-Customer Care)*
Steven Tunney *(Exec VP-Plng & Strategy)*
Joseph Farano *(Gen Counsel)*
Ted Salame *(VP-Bus Dev)*
Lori Thomas *(VP-Client Engagement)*
Will Prince *(VP-Ops)*
Eddie Rishty *(VP-Enterprise Sls)*
Tim Hanley *(VP-Strategic Sls)*
David Mitchell *(VP-Sls-Agent Channel)*
Keith Hochstin *(VP-Strategic Client Dev)*
James Salame *(Exec Dir-Bruin)*
Orest Siryj *(VP-Risk & Cost Mgmt)*
Wilma Killgo *(VP-Strategic Client Dev)*
Peter Bell *(Sr VP-Sls-Digital Transformation)*
David Dickson *(Exec Dir-Unified Comm Solutions)*
Diana Gowen *(Sr VP-Federal Program & Gen Mgr)*
Robert Dapkiewicz *(Sr VP-Federal Program & Gen Mgr-Federal Program)*
Don Parente *(VP-Federal Practice)*
Edward J. Fox III *(VP-Network Svcs)*

METROPOLITAN THEATRES CORPORATION
8727 W Third St, Los Angeles, CA 90048-3843
Tel.: (310) 858-2800   CA
Web Site: http://www.metrotheatres.com
Year Founded: 1923
Exhibition, Cinema & Movie Theatre Operator
N.A.I.C.S.: 512131
Bruce Corwin *(Chm & CEO)*
David Corwin *(Pres)*
Phillip Hermann *(CFO)*
Dale Davison *(Sr VP-Ops & Dev)*
Victoria Uy *(VP-Fin & HR)*
James Pope *(VP-IT)*
Kim Tucker *(Dir-Ops)*
Natalie Eig *(Dir-Mktg & Comm)*
Thanasi Papoulias *(Dir-Food & Bev)*
Robert Macias *(Mgr-Content Administration)*

METROPOLITAN TRANSIT AUTHORITY OF HARRIS COUNTY
Lee P Brown Metro Admin Bldg 1900 Main St, Houston, TX 77002
Tel.: (713) 739-4000
Web Site: http://www.ridemetro.org
Year Founded: 1979
Sales Range: $50-74.9 Million
Emp.: 3,473
Bus & Rail Transit Operations
N.A.I.C.S.: 485113
Thomas C. Lambert *(Pres & CEO)*
Christof Spieler *(Sec)*
David W. Couch *(Sr VP-Capital Programs)*
Jerome Gray *(Officer-Press & VP)*
Tom Jasien *(Deputy CEO)*
Tim Kelly *(Exec VP-Ops, Pub Safety & Customer Svc)*
Margaret Menger *(Dir-Bd Rels)*
Raequel Roberts *(VP-Mktg & Corp Comm)*
Alva I. Trevino *(Gen Counsel)*
Gilbert Andrew Garcia *(Chm)*
Rosa Diaz *(Dir-Board Support)*
Arthur C. Smiley III *(VP-Audit)*

METROPOLITAN TRANSIT SYSTEM
1255 Imperial Ave Ste 1000, San Diego, CA 92101
Tel.: (619) 231-1466
Web Site: http://www.sdcommute.com
Sales Range: $100-124.9 Million
Emp.: 2,000
Bus & Rail Services
N.A.I.C.S.: 485113
Emma Aguilera *(Mgr-Payroll)*
Rob Schupp *(Dir-Mktg & Comm)*
Sharon Cooney *(Interim CEO)*

Subsidiaries:

San Diego Transit Corporation   (1)
1255 Imperial Ave, San Diego, CA 92101-7602
Tel.: (619) 238-0100
Web Site: http://www.sdmts.com
Sales Range: $25-49.9 Million
Emp.: 900
Local & Suburban Transit
N.A.I.C.S.: 485113
Larry Marnesi *(CFO)*

San Diego Trolley Inc.   (1)
1255 Imperial Ave Ste 900, San Diego, CA 92101
Tel.: (619) 595-4949
Web Site: http://www.sdmts.com
Rev.: $20,940,890
Emp.: 300
Trolley Operation
N.A.I.C.S.: 485119

METROPOLITAN TRANSPORTATION AUTHORITY
333 W 34th St 9th Fl, New York, NY 10001-2402
Tel.: (212) 878-7000   NY
Web Site: http://www.new.mta.info
Year Founded: 1965
Sales Range: $5-14.9 Billion
Emp.: 68,313
Integrated Transportation Network
N.A.I.C.S.: 485119
Patrick J. Foye *(Chm & CEO)*
Fernando Ferrer *(Vice Chm)*
Janno Lieber *(Chief Dev Officer)*
Veronique Hakim *(Mng Dir)*
Thomas J. Quigley *(Gen Counsel)*
Patrick Warren *(Chief Safety Officer)*
Abbey Collins *(Chief Comm Officer)*
Sarah E. Feinberg *(Interim Pres)*
Seleta Reynolds *(Chief Innovation Officer)*
Jennifer Vides *(Chief Customer Experience Officer)*
Sharon Gookin *(Deputy CEO)*

Subsidiaries:

Long Island Rail Road   (1)
Jamaica Sta, Jamaica, NY 11435
Tel.: (718) 558-7400
Web Site: http://mta.info
Sales Range: $350-399.9 Million
Emp.: 6,381
Local Railroad Operator
N.A.I.C.S.: 485119
Phil Eng *(Pres)*

MTA Bus Company   (1)
2 Broadway, New York, NY 10004-2207
Tel.: (212) 878-7000
Web Site: http://www.mta.info
Sales Range: $650-699.9 Million
Emp.: 5,000
Passenger Buses Operator
N.A.I.C.S.: 485999
Darryl C. Irick *(Pres)*

New York City Transit Authority   (1)
370 Jay St, Brooklyn, NY 11201
Tel.: (718) 330-3000
Web Site: http://mta.info
Sales Range: $200-249.9 Million
Emp.: 2,000
Bus Transportation Systems
N.A.I.C.S.: 485999
Lynne Troy Henderson *(Asst Gen Counsel)*
Jeffrey Erlitz *(Asst Mgr-Schedule)*
Frank Benenati *(Engr-Electrical Inspector)*
Andy Byford *(Pres)*

METROPOLITAN UTILITIES DISTRICT
1723 Harney St, Omaha, NE 68102-1960
Tel.: (402) 554-6666
Web Site: http://www.mudomaha.com
Year Founded: 1913
Sales Range: $300-349.9 Million
Emp.: 856
Utility Services
N.A.I.C.S.: 221210
Ronald E. Bucher *(Gen Counsel & Sr VP)*
Scott L. Keep *(Pres & Sec)*
Mark E. Doyle *(CIO & Sr VP)*
Debra A. Schneider *(CFO & Sr VP)*
James P. Begley *(Vice Chm)*
Ron Reisner *(COO & Sr VP)*

METROPOLITAN WASHINGTON AIRPORTS AUTHORITY
1 Aviation Cir, Washington, DC 20001
Tel.: (703) 417-8600
Web Site: http://www.mwaa.com
Year Founded: 1938
Sales Range: $75-99.9 Million
Emp.: 1,100
Provider of Management Services
N.A.I.C.S.: 488119
David Mould *(VP-Comm)*
William Shaw McDermott *(Chm)*
John E. Potter *(Pres & CEO)*
Warner H. Session *(Vice Chm)*

METROPOLITAN WASHINGTON AIRPORTS AUTHORITY U.S. PRIVATE

Metropolitan Washington Airports Authority—(Continued)

Jerome L. Davis *(Chief Revenue Officer & Exec VP)*
Carl Schultz *(Dir-Airline Bus Dev)*
Monica R. Hargrove *(Sec & VP)*
Yil Surehan *(VP-Airline Bus Dev)*
John E. Potter *(Pres & CEO)*

METROPOLITAN WHOLESALE & RETAIL BEER

2503 3rd Ave, Bronx, NY 10451
Tel.: (718) 993-2454
Rev.: $20,400,000
Emp.: 40
Beer & Liquor Distr
N.A.I.C.S.: 424810
Paul Bleich *(Owner)*

METROPOLITAN-SAINT LOUIS SEWER DISTRICT INC.

2350 Market St, Saint Louis, MO 63103-2555
Tel.: (314) 768-6200   MO
Web Site: http://www.stlmsd.com
Year Founded: 1954
Sales Range: $150-199.9 Million
Emp.: 981
Provider of Sewerage Systems
N.A.I.C.S.: 561110
Randy Hayman *(Gen Counsel)*

METROPOULOS & CO.

200 Greenwich Ave, Greenwich, CT 06830
Tel.: (310) 695-1941
Web Site: http://www.metropoulos.com
Privater Equity Firm
N.A.I.C.S.: 523999
C. Dean Metropoulos *(Owner, Chm & CEO)*
Daren Metropoulos *(Principal)*
Evan Metropoulos *(Principal)*
Russell Leto *(CFO)*
Howard Altman *(Chief Investment Officer)*

Subsidiaries:

BlueTriton Brands, Inc.   (1)
900 Long Ridge Rd Bldg 2, Stamford, CT 06902-1138
Tel.: (203) 629-7802
Web Site: http://www.nestle-watersna.com
Emp.: 650
Mineral Water & Domestic Water Bottling Services
N.A.I.C.S.: 424490
Charlie Broll *(Gen Counsel, Sec & Exec VP)*
Tom Smith *(Pres-Customer Dev & Sls Ops)*
Tara Carraro *(Chief Corp Affairs Officer & Exec VP)*
Henrik Jelert *(Exec VP-ReadyRefresh)*
Bill Trackim *(Exec VP-Technical & Production, Supply Chain & Procurement)*
David Tulauskas *(Chief Sustainability Officer & VP)*
Lisa Walker *(Chief HR Officer & Exec VP)*
Dean Metropoulos *(Chm)*
Javier Idrovo *(CFO)*
Paul Norman *(Pres-Retail)*
Kheri Holland Tillman *(CMO)*

Subsidiary (Domestic):

Arrowhead Mountain Spring Water Company   (2)
900 Long Ridge Rd Building 2, Stamford, CT 06902
Tel.: (203) 531-4100
Web Site: http://www.nestle-watersna.com
Sales Range: $125-149.9 Million
Emp.: 600
Water Purification Systems for Home & Office, Bottled Water Service, Drinking Cups, Electric Water Coolers
N.A.I.C.S.: 424490
Bill Pearson *(CFO)*

Arrowhead Mountain Spring Water Company   (2)
5772 Jurupa St, Ontario, CA 91761-3643
Tel.: (909) 974-0600
Web Site: http://www.nestlewatersnorthamerica.com
Sales Range: $25-49.9 Million
Emp.: 100
Water Quality Monitoring & Control Systems
N.A.I.C.S.: 424490

Arrowhead Mountain Spring Water Company   (2)
1566 E Washington Blvd, Los Angeles, CA 90021
Tel.: (213) 763-1383
Web Site: http://www.arrowheadwater.com
Sales Range: $50-74.9 Million
Emp.: 4
Mineral or Spring Water Bottling
N.A.I.C.S.: 424490

Arrowhead Mountain Spring Water Company   (2)
130 Fogg St, Colton, CA 92324-3563
Tel.: (909) 825-8543
Web Site: http://www.arrowheadwater.com
Sales Range: $25-49.9 Million
Emp.: 50
Mfr of Distilled Mineral & Spring Water
N.A.I.C.S.: 445298

Arrowhead Water   (2)
52 Julian St, Ventura, CA 93001-2506
Tel.: (805) 653-0253
Web Site: http://www.arrowheadwater.com
Sales Range: $25-49.9 Million
Emp.: 24
Mineral & Spring Water Distribution
N.A.I.C.S.: 424490

Arrowhead Water   (2)
3230 E Imperial Hwy Ste 100, Brea, CA 92821
Tel.: (714) 792-2100
Web Site: http://www.arrowheadwater.com
Sales Range: $50-74.9 Million
Emp.: 40
Provider of Bottled Water
N.A.I.C.S.: 424490
Rick Croarkin *(CFO & VP)*

Ice Mountain Spring Water   (2)
4231 C Leap Rd, Hilliard, OH 43026-1125
Tel.: (614) 876-0626
Web Site: http://www.nestlewatersnorthamerica.com
Sales Range: $25-49.9 Million
Emp.: 40
Bottled Water Delivery
N.A.I.C.S.: 445298

Division (Non-US):

Nestle Water Canada Ltd.   (2)
3440 Francis Hughes Ave, Ville de Laval, H7L 5A9, QC, Canada
Tel.: (450) 629-8543
Sales Range: $25-49.9 Million
Emp.: 25
Groceries & Related Products
N.A.I.C.S.: 445110
Adam Graves *(Pres)*

Nestle Waters Canada Inc.   (2)
101 Brock Rd South, Puslinch, N0B 2J0, ON, Canada
Tel.: (519) 763-9462
Web Site: https://bluetriton.ca
Sales Range: $25-49.9 Million
Emp.: 220
Bottled Waters Production & Distribution
N.A.I.C.S.: 312112

Nestle Waters Canada Inc.   (2)
101 Brock Road South, Puslinch, N0B 2J0, ON, Canada
Tel.: (604) 860-4888
Web Site: http://www.nestle-waters.com
Sales Range: $25-49.9 Million
Emp.: 100
Distribution of Bottled & Canned Soft Drinks
N.A.I.C.S.: 312111

Subsidiary (Domestic):

Nestle Waters North America Holdings, Inc.   (2)
900 Long Rdg Rd Bldg 2, Stamford, CT 06902
Tel.: (203) 531-4100
Web Site: http://www.nestle-watersna.com
Emp.: 8,000
Investment Management Service
N.A.I.C.S.: 523999

Plant (Domestic):

Nestle Waters North America Inc. - Brea   (2)
3230 E Imperial Hwy, Brea, CA 92821
Tel.: (714) 792-2100
Web Site: http://www.arrowheadwater.com
Sales Range: $25-49.9 Million
Emp.: 40
Mineral or Spring Water Bottling
N.A.I.C.S.: 424490

Nestle Waters North America Inc. - Breinigsville   (2)
405 Nestle Way, Breinigsville, PA 18031
Tel.: (610) 530-7301
Mfr of Bottled Water
N.A.I.C.S.: 424490

Nestle Waters North America Inc. - Coppell   (2)
1322 Crestside Dr, Coppell, TX 75019
Tel.: (972) 462-3600
Web Site: http://www.nestle-waters.com
Sales Range: $25-49.9 Million
Emp.: 200
Coffee & Tea Mfr
N.A.I.C.S.: 311920

Nestle Waters North America Inc. - Dracut   (2)
32 Commercial Dr, Dracut, MA 01826-2836
Tel.: (978) 970-5656
Sales Range: $25-49.9 Million
Emp.: 58
Mineral & Spring Water Bottling
N.A.I.C.S.: 424490

Nestle Waters North America Inc. - Fort Lauderdale   (2)
10599 Northwest 67th St, Fort Lauderdale, FL 33321-6407
Tel.: (954) 597-7852
Web Site: http://www.perrier.com
Sales Range: $25-49.9 Million
Emp.: 100
Home & Office Water & Coffee Delivery
N.A.I.C.S.: 312112

Nestle Waters North America Inc. - Greenwich   (2)
900 Long Ridge Rd, Stamford, CT 06902
Tel.: (203) 629-7802
Web Site: http://www.nestle-watersna.com
Sales Range: $125-149.9 Million
Emp.: 600
Mineral Water
N.A.I.C.S.: 424490
Susan Vinales *(Mgr-Facilities)*

Nestle Waters North America Inc. - Jacksonville   (2)
7035 Davis Creek Rd, Jacksonville, FL 32256-3027
Tel.: (904) 268-5152
Web Site: http://www.zephyrhillswater.com
Sales Range: $25-49.9 Million
Emp.: 20
Bottled Water Distr
N.A.I.C.S.: 445298

Nestle Waters North America Inc. - Lanham   (2)
9921 Business Pkwy, Lanham, MD 20706-1836
Tel.: (301) 731-3448
Sales Range: $25-49.9 Million
Emp.: 60
Distilled Mineral & Spring Water
N.A.I.C.S.: 312112

Nestle Waters North America Inc. - Northbrook   (2)
310 Huehl Rd, Northbrook, IL 60062-1918
Tel.: (847) 400-3657
Sales Range: $25-49.9 Million
Emp.: 10
Water Bottling
N.A.I.C.S.: 312112

Nestle Waters North America Inc. - Raynham   (2)
375 Paramount Dr, Raynham, MA 02767

Tel.: (508) 977-9696
Sales Range: $50-74.9 Million
Emp.: 175
Natural Water Packaged In Cans
N.A.I.C.S.: 424490

Nestle Waters North America Inc. - Rochester   (2)
146 Halstead St, Rochester, NY 14610-1946
Tel.: (585) 288-7241
Web Site: http://www.perriergroup.com
Sales Range: $25-49.9 Million
Emp.: 17
Mineral or Spring Water Bottling
N.A.I.C.S.: 325998

Nestle Waters North America Inc. - Thousand Palms   (2)
72242 Varner Rd, Thousand Palms, CA 92276-3341
Tel.: (760) 343-3125
Web Site: http://www.perriergroup.com
Sales Range: $50-74.9 Million
Emp.: 10
Mineral or Spring Water Bottling
N.A.I.C.S.: 424490

Nestle Waters North America Inc. - Woodridge   (2)
10335 Argon Woods Dr Ste 200, Woodridge, IL 60517
Tel.: (630) 271-7300
Sales Range: $25-49.9 Million
Emp.: 15
Bottled Water
N.A.I.C.S.: 424490

Nestle Waters North America Inc. - Zephyrhills   (2)
4330 20th St, Zephyrhills, FL 33540-6703
Tel.: (813) 783-1959
Web Site: http://www.nestlewatersna.com
Sales Range: $125-149.9 Million
Emp.: 300
Mfr of Water Bottling Services
N.A.I.C.S.: 424490

Subsidiary (Domestic):

Ozarka Water   (2)
PO Box 628, Wilkes Barre, PA 18703
Sales Range: $25-49.9 Million
Emp.: 15
Water Distilled
N.A.I.C.S.: 312112

Ozarka Water   (2)
9351 E Point Dr, Houston, TX 77054-3715
Tel.: (713) 799-1452
Web Site: http://www.ozarkawater.com
Sales Range: $50-74.9 Million
Emp.: 200
Groceries & Related Products
N.A.I.C.S.: 424490

Poland Spring Corporation   (2)
900 Long Ridge Rd Buld-2, Stamford, CT 06902-5091
Tel.: (203) 531-4100
Web Site: http://www.nestle-watersna.com
Sales Range: $250-299.9 Million
Emp.: 700
Bottler of Spring Water
N.A.I.C.S.: 424490

Division (Domestic):

Poland Spring Bottling   (3)
109 Poland Spring Dr, Poland Spring, ME 04274-5327
Tel.: (207) 998-4315
Web Site: http://www.polandspring.com
Sales Range: $125-149.9 Million
Emp.: 300
Storage Services for Bottled & Canned Soft Drinks
N.A.I.C.S.: 424490

Plant (Domestic):

Poland Spring Corporation   (3)
111 Thomas Mcgovern Dr, Jersey City, NJ 07305-4620
Tel.: (201) 531-2044
Web Site: http://www.polandspring.com
Sales Range: $25-49.9 Million
Emp.: 85
Water Distilled

N.A.I.C.S.: 424490

Poland Spring Corporation (3)
109 Poland Spring Dr, Poland Spring, ME 04274-5327
Tel.: (207) 998-4315
Web Site: http://www.polandspring.com
Sales Range: $50-74.9 Million
Emp.: 300
Bottled Water Mfr
N.A.I.C.S.: 312112

Subsidiary (Domestic):

Saratoga Spring Water Company (2)
11 Geyser Rd, Saratoga Springs, NY 12866-9038
Tel.: (518) 584-6363
Web Site:
   http://www.saratogaspringwater.com
Bottler of Mineral & Spring Water
N.A.I.C.S.: 312112
Adam Madkour (CEO)

Zephyrhills Spring Water Company (2)
6403 Harney Rd, Tampa, FL 33610
Tel.: (813) 621-2025
Web Site: http://www.zephyrhillswater.com
Spring Water Producer
N.A.I.C.S.: 312112

METROPOWER INC.
800 21st Ave, Albany, GA 31706
Tel.: (229) 432-7345   GA
Web Site:
   http://www.metropower.com
Year Founded: 1983
Sales Range: $25-49.9 Million
Emp.: 500
Electrical Work
N.A.I.C.S.: 238210
Ronnie T. Hinson (CEO)
Danny Gibson (Pres & COO)
Todd Stevens (VP-Industrial Construction)

METROSPEC TECHNOLOGY LLC
2401 Pilot Knob Rd Ste 108, Mendota Heights, MN 55120
Tel.: (651) 452-4800
Web Site: http://www.flexrad.com
Year Founded: 2001
Sales Range: $1-9.9 Million
Emp.: 24
Mfr of LED Light Sources
N.A.I.C.S.: 335139
Vic Holec (Pres)
Curtis Romano (VP)

METROSTAR SYSTEMS
1856 Old Reston Ave Ste 100, Reston, VA 20190
Tel.: (703) 481-9581
Web Site:
   http://www.metrostarsystems.com
Year Founded: 1999
Rev.: $7,700,000
Emp.: 70
Custom Computer Programming Services
N.A.I.C.S.: 541511
Ali Reza Manouchehri (CEO)
Robert Jason Santos (Co-Founder & Pres)
Herman Hewitt (Sr VP-Bus Dev)
Vy Truong (VP-Civilian Strategy & Ops)
Jorge Vasquez (Dir-Product Dev)
Mo Hessabi (Dir-Bus Dev)
Mona Lutnes (Mgr-Facility & Security)
Anthony Salvi (COO)
Joseph Kinder (Dir-Cyber Ops & Tactics)
Ricardo Palhano (Dir-Collaboration)
Clay Calvert (Dir-Cybersecurity)
Jason Stoner (Dir-Digital)
Maureen Tepe (Dir-Fin & Acctg)
Matt Louderback (Dir-Mobile)

Fred Ferares (VP-Bus Dev-Defense)
Ron Dahart (VP-Defense Strategy & Ops)
Christine Couch (Sr VP-Defense & Intelligence Grp)
Robert Wren (Dir-IT Transformation & Enterprise Architecture)
Todd Morris (VP-Homeland Svcs)
Rachel F. Cohen (Chief Growth Officer)
Pete Nelson (Chief Growth Officer)

METRUM RESEARCH GROUP LLC
2 Tunxis Rd, Tariffville, CT 06081
Tel.: (860) 735-7043
Web Site: http://www.metrumrg.com
Year Founded: 2004
Sales Range: $1-9.9 Million
Emp.: 21
Technical Consulting
N.A.I.C.S.: 541690
Marc R. Gastonguay (Pres & CEO)
Jeffrey T. Hane (COO & CIO)
Jonathan French (Dir-Innovation)

METSOVO BAKING COMPANY
290 Madsen Dr Ste 101, Bloomingdale, IL 60108
Tel.: (630) 380-5100
Web Site:
   http://www.metsovobaking.com
Sales Range: $25-49.9 Million
Emp.: 185
Frozen Specialty Food Mfr
N.A.I.C.S.: 311412
Paul Vadevoulis (Pres)

METTERS INDUSTRIES, INC.
8200 Greensboro Dr Ste 525, McLean, VA 22102-3803
Tel.: (703) 821-3300
Web Site: http://www.metters.com
Year Founded: 1981
Telecommunications & Network Security; Database Design & Administration
N.A.I.C.S.: 541512
Samuel Metters (Founder, Chm, Pres & CEO)
Will Dolan (Dir-Contracts & Pricing)

METUCHEN COMMUNITY SERVICES CORPORATION
319 Maple St, Perth Amboy, NJ 08861
Tel.: (732) 324-8200   NJ
Year Founded: 1995
Sales Range: $1-9.9 Million
Emp.: 2
Rental Space Provider
N.A.I.C.S.: 531190
Douglas J. Susan (Treas & Sec)
Gary Hoagland (Chm)

METUCHEN SAVINGS BANK
429 Main St, Metuchen, NJ 08840
Tel.: (732) 548-7400
Web Site:
   http://www.metuchensavingsbank.com
Year Founded: 1897
Sales Range: $10-24.9 Million
Emp.: 36
Provider of Banking Services
N.A.I.C.S.: 522110
Joseph Razzano (VP)
Katherine J. Liseno (Pres & CEO)
Lorraine Mulligan (VP-Bus Dev & Mktg)
Ed McGovern (CFO)
Manny Deleon (Controller)
Jennie Piperi (COO & Exec VP)

METWEST REALTY ADVISORS LLC
11100 Santa Monica Blvd Ste 1700, Los Angeles, CA 90025
Tel.: (310) 893-0200
Web Site:
   http://www.metwestrealtyadvisors.com
Emp.: 4
Real Estate Investment Services
N.A.I.C.S.: 525990
Richard S. Hollander (Founder, Chm & CEO)

Subsidiaries:

Casa Madrona Hotel & Spa (1)
801 Bridgeway, Sausalito, CA 94965
Tel.: (415) 332-0502
Web Site: http://www.casamadrona.com
Hotel Operator
N.A.I.C.S.: 721110
Carmen Cruz (Gen Mgr)

METZ ENTERPRISES INC.
2 Woodland Dr, Dallas, PA 18612
Tel.: (570) 675-8100
Web Site: http://www.metzltd.com
Sales Range: $75-99.9 Million
Emp.: 3,500
Restaurant & Hotel Owner & Operator
N.A.I.C.S.: 722511
John C. Metz (Chm)
Greg Polk (VP-Fin & Admin)
Cheryl McCann (VP-HR)
John Geronimo (VP-Sls)
Jim Dickson (Sr VP-Education & Corp Dining)
Jack Brill (VP-Bus Dev)
Craig Solomon (VP-Healthcare & Support Svcs)
Dennis Daley (VP-Higher Education & Independent Schools)
Brian Bachman (VP-Pur)

Subsidiaries:

Metz & Associates, Ltd. (1)
2 Woodland Dr, Dallas, PA 18612
Tel.: (570) 675-8100
Web Site: http://www.metzculinary.com
Rev.: $37,040,200
Emp.: 35
Food Management & Brokerage Services
N.A.I.C.S.: 541990
Ryan McNulty (Dir-Culinary Dev)
Brian Bachman (VP-Pur)
Jack Brill (VP-Bus Dev)
Mike Gallagher (Dir-IT)
John Geronimo (VP-Sls)
Cheryl McCann (VP-HR)
Maureen Metz (VP-Mktg)
Greg Polk (VP-Fin & Admin)
Craig Solomon (VP-Healthcare & Support Svcs)

Subsidiary (Domestic):

Smith & Sons Foods, Inc. (2)
2124 Riverside Dr, Macon, GA 31204-1747
Tel.: (478) 745-4759
Web Site: http://www.sscafeterias.com
Sales Range: $25-49.9 Million
Restaurants & Cafeterias
N.A.I.C.S.: 722310
Robert A. Smith (Exec VP)
David R. Johnson (Treas, Sec & VP)
Melissa C. Smith (Dir-HR)
Sheryl Skidmore (Dir-Computer Ops)
Raylon Soles (Gen Mgr-State Wholesale Food)
James A. Smith III (Chm & CEO)
James A. Smith IV (Pres)

Northeast Concepts Inc. (1)
2 Woodland Dr, Dallas, PA 18612
Tel.: (570) 675-8100
Web Site: http://www.metzcorp.com
Rev.: $1,100,000
Emp.: 30
Bond Brokers
N.A.I.C.S.: 424410
John C. Metz (Pres)

South Jersey Pubs Inc (1)
1279 Hooper Ave, Toms River, NJ 08753
Tel.: (732) 914-1113
Rev.: $5,000,000
Emp.: 130
Drinking Places
N.A.I.C.S.: 722410

METZGAR CONVEYOR COMPANY
901 Metzgar Dr, Comstock Park, MI 49321-9758
Tel.: (616) 784-0930
Web Site:
   http://www.metzgarconveyors.com
Year Founded: 1933
Sales Range: $50-74.9 Million
Emp.: 75
Line-Shaft Driven Conveyors
N.A.I.C.S.: 333922
Rob Metzgar (Owner & Pres)

METZGER ASSOCIATES
5733 Central Ave, Boulder, CO 80301
Tel.: (303) 786-7000
Web Site: http://www.metzger.com
Year Founded: 1991
Sales Range: $1-9.9 Million
Emp.: 12
Public Relations
N.A.I.C.S.: 541820
John Metzger (Founder)
Doyle Albee (Pres & COO)
Sarah Engle (CFO)
Stephanie Vanderholme (VP)
Amy Little (Mgr-Digital Svcs)

METZGERMEISTER & RESEARCH CORP.
PO Box 1338, Ciales, PR 00638
Tel.: (787) 871-6363
Year Founded: 2003
Sales Range: $10-24.9 Million
Emp.: 160
Meat Packing Services
N.A.I.C.S.: 311611
Jose R. Ayala (Pres)
Wilmet Pagan (Controller)
Lilibeth Rojas (Sec)
Charles Conwell Jr. (Gen Mgr)

MEVION MEDICAL SYSTEMS, INC.
300 Foster St, Littleton, MA 01460
Tel.: (978) 540-1500   DE
Web Site: http://www.mevion.com
Year Founded: 2004
Proton Therapy Systems Mfr
N.A.I.C.S.: 334510
Joseph K. Jachinowski (Pres & CEO)
Donald B. Melson (CFO & VP)
Robert N. Wilson (Chm)
Stanley Rosenthal (VP-Clinical Sys)
Mark Jones (VP-Engrg)
Bill Alvord (VP-Ops)
George L. Rugg (VP-Global Svc)
Thomas Faris (VP-Regulatory Affairs, Quality Assurance & Admin)
Lionel G. Bouchet (VP-Mktg)
Patricia A. Davis (Gen Counsel, Sec & VP)

MEWBOURNE HOLDINGS INC.
3901 S Bdwy Ave, Tyler, TX 75701-8716
Tel.: (903) 561-2900
Web Site:
   http://www.mewbourne.com
Year Founded: 1965
Sales Range: $1-9.9 Million
Emp.: 150
Provider of Petroleum Services
N.A.I.C.S.: 211120
Curtis W. Mewbourne (Founder)

Subsidiaries:

Mewbourne Oil Co. Inc. (1)
PO Box 7698, Tyler, TX 75711
Tel.: (903) 561-2900

MEWBOURNE HOLDINGS INC.

Mewbourne Holdings Inc.—(Continued)
Web Site: http://www.mewbourne.net
Emp.: 400
Provider of Petroleum Services
N.A.I.C.S.: 211120
Curtis Mewbourne (Pres)

MEXICAN AMERICAN OPPORTUNITY FOUNDATION
401 N Garfield Ave, Montebello, CA 90640
Tel.: (323) 890-9600   CA
Web Site: http://www.maof.org
Year Founded: 1963
Sales Range: $50-74.9 Million
Emp.: 805
Community Action Services
N.A.I.C.S.: 624190
Vicky Santos (VP-Ops)
Claudia Rufino (Dir-HR)
Suzanne Gonzalez (Chief Dev Officer)
Orlando M. Sayson (CFO)

MEXICAN GOVERNMENT TOURISM OFFICES
400 Madison Ave Ste 11C, New York, NY 10017
Tel.: (212) 308-2110
Web Site: http://www.visitmexico.com
Year Founded: 1930
Emp.: 10
Tourism Administrative Services
N.A.I.C.S.: 561591
Rodrigo Esponda (Reg Dir)
Ivan Martinez-Vega (Dir-Northeast)

Subsidiaries:

Mexico Tourism Board-Los Angeles   (1)
2401 W 6th St, Los Angeles, CA 90057
Tel.: (213) 739-6336
Web Site: http://www.visitmexico.com
Emp.: 3
Tourism Administrative Services
N.A.I.C.S.: 561591
Jorge Gamboa Patron (Dir-Strategy, Mktg & Consulting)
Gerardo Llanes (CMO)

MEXICO SALES MADE EASY, INC.
1785 E Sahara Ave Ste 490-941, Las Vegas, NV 89104
Tel.: (619) 616-2973   NV
Web Site: http://www.mexicosalesmadeeasy.com
Year Founded: 2012
Sales Range: Less than $1 Million
Business Consulting Services
N.A.I.C.S.: 541611
Sandro Piancone (CEO)

MEYCO PRODUCTS INC.
1225 Walt Whitman Rd, Melville, NY 11747
Tel.: (631) 421-9800
Web Site: http://www.meycoproducts.com
Sales Range: $10-24.9 Million
Emp.: 100
Mfr of Fabric Liners & Covers
N.A.I.C.S.: 314910
David W. Weissner (Pres)

MEYDA STAINED GLASS STUDIO & LIGHTING CORP.
55 Oriskany Blvd, Yorkville, NY 13495
Tel.: (315) 768-3711
Web Site: http://www.meyda.com
Year Founded: 1975
Rev.: $11,000,000
Emp.: 65
Whslr of Novelty Glassware
N.A.I.C.S.: 238150

Robert Cohen (Pres)
Joe Babicz (Controller)

MEYER & NAJEM INC.
11787 Lantern Rd Ste 100, Fishers, IN 46038
Tel.: (317) 577-0007   IN
Web Site: http://www.meyer-najem.com
Year Founded: 1987
Sales Range: $10-24.9 Million
Emp.: 70
Provider of Nonresidential Construction Services
N.A.I.C.S.: 236220
Karl Meyer (Chm)
Sam Mishelow (Chief Strategy Officer)
Anthony Najem (CEO)
Tim Russell (Pres)
Robert Lawyer (CFO)
Chris McCracken (Exec VP)
Kevin McGovern (Exec VP)
Toby Holcomb (Exec VP-Field Ops)
Matt Weaver (Exec VP-IT)
Nate Lelle (Exec VP)
Traci Hardin (VP-Safety & Compliance)

MEYER & WALLIS, INC.
731 N Jackson St Fl 7, Milwaukee, WI 53202-4615
Tel.: (414) 224-0212   WI
Year Founded: 1967
Rev.: $25,000,000
Emp.: 25
Fiscal Year-end: 12/31/04
N.A.I.C.S.: 541810
Tom Dixon (VP & Dir-Creative)
Fran Weber (CFO)
Cathleen Looze (VP & Media Dir)
Cathy Pritzl (Assoc Dir-Art)
Lynn Becker (Production Mgr)
Tim Wallis (Exec VP & Creative Dir)
Chris Mortenson (CEO)
Shannon Safar (Exec VP-Acct Mgmt)
Lisa Liljegren (Dir-Comm)
Brett Liljegren (Grp Acct Dir)
Jeff McCarthy (Acct Dir)
Betsy Wyant (VP-Acct Svcs)
Karyn Soergel (VP)

Subsidiaries:

Meyer & Wallis, Inc.   (1)
233 McCrae St 12 Fl, Indianapolis, IN 46225-1067
Tel.: (317) 955-9414
Sales Range: $10-24.9 Million
Emp.: 13
Full Service
N.A.I.C.S.: 541810
Tim Wallis (Exec VP & Exec Creative Dir)
Greg Huff (Assoc Dir-Creative)
Betsy Allen (Acct Dir)
Megan Snow (Dir-Art)

MEYER BROTHERS AUTOMOTIVE CO.
1268 Central Park Dr, O'Fallon, IL 62269
Tel.: (618) 622-0588
Web Site: http://www.meyerhonda.com
Sales Range: $25-49.9 Million
Emp.: 40
New & Used Automobiles
N.A.I.C.S.: 441110
Charles H. Meyer (Owner)

MEYER EQUIPMENT, CO.
US Rt 6, Ridgeville Corners, OH 43555
Tel.: (419) 267-3848
Web Site: https://www.meyereq.com
Rev.: $1,400,000
Emp.: 10
Fiscal Year-end: 12/31/10

Farm & Garden Machinery & Equipment Merchant Whslr
N.A.I.C.S.: 423820

MEYER INDUSTRIES INC.
3528 Fredericksburg Rd, San Antonio, TX 78201
Tel.: (210) 736-1811
Web Site: http://www.meyer-industries.com
Sales Range: $25-49.9 Million
Emp.: 95
Conveyors & Conveying Equipment
N.A.I.C.S.: 333922
Julia O'Meara (Mgr-Acctg)

MEYER JABARA HOTELS, LLC
7 Kenosia Ave Ste 2A, Danbury, CT 06810
Tel.: (203) 798-1099
Web Site: http://www.meyerjabarahotels.com
Year Founded: 1977
Sales Range: $150-199.9 Million
Emp.: 1,400
Hotel Owner & Operator
N.A.I.C.S.: 721110
Richard Jabara (Pres & CEO)
William A. Meyer (Chm)
Daroyl McDonald (Sr VP-Pur)
Gail Clarke (Sr VP-HR)
Justin Jabara (VP-Dev & Acquisitions)
George Rendell (Sr VP-Architecture & Construction)
Alan Chandler (CIO)
Bob Hartman (Chief Cultural Officer)
Eric Churchill (Sr VP-Ops)
Henry V. Kelley (CFO)
Mark McGehee (Sr VP-Sls & Mgr-Revenue)
Rick Odorisio (Sr VP)
Ron Antonucci (Sr VP-Ops)

Subsidiaries:

HD Hotel LLC   (1)
7 Kenosia Ave Ste 2A, Danbury, CT 06810
Tel.: (203) 798-1099
Rev.: $11,700,000
Emp.: 25
Hotels & Motels
N.A.I.C.S.: 721110

MEYER NATURAL ANGUS, LLC
1990 Rocky Mountain Ave, Loveland, CO 80538
Tel.: (970) 292-5006
Web Site: http://www.meyernaturalangus.com
Year Founded: 1990
Sales Range: $25-49.9 Million
Emp.: 30
Beef Cattle Ranching, Processing & Whslr
N.A.I.C.S.: 311612
Robert E. Meyer (Founder & Owner)
Bob Meyer (Pres)

Subsidiaries:

Laura's Lean Beef Company   (1)
1792 Alysheba Way Ste 350, Lexington, KY 40509
Tel.: (859) 299-7707
Web Site: http://www.laurasleanbeef.com
Beef Cattle Ranching Processing Mfr
N.A.I.C.S.: 311612
Jeff Tanner (Mgr)

MEYER OIL CO.
1505 W Main St, Teutopolis, IL 62467
Tel.: (217) 857-3163
Web Site: http://www.mach1foodshops.com
Sales Range: $10-24.9 Million
Emp.: 30

U.S. PRIVATE

Owner & Operator of Convenience Stores; Retailer of Petroleum Products
N.A.I.C.S.: 424720
Randy Meyer (Pres)
Terry Meyer (Sec)

MEYER PLASTICS INC.
5167 E 65th St, Indianapolis, IN 46220
Tel.: (317) 259-4131
Web Site: http://www.meyerplastics.com
Sales Range: $10-24.9 Million
Emp.: 65
Plastics Materials & Basic Shapes
N.A.I.C.S.: 424610
Steve Covert (Mgr-Acct)
Larry Pike (Controller)
Chad Becker (VP-Bus Dev)

MEYER PROPERTIES CORP.
4320 Von Karman Ave, Newport Beach, CA 92660-2004
Tel.: (949) 862-0500   CA
Web Site: http://www.meyerprop.com
Year Founded: 1977
Sales Range: $25-49.9 Million
Emp.: 150
Subdividers & Developers
N.A.I.C.S.: 237210
Jim Hasty (Sr VP)

MEYER SERVICE, INC.
6733 Leopard St, Corpus Christi, TX 78409
Tel.: (361) 289-2130   TX
Web Site: http://www.meyernow.com
Year Founded: 2006
Oil Field Machinery & Equipment Mfr
N.A.I.C.S.: 333132

Subsidiaries:

Texas West BOP Sales & Service LLC   (1)
2414 W 49th St, Odessa, TX 79764-3931
Tel.: (432) 366-1133
Oil & Gas Operations
N.A.I.C.S.: 213112
James Rankin (Mgr)

MEYER SOUND LABORATORIES INC.
2832 San Pablo Ave, Berkeley, CA 94702
Tel.: (510) 486-1166
Web Site: http://www.msli.com
Sales Range: $10-24.9 Million
Emp.: 200
Provider of Sound Equipment
N.A.I.C.S.: 334310
John Meyer (CEO)
Cliff Eldridge (CFO)
Michael Maxson (Mgr-Tech Support)
Luke Jenks (Dir-Product Mgmt)
Helen Meyer (Exec VP)
Michael Bogden (Mgr-Sls-Midwest)

MEYER STEEL DRUM INC.
3201 S Millard Ave, Chicago, IL 60623-5028
Tel.: (773) 376-8376   IL
Web Site: http://www.meyersteeldrum.com
Year Founded: 1976
Sales Range: $50-74.9 Million
Emp.: 200
Metal Barrels, Drums & Pails
N.A.I.C.S.: 332439
Ed Meyer (Founder & Pres)
Gregory Rapacz (Plant Mgr)
Cesar Gallardo (Mgr-Maintenance)
O. Joyner (Mgr-HR)

MEYER TOOL INC.

3055 Colerain Ave, Cincinnati, OH 45225-1827
Tel.: (513) 853-4400 — OH
Web Site: http://www.meyertool.com
Year Founded: 1973
Sales Range: $75-99.9 Million
Emp.: 1,000
Aircraft Engines & Engine Parts Mfr
N.A.I.C.S.: 336412
Denise Kohl (Controller)

Subsidiaries:

Florida Aero Precision Inc. (1)
120 Reed Rd, West Palm Beach, FL 33403-3015
Tel.: (561) 848-6248
Web Site: http://www.flaero.com
Sales Range: $10-24.9 Million
Emp.: 30
Aircraft Engines & Engine Parts
N.A.I.C.S.: 336412
Gary Bishop (Engr-Facilities)

MT R&O LLC. (1)
3055 Colerain Ave, Cincinnati, OH 45225
Tel.: (513) 853-4544
Precision Component Mfr
N.A.I.C.S.: 332721
Rose Lawless (Mgr-Quality)

MT Texas LLC. (1)
3614 Highpoint St, San Antonio, TX 78217
Tel.: (210) 599-0060
Web Site: http://www.mt-texas.com
Metallurgical Engineering Services
N.A.I.C.S.: 541330

Meyer Canada Inc. (1)
88 de Vaudreuil, Boucherville, J4B 5G4, QC, Canada
Tel.: (450) 449-5440
Web Site: http://www.meyertool.com
Emp.: 20
Precision Component Mfr
N.A.I.C.S.: 332721

Meyer Tool Poland Sp. z o. o. (1)
Ul Inwestorska 7, 62-800, Kalisz, Poland
Tel.: (48) 62 75 25 101
Web Site: http://www.meyertool.pl
Emp.: 100
Precision Component Mfr
N.A.I.C.S.: 332721
Doug Lang (Gen Mgr-USA)
Slawomir Zdyb (Gen Mgr)

MEYER WIRE & CABLE COMPANY, LLC
1072 Sherman Ave, Hamden, CT 06514-1337
Tel.: (203) 281-0817 — CT
Web Site: http://www.meyerwire.com
Year Founded: 1972
Cable & Coil Cords Designer & Mfr
N.A.I.C.S.: 335931
Brian Meyer (Co-Owner & Pres)

MEYERS PRINTING COMPANY INC.
7277 Boone Ave N, Minneapolis, MN 55428-1519
Tel.: (763) 533-9730 — MN
Web Site: http://www.meyers.com
Year Founded: 1949
Sales Range: $25-49.9 Million
Emp.: 265
Provider of Commercial Printing & Lithographic Services
N.A.I.C.S.: 323111
Micheal Lane (CEO)

MFA INCORPORATED
201 Ray Young Dr, Columbia, MO 65201
Tel.: (573) 874-5111 — MO
Web Site: http://www.mfa-inc.com
Year Founded: 1914
Sales Range: $600-649.9 Million
Emp.: 1,400
Farm Cooperative; Mfr & Marketer of Animal Feeds, Plant Food, Hybrid Seeds; Marketer of Farm Supply Equipment & Grain
N.A.I.C.S.: 459999
Mike John (Dir-Health Track Ops)
Don Mills (Chm)
John Moffitt (Vice Chm)
Ernie Verslues (Pres & CEO)
Stefan Knudsen (Gen Counsel, Sec & VP)
Craig Childs (Sr VP-Agri Svcs)
John Akridge (Treas)
Don Houston (VP-Supply Ops & Mktg)
Wayne Nichols (Co-Chm)

Subsidiaries:

Agmo Corporation (1)
201 Ray Young Dr, Columbia, MO 65201-3568
Tel.: (573) 876-5405
Financial Advisory Services
N.A.I.C.S.: 523940
Mary Poland (Gen Mgr)

MFA Enterprises, Inc. (1)
201 Ray Young Dr, Columbia, MO 65201-3568
Tel.: (573) 874-5111
Web Site: http://www.mfa-inc.com
Farm Supplies Whslr
N.A.I.C.S.: 424910

MFA OIL COMPANY
1 Ray Young Dr, Columbia, MO 65201
Tel.: (573) 442-0171 — MO
Web Site: http://www.mfaoil.com
Year Founded: 1929
Sales Range: $450-499.9 Million
Emp.: 1,500
Fuel & Lubrication Products Mfr; Petroleum & Propane Refiner; Convenience Store Operator
N.A.I.C.S.: 424710
Jon Ihler (CEO)
Janice Serpico (Chief HR Officer)
Curtis Chaney (Sr VP-Retail)
Kenny Steeves (VP-Bulk & Propane Plant Ops)
James Greer (VP-Supply & Distr)
Tami Ensor (Sec)
Marion Kertz (Chm)
Jeff Raetz (CFO)

Subsidiaries:

Brownfield Oil Company, Inc. (1)
1415 Riley Industrial Dr, Moberly, MO 65270-3181
Tel.: (660) 263-7711
Web Site: http://www.brownfieldoil.com
Emp.: 50
Fuel & Lubricants, Branding Options & Transportation Services
N.A.I.C.S.: 424710
Terry Frost (Supvr-HR)

MFA Oil Biomass LLC (1)
1 Ray Young Dr, Columbia, MO 65203
Tel.: (573) 876-0381
Perennial Grass Farming Services
N.A.I.C.S.: 111998

MFG PARTNERS LLC
135 E 57th St 14th Fl, New York, NY 10022
Tel.: (212) 651-4615
Web Site: http://www.mfgpartners.com
Year Founded: 2016
Holding Company
N.A.I.C.S.: 551112
Jeff Mizrahi (Partner)

Subsidiaries:

Miller Advisors Inc. (1)
11 10th Ave, Kirkland, WA 98033-5406
Tel.: (425) 822-8122
Web Site: https://www.milleradvisors.com
Administrative Management & General Management Consulting Services
N.A.I.C.S.: 541611
Nicole Miller (Mng Partner)

Storage Solutions Inc. (1)
910 E 169th St, Westfield, IN 46074
Tel.: (317) 867-2001
Web Site: http://www.storage-solutions.com
Shelving, Commercial & Industrial
N.A.I.C.S.: 423440
Craig R. McElheny (CEO)
Kevin Rowles (Pres)

MFG.COM, INC.
1165 Northchase Pkwy SE Ste 250, Marietta, GA 30067
Tel.: (770) 444-9686 — GA
Web Site: http://www.mfg.com
Year Founded: 2000
Sales Range: $10-24.9 Million
Emp.: 200
Online Marketplace Offering Proprietary Manufacturing Services & Industrial Components
N.A.I.C.S.: 425120
Olivier Gavillot (VP-Ops)
Jean-Francois Blachon (CTO)
Bo Hagler (CEO)
Howard Hoover (CFO)
Allan Sweatt (VP-Product Strategy)
Mike Stein (Dir-Mktg)
Michael Vining (VP-Marketplace Ops)

Subsidiaries:

MFG.com China (1)
9/F The Exchange, No 299 Tongren Rd, Shanghai, 200040, China (100%)
Tel.: (86) 2132039588
Web Site: http://www.mfg.com
Sales Range: $10-24.9 Million
Emp.: 100
Online Seller of Industrial Components
N.A.I.C.S.: 517810
James Jin (Pres-Asia Pacific)

MFJ ENTERPRISES INC.
300 Indus Park Rd, Starkville, MS 39759
Tel.: (662) 323-5869
Web Site: http://www.mfjenterprises.com
Sales Range: $10-24.9 Million
Emp.: 150
Transmitter-Receivers, Radio
N.A.I.C.S.: 334220
Martin F. Jue (Founder & Pres)
Steven Pan (VP)
Richard Stubbs (Mgr-PR & Customer Svcs)

MFM DELAWARE INC.
3951 NW County Line Rd Hwy 329, Reddick, FL 32686
Tel.: (352) 854-0070
Rev.: $16,727,846
Emp.: 80
Fuller's Earth Mining
N.A.I.C.S.: 424690
Ann Chaffin (Controller)

MFORMATION TECHNOLOGIES, INC.
379 Thornall St 10th Fl, Edison, NJ 08837
Tel.: (732) 692-6200 — DE
Web Site: http://www.mformation.com
Year Founded: 2000
Sales Range: $10-24.9 Million
Emp.: 44
Developer of Mobile Device Management Software
N.A.I.C.S.: 513210
Mark Edwards (Co-Founder)
Rakesh Kushwaha (Co-Founder & CTO)
Kevin A. Wood (CEO)
Christine Bolles (VP-Mktg & Product Mgmt)
Luca Ferrari (VP-Sls-EMEA)
Sean Fleming (VP-Bus Dev)

MFS CONSULTING ENGI-

NEERS & SURVEYOR CORPORATION
2780 Hamilton Blvd, South Plainfield, NJ 07080
Tel.: (908) 922-4622
Web Site: http://www.mfsengineers.com
Year Founded: 2009
Civil Engineering & Design Consulting Firm
N.A.I.C.S.: 237990
Michael Mudalel (Mng Partner & Principal Engr)

Subsidiaries:

GEOD Corporation (1)
24 Kanouse Rd, Newfoundland, NJ 07435
Tel.: (973) 697-2122
Web Site: http://www.geodcorp.com
Surveying Services, Nsk
N.A.I.C.S.: 541370
Christopher Emilius (Sec)
John Emilius (Mgr-Bus Dev)

MFS SUPPLY, LLC.
31100 Solon Rd Ste 16, Solon, OH 44139
Tel.: (440) 248-5300
Web Site: http://www.mfssupply.com
Sales Range: $25-49.9 Million
Emp.: 80
Lockbox Contractors & Suppliers
N.A.I.C.S.: 423440
Mike Hajec (Dir-Ops)
Brandon Guzman (Pres)
David Stone (Acct Mgr-Svcs)
Jay Klein (Gen Mgr)
Jonathan Zilber (Dir-Sls)
Kevin Elvington (Mgr-Mktg)
Jeffrey Muencz (CFO)

MFS, INC.
605 Pinetree Cir, Virginia Beach, VA 23452-2638
Tel.: (757) 340-7015
Web Site: http://www.mfsi.com
Year Founded: 1987
Sales Range: $1-9.9 Million
Emp.: 20
Provider of Computer Related Services
N.A.I.C.S.: 811210
Derek Fick (Pres)

MG BUILDING MATERIALS
2651 SW Military Dr, San Antonio, TX 78224-1048
Tel.: (210) 924-8604 — TX
Web Site: http://www.mgbuildingmaterials.com
Year Founded: 1972
Sales Range: $100-124.9 Million
Emp.: 300
Building Materials & Home Improvement Supplies Retailer
N.A.I.C.S.: 423310

Subsidiaries:

MG Building Materials - Truss Division (1)
9405 Highway 81 S, San Antonio, TX 78211
Tel.: (210) 798-0650
Building Materials Distr
N.A.I.C.S.: 423320

MG DESIGN ASSOCIATES CORP.
8778 100th St, Pleasant Prairie, WI 53158
Tel.: (262) 947-8890
Web Site: http://www.mgdesign.com
Sales Range: $1-9.9 Million
Emp.: 80
Showcase, Partition, Shelving & Locker Mfr
N.A.I.C.S.: 337215

MG DESIGN ASSOCIATES CORP.

MG Design Associates Corp.—(Continued)
Mike Grivas (CEO)
Betty Kasper (Exec VP)
Ben Olson (VP-Mktg)
Rob Majerowski (VP-New Bus Strategy)
Kristin Castelli (Mng Dir-West Coast & VP)
Kelli Steckbauer (VP-Ops)
Nicole Magdovitz (Project Mgr)
Josh Melcher (Mgr-Graphic Production)
Tim Stefaniak (Dir-Rental Solutions)
Cindy Yi (VP-IT)
Brook Redemann (VP-Special Projects & Technologies)
Ed Jacquest (Mgr-Transportation)
John Henken (Dir-Design)
Matthew Buchmeyer (Controller)
Sheila Bryant (Mng Dir-Client Experiences)
Paul Fowler (Project Mgr)
Nancy Johnson (Asst VP-Client Experience)
Bunny Hoskins (Acct Mgr)
Jennifer Hinkle (Acct Dir)
Mike Lembrich (Project Mgr)
Steven Wu (Project Mgr)
Bonnie Hansen (Dir-Events)

MG ELECTRIC SERVICE COMPANY
1450 E Algonquin Rd, Arlington Heights, IL 60005
Tel.: (847) 439-7500
Sales Range: $10-24.9 Million
Emp.: 78
General Electrical Contractor
N.A.I.C.S.: 238210
Thomas Desideri (VP)
George Frydrych (Controller)

MG GOLF INC.
3410 Century Cir, Irving, TX 75062
Tel.: (972) 554-4450
Web Site: http://www.mggolf.com
Year Founded: 1965
Sales Range: $10-24.9 Million
Emp.: 40
Golf Equipment
N.A.I.C.S.: 423910
Richard Card (Pres)

MG OIL INC.
1180 Creek Dr, Rapid City, SD 57701
Tel.: (605) 342-0527
Web Site: http://www.mgoil.com
Year Founded: 1976
Sales Range: $50-74.9 Million
Emp.: 200
Gasoline
N.A.I.C.S.: 424720
Marlyn G. Erickson (Pres)

MG PRODUCTS COMPANY
6825 Cielo Vista Dr Ste 25, El Paso, TX 79925
Tel.: (915) 541-8950
Web Site: http://www.mg-products.com
Rev.: $67,400,000
Emp.: 220
Foundry Products
N.A.I.C.S.: 331529

MG WEST COMPANY
2 Shaw Aly Fl 3, San Francisco, CA 94105-0904
Tel.: (415) 284-4800
Web Site: http://www.mgwest.com
Sales Range: $10-24.9 Million
Emp.: 30
Office Furniture
N.A.I.C.S.: 423210
Katy Baroni (Principal)
Melissa Henry (Project Coord)

Lili Hu (Principal-Fin & Ops)
Cristina Figone (Dir-Bus Dev & Mktg)
Brenna Bianchi (Dir-Acct Mgmt)
Jaime Swickward (Principal)
Hilary Hanhan (Acct Mgr)

MGA EMPLOYEE SERVICES INC.
3131 E Camelback Rd, Phoenix, AZ 85016
Tel.: (602) 508-1883
Web Site: http://www.mgasearch.com
Rev.: $12,045,711
Emp.: 200
Help Supply Services
N.A.I.C.S.: 561320
Dave Zowine (Owner)

MGA ENTERTAINMENT, INC.
16300 Roscoe Blvd Ste 150, Van Nuys, CA 91406
Tel.: (818) 894-2525
Web Site: http://www.mgae.com
Year Founded: 1979
Sales Range: $1-9.9 Million
Emp.: 1,600
Toy Developer & Licensor
N.A.I.C.S.: 423920
Isaac Larian (Founder & CEO)
Bruce Morrison (Exec VP-Sls & Licensing)
Sapienza Salerno (Mng Dir-Sydney)
Sandrine De Rasped (Gen Mgr-Intl Sls & Licensing)
Martin J. Elliott (CFO)

Subsidiaries:

MGA Entertainment (UK) Ltd. (1)
50 Presley Way Crownhill, Milton Keynes, MK8 0ES, Buckinghamshire, United Kingdom
Tel.: (44) 1908 268480
Emp.: 30
Game & Toy Product Retailer
N.A.I.C.S.: 459120
Sarah Walker (Mgr-HR)

MGA Zapf Creation GmbH (1)
Monchrodener Str 13, 96472, Rodental, Germany (100%)
Tel.: (49) 95637250
Web Site: http://www.zapf-creation.com
Sales Range: $75-99.9 Million
Emp.: 69
Dolls & Doll Accessories Mfr
N.A.I.C.S.: 339930
Thomas Eichhorn (Pres)

Subsidiary (Non-US):

Zapf Creation (Polska) Sp. z o.o. (2)
Poleczki Street 23, Platan Park II Building, 02-822, Warsaw, Poland
Tel.: (48) 223352171
Hobby Toy & Game Stores
N.A.I.C.S.: 459120

Zapf Creation (U.K.) Ltd. (2)
6 Presley Way, Crownhill, Milton Keynes, MK8 0ES, United Kingdom
Tel.: (44) 1908268480
Web Site: http://www.zapfcreation.co.uk
Emp.: 30
Doll & Stuffed Toy Mfr
N.A.I.C.S.: 339930
Andrew Lotten (Mng Dir)

Subsidiary (Domestic):

Zapf Creation Logistics GmbH & Co. KG (2)
Monchrodener Strabe 13, 96472, Rodental, Germany
Tel.: (49) 956372530
Web Site: http://www.zapf-creation.com
Process Physical Distribution & Logistics Consulting Services
N.A.I.C.S.: 541614

The Little Tikes Company (1)
2180 Barlow Rd, Hudson, OH 44236-4108
Tel.: (330) 650-3000
Web Site: http://www.littletikes.com
Rev.: $12,000,000

Emp.: 600
Toy Mfr
N.A.I.C.S.: 339930
Laurie Frankino (Coord-Mktg)

Division (Domestic):

Iron Mountain Forge Corporation (2)
PO Box 897, Farmington, MO 63640-0897
Tel.: (573) 756-4591
Commercial Playground Systems
N.A.I.C.S.: 339930

MGB BANCSHARES, INC.
511 Lake Land Blvd, Mattoon, IL 61938
Tel.: (217) 234-7900   DE
Web Site: http://www.fnbbankingcenters.com
Bank Holding Company
N.A.I.C.S.: 551111
Preston G. Smith (CEO-First National Bank)

Subsidiaries:

The First National Bank (1)
511 Lake Land Blvd, Mattoon, IL 61938
Tel.: (217) 234-7900
Web Site: http://www.fnbbankingcenters.com
Sales Range: $1-9.9 Million
Emp.: 20
Commericial Banking
N.A.I.C.S.: 522110
Preston G. Smith (CEO)
John Covington (Pres)

MGDM HOLDINGS CO.
9301 Marine City Hwy, Fair Haven, MI 48023
Tel.: (586) 725-8227   MI
Web Site: http://www.modinteriors.com
Year Founded: 1982
Sales Range: $1-9.9 Million
Emp.: 27
Millwork (including Flooring)
N.A.I.C.S.: 321918

MGE MANAGEMENT EXPERTS, INC.
11800 30th Ct N, Pinellas Park, FL 33716
Tel.: (727) 530-4277
Web Site: http://www.mgeonline.com
Year Founded: 2007
Sales Range: $10-24.9 Million
Emp.: 40
Management Development Training Services
N.A.I.C.S.: 611430
Luis A. Colon (Owner, Chm & CEO)
Gregory A. Winteregg (Owner)

MGG INVESTMENT GROUP, LP
1 Penn Plz 53rd Fl, New York, NY 10119
Tel.: (212) 356-6100
Web Site: http://mgginv.com
Financial Services
N.A.I.C.S.: 541611
Kevin F. Griffin (CEO & Chief Investment Officer)
Gregory Racz (Pres)
Mustafa Tayeb (CFO)
Eran Cohen (Mng Dir)
Kevin Griffin (Founder, CEO, Mng Partner & CIO)
Dale Stohr (Mng Dir)

Subsidiaries:

Spring Mountain Vineyards, Inc. (1)
2805 Spring Mountain Rd, Saint Helena, CA 94574-1775
Tel.: (707) 967-4188
Web Site: https://www.springmountainvineyard.com

U.S. PRIVATE

Sales Range: $1-9.9 Million
Emp.: 42
Farm Management Services
N.A.I.C.S.: 115116
Don Yannias (Chm & Pres)
Kenneth Barbour (Dir-Intl Sls, Strategy & Key Accts)
Ron Rosenbrand (Mgr-Vineyard)
Valli Ferrell (Dir-PR)
Leah Smith (Dir-Customer Rels & Events)
Marilyn Ferrante (Asst Mgr-Tasting Room)
Doris Capovilla (Coord-Wine Club)
Lindsay McArdle (Mgr-Tasting Room)
Samantha Francis (Mgr-Wine Club, E-Commerce & Social Media)
Susan Doyle (Dir-Technical-Vineyards & Winemaking)

MGH, INC.
100 Painters Mill Rd Ste 600, Owings Mills, MD 21117-7305
Tel.: (410) 902-5000   MD
Web Site: http://www.mghus.com
Year Founded: 1995
Sales Range: $50-74.9 Million
Emp.: 80
Advetising Agency
N.A.I.C.S.: 541810
Andy Malis (CEO)
John Patterson (Exec VP & Dir-Creative)
Jane Goldstrom (Pres, COO & Dir-Media)
Mike Skandalis (Exec VP & Dir-Plng)
Shelley Welsh (CFO & Exec VP)
Chris McMurry (VP & Dir-PR)
Kristi Betz (VP-PR & Dir-Acct)
Cheryl Peluso (Sr VP & Dir-Acct Svcs)
Marah Schmitz (Acct Mgr)
Lindsey Halpin (Acct Dir)
Allison Randall (Sr Dir-Interactive Art)
Melissa Gray (VP-Integrated Media)
Katie Cresswell (VP & Dir-Interactive Ops)
Paul Didwall (Acct Coord-Social Media Mktg)
Kerry Owens (VP & Dir-PR Acct)
Ed Repasky (Sr VP & Dir-Acct)

MGM GOLD COMMUNICATIONS
228 E 45th St Rm 601, New York, NY 10017-3335
Tel.: (212) 869-7323   NY
Web Site: http://www.mgmgoldcommunications.com
Year Founded: 1980
Rev.: $18,000,000
Emp.: 12
Advertising Agency
N.A.I.C.S.: 541810
Mario G. Messina (Pres & Exec Dir-Creative)
Ronald D. Gold (Partner & Exec Dir-Creative)

MGM INDUSTRIES, INC.
287 Freehill Rd, Hendersonville, TN 37075-2136
Tel.: (615) 824-6572
Web Site: http://www.mgmindustries.com
Year Founded: 1965
Sales Range: $10-24.9 Million
Emp.: 130
Metal Window & Door Mfr
N.A.I.C.S.: 332321
Lisa Dill (Office Mgr)

MGM WINE & SPIRITS INC.
2550 University Ave W Ste 230 S, Saint Paul, MN 55113
Tel.: (651) 487-1006
Web Site: http://www.mgmwineandspirits.com
Year Founded: 1970
Rev.: $12,700,000
Emp.: 41

Hard Liquor
N.A.I.C.S.: 445320
Paul Setter (Gen Mgr)
Dana Mudgett (Controller)
Mike Behrendt (Owner & CEO)

MGN & ASSOCIATES INC.
11 Dana Hill Rd, Sterling, MA 01564
Tel.: (978) 422-0292
Web Site: http://www.mgn-assoc.com
Rev.: $20,000,000
Emp.: 7
Wire & Cable
N.A.I.C.S.: 423610
Robert J. Gingras (Pres)

MGR EQUIPMENT CORP.
22 Gates Ave, Inwood, NY 11096-1612
Tel.: (516) 239-3030
Web Site: http://www.mgrequip.com
Sales Range: $10-24.9 Million
Emp.: 38
Mfr of Refrigeration, Ice & Air Conditioning Equipment
N.A.I.C.S.: 333415
Gerald Ross (CEO & CFO)
George Mauder (VP)

MGS MACHINE CORPORATION
9900 85th Ave N, Maple Grove, MN 55369
Tel.: (763) 425-8808   MN
Web Site:
   http://www.mgsmachine.com
Year Founded: 1979
Sales Range: $10-24.9 Million
Emp.: 90
Packaging Machinery
N.A.I.C.S.: 333993
Richard Bahr (CEO)
Richard Bahr (Pres & CEO)
Bob King (Engr-Applications)
Ross Dalheimer (Mgr-Mfg)
Tim Allen (Reg Mgr-Sls)
Travis Dreier (Engr-Controls)
Casey DiChiria (Mgr-Sls-Western United States & Intl)
Steve Hallblade (Dir-Bus Dev)

MGS MANUFACTURING GROUP, INC.
W 188 N 11707 Maple Rd, Germantown, WI 53022-2409
Tel.: (262) 255-5790   WI
Web Site: http://www.mgstech.com
Year Founded: 1982
Sales Range: $125-149.9 Million
Emp.: 800
Engineering, Design & Production of Plastic Injection Molding Tools & Parts
N.A.I.C.S.: 326199
Mark Sellers (CEO)
John Berg (Dir-Mktg)
Subsidiaries:

Moldmakers Incorporated   (1)
W188 N 11707 Maple Rd, Germantown, WI 53022
Tel.: (262) 255-5790
Rev.: $28,444,978
Emp.: 500
Designs & Builds Plastic Injection Molds
N.A.I.C.S.: 333511

Moldmakers Management Inc.   (1)
W188n11707 Maple Rd, Germantown, WI 53022-2409
Tel.: (262) 255-5790
Web Site: http://www.mgstech.com
Sales Range: $25-49.9 Million
Emp.: 260
Special Dies, Tools, Jigs & Fixtures
N.A.I.C.S.: 551112

Subsidiary (Domestic):
Caddplus Inc.   (2)
W188 N 11707 Maple Rd, Germantown, WI 53022-2409
Tel.: (262) 255-5790
Web Site: http://www.mgstech.com
Rev.: $650,000
Emp.: 15
Computer Integrated Systems Design
N.A.I.C.S.: 541512

Moldmakers Die Cast Tooling Division Inc.   (2)
W188 N11707 Maple Rd, Germantown, WI 53022
Tel.: (262) 255-5790
Web Site: http://www.mgsmfg.com
Rev.: $2,931,874
Emp.: 20
Special Dies, Tools, Jigs & Fixtures
N.A.I.C.S.: 333514

O & S Designs Inc.   (2)
W 188 N 11707 Maple Rd, Germantown, WI 53022-2409
Tel.: (262) 255-5790
Web Site: http://www.mgstech.com
Rev.: $4,206,915
Emp.: 100
Business Services
N.A.I.C.S.: 541420

Tecstar Mfg. Group, Inc.   (1)
W 190 N 11701 Moldmakers Way, Germantown, WI 53022-2463
Tel.: (262) 250-2950
Web Site: http://www.mgstech.com
Rev.: $30,000,000
Emp.: 400
Plastic Injection Molding Production Company
N.A.I.C.S.: 326199
Paul Manley (Pres)

MH EQUIPMENT COMPANY
2001 E Hartman Rd, Chillicothe, IL 61523
Tel.: (309) 579-8020
Web Site:
   http://www.mhequipment.com
Sales Range: $50-74.9 Million
Emp.: 400
Industrial Machinery & Equipment Sales & Rentals
N.A.I.C.S.: 423830
John S. Wieland (Owner & CEO)
Randy Kaluza (Pres)
Subsidiaries:

MH Equipment   (1)
106 Cir Freeway Dr, Cincinnati, OH 45246-1204
Tel.: (513) 681-2200
Web Site: http://www.mhequipment.com
Sales Range: $50-74.9 Million
Emp.: 62
Industrial Machinery & Equipment Sales & Rentals
N.A.I.C.S.: 423830
Paul Hagedorn (Mgr)

MH Equipment   (1)
3306 Gilmore Industrial Blvd, Louisville, KY 40213-2173
Tel.: (502) 962-6560
Web Site: http://www.mhequipment.com
Sales Range: $50-74.9 Million
Emp.: 50
Industrial Machinery & Equipment Sales & Rentals
N.A.I.C.S.: 423830
Bill Meek (Pres)

MH PRIVATE EQUITY FUND, LLC
6270 Corporate Dr Ste 200, Indianapolis, IN 46278
Tel.: (317) 582-2100   IN
Privater Equity Firm
N.A.I.C.S.: 523999
Stephen H. Hilbert (CEO)

MHC SYSTEMS, LLC
8818 Washington Cir, Omaha, NE 68127
Tel.: (402) 339-2110   NE
Web Site:
   http://www.mhcsystems.com
Year Founded: 1973
Sales Range: $1-9.9 Million
Emp.: 42
Industrial Machinery & Equipment Merchant Whslr
N.A.I.C.S.: 423830
Paul Mecklenburg (Owner)

MHD ENTERPRISES
9715A Burnet Rd Ste 125, Austin, TX 78758
Tel.: (512) 992-2565
Web Site:
   http://www.mhdenterprises.com
Year Founded: 2007
Sales Range: $1-9.9 Million
Emp.: 17
Electronic Product Logistics Consulting Services
N.A.I.C.S.: 541614
Michael Dadashi (CEO)

MHF INC.
2328 Evans City Rd, Zelienople, PA 16063
Tel.: (724) 452-3900
Year Founded: 1983
Sales Range: $1-9.9 Million
Emp.: 55
Trucking Except Local
N.A.I.C.S.: 484121
Thomas B. Wylie (Pres)

MHI HOTELS LLC
6411 Ivy Ln Ste 510, Greenbelt, MD 20770
Tel.: (301) 474-3307
Web Site:
   http://www.chesapeakehospitality.com
Rev.: $12,000,000
Emp.: 15
Hotels & Motels
N.A.I.C.S.: 721110
Kim E. Sims (Pres)

MHI PARTNERSHIP LTD.
7676 Woodway Dr Ste 104, Houston, TX 77063-1521
Tel.: (713) 260-4141   TX
Web Site:
   http://www.mcguyerhomebuilders.com
Year Founded: 1991
Sales Range: $10-24.9 Million
Emp.: 347
Provider of Building Services
N.A.I.C.S.: 236115
Frank B. McGuyer (Chm & CEO)
Gary Tesch (Pres)
William McKinnie (Gen Counsel)
David Bruning (CFO)
Keith Faseler (Pres-Land Div)
Denny Garrett (Pres-Dallas Fort Worth, Austin & San Antonio Reg)

MHJ GROUP INC.
3666 Debby Dr Ste B, Montgomery, AL 36108
Tel.: (334) 281-0097
Web Site: http://www.mhjgroup.com
Rev.: $15,000,000
Emp.: 6
Millwork
N.A.I.C.S.: 321918

MHR FUND MANAGEMENT LLC
40 W 57th St Ste 24, New York, NY 10019-4009
Tel.: (212) 262-0005

Web Site: http://www.mhrfund.com
Investment Banking & Securities Dealing
N.A.I.C.S.: 523150
Janet T. Yeung (Principal & Gen Counsel)
Hillel Y. Goldstein (Co-Founder & Mng Principal)
Mark H. Rachesky (Co-Founder & Mng Principal)

MHR MANAGEMENT LLC
33 Silver St, Portland, ME 04101
Tel.: (207) 358-7888   ME
Web Site:
   https://www.mhrmanagement.com
Year Founded: 2010
Parking Garage Operator
N.A.I.C.S.: 812930
Steven P. Kalisz (Gen Mgr)

MHT HOUSING, INC.
32600 Telegraph Rd Ste 102, Bingham Farms, MI 48025
Tel.: (248) 833-0550   MI
Web Site: http://www.mhthousing.net
Sales Range: $25-49.9 Million
Emp.: 10
Apartment Building Construction
N.A.I.C.S.: 236116
Timothy Van Fox (Chm)
Christopher Bric (Exec VP)
Chad Joseph (Dir-Dev)
Aimee Vito (Project Coord)
Subsidiaries:

MHT Properties VII Inc.   (1)
20505 W 12 Mi Rd, Southfield, MI 48076
Tel.: (248) 352-0380
Rev.: $180,000
Emp.: 3
Investor
N.A.I.C.S.: 523999

MHW LTD.
1129 Northern Blvd Ste 312, Manhasset, NY 11030
Tel.: (516) 869-9170
Web Site: http://www.mhwltd.com
Rev.: $31,000,000
Emp.: 80
Retail Wine
N.A.I.C.S.: 424820
John F. Beaudette (Pres & CEO)
Scott L. Saul (Exec VP)
MaryAnn Pisani (VP)
Hilary Rick (Controller)

MHZ NETWORKS
8101A Lee Hwy, Falls Church, VA 22042
Tel.: (703) 770-7100   VA
Web Site:
   http://www.mhznetworks.org
Year Founded: 2010
Sales Range: $10-24.9 Million
Television Professional Association
N.A.I.C.S.: 813920
Frederick Thomas (CEO)
Lisa Murphy (Treas & Dir-Acctg)
Nigeen Sadozai (Sec)

MI TECHNOLOGIES, INC.
2215 Paseo De Las Americas Ste 30, San Diego, CA 92154
Tel.: (858) 779-9045
Web Site:
   http://www.mitechnologiesinc.com
Year Founded: 2004
Sales Range: $10-24.9 Million
Emp.: 85
Industrial Supplies Whslr
N.A.I.C.S.: 424130
Ankit Gulati (Project Mgr)

MI-MED SUPPLY CO. INC.
1390 Decision St Ste B, Vista, CA 92081

MI-MED SUPPLY CO. INC.

Mi-Med Supply Co. Inc.—(Continued)
Tel.: (760) 734-6648　　CA
Web Site: http://www.mimedsupply.com
Year Founded: 1999
Medical Supplies Distr
N.A.I.C.S.: 423450
Robert Wolf Jr. (Pres & CEO)

Subsidiaries:

Peaks & Plains Medical, Inc. (1)
6326 E Trent Ave Ste A, Spokane Valley, WA 99212-1220
Tel.: (509) 922-1572
Web Site: http://www.peaks-plains.com
Medical Supplies Distr & Retailer
N.A.I.C.S.: 423450
Leigh McNellis (VP)

Rocklyn Medical Supply, Inc. (1)
505 1st St, Davenport, WA 99122
Tel.: (509) 786-3432
Web Site: http://www.rocklynmedical.com
Medical Supplies Distr
N.A.I.C.S.: 423450
Dian S. Jones (VP)

MI-T-M CORPORATION

8650 Enterprise Dr, Peosta, IA 52068
Tel.: (563) 556-7484　　IA
Web Site: http://www.mitm.com
Year Founded: 1971
Sales Range: $10-24.9 Million
Emp.: 312
Provider of Industrial Machinery Products & Services
N.A.I.C.S.: 333998
A. J. Spiegel (Founder & CEO)
Dana Schrack (VP)
Sam Humphrey (Pres)
Tom Allendorf (Mng Dir-Ops)
Pat White (Dir-Production)
Steve Gaul (Dir-Matls)
Karen Anderson (Mgr-Mktg)
Barry McDermott (Mgr-Pur)
Susan Haxmeier (Mgr-HR)
John Lembezeder (Dir-Fabrication)
Bryan McCarron (Mgr-Air Compressor Div)
Dennis Waller (Mgr-Consumer Div)
Matt Hoefer (Mgr-Equipment Div)
Vaughn Grimm (Mgr-Govt Div)
Rich Zurcher (Mgr-Ops-Engrg)
Jeff Schlichte (Mgr-Paint Div)
Brian Ruden (Mgr-Quality Control)
Laura Runde (Mgr-Sls Ops)
Aaron Auger (Mgr-Water Treatment)
David Nelson (Mgr-Credit)

MI5 PRINT & DIGITAL COMMUNICATIONS

757 Third Ave, New York, NY 10017
Tel.: (212) 376-6223
Web Site: http://www.mi5print.com
Year Founded: 2002
Printing Solutions Services
N.A.I.C.S.: 323120
Derek McGeachie (Pres & CEO)
Sheryk Sauder (Partner)
Steve Tahk (Exec VP & Gen Mgr)

MI9 RETAIL, INC.

12000 Biscayne Blvd Ste 600, Miami, FL 33181
Web Site: http://www.mi9retail.com
Year Founded: 2001
Enterprise Retail Merchandising, Business Intelligence & Store Operations Software & Services
N.A.I.C.S.: 513210
Neil Moses (CEO)
Jason Williams (Pres & COO)
Charles Kaplan (Chief Revenue Officer)
John Sarvari (CTO)
Karina DuQuesne (Gen Counsel & Sr VP-Admin)

Subsidiaries:

MyWebGrocer Inc. (1)
20 Winooski Falls Way 5th Fl, Winooski, VT 05404
Tel.: (888) 662-2284
Web Site: http://www.mywebgrocer.com
Online Groceries Services
N.A.I.C.S.: 424490
Jaclyn Nix (VP-CPG Sls & Shopper Mktg)

Raymark Xpert Business Systems Inc. (1)
5460 Cote de Liesse Rd, Montreal, H4P 1A5, QC, Canada
Tel.: (514) 737-0941
Web Site: http://www.raymark.com
Emp.: 110
Enterprise Retail Software Solutions
N.A.I.C.S.: 513210
Marc Chriqui (Pres)
Claude Chriqui (CEO)
Danielle Chagnon (CFO)
Claude Roberge (Dir-Ops)
Sherry Egerton (VP-Bus Dev & Dir-Sls)

Subsidiary (Non-US):

Raymark Asia Limited (2)
2705 27F 600 Luban Road, Huangpu District, Shanghai, 200023, China
Tel.: (86) 2168869980
Software Development Services
N.A.I.C.S.: 541511

Raymark Europe (2)
24-26 rue des Gaudines, Saint Germain-en-Laye, 78100, France
Tel.: (33) 1 39 04 00 40
Software Development Services
N.A.I.C.S.: 541511
Marika Fassone (Mgr-Mktg & Comm)

Subsidiary (US):

Retaligent Solutions, Inc. (2)
1050 Crown Pointe Pkwy, Atlanta, GA 30338
Tel.: (770) 379-0440
Web Site: http://www.retaligent.com
Sales Range: $25-49.9 Million
Emp.: 15
Computer & Computer Peripheral Equipment & Software Merchant Whslr
N.A.I.C.S.: 423430

MIACO MEDIA INC.

PO Box 1286, Aliquippa, PA 15001
Tel.: (412) 848-7788
Web Site: http://miacomedia.com
Year Founded: 2003
Sales Range: $1-9.9 Million
Emp.: 8
Media Buying Services
N.A.I.C.S.: 541810
Mike Sutherland (Owner)

MIAMI AUTOMOTIVE RETAIL, INC.

665 SW 8th St, Miami, FL 33130
Tel.: (305) 856-3000
Web Site: http://www.brickellmotors.com
Year Founded: 1981
Sales Range: $75-99.9 Million
Emp.: 200
Car Dealership Owner & Operator
N.A.I.C.S.: 441110
Mario Murgado (Pres & CEO)

MIAMI BEACH COMMUNITY HEALTH CENTER, INC.

11645 Biscayne Blvd Ste 207, Miami, FL 33181
Tel.: (305) 538-8835　　FL
Web Site: http://www.miamibeachhealth.org
Year Founded: 1977
Sales Range: $25-49.9 Million
Emp.: 316
Community Health Care Services
N.A.I.C.S.: 622110
Sorangely Menjivar (Sr Exec VP-Patient Svcs)
Orlando Taquechel (Sr Exec VP-Project Mgmt)
Mark L. Rabinowitz (CEO & Chief Medical Officer)
Jose Ortega (Exec VP-HIV & AIDS Svcs)
Mark Delvaux (CFO)
Dennis Cadiz (Chief Compliance Officer & Sr Exec VP-IT)
David Chamberlain (Treas)
Mitchell Rubinson (Chm)
Therese Gibb (VP)
Myriam Notkin (Sec)

MIAMI CHILDREN'S HOSPITAL

3100 SW 62nd Ave, Miami, FL 33155
Tel.: (305) 666-6511
Web Site: http://www.mch.com
Year Founded: 1950
Sales Range: $450-499.9 Million
Emp.: 3,200
Children's Hospital
N.A.I.C.S.: 622310
Deise Granado-Villar (Chief Medical Officer & Sr VP-Medical & Academic Affairs)
M. Narendra Kini (Pres & CEO)
Edward Martinez (CIO & Sr VP)
Keith Ward (Sec)
Jefry L. Biehler (Sec)
Jaret L. Davis (Vice Chm)
Alex Soto (Chm)
Timothy Birkenstock (CFO & Treas)

MIAMI CITY BALLET, INC.

2200 Liberty Ave, Miami Beach, FL 33139
Tel.: (305) 929-7000　　FL
Web Site: http://www.miamicityballet.org
Year Founded: 1985
Sales Range: $10-24.9 Million
Emp.: 100
Ballet Production Services
N.A.I.C.S.: 711120
Abram Best (Mgr)
Nicole M. Mitchell (Mgr-Production Stage)
Haydee Morales (Designer-Costume)
Caroline Murray (Asst Mgr-Mktg)
Michelle Cote (Asst Mgr-Stage)
Lourdes Lopez (Dir-Artistic)
Eva Silverstein (Dir-Dev)
Jeffrey Parks (Dir-Mktg & Comm)
Terry Schechter (Dir-Outreach & Special Projects)
Andrea Arauz (Mgr-Membership)
Stella Braudy (Mgr-School Programs & Intl Rels)
Michael Tiknis (Interim Exec Dir)
Katia Carranza (Principal)
Renan Cerdeiro (Principal)
Tricia Albertson (Principal)
Tania Castroverde Moskalenko (Exec Dir)
AnaMaria Correa (Sr Dir-Community Engagement)
Kristi Jernigan (Chm)
Meghan Bulfin Monteiro (Mgr-Dev & Outreach-Palm Beach)
Jonah Pruitt III (CFO)

MIAMI CORP.

720 Anderson Ferry Rd, Cincinnati, OH 45238
Tel.: (513) 451-6700
Web Site: http://www.miamicorp.com
Sales Range: $10-24.9 Million
Emp.: 50
Automotive & Marine Trim Products Distr
N.A.I.C.S.: 424310
Tim Niehaus (CEO)
Dan Niehaus (VP-Acctg & IT)
Kevin P. Niehaus (VP-Ops)
Michael Lindemuth (Controller)
Robert Lippert (Gen Mgr-Jacksonville)
John E. Rau (Pres & CEO)
Joe Taylor (Mgr-Warehouse-Cincinnati)
Larry Sherwood (Dir-Mktg)

MIAMI DOWNTOWN DEVELOPMENT AUTHORITY

200 S Biscayne Blvd Ste 2929, Miami, FL 33131
Tel.: (305) 579-6675
Web Site: http://www.miamidda.com
Sales Range: $1-9.9 Million
Emp.: 26
Urban Development
N.A.I.C.S.: 925120
Alyce Robertson (Exec Dir)

MIAMI FOUNDATION

40 NW 3rd St Ste 305, Miami, FL 33128
Tel.: (305) 371-2711　　FL
Web Site: http://www.miamifoundation.org
Year Founded: 1967
Sales Range: $25-49.9 Million
Emp.: 21
Grantmaking Services
N.A.I.C.S.: 813211
Matthew Beatty (Dir-Comm)
Pamela Olmo (CFO & VP-Fin & Admin)
Javier Alberto Soto (Pres & CEO)
Charisse Grant (Sr VP-Programs)
Rebecca Mandelman (VP-Strategy & Engagement)
Juan Martinez (Treas & Sec)

MIAMI INDUSTRIAL TRUCKS INC.

2830 E River Rd, Dayton, OH 45439-1538
Tel.: (937) 396-6382　　OH
Web Site: http://www.mitlift.com
Year Founded: 1956
Sales Range: $25-49.9 Million
Emp.: 150
Provider of Industrial Machinery & Equipment
N.A.I.C.S.: 423830
Mark G. Jones (Pres & CEO)

Subsidiaries:

Miami Industrial Trucks Inc. (1)
3485 Silica Rd Ste D, Sylvania, OH 43560　　(100%)
Tel.: (419) 841-1380
Web Site: http://www.mitlift.com
Sales Range: $10-24.9 Million
Emp.: 10
Material Handling Rental & Distr
N.A.I.C.S.: 532120
Jim Shriner (Mgr-Ops)

MIAMI INTERNATIONAL AIRPORT

PO Box 592075, Miami, FL 33159
Tel.: (305) 876-7000
Web Site: http://www.miami-airport.com
Sales Range: $650-699.9 Million
Emp.: 1,435
Airport Transportation Services
N.A.I.C.S.: 488119
Chris Mangos (Dir-Mktg Div)
Ken Pyatt (Deputy Dir-Miami-Dade Aviation Dept)
Milton Collins (Assoc Dir-Minority Affairs)
Tony Quintero (Assoc Dir-Govt Affairs)
Dickie K. Davis (Dir-Pub & Customer Rels)
Evelyn Campos (Dir-Pro Compliance Div)

Gregory C. Owens *(Asst Dir-Bus Retention & Dev)*
Irving A. Fourcand *(Dir-Protocol & Intl Affairs Div)*
Ivonne M. Davila *(Dir-Fin Plng & Performance Analysis Div)*
Jeff Bunting *(Dir-Noise Abatement & Gen Aviation Airports Div)*
Lonny Craven *(Dir-Airside Ops Div)*
Marie Clark-Vincent *(Dir-Contracts Admin Div)*
Maurice Jenkins *(Dir-Info Sys & Telecomm Div)*
Neivy Garcia *(Dir-Commodities Mgmt Div)*
Pedro Hernandez *(Asst Dir-Facilities Dev)*
Sandra Bridgeman *(CFO)*
Jose A. Ramos *(Dir-Aviation Plng, Land Use & Grants Div)*
Yolanda Sanchez *(Dir-Fine Arts & Cultural Affairs Div)*
Barbara Jimenez *(Asst Dir-Admin)*
Daniel J. Agostino *(Asst Dir-Ops)*
Wallace Madry Jr. *(Dir-HR Div)*

MIAMI INTERNATIONAL HOLDINGS, INC.
7 Roszel Rd, Princeton, NJ 08540
Tel.: (609) 987-0100
Web Site: http://www.miaxoptions.com
Custom Computer Programming Services
N.A.I.C.S.: 541511
Thomas P. Gallagher *(Pres)*

Subsidiaries:

Bermuda Stock Exchange (1)
30 Victoria Street, PO Box HM 1369, Hamilton, HM FX, Bermuda
Tel.: (441) 292 7212
Web Site: http://www.bsx.com
Stock Exchange Services
N.A.I.C.S.: 523210
Greg Wojciechowski *(Pres & CEO)*
Neville Caines *(Mgr-Ops)*
Ian Havercroft *(Mgr-IT)*
James McKirdy *(Chief Compliance Officer)*
David A. Brown *(Chm)*

Dorman Trading Company, Inc. (1)
141 W Jackson Blvd, Chicago, IL 60604
Tel.: (312) 341-7070
Web Site: http://www.dormantrading.com
Rev.: $1,200,000
Emp.: 8
Wholesale Trade Agents & Brokers
N.A.I.C.S.: 425120

Minneapolis Grain Exchange, Inc. (1)
400 S 4th St Ste 130 Grain Exchange Bldg, Minneapolis, MN 55415
Tel.: (612) 321-7101
Web Site: http://www.mgex.com
Sales Range: $1-9.9 Million
Emp.: 37
Securities & Commodity Exchanges
N.A.I.C.S.: 523210
Mark G. Bagan *(Pres & CEO)*
Layne G. Carlson *(Treas & Sec)*

MIAMI SUBS CAPITAL PARTNERS I, INC.
901 Clint Moore Rd Ste A, Boca Raton, FL 33487
Tel.: (954) 973-0000
Web Site: http://mymiamigrill.com
Investment Services
N.A.I.C.S.: 523999

Subsidiaries:

Miami Subs Corporation (1)
891 W Commercial Blvd, Fort Lauderdale, FL 33309
Tel.: (954) 768-9100
Web Site: http://mymiamigrill.com
Operates & Franchises Miami Subs Restaurants
N.A.I.C.S.: 722513

Subsidiary (Domestic):

Miami Subs USA, Inc. (2)
828 W Oakland Park Blvd, Fort Lauderdale, FL 33311 (100%)
Tel.: (954) 561-5055
Web Site: http://www.miamisubs.com
Sales Range: $10-24.9 Million
Emp.: 20
Manages Mr. Submarine/Miami Subs Restaurants
N.A.I.C.S.: 722513

MIAMI VALLEY CHILD DEVELOPMENT CENTERS, INC.
215 Horace St, Dayton, OH 45402-8318
Tel.: (937) 226-5664 OH
Web Site: http://www.mvcdc.org
Year Founded: 1964
Sales Range: $25-49.9 Million
Emp.: 550
Child Development Services
N.A.I.C.S.: 624110
Mary Burns *(Pres & CEO)*
Dayvenia Chesney *(COO)*
Jeffrey Lakes *(CFO)*
Anthony Cruz *(Vice Chm)*
Steve Goubeaux *(Chm)*

MIAMI-LUKEN INC.
265 S Pioneer Blvd, Springboro, OH 45066-1180
Tel.: (937) 743-7775 OH
Web Site: http://www.miamiluken.com
Year Founded: 1968
Sales Range: $10-24.9 Million
Emp.: 68
Drugs, Proprietaries & Sundries
N.A.I.C.S.: 424210
Jim Lyons *(Controller)*
Anthony Rattini *(Pres & CEO)*

MIB GROUP INC.
50 BrainTree Hillpark St 400, Braintree, MA 02184
Tel.: (781) 329-4500
Web Site: http://www.mib.com
Rev.: $26,000,000
Emp.: 175
Information Bureaus, Insurance
N.A.I.C.S.: 524298
Brian Millman *(Head-Electronic Health Records Solutions Platform)*
David Acselrod *(Vice Chm)*
Arthur J. Roberts *(Chm)*
Brian Winikoff *(Pres & CEO)*
Trey Reynolds *(Exec VP-Strategy & Bus Dev)*
Andrea Caruso *(COO & Exec VP)*
Christie Corado *(Chief Privacy Officer, Gen Counsel & Sec)*
Tracy S. Harris *(CFO, Treas & Exec VP)*

Subsidiaries:

Apexa Corp. (1)
60 Adelaide Street East Suite 1300, Toronto, M5C 3E4, ON, Canada
Tel.: (647) 800-8679
Web Site: http://www.apexa.ca
Insurance Services
N.A.I.C.S.: 524113
Tonya Blackmore *(CEO)*
Dylan Friedmann *(VP-Client & Partner Experience & Engagement)*
Kelsi Van Kruistum *(VP-Product Mgmt)*
Barb Boothe *(Dir-Trng)*
Wasif Syed *(Dir-Infrastructure & Security)*
Josephine Moser *(Mgr-Customer Support)*
Sebastien Rocco *(Mgr-Sls & Relationship)*

MIC INDUSTRIES INC.
11911 Freedom Dr Ste 1000, Reston, VA 20190
Tel.: (703) 318-1900

Web Site: http://www.micindustries.com
Rev.: $250,000,000
Emp.: 30
Construction Machinery
N.A.I.C.S.: 333120
Michael S. Ansari *(Founder, Chm & CEO)*
Eileen Pendleton *(CFO & Exec VP)*
Anatoly Rosenzweig *(Mgr-Mktg-Intl)*
Donald Bowen *(Mgr-Production)*

MIC-RON GENERAL CONTRACTORS INC.
321 W 44th St Ste 601, New York, NY 10036
Tel.: (212) 581-5333
Web Site: http://www.microngc.net
Sales Range: $10-24.9 Million
Emp.: 75
Nonresidential Construction Services
N.A.I.C.S.: 236220
Ronald Franco *(Owner)*

MICA CORPORATION
5750 N Riverside Dr, Fort Worth, TX 76137
Tel.: (817) 577-2088
Web Site: http://www.micacorporation.com
Sales Range: $25-49.9 Million
Emp.: 200
Highway Signs & Guard Rails Mfr
N.A.I.C.S.: 237310
Carla Danford *(VP)*
Jack Davis *(Treas & VP)*
Roy Mullins *(VP & Mgr-Risk)*
Mike Tanner *(VP)*
Mike Walsh *(VP & Area Mgr-South Texas)*
L. C. Tubb Jr. *(Pres & CEO)*

MICAH GROUP ENERGY AND ENVIRONMENTAL
389 Waller Ave Ste 210, Lexington, KY 40504
Tel.: (859) 260-7760
Web Site: http://www.micahgroup.com
Year Founded: 1998
Rev.: $6,300,000
Emp.: 20
Environmental Remediation Services
N.A.I.C.S.: 541620
Aaron M. Jamison *(Pres & CEO)*
Craig Music *(Mgr-Program-Ops)*
Gary W. Stone *(Dir-Bus Dev)*
Mark E. Stafford *(Mgr-Construction Quality Control & Subsurface)*

MICAMP SOLUTIONS, LLC
4021 N 75th St, Scottsdale, AZ 85251
Tel.: (888) 552-1522
Web Site: http://www.micamp.com
Emp.: 300
Merchant Processing Business Solutions
N.A.I.C.S.: 522320
Stephen Campbell *(Co-Founder & CEO)*
Micah Kinsler *(Co-Founder & Pres)*
Russell Hibbert *(Exec VP)*

MICELI DAIRY PRODUCTS CO.
2721 E 90th St, Cleveland, OH 44104
Tel.: (216) 791-6222
Web Site: http://www.miceli-dairy.com
Rev.: $49,500,000
Emp.: 90
Natural Cheese
N.A.I.C.S.: 311513
Joseph D. Miceli *(Chm)*

MICELLO, INC.

465 S Mathilda Ave Ste 104, Sunnyvale, CA 94086
Tel.: (408) 739-2738
Web Site: http://www.micello.com
Software Publisher
N.A.I.C.S.: 513210
Anil Agarwal *(VP-Bus Dev)*

MICHAEL C. FINA CO. INC.
545 5th Ave, New York, NY 10017
Tel.: (212) 557-2500
Web Site: http://www.mcfina.com
Year Founded: 1937
Sales Range: $25-49.9 Million
Emp.: 300
Sales of China, Silver, Jewelry & Corporate Recognition Programs
N.A.I.C.S.: 449129
George Fina *(Pres)*
Mark Ellis *(CFO)*
Ashley Ruth Fina *(Pres)*
Steve Linn *(VP-Sls)*

MICHAEL CADILLAC INC.
5737 N Blackstone, Fresno, CA 93710
Tel.: (559) 431-6000
Web Site: http://www.michaelautomotive.com
Rev.: $105,700,000
Emp.: 300
Automobiles, New & Used
N.A.I.C.S.: 441110
Michael Rosvold *(Pres)*
Bruce Kane *(Gen Mgr-Sls)*
Jeffrey A. Moore *(Controller)*

MICHAEL COLLARD PROPERTIES INC.
1131 Symonds Ave, Winter Park, FL 32789
Tel.: (407) 599-4444
Web Site: http://www.collardproperties.com
Sales Range: $1-9.9 Million
Emp.: 4
Property Development, Investment, Leasing & Brokerage Services
N.A.I.C.S.: 237210
Michael A. Collard *(Founder & Pres)*
David W. Marks *(Principal-Retail Dev)*
David Beyer *(Mgr-Dev)*

MICHAEL DUNN CENTER
629 Gallaher Rd, Kingston, TN 37763
Tel.: (865) 376-3416 TN
Web Site: http://www.michaeldunncenter.org
Year Founded: 1973
Sales Range: $10-24.9 Million
Emp.: 506
Developmental Disability Assistance Services
N.A.I.C.S.: 623210
Mike McElhinney *(Pres & CEO)*

MICHAEL FLORA & ASSOCIATES INC.
2600 W Big Beaver Rd Ste 540, Troy, MI 48084-3337
Tel.: (248) 643-6431 MI
Web Site: http://www.michaelflora.com
Year Founded: 1979
Rev.: $21,000,000
Emp.: 25
Advetising Agency
N.A.I.C.S.: 541810
Michael Flora *(CEO)*
Sal Venti *(VP & Controller)*
David Craffey *(VP & Assoc Dir-Creative)*
Tom Brzezina *(Pres)*
Marci Grzelecki *(New Bus Mgr)*

MICHAEL GERALD LTD. INC.

MICHAEL GERALD LTD, INC.

Michael Gerald Ltd, Inc.—(Continued)
12836 Alondra Blvd, Cerritos, CA 90703-2107
Tel.: (562) 921-9611
Web Site:
http://www.michaelgerald.com
Year Founded: 1983
Sales Range: $10-24.9 Million
Emp.: 15
Men's & Boy's Clothing Distr
N.A.I.C.S.: 424350
Gerald Barnes *(Chm & Pres)*
Robert Sawyer *(CFO)*
Howaida Thomas-Willett *(Dir-Production)*

MICHAEL GRAVES & ASSOCIATES, INC.
341 Nassau St, Princeton, NJ 08540
Tel.: (609) 924-6409   NJ
Web Site:
http://www.michaelgraves.com
Year Founded: 1964
Architectural Services
N.A.I.C.S.: 541310
Ravi Waldon *(Principal)*
Julie Yurasek *(Dir-Interior Design)*
Thomas P. Rowe *(Principal-Architecture)*
Patrick Burke *(Principal-Architecture)*
Karen Nichols *(Principal-Architecture)*
Donald Strum *(Principal-Product Design)*
Rob Van Varick *(Principal-Design, Insights & Strategy)*
Ben Wintner *(Principal-Mktg & Bus Dev)*
Gordon Horvath *(CFO)*

Subsidiaries:

Studio Four Design Inc.   (1)
414 Clinch Ave, Knoxville, TN 37902
Tel.: (865) 523-5001
Web Site: http://www.studiofourdesign.com
Sales Range: $1-9.9 Million
Architectural Services
N.A.I.C.S.: 541310
Michelle Barton *(Coord-Design)*
Gigi Carpenter *(Office Mgr)*
Stacy Cox *(Principal & Dir-Bus Dev)*
Kevin Diegel *(Principal & Dir-Ops)*
Kimberlee Firkins *(Coord-Design)*
Mike Keller *(CFO & Principal)*
Katie Moran *(Project Mgr)*
Brian Nicholson *(Sr Project Mgr)*
Jacene Phillips *(Sr Project Mgr)*
Ana Smetana *(Coord-Design)*
Greg Terry *(Principal & Dir-Design)*

Waldon Studio Architects & Planners, PC   (1)
6325 Woodside Ct Ste 310, Columbia, MD 21046-1073
Tel.: (410) 290-9680
Web Site: http://www.waldonstudio.com
Architectural Services
N.A.I.C.S.: 541310
Ravi Waldon *(Principal)*
Kirk Guillory *(VP-Ops)*

MICHAEL HOHL MOTOR COMPANY
3700 S Carson St, Carson City, NV 89701
Tel.: (775) 883-5777
Web Site: http://www.hohlrv.com
Rev.: $22,100,000
Emp.: 60
Automobiles, New & Used
N.A.I.C.S.: 441110
Michael Hohl III *(Pres)*

MICHAEL HYATT & COMPANY LLC
PO Box 1221, Franklin, TN 37065
Web Site:
http://www.michaelhyatt.com
Year Founded: 2012
Sales Range: $10-24.9 Million
Emp.: 50
Event Management Services
N.A.I.C.S.: 711310
Michael Hyatt *(CEO)*
Megan Hyatt Miller *(COO)*
Courtney Baker *(CMO)*
Megan Greer *(Sr Project Mgr-Mktg)*
Sarah Mcelroy *(Specialist-Mktg Automation)*

MICHAEL J. LONDON & ASSOCIATES
929 White Plains Rd Ste 330, Trumbull, CT 06611
Tel.: (203) 261-1549
Web Site: http://www.mjlondon.com
Year Founded: 1990
Sales Range: Less than $1 Million
Emp.: 6
Public Relations
N.A.I.C.S.: 541820
Michael J. London *(Owner)*

MICHAEL LEWIS COMPANY
8900 W 50th St, McCook, IL 60525-6005
Tel.: (708) 688-2200   IL
Web Site: http://www.mlco.com
Year Founded: 1928
In-flight & Catering Products, Global Logistics & Supply Chain Management Services
N.A.I.C.S.: 722320

MICHAEL MALTZAN ARCHITECTURE, INC.
2801 Hyperion Ave Ste 107, Los Angeles, CA 90027
Tel.: (323) 913-3098   CA
Web Site: http://www.mmaltzan.com
Year Founded: 1995
Sales Range: $1-9.9 Million
Emp.: 14
Architectural Services
N.A.I.C.S.: 541310
Michael Maltzan *(Founder & Principal)*
Tim Williams *(Mng Principal)*
Betty Tanaka *(Mng Principal)*

MICHAEL O'BRIEN ENTERPRISES, INC.
101 116th Ave SE, Bellevue, WA 98004
Tel.: (425) 455-9995   WA
Web Site:
http://www.obrienautogroup.com
Year Founded: 1986
Sales Range: $600-649.9 Million
Emp.: 750
Holding Company; New & Used Automobile Dealers
N.A.I.C.S.: 551112
Michael P. O'Brien *(Owner)*

Subsidiaries:

Acura of Seattle at Southcenter   (1)
301 Baker Blvd, Seattle, WA 98188   (100%)
Tel.: (206) 433-1000
Web Site: http://www.acuraofseattle.com
Sales Range: $25-49.9 Million
Emp.: 100
New & Used Automobile Dealer
N.A.I.C.S.: 441110
Todd Guthrie *(Gen Mgr)*

Jaguar-Land Rover of Tacoma   (1)
1601 40th Ave Ct E, Fife, WA 98424   (100%)
Tel.: (253) 896-4200
Web Site: http://www.jaguaroftacoma.com
Sales Range: $25-49.9 Million
Emp.: 80
New & Used Automobile Distr
N.A.I.C.S.: 441110
Frank Lee *(Gen Mgr)*

Lexus of Bellevue   (1)
101 116th Ave SE, Bellevue, WA 98004   (100%)
Tel.: (425) 455-9995
Web Site: http://www.lexusofbellevue.com
Sales Range: $50-74.9 Million
Emp.: 170
New & Used Automobile Dealers
N.A.I.C.S.: 441110
Derrick Albrecht *(Dir-Svc & Parts)*
Patrick Nove *(Mgr-Parts Dept)*

Lexus of Tacoma   (1)
1708 40th Ave Ct E, Fife, WA 98424   (100%)
Tel.: (253) 922-7100
Web Site: http://www.lexusoftacomafife.com
Sales Range: $25-49.9 Million
Emp.: 75
New & Used Automobile Distr
N.A.I.C.S.: 441110
Frank Lee *(Gen Mgr)*
Don Pelley *(Dir-Pre-Owned Sls)*
Jeff Smyth *(Mgr-Svc)*
Ed Guthrie *(Sls Mgr)*
Duane Heitzman *(Mgr-Parts)*
Amy Hansen *(Mgr-Fin Svcs)*
Dwight Hurn *(Sls Mgr)*
Tiffany King *(Fin Dir)*

Toyota of Kirkland   (1)
12612 NE 124th St, Kirkland, WA 98034   (100%)
Tel.: (425) 814-9696
Web Site: http://www.toyotaofkirkland.com
New & Used Automobile Dealer
N.A.I.C.S.: 441110
Jim Roes *(Gen Mgr)*

Toyota of Renton   (1)
150 SW 7th St, Renton, WA 98057
Tel.: (425) 228-4700
Web Site: http://www.toyotaofrenton.com
Sales Range: $25-49.9 Million
Emp.: 100
New Car Dealers
N.A.I.C.S.: 441110
John North *(Gen Mgr)*
Thomas Maceda *(Mgr-Sls-Pre-Owned & Certified)*
Dinh Mai *(Mgr-Sls)*
Fred Johnson *(Dir-Fin)*
Dwight Haughton *(Mgr-Sls)*
Buddy Bobadilla *(Mgr-New Car)*

MICHAEL RIESZ & CO. INC.
588 New Brunswick Ave, Fords, NJ 08863-2128
Tel.: (732) 738-8100
Web Site: http://www.rieszco.com
Sales Range: $10-24.9 Million
Emp.: 26
Industrial Buildings & Warehouses
N.A.I.C.S.: 236220
Gina Rosar *(Office Mgr)*

MICHAEL SAUNDERS & COMPANY
100 S Washington Blvd, Sarasota, FL 34236
Tel.: (941) 953-7900
Web Site:
http://www.michaelsaunders.com
Year Founded: 1976
Sales Range: $1-4.9 Billion
Emp.: 550
Real Estate Brokerage Services
N.A.I.C.S.: 531210
Michael Saunders *(Founder & CEO)*
Paula Rees *(VP-Ops)*
David Gumpper *(Dir-Info Sys)*
Drayton Saunders *(Pres)*
Tom Heatherman *(Dir-Comm)*
Jennifer Horvat *(Dir-Mktg)*
Matt Drews *(Dir-Comml)*
Christine Johns *(Comptroller)*
Ronnie Nelson *(Dir-Appointment Center)*
Susie Rosario *(Dir-Relocation & Referral Svcs)*
Jamie Styers *(Dir-Rental Div)*
Ann Fontanetta *(Mgr-MSCMortgage)*
Nancy Arbuckle *(Mng Dir-New Homes & Condominiums)*
Peter McGarry *(Chief Bus Dev Officer)*

MICHAEL SIMON INC.
250 39th St, New York, NY 10018
Tel.: (212) 575-9222
Web Site:
http://www.michaelsimon.com
Sales Range: $10-24.9 Million
Emp.: 10
Clothing Designers
N.A.I.C.S.: 315120
Michael Petito *(Pres)*
Daniel Lonergan *(VP-Mktg)*

MICHAEL SKURNIK WINES, INC.
48 W 25th St 9th Fl, New York, NY 10010   NY
Tel.: (212) 273-9463
Web Site: https://www.skurnik.com
Year Founded: 1987
Wine & Distilled Alcoholic Beverage Merchant Whslr
N.A.I.C.S.: 424820
Michael Skurnik *(Founder & CEO)*
Harmon Skurnik *(Pres)*

Subsidiaries:

Vintner Select, Inc.   (1)
6215 Hi Tek Ct, Mason, OH 45040
Tel.: (513) 229-3630
Web Site: https://www.skurnik.com
Wine & Distilled Alcoholic Beverage Merchant Whslr
N.A.I.C.S.: 424820

MICHAEL STARS, INC.
12955 Chadron Ave, Hawthorne, CA 90250
Tel.: (310) 263-7375
Web Site:
http://www.michaelstars.com
Year Founded: 1986
Sales Range: $10-24.9 Million
Emp.: 100
Womens Clothing
N.A.I.C.S.: 424350
Michael Cohen *(Co-Founder & Chm)*
Suzanne Lerner *(Co-Founder & Pres)*
Brenda Sadler *(Mgr-Sampling)*
Jasmin Cerda *(Mgr-Retail Warehouse)*

MICHAEL STEADS HILLTOP FORD KIA
3280 Auto Plz, Richmond, CA 94806-1932
Tel.: (510) 222-4444
Web Site: http://www.hilltopford.com
Year Founded: 1995
Sales Range: $25-49.9 Million
Emp.: 85
New Car Whslr
N.A.I.C.S.: 441110
Leon Thomas *(Gen Mgr)*

MICHAEL THOMAS FURNITURE INC.
211 Old Thomasville Rd, High Point, NC 27260
Tel.: (336) 622-3075
Web Site:
http://www.themtcompany.com
Sales Range: $10-24.9 Million
Emp.: 30
Living Room Furniture: Upholstered On Wood Frames
N.A.I.C.S.: 337121
Thomas A. Jordan *(Pres)*
Jerry McKenzie *(VP-Logistics)*

MICHAEL THRASHER TRUCKING CO.

COMPANIES

MICHELMAN-CANCELLIERE IRON WORKS, INC.

1500 Marietta Rd Northwest, Atlanta, GA 30318
Tel.: (404) 799-7200
Rev.: $12,718,007
Emp.: 45
Local Trucking without Storage
N.A.I.C.S.: 238910
Michael Thrasher *(Pres)*

MICHAEL WALTERS ADVERTISING

444 N Wabash Ste 4W, Chicago, IL 60030
Tel.: (312) 467-5550
Web Site:
http://www.michaelwaltersadvertising.com
Year Founded: 1998
Rev.: $25,000,000
Advetising Agency
N.A.I.C.S.: 541810
Greg Kosinski *(Dir-Creative)*
Jim Lake *(VP)*
Ken Lakowske *(Pres)*

MICHAEL'S CARPET INC.

237 Belwood Rd SE, Calhoun, GA 30701
Tel.: (706) 629-1242
Web Site:
http://www.michaelscarpets.com
Sales Range: $10-24.9 Million
Emp.: 40
Floor Covering Stores
N.A.I.C.S.: 449121
James Michael Meadows *(Pres)*

MICHAEL, BEST & FRIEDRICH LLP

100 E Wisconsin Ave Ste 3300, Milwaukee, WI 53202
Tel.: (414) 271-6560
Web Site:
http://www.michaelbest.com
Year Founded: 1848
Legal Advisory Services
N.A.I.C.S.: 541110
Michael H. Altman *(Partner-Transactional Grp)*
Christopher B. Austin *(Co-Partner)*
Scott C. Beightol *(Co-Partner)*
Alan W. Ciochon *(CIO)*
L. David Lentz *(COO)*
Peter L. Coffey *(Co-Partner)*
Sarah N. Ehrhardt *(Partner-Wealth Plng Practice Grp)*
Kelly M. Fortier *(Partner-Employment Rels Practice Grp)*
Robert L. Gordon *(Partner-Tax Practice Grp)*
F. William Haberman *(Partner-Wealth Plng Svcs Grp)*
Kevin Barner *(Partner)*
Eric Callisto *(Partner)*
Yoichiro Yamaguchi *(Partner)*
Barry W. Sufrin *(Partner)*
John P. Huber *(CFO)*
Kay D. Cheng *(Mgr-Practice Grp)*
Michel J. Danahar *(Mgr-Practice Grp-Intellectual Property)*
Susan L. Hollender *(Chief Mktg & Bus Dev Officer)*
Tom E. Havas *(Mgr-Practice Grp-Transactional)*
William G. Kellner *(Chief HR Officer)*
Sean Van Eysden *(Engr-Patent)*
Abigail Griffin *(Engr-Patent)*
Luis I. Arroyo *(Partner)*
Adam E. Witkov *(Partner)*
Molly S. Lawson *(Partner)*
Denise Greathouse *(Partner)*
Michelle Wagner Ebben *(Partner)*
Stephen A. Mason *(Partner-Intellectual Property Practice Grp-Austin)*
Maryelena Zaccardelli *(Sr Dir-Affirmative Action Plans & Contractor Compliance)*
John Sheehan *(Partner-Environmental & Natural Resources Practice Grp-Washington)*
Conny Ruthven *(Partner-Corp & Transactional Practice Grp-Austin)*
Meghan Froehlich *(Mgr-Bus Dev)*
Andrew Eisenberg *(Partner-Intellectual Property & Corp Practice Grps-Austin)*
Michael Graham *(Partner)*
Paulette Mara *(Partner)*
Peter Huh *(Partner)*
Mircea Tipescu *(Partner)*
John Scheller *(Chm-Litigation Practice Grp)*
Kerryann Haase Minton *(Mng Partner-Chicago)*
James Fieweger *(Partner-Litigation Practice Grp-Chicago)*
David Krutz *(Mng Partner)*
Reince Priebus *(Pres-Washington)*
Elizabeth A. Rogers *(Partner-Data Privacy & Cybersecurity Grp-Austin)*
Ryan Sulkin *(Partner)*
Arimi Yamada *(Partner-Intellectual Property Practice-Washington)*
Phillip R. Maples *(Partner-Wealth Plng Svcs Grp-Manitowoc)*
John D. Finerty Jr. *(Partner-Litigation Practice Grp)*

Subsidiaries:

Bottom Line Marketing & Public Relations, Inc. (1)
600 W Virginia St Ste 100, Milwaukee, WI 53204-1556
Tel.: (414) 270-3000
Web Site: http://www.blmpr.com
Marketing & Public Relation Services
N.A.I.C.S.: 561312

MICHAELKATE INTERIORS AND GALLERY

132 Santa Barbara St, Santa Barbara, CA 93101
Tel.: (805) 963-1411
Web Site:
http://www.michaelkate.com
Home & Office Interior Design & Furnishings
N.A.I.C.S.: 541410
Kirk Sandland *(Sls Mgr)*

Subsidiaries:

Neuvie (1)
132 Santa Barbara St, Santa Barbara, CA 93101
Tel.: (805) 564-3396
Web Site: http://www.michaelkate.com
Furniture Retailer
N.A.I.C.S.: 449110

MICHAELS ENTERPRISES INC.

150 Mattatuck Hts Rd, Waterbury, CT 06705
Tel.: (203) 597-4942
Web Site:
http://www.michaelsjewelers.com
Sales Range: $10-24.9 Million
Emp.: 130
Jewelry Stores
N.A.I.C.S.: 458310

Subsidiaries:

Michaels Inc. (1)
150 Mattatuck Hts Rd, Waterbury, CT 06705
Tel.: (203) 597-4942
Web Site: http://www.michaelsjewelers.com
Jewelry Stores
N.A.I.C.S.: 458310

MICHAELS GROUP, LLC

1 Marions Way, Mechanicville, NY 12118
Tel.: (518) 899-6311 NY
Web Site:
http://www.michaelsgroup.com
Year Founded: 1981
Sales Range: $75-99.9 Million
Emp.: 12
Contractor For Single Family Homes, Townhouses & Condominiums
N.A.I.C.S.: 236116
Tom Tallman *(Project Mgr)*
Eric Willson *(Principal)*
Tony LoCascio *(Project Mgr)*
Joe Dolan *(Mgr-Pur)*

MICHAELSON GROUP REAL ESTATE, LLC

12443 San Jose Blvd Ste 604, Jacksonville, FL 32223
Tel.: (904) 880-0000
Web Site:
http://www.michaelsongroup.com
Sales Range: $10-24.9 Million
Emp.: 80
Property Management
N.A.I.C.S.: 531311
Michael N. Moses *(Founder, Chm, CEO & Principal)*
Alfonso Restrepo *(CFO)*
Janice Bryant *(VP-Ops)*
Elizabeth Libby Moses *(Corp Counsel)*
Chelsey Moses *(Dir-HR)*
Debbie Mccoy *(Reg Dir)*

MICHAELSON, CONNOR & BOUL, INC.

5312 Bolsa Ave Ste 200, Huntington Beach, CA 92649
Tel.: (714) 230-3600
Web Site: http://www.mcbreo.com
Rev.: $60,000,000
Emp.: 150
Real Estate Services
N.A.I.C.S.: 531390
Firmin Boul *(Treas & Sec)*
Joan Heid *(CEO)*
Gail Hyland-Savage *(COO)*
Michael Ryan *(VP)*

MICHAELSWILDER

7773 W Golden Ln, Peoria, AZ 85345-7977
Tel.: (623) 334-0100
Year Founded: 1989
Rev.: $17,000,000
Emp.: 40
Advertising Specialties, Internet/Web Design, Media Buying Services, Recruitment, Yellow Pages Advertising
N.A.I.C.S.: 541810
Ralph Knight *(VP)*
Shelly Little *(Exec VP)*
Sue Weinman *(Sr Acct Exec)*
Stacey Shaw *(VP-Recruitment Client Svcs)*
Paul Wills *(Sr VP & Gen Mgr-Recruitment Svcs)*

MICHAUD & SAMMON INSURANCE, INC.

107 Broad St, Claremont, NH 03743
Tel.: (603) 542-2551
Web Site:
http://www.insurancecenterinc.com
Year Founded: 1979
Sales Range: $1-9.9 Million
Emp.: 12
Insurance Agencies & Brokerages
N.A.I.C.S.: 524210
Robert Sammon *(Pres)*

Subsidiaries:

McCrillis & Eldredge Insurance, Inc. (1)
2 N Main St, Newport, NH 03773
Tel.: (603) 863-3636
Insurance Agents
N.A.I.C.S.: 524210

MICHELETTI & ASSOCIATES INC.

99 Almaden Blvd Ste 800, San Jose, CA 95113
Tel.: (408) 292-4900
Web Site:
http://www.michelettiins.com
Rev.: $25,000,000
Emp.: 30
Insurance Services
N.A.I.C.S.: 524210
Robert Micheletti *(Principal)*

MICHELMAN INC.

9080 Shell Rd, Cincinnati, OH 45236-1232
Tel.: (513) 793-7766 OH
Web Site: http://www.michem.com
Year Founded: 1949
Sales Range: $50-74.9 Million
Emp.: 200
Industrial Organic Chemicals Mfr
N.A.I.C.S.: 325199
Steven Wong *(Mng Dir-Asia Pacific)*
Steven Shifma *(Pres & CEO)*
Rick Michelman *(CTO & Exec VP)*
Ginger Merritt *(VP-Coatings)*
Lisa DiGate *(VP-Printing & Pkg)*
Jason Wise *(CFO)*
Ralph Giammarco *(Dir-Global Bus Dev & Applications-Printing & Packaging)*

Subsidiaries:

Ecronova Polymer GmbH (1)
Alte Grenzstrasse 153, D 45663, Recklinghausen, Alemania, Germany
Tel.: (49) 236166050
Web Site: http://www.ecronova.de
Sales Range: $25-49.9 Million
Emp.: 15
Water-Based Polymer Mfr
N.A.I.C.S.: 325998
Peter Montag *(Mng Dir)*
Anton Solich *(Mng Dir)*

Michelman (Shanghai) Chemical Trading Co., Ltd. (1)
Room 212 Building 3 Zhongtian Science & Technology Park, No 787 Kangqiao Road, Shanghai, 201315, China
Tel.: (86) 21 2098 6880
Web Site: http://www.michelman.com
Chemical Products Mfr
N.A.I.C.S.: 325998
Ginger Merritt *(Gen Mgr)*
James Xue *(Mgr-Greater China)*

Michelman Asia-Pacific Pte. Ltd. (1)
2A Tuas Avenue 12, Singapore, 639023, Singapore
Tel.: (65) 6861 2822
Chemical Products Mfr
N.A.I.C.S.: 325998
Richard Yang *(Mgr-Sls-Chemical Specialties)*

Michelman Chemicals Pvt. Ltd. (1)
Advaya Legal 1 Lalani Aura 34th Road, Bandra, Mumbai, 400050, India
Tel.: (91) 9987815193
Chemical Product Whslr
N.A.I.C.S.: 424690

Michelman SARL (1)
11 rue de l'Industrie, 8399, Windhof, Luxembourg
Tel.: (352) 2639441
Chemical Product Whslr
N.A.I.C.S.: 424690

MICHELMAN-CANCELLIERE IRON WORKS, INC.

7230 Beth Bath Pike, Bath, PA 18014
Tel.: (610) 837-9914
Web Site:
http://www.mcironworks.com
Year Founded: 1992
Sales Range: $10-24.9 Million
Emp.: 110

MICHELMAN-CANCELLIERE IRON WORKS, INC.

U.S. PRIVATE

Michelman-Cancelliere Iron Works, Inc.—(Continued)
Fabricated Structural Metal Mfr
N.A.I.C.S.: 332312
John Cancelliere (Pres & CEO)
Michael Cancelliere (VP-Production)
Samy Elsayed (VP-Engrg & Chief Engr)
Keith Harper (Controller & Treas)

MICHELS CORPORATION
817 Main St, Brownsville, WI 53006-0128
Tel.: (920) 583-3132
Web Site: https://www.michels.us
Year Founded: 1960
Sales Range: $300-349.9 Million
Emp.: 8,000
Water & Sewer Line & Related Structures Construction
N.A.I.C.S.: 237110
Herb Miller (Mgr-Supplier Diversity Program)
Patrick D. Michels (Pres & CEO)
Benjamin Ploederl (Gen Mgr-Estimating & Project Controls-Pipeline Construction)

Subsidiaries:

Heitkamp, Inc. (1)
99 Callender Rd, Watertown, CT 06795
Tel.: (860) 274-5468
Web Site: www.eheitkamp.com
Water & Sewage Pipe Maintenance Services
N.A.I.C.S.: 237110

MICHELSEN PACKAGING CO. INC.
202 N 2nd Ave, Yakima, WA 98902-2625
Tel.: (509) 248-6270 **WA**
Web Site: http://www.mpchome.com
Year Founded: 1964
Sales Range: $10-24.9 Million
Emp.: 200
Industrial & Personal Service Paper Mfr
N.A.I.C.S.: 424130
Dan Heck (Pres)

Subsidiaries:

Michelsen Packaging of California Inc. (1)
PO Box 10109, Fresno, CA 93745-0109
Tel.: (559) 237-3819
Web Site: http://www.mpcfresno.com
Sales Range: $10-24.9 Million
Emp.: 30
Corrugated & Solid Fiber Boxes Mfr
N.A.I.C.S.: 322220
Debbie Falcon (Office Mgr)

Sims Manufacturing Co. Inc. (1)
134 N 1st Ave, Yakima, WA 98902-1416
Tel.: (509) 453-7690
Web Site: http://www.simsmfg.com
Sales Range: $10-24.9 Million
Emp.: 29
Packaging Machinery Mfr
N.A.I.C.S.: 333993

MICHELSON ENERGY COMPANY
4940 Broadway St Ste 200, San Antonio, TX 78209
Tel.: (210) 826-0681
Web Site: http://www.bengalenergy.com
Rev.: $49,761,255
Emp.: 7
Gas Transmission & Distribution
N.A.I.C.S.: 221210
Calvin Michelson (Pres)
Mitch Michelson (VP)

Subsidiaries:

United Energex LP (1)

4940 Broadway St Ste 200, San Antonio, TX 78209
Tel.: (210) 826-0681
Rev.: $2,694,456
Emp.: 6
Servicing Oil & Gas Wells
N.A.I.C.S.: 213112

MICHELSON JEWELERS
1 Executive Blvd Ste 335, Paducah, KY 42001
Tel.: (270) 444-0800
Web Site: http://www.michelson-jewelers.com
Rev.: $12,500,000
Emp.: 25
Jewelry Stores
N.A.I.C.S.: 458310
Louis M. Michelson (Pres & CEO)

MICHIGAN AIR PRODUCTS CO.
1185 Equity Dr, Troy, MI 48099-1155
Tel.: (248) 837-7000
Web Site: http://www.michiganair.com
Year Founded: 1973
Sales Range: $10-24.9 Million
Emp.: 40
Heating Equipment Mfr
N.A.I.C.S.: 423720
Jim Kutil (Co-Owner)
Paul Joliat (Co-Owner)
Steve Mollison (Controller)

MICHIGAN ARC PRODUCTS
2040 Austin Dr, Troy, MI 48083
Tel.: (248) 740-8066
Web Site: http://www.micharc.com
Year Founded: 1970
Sales Range: $10-24.9 Million
Emp.: 35
Welding Machinery & Equipment
N.A.I.C.S.: 423830
James M. Colosimo (Pres)
Liz Crawford (Gen Mgr-Weld Wire, Pur & Sls Support)
Gary Baum (Mgr-SKS Sls)

MICHIGAN BASIC PROPERTY INSURANCE ASSOCIATION
3245 E Jefferson Ave, Detroit, MI 48207
Tel.: (313) 877-7400
Web Site: http://www.mbpia.com
Rev.: $78,800,000
Emp.: 101
Direct Property & Casualty Insurance Carriers
N.A.I.C.S.: 524126
Robert Hoffman (Gen Mgr)

MICHIGAN BOX COMPANY
1910 Trombly St, Detroit, MI 48211
Tel.: (313) 873-9500
Web Site: http://www.michiganbox.com
Year Founded: 1970
Rev.: $15,581,533
Emp.: 35
Boxes, Wood
N.A.I.C.S.: 321920

MICHIGAN CATASTROPHIC CLAIMS ASSOCIATION
17584 Laurel Park Dr N, Livonia, MI 48152-3982
Tel.: (734) 953-2779 **MI**
Web Site: http://www.michigancatastrophic.com
Year Founded: 1978
Sales Range: $1-4.9 Billion
Emp.: 23
Personal Protection Insurance Coverage Services
N.A.I.C.S.: 524291

James Lunsted (Controller)
Gloria Freeland (Exec Dir)

MICHIGAN COMMUNITY ACTION AGENCY ASSOCIATION
2173 Commons Pkwy, Okemos, MI 48864
Tel.: (517) 321-7500 **MI**
Web Site: http://www.mcac.memberclicks.net
Year Founded: 1975
Sales Range: $10-24.9 Million
Emp.: 14
Community Action Services
N.A.I.C.S.: 624190
Keith Schafer (Dir-IT & Facility Mgmt)
Mike Shalley (Dir-Member Svcs)
Kate White (Exec Dir)
Chere Coleman (Dir-Policy & Program)
Jill Sutton (Treas & Sec)
John Stephenson (Chm)
Louis Piszker (Vice Chm)
Heather Badder (Dir-Fin & HR)

MICHIGAN COMMUNITY DENTAL CLINICS, INC.
1 Water St Ste 200, Boyne City, MI 49712
Tel.: (231) 547-7638 **MI**
Web Site: http://www.midental.org
Year Founded: 2006
Sales Range: $25-49.9 Million
Emp.: 384
Health Care Srvices
N.A.I.C.S.: 622110
Keith Sherwood (CFO)
Kimberly Singh (Dir-Community & Govt Affairs)
David Murphy (Dir-Provider Rels & Quality Improvement)
Amanda DesJardins (Chief Dental Officer)
Danial Redifer (COO)
Gregory P. Heintschel (Pres & CEO)
Larry Keys (Dir-Info Sys & Tech)
Rob Kowalski (Dir-Talent, Support & Recruitment)

MICHIGAN CRYSTAL FLASH PETRO
1754 Alpine Ave NW, Grand Rapids, MI 49504
Tel.: (616) 363-4851
Web Site: http://www.crystalflash.com
Sales Range: $10-24.9 Million
Emp.: 5
Commercial & Industrial Building Operation
N.A.I.C.S.: 551112
Thomas V. Fehsenfeld (Pres)

MICHIGAN CUSTOM MACHINES, INC.
22750 Heslip Dr, Novi, MI 48375
Tel.: (248) 347-7900 **MI**
Web Site: http://www.mcm1.com
Year Founded: 1994
Sales Range: $1-9.9 Million
Emp.: 35
Specialty Test Machines for Diesel Fuel Systems
N.A.I.C.S.: 333998
Mike Schena (Pres & CEO)
Steven Hobson (Engr-Electrical)
Craig Antenucci (VP-Sls & Mktg)

MICHIGAN DRILL CORPORATION
1863 Larchwood Dr, Troy, MI 48083
Tel.: (248) 689-5268
Web Site: http://www.michigandrill.com
Rev.: $18,000,000
Emp.: 120

Mfr of Drills, Reamers, End Mills, Taps & Dies; Indexable, Solid Carbide & Carbide-Tipped Cutting Tools
N.A.I.C.S.: 333515
Hyman Ash (Pres)

MICHIGAN EDUCATION ASSOCIATION
1216 Kendale Blvd, East Lansing, MI 48826-2573
Tel.: (517) 332-6551 **MI**
Web Site: http://www.mea.org
Year Founded: 1914
Sales Range: $50-74.9 Million
Emp.: 869
Educational Support Services
N.A.I.C.S.: 611710
Doug Pratt (Dir-Member Benefits)
Gretchen Dziadosz (Exec Dir)
Paula Herbart (Pres)
Chandra Madafferi (VP)
Mike Shoudy (Exec Dir)

MICHIGAN ELECTRIC SUPPLY CO.
4060 Summers Dr, Burton, MI 48529
Tel.: (810) 234-8661
Web Site: http://www.michiganelectricsupply.com
Rev.: $23,300,000
Emp.: 16
Distribute Electrical Apparatus & Equipment
N.A.I.C.S.: 423610
Don Marlinga (Pres)

MICHIGAN ELECTRICAL EMPLOYEES HEALTH PLAN
6525 Centurion, Lansing, MI 48917-9275
Tel.: (517) 321-7502 **MI**
Web Site: http://www.mielectricalhealth.org
Sales Range: $25-49.9 Million
Health & Welfare Benefits Services
N.A.I.C.S.: 525120
Robert Schumaker (Chm)
Steve Claywell (Sec)
Sean Egan (Vice Chm)
James E. Schreiber (Mgr-Admin)
Barbara Alexander (Mgr-Contribution Entry)
Brian Nowosacki (Supvr-Contribution Entry)
Marlene McDiarmid (Mgr-Medical Claims & Eligibility)
Nicole Donald (Supvr-Medical Claims & Eligibility)
Laurie Savage (Supvr-Medical Claims & Eligibility)
Amy Appleyard (Coord-Lead Eligibility)
Steve Homer (Mgr-Payroll Auditing)

MICHIGAN FAMILY RESOURCES
2626 Walker Ave NW, Walker, MI 49544
Tel.: (616) 453-4145 **MI**
Web Site: http://www.hs4kc.org
Year Founded: 1989
Sales Range: $10-24.9 Million
Emp.: 323
Child & Family Care Services
N.A.I.C.S.: 624190
Mary L. Hockwalt (Exec Dir)

MICHIGAN HISTORIC PRESERVATION NETWORK
313 E Grand River Ave, Lansing, MI 48906
Tel.: (517) 371-8080 **MI**
Web Site: http://www.mhpn.org
Year Founded: 1981

Sales Range: $10-24.9 Million
Historical Resource Preservation Services
N.A.I.C.S.: 712110
Gary Scheuren (Dir-MHPN Programs)
Nancy Finegood (Exec Dir)

MICHIGAN IMPLEMENT INC.
515 South St W, Michigan, ND 58259
Tel.: (701) 259-2115 ND
Web Site:
http://www.leadingedgeequip.com
Year Founded: 1963
Sales Range: $10-24.9 Million
Emp.: 75
Farm & Construction Equipment Dealerships Owner & Operator
N.A.I.C.S.: 441227
Jay Vasichek (Co-Owner & Gen Mgr-Michigan Store)
James A. Vasichek (Co-Owner & Gen Mgr-Devils Lake)
Don Staniszewski (Mgr-Corp Parts)
Lenny Tufte (Mgr-Svc-Michigan Store)
Subsidiaries:

Michigan Implement Inc. - Devils Lake (1)
506 Hwy 2 W, Devils Lake, ND 58301
Tel.: (701) 662-4948
Web Site: http://www.leadingedgeequip.com
Farm & Construction Equipment Dealerships Operator
N.A.I.C.S.: 441227
Gary Kurtz (Mgr-Parts)
Don Staniszewski (Mgr-Corp Parts)

MICHIGAN KENWORTH, INC.
7393 Expressway Ct SW, Grand Rapids, MI 49548-7967
Tel.: (616) 281-8610
Web Site:
http://www.michigankenworth.com
Sales Range: $10-24.9 Million
Emp.: 85
Car Whslr
N.A.I.C.S.: 441110
Jim Kamps (Branch Mgr)
Pat Mosketti (Gen Mgr & VP)

MICHIGAN LABORERS FRINGE BENEFIT FUNDS
6525 Centurion Dr, Lansing, MI 48917-9275
Tel.: (517) 321-7502 MI
Web Site:
http://www.michiganlaborers.org
Year Founded: 1952
Sales Range: $50-74.9 Million
Emp.: 7,000
Health & Welfare Benefits Services
N.A.I.C.S.: 525120
Geno Alessandrini (Chm)
Wa Hendrick Jr. (Sec)

MICHIGAN MULTI-KING INC.
4897 Rochester Rd, Troy, MI 48085
Tel.: (248) 528-2860
Web Site: http://www.multiking.com
Year Founded: 1978
Sales Range: $200-249.9 Million
Emp.: 350
Fast Food Services
N.A.I.C.S.: 722513
Anthony Versaci (Pres & CEO)
Robert W. Nicolai (CFO)
Subsidiaries:

King of Sterling Heights Inc. (1)
44805 Schoenherr Rd, Sterling Heights, MI 48313
Tel.: (586) 739-7690
Rev.: $1,500,000
Emp.: 15
Provider of Fast-Food Services
N.A.I.C.S.: 722513
Anthony Versaci (Pres)

MICHIGAN OFFICE SOLUTIONS
2859 Walkent Dr NW, Grand Rapids, MI 49514-0587
Tel.: (616) 459-1161 MI
Web Site:
http://www.miofficesolutions.com
Year Founded: 1957
Sales Range: $25-49.9 Million
Emp.: 270
Provider of Office Forms & Supplies
N.A.I.C.S.: 459410
Bill Orr (Exec VP-Sls)
Kevin Minzlaff (Reg Mgr-Sls)
Paul Hartley (Pres)

MICHIGAN PIZZA HUT INC.
2053 Niles Rd, Saint Joseph, MI 49085
Tel.: (269) 983-3888
Web Site:
http://www.michiganpizzahut.com
Rev.: $65,100,000
Emp.: 20
Pizzeria Chain
N.A.I.C.S.: 722513
John C. Brinker (COO)

MICHIGAN PROPERTY & CASUALTY GUARANTY ASSOCIATION
39810 Grand River Ave Ste 120, Novi, MI 48375-2139
Tel.: (248) 482-0381 MI
Web Site: http://www.mpcga.com
Year Founded: 1969
Sales Range: $10-24.9 Million
Emp.: 15
Property & Casualty Insurance Services
N.A.I.C.S.: 524126
James W. Webb (Vice Chm)

MICHIGAN PUBLIC HEALTH INSTITUTE
2436 Woodlake Cir Ste 300, Okemos, MI 48864
Tel.: (517) 324-8300 MI
Web Site: http://www.mphi.org
Year Founded: 1990
Sales Range: $25-49.9 Million
Emp.: 504
Medical Educational Support Services
N.A.I.C.S.: 611310
Heather White (Chief Admin Officer)
Dean G. Smith (VP)
Nick Lyon (Pres)
Renee Branch Canady (CEO)
Jeff Ott (CIO)

MICHIGAN ROD PRODUCTS INC.
1326 Grand Oaks Dr, Howell, MI 48843
Tel.: (517) 552-9812
Web Site: http://www.michrod.com
Rev.: $18,000,000
Emp.: 110
Miscellaneous Fabricated Wire Products
N.A.I.C.S.: 332618
Tim Brown (VP)
Tony Schwerin (Mgr-Production Control)
Scott Sherman (Mgr-Quality Control)

MICHIGAN SPORTING GOODS DISTRIBUTORS INC.
3070 Shaffer Ave SE, Grand Rapids, MI 49512-1710
Tel.: (616) 942-2600 MI
Web Site: http://www.mcsports.com
Year Founded: 1940
Sales Range: $75-99.9 Million
Emp.: 1,500
Sporting Goods Retailer

N.A.I.C.S.: 459110
Bruce Ullery (Pres & CEO)

MICHIGAN STATE UNIVERSITY FEDERAL CREDIT UNION
3775 Coolidge Rd, East Lansing, MI 48823
Tel.: (517) 333-2424
Web Site: https://www.msufcu.org
Year Founded: 1937
Credit Union Services
N.A.I.C.S.: 522130
April Clobes (Pres & CEO)

MICHIGAN SUGAR COMPANY
2600 S Euclid Ave, Bay City, MI 48706
Tel.: (989) 686-0161 MI
Web Site:
http://www.michigansugar.com
Rev.: $300,000,000
Emp.: 450
Beet Sugar Refinery
N.A.I.C.S.: 311313
David Noble (VP-Ops)
Subsidiaries:

Michigan Sugar Company (1)
1101 N Front St, Fremont, OH 43420
Tel.: (419) 332-1501
Web Site: http://www.michigansugar.com
Emp.: 9
Sugar Production Mfr
N.A.I.C.S.: 311314

Michigan Sugar Company (1)
122 Uptown Dr Ste 300, Bay City, MI 48708
Tel.: (989) 686-0161
Web Site: http://www.michigansugar.com
Sales Range: $25-49.9 Million
Emp.: 150
Sugar Refinery
N.A.I.C.S.: 311313

Midwest Agri-Commodities (1)
999 5th Ave Ste 500, San Rafael, CA 94901
Tel.: (415) 259-2720
Web Site: http://www.mwagri.com
Sales Range: $250-299.9 Million
Emp.: 60
Sugar Beet Pulp, Molasses & Raffinates Whslr
N.A.I.C.S.: 424490
Jim Eichenberger (Pres)
Tim Klovstad (Mgr-Natl Sls)
Roger Roslund (Mgr-Sls)
Kevin Christensen (VP-Fin)

MICHIGAN SURGERY SPECIALISTS PC.
11012 E 13 Mile Rd, Warren, MI 48093
Tel.: (586) 573-6880
Web Site: http://www.msspc.org
Rev.: $10,000,000
Emp.: 150
Office Of Physician
N.A.I.C.S.: 621111
Edward Burke (Pres)
Richard Singer (Treas)

MICHIGAN TRACTOR & MACHINERY CO.
24800 Novi Rd, Novi, MI 48375
Tel.: (248) 349-4800 MI
Web Site:
http://www.michigancat.com
Year Founded: 1943
Sales Range: $200-249.9 Million
Emp.: 775
Construction & Paving Equipment Distr
N.A.I.C.S.: 423810
Bill Hodges (Pres)
Jim Damron (Product Mgr)
Ken Meerschaert (Gen Mgr-Ops)
Erv Gambee (VP-Sls)

Jeff Lefebvre (Dir-HR)
Kevin O. Connel (VP & Gen Mgr)
Clay Cutchins (Dir-Mktg)

MICHIGAN TUBE SWAGERS SEATING
7100 Indus Dr, Temperance, MI 48182-9105
Tel.: (734) 847-3875 MI
Web Site: http://www.mtsseating.com
Year Founded: 1955
Sales Range: $25-49.9 Million
Emp.: 350
Hospital Seating
N.A.I.C.S.: 337214
Phil Swy (CEO)
Bart Kulish (Pres)

MICHIGAN WEST SHORE NURSERY, LLC.
201 W Washington Ave Ste 270, Zeeland, MI 49464
Tel.: (616) 772-2126
Web Site:
http://www.michiganwestshore.com
Year Founded: 1960
Sales Range: $10-24.9 Million
Emp.: 9
Floriculture Production Services
N.A.I.C.S.: 111422
Jeffrey Palsrok (Gen Mgr)
Dan Palsrok (Mgr-Sls)

MICHLIG AGRICENTER INC.
105 1st St, Manlius, IL 61338
Tel.: (815) 445-6921
Web Site: http://www.michligag.com
Sales Range: $25-49.9 Million
Emp.: 35
Chemicals, Agricultural
N.A.I.C.S.: 424910
Donald King (Owner & Pres)

MICKELBERRY COMMUNICATIONS INC.
445 Park Ave Ste 1400, New York, NY 10022-8625
Tel.: (212) 832-0303
Rev.: $64,500,000
Emp.: 8
Commercial Printing, Lithographic
N.A.I.C.S.: 323111

MICKEY FINN STORES INC.
874 Berlin Tpke, Berlin, CT 06037
Tel.: (860) 829-3538 CT
Web Site:
http://www.mickeyfinnstores.com
Year Founded: 1968
Sales Range: $10-24.9 Million
Emp.: 115
Retailer of Men's, Women's & Children's Outer Wear
N.A.I.C.S.: 459110
Jerome E. Skolnick (Pres)

MICKEY TRUCK BODIES INC.
1305 Trinity Ave, High Point, NC 27260-8357
Tel.: (336) 882-6806 DE
Web Site:
http://www.mickeybody.com
Year Founded: 1904
Sales Range: $10-24.9 Million
Emp.: 300
Truck & Body Repair Services
N.A.I.C.S.: 336611
Jim Hiatt (VP-Van Division Sls)
Wayne Childress (VP-Corp Sls)
Greg McLaughlin (VP-Reconditioning)
Matt Sink (CEO)
Josh Reed (Dir-Mfg Ops)
Tom Arland (Pres)
Martin Skurka (VP-Ops, Engrg, Mfg & Pur)

MICKEYS ENTERPRISES INC.

Mickey Truck Bodies Inc.—(Continued)
MICKEYS ENTERPRISES INC.
1008 Illinois Ave, Killeen, TX 76541
Tel.: (254) 628-0343
Web Site:
http://www.mickeyscstores.com
Rev: $20,718,209
Emp.: 300
Convenience Store
N.A.I.C.S.: 445131
Karen Walinder *(Owner)*

MICKEYS LINEN & TOWEL SUPPLY
4601 W Addison St, Chicago, IL 60641
Tel.: (773) 545-7296
Web Site:
http://www.mickeyslinen.com
Rev: $12,200,000
Emp.: 175
Linen Supply
N.A.I.C.S.: 812331
Gregory M. Brown *(Pres)*
Greg Guido *(Mgr-Sls)*

MICKS EXTERMINATING
8491 Veterans Memorial Park, O'Fallon, MO 63366-3085
Tel.: (636) 978-5700
Web Site:
http://www.micksexterminating.com
Exterminating & Pest Control Services
N.A.I.C.S.: 561710
Charles Ostrander *(Pres)*

MICOBE INC.
1302 E Main St, Hamilton, TX 76531
Tel.: (254) 386-0073
Web Site: http://www.micobe.com
Sales Range: $10-24.9 Million
Emp.: 20
Animal Feed Mfr
N.A.I.C.S.: 311119
Mark Drewes *(COO)*
Joanna Wasson *(Treas)*

MICRO 2000, INC.
600 N Central Ave, Glendale, CA 91203
Tel.: (818) 547-0125 CA
Web Site: http://www.micro2000.com
Year Founded: 1990
Sales Range: $10-24.9 Million
Emp.: 15
Computer Equipment Retailer
N.A.I.C.S.: 423430
Rob McFarlane *(CEO)*

MICRO CONTROL SYSTEMS INC.
5580 Enterprise Pkwy, Fort Myers, FL 33905
Tel.: (239) 694-0089
Web Site:
http://www.mcscontrols.com
Year Founded: 1994
Sales Range: $1-9.9 Million
Emp.: 30
Microprocessor Based Controllers Mfr
N.A.I.C.S.: 334513
Brian W. Walterick *(Co-Owner & Pres)*
John G. Walterick *(Co-Owner & VP-Sls & Mktg)*
Kelly Mitchell *(Mgr-Inside Sls Support)*
Lisa A. Waterick *(Owner & Office Mgr-HR)*
Brenda L. Davila *(Mgr-Pur-Production)*

MICRO CRAFT INC.
207 Big Springs Ave, Tullahoma, TN 37388-3390
Tel.: (931) 455-2617 TN
Web Site: http://www.microcraft.aero
Year Founded: 1958
Sales Range: $25-49.9 Million
Emp.: 55
Engineeering Services
N.A.I.C.S.: 541330
Jim Herron *(Pres & CEO)*
Marty Smith *(Mgr-Engrg)*
Don Walls *(Mgr-Mfg)*
Malinda Gibson *(Mgr-Security & Contracts)*

MICRO ELECTRONICS, INC.
4119 Leap Rd, Hilliard, OH 43026-1117
Tel.: (614) 850-3000 OH
Web Site:
https://www.microcenter.com
Year Founded: 1980
Sales Range: $1-4.9 Billion
Emp.: 27,000
Electronic Parts Distr
N.A.I.C.S.: 423430
Rick Mershad *(Pres & CEO)*
Peggy Wolfe *(COO)*
Sean Beaupre *(Mgr-Mdsg)*
Paul Pepper *(Mgr-IT Ops)*
James Hefty *(Asst Controller)*

MICRO INDUSTRIES CORPORATION
8399 Green Meadows Dr N, Westerville, OH 43081-9486
Tel.: (740) 548-7878
Year Founded: 1979
Sales Range: $25-49.9 Million
Emp.: 98
Computer Processor, Touch-Screen Computer & Custom Computer System Mfr
N.A.I.C.S.: 334413
Brian Eirich *(Mgr-Credit)*
Jim Hogan *(Mgr-Dev Engrg)*

MICRO MAN DISTRIBUTORS, INC.
166 Douglas Rd E, Oldsmar, FL 34677
Tel.: (727) 736-2700 FL
Year Founded: 1997
Sales Range: $1-9.9 Million
Emp.: 45
Beer Distr
N.A.I.C.S.: 424810
Ian McCarthy *(Owner)*
Bethany Elder *(Office Mgr)*

MICRO MATIC USA, INC.
19791 Bahama St, Northridge, CA 91324
Tel.: (818) 882-8012 DE
Web Site: http://www.micromatic.com
Year Founded: 1988
Sales Range: $10-24.9 Million
Emp.: 157
Refrigeration & Heating Equipment Supplier
N.A.I.C.S.: 333415
Peter Muzzonigro *(Pres)*
Cian Hickey *(Dir-Natl Accts & Certified Installers)*
John Hickey *(Dir-Foodservice)*
John Soler *(Mng Dir)*

MICRO PRODUCTS COMPANY
1886 E Fabyan Pkwy, Batavia, IL 60510
Tel.: (630) 787-9350
Web Site: http://www.micro-weld.com
Year Founded: 1928
Sales Range: $10-24.9 Million
Emp.: 75
Electric Welding Equipment Whslr
N.A.I.C.S.: 423830

Gerri Osberg *(Mgr-Inside Sls & Customer Svc)*
Ed Harrington *(Mgr-Engrg & Customer Technical Svcs)*
H. Dayal *(Mng Dir-Intl Markets)*

MICRO SMART INC.
3602 Kennedy Rd, South Plainfield, NJ 07080
Tel.: (908) 222-4070
Web Site:
http://www.emicrosmart.com
Sales Range: $25-49.9 Million
Emp.: 43
Computer Peripheral Equipment
N.A.I.C.S.: 423430
Mie Mie Wong *(Pres)*

MICRO STAMPING CORP.
140 Belmont Dr, Somerset, NJ 08873-1204
Tel.: (732) 302-0800 NJ
Web Site:
http://www.microstamping.com
Year Founded: 1945
Sales Range: $75-99.9 Million
Emp.: 335
Metal Stampings, Medical & Surgical Instrument Mfr
N.A.I.C.S.: 332119
Mario Cappuccio *(Dir-Matls)*

Subsidiaries:

Micro Stamping Corp. - Florida Facility (1)
12955 Starkey Rd, Largo, FL 33773
Tel.: (727) 539-7200
Web Site: http://www.micro-co.com
Emp.: 40
Medical & Surgical Instrument Mfr
N.A.I.C.S.: 339112
Bob Harcielode *(Mgr-Ops)*

MICRO STRATEGIES INC.
1140 Parsippany Blvd, Parsippany, NJ 07054
Tel.: (973) 625-7721 NJ
Web Site: http://www.microstrat.com
Year Founded: 1983
Computer Software Related Services
N.A.I.C.S.: 541511
Anthony L. Bongiovanni *(Founder & CEO)*
Liam O'Heir *(Dir-New England Region)*

Subsidiaries:

Micro Strategies Inc. (1)
1200 Atwater Dr Suite 165, Malvern, PA 19355
Tel.: (484) 320-8932
Web Site: http://www.microstrat.com
Information Technology Services
N.A.I.C.S.: 519290

New England Systems Inc. (1)
200 Center St, Ludlow, MA 01056
Tel.: (413) 589-7565
Web Site: http://www.nesystems.com
Custom Computer Programming Services
N.A.I.C.S.: 541511
Liam O'Heir *(VP)*

MICRO VIDEO INSTRUMENTS INC.
11 Robbie Rd, Avon, MA 02322
Tel.: (508) 580-0080
Web Site: http://www.mvi-inc.com
Sales Range: $10-24.9 Million
Emp.: 25
Scientific Instruments
N.A.I.C.S.: 423490
Victor Laronga *(Pres)*
David Claypool *(Product Mgr-Digital Imaging)*

MICRO VOICE APPLICATIONS, INC.

U.S. PRIVATE

5100 Gamble Dr Ste 375, Minneapolis, MN 55416-1565
Tel.: (612) 373-9300 MN
Web Site: http://www.mva.com
Year Founded: 1989
Sales Range: $25-49.9 Million
Emp.: 80
Telephone Voice Directory & Voice Recognition Software Developer
N.A.I.C.S.: 334210
Steve Lazar *(Co-Founder & Exec VP)*
Connie Nicholls *(Controller)*

MICRO-CLEAN INC.
177 N Commerce Way, Bethlehem, PA 18017
Tel.: (610) 867-5302
Web Site: http://www.microcln.com
Year Founded: 1974
Sales Range: $10-24.9 Million
Emp.: 115
Performance Testing & Consulting
N.A.I.C.S.: 541380
Cory Kunkle *(VP)*

MICRO-OHM CORPORATION
1088 Hamilton Rd, Duarte, CA 91010
Tel.: (626) 357-5377
Web Site: http://www.micro-ohm.com
Year Founded: 1960
Sales Range: $50-74.9 Million
Emp.: 25
Precision Wire Wound & Power Resistors Mfr
N.A.I.C.S.: 334416
Charles Schwab *(Pres)*
Byron Ritchey *(CEO)*
Barbette Bowers *(Controller)*

MICRO-WORLD, INC.
414 Alaska Ave, Torrance, CA 90503
Tel.: (310) 533-1177
Web Site: http://www.micro-world.com
Sales Range: $10-24.9 Million
Emp.: 20
Computer System Design Services
N.A.I.C.S.: 541512
Biren Lalchandani *(Pres)*
Jeevan Kamnani *(VP-Sls)*

MICROBAC LABORATORIES, INC.
One Allegheny Sq Ste 400, Pittsburgh, PA 15212
Tel.: (412) 459-1060
Web Site: http://www.microbac.com
Sales Range: $25-49.9 Million
Emp.: 600
Testing Laboratories
N.A.I.C.S.: 541715
J. Trevor Boyce *(Chm & CEO)*
Sean P. Hyde *(Sr VP-Operational Affairs)*
Karen Ziolkowski *(Sr Project Mgr)*

MICROBIOLOGY RESEARCH ASSOCIATES, INC.
33 Nagog Pk, Acton, MA 01720
Tel.: (978) 263-2624
Web Site: http://www.mra-bact.com
Year Founded: 1993
Microbiology Testing Laboratories
N.A.I.C.S.: 541380
Francis McAteer *(Pres)*
Kelly Hagen *(Dir-Bus Dev)*
Darcy Sidwell *(VP)*

Subsidiaries:

Microbiology & Quality Associates, Inc. (1)
2341 Stanwell Dr, Concord, CA 94520-4808
Tel.: (925) 270-3800
Web Site: http://www.microqa.com
Microbiology Testing Laboratories
N.A.I.C.S.: 541380
Juan Munoz *(Pres)*

COMPANIES / MICROMERITICS INSTRUMENT CORPORATION, INC.

MICROBOARDS TECHNOLOGY, LLC
8150 Mallory Ct, Chanhassen, MN 55317-0846
Tel.: (952) 556-1600 MN
Web Site: http://www.microboards.com
Year Founded: 1996
Sales Range: $50-74.9 Million
Emp.: 25
Computer Storage Devices, DVD & CD Duplication Services
N.A.I.C.S.: 334112
Mitch Ackmann (Pres)
Brian Towey (Mgr-Sls)

MICROCARE, LLC
595 John Downey Dr, New Britain, CT 06051
Tel.: (860) 827-0626
Web Site: http://www.microcare.com
Rev.: $2,300,000
Emp.: 15
Polish & Other Sanitation Good Mfr
N.A.I.C.S.: 325612
Christopher Jones (Pres)
Heather Gombos (VP-Bus Ops)
Michael Jones (VP-Intl Sls)
Brian King (VP-Mfg & IT)
Steven Lefebvre (CFO)
Thomas Tattersall (CEO)
Ray Bellavance (VP-Global Sls & Mktg)
Marufur Rahim (Dir-Technical)

Subsidiaries:

Certol International, LLC (1)
6120 E 58th Ave, Commerce City, CO 80022
Tel.: (303) 799-9401
Web Site: http://www.certol.com
Sales Range: $1-9.9 Million
Emp.: 35
Soap & Other Detergent Mfr
N.A.I.C.S.: 325611

MICROCAST TECHNOLOGIES INC.
1611 W Elizabeth Ave, Linden, NJ 07036
Tel.: (908) 523-9503
Web Site: http://www.mtcnj.com
Rev.: $34,612,107
Emp.: 100
Zinc & Zinc-Base Alloy Die-Castings
N.A.I.C.S.: 331523
Kasia Kozlowski (VP-Ops)

MICROCOM TECHNOLOGIES, INC.
26635 Agoura Rd Ste 109, Calabasas, CA 91302
Tel.: (818) 880-8008 CA
Web Site: http://www.microcomtec.com
Year Founded: 1999
Sales Range: $10-24.9 Million
Emp.: 15
Electronic Parts & Equipment
N.A.I.C.S.: 423690
David Golob (Pres)

MICROCOSM, INC.
3111 Lomita Blvd, Torrance, CA 90505
Tel.: (310) 539-2306
Web Site: http://www.smad.com
Year Founded: 1984
Sales Range: $1-9.9 Million
Space Mission Engineering & Vehicle Components Mfr
N.A.I.C.S.: 336419
James Wertz (Pres)

MICRODYNAMICS GROUP
1400 Shore Rd, Naperville, IL 60563-8765
Tel.: (630) 527-8400
Web Site: http://www.microdg.com
Year Founded: 1974
Sales Range: $75-99.9 Million
Emp.: 193
Prepress Services
N.A.I.C.S.: 323120
Dave Baker (CFO)
Rick Schaltegger (VP-Admin)
Darrell Zolezzi (Sr VP)
Thomas Harter Sr. (Chm & CEO)

MICRODYNE PLASTICS, INC.
1901 E Cooley Dr, Colton, CA 92324
Tel.: (909) 503-4010 CA
Web Site: http://www.microdyneplastics.com
Year Founded: 1975
Rev.: $13,126,229
Emp.: 63
Precision Plastics Molding
N.A.I.C.S.: 326199
Ron D. Brown (Owner & Pres)
Judy Lopez (Project Mgr)
Harry Kline (Mgr-Production)

MICROELECTRONICS TECHNOLOGY COMPANY
500 N Rainbow Blvd, Ste 300, Las Vegas, NV 89107
Tel.: (702) 221-1938 NV
Web Site: http://www.mtigroup.com
Year Founded: 2005
Sales Range: Less than $1 Million
Emp.: 1
Online Video Sharing Services
N.A.I.C.S.: 541810
Allen Yen (Pres & CEO)
Chi Hsieh (Founder & Chm)
Dunga Wu (VP-SCM)
Eugene Wu (VP-Sls)
Hualin Chi (CFO & Sec)
Hunter Huang (Exec VP)

Subsidiaries:

Cloud Data Corporation (1)
500 N Rainbow Blvd Ste 300, Las Vegas, NV 89107 (100%)
Tel.: (702) 221-1938
Dedicated Server Hosting Services
N.A.I.C.S.: 541513
Shone Anstey (Pres)

Jupiter Technology (Wuxi) Co., Ltd. (1)
No 13 Minjiang Road Wuxi State High and New Technology, Industry Development Zone, Wuxi, 214028, Jiangsu, China
Tel.: (86) 51085228800
Web Site: http://www.mtiw.com.cn
Satellite Communication Equipment Mfr
N.A.I.C.S.: 334290

Microelectronics Technology Inc. (MTI) (1)
No 1 Innovation Rd II Hsinchu Science Park, Hsinchu, 300, Taiwan
Tel.: (886) 35773335
Web Site: http://www.mtigroup.com
Wireless Communication Equipment Mfr
N.A.I.C.S.: 334220
Chi Chia Hsieh (Chm)

MICROEXCEL, INC.
400 Plz Dr, Secaucus, NJ 07094
Tel.: (201) 866-6789
Web Site: http://www.microexcel.com
Year Founded: 2001
Sales Range: $10-24.9 Million
Emp.: 70
Computer System Design Services
N.A.I.C.S.: 541512
Nirmal Mehta (Founder & Pres)
Paul Simon (CEO & Dir-Sls)
Shekhar Bhole (VP-Quality Assurance Svcs)
Geoff Obeney (COO)
Wade Dalton (VP-Engrg & CSD Svcs)

MICROFIBRES INC.
1 Moshassuck St, Pawtucket, RI 02860-4873
Tel.: (401) 725-4883 RI
Web Site: http://www.microfibres.com
Year Founded: 1926
Sales Range: $25-49.9 Million
Emp.: 457
Fabrics Supplier
N.A.I.C.S.: 313210
Jim McCulloch (Pres & CEO)
Michael Czarnecki (VP-Sls & Mktg)
Maryann Beirne (CFO)

MICROFLEX INC.
1800 N US Hwy 1, Ormond Beach, FL 32174
Tel.: (386) 677-8100
Web Site: http://www.microflexinc.com
Year Founded: 1975
Sales Range: $25-49.9 Million
Emp.: 150
Wire Braids, Hoses & Flexible Metal-Related Products Mfr
N.A.I.C.S.: 332919
George Atanasoski (Co-Founder & VP)
Jim Greenlees (Dir-Pur)
Joseph Rushton (Dir-Mktg)
Gene Schiavone (Controller)

MICROLAND ELECTRONICS CORP.
1883 Ringwood Ave, San Jose, CA 95131-1721
Tel.: (408) 441-1688 CA
Web Site: http://www.microlandusa.com
Year Founded: 1986
Sales Range: $10-24.9 Million
Emp.: 70
Computers Peripherals & Software
N.A.I.C.S.: 423430
Abraham Chen (Pres & CEO)
Randy Yuan (VP-Sls)
George Silva (VP-Bus Dev)
Helen Muljadi (Mgr-Credit)
Carol Shi (Acct Mgr)
Ashish Mahadwar (COO)

MICROLOGIC BUSINESS SYSTEMS, INC.
2745 W Clay St Ste C, Saint Charles, MO 63301
Tel.: (636) 946-6681 MO
Web Site: http://www.mbstp.com
Year Founded: 1992
Sales Range: $10-24.9 Million
Emp.: 10
Information Technology Products & Services
N.A.I.C.S.: 541512
Rich Hollander (Owner)

MICROLUMEN, INC.
1 MicroLumen Way, Oldsmar, FL 34677
Tel.: (813) 886-1200
Web Site: http://www.microlumen.com
Year Founded: 1987
Sales Range: $10-24.9 Million
Emp.: 80
Medical Tube Mfr
N.A.I.C.S.: 339112
Roger Roberds (Founder & CEO)
Tim Lynch (VP-Ops)
M. Scott Roberds (Pres)
Rod Peifer (VP-R&D)
Robin Reynolds (VP-Fin)
Joe Slaven (VP-Materials)
Sara Kaplan (Mgr-Quality)

MICROMAN, INC.
4393 Tuller Rd Ste A, Dublin, OH 43017
Tel.: (614) 573-6113
Web Site: http://www.microman.com
Year Founded: 1987
Rev.: $19,490,073
Emp.: 65
Computers Dealer, Service & Repair
N.A.I.C.S.: 449210
Bradford J. Mandell (Pres)

MICROMATIC SPRING STAMPING CO.
45 N Church St, Addison, IL 60101
Tel.: (630) 607-0141
Web Site: http://www.micromaticspring.com
Sales Range: $10-24.9 Million
Emp.: 65
Wire Springs & Stampings Mfr
N.A.I.C.S.: 332613
George Zajack (Gen Mgr)
Walter Prociuk (Pres)

MICROMATIC, LLC
525 Berne St, Berne, IN 46711-1246
Tel.: (260) 589-2136
Web Site: http://www.micromaticllc.com
Year Founded: 1929
Rotary Actuator & Automated Assembly Equipment Mfr
N.A.I.C.S.: 333517
Rick Bush (Pres & CEO)
Tim Grover (Mgr-Automation Sls & Mktg)
Janet Honeywell (Cost Mgr)
Lisa Moore (Mgr-Fin)

MICROMENDERS INC.
1388 Sutter St Ste 650, San Francisco, CA 94109
Tel.: (415) 808-0600
Web Site: http://www.micromenders.com
Year Founded: 1985
Sales Range: $10-24.9 Million
Emp.: 70
Network Systems & Information Technology Consultants
N.A.I.C.S.: 541512
Dave Sperry (Pres)
Cory Choi (Partner)
Steven Liu (Controller)

MICROMERITICS INSTRUMENT CORPORATION, INC.
4356 Communications Dr, Norcross, GA 30093-2901
Tel.: (770) 662-3636 GA
Web Site: http://www.micromeritics.com
Year Founded: 1963
Sales Range: $10-24.9 Million
Emp.: 300
Analytical Instruments Researcher & Mfr
N.A.I.C.S.: 334516

Subsidiaries:

Micromeritics China (1)
Apt 5H No 1 Bldg Hua Ao Ctr Epoch Ctr, No 31 Zi Zhu Yuan Rd Hai Dian, Beijing, 100081, China (100%)
Tel.: (86) 68489371
Web Site: http://www.micromeritics.com
Sales Range: $10-24.9 Million
Emp.: 11
Analytical Instrument Mfr
N.A.I.C.S.: 334516

Micromeritics France S.A. (1)
Parc Alata Rue Antoine Laurent Lavoisier, 60550, Verneuil-en-Halatte, France (100%)
Tel.: (33) 344646080
Web Site: http://www.micromeritics.fr

MICROMERITICS INSTRUMENT CORPORATION, INC.　　　　　　　　　　　　　　　　　　　　　　　U.S. PRIVATE

Micromeritics Instrument Corporation, Inc.—(Continued)
Sales Range: $10-24.9 Million
Emp.: 6
Analytical Instrument Mfr
N.A.I.C.S.: 334516
Francine Le Merlus (Sec)

Micromeritics Germany GmbH (1)
Einsteinstrasse 14, 85716, Unterschleissheim, Germany (100%)
Tel.: (49) 89954537780
Web Site: http://micromeritics.de
Sales Range: $10-24.9 Million
Emp.: 7
Analytical Instrument Mfr
N.A.I.C.S.: 334516
Ton Hastings (Mng Dir)

Micromeritics Italy SRL (1)
Via W Tobagi n 26/7, Peschiera Borromeo, Milan, 20068, Italy (100%)
Tel.: (39) 0255302833
Web Site: http://www.micromeritics.it
Sales Range: $10-24.9 Million
Emp.: 3
Analytical Instrument Mfr
N.A.I.C.S.: 334516
Orazior Russo (Mgr)

Micromeritics Japan, G.K. (1)
5F Tokatsu Techno Plaza 501 5-4-6 Kashiwanoha, Kashiwa, 277-0882, Chiba, Japan
Tel.: (81) 4 7128 5051
Web Site: http://www.microjp.com
Laboratory Instrument Mfr
N.A.I.C.S.: 334516

Micromeritics NV/SA (1)
BDC -Esplanade 1 box 95, 1030, Brussels, Belgium (100%)
Tel.: (32) 27433974
Web Site: http://www.micromeritics.com
Sales Range: $10-24.9 Million
Emp.: 4
Analytical Instrument Mfr
N.A.I.C.S.: 334516
Tom Hustings (Gen Mgr)

Micromeritics U.K. Ltd. (1)
Ste 2 The Stables, Hexton Manor, Hexton, SG5 3JH, Herts, United Kingdom (100%)
Tel.: (44) 1582 881164
Web Site: http://www.micromeritics.com
Sales Range: $10-24.9 Million
Emp.: 5
Analytical Instrument Mfr
N.A.I.C.S.: 334516
Steve Coulson (Gen Mgr)

Micromeritics Comercio e Representacoes Ltda (1)
Rua Jose Getulio 360-Suites 62 63 e 64, 01509-000, Sao Paulo, Brazil
Tel.: (55) 11 3107 6843
Web Site: http://www.micrometics.com.br
Emp.: 4
Laboratory Instrument Mfr
N.A.I.C.S.: 334516
Luiz Pias (Mng Dir)

PoroTechnology, Inc. (1)
4356 Communications Dr, Norcross, GA 30093
Tel.: (770) 662-3630
Web Site: http://www.porotechnology.com
Emp.: 400
Industrial Supplies Whslr
N.A.I.C.S.: 423840
Myke Scoggins (Mgr-Lab)
Greg Thiele (Gen Mgr)

MICROMETALS INC.
5615 E La Palma Ave, Anaheim, CA 92807
Tel.: (714) 970-9400
Web Site: http://www.micrometals.com
Sales Range: $10-24.9 Million
Emp.: 150
Iron Cores Mfr
N.A.I.C.S.: 334419
Jim Cox (Pres)
Joseph Barbeito (Dir-Sls & Mktg)
Richard H. Barden Sr. (Chm)

MICROMETL CORP.
3035 N Shadeland Ave Ste 300, Indianapolis, IN 46226-6231
Tel.: (317) 543-5980　　　　IN
Web Site: http://www.micrometl.com
Year Founded: 1964
Sales Range: $10-24.9 Million
Emp.: 200
Iron Powder Cores
N.A.I.C.S.: 332322
Mark Webber (VP & Gen Mgr)

MICROMICR CORPORATION
35 SW 12th Ave Ste 112, Dania, FL 33004
Tel.: (954) 922-8044
Web Site: http://www.micro-micr.com
Year Founded: 1988
Sales Range: $1-9.9 Million
Emp.: 17
Mfr of Products for Laser Check Printing & Other Magnetic Ink Character Recognition (MICR) Encoded Products
N.A.I.C.S.: 334118
Michael Axelrod (Pres)

MICROMOLD, INC.
2100 Iowa Ave, Riverside, CA 92507
Tel.: (951) 684-7130　　　　CA
Web Site: http://www.micromoldinc.com
Year Founded: 1980
Sales Range: $1-9.9 Million
Emp.: 25
Mfg Plastic Molding
N.A.I.C.S.: 326199
Brenda DeWees (Office Mgr)
Bill Tischler (Mgr-QA)
Dave Dunn (Dir-Mktg)
Ron Peterson (Pr)
Steve Wilbur (Plant Mgr)
Melissa Aust (Mgr-Production Control)

MICRON CORPORATION
89 Access Rd Ste 5, Norwood, MA 02062-5234
Tel.: (781) 769-5771
Web Site: http://www.microncorp.com
Year Founded: 1982
Sales Range: $10-24.9 Million
Emp.: 24
Printed Circuit Board Assemblies Mfr
N.A.I.C.S.: 334412
William Theos (Pres)
James Theos (VP-Mktg)

MICROPRECISION INC.
1206 Ann St, Delavan, WI 53115
Tel.: (262) 728-5262
Web Site: http://www.micro-precision.com
Year Founded: 1953
Sales Range: $10-24.9 Million
Emp.: 110
Screw Machine Products, Metal Cutting Machine Tools & Metal Stampings Mfr
N.A.I.C.S.: 332721
Joseph Moser (Pres)
Jeff Graske (Mgr-Mfg & Engrg)

MICRORAM ELECTRONICS INC.
222 Dunbar Ct, Oldsmar, FL 34677
Tel.: (813) 854-5500
Web Site: http://www.microram.com
Rev.: $20,000,000
Emp.: 20
Electronic Parts & Equipment Merchant Whslr
N.A.I.C.S.: 423690
Brian Wilson (Exec VP-Electronics)
Beth Markle (Mgr-Acctg)
Lauren Petollino-Sawicki (Acct Mgr)

MICROSEISMIC, INC.
10777 Westheimer Ste 500, Houston, TX 77042
Tel.: (713) 781-2323
Web Site: http://www.microseismic.com
Year Founded: 2003
Sales Range: $50-74.9 Million
Emp.: 175
Geophysical Mapping Services
N.A.I.C.S.: 541360
Peter M. Duncan (Pres & CEO)
Terry Jbeili (COO)
Michael Thornton (CTO)
Greg Burns (VP-HR)
Ganesh Murdeshwar (Gen Mgr-Canada)
Sarah Groen (VP-Strategic Mktg)
Sudhendu Kashikar (VP-Completions Evaluation)
Jeff Foster (Pres & CEO)
Rick Luke (CFO)
Rip Stringer (VP-Sls)
Eric Bourdages (VP-Ops)
Bill Barker (VP-Analysis)
Carl Neuhaus (VP-Engrg)

MICROSYSTEMS
3025 Highland Pkwy Ste 450, Downers Grove, IL 60515
Tel.: (630) 598-1100
Web Site: http://www.microsystems.com
Sales Range: $75-99.9 Million
Emp.: 65
Document Lifecycle Software; Document Creation, Productivity & Control
N.A.I.C.S.: 513210
Tom O'Sullivan (Founder)
Nasser Amer (VP-Engrg)
Jody Cosgrove (VP-Customer Success)
Avaneesh Marwaha (Pres & CEO)

MICROSYSTEMS AUTOMATION GROUP
2785 B Hartland Rd, Falls Church, VA 22043
Tel.: (703) 538-0807
Web Site: http://www.msag.net
Year Founded: 1986
Sales Range: $1-9.9 Million
Emp.: 25
Technology Solution Service
N.A.I.C.S.: 541511
Robert Reznikoff (CEO)
Steve Reznikoff (Sr VP-Bus Dev)
Jim Reznikoff (Sr VP-Ops)

MICROTECH COMPUTERS INC.
4921 Legends Dr, Lawrence, KS 66049-5800
Tel.: (785) 841-9513　　　　KS
Web Site: http://www.microtechcomp.com
Year Founded: 1986
Sales Range: $25-49.9 Million
Emp.: 10
Computers & Peripherals
N.A.I.C.S.: 423430
Mike Zheng (Pres)
Qiuu Liu (VP)

MICROTECH STAFFING GROUP INC.
5 Cabot Pl, Stoughton, MA 02072
Tel.: (617) 657-0600
Web Site: http://www.mtsg.com
Sales Range: $10-24.9 Million
Emp.: 20
Temporary Staffing Services
N.A.I.C.S.: 561320
Bernie Cavanaugh (Mng Partner)
Dustin Chece (Mgr-Staffing)

MICROTECHNOLOGIES LLC
8330 Boone Blvd Ste 600, Vienna, VA 22182
Tel.: (703) 891-1073
Web Site: http://www.microtech.net
Sales Range: $150-199.9 Million
Emp.: 400
IT Support Services
N.A.I.C.S.: 541512
Anthony R. Jimenez (Founder, Pres & CEO)

MICROTEK
2001 Butterfield Rd Ste 1500, Downers Grove, IL 60515
Tel.: (630) 719-0211
Web Site: http://www.mclabs.com
Year Founded: 1991
Sales Range: $25-49.9 Million
Emp.: 100
Computer Training
N.A.I.C.S.: 611420
Bill Taylor (VP)
Kim Markovich (VP-Fin)
Don Slivensky (CEO)

Subsidiaries:

Access Event Network, Inc. (1)
2001 Butterfield Rd Ste 1500, Downers Grove, IL 60515
Tel.: (630) 719-0277
Web Site: http://www.accesseventnetwork.com
Rev.: $3,400,000
Emp.: 13
School & Educational Services
N.A.I.C.S.: 611699

MICROWAVE TRANSMISSION SYSTEMS, INC.
541 Sterling Dr, Richardson, TX 75081
Tel.: (972) 669-0591
Web Site: http://www.mtsi.com
Sales Range: $25-49.9 Million
Emp.: 199
Communications Specialization Services
N.A.I.C.S.: 238210
Preston D. Spurlin (Founder, Pres & CEO)
Derek Miller (CFO)

Subsidiaries:

CKS Management Inc. (1)
101 Nance St, Jacksonville, TX 75766-5522
Tel.: (903) 589-5369
Web Site: http://www.mtsi.com
Sales Range: $10-24.9 Million
Emp.: 6
Transmitting Tower (Telecommunication) Construction
N.A.I.C.S.: 237130
Butch Kelly Kelly (Gen Mgr)

Epic Communications, Inc. (1)
18131 FM 150 W, Driftwood, TX 78619
Tel.: (512) 858-2200
Emp.: 30
Wireless Telecommunication Services
N.A.I.C.S.: 517112
Dwayne Griffin (Pres)

MTSI, Northeast Division, Inc. (1)
8100 Avon Rd, Mechanicsburg, OH 44651
Tel.: (330) 738-3335
Wireless Telecommunication Services
N.A.I.C.S.: 517112

Site Communications, Inc. (1)
171 W Factory St, Gallatin, TN 37066
Tel.: (615) 452-1850
Wireless Telecommunication Services
N.A.I.C.S.: 517112

The Celeris Group, LLC (1)
2000 E Lamar Blvd Ste 550, Arlington, TX 76006
Tel.: (817) 446-1700
Web Site: http://www.celerisgroup.com
Emp.: 14
Wireless Telecommunication Services

COMPANIES

N.A.I.C.S.: 517112
Gabe Cobb (Sr Project Mgr)
Katie Stapleton (VP)
Mark Stapleton (Pres)

Triple S Towers, Inc. (1)
6478 Wagons East Trl, Las Cruces, NM 88012
Tel.: (575) 373-1018
Wireless Telecommunication Services
N.A.I.C.S.: 517112

Viper Communication Systems (1)
4211 SW 13th St, Ocala, FL 34474
Tel.: (352) 694-7030
Web Site:
http://www.microwavetransmission.com
Rev: $3,100,000
Emp.: 20
Visual Communication Systems
N.A.I.C.S.: 334290
James Conant (Pres)

MICROWAY, INC.
Plymouth Industrial Park 12 Richards Rd, Plymouth, MA 02360
Tel.: (508) 746-7341   MA
Web Site: http://www.microway.com
Year Founded: 1982
Sales Range: $10-24.9 Million
Emp.: 40
Computer Related Services
N.A.I.C.S.: 334111
Stephen Fried (Pres)
Ann Fried (Chm)
Eliot Eshelman (Sr Acct Mgr-Tech)
Terri Klaila (VP-Sys Div)

MID AMERICA CORP.
2812 North Broadway St, Knoxville, TN 37917
Tel.: (865) 524-3477
Rev.: $21,700,000
Emp.: 3
Fast-Food Restaurant, Chain
N.A.I.C.S.: 722513

MID AMERICA HARDWOODS INC.
Hwy 37, Sarcoxie, MO 64862
Tel.: (417) 548-2191   MO
Web Site: http://www.mid-americahardwoods.com
Year Founded: 1979
Sales Range: $10-24.9 Million
Emp.: 100
Millwork Services
N.A.I.C.S.: 321918
Robert Shepherd (Pres)
Melaine Caddick (CFO)

Subsidiaries:

Heritage Oak Flooring (1)
Hwy 37 S, Sarcoxie, MO 64862
Tel.: (417) 548-2191
Provider of Hardwood Flooring
N.A.I.C.S.: 321918

MID AMERICA MORTGAGE, INC.
15301 Spectrum Dr Ste 405, Addison, TX 75001
Tel.: (214) 261-3300
Web Site: http://www.midamericamortgage.com
Year Founded: 1940
Mortgage Lending Services
N.A.I.C.S.: 522310
Jeffrey E. Bode (Owner, Chm, Pres & CEO)
Michael L. Kennemer (CFO)
Michael Cooksey (Exec Mng Dir-Production & Mgr-The Cooksey Team)
Jemma Pachiano (COO)

MID AMERICA MOTORWORKS
2900 N 3rd St, Effingham, IL 62401
Tel.: (217) 540-4200

Web Site:
http://www.mamotorworks.com
Sales Range: $25-49.9 Million
Emp.: 130
Automotive Supplies & Parts
N.A.I.C.S.: 423120
Michael Yager (Pres)

MID AMERICA PET FOOD LLC.
2024 N Frontage Rd, Mount Pleasant, TX 75455
Tel.: (903) 572-5900
Web Site:
http://www.midamericapetfood.com
Sales Range: $1-9.9 Million
Emp.: 20
Dog & Cat Food Mfr
N.A.I.C.S.: 311111
Scott Glover (Pres)
Antoine Albin (Gen Mgr)
Kevin Barrett (Dir-Sls & Mktg)
Mark L. Schiller (Interim CEO)
Greg Cyr (CEO)

Subsidiaries:

NL Enterprises LLC (1)
PO Box 67224, Lincoln, NE 68506-7224
Web Site: http://www.natureslogic.com
Sales Range: $1-9.9 Million
Emp.: 50
Pet Food Mfr
N.A.I.C.S.: 311111
David Yaskulka (CEO)
Scott Freeman (Founder & Chief Product Dev Officer)
Marilyn Sherwin (Sr VP-Fin & Strategy)
Caroline Golon (VP-Mktg)
Donna Bowden (VP-Ops & Sustainability)

MID AMERICA STEEL, INC.
92 NP Ave N, Fargo, ND 58102-4832
Tel.: (701) 232-8831   ND
Web Site:
http://www.midamericasteelfargo.com
Year Founded: 1905
Sales Range: $75-99.9 Million
Emp.: 165
Structural Steel Fabrication
N.A.I.C.S.: 332312
George Cook (Pres & CEO)
John Simonson (Mgr-HR)
Aric Rude (VP-Production & Engrg)

MID ATLANTIC CAPITAL GROUP, INC.
1251 Waterfront Pl Ste 510, Pittsburgh, PA 15222
Tel.: (412) 391-7077   DE
Web Site: http://www.macg.com
Holding Company; Financial & Brokerage Advisory Services
N.A.I.C.S.: 551112
Charles A. Warden (Chm)
Paul Schneider (CEO)
Joseph F. Banco (CFO)

Subsidiaries:

Mid Atlantic Capital Corporation (1)
336 4th Ave, Pittsburgh, PA 15222
Tel.: (412) 391-7077
Web Site: http://www.macg.com
Rev.: $8,700,000
Emp.: 50
Portfolio Management
N.A.I.C.S.: 523940
David J. Down (Pres)
Joseph F. Banco (Sr VP & Mgr-Fin Grp)
Michael S. Brownlee (Sr VP & Mgr-Trading Grp)
Amy E. Chalmers (Sr VP & Mgr-Tech Grp)
Michele A. Coletti (Sr VP-Retirement Plan Svcs)
Erin N. Fischer (Gen Counsel & VP)
Gretchen A. Friday (Sr VP-Trust Ops)
Jean Sesler (Sr VP & Mgr-Ops Grp)
Nicholas B. Ventura (VP-Trust Trading)
Charles A. Warden (Chm & CEO)
William J. Woods (VP & Dir-Res)

The First Mercantile Trust Company (1)
57 Germantown Ct 4th Fl, Cordova, TN 38018
Tel.: (901) 753-9080
Web Site: http://www.firstmerc.com
Emp.: 100
Investment Management Service
N.A.I.C.S.: 523940
James Pratt (Pres)
Edwin C. Riley (Chief Investment Officer)

Division (Domestic):

American Trust (2)
855 Main St 4th Fl, Dubuque, IA 52001
Tel.: (800) 548-2993
Retirement Plan Solutions
N.A.I.C.S.: 525110
Micah DiSalvo (Chief Revenue Officer)

Division (Domestic):

Stanley Benefit Services, Inc. (3)
7800 McCloud Rd Ste 200, Greensboro, NC 27409
Tel.: (336) 271-4450
Web Site: http://www.stanleybenefits.com
Administrative Management & General Management Consulting Service
N.A.I.C.S.: 541611
William Stanley (Sr VP)
Allison Grimm (Sr VP-Compliance Svcs)
Amy Robinson (Sr VP-Flex, HSA & Admin)
Chris Francis (Sr VP-Defined Contribution)
Craven Lowe (VP)
Cynthia Richter (VP-Compliance Svcs)
Kenneth W. Miller (VP & Mgr-Ops & Defined Contribution)
Patrick Meehan (Sr VP-IT)

MID ATLANTIC CONSTRUCTION GROUP INC.
505 Lendall Ln, Fredericksburg, VA 22405
Tel.: (540) 368-0540
Web Site: http://www.macgrp.net
Sales Range: $10-24.9 Million
Emp.: 35
Commercial & Office Building Construction
N.A.I.C.S.: 236220
Dan Wight (Pres)
Ruth Cook (Office Mgr)
Mike Waniel (VP-Construction)

MID ATLANTIC CONTRACTING INC.
909 Highams Ct, Woodbridge, VA 22191
Tel.: (703) 492-4663
Web Site:
http://www.macontracting.com
Year Founded: 1979
Sales Range: $1-9.9 Million
Emp.: 7
Construction Engineering & Home Improvement Services
N.A.I.C.S.: 237990
Eric Fletcher (Pres)

MID ATLANTIC PETROLEUM PROPERTIES LLC
12311 Middlebrook Rd Ste 110, Germantown, MD 20874-1512
Tel.: (301) 972-4116
Rev.: $35,000,000
Emp.: 100
Property Operation, Retail Establishment
N.A.I.C.S.: 531120
Maymay Huie (CFO)

MID ATLANTIC STORAGE SYSTEMS
1551 Robinson Rd SE, Washington Court House, OH 43160
Tel.: (740) 335-2019
Web Site:
http://www.midatlanticstorage.com
Sales Range: $25-49.9 Million

Emp.: 70
Erector of Metal Storage Tanks
N.A.I.C.S.: 238120
Jerry Morris (Founder & CEO)
Gary Mann (VP-Construction)
Larry Morris (VP)
Greg Mullins (Reg Mgr-Sls)
John Fox (Pres)
Kyle Butts (Project Mgr)
Kevin Wilkerson (Dir-Field Svcs)
James Baughn (Project Mgr)
Luke Bihl (Project Mgr)
Ryan Lynch (Project Mgr)
Barbara Baker (Sec & Mgr-Acctg)

MID CITY FOUNDRY CO.
1521 W Bruce St, Milwaukee, WI 53204
Tel.: (414) 645-0840
Web Site:
http://www.midcityfoundry.com
Rev.: $14,000,000
Emp.: 85
Gray Iron Castings
N.A.I.C.S.: 331511
Darren Castello (Dir-Ops)
Tom Irvine (Dir-Quality)
Bob Miller (Mgr-Supply Chain)

MID CITY STEEL CORP.
275 State Rd, Westport, MA 02790
Tel.: (508) 675-7833
Web Site:
http://www.midcitysteel.com
Sales Range: $10-24.9 Million
Emp.: 51
Metal Whslr
N.A.I.C.S.: 423510
Louis Gitlin (Pres)
Lenny Reis (Dir-IT)
David Medeiros (Gen Mgr)
Laine Raposa (VP-Sls)
Steve Quinn (CFO)
Rick Mello (Mgr-Bozrah)

MID COAST ELECTRIC SUPPLY INC.
1801 Stolz St, Victoria, TX 77901
Tel.: (361) 575-6311
Web Site: http://www.mcesi.com
Year Founded: 1968
Sales Range: $25-49.9 Million
Emp.: 250
Electrical Supplies Whslr
N.A.I.C.S.: 423610
Thomas Barker (Owner)

MID COLUMBIA ENGINEERING INC.
2155 Robertson Dr, Richland, WA 99354
Tel.: (509) 943-6706
Web Site: http://www.mceng.com
Year Founded: 1980
Emp.: 100
Design & Build Engineering & Construction
N.A.I.C.S.: 237990
Karen Litts-Killoy (CFO)
Julie Lingle (VP-MCE Technical Svcs)
Lawrnel Harrison (COO)
Fred Yapuncich (Pres & CEO)

MID COLUMBIA FORKLIFT, INC.
1007 N 16th Ave, Yakima, WA 98902
Tel.: (509) 457-5137
Web Site:
http://www.midcolumbiaforklift.com
Rev.: $12,300,000
Emp.: 63
Industrial Machinery & Equipment Merchant Whslr
N.A.I.C.S.: 423830
Duane Bolinger (Pres)

MID COLUMBIA PRODUCERS, INC.

Mid Columbia Producers, Inc.—(Continued)

MID COLUMBIA PRODUCERS, INC.
2003 1st St, Moro, OR 97039-0344
Tel.: (541) 565-3737 OR
Web Site: http://www.mcpcoop.com
Year Founded: 1988
Sales Range: $10-24.9 Million
Emp.: 22
Grain & Seeds
N.A.I.C.S.: 424510
Jill Harrison (Controller)

Subsidiaries:

Mid Columbia Producers, Inc. - Wasco Seed Plant (1)
916 Highway 206, Wasco, OR 97065
Tel.: (541) 442-5555
Web Site: http://www.mcpcoop.com
Emp.: 4
Grain & Seed Product Distr
N.A.I.C.S.: 424510
Jeff Kaser (Gen Mgr)

MID CONTINENT AIRCRAFT CORP.
1601 Hwy 84, Hayti, MO 63851
Tel.: (573) 359-0500
Web Site: http://www.midcont.net
Sales Range: $10-24.9 Million
Emp.: 45
Retailers Of Aircrafts
N.A.I.C.S.: 441227
Richard Reade (Pres)
Chris Cobb (VP)
Terri Strawn (Coord-Aircraft Sls)
Sharon Watkins (Mgr-Aviation Insurance Agency)

MID DEL CONSULTING NETWORK
1660 S Hwy 100 Ste 201, Saint Louis Park, MN 55416
Tel.: (952) 500-9340
Web Site:
http://www.middelconsulting.com
Year Founded: 2005
Sales Range: $1-9.9 Million
Emp.: 9
Information Technology Consulting Services
N.A.I.C.S.: 541512
Scott Levin (Mng Partner)
Jed Marquisee (Dir-Bus Dev)

MID EASTERN BUILDERS, INC.
4016 Holland Blvd, Chesapeake, VA 23323
Tel.: (757) 487-5858
Web Site: http://www.meb-inc.com
Year Founded: 1982
Rev.: $40,000,000
Emp.: 200
Bridge Construction Services
N.A.I.C.S.: 237310
Eric Keplinger (VP)
William R. Blowe (VP)
David M. Ervin (VP)
Mark F. Olmstead (Sr VP)
George B. Clarke (Pres)

MID IOWA TOOLS INCORPORATED
3350 Square D Dr SW, Cedar Rapids, IA 52404
Tel.: (319) 366-8363
Web Site:
http://www.midiowatools.com
Year Founded: 1974
Sales Range: $10-24.9 Million
Emp.: 25
Tools
N.A.I.C.S.: 423840

Greg Harvieux (Pres)
John Stewart (VP-Sls)
Chris Ernberger (Mgr-Svcs)
Melissa McVeigh (Controller)

MID OAKS INVESTMENTS LLC
750 Lake Cook Rd Ste 460, Buffalo Grove, IL 60089
Tel.: (847) 215-3475
Web Site: http://www.midoaks.com
Privater Equity Firm
N.A.I.C.S.: 523999
Wayne C. Kocourek (Chm & CEO)
Michael A. Kocourek (Pres)
David L. Crouch (Mng Dir)
Donald F. Piazza (Sr Mng Dir)
David A. Boyle (Mng Dir & CFO)
Nicolas J. Gallo (VP)

Subsidiaries:

D&W Fine Pack LLC (1)
1900 Pratt Blvd, Elk Grove Village, IL 60007
Tel.: (847) 378-1200
Web Site: http://www.dwfinepack.com
Aluminum & Plastic Food Containers & Packaging Mfr
N.A.I.C.S.: 322220
Clay Davis (Sr VP)
Jay DuBois (Sr VP-Ops)
Michael Casula (CIO & VP)
Russ Stephens (VP-Engrg)
Mike Wenzel (VP-Supply Chain)
Debra Onken (VP-Natl Accts)
Rick Barton (VP-Sls-Grocery & Processor)
Jim Japczyk (CFO)

Plant (Domestic):

D&W Fine Pack LLC - Fort Calhoun (2)
1112 Madison St, Fort Calhoun, NE 68023
Tel.: (402) 468-5511
Web Site: http://www.dwfinepack.com
Producer & Supplier of Metal & Plastic Food Containers
N.A.I.C.S.: 326199

D&W Fine Pack LLC - Fountain Inn (2)
1372 N Old Laurens Rd, Fountain Inn, SC 29644
Web Site: http://www.dwfinepack.com
Aluminum & Plastic Food Container & Packaging Mfr
N.A.I.C.S.: 322220
Clay Davis (VP-Sls & Mktg)
David Randall (Pres & CEO)
Michael Casula (CIO)

Subsidiary (Domestic):

C.M. Holding Co., Inc. (3)
800 Ela Rd, Lake Zurich, IL 60047-2340
Tel.: (847) 438-2171
Web Site: http://www.cmpackaging.com
Sales Range: $50-74.9 Million
Holding Company; Metal & Plastic Food Packaging Mfr
N.A.I.C.S.: 551112
Kevin Andrews (Pres)

Plant (Domestic):

D&W Fine Pack LLC - Lake Zurich (2)
800 Ela Rd, Lake Zurich, IL 60047-2340 (100%)
Tel.: (847) 438-2171
Web Site: http://www.dwfinepack.com
Metal & Plastic Food Packaging Product Mfr
N.A.I.C.S.: 322220

MID SOUTH BUILDING SUPPLY
5640 P Sunnyside Ave Ste, Beltsville, MD 20705
Tel.: (301) 513-9000
Web Site:
http://www.midsouthsupply.com
Year Founded: 1965
Sales Range: $25-49.9 Million
Emp.: 70
Kitchen Cabinets

N.A.I.C.S.: 423310
John Briggs (Pres)
Scott Bibb (Mgr-Sls)
Kevin Taimanglo (Mgr-Warehouse)
Brenda Jenkins (Mgr-Credit Branch)
Diane Arch (Mgr-Credit)
Melissa Myers (Acct Mgr)

Subsidiaries:

Mid South Building Supply, Commercial Division (1)
5640 Sunnyside Ave Ste P, Beltsville, MD 20705
Tel.: (301) 513-9000
Web Site: http://www.msbs.com
Sales Range: $25-49.9 Million
Emp.: 40
Kitchen Cabinets
N.A.I.C.S.: 423310
John Briggs (Pres)

MID SOUTH MACHINERY INC.
3233 Hwy 80 W, Jackson, MS 39204
Tel.: (601) 948-6740
Rev.: $15,000,000
Emp.: 25
Heavy Construction Equipment Rental
N.A.I.C.S.: 532412
Ralph Henry (Pres)

MID SOUTH RADIOLOGY PARTNERS, LLC
747 Plaza Blvd Ste 100, Coppell, TX 75019
Tel.: (972) 459-3400
Sales Range: $10-24.9 Million
Emp.: 50
Radiology Services
N.A.I.C.S.: 621111
Daryl Miller (VP-Clinical Ops)
Robert Lapidus (Owner)

MID SOUTH SALES, INC.
243 County Rd 414, Jonesboro, AR 72404
Tel.: (870) 933-6457 AR
Web Site:
http://www.midsouthsales.com
Year Founded: 1962
Sales Range: $25-49.9 Million
Emp.: 60
Whslr & Retailer of Oil Products & Fuels
N.A.I.C.S.: 424720
Murray Benton (Pres)
Ed Gibson (Controller)
Thomas Handy (Plant Mgr)
William G. Benton (Chm)

MID SOUTH TRANSPORT INC.
2765 Profit Dr, Memphis, TN 38132
Tel.: (901) 332-8600
Web Site:
http://www.midsouthtransport.com
Year Founded: 1982
Sales Range: $10-24.9 Million
Emp.: 115
Trucking
N.A.I.C.S.: 484121
Ronnie Lancaster (Pres)

MID STATE DISTRIBUTING COMPANY
2600 Bell Ave, Des Moines, IA 50321
Tel.: (515) 244-7231
Web Site:
http://www.midstatedistributing.com
Year Founded: 1948
Consumer Electronics & Service Parts Distr
N.A.I.C.S.: 423690
Jeff Hedden (Exec VP)

MID STATES CONSTRUCTION INC.
53697 County Rd 9 N, Elkhart, IN 46514
Tel.: (574) 264-9547
Web Site:
http://www.midstatesconstruction.com
Year Founded: 1975
Rev.: $18,000,000
Emp.: 35
Industrial Buildings New Construction
N.A.I.C.S.: 236210
Donald L. Shaum Sr. (Pres)

MID STATES UTILITY TRAILER SALES, INC.
4550 S 96th St, Omaha, NE 68127
Tel.: (402) 331-4740 NE
Web Site: http://www.keizerco.biz
Year Founded: 1957
Sales Range: $10-24.9 Million
Emp.: 25
Sales of New & Used Trailers for Trucks
N.A.I.C.S.: 423110
Stacey Bricker (Owner)

MID VALLEY AGRICULTURAL SERVICES, INC.
PO Box 593, Linden, CA 95236
Tel.: (209) 931-7600 CA
Web Site:
http://www.midvalleyag.com
Year Founded: 1983
Sales Range: $10-24.9 Million
Emp.: 200
Provider of Farm Supply Services
N.A.I.C.S.: 424910
Larry Beck (Owner)

Subsidiaries:

BG Agri Sales & Service Inc. (1)
16299 East Hwy 26, Linden, CA 95236-9746
Tel.: (209) 931-7650
Sales Range: $10-24.9 Million
Emp.: 7
Provider of Hardware Store Services
N.A.I.C.S.: 423710
Anthony Davalle (Mgr)

MID WEST FABRICATING COMPANY, INC.
313 N Johns St, Amanda, OH 43102
Tel.: (740) 969-4411 OH
Web Site:
http://www.midwestfab.com
Year Founded: 1945
Sales Range: $10-24.9 Million
Emp.: 250
Motor Vehicle Parts & Accessories Mfr
N.A.I.C.S.: 336330
Ann Custer (VP-Fin)
Jennifer Friel (Pres)

MID WESTERN AUTOMOTIVE LLC
3320 S Outer Belt Rd, Grain Valley, MO 64029 MO
Web Site: http://www.magtrucks.com
Year Founded: 2007
Sales Range: $1-9.9 Million
Emp.: 25
New & Used Commercial Trucks & Vans Dealer & Upfitter
N.A.I.C.S.: 423110
Brad Carlson (CEO)
Heather Raleigh (Mgr-Ops)

Subsidiaries:

MAG Capital, LLC (1)
3320 S Outer Belt Rd, Grain Valley, MO 64029 (100%)
Web Site: http://www.magtrucks.com
Commercial Trucks & Equipment Sales Financing
N.A.I.C.S.: 522220
Brad Carlson (CEO)

COMPANIES

MAG Specialty Vehicles (1)
3320 S Outer Belt Rd, Grain Valley, MO 64029
Tel.: (800) 805-6818
Web Site: http://www.magspecialty.com
Commercial Trucks & Trailers Customization Services
N.A.I.C.S.: 811121
Brad Carlson *(Principal)*

MAG Transport, LLC (1)
3320 S Outer Belt Rd, Grain Valley, MO 64029 **(100%)**
Web Site: http://www.magtrucks.com
Regular Truck Delivery, Fleet Shipping & Management & Truck Transportation Services
N.A.I.C.S.: 484121
Brad Carlson *(CEO)*

MID-AMERICA CABINETS INC.
20980 Marion Lee Rd, Gentry, AR 72734
Tel.: (479) 736-2671
Web Site: http://www.midamericacabinets.com
Year Founded: 1982
Sales Range: $10-24.9 Million
Emp.: 75
Wood Kitchen Cabinets
N.A.I.C.S.: 337110
Robert J. Hosteter *(Pres)*
Robert Sample *(Treas & Sec)*
Charlie Keesee *(Plant Mgr)*
Bryan Yeagley *(Mgr-Direct Sls-Natl)*
Dennis Pierson *(Coord-Logistics)*

MID-AMERICA FEED YARD
2350 Rd 6950, Ohiowa, NE 68416-9504
Tel.: (402) 295-2216 NE
Web Site: http://www.midamericafeedyard.com
Year Founded: 1986
Sales Range: $50-74.9 Million
Emp.: 20
Commercial Feed Yard
N.A.I.C.S.: 112112
Dave McCoy *(Dir-Mktg)*
Doug Karl *(Gen Mgr)*
Pat Bentley *(Asst Mgr)*

MID-AMERICA OVERSEAS INC.
333 Pierce Rd Ste 400, Itasca, IL 60143
Tel.: (630) 285-9083 IL
Web Site: http://www.maoinc.com
Year Founded: 1976
Sales Range: $150-199.9 Million
Emp.: 400
Freight Transportation & Logistics Services
N.A.I.C.S.: 488510
Burkard M. Schmitt *(Founder & Pres)*
Hubert Elsen *(Sr VP-Midwest)*
Gene Cushing *(VP-Sea Freight Ops & Branch Mgr)*
Casey Davis *(Mgr-Import-Los Angeles)*
Donna Palermo *(VP-Customs Compliance & Branch Mgr-Newark)*
Gene Cuhing *(Branch Mgr)*

Subsidiaries:

LOGISTIC MAO DE MEXICO, S.A. DE C.V. (1)
C Insurgentes Sur 1690 Piso 2 Col Florida, Federal District, Mexico, 01030, Mexico
Tel.: (52) 5556629885
Logistics Consulting Servies
N.A.I.C.S.: 541614
Guadalupe Serrano *(Mgr-Ops)*

Mid-America Overseas (China) Ltd. (1)
Room 603 Beijing Yulin Plaza No 5 Second Alley Xiang Junnanli, Chaoyang District, Beijing, 100020, China
Tel.: (86) 10 6508 3577

Web Site: http://www.maonic.com
Freight Transportation Services
N.A.I.C.S.: 488510
Charles Liu *(Branch Mgr)*

Mid-America Overseas (M) Sdn. Bhd. (1)
41C Jalan Anggerik Vanilla N 31/N Kota Kemuning Seksyen 31, 40460, Shah Alam, Selangor, Malaysia
Tel.: (60) 351217020
Freight Transportation Services
N.A.I.C.S.: 488510

Mid-America Overseas (S) Pte. Ltd. (1)
No 9 Airline Road 04-26 Cargo Agent Building D, Singapore, 819827, Singapore
Tel.: (65) 65434424
Web Site: http://www.maoinc.com
Emp.: 5
Freight Transportation Services
N.A.I.C.S.: 488510
Michelle Tan *(Mgr-Branch)*

Mid-America Overseas (The Netherlands) B.V. (1)
Albert Plesmanweg 39A, 3088 GB, Rotterdam, Netherlands
Tel.: (31) 104296622
Web Site: http://www.midamericaoverseas.com
Freight Transportation Services
N.A.I.C.S.: 488510
Dennis de Ruiter *(Mgr-Bus Dev)*
Patrick Edelaar *(Mng Dir)*

Mid-America Overseas de Venezuela, C.A. (1)
Av Fco Solano Lopez con Calle la Iglesia Piso 3 Oficinas 3c y 3d, Sabana Grande, Caracas, 1050, Venezuela
Tel.: (58) 212 761 0728
Freight Transportation & Logistics Services
N.A.I.C.S.: 488510
Alicia Goudet *(Gen Mgr)*

Mid-America Overseas do Brasil Logistica Ltda. (1)
Rua Pascal 791-Campo Belo, Sao Paulo, 04616-002, Brazil
Tel.: (55) 11 5094 2020
Logistics Consulting Servies
N.A.I.C.S.: 541614
Rita Enei *(Branch Mgr)*

Mid-America Overseas, Ltd. (1)
9F 5 No 1 Fu-Hsing N Road, Taipei, 10595, Taiwan
Tel.: (886) 2 2731 0328
Freight Transportation Services
N.A.I.C.S.: 488510

MID-AMERICA STEEL CORP.
20900 Saint Clair Ave, Cleveland, OH 44117
Tel.: (216) 692-3800
Web Site: http://www.mastainless.com
Sales Range: $10-24.9 Million
Emp.: 60
Metals Service Centers & Offices
N.A.I.C.S.: 423510
Morton Kaufman *(Pres)*

MID-AMERICA WHOLESALE INCORPORATED
3101 S Van Buren St, Enid, OK 73702
Tel.: (580) 237-1040
Web Site: http://www.mid-america-online.com
Sales Range: $25-49.9 Million
Emp.: 60
Tobacco & Tobacco Products
N.A.I.C.S.: 424940
Roger Beagle *(Controller)*

MID-AMERICAN CLEANING CONTRACTORS
447 N Elizabeth St, Lima, OH 45801
Tel.: (419) 229-3899
Web Site: http://www.macc.net
Rev.: $10,409,475

Emp.: 1,200
Provider of Contract Janitorial Services
N.A.I.C.S.: 561720
Bob Swan *(Owner)*

MID-AMERICAN ELEVATOR EQUIPMENT CO., INC.
820 N Wolcott, Chicago, IL 60622
Tel.: (773) 486-6900 DE
Web Site: http://www.mid-americanelevator.com
Year Founded: 1974
Sales Range: $25-49.9 Million
Emp.: 135
Installation, Repair & Maintenance of Elevators
N.A.I.C.S.: 238290
Jack Luchewki *(VP)*
Peter Pold *(Controller)*
Robert Bailey II *(CEO & CFO)*
Robert Bailey III *(Pres)*

Subsidiaries:

USA Hoist Co., Inc. (1)
820 N Wolcott Ave, Chicago, IL 60622
Tel.: (773) 486-6900
Web Site: http://www.usahoist.com
Emp.: 70
Construction Elevator Leasing Services
N.A.I.C.S.: 532490
Robby Bailey *(VP)*
David Montijo *(Mgr-West Coast)*

MID-AMERICAN MACHINE & EQUIPMENT, LLC.
815 E 6th St, Le Roy, KS 66857
Tel.: (620) 964-2156
Web Site: http://www.mid-americanmachine.com
Sales Range: $10-24.9 Million
Emp.: 45
Machine Retailer
N.A.I.C.S.: 332710
Shane Sutherland *(Co-Partner)*
John Tindal *(Co-Partner)*
Johnny Guy *(Co-Partner)*

MID-AMERICAN RESTAURANTS INC.
1650 Gladewood Dr, Alpharetta, GA 30005
Tel.: (770) 752-9530
Sales Range: $10-24.9 Million
Emp.: 450
Family Restaurants
N.A.I.C.S.: 722511
Haig Antranikian *(Pres)*
John Girma *(Controller)*

MID-ATLANTIC HEALTH CARE, LLC
1922 Greenspring Dr Ste 6, Timonium, MD 21093-7603
Tel.: (410) 308-2300 MD
Web Site: http://www.mahchealth.com
Year Founded: 2003
Skilled Nursing Care Facilities Operator
N.A.I.C.S.: 623110
Scott Rifkin *(Co-Founder & CEO)*
Jeff Grillo *(COO)*
Sonny Taragin *(CTO)*
Howard Friner *(Co-Founder & Sr VP)*
Alan Kimmel *(Chief Medical Officer)*
Scott Potter *(CFO & Pres-Acctg & Fin)*

Subsidiaries:

Forest Haven, Inc. (1)
701 Edmonson Ave, Catonsville, MD 21228
Tel.: (410) 747-7425
Web Site: http://www.foresthavennursingcenter.com

Sales Range: $1-9.9 Million
Nursing Care Facility Operator
N.A.I.C.S.: 623110
Ebony Bostic *(Dir-Activity)*
Roslyn Delane *(Dir-Nursing)*
Jill Bohn *(Dir-Fin)*
Kaaren Patton *(Dir-Social Work)*

MID-ATLANTIC PRINTERS LTD.
503 3rd St, Altavista, VA 24517
Tel.: (434) 369-6633
Web Site: http://www.mapl.net
Sales Range: $10-24.9 Million
Emp.: 100
Offset Printing
N.A.I.C.S.: 323111
Charles R. Edwards *(Pres)*
Larry Connor *(Acct Exec)*
Rusty Giles *(Acct Exec)*
Jerry Kiser *(Acct Exec)*
Tim McCarthy *(Acct Exec)*
Margo Patrick *(Acct Exec)*
Mark Peters *(Mgr-Sls-Northern Virginia & DC)*
Mike Hudgins *(Acct Exec)*
Levenie Hughes *(Acct Exec)*
Guy Neal *(Mgr-Bindery & Shipping)*

MID-CAROLINA ELECTRIC COOPERATIVE, INC.
254 Longs Pond Rd, Lexington, SC 29072-9378
Tel.: (803) 749-6555 SC
Web Site: http://www.mcecoop.com
Year Founded: 1940
Sales Range: $1-9.9 Million
Emp.: 140
Electricity Distribution Services
N.A.I.C.S.: 221122
Clifford B. Shealy *(Vice Chm)*
Theresa Crepes *(VP-Fin & Acctg)*
Lavenia D. Hentz *(Sec)*
Allan Risinger *(Treas)*
Marvin W. Sox *(Chm)*
Keith Sturkie *(VP-IT)*
B. Robert Paulling *(Pres & CEO)*
Lee Ayers *(VP-Engrg)*
Troy Simpson *(VP-Member Svcs)*
Bobby Wilbur *(VP-Ops)*

MID-CITY LUMBER COMPANY LTD.
4709 Paris Rd, Columbia, MO 65202
Tel.: (573) 474-6139
Web Site: http://www.mclumber.com
Year Founded: 1969
Sales Range: $25-49.9 Million
Emp.: 60
Provider of Lumber & Other Building Materials
N.A.I.C.S.: 423310
Michael Teel *(Pres)*

MID-CITY SUPPLY CO. INC.
940 Industrial Pkwy, Elkhart, IN 46516
Tel.: (574) 294-5551
Web Site: http://www.mid-city.com
Sales Range: $10-24.9 Million
Emp.: 48
Plumbing Fittings & Supplies
N.A.I.C.S.: 423720
Jeffrey New *(Pres)*
Gail Sager *(Mgr-Showroom)*
Luke Hostetler *(Product Mgr-HVAC)*
Mike L. Smith *(Mgr-Plumbing Products)*

MID-COLUMBIA MEDICAL CENTER
1700 E 19th St, The Dalles, OR 97058
Tel.: (541) 296-1111 OR
Year Founded: 1984
Sales Range: $1-4.9 Billion

MID-COLUMBIA MEDICAL CENTER

MID-COLUMBIA MEDICAL CENTER—(Continued)
Emp.: 1,048
Community Health Plan Promotion Services
N.A.I.C.S.: 624190
William Hamilton (VP-Medical Affairs)
Regina Rose (Chief Nursing Officer & VP)
Donald Arbon (CFO & VP-Fin)
Dan Boldt (Vice Chm)
Paul Cardosi (Chm)
Rob Carnahan (Sec)

MID-CONTINENT INSTRUMENT CO., INC.
9400 E 34th St N, Wichita, KS 67226
Tel.: (316) 630-0101
Web Site: http://www.mcico.com
Year Founded: 1964
Sales Range: $10-24.9 Million
Emp.: 160
Aircraft Instrument Mfr, Repairer, Overhauler & Exchanger
N.A.I.C.S.: 336413
J. Todd Winter (Pres)
Julie Lowrance (Dir-Comm)
Hanna Simon (Mgr-HR)
Chad Ohl (Mgr-Ops)
Rick Slater (Dir-True Blue Power)
David Copeland (Dir-Sls)

MID-CONTINENT MINERALS CORPORATION
1058 County Rd 100, Carbondale, CO 81623-9531
Tel.: (970) 963-2581   DE
Year Founded: 1975
Sales Range: $10-24.9 Million
Emp.: 100
Mfr of Coal & Other Minerals
N.A.I.C.S.: 423620
Thomas E. Gibbs (Pres)

Subsidiaries:

Mid-Continent Coal & Coke Company   (1)
20600 Chagrin Blvd Ste 850, Cleveland, OH 44122-5327
Tel.: (216) 283-5700
Web Site: http://www.midcontinentcoke.com
Sales Range: $10-24.9 Million
Emp.: 12
Coal & Other Minerals Mfr & Distr
N.A.I.C.S.: 324199
Donald J. Joyce (CEO)
David Herman (Pres)

MID-CONTINENTAL RESTORATION CO.
400 E Hudson St, Fort Scott, KS 66701
Tel.: (620) 223-3700
Web Site: http://www.midcontinental.com
Sales Range: $25-49.9 Million
Emp.: 140
Masonry & Other Stonework
N.A.I.C.S.: 238140
J. Frank Halsey (Pres)
Steve Floyd (CFO)

MID-FLORIDA AREA AGENCY ON AGING, INC.
100 SW 75th St Ste 301, Gainesville, FL 32607
Tel.: (352) 378-6649   FL
Web Site: http://www.agingresources.org
Year Founded: 1977
Sales Range: $10-24.9 Million
Emp.: 44
Elder Care Services
N.A.I.C.S.: 623312
Major Stroupe (Treas)
Adelia Vachon (Sec)
Charles Miller (Pres)
Allison Thall (VP)

MID-FLORIDA FREEZER WAREHOUSES, LTD.
2560 W Orange Blossom Trl, Apopka, FL 32712
Tel.: (407) 886-7730
Web Site: http://www.mffreezer.com
Sales Range: $10-24.9 Million
Emp.: 60
Cost-Effective, Turnkey Warehousing Solutions
N.A.I.C.S.: 493120
Patrick T. Lee (Owner)

MID-ILLINOIS CONCRETE INC.
1805 S 4th St, Effingham, IL 62401
Tel.: (217) 342-2115
Web Site: http://www.mid-illinoisconcrete.com
Sales Range: $10-24.9 Million
Emp.: 95
Concrete Products, Precast
N.A.I.C.S.: 327390
Pete Robinson (CEO)

MID-IOWA COOPERATIVE INC.
101 S Main, Beaman, IA 50609
Tel.: (641) 366-2740   IA
Web Site: http://www.midiowacoop.com
Year Founded: 1942
Sales Range: $10-24.9 Million
Emp.: 56
Grain & Field Beans
N.A.I.C.S.: 424510
Mark Kistenmacher (Gen Mgr)
Linda Kuhl (Mgr-Commodity & Mktg)
Denny Hines (Mgr-Ops)
Shane Coughenour (CFO)
Susie Petersen (Mgr-Sls & Mktg)

MID-KANSAS CO-OP ASSOCIATION
307 W Cole, Moundridge, KS 67107
Tel.: (620) 345-6328   KS
Web Site: http://www.mkcoop.com
Year Founded: 1965
Sales Range: $75-99.9 Million
Emp.: 160
Grain Elevators & Service Stations Owner & Operator; Feeds & Fertilizers Retailer
N.A.I.C.S.: 424510
Dave Christiansen (Pres & CEO)
Jon Brown (Dir-Facilities Mgmt)
Myron Voth (Vice Chm)

Subsidiaries:

Haven Commodities LLC   (1)
307 W Cole, Moundridge, KS 67107-0582   (99%)
Tel.: (620) 345-6328
Web Site: http://www.mkcoop.com
Sales Range: $25-49.9 Million
Emp.: 42
Commodity Trading
N.A.I.C.S.: 523160
Dave Christiansen (Pres)

Mid-Kansas Coop   (1)
307 W Cole, Moundridge, KS 67107-0582   (100%)
Tel.: (620) 345-6328
Web Site: http://www.mkcoop.com
Sales Range: $10-24.9 Million
Emp.: 325
Operating Convenience Stores
N.A.I.C.S.: 445131
Dave Christiansen (Pres & CEO)
Danny Posch (CFO & Sr VP)
Dave Spears (CMO & Sr VP)
Erik Lange (COO & Sr VP)
Anne Warren (Chief HR Officer & Sr VP)
Allan Wegner (Chm)
Jason Gaeddert (Vice Chm)
David Mills (Sec)
Kenny Carlton (Assoc Dir)
Ben Schrag (Assoc Dir)

MID-MINNESOTA LEGAL AID
430 1st Ave N Ste 300, Minneapolis, MN 55401-1780
Tel.: (612) 332-1441   MN
Web Site: http://www.mylegalaid.org
Year Founded: 1980
Sales Range: $10-24.9 Million
Emp.: 177
Law firm
N.A.I.C.S.: 541110
Andrea Kaufman (Dir-Dev)
Galen Robinson (Dir-Litigation & Advocacy)
Cathy Haukedahl (Exec Dir)
Lisa Cohen (Deputy Dir-Ops)

MID-MISSOURI HOLDING COMPANY, INC.
318 W Main St, Sullivan, MO 63080
Tel.: (573) 468-3191   MO
Web Site: http://www.bankofsullivan.com
Year Founded: 1993
Sales Range: $10-24.9 Million
Emp.: 130
Bank Holding Company
N.A.I.C.S.: 551111
Michael P. Hoffman (Pres & CEO)
Milt Branum Jr. (Chm)

Subsidiaries:

Sullivan Bank   (1)
318 W Main St, Sullivan, MO 63080
Tel.: (573) 468-3191
Web Site: http://www.bankofsullivan.com
Sales Range: $10-24.9 Million
Emp.: 91
Retail & Commercial Banking
N.A.I.C.S.: 522110
Michael P. Hoffman (Pres & CEO)
Trenton Carey (VP)
Linda Weiskopf (VP)
Dale Cottrell (CFO & Exec VP)
Clifton Dudley (CFO, Exec VP & Branch Mgr)
Jon Downard (Chm)

MID-OHIO MECHANICAL, INC.
PO Box 418, Granville, OH 43023
Tel.: (740) 587-3362
Web Site: http://www.midohiomechanical.com
Year Founded: 1974
Sales Range: $10-24.9 Million
Emp.: 45
Plumbing Installation Services
N.A.I.C.S.: 238220
Neal T. Hartfield (Pres)
Dianna Boeshart (Sec)
Mark Hartfield (VP-Ops)
Brek Wildermuth (Mgr-Sheet Metal Div)
Mike Scott (Superintendent-Craft)
Robert Norman (Project Engr)
Sue W. Hartfield (VP)

Subsidiaries:

Mid-Ohio Mechanical, Inc. - Sheetmetal Division   (1)
2588 Johnstown Rd, Columbus, OH 43219
Tel.: (614) 258-5716
Web Site: http://www.midohiomechanical.com
Mechanical Contractor Specializing in Sheetmetal Fabrication & Installation, Ductwork, HVAC & Paint Booths
N.A.I.C.S.: 238220
G. Edward Beckett (Founder & Chief Creative Officer)
Gina Cansino (VP-Media Rels & Data Resources)
Kevin McLaughlin (VP & Controller)
John Schiavone (Dir-Art)
David Phelps Zink (VP)

MID-PARK INC.
1021 Salt River Rd, Leitchfield, KY 42754
Tel.: (812) 284-6430
Web Site: http://www.mid-park.com
Sales Range: $10-24.9 Million
Emp.: 130
Guard Rails, Highway; Sheet Metal
N.A.I.C.S.: 332322
Chad Patterson (Mgr-Quality & Safety)
Larry Vogt (CFO)
Mike Snell (Mgr-Ops)

MID-RIVERS TELEPHONE CO-OPERATIVE
904 C Ave, Circle, MT 59215
Tel.: (406) 485-3301
Web Site: http://www.midrivers.com
Sales Range: $10-24.9 Million
Emp.: 130
Local & Long Distance Telephone Communications
N.A.I.C.S.: 517121
Barb Stairs (Dir-HR)
Gene Engen (Treas & Sec)

MID-SOUTH BUILDING SUPPLY CO., INC.
7940 Woodruff Ct, Springfield, VA 22151-2107
Tel.: (703) 321-8500   VA
Web Site: http://www.msbs.net
Year Founded: 1985
Sales Range: $75-99.9 Million
Emp.: 100
Provider of Building Supplies
N.A.I.C.S.: 423310
Andrew R. Tavss (Pres)
Jim Roland (VP)
Mike Litinen (VP-Sls-Mktg)

MID-SOUTH INDUSTRIES, INC.
2620 E Meighan Blvd, Gadsden, AL 35903-1924
Tel.: (256) 492-8997   AL
Web Site: http://www.msi-mfg.com
Year Founded: 1964
Sales Range: $75-99.9 Million
Emp.: 2,000
Mfr of Printed Circuit Boards
N.A.I.C.S.: 541330
David Rickel (Mgr-Engrg)

Subsidiaries:

Mid-South Electronics, Inc.   (1)
2620 E Meighan Blvd, Gadsden, AL 35903-3459
Tel.: (256) 492-8997
Web Site: http://www.msi-mfg.com
Sales Range: $25-49.9 Million
Emp.: 450
Printed Circuit Board Assembly & Plastic Injection Molding
N.A.I.C.S.: 334412
E. Ricky Gibson (Executives)

Mid-South Products Engineering, Inc.   (1)
2600 E Meighan Blvd, Gadsden, AL 35903-1924
Tel.: (256) 494-1302
Web Site: http://www.msi-mfg.com
Sales Range: $10-24.9 Million
Emp.: 18
Provider of Engineering Services
N.A.I.C.S.: 541330

Stamped Products Inc.   (1)
201 Industrial Pkwy, Gadsden, AL 35903
Tel.: (256) 492-8890
Web Site: http://www.stamped.com
Sales Range: $25-49.9 Million
Emp.: 198
Supplier for Metal Stampings
N.A.I.C.S.: 332710

MID-SOUTH LUMBER AND SUPPLY
107 Emmett Ave, Bowling Green, KY 42101
Tel.: (270) 843-0194
Web Site: http://www.midsouthlumber.com
Sales Range: $10-24.9 Million

Emp.: 26
Lumber & Other Building Materials
N.A.I.C.S.: 423310
Sharon Cook (Office Mgr)
Ronnie Kiper (Mgr-Pur)
Vanessa Jo Walker (CFO)

MID-SOUTH LUMBER COMPANY OF GEORGIA INC.
6595 Marshall Blvd, Lithonia, GA 30058-8973
Tel.: (770) 318-3274 GA
Web Site: http://www.mid-southlumber.com
Year Founded: 1985
Sales Range: $10-24.9 Million
Emp.: 30
Provider Of Lumber Plywood & Millwork
N.A.I.C.S.: 423310
Marc Johns (VP-Ops)
Ernie Montgomery (Mgr-Accts-Natl)

MID-SOUTH MAINTENANCE, INC.
1449 Thomas St, Memphis, TN 38107
Tel.: (901) 527-1570 TN
Web Site: http://www.mid-southmaintenance.com
Sales Range: $25-49.9 Million
Emp.: 80
Renovation, Remodeling & Repairs: Industrial Buildings
N.A.I.C.S.: 236220
Bill Shirley (Mgr-Quality Assurance & Quality Control)

MID-SOUTH MANAGEMENT CO. INC.
314 S Pine St PO Box 1634, Spartanburg, SC 29302
Tel.: (864) 583-2907
Rev.: $12,200,000
Emp.: 10
Newspapers, Publishing & Printing
N.A.I.C.S.: 513110
Loretta Conner (VP & Dir)

MID-SOUTH MILLING COMPANY, INC.
710 Oakleaf Office Ln, Memphis, TN 38117-4800
Tel.: (901) 767-0071 TN
Web Site: http://www.msmilling.com
Year Founded: 1961
Sales Range: $75-99.9 Million
Emp.: 75
Animal Feed Ingredient Mfr
N.A.I.C.S.: 311119
John L. Petty (Pres & CEO)
Jackie Hall (Controller)

Subsidiaries:

ComTran Inc. (1)
710 Oakleaf Office Ln, Memphis, TN 38117
Tel.: (901) 681-4327
General Freight Trucking Services
N.A.I.C.S.: 484110
Nathan Pappas (Pres)

Mid-South Milling Company, Inc. - Kansas Plant (1)
213 Central Ave, Kansas City, KS 66118
Tel.: (913) 621-5442
Web Site: http://www.msmilling.com
Animal Feed Mfr
N.A.I.C.S.: 311119

MID-SOUTH RESTAURANTS INC.
300 W Wieuca Rd NE, Atlanta, GA 30342
Tel.: (404) 303-9133
Sales Range: $10-24.9 Million
Emp.: 260
Fast-Food Restaurant, Chain

N.A.I.C.S.: 722513
William D. Perkins (Pres)
James Clark (VP)

MID-SOUTH STEEL INC.
15 Welborn St, Pelham, AL 35124
Tel.: (205) 663-1750
Web Site: http://www.midsouthsteelinc.com
Year Founded: 1978
Sales Range: $10-24.9 Million
Emp.: 90
Industrial Fabrication & Machining Services
N.A.I.C.S.: 332312
Craig Farris (Pres)
Robert Laswell (Project Mgr-Sls)
Mike Shoop (VP)

MID-SOUTH SYNERGY
7625 Hwy 6, Navasota, TX 77868
Tel.: (936) 825-5100
Web Site: http://www.midsouthsynergy.com
Sales Range: $25-49.9 Million
Emp.: 100
Distribution, Electric Power
N.A.I.C.S.: 221122
Kerry Kelton (CEO & Gen Mgr)
Jack Shepherd (Sec)
James Morrison (VP)
Mike McDougale (VP-Admin)

MID-SOUTH WIRE COMPANY, INC.
1070 Visco Dr, Nashville, TN 37210
Tel.: (615) 743-2850
Web Site: http://www.midsouthwire.com
Year Founded: 1967
Sales Range: $10-24.9 Million
Emp.: 125
Fabricated Wire Product Mfr
N.A.I.C.S.: 332618
John T. Johnson (Gen Mgr)
Stan Fossick (VP-Sls)
John T. Johnson Jr. (Pres)

MID-STATE BOLT & NUT CO., INC.
1575 Alum Creek Dr, Columbus, OH 43209
Tel.: (614) 253-8631
Web Site: http://www.msbolt.com
Sales Range: $25-49.9 Million
Emp.: 55
Bolts
N.A.I.C.S.: 423710
Dave Broehm (Pres)
Curt McCullough (VP-Sls)
Steve English (VP)

MID-STATE COMMUNICATIONS & ELECTRONICS, INC.
185 Clear Rd, Oriskany, NY 13424
Tel.: (315) 736-3061
Web Site: http://www.midstatecomm.com
Sales Range: $1-9.9 Million
Emp.: 43
Electronic Parts & Equipment
N.A.I.C.S.: 423690
Sandra L. Corney (Pres & CEO)

MID-STATE CONTRACTING LLC
2001 County Hwy U, Wausau, WI 54401
Tel.: (715) 675-2388
Web Site: http://www.midstatecontracting.com
Sales Range: $10-24.9 Million
Emp.: 75
Provider of Mechanical Contracting Services
N.A.I.C.S.: 238220

Roy Mumper (Pres)
John Teske (VP)
Mike Aschenbrenner (Project Mgr)
Todd Swatzina (Project Mgr)

MID-STATE ENERGY INCORPORATED
1130 N Scenic Hwy, Lake Wales, FL 33853
Tel.: (863) 676-3910
Web Site: http://www.midstateenergy.com
Sales Range: $150-199.9 Million
Emp.: 40
Gasoline
N.A.I.C.S.: 424720
Sam Askar (Pres)

MID-STATE PETROLEUM INC.
4192 Mendenhall Oaks Pkwy, High Point, NC 27265
Tel.: (336) 841-3000 NC
Web Site: http://www.midstatepetroleum.com
Year Founded: 1993
Sales Range: $75-99.9 Million
Emp.: 200
Petroleum Services
N.A.I.C.S.: 424710
Nelson J. Perez (Pres)
Jerry Rose (VP-Sls)

MID-STATE TRUCK SERVICE INC.
2100 E 29th St, Marshfield, WI 54449
Tel.: (715) 406-4266
Web Site: http://www.midstatetruck.com
Sales Range: $25-49.9 Million
Emp.: 200
New & Used Commercial Truck Sales
N.A.I.C.S.: 423110
John Vandehey (CEO)
Tom Vandehey (COO)

MID-STATES DISTRIBUTORS
1201 Sheffler Dr, Chambersburg, PA 17201
Tel.: (717) 263-2413
Rev.: $27,500,000
Emp.: 39
Magazines
N.A.I.C.S.: 424920

MID-STATES ENERGY WORKS, INC.
618 N Santa Fe, Salina, KS 67401
Tel.: (785) 827-3631
Web Site: http://www.msew.biz
Year Founded: 1952
Provider of Electrical Construction Services
N.A.I.C.S.: 541690
Mike Schmaderer (Pres)
Bruce Marihugh (VP)
Sharon Schmaderer (Sec & Treas)

MID-STATES GENERAL & MECHANICAL CONTRACTING
4170 N Bearsdale Rd, Decatur, IL 62526
Tel.: (217) 875-1260
Web Site: http://www.midstatescontracting.com
Sales Range: $10-24.9 Million
Emp.: 60
Commercial & Office Building, New Construction
N.A.I.C.S.: 236220
George Hill (Pres)

MID-STATES SUPPLY COMPANY, INC.
1716 Guinotte Ave, Kansas City, MO 64120

Tel.: (816) 842-4290 MO
Web Site: http://www.midcoonline.com
Emp.: 100
Industrial Supplies Distr & Mfr
N.A.I.C.S.: 423840
Andy Brown (Co-Pres & Sec)
Robert Brown (Co-Pres)

MID-TEX OF MIDLAND, INC.
5206 W Wadley Ave, Midland, TX 79707
Tel.: (432) 697-2282
Web Site: http://www.midtexofmidland.com
Sales Range: $25-49.9 Million
Emp.: 40
Nonresidential Construction Services
N.A.I.C.S.: 236220
Paul Renz (VP)

MID-USA CYCLE PARTS INC.
5928 N Lindbergh Blvd, Hazelwood, MO 63042
Tel.: (314) 595-5555
Web Site: http://www.mid-usa.com
Sales Range: $10-24.9 Million
Emp.: 62
Motorcycle Parts
N.A.I.C.S.: 423120
John Stdko (Pres)

MID-VALLEY COMMUNITY ACTION AGENCY
2475 Center St NE, Salem, OR 97301
Tel.: (503) 585-6232 OR
Web Site: http://www.mwvcaa.org
Year Founded: 1967
Sales Range: $10-24.9 Million
Emp.: 385
Community Action Services
N.A.I.C.S.: 624190
Teresa Cox (Exec Dir)

MID-WAY SUPPLY INC.
2502 Deborah Ave, Zion, IL 60099-2708
Tel.: (847) 872-5481 IL
Year Founded: 1951
Sales Range: $10-24.9 Million
Emp.: 99
Provider of Heating & Air Conditioning Services
N.A.I.C.S.: 423730
Kenneth Sisson (Owner & Pres)
Michael LaBelle (Mgr-Warehouse)

MID-WEST FERTILIZER INC.
1105 Baptiste Dr, Paola, KS 66071
Tel.: (913) 294-5555
Web Site: http://www.midwestfertilizerinc.com
Rev.: $11,300,000
Emp.: 6
Fertilizer & Fertilizer Materials
N.A.I.C.S.: 424910
Jeff Novotny (Mgr)
Ashton Clemens (Mgr-IT)
Lucas Coppinger (Mgr)

MID-WEST FORGE CORPORATION
17301 St Clair Ave, Cleveland, OH 44110-2508
Tel.: (216) 481-3030 OH
Web Site: http://www.mid-westforge.com
Year Founded: 1925
Sales Range: $10-24.9 Million
Emp.: 160
Iron & Steel Forging
N.A.I.C.S.: 332111
Robert Dems (CFO)
Phil Calderone (Mgr-IT)
Robert I. Gale III (Chm)

Mid-West Forge Corporation—(Continued)

MID-WEST MANAGEMENT INC.
730 Rayovac Dr, Madison, WI 53711
Tel.: (608) 273-1000
Web Site: http://www.magic98.com
Rev.: $11,293,000
Emp.: 85
Radio Broadcasting Stations
N.A.I.C.S.: 516110
Tom Walker (Pres & CEO)

MID-WEST MATERIALS, INC.
3687 Shepard Rd, Perry, OH 44081
Tel.: (440) 259-5200
Web Site:
  http://www.midwestmaterials.com
Year Founded: 1952
Sales Range: $10-24.9 Million
Emp.: 49
Steel Processing & Distribution Services
N.A.I.C.S.: 331110
Joseph Koppelman (Chm)
Noreen Koppelman Goldstein (Pres)
Brian Robbins (CEO)

MID-WEST METAL PRODUCTS COMPANY INC.
4211 E Jackson St, Muncie, IN 47303-4423
Tel.: (765) 289-3355
Web Site:
  http://www.midwestmetal.com
Year Founded: 1953
Sales Range: $10-24.9 Million
Emp.: 300
Provider of Fabricated Wire Products
N.A.I.C.S.: 332618
Steven M. Smith (Pres & CEO)
Chip Rolfsen (CFO)
Martyn Woolley (Mgr-Mfg Ops)

MID-WEST OIL COMPANY INCORPORATED
301 S 3rd St, Terre Haute, IN 47807
Tel.: (812) 234-2844
Web Site: http://www.midwestoil.com
Sales Range: $10-24.9 Million
Emp.: 6
Provider of Independent Convenience Stores
N.A.I.C.S.: 445131
Missi Sandtee (Gen Mgr)

MID-WEST SPRING & STAMPING, INC.
1404 Joliet Rd Ste C, Romeoville, IL 60446-4066
Tel.: (630) 739-3800   DE
Web Site: http://www.mwspring.com
Year Founded: 1928
Wire Spring & Metal Stamping Mfr
N.A.I.C.S.: 332613
CJ Overmyer (Pres)

MID-WEST WHOLESALE LIGHTING CORP.
5250 Hollywood Blvd, Los Angeles, CA 90027
Tel.: (323) 469-1641
Web Site:
  http://www.midwestlighting.com
Sales Range: $25-49.9 Million
Emp.: 55
Lighting Fixtures
N.A.I.C.S.: 423610
John Thief (Gen Mgr)

MID-WOOD INC.
12965 Defiance Pike, Cygnet, OH 43413
Tel.: (419) 352-5231   OH
Web Site: http://www.mid-wood.com
Year Founded: 1967
Sales Range: $10-24.9 Million
Emp.: 60
Cooperative Supplier of Grain & Field Beans
N.A.I.C.S.: 424510
Thomas Dorman (Pres & CEO)
Kurt Dickey (Branch Mgr)
Edward Miller (VP-Agronomy)

MIDAMERICA HOTELS CORPORATION
105 S Mt Auburn Rd, Cape Girardeau, MO 63703-4915
Tel.: (573) 334-0546   MO
Web Site: http://www.midamcorp.com
Year Founded: 1968
Sales Range: $50-74.9 Million
Emp.: 1,400
Provider of Dining, Hotel & Motel Services
N.A.I.C.S.: 722513
Joel Neikirk (VP-Ops)
Diane Edwards (VP)

MIDAMERICA NATIONAL BANCSHARES, INC.
100 W Elm St, Canton, IL 61520
Tel.: (309) 647-5000
Web Site:
  http://www.midnatbank.com
Year Founded: 1982
Sales Range: $10-24.9 Million
Emp.: 50
Bank Holding Company
N.A.I.C.S.: 551111
Rick R. Klinedinst (Pres & CEO)
Subsidiaries:
MidAmerica National Bank   (1)
100 W Elm St, Canton, IL 61520
Tel.: (309) 647-5000
Sales Range: $10-24.9 Million
Emp.: 98
Commercial Banking Services
N.A.I.C.S.: 522110
Rick R. Klinedinst (Pres & CEO)

MIDAS AUTO SYSTEMS EXPERTS INC.
4537 N Brady St, Davenport, IA 52806
Tel.: (563) 386-0664
Web Site: http://www.midas.com
Sales Range: $10-24.9 Million
Emp.: 22
Providers of Automotive Brake Repair.
N.A.I.C.S.: 811114
Susan Blazer (VP-Ops)

MIDAS COMPANIES
9200 Edgeworth Dr, Capitol Heights, MD 20743
Tel.: (301) 474-4888
Web Site:
  http://www.midascompanies.com
Utility Construction & Repair Services
N.A.I.C.S.: 237110
Dan Cathell (CEO)
Matt Moser (COO)
Hank Norris (VP-Ops)
Chris Englebrake (VP-Flow Control)
Mike Trail (Gen Mgr-Utilities)

MIDCAP FINANCIAL SERVICES, LLC
7255 Woodmont Ave Ste 200, Bethesda, MD 20814
Tel.: (301) 760-7600
Web Site:
  http://www.midcapfinancial.com
Private Investment Firm
N.A.I.C.S.: 523999
Steve Curwin (CEO)
David Moore (CFO)
Bobe Goodridge (Gen Counsel)
Randall Feldner (Mng Dir-Fin & Acctg)
Jeffrey L. Shekell (Mng Dir-Leveraged Fin)

MIDCENTRAL ENERGY SERVICES, LLC
727 N Morgan Rd, Oklahoma City, OK 73127
Tel.: (405) 815-4041
Web Site:
  http://www.midcentralenergy.com
Year Founded: 2013
Energy Product Whslr
N.A.I.C.S.: 424720
Dikran Tourian (Co-CEO)
Avery Cruz (Mgr-Shop)

MIDCO CONSTRUCTION CORPORATION
22260 Illinois Rte 9, Tremont, IL 61568
Tel.: (309) 264-2857   DE
Web Site:
  http://www.midwestfoundation.com
Year Founded: 1985
Sales Range: $25-49.9 Million
Emp.: 50
Heavy Construction Contractor & Equipment Rental Services
N.A.I.C.S.: 237310
Jerome A. Greene (Chm)
Judy Woods (Sec)
Barry Roman (CFO)
Timothy Troyer (Pres)
Rick Tockes (Exec VP)
Tom Clark (Chief Engr)
Subsidiaries:
Midwest Equipment Leasing Corp.   (1)
22260 Illinois Rte 9, Tremont, IL 61568   (100%)
Tel.: (309) 925-2831
Web Site:
  http://www.midwestfoundation.com
Sales Range: $10-24.9 Million
Emp.: 12
Heavy Construction Equipment Rental Services
N.A.I.C.S.: 532412
Barry Roman (CFO & Treas)
Timothy Troyer (Pres)

Midwest Foundation Corporation   (1)
22260 Illinois Rte 9, Tremont, IL 61568
Tel.: (309) 925-2831
Web Site:
  http://www.midwestfoundation.com
Sales Range: $10-24.9 Million
Emp.: 10
Provider of Heavy Construction Services
N.A.I.C.S.: 236210
Judy Woods (Sec)
Barry Roman (CFO)
Timothy Troyer (Pres)
Rick Tockes (Exec VP)
Dick Wurster (VP-Field Ops & Mgr-Equipment & Warehouse)

MIDCO INTERNATIONAL, INC.
4140 W Victoria St, Chicago, IL 60646
Tel.: (773) 604-8700   IL
Web Site:
  http://www.midcointernational.com
Year Founded: 1941
Sales Range: $50-74.9 Million
Emp.: 50
Power Gas Burners Mfr
N.A.I.C.S.: 333414
Stan Beinarauskas (COO)
Hal Beyer (Owner & Chm)
Rutilio Delgado (Mgr-IT)
Karen Trice (Mgr-Sls)

MIDCON CABLES LLC
2500 Davis Blvd, Joplin, MO 64802
Tel.: (417) 781-4331   DE
Web Site:
  http://www.midconcables.com
Year Founded: 1972
Mfr of Electronic Cables & Wire Harnesses
N.A.I.C.S.: 334419
Jack Walling (CFO)

MIDCON DATA SERVICES LLC
13431 Broadway Extension Ste #115, 73114, Oklahoma City, OK
Tel.: (405) 478-1234   OK
Web Site:
  https://www.midcondata.com
Year Founded: 1991
Data Management & Strorage Services
N.A.I.C.S.: 518210
Austin Fugitt (Controller)
Randal Allen (Founder, Pres & CEO)
Darren Helm (Mgr-MIDCON Selsmic Data Brokerage)
Subsidiaries:
GET Imaging, Inc.   (1)
2932 NW 156th St, 73013, Edmond, OK
Tel.: (405) 415-8400
Web Site: http://www.getimaging.com
Document Conversion, Scanning & Imaging Services
N.A.I.C.S.: 518210

MIDCON INVESTORS INC.
401 S Boston Ave Ste 1200, Tulsa, OK 74103
Tel.: (918) 587-7325
Web Site: http://www.bfpna.com
Sales Range: $100-124.9 Million
Emp.: 112
Holding Company; Industrial Machinery & Equipment-Wholesale
N.A.I.C.S.: 423830
Ian H. Hill (Pres)

MIDCONTINENT INDEPENDENT SYSTEM OPERATOR, INC.
720 City Center Dr, Carmel, IN 46032-7574
Tel.: (317) 249-5400   DE
Web Site: http://www.misoenergy.org
Year Founded: 1998
Rev.: $380,341,000
Assets: $1,594,890,000
Liabilities: $1,594,889,999
Net Worth: $1
Emp.: 903
Fiscal Year-end: 12/31/18
Electric Power Transmission Services
N.A.I.C.S.: 221122
Jennifer Curran (Chief Compliance Officer & VP-Sys Plng)
Richard Doying (Exec VP-Market & Grid Strategy)
John Goode (CIO & Sr VP)
John R. Bear (CEO)
Andre T. Porter (Gen Counsel, Sec & VP)
Keri Glitch (Chief Information Security Officer & VP)
Todd Ramey (VP-Market Sys Enhancement)
Clair J. Moeller (Pres & COO)
Melissa Brown (CFO & Sr VP)
Todd Hillman (Chief Customer Officer & Sr VP)
Greg Powell (VP-HR)
Wayne Schug (VP-Strategy & Bus Dev)
Allegra Nottage (Chief Diversity Officer)
Andre T. Porter (Gen Counsel, Sec & VP)

MIDCONTINENT MEDIA INC.

COMPANIES

3600 Minnesota Dr Ste 700, Minneapolis, MN 55435
Tel.: (952) 844-2600   DE
Year Founded: 1933
Sales Range: $25-49.9 Million
Emp.: 650
Provider of Cable TV, Telephone, Paging, Radio, Advertising & Software Services
N.A.I.C.S.: 516210
Steve Grosser *(CFO)*
Patrick McAdaragh *(Pres & CEO)*
Dick Busch *(COO)*
W. Thomas Simmons *(Sr VP-Pub Policy)*

Subsidiaries:

Dataware, LLC   (1)
5841 S Corporate Place, Sioux Falls, SD 57108
Tel.: (605) 336-0820
Web Site: http://www.datawareservices.com
Data Center & Cloud Based Management Services
N.A.I.C.S.: 518210
Joe Krizan *(Pres & CEO)*

Midco of South Dakota, Inc.   (1)
5111 S Louise Ave, Sioux Falls, SD 57106
Tel.: (605) 334-1200
Web Site: http://www.midco.net
Sales Range: $10-24.9 Million
Emp.: 10
Cable & Other Pay Television Services
N.A.I.C.S.: 561422
Eyabane Patasse *(VP-Tech)*
Jonathan Pederson *(CTO)*

Midcontinent Business Systems Inc.   (1)
6600 France Ave, Minneapolis, MN 55435
Tel.: (952) 844-2626
Web Site: http://www.mbstechnologies.com
Sales Range: $1-9.9 Million
Emp.: 12
Computer Integrated Systems Design
N.A.I.C.S.: 516210

Midcontinent Cable Co. Inc.   (1)
PO Box 5010, Sioux Falls, SD 57117-5010
Tel.: (605) 229-1775
Sales Range: $10-24.9 Million
Emp.: 44
Cable & Other Pay Television Services
N.A.I.C.S.: 516210

Midcontinent Communications   (1)
3901 N Louise Ave, Sioux Falls, SD 57107   (50%)
Web Site: http://www.midco.com
Cable Television, Telephone, High-speed Internet Access, Cable Advertising & Data Network Services
N.A.I.C.S.: 517121

Midcontinent Communications Investor LLC   (1)
3600 Minnesota Dr, Minneapolis, MN 55435
Tel.: (952) 844-2600
Sales Range: $10-24.9 Million
Emp.: 4
Holding Company
N.A.I.C.S.: 541840

Midcontinent Media Inc.   (1)
3600 Minnesota Dr Ste 700, Minneapolis, MN 55435
Tel.: (952) 844-2600
Web Site: http://www.midco.net
Sales Range: Less than $1 Million
Emp.: 50
Radio Broadcasting Stations
N.A.I.C.S.: 516110
Steven Schuster *(Dir-Treasury & Risk)*

MIDCOUNTRY ACQUISITION CORP.

7825 Washington Ave S Ste 120, Bloomington, MN 55439
Tel.: (952) 698-6274   DE
Web Site: http://www.midcountrybank.com
Year Founded: 2018
Bank Holding Company
N.A.I.C.S.: 551111

James Charles Hays *(Chm & CEO)*

Subsidiaries:

MidCountry Bank   (1)
7825 Washington Ave S Ste 120, Bloomington, MN 55439
Tel.: (952) 698-6274
Web Site: http://www.midcountrybank.com
Sales Range: $50-74.9 Million
Emp.: 332
Federal Savings Bank
N.A.I.C.S.: 522180
Todd Streed *(Sr VP & Mgr-Comml Lending)*
Steve Meads *(Pres & CEO)*
Dave Thompson *(Chief Comml Banking Officer)*
Carol Kollodge *(Chief HR Officer)*
Bret Green *(Branch Mgr)*
Denise Koch *(Branch Mgr-Bloomington)*
Kurt Egertson *(Chief Credit Officer)*
Maureen O'Brien Wieser *(COO)*
Andrew Gruber *(VP)*
Chris Vosbeek *(CFO)*

Subsidiary (Domestic):

Pioneer Services Corp.   (2)
4700 Belleview Ave Ste 300, Kansas City, MO 64112
Tel.: (816) 756-2020
Web Site: http://www.pioneermilitaryloans.com
Military Personnel Loan Brokerage Services
N.A.I.C.S.: 522310
Jodi Vickery *(Pres)*

Subsidiary (Domestic):

Pioneer Services Sales Finance, Inc.   (3)
3240 E Tropicana, Las Vegas, NV 89121
Tel.: (702) 821-3100
Web Site: http://www.pioneermilitaryloans.com
Military Personnel Consumer Loan Sales Financing
N.A.I.C.S.: 522220

MIDCOUNTRY FINANCIAL CORP.

201 2nd St Ste 950, Macon, GA 31201
Tel.: (478) 746-8222
Web Site: http://www.midcountryfinancial.com
Sales Range: $300-349.9 Million
Emp.: 1,200
Financial Services Holding Company
N.A.I.C.S.: 551111
Timothy L. Stanley *(Pres & CEO)*
Sandra Laughlin *(Chief Risk Mgmt Officer & Sr VP)*
Gary McQuain *(Exec VP-Ops)*

Subsidiaries:

Pioneer Financial Services, Inc.   (1)
4700 Belleview Ave Ste 300, Kansas City, MO 64112
Tel.: (816) 756-2020
Web Site: http://www.investpioneer.com
Rev.: $70,761,000
Assets: $222,556,000
Liabilities: $142,765,000
Net Worth: $79,791,000
Earnings: $2,759,000
Fiscal Year-end: 09/30/2018
Credit & Loan Services
N.A.I.C.S.: 522210
Timothy L. Stanley *(CEO & Vice Chm)*
Robert F. Hatcher *(Chm)*

MIDDLE EAST INVESTMENT INITIATIVE

500 8th St NW, Washington, DC 20004
Tel.: (202) 799-4345   DC
Web Site: http://www.meiinitiative.org
Year Founded: 2005
Sales Range: $1-9.9 Million
Emp.: 7
Economic Development Services
N.A.I.C.S.: 813319

William E. Mayer *(Vice Chm)*
James Pickup *(Pres)*

MIDDLE EAST MARKETING GROUP

266 S Dean St, Englewood, NJ 07631
Tel.: (201) 503-0150
Sales Range: $10-24.9 Million
Emp.: 7
Bric-A-Brac
N.A.I.C.S.: 339999
Henri Dimidjian *(Pres)*

MIDDLE TENNESSEE ELECTRIC MEMBERSHIP CORPORATION

555 New Salem Rd, Murfreesboro, TN 37129-3390
Tel.: (615) 890-9762   TN
Web Site: http://www.mtemc.com
Year Founded: 1936
Sales Range: $250-299.9 Million
Emp.: 375
Providers of Electrical Services
N.A.I.C.S.: 221122
Bernie Steen *(CFO & VP-Fin)*
Chris Jones *(Pres)*
Tom Suggs *(COO)*
John Florida *(VP-Info Sys)*
William P. Jordan *(Vice Chm)*
Steve Seger *(Treas & Sec)*
Tom Purkey *(Vice Chm)*
Brad Gibson *(Chief Cooperative Bus Officer)*
Keith Thomason *(VP-Engrg)*

MIDDLE TENNESSEE NATURAL GAS UTILITY DISTRICT INC.

1030 W Broad St, Smithville, TN 37166-2501
Tel.: (615) 597-4300   TN
Web Site: http://www.mtng.com
Year Founded: 1955
Sales Range: $25-49.9 Million
Emp.: 200
Natural Gas Distribution
N.A.I.C.S.: 221210
Ed Kelley *(VP-Ops & Customer Svc)*

MIDDLEGROUND MANAGEMENT, LP

1500 Aristides Blvd, Lexington, KY 40511
Tel.: (646) 722-6530   DE
Web Site: http://www.middlegroundcapital.com
Year Founded: 2018
Privater Equity Firm
N.A.I.C.S.: 523940
John Stewart *(Co-Founder & Mng Partner)*
Monica McClinton *(Partner & Chief Compliance Officer)*
Lauren Mulholland *(Founder & Partner)*
Scot Duncan *(Founder & Partner)*
Alex Van Der Have *(Head-Investments-Amsterdam)*
Anthony Denaix *(Head-Bus Dev-Amsterdam)*
Robert Jonkers *(Head-Ops-Amsterdam)*

Subsidiaries:

Alco Manufacturing Corporation LLC   (1)
10584 Middle Ave, Elyria, OH 44035
Tel.: (440) 458-3040
Web Site: http://www.alco.com
Precision Machined Metal Components Mfr
N.A.I.C.S.: 332721
D.J. Mumma *(Pres)*

Subsidiary (Domestic):

Lakeshore Fittings, Inc.   (2)
1865 Industrial Park Dr, Grand Haven, MI 49417
Tel.: (616) 846-5090
Web Site: http://www.alco.com
Machining Specialists in Brass & Aluminum Components & Fittings
N.A.I.C.S.: 333248
Sarah Ordish *(Controller)*
Bud Hoffman *(Pres)*
Scott Reus *(Gen Mgr)*
Sheri Porter *(Office Mgr)*

Manth-Brownell Inc.   (2)
1120 Fyler Rd, Kirkville, NY 13082
Tel.: (315) 687-7263
Web Site: http://www.alco.com
Precision Turned Product Mfr
N.A.I.C.S.: 332721
Wesley R. Skinner *(CEO)*

Arrow Tru-Line, Inc.   (1)
2211 S Defiance St, Archbold, OH 43502-9151
Tel.: (419) 446-2785
Web Site: http://www.arrowtruline.com
Rollforming & Stamping Metal Hardware Parts Mfr
N.A.I.C.S.: 332510
John McLaughlin *(VP-Sls & Mktg)*
Randy Ordway *(VP-Ops & Materials)*
Stacy Sauber *(CFO)*
Jill Jacoby *(Dir-HR)*
Jack Francis *(Plant Mgr)*
Alan Elliot *(Dir-Mfg Svcs)*
Jerry Schutt *(Dir-Engrg)*
Jim Aschliman *(Mgr-Materials)*
Don Brenner *(Mgr-Quality)*
Dave Wilson *(Mgr-Shipping & Traffic)*
Alex Brandt *(Controller)*
Darren Bonar *(Sls Mgr-Midwest Reg)*
Ernie Wilson *(Dir-Reg Mfg)*
Kirk Wanstedt *(Sls Mgr-East Coast)*
Steven Trepanier *(Sls Mgr-Canada & Mgr-Distr Centre-Canadian Ops)*
Travis Nowak *(Mgr-Dallas & Texas Distr Centre)*
Thomas Brockley *(CEO)*

Banner Service Corporation   (1)
494 E Lies Rd, Carol Stream, IL 60188-9425
Tel.: (630) 653-7500
Web Site: http://www.banner-servicecorp.com
Mfr & Supplier of Precision Ground, Centerless Grinding, Turning & Straightened Bars
N.A.I.C.S.: 423510
Mark Redding *(Pres)*
Dan Stoettner *(VP-Sls)*

Subsidiary (Domestic):

Banner Medical Inc.   (2)
104 Smith Ave, Sikeston, MO 63801-5240
Tel.: (630) 868-1229
Web Site: http://www.banner-medical.com
Chemical & Allied Products Merchant Whslr
N.A.I.C.S.: 424690
Steve Lancaster *(Pres)*

Capitol Stampings Corp.   (1)
2700 W N Ave, Milwaukee, WI 53208-3208
Tel.: (414) 372-3500
Web Site: http://www.capitolstampings.com
Sheet Metal Work Mfg
N.A.I.C.S.: 332322
Gary Wenzel *(Pres)*

Dura Automotive Systems, Inc.   (1)
1780 Pond Run, Auburn Hills, MI 48326
Tel.: (248) 299-7500
Web Site: http://www.duraauto.com
Sales Range: $1-4.9 Billion
Emp.: 6,700
N.A.I.C.S.: 336390
Kevin Grady *(CFO & Exec VP)*
Francois Stouvenot *(Chief Comml Officer & Exec VP)*
David Pettyes *(Exec VP-HR-Global)*
Jonathan Greenberg *(Gen Counsel & Sec)*
Sanjay Singh *(CTO & Exec VP)*
Kimberly Rodriguez *(CEO)*

Subsidiary (Domestic):

Dura Automotive   (2)

MIDDLEGROUND MANAGEMENT, LP

U.S. PRIVATE

MiddleGround Management, LP—(Continued)

1780 Pond Run, Auburn Hills, MI 48326 **(100%)**
Tel.: (248) 299-7500
Web Site: http://www.duraauto.com
Sales Range: $150-199.9 Million
Mfr of Brake Cables
N.A.I.C.S.: 336340
David Pettyes *(Exec VP-HR-Global)*
Francois Stouvenot *(Chief Comml Officer & Exec VP)*
Jonathan Greenberg *(Gen Counsel & Sec)*
Kevin Grady *(CFO & Exec VP)*
Sanjay Singh *(CTO & Exec VP)*

HLC, Inc. **(1)**
1000 rue des Riveurs, Levis, G6V 9G3, QC, Canada
Tel.: (418) 835-1685
Web Site: https://www.hlc.bike
Sales Range: $10-24.9 Million
Cycling Products Distr
N.A.I.C.S.: 423910
Tracey Lee Batsford *(Dir-Mktg)*
Pat McGinnis *(Pres)*

Megatech A.Q. Inc. **(1)**
340 ave Galilee, Quebec, G1P 4M9, Canada
Web Site: http://www.megatechaq.com
Precision Metal & Machining Services
N.A.I.C.S.: 332710
Jean Blanchet *(CEO)*

Subsidiary (US):

Segundo Metal Products, Inc. **(2)**
7855 S Front Rd, Livermore, CA 94551
Tel.: (925) 455-8789
Web Site: http://www.advantagemetal.com
Sales Range: $1-9.9 Million
Emp.: 45
Sheet Metal Work Mfg
N.A.I.C.S.: 332322
Mike Segundo *(CEO & Co-Founder)*
Phil Segundo *(Co-Founder & VP-Sls)*

PVI Holdings Inc. **(1)**
840 Gessner Rd Ste 950, Houston, TX 77024
Tel.: (713) 365-6805
Holding Company; Industrial Service Companies
N.A.I.C.S.: 551112
Brad Bergeron *(CEO)*
Jack B. Guidry *(CTO)*
David Watkins *(CFO, Sec & Treas)*
David Turner *(Dir)*

Subsidiary (Domestic):

A-T Controls, Inc **(2)**
9955 Intl Blvd, Cincinnati, OH 45246
Tel.: (513) 530-5175
Web Site: http://www.a-tcontrols.com
Sales Range: $25-49.9 Million
Emp.: 40
Actuation Systems & Valve Mfr
N.A.I.C.S.: 333995
Brian Wright *(Pres)*

Setpoint Integrated Solutions, Inc. **(2)**
19011 Highland Rd, Baton Rouge, LA 70809-1363
Tel.: (225) 753-3290
Web Site: http://www.setpointis.com
Sales Range: $75-99.9 Million
Emp.: 500
Provider of Industrial Machinery & Equipment
N.A.I.C.S.: 423830
Joey Jobe *(CEO)*

Subsidiary (Domestic):

Louisiana Valve Source Inc. **(3)**
101 Metals Dr & Hwy 92, Youngsville, LA 70592
Tel.: (337) 856-9100
Web Site: http://www.lavalve.com
Emp.: 200
Repair & Remanufacturing of Industrial Machinery
N.A.I.C.S.: 811310
Brad Bergeron *(CEO)*
Ryan Ardoin *(Product Mgr-Design)*
Amy Gilliland *(Mgr-HR)*
Kirt Hebert *(Dir-Sls & Bus Dev)*

Subsidiary (Domestic):

W. & O. Supply, Inc. **(2)**
2677 Port Industrial Dr, Jacksonville, FL 32226 **(100%)**
Tel.: (904) 354-3800
Web Site: http://www.wosupply.com
Sales Range: $50-74.9 Million
Emp.: 80
Marine Supply Whslr
N.A.I.C.S.: 423840
Michael Hume *(Pres & CEO)*
Michael Page *(VP-Ops-East & West Coast Ops)*
Greg Lechwar *(CFO)*
Fred Loomis *(VP-Technical Projects)*
Todd Nestel *(COO)*

Subsidiary (Domestic):

Engine Monitor, Inc. **(3)**
191 James Dr W, Saint Rose, LA 70087 **(100%)**
Tel.: (504) 620-9800
Web Site: http://www.emi-marine.com
Rev.: $3,500,000
Emp.: 40
Specialized Control Products Mfr
N.A.I.C.S.: 334519
Kevin Kentner *(Mgr-Production & Quality)*
Scott Petty *(Mgr-Engrg)*
Ken Cognevich *(CEO)*
Craig Cabiro *(COO)*

Peterson American Corporation **(1)**
21200 Telegraph Rd, Southfield, MI 48033-4243
Tel.: (248) 799-5400
Web Site: http://www.pspring.com
Sales Range: $125-149.9 Million
Emp.: 1,000
Springs, Wire Forms, Hose Clamps, Engine Valve Springs, Brake Springs & Retaining Rings Mfr
N.A.I.C.S.: 332613
Daniel E. Sceli *(CEO)*

Subsidiary (Non-US):

Peterson Spring Europe Ltd. **(2)**
Heath House Hewell Road, Redditch, B97 6AY, Worcestershire, United Kingdom **(100%)**
Tel.: (44) 152761952
Web Site: http://www.pspring.com
Rev.: $7,000,000
Emp.: 78
Springs, Stampings, Wire Forms & Fourslide Products Mfr
N.A.I.C.S.: 332613
Richard Bray *(Plant Mgr)*

Plant (Domestic):

Peterson Spring-CIMA Plant **(2)**
16805 Heimbach Rd, Three Rivers, MI 49093 **(100%)**
Tel.: (269) 279-7421
Web Site: http://www.pspring.com
Rev.: $4,000,000
Emp.: 75
Mfr Of Hose Clamps, Wire Forms & Fourslide Products
N.A.I.C.S.: 332510
Bill Platco *(Gen Mgr)*

Peterson Spring-Commonwealth Plant **(2)**
40 Bearfoot Rd, Northborough, MA 01532-1514
Tel.: (248) 799-5400
Web Site: http://www.pspring.com
Sales Range: $25-49.9 Million
Emp.: 20
Mfr of Overhead Door Springs Agriculture Tines Large Wire Compression & Extension Springs
N.A.I.C.S.: 811114

Peterson Spring-Georgia Plant **(2)**
600 Old Hull Rd, Athens, GA 30601-1572 **(100%)**
Tel.: (706) 549-3400
Web Site: http://www.pacaloy.com
Rev.: $10,000,000
Emp.: 90
Mfr of Miscellaneous Springs, Wire Forms & Stampings
N.A.I.C.S.: 332613
Cary Foster *(Gen Mgr)*

Peterson Spring-Greenville Plant **(2)**
1375 Peterson Industrial Dr, Greenville, IL 62246-2401
Tel.: (618) 664-1500
Web Site: http://www.pspring.com
Sales Range: $1-9.9 Million
Emp.: 20
Miscellaneous Springs, Overhead Garage Door Springs & Sewer Cable Mfr
N.A.I.C.S.: 332613
Denzil Ramdant *(Gen Mgr)*

Plant (Non-US):

Peterson Spring-Kingsville Plant **(2)**
208 Wigle Ave, Kingsville, N9Y 2J9, ON, Canada **(100%)**
Tel.: (519) 733-2358
Sales Range: $25-49.9 Million
Emp.: 75
Mfr of Automotive Engine Valve Springs, High Performance Valve Springs & Replacement Valve Springs
N.A.I.C.S.: 334519

Plant (Domestic):

Peterson Spring-Madison Heights Plant **(2)**
32601 Industrial Dr, Madison Heights, MI 48071-1517
Tel.: (248) 588-4860
Web Site: http://www.pacaloy.com
Rev.: $4,000,000
Emp.: 40
Mfr of Fuel System Springs
N.A.I.C.S.: 332613

Peterson Spring-Maumee Plant **(2)**
1625 Commerce Rd, Holland, OH 43528-8689 **(100%)**
Tel.: (419) 867-8711
Web Site: http://www.pspring.com
Sales Range: $25-49.9 Million
Emp.: 60
Retaining Ring Bearing Spacer & Wave Ring Mfr
N.A.I.C.S.: 332618

Peterson Spring-Packaging & Distribution **(2)**
800 W Broadway, Three Rivers, MI 49093 **(100%)**
Tel.: (269) 279-7136
Sales Range: $25-49.9 Million
Emp.: 50
Packaging, Bar Code Labels & Assemblies
N.A.I.C.S.: 493110

Peterson Spring-Three Rivers Plant **(2)**
800 W Broadway St, Three Rivers, MI 49093-1946
Tel.: (269) 279-3707
Web Site: http://www.pacaloy.com
Sales Range: $25-49.9 Million
Emp.: 12
Mfr of Transmission Rings, Miscellaneous Springs, Stampings & Die Springs
N.A.I.C.S.: 332613

Plant (Non-US):

Peterson Spring-Windsor Plant **(2)**
Kingsville Plant 208 Wigle Ave, Kingsville, N9Y 2J9, ON, Canada **(100%)**
Tel.: (519) 733-2358
Web Site: http://www.petersonspring.com
Sales Range: $1-9.9 Million
Emp.: 55
Mfr of Automotive Engine Valve Springs
N.A.I.C.S.: 334519
Kathy Bechard *(Mgr-HR)*

Resortes y Productos Metalicos S.A.-Queretaro Plant **(2)**
Av Del Virrey No 3 Parque Industrial El Marques, Municipio El Marques, Queretaro, Mexico **(100%)**
Tel.: (52) 4421533800
Web Site: http://www.pspring.com
Sales Range: $1-9.9 Million
Emp.: 55
Mfr of Automotive Engine Valve Springs
N.A.I.C.S.: 334519
Merces Trindade *(Gen Mgr)*

Race Winning Brands, Inc. **(1)**
7201 Industrial Pk Blvd, Mentor, OH 44060
Tel.: (440) 951-6600

Web Site: http://www.racewinningbrands.com
Motor Vehicle Engine Component Mfr
N.A.I.C.S.: 336310

Subsidiary (Domestic):

Rekluse Motor Sports, Inc. **(2)**
12000 W Franklin St, Boise, ID 83709-0145
Tel.: (208) 426-0659
Web Site: http://www.rekluse.com
Motorcycle, Bicycle & Parts Mfr
N.A.I.C.S.: 336991

Victory 1 Performance, Inc. **(2)**
159 Lugnut Ln, Mooresville, NC 28117
Tel.: (704) 799-1955
Rev.: $4,000,000
Emp.: 15
Steel Foundries, except Investment
N.A.I.C.S.: 331513
Derek Dahl *(Pres)*

Steel Craft Corp **(1)**
105 Steel Craft Dr, Hartford, WI 53027
Tel.: (262) 673-6770
Web Site: http://www.steelcraftwi.com
Sales Range: $25-49.9 Million
Emp.: 250
Miscellaneous Metalwork
N.A.I.C.S.: 332322
Gene Wendorff *(CEO)*
Jeff Sass *(Engr-Tool Design)*
Dave Wolff *(Engr-Process Automation)*
Denny Lawson *(VP-Sls & Mktg)*

Stemmer Imaging AG **(1)**
Gutenbergstr 9-13, 82178, Puchheim, Germany **(83.54%)**
Tel.: (49) 89809020
Web Site: https://www.stemmer-imaging.com
Rev.: $167,677,531
Assets: $130,104,684
Liabilities: $39,365,422
Net Worth: $90,739,262
Earnings: $19,396,719
Emp.: 310
Fiscal Year-end: 12/31/2022
Industrial Equipment Mfr & Distr
N.A.I.C.S.: 334512
Klaus Weinmann *(Chm-Supervisory Bd)*
Stefan Kobe *(Deputy Chm-Supervisory Bd)*
Arne Deh *(CEO & Member-Exec Bd)*
Uwe Kemm *(COO & Member-Exec Bd)*
Peter Kepple *(Dir-Corp Sls Enablement)*
Johannes Hiltner *(Dir-Product Mgmt)*

Subsidiary (Non-US):

Infaimon Do Brasil Visao Artificial Ltda **(2)**
Jose Versolato 111 Sala 1421 Ed Domo Business-Centro, Sao Bernardo do Campo, 09751-020, SP, Brazil
Tel.: (55) 1143143545
Machine Vision Component Mfr
N.A.I.C.S.: 333998

Infaimon Mexico S.A.DE C.V. **(2)**
Av Colinas del Cimatario 435 Piso 2 Int 306, Fracc Colinas del Cimatario, 76090, Queretaro, Mexico
Tel.: (52) 4422151415
Machine Vision Component Mfr
N.A.I.C.S.: 333998

Infaimon S.L.U. **(2)**
Plaza Europa 10 Floor 1, 08902, Barcelona, Spain
Tel.: (34) 932525757
Web Site: http://www.infaimon.com
Machine Vision Component Mfr
N.A.I.C.S.: 333998

Infaimon Unipessoal, Lda. **(2)**
Avenida Europa 437, 3800-228, Aveiro, Portugal
Tel.: (351) 234312034
Machine Vision Component Mfr
N.A.I.C.S.: 333998

Stemmer Imaging A/S **(2)**
Vesterbrogade 149 5th floor Building 12, 1620, Copenhagen, Denmark
Tel.: (45) 33730000
Machine Vision Component Mfr
N.A.I.C.S.: 333998

Stemmer Imaging AB **(2)**
Sandhamnsgatan 63C 3 tr, 115 28, Stock-

holm, Sweden
Tel.: (46) 855511000
Machine Vision Component Mfr
N.A.I.C.S.: 333998

Stemmer Imaging AG (2)
Eichenstr 2, 8808, Pfaffikon, Switzerland
Tel.: (41) 554159090
Machine Vision Component Mfr
N.A.I.C.S.: 333998

Stemmer Imaging B.V. (2)
Zonnehorst 17, 7207 BT, Zutphen, Netherlands
Tel.: (31) 575798888
Machine Vision Component Mfr
N.A.I.C.S.: 333998

Stemmer Imaging Ges.m.b.H. (2)
Liebenauer Hauptstr 2-6, 8041, Graz, Austria
Tel.: (43) 3162696090
Machine Vision Component Mfr
N.A.I.C.S.: 333998

Stemmer Imaging Ltd. (2)
The Old Barn Grange Court, Tongham, Farnham, GU10 1DW, Surrey, United Kingdom
Tel.: (44) 1252780000
Machine Vision Component Mfr
N.A.I.C.S.: 333998
Chris Pitt *(Sls Dir-UK)*

Stemmer Imaging Oy (2)
Keilaranta 16, 02150, Espoo, Finland
Tel.: (358) 94355500
Machine Vision Component Mfr
N.A.I.C.S.: 333998

Stemmer Imaging S.A.S. (2)
13-15 rue Jean Jaures, 92800, Puteaux, France
Tel.: (33) 145069560
Machine Vision Component Mfr
N.A.I.C.S.: 333998

Stemmer Imaging S.r.l. (2)
Via Guerrazzi n 1/A, 40125, Bologna, Italy
Tel.: (39) 04533730000
Machine Vision Component Mfr
N.A.I.C.S.: 333998

Stemmer Imaging Sp.z o.o. (2)
3 Maja 6A, 99-400, Lowicz, Poland
Tel.: (48) 664921922
Machine Vision Component Mfr
N.A.I.C.S.: 333998

The L.S. Starrett Company (1)
121 Crescent St, Athol, MA 01331-1915
Tel.: (978) 249-3551
Web Site: https://www.starrett.com
Rev.: $253,701,000
Assets: $199,554,000
Liabilities: $97,125,000
Net Worth: $102,429,000
Earnings: $14,878,000
Emp.: 1,493
Fiscal Year-end: 06/30/2022
Precision Measuring Tools, Saw Blades, Optical & Vision Measuring Equipment & Hand Tools Mfr
N.A.I.C.S.: 332216
John Stewart *(Pres)*
Douglas A. Starrett *(CEO)*
John C. Tripp *(CFO & Treas)*
Christian Arnsten *(VP & Gen Mgr-Industrial Products-Intl)*
Charles Starrett *(Product Mgr-Saws & Hand Tools)*
Michael Connor *(Dir-Sls & Mktg-Industrial Products-North America)*
Justin Steil *(Sec & VP)*

Division (Domestic):

Bytewise Measurement Systems (2)
1150 Brookstone Ctr Pkwy, Columbus, GA 31904
Tel.: (706) 323-5142
Web Site: https://www.bytewise.com
Sales Range: $25-49.9 Million
Emp.: 24
Electrical Contractor
N.A.I.C.S.: 238210
Andy Hidle *(CEO)*

Subsidiary (Domestic):

Evans Rule Company, Inc. (2)
5965 Core Ave Ste 618, North Charleston, SC 29406-4909 (100%)
Tel.: (843) 797-2500
Web Site: https://www.starrett.com
Sales Range: $25-49.9 Million
Emp.: 10
Folding Rulers, Steel Measuring Tapes & Chalkline Reels Mfr
N.A.I.C.S.: 332216

Division (Domestic):

L.S. Starrett Company - Saw Division (2)
1372 Boggs Dr, Mount Airy, NC 27030-1268
Tel.: (336) 789-5141
Web Site: https://www.starrett.com
Stone Product Mfr
N.A.I.C.S.: 327991

Precision Ground Flat Stock Division (2)
1372 Boggs Dr, Mount Airy, NC 27030
Tel.: (336) 789-5141
Web Site: https://www.starrett.com
Sales Range: $25-49.9 Million
Emp.: 100
Stone Product Mfr
N.A.I.C.S.: 327991

Subsidiary (Non-US):

Starrett (Asia) Pte. Ltd. (2)
35 Marsiling Industrial Estate Road 3 05-04, Singapore, 739257, Singapore
Tel.: (65) 63651088
Web Site: https://www.starrett.com.sg
Emp.: 10
Saw Blades & Hand Tools Distr
N.A.I.C.S.: 423830

Starrett (New Zealand) Limited (2)
Unit D 61-63 Hugo Johnston Drive, Penrose, 1061, Auckland, New Zealand
Tel.: (64) 95891429
Web Site: https://nz.starrett.com
Hand Tools Distr
N.A.I.C.S.: 423830

Subsidiary (Domestic):

Starrett Bytewise Development, Inc. (2)
1245 Broadway, Columbus, GA 31901
Tel.: (706) 323-5142
Web Site: https://www.starrett.com
Emp.: 25
Software Publishing Services
N.A.I.C.S.: 513210

Division (Domestic):

Starrett Granite Surface Plate Division (2)
1101 Proster Dr, Waite Park, MN 56387 (100%)
Tel.: (320) 251-7171
Web Site: https://www.starrett.com
Sales Range: $25-49.9 Million
Emp.: 70
Granite Surface Plates Mfr
N.A.I.C.S.: 327991

Subsidiary (Non-US):

Starrett Industria e Comercio Ltda. (2)
Avenida Laroy S Starrett 1880, PO Box 171, Itu, 13300-000, Sao Paulo, Brazil (100%)
Tel.: (55) 1121188200
Web Site: https://www.starrett.com.br
Sales Range: $75-99.9 Million
Emp.: 500
Saw Blades & Hand Tools Mfr
N.A.I.C.S.: 332216

Subsidiary (Domestic):

Starrett Kinemetric Engineering, Inc. (2)
26052 Merit Cir Ste 103, Laguna Hills, CA 92653
Tel.: (949) 348-1213
Web Site: https://www.starrett.com
Emp.: 25
Video & Multi-Sensor Measurement Systems Mfr
N.A.I.C.S.: 333248

Subsidiary (Non-US):

Starrett Tools (Suzhou) Co. Ltd. (2)
N 339 Su Hong Zhong Road, Suzhou Industrial Park, Suzhou, 215021, Jiangsu, China
Tel.: (86) 51267411940
Web Site: https://www.starrett.com.cn
Saw Blades & Precision Tools Mfr
N.A.I.C.S.: 332216

The L.S. Starrett Company Limited (2)
Oxnam Road, Jedburgh, TD8 6LR, Roxburghshire, United Kingdom (100%)
Tel.: (44) 1835863501
Web Site: https://www.starrett.co.uk
Sales Range: $25-49.9 Million
Emp.: 200
Saw Blades & Hand Tools Mfr & Distr
N.A.I.C.S.: 332216
Ralph Nagle *(Mng Dir)*

Subsidiary (Non-US):

Starrett GmbH (3)
Feldwies 12, Taunus, 61389, Schmitten, Germany
Tel.: (49) 6084959510
Web Site: https://www.starrett.com
Saw Blades & Hand Tools Distr
N.A.I.C.S.: 423830

Subsidiary (Domestic):

Starrett Precision Optical Limited (3)
Oxnam Road, Jedburgh, TD8 6LR, United Kingdom (100%)
Tel.: (44) 1835863501
Web Site: http://www.starrett-precision.co.uk
Optical Profile Projectors & Video Measuring Systems Mfr
N.A.I.C.S.: 333310

Subsidiary (Non-US):

The L.S. Starrett Company of Australia Pty Ltd (2)
Unit 2 57 Prince William Drive, Seven Hills, 2147, NSW, Australia
Tel.: (61) 296206944
Web Site: https://www.starrett.com.au
Saw Blades & Hand Tools Warehouse & Distr
N.A.I.C.S.: 423830

The L.S. Starrett Company of Canada Limited (2)
1244 Kamato Rd, Mississauga, L4W 1Y1, ON, Canada (100%)
Tel.: (905) 624-2750
Web Site: https://www.starrett.com
Sales Range: $25-49.9 Million
Emp.: 20
Saw Blades & Hand Tools Distr
N.A.I.C.S.: 423830

The L.S. Starrett Company of Mexico S. de R.L. de C.V. (2)
Prolongacion Irlanda 901, Colonia Privadas de Luxemburgo, Saltillo, CP 25240, Coahuila, Mexico (100%)
Tel.: (52) 8444324660
Web Site: https://www.starrett.com.mx
Emp.: 20
Saw Blades & Hand Tools Distr
N.A.I.C.S.: 423830

Subsidiary (Domestic):

Tru-Stone Technologies, Inc. (2)
1101 Prosper Dr, Waite Park, MN 56387
Tel.: (320) 251-7171
Web Site: https://www.tru-stone.com
Emp.: 70
Mfr of Custom Precision Granite Machine Bases & Accessories
N.A.I.C.S.: 333248

Division (Domestic):

Webber Gauge Division (2)
24500 Detroit Rd, Cleveland, OH 44145-2521
Tel.: (440) 835-0001
Web Site: https://www.starrett-webber.com
Sales Range: $50-74.9 Million
Emp.: 80
Mfr of Precision Gauge Blocks & Machinists Tools
N.A.I.C.S.: 332216

Xtrac Group Limited (1)
Gables Way Kennet Park, Thatcham, RG19 4ZA, Berks, United Kingdom
Tel.: (44) 1635293800
Web Site: http://www.xtrac.com
Emp.: 330
Holding Company; Automotive Transmission Systems Designer & Mfr
N.A.I.C.S.: 551112
Peter Digby *(Chm)*
Adrian Paul Moore *(CEO & Mng Dir)*
Stephen John Roger Lane *(Fin Dir)*
Clifford Arthur Hawkins *(Dir-Dev)*

Subsidiary (Domestic):

Xtrac Limited (2)
Gables Way Kennet Park, Thatcham, RG19 4ZA, Berks, United Kingdom
Tel.: (44) 1635 293 800
Web Site: http://www.xtrac.com
Automotive Transmission Systems Designer, Mfr & Whslr
N.A.I.C.S.: 336350
Peter Digby *(Chm)*
Adrian Paul Moore *(Mng Dir)*
Stephen John Roger Lane *(Fin Dir)*
Martin Halley *(Dir-Ops)*
Clifford Arthur Hawkins *(Dir-Dev)*
James Setter *(Head-High Performance Automotive)*
Jane Gilham *(Head-HR)*
Peter Ayling *(Controller-Fin)*
Martyn Silby *(Head-Mfg)*
Dominic Smith *(Head-Advanced Engrg)*
Stuart Croot *(Mgr-Engrg)*
Jon Marsh *(Chief Designer)*

Subsidiary (US):

Xtrac, Inc. (2)
6183 W 80th St, Indianapolis, IN 46278
Tel.: (317) 472-2454
Web Site: http://www.xtrac.com
Automotive Transmission Systems Mfr & Whslr
N.A.I.C.S.: 336350
Dolev Rafaeli *(Founder)*
Andrew Heard *(VP)*
Jeff Kitchen *(Gen Mgr)*
Lisa Lamott *(Controller)*

MIDDLEKAUFF AUTOMOTIVE INC.
1243 Blue Lakes Blvd N, Twin Falls, ID 83301
Tel.: (208) 736-2480
Web Site: http://www.bigmdirect.com
Rev.: $49,000,000
Emp.: 140
Owner & Operator of Car Dealerships
N.A.I.C.S.: 441110
Dave Mace *(Gen Mgr)*
Rick Rojas *(Mgr-Fin)*

MIDDLEPORT FAMILY HEALTH CENTER
81 Rochester Rd, Middleport, NY 14105
Tel.: (716) 735-3261
Web Site: http://www.middleportfamilyhealthcenter.com
Year Founded: 1983
Sales Range: $10-24.9 Million
Emp.: 40
Pharmaceutical Product Whslr
N.A.I.C.S.: 424210
Stephen L. Giroux *(Owner & Pres)*

MIDDLESBORO COCA-COLA BOTTLING
1324 Cumberland Ave, Middlesboro, KY 40965
Tel.: (606) 248-2660
Web Site: http://www.mccbw.com
Year Founded: 1904
Sales Range: $25-49.9 Million
Emp.: 100
Spring Water & Beverage Bottling Services
N.A.I.C.S.: 312112

MIDDLESBORO COCA-COLA BOTTLING
U.S. PRIVATE

Middlesboro Coca-Cola Bottling—(Continued)
Jill Barry (VP)
Linvil Day (VP-Sls & Mktg)
Patrick Forster (CFO)
Brenda Bailey (Dir-HR)
Glenn Hoskins (Mgr-Production)
Ed Jones (Dir-Safety & Coord-Food Safety)
Lisa Moyers (Mgr-Data Sys)
Neil Barry Jr. (Pres)
Neil G. Barry IV (Acct Exec)

MIDDLESEX BANCORP, MHC
6 Main St, Natick, MA 01760
Tel.: (508) 653-0300
Web Site:
http://www.middlesexbank.com
Sales Range: $150-199.9 Million
Bank Holding Company
N.A.I.C.S.: 551111

Subsidiaries:

Middlesex Savings Bank (1)
6 Main St, Natick, MA 01760
Tel.: (508) 653-0300
Web Site: http://www.middlesexbank.com
Sales Range: $150-199.9 Million
Emp.: 16
Savings Institutions, Except Federal
N.A.I.C.S.: 522180
John R. Heerwagen (CEO)
Timothy P. Fahey (Officer-Comml Lending & Sr VP)
David M. Bennett (Sr VP)
Brian K. Hanley (Officer-Community Bus Banking & Sr VP)
Bruce A. Miccile (Officer-Bus Banking & VP)
Susan J. Johnson (Officer-Bus Banking & Sr VP)
Kathleen A. Maroney (VP-Govt Assisted Lending & Underwriting)
Julie St. Pierre (Branch Mgr)
Thomas F. Farley (Chief Comml Banking Officer & Exec VP)
Jon C. Auger (Chief Retail Lending Officer & Exec VP)
Jami Eycleshymer (Officer-Bus Banking Lending)
Greg Pater (Officer-Bus Banking Lending)

MIDDLESEX COUNTY UTILITIES AUTHORITY
2571 Main St, Sayreville, NJ 08872
Tel.: (732) 721-3800
Web Site: http://www.mcua.com
Year Founded: 1950
Sales Range: $25-49.9 Million
Emp.: 180
Sewerage Systems
N.A.I.C.S.: 221320
Richard L. Fitamant (Exec Dir)
Ted Light (Chm)
Samuel Chiaravalli (Vice Chm)
John A. Hila (Gen Counsel)

MIDDLESEX FEDERAL SAVINGS F.A.
1 College Ave, Somerville, MA 02144-1961
Tel.: (617) 666-4700
Web Site:
http://www.middlesexfederal.com
Year Founded: 1890
Sales Range: $25-49.9 Million
Emp.: 40
Federal Savings Institutions
N.A.I.C.S.: 522180
John R. Wiseman (Pres & CEO)
Ronald J. Gauthier (Portfolio Mgr-Comml)
Peter A. Bazinotti (Sr VP)
Barbara Sartanowicz (Sr VP-Retail Banking)
Daniel Devine (CFO & Sr VP)

MIDDLESEX LLC.
1335 Thomas Ave, Leesburg, FL 34748
Tel.: (352) 728-2800
Web Site:
http://www.middlesexcompany.com
Rev.: $12,600,000
Emp.: 99
Highway, Street & Bridge Construction
N.A.I.C.S.: 237310
Alfred A. Aponas (Pres)

MIDDLETON BUILDING SUPPLY INC.
5 Kings Hwy, Union, NH 03887
Tel.: (603) 473-2314
Web Site: http://www.lavalleys.com
Sales Range: $25-49.9 Million
Emp.: 99
Retail & Manufacture Lumber & Other Building Materials
N.A.I.C.S.: 423310
Lawrence Huot (Owner)
Ron Godfrey (Mgr)
Jim Bruneau (Mgr)

MIDDLETON FORD INC.
7520 Century Ave, Middleton, WI 53562
Tel.: (608) 831-7725
Web Site:
http://www.middletonford.com
Sales Range: $10-24.9 Million
Emp.: 60
New Car Dealers
N.A.I.C.S.: 441110
Bob Hudson (Pres)
David James (Mgr-Sls)
Jeff Helm (Mgr-Parts)
Russel Zimmerman (Mgr-Svc)
Chuck Polley (Gen Mgr)
Dave Hudson (VP)
Jessica Flemming (Asst Mgr-Parts)
Ralph Norton (Mgr-Used Car)
Stacey Ambort (Mgr-Fin)
Will Hudson (Mgr-Internet)
Andrew Hudson (Owner & VP)

MIDDLETON INC.
22039 Interstate 30, Bryant, AR 72022
Tel.: (501) 847-0371
Web Site:
http://www.middletoninc.com
Year Founded: 1976
Sales Range: $10-24.9 Million
Emp.: 20
HVAC Contractors
N.A.I.C.S.: 238220
Matt McElhaney (Gen Mgr-Svcs)

MIDDLETON OIL CO. INC.
420 Bolling St, Greenville, AL 36037
Tel.: (334) 382-2627
Sales Range: $10-24.9 Million
Emp.: 7
Petroleum Bulk Stations
N.A.I.C.S.: 424710
William L. Coon Sr. (Pres)

MIDDLETOWN FORD
237 Wickham Ave, Middletown, NY 10940
Tel.: (845) 343-3135
Sales Range: $10-24.9 Million
Emp.: 52
Car Whslr
N.A.I.C.S.: 441110

MIDDLETOWN FORD SALES INC.
2 Walnut St, Middletown, MD 21769
Tel.: (301) 698-6200
Sales Range: $10-24.9 Million
Emp.: 22
New & Used Car Dealers
N.A.I.C.S.: 441110

Frank Kennedy (Gen Mgr)
Roger A. East (Fin Dir)

MIDDLETOWN HOME SALES
53 Middletown Rd, Fairmont, WV 26554
Tel.: (304) 363-8565
Web Site:
http://www.middletownhomes.com
Year Founded: 1994
Sales Range: $10-24.9 Million
Emp.: 44
Provider of Mobile Home Dealer Services
N.A.I.C.S.: 459930
Kevin D. Wilfong (Pres)

MIDDOUGH, INC.
1901 E 13th St Ste 400, Cleveland, OH 44114
Tel.: (216) 367-6000
Web Site: http://www.middough.com
Year Founded: 1950
Rev.: $38,100,000
Emp.: 650
Full Engineering Service; Consulting Architectural, Environmental & Construction Services Firm
N.A.I.C.S.: 541330
Ronald Ledin (Chm & CEO)
James J. Volk (Sr VP & Gen Mgr-Midwest)
Carl E. Wendell (Pres & COO)
Daniel P. Lowry Jr. (Sr VP & Gen Mgr-Midwest)

Subsidiaries:

Microtech Systems, Inc. (1)
5617 Scotts Valley Dr Suite 100, Scotts Valley, CA 95066
Tel.: (650) 596-1900
Web Site: http://www.microtech.com
Sales Range: $10-24.9 Million
Emp.: 25
Producer of Innovative CD/DVD/Blu-ray Disc Duplicators & Disc Publisher
N.A.I.C.S.: 513210
Corwin Nichols (Founder & CEO)
Michael Fallavollita (VP-R&D)

Middough Consulting, Illinios (1)
700 Commerce Dr Ste 200, Oak Brook, IL 60523-5516
Tel.: (630) 734-7000
Web Site: http://www.milbankmfg.com
Rev.: $7,300,000
Emp.: 110
Engineering Services
N.A.I.C.S.: 541330

Middough Consulting, Inc (1)
6135 Trust Dr Ste 102, Holland, OH 43528-9129
Tel.: (216) 367-6000
Web Site: http://www.middough.com
Sales Range: $10-24.9 Million
Emp.: 100
Engineering Design & Consultancy
N.A.I.C.S.: 541330

Middough Consulting, Kentucky (1)
1212 Bath Ave, Ashland, KY 41101-2664
Tel.: (216) 367-6000
Web Site: http://www.middough.com
N.A.I.C.S.: 541330

Middough Consulting, West Virginia (1)
1212 Bath Ave, Ashland, KY 41101 (100%)
Tel.: (606) 920-7700
Web Site: http://www.middough.com
Sales Range: $10-24.9 Million
Emp.: 12
Engineeering Services
N.A.I.C.S.: 541420

MIDFLORIDA CREDIT UNION
PO Box 8008, Lakeland, FL 33802-8008
Tel.: (863) 688-3733 FL
Web Site: http://www.midflorida.com
Year Founded: 1954
Sales Range: $100-124.9 Million
Emp.: 604
Credit Union Operator
N.A.I.C.S.: 522130
D. Kevin Jones (Pres & CEO)
Kathy Britt (COO)
Dennis Pershing (Chief Lending Officer)

MIDGLEY-HUBER INC.
2465 Progress Dr, Salt Lake City, UT 84119
Tel.: (801) 972-5011
Web Site: http://www.midgley-huber.com
Sales Range: $10-24.9 Million
Emp.: 22
Distr of Air Conditioning Equipments
N.A.I.C.S.: 423730
Sean Petersen (Mgr-Acctg)
Amy Myers (Mgr-Credit)
Terry B. Shields (Pres)

MIDLAND ATLANTIC PROPERTIES, LLC
310 Montgomery Rd Ste 710, Cincinnati, OH 45236
Tel.: (513) 792-5000
Web Site:
http://www.midlandatlantic.com
Sales Range: $25-49.9 Million
Emp.: 15
Real Estate Development & Management
N.A.I.C.S.: 237210
Nicole Chimento (Dir-Leasing)
Sandy King (Controller)
Ryan Kyte (CFO)
David P. Woodke (Dir-Construction)
John Silverman (Mng Principal)
William Mees (Dir-Dev)
Chris Palermo (Dir-Acq)
Julie Krause (Mgr-Property)

Subsidiaries:

Midland Atlantic Properties, LLC (1)
9000 Keystone Crossing Ste 850, Indianapolis, IN 46240
Tel.: (317) 580-9900
Web Site: http://www.midlandatlantic.com
Emp.: 9
Real Estate Development & Management
N.A.I.C.S.: 237210
Aaron Boyle (Mng Partner)
Kelly Boyle (Principal)
Kelly Skeens (Dir-Mktg)
Amy Martikke (Mgr-Property)

Midland Atlantic Properties, LLC (1)
406 Hogans Valley Way, Cary, NC 27513
Tel.: (919) 349-0944
Real Estate Development & Management
N.A.I.C.S.: 237210

MIDLAND CAPITAL HOLDINGS CORP.
8929 S Harlem Ave, Bridgeview, IL 60455
Tel.: (708) 598-9400
Web Site:
https://www.midlandfederal.com
MCPH—(OTCIQ)
Emp.: 100
Offices of Bank Holding Companies
N.A.I.C.S.: 551111
Paul M. Zogas (Chm, Pres & CEO)

Subsidiaries:

Midland Federal Savings and Loan Association (1)
8929 S Harlem Ave, Bridgeview, IL 60455
Tel.: (708) 598-9400
Web Site: http://www.midlandfederal.com
Rev.: $4,234,000
Assets: $124,044,000
Liabilities: $112,791,000
Net Worth: $11,253,000
Earnings: ($51,000)
Emp.: 20

COMPANIES MIDMARK CAPITAL

Fiscal Year-end: 12/31/2013
Banking Services
N.A.I.C.S.: 522110
Paul M. Zogas *(Chm, Pres & CEO)*

MIDLAND CARE CONNECTION, INC.
200 SW Frazier Cir, Topeka, KS 66606
Tel.: (785) 232-2044 KS
Web Site: http://www.midlandcare.org
Year Founded: 1978
Sales Range: $25-49.9 Million
Emp.: 250
Health Care Srvices
N.A.I.C.S.: 622110
Charles Gregory Nelson *(Dir-Medical)*
Karren Weichert *(Pres & CEO)*
Harmony Hines *(VP-Compliance)*
Marsha Kent *(VP-Clinical Svcs)*
Chad Wilkins *(CFO & VP-Fin)*
Brenden Long *(VP-HR)*
Greg Reser *(VP-Sr Svcs)*
Mike Dunnaway *(Chm)*
Keith Warta *(Vice Chm)*

MIDLAND COMPUTER INC.
11011 Q St Ste 104C, Omaha, NE 68137
Tel.: (402) 691-8900
Web Site: http://www.midcomp.com
Year Founded: 1979
Sales Range: $10-24.9 Million
Emp.: 15
Computers Peripherals & Software
N.A.I.C.S.: 423430
Wayne Clure *(Pres)*
William Bennett Sr. *(COO)*

MIDLAND ENGINEERING COMPANY
52369 State Rd 933 Indiana State Rte, South Bend, IN 46637
Tel.: (574) 272-0200
Web Site:
  http://www.midlandengineering.com
Sales Range: $10-24.9 Million
Emp.: 195
Roofing Contractors
N.A.I.C.S.: 238160
Ken Sage *(Mgr-Sls & Mktg)*

MIDLAND FINANCIAL CO.
MidFirst Plz 501 NW Grand Blvd, Oklahoma City, OK 73118
Tel.: (405) 767-7000 OK
Web Site: http://www.midfirst.com
Year Founded: 1981
Sales Range: $650-699.9 Million
Emp.: 2,433
Bank Holding Company
N.A.I.C.S.: 551111
Todd A. Dobson *(CFO)*
G. Jeffrey Records Jr. *(Chm, Pres & CEO)*

Subsidiaries:

MidFirst Bank (1)
MidFirst Plz 501 NW Grand Blvd, Oklahoma City, OK 73118-6054
Tel.: (405) 767-7000
Web Site: http://www.midfirst.com
Sales Range: $650-699.9 Million
Federal Savings Bank
N.A.I.C.S.: 522180
Daniel Adams *(Sr VP)*
Todd A. Dobson *(Pres)*
K. Randy Roper *(Chief Credit Officer & First Exec VP)*
Garland W. Wilkinson *(COO & Sr Exec VP)*
Timothy M. Schneider *(CIO & Exec VP)*
Dana M. Lorenson *(Sr VP-HR)*
Kevin Wilson *(Sr VP-Tax Acctg)*
Grant Griswold *(VP & Dir-Media Rels)*
Brian Wilkinson *(Pres-Colorado Market)*
L. J. Willis *(VP & Mgr-Bus Banking Relationship)*
Drew Burlak *(Sr VP & Mng Dir-Chicago)*
Jeff Lowe *(Pres-Arizona Market)*

Melody Stallings *(VP-Comml Lending)*
Gretchen Wahl *(Sr VP-Comml Lending)*
Leslie Wilkerson *(Sr VP & Dir-Treasury Mgmt)*
Greg Schaefer *(CFO & Exec VP)*
D. J. Morgan *(Chief Comml Banking Officer & Sr Exec VP)*
G. Jeffrey Records Jr. *(Chm & CEO)*
Roger DiSalvatore Jr. *(Exec VP & Mng Dir-Natl Lending)*

Division (Domestic):

1st Century Bank (2)
1875 Century Park E Ste 100, Los Angeles, CA 90067-2535
Tel.: (310) 270-9500
Web Site: http://www.1cbank.com
Sales Range: $10-24.9 Million
Commercial Banking Services
N.A.I.C.S.: 522110
Jason Omega Philip DiNapoli *(Pres & CEO)*
George A. Perez *(Mng Dir & Sr VP)*
Robert Rodriguez *(Sr VP & Dir-Sls)*
Bonnie Rubin *(Exec VP & Reg Dir)*
Justin Weissman *(Sr VP-Bus Banking)*
Richard Rothenberg *(Mng Dir)*
Carlos Payan *(Sr VP & Reg Mgr)*
Alan I. Rothenberg *(Founder & Chm)*

Subsidiary (Domestic):

MidFirst Trust Co. (2)
MidFirst Plz 501 NW Grand Blvd, Oklahoma City, OK 73118-6054
Tel.: (405) 767-7506
Trust & Wealth Management Services
N.A.I.C.S.: 523991

Midland Mortgage Co. (2)
MidFirst Plz 501 NW Grand Blvd, Oklahoma City, OK 73118-6054
Tel.: (405) 840-7600
Web Site:
  http://www.mymidlandmortgage.com
Mortgage Broker Services
N.A.I.C.S.: 522310

Presidential Financial Corporation (2)
3460 Preston Rdg Rd Ste 550, Alpharetta, GA 30084-5851
Tel.: (770) 491-8345
Web Site:
  http://www.presidentialfinancial.com
Sales Range: $10-24.9 Million
Emp.: 70
Commercial Lending Services
N.A.I.C.S.: 522299
Lewis Chan *(Mng Dir & Sr VP)*
Frank Palmieri *(Sr VP & Portfolio Mgr)*
Jeffrey L. Guldner *(Sr VP & Dir-Loan Admin)*
Dennis Schlesner *(Pres)*

MIDLAND FOOD SERVICES
6200 Rockside Woods Blvd, Cleveland, OH 44131-7303
Tel.: (216) 524-2251 DE
Web Site:
  http://www.midlandfoodservice.com
Year Founded: 1995
Sales Range: $350-399.9 Million
Emp.: 6,000
Operator of Franchised Pizza Restaurants
N.A.I.C.S.: 722513
Charlie Hudson *(Pres)*
Christopher Flocken *(CFO)*

MIDLAND IMPLEMENT COMPANY, INC.
402 Daniel St, Billings, MT 59101
Tel.: (406) 248-7771
Web Site:
  http://www.midlandimplement.com
Year Founded: 1920
Emp.: 100
Marketing & Distribution of Agricultural, Irrigation & Landscaping Machinery & Equipment
N.A.I.C.S.: 423820
Gary Pates *(Co-Owner & Mgr-Irrigation & Pump Div)*

Randall Pates *(Co-Owner & Mgr-Golf Dv)*
Doug Leischner *(Mgr-Shop & Svc)*
Perry Hilderman *(Mgr-Inside Sls)*
Guy Raidiger *(Mgr-Ag & Turf-Billings)*
Bryan Lucas *(Branch Mgr-Bozeman)*
Ryan Susott *(Branch Mgr-Missoula)*

MIDLAND MARKETING COOP, INC.
219 E 9th St, Hays, KS 67601-4122
Tel.: (785) 628-3221 KS
Web Site:
  http://www.midlandmarketing.org
Year Founded: 1915
Sales Range: $10-24.9 Million
Emp.: 41
Farm Supplies & Gasoline Service Stations
N.A.I.C.S.: 424510
Vance Westhusin *(Gen Mgr)*
Kevin Royer *(Asst Mgr)*
Randy Schoenthaler *(Office Mgr)*
Brian Witt *(Coord-Hays Feedmill)*
Doug Dreiling *(Mgr-Central)*
Matt Benoit *(Mgr-South)*
Nathan Felder *(Coord-Brownell)*
Steve Hageman *(Mgr-Petroleum)*

MIDLAND PAPER COMPANY
101 E Palatine Rd, Wheeling, IL 60090-6500
Tel.: (847) 777-2700 IL
Web Site:
  http://www.midlandpaper.com
Year Founded: 1907
Sales Range: $800-899.9 Million
Emp.: 400
Wholesale Paper Distributor
N.A.I.C.S.: 424110
E. Stanton Hooker *(Co-Owner)*
Ralph Deletto *(CFO & Exec VP)*
Mike Graves *(CEO)*
Jim O'Toole *(Co-Owner & Pres-Midland Natl)*

Subsidiaries:

Midland Paper (1)
8305 B Stewart Ave, Wausau, WI 54401-9038
Tel.: (847) 777-2640
Web Site: http://www.midlandpaper.com
Sales Range: $10-24.9 Million
Emp.: 30
Provider of Printing & Writing Paper
N.A.I.C.S.: 424110
Wally Haglund *(Gen Mgr)*

Midland Paper Co. (1)
101 E Palatine Rd, Wheeling, IL 60090 (100%)
Tel.: (847) 777-2700
Web Site: http://www.midlandpaper.com
Sales Range: $10-24.9 Million
Emp.: 20
Wholesale Distributor of Paper Products
N.A.I.C.S.: 424130
Dan Denz *(Asst Mgr-Warehouse)*
Bill Blocker *(Gen Mgr)*
Bob Knuerr *(Mgr-IS)*
Tom Edwards *(Sr VP)*
Rich Goodwin *(VP-Logistics)*

Midland Paper Co. (1)
8601 N 91st St, Milwaukee, WI 53224-2405
Tel.: (847) 777-2920
Sales Range: $10-24.9 Million
Emp.: 32
Fine Paper Distributors
N.A.I.C.S.: 424110
Brit Swisher *(Gen Mgr)*

Midland Paper Co. (1)
19 Ludlow Rd Ste 102, Westport, CT 06880-3040
Tel.: (203) 222-0076
Rev.: $120,000,000
Emp.: 5
Paper Merchants
N.A.I.C.S.: 424110

Midland Paper Co. (1)

4826 W Converters Dr, Appleton, WI 54913
Tel.: (847) 777-2675
Web Site: http://www.midlandpaper.com
Sales Range: $10-24.9 Million
Emp.: 25
Paper Distributor
N.A.I.C.S.: 424110
Barry Hammershoy *(Mgr-Distr)*

MIDLAND PLASTICS INC.
5405 S Westridge CT, New Berlin, WI 53151
Tel.: (920) 336-4464
Web Site:
  http://www.midlandplastic.com
Rev.: $31,000,000
Emp.: 77
Plastics Sheets & Rods
N.A.I.C.S.: 424610
Jamie Carriveau *(Supvr-Forming Dept)*
Michael Crowley *(VP-Tech Svcs)*
Sally Giese *(Dir-HR)*
Stacy Thoreson *(Asst Controller)*
Jeff Smoot *(Mgr-Mktg)*
Roger Stoltenberg *(VP-Sls & Mktg)*
Terry Stephens *(Mgr-Mfg Ops)*
Monica Dinauer *(Mgr-HR)*
Daniel Pitterle *(Mgr-Sls)*

MIDLAND STEEL COMPANY
202 Boeh Ln, Wathena, KS 66090
Tel.: (785) 989-4442
Web Site:
  http://www.midlandsteelco.com
Year Founded: 1961
Sales Range: $10-24.9 Million
Emp.: 75
Fabricator of Structural Steel
N.A.I.C.S.: 332312
Donald Jones *(VP-Production)*
Doug Bibens *(Pres)*

MIDLANDS MECHANICAL INC.
8425 Wirt St, Omaha, NE 68134
Tel.: (402) 571-4258
Web Site:
  http://www.midmechinc.com
Sales Range: $10-24.9 Million
Emp.: 75
Provider of Mechanical Contracts
N.A.I.C.S.: 238220
Doug Brummer *(VP)*
Chris Sills *(Pres)*
Gil Balboa *(Officer-Safety & Compliance)*

MIDLANDS ORTHOPAEDICS SURGERY CENTER, LLC
1930 Blanding St, Columbia, SC 29201
Tel.: (803) 461-4740
Web Site:
  http://www.surgerycenteratmidortho neuro.com
Hospital & Health Care Services
N.A.I.C.S.: 622110
Janet L. Carlson *(CEO)*
Coleman D. Fowble *(Dir-Medical)*
Kelly Easley *(Dir-Nursing)*

MIDMARK CAPITAL
177 Madison Ave, Morristown, NJ 07960
Tel.: (973) 971-9960
Web Site:
  http://www.midmarkcapital.com
Year Founded: 1989
Sales Range: $25-49.9 Million
Emp.: 10
Private Equity Firm
N.A.I.C.S.: 523999
Wayne L. Clevenger *(Co-Founder & Mng Dir)*
Denis Newman *(Co-Founder & Mng Dir)*
Joseph R. Robinson *(Co-Founder & Mng Dir)*

MIDMARK CAPITAL

MidMark Capital—(Continued)
Judith S. Werner (Controller)
Douglas A. Parker (Mng Dir)
Matthew W. Finlay (Mng Dir)

Subsidiaries:

The McPherson Companies, Inc. (1)
5051 Cardinal St, Trussville, AL 35173
Tel.: (205) 661-4400
Web Site: http://www.mcphersonoil.com
Petroleum Products & Oil Collection Services
N.A.I.C.S.: 424710
Ken McPherson (Pres)
Wendi Allen (Dir-Fuelz Mktg & Svcs)
Andy Bass (VP-Supply Chain)
Anna Marie Chapman (VP-HR & Corp Admin)
Brant Holladay (VP-Fin)

MIDMARK CORPORATION

1700 S Patterson Blvd Ste 400, Dayton, OH 45409
Tel.: (937) 526-3662   OH
Web Site: http://www.midmark.com
Year Founded: 1915
Medical, Dental & Health Diagnostic Equipment Mfr
N.A.I.C.S.: 339112
Susan Kaiser (Mgr-Media & Comm)
John Q. Baumann (Pres & CEO)
Robert Morris (CFO)
Matt Bourne (VP-Sls-Global)
Mike Walker (COO)
Stephanie Muir (CTO)
Shawn Ashcraft (VP-Info Tech)
Randy Burton (VP-Mktg)
Chris Grenier (VP-Sls-Animal Health)
Crissy Treon (Dir-Downstream Mktg-Animal Health)

Subsidiaries:

Matrx by Midmark (1)
60 Vista Dr, Versailles, OH 45380-9488
Tel.: (716) 662-6650
Web Site: http://www.matrxmedical.com
Sales Range: $25-49.9 Million
Emp.: 150
Dental Gas & Veterinary Anesthesia Equipment Mfr
N.A.I.C.S.: 339114

Midmark Animal Health (1)
10010 N Dale Mabry Hwy Ste 110, Tampa, FL 33618
Tel.: (813) 962-6664
Sales Range: $10-24.9 Million
Emp.: 10
Veterinary Monitoring Product Mfr
N.A.I.C.S.: 339112
Andrew Schultz Jr. (Dir-Bus Dev)

Midmark Diagnostics Group (1)
1125 W 190 St, Gardena, CA 90248   (100%)
Tel.: (310) 530-5955
Sales Range: $10-24.9 Million
Emp.: 60
Ambulatory Care Digital Diagnostic Products Mfr
N.A.I.C.S.: 334510
Ruomei Zhang (CTO)

Schroer Manufacturing Company (1)
511 Osage Ave, Kansas City, KS 66105
Tel.: (913) 281-1500
Web Site: http://www.shor-line.com
Sales Range: $10-24.9 Million
Emp.: 150
Laboratory Apparatus & Furniture
N.A.I.C.S.: 337127
Richard E. Donahue II (Chm)

The Mason Company, LLC (1)
260 Depot St, Leesburg, OH 45135
Tel.: (937) 780-2321
Web Site: http://www.masonco.com
Animal Shelters & Containment Solutions, Pet Resorts & Veterinary Hospitals
N.A.I.C.S.: 541940
Elaine Schmidt (Office Mgr)

MIDNIGHT GAMING CORP.

1900 E Golf Rd Ste 950, Schaumburg, IL 60173
Tel.: (888) 525-0010   DE
Web Site: https://midnightgtv.com
eSports & Technology Services
N.A.I.C.S.: 339930
Ken McGraw (CEO)

MIDNIGHT OIL CREATIVE

3800 W Vanowen St, Burbank, CA 91505
Tel.: (818) 295-6300
Sales Range: $10-24.9 Million
Emp.: 47
Commercial Art & Graphic Design
N.A.I.C.S.: 541430
Al Shatiro (Owner)
Tom Stillwell (Owner & CEO)
Sean Krankel (Dir-Creative)
Monica Hare (Pres & Mng Dir-Digital)

MIDOCEAN PARTNERS, LLP

245 Park Ave 38th Fl, New York, NY 10167
Tel.: (212) 497-1400   Ky
Web Site: http://www.midoceanpartners.com
Year Founded: 2003
Private Equity Investment Firm
N.A.I.C.S.: 551112
Steven J. Gilbert (Vice Chm-Exec Bd-Exec Bd)
Ted Virtue (CEO)
Deborah Hodges (Mng Dir & COO)
Graham Clempson (Co-Founder & Vice Chm-Exec Bd)
Graham Clempson (Vice Chm-Exec Bd)
Steven L. Spinner (Operating Partner)
Daniel Penn (Mng Dir-Consumer)
Dana Carey (Mng Dir & Chief Investment Officer)
Steve Shenfeld (Chm-Credit)
Marc Graham (Operating Partner)
Steve Loeffler (Principal)
Tony DeLio (Operating Partner)
Lisa Mann (Operating Partner)
Matthew E. Rubel (Chm)

Subsidiaries:

Arnott, Inc. (1)
100 Sea Ray Dr, Merritt Island, FL 32953-4104
Tel.: (321) 868-3016
Web Site: http://www.arnottinc.com
Sales Range: $1-9.9 Million
Emp.: 27
Automotive Repair & Maintenance Services
N.A.I.C.S.: 811198
Doug Taylor (Mgr-Ops)
Jenni Dill (CMO)

Subsidiary (Domestic):

AccuAir Control Systems LLC (2)
888 Ricardo Ct, San Luis Obispo, CA 93401-7174
Tel.: (805) 481-6500
Web Site: http://www.accuair.com
Motor Vehicle Parts Merchant Whslr
N.A.I.C.S.: 423140

Casper's Ice Cream, Inc. (1)
11805 N 200 E, Richmond, UT 84333
Tel.: (435) 258-2477
Web Site: http://www.caspersicecream.com
Sales Range: $1-9.9 Million
Emp.: 60
Ice Cream & Frozen Dessert Mfr
N.A.I.C.S.: 311520
Ezra Farmer (Plant Mgr)
McLain Knutson (Mgr-Quality Assurance)
Kyle Smith (CEO)
Keith Lawes (Exec VP)
Shane Petersen (Exec VP)
Steve Spinner (Chm)

Cloyes Gear & Products, Inc. (1)
7800 Ball Rd, Fort Smith, AR 72908
Tel.: (479) 646-1662
Web Site: https://www.cloyes.com
Motor Vehicle Parts & Accessories Mfr
N.A.I.C.S.: 336350
John Hanighen (Pres & CEO)

Subsidiary (Non-US):

Cloyes Dynagear Mexicana S. de R.L. de C.V. (2)
Av Mexico 208-A Parque Industrial San Francisco, San Francisco de los Romo, 20300, Mexico
Tel.: (52) 4499103990
Motor Vehicle Parts Distr
N.A.I.C.S.: 423120

Cloyes Dynagear Mexicana S. de R.L. de C.V. (2)
Av Mexico 208-A Parque Industrial San Francisco, San Francisco de los Romo, Aguascalientes, 20300, Mexico
Tel.: (52) 4499103990
Motor Vehicle Parts Distr
N.A.I.C.S.: 423120
Pamela Carrillo (Sls Mgr)

Cloyes Dynagear Mexicana S. de R.L. de C.V. (2)
Av Mexico 208-A Parque Industrial San Francisco, San Francisco de los Romo, Aguascalientes, 20300, Mexico
Tel.: (52) 4499103990
Motor Vehicle Parts Distr
N.A.I.C.S.: 423120
Pamela Carrillo (Sls Mgr)

Global Knowledge Training LLC (1)
9000 Regency Pkwy Ste 500, Cary, NC 27518
Tel.: (919) 461-8600
Web Site: http://www.globalknowledge.com
Sales Range: $25-49.9 Million
Computer & IT Training Services
N.A.I.C.S.: 611420
Brian G. Holland (Gen Counsel & Sec)
Michael K. Fox (Sr VP-Product Mgmt)
Robert A. Kalainikas (CFO & Treas)
Donna B. Peffley (VP-HR)
Sean J. Dolan (Pres)
Satish Shetty (CIO-Global)
Frank Anastasio (CIO)
Christopher L. Barefoot (Sr Dir-Ops)
Travis L. Brisbon (Dir-Project Mgmt Office)
Daniel J. Endres (VP-Sls-US)
Lawrence Franco (Pres-Canada)
David D. Knier (VP-Mktg)
Volker Wetekam (Chm)
Nurali Jamani (COO)

Subsidiary (Domestic):

Education Experiences, Inc. (2)
5777 W Century Blvd, Los Angeles, CA 90045
Tel.: (310) 988-7700
Sales Range: $10-24.9 Million
Emp.: 32
Computer Training
N.A.I.C.S.: 611420

Branch (Non-US):

Global Knowledge Training Center-Victoria
838 Fourt St Suite 200, Victoria, V8W 1H8, BC, Canada
Tel.: (250) 383-9388
Web Site: http://www.globalknowledge.ca
Sales Range: $25-49.9 Million
Emp.: 3
Computer Training Services
N.A.I.C.S.: 611420
Lawrence Franco (Pres)

Grease Monkey International, LLC (1)
5575 DTC Pkwy Ste 100, Greenwood Village, CO 80111
Tel.: (303) 308-1660
Web Site: http://www.greasemonkeyauto.com
Quick Lubrication Centers
N.A.I.C.S.: 811191

Subsidiary (Domestic):

American LubeFast LLC (2)
1550 N Brown Rd Ste 140, Lawrenceville, GA 30043
Tel.: (770) 995-6312
Web Site: http://www.lubefast.com
Oil Change & Preventative Automotive Maintenance Services
N.A.I.C.S.: 811191
Scott Hesprich (CFO)
Tim Embry (CEO)
Joe Johnson (Reg VP)

InterVision Systems, LLC (1)
2250 Walsh Ave, Santa Clara, CA 95050
Tel.: (408) 980-8550
Web Site: http://www.intervision.com
IT Infrastructure Solutions & Consulting
N.A.I.C.S.: 541512
Jonathan Lerner (Pres & CEO)
Jim Zaloudek (CFO & Interim COO)
Tony Bailey (Sr VP-Alliances)

Subsidiary (Domestic):

SyCom Technologies, L.L.C. (2)
1802 Bayberry Ct Ste 201, Richmond, VA 23226
Tel.: (804) 262-7100
Web Site: http://www.sycomtech.com
Sales Range: $50-74.9 Million
Emp.: 124
System Integration & Consulting Services
N.A.I.C.S.: 541512
Thomas J. Cricchi (Pres & CEO)
Renee L. Symons (VP-Strategic Ops)
Tom Carr (Sr VP-Sls & Emerging Markets)
Patrick Miller (VP-Tech)
John Schmohl (CFO)

JF Corp. (1)
100 Perimeter Park Dr Ste H, Morrisville, NC 27560
Tel.: (919) 838-7555
Web Site: http://www.jfpetrogroup.com
Emp.: 560
Fuel & Fluid Handling Equipment Distr & Installation Services
N.A.I.C.S.: 423830
Joe Wrightson (Exec VP-Regl-Ops)
Drew Tyo (VP-Construction)
Christa Miller (Co-CFO)
John Sauers (Exec VP-Sls)
Keith Shadrick (CEO)
Wassie Lind (VP-Svc)
Wayne Morrison (Co-CFO)

Subsidiary (Domestic):

ANS Distributing LLC (2)
407 S 107th Ave Bldg C Ste 42, Tolleson, AZ 85353
Tel.: (520) 623-9300
Web Site: http://www.ansdistributing.com
Industrial Machinery & Equipment
N.A.I.C.S.: 423830
John Sauers (Pres & CEO)
Todd Olson (Mgr-Vendor)
Joe Kozak (Mgr-Customer Svc-Natl)

Dykstra Construction, Inc. (2)
50181 State Highway 13, Ashland, WI 54806
Tel.: (715) 682-9599
Web Site: http://www.dykstraconstructioninc.com
Rev: $1,180,000
Emp.: 100
Residential Remodeler
N.A.I.C.S.: 236118

McCon Building & Petroleum Services, Inc. (2)
8426 Sterling St, Irving, TX 75063
Tel.: (972) 929-0646
Web Site: http://www.mcconbuilding.com
Sales Range: $1-9.9 Million
Emp.: 18
Petroleum Equipment Distr
N.A.I.C.S.: 423830
Angela Nuno (Mgr)
Rhett Stokes (Dir-Sls & Svc)
Christopher Lawson (Pres)

Petroleum Solutions Inc. (2)
3702 S Expy 281, Edinburg, TX 78542
Tel.: (956) 686-9582
Web Site: http://www.petroleumsolutionsinc.com
Sales Range: $10-24.9 Million
Emp.: 200
Service Station Equipment
N.A.I.C.S.: 238990

COMPANIES | MIDSTATE BANCORP, INC.

Mark Barron (Pres)
John Keller (VP)
Stan Spofford (Mgr-Corp Acct Sls)
Dru Hall (Branch Mgr)
Michael Jorgenson (Branch Mgr)
Marge Newton (Dir-Field Svc)
Robert Wileman (Dir-Field Svc)
Red Kluck (Mgr-Acct)
Kevin Marks (Mgr-Automotive & Electrical Dept)
George Mesquita (Mgr-Automotive Svc)
Larry Wileman (Mgr-Construction)
Mike Molina (Mgr-Property Maintenance)
James Droddy (Mgr-Svc)
Jimmy Klyberg (Mgr-Svc)
Maria Mendez (Mgr-Svc)
Wes Nance (Mgr-Svc)
Randy Ward (VP-Ops)

Star Construction, Inc. (2)
8912 Adams St NE, Albuquerque, NM 87113
Tel.: (505) 823-1100
Web Site: http://www.starconstruction.com
Sales Range: $10-24.9 Million
Emp.: 35
Nonresidential Construction, Nec, Nsk
N.A.I.C.S.: 236220
Clayton Gooden (Pres)

KidKraft Inc. (1)
4630 Olin Rd, Dallas, TX 75244-4615
Tel.: (469) 374-0985
Web Site: http://www.kidkraft.com
Children's Furniture & Toys Mfr
N.A.I.C.S.: 339930
Charmaine Lampert (Chief Creative Officer)
George Benz (Sr VP-Mktg & ECommerce)
Martijn de Bruijn (Dir-Comml-Europe)
Debra Berman (Chief Mktg Officer)
Geoff Walker (Pres & CEO)

LYNX Franchising, LLC (1)
2520 Northwinds Pkwy Ste 375, Alpharetta, GA 30009
Tel.: (678) 336-1780
Web Site: https://empowerfranchising.com
Consumer Services & Franchising
N.A.I.C.S.: 533110
Michael Borreca (CFO & Sr VP)
Scott Zide (CEO)
Tom O'Hare (COO-Comml Div)
Tom Welter (COO-Residential Div)
Scott Sutton (Chief Dev Officer)
Sanjay Malhotra (Gen Counsel & VP)
Zach Peyton (Pres-Superior Fence & Rail Brand)

Subsidiary (Domestic):

FRSTeam, Inc. (2)
3201B Investment Blvd, Hayward, CA 94545
Tel.: (510) 723-1000
Web Site: http://www.frsteam.com
Sales Range: $1-9.9 Million
Emp.: 14
Restoration Services
N.A.I.C.S.: 236118
Jim Nicholas (Pres)
Courtney Nicholas (CEO)
Ryan Meekma (VP & Dir-Trng)
Holly Murry (Pres-Brand)
Lenny Towle (Dir-Natl Sls)

The Intelligent Office, Inc. (2)
4450 Arapahoe Ave Ste 100, Boulder, CO 80303
Tel.: (720) 868-9739
Web Site: http://www.intelligentoffice.com
Virtual Office, Receptionist Services & Custom Business Services & Executive Suites
N.A.I.C.S.: 561499

MPearlRock LP (1)
3835 PGA Blvrd, Ste 901 Palm, Beach Gardens, FL 33410
Tel.: (212) 497-1400
Web Site: https://www.mpearlrock.com
Food & Beverage
N.A.I.C.S.: 311999

Subsidiary (Domestic):

Green Grass Foods, Inc. (2)
15900 SE Eastgate Way Bldg B Ste 125, Bellevue, WA 98004
Web Site: http://www.nutpods.com
Sales Range: $10-24.9 Million
Emp.: 23
Dairy Products Distr

N.A.I.C.S.: 424430
Geoff Haydon (CFO)
Emi Ha (Coord-Logistics)
Andrew Prentice (Coord-Key Accts)
Natalie Esteb (Coord-Mktg)

Meyers Research, LLC (1)
3200 Bristol St Ste 640, Costa Mesa, CA 92626
Tel.: (714) 619-7800
Web Site: http://www.meyersresearchllc.com
Residential Housing Research & Information Services
N.A.I.C.S.: 519290
Jeff Meyers (CEO)
Melissa Billiter (CFO)
Hamin Balaporia (Exec VP-Tech)
Ludmilla Schappert (Exec VP-Product Dev)
Amy Dudley (Exec VP-Natl Sls)
Tim Sullivan (Mng Principal)
Kimberly Byrum (Principal)
Mollie Carmichael (Principal)
Steve LaTerra (Mng Dir-Phoenix)

Subsidiary (Domestic):

Hanley Wood Media, Inc. (2)
1 Thomas Cir NW Ste 600, Washington, DC 20005
Tel.: (202) 452-0800
Web Site: http://www.hanleywood.com
Sales Range: $150-199.9 Million
Emp.: 200
Information, Media, Event & Marketing Services for Residential & Commercial Design & Construction Industries
N.A.I.C.S.: 541613
Matthew Flynn (CFO)
Peter Goldstone (CEO)
Frank Anton (Vice Chm)
Andrew Reid (Pres-Digital & Head-Strategic Dev)
Jeanne Milbrath (Pres-Mktg)
Christopher Veator (Pres)
David Colford (Pres-Media)
Paul Mattioli (Sr VP-Corp Sls)

Subsidiary (Domestic):

Metrostudy, Inc. (3)
2211 Michelson Dr Ste 810, Irvine, CA 92612
Tel.: (714) 540-8500
Web Site: http://www.metrostudy.com
Housing Market Research
N.A.I.C.S.: 541910
Robb Coltrin (VP-Sls-East & Gen Mgr-Consulting)
Paige Shipp (Dir-Dallas & Fort Worth)
Justin Caron (VP-Membership Svc-Washington D.C.)
Mike Overley (Dir-Bus Dev-Atlanta)
Penny Arensdorf (VP-Consumer Segmentation)
David Brown (Sr VP)
David MacIntosh (Chief Revenue Officer & Sr VP-Sls & Membership Svcs)
Scott Artis (CTO)
John Cosenza (Dir-Bus Dev-Dallas)
Sean Wilt (Reg VP-Sls)
John Mulville (Dir-South California)
Wayne Norris (Dir-Institutional Investment Segment)
Ryan Brault (Dir-Phoenix & Tucson)
Jenifer Gooch (Dir-Charlotte)
Andy Reid (Pres)

Division (Domestic):

Real Estate Economics (4)
905 Calle Amanecer #200, San Clemente, CA 92673
Tel.: (949) 502-5151
Web Site: http://www.realestateeconomics.com
Sales Range: $1-9.9 Million
Emp.: 14
Economic & Housing Information & Statistics Data Research
N.A.I.C.S.: 531390
Mark Robbins Boud (Founder & Principal)
Gail Lottie (COO)
John Knaack (Dir-IT)
John Mulville (VP-Consulting)
Lou Davis (Office Mgr)

MidOcean Partners, LLP - London Office (1)

Cardinal Pl 80 Victoria St, London, SW1E 5JL, United Kingdom
Tel.: (44) 2031788492
Web Site: http://www.midoceanpartners.com
Sales Range: $50-74.9 Million
Emp.: 20
Private Equity Investment Firm

Music Reports, Inc. (1)
21122 Erwin St, Woodland Hills, CA 91367
Tel.: (818) 558-1400
Web Site: http://www.musicreports.com
Sales Range: $1-9.9 Million
Administrative Management Consulting Services
N.A.I.C.S.: 541611
Karyan Ulman (VP-Licensing)
William B. Colitre (Gen Counsel & VP)
Michael Shanley (VP-IT Bus Dev)
Cathy Nolan (Dir-Copyright Res)
Dhruv Prasad (Pres & CEO)

Pragmatic Institute, LLC (1)
8910 E Raintree Dr, Scottsdale, AZ 85260
Tel.: (480) 515-1411
Web Site: http://www.pragmaticmarketing.com
Sales Range: $10-24.9 Million
Emp.: 24
Product Management & Marketing Training Services
N.A.I.C.S.: 541613
Todd Davis (VP-Sls)

Quali Tech LLC (1)
318 Lk Hazeltine Dr, Chaska, MN 55318-1034
Tel.: (952) 448-5151
Web Site: http://www.qualitechco.com
Animal Nutrition & Food Ingredient Products Mfr
N.A.I.C.S.: 311119
Mark Ploen (VP)
Mike Hodgens (CEO)

Subsidiary (Domestic):

Ellison Bakery Inc. (2)
4108 W Ferguson Rd, Fort Wayne, IN 46809
Tel.: (800) 711-8091
Web Site: http://www.ebakery.com
Commercial Bakeries
N.A.I.C.S.: 311812
Jon Ellis (Plant Mgr)

Questex Media Group LLC (1)
275 Grove St Ste 2-130, Newton, MA 02466
Tel.: (617) 219-8300
Web Site: http://www.questex.com
Sales Range: $75-99.9 Million
Emp.: 350
Business Information Services
N.A.I.C.S.: 513120
Michael Driscoll (VP-Bus Dev)
John Mcmahon (Exec VP-Travel)
Dana E. Lupton (Exec VP-Beauty & Wellness)
Alexi Huntley Khajavi (Exec VP-Hospitality)
Jack Fordi (Sr VP & Publr-Healthcare & Life Sciences)
Jason Nelson (Sr VP & Publr-Tech, Telecom, & Emerging Markets)
Rebecca Willumson (Publr-Life Sciences)
Heather Martin (Publr-Tech Grp)
Liza Wylie (VP-Events, Beauty, Spa & Wellness Grp)
Amy Vaxman (Publr-Hospitality)
John Yarrington (Publr-Response)
Thomas Arnold (Publr-Home Media)
Matt Kavney (VP-Bus Dev-Questec Digital)
Julie Keller Callaghan (Publr-America Spa)
Auseh Britt (VP-Mktg & Client Svcs)
Kate Spellman (CMO)
Paul Miller (CEO)

Smith System Driver Improvement Institute Inc. (1)
2301 E Lamar Blvd Ste 250, Arlington, TX 76006
Tel.: (817) 652-6969
Web Site: http://www.drivedifferent.com
Driver Training Services
N.A.I.C.S.: 611430
Anthony S. Douglas (Pres & CEO)
Derek Dunaway (Chm)

Subsidiary (Domestic):

Drivers Alert, LLC (2)

5340 N Federal Hwy, Pompano Beach, FL 33064
Tel.: (954) 421-0400
Web Site: http://www.driversalert.com
Sales Range: $1-9.9 Million
Emp.: 18
Management Consulting Services
N.A.I.C.S.: 541614
John Diprato (Pres)

Travelpro Products, Inc. (1)
700 Banyan Trl, Boca Raton, FL 33431
Tel.: (561) 998-2824
Web Site: http://www.travelpro.com
Luggage, Bags & Travel Accessories Design & Marketer
N.A.I.C.S.: 423990
Ron Wood (Exec VP-Global Sls)
John Gualtieri (VP & Dir-Sls)
Robin Klenetsky (Dir-HR)

MIDPAC AUTO CENTER, INC.
3050 Hoolako St, Lihue, HI 96766-1424
Tel.: (808) 245-3673
Web Site: http://www.midpackauai.com
Year Founded: 1983
Sales Range: $10-24.9 Million
Emp.: 51
Car Whslr
N.A.I.C.S.: 441110
Aaris Berry (Mgr-Sls)
Ryan MacKey (Gen Mgr & VP)
Dan Mackey (Pres)
Dana Temme (Treas & Sec)

MIDPEN HOUSING CORPORATION
303 Vintage Park Dr Ste 250, Foster City, CA 94404
Tel.: (650) 356-2900   CA
Web Site: http://www.midpen-housing.org
Year Founded: 1970
Sales Range: $10-24.9 Million
Community Housing Services
N.A.I.C.S.: 624229
Jan M. Lindenthal (VP-Real Estate Dev)
Richard S. Chapura (VP-HR)
Matthew O. Franklin (Pres)
Beth Bartlett (Chm)
Daniel Seubert (Sec)
Monique Moyer (Treas)
Paul Staley (Vice Chm)
Annette Billingsley (Sr VP)
Janine Lind (COO)
Marvin Williams (VP-Property Mgmt)
Mick Vergura (CFO)

MIDSOUTH FARMERS CO-OP
14840 Hwy 18 S, Bolivar, TN 38008
Tel.: (731) 658-3931
Web Site: http://www.midsouthcoop.com
Sales Range: $10-24.9 Million
Emp.: 20
Farm Supplies & Feed Stores
N.A.I.C.S.: 424910
Jamie Perry (Gen Mgr)
Sam Tinsley (Mgr)

MIDSTATE BANCORP, INC.
101 W Main St, Hinton, OK 73047
Tel.: (405) 542-3101
Web Site: http://www.legacybank.com
Sales Range: $25-49.9 Million
Emp.: 25
Bank Holding Company
N.A.I.C.S.: 551111
R. Stephen Carmack (CEO)

Subsidiaries:

Legacy Bank (1)
101 W Main St, Hinton, OK 73047 (100%)
Tel.: (405) 542-3101
Web Site: http://www.legacybank.com

MIDSTATE BANCORP, INC.

Midstate Bancorp, Inc.—(Continued)
Commercial Bank
N.A.I.C.S.: 522110
Kaci Barrett (Mgr-Store)
Jamie Allison (VP-May & Memorial)
Steven Suellentrop (Asst VP-Retail Ops)
Kristen Wesolowsky (VP-Mktg)
Jeffrey Wolfe (Sr VP)
Grady Trumble (CFO & Sr VP-Fin)
Brad E. Yaeger (Pres)
Brice Malloy (Exec VP)

MIDSTATE ELECTRIC COOPERATIVE, INC.
16755 Finley Butte Rd, La Pine, OR 97739
Tel.: (541) 536-2126   OR
Web Site:
http://www.midstateelectric.coop
Year Founded: 1948
Sales Range: $25-49.9 Million
Emp.: 59
Electric Power Transmission Services
N.A.I.C.S.: 221122
Dave Schneider (CEO & Gen Mgr)
Jami Bartunek (Mgr-Acctg)
Teresa Lackey (Mgr-Mktg & Comm)
Steve Hess (Mgr-Engrg & Ops)

MIDSTATE RADIOLOGY ASSOCIATES LLC
435 Lewis Ave, Meriden, CT 06451
Tel.: (203) 694-8406
Web Site:
https://www.midstateradiology.com
Year Founded: 1955
Emp.: 100
Diagnostic & Therapeutic Radiology Services
N.A.I.C.S.: 621512
Gary Havican (Pres & Pres-Central Reg)
Subsidiaries:
New Haven Radiology Associates, P.C. (1)
PO Box 8416, New Haven, CT 06530
Tel.: (203) 732-7101
Web Site: http://www.nhrad.com
Emp.: 100
Offices of All Other Miscellaneous Health Practitioners
N.A.I.C.S.: 621399
Stacey Lipp (Office Mgr)

MIDSTATES GROUP COMPANY
4820 Capital Ave NE PO Box 940, Aberdeen, SD 57401
Tel.: (605) 225-5287
Web Site:
http://www.midstatesgroup.com
Year Founded: 1893
Emp.: 300
Print & Media Solutions
N.A.I.C.S.: 541840
Roger Feickert (Pres & CEO)
Justin Feickert (VP-Sls & Mktg)
Peter Yovetich Jr. (Dir-Production)
Subsidiaries:
Jacob North LLC (1)
4820 Capital Ave NE, Aberdeen, SD 57401
Tel.: (605) 225-5287
Web Site: http://www.jacobnorth.com
Emp.: 80
Print & Media Solutions
N.A.I.C.S.: 323111
Charles Calhoun (Pres & CEO)

MIDSTATES PRINTING INC.
4820 Capital Ave NE, Aberdeen, SD 57401
Tel.: (605) 226-2541
Web Site: http://www.mqprint.com
Sales Range: $10-24.9 Million
Emp.: 325
Printing Services
N.A.I.C.S.: 323111
Roger Feickert (Pres)

MIDTEX OIL, LP
3455 Interstae 35 S, New Braunfels, TX 78132-5039
Tel.: (830) 625-8042   TX
Web Site: http://www.midtexoil.com
Year Founded: 1966
Sales Range: $25-49.9 Million
Emp.: 250
Gasoline Service Stations
N.A.I.C.S.: 457120
Charlene Fischer (Treas & Sec)
Scott Schwind (CFO)
Pedro Jimenez (Dir-Wholesale Ops)
Rotney Fischer (Pres & CEO)

MIDTOWN CONSULTING GROUP, INC.
75 5th St NW Ste 342, Atlanta, GA 30308
Tel.: (404) 526-6205
Web Site: http://www.midtowncg.com
Year Founded: 2004
Sales Range: $10-24.9 Million
Emp.: 92
Management Consulting Services
N.A.I.C.S.: 541611
Jeff Elam (Mng Dir)
Ellen Bailey (Mng Dir)
David Smith (Mng Dir & CFO)

MIDTOWN ELECTRIC SUPPLY CORP.
157 W 18th St, New York, NY 10011
Tel.: (212) 255-3388
Web Site:
http://www.midtownelectric.com
Rev.: $22,000,000
Emp.: 55
Electrical Apparatus & Equipment
N.A.I.C.S.: 423610
Matthew Gold (Pres)
John Gold (Asst VP)

MIDTOWN FOOD STORES INCORPORATION
18850 Cox Ave, Saratoga, CA 95070
Tel.: (408) 379-8300
Sales Range: $10-24.9 Million
Emp.: 85
Grocery Stores, Independent
N.A.I.C.S.: 445110
Richard Giomi (Pres)

MIDTOWN PARTNERS & CO., LLC
380 Lexington Ave Ste 3000, New York, NY 10168
Tel.: (212) 939-6430   FL
Web Site:
http://www.midtownpartners.com
Year Founded: 2004
Emp.: 20
Securities Brokerage Services
N.A.I.C.S.: 523150
Rory McAdam (Sr VP)
John Clarke (CEO & Mng Dir)
Bill Relyea (Dir-Res)
Daniel Kazimierz Krzyzanowski (Sr VP)
Victor Greene (Dir)
Prakash Mandgi (Dir)
Tony Beggio (VP-Sls)

MIDTOWN TOYOTA
2700 N Cicero Ave, Chicago, IL 60639-1702
Tel.: (773) 622-6300
Web Site:
http://www.midtowntoyota.com
Sales Range: $10-24.9 Million
Emp.: 48
Car Whslr
N.A.I.C.S.: 441110

Lynn Bowman (CFO)
Phillip H. Resnick (Owner)
Lee Wulbert (VP-Ops)
Guy Drake (Gen Mgr)

MIDVALE TRUCK SALES & SERVICE INC.
3429 Brightwood Rd, Midvale, OH 44653
Tel.: (740) 922-3412
Web Site: http://www.trksls.com
Year Founded: 1990
Sales Range: $25-49.9 Million
Emp.: 175
Distr of Trucks
N.A.I.C.S.: 423110
Rod Rafael (Pres)
Subsidiaries:
Truck Sales & Service Inc.- Mansfield (1)
85 E Longview Ave, Mansfield, OH 44903
Tel.: (419) 522-9811
Web Site: http://www.trksls.com
Truck Dealer
N.A.I.C.S.: 423110
Doug Dye (Mgr-Svc)

MIDVALLEY HEALTHCARE
2321 E Gala St Ste 3, Meridian, ID 83642
Tel.: (208) 888-5848   OR
Web Site:
http://www.midvalleyhealthcare.com
Year Founded: 1950
Sales Range: $75-99.9 Million
Emp.: 769
Community Health & Welfare Services
N.A.I.C.S.: 624190
Daniel B. Smith (CFO & VP-Fin)
Becky A. Pape (CEO)
Joseph M. Cahill (COO)

MIDWAY AIRLINES' TERMINAL CONSORTIUM
5757 S Cicero Ave Ste TU2-322B, Chicago, IL 60638
Tel.: (773) 948-6630   IL
Year Founded: 2001
Sales Range: $10-24.9 Million
Airport Terminal Maintenance Services
N.A.I.C.S.: 488119
Peter Houghton (Pres)
Blaine Peters (Sec)
James Story (Treas)

MIDWAY CHEVROLET COMPANY
2323 W Bell Rd, Phoenix, AZ 85023
Tel.: (602) 866-0102
Web Site:
http://www.midwaychevy.com
Rev.: $84,000,000
Emp.: 400
New & Used Car Dealers
N.A.I.C.S.: 441110
Johnny Bhatt (Controller)

MIDWAY COOP INC.
210 Harrison St, Osborne, KS 67473
Tel.: (785) 346-5451
Web Site:
http://www.midwaycoop.com
Year Founded: 1908
Sales Range: $10-24.9 Million
Emp.: 70
Provider of Farm Supplies
N.A.I.C.S.: 424510
Dell Prince (Gen Mgr)
Larry Stanley (Pres)

MIDWAY DODGE INC.
4747 S Pulaski Rd, Chicago, IL 60632

Tel.: (773) 376-8060
Web Site: http://www.midwaydodge.com
Rev.: $13,200,000
Emp.: 43
New Car Dealers
N.A.I.C.S.: 441110
Mario Weber (Gen Mgr)
Al J. Weber (Pres & CEO)
Karen Schaffert (Office Mgr)

MIDWAY FORD TRUCK CENTER INC.
7601 NE 38th St, Kansas City, MO 64161-9457
Tel.: (816) 455-3000   DE
Web Site:
http://www.midwaytrucks.com
Year Founded: 1961
Sales Range: $200-249.9 Million
Emp.: 250
Retailer of New & Used Trucks & Truck Parts
N.A.I.C.S.: 423110
Trey Meyer (Pres)
Subsidiaries:
Midway U.S.A. Inc. (1)
5875 W Van Horn Tavern Rd, Columbia, MO 65203
Tel.: (573) 445-6363
Web Site: http://www.midwayusa.com
Shooting, Hunting & Outdoor Product Retailer
N.A.I.C.S.: 423910
Larry Potterfield (Founder & CEO)
Deanna Herwald (VP-Quality Mgmt Sys)
Tim Holtsman (Mgr-Engrg)

MIDWAY GAMES INC.
2704 W Roscoe St, Chicago, IL 60618
Tel.: (773) 961-2222   DE
Web Site: http://www.midway.com
Year Founded: 1941
Sales Range: $200-249.9 Million
Emp.: 540
Video Games Designer & Distr
N.A.I.C.S.: 513210
Deborah K. Fulton (Gen Counsel, Sec & Sr VP)
Subsidiaries:
Midway Amusement Games LLC (1)
2727 W Roscoe St, Chicago, IL 60618-5910
Tel.: (773) 961-2222
Web Site: http://www.midway.com
Sales Range: $100-124.9 Million
Emp.: 400
Designing & Distribution of Home Video Games
N.A.I.C.S.: 339930

MIDWAY GOLD CORP.
8310 S Valley Hwy Ste 280, Englewood, CO 80112
Tel.: (720) 979-0900   BC
Web Site:
http://www.midwaygold.com
Year Founded: 1996
Sales Range: Less than $1 Million
Gold Mining Services
N.A.I.C.S.: 212220
William M. Zisch (Pres & CEO)
Daniel Brosious (Chief Restructuring Officer)
Subsidiaries:
MDW Gold Rock LLP (1)
8310 S Valley Hwy Ste 280, Englewood, CO 80112
Tel.: (720) 979-0900
Gold Ore Mining Services
N.A.I.C.S.: 212220

MIDWAY INC.
220 Sandusky St, Monroeville, OH 44847

Tel.: (419) 465-2551
Web Site: http://www.midwayinc.com
Sales Range: $25-49.9 Million
Emp.: 115
Provider of Restaurant Services
N.A.I.C.S.: 722511
David Hasselbach (Mgr)

MIDWAY INDUSTRIES INC.
51 Wurz Ave, Utica, NY 13502
Tel.: (315) 797-6660
Web Site:
http://www.midwayindustries.net
Rev.: $21,554,615
Emp.: 40
Power Transmission Equipment & Apparatus
N.A.I.C.S.: 423840
Richard H. Legro (Chm)
Paul Rocwell (Pres)

MIDWAY OIL CORP.
217 N Main St, Rutland, VT 05701
Tel.: (802) 775-5534
Web Site: http://www.midwayoil.biz
Rev.: $35,590,766
Emp.: 10
Gasoline
N.A.I.C.S.: 424720
Frank Trombetta (Pres)

MIDWAY PETROLEUM CO. INC.
5140 Hwy 79, Brandenburg, KY 40108
Tel.: (270) 422-2992
Rev.: $24,504,513
Emp.: 2
Petroleum Bulk Stations & Terminals
N.A.I.C.S.: 424710
Allen Hicks (Pres)

MIDWAY PRODUCTS GROUP, INC.
1 Lymon E Hoyt Dr, Monroe, MI 48161-9607
Tel.: (734) 241-7242
Web Site:
http://www.midwayproducts.com
Year Founded: 1956
Sales Range: $1-4.9 Billion
Emp.: 2,500
Mfr of Automotive Stampings & Assemblies
N.A.I.C.S.: 541611
Robert Trowbridge (Mgr-Bus Unit)

Subsidiaries:

Findlay Products Corp. (1)
2045 Industrial Dr, Findlay, OH 45840
Tel.: (419) 423-3324
Automotive Stamping Mfr
N.A.I.C.S.: 336370

Hudson Industries, Inc. (1)
105 W State Rd 4, Hudson, IN 46747
Tel.: (260) 587-3288
Web Site: http://www.midwayproducts.com
Emp.: 150
Automotive Stamping Mfr
N.A.I.C.S.: 336370
Jeff Price (Plant Mgr)
Larry Wojciechowski (Plant Mgr)

Lakepark Industries of Indiana, Inc. (1)
750 E Middlebury St, Shipshewana, IN 46565
Tel.: (260) 768-7411
Web Site: http://www.midwayproducts.com
Emp.: 150
Automotive Stamping Mfr
N.A.I.C.S.: 336370
Terry Williams (Gen Mgr)

Lakepark Industries, Inc. (1)
40 Seminary St, Greenwich, OH 44837
Tel.: (419) 752-4471
Web Site: http://www.midwayproducts.com

Sales Range: $10-24.9 Million
Emp.: 120
Automotive Stamping Mfr
N.A.I.C.S.: 336370
Steve Anderson (Gen Mgr)

P&A Industries, Inc. (1)
600 Crystal Ave, Findlay, OH 45840
Tel.: (419) 422-7070
Sales Range: $25-49.9 Million
Emp.: 125
Automotive Stamping Mfr
N.A.I.C.S.: 336370
Dean Treier (Controller)

Production Products, Inc. (1)
200 Sugar Grove Ln, Columbus Grove, OH 45830
Tel.: (419) 659-4150
Web Site: http://www.midwayproducts.com
Sales Range: $25-49.9 Million
Emp.: 200
Automotive Stamping Mfr
N.A.I.C.S.: 336370
Nicole Latham (Mgr-HR)

Progressive Stamping, Inc. (1)
200 Progressive Dr, Ottoville, OH 45876
Tel.: (419) 453-1111
Automotive Stamping Mfr
N.A.I.C.S.: 336370
Melanie Roethlisberger (Mgr-HR)

MIDWAY RENT-A-CAR INC.
4751 Wilshire Blvd Ste 120, Los Angeles, CA 90010
Tel.: (323) 692-4000
Web Site:
http://www.midwaycarrental.com
Rev.: $14,000,000
Emp.: 250
Rent-A-Car Service
N.A.I.C.S.: 532111
Gary Mac Donald (Pres)
Serena Ho (Bus Mgr)

MIDWAY SALES & DISTRIBUTING, INC.
218 SE Branner St, Topeka, KS 66607
Tel.: (785) 232-4572
Web Site:
http://www.midwaywholesale.com
Sales Range: $25-49.9 Million
Emp.: 40
Roofing & Siding Materials Distr
N.A.I.C.S.: 423330
Bruce Myers (Pres)
John Oseillo (VP)
Kenneth L. Daniel Jr. (Founder & Chm)

MIDWAY STAFFING, INC.
2137 Euclid Ave Ste 1-2, Berwyn, IL 60402
Tel.: (708) 393-3781
Web Site:
http://www.midwaystaffing.com
Year Founded: 2015
Sales Range: $25-49.9 Million
Emp.: 2,330
Staffing & Recruitment Services
N.A.I.C.S.: 541612
RJ Parrilli (CEO)

MIDWAY TRAILERS, INC.
2650 County Hwy 401, Benton, MO 63736
Tel.: (573) 545-3065
Web Site:
http://www.missourigreatdane.com
Year Founded: 1980
Sales Range: $10-24.9 Million
Emp.: 38
Providers of Trailer Repair
N.A.I.C.S.: 811114
Steven W. Jones (Pres)

Subsidiaries:

Missouri Great Dane (1)

404 S Cool Springs Rd, Saint Louis, MO 63366
Tel.: (636) 980-9429
Web Site:
http://www.missourigreatdane.com
Sales Range: $10-24.9 Million
Emp.: 15
Provider of Trucking Services
N.A.I.C.S.: 811114
Mike Bigelow (Mgr-Sls)
Joe Goodall (Mgr-Svcs)

MIDWAY TRUCK PARTS INC.
7400 W 87th St, Bridgeview, IL 60455
Tel.: (708) 430-2081
Web Site: http://www.sleeppride.com
Sales Range: $50-74.9 Million
Emp.: 300
Truck Parts & Accessories
N.A.I.C.S.: 423120
Lee Schille (CFO)
Douglas Smith (Mgr-Sls)
Chuck Herman (Mgr-Facility)

MIDWAYUSA FOUNDATION, INC.
6001 W Van Horn Tavern Rd Ste C, Columbia, MO 65203-9274
Tel.: (573) 445-6363
Web Site:
http://www.midwayusafoundation.org
Year Founded: 2007
Sales Range: $25-49.9 Million
Emp.: 10
Fundraising Services
N.A.I.C.S.: 813211
Terri DeWitt (Mgr-Program-East)
Jay McClatchey (COO)
Jeff McClure (Mgr-Program-West)
Jan Ruess (Controller)
Brenda Potterfield (Treas & Sec)
Ron Utterback (VP)
Randy Moeller (Exec Dir)

MIDWESCO INDUSTRIES INC.
2119 S Union Ave, Tulsa, OK 74107-2703
Tel.: (918) 858-4200
Web Site:
http://www.midwescoind.com
Year Founded: 1972
Rev.: $35,000,000
Emp.: 130
Industrial Supplies Mfr
N.A.I.C.S.: 423840
James A. Bost (Chm)
Jim Shelly (Gen Mgr)

Subsidiaries:

Hi-Way Equipment Company Inc. (1)
926 N Sam Houston Pkwy E, Houston, TX 77032
Tel.: (281) 987-1990
Web Site: http://www.ascoequipment.com
Sales Range: $10-24.9 Million
Emp.: 38
Construction & Mining Machinery Rental Services
N.A.I.C.S.: 423810

Midwestern Manufacturing Co. Inc. (1)
2119 S Union Ave, Tulsa, OK 74107-2703 (100%)
Tel.: (918) 858-4200
Web Site: http://www.sidebooms.com
Rev.: $3,500,000
Emp.: 10
Oil & Gas Field Machinery
N.A.I.C.S.: 333132
James A. Bost (Chm)

Midwestern Pipe Line Products Co. Inc. (1)
3601 W 48th St, Tulsa, OK 74107
Tel.: (918) 447-8652

Web Site:
http://www.midwesternpipeline.com
Rev.: $1,500,000
Emp.: 10
Industrial Supplies
N.A.I.C.S.: 423840
James A. Bost (Chm)

MIDWEST ACOUST-A-FIBER INC.
759 Pittsburgh Dr, Delaware, OH 43015
Tel.: (740) 369-3624
Web Site: http://www.acoust-a-fiber.com
Sales Range: $25-49.9 Million
Emp.: 200
Acoustical Board & Tile, Mineral Wool
N.A.I.C.S.: 327993
Judy Evans (Controller)
Jerry M. Wolf (Founder, Chm & CEO)
Skip Allan (Pres)

MIDWEST AIR TECHNOLOGIES INC.
6700 Rfd, Long Grove, IL 60047-9596
Tel.: (847) 821-9630
Web Site: http://www.midwest-air.com
Year Founded: 1984
Sales Range: $10-24.9 Million
Emp.: 200
Motor Vehicle Supplies & New Parts
N.A.I.C.S.: 423120
Steve Wang (Chm & CEO)
Heather Malo (Coord-Mktg)
Terry O'Brien (CEO)
Ron Sherman (Mgr-Engrg)
Paul Thomas (COO)
Charles Walker (Sr VP-Sls & Mktg)
Kurt Wiesner (Dir-Sls)
Jay King (VP & Gen Mgr)
Marianne Andrews (Asst Mgr-Ops)
Janis Nebel (Dir-HR)
Andrew Fauth (Dir-Sls)

MIDWEST AIR TRAFFIC CONTROL SERVICE
7285 W 132nd St Ste 340, Shawnee Mission, KS 66213
Tel.: (913) 782-7082
Web Site: http://www.atctower.com
Sales Range: $50-74.9 Million
Emp.: 800
Airport Control Tower Operation, Except Government
N.A.I.C.S.: 488111
Shane Cordes (Owner)

MIDWEST AORTIC & VASCULAR INSTITUTE, P.C.
2750 Clay Edwards Dr Ste 304, Kansas City, MO 64116-3256
Tel.: (816) 842-5555
Web Site: http://www.kcvascular.com
Year Founded: 2016
Aortic & Vascular Surgeon Professional Organization
N.A.I.C.S.: 813920
Annette Small (CEO)
Ginger L. Bliss (COO)
Thomas J. Giald (Dir-Technical)
Taia Bringus (Mgr-Quality & Safety)
Nicole Kramer (Mgr-Clinical Res)
Terri Self (Mgr-Revenue Cycle)

MIDWEST APPAREL GROUP INC.
2301 Frnt St, Kansas City, MO 64120-1431
Tel.: (816) 421-2800
Year Founded: 1981
Sales Range: $10-24.9 Million
Emp.: 40

MIDWEST APPAREL GROUP INC. U.S. PRIVATE

Midwest Apparel Group Inc.—(Continued)
Retail Sales of Womens Childrens & Infants Clothing
N.A.I.C.S.: 424350
Jonathon Wiesner (Pres & CEO)
Sue McDonald (Controller)

MIDWEST ASPHALT CORP.
6340 Industrial Dr Ste 200, Eden Prairie, MN 55346
Tel.: (952) 937-8033
Web Site:
http://www.midwestasphalt.net
Year Founded: 1968
Sales Range: $10-24.9 Million
Emp.: 102
Highway, Street & Bridge Construction Services
N.A.I.C.S.: 237310
Blair B. Bury (Pres)
Gregg Prest (CFO & Treas)
Matt Timmers (VP-Construction)
Paul Hoffer (Sec)

MIDWEST AUTOMATION INC.
11872 Adie Rd, Maryland Heights, MO 63043
Tel.: (314) 432-8111
Web Site:
http://www.midwestautomation.com
Sales Range: $10-24.9 Million
Emp.: 25
Mfr of Industrial Machinery & Equipment
N.A.I.C.S.: 423830
Bernard Keusenkothen (Pres)

Subsidiaries:

Durkin Equipment Co. Inc. (1)
2383 Chaffee Dr, Saint Louis, MO 63146
Tel.: (314) 432-2040
Web Site: http://www.durkininc.com
Sales Range: $1-9.9 Million
Emp.: 22
Industrial Machinery & Equipment
N.A.I.C.S.: 423830
Jere Fulghum (Pres)

MIDWEST BANCO CORPORATION
747 Meridian, Cozad, NE 69130
Tel.: (308) 784-2515 NE
Web Site:
http://www.firstbankandtrust.com
Year Founded: 1953
Bank Holding Company
N.A.I.C.S.: 551111
Alan J. Svajgr (Pres & CEO)

Subsidiaries:

First Bank & Trust Company (1)
747 Meridian, Cozad, NE 69130
Tel.: (308) 784-2515
Web Site:
http://www.firstbankandtrustcozad.com
Emp.: 20
Commericial Banking
N.A.I.C.S.: 522110
Alan J. Svajgr (Pres & CEO)

MIDWEST BANCORPORATION, INC.
250 Prairie Ctr Dr, Eden Prairie, MN 55344
Tel.: (952) 358-2265 MN
Bank Holding Company
N.A.I.C.S.: 551111

Subsidiaries:

Star Bank (1)
228 Studdart Ave, Graceville, MN 56240
Tel.: (320) 748-7239
Web Site: http://www.starbank.net
Rev.: $2,408,000
Emp.: 8
Banking Services
N.A.I.C.S.: 522110

Jean Lupkes (VP)
Harold G. Wahlquist (Chm, Pres & CEO)

MIDWEST BANK NATIONAL ASSOCIATION
114 W Main St, Pierce, NE 68767
Tel.: (402) 329-6221
Web Site:
http://www.midwestbanks.com
Year Founded: 1882
Sales Range: $10-24.9 Million
Emp.: 130
Retail & Commercial Banking
N.A.I.C.S.: 522110
Russ Wilcox (Sr VP)

MIDWEST BLOCK & BRICK INC.
2203 E McCarty St, Jefferson City, MO 65101
Tel.: (573) 635-7119
Web Site:
http://www.midwestblock.com
Concrete Block, Retaining Walls, Pavers, Brick, Stone & Other Masonry & Landscape Products Mfr & Distr
N.A.I.C.S.: 423320
Mark Wilhelms (VP-Architectural Sls)

MIDWEST BUS SALES INC.
313 E Frnt St, Bonner Springs, KS 66012-1008
Tel.: (913) 422-1000 KS
Web Site:
http://www.midwestbussales.com
Year Founded: 1979
Sales Range: $10-24.9 Million
Emp.: 25
Provider of New & Used School Busses & Automobile Spare Parts for Busses
N.A.I.C.S.: 423110
Scott Kintaid (CFO)
Dawn Kelley (Coord-Sls)
Scott Bruegge (Mgr-Sls-Missouri & Kansas)
Graydon J. Kincaid Jr. (Pres)

MIDWEST CAR CORPORATION
1450 Delanglade St, Kaukauna, WI 54130
Tel.: (920) 766-0123
Web Site: http://www.nationalcar.com
Sales Range: $50-74.9 Million
Emp.: 500
Provider of Car Rental Services
N.A.I.C.S.: 532111
Thomas Gustman (Treas & VP)

MIDWEST COMMUNICATIONS & MEDIA
2015 Roundwyck Ln, Powell, OH 43065
Tel.: (614) 440-4449
Web Site:
http://www.midwestcommunicationsandmedia.com
Year Founded: 1982
Sales Range: $10-24.9 Million
Emp.: 10
Media Buying Services
N.A.I.C.S.: 541830
Patty Russell (Pres)
Robert Clegg (Sr VP)
Terry Eyears (Media Buyer)

MIDWEST COMMUNICATIONS, INC.
904 Grand Ave, Wausau, WI 54403-6420
Tel.: (715) 842-1437
Web Site: http://www.mwcradio.com
Year Founded: 1958
Emp.: 700

Holding Company; Radio Broadcasting Stations Owner & Operator
N.A.I.C.S.: 551112
Duke Wright (Pres & CEO)
Paul Rahmlow (CFO, Treas & Sec)
Michael Wright (COO)
Mary Kay Wright (CMO)
Jeff Wright (Chief Sls Officer)
Peter Tanz (Sr VP)
Andrew Gille (VP-Digital Ops)
Esther Gillis (VP-HR)
Jeff McCarthy (VP-Programming)
Tyson Hinsdill (Dir-IT)
Tim Laes (Engr-Corp)

Subsidiaries:

WRIG, Inc. (1)
557 Scott St, Wausau, WI 54403
Tel.: (715) 842-1672
Web Site: http://www.foxsportswausau.com
Sales Range: $10-24.9 Million
Radio Broadcasting Stations
N.A.I.C.S.: 516110

WTHI-FM (1)
824 S 3rd St, Terre Haute, IN 47807
Tel.: (812) 232-4161
Web Site: http://www.hi99.com
Emp.: 30
Radio Broadcasting Stations
N.A.I.C.S.: 516110
James Conner (VP & Gen Mgr)

Wkzo Am 590 (1)
4200 W Main St, Kalamazoo, MI 49006
Tel.: (269) 382-4280
Web Site: http://www.wkzo.com
Radio Stations
N.A.I.C.S.: 516110

MIDWEST COMMUNITY BANCSHARES, INC.
300 Tower Sq Plz, Marion, IL 62959
Tel.: (618) 997-4341
Web Site:
http://www.bankofmarion.com
Sales Range: $10-24.9 Million
Emp.: 100
Bank Holding Company
N.A.I.C.S.: 551111
Raymond Altmix (Pres & CEO)
Mitzi Calhoon Moore (CFO, Sec & Sr VP)
Robert Kincheloe (Sr VP)
Stacey Cobb (Asst VP & Mgr-Loan Ops)
Gene Watson (Vice Chm)
Susan Reams (Mgr-Facility)
Tracey Doss (Mgr-Facility)

Subsidiaries:

First Southern Bank (1)
300 Tower Sq Plz, Marion, IL 62959
Tel.: (618) 997-4341
Web Site: http://www.firstsouthernbank.net
Rev.: $9,400,000
Emp.: 30
Commericial Banking
N.A.I.C.S.: 522110
Raymond Altmix (Pres & CEO)
Tara Broy (Asst VP)
Mitzi Moore (CFO & Sr VP)

MIDWEST COMMUNITY BANK
510 S Park Crest Dr, Freeport, IL 61032
Tel.: (815) 235-6137
Web Site: http://www.mwbonline.com
Year Founded: 1965
Commericial Banking
N.A.I.C.S.: 522110
Laura Reynolds (Officer)
Karen Gorseline (Branch Mgr)
Mark Wright (Co-CEO)
Larry Feiner (VP)
Todd Wright (Co-CEO)

MIDWEST CONTROL PRODUCTS CORP.
590 E Main St, Bushnell, IL 61422

Tel.: (309) 772-3163
Web Site:
http://www.midwestcontrol.com
Sales Range: $10-24.9 Million
Emp.: 110
Rods, Iron & Steel: Made In Steel Mills
N.A.I.C.S.: 331110
Mark C. Rauschert (Pres)
Michael Bartlett (Mgr-Inside Sls)
Min Htway (Engr-Methods)

MIDWEST CONTROLS INC.
15475 Endeavor Dr, Noblesville, IN 46060-4921
Tel.: (317) 776-2600
Web Site:
http://www.midwestcontrolsinc.com
Rev.: $17,000,000
Emp.: 4
Motor Controls, Starters & Relays: Electric
N.A.I.C.S.: 423610
Mark Rodman (Pres)

MIDWEST COOPERATIVES
1919 E Sioux Ave, Pierre, SD 57501
Tel.: (605) 224-5935
Web Site:
http://www.ehsmidwestcooperative.com
Sales Range: $10-24.9 Million
Emp.: 85
Grain Elevators
N.A.I.C.S.: 424510
Russ Daley (Asst Gen Mgr-Agronomy)

MIDWEST DAIRY ASSOCIATION
2015 N Rice St, Saint Paul, MN 55113
Tel.: (651) 488-0261 MN
Web Site:
http://www.midwestdairy.com
Year Founded: 1937
Sales Range: $10-24.9 Million
Emp.: 65
Dairy Farmer Welfare Services
N.A.I.C.S.: 445298
Nancy Behrends (Office Mgr)
Molly Pelzer (CEO)
Allen Merrill (Chm)

MIDWEST DESIGNER SUPPLY, INC.
N30 W22377 Green Rd Ste C, Waukesha, WI 53186
Tel.: (888) 523-2611
Web Site:
http://www.midwestdesignersupply.com
Year Founded: 1963
Emp.: 55
Home Furnishing Merchant Whslr
N.A.I.C.S.: 423220
John A. Graber (Pres)

MIDWEST DIRECT
2222 W 110th St, Cleveland, OH 44102
Tel.: (216) 472-4922
Web Site: http://www.mw-direct.com
Sales Range: $125-149.9 Million
Emp.: 250
Printing & Mailing Services
N.A.I.C.S.: 423440
Mary Ann Yandek (Sec-Lettershop)
Robert Schieb (Mgr-DP)
Sam Mazzolla (Mgr-Lettershop)
Steve Tillinger (Mgr-Transportation)

MIDWEST DRYWALL CO., INC.
1351 S Reca Ct, Wichita, KS 67209-1848
Tel.: (316) 722-9559 KS
Web Site: http://www.mwdw.com
Year Founded: 1972

Sales Range: $10-24.9 Million
Emp.: 800
Provider of Plastering Drywall & Insulation Services
N.A.I.C.S.: 238310
Steven A. Nienke (Pres)
Denis H. Dieker (CFO)
Randy Cantrell (Mgr-Harrison Div)
Mike Wilson (Mgr-Tulsa)
Keith Ewing (Mgr-Dallas)
Marv Vanlingen (Mgr-Div)

MIDWEST ELECTRIC
4601 Homer Ohio Ln, Groveport, OH 43125
Tel.: (614) 482-8008
Year Founded: 1981
Sales Range: $25-49.9 Million
Emp.: 200
Electrical Contractor for Industrial Companies & Utilities
N.A.I.C.S.: 238210
R.J. Nicolosi (Pres)
Jeff Wachter (VP-Ops)
Dave Speas (Controller)
Ed Beemiller (CFO & VP-Strategic Growth)

MIDWEST ELECTRIC COOP CORP.
104 Washington St, Grant, NE 69140
Tel.: (308) 352-4356
Web Site:
http://www.midwestecc.com
Sales Range: $10-24.9 Million
Emp.: 30
Distribution, Electric Power
N.A.I.C.S.: 221122
Dick Hasenauer (Pres)

MIDWEST ENERGY COOPERATIVE INC.
901 E State St, Cassopolis, MI 49031-9339
Tel.: (269) 445-1000 MI
Web Site:
http://www.teammidwest.com
Year Founded: 1937
Sales Range: $25-49.9 Million
Emp.: 110
Electric Power Distribution
N.A.I.C.S.: 221122
Angie Edge (Controller)
Kerri Wade (VP-Admin Resources)
Bob Hance (Pres & CEO)
Andy Badner (Mgr-Ops-Propane)
Patty Nowlin (Dir-Comm & Community Rels)

Subsidiaries:

Midwest Connections, Inc. (1)
402 E Main St, Chanute, KS 66720
Tel.: (913) 294-3612
Electric Power Distribution Services
N.A.I.C.S.: 221122
Josh White (Gen Mgr)

MIDWEST ENERGY INC.
1330 Canterbury Dr, Hays, KS 67601
Tel.: (785) 625-3437 KS
Web Site: http://www.mwenergy.com
Year Founded: 1979
Sales Range: $150-199.9 Million
Emp.: 282
Provider of Electric & Gas Services
N.A.I.C.S.: 221118
Pat Parke (VP-Customer Svc)
Bill Dowling (VP-Engrg & Energy Supply)
Earnie Lehman (Pres & Gen Mgr)
Chuck Moore (Sec)
Tom Meis (CFO & VP-Fin)
Sharon Dreher (VP-Admin Svcs)
John Blackwell (Chm)
Juanita Stecklein (Vice Chm)

Louise Berning (Treas)
Fred Taylor (VP-Ops)
Michael Morley (Mgr-Corp Comm)

MIDWEST FARM MANAGEMENT, INC.
203 N Main St, Maquoketa, IA 52060
Tel.: (563) 652-2491
Web Site:
http://www.maquoketasb.com
Rev.: $28,400,000
Emp.: 107
Farm Operations & Management
N.A.I.C.S.: 115116
Alan R. Tubbs (Pres)
Edward Tubbs (Vice Chm)
Kendra Beck (VP)

MIDWEST FASTENER CORPORATION
9031 Shaver Rd, Kalamazoo, MI 49024-6164
Tel.: (269) 327-6917 MI
Web Site: http://www.mwf.net
Year Founded: 1975
Sales Range: $25-49.9 Million
Emp.: 85
Distr of Hardware & Fasteners
N.A.I.C.S.: 423710
Henry De Vries (Pres & CFO)
Robert De Vries (VP)
Chris Chase (Mgr-Inside Sls)
Clair Carr (Mgr-Ops)
Kees Kleppe (VP-Pur)
Tom Darling (Reg Mgr-Sls)
Jeff Moug (Mgr-Territory Acct)

MIDWEST FLOOR COVERINGS
810 W 2500 S, Salt Lake City, UT 84119
Tel.: (801) 972-1125
Web Site:
http://www.midwestfloors.com
Rev.: $12,600,000
Emp.: 60
Floor Coverings
N.A.I.C.S.: 423220
Bryan Paxton (Mgr-Cabinets)
Clint Beckstead (VP-Flooring)
Nate Noel (Mgr)
Spencer Egan (VP-Countertops, Cabinets & Millworks)
Eric Parrish (Pres)
Adam Jensen (CFO)

MIDWEST FOOD & POULTRY INC.
1330 Copper Dr, Cape Girardeau, MO 63701-2169
Tel.: (573) 651-3940 MO
Year Founded: 1980
Sales Range: $10-24.9 Million
Emp.: 15
Wholesale Distributors of Poultry & Poultry Products
N.A.I.C.S.: 424440
Kenneth H. Ochs (Pres)
Matt Ochs (VP)
Celinda Tankersley (Controller)

MIDWEST FOOD BANK
2031 Warehouse Rd, Normal, IL 61761
Tel.: (309) 663-5350 IL
Web Site:
http://www.midwestfoodbank.org
Year Founded: 2003
Sales Range: $25-49.9 Million
Emp.: 16
Hunger Relief Services
N.A.I.C.S.: 624210
Michael Hoffman (Dir-Supply Chain & Logistics)
Peter Goddard (Comptroller)
David Kieser (Founder & Pres)

John Feit (Second VP)
Ralph Endress (Asst Sec)
David Hodel (Treas)
Dennis Mott (Asst Treas)
Larry Herman (First VP)
Merry Anne Schmied (Sec)
Chad Bevers (Exec Dir-Bloomington-Normal)
Eric Hodel (CEO)

MIDWEST FORESTREE LLC.
566 Rock Rd Dr, Dundee, IL 60118
Tel.: (847) 426-6354
Web Site:
http://www.mwcompanies.com
Rev.: $16,500,000
Emp.: 150
Industrial Building Construction
N.A.I.C.S.: 236210

MIDWEST GLASS, INC.
1333 Main Ave S, Brookings, SD 57006
Tel.: (605) 692-7251 SD
Web Site:
http://www.midwestglass.net
Year Founded: 1974
Sales Range: $1-9.9 Million
Emp.: 22
Automotive, Residential & Commercial Windows, Doors & Related Products Whslr
N.A.I.C.S.: 238150
James Skyberg (Pres)

MIDWEST GROWTH PARTNERS, LLLP
7049 Vista Dri, West Des Moines, IA 50266
Tel.: (515) 309-3018
Web Site: http://www.mgpfund.com
Privater Equity Firm
N.A.I.C.S.: 523999
John Mickelson (Mng Partner)
Mike Taylor (Partner)

Subsidiaries:

Inland Coatings Corporation (1)
2619 Highway 6, Adel, IA 50003
Tel.: (515) 993-4524
Web Site: http://www.inlandcoatings.com
Sales Range: $1-9.9 Million
Emp.: 8
Asphalt Shingle & Coating Materials Mfr
N.A.I.C.S.: 324122
Doug Walmsley (Pres)

MIDWEST HARDWOOD CORPORATION
9540 83rd Ave N, Maple Grove, MN 55369-4567
Tel.: (763) 425-8700 WI
Web Site:
http://www.midwesthardwood.com
Year Founded: 1981
Sales Range: $50-74.9 Million
Emp.: 550
Lumber, Plywood & Millwork
N.A.I.C.S.: 423310
Michael D. Flynn (Pres & CEO)
Mike Mallin (Mgr-Sls)
Dan Marks (Mgr-Acctg)
Ben Laski (Mgr-Pur)
Todd Copley (Mgr-HR)
Jim Finnegan (Mgr-Credit)

Subsidiaries:

Buffalo Lumber & Tie Co. (1)
S2941 Indian Creek Rd, Fountain City, WI 54629
Tel.: (608) 687-7681
Web Site: http://www.buffalolumbertie.com
Lumber & Plywood Mfr
N.A.I.C.S.: 321113

Daniels-Olsen Bldg Products Inc (1)
815 W Blackhawk St, Sioux Falls, SD 57104

Tel.: (605) 336-3588
Web Site: http://www.danielsolsen.com
Hardwood Distr
N.A.I.C.S.: 423310

Meister Log & Lumber Co. (1)
1440 Laukant St, Reedsburg, WI 53959
Tel.: (608) 524-4412
Web Site: http://www.midwesthardwood.com
Emp.: 50
Lumber & Plywood Mfr
N.A.I.C.S.: 321113
Mike Flynn (Owner)

Midwest Hardwood Corporation - Little River Hardwoods Facility (1)
141 Cerulean Rd, Cadiz, KY 42211
Tel.: (270) 522-5959
Web Site: http://www.midwesthardwood.com
Lumber Mfr
N.A.I.C.S.: 321912

Midwest Hardwood Corporation - Park Falls Hardwoods Facility (1)
307 N 5th Ave, Park Falls, WI 54552
Tel.: (715) 762-5600
Web Site: http://www.midwesthardwood.com
Emp.: 50
Lumber Mfr
N.A.I.C.S.: 321912

Midwest Hardwood Corporation - Reedsburg Hardwoods Facility (1)
1580 Laukant St, Reedsburg, WI 53959
Tel.: (608) 524-2422
Web Site:
http://www.reedsburghardwoods.com
Hardwood Products Mfr
N.A.I.C.S.: 321912

Midwest Hardwood Corporation - Westby Hardwood Products Facility (1)
105 Webster St, Westby, WI 54667
Tel.: (608) 634-3072
Web Site:
http://www.westbyhardwoodproducts.com
Hardwood Products Mfr
N.A.I.C.S.: 321912

Superior Kilns, Inc. (1)
Hwy 77 E, Mellen, WI 54546
Tel.: (715) 274-4211
Web Site: http://www.superiorkilns.com
Wood Product Mfr & Distr
N.A.I.C.S.: 321999

MIDWEST HEME MANAGEMENT, INC.
8625 Oakmont Dr, Lincoln, NE 68526
Tel.: (402) 484-5889
Web Site:
http://www.hemeperfusion.com
Year Founded: 2001
Sales Range: $1-9.9 Million
Emp.: 19
Perfusion Services
N.A.I.C.S.: 423450
Michael Springer (Pres)

MIDWEST IMPRESSIONS INC.
1837 N 203rd St, Elkhorn, NE 68022
Tel.: (402) 289-9583
Web Site:
http://www.midwestimpressions.com
Year Founded: 2000
Sales Range: $1-9.9 Million
Emp.: 18
Custom Apparel for High Schools
N.A.I.C.S.: 315990
Jayne Balch (Co-Owner)
Eric Balch (Co-Owner)

MIDWEST INDUSTRIAL METALS CORPORATION
615 NW Ave, North Lake, IL 60164
Tel.: (773) 202-8202 IL
Web Site:
http://www.mimrecycles.com
Year Founded: 1981
Sales Range: $10-24.9 Million
Emp.: 20
Whslr of Scrap & Waste Materials

MIDWEST INDUSTRIAL METALS CORPORATION — U.S. PRIVATE

Midwest Industrial Metals Corporation—(Continued)
N.A.I.C.S.: 561499
Steven Cadkin (Pres)

MIDWEST INDUSTRIAL SUPPLY, INC.
1101 3rd St SE, Canton, OH 44707
Tel.: (330) 456-3121
Web Site: http://www.midwestind.com
Year Founded: 1975
Sales Range: $10-24.9 Million
Emp.: 58
Specialty Chemicals Mfr
N.A.I.C.S.: 325998
Robert Vitale (CEO)
Steven Vitale (Pres)
Lynn Edwards (VP-Sls)

MIDWEST INDUSTRIES, INC.
122 E Hwy 175, Ida Grove, IA 51445
Tel.: (712) 364-3365   DE
Web Site:
  http://www.midwestindustries.com
Year Founded: 1954
Sales Range: $100-124.9 Million
Emp.: 200
Mfr & Retailer of Boat Hoists, Docks & Trailers
N.A.I.C.S.: 336214
Andy Brosius (Pres)
Valerie Krager (Mgr-Payroll & Benefit)
Jon Devitt (VP-Engrg)

MIDWEST INTERNATIONAL STANDARD PRODUCTS, INC.
105 Stover Rd, Charlevoix, MI 49720-1756
Tel.: (231) 547-4000   MI
Web Site:
  http://www.midwestmagic.com
Year Founded: 1968
Sales Range: $50-74.9 Million
Emp.: 18
Air Pollution Equipment, Truck & Railcar Loading Equipment & Ship Loading Equipment Mfr
N.A.I.C.S.: 333413
Walter Pair (Dir-Adv & Mktg)

MIDWEST MEDIA GROUP INC.
135 E Algonquin Rd Ste B, Arlington Heights, IL 60005-5322
Tel.: (847) 228-5588
Web Site: http://www.mwmg.com
Sales Range: $10-24.9 Million
Emp.: 20
Retailer of Electronic Video Equipment
N.A.I.C.S.: 423690
Michael McDonald (Principal)

MIDWEST METALS CORPORATION
13051 Forest Center Ct, Louisville, KY 40223
Tel.: (502) 244-6063
Web Site: http://www.mwmcorp.com
Sales Range: $100-124.9 Million
Emp.: 16
Aluminum Bars, Rods, Ingots, Sheets, Pipes & Plates
N.A.I.C.S.: 423510
Larry Wence (Chm)
Steve Syms (Controller)
Patrick Debes (Exec VP)
Debbie Matthews (Mgr-Traffic)
Don Blackwood (Dir-Technical)
James Endsley (Mgr-Warehouse)
Jamie Hoskins (Gen Mgr)
Jimmy Renfroe (Gen Mgr)
Michael Carter (Supvr-Warehouse)
Mike Carroll (CFO)

MIDWEST MINNESOTA COMMUNITY DEVELOPMENT CORPORATION
119 Graystone Plz Ste 100, Detroit Lakes, MN 56501
Tel.: (218) 847-3191   MN
Web Site: https://www.mmcdc.com
Bank Holding Company; Commercial & Home Mortgage Lending Services
N.A.I.C.S.: 551111
Subsidiaries:
Community Development Bank, FSB   (1)
516 Main St W, Ogema, MN 56569
Tel.: (218) 983-3241
Web Site: http://www.comdevbank.com
Sales Range: $1-9.9 Million
Emp.: 8
Commercial Banking Services
N.A.I.C.S.: 522110
Nick Shultz (Pres & CEO)
Paul Weber (Sr VP-Comml Lending)
Brenda Hayle (Sr VP-Retail Banking)
Justin Cronen (COO)
Beth Crockett (Officer-IT & Ops)

MIDWEST MONITORING & SURVEILLANCE INC.
2500 County Rd 42 W Ste 5, Burnsville, MN 55337
Tel.: (952) 435-9300
Web Site:
  http://www.midwestmonitoring.com
Year Founded: 1997
Correctional Technology Products & Services
N.A.I.C.S.: 561621
Gary Shelton (CEO)

MIDWEST MOTOR SUPPLY CO.
4800 Roberts Rd, Columbus, OH 43228-1105
Tel.: (614) 219-6100
Web Site:
  http://www.kimballmidwest.com
Year Founded: 1923
Sales Range: $50-74.9 Million
Emp.: 550
Motor Vehicle Supplies & New Parts
N.A.I.C.S.: 423120
Patrick J. Mccurdy (Pres)
David Mccurdy (VP)

MIDWEST NATURAL GAS CORP.
101 SE 3rd St, Washington, IN 47501-0520
Tel.: (812) 254-5087
Web Site: http://www.midnatgas.com
Sales Range: $25-49.9 Million
Emp.: 35
Natural Gas Distr
N.A.I.C.S.: 221210
Michael Crouch (Pres & CEO)
Dave Osmon (Exec VP)
Subsidiaries:
Indiana Natural Gas Corp.   (1)
1080 W Hospital Rd, Paoli, IN 47454
Tel.: (812) 723-2151
Web Site: http://www.indiananatural.com
Sales Range: $10-24.9 Million
Natural Gas Distr
N.A.I.C.S.: 221210
Phil Ross (Gen Mgr-Natural Gas-Indiana)

MIDWEST PACKAGING SOLUTIONS
322 Ryder Rd, Toledo, OH 43607-3104
Tel.: (419) 536-1212   OH
Web Site:
  http://www.mwpackaging.com
Year Founded: 1968
Sales Range: $10-24.9 Million
Emp.: 17
Mfr of Industrial & Personal Service Paper & Boxes
N.A.I.C.S.: 424130
Lou Galambos (CEO)
Jeffrey Pierce (Exec VP)
Sukhdeep O'Loughlin (Controller)

MIDWEST PALLIATIVE & HOSPICE CARECENTER
2050 Claire Ct, Glenview, IL 60025
Tel.: (847) 467-7423   IL
Web Site: http://www.carecenter.org
Year Founded: 1978
Sales Range: $25-49.9 Million
Emp.: 383
Hospice Care Services
N.A.I.C.S.: 621610
Jamie M. O'Malley (Pres & CEO)
Jill Koons (Sr Dir-Quality & Compliance)
Miriam Mollin (VP-HR & Info Sys)
Kristin Gover (VP-Community Dev & Mktg Comm)

MIDWEST PERISHABLES INC.
4850 Helgesen Dr, Madison, WI 53718-3254
Tel.: (608) 273-8000   WI
Web Site:
  http://www.meatsandmore.com
Year Founded: 1993
Sales Range: $10-24.9 Million
Emp.: 40
Meats & Meat Products
N.A.I.C.S.: 424470
Jeff White (Controller)
Dan Roberts (Pres, VP & Treas)

MIDWEST PETROLEUM CO.
220 Old Mearmax Staton Rd, Ballwin, MO 63143-2624
Tel.: (314) 647-5550   MO
Web Site:
  http://www.midwestpetro.com
Year Founded: 1946
Sales Range: $100-124.9 Million
Emp.: 75
Petroleum Product Distr
N.A.I.C.S.: 457120
Mike McNutt (VP)
Jeff Ziegler (VP-Fin)
Tiffany Akers (Mgr-Store)

MIDWEST PIPE & STEEL INC.
323 E Berry St, Fort Wayne, IN 46802-2707
Tel.: (260) 422-6541   IN
Web Site:
  http://www.midwestpipe.com
Year Founded: 1972
Sales Range: $10-24.9 Million
Emp.: 50
Metals Service Centers & Offices
N.A.I.C.S.: 423510
Jerome F. Henry Jr. (Pres)
Dorina Feher (CFO)
Subsidiaries:
Paragon Steel Inc   (1)
4211 County Rd 61, Butler, IN 46721
Tel.: (260) 868-1100
Web Site: http://www.pstparagonsteel.com
Steel Pipe & Tube Mfr
N.A.I.C.S.: 331210
Bruce Whitman (Gen Mgr)
Paragon Tube Corp.   (1)
1605 Winter St, Fort Wayne, IN 46803
Tel.: (260) 424-1266
Web Site: http://www.paragontube.com
Steel Pipe & Tube Mfr
N.A.I.C.S.: 331210

MIDWEST PMS
11347 Business Park Cir, Frederick, CO 80504-5270
Tel.: (308) 635-3031
Sales Range: $10-24.9 Million
Emp.: 15
Feed Supplements
N.A.I.C.S.: 311119
Kenneth M. Green (Pres)

MIDWEST PRODUCTS & ENGINEERING, INC.
10597 W Glenbrook Ct, Milwaukee, WI 53224
Tel.: (414) 355-0310   WI
Web Site: http://www.mpe-inc.com
Year Founded: 1978
Medical Equipment Mfr
N.A.I.C.S.: 335999
Don Kubiak (Mgr-HR)
John Hart (VP-Strategic Accts)
Hank Kohl (Pres & CEO)
Tom Weiss (Sr Dir-Strategic Accts)
Subsidiaries:
MindFlow Design LLC   (1)
2036 Corte Del Nogal, Carlsbad, CA 92011
Tel.: (760) 930-9285
Web Site: http://www.mindflowdesign.com
Engineering Design Services
N.A.I.C.S.: 541330
Andy Moulds (Principal)
Chris Ross (Founder)

MIDWEST PROTOTYPING LLC
10949 Blackhawk Dr, Blue Mounds, WI 53517
Tel.: (608) 437-1400
Web Site:
  http://www.midwestproto.com
Year Founded: 2001
Sales Range: $1-9.9 Million
Emp.: 16
Industrial & Consumer Prototypes
N.A.I.C.S.: 339999
Steve Grundahl (Founder & Pres)
Bill Isermann (Gen Mgr)
Trent Appleby (Mgr-Production)
Mitch Ziegler (Project Coord)
Cheryl Kotlowski (Mgr-Shipping)

MIDWEST PUBLISHING, INC.
10844 N 23rd Ave, Phoenix, AZ 85029
Tel.: (602) 943-1244
Web Site: http://www.mpi-services.com
Year Founded: 1974
Sales Range: $10-24.9 Million
Emp.: 275
Periodical Publishers
N.A.I.C.S.: 513120
John F. McCallum (Pres)

MIDWEST QUALITY GLOVES, INC.
835 Indus Rd, Chillicothe, MO 64601
Tel.: (660) 646-2165   MO
Web Site:
  http://www.midwestglove.com
Year Founded: 1984
Sales Range: $25-49.9 Million
Emp.: 200
Producer of Leather Gloves & Mittens
N.A.I.C.S.: 315990
Stephen J. Franke (Pres & CEO)
Anne Whiteside (Dir-Mktg)

MIDWEST RAILROAD TIE SALES
6755 S Old State Rd 37 S, Bloomington, IN 47401
Tel.: (812) 339-9000
Web Site: http://www.nssccorp.com
Sales Range: $10-24.9 Million
Emp.: 60
Transportation Equipment & Supplies Merchant Whslr
N.A.I.C.S.: 423860
Victoria Schopp (Pres)
Curtis Schopp (VP)

MIDWEST REAL ESTATE DEVELOPMENT
2990 Universal St Ste B, Oshkosh, WI 54904
Tel.: (920) 426-2001
Web Site:
http://www.midwestrents.com
Year Founded: 1953
Sales Range: $10-24.9 Million
Emp.: 20
Developers of Single & Multi-Family Construction & Property Management: Residential Subdividers & Developers
N.A.I.C.S.: 531110
Jerry Kueller *(Controller)*
Tom Amack *(Dir-Property Mgmt)*
Tracey Okon *(Mgr-Property)*
Subsidiaries:

M.A. Inc. (1)
2990 Universal St Ste B, Oshkosh, WI 54904
Tel.: (920) 426-2001
Web Site: http://www.mwdevelopment.com
Sales Range: $10-24.9 Million
Emp.: 15
Aircraft Servicing & Repairing
N.A.I.C.S.: 424990
John Mark *(Pres)*

MIDWEST REMEDIATION INC.
5858 Thunderbird Rd, Indianapolis, IN 46236
Web Site:
http://www.mwremediation.com
Other Commercial & Service Industry Machinery Mfr
N.A.I.C.S.: 333310
Greg Rosebrough *(Dir-Sls)*
Subsidiaries:

Americlean Tile & Grout, LLC (1)
2315 Southyard Ct, Fort Wayne, IN 46818
Tel.: (260) 489-2070
Web Site:
http://www.wateroutfortwayne.com
Residential Remodeler
N.A.I.C.S.: 236118
Christopher M. Laney *(CEO)*

MIDWEST RUBBER COMPANY
3525 Range Line Rd, Deckerville, MI 48427-0098
Tel.: (810) 376-2085
Web Site: http://www.mwrco.com
Year Founded: 1946
Sales Range: $75-99.9 Million
Emp.: 100
Plastics Product Mfr
N.A.I.C.S.: 326291

MIDWEST SIGN & SCREEN PRINTING SUPPLY COMPANY, INC.
45 Maryland Ave E, Saint Paul, MN 55117-4610
Tel.: (651) 489-9999   MN
Web Site:
http://www.midwestsign.com
Year Founded: 1932
Sales Range: $25-49.9 Million
Emp.: 200
Distr of Sign & Screen Printing Supplies
N.A.I.C.S.: 423830
Nancy J. P. Anderson *(CEO)*

MIDWEST SINGLE SOURCE INC.
1501 E 1st St N, Wichita, KS 67214
Tel.: (316) 267-6333
Web Site: http://www.ssource.com
Sales Range: $10-24.9 Million
Emp.: 80
Business Forms
N.A.I.C.S.: 424120

Kevin Ulweling *(Pres)*
Chris Eckhoff *(VP-Equipment Div)*
Eva Mora *(Supvr-Warehouse)*

MIDWEST SPECIALIZED TRANSPORTATION, INC.
4515 Hwy 63 N, Rochester, MN 55906
Tel.: (507) 288-5649
Web Site: http://www.midspec.com
Year Founded: 1967
Rev.: $23,000,000
Emp.: 40
Specialized Trucking Services
N.A.I.C.S.: 484121
Allen I. Koenig *(Pres)*

MIDWEST STEEL INC.
2525 E Grand Blvd, Detroit, MI 48211
Tel.: (313) 873-2220
Web Site:
http://www.midweststeel.com
Year Founded: 1968
Rev.: $70,000,000
Emp.: 175
Structural Steel Erection
N.A.I.C.S.: 238120
Gary R. Broad *(Pres)*

MIDWEST SUPERSTORE
1100 E 30th Ave, Hutchinson, KS 67502-4229
Tel.: (620) 662-6631
Web Site:
http://www.midwestsuperstore.com
Year Founded: 1982
Sales Range: $10-24.9 Million
Emp.: 90
New Car Whslr
N.A.I.C.S.: 441110
Les Eck *(Owner)*
Sarah Grant *(Principal)*
Wes Thomas *(Gen Mgr)*

MIDWEST TELEMARK INTERNATIONAL INC
112 W Main St, Mohall, ND 58761
Tel.: (701) 756-6483
Web Site: http://www.MTInd.com
Rev.: $12,500,089
Emp.: 450
Inbound & Outbound Contact Center Services
N.A.I.C.S.: 561499
Marvin Thom *(VP)*
Muriel V. Leavitt *(Sec & Treas)*
Kathy Hett *(Pres)*

MIDWEST TIRE & MUFFLER, INC.
4700 N I-90 Service Rd, Rapid City, SD 57709
Tel.: (605) 348-2160   SD
Web Site: http://www.midwesttire.net
Year Founded: 1969
Sales Range: $100-124.9 Million
Emp.: 120
Retailer of Tires, Wheels & Accessories
N.A.I.C.S.: 441340
Larry W. Haley *(Chm & Pres)*
Scott Kudlock *(Mgr-Warehouse)*

MIDWEST TOOL AND CUTLERY CO.
1210 Progress St, Sturgis, MI 49091
Tel.: (269) 651-2476   MI
Web Site:
http://www.midwestsnips.com
Year Founded: 1960
Rev.: $10,000,000
Emp.: 80
Shears, Clippers, Snips & Similar Tools
N.A.I.C.S.: 332215

Steven Peter *(Pres)*
Raymond Dresser *(Sec)*

MIDWEST TOWERS INC.
1156 Hwy 19 E, Chickasha, OK 73018
Tel.: (405) 224-4622
Web Site:
http://www.midwesttowers.com
Year Founded: 1987
Sales Range: $125-149.9 Million
Emp.: 450
Mfr & Supplier of Components for Cooling Towers Construction & Repair
N.A.I.C.S.: 321999
Terry Ogburn *(VP & Mgr-Sls)*
Shane Schimdt *(Mgr-Sls-Southwest Reg)*
Subsidiaries:

Beetle Plastics, LLC (1)
601 Beetle St Ardmore Industrial Airpark, Ardmore, OK 73401-1192
Tel.: (580) 389-5421
Web Site: http://www.beetleplastics.com
Sales Range: $10-24.9 Million
Emp.: 44
Fiberglass Pipe, Duct & Tanks Mfr
N.A.I.C.S.: 326122
Bill Daugherty *(Mgr-Sls-Texas)*

MIDWEST TRAILER SALES INC.
4107 Terminal Dr, McFarland, WI 53558
Tel.: (608) 838-4164
Web Site:
http://www.midwesttrailersales.com
Sales Range: $10-24.9 Million
Emp.: 40
Sales & Service of Truck Trailers
N.A.I.C.S.: 423110
Robert Zurbuchen *(Owner)*

MIDWEST TRANSIT EQUIPMENT, INC.
146 W Issert Dr, Kankakee, IL 60901
Tel.: (815) 933-2412   IL
Web Site:
http://www.midwesttransit.com
Year Founded: 1973
Sales Range: $10-24.9 Million
Emp.: 100
Whslr of Buses
N.A.I.C.S.: 423110
Stephen Ball *(Dir-School Bus Sls)*
Tom Boldwin *(Dir-Govt Sls)*
Ray Nichols *(Mgr-Svc)*
John M. Keigher *(Dir-Sys & HR)*
Chris Lounsbury *(Dir-Bus Orders & Fin)*
Joel Oliva *(Mgr-Warehouse)*
Kevin Mansfield *(Asst Dir-Govt Sls)*
Michael Woodworth *(Mgr-Body Shop)*

MIDWEST TRANSPLANT NETWORK
1900 W 47th Pl Ste 400, Westwood, KS 66205
Tel.: (913) 262-1668   KS
Web Site: http://www.mwtn.org
Year Founded: 1973
Sales Range: $25-49.9 Million
Emp.: 158
Organ & Tissue Donation Services
N.A.I.C.S.: 621991
Steve Reintjes *(Vice Chm)*
Richard Muther *(Chm)*
Ken Powell *(Sec)*
James Boyd *(CFO)*

MIDWEST UNDERGROUND TECHNOLOGIES, INC.
2626 Midwest Ct, Champaign, IL 61822

Tel.: (217) 819-3040
Web Site: http://www.mutionline.com
Year Founded: 2000
Rev.: $23,800,000
Emp.: 97
Electrical Contractor
N.A.I.C.S.: 238210
Barry Schlickman *(VP-Ops-Central Reg)*
Darrin Peters *(Pres)*
Darrin Peters *(Pres)*
Kyle Fulton *(Dir-Health & Safety)*
Kyle Fulton National *(Dir-Health & Safety)*
Aaron Wagener National *(Dir-IT)*
Aaron Wagener *(Dir-IT)*
Richard Lazarski National *(Program Dir)*
Scott Kisting National *(Sr VP)*
Doug Poe *(Sr VP)*
Chad Sumner *(VP-Facility Svcs)*

MIDWEST VETERINARY SUPPLY, INC.
21467 Holyoke Ave, Lakeville, MN 55044
Tel.: (952) 894-4350   ND
Web Site: http://www.midwestvet.net
Year Founded: 1961
Sales Range: $10-24.9 Million
Emp.: 50
Drugs, Proprietaries & Sundries
N.A.I.C.S.: 424210
Guy Flickenger *(Pres)*
Scott Davis *(Dir-Pur)*
Kevin Ebel *(Mgr-Sls-Natl)*
Pam Koopman *(Dir-e-Business)*
Subsidiaries:

JAT Pharmacy, LLC (1)
5374 Maly Rd, Sun Prairie, WI 53590
Tel.: (608) 834-2815
Web Site: http://www.jatpharmacy.com
Emp.: 7
Pharmaceutical Products Distr
N.A.I.C.S.: 424210

MIDWEST WALNUT COMPANY
1914 Tostevin St, Council Bluffs, IA 51503
Tel.: (712) 325-9191
Web Site:
http://www.midwestwalnut.com
Year Founded: 1931
Sales Range: $10-24.9 Million
Emp.: 50
Rough, Dressed & Finished Lumber
N.A.I.C.S.: 423310
James D. Plowman *(Pres)*
Bruce Stevenson *(Controller)*
Mike McDaniel *(VP-Matls)*

MIDWEST WAREHOUSE & DISTRIBUTION SYSTEMS
5967 W 65th St, Chicago, IL 60638
Tel.: (708) 563-1626
Web Site:
http://www.midwestwarehouse.com
Rev.: $27,921,438
Emp.: 5
General Warehousing
N.A.I.C.S.: 493110
Radmila Geever *(Dir-HR)*
John Rowan *(VP)*
Edward J. Borkowski *(Pres)*

MIDWEST WHEEL COMPANY
1436 E Ovid Ave, Des Moines, IA 50316
Tel.: (515) 265-1491
Web Site:
http://www.midwestwheel.com
Rev.: $21,016,394
Emp.: 200
Automotive Supplies & Parts
N.A.I.C.S.: 423120
Michael Callison *(Pres)*

MIDWEST WOODWORKING & FIXTURE CORP.

U.S. PRIVATE

Midwest Woodworking & Fixture Corp.—(Continued)

MIDWEST WOODWORKING & FIXTURE CORP.
11634 Gravois Rd, Saint Louis, MO 63126
Tel.: (314) 843-3001
Web Site:
http://www.midwestwoodworking.com
Sales Range: $1-9.9 Million
Emp.: 5
Fixtures, Store: Except Wood
N.A.I.C.S.: 337126
Andrew Depke (Chm)
Donald Depke (Pres)
Jackie Kohsier (Controller)

MIDWESTERN BIOAG, INC.
10955 Blackhawk Dr, Blue Mounds, WI 53517
Tel.: (608) 437-4994 DE
Web Site:
http://www.midwesternbioag.com
Year Founded: 1984
Sales Range: $10-24.9 Million
Emp.: 43
Crop Farming & Livestock Mfr
N.A.I.C.S.: 111998
Gary Zimmer (Co-Founder & Pres)
Duane Siegenthaler (Chief Sls Officer)
Ronnie Kurschner (VP-Ops)
Douglas C. Rosenberg (Chm)
Jennifer Hasburgh (Asst Sec & Project Mgr)
Sue Gullickson (CFO & Treas)
Mike Beringer (Dir-HR)
Leilani Zimmer-Durand (VP)
Tom Vander Heiden (VP-Growth & Dev)
Bob Yanda (VP-Growth & Dev)
Mark Halton (VP-Ops)
Steve Slater (VP-R&D)

MIDWESTERN CONNECTICUT COUNCIL OF ALCOHOLISM
38 Old Ridgebury Rd, Danbury, CT 06810
Tel.: (203) 792-4515 CT
Web Site:
http://www.mccaonline.com
Year Founded: 1972
Sales Range: $10-24.9 Million
Emp.: 234
Alcohol & Drug Abuse Rehabilitation Services
N.A.I.C.S.: 622210
Joe Sullivan (Pres & CEO)
Glenn Connan (CFO & VP)
Jaya Daptardar (COO)
Jennifer Ballew (Chief Medical Officer)
Richard A. Radocchia (Chief Clinical Officer)

MIDWESTERN INDUSTRIES INC.
915 Oberlin Rd SW, Massillon, OH 44647
Tel.: (330) 837-4203
Web Site:
http://www.midwesternind.com
Year Founded: 1953
Sales Range: $10-24.9 Million
Emp.: 95
Mfr of Vibrating Screening Equipment & Industrial Wire Cloth
N.A.I.C.S.: 332618
Harold I. Painter (Pres)
David Weaver (Treas & VP-Fin)

MIDWESTERN MACHINE & HYDRAULICS, INC.
17265 N Timberline Ln, Mount Vernon, IL 62864

Tel.: (618) 246-9440 IL
Web Site:
http://www.midwesternmachinehydraulics.com
Year Founded: 1998
Sales Range: $1-9.9 Million
Emp.: 14
Hydraulic Equipment Repair Shops & Related Services
N.A.I.C.S.: 811210
Robin Stowers (Pres)
Jim Stowers (Owner)

MIDWESTERN RUST PROOF CO.
3636 North Kilbourn Ave, Chicago, IL 60641
Tel.: (773) 725-6636
Web Site:
http://www.midwesternrustproof.com
Metal Coating, Engraving, except Jewelry & Silverware & Allied Services to Manufacturers
N.A.I.C.S.: 332812
Garth Davies (Pres)

Subsidiaries:

Arlington Plating Company (1)
600 S Vermont St, Palatine, IL 60078-0974
Tel.: (847) 359-1490
Web Site: http://www.arlingtonplating.com
Electroplating, Plating, Polishing, Anodizing & Coloring
N.A.I.C.S.: 332813
Jay Ramp (Dir-Sls & Mktg)

MIDWESTERN WHEELS INC.
1611 E Amelia St, Appleton, WI 54911
Tel.: (920) 730-7560
Web Site: http://www.aviswi.com
Rev.: $11,800,000
Emp.: 200
Rent-A-Car Service
N.A.I.C.S.: 532111
William J. Wallschlaeger (Pres)

MIE PROPERTIES INC.
2560 Lord Baltimore Dr, Baltimore, MD 21244-2666
Tel.: (410) 788-0100
Web Site:
http://www.mieproperties.com
Year Founded: 1971
Rev.: $128,000,000
Emp.: 100
Commercial & Industrial Building Operation
N.A.I.C.S.: 531120
Edward A. St. John (Pres)
Lawrence Maykrantz (CFO & Sr VP)
Stan Meros (Sr VP-Property Mgmt)
Richard Williamson (Sr VP-Leasing)
Robert Becker (Sr VP-Tenant Retention)
Gerard J. Wit (Sr VP-Mktg)

MIF CONSTRUCTION, INC.
148 Perrysville Ave, Pittsburgh, PA 15229
Tel.: (412) 931-7444
Sales Range: $10-24.9 Million
Emp.: 200
Masonry Services
N.A.I.C.S.: 238140
Mark E. Friday (Pres)

MIFFLINBURG BANCORP, INC.
250 E Chestnut St, Mifflinburg, PA 17844
Tel.: (570) 966-1041
Web Site: https://www.mbtc.com
Year Founded: 1872
Bank Holding Company
N.A.I.C.S.: 551111

Subsidiaries:

Mifflinburg Bank & Trust Co. (1)
250 E Chestnut St, Mifflinburg, PA 17844
Tel.: (570) 966-1041
Web Site: http://www.mbtc.com
State Commercial Banks
N.A.I.C.S.: 522110
Andrea Long (VP & Dir-HR)
Jeffrey J. Kapsar (Pres & CEO)
Garry Benfer (Sr VP-Loan Admin)
Thomas Beck (Pres-Internal Audit & Compliance)
Thomas Eberhart (COO & Sr VP)
Thomas Graver Jr. (CFO & Sr VP)

MIG & CO.
60 E 42nd St Ste 2137, New York, NY 10165
Tel.: (212) 681-1400
Web Site: http://www.mig.com
Year Founded: 1998
Sales Range: Less than $1 Million
Emp.: 35
Computer Consulting Services
N.A.I.C.S.: 541519
Eric Mcguardian (Pres & CEO)
Daron Migirdeyan (VP)
Greg Besso (Engr-Sys)

MIGHTY DISTRIBUTING SYSTEM OF AMERICA
650 Engineering Dr, Norcross, GA 30092-2821
Tel.: (770) 448-3900 GA
Web Site:
http://www.mightyfranchise.com
Year Founded: 1970
Rev.: $76,000,000
Emp.: 50
Franchise System of Distributing Automotive Parts to Professional Shops
N.A.I.C.S.: 533110
Ken Voelker (Pres & CEO)
Gary Vann (Sr VP-Sls & Mktg)
Brad Bradshaw (VP-Product Mgmt)
Barry Teagle (VP-Franchising)
Josh D'Agostino (Pres-Auto Parts & CEO-Auto Parts)
Sean Milligan (VP-Ops-Auto Parts)
Mike Dallin (Dir-Product Info-Auto Parts)
Carmen Strickland (VP-Franchise Ops)
Chris Adams (VP-Franchise Dev & Ops)
Matt Shaw (VP-Sls-Auto Parts)
Ronnie Barassi (VP-Intl Dev & Strategic Accounts-Auto Parts)

MIGHTY USA, INC.
19706 S Normandie Ave, Torrance, CA 90502
Tel.: (310) 516-7478
Web Site: http://www.mightyusa.com
Sales Range: $25-49.9 Million
Emp.: 30
Industrial Machinery & Equipment Merchant Whslr
N.A.I.C.S.: 423830
Peter Tsai (Pres)

MIHLFELD & ASSOCIATES INC.
2841 E Division St, Springfield, MO 65803
Tel.: (417) 831-6727
Web Site: http://www.mihlfeld.com
Sales Range: $150-199.9 Million
Emp.: 80
Office Administrative Services
N.A.I.C.S.: 561110
Marshall Mihlfeld (Pres)

MIKARA CORPORATION
3109 Louisiana Ave N, Minneapolis, MN 55427-2918
Tel.: (763) 541-1000

Web Site:
http://www.nationalsalon.com
Sales Range: $10-24.9 Million
Emp.: 55
Mfr of Salon Products & Equipment
N.A.I.C.S.: 423850

Subsidiaries:

National Salon Resources (1)
3109 Louisiana Ave N, Minneapolis, MN 55427-2918
Tel.: (763) 546-9500
Web Site: http://www.nationalsalon.com
Mfr of Salon Products & Equipment
N.A.I.C.S.: 423850

MIKART INC.
1750 Chattahoochee Ave NW, Atlanta, GA 30318-2112
Tel.: (404) 351-4510 GA
Web Site: http://www.mikart.com
Year Founded: 1975
Sales Range: $25-49.9 Million
Emp.: 170
Provider of Pharmaceutical Preparations
N.A.I.C.S.: 325412
Miguel Arteche (Chm & CEO)
Tom Head (VP)
Larry Gunnin (CFO)
Blair Jones (VP-Sls & Mktg)
Judy Howard (VP-Scientific Affairs)

MIKE ALBERT LEASING, INC.
10340 Evendale Dr, Cincinnati, OH 45241-2512
Tel.: (513) 563-1400 OH
Web Site: http://www.mikealbert.com
Year Founded: 1928
Sales Range: $25-49.9 Million
Emp.: 350
Automobile Leasing Services
N.A.I.C.S.: 532112
John Betagole (VP)
Marty Betagole (CEO)
Sheri J. Hardesty (VP-Bus Intelligence & Quality Assurance)
Keith R. Miller (Treas)
W. Bruce Shaffer (Co-COO)
Barbara Heyn (Dir-HR)
John Groene (Dir-Mktg)
Anne Pezel (COO)
Jeff Hart (Pres)
Ted Cain (Exec VP-Sls)
Susan Fulmer (VP & Controller)
Phillip J. Schneider Jr. (VP-Sls, Mktg & Customer Svc)

MIKE ANDERSON CHEVROLET BUICK GMC TRUCK, INC.
4301 E Market St, Logansport, IN 46947
Tel.: (574) 753-6285
Web Site:
http://www.mikeanderson.com
Sales Range: $100-124.9 Million
New & Used Automobiles Whslr & Distr
N.A.I.C.S.: 441110
Greg Dieterly (Gen Mgr)

MIKE BARNEY NISSAN
3676 Sheridan Dr, Amherst, NY 14226
Tel.: (716) 833-9888
Web Site:
http://www.mikebarneynissan.com
Year Founded: 1979
Sales Range: $10-24.9 Million
Emp.: 45
Car Whslr
N.A.I.C.S.: 441110
Joe Caldarelli (Pres)
Mike Tohl (Mgr-Fin)

MIKE BROWN ELECTRIC CO.
561-A Mercantile Dr, Cotati, CA 94931-3040
Tel.: (707) 792-8100

Web Site: http://www.mbelectric.com
Year Founded: 1979
Sales Range: $25-49.9 Million
Emp.: 100
Electrical Wiring Services
N.A.I.C.S.: 238210
James G. Brown *(Pres)*
Tami Erhardt *(Acct Mgr)*
Tiffany Howe *(Controller)*
Sean Hartnett *(Mgr-Warehouse)*

MIKE BURKART FORD MERCURY INC.
3110 County Rd PP, Plymouth, WI 53073
Tel.: (920) 893-6961
Web Site: http://www.burkartford.com
Sales Range: $10-24.9 Million
Emp.: 40
Car Whslr
N.A.I.C.S.: 441110
Michael Burkart *(Owner)*

MIKE CARTER CONSTRUCTION INC.
435 12th St W, Bradenton, FL 34205-7301
Tel.: (941) 745-1700 FL
Web Site: http://www.carterconst.com
Year Founded: 1977
Sales Range: $1-9.9 Million
Emp.: 6
Nonresidential Construction
N.A.I.C.S.: 236220
Kris Merritt *(Asst Controller)*

MIKE CASTRUCCI, LLC
1099 Lila Ave, Milford, OH 45150
Tel.: (513) 334-0400 OH
Web Site: http://mikecastrucciformilford.com
Sales Range: $25-49.9 Million
Holding Company; New & Used Car Dealerships Owner & Operator
N.A.I.C.S.: 551112
Michael Castrucci *(Founder, Owner & Pres)*

Subsidiaries:

Mike Castrucci Chevrolet Sales, Inc. (1)
1099 Lila Ave, Milford, OH 45150-1684
Tel.: (513) 831-5555
Web Site: http://www.mikecastruccichevrolet.com
Sales Range: $25-49.9 Million
Emp.: 45
New & Used Car Dealer
N.A.I.C.S.: 441110
Jerome Fix *(Mgr-Corp Fin)*
Sean Stevenson *(Mgr-Sls-New Cars)*
Rick Loomis *(Mgr-Fin)*
Bill Lykins *(Mgr-Svcs)*
Terry Moore *(Mgr-Parts)*
Rebecca Rush *(Mgr-Fleet)*

MIKE D. DIMICH & SONS, INC.
344 Howard Ave, Billings, MT 59101
Tel.: (406) 252-9355
Sales Range: $10-24.9 Million
Emp.: 75
Soft Drink Bottler
N.A.I.C.S.: 312111
Tom Dimich *(Controller)*
William Dimich Sr. *(Pres)*

MIKE DUMAN AUTO SALES, INC.
2300 Godwin Blvd, Suffolk, VA 23434
Tel.: (757) 539-1000
Year Founded: 1980
Sales Range: $25-49.9 Million
Emp.: 73
Used Car Whslr
N.A.I.C.S.: 441120
Michael D. Duman *(Owner)*

MIKE ERDMAN MOTORS INC.
445 E Merritt Island Causeway, Merritt Island, FL 32952
Tel.: (321) 453-2050
Web Site: http://www.mikeerdmanmotors.com
Rev.: $37,000,000
Emp.: 100
Owner & Operator of Car Dealerships
N.A.I.C.S.: 441110
Michael Erdman *(Pres)*

MIKE FINNIN MOTORS INC.
3600 Dodge St, Dubuque, IA 52003-5251
Tel.: (563) 583-8825
Web Site: http://www.mikefinnin.com
Year Founded: 1993
Sales Range: $10-24.9 Million
Emp.: 70
Car Whslr
N.A.I.C.S.: 441110
Sharon Finnin *(Sec)*

MIKE GARCIA MERCHANT SECURITY, INC.
6000 Welch Ave Ste 11, El Paso, TX 79905
Tel.: (915) 772-7047
Web Site: http://www.merchant-security.com
Sales Range: $10-24.9 Million
Emp.: 400
Protective Services, Guard
N.A.I.C.S.: 561612
Miguel U. Garcia *(Pres & CEO)*
Evangelina G. Garcia *(CFO & VP)*
Yevtte Garcia *(Mgr-Ops)*

MIKE GATTO INC
15 W Hibiscus Blvd, Melbourne, FL 32901
Tel.: (321) 676-2710
Web Site: http://www.gattos.com
Sales Range: $10-24.9 Million
Emp.: 11
Automotive Tires
N.A.I.C.S.: 441340
Pam Gatto *(Owner)*
Mike Gatto *(Founder)*
Scott McHenry *(Mgr-Ops)*
Mike McHenry *(Mgr-Adv & Mktg)*
Mike Nevin *(Mgr-Sls & Supvr-Store)*

MIKE JORDAN CO. INC.
6305 Cliff Dr, Fort Smith, AR 72903
Tel.: (479) 484-5059
Sales Range: $10-24.9 Million
Emp.: 12
Oil Well Machinery, Equipment & Supplies
N.A.I.C.S.: 423830
Mike Jordan *(Owner & CEO)*
Alan Van Hook *(Pres)*
Fred Jordan *(Office Mgr)*

MIKE MURPHY FORD INC.
565 W Jackson St, Morton, IL 61550
Tel.: (309) 263-2311
Web Site: http://www.mikemurphyford.com
Rev.: $35,935,567
Emp.: 32
Automobiles, New & Used
N.A.I.C.S.: 441110
Michael Murphy *(Pres)*
Levi Smith *(Mgr-Fin)*

MIKE MYERS REALTY INC.
92 E Main St, Norwalk, OH 44857
Tel.: (419) 668-2585
Web Site: http://www.mikemyersrealtyinc.com
Rev.: $33,000,000
Emp.: 25
Real Estate Agents & Managers
N.A.I.C.S.: 531210

Mike Myers *(Pres)*

MIKE PATTON AUTO
1406 Lafayette Pkwy, Lagrange, GA 30241
Tel.: (706) 882-2931
Web Site: http://www.mikepattonauto.com
Sales Range: $10-24.9 Million
Emp.: 75
Automobiles, New & Used
N.A.I.C.S.: 441110
Mary White *(Office Mgr)*
Chris Patton *(Mgr-Recon Inventory)*
Allen Bruce *(Dir-Svcs)*
Tim Wilson *(CFO)*
Britt Gilmore *(COO)*

MIKE PERRY MOTOR CO.
3828 S St, Nacogdoches, TX 75964-7250
Tel.: (936) 564-7353
Web Site: http://www.mikeperrymotor.com
Sales Range: $10-24.9 Million
Emp.: 50
Car Whslr
N.A.I.C.S.: 441110
Mark Mitchell *(Mgr-Svc)*
Ray Perry *(Owner)*

MIKE PIAZZA HONDA
1908 E Lincoln Hwy, Langhorne, PA 19047
Tel.: (215) 702-1500
Web Site: http://www.mikepiazzahonda.com
Sales Range: $10-24.9 Million
Emp.: 60
Car Whslr
N.A.I.C.S.: 441110
Gary Berlin *(Principal)*

MIKE PILE BMW
2401 W Southwest Loop 323, Tyler, TX 75701-9208
Tel.: (903) 561-7049
Web Site: http://www.mikepilebmw.com
Year Founded: 1995
Sales Range: $10-24.9 Million
Emp.: 36
Car Whslr
N.A.I.C.S.: 441110
Bob Murray *(Controller)*
Rick Odette *(Mgr-Svc)*
Mike Pile *(Owner)*

MIKE REICHENBACH FORD LINCOLN MERCURY
600 N Coit St, Florence, SC 29501
Tel.: (843) 664-4141
Web Site: http://www.toughnameeasydeal.com
Sales Range: $25-49.9 Million
Emp.: 87
New & Used Car Dealers
N.A.I.C.S.: 441110
Mike Reichenbach *(Owner & Pres)*
Charisse Reichenbach *(Dir-Mktg)*
John Pinel *(Gen Mgr)*
Pearl Wallace *(Comptroller)*

MIKE ROCHE INC.
8445 Atlantic Ave, Bell, CA 90201
Tel.: (323) 773-4923
Rev.: $13,000,000
Emp.: 29
Petroleum Products
N.A.I.C.S.: 424720
Patrick Roche *(Pres)*
Fiona Roche *(CFO)*

MIKE RYAN TREE SERVICE INC.
235 County Line Rd, Amityville, NY 11701
Tel.: (631) 691-2381
Sales Range: $50-74.9 Million
Emp.: 150
Civil Engineering Services
N.A.I.C.S.: 237310
Mike Ryan *(Pres)*

MIKE SAVOIE CHEVROLET INC.
1900 W Maple Rd PO Box 520, Troy, MI 48084-7105
Tel.: (248) 643-8000 DE
Web Site: http://www.mikesavoie.com
Year Founded: 1966
Sales Range: $100-124.9 Million
Emp.: 75
Sales of Automobiles
N.A.I.C.S.: 441110
Tom Marion *(Mgr-Parts)*

MIKE SHAW BUICK GMC
1313 Motor City Dr, Colorado Springs, CO 80905-7316
Tel.: (719) 636-3881
Web Site: http://www.mikeshawbuickgmc.com
Sales Range: $10-24.9 Million
Emp.: 65
Car Whslr
N.A.I.C.S.: 441110
Scott James *(COO)*
Mike Shaw *(Pres)*
Anthony Downs *(Gen Mgr)*

MIKE SMITH TOYOTA MITSUBISHI KIA
3941 Mike Smith Dr, Paducah, KY 42001
Tel.: (270) 442-5461
Year Founded: 1991
Sales Range: $10-24.9 Million
Emp.: 40
Car Whslr
N.A.I.C.S.: 441110
Jerry Washer *(Gen Mgr)*

MIKE STEVEN AUTO GROUP INC.
6631 E Kellogg Dr, Wichita, KS 67207-1505
Tel.: (316) 652-2277
Web Site: http://www.stevenmotors.com
Rev.: $60,000,000
Emp.: 100
New Car Dealers
N.A.I.C.S.: 441110
Michael Steven *(Pres-Fin)*

MIKE THOMPSON'S RECREATIONAL VEHICLES
1394 Firestone Blvd, Santa Fe Springs, CA 90670
Tel.: (562) 921-0955
Web Site: http://www.mikethomson.com
Rev.: $33,300,000
Emp.: 85
Dealership Of Motor Homes
N.A.I.C.S.: 441210
Frank B. Degelas *(Pres)*

MIKE VASILINDA PRODUCTIONS, INC.
310 N Monroe St, Tallahassee, FL 32301
Tel.: (850) 224-5420
Web Site: http://www.mvptv.tv
Year Founded: 1973
Sales Range: $1-9.9 Million
Emp.: 6
High Definition Television & Video Production
N.A.I.C.S.: 512110

MIKE VASILINDA PRODUCTIONS, INC.

U.S. PRIVATE

Mike Vasilinda Productions, Inc.—(Continued)
Mike Vasilinda (Pres & CEO)

MIKE WILSON PUBLIC RELATIONS, INC.
1521 Laurel Park Cir NE, Atlanta, GA 30329
Tel.: (404) 325-5550 GA
Web Site:
http://www.mikewilsonpr.com
Year Founded: 1977
Sales Range: Less than $1 Million
Emp.: 1
Public Relations Agency
N.A.I.C.S.: 541820
Thomas Wilson (Pres)

MIKE'S AUTO GLASS INC.
4721 N Thatcher Ave Ste B, Tampa, FL 33614-6903
Tel.: (813) 876-4115
Web Site:
http://www.mikesautoglassinc.com
Year Founded: 1989
Sales Range: $1-9.9 Million
Auto Glass Replacement & Repair
N.A.I.C.S.: 811122
Michael Cumbie (Pres)
Les Henley (VP)

MIKE'S CAMERA INC.
2500 Pearl St, Boulder, CO 80302
Tel.: (303) 443-1715
Web Site:
http://www.mikescamera.com
Rev.: $11,000,000
Emp.: 135
Retailer of Cameras & Related Equipment & Supplies
N.A.I.C.S.: 449210
Kaloust Christianian (Pres)
Alex Christianian (VP)
Aroussiag Christianian (Sec & VP)
Brian Rabin (Acct Mgr)

MIKE'S CIGARS DISTRIBUTORS, INC.
1030 Kane Concourse, Bay Harbor Islands, FL 33154
Tel.: (305) 866-2277
Web Site:
http://www.mikescigars.com
Year Founded: 1985
Sales Range: $1-9.9 Million
Emp.: 29
Tobacco & Tobacco Product Merchant Whslr
N.A.I.C.S.: 424940
Oded Ben-Arie (Pres & CEO)
Rose Boruchin (Treas)

MIKE'S FLOORING COMPANIES
4425 Brookfield Corporate Dr Ste 300, Chantilly, VA 20151
Tel.: (703) 802-3485
Web Site:
http://www.mikesfloorco.com
Sales Range: $10-24.9 Million
Emp.: 20
Carpeting & Flooring
N.A.I.C.S.: 449121
Michael Schreiber (CEO)

MIKE'S INC.
109 Velma Ave, South Roxana, IL 62087
Tel.: (618) 254-4491
Web Site: http://www.mikesinc.com
Year Founded: 1965
Sales Range: $10-24.9 Million
Emp.: 50

Provider of Heavy Equipment & Truck Repairs, Workboat Repairs & Specialized Heavy Equipment Rentals; Wholesaler & Retailer of Heavy Equipment Parts
N.A.I.C.S.: 336611
Michael J. Marko (Owner & Pres)

MIKELE INTERNATIONAL GROUP, LLC
2211 W Washington St, Orlando, FL 32805
Tel.: (407) 968-7195
Web Site:
http://www.davilacustomhomes.com
Year Founded: 2010
Sales Range: $1-9.9 Million
Construction Services
N.A.I.C.S.: 236220
Thiago Davila (CEO)

MIKEN BUILDERS, INC.
32782 Cedar Dr Unit 1, Millville, DE 19967-6919
Tel.: (302) 537-4444
Web Site:
http://www.mikenbuilders.com
Sales Range: $10-24.9 Million
Emp.: 25
New Home Construction
N.A.I.C.S.: 236115
Michael Cummings (Principal)
Michael McKone (Principal)

MIKEN SALES INC.
7230 Oxford Way, Commerce, CA 90040
Tel.: (323) 266-2560
Web Site: http://www.mikenusa.com
Sales Range: $10-24.9 Million
Emp.: 45
Women's & Children's Clothing
N.A.I.C.S.: 424350
Michael Bobbitt (Pres)
Ada Wu (Mgr)

MIKEN SPECIALTIES, LTD
431 Commerce St, Clute, TX 77531-5607
Tel.: (979) 265-9599 TX
Web Site: http://www.brockgroup.com
Year Founded: 1996
Sales Range: $50-74.9 Million
Emp.: 634
Provider of Insulation, Industrial Roofing & Scaffolding
N.A.I.C.S.: 238310
Mike Scarborough (Gen Mgr)
Kendra White (Office Mgr & Mgr-Billing)
Royce Branch (Mgr-EH&S Site)

MIKES COLLIERVILLE BIG STAR 52
1415 Goodman Rd, Horn Lake, MS 38637
Tel.: (662) 393-9708
Rev.: $43,000,000
Emp.: 60
Grocery Stores, Independent
N.A.I.C.S.: 445110
Michael Gordin (Pres)
Rita Salf (Sec)

MIKESELL'S POTATO CHIP CO.
333 Leo St, Dayton, OH 45404-0115
Tel.: (937) 228-9400 OH
Web Site: http://www.mikesells.com
Year Founded: 1910
Potato Chip Mfr
N.A.I.C.S.: 311919

MIKHAIL DARAFEEV INC.
5075 Edison Ave, Chino, CA 91710
Tel.: (909) 613-1818

Web Site: http://www.darafeev.com
Sales Range: $10-24.9 Million
Emp.: 45
Mfr & Designer of Custom Made Gameroom Furniture
N.A.I.C.S.: 337122
Antonina Darafeev (Pres)
Carol Young (Controller)

MIKROCOZE INC.
1545 Crossways Blvd Ste 250, Chesapeake, VA 23320-0210 NV
Web Site:
http://www.mikrocozeinc.com
Year Founded: 2016
Assets: $65
Liabilities: $82,423
Net Worth: ($82,358)
Earnings: ($25,657)
Emp.: 1
Fiscal Year-end: 11/30/20
Furniture Mfr & Distr
N.A.I.C.S.: 337121
Terry Wilshire (Pres, CEO, CFO, Principal Acctg Officer, Treas & Sec)
Robert Dickenson (VP)

MIL CORPORATION
4000 Mitchellville Rd Ste A 210, Bowie, MD 20716
Tel.: (301) 805-8500
Web Site: http://www.milcorp.com
Year Founded: 1980
Rev.: $18,214,912
Emp.: 350
Provider of Computer Software Systems Analysis & Design Services
N.A.I.C.S.: 541511
Maurice I. Long (Co-Founder, Pres & CEO)
Ed Greer (COO)
Larry Hollingsworth (VP-Corp Bus Dev Sector)
Marisa Daley (Exec VP)
Joel Melville (Officer-Executive Action)
Leslie Taylor (VP-Defense Bus)

MILAEGERS INC.
4838 Douglas Ave, Racine, WI 53402
Tel.: (262) 639-2040
Web Site: http://www.milaegers.com
Sales Range: $10-24.9 Million
Emp.: 200
Retail Nurseries & Garden Stores
N.A.I.C.S.: 444240
David Bennett (Controller)
Kris Reisdorf (Pres)
Kevin Milaeger (Owner)
Kara Kading (Mgr)

MILAGRO EXPLORATION, LLC
1301 McKinney Ste 500, Houston, TX 77010
Tel.: (713) 750-1600 DE
Web Site:
http://www.milagroexploration.com
Year Founded: 2005
Sales Range: $125-149.9 Million
Emp.: 103
Oil & Gas Exploration Services
N.A.I.C.S.: 211120
Gary J. Mabie (Pres & COO)
Marshall L. Munsell (Exec VP-Bus Dev & Land)
Lloyd Armstrong (VP-Production Logistics)
Scott Winn (CFO & Chief Restructuring Officer)

MILAGRO PACKAGING, LLC
1585 Wells Rd, Dundee, MI 48131
Tel.: (734) 777-1744
Web Site: http://www.milagro-pkg.com
Year Founded: 2001

Sales Range: $10-24.9 Million
Emp.: 150
Packaging Solutions
N.A.I.C.S.: 561910
Dolores Rodriguez (Pres)

MILAM OIL CORPORATION
1605 Haynesville Hwy, El Dorado, AR 71730
Tel.: (870) 862-4258
Web Site:
http://www.milamconst.com
Sales Range: $25-49.9 Million
Emp.: 225
Oil & Gas Pipeline & Related Structures Construction
N.A.I.C.S.: 237120
John Milam (Chm)
Mike Nutter (Mgr-Pur)
Johnny Joseph (Mgr-HR)

MILAN EXPRESS CO., INC.
1091 Kefauver Dr, Milan, TN 38358-3412
Tel.: (731) 686-7428 TN
Web Site:
http://www.milanexpress.com
Year Founded: 1969
Sales Range: $150-199.9 Million
Emp.: 1,850
Local & Interstate Trucking
N.A.I.C.S.: 484110
Brad Morris (VP-Sls)

MILANO BROTHERS INTERNATIONAL CORPORATION
1456 Newport Ctr Dr, Deerfield Beach, FL 33442
Tel.: (954) 420-5000
Web Site: http://www.milanobro.com
Rev.: $16,158,687
Emp.: 10
Electronic Parts & Equipment
N.A.I.C.S.: 423690
Piero Guidughi (Pres)

MILBANK MANUFACTURING COMPANY INC.
4801 Deramus Ave, Kansas City, MO 64120-1103
Tel.: (816) 483-5314 MO
Web Site:
http://www.milbankworks.com
Year Founded: 1913
Rev.: $68,600,000
Emp.: 1,107
Provider of Electricity Measurement Instruments
N.A.I.C.S.: 334515
Brad Skinner (Pres & CEO)
Jay McMullen (Dir-Metering & Comml Enclosures)
Adrienne Sander (VP-Sls)

Subsidiaries:

Milbank Manufacturing Company Inc. (1)
195 Prescolite, El Dorado, AR 71730 (100%)
Tel.: (870) 862-6601
Web Site: http://www.milbankworks.com
Sales Range: $10-24.9 Million
Emp.: 120
Instruments to Measure Electricity
N.A.I.C.S.: 335312
Robert Waldrop (Chm)

Milbank Manufacturing Company Inc. (1)
1400 E Havens St, Kokomo, IN 46901-3184
Tel.: (765) 452-5694
Web Site: http://www.milbankmfg.com
Rev.: $7,300,000
Emp.: 125
Sheet Metalwork
N.A.I.C.S.: 332322

Milbank Manufacturing Company Inc. - Concordia Facility (1)

COMPANIES

1601 S St Louis St, Concordia, MO 64020
Tel.: (660) 463-7994
Electrical Component Mfr
N.A.I.C.S.: 335999

MILBANK, TWEED, HADLEY & MCCLOY LLP
28 Liberty St, New York, NY 10005
Tel.: (212) 530-5000   NY
Web Site: http://www.milbank.com
Year Founded: 1866
Sales Range: $650-699.9 Million
Emp.: 501
Legal Advisory Services
N.A.I.C.S.: 541110
Thomas A. Arena *(Co-Partner)*
Wayne M. Aaron *(Co-Partner)*
Daniel D. Bartfeld *(Co-Partner)*
Michael J. Bellucci *(Co-Partner)*
William B. Bice *(Co-Partner)*
Austin Bramwell *(Co-Partner)*
James G. Cavoli *(Co-Partner)*
Charles J. Conroy *(Co-Partner)*
Paul Denaro *(Co-Partner)*
Antonia M. Apps *(Partner)*
Aaron Renenger *(Partner)*
Scott A. Edelman *(Chm)*
Robert Kennedy *(Partner)*
Jay Grushkin *(Head-Collateralized Loan Obligation Practice)*
Sean Solis *(Partner-Structured Fin & Securitization Practice-Collateralized)*
James H. Ball Jr. *(Co-Partner)*

MILBERG FACTORS, INC.
99 Park Ave Fl 21, New York, NY 10016
Tel.: (212) 697-4200
Web Site: http://www.milbergfactors.com
Year Founded: 1936
Sales Range: $50-74.9 Million
Emp.: 90
Provider of Factoring & Commercial Finance Services
N.A.I.C.S.: 522299
Leonard L. Milberg *(Chm)*
William A. Zisfein *(Exec VP)*
Daniel R. Milberg *(Pres)*
Barry MacHowsky *(Sr VP)*
Neil R. Desai *(Partner & Sr VP)*
Paul D. Pagano *(VP)*
Jeffrey S. Sesko *(VP)*
David M. Reza *(Sr VP)*
Ernest B. White *(Sr VP)*
Stanley M. Joseph *(Sr VP)*
Peter Austin *(Sr VP)*

MILCO INDUSTRIES INC.
550 E 5th St, Bloomsburg, PA 17815-2301
Tel.: (570) 784-0400   PA
Web Site: http://www.milcoind.com
Year Founded: 1979
Sales Range: $25-49.9 Million
Emp.: 250
Women's Lingerie Mfr
N.A.I.C.S.: 315250
Lenny Comerchero *(Pres)*
Tony Peluso *(CFO)*
Bessie Paden *(Coord-Production)*
David Mosteller *(Mgr-IT)*
Julie Ezzyk *(Sec)*

MILE 9
23622 Calabasas Rd Ste 323, Calabasas, CA 91302
Tel.: (818) 876-7100
Web Site: http://www.mile9agency.com
Sales Range: $10-24.9 Million
Emp.: 15
Advetising Agency
N.A.I.C.S.: 541810

Jeff Smaul *(Pres & Dir-Creative)*
Izabela Drodge *(Mgr-Admin)*
Adel Jalili *(Dir-Art)*
Katy Thomas *(Acct Exec)*

MILE HI FROZEN FOODS CO.
4770 E 51st Ave, Denver, CO 80216
Tel.: (303) 399-6066
Web Site: http://www.milehifoods.com
Year Founded: 1974
Rev.: $20,600,000
Emp.: 180
Restaurant Supplies Whslr
N.A.I.C.S.: 423850
Tony M. Taddonio *(Pres)*
Pamela Taddonio *(Sec)*
Ray Lyons *(CFO)*
Mike Planton *(Mgr-Ops)*

MILE MARKER INTERNATIONAL INC.
2121 Blount Rd, Pompano Beach, FL 33069
Tel.: (954) 782-0604   FL
Web Site: http://www.milemarker.com
Year Founded: 1980
Sales Range: $10-24.9 Million
Emp.: 12
Automotive Supplies & Parts Mfr & Distr
N.A.I.C.S.: 336390
Stacy Edelson *(Dir-Sls)*

Subsidiaries:

Mile Marker Inc.   (1)
2121 Blount Rd, Pompano Beach, FL 33069-5112
Tel.: (954) 782-0604
Web Site: http://www.milemarker.com
Automotive Supplies & Parts
N.A.I.C.S.: 423120

MILEA TRUCK SALES CORP.
885 E 149th St, Bronx, NY 10455
Tel.: (718) 292-6200
Web Site: http://www.mileatruck.com
Rev.: $54,022,029
Emp.: 85
Trucks, Tractors & Trailers: New & Used
N.A.I.C.S.: 441110
Barry Milea *(Pres)*
George Lin *(VP)*
Lisa Sanfilippo *(Mgr)*

MILEND, INC.
400 Northridge Rd Ste 600, Atlanta, GA 30350
Tel.: (855) 645-3631
Web Site: http://www.milend.com
Year Founded: 1994
Sales Range: $10-24.9 Million
Emp.: 86
Mortgage Lender & Refinancing Services
N.A.I.C.S.: 522310
Mark Granigan *(Pres)*
Sam Morano *(Mng Dir)*
Jason Breeland *(COO)*
Ali Khademi *(Reg Mgr)*

MILENDER WHITE CONSTRUCTION CO.
12655 W 54th Dr, Arvada, CO 80002
Tel.: (303) 216-0420
Web Site: http://www.milenderwhite.com
Year Founded: 1997
Sales Range: $75-99.9 Million
Emp.: 60
Construction Services
N.A.I.C.S.: 236115
Bryon White *(Pres & CEO)*
Mike Milender *(Exec VP)*
Darren Hinton *(Sr VP)*
Shane Fobes *(Sr VP)*

MILEPOST INDUSTRIES
Apt 301 1081 Pine St, San Francisco, CA 94109-5099
Tel.: (415) 346-0370
Rev.: $19,800,000
Emp.: 12
Railroad & Railway Roadbed Construction
N.A.I.C.S.: 236210

MILES CHEVROLET INC.
150 W Pershing Rd, Decatur, IL 62526
Tel.: (217) 877-4440
Web Site: http://www.milesnissan.com
Sales Range: $100-124.9 Million
Emp.: 200
Automobiles, New & Used
N.A.I.C.S.: 441110
Vic Castelli *(Controller)*
Pat Dawson *(Owner & Gen Mgr)*

MILES CONSULTING CORP.
193 Blue Ravine Rd Ste 160, Folsom, CA 95630
Web Site: http://www.milesconsultingcorp.com
Year Founded: 2002
Sales Range: $1-9.9 Million
Emp.: 29
Information Technology Services
N.A.I.C.S.: 541519
Miles Feinberg *(Founder & Pres)*

MILES ENTERPRISES, INC.
2760 Keller Rd, Owensboro, KY 42301
Tel.: (270) 926-1786
Gas Distr; Grain Storage; Tire Retailer
N.A.I.C.S.: 221210
Debra Seymour *(Pres)*
Ray Turk *(CEO)*

MILES FIBERGLASS & COMPOSITES, INC.
8855 SE Otty Rd, Portland, OR 97086
Tel.: (503) 775-7755
Web Site: http://www.milesfiberglass.com
Year Founded: 1963
Sales Range: $10-24.9 Million
Emp.: 200
Fiberglass & Composite Mfr
N.A.I.C.S.: 327212
Lowell Miles *(CEO)*
Lori Miles-Olund *(Pres)*
Joe Luchak *(CFO & Gen Mgr)*
Craig Hinkle *(COO)*
Forrest Olund *(Mgr-Ops)*
Mark Martens *(Mgr-Quality Assurance)*
Mollie LeClaire *(Acct Mgr)*

MILES MEDIA GROUP, LLLP
6751 Professional Pkwy W Ste 200, Sarasota, FL 34240
Tel.: (941) 342-2300
Web Site: http://www.milespartnership.com
Year Founded: 1990
Sales Range: $25-49.9 Million
Emp.: 170
Marketing Solutions; Magazine Publisher
N.A.I.C.S.: 541613
Roger W. Miles *(Founder & CEO)*
Nate Huff *(Sr VP)*
Dianne Gates *(CFO)*
Elena Prostova *(VP-New Bus Dev)*
Paul Winkle *(Sr VP-Global Mktg)*
Angie Briggs *(VP-New Bus Dev)*
Doug Luciani *(COO)*
Ben Miles *(VP-HR & Ops)*

Chris Adams *(Dir-Online Res & Mktg)*
Gray Lawry *(VP-Strategy & Insights)*
Carrie Koenig *(VP-Sls & Mktg)*
Karin Mast *(VP-New Bus Dev & Hospitality)*
Rachael Root *(Acct Dir)*
Camron Reid *(Dir-Comm-Hospitality Div)*
Chad Ketchum *(Mgr-Web Project)*
Greg Insco *(Dir-Art)*
Hannah Kelbaugh *(Acct Dir)*
Karen Galvin *(Mgr-Content)*
Kim Hanrahan *(Dir-Creative)*
Lauren Bourgoing *(VP)*
Neal Alfano *(Dir-Creative)*
Rebecca Jones *(Dir-Art)*
Scott Bacon *(VP-New Bus Dev & Hospitality)*
Stacia Franke *(VP-Product Dev)*

Subsidiaries:

Miles South Pacific   (1)
2 Ngaire Avenue, PO Box 9390, Newmarket, Auckland, 1149, New Zealand
Tel.: (64) 9 974 2452
Marketing Solutions; Magazine Publisher
N.A.I.C.S.: 541613

MILES PROPERTIES INC.
3379 Peachtree Rd Northeast Ste 500, Atlanta, GA 30326-1418
Tel.: (404) 965-3300   GA
Web Site: http://www.milesproperties.com
Year Founded: 1989
Sales Range: $50-74.9 Million
Emp.: 400
Apartment Building Owners
N.A.I.C.S.: 531311
Angie Smith *(Reg VP)*
Barbara Young *(Asst Controller)*
Danette Vaughan *(Dir-Payroll Svcs)*
Shaun Shaw *(Mgr-Bus)*
Tara Oliver *(Mgr-HR)*
Becky Register *(Mgr-Ops)*

MILES SAND & GRAVEL COMPANY
400 Valley Ave NE, Puyallup, WA 98372
Tel.: (253) 833-3705   WA
Web Site: http://www.miles.rocks
Year Founded: 1943
Sales Range: $100-124.9 Million
Emp.: 175
Provider of Ready Mixed Concrete & Sand & Gravel
N.A.I.C.S.: 327320
Walter Miles *(Pres)*
Lisa Kittilsby *(VP)*
Marjean Davis *(Mgr-Payroll & HR)*
Erica Sorensen *(Asst Mgr-Credit)*
Ray Shaak *(Office Mgr)*

Subsidiaries:

Port Orchard Sand & Gravel Company, Inc.   (1)
7000 Werner Rd, Bremerton, WA 98312
Tel.: (360) 479-4626
Sales Range: $1-9.9 Million
Construction Materials Distr
N.A.I.C.S.: 423320

MILES TECHNOLOGIES, INC.
300 W Rte 38, Moorestown, NJ 08057
Tel.: (856) 439-0999
Web Site: http://www.milestechnologies.com
Year Founded: 1997
Sales Range: $10-24.9 Million
Emp.: 130
IT Support Services
N.A.I.C.S.: 541512
Chris Miles *(CEO)*
John Bialous *(COO)*

MILES TECHNOLOGIES, INC.

U.S. PRIVATE

Miles Technologies, Inc.—(Continued)
Dan Carpenter (Pres)
John Horner (VP-Strategic Consulting Svcs)
Andrew Elia (VP-IT)

MILES-MCCLELLAN CONSTRUCTION COMPANY
2100 Builders Pl, Columbus, OH 43204
Tel.: (614) 487-7744
Web Site: http://www.miles-mcclellan.com
Year Founded: 1978
Rev.: $86,400,000
Emp.: 107
Commercial & Institutional Building Construction
N.A.I.C.S.: 236220
Terry McClellan (Principal & Dir-Pre-Construction Svcs)
Aubrey Harless (VP)
David McIntosh (VP)
Mike Rodriguez (VP)
Ted Tinkler (VP)
Tim Bourke (Asst Controller)
Alex Bailey (Project Mgr-Charlotte)
Micah Byler (Asst Project Mgr)

MILESBRAND, INC.
1101 Bannock St, Denver, CO 80204
Tel.: (303) 293-9191
Web Site: http://www.milesbrand.com
Year Founded: 1986
Rev.: $15,000,000
Emp.: 20
Advetising Agency
N.A.I.C.S.: 541810
Harris Wilkinson (Dir-Creative & Copywriter)
Jaimee Woodruff (Partner & VP)

Subsidiaries:

Milesbrand Sales (1)
10025 E 96th St, Indianapolis, IN 46256
Tel.: (317) 682-8407
N.A.I.C.S.: 541810

MILESTONE BROADCAST
33 Flatbush Ave 4th Fl, Brooklyn, NY 11217
Tel.: (212) 647-1212
Web Site: http://www.goodnewsbroadcast.com
Year Founded: 1985
Sales Range: Less than $1 Million
Emp.: 11
African-American Market, Asian Market, Event Marketing, Full Service, Hispanic Marketing, Internet/Web Design
N.A.I.C.S.: 541810
Paul H. Sladkus (Co-Pres)
Jennifer Sladkus (Co-Pres)
Greg Sullivan (Dir-New Bus Dev)
Douglas McGann (Partner)

MILESTONE CAPITAL, INC.
Three Riverway Ste 1010, Houston, TX 77056
Tel.: (713) 993-0303
Web Site: http://www.milestonevg.com
Privater Equity Firm
N.A.I.C.S.: 523999
A. Kelly Williams (Founder & Mng Dir)

Subsidiaries:

Aztec Events & Tents, Inc. (1)
601 W 6th St, Houston, TX 77007
Tel.: (713) 699-0088
Web Site: http://www.aztecusa.com
Emp.: 200
Party Supplies Rental Services
N.A.I.C.S.: 532490

Todd M. Johnson (Pres)
Ashley Blake (Sls Mgr)

MILESTONE CENTERS, INC.
600 Ross Ave, Pittsburgh, PA 15221
Tel.: (412) 243-3400 PA
Web Site: http://www.milestonecentersinc.org
Year Founded: 1969
Sales Range: $10-24.9 Million
Emp.: 759
Community Health Care Services
N.A.I.C.S.: 621498
Roseland Bainum (Chief HR Officer)
Scott Douglass (Dir-Quality)
David Gigliotti (Dir-Mental Health Rehabilitation)
Ken Wood (COO)
Michael Laffey (VP)
Joan Eichner (Sec)
Greg Gendron (Pres)
Gary Bell (CFO)
David Fath (Dir-Svc Coordination Unit)
Stacey Dowden (Dir-Intellectual & Developmental Disabilities)
Natalie Symons (Dir-Health Care Quality Unit West)
Darryl Bergstrom (Dir-Health Care Quality-Northwest)

MILESTONE COMMUNITY BUILDERS LLC.
9111 Jollyville Rd Ste 111, Austin, TX 78759
Tel.: (512) 686-4986
Web Site: http://www.mymilestone.com
Year Founded: 2009
Sales Range: $25-49.9 Million
Emp.: 63
Residential Building Construction Services
N.A.I.C.S.: 236117
Garrett Martin (Pres & CEO)

MILESTONE CONSTRUCTION SERVICES, INC.
21495 Ridgetop Cir Ste 300, Sterling, VA 20166
Tel.: (703) 406-0960
Web Site: http://www.milestoneconstruction.com
Year Founded: 1998
Sales Range: $10-24.9 Million
Emp.: 30
Construction Management, Consulting & General Contracting Services
N.A.I.C.S.: 236220
Keith A. Whitener (Pres)
Mimi Phan (CFO)
William N. Colonna III (VP-Project Mgmt & Consulting)

MILESTONE CONTRACTORS, LP
5950 S Belmont Ave, Indianapolis, IN 46217-9757
Tel.: (317) 788-6885 IN
Web Site: http://www.milestonelp.com
Year Founded: 1955
Sales Range: $10-24.9 Million
Emp.: 200
Provider of Highway & Street Paving Contracting Services
N.A.I.C.S.: 237310
Pat Walters (Controller)

Subsidiaries:

Wabash Valley Asphalt Co., LLC (1)
400 North Tenth St, Terre Haute, IN 47807
Tel.: (812) 232-6094

Web Site: http://www.wabashvalleyasphalt.com
Rev.: $2,333,333
Emp.: 12
Asphalt Paving Mixture & Block Mfr
N.A.I.C.S.: 324121
Luann Bolk (Controller)
Darryl Huyett (Area Mgr)
John Collett (Pres)
Dan Conley (VP-Ops)
Jay Atkinson (Superintendent-Equipment)
Charles Kinzer (Mgr-Hma Field Density)
Harry Crossley (Project Mgr)
Keith McMahon (Mgr-Qc Lab)
Tom McCullough (Mgr-Hma Quality)

Walsh & Kelly, Inc. (1)
1700 E Main St, Griffith, IN 46319
Tel.: (219) 924-5900
Web Site: http://www.walshkelly.com
Sales Range: $50-74.9 Million
Emp.: 250
Mfr of Asphalt Paving Mixtures & Blocks
N.A.I.C.S.: 324121
Kevin J. Kelly (Pres)
Nick Relias (Mgr-Projects)

MILESTONE DISTRIBUTORS INC.
2615 E Belt Ln Rd, Carrollton, TX 75006
Tel.: (972) 466-4660
Web Site: http://www.milestonedist.com
Sales Range: $10-24.9 Million
Emp.: 10
Wholesale Distributor
N.A.I.C.S.: 423620
Teena Jinenez (Controller-Fin)

MILESTONE ELECTRIC & SECURITY
5150 Grisham Dr, Rowlett, TX 75088
Tel.: (214) 348-5100
Web Site: http://www.milestoneelectricdfw.com
Year Founded: 2004
Sales Range: $10-24.9 Million
Emp.: 85
Electrical Repair & Installation
N.A.I.C.S.: 238210
Joe DeCaria (Gen Mgr)

MILESTONE MARKETING ASSOCIATES, INC.
PO Box 19947, Sarasota, FL 34276-2947
Tel.: (941) 306-3602
Web Site: http://www.milestone-marketing.com
Year Founded: 2009
Sales Range: Less than $1 Million
Emp.: 2
Marketing & Advertising Services
N.A.I.C.S.: 541613
Matthew Anderson (Pres)

MILESTONE METALS INC.
12587 Fair Lakes Cir Ste 344, Fairfax, VA 22033
Tel.: (703) 222-0074
Web Site: http://www.milestonemetal.com
Year Founded: 2002
Sales Range: $25-49.9 Million
Emp.: 25
Scrap Metal Trading
N.A.I.C.S.: 332999
Ram Prasad (Pres)

MILESTONE PARTNERS LTD.
555 E Lancaster Ave Ste 500, Radnor, PA 19087
Tel.: (610) 526-2700 PA
Web Site: http://www.milestonepartners.com
Year Founded: 1995
Sales Range: $25-49.9 Million
Emp.: 22

Privater Equity Firm
N.A.I.C.S.: 523999
W. Scott Warren (Mng Partner)
John P. Shoemaker (Mng Partner)
Brooke B. Hayes (Partner)
John J. Nowaczyck (Partner)
Adam H. Curtin (Partner)
Daniel F. Ryan (Partner & Head-Bus Dev)
David G. Proctor (Partner)
Paul Slaats (Partner)
Pete Lloyd (Partner, CFO & Chief Compliance Officer)

Subsidiaries:

Black Letter Discovery, Inc. (1)
2 Embarcadero Ctr Ste 2350, San Francisco, CA 94111
Tel.: (415) 439-4883
Sales Range: $10-24.9 Million
Legal & Corporate Document Review Services
N.A.I.C.S.: 541199
Ki Yun Hwang (CEO & Gen Counsel)
Zain Ali (Mgr-Payroll)
Bob Roberts (Mng Partner)
Jason Hager (VP)
Brock Towler (Dir-Discovery Ops)
Christine Wang (Mng Dir)
Jessica Allman (Mng Dir)
June Dang (Dir-Recruiting)
Tammy Hiland (Dir-Recruiting)
Tommy Fenton (Mgr-Facilities)
Trisha Textor-Gerrity (Dir-Recruiting)

Cafe Enterprises, Inc. (1)
4324 Wade Hampton Blvd Ste B, Taylors, SC 29687
Tel.: (864) 322-1331
Web Site: http://www.fatzcafe.com
Sales Range: $10-24.9 Million
Full-Service Restaurant Owner & Operator
N.A.I.C.S.: 722511
Richie Cannon (COO)
Bruce Dressler (Operating Partner)
Don Camacho (CFO-Fatz)
Katie Batista (Dir-Mktg)
Jim Mazany (Pres & CEO)

Cde Services, Inc. (1)
1200 Williams Dr Ste 1210, Marietta, GA 30066
Tel.: (770) 499-5000
Web Site: https://www.cdesolutions.com
Rev.: $5,000,000
Emp.: 22
Computer & Computer Peripheral Equipment & Software Merchant Whslr
N.A.I.C.S.: 423430
Daniel Merchant (VP-Bus Analytics)
Joe Cohane (CEO)
Stephanie Sharp (CFO)
Dorota Castillo (VP)
Mark Buckner (CIO)

D.A. Kopp & Associates, Inc. (1)
9 Campus Dr, Parsippany, NJ 07054
Tel.: (973) 237-9415
Web Site: http://www.dydacomp.com
Sales Range: $25-49.9 Million
Mail Order & E-Commerce Management Software Publisher
N.A.I.C.S.: 513210
Robert Coon (Sr VP-Mktg & Bus Dev)
Kevin Loo (Sr VP-Product Dev)
Fred Lizza (CEO)
Julie Bilinkas (VP-Customer Svcs)
Mike Nardini (VP-Bus Partner Solutions)

Global Connection Inc. of America (1)
5555 Oakbrook Pkwy Ste 620, Norcross, GA 30093
Tel.: (678) 741-6200
Web Site: http://www.connectwithglobal.com
Prepaid Home Telecommunications Marketer
N.A.I.C.S.: 517121
Michael Khoury (Dir-Admin)
Dave Skogen (CEO)
Ed Smith (CFO)

Pancon Corporation (1)
1490 Central St, Stoughton, MA 02072-4414
Tel.: (800) 225-3296
Web Site: http://www.panconcorp.com
Holding Company
N.A.I.C.S.: 551112

COMPANIES

Mike Savage *(VP-Sls & Mktg)*

Division (Domestic):

Ark-Les Connectors (2)
350 Revolutionary Dr, East Taunton, MA 02718
Tel.: (781) 297-6000
Web Site: http://www.panconcorp.com
Sales Range: $450-499.9 Million
Mfr of Electric Switches & Interconnect Devices
N.A.I.C.S.: 335931

Paktron Capacitors (2)
1205 McConville Rd, Lynchburg, VA 24502-4535
Tel.: (434) 239-6941
Web Site: http://www.paktron.com
Sales Range: $25-49.9 Million
Emp.: 17
Film Capacitor Mfr
N.A.I.C.S.: 334419
Terry Martin *(Plant Mgr)*

Pancon Connectors (2)
440 Quadrangle Dr, Bolingbrook, IL 60440
Tel.: (630) 972-6400
Web Site: http://www.panconconnectors.com
Sales Range: $10-24.9 Million
Emp.: 5
Electronic Connector Mfr
N.A.I.C.S.: 335931
Tom Gerringer *(Mgr-Technical Sls)*

PayLink Payment Plans, LLC (1)
150 N Wacker D Ste 2700, Chicago, IL 60606
Tel.: (312) 261-4860
Web Site: http://www.paylinkdirect.com
Diversified Financial Services Firm
N.A.I.C.S.: 522320
Rebecca Howard *(CEO)*

Subsidiary (Domestic):

Omnisure Group, LLC (2)
205 W Wacker Dr 15th Fl, Chicago, IL 60606
Tel.: (855) 310-2653
Web Site: http://www.omnisuregroup.com
Finance Company & Customized Payment Plan Services
N.A.I.C.S.: 522320
Martha Choromanska *(VP-Bus & Legal Affairs)*

Southern Management Corporation (1)
101 N Main St Ste 600, Greenville, SC 29601
Tel.: (866) 413-1836
Loan Consumer Finance Services
N.A.I.C.S.: 522310
John Keilholz *(CEO)*

Strucsure Home Warranty, LLC (1)
6825 E Tennessee Ave Ste 410, Denver, CO 80224
Tel.: (303) 806-8688
Web Site: http://www.strucsure.com
Sales Range: $1-9.9 Million
Emp.: 15
Direct Insurance (except Life, Health & Medical) Carriers
N.A.I.C.S.: 524128
Christopher Macaulay *(Pres)*
Jerry Thompson *(CEO)*
Adria Ellerbrock *(VP-Mktg)*
Stacie Locke *(VP-Sls-Rocky Mountain)*
Jerrell Bass *(VP-Sls-Florida)*

MILESTONE PROPERTIES INC.
200 Congress Park Dr Ste205, Delray Beach, FL 33445-4827
Tel.: (561) 394-9260 FL
Web Site: http://www.milestoneproperties.com
Year Founded: 1990
Sales Range: $75-99.9 Million
Emp.: 18
Real Estate & Leasing Services
N.A.I.C.S.: 531120

Subsidiaries:

Milestone Property Management, Inc. (1)
1710 S 145 E, Orem, UT 84058-7891
Tel.: (801) 765-0796
Commercial Property Management Services
N.A.I.C.S.: 531312

MILFORD BANK
33 Broad St, Milford, CT 06460
Tel.: (203) 783-5700
Web Site: http://www.milfordbank.com
Sales Range: $10-24.9 Million
Emp.: 21
Savings Institutions, Except Federal
N.A.I.C.S.: 522180
John Darin *(Sr VP)*
Lynda Mason *(Asst VP & Mgr-Woodmont)*
Susan L. Shields *(Pres & CEO)*
Jorge Santiago *(Exec VP)*

MILFORD FEDERAL SAVINGS & LOAN ASSOCIATION
246 Main St, Milford, MA 01757
Tel.: (508) 634-2500
Web Site: http://www.milfordfederal.com
Sales Range: $50-74.9 Million
Emp.: 100
Federal Savings & Loan Associations
N.A.I.C.S.: 522180
Cynthia Casey *(Pres & CEO)*
Michael DiCicco *(Branch Mgr)*
Patricia A. Matos *(Branch Mgr-Milford)*
Robert Bodio *(Sr VP-Ops)*
Joseph Fournier *(CFO, Treas & VP)*

MILFORD REGIONAL MEDICAL CENTER, INC.
14 Prospect St, Milford, MA 01757
Tel.: (508) 473-1190 MA
Web Site: http://www.milfordregional.org
Year Founded: 1903
Sales Range: $250-299.9 Million
Emp.: 1,844
Community Health Care Services
N.A.I.C.S.: 621498
Andrew L. Salmon *(Vice Chm)*
Edward J. Kelly *(Co-Pres & Treas)*

MILFORD REGIONAL PHYSICIAN GROUP
9 Industrial Rd Ste 5, Milford, MA 01757
Tel.: (508) 473-1480 MA
Web Site: http://www.tricountymedical.org
Year Founded: 1992
Sales Range: $50-74.9 Million
Emp.: 420
Community Health Care Services
N.A.I.C.S.: 621498
Zofia Bibeault *(Dir-Ops)*
Martha Lingard *(Dir-Risk Mgmt)*
Susan Navien *(Dir-HR)*
Carman Yee *(Controller)*
Kevin Parker *(Dir-IT)*

MILFORD SUPPLY CO. INC.
10943 Lin Valle Dr, Saint Louis, MO 63123
Tel.: (314) 894-1991 MO
Web Site: http://www.milfordsupply.com
Sales Range: $10-24.9 Million
Emp.: 50
Whslr of Plumbing & Hydronic Heating Supplies
N.A.I.C.S.: 423720
Timothy Milford *(Treas & Sec)*
Betsy Keith *(Mgr)*
Justin Bethel *(Branch Mgr)*
Daniel Milford *(Branch Mgr)*

MILHOUSE ENGINEERING & CONSTRUCTION, INC.
60 E Van Buren St Ste 1501, Chicago, IL 60605
Tel.: (312) 987-0061 IL
Web Site: http://www.milhouseinc.com
Year Founded: 2001
Sales Range: $10-24.9 Million
Emp.: 120
Engineering & Construction Services
N.A.I.C.S.: 541330
Dolla Crater *(Pres-Bus Ops)*
Joseph T. Zurad *(Pres-Engrg Construction & Mep)*
Jean Gibbons *(Mgr-Mechanical)*
David Sawicki *(Dir-Environmental Engrg)*
Tom Mayer *(Mgr-Construction)*
Brian Registe *(CFO)*
Fred Owens *(Sr VP)*
Robert Smith *(Sr VP)*
Robert Bohnak *(Mgr-Water Section-Civil & Transportation Team)*
Chrissy Carr *(Chief Engrg Officer-Industries)*
Anna Vargas *(VP-Power Engrg-Midwest)*
Wilbur C. Milhouse III *(Founder, Chm & CEO)*

Subsidiaries:

Zroka Engineering, P.C. (1)
4216 N Hermitage Ave, Chicago, IL 60613
Tel.: (773) 935-6376
Web Site: http://www.zrokaengineering.com
Sales Range: Less than $1 Million
Architectural Engineering Services
N.A.I.C.S.: 541310
Scott Whitney *(Engr)*
Deborah Zroka *(Founder & Engr)*

MILITARY CONSTRUCTION CORPORATION
6142 Lake Gray Blvd, Jacksonville, FL 32244
Tel.: (904) 317-5601
Web Site: http://www.mil-con.com
Year Founded: 1984
Sales Range: $25-49.9 Million
Emp.: 168
Nonresidential Construction
N.A.I.C.S.: 236220
Kerry Bentley *(Chm)*
Walt Hetz *(Sec)*
Mark Thompson *(Pres & CEO)*
Jerry Robinson *(VP)*
Richard Methe *(Exec VP & Controller)*

MILITARY PARK PARTNERSHIP
51 Park Pl Ste 1431, Newark, NJ 07102
Tel.: (973) 596-6400 NJ
Web Site: http://www.militarypark.com
Year Founded: 2011
Sales Range: $1-9.9 Million
Park Maintenance Services
N.A.I.C.S.: 712190
Ommeed Sathe *(Chm)*
Dan Biederman *(Pres)*
Ben Donsky *(VP)*

MILITARY PRODUCTS GROUP, INC.
100 Industrial Dr, New London, OH 44851
Tel.: (419) 929-7000
Year Founded: 2001
Sales Range: $1-9.9 Million
Emp.: 15
Mfr & Sales of Military & Aerospace Tie-Down, Lifting & Towing Hardware & Assemblies
N.A.I.C.S.: 333248

Amarbayasgalan Amar *(Staff Officer)*
Bud Leinenger *(Pres & CEO)*

MILITARY WARRIORS SUPPORT FOUNDATION
2511 N Loop 1604 W Ste 201, San Antonio, TX 78258
Tel.: (210) 615-8973 TX
Web Site: http://www.militarywarriors.org
Year Founded: 2007
Sales Range: $25-49.9 Million
Emp.: 17
Veteran Support Services
N.A.I.C.S.: 813410
Burton Ken Eakes *(Exec Dir)*
Ken Eakes *(Exec Dir)*

MILK + HONEY DAY SPA
100A Guadalupe St, Austin, TX 78701
Tel.: (512) 236-1115
Web Site: http://www.milkandhoneyspa.com
Year Founded: 2006
Sales Range: $1-9.9 Million
Emp.: 150
Day Spa
N.A.I.C.S.: 812112
Alissa Bayer *(Founder)*

MILK INDUSTRY MANAGEMENT CORP.
4 Mahattan Dr, Burlington, NJ 08016
Tel.: (609) 699-2630
Web Site: http://www.balford.com
Sales Range: $10-24.9 Million
Emp.: 100
Distr of Dairy Products
N.A.I.C.S.: 111998
Daniel T. Smith *(VP-Ops)*
Larry Bowes *(Pres)*
Donald Hartnett *(Dir-Sls & Mktg)*

Subsidiaries:

Balford Farms (1)
4 Manhattan Dr, Burlington, NJ 08016
Tel.: (609) 699-2630
Web Site: http://www.balford.com
Emp.: 250
Distr of Dairy Products
N.A.I.C.S.: 424430
Robert E. Venafra *(CFO & Treas)*
Pamela Bilger *(VP-HR)*
Laurence E. Bowes *(CEO)*
Daniel T. Smith *(VP-Fleet Maintenance & Facilities)*
Larry Walker *(Pres)*

MILKY WAY INTERNATIONAL TRADING
15203 Shoemaker Ave, Norwalk, CA 90650
Tel.: (562) 921-2800
Web Site: http://www.mwpolar.com
Sales Range: $10-24.9 Million
Emp.: 20
Seafoods & Canned Foods
N.A.I.C.S.: 424460
Fred Chiu *(VP)*

MILL CITY CAPITAL, L.P.
50 S 6th St Ste 1390, Minneapolis, MN 55402
Tel.: (612) 238-9500 DE
Web Site: http://www.millcitycapital.com
Year Founded: 2010
Emp.: 9
Privater Equity Firm
N.A.I.C.S.: 523999
Gary J. Obermiller *(Co-Founder & Operating Partner)*
Lisa A. Kro *(Executives)*
Gary J. Obermiller *(Co-Founder & Operating Partner)*
Alexander Rutlin *(Mng Dir)*

MILL CITY CAPITAL, L.P.

Mill City Capital, L.P.—(Continued)

Angela Wood (VP-Fin)
Dianna Seltz (VP)
Lisa Molitor (Office Mgr)
Michael S. Israel (Co-Founder)
Darren L. Acheson (Co-Founder & Mng Dir)

Subsidiaries:

Behrens Manufacturing, LLC (1)
1250 E Sanborn Rd, Winona, MN 55987
Tel.: (507) 454-4664
Web Site: http://www.behrensmfg.com
Steel Container Mfr & Distr
N.A.I.C.S.: 332439
Stephen L. Tuscic (Pres & CEO)

Renaissance Power Systems, LLC (1)
222 E Erie St Ste 320, Milwaukee, WI 53202
Tel.: (414) 732-2400
Web Site: http://www.renaissancepowersystem.com
Holding Company; Industrial Gear & Rotating Component Mfr
N.A.I.C.S.: 551112
Mark Readinger (Pres & CEO)

Subsidiary (Non-US):

Havlik International Machinery Inc. (2)
455 Sheldon Dr, Cambridge, N1T 2B7, ON, Canada
Tel.: (519) 624-6240
Web Site: http://www.havlikinternational.com
Emp.: 30
Machine Tools, Presses & Parts Distr; Gear Mfr & Distr
N.A.I.C.S.: 423830
John Havlik Sr. (Founder & CEO)

Division (Domestic):

Havlik Gear (3)
455 Sheldon Dr, Cambridge, N1T 2B7, ON, Canada
Tel.: (519) 624-6240
Web Site: http://www.havlikgear.com
Industrial Gear Mfr & Distr
N.A.I.C.S.: 333612
Rob Borrelli (Mgr-Ops)
John Havlik (Pres)

MILL POND HOLDINGS LLC
250 Center Ct Unit A, Venice, FL 34285-5548
Tel.: (941) 497-6020
Web Site: http://www.millpond.com
Sales Range: $10-24.9 Million
Emp.: 30
Holding Company
N.A.I.C.S.: 513199
Linda Schaner (Pres)

Subsidiaries:

The Mill Pond Press Companies, Inc. (1)
250 Ctr Ct Unit A, Venice, FL 34285
Tel.: (941) 497-6020
Web Site: http://www.millpond.com
Sales Range: $10-24.9 Million
Emp.: 5
Publishers of Fine Art
N.A.I.C.S.: 323119
Linda Schaner (Pres)
Linda Sthaner (Dir-Mktg)

MILL ROAD CAPITAL MANAGEMENT LLC
382 Greenwich Ave Ste 1, Greenwich, CT 06830
Tel.: (203) 987-3500 DE
Web Site: http://www.millroadcapital.com
Year Founded: 2004
Privater Equity Firm
N.A.I.C.S.: 523999
Justin C. Jacobs (Mng Dir)
Eric Yanagi (Mng Dir)
Thomas E. Lynch (Sr Mng Dir)

Scott P. Scharfman (Mng Dir)
Ann Marie Hendry (Dir-Fin & Admin)
Sarah Heberle (Principal)
James Zivin (Principal)
Lisa McGovern (Mng Dir, CFO & Chief Compliance Officer)
Sean Quinn (Principal)

Subsidiaries:

EDC Communications Limited (1)
172 Drury Lane, London, WC2B 5QR, United Kingdom
Tel.: (44) 20 3150 2100
Holding Company; Advertising Services
N.A.I.C.S.: 551112
Gregor Angus (Pres)

PRT Growing Services Ltd. (1)
101-1006 Fort Street, Victoria, V8V 3K4, BC, Canada
Tel.: (250) 381-1404
Web Site: http://www.prtgroup.com
Sales Range: $25-49.9 Million
Emp.: 375
Container-Grown Forest Seedling Producer
N.A.I.C.S.: 111998
Collin Phillip (Chief Comml Officer)
Keith Grauman (VP & Grp Dir-PR)
Randy Fournier (CEO)
Marlene Higgins (Chief People Officer)

R.G. Barry Corporation (1)
13405 Yarmouth Rd NW, Pickerington, OH 43147
Tel.: (614) 864-6400
Web Site: http://www.rgbarry.com
Sales Range: $125-149.9 Million
Emp.: 154
Accessory Footwear & Comfort Products Designer & Marketer
N.A.I.C.S.: 316210
Lee F. Smith (Pres-Footwear)
Tom Stoughton (Dir-IT)
Jeffrey R. Cosgrove (Pres-Foot Petals)
Dru Williams (Dir-HR)
Bob Mullaney (Pres & CEO)
Joseph Bean (Sr VP-Ecommerce Wholesale)

Subsidiary (Domestic):

baggallini Inc. (2)
13405 Yarmouth Rd NW, Pickerington, OH 43147
Web Site: http://www.baggallini.com
Sales Range: $10-24.9 Million
Emp.: 18
Luggage Mfr
N.A.I.C.S.: 316990
Scott Erdman (Pres)

Rubio's Restaurants, Inc. (1)
2200 Faraday Avenue Ste 250, Carlsbad, CA 92008
Tel.: (760) 929-8226
Web Site: http://www.rubios.com
Sales Range: $150-199.9 Million
Restaurant Operators
N.A.I.C.S.: 722511
Ralph Rubio (Co-Founder)
Frank E. Henigman (CFO & Sr VP)

Skullcandy, Inc. (1)
6301 N Landmark Dr, Park City, UT 84098
Tel.: (435) 940-1545
Web Site: http://www.skullcandy.com
Holding Company; Headphones & Other Audio Accessories Mfr & Distr
N.A.I.C.S.: 551112
Jason Hodell (CEO)
Holly N. Alden (Founder)

Subsidiary (Non-US):

Skullcandy Audio (Shenzhen) Co., Ltd. (2)
RM503 A3 Building East Industrial Area OCT, Nanshan District, Shenzhen, 518053, China
Tel.: (86) 2034812000
Web Site: http://www.skullcandy.eu
Headphone & Audio Accessories Mfr
N.A.I.C.S.: 334310

Skullcandy International GmbH (2)
Heinrichstrasse 235, 8005, Zurich, Switzerland
Tel.: (41) 442747000

Web Site: http://www.skullcandy.eu
Headphones & Other Audio Accessories Mfr & Distr
N.A.I.C.S.: 334310

Skullcandy Nordic AB (2)
Sergels Torg, SE 111 57, Stockholm, Sweden
Tel.: (46) 707290800
Headphones & Other Audio Accessories Mfr & Distr
N.A.I.C.S.: 334310

MILL STREET PARTNERS LLC
1213 Path St, Santa Barbara, CA 93101
Tel.: (805) 346-3700 DE
Web Site: http://www.millstreetpartners.com
Year Founded: 2011
Privater Equity Firm
N.A.I.C.S.: 523999
Steven J. Semmelmayer (Co-Founder & Mng Partner)
Robert Cartagena (Co-Founder & Mng Partner)
Todd J. Tiberi (Co-Founder & Mng Partner)

Subsidiaries:

Den-Mat Holdings, LLC (1)
1017 W Central Ave, Lompoc, CA 93436-2701
Tel.: (805) 346-3700
Web Site: http://www.denmat.com
Emp.: 300
Dental Product Mfr
N.A.I.C.S.: 339114
Robert Cartagena (COO)
Rich Hallworth (Chm)
David Casper (CEO)
Felix Silva (Dir-Laboratory Ops)

Subsidiary (Domestic):

PeriOptix, Inc. (2)
1017 W Central Ave, Lompoc, CA 93436
Tel.: (805) 922-8491
Web Site: http://www.perioptix.com
Sales Range: $10-24.9 Million
Medical & Dental Magnification & Illumination Equipment Developer & Mfr
N.A.I.C.S.: 339113
Keith Tholin (Co-Founder & Pres)

MILL SUPPLIES INC.
5105 Industrial Rd, Fort Wayne, IN 46825
Tel.: (260) 484-8566
Web Site: http://www.millsupplies.com
Sales Range: $10-24.9 Million
Emp.: 45
Industrial Supplies
N.A.I.C.S.: 423840
Jeff Botorf (Dir-Mktg)
Karen Beckstein (CEO)
Andy Beckstein (Pres & Mgr-Outside Sls)

MILL-RITE WOODWORKING COMPANY, INC.
6401 47th St N, Pinellas Park, FL 33781
Tel.: (727) 527-7808 FL
Web Site: http://www.mill-rite.com
Year Founded: 1966
Sales Range: $1-9.9 Million
Emp.: 60
Architectural Millwork Mfr
N.A.I.C.S.: 337212
Jennifer Clark (Owner)
Robert D. Clark (VP)
Dale Johannes (Project Mgr)

MILL-ROSE COMPANY
7995 Tyler Blvd, Mentor, OH 44060-4896
Tel.: (440) 255-9171 OH
Web Site: http://www.millrose.com
Year Founded: 1920

Sales Range: $10-24.9 Million
Emp.: 170
Mfr of Industrial Brushes
N.A.I.C.S.: 339994
Vince Pona (CFO)

Subsidiaries:

Mill-Rose Clean-Fit (1)
7310 Corporate Blvd, Mentor, OH 44060
Tel.: (800) 321-3598
Web Site: http://www.cleanfit.com
Industrial Supplies Whslr
N.A.I.C.S.: 423840

MILL-RUN TOURS INC.
424 Madison Ave Fl 12, New York, NY 10017-1106
Tel.: (212) 486-9840 NY
Web Site: http://www.millrun.com
Year Founded: 1975
Sales Range: $10-24.9 Million
Emp.: 150
Travel Agencies
N.A.I.C.S.: 561510
Issam Sawaya (Pres)
Ibrahim Akaki (CFO)
John Huynh (Mgr-IT)
Philip Badu (Mgr-Sls)
Rajni Shivdasani (Mgr-Admin)

MILLARD BOWEN COMMUNITIES, LLC
5072 Bristol Indus Way, Buford, GA 30518
Tel.: (770) 271-4414 GA
Web Site: http://www.bowenhomes.com
Sales Range: $25-49.9 Million
Emp.: 10
New Construction, Single-Family Houses
N.A.I.C.S.: 236115
Melissa Kibbe (Coord-Closing)

MILLARD LUMBER INC.
12900 I St, Omaha, NE 68137
Tel.: (402) 896-2800 NE
Web Site: http://www.millardlumber.com
Year Founded: 1948
Sales Range: $125-149.9 Million
Emp.: 300
Lumber, Plywood, Millwork & Building Material Mfr & Distr
N.A.I.C.S.: 321920
Richard G. Russell (Founder & Pres)
Cheri Purdue (Mgr-Comm & Mktg)

MILLBROOK CAPITAL MANAGEMENT, INC.
570 Lexington Ave 46th Fl, New York, NY 10022
Tel.: (212) 586-4333 NY
Web Site: http://www.millcap.com
Year Founded: 1981
Privater Equity Firm
N.A.I.C.S.: 523999
Alan L. Rivera (Pres)
John S. Dyson (Founder & Chm)
Drew H. Sitten (Controller)
John W. Powers (Sr VP)

MILLBURN RIDGEFIELD CORPORATION
411 W Putnam Ave, Greenwich, CT 06830
Tel.: (203) 625-8211
Web Site: http://www.millburncorp.com
Sales Range: $75-99.9 Million
Emp.: 50
Investment Management, Banking & Portfolio Services

N.A.I.C.S.: 523150
Gregg Richard Buckbinder *(Pres, CFO & COO)*
Harvey Beker *(Co-Chm)*
George E. Crapple *(Co-Chm)*
Grant Norman Smith *(CIO)*
Barry Alan Goodman *(CEO & Exec Dir-Trading)*
Mark B. Fitzsimmons *(Sr VP)*
Dennis B. Newton *(Sr VP)*
Michael W. Carter *(Chief Acctg Officer)*
Irina Bogacheva *(Dir-Res)*
Michael Soss *(Deputy Chief Investment Officer)*
Craig Gilbert *(Head-Bus Dev-Global)*
Subsidiaries:

MILLBURN MULTI-MARKETS FUND L.P. (1)
55 W 46th St 31st Fl, New York, NY 10036
Tel.: (212) 332-7300
Rev.: $5,821,882
Assets: $124,119,357
Liabilities: $189,580
Net Worth: $123,929,777
Earnings: ($11,150,276)
Fiscal Year-end: 12/31/2023
Portfolio Management Services
N.A.I.C.S.: 523940
Harvey Beker *(Chm)*

MILLBURY NATIONAL BANK
18 Main St, Millbury, MA 01527
Tel.: (508) 865-9521
Web Site: http://www.mnbonline.com
Sales Range: $25-49.9 Million
Emp.: 24
Banking Services
N.A.I.C.S.: 522110
Kathleen C. Marcum *(Pres)*
Garr Donna *(COO & VP)*
John Latino *(VP)*
Suzanne C. Nydam *(CFO & VP)*

MILLCRAFT INDUSTRIES INC.
95 W Beau St Ste 600, Washington, PA 15301
Tel.: (724) 743-3400   PA
Web Site: http://www.millcraftinv.com
Year Founded: 1971
Sales Range: $10-24.9 Million
Emp.: 25
Real Estate Development
N.A.I.C.S.: 531390
Jack B. Piatt *(Founder & Chm)*
Brian R. Walker *(CFO)*
Subsidiaries:

Millcraft Investments Inc. (1)
95 W Beau St Ste 600 Wasihngton P, Washington, PA 15301
Tel.: (724) 743-3400
Web Site: http://www.millcraftinv.com
Rev.: $568,142
Emp.: 3
Subdividers & Developers
N.A.I.C.S.: 531190
Lucas B. Piatt *(COO)*
Mary Jo Vicario *(Sr Mgr-Property)*
Louie Calabria *(Dir-Hotel Construction)*
Joe Celender *(Asst Controller-Millcraft Hospitality)*

MILLE LACS BANCORPORATION, INC.
424 Main St, Onamia, MN 56359
Tel.: (320) 532-4142   DE
Web Site:
 https://www.woodlandsnational bank.com
Year Founded: 1995
Bank Holding Company
N.A.I.C.S.: 551111
Joel Braun *(Pres & CEO)*
Subsidiaries:

Woodlands National Bank (1)
122 E Main St, Hinckley, MN 55037
Tel.: (320) 532-4142
Web Site:
 https://www.woodlandsnationalbank.com
Commericial Banking
N.A.I.C.S.: 522110
Joel Braun *(Pres & CEO)*
Kara Ketola *(Sr VP-Comml Banking)*
Karen Butterfield *(VP & Mgr-HR)*
Amanda Tretter Meyer *(VP-Mortgage Dept)*
Michelle Starr *(VP & Ops Mgr)*

MILLEN INDUSTRIES INCORPORATED
108 Main St, Norwalk, CT 06851
Tel.: (203) 847-8500
Web Site: http://www.mafcote.com
Rev.: $13,500,000
Emp.: 5
Setup Paperboard Boxes
N.A.I.C.S.: 322219

MILLENIUM BROKERAGE GROUP, LLC
100 Winners Cir Ste 410, Brentwood, TN 37027
Tel.: (615) 259-9355
Web Site: http://www.mbgnow.com
Year Founded: 1998
Emp.: 112
Planning, Insurance & Financial Services Solutions
N.A.I.C.S.: 523999
William L. Zelenik *(CEO)*
Kerri Zelenik Burton *(Mgr-Media Rels)*

MILLENIUM MILLWORK CORP.
250 Ballardvale St, Wilmington, MA 01887
Tel.: (978) 658-8911
Rev.: $17,100,000
Emp.: 53
Millwork
N.A.I.C.S.: 423310

MILLENNIA GROUP INC.
1105 Pittsburgh St, Cheswick, PA 15024
Tel.: (724) 274-2222
Web Site: http://www.1tmg.com
Year Founded: 2000
Sales Range: $10-24.9 Million
Emp.: 110
Provider of Electronic Assembly Services; Electronic Circuits
N.A.I.C.S.: 334419
Michael D'Ambrosio *(Chm, Pres & CEO)*
Subsidiaries:

The Millennia Design (1)
1105 Pittsburgh St, Cheswick, PA 15024
Tel.: (724) 274-2222
Provider of Electronic Assembly Services; Electronic Circuits
N.A.I.C.S.: 334419

MILLENNIUM 3 MANAGEMENT INC.
2001 Market St Ste 2920, Philadelphia, PA 19103
Tel.: (215) 922-7184
Web Site:
 http://www.millennium3management.com
Year Founded: 1989
Sales Range: $10-24.9 Million
Emp.: 8
African-American Market
N.A.I.C.S.: 541810
A. Bruce Crawley *(Pres)*
Anthony Marc Fullard *(Exec VP)*

MILLENNIUM AUTOMOTIVE LOGISTICS INC.
1820 Spencer Mtn Rd Ranlo, Gastonia, NC 28054
Tel.: (704) 824-9079
Web Site:
 http://www.napaautopartscarolina.com
Sales Range: $10-24.9 Million
Emp.: 75
Automotive Parts
N.A.I.C.S.: 441330
Ralph A. Dickson Jr. *(Pres)*
Ralph Dickson III *(VP)*

MILLENNIUM BUSINESS SYSTEMS, LLC
38281 Schoolcraft Rd, Livonia, MI 48150
Tel.: (734) 591-3100
Year Founded: 1997
Sales Range: $1-9.9 Million
Emp.: 14
Office Equipment Merchant Whslr
N.A.I.C.S.: 423420
Michael Neu *(Pres)*

MILLENNIUM COMMUNICATIONS GROUP LLC
1 Gatehall Dr Ste 210, Parsippany, NJ 07054
Tel.: (201) 327-1260
Web Site:
 http://www.milcomgroup.com
Year Founded: 1995
Sales Range: $1-9.9 Million
Emp.: 15
Marketing, Training & Communications Programs for the Medical & Pharmaceutical Industries
N.A.I.C.S.: 611430
Michael Fernandez *(Founder & Pres)*
Eric Olinger *(Sr Acct Mgr)*

MILLENNIUM COMMUNICATIONS, INC.
6900 Jericho Tpke Ste 100LL, Syosset, NY 11791
Tel.: (516) 682-8080   NY
Web Site:
 http://www.millenniumweb.com
Rev.: $2,700,000
Emp.: 25
Fiscal Year-end: 12/31/06
Advetising Agency
N.A.I.C.S.: 541810
Patrick Macri *(Pres & CEO)*
Theresa Macri *(CFO)*
David Denara *(CIO & CTO)*
Jeffrey Maldavir *(Client Svcs Dir)*
John Murphy *(Dir-Creative)*

MILLENNIUM ENGINEERING & INTEGRATION COMPANY
1400 Crystal Dr Ste 800, Arlington, VA 22202
Tel.: (703) 413-7750   MD
Web Site:
 http://www.meicompany.com
Year Founded: 1995
Sales Range: $50-74.9 Million
Emp.: 259
Engineering & Software Development Services
N.A.I.C.S.: 541330
Kerry Wisnosky *(Founder)*
Brian McKee *(Chm)*
Susan Hall *(Founder)*
Patrick Murphy *(Pres & CEO)*
Dan Deans *(COO & Exec VP)*
Kenneth A. Baird *(VP-Corp Ops)*
Larry Foor *(Pres-Bus Unit & Gen Mgr-Aerospace Sys)*
Carlton M. Bourne *(VP-Strategies & Analysis)*
Dianne Thomas *(VP-Contracts)*
Michele Hargis *(VP)*
Al Wassel *(VP-Integrated Sys)*
Porf Dubon *(VP-Strategies & Analysis)*
Kylie Allen *(CFO & Exec VP)*
Kathryn Gaulke *(VP)*
Subsidiaries:

Millennium Engineering & Integration Company (1)
1333 Enterprise Way NW, Huntsville, AL 35806
Tel.: (256) 489-7817
Web Site: http://www.meicompany.com
Sales Range: $10-24.9 Million
Emp.: 30
Engineeering Services
N.A.I.C.S.: 541330

QuantiTech LLC (1)
360A Quality Cir Ste 100, Huntsville, AL 35806
Tel.: (256) 650-6263
Web Site: http://www.quantitech.com
Rev.: $2,550,000
Emp.: 15
Systems Engineering, Information Technology & Business Management Services
N.A.I.C.S.: 541611
Sheila Brown *(Founder)*
Randy Allen *(Dir-Bus & Analytical Div)*
Tucker Brown *(Exec VP-Force Protection)*
Darryl Wortman *(Pres & CEO)*
Tina Leighty *(VP-Quality & Change Mgmt)*
Byran West *(VP-Logistics & Engrg)*
Subsidiary (Domestic):

Dynamic Concepts, Inc. (2)
6700 Odyssey Dr Ste 202, Huntsville, AL 35806
Tel.: (256) 922-9888
Web Site: http://www.dynamic-concepts.com
Sales Range: $1-9.9 Million
Emp.: 32
Custom Computer Programming Services
N.A.I.C.S.: 541511
Thomas Howsman *(CEO)*
Patrick Tobbe *(VP)*
Joseph Clayton *(Pres)*

MILLENNIUM INDUSTRIAL TIRES LLC.
433 Ln Dr, Florence, AL 35630
Tel.: (256) 764-2900
Web Site:
 http://www.millenniumtire.com
Rev.: $13,200,000
Emp.: 140
Tiles Mfr
N.A.I.C.S.: 326211
Le R. Bess *(Gen Mgr)*

MILLENNIUM INTEGRATED MARKETING
150 Dow St 3rd Fl, Manchester, NH 03101
Tel.: (603) 792-2200
Web Site: http://www.mill-im.com
Sales Range: Less than $1 Million
Emp.: 10
Public Relations
N.A.I.C.S.: 541810
Jessica Chabot *(Dir-Client Svcs)*
Linda Fanaras *(Pres)*
Samantha J. Mahoney *(Acct Mgr)*

MILLENNIUM MANAGEMENT INC.
1995 Broadway, New York, NY 10023
Tel.: (212) 875-4900   NY
Web Site:
 http://www.millenniumptrs.com
Year Founded: 1991
Mixed-use Property Developer
N.A.I.C.S.: 237210
Philip E. Aarons *(Co-Founder & Partner)*
Christopher M. Jeffries *(Co-Founder & Partner)*
Subsidiaries:

Lincoln Triangle Partners L.P. (1)
1995 Broadway 3rd Fl, New York, NY 10023
Tel.: (212) 875-4900
Web Site: http://www.millenniumptrs.com

MILLENNIUM MANAGEMENT INC.   U.S. PRIVATE

Millennium Management Inc.—(Continued)
Sales Range: $10-24.9 Million
Emp.: 20
Mixed-use Property Developer
N.A.I.C.S.: 237210
Philip H. Lovett *(Co-Founder, Partner & Principal)*
Steven L. Hoffman *(Partner)*
Pamela Malkani *(Partner & Head-Hotel Ops)*

MILLENNIUM MANAGEMENT LLC
666 Fifth Ave 8th Fl, New York, NY 10103
Tel.: (212) 841-4100
Web Site: http://www.mlp.com
Year Founded: 1989
Rev.: $35,070,000,000
Emp.: 2,200
Investment Management Service
N.A.I.C.S.: 523940
Simon M. Lorne *(Vice Chm & Chief Legal Officer)*
Vladimir Torgovnik *(CIO)*
Stacey Gurney *(Head-Recruiting)*
Ajay Nagpal *(COO)*
Israel Englander *(Chm & CEO)*
Mark Meskin *(Chief trading Officer)*
John Anderson *(Head-Global Commodities)*
David Nolan *(Vice Chm)*
John Novogratz *(Head-Global Capital Dev & IR)*
Mark Tsesarsky *(Head-Fixed Income & Commodities)*

MILLENNIUM MARKETING CONSULTANTS, INC.
103 Clinton Rd, Fairfield, NJ 07004
Tel.: (973) 244-0505   NJ
Web Site: http://www.mmdirect.com
Year Founded: 1903
Sales Range: $10-24.9 Million
Emp.: 13
Rubber Stamps Mfr
N.A.I.C.S.: 423990
Neil Rubin *(Pres)*
Ashley Donohue *(Acct Exec)*

MILLENNIUM MARKETING GROUP, LLC
11313 Chicago Cir, Omaha, NE 68154-2633
Tel.: (402) 390-0433
Web Site: http://www.mmginsurance.com
Sales Range: Less than $1 Million
Emp.: 5
Annuity, Life & Long-Term Care Services
N.A.I.C.S.: 524298
Steve Pennella *(Pres)*
Lindsey Pennella *(VP)*

MILLENNIUM MEDICAL MEDICAL PRODUCTS INC.
1346 S Shore Dr, Saint Cloud, FL 34771
Tel.: (407) 791-6161
Web Site: http://www.medcompnet.com
Year Founded: 2001
Sales Range: $1-9.9 Million
Emp.: 14
Medical Devices for Hospitals & Surgical Centers
N.A.I.C.S.: 423450
Darryn Dierickx *(Pres)*

MILLENNIUM PHYSICIAN GROUP LLC
6321 Daniels Pkwy Ste 200, Fort Myers, FL 33912
Web Site: http://www.millenniumphysical.org

Emp.: 700
Physicians Offices & Medical Clinics
N.A.I.C.S.: 621111
Guert Peet *(CEO)*

MILLENNIUM STEEL SERVICE LLC.
300 E 350 S, Princeton, IN 47670
Tel.: (812) 385-1122
Web Site: http://www.millenniumsteelservice.com
Rev.: $164,000,000
Emp.: 62
Commercial & Institutional Building Construction
N.A.I.C.S.: 236220
Henry Jackson *(Pres & CEO)*

MILLENNIUM TOURS
3312 Pearce Rd, Austin, TX 78730
Tel.: (800) 929-9330
Web Site: http://www.mltours.com
Year Founded: 1973
Sales Range: $1-9.9 Million
Emp.: 7
Group Travel Planning Consultants
N.A.I.C.S.: 561510
Mohib Mamujee *(Pres)*
Hasnain Mamujee *(VP)*

MILLENNIUM TOYOTA
257 N Franklin St, Hempstead, NY 11550
Tel.: (516) 485-1400
Web Site: http://www.millenniumtoyota.com
Sales Range: $25-49.9 Million
Emp.: 175
New & Used Car Dealers
N.A.I.C.S.: 441110
John Staluppi *(Pres)*

MILLENNIUM, CORP.
1401 S Clark St Ste 810, Arlington, VA 22202
Tel.: (703) 436-1343
Web Site: http://www.millgroupinc.com
Year Founded: 2004
Sales Range: $1-9.9 Million
Emp.: 160
Administrative Management & General Management Consulting Service
N.A.I.C.S.: 541611
Kevin N. Jennings *(Pres & CEO)*
Roy Maday *(Project Mgr)*
Steve Ware *(Exec VP)*
Traviss Green *(COO)*
Christina Mansfield *(Chief Admin Officer)*
Carmen Santos-Logan *(VP-Bus Dev)*

MILLER & ANDERSON INC.
4150 Martinsburg Pike, Clear Brook, VA 22624
Tel.: (540) 667-4757
Web Site: http://www.millerandanderson.com
Rev.: $12,700,000
Emp.: 117
Plumbing, Heating & Air-Conditioning Services
N.A.I.C.S.: 238220

Subsidiaries:
Miller & Anderson   (1)
920 Eldridge Dr E, Hagerstown, MD 21740
Tel.: (301) 733-6695
Web Site: http://www.millerandanderson.com
Sales Range: $25-49.9 Million
Emp.: 12
Plumbing, Heating, Air-Conditioning Services
N.A.I.C.S.: 238220

MILLER & COMPANY, INC.
500 Hooper Dr, Selma, AL 36701-6444
Tel.: (334) 874-8271   AL
Web Site: http://www.millerlbr.com
Year Founded: 1929
Sales Range: $150-199.9 Million
Emp.: 400
Provider of Hardwood Lumber, Logs & Oak Flooring
N.A.I.C.S.: 321113
Bobby Buchanan *(Gen Mgr)*

MILLER & HOLMES INC.
2311 Oneil Rd, Hudson, WI 54016
Tel.: (715) 377-1730
Web Site: http://www.mhgas.com
Sales Range: $10-24.9 Million
Emp.: 15
Convenience Stores, Independent
N.A.I.C.S.: 445131
Gerald T. Peterson *(Chm)*

MILLER & LONG COMPANY, INC.
7101 Wisconsin Ave Ste 800, Bethesda, MD 20814
Tel.: (301) 657-8000   MD
Web Site: http://www.millerandlong.com
Year Founded: 1947
Sales Range: $450-499.9 Million
Emp.: 2,000
Concrete Construction Services
N.A.I.C.S.: 238110
John M. McMahon *(Chm)*
Tom Fitzgerald *(Sec & Controller)*
Otto Girr *(VP-HR)*

MILLER & RAVED INC.
2 Hamilton Ave Ste 207, New Rochelle, NY 10801-3523
Tel.: (914) 632-3555
Year Founded: 1963
Sales Range: $10-24.9 Million
Emp.: 6
Single-Family Housing Construction/Renovations
N.A.I.C.S.: 236115
Roy Raved *(Pres)*

MILLER & SMITH HOLDING COMPANY INC.
8401 Greensboro Dr Ste 300, McLean, VA 22102-3016
Tel.: (703) 821-2500   VA
Web Site: http://www.millerandsmith.com
Year Founded: 1964
Sales Range: $10-24.9 Million
Emp.: 100
Operative Builder Services
N.A.I.C.S.: 236115
Gordon V. Smith *(Chm)*

Subsidiaries:
Miller & Smith Co.   (1)
8401 Greensboro Dr Ste 450, McLean, VA 22102-3016   (100%)
Tel.: (703) 821-2500
Web Site: http://www.millerandsmith.com
Sales Range: Less than $1 Million
Emp.: 97
Investor
N.A.I.C.S.: 236115
Gordon V. Smith *(Chm)*
Joe Parker *(Controller)*

Miller and Smith Homes, Inc.   (1)
8401 Greensboro Dr Ste 450, McLean, VA 22102-3054
Tel.: (703) 468-8659
Web Site: http://www.millerandsmith.com
Sales Range: $10-24.9 Million
Emp.: 75
Home Builder & Developer Services
N.A.I.C.S.: 236220

Gordon V. Smith *(Founder & Chm)*
Alvin D. Hall *(CFO)*
Richard J. North *(Partner)*

MILLER & SON PAVING CO. INC.
6100 No Eastern Rd, Warminster, PA 18974
Tel.: (215) 766-2653   PA
Web Site: http://www.millersonpaving.com
Year Founded: 1940
Sales Range: $10-24.9 Million
Emp.: 100
Provider of Parking Lot Construction
N.A.I.C.S.: 238990
Robert Miller *(Pres)*
George Miller III *(VP)*

MILLER - EDWARDS BUICK GMC
1600 N Main St, Muskogee, OK 74401
Tel.: (918) 687-4441
Web Site: http://www.miller-edwardsgmc.com
Sales Range: $10-24.9 Million
Emp.: 52
Sales of New & Used Cars
N.A.I.C.S.: 441110
Susan Myers *(Office Mgr)*

MILLER ADVERTISING AGENCY INC.
71 5th Ave 5th Fl, New York, NY 10003-3004
Tel.: (212) 929-2200
Web Site: http://www.milleradvertising.com
Year Founded: 1919
Sales Range: $10-24.9 Million
Emp.: 125
Leonard J. Miller *(Chm)*
Robert Miller *(Pres)*
Andrew Miller *(VP)*
San Miller *(VP & Classified Supvr)*
James T. Curry *(Controller)*
Nicole Miller *(Principal)*

Subsidiaries:
G&B/Miller Advertising   (1)
71 5th Ave, New York, NY 10003-3004
Tel.: (212) 366-0901
Emp.: 20
N.A.I.C.S.: 541810
Rich Guggenheim *(Pres)*
Gene Bell *(CEO)*

Miller Adv.   (1)
195 Froehlich Farm Blvd, Woodbury, NY 11797-2928
Tel.: (516) 364-9696
Web Site: http://www.milleradvertising.com
Sales Range: $10-24.9 Million
Emp.: 25
N.A.I.C.S.: 541810
Carol Young *(Mgr)*

Miller Advertising Agency Inc.   (1)
8190-A Beechmont Ave Ste 137, Cincinnati, OH 45255-6117
Tel.: (513) 528-3331
Web Site: http://www.milleradvertising.com
Sales Range: $10-24.9 Million
Emp.: 1
N.A.I.C.S.: 541810
Bill Rilling *(VP)*

Miller Advertising Agency Inc.-Chicago   (1)
1 Northfield Plz Ste 300, Northfield, IL 60093-1214
Tel.: (847) 441-2618
Web Site: http://www.milleraa.com
Emp.: 5
N.A.I.C.S.: 541810
Steve Brown *(Mng Dir)*

Miller Legal Services   (1)
2442 N Lincoln Ave, Chicago, IL 60614
Tel.: (773) 388-3393

COMPANIES

Emp.: 5
Law firm
N.A.I.C.S.: 541810
Adam B. Levin *(Acct Exec)*

MILLER AUTO GROUP
145 Rte 1120, Lebanon, NH 03766
Tel.: (603) 448-3770
Web Site: http://www.millerautogroup.com
Sales Range: $75-99.9 Million
Emp.: 50
New & Used Automobile Sales
N.A.I.C.S.: 441110
Jo Cicotte *(Owner & Pres)*
Keith Higgs *(Gen Mgr)*
Jaime Lanfranconi *(Office Mgr)*
Luke Walthour *(Dir-Mktg)*
Kevin Lyons *(Mgr-Wholesale)*
Phil Maheu *(Mgr-Facilities)*

MILLER AUTO SALES INC.
3985 Valley Pike, Winchester, VA 22602
Tel.: (540) 869-5000
Web Site: http://www.drivemiller.com
Rev.: $17,200,000
Emp.: 200
Automobiles, New & Used
N.A.I.C.S.: 441110
John Grist *(VP)*
John Miller *(Owner)*

MILLER AUTOMOBILE CORPORATION
1335 post Rd, Darien, CT 06820
Tel.: (203) 655-7451
Web Site: http://www.darienautomotivegroup.com
Sales Range: $25-49.9 Million
Emp.: 70
Sales of New & Used Automobiles
N.A.I.C.S.: 441110
William Steinmetz *(Pres)*
Darlene Renos *(Controller)*

MILLER BROTHERS EXPRESS LLC
560 W 400 N, Hyrum, UT 84319
Tel.: (435) 245-6025
Web Site: http://www.mbexlc.com
Sales Range: $10-24.9 Million
Emp.: 150
Provider of Trucking Services: Transporter of General Commodities, Frozen Foods & Hazardous Materials
N.A.I.C.S.: 484121
Mike Simpson *(VP-Transportation)*
Zan Baer *(Controller)*

MILLER BROTHERS GROCERY INC.
166 W Main St, New London, OH 44851
Tel.: (419) 929-1591
Web Site: http://www.celinea.com
Sales Range: $10-24.9 Million
Emp.: 75
Grocery Stores
N.A.I.C.S.: 445110
Michael Miller *(Pres)*
Patty Porter *(Mgr-Customer Svc)*
Annette Myers *(Office Mgr)*

MILLER BUCKFIRE & CO., LLC
601 Lexington Ave, New York, NY 10022
Tel.: (212) 895-1800
Web Site: http://www.millerbuckfire.com
Year Founded: 2002
Financial Consulting Services
N.A.I.C.S.: 541611
Kenneth A. Buckfire *(Co-Pres)*
James Doak *(Co-Mng Dir)*
Stuart E. Erickson *(Mng Dir)*
Richard Klein *(Mng Dir)*
Kevin Haggard *(Mng Dir)*
Matthew Rodrigue *(Mng Dir)*
John A. McKenna Jr. *(Co-Mng Dir)*

MILLER BUICK-PONTIAC-GMC CO.
920 Rte 1 N, Woodbridge, NJ 07095
Tel.: (732) 596-1955
Web Site: http://www.autobymiller.com
Rev.: $13,600,000
Emp.: 45
New & Used Car Dealers
N.A.I.C.S.: 441110
Steve Danach *(Mgr-Parts)*

MILLER BUILDINGS INC.
311 W Lincoln Ave, Myerstown, PA 17067
Tel.: (717) 866-2319
Web Site: http://www.millerbldgs.com
Sales Range: $10-24.9 Million
Emp.: 20
Mfr of Portable Buildings & Prefabricated Metal
N.A.I.C.S.: 332311
Paul Frantz *(VP)*

MILLER COMPRESSING CO., INC.
1640 W Bruce St, Milwaukee, WI 53204-1103
Tel.: (414) 671-5980   WI
Web Site: http://www.millercompressing.com
Year Founded: 1950
Sales Range: $25-49.9 Million
Emp.: 280
Provider of Scrap, Waste Materials & Recycling Services
N.A.I.C.S.: 423930
Phil Heston *(Mgr-Mktg)*

MILLER CONSOLIDATED INDUSTRIES INC.
2221 Arbor Blvd, Dayton, OH 45439-1521
Tel.: (937) 294-2681   OH
Web Site: http://www.millerconsolidated.com
Year Founded: 1969
Sales Range: $10-24.9 Million
Emp.: 49
Metal Heat Treating
N.A.I.C.S.: 332811
Tom R. Miller *(Pres)*

Subsidiaries:

Day-Met Finishing Co. Inc. (1)
2221 Arbor Blvd, Dayton, OH 45439-1521 (100%)
Tel.: (937) 294-0155
Sales Range: $10-24.9 Million
Emp.: 2
Plating & Polishing
N.A.I.C.S.: 332813
Nick Millon *(Branch Mgr)*
Larry Cartwright *(Branch Mgr)*

Metallurgical & Environmental Testing Laboratories Inc. (1)
2681 E River Rd, Dayton, OH 45439-1533
Tel.: (937) 293-1621
Sales Range: $10-24.9 Million
Emp.: 6
Testing Laboratories
N.A.I.C.S.: 541380
Larry Cartwright *(Gen Mgr)*

Metallurgical Service Inc. (1)
2681 E River Rd, Dayton, OH 45439-1533
Tel.: (937) 294-3212
Sales Range: $10-24.9 Million
Metal Heat Treating
N.A.I.C.S.: 332811
Thomas Miller *(Pres)*

Quality Steels Corporation (1)
2221 Arbor Blvd, Dayton, OH 45439-1521
Tel.: (937) 294-4133
Sales Range: $10-24.9 Million
Emp.: 26
Metals, Service Centers & Offices
N.A.I.C.S.: 423510
Tom R. Miller *(CEO)*

MILLER CONSTRUCTION COMPANY
614 S Federal Hwy, Fort Lauderdale, FL 33301
Tel.: (954) 764-6550
Web Site: http://www.millerconstruction.com
Year Founded: 1973
Sales Range: $1-9.9 Million
Emp.: 35
Commercial, Retail & Office Building Construction Services
N.A.I.C.S.: 236220
Thomas J. Miller *(CEO)*
Harley W. Miller *(Pres)*
Brian Sudduth *(Sr VP)*
Traci Miller *(VP-Bus Dev)*
Kim Riehn *(CFO)*
Preeti Jain *(Controller)*
Ankit Patel *(Sr Mgr-Preconstruction)*
William Jessee *(Superintendent)*
Rich Smolich *(Mgr-Preconstruction)*
Jeff Slade *(VP-Ops)*

MILLER CONTAINER CORPORATION
340278 Ave W, Rock Island, IL 61264-1130
Tel.: (309) 787-6161   IL
Web Site: http://www.millercontainer.com
Year Founded: 1959
Sales Range: $25-49.9 Million
Emp.: 250
Corrugated & Solid Fiber Boxes
N.A.I.C.S.: 322211
Gerry Chretien *(Mgr)*

Subsidiaries:

Miller Container Corporation - Clinton Division (1)
PO Box 443, Clinton, IL 61727-0443
Tel.: (217) 935-8361
Web Site: http://www.millercontainer.com
Emp.: 15
Corrugated Box Mfr
N.A.I.C.S.: 322211
Doug McNamara *(Gen Mgr)*

MILLER CURTAIN CO., INC.
211 New Laredo Hwy, San Antonio, TX 78211-1905
Tel.: (210) 483-1000   TX
Year Founded: 1947
Sales Range: $50-74.9 Million
Emp.: 500
Mfr of Drapes, Curtains & Bedspreads
N.A.I.C.S.: 314120
Gerd Miller *(Pres & Treas)*
Vicki Bates *(Controller)*

MILLER DISTRIBUTING INC.
300 S 4th St, Saint Clair, PA 17970
Tel.: (570) 429-1191   PA
Year Founded: 1973
Sales Range: $10-24.9 Million
Emp.: 50
Tobacco & Tobacco Products
N.A.I.C.S.: 424940
W. Fred Miller *(Pres)*

MILLER DIVERSIFIED INC.
1656 Henthome Dr, Maumee, OH 43537
Tel.: (419) 867-9119
Web Site: http://www.millerdiversified.com
Year Founded: 1920
Land Subdivision
N.A.I.C.S.: 237210
Kurt Miller *(Pres)*
Dave Spalding *(VP-Field Ops)*
Lisa Babich *(Sr Project Mgr)*
Jerry Miller *(VP)*

Subsidiaries:

The Danberry, Co. (1)
3242 Executive Pkwy # 203, Toledo, OH 43606
Tel.: (419) 534-6592
Web Site: http://www.danberry.com
Sales Range: $1-9.9 Million
Emp.: 300
Offices of Real Estate Agents & Brokers
N.A.I.C.S.: 531210
Dick Baker *(Pres)*
Joann Amos *(Mgr)*

MILLER DRUG
210 State St, Bangor, ME 04401
Tel.: (207) 947-8369
Web Site: http://www.millerdrug.com
Sales Range: $25-49.9 Million
Emp.: 90
Pharmaceutical Product Whslr
N.A.I.C.S.: 424210
Bernard W. Miller *(Pres)*
Brenda St. Amand *(Mgr-Admin)*
Kirk Bridges *(Project Mgr-Pur)*

MILLER ELECTRIC COMPANY
2251 Rosselle St, Jacksonville, FL 32204-3125
Tel.: (904) 388-8000   FL
Web Site: http://www.mecojax.com
Year Founded: 1928
Sales Range: $250-299.9 Million
Emp.: 1,200
Electrical Contracting Services
N.A.I.C.S.: 238210
H. E. Autrey *(Chm)*
Ronald A. Autrey *(Chm)*
Susan A. Walden *(CFO, Treas, Sec & Exec VP)*
Henry Brown *(CEO)*
Daniel A. Brown *(COO & VP-Ops)*
David Long *(Pres)*
James McDonald *(VP-Corp Svcs)*
Robert Tesney *(VP-Projects)*
Donnie Smith *(VP-Corp Svcs)*
David Stallings *(VP)*
Kevin Hebert *(VP-Atlantic Coast Reg)*
Alan Creel *(VP-Pre-Construction Svcs)*
Brian Seay *(Sr VP-Healthcare & Construction Ops)*
Mike Brannen *(VP-Indus)*
Russell W. Oden *(VP-Projects)*
Jonathan Bolen *(Sr Project Mgr-Birmingham)*
Craig Bowman *(Dir-Security Solutions)*
James MacDonald *(Sr VP-Svc & Branch Ops)*
Andy Bowman *(VP-Integrated Solutions)*
Rochelle Price *(VP-Shared Svcs)*
Kevin Flanigan *(VP-Network Svcs)*
Edward Witt Jr. *(Sr VP)*
Bill Foley Jr. *(VP-Indus)*

MILLER ELECTRIC CONSTRUCTION INC.
4377 William Flynn Hwy, Allison Park, PA 15101
Tel.: (412) 487-1044
Web Site: http://www.millerelectric.com
Rev.: $22,279,627
Emp.: 25
General Electrical Contractor
N.A.I.C.S.: 238210
Richard R. Miller *(Founder)*
Greg McQuaide *(Chm & Dir-Safety)*

MILLER ELECTRIC CONSTRUCTION INC. — U.S. PRIVATE

Miller Electric Construction Inc.—(Continued)

Subsidiaries:

Miller Electric Construction (1)
4377 William Flynn Hwy, Allison Park, PA 15101
Tel.: (412) 487-1044
Web Site: http://www.millerelectric.com
Sales Range: $25-49.9 Million
General Electrical Contractor
N.A.I.C.S.: 238210

MILLER ENTERPRISES
2930 2nd St S, Saint Cloud, MN 56301
Tel.: (320) 251-1363
Web Site:
http://www.millerautoplaza.com
Rev.: $99,700,000
Emp.: 95
Automobiles, New & Used
N.A.I.C.S.: 441110
Thomas R. Miller (Pres)

Subsidiaries:

Miller All Line Leasing Inc. (1)
2930 2nd St S, Saint Cloud, MN 56301
Tel.: (320) 251-1363
Web Site: http://www.minnesotagmc.com
Emp.: 200
Passenger Car Leasing
N.A.I.C.S.: 532112
Thomas R. Miller (Pres)

Miller Auto Club (1)
2930 2nd St S, Saint Cloud, MN 56301
Tel.: (320) 251-1363
Emp.: 200
Automobiles, New & Used
N.A.I.C.S.: 441110
Thomas R. Miller (Pres)

Miller Marine (1)
2930 2nd St S, Saint Cloud, MN 56301
Tel.: (320) 252-8747
Web Site: http://www.millermarine.com
Rev.: $10,200,000
Emp.: 9
Boat Distr
N.A.I.C.S.: 441222
Thomas R. Miller (Pres)

Miller Pontiac-Buick-GMC Inc. (1)
2900 2nd St S, Saint Cloud, MN 56301
Tel.: (320) 251-1363
Web Site: http://www.millerautoplaza.com
Rev.: $29,600,000
Emp.: 200
Automobiles, New & Used
N.A.I.C.S.: 441110
Thomas R. Miller (Pres)

MILLER ENTERPRISES OF MANATEE, INC.
1200 1st Ave W Ste 200, Bradenton, FL 34205
Tel.: (941) 748-3433   FL
Web Site:
http://www.millerinvesting.com
Year Founded: 1963
Sales Range: $75-99.9 Million
Emp.: 168
Holding Company; Marina & Restaurant Owner; Real Estate Broker
N.A.I.C.S.: 551112
C. Donald Miller (Pres)

Subsidiaries:

Twin Dolphin Marina (1)
1000 1st Ave W, Bradenton, FL 34205-7852
Tel.: (941) 747-8300
Web Site: http://www.twindolphinmarina.com
Emp.: 5
Marinas
N.A.I.C.S.: 713930
Cynthia Belfatto (Pres)

MILLER ENTERPRISES, INC.
1120 W Goshen Ave, Visalia, CA 93291
Tel.: (559) 732-8371

Web Site:
http://www.dignitymemorial.com
Year Founded: 1962
Funeral Homes & Funeral Services
Rhonda S. Wright (Dir-Funeral)
Kera Dawn Dugan (Mgr)

MILLER FABRICATION & CONSTRUCTION, INC.
80 Hwy 14A E, Lovell, WY 82431-0248
Tel.: (307) 548-6346   WY
Web Site: http://www.millersfab.com
Year Founded: 1980
Sales Range: $10-24.9 Million
Emp.: 15
Metal Fabrication & Construction Services
N.A.I.C.S.: 332999
Linda J. Miller (Pres)

MILLER FELPAX CORPORATION
1155 E 8th St, Winona, MN 55987
Tel.: (507) 452-2461   MN
Web Site:
http://www.milleringenuity.com
Year Founded: 1947
Railroad Rolling Stock Mfr
N.A.I.C.S.: 336510
Paul van Dyck (CFO)
Steven Blue (CEO)
Randy J. Skarlupka (VP-Ops)
Kevin SMith (Sr VP-Global Sls & Mktg)
Matt Edmonds (Dir-Technical Sls)

MILLER FORD SALES INC.
1594 Rte 38, Lumberton, NJ 08048
Tel.: (609) 267-0476
Web Site: http://www.millerford.net
Sales Range: $100-124.9 Million
Emp.: 150
Sales of New & Used Automobiles
N.A.I.C.S.: 441110
Charles S. Miller (Principal)
Ross Contiliano (Controller)
Marc Kweeder (Mgr-Sls-New Car)
Jim Visco (Dir-Svc)
Tony DiMartino (Asst Mgr-Svc)
Tony Oliveri (Mgr-Parts)
John McDonald (Gen Mgr-Sls)
Andrew Buchanan (Asst Mgr-Svc)
Travis King (Dir-Mktg & Bus Dev)
Don Ratcliffe (Mgr-Bus)
Rick Damush (Mgr-Comml Truck Sls)
Mike Simon (Mgr-Sls)
Sean Hartman (Mgr-Sls-Used Car)

MILLER HARDWARE COMPANY
2 E Necessity Ave, Harrison, AR 72601
Tel.: (870) 741-3493
Web Site:
http://www.millerhardware.com
Sales Range: $10-24.9 Million
Emp.: 75
Hardware Stores
N.A.I.C.S.: 444140
T. Meredith Miller (Pres)
Rachel Bailey (Treas)
Matt Miller (Mgr-Store)

MILLER HOLDING CORP.
105 N 8th Ave, Stroud, OK 74079-4021
Tel.: (918) 447-2100   OK
Web Site: http://www.millertl.com
Sales Range: $200-249.9 Million
Emp.: 350
Trucking Service
N.A.I.C.S.: 484121

Subsidiaries:

Miller Truck Lines Inc. (1)
105 N 8th Ave, Stroud, OK 74079-4021   (100%)
Tel.: (918) 968-3584
Web Site: http://www.millertrucklines.com
Sales Range: $25-49.9 Million
Emp.: 50
Trucking Except Local Distr
N.A.I.C.S.: 484121
Houston Brittain (Dir-Risk Mgmt)
Sara Carter (Dir-HR)
Mark Clutter (Gen Mgr)
Roger Johnson (Dir-Claims)
Joe Taylor V (VP-Pricing & Bus Analytics)

Unit (Domestic):

Miller Truck Lines Inc. - Tulsa (2)
4231 S Elwood, Tulsa, OK 74107
Tel.: (918) 439-4165
Web Site: http://www.millertrucklines.com
Sales Range: $10-24.9 Million
Emp.: 15
General Freight Trucking, Long-Distance, Truckload
N.A.I.C.S.: 484121
Bobby Miller (VP-HR & IT)

MILLER INDUSTRIES, INC.
1521 NW 165th St, Miami Gardens, FL 33169
Tel.: (305) 621-0501   FL
Year Founded: 1963
Rev.: $621,867
Assets: $2,322,220
Liabilities: $1,223,079
Net Worth: $1,099,141
Earnings: $115,433
Fiscal Year-end: 04/30/18
Warehousing & Storage Services
N.A.I.C.S.: 531130
Jeffrey I. Badgley (Co-CEO)
Deborah L. Whitmire (CFO, Treas & Exec VP)
William G. Miller (Chm)
Frank Madonia (Gen Counsel, Sec & Exec VP)
Josias W. Reyneke (CIO)
William G. Miller II (Pres & Co-CEO)

MILLER INSULATION CO. INC.
3520 E Century Ave, Bismarck, ND 58503
Tel.: (701) 258-4323
Web Site:
http://www.millerinsulation.com
Year Founded: 1972
Sales Range: $10-24.9 Million
Emp.: 25
Installs Residential, Commercial & Industrial Building Insulation
N.A.I.C.S.: 238310
Bradley Miller (Pres & CEO)
Dwight Miller (VP)
Rick Thompson (Controller)

MILLER INTERNATIONAL, INC.
8500 Zuni St, Denver, CO 80260-5007
Tel.: (303) 428-5696
Web Site: http://www.miller-international.com
Sales Range: $100-124.9 Million
Emp.: 200
Mfr of Western Apparel
N.A.I.C.S.: 315250
David Wooten (Mgr-Distr & Property Mgmt)
Pat Hurley (CFO)
Jill Gechter (Mgr)

Subsidiaries:

Miller International, Inc. - Cinch Jeans and Shirts Division (1)
8500 Zuni St, Denver, CO 80260
Tel.: (786) 391-4868
Web Site: http://www.cinchjeans.com

Sales Range: $25-49.9 Million
Emp.: 100
Jean Apparel Mfr
N.A.I.C.S.: 315210
David Dean (CEO)

Rocky Mountain Clothing Co. (1)
8500 Zuni St, Denver, CO 80260-5007
Tel.: (303) 428-5696
Sales Range: $25-49.9 Million
Emp.: 150
Mfr of Western Apparel
N.A.I.C.S.: 315250
David Dean (CEO)

MILLER INVESTMENT MANAGEMENT, LLC
1 Tower Bridge 100 Front St Ste 1500, West Conshohocken, PA 19428
Tel.: (610) 834-9820   PA
Web Site: http://www.millerinv.com
Year Founded: 1998
Investment Management, Private Equity & Real Estate Investment Services
N.A.I.C.S.: 523940
H. Scott Miller (Mng Dir)
Christine M. Dostillio (CFO)
Jessica A. Yeich (Controller & Accountant)
Elwyn Evans III (Partner)

MILLER LAW GROUP
111 Sutter St Ste 700, San Francisco, CA 94104
Tel.: (415) 464-4300
Web Site:
http://www.millerlawgroup.com
Year Founded: 1998
Sales Range: $1-9.9 Million
Emp.: 38
Legal Advisory Services
N.A.I.C.S.: 541199
Michele Ballard Miller (Co-Founder)
Dax Lovett (Mgr-Mktg)
Theresa Telford (Controller)
Lisa Hamasaki (Atty)
Kerry McInerney Freeman (Atty)
Holly R. Lake (Atty)
Janine S. Simerly (Atty)
Jennifer R. Cotner (Atty)
Walter M. Stella (Atty)
Crista Davis (Office Mgr)
Melvin Hollowell (Mng Partner-Detroit)
E. Powell Miller (Co-Founder & Partner)

MILLER LEGG & ASSOCIATES INC.
5747 N Andrews Way, Fort Lauderdale, FL 33301
Tel.: (954) 436-7000
Web Site: http://www.millerlegg.com
Rev.: $11,400,000
Emp.: 80
Architectural Services
N.A.I.C.S.: 541310
Dylan Larson (COO & Principal)
Leslie Hernandez (CFO & Principal)
Michael Kroll (Pres & Principal)

MILLER LIVESTOCK MARKETS INC.
100 Salebarn Rd, Dequincy, LA 70633
Tel.: (337) 786-2995
Web Site:
http://www.millerlivestock.com
Sales Range: $25-49.9 Million
Emp.: 10
Livestock Auction
N.A.I.C.S.: 424520
James J. Miller (Pres)

MILLER MANUFACTURING, INC.
165 Cascade Ct, Rohnert Park, CA 94928
Tel.: (707) 584-9528 — CA
Web Site: http://windowwand.net
Year Founded: 1983
Sales Range: $1-9.9 Million
Emp.: 12
Blind & Shade Mfr
N.A.I.C.S.: 337920
Joanne Miller (VP)

Subsidiaries:

Miller Powder Coating (1)
165 Cascade Ct, Rohnert Park, CA 94928
Tel.: (707) 584-9528
Web Site: http://www.gompc.com
Powder Coating Mfr
N.A.I.C.S.: 332117

MILLER MANUFACTURING, INC.
3301 Castlewood Rd, Richmond, VA 23234
Tel.: (804) 232-4551 — VA
Web Site: http://www.miller-group.com
Year Founded: 1898
Sales Range: $150-199.9 Million
Emp.: 450
Mfr of Store Fixtures & Displays
N.A.I.C.S.: 337212
Tucker Grigg (Pres)

Subsidiaries:

Miller Multiplex Display Fixture Co. (1)
1610 Design Way, Dupo, IL 62239
Tel.: (636) 343-5700
Web Site: http://www.multiplexdisplays.com
Sales Range: $10-24.9 Million
Emp.: 50
Custom Store Fixtures Mfr
N.A.I.C.S.: 337110
Kathy Webster (Dir-Mktg)
Ryandy Cascoe (Pres)

MILLER MECHANICAL SERVICES, INC.
55-57 Walnut St, Glens Falls, NY 12801
Tel.: (518) 792-0430 — GA
Web Site: http://www.millermech.com
Year Founded: 1988
Sales Range: $1-9.9 Million
Emp.: 20
Metal Fabrication & Installation Services
N.A.I.C.S.: 332710
Elizabeth A. Miller (Pres & CEO)
Frank Burkhardt (Mgr-Engrg)
Bill Batkay (Controller)

Subsidiaries:

Doty Machine Works, Inc. (1)
35 Sullivan Pkwy, Fort Edward, NY 12828
Tel.: (518) 747-5326
Web Site: http://www.dotymachine.com
Sales Range: $1-9.9 Million
Emp.: 50
Metal Machine Shops
N.A.I.C.S.: 332710
Elizabeth A. Miller (Chm)
Mark Moulton (Mgr-Tool Room & Safety)
Bill Batkay (CFO)
Jim Beames (Sr Project Mgr)
Bill Smith (Gen Mgr)

MILLER MFG, CO.
1450 13th St W, Glencoe, MN 55336
Tel.: (320) 864-3564
Web Site: http://www.miller-mfg.com
Miscellaneous Mfr
N.A.I.C.S.: 339999
Mark Heruth (Principal)

MILLER MOTOR CAR CORP.
4455 Vestal Pkwy E, Vestal, NY 13850
Tel.: (607) 797-1221
Web Site: http://www.millerautoteam.com
Sales Range: $25-49.9 Million
Emp.: 110
Automobiles, New & Used
N.A.I.C.S.: 441110
Kenneth Miller (Owner)
Steve Miller Sr. (Owner)

MILLER MOTORCARS INC.
342 W Putnam Ave, Greenwich, CT 06830
Tel.: (203) 629-3890
Web Site: http://www.millermotorcars.com
Sales Range: $75-99.9 Million
Emp.: 30
Automobiles, New & Used
N.A.I.C.S.: 441110
Richard Koppelman (Pres)
Janet Jefferson (Controller)
Evan Cygler (Dir-Special Projects)
Joseph Tambini (Dir-Parts)

MILLER OF DENTON LTD.
2421 Interstate 35 W North, Denton, TX 76207
Tel.: (940) 566-6717
Web Site: http://www.millerofdenton.com
Sales Range: $25-49.9 Million
Emp.: 250
Beer Distr
N.A.I.C.S.: 424810
Dan Fisher (Chm)

MILLER OIL CO., INC.
1000 E City Hall Ave, Norfolk, VA 23504-4214
Tel.: (757) 623-6600 — VA
Web Site: http://www.milleroil.com
Year Founded: 1977
Sales Range: $200-249.9 Million
Emp.: 480
Distr of Petroleum Products
N.A.I.C.S.: 445111
Augustus C. Miller (Chm)
Jeffrey G. Miller (Pres)
Mike J. Miller (CFO)

MILLER PLASTERING & STUCCO, INC.
15841 Old US Hwy 441, Tavares, FL 32778
Tel.: (352) 343-8199 — FL
Year Founded: 1978
Sales Range: $10-24.9 Million
Emp.: 56
Stucco Work, Interior
N.A.I.C.S.: 238310
James T. Miller (Pres)

MILLER PROCTOR NICKOLAS INC.
2 Hudson St, Tarrytown, NY 10591
Tel.: (914) 332-0088
Web Site: http://www.mpnboilers.com
Sales Range: $10-24.9 Million
Emp.: 40
Heat Exchange Equipment, Industrial
N.A.I.C.S.: 423830
Duncan Mitchell (Pres)
Paul Triana (VP)
Bill Mack (Controller)

Subsidiaries:

Mobile Steam Boiler Rental Corp. (1)
182 Montrose Ave, Brooklyn, NY 11206
Tel.: (718) 384-1110
Web Site: http://www.mobilesteam.com
Sales Range: $1-9.9 Million
Emp.: 16
Equipment Rental And Leasing, Nec
N.A.I.C.S.: 532490
Jeff Moskowitz (VP)

MILLER PRODUCTS COMPANY, INC.
2511 S TriCenter Blvd, Durham, NC 27713
Tel.: (919) 313-2100 — NJ
Web Site: http://www.millerproducts.com
Year Founded: 1930
Rev.: $10,000,000
Emp.: 23
Mfr of Rubber & Synthetic Rubber Products & Plastic Molded Products
N.A.I.C.S.: 326299

Subsidiaries:

Miller Rubber Products Company (1)
2511 S Tricenter Blvd, Durham, NC 27713
Tel.: (919) 313-2100
Rubber Products Mfr
N.A.I.C.S.: 326299

MILLER PUBLISHING GROUP, LLC
814 S Westgate Ste 100, Los Angeles, CA 90049
Tel.: (310) 893-5300 — CA
Web Site: http://www.tennis.com
Sales Range: $50-74.9 Million
Emp.: 50
Publishing Company
N.A.I.C.S.: 513120
Robert L. Miller (Pres & CEO)

Subsidiaries:

Miller Sports Group (1)
79 Madison Ave Fl 8, New York, NY 10016-5818
Tel.: (212) 636-2700
Web Site: http://www.tennis.com
Sales Range: $10-24.9 Million
Publisher of Sports Magazines
N.A.I.C.S.: 513120

Subsidiary (Domestic):

Tennis Magazine (2)
79 Madison Ave 8th Fl, New York, NY 10016-7802 (100%)
Tel.: (212) 636-2700
Web Site: http://www.tennis.com
Sports Magazine
N.A.I.C.S.: 513120

WHERE International LP (1)
11100 Santa Monica Blvd, Los Angeles, CA 90025
Tel.: (310) 893-5400
Web Site: http://www.wheremagazine.com
Rev.: $21,000,000
Magazines: Publishing & Printing
N.A.I.C.S.: 513120

MILLER RESOURCES INTERNATIONAL, INC.
2525 Route 130 Bldg A, Cranbury, NJ 08512
Tel.: (609) 395-1800 — NJ
Web Site: http://www.millerstaffing.com
Year Founded: 1974
Employment Services
N.A.I.C.S.: 561311
Ronni Hyman (VP)
Francisco Perez (Mgr-Acct)
Danny Willins (Exec VP)

Subsidiaries:

Miller Personnel Inc. (1)
83 Stultes Rd, Dayton, NJ 08810
Tel.: (609) 395-1800
Web Site: http://www.millerjobs.com
Sales Range: $25-49.9 Million
Full Service Employment Agency
N.A.I.C.S.: 441110

MILLER SELLNER IMPLEMENT INC.
22024 State Hwy 4 S, Sleepy Eye, MN 56085
Tel.: (507) 831-1106
Web Site: http://www.millersellner.com
Sales Range: $10-24.9 Million
Emp.: 44
Farm Implements
N.A.I.C.S.: 423820
Doug Miller (Pres)

MILLER SHINGLE COMPANY INC.
20820 Gun Club, Granite Falls, WA 98252
Tel.: (360) 691-7727 — WA
Web Site: http://www.millershingle.com
Year Founded: 1946
Rev.: $11,000,000
Emp.: 190
Provider of Logging Camps & Contracts
N.A.I.C.S.: 113310
Bruce L. Miller II (Pres)

MILLER SUPPLY OF WEST VIRGINIA INCORPORATED
1537 Blachleyville Rd, Wooster, OH 44691
Tel.: (330) 264-9146
Web Site: http://www.kenmillersupply.com
Sales Range: $10-24.9 Million
Emp.: 55
Oil Well Machinery Equipment Supplier
N.A.I.C.S.: 423830
Joe Zehnder (Controller)

MILLER SURFACE GALLERY
1460 W Bay St, Savannah, GA 31415
Tel.: (912) 341-0435
Web Site: http://www.millersurfacegallery.com
Brick Stone & Related Construction Material Merchant Whslr
N.A.I.C.S.: 423320
Darren L. Miller (Owner)

MILLER TECHNOLOGIES INTERNATIONAL
3928 McGregor CT, Mobile, AL 36608
Tel.: (251) 343-9101
Web Site: http://www.millertechintl.com
Sales Range: $10-24.9 Million
Emp.: 150
Pharmaceuticals Product Mfr
N.A.I.C.S.: 325412
Drayton Miller (Pres & CEO)

MILLER WASTE MILLS, INC.
580 E Front St, Winona, MN 55987-4256
Tel.: (507) 454-6906 — MN
Web Site: http://www.millerwastemills.com
Year Founded: 1927
Sales Range: $25-49.9 Million
Emp.: 600
Custom Compound Purchased Resins
N.A.I.C.S.: 325991
Hugh Miller (CEO)

MILLER YACHT SALES, INC.
200 State Hwy 166, Toms River, NJ 08757
Tel.: (732) 349-6800 — NJ
Web Site: http://www.milleryachtsales.com
Sales Range: $1-9.9 Million
Emp.: 25

MILLER YACHT SALES, INC.

Miller Yacht Sales, Inc.—(Continued)
Mfr & Retailer of Yachts
N.A.I.C.S.: 441222
Ed Trengrove (Mgr-Svcs)
Subsidiaries:

Lighthouse Point Marina (1)
200 Atlantic City Blvd, Toms River, NJ 08757
Tel.: (732) 349-6600
Yacht Club & Docking Facilities
N.A.I.C.S.: 713930

Marine Trading International, Inc. (1)
200 State Hwy 166 S, Toms River, NJ 08757
Tel.: (732) 286-4000
Provider of Boat Building & Repairing Services
N.A.I.C.S.: 336612

Trader's Cove (1)
Mantoloking Rd., Mantoloking, NJ 08738
Tel.: (732) 295-2500
Marina & Park
N.A.I.C.S.: 713930

MILLER'S CHRYSLER-PLYMOUTH JEEP
48 Kelly Island Rd, Martinsburg, WV 25401
Tel.: (304) 263-8821
Sales Range: $10-24.9 Million
Emp.: 40
Car Whslr
N.A.I.C.S.: 441110
John Miller (CEO)

MILLER'S OF COLUMBIA, INC.
2905 2 Notch Rd, Columbia, SC 29204
Tel.: (803) 254-1656
Web Site: http://www.millersinc.com
Sales Range: $10-24.9 Million
Emp.: 23
Office Furniture Whslr
N.A.I.C.S.: 423210
David E. Olsen (Co-Pres)
Betty B. Olsen (VP)
Barbara H. Olsen (Co-Pres)

MILLER, CANFIELD, PADDOCK AND STONE, P.L.C.
150 W Jefferson Ste 2500, Detroit, MI 48226
Tel.: (313) 963-6420   MI
Web Site: http://www.millercanfield.com
Year Founded: 1852
Sales Range: $125-149.9 Million
Emp.: 501
Legal Advisory Services
N.A.I.C.S.: 541110
Elisa M. Angeli (Principal)
Frederick A. Acomb (Principal)
Michael P. McGee (CEO & Principal)
David A. Robson (COO)
N. Clark Campbell (Dir-IT)
David R. Hoin (Dir-Fin)
Catherine R. Mulla (Dir-Library Svcs)
Elizabeth K. Needleman (Dir-HR)
Robin W. Asher (Principal)
Kimberly A. Berger (Principal)
Brad B. Arbuckle (Mng Dir & Principal)
Danielle Mason Anderson (Pres & Dir-Kalamazoo Resident)
James L. Allen (Principal)
Matthew P. Allen (Principal)
Thomas G. Appleman (Principal)
Ann Arbor (Principal)
Thomas D. Colis (Mng Dir & Principal)
Michelle P. Crockett (Principal-Diversity & Prof Dev)
Darryl R. Davidson (Principal & Dir-Chicago)
Robert L. DeJong (Principal)
Gregory V. Di Censo (Principal)
Marco Dolfi (Principal-Windsor)
Donna J. Donati (Principal)
Jeffrey M. Drake (Principal)
Lawrence M. Dudek (Principal)
Lawrence W. Falbe (Principal)
Joseph M. Fazio (Mng Dir, Principal & Dir-Ann Arbor)
Gary R. Glenn (Principal)
Leo P. Goddeyne (Principal)
Joseph D. Gustavus (Principal)
Jeffrey L. LaBine (Partner-Ann Arbor & New York, Principal & Dir-Resident-New York)
Stephen S. LaPlante (Principal)
Thomas W. Linn (Principal)
Steven D. Mann (Principal)
Christina J. Marshall (Principal)
Jeffrey M. McHugh (Principal)
Megan P. Norris (Mng Dir & Principal)
Larry J. Saylor (Principal)
Richard A. Walawender (Principal)
LeRoy L. Asher Jr. (Principal)

MILLER, MILLER & MCLACHLAN CONSTRUCTION, INC.
1249 Newport Ave, Northampton, PA 18067
Tel.: (610) 262-2220
Web Site: http://www.m-3.cc
Year Founded: 1986
Sales Range: $1-9.9 Million
Emp.: 18
Commercial, Industrial & Institutional General Construction & Construction Management
N.A.I.C.S.: 236220
Barry D. Miller (Co-Founder & Pres)
Mark C. Miller (CO-Founder)
D. Scott McLachlan (Pres)

MILLER-BOWIE SUPPLY CO.
1007 W 3rd St, Texarkana, TX 75504
Tel.: (903) 794-3631
Web Site: http://www.millerbowiesupply.com
Rev.: $15,886,532
Emp.: 40
Farm Products Supplier
N.A.I.C.S.: 424910
Ed Smith (Asst Mgr)
Curtis Olson (CEO)

MILLER-BRADFORD & RISBERG, INC.
W 250 N 6851 Hwy 164, Sussex, WI 53089
Tel.: (262) 246-5700   WI
Web Site: http://www.miller-bradford.com
Year Founded: 1944
Equipment Dist & Construction, Forestry, Industry & Municipalities Supplies
N.A.I.C.S.: 423810
Dan Soley (Exec VP-Sls & Mktg)
Bill Arnold (Treas)
Mike Soley Jr. (Pres & CEO)

MILLER-DAVIS COMPANY INC.
1029 Portage St, Kalamazoo, MI 49001
Tel.: (269) 345-3561   MI
Web Site: http://www.miller-davis.com
Year Founded: 1936
Rev.: $35,000,000
Emp.: 35
Management Services
N.A.I.C.S.: 541618
Rex Bell (Pres)
Dan Coffman (CFO)

MILLER-REID, INC.
1200 Mountain Creek Rd Ste 480, Chattanooga, TN 37405
Tel.: (423) 875-5868
Web Site: http://www.miller-reid.com
Year Founded: 1979
Sales Range: $25-49.9 Million
Emp.: 7
N.A.I.C.S.: 541810
Kent Keasler (Pres)
Jeanie Camp (Media Dir)
Sam Turner (Creative Dir)

MILLER-STEPHENSON CHEMICAL COMPANY, INC.
55 Backus Ave, Danbury, CT 06810-7328
Tel.: (203) 743-4447   CT
Web Site: http://www.miller-stephenson.com
Year Founded: 1955
Sales Range: $10-24.9 Million
Emp.: 50
Supplier of High Purity Chemicals
N.A.I.C.S.: 325612
Bob Wilcox (Mgr-Mktg)
Mourad Fahmi (Pres)

MILLER/RUSSELL & ASSOCIATES LLC
3200 E Camelback Rd Ste 300, Phoenix, AZ 85018
Tel.: (602) 737-2750
Web Site: http://www.mraassociates.com
Year Founded: 1991
Investment Advisory & Wealth Management Services
N.A.I.C.S.: 523940
Mark Feldman (Mng Partner & CEO)
Brad Lemon (Mng Partner)
Christina Burroughs (Mng Partner)
Maureen Rzeppa (Mng Partner & Chief Admin Officer)
Nathan Erickson (Mng Partner & Chief Investment Officer)
Ken Garrett (Sr Dir)
Russ Bucklew (Partner)
Dave Westra (Partner)
Eric Ensign (Partner)
Brenda Bernardi (Dir-Bus Ops)
Eric Nystrom (Dir-Process & Tech)
Jo Leong (Dir-Project Mgmt)
Danielle Robinson (Team Mgr-Client Support Svcs)
Jessica Cobb (Process & Project Mgr)
Ron McKee (Sr Mgr-Client Admin/Alternatives)
Natalie Phillips (Mgr-Tax Ops)
Stephanie Harrer (Controller)
Kelly Inglhofer (Coord-Mktg & Comms)
Mike Hirte (Mng Dir)

MILLER/ZELL, INC.
6100 Fulton Industrial Blvd SW, Atlanta, GA 30336-0607
Tel.: (404) 691-7400   GA
Web Site: http://www.millerzell.com
Year Founded: 1972
Sales Range: $150-199.9 Million
Emp.: 400
Integrated Retail Store Development Agency
N.A.I.C.S.: 541990
Sandy Miller (Founder)
Andrew Gaillard (Dir-Production-Digital Media)
Ford Bowers (Gen Mgr-Graphic Center)
Paul Wolski (VP & Dir-Design)
Lavina Moss (Dir-HR)
Bob DeGroff (VP-Design Dev)
Paul Papantonis (Pres)
Gina Strickland (VP-IT)
Horace Hume (Sr VP & Dir-Design)
Howard Marx (Dir-Retail Svcs)
Mike Albuquerque (Dir-Art)
Patrick Hudson (Acct Mgr)
Rodney Mull (Dir-Ops-Digital Media)
Tom Ertler (Sr VP & Dir-Design)
Walt Murphy (Dir-Design Dev)
William Wu (Dir-Engrg-Digital Media)
Jeremy Buttson (VP-Natl Accts)

MILLERBERND MANUFACTURING CO.
622 6th St S, Winsted, MN 55395
Tel.: (320) 485-2111
Web Site: http://www.millerberndmfg.com
Sales Range: $10-24.9 Million
Emp.: 380
Stainless Steel Producer
N.A.I.C.S.: 331110
Trevor Millerbernd (CEO)

MILLERS CAPITAL INSURANCE CO.
3815 Tecport Dr, Harrisburg, PA 17111
Tel.: (717) 232-3211
Web Site: http://www.millersinsurance.com
Sales Range: $10-24.9 Million
Emp.: 50
Property Damage Insurance
N.A.I.C.S.: 524126
Scott Orndorff (Mgr)

MILLERS FORGE INC.
1411 Capital Ave, Plano, TX 75074-8119
Tel.: (972) 422-2145
Web Site: http://www.millersforge.com
Rev.: $5,000,000
Emp.: 3
Mfr of Manicure Cutlery, Surgical Tools, Pet Grooming Tools & Scissors
N.A.I.C.S.: 424990
Ted Hughes (Pres & COO)
Mike Engels (CEO)

MILLERS INC.
610 E Jefferson St, Pittsburg, KS 66762
Tel.: (620) 231-8050
Web Site: http://www.millerslab.com
Sales Range: $125-149.9 Million
Emp.: 380
Film Developing & Printing
N.A.I.C.S.: 812921
Richard Miller (CEO)
Dick Coleman (VP)

MILLHOUSE GROUP, INC.
791 Park of Commerce Dr, Boca Raton, FL 33487
Tel.: (561) 988-9220   FL
Sales Range: $125-149.9 Million
Emp.: 10
Holding Company
N.A.I.C.S.: 551112
Paul Millhouse (Pres)

MILLIKEN & COMPANY
920 Milliken Rd, Spartanburg, SC 29303
Tel.: (864) 503-2020   DE
Web Site: http://www.milliken.com
Year Founded: 1865
Textiles & Chemicals Mfr
N.A.I.C.S.: 313210
J. Harold Chandler (Chm)
Jim McCallum (Pres-Flooring Div)
Bob Hutchinson (VP-Global Design)
Jennifer K. Harmon (VP-Specialty Interiors)
Jeff Price (Pres-Specialty Fabrics Div)

COMPANIES

Dana Claire Larson *(Dir-Design & Dev-Specialty Interiors)*
Rene Vaughn *(Dir-Sls & Mktg)*
LeAnne Flack *(Mgr-Mktg)*
Debra Clements *(Chief Admin Officer, Sec & Sr Gen Counsel)*
Halsey M. Cook *(Pres & CEO)*
Brock Henderson *(Acct Mgr-Specialty Interiors)*
Shri Parikh *(Pres-Healthcare Bus & Exec VP)*
Patrick Keese *(Pres/Exec VP-Flooring)*

Subsidiaries:

Andover Healthcare, Inc. (1)
9 Fanaras Dr, Salisbury, MA 01952
Tel.: (978) 465-0044
Web Site: http://www.andoverhealthcare.com
Metal Coating, Engraving, except Jewelry & Silverware & Allied Services Mfr
N.A.I.C.S.: 332812
Thomas S. Murphy *(CEO)*

Keystone Aniline Corp. (1)
2501 W Fulton St, Chicago, IL 60612
Tel.: (312) 666-2015
Web Site: http://www.dyes.com
Chemicals & Allied Products Mfr
N.A.I.C.S.: 424690
John Andrews *(CEO)*
Osvaldo Velasquez *(Dir-MIS)*
Brian Foley *(Mgr-Bus Unit-Inks, Coatings & Paper)*

Plant (Domestic):

Keystone Aniline Corp. - Liquid Manufacturing Technical Facility (2)
2165 Hwy 292, Inman, SC 29349
Tel.: (864) 473-1601
Web Site: http://www.dyes.com
Synthetic Dye Mfr
N.A.I.C.S.: 325130

Division (Domestic):

Keystone Aniline Corp. - Pacific Division (2)
3002 W Weldon Ave, Phoenix, AZ 85017
Tel.: (800) 522-4393
Web Site: http://www.dyes.com
Synthetic Dye Mfr
N.A.I.C.S.: 325130

Milliken (Australia) P/L (1)
171 Briens Rd, Northmead, 2152, NSW, Australia
Tel.: (61) 288382500
Web Site: http://www.ontera.com.au
Carpet Tile Mfr
N.A.I.C.S.: 314110
Graeme Catt *(Mgr-Key Acct-Trade Sls)*
John Monroe *(Mgr-Sls-Natl)*
Damon Bennett *(Mgr-Key Acct)*
Joe Sciberras *(Mgr-Key Acct)*

Milliken Fine Goods Div. (1)
PO Box 1926, Spartanburg, SC 29304-1926
Tel.: (864) 503-2020
Web Site: http://www.milliken.com
R&D & Mfr of Flame Resistant Fabrics & Floor Coverings
N.A.I.C.S.: 313210

Milliken Finished Apparel Div. (1)
920 Milliken Rd, Spartanburg, SC 29304-1926
Tel.: (864) 503-2020
Web Site: http://www.milliken.com
R&D & Mfr of Flame Resistant Fabrics & Floor Coverings
N.A.I.C.S.: 313210

Milliken Industrial Div. (1)
920 Milliken Rd, Spartanburg, SC 29304-1926
Tel.: (864) 503-2020
Web Site: http://www.milliken.com
R&D & Mfr of Flame Resistant Fabrics & Floor Coverings
N.A.I.C.S.: 313210

Milliken Interior Furnishings Div. (1)
PO Box 1926, Spartanburg, SC 29304-1926

Tel.: (864) 503-2020
R&D & Mfr of Flame Resistant Fabrics & Floor Coverings
N.A.I.C.S.: 313210

Polartec LLC (1)
300 Brickstone Sq, Andover, MA 01810
Tel.: (978) 685-6341
Web Site: http://www.polartec.com
Sales Range: $250-299.9 Million
Outdoor Apparel Fabrics
N.A.I.C.S.: 313210
Gary Smith *(CEO)*

Product Concepts Residential LLC (1)
525 Callahan Rd SE, Dalton, GA 30721 (100%)
Tel.: (706) 277-7141
Sales Range: $25-49.9 Million
Emp.: 173
Carpet & Rug Mfr
N.A.I.C.S.: 423220

Springfield LLC (1)
30 Jericho Executive Plz #500e, Jericho, NY 11753
Tel.: (917) 421-6000
Web Site: http://www.springfieldllc.com
Rev.: $1,295,000
Emp.: 5
Piece Goods, Notions & Other Dry Goods Merchant Whslr
N.A.I.C.S.: 424310
Edward Shogan *(CEO)*

Westex Inc. (1)
122 W 22nd St, Oak Brook, IL 60523
Tel.: (773) 523-7000
Web Site: http://www.westex.com
Flame Resistant Fabrics Mfr & Distr
N.A.I.C.S.: 424310
Daniel Bischoff *(Pres)*
Andrew Antala *(Reg Mgr-Market)*
Steve Layton *(Dir-Intl Sls)*
Scott Margolin *(Dir-Technical-Intl)*
Josh Moody *(VP-Technical Svcs)*

MILLIMAN, INC.
1301 5th Ave Ste 3800, Seattle, WA 98101-2635
Tel.: (206) 624-7940 WA
Web Site: http://www.milliman.com
Year Founded: 1947
Sales Range: $75-99.9 Million
Emp.: 1,300
Actuarial & Consulting Services
N.A.I.C.S.: 541612
Bill Pedersen *(CFO)*
Bradley M. Smith *(Chm)*
Dennis Sain *(Head-Defined Contribution Sls & Mktg-North)*
Gerald Erickson *(Principal)*
Gary Setterberg *(Sr Mng Dir-Higher Education Practice-Global)*
Steve White *(CEO)*
Bret Linton *(Dir-Employee Benefits Practice-Global)*

Subsidiaries:

Milliman GmbH (1)
Grand Bateau Zollhof 4, Dusseldorf, 40221, Germany
Tel.: (49) 211 93886 610
Actuarial Services
N.A.I.C.S.: 524298

Milliman, Inc. (1)
Urbannet Kojimachi Bldg 8F 1-6-2 Kojimachi, Chiyoda-ku, Tokyo, 102-0083, Japan
Tel.: (81) 3 5211 7031
Web Site: http://www.milliman.com
Actuarial Services
N.A.I.C.S.: 524298

MILLINGTON LOCKWOOD INC.
3901 Genesee St Ste 800, Buffalo, NY 14225
Tel.: (716) 633-5600
Web Site: http://www.millingtonlockwood.com
Sales Range: $10-24.9 Million
Emp.: 29

Office Furniture Distr
N.A.I.C.S.: 423210
Michael Bonitatibus *(Owner & CEO)*
David Macro *(VP-Structures Grp)*

MILLION DOLLAR BABY
855 Washington Blvd, Montebello, CA 90640-6123
Tel.: (323) 728-9988
Web Site: http://www.milliondollarbaby.com
Sales Range: $25-49.9 Million
Emp.: 45
Toy Furniture Mfr
N.A.I.C.S.: 339930
Teddy Fong *(VP-Sls & Mktg)*
Julia Fong Yip *(Dir-Ops Support Grp)*
Staci Wong *(Mgr-Online Specialty Sls)*

MILLION DOLLAR ROUND TABLE THE PREMIER ASSOCIATION OF FINANCIAL PROFESSIONALS
325 W Touhy Ave, Park Ridge, IL 60068
Tel.: (847) 692-6378 IL
Web Site: http://www.mdrt.org
Year Founded: 1969
Sales Range: $25-49.9 Million
Emp.: 86
Professional Organizations
N.A.I.C.S.: 813920
Brian Heckert *(Sec)*
Joe Ferrazza *(Dir-Channel Rels-North America)*

MILLMAN LUMBER COMPANY
9264 Manchester Rd, Saint Louis, MO 63144
Tel.: (314) 968-1700
Web Site: http://www.millmanlumber.com
Year Founded: 1932
Sales Range: $10-24.9 Million
Emp.: 400
Lumber, Rough, Dressed & Finished
N.A.I.C.S.: 423310
Robert L. Millman *(Owner & Chm)*
Mike Henson *(Dir-IT)*

Subsidiaries:

Great Central Lumber Company (1)
137 Ecology Dr, Saint Peters, MO 63376 (100%)
Tel.: (636) 970-7040
Web Site: http://www.gclumber.com
Rev.: $50,006,191
Emp.: 10
Lumber & Other Building Materials
N.A.I.C.S.: 423310

MILLMAN SURVEYING, INC.
4111 Bradley Cir NW Ste 240, Canton, OH 44718
Tel.: (330) 342-0723 OH
Web Site: http://www.millmansurveying.com
Year Founded: 1996
Sales Range: $1-9.9 Million
Emp.: 45
Surveying Services
N.A.I.C.S.: 541370
Deron Millman *(CEO)*
Vincent Macauda *(Pres & COO)*
Scott Clark *(Acct Exec-Natl)*

MILLS CHEVROLET CO., INC.
1610 39th Ave, Moline, IL 61265
Tel.: (309) 797-1241
Web Site: http://www.millschevy.com
Sales Range: $10-24.9 Million
Emp.: 60
New & Used Car Dealer
N.A.I.C.S.: 441110
David Mills *(Owner)*
Nancy Hill *(Controller)*

MILLS FORD OF WILLMAR

Shane Anthony *(Mgr-Sls)*
Andy Maberry *(Mgr-Fin & Sls)*
Tobias Baskind *(Dir-Parts & Svc)*
Marty Houlihan *(Mgr-Fin)*
Tom Walker *(Mgr-Svc)*
Dean Wallarab *(Mgr-Used Cars)*
Elizabeth Weber *(Mgr-Internet Sls)*
Jeremy Howard *(Mgr-Fin)*

MILLS FENCE CO. INC.
6315 Wiehe Rd, Cincinnati, OH 45237
Tel.: (513) 631-0333
Web Site: http://www.millsfence.com
Sales Range: $10-24.9 Million
Emp.: 56
Wire Fence, Gates & Accessories
N.A.I.C.S.: 423390
Kenneth Mills *(Pres)*

MILLS FLEET FARM, INC.
512 Laurel St, Brainerd, MN 56401
Tel.: (218) 829-3521 MN
Web Site: http://www.fleetfarm.com
Year Founded: 1922
Holding Company; General Merchandise Stores & Auto Dealerships Owner & Operator
N.A.I.C.S.: 551112
Alanna Lundstrom *(Asst Mgr)*
Susan Kimman *(Coord-Electronic Media)*
Hugh Leasum *(COO)*
Mike Sidders *(Dir-Mktg & Adv)*
Derick Prelle *(Pres & CEO)*

Subsidiaries:

Mills Auto Group, Inc. (1)
512 Laurel St, Brainerd, MN 56401
Tel.: (218) 825-3574
Web Site: http://www.millsauto.com
Holding Company; New & Used Car Dealerships Owner & Operator
N.A.I.C.S.: 551112
Marisa Mae Mills *(Gen Mgr-Grp)*
Ronald D. Obeidzinski *(CFO)*
Patrick Weideman *(Dir-Admin)*
Kathleen Baumann *(Office Mgr)*
Bret Mattheisen *(Mgr-IT)*
Dawn Rasmussen *(Mgr-Customer Care Center)*
Bart Harmer *(Mgr-Dealership Ops)*
Chad Karas *(Mgr-Facilities & Construction)*
Al Porta *(Mgr-Parts & Svc)*
Danny Sargent *(Sls Mgr-New Vehicle-GMC Buick Brainerd)*
Brady Sladek *(Gen Mgr-Sls)*
Brian Smith *(Sls Mgr-New Vehicle-GMC Buick Brainerd)*

Subsidiary (Domestic):

Mills Auto Enterprises, Inc. (2)
14138 Dellwood Dr, Baxter, MN 56425
Tel.: (218) 829-3504
Web Site: http://www.millsgm.com
Sales Range: $10-24.9 Million
Emp.: 90
New & Used Car Dealer
N.A.I.C.S.: 441110
Ray Giles *(Bus Mgr)*
Paul Larson *(Mgr-Sls)*
Brent Mackcow *(Mgr-Svc)*
Monique Southard *(Mgr-Fin)*

Mills Motor, Inc. (2)
14858 Dellwood Dr, Baxter, MN 56425
Tel.: (218) 829-2893
Web Site: http://www.millsford.com
Sales Range: $10-24.9 Million
Emp.: 50
New & Used Car Dealership
N.A.I.C.S.: 441110
Brady Sladek *(Gen Mgr-Sls)*
Mike Brown *(Mgr-Sls)*
Al Porta *(Mgr-Parts & Svc)*
Kyle Holm *(Bus Mgr)*
Marvin Schmaltz *(Mgr-Parts)*
Monty Becker *(Mgr-Quick Lane)*
Tom Hice *(Mgr-Sls)*

MILLS FORD OF WILLMAR
4100 Hwy 71 S, Willmar, MN 56201

MILLS FORD OF WILLMAR

Mills Ford of Willmar—(Continued)
Tel.: (320) 235-0654
Web Site: http://www.millsfordwil.com
Sales Range: $10-24.9 Million
Emp.: 70
Car Dealership Owner & Operator
N.A.I.C.S.: 441110
Henry Mills (Pres)

MILLS GROUP INC.
9225 King James Dr, Dallas, TX 75247
Tel.: (214) 879-9881
Web Site: http://www.millsgroupinc.com
Year Founded: 2008
Sales Range: $1-9.9 Million
Emp.: 22
Specialty Construction & Insulation
N.A.I.C.S.: 238310
Cameron Leggett (CEO)

MILLS PRODUCTS INC.
7003 Chadwick Dr Ste 153, Brentwood, TN 37027-5288
Tel.: (615) 661-6570
Web Site: http://www.millsproducts.com
Sales Range: $10-24.9 Million
Emp.: 4
Metal Household Articles
N.A.I.C.S.: 332999
Bob D. Mills (CEO)
David Sampson (Mgr-Quality-North America)
Kristy Johnson (Mgr-Matls)
Darrell Adcock (Pres)

MILLWOOD INC.
3708 International Blvd, Vienna, OH 44473
Tel.: (330) 539-5460
Web Site: http://www.millwoodinc.com
Sales Range: $25-49.9 Million
Emp.: 700
Pallets, Wood
N.A.I.C.S.: 321920
Steve Miller (Co-Pres & Partner)
Lionel W. Trebilcock (Co-Pres & Partner)
Craig Gretter (CFO)

Subsidiaries:

Liberty Technologies (1)
840 McClurg Rd, Youngstown, OH 44512
Tel.: (330) 729-2120
Web Site: http://www.libertytechnologies.com
Pallets, Wood
N.A.I.C.S.: 321920
Judy Gaither (Mgr-Customer Svc & Inside Sls)
Keith Countryman (VP-Natl Accts)
Phillip Fong (Controller)
Rick Lombardo (Dir-HR)
Tom Paskert (CFO & Exec VP)
Brad Arnold (VP-Engrg)
Jake Bennett (Dir-Engrg)

MILLWORK DISTRIBUTORS INC.
2751 Universal St, Oshkosh, WI 54904
Tel.: (920) 235-8110
Web Site: http://www.mdi-oshkosh.com
Sales Range: $25-49.9 Million
Emp.: 80
Lumber Plywood Millwork & Wood Panel Merchant Whslr
N.A.I.C.S.: 423310
Michael C. Huszar (COO)
Stephen R. Huszar (CFO)

MILLWRIGHT HOLDINGS LLC

755 Sansome St Ste 360, San Francisco, CA 94111
Web Site: http://www.millwrightholdings.com
Holding Company
N.A.I.C.S.: 551112
Michael Young (Pres & CEO)
Greg Porto (Partner)
Eileen Rochford (Partner & Head-Agency Ops)
Rick Belgarde (CFO & Partner)

Subsidiaries:

Warner Communications (1)
41 Raymond St, Manchester, MA 01944
Tel.: (978) 526-1960
Web Site: http://www.warnerpr.com
Emp.: 15
Public Relations Agency
N.A.I.C.S.: 541820
Carin Warner (Founder & Pres)
Dawn Ringel (Exec VP)
Erin Vadala (Sr VP)

MILNE CONSTRUCTION CO.
6420 SW McAdam Ste 300, Portland, OR 97239
Tel.: (503) 222-9836
Web Site: http://www.milneconstruction.com
Sales Range: $25-49.9 Million
Emp.: 15
Mausoleum Construction
N.A.I.C.S.: 236220
Clinton Pearson (Mgr-Design)

MILNE RUSS FORD INC.
24777 Hall Rd, Macomb, MI 48042
Tel.: (586) 948-7700
Web Site: http://www.russmilneford.com
Sales Range: $25-49.9 Million
Emp.: 90
Car Whslr
N.A.I.C.S.: 441110
Russell G (Pres)

MILNER DOCUMENT PRODUCTS, INC.
5125 Peachtree Indus Blvd, Norcross, GA 30092-3027
Tel.: (770) 263-5300 GA
Web Site: http://www.milner.com
Year Founded: 1987
Sales Range: $25-49.9 Million
Emp.: 185
Electronic Document Management Software Mfr & Document Imaging Service
N.A.I.C.S.: 561410
Charlie Gibson (VP-Sls)
Gene Milner Jr. (Pres)

Subsidiaries:

Milner Document Products, Inc. (1)
3200 Gateway Centre Blvd Ste 140, Morrisville, NC 27560-9236 (100%)
Tel.: (919) 781-1220
Sales Range: $10-24.9 Million
Emp.: 50
Retailer of Business Machines & Office Equipment
N.A.I.C.S.: 532420

MILNER ELECTRICAL COMPANY
817 Winchester Rd Ste 100, Lexington, KY 40505
Tel.: (859) 254-0213
Year Founded: 1986
Sales Range: $10-24.9 Million
Emp.: 60
General Electrical Contractor
N.A.I.C.S.: 238210
James I. Milner Sr. (Pres)

MILO C. COCKERHAM INC.
388 N Railroad Ave, Galax, VA 24333

Tel.: (276) 236-5194
Rev.: $23,935,242
Emp.: 25
Fuel Oil Dealers
N.A.I.C.S.: 423130

MILO GORDON CHRYSLER ISUZU MITSUBISHI
5002 Cache Rd, Lawton, OK 73505
Tel.: (580) 355-2464
Web Site: http://www.milogordon.com
Sales Range: $100-124.9 Million
Emp.: 45
Automobiles, New & Used
N.A.I.C.S.: 441110
Brooke Rooney (Dir-Mktg & Fin)
Nic Sigala (Mgr-Bus Dev)

MILO PETERSON FORD
3020 457th St Way, Kenyon, MN 55946
Tel.: (507) 789-6113 MN
Year Founded: 1961
Emp.: 25
New & Used Car Dealer
N.A.I.C.S.: 441110
Paul Peterson (Pres & Owner)
Tim Struve (Mgr-Svc & Parts)
Gerald Peterson (Owner)
Jeremy Horn (Mgr-Fin)

MILOSI, INC.
655 New Shackle Island Rd, Hendersonville, TN 37077
Tel.: (615) 239-6056
Web Site: http://www.milosilandscape.com
Year Founded: 2001
Sales Range: $1-9.9 Million
Emp.: 50
Design & Construction Services
N.A.I.C.S.: 541310
Taylor D. Milliken (Owner & Pres)
Tina Kizer (Office Mgr)
June Hawkins (Project Mgr)
Chris Williams (Sr Mgr-Client Relationship)
Todd Marasi (Mgr-Nashville Client Relationship)

MILROD ENTERPRISES
600 Ave Hipodromo, San Juan, PR 00909
Tel.: (787) 721-1717
Sales Range: $10-24.9 Million
Emp.: 15
Sell Shoes
N.A.I.C.S.: 458210

MILSOFT UTILITY SOLUTIONS, INC.
4400 Buffalo Gap Rd Ste 5150, Abilene, TX 79606
Tel.: (325) 695-1642 TX
Web Site: http://www.milsoft.com
Year Founded: 1989
Sales Range: $10-24.9 Million
Emp.: 78
Prepackaged Software
N.A.I.C.S.: 513210
Josh Wolf (Mgr-Acct)
Bart Brockway (Dir-Sls)
Angela Hare (Dir-IT)
David Kelley (Dir-Mapping)
Leon Daggett (Dir-Power & Light)
Ryan Hart (Mgr-Engrg)
Derek Howe (Mgr-Engrg)
Eric Jung (Mgr-Engrg)
George Buckner (Mgr-IT)
Margaretta Mayes (Mgr-IT)
Philip Caskey (VP-Engrg & Ops)
Marvin Denzer (VP-Engrg Svcs)
Chris Brewer (VP-Power Delivery)

MILTEC UV

U.S. PRIVATE

146 Log Canoe Cir, Stevensville, MD 21666
Tel.: (410) 604-2900
Web Site: http://www.miltec.com
Year Founded: 1989
Sales Range: $10-24.9 Million
Emp.: 59
Industrial Machinery Whslr
N.A.I.C.S.: 423830
Bob Blandford (Pres)
Timothy Kerr (Engr-Mechanical)
Oliver Hamann (Dir-Ops)
Mark Walter (Dir-Engrg)

MILTIMORE SALES, INC.
22765 Heslip Dr Ste 101, Novi, MI 48375-4144
Tel.: (248) 349-0260 MI
Web Site: http://www.miltimore.com
Year Founded: 1969
Sales Range: $10-24.9 Million
Emp.: 20
Electronic Parts & Equipment
N.A.I.C.S.: 423690
Colin L. Miltimore (CEO)
Bob Kelly (Sr VP)
Rick Arnold (Pres)
Jennifer Gilhuly (Acct Mgr)
Jon Woods (Acct Mgr)

MILTON J. WOOD COMPANY
3805 Faye Rd, Jacksonville, FL 32226
Tel.: (904) 353-5527 FL
Web Site: http://www.mjwood.com
Year Founded: 1969
Sales Range: $10-24.9 Million
Emp.: 50
General Contracting Services
N.A.I.C.S.: 236210
Mark S. Wood (Chm)
Annmarie Nemeth (CFO)
Zarko Ognjenovic (CEO)

MILTON MANUFACTURING, INC.
301 East Grixdale St, Detroit, MI 48203
Tel.: (313) 366-2450 MI
Web Site: http://www.miltonmfg.com
Metal Stamping
N.A.I.C.S.: 332119
Neil Vanhecke (Coord-Sys & ISO)
Paul Mukhtar (Engr-Indus & Quality)

MILTON RUBEN CHEVROLET
3514 Washington Rd, Augusta, GA 30907
Tel.: (706) 868-0588
Web Site: http://www.buybuybaby.com
Rev.: $74,050,643
Emp.: 100
Automobiles, New & Used
N.A.I.C.S.: 441110
James J. Bernstein (Mng Partner)
Milton Ruben (Pres)
Robbie Newman (Gen Mgr-Sls)
Mike McNutt (Mgr-Svc)
Clay Woodward (Mgr-Parts)

Subsidiaries:

Milton Ruben Leasing Company (1)
3514 Washington Rd, Augusta, GA 30907
Tel.: (706) 868-0588
Web Site: http://www.miltonruben.com
Provider of Automobile Finance Leasing Services
N.A.I.C.S.: 441110
Milton Ruben (Pres)

Milton Ruben Motors, Inc. (1)
3512 Washington Rd, Augusta, GA 30907
Tel.: (706) 250-6110
Web Site: http://www.miltonruben.com
Rev.: $39,619,044
Emp.: 48
Automotive Distr

N.A.I.C.S.: 441110
James J. Bernstein (Mng Partner)
Milton Ruben (Pres)

MILTON STREET CAPITAL, LLC
3131 Eastside St #300, Houston, TX 77098
Web Site: http://miltonstreetcap.com
Privater Equity Firm
N.A.I.C.S.: 523940
Francis Carr (Mng Partner)
Bob Hogan (Mng Partner)

MILTON TRANSPORTATION INC.
Route 405 S, Milton, PA 17847
Tel.: (570) 742-8774   PA
Web Site: http://www.miltontrans.com
Year Founded: 1969
Sales Range: $10-24.9 Million
Emp.: 60
Provider of Trucking Services
N.A.I.C.S.: 459110
Ray B. Bowersox (Pres)
Richard Bowersox (VP)

MILTONS INC.
250 Granite St Ste 208, Braintree, MA 02184
Tel.: (781) 848-1880
Web Site: http://www.miltons.com
Rev.: $16,667,229
Emp.: 85
Clothing, Male: Everyday, Except Suits & Sportswear
N.A.I.C.S.: 458110
Dana Katz (Pres)
Mark Sarkis (Gen Mgr)

MILWAUKEE AREA WORKFORCE INVESTMENT BOARD INC.
2338 N 27th St, Milwaukee, WI 53210
Tel.: (414) 270-1700   WI
Web Site: http://www.milwaukeewib.org
Year Founded: 1989
Sales Range: $10-24.9 Million
Emp.: 1,624
Employment Placement Services
N.A.I.C.S.: 561311
Earl Buford (Pres & CEO)

MILWAUKEE BREWERS BASEBALL CLUB, INC.
1 Brewers Way, Milwaukee, WI 53214-3651
Tel.: (414) 902-4400   WI
Web Site: http://www.brewers.com
Year Founded: 1970
Sales Range: $50-74.9 Million
Emp.: 100
Professional Baseball Club
N.A.I.C.S.: 711211
Rick Schlesinger (COO)
Gord Ash (VP & Asst Gen Mgr)
Mark L. Attanasio (Owner, Chm & Principal)
Mike Vassallo (Dir-Media Rels)
Billy Friess (VP-Ticket Sls)
Zack Minasian (Dir-Pro Scouting)
Chris Kimball (Dir-Grp Ticket Sls)
Bob Bowman (Pres-Bus & Media)
Pats Courtney (Chief Comm Officer)
Dan Halem (Chief Legal Officer)
Tony Petitti (COO)
Bob Starkey (CFO)
Joe Torre (Chief Baseball Officer)
Octavio Castro (VP-HR)
Kevin Babusiak (VP-Partnership Activation & Strategy)
Jason Hartlund (Chief Revenue Officer)

MILWAUKEE BUCKS, INC.
1001 N 4th St, Milwaukee, WI 53203-1314
Tel.: (414) 227-0500   WI
Web Site: http://www.bucks.com
Year Founded: 1968
Sales Range: $50-74.9 Million
Emp.: 75
Professional Basketball Team
N.A.I.C.S.: 711211
Jim Woloszyk (Sr VP-Fin & Admin)
Dave Babcock (VP-Player Personnel)
Steve Tarachow (Mgr-Grp Sls)
Sue Thompson (Mgr-Ticket Ops)
Kareeda Chones-Aguam (VP-Bus Strategy & Activation)
Skip Robinson (Dir-Community Rels & Player Dev)
Ron Kiepert (Dir-IT)
Clark Hillery (Dir-Facilities)
Dan Smyczek (VP-PR)
John Hammond (Gen Mgr)
David Dean (Dir-Basketball Admin)
Jon Horst (Dir-Basketball Ops)
Jeffrey A. Joerres (Owner-Minority)
Patrick McDonough (CFO & Sr VP)
Peter Feigin (Pres)
Marc Lasry (Co-Owner)
Wes Edens (Co-Owner)
Kelly Kauffman (Sr VP-HR)
Matt Pazaras (Sr VP-Bus Dev)
Andrea Zahn (Sr Dir-Fan Experience)
Jamie Morningstar (VP-Ticket Sls & Svc)
Alicia Dupies (VP-Community Rels)
Justin Zanik (Asst Gen Mgr)
Craig Robinson (VP-Player & Organizational Dev)
Mike McCarthy (COO)
Barry Baum (Sr VP-Comm)
Aaron Rodgers (Partner-Limited)

MILWAUKEE CENTER FOR INDEPENDENCE, INC.
2020 W Wells St, Milwaukee, WI 53233-2720
Tel.: (414) 937-2083
Web Site: http://www.mcfi.net
Refrigerated Warehousing & Storage
N.A.I.C.S.: 493120
Raymond J. Zastrow (Dir-Medical)

Subsidiaries:

Independent Care Health Plan, Inc. (1)
1555 River Ctr Dr Ste 206, Milwaukee, WI 53212
Tel.: (414) 223-4847
Web Site: https://www.icarehealthplan.org
Sales Range: $75-99.9 Million
Emp.: 150
Health Care Insurance Services
N.A.I.C.S.: 524114
Bill Jensen (VP-Sls & Mktg)
Tom Lutzow (Pres & CEO)
Lisa Holden (VP-Accountable Care)
Mary Ellen Benzik (Chief Medical Officer)
Margaret Kristan (VP-Long Term Care & Community Inclusion)

MILWAUKEE COUNTY TRANSIT SYSTEM
1942 N 17th St, Milwaukee, WI 53205-1652
Tel.: (414) 344-4550   WI
Web Site: http://www.ridemcts.com
Year Founded: 1975
Sales Range: $75-99.9 Million
Emp.: 1,500
Provider of Local & Suburban Transit Services
N.A.I.C.S.: 485210
Mike Giugno (Mng Dir)
Sandra Kellner (COO)

MILWAUKEE FORGE, INC.
1532 E Oklahoma Ave, Milwaukee, WI 53207-2433
Tel.: (414) 744-4565   WI
Web Site: http://www.milwaukeeforge.com
Year Founded: 1913
Sales Range: $10-24.9 Million
Emp.: 200
Iron & Steel Forgings
N.A.I.C.S.: 332111
Dave Mesick (Pres)

MILWAUKEE JEWISH FEDERATION, INC.
1360 N Prospect Ave, Milwaukee, WI 53202-3094
Tel.: (414) 390-5700   WI
Web Site: http://www.milwaukeejewish.org
Year Founded: 1902
Rev: $27,126,683
Assets: $234,307,816
Liabilities: $100,918,824
Net Worth: $133,388,992
Emp.: 66
Fiscal Year-end: 06/30/18
Jewish Community Support Services
N.A.I.C.S.: 813410
Tom Lindow (CFO & COO-Bus Svcs)
Hannah Rosenthal (Pres & CEO)
Stephanie Wagner (VP-Comm & Strategy)
Susan Lubar Solvang (Vice Chm)
Andrea Schneider (Chm)
Joan Lubar (Vice Chm)
Stephen L. Chernof (Vice Chm)
Marci Taxman (Sec)
Moshe Katz (Vice Chm)
Lisa Hiller (Vice Chm)
Pat Cornett (Dir-Acctg-Bus Svcs)
Ellie Gettinger (Dir-Education)
Shay Pilnik (Exec Dir)
Hannah Greenstein (VP-Outreach, Israel & Overseas)
Lauren Berger (Dir-Young Leadership)
Michelle Brookshire (Accountant)
Caren Goldberg (Chief Dev Officer)
Eileen Graves (Vice Chm)
Sharyl Paley (Vice Chm)
Michael Pollack (Vice Chm)

MILWAUKEE METROPOLITAN SEWERAGE DISTRICT
260 W Seeboth St, Milwaukee, WI 53204-1446
Tel.: (414) 272-5100
Web Site: http://www.mmsd.com
Year Founded: 1913
Sales Range: $25-49.9 Million
Emp.: 232
Sewerage Systems
N.A.I.C.S.: 221320
Kevin Shafer (Exec Dir)
Shelley Mazurek (Coord-Customer Svc)
Jeff Spence (Dir-Agency Svcs)
Susan Anthony (Dir-Legal Svcs)
Peter R. Topczewski (Dir-Water Quality Protection)
Gregory Hottinger (Mgr-CMOM & Asset Mgmt Program)
Patrick Obenauf (Mgr-Contract Compliance)
Candace M. Richards (Mgr-HR)
Robert Carroll (Mgr-Info Sys)
David Kasper (Mgr-Section)
Urbain Boudjou (Project Mgr)

MILWAUKEE PC INC.
6013 W Bluemound Rd, Milwaukee, WI 53213
Tel.: (414) 258-2275
Web Site: http://www.milwaukeepc.com
Rev.: $15,000,000
Emp.: 100
Computer Terminal Mfr
N.A.I.C.S.: 334118
Jim Petr (CEO)

MILWAUKEE REGIONAL MEDICAL CENTER, INC.
9000 W Wisconsin Ave Ste C165, Milwaukee, WI 53226
Tel.: (414) 778-4570   WI
Web Site: http://www.mrmccampus.org
Year Founded: 1977
Sales Range: $10-24.9 Million
Emp.: 69
Health Care Srvices
N.A.I.C.S.: 622110
Bob Simi (Exec Dir)
Bob Mlynarek (VP-Fin)

MILWAUKEE SYMPHONY ORCHESTRA INC.
1101 N Market St Ste 100, Milwaukee, WI 53202
Tel.: (414) 291-6010
Web Site: http://www.mso.org
Sales Range: $10-24.9 Million
Emp.: 120
Symphony Orchestra
N.A.I.C.S.: 711110
Luther Gray (Mgr-Patron Svcs)
Renee Logee (Gen Mgr)
Mary Novak (Mgr-HR)
Linda Unkefer (Mgr-Orchestra Personnel)
Catherine Kiekhofer (CFO & VP-Fin & Admin)
Karli Larsen (Dir-Education)
Jennifer Samuelson (Dir-Mktg)
John Roloff (Dir-Ops)
Jenene Cherney (Dir-Production)
Maggey Oplinger (Dir-Shared Experiences)
Kathryn Reinardy (Mgr-Digital Comm)
Mark Niehaus (Pres & Exec Dir)
Pam Garvey (VP-Dev)
Susan Loris (Exec VP & Gen Mgr)
Ken-David Masur (Dir-Music)

MILWAUKEE VALVE COMPANY, INC.
16550 W Stratton Dr, New Berlin, WI 53151-7301
Tel.: (262) 432-2800   WI
Web Site: http://www.milwaukeevalve.com
Year Founded: 1901
Sales Range: $150-199.9 Million
Emp.: 640
Mfr of Specialty Valves
N.A.I.C.S.: 332919
Tom Laguardia (VP-Sls & Mktg)
Ricky Seward (VP-Sls)
Joe Myers (Reg Mgr)
Chris Tarantello (Reg Mgr)
Elias Rizk (VP-Marine)
Tammy Wallch (Head-HR)
Glenn Whelan (Mgr-Customer Svc)
Julie Olson (Mgr-Govt Sls)

Subsidiaries:

Hammond Valve Corp. (1)
16550 W Stratton Dr, New Berlin, WI 53151
Tel.: (262) 432-2702
Web Site: http://www.hammondvalve.com
Sales Range: $25-49.9 Million
Emp.: 200
Plumbing & Heating; Industrial Bronze; Iron; Ball & Butterfly; Cast Carbon & Stainless Steel Valves
N.A.I.C.S.: 332919
Tom Laguardia (VP-Sls & Mktg)
Glenn Whelan (Mgr-Customer Svc)

MILWAUKIE LUMBER COMPANY

MILWAUKIE LUMBER COMPANY

Milwaukie Lumber Company—(Continued)
10998 SE 21st Ave, Portland, OR 97222
Tel.: (503) 654-5417
Web Site:
http://www.milwaukielumber.com
Sales Range: $10-24.9 Million
Emp.: 92
Lumber & Building Material Whslr
N.A.I.C.S.: 444110
Steve Morse (Pres)

MILWHITE INC.
5487 S Padre Island Hwy, Brownsville, TX 78521
Tel.: (956) 547-1970
Web Site: http://www.milwhite.com
Rev.: $20,463,934
Emp.: 10
Specialty Earth Mining
N.A.I.C.S.: 493110
Orlando Osuna (Dir-Health Science Div)
Hector Guerrero (Mgr-Fin)

MIMEO.COM, INC.
460 Park Ave S Fl 8, New York, NY 10016
Tel.: (212) 847-3000
Web Site: http://www.mimeo.com
Year Founded: 1999
Sales Range: $10-24.9 Million
Emp.: 160
Document Printing & Delivery Services
N.A.I.C.S.: 561410
David Uyttendaele (Co-Founder & CTO)

Subsidiaries:

HubCast, Inc. (1)
701 Edgewater Dr Ste 150, Wakefield, MA 01880
Tel.: (781) 221-7200
Web Site: http://www.hubcast.com
Emp.: 300
Commercial Print & Shipping
N.A.I.C.S.: 323111
Aron Blume (VP-Ops)
Timothy Corkery (Pres & CEO)
Adam Bellusci (VP-Products & Tech)

MINACT INC.
5220 Keele St, Jackson, MS 39206-4302
Tel.: (601) 362-1631 MI
Web Site: http://www.minact.com
Year Founded: 1978
Sales Range: $75-99.9 Million
Emp.: 1,200
Provider of Job Training & Related Services
N.A.I.C.S.: 624310
Booker Jones (Founder & Pres)
Jacqueline Beasley (Sr VP-Admin)
Patrick Smith (VP-Ops)
Mark Brantley (VP-Fiscal Svcs)
Lyn Dockter-Pinnick (VP-Ops)
Reuben V. Anderson (Chm)
Augustus Leon Collins (CEO)
Delois White (VP-Ops)
Kabah S. Ealy (VP-HR)

MINARD RUN OIL COMPANY
609 South Ave, Bradford, PA 16701
Tel.: (814) 362-3531
Web Site:
http://www.minardrunoil.com
Sales Range: $10-24.9 Million
Emp.: 61
Oil & Gas Drilling Services
N.A.I.C.S.: 213111
Jim MacFarlane (CEO)

MINARDOS CONSTRUCTION & ASSOCIATES
2800 28th St Ste 170, Santa Monica, CA 90405
Tel.: (310) 450-6900 CA
Year Founded: 1996
Sales Range: $1-9.9 Million
Emp.: 17
Commercial & Institutional Building Construction
N.A.I.C.S.: 236220
George Minardos (Founder & CEO)
Brett Butler (Pres & Gen Mgr)
Larry Adkins (Sr Project Mgr & Mgr-Building Grp)

MINCO MANUFACTURING, LLC
4194 Center Park Dr, Colorado Springs, CO 80916
Tel.: (719) 550-1223
Web Site: http://www.mincomfg.com
Year Founded: 1992
Printing Roller & Sleeve Mfr
N.A.I.C.S.: 333310
Mark Flesher (VP-Sls)
Judy Holt (Mgr-HR & Safety)

MINCO PRODUCTS, INC.
7300 Commerce Ln NE, Minneapolis, MN 55432-3113
Tel.: (763) 571-3121 MN
Web Site: http://www.minco.com
Year Founded: 1956
Sales Range: $50-74.9 Million
Emp.: 600
Flexible Interconnect Circuits & Temperature Detecting Instruments Mfr
N.A.I.C.S.: 334412
Dana Schurr (Pres & CEO)

Subsidiaries:

Minco EC AG (1)
Poststrasse 5, CH 9500, Wil, Switzerland
Tel.: (41) 719527989
Sales Range: $10-24.9 Million
Emp.: 3
Flexible Interconnect Circuits & Temperature Detecting Instruments Mfr
N.A.I.C.S.: 334412

Minco GmbH (1)
Lebacher Strasse 4, 66113, Saarbrucken, Germany
Tel.: (49) 6819963630
Sales Range: $10-24.9 Million
Emp.: 2
Flexible Interconnect Circuits & Temperature Detecting Instruments Mfr
N.A.I.C.S.: 334412

Minco Ltd (1)
Endeavour House, London Stansted Airport, London, CM24 1SJ, Essex, United Kingdom
Tel.: (44) 1279669464
Flexible Interconnect Circuits & Temperature Detecting Instruments Mfr
N.A.I.C.S.: 334412

Minco SA (1)
Zone Industrielle, 09310, Aston, France
Tel.: (33) 561032401
Web Site: http://www.ap.minco.com
Sales Range: $25-49.9 Million
Electronics Mfr
N.A.I.C.S.: 334417

MIND OVER MACHINES, INC.
10451 Mill Run Cir Ste 900, Owings Mills, MD 21117
Tel.: (410) 321-4700
Web Site:
http://www.mindovermachines.com
Year Founded: 1989
Rev.: $8,100,000
Emp.: 49
Custom Computer Programming Services
N.A.I.C.S.: 541511
Tom Loveland (Founder & CEO)
Dmitry Cherches (CTO)
Paul-Sean Gray (COO)
Rick Mosca (VP-Consulting Svcs)

Dustin Sitton (Co-CTO)
Brenda Kahler (Dir-Recruiting)
Brian Bailey (Dir-Solutions Engrg)
Stefan Subotich (Dir-Strategic Partnerships)
Lisa Nugent (VP-HR)
Ed Mullin (VP-IT Strategy)
Tim Kulp (Chief Innovation Officer)
Steve Navarro (Chief Revenue Officer & Gen Mgr)

MIND RESEARCH INSTITUTE
111 Academy Dr Ste 100, Irvine, CA 92617
Tel.: (949) 345-8700 CA
Web Site:
http://www.mindresearch.net
Year Founded: 1998
Rev.: $7,812,431
Assets: $8,318,845
Liabilities: $8,229,605
Net Worth: $89,240
Earnings: ($4,743,584)
Fiscal Year-end: 06/30/14
Educational Support Services
N.A.I.C.S.: 611710
Greg Blevins (CFO)
Jason Brown (CTO)
Janine Ingram (VP-Philanthropic Partnerships)
Jim Lund (VP-Education Svcs)
Art McCoy (Chief Academic Officer)
Matthew Peterson (Co-Founder & CEO)
Nigel Nisbet (VP-Content Creation)
Kathy Naylor (VP-HR & Talent)
Theresa Poprac (Chief Partnerships Officer)
Mark Bodner (Co-Founder & Pres-Res Div)
Karin Wu (VP-Engagement)
John Phelan (Chm)

MIND YOUR BUSINESS, INC.
305 8th Ave E, Hendersonville, NC 28792
Web Site: http://www.mybinc.com
Year Founded: 1996
Sales Range: $1-9.9 Million
Emp.: 50
Human Resource Consulting Services
N.A.I.C.S.: 541612
Karen Caruso (Founder & CEO)
Mabel Machin (CFO)
Renee Heider (Mgr-EEO Program)

MINDBANK CONSULTING GROUP OF VIRGINIA, INC.
10780 Pkrdg Blvd Ste 150, Reston, VA 20191
Tel.: (703) 893-4700 VA
Web Site: http://www.mindbank.com
Year Founded: 1986
Sales Range: $25-49.9 Million
Emp.: 200
Computer Hardware & Software Consulting Services
N.A.I.C.S.: 541512
Judy Perrault (CEO)

MINDCOMET CORPORATION
385 Pearl Lk Causeway, Altamonte Springs, FL 32714
Tel.: (407) 838-1010 FL
Sales Range: $10-24.9 Million
Emp.: 50
Advertising Services
N.A.I.C.S.: 541810
Jennifer Carey (VP-Ops)
Marcelle Turner (Pres & CEO)

Subsidiaries:

MindComet (1)
260 Madison Ave 8th Fl, New York, NY 10016

Tel.: (646) 216-2195
Sales Range: $10-24.9 Million
Emp.: 25
N.A.I.C.S.: 541810

MindComet (1)
6080 Center Dr 6th Fl, Los Angeles, CA 90045
Tel.: (310) 242-6732
N.A.I.C.S.: 541810

MINDFIRE ENTERTAINMENT
3740 Overland Ave Ste E, Los Angeles, CA 90034
Tel.: (310) 204-4481
Year Founded: 1997
Sales Range: $10-24.9 Million
Emp.: 100
Film, Television, Multi-Media & Music Publisher & Producer
N.A.I.C.S.: 512110
Mark A. Altman (CEO)
Mark Gottwald (Chm)

Subsidiaries:

CFQ Media, LLC (1)
29219 Canwood St Ste 100, Agoura Hills, CA 91301-1582
Tel.: (310) 204-2029
Sales Range: Less than $1 Million
Emp.: 10
Genre Film Magazines Publisher
N.A.I.C.S.: 513120

MINDLANCE, INC.
80 River St 4a, Hoboken, NJ 07030
Tel.: (201) 386-5400
Web Site: http://www.mindlance.com
Sales Range: $10-24.9 Million
Emp.: 225
IT Consulting & Staffing Services
N.A.I.C.S.: 541690
Vikram Kalra (Co-Pres & Mng Dir)
Rajad Dhall (Co-Pres)
Ishrat Jan (Acct Mgr-Sls)
Pankaj Gupta (Sr Acct Mgr)
Rahul Srivastava (Sr Acct Mgr)
Cory Goldstein (Sr Mgr-Delivery)
Shanta Lama (Mgr-Talent Acq & Assoc Acct Mgr)
Vineet Tripathi (Sr Acct Mgr)

MINDLEAF TECHNOLOGIES, INC.
19B Crosby Dr Ste 330, Bedford, MA 01730
Tel.: (781) 275-1845
Web Site: http://www.mindleaf.com
Year Founded: 1993
Sales Range: $1-9.9 Million
Emp.: 140
Information Technology Services for Hospitals
N.A.I.C.S.: 541519
Paresh Shah (Pres)

MINDPATH CARE CENTERS PLLC
4220 Apex Hwy Ste 200, Durham, NC 27713
Tel.: (919) 354-0850
Web Site: https://www.mindpath.com
Year Founded: 1994
Emp.: 299
Health Provider Services
N.A.I.C.S.: 621112

Subsidiaries:

Psychiatric Centers At San Diego, Inc. (1)
6153 Fairmount Ave # 140, San Diego, CA 92120
Tel.: (619) 460-2675
Web Site: http://www.psychiatriccenters.com
Sales Range: $1-9.9 Million
Emp.: 80
Offices of Physicians, Mental Health Specialists
N.A.I.C.S.: 621112

MINDPETAL SOFTWARE SOLUTIONS, INC.
1604 Spring Hill Rd Ste 100, Vienna, VA 22182
Tel.: (703) 546-8527
Web Site: http://www.mindpetal.com
Sales Range: $1-9.9 Million
Emp.: 7
Software Solutions Provider
N.A.I.C.S.: 513210
Paul Grace (CFO)
Sony George (CEO)
Josiah Cushing (VP)
Sam Gupta (Dir-Forms Delivery)
Mukta Noori (VP-HR)
William Wilkey (Sr Dir)
Shankar Pillai (VP-Corp Dev)
Will Choi (COO)
Michael Grace (Sr VP-Program Delivery)
Michael Agrillo (Pres)

Subsidiaries:

Vertical Applications, Inc. (1)
42694 Middle Rdg Pl, Ashburn, VA 20148-5512 **(100%)**
Tel.: (571) 213-9192
Web Site: https://www.verticalapps.com
General Management Consulting Services
N.A.I.C.S.: 541611

MINDPOWER INC
337 Georgia Ave SE, Atlanta, GA 30312
Tel.: (404) 581-1991
Web Site: http://www.mindpowerinc.com
Year Founded: 1994
Sales Range: $1-9.9 Million
Emp.: 18
Advertising Agency & Marketing Consulting Services
N.A.I.C.S.: 541810
Donna Bowling (VP)
Bo Uzzle (Dir-Art)
Lisa Jordan (Pres)
Preetam Printz (Acct Dir)

MINDS-EYE-VIEW, INC.
48 Western Ave, Cohoes, NY 12047
Tel.: (518) 237-1975
Web Site: http://www.ipix.com
Year Founded: 1989
Sales Range: $10-24.9 Million
Emp.: 4
Spherical Photography Products
N.A.I.C.S.: 333310
Ford Oxaal (Founder & Pres)

MINDSEED CORPORATION
926 85th Ave, Oakland, CA 94621
Tel.: (510) 957-1240
Year Founded: 1979
Sales Range: $1-9.9 Million
Emp.: 5
Mfr & Producer of Multimedia
N.A.I.C.S.: 336510
Joanne Anderson (Pres)
Edwin Anderson (CEO)

MINDSEEKER, INC.
20130 Lakeview Centre Plz Ste 320, Ashburn, VA 20147
Tel.: (571) 313-5950
Web Site: http://www.mindseeker.com
Year Founded: 2000
Sales Range: $10-24.9 Million
Emp.: 135
Information Technology & Enterprise Performance Management Services & Solutions to Commercial & Government Clients
N.A.I.C.S.: 561311

Chris Dobson (Founder & Pres)
Tom Lamendola (Mng Partner)
Don Muse (Mgr-Acct)
Andy Zeweri (CFO)

MINDSHARE TECHNOLOGIES, INC.
310 E 4500 South Ste 450, Salt Lake City, UT 84107
Tel.: (801) 263-2333
Web Site: http://www.mshare.net
Year Founded: 1996
Sales Range: $10-24.9 Million
Emp.: 100
Enterprise Feedback Management Software
N.A.I.C.S.: 513210
John Sperry (CEO)
Derek Newbold (CTO)
Jon Sanderson (VP-Mktg)
John Crofts (VP-Text Analytics)
Brad Clark (COO)
Chadly D. Hortin (Sr VP-Mktg Insights)
Kurt Williams (Chief Product Officer)
Lonnie Mayne (Pres)
Greg Lloyd (VP-Customer Experience Strategy)
Sandra Tamburino (Sr Dir-Mktg Insights)
Randy Jordan (Sr VP-Bus Solutions-Food Svc)
Erich Dietz (VP-Bus Solutions-Contact Centers)
Mark Heap (CEO-Europe, Middle East & Africa)

Subsidiaries:

InMoment Mississauga (1)
2121 Argentia Road Suite 200, Mississauga, L5N 2X4, ON, Canada
Tel.: (905) 542-9001
Web Site: http://www.inmoment.com
Sales Range: $10-24.9 Million
Cloud-Based Customer Experience Management Solutions Software Developer
N.A.I.C.S.: 513210
Bandi Smith (VP-Demand Mktg)

MINDSMACK
311 W 43rd St, New York, NY 10036
Tel.: (732) 348-8785
Web Site: http://www.mindsmack.com
Year Founded: 1997
Sales Range: $10-24.9 Million
Emp.: 40
Advertising Services
N.A.I.C.S.: 541810
Samuel Feuer (CEO)
Marcelo Moyano (Owner)
Vanessa Branco (VP-Adv & Sls)

MINDSPACE
2402 S Rural Rd Ste 201, Tempe, AZ 85282
Tel.: (480) 941-8497
Web Site: http://www.mindspace.net
Sales Range: $1-9.9 Million
Emp.: 25
Advetising Agency
N.A.I.C.S.: 541810
Brent Shetler (Founder, Principal & Dir-Creative)
Erik Rich (Dir-Video)
Todd Young (Dir-Client Svcs)
Meghan Freeney (Mgr-Ops)

MINDSPARK INTERNATIONAL INC.
3860 Windermere Pkwy Ste 204, Cumming, GA 30041
Tel.: (770) 886-9800
Web Site: http://www.mindsparkit.com
Year Founded: 2000
Sales Range: $1-9.9 Million

Emp.: 30
It Consulting
N.A.I.C.S.: 541519
Hema Puvvada (CEO)

MINDSTORM COMMUNICATIONS GROUP, INC.
10316 Feld Farm Ln Ste 200, Charlotte, NC 28210
Tel.: (704) 331-0870
Web Site: http://www.gomindstorm.com
Year Founded: 1999
Sales Range: Less than $1 Million
Emp.: 3
Advertising Services
N.A.I.C.S.: 541810
Jeff Masilun (Partner & Dir-Creative)

MINE SERVICE COMPANY INC.
Hwy 15 S, Hazard, KY 41701
Tel.: (606) 436-3191
Web Site: http://www.mineservicesale.com
Sales Range: $10-24.9 Million
Emp.: 29
Industrial Supplies
N.A.I.C.S.: 423840
Wallace E. Cornett (Pres)

MINE SERVICE INC.
PO Box 32, Rockdale, TX 76567
Tel.: (512) 446-7011
Rev.: $11,000,000
Emp.: 150
Highway Construction
N.A.I.C.S.: 237310
Keith Debault (Pres)

MINE SUPPLY COMPANY INC.
402 South Main St, Carlsbad, NM 88220
Tel.: (505) 887-2888
Web Site: http://www.theminesupplyco.com
Sales Range: $10-24.9 Million
Emp.: 50
Industrial Supplies Distr
N.A.I.C.S.: 423840
Mike Adorjan (Pres)

MINELLA CAPITAL MANAGEMENT LLC
9864 Brassie Bend, Naples, FL 34109
Tel.: (203) 979-2776
Web Site: http://www.minellacap.com
Private Investment Firm
N.A.I.C.S.: 523999
David A. Minella (Mng Member)

Subsidiaries:

W.E. Donoghue & Co., Inc. (1)
One International Pl Ste 2920, Boston, MA 02110
Tel.: (800) 642-4276
Web Site: http://www.donoghue.com
Emp.: 9
Investment Advice
N.A.I.C.S.: 523940
Jeff Thompson (Pres)

MINELLI CONSTRUCTION CO., INC.
300 Corporate Plz, Islandia, NY 11749
Tel.: (631) 232-0222 NY
Web Site: http://www.minelliconstruction.com
Year Founded: 1975
Sales Range: $10-24.9 Million
Emp.: 100
Contractor of Nonresidential Construction
N.A.I.C.S.: 236220
Joseph Spano (VP)

MINER ENTERPRISES, INC.
1200 E State St, Geneva, IL 60134-2440
Tel.: (630) 232-3000 DE
Web Site: http://www.minerent.com
Year Founded: 1894
Sales Range: $75-99.9 Million
Emp.: 120
Transportation & Material Handling Equipments Mfr
N.A.I.C.S.: 336510
Ingrid McClure (Gen Mgr-Mktg)
Chuck Montgomery (Mgr-Engrg Admin)
Andy Kries (Mgr-Mechanical Testing)
Christopher Gaydos (Mgr-Mechanisms Engrg)
Ken James (Mgr-Testing Svcs)
Ric Biehl (Pres & Gen Mgr)
Eric Graves (Reg Mgr-Sls)

Subsidiaries:

Autoquip Corporation (1)
1058 West Industrial Rd, Guthrie, OK 73044
Tel.: (405) 282-5200
Web Site: http://www.autoquip.com
Sales Range: $10-24.9 Million
Emp.: 100
Industrial Equipment & Machinery Mfr
N.A.I.C.S.: 333248
Joe Robillard (Pres)
Steve Castle (Reg Mgr-Sls)
Chris Kuehni (Dir-Ops)
Louis Coleman (Dir-Sls & Mktg)
Julie Rice (Coord-Mktg)

Miner Elastomer Products Corp. (1)
1200 E State St, Geneva, IL 60134
Tel.: (630) 232-3000
Web Site: http://www.minerelastomer.com
General Merchandise Retailer
N.A.I.C.S.: 455219

Powerbrace Corporation (1)
7640 60th Ave, Kenosha, WI 53142-4098
Tel.: (262) 694-3202
Web Site: http://www.powerbrace.com
Emp.: 47
Motor Vehicle Parts Mfr
N.A.I.C.S.: 336390
John Swezey (Pres & Gen Mgr-Bus Dev)
Brian Senn (Dir-Bus Dev)

MINER'S INCORPORATED
5065 Miller Trunk Hwy, Hermantown, MN 55811-1442
Tel.: (218) 729-5882 MN
Web Site: http://www.superonefoods.com
Year Founded: 1957
Sales Range: $100-124.9 Million
Emp.: 2,500
Owner & Operator of Grocery Stores
N.A.I.C.S.: 445110
Teresa Lorentz (Controller)
Gregory Borash (CFO)

MINERALLAC CO.
100 Gast Rd, Hampshire, IL 60140-7654
Tel.: (630) 543-7080 IL
Web Site: http://www.minerallac.com
Year Founded: 1894
Sales Range: $75-99.9 Million
Emp.: 50
Steel & Plastic Fasteners Mfr for Electrical Telecommunications & Utility Industry
N.A.I.C.S.: 335932
Steve Yoder (VP-Natl Accts)
James Hlavacek (Pres)
Stan Hilty (Exec VP)
Torrie Palumbo (VP-Bus Dev)

MINERALTECH GULF COAST ABRASIVES, LLC
11501 Crosby Lynchburg Rd, Highlands, TX 77562

MineralTech Gulf Coast Abrasives, LLC—(Continued)
Tel.: (281) 462-4220
Web Site: http://www.mineraltechllc.com
Abrasive Product Mfr
N.A.I.C.S.: 327910
Alecia Barbo (Office Mgr)
Alecia Y'Barbo (Office Mgr)

Subsidiaries:

Specialty Sand Co. (1)
16601 Garrett Rd, Houston, TX 77044-5957
Tel.: (409) 746-2290
Web Site: http://www.specialtysand.com
Mining
N.A.I.C.S.: 212312
Bill Keckley (Pres)

MINERS AND MERCHANTS BANCORP, INC.
20089 Riverside Dr, Grundy, VA 24614
Tel.: (276) 935-8161
Web Site: http://www.trupointbank.com
Sales Range: $25-49.9 Million
Emp.: 50
Bank Holding Company
N.A.I.C.S.: 551111
Susan Paris (Mgr-Mktg)
Barry C. Elswick (Pres & CEO)

MING CORPORATION
34 53rd Southwest Temple, Murray, UT 84107-3816
Tel.: (801) 281-8585   NE
Year Founded: 1935
Sales Range: $50-74.9 Million
Emp.: 10
Franchiser of Auto Detailing & Protection Centers
N.A.I.C.S.: 722511
Tony Noonan (VP)
Mark Cunha (Pres)

MINGLE, LLC
701 B St Ste 540, San Diego, CA 92101
Tel.: (619) 618-4200
Web Site: http://www.minglellc.com
Year Founded: 2005
Sales Range: $1-9.9 Million
Emp.: 16
Career Counselling & Recruiting Services
N.A.I.C.S.: 561311
Nicholas M. Jimenez (COO & Exec VP)
Michael C. O'Brien (CEO)

Subsidiaries:

Climber.com (1)
701 B Street Suite 520, San Diego, CA 92101
Tel.: (619) 618-4205
Web Site: http://www.climber.com
Sales Range: $1-9.9 Million
Emp.: 40
Networks & Connects Professionals with Hiring Managers & Recruiters
N.A.I.C.S.: 561311
Michael C. O'Brien (Co-Founder & CEO)
Nicholas M. Jimenez (Pres & Exec VP)
Casey R. Gustus (Exec VP)

MINGLEDORFF'S INC.
6675 Jones Mill Ct, Norcross, GA 30092-3622
Tel.: (770) 446-6311
Web Site: http://www.mingledorffs.com
Sales Range: $10-24.9 Million
Emp.: 450
Whslr of Air Conditioning & Heating Equipment
N.A.I.C.S.: 423730
David R. Kesterton (Pres & CEO)

Subsidiaries:

Mechanical Equipment Co. Inc. (1)
111-B Tanner St, Lawrenceville, GA 30046
Tel.: (770) 963-6226
Web Site: http://www.mechanicalequipment.net
Warm Air Heating & Air Conditioning
N.A.I.C.S.: 423730
Brandon Childress (Pres & CEO)
Louise Barber (Sec)

MINGS SUPERMARKET INC.
1102 Washington St, Boston, MA 02118
Tel.: (617) 338-1588
Rev.: $15,858,927
Emp.: 50
Grocery Stores, Independent
N.A.I.C.S.: 445110
Chin Lee (Pres)

MINGUS CONSTRUCTORS INCORPORATED
917 Main St, Clarkdale, AZ 86324
Tel.: (928) 634-9556   AZ
Year Founded: 1978
Sales Range: $10-24.9 Million
Emp.: 60
Water Main Construction
N.A.I.C.S.: 237110
Eric Arnett (Controller-Acctg)
Guy Bluff (Treas)

MINI CENTER OF SAN ANTONIO
8434 Airport Blvd, San Antonio, TX 78216
Tel.: (210) 732-7121
Web Site: http://www.principalauto.com
Sales Range: $10-24.9 Million
Emp.: 70
Car Whslr
N.A.I.C.S.: 441110
Nick Vanderpool (Gen Mgr)

MINI MELTS INC.
245 Asylum St, Norwich, CT 06360
Tel.: (860) 889-7300
Web Site: http://www.minimelts.com
Year Founded: 2000
Sales Range: $1-9.9 Million
Emp.: 25
Cryogenically Frozen Desserts
N.A.I.C.S.: 311520
Tom Mosey (Owner, Pres & CEO)

MINI-GOLF, INC.
202 Bridge St, Jessup, PA 18434-1302
Tel.: (570) 489-8623
Web Site: http://www.minigolfinc.com
Year Founded: 1981
Sales Range: Less than $1 Million
Emp.: 32
Portable, Pre-Fabricated Miniature Golf Course Mfr
N.A.I.C.S.: 339920
Joseph Buckshon Jr. (Pres)

MINI-SYSTEMS, INC.
20 David Rd, North Attleboro, MA 02760
Tel.: (508) 695-0203   MA
Web Site: http://www.mini-systemsinc.com
Rev.: $20,000,000
Emp.: 200
Electronic Resistor Mfr
N.A.I.C.S.: 334416
Richard Charbonneau (Pres)
Rana Duff (Ops Mgr)
Heather Edwards (Mgr-Sls)

Subsidiaries:

Mini-Systems, Inc. - Electronic Package Division (1)
168 E Bacon St, Plainville, MA 02762
Tel.: (508) 695-2000
Web Site: http://www.mini-systemsinc.com
Rev.: $5,152,000
Emp.: 23
Radio & Television Broadcasting & Wireless Communications Equipment Mfr
N.A.I.C.S.: 334220
Richard Charbonneau (VP & Gen Mgr)

MINILEC SERVICE INCORPORATED
9207 Dering Ave, Chatsworth, CA 91311
Tel.: (818) 773-6300
Web Site: http://www.minilec.com
Sales Range: $10-24.9 Million
Emp.: 60
Intercommunication Equipment Repair
N.A.I.C.S.: 811210
Martin A. Schwartz (Pres)

MINING MACHINERY INC.
1512 N Big Run Rd, Ashland, KY 41102
Tel.: (606) 928-0490
Web Site: http://www.mining-machinery.com
Emp.: 30
Industrial Machinery & Equipment Repair
N.A.I.C.S.: 811210
Shane Willis (Owner & Pres)

Subsidiaries:

MMI Services LLC (1)
1512 N Big Run Rd, Ashland, KY 41102
Tel.: (606) 928-3433
Rev.: $5,000,000
Emp.: 40
Equipment Rental & Leasing
N.A.I.C.S.: 532490

MINIT STOP
385 Hukilike St, Kahului, HI 96732
Tel.: (808) 270-2870
Web Site: http://www.minitstop.com
Sales Range: $10-24.9 Million
Emp.: 150
Convenience Store
N.A.I.C.S.: 445131
Kim Robello (Mgr-Mktg)
Larry Broadstone (Project Mgr-Facilities)

MINKA LIGHTING INC.
1151 Bradford Ct, Corona, CA 92882
Tel.: (951) 735-9220
Web Site: http://www.minkagroup.net
Rev.: $36,000,000
Emp.: 500
Lighting Fixtures
N.A.I.C.S.: 423610
Marian Tang (CEO)
Allan Ashley (Mgr-Sls-Natl)

Subsidiaries:

Metropolitan Lighting Fixture Co. (1)
200 Lexington Ave Rm 512, New York, NY 10016
Tel.: (212) 545-0032
Web Site: http://www.minkagroup.net
Rev.: $6,100,000
Emp.: 16
Lighting Fixtures
N.A.I.C.S.: 423610

MINKOFF COMPANY INC.
11716 Baltimore Ave, Beltsville, MD 20705-1850
Tel.: (301) 652-8711
Web Site: http://www.minkoff.com
Year Founded: 1949
Sales Range: $10-24.9 Million

Commercial & Office Building Contractors
N.A.I.C.S.: 236220
Barry Minkoff (Pres)

MINMOR INDUSTRIES LLC
6010 Earle Brown Dr, Minneapolis, MN 55430
Tel.: (763) 504-5400
Web Site: http://www.minmor.com
Year Founded: 1980
Prepackaged Food, Lunch Sacks & Food Service Promotional Items; Printing & Packaging
N.A.I.C.S.: 311991
Mark Miner (Pres)
Andrew Clark (Mgr-Digital Mktg)
Michael Mathisen (Sr VP & Gen Mgr)

MINN-DAK FARMERS COOPERATIVE
7525 Red River Rd, Wahpeton, ND 58075-9705
Tel.: (701) 642-8411   ND
Web Site: http://www.mdf.coop
Year Founded: 1972
Sales Range: $300-349.9 Million
Emp.: 315
Beet Sugar Mfr
N.A.I.C.S.: 311313
Thomas D. Knudsen (VP-Agriculture)
John S. Nyquist (Mgr-Pur)
John Wieser (Mgr-IT)
Richard J. Kasper (CFO & Exec VP)
Daniel Otto (Controller)
Kurt Wickstrom (Pres & CEO)

Subsidiaries:

Midwest Agri-Commodities (1)
999 5th Ave Ste 500, San Rafael, CA 94901
Tel.: (415) 259-2720
Web Site: http://www.mwagri.com
Sales Range: $250-299.9 Million
Emp.: 60
Sugar Beet Pulp, Molasses & Raffinates Whslr
N.A.I.C.S.: 424490
Jim Eichenberger (Pres)
Tim Klovstad (Mgr-Natl Sls)
Roger Roslund (Mgr-Sls)
Kevin Christensen (VP-Fin)

Minn-Dak Yeast Company Inc. (1)
18175 Red River Rd W, Wahpeton, ND 58075-9706
Tel.: (701) 642-3300
Web Site: http://www.mdyc.com
Sales Range: $10-24.9 Million
Emp.: 20
Food Preparations
N.A.I.C.S.: 311999
Richard Ames (Mgr-Factory)

United Sugars Corp. (1)
524 Center Ave, Moorhead, MN 56560
Tel.: (218) 236-4740
Web Site: http://www.unitedsugars.com
Rev.: $16,500,000
Emp.: 30
Beet Sugar Manufacturing
N.A.I.C.S.: 424590
Lee Glass (Dir-Transportation)
Christi Thielke (Mgr-Customer Svc)

MINN-DAK GROWERS, LTD.
Hwy 81 N, Grand Forks, ND 58208-3276
Tel.: (701) 746-7453   ND
Web Site: http://www.minndak.com
Year Founded: 1967
Sales Range: $50-74.9 Million
Emp.: 28
Miller of Buckwheat & Mustard
N.A.I.C.S.: 115114
Harris A. Peterson (Pres & Gen Mgr)

MINN-DAK INC.
3440 36th St SW, Fargo, ND 58104
Tel.: (701) 293-9133

Web Site:
http://www.fargofreightliner.com
Sales Range: $10-24.9 Million
Emp.: 65
Trucks, Commercial
N.A.I.C.S.: 423110
Ron W. Ristvedt (Pres)
Shane Giesen (Controller)

MINN-KOTA AG PRODUCTS, INC.
90 8th St N, Breckenridge, MN 56520-1556
Tel.: (218) 643-8464   MN
Web Site: http://www.mkap.com
Year Founded: 1990
Sales Range: $10-24.9 Million
Emp.: 50
Grain Elevator & Field Beans
N.A.I.C.S.: 424510
Marlyn Anderson (Controller)
Brian Arnhalt (Treas)
George M. Schuler III (Pres)

MINNEAPOLIS PUBLIC HOUSING AUTHORITY
1001 Washington Ave N, Minneapolis, MN 55401
Tel.: (612) 342-1400
Web Site: http://www.mphaonline.org
Sales Range: $50-74.9 Million
Emp.: 280
Housing Authority Operator
N.A.I.C.S.: 925110
Betty Battle (Mgr-Leasing & Occupancy)
Dennis A. Goldberg (COO & Deputy Exec Dir)
Jan Hughes (Mgr-Pub Housing)
Carol Kubic (Gen Counsel)
Kari Lee (Mgr-Property)
Susan Norby (Mgr-HR & EEO)
Bradley Scott (Coord-Community Svcs)
Mary Smalls (Reg Mgr-Property)

MINNEAPOLIS RAG STOCK CO. INC.
113 27th Ave NE Ste I, Minneapolis, MN 55418
Tel.: (612) 333-6576
Web Site: http://www.ragstock.com
Sales Range: $10-24.9 Million
Emp.: 87
Clothing, Secondhand
N.A.I.C.S.: 459510
Mike Finn (Pres)

MINNEAPOLIS SOCIETY OF FINE ARTS
2400 3rd Ave S, Minneapolis, MN 55404
Tel.: (612) 870-3000   MN
Web Site: http://www.artsmia.org
Year Founded: 1883
Sales Range: $25-49.9 Million
Emp.: 361
Art Exhibition Organizer
N.A.I.C.S.: 561920
Kevin Feldman (Dir-Institutional Bus)

MINNEAPOLIS-SAINT PAUL INTERNATIONAL AIRPORT
6040 28th Ave S, Minneapolis, MN 55450
Tel.: (612) 726-8100
Web Site: http://www.mspairport.org
Year Founded: 1923
Sales Range: $25-49.9 Million
Emp.: 500
Airport
N.A.I.C.S.: 488119
Jeffrey W. Hamiel (CEO)
Bob Schauer (Controller)
Tim Anderson (Vice Chm)
Brian Ryks (CEO)

MINNESOTA AG GROUP INC.
32907 Northfield Blvd, Northfield, MN 55057-1492
Tel.: (507) 645-6643   MN
Web Site: http://www.mnaggroup.com
Year Founded: 1996
Sales Range: $25-49.9 Million
Emp.: 87
Retailer of Farm & Garden Machinery
N.A.I.C.S.: 423820
Bob Shanks (Pres)
Carolyn Koziolek (Controller)

Subsidiaries:

Bishop & Wachholz Inc.   (1)
601 8th St SE, Kasson, MN 55944-1807
Tel.: (507) 634-4388
Web Site: http://www.mnaggroup.com
Sales Range: $10-24.9 Million
Emp.: 10
Farm & Garden Machinery
N.A.I.C.S.: 423820
Craig Poppie (Mgr)

Larson Implement Inc.   (1)
32907 Northfield Blvd, Northfield, MN 55057-1492
Tel.: (507) 645-6643
Web Site: http://www.mnaggroup.com
Sales Range: $10-24.9 Million
Emp.: 20
Farm & Garden Machinery Retail
N.A.I.C.S.: 423820

Plainview Agri Power Inc.   (1)
400 10th St SW, Plainview, MN 55964
Tel.: (507) 534-3195
Web Site: http://www.mnaggroup.com
Sales Range: $1-9.9 Million
Emp.: 21
Farm & Garden Machinery
N.A.I.C.S.: 423820
Susan Shanks (Mgr-Mktg)

MINNESOTA COMMERCIAL RAILWAY CO.
508 Cleveland Ave N, Saint Paul, MN 55114
Tel.: (651) 646-2010   MN
Web Site: http://www.mnnr.net
Year Founded: 1987
Sales Range: $10-24.9 Million
Emp.: 75
Railroad Terminals
N.A.I.C.S.: 488101
Wayne Hall (Co-Pres & COO)
Bryan Tschudy (Dir-HR)
Mike Lebakken (Co-Pres & CFO)
Robert Johnson (Dir-Ops)
Robert Johnson (Dir/Asst Dir-Ops)
Mike Lebakken (Co-Pres, CFO & Mgr-Acctg)
Bryan Tschudy (Dir/Mgr-HR)
Ken Noren (Chief Mechanical Officer-)
Josh Waltman (Chief Mechanical Officer-)
Dave Sanders (Chief Mechanical Officer-)
Robert Bagaus (Chief Maintenance of Way & Signals Officer)
Wayne Hall Jr. (Dir-Ops & Indus Dev)

MINNESOTA DEHYDRATED VEGETABLES, INC.
915 Omland Ave N, Fosston, MN 56542
Tel.: (218) 435-1997
Web Site: http://www.mdvcorp.com
Year Founded: 1990
Sales Range: $10-24.9 Million
Emp.: 82
Dried & Dehydrated Food Mfr
N.A.I.C.S.: 311423
Larry Altringer (Owner)
Tom Erhart (Mgr-Packaging)
John Goehke (Dir-Quality Control)
Karla Holm (Controller-Inventory)

MINNESOTA DIVERSIFIED INDUSTRIES
3501 Broadway St NE Ste 100, Minneapolis, MN 55413
Tel.: (651) 999-8200
Web Site: http://www.mdi.org
Sales Range: $25-49.9 Million
Emp.: 138
Packaging & Shipping Materials, Foamed Plastics
N.A.I.C.S.: 561910
Peter McDermott (Pres & CEO)
Rod Wood (VP-Ops)
Barb Majerus (VP-Sls)
Marv Hannon (CFO)
Debi Thompson (Dir-HR)
John Stemper (Dir-Mktg & New Ventures)

MINNESOTA ELEVATOR INC.
19336 607th Ave, Mankato, MN 56001
Tel.: (507) 245-3060
Web Site: http://www.meielevatorsolutions.com
Year Founded: 1971
Sales Range: $10-24.9 Million
Emp.: 200
Elevators & Equipment
N.A.I.C.S.: 333921
Rick Lowenberg (Pres)
Roxie Weingartz (Supvr-Supply Chain)
Bern Beckman (Product Mgr-Line)
Don Goltz (Mgr-Field Ops)
Kevin Peterson (Supvr-Paint)
Kirk Yungerberg (Acct Mgr)
Mike Klehr (VP-Sls)
Paul Rollenhagen (Supvr-Cab Engrg)

MINNESOTA EQUIPMENT, INC.
13725 Main St, Rogers, MN 55374
Tel.: (763) 428-4107
Web Site: http://minnesotaequipment.com
Year Founded: 1916
Lawn & Garden Equipment Sales
N.A.I.C.S.: 444230
Mike Scharber (Owner)

MINNESOTA FLEXIBLE CORP.
803 Transfer Rd, Saint Paul, MN 55114
Tel.: (651) 645-7522   MN
Web Site: http://www.mfchose.com
Year Founded: 1969
Sales Range: $10-24.9 Million
Emp.: 60
Metal Hose & Tubing Mfr & Distr
N.A.I.C.S.: 423840
Terry Kelly (VP-Ops)
Will Stewart (CEO)

Subsidiaries:

General Rubber Co.   (1)
16988 W Victor Rd, New Berlin, WI 53151
Tel.: (262) 754-5522
Web Site: http://www.generalrubber.com
Sales Range: $1-9.9 Million
Emp.: 11
Rubber Products Mfr
N.A.I.C.S.: 339991
Will Stewart (Gen Mgr)
Andy Larsen (Mgr-Sls)

MINNESOTA HISTORICAL SOCIETY
345 W Kellogg Blvd, Saint Paul, MN 55102
Tel.: (651) 259-3000   MN
Web Site: http://www.mnhs.org
Year Founded: 1849
Sales Range: $50-74.9 Million
Emp.: 746
Historical Society Preservation Services
N.A.I.C.S.: 712110

Jill Rudnitski (Chief Dev Officer)
Peggy Ingison (CFO)
Phyllis Rawls Goff (Pres)
Andrea Kajer (Deputy Dir-External Rels)
Chris Taylor (Dir-Inclusion & Community Engagement)
William D. Green (First VP)

MINNESOTA HOCKEY VENTURES GROUP, LP
317 Washington St, Saint Paul, MN 55102-1609
Tel.: (651) 602-6000   MN
Web Site: http://wild.nhl.com
Year Founded: 1997
Holding Company; Professional Hockey Club & Sporting Arena Owner & Operator
N.A.I.C.S.: 551112
Craig Leipold (Co-Owner & Chm)
Robert Naegele Jr. (Founder)

Subsidiaries:

Minnesota Wild Hockey Club, LP   (1)
317 Washington St, Saint Paul, MN 55102-1609
Tel.: (651) 602-6000
Web Site: http://www.wild.nhl.com
Sales Range: $10-24.9 Million
Emp.: 300
Professional Hockey Club Operator
N.A.I.C.S.: 711211
Matt Majka (Pres)
Jim Ibister (VP-Facility Admin & Gen Mgr-RiverCentre)
Sheldon Burns (Dir-Medical)
Craig Leipold (Owner)
Chuck Fletcher (Exec VP & Gen Mgr)
Jeffrey Pellegrom (CFO & Exec VP)
John Maher (VP-Brand, Brdcst & Production)
Carin Anderson (Sr VP-Corp Partnerships & Retail Mgmt)
Brad Bombardir (Dir-Player Dev)
Shep Harder (Asst Gen Mgr)
Andrew Heydt (Dir-Team Ops & Player Rels)
Maria Troje (VP-Customer Svc & Retention)
Steven Weinreich (Gen Counsel & VP)
Mitch Helgerson (Sr VP-Mktg & Ticket Sls)

MINNESOTA SUPPLY COMPANY
6470 Flying Cloud Dr, Eden Prairie, MN 55344
Tel.: (952) 828-7300
Web Site: http://www.mnsupply.com
Rev.: $27,126,310
Emp.: 115
Industrial Machinery & Equipment
N.A.I.C.S.: 423830
Jim Oberg (Mgr-Credit)
Mark Olsen (CFO & COO)

MINNESOTA TEEN CHALLENGE INC
740 E 24th St, Minneapolis, MN 55404
Tel.: (612) 373-3366   MN
Web Site: http://www.mntc.org
Year Founded: 1983
Sales Range: $25-49.9 Million
Emp.: 579
Alcohol & Drug Rehabilitation Services
N.A.I.C.S.: 623220
Jay Coughlan (Chm)
Richard Scherber (Pres)
Eric Vagle (Sec)
Ann Morse (Treas)
Randy Schmidt (Dir-AfterCare)
Tim Walsh (VP-Programs)
Saul Selby (VP-Clinical & Transitional Svcs)
Barry Haglund (VP-Strategic Partnerships)
Laura Zabinski (Mgr-Prevention)
Rafe Ronning (Dir-TCLI)

MINNESOTA TEEN CHALLENGE INC

Minnesota Teen Challenge Inc—(Continued)
Seth Currier (Dir-Northland Duluth Center)
Tom Truszinski (Dir-Rochester Center)
Sarah Gustafson (VP-Fin & Admin)
Mary Brown (VP-Mktg & Events)
Sam Anderson (Dir-Central Minnesota Brainerd Campus)

MINNESOTA TIMBERWOLVES BASKETBALL LIMITED PARTNERSHIP
600 Hennepin Ave Ste 300, Minneapolis, MN 55403-1400
Tel.: (612) 673-1600 MN
Year Founded: 1989
Sports Team & Ticket Distr
N.A.I.C.S.: 711211
Scott Hebert (Sls Mgr-Inside)

MINNESOTA VIKINGS FOOTBALL LLC
9520 Viking Dr, Eden Prairie, MN 55344
Tel.: (952) 828-6500 MN
Web Site: http://www.vikings.com
Year Founded: 1961
Sales Range: $75-99.9 Million
Emp.: 200
Professional Football Franchise
N.A.I.C.S.: 711211
Bob Hagan (Exec Dir-PR)
Rob Brzezinski (Exec VP-Football Ops)
Cheryl Nygaard (Dir-IT)
Dannon Hulskotter (VP-Mktg & Fan Engagement)
Tom West (Asst Dir-PR)
Luther Hippe (Dir-Ops-Team Travel)
Phil Huebner (VP-Ticket Sls & Ops)
Steve Poppen (Chief Bus Admin Officer & Exec VP)
Zygi Wilf (Co-Owner & Chm)
Mark Wilf (Co-Owner & Pres)
Leonard Wilf (Co-Owner & Vice Chm)
David Mandelbaum (Partner-Ownership)
Lester Bagley (Exec VP-Pub Affairs)
George Paton (Asst Gen Mgr)
Paul Nelson (Dir-Football Info Sys)
Dennis Ryan (Mgr-Equipment)
Kim Klawiter (Dir-Security)
Chad Lundeen (VP-Ops & Facilities)
Les Pico (Exec Dir-Player Dev & Legal)
Debra Jones (Sr Mgr-Special Events & Alumni Affairs)
Bryan Harper (VP-Content & Production)
Erin Swartz (Dir-Brand & Creative)
Jeff Anderson (Exec Dir-Comm)
Joe Mee (Sr Mgr-Ticket Ops)
John Neppl (Mgr-Ticket Sls)
Mike Manahan (Mgr-Team Facilities Project)
Jonathan Wilf (Co-Owner & Exec VP-Strategic Plng & Bus Initiatives)
Ryan Monnens (Dir-Pro Scouting)
Bob Marcus (Dir-Video)
John Penhollow (Chief Revenue Officer & Exec VP)
Karin Nelsen (Chief Legal Officer & Exec VP)
Jamaal Stephenson (Dir-College Scouting)
Jon Ekstrom (Mgr-PR)
Justin Miner (Mgr-Facilities)
Natalie Kolander (Mgr-Corp Sls)
Rich Wang (Dir-Sls Analytics & Engagement)
Skip Krueger (Dir-Brdcst)
Andrew Miller (COO)
Scott Landis (Partner-Ownership)
Steven Wilf (Co-Owner & Exec VP-Innovation & Strategy)
Kate Shibilski (CFO & Exec VP)
Martin Nance (CMO & Exec VP)

MINNESOTA VISITING NURSE AGENCY
2000 Summer St Ste 100, Minneapolis, MN 55413
Tel.: (612) 617-4600 MN
Web Site: http://www.mvna.org
Year Founded: 1934
Sales Range: $10-24.9 Million
Emp.: 378
Community Health Care Services
N.A.I.C.S.: 621498
Jeanette Van Liew (Pres & CEO)
Pamela Schaid (COO)
Caren Gaytko (Sr VP-Clinical Svcs)
Dan Smith (CFO)

MINNESOTA WIRE & CABLE COMPANY
1835 Energy Park Dr, Saint Paul, MN 55108
Tel.: (651) 642-1800
Web Site: http://www.mnwire.com
Sales Range: $10-24.9 Million
Emp.: 200
Current-Carrying Wiring Devices
N.A.I.C.S.: 335931
Tom Kukowski (Mgr-R&D)
Bob Pope (Mgr-Accts)
Chris Howells (Mgr-Engrg)
Michelle Westberg (Dir-Quality)
Molly Hackman (Mgr-Bus Dev)

MINNIE HAMILTON HEALTH CARE CENTER INC.
186 Hospital Dr, Grantsville, WV 26147
Tel.: (304) 354-9244 WV
Web Site: http://www.minniehamilton.com
Year Founded: 1983
Sales Range: $10-24.9 Million
Emp.: 299
Health Care Srvices
N.A.I.C.S.:
Stephen S. Whited (CEO)
Dan Given (CFO)

MINNKOTA POWER COOPERATIVE, INC.
5301 32nd Ave S, Grand Forks, ND 58201
Tel.: (701) 795-4000 MN
Web Site: http://www.minnkota.com
Year Founded: 1940
Rev.: $406,396,814
Assets: $1,060,797,950
Liabilities: $910,601,143
Net Worth: $150,196,807
Earnings: $10,099,000
Emp.: 386
Fiscal Year-end: 12/31/18
Electric Power Distr
N.A.I.C.S.: 221122
Steve Arnesen (Vice Chm)
Robert McLennan (Pres & CEO)
Gerad Paul (Gen Counsel & VP-Legal Affairs)
Lowell Stave (COO & VP)
Karen Thingelstad (CFO & VP)
Colette Kujava (Treas & Sec)
Gerry Pfau (Sr Mgr-Project Dev)
Stacey Dahl (Sr Mgr-External Affairs)
Dan Inman (Chief Information Security Officer & VP)
Les Windjue (Chm)
Jami Hovet (VP-Admin)
Craig Bleth (Sr Mgr-Power Production)

Subsidiaries:
Square Butte Electric Cooperative (1)
1822 Mill Rd, Grand Forks, ND 58203 (100%)
Tel.: (701) 795-4000
Web Site: http://www.minnekota.com
Sales Range: $50-74.9 Million
Emp.: 175
Utility
N.A.I.C.S.: 221118

MINNOTTE MANUFACTURING CORPORATION
1 Minnotte Sq, Pittsburgh, PA 15220
Tel.: (412) 922-1633 PA
Web Site: http://www.minnotte.com
Year Founded: 1959
Fabricated Plate Work (Boiler Shop)
N.A.I.C.S.: 332313
Joseph Martin (Reg Mgr-Sls)
Erik Galis (VP-Ops)
Jeff Kiley (Mgr-Construction)
John Lucas (Reg Mgr-Boiler Tube Sls)

MINNWEST CORPORATION
14820 Hwy 7, Minnetonka, MN 55345
Tel.: (952) 545-8815 MN
Web Site: https://www.minnwestbank.com
Year Founded: 1986
Sales Range: $25-49.9 Million
Emp.: 15
Bank Holding Company
N.A.I.C.S.: 551111
John Welle (VP)
Steven Jesme (Sr VP)
Gary Kluthe (Sr VP)

Subsidiaries:
Minnwest Bank (1)
300 S Washington St, Redwood Falls, MN 56283
Tel.: (507) 637-5731
Web Site: https://www.minnwestbank.com
Sales Range: $10-24.9 Million
Emp.: 350
Commercial Banking Services
N.A.I.C.S.: 522110
Douglas Karsky (Pres)
Gale Ripka (Dir-Ops)
Evan Ingebrigtson (Pres)

MINOL USA
15280 Addison Rd Ste 100, Addison, TX 75001
Tel.: (972) 386-6611
Web Site: http://www.minolusa.com
Year Founded: 1999
Sales Range: $1-9.9 Million
Emp.: 100
Energy & Property Management, Conservation & Billing Services
N.A.I.C.S.: 924120
Jeff Boyd (Mgr-Portfolio Rels)

Subsidiaries:
Master Tek International, Inc. (1)
15280 Addison Rd Ste 100, Addison, TX 75001
Tel.: (303) 650-6700
Web Site: http://www.minol.com
Submetering & Utility Billing Services
N.A.I.C.S.: 238290

MINOR RUBBER CO., INC.
49 Ackerman St, Bloomfield, NJ 07003
Tel.: (973) 338-6800 NJ
Web Site: http://www.minorrubber.com
Year Founded: 1914
Sales Range: $75-99.9 Million
Emp.: 120
Molded, Dipped, Extruded, Industrial Rubber & Synthetic Rubber Components & Assembly Mfr

U.S. PRIVATE

N.A.I.C.S.: 326291
R.W. Krumscheid Jr. (Pres)

Subsidiaries:
Minor Rubber Co. (1)
49 Ackerman St, Bloomfield, NJ 07003
Tel.: (972) 484-6477
Web Site: http://www.minorrubber.com
Sales Range: $25-49.9 Million
Emp.: 6
Mfr of Molded, Extruded, Industrial Rubber & Synthetic Rubber Components & Assemblies
N.A.I.C.S.: 423840

MINOT AUTOMOTIVE CENTER
3615 S Broadway, Minot, ND 58701
Tel.: (701) 852-0151
Web Site: http://www.minotautomotive.com
Sales Range: $10-24.9 Million
Emp.: 81
Car Whslr
N.A.I.C.S.: 441110
Larry Durand (Owner)
Jerry Leiss (Mgr-Gen Sls)
Andrea Edwards (Mgr-Recon)
Ryan Schoenwald (Mgr-Svc)

MINOT BUILDERS SUPPLY ASSOCIATION
2626 Burdick Expy W, Minot, ND 58701-5658
Tel.: (701) 852-1301 ND
Year Founded: 1946
Sales Range: $75-99.9 Million
Emp.: 85
Wholesale Distribution of Rough, Dressed & Finished Lumber; Millwork; Building Material
N.A.I.C.S.: 423310
Joel Bosch (Treas & Sec)
Tom Philion (Pres)

MINSON CORPORATION
1 Minson Way, Montebello, CA 90640-6727
Tel.: (323) 513-1041
Web Site: http://www.minson.com
Year Founded: 1980
Sales Range: $10-24.9 Million
Emp.: 150
Mfr & Distributor of Household Wood & Plastic Furniture
N.A.I.C.S.: 337126
Kenneth Chen (Pres)
Ben Hwang (Plant Mgr)

MINSTER BANK
95 W 4th St, Minster, OH 45865
Tel.: (419) 628-2351 OH
Web Site: http://www.minsterbank.com
Year Founded: 1914
Sales Range: $50-74.9 Million
Emp.: 100
Provider of State Commercial Banks
N.A.I.C.S.: 522110
Ken Wuebker (CFO)
Lorrie Loughridge (Mgr-Ops)
Dave Kelch (Branch Mgr)
Daniel Heitmeyer (VP-Comml Banking)
Rhonda Keister (Branch Mgr)
Rex Lippincott (Branch Mgr)
Mark A. Henschen (Pres & CEO)
Steven M. Eiting (Mgr-Private Health Mgmt Dept)

MINT ADVERTISING
120 W Main St, Clinton, NJ 08809
Tel.: (908) 722-9400
Web Site: http://www.mintadvertising.com
Sales Range: $1-9.9 Million
Emp.: 18
Advetising Agency

N.A.I.C.S.: 541810
Eric W. Schoenfeld (CEO)
Al Navarro (Chief Creative Officer)
Billy Joe Pyle III (Dir-Creative)

MINTAKA FINANCIAL, LLC
5403 Olympic Drive NW Ste 200, Gig Harbor, WA 98335-4149
Tel.: (855) 223-6544
Web Site: http://www.mintakafinancial.com
Year Founded: 2004
Commercial Finance Company
N.A.I.C.S.: 522291
Quentin Cote (Pres)
Curtis Costner (VP-Mktg)

Subsidiaries:

Summit Commercial Finance Company (1)
14614 N Kierland Blvd Ste N100, Scottsdale, AZ 85254
Tel.: (480) 348-3777
Web Site: http://www.summitcommercialfinance.com
Equipment Rental & Leasing
N.A.I.C.S.: 532490
Kathy Bytnar (Dir-Ops)
Scott C. Forrest (Pres & CEO)
Jeff Hayes (Sr VP-Lessee Svcs)
Jermane Cheathem (VP-Vendor Svcs)

MINTED LLC.
747 Front St Ste 200, San Francisco, CA 94111
Tel.: (415) 528-2708
Web Site: http://www.minted.com
Year Founded: 2007
Internet & Catalog Online Retailer
N.A.I.C.S.: 449210
Melissa Kim (Founder & Pres)
Jason Eyler (VP-Product Mgmt)
Brady Wood (Sr VP-Artists & Partnerships)
Mariam Naficy (CEO)
Jennifer Gosselin (Sr VP-Mdsg)
Wendy Bergh (Sr VP-Ops & Gen Mgr-Art)
Spencer Lee (CFO & VP-Fin)
Jordan Zamir (Gen Counsel & VP)

Subsidiaries:

Hitched Weddings & Events LLC (1)
923 W 17th St, Kansas City, MO 64108
Tel.: (913) 909-1194
Web Site: http://www.hitchedinkc.com
Event Design Services
N.A.I.C.S.: 711310
Luis Marques (Owner)

MINTON-JONES CO. INC.
1325 Oakbrook Dr, Norcross, GA 30093
Tel.: (770) 449-4787
Web Site: http://www.mintonjones.com
Sales Range: $10-24.9 Million
Emp.: 20
Social Stationery & Greeting Cards
N.A.I.C.S.: 424120
Susan Bauer (CFO)
Ulf Rheborg (VP-Mktg)
Travis W. Jones Jr. (Pres)

MINTZ & HOKE, INC.
40 Tower Ln, Avon, CT 06001-4222
Tel.: (860) 678-0473 CT
Web Site: http://www.mintz-hoke.com
Year Founded: 1971
Sales Range: $10-24.9 Million
Emp.: 45
Advertising & Public Relations Agency
N.A.I.C.S.: 541810
Chris Knopf (CEO)
Mary Farrell (Chief Corp Officer)
Ron Perine (Pres)
Andrew Wood (Sr VP-Strategy & Plng)

Su Strawderman (Sr VP-Creative)
Sara-Beth Donovan (Sr VP-Media)
Grant Sanders (Dir-Creative)

MINTZ, LEVIN, COHN, FERRIS, GLOVSKY & POPEO, P.C.
One Financial Ctr, Boston, MA 02111
Tel.: (617) 542-6000 MA
Web Site: http://www.mintz.com
Year Founded: 1933
Sales Range: $250-299.9 Million
Emp.: 501
Legal Advisory Services
N.A.I.C.S.: 541110
R. Robert Popeo (Chm)
Amy M. Fowler (CMO)
David A. Ballinger (COO)
Andrew R. Urban (Vice Chm)
Carolyn M. Manning (Dir-Bus Dev)
Gina P. Addis (Dir-PR)
Brian K. Mantarian (Dir-Fin)
Wendy L. Starr (Dir-HR)
Fred Pretorius (Dir-IT)
Lori Tarpinian (Dir-Library & Res Svcs)
Alan M. Hertz (Dir-Ops)
David P. Salisbury (Dir-Bus Dev-West Coast)
Jessica L. Clifton (Dir-IP Ops & Practice Mgmt)
Shannon Davis (Dir-Legal Recruiting)
William J. Kyrouz III (Dir-Info Security)

MINUTE KEY, INC.
4760 Walnut St Ste 105, Boulder, CO 80301 DE
Web Site: http://www.minutekey.com
Year Founded: 2008
Sales Range: $10-24.9 Million
Self-Service Key-Making Kiosks Mfr
N.A.I.C.S.: 333310
Randy Fagundo (CEO)
Britain White (VP-Sls-Walmart & Bus Dev)

MINUTEMAN DISTRIBUTORS INC.
4810 Clover Rd, Greensboro, NC 27405
Tel.: (508) 223-5500
Web Site: http://www.eagleequip.com
Rev.: $10,900,000
Emp.: 20
Machine Tools & Accessories
N.A.I.C.S.: 423830

MINUTEMAN PRESS INTERNATIONAL, INC.
61 Exec Blvd, Farmingdale, NY 11735-1510
Tel.: (631) 249-1370 NY
Web Site: http://minutemanpress.com
Year Founded: 1973
Sales Range: $10-24.9 Million
Emp.: 125
Provider of Printing & Copying Services
N.A.I.C.S.: 533110
Roy W. Titus (Chm)
Robert Meyer (Controller)
Stanley M. Katz (Treas & Sec)

MINUTI-OGLE CO. INC.
7030 6th St N, Saint Paul, MN 55128
Tel.: (651) 735-5800
Web Site: http://www.minuti-ogle.com
Year Founded: 1910
Sales Range: $10-24.9 Million
Emp.: 100
Provider of Insulation Services
N.A.I.C.S.: 238310
David Sauter (CEO)

MINYARD FOOD STORES, INC.

8304 Esters Blvd Ste 860, Irving, TX 75063
Tel.: (972) 393-8700 TX
Year Founded: 1932
Rev.: $900,000,000
Emp.: 230
Operator of Retail Groceries & Warehouse Distribution Center
N.A.I.C.S.: 445110
John Piper (Mgr-Pharmacy)
Sylvia Clayton (Office Mgr)

MIPRO CONSULTING, LLC.
1100 Corporate Office Dr Ste 100, Milford, MI 48381
Tel.: (248) 684-1900
Web Site: http://www.miproconsulting.com
Year Founded: 2005
Sales Range: $10-24.9 Million
Emp.: 97
Information Technology Consulting Services
N.A.I.C.S.: 541512
James Allen Prokes (CEO & Mng Partner)
Jeffery V. Micallef (Mng Partner & Exec VP)
Bernadette Sprawka (CFO & Mng Partner)
Larry Zagata (Mng Partner & VP)
Jeff Keller (VP-Talent Acq)
Jennifer Berry (Dir-HR)
Gayla Burns (Dir-Central Reg)
Bob Neely (Dir-Southeast Reg)
David Scott (Dir-Northeast Reg)
Michael Rigano (Dir-Northwest Reg)
Shannon Roche (Dir-PeopleSoft Practice)
Troy Richardson (Sr VP-Oracle Strategic Alliances)

MIR, MITCHELL & COMPANY, LLP
105 Decker Ct Ste 1100, Irving, TX 75062-2211
Tel.: (972) 893-0300
Web Site: http://www.mmcgrp.com
Year Founded: 1992
Sales Range: $25-49.9 Million
Emp.: 200
Professional Contract Services
N.A.I.C.S.: 541219
Michelle Smallwood (Gen Mgr)

MIRABILE INVESTMENT CORP.
1900 Whitten Rd, Memphis, TN 38133-4713
Tel.: (901) 324-0450 TN
Web Site: http://www.micmemphis.com
Year Founded: 1978
Sales Range: $50-74.9 Million
Emp.: 1,200
Operator of Franchised Convenience Stores
N.A.I.C.S.: 722513
Joseph W. Mirabile (Pres)
Edward Czmut (VP-Engrg & Dev)
Misty Walker (Dir-Mgmt Info Sys)

MIRABITO FUEL GROUP
44 Grand St, Sidney, NY 13838-1141
Tel.: (607) 561-2700 NY
Web Site: http://www.mirabitofuel.com
Year Founded: 1927
Sales Range: $50-74.9 Million
Emp.: 400
Fuel Oil Dealers
N.A.I.C.S.: 424720
Tom Mirabito Jr. (VP)

MIRACLE FLIGHTS

5740 S Eastern Ave Ste 240, Las Vegas, NV 89119
Tel.: (702) 261-0494 NV
Web Site: http://www.miracleflights.org
Year Founded: 1985
Sales Range: $1-9.9 Million
Emp.: 13
Commercial Air Travel
N.A.I.C.S.: 923130
Ann D. McGee (Founder)
Christopher Khorsandi (Chm)
Mark E. Brown (CEO)
Rebecca Boyce (Dir-Flight Ops)
Jessica Cardenas (Specialist-Flight)
Debra Alston (Specialist-Flight)
Christina Moon (Dir-Programs & Dev)
Melanie Marcano (Mgr-R&D)
Charles Courtney (Dir-Special Projects)
Denyce Tuller (Dir-Mktg & PR)
Robert Sanchez (VP-Corp Alliances)

MIRACLE MILE ADVISORS, LLC
11300 W Olympic Blvd Ste 800, Los Angeles, CA 90064-1657
Tel.: (310) 246-1243
Web Site: http://www.miraclemileadvisors.com
Year Founded: 2007
Investment Advice
N.A.I.C.S.: 523940
Matt Granski (Pres)
Kevin Barlow (Mng Dir)
Ted Bloomberg (Chm)
Duncan Rolph (Mng Partner)

MIRACLE SIGNS, INC.
3611 N Broadway St, Wichita, KS 67219
Tel.: (316) 832-1177
Web Site: http://www.miraclesigns.biz
Rev.: $5,572,000
Emp.: 17
Other Commercial Equipment Merchant Whslr
N.A.I.C.S.: 423440
Jason Ridder (Creative Dir)
Joe Poston (Owner)

Subsidiaries:

George Lay Signs, Inc. (1)
1016 North Waco St, Wichita, KS 67203
Tel.: (316) 262-0433
Web Site: http://www.laysigns.com
Rev.: $2,333,333
Emp.: 25
Sign Mfr
N.A.I.C.S.: 339950
Deborah Bryant (Mgr-Fin)

MIRACLE SOFTWARE SYSTEMS INC.
45625 Grand River Ave, Novi, MI 48374
Tel.: (248) 350-1515
Web Site: http://www.miraclesoft.com
Sales Range: $10-24.9 Million
Emp.: 200
Custom Computer Programming Services
N.A.I.C.S.: 541511
Prasad V. Lokam (Pres & CEO)
Sai Kastury (Dir-Bus Integration)

MIRACLE SUPPLY CO. INC.
1580 N & S Rd, Saint Louis, MO 63130
Tel.: (314) 426-4455
Web Site: http://www.miraclesupply.com
Sales Range: $10-24.9 Million
Emp.: 25
Industrial Supplies
N.A.I.C.S.: 423840
Mike Dattilo (Pres)

MIRACLE TRANSPORTATION, INC. — U.S. PRIVATE

Miracle Transportation, Inc.—(Continued)

MIRACLE TRANSPORTATION, INC.
9383 E Bahla Dr, Scottsdale, AZ 85260
Tel.: (480) 563-0770
Web Site: http://www.miracletransportation.com
Year Founded: 2000
Sales Range: $25-49.9 Million
Emp.: 7
Freight Transportation Arrangement Services
N.A.I.C.S.: 488510
Gary D. Flosi (Pres)

MIRACORP INC.
6634 E Baseline Rd Unit 101 Bldg 5, Mesa, AZ 85206
Tel.: (480) 726-7747
Web Site: http://www.miracorp.us
Year Founded: 1999
Sales Range: $1-9.9 Million
Emp.: 100
Government Support
N.A.I.C.S.: 921190
Cynthia M. Reed (Pres & CEO)
Laura Lyon (Mgr-Ops)

MIRAK CHEVROLET-HYUNDAI, INC.
1125 Massachusetts Ave, Arlington, MA 02476
Tel.: (781) 643-8000
Web Site: http://www.mirak.com
Year Founded: 1936
Sales Range: $75-99.9 Million
Emp.: 110
New Car Retailer
N.A.I.C.S.: 441110
Robert Mirak (VP)

MIRAMAR EVENTS
PO Box 27, El Granada, CA 94018-0027
Tel.: (650) 726-3491 CA
Web Site: http://www.miramarevents.com
Year Founded: 1986
Sales Range: $10-24.9 Million
Emp.: 6
Public Relations Agency
N.A.I.C.S.: 541820
Timothy R. Beeman (Chm & CEO)

MIRANTIS, INC.
615 National Ave Ste 100, Mountain View, CA 94043
Tel.: (650) 963-9828 CA
Web Site: http://www.mirantis.com
Year Founded: 2000
Sales Range: $10-24.9 Million
Emp.: 250
Computer Infrastructure & Applications Services
N.A.I.C.S.: 541519
Alex Freedland (Co-Founder & Pres)
Boris Renski (Co-Founder & CMO)
Adrian Ionel (Pres & CEO)

MIRENCO, INC.
206 May St, Radcliffe, IA 50230
Tel.: (515) 899-2164 IA
Web Site: http://www.mirenco.com
Year Founded: 1997
Sales Range: Less than $1 Million
Emp.: 10
Engine Combustion & Equipment Mfr
N.A.I.C.S.: 336310
Dwayne L. Fosseen (Chm, Pres & CEO)
Daniel Bina (COO)

MIRESBALL
2605 State St, San Diego, CA 92103-6419
Tel.: (619) 234-6631
Web Site: http://www.miresball.com
Year Founded: 1985
Rev.: $5,000,000
Emp.: 20
Fiscal Year-end: 08/31/00
Advetising Agency
N.A.I.C.S.: 541810
John Ball (Principal & Dir-Creative)
Scott Mires (Principal & Dir-Creative)

MIRIFEX SYSTEMS, LLC
1383 Sharon Copley Rd PO Box 328, Sharon Center, OH 44274
Tel.: (440) 891-1210
Web Site: http://www.mirifex.com
Year Founded: 1999
Sales Range: $10-24.9 Million
Emp.: 216
Information Technology, Outsourcing & Strategic Marketing Services
N.A.I.C.S.: 561499
William Nemeth (Pres & CEO)
Dennis Langdon (CFO)

MIRO CONSULTING, INC.
167 Main St, Woodbridge, NJ 07095
Tel.: (732) 738-8511
Web Site: http://www.miroconsulting.com
Year Founded: 2000
Sales Range: $10-24.9 Million
Emp.: 20
Software Consulting Services
N.A.I.C.S.: 561499
Scott D. Rosenberg (Pres & CEO)
Robert Kinkade (VP-Fin & Admin)
Gary Coleman (Acct Exec)
Wayne Federico (CIO)

MIROMAR DEVELOPMENT CORPORATION
10801 Corkscrew Rd Ste 305, Estero, FL 33928
Tel.: (239) 390-5100
Web Site: http://www.miromar.com
Year Founded: 1988
Commercial Developer
N.A.I.C.S.: 237210
Mark Geschwendt (Gen Counsel)
Logan Peters (Coord-PR)

Subsidiaries:

Miromar Outlet East, LLC (1)
10801 Corkscrew Rd Ste 199, Estero, FL 33928
Tel.: (239) 948-3766
Web Site: http://www.miromaroutlets.com
Sales Range: $1-9.9 Million
Emp.: 10
Land Subdivision
N.A.I.C.S.: 237210
Margaret Miller (Owner)

MIRON CONSTRUCTION CO. INC.
1471 McMahon Dr, Neenah, WI 54956-6305
Tel.: (920) 969-7000 DE
Web Site: http://www.miron-construction.com
Year Founded: 1918
Sales Range: $100-124.9 Million
Emp.: 1,200
Provider of Construction Services
N.A.I.C.S.: 236220
Dean J. Basten (CFO, Treas & Sec)
Timothy A. Kippenhan (COO & VP)
Steve Tyink (VP-Bus Innovation)
Steve Wilz (Dir-Conceptual Estimating)
Dan Goymerac (VP-Industrial Bus Dev)
Patrick Nate (VP-Industrial Ops)

Craig Uhlenbrauck (VP-Education & Comml)
David G. Voss Jr. (Pres & CEO)

MIRON ENTERPRISES LLC
4780 Ashford Dunwoody Rd Ste A 236, Atlanta, GA 30338
Web Site: http://www.keepcalling.net
Year Founded: 2002
Sales Range: $1-9.9 Million
Emp.: 35
Prepaid International Phone Services
N.A.I.C.S.: 517112
Florin Miron (Founder & Pres)
Abdul Tawab Qadir (CFO)
Daniel Faur (Dir-IT)

MIRSA MANUFACTURING LLC
501 N Bridge St Ste 148, Hidalgo, TX 78557
Tel.: (956) 345-6656
Web Site: http://www.mirsamfg.com
Rev.: $22,200,000
Emp.: 30
Plastics Processing
N.A.I.C.S.: 326199

MIRTEC CORP
3 Morse Rd, Oxford, CT 06478
Tel.: (203) 881-5559
Web Site: http://www.mirtecusa.com
Year Founded: 2004
Sales Range: $1-9.9 Million
Emp.: 9
Communication Equipment Mfr
N.A.I.C.S.: 332321
Brian D'Amico (Pres)
Frank Cormier (Reg Mgr-Sls)
Robert Horowitz (Reg Mgr-Sls)
Stephen Nigro (Mgr-Tech Support)
Henry Cho (Gen Mgr)

MIRTH INCORPORATED
1422 Burtonwood Rd Ste 100, Gastonia, NC 28054
Tel.: (704) 824-4915
Sales Range: $10-24.9 Million
Emp.: 10
Leather Goods Sales
N.A.I.C.S.: 424990
Rafi H. Lakhany (Chm)

MISCELLANEOUS METALS INC.
8301 Retreat Rd, Walkersville, MD 21793
Tel.: (301) 695-8820
Web Site: http://www.miscmet.com
Year Founded: 1978
Sales Range: $10-24.9 Million
Emp.: 100
Architectural & Ornamental Metal Work
N.A.I.C.S.: 332323
Kenneth G. McCombs (Pres)
Tim Morgan (Asst Mgr-Field Dept)

MISERICORDIA
6300 N Ridge Ave, Chicago, IL 60660
Tel.: (773) 973-6300 IL
Web Site: http://www.misericordia.com
Year Founded: 1921
Sales Range: $75-99.9 Million
Emp.: 1,212
Developmental Disability Assistance Services
N.A.I.C.S.: 623210
Rosemary Connelly (Treas & Gen Mgr)
Margaret Murphy (Sec)
Michael Boland (Pres)
Kevin Connelly (CFO)

MISHA CONSULTING GROUP INC.
111 W Saint John St Ste 1100, San Jose, CA 95113
Tel.: (408) 654-7900
Web Site: http://www.ebusinessdesign.com
Sales Range: $10-24.9 Million
Emp.: 50
Computer Related Consulting Services
N.A.I.C.S.: 541512
Amardeep Misha (Pres & CEO)
Sudhir Arora (CTO)

MISKELLY FURNITURE WAREHOUSE INC.
101 Airport Rd, Jackson, MS 39208-6655
Tel.: (601) 939-6288 MS
Web Site: http://www.miskellys.com
Year Founded: 1978
Sales Range: $25-49.9 Million
Emp.: 300
Retail of Furniture Stores
N.A.I.C.S.: 449110
Debra Watson (COO)
Andrea Adams (Mgr-IT)

MISOURCE INC.
2002 N Lois Ave, Tampa, FL 33607
Tel.: (813) 286-9888 FL
Web Site: http://www.misource.net
Year Founded: 1999
Sales Range: $10-24.9 Million
Emp.: 65
Staffing & Technical Recruiting
N.A.I.C.S.: 561311
Cory Jensen (Co-CEO)
Darvin Boothe (Co-CEO)
John Freeman (Co-CEO)
Brian K. Cabral (Project Mgr-Satellite & Cable Div)
Stacey Becker (Mgr-Revenue)
Jason Blake (Acct Mgr)
Chris Cosentino (Dir-Natl)
Mark Schlein (Mgr-Acctg)
Anthony Lechich (Sr Mgr-Natl Accts)

MISS ELAINE INC.
8430 Valcour Ave, Saint Louis, MO 63123
Tel.: (314) 631-1900 MO
Web Site: http://www.misselaine.com
Year Founded: 1927
Sales Range: $75-99.9 Million
Emp.: 100
Women's Sleepwear
N.A.I.C.S.: 315990
James Seldin (Pres)
Alison Talbot (VP-Ops)
Michael R. Brand (Controller)
Elizabeth Cromwell (Mgr-Import)

MISS PAIGE LTD.
8430 W Bryn Mawr Ste 777, Chicago, IL 60631
Tel.: (773) 693-0480
Web Site: http://www.jobgiraffe.com
Sales Range: $25-49.9 Million
Emp.: 20
Temporary Help Service
N.A.I.C.S.: 561320
Karen Rae Horwitz (Pres)

MISS SPORTSWEAR INC.
117 9th St, Brooklyn, NY 11215
Tel.: (718) 369-6012
Web Site: http://www.themissgroup.com
Sales Range: $25-49.9 Million
Emp.: 70
Clothing & Sportswear Importer
N.A.I.C.S.: 424350
Moey Fallas (Owner & Pres)
Elise Quintada (Office Mgr)
Ike Fallas (VP)
Allen Fallas (Controller)

COMPANIES

MISSCO CONTRACT SALES
2001 Airport Rd Ste 102, Flowood, MS 39232-8846
Tel.: (601) 987-8600   MS
Web Site: http://www.missco.com
Year Founded: 1919
Sales Range: $25-49.9 Million
Emp.: 200
Mfr of Furniture
N.A.I.C.S.: 423210
Mark Sorgenfrei *(Controller)*
Bill Luter *(Project Mgr)*

Subsidiaries:

Sheldon Laboratory Systems Inc. (1)
102 Kirk St, Crystal Springs, MS 39059-2850
Tel.: (601) 892-2731
Web Site: http://www.sheldonlabs.com
Rev.: $6,300,000
Emp.: 30
Laboratory Apparatus & Furniture Mfr
N.A.I.C.S.: 337127
Eddie Adkins *(Pres)*
Jenny Phillips *(COO)*

MISSION BROADCASTING, INC.
901 Indiana Ave Ste 375, Wichita Falls, TX 76301
Tel.: (940) 228-7861   DE
Rev.: $112,243,000
Assets: $205,679,000
Liabilities: $255,479,000
Net Worth: ($49,800,000)
Earnings: ($28,663,000)
Emp.: 42
Fiscal Year-end: 12/31/19
Holding Company; Television Broadcasting Stations Owner & Operator
N.A.I.C.S.: 551112
Nancie J. Smith *(Chm & Sec)*
Dennis P. Thatcher *(Pres & Treas)*
Lance Carwile *(VP)*
Sharon Moser *(VP)*

Subsidiaries:

KAMC-TV (1)
7403 S University Ave, Lubbock, TX 79423
Tel.: (806) 745-2345
Web Site: http://www.everythinglubbock.com
Emp.: 50
Television Broadcasting Station
N.A.I.C.S.: 516120

KLRT-TV (1)
1401 W Capitol Ave Ste 104, Little Rock, AR 72201
Tel.: (501) 340-4439
Web Site: http://www.fox16.com
Sales Range: $1-9.9 Million
Television Broadcasting Station
N.A.I.C.S.: 516120

KODE-TV (1)
1502 S Cleveland Ave, Joplin, MO 64801
Tel.: (417) 781-2345
Web Site: http://www.fourstateshomepage.com
Emp.: 2
Television Broadcasting Station
N.A.I.C.S.: 516120
Shirley Morton *(Gen Mgr & Mgr-Station)*
John Emrich *(Sls Mgr-Local)*
Jenna Bontrager-Parker *(Sls Mgr-Local)*
Calin Adams *(Mgr-IT & Engr-Brdcst)*

KTVE-TV (1)
200 Pavilion Rd, West Monroe, LA 71292
Tel.: (318) 323-1972
Web Site: http://www.myarklamiss.com
Sales Range: $10-24.9 Million
Emp.: 55
Television Broadcasting Station
N.A.I.C.S.: 516120
Randy Stone *(Gen Mgr)*
Scott Oglesbee *(Mgr-Station)*
Carolyn Clampit *(Sls Dir)*
Alyson Futch *(Sls Mgr-Local)*
Andy Pederson *(Dir-News)*
Ashlee Clampit *(Mgr-Digital Media)*
Michael Thompson *(Dir-News)*
Billy Brown *(Dir-Ops)*

WTVO-TV (1)
1917 N Meridian Rd, Rockford, IL 61101-9215
Tel.: (815) 963-5413
Web Site: http://www.mystateline.com
Sales Range: $10-24.9 Million
Television Broadcasting Station
N.A.I.C.S.: 516120
Scott Leber *(Dir-Sports)*
Jose Cabezas *(Mgr-Station)*

WYOU-TV (1)
62 S Franklin St, Wilkes Barre, PA 18701
Tel.: (570) 961-2222
Web Site: http://www.pahomepage.com
Emp.: 120
Television Broadcasting Station
N.A.I.C.S.: 516120
Sue Kalinowski *(Program Dir)*
Stephanie Cielski *(Dir-Sls)*

MISSION CONSUMER CAPITAL
201 Main St Ste 1310, Fort Worth, TX 76102
Tel.: (817) 953-5799
Web Site: http://www.missionconsumercapital.com
Privater Equity Firm
N.A.I.C.S.: 523999
Robert J. McGee *(Mng Partner)*
Richard Gardland *(Partner)*

Subsidiaries:

Garcia Foods, Inc. (1)
1802 Jackson Keller Rd, San Antonio, TX 78213
Tel.: (210) 349-6262
Web Site: http://www.garciafoods.com
Rev.: $11,500,000
Emp.: 120
Mexican Food Products Distr
N.A.I.C.S.: 445298
Andy E. Garcia *(Chm)*

MISSION CRITICAL GROUP
21301 HWY 71 W, Spicewood, TX 78669
Tel.: (866) 202-2210
Web Site: https://missioncriticalgroup.com
Power Solutions Mfg.
N.A.I.C.S.: 335311

Subsidiaries:

Johnson Thermal Systems Inc. (1)
1505 Industrial Way Ste 1, Caldwell, ID 83605-6908
Tel.: (208) 453-1000
Web Site: http://www.johnsonthermal.com
Wholesale Trade Agents & Brokers
N.A.I.C.S.: 425120
Glen Wagoner *(Mgr-Ops & Pur)*

Subsidiary (Domestic):

Superior Systems & Technologies, Llp. (2)
515 N Cedar Ridge Dr, Duncanville, TX 75116
Tel.: (972) 572-6110
Web Site: http://www.superior-technologies.blogspot.com
Sales Range: $1-9.9 Million
Emp.: 25
Miscellaneous Chemical Product & Preparation Mfr
N.A.I.C.S.: 325998
Steve Percival *(Dir)*

Mission Critical Facilities International LLC (1)
2802 Flintrock Trce, Austin, TX 78738-1743
Tel.: (512) 402-7258
Web Site: http://www.mcfintl.com
Oil & Gas Operations
N.A.I.C.S.: 213112
Thane Newman *(Dir-Fin & Admin)*

Point Eight Power Inc. (1)
1510 Engineers Rd, Belle Chasse, LA 70037
Tel.: (504) 394-6100
Web Site: http://www.pointeightpower.com
Rev.: $20,969,977
Emp.: 134
Control Panels, Electric
N.A.I.C.S.: 335313
Angela Londot *(Coord-Learning & Growth Theme Team)*
Carlis Gross *(Pres)*

MISSION CRITICAL PARTNERS
690 Gray's Woods Blvd, Port Matilda, PA 16870
Tel.: (888) 862-7911
Web Site: http://www.mcp911.com
Year Founded: 2009
Sales Range: $1-9.9 Million
Emp.: 60
Consulting Services to the Public Safety Communications Industry
N.A.I.C.S.: 921190
R. Kevin Murray *(Founder, Chm & CEO)*
Leonard F. Kowalski *(Sr VP & Mgr-Programs)*
David F. Jones *(Principal & Sr VP)*
David W. Boyce *(VP-Tech Svcs & Specialist-Tech)*
Sidney M. McConahy *(Dir-Ops)*
John L. Spearly *(Dir-Admin Svcs)*
Darrin Reilly *(Pres & COO)*

MISSION ESSENTIAL PERSONNEL, LLC
6525 W Campus Oval Ste 101, New Albany, OH 43054
Tel.: (614) 416-2345
Web Site: http://www.missionessential.com
Year Founded: 2004
Sales Range: $150-199.9 Million
Emp.: 5,000
Civilian Language Interpreter Staffing for Military & Government
N.A.I.C.S.: 541930
Chad A. Monnin *(Founder)*
Gregory K. Miller *(Chm)*

Subsidiaries:

IMT Corporation (1)
530 Manitou Drive, Kitchener, N2C 1L3, ON, Canada
Tel.: (519) 748-0848
Web Site: https://imtcorporation.com
Precision Machined Component & Axles Mfr
N.A.I.C.S.: 336350
Cheryl Hacking *(CEO)*

Subsidiary (US):

IMT Defence Corp (2)
5386 Club Dr, Westerville, OH 43082-8312
Tel.: (614) 891-8888
Military Equipment Distr
N.A.I.C.S.: 423860

Subsidiary (Domestic):

IMT Forge Group (2)
837 Reuter Road, Port Colborne, L3K 5V7, ON, Canada
Tel.: (905) 834-7211
Web Site: http://www.imtforgegroup.com
Metal Forging Services
N.A.I.C.S.: 333517

Subsidiary (US):

Clifford-Jacobs Forging Company (3)
2410 N 5th St, Champaign, IL 61822
Tel.: (217) 352-5172
Web Site: http://www.clifford-jacobs.com
Metal Forging Services
N.A.I.C.S.: 333517
Jason Ray *(Gen Mgr)*
Gordon Glosser *(Mgr-Quality)*
Mike Snell *(Mgr-Engrg & Ops)*
Lindsay Carney *(Mgr-Acctg)*

Division (Domestic):

Port Colborne Drop Forge (2)
837 Reuter Road, PO Box 100, Port Colborne, L3K 5V7, ON, Canada
Tel.: (905) 834-7211
Web Site: http://www.imtcorporation.com
Sales Range: $25-49.9 Million
Emp.: 100
Steel Forging
N.A.I.C.S.: 332111

MISSION FEDERAL CREDIT UNION
4250-B Clairemont Mesa Blvd, San Diego, CA 92117
Tel.: (858) 524-2850
Web Site: http://www.missionfed.com
Emp.: 320
Credit Union
N.A.I.C.S.: 522130
Debra Schwartz *(Pres & CEO)*
Wayne Oetken *(Co-Vice Chm)*
Lora L. Duzyk *(Chm)*
Richard L. Pepper *(Co-Vice Chm)*
Jojo Seva *(CIO)*

Subsidiaries:

Autoland, Inc. (1)
9121 Oakdale Ave, Chatsworth, CA 91311
Tel.: (818) 501-2222
Web Site: http://www.advocar.com
Sales Range: $250-299.9 Million
Emp.: 200
Automobile Brokerage & Sales Financing Services
N.A.I.C.S.: 812990
Marisol Winter *(CFO)*
Jeffry Martin *(Pres)*
Beth Hope *(Sr VP-Sls)*

MISSION HEALTH SERVICES
2825 Virginia Way, Ogden, UT 84401
Tel.: (801) 745-2348   UT
Web Site: http://www.missionhealthservices.org
Year Founded: 1990
Sales Range: $10-24.9 Million
Emp.: 529
Developmental Disability & Elderly People Assistance Services
N.A.I.C.S.: 624120
Marion Sodergren *(VP-Clinical Svcs)*
Gary Kelso *(Pres & CEO)*

MISSION INN RESORTS INC.
10400 County Rd 48, Howey in the Hills, FL 34737
Tel.: (352) 324-3101
Web Site: http://www.missioninnresort.com
Sales Range: $10-24.9 Million
Emp.: 250
Golf Course, Hotel & Resort Owner & Operator
N.A.I.C.S.: 713910
Robert Beucher *(Pres)*
Vicki Ford *(Dir-Sls)*
Jan T. Vicale *(Dir-Conference Svcs)*

MISSION NEIGHBORHOOD HEALTH CENTER
240 Shotwell St, San Francisco, CA 94110
Tel.: (415) 552-1013   CA
Web Site: http://www.mnhc.org
Year Founded: 1974
Sales Range: $10-24.9 Million
Emp.: 235
Health Advocacy Services
N.A.I.C.S.: 813319
Dolores Ramirez *(Dir-Patient Svcs)*
Patty Caplan *(COO)*
Joanie Pacheco *(Dir-HR)*
Angela Robinson *(CFO)*
Ricardo Alvarez *(Dir-Medical)*
Charles Moser *(Pres)*
Amelia Martinez *(VP)*
Ricardo Wohler *(Treas)*
Rita Franklin *(Sec)*
Brenda Storey *(CEO & Exec Dir)*

MISSION PHARMACAL COMPANY INC.

U.S. PRIVATE

Mission Neighborhood Health Center—(Continued)

MISSION PHARMACAL COMPANY INC.
10999 IH 10 W Ste 1000, San Antonio, TX 78230-1355
Tel.: (210) 696-8400   TX
Web Site:
http://www.missionpharmacal.com
Year Founded: 1946
Sales Range: $25-49.9 Million
Emp.: 461
Pharmaceutical Preparations
N.A.I.C.S.: 325412
Thomas Dooley *(CFO)*
Neill Walsdorf Sr. *(CEO)*
Neill Walsdorf Jr. *(Pres)*

MISSION POOLS OF ESCONDIDO
755 W Grand Ave, Escondido, CA 92025
Tel.: (760) 743-2605
Web Site:
http://www.missionpools.com
Sales Range: $10-24.9 Million
Emp.: 100
Swimming Pool Construction
N.A.I.C.S.: 238990
Bruce Dunn *(Pres)*
Jeff Dunn *(Exec VP)*
Brad Cotton *(CFO)*
Jack Tone *(VP)*

MISSION WEALTH MANAGEMENT, LLC
1123 Chapala St Ste 202, Santa Barbara, CA 93101
Tel.: (805) 882-2360
Web Site:
http://www.missionwealth.com
Year Founded: 2000
Sales Range: $1-9.9 Million
Emp.: 11
Insurance Agencies & Brokerages
N.A.I.C.S.: 524210
Matthew Adams *(Pres & Mng Partner)*
Renee Hennessee *(Coord-Mktg)*
Marcie Lund *(Coord-Mktg)*
Diane Williamson *(Dir-Ops)*

Subsidiaries:

AHC Advisors, Inc.   (1)
303 N 2nd St Ste 28, Saint Charles, IL 60174-1804
Tel.: (630) 762-8185
Web Site: http://www.ahcadvisors.com
Investment Advice
N.A.I.C.S.: 523940
Craig Larsen *(Mgr)*

MISSISSIPPI ARTS AND ENTERTAINMENT CENTER
2118 Front St, Meridian, MS 39301
Tel.: (601) 581-1550
Web Site: http://www.msarts.org
Sales Range: $10-24.9 Million
Emp.: 2
Arts Promotion Services
N.A.I.C.S.: 711310
Paul Ott *(VP)*
Alan Lamar *(Treas)*
Dede B. Mogollon *(Sec)*
Tommy Dulaney *(Pres)*

MISSISSIPPI BLOOD SERVICES
115 Tree St, Flowood, MS 39232
Tel.: (601) 981-3232   MA
Web Site: http://www.msblood.com
Year Founded: 1979
Sales Range: $10-24.9 Million
Emp.: 217
Blood Collection & Distr Services
N.A.I.C.S.: 621991

Dan Modisett *(Vice Chm)*
Kenny Windham *(Chm)*
David Allen *(Pres & CEO)*
Phil Posey *(Treas)*
Barney Daly *(Sec)*

MISSISSIPPI CHILDREN'S HOME SERVICES
PO Box 1078, Jackson, MS 39215
Tel.: (601) 352-7784   MS
Web Site: http://www.mchscares.org
Year Founded: 1912
Sales Range: $10-24.9 Million
Emp.: 255
Child Care Services
N.A.I.C.S.: 624110
John D. Damon *(CEO)*
Terry L. Hight *(COO)*
Angela L. Sumrall *(CFO)*

MISSISSIPPI COMPREHENSIVE HEALTH INSURANCE RISK POOL ASSOCIATION
PO Box 13748, Jackson, MS 39236
Tel.: (601) 362-0799   MS
Web Site:
http://www.mississippihealthpool.org
Year Founded: 1991
Sales Range: $25-49.9 Million
Health Insurance Services
N.A.I.C.S.: 524114
Lanny Craft *(Exec Dir)*

MISSISSIPPI COUNTY, ARKANSAS, ECONOMIC OPPORTUNITY COMMISSION, INC.
1400 N Division, Blytheville, AR 72316
Tel.: (870) 776-1054
Web Site: http://www.mcaeoc.com
Year Founded: 1965
Sales Range: $10-24.9 Million
Emp.: 439
Economic Development Services
N.A.I.C.S.: 926110
Samuel Scruggs *(Exec Dir)*

MISSISSIPPI DISTRIBUTORS
401 Indus Dr, Batesville, MS 38606
Tel.: (662) 578-7400
Sales Range: $10-24.9 Million
Emp.: 57
Beer & Other Fermented Malt Liquors
N.A.I.C.S.: 424810

MISSISSIPPI FARM BUREAU INSURANCE COMPANIES
6311 Ridgewood Rd, Jackson, MS 39211
Tel.: (601) 957-3200   MS
Web Site: http://www.msfbins.com
Year Founded: 1952
Sales Range: $10-24.9 Million
Emp.: 300
Provider of Fire, Marine & Casualty Insurance
N.A.I.C.S.: 813910
Randy Knight *(Pres)*

MISSISSIPPI INDUSTRIES FOR THE BLIND
2501 NW St, Jackson, MS 39216
Tel.: (601) 984-3200
Web Site: http://www.msblind.org
Sales Range: $10-24.9 Million
Emp.: 150
Job Training & Support for Blind & Visually Impaired; Office Furnishings Whslr
N.A.I.C.S.: 423420
Michael Chew *(Exec Dir)*
Bob Coy *(Mgr-Acct)*
George Aarons *(Mgr-Bus Dev)*
Ken Maddox *(Asst Mgr-Warehouse)*
Roy Granger *(Dir-Ops)*

David Brister *(Mgr-Technical)*
Cheri Russell *(Mgr-Customer Svc)*
Cheryle Burrow *(Supvr-Acct)*

MISSISSIPPI MARINE CORPORATION
2219 Harbor Front Rd, Greenville, MS 38701
Tel.: (662) 332-5457
Web Site: http://www.msmarine.net
Year Founded: 1972
Sales Range: $10-24.9 Million
Emp.: 100
Shipbuilding & Repairing
N.A.I.C.S.: 336611
Bob Jones *(Exec VP)*
David Turner *(Pres)*
Kenny Schoffstall *(Asst Mgr)*
Steven Millwood *(Pres)*

MISSISSIPPI METHODIST SENIOR SERVICES
109 S Broadway St, Tupelo, MS 38804
Tel.: (662) 844-8977
Web Site: http://www.mss.org
Sales Range: $10-24.9 Million
Emp.: 1,000
Retirement Hotel Operation
N.A.I.C.S.: 531110
Alan Brown *(COO & VP-Ops)*
Christie Vance *(CFO & VP-Fin)*
Cathy Coleman *(VP-Donor Rels)*
Catherine Bradley *(Exec Dir-Turner Duvall)*
Kim Pittman *(Exec Dir)*
Stan Maynard *(Exec Dir-Trinity Retirement Community)*
Renee Reid *(Dir-PR)*
Jim Zuelzke *(Dir-Acctg)*
Jon Stirewalt *(Exec Dir-Traceway)*
Lawona Broadfoot *(Exec Dir-Aldersgate)*
Mary Wilkinson *(Exec Dir-Flowers Manor)*
Sacha MacGown *(Dir-Rehabilitative Svcs)*
Teresa Baker *(Dir-Clinical Support)*
Valerie Sullivan *(Dir-Pharmacy Svcs)*
Cynthia Parker *(Vice Chm)*
Lloyd Gray *(Chm)*
Van Ray *(Sec)*
Merrin Cantin *(VP-HR)*

MISSISSIPPI ORGAN RECOVERY AGENCY
4400 Lakeland Dr, Flowood, MS 39232
Tel.: (601) 933-1000   MS
Web Site: http://www.msora.org
Year Founded: 1994
Sales Range: $10-24.9 Million
Emp.: 69
Organ Recovery Services
N.A.I.C.S.: 621991
Christina Williams-Paige *(Mgr-Accts Receivable)*
Memorie Hood *(Mgr-Accts Payable)*
Kevin Stump *(CEO)*
Ava Williams *(Dir-HR)*
Bill Hillman *(CFO)*
Wauline Carter *(Dir-Fin)*

MISSISSIPPI POLYMERS, INC.
6750 Poplar Ave, Memphis, TN 38138
Year Founded: 2003
Plastic Mfr
N.A.I.C.S.: 513210

Subsidiaries:

Mississippi Polymers   (1)
2733 S Harper Rd, Corinth, MS 38834
Tel.: (662) 287-1401
Web Site:
http://www.mississippipolymers.com

Sales Range: $25-49.9 Million
Emp.: 250
Mfr of Vinyl Calendar Sheeting, Printing & Laminating
N.A.I.C.S.: 326199
Terry Emmons *(Mgr-Tech Svc)*
Luis Alberto Albarracin *(Mgr-Safety & Environmental)*
Tee Nhek *(Mgr-Tech Svc)*
Leigh Ann Green *(Dir-Technical)*

MISSISSIPPI PRESS SERVICES
371 Edgewood Ter, Jackson, MS 39206
Tel.: (601) 981-3060   MS
Web Site: http://www.mspress.org
Year Founded: 1978
Sales Range: $10-24.9 Million
Emp.: 12
Media Buying Services
N.A.I.C.S.: 541810
Kimberly Haydu *(Mgr-Bus & Event)*
Layne Bruce *(Exec Dir)*
David Gillis *(Dir-Sls)*

MISSISSIPPI VALLEY REGIONAL BLOOD CENTER
5500 Lakeview Pkwy, Davenport, IA 52807
Tel.: (563) 359-5401   IA
Web Site: http://www.bloodcenter.org
Year Founded: 1974
Sales Range: $50-74.9 Million
Emp.: 703
Blood Product Provider
N.A.I.C.S.: 334510
Yasuko Erickson *(Chief Medical Officer & Exec VP)*
Darren Klocke *(CFO & Exec VP-Admin)*
Jeannine McCullough *(Chief Quality Officer & Exec VP)*
Susan Blaskovich *(Pres & COO)*
Jennifer Feeney *(VP-HR)*
Mike Parejko *(CEO)*
Barney Daly *(Sec)*
Nancy Kelting *(VP-Bus Dev & Client Svcs)*

MISSISSIPPI WELDERS SUPPLY CO.
5150 W 6th St, Winona, MN 55987
Tel.: (507) 454-5231
Web Site: http://www.mwsco.com
Year Founded: 1939
Sales Range: $10-24.9 Million
Emp.: 160
Welding Machinery & Equipment
N.A.I.C.S.: 423830
Sue Ryan *(Office Mgr)*
John Tomten *(Mgr-Cryogenics)*
Scott Myran *(Mgr-Ops)*
Bruce Nuttall *(Mgr-Sls)*
Scott Good *(Plant Mgr)*

MISSOULA CARTAGE CO. INC.
9300 Cartage Rd, Missoula, MT 59808-9758
Tel.: (406) 542-2114   MT
Year Founded: 1958
Sales Range: $25-49.9 Million
Emp.: 110
Trucking Leasing
N.A.I.C.S.: 484121
Allan Williams *(Pres)*

Subsidiaries:

Triple W. Equipment Inc.   (1)
8571 Running W Rd, Missoula, MT 59808-1611
Tel.: (406) 549-4171
Web Site: http://www.triplewequipment.com
Rev.: $22,500,000
Emp.: 30
Agricultural, Commercial, Construction & Garden Machinery Rental

N.A.I.C.S.: 423820
Glen Richard (Mgr-Parts)
Rodger Otten (Controller)

MISSOULA ELECTRIC CO-OP INC.
1700 W Broadway St, Missoula, MT 59808
Tel.: (406) 541-4433
Web Site:
  htttp://www.missoulaelectric.com
Sales Range: $10-24.9 Million
Emp.: 40
Distribution, Electric Power
N.A.I.C.S.: 221122
Mark Hayden (Gen Mgr)

MISSOURI ATHLETIC CLUB
405 Washington Ave, Saint Louis, MO 63102
Tel.: (314) 231-7220 MO
Web Site: http://www.mac-stl.org
Year Founded: 1903
Sales Range: $10-24.9 Million
Emp.: 391
Athlete Club Operator
N.A.I.C.S.: 713940
Larry Absheer (CFO)
Wallace Smith (COO & Gen Mgr)
Christine Maurer (Dir-HR)
Joe Dietz (Dir-Ops)
Angie Minges (Pres)
Aaron Pawlitz (First VP)
Julie Ahrling (Second VP)
Duke Niedringhaus (Sec)
Matt Gross (Treas)

MISSOURI BASIN WELL SERVICE, INC.
12980 35th St SW, Belfield, ND 58622
Tel.: (701) 575-8242 ND
Web Site:
  http://www.mbienergyservices.com
Year Founded: 1979
Oil Well Drilling, Facilities Construction, Environmental Remediation & Other Ancillary Well-Site Support Services
N.A.I.C.S.: 213112
Jim Arthaud (Co-Founder & CEO)
Jason Homiston (VP-Dev)

MISSOURI BOTANICAL GARDEN
4344 Shaw Blvd, Saint Louis, MO 63110
Tel.: (314) 577-5100 MO
Web Site: http://www.mobot.org
Year Founded: 1859
Sales Range: $25-49.9 Million
Emp.: 563
Garden Preservation Services
N.A.I.C.S.: 712130
Sheila Voss (VP-Education)
Rebecca Ingram (VP-HR)
Charles K. Miller (CIO & VP-IT)
Daniel A. Burkhardt (Vice Chm)
David M. Hollo (Vice Chm)
Lelia J. Farr (Chm)
Peter Wyse Jackson (Pres)
Deborah Frank (VP-Sustainability)
John W. Behrer (Dir-Shaw Nature Reserve)
Olga Martha Montiel (VP-Conservation & Sustainable Dev)
Paul W. Brockmann (Sr VP-Gen Svcs)
Robert Woodruff (COO)
Vickie Campbell (Sr VP-Ops)
Andrew Wyatt (Sr VP-Horticulture & Living Collections)
Dianne Johnson (VP-Institutional Advancement)
James S. Miller (Sr VP-Science & Conservation)

MISSOURI DELTA MEDICAL CENTER
1008 N Main St, Sikeston, MO 63801
Tel.: (573) 471-1600 MO
Web Site:
  http://www.missouridelta.com
Year Founded: 1948
Sales Range: $75-99.9 Million
Emp.: 1,023
Health Care Srvices
N.A.I.C.S.: 622110
Jason Schrumpf (Pres)

MISSOURI DEPARTMENT OF TRANSPORTATION
105 W Capitol, Jefferson City, MO 65102
Tel.: (573) 751-2551
Web Site: http://www.modot.org
Sales Range: $450-499.9 Million
Emp.: 6,200
Transportation Services
N.A.I.C.S.: 926120
Roberta Broeker (CFO)
Deanne Rickabaugh (Project Mgr)
Randy Johnson (Mgr-Traffic Center)
Jim True (Dir-Motor Carrier Svcs Div)

MISSOURI EAGLE LLC
242 Hwy MM, Lebanon, MO 65536
Tel.: (417) 532-6157
Web Site: http://www.moeagle.com
Sales Range: $10-24.9 Million
Emp.: 150
Beer & Other Fermented Malt Liquors
N.A.I.C.S.: 424810
Keith Strickland (Mgr-Ops)
Allen Beaver (Gen Mgr)

MISSOURI EMPLOYERS MUTUAL INSURANCE CO., INC.
101 N Keene St, Columbia, MO 65201-6619
Tel.: (573) 499-9714 MO
Web Site: http://www.mem-ins.com
Year Founded: 1993
Sales Range: $125-149.9 Million
Emp.: 200
Provider of Fire, Marine & Casualty Insurance Services
N.A.I.C.S.: 524126
Timothy D. Jackman (COO & Sr VP-Ops)
James C. Owen (Pres & CEO)
Bob Steinmetz (Dir-IT Ops)
Debbra Keener (Mgr-HR)
Doug Phillips (CFO & VP-Fin)

MISSOURI FARM BUREAU
701 S Country Club Dr, Jefferson City, MO 65109
Tel.: (573) 893-1400 MO
Web Site: http://www.mofb.com
Year Founded: 1915
Sales Range: $250-299.9 Million
Emp.: 885
In-State Federation of Companies
N.A.I.C.S.: 524113
Kelly Smith (Dir-Mktg & Commodities)
Dan Cassidy (Chief Admin Officer)
Randy Campbell (CFO)
Garrett Hawkins (Pres)

Subsidiaries:

Farm Bureau Life Insurance Company of Missouri, Inc. (1)
701 S Country Club Dr, Jefferson City, MO 65102
Tel.: (573) 893-1400
Web Site: http://www.mofbinsurance.com
Sales Range: $75-99.9 Million
Emp.: 250
Fire Insurance Services
N.A.I.C.S.: 524113
Dan Cassidy (VP)
Blake Hurst (Pres)

Farm Bureau Town & Country Insurance Co. of Missouri (1)
701 S Country Club Dr, Jefferson City, MO 65109-5102
Tel.: (573) 893-1400
Web Site: http://www.farmbureau.com
Sales Range: $50-74.9 Million
Emp.: 250
Fire, Marine & Casualty Insurance Services
N.A.I.C.S.: 524126
Blake Hurst (Pres)

Missouri Agricultural Marketing Association (1)
701 S Country Club Dr, Jefferson City, MO 65109-0348 (100%)
Tel.: (573) 893-1400
Web Site: http://www.mofb.org
Rev.: $1,171,012
Emp.: 250
Commodity Contracts Brokers & Dealers
N.A.I.C.S.: 523160

Missouri Farm Bureau Services (1)
701 S Country Club Dr, Jefferson City, MO 65102
Tel.: (573) 893-1400
Web Site: http://www.mofbinsurance.com
Rev.: $194,500,000
Emp.: 250
Fire Insurance Services
N.A.I.C.S.: 524113
Randy Campbell (Mng Dir)

MISSOURI FURNITURE INC.
Hwy 5 N, Camdenton, MO 65020
Tel.: (573) 346-3533
Web Site:
  http://www.missourifurniture.com
Rev.: $10,500,000
Emp.: 50
Furniture Retailer
N.A.I.C.S.: 449110
David Faiferlick (Sec & VP)

MISSOURI SLOPE LUTHERAN CARE CENTER
2425 Hillview Ave, Bismarck, ND 58501
Tel.: (701) 223-9407 ND
Web Site: http://www.mslcc.com
Year Founded: 1962
Sales Range: $25-49.9 Million
Emp.: 655
Health Care Srvices
N.A.I.C.S.: 621498
Jonathan P. Spilde (Vice Chm)
Duane Bergeson (Chm)
Don Walz (Treas & Sec)

MISSOURI TOOLING & AUTOMATION, LLC
1235 Beck Ln, Lebanon, MO 65536
Tel.: (417) 533-7007 MO
Web Site:
  http://www.mtautomation.com
Year Founded: 2004
Sales Range: $1-9.9 Million
Management Consulting Services
N.A.I.C.S.: 541611
Bryan Root (VP)

MISSOURI VALLEY INC.
4614 McCarty Blvd, Amarillo, TX 79110
Tel.: (806) 352-2765
Web Site:
  http://www.industrialcontractoramarillo.com
Sales Range: $10-24.9 Million
Emp.: 50
Power Plant Construction
N.A.I.C.S.: 237990
George Cumming (Pres)
Shannon Lusk (Dir-Safety)

MISSOURI-PACIFIC LUMBER COMPANY
694 State Rte Rd Dd, Fayette, MO 65248
Tel.: (660) 248-3000
Web Site:
  http://www.mopaclumber.com
Year Founded: 1935
Sales Range: $10-24.9 Million
Lumber Mfr & Distr
N.A.I.C.S.: 321912
Bucky Pescaglia (Pres)
Grafton Cook (Sls Mgr)
Ryan Pescaglia (VP)
Lori Kopp (Mgr-Traffic)

MISSRY ASSOCIATES INC.
100 S Washington Ave, Dunellen, NJ 08812
Tel.: (732) 752-7500
Web Site:
  http://www.miscohomeandgarden.com
Sales Range: $10-24.9 Million
Emp.: 90
Phosphatic Fertilizers
N.A.I.C.S.: 424930
Morris Missry (Pres)

MISTAMERICA CORPORATION
15855 N Greenway Hayden Loop Ste 180, Scottsdale, AZ 85260
Tel.: (602) 255-0500 AZ
Web Site:
  http://www.mistamerica.com
Year Founded: 1994
Sales Range: $1-9.9 Million
Emp.: 15
Misting & Fogging Equipment Mfr
N.A.I.C.S.: 333415
Jonathan Marsh (Founder & Owner)
Dave Johnson (Pres)
Peter Rambo (Mgr-Sls)
Robert Lank (Engr-Sls)

MISTEQUAY GROUP LTD.
1212 N Niagara St, Saginaw, MI 48602
Tel.: (989) 752-7700
Web Site:
  http://www.mistequaygroup.com
Rev.: $15,000,000
Emp.: 200
Mfr of Special Dies, Tools, Jigs & Fixtures
N.A.I.C.S.: 333514
R. James Paas (Pres)
Tim Matuszewski (Mgr-Ops)
Gary Steele (CFO & VP)

Subsidiaries:

Aero Precision Products, Inc. (1)
230 Deming Way, Summerville, SC 29483
Tel.: (843) 821-9720
Web Site: http://www.aeropp.com
Ball Screw Mfr
N.A.I.C.S.: 332722
Darwin Eschenbacher (Sr Engr-Project)
John Kinney (Gen Mgr)
Ryan West (Sr Engr-Design)
Josh Reynolds (Mgr-Quality & Procurement)

Mistequay (1)
126 N Main St, Frankenmuth, MI 48734-1196
Tel.: (989) 652-9911
Machine Tools, Metal Forming Types
N.A.I.C.S.: 333515

Mistequay Group Ltd. - Bay Road Plant (1)
3071 Bay Rd, Saginaw, MI 48603
Tel.: (989) 754-0175
Industrial Machinery Mfr
N.A.I.C.S.: 333248

Mistequay Group Ltd. - Standish Plant (1)
1015 W Cedar St, Standish, MI 48658
Tel.: (989) 846-1000
Industrial Machinery Mfr
N.A.I.C.S.: 333248

Mistequay International (Pvt) Limited (1)
11 Liaqat Rd, Faisalabad, 38000, Pakistan

MISTEQUAY GROUP LTD. U.S. PRIVATE

Mistequay Group Ltd.—(Continued)
Tel.: (92) 41 8797971
Web Site:
http://www.mistequayinternational.com
Industrial Machinery Mfr
N.A.I.C.S.: 333248

Precision Machined Products (1)
1017 Smithfield Dr, Fort Collins, CO 80524
Tel.: (970) 482-7676
Sales Range: $10-24.9 Million
Emp.: 40
Mfr of Industrial Machinery
N.A.I.C.S.: 332710
Andy Newcomb (Mgr-Ops)
Ben Cox (Product Mgr)

Universal / DeVlieg LLC (1)
1156 N Niagara St, Saginaw, MI 48602
Tel.: (989) 752-3077
Web Site: http://www.universaldevlieg.com
Machine Tools Mfr
N.A.I.C.S.: 333515

MISTICO ACQUISITION CORP.
4 Four Embarcadero Ctr Ste 2100,
San Francisco, CA 94111
Tel.: (415) 780-9975 DE
Year Founded: 2021
Investment Services
N.A.I.C.S.: 523999
Rufina A. Adams (CFO & Sec)
James H. Greene Jr. (Chm & CEO)

MISTLIN HONDA INC.
4754 McHenry Ave, Modesto, CA 95356
Tel.: (209) 549-5000
Web Site:
http://www.mistlinhonda.com
Sales Range: $25-49.9 Million
Emp.: 75
Automobiles, New & Used
N.A.I.C.S.: 441110
Anthony A. Mistlin (Pres)
Henry Rodriguez (Mgr-Internet Sls)
Jim Lemmons (Mgr-Sls)

MISTRAL EQUITY PARTNERS LLC
650 5th Ave 31st Fl, New York, NY 10019
Tel.: (212) 616-9600
Web Site:
http://www.mistralequity.com
Sales Range: $10-24.9 Million
Emp.: 6
Privater Equity Firm
N.A.I.C.S.: 523999
William P. Phoenix (Mng Dir)
Christopher Bradley (Mng Dir)
Andrew R. Heyer (CEO, Mng Partner & Mng Dir)

MISYD CORP.
1411 Wilson St, Los Angeles, CA 90021
Tel.: (213) 742-1800
Web Site: http://www.rubyrox.com
Rev.: $13,255,907
Emp.: 49
Mfr of Blouses & Shirts
N.A.I.C.S.: 315250
Robert Borman (Pres)
Colina Tang (Coord-Import Production)

MITCH CRAWFORD'S HOLIDAY MOTORS CO.
10807 E State Rte 350 Hwy, Raytown, MO 64138
Tel.: (816) 356-9500
Web Site:
http://www.mitchcrawfordholidaymotors.com
Sales Range: $10-24.9 Million
Emp.: 2
Automobiles, New & Used
N.A.I.C.S.: 441110

James Michael Crawford (Owner)

MITCHCO INTERNATIONAL INC.
4801 Sherburn Ln, Louisville, KY 40207
Tel.: (502) 896-9653
Web Site:
http://www.mitchcointernational.com
Year Founded: 1985
Sales Range: $10-24.9 Million
Emp.: 1,000
Provider of Eating Places
N.A.I.C.S.: 722511

MITCHEL & SCOTT MACHINE COMPANY, INC.
1841 Ludlow Ave, Indianapolis, IN 46201-1035
Tel.: (317) 639-5331 IN
Web Site:
http://www.mitchelandscott.com
Year Founded: 1933
Sales Range: $25-49.9 Million
Emp.: 190
Mfg Of Screw Machine Products
N.A.I.C.S.: 332711
Thomas L. Mitchel (Pres)
David Mitchel (VP)

MITCHELL & RESNIKOFF
8003 Old York Rd, Elkins Park, PA 19027-1410
Tel.: (215) 635-1000
Year Founded: 1970
Sales Range: $10-24.9 Million
Emp.: 13
Advertising Agencies
N.A.I.C.S.: 541810
Ronald B. Resnikoff (CEO)
John Byrnes (Exec Art Dir)
Lynette Byrnes (Sr Acct Exec)

MITCHELL & STARK CONSTRUCTION CO. INC.
170 W 1st St, Medora, IN 47260
Tel.: (812) 966-2151 IN
Year Founded: 1955
Sales Range: $25-49.9 Million
Emp.: 250
Provider of Water, Sewer & Utility Lines
N.A.I.C.S.: 237110
Connie Sparks (Controller & Mgr-Indiana Office)

MITCHELL & TITUS LLP
1 Battery Park Plz FL 27, New York, NY 10004
Tel.: (212) 709-4500
Web Site:
http://www.mitchelltitus.com
Rev.: $13,200,000
Emp.: 125
Certified Public Accountants
N.A.I.C.S.: 541211
Bert N. Mitchell (Founder)
Anthony S. Kendall (Chm & CEO)
Kwabina Appiah (Vice Chm & COO)
Terry Lamantia (Partner)

MITCHELL AUTOMOTIVE, INC.
1522 Hwy 45 N Altn, West Point, MS 39773
Tel.: (662) 494-4344
Web Site:
http://www.mitchellautomotive.com
Rev.: $11,100,000
Emp.: 40
New & Used Automobile Dealer
N.A.I.C.S.: 441110
Mike McGill (Gen Mgr)
Bonnie Thompson (Office Mgr)
Mark Alexander (Pres)

MITCHELL COMMUNICATIONS GROUP
2 North College Ave, Fayetteville, AR 72701
Tel.: (479) 443-4673
Web Site:
http://www.mitchcommgroup.com
Year Founded: 1995
Sales Range: $1-9.9 Million
Emp.: 40
Communication Service
N.A.I.C.S.: 517810
Michael Clark (COO)
Elise Mitchell (CEO)
Brett Carrey (Sr VP & Gen Mgr-New York)
Sarah Clark (Pres)

MITCHELL COMPANIES
3200 Hwy 45 N, Meridian, MS 39301
Tel.: (601) 482-7471
Web Site:
http://www.mitchellcompanies.com
Sales Range: $10-24.9 Million
Emp.: 50
Diversified Holding Company
N.A.I.C.S.: 551112
Manny Mitchell (CEO)

Subsidiaries:

Burkhardt Distributing Company (1)
3935 Inman Rd, Saint Augustine, FL 32084
Tel.: (904) 829-3008
Web Site: https://www.burkhardtsales.com
Sales Range: $10-24.9 Million
Emp.: 110
Beer & Malt Liquor Distr
N.A.I.C.S.: 424810
Brookes Burkhardt (Pres & Mgr-Equity-Gainesville & St Augustine)

Mitchell Beverage, LLC (1)
227 C D F Blvd, Shannon, MS 38868
Tel.: (662) 328-3551
Web Site:
http://www.mitchellcompanies.com
Emp.: 88
Beer Distr
N.A.I.C.S.: 424810
Tony Carley (Mgr-Sls)

Mitchell Distributing Company, Inc. (1)
100 49th Ave, Meridian, MS 39307
Tel.: (601) 482-6161
Web Site:
http://www.mitchelldistributing.com
Emp.: 550
Beer Distr
N.A.I.C.S.: 424810
Jon Hamm (Mgr-Sls)
Adam Mitchell (Pres)
Manny Mitchell (Owner & CEO)

MITCHELL ELECTRIC MEMBERSHIP CORPORATION
475 Cairo Rd, Camilla, GA 31730
Tel.: (229) 336-5221 GA
Web Site:
http://www.mitchellemc.com
Sales Range: $25-49.9 Million
Emp.: 100
Supplier of Electric Power
N.A.I.C.S.: 221122
Tony Tucker (CEO)

MITCHELL ENTERPRISES INC.
700 N Crockett St, Sherman, TX 75090
Tel.: (903) 893-6593
Web Site: http://www.mitchellent.com
Rev.: $78,000,000
Emp.: 18
Commercial & Office Building, New Construction
N.A.I.C.S.: 236220
Steve Mitchell (Pres)

MITCHELL GROCERY CORP.
550 Railroad Ave, Albertville, AL 35950
Tel.: (256) 878-4211 AL
Web Site:
http://www.mitchellgrocery.com
Year Founded: 1945
Sales Range: $50-74.9 Million
Emp.: 450
Provider of Grocery Services
N.A.I.C.S.: 424410
David Mitchell (Pres)

Subsidiaries:

Little Giant Farmers Market Corp. (1)
399 Uppr Riverdale Rd, Jonesboro, GA 30236
Tel.: (770) 996-5220
Web Site:
http://www.littlegiantfarmersmarket.com
Rev.: $8,500,000
Emp.: 160
Fruit & Vegetable Markets
N.A.I.C.S.: 445230

MITCHELL INDUSTRIAL CONTRACTORS, INC.
188 Westchester Dr, Madison, AL 35758
Tel.: (256) 772-5554
Web Site:
http://www.mitchellindustrialcontractors.com
Year Founded: 2002
Sales Range: $10-24.9 Million
Emp.: 80
Construction Services
N.A.I.C.S.: 238990
Alan Mitchell (Pres & CEO)

MITCHELL LEWIS & STAVER CO.
9925 SW Commerce Cir, Wilsonville, OR 97070
Tel.: (503) 682-1800
Web Site:
http://www.mitchelllewis.com
Sales Range: $10-24.9 Million
Emp.: 44
Water Pumps Mfr
N.A.I.C.S.: 423830
David Brown (CEO)
Ean Reves (CFO & COO)
Matt Johnson (VP-Bus Dev)

MITCHELL MANNING ASSOCIATES, LTD.
155 E 55th St Apt 6k, New York, NY 10022-4051
Tel.: (212) 980-1711 NY
Web Site:
http://www.mitchellmanning.com
Year Founded: 1993
Sales Range: $1-9.9 Million
Emp.: 4
Public Relations Agency
N.A.I.C.S.: 541820
Anthony C. Manning (Pres & CEO)

MITCHELL MARTIN, INC.
307 W 38th St Ste 1305, New York, NY 10018
Tel.: (212) 943-1404
Web Site: http://www.itmmi.com
Year Founded: 1984
Sales Range: $125-149.9 Million
Emp.: 1,000
Recruitment Services
N.A.I.C.S.: 561311
Eugene Holtzman (Founder & Pres)
Matthew Franklin (Dir-Recruiting)
Joseph Schimpf (CFO)
Marie Romano (Pres-Health Care)
Junette Eng (Dir-Ops)
Stephen Ryerson (Chief Admin Officer)
Maria Paccione (Controller)
Kathy Koutsodontis (Mgr-Trng)

COMPANIES

Tim Fischer (COO)
Kathy Kholdani (Dir-Trng)
Dawn Ponico (Mgr-HR)
Jim Michalak (Mgr-IT & Infrastructure)
Robert Tutein (Mgr-Payroll & Billing)
Brett Buttacavoli (Mgr-Recruiting)
Paul Casale (Mgr-Recruiting)
Michael Reyes (Sr VP-Strategic Accts)
Joanne Russo (VP-Healthcare Div)

Subsidiaries:

Spring Lake Consulting (1)
1120 Ave of the Americas, New York, NY 10036-6700
Tel.: (212) 389-2300
Web Site:
http://www.springlakeconsulting.com
Staff Augmentation, Payroll & Information Technology Services
N.A.I.C.S.: 561311
Robert Cozzi (Mgr)

MITCHELL MOTORS INC.
1500 Knickerbocker Rd, San Angelo, TX 76904
Tel.: (325) 653-2302
Web Site:
http://www.mitchelltoyota.com
Year Founded: 1987
Sales Range: $10-24.9 Million
Emp.: 50
New & Used Car Dealers
N.A.I.C.S.: 441110
Michael D. Mitchell (Pres)

MITCHELL PONTIAC INC.
384 Hopmeadow St, Weatogue, CT 06089
Tel.: (860) 408-6056
Sales Range: $25-49.9 Million
Emp.: 90
Automobiles, New & Used
N.A.I.C.S.: 441110
Walter Mitchell (Owner)

MITCHELL RUBBER PRODUCTS INC.
491 Wilson Way, La Puente, CA 91744-3935
Tel.: (626) 961-9711
Web Site:
http://www.mitchellrubber.com
Year Founded: 1967
Sales Range: $10-24.9 Million
Emp.: 235
Fabricated Rubber Product Mfr
N.A.I.C.S.: 326299
David Schlothauer (CFO)
Marcey Lundy (Controller)
Kimberly Ljungstrom (Asst Controller)
Trevor Ballou (Product Mgr)
Celia Paterson (Dir-Specifications & Estimating)

MITCHELL SILBERBERG & KNUPP LLP
11377 W Olympic Blvd, Los Angeles, CA 90064
Tel.: (310) 312-2000
Web Site: http://www.msk.com
Year Founded: 1908
Emp.: 120
Law firm
N.A.I.C.S.: 541110
Anthony A. Adler (Co-Partner)
Anthony J. Amendola (Co-Partner)
Patricia H. Benson (Co-Chm & Co-Partner)
Jean P. Nogues (Atty)
Lawrence A. Michaels (Partner)
Richard B. Sheldon (Atty)
William Cole (Partner)
Kevin E. Gaut (Partner-Los Angeles)
Nimesh Patel (Partner)
Kevin Friedmann (Chm & Partner-Los Angeles)

Jonathan Turner (Partner-Labor & Employment Practice)
Matthew Williams (Partner)
Andrew Spitser (Partner)
Mark Hiraide (Partner-Corp & Bus Transactions Grp)
Mark Bravin (Partner-Intl Dispute Relation & Intl Trade)
John Durrant (Partner)
Gilbert S. Lee (Partner)
Emily F. Evitt (Partner)

MITCHELL, LINDBERG & TAYLOR, INC.
4020 E Ponce De Leon Ave, Clarkston, GA 30021
Tel.: (404) 292-4502 GA
Web Site: http://www.mltcreative.com
Year Founded: 1984
Sales Range: $10-24.9 Million
Emp.: 25
Advertising Agencies
N.A.I.C.S.: 541810
William C. Mitchell (Partner & Sr Dir-Creative)
Glenn Taylor (Partner & Sr Dir-Creative)
Matt Albert (Dir-Art)
Chris Davis (Dir-Production)
Sonya Stoudemire (Office Mgr-Bus)
Tom Webster (VP-Strategy)

MITCHELLS SALON & DAY SPA
5901 E Galbraith Rd, Cincinnati, OH 45236
Tel.: (513) 793-0900
Web Site:
http://www.mitchellssalon.com
Rev.: $12,000,000
Emp.: 100
Beauty Shops
N.A.I.C.S.: 812112
Deborah M. Schmidt (Pres)
Christine Gilbert (Mng Dir)
Jeanine Kreimer (Mng Dir)
Sherry Williams (VP-Client Rels)
Nicholena Thompson (Mng Dir)

MITEK CORPORATION
4545 E Baseline Rd, Phoenix, AZ 85042-6400
Tel.: (602) 438-4545 AZ
Web Site: http://www.mitekusa.com
Sales Range: $150-199.9 Million
Emp.: 500
Loudspeakers, Speaker Systems, Amplifiers & Related Accessory Mfr
N.A.I.C.S.: 334310
Loyd Ivey (Founder & CEO)
Dan Murphy (Sr VP-Digital Sys)
Jason Fickas (Mgr-Sls-Natl)

Subsidiaries:

Atlas Sound (1)
1601 Jack McKay Blvd, Ennis, TX 75119-6507
Tel.: (972) 875-8413
Web Site: http://www.atlasied.com
Sales Range: $25-49.9 Million
Emp.: 140
Mfr of Loudspeakers, Emergency Communication Systems, Intercom & Telecom Products
N.A.I.C.S.: 334310

Innovative Electronic Designs, Inc. (1)
9701 Taylorsville Rd, Louisville, KY 40299
Tel.: (502) 267-7436
Web Site: http://www.iedaudio.com
Emp.: 75
Electronic Components Mfr
N.A.I.C.S.: 334419
Mike Abernathy (Mgr-Intl Sls)
Steve Youngson (Mgr-Sls-Intl)
Dave Moriarty (Mgr-Sls-US North Central)
Charles Kowalczyk (Mgr-Sls-US South Central)

Thomas Ahern (Mgr-Sls-US Southeast)
Jeff Mason (Mgr-Sls-US Northeast)
Norm Ross (Mgr-Sls Intl)
Olivier Savoie (Mgr-Sls Intl)

MiTek Corporation - Monroe Facility (1)
700 30th St, Monroe, WI 53566
Tel.: (608) 328-5560
Web Site: http://www.mitekusa.com
Audio Speakers Mfr
N.A.I.C.S.: 334310

MITEM CORPORATION
640 Menlo Ave, Menlo Park, CA 94025
Tel.: (650) 323-1500
Web Site: http://www.mitem.com
Year Founded: 1985
Sales Range: $10-24.9 Million
Emp.: 40
Computer Software Development
N.A.I.C.S.: 541511
Aurel Kleinerman (Founder & CEO)
Lawrence White (VP-Pro Svcs)
Andrei M. Manoliu (Sec)

MITHOFF BURTON PARTNERS
123 W Mills Ave Ste 500, El Paso, TX 79901
Tel.: (915) 544-9400
Web Site:
http://www.mithoffburton.com
Year Founded: 1931
Rev.: $65,000,000
Emp.: 22
Advetising Agency
N.A.I.C.S.: 541810
Bill Burton Jr. (CEO)

MITHUN INC.
660 Market St Ste 300, San Francisco, CA 94104-5012
Tel.: (415) 956-0688
Web Site: http://www.mithun.com
Architectural Services
N.A.I.C.S.: 541310
Dave Goldberg (Pres)

MITO CORPORATION
213 County Rd 17, Elkhart, IN 46516
Tel.: (574) 295-2441
Web Site: http://www.mitocorp.com
Rev.: $18,600,000
Emp.: 35
Electrical & Electronic Appliance, Television & Radio Set Merchant Whslr
N.A.I.C.S.: 423620
Ken Smith (Mgr-HR)
Michael Stock (Pres)
Dan Maloney (VP-Sls)

MITSUSHIBA INTERNATIONAL INC.
2300 E Walnut Ave, Fullerton, CA 92831
Tel.: (714) 870-1900
Web Site: http://www.mitsushiba.com
Year Founded: 1943
Sales Range: $10-24.9 Million
Emp.: 20
Golf Equipment
N.A.I.C.S.: 423910
Richard P. Tcheng (Pres)

MITTEN FLUIDPOWER INC.
5960 Ct St Rd, Syracuse, NY 13206
Tel.: (315) 437-7563
Web Site: http://www.mitten.com
Year Founded: 1971
Sales Range: $10-24.9 Million
Emp.: 60
Industrial Supplies
N.A.I.C.S.: 423840
John Mitten (Pres)
Brent Weicht (VP-Sls)

MITTERA GROUP, INC.

MITTERA GROUP, INC.
1312 Locust St Ste 202, Des Moines, IA 50309
Tel.: (515) 343-5359
Web Site:
http://www.mitteragroup.com
Holding Company
N.A.I.C.S.: 551112
Jon Troen (Pres & CEO)
Tom L. Slaughter (Chief Strategy Officer & Gen Counsel)
Dave Fehrer (COO)
Perry Klein (CTO)
Hilary Warner (CFO)
Emily Lyons (Dir-HR)
Darby Oppold (VP-Creative Svcs)

Subsidiaries:

Angstrom Graphics Inc. (1)
4437 E 49th St, Cleveland, OH 44125
Tel.: (216) 271-5300
Web Site: http://www.angstromgraphics.com
Sales Range: $150-199.9 Million
Emp.: 250
Web Offset, Sheetfed & Digital Printing Services
N.A.I.C.S.: 323111
Mark Angstrom (Dir-Sales-Print)
David Angstrom (Pres & CEO)

Division (Domestic):

Angstrom Graphics Inc. - Angstrom Graphics Creative Division (2)
2025 McKinley St, Hollywood, FL 33020
Tel.: (954) 926-5000
Digital Printing Services
N.A.I.C.S.: 323111

Subsidiary (Domestic):

Angstrom Graphics Inc.-Midwest (2)
4437 E 49th St, Cleveland, OH 44125-1005 (100%)
Tel.: (216) 271-5300
Web Site: http://www.angstromgraphics.com
Sales Range: $25-49.9 Million
Web Offset, Sheetfed & Digital Printing Services
N.A.I.C.S.: 323111
Bruce MacDonald (Sr VP-Sls)

Colorfx LLC (1)
10776 Aurora Ave, Des Moines, IA 50322
Web Site: http://www.mittera.com
Web Printing & Finishing Services
N.A.I.C.S.: 323111
Karen Handeland (Gen Mgr-Waverly)
Harry Matternas (Gen Mgr-Urbandale)
Mark Nilles (Gen Mgr-Boyden)

EarthColor, Inc. (1)
249 Pomeroy Rd, Parsippany, NJ 07054
Tel.: (973) 884-1300
Web Site: http://www.earthcolor.com
Commercial Printing Services
N.A.I.C.S.: 323111
Bruce Wexler (Pres)

Unit (Domestic):

Earth Thebault (2)
249 Pomeroy Rd, Parsippany, NJ 07054
Tel.: (973) 884-1300
Web Site: http://earthcolor.com
Sheetfed & Web-Printing, Digital Printing & Prepress Services
N.A.I.C.S.: 323111
Robert Kashan (CEO)

EarthDigital (2)
7021 Portwest Dr Ste 190, Houston, TX 77024
Tel.: (713) 861-8159
Web Site: http://www.earthcolor.com
Digital Printing Services
N.A.I.C.S.: 323111

Earthintegrate (2)
7021 Portwest DrSte190, Houston, TX 77024-8015 (100%)
Tel.: (713) 589-7160
Web Site: http://www.earthintegrate.com
Emp.: 50
Marketing Applications Through Innovative Technological Solutions
N.A.I.C.S.: 541690

MITTERA GROUP, INC.

Mittera Group, Inc.—(Continued)
Ryan Farris (Pres)
Patricia Bourassa (VP-Client Svcs)
Tara Drago (Dir-Sls-Natl)
Kay To (VP-Product Svcs)
Keith Watt (VP-Tech)

Nicholas Earth Printing (2)
7021 Portwest Dr Ste 100, Houston, TX 77024
Tel.: (713) 880-0195
Web Site: http://www.nicholasearth.com
Commercial Printing
N.A.I.C.S.: 323111
Arita Nicholas (Founder & CEO)

Trend Offset Printing Services, Inc. (1)
3791 Catalina St, Los Alamitos, CA 90720-2402
Tel.: (562) 598-2446
Web Site: http://www.trendoffset.com
Sales Range: $125-149.9 Million
Emp.: 900
Offset Printing, Bookbinding & Related Services
N.A.I.C.S.: 323111
Todd Nelson (CEO)
Jeff Sweetman (Principal)

Division (Domestic):

Trend Offset Printing Services - Southeast Division (2)
10301 Busch Dr N, Jacksonville, FL 32218
Tel.: (904) 696-8675
Emp.: 1,000
Commercial Printing Services
N.A.I.C.S.: 323111
Charlotte Troilo (Mgr-HR)

Trend Offset Printing Services - Southwest Division (2)
2323 McDaniel Dr, Carrollton, TX 75006
Tel.: (972) 243-3556
Web Site: http://www.trendoffset.com
Emp.: 220
Commercial Printing Services
N.A.I.C.S.: 323113
Jeff Thompson (Gen Mgr)

MITTERNIGHT, INC.
5301 Hwy 43 N, Satsuma, AL 36572
Tel.: (251) 675-2550
Web Site: http://www.mitternight.com
Sales Range: $25-49.9 Million
Emp.: 60
Pressure Vessels & Heat Exchangers Mfr
N.A.I.C.S.: 332313
Norbert Long (CFO)
F. Todd Burkhalter (CEO & Mng Partner)

MITUTOYO AMERICA CORPORATION
965 Corporate Blvd, Aurora, IL 60502
Tel.: (630) 820-9666   NY
Web Site: http://www.mitutoyo.com
Year Founded: 1963
Precision Measuring Tools, Training & Micrometers Marketer
N.A.I.C.S.: 811210
Robert Dillon (Gen Mgr-Logistics)
Mark Izumi (Mgr-Mktg)

MIVA MERCHANT, INC.
5060 Shoreham Pl Ste 130, San Diego, CA 92122
Tel.: (858) 490-2570
Web Site: http://www.mivamerchant.com
Year Founded: 1995
Sales Range: $1-9.9 Million
Emp.: 70
Electronic Commerce Software Development Services
N.A.I.C.S.: 541511
Jon Burchmore (CTO)
Nathan Osborne (COO)
David Hubbard (CIO)
Jen Ferraz (Sr VP-Hosting Ops)
Rick Wilson (CEO)

MIXBOOK INC.
409 Sherman Ave, Palo Alto, CA 94306
Tel.: (408) 955-9151
Web Site: http://www.mixbook.com
Year Founded: 2006
Sales Range: $25-49.9 Million
Emp.: 60
Software Product Development Services
N.A.I.C.S.: 541511
Andrew Laffoon (Founder & CEO)

MIXER SYSTEMS INC.
190 Simmons Ave, Pewaukee, WI 53072
Tel.: (262) 691-3100
Web Site: http://www.mixersystems.com
Sales Range: $10-24.9 Million
Emp.: 50
Manufacture Cement Mixers
N.A.I.C.S.: 333120
Doug Dooley (VP & Dir-Part & Pur)
Al Wegner (Dir-Sls & Mktg-Concrete Equipment)
Doug Duley (Chm & CEO)

MIXON FRUIT FARMS, INC.
2525 27th St E, Bradenton, FL 34208
Tel.: (941) 748-5829   FL
Web Site: http://www.mixon.com
Year Founded: 1997
Sales Range: $1-9.9 Million
Emp.: 100
Fresh Fruits And Vegetables
N.A.I.C.S.: 424480
Dean Mixon (Co-Owner & Gen Mgr)
Janet Mixon (Co-Owner)

MIXON SEED CO., INC.
PO Box 1652, Orangeburg, SC 29116-1652
Tel.: (803) 531-1777   SC
Year Founded: 1985
Sales Range: $10-24.9 Million
Emp.: 35
Provider of Farm Supplies
N.A.I.C.S.: 424910
Daniel A. Mixon (Pres)

MIXON-NOLLNER OIL CO.
30 Cookeville Hwy, Carthage, TN 37030
Tel.: (615) 735-2750
Sales Range: $10-24.9 Million
Emp.: 4
Engine Fuels & Oils
N.A.I.C.S.: 424720
Donnie Apple (VP)
Mary Helen Apple (Pres)

MIXSON OIL CO. INC.
4301 Allendale Fairfax Hwy, Allendale, SC 29810
Tel.: (803) 584-2398
Sales Range: $10-24.9 Million
Emp.: 2
Petroleum Bulk Stations
N.A.I.C.S.: 424710
Miriam Cook (Sec)
Richard Mixon Jr. (Owner & Pres)

MIXT SOLUTIONS LLC
8050 Corp Blvd Ste A, Plain City, OH 43064
Web Site: http://www.mixtsolutions.com
Year Founded: 2014
Sales Range: $1-9.9 Million
Emp.: 5
Online Shopping Services
N.A.I.C.S.: 541511
Austin T. Keller (Co-Founder)
Alexander V. Johnson (Co-Founder)
Benjamin Johnson (COO)

MIYAMOTO INTERNATIONAL, INC.
1450 Halyard Dr Ste 1, West Sacramento, CA 95691
Tel.: (916) 373-1995   CA
Web Site: http://www.miyamotointernational.com
Year Founded: 1976
Sales Range: $10-24.9 Million
Emp.: 80
Earthquake & Structural Engineering Services
N.A.I.C.S.: 237990
H. Kit Miyamoto (Pres, CEO & Principal)
Marco Cossu (Principal)
Jeff Crosier (Principal)
Lon M. Determan (Principal)
Bob S. Glasgow (Principal)
Francis Lo (Principal)
Sara Nim (Mgr-Fin)
Jason Reiser (Principal)
Devis Sonda (Principal)
Guilaine Victor (Mgr-Haiti)
Richard Chen (Principal)
Josh Reynolds (Principal-San Jose)
Casey Lubawy (Assoc Principal)
Tim Tsukamoto (Assoc Principal)

MIZE HOUSER & CO., P.A.
534 S Kansas Ave Ste 700, Topeka, KS 66603
Tel.: (785) 233-0536
Web Site: http://www.mizehouser.com
Sales Range: $10-24.9 Million
Emp.: 170
Certified Public Accountants
N.A.I.C.S.: 541211
Duane Bond (Partner)
Keith Olson (Owner & VP)
Marsha Oliver (Owner & Dir-Mktg)

MIZE INC.
8610 Hidden River Pkwy Ste 200, Tampa, FL 33637
Tel.: (813) 971-2666
Web Site: http://www.m-ize.com
Sales Range: $1-9.9 Million
Emp.: 150
Software Publisher
N.A.I.C.S.: 513210
Ashok Kartham (CEO)
Bruce Burke (CMO)
Stuart Ransom (Chief Revenue Officer)

MIZNER COUNTRY CLUB, INC.
16104 Mizner Club Dr, Delray Beach, FL 33446
Tel.: (561) 638-5600
Web Site: http://www.miznercc.org
Real Estate Development & Management Services
N.A.I.C.S.: 236115
Larry S. Savvides (COO & Gen Mgr)

MIZRAHI ENTERPRISES INC.
464 W 11th St, San Pedro, CA 90731
Tel.: (310) 832-7519
Rev.: $21,000,000
Emp.: 18
Children's & Infants' Wear Whslr
N.A.I.C.S.: 424350
Silvano Mizrahi (Pres)

MJ BASKETBALL HOLDINGS, LLC
333 E Trade St, Charlotte, NC 28202
Tel.: (704) 688-8600   DE
Year Founded: 2006
Holding Company
N.A.I.C.S.: 551112
Michael J. Jordan (Founder & Owner)

Subsidiaries:

Hornets Sports & Entertainment (1)
333 E Trade St, Charlotte, NC 28202
Tel.: (704) 688-8600
Web Site: http://www.nba.com
Holding Company; Professional Basketball Team & Entertainment Arena Owner & Operator
N.A.I.C.S.: 551112
Michael J. Jordan (Chm)
Rich Cho (Exec VP & Gen Mgr)
Chad Buchanan (Asst Gen Mgr)
Pete Guelli (Chief Sls & Mktg Officer & Exec VP)
James R. Jordan (Exec VP-Ops)
Seth Benett (Sr VP-Mktg, Entertainment & Interactive Media)
Mike Cristaldi (VP-Comm)
Rhonda Curry (VP-HR)
Marlene Hendricks (VP-Guest Svcs & Event Staffing)
Joe Pierce (Gen Counsel & VP)
Andrew Shure (VP-Ticket Sls)
Fred Whitfield (Owner-Minority, Vice Chm, Pres & COO)

Subsidiary (Domestic):

Bobcats Basketball Center, LLC (2)
333 E Trade St, Charlotte, NC 28202
Tel.: (704) 688-9000
Web Site: http://www.timewarnercablearena.com
Sports & Entertainment Arena Operator
N.A.I.C.S.: 711310

MJ BIOTECH, INC.
4781 N Congress Ave Ste 1102, Boynton Beach, FL 33426
Tel.: (561) 563-3830   DE
Web Site: http://www.mjbiotech.us
Year Founded: 2010
Assets: $1
Liabilities: $2,476,449
Net Worth: ($2,476,448)
Earnings: ($837,760)
Emp.: 2
Fiscal Year-end: 12/31/18
Pharmaceutical Products Developer & Marketer
N.A.I.C.S.: 325412
Maxine C. Pierson (CEO, CFO & Chief Acctg Officer)

MJ OPTICAL INC.
8838 Washington Cir, Omaha, NE 68127
Tel.: (402) 339-4029
Web Site: http://www.mjoptical.com
Sales Range: $10-24.9 Million
Emp.: 90
Provider of Frames
N.A.I.C.S.: 423460
Park Wilkinson (Mgr-Sls)

MJ SIMPSON CORPORATION
Ste A 400 E Atlantic Blvd, Pompano Beach, FL 33060-6263
Tel.: (954) 941-0341
Sales Range: $10-24.9 Million
Emp.: 7
Commercial & Office Building Contractors
N.A.I.C.S.: 236220
James Fry (Pres)
Troy Parra (VP)
Terri Simpson (VP-Fin)
Mike Knapik (Superintendent)

MJB REALTY INC.
3300 Sunset Blvd Ste 230, Rocklin, CA 95677
Tel.: (916) 624-9725
Web Site: http://www.mjbrealty.net
Rev.: $12,500,000
Emp.: 18
Real Estate Brokers & Agents
N.A.I.C.S.: 531210
Mike Bouchard (Gen Mgr)

MJB WOOD GROUP INC.
2201 W Royal Ln Ste 250, Irving, TX 75063
Tel.: (972) 401-0005 TX
Web Site: http://www.mjbwood.com
Year Founded: 1998
Sales Range: $10-24.9 Million
Emp.: 60
Lumber, Plywood & Millwork
N.A.I.C.S.: 423310
Pete Little *(CFO)*
Mark Butler *(Mgr-Div)*
William Corbo *(Mgr-Div)*
Brent Monroe *(Mgr-Div)*

MJE MARKETING SERVICES
3111 Camino del Rio N Ste 100, San Diego, CA 92108
Tel.: (619) 682-3841
Year Founded: 1994
Sales Range: Less than $1 Million
Emp.: 10
Financial, Government/Political/Public Affairs, High Technology, Travel & Tourism
N.A.I.C.S.: 541810
Marlee J. Ehrenfeld *(Pres & Dir-Creative)*
Susan Smith *(Chief Mktg Strategist)*
Nancy Mumford *(Mgr-Mktg Commun)*
Aaron Ishaeik *(Dir-Art)*
Robb Henderson *(Mgr-Client Svcs)*
Kristen McDade Byrne *(VP)*

MJG CORPORATION
204 W 4th St, Roswell, NM 88201
Tel.: (575) 622-8711 NM
Web Site:
   http://www.mjgcorpbys.com
Year Founded: 1979
Sales Range: $200-249.9 Million
Emp.: 1,000
Fast-Food Restaurants Owner & Operator
N.A.I.C.S.: 722513
Jay Gluck *(Pres & CEO)*

MJM ASSOCIATES, LLC
301 E 66th St Ste 4K, New York, NY 10065
Tel.: (212) 517-5885
Web Site:
   http://www.mjmassocllc.com
Emp.: 1,500
Nursing Care Facilities Management
N.A.I.C.S.: 623110
Martin D. Hamburg *(Pres)*
Jeanette Perlman *(COO & Sr VP)*
Mark J. Nunheimer *(Sr VP-Fin & Acctg)*
Andrea Ellen *(VP & Dir-Mktg)*
Robert Steiner *(VP & Dir-Assset Mgmt)*
Myra B. Richardson *(Dir-Trng)*
Jacqueline Hurt *(Sr VP-Ops)*

MJM ELECTRIC COOPERATIVE, INC.
264 N East St, Carlinville, IL 62626
Tel.: (217) 854-3137 IL
Web Site: http://www.mjmec.coop
Year Founded: 1939
Sales Range: $10-24.9 Million
Emp.: 31
Electric Power Distr
N.A.I.C.S.: 221122
Laura Cutler *(Dir-Fin & Admin)*
Robert Lehmann *(Chm)*

MJM ELECTRIC, INC.
3225 E 4th Ave, Tampa, FL 33605-5715
Tel.: (813) 248-1711
Web Site: http://www.mjmelect.com
Sales Range: $1-9.9 Million
Emp.: 80

Electrical Contractor
N.A.I.C.S.: 238210
Mark Mazur *(Pres)*
Lisa S. Pink *(Comptroller)*
Joy Parshell *(Mgr-Payroll)*
Scott Humenansky *(Project Mgr-Svc)*
Eric Hott *(Mgr-Svc & Superintendent-Shop)*
Jim Horton *(Project Mgr)*
Tony Grieco *(Project Mgr)*
Ray Dykes *(Project Mgr)*

MJM HOLDINGS INC.
130 N Main St, Lisbon, NH 03585-6603
Tel.: (603) 838-6624 NH
Web Site:
   http://www.newenglandwire.com
Year Founded: 1985
Sales Range: $10-24.9 Million
Emp.: 300
Nonferrous Wiredrawing & Insulating
N.A.I.C.S.: 332618
Wendell W. Jesseman *(Chm & Pres)*
Bette Liveston *(Dir-HR)*

Subsidiaries:

New England Wire Technologies (1)
130 N Main St, Lisbon, NH 03585-6603 (100%)
Tel.: (603) 838-6624
Web Site: http://www.newenglandwire.com
Nonferrous Wiredrawing & Insulating
N.A.I.C.S.: 335929
Rick Jesseman *(Dir-Mktg)*
Robert F. Meserve *(VP)*
Kelly MacKay *(Dir-Sls)*
Kathy Stevens *(Mgr-Bus Dev)*

Subsidiary (Domestic):

Bay Associates Wire Technologies Inc. (2)
150 Jefferson Dr, Menlo Park, CA 94025
Tel.: (650) 847-3900
Web Site: http://www.baycable.com
Emp.: 50
Coaxial Cable Mfr
N.A.I.C.S.: 335929
Jack Sanford *(Gen Mgr)*

New England Catheter Corp. (2)
130 N Main St, Lisbon, NH 03585
Tel.: (603) 838-2261
Web Site: http://www.necatheter.com
Surgical Supplies Mfr
N.A.I.C.S.: 339113

MJN SERVICES INC.
534 E 800 N, Orem, UT 84097-4146
Tel.: (801) 705-9030
Web Site:
   http://www.mjnservices.com
Year Founded: 2000
Sales Range: $10-24.9 Million
Emp.: 5
Freight Transportation Arrangement Services
N.A.I.C.S.: 488510
Michael L. Jardine *(Owner)*

MJO INDUSTRIES, INC.
8000 Technology Blvd, Huber Heights, OH 45424
Tel.: (937) 235-7100 PA
Web Site:
   http://www.hughespeters.com
Year Founded: 1921
Emp.: 50
Electronic Components Distr
N.A.I.C.S.: 334413
Don Guy *(CFO)*
Dawn Pribbernow *(Acct Mgr)*

MJS COMMUNICATIONS
358 Chesnut Hill Ave Ste 201, Brighton, MA 02135
Tel.: (617) 566-2454
Web Site: http://www.mjscom.com
Year Founded: 1993

Sales Range: $1-9.9 Million
Emp.: 25
Media Buying Services
N.A.I.C.S.: 541830
Matt Sacher *(Pres)*
Tonia Gracie *(VP-Sls)*
John Vellela *(Dir-Mktg)*

MJT ENTERPRISES INC.
PO Box 993, Provincetown, MA 02657
Tel.: (508) 487-0205
Web Site: http://www.capecodoil.com
Sales Range: $10-24.9 Million
Emp.: 20
Whslr of Fuel & Oil
N.A.I.C.S.: 457210
Halcyine Tasha *(Owner)*

MJV HOLDINGS, LLC
13613 S US 71 Hwy, Grandview, MO 64030
Tel.: (816) 442-8555
Web Site:
   http://www.pridecleanerss.com
Year Founded: 2008
Emp.: 240
Holding Company
N.A.I.C.S.: 551112
Dominic Brancato *(CEO)*

Subsidiaries:

Pride Cleaners Inc. (1)
13613 S US Hwy 71, Grandview, MO 64030-3659
Tel.: (816) 442-8555
Web Site: http://www.pridecleaners.com
Sales Range: $10-24.9 Million
Emp.: 180
Dry Cleaning & Laundry Services
N.A.I.C.S.: 812320
Dominic Brancato *(Owner)*

MK CHAMBERS COMPANY
2251 Johnson Mill Rd, North Branch, MI 48461
Tel.: (810) 688-3750
Web Site:
   http://www.mkchambers.com
Sales Range: $10-24.9 Million
Emp.: 120
Automobile Parts Mfr
N.A.I.C.S.: 332721
Gerald Chambers *(Pres)*
Bob Chambers *(Sr VP-Ops)*
Harvey Nelson *(Mgr-Sls)*
Jeff Weingartz *(Dir-Quality)*

MK DIAMOND PRODUCTS, INC.
1315 Storm Pkwy, Torrance, CA 90501-5041
Tel.: (310) 257-2800 CA
Web Site:
   http://www.mkdiamond.com
Year Founded: 1860
Sales Range: $100-124.9 Million
Emp.: 200
Mfr of Diamond Cutting Wheels & Saws
N.A.I.C.S.: 332216

Subsidiaries:

Barranca Diamond Products, Inc. (1)
1315 Storm Pkwy, Orange, CA 90501
Tel.: (310) 523-5867
Web Site: http://www.barrancadiamond.com
Emp.: 100
Polishing Equipment Mfr
N.A.I.C.S.: 333517
Dean Delauhaut *(CEO)*

MK DISTRIBUTORS INC.
310 S Linden St, Pine Bluff, AR 71601
Tel.: (870) 534-0364
Web Site:
   http://www.abwholesaler.com

Sales Range: $10-24.9 Million
Emp.: 40
Whslr Of Beer & Other Fermented Malt Liquors
N.A.I.C.S.: 424810
George A. Makris Jr. *(Pres)*
Duke Fakouri *(Pres)*

MKS INDUSTRIES INCORPORATED
5801 Ct St Rd, Syracuse, NY 13206
Tel.: (315) 437-1511
Web Site:
   http://www.modernkitchens.com
Rev.: $17,400,000
Emp.: 35
Electrical Appliances, Major
N.A.I.C.S.: 423620
Mark Martino *(Pres)*
Kirby Holekamp *(Mgr-Sls)*
James Marrocco *(Branch Mgr-Albany)*

MKSD ARCHITECTS
1209 Hausman Rd Ste A, Allentown, PA 18104
Tel.: (610) 366-2081
Web Site:
   http://www.mksdarchitects.com
Year Founded: 2005
Sales Range: $1-9.9 Million
Emp.: 15
Architectural Services
N.A.I.C.S.: 541310
Sylvia Hoffman *(Partner)*

MKTG INC.
200 Carleton Ave, East Islip, NY 11730
Tel.: (631) 277-7000
Web Site: http://www.mktginc.com
Rev.: $16,700,000
Emp.: 50
Market Analysis Or Research
N.A.I.C.S.: 541910
Elaine Trimarchi *(Exec VP)*
Bob Granger *(Dir-Online Svcs)*
Howard Gershowitz *(Sr VP)*

MKTWORKS, INC.
292 Main St, Cold Spring, NY 10516
Tel.: (845) 265-7000
Web Site:
   http://www.marketingworksnow.com
Year Founded: 2002
Sales Range: Less than $1 Million
Emp.: 10
Advetising Agency
N.A.I.C.S.: 541810
Debbie Darman *(Corp Responsibility Officer)*
Chris Nelson *(Dir-Creative)*
Marc Sabin *(Exec VP)*
Ron Hill *(Mgr-Media)*
Marshall Mermell *(Pres)*

ML MULTISERVICE EXPRESS, INC.
2695 Imperial Ave, San Diego, CA 92102
Tel.: (619) 234-4800
Year Founded: 1998
Sales Range: $10-24.9 Million
Emp.: 200
Courier & Express Delivery Services
N.A.I.C.S.: 492110
Mario Lopez *(Pres)*

MLB CAPITAL PARTNERS, LLC
7026 Old Katy Rd Ste 274, Houston, TX 77024
Tel.: (713) 588-0144 TX
Web Site:
   http://mlbcapitalpartners.com
Year Founded: 2010

MLB CAPITAL PARTNERS, LLC

MLB Capital Partners, LLC—(Continued)
Commercial Real Estate Investment
N.A.I.C.S.: 531190
Todd Mason (Co-Founder)
Jeff Lindenberger (Co-Founder & Mng Partner)

Subsidiaries:

Farmers Marketing Association of Houston Texas, Inc. (1)
2520 Airline Dr Ste 1, Houston, TX 77009
Tel.: (713) 862-8866
Web Site:
http://thehoustonfarmersmarket.co
Farmers Market/Cooperative
N.A.I.C.S.: 531120

MLO PRODUCTS INCORPORATED
100 W. 5th St, Ste 700, Tulsa, OK 74103
Web Site:
http://www.mloproducts.com
Year Founded: 1974
Sales Range: $25-49.9 Million
Emp.: 200
Mfr of Sports Nutrition & Natural Nutrition Products
N.A.I.C.S.: 311999

MLP STEEL COMPANY
18 Mount Pleasant Rd, Scottdale, PA 15683
Tel.: (724) 887-8100
Web Site: http://www.mlpsteel.com
Rev.: $19,521,521
Emp.: 65
Steel Wire & Related Products Mfr
N.A.I.C.S.: 332618

MLT CREATIVE
4020 E Ponce de Leon Ave, Clarkston, GA 30021
Tel.: (404) 292-4502
Web Site: http://www.mltcreative.com
Sales Range: $10-24.9 Million
Emp.: 15
N.A.I.C.S.: 541810
Craig Lindberg (Partner & Exec VP)
Billy Mitchell (Partner & Sr Dir-Creative)
Glen Taylor (Partner & Sr Dir-Creative)
Brian Sheppard (Dir-Creative-Interactive Media)
Kelly Pires (Acct Exec)
Vann Morris (Dir-Buyer Behavior Studies)

MM SYSTEMS CORPORATION
50 MM Way, Pendergrass, GA 30567-0098
Tel.: (706) 824-7500 GA
Web Site:
http://www.mmsystemscorp.com
Year Founded: 1960
Sales Range: $75-99.9 Million
Emp.: 150
Provider of Metal Building Products
N.A.I.C.S.: 332322
Carl Bussey (Project Mgr)

MMB
580 Harrison Ave, Boston, MA 02118
Tel.: (617) 670-9700
Web Site: http://www.mmb580.com
Year Founded: 2001
Sales Range: $10-24.9 Million
Emp.: 42
N.A.I.C.S.: 541810
Fred Bertino (Pres & Chief Creative Officer)
Jamie Mambro (Partner & Dir-Creative)
Chad Caufield (Mng Partner)
Jerry Cronin (Partner, Dir-Creative)

Matt Fallon (Supvr-Mgmt)
Kerry Park (Sr Acct Dir)
Lance Smith (Mng Dir)
Liz Vanzura (CMO)
Carrie Parks (Grp Acct Dir)

MMC CORP.
10955 Lowell Ave Ste 350, Overland Park, KS 66210-2326
Tel.: (913) 469-0101 KS
Web Site: http://www.mmcorps.com
Year Founded: 1932
Sales Range: $350-399.9 Million
Emp.: 525
Holding Company; General & Mechanical Construction
N.A.I.C.S.: 238220
David Cimpl (CFO & VP)
Jason Evelyn (COO)
Craig Woodson (VP-Talent)
David Lauck (VP-Info Sys & Tech)
Tate Tyree (Dir-Corp Risk Mgmt)
Tim Chadwick (CEO)

Subsidiaries:

M.W. Builders Inc. (1)
13725 W 109th St, Lenexa, KS 66215
Tel.: (913) 317-3700
Web Site: http://www.mwbuilders.com
Sales Range: $200-249.9 Million
Emp.: 31
Provider of Nonresidential Construction Services
N.A.I.C.S.: 236220
R. Jason Evelyn (COO)
Mark Hegarty (VP-Ops)
Austin Shepherd (Sr Project Mgr)
Eric Bebermeyer (Sr Project Mgr)
Todd Winnerman (Pres)
Kip Maxwell (Mgr-Design)
Isaac Byers (Mgr-Jacksonville)

Midwest Mechanical Contractors, Inc. (1)
13800 Wyandotte St, Kansas City, MO 64145 (100%)
Tel.: (816) 333-8484
Sales Range: $10-24.9 Million
Emp.: 60
Plumbing, Heating & Air-Conditioning
N.A.I.C.S.: 238220
Michael J. Kotubey (Pres)
Keith E. Andrews (Exec VP)
Michael J. Teahan (Treas & VP)
Kim Caddell (Office Mgr)

Subsidiary (Domestic):

MMC Contractors Northeast, Inc. (2)
114 Almond Dr, Somerset, NJ 08873
Tel.: (732) 412-7800
Web Site: http://www.mmccontractors.com
Emp.: 25
Plumbing Services
N.A.I.C.S.: 238220
Daniela Paulson (Pres)

MMC Contractors West, Inc. (2)
5080 Cameron St, Las Vegas, NV 89118-1553
Tel.: (702) 889-6800
Air Conditioning & Heating Contract Services
N.A.I.C.S.: 238220

MMC Mechanical Contractors North Central, Inc. (2)
4717 F St, Omaha, NE 68117-1404
Tel.: (402) 861-0681
Web Site: http://www.mmccontractors.com
Construction Management Services
N.A.I.C.S.: 541330
Jacob Vogel (Gen Mgr)

Midwest Mechanical Contractors, Inc. (1)
144 Belmont Dr, Somerset, NJ 08873
Tel.: (973) 560-0100
Web Site: http://www.mmccontractors.com
Rev.: $15,000,000
Emp.: 100
Plumbing Heating & Air Conditioning Services
N.A.I.C.S.: 238220
Thomas Powers (Pres)

Stroh Corporation (1)
5000 Park Ave, Des Moines, IA 50321 (100%)
Tel.: (515) 244-8177
Web Site: http://www.strohcorp.com
Rev.: $10,000,000
Emp.: 20
Mechanical, Electrical, Plumbing & Energy Services
N.A.I.C.S.: 238210
Bob Blaskovich (VP & Gen Mgr)
Clint Trebon (Mgr-Svc)

MMC SYSTEMS INC.
13800 Coppemine Rd 3rd FL, Herndon, VA 20171
Tel.: (703) 463-9671
Web Site:
http://www.mmcsystemsinc.com
Year Founded: 2004
Sales Range: $1-9.9 Million
Emp.: 84
Professional Consulting & Software Support Services to Professional Consulting & Software Support Services to Government Agencies & Corporations
N.A.I.C.S.: 519290
Shashi Sharma (VP-Legal & Ops)

MME INC.
5015 E Main Ave, Bismarck, ND 58502
Tel.: (701) 223-1880 ND
Web Site: http://www.mmeinc.com
Year Founded: 1984
Rev.: $46,877,545
Emp.: 550
Provider of Trucking Services, Except Local
N.A.I.C.S.: 484121
John T. Roswick (CEO)
Marlin Kling (Pres)

Subsidiaries:

Midnite Express Inc. (1)
448 7th St NW, West Fargo, ND 58078-1150
Tel.: (701) 281-2511
Web Site: http://www.mmeinc.com
Sales Range: $10-24.9 Million
Emp.: 80
Trucking Except Local
N.A.I.C.S.: 484121

Midwest Motor Express Inc. (1)
5015 E Main Ave, Bismarck, ND 58502 (100%)
Tel.: (701) 223-1880
Web Site: https://www.mmeinc.com
Rev.: $27,213,636
Emp.: 100
Trucking Except Local
N.A.I.C.S.: 484121

MMF CAPITAL MANAGEMENT LLC
55 W Monroe St Ste 3650, Chicago, IL 60603
Tel.: (312) 291-7300 IL
Web Site: http://www.mmfcapital.com
Year Founded: 1992
Equity Investment Firm
N.A.I.C.S.: 523999
David A. Gezon (Co-Founder & Sr Mng Dir)
C. Michael Foster (Sr Mng Dir)
Paul G. Kreie (Mng Dir)
Ana M. Winters (Mng Dir)
Elizabeth E. Milz (Dir-Fin)
Elliott B. Linsley (VP)
Rachel White (Officer Mgr)
Michael Feola (Co-Founder)

Subsidiaries:

Dorsett Technologies Inc. (1)
100 Woodlyn Dr, Yadkinville, NC 27055
Tel.: (855) 387-2232
Web Site: http://www.dorsett-tech.com

U.S. PRIVATE

SCADA Hardware & Software Designer & Mfr
N.A.I.C.S.: 513210

Icat Logistics, Inc. (1)
6805 Douglas Legum Dr, Elkridge, MD 21075
Tel.: (443) 891-2000
Web Site: https://www.icatlogistics.com
Sales Range: $25-49.9 Million
Emp.: 35
Freight Forwarding Services
N.A.I.C.S.: 488510
Rick Campbell (Founder & CEO)
Jim Vespa (VP-Fin)
Ray Smith (Sr VP)
Hann Livinston (Chief Growth Officer)

MMG CORPORATION
1717 Olive St, Saint Louis, MO 63103
Tel.: (314) 421-2182
Sales Range: $10-24.9 Million
Emp.: 140
Neckties, Men's & Boys': Made From Purchased Materials
N.A.I.C.S.: 315990
Lisa Edwards (Office Mgr)
Maria Humphrey (Dir-Design)
Terri Jentilucci (VP-Mdsg)
Tom Kroner (VP-Sls)
Gary Lerner (VP)
David Klaus (VP-Sls)

MMG INSURANCE COMPANY
44 Maysville St PO Box 729, Presque Isle, ME 04769-0729
Tel.: (207) 764-6611
Web Site:
http://www.mainemutual.com
Year Founded: 1897
Sales Range: $25-49.9 Million
Emp.: 100
Provider of Fire, Marine & Casualty Insurance
N.A.I.C.S.: 524126
Larry M. Shaw (Pres & CEO)
Michael M. Young (CFO, Treas & Sr VP)
Timothy W. Vernon (VP & Mgr-Property Claims)
Pamela G. Johnson (VP & Mgr-Comml Lines)
Matthew R. McHatten (COO, Sec & Exec VP)
Lynn M. Lombard (VP & Dir-HR)
Michael D. MacPherson (Vice Chm)
Terri L. Ouellette (Asst Mgr-Acctg)
Stephen H. Morgan (Asst Mgr-Casualty Claims)
Andrew J. Grass (Asst Mgr-Comml Lines)
Chad M. Brewer (Asst Mgr-Info Sys)
Keith D. Sperrey (Dir-Mktg)
Michael A. Thibodeau (Mgr-Acctg)
Dianne C. Collins (Mgr-Customer Svc)
Douglas R. Hazlett (VP & Mgr-Personal Lines)
Eric Tawfall (VP-Personal Lines)
Kayla O'Malley Dill (VP-Mktg & Bus Dev)
Julia Clukey (VP-People, Engagement, and HR)
John H. Cashwell III (Chm)

MMI HOTEL GROUP INC.
1000 Red Fern Pl, Flowood, MS 39232
Tel.: (601) 936-3666
Web Site:
http://www.mmihotelgroup.com
Year Founded: 1956
Sales Range: $10-24.9 Million
Emp.: 300
Motel, Franchised
N.A.I.C.S.: 721110

Gaines Sturdivant *(CEO-MMI Hospitality Grp)*
Michael J. Hart *(CFO)*
David McEwen *(District Mgr)*
Len E. Shannon *(Controller)*
Jessica Humphreys *(Asst Controller)*
Laura Rabalais *(Asst Controller)*
Melissa Rogers *(Coord-Support Svcs)*
Susan Sparkman Smith *(Dir-Bus Dev)*
Daniel MacGregor *(Dir-IT)*
Lindsay Hamm *(Dir-Revenue Performance)*
Bob Gilstrap *(Mgr-District)*
Cynde Houston *(Mgr-District)*
Tina Presley *(Mgr-Payroll)*
Micajah Sturdivant *(Co-Pres)*
Dave Jenner *(Co-CFO)*

Subsidiaries:

MMI Dining Systems (1)
1000 Red Fern Pl, Flowood, MS 39232
Tel.: (601) 936-3666
Web Site: http://www.mmihotelgroup.com
N.A.I.C.S.: 722511
Bob Gilstrap *(District Mgr)*
David McEwen *(District Mgr)*
Michael J. Hart *(Sr VP-Fin-Hospitality)*
Cynde Houston *(District Mgr)*
Scott Reese *(Mgr-Area Healthcare)*
Susan Sparkman Smith *(Dir-Bus Dev)*
David Jenner *(CFO)*
Ronald James Cockayne Jr. *(Pres)*

MMI PUBLIC RELATIONS
223 E Chatham St, Cary, NC 27511-3475
Tel.: (919) 233-6600
Web Site:
http://www.mmipublicrelations.com
Year Founded: 1994
Sales Range: $10-24.9 Million
Emp.: 25
Public Relations
N.A.I.C.S.: 541820
Jennifer Fair *(Sr Acct Mgr)*
Michelle Fowler *(Exec VP)*
Erin Smith *(VP)*
Robert Buhler *(Chm)*
Kathleen Donnelly *(Acct Exec)*
Jennifer Evans *(Acct Exec)*
Alfred Leach *(Pres)*
Amanda Romano *(Sr Acct Exec)*
Kelsie Murdock *(Dir-Analytics)*
Ashley Warren *(Acct Exec)*
Chris Buhler *(Dir-Multimedia Svcs)*
Danni Dichito *(Asst Acct Exec)*
Finn Winterson *(Dir-Creative)*
Jeanne Yacono *(Acct Exec)*
Jim Cyphert *(Dir-PR)*

Subsidiaries:

MMI Public Relations (1)
5420 Wade Park Blvd Ste 204, Raleigh, NC 27607 **(100%)**
Tel.: (704) 644-4284
Web Site:
http://www.mmipublicrelations.com
Emp.: 20
Public Relations
N.A.I.C.S.: 541820
Al Leach *(Pres)*

MMI SERVICES, INC.
4042 Patton Way, Bakersfield, CA 93308
Tel.: (661) 589-9366
Web Site: http://www.mmi-services.com
Year Founded: 1970
Sales Range: $25-49.9 Million
Emp.: 175
Oil & Gas Field Services
N.A.I.C.S.: 213112
Mel McGowan *(CEO)*
Eric Olson *(VP-Ops)*
Kent Finney *(Mgr-Wireline)*
Steve McGowan *(CEO)*
Anthony Hernandez *(Dir-Bus Dev)*

MMIX BISCOM INC.
321 Billerica Rd, Chelmsford, MA 01824
Tel.: (978) 250-1800
Web Site: http://www.biscom.com
Year Founded: 1986
Sales Range: $10-24.9 Million
Emp.: 63
Document Delivery Software Development Services
N.A.I.C.S.: 541511
S. K. Ho *(Founder & Chm)*
Don Dunning *(COO)*
Bill Ho *(CEO)*
Bill Agudelo *(Co-Founder & Sr VP)*
Carlos Mainemer *(VP-Tech)*
George S. Bartley *(VP-Engrg)*
John Lane *(Chief Info Security Officer)*
Neal B. McCann *(VP-Strategic Partnerships)*
Michael Gayowski *(Sr VP-Biscom Hosted Fax Svcs)*
Charlie Magliato *(VP-Channel Dev)*
Sharif Rahman *(VP-Engrg)*

MMLJ, INC.
5711 Schurmier Rd, Houston, TX 77048
Tel.: (713) 869-2227 TX
Web Site: http://www.mmlj.com
Year Founded: 1976
Sales Range: $50-74.9 Million
Emp.: 80
Blast Cleaning Equipment & Machines Mfr
N.A.I.C.S.: 333998

MMM SALES, INC.
14314 Lomitas Ave, City of Industry, CA 91746
Tel.: (626) 968-9621 CA
Web Site:
http://www.batoryfoods.com
Year Founded: 1966
Sales Range: $75-99.9 Million
Emp.: 18
Wholesale Distributor of Dairy Products & Food Ingredients
N.A.I.C.S.: 424430
Ron Friedman *(Pres)*

MMR GROUP INC.
15961 Airline Hwy, Baton Rouge, LA 70817-7412
Tel.: (225) 756-5090 LA
Web Site: http://www.mmrgrp.com
Year Founded: 1985
Sales Range: $50-74.9 Million
Emp.: 500
Electrical Work
N.A.I.C.S.: 238210
James Rutland *(Pres & CEO)*

Subsidiaries:

MMR Canada, Limited (1)
11083 48th Street SE, Calgary, T2C 1G8, AB, Canada
Tel.: (403) 720-9000
Web Site: http://www.mmrcdn.com
Electrical Engineering Services541330
N.A.I.C.S.: 541330

MMR Caribbean, Limited (1)
PO Box 2291, Chaguanas, Trinidad & Tobago
Tel.: (868) 637 3704
Electrical Engineering Services
N.A.I.C.S.: 541330

MMR Colombia, S.A.S. (1)
Carrera 2 No 11-33 and 11-41 Building Grupo Area Office No 702, Bocagrande, Cartagena, Colombia
Tel.: (57) 5 655 2122
Electrical Engineering Services
N.A.I.C.S.: 541330

MMR Constructors Inc. (1)
15961 Airline Hwy, Baton Rouge, LA 70817 **(100%)**
Tel.: (225) 756-5090
Web Site: http://www.mmrgrp.com
Rev.: $38,881,389
Emp.: 150
Electrical Work
N.A.I.C.S.: 238210
Darryl Clark *(VP & Mgr-Estimating)*
Jeffrey Escue *(Asst Mgr-Estimating)*

Branch (Domestic):

MMR Constructors Inc. - Corpus Christi (2)
2033 FM 2725, Ingleside, TX 78362
Tel.: (361) 758-4019
Web Site: http://www.mmrgrp.com
Emp.: 10
Electrical Contractor
N.A.I.C.S.: 238210
Adam Philippi *(Mgr)*

MMR Offshore Services, Inc. (1)
1135 Highway 90 East, Broussard, LA 70518
Tel.: (337) 367-5494
Web Site: http://www.mmrgrp.com
Emp.: 50
Vitreous China, Fine Earthenware & Other Pottery Product Mfr
N.A.I.C.S.: 327110

MMR ProCom, LLC (1)
19500 State Hwy 249 Ste 365, Houston, TX 77070
Tel.: (832) 237-9800
Emp.: 15
Electrical Engineering Services
N.A.I.C.S.: 541330
Jim Honald *(Gen Mgr)*

MMR Technical Services, Inc. (1)
4064 9 McFarland Dr Ste A, Alpharetta, GA 30004
Tel.: (770) 664-9137
Electrical Engineering Services
N.A.I.C.S.: 541330

MMR Venezuela, S.A. (1)
Edificio Leif-Piso 2 Av Intercomunal Jorge Rodriquez Sector Las Garzas, Frente Al Deposito Del Inos, Barcelona, Anzoategio, Venezuela
Tel.: (58) 281 265 9222
Web Site: http://www.mmrvzl.com
Electrical Engineering Services
N.A.I.C.S.: 541330
Arturo Pinzon *(Project Mgr)*
Dante Osteicoechea *(Bus Mgr)*
Richard Gibb *(Mgr-Ops)*

SouthWestern Power Group II LLC (1)
3610 N 44th S Ste 250, Phoenix, AZ 85018
Tel.: (602) 808-2004
Web Site:
http://www.southwesternpower.com
Emp.: 9
Power Plant Construction Services
N.A.I.C.S.: 237990
David Getts *(Gen Mgr)*
Gary Crane *(Mgr-Environmental)*
Lori Schleier *(Dir-Land Plng & Entitlements)*
Martin Bailey *(Mgr-Real Estate)*
Tom Wray *(Mgr-Generation & Transmission Projects)*

MMRGLOBAL, INC.
4401 Wilshire Blvd Ste 200, Los Angeles, CA 90010
Tel.: (310) 476-7002 DE
Web Site:
http://www.mymedicalrecords.com
Year Founded: 2000
MMRF—(OTCBB)
Sales Range: Less than $1 Million
Emp.: 4
Computer Information Storage Products
N.A.I.C.S.: 334112
Bernard Stolar *(Acting CFO & Chief Acctg Officer)*
Rafael Salazar *(Exec VP-Telecomm & Carrier Rels)*
Richard M. Lagani *(Exec VP)*

Lisa L. Dahm *(VP-Healthcare Regulatory Affairs)*
Scott C. Kline *(Gen Counsel & Sec)*
Jason R. Pfeiffer *(Interim Pres)*

MMS TRADING INC.
5390 Rickenbacker Rd, Bell, CA 90201
Tel.: (323) 587-1082
Web Site:
http://www.mmstradinginc.com
Year Founded: 2006
Sales Range: $10-24.9 Million
Emp.: 6
Fashion Accessories
N.A.I.C.S.: 315990
Sumir Kaytee *(Owner)*

MMW FABRICATION, LTD.
1155 W Hurst Blvd, Hurst, TX 76053
Tel.: (817) 284-4978 TX
Web Site:
http://www.mmwfabrication.com
Year Founded: 1970
Sales Range: $10-24.9 Million
Emp.: 30
Structural Steel Fabrication
N.A.I.C.S.: 332312
Jimmy R. Miller *(Chm)*
Rick Miller *(Pres & CEO)*

MNB BANCSHARES, INC.
1 Money Pl, Malvern, AR 72104
Tel.: (501) 332-6955 AR
Web Site: http://www.mnbbank.com
Bank Holding Company
N.A.I.C.S.: 551111
Claud A. Davis *(Pres & CEO)*
Mark Roberts *(Pres-Bank)*

Subsidiaries:

The Malvern National Bank (1)
1 Money Pl, Malvern, AR 72104
Tel.: (501) 332-6955
Web Site: http://www.mnbbank.com
Banking Services
N.A.I.C.S.: 522110
Mark Roberts *(Pres)*
Brian Coker *(COO)*
Kyle Keeney *(Chief Credit Officer)*
John Fowler *(Pres-Market-Little Rock)*
Mike Rushing *(Pres-Market-Saline County)*
Brent Godwin *(Chief Risk Officer)*

MNDUSTRIES, INC.
3625 Swiftwater Park Dr, Suwanee, GA 30024
Tel.: (770) 831-0760
Web Site: http://www.mndustries.com
Sales Range: $1-9.9 Million
Emp.: 50
Sheet Metal Cutting, Forming & Painting Services
N.A.I.C.S.: 332322
Mike Nance Sr. *(CEO)*

MNJ TECHNOLOGIES DIRECT, INC.
1025 E Busch Pkwy, Buffalo Grove, IL 60089
Tel.: (847) 634-0700
Web Site: http://www.mnjtech.com
Sales Range: $10-24.9 Million
Emp.: 50
Computer Hardware & Software Distr
N.A.I.C.S.: 423430
Susan Kozak *(Pres)*
Ron Kelly *(Sr Acct Mgr)*
Vanessa Lubinski *(Sr Acct Mgr)*

MNP CORPORATION
44225 Utica Rd, Utica, MI 48317-5464
Tel.: (586) 254-1320 MI
Web Site: http://www.mnp.com
Year Founded: 1970
Sales Range: $350-399.9 Million

MNP CORPORATION — U.S. PRIVATE

MNP Corporation—(Continued)
Emp.: 1,200
Mfr of Fasteners, Screws & Washers
N.A.I.C.S.: 332722
Larry S. Berman *(Chm)*
Tom Klein *(Pres)*
Craig L. Stormer *(CFO)*

Subsidiaries:

Beta Steel (1)
44225 Utica Rd, Utica, MI 48317
Tel.: (586) 323-6800
Web Site: http://www.betasteel.com
Sales Range: $25-49.9 Million
Emp.: 11
Producer of Products for Fastener & Wire Forming Industries
N.A.I.C.S.: 423510
Scott Bernstein *(Pres)*

Delaware Steel Co. (1)
535 102 Pennsylvania, Fort Washington, PA 19034
Tel.: (215) 654-8285
Web Site: http://www.delawaresteel.com
Sales Range: $25-49.9 Million
Emp.: 10
Producer of Products for Fastener & Wire Forming Industries
N.A.I.C.S.: 423510
Lisa Goldenberg *(Pres)*

Highland Bolt & Nut (1)
44225 Utica Rd, Utica, MI 48318
Tel.: (586) 654-8285
Producer of Metal Products
N.A.I.C.S.: 332722

Link Tool & Die (1)
9495 Inkster Rd, Taylor, MI 48180
Tel.: (734) 946-1040
Web Site: http://www.linktoolmfg.com
Mfr of Metal Products
N.A.I.C.S.: 333514

MNP Aerospace, LLC. (1)
44225 Utica Rd, Utica, MI 48317
Tel.: (586) 254-1320
Web Site: http://www.mnp-aerospace.com
Fastener Mfr & Distr
N.A.I.C.S.: 339993
Ted Davis *(Dir-Special Applications & New Dev)*
Chad Clifford *(VP-Engrg, Quality, Reliability & Environmental Quality)*

MNP Corporation - MNP Plant I (1)
44225 Utica Rd, Utica, MI 48317
Tel.: (586) 254-1320
Fastener Mfr
N.A.I.C.S.: 339993

MNP Corporation - MNP Plant II (1)
1524 E 14 Mile Rd, Madison Heights, MI 48071
Tel.: (248) 585-5010
Fastener Mfr
N.A.I.C.S.: 339993

MNP Steel & Wire Division (1)
44225 Utica Rd, Utica, MI 48317
Tel.: (586) 254-1320
Web Site: http://www.mnp.com
Sales Range: $50-74.9 Million
Emp.: 600
Mfr of Metal Products
N.A.I.C.S.: 332722
Tom Klein *(Pres)*

MNP Steel & Wire/Utica Washer Division (1)
122 Prairie View Ste H, Grayslake, IL 60030
Tel.: (847) 223-6358
Mfr of Metal Products
N.A.I.C.S.: 561499

MNP Steel Services & Warehousing Division (1)
3401 Martin, Detroit, MI 48210
Tel.: (313) 843-7152
Sales Range: $10-24.9 Million
Emp.: 30
Provider of Metals Services
N.A.I.C.S.: 493110

Marathon Metals LLC (1)
6440 Mack Ave, Detroit, MI 48207
Tel.: (313) 571-9544
Web Site: http://www.marathonmetalsllc.com
Sales Range: $25-49.9 Million
Emp.: 30
Metal Services
N.A.I.C.S.: 423510
Al Pace *(Gen Mgr)*

Michigan Wire Die Company (1)
22903 Industrial Dr E, Saint Clair Shores, MI 48080
Tel.: (586) 777-1900
Sales Range: $10-24.9 Million
Emp.: 10
Mfr of Metal Products
N.A.I.C.S.: 327910

New Craft Tool & Die (1)
13501 Ashurst, Livonia, MI 48150
Tel.: (734) 522-3350
Web Site: http://www.mnp.com
Mfr of Metal Products
N.A.I.C.S.: 333514
William Neubecker *(Pres)*

Ohio Pickling & Processing (1)
1149 Campbell St, Toledo, OH 43607
Tel.: (419) 241-9601
Web Site: http://www.ohiopickling.com
Sales Range: $10-24.9 Million
Emp.: 50
Provider of Metals Services
N.A.I.C.S.: 333519
Rick Vella *(VP-Processing Equipment)*

Perfection Steel Treating (1)
24200 Plymouth Rd, Redford, MI 48239
Tel.: (313) 538-4600
Sales Range: $10-24.9 Million
Emp.: 100
Provider of Metals Services
N.A.I.C.S.: 332811

Sombur Tool & Die (1)
2305 Beard St, Port Huron, MI 48060
Tel.: (810) 982-8996
Web Site: http://www.somburtool.com
Sales Range: $10-24.9 Million
Emp.: 17
Mfr of Metal Products
N.A.I.C.S.: 333517
Bruce Miler *(Plant Mgr)*

Utica Washers (1)
3105 Beaufait, Detroit, MI 48207
Tel.: (313) 571-1568
Web Site: http://www.mnp.com
Sales Range: $10-24.9 Million
Emp.: 10
Metal Products Mfr
N.A.I.C.S.: 332722
Chris Yoon *(Mgr-Acctg)*

MNS1 EXPRESS, INC.
335 Remington Blvd, Bolingbrook, IL 60440
Tel.: (630) 246-3280
Web Site: http://www.mns1express.com
Year Founded: 2011
Sales Range: $25-49.9 Million
Emp.: 15
Freight Transportation Services
N.A.I.C.S.: 488510
Mindaugas Narkys *(Pres)*

MOAB REGIONAL HOSPITAL
450 W Williams Way, Moab, UT 84532
Tel.: (435) 719-3500   UT
Web Site: http://www.amhmoab.org
Year Founded: 1995
Sales Range: $25-49.9 Million
Emp.: 187
Health Care Srvices
N.A.I.C.S.: 622110
Robert Austin *(CEO)*
Craig Daniels *(CFO)*
Victoria Gigliotti *(Chief Compliance Officer)*
James L. Walling *(Dir-Ancillary Svcs)*

MOAI TECHNOLOGIES INC.
100 1st Ave 9th Fl, Pittsburgh, PA 15222
Tel.: (412) 454-5550
Web Site: http://www.moai.com
Rev.: $10,080,000
Emp.: 20
Business Oriented Computer Software
N.A.I.C.S.: 513210
Ramesh Mehta *(Pres & CEO)*
Ravi Ghai *(VP-Bus Dev)*
Michael J. Kulmoski *(VP-Fin)*
Michael B. Nelson *(Mng Dir)*

MOANA NURSERY INC.
1100 W Moana Ln, Reno, NV 89509
Tel.: (775) 825-0600
Web Site: http://www.moananursery.com
Rev.: $10,485,032
Emp.: 150
Nursery Stock, Seeds & Bulbs
N.A.I.C.S.: 444240
Scott Gescheider *(Pres & CEO)*
Matt Pulliam *(Gen Mgr-Retail Svcs)*

MOARK PRODUCTIONS INC.
1100 Blair Ave, Neosho, MO 64850-9117
Tel.: (417) 451-3353   MO
Web Site: http://www.moarkllc.com
Year Founded: 1957
Sales Range: $25-49.9 Million
Emp.: 320
Poultry & Poultry Products
N.A.I.C.S.: 424440
Jerry Welch *(Pres)*

Subsidiaries:

Classic Egg Products Inc. (1)
409 N Wood St, Neosho, MO 64850-1541   (100%)
Tel.: (417) 451-2050
Sales Range: $10-24.9 Million
Emp.: 55
Poultry Slaughtering & Processing
N.A.I.C.S.: 311999

McNally Enterprises, Inc (1)
12005 Cabernet Dr, Fontana, CA 92337-7703
Tel.: (909) 797-0144
Sales Range: $25-49.9 Million
Producer, Processor & Sales of Chicken Eggs
N.A.I.C.S.: 112310

MOB MEDIA
27121 Towne Centre Dr Ste 260, Foothill Ranch, CA 92610
Tel.: (949) 222-0220
Web Site: http://www.mobmedia.com
Year Founded: 1989
Sales Range: $10-24.9 Million
Emp.: 20
N.A.I.C.S.: 541810
Paul Otis *(CEO)*
Jeffrey Monroe *(Pres)*
Alan Whetzel *(Dir-Client Svcs)*
Nan Paturzo *(Dir-Media)*

MOBEL INCORPORATED
2130 Industrial Park Rd, Ferdinand, IN 47532
Tel.: (812) 367-1214
Web Site: http://www.mobelinc.com
Rev.: $27,864,629
Emp.: 140
Wood Bedroom Furniture
N.A.I.C.S.: 337122
Paul Ruhe *(CEO)*

MOBERLY MOTOR
1520 N Morley St, Moberly, MO 65270
Tel.: (660) 263-6000
Web Site: http://www.moberlymotors.com
Sales Range: $10-24.9 Million
Emp.: 50
Car Whslr
N.A.I.C.S.: 441110
Dean Miller *(Gen Mgr)*

MOBEX COMMUNICATIONS INC.
1601 Greentree Ct Ste 3, Clarksville, IN 47129-2367
Tel.: (812) 288-0401
Sales Range: $50-74.9 Million
Emp.: 25
Provider of Wireless Communication Systems & Services
N.A.I.C.S.: 517112

MOBIENTS INC.
1425 Ellsworth Industrial Dr Ste 12, Atlanta, GA 30318
Tel.: (678) 705-3614
Web Site: http://www.mobients.com
Year Founded: 2007
Sales Range: $1-9.9 Million
Emp.: 14
Mobile Application Software Development Services
N.A.I.C.S.: 541511
Eric Irvin *(Exec Dir-Design Strategy)*
Matthew Perry *(CEO)*

MOBIFUSION, INC.
39270 Paseo Padre Parkway #401, Fremont, CA 94538
Tel.: (510) 870-1546
Web Site: http://www.mobifusion.com
Year Founded: 2005
Sales Range: $1-9.9 Million
Emp.: 57
Develops Mobile Content Apps for Operating Systems, Platforms, Protocols & Handsets
N.A.I.C.S.: 513210
Pavan Mandhani *(Co-Founder, Pres & CEO)*
Chris McKenney *(Co-Founder & COO)*

MOBILE AIR TRANSPORT, INC.
12 Runway Ave, Latham, NY 12110
Tel.: (518) 783-5111   NY
Web Site: http://www.mobileairtrans.com
Year Founded: 1981
Sales Range: $1-9.9 Million
Emp.: 60
Air Courier Services
N.A.I.C.S.: 492110
John J. Ingemie *(Pres)*
Lee Horton *(COO & VP)*
Phil Pfeiffenberger *(CFO & VP)*

MOBILE AIRPORT AUTHORITY
1891 9th St, Mobile, AL 36615
Tel.: (251) 438-7334   AL
Web Site: http://www.mobileairportauthority.com
Year Founded: 1927
Sales Range: $25-49.9 Million
Emp.: 14
Airport Owner & Operator
N.A.I.C.S.: 488119
Michael Pierce *(Treas & Asst Sec)*
Elliot B. Maisel *(Chm)*
Thomas Curry *(Exec Dir)*
Brian Belcher *(Dir-Mktg & Air Svc Dev)*

MOBILE AREA WATER & SEWER SYSTEM
207 N Catherine St, Mobile, AL 36604
Tel.: (251) 694-3100
Web Site: http://www.mawss.com
Year Founded: 1952
Rev.: $60,893,484

COMPANIES

Emp.: 370
Sewerage Systems
N.A.I.C.S.: 221320
Sharon King (HR Officer)
Doug Cote (Asst Dir-Ops)
James W. Bell (Vice Chm, Treas & Sec)
Maynard V. Odom (Chm)
Pat Tyrrell (Treas & Sec)
Barbara Shaw (Officer-HR)

MOBILE ASPHALT CO., LLC
3151 Hamilton Blvd, Theodore, AL 36582-8500
Tel.: (251) 408-0770
Web Site:
http://www.mobileasphalt.com
Year Founded: 1991
Sales Range: $10-24.9 Million
Emp.: 150
Asphalt Paving Mixtures & Blocks
N.A.I.C.S.: 324121
Jimmy Loften (Pres)

Subsidiaries:

Mobile Asphalt Co., LLC - Atmore Plant (1)
1088 Old Jack Springs Rd, Atmore, AL 36502
Tel.: (251) 368-5087
Asphalt Product Mfr
N.A.I.C.S.: 324121
Randy Hardy (Plant Mgr)

Mobile Asphalt Co., LLC - Bay Minette Plant (1)
43385 Nicholsville Rd, Bay Minette, AL 36507
Tel.: (251) 580-0095
Asphalt Product Mfr
N.A.I.C.S.: 324121
Richard Moye (Plant Mgr)

Mobile Asphalt Co., LLC - Foley Plant (1)
21650 Doc McDuffie Rd, Foley, AL 36535
Tel.: (251) 943-9241
Asphalt Product Mfr
N.A.I.C.S.: 324121
Randy Hardy (Plant Mgr)

Mobile Asphalt Co., LLC - Saraland Plant (1)
1370 Highway 43 S, Saraland, AL 36571
Tel.: (251) 679-9783
Asphalt Product Mfr
N.A.I.C.S.: 324121
Stoney Norred (Plant Mgr)

Mobile Asphalt Co., LLC - Summerdale Plant (1)
17751 Vaughn Rd, Summerdale, AL 36580
Tel.: (251) 989-2405
Asphalt Product Mfr
N.A.I.C.S.: 324121
Mike Parker (Plant Mgr)

Mobile Asphalt Co., LLC - Whatley Plant (1)
1110 Main St, Whatley, AL 36482
Tel.: (251) 275-3833
Asphalt Product Mfr
N.A.I.C.S.: 324121
Mike Grayson (Plant Mgr)

MOBILE CARDIAC IMAGING, LLC.
7018 S Utica Ave, Tulsa, OK 74136
Tel.: (918) 744-1001 OK
Web Site:
http://www.mobilecardiac.com
Year Founded: 1998
Sales Range: $1-9.9 Million
Emp.: 23
Diagnostic Imaging
N.A.I.C.S.: 621512
Colleen Payne (Owner, Pres & CEO)

MOBILE EDGE, LLC
1150 N Miller St, Anaheim, CA 92806
Tel.: (714) 399-1400 CA
Web Site:
http://www.mobileedge.com
Year Founded: 2002
Sales Range: $10-24.9 Million
Emp.: 23
Laptop Computer Cases Designer, Mfr & Marketer
N.A.I.C.S.: 423990
G. David Cartwright (Owner, Pres & CEO)
Matthew Olivolo (Dir-PR)

MOBILE EIGHT HOLDING LTD.
501 7th Ave, New York, NY 10008
Tel.: (212) 629-3883
Rev.: $60,000,000
Emp.: 25
Men's & Boys' Sportswear
N.A.I.C.S.: 315250

Subsidiaries:

Mobile Eight Apparel Corp (1)
1407 Broadway Rm 2108, New York, NY 10018
Tel.: (917) 342-9178
Sales Range: $10-24.9 Million
Sportswear, Men's & Boys'
N.A.I.C.S.: 424350

MOBILE FLEET SERVICE INC.
2003 E Viola Ave, Yakima, WA 98901
Tel.: (509) 575-8888
Web Site:
http://www.mobilefleetservice.com
Rev.: $15,449,795
Emp.: 50
Trucks, Tractors & Trailers: New & Used
N.A.I.C.S.: 811111
Douglas Edler (Pres)
Connie Frazier (CFO)

MOBILE FOREST PRODUCTS INC.
3151b S Midtown Pk, Mobile, AL 36606
Tel.: (251) 476-8184
Web Site:
http://mobileforestproducts.com
Sales Range: $10-24.9 Million
Emp.: 54
Whslr of Timber & Trucking Products
N.A.I.C.S.: 423990
John Zuckley (Pres)

MOBILE GLOBAL EXPORTS INC.
616 S El Camino Real Ste H, San Clemente, CA 92672-4294
Tel.: (949) 573-0628 DE
Web Site:
https://www.mogoesports.com
Year Founded: 2021
Online Game Development Services
N.A.I.C.S.: 541511
Marco Welch (Chm)

MOBILE LUMBER & MILLWORK INC.
5229 Hwy 90 W, Mobile, AL 36619
Tel.: (251) 660-0400
Web Site:
http://www.mobilelumber.com
Sales Range: $10-24.9 Million
Emp.: 140
Planing Mill Products & Lumber
N.A.I.C.S.: 423310
Paul Collier (Mgr-Ops)

MOBILE MARK, INC.
1140 W Thorndale Ave, Itasca, IL 60143
Tel.: (847) 671-6690
Web Site:
http://www.mobilemark.com
Year Founded: 1984
Sound Recording Studios
N.A.I.C.S.: 512240
Chris Wallgren (Mgr-Reg Acct)

MOBILE MEALS
8909 Magnolia Chase Cir, Tampa, FL 33647
Tel.: (813) 907-6325
Web Site:
http://www.mobilemeals.com
Sales Range: $1-9.9 Million
Catering & Food Delivery Services
N.A.I.C.S.: 722320
Elizabeth Mekdeci (CEO)

MOBILE ONE COURIER CARGO & LOGISTICS
1619 Diamond Springs Rd, Virginia Beach, VA 23455
Tel.: (757) 622-9500
Web Site:
http://www.mobileonecourier.com
Sales Range: $1-9.9 Million
Emp.: 50
Courier & Logistics Consulting Services
N.A.I.C.S.: 492110
Eric Brown (Pres & CEO)
Teresa Scarano (Dir-Ops)

MOBILE PAINT MANUFACTURING COMPANY OF DELAWARE INC.
4775 Hamilton Blvd, Theodore, AL 36582-8509
Tel.: (251) 443-6110
Web Site:
http://www.blpmobilepaint.com
Year Founded: 1921
Sales Range: $25-49.9 Million
Emp.: 480
Mfr of Paints
N.A.I.C.S.: 325510
Robert A. Williams (Pres & CEO)
Gary Meaut (VP-Sls & Mktg)
John Wilson (VP)
Louis Petit (VP & Gen Mgr)
Mark Dix (Mgr-Sls)

Subsidiaries:

Key Wallcovering Inc. (1)
PO Box 717, Theodore, AL 36590
Tel.: (251) 443-6110
Web Site: http://www.keywallcovering.com
Sales Range: $10-24.9 Million
Emp.: 100
Mfr of Wallcoverings
N.A.I.C.S.: 424950

Mobile Paint Carribbean (1)
4775 Hamilton Blvd, Theodore, AL 36582
Tel.: (251) 443-6110
Web Site: http://www.blpmobilepaint.com
Sales Range: $10-24.9 Million
Emp.: 5
Mfr of Paints
N.A.I.C.S.: 424950
John Wilson (VP-Fin)

Mobile Paint Manufacturing Company of Puerto Rico Inc. (1)
4775 Hamilton Blvd, Theodore, AL 36582
Tel.: (251) 443-6110
Sales Range: $10-24.9 Million
Emp.: 2
Mfr of Paints
N.A.I.C.S.: 424950
Elba Hernandez (Gen Mgr)

MOBILE RADIO COMMUNICATIONS INC.
1925 Baltimore Ave, Kansas City, MO 64108
Tel.: (816) 221-2720
Web Site: http://www.mobilfone.com
Rev.: $13,000,000
Emp.: 10
Provider of Wireless Communication Services
N.A.I.C.S.: 517112

MOBILEDATAFORCE, INC.

Elizabeth Ann Phillips (Pres)

MOBILE STRUCTURES INC.
2405 Cassopolis St, Elkhart, IN 46514
Tel.: (574) 264-6000
Web Site:
http://www.mobilestructures.com
Sales Range: $1-9.9 Million
Emp.: 4
Other Construction Material Merchant Whslr
N.A.I.C.S.: 423390
Cindy Smith (VP)

MOBILE SYSTEMS WIRELESS LLC
3195 Independence Dr, Livermore, CA 94551
Tel.: (510) 324-3420
Web Site: http://www.mswireless.com
Sales Range: $25-49.9 Million
Emp.: 120
Telephone & Communication Equipment
N.A.I.C.S.: 449210

MOBILE TV GROUP
8455 Highfield Pkwy, Englewood, CO 80112
Tel.: (303) 388-8500
Web Site:
http://www.mountainmobiletv.com
Year Founded: 1994
Sales Range: $10-24.9 Million
Emp.: 150
Mobile Production Services
N.A.I.C.S.: 512110
Philip Garvin (Founder & Gen Mgr)
Peter Wehner (Dir-Engrg)
Nick Garvin (COO)
Ryan Hatch (Dir-Ops)

MOBILE-ONE AUTO SOUND INC.
3000 Clearview Pkway, Metairie, LA 70006
Tel.: (504) 888-4922
Web Site: http://www.mobileone.com
Sales Range: $25-49.9 Million
Emp.: 60
Provider of Automotive Sound Equipment Services
N.A.I.C.S.: 441330
Paul M. Campo (Pres)

MOBILEATION, INC.
3655 W Anthem Way Ste A-109 171, Anthem, AZ 85086
Tel.: (928) 567-1228
Web Site:
http://www.mobileation.com
Sales Range: $1-9.9 Million
Emp.: 3
Mail-Order & Internet Retailer of Toys
N.A.I.C.S.: 459120

MOBILEBITS HOLDINGS CORPORATION
5901 N Honore Ave Ste 110, Sarasota, FL 34243
Tel.: (941) 225-6115 NV
Year Founded: 2008
Sales Range: Less than $1 Million
Emp.: 9
Mobile Marketing Services
N.A.I.C.S.: 517112
Hussein Abu Hassan (Chm)

MOBILEDATAFORCE, INC.
943 W Overland, Meridian, ID 83642-8917
Tel.: (208) 384-1200
Web Site:
http://www.mobiledataforce.com

MOBILEDATAFORCE, INC.

MobileDataforce, Inc.—(Continued)
Sales Range: $10-24.9 Million
Emp.: 15
Business Software Services
N.A.I.C.S.: 513210
Kevin Benedict (CEO)
David Cohen (CEO)
Kathleen Obrien (Office Mgr-HR)
Ryan Thompson (Engr-Software)

Subsidiaries:

Treetop Technologies, Inc. (1)
6148 Discovery Way Ste 107, Boise, ID 83713
Tel.: (208) 830-1875
Web Site: http://www.treetoptech.com
Sales Range: $1-9.9 Million
IT Outsource Consulting Services
N.A.I.C.S.: 541690

MOBILEDEMAND, LC

1501 Boyson Square Dr Ste 101, Hiawatha, IA 52233
Tel.: (319) 363-4121
Web Site:
http://www.ruggedtabletpc.com
Year Founded: 2003
Rev.: $3,600,000
Emp.: 30
Electronic Computer Mfr
N.A.I.C.S.: 334111
Matt Miller (Founder & CEO)
Christie Bielenberg (Dir-HR)

MOBILEIRON, INC.

490Å E Middlefield Rd, Mountain View, CA 94043
Tel.: (650) 919-8100   DE
Web Site: http://www.mobileiron.com
Year Founded: 2007
Rev.: $205,236,000
Assets: $212,430,000
Liabilities: $176,432,000
Net Worth: $35,998,000
Earnings: ($48,846,000)
Emp.: 870
Fiscal Year-end: 12/31/19
Information Technology Services
N.A.I.C.S.: 541512
Suresh Batchu (Co-Founder & CTO)
Ajay Mishra (Co-Founder)
Tae Hea Nahm (Chm)
Simon Biddiscombe (Pres & CEO)
Dilip Patel (Sr VP-Customer Success)
Jared Lucas (Chief People Officer)
Scott D. Hill (CFO)
Rhonda Shantz (CMO)
Brian Foster (Sr VP-Product Mgmt)
Renchi Raju (VP-Engrg)

Subsidiaries:

MobileIron Australia (1)
Level 57 MLC Centre 19-29 Martin Place, Sydney, 2000, NSW, Australia
Tel.: (61) 2 9238 1907
Information Technology Services
N.A.I.C.S.: 541512

MobileIron EMEA (1)
Marathon 2, 1213 PH, Hilversum, Netherlands
Tel.: (31) 35 5288 170
Web Site: http://www.mobileiron.com
Emp.: 25
Information Technology Services
N.A.I.C.S.: 541512

Branch (Non-US):

MobileIron Central & Eastern Europe (2)
Balanstrasse 73 Building 8, 81541, Munich, Germany
Tel.: (49) 89 12503644 0
Web Site: http://www.mobileiron.com
Information Technology Services
N.A.I.C.S.: 541512

MobileIron France (2)
171 Bis Avenue Charles de Gaulle, Bureau 302, 92200, Neuilly-sur-Seine, France

Tel.: (33) 1 40 88 11 45
Information Technology Services
N.A.I.C.S.: 541512

MobileIron UK & Ireland (2)
200 Brook Dr Green Park, Reading, RG2 6UB, United Kingdom
Tel.: (44) 0118 949 7571
Information Technology Services
N.A.I.C.S.: 541512

MobileIron Hong Kong (1)
Level 23 1 Island East, Quarry Bay, China (Hong Kong)
Tel.: (852) 3750 7464
Information Technology Services
N.A.I.C.S.: 541512

MobileIron Japan (1)
Shima Akasaka Building 4-1-1 Akasaka Minato-ku, Tokyo, 107-0052, Japan
Tel.: (81) 3 6234 4962
Information Technology Services
N.A.I.C.S.: 541512
Matt Bennett (VP-Sls-Asia Pacific & Japan)

MobileIron Singapore (1)
Level 42 Suntec Tower 3 8 Temasek Boulevard, Singapore, 038988, Singapore
Tel.: (65) 6829 2186
Information Technology Services
N.A.I.C.S.: 541512
Frederic Gillant (VP-Sls-Asia Pacific)
Jeroen Nooijen (VP-Sls-Asia Pacific & Japan)

MOBILEONE LLC

4655 Cass St Ste 304, San Diego, CA 92109
Tel.: (858) 270-2500
Web Site:
http://www.mobileonellc.com
Year Founded: 2008
Sales Range: $1-9.9 Million
Emp.: 150
T-Mobile Premium Retail Stores
N.A.I.C.S.: 517121
Heang Kao (Owner)

MOBILESTORM, INC.

16530 Ventura Blvd Ste 502, Encino, CA 91436
Tel.: (818) 465-6500   DE
Web Site:
http://www.mobilestorm.com
Year Founded: 1999
Sales Range: $1-9.9 Million
Emp.: 12
Email Marketing Software
N.A.I.C.S.: 513210
Jared E. Reitzin (Co-Founder, Chm & CEO)
Doug Schiller (CFO)
Joseph Shavit (VP-Product)
Ojas Amin (Co-Founder & VP-Product & Tech)

MOBILITY SERVICES INTERNATIONAL LLC

260 Merrimac St, Newburyport, MA 01950-2192
Tel.: (978) 462-9011   MA
Web Site: http://www.msimobility.com
Year Founded: 1981
Sales Range: $25-49.9 Million
Emp.: 70
Provider of Worldwide Employee Relocation Services
N.A.I.C.S.: 561990
Timm T. Runnion (CEO)
Gail Rabasca (Mng Dir & VP-Worldwide Ops)
Elaine Phipps (Reg Dir)
Kate DeFrancisco (Dir-Client Engagement)
Melissa Graber (Dir-Client Svcs)
Paul Neve (Dir-Client Engagement)
Sharon Leong (Dir-Client Engagement-Asia Pacific)
Val Dean (VP-Client Mgmt)

Liz Schulze (CFO)
Eric Egnet (COO & CIO)
Laurie Allen (VP-Client Ops)

MOBITV, INC.

6425 Christie Ave 5th Fl, Emeryville, CA 94608
Tel.: (510) 450-5000   DE
Web Site: http://www.mobitv.com
Sales Range: $50-74.9 Million
Emp.: 258
Mobile Device Television Broadcasting Services
N.A.I.C.S.: 517810
Charlie Nooney (Chm & CEO)
Paul M. Scanlan (Founder & Pres)
Bill Routt (COO)
Cedric Fernandes (CTO)

MOBIUS PARTNERS ENTERPRISE SOLUTIONS

1711 Citadel Plz, San Antonio, TX 78209-1001
Tel.: (210) 979-0380
Web Site:
http://www.mobiuspartners.com
Year Founded: 2000
Sales Range: $10-24.9 Million
Emp.: 14
Computer Server Seller & Installer
N.A.I.C.S.: 334118
J. Jaiver Uribe (Co-Founder & Pres)
Rosemary Elizalde (CFO)
Liz Masters Lovelace (Dir-Mktg)
Scott King (CTO)
Rob Vazzola (VP-Sls)
Junab Ali II (Co-Founder & Co-Pres)

Subsidiaries:

Pervigil, Inc. (1)
1711 Citadel Plz, San Antonio, TX 78209
Tel.: (210) 979-0380
Sales Range: $10-24.9 Million
Emp.: 10
Computer System Design Services
N.A.I.C.S.: 541512

MOBIUS VENTURE CAPITAL, INC.

1050 Walnut St Ste 210, Boulder, CO 80302
Tel.: (303) 642-4000   CA
Web Site: http://www.mobiusvc.com
Year Founded: 1996
Venture Capital Firm
N.A.I.C.S.: 523999
Becky Cooper (VP-Ops)
Jill Spruiell (Exec Asst & Office Mgr)

MOBLEY CONTRACTORS INC.

952 Hwy 287 E, Morrilton, AR 72110
Tel.: (501) 354-2510
Web Site:
http://www.mobleycontractors.com
Sales Range: $10-24.9 Million
Emp.: 130
Heavy Construction
N.A.I.C.S.: 237110
Ronald F. Mobley (Founder, Owner & Pres)
Donald Depriest (VP & Controller)
William K. French (VP-Ops)
Janice Mobley (Treas & Sec)

MOBLEY HOMES OF FLORIDA INC.

14824 N Florida Ave, Tampa, FL 33613
Tel.: (813) 960-8966
Web Site:
http://www.mobleyhousing.com
Year Founded: 1976
Sales Range: $10-24.9 Million
Emp.: 50
Builder of Single-Family Houses
N.A.I.C.S.: 236115

Timothy F. Mobley (Pres)

Subsidiaries:

M Tampa Corp. (1)
14824 N Flaave, Tampa, FL 33613
Tel.: (813) 960-8966
Web Site: http://www.mobleyhousing.com
Rev.: $15,000,000
Emp.: 30
New Construction, Single-Family Houses
N.A.I.C.S.: 236115

MOBOMO

6707 Democracy Blvd Ste 104, Bethesda, MD 20817-1129
Tel.: (240) 244-9662
Web Site: http://www.mobomo.com
Year Founded: 2009
Sales Range: $1-9.9 Million
Emp.: 14
Global Full-Service Mobile Developer
N.A.I.C.S.: 517810
Brian Lacey (COO)

MOC PRODUCTS COMPANY, INC.

12306 Montague St, Pacoima, CA 91331
Tel.: (818) 896-2258   CA
Web Site:
http://www.mocproducts.com
Year Founded: 1954
Sales Range: $25-49.9 Million
Emp.: 200
Mfr & Distr Automotive Care Products; Automotive Industry Solutions
N.A.I.C.S.: 325612
Dave Waco (VP-Sls)
Michael Camacho (Gen Mgr-Equipment Dev)
Chuck Chalfin (Mgr)
Ed Love (Reg Mgr-Sls)
John Allyn (Acct Mgr)
Kevin Bisson (Acct Mgr)

MOCAP INC.

409 Parkway Dr, Park Hills, MO 63601-4435
Tel.: (314) 543-4000   MO
Web Site: http://www.mocap.com
Year Founded: 1967
Sales Range: $10-24.9 Million
Emp.: 45
Mfr of Vinyl Dip Molded & Rubber Injection Molded Caps, Plugs, Grips & High Temperature Masking Products
N.A.I.C.S.: 326199
Joseph Miller (Pres)
Greg Miller (VP)
Paul Miller (VP)

Subsidiaries:

MOCAP France (1)
PO Box 8, F 28330, Authon-du-Perche, France (100%)
Tel.: (33) 237491902
Sales Range: $10-24.9 Million
Emp.: 1
Mfr of Plastic & Rubber Products
N.A.I.C.S.: 326199

MOCAP Limited (1)
Hortonwood 35, Telford, TF1 7YW, Shropshire, United Kingdom
Tel.: (44) 1952 670247
Web Site: http://www.mocap.co.uk
Plastic Product Mfr & Distr
N.A.I.C.S.: 326199
Nicola Meir (Dir-Fin)

MOCAP Srl (1)
Via GB Bonaita 219, Urgnano, 24059, Bergamo, Italy (100%)
Tel.: (39) 0354872020
Web Site: http://www.mocap.it
Sales Range: Less than $1 Million
Emp.: 18
Mfr of Plastic Products

N.A.I.C.S.: 326199
Cezeama Comencha *(Mgr)*

Productos MOCAP S. de R.L. de C.V. (1)
Serafin Pena No 745 Sur Col Centro, 64000, Monterrey, Mexico
Tel.: (52) 8183441843
Web Site: http://www.mocap.com.mx
Sales Range: $10-24.9 Million
Plastic Products Mfr & Whslr
N.A.I.C.S.: 326199

MOCHILA, INC.
100 Church St, New York, NY 10007
Tel.: (212) 587-5151
Web Site: http://www.mochila.com
Rev.: $4,500,000
Emp.: 40
Fiscal Year-end: 12/31/06
Audio/Visual, E-Commerce, Media Relations, New Technologies, Web (Banner Ads, Pop-ups, etc.)
N.A.I.C.S.: 541810
Benjamin Chen *(Chm & CEO)*
Carolyn Bekkedahl *(Pres & Chief Revenue Officer)*
Bill Lindsey *(CTO)*

MOCK PLUMBING & MECHANICAL, INC.
67 Ross Rd, Savannah, GA 31405
Tel.: (912) 232-1104
Web Site:
http://www.mocksavannah.com
Year Founded: 1946
Rev.: $22,094,848
Emp.: 110
Plumbing Contractor
N.A.I.C.S.: 238220
Ronald A. Tucker *(VP & Mgr-Contract Ops)*
Gary Cail *(Controller)*
William H. Mock Jr. *(Pres & Gen Mgr)*

MOCKLER BEVERAGE CO. LP
11811 Reiger Rd., Baton Rouge, LA 70809
Tel.: (225) 408-4283
Web Site:
https://www.mocklerbeverage.com
Emp.: 100
Food Service
N.A.I.C.S.: 311999

Subsidiaries:

Southwest Beverage Co. Inc. (1)
108 E Franklin St, Leesville, LA 71446
Tel.: (337) 478-6211
Web Site:
http://www.southwestbeverage.com
Grocery & Related Products Merchant Whslr
N.A.I.C.S.: 424490
Russ Fetting *(Mgr)*

MOD MEDIA LLC
11 Park St Ste 2F, Montclair, NJ 07042
Tel.: (973) 249-6157
Web Site: http://hudsonmod.com
Year Founded: 2012
Magazine Publisher; Marketing & Branding Solutions Services
N.A.I.C.S.: 513199
Shannon Steitz *(Founder, Pres & Publisher)*

Subsidiaries:

New York Spaces, Inc. (1)
520 8th Ave Fl 16, New York, NY 10018
Tel.: (212) 799-5433
Web Site: http://www.newyorkspaces.com
Magazine Publisher
N.A.I.C.S.: 513120
Patricia Ripley *(CEO)*

MOD SUPER FAST PIZZA, LLC
2035 158th CT NE Ste 200, Bellevue, WA 98004
Tel.: (206) 332-0200
Web Site:
http://www.modsuperfast.com
Year Founded: 2008
Perishable Prepared Food Mfr
N.A.I.C.S.: 722513
Robin Hamm *(VP-Culinary)*
John Maguire *(COO)*
Scott Svenson *(Founder & CEO)*

MOD-PAC CORP.
1801 Elmwood Ave, Buffalo, NY 14207
Tel.: (716) 873-0640
Web Site: http://www.modpac.com
Year Founded: 1881
Sales Range: $50-74.9 Million
Emp.: 370
Paperboard Packaging Printer, Designer & Mfr
N.A.I.C.S.: 561910
Daniel G. Keane *(Pres & CEO)*
Philip C. Rechin *(VP-Sls)*
David B. Lupp *(CFO & COO)*

Subsidiaries:

Krepe-Kraft, Inc. (1)
4199 Bayview Rd, Blasdell, NY 14219-2732
Tel.: (716) 826-7086
Web Site: http://www.krepekraft.com
Sales Range: $25-49.9 Million
Emp.: 110
Specialized Printing
N.A.I.C.S.: 323111
Katie Niedermeier *(Mgr-Sls)*

MODAGRAFICS INC.
5300 Newport Dr, Rolling Meadows, IL 60008
Tel.: (847) 392-3980
Web Site:
http://www.modagrafics.com
Year Founded: 1973
Sales Range: $10-24.9 Million
Emp.: 95
Provider of Screen Printing Services
N.A.I.C.S.: 323113
Ben Berning *(Dir-Creative)*
Brian Leyden *(Dir-Retail Sls)*
Jeff Rychlewski *(Dir-Installation Svcs)*

MODBE, INC.
1499 W 105 N, Orem, UT 84057-5112
Web Site:
http://www.modbeclothing.com
Year Founded: 2005
Sales Range: $1-9.9 Million
Emp.: 17
Women's Clothing Designer
N.A.I.C.S.: 315250
Jeff Wilhite *(Chm, Pres & CEO)*
Tricia Wilhite *(VP-Mktg)*

MODCO CREATIVE INC.
102 Madison Ave 10th Fl, New York, NY 10016
Tel.: (212) 686-0006
Web Site:
http://www.modcomedia.com
Year Founded: 1991
Advetising Agency
N.A.I.C.S.: 541810
Erik Dochtermann *(CEO)*
John Derisi *(VP & Creative Dir)*
Margie Cooper *(VP & Dir-Media)*
Jackie Santora *(VP)*
Felicia McCleary *(Supvr-Media)*
Daniel Cartwright *(Media Buyer)*
Adriana Pina *(Acct Coord)*
David Handog *(Buyer-Online Media)*
Frederick Navarrete *(Acct Exec)*
Deborah Kenney *(Buyer-Media)*

MODE GLOBAL, LLC
14785 Preston Rd Ste 850, Dallas, TX 75254
Web Site:
https://www.modeglobal.com
Year Founded: 1989
Emp.: 500
Transportation Services
N.A.I.C.S.: 484121
Lance Malesh *(Pres & CEO)*
Gene Welsh *(Chief Transportation Officer)*
Normand Frigon *(COO)*
Max Slivka *(CFO)*
Ajit Jagtap *(CIO)*

MODEA CORP
117 Washington St SW, Blacksburg, VA 24060
Tel.: (540) 552-3210
Web Site: http://www.modea.com
Year Founded: 2006
Sales Range: $1-9.9 Million
Emp.: 95
Advetising Agency
N.A.I.C.S.: 541810
David Catalano *(Co-Founder)*
Ted Boezaart *(CEO)*
Aaron Herrington *(Co-Founder)*

MODELS & TOOLS INC.
51400 Beloestri Ct, Shelby, MI 48315
Tel.: (248) 585-4540
Web Site:
http://www.modelsandtools.net
Year Founded: 1974
Sales Range: $10-24.9 Million
Emp.: 100
Industrial Molds
N.A.I.C.S.: 333511
Phil Neale *(Pres)*

MODERA WEALTH MANAGEMENT, LLC
56 Jefferson Ave 2nd Fl, Westwood, NJ 07675
Tel.: (201) 768-4600
Web Site:
http://www.moderawealth.com
Year Founded: 1983
Sales Range: $1-9.9 Million
Emp.: 50
Financial Advisory & Portfolio Management Services
N.A.I.C.S.: 523940
Rick Manske *(Chief Growth Officer)*
Bill Hansen *(Chief Investment Officer)*
Harli Palme *(COO)*
Adam Leone *(Principal & Mgr-Wealth-New Jersey)*
Bill Houck *(Mgr-Wealth)*
Greg Plechner *(Principal & Mgr-Wealth-New Jersey)*
Jeanne Owens *(Mgr-Ops)*
Robert Dowling *(Mgr-Wealth)*
Laurie Kane Burkhardt *(Mgr-Wealth)*
Karl H. Graf *(Principal & Mgr-Wealth)*
Peter Somich *(Principal & Mgr-Wealth)*
Tom Orecchio *(CEO)*

Subsidiaries:

Parsec Financial Management, Inc. (1)
6 Wall St, Asheville, NC 28801
Tel.: (828) 255-0271
Web Site: http://www.parsecfinancial.com
Rev.: $2,600,000
Emp.: 22
Investment Advice
N.A.I.C.S.: 523940

MODERN AMERICAN RECYCLING SERVICES, INC.
PO Box 1163, Amelia, LA 70340
Tel.: (985) 630-7002
Web Site:
http://www.modernamericanrecyclingservices.com
Year Founded: 1991
Rev.: $26,300,000
Emp.: 110
Recyclable Material Merchant Whslr
N.A.I.C.S.: 423930
Dwight Caton *(Pres)*

MODERN ART MUSEUM OF FORT WORTH
3200 Darnell St, Fort Worth, TX 76107
Tel.: (817) 738-9215
Web Site: http://www.themodern.org
Year Founded: 1961
Sales Range: $10-24.9 Million
Emp.: 146
Art Collection & Presentation Services
N.A.I.C.S.: 459920
Joanette Garwood *(Controller)*
Marla J. Price *(Dir-Museum)*

MODERN AUTOMOTIVE PERFORMANCE
9800 Hemingway Ave S, Cottage Grove, MN 55016
Tel.: (763) 545-3800
Web Site:
http://www.maperformance.com
Year Founded: 2006
Sales Range: $1-9.9 Million
Emp.: 24
New & Used Car Dealers
N.A.I.C.S.: 441110
Bill Tschida *(VP-Ops)*
Chris Carey *(Founder & Pres)*
Dan Carey *(Dir-Mktg)*
James Anderson *(Mgr-Logistics)*

MODERN BANK
250 W 55 St Fl 15, New York, NY 10019
Tel.: (212) 605-6500
Web Site:
http://www.modernbank.com
Sales Range: $25-49.9 Million
Emp.: 45
National Commercial Banks
N.A.I.C.S.: 522110
Bippy Siegal *(Founder & Chm)*
Joe Montana *(Vice Chm)*

MODERN BUILDERS, INC.
202 Main St, Janesville, IA 50647
Tel.: (319) 987-2911
Web Site:
http://www.moderniowa.com
Year Founded: 1967
Sales Range: $10-24.9 Million
Emp.: 15
Commercial & Industrial Building Construction
N.A.I.C.S.: 236220
Tami Mauer *(Office Mgr)*

MODERN BUSINESS ASSOCIATES, INC.
9455 Koger Blvd N Ste 200, Saint Petersburg, FL 33702
Tel.: (727) 563-1500
Web Site: http://www.mbahro.com
Year Founded: 1997
Sales Range: $350-399.9 Million
Emp.: 100
Benefits, Human Resource & Payroll Services
N.A.I.C.S.: 561330
Mark P. Lettelleier *(Pres & CEO)*
Sean McConnell *(Chief Legal Officer & VP-HR)*
Ellie Finehout *(VP-Sls & Mktg)*
Kris L. Simonsen *(VP-Fin)*

MODERN BUSINESS ASSOCIATES, INC. U.S. PRIVATE

Modern Business Associates, Inc.—(Continued)
Jim Hundley *(Dir-IT)*
Edwina Maxwell *(Dir-HR)*
Brady Diggs *(Sr Dir-Bus Dev)*

MODERN CLIMATE
800 Hennepin 8th Fl, Minneapolis, MN 55403
Tel.: (612) 343-8180
Web Site: http://modernclimate.com
Year Founded: 1998
Sales Range: $10-24.9 Million
Emp.: 25
Brand Development & Integration
N.A.I.C.S.: 541810
Jason Tell *(Chief Knowledge Officer)*
Geoff Bremner *(Pres & CEO)*
Keith Wolf *(Chief Creative Officer)*
John Moberg *(COO & CTO)*
Brant Haenel *(Exec VP-Client Svcs)*
Jim Toth *(Dir-Tech)*

MODERN COIN WHOLESALE INC.
PO Box 110159, Lakewood Ranch, FL 34211
Tel.: (941) 907-8484
Web Site:
  http://www.moderncoinwholesale.com
Sales Range: $1-9.9 Million
Coin Dealer
N.A.I.C.S.: 423940
Ron Drzewucki *(CEO)*

MODERN CONCRETE, INC.
1777 Sharps Access, Elko, NV 89802
Tel.: (775) 753-5100
Web Site:
  http://www.modernconcrete.net
Year Founded: 1997
Rev.: $7,300,000
Emp.: 29
Brick, Stone & Related Construction Material Merchant Whslr
N.A.I.C.S.: 423320
Scott W. Reutner *(Pres)*
Michael Shanks *(Treas & Sec)*

MODERN CONSTRUCTION INC.
2120 Blaine St, Laredo, TX 78043
Tel.: (956) 724-9001
Web Site:
  http://www.modernconstruction.com
Sales Range: $10-24.9 Million
Emp.: 30
General Contractors For Prefabricated Building For Industrial Use
N.A.I.C.S.: 236220
Jose E. Garcia *(Pres)*
Hector G. Garcia Jr. *(Project Mgr)*

MODERN CORPORATION
4746 Model City Rd, Model City, NY 14107
Tel.: (716) 754-8226
Web Site:
  http://www.moderncorporation.com
Year Founded: 1964
Sales Range: $50-74.9 Million
Emp.: 500
Refuse Collection & Disposal Services
N.A.I.C.S.: 562212
Kevin Doyle *(Mgr-IT)*

Subsidiaries:

Modern Landfill, Inc. (1)
4746 Model City Rd, Model City, NY 14107
Tel.: (716) 754-8226
Web Site:
  http://www.moderncorporation.com
Rev.: $16,012,300
Emp.: 60
Sanitary Landfill Operator

N.A.I.C.S.: 562212
Richard Washuta *(Pres)*

MODERN DEVELOPMENT COMPANY
3333 West Coast Hwy Ste 400, Newport Beach, CA 92663
Tel.: (949) 646-6400
Web Site:
  http://www.bianchiwine.com
Sales Range: $10-24.9 Million
Emp.: 10
Open Marketplace Operator
N.A.I.C.S.: 531190
Mike Gardner *(VP-Fin)*
Beau Bianchi *(VP-Mktg & Sls)*

Subsidiaries:

Bianchi Vineyards (1)
3333 W Coast Hwy Ste 400, Newport Beach, CA 92663
Tel.: (949) 646-9100
Web Site: http://www.bianchiwine.com
Sales Range: $1-9.9 Million
Wine Producer, Bottler & Supplier
N.A.I.C.S.: 312130
Glenn Bianchi *(Chm & Pres, Mng Gen Partner)*

MODERN DISPERSIONS, INC.
78 Marguerite Ave, Leominster, MA 01453-4222
Tel.: (978) 534-3370   MA
Web Site:
  http://www.moderndispersions.com
Year Founded: 1967
Emp.: 250
Thermoplastic Compounder & Concentrate Mfr
N.A.I.C.S.: 325991
Janos Kozma Sr. *(Founder)*

Subsidiaries:

Modern Dispersions South, Inc. (1)
302 Ed Ward Rd, Fitzgerald, GA 31750-0787
Tel.: (229) 423-9141
Thermoplastic Product Mfr
N.A.I.C.S.: 325211

MODERN DISTRIBUTORS INC.
817 W Columbia St, Somerset, KY 42501
Tel.: (606) 679-1178   KY
Web Site:
  http://www.moderndistributors.com
Year Founded: 1965
Sales Range: $25-49.9 Million
Emp.: 200
Tobacco & Tobacco Products & Food Products Whslr
N.A.I.C.S.: 445132
Robert M. Ray *(Treas & Sec)*
Gerald Ray *(Pres)*

MODERN DOOR & EQUIPMENT SALES INC.
4301 Charles Crossing Dr, White Plains, MD 20695
Tel.: (301) 843-5255
Web Site:
  http://www.moderndoor.com
Year Founded: 1985
Emp.: 30
Dist of Doors & Partitions
N.A.I.C.S.: 321911
William J. Dotson *(Pres)*
Phil Pasini *(VP & Gen Mgr)*
Steve Schjenken *(Mgr-Ops)*
Janice Haupt *(Controller)*

MODERN DROP FORGE CO.
13810 S Western Ave, Blue Island, IL 60406-3229
Tel.: (708) 388-1806   IL
Web Site:
  http://www.modernforge.com

Year Founded: 1914
Sales Range: $100-124.9 Million
Emp.: 300
Steel Drop Forgings Mfr
N.A.I.C.S.: 332111
Gregory Heim *(Pres & CEO)*
Ruth Genova *(Controller)*

Subsidiaries:

Mid-States Forging Die & Tool Co. (1)
2844 Eastrock Dr, Rockford, IL 61109-1736   (100%)
Tel.: (815) 226-2313
Web Site: http://www.modernforge.com
Sales Range: $10-24.9 Million
Emp.: 20
Sinking of Forging Dies
N.A.I.C.S.: 333514

Modern Forge/Tennessee (1)
501 Rock Ln Tri County Industrial Park, Piney Flats, TN 37686   (100%)
Tel.: (423) 282-0327
Web Site: http://www.modernforge.com
Sales Range: $25-49.9 Million
Emp.: 250
Mfr of Steel Drop Forgings
N.A.I.C.S.: 332111

MODERN ELECTRIC CO.
246 W 1st St, Casper, WY 82601
Tel.: (307) 266-1711
Web Site: http://www.modern-electric.com
Sales Range: $10-24.9 Million
Emp.: 60
General Electrical Contractor
N.A.I.C.S.: 238210
Dawn Clair *(Sec)*
Kristen Wilson *(Treas)*
Richard Vignaroli *(Pres & CEO)*

MODERN ENTERPRISE SOLUTIONS INC.
6026 Jet Port Industrial Blvd, Tampa, FL 33634
Tel.: (813) 673-8886
Web Site:
  http://www.modernenterprise.com
Year Founded: 2003
Sales Range: $10-24.9 Million
Emp.: 67
Networking, Transport, Switching & Central Office Equipment Distr
N.A.I.C.S.: 423690
Neil Birner *(Co-Founder)*
Steven Elia *(Co-Founder)*
Mike Herzog *(Co-Founder)*
Zarko Stanimirovic *(Asst Controller)*
Frank Janusas *(Dir-IT)*
Nick Scarsella *(VP-Sls Ops)*
David Pope *(Mgr-Channel Sls)*
Jimmy Whitman *(Partner-Channel & Mgr)*
Michael Algawani *(Reg Mgr)*

MODERN EXPLORATION INC.
213 N Travis St Ste 311, Sherman, TX 75090
Tel.: (903) 893-1129
Web Site:
  http://www.modernexploration.com
Sales Range: $10-24.9 Million
Emp.: 15
Crude Petroleum Production
N.A.I.C.S.: 211120
Gary Yost *(Pres)*
Walter Brice *(Sec)*
Charles Holcomb *(VP)*
John R. Murphy *(Mgr-Acctg)*

MODERN FARM EQUIPMENT CORP.
PO Box 467, Gordon, NE 69343-0467
Tel.: (308) 282-2368

Web Site:
  http://www.modernfarm.com
Sales Range: $25-49.9 Million
Emp.: 20
Farm & Garden Machinery
N.A.I.C.S.: 423820
Tim Bounous *(Gen Mgr)*
Roger Rosane *(Mgr-Svc)*
Brett Kersey *(Mgr-Parts)*

MODERN FOODS LLC
4926 Roberts Dr, Ashland, KY 41102
Tel.: (606) 928-4590
Sales Range: $10-24.9 Million
Emp.: 39
Dairy Products Mfr & Distr
N.A.I.C.S.: 424430
Michael Blair *(Gen Mgr)*

MODERN GAS SALES INC.
Rte 502, Avoca, PA 18641
Tel.: (570) 457-5311
Web Site: http://www.moderngas.com
Rev.: $490,000,000
Emp.: 35
Propane Gas, Bottled
N.A.I.C.S.: 484121
Edward Gorzkowski Sr. *(Pres)*

MODERN GROUP LTD.
2501 Durham Rd, Bristol, PA 19007
Tel.: (215) 943-9100   PA
Web Site:
  http://www.moderngroup.com
Year Founded: 1946
Sales Range: $50-74.9 Million
Emp.: 300
Holding Company; Forklift & Material Handling Equipment Sales, Rental, Parts & Repair Services
N.A.I.C.S.: 551112
David E. Griffith *(Chm)*
Ray Wiley *(VP-Forklift Sls)*
Paul Farrell *(Pres & CEO)*
Steve Seminack *(CFO & VP)*
Chris O'Connor *(Mgr-Forklift Tire)*
Eric Walker *(VP-Parts Ops & Modern Indus Cleaning Equipment)*

Subsidiaries:

Modern Handling Equipment Company (1)
2501 Durham Rd, Bristol, PA 19007-6923   (100%)
Tel.: (215) 943-9100
Web Site: http://www.moderngroup.com
Sales Range: $50-74.9 Million
Emp.: 100
Forklift & Material Handling Equipment Sales, Rental, Parts & Repair Services
N.A.I.C.S.: 423830
Paul Farrell *(Pres & CEO)*

Division (Domestic):

Modern Equipment Sales & Rental Co. (2)
2501 Durham Rd, Bristol, PA 19007
Tel.: (215) 943-9100
Web Site: http://www.moderngroup.com
Forklift & Material Handling Equipment Sales & Rental Services
N.A.I.C.S.: 423830
David E. Griffith *(Pres & CEO)*
Steve Lecatsas *(Branch Mgr)*

Branch (Domestic):

Modern Equipment Sales & Rental Co. - King of Prussia (3)
2501 Durham Rd, Bristol, PA 19007
Tel.: (610) 825-6010
Web Site: http://www.moderngroup.com
Sales Range: $25-49.9 Million
Emp.: 35
Forklift & Material Handling Equipment Sales & Rental Services
N.A.I.C.S.: 423830

Modern Equipment Sales & Rental Co. - Wilmington (3)
24 Brookside Dr, Wilmington, DE 19804-1102

Tel.: (302) 658-5257
Web Site: http://www.moderngroup.com
Sales Range: $25-49.9 Million
Emp.: 56
Forklift & Material Handling Equipment Sales & Rental Services
N.A.I.C.S.: 423830

Subsidiary (Domestic):

Modern Handling Equipment of N.J., Inc. (2)
75 New St, Edison, NJ
08837-3563 (100%)
Tel.: (732) 738-9200
Web Site: http://www.moderngroup.com
Sales Range: $50-74.9 Million
Forklift & Material Handling Equipment Sales, Rental, Parts & Repair Services
N.A.I.C.S.: 423830
Paul Van Nocker *(Gen Mgr)*

Moreco, Inc. (1)
2501 Durham Rd, Bristol, PA
19007-6923 (100%)
Tel.: (215) 943-9100
Web Site: http://www.moderngroup.com
Sales Range: $25-49.9 Million
Real Estate
N.A.I.C.S.: 531210
Don Sherow *(Dir-Mktg)*

Seely Equipment & Supply Co., Inc. (1)
1325 Hwy 34, Farmingdale, NJ 07727
Tel.: (732) 938-2900
Sales Range: $10-24.9 Million
Emp.: 60
Distr of Ice Equipment & Supplies Signs & Safety Items
N.A.I.C.S.: 423810

MODERN GROUP, LTD.
1655 Louisiana St, Beaumont, TX 77701
Tel.: (409) 833-2665
Web Site: http://www.modernusa.com
Rev: $24,209,751
Emp.: 13
Fabricated Structural Metal
N.A.I.C.S.: 332312
Casey J. Crenshaw *(Pres)*
Will Crenshaw *(Chm & CEO)*

Subsidiaries:

Dragon Products Ltd. (1)
1655 Louisiana St, Beaumont, TX 77701
Tel.: (844) 423-7246
Web Site: http://dragonproductsltd.com
Industrial Equipment Mfr
N.A.I.C.S.: 333248
Will Crenshaw *(Chm & CEO)*
Tom Inman *(VP-Pumps & Sitimulation Equipment)*
Johnny Tennison *(VP-Southeast Sls, Tanks & Trailers)*
Casey Crenshaw *(Pres)*
Todd Henning *(VP-Northwest Sls, Tanks & Trailers)*
Jimmy Jones *(VP-Rigs Sls & Svc)*
Ricky Plymell *(Sls Mgr-Rigs Sls & Svc)*

Division (Domestic):

Nalco Fab-Tech LLC (2)
4500 33 Mile Rd, Casper, WY 82604
Tel.: (307) 472-9740
Oil Recovery & Injection Equipment Distr
N.A.I.C.S.: 423830

MODERN HOLDINGS INCORPORATED
89 Summit Ave, Summit, NJ 07901
Tel.: (908) 378-2867 DE
Year Founded: 1994
Sales Range: $10-24.9 Million
Diverse Holding Company
N.A.I.C.S.: 551112
Henry L. Guy *(Pres & CEO)*
David Marcus *(Chm)*
Jay Murray *(CFO)*

MODERN ICE EQUIPMENT & SUPPLY CO.
5709 Harrison Ave, Cincinnati, OH 45248
Tel.: (513) 367-2101
Web Site: http://www.modernice.com
Sales Range: $25-49.9 Million
Emp.: 50
Refrigeration Equipment & Supplies
N.A.I.C.S.: 423740
Gary Jerow *(Pres & CEO)*
John Murphy *(Exec VP)*
Allen Butcher *(Mgr-Sls-Arizona)*
Mike Ringstaff *(Dir-Sls)*
Andrew Goderwis *(Project Engr)*
Brian Ballman *(Dir-Technical Svcs)*
Brian Bloch *(Project Mgr & Designer-CAD)*
Dan Graham *(Mgr-Bus Sys)*
Drew Johnson *(Supvr-Warehouse-Greendale)*
Jason Dulle *(Mgr-Sls-Alaska)*
Philip Brasher *(Mgr-Sls-Alabama)*

Subsidiaries:

Modern Fabricating Inc. (1)
5709 Harrison Ave, Cincinnati, OH 45248
Tel.: (513) 367-2101
Web Site: http://www.modernice.com
Rev: $180,000
Emp.: 3
Sheet Metalwork
N.A.I.C.S.: 332322
Gary Jerow *(Pres & CEO)*
John Murphy *(Exec VP)*
Allen Butcher *(Reg Mgr-Sls)*
Andrew Goderwis *(Sr Engr-Design)*
Brian Ballman *(Dir-Engrg & Product Dev)*
Brian Bloch *(Project Mgr & Designer-CAD)*
Jason Dulle *(Reg Mgr-Sls)*
Philip Brasher *(Reg Mgr-Sls)*
Tom Howat *(Reg Mgr-Sls)*

MODERN INDUSTRIES INC.
613 W 11th St, Erie, PA 16501
Tel.: (814) 455-8061
Web Site: http://www.modernind.com
Year Founded: 1946
Sales Range: $25-49.9 Million
Emp.: 355
Machine Shop, Jobbing & Repair
N.A.I.C.S.: 332811
Herb S. Sweny *(Founder)*
Mitch Willis *(CFO)*
Dennis Sweny *(Co-Pres)*
Tim Sweny *(Co-Pres)*

Subsidiaries:

Free-Col Laboratories (1)
11618 Cotton Rd, Meadville, PA 16335
Tel.: (814) 724-6242
Web Site: http://www.mi-erie.com
Sales Range: $10-24.9 Million
Emp.: 42
Environmental Testing
N.A.I.C.S.: 541380
Tim Sweaney *(Pres)*

Modern Industries Inc. - Kersey Plant (1)
135 Greens Rd, Kersey, PA 15846
Tel.: (814) 885-8514
Web Site: http://www.modernind.com
Heat Treating Services
N.A.I.C.S.: 332811

Modern Industries Inc., Heat Treat Division (1)
613 W 11th St, Erie, PA 16501
Tel.: (814) 455-8061
Web Site: http://www.modernind.com
Sales Range: $10-24.9 Million
Emp.: 120
Heat Treating Services
N.A.I.C.S.: 332811

MODERN INDUSTRIES, INC.
4755 E Beautiful Ln, Phoenix, AZ 85044
Tel.: (602) 427-1000
Web Site: http://www.modinds.com
Year Founded: 1969
Sales Range: $25-49.9 Million
Emp.: 350
Mfr of Precision Machine Components
N.A.I.C.S.: 332710
Dan Yahraus *(Pres)*

MODERN LANGUAGE ASSOCIATION
85 Broad St Ste 500, New York, NY 10004-2434
Tel.: (646) 576-5000 MD
Web Site: http://www.mla.org
Year Founded: 1883
Sales Range: $10-24.9 Million
Emp.: 116
Professional Organizations
N.A.I.C.S.: 813920
Arlene M. Barnard *(Controller)*
Kathleen Fitzpatrick *(Dir-Admin & Fin)*
Terrence Callaghan *(Dir-Admin & Fin)*
Cheri A. Smith *(Mgr-Adv)*
David E. Laurence *(Dir-Res & ADE)*
David W. Wright *(Editor-Directory Periodicals)*
Dennis Looney *(Dir-Programs & ADFL)*
June DiMarzo *(Asst Exec Dir)*
Mara Naaman *(Asst Dir-Programs)*
Micki Kaufman *(Dir-Info Sys)*
Rosemary G. Feal *(Exec Dir)*
Siovahn Walker *(Dir-Outreach)*

MODERN LITHO-PRINT CO.
6009 Stertzer Rd, Jefferson City, MO 65101
Tel.: (573) 635-6119
Web Site: http://www.modernlitho.com
Year Founded: 1937
Printing
N.A.I.C.S.: 323111

Subsidiaries:

Modern Litho - St Louis (1)
5111 Southwest Ave, Saint Louis, MO 63110
Tel.: (314) 781-6505
Web Site: https://modernlitho.com
Commercial Printing
N.A.I.C.S.: 323111
Skip Bray *(Pres)*

Modern Litho-Kansas City (1)
1340 Taney St, Kansas City, MO 64116
Tel.: (816) 561-6211
Web Site: http://www.modernlitho.com
Commercial Printing, Lithographic
N.A.I.C.S.: 323111
Evan James *(Pres)*
Tim Robertson *(Mgr)*

MODERN MARKET MASTER INC.
796 Bill Rutledge Rd, Winder, GA 30680
Tel.: (470) 558-2848
Web Site: http://www.mmm-express.com
Year Founded: 2006
Sales Range: $10-24.9 Million
Emp.: 101
Freight Trucking Services
N.A.I.C.S.: 484110
Vladimir L. *(Founder)*
Max L. *(CEO)*
Roman A. *(COO)*
Vick M. *(VP-Expedite Division)*
Tony Z. *(VP-Sls)*

MODERN MARKETING PARTNERS
1220 Iroquois Ave Ste 210, Naperville, IL 60563
Tel.: (630) 868-5060
Web Site: http://www.modernmarketingpartners.com
Sales Range: $1-9.9 Million
Emp.: 13
Advertising & Marketing Services
N.A.I.C.S.: 541810
Neil M. Brown *(Partner)*

MODERN MASS MEDIA INC.
Ste 4 100 Passaic Ave, Chatham, NJ 07928-2848
Tel.: (973) 635-6000
Web Site: http://www.mmmusa.com
Year Founded: 1970
Sales Range: $25-49.9 Million
Emp.: 10
Provider of Electronic Communication Equipment
N.A.I.C.S.: 423690

MODERN MUSHROOM FARMS, INC.
1330 Newark Rd, Toughkenamon, PA 19374
Tel.: (610) 268-3535 PA
Web Site: http://www.modernmush.com
Year Founded: 1970
Rev: $25,000,000
Emp.: 350
Mushrooms Producer
N.A.I.C.S.: 111411
Charles J. Ciarrocchi Jr. *(Pres)*
Gene Gtgene *(Mgr-Farm)*
Ruth Andrews *(Mgr-Payroll)*
William Chalupa *(VP-Res & Quality Assurance)*

Subsidiaries:

Modern Mushroom Sales (1)
1330 Newark Rd, Toughkenamon, PA 19374 (100%)
Tel.: (610) 268-3535
Web Site: http://www.modernmush.com
Sales Range: $100-124.9 Million
Fresh & Processed Mushroom
N.A.I.C.S.: 111411
Charles J. Ciarrocchi Jr. *(Pres)*

The California Mushroom Farm, Inc. (1)
4440 Olivas Park Dr, Ventura, CA 93001-4310
Tel.: (805) 642-3253
Mushroom Farming Services
N.A.I.C.S.: 111411

MODERN NISSAN OF CONCORD, INC.
967 Concord Pkwy S, Concord, NC 28027-9061
Tel.: (704) 788-2110
Web Site: http://www.modernnissanofconcord.com
Sales Range: $10-24.9 Million
Emp.: 45
Car Whslr
N.A.I.C.S.: 441110
Gary Frazier *(Gen Mgr)*
Jim Whitner *(Controller)*
John Bratton *(Asst Gen Mgr)*

MODERN OFFICE METHODS INC.
4747 Lake Forest Dr, Cincinnati, OH 45242
Tel.: (513) 791-0909
Web Site: http://www.momnet.com
Year Founded: 1957
Sales Range: $25-49.9 Million
Emp.: 170
Office Equipment Merchant Whslr
N.A.I.C.S.: 423420
Kevin McCarthy *(Pres & CEO)*
Brad Jones *(Mgr-Client Loyalty)*
Ken Staubitz *(VP-Ops & Gen Mgr-Full Svc Networking)*
Ron Slageter *(CFO)*
Steve Bandy *(Sr VP-Sls & Mktg)*

MODERN OFFICE METHODS INC.

Modern Office Methods Inc.—(Continued)

Subsidiaries:

Document Solutions LLC (1)
100 E Campus View Blvd Ste 105, Columbus, OH 43235
Tel.: (614) 846-2400
Web Site: http://www.docsol.net
Office Equipment Merchant Whslr
N.A.I.C.S.: 423420
Karen Leeth (Sr Mgr-Acct)
Leah Seymour (Sr Mgr-Acct-Major Markets)
Jessica Shrader (Acct Mgr)
Heather Bower (Mgr-Acct)

FSN, Inc. (1)
4747 Lk Forest Dr Ste 100, Cincinnati, OH 45242
Tel.: (513) 782-4200
Web Site: https://www.momnet.com
IT Consulting Services
N.A.I.C.S.: 541519

Subsidiary (Domestic):

Connective Computing Inc. (2)
2200 Victory Pkwy Ste 525, Cincinnati, OH 45206-2837
Tel.: (513) 475-5660
Web Site:
  http://www.connectivecomputing.com
Computer Related Services
N.A.I.C.S.: 541519

MODERN OIL COMPANY INC.
39103 MacArthur St, Shawnee, OK 74804
Tel.: (405) 273-5735
Rev: $44,300,000
Emp.: 12
Gases, Liquefied Petroleum
N.A.I.C.S.: 424720
Pat Sparkman (Pres)
Bud Phelps (Controller)

MODERN PARKING INC.
303 S Union Ave 1st Fl, Los Angeles, CA 90017
Tel.: (213) 482-8400
Web Site:
  http://www.modernparking.com
Year Founded: 1993
Sales Range: $1-9.9 Million
Emp.: 450
Parking Management Company
N.A.I.C.S.: 812930
M. J. Islam (CEO)
Dolan Islam (VP)
Lori R. Pinson (Sr VP)
Gary Pitts (Pres)
Manuel Rubio (VP-Quality & Revenue)
Raymond Abarca (Asst VP)

MODERN POURED WALLS INC.
41807 State Rte 18, Wellington, OH 44090
Tel.: (440) 647-6661
Web Site: http://www.mpwcs.com
Year Founded: 1976
Sales Range: $10-24.9 Million
Emp.: 120
Concrete Work
N.A.I.C.S.: 238110
Scott Smith (Owner)

MODERN PRECAST CONCRETE
210 Durham Rd, Ottsville, PA 18942-1723
Tel.: (610) 847-5112 PA
Web Site: http://www.modcon.com
Year Founded: 1946
Sales Range: $100-124.9 Million
Emp.: 160
Mfr of Concrete Septic Tanks & Wall Panels; Headwalls; Seepage Tanks, Sewer Manholes & Inlets; Plumbing Supplies; Wastewater Treatment Plants, Buildings, Durarest Restrooms
N.A.I.C.S.: 562991
James P. Loew (CFO & VP)
Jason Wehrung (Owner & Pres)
Brad Jacobs (Dir-Pur)

Subsidiaries:

Wehrung's Lumber & Home Center (1)
7711 Easton Rd, Ottsville, PA 18942
Tel.: (610) 847-2066
Web Site: http://www.wehrungs.com
Sales Range: $10-24.9 Million
Emp.: 60
Lumber Processing
N.A.I.C.S.: 327390
Jim Loew (CFO)

MODERN PRODUCTS, INC.
6425 W Executive Dr, Mequon, WI 53092-0248
Tel.: (262) 242-2400 WI
Web Site:
  http://www.modernfearn.com
Year Founded: 1925
Sales Range: $75-99.9 Million
Emp.: 25
Special Diet Foods & Health Food Seasoning Mfr
N.A.I.C.S.: 311942
Gaylord G. Palermo (Pres)
Anthony A. Palermo (CEO)
James Kohnke (Controller)

MODERN SUPPLY COMPANY INC.
525 Lovell Rd, Knoxville, TN 37932-3216
Tel.: (865) 966-4567 TN
Web Site:
  http://www.modernsupplyco.com
Year Founded: 1949
Sales Range: $10-24.9 Million
Emp.: 100
Plumbing Fixtures, Equipment & Supplies
N.A.I.C.S.: 423720
Pace Robinson (Pres & CEO)
Dottie Ramsey (COO)
Jason Carnley (Mgr-Warehouse)

MODERN TECHNOLOGY SOLUTIONS, INC.
Poplar Run Ofc Park 5285 Shawnee Rd Ste 400, Alexandria, VA 22312
Tel.: (703) 564-3800
Web Site: http://www.mtsi-va.com
Year Founded: 1993
Sales Range: $75-99.9 Million
Emp.: 428
Scientific & Technical Consulting Services
N.A.I.C.S.: 541690
Phil Suocy (Co-Founder & Chm)
Tom McMahan (Co-Founder)
Kevin Robinson (Pres & CEO)
Steve Trieber (VP-Strategic Dev)

MODERN TOYOTA
3178 Peters Creek Pkwy, Winston Salem, NC 27127-4755
Tel.: (336) 785-3100 NC
Web Site:
  http://www.modernautomotive.com
Year Founded: 1990
Sales Range: $25-49.9 Million
Emp.: 200
New & Used Car Dealers
N.A.I.C.S.: 441110
Daniel Derrick (Mgr-Sls)
Dawn Hernandez (Office Mgr)
James Flippin (Mgr-Svcs)
Paul Stack (Mgr-Body Shop Parts)
Steve Barton (Mgr-Pre-Owned Sls)
Mark Thompson (Mgr-Svc)
Jerry Hollifield (CFO)
Mike Feiereisel (Gen Counsel & Dir-Compliance)
Rob Fowler (Pres)
Fred Fowler (VP)
Brad Fowler (VP-Corp Ops)

MODERN TOYOTA OF BOONE INC.
665 E King St, Boone, NC 28607
Tel.: (828) 264-1491
Web Site: http://www.moderntoyotaofboone.com
Sales Range: $25-49.9 Million
Emp.: 30
Car Dealership Owner & Operator
N.A.I.C.S.: 441110
Drew Johnson (Controller)
Linda Day (Controller)
Steve Carson (Mgr-Sls)
Rob Fowler (Pres)

MODERN TRANSPORTATION SERVICES INC.
2605 Nicholson Rd Ste 110, Sewickley, PA 15143-8896
Tel.: (412) 489-4800 DE
Web Site:
  http://www.moderntrans.com
Year Founded: 1987
Sales Range: $25-49.9 Million
Emp.: 258
Provider of Trucking Services
N.A.I.C.S.: 484110
Patrick Cozzens (Pres)
Tammy Evans (VP-Ops)
Ken Klinvex (Dir-HR)

MODERN WELDING COMPANY, INC.
2880 New Hartford Rd, Owensboro, KY 42303-1321
Tel.: (270) 685-4400 KY
Web Site:
  http://www.modweldco.com
Year Founded: 1932
Sales Range: $150-199.9 Million
Emp.: 775
Custom Metal Mfr
N.A.I.C.S.: 332420
Jim Prindle (VP & Mgr-Subsidiary)
John G. Bernard (Founder)

Subsidiaries:

Modern Custom Fabrication, Inc. (1)
2421 E California Ave, Fresno, CA 93721
Tel.: (559) 264-4741
Metal Tank Mfr
N.A.I.C.S.: 332420
James Gray (VP & Mgr-Subsidiary)

Modern Supply Co., Inc. (1)
5255 Modern Way, Bowling Green, KY 42101-4837 (100%)
Tel.: (270) 781-2900
Web Site: http://www.modernsupplyco.com
Sales Range: $10-24.9 Million
Emp.: 12
Welding Supply Distr
N.A.I.C.S.: 811490
Ricky Peebles (Gen Mgr)

Modern Supply Co., Inc. (1)
307 Steel Dr, Elizabethtown, KY 42701 (100%)
Tel.: (270) 769-5588
Sales Range: $10-24.9 Million
Emp.: 6
Welding Industrial Supplier
N.A.I.C.S.: 459999
Philip Crady (Mgr)

Modern Supply Co., Inc. (1)
2905 Nebo Rd, Madisonville, KY 42431 (100%)
Tel.: (270) 821-8652
Web Site: http://www.modernsupplyco.com
Sales Range: $10-24.9 Million
Emp.: 4
Industrial Gases & Welding Supplies Distr
N.A.I.C.S.: 459999
Lavalton Humphrey (Gen Mgr)

Modern Supply Co., Inc. (1)
1507 E 15th St, Owensboro, KY 42303-1068 (100%)
Tel.: (270) 684-1449
Sales Range: $10-24.9 Million
Emp.: 30
Welding Supplies Distr
N.A.I.C.S.: 459999
Mark Pike (Gen Mgr)

Modern Supply Co., Inc. (1)
818 Division St, Evansville, IN 47711-5664 (100%)
Tel.: (812) 425-1265
Web Site: http://www.modernwelding.com
Sales Range: $10-24.9 Million
Emp.: 7
Welding Supply
N.A.I.C.S.: 423840

Modern Welding Company of California, Inc. (1)
4141 N Brawley Ave, Fresno, CA 93722-3915 (100%)
Tel.: (559) 275-9353
Web Site: http://www.modweldco.com
Sales Range: $10-24.9 Million
Emp.: 18
Metal Fabricators
N.A.I.C.S.: 332312
Bob Bartlett (VP)

Modern Welding Company of Florida, Inc. (1)
1801 Atlanta Ave, Orlando, FL 32806 (100%)
Tel.: (407) 843-1270
Web Site: http://www.modweldco.com
Sales Range: $25-49.9 Million
Emp.: 50
Tanks Mfr
N.A.I.C.S.: 332313

Modern Welding Company of Georgia, Inc. (1)
300 Prep Phillips Dr, Augusta, GA 30901-1772 (100%)
Tel.: (706) 722-3411
Web Site: http://www.modernwelding.com
Sales Range: $25-49.9 Million
Emp.: 40
Metal Fabricator
N.A.I.C.S.: 332313
Gary Harvel (Mgr-Pur)
Steve Fort (Gen Mgr)

Modern Welding Company of Kentucky, Inc. (1)
303 Steel Dr, Elizabethtown, KY 42701-9063 (100%)
Tel.: (270) 769-1368
Web Site: http://www.modernwelding.com
Sales Range: $10-24.9 Million
Emp.: 35
Structural Steel Mfr
N.A.I.C.S.: 332420

Modern Welding Company of Kentucky, Inc. (1)
155 Ben Chemetry Rd, Madisonville, KY 42431 (100%)
Tel.: (270) 821-3575
Sales Range: $10-24.9 Million
Emp.: 26
Steel Fabrication
N.A.I.C.S.: 332312
Mike Eddings (Gen Mgr)

Modern Welding Company of Ohio, Inc. (1)
1 Modern Way, Newark, OH 43058-4430 (100%)
Tel.: (740) 344-9425
Sales Range: $25-49.9 Million
Emp.: 38
Tank Mfr
N.A.I.C.S.: 332313
Douglas Rothert (VP & Mgr-Subsidiary)

Modern Welding Company of Owensboro, Inc. (1)
1450 E Parrish Ave, Owensboro, KY 42303-0837 (100%)
Tel.: (270) 683-5323
Web Site: http://www.modweldco.com
Sales Range: $10-24.9 Million
Emp.: 51
Steel Fabrication

N.A.I.C.S.: 332420
John Austin (VP & Mgr-Subsidiary)

Modern Welding Company of Texas, Inc. (1)
715 Sakowitz St, Houston, TX 77020-8021 (100%)
Tel.: (713) 675-4211
Web Site: http://www.modweldco.com
Sales Range: $10-24.9 Million
Emp.: 30
Underground Storage Tanks Mfr
N.A.I.C.S.: 332420
Randy Hill (VP & Plant Mgr)

Modern Welding Company of Texas, Inc. (1)
200 N Main St, Rhome, TX 76078 (100%)
Tel.: (817) 636-2215
Sales Range: $25-49.9 Million
Emp.: 20
Tanks Mfr
N.A.I.C.S.: 332313
W. E. Hill (VP & Mgr-Subsidiary)

Modern Welding Company, Inc. (1)
2818 Mt Pleasant Rd, Burlington, IA 52601-2001 (100%)
Tel.: (319) 754-6577
Sales Range: $10-24.9 Million
Emp.: 39
Underground Tanks Mfr
N.A.I.C.S.: 332420
Crystal Harris (Dir-Pur)

MODERN WOODCRAFTS LLC
72 NW Dr, Plainville, CT 06062
Tel.: (860) 677-7371
Web Site:
   http://www.modernwoodcrafts.com
Sales Range: $10-24.9 Million
Emp.: 100
Wood Partitions & Fixtures
N.A.I.C.S.: 337110
Gerald L. Pelletier (Owner)
Philip Shoeman (CEO)
Joe Legere (VP-Mfg)
Lisa Fekete (Pres)

MODERN WOODMEN OF AMERICA
1701 1st Ave, Rock Island, IL 61201-8724
Tel.: (309) 786-6481   IL
Web Site:
   http://www.modernwoodmen.org
Year Founded: 1883
Sales Range: $450-499.9 Million
Emp.: 500
Fraternal Life Insurance Services
N.A.I.C.S.: 524113
W. Kenny Massey (Pres & CEO)

Subsidiaries:

MWAGIA, Inc. (1)
1701 1st Ave, Rock Island, IL 61201
Tel.: (309) 786-6481
Financial Management Services
N.A.I.C.S.: 523940

MODERNE COMMUNICATIONS INC.
49 Front St, Rockville Centre, NY 11570
Tel.: (516) 594-1100
Web Site:
   http://www.modernecomm.com
Sales Range: $1-9.9 Million
Marketing Software
N.A.I.C.S.: 513210
Joe Mastrocovi (Pres)
Andrea Maria Urioste (VP-Mktg, Social & Digital Strategy)

MODERNFOLD/STYLES INC.
15 Empire Blvd, South Hackensack, NJ 07606
Tel.: (201) 329-6226
Web Site:
   http://www.modernfoldstyles.com
Sales Range: $10-24.9 Million

Emp.: 50
Demountable Partition Installation
N.A.I.C.S.: 423440
Rich Leahy (Project Mgr)
Terry Shoebridge (CFO)
Tim Vasile (Project Mgr)
Robert Styles Jr. (Pres)

MODERNISTA!
109 Kingston St Fl 2, Boston, MA 02111-2134
Tel.: (617) 451-1110
Year Founded: 2000
Emp.: 150
N.A.I.C.S.: 541810
Gary Koepke (Founder)
Joe Fallon (Dir-Creative)
Thom Donahue (Sr Studio Designer)
Clift Jones (COO-Worldwide)
Kapil Kachru (Copywriter)
Will Uronis (Dir-Art)
Matthew Charlton (Pres-Worldwide)
Chris Wallrapp (CMO)
Davi Liu (Dir-Creative)
Xavier Teo (Dir-Creative & Digital)
Darren Crawforth (Dir-Design)
Alex Hesz (Mng Dir)

Subsidiaries:

Modernista! (1)
Keizersgracht 534-5, 1017 EK, Amsterdam, Netherlands
Tel.: (31) 20 530 7979
N.A.I.C.S.: 541810

MODERNISTIC INC.
1987 Industrial Blvd S, Stillwater, MN 55082
Tel.: (651) 291-7650
Web Site: http://www.modprit.com
Rev.: $14,000,000
Emp.: 200
Converted Paper Products
N.A.I.C.S.: 322299
Doug Rausch (Dir-Art)

MODERNIZING MEDICINE, INC.
4850 Network Way Ste 200, Boca Raton, FL 33431
Tel.: (561) 880-2998
Web Site:
   http://www.modernizingmedicine.com
Sales Range: $1-9.9 Million
Emp.: 70
Medical Software
N.A.I.C.S.: 513210
Daniel Cane (Founder & CEO)
Michael Sherling (Chief Medical Officer)
Karen O'Byrne (CFO & COO)
Nadeem Dhanani (Dir-Medical-Urology)
Ida Mantashi (Sr Product Mgr & Chm-Quality Measurement Workgroup-Electronic Hea)
Brian Boyd (Chief Revenue Officer)
Venkatesh Jayaraman (CTO)
Jody Beaverson (Chief People Officer)

Subsidiaries:

Exscribe, Inc. (1)
5 W 4th St, Bethlehem, PA 18015
Tel.: (610) 419-2050
Web Site: http://www.exscribe.com
Rev.: $5,000,000
Emp.: 12
Custom Computer Programming Services
N.A.I.C.S.: 541511
Ranjan Sachdev (Pres)
Brandon Hanf (Project Mgr)
Andrew Frankenfield (Exec VP)
Richard McCormick (COO)

General Medical Applications, Inc. (1)

2700 S Commerce Pkwy Ste 400, Weston, FL 33331
Tel.: (954) 659-9310
Web Site: http://www.gmed.com
Sales Range: $1-9.9 Million
Emp.: 60
Electronic Medical Record Systems
N.A.I.C.S.: 541519
Daniel Cane (CEO)

MODESTO IRRIGATION DISTRICT INC.
1231 11th St, Modesto, CA 95354-0701
Tel.: (209) 526-7373
Web Site: http://www.mid.org
Year Founded: 1887
Sales Range: $75-99.9 Million
Emp.: 400
Provider of Irrigation & Electrical Services
N.A.I.C.S.: 221118
Scott Furgerson (Gen Mgr)
Nick Blom (Chm)
Greg Salyer (Asst Gen Mgr)
John David (Asst Gen Mgr-Water Ops)

MODESTO MOTOR CARS INC.
4701 McHenry Ave, Modesto, CA 95356
Tel.: (209) 575-3987
Web Site: http://www.valleylexus.com
Sales Range: $10-24.9 Million
Emp.: 30
New & Used Car Dealers
N.A.I.C.S.: 441110
B. E. Fitzpatrick (Pres)

MODESTO STEEL CO INC.
1424 N Emerald Ave, Modesto, CA 95352
Tel.: (209) 526-5306
Web Site:
   http://www.modestosteel.com
Year Founded: 1972
Sales Range: $10-24.9 Million
Emp.: 35
Steel & Steel Related Products
N.A.I.C.S.: 423510
Don Wenstrand (Pres)

MODIGENT LLC
3930 E Watkins St Ste 300, Phoenix, AZ 85034
Tel.: (800) 840-9170
Web Site: https://modigent.com
Infrastructure, Technology & Energy Solutions & Services
N.A.I.C.S.: 561210
Daniel Bueschel, (CEO)

Subsidiaries:

Tebarco Mechanical Corp. (1)
1690 Bluegrass Lk, Alpharetta, GA 30004
Tel.: (770) 475-5552
Web Site: http://www.tebarco.com
Rev.: $5,000,000
Emp.: 30
Plumbing, Heating & Air-Conditioning Contractors
N.A.I.C.S.: 238220
Terrell Barden (Owner)
Tony Adams (Pres)
Mike Rahn (Project Mgr)

MODINEER COMPANY INC.
2190 Indus Dr, Niles, MI 49120
Tel.: (269) 683-2550   IN
Web Site: http://www.modineer.com
Year Founded: 1940
Sales Range: $25-49.9 Million
Emp.: 380
Metal Stamping Services
N.A.I.C.S.: 332119
P. Michael Dreher (Chm)
Gary Dreher (VP-Sls)
Michael J. Dreher (Pres)

MODOP, LLC
444 Brickell Ave Ste 900, Miami, FL 33131
Tel.: (212) 431-5324
Web Site: https://www.modop.com
Year Founded: 2017
Emp.: 145
Advertising Services
N.A.I.C.S.: 541810
Dorothy Crenshaw (Chief Public Relations Officer)
Eric J. Bertrand (CEO)

Subsidiaries:

Crenshaw Communications, LLC (1)
36 W 20th St Fl 5, New York, NY 10011-4330
Tel.: (212) 367-9700
Web Site: https://www.crenshawcomm.com
Sales Range: $1-9.9 Million
Emp.: 15
Public Relations Agency
N.A.I.C.S.: 541820

MODUFORM, INC.
172 Industrial Rd, Fitchburg, MA 01420
Tel.: (978) 345-7942
Web Site: http://www.moduform.com
Year Founded: 1976
Sales Range: $10-24.9 Million
Emp.: 90
Public Building & Related Furniture
N.A.I.C.S.: 337127
Thomas Hurd (Exec VP)

MODULAR MANUFACTURING HOLDINGS
11701 6th St, Rancho Cucamonga, CA 91730
Tel.: (909) 476-4200
Web Site:
   http://www.modularsolutions.com
Sales Range: $10-24.9 Million
Emp.: 100
Remanufacturer of Modular Office Work Stations
N.A.I.C.S.: 337211
Daniel Coelho (CEO)
Rick Emmett (Treas)
George Robles (Pres)

MODULAR TECHNOLOGIES INC.
101J N Heritage St, Kinston, NC 28501
Tel.: (252) 522-5770
Web Site:
   http://www.mtimodtech.com
Rev.: $16,124,932
Emp.: 9
Prefabricated Buildings
N.A.I.C.S.: 444180
Patricia Jones (Sec)

MODULAR THERMAL TECHNOLOGIES, LLC
935 Roger Williams Way, North Kingstown, RI 02852
Tel.: (401) 667-7401   DE
Web Site: http://www.cryomax.com
Year Founded: 2004
Therapeutic Cold Pack & Sports Medicine Products Developer, Mfr & Marketer
N.A.I.C.S.: 339113
Brad Waugh (CEO)

Subsidiaries:

Life Wear Technologies, Inc. (1)
1620 SW 5th Ct, Pompano Beach, FL 33069
Tel.: (954) 785-1055
Web Site:
   http://www.lifeweartechnologies.com
Sports Medicine Products Developer, Mfr & Marketer
N.A.I.C.S.: 339113

MODULAR THERMAL TECHNOLOGIES, LLC   **U.S. PRIVATE**

Modular Thermal Technologies, LLC—(Continued)
Colin Hall *(Pres-Sls & Mktg)*
Lee Epstein *(VP-Ops)*
David Bass *(VP-Mktg)*

MODULEMD LLC
8359 Office Park Dr., Grand Blanc, MI 48439
Tel.: (877) 347-7978
Web Site:
https://www.modulemd.com
Year Founded: 2000
Emp.: 105
Technology Services
N.A.I.C.S.: 513210
Abhinay Rao Penugonda *(CEO)*

Subsidiaries:

Diversified Health Care Management, Inc. (1)
4141 B St Ste 301, Anchorage, AK 99503
Tel.: (907) 562-7536
Web Site: https://www.dhcmak.com
Emp.: 100
Accounting, Auditing & Bookkeeping Services
N.A.I.C.S.: 541219
Joseph Beatty *(Pres)*

MODUS CREATE, LLC
12355 Sunrise Vly Dr Ste 170, Reston, VA 20191-3491
Web Site:
http://www.moduscreate.com
Custom Computer Programming Services
N.A.I.C.S.: 541511
Bogdan Bucura *(Dir-Sls & Dev)*
Patrick Sheridan *(Co-Founder & Mng Partner)*
Jay Garcia *(Co-Founder & Mng Partner)*
Sarah McCasland *(Chief Strategy Officer)*

Subsidiaries:

Clarisoft Technologies, LLC (1)
640 Kreag Rd Ste 301, Pittsford, NY 14534
Tel.: (585) 310-7668
Web Site: http://www.clarisoft.com
Sales Range: $1-9.9 Million
Software Development Services
N.A.I.C.S.: 541511
Mircea Enache *(COO)*
Marius Cara *(Partner)*
Robert Benea *(Partner)*
Adrian Dobre *(Mgr)*
Adrian Morariu *(Mgr)*
Andrei Bouariu *(Mgr)*
George Craciun *(Mgr)*

Promptworks LLC (1)
123 S Broad St Ste 2400, Philadelphia, PA 19109
Web Site: http://www.promptworks.com
Sales Range: $1-9.9 Million
Emp.: 50
Software Development Services
N.A.I.C.S.: 541511
Jason Garber *(Co-Founder & COO)*
Mike Nicholaides *(Co-Founder & CTO)*
Greg Sterndale *(Co-Founder & CEO)*
Christine Olivas *(Dir-Sls & Mktg)*
Matt Riedel *(Dir-Engrg)*

MODUS OPERANDI PARTNERS, LLC
444 Gulf of Mexico Dr Ste 101, Longboat Key, FL 34228
Tel.: (941) 487-8504
Web Site: http://www.modusfl.com
Year Founded: 2007
Sales Range: $10-24.9 Million
Emp.: 5
Real Estate Development
N.A.I.C.S.: 237210
Steven Hanson *(Owner)*
Rob Knowlton *(Sr Project Mgr)*
Gunnar Barcomb *(Project Mgr)*

MOEHL MILLWORK INC.
5150 Southeast Rio Ct, Ankeny, IA 50021
Tel.: (515) 276-6791
Web Site:
http://www.moehlmillwork.com
Sales Range: $50-74.9 Million
Emp.: 80
Operators of Mills
N.A.I.C.S.: 423310
Bob Lane *(VP-Sls)*

MOEHN ART CHEVROLET CO.
2200 Seymour Rd, Jackson, MI 49201
Tel.: (517) 787-7700
Web Site: http://www.artmoehn.com
Sales Range: $50-74.9 Million
Emp.: 100
Sales of New & Used Automobiles
N.A.I.C.S.: 441110
John Kudner *(Owner & Pres)*

MOELIS ASSET MANAGEMENT LP
399 Park Ave 6th Fl, New York, NY 10022
Tel.: (917) 719-5700   DE
Web Site:
http://www.moelisassetmanagement.com
Holding Company; Investment Banking Services
N.A.I.C.S.: 551112
Frank Benevento *(Head-Bus Dev)*
Eric Felder *(CEO)*
Christopher Ryan *(Mng Dir)*

Subsidiaries:

Moelis & Company LLC (1)
399 Park Ave 5th Fl, New York, NY 10022
Tel.: (212) 883-3800
Web Site: https://www.moelis.com
Financial Advisory Services & Capital Raising Solutions
N.A.I.C.S.: 523940
Kenneth D. Moelis *(Chm & CEO)*
Joseph W. Simon *(Mng Dir & CFO)*
Osamu R. Watanabe *(Gen Counsel)*
Anton Sahazizian *(Mng Dir)*
James Schiro *(Mng Dir)*
Peijie Shiu *(Mng Dir)*
Margot Shoshan *(Mng Dir-Marketing)*
Greg Starkins *(Mng Dir)*
Adam Steinberg *(Mng Dir)*
Andrew Swift *(Mng Dir)*
Brian Tichenor *(Mng Dir)*
Carl Torrillo *(Mng Dir)*
Mark Webber *(Mng Dir)*
Angus Whelchel *(Mng Dir)*
Irene Zhang *(Mng Dir)*
Justin Craig *(Mng Dir)*
Dennis Crandall *(Mng Dir)*
Brad Davis *(Mng Dir)*
Francesco Del Vecchio *(Mng Dir)*
Jared Dermont *(Mng Dir)*
William Q. Derrough *(Mng Dir)*
Michael DiYanni *(Mng Dir)*
Jugjeev Duggal *(Mng Dir)*
Liz Eberhart *(Mng Dir)*
David P. Faris *(Mng Dir)*
Ted Ferguson *(CIO)*

Moelis & Company UK LLP (1)
First Floor Condor House 10 St Pauls Churchyard, London, EC4M 8AL, United Kingdom
Tel.: (44) 2076343500
Emp.: 100
Investment Bank & Financial Advisory Services
N.A.I.C.S.: 523940
Mark Aedy *(Head-Investment Banking-EMEA)*
Alexandra Oldroyd *(Mng Dir-Consumer Practice)*
David Cheyne *(Vice Chm-Investment Banking-EMEA)*
Robert Sorrell *(Mng Dir)*
Philip Smith *(Mng Dir-EMEA)*

Moelis Capital Partners LLC (1)
399 Park Ave 5th Fl, New York, NY 10022

Tel.: (212) 883-3800
Web Site:
http://www.moeliscapitalpartners.com
Rev.: $700,000,000
Emp.: 17
Privater Equity Firm
N.A.I.C.S.: 523999
Kurt Larsen *(Mng Partner)*

Holding (Domestic):

CyberCore Technologies LLC (2)
Meadowridge Bus Park 6605 Business Pkwy, Elkridge, MD 21075
Tel.: (410) 560-7177
Web Site: http://www.cybercoretech.com
Sales Range: $75-99.9 Million
Information Technology Services
N.A.I.C.S.: 541512
Kevin Powderly *(Chm)*
Jennifer Kauffman *(VP-Bus Dev)*
Neal Frick *(CEO)*

NexPhase Capital, LP (1)
600 Lexington Ave 12th Fl, New York, NY 10022
Tel.: (212) 878-6000
Web Site: http://www.nexphase.com
Emp.: 20
Privater Equity Firm
N.A.I.C.S.: 523999
Barbara B. Hill *(Operating Partner)*
Kurt Larsen *(Mng Partner)*
Ted Yun *(Mng Partner)*
Andrew Goldfarb *(CFO)*
Andy Kieffer *(Partner)*
Joel Killion *(Partner)*
Lex Leeming *(Partner & Head-Bus Dev)*
Doug Corbett *(Operating Partner)*
Ned Stringham *(Operating Partner)*
Robert Gartland *(Principal)*
Jamie Kaufman *(Partner)*
George Zahringer *(Principal)*

Holding (Domestic):

American Global Logistics, LLC (2)
3399 Peachtree Rd NE Ste 1130, Atlanta, GA 30326
Tel.: (866) 285-9610
Web Site:
http://www.americangloballogistics.com
Warehousing & Logistics Solutions
N.A.I.C.S.: 541614
Blake Shumate *(COO)*
Jon W. Slangerup *(Chm & CEO)*
Darren Brown *(CTO)*
Tania Garcia *(Sr VP & Head-Mktg)*
Doug McBee *(Sr VP & Head-Sls)*
Lori Fox *(VP-Customs Brokerage Svcs)*
Brad Ferguson *(VP-Ops)*
Timothy W. Henry *(CFO)*

Hawthorne Corporation (2)
3955 Faber Pl Ste 301, Charleston, SC 29405
Tel.: (843) 553-2203
Web Site: http://www.hawthornecorp.com
Sales Range: $150-199.9 Million
Emp.: 200
Aviation Facility & Real Estate Equity Investment Firm
N.A.I.C.S.: 523999
William E. Harton *(VP-Dev)*

Subsidiary (Domestic):

Hawthorne Global Aviation Services, LLC (3)
3955 Faber Place Dr Ste 301, North Charleston, SC 29405
Tel.: (843) 553-2203
Web Site: http://www.hawthorne.aero
Aviation Services & Aircraft Management
N.A.I.C.S.: 488190
W. Bryon Burbage *(Pres & CEO)*
William E. Harton *(Sr VP-Dev)*
Ralph Michielli *(COO)*
Keith Ruggirello *(VP-Sls & Mktg)*
Scott M. Zimmerman *(VP-Operational Fin)*
Denise Del Pino *(Dir-HR)*
Cameron Burr *(Chm)*
Dave Hurley *(Vice Chm)*
James W. Kaler II *(Dir-Ops)*

Subsidiary (Domestic):

Bama Air, Inc. (4)
4800 Carter Dr, Tuscaloosa, AL 35401
Tel.: (205) 349-3991

Web Site: http://www.bamaair.com
Sales Range: $1-9.9 Million
Emp.: 17
Airport Maintenance & Repair Services
N.A.I.C.S.: 488190
Wayne Dubose *(Pres)*

Heartland Aviation, LLC (4)
3800 Starr Ave, Eau Claire, WI 54703
Tel.: (715) 835-3181
Emp.: 32
Aircraft Charter & Aviation Maintenance Services
N.A.I.C.S.: 488190
Bill Thomas *(Dir-Maintenance)*

Holding (Domestic):

Surgent Holding Corp (2)
201 N King of Prussia Rs Ste 370, Radnor, PA 19087
Tel.: (800) 778-7436
Web Site: http://www.knowfully.com
Administration of Education Programs
N.A.I.C.S.: 923110
Eric Cantor *(CEO)*
Amy Burmeister *(Exec VP-Healthcare Direct Div)*

Subsidiary (Domestic):

American Fitness Professionals & Associates, LLC (3)
1601 Long Beach Blvd, Ship Bottom, NJ 08008
Web Site: http://www.afpafitness.com
Sales Range: $1-9.9 Million
Emp.: 10
Physical Fitness Coaching Services
N.A.I.C.S.: 713940
Mark J. Occhipinti *(Co-Founder & CEO)*
Amy L. Occhipinti *(Co-Founder & COO)*
Rebecca Binford *(VP-Comm)*
Sig Watkins *(Dir-Digital Mktg)*
Ruth-Ann Solomon *(Mgr-Admin)*

Pharmcon, Inc. (3)
201 N King of Prussia Rd Ste 370, Radnor, PA 19087
Tel.: (844) 566-3559
Web Site: http://www.pharmcon.com
Administration of Education Programs
N.A.I.C.S.: 928110
Kevin Hope *(Dir-Content Dev)*

Subsidiary (Domestic):

Continuing Education Network, Inc. (4)
628 D St, Martinez, CA 94553-3206
Tel.: (925) 229-5440
Web Site: http://www.rxconsultant.com
Periodical Publishers
N.A.I.C.S.: 513120

Subsidiary (Domestic):

Psychotherapy.Net LLC (3)
4625 California St, San Francisco, CA 94118-1224
Tel.: (415) 332-3232
Web Site: http://www.psychotherapy.net
Motion Picture & Video Production
N.A.I.C.S.: 512110
Victor Yalom *(Founder & CEO)*

MOELLERING INDUSTRIES CO. INC.
6325 Este Ave, Cincinnati, OH 45232
Tel.: (513) 651-3510
Web Site:
http://www.moelleringindustries.com
Year Founded: 1972
Sales Range: $25-49.9 Million
Emp.: 235
Kitchen Cabinets
N.A.I.C.S.: 423310
Steve Steinman *(Pres)*
Connie Orr *(HR Dir)*
John Beiersdorfer *(Gen Mgr)*
Roger Ollila *(Controller)*

MOEWS SEED CO., INC.
Rte 89 S, Granville, IL 61326
Tel.: (815) 339-2201   IL
Web Site: http://www.moews.com

Year Founded: 1927
Sales Range: $1-9.9 Million
Emp.: 50
Hybrid Seed Corn & Field Seeds Whslr
N.A.I.C.S.: 111150
Bettina M. Moews (CEO)
David Trapkus (VP & Controller)

MOFFETT TURF EQUIPMENT, INC.
33 Thruway Park Dr, West Henrietta, NY 14586
Tel.: (585) 334-0100
Web Site: http://www.mte.us.com
Sales Range: $10-24.9 Million
Emp.: 52
Turf & Irrigation Systems Mfr
N.A.I.C.S.: 444230
Ben Mancuso (VP-Sls)
Thomas Houseknecht (Owner)
Patti Nicosia (Controller)

MOFFITT VOLKSWAGON -MAZDA
1960 Old Minden Rd, Bossier City, LA 71111-4912
Tel.: (318) 746-2175
Web Site: http://www.moffittvw.com
Year Founded: 1964
Sales Range: $10-24.9 Million
Emp.: 60
Car Whslr
N.A.I.C.S.: 441110
Fred Moffitt (Pres)

MOFFITTS INCORPORATED
1819 SE Marshall St, Boone, IA 50036
Tel.: (515) 432-6336
Web Site: http://www.moffitts.com
Year Founded: 1928
Sales Range: $10-24.9 Million
Emp.: 32
Sales of New & Used Automobiles
N.A.I.C.S.: 441110
Stan L. Moffitts (Owner)
Chris Moffitts (Gen Mgr)

MOHAR INCORPORATED
550 Gravenstein Hwy N, Sebastopol, CA 95472
Tel.: (707) 823-1418
Web Site: http://www.pacificmkt.com
Sales Range: $10-24.9 Million
Emp.: 130
Independent Supermarket
N.A.I.C.S.: 445110
Kenneth J. Silveira (Owner & Pres)
Vasu Narayanan (Owner)

MOHAVE CELLULAR LTD. PARTNER
3707 Stockton Hill Rd B, Kingman, AZ 86409
Tel.: (928) 681-0320
Web Site: http://www.mohavewireless.com
Sales Range: $10-24.9 Million
Emp.: 25
Cellular Telephone Communication
N.A.I.C.S.: 517112
Clive Weitzel (Mgr-Ops)
Charlie Peagern (VP-Networks)

MOHAVE ELECTRIC COOP INC.
1999 Arena Dr, Bullhead City, AZ 86442
Tel.: (928) 763-4115
Web Site: http://www.mohaveelectric.com
Sales Range: $50-74.9 Million
Emp.: 75
Distribution, Electric Power
N.A.I.C.S.: 221122

Tyler Carlson (CEO)

MOHAWK ENERGY LTD.
5440 Guhn Rd, Houston, TX 77040
Tel.: (713) 956-7473
Web Site: http://www.mohawkenergy.com
Year Founded: 2004
Expandable Tubular Mfr
N.A.I.C.S.: 331210
Scott Benzie (CEO)

MOHAWK LTD.
1 Newell Ln, Chadwicks, NY 13319
Tel.: (315) 737-7328
Web Site: http://www.mohawkltd.com
Year Founded: 1959
Sales Range: $10-24.9 Million
Emp.: 52
Electronic Equipment Repair
N.A.I.C.S.: 811210
Cathy Newell (Pres & CEO)

MOHAWK NORTHEAST, INC.
170 Canal St, Plantsville, CT 06479
Tel.: (860) 621-1451
Web Site: http://www.mohawknortheast.com
Year Founded: 1968
Rev.: $23,000,000
Emp.: 20
Bridge Construction
N.A.I.C.S.: 237310
Allan R. Heinke (Pres)
Chris Barnwell (Project Mgr)
Tim O'Connell (Project Mgr)
Steven Stanton (Chief Engr)

MOHEGAN LAKE MOTORS
1791 E Main St, Mohegan Lake, NY 10547
Tel.: (914) 528-8076
Web Site: http://www.moheganlakemotors.com
Year Founded: 1969
Sales Range: $10-24.9 Million
Emp.: 40
New Car Dealers
N.A.I.C.S.: 441110
Barry E. Rost (Pres)

MOHEGAN TRIBAL GAMING AUTHORITY
1 Mohegan Sun Blvd, Uncasville, CT 06382
Tel.: (860) 862-8000
Web Site: https://www.mohegangaming.com
Year Founded: 1996
Rev.: $1,590,511,000
Assets: $3,048,917,000
Liabilities: $3,262,816,000
Net Worth: ($213,899,000)
Earnings: $74,651,000
Emp.: 9,660
Fiscal Year-end: 09/30/22
Casino Hotel & Resort Owner & Operator
N.A.I.C.S.: 721120
George Galinsky (Sr VP-Mktg Comm)
Raymond Pineault (Pres & CEO)
Tom Cantone (Sr VP-Sports & Entertainment)
Jody Madigan (COO)
Kathleen M. Regan-Pyne (Member-Mgmt Bd)
Sarah E. Harris (Vice Chm-Mgmt Bd)
Anthony Casdia (Sr VP-Bus Dev)
Richard Lindsay (Chief Dev Officer & Sr VP)
Aviram Alroy (VP-Interactive Gaming)
Marc Comella (Chief Compliance Officer & VP)
Christopher Jones (VP-Corp Fin)
David Rome (VP)

Helen Ann Shockey (VP-Retail & Supply Chain Mgmt)
Scott Wells (Gen Counsel-Corp & VP)
Jennifer Ballester (Dir-Corp Comm)
Fouad Kheir (Dir-Project Cost Control)
Mary Lou Morrissette (Dir-Risk Mgmt)
Kelly Sullivan (Dir-Organizational Dev)
Paul Surprenant (Dir-Corp Pur)
Paul Toennes (Dir-Corp Mktg Strategy)
Patricia A. LaPierre (Member-Mgmt Bd)
John G. Harris (Member-Mgmt Bd)
Joseph M. Soper (Member-Mgmt Bd)
Tom Smock (Gen Counsel/Sr VP-Mohegan Gaming & Entertainment)
Christian Block (Reg Pres)
Erica Tessier (VP-Corp Mktg)
Paul Tresnan (VP-Project Mgmt)
Paula Tycienski-Russo (Dir-Brand Mktg)
Kenneth Davison (Member-Mgmt Bd)
David Martinelli (CMO)
Patricia Smith (Chief HR Officer & Sr VP)
Mark Rosa (CIO & Sr VP)
Judy NewmanLocke (VP-HR Mgmt)
Nick Gilham (Dir-Social Media)
Greg Romeyn (Dir-Sports & Entertainment)
Ian Connelly (VP-Dev)
Dario Johnson (Dir-Venue Mgmt)
Carol K. Anderson (CFO)
Haven Pope (Chief Acctg Officer)
Raymond Lin (Chief Legal Officer)
Richard Roberts (Pres & Chief Legal Officer)
Nelson Parker (Pres, Chief Legal Officer & Sr VP)
William Quidgeon Jr. (Member-Mgmt Bd)
Thayne D. Hutchins Jr. (Member-Mgmt Bd & Treas)
Ralph James Gessner Jr. (Chm-Mgmt Bd)

Subsidiaries:

Mohegan Commercial Ventures-PA, LLC (1)
1280 Highway 315, Wilkes Barre, PA 18702
Tel.: (570) 825-6681
Casino Operator
N.A.I.C.S.: 713210

MOHLER MATERIAL HANDLING, INC.
4514 McDonnell Blvd, Saint Louis, MO 63134
Tel.: (314) 743-4500
Web Site: http://www.mmhcorp.com
Year Founded: 2003
Rev.: $5,600,000
Emp.: 8
Conveyor & Conveying Equipment Mfr
N.A.I.C.S.: 333922
John Mohler (Pres)
Brad Ebner (Engr-Sls)

MOHR CONSTRUCTION CO. INC.
1420 S Union St, Kokomo, IN 46902
Tel.: (765) 459-3111
Web Site: http://www.ebpaving.com
Sales Range: $25-49.9 Million
Emp.: 100
Highway & Street Paving Contractor
N.A.I.C.S.: 237310
Stanton D. Mohr (Pres)

MOHR DAVIDOV VENTURES
3000 Sand Hill Rd Bldg 3 Ste 290, Menlo Park, CA 94025

Tel.: (650) 854-7236
Web Site: http://www.mdv.com
Year Founded: 1983
Sales Range: $1-4.9 Billion
Emp.: 40
Venture Capital Company
N.A.I.C.S.: 523999
William H. Davidow (Founder & Partner)
Katherine Barr (Partner)
Will Coleman (Partner)
Alex de Winter (Partner)
Geoffrey A. Moore (Venture Partner)

MOHR OIL COMPANY
7340 Harrison St, Forest Park, IL 60130
Tel.: (708) 366-2900
Web Site: http://www.mohroil.com
Sales Range: $10-24.9 Million
Emp.: 8
Gasoline & Diesel Fuel Distr
N.A.I.C.S.: 424720
Michael H. Mohr (Pres)

MOISHE HOUSE
441 Saxony Rd Barn 2, Encinitas, CA 92024-2725
Tel.: (855) 598-5509
Web Site: http://www.moishehouse.org
Year Founded: 2008
Sales Range: $1-9.9 Million
Emp.: 23
Community Support Services
N.A.I.C.S.: 813219
Alejandro Okret (Chief Global Officer)
Jen Kraus Rosen (COO)
Jordan Fruchtman (Chief Program Officer)
Jena Coen (Dir-Dev Ops & Mgr-Dev)
Jason Boschan (Dir-Mktg & Comm)
Jena Coen (Mgr-Dev)
Kevin Waldman (Chm)
Jaynie Schultz (Vice Chm)
Kenneth Weiner (Treas)
Spencer Kallick (Sec)
David Cygielman (Founder & CEO)

MOJACK DISTRIBUTORS
3535 N Rock Rd Ste 300, Wichita, KS 67226
Tel.: (316) 425-8187
Web Site: http://www.themojack.com
Year Founded: 2007
Sales Range: $10-24.9 Million
Emp.: 19
Lawn Mower Lifts
N.A.I.C.S.: 333112
Dan Drake (Co-Founder & Chm)
Alan Harr (Mgr-Warehouse)
Audra Hanson (Mgr-Mdse)

MOJAVE AUTO GROUP
1010 W Main St, Barstow, CA 92311-2694
Tel.: (760) 256-2241
Web Site: http://www.mojaveautogroup.com
Year Founded: 1964
Sales Range: $10-24.9 Million
Emp.: 65
New Car Dealers
N.A.I.C.S.: 441110
John Jomehri (Co-Pres & Co-Owner)
Connie Jomehri (Co-Pres & Co-Owner)
Lester Hui (Gen Sls Mgr)

MOJAVE MOTORS LTD.
16400 Sierra Hwy, Mojave, CA 93501
Tel.: (661) 824-2477
Web Site: http://www.kieffeandsons.com
Sales Range: $10-24.9 Million
Emp.: 43

MOJAVE MOTORS LTD.

Mojave Motors Ltd.—(Continued)
Automobiles, New & Used
N.A.I.C.S.: 441110
Richard Kieffe (Pres)

MOJIVA INC.
136 Baxter St Ste A, New York, NY 10013
Tel.: (646) 862-6201
Web Site: http://www.mojiva.com
Emp.: 100
Mobile Advertising Services
N.A.I.C.S.: 541890
David Gwozdz (CEO)
Krish Arvapally (Chief Innovation Officer)
Dan Goikhman (Founder & Sr VP-Strategic Alliances)
Frank O'Donnell (CTO)
Tony Nethercutt (Gen Mgr-North America)
Amy Vale (VP-Global Res & Strategic Comm)
Denise Fiore (VP-HR)
Julie Preis (VP-Product Mktg)
Peter Roper (VP-Sls-Central & East)
Jack Hallahan (VP-Mobile Innovations)
Carrie Coffee (VP-Sls-West Coast)
Miles Spencer (Chm)
Richie Hecker (Partner)

Subsidiaries:

Mojiva UK Ltd. (1)
14 Hanover Square, London, W1S 1HP, United Kingdom
Tel.: (44) 207 665 4079
Mobile Advertising Services
N.A.I.C.S.: 541890

MOJO BRANDS MEDIA, LLC
3260 University Blvd Ste 100, Winter Park, FL 32792
Tel.: (407) 673-5400
Web Site: http://www.mojobrandsmedia.com
Year Founded: 2013
Media Holding Company
N.A.I.C.S.: 551112
Marc Jaromin (Pres)
Troy McGuire (COO)
Sharon Weiler (Chief Revenue Officer)

Subsidiaries:

The Daily Buzz, LLC (1)
3260 University Blvd, Winter Park, FL 32792
Tel.: (407) 673-5400
Web Site: http://www.thedbz.com
Sales Range: $10-24.9 Million
Emp.: 30
Syndicated Television News Program Production & Distribution
N.A.I.C.S.: 516210
Troy McGuire (COO)
Marc Jaromin (Pres)

MOJOTECH, LLC
56 Exchange Ter Ste 210, Providence, RI 02903
Tel.: (401) 400-1970
Web Site: http://www.mojotech.com
Year Founded: 2008
Sales Range: $1-9.9 Million
Emp.: 35
Web & Mobile App Design & Development Services
N.A.I.C.S.: 541490
Nick Kishfy (Founder & CEO)
Chris Shoemaker (Partner & CTO)
Duncan Shaw (Pres)
Andrew Shedd (Mng Dir)
Paul Lanyon (Product Mgr)
Jacob Brier (Dir-Ops)
Neal Shoemaker (Mgr-Quality)
Bing Chou (Mng Dir)

Subsidiaries:

MojoTech (1)
175 Varick St, New York, NY 10014
Tel.: (212) 203-5526
Web Site: http://www.mojotech.com
Web & Mobile App Design & Development
N.A.I.C.S.: 513210
Duncan Shaw (Mng Dir)

MojoTech (1)
4-5 Bonhill Street, London, EV2A 4BX, United Kingdom
Tel.: (44) 20 3519 7750
Web Site: http://www.mojotech.com
Web & Mobile App Design & Development
N.A.I.C.S.: 513210
Nick Kishfy (Founder & CEO)

MOKA CORPORATION
715 Terrace Ste 201, Muskegon, MI 49440
Tel.: (231) 830-9376
Web Site: http://www.moka.org
Year Founded: 1978
Sales Range: $10-24.9 Million
Emp.: 745
Disability Assistance Services
N.A.I.C.S.: 624120
Christopher Benedict (Dir-Fin)
Dorothy Bowne (Dir-HR)
Thomas Zmolek (Exec Dir)
Tracey Hamlet (Dir-Programs)
Leon Stedman (Pres)
Chuck Zamiara (Sec)
Joshua Canale (Dir-Property)

MOLBAKS LLC
13625 NE 175th St, Woodinville, WA 98072
Tel.: (425) 483-5000
Web Site: http://www.molbaks.com
Year Founded: 1956
Sales Range: $10-24.9 Million
Emp.: 150
Provider of Nursery Stock, Seeds & Bulbs
N.A.I.C.S.: 444240
Jens Molbak (Owner)

MOLD BASE INDUSTRIES INC.
7501 Derry St, Harrisburg, PA 17111
Tel.: (717) 564-7960
Web Site: http://www.moldbase.com
Year Founded: 1972
Sales Range: $75-99.9 Million
Emp.: 80
Industrial Molds
N.A.I.C.S.: 333511
Richard Shiffler (Owner & Mgr-Estimating)
Samuel Shiffler Sr. (Owner & Mgr-Sls)

MOLD MASTERS INTL. LLC
7500 Clover Ave, Mentor, OH 44060
Tel.: (440) 953-0220
Web Site: http://www.moldmastersintl.com
Year Founded: 1961
Sales Range: $10-24.9 Million
Emp.: 170
Industrial Mold Mfr
N.A.I.C.S.: 333511
Anna Gennert (Mgr-Fin)
Jim Allen (Chm & CEO)
Vic Sirotek (Mgr-Sls)

MOLDAMATIC INC.
29 Noeland Ave, Langhorne, PA 19047
Tel.: (215) 757-4819
Web Site: http://www.moldamatic.com
Year Founded: 1967
Rev.: $23,000,000
Emp.: 135
Mfr of Plastic Products
N.A.I.C.S.: 326199

Thomas Wright (Mgr-Matls)

MOLDED DIMENSIONS INC.
701 Sunset Rd, Port Washington, WI 53074
Tel.: (262) 284-9455
Web Site: http://www.moldeddimensions.com
Rev.: $13,400,000
Emp.: 65
Rubber Products Mfr
N.A.I.C.S.: 326299
Patrick Roddy (VP-Sls & Mktg)
Carol Nikolaus (VP-Tech Svcs)
Kevin Kuhagen (Bus Mgr)

MOLDED FIBER GLASS COMPANIES
2925 MFG Pl, Ashtabula, OH 44005-0675
Tel.: (440) 997-5851
Web Site: http://www.moldedfiberglass.com
Year Founded: 1948
Sales Range: $400-449.9 Million
Emp.: 2,000
Custom Fiber Glass Products Mfr
N.A.I.C.S.: 326199
Richard S. Morrison (CEO)
Carolyn J. Turk (CFO & Treas)
Dan Plona (Dir-Pur)
Peter Emrich (Sr VP-Tech)
Dennis Vorse (Sr VP)
Andy Juhola (VP-HR)
Terry Weddle (Dir-Quality)

Subsidiaries:

MFG de Mexico (1)
Ecologia 111 Parque Industrial La Silla Apodaca, Apodaca, 66600, Nuevo Leon, Mexico
Tel.: (52) 81 8288 6800
Molded Fiber Glass Mfr
N.A.I.C.S.: 326199

Molded Fiber Glass Companies - MFG Alabama Factory (1)
200 Hattaway Rd, Opp, AL 36467
Tel.: (334) 493-1253
Sales Range: $25-49.9 Million
Emp.: 125
Molded Fiber Glass Mfr
N.A.I.C.S.: 326199

Molded Fiber Glass Companies - MFG Construction Products Factory (1)
1018 W Sycamore St, Independence, KS 67301
Tel.: (620) 331-7366
Web Site: http://www.mfgcp.com
Fiber Glass Construction Product Mfr
N.A.I.C.S.: 326199
Jon Alloway (Mgr-Ops)

Molded Fiber Glass Companies - MFG South Dakota Factory (1)
1401 Brown County 19 N, Aberdeen, SD 57401-1730
Tel.: (605) 725-9463
Sales Range: $25-49.9 Million
Emp.: 250
Molded Fiber Glass Mfr
N.A.I.C.S.: 326199
David Giovannini (Gen Mgr)

Molded Fiber Glass Companies - MFG Southeast Factory (1)
18361 Galileo Dr, Opp, AL 36467
Tel.: (334) 493-8040
Sales Range: $25-49.9 Million
Emp.: 50
Molded Fiber Glass Mfr
N.A.I.C.S.: 326199
Charles Hawkins (Gen Mgr)

Molded Fiber Glass Composite Systems Co. (1)
2925 MFG Pl, Ashtabula, OH 44005-0675 (100%)
Tel.: (440) 997-5851
Web Site: http://www.moldedfiberglass.com
Rev.: $31,000,000

Emp.: 550
Composite Products, Systems & Services
N.A.I.C.S.: 326199
Richard S. Morrison (CEO)

Molded Fiber Glass North Carolina (1)
213 Reep Dr, Morganton, NC 28655-8253 (100%)
Tel.: (828) 584-4974
Web Site: http://www.moldedfiberglass.com
Sales Range: $25-49.9 Million
Emp.: 150
Supplies Contractors With Fiberglass, Plastic, Standard & Special Forms & Custom Molding
N.A.I.C.S.: 326199
Joe Wilk (Sr VP)
Nicole Connor (Mgr-IT)

Molded Fiber Glass Northwest (1)
PO Box 675, Ashtabula, OH 44005-0675
Tel.: (509) 427-7755
Web Site: http://www.moldedfiberglass.com
Sales Range: $50-74.9 Million
Emp.: 55
Heavy Truck Exterior Fiberglass Assemblies Mfr
N.A.I.C.S.: 326199

Molded Fiber Glass Texas (1)
3333 N Interstate 35 Bldg 5, Gainesville, TX 76240 (100%)
Tel.: (940) 668-0302
Web Site: http://www.moldedfiberglass.com
Sales Range: $50-74.9 Million
Emp.: 100
Mfr of Fiberglass-Plastic Custom Molding
N.A.I.C.S.: 238130
Gary Kanaby (Dir-Sls-Wind Energy)
Matthew Chambers (Gen Mgr)

Molded Fiber Glass Tray Co. (1)
6175 US Hwy 6, Linesville, PA 16424
Tel.: (814) 683-4500
Web Site: http://www.mfgtray.com
Sales Range: $25-49.9 Million
Emp.: 150
Plastic Trays Mfr
N.A.I.C.S.: 326199
Mike Carr (Gen Mgr-Sls)
John Thompson (Gen Mgr)
Stephanie Goss (Mgr-Mktg)
Linda Noles (Mgr-Food Svc Product Line)
Tom Woods (Mgr-Confectionery Product Line)

Molded Fiber Glass Union City (1)
55 4th Ave, Union City, PA 16438-1247
Tel.: (814) 438-3841
Web Site: http://www.moldedfiberglass.com
Sales Range: $25-49.9 Million
Emp.: 120
Mfr of Fiberglass-Plastic Custom Molding
N.A.I.C.S.: 326199

Molded Fiber Glass Water Treatment Products (1)
55 4th Ave, Union City, PA 16438-1247 (100%)
Tel.: (814) 438-3959
Web Site: http://www.mfgcwp.com
Sales Range: $10-24.9 Million
Emp.: 8
Water Treatment Mfr
N.A.I.C.S.: 333310
Mike Sjostrom (Bus Mgr)

Molded Fiber Glass West (1)
9400 Holly Rd, Adelanto, CA 92301-3900 (100%)
Tel.: (760) 246-4042
Web Site: http://www.moldedfiberglass.com
Sales Range: $1-9.9 Million
Emp.: 125
Reinforce Plastic & Composite Products & Structures
N.A.I.C.S.: 326199
Jeff Burguss (Gen Mgr)

MOLDED RUBBER & PLASTIC CORPORATION
13161 W Glendale Ave, Butler, WI 53007
Tel.: (262) 781-7122
Web Site: http://www.mrpcorp.com
Year Founded: 1921
Sales Range: $10-24.9 Million

Emp.: 140
Molded Rubber & Plastic Medical Devices & Components Mfr
N.A.I.C.S.: 339112
Greg Riemer (Pres)

MOLDING BOX INC.
2625 S 600 W, Salt Lake City, UT 84115
Tel.: (801) 307-2224
Web Site: http://www.moldingbox.com
Year Founded: 2005
Sales Range: $1-9.9 Million
Emp.: 25
Fulfillment, Printing & Disc Duplication Services
N.A.I.C.S.: 541614
Jesus Rodriguez (Engr-Software)

MOLE-RICHARDSON CO.
12154 Montague St, Pacoima, CA 91331
Tel.: (323) 851-0111
Web Site: http://www.mole.com
Year Founded: 1927
Sales Range: $10-24.9 Million
Emp.: 150
Lighting & Power Equipment Mfr
N.A.I.C.S.: 335139
Larry Parker (Exec VP)

MOLECU WIRE CORPORATION
6 Shirley Ave, Somerset, NJ 08873
Tel.: (732) 296-9473   NJ
Web Site: http://www.molecu.com
Year Founded: 1958
Sales Range: $10-24.9 Million
Emp.: 75
Nonferrous Wiredrawing & Insulating
N.A.I.C.S.: 332618
Vinod K. Barot (Pres)
Hung Chan (Owner)

MOLECULAR BIOLOGY RESOURCES
6143 N 60th St, Milwaukee, WI 53218
Tel.: (414) 535-8585
Web Site: http://molbiores.com
Year Founded: 1973
Sales Range: $10-24.9 Million
Emp.: 50
Research of Enzymes
N.A.I.C.S.: 325199
Peter J. Smyczek (Pres)
James Wick (VP)

Subsidiaries:

Wisconsin Bioproducts   (1)
6143 N 60th St, Milwaukee, WI 53218
Tel.: (414) 535-7367
Web Site: http://www.wisbio.com
Provider of Contract Fermentation
N.A.I.C.S.: 325199
Pete Smyczek (Owner)

MOLLE TOYOTA INCORPORATED
601 W 103rd St, Kansas City, MO 64114
Tel.: (816) 942-5200
Web Site: http://www.molletoyota.com
Rev.: $20,000,000
Emp.: 76
Sales of Automobiles, New & Used
N.A.I.C.S.: 441110
John Carlin (Mgr-IT & Inventory)

MOLLE VOLKSWAGON AUDI
10344 Summit St, Kansas City, MO 64114
Tel.: (816) 941-9500
Web Site: http://www.molleaudi.com
Sales Range: $25-49.9 Million

Emp.: 56
Car Whslr
N.A.I.C.S.: 441110
John Molle (Owner)
Kevin Young (Mgr-Sls)

MOLLENBERG-BETZ INC.
300 Scott St, Buffalo, NY 14204-2268
Tel.: (716) 614-7473   NY
Web Site: http://www.mollenbergbetz.com
Year Founded: 1910
Sales Range: $75-99.9 Million
Emp.: 110
Mfr & Designer of Refrigeration Systems; Process Piping; HVAC Service Work; Boiler Plants; Heat Vent & Air Handling Installation
N.A.I.C.S.: 238220
H. Van Mollenberg (Pres & CEO)
Joe Kilijanski (Exec VP)
Jim Camarre (Controller)
Mike Balsavage (Mgr-Svc)
Paul Schiffhauer (Mgr-Safety)

MOLLENHOUR GROSS LLC
11409 Municipal Ctr Dr Ste 23434, Knoxville, TN 37933-1434
Tel.: (865) 280-1748
Web Site: http://www.mollenhourgross.com
Year Founded: 2004
Private Investment Firm
N.A.I.C.S.: 523999
Jordan Mollenhour (Co-CEO)
Dustin Gross (Co-CEO)

Subsidiaries:

PTAC 4 Less Inc.   (1)
7450 Chapman Hwy 303, Knoxville, TN 37920
Tel.: (855) 694-5210
Web Site: http://www.ptac4less.com
Plumbing, Heating & Air-Conditioning Contractors
N.A.I.C.S.: 238220

MOLLER INTERNATIONAL, INC.
1222 Research Park Dr, Davis, CA 95618
Tel.: (530) 756-5086   CA
Web Site: http://www.moller.com
Year Founded: 1983
Sales Range: Less than $1 Million
Emp.: 1
Aircraft Mfr
N.A.I.C.S.: 336411
Paul S. Moller (Founder, Pres & CEO)
Robert Churchill (Controller)

MOLLY MAID, INC.
7801 N Lamar Blvd Ste D82, Austin, TX 78752
Tel.: (512) 323-6400
Web Site: http://www.mollymaid.com
Year Founded: 1994
Sales Range: $1-9.9 Million
Emp.: 85
Residential Cleaning Services
N.A.I.C.S.: 561720
Meg Roberts (Pres)

MOLO OIL COMPANY INC.
123 Southern Ave, Dubuque, IA 52003-7847
Tel.: (563) 557-7540   IA
Web Site: http://www.molocompanies.com
Year Founded: 1927
Sales Range: $25-49.9 Million
Emp.: 300
Petroleum Bulk Stations & Terminals
N.A.I.C.S.: 424710
Mark Molo (Pres & CEO)
Nicole Johnson (CFO-Dubuque)

Subsidiaries:

The Independent Oil Corporation   (1)
1400 Lancer Ct, Eldridge, IA 52748-1406
Tel.: (309) 787-2081
Sales Range: $10-24.9 Million
Emp.: 10
Petroleum Products
N.A.I.C.S.: 424720

MOLON MOTOR & COIL CORPORATION
300 N Ridge Ave, Arlington Heights, IL 60005-1376
Tel.: (847) 253-6000   IL
Web Site: http://www.molon.com
Year Founded: 1954
Sales Range: $75-99.9 Million
Emp.: 200
Mfr of Subfractional Horsepower Motors
N.A.I.C.S.: 335312
Earle S. Moloney (CEO)
Bob Clancy (VP)
Bill Kennedy (VP-Mktg)

MOLPUS COMPANY
654 N State St, Jackson, MS 39202
Tel.: (601) 656-3373
Web Site: http://www.molpus.com
Sales Range: $25-49.9 Million
Real Estate Brokers & Agents
N.A.I.C.S.:
Terrell E. Winstead (Exec VP)
Dick Molpus (Pres)
Bob Lyle (Exec VP)

MOLSBERRY MARKETS INC.
522 Larkfield Ctr, Santa Rosa, CA 95403
Tel.: (707) 546-5041
Web Site: http://www.molsberrymarkets.com
Sales Range: $10-24.9 Million
Emp.: 80
Supermarkets, Chain
N.A.I.C.S.: 445110
Brian Molsbery (Pres)

MOLYE CHEVROLET OLDSMOBILE SALES
115 W Main St, Honeoye Falls, NY 14472
Tel.: (585) 624-2818
Web Site: http://www.molye.com
Rev.: $23,500,000
Emp.: 25
Automobiles, New & Used
N.A.I.C.S.: 441110
Chuck Jansen (Owner)

MOLZEN-CORBIN & ASSOCIATES, P.A.
2701 Miles Rd SE, Albuquerque, NM 87106
Tel.: (505) 242-5700   NM
Web Site: http://www.molzencorbin.com
Sales Range: $10-24.9 Million
Emp.: 70
Architectural & Engineering Services
N.A.I.C.S.: 541310
Adelmo E. Archuleta (Owner & Pres)
Kent S. Freier (VP)
Daniel Gonzales (VP-Electrical Engrg)
Wyatt D. Kartchner (VP)
Clayton H. Ten Eyck (VP-Water Resources)
Jerry B. Paz (Exec VP)
Kevin W. Eades (Exec VP)
Robert Robeda (Chief Admin Officer & VP)
Mike Provine (VP-Airport Engrg)
John Quinn Pate (VP-Landscape Architecture)
John Montoya (VP-Surveying)

Subsidiaries:

Molzen-Corbin & Associates, P.A.   (1)
1155 Commerce Dr Ste F, Las Cruces, NM 88011
Tel.: (575) 522-0049
Sales Range: $10-24.9 Million
Emp.: 11
Architectural & Engineering Services
N.A.I.C.S.: 541310
Jerry Paz (Branch Mgr)

MOM CENTRAL CONSULTING
55 Chapel St, Newton, MA 02458
Tel.: (617) 244-3002
Web Site: http://www.momcentralconsulting.com
Year Founded: 2007
Sales Range: $1-9.9 Million
Emp.: 24
Advertising & Marketing
N.A.I.C.S.: 541613
Stacy DeBroff (Founder & CEO)
Maria Guerra (Sr VP)
Stacey Smith (Sr VP-Mktg)

MOM365, INC.
3613 Mueller Rd, Saint Charles, MO 63301
Tel.: (636) 946-5115   MO
Web Site: http://www.mom365.com
Year Founded: 1981
Sales Range: $50-74.9 Million
Emp.: 400
In-Hospital Newborn Photographic Portrait Services
N.A.I.C.S.: 541922

MOMAR, INC.
1830 Ellsworth Industrial Dr NW, Atlanta, GA 30318-3746
Tel.: (404) 355-4580   GA
Web Site: http://www.momar.com
Year Founded: 1947
Specialty Cleaning, Polishing & Sanitation Preparations; Insecticides & Pesticides; Water Treating Compound Mfr
N.A.I.C.S.: 325612
Bill Buckley (Mgr-Natl Sls)

Subsidiaries:

Aquatrol   (1)
1830 Ellsworth Industrial Dr NW, Atlanta, GA 30318   (100%)
Tel.: (404) 355-4580
Web Site: http://www.momar.com
Emp.: 100
Water Treatment Products Mfr
N.A.I.C.S.: 221310
Teresa Brown (Sr VP & Tech Dir)
George Grabow (Gen Mgr)

Best Chem, Ltd.   (1)
Barracks Road Sandy Lane Industrial Estate, Stourport-on-Severn, DY13 9QB, Worchestershire, United Kingdom
Tel.: (44) 1 29982 7232
Web Site: http://www.best-chem.co.uk
Mfr of Specialty Chemicals for Commercial & Industrial Cleaning Products & Dust Suppression
N.A.I.C.S.: 325998
Raj Naik (Gen Mgr)

Brilliant Lavender Sdn Bhd   (1)
Kawasan Perindustrian Chendering, 21080, Kuala Terengganu, Malaysia
Tel.: (60) 17 971 1353
Web Site: http://www.momar.com
Specialty Chemical Mfr & Distr
N.A.I.C.S.: 325998
Othman Bin Chani (Gen Mgr)

CANSA Pty Ltd.   (1)
Induland Crescent, Landsdowne, 7780, Cape Town, South Africa
Tel.: (27) 21 692 1295

MOMAR, INC.
U.S. PRIVATE

Momar, Inc.—(Continued)
Web Site: http://www.momar.co.za
Sales Range: $10-24.9 Million
Emp.: 5
Specialty Chemicals Distribution
N.A.I.C.S.: 325998
Dennis B. Hammar *(Gen Mgr)*

Frens Specialty Chemicals & Equipment Ltd. (1)
Lot 13 Industrial Zone Geoffroy, Bambous, Mauritius
Tel.: (230) 452 0714
Web Site: http://www.momar.com
Specialty Chemicals Mfr
N.A.I.C.S.: 325998
Francois Langlois *(Gen Mgr)*

Handyman (1)
1830 Ellsworth Industrial Dr NW, Atlanta, GA 30318-3746 **(100%)**
Tel.: (404) 355-4580
Web Site: http://www.momar.com
Mfr of Comprehensive Line of Specialty Supplies for all Industries
N.A.I.C.S.: 325998

LuBest (1)
1830 Ellsworth Industrial Dr NW, Atlanta, GA 30318-3746 **(100%)**
Tel.: (404) 355-4580
Web Site: http://www.momar.com
Emp.: 80
Synthetic Lubricants Mfr
N.A.I.C.S.: 325998

MinTech (1)
1830 Ellsworth Industrial Dr NW, Atlanta, GA 30318 **(100%)**
Tel.: (404) 355-4580
Web Site: http://www.momar.com
Emp.: 3
Mineral Handling & Consulting Engineering Services
N.A.I.C.S.: 541330
Jeff Sparks *(Sr VP & Mgr-Natl Sls)*

MoChem (1)
1830 Ellsworth Industrial Dr NW, Atlanta, GA 30318 **(100%)**
Tel.: (404) 355-4580
Web Site: http://www.momar.com
Emp.: 85
Mfr of Cleaning, Sanitizing & Maintenance Products
N.A.I.C.S.: 811490
West Gary *(VP & Dir-Tech)*

MoMarket (1)
1830 Ellsworth Industrial Dr NW, Atlanta, GA 30318 **(100%)**
Tel.: (404) 355-4580
Web Site: http://www.momar.com
Emp.: 100
Food Processing Products
N.A.I.C.S.: 311999
West Gary *(VP & Dir-Tech)*

Momar Australia Pty Ltd. (1)
30 Binney Road, Kings Park, 2148, NSW, Australia
Tel.: (61) 29 831 4311
Web Site: http://www.momar.com.au
Emp.: 5
Specialty Chemical Mfr & Distr
N.A.I.C.S.: 325998
Mark Moskow *(Gen Mgr)*

Momar, Inc. - SafetyMan Division (1)
1830 Ellsworth Industrial Dr, Atlanta, GA 30318-3746
Tel.: (404) 355-4580
Web Site: http://www.momar.com
Safety Products Distr
N.A.I.C.S.: 423840
Julian Mohr Jr. *(Pres)*

Superco Specialty Products (1)
25041 Anza Dr, Santa Clarita, CA 91355
Tel.: (661) 775-8877
Web Site: http://www.supercoproducts.com
Specialty Maintenance & Products Mfr
N.A.I.C.S.: 459999
Steve Cina *(Pres)*

MOMENCE PALLET CORPORATION
PO Box 708, Momence, IL 60954
Tel.: (815) 472-6451
Sales Range: $10-24.9 Million
Emp.: 40
Wood Container & Pallet Mfr
N.A.I.C.S.: 321920
Andrew Cryer *(Pres & Treas)*
Patrick Cryer *(Sec & VP)*

MOMENI INC.
60 Broad St, Carlstadt, NJ 07072
Tel.: (212) 532-9577
Web Site: http://www.momeni.com
Rev.: $17,750,864
Emp.: 40
Retail Manufacturing Rugs
N.A.I.C.S.: 423220
Douglas Tashjian *(Dir-Custom Program)*
Hadi Sattari *(Mgr-Natl Sls)*

MOMENTUM AUTO GROUP
4325 Sonoma Blvd, Vallejo, CA 94589-2243
Tel.: (707) 651-7000 CA
Web Site: http://www.momentumautogroup.com
Sales Range: $50-74.9 Million
Emp.: 100
New & Used Automobiles Sales, Service, Parts & Financing
N.A.I.C.S.: 441110
Scott Thomason *(Pres)*
Akie Alifragis *(Mgr-Customer Rels)*
Kenny Cramer *(Mgr-Svcs)*
Michael Abratique *(Mgr-Sls)*
Rahim Hassanally *(Pres)*

MOMENTUM ECM, LLC
27 Miller St Ste B, Lemoyne, PA 17043
Tel.: (833) 585-7474 PA
Web Site: http://www.momentumecm.com
Year Founded: 2018
Business Process Automation & Software Development Services
N.A.I.C.S.: 423430
Corey Robert *(Ops Mgr)*
Tom Hogue *(CEO)*

MOMENTUM TEXTILES INC.
17811 Fitch, Irvine, CA 92614-6001
Tel.: (949) 833-8886 CA
Web Site: http://www.memosamples.com
Year Founded: 1993
Sales Range: $10-24.9 Million
Emp.: 100
Piece Goods & Notions
N.A.I.C.S.: 424310
Kathy Gowdy *(VP)*
J. V. Kennedy *(Dir-Art)*

Subsidiaries:

Sina Pearson Textiles, Inc. (1)
150 Varick St, New York, NY 10013 **(100%)**
Tel.: (212) 366-1146
Web Site: http://www.themomgroup.com
Sales Range: $1-9.9 Million
Emp.: 12
Designs & Distributes Upholstery Fabrics
N.A.I.C.S.: 313310
Sina Pearson *(Gen Mgr & Designer)*

MOMENTUM VOLKSWAGEN OF JERSEY VILLAGE
19550 Northwest Freeway, Houston, TX 77065
Tel.: (281) 925-5000
Web Site: http://www.jerseyvillagevw.com
Rev.: $58,100,000
Emp.: 50
Automobiles & Other Motor Vehicles
N.A.I.C.S.: 423110
Stephen Ruiz *(Mgr-Internet)*

MOMENTUM, INC.
Seattle $ Pittsburgh 1520 4th Ave Ste 300, Seattle, WA 98101-1129
Tel.: (206) 267-1900
Web Site: http://www.momentumbuilds.com
Year Founded: 1977
Sales Range: $10-24.9 Million
Emp.: 22
Personal Services
N.A.I.C.S.: 812990
Jim Haack *(Co-Founder & Pres)*
Bob Saunders *(Co-Founder & Exec VP)*
Ben Warren *(Project Mgr)*
Jim Corle *(On-Site Superintendent)*
Jay Speidell *(Coord-Sls & Mktg)*
Jay-E Emmingham *(Mktg Dir)*
Jim Tarte *(CFO)*
Michael Ward *(On-Site Superintendent)*
Frank Torhan *(Superintendent-Onsite)*
Mitch Gibbs *(Superintendent-Onsite)*
Deb Seatter *(Accountant)*

MON CHERI BRIDALS INC.
1018 Whitehead Rd Ext, Trenton, NJ 08638
Tel.: (609) 530-1900
Web Site: http://www.moncheribridals.com
Rev.: $25,000,000
Emp.: 50
Bridal Supplies
N.A.I.C.S.: 424310
Stephen Lang *(CEO)*
Stewart Steinman *(Controller)*

MON CHONG LOONG TRADING CORP.
5672 49th Pl, Maspeth, NY 11378
Tel.: (718) 417-1668
Web Site: http://www.monchongloong.com
Year Founded: 1984
Sales Range: $10-24.9 Million
Emp.: 35
Whslr & Importer of Asian Groceries
N.A.I.C.S.: 424410
Jeffrey Wu *(Pres)*
Richard Tang *(Controller)*

MON SPACE NET INC.
3651 LINDELL ROAD, D407, LAS VEGAS, NV 89103
Tel.: (702) 473-8226
N.A.I.C.S.:

MON VALLEY PETROLEUM INC.
5515 W Smithfield St, McKeesport, PA 15135-1261
Tel.: (412) 751-5210 PA
Year Founded: 1928
Sales Range: $25-49.9 Million
Emp.: 115
Provider of Petroleum Products
N.A.I.C.S.: 457120
Hartley King *(Owner)*

MON YOUGH COMMUNITY SERVICES, INC.
500 Market St 3rd Fl, McKeesport, PA 15132
Tel.: (412) 675-6927 PA
Web Site: http://www.mycs.org
Year Founded: 1969
Sales Range: $10-24.9 Million
Emp.: 541
Disability Assistance Services
N.A.I.C.S.: 624120
David Bobrzynski *(Treas)*
Carol Gross *(Exec Dir)*
William Latta *(Dir-Fin & Admin)*
Noreen Fredrick *(Pres)*

MONA ELECTRIC GROUP INC.
7915 Malcolm Rd Ste 102, Clinton, MD 20735
Tel.: (301) 868-8400
Web Site: http://www.getmona.com
Sales Range: $10-24.9 Million
Emp.: 35
Electrical Work
N.A.I.C.S.: 238210
Elliott Hayward *(Sr Mgr-Field Safety)*
Agnolutto Walt *(Mgr-Pur)*
Brian R. Moorefield *(COO)*

MONADNOCK PAPER MILLS, INC.
117 Antrim Rd, Bennington, NH 03442-4205
Tel.: (603) 588-3311 NH
Web Site: http://www.mpm.com
Year Founded: 1948
Rev.: $58,826,253
Emp.: 230
Paper Mills
N.A.I.C.S.: 322120
Richard G. Verney *(Chm & CEO)*
Fuushern Wuu *(Sr Product Mgr-R&D & Technical Svcs Dept)*
Lee Corson *(Dir-Supply Chain Logistics)*
Dawn Soucek *(Sr Mgr-Technical Sls)*
James Cree *(Pres-Monadnock Non-Wovens)*
Lisa Taylor *(VP-Sls & Mktg)*
Brigitte O'Connor *(Reg Sls Mgr-Southeast)*

MONARCH ART PLASTICS LLC
3838 Church Rd, Mount Laurel, NJ 08054
Tel.: (856) 235-5151
Web Site: http://www.monarchplastics.com
Rev.: $10,000,000
Emp.: 70
Commercial Printing
N.A.I.C.S.: 323111
William C. Shanley IV *(Pres & CEO)*

MONARCH BEVERAGE CO. INC.
9347 E Pendelton Pke, Indianapolis, IN 46236
Tel.: (317) 612-1310 IN
Web Site: http://www.monarch-beverage.com
Year Founded: 1947
Sales Range: $100-124.9 Million
Emp.: 600
Beer & Other Fermented Malt Liquors Distr
N.A.I.C.S.: 424810
Phillip A. Terry *(CEO)*
John Xenos *(Gen Mgr)*
Fred Dufour *(Sr VP)*
Natalie Roberts *(Sr VP)*

MONARCH COLOR CORPORATION
5327 Brookshire Blvd, Charlotte, NC 28216
Tel.: (704) 394-4626
Web Site: http://www.monarchcolor.com
Year Founded: 1977
Sales Range: $10-24.9 Million
Emp.: 53
Letterpress Or Offset Ink
N.A.I.C.S.: 325910
Greg West *(Pres)*

MONARCH CONSTRUCTION COMPANY
1654 Sherman Ave, Cincinnati, OH 45212-2544
Tel.: (513) 351-6900 KY

Web Site:
http://www.monarchconstruction.cc
Year Founded: 1963
Sales Range: $75-99.9 Million
Emp.: 100
Provider of Contracting & Construction Services
N.A.I.C.S.: 236220
Tom Butler (Pres)

MONARCH CONSTRUCTION CORP.
7 Aerial Way, Syosset, NY 11791
Tel.: (516) 827-1900
Web Site:
http://www.monarchbuilt.com
Sales Range: $10-24.9 Million
Emp.: 49
Commercial & Office Buildings, Renovation & Repair
N.A.I.C.S.: 236220
Charles J. Saliba (Owner)

MONARCH KNITTING MACHINERY CORP.
115 N Secrest Ave, Monroe, NC 28110
Tel.: (718) 231-2321 NY
Web Site:
http://www.monarchknittingmachinery.com
Year Founded: 1964
Sales Range: $100-124.9 Million
Emp.: 500
Industrial Machinery & Equipment
N.A.I.C.S.: 423830
Bruce Pernick (Chm, Pres & CEO)

Subsidiaries:

Monarch Knitting Machinery (UK) Ltd. (1)
74 Boston Rd, Beaumont Leys, Leicester, LE4 1BG, United Kingdom (100%)
Tel.: (44) 1162351502
Web Site: http://www.monarchknitting.co.uk
Sales Range: $10-24.9 Million
Emp.: 45
Industrial Machinery & Equipment
N.A.I.C.S.: 333248
David J. Brunton (Mng Dir)

Monarch Manufacturing Corp. (1)
115 N Secrest Ave, Monroe, NC 28110-3622
Tel.: (704) 291-3300
Web Site:
http://www.monarchmanufacturing.com
Rev.: $17,100,000
Emp.: 30
Textile Machinery
N.A.I.C.S.: 333248

MONARCH LEASING INC.
195 N 30th St, San Jose, CA 95116
Tel.: (408) 275-0500
Web Site:
http://www.monarchtruck.com
Sales Range: $10-24.9 Million
Emp.: 65
Trucks, Tractors & Trailers: New & Used
N.A.I.C.S.: 441110
Dinh Nguyen (Mgr-Fin)
Gary Davidson (Mgr-Mktg)

MONARCH LIFE INSURANCE CO.
330 Witney Ave Ste 500, Holyoke, MA 01040
Tel.: (413) 784-2000
Sales Range: $75-99.9 Million
Emp.: 140
Life Insurance Carrier
N.A.I.C.S.: 524113
Kevin Mcadoo (Pres & CEO)

MONARCH LITHO INC.
1501 Date St, Montebello, CA 90640
Tel.: (323) 727-0300
Web Site:
http://www.monarchlitho.com
Sales Range: $500-549.9 Million
Emp.: 280
Offset Printing
N.A.I.C.S.: 323111
Robert Lopez (Pres)
Enrique Jimenez (Coord-Production)
Manuel Franco (Dir-Creative Svcs)
Tony Green (Superintendent-Prepress)
Hugo Vieyra (Coord-Production)
Demo Diaz (Mgr-QC)

MONARCH MATERIALS GROUP INC.
28972 R Ave, Adel, IA 50003
Tel.: (515) 993-4561
Web Site:
http://www.monmatgrp.com
Year Founded: 1960
Sales Range: $10-24.9 Million
Emp.: 50
Mfr of Basement Windows, Frames, Wells, Covers & Egress Products & Accessories
N.A.I.C.S.: 332321
David Stephen Mulcahy (Chm)

MONARCH MEDIA, INC.
406 Mission St Ste J, Santa Cruz, CA 95060
Tel.: (831) 457-4414
Web Site:
http://www.monarchmedia.com
Sales Range: $1-9.9 Million
Emp.: 16
Online Training Services
N.A.I.C.S.: 611420
Chris Bush (Co-CEO)
Claire Schneeberger (Founder & Co-CEO)
Nandu Madimchetty (CTO)

MONARCH NC
350 Pee Dee Ave, Albemarle, NC 28001
Tel.: (704) 986-1500 NC
Web Site: http://www.monarchnc.org
Year Founded: 1981
Sales Range: $75-99.9 Million
Emp.: 2,040
Developmental Disability Assistance Services
N.A.I.C.S.: 623210
James Kelley (COO)
Peggy S. Terhune (Pres & CEO)
Caroline Z. Fisher (Dir-Quality Mgmt)
Robert McHale (Dir-Medical)
Cindy Jones (CFO)
Alexandra Spessot (Chief Medical Officer)

MONARCH RECOVERY MANAGEMENT INC.
10965 Decatur Rd, Philadelphia, PA 19154
Tel.: (215) 281-7500
Web Site:
http://www.monarchrecoverymanagement.com
Sales Range: $25-49.9 Million
Emp.: 500
Collection Agency, Except Real Estate
N.A.I.C.S.: 561440
Diane Green (Mgr-HR)
Aleah Raymond (Dir-Bus Dev)

MONARCH SITE SERVICES
1220 E Hampden Ave, Englewood, CO 80113
Tel.: (303) 355-1778
Web Site:
http://monarchsiteservices.com
Year Founded: 2006
Sales Range: $1-9.9 Million
Emp.: 18
Specialists in Sustainable Design-Build Construction, Construction Management & Comprehensive Environmental Remediation
N.A.I.C.S.: 541620
Jon Neil (Mgr-Projects)

MONARCH WELDING & ENGINEERING
23635 Mound Rd, Warren, MI 48091
Tel.: (586) 754-5400
Web Site:
http://www.monarchwelding.com
Sales Range: $25-49.9 Million
Emp.: 100
Mechanical Contractor
N.A.I.C.S.: 238220
Dave Rutledge (Mgr-Ironwork Div)
Brian Wimmer Jr. (Pres)

MONARCH, LLC.
7050 N 76th St, Milwaukee, WI 53223
Tel.: (414) 353-8820
Web Site:
http://www.monarchcorp.com
Year Founded: 1933
Sales Range: $1-9.9 Million
Emp.: 78
Fabrication, Machining & Assembly Supplier
N.A.I.C.S.: 423830
David M. Mitchell (Pres & Owner)
Amber Stevens (Office Mgr)

MONDERA.COM
45 W 45th St, New York, NY 10036-4602
Tel.: (800) 666-3372
Year Founded: 1998
Sales Range: $10-24.9 Million
Emp.: 100
Online Retailer of Jewelry & Luxury Items
N.A.I.C.S.: 458310
Fred Mouawad (Chm & CEO)
Marla Nitke (Dir-Mktg Comm)
Kyaw Thu (Mgr-Fulfillment)

Subsidiaries:

Mouawad International Gold Jewellery Company (1)
Al Hamra Luxury Center Ground Floor Shop No G6, PO Box 15462, Sharq, Kuwait, Kuwait
Tel: (965) 2227 0204
Jewelry Mfr
N.A.I.C.S.: 339910

MONDIAL INTERNATIONAL CORPORATION
PO Box 8369, Pelham Manor, NY 10803
Tel.: (914) 738-7411 NY
Web Site:
http://www.mondialgroup.com
Year Founded: 1952
Coin-Operated Machines & Mechanisms International Trade Whslr & Group Administrative Services
N.A.I.C.S.: 425120
Robert Fesjian (Pres)

MONDIAL VENTURES, INC.
6564 Smoke Tree Ln, Scottsdale, AZ 85253
Tel.: (480) 948-6581 NV
Web Site:
http://www.mondialventures.com
Year Founded: 2002
Sales Range: Less than $1 Million
Oil & Gas Exploration Services
N.A.I.C.S.: 213112

Dennis R. Alexander (Chm, Pres & CEO)
Joanne M. Sylvanus (CFO, Treas & Sec)

MONDICS INSURANCE GROUP INC
6900 N Dallas Pkwy Ste 425, Plano, TX 75024
Tel.: (214) 739-4800
Web Site:
http://www.mondicsinsurance.com
Rev.: $12,000,000
Emp.: 8
Insurance Agents & Brokers
N.A.I.C.S.: 524210
John Monvics (Owner)
Barbara Sullivan (Office Mgr)

MONDO MEDIA CORPORATION
550 15th St Ste 31, San Francisco, CA 94103
Tel.: (415) 865-2700
Web Site:
http://www.mondomedia.com
Year Founded: 1989
Sales Range: $1-9.9 Million
Emp.: 20
Animated Entertainment Services
N.A.I.C.S.: 541430
Douglas S. Kay (CFO)
Dean MacDonald (Dir-Creative)
Aaron Simpson (VP-Animation & Bus Dev)
April Pesa (Dir-Dev)
Kris Fragomeni (Mgr-Fin)
Stevie Levine (Mgr-Animation Production)
Eunice Budarara (Mgr-Adv & Bus Dev)
Zdravomir Staykov (Mgr-Media)
Damian Nelson (Engr-Web)
Cliff Malloy (Mgr-Web)
Brendan Burch (CEO)

MONETA GROUP, LLC.
100 S Brentwood Blvd Ste 500, Saint Louis, MO 63105-1695
Tel.: (314) 726-2300
Web Site:
http://www.monetagroup.com
Year Founded: 1869
Sales Range: $10-24.9 Million
Emp.: 142
Investment Management Service
N.A.I.C.S.: 523940
Gene Diederich (CEO)
Luke Ferraro (Dir-Investment Res)
Rich McDonald (Dir-Fixed Income)
Jane Heine (Mgr-Ops)
Carolyn Duggan (Mgr-Client Svc)
Alicia Faerber (Mgr-Client Svc)
Ingrid Lee (Mgr-Client Svc)
Stephanie Martin (Mgr-Client Svc)
Hunter Brown (Principal)
Patrick McGinnis (Principal)
Donald Poling (Principal)
Kim Johnson (Principal)
David Curtis (Principal)
Bryan Krueger (Dir-Tax Strategies)
Keith Bowles (COO)
Emily Haislar (Mgr-Client Svc)
Leslie Hubbs (Chief Compliance Officer)
Mark Conrad (Partner-Compardo Team)
Jake Winegrad (Partner)
Jordan Janes (Partner)
Aoifinn Devitt (Chief Investment Officer)
Deborah Dubin (Chief Philanthropy Officer)

MONETIVA, INC.

MONETIVA, INC.

Monetiva, Inc.—(Continued)
5000 Birch St West Tower Ste 3000, Newport Beach, CA 92660
Tel.: (949) 260-2085 DE
Year Founded: 2016
Rev.: $61,625
Assets: $1,295,380
Liabilities: $368,834
Net Worth: $926,546
Earnings: ($782,831)
Emp.: 1
Fiscal Year-end: 12/31/19
Money Remittance Services
N.A.I.C.S.: 522390
Pierre Sawaya *(Chm, Pres, CEO & Sec)*

MONEX DEPOSIT COMPANY

4910 Birch St, Newport Beach, CA 92660-8100
Tel.: (949) 752-1400 CA
Web Site: http://www.monex.com
Year Founded: 1967
Sales Range: $125-149.9 Million
Emp.: 200
Precious Metals Trading
N.A.I.C.S.: 458310
Louis E. Carabini *(Founder)*
Geoffrey Hodes *(Dir-Adv & Mktg)*

MONEY ATUOMOTIVE CENTER INC.

2222 S 9th St, Salina, KS 67401
Tel.: (785) 827-4451
Web Site: http://www.moneyautomotive.com
Sales Range: $10-24.9 Million
Emp.: 25
Car Dealership
N.A.I.C.S.: 441110
Carolyn Money *(Owner)*
Mike Wernecke *(Mgr-Sls)*

MONEY CLIP MAGAZINE

105 S 1st Colonial Rd Ste 115, Virginia Beach, VA 23454
Tel.: (757) 428-2287
Web Site: http://www.moneyclipmagazine.com
Year Founded: 1998
Rev.: $3,800,000
Emp.: 25
Advertising Material Distr
N.A.I.C.S.: 541870
Randy Harris *(Acct Exec)*

MONEY MANAGEMENT INTERNATIONAL

14141 SW Fwy Ste 1000, Sugar Land, TX 77478-3494
Tel.: (713) 394-5927
Web Site: http://www.moneymanagement.org
Year Founded: 1997
Sales Range: $10-24.9 Million
Emp.: 300
Non-Profit Credit Counseling
N.A.I.C.S.: 812990
Lester E. Dees *(Chm)*
John J. Fisher *(Chief Relationship Officer)*
Anthony Scataglia *(COO)*
Marianne Gray D'Aquila *(Chief Talent Officer)*
Lyle Lansdell *(CFO)*
Zynda Sellers *(Gen Counsel)*
Michelle Jones *(Chief Dev Officer)*
Ivan L. Hand Jr. *(Pres & CEO)*

Subsidiaries:

Consumer Credit Counseling Service of Greater Atlanta, Inc. (1)
270 Peachtree St NW, Atlanta, GA 30303
Tel.: (800) 750-2227
Web Site: http://www.clearpointcreditcounselingsolutions.org
Credit Counseling Services
N.A.I.C.S.: 522390
Michelle Jones *(Exec VP, Chief Bus Dev Officer)*
Kevin Keeney *(Sr VP-IT)*
Ray Pennie *(VP-Bus Dev)*
Charles Bruen *(Chm)*
Larry Hoskins *(Vice Chm)*
Greg McBride *(Treas)*

MONEY SAVER COUPON BOOK INC.

11471 W Sample Rd, Coral Springs, FL 33065
Tel.: (954) 747-4898
Web Site: http://www.moneysaverfl.com
Sales Range: $1-9.9 Million
Emp.: 13
Coupon Direct Mail & Internet Publisher
N.A.I.C.S.: 541860
Brian Squires *(Pres)*
Sharon Squires *(VP)*
Adam Squires *(VP)*

MONEY STORE LP

1114 Lost Creek Blvd Ste 310, Austin, TX 78746
Tel.: (512) 306-0341
Web Site: http://www.themoneybox.com
Sales Range: $10-24.9 Million
Emp.: 235
Check Cashing Agencies
N.A.I.C.S.: 522390
Sherry Allen *(Mgr-Northern California)*

MONEY.NET, INC.

333 Hudson St 8th Fl, New York, NY 10013
Tel.: (212) 334-2000
Web Site: http://www.money.net
Year Founded: 1997
Sales Range: $1-9.9 Million
Emp.: 30
Real-Time Market Data Direct to Individual Investors & Customized Software Systems
N.A.I.C.S.: 517810
Harold L. Van Arnem *(COO)*
Janet Christofano *(CFO)*
Salil Pitkar *(CTO)*

Subsidiaries:

PCQuote.com, Inc. (1)
155 Spring St 3rd Fl, New York, NY 10012
Tel.: (888) 860-4800
Web Site: http://www.pcquote.com
Real-Time Securities Quotations, News & Investment Tools Via the Internet
N.A.I.C.S.: 561499

MONEYSHOW.COM, LLC

1626 Ringling Blvd 400, Sarasota, FL 34236-5604
Tel.: (941) 955-0323
Web Site: http://www.moneyshow.com
Sales Range: $10-24.9 Million
Emp.: 70
Convention & Trade Show Organizer; Web Seminars
N.A.I.C.S.: 561920
Kim Githler *(Chm & CEO)*
Deborah Rossard *(Exec VP)*
Johnny Antolak *(COO, CTO & Sr VP)*
Marie Mowbray *(Sr VP-Editorial)*
Greg Huffman *(Sr VP-Bus Dev & Media)*
Michele Ress *(CFO & Sr VP)*
John Kroll *(Sr VP-IT & Site Dev)*
Aaron West *(Pres)*
Debbie Osborne *(VP-Programming)*
Steven Halpern *(Editor)*
Paul Mackler *(COO)*

MONEYTREE, INC.

6720 Fort Dent Way Ste 230, Seattle, WA 98188
Tel.: (206) 246-3500 WA
Web Site: http://www.moneytreeinc.com
Rev.: $70,000,000
Emp.: 1,200
Check Cashing & Payday Lending Services
N.A.I.C.S.: 522390
Dennis Bassford *(Owner & CEO)*
Tom King *(CFO)*
Beau Cline *(Controller)*

MONEYWISE WEALTH MANAGEMENT

8700 Stockdale Hwy Ste 100, Bakersfield, CA 93311
Tel.: (661) 847-1000
Web Site: http://www.moneywiseguys.com
Year Founded: 2003
Sales Range: $1-9.9 Million
Emp.: 12
Financial Management Services
N.A.I.C.S.: 523999
David Anderson *(Owner)*

MONGOLIA HOLDINGS, INC.

2300 W Sahara Ave Ste 800, Las Vegas, NV 89012
Tel.: (702) 949-9449 NV
Web Site: http://www.consolidation-services.net
Year Founded: 2007
Sales Range: Less than $1 Million
Emp.: 6
Industrial Equipment Rental Services
N.A.I.C.S.: 532490
Gary D. Kucher *(CEO)*
Michael Telford *(Exec VP)*
Bradley Siniscalchi *(Pres)*
E. Michael Ussery *(Chm)*
Jeffrey R. Leach *(COO)*
Tadd McKenzie *(Interim CFO)*

MONICO ALLOYS, INC.

3039 Ana St, Rancho Dominguez, CA 90221
Tel.: (213) 629-4767 CA
Web Site: http://www.monicoalloys.com
Year Founded: 1979
Sales Range: $75-99.9 Million
Emp.: 65
Mfr & Recycler of Metal Metal Alloys
N.A.I.C.S.: 423510
Barbara Zenk *(Chm)*
Saul Zenk *(CFO)*
Kenneth Larson *(Exec VP)*
Jason Zenk *(Pres)*
Bruce Botansky *(VP)*

MONICO INC.

2703 Bernice Rd, Lansing, IL 60438-1011
Tel.: (708) 474-8300
Web Site: http://www.monicoinc.com
Year Founded: 1979
Sales Range: $50-74.9 Million
Emp.: 450
Provider of Plumbing Heating & Air Conditioning Product & Services
N.A.I.C.S.: 238220
Bill Dicken *(Mgr-Technical Support)*

Subsidiaries:

Electrical Systems Inc. (1)
2725 Bernice Rd, Lansing, IL 60438-1011
Tel.: (708) 474-3710
Sales Range: $10-24.9 Million
Emp.: 10
Providers of Electrical Services
N.A.I.C.S.: 238210
Robert J. Bergeron *(Pres)*

Meccon Industries Inc. (1)
2703 Bernice Rd, Lansing, IL 60438-1011
Tel.: (708) 474-8300
Web Site: http://www.meccon.com
Sales Range: $25-49.9 Million
Emp.: 250
Provider of Plumbing, Heating & Air Conditioning Products & Services
N.A.I.C.S.: 238220
Kim Seyforth *(Asst Controller)*
Timothy McGlennon *(Project Mgr)*
Paul Beugel *(VP)*
Dale Johnson *(Project Mgr)*
Gary Kebert *(VP)*
John P. Starkman *(Dir-Corp Safety)*

MONITOR CLIPPER PARTNERS, LLC

116 Huntington Ave 9th Fl, Boston, MA 02116
Tel.: (617) 638-1100
Web Site: http://www.monitorclipper.com
Sales Range: $25-49.9 Million
Emp.: 50
Private Equity Investment Firm
N.A.I.C.S.: 523999
April Evans *(COO, CFO & Partner)*
Travis R. Metz *(Partner)*
Mark T. Thomas *(Partner)*
Adam S. Doctoroff *(Partner)*
Charles Yoon *(Partner)*
Jennifer He *(Dir-Tax)*
Matthew Fox *(Dir-Acctg)*
Michael A. Bell *(Founder)*

Subsidiaries:

Access Communications LLC (1)
400 Connell Dr Ste 2, Berkeley Heights, NJ 07922-2739
Tel.: (908) 508-6700
Web Site: http://www.acinj.com
Sales Range: $25-49.9 Million
Healthcare Marketing & Communications Agency
N.A.I.C.S.: 541810
Michael Webster *(Mng Partner)*
Eric Bishea *(Co-CEO)*
Seth Gordon *(Mng Partner)*
Adam Doctoroff *(Partner)*
Daniel Jang *(Principal)*
John D. McClellan *(Co-CEO)*
Mark Thomas *(Founder & Partner)*
Chris Abtahi *(Exec VP)*
Kevin Barnett *(Mng Partner)*
Jill Cantelmo *(Exec VP-Clinical Svcs)*
Jeffrey Gruenglas *(Sr VP-Bus Dev)*
Bryan Horveath *(Exec VP)*
Jessica Kalbach *(Sr VP-Ops)*
Jennifer Richardson *(Sr Dir-Meeting Svcs)*
Frank Scott *(CFO)*
Richard G. Stefanacci *(CMO)*
Leana Wood *(Mng Partner)*

Microgame S.p.A. (1)
Via Giovanni Agnelli Peoples House, zona ind Olivola, Lotto D/4, 82100, Benevento, BN, Italy (70%)
Tel.: (39) 08 24 56 54 01
Web Site: http://www.web.microgame.it
Designs & Develops Gaming Application Platforms for Gaming Operators
N.A.I.C.S.: 541511

Monitor Clipper Partners (UK), LLC (1)
Michelin House, 81 Fulham Road, London, SW3 6RD, United Kingdom
Tel.: (44) 2078386600
Privater Equity Firm
N.A.I.C.S.: 523999

Monitor Clipper Partners GmbH (1)
Muhlebachstrasse 173, Zurich, 8034, Switzerland
Tel.: (41) 443897150
Web Site: http://www.monitorclipper.com
Sales Range: $50-74.9 Million
Emp.: 10
Privater Equity Firm

N.A.I.C.S.: 523999
Peter S. Laino *(Mng Partner)*
Stephen Lehman *(Mng Partner)*

Pharmetics, Inc. (1)
3695 Autoroute des Laurentides, Laval, H7L 3H7, QC, Canada
Tel.: (450) 682-8580
Web Site: http://www.pharmetics.com
Over-the-Counter Drugs & Private Label Vitamins, Minerals & Supplements Mfr
N.A.I.C.S.: 325412

Plant (Domestic):

Pharmetics - Burlington Operations (2)
921 Gateway Dr, Burlington, L7L 5K5, ON, Canada **(100%)**
Tel.: (905) 639-4933
Web Site: http://www.pharmetics.com
Sales Range: $50-74.9 Million
Mfr & Packaging of Powder Sachets
N.A.I.C.S.: 325411

Reverse Logistics GmbH (1)
Karl-Hammerschmidt-Str 36, 85609, Dornach, Germany
Tel.: (49) 89 49049 100
Web Site: http://www.rev-log.com
Emp.: 10
Collection & Recycling Services
N.A.I.C.S.: 562219
Patrick Wiedemann *(CEO)*

Subsidiary (Domestic):

CCR Logistics Systems AG (2)
Karl-Hammerschmidt-Str 36 Eingang Haus Nr 42, D 85609, Dornach, Germany
Tel.: (49) 89 49049 100
Web Site: http://www.ccr-revlog.com
Sales Range: $100-124.9 Million
Emp.: 81
Waste Collection Logistics Services
N.A.I.C.S.: 541614
Patrick Wiedemann *(Co-CEO)*
Andreas Kroniger *(Exec VP-Environmental Compliance Svcs)*
Matthias Burger *(Mng Dir)*
Stefan Macheleidt *(Mng Dir)*

STS Medical Group SARL (1)
A Rue Robert Stumper, L-2557, Luxembourg, Luxembourg
Tel.: (352) 26 495 842 95
Surgical Product Mfr
N.A.I.C.S.: 339112

Subsidiary (Non-US):

Sengewald Klinikprodukte GmbH (2)
Adlerstrasse 2, 83101, Rohrdorf, Thansau, Germany
Tel.: (49) 803172240
Web Site: http://www.sengewald.de
Disposable Operating Room & Hospital Supply Mfr
N.A.I.C.S.: 423450

MONITOR PRODUCTS INC.
15400 Flight Path Dr, Brooksville, FL 34604
Tel.: (352) 544-2620
Web Site: http://www.monitorpro.com
Rev.: $11,000,000
Emp.: 30
Heat Exchangers; Plate Type
N.A.I.C.S.: 332410
Carl H. Sunden *(Pres)*

MONITORING SOLUTIONS, INC.
78 Rte 173 Ste 7, Hampton, NJ 08827
Tel.: (908) 713-0172 IN
Web Site: http://www.monsol.com
Year Founded: 1997
Sales Range: $25-49.9 Million
Emp.: 25
Air Emissions Monitoring Equipment
N.A.I.C.S.: 333310
Mike Sroka *(Pres & CEO)*
Naga Kadiyala *(Engr-Software)*

MONK DEVELOPMENT, INC.
2707 Congress St Suite 2G, San Diego, CA 92110
Tel.: (877) 452-0015 CA
Web Site: http://www.monkdevelopment.com
Year Founded: 2006
Sales Range: $1-9.9 Million
Emp.: 25
Web-Based Content Management Systems, Software & Social Media & Mobile Integration to Churches & Other Organizations
N.A.I.C.S.: 513210
Drew Goodmanson *(CEO)*
James Martin *(Pres & COO)*
Etienne de Bruin *(CTO)*
Jesse Craycraft *(Mgr-Customer Experience)*

MONKEDIA LLC
350 E Royal Ln Ste 150, Irving, TX 75039
Web Site: http://www.monkedia.com
Year Founded: 2014
Sales Range: $10-24.9 Million
Emp.: 54
Online Shopping Services
N.A.I.C.S.: 541511
Noah Curran *(CEO)*

MONKS' BREAD
Abbey of the Genesee, Piffard, NY 14533
Tel.: (585) 243-0660
Web Site: http://www.geneseeabbey.org
Year Founded: 1959
Sales Range: $10-24.9 Million
Emp.: 47
Monastery & Bread Bakers
N.A.I.C.S.: 813110
Randy Colvin *(Product Mgr)*

MONMOUTH CUSTOM BUILDERS
259 Monmouth Rd, Deal, NJ 07723
Tel.: (732) 517-0400
Web Site: http://www.monmouthcustombuilders.com
Year Founded: 1996
Rev.: $6,700,000
Emp.: 15
Construction Services
N.A.I.C.S.: 236118
Ike Levy *(Pres)*
Lauren Levy *(Sec)*
Audrey Clarkin *(Office Mgr)*

MONMOUTH PETROLEUM CO. INC.
Nine Central Ave, Long Branch, NJ 07740-3128
Tel.: (732) 446-7722
Year Founded: 1946
Sales Range: $10-24.9 Million
Emp.: 20
Petroleum Products Distr
N.A.I.C.S.: 457210
Pat Mazzucca *(Pres)*

MONMOUTH-OCEAN HOSPITAL SERVICE CORPORATION
4806 Megill Rd, Wall Township, NJ 07753
Tel.: (732) 919-3045 NJ
Web Site: http://www.monoc.org
Year Founded: 1984
Sales Range: $25-49.9 Million
Emp.: 791
Emergency Medical Services
N.A.I.C.S.: 621493
Vincent Robbins *(Pres & CEO)*
John Brennan *(Chm)*
Jeff Behm *(COO & Sr VP)*
Margaret Keavney *(Gen Counsel)*
Scott Matin *(VP-Clinical & Bus Svcs)*
Brian Hector *(CFO & VP)*
Stacy Quagliana *(VP-Admin)*

MONNEX INTERNATIONAL INC.
700 Hickory Hill Dr, Vernon Hills, IL 60061
Tel.: (847) 478-1800
Year Founded: 1989
Sales Range: $10-24.9 Million
Emp.: 20
Mfr of Electronic & Industrial Products: Contract Manufacturing
N.A.I.C.S.: 423830
Moon S. Yun *(Pres)*
Tony Yewb *(Vice Chm)*

Subsidiaries:

Monnex Industries Inc. (1)
476 Diens Dr, Wheeling, IL 60090
Tel.: (847) 478-1800
Web Site: http://www.monnex.com
Rev.: $1,700,000
Emp.: 13
Industrial Machinery & Equipment
N.A.I.C.S.: 423830

MONO
3036 Hennepin Ave, Minneapolis, MN 55408
Tel.: (612) 822-4135
Web Site: http://www.mono-1.com
Year Founded: 2004
Sales Range: $10-24.9 Million
Emp.: 40
Advertising Agencies
N.A.I.C.S.: 541810
Michael Hart *(Co-Founder & Mng Dir-Creative)*
Chris Lange *(Founder & Mng Dir-Creative)*
T. Scott Major *(Dir-Creative)*
Erin Keeley *(CMO)*
Tracy Tabery-Weller *(Dir-Content Production)*
Bill Lee *(Dir-Creative)*
Joel Stacy *(Dir-Creative)*
Julie Vessel *(Dir-Talent)*
Steve Lynch *(Dir-Comm Strategy)*
Becca Tlustosch *(CFO)*
Andie Peterson *(Acct Dir)*
Britta Savik *(Acct Dir)*
Stephanie Schafer *(Acct Dir)*
Erika Schumacher *(Dir-Art Production)*
Dave Bullen *(Dir-Creative)*
Jolene Lew *(Dir-Creative Resource)*
Peter Huxmann *(Dir-Studio Production)*
Joe King *(Grp Acct Dir)*
Seth Thompson *(Mgr-Billing)*
Ellen Gospodarek *(Mgr-Bus)*
Jane Delworth *(Mng Dir-San Francisco)*
Paula Maki *(Mng Dir-Creative)*
Andrew Voss *(Dir-Design)*

MONO MACHINES LLC.
1133 Broadway Ste 706, New York, NY 10010
Tel.: (646) 820-2386
Web Site: http://www.monomachines.com
Year Founded: 2006
Sales Range: $1-9.9 Million
Emp.: 7
Writing Paper Whslr
N.A.I.C.S.: 424110
Isaac de la Fuente *(CEO)*

MONO-SYSTEMS, INC.
4 International Dr, Port Chester, NY 10573
Tel.: (914) 934-2075
Web Site: http://www.monosystems.com
Sales Range: $10-24.9 Million
Emp.: 65
Metal Plate Cable Trays Mfr
N.A.I.C.S.: 332313
Jordan Handler *(Pres)*

MONOCACY HEALTH PARTNERS
400 W 7th St, Frederick, MD 21701
Tel.: (240) 566-3300 MD
Web Site: http://www.monocacyhealthpartners.org
Year Founded: 2011
Sales Range: $10-24.9 Million
Health Care Srvces
N.A.I.C.S.: 622110
E. James Reinsch *(Chm)*
Gregory Powell *(Sec)*

MONOGRAM FOOD SOLUTIONS, LLC
530 Oak Court Dr Ste 400, Memphis, TN 38117
Tel.: (901) 685-7167
Web Site: http://www.monogramfoods.com
Year Founded: 2004
Sales Range: $150-199.9 Million
Emp.: 810
Packaged Processed Meat Products & Appetizers Mfr & Distr
N.A.I.C.S.: 424470
Karl Schledwitz *(Co-Founder, Chm & CEO)*
Wes Jackson *(Co-Founder & Pres)*
David Dunavant *(CFO)*
Don Brunson *(COO)*
Raymond R. Stitle *(Chief People Officer)*
Ches Jackson *(Pres-Supply Chain)*
Rick Goodman *(Chief Customer Officer)*
Jeff Johnson *(Chief Ops Strategy Officer)*
Gary Brooks *(VP-Technical Svcs)*
Brett Elliott *(VP & Gen Mgr-Prepared Meats)*
Joan Vanness *(CIO)*
Matt Arinder *(Chief Acctg Officer)*
Cheryl Duffy-Geiger *(Co-CFO)*
Scott Torrey *(Sr VP-Sls & Mktg)*

Subsidiaries:

Monogram Appetizers, LLC (1)
300 Moore Rd, Plover, WI 54467
Tel.: (715) 341-3191
Web Site: http://www.monogramfoods.com
Frozen Specialty Foods Mfr
N.A.I.C.S.: 311412

Monogram Comfort Foods, LLC (1)
605 Kesco Dr, Bristol, IN 46507
Tel.: (574) 848-0344
Web Site: http://www.hinsdalefarms.com
Emp.: 300
Processed Meat Product Mfr
N.A.I.C.S.: 311999
Gary L. Byrd *(VP-Retail Sls)*

Monogram Meat Snacks, LLC (1)
521 5th St, Chandler, MN 56122
Tel.: (507) 677-2291
Web Site: http://www.monogramfoods.com
Emp.: 250
Sausages & Prepared Meats Mfr
N.A.I.C.S.: 311612
Pat Tocco *(Plant Mgr)*

MONOMOY CAPITAL PARTNERS LLC
600 3rd Ave 27th Fl, New York, NY 10016
Tel.: (212) 699-4000 DE
Web Site: http://www.mcpfunds.com
Year Founded: 2004
Private Equity Firm
N.A.I.C.S.: 523999

MONOMOY CAPITAL PARTNERS LLC

Monomoy Capital Partners LLC—(Continued)

Stephen W. Presser *(Partner)*
Daniel Collin *(Co-CEO & Partner)*
Justin Hillenbrand *(Co-CEO & Partner)*
Lee Mlotek *(Mng Dir)*
David Robbins *(Partner & Head-Credit Strategies)*
Ashley Johansen *(Mng Dir & Head-IR)*
Guy Lotem *(CFO & Chief Compliance Officer)*
Jordan Matusow *(Mng Dir-Bus Dev & Capital Markets)*
Keith Motelson *(Mng Dir)*
Stephen Madsen *(Dir-Bus Dev & Capital Markets)*
Greg Ethridge *(Chm)*

Subsidiaries:

American Textile Holdings, LLC (1)
1926 FM 54 E, Littlefield, TX 79339-0430
Tel.: (806) 385-6401
Emp.: 2,200
Holding Company; Textile Mills
N.A.I.C.S.: 551112
Robert Fowler *(CEO)*

Subsidiary (Domestic):

American Textile Industries, LLC (2)
1926 FM 54 E, Littlefield, TX 79339-0430
Tel.: (806) 385-6401
Sales Range: $50-74.9 Million
Emp.: 320
Textile Mill
N.A.I.C.S.: 313310
Bryan Gregory *(VP & Gen Mgr)*

Subsidiary (Non-US):

Denimatrix S.A. (2)
37 Avenida 2-77 zona 7, Colonia El Rodeo, Guatemala, Guatemala
Tel.: (502) 2420 4600
Web Site: http://www.denimatrix.com
Denim Jeans Mfr
N.A.I.C.S.: 315250

Carlton Creek Ironworks Inc. (1)
801 W Norton Ave Ste 300, Muskegon, MI 49441-4155
Tel.: (231) 739-4349
Web Site: http://www.kurdziel.com
Gray Iron Counterweight Castings
N.A.I.C.S.: 331511

Branch (Domestic):

Carlton Creek Ironworks (2)
2625 W Winston Rd, Rothbury, MI 49452-9777
Tel.: (231) 893-1415
Mfr of Gray & Duct Iron
N.A.I.C.S.: 331511

Casting Technology Company (1)
1450 Musicland Dr, Franklin, IN 46131-7922
Tel.: (317) 738-0282
Web Site: http://www.amcast.com
Sales Range: $25-49.9 Million
Aluminum Castings
N.A.I.C.S.: 331524

Cobra Electronics Corporation (1)
6500 W Cortland St, Chicago, IL 60707
Tel.: (773) 889-3087
Web Site: http://www.cobra.com
Consumer Electronic Products Designer & Marketer
N.A.I.C.S.: 334220
Sally A. Washlow *(Pres)*

Subsidiary (Non-US):

Cobra Electronics (HK) Limited (2)
Suites 2501-2 25/F AXA Tower Landmark East 100 How Ming Street, Kwun Tong, China (Hong Kong)
Tel.: (852) 23690211
Web Site: http://www.cobra.com
Electronic Entertainment Products Whslr
N.A.I.C.S.: 449210

Cobra Electronics EMEA (2)
Cleaver House Sarus Court Manor Park,
Runcorn, WA7 1UL, United Kingdom
Tel.: (44) 1928595494
Web Site: http://www.cobraelectronics.co.uk
Broadcast & Wireless Communications Equipment Mfr & Marketer
N.A.I.C.S.: 423690

Edsal Manufacturing Company, Inc. (1)
1555 West 44th St, Chicago, IL 60609
Tel.: (773) 475-3000
Web Site: http://www.edsal.com
Steel Shelving & Lockers Mfr
N.A.I.C.S.: 337215
Yale Mappa *(Controller)*
Scott White *(Pres & CEO)*
Scott White *(CEO)*
Stephen Presser *(Chm)*

EnviroTech Services Inc. (1)
910 54th Ave Ste 230, Greeley, CO 80634
Tel.: (970) 346-3900
Web Site: https://www.envirotechservices.com
Rev.: $15,000,000
Emp.: 25
Highway & Street Maintenance & Safety Solutions
N.A.I.C.S.: 488490
Kevin Whyrick *(CFO)*
Charles Dickson *(Gen Counsel & Sec)*
Matt Duran *(VP-Corp Rels)*
Steve Bytnar *(Pres)*
Neil Parker *(VP-Ops)*

Escort, Inc. (1)
5440 W Chester Rd, West Chester, OH 45069-2950
Tel.: (513) 870-8500
Web Site: http://www.escortradar.com
Sales Range: $50-74.9 Million
Emp.: 230
Radar & Laser Detectors Mfr
N.A.I.C.S.: 334511
Tim Coomer *(VP-Product Dev)*
Blake Thomas *(Mgr-Comm)*
David Thornhill *(Pres & CEO)*

Fortis Plastics LLC (1)
3615 Voorde Dr, South Bend, IN 46628
Tel.: (574) 485-1100
Web Site: http://www.fortisplasticsgroup.com
Sales Range: $100-124.9 Million
Molded Plastics Mfr
N.A.I.C.S.: 326199

Japs-Olson Company (1)
7500 Excelsior Blvd, Saint Louis Park, MN 55426
Tel.: (952) 932-9393
Web Site: http://www.japsolson.com
Sales Range: $25-49.9 Million
Emp.: 750
Printing, Packaging & Mailing Services
N.A.I.C.S.: 323111
Robert E. Murphy *(Chm)*
Michael W. Beddor *(CEO)*
Michael R. Murphy *(Pres)*
Kevin J. Beddor *(Pres-JO Direct)*
Gary Petrangelo *(CFO)*

Kauffman Engineering, Inc. (1)
701 Ransdell Rd, Lebanon, IN 46052
Tel.: (765) 482-5640
Web Site: http://www.kewire.com
Electrical Harnesses, Lead Wires, Cable Assemblies & Molded Plugs Mfr
N.A.I.C.S.: 335999
Micahel Buis *(CEO)*

Klaussner Furniture Industries, Inc. (1)
PO Box 220, Asheboro, NC 27204
Tel.: (336) 625-6174
Web Site: http://www.klaussner.com
Upholstered Household Furniture Mfr
N.A.I.C.S.: 337121
Jay Foscue *(Sr VP-Mdsg)*
Geoff Beaston *(Sr VP-Case Goods)*
Bill Wittenberg *(Pres & CEO)*
Keith Bolt *(CFO)*
Brandunn Rush *(Sr VP-Sls & Mktg)*

Subsidiary (Domestic):

Prestige Fabricators Inc. (2)
2206 Dumont St, Asheboro, NC 27203-2909
Tel.: (336) 672-3383
Web Site: http://www.prestigefab.com
Sales Range: $25-49.9 Million
Emp.: 275
Foam Mfr
N.A.I.C.S.: 326150
Joseph R. Wingfield *(Pres)*
David Bryant *(VP)*

Kurz-Kasch, Inc. (1)
511 Byers Rd, Miamisburg, OH 45342
Tel.: (937) 299-0990
Web Site: http://www.kurz-kasch.com
Sales Range: $75-99.9 Million
Electrical & Mechanical Components & Devices Mfr
N.A.I.C.S.: 335999
Chad Merkel *(Mng Dir)*

Division (Domestic):

Kurz-Kasch Wabash (2)
511 Byers Rd, Miamisburg, OH 45342
Tel.: (888) 587-9527
Web Site: http://www.kurz-kasch.com
Sales Range: $25-49.9 Million
Engineered Composite Components, Subassemblies, Sensing Devices & Solenoids Mfr
N.A.I.C.S.: 334416
Jan Harris *(Mgr-HR)*
Bob Sheridan *(Plant Mgr)*
George Kochanowski *(CEO)*

MAC Papers, Inc. (1)
3300 Phillips Hwy, Jacksonville, FL 32207
Tel.: (904) 348-3300
Web Site: http://www.macpapers.com
Emp.: 200
Printing Paper Products Whslr
N.A.I.C.S.: 424110
Craig Boortz *(Exec VP-Paper)*
Rick Mitchell *(Pres & COO)*
Greg Gay *(CFO)*

Subsidiary (Domestic):

Boxes Etc. II, LLC (2)
1150 Antioch Pike Ste 250, Nashville, TN 37211-3170
Tel.: (615) 399-7070
Web Site: http://www.boxesetc.biz
Packaging Boxes Whslr
N.A.I.C.S.: 424130

Florida Graphic Services, Inc. (2)
1351 N Arcturas Ave, Clearwater, FL 33765
Tel.: (877) 447-9780
Web Site: http://www.fgs2.com
Inkjet Printing Equipment Whslr
N.A.I.C.S.: 423840
Santiago Jarrin *(Gen Mgr)*
Lorena Cabezas *(Office Mgr)*

Branch (Domestic):

MAC Papers, Inc. (2)
801 Edwards Ave, Harahan, LA 70123
Tel.: (504) 733-7559
Web Site: http://www.macpapers.com
Sales Range: $10-24.9 Million
Emp.: 20
Mfr & Sales of Printing Paper
N.A.I.C.S.: 424110

Marquis Corp. (1)
596 Hoffman Rd, Independence, OR 97351
Tel.: (503) 838-0888
Web Site: http://www.marquisspas.com
Hot Tubs
N.A.I.C.S.: 339999
John Schrenk *(CEO)*
Aaron Hinton *(Controller)*

Nordic Products, Inc. (1)
4655 Patterson Ave SE, Grand Rapids, MI 49512-5337
Tel.: (616) 940-4036
Web Site: http://www.nordichottubs.com
Rev.: $9,758,082
Emp.: 49
Wood Container & Pallet Mfr
N.A.I.C.S.: 321920
Todd Gibson *(Plant Mgr)*
William Gibson *(Pres)*
Barbara Sisung *(Bus Mgr)*

Sportech, LLC (1)
10800 175th Ave NW, Elk River, MN 55330
Tel.: (763) 712-3965
Web Site: http://www.sportechinc.com
Cab Component & System Designer & Mfr
N.A.I.C.S.: 336390

Paul DeVault *(Mgr-Site)*
Jim Glomstad *(CEO)*

Steel Parts Manufacturing, Inc. (1)
801 Berryman Pike, Tipton, IN 46072-8492
Tel.: (765) 675-2191
Web Site: http://www.steelparts.com
Sales Range: $75-99.9 Million
Automotive Precision Stampings & Metal Parts Mfr
N.A.I.C.S.: 336370

Waupaca Foundry, Inc. (1)
1955 Brunner Dr, Waupaca, WI 54981-1664
Tel.: (715) 258-6611
Web Site: https://www.waupacafoundry.com
Gray Iron & Modular Castings Mfr
N.A.I.C.S.: 331511
Michael Nikolai *(Pres, CEO & COO)*
Todd Pagel *(VP)*
Jarrod Osborn *(VP)*
James Newsome *(VP)*

West Marine, Inc. (1)
500 Westridge Dr, Watsonville, CA 95076
Tel.: (831) 728-2700
Web Site: http://www.westmarine.com
Sales Range: $700-749.9 Million
Boating Supplies Retailer
N.A.I.C.S.: 441222
Barry Kelley *(Exec VP-Stores & Wholesale)*
Bob Buckborough *(VP-Mktg)*
Deborah Ajeska *(CFO, Divisional VP & Controller)*
Virginia Wright *(CIO & Sr VP-IT & E-Commerce)*
Ron Baime *(Chief Mdse Officer)*

Women's Apparel Group, LLC (1)
35 United Dr, West Bridgewater, MA 02379
Tel.: (508) 583-8110
Web Site: http://www.bostonapparel.com
Sales Range: $200-249.9 Million
Women's Apparel Catalog & Online Retailer
N.A.I.C.S.: 458110

MONONA BANKSHARES, INC.
5515 Monona Dr, Monona, WI 53716
Tel.: (608) 310-1244   WI
Web Site:
http://www.mononabank.com
Year Founded: 1991
Rev.: $40,414,000
Assets: $914,596,000
Liabilities: $825,942,000
Net Worth: $88,654,000
Earnings: $7,469,000
Emp.: 90
Fiscal Year-end: 12/31/18
Bank Holding Company
N.A.I.C.S.: 551111
Paul Hoffmann *(Pres & CEO)*

Subsidiaries:

Monona State Bank (1)
5515 Monona Dr, Monona, WI 53716-3130
Tel.: (608) 223-3000
Web Site: http://www.mononabank.com
Sales Range: $10-24.9 Million
Commericial Banking
N.A.I.C.S.: 522110
Paul Hoffmann *(Pres & CEO)*

MONROE CAPITAL INCOME PLUS CORPORATION
311 S Wacker Dr Ste 6400, Chicago, IL 60606
Tel.: (312) 258-8300   MD
Year Founded: 2018
Rev.: $91,675,000
Assets: $1,544,642,000
Liabilities: $789,726,000
Net Worth: $754,916,000
Earnings: $49,816,000
Emp.: 121
Fiscal Year-end: 12/31/22
Financial Investment Services
N.A.I.C.S.: 523940
Theodore L. Koenig *(Chm & CEO)*
Lewis W. Solimene Jr. *(CFO, Chief Investment Officer & Sec)*

MONROE CAPITAL LLC

COMPANIES — MONROE STREET PARTNERS LLC

311 S Wacker Dr Ste 6400, Chicago, IL 60606
Tel.: (312) 258-8300 MD
Web Site:
   https://www.monroecap.com
Rev.: $45,018,000
Assets: $424,545,000
Liabilities: $183,695,000
Net Worth: $240,850,000
Earnings: $22,506,000
Fiscal Year-end: 12/31/16
Investment Services
N.A.I.C.S.: 523999
Theodore L. Koenig *(Chm & CEO)*
Aaron D. Peck *(Mng Dir & Co-Head-Opportunistic Private Credit Grp)*
Lewis W. Solimene Jr. *(Mng Dir & . Portfolio Mgr)*
David H. Jacobson *(Chief Compliance Officer)*
Zia Uddin *(Pres & Co-Portfolio Mgr-Institutional Portfolios)*
Sweta Chanda *(Mng Dir & Head-Bus Strategy)*
Chris Lund *(Co-Portfolio Mgr-Institutional Portfolios)*
Gordon Saint-Denis *(Mng Dir & Head-Sports Fin)*
Matt Rosenberg *(Mng Dir & Head-Media Fin)*
Amanda Tallman *(VP-Direct Originations)*
Caroline B. Davidson *(Mng Dir & Head-Capital Markets)*

Subsidiaries:

Horizon Technology Finance Management LLC (1)
312 Farmington Ave, Farmington, CT 06032
Tel.: (860) 676-8654
Investment Services
N.A.I.C.S.: 523999

LAI International, Inc. (1)
708 W 22nd St, Tempe, AZ 85282
Tel.: (480) 968-6228
Web Site: http://www.laico.com
Sales Range: $25-49.9 Million
Emp.: 250
Precision-Finished Components & Subassemblies Mfr
N.A.I.C.S.: 332999
Stewart Cramer *(Pres)*
Vinnie Caliendo *(CFO)*
John Rogers *(VP & COO)*
Darcy Dodge *(VP-Strategic Markets & Products)*
Jim Corrao *(CIO)*
Joe Beauchemin *(Dir-Quality)*
Patrick J. Gruetzmacher *(Pres & CEO)*
Michael Koesling *(VP-Engrg)*
Gary Thornton *(VP-HR)*
Kevin McGlinch *(CFO)*

Branch (Domestic):

LAI International, Inc.-Minneapolis (2)
7645 Baker St NE, Minneapolis, MN 55432
Tel.: (763) 780-0060
Web Site: http://www.laico.com
Sales Range: $10-24.9 Million
Emp.: 35
Precision-Finished Components & Subassemblies Mfr
N.A.I.C.S.: 332999
Patrick J. Gruetzmacher *(Pres)*

LAI International, Inc.-Westminster (2)
1110 Business Pkwy S, Westminster, MD 21157
Tel.: (410) 857-0770
Web Site: http://www.laico.com
Sales Range: $10-24.9 Million
Emp.: 50
Precision-Finished Component & Subassemble Mfr
N.A.I.C.S.: 332999
Steve Jones *(Mgr-Site)*

Vice Media LLC (1)
90 N 11th St, Brooklyn, NY 11211
Tel.: (718) 599-3101
Web Site: http://www.vice.com
Sales Range: $150-199.9 Million
Emp.: 750
Magazine & Internet Publishing
N.A.I.C.S.: 513120
Shane Smith *(Co-Founder)*
Suroosh Alvi *(Co-Founder)*
Andrew Creighton *(Co-Pres)*
Eddy Moretti *(Pres-Viceland)*
James Schwab *(Co-Pres)*
Alex Miller *(Dir-Creative-EMEA-Viceland)*
Nick Weidenfeld *(Pres-Programming)*
Cristian Jofre *(Dir-Creative-Viceland Intl)*
Guy Slattery *(Gen Mgr-Viceland)*
Ciel Hunter *(Head-Content)*
James Rosenstock *(Chief Corp Dev Officer & Pres-Viceland Intl)*
Tom Punch *(Chief Comml & Creative Officer)*
Mimi Turner *(Sr VP-Strategy-UK)*
Matt O'Mara *(Mng Dir-UK)*
Sam Bergen *(Exec Dir-Creative-West Coast)*
Nicolas Bonard *(CEO-France)*
Benjamin Lassale *(Gen Mgr)*
Tammy Smulders *(Pres-Fashion Grp)*
Matt Elek *(CEO-EMEA)*
Nilesh Zaveri *(CFO/COO-Asia Pacific)*
Hosi Simon *(CEO-Asia Pacific)*
Lucy Delacherois-Day *(Dir-Comml-Fashion Grp)*
Dominique Delport *(Chief Revenue Officer & Pres-Intl)*
Rohit Tugnait *(Comml Dir-India)*
Samira Kanwar *(Head-Content-Asia Pacific)*
Susie Banikarim *(Exec VP & Head-Newsgathering-Global-Vice News)*
Daisy Auger-Dominguez *(Chief People Officer)*
Jannat Gargi *(VP & Head-Documentaries-Vice Studios)*
Danny Gabai *(Exec VP & Head-Vice Studios-US)*
Nadja Bellan-White *(CMO-Global)*
Jonathan Bing *(Chief Comm Officer)*

Subsidiary (Domestic):

Carrot Creative LLC (2)
55 Washington St Ste 900, Brooklyn, NY 11201
Tel.: (718) 395-7934
Web Site: http://www.carrot.is
Emp.: 70
Advetising Agency
N.A.I.C.S.: 541810
Mike Germano *(Co-Founder & CEO)*
Chris Petescia *(Co-Founder & Chief Experience Officer)*
Kyle MacDonald *(CTO)*
Tim Nolan *(Chief Creative Officer)*

Subsidiary (Non-US):

Pulse Films Limited (2)
17 Hanbury Street, London, E1 6QR, United Kingdom
Tel.: (44) 20 7426 5700
Web Site: http://www.pulsefilms.co.uk
Motion Picture Production Services
N.A.I.C.S.: 512110
Thomas Benski *(Co-Founder & CEO)*
Marisa Clifford *(Co-founder & CEO-Europe)*
Davud Karbassioun *(Pres-Commercials & Branded Entertainment)*
Jade Maxwell *(Head-HR)*
Rik Green *(Head-Music Videos)*
Julia Nottingham *(Head-Documentary)*
Emma Cooper *(Pres-Global)*
Jon Alwen *(Sr VP-Non-Fiction TV-UK)*
Nelesh Dhand *(Head-Dev-Global)*
Bianca Gavin *(Head-Production-Scripted Television & Film)*
Jamie Hall *(COO-Scripted Television & Film)*

Subsidiary (Domestic):

Refinery 29, Inc. (2)
225 Broadway 23rd Fl, New York, NY 10007
Tel.: (212) 966-3112
Web Site: http://www.refinery29.com
Sales Range: $1-9.9 Million
Emp.: 59
Fashion, Beauty & Entertainment Website
N.A.I.C.S.: 519290
George Mitchell *(VP-Bus Affairs & Ops)*
Jenny Gorenstein *(Dir-Fashion)*
Kirsty Hathaway *(Creative Dir-Europe)*
Kristin Cardwell *(VP-Strategy & Bus Dev-Intl)*
Nina Joyce *(Dir-PR-Europe)*
Kate Ward *(Sr VP & Head-Intl)*
Simone Oliver *(Editor-in-Chief)*

MONROE CLINIC
515 22nd Ave, Monroe, WI 53566
Tel.: (608) 324-2000
Web Site:
   http://www.monroeclinic.org
Year Founded: 1939
Sales Range: $1-9.9 Million
Medical Health Network
N.A.I.C.S.: 622110
Mike Sanders *(Pres & CEO)*
Mark Thompson *(Chief Medical Officer)*
Christine Wellington *(Chm)*
Marilyn Pfarr *(Vice Chm)*
Michelle Brukwicki *(Treas)*
Shelley Muranyi *(CFO)*
Tracey Pederson *(Exec Dir)*

MONROE COUNTY BAR ASSOCIATION
913 Main St, Stroudsburg, PA 18360
Tel.: (570) 424-7288 PA
Web Site: http://www.monroebar.org
Year Founded: 1915
Rev.: $1,043,319
Assets: $2,697,896
Liabilities: $149,917
Net Worth: $2,547,979
Earnings: $481,290
Emp.: 5
Fiscal Year-end: 12/31/14
Bar Association
N.A.I.C.S.: 813910
Denise M. Burdge *(Exec Dir)*
Elizabeth Bensinger Weekes *(Treas)*
Jeffrey A. Durney *(Pres)*
Mark A. Primrose *(Sec)*
Timothy J. McManus *(VP)*
Denise M. Burdge *(Exec Dir)*
Elizabeth Bensinger Weekes *(Treas)*
Jeffrey A. Durney *(Pres)*
Mark A. Primrose *(Sec)*
Timothy J. McManus *(VP)*
Elizabeth M. Field *(Pres-Young Lawyers Div)*

MONROE COUNTY WATER AUTHORITY
475 Norris Dr, Rochester, NY 14610-0999
Tel.: (585) 442-2000 NY
Web Site: http://www.mcwa.com
Year Founded: 1950
Sales Range: $10-24.9 Million
Emp.: 225
Water Service Provider
N.A.I.C.S.: 221310
Raymond W. Benshoff *(Exec Dir-Ops)*
Richard J. Metzger *(Exec Engr)*
Nicholas A. Noce *(Exec Dir)*
Joseph R. Rulison *(Treas)*
Larry M. Magguilli *(Chm)*
Stephen M. Savage *(Dir-Engrg)*
Scott D. Nasca *(Vice Chm)*
Kathleen A. Prestidge *(Dir-Fin & Bus Svcs)*

MONROE EQUIPMENT, INC.
N50 W13941 Overview Dr, Menomonee Falls, WI 53051
Tel.: (262) 783-8190
Web Site:
   http://www.theheatingsource.com
Rev.: $19,600,000
Emp.: 30
Warm Air Heating & Air Conditioning Equipment & Supplies Merchant Whslr
N.A.I.C.S.: 423730
Randy Schneider *(Pres)*
Larry Bellman *(Mgr-Parts-Columbus)*
Greg Olszowy *(Mgr-Warehouse & Shipping)*
Fred Lewis *(Asst Mgr-Warehouse)*
Lisa Swance *(Mgr-Credit & Office Mgr-Computer & Website Issues)*

MONROE GAS STORAGE COMPANY LLC
1200 17th St, Denver, CO 80202
Tel.: (303) 951-4284
Web Site:
   http://www.monroegasstorage.com
Natural Gas Storage & Consulting Services
N.A.I.C.S.: 457110

MONROE GROUP INC.
500 Purdy Hill Rd, Monroe, CT 06468
Tel.: (203) 268-8624
Web Site:
   http://www.monroestaffing.com
Year Founded: 1969
Sales Range: $25-49.9 Million
Emp.: 20
Provider of Employment Services
N.A.I.C.S.: 561311
Matthew Briand *(Pres & CEO)*
Steve Miller *(CFO)*

MONROE HARDWARE COMPANY
101 N Sutherland Ave, Monroe, NC 28110
Tel.: (704) 289-3121 NC
Web Site:
   http://www.monroehardware.com
Year Founded: 1886
Sales Range: $100-124.9 Million
Emp.: 200
Hardware Distr
N.A.I.C.S.: 423710
Carl G. Belk *(Chm)*

MONROE MACHINED PRODUCTS, INC.
1422 S 192nd St, Seattle, WA 98148
Tel.: (206) 242-4898 WA
Web Site:
   http://www.monroemachinedproducts.com
Year Founded: 1957
Sales Range: $10-24.9 Million
Precisioned Machined Products Mfr
N.A.I.C.S.: 332710
Bhrett A. Monroe *(Pres)*

MONROE PIPING & SHEET METAL LLC
68 Humboldt St, Rochester, NY 14609
Tel.: (585) 482-0200
Web Site:
   http://www.monroepiping.com
Year Founded: 1967
Emp.: 115
Mechanical Contractor
N.A.I.C.S.: 238220
Dan Englert *(Pres & CEO)*
Phil Somers *(CFO & Sec)*
Jeff Turner *(VP & Partner)*

MONROE STREET PARTNERS LLC
100 S State St Ste 454, Chicago, IL 60603
Tel.: (630) 699-9947
Web Site: https://www.monroestreetpartners.com
Private Equity Firm
N.A.I.C.S.: 523940
Alexander Foshager *(Co-Founder & Mng Partner)*
Ken Mill *(Co-Founder & Mng Partner)*

MONROE STREET PARTNERS LLC — U.S. PRIVATE

Monroe Street Partners LLC—(Continued)

Subsidiaries:

Brandito, LLC (1)
2100 Tomlynn St, Richmond, VA 23230
Tel.: (804) 747-6721
Web Site: https://brandito.net
Advertising Services
N.A.I.C.S.: 541810
Michael Lovern *(Pres)*

MONROE TRACTOR & IMPLEMENT CO., INC.
1001 Lehigh Station Rd, Henrietta, NY 14467-9374
Tel.: (585) 334-3867   NY
Web Site: http://www.monroetractor.com
Year Founded: 1951
Sales Range: $25-49.9 Million
Emp.: 135
Construction & Agricultural Equipment Dealer & Rental Services
N.A.I.C.S.: 441227
Janet Felosky *(Pres)*
John Dancy *(Mgr-Rochester)*
Chris Felosky *(Gen Mgr-Agriculture)*
Chuck Miller *(Gen Mgr-Construction & Mgr-Elmira)*
Laura Wilkas *(Mgr-Mktg)*

MONROE TRANSPORTATION SERVICES
1051 S Westwood Ave, Addison, IL 60101
Tel.: (630) 543-4650
Web Site: http://www.monroe-trans.com
Sales Range: $10-24.9 Million
Emp.: 120
Local Trucking without Storage
N.A.I.C.S.: 484110
Jack Swierenga *(Pres & CEO)*

MONROE TRUCK EQUIPMENT, INC.
1051 W 7th St, Monroe, WI 53566-9102
Tel.: (608) 328-8127   WI
Web Site: http://www.monroetruck.com
Year Founded: 1958
Motor Vehicle Supplies & New Parts Mfr
N.A.I.C.S.: 423120
David Quade *(Pres)*
Jim Schneider *(Mgr-Sls)*

Subsidiaries:

Kandi Kountry Express, Ltd. (1)
61381 US Highway 12, Litchfield, MN 55355
Tel.: (320) 693-7900
Web Site: http://www.towmaster.com
Truck Trailer Mfr
N.A.I.C.S.: 336212
Chris Pokornowski *(Mgr-Sls)*

MONROEVILLE CHRYSLER JEEP
3651 William Penn Hwy, Monroeville, PA 15146
Tel.: (888) 856-1441
Web Site: http://www.monroevillechryslerjeep.net
Emp.: 67
New & Used Car Dealer
N.A.I.C.S.: 441110
Chad Guerzo *(Gen Sls Mgr)*
Chris Takach *(Mgr-Vehicle Upgrade)*
Josh Finnagan *(Sls Mgr)*
Robert Manning *(Gen Mgr)*
Carol Noel *(Dir-Bus Dev Center)*
Kristie Fularz *(Mgr-Customer Care)*

Robin Lightfoot *(Mgr-Customer Care Center)*
Chiffon Allen *(Dir-Internet Care Center)*

MONROEVILLE DODGE
3633 William Penn Hwy, Monroeville, PA 15146
Tel.: (412) 856-1700
Web Site: http://www.monroevilledodge.com
Year Founded: 1994
Sales Range: $10-24.9 Million
Emp.: 65
Car Whslr
N.A.I.C.S.: 441110
Michael C. Auffenberg *(Pres)*
Blancy Mitchell *(Gen Mgr)*

MONROVIA GROWERS COMPANY
817 E Monrovia Pl, Azusa, CA 91702-1385
Tel.: (626) 334-9321   CA
Web Site: http://www.monrovia.com
Year Founded: 1926
Sales Range: $125-149.9 Million
Emp.: 2,100
Ornamental Nursery Stock Grower & Whslr
N.A.I.C.S.: 111421
Miles Rosedale *(CEO)*
Tristan Simpson *(CMO)*

Subsidiaries:

Monrovia Growers-Oregon (1)
13455 SE Lafayette Hwy, Dayton, OR 97114-8600
Tel.: (503) 868-7941
Web Site: http://www.monrovia.com
Sales Range: $50-74.9 Million
Emp.: 450
Plant Nursery
N.A.I.C.S.: 111421
Rick Wells *(Gen Mgr)*

MONSEN ENGINEERING COMPANY
6 Daniel Rd E, Fairfield, NJ 07004
Tel.: (973) 227-1880
Web Site: http://www.monsen.com
Rev.: $20,274,702
Emp.: 112
Warm Air Heating & Air Conditioning Contractor
N.A.I.C.S.: 238220
Eric Monsen *(Pres)*
Donald Long *(VP-Sls)*

MONSMA MARKETING CORPORATION
2450 Buchanan Ave SW, Grand Rapids, MI 49548
Tel.: (616) 245-8714
Web Site: http://www.monsma.com
Year Founded: 1923
Sales Range: $25-49.9 Million
Emp.: 54
Building Materials Whslr
N.A.I.C.S.: 423330
Jane Lovell *(Chm & CEO)*
Brian Stephens *(Dir-Product Dev)*

MONSTER MEDIA, LLC
517 S Lake Destiny Rd, Orlando, FL 32810
Tel.: (407) 478-8163
Web Site: http://www.monstermedia.net
Year Founded: 2006
Rev.: $2,600,000
Emp.: 25
Fiscal Year-end: 12/31/06
Media Advertising
N.A.I.C.S.: 541840

Pedro Sanchez *(Dir-Interactive Art)*
Natalie Brokaw *(VP-Mktg & Client Svcs)*

MONSTER PRODUCTS, INC.
15321 NW 60th Ave 51 St Ste 109, South San Francisco, CA 94080
Tel.: (415) 330-3479   NV
Web Site: http://www.monsterstore.com
Year Founded: 2015
Holding Company
N.A.I.C.S.: 551112
Noel Lee *(CEO)*

Subsidiaries:

Monster, Inc. (1)
601 Gateway Blvd Ste 900, South San Francisco, CA 94080
Tel.: (415) 840-2000
Web Site: http://www.monsterstore.com
Sales Range: $550-599.9 Million
Emp.: 650
Holding Company; Audio Equipment & Related Accessories Mfr & Whslr
N.A.I.C.S.: 551112
Noel Lee *(Founder, Pres & CEO)*
Dan Dougherty *(Gen Counsel)*

Subsidiary (Domestic):

Monster, LLC (2)
601 Gateway Blvd Ste 900, South San Francisco, CA 94080
Tel.: (415) 840-2000
Web Site: http://www.monsterstore.com
Audio Equipment & Related Accessories Mfr & Whslr
N.A.I.C.S.: 334310
Noel Lee *(CEO)*

MONSTER SCOOTER PARTS
5045 Galley Rd, Colorado Springs, CO 80915
Tel.: (800) 798-0325
Web Site: http://www.monsterscooterparts.com
Year Founded: 2005
Sales Range: $1-9.9 Million
Emp.: 12
Resells Replacement Parts for Mobility, Recreational & Street Scooters & Power Wheelchairs
N.A.I.C.S.: 336991
Glenn Alvey *(Co-Founder)*
Kevin Alvey *(Co-Founder)*

MONSTER TRANSMISSION & PERFORMANCE
19370 Oliver St, Brooksville, FL 34601
Web Site: http://www.monstertransmission.com
Year Founded: 2003
Sales Range: $1-9.9 Million
Emp.: 25
Transmission Products
N.A.I.C.S.: 811114
Achilles Thomas *(Owner)*

MONT BLANC GOURMET
2925 E Colfax Ave, Denver, CO 80206
Tel.: (303) 755-1100
Web Site: http://www.montblancgourmet.com
Sales Range: $10-24.9 Million
Emp.: 8
Chocolate Powders & Flavored Syrups
N.A.I.C.S.: 311930
Michael Szyliowicz *(Co-Founder)*
Irene Szyliowicz *(Founder)*
Paul Groh *(Controller)*

MONTACHUSETT OPPORTUNITY COUNCIL, INC.
601 River St, Fitchburg, MA 01420

Tel.: (978) 345-7040   MA
Web Site: http://www.mocinc.org
Year Founded: 1966
Sales Range: $10-24.9 Million
Emp.: 334
Individual & Family Support Services
N.A.I.C.S.: 624190
Linda Duffy *(Dir-Admin & Fin)*
Tammy Maxwell *(Dir-HR)*
Leona Shaw *(Dir-Ops)*
Kevin Reed *(Exec Dir)*
Oscar O'Connor *(Pres-Board)*

MONTAGE PARTNERS, INC.
7150 E Camelback Rd Ste 230, Scottsdale, AZ 85251
Tel.: (480) 675-5000
Web Site: http://www.montagepartners.com
Private Investment Firm
N.A.I.C.S.: 523999
Chris Brown *(VP-Bus Dev)*
Chris Young *(CFO & Dir-Ops)*

Subsidiaries:

Advanced Manufacturing & Development, Inc. (1)
200 N Lenore Ave, Willits, CA 95490-3209
Tel.: (707) 459-9451
Web Site: http://www.metalfx.com
Mfr of Electronic Enclosures, Parts & Systems; Precision Sheet Metal Shop For High Volume Stamping Electronics Industry & Electric Mechanic Assembly
N.A.I.C.S.: 332322

Division (Domestic):

Interactive Technologies (2)
300 E Commercial St, Willits, CA 95490-3202
Tel.: (707) 459-7560
Sales Range: $10-24.9 Million
Emp.: 100
Sheet Metal Fabrication
N.A.I.C.S.: 332322

METAL fx (2)
200 N Lenore Ave, Willits, CA 95490-3209
Tel.: (707) 459-9451
Web Site: http://www.metalfx.com
Sales Range: $25-49.9 Million
Sheet Metal Manufacturing Warehouse Distributor
N.A.I.C.S.: 332322
Gordon Short *(Pres)*

MONTALBANO INC.
780 Serramonte Blvd, Colma, CA 94014
Tel.: (650) 994-2400
Web Site: http://www.stewartcars.com
Rev.: $60,473,319
Emp.: 80
Automobiles Dealer
N.A.I.C.S.: 441110
Paul Montalbano *(Owner)*
Frank Fragomei *(Gen Mgr)*

MONTALBANO LUMBER COMPANY INC.
1309 Houston Ave, Houston, TX 77007
Tel.: (713) 228-9011
Web Site: http://www.montalbanolumber.com
Sales Range: $25-49.9 Million
Emp.: 103
Lumber & Other Building Materials
N.A.I.C.S.: 423310
Michael J. Montalbano *(Pres)*

MONTALVO SPIRITS, INC.
13092 Caminito Del Rocio, Del Mar, CA 92014
Tel.: (858) 262-1810
Year Founded: 2010
Alcoholic Beverage Mfr & Distr

N.A.I.C.S.: 312140
Isaac Gilmore *(Chm & CEO)*

MONTANA COFFEE TRADERS INC.
5810 Hwy 93 S, Whitefish, MT 59937
Tel.: (406) 862-7633
Web Site: http://www.coffeetraders.com
Year Founded: 1981
Sales Range: $1-4.9 Billion
Emp.: 98
Roasted Coffee & Tea Mfr & Whslr
N.A.I.C.S.: 311920
Heather Vrentas *(Mgr)*

MONTANA ECONOMIC REVITALIZATION & DEVELOPMENT INSTITUTE INC.
65 E Broadway St, Butte, MT 59701
Tel.: (406) 533-6700
Web Site: http://www.merdi.org
Year Founded: 1974
Sales Range: $10-24.9 Million
Emp.: 10
Research Services
N.A.I.C.S.: 541715
Jim Kambich *(Pres & CEO)*
Gary Rowe *(CFO)*

Subsidiaries:

MSE Technology Applications Inc. (1)
200 Technology Way, Butte, MT 59701-9795
Tel.: (406) 494-7100
Web Site: http://www.mse-ta.com
Sales Range: $10-24.9 Million
Commercial Physical Research
N.A.I.C.S.: 541715
Helen Joyce *(CEO)*

MONTANA METAL PRODUCTS LLC
25 E Howard St, Des Plaines, IL 60018
Tel.: (847) 803-6600
Web Site: http://www.mmpllc.com
Rev.: $15,000,000
Emp.: 116
Sheet Metalwork
N.A.I.C.S.: 332322
Charles Kelley *(VP-Ops)*

MONTANO CIGARETTE CANDY & TOBACCO COMPANY INC.
290 Boston Post Rd, Milford, CT 06460-2527
Tel.: (203) 877-0341
Web Site: http://www.montano.biz
Year Founded: 1953
Sales Range: $10-24.9 Million
Emp.: 50
Tobacco & Tobacco Products
N.A.I.C.S.: 424940
Gary Montano *(Pres & CEO)*

MONTANO MOTORS, INC.
1200 S Renaissance Blvd NE, Albuquerque, NM 87107
Tel.: (505) 345-8741
Year Founded: 1986
Sales Range: $10-24.9 Million
Emp.: 25
Car Whslr
N.A.I.C.S.: 441110
James Edens *(Pres)*

MONTAUK RUG & CARPET CORP.
65 Price Pkwy, Farmingdale, NY 11735
Tel.: (631) 293-3900
Web Site: http://www.montaukcarpet.com

Sales Range: $10-24.9 Million
Emp.: 70
Carpets
N.A.I.C.S.: 449121
Stephen Fruchter *(Pres)*
Lorraine Bair *(Mgr)*

MONTAVISTA SOFTWARE LLC
5201 Great America Pkwy Ste 432, Santa Clara, CA 95054
Tel.: (408) 520-1591
Web Site: http://www.mvista.com
Year Founded: 1999
Software Publisher
N.A.I.C.S.: 513210

Subsidiaries:

MontaVista Software Japan, Inc. (1)
Shibuya Mark City West 22F 1-12-1 Dogenzaka, Shibuya-ku, Tokyo, 150-0043, Japan
Tel.: (81) 3 4360 5405
Web Site: http://www.mvista.com
Software Development Services
N.A.I.C.S.: 513210

MontaVista Software Korea LLC (1)
9F West Wing IT Venture Tower 135, Jungdae-ro Songpa-gu, Seoul, 05717, Korea (South)
Tel.: (82) 2 2142 3773
Web Site: http://www.mvista.com
Software Development Services
N.A.I.C.S.: 513210

MONTAVO, INC.
4957 Lakemont Blvd Ste 239, Bellevue, WA 98006
Tel.: (425) 747-5500
Web Site: http://www.montavo.com
Year Founded: 2005
Software Applications; Mobile Marketing & Advertising Solutions
N.A.I.C.S.: 513210
Brook W. Lang *(CEO)*

MONTBLEAU & ASSOCIATES INC
555 Raven St, San Diego, CA 92102
Tel.: (619) 263-5550
Web Site: http://www.montbleau.com
Year Founded: 1980
Rev.: $28,100,000
Emp.: 120
Wood Office Furniture
N.A.I.C.S.: 337211
Ron P. Montbleau *(Pres)*
Sophie Tejada *(Controller)*

MONTCLAIR GOLF CLUB
25 Prospect Ave, West Orange, NJ 07052
Tel.: (973) 239-1800
Web Site: http://www.montclairgolfclub.org
Year Founded: 1893
Sales Range: $10-24.9 Million
Emp.: 350
Golf Club
N.A.I.C.S.: 713910
Daniel Somogyl *(Gen Mgr)*

MONTCLAIR HOTEL INVESTORS, INC.
2801 Lakeside Dr Ste 208, Bannockburn, IL 60015
Tel.: (847) 457-3900
Web Site: http://www.montclairhotels.com
Year Founded: 1995
Hotel Investment & Management
N.A.I.C.S.: 721110
Ata Kashanian *(VP-Ops)*
Scott Warren *(VP-Ops)*
Richard Roller *(VP-Fin)*
Tom North *(VP)*

Subsidiaries:

Glen Cove Mansion Hotel & Conference Center (1)
200 Dosoris Ln, Glen Cove, NY 11542
Tel.: (516) 671-6400
Web Site: http://www.glencovemansion.com
Sales Range: $10-24.9 Million
Emp.: 160
Conference Center & Hotel
N.A.I.C.S.: 721110
Ata Kashanian *(VP & Gen Mgr)*
Gus Montesantos *(Dir-Food & Beverage)*

MONTCLAIR STATE UNIVERSITY
1 Normal Ave, Montclair, NJ 07043
Tel.: (973) 655-4000
Web Site: http://www.montclair.edu
Year Founded: 1908
Colleges & Universities
N.A.I.C.S.: 611310
Stephen G. Sudovar *(Adjunct Professor-Mgmt)*
Edward V. Chapel *(VP-IT)*
Donald D. Cipullo *(Treas & VP-Fin)*
Gregory W. Bressler *(VP-University Facilities)*
Samir Bakane *(Exec Dir-Enterprise Sys Implementation)*
Shivaun Gaines *(Dir-Govt Rels)*
David Josephson *(Exec Dir-Budget & Plng)*
Jerry M. Cutler *(VP-HR)*
Karen L. Pennington *(VP-Student Dev & Campus Life)*
George J. Hiltzik *(Vice Chm)*
Susan L. Blount *(Sec)*
Junius Gonzales *(Sr VP & Provost)*
Kimberly Kilmer Hollister *(VP-Academic Affairs)*
Jonathan Koppell *(Pres)*
Ralph A. Larossa *(Bd of Trustees, Executives)*
John T. Shannon Jr. *(VP-University Advancement)*

Subsidiaries:

Bloomfield College (1)
467 Franklin St, Bloomfield, NJ 07003
Tel.: (973) 748-9000
Web Site: http://www.bloomfield.edu
Graduate & Undergraduate College
N.A.I.C.S.: 611310
Howard Buxbaum *(VP-Admin & Fin)*
Marion Terenzio *(VP-Academic Affairs)*
Patrick Lamy *(VP-Student Affairs)*
Jacqueline Bartley-Oxley *(VP-Institutional Advancement)*
Peter K. Jeong *(VP-Global Programs & Pro Studies)*
Adam J. Castro *(VP-Enrollment Mgmt)*
William McDonald *(VP-Campus Plng & Assoc VP-Fin & Admin)*
Martin McKerrow *(Chm)*
John J. Delucca *(Vice Chm)*
Stephen A. Glasser *(Vice Chm)*
Adrian A. Shelby *(Sec)*
Gerald Holmes *(Asst Dir-Athletics)*
Rocco Constantino *(Asst Dir-Athletics)*
Jennifer Virgil *(Coord-Compliance)*
Sheila Wooten *(Dir-Athletic)*
Gladstone Harris *(Dir-Sports Info)*
Denise Wilburn *(Sec)*
Dan Figueredo *(Dir-Library)*
Julia Del Bagno *(Asst Dir-Admission)*
Lisa Shaheen *(Dir-Student Fin Svcs)*
Marcheta P. Evans *(Pres)*

MONTE RESOURCES INC.
1002 Ermine Ct, South Lake Tahoe, CA 96150
Tel.: (530) 577-4141
Year Founded: 2010
Sales Range: $25-49.9 Million
Emp.: 1
Molybdenite & Other Mineral Mining Services
N.A.I.C.S.: 212290

Edwin G. Morrow *(Pres, CEO, CFO, Chief Acctg Officer, Treas & Sec)*

MONTE SHELTON JAGUAR
1638 W Burnside St, Portland, OR 97209-2106
Tel.: (503) 224-3232
Web Site: http://www.monteshelton.com
Sales Range: $25-49.9 Million
Emp.: 33
Car Whslr
N.A.I.C.S.: 441110
Monte Shelton *(CEO)*

MONTE VISTA CO-OP ASSOCIATION, INC.
1901 US Hwy 160 E, Monte Vista, CO 81144-9344
Tel.: (719) 852-5181
Web Site: http://www.mvcoop.com
Year Founded: 1949
Sales Range: $25-49.9 Million
Emp.: 100
Retailer & Distributor of Fertilizer & Fertilizer Materials; Operator of Gasoline Filling Stations; Manufacturer of Agricultural Machinery & Equipment
N.A.I.C.S.: 424910
Mike Boothe *(Dir-Fin)*
Alvin Kunugi *(Sec)*
Matt Seger *(Pres)*

MONTEBELLO BRANDS INC.
1919 Willow Spring Rd, Baltimore, MD 21222-2939
Tel.: (410) 282-8800
Year Founded: 1933
Sales Range: $10-24.9 Million
Emp.: 20
Mfr of Spirits
N.A.I.C.S.: 312140
Leo Conte *(Pres & CEO)*
Nancy Hogan *(Office Mgr)*

MONTECITO BANCORP
1010 State St, Santa Barbara, CA 93101
Tel.: (805) 963-7511
Web Site: http://www.montecito.bank
Year Founded: 1982
Sales Range: $25-49.9 Million
Emp.: 185
State Commercial Banks
N.A.I.C.S.: 522110
Michael Towbes *(Chm)*
Scott Estby *(VP & Portfolio Mgr)*
Carolyn Tulloh *(Dir-Mktg)*

Subsidiaries:

Montecito Bank & Trust (1)
1000 State St, Santa Barbara, CA 93101
Tel.: (805) 963-7511
Web Site: http://www.montbank.com
Sales Range: $50-74.9 Million
Emp.: 150
State Commercial Banks
N.A.I.C.S.: 522110
Janet Garufis *(Chm & CEO)*
Jeff Pittman *(Sr VP & Dir-Wealth)*
Suzi Schomer *(VP-Wealth Mgmt)*
Drew Brahos *(VP & Sr Portfolio Mgr-Wealth Mgmt)*
Peter Madlem *(Chief Investment Officer & Sr VP)*
Justin Mendoza *(VP & Mgr-Goleta)*
John Braunschweiger *(VP & Mgr-Relationship-Community Lending)*
Stephen Mihalic *(Sr VP & Dir-Community Lending)*
George Leis *(Pres & COO)*
Michele Shipp *(VP)*

MONTECITO RETIREMENT ASSOCIATION
300 Hot Springs Rd, Montecito, CA 93108
Tel.: (805) 969-8011

MONTECITO RETIREMENT ASSOCIATION

Montecito Retirement Association—Continued

Web Site: http://www.casadorinda.org
Year Founded: 1970
Sales Range: $10-24.9 Million
Emp.: 315
Elder Care Services
N.A.I.C.S.: 623312
Carol Whitehurst (Dir-Nursing)

MONTEFIORE MEDICAL CENTER
111 E 210 St, Bronx, NY 10467-2662
Tel.: (718) 920-4321 NY
Web Site: http://www.montefiore.org
Year Founded: 1884
Non-Profit Hospital Administration Organization
N.A.I.C.S.: 813910
Steven M. Safyer (Pres & CEO)
Philip O. Ozuah (Pres & CEO)
Susan Green-Lorenzen (Sr VP-Ops)
Philip O. Ozuah (Pres)
Andrew Racine (Chief Medical Officer & Sr VP-Sys)
Christopher S. Panczner (Gen Counsel & Sr VP)
Richard T. Celiberti (Sr VP-Network Dev)
Alfredo Cabrera (Chief HR Officer & Sr VP-Sys)
Oded Aboodi (Vice Chm & Treas)
Colleen M. Blye (CFO & Exec VP)
Edward Pfleging (Sr VP-Facilities & Real Estate)
Lynn Richmond (Chief Strategy Officer & Exec VP)
Stephen Rosenthal (Sr VP-Population Health Mgmt)

Subsidiaries:

St. Luke's Cornwall Hospital (1)
70 Dubois St, Newburgh, NY 12550
Tel.: (845) 561-4400
Web Site: http://www.montefiore.org
Health Care Srvices
N.A.I.C.S.: 622110

MONTEREY BAY AQUARIUM FOUNDATION
886 Cannery Row, Monterey, CA 93940
Tel.: (831) 648-4800 CA
Web Site: http://www.mbayaq.org
Year Founded: 1978
Sales Range: $50-74.9 Million
Emp.: 604
Aquarium
N.A.I.C.S.: 712130
Jim Hekkers (Mng Dir)
Don Hughes (VP-Exhibitions)
Brendan P. Kelly (Dir-Conservation Res)
Teresa Merry (VP-HR)
Michael J. Murray (Dir-Veterinary Svcs)
Aimee David (Dir-Ocean Conservation Policy & Initiatives)
Wendy Norden (Dir-Seafood Watch Science)
Andrew Johnson (Mgr-Sea Otter Research & Conservation)
Shawn Cronin (Mgr-Seafood Watch Business Program)

MONTEREY BAY BEVERAGE, INC.
14535 Benefit St Unit 4, Sherman Oaks, CA 91403-3741
Tel.: (818) 784-4885
Sales Range: $50-74.9 Million
Emp.: 60
Fruit & Vegetable Canning Services
N.A.I.C.S.: 311421
Mark Fields (CEO)

MONTEREY FISH COMPANY INC.
960 S Sanborn Rd, Salinas, CA 93901-4530
Tel.: (831) 775-0522 CA
Web Site: http://www.montereyfishcompany.com
Year Founded: 1938
Sales Range: $10-24.9 Million
Emp.: 30
Packer & Importer of Canned & Cured Fish & Seafoods
N.A.I.C.S.: 311710
Sal Tringali (Pres)

MONTEREY INC.
1725 E Delavan Dr, Janesville, WI 53546
Tel.: (608) 754-2866 WI
Web Site: http://www.montereymills.com
Year Founded: 1966
Sales Range: $25-49.9 Million
Emp.: 200
Broadwoven Fabric Mills
N.A.I.C.S.: 313210
John Janke (Dir-Fin & Acctg)
Dan Sinykin (Pres & CEO)
Daniel Yung (Chief Mktg Officer & VP-Sls)

MONTEREY MECHANICAL COMPANY
8275 San Leandro St, Oakland, CA 94621-1901
Tel.: (510) 632-3173 CA
Web Site: http://www.montmech.com
Year Founded: 1942
Sales Range: $125-149.9 Million
Emp.: 250
Provider of Contracting & Metal Fabrication Services
N.A.I.C.S.: 236210
Richard F. Hamilton (Chm & CEO)
Milt Burleson (Pres)
Jim Troupe (VP-Gen Engrg)
Paul Moreira (CFO)

MONTEREY MUSHROOMS, INC.
260 Westgate Dr, Watsonville, CA 95076
Tel.: (831) 763-5300 CA
Web Site: http://www.montmush.com
Year Founded: 1971
Sales Range: $350-399.9 Million
Emp.: 4,000
Marketing, Growing & Processing of Mushrooms
N.A.I.C.S.: 111411
Mike Stephan (Dir-Sls-Eastern)

Subsidiaries:

Amycel, Inc. (1)
553 Mission Vineyard Rd, San Juan Bautista, CA 95045-1360 (100%)
Tel.: (831) 623-7400
Web Site: http://www.amycel.com
Sales Range: $10-24.9 Million
Emp.: 35
Production & Mushroom Spawn Sale Distr
N.A.I.C.S.: 311421

MONTEREY PENINSULA COUNTRY CLUB
3000 Club Rd, Pebble Beach, CA 93953
Tel.: (831) 373-1556 CA
Web Site: http://www.mpccpb.org
Year Founded: 1925
Sales Range: $10-24.9 Million
Emp.: 220
Country Club
N.A.I.C.S.: 713910

Susan Fain (Dir-HR)
Richard Busman (Controller)
Brian Hein (Mgr-Clubhouse)
Rachel Carter (Dir-Member Svc)
Michael Bowhay (Gen Mgr)
Frank C. Amato (VP)
Bob Perry-Smith (Pres)

MONTEREY PLAZA HOTEL
400 Cannery Row, Monterey, CA 93940
Tel.: (831) 646-1700
Web Site: http://www.montereyplazahotel.com
Year Founded: 1993
Sales Range: $10-24.9 Million
Emp.: 360
Hotel & Motel Operating Services
N.A.I.C.S.: 721110
John V. Narigi (VP & Gen Mgr)

MONTEREY REGIONAL WATER POLLUTION CONTROL
5 Harris CT Bldg D, Monterey, CA 93940
Tel.: (831) 372-3367
Web Site: http://www.mrwpca.org
Sales Range: $10-24.9 Million
Emp.: 80
Sewerage Systems
N.A.I.C.S.: 221320
Bret Boatman (Supvr-Maintenance)
Brad Hagemann (Asst Gen Mgr)
Paul Sciuto (Gen Mgr)

MONTEREY-SALINAS TRANSIT
19 Upper Ragsdale Dr Ste 200, Monterey, CA 93940
Tel.: (831) 899-2558
Web Site: http://www.mst.org
Sales Range: $10-24.9 Million
Emp.: 240
Bus Line Operations
N.A.I.C.S.: 485113
Carl Sedoryk (Gen Mgr)
Kelly Halcon (Dir-HR)
Sandra Amorim (Mgr-Pur)

MONTESI MOTORS, INC.
444 State St, North Haven, CT 06473
Tel.: (203) 281-0481
Web Site: http://www.montesivolkswagen.com
Year Founded: 1964
Sales Range: $10-24.9 Million
Emp.: 45
Car Dealer
N.A.I.C.S.: 441110

MONTESQUIEU
8221 Arjons Dr Ste F, San Diego, CA 92126
Tel.: (877) 705-5669
Web Site: http://www.montesquieu.com
Year Founded: 1991
Sales Range: $10-24.9 Million
Emp.: 10
Full Service Wine Group
N.A.I.C.S.: 424820
Tom Peters (Mgr-Wine Pur)
Cathrow Zishka (Mgr-Sls)

MONTGOMERY BANCORPORATION INC.
1 Montgomery Bank Plz, Sikeston, MO 63801
Tel.: (573) 471-2275
Web Site: http://www.montgomerybank.com
Sales Range: $10-24.9 Million
Emp.: 240
State Commercial Banks
N.A.I.C.S.: 522110

Bryan Harper (VP-Risk)
Ken Witbrodt (CEO)

Subsidiaries:

Montgomery Bank (1)
1 Montgomery Bank Plz, Sikeston, MO 63801
Tel.: (573) 471-2275
Web Site: http://www.montgomerybank.com
Sales Range: $50-74.9 Million
Emp.: 105
National Commercial Banks
N.A.I.C.S.: 522110

MONTGOMERY BAPTIST OUTREACH SERVICES CORPORATION
PO Box 244030, Montgomery, AL 36124-4030
Tel.: (334) 273-4258 AL
Year Founded: 1981
Sales Range: $10-24.9 Million
Healthcare Services
N.A.I.C.S.: 622110
W. Russell Tyner (Pres & CEO)
Robin Barca (Chm)
Katrina Belt (Treas)
Julia S. Ventress-Henig (Vice Chm)
B. Blaine Brown III (Sec)

MONTGOMERY CHEVROLET
5325 Preston Hwy, Louisville, KY 40213-2772
Tel.: (502) 968-6111
Web Site: http://www.montgomery-chevrolet.com
Rev.: $60,000,000
Emp.: 100
New & Used Automobiles; Automobile Service Department & Body Shop
N.A.I.C.S.: 441110

Subsidiaries:

JHS Corporation (1)
1501 N Dixie Hwy, Elizabethtown, KY 42701
Tel.: (270) 737-0005
Web Site: http://www.montgomeryimports.com
Sales Range: $300-349.9 Million
Emp.: 50
Automobiles, New & Used
N.A.I.C.S.: 441110
Rodney Chancey (Gen Mgr-Montgomery Chevrolet)

MONTGOMERY COALITION FOR ADULT ENGLISH LITERACY
12320 Parklawn Dr, Rockville, MD 20852
Tel.: (301) 881-1338 MD
Web Site: http://www.mcael.org
Year Founded: 2006
Rev.: $1,004,698
Assets: $146,865
Liabilities: $10,090
Net Worth: $136,775
Earnings: $20,643
Emp.: 3
Fiscal Year-end: 06/30/14
Literary Support Services
N.A.I.C.S.: 611691
Charlotte Van Londen (Mgr-ESOL Program & Instructional)
Kathy Stevens (Exec Dir)
Martin Yescas (Treas)

MONTGOMERY COUNTY EMERGENCY SERVICE, INC.
50 Beech Dr, Norristown, PA 19403-5421
Tel.: (610) 279-6100 PA
Web Site: http://www.mces.org
Year Founded: 1974
Sales Range: $10-24.9 Million
Emp.: 305
Behavioral Healthcare Services
N.A.I.C.S.: 621420

William Myers (CEO)
Debbie Shanley (Dir-Medical Records)
Anthony Salvatore (Dir-Dev)
Naomi Finkel (Mgr-Nurse)

MONTGOMERY GENERAL HOSPITAL, INC.
401 6th Ave, Montgomery, WV 25136
Tel.: (304) 442-5151   WV
Web Site: http://www.mghwv.com
Year Founded: 1970
Sales Range: $25-49.9 Million
Emp.: 290
Health Care Srvices
N.A.I.C.S.: 622110
Robin McDaniel (Chief Nursing Officer)
Sherri Murray (CFO)
Denzil Blevins (CIO)
Vickie Gay (Pres & CEO)

MONTGOMERY HOSPICE, INC.
1355 Piccard Dr Ste 100, Rockville, MD 20850
Tel.: (301) 921-4400   MD
Web Site: http://www.montgomeryhospice.org
Year Founded: 1979
Sales Range: $10-24.9 Million
Emp.: 290
Hospice Care Services
N.A.I.C.S.: 621610
Monica Escalante (CFO & VP-Community Education & Outreach)
Ann Mitchell (Pres & CEO)
Marlene Bradford (VP-Philanthropy)
Aziza Owusu (VP-HR)

MONTGOMERY MANUFACTURING CO.
118 Industrial Dr, Kennedale, TX 76060
Tel.: (817) 478-3221   TX
Web Site: http://www.montgomerymfg.com
Year Founded: 1980
Chemical Blending Services
N.A.I.C.S.: 325199
Peter Zehr (Pres)

Subsidiaries:

Carroll Company   (1)
2900 W Kingsley Rd, Garland, TX 75041
Tel.: (972) 278-1304
Web Site: http://www.carrollco.com
Industrial Cleaners & Maintenance Products Mfr
N.A.I.C.S.: 325612
Peter Zehr (CEO)
Troy Kloewer (Pres-Sls & Mktg)
Tony Casmus (Dir-Technical-R&D-Regulatory)
Sharnett Robinson (VP-Plng)
Mark Stephens (Dir-Quality Assurance)
Edward McGuire (VP-IT)

Division (Domestic):

Carroll Company - cleanworks Division   (2)
2900 W Kingsley Rd, Garland, TX 75041
Tel.: (800) 527-5722
Industrial Cleaners & Maintenance Products Mfr
N.A.I.C.S.: 325612

Subsidiary (Domestic):

Cello Professional Products   (2)
1354 Post Rd, Havre De Grace, MD 21078
Tel.: (410) 939-1234
Web Site: http://www.cello-online.com
Industrial Cleaning Products Mfr
N.A.I.C.S.: 325612

MONTGOMERY MARTIN CONTRACTORS, LLC
8245 Tournament Dr Ste 300, Memphis, TN 38125-8874
Tel.: (901) 374-9400   TN
Web Site: http://www.montgomerymartin.com
Year Founded: 1995
Sales Range: $50-74.9 Million
Emp.: 175
Nonresidential Construction
N.A.I.C.S.: 236220
H. Montgomery Martin (Founder & CEO)
Richard T. Meena (VP)
Joel M. Thomas (CFO & VP)
Randy Bratton (VP)
Jeffrey J. Emerson (VP)
Margaret Manifold (Coord-Comm)
April Hitzfeld (Coord-Construction Compliance)
R. J. Bass (Superintendent)

MONTGOMERY MARTIN CONTRACTORS, LLC.
8245 Tournament Dr Ste 300, Memphis, TN 38125-8874
Tel.: (901) 374-9400
Web Site: http://www.montgomerymartin.com
Year Founded: 1995
Sales Range: $25-49.9 Million
Emp.: 175
Civil Engineering Services
N.A.I.C.S.: 237310
H. Montgomery Martin (Owner & CEO)
Joel M. Thomas (Co-Owner)

MONTGOMERY PLACE RETIREMENT COMMUNITY
5550 S Shore Dr, Chicago, IL 60637
Tel.: (773) 753-4102   IL
Web Site: http://www.montgomeryplace.org
Year Founded: 1987
Sales Range: $10-24.9 Million
Emp.: 312
Continuing Care Retirement Community Operator
N.A.I.C.S.: 623311
Beverly Covington (Dir-Nursing)
Debra Hart (CEO)
Art Carr (CFO)

MONTGOMERY TRUSS AND PANEL
803 W Main St, Grove City, PA 16127
Tel.: (724) 458-7500
Web Site: http://www.montgomerytruss.com
Rev.: $10,200,000
Emp.: 125
Structural Wood Members
N.A.I.C.S.: 321215
Charles B. Montgomery Jr. (Pres)

MONTGOMERY WATER WORKS & SANITARY SEWER BOARD
22 Bibb St, Montgomery, AL 36104-2503
Tel.: (334) 206-1600
Web Site: http://www.mwwssb.com
Rev.: $70,300,000
Emp.: 280
Water Supply & Irrigation Systems
N.A.I.C.S.: 221310
Thomas R. Morgan (Gen Mgr)
Keith Yarbrough (Dir-Water Production)
Mindy Porter (Asst Comptroller-Utility)
Charlene Wachs (Asst Gen Mgr)
Pete McCord (Supvr-Maintenance)
Steve Rodopoulos (Mgr-Lab)
William R. Henderson (Asst Gen Mgr-Engrg & Ops)

MONTI INCORPORATED
333 W Seymour Ave, Cincinnati, OH 45216
Tel.: (513) 761-7775
Web Site: http://www.monti-inc.com
Rev.: $14,624,630
Emp.: 90
Insulators & Insulation Materials, Electrical
N.A.I.C.S.: 335932
Gavin J. Narburgh (Pres)
Andy Franklin (Engr-Mfg)
Linda Corwin (Controller-HR)
Stephen Hess (Acct Mgr)

MONTICELLO MANAGEMENT CO.
2505 Congress St Ste 220, San Diego, CA 92110-2847
Tel.: (619) 298-9877   CA
Year Founded: 1984
Sales Range: $75-99.9 Million
Emp.: 100
Provider of Contracting Services
N.A.I.C.S.: 531210
Tawfig N. Khoury (Founder & Pres)

MONTICELLO SPRING CORPORATION
3137 S Freeman Rd, Monticello, IN 47960
Tel.: (574) 583-8090
Web Site: http://www.monticellospring.com
Sales Range: $10-24.9 Million
Emp.: 150
Mfr of Wire Springs
N.A.I.C.S.: 332613
Thomas H. Pimmler (Pres & CEO)
Paul Wing (Mgr-Production & R&D)

MONTREUX GOLF CLUB LIMITED
18077 Bordeaux Dr, Reno, NV 89511
Tel.: (775) 849-1090
Web Site: http://www.montreuxgolf.com
Sales Range: $10-24.9 Million
Emp.: 100
Subdividers & Developers
N.A.I.C.S.: 237210
Stan Jaksick (Pres)
Doug Heinrichs (Superintendent-Golf Course)

MONTROSE ENVIRONMENTAL CORP.
1631 E St Andrew Pl, Santa Ana, CA 92705
Tel.: (714) 282-8240   CA
Web Site: http://www.scec.com
Year Founded: 1989
Sales Range: $1-9.9 Million
Emp.: 18
Professional, Scientific & Technical Services
N.A.I.C.S.: 541990
Leslie Johnson (Pres)

Subsidiaries:

Enthalpy Analytical, Inc.   (1)
2202 Ellis Rd, Durham, NC 27703
Tel.: (919) 850-4392
Web Site: http://www.enthalpy.com
Rev.: $5,515,000
Emp.: 47
Testing Laboratories
N.A.I.C.S.: 541380
Steven J. Eckard (Pres)
Bryan Tyler (Mgr-Sls)

Subsidiary (Domestic):

Frontier Analytical Laboratory   (2)
5172 Hillsdale Cir, El Dorado Hills, CA 95762
Tel.: (916) 934-0900
Web Site: http://www.frontieranalytical.com
Analytical Laboratory Instrument Mfr

N.A.I.C.S.: 334516
Tom Crabtree (Dir-Mass Spectrometry)
Bradley Silverbush (VP & Dir-Laboratory)

MONTROSE FORD LINCOLN
100 Merchant Dr, Montrose, CO 81401
Tel.: (970) 249-4576
Web Site: http://www.montroseford.com
Sales Range: $10-24.9 Million
Emp.: 40
New Car Retailer
N.A.I.C.S.: 441110
Thomas Abbott (Pres)
Jack Weyers (Dir-Svcs & Parts)
Nick Klahrs (Mgr-Sls)
Tim Bergman (Mgr-Sls)

MONTROSE MEMORIAL HOSPITAL
800 S 3rd St, Montrose, CO 81401
Tel.: (970) 249-2211   CO
Web Site: http://www.montrosehospital.com
Year Founded: 2010
Sales Range: $75-99.9 Million
Emp.: 679
Health Care Srvices
N.A.I.C.S.: 621610
Joan Napolilli (Chief Nursing Officer)
Joyce Beck (COO)
Al White (CFO)
Julie Disher (Dir-Medical Staff Svcs)
Leann Tobin (Dir-Community Engagement)
Louis H. Winkler (Treas & Sec)
Rob Ruyle (Vice Chm)
Ron Courtney (Chm)
Kathy McKie (Dir-HR)
James Kiser (CEO)

MONTY MEX CORP.
4130 Wall St, Montgomery, AL 36106
Tel.: (334) 244-7770
Web Site: http://www.tacobell.com
Sales Range: $10-24.9 Million
Emp.: 340
Fast-Food Restaurant, Chain
N.A.I.C.S.: 722513
Phillip Festoso (Pres)
Fred Abrahamson (VP)

MONUMENT & CATHEDRAL HOLDINGS, LLC
14 W Mount Vernon Pl, Baltimore, MD 21201
Tel.: (410) 230-1263   MD
Web Site: http://www.agora-inc.com
Year Founded: 1978
Holding Company; Newsletter Publishing
N.A.I.C.S.: 551112
William Bonner (Pres)

MONUMENT OIL COMPANY
560 Colorado Ave, Grand Junction, CO 81501
Tel.: (970) 245-3440
Rev.: $15,000,000
Emp.: 20
Diesel Fuel
N.A.I.C.S.: 424720
Cullen R. Brown (Pres)

MONUMENTAL SUPPLY CO. INC.
401 S Haven St, Baltimore, MD 21224
Tel.: (410) 732-9300
Web Site: http://www.monumentalsupply.com
Rev.: $14,843,017
Emp.: 60
Valves & Fittings
N.A.I.C.S.: 423830

MONUMENTAL SUPPLY CO. INC.   U.S. PRIVATE

Monumental Supply Co. Inc.—(Continued)
David Coarts *(Controller)*
Susan Kirchner *(Pres & CEO)*

MONUMETRIC, LLC
42 N 650 W, Farmington, UT 84025
Web Site:
http://www.monumetric.com
Year Founded: 2013
Sales Range: $10-24.9 Million
Emp.: 36
Advertising Agency Services
N.A.I.C.S.: 541810
Nathan Putnam *(CEO)*

MOO & OINK INC.
7158 S Stony Ist Ave, Chicago, IL 60649
Tel.: (773) 493-7100
Web Site: http://www.moo-oink.com
Sales Range: $10-24.9 Million
Emp.: 150
Meat & Fish Markets
N.A.I.C.S.: 445240
Catherine Taylor *(VP)*

MOODY BANCSHARES, INC.
2302 Post Office, Galveston, TX 77550
Tel.: (409) 765-5561   TX
Web Site:
http://www.moodybank.com
Sales Range: $25-49.9 Million
Emp.: 270
Bank Holding Company
N.A.I.C.S.: 551111
Robert Lee Moody Sr. *(Pres)*
Victor Pierson *(Pres)*
Craig Barker *(Chief Risk Officer & Exec VP)*
Katherine Rodriguez *(CFO & Exec VP)*
Mark Wilson *(Chief Credit Officer & Exec VP)*
Michael Christiansen *(Chief Admin Officer & Exec VP)*
Michael Wisner *(Chief Lending Officer & Exec VP)*

Subsidiaries:

Moody National Bank   (1)
2302 Post Office St, Galveston, TX 77550   (100%)
Tel.: (409) 765-5561
Web Site: http://www.moodybank.com
Sales Range: $25-49.9 Million
Commercial Banking & Treasury Management Services
N.A.I.C.S.: 522110
Victor R. Pierson *(Pres)*
Craig Barker *(Exec VP & Chief Credit Officer)*
Michael Wisner *(Exec VP & Chief Lending Officer)*
Richard Cardner *(Exec VP & Chief Trust Officer)*
Michael Christiansen *(Chief Admin Officer & Exec VP-Branch Admin/Ops)*
Owen Cheney *(CIO & Exec VP)*
Dan Walsh *(Chief Lending Officer & Exec VP)*
Josh Hernandez *(Sr VP-HR)*
Bradley Gregory *(Chief Risk Officer & Exec VP)*
Mike Cooper *(Exec VP-Comml Lending)*
Jeff Hutchens *(Exec VP-Comml Lending)*
Katherine Rodriguez *(CFO & Exec VP)*
Ken Wesson *(Exec VP-Comml Lending)*
Mark Wilson *(Chief Credit Officer & Exec VP)*

MOODY BIBLE INSTITUTE
820 N La Salle Blvd, Chicago, IL 60610-3214
Tel.: (312) 329-4000
Web Site: http://www.moody.edu
Year Founded: 1886
Sales Range: $150-199.9 Million
Emp.: 650

Bible Centered Education; Publishers of Books; Educational & Religious Broadcasting
N.A.I.C.S.: 813110
Kenneth D. Heulitt *(CFO)*
Janet A. Stiven *(Gen Counsel & VP)*
Larry J. Davidhizar *(VP)*
John Jelinek *(VP)*
Bruce Everhart *(VP-Donor Dev & Channel Strategy)*
Debbie Zelinski *(VP-HR)*
Paul Santhouse *(VP-Moody Publishers)*
James G. Elliott *(VP-Stewardship)*
Randy Fairfax *(Chm)*
Mark Jobe *(Pres)*
Richard E. Warren *(Vice Chm)*
T. Randall Fairfax *(Chm)*

Subsidiaries:

Moody Publishers   (1)
820 N La Salle Blvd, Chicago, IL 60610-3214
Tel.: (312) 329-2101
Web Site: http://www.moodypublishers.com
Sales Range: $10-24.9 Million
Emp.: 75
Publisher of Books & Bibles
N.A.I.C.S.: 561110
Greg Thornton *(VP-Publ)*
Duane Koenig *(Bus Mgr)*
Elizabeth Newenhuyse *(Dir-Editorial)*
Zack Williamson *(Mgr-Audience Dev)*

MOODY DUNBAR INC.
2000 Waters Edge Dr, Johnson City, TN 37604
Tel.: (423) 952-0100   TN
Web Site:
http://www.moodydunbar.com
Year Founded: 1933
Sales Range: $25-49.9 Million
Emp.: 200
Canned Fruits & Specialties
N.A.I.C.S.: 311421
Stanley K. Dunbar *(CEO)*
Dawn Young *(Controller)*
Terri Sams *(Dir-Sls Svcs)*

Subsidiaries:

Moody Dunbar Foods Corporation   (1)
1000 S Fayetteville Ave, Dunn, NC 28334-6213
Tel.: (910) 892-3175
Web Site: http://www.moodydunbar.com
Rev.: $6,300,000
Emp.: 150
Canned Fruits & Specialties
N.A.I.C.S.: 311421
Ron Austin *(Gen Mgr)*

Saticoy Foods Corporation   (1)
554 S Todd Rd, Santa Paula, CA 93060-9725
Tel.: (423) 952-0100
Sales Range: $10-24.9 Million
Emp.: 38
Canned Fruits & Specialties
N.A.I.C.S.: 311421

MOODY NATIONAL REIT I, INC.
6363 Woodway Dr Ste 110, Houston, TX 77057
Tel.: (713) 977-7500   MD
Web Site:
http://www.moodynationalreit.com
Year Founded: 2008
Rev.: $61,930,033
Assets: $267,249,966
Liabilities: $176,674,041
Net Worth: $90,575,925
Earnings: ($4,173,551)
Fiscal Year-end: 12/31/16
Real Estate Investment Trust
N.A.I.C.S.: 525990
Robert W. Engel *(Chief Fin & Acctg Officer & Treas)*

MOODY NATIONAL REIT II, INC.
9655 Katy Fwy Ste 600, Houston, TX 77024
Tel.: (713) 977-7500   MD
Web Site:
https://www.moodynationalreit.com
Year Founded: 2014
Rev.: $82,368,000
Assets: $415,858,000
Liabilities: $301,452,000
Net Worth: $114,406,000
Earnings: ($20,437,000)
Emp.: 5
Fiscal Year-end: 12/31/23
Real Estate Investment Trust
N.A.I.C.S.: 525990
Brett C. Moody *(Chm, Pres & CEO)*
Robert W. Engel *(CFO & Treas)*

MOODY'S JEWELRY INC.
1137 S Harvard Ave, Tulsa, OK 74112
Tel.: (918) 834-3371
Web Site:
http://www.moodysjewelry.com
Rev.: $14,000,000
Emp.: 90
Jewelry Stores
N.A.I.C.S.: 458310
Craig Ehrman *(Dir-Mktg & Adv)*
Ernest L. Moody III *(Pres)*

MOODY'S MARKET INC.
50389 US Hwy 93, Polson, MT 59860
Tel.: (406) 883-1500
Rev.: $34,152,988
Emp.: 6
Grocery Stores, Independent
N.A.I.C.S.: 445110
Greg Hertz *(Pres)*

MOODY-PRICE INC.
18320 Petroleum Dr, Baton Rouge, LA 70809-6123
Tel.: (225) 767-7755
Web Site:
http://www.moodyprice.com
Rev.: $36,000,000
Emp.: 100
Industrial Machinery & Equipment
N.A.I.C.S.: 423830
Blake Aucoin *(VP)*
Kenny LeBleu *(Sr VP-Sls)*
Danny Daniel Jr. *(Pres & COO)*

MOODY.NOLAN, INC
300 Spruce St Ste 300, Columbus, OH 43215
Tel.: (614) 461-4664
Web Site:
http://www.moodynolan.com
Year Founded: 1982
Rev.: $31,300,000
Emp.: 162
Architectural Engineering Services
N.A.I.C.S.: 541310
Robert K. Larrimer *(Partner & Exec Dir-Architecture)*
Curtis J. Moody *(Pres & CEO)*
Paul F. Pryor *(Partner & Dir-Construction Admin)*
David King *(CFO)*
Allen Schaffer *(Dir-Sustainable Design)*
Yanitza Brongers-Marrero *(Dir-Housing Studio)*
Daniel Pickett *(Partner & Dir-Southwest Ops)*
D. Brent Wilcox *(Dir-Healthcare Architecture)*
Todd B. Dove *(Dir-Retail Studio)*
Eileen M. Goodman *(Partner & Dir-Construction & Admin)*
Renauld D. Mitchell *(Partner & Dir-Ops-Nashville)*

Elizabeth A. Thompson *(Partner & Dir-Ops-Nashville)*
Brian Tibbs *(Partner)*
Jonathan Moody *(CEO)*

MOOERS MOTOR CAR COMPANY INC.
7211 W Broad St, Richmond, VA 23294
Tel.: (804) 755-6666
Web Site:
http://www.mooersvolvo.com
Year Founded: 1924
Rev.: $26,600,000
Emp.: 98
Car Dealership Owner & Operator
N.A.I.C.S.: 441110
Kirby Fields *(Gen Mgr-Sls)*
Mike Lawrence *(Mgr-Pre-Owned)*
Wayne Edgerton *(Mgr-Sls)*
Mark Rogers *(Dir-Svcs)*
Ron Ferguson *(Pres)*

MOOG LOUISVILLE WAREHOUSE INC.
1421 Magazine St, Louisville, KY 40203
Tel.: (502) 583-7795
Web Site: http://www.mlwky.com
Sales Range: $25-49.9 Million
Emp.: 200
Automotive Supplies & Parts
N.A.I.C.S.: 423120
Douglas Washbish *(Pres)*

MOON DISTRIBUTORS, INC.
2800 Vance St, Little Rock, AR 72206-3338
Tel.: (501) 375-8291   AR
Web Site: http://www.moondist.com
Year Founded: 1932
Sales Range: $25-49.9 Million
Emp.: 120
Wine & Distilled Beverages Distr
N.A.I.C.S.: 424820
Harry L. Hastings Jr. *(Chm)*
Stanley Hastings *(CEO)*
Mickey Nottingham *(Pres-Central)*

Subsidiaries:

Central Distributors Inc.   (1)
2805 Vance St, Little Rock, AR 72206-3316
Tel.: (501) 372-3158
Rev.: $6,900,000
Emp.: 35
Wine & Distilled Beverages
N.A.I.C.S.: 424820

MOON LAKE ELECTRIC ASSOCIATION INC.
800 W Highway 40, Roosevelt, UT 84066
Tel.: (435) 722-5400
Web Site: http://www.mleainc.com
Year Founded: 1938
Sales Range: $25-49.9 Million
Emp.: 81
Distribution, Electric Power
N.A.I.C.S.: 221122
Grant J. Earl *(CEO & Gen Mgr)*
Yankton Johnson *(Mgr-Personnel & Member Rels)*

MOON MANAGEMENT, INC.
1105 E Lafayette St, Tallahassee, FL 32301
Tel.: (850) 878-6900   FL
Web Site: http://moonevents.com
Year Founded: 1987
Sales Range: $1-9.9 Million
Emp.: 50
Drinking Places (Alcoholic Beverages)
N.A.I.C.S.: 722410
Scott Carswell *(Owner & Gen Mgr)*

MOON VALLEY NURSERY, INC.
19820 N 7th St Ste 260, Phoenix, AZ 85024-1696
Tel.: (480) 778-0611
Web Site:
   http://www.moonvalleynursery.com
Year Founded: 1995
Sales Range: $10-24.9 Million
Emp.: 200
Retail Nurseries
N.A.I.C.S.: 444240
John Marshall (VP-Fin & Admin)
Brian Flood (Mgr-Wholesale)
Tom Berryhill (Mgr-Internet)

MOONBEAM CAPITAL INVESTMENTS, LLC
9103 Alta Dr Ste 204, Las Vegas, NV 89145
Tel.: (702) 968-2474
Web Site:
   http://www.moonbeamci.com
Sales Range: $75-99.9 Million
Emp.: 20
Real Estate Investment, Management & Leasing Services
N.A.I.C.S.: 523999
Steven V. Maksin (Founder & CEO)
Natalie C. Maksin (Chief Legal Officer & Exec VP)
Shawl Pryor (Sr VP)
Anna Khavulya (Dir-Mktg & Specialty Leasing)
Gennady Ratin (CFO)

MOONBLINK COMMUNICATIONS
1211 Alderwood Ave, Sunnyvale, CA 94089
Tel.: (408) 580-1143
Web Site: http://www.moonblink.com
Year Founded: 2004
Sales Range: $1-9.9 Million
Emp.: 12
Wireless & Video Surveillance
N.A.I.C.S.: 334310
Daniel Redmond (Co-Founder)
Kevin Sitzes (Co-Founder)
Sean Nolan (Mgr-Inside Partner Dev)
Jarrod Washington (Mgr-Partner Dev-Northeast United States & Eastern Canada)
Dude Decker (Mgr-Ops)

MOONEY AEROSPACE GROUP, LTD.
1165 Al Mooney Rd N, Kerrville, TX 78028
Tel.: (830) 896-6000
Web Site: http://www.mooney.com
Year Founded: 1990
Sales Range: $25-49.9 Million
Emp.: 400
Holding Company
N.A.I.C.S.: 551112
Richard A. Kravit (Gen Counsel & Dir-Contracts)

Subsidiaries:

Mooney Airplane Company, Inc. (1)
165 Al Mooney Rd N, Kerrville, TX 78028
Tel.: (830) 896-6000
Web Site: http://www.mooney.com
Sales Range: $25-49.9 Million
Emp.: 300
4-Place Single Engine High Performance Aircraft & Parts Mfr
N.A.I.C.S.: 336411
Steven E. Karol (Chm)

MOONLIGHT BPO
2491 NE Twin Knolls Dr Ste 102, Bend, OR 97701
Tel.: (541) 382-8402
Web Site:
   http://www.moonlightbpo.com
Sales Range: $1-9.9 Million
Emp.: 15
Consulting Services
N.A.I.C.S.: 541618
Brenda Grigsby (Pres)

MOONLIGHT PACKING CORPORATION
17719 E Huntsman Ave, Reedley, CA 93654
Tel.: (559) 638-7799
Web Site:
   http://www.moonlightcompany.com
Year Founded: 1918
Rev.: $83,600,000
Emp.: 185
Frozen Vegetables & Fruit Products
N.A.I.C.S.: 424420
Ty Tavlan (Controller)

Subsidiaries:

Royal Moonlight Corporation (1)
PO Box 846, Reedley, CA 93654
Tel.: (559) 637-7799
Web Site:
   http://www.moonlightcompanies.com
Sales Range: $10-24.9 Million
Emp.: 13
Frozen Vegetables & Fruit Products
N.A.I.C.S.: 115114
Russ Tavlan (Pres)

MOONWORKS, INC.
1137 Park E Dr, Woonsocket, RI 02895
Web Site:
   http://www.moonworkshome.com
Sales Range: $10-24.9 Million
Emp.: 60
Home Products Distr & Service
N.A.I.C.S.: 444110
Jim Moon (Founder & Pres)

MOORADIANS INC.
800 Central Ave, Albany, NY 12206-1602
Tel.: (518) 489-2529
Web Site:
   http://www.mooradians.com
Rev.: $11,238,668
Emp.: 14
Furniture Retailer
N.A.I.C.S.: 449110
Bill Fluty (VP)
David Mooradian (Owner)

MOORE & SCARRY ADVERTISING, INC.
1521 Commerce Creek Blvd, Cape Coral, FL 33909
Tel.: (239) 689-4000
Web Site:
   http://www.ckadvertising.com
Year Founded: 2002
Sales Range: $75-99.9 Million
Emp.: 125
Advetising Agency
N.A.I.C.S.: 541810
Ed Kiesel (Dir-Creative)
Tom Kerr (Partner)
Jacquie Miller (Gen Mgr)
Kayla Judd (Acct Exec)
Karyn Cardona (Dir-Media)
Lucero Ruiz (Dir-Production)
Paul Caldwell (Partner)

MOORE & VAN ALLEN PLLC
100 N Tryon St Ste 4700, Charlotte, NC 28202-4003
Tel.: (704) 331-1000
Web Site: http://www.mvalaw.com
Year Founded: 1949
Sales Range: $150-199.9 Million
Emp.: 501
Legal Advisory Services
N.A.I.C.S.: 541110
Maggie Akers (Dir-Pub Affairs & Event Mgmt)
Steven Allison (Deputy Dir-Pub Affairs)
Matthew R. French (Dir-Pub Affairs Comm)
Katie Hallaway (Dir-Comm & Media Rels)
John D. Hofland (Dir-Pub Affairs)
Walter S. Price (Mng Dir & Co-Head-Pub Affairs)
Christopher A. Yountz (Dir-Creative)
Myrna Charlot (Mgr-Pro Recruiting)
Clinton M. Gandy (Project Mgr-Info Sys)
Hayley M. Hayes (Mgr-HR)
James Douglas Harper (Atty)
Jennifer E. Braccia (Atty)
Martha J. Efird (Atty)
Stephanie Gryder (Mgr-Diversity & Community Initiatives)
William L. Ferguson (Dir-Info Sys)
Lehlan M. Decker (Mgr-Network Svcs)
Tamara S. Acevedo (Mgr-Res & Knowledge Mgmt)
Andy Munn (Dir-State Pub Affairs)
Ashley Simmons (Dir-PR & Pub Affairs)

MOORE BROTHERS ASPHALT INC.
John S Moore Bldg 211 E Shepherd Ave Ste 101, Lufkin, TX 75901
Tel.: (936) 699-2960
Year Founded: 1993
Rev.: $30,000,000
Emp.: 150
Asphalt Paving Mixtures & Blocks
N.A.I.C.S.: 324121
Dale Moore (CEO & Treas)

Subsidiaries:

Fort Dodge Asphalt Co. (Inc.) (1)
2516 Seventh Ave S, Fort Dodge, IA 50501-5505 (100%)
Tel.: (515) 573-3124
Sales Range: $1-9.9 Million
Emp.: 5
Highway & Street Construction
N.A.I.C.S.: 237310

Jensen Builders Ltd. (Inc.) (1)
1175 S 32nd St, Fort Dodge, IA 50501-6430
Tel.: (515) 573-3292
Web Site: http://www.jensenbuildersltd.com
Sales Range: $10-24.9 Million
Emp.: 50
Nonresidential Construction Services
N.A.I.C.S.: 236220
Dale Jensen (Pres)

Moore Brothers Paving Inc. (1)
264 Williamsburg Cir, McDonough, GA 30253-6473
Tel.: (770) 506-9028
Rev.: $13,000,000
Emp.: 55
Highway & Street Construction
N.A.I.C.S.: 237310

MOORE BROTHERS CONSTRUCTION CO.
813 N Timberland Dr, Lufkin, TX 75902
Tel.: (936) 639-2261
Web Site: http://www.moorebro.com
Sales Range: $10-24.9 Million
Emp.: 35
General Contractor, Highway & Street Construction
N.A.I.C.S.: 237310

MOORE BUSINESS SERVICE INC.
1701 S Florida Ave, Lakeland, FL 33803
Tel.: (863) 688-4060   FL
Sales Range: $25-49.9 Million
Emp.: 4
Operators of Tax Agencies
N.A.I.C.S.: 541219

MOORE CADILLAC HUMMER OF DULLES, LLC.
25450 Pleasant Valley Rd, Chantilly, VA 20152
Tel.: (703) 674-5900
Web Site:
   http://www.moorecadillac.com
Year Founded: 1977
Sales Range: $25-49.9 Million
Emp.: 110
Car Whslr
N.A.I.C.S.: 441110
Michael Korelitz (Dir-Fixed Ops)
Jacques J. Moore (Owner)

MOORE CHRYSLER, INC.
1523 W 3rd Ave, Williamson, WV 25661
Tel.: (304) 235-8040
Web Site:
   http://www.moorechrysler.net
Sales Range: $10-24.9 Million
Emp.: 80
Car Whslr
N.A.I.C.S.: 441110
Angel Mick (Mgr)
Sharon May (Mgr-Ops)

MOORE COMMUNICATIONS GROUP
2011 Delta Blvd, Tallahassee, FL 32303
Tel.: (850) 224-0174
Web Site:
   http://www.moorecommgroup.com
Year Founded: 1992
Sales Range: $1-9.9 Million
Emp.: 30
Advertising Agency
N.A.I.C.S.: 541810
Karen B. Moore (Founder & CEO)
Terrie Glover Ard (Pres)
Nanette M. Schimpf (VP)
Jamie Fortune (Mng Dir)
Justin Smith (Dir-Art)
Andrea Blount (Bus Mgr)
Darren Allen (Mng Dir)
Danelle Amos (Acct Exec)
Jordan Jacobs (VP-Client Servicing)
Courtney Cox (Acct Exec)
Rachel Fackender (Acct Exec)
Adam Montgomery (Acct Exec)
Whitney Pickett (Coord-Comm)
Kayla Preston (Coord-Social Media Acct)
Patrick Sheffield (Sr Acct Exec)
Fern Senra James (Mng Dir)
Melissa Wisehart (Mng Dir)

MOORE COMPANY
36 Beach St, Westerly, RI 02891
Tel.: (401) 596-2816   RI
Web Site:
   http://www.themooreco.com
Year Founded: 1909
Sales Range: $450-499.9 Million
Emp.: 1,500
Fabric Finishing; Warp Knit, Man-made Fiber, Narrow Woven Fabrics, Pressure Sensitive Tape, Rubber, Thread, Mechanical Rubber Goods, Battery Separators & Wood
N.A.I.C.S.: 313310
Thomas F. Moore (Chm)
Dana Barlo (Pres & CEO)

Subsidiaries:

Darlington Fabrics Corporation (1)
36 Beach St, Westerly, RI 02891
Tel.: (401) 596-2816
Web Site: http://www.darlingtonfabrics.com

MOORE COMPANY — U.S. PRIVATE

Moore Company—(Continued)

Elastic Fabric Mfr
N.A.I.C.S.: 313210

MOORE DM GROUP, LLC
2900 E Apache St, Tulsa, OK 74110
Tel.: (918) 295-0112
Web Site:
  http://www.mooredmgroup.com
Holding Company; Direct Marketing Services
N.A.I.C.S.: 551112
James Moore (Owner)
Gary Kirk (CTO)
Gretchen Littlefield (CEO)
Greg Fox (Chief Strategy Officer)
Kelly Navarro (Chief People Officer)
Heather Philpot (Exec VP)

Subsidiaries:

Amergent, Inc. (1)
9 Centennial Dr Unit 201, Peabody, MA 01960-7940
Web Site: http://www.amergent.com
Professional, Scientific & Technical Services
N.A.I.C.S.: 541990
Mark Connors (VP)
Jack Doyle (CEO)
George Whelan (Sr VP-Bus Dev)
Rick Hohman (COO)

Barton Cotton (1)
3030 Waterview Ave Ste 100, Baltimore, MD 21230-3520
Web Site: http://www.bartoncotton.com
Sales Range: $50-74.9 Million
Emp.: 200
Direct Marketing Fundraising Products & Services
N.A.I.C.S.: 561499
Larry Vogel (COO)
Denise Payne (Sr VP-Religious Products & Svcs)
John Hall (Sr VP-Bus Dev)
Becky Odum (VP-Strategic Svcs)
Karen Jones (VP-Client Svcs)
Tammy Severe (VP-Creative Svcs & Art Acq)
Laura Thompson (VP-Data Svcs)
Kathy Calta (Pres)
Margaret Chialastri (VP-Dev & Integrated Direct Response)

CDR Fundraising Group (1)
16900 Science Dr Ste 210, Bowie, MD 20715
Tel.: (301) 858-1500
Web Site: http://www.cdrfg.com
Emp.: 50
Direct Mailing & Marketing Services
N.A.I.C.S.: 541860
Donna Shortz (CIO & Sr VP-Admin)
Angela Brightman Struebing (Pres)
Lenka Krejcova-Sloan (Dir-HR)
Kojo Duncan (Dir-Product Dev)
DeDi Oxenberg (VP)
Katy Jordan (VP-Integrated Mktg)
Janet Tonner (VP-Data & Analytics)

Merkle Response Management Group (1)
100 Jamison Ct, Hagerstown, MD 21740
Tel.: (301) 790-3100
Web Site: http://www.merkleresponse.com
Donation & Remittance Processing & Other Fulfillment Services
N.A.I.C.S.: 561499
Bill Sayre (Pres)
Jim Stouffer (VP-Tech Svcs)
Scott Ryan (VP-Ops)
Steven L. Gregg (VP-Sls & Mktg)
Amy Bobrick (VP-Strategy)
Jann Schultz (VP-Client Svcs)

Resource One (1)
2900 E Apache St, Tulsa, OK 74110
Tel.: (918) 295-0112
Web Site: http://www.resource-one.us
Sales Range: $1-9.9 Million
Emp.: 19
Direct Mailing, Printing, Fundraising & Data Management Services
N.A.I.C.S.: 323111
James Moore (CEO)
Jeff Pelcher (Pres)
Holly Weinzapfel (VP)

Southwest Publishing & Mailing Corp. (1)
4000 SE Adams, Topeka, KS 66609
Tel.: (785) 233-5662
Web Site: http://www.swpks.com
Emp.: 350
Direct Mail Advertising
N.A.I.C.S.: 541860
Shane Hillmer (Pres)
Angie McAtee (VP)

Worcester Envelope Company (1)
22 Millbury St, Auburn, MA 01501
Tel.: (508) 832-5394
Web Site:
  http://www.worcesterenvelope.com
Corrugated & Solid Fiber Box Mfr
N.A.I.C.S.: 322211
Derek Waterhouse (Pres)

MOORE FANS LLC
800 S Missouri Ave, Marceline, MO 64658-1602
Tel.: (660) 376-3575
Web Site: http://www.moorefans.com
Year Founded: 1939
Sales Range: $50-74.9 Million
Emp.: 60
Industrial Air Moving Equipment, Louvers, Dampers, Storm Louvers, Solar Shades, Lighting Control Electronics Mfr
N.A.I.C.S.: 333413
John D. Moore (Pres & CEO)
Randy Ward (VP-Sls)
Carol Schreckhise (Dir-Fin)

Subsidiaries:

Moore Fans Ltd (1)
Grosvenor Mansions 2-3 Claremont, Hastings, TN34 1HA, East Sussex, United Kingdom
Tel.: (44) 1424436815
Web Site: http://www.moorefans.com
Sales Range: $10-24.9 Million
Emp.: 3
Appliance Sales & Distr
N.A.I.C.S.: 423620

MOORE GRAHAM SALES, INC.
6411 Colonial Dr, Granbury, TX 76049-4118
Tel.: (682) 936-4626
Web Site:
  http://www.mooregraham.com
Year Founded: 1996
Sales Range: $10-24.9 Million
Emp.: 2
Roofing, Siding & Insulation Material Whslr
N.A.I.C.S.: 423330
Lee Moore (Co-Founder)
Paul Graham (Co-Founder)

MOORE HOLDINGS INC.
5320 N Franklin St, Denver, CO 80216-1506
Tel.: (303) 294-0026
Year Founded: 1993
Sales Range: $75-99.9 Million
Emp.: 300
Holding Company; Natural Meats Supplier
N.A.I.C.S.: 551112
Roy R. Moore Jr. (Founder & CEO)

Subsidiaries:

Mountain Man Resorts Inc. (1)
5360 N Franklin St, Denver, CO 80216-1506
Tel.: (303) 294-0146
Sales Range: $10-24.9 Million
Emp.: 4
Provider of Resort Services
N.A.I.C.S.: 721110

TLC Wildlife Ranches Inc. (1)
5360 N Franklin St, Denver, CO 80216-1506
Tel.: (303) 294-0146

Sales Range: $25-49.9 Million
Emp.: 250
Provider of Property Services
N.A.I.C.S.: 531190

MOORE INDUSTRIES INTERNATIONAL INC.
16650 Schoenborn St, North Hills, CA 91343-6106
Tel.: (818) 894-7111
Web Site: http://www.miinet.com
Year Founded: 1965
Rev.: $26,000,000
Emp.: 260
Provider of Process Control Instruments
N.A.I.C.S.: 334513
Leonard Moore (Founder, Pres & CEO)
Ameen Hossain (CIO)
Gilbert Perez (Mgr-Fabrication)
Gonzalo Caldera (Supvr-E&A)
Yong Park (Controller)
Matt Moren (Dir-Sls Support)
Gregory Shaw (Engr-Application)
Hernan Fontana (Engr-Hardware)
Juan Arellano (Supvr)

Subsidiaries:

Moore Industries-Europe Inc. (1)
16650 Schoenborn St, North Hills, CA 91343
Tel.: (818) 894-7111
Web Site: http://www.miinet.com
Sales Range: $25-49.9 Million
Emp.: 160
Electronic Parts & Equipment Service
N.A.I.C.S.: 334513
Leonard Moore (Founder & Pres)

MOORE OIL CO., INC.
1800 Ctr Point Rd, Birmingham, AL 35215
Tel.: (205) 853-1533
Web Site:
  http://www.mooreoilcompany.com
Sales Range: $200-249.9 Million
Emp.: 19
Fuel Distr
N.A.I.C.S.: 424720
Joey Moore (VP)
Ronald J. Moore (Pres)
Ed Harding (Gen Mgr)

Subsidiaries:

Moore Oil Co., Inc. - Montgomery (1)
853 Taylor Rd, Montgomery, AL 36117
Tel.: (334) 244-6558
Web Site: http://www.mooreoilcompany.com
Emp.: 12
Fuel Distr
N.A.I.C.S.: 424720
David Owen (Gen Mgr)

MOORE OIL INC.
18 Tradewinds Dr, Thompson Falls, MT 59873
Tel.: (406) 827-4314
Year Founded: 1976
Sales Range: $25-49.9 Million
Emp.: 4
Petroleum Bulk Stations
N.A.I.C.S.: 424710
Bary C. Moore (Pres)

MOORE SUPPLY CO. INC.
4332 W Ferdinand St, Chicago, IL 60624
Tel.: (773) 638-5930
Web Site: http://www.mooresc.com
Rev.: $10,542,834
Emp.: 12
Heating Equipment (Hydronic)
N.A.I.C.S.: 423720
Dick Moore (Mgr)

MOORE TRANSPORT

1111 Jupiter Rd Ste 118E, Plano, TX 75074-8401
Tel.: (972) 578-0606
Web Site:
  http://www.mooretransport.com
Year Founded: 2005
Sales Range: $1-9.9 Million
Emp.: 45
Automotive Logistics Consulting Services
N.A.I.C.S.: 541614
Bryan Stewart (Dir-Safety)
Gary Moore (CEO)
Dan Faircloth (COO)

MOORE'S ELECTRICAL & MECHANICAL CONSTRUCTION, INC.
101 Edgewood Ave, Altavista, VA 24517
Tel.: (434) 369-4374
Web Site:
  http://www.mooreselectric.com
Year Founded: 1985
Sales Range: $25-49.9 Million
Emp.: 350
Contractor of Electrical & Mechanical Construction
N.A.I.C.S.: 238210
Steve Rogers (Dir-Safety)
George Coleman (VP-Fin Ops)

MOORE'S RETREAD & TIRE CO.
6425 Youree Dr Ste 260, Shreveport, LA 71105
Tel.: (318) 798-0770
Rev.: $13,356,032
Emp.: 2
Truck Tires & Tubes
N.A.I.C.S.: 423130

MOORE, EPSTEIN, MOORE
442 W Kennedy Blvd Ste 200, Tampa, FL 33606
Tel.: (813) 286-6500
Year Founded: 1983
Rev.: $21,000,000
Emp.: 15
N.A.I.C.S.: 541810
Marianne Moore (Exec VP)
Ted Moore (Partner)
Barbara Melindi (Production Mgr)
Philip Bennett (VP & Creative Dir)

MOOREFIELD CONSTRUCTION INC.
600 N Tustin Ave Ste 210, Santa Ana, CA 92705
Tel.: (714) 972-0700
Web Site:
  http://www.moorefieldconst.com
Rev.: $104,376,310
Emp.: 40
Shopping Center Construction
N.A.I.C.S.: 236220
Mike Moorefield (Pres)
Hal Moorefield (VP)
Larry Moorefield (VP)

MOORES TIRE SALES INC.
1436 Taylor Rd, Owego, NY 13827
Tel.: (607) 687-3275
Web Site:
  http://www.moorestiresales.com
Sales Range: $50-74.9 Million
Emp.: 172
Tires & Tubes Whslr
N.A.I.C.S.: 423130
Bill Watkins (Gen Mgr)
Tim Mathewson (Mgr-Sls)

MOORESTOWN VISITING NURSE ASSOCIATION
300 Harper Dr, Moorestown, NJ 08057

Tel.: (856) 552-1300 NJ
Web Site:
http://www.moorestownvna.org
Year Founded: 1904
Sales Range: $25-49.9 Million
Emp.: 269
Health Care Srvices
N.A.I.C.S.: 622110
Kathleen Miller *(CFO & VP-Fin)*
Michele Fiore *(VP-Clinical Svcs)*
Sean Rabindranauth *(Dir-IT & Patient Acct)*
Kim Plasket *(Dir-Pub Comm)*
Jeffrey DeFrehn *(VP-Bus Dev)*

MOORETOWN RANCHERIA
1 Alverda Dr, Oroville, CA 95966
Tel.: (530) 533-3625
Web Site:
http://www.mooretownrancheria.org
Sales Range: $10-24.9 Million
Emp.: 500
Casino Hotels
N.A.I.C.S.: 721120
Gary Archuleta *(Chm)*
Coquette Elliott *(Dir-Education)*
Kayla Lobo *(Treas-Tribal Council)*

MOORINGS PARK INSTITUTE INC.
120 Moorings Park Dr, Naples, FL 34105
Tel.: (239) 643-9111 FL
Web Site:
http://www.mooringspark.org
Year Founded: 2004
Sales Range: $50-74.9 Million
Emp.: 800
Senior Living Retirement Communities
N.A.I.C.S.: 623311
Daniel Lavender *(CEO)*
Mary Morton *(CFO)*

MOORS & CABOT INC.
111 Devonshire St Ste 100, Boston, MA 02109
Tel.: (617) 426-0500
Web Site:
http://www.moorscabot.com
Year Founded: 1890
Sales Range: $10-24.9 Million
Emp.: 250
Security Brokerage Services
N.A.I.C.S.: 523150
Robert W. Morey *(Owner)*
Michael J. Egan *(Mng Dir-Wealth Mgmt)*
Brad East *(Mng Dir-Investments)*
James Pillow *(Mng Dir)*

MOOSE CHARITIES, INC.
155 S International Dr, Mooseheart, IL 60539-1100
Tel.: (630) 966-2200 IL
Web Site:
http://www.moosecharities.org
Year Founded: 1994
Sales Range: $10-24.9 Million
Emp.: 5
Fundraising Services
N.A.I.C.S.: 561499
Janet Fregulia *(Exec Dir)*
Pamela Amundsen *(Dir-Dev)*

MOOSYLVANIA MARKETING
7303 Marietta, Saint Louis, MO 63143
Tel.: (314) 533-5800
Web Site:
http://www.moosylvania.com
Rev.: $2,800,000
Emp.: 45
Fiscal Year-end: 12/31/06
Management Consulting Services
N.A.I.C.S.: 541613

Norty Cohen *(CEO)*
AnneMarie Greene *(VP-Client Svcs)*
Gus Hattrich *(Pres)*
Lynn Ullman *(VP & Sr Dir-Creative)*
Mary Behrman *(Dir-Plng & Emerging Media)*
Mike Wienke *(Dir-Creative)*
Rob Brooks *(VP & Dir-Creative)*
Sharon Ayres *(VP-HR)*
Teresa Sausville *(VP & Dir-Creative)*
Nick Foppe *(Exec VP & Dir-Client Svcs)*
Brooke Friedman *(VP-Acct Svcs)*
Abby Luther *(VP-Media & Consumer Insights)*

MOOVE AND OINK INC.
3330 183rd St, Hazel Crest, IL 60429
Tel.: (708) 206-0308
Sales Range: $10-24.9 Million
Emp.: 100
Convenient Store Owner & Operator
N.A.I.C.S.: 445131
Fred Garner *(CEO)*

MOR FURNITURE FOR LESS
8996 Miramar Rd #300, San Diego, CA 92126
Tel.: (866) 466-7435
Web Site:
http://www.morfurniture.com
Year Founded: 1977
Furniture Retailer
N.A.I.C.S.: 449110
Jeffrey Haux *(Pres)*
Matt Tranchina *(CFO)*

MORA ENGINEERING CONTRACTORS, INC.
1548 Seminola Blvd Unit 120, Casselberry, FL 32707-3648
Tel.: (321) 972-9908
Web Site: http://mecinc.net
Sales Range: $50-74.9 Million
Emp.: 3
Industrial Building Construction
N.A.I.C.S.: 236210
Monica S. Mora *(Treas & VP)*

MORA-SAN MIGUEL ELECTRIC COOPERATIVE, INC.
Highway 518 Main St, Mora, NM 87732
Tel.: (575) 387-2205 NM
Web Site: http://www.moraelectric.org
Year Founded: 1940
Sales Range: $10-24.9 Million
Emp.: 45
Electric Power Distr
N.A.I.C.S.: 221122
Alex C. Romero *(CEO & Gen Mgr)*
Roy Montoya *(Superintendent-Line)*
Larry Barela *(Mgr-Ops)*
LaDonna LaRan *(CFO)*
Gwen Mascarenas *(COO)*

MORAE GLOBAL CORP.
1000 Louisiana St 65th Fl, Houston, TX 77002
Tel.: (713) 244-6000
Web Site:
http://www.moraeglobal.com
Commercial Services
N.A.I.C.S.: 926150
Shahzad Bashir *(Chm & CEO)*

Subsidiaries:

Adaptive Solutions, Inc. (1)
516 DeKalb St, Norristown, PA 19401
Tel.: (610) 489-9872
Web Site: http://www.adaptivesolutions.com
Sales Range: $10-24.9 Million
Emp.: 53
IT Services for Law Firms & Corporate Legal
N.A.I.C.S.: 541511

Charles Davis *(Pres)*
Todd Baratz *(CTO)*
Brad Ebright *(Engr-Help Desk)*
Matthew McGowan *(Engr-Help Desk)*
Peter Huang *(Engr-Sys)*
Brian Albert *(Mgr-Help Desk)*
Raza Imam *(Mng Partner)*

MORALES GROUP INC.
5628 W 74th St, Indianapolis, IN 46278
Tel.: (317) 472-7600
Web Site:
http://www.moralesgroup.net
Year Founded: 2003
Sales Range: $25-49.9 Million
Emp.: 32
Employment Placement
N.A.I.C.S.: 561311
Tom Morales *(Co-Founder, Pres & CEO)*

MORALLY WHOLESALE, INC.
4695 N Ave, Oceanside, CA 92056
Tel.: (760) 726-3996
Web Site:
http://www.mwiplumbing.com
Year Founded: 1993
Sales Range: $10-24.9 Million
Emp.: 40
Plumbing Fittings & Supplies
N.A.I.C.S.: 423720
Mark Walton *(Co-Owner & Gen Mgr)*

MORAN CHEVROLET INC.
35500 Gratiot Ave, Clinton Township, MI 48035-2847
Tel.: (586) 791-1010 DE
Web Site:
http://www.moranautomotive.com
Sales Range: $10-24.9 Million
Emp.: 80
New & Used Car Dealer
N.A.I.C.S.: 441110
Patrick Moran *(Pres)*
Chris Aleksander *(Dir-Adv & Mktg)*
Ed Koury *(Asst Mgr-Sls)*
Dan Cohen *(Gen Mgr-New & Used Sls Cars)*
Dan Perini *(Bus Mgr-New Car Sls)*

MORAN EDWARDS ASSET MANAGEMENT GROUP
5801 Pelican Bay Blvd Ste 200, Naples, FL 34108
Tel.: (239) 254-2200
Web Site:
http://morangroup.wfadv.com
Rev.: $2,000,000,000
Investment Management
N.A.I.C.S.: 523150
Thomas M. Moran *(Founder & Mng Member)*
Robert T. Edwards *(Sr Member)*
Earl Sistrunk *(Sr VP & Fin Consultant)*
Julie Cusson *(VP-Investments)*

MORAN PRINTING INC.
5425 Florida Blvd, Baton Rouge, LA 70806
Tel.: (225) 923-2550
Web Site:
http://www.moranprinting.com
Rev.: $13,275,000
Emp.: 77
Offset Printing
N.A.I.C.S.: 323111
Courtney B. Westbrook *(Owner & CEO)*
Neill Cato *(CIO)*
Andrea Duroncelet *(Acct Mgr)*
Morgan Esser *(Plant Mgr)*
Randy Norwood *(Dir-HR)*
Greg Thompson *(Mgr-Production)*
Rebecca Vance *(Pres & COO)*

MORAN TOWING CORPORATION
50 Locust Ave, New Canaan, CT 06840-4737
Tel.: (203) 442-2800
Web Site: http://www.morantug.com
Year Founded: 1860
Sales Range: $350-399.9 Million
Emp.: 1,000
Towing, Tugboat & Water Transportation Services Operator
N.A.I.C.S.: 488999
Bruce D. Richards *(VP-Barges)*
Peter R. Keyes *(VP-Tugs)*

Subsidiaries:

Moran Environmental Recovery, LLC (1)
251 Levy Rd, Atlantic Beach, FL 32233
Tel.: (904) 241-2200
Web Site:
http://www.moranenvironmental.com
Emp.: 55
Environmental Field Service Solutions
N.A.I.C.S.: 541620
Brian J. House *(Pres)*

Moran Shipyard Corporation (1)
2015 Richmond Terr, Staten Island, NY 10302
Tel.: (718) 981-5600
Ship Building & Repairing Services
N.A.I.C.S.: 336611
Vincent Borello *(Mgr)*

Moran Towing and Transportation, LLC (1)
50 Locust Ave, New Canaan, CT 06840-4737
Tel.: (203) 442-2800
Web Site: http://www.morantug.com
Sales Range: $10-24.9 Million
Emp.: 100
Towing & Water Transportation Services
N.A.I.C.S.: 488330
Bruce D. Richards *(VP-Barges)*

Moran Towing of Charleston (1)
2075 Thompson Ave Ste 200, North Charleston, SC 29405
Tel.: (843) 529-3000
Web Site: http://www.morantug.com
Sales Range: $25-49.9 Million
Emp.: 50
Towing, Tugboat & Water Transportation Services Operator
N.A.I.C.S.: 488390
Jonathan Archer *(VP & Gen Mgr)*

Moran Towing of Florida (1)
9051 Dames Point Rd, Jacksonville, FL 32226-2911 (100%)
Tel.: (904) 757-6900
Web Site: http://www.morantug.com
Sales Range: $10-24.9 Million
Emp.: 40
Towing, Tugboat & Water Transportation Services Operator
N.A.I.C.S.: 488999
Thomas Craighead *(Gen Mgr)*

Moran Towing of Maryland (1)
1820 S Clinton St, Baltimore, MD 21224
Tel.: (410) 732-9600
Web Site: http://www.morantowing.com
Sales Range: $25-49.9 Million
Emp.: 12
Towing, Tugboat & Water Transportation Services Operator
N.A.I.C.S.: 488390
Paul P. Swenson *(VP & Gen Mgr)*

Moran Towing of Miami (1)
1015 N America Way Ste 121, Miami, FL 33132-2017
Tel.: (305) 375-0455
Web Site: http://www.morantug.com
Sales Range: $25-49.9 Million
Emp.: 15
Towing, Tugboat & Water Transportation Services Operator
N.A.I.C.S.: 488390
Jamie Scott *(Gen Mgr)*

Moran Towing of New Hampshire (1)
34 Ceres St, Portsmouth, NH 03801

MORAN TOWING CORPORATION   U.S. PRIVATE

Moran Towing Corporation—(Continued)
Tel.: (603) 436-0556
Web Site: http://www.morantowing.com
Sales Range: $25-49.9 Million
Emp.: 12
Towing, Tugboat & Water Transportation Services Operator
N.A.I.C.S.: 488390
Richard Holt (VP & Gen Mgr)

Moran Towing of Pennsylvania (1)
1411 Admiral Peary Way, Philadelphia, PA 19112-1800 (100%)
Tel.: (215) 755-4706
Web Site: http://www.morantug.com
Sales Range: $50-74.9 Million
Emp.: 90
Towing, Tugboat & Water Transportation Services Operator
N.A.I.C.S.: 488330

Moran Towing of Savannah (1)
504 E River St, Savannah, GA 31401
Tel.: (912) 232-8103
Sales Range: $25-49.9 Million
Emp.: 40
Towing, Tugboat & Water Transportation Services Operator
N.A.I.C.S.: 488999
Ron Droop (VP & Gen Mgr)

Moran Towing of Texas Inc. (1)
8740 Old Yacht Club Rd, Port Arthur, TX 77642 (100%)
Tel.: (409) 962-0591
Web Site: http://www.morantug.com
Sales Range: $25-49.9 Million
Emp.: 50
Towing, Tugboat & Water Transportation Services Operator
N.A.I.C.S.: 483113
Stephen M. Kelly (VP & Gen Mgr)

Moran Towing of Virginia Inc. (1)
1901 Brown Ave, Norfolk, VA 23504 (100%)
Tel.: (757) 625-6000
Web Site: http://www.morantug.com
Sales Range: $25-49.9 Million
Emp.: 100
Towing, Tugboat & Water Transportation Services Operator
N.A.I.C.S.: 488330
Mark Vanty (VP & Gen Mgr)

MORAN TRANSPORTATION CORP.
1000 Estes Ave, Elk Grove Village, IL 60007
Tel.: (847) 439-0000
Web Site: http://www.morandist.com
Rev.: $10,555,653
Emp.: 70
Local Freight Trucking Services
N.A.I.C.S.: 484110
Michael J. Moran (Chm & CEO)
Robert Beatty (Sr Mgr-Tech Sys)

Subsidiaries:

Mats, Inc. (1)
940 Aldrin Dr Ste 100, Saint Paul, MN 55121
Tel.: (651) 406-8300
Web Site: http://www.matstrucking.com
Sales Range: $1-9.9 Million
Emp.: 65
Local Freight Trucking Services
N.A.I.C.S.: 484110
John Dawson (Pres)

MORAVIAN HOME INCORPORATED
190 Moravian Way Dr, Winston Salem, NC 27106
Tel.: (336) 767-8130 NC
Web Site: http://www.salemtowne.org
Year Founded: 1971
Sales Range: $10-24.9 Million
Retirement Care Services
N.A.I.C.S.: 623311
Joseph Lydon (Pres)

MORAVIAN MANORS, INC.
300 W Lemon St, Lititz, PA 17543
Tel.: (717) 626-0214 PA
Web Site: http://www.moravianmanor.org
Year Founded: 1975
Sales Range: $10-24.9 Million
Emp.: 470
Lifecare Retirement Community Operator
N.A.I.C.S.: 623311
Peggy Kammerer (Dir-Community Svcs)
Mary Jane Hudock (Dir-Children's Corner Program)
J. David Swartley (Pres & CEO)
Amy L. Blough (VP-HR)
Cindy Meier (VP-Fin)
Gary Gaissert (VP-Ops)
Joyce Krushinski (VP-Health Svcs)

MORAVIAN VILLAGE OF BETHLEHEM
526 Wood St, Bethlehem, PA 18018
Tel.: (610) 625-4885 PA
Web Site: http://www.moravianvillage.com
Year Founded: 1999
Sales Range: $10-24.9 Million
Emp.: 434
Lifecare Retirement Community Operator
N.A.I.C.S.: 623311
Valerie Stumer-Heller (Dir-Mktg)
Tracy Patton (Exec VP)
John Calzola (VP-Resident & Employee Svcs)
Deborah Ellis (Dir-Admissions)

MORBELLI, RUSSO & PARTNERS ADVERTISING, INC.
55 Madison Ave Ste 400, Morristown, NJ 07960
Tel.: (973) 644-9663
Web Site: http://www.morbelli-russo.com
Year Founded: 1987
Sales Range: $10-24.9 Million
Emp.: 10
Fiscal Year-end: 12/31/15
Advertising Services
N.A.I.C.S.: 541810
Kathy Brennan (Office Mgr)
Eric Ortiz (VP & Supvr-Creative)
Joseph DeFalco (Dir-Acct Svcs)
Christina Murphy (Asst Dir-Art)
Eric Ortez (VP-Creative)
Mario J. Morbelli Jr. (Pres & Chief Creative Officer)

MORCOM INTERNATIONAL, INC.
3656 Centerview Dr Unit 1, Chantilly, VA 20151
Tel.: (703) 263-9305
Web Site: http://www.morcom.com
Year Founded: 1984
Sales Range: $10-24.9 Million
Emp.: 20
Electronic Parts & Equipment Merchant Whslrs
N.A.I.C.S.: 423690
Francisco Ojeda (Treas)
Jose Pacheco (Engr-RF)

MORCON CONSTRUCTION INC.
5905 Golden Valley Rd Ste 231, Minneapolis, MN 55422-4475
Tel.: (763) 546-6066
Web Site: http://www.morcon.com
Year Founded: 1982
Sales Range: $10-24.9 Million
Emp.: 75
Nonresidential Construction Services
N.A.I.C.S.: 236220
Jerry Jullie (Owner)
Carl Hoikka (Project Mgr)

Louise Pickering (Office Mgr)
Heidi Smith (Project Coord)
Max Mallery (Superintendent)

MORCON, INC.
879 State Rte 22, Cambridge, NY 12816
Tel.: (518) 677-8511 NY
Year Founded: 1987
Sales Range: $10-24.9 Million
Emp.: 205
Sanitary Paper Product Mfr
N.A.I.C.S.: 322291
Wayne R. Morris (Founder & Pres)
Joseph F. Raccuia (Owner & CEO)

MOREFIELD COMMUNICATIONS INC.
35 N 35th St, Camp Hill, PA 17011
Tel.: (717) 761-6170
Web Site: http://www.morefield.com
Sales Range: $10-24.9 Million
Emp.: 115
Telephone & Telephone Equipment Installation
N.A.I.C.S.: 238210
Michael Whiteman (Exec VP-Sls & Mktg)
Wes Kelly (VP-Svcs)
Brian Valentine (Engr-Network)

MOREHART CHEVROLET CO
31 Parker Ave, Durango, CO 81303
Tel.: (970) 247-2121
Rev.: $19,000,000
Emp.: 75
Automobiles, New & Used
N.A.I.C.S.: 441110
James E. Morehart II (Pres)

MOREIN MOTOR COMPANY INC.
1019 W Magnolia St, Ville Platte, LA 70586
Tel.: (337) 363-6627
Year Founded: 1958
Sales Range: $10-24.9 Million
Emp.: 19
New & Used Car Dealers
N.A.I.C.S.: 441110
Randall Morein (Pres)
Carla Lafleur (Sec-Tres)

MORELANDS INC.
Hwy 12 W, Starkville, MS 39759
Tel.: (662) 323-4892
Sales Range: $10-24.9 Million
Emp.: 3
Convenience Store
N.A.I.C.S.: 445131
Dan W. Moreland (Pres)
Sherry Moreland (VP)

MORENO TRENCHING, LTD.
1015 B Airport Rd, Rio Vista, CA 94571
Tel.: (707) 374-5075
Web Site: http://www.morenotrenching.com
Rev.: $25,000,000
Emp.: 60
Water & Sewer Line & Related Structures Construction
N.A.I.C.S.: 237110
Jon Moreno (Pres)
J. Lavagnino (Superintendent)

MORENO, PEELEN, PINTO & CLARK (MPC)
111 N Magnolia Ave Ste 1025, Orlando, FL 32801
Tel.: (407) 246-1515
Web Site: http://www.mpc-wm.com
Year Founded: 1960
Sales Range: $1-9.9 Million
Emp.: 20

Financial Planning Services
N.A.I.C.S.: 525990
Sarah Lapham (Office Mgr)
Scott Peelen (Sr Partner)

MORET CONSTRUCTION
3341 Riverview St, Lower Burrell, PA 15068
Tel.: (724) 339-0500
Sales Range: $1-9.9 Million
Emp.: 20
Commercial & Institutional Building Construction Services
N.A.I.C.S.: 236220
August R. Moret (Owner)

MORETTE COMPANY, INC.
1201 N Tarragona St, Pensacola, FL 32501-2658
Tel.: (850) 432-4084
Web Site: http://www.moretteco.com
Year Founded: 1978
Sales Range: $25-49.9 Million
Emp.: 28
Nonresidential Construction Services
N.A.I.C.S.: 236220
Nicole Bell (Comptroller)
Michael Morette (Pres)
Gidget Mott (Acct Mgr)

MOREVISIBILITY.COM, INC.
Wachovia Plz 925 S Federal Hwy Ste 750, Boca Raton, FL 33432
Tel.: (561) 620-9682
Web Site: http://www.morevisibility.com
Year Founded: 1999
Sales Range: $1-9.9 Million
Emp.: 35
Internet Search-Engine Marketing
N.A.I.C.S.: 425120
Andrew Wetzler (Co-Founder & Pres)
Dennis Pushkin (Co-Founder & CEO)
Danielle Leitch (Exec VP-Client Strategy)

MOREY EVANS
620 16th St Ste 200, Denver, CO 80202
Tel.: (303) 296-8011
Year Founded: 1989
Sales Range: $25-49.9 Million
Emp.: 20
Advertising Services
N.A.I.C.S.: 541810
Glenn Morey (Pres)
Krista Nicholson (VP & Dir-Acct Svcs)

MOREY'S PIERS INCORPORATED
3501 Boardwalk, Wildwood, NJ 08260
Tel.: (609) 522-3900
Web Site: http://www.moreyspiers.com
Year Founded: 1969
Amusement Park
N.A.I.C.S.: 713110
George E. Rohman (Mgr-Sr Ops)

Subsidiaries:

Morey Development Co. Inc. (1)
3501 Boardwalk, Wildwood, NJ 08260
Tel.: (609) 729-0022
Web Site: http://www.moreyspiers.com
Sales Range: $10-24.9 Million
Emp.: 50
Townhouse Construction
N.A.I.C.S.: 236115

MOREY'S SEAFOOD INTERNATIONAL LLC
742 Decatur Ave N, Minneapolis, MN 55427
Tel.: (763) 541-0129
Web Site: http://www.moreys.com

Year Founded: 1891
Rev.: $60,000,000
Emp.: 400
Whslr of Fish & Seafoods
N.A.I.C.S.: 424460
Gary Ziolkowski (CFO)
Patti Zahler (Plant Mgr)
Scott Wickert (VP-Sls)

MORGAL MACHINE TOOL COMPANY, INC.
2100 S Yellow Springs St, Springfield, OH 45506
Tel.: (937) 325-5561
Web Site:
 http://www.mcgregormetal.com
Year Founded: 1939
Rev.: $30,000,000
Emp.: 100
Metal Stamping Mfr
N.A.I.C.S.: 332119
Daniel P. McGregor (Chm & CEO)
Tom Wright (Pres)

MORGAN & BROTHER MANHATTAN STORAGE INC.
16 Bruce Park Ave, Greenwich, CT 06830
Tel.: (203) 446-5556
Web Site:
 http://www.morganmanhattan.com
Year Founded: 1851
Sales Range: $10-24.9 Million
Emp.: 80
Moving Company
N.A.I.C.S.: 493110
Jeffrey S. Morgan (Pres)
Brian G. Clark (VP)
Anthony Parisi (Controller)

MORGAN & COMPANY
4407 Canal St, New Orleans, LA 70119-5946
Tel.: (504) 523-7734
Web Site:
 http://www.morganandco.com
Year Founded: 1997
Sales Range: $10-24.9 Million
Emp.: 9
Advertising & Marketing
N.A.I.C.S.: 541810
Renee Stuart (Dir-Media Buying)
Jennifer Huber (Dir-Comm Plng)
Brenda Cole (CFO)
Jennifer Huber (Dir-Comm Plng)
Renee Cobb-Stuart (Dir-Media Buying)
Britt Hafstad (Acct Coord)

MORGAN & SAMPSON USA
11155 Dana Cir, Cypress, CA 90630-5133
Tel.: (714) 894-0646
Web Site:
 http://www.morgansampson.com
Year Founded: 1921
Sales Range: $10-24.9 Million
Emp.: 75
Manufacturers' Representative for Hardware, Household Appliances, Homeopathic Pharmaceuticals & Various Other Consumer Products
N.A.I.C.S.: 423710
Ralph Carter (CEO)

MORGAN & THORNBURG, INC.
4076 Hatcher Cir, Memphis, TN 38118
Tel.: (901) 365-4936
Year Founded: 1976
Sales Range: $25-49.9 Million
Emp.: 140
Plumbing Services
N.A.I.C.S.: 238220

Wes Thornburg (Pres)
Joseph R. Thornburg (VP)
Stephen R. Thornburg (VP)

MORGAN AUTO GROUP, LLC
3031 N Rocky Point Dr W Ste 770, Tampa, FL 33607
Tel.: (813) 434-1967 FL
Web Site:
 http://www.morganautogroup.com
Year Founded: 2010
Holding Company; New & Used Car Dealerships Owner & Operator
N.A.I.C.S.: 551112
Larry C. Morgan (Chm)
Mark Schols (Gen Mgr)
Brett Morgan (CEO)
Kelly Ross (CFO)
Bennett Acuff (Gen Counsel & Exec VP)
Tom Moore (COO)
Joerg Schlueter (VP-Fixed Ops)
Tanner Boyle (CIO)
Tim Desmond (VP-HR)
Jason Hillman (Dir-HR)
Michelle Whidden (Dir-Social Media & Reputation)
Jennifer Sharp (Office Mgr)
Pam Prue (Chief Learning Officer)
Subsidiaries:

Brandon Honda (1)
9209 E Adamo Dr, Tampa, FL 33619
Tel.: (813) 664-1234
Web Site: http://www.brandonhonda.com
Emp.: 100
New & Used Car Dealer
N.A.I.C.S.: 441110
John Marazzi (Mng Partner)
Jerry Meany (Asst Mgr-Used Car)
Neil Cann (Mgr-Svc)

Hollywood Kia, Inc. (1)
6011 Pembroke Rd, Hollywood, FL 33023
Tel.: (954) 967-5665
Web Site: https://www.hollywoodkia.com
Emp.: 100
New Car Dealers
N.A.I.C.S.: 441110
Steve Gutstein (Gen Mgr)

Rountree Moore Toyota (1)
1232 W US Hwy 90, Lake City, FL 32055-3733
Tel.: (386) 755-0631
Web Site:
 http://www.rountreemooretoyota.com
New & Used Car Dealer
N.A.I.C.S.: 441110
Ali Ansari (Gen Mgr)
Phil Kuhn (Gen Sls Mgr)
Matt Like (Dir-Internet Sls)

Sun Automotive, Inc. (1)
3001 US Hwy 19, Holiday, FL 34691
Tel.: (727) 842-9735
Web Site: http://www.suntoyota.com
Sales Range: $100-124.9 Million
Emp.: 200
Automobiles, New & Used
N.A.I.C.S.: 441110
Joe Reth (Mgr-Preowned Sls)
Michael Sturm (Mgr-Parts)
Stephanie Durbin (Mgr-Inventory)
Robbie Boston (Gen Mgr)
Rick Fowler (Dir-Fixed Ops)
Frank Vitale (Mgr-Fin)
John Ancona (Dir-Fin)
John Marazzi (Mng Partner)

MORGAN AUTO PARTS INC.
PO Box 1917, Fairmont, WV 26554
Tel.: (304) 366-3884
Sales Range: $10-24.9 Million
Emp.: 100
Whslr of Automotive Supplies & Parts
N.A.I.C.S.: 423120
Marty L. Morgan (Pres)

MORGAN BORSZCZ CONSULTING
42395 Ryan Rd Ste 112-805, Brambleton, VA 20148
Tel.: (866) 455-2424
Web Site: http://www.mbc360.com
Year Founded: 2001
Sales Range: $10-24.9 Million
Emp.: 170
Business Consultants
N.A.I.C.S.: 541618
Christine Morgan (Pres & CEO)
Michael Morgan (COO & VP)
Matthew Borszcz (VP)
Alex Amenabar (VP)
Mark Danis (Principal)
Andy Higgins (Principal)
Brittney Killen (Principal)

MORGAN CONCRETE COMPANY INC
350 Locust St, Toccoa, GA 30577
Tel.: (706) 886-0431
Web Site:
 http://www.morganconcrete.com
Sales Range: $10-24.9 Million
Emp.: 40
Manufactures Ready-Mixed Concrete
N.A.I.C.S.: 327320
Scott Morgan (Pres)
Chad Herron (Mgr-Quality Control)

MORGAN CORP.
1800 E Main St, Duncan, SC 29334
Tel.: (864) 433-8800
Web Site: http://www.morgan-corp.com
Sales Range: $25-49.9 Million
Emp.: 300
Excavation & Grading, Building Construction
N.A.I.C.S.: 238910
Stewart H. Johnson (Chm)
Robert P. Mina (VP-Estimating)
Larry Tate (Mgr-IT)
Arnie Applebaum (VP-HR)
Jeff Howell (Mgr-Ops)
Jacob Hansen (Project Mgr)
Jay Lynch (Pres-Charlotte Div)
Matt Simon (Pres-Savannah Div)
Tommy Harrill (VP-Estimating)

MORGAN COUNTY RURAL ELECTRIC ASSOCIATION
734 Barlow Rd, Fort Morgan, CO 80701
Tel.: (970) 867-5688 CO
Web Site: http://www.mcrea.org
Year Founded: 1937
Sales Range: $25-49.9 Million
Emp.: 50
Electric Power Transmission Services
N.A.I.C.S.: 221121
David P. Frick (Gen Mgr)
Stephan T. Sundet (Mgr-Engrg)
David E. Henderson (Dir-External Affairs)
Bobby J. Brenton (Ops Mgr)
Robb L. Shaver (Mgr-Office Svcs)

MORGAN DISTRIBUTING COMPANY INC.
3425 N 22nd St, Decatur, IL 62526
Tel.: (217) 877-3570 AL
Web Site: http://www.mdilubes.com
Year Founded: 1947
Rev.: $30,000,000
Emp.: 70
Petroleum Products
N.A.I.C.S.: 424720
Brad Pugh (Mgr-Lubrication)
Ken Copenbarger (Mgr-Liquid Fuels)
Gary Morgan (CEO)
Dan Butler (Pres)
Beverly Evitt (CFO)
Joe Hodge (Mgr-Ops)

Kim Grant (Office Mgr)
Jeanne Baietto (Mgr-Customer Svc)
Allison Matusin (VP)
Subsidiaries:

All Star Marketing Inc. (1)
9801 Bluejacket Dr, Overland Park, KS 66214
Tel.: (913) 499-1758
Rev.: $16,860,516
Gasoline Distribution
N.A.I.C.S.: 445131

MORGAN DISTRIBUTION
4930 Old Maumee Rd, Fort Wayne, IN 46803
Tel.: (260) 748-2300
Web Site: http://www.morgandist.com
Year Founded: 1929
Sales Range: $10-24.9 Million
Emp.: 25
Paints
N.A.I.C.S.: 424950
Perry Morgan (Owner & Pres)
Chris Breuning (Controller)

MORGAN FOODS, INC.
90 W Morgan St, Austin, IN 47102-1741
Tel.: (812) 794-1170 IN
Web Site:
 http://www.morganfoods.com
Year Founded: 1899
Sales Range: $200-249.9 Million
Emp.: 400
Food Processing Services
N.A.I.C.S.: 311422
John S. Morgan (Chm & CEO)
Daniel R. Slattery (CFO & Sr VP)
Mary Grander (Mgr-Quality Assurance)
Mark Hartman (VP-Pur)

MORGAN GMC-BUICK
8757 Business Park Dr, Shreveport, LA 71105-5612
Tel.: (318) 798-1600
Web Site:
 http://www.mikemorgan.com
Year Founded: 1986
Sales Range: $50-74.9 Million
Emp.: 130
Car Whslr
N.A.I.C.S.: 441110
Keith Marcott (Gen Mgr)
Michael Morgan (Pres)

MORGAN INDUSTRIAL INC.
23810 NW Huffman St, Hillsboro, OR 97124
Tel.: (503) 647-7474
Web Site:
 http://www.omegamorgan.com
Sales Range: $10-24.9 Million
Emp.: 100
Machine Moving & Rigging
N.A.I.C.S.: 238290
Tom Walker (VP)
Troy Tallent (VP)

MORGAN JEWELERS OF SALT LAKE CITY
545 E 300 S, Salt Lake City, UT 84102
Tel.: (801) 328-8511
Web Site:
 http://www.morganjewelers.com
Sales Range: $75-99.9 Million
Emp.: 150
Jewelry, Precious Stones & Precious Metals
N.A.I.C.S.: 458310
Julianne Lintz (Mgr)
Arnold Prepena (Mgr)

MORGAN JEWELERS OF SALT LAKE CITY — U.S. PRIVATE

Morgan Jewelers of Salt Lake City—(Continued)
Josh Wickersham *(Mgr)*
Larry VanWagoner *(Mgr)*
Susan Muccigrosso *(Mgr)*
Zack Phillips *(Mgr)*

MORGAN JOSEPH TRIARTISAN GROUP INC.
600 5th Ave 14th Fl, New York, NY 10020
Tel.: (212) 218-3700
Web Site: http://www.mjta.com
Sales Range: $75-99.9 Million
Emp.: 140
Holding Company; Investment Banking
N.A.I.C.S.: 551112
Gerald H. Cromack *(Co-Pres)*
Rohit Manocha *(Co-Pres)*
John F. Sorte *(Chm)*
Steven D. Blecher *(Vice Chm)*

Subsidiaries:

Morgan Joseph TriArtisan LLC (1)
600 Fifth Ave 14th Fl, New York, NY 10020-2302
Tel.: (212) 218-3700
Web Site: http://www.mjta.com
Sales Range: $50-74.9 Million
Emp.: 100
Investment Banking
N.A.I.C.S.: 523150
Gerald H. Cromack *(Co-Pres)*
Rohit Manocha *(Co-Pres)*
Steven D. Blecher *(Vice Chm)*

Subsidiary (Domestic):

Karis Capital Partners, LLC
4 High Ridge Park Rd, Stamford, CT 06905
Tel.: (203) 724-9900
Web Site: http://www.kariscp.com
Emp.: 5
Capital Advisory Services
N.A.I.C.S.: 523940
Gregory Neumann *(Co-Mng Dir)*
Kevin Keady *(Co-Mng Dir)*
Meaghan Anderson *(Asst VP)*

Tri-Artisan Partners Advisors Europe LLP (1)
26 Dover Street 2nd Floor, London, W1S 4LY, United Kingdom
Tel.: (44) 20 7518 1650
Financial Advisory Services
N.A.I.C.S.: 523940

MORGAN LINEN SERVICE INC.
145 Broadway, Menands, NY 12204
Tel.: (518) 465-3337
Web Site: http://www.morganlinenservice.com
Rev: $11,313,589
Emp.: 95
Linen Supply
N.A.I.C.S.: 812331
Micmactom Julian *(Mgr-Fleet)*
Anthony Sloane *(Mgr-Saugerties)*
David P. Cesari Jr. *(Pres)*

MORGAN MARKETING & PUBLIC RELATIONS LLC
1231 E Dyer Rd Ste 238, Santa Ana, CA 92705
Tel.: (949) 261-2216
Web Site: http://www.mmpr.biz
Year Founded: 1991
Sales Range: $1-9.9 Million
Emp.: 7
Crisis Communications, Event Planning, Strategic Solutions, Marketing & Communications
N.A.I.C.S.: 541820
Kristin Daher *(Owner)*
Samantha Tyson *(Asst Acct Exec)*

MORGAN OIL COMPANY INCORPORATED
4921 NW Stallings, Nacogdoches, TX 75964
Tel.: (936) 564-4801
Sales Range: $25-49.9 Million
Emp.: 100
Petroleum Bulk Stations
N.A.I.C.S.: 424710
Doug Jordan *(VP)*
Eddie Matts *(Asst Mgr)*
Ed Morgan Jr. *(Pres)*

MORGAN OIL COMPANY, INC.
151 Southwire Dr, Carrollton, GA 30117
Tel.: (770) 832-2311
Web Site: http://www.morganoil.com
Year Founded: 1933
Sales Range: $10-24.9 Million
Emp.: 48
Petroleum Products Mfr & Distr
N.A.I.C.S.: 424710
James P. Morgan *(Owner)*
Pam Dematteis *(Treas & Sec)*

MORGAN PARK SUMMER MUSIC FESTIVAL ASSOCIATION INC.
9 September Ln, Glen Cove, NY 11542
Tel.: (516) 676-7668 NY
Year Founded: 1958
Sales Range: $1-9.9 Million
Musical Concert Organizer
N.A.I.C.S.: 711130
Margaret Minnick *(Treas)*
Nancy Epstein *(Sec)*
Marguerite Suozzi *(Chm)*

MORGAN PROPERTIES TRUST
160 Clubhouse Rd, King of Prussia, PA 19406
Tel.: (610) 265-2800 MD
Web Site: http://www.morgan-properties.com
Sales Range: $125-149.9 Million
Emp.: 770
Real Estate Investment Services
N.A.I.C.S.: 525990
Rimas Petrulis *(Sr VP-Acq & Asset Mgmt)*
Jeffrey Weissman *(Sr VP-Ops)*

MORGAN SAMUELS COMPANY
6420 Wilshire Blvd Ste 1240, Los Angeles, CA 90035
Tel.: (310) 205-2200
Web Site: http://www.morgansamuels.com
Year Founded: 1969
Sales Range: $10-24.9 Million
Emp.: 30
Executive Recruitment Services
N.A.I.C.S.: 541612
Bert C. Hensley *(Chm & CEO)*
Monica L. Bua *(Sr Partner-Client)*
Janice DiPietro *(Pres)*
Todd Wyles *(Partner)*
Marie Martini *(VP-Client Svcs)*
Ali Brainard *(Dir-Recruiting)*
Anne Hoversten *(Dir-Admin)*
Kinohi Orme *(Dir-Org Effectiveness)*
T. J. Zientek *(Dir-IT)*
Udo Eberlein *(Sr Partner-Client-Sausalito)*
Celine Fintzi *(VP-Recruiting & Res)*
Elizabeth S. Thimme *(Principal)*
Lynn Wu *(Principal)*

MORGAN STREET BREWERY & TAVERN INC.
721 N 2nd St, Saint Louis, MO 63102
Tel.: (314) 231-9970
Web Site: http://www.morganstreetbrewery.com
Year Founded: 1993
Sales Range: $10-24.9 Million
Emp.: 100
Brewery Mfr
N.A.I.C.S.: 312120
Dennis Harper *(Pres)*
Steve Owens *(VP)*

MORGAN WHITE GROUP, INC.
5722 I-55 N, Jackson, MS 39211
Tel.: (601) 956-2028
Web Site: http://www.morganwhite.com
Sales Range: $50-74.9 Million
Emp.: 169
Payroll Processing Services
N.A.I.C.S.: 541214
John J. Morgan *(Founder & VP)*
David R. White *(CEO)*
Lynn Flynt *(Suprv-Policy Issue)*
Jason Peets *(Chief Admin Officer)*
Ryan Eaton *(CMO)*
Leigh Ann Ramsey *(Coord-Market)*

MORGAN, LEWIS & BOCKIUS LLP
2222 Market St, Philadelphia, PA 19103-3007
Tel.: (215) 963-5000
Web Site: https://www.morganlewis.com
Year Founded: 1873
Sales Range: Less than $1 Million
Emp.: 2,200
Law firm
N.A.I.C.S.: 541110
Anthony A. Licata *(COO)*
Francis M. Milone *(Partner)*
Steven R. Wall *(Mng Partner)*
David W. Pollak *(Mng Partner)*
Jami Wintz McKeon *(Chm)*
Michael J. Ossip *(Partner)*
Michele E. Martin *(Partner)*
John G. Ferreira *(Partner)*
Laurie A. Dee *(Partner)*
David Sean Cox *(Partner)*
Tae-Woong Koo *(Partner)*
Julie L. Davies *(Partner)*
Sharon R. Smith *(Partner)*
Zane Memeger *(Partner-Litigation)*
Kenneth Nunnenkamp *(Partner-Intl Trade, Natl Security & Economic Sanctions Practic)*
Giovanna Cinelli *(Partner)*
Robert D.#sthash.qlj8i0ag.dpuf Goldbaum *(Partner-Investment Mgmt Transactions Practice)*
Nathan R. Pusey *(Partner-Investment Mgmt Transactions Practice)*
Thomas V. Linguanti *(Partner-Chicago)*
Barton W.S. Bassett *(Head-Tax Practice)*
Jenny A. Austin *(Partner-Chicago)*
James M. Diasio *(CFO)*
Debra S. Lawrence *(Chief Strategy Officer)*
Colleen F. Nihill *(Chief Admin Officer)*
Michael Shea *(CIO)*
Valerie R. Wandler *(Chief HR Officer)*
Mona C. Zeiberg *(CMO)*
Philip Miscimarra *(Partner-Washington)*
Rick Denhup *(Partner-New York)*
Natalie Bennett *(Partner-Washington)*
Adam P. Beckerink *(Partner-Chicago)*
Asem B. Bakenova *(Partner-Astana)*
Carter Brod *(Partner-London)*
Casey S. August *(Partner-Philadelphia)*
Charles R. Bogle *(Partner-New York)*
Edward Bennett *(Partner-Singapore)*
Elizabeth Khoury Ali *(Partner-Houston & New York)*
Ellen S. Bancroft *(Partner-Orange Country)*
Felipe Alice *(Partner-Houston)*
Gitte J. Blanchet *(Partner-Boston)*
J. Goodwin Bland *(Partner-New York)*
James D. Bridgeman *(Partner-Washington)*
Jane Accomando *(Partner-Washington)*
Jeffrey P. Bodle *(Partner-Philadelphia)*
Jennifer Breen *(Partner-Washington)*
Jonathan K. Bernstein *(Partner-Boston)*
Karen A. Abesamis *(Partner)*
Michael K. Barron *(Partner-Boston)*
Michael N. Baxter *(Partner-Philadelphia)*
Patricia F. Brennan *(Partner-New York)*
Paul M. Bessette *(Partner-Washington)*
Richard B. Aldridge *(Partner-Philadelphia)*
Robert A. J. Barry *(Partner-New York & Boston)*
Stephen J. Burdick *(Partner-Washington)*
Wendy Abkin *(Partner-San Francisco)*
Michelle McCarthy *(Partner-Employee Benefits & Exec Compensation Practice)*
Douglas Baruch *(Partner-Washington)*
Jennifer Wollenberg *(Partner-Washington)*
Collie James *(Mng Partner)*
J. Gordon Cooney Jr. *(Partner)*

MORGAN-MCCLURE CHEVY BUICK CADILLAC, INC.
11147 Norton Coeburn Rd, Coeburn, VA 24230
Tel.: (276) 395-3333
Year Founded: 1980
Sales Range: $10-24.9 Million
Emp.: 48
Car Whslr
N.A.I.C.S.: 441110
Timothy Morgan *(Pres & Sec)*

MORGAN-WIGHTMAN SUPPLY COMPANY
739 Goddard Ave, Chesterfield, MO 63005
Tel.: (636) 536-9729
Web Site: http://www.morgan-wightman.com
Sales Range: $10-24.9 Million
Emp.: 13
Millwork
N.A.I.C.S.: 423310
Sandy Brewer *(Mgr-HR)*

MORGAN/HARBOUR CONSTRUCTION, LLC.
390 Internationale Dr, Bolingbrook, IL 60440
Tel.: (630) 734-8800
Web Site: http://www.morganharbour.com
Sales Range: $10-24.9 Million
Emp.: 20
Civil Engineering Services
N.A.I.C.S.: 237310
Warren Seil *(Pres)*
Drue Stoehr *(VP)*

MORGANFRANKLIN CORPORATION
1753 Pinnacle Dr Ste 1200, McLean, VA 22102
Tel.: (703) 564-7525

Web Site:
http://www.morganfranklin.com
Year Founded: 1998
Sales Range: $75-99.9 Million
Emp.: 4,000
Business Software Consulting Services
N.A.I.C.S.: 541512
Robert Morgan (Co-Founder)
Ron Morgan (Co-Founder & Chm)
Ashley Baquie (Chief HR Officer & VP)
Ross Creasy (Mng Dir)
Jim Burns (Mng Dir)
Geoff Harkness (Mng Dir)
Frank Landefeld (Mng Dir)
Barbara Ard (Mng Dir-Acctg & Transaction Svcs)
Fred Hargrove (Mng Dir-Info Mgmt & Tech)
Kenneth Merritt (Mng Dir-Strategy, Fin & Ops)
Eric Reicin (Gen Counsel, Sec & VP)
Shawn Degnan (Mng Dir)
Chris Mann (CEO & Mng Partner)
Amanda Mitchell (Dir-Client Relationships)
Steve Boyce (Mng Dir & CFO)
Stephanie Irby (Dir-Pub Sector Practice)
Steve Balistreri (Mng Dir)
Charles E. Price II (Mng Dir-Risk & Compliance)

MORGANTI GROUP/SKH HOLDINGS INC.
100 Mill Plain Rd, Danbury, CT 06811
Tel.: (203) 743-2675
Web Site: http://www.morganti.com
Year Founded: 1988
Sales Range: $25-49.9 Million
Emp.: 233
Holding Company
N.A.I.C.S.: 551112
Nabil Takla (Pres)

Subsidiaries:

The Morganti Group, Inc. (1)
100 Mill Plain Rd, Danbury, CT 06811-5178
Tel.: (203) 743-2675
Web Site: https://morganti.com
Sales Range: $25-49.9 Million
Commercial & Institutional Building Construction Services
N.A.I.C.S.: 236220
Maria Woods (Mgr-Payroll)
Bob Zaccagnino (Project Mgr)
David Bielawski (Project Mgr)
Mark Schweitzer (Project Mgr)
Charles Blaszka (Superintendent)
John Moore (Superintendent)
Collin Majev (Coord-Bus Dev)
Jason M. Crumbling (VP & Controller)
Cyril J. Greenya (Chief Underwriting Officer & Sr VP)
Jeffrey A. Jacobsen (Sr VP-Personal Lines Underwriting)
David S. Krenkel (VP-Mktg & Adv)
Sanjay Pandey (CIO & Sr VP)
Charles E. Smith (VP-HR)
Christina M. Springer (Sr VP-Internal Audit)
Daniel J. Wagner (Treas & Sr VP)
Thamer Rushaidat (Pres & CEO)

Subsidiary (Domestic):

Morganti Florida Inc. (2)
1450 Centrepark Blvd Ste 260, West Palm Beach, FL 33401-6450
Tel.: (561) 689-0200
Web Site: http://www.morganti.com
Sales Range: $10-24.9 Million
Emp.: 20
Provider of Nonresidential Construction Services
N.A.I.C.S.: 236220

Morganti Texas Inc. (2)
350 N Sam Houston Pkwy E Ste 121, Houston, TX 77060-3306
Tel.: (203) 743-2675

Web Site: http://www.morganti.com
Sales Range: $10-24.9 Million
Emp.: 12
Provider of Nonresidential Construction Services
N.A.I.C.S.: 236220
Joe Kummer (VP)

MORGENS WATERFALL VINTIADIS & CO. INC.
600 5th Ave, New York, NY 10020
Tel.: (212) 218-4100
Year Founded: 1970
Sales Range: $10-24.9 Million
Emp.: 10
Investment Firm
N.A.I.C.S.: 523999
Edwin Huffman Morgens (Chm)
Morgen Edwin (Pres)

MORGENTHALER MANAGEMENT CORPORATION
3200 Alpine Rd, Portola Valley, CA 94028
Tel.: (650) 388-7600 OH
Web Site:
http://www.morgenthaler.com
Year Founded: 1968
Venture Capital & Private Equity Investment Management Firm
N.A.I.C.S.: 523940
Gary Little (Partner-IT)
Gary Morgenthaler (Partner-IT)
Robin Bellas (Partner-Life Sciences)
Ralph E. Christoffersen (Partner-Life Sciences)
Rebecca Lynn (Partner-IT)
Hank Plain (Partner-Life Sciences)
Travis Boettner (CFO & Chief Compliance Officer)

MORGRO, INC.
145 W Central Ave, Salt Lake City, UT 84107-1418
Tel.: (801) 266-1132 UT
Web Site: http://www.morgro.com
Year Founded: 1980
Sales Range: $10-24.9 Million
Emp.: 12
Fertilizers, Wasp Traps, Garden Products & Log Fire Starters Mfr
N.A.I.C.S.: 325998
Delbert Davis (Pres)
Steven Martin (VP & Controller)
Rick Jensen (Gen Mgr)

MORI LUGGAGE AND GIFTS INC.
3595 McCall Pl, Atlanta, GA 30340
Tel.: (770) 451-6674
Web Site:
http://www.moriluggage.com
Sales Range: $10-24.9 Million
Emp.: 250
Luggage, Except Footlockers & Trunks
N.A.I.C.S.: 458320
Kim Rowan (Controller)
John Mori (CEO)

MORIN BRICK CO.
130 Morin Brick Rd, Auburn, ME 04211
Tel.: (207) 784-9375
Web Site: http://www.morinbrick.com
Sales Range: $10-24.9 Million
Emp.: 55
Brick, Concrete
N.A.I.C.S.: 327331
Jason Lachance (Dir-Sls)

MORITZ KIA F.T. WORTH
8501 W West Freeway, Fort Worth, TX 76116
Tel.: (817) 560-6000
Web Site: http://www.moritzkiafw.com
Year Founded: 2002

Sales Range: $10-24.9 Million
Emp.: 60
Car Whslr
N.A.I.C.S.: 441110
Matt Ducote (Gen Mgr)

MORLEY BANCSHARES CORPORATION
502 N Merchant St, Belle Plaine, KS 67013
Tel.: (620) 488-2211 KS
Web Site:
http://www.valleystatebank.com
Year Founded: 1990
Sales Range: $1-9.9 Million
Emp.: 32
Bank Holding Company
N.A.I.C.S.: 551111
Douglas M. Morley (Pres)
Randal D. Morley (Chm)

Subsidiaries:

The Valley State Bank (1)
502 N Merchant St, Belle Plaine KS 67013
Tel.: (620) 488-2211
Web Site: http://www.valleystatebank2.com
Sales Range: $1-9.9 Million
Emp.: 30
Commericial Banking
N.A.I.C.S.: 522110
Douglas M. Morley (Pres & CEO)
Randal D. Morley (Chm)
Melissa Morgan (Asst VP)
Sandra Wharton (VP-NMLS)
Stacey Clark (CFO & VP-Ops)
Chad Allen (VP)
Matt Canfield (VP-NMLS)
Jonathan Holmes (Exec VP)

MORLEY BUILDERS
3330 Ocean Pk Blvd, Santa Monica, CA 90405-2938
Tel.: (310) 399-1600 CA
Web Site:
http://www.morleybuilders.com
Year Founded: 1947
Sales Range: $250-299.9 Million
Emp.: 300
General Contractors, Concrete Work, New Construction of Condominiums, Commercial & Office Building Construction
N.A.I.C.S.: 236220
Charles Muttillo (Pres)
Eric Garcia (CFO)
Jan Karl (VP-Project Dev)
Ron Elazar (VP-Construction Ops)
Jeff Simonson (VP-Preconstruction & Estimating)

Subsidiaries:

Benchmark Contractors, Inc. (1)
3330 Oceanpark Blvd, Santa Monica, CA 90405 (100%)
Tel.: (310) 399-1600
Web Site: http://www.morleybuilders.com
Sales Range: $10-24.9 Million
Emp.: 100
General Contractors
N.A.I.C.S.: 236116
Charlie Muttillo (Pres)

Morley Construction Co., Inc. (1)
3330 Ocean Park Blvd, Santa Monica, CA 90405-2938 (100%)
Tel.: (310) 392-7272
Web Site: http://www.morelybuilders.com
Sales Range: $25-49.9 Million
Emp.: 100
Sub Contractors of Concrete Works
N.A.I.C.S.: 238110
Chris Lopez (Office Mgr)

MORMAC MARINE GROUP, INC.
1 Landmark Sq Ste 710, Stamford, CT 06901-2620
Tel.: (440) 260-6900 DE
Year Founded: 1987
Sales Range: $10-24.9 Million

Emp.: 8
Deep Sea Foreign Transportation Of Freigh
N.A.I.C.S.: 483111
Paul R. Tregurtha (Chm & CEO)
James R. Barker (Vice Chm)
Thomas W. Wynne (Gen Counsel)

Subsidiaries:

Interlake Steamship Company Inc. (1)
7300 Engle Rd, Middleburg Heights, OH 44130 (100%)
Tel.: (440) 260-6900
Web Site: http://www.interlake-steamship.com
Inland Water Freight Transportation
N.A.I.C.S.: 483211
James R. Barker (Chm & CEO)
Robert Born (VP)

MORNING LAVENDER LLC
330 El Camino Real, Tustin, CA 92780
Tel.: (714) 486-1429
Web Site:
http://www.morninglavender.com
Year Founded: 2014
Sales Range: $1-9.9 Million
Fashion Garment Distr
N.A.I.C.S.: 424350
Kim Le Pham (Founder)

MORNING STAR PACKING CO. LP
13448 Volta Rd, Los Banos, CA 93635
Tel.: (209) 826-8000
Web Site:
http://www.morningstarco.com
Sales Range: $200-249.9 Million
Emp.: 35
Mfr of Canned Tomato Paste
N.A.I.C.S.: 311421
Chris Rufer (Founder & Owner)

MORNINGSIDE MINISTRIES
700 Babcock Rd, San Antonio, TX 78201
Tel.: (210) 734-1000 TX
Web Site: http://www.mmliving.org
Year Founded: 1959
Sales Range: $25-49.9 Million
Emp.: 1,080
Lifecare Retirement & Elderly People Assisted Living Services
N.A.I.C.S.: 623312
Joan Dixon (VP-Fin)
Maria Wellisch (VP-Corp Education)
Jordan Lovelady (COO)

MOROCH PARTNERS
3625 N Hall St Ste 1100, Dallas, TX 75219-5122
Tel.: (214) 520-9700 DE
Web Site: http://www.moroch.com
Year Founded: 1981
Sales Range: $10-24.9 Million
Emp.: 250
Advertising Services
N.A.I.C.S.: 541810
Pat Kempf (Co-Founder & Vice Chm)
Rob Boswell (CEO)
Thomas F. Moroch (Co-Founder & Chm)
Kevin Sutton (Exec Dir-Creative)
Brad B. McCormick (Chief Integrated Strategy Officer)
Doug Martin (Pres)
Candyce Vanterpool (Dir-Creative)
Elijah Farmer (Dir-Creative)
Yolanda Cassity (Chief Brand Mgmt & Integration Officer)
Colin Turney (Chief Creative Svcs Officer)
Jessica Anderson (Mng Dir-Brand Rels)

MOROCH PARTNERS

U.S. PRIVATE

Moroch Partners—(Continued)
Kelly Correia *(Exec VP)*
Lindsay Weeks *(Mng Dir-Digital Media-Bloodhound)*

Subsidiaries:

Moroch (1)
2601 Nw Expressway Ste 500e, Oklahoma City, OK 73112-7266
Tel.: (405) 848-6800
Sales Range: $10-24.9 Million
Emp.: 11
Advertising Services
N.A.I.C.S.: 541810

Moroch (1)
2450 Ste 230, Sacramento, CA 95833-4333
Tel.: (916) 929-9100
Web Site: http://www.moroch.com
Sales Range: $10-24.9 Million
Emp.: 10
Advertising Services
N.A.I.C.S.: 541810
Clay Merrill *(Acct Exec)*

Moroch (1)
1801 Broadway Ste 1050, Denver, CO 80202-3809
Tel.: (801) 487-6773
Sales Range: $10-24.9 Million
Emp.: 3
Advertising Services
N.A.I.C.S.: 541810

Moroch (1)
201 McCullough Dr Ste 380, Charlotte, NC 28262
Tel.: (704) 503-5120
Sales Range: $10-24.9 Million
Emp.: 4
Advertising Services
N.A.I.C.S.: 541810
Anne Hylton *(Acct Supvr)*

Moroch (1)
590 Means St, Atlanta, GA 30318
Tel.: (404) 607-8822
Sales Range: $10-24.9 Million
Emp.: 20
Advertising Services
N.A.I.C.S.: 541810
Pat Kempf *(Chm & CEO)*
Andrew Lamar *(Acct Exec)*

Moroch (1)
10809 Executive Ctr Dr Ste Plz 7, Little Rock, AR 72211
Tel.: (501) 225-9537
Web Site: http://www.moroch.com
Sales Range: $10-24.9 Million
Emp.: 3
Advertising Services
N.A.I.C.S.: 541810
Chris White *(Asst Acct Exec)*

Moroch (1)
9020 Stoney Point Pkwy Ste 370, Richmond, VA 23235
Tel.: (804) 320-6376
Web Site: http://www.moroch.com
Sales Range: Less than $1 Million
Emp.: 3
Advertising Services
N.A.I.C.S.: 541810
Dionne Kumpe *(Acct Dir)*
Andrew LaMar *(Acct Supvr)*

Moroch (1)
5400 Glenwood Ave Ste G05, Raleigh, NC 27612
Tel.: (919) 881-7880
Sales Range: $10-24.9 Million
Emp.: 3
Advertising Services
N.A.I.C.S.: 541810

Moroch (1)
81 SW 10th St Ste 2200, Lauderdale, FL 33324
Tel.: (214) 560-9700
Sales Range: $10-24.9 Million
Emp.: 2
Advertising Services
N.A.I.C.S.: 541810

Moroch (1)
39500 High Pointe Blvd Ste 450, Novi, MI 48375-1240
Tel.: (248) 348-9095
Web Site: http://www.moroch.com
Sales Range: $10-24.9 Million
Emp.: 10
Advertising Services
N.A.I.C.S.: 541810
Steve Barry *(Acct Dir)*

Moroch (1)
3901 Brisco Rd Ste 12, Parkersburg, WV 26104
Tel.: (304) 424-7134
Web Site: http://www.moroch.com
Sales Range: $10-24.9 Million
Emp.: 5
Advertising Services
N.A.I.C.S.: 541810

Moroch (1)
115 Gold Ave SW Ste 205, Albuquerque, NM 87102
Tel.: (505) 836-1823
Advertising Services
N.A.I.C.S.: 541810

Moroch (1)
4074 Overlook Trail Dr, Roanoke, VA 24014
Tel.: (540) 725-1860
Advertising Services
N.A.I.C.S.: 541810

Moroch (1)
135 N Meramec Ave Ste 405, Clayton, MO 63105
Tel.: (314) 878-8311
Web Site: http://www.moroch.com
Sales Range: Less than $1 Million
Emp.: 6
Advertising Services
N.A.I.C.S.: 541810
Jack Phifer *(Chief Mktg Officer)*

Moroch (1)
70 Office Pkwy, Rochester, NY 14534
Tel.: (585) 586-6320
Advertising Services
N.A.I.C.S.: 541810

Moroch (1)
402 Main St 5th Fl, Houston, TX 77002
Tel.: (713) 223-2788
Web Site: http://www.moroch.com
Sales Range: $10-24.9 Million
Emp.: 10
Advertising Services
N.A.I.C.S.: 541810
Kesha Willaford *(Acct Supvr)*
Jason Price *(Sr Acct Exec)*
Sonya Sauceda *(Sr Partner)*

Moroch (1)
901 NE Loop 410 Ste 826, San Antonio, TX 78209-1310
Tel.: (210) 822-4840
Web Site: http://www.moroch.com
Sales Range: $10-24.9 Million
Emp.: 8
Advertising Services
N.A.I.C.S.: 541810

Moroch (1)
3500 N Causeway Blvd Ste 1405, Metairie, LA 70002
Tel.: (504) 833-8399
Advertising Services
N.A.I.C.S.: 541810

MORONEY & GILL, INC.
245 Park Ave 39th Fl, New York, NY 10167
Tel.: (212) 672-1675
Web Site: http://www.moroneyandgill.com
Year Founded: 1991
Rev: $20,000,000
Emp.: 60
Consulting, Pharmaceutical
N.A.I.C.S.: 541810
Kevin Moroney *(Pres & CEO)*

MOROSO PERFORMANCE PRODUCTS, INC.
80 Carter Dr, Guilford, CT 06437
Tel.: (203) 453-6571
Web Site: http://www.moroso.com
Year Founded: 1968
Sales Range: $10-24.9 Million
Emp.: 190
Supplier of Automotive Equipment for Racing & Street Performance Applications
N.A.I.C.S.: 336390
Richard B. Moroso *(Pres)*
John Ferretti *(CFO)*
Gail Anderson *(Office Mgr)*
Gary Burkle *(Dir-Ops)*
John Galayda *(Engr-Mfg)*
Paul Minroe *(Mgr-Shop)*

MORRELL INCORPORATED
3333 Bald Mtn Rd, Auburn Hills, MI 48326
Tel.: (248) 373-1600
Web Site: http://www.morrellinc.com
Year Founded: 1976
Sales Range: $50-74.9 Million
Emp.: 320
Provider of Hydraulic Systems Equipment & Supplies
N.A.I.C.S.: 423830
Steven L. Tallman *(Pres)*
Richard Dunnigan *(Product Mgr-Hydraulic)*

MORRIE'S IMPORTS, INC.
12550 Wayzata Blvd, Minnetonka, MN 55305
Tel.: (952) 544-0096
Web Site: http://www.morries.com
Sales Range: $600-649.9 Million
Emp.: 845
Holding Company; New & Used Car Dealerships Operator
N.A.I.C.S.: 551112
John Aretz *(Gen Mgr)*
Nancy Erickson *(Controller)*
Daniel Hegge *(Mgr-Sls)*
Jess Vraspir *(Mgr-Parts)*
Joe Weil *(Mgr-Internet Sls)*
Kevin Schiltz Schiltz *(Mgr-Used Car)*
Patrick Kyes *(Mgr-Sls)*
Rich Adamson *(Mgr-Internet)*
Steven Lovel *(Mgr-Parts)*
Toulong Yang *(Mgr-F&I)*
Jennifer Zuniga *(Office Mgr)*
Brian D. Kruschke *(Bus Mgr-Fin)*
Chris Johnston *(Dir-Fin)*
Brooke Robbins *(Mgr-CRM Performance)*
David Ahlm *(Mgr-Sls)*
Kim Berbaum *(Mgr-Sls)*
Bill Bertrand *(Gen Mgr)*
Karl Schmidt *(CEO)*
Ron Budhram *(Dir-Svc)*
Curt Bjorklund *(Mgr-Fleet & Lease)*
Jesse Howard *(Mgr-Internet Sls)*
Dan Epp *(Mgr-Sls)*
Michael Iverson *(Mgr-Sls)*
Mike Popp *(Mgr-Sls)*
Steve Olson *(Mgr-Sls)*
Shawn Sodren *(Mgr-Svc)*
Jan Seeman *(Office Mgr)*

Subsidiaries:

Morrie's Buffalo Ford (1)
702 E Hwy 55, Buffalo, MN 55313
Tel.: (763) 248-7879
Web Site: http://www.morriesbuffalofordstore.com
Emp.: 75
New & Used Car Dealer
N.A.I.C.S.: 441110
Brett Kramer *(Gen Mgr)*

Morrie's Cadillac (1)
7400 Wayzata Blvd, Golden Valley, MN 55426
Tel.: (763) 248-7859
Web Site: http://www.morriescadillac.com
Sales Range: $25-49.9 Million
Emp.: 65
New Car Dealers
N.A.I.C.S.: 441110
Steve Lee *(Mgr-Parts)*

MORRIS & DICKSON CO., LLC
410 Kay Ln, Shreveport, LA 71115-3604
Tel.: (318) 797-7900
Web Site: http://www.morrisdickson.com
Year Founded: 1896
Sales Range: $1-9.9 Million
Emp.: 400
Pharmaceutical Services
N.A.I.C.S.: 424210
Paul Dickson *(Pres)*

Subsidiaries:

Morris & Dickson Co., LLC - Retail and Hospital Division (1)
1776 Woodstead Ct Ste 125, The Woodlands, TX 77380
Tel.: (281) 292-9180
Pharmaceutical Product Whslr
N.A.I.C.S.: 424210

New Tech Computer Systems Inc. (1)
410 Kay Ln, Shreveport, LA 71115-3604
Web Site: http://www.newtechsys.com
Sales Range: $50-74.9 Million
Emp.: 350
Computer Peripheral & Software Distr
N.A.I.C.S.: 423430
Markham Allen Dickson Jr. *(Pres)*

MORRIS BEAN & COMPANY
777 E Hyde Rd, Yellow Springs, OH 45387
Tel.: (937) 767-7301
Web Site: http://www.morrisbean.com
Year Founded: 1946
Sales Range: $10-24.9 Million
Emp.: 94
Aluminum Foundries
N.A.I.C.S.: 331524
William Magro *(CFO)*

MORRIS BLACK & SONS INC.
984 Marcon Blvd LVIP III, Allentown, PA 18109
Tel.: (610) 264-2700
Web Site: http://www.morrisblackinc.com
Year Founded: 1908
Custom-Fabricated Casework, Architectural Millwork, Kitchens & Baths & Residential Insulation Contracting Services
N.A.I.C.S.: 423310
Robert Black *(VP)*

MORRIS CAPITAL MANAGEMENT, LLC
1200 Mountain Creek Rd Ste 150, Chattanooga, TN 37405
Tel.: (423) 870-0800
Web Site: http://www.morriscapitalmanagement.com
Year Founded: 2002
Investment Advisory & Fund Management Services
N.A.I.C.S.: 523940
Tim T. Morris *(Mng Partner)*
Ricky Sanders *(Partner)*
Larry Hughes *(Partner)*
Tim T. Morris Jr. *(Partner)*

MORRIS CERULLO WORLD EVANGELISM
3545 Aero Ct, San Diego, CA 92123-1710
Tel.: (858) 277-2200
Web Site: http://www.mcwe.com
Sales Range: $50-74.9 Million
Emp.: 100
Religious Services
N.A.I.C.S.: 813110
Morris Cerullo *(Pres)*
Theresa Cerullo *(Treas & Sec)*

COMPANIES

Subsidiaries:

Morris Cerullo World Evangelism (1)
Unit 10 Sovereign Park Cleveland Way, PO Box 277, Hemel Hempstead, HP2 7BR, Herts, United Kingdom
Tel.: (44) 1442232432
Web Site: http://www.mcwe.co.uk
Sales Range: $10-24.9 Million
Emp.: 9
Religious Services
N.A.I.C.S.: 813110

Morris Cerullo World Evangelism (1)
PO Box 3600, Concord, L4K 1B6, ON, Canada
Tel.: (905) 669-1788
Web Site: https://mcwe.com
Sales Range: $10-24.9 Million
Emp.: 4
Religious Services
N.A.I.C.S.: 813110
Morris Cerullo (CEO)

MORRIS COMMUNICATIONS, INC.
533 Woodruff Rd, Greenville, SC 29607
Tel.: (864) 234-7309   SC
Web Site:
  http://www.morriswireless.com
Sales Range: $10-24.9 Million
Emp.: 80
Provider of Wireless Communication Services
N.A.I.C.S.: 517112
Trace Morris (Pres & CEO)
Mary Beth Van Meter (Controller)

MORRIS CORPORATION
145 Ridgeland Plz, Ridgeland, MS 39157
Tel.: (601) 856-3005
Web Site: http://www.strintnart.com
Rev.: $17,900,000
Emp.: 15
Convenience Stores, Independent
N.A.I.C.S.: 445131
Charles Morris (Pres)

MORRIS COUNTY LIBRARY
30 E Hanover Ave, Whippany, NJ 07981
Tel.: (973) 285-6930
Web Site: https://www.mclib.info
Year Founded: 1922
Educational Support Services
N.A.I.C.S.: 611710

MORRIS COUNTY MUNICIPAL UTILITIES AUTHORITY
300 Mendham Rd, Morristown, NJ 07960
Tel.: (973) 285-8383
Web Site: http://www.mcmua.com
Rev.: $35,903,054
Emp.: 20
Provider of Municipal Water Supply Services
N.A.I.C.S.: 221310
Glenn Schweizer (Exec Dir)
Robert Ross (Mgr-Transfer Station)
John Scarmozza (Chief Water Engr)
Mike Bonefede (Mgr-Ops)

MORRIS COUPLING COMPANY
2240 W 15th St, Erie, PA 16505
Tel.: (814) 459-1741   PA
Web Site:
  http://www.morriscoupling.com
Year Founded: 1941
Sales Range: $500-549.9 Million
Emp.: 250
Mfr of Piping Components for the Pneumatic Conveying Industry
N.A.I.C.S.: 522110

Robert Shreve (VP-Sls & Mktg)
Barbara R. Pollock (Treas)
John McUmber (Mgr-Sls-Midwest)

Subsidiaries:

Tennessee Tubebending Inc. (1)
5112 N National Dr, Knoxville, TN 37914-6511   (100%)
Tel.: (865) 546-6511
Web Site: http://www.morriscoupling.com
Sales Range: $10-24.9 Million
Emp.: 60
Pipe And Tube Bending & Vaccum Products
N.A.I.C.S.: 332996
Howard Pollock (Pres)
Jan Campbell (Office Mgr)
Jerry Fialkowski (Mgr-Sls-Midwest)
John McUmber (Mgr-Sls-Midwest)

MORRIS FURNITURE CO. INC.
2377 Commerce Center Blvd, Fairborn, OH 45324
Tel.: (937) 874-7100   OH
Web Site:
  http://www.morrisathome.com
Year Founded: 1948
Sales Range: $25-49.9 Million
Emp.: 300
Provider of Home Furnishings, Mattresses, Appliances & Electronics
N.A.I.C.S.: 449110
Lewis Thorp (Coord-IST)
Matthew Ball (Mgr-Bedding)
Ed Adams (Mgr-Show Room)

MORRIS GROUP, INC.
910 Day Hill Rd, Windsor, CT 06095
Tel.: (860) 687-3475
Web Site:
  http://www.morrisgroupinc.com
Year Founded: 1941
Sales Range: $550-599.9 Million
Emp.: 500
Machine Tool Distr
N.A.I.C.S.: 423830
Lee Morris (Founder & Chm)
Bradley R. Morris (Pres & CEO)
Stephen Boyd (CFO)

Subsidiaries:

HFO Chicago, LLC (1)
555 Busse Rd, Elk Grove Village, IL 60007
Tel.: (877) 440-4227
Web Site: http://www.hfochicago.com
Emp.: 25
Industrial Machinery Whslr
N.A.I.C.S.: 423830
Jeff Holtzapple (VP & Gen Mgr)

Haas Factory Outlet LLC (1)
913 US Hwy 301 S, Tampa, FL 33619
Tel.: (813) 628-0665
Web Site: http://www.haasflorida.com
Emp.: 15
Industrial Machinery Whslr
N.A.I.C.S.: 423830

MP Systems, Inc. (1)
34 Bradley Park Rd, East Granby, CT 06026
Tel.: (877) 689-1860
Web Site: http://www.mp-systems.net
Emp.: 30
Industrial Machinery Whslr
N.A.I.C.S.: 423830
Graham Noake (Pres)
Mike Sayers (Gen Mgr)
Kermit Wright (Mgr-Sls)
Maura Thompson (Mgr-Ops)

Machinery Finance Resources, LLC (1)
651 Day Hill Rd, Windsor, CT 06095
Tel.: (860) 687-3375
Web Site: http://www.mfresources.com
Emp.: 9
Financial Management Services
N.A.I.C.S.: 523940
John Fitzgerald (Pres)

Midwest Manufacturing Resources, Inc. (1)
1993 Case Pwy N, Twinsburg, OH 44087
Tel.: (330) 405-4227
Emp.: 30
Industrial Machinery Whslr
N.A.I.C.S.: 423830

Division (Domestic):

Midwest Manufacturing Resources, Inc. - Haas Factory Outlet Midwest Division (2)
1993 Case Pwy N, Twinsburg, OH 44087
Tel.: (330) 405-4227
Web Site: http://www.hfomidwest.com
Industrial Machinery Whslr
N.A.I.C.S.: 423830
David M. Kerr (VP-Tech Ops)

Morris Group, Inc. - Morris Great Lakes Division (1)
9151 Marshall Rd, Cranberry Township, PA 16066
Tel.: (877) 373-8906
Web Site: http://www.morrisgreatlakes.com
Industrial Machinery Whslr
N.A.I.C.S.: 423830

Morris Group, Inc. - Morris South Division (1)
12428 Sam Neely Rd, Charlotte, NC 28278
Tel.: (704) 523-6008
Web Site: http://www.morrissouth.com
Emp.: 50
Industrial Machinery Whslr
N.A.I.C.S.: 423830
Kevin Wigington (Pres)

Morris Group, Inc. - Morris Turbine Group Division (1)
910 Day Hill Rd, Windsor, CT 06095
Tel.: (860) 687-3300
Aircraft Turbine Mfr
N.A.I.C.S.: 336412

Morris Group, Inc. - Velocity Products Division (1)
350 Electronic Blvd, Huntsville, AL 35824
Tel.: (860) 687-3530
Web Site: http://www.velocityproducts.com
Emp.: 5
Industrial Machinery Whslr
N.A.I.C.S.: 423830
Bob Bauer (VP)

Morris Midwest, LLC (1)
8718 Monticello Ln N, Maple Grove, MN 55369
Tel.: (763) 424-5622
Web Site: http://www.morrismidwest.com
Industrial Machinery Whslr
N.A.I.C.S.: 423830
Amenda Nagy (Controller)
Craig Hahne (Sls Mgr)

Morris Midwest, LLC (1)
9300 W Heather Ave, Milwaukee, WI 53224
Tel.: (414) 586-0450
Web Site: http://www.morrismidwest.com
Industrial Machinery Whslr
N.A.I.C.S.: 423830
Corey Johnson (Pres)
Eric Grob (Sls Mgr)
Doug Pence (Mgr-Engrg & Svc)
Ron Boudreau (Mgr-Engrg & Svc)
Mike James (Sls Mgr-IL)

Morris South, LLC (1)
12428 Sam Neely Rd, Charlotte, NC 28278
Tel.: (704) 523-6008
Web Site: http://www.morrissouth.com
Sales Range: $25-49.9 Million
Emp.: 40
Industrial Machinery & Equipment Distr
N.A.I.C.S.: 423830
Dan Danese (VP)
Kevin Wigington (Pres)
Craig Baye (Mgr-Engrg-Huntsville)
Glenn Cave (VP-Sls-Charlotte)
Joe Hunt (VP-Sls-Georgia)
Keith Wilson (VR-Sls)

Subsidiary (Domestic):

Morris South, LLC-Huntsville (2)
350 Electronics Blvd, Huntsville, AL 35824-2218   (100%)
Tel.: (256) 461-8111
Web Site: http://www.morrisgroupinc.com
Sales Range: $1-9.9 Million
Emp.: 31
Industrial Machinery & Equipment

N.A.I.C.S.: 423830
Lee Morris (Chm)

REM Sales, LLC (1)
910 Day Hill Rd, Windsor, CT 06095
Tel.: (860) 687-3400
Web Site: http://www.remsales.com
Sales Range: $25-49.9 Million
Emp.: 38
Industrial Machinery & Equipment
N.A.I.C.S.: 423830
Ron Gainer (Mgr-North East)
Frank Maiocco (Mgr-South East)
Stefan Brusky (Mgr-Midwest)
George Media (Mgr-North Central)
John Traver (Mgr-West)

Technical Equipment Sales Company (1)
10165 International Blvd, Cincinnati, OH 45246
Tel.: (513) 874-0160
Web Site: http://www.techequip.com
Emp.: 60
Industrial Machinery Whslr
N.A.I.C.S.: 423830
Lou Olson (Pres-Tech Equipment Sls)

The Robert E. Morris Company (1)
910 Day Hill Rd, Windsor, CT 06095
Tel.: (860) 687-3300
Web Site: http://www.robertemorris.com
Sales Range: $25-49.9 Million
Emp.: 150
Machine Tool Distr
N.A.I.C.S.: 423830
Lee B. Morris (Chm)
Todd W. Campbell (Mgr-Sls-New England)
Aaron Hornyak (Pres)
Reid Gibson (VP-Ops)
Andy Piccus (Head-Engrg & Contracts Admin)
John Sadowski (Mgr-Engrg)

Trident Machine Tools, LLC (1)
790 Marshall Phelps Rd, Windsor, CT 06095
Tel.: (860) 687-2466
Web Site: http://www.hfotrident.com
Industrial Machinery Whslr
N.A.I.C.S.: 423830
Kirk DeRousse (Pres)
Dino Baldoni (Mgr-Svc)
Chris Cook (Engr-Sls)

MORRIS HARDWICK SCHNEIDER & LANDCASTLE TITLE
120 Interstate N Pkwy SE Suite 110, Atlanta, GA 30339
Tel.: (678) 298-2100
Web Site:
  http://www.closingsource.net
Year Founded: 2005
Sales Range: $50-74.9 Million
Emp.: 709
Attorney & Title Services to Real Estate Companies
N.A.I.C.S.: 524127
Lisa Edwards Anderson (Partner)
Natalie Nell Hardwick (Partner)
Arthur J. Morris (Mng Partner)
Frederick G. Boynton (Partner)
James J. Cooney (Partner)
Nathan E. Hardwick IV (Mng Partner)

MORRIS HEIGHTS HEALTH CENTER, INC.
85 W Burnside Ave, Bronx, NY 10453
Tel.: (718) 483-1270   NY
Web Site: http://www.mhhc.org
Year Founded: 1984
Sales Range: $25-49.9 Million
Emp.: 533
Healtcare Services
N.A.I.C.S.: 622110
Tosan Oruwariye (Chief Medical Officer & Exec VP)
Judith Fairweather (Exec VP-Regulatory & Bus Affairs)
Pamela Smith (Chief HR Officer & VP)
Marcus Freeman (VP-Fin)

MORRIS INDUSTRIES INC.

Morris Industries Inc.—(Continued)

MORRIS INDUSTRIES INC.
777 State Rt 23, Pompton Plains, NJ 07444
Tel.: (973) 835-6600
Web Site: http://www.morrispipe.com
Year Founded: 1958
Sales Range: $10-24.9 Million
Steel Pipe & Water Well Casing Mfr
N.A.I.C.S.: 331210
Robert Nochenson (Pres)
Mike Stern (VP)

MORRIS INTERNATIONAL, INC.
100-H N Harbor Pl, Davidson, NC 28036
Tel.: (704) 896-3350
Web Site: http://www.morrisinternational.com
Year Founded: 1972
Sales Range: $50-74.9 Million
Emp.: 20
N.A.I.C.S.: 541810
Sid Morris (CEO)
Deb Cameron (Mgr-HR)

MORRIS LEVIN AND SON
1816 S K St, Tulare, CA 93274
Tel.: (559) 686-8665
Web Site: http://www.morrislevin.com
Sales Range: $10-24.9 Million
Emp.: 125
Lumber & Other Building Materials
N.A.I.C.S.: 423310
Paul Atlas (Pres & CEO)
Tom Colesberry (CFO)
David Atlas (VP)

MORRIS MOORE CHEVROLET-BUICK, INC.
1415 Hwy 96 Bypass, Silsbee, TX 77656-6267
Tel.: (409) 385-5221
Sales Range: $50-74.9 Million
Emp.: 100
Car Whslr
N.A.I.C.S.: 441110
Greg Butts (Gen Mgr-Sls)
Gary Gerngross (Mgr-Svc)
Fabian Gonzalez (Treas & Sec)
Morris Moore (Co-Owner)
Tommy Moore (Co-Owner)
Paul Palumbo (Mgr-Used Car)
Rita Peyres (Comptroller)

MORRIS MULTIMEDIA, INC.
27 Abercorn, Savannah, GA 31401
Tel.: (912) 233-1281
Web Site: http://www.morrismultimedia.com
Year Founded: 1970
Sales Range: $400-449.9 Million
Emp.: 1,000
Newspaper Publishers
N.A.I.C.S.: 513110
Jeffrey R. Samuels (CFO & VP)
Joe McGlamery (Reg Mgr)
Lori Maxim (Dir-Revenue)
Bobby Berry (COO)
Charles Hill Morris Jr. (CEO)
Charles H. Morris Sr. (Pres)

Subsidiaries:

Morris Network, Inc. (1)
301 Poplar St, Macon, GA 31201
Tel.: (478) 745-4141
Emp.: 50
Television Broadcasting Stations Operator
N.A.I.C.S.: 516120
Bobby Berry (Pres & CEO)

Morris Newspaper Corporation (1)
27 Abercorn St, Savannah, GA 31401
Tel.: (912) 233-1281
Web Site: http://www.morrismultimedia.com

Sales Range: $10-24.9 Million
Emp.: 8
Newspaper Publishers
N.A.I.C.S.: 513110
Charles H. Morris (Pres)
Randy Morton (Dir-Strategic Multimedia-Southeast Georgia & Southern California)

WDEF-TV (1)
3300 Broad St, Chattanooga, TN 37408
Tel.: (423) 785-1200
Web Site: http://www.wdef.com
Sales Range: $10-24.9 Million
Emp.: 60
Television Broadcasting Station
N.A.I.C.S.: 516120
Phillip Cox (Gen Mgr)

WTVQ-TV (1)
6940 Man O War Blvd, Lexington, KY 40509
Tel.: (859) 299-3636
Web Site: http://www.wtvq.com
Sales Range: $10-24.9 Million
Emp.: 200
Television Station
N.A.I.C.S.: 516120
Chris Aldridge (Gen Mgr)

MORRIS MURDOCK, LLC
515 S 700 E Ste 1B, Salt Lake City, UT 84102
Tel.: (801) 487-9731 NV
Web Site: http://www.morrismurdock.com
Year Founded: 2000
Sales Range: $10-24.9 Million
Emp.: 200
Travel Agency Services
N.A.I.C.S.: 561510
Brian Hollien (Pres)

MORRIS OIL CO. INC.
420B W Walnut Ln, Springfield, MO 65807
Tel.: (417) 889-1222
Year Founded: 1958
Sales Range: $10-24.9 Million
Emp.: 32
Provider of Gasoline Station Services
N.A.I.C.S.: 457120
Jim Morris (Pres)

MORRIS OIL OF MISSISSIPPI
409 S High School Ave, Columbia, MS 39429
Tel.: (601) 736-2634
Sales Range: $10-24.9 Million
Emp.: 12
Petroleum Products
N.A.I.C.S.: 424720
Bradley Morris (Pres)
Steve Morris (Treas & Sec)

MORRIS PONTIAC GMC INC.
26100 Lorain Rd, North Olmsted, OH 44070-2740
Tel.: (440) 327-4181
Web Site: http://www.drivemorris.com
Rev: $32,000,000
Emp.: 40
Car Dealership
N.A.I.C.S.: 441110
Robert J. Morris Jr. (Pres)

MORRIS PRINTING GROUP, INC.
3212 E Hwy 30, Kearney, NE 68847
Tel.: (308) 236-7888
Web Site: http://www.morriscookbooks.com
Year Founded: 1933
Sales Range: $25-49.9 Million
Commercial Printing & Publishing Services
N.A.I.C.S.: 323111
Tamara Omtvedt (Dir-Mktg & Product Dev)

MORRIS SHEET METAL CORP.

6212 Highview Dr, Fort Wayne, IN 46818
Tel.: (260) 497-1300
Web Site: http://www.morrissheetmetal.com
Sales Range: $10-24.9 Million
Emp.: 110
Warm Air Heating & Air Conditioning Contractor
N.A.I.C.S.: 238220
James Morris (Owner)
Daniel T. Morris (Owner)

MORRIS TILE DISTRIBUTORS INC.
2525 Kenilworth Ave, Hyattsville, MD 20781
Tel.: (301) 772-2820
Web Site: http://www.morristile.com
Sales Range: $10-24.9 Million
Emp.: 30
Clay or Other Ceramic Tile Mfr & Distr
N.A.I.C.S.: 423320
Edward J. Condolon (Pres)

MORRIS, MANNING & MARTIN LLP
1600 Atlanta Financial Ctr 3343 Peachtree Rd NE, Atlanta, GA 30326
Tel.: (404) 233-7000
Web Site: http://www.mmmlaw.com
Year Founded: 1976
Sales Range: $75-99.9 Million
Emp.: 300
Legal Advisory Services
N.A.I.C.S.: 541110
Bob Alpert (Partner)
Paul H. Arne (Co-Partner)
Scott L. Allen (Co-Partner)
Ward Bondurant (Partner)
G. Brian Butler (Partner)
David Calhoun (Partner)
David Cranshaw (Partner)
Jason D'Cruz (Partner)
Frank W. DeBorde (Partner)
Jeffrey Douglass (Partner)
C. Glenn Dunaway (Partner)
Charles Beaudrot (Partner)
Carol Weld King (Partner)
Owen Pinkerton (Partner)
Lynn Wilson (Partner)
Daniel Sineway (Partner)
Edgar Bueno (Partner)
Mary Anthony Merchant (Partner-IP)
John Morris (Chm)
Louise M. Wells (Mng Partner)
Daniel Prywes (Partner-Litigation)
L. Craig Dowdy (Partner)
Mark Zisholtz (Partner-Contingent Labor Practice)
Matthew Peurach (Partner-Corp, Funds & Alternative Investments, Real Estate Grp)
Marc Bulson (Partner-Real Estate Dev & Fin Practice)
Justin Barry (Partner-Comml Real Estate Dev, Fin & Comml Lending Grps)
Mark A. Block (Partner-Real Estate Dev, Fin & Capital Markets Groups)
Tony Roehl (Chm-Insurance & Reinsurance Grp)
Simon Malko (Mng Partner-Washington)
Aresh Homayoun (Partner-Washington)
Brett Lavoie (Partner-Comml Real Estate Dev & Fin Practice)
Eric Larson (Partner-Comml Litigation Practice)
Larkin Ellzey (Partner-Corp Practice)
Meredith Caiafa (Partner-Employment & Litigation Practices)
Scott Wagner (Partner-Employment, Employee Benefits & Tax Practices)

U.S. PRIVATE

Stephen Vaughn (Partner-Comml & Intellectual Property Litigation Practice)
Austin Mills (Partner-Corp Tech Practice)
Bonnie Hochman Rothell (Chm-Litigation Grp-Washington)
Daniel Huynh (Partner-Intellectual Property & Tech Litigation Grp)
Seslee S. Smith (Gen Counsel)
Frederick C. C. Boyd III (Partner)
Edmund Emerson III (Chm-Benefits & Employment Grp)

MORRIS-SHEA BRIDGE COMPANY, INC.
609 S 20th St, Irondale, AL 35210
Tel.: (205) 956-9518
Web Site: http://www.morrisshea.com
Year Founded: 1969
Sales Range: $10-24.9 Million
Emp.: 80
Provider of Construction Services
N.A.I.C.S.: 236210
Richard J. Shea Jr. (Pres)

MORRISETTE PAPER COMPANY INC.
5925 Summit Ave, Browns Summit, NC 27214-9704
Tel.: (336) 375-1515 NC
Web Site: http://www.morrisettepaper.com
Year Founded: 1962
Sales Range: $25-49.9 Million
Emp.: 150
Distr Of Paper For Industrial & Personal Service
N.A.I.C.S.: 424130
Marie Morrisette Sartin (Exec VP)
Cary Duley (Gen Mgr)

MORRISON & FOERSTER LLP
425 Market St, San Francisco, CA 94105-2482
Tel.: (415) 268-7000 CA
Web Site: http://www.mofo.com
Year Founded: 1883
Sales Range: $1-4.9 Billion
Emp.: 1,001
Legal Advisory Services
N.A.I.C.S.: 541110
Philip T. Besirof (Partner)
James P. Bennett (Partner)
Michael J. Agoglia (Partner)
Pat Cavaney (COO)
Eric R. Roberts (Dir-Forensic Acctg Svcs)
Paul Borden (Partner)
Christopher J. Carr (Partner)
Somnath Raj Chatterjee (Partner)
Tiffany Cheung (Partner)
Shirin Tang (Partner-Singapore)
Paul T. Friedman (Mng Partner-Europe)
James Robinson (Partner-Tokyo)
Jeremy M. Schropp (Partner)
Nathan D. Taylor (Partner)
Marc Hearron (Partner)
Thomas J. Knox (Partner)
Nicholas J. Spiliotes (Partner)
James M. Koukios (Partner-Washington)
Adrian Yip (Partner-Hong Kong)
David Cross (Partner-Global Antitrust Practice Grp-Washington)
Lauren C. Bellerjeau (Partner-Corp Dept-Washington)
Vladimir Maly (Partner-Corp Practice-London)
Jason R. Nelms (Partner-Hong Kong)
Alexis Amezcua (Partner)
Matthew Chivvis (Partner)
Diana Kruze (Partner)
Tessa Schwartz (Mng Partner)
Erik Knudsen (Partner)

COMPANIES

Shannon Reaney *(Partner)*
John Pintarelli *(Partner-Bus Restructuring & Insolvency Practice Grp)*
Joshua Isenberg *(Partner-Tokyo)*
Jonathan Levine *(Partner-Bus Restructuring & Insolvency Grp)*
Vivian Yiu *(Partner-Hong Kong)*
Damien Specht *(Partner-Washington)*
Daniel Chudd *(Partner-Washington)*
Jessie Liu *(Partner)*
Kevin Dwyer *(Partner)*
Kevin Mullen *(Partner)*
J. Alex Ward *(Co-Chm-Govt Contracts & Pub Procurement Parctice & Partner)*
W. Jay DeVecchio *(Co-Chm-Govt Contracts & Pub Procurement Practice & Partner)*
Carrie H. Cohen *(Partner-New York)*
Ben Fox *(Chm-Global Litigation Dept)*
Jordan Eth *(Chm-SLEW Grp)*
Angela Kerek *(Partner-Fin-Berlin)*
Hanno Timner *(Co-Mng Partner-Berlin)*
Jens-Uwe Hinder *(Co-Mng Partner-Berlin)*
Sun Chuan *(Partner-Hong Kong)*
Yiu Vivian *(Partner-Hong Kong)*
Tepe Yemi *(Partner-Singapore)*
Eric Piesner *(Mng Partner-Asia & Singapore)*
Ven Tan *(Mng Partner-Hong Kong)*
Brian A. Bates *(Partner)*
Charles S. Barquist *(Partner)*
Dale D. Araki *(Partner)*
Eric M. Acker *(Partner)*
Jay G. Baris *(Partner)*
Kei Amemiya *(Partner)*
Motonori Araki *(Partner)*
Mehran Arjomand *(Partner)*
Scott D. Ashton *(Partner)*
Sara Terheggen *(Partner-Corp Dept)*
Alex Kaufman *(Partner-Private Equity Investments & Buyouts Grp)*
Dario Avram *(Partner-Private Equity Investments & Buyouts Grp)*
Patrick Huard *(Partner-Private Equity Investments & Buyouts Grp)*
Oliver Rochman *(Partner-Corp Practice-London)*
Katie Thomson *(Partner-Washington)*
Larren M. Nashelsky *(Chm)*
Bill O'Connor *(Chm-Airports, Aviation, Drones & Unmanned Aircraft Sys Grp)*
Tracy Bacigalupo *(Partner-New York)*
Dennis Jenkins *(Partner-Bus Restructuring & Insolvency Grp-New York)*
Brett Miller *(Mng Partner-New York & Partner-Bus Restructuring & Insolvency Grp)*
James Peck *(Chm-Bus Restructuring & Insolvency Grp-Global)*
Tina Reynolds *(Partner-Govt Contracts Practice)*
Natalie Fleming Nolen *(Partner-Litigation Dept-Washington)*
Julie O'Neill *(Partner)*
Kenichi Ko *(Partner-Tokyo)*
Amit Kataria *(Partner-Hong Kong)*
Michael Krigbaum *(Partner-Palo Alto)*
Matthew Lau *(Partner-Hong Kong)*
Tyler Sewell *(Partner-Denver)*
Joshua Hill *(Partner)*
Florian Ehrich *(Partner- Real Estate Practice-Berlin)*
Mark Edelstein *(Chm-Real Estate Grp-Global)*
Jesse Gillespie *(Partner-Corp Practice-Tokyo)*
Ken Siegel *(Mng Partner-Tokyo)*
Khoa Do *(Partner-Corp Practice & Mergers & Acq Grp-Palo Alto)*
Eric McCrath *(Chm-Mergers & Acq Grp & Private Equity Investments & Buyouts Grp)*
Timothy Harris *(Mng Partner-Palo Alto)*
Lucy Lu *(Partner-Beijing)*
Susan Gault-Brown *(Partner-Fin Svcs-Washington)*
Gary Lee *(Co-Chm-Fin Dept-Global)*
Joseph Palmore *(Mng Partner-Washington)*
John Carlin *(Partner-Risk & Crisis Mgmt-Gobal & Security Groups-Natl)*
David Newman *(Partner-Washington)*
Caroline Jury *(Partner-Fin-London)*
Blaivas Blaivas *(Partner-Tax-New York)*
David Slotkin *(Chm-Real Estate Investment Trust Grp)*
Michael Birnbaum *(Partner-Litigation)*
Dan Coppel *(Partner-London)*
Benoit Lavigne *(Partner-Fin Practice-London)*
John Smith *(Partner-Washington)*
Lisa Phelan *(Partner-Antitrust Law Practice, Investigations & White Collar Grp)*
Jeff Jaeckel *(Chm-Antitrust Law Practice-Global)*
Andy Campbell *(Partner-Washington)*
Alice Connaughton *(Partner-Real Estate Investment Trust Grp-Washington)*
Heath Linsky *(Partner-Real Estate Investment Trust Grp)*
Christopher Kandel *(Partner-Fin Practice-London)*
Jon Ornolfsson *(Partner-Global Project Fin Grp)*
Tessa Davis *(Partner-Project Fin Grp-Singapore)*
Daiske Yoshida *(Partner-Antitrust & Investigations-Tokyo)*
Ke Huang *(Partner-Capital Markets-Hong Kong)*
Ruomu Li *(Partner-Shanghai)*
Jay Gavigan *(Partner-Lending & Fin Transactions Grp-New York)*
Jennifer L. Marines *(Co-Chm-Fin Dept-Global)*
Natalie Kernisant *(Chief Diversity & Inclusion Officer)*
Maria B. Earley *(Partner-Fin Svcs & FinTech Grps-Washington D.C.)*
John W. Campbell III *(Partner)*

MORRISON & SYLVESTER INC.

1175 Minot Ave, Auburn, ME 04210
Tel.: (207) 783-8548   ME
Web Site:
   http://www.morrisontruck.net
Year Founded: 1956
Sales Range: $10-24.9 Million
Emp.: 17
Sales of Trucks, Tractors & Trailers
N.A.I.C.S.: 441110
Keith F. Morrison *(Owner & Chm)*
Richard Morrison *(Pres)*
Jennifer Potter *(Treas)*

MORRISON BERKSHIRE INC.

865 S Church St, North Adams, MA 01247-0958
Tel.: (413) 663-6501   MA
Web Site:
   http://www.morrisonberkshire.com
Year Founded: 1983
Sales Range: $1-9.9 Million
Emp.: 40
Machine Shop; Contract Manufacturing
N.A.I.C.S.: 332710
Jim White *(Pres)*

MORRISON BROTHERS COMPANY

570 E 7th St, Dubuque, IA 52001
Tel.: (563) 583-5701
Web Site: http://www.morbros.com
Rev.: $10,700,000
Emp.: 130
Plumbing & Heating Valves
N.A.I.C.S.: 332919
Charlie Glab *(Pres)*
Jerry Schollmeyer *(Mgr-Sls)*

MORRISON CHEVROLET INC.

121 Downeast Hwy, Ellsworth, ME 04605
Tel.: (207) 667-2512   ME
Web Site:
   http://www.morrisonchevrolet.com
Year Founded: 1946
Sales Range: $10-24.9 Million
Emp.: 200
New & Used Automobiles
N.A.I.C.S.: 441110
Sandy Salsbury *(Coord-Bus Dev)*

MORRISON COMMUNICATIONS, INC.

1039 Walters Dr, Morristown, TN 37814-6133
Tel.: (423) 586-4812
Web Site: http://www.morriscom.com
Sales Range: $10-24.9 Million
Emp.: 60
Commercial Printing Services
N.A.I.C.S.: 323111
Mary Maude Briggs *(Pres & CEO)*
Linda Ketner *(Mgr-IT)*

MORRISON CONSTRUCTION COMPANY

1834 Summer St, Hammond, IN 46320-2236
Tel.: (219) 932-5036   IN
Web Site:
   http://www.morrisonconst.com
Year Founded: 1925
Sales Range: $200-249.9 Million
Emp.: 450
Provider of Contracting Services
N.A.I.C.S.: 238220
Daniel J. Sharpe *(Pres)*

MORRISON DISTRIBUTION & MARKETING

3601 S Broadway Ste 1000, Edmond, OK 73013
Tel.: (405) 946-1900
Web Site:
   http://www.morrisononline.com
Rev.: $10,000,000
Emp.: 30
Disposable Plates, Cups, Napkins & Eating Utensils
N.A.I.C.S.: 424130
Michael D. Morrison *(Pres)*

MORRISON ENTERPRISES

3303 W 12th St, Hastings, NE 68901-3446
Tel.: (402) 463-3191
Year Founded: 1954
Sales Range: $10-24.9 Million
Emp.: 20
Provider of General Farm Services
N.A.I.C.S.: 111998
Kenneth Morrison *(Gen Mgr)*
Scott Kummer *(CFO)*

MORRISON EXPRESS CORPORATION USA

2000 S Hughes Way, El Segundo, CA 90245-4730
Tel.: (310) 322-8999   CA
Web Site:
   http://www.morrisonexpress.com
Year Founded: 1972
Sales Range: $50-74.9 Million
Emp.: 150
Provider of Freight Transportation Services
N.A.I.C.S.: 488510
Danny Chiu *(Chm & CEO)*
Stefan Vogt *(VP)*
Lily Chiu *(Chm)*
Ron Krajniak *(VP/Gen Mgr-Americas)*

MORRISON INDUSTRIAL EQUIPMENT COMPANY

1825 Monroe Ave NW, Grand Rapids, MI 49505
Tel.: (616) 447-3800
Web Site: http://www.morrison-ind.com
Year Founded: 1953
Sales Range: $25-49.9 Million
Emp.: 350
Distr of Industrial Machinery & Equipment
N.A.I.C.S.: 423830
Roger Troost *(CEO)*

Subsidiaries:

Cisco, Inc.   (1)
4565 Herman Ave SW, Grand Rapids, MI 49509-5134
Tel.: (616) 534-8651
Web Site: http://www.pmlight.com
Sales Range: $10-24.9 Million
Emp.: 20
Distr of Industrial Machinery & Equipment
N.A.I.C.S.: 423830

Mor-Son Leasing Inc.   (1)
1825 Monroe Ave NW, Grand Rapids, MI 49505-6240
Tel.: (616) 447-3840
Web Site: http://www.morrison.com
Sales Range: $10-24.9 Million
Emp.: 4
Provider of Equipment Rental & Leasing Services
N.A.I.C.S.: 532490
Bob Veldkamp *(Office Mgr)*

Morrison Industrial Equipment Company   (1)
1183 S Old US Hwy 23, Brighton, MI 48114-9681
Tel.: (810) 227-6311
Web Site: http://www.morrison-ind.com
Sales Range: $10-24.9 Million
Emp.: 14
Distr of Industrial Fork Lifts
N.A.I.C.S.: 423830

MORRISON PRODUCTS INC.

16900 S Waterloo Rd, Cleveland, OH 44110
Tel.: (216) 486-4000
Web Site:
   http://www.morrisonfan.com
Rev.: $47,000,000
Emp.: 350
Blowers & Fans
N.A.I.C.S.: 333413
Harry Holmes *(Pres)*
Joe Militello *(Controller)*
Daniel W. Holmes Jr. *(Chm)*

MORRISON TEXTILE MACHINERY CO.

6044 Lancaster Hwy, Fort Lawn, SC 29714-8803
Tel.: (803) 872-4401   SC
Web Site:
   http://www.morrisontexmach.com
Year Founded: 1959
Sales Range: $75-99.9 Million
Emp.: 100
Textile Machinery Mfr; Textile Wet Finishing Equipment Distr
N.A.I.C.S.: 333248
W.H. Maesalu *(CFO)*
Kevin O'Neill *(Controller)*
David Emrey *(VP-Sls)*
John M. White Jr. *(Chm & Pres)*

MORRISON TEXTILE MACHINERY CO.

U.S. PRIVATE

Morrison Textile Machinery Co.—(Continued)

Subsidiaries:

Morrison Textile Machinery Co. - Morrison Contract Manufacturing Division (1)
6044 Lancaster Hwy, Fort Lawn, SC 29714
Tel.: (803) 872-4401
Web Site: http://www.morrisoncm.com
Fabricated Steel Product Mfr
N.A.I.C.S.: 332312
Scott Threatt *(Mgr-Engrg)*

MORRISONVILLE FARMERS COOP CO
6th St & Vandeveer St, Morrisonville, IL 62546
Tel.: (217) 526-3123
Web Site: http://www.morrisonvillecoop.com
Sales Range: Less than $1 Million
Emp.: 3
Grain Elevators
N.A.I.C.S.: 922120
Dan Litteken *(Gen Mgr)*

MORRISSEY & COMPANY
6 Edgerly Pl, Boston, MA 02116
Tel.: (617) 523-4141
Web Site: http://www.morrisseyco.com
Year Founded: 1999
Sales Range: $10-24.9 Million
Emp.: 10
Public Relations Agency
N.A.I.C.S.: 541820
Peter A. Morrissey *(Pres & CEO)*
Margaret Brady *(Sr Dir)*
Megan Page *(VP)*
Laura DiGeronimo *(Dir-Healthcare, Fin, Corp & Tech Expertise)*

MORRISTOWN DRIVERS SERVICE INC.
1111 Gateway Service Park Rd, Morristown, TN 37813
Tel.: (423) 318-9417
Web Site: http://www.mdstrucking.com
Sales Range: $10-24.9 Million
Emp.: 150
Trucking Except Local
N.A.I.C.S.: 484121
Denise Miller *(Controller)*
Mike Morgan *(VP-Sls)*
Terry K. Wolfe *(Pres)*
Tracy Cutshall *(Mgr-Ops)*

MORRISTOWN UTILITY COMMISSION
441 W Main St, Morristown, TN 37814
Tel.: (423) 586-4121
Web Site: http://www.morristownutilities.org
Year Founded: 1901
Rev.: $51,034,154
Emp.: 105
Electric & Other Services Combined
N.A.I.C.S.: 221118
Joseph S. Wigington *(CEO & Gen Mgr)*
Clark H. Rucker *(CFO & Asst Gen Mgr)*
Bryan J. Delozier *(Mgr-Power Sys)*
George A. Benjamin *(Mgr-Telecom)*
Michael R. Howard *(Mgr-Water Sys)*
George McGuffin *(Chm)*

MORROW CONSTRUCTION COMPANY
1050 Eagles Landing Pkwy, Stockbridge, GA 30281
Tel.: (770) 474-4345
Web Site: http://www.davisdevelopment.info
Rev.: $10,000,000
Emp.: 60
Provider of Renovation & Repair Services of Commercial & Office Buildings
N.A.I.C.S.: 236220

MORROW CONTROL & SUPPLY CO
810 Marion Motley, Canton, OH 44705
Tel.: (330) 452-9791
Web Site: http://www.morrowcontrol.com
Sales Range: $10-24.9 Million
Emp.: 45
Heating Equipment (Hydronic)
N.A.I.C.S.: 423720
Richard Schwane *(Pres)*

MORROW COUNTY GRAIN GROWERS
350 E Main St, Lexington, OR 97839
Tel.: (541) 989-8221
Web Site: http://www.mcgg.net
Rev.: $35,381,728
Emp.: 30
Grains
N.A.I.C.S.: 424510
John Ripple *(Gen Mgr)*
Mike Walker *(Mgr-Sls)*
Jamie Helfrecht *(Mgr-Feed Store)*

MORROW EQUIPMENT CO. LLC
3218 Pringle Rd SE, Salem, OR 97302
Tel.: (503) 585-5721
Web Site: http://www.morrow.com
Sales Range: $50-74.9 Million
Emp.: 120
Heavy Construction Equipment Rental
N.A.I.C.S.: 532412
Christian Chalupny *(Pres)*
Mark Beals *(Controller)*
Peter Juhren *(VP-Ops)*
Rick Morrow *(Vice Chm)*

MORROW FAMILY MEDICINE, LLC
3970 Deputy Bill Cantrell Memorial Rd Ste 150, Cumming, GA 30040
Tel.: (770) 781-8004
Web Site: http://www.morrowfammed.com
Year Founded: 2011
Sales Range: $1-9.9 Million
Emp.: 27
Healthcare Services
N.A.I.C.S.: 621999
Peggie Morrow *(Mgr-Mktg)*

MORROW MOTOR SALES INC.
6865 Jonesboro Rd, Morrow, GA 30260
Tel.: (770) 961-0225
Web Site: http://www.toyotasouthatlanta.com
Sales Range: $25-49.9 Million
Emp.: 115
New & Used Car Dealers
N.A.I.C.S.: 441110
Greg Sorrell *(Mgr-Parts)*
Kyle Edwards *(Mgr-Parts)*

MORROW MOTORS INC.
201 7th Ave, Beaver Falls, PA 15010
Tel.: (724) 843-1000
Web Site: http://www.ronlewisford.com
Rev.: $52,000,000
Emp.: 60
Automobiles, New & Used
N.A.I.C.S.: 441110
Diane Davic *(Controller)*

MORROW-MEADOWS CORPORATION
231 Benton Ct, City of Industry, CA 91789
Tel.: (909) 598-7700   CA
Web Site: http://www.morrow-meadows.com
Year Founded: 1964
Sales Range: $50-74.9 Million
Emp.: 820
Electrical Work
N.A.I.C.S.: 238210
Karen V. Price *(Pres)*

Subsidiaries:

Morrow-Meadows Corp (1)
1050 Bing St, San Carlos, CA 94070   (100%)
Tel.: (650) 634-0682
Web Site: http://www.morrowmeadows.com
Sales Range: $10-24.9 Million
Emp.: 75
Electrical Work
N.A.I.C.S.: 238210
Kathleen Richards *(Controller)*
John Menicucci *(Project Mgr)*

Morrow-Meadows Corporation - Alternative Energy Division
231 Benton Ct, City of Industry, CA 91789
Tel.: (909) 598-7700
Eletric Power Generation Services
N.A.I.C.S.: 221118

Morrow-Meadows Corporation - Cherry City Electric Division (1)
1596 22nd St SE, Salem, OR 97302
Tel.: (503) 566-5600
Web Site: http://www.cherrycityelectric.com
Emp.: 25
Eletric Power Generation Services
N.A.I.C.S.: 221118
Kurt Hamilton *(Dir-Estimating)*
Mike Guinn *(VP-Construction)*
Joe Janssen *(Gen Counsel & CMO)*
Matt Jones *(Dir-Design Build)*

MORSE CHEVROLET INC.
9201 Metcalf Ave, Overland Park, KS 66212
Tel.: (913) 649-6000
Web Site: http://www.morsechevrolet.com
Rev.: $23,700,000
Emp.: 80
Automobiles, New & Used
N.A.I.C.S.: 441110
John McCarthy *(Pres)*
Becky Davis *(Controller)*

MORSE DISTRIBUTION INC.
3006 W Illinois St, Bellingham, WA 98225-5011
Tel.: (360) 756-6200   WA
Web Site: http://www.morsesteel.com
Year Founded: 1884
Sales Range: $10-24.9 Million
Emp.: 48
Mfr & Retailer of Industrial Supplies & Steel Products
N.A.I.C.S.: 423510
Rich Olson *(CFO)*
Mike Morse *(Pres)*

MORSE ELECTRIC INCORPORATED
500 W S St, Freeport, IL 61032-6042
Tel.: (815) 266-4200   IL
Web Site: http://www.morselec.com
Year Founded: 1977
Sales Range: $25-49.9 Million
Emp.: 350
Providers of Electrical Services
N.A.I.C.S.: 238210
Brian Scott *(CFO & Controller)*
Lou Rotello *(Pres)*
Dennis Dietzel *(Mgr)*

Subsidiaries:

AMP Electric Inc. (1)
1390 Gateway Blvd, Beloit, WI 53511
Tel.: (815) 266-4200
Web Site: http://www.themorsegroup.com
Sales Range: $10-24.9 Million
Emp.: 90
Electronic Services
N.A.I.C.S.: 238210
Brian Scott *(CFO)*
Janey Morse *(CEO)*
Lou Rotello *(Pres)*
Joy A. Morse-Fritz *(Sec)*

MORSE INDUSTRIES INC.
25811 74th Ave S, Kent, WA 98032
Tel.: (800) 325-7513
Web Site: http://www.morseindustries.com
Rev.: $10,800,000
Emp.: 35
Metal Service Centers & Other Metal Merchant Whslr
N.A.I.C.S.: 423510
Larry Larsen *(CFO)*
Terry Morse *(Pres & Treas)*
Larry Morse *(Sec & VP)*
Jeremy Nolan *(Mgr-Mktg)*

MORSE OPERATIONS INC.
2850 S Federal Hwy, Delray Beach, FL 33483-3216
Tel.: (561) 455-1111   FL
Web Site: http://www.edmorse.com
Year Founded: 1968
Sales Range: $900-999.9 Million
Emp.: 1,500
Owner & Operator of Car Dealerships
N.A.I.C.S.: 441110
Edward J. Morse *(Founder & Chm)*
Ted Morse *(Chm & CEO)*
Dennis MacInnes *(CFO, Treas & VP)*

Subsidiaries:

Crowe Ford Sales Co (1)
1041 S State St, Geneseo, IL 61254
Tel.: (309) 944-2127
Web Site: http://www.crowefordsales.com
Rev.: $8,411,000
Emp.: 13
New Car Dealers
N.A.I.C.S.: 441110
Gary Crowe *(Owner)*

Grand Junction Harley Davidson (1)
2747 Crossroads Blvd, Grand Junction, CO 81506-3954
Tel.: (970) 245-0812
Web Site: http://www.gjharley.com
Motorcycle, ATV & All Other Motor Vehicle Dealers
N.A.I.C.S.: 441227
Scott Lindsay *(Mgr)*

Putnam Chevrolet Inc.
500 W Buchanan St, California, MO 65018
Tel.: (573) 796-2131
Sales Range: $1-9.9 Million
Emp.: 30
New And Used Car Dealers, Nsk
N.A.I.C.S.: 441110
Penny Campbell *(Treas)*

Sellers-Sexton Inc. (1)
341 VFW Memorial Dr, Saint Robert, MO 65584
Tel.: (573) 336-2000
Web Site: http://www.sellerssexton.com
Car Dealerships & Parts Center
N.A.I.C.S.: 441110
Michael Friedman *(Gen Mgr)*

Thomas Motors, Inc. (1)
Hwy 63, Moberly, MO 65270
Tel.: (660) 263-4560
Sales Range: $1-9.9 Million
Emp.: 25
Ret Automobiles
N.A.I.C.S.: 441110
Donald Thomas *(Pres)*

MORSE PROPERTIES, INC.

200 Ocean Ave Ste 202, Melbourne Beach, FL 32951
Tel.: (321) 728-8938
Web Site:
http://www.morseproperties.net
Year Founded: 2002
Sales Range: $1-9.9 Million
Commercial Real Estate Development & Brokerage
N.A.I.C.S.: 531210
William Morse (*Co-Founder & Pres*)
Robert Morse (*Co-Founder*)
David Morse (*Co-Founder*)

MORSE WATCHMANS INC.
2 Morse Rd, Oxford, CT 06478-1040
Tel.: (203) 264-4949   CT
Web Site:
http://www.morsewatchman.com
Year Founded: 1882
Rev.: $8,000,000
Emp.: 45
Mfr & Sale of Guard Tour Systems & Key Management Systems
N.A.I.C.S.: 335999
Fernando Pires (*VP-Sls & Mktg*)
Mary Ellen Orsini (*Acct Exec*)
Joseph Granitto (*Dir-Ops*)
Tim Purpura (*VP-Sls & Mktg*)

MORSEKODE
7900 International Dr Ste 140, Minneapolis, MN 55425
Tel.: (952) 853-9555
Web Site: http://www.morsekode.com
Sales Range: $10-24.9 Million
Emp.: 12
Advertising Agencies, Brand Development, Entertainment, Graphic Design, Health Care, High Technology, Interactive Agencies, Internet/Web Design, Retail, Strategic Planning/Research
N.A.I.C.S.: 541810
Mark Morse (*Principal*)
Becky Ewert (*Dir-Client Strategy*)
Denise Bornhausen (*Sr Project Mgr*)
Paul Jongeward (*Partner*)
Melissa Sonnek (*Designer*)
Jesse Sutherland (*Designer*)
Joe Beard (*Dir-Brand Motion*)
Paul Afong (*Dir-Creative*)
Chuck Swensson (*Pres*)
Matt Boswell (*Dir-Art*)
Clare Gardner (*Mgr-Interactive Project*)
Mark Kasper (*Editor-Brand Motion*)
Matt Horton (*Exec Dir-Creative*)

MORTAR ADVERTISING
25 Maiden Ln 6th Fl, San Francisco, CA 94108
Tel.: (415) 772-9907
Web Site:
http://www.mortaradvertising.com
Year Founded: 2002
Rev.: $22,000,000
Emp.: 20
N.A.I.C.S.: 541810
C. Todd Rasnick (*Principal*)
Tim Spry (*Principal & Dir-Creative*)
Mark Williams (*Principal & Dir-Brand Strategy*)
Ben Klau (*Gen Mgr*)
Jonathan Harrison (*Jr Acct Coord*)
Sylvie Lee (*Jr Acct Exec*)
Daniel Ray (*Asst Acct Exec-PR & Social Media*)

MORTEN ENTERPRISES INC.
12350 US Hwy 19 N, Clearwater, FL 33764
Tel.: (727) 531-8957
Web Site: http://www.printerusa.com
Sales Range: $10-24.9 Million
Emp.: 100
Provider of Offset Printing Services
N.A.I.C.S.: 323111
James E. Morten (*Chm & CEO*)
James A. Morten (*Pres-Sls*)

Subsidiaries:

Interprint Incorporated (1)
12350 US Hwy 19 N, Clearwater, FL 33764
Tel.: (727) 531-8957
Web Site: http://www.printerusa.com
Rev.: $10,600,221
Emp.: 60
Commercial Printing, Lithographic
N.A.I.C.S.: 323111

MORTENSEN WOODWORK INC.
4920 Baker St, Union City, GA 30291
Tel.: (770) 969-1475
Web Site:
http://www.mortensenwoodwork.com
Rev.: $17,572,811
Emp.: 45
Millwork
N.A.I.C.S.: 321918
Greg Kesten (*Pres*)
Frederick J. Mortensen (*Chm & CEO*)

MORTEX CORPORATION
4251 Wendell Blvd, Wendell, NC 27591
Tel.: (919) 365-9805
Web Site:
http://www.eaglesportswear.com
Sales Range: $10-24.9 Million
Emp.: 90
Mfr of Sportswear & Athletic Clothing
N.A.I.C.S.: 315250
Edward Morrell (*Pres*)

MORTGAGE CAPITAL ASSOCIATES, INC.
11150 W Olympic Blvd Ste 1160, Los Angeles, CA 90064
Tel.: (310) 477-6877
Web Site: http://www.mtgcapital.com
Sales Range: $10-24.9 Million
Emp.: 50
Mortgage Banker
N.A.I.C.S.: 522310
Jay Stern (*CEO*)

MORTGAGE CONNECT, LP
260 Airside Drive, Moon Township, PA 15108
Tel.: (866) 789-1814
Web Site:
http://www2.mortgageconnectlp.com
Year Founded: 2008
Sales Range: $50-74.9 Million
Emp.: 433
Mortgage Services
N.A.I.C.S.: 522310
Jeff Coury (*CEO*)
Robert Franco (*Pres-Originations Div*)

Subsidiaries:

Adfitech, Inc. (1)
3001 Technology Dr, Edmond, OK 73013
Tel.: (405) 715-8000
Web Site: http://www.adfitech.com
Outsource Services
N.A.I.C.S.: 561499
Samuel A. Meek (*Pres*)
Thomas G. Apel (*Founder*)

MORTGAGE INVESTMENT CORPORATION
1808 Spring Garden St, Greensboro, NC 27403
Tel.: (336) 274-7651
Web Site:
http://www.magentainvestment.com
Sales Range: $10-24.9 Million
Emp.: 50
Residential Building Lessor Services
N.A.I.C.S.: 531110
Stuart Austin (*VP*)
Eli Dadouch (*Pres & CEO*)
Stanley Goldfarb (*Chm*)

MORTGAGE INVESTORS CORPORATION
6090 Central Ave, Saint Petersburg, FL 33707
Tel.: (727) 347-1930   OH
Web Site:
http://www.mortgageinvestors.com
Year Founded: 1938
Sales Range: $50-74.9 Million
Emp.: 10
Veterans' Mortgage Refinancing Services
N.A.I.C.S.: 522292
David Lattner (*CFO*)

MORTGAGE INVESTORS GROUP, INC.
8320 E Walker Springs Ln, Knoxville, TN 37923
Tel.: (865) 691-8910   TN
Web Site: http://www.migonline.com
Sales Range: $10-24.9 Million
Emp.: 300
Mortgage Banker
N.A.I.C.S.: 522292
Chrissi Rhea (*Co-Founder & Co-Pres*)
Chuck Tonkin (*Co-Founder & Pres*)
Tandy Shuler (*Branch Mgr*)
John Bruington (*Branch Mgr*)
Terre Webb (*Branch Mgr*)
Chris White (*Branch Mgr*)
Gary Sturm (*Branch Mgr*)
Jennifer Torgeson (*Branch Mgr*)
John Burns (*Dir-Direct Lending Div*)
Ed Sauer (*CFO*)
Jesse A. Lehn (*Exec VP-Ops*)
Darin Anderson (*Mgr-Bridgeport*)
Todd Brown (*Mgr-Bridgeport*)
John Parrish (*Mgr-Bridgeport*)
Jeannie Sidwell (*Mgr-Bridgeport*)
Cathy Neubert (*Sr VP & Dir-Ops*)
Sharon Rivers (*Sr VP-Closing & Post Closing Ops*)
Kevin Rhea (*Sr VP & Dir-Bus Dev*)

MORTGAGE LENDERS OF AMERICA, LLC
10975 El Monte St, Overland Park, KS 66211
Tel.: (913) 491-4299
Web Site:
http://www.mortgagelendersofamerica.com
Year Founded: 2000
Sales Range: $10-24.9 Million
Emp.: 115
Mortgage Loan Brokerage Services
N.A.I.C.S.: 522310
Paula Acree (*Acct Mgr*)
Philip Kneibert (*Pres*)

MORTGAGE OUTLET INC.
1800 Sandy Plains Pkwy Ste 306, Marietta, GA 30066
Tel.: (770) 795-9959
Web Site:
http://www.moneyoutlet.com
Sales Range: $10-24.9 Million
Emp.: 20
Mortgage Loan Brokerage Services
N.A.I.C.S.: 522310
Steve Myers (*VP*)
Frank Losito (*Pres*)

MORTGAGE SUCCESS SOURCE, LLC
24 SHolmdel Rd, Holmdel, NJ 07733
Web Site:
http://www.mortgagesuccesssource.com
Year Founded: 2007
Sales Range: $25-49.9 Million
Emp.: 50
Loan Services
N.A.I.C.S.: 522310
Mike Sepesi (*CFO*)
Bill Bodnar (*Pres-Sls & Corp Dev*)
Sue Woodard (*Pres-Content & Publ*)
Torry Burdick (*Sr VP-Mktg*)
Mark Teteris (*VP-Banking Solutions*)
Ryan Stillwell (*VP-Ops*)
Paul Harrison (*VP-Tech & Product Dev*)
Laura Smith (*Dir-Member Svcs*)
Devin Daly (*Exec VP-Sls & Svc*)
Paul Zoukis (*CEO*)

MORTGAGE WAREHOUSE, LLC
2011 Lake Point Way Ste 101, Louisville, KY 40223-4221
Tel.: (502) 429-9040
Web Site:
http://www.mortgagewarehouse.com
Year Founded: 2003
Sales Range: $1-9.9 Million
Mortgage Lending
N.A.I.C.S.: 522310
Scott Riley (*Founder*)
Mike Roberts (*VP*)

MORTGAGEFLEX SYSTEMS INC.
1200 Riverplace Blvd Ste 650, Jacksonville, FL 32207
Tel.: (904) 356-2490
Web Site:
http://www.mortgageflex.com
Sales Range: $10-24.9 Million
Emp.: 45
Computer Software Development
N.A.I.C.S.: 541511
Lester Dominick (*Pres*)
Craig Bechtle (*COO & Exec VP*)
Steve Shore (*CIO*)

MORTIMER & SON LUMBER CO. INC.
2307 Lapeer Ave, Port Huron, MI 48060-4159
Tel.: (810) 987-3020   MI
Web Site:
http://www.mortimerlumber.com
Year Founded: 1919
Sales Range: $10-24.9 Million
Emp.: 120
Sale of Lumber & Other Building Materials
N.A.I.C.S.: 423310
Franklin Mortimer (*Pres*)

MORTON AUTO AUCTION INC.
410 Erie Ave, Morton, IL 61550
Tel.: (309) 263-7467
Web Site: http://www.mortonaa.com
Rev.: $22,200,000
Emp.: 90
Automobile & Other Motor Vehicle Merchant Whslr
N.A.I.C.S.: 423110
S. Hay (*Gen Mgr*)
C. Hall (*Asst Gen Mgr*)

MORTON BUILDINGS INC.
252 W Adams St, Morton, IL 61550-1804
Tel.: (309) 263-7474   IL
Web Site:
http://www.mortonbuildings.com
Year Founded: 1903
Sales Range: $300-349.9 Million
Emp.: 3,000
Prefabricated Buildings Mfr
N.A.I.C.S.: 332311
Stephanie Cobb (*Coord-Crew Dev*)
Clint Cowley (*Supvr-Pricing & Product*)
Justin Dentino (*Project Mgr*)

MORTON BUILDINGS INC.

Morton Buildings Inc.—(Continued)
Tim Duffy *(Coord-Construction)*
Chris McLean *(Mgr-Product & Process)*
Pat Mooney *(Mgr-Risk Assessment & Compliance)*
Sharon Sering *(Sec)*
James Willms *(Supvr-Area Construction)*
Steve Mauer *(Mgr-Sls)*
David Balkema *(Mgr-Customer Svc)*
Joel Hasse *(Project Mgr)*
Julian King *(Engr-Tech Sys)*
Sean Marcotte *(Gen Mgr-Design Build)*
Troy Erickson *(Project Mgr)*
John Russell *(CEO)*

Subsidiaries:

Classic Equine Equipment, LLC (1)
100 Wulfert Dr, Fredericktown, MO 63645
Tel.: (573) 783-2999
Web Site: http://www.classic-equine.com
Sales Range: $1-9.9 Million
Emp.: 29
Stall & Barn Equipment Mfr
N.A.I.C.S.: 321992
Terry Westrich *(Dir-Sls & Mktg)*
Tyler Henson *(Engr-Design)*
Tom Knott *(Mgr-Reg Sls)*
Scott Lix *(Pres)*

MORTON COMPREHENSIVE HEALTH SERVICES, INC.
1334 N Lansing Ave, Tulsa, OK 74106
Tel.: (918) 587-2171
Web Site:
   http://www.mortonhealth.com
Year Founded: 1983
Sales Range: $10-24.9 Million
Emp.: 200
Health Care Srvices
N.A.I.C.S.: 622110
John M. Silva *(CEO)*
Stan Fosburg *(CIO)*
Larry Tease *(CFO)*
Maiuri Ranchhod *(COO)*
Barbara Cannady *(Vice Chm)*
Ray Hatton *(Treas)*
Dewitt Lucas *(Sec)*
Edward Thomas *(Chm & Pres)*
Cassie Clayton *(Chief Nursing Officer)*

MORTON CONSULTING LLC
4701 Cox Rd Ste 135, Glen Allen, VA 23060
Tel.: (804) 290-4272
Web Site:
   http://www.mortonconsulting.com
Year Founded: 2006
Sales Range: $1-9.9 Million
Emp.: 50
IT & Project Management
N.A.I.C.S.: 541618
Mark Morton *(Founder & Pres)*

MORTON INDUSTRIES LLC
70 Commerce Dr, Morton, IL 61550
Tel.: (309) 263-2590
Web Site: http://www.mortonind.com
Year Founded: 1946
Sales Range: $50-74.9 Million
Emp.: 320
Metal Tube Fabrication & Sheet Metal Component Mfr
N.A.I.C.S.: 332999
Chris Ober *(Pres & CEO)*
Gary Schmitt *(Mgr-Quality)*
Rod Miller *(CIO)*
Kevin Baughman *(Dir-Sls & Mktg)*
Robb Herbig *(Dir-Bus Dev)*
Russ Argadine *(VP-Ops)*
Nathan Gillespie *(CFO)*
James Knepp *(Mgr-Engrg)*
Brent R. Cobb *(Chm)*

MORTON TRUCKING, INC.
121 Garnet Ln, Jacksonville, NC 28546-8801
Tel.: (910) 346-9068
Web Site:
   http://www.mortontrucking.com
Sales Range: $10-24.9 Million
Emp.: 85
Excavation Services
N.A.I.C.S.: 238910
Elijah T. Morton *(Pres & CEO)*

MORTON'S RESTAURANT GROUP, INC.
325 N LaSalle St Ste 500, Chicago, IL 60654
Tel.: (312) 923-0030   DE
Web Site: http://www.mortons.com
Year Founded: 1978
Sales Range: $250-299.9 Million
Emp.: 4,154
Holding Company; Restaurants Owner & Operator
N.A.I.C.S.: 551112
Klaus W. Fritsch *(Founder & Vice Chm)*
Leandra Pavlik *(Mgr-Sls & Event)*

Subsidiaries:

Morton's of Chicago, Inc. (1)
325 N LaSalle Dr Ste 500, Chicago, IL 60654
Tel.: (312) 923-0030
Web Site: http://www.mortons.com
Sales Range: $200-249.9 Million
Emp.: 1,500
Steakhouse Restaurant Chain Operator
N.A.I.C.S.: 722511

MOSAIC
4801 Viewpoint Pl, Cheverly, MD 20781
Tel.: (301) 927-3800
Web Site:
   http://www.mosaicprint.com
Sales Range: $25-49.9 Million
Emp.: 120
Commercial Lithographic Printing Services
N.A.I.C.S.: 323111
Mike Stief *(COO)*
Patti Dumas *(Sr VP-Sls)*
Brendan Connors *(Co-CEO)*

MOSAIC ATM, INC.
801 Sycolin Rd Ste 212, Leesburg, VA 20175
Tel.: (703) 737-7637
Web Site: http://www.mosaicatm.com
Year Founded: 2004
Rev: $5,400,000
Emp.: 27
Scientific & Technical Consulting Services
N.A.I.C.S.: 541690
Chris Stevenson *(Bus Mgr)*

MOSAIC CAPITAL PARTNERS
101 S Tryon Street Ste 2620, Charlotte, NC 28280
Tel.: (704) 626-6419
Web Site: http://www.mosaic-cp.com
Portfolio Management
N.A.I.C.S.: 523940
Ian Mohler *(Principal)*

Subsidiaries:

Boston Barricade Co., Inc. (1)
1151 19th St, Vero Beach, FL 32960
Tel.: (772) 569-7202
Web Site: http://www.bostonbarricade.com
Sales Range: $1-9.9 Million
Commercial & Industrial Machinery & Equipment Rental & Leasing
N.A.I.C.S.: 532490

David Chase *(Gen Mgr)*
Randy Ahlm *(COO)*
Bob Putnam *(Pres & CEO)*
Adam Acosta *(Mktg Dir)*

MOSAIC INTERACTIVE
301 Broadway 2nd Fl, Bethlehem, PA 18015
Tel.: (610) 694-8818
Web Site:
   http://www.mosaicwebsite.com
Year Founded: 2006
Sales Range: $10-24.9 Million
Emp.: 11
Integrated Marketing & Interactive Services
N.A.I.C.S.: 541830
Matthew McKernan *(Pres)*

MOSAIC LIFE CARE
5325 Faraon St, Saint Joseph, MO 64506
Tel.: (816) 271-6000
Web Site:
   http://www.mymosaiclifecare.org
Health Care Srvices
N.A.I.C.S.: 621610
Mark Laney *(Pres & CEO)*
Michael Pulido *(COO)*
Dwain Stilson *(CFO)*
Brennan Lehman *(CIO)*
Edward Kammerer *(Chief Quality Officer)*
Brady Dubois *(Pres-Medical Center)*
Jon Doolittle *(Pres-Northwest Medical Center)*
Davin Turner *(Pres-MLC Clinics)*
Barbara Wurtzler *(Chm)*

MOSAIC MEDIA INVESTMENT PARTNERS LLC
9200 W Sunset Blvd 10th Fl, Los Angeles, CA 90069
Tel.: (310) 786-4900
Financial Investment
N.A.I.C.S.: 523999
Allen Shapiro *(Mng Partner)*

Subsidiaries:

Direct Holdings Americas Inc. (1)
8280 Willow Oaks Corporate Dr Ste 800, Fairfax, VA 22031-4511
Tel.: (703) 663-4500
Web Site: http://www.timelife.com
Sales Range: $400-449.9 Million
Emp.: 75
Book, Music & Video Product Direct Marketing & Retail Services
N.A.I.C.S.: 541990
Chris Hearing *(Pres)*
Jennifer Smith *(Dir-Mktg)*
Paul Crocker *(Dir-Mktg & E-Commerce)*
John Bonfield *(VP-E-Commerce)*
Lange Johnson *(VP-Ops)*
Michael Mitchell *(VP-Strategic Mktg & Partnerships)*
Tim Pearson *(Sr VP-Mktg-Household)*
Michele Adamson *(Dir-Mktg-Multi-Channel)*

Subsidiary (Domestic):

Direct Holdings Libraries Inc. (2)
8280 Willow Oaks Corporate Dr Ste 800, Fairfax, VA 22031-4511
Tel.: (703) 663-4500
Web Site: http://www.timelife.com
Book Direct Marketing Services
N.A.I.C.S.: 541990
Chris Hearing *(Pres)*

Saguaro Road Records, Inc. (1)
8280 Willow Oaks Corporate Dr Ste 800, Fairfax, VA 22031
Tel.: (703) 663-4500
Web Site: http://www.saguaroroad.com
Audio & Video Entertainment Products Marketer
N.A.I.C.S.: 334610
Elaine Anoriscat *(Sr VP)*

U.S. PRIVATE

MOSAIC TECHNOLOGIES GROUP, LLC
8135 Maple Lawn Blvd Ste 450, Fulton, MD 20759-2571
Tel.: (301) 725-0925
Web Site:
   http://www.mosaicsgroup.com
Year Founded: 2005
Sales Range: $25-49.9 Million
Emp.: 235
Management Consulting Services
N.A.I.C.S.: 541618
Michael Grier *(Founder, Pres & CEO)*
Sandra Grier *(COO & VP)*
Dave P. Quinn *(Chief Quality Officer)*
Paul Mays *(Dir-Mgmt Solutions Grp)*
Tim Newell *(Dir-Tech Solutions Grp)*

MOSAICA EDUCATION
3400 Peachtree Rd NE Ste 550, Atlanta, GA 30326
Tel.: (404) 841-2305
Web Site:
   http://www.mosaicaeducation.com
Year Founded: 1997
Sales Range: $75-99.9 Million
Emp.: 1,200
Public Grade School Administration Services
N.A.I.C.S.: 923110
Dawn Eidelman *(Co-Founder & Pres-Paragon Div)*
Gene Eidelman *(Co-Founder & Pres)*
Michael J. Connelly *(CEO)*

MOSBACHER ENERGY COMPANY
712 Main St Ste 2200, Houston, TX 77002
Tel.: (713) 546-2500
Sales Range: $10-24.9 Million
Emp.: 50
Crude Petroleum Production
N.A.I.C.S.: 211120

MOSCOT OPTICAL CORP.
108 Orchard St, New York, NY 10002
Tel.: (212) 477-3796   NY
Web Site: http://www.moscot.com
Year Founded: 1915
Sales Range: $1-9.9 Million
Emp.: 40
Optical Goods Stores Owner & Operator
N.A.I.C.S.: 456130
Harvey Moscot *(CEO)*

MOSCOW BANCSHARES, INC.
1265 Hwy 57 E, Collierville, TN 38017
Tel.: (901) 854-2265   TN
Web Site:
   http://www.thebank1905.com
Year Founded: 1983
Sales Range: $10-24.9 Million
Bank Holding Company
N.A.I.C.S.: 551111
H. McCall Wilson Jr. *(Pres & CEO)*

Subsidiaries:

The Bank of Fayette County (1)
1265 Hwy 57 E, Collierville, TN 38017
Tel.: (901) 854-2265
Web Site: http://www.thebank1905.com
Sales Range: $10-24.9 Million
Emp.: 97
Federal Savings Bank
N.A.I.C.S.: 522180
H. McCall Wilson Jr. *(Pres & CEO)*

MOSCOW MILLS LUMBER COMPANY
250 Main St, Moscow Mills, MO 63362
Tel.: (636) 366-4221
Sales Range: $10-24.9 Million
Emp.: 23

Lumber & Other Building Materials
N.A.I.C.S.: 423310
Dan Prendergast (Pres)

MOSELEY ARCHITECTS P.C.
3200 Norfolk St, Richmond, VA 23230
Tel.: (804) 794-7555
Web Site: http://www.moseleyarchitects.com
Rev.: $13,700,000
Emp.: 200
Architectural Design Services
N.A.I.C.S.: 541310
Stewart D. Roberson (Chm, Pres & CEO)

MOSELEY ASSOCIATES, INC.
82 Coromar Dr, Santa Barbara, CA 93117-3025
Tel.: (805) 968-9621   CA
Web Site: http://www.moseleysb.com
Year Founded: 1960
Sales Range: $10-24.9 Million
Emp.: 40
Designs, Manufactures & Markets Digital Transmission Systems for the Telecommunications Industry & the Radio & TV Broadcast Industry
N.A.I.C.S.: 334220
Jamal N. Hamdani (Pres & CEO)
Bruce Tarr (CFO)

Subsidiaries:

Axxcelera Broadband Wireless Inc.   (1)
82 Coromar Dr, Santa Barbara, CA 93117
Tel.: (408) 894-7045
Web Site: http://www.axxcelera.com
Sales Range: $10-24.9 Million
Supplier of Telecommunications Equipment, Earth Stations & Microwave Radios Used in Wireless Communications
N.A.I.C.S.: 334220
Jamal N. Hamdani (Pres & CEO)
Jerry Kollman (Sr VP-Sls, Mktg & Customer Support-Worldwide)
Tony Masters (CTO & Sr VP)
Philip Rushton (Sr VP-Ops)

CarrierComm Inc.   (1)
111 Castilian Dr, Santa Barbara, CA 93117
Tel.: (760) 634-6200
Web Site: http://www.carriercom.com
Sales Range: $10-24.9 Million
Emp.: 30
Broadband & Wireless Network Systems Provider
N.A.I.C.S.: 334220

E-Band Communications, LLC   (1)
10095 Scripps Ranch Ct Ste A, San Diego, CA 92131
Tel.: (858) 408-0660
Web Site: http://www.e-band.com
Emp.: 25
Communication Equipment Mfr
N.A.I.C.S.: 334220
Sam Smookler (Co-Founder, Pres & CEO)
Saul Umbrasas (Co-Founder & Sr VP-Sls & Mktg)
Andrew Pavelchek (VP-Engrg)

MOSER CORPORATION
601 N 13th St, Rogers, AR 72756
Tel.: (479) 636-3481   AR
Web Site: http://www.mosercorporation.com
Year Founded: 1950
Sales Range: $50-74.9 Million
Emp.: 80
Wood Office Furniture
N.A.I.C.S.: 449110
Clarence Sears (Mgr)

MOSES ANSHELL, INC.
20 W Jackson St, Phoenix, AZ 85003
Tel.: (602) 254-7312
Web Site: http://www.mosesanshell.com
Year Founded: 1981
Sales Range: $25-49.9 Million
Emp.: 35
Full Service
N.A.I.C.S.: 541810
Jos Anshell (CEO)
Louis S. Moses (Pres & Exec Dir-Creative)
Diana Moore (VP-Admin & HR)
Kat Langman (VP-Strategy-Ops)
Annettee Kracht (Dir-Interactive-Digital Mktg)
Craig Hedges (VP & Dir-Creative)
Jason Scott (Dir-Bus Dev)
Chris Fiscus (Dir-PR)
Gary Gauthier (CFO)
Ginelle Howard (Mgr-Bus Dev)

MOSEY MANUFACTURING COMPANY INCORPORATED
262 Fort Wayne Ave, Richmond, IN 47374
Tel.: (765) 983-8800
Web Site: http://www.moseymfg.com
Sales Range: $25-49.9 Million
Emp.: 400
Machine Tools, Metal Cutting Type
N.A.I.C.S.: 333517
Dean Combs (Mgr-Environmental & Safety)

MOSIER & COMPANY, INC.
3151 Airway Ave Ste A-1, Costa Mesa, CA 92626
Tel.: (714) 432-0800
Web Site: http://www.mosierco.com
Year Founded: 1980
Emp.: 10
Corporate Crisis Management Services
N.A.I.C.S.: 541611
Robert P. Mosier (Founder, Pres & CEO)
Craig Marshall Collins (CFO & Controller)

MOSIER FLUID POWER OF INDIANA
9851 Park Davis Dr, Indianapolis, IN 46235
Tel.: (317) 895-6200
Web Site: http://www.mosierautomation.com
Rev.: $10,113,698
Emp.: 60
Pneumatic Tools & Equipment
N.A.I.C.S.: 423830
Jeff Hardwick (VP)

MOSLEY HOLDINGS LIMITED PARTNERSHIP
101 S Oak St Ste A, Sheridan, AR 72150-2436
Tel.: (870) 942-2662
Rev.: $11,700,000
Emp.: 8,000
Holding Company
N.A.I.C.S.: 325910
Rob Raeke (Controller)

Subsidiaries:

American Inks & Coatings Corporation   (1)
114 S Washington St, Pottstown, PA 19464
Tel.: (336) 880-8513
Sales Range: $10-24.9 Million
Emp.: 28
Coatings & Inks for the Printing Trade Mfr
N.A.I.C.S.: 325910

MOSQUITO SQUAD FRANCHISING CORPORATION
2924 Emerywood Pkwy, Richmond, VA 23294
Tel.: (804) 353-6999
Web Site: http://www.mosquitosquad.com
Year Founded: 2005
Sales Range: $1-9.9 Million
Emp.: 27
Pest Control
N.A.I.C.S.: 561710
Michael Nevarr (Owner)
Amy Lawhorne (VP)

MOSQUITONIX FRANCHISE SYSTEMS, LTD.
12655 N Central Expy Ste 425, Dallas, TX 75243
Tel.: (972) 934-3131
Web Site: http://www.mosquitonix.com
Year Founded: 2002
Sales Range: $1-9.9 Million
Emp.: 21
Pest Control & Pesticide Services
N.A.I.C.S.: 561710
Dan O'Neal (CEO)

MOSS & ASSOCIATES, LLC
2101 N Andrews Ave, Fort Lauderdale, FL 33311
Tel.: (954) 524-5678
Web Site: http://www.mosscm.com
Year Founded: 2004
Sales Range: $300-349.9 Million
Emp.: 600
Construction Services
N.A.I.C.S.: 236220
Bob L. Moss (Chm & CEO)
Scott R. Moss (Pres)
Brett Atkinson (Exec VP)
Mike Mazza (Exec VP)
Andrew McAllister (Exec VP)
Scott Desharnais (Exec VP)
Mike Little (Exec VP)
Chad Moss (Exec VP)
Joe Harris (Exec VP)
Bruce Moldow (Exec VP)
Ed Baro (VP)
Dave Ciampini (VP)
Dick Slater (VP)
Joanna Clarkson (VP-Fin)
Guy Reese (VP)
David Greer (Chief Investment Officer & VP)
Doug Rogers (VP)
J. T. Sayfie (CIO)
Tom Philley (Exec VP)
Stephen Chang (VP)
David Fellows (Exec VP)
John Bowden (VP-Tampa)
Joe Broom (Sr VP)
David Burton (VP-Criminal Justice)
Robert Cabello (VP-Preconstruction-West)
David Cooper (VP)
Chris Dorman (VP)
Scott Gerard (VP-Environmental, Health & Safety)
Todd Rogers (VP-HR)
Dan Wobby (Sr VP)
Brian Wetherington (VP)
Toby Manulak (VP)
Marty Strype (VP-Preconstruction-Mid-Florida)

MOSS ADAMS LLP
999 3rd Ave Ste 2800, Seattle, WA 98104-4057
Tel.: (206) 302-6500   WA
Web Site: http://www.mossadams.com
Year Founded: 1913
Emp.: 2,200
Accounting, Tax, Auditing, Bookkeeping, Wealth Management & Advisory Services
N.A.I.C.S.: 541211
Robb McEachran (Partner)
Pam Cleaver (Partner)
Louise Hanson (Partner)
Mark Thoma (Partner)
Mary Wright (Partner)
Jarret Rea (Partner)
Jason Lukaszewicz (Partner)
Jeff Dieleman (Partner)
Jeff Green (Partner)
Carol Suruki (Partner)
Don Greear (Partner)
Eric Miles (Chm & CEO)
Ernesto Vallejo (Partner)
Dan Cheyney (Partner)
Aaron Faulk (Partner)
Ben Mack (Partner)
Brandon Hansen (Partner)
Bruce Knowlton (Partner)
Todd Kooiman (Partner)
Tony Andrade (Partner)
Shannan Gardner (Partner)
Stacey Dell (Partner)
Kristine Hoeflin (Partner)
Star Fischer (Partner)
Dan Evans (Partner)
Dave Follett (Pres, Partner & COO)
Rhonda Powell (Partner & Dir-Tax Svcs)
Scott Kallander (Gen Counsel)
Jen Wyne (Exec Dir-HR)
Piper Turner (Exec Dir-Mktg)
Jason Delles (Dir-Sls)
Eve Dreyfuss (Partner)
Adam Cline (Partner)
Mark Steranka (Partner)
Mike Zelda (Partner)
Mei Xu (Partner-Silicon Valley)
Mike Simone (Dir-IT Consulting-Dallas)
Alan Hungate (Partner)
Alan Villanueva (Partner)
Amanda McCleary-Moore (Partner)
Andy Cates (Partner)
Andy Mattson (Partner)
Barbara Mead (Partner)
Bertha Minnihan (Partner)
Erica Coogan (Partner)
Sharon Gregory (Partner)
Jason Thompson (Partner)
Olga Darlington (Partner)
Aaron Sedler (Partner-Kansas City)
Matthew McKittrick (Mng Dir)
Mark Zilberman (Partner)
Sarah Ratra (Partner-Tech & Life Sciences Practice)
Weston Nelson (Partner-IT Advisory Practice)
Paul Holden (Partner-Health Care Consulting Practice)
Kyle Boast (Partner)
Kelsey Head (Partner-Dallas)
Jamie Simmons (CIO)
Jennifer Schmidt (Partner-Natl)
Mark Hurst (Partner-Dallas)
Curtis Abramson (Partner)
Jason Adkins (Partner)
Craig Anderson (Partner)
Dave Anderson (Partner)
Amy Apiado (Partner)
Bill Armstrong (Partner)
Luc Arsenault (Partner)
Chad Averill (Partner)
Jack Baker (Partner)
Eric Balentine (Partner)
Bill Barnard (Partner)
Jode Beauvais (Partner)
Chris Bell (Partner)
Rick Betts (Partner)
Dustin Birashk (Partner)
Catrina Blackwell (Partner)
Marcy Boyd (Partner)
Letizia Brentano (Partner)
Cheri Burnham (Partner)
Wendy Campos (Partner)
Bryan Cartwright (Partner)
Ryan Curie (Partner-Tax Svcs)

Subsidiaries:

Mengali Accountancy   (1)

MOSS ADAMS LLP

Moss Adams LLP—(Continued)

205 Foss Creek Cir, Healdsburg, CA 95448-4298
Tel.: (707) 431-0600
Web Site: http://www.mengali.com
Offices of Certified Public Accountants
N.A.I.C.S.: 541211
Renee Mengali *(Pres)*
Keith Hollander *(CFO & Principal)*
Katie Olsen *(Dir-Real Estate)*

Moss Adams LLP - Bellingham (1)
2219 Rimland Dr Ste 215, Bellingham, WA 98226-6641
Tel.: (360) 676-1920
Web Site: http://www.mossadams.com
Sales Range: $25-49.9 Million
Emp.: 50
Accounting Auditing & Bookkeeping
N.A.I.C.S.: 541219
Michelle VanDellen *(Partner)*

Moss Adams LLP - Eugene (1)
975 Oak St Ste 500, Eugene, OR 97401-3119
Tel.: (541) 686-1040
Web Site: http://www.mossadams.com
Sales Range: $25-49.9 Million
Emp.: 70
Accounting Auditing & Bookkeeping
N.A.I.C.S.: 541219
Christine Toreson *(Office Mgr)*
Brad Smith *(Partner)*

Moss Adams LLP - Everett (1)
2707 Colby Ave Ste 801, Everett, WA 98201-3565
Tel.: (425) 259-7227
Web Site: http://www.mossadams.com
Sales Range: $25-49.9 Million
Emp.: 120
Accounting, Auditing & Bookkeeping
N.A.I.C.S.: 541219
Phillip Knudson *(Partner)*
Rob Grannum *(Partner)*

Moss Adams LLP - Fresno (1)
265 E River Park Cir Ste 110, Fresno, CA 93720
Tel.: (559) 389-5700
Web Site: http://www.mossadams.com
Accounting, Tax, Auditing, Bookkeeping, Wealth Management & Advisory Services
N.A.I.C.S.: 541211
Chris Morse *(Partner & Head-Fresno Office)*
Sheryl Morse *(Partner)*
Doug Sampson *(Partner)*
Ken Wittwer *(Partner)*

Moss Adams LLP - Issaquah (1)
385 Front St N, Issaquah, WA 98027
Tel.: (425) 369-2500
Web Site: http://www.mossadams.com
Sales Range: $1-9.9 Million
Emp.: 24
Information Technology Consulting Services
N.A.I.C.S.: 541690
Mark Curtis *(Partner)*

Moss Adams LLP - Los Angeles (1)
10960 Wilshire Blvd Ste 1100, Los Angeles, CA 90024
Tel.: (310) 477-0450
Web Site: http://www.mossadams.com
Sales Range: $25-49.9 Million
Emp.: 100
Accounting, Auditing & Bookkeeping
N.A.I.C.S.: 541219
Todd Zanderwel *(Gen Mgr)*

Moss Adams LLP - Orange County (1)
2030 Main St Ste 1400, Irvine, CA 92614
Tel.: (949) 221-4000
Web Site: http://www.mossadams.com
Sales Range: $25-49.9 Million
Emp.: 90
Accounting, Auditing & Bookkeeping
N.A.I.C.S.: 541219
Chris L'Heureux *(Partner)*

Moss Adams LLP - Portland (1)
Fox Twr 805 SW Broadway Ste 1200, Portland, OR 97205
Tel.: (503) 242-1447
Web Site: http://www.mossadams.com
Sales Range: $25-49.9 Million
Emp.: 200
Accounting, Auditing & Bookkeeping

N.A.I.C.S.: 541219
Matthew Montez *(Partner)*
Steve Fein *(Partner)*

Moss Adams LLP - Sacramento (1)
2882 Prospect Park Dr Ste 300, Rancho Cordova, CA 95670-6019
Tel.: (916) 503-8100
Web Site: http://www.mossadams.com
Sales Range: $25-49.9 Million
Emp.: 75
Accounting, Auditing & Bookkeeping
N.A.I.C.S.: 541211
Stephen Fineberg *(Partner)*
Brian Conner *(Partner)*

Moss Adams LLP - San Francisco (1)
101 2nd St Ste 900, San Francisco, CA 94105
Tel.: (415) 956-1500
Web Site: http://www.mossadams.com
Sales Range: $10-24.9 Million
Emp.: 55
Accounting, Auditing & Bookkeeping
N.A.I.C.S.: 541219
Kinman Tong *(Partner)*
Wenli Wang *(Partner)*
Francisco Sarmiento Jr. *(Partner)*

Moss Adams LLP - Santa Rosa (1)
3700 Old Redwood Hwy Ste 200, Santa Rosa, CA 95403
Tel.: (707) 527-0800
Web Site: http://www.mossadams.com
Sales Range: $10-24.9 Million
Emp.: 55
Accounting, Auditing & Bookkeeping
N.A.I.C.S.: 541219
Bill Vyenielo *(Sr Mgr-Bus Consulting)*
Dmitri Alexeev *(Sr Mgr-Tax)*
Joe Hester *(Mgr-Tax)*

Moss Adams LLP - Spokane (1)
601 W Riverside Ave Ste 1800, Spokane, WA 99201-0663
Tel.: (509) 747-2600
Web Site: http://www.mossadams.com
Sales Range: $25-49.9 Million
Emp.: 86
Accounting, Bookkeeping, Human Resources & Information Technology Consultancy Services
N.A.I.C.S.: 541211
Rick Betts *(Mng Partner)*
Camille Christiansen *(Partner)*

Moss Adams LLP - Tacoma (1)
1301 A St Ste 600, Tacoma, WA 98402-4205
Tel.: (253) 572-4100
Web Site: http://www.mossadams.com
Sales Range: $10-24.9 Million
Emp.: 50
Accounting, Auditing & Taxes
N.A.I.C.S.: 541219
Torre Hammer *(Partner)*

Moss Adams LLP - Yakima (1)
402 E Yakima Ave Ste 110, Yakima, WA 98901
Tel.: (509) 248-7750
Web Site: http://www.mossadams.com
Sales Range: $25-49.9 Million
Emp.: 60
Accounting Firm
N.A.I.C.S.: 541211
Rick Anderson *(Pres)*

Moss Adams Wealth Advisors LLC (1)
999 3rd Ave St 2800, Seattle, WA 98104
Tel.: (206) 302-6717
Web Site: http://www.mossadamswealthadvisors.com
Sales Range: $25-49.9 Million
Emp.: 300
Wealth & Investment Advisory Services
N.A.I.C.S.: 523940
Gidget Furness *(Chief Compliance Officer)*
Rebecca Pomering *(CEO)*
Jim Schlager *(Principal)*
John Whiting *(Principal)*
Ken Evans *(Partner)*
Heather Hagen *(Portfolio Mgr)*
George L. Taylor *(Portfolio Mgr)*

MOSS BROS. CHRYSLER JEEP DODGE RAM

8151 Auto Dr, Riverside, CA 92504-4190
Tel.: (951) 688-6200
Web Site: http://www.mossbroscjdrriverside.com
Year Founded: 1938
Sales Range: $75-99.9 Million
Emp.: 200
Car Whslr
N.A.I.C.S.: 441110
Shirley Aplin *(Pres & Sec)*

MOSS BROS. TOYOTA, INC.

12630 Motorway, Moreno Valley, CA 92555
Tel.: (951) 247-8000
Web Site: http://www.mossbrostoyotamorenovalley.com
Sales Range: $75-99.9 Million
Emp.: 150
Car Whslr
N.A.I.C.S.: 441110
Bill Camp *(CFO)*

MOSS LUMBER CO. INC.

5321 Eastside Rd, Redding, CA 96001
Tel.: (530) 244-0700
Web Site: http://www.mosslumber.com
Year Founded: 1976
Sales Range: $25-49.9 Million
Emp.: 140
Retailer of Lumber & Other Building Materials
N.A.I.C.S.: 423310
Gregory Moss *(Pres)*
Darren Moss *(VP)*

MOSS MOTORS

1401 Surrey St, Lafayette, LA 70501
Tel.: (337) 235-9086
Web Site: http://www.mossisboss.com
Year Founded: 1979
Sales Range: $25-49.9 Million
Emp.: 142
New Car Whslr
N.A.I.C.S.: 441110
Sharon Moss *(Owner)*
Eric Robicheaux *(Mgr-Adv)*

MOSS SUPPLY COMPANY

5001 N Graham St, Charlotte, NC 28221
Tel.: (704) 596-8717
Web Site: http://www.mosssupply.com
Sales Range: $25-49.9 Million
Emp.: 350
Windows, Plastics
N.A.I.C.S.: 326199
Ralph Wearsch *(Pres)*
Fred Rymer III *(Plant Mgr)*

MOSS TELECOMMUNICATIONS SERVICES

561 Century Ave SW, Grand Rapids, MI 49503-4903
Tel.: (616) 451-9933
Web Site: http://www.mosstele.com
Year Founded: 1977
Sales Range: $75-99.9 Million
Emp.: 60
Provider of Telecommunications Systems
N.A.I.C.S.: 238210
Gerard J. Schaefer *(Pres & CEO)*
Paul Hinkley *(VP-Ops)*

MOSS WARNER INC.

33332 Valle Rd Ste 200, San Juan Capistrano, CA 92765
Tel.: (949) 429-2266

Web Site: http://www.mosswarner.com
Sales Range: $10-24.9 Million
Emp.: 20
Marketing/Communications
N.A.I.C.S.: 541810
Lee Nichols *(CEO)*
Bob Smithers *(Pres)*
Marcy Kalina *(VP)*
Douglas Blecher *(VP)*
Rusty Forman *(Dir-Creative)*
Jack Fearing *(Creative Dir-Interactive & Design)*
Lisa Smith *(Creative Dir-Design)*

MOSSBERG CORPORATION

7 Grasso Ave, North Haven, CT 06473
Tel.: (203) 230-5300
Web Site: http://www.mossberg.com
Sales Range: $150-199.9 Million
Emp.: 515
Firearm Manufacturing
N.A.I.C.S.: 332994

Subsidiaries:

Maverick Arms, Inc. (1)
1001 Industrial Blvd, Eagle Pass, TX 78852
Tel.: (830) 773-9007
Web Site: http://www.maverickarms.com
Rev.: $10,000,000
Emp.: 300
Shotguns Or Shotgun Parts, 30 Mm. & Below
N.A.I.C.S.: 332994

O.F. Mossberg & Sons, Inc. (1)
7 Grasso Ave, North Haven, CT 06473-3237
Tel.: (203) 230-5300
Web Site: http://www.mossberg.com
Sales Range: $25-49.9 Million
Emp.: 285
Shotguns & Sporting Arms Mfr.
N.A.I.C.S.: 332994
Alan I. Mossberg *(Owner & Chm)*
Iver Mossberg *(CEO)*

MOSSBERG INDUSTRIES, INC.

204 N 2nd St, Garrett, IN 46738-1600
Tel.: (260) 357-5141
Web Site: http://www.mossbergind.com
Year Founded: 1970
Sales Range: $10-24.9 Million
Emp.: 150
Plastic Spool Mfr
N.A.I.C.S.: 321999
Greg Baker *(Controller)*
Michael Khorshid *(Pres)*

Subsidiaries:

Mossberg Industries - Hubbard Division (1)
204 N 2nd St, Garrett, IN 46738
Tel.: (260) 357-5141
Web Site: http://www.mossbergind.com
Mfr of Plastic Spools
N.A.I.C.S.: 321999

MOSSER CONSTRUCTION INC.

122 S Wilson Ave, Fremont, OH 43420-2725
Tel.: (419) 334-3801
Web Site: http://www.mosserconstruction.com
Year Founded: 1974
Sales Range: $50-74.9 Million
Emp.: 500
Building Construction Services
N.A.I.C.S.: 236220
Kevin Wenning *(VP-Comml & Indus Div)*
Brain R. Geffe *(Pres & CEO)*

Subsidiaries:

Contractors Equipment Inc. (1)
201 S Stone St, Fremont, OH 43420-2653
Tel.: (419) 334-3801

Sales Range: $10-24.9 Million
Emp.: 70
Provider of Equipment Rental & Leasing Services, Commercial & Industrial Construction
N.A.I.C.S.: 532490
Vic Coleman (Exec VP)
Chuck Mooreman (Sr VP)

Telamon Construction Inc. (1)
5505 Milan Rd, Sandusky, OH 44870 (100%)
Tel.: (419) 626-1111
Web Site:
 http://www.telamonconstruction.com
Sales Range: $10-24.9 Million
Emp.: 50
Builder of Industrial Buildings
N.A.I.C.S.: 236220
Michael Bossetti (Pres)
James Brossia (CEO)

MOSSO'S MEDICAL SUPPLY COMPANY
5103 Ctr Dr, Latrobe, PA 15650
Tel.: (800) 555-4951
Web Site:
 http://www.airproductshealthcare.com
Year Founded: 1999
Sales Range: $10-24.9 Million
Emp.: 130
Home Medical Equipment
N.A.I.C.S.: 621610
William J. McGinnis (Chief Devel Dir)
Joey Ryan (Sr VP-Reimbursement & Compliance)
Jennifer Woo (VP-HR)

MOSSY NISSAN INC.
2700 National City Blvd, National City, CA 91950
Tel.: (619) 870-8384
Web Site:
 http://www.mossynissannationalcity.com
Year Founded: 1982
Sales Range: $25-49.9 Million
Emp.: 70
Sales of New & Used Cars
N.A.I.C.S.: 441110
Gary Williams (Mgr-Inventory)
Kenny Afshar (Gen Mgr)

MOSSY TOYOTA INC.
4555 Mission Bay Dr, San Diego, CA 92109
Tel.: (858) 581-4000
Web Site: http://www.mossy.com
Rev.: $42,000,000
Emp.: 100
New & Used Car Dealers
N.A.I.C.S.: 441110
Christian Coburn (Mgr-Bus Dev)
Dale Snow (Dir-Fixed Ops)
Kelsie Roiz (Asst Mgr-Fleet)
Richard Carver (Asst Mgr-Svc)
Steve Sawyer (Sr Mgr-Sls)
Thomas Nguyen (Mgr-Internet Sls)

MOST BRAND DEVELOPMENT + ADVERTISING
25 Enterprise Ste 250, Aliso Viejo, CA 92656
Tel.: (949) 475-4050
Web Site:
 http://www.mostagency.com
Year Founded: 2005
Sales Range: $50-74.9 Million
Emp.: 15
Advetising Agency
N.A.I.C.S.: 541810
John G. Most (Pres & CEO)
Mike Burkhart (Assoc Dir-Creative)
Joel Tarman (Dir-Creative)
Jodi A. Most (Dir-Ops)
Marci Grzelecki (Dir-Bus Dev)

Lisa Lindsay (Mgr-Digital Media)
Jon Grenier (Sr Dir-Art)
Dave MacLeod (VP & Acct Dir)

MOSTCHOICE.COM
5600 Roswell Rd 275, Atlanta, GA 30342
Tel.: (404) 531-9858
Year Founded: 2000
Sales Range: $1-9.9 Million
Emp.: 10
Real Estate Industry Suppport Services
N.A.I.C.S.: 531390

MOTA GROUP, INC.
81 Daggett Dr, San Jose, CA 95134
Tel.: (408) 370-1248 DE
Web Site: http://www.mota.com
Year Founded: 2003
Sales Range: $1-9.9 Million
Emp.: 21
Unmanned Commercial Drone Mfr & Distr
N.A.I.C.S.: 333923
Michael Faro (Chm, Pres, CEO & CFO)
Lily Q. Ju (Chief Product Officer & VP)

MOTAN, INC.
320 N Acorn St, Plainwell, MI 49080
Tel.: (269) 685-1050
Web Site: http://www.motan.com
Year Founded: 1980
Sales Range: $10-24.9 Million
Emp.: 15
Plastic Pellet Material Handling & Drying Equipment
N.A.I.C.S.: 333922
Mark McKibbin (Pres)

MOTAWI TILEWORKS, INC.
170 Enterprise Dr, Ann Arbor, MI 48103
Tel.: (734) 213-0017
Web Site: http://www.motawi.com
Year Founded: 1992
Sales Range: $1-9.9 Million
Emp.: 35
Ceramic Tile Mfr
N.A.I.C.S.: 327120
Nawal Motawi (Founder & Owner)
Dave Weber (Mgr-Production)

MOTCO, INC.
10900 NW 27 St, Miami, FL 33172
Tel.: (305) 591-3993
Sales Range: $10-24.9 Million
Emp.: 100
Consumer Goods Wholesale Trade Distr
N.A.I.C.S.: 425120
Mari Sousa (Sec)

Subsidiaries:

Carisam-Samuel Meisel (MD), Inc. (1)
2707 Rolling Rd Ste 120, Baltimore, MD 21244
Tel.: (443) 348-1414
Sales Range: $10-24.9 Million
Emp.: 50
Consumer Goods Wholesale Trade Distr
N.A.I.C.S.: 425120
David Granek (CEO)
Harold Rifas (Treas & Sec)
Rusell Davis (Mgr-Sls)

MOTE MARINE LABORATORY, INC.
1600 Ken Thompson Pkwy, Sarasota, FL 34236
Tel.: (941) 388-4441
Web Site: http://www.mote.org
Year Founded: 1955
Sales Range: $10-24.9 Million

Emp.: 200
Marine Laboratory & Aquarium
N.A.I.C.S.: 712130
Kevan Main (Mgr-Program)
Randall S. Wells (Mgr-Program)
Dena Smith (CFO & VP-Admin)
Michael P. Crosby (Pres & CEO)
Dan Bebak (VP-Aquarium)
Derek A. Templeton (VP-Facilities)
Peter T. Hull (VP-Marine Ops)
Robert Essner (Vice Chm)
Peter Rosasco (Chm)
Erin Kabinoff (Chief Dev Officer)
Pam Baker (Sec)
Bob Whyte (Treas)
Anna Marie Martin (VP)
Andria Piekarz (Dir-Dev)
Kevin Claridge (Assoc VP-Sponsored Res & Coastal Policy Programs)

MOTEN TATE, INC. (MTI)
390 N Orange Ave Suite 1890, Orlando, FL 32801
Tel.: (407) 843-3277
Web Site: http://www.motentate.com
Year Founded: 1997
Sales Range: $1-9.9 Million
Emp.: 50
IT & Engineering Staffing Services
N.A.I.C.S.: 561311

MOTENG INTERNATIONAL INCORPORATED
7220 Trade St Ste 100, Poway, CA 92121
Tel.: (858) 715-2500
Web Site: http://www.moteng.com
Rev.: $11,800,000
Emp.: 40
Clothing Mfr
N.A.I.C.S.: 424350
Leslie Edelstein (Founder & Pres)

MOTHER ANGELINE MCCRORY MANOR
5199 E Broad St, Columbus, OH 43213
Tel.: (614) 751-5700 OH
Web Site:
 http://www.mangelinemanor.org
Year Founded: 2001
Sales Range: $10-24.9 Million
Emp.: 364
Community Health Care Services
N.A.I.C.S.: 621498
Pauline Ross (Treas)

MOTHERNATURE.COM, INC.
322 7th Ave Fl 3, New York, NY 10001
Tel.: (212) 279-4350
Web Site:
 http://www.mothernature.com
Sales Range: $10-24.9 Million
Emp.: 40
Online Health Supplement Store
N.A.I.C.S.: 456191

MOTHERS NUTRITIONAL CENTER
13635 Freeway Dr, Santa Fe Springs, CA 90670-5622
Tel.: (562) 293-4280
Web Site: http://www.mncinc.com
Sales Range: $25-49.9 Million
Emp.: 50
Grocery Stores
N.A.I.C.S.: 445110
Richard Flores (Pres)
Jasmin Fajardo (Mgr-Mktg)

MOTIF BIO PLC
5 Independence Way Ste 300, Princeton, NJ 08540
Tel.: (609) 608-0032
Web Site: http://www.motifbio.com

Year Founded: 2014
Rev.: $113,000
Assets: $18,724,000
Liabilities: $27,650,000
Net Worth: ($8,926,000)
Earnings: ($13,985,000)
Emp.: 7
Fiscal Year-end: 12/31/18
Product Research Services
N.A.I.C.S.: 325412
Graham George Lumsden (CEO)

MOTIFWORKS, INC.
222 Courthouse Ct Ste 3G, Towson, MD 21204
Tel.: (443) 424-2340
Web Site: http://www.motifworks.com
Year Founded: 2010
Sales Range: $1-9.9 Million
Software Development Services
N.A.I.C.S.: 541511
Nitin Agarwal (Founder & CEO)
Vikas Agarwal (COO)
Kirk Pawlak (VP-Sls)

MOTION ANALYSIS CORPORATION
3617 Westwind Blvd, Santa Rosa, CA 95403
Tel.: (707) 579-6500
Web Site:
 http://www.motionanalysis.com
Sales Range: $10-24.9 Million
Emp.: 35
Measuring & Controlling Devices
N.A.I.C.S.: 334519
Tom D. Whitaker (CEO)
Brian Leedy (Pres)

Subsidiaries:

Performance Capture Studios (1)
1041 N Mansfield Ave, Hollywood, CA 90038
Tel.: (323) 461-3835
Web Site: http://www.mastudios.com
Rev.: $1,200,000
Emp.: 10
Visual Effects Production
N.A.I.C.S.: 512191

MOTION PICTURE ASSOCIATION OF AMERICA, INC.
15301 Ventura Blvd Bldg E, Sherman Oaks, CA 91403
Tel.: (818) 995-6600 NY
Web Site: http://www.mpaa.org
Year Founded: 1922
Emp.: 216
Motion Picture Industry Association
N.A.I.C.S.: 813910
Christopher J. Dodd (Chm)
David F. England (CFO & Exec VP)
Matt Bennett (Exec VP-Comm-Global)
Gail MacKinnon (Exec VP-Govt Affairs)
Charles H. Rivkin (CEO)
Mike Ellis (Pres & Mng Dir-Asia-Pacific)
Stan McCoy (Pres & Mng Dir-EMEA)
Steve Fabrizio (Gen Counsel-Global & Sr Exec VP)
Brandon Reese (VP-State Govt Affairs-Southeast)
Patrick Kilcur (Exec VP-Govt Affairs)
Kathy Banuelos (Sr VP-State Govt Affairs)

MOTION PICTURE INDUSTRY PENSION & HEALTH PLANS
11365 Ventura Blvd, Studio City, CA 91614-3161
Tel.: (818) 769-0007 CA
Web Site: http://www.mpiphp.org
Year Founded: 1952
Sales Range: $550-599.9 Million
Emp.: 271
Health & Pension Benefit Services
N.A.I.C.S.: 525120

MOTION PICTURE INDUSTRY PENSION & HEALTH PLANS — U.S. PRIVATE

Motion Picture Industry Pension & Health Plans—(Continued)
Michael Miller (Co-Sec)
Helayne Antler (Co-Sec)
Thom Davis (Chm)

MOTION WATER SPORTS INC.
14615 NE 91st, Snoqualmie, WA 98065
Tel.: (425) 202-2100
Web Site: http://www.obrien.com
Sales Range: $10-24.9 Million
Emp.: 91
Water Sports Equipment
N.A.I.C.S.: 339920
Charlie Mehrmann (VP-Mfg)

Subsidiaries:
O'Brien International, Inc. (1)
14615 NE 91st St, Redmond, WA 98052-3459
Tel.: (425) 202-2100
Web Site: http://www.obrien.com
Sales Range: $10-24.9 Million
Mfr & Retailer of Slalom Skis, Sailboards & Accessories
N.A.I.C.S.: 339920

MOTIONPOINT CORP.
4661 Johnson Rd Ste 14, Coconut Creek, FL 33073
Tel.: (954) 421-0890
Web Site:
  http://www.motionpoint.com
Year Founded: 2000
Sales Range: $25-49.9 Million
Emp.: 200
Website Translation Services
N.A.I.C.S.: 541930
Adam Rubenstein (COO)
Ben Field (VP-Sls)
Charles Whiteman (Sr VP-Client Svcs)
Enrique Travieso (CTO)
Arcadio Andrade (VP-Translation)
Darren Burris (VP-Channels & Alliances)
Jimmy Hale (VP-Solutions)
Craig Witt (Exec VP-Worldwide Sls)
Evan Kramer (CEO)

MOTIV, INC.
2226 3rd Ave Ste 200, Seattle, WA 98121
Tel.: (206) 407-3173
Web Site: http://www.motivworks.com
Year Founded: 2013
Sales Range: $10-24.9 Million
Emp.: 86
Digital Marketing Services
N.A.I.C.S.: 541613
David Graves (CEO)

MOTIVATION DESIGN LLC
2D Fanaras Dr, Salisbury, MA 01952
Tel.: (978) 465-5678
Web Site: http://www.kurgostore.com
Year Founded: 2003
Sales Range: $1-9.9 Million
Emp.: 12
Pet Travel Products
N.A.I.C.S.: 459910
Kitter Spater (Co-Founder & Chief Creative Officer)
Gordie Spater (Co-Founder & Chief Bus Officer)
Brett Tetley (Dir-Art)
Chris Smith (Mgr-Sls-Western)
Jen Joyce (VP-Mktg)
Joe Graves (Dir-Ops & Fin)
Kevin Waller (VP-Sls)

MOTIVATIONAL SYSTEMS INC.
2200 Cleveland Ave, National City, CA 91950
Tel.: (619) 474-8246
Web Site:
  http://www.motivationalsystems.com
Sales Range: $10-24.9 Million
Emp.: 100
Signs & Advertising Specialties
N.A.I.C.S.: 541430
Robert D. Young (Founder & Pres)
Tony F. Young (Exec VP)
Joe Jordan (CFO & VP)
Bonny Franklin (Acct Exec)

MOTIVATORS INC.
123 Frost St Ste 204, Westbury, NY 11590
Tel.: (516) 735-9600
Web Site: http://www.motivators.com
Year Founded: 1979
Sales Range: $1-9.9 Million
Emp.: 40
Promotional Products
N.A.I.C.S.: 541890
Kenneth Laffer (Pres & CEO)
Tony McNally (Mgr-Ops)

MOTIVE INTERACTIVE INC.
6020 Cornerstone Ct W Ste 280, San Diego, CA 92121
Tel.: (858) 677-0792
Web Site:
  http://www.motiveinteractive.com
Year Founded: 2003
Sales Range: $1-9.9 Million
Emp.: 30
Interactive Advertising Services
N.A.I.C.S.: 541890
Luke Smith (Mgr-Network)
Ryan Berger (Mgr-Affiliate)
Mike Schwartzberg (VP-Sls)
Sean E. Duggan (Chm)
Brendan J. Smith (CEO)
John Teotico (CFO & VP)

MOTIVE PARTNERS GP, LLC
7 World Trade Ctr 250 Greenwich ST FL47, New York, NY 10007
Tel.: (212) 651-0200
Web Site:
  http://www.motivepartners.com
Investment Firm
N.A.I.C.S.: 523999
Bob Brown (Partner)
Andy Stewart (Partner)
Blythe Masters (Partner)
Jeffery W. Yabuki (Founding Partner)

MOTIVE PARTS COMPANY FMP
1380 Corporate Center Curve Ste 200, Eagan, MN 55121
Tel.: (651) 405-3610
Web Site:
  http://www.factorymotorparts.com
Sales Range: $10-24.9 Million
Emp.: 75
Automotive Supplies & Parts Distr
N.A.I.C.S.: 423120
Elliot Badzin (Pres)

MOTO, INC.
721 W Main St, Belleville, IL 62220
Tel.: (618) 233-6754
Web Site: http://www.motomart.net
Year Founded: 1974
Sales Range: $75-99.9 Million
Emp.: 700
Holding Company; Operator of Gasoline Service Stations
N.A.I.C.S.: 457120
Jim Forsyth (Pres)

Subsidiaries:
FKG Oil Company (1)
721 W Main, Belleville, IL 62220
Tel.: (618) 233-6754
Web Site: http://www.mymotomart.com
Sales Range: $10-24.9 Million
Emp.: 45
Operator of Gasoline Service Stations & Convenience Store Chain
N.A.I.C.S.: 457120
Timothy Horan (CFO)

MOTOCROSS TOYOTA
2950 Mayfield Rd, Cleveland Heights, OH 44118
Tel.: (216) 321-0102
Web Site:
  http://www.motorcarstoyota.com
Sales Range: $10-24.9 Million
Emp.: 69
New Car Dealers
N.A.I.C.S.: 441110
Steve Walcoff (Mgr-Svc)
Don Shaffer (Mgr-Svc)

MOTOMCO
3699 Kinsman Blvd, Madison, WI 53704
Tel.: (608) 244-2904
Web Site: http://www.motomco.com
Sales Range: $25-49.9 Million
Emp.: 375
Rodent Control Supplies Mfr
N.A.I.C.S.: 561710
Todd Butzow (Dir-Mktg)

MOTOR
215 Ferndale Rd S, Wayzata, MN 55391
Tel.: (612) 234-5520
Web Site: http://www.motor247.net
Year Founded: 1996
Rev.: $10,000,000
Emp.: 10
Advertising, Broadcast, Print
N.A.I.C.S.: 541810
John Henning (CEO & Dir-Creative)
Jean Koelz (VP-Strategic Plng)
Adam Lindquist (VP-New Bus Dev)
Josh Fait (CIO)

MOTOR & EQUIPMENT MANUFACTURERS ASSOCIATION
10 Laboratory Dr, Research Triangle Park, NC 27709
Tel.: (919) 549-4800
Web Site: http://www.mema.org
Year Founded: 1904
Sales Range: $10-24.9 Million
Motor Vehicle Component & System Manufacturer Association
N.A.I.C.S.: 813910
Julie A. Fream (Pres & CEO)
Wendy T. Earp (CFO, Sec & Sr VP)
Paul McCarthy (Sr VP-Strategy, Plng & Info Svcs)
Brian Daugherty (CTO)
Daniel E. Sceli (Chm)

MOTOR APPLIANCE CORPORATION
601 International Ave, Washington, MO 63090
Tel.: (636) 532-3406
Web Site: http://www.macmc.com
Rev.: $20,752,000
Emp.: 100
Battery Charging Generators, Automobile & Aircraft
N.A.I.C.S.: 336320

MOTOR CAR AUTO CARRIERS, INC.
8641 Rosemary St, Commerce City, CO 80022-5052
Tel.: (303) 288-6699
Web Site:
  http://www.motorcarautocarriers.com
Sales Range: $1-9.9 Million
Emp.: 33
Automobile Transport Services
N.A.I.C.S.: 488490

Bruce Balsley (CEO)

MOTOR CITY ELECTRIC CO., INC.
99440 Grennell St, Detroit, MI 48213-1815
Tel.: (313) 921-5300
Web Site: http://www.mceco.com
Year Founded: 1952
Sales Range: $25-49.9 Million
Emp.: 600
Electrical Work Services
N.A.I.C.S.: 335313
Dale Wieczorek (Pres & CEO)
Patrick Mitchell (Controller)
Dick Martin (VP)
Denise Hodgins (CFO & Exec VP)
Kevin Wieczorek (Exec VP)
Paul Gillespie (Sr VP)
Steve Frantz (Exec VP)
Thomas McGrail (Exec VP)
David Krausman (Gen Mgr)
Bob Nichols (Mgr-Ops)

Subsidiaries:
Apex Electric (1)
6385 Montessouri St Ste 120, Las Vegas, NV 89113-1186
Tel.: (702) 791-2739
Web Site: http://www.apexelectriclv.com
Emp.: 30
Electrical Contracting Services
N.A.I.C.S.: 238210
Dale Wieczorek (Pres)
Josh Wozniak (Gen Mgr)
Jeff Zwiesler (Controller)

Detroit Excavation, Inc. (1)
9440 Grennell St, Detroit, MI 48213-1151
Tel.: (313) 921-5300
Excavation Contracting Services
N.A.I.C.S.: 238910

Huron Valley Electric, Inc. (1)
425 Jackson Plz, Ann Arbor, MI 48103-1960
Tel.: (734) 747-8840
Emp.: 20
Electrical Contracting Services
N.A.I.C.S.: 238210
Thomas Kittel (Pres)

Iowa City Electric Company (1)
2474 Feedom Ct, Iowa City, IA 52240
Tel.: (319) 354-3900
Web Site: http://www.mceco.com
Electrical Contracting Services
N.A.I.C.S.: 238210
Steve Frantz (Exec VP)

Mid South Contractors LTD. (1)
3110 Devon Drive, Windsor, N8X 4L2, ON, Canada
Tel.: (519) 966-6163
Web Site: https://www.midsouthulc.com
Electrical Contracting Services
N.A.I.C.S.: 238210
John Salvatore (Pres)

Motor City Electric Technology (1)
9440 Grennell St, Detroit, MI 48213-1151 (100%)
Tel.: (313) 957-3696
Web Site: http://www.cadrecorp.com
Sales Range: $10-24.9 Million
Emp.: 70
Mfr of Switchgear & Switchboard Apparatus
N.A.I.C.S.: 335313

Motor City Electric Utilities Co., Inc. (1)
9440 Grennell St, Detroit, MI 48213-1151
Tel.: (313) 921-5300
Web Site: http://www.mceco.com
Sales Range: $10-24.9 Million
Emp.: 70
Utility Construction & Maintenance
N.A.I.C.S.: 238210

Rotor Electric LLC. (1)
9522 Grinnell Ave, Detroit, MI 48213-1151
Tel.: (313) 891-0331
Sales Range: $1-9.9 Million
Emp.: 20
Electrical Contracting Services
N.A.I.C.S.: 238210

Benjamin Rosenberg *(Pres)*

Stelko Electric, Inc. (1)
2529 N Washington St, Kokomo, IN 46901-5847
Tel.: (765) 452-2090
Web Site: http://www.stelkoelectric.com
Emp.: 100
Electrical Contracting Services
N.A.I.C.S.: 238210
Steve Frantz *(Exec VP)*

Telecom Technicians Inc. (1)
34000 Mound Rd, Sterling Heights, MI 48310-6609
Tel.: (586) 268-7000
Web Site: http://www.telecomtech.com
Sales Range: $25-49.9 Million
Emp.: 305
Provider of Electrical Work Services
N.A.I.C.S.: 238210
Brett Quantz *(Mgr-Pur)*
Tony Salinaz *(Mgr-Svc)*
David McMullen *(Supvr-Warehouse)*

MOTOR CITY POWERSPORTS, LLC
1645 S Telegraph Rd, Bloomfield Hills, MI 48302
Tel.: (248) 858-2300
Web Site: http://www.motorcitypowersport.com
Sales Range: $25-49.9 Million
Emp.: 50
Motorcycle Dealers
N.A.I.C.S.: 441227
Tom Celani *(Pres)*

MOTOR CITY STAMPING, INC.
47783 Gratiot Ave, Chesterfield, MI 48051
Tel.: (586) 949-8420
Web Site: http://www.mcstamp.com
Year Founded: 1969
Sales Range: $50-74.9 Million
Emp.: 350
Mfr of Automotive Stampings
N.A.I.C.S.: 336370
Judith Kucway *(CEO)*
Roger Kucway *(Pres)*
Paul Lachowicz *(Controller)*

MOTOR CONTROLS, INC.
10661 Newkirk St, Dallas, TX 75220
Tel.: (972) 247-8991
Web Site: http://www.motorcontrols.com
Year Founded: 1980
Sytems & Control Solutions; Pumping Systems Mfr
N.A.I.C.S.: 334519
Craig Carter *(Pres)*
Carson Keifer *(VP-Sls)*
Jeff Hains *(VP-Engrg)*
John Murtaugh *(VP-Water Products)*

Subsidiaries:

Flowtronex PSI, LLC (1)
10661 Newkirk St, Dallas, TX 75220
Tel.: (469) 221-1200
Web Site: http://www.motorcontrols.com
Irrigation Equipment Mfr
N.A.I.C.S.: 333914

MOTOR MART AUTO SALES
800 Washington St, South Attleboro, MA 02703
Tel.: (508) 761-5400
Web Site: http://www.motormartautosales.com
Year Founded: 1964
Sales Range: $10-24.9 Million
Emp.: 30
New Car Dealers
N.A.I.C.S.: 441110
Donald Cerrone *(Pres)*

MOTOR TRUCK EQUIPMENT COMPANY
198 Kost Rd, Carlisle, PA 17013-0922
Tel.: (717) 766-8000   PA
Web Site: http://www.kwofpa.com
Year Founded: 1969
Sales Range: $25-49.9 Million
Emp.: 150
Provider of Automobiles & Other Motor Vehicle Supplies
N.A.I.C.S.: 423110
Gareth Mitchell *(Chm)*
Timothy Mitchell *(VP & Gen Mgr)*

MOTOR TRUCKS INC.
315 Riverside Rd, Everett, WA 98201-1275
Tel.: (425) 258-2691
Web Site: http://www.motortrucksinc.com
Sales Range: $25-49.9 Million
Emp.: 125
Heavy Duty Repair Shops
N.A.I.C.S.: 811111
Marshall Cymbaluk *(Pres)*

MOTOR VEHICLE ACCIDENT INDEMNIFICATION CORPORATION
100 William St 14th Fl, New York, NY 10038
Tel.: (646) 205-7800   NY
Web Site: http://www.mvaic.com
Year Founded: 1959
Sales Range: $25-49.9 Million
Emp.: 79
Vehicle Accident Insurance Assistance Services
N.A.I.C.S.: 524298
Fred Fossett *(CFO & Treas)*
Frank Marzulo *(Mgr-Claim)*

MOTOR WERKS PARTNERS LP
1475 S Barrington Rd, Barrington, IL 60010
Tel.: (847) 381-8900
Web Site: http://www.motorwerks.com
Rev.: $250,000,000
Emp.: 215
Automobiles, New & Used
N.A.I.C.S.: 441110
Paul Tamraz *(Owner)*

MOTORCARS INTERNATIONAL INC.
3015 E Cairo St, Springfield, MO 65802
Tel.: (417) 831-9999
Web Site: http://www.motorcars-intl.com
Rev.: $30,000,000
Emp.: 6
New & Used Car Dealers
N.A.I.C.S.: 441110
Bob Cann *(Pres & CEO)*
Steve Burks *(Dir-Mktg)*

MOTORCYCLE SAFETY FOUNDATION, INC.
2 Jenner Ste 150, Irvine, CA 92618
Tel.: (949) 727-3227   DC
Web Site: http://www.msf-usa.org
Year Founded: 1973
Sales Range: $10-24.9 Million
Emp.: 40
Safety Professional Association
N.A.I.C.S.: 813920
Amy Garton *(Dir-Interactive Media)*
Tim Buche *(Pres)*

MOTORISTS MUTUAL INSURANCE CO.
471 E Broad St Ste 200, Columbus, OH 43215
Tel.: (614) 232-1700   OH

Web Site: http://www.motoristsgroup.com
Year Founded: 1965
Sales Range: $500-549.9 Million
Emp.: 1,144
Property, Casualty & Life Insurance Services
N.A.I.C.S.: 524126
Michael L. Wiseman *(CFO & Treas)*
Grady Campbell *(VP)*
Shawn Kimmes *(VP-Sls)*
Joe Fullenkamp *(VP-Personal Lines)*

Subsidiaries:

American Merchants Casualty Co. (1)
5605 Green Cir Dr, Minnetonka, MN 55343   (100%)
Tel.: (952) 835-1400
Property & Casualty Insurance
N.A.I.C.S.: 524126

MICO Insurance Company (1)
471 E Broad St, Columbus, OH 43215-3842   (100%)
Tel.: (614) 225-8211
Web Site: http://www.motoristmutual.com
Sales Range: $1-9.9 Million
Emp.: 869
Property & Casualty Insurer
N.A.I.C.S.: 524126
Dave Kaufman *(CEO)*

Motorists Life Insurance Company (1)
471 E Broad St, Columbus, OH 43215-3842   (70%)
Tel.: (614) 225-8211
Web Site: http://www.motoristsgroup.com
Sales Range: $50-74.9 Million
Emp.: 250
Life, Accident & Health Insurance
N.A.I.C.S.: 524113
Charles Stapleton *(Sr VP-Agency-Mktg)*

MOTORS & ARMATURES, INC.
250 Rabro Dr E, Hauppauge, NY 11788
Tel.: (631) 348-0200
Web Site: http://www.marsm-a.com
Year Founded: 1946
Sales Range: $25-49.9 Million
Emp.: 150
Distr of Refrigeration, Heating & Air Conditioning Replacement Parts
N.A.I.C.S.: 423740
Therese Deangelis *(CFO)*
Mary Ellen Coady *(Mgr-Inside Sls)*

Subsidiaries:

Heat Controller, Inc. (1)
1900 Wellworth, Jackson, MI 49203-6428
Tel.: (517) 787-2100
Web Site: http://www.heatcontroller.com
Sales Range: $10-24.9 Million
Emp.: 50
Air Conditioning & Heating Equipment Mfr
N.A.I.C.S.: 333415
Dave Duane *(VP-Fin)*

MOTT & CHACE SOTHEBY'S INTERNATIONAL REALTY
5280 Post Rd, Charlestown, RI 02813
Tel.: (401) 364-6700
Web Site: http://www.mottandchance.com
Year Founded: 2013
Real Estate Agency
N.A.I.C.S.: 531210
Raymond Mott *(Co-Owner)*
Judy Chace *(Co-Owner)*
Geer Messinger *(COO)*
Jeni Pardo de Zela *(CMO)*
Benjamin Scungio *(Office Mgr)*

MOTT CHILDREN'S HEALTH CENTER
806 Tuuri Pl, Flint, MI 48503
Tel.: (810) 767-5750   MI

Web Site: http://www.mottchc.org
Year Founded: 1939
Sales Range: $10-24.9 Million
Emp.: 126
Child Health Care Services
N.A.I.C.S.: 622110

MOTT'S HOLDINGS, INC.
701 Hebron Ave, Glastonbury, CT 06033-4337
Tel.: (860) 682-1020   CT
Year Founded: 1989
Sales Range: $125-149.9 Million
Emp.: 5
Investment & Insurance
N.A.I.C.S.: 551112
Barry Baskind *(Pres & CEO)*
Christine Reed *(Sec)*

Subsidiaries:

Motts Supermarkets (1)
701 Hebron Ave, Glastonbury, CT 06033-4337
Tel.: (860) 682-1020
Sales Range: $25-49.9 Million
Emp.: 2
Basic Insurance
N.A.I.C.S.: 551112

MOUAT COMPANY INC.
1950 Stonegate Dr Ste 150, Birmingham, AL 35242
Tel.: (205) 951-1815
Web Site: http://www.mouat.com
Year Founded: 1924
Rev.: $25,000,000
Emp.: 10
Engineering & Design of Forklift Parts
N.A.I.C.S.: 333922
John Michael Morris *(CFO & Pres)*

MOULDAGRAPH CORPORATION
4134 1st Ave, Nitro, WV 25143
Tel.: (304) 759-2150
Web Site: http://www.mouldagraph.com
Sales Range: $100-124.9 Million
Emp.: 70
Construction, Mining & Forestry Machinery & Equipment Rental & Leasing
N.A.I.C.S.: 532412
Gordon Robinson *(Mgr-Centrifuge)*
Rudy Moulder *(Mgr-Field Svc)*
Jeff Holstein *(Mgr-Plastics Sls)*
Nancy Moulder *(Owner)*

MOULTON-NIGUEL WATER DISTRICT
27500 La Paz Rd, Laguna Niguel, CA 92677-3402
Tel.: (949) 831-2500   CA
Web Site: http://www.mnwd.com
Year Founded: 1960
Sales Range: $25-49.9 Million
Emp.: 100
Water Supply
N.A.I.C.S.: 221310
Mark Mountford *(Project Mgr)*
Jane Nguyen *(Supvr-IT)*
Ronin Goodall *(Supvr-Water Distr)*

MOUNT AUBURN CEMETERY
580 Mount Auburn St, Cambridge, MA 02138
Tel.: (617) 547-7105   MA
Web Site: http://www.mountauburn.org
Year Founded: 1831
Sales Range: $10-24.9 Million
Emp.: 96
Cemetery Services
N.A.I.C.S.: 812220
Bree D. Harvey *(VP-Cemetery & Visitors)*
Jane M. Carroll *(VP-Dev)*

MOUNT AUBURN CEMETERY U.S. PRIVATE

Mount Auburn Cemetery—(Continued)
Kimberly D. Gluck (Treas)
Michael A. Albano (Exec VP)
Oliver C. Scholle Jr. (Vice Chm)

MOUNT CLEMENS KIA
43774 N Gratiot Ave, Clinton Township, MI 48036
Tel.: (586) 463-1521
Web Site: http://www.clemenskia.com
Sales Range: $10-24.9 Million
Emp.: 70
Car Dealership
N.A.I.C.S.: 441110
Jill Kapeluch (Controller)

MOUNT DESERT ISLAND BIOLOGICAL LABORATORY
159 Old Bar Harbor Rd, Salsbury Cove, ME 04672
Tel.: (207) 288-9880
Web Site: http://www.mdibl.org
Year Founded: 1898
Sales Range: $10-24.9 Million
Emp.: 88
Biomedical Research Services
N.A.I.C.S.: 541715
Jerilyn M. Bowers (Dir-Dev & PR)
Patricia Hand (VP-Admin)
Claudine Lurvey (Dir-Fin)
Roy McMorran (Dir-IT)
Mark Nicknair (Asst Dir-Facilities)
Judy Sproule (Deputy Dir-Dev)
Jilliane Sawyer (Coord-Payroll & Billing)

MOUNT FRANKLIN FOODS, LLC
1800 Northwestern Dr, El Paso, TX 79912
Web Site: http://www.mountfranklinfoods.com
Year Founded: 1907
Food Mfr
N.A.I.C.S.: 311999
Curtis Whetten (Sr VP-Sls)

Subsidiaries:
Hospitality Mints LLC (1)
213 Candy Ln, Boone, NC 28607
Tel.: (828) 264-3045
Web Site: http://www.hospitalitymintspromo.com
Candy & Other Confectionery Products
N.A.I.C.S.: 311340
Conley Stegal (VP-Admin)

MOUNT HAMILL ELEVATOR
1564 143rd St, Donnellson, IA 52625
Tel.: (319) 469-2531
Sales Range: $10-24.9 Million
Emp.: 40
Provider of Grains & Lumber
N.A.I.C.S.: 424510
Jerry Bentler (Pres)

MOUNT HOOD MEADOWS OREGON LTD. PARTNERSHIP
Hwy 35, Mount Hood Parkdale, OR 97041
Tel.: (503) 337-2222
Web Site: http://www.skihood.com
Sales Range: $10-24.9 Million
Emp.: 40
Owner & Operator of Ski Resort
N.A.I.C.S.: 487990
Matthew Drake (CEO)

MOUNT KELLETT CAPITAL MANAGEMENT LP
1345 6th Ave Fl 46, New York, NY 10105
Tel.: (212) 588-6100
Web Site: http://www.mountkellett.com
Rev.: $6,000,000,000

Emp.: 100
Privater Equity Firm
N.A.I.C.S.: 523999
James E. Maynard (Co-Founder)
Mark E. McGoldrick (Co-Founder)
Timothy Grady (Mng Dir)

MOUNT NITTANY HEALTH SYSTEM
1800 E Park Ave, State College, PA 16803
Tel.: (814) 231-7170
Web Site: http://www.mountnittany.org
Year Founded: 2011
Sales Range: $10-24.9 Million
Healthcare Services
N.A.I.C.S.: 622110
Tom Charles (Chief Strategy Officer & Exec VP-Sys Dev)
Patty Watson (Chief Nursing Officer & Sr VP-Interim-Patient Care Svcs)
Wayne Thompson (CIO & Exec VP)
Gerald Dittmann (VP-HR)
Gail A. Miller (VP-Quality)
James B. Thomas (Chm)
Patricia L. Best (Vice Chm)
Lou Brungard (VP-Facilities & Plant Svcs)
Maureen Karstetter (VP-Mktg, Comm & Community Outreach)
Jeffrey A. Ratner (Sr VP-Medical Affairs)
Kathleen Rhine (Pres & CEO)
Pete Roy (Sec)
Randy Tewksbury (CFO & Sr VP-Fin)
Charles L. Witmer (Treas)
Roger C. Yost (VP-Fin)
Nirmal Joshi (Chief Medical Officer)
Damon D. Sorensen (Exec VP-Fin & Admin Svcs)

MOUNT NITTANY MEDICAL CENTER
1800 E Park Ave, State College, PA 16803
Tel.: (814) 231-7000
Web Site: https://www.mountnittany.org
Year Founded: 1902
Health Care Srvices
N.A.I.C.S.: 621610

MOUNT OLIVE LIVESTOCK MARKET
201 Bert Martin Rd, Mount Olive, NC 28365
Tel.: (919) 658-6601
Sales Range: $10-24.9 Million
Emp.: 20
Auctioning Livestock Hogs
N.A.I.C.S.: 424520
Charles O. Sykes (Pres)
Marion Sykes (VP)
Dorothy Sykes (Treas & Sec)

MOUNT OLIVET ROLLING ACRES
18986 Lake Dr E, Chanhassen, MN 55317-9348
Tel.: (952) 474-5974
Web Site: http://www.mtolivetrollingacres.org
Year Founded: 1965
Sales Range: $10-24.9 Million
Emp.: 524
Disability Assistance Services
N.A.I.C.S.: 624120
Peter Leneau (Controller)

MOUNT PLEASANT CAPITAL CORP.
103 N Meadows Dr Ste 315, Wexford, PA 15090
Tel.: (724) 934-7600

Web Site: http://www.mountpleasantcapital.com
Sales Range: $10-24.9 Million
Emp.: 6
Equipment & Vehicle Finance Leasing Companies
N.A.I.C.S.: 522220
Robert Rodi (Pres)
Marina Rodi (Treas-Fin)

MOUNT PLEASANT WATERWORKS
1619 Rifle Range Rd, Mount Pleasant, SC 29464
Tel.: (843) 884-9626
Web Site: http://www.mountpleasantwaterworks.com
Sales Range: $10-24.9 Million
Emp.: 150
Supplier of Water
N.A.I.C.S.: 921110
H. Clay Duffie (Gen Mgr)
Tom Wright (Mgr-Wastewater Dept)
Brian Head (Dept Head-Mgmt Info Sys)

MOUNT ROYAL PRINTING & COMMUNICATIONS, INC.
6310 Blair Hill Ln, Baltimore, MD 21209
Tel.: (410) 296-1117
Web Site: http://mtroyalprinting.com
Print Production Services
N.A.I.C.S.: 323120
Gary Cayce (Pres)

Subsidiaries:
Shuman-Heritage Printing Co. LLC (1)
725 Bierman Ave, York, PA 17401-2210
Tel.: (717) 854-0769
Web Site: http://www.shumanheritage.com
Printing
N.A.I.C.S.: 323120
John Schafer (Owner)

Spectrum Printing Inc. (1)
1160 Enterprise Ct, East Petersburg, PA 17520
Tel.: (717) 569-3200
Rev.: $4,400,000
Emp.: 47
Commercial Lithographic Printing
N.A.I.C.S.: 323111
Nicholas Schafer (Pres)

MOUNT SAINT JOSEPH
7 Highwood St, Waterville, ME 04901
Tel.: (207) 873-0705
Web Site: http://www.mtsj.org
Year Founded: 1965
Sales Range: $10-24.9 Million
Emp.: 370
Home & Rehabilitation Center Operator
N.A.I.C.S.: 551114
Claudette Poulin (VP)

MOUNT SINAI MEDICAL CENTER
4300 Alton Rd, Miami Beach, FL 33140-2910
Tel.: (305) 674-2064
Web Site: http://www.msmc.org
Year Founded: 1946
Sales Range: $1-4.9 Billion
Emp.: 3,000
Medical Center
N.A.I.C.S.: 622110
Gino R. Santorio (CEO)

MOUNT ST. MARY'S HOSPITAL OF NIAGARA FALLS
5300 Military Rd, Lewiston, NY 14092
Tel.: (716) 297-4800
Web Site: http://www.chsbuffalo.org

Year Founded: 1996
General Hospital Operator
N.A.I.C.S.: 622110
Gary C. Tucker (Pres & CEO)
Jessica Visser (Chief Nursing Officer)

Subsidiaries:
Catholic Medical Partners - Accountable Care IPA, Inc. (1)
1083 Delaware Ave, Buffalo, NY 14209
Tel.: (716) 862-2161
Web Site: http://www.catholicmedicalpartners.org
Healthcare Services Professional Organization
N.A.I.C.S.: 813920
Michael Edbauer (Chief Medical Officer)
Dennis Horrigan (Pres & CEO)
Kristin Cortese (Coord-Clinical Transformation)
Desiree Corrao (Mgr-Care Mgmt)
Dapeng Cao (Mgr-Healthcare Analytics)
Paula Conti (Dir-Clinical Transformation)
Sarah Cotter (VP-Clinical Transformation)
Barry Stelmach (CFO)
Lisa Hoffman (Chm)
David Martinke (Chief Medical Officer)
James Rycyna (Chm)
David Serra (Assoc Dir-Medical)
James Dunlop Jr. (Treas)

MOUNT VERNON NEIGHBORHOOD HEALTH CENTER
107 W 4th St, Mount Vernon, NY 10550
Tel.: (914) 699-7200
Web Site: http://www.mountvernonhealthcenter.org
Year Founded: 1985
Sales Range: $25-49.9 Million
Emp.: 533
Health Care Association
N.A.I.C.S.: 813910
Steven Horowitz (CFO)
Sangeeta Ahuja (Dir-Nutrition Svcs)
Opal Dunstan (CEO)

MOUNT WHEELER POWER INC.
1600 Great Basin Blvd, Ely, NV 89315
Tel.: (775) 289-8981
Web Site: http://www.mwpower.net
Year Founded: 1963
Sales Range: $10-24.9 Million
Emp.: 30
Distribution, Electric Power
N.A.I.C.S.: 221122
Brandy Ewell (Gen Mgr)

MOUNTAIN ACQUISITION COMPANY, LLC
1429 Grand Ave Ste 103, Glenwood Springs, CO 81601
Tel.: (970) 945-2152
Investment Holding Company
N.A.I.C.S.: 551112
Christopher A. Heath (Mng Partner)

Subsidiaries:
Western Security Systems, Inc. (1)
1206 Lincoln Ave, Steamboat Springs, CO 80487
Tel.: (970) 879-5281
Web Site: http://www.westernsecuritysys.com
Electronic Parts & Equipment Merchant Whslr
N.A.I.C.S.: 423690

MOUNTAIN AGENCY INC.
829 Eastgate S Dr, Cincinnati, OH 45245
Tel.: (513) 752-7450
Sales Range: $75-99.9 Million
Emp.: 150
Real Estate Investment Trust
N.A.I.C.S.: 525990
Jeff Wyler (Pres)

MOUNTAIN AREA HEALTH

COMPANIES

EDUCATION CENTER
121 Hendersonville Rd, Asheville, NC 28803-2868
Tel.: (828) 257-4400 NC
Web Site: http://www.mahec.net
Year Founded: 1974
Sales Range: $25-49.9 Million
Emp.: 506
Community Health & Educational Support Services
N.A.I.C.S.: 611310
Ed Coryell *(Dir-Dentistry & Dental Residency Program)*
Suzanne Landis *(Dir-Healthcare Innovation Div)*
Frank Castelblanco *(Dir-Reg Svcs Div)*
Steve Hulkower *(Dir-Family Medicine Div)*
Dale Fell *(Chm)*
Gary Bowers *(Vice Chm)*
Jeffery Heck *(Pres & CEO)*

MOUNTAIN CAPITAL PARTNERS, LP
811 Louisiana St Ste 2550, Houston, TX 77002
Tel.: (713) 357-9660 DE
Web Site: http://mountainlp.com
Year Founded: 2015
Privater Equity Firm
N.A.I.C.S.: 523999
Sam Oh *(Founder, Pres & Chief Investment Officer)*
John Wehrle *(Mng Dir)*

Subsidiaries:

Revolution II WI Holding Company, LLC (1)
14301 Caliber Dr Ste 110, Oklahoma City, OK 73134
Tel.: (405) 534-5232
Investment Services
N.A.I.C.S.: 523999
Scott Van Sickle *(CEO)*

MOUNTAIN COMPANY INC.
166 60th St, Vienna, WV 26105
Tel.: (304) 295-3311
Web Site: http://www.tri-stateservicegroup.com
Rev: $18,300,000
Emp.: 7
Roofing Contractors
N.A.I.C.S.: 238160
Bryan Ream *(Controller)*
Harry H. Esbenshade Sr. *(Chm)*

MOUNTAIN DEVELOPMENT CORP.
100 Delawana Ave, Clifton, NJ 07014
Tel.: (973) 279-9000
Web Site: http://www.mountaindevelopment.com
Year Founded: 1979
Sales Range: $10-24.9 Million
Emp.: 100
Property Management
N.A.I.C.S.: 531312
L. Robert Lieb *(Chm & CEO)*
Michael Allen Seeve *(Pres)*
Chuck Breidenbach *(Mng Dir-Retail Properties Grp)*
Irene Fitzgerald *(CFO)*
Michael Donohue *(Dir-Ops)*
Joseph Coci III *(Mng Dir-Connecticut Properties)*
William J. Martini Jr. *(Dir-Acq)*

Subsidiaries:

Eastfield Associates, LLC (1)
1655 Boston Rd, Springfield, MA 01129-1148 (100%)
Tel.: (413) 543-8000
Web Site: http://www.eastfieldmall.com
Sales Range: $10-24.9 Million
Emp.: 40
Property Management Services
N.A.I.C.S.: 531120
Melinda Graulau *(Gen Mgr)*

MOUNTAIN ELECTRIC COOPERATIVE INC.
604 S Church St, Mountain City, TN 37683-1844
Tel.: (423) 727-1800 TN
Web Site: http://www.mountain.coop.com
Year Founded: 1941
Sales Range: $25-49.9 Million
Emp.: 41
Electronic Services
N.A.I.C.S.: 221122
Joseph Thacker *(Gen Mgr)*
Richard Grubb *(Dir-Ops)*
Judy Walsh *(Dir-Acctg)*
Ross Dowell *(Treas & Sec)*
Danny Cuthbertson *(District Mgr)*
Charlie Dunn *(Dir-Customer Svcs)*

MOUNTAIN EMPIRE OIL COMPANY INC.
282 Christian Church Rd, Johnson City, TN 37615
Tel.: (423) 928-7241 TN
Web Site: http://www.meoc.com
Year Founded: 1977
Sales Range: $50-74.9 Million
Emp.: 400
Gasoline Service Stations
N.A.I.C.S.: 457120
Warren K. Broyles *(CEO)*
Ralph Fellars *(VP-Fin)*
John Kelly *(VP-Ops)*
Heather DePriest *(Acct Mgr)*
Billy Broyles *(Dir-Mktg)*

MOUNTAIN HIGH PRODUCTS, LLC
Arapahoe Ave, Boulder, CO 80302
Web Site: http://www.wanabrands.com
Year Founded: 2010
Sales Range: $10-24.9 Million
Emp.: 200
Cannabis Related Capsule Product Mfr
N.A.I.C.S.: 325412
Nancy Whiteman *(CEO)*

MOUNTAIN MAN NUT & FRUIT CO.
10338 S Progress Way, Parker, CO 80134
Tel.: (303) 841-4041
Web Site: http://www.mountainmannut.com
Sales Range: $10-24.9 Million
Emp.: 57
Marzipan (Candy)
N.A.I.C.S.: 311340
David D. Conner *(Pres & CEO)*

MOUNTAIN MECHANICAL CONTRACTORS INC.
903 S School, Fayetteville, AR 72701
Tel.: (479) 521-4886 AR
Web Site: http://www.mountainmech.com
Year Founded: 1980
Plumbing, Heating & Process Piping Services
N.A.I.C.S.: 238220
Gary Harvey *(CEO)*
Chris Harvey *(Pres)*
John Overton *(Controller)*
Bill Dewberry *(Dir-Safety)*
Robert Harvey *(VP-Ops)*
Becky Myers *(Office Mgr)*
Jason Lane *(Project Mgr)*
Lon Bugg *(Project Mgr)*

MOUNTAIN ONE FINANCIAL PARTNERS
93 Main St, North Adams, MA 01247
Tel.: (413) 663-5353
Web Site: http://www.mountainone.com
Sales Range: $10-24.9 Million
Emp.: 150
Bank Holding Company
N.A.I.C.S.: 541611
Steven J. Owens *(CFO)*
Thomas S. Leavitt *(Pres & CEO)*

Subsidiaries:

MountainOne Bank (1)
93 Main St, North Adams, MA 01247-9924
Web Site: http://www.mountainone.com
Sales Range: $25-49.9 Million
Commercial Banking Services
N.A.I.C.S.: 522110
Robert J. Fraser *(Pres & CEO)*
Steven J. Owens *(CFO, COO, CIO, Treas & Exec VP)*
Lynne M. Carlotto *(Officer-Risk Mgmt & CRA & Exec VP)*
Stacy D. Litke *(Officer-Ops & Sr VP)*
Richard W. Bromberg *(Officer-Information Security, Sr VP & Dir-IT)*
Timothy P. Rhuda *(Officer-Comml Banking & Sr VP)*
Debra A. Wooley *(Sr VP & Controller)*
Lynn Sullivan *(Officer-Cash Mgmt & Sr VP)*
Jill K. Amato *(Officer-Mktg & Sr VP)*
Melissa E. Weber *(Officer-Mortgage Banking & Consumer Lending & Sr VP)*
Elizabeth A. Petropulos *(Officer-HR & Sr VP)*
Peter M. Fortier *(Officer-Security & Facilities)*
Michael Z. Pang *(Officer-Credit Admin & Sr VP)*
Kim E. Anderson *(Officer-Loan Compliance & VP)*
Kelly C. Grant *(Officer-Reg Community Banking)*
Kelli E. Kozak *(Officer-Community Engagement & VP)*
Matthew B. Kreiser *(Officer-Comml Banking & VP)*
Kevin M. McGowan *(Officer-Comml Banking & VP)*
Alicia A. Benoit *(Officer-Electronic Banking & Asst VP)*
Kelly L. Dubie *(Officer-Customer Care & Asst VP)*
Lisa J. Mineau *(Officer-HR & Asst VP)*
Rebecca L. Oregan *(Officer-Consumer Credit & Asst VP)*
Timothy J. Shepard *(Officer-IT & Asst VP)*
Lucille A. Weare *(Officer-Community Banking & Asst VP)*
Nancy C. Baran *(Officer-Deposit Ops)*
Noelle M. Pandell *(Sec)*
Meghan L. Dunphy *(Officer-Community Banking)*
Sonia M. Figueira *(Officer-Community Banking)*
Greg Marchion *(Officer-Community Banking)*
Jacob Phillips *(Officer-Community Banking)*
Stephanie Scott *(Officer-Deposit Compliance & VP-BSA, AML & OFAC)*
Steven Munger *(Officer-Comml Banking & VP)*

MOUNTAIN PACIFIC MACHINERY
11705 SW 68th Ave, Portland, OR 97223
Tel.: (503) 639-7635
Web Site: http://www.mountpac.com
Year Founded: 1969
Sales Range: $100-124.9 Million
Emp.: 10
Food Product Manufacturing Machinery
N.A.I.C.S.: 423830
Jeudi Chilson *(Bus Mgr)*

MOUNTAIN PARK HEALTH CENTER
2702 N 3rd St Ste 4020, Phoenix, AZ 85004-4608
Tel.: (602) 323-3477 AZ
Web Site: http://www.mountainparkhealth.org
Year Founded: 1984
Sales Range: $25-49.9 Million
Emp.: 580
Community Health Care Services
N.A.I.C.S.: 621498
John Swagert *(CEO)*
Jarret Sharp *(Vice Chm)*
Alana Podwika *(CIO)*
Kevin Camberg *(Treas)*
Kristin Gubser *(Chm)*
Davinder Singh *(Chief Medical Officer)*
Rachel Lambert *(COO)*

MOUNTAIN PRODUCTIONS, INC.
80 New Frederick St, Wilkes Barre, PA 18702
Tel.: (570) 826-5566
Web Site: http://www.mountainproduction.com
Rev: $2,000,000
Emp.: 67
Other Commercial & Industrial Machinery & Equipment Rental & Leasing
N.A.I.C.S.: 532490
Ronald W. Simms *(Chm & Pres)*
Ricky Rose *(CEO)*
Jeffrey Goldenberg *(COO)*
Andrew Hawk *(Dir-Installs)*

Subsidiaries:

Roc-Off Productions, Inc. (1)
15350 Park of Commerce Blvd, Jupiter, FL 33478
Tel.: (954) 436-2118
Web Site: http://www.roc-off.com
Lighting Equipment Mfr
N.A.I.C.S.: 335139

MOUNTAIN PURE BEVERAGE COMPANY
6921 Interstate 30, Little Rock, AR 72209
Tel.: (501) 568-3540
Web Site: http://www.shootingstarbeverages.com
Sales Range: $10-24.9 Million
Emp.: 75
Bottled Water & Canned Soft Drink Mfr
N.A.I.C.S.: 312112
Hank Bird *(Owner)*

MOUNTAIN RANGE RESTAURANT LLC
825 S 48th St, Tempe, AZ 85281
Tel.: (480) 829-5090
Year Founded: 2001
Sales Range: $25-49.9 Million
Emp.: 950
Operator of Restaurants
N.A.I.C.S.: 722511
Bob Jensen *(Co-Owner)*
Bill Cox *(Co-Owner)*
William Cox Jr. *(Mgr-AP Dept)*

MOUNTAIN RURAL TELEPHONE COOPERATIVE CORPORATION, INC.
425 Main St, West Liberty, KY 41472
Tel.: (606) 743-3121 KY
Web Site: http://www.mountaintelephone.com
Year Founded: 1950
Telephone Service Provider
N.A.I.C.S.: 517111
Steven Gullett *(Mgr-Plant)*
Sarah Couch *(Mgr-Client Svcs)*

MOUNTAIN STATE AUTO AUCTION INC.

MOUNTAIN STATE AUTO AUCTION INC.   U.S. PRIVATE

Mountain State Auto Auction Inc.—(Continued)
5546 Benedum Dr, Shinnston, WV 26431
Tel.: (304) 592-5300
Web Site: http://www.mtstateaa.com
Rev.: $60,400,000
Emp.: 200
Automobile & Other Motor Vehicle Merchant Whslr
N.A.I.C.S.: 423110
Charlotte Pyle (Co-Owner)
Joseph Pyle (Co-Owner)
Margie Wills (Controller)
Chad Garrison (Gen Mgr)
Brad Hollar (Asst Gen Mgr)
Wayne Bowman (Mgr-Arbitration)
Courtney Thompson (Office Mgr)
Andrew Pyle (Chief Sls Officer)

MOUNTAIN STATES EMPLOYERS COUNCIL, INC.
1799 Pennsylvania St, Denver, CO 80203
Tel.: (303) 839-5177   CO
Web Site: http://www.msec.org
Year Founded: 1939
Sales Range: $10-24.9 Million
Emp.: 216
Management Consulting Services
N.A.I.C.S.: 541612
Deborah Dale Brackney (Exec VP)
Julie A. McLaughlin (CFO)
Michael G. Severns (Pres & CEO)
Mark Driscoll (Chm)
Linda Childears (Treas)
William L. Smith Jr. (Pres-Arizona)

MOUNTAIN STATES HEALTH ALLIANCE
400 N State of Franklin Rd, Johnson City, TN 37604-6094
Tel.: (423) 431-1313
Web Site: http://www.mountainstateshealth.com
Year Founded: 1998
Healthcare System Hospitals & Clinics Owner & Operator
N.A.I.C.S.: 622110
Marvin Eichorn (COO & Exec VP)
Morris Seligman (Chief Medical Officer & Exec VP)
Tony Keck (Chief Dev Officer & Sr VP)
Lynn Krutak (CFO & Sr VP)
Steve Kilgore (Sr VP-Outpatient & Retail Ops)
Tim Belisle (Gen Counsel & Sr VP-Corp Compliance)

Subsidiaries:

Laughlin Memorial Hospital   (1)
1420 Tusculum Blvd, Greeneville, TN 37745
Tel.: (423) 787-5000
Web Site: http://www.balladhealth.org
Health Care Srvices
N.A.I.C.S.: 622110
Charles Whitfield (Pres)

Wellmont Health System   (1)
PO Box 238, Kingsport, TN 37662-0238
Tel.: (226) 382-5271
Web Site: http://www.wellmont.org
Offices of Other Holding Companies
N.A.I.C.S.: 551112
Todd Dougan (Interim CFO)
Bart Hove (Pres & CEO)

MOUNTAIN STATES PIPE & SUPPLY COMPANY
111 W Las Vegas St, Colorado Springs, CO 80903
Tel.: (719) 634-5555   CO
Web Site: http://www.msps.com
Year Founded: 1986
Sales Range: $75-99.9 Million
Emp.: 40
Plumbing & Hydronic Heating Supplies Whslr
N.A.I.C.S.: 423720
Paul Carroll (CEO)
Elizabeth Carroll (Pres)
Jerry Uhlman (VP)
Scott Zanteylinger (COO)

MOUNTAIN SUPPLY CO
2101 Mullan Rd, Missoula, MT 59808
Tel.: (406) 543-8255
Web Site: http://www.mountainsupply.com
Sales Range: $10-24.9 Million
Emp.: 50
Plumbing & Hydronic Heating Supplies
N.A.I.C.S.: 423720
Mike Rubie (Chm)
Doug Tallent (Controller)
Craig Bolenbaugh (Branch Mgr)

MOUNTAIN TELECOMMUNICATIONS SALES INC.
12687 W Cedar Dr Ste 350, Lakewood, CO 80228
Tel.: (303) 683-6344
Web Site: http://www.triwestsalesinc.com
Rev.: $25,000,000
Emp.: 3
Communications Equipment
N.A.I.C.S.: 423690
Richard Perrigo (Co-Owner)
Warren West (Co-Owner)

MOUNTAIN VALLEY EXPRESS CO
1019 Bessemer Ave, Manteca, CA 95337
Tel.: (209) 823-2168
Web Site: http://www.mountainvalleyexpress.com
Sales Range: $25-49.9 Million
Emp.: 400
Trucking Except Local
N.A.I.C.S.: 484121
James Scott Blevins (Pres)
Ken Brandon (Dir-Mktg & Sls)

MOUNTAIN VALLEY PRODUCE, LLC.
3501 County Rd 53, Center, CO 81125
Tel.: (719) 754-2139
Web Site: http://www.mvproduce.com
Sales Range: $10-24.9 Million
Emp.: 65
Seed Potato Production Services
N.A.I.C.S.: 111211
Virginia Myers (Mgr)
Ernest M. Meyers (Mgr)
Zach Gillespie (Mgr-Transportation)

MOUNTAIN VIEW CO-OP
2200 Old Havre Hwy, Black Eagle, MT 59414
Tel.: (406) 453-5900
Web Site: http://www.mountainviewcoop.com
Sales Range: $50-74.9 Million
Emp.: 140
Agricultural Services
N.A.I.C.S.: 424510
Art Schmidt (CEO & Gen Mgr)
Terry Allen (VP)
Del Styren (Pres)
John Goodmunson (Treas & Sec)

MOUNTAIN VIEW ELECTRIC ASSOCIATION
1655 5th St, Limon, CO 80828
Tel.: (719) 775-2861
Web Site: http://www.mvea.coop
Sales Range: $50-74.9 Million
Emp.: 135
Electronic Services
N.A.I.C.S.: 551112
Jim C. Herron (Gen Mgr)
Dave Waldner (Mgr-Engrg)

MOUNTAIN VIEW EQUIPMENT CO. INC.
700 W Overland Rd, Meridian, ID 83642-6510
Tel.: (208) 888-1593   ID
Web Site: http://www.mtvieweq.com
Year Founded: 1981
Sales Range: $25-49.9 Million
Emp.: 65
Retail of Farm & Garden Machinery
N.A.I.C.S.: 423820
Tom Nicholson (Owner)

MOUNTAIN VIEW FORD LINCOLN
301 E 20th St, Chattanooga, TN 37408
Tel.: (423) 756-1331
Web Site: http://www.mvford.com
Sales Range: $25-49.9 Million
Emp.: 110
Car Whslr
N.A.I.C.S.: 441110
Geneen Clark (Principal)
Mike Thornton (Gen Mgr)
Andrew Watson (Pres)
Clay Watson (CEO)
David N. Watson (Principal)
Todd Lander (Mgr-Svc)

MOUNTAIN VIEW MARKETING INC.
215 N 1800 W, Lindon, UT 84042
Tel.: (801) 785-8801
Web Site: http://www.pugsgear.com
Rev.: $14,700,000
Emp.: 200
Markets Sunglasses & Novelty Items for Convenience Stores
N.A.I.C.S.: 424210
Darrin Eisele (Pres)
Estuardo Moran (Supvr-Inventory Control)

MOUNTAIN VIEW RENDERING COMPANY
173 Rocco Rd, Edinburg, VA 22824
Tel.: (540) 984-4158
Rendering & Meat Byproduct Processing Services
N.A.I.C.S.: 311613
Hannah Bowers (Office Mgr)

MOUNTAIN VIEW TIRE & SERVICE CO
8548 Utica Ave, Rancho Cucamonga, CA 91730
Tel.: (909) 484-9497
Web Site: http://www.mountainviewtire.com
Rev.: $11,700,000
Emp.: 6
General Automotive Repair Shops
N.A.I.C.S.: 811111
Nicholas Mitsos (Pres)
Chris Mitsos (VP)
Michael Mitsos (VP)
Mike Bakalian (Mgr-Store-Retail)
Efrain Lopez (Mgr)
Henry Montes (Mgr-Rancho Cucamonga)
Paul Mitsos (VP)
Bruce Sims (Asst Mgr-Woodworking)

MOUNTAIN WEST AVIATION, LLC
PO Box 1695, Crystal Bay, NV 89402
Tel.: (530) 582-1717   NV
Web Site: http://www.mountainwestaviation.com
Airplane & Flight Support Services
N.A.I.C.S.: 488119
Michael Golden (Owner)

MOUNTAIN WEST DISTRIBUTORS
2889 S 900 W, Salt Lake City, UT 84119
Tel.: (801) 487-5694
Web Site: http://www.mountainwestdistributors.com
Year Founded: 1977
Sales Range: $10-24.9 Million
Emp.: 20
Electrical Appliances Mfr & Distr
N.A.I.C.S.: 423620
Rick Reynolds (Pres)
Craig B. Holt (VP)

MOUNTAIN WEST FARM BUREAU MUTUAL INSURANCE COMPANY INC.
931 Boulder Dr, Laramie, WY 82072
Tel.: (307) 745-4835   WY
Web Site: http://www.mwfbi.com
Year Founded: 1948
Sales Range: $25-49.9 Million
Emp.: 110
Provider of Fire, Marine & Casualty Insurance Services
N.A.I.C.S.: 524126
Dave Perdue (CFO)
Jim Geesey (CEO & VP)

Subsidiaries:

Western Farm Bureau Service Co., Inc.   (1)
931 Boulder Dr, Laramie, WY 82070-4324
Tel.: (307) 745-4835
Sales Range: $50-74.9 Million
Emp.: 90
Provider of Insurance Agency & Broker Services
N.A.I.C.S.: 524126
Katherine Shoefelt (Mgr-Mktg)
Roy Schmidt (CEO)
Jim Geesey (CEO)

MOUNTAIN WEST TELECOM INC.
17 E Vine St, Salt Lake City, UT 84107
Tel.: (801) 265-0505
Web Site: http://www.mtnwesttelecom.com
Year Founded: 1947
Sales Range: $75-99.9 Million
Emp.: 45
Telecommunication Equipment Whslr
N.A.I.C.S.: 423690
Jaron S. Payzant (CEO)
Craig Allan (Pres)
Paul Rengers (Engr-NOC)

MOUNTAIN WEST, LLC
4212 S Hwy 191, Rexburg, ID 83440-4251
Tel.: (208) 359-5641
Web Site: http://www.mountainwestbark.com
Year Founded: 1981
Marketer of Volcanic Stone, Western Bark, Aquarium Gravel, Gas Grill Lava Rock
N.A.I.C.S.: 212319
Byron Morgan (Gen Mgr)
Jeff Rydalch (CFO)
Lyle Jeppesen (Mgr-Ops)

MOUNTAIN-VALLEY BANCSHARES, INC.
317 Davis Ave, Elkins, WV 26241
Tel.: (304) 637-2265   WV
Web Site: http://www.mountainvalleybank.com
Year Founded: 1988

COMPANIES

Sales Range: $1-9.9 Million
Emp.: 42
Bank Holding Company
N.A.I.C.S.: 551111
David J. Orr *(Exec VP)*
Joan E. Hostetler *(Mgr-HR & Mktg)*
T. Richard Harvey *(Pres & CEO)*
Anthony N. Ricottilli *(Treas & Controller)*
Shannon G. Titchnell *(Compliance Officer & Sec)*

Subsidiaries:

Mountain Valley Bank, N.A. (1)
317 Davis Ave, Elkins, WV 26241
Tel.: (304) 637-2265
Web Site:
    http://www.mountainvalleybank.com
Sales Range: $1-9.9 Million
Savings Bank
N.A.I.C.S.: 522180
T. Richard Harvey *(Pres & CEO)*
Rebecca L. McClung *(VP & Sr Loan Officer)*
Anthony N. Ricottilli *(Controller)*
Joan E. Hostetler *(Mgr-Mktg & HR)*
Kimberly S. Been *(Ops Officer)*

MOUNTAINEER CONTRACTORS INC.

15237 S Preston Hwy, Kingwood, WV 26537
Tel.: (304) 329-2129
Web Site: http://www.mciwv.com
Sales Range: $10-24.9 Million
Emp.: 75
Surfacing & Paving
N.A.I.C.S.: 237310
William Boyle *(Pres)*
Bob Leigh *(VP)*
Denise Good *(Treas)*

MOUNTAINEER FABRICATORS INC.

9 McJunkin Rd PO Box 37, Nitro, WV 25143
Tel.: (304) 204-1482
Web Site:
    http://www.mountaineerfabricators.com
Rev.: $10,600,000
Emp.: 46
Fabricated Pipe & Pipe Fitting Mfr
N.A.I.C.S.: 332996
Tony Christian *(Mgr-Ops)*
Gordon Snodgrass *(Mgr-Sls)*
Bob Hammack Jr. *(CEO)*

MOUNTAINGATE CAPITAL MANAGEMENT, L.P.

1800 Larimer St Ste 2200, Denver, CO 80202
Tel.: (303) 390-5001
Web Site: http://mountaingate.com
Private Investment Firm
N.A.I.C.S.: 523999
Bruce Rogers *(Mng Dir)*
Stew Fisher *(Mng Dir)*
Sue Cho *(Principal)*
Ben McCown *(Principal)*
Trent Sisson *(Principal)*
Molly Fitzpatrick *(VP)*
Will Benton *(VP)*
Jay Royston *(VP)*
Bennett Thompson *(Mng Dir)*

Subsidiaries:

Acceleration Partners LLC (1)
16 Rae Ave, Needham, MA 02492
Tel.: (617) 963-0839
Web Site:
    http://www.accelerationpartners.com
Sales Range: $1-9.9 Million
Emp.: 15
Advetising Agency
N.A.I.C.S.: 541810
Robert Glazer *(Founder & Mng Dir)*
Helen Southgate *(Mng Dir-UK & Europe)*
Emily Tetto *(VP-Talent & Culture)*

Subsidiary (Domestic):

Streamline Marketing, LLC (2)
3131 Elliott Ave Ste 700, Seattle, WA 98121
Tel.: (206) 899-4650
Web Site: http://www.streamline-marketing.com
Sales Range: $1-9.9 Million
Emp.: 23
Advertising Agency Services
N.A.I.C.S.: 541810
Jonathan Claydon *(Founder & CEO)*

Relevate Health, LLC (1)
4270 Ivy Pointe Blvd Ste 220, Cincinnati, OH 45245
Tel.: (513) 864-8900
Web Site: https://www.relevatehealth.com
Emp.: 143
Agency Services
N.A.I.C.S.: 541890
Jeff Spanbauer *(CEO)*
Hans Kaspersetz *(Chief Innovation Officer)*

Subsidiary (Domestic):

Axon Communications Inc. (2)
35 Braintree Hill Ofc Park, Braintree, MA 02184-8719
Tel.: (781) 849-6700
Web Site: http://www.axonrx.com
Chemicals Mfr
N.A.I.C.S.: 325411
Christopher S. Mutkoski *(Pres, Treas & Sec)*
Antonia Katsambis *(Dir-HR)*
Miranda Dini *(Mng Partner)*

MOUNTAINLAND SUPPLY COMPANY

184 W 3300 S, Salt Lake City, UT 84115-3704
Tel.: (801) 484-8885 UT
Web Site:
    http://www.mountainlandsupply.com
Year Founded: 1947
Provider of Plumbing Fixtures & Supplies
N.A.I.C.S.: 423720
Brent Anderson *(CEO)*
Mike Edwards *(Pres)*
Ben Mecham *(VP-Ops)*

MOUNTAINS PLUS OUTDOOR GEAR

2557 76th Ave SE, Mercer Island, WA 98040
Tel.: (206) 686-8002
Web Site: http://www.mpgear.com
Year Founded: 1995
Sales Range: $1-9.9 Million
Emp.: 10
Outdoor Apparel & Equipment
N.A.I.C.S.: 423910
Erik Viafore *(Pres & CEO)*

MOUNTAIRE CORPORATION

PO Box 1320, Millsboro, DE 19966
Tel.: (302) 934-1100
Web Site: https://www.mountaire.com
Year Founded: 1914
Sales Range: Less than $1 Million
Emp.: 10,000
Poultry Processing
N.A.I.C.S.: 311615
Carolyn Bishop *(Supvr-Benefits)*

Subsidiaries:

Star Milling Company Inc (1)
2206 W Frnt St, Statesville, NC 28677
Tel.: (704) 873-9561
Web Site: http://www.starmills.com
Sales Range: $10-24.9 Million
Emp.: 25
Livestock Feeds
N.A.I.C.S.: 311119
Robert B. Cashion *(Pres)*
Jimmy Cashion *(Treas & Sec)*
Burney Paslay *(Mgr)*
Jimmy Howard *(Mgr-Sls)*

MOUNTCASTLE VEIN CEN-

TERS INTERNATIONAL, INC.
5901 Sun Blvd Ste 113 & Ste 201, Saint Petersburg, FL 33715
Tel.: (727) 865-6941
Web Site:
    http://www.mountcastleveincenters.com
Sales Range: $1-9.9 Million
Emp.: 25
Vein Treatment Services
N.A.I.C.S.: 621111
Daniel Mountcastle *(Owner)*

MOUNTJOY CHILTON MEDLEY LLP

2600 Meidinger Twr 462 S 4th St, Louisville, KY 40202
Tel.: (502) 749-1900 KY
Web Site: http://www.mcmcpa.com
Emp.: 350
Accounting, Tax & Consulting Services
N.A.I.C.S.: 541211
Michael B. Mountjoy *(Partner)*
Diane B. Medley *(Mng Partner)*
Kelley T. Helgeson *(Principal)*
Barry R. Pennybaker *(Partner)*
Rebecca L. Phillips *(Partner)*
Cristine M. Miller *(Partner)*
Debbie C. Smith *(Partner)*
John C. Pieper *(Partner)*
Mark A. Schmitt *(Partner)*
E. Shane Satterly *(Partner)*
Stephen M. Lukinovich *(Partner)*
Stephen F. Schulz *(Partner)*
J. Todd Rosenbaum *(Partner)*
Theresa J. Batliner *(Principal)*

MOUNTRAIL-WILLIAMS ELECTRIC COOPERATIVE

4904 2nd Ave W, Williston, ND 58802
Tel.: (701) 577-3765 ND
Web Site: http://www.mwec.com
Sales Range: $150-199.9 Million
Electric Distr Cooperative
N.A.I.C.S.: 818990
Dale Haugen *(Gen Mgr)*
Blaine Jorgenson *(Sec)*
Robert Grant *(VP)*
Cheryl Hartsoch *(Treas)*
Roger Sorenson *(Chm)*

MOUNTVILLE MILLS INC.

1729 S Davis Rd, Lagrange, GA 30241
Tel.: (706) 882-2961
Web Site: http://www.mountville.com
Sales Range: $10-24.9 Million
Emp.: 500
Door Mats: Paper, Grass, Reed, Coir, Sisal, Jute, Rags, Etc.
N.A.I.C.S.: 314110
David Watterson *(VP-Sls-Intl)*
Heather Paschal *(Project Mgr)*
Tyler Fowler *(Pres)*
Brandon Bennett *(VP-HR)*

Subsidiaries:

Mountville Mills Canada (1)
6970 Pacific Circle, Mississauga, L5T 1N8, ON, Canada (100%)
Tel.: (905) 795-1595
Web Site: http://www.mountvillecanada.com
Sales Range: $10-24.9 Million
Emp.: 6
Textiles & Rubber Products Mfr
N.A.I.C.S.: 314110

Mountville Mills China Co. (1)
Rm 2911 RenFeng DaSha 490 TianHe Road, TianHe District, Guangzhou, 510620, China
Tel.: (86) 20 38038163
Web Site: http://www.mountville.com.cn
Floor Mat Mfr
N.A.I.C.S.: 326299

Mountville Mills Europe BVBA (1)
Klien Frankrijkstraat 14, 9600, Ronse, Belgium
Tel.: (32) 55319597
Web Site: http://www.mountville.eu
Emp.: 40
Floor Mat Mfr
N.A.I.C.S.: 326299
Kirk Boster *(Mng Dir)*

Mountville Rubber Company, LLC (1)
1602 Orchard Hill Rd, LaGrange, GA 30240
Tel.: (706) 882-8134
Web Site: http://www.mountvillerubber.com
Floor Mat Mfr
N.A.I.C.S.: 326299
Bud Paulk *(Pres)*
Tony Johnson *(Mgr-Lab)*

U.S. Micro Corporation - Dallas Facility (1)
1075 S Beltline Ste 500, Coppell, TX 75019
Tel.: (469) 293-0800
Information Technology Consulting Services
N.A.I.C.S.: 541512

U.S. Micro Corporation - Toronto Facility (1)
3620B Laird Road Unit 8, Mississauga, L5L 6A9, ON, Canada
Tel.: (905) 607-5999
Information Technology Consulting Services
N.A.I.C.S.: 541512

MOUSAM VENTURES LLC

141 Sea Rd, Kennebunk, ME 04043
Tel.: (978) 257-1508 ME
Web Site:
    http://www.mousamventures.com
Sales Range: $25-49.9 Million
Emp.: 1
Private Investments & Growth Capital Firm
N.A.I.C.S.: 525910

MOVABLE, INC.

5 Bryant Park 9th Fl, New York, NY 10018
Tel.: (800) 270-6033
Web Site:
    http://www.movableink.com
Year Founded: 2010
Sales Range: $10-24.9 Million
Marketing Consulting Services
N.A.I.C.S.: 541613
Vivek Sharma *(Co-Founder & CEO)*
Michael Nutt *(Co-Founder & CTO)*
John Herman *(CFO)*
Matt Potter *(VP-EMEA)*
Miles Williams *(CMO)*
Adam Stambleck *(Chief Revenue Officer)*
Jeremy Seltzer *(VP-Worlwide Sls)*
Lee Bankewitz *(VP-Engrg)*
Louise Peddell *(VP-Talent)*
Andi Mignolo *(Head-Design & UX)*
Larry Geller *(VP-Partnerships)*
Rob Brosnan *(VP-Strategy)*
Michelle Friend *(Gen Counsel)*
Bridget Bidlack *(Sr VP-Product)*
Dee Anna McPherson *(Sr VP-Mktg)*

Subsidiaries:

Coherent Path Inc. (1)
23 Russell St, Arlington, MA 02474
Tel.: (617) 588-1722
Web Site: http://www.coherentpath.com
Custom Computer Programming Services
N.A.I.C.S.: 541511
Greg Leibon *(Founder & CTO)*

MOVE SOLUTIONS LTD.

1473 Terre Colony Ct, Dallas, TX 75212
Tel.: (214) 630-3607
Web Site:
    http://www.movesolutions.org
Sales Range: $10-24.9 Million
Emp.: 225
Provider of Moving Services
N.A.I.C.S.: 484210

MOVE SOLUTIONS LTD.

Move Solutions Ltd.—(Continued)
Michael A. Monette (Pres)
Beverly Bright (Acct Mgr)
John Conway (Acct Mgr)

MOVEMENT MORTGAGE, LLC
841 Seahawk Cir, Virginia Beach, VA 23452
Tel.: (757) 227-3385
Web Site: http://www.movementmortgage.com
Sales Range: $75-99.9 Million
Emp.: 1,200
Mortgage Services
N.A.I.C.S.: 522310
Casey S. Crawford (Co-Founder & CEO)
William Harris (Co-Founder & Exec VP)
John Third (COO)
Gregory Richardson (Exec VP-Capital Markets)
Aimee Dodson (Dir-Thrive)
Chris Allen (Chief Talent Officer)
Deran Pennington (Dir-Sls-Natl)
Ignacio Metcalf (Dir-Sls-Natl)
Laura Bowles (CFO)
Toby Harris (Exec VP)
Kelly Lindsay Rogers (Mgr-Woodlands)
Michelle Donnelly (Chief Comml Officer)
Henry Santos (CIO)
Subsidiaries:
Mortgage Service Network, Inc. (1)
171 Saxony Rd Ste 105B, Encinitas, CA 92024
Tel.: (760) 634-4165
Web Site: http://www.mortgagenetwork.com
Sales Range: $1-9.9 Million
Emp.: 18
Mortgage & Nonmortgage Loan Brokers
N.A.I.C.S.: 522310
Brian Koss (Exec VP)
Chris Blanchard (District Mgr)
Jane Stanton (Branch Mgr)
Ryan Leahy (Mgr-Sls)
Robert McInnes (Pres)
Carrie A. Hamel (Branch Mgr)
Thomas A. Popson (Branch Mgr)
Hope E. Morgan (Branch Mgr)
Carolyn E. Smith (Branch Mgr)
Jane F. Jordan (Branch Mgr)
Leslie Kuffel McLaughlin (Mgr-Sls)
Fred Allard (Mgr-Sls)
Brian Anger (Branch Mgr)
Emma Bodwell (Branch Mgr)
Linda Browning (Branch Mgr)
David Crowell (Reg Mgr)
Kevin Downs (Branch Mgr)
Maureen Elliot (Mgr-NE)
Kevin Gaffney (Branch Mgr)
Steven Gaziano (Branch Mgr)
John Holian (Mgr-Sls)
Jesse Kenner (Branch Mgr)
Craig J. LeBoeuf (Branch Mgr)
James Loughrey (Mgr-Sls)
Brian Moloney (Branch Mgr)
Timothy Moore (Branch Mgr)
Billy Pierce (Branch Mgr)
Jeff Rae (Branch Mgr)
Ellen Roche (Branch Mgr)
Wes Sellew (Branch Mgr)
Jola Smith (Mgr-Sls)
Kirk Todd (Branch Mgr)
Lorimer Trafton (Mgr-District)
Adam Lynds (Mgr-Sls)
Brian Pollard (Mgr-Sls)
Chari Goodman (Mgr-Sls)
Chris Fretz (Mgr-Sls)
Christopher Wall (Mgr-Sls)
Daphne Hayman (Mgr-Sls)
Elisa D. Balboni (Mgr-Sls)
Evan Shenkman (Mgr-Sls)
Sally Herreid (Mgr-Sls)
Shelley Kennagh (Officer-Loan)

MOVERO, INC.
5901 C Peachtree Dunwoody Rd Ste 300, Atlanta, GA 30328
Tel.: (678) 507-1220
Web Site: http://www.moveroinc.com
Year Founded: 2001
Sales Range: $10-24.9 Million
Emp.: 125
Telecommunications Expense Tracking Services
N.A.I.C.S.: 561499
Alan Powell (Sr VP-Sls & Bus Dev)
Michele Bell (VP-Fin)
Michael Lustig (CEO)
Michelle Russell (CTO)
Subsidiaries:
Movero, Inc. - Columbus (1)
8889 Commerce Loop Dr, Columbus, OH 43240
Tel.: (513) 770-0460
Web Site: http://www.moveroinc.com
Sales Range: $1-9.9 Million
Emp.: 18
Wireless Information Technology Services
N.A.I.C.S.: 541519

MOVEX, INC.
12183 W Linebaugh Ave, Tampa, FL 33626-1732
Tel.: (813) 908-5557
Web Site: http://www.movex.com
Rev.: $14,000,000
Emp.: 35
Moving Services
N.A.I.C.S.: 488999
Stuart Suddath (CEO)

MOVIE BRANDS INC.
7400 Metro Blvd Ste 190, Edina, MN 55439
Tel.: (952) 835-3321
Sales Range: $100-124.9 Million
Emp.: 300
Video Tape & Disc Rental Services
N.A.I.C.S.: 532282
Lonnie Strong (Pres)

MOVIE FACTS INC.
542 Busse Hwy Ste 1, Park Ridge, IL 60068
Tel.: (847) 299-9700
Web Site: http://www.moviefactsinc.com
Year Founded: 1972
Sales Range: $25-49.9 Million
Emp.: 150
Pamphlet Publishing Services
N.A.I.C.S.: 513130
Jill Kab (Pres)

MOVIES UNLIMITED INC.
3015 Darnell Rd, Philadelphia, PA 19154-3201
Tel.: (215) 637-4444
Web Site: http://www.moviesunlimited.com
Year Founded: 1978
Sales Range: $25-49.9 Million
Emp.: 40
Video Tapes & DVDs Mail Order, Retailer & Rental Services
N.A.I.C.S.: 449210
Jerry Frebowitz (Pres)
Ed Weiss (Gen Mgr)
Ava Leas (Sec)

MOVISTA INC.
406 SE 5th St #12, Bentonville, AR 72712
Tel.: (888) 686-6245
Web Site: http://movista.com
Year Founded: 2010
Software Developer
N.A.I.C.S.: 513210
Stan Zylowski (CEO)
April Seggebruch (COO)
Stefan Midford (Chief Customer Officer)

Subsidiaries:
South49 Solutions, Inc. (1)
20098 Ashbrook Pl Ste 195, Ashburn, VA 20147
Tel.: (888) 686-6245
Web Site: https://www.naturalinsight.com
Software Publisher
N.A.I.C.S.: 513210

MOVIUS INTERACTIVE CORPORATION
4450 River Green Pkwy Ste 300, Duluth, GA 30096
Tel.: (770) 283-1000
Web Site: http://www.moviuscorp.com
Sales Range: $10-24.9 Million
Emp.: 120
Messaging, Collaboration & Mobile Media Solutions
N.A.I.C.S.: 517112
Leonardo Vidal (VP-Sls-EMEA, Central & Latin America)
Troy McKaskle (Sr VP-SaaS & Ops)
Amit Modi (CTO & Chief Product Officer)
Bill Pettit (VP-Svc Delivery)
Krish Panu (Chm)
Ananth Siva (CEO)
Rahul Rana (VP-Engrg)
Tara Panu (VP-Mktg & Customer Experience)
Carol Gray (CFO)
Subsidiaries:
Movius Interactive Corporation (1)
1 Glenayre Way, Quincy, IL 62305-7616
Tel.: (217) 223-3211
Web Site: http://www.glenayre.com
Sales Range: $10-24.9 Million
Emp.: 16
Unified Messaging Services & Consumer Wireless Messaging Devices
N.A.I.C.S.: 334220

MOVOTO LLC
1900 S Norfolk Ste 310, San Mateo, CA 94403
Web Site: http://www.movoto.com
Year Founded: 2005
Sales Range: $1-9.9 Million
Online Real Estate Brokerage Services
N.A.I.C.S.: 531210
Imtiyaz Haque (CEO)
Yuji Horiguchi (Owner)
Maximillian Diez (VP-Ops-Real Estate)
Mark Frederick (Head-Sls Ops)
Maricela Prado (Ops Mgr-People)

MOWAT CONSTRUCTION COMPANY
20210 142nd Ave NE, Woodinville, WA 98072
Tel.: (425) 398-0205
Web Site: http://www.mowatco.com
Year Founded: 1994
Sales Range: $10-24.9 Million
Emp.: 150
Highway & Street Construction
N.A.I.C.S.: 237310
Gary Smith (Project Mgr)
Dave Banke (Mgr-Construction-Alaska)

MOWREY ELEVATOR CO., INC.
4518 Lafayette St, Marianna, FL 32446-3418
Tel.: (850) 526-4111
Web Site: http://www.mowreyelevator.com
Year Founded: 1976
Sales Range: $10-24.9 Million
Emp.: 120
Commercial & Residential Elevator Inspection, Service & Repair
N.A.I.C.S.: 811310
Timothy Mowrey Sr. (Founder)

MOXIE SOZO
1140 Pearl St, Boulder, CO 80302-5253
Tel.: (720) 304-7210
Web Site: http://www.moxiesozo.com
Sales Range: $10-24.9 Million
Emp.: 12
Advetising Agency
N.A.I.C.S.: 541810
Teri Gosse (VP-Ops)

MOYER & SON INC.
113 E Reliance Rd, Souderton, PA 18964
Tel.: (215) 723-6000
Web Site: http://www.emoyer.com
Year Founded: 1869
Rev.: $60,400,000
Emp.: 220
Animal Feed
N.A.I.C.S.: 424910
John Moyer (Pres)

MOYER VINEYARDS INC.
3859 US Hwy 52, Manchester, OH 45144-8338
Tel.: (937) 549-2957
Web Site: http://www.moyerwineryrestaurant.com
Sales Range: $1-4.9 Billion
Emp.: 22
Winery & Restaurant Services
N.A.I.C.S.: 312130
Rebecca Hardymon (Gen Mgr)

MOYLE PETROLEUM COMPANY INC.
2504 W Main St, Rapid City, SD 57702
Tel.: (605) 343-1966
Web Site: http://www.commoncentsstores.com
Year Founded: 1957
Sales Range: $10-24.9 Million
Emp.: 300
Gas Station & Convenience Store Owner & Operator
N.A.I.C.S.: 457120
Gilbert D. Moyle (Pres)
Chris Metras (Mgr-Store)

MOZEL DEVELOPMENT CORP.
6031 Leesburg Pke, Baileys Crossroads, VA 22041-2203
Tel.: (703) 578-4000
Year Founded: 1949
Sales Range: $75-99.9 Million
Emp.: 25
General Building Contracting Services
N.A.I.C.S.: 236117
Cyrus Katzen (Pres & CEO)

MOZILLA FOUNDATION
331 E Evelyn Ave, Mountain View, CA 94041
Tel.: (650) 903-0800
Web Site: http://www.mozilla.org
Year Founded: 2003
Open Internet Advocacy Organization
N.A.I.C.S.: 813319
Mitchell Baker (Chm)
Ashley Boyd (VP-Advocacy)
Mark Surman (Pres & Exec Dir)
Angela Plohman (Exec VP-Ops)
Chris Lawrence (VP-Leadership Network)
Alan Davidson (VP-Policy, Trust & Security-Global)

COMPANIES

Subsidiaries:

Mozilla Corporation (1)
331 E Evelyn Ave, Mountain View, CA 94041
Tel.: (650) 903-0800
Web Site: http://www.mozilla.org
Internet Search Engine & Application Developer
N.A.I.C.S.: 518210
Mitchell Baker (Chm)
Chris Beard (CEO)
Jascha Kaykas-Wolff (CMO)
Katharina Borchert (Chief Open Innovation Officer)
Mark Mayo (Chief Product Officer)
Sean White (Chief R&D Officer)
Susan Chen (VP-Bus Dev)
Mary Ellen Muckerman (VP-Brand Engagement)
Nick Nguyen (VP-Firefox Product)
Michael DeAngelo (Chief People Officer)
Amy Keating (Gen Counsel)
Eric Rescorla (CTO-Firefox)
Heather West (Head-Pub Policy-Americas)

MP DISPLAYS, LLC
704 Executive Blvd Ste 1, Valley Cottage, NY 10989
Tel.: (845) 268-4113
Web Site: http://www.mpdisplays.com
Sales Range: $100-124.9 Million
Emp.: 25
Point-of-Purchase Display Services
N.A.I.C.S.: 541890
Michael Parkes (Pres)

MP ENVIRONMENTAL SERVICES
3400 Manor St, Bakersfield, CA 93308
Tel.: (661) 393-1151
Web Site: http://www.mpenviro.com
Rev.: $28,633,285
Emp.: 117
Hazardous Waste Collection & Disposal
N.A.I.C.S.: 562211
Dawn Calderwood (Owner & Pres)
Angie Carrasco (Supvr-Accts Receivable)

MP VENTURES, INC.
310 Olive St, Long Beach, NY 11561
Tel.: (516) 247-1917   NV
Year Founded: 2014
Sales Range: Less than $1 Million
Property Management & Consulting Services
N.A.I.C.S.: 531390
Mark Poretsky (Pres, CEO, CFO, Principal Acctg Officer, Treas & Sec)

MPACT STRATEGIC CONSULTING LLC
3209 Drake Springs Ln, Pearland, TX 77584-8013
Tel.: (832) 563-1885
Web Site: http://www.mpact-consulting.com
General Management Consulting Services
N.A.I.C.S.: 541611
Spurgeon Robinson (Mgr)

Subsidiaries:

Designing Success, Inc. (1)
433 Plz Real Ste 275, Boca Raton, FL 33432
Tel.: (954) 457-3330
Web Site: http://www.designingsuccess.us
Custom Computer Programming Services
N.A.I.C.S.: 541511
Cheryl Wachtel (Co-Founder & Principal)
Samuel Wachtel (Co-Founder & Principal)

MPAY, INC.
400 5th Ave Ste 410, Waltham, MA 02451
Tel.: (781) 810-9000
Web Site: http://www.mpay.com
Year Founded: 1996
Rev.: $8,100,000
Emp.: 52
Accounting, Auditing & Payroll Services
N.A.I.C.S.: 541214
Dennis Donohue (Dir-Customer Support)
Geoffrey R. Duke (Pres & CEO)
John Berube (VP)

MPC CASH-WAY LUMBER CO., INC.
5401 W Grand River Ave, Lansing, MI 48906-9117
Tel.: (517) 321-7766
Web Site: http://www.mpccashlumber.com
Year Founded: 1981
Sales Range: $10-24.9 Million
Emp.: 50
Provider of Lumber & Other Building Material Services
N.A.I.C.S.: 423310
Ed Bailey (Mgr-Store)
Mark Piggott (Owner)
Mathew Piggott (Controller)

Subsidiaries:

MPC Cash-Way Lumber Co. Williamston, Inc. (1)
1191 E Grand River, Williamston, MI 48895
Tel.: (517) 655-4641
Web Site: http://www.mpccashwaylumber.com
Sales Range: $10-24.9 Million
Emp.: 42
Producer of Lumber & other Building Materials
N.A.I.C.S.: 423310
Thomas Wolfe (Gen Mgr)
Matt Pigott (Gen Mgr)

MPD, INC.
316 E 9th St, Owensboro, KY 42303
Tel.: (270) 685-6200   KY
Web Site: http://www.mpdinc.com
Year Founded: 1987
Sales Range: $100-124.9 Million
Emp.: 230
Microwave Components Mfr
N.A.I.C.S.: 334519
Gary Braswell (Pres & CEO)
David Blythe (Mgr-IT)
Bruce Law (Supvr-Incoming Matl & Calibration)
John W. Noblitt (Mgr-Sls)

Subsidiaries:

CMI Limited (1)
PD-II Jhilmil Metro Station Jhilmil Industrial Area, Delhi, 110095, India
Tel.: (91) 1149570000
Web Site: https://www.cmilimited.in
Rev.: $28,135,503
Assets: $78,569,973
Liabilities: $61,566,619
Net Worth: $17,003,355
Earnings: ($26,563,323)
Emp.: 127
Fiscal Year-end: 03/31/2021
Electrical Cable Mfr & Distr
N.A.I.C.S.: 335921
Munishvar Gaur (Pres-Marketing)
Tanya Kukreja (Sec)
Amit Jain (Chm & Mng Dir)

CMI, Inc. (1)
316 E 9th St, Owensboro, KY 42303-3511   (100%)
Tel.: (270) 685-6545
Web Site: http://www.alcoholtest.com
Sales Range: $25-49.9 Million
Alcohol Breath Analyzers, Speed Radar Guns & Mobile Videos Mfr
N.A.I.C.S.: 334519
Tom Settles (Mgr-Sls)
Pam Hagan (Mgr-Technical Sls)
Toby Dyas (Mgr-Program Support)

Lion Laboratories Limited (1)
Ty Verlon Industrial Estate, Barry, CF63 2BE, Vale of Glamorgan, United Kingdom
Tel.: (44) 1446 724500
Web Site: http://www.lionlaboratories.com
Sales Range: $10-24.9 Million
Emp.: 78
Breath Alcohol Analyzer Mfr
N.A.I.C.S.: 334513
Patrick Martin (Mng Dir)

MPD Components (1)
316 E 9th St, Owensboro, KY 42303-3511
Tel.: (270) 685-6200
Web Site: http://www.mpdinc.com
Mfr of Microwave Components
N.A.I.C.S.: 334519
Donna Parks (Sec)
Gary Braswell (Pres)

MPH Industries, Inc. (1)
316 E 9th St, Owensboro, KY 42303
Tel.: (270) 685-6545
Web Site: http://www.mphindustries.com
Speed Monitoring Device Mfr
N.A.I.C.S.: 334519
John Broxon (Mgr-Intl Sls)

MPE PARTNERS, LLC
3 Post Ofc Sq Ste 200, Boston, MA 02109
Tel.: (617) 587-7800
Web Site: https://www.mpepartners.com
Year Founded: 2012
Private Equity Firm
N.A.I.C.S.: 523999
Peter Taft (Partner)
Charlie Rossetti (Principal)
Michael Duffy (VP)
Barb Neifach (Dir-Ops)
Travis Boettner (CFO & Chief Compliance Officer)
Constantine Elefter (Partner)
Karen Tuleta (Partner)

Subsidiaries:

DecoArt Inc (1)
49 Cotton Avenue, Stanford, KY 40484
Tel.: (800) 367-3047
Web Site: https://decoart.com
Paint Product Mfr
N.A.I.C.S.: 325510

Subsidiary (Domestic):

Jack Richeson & Co., Inc. (2)
557 Marcella St, Kimberly, WI 54136
Tel.: (920) 735-5820
Web Site: http://www.richesonart.com
Sales Range: $1-9.9 Million
Emp.: 70
Non-Durable Goods Whslr
N.A.I.C.S.: 424990
Jack Richeson (CEO)

Formed Fiber Technologies, Inc. (1)
125 Allied Rd, Auburn, ME 04211-1300
Tel.: (207) 784-1118
Web Site: http://www.formedfiber.com
Sales Range: $75-99.9 Million
Molded Structures Mfr for Automotive & Aircraft Applications
N.A.I.C.S.: 326199
Marc Lachance (Dir-Sls)
Jessica Palladino (Mgr-HR)

Mid-States Bolt & Screw Co. (1)
4126 Somers Dr, Burton, MI 48529
Tel.: (810) 744-0123
Web Site: http://www.midstatesbolt.com
Sales Range: $10-24.9 Million
Emp.: 100
Bolts Distr
N.A.I.C.S.: 423710
Marc Somers (VP)
Rick Rudbal (Dir-Pur & Inventory Plng)
Jim Baker (VP-Sls & Branch Ops)

RBL Products, Inc. (1)
6040 Russell St, Detroit, MI 48211
Tel.: (313) 873-8800
Web Site: http://www.rblproducts.com
Sales Range: $1-9.9 Million
Emp.: 17
Plastics Product Mfr
N.A.I.C.S.: 326199
Ron Lipson (Founder & CEO)

Rotometrics, Inc. (1)
800 Howerton Ln, Eureka, MO 63025
Tel.: (636) 587-3600
Web Site: http://www.rotometrics.com
Machine Tool Mfr & Distr
N.A.I.C.S.: 333517
Bob Spiller (CEO)
Paul McKay (Gen Mgr-Asia)
Kerry Beaver (VP/Gen Mgr-US & Canada)
Molly Moroni (VP/Gen Mgr-Asia Pacific)

Subsidiary (Non-US):

Rotary Dies, S.L. (2)
Avda Industria 37 2nd Flr, 28108, Alcobendas, Spain
Tel.: (34) 91 657 34 64
Emp.: 3
Machine Tool Distr
N.A.I.C.S.: 423840
Maria Veguillas (Mgr-HR)

RotoMetrics (SE Asia) Co., Ltd. (2)
Amata Nakorn Industrial Estate 700/714 Moo 1 T Panthong, A Panthong, Chon Buri, 20160, Thailand
Tel.: (66) 38 447487
Machine Tool Distr
N.A.I.C.S.: 423840

RotoMetrics Australia Pty. Ltd. (2)
65 Northcorp Boulevard, Broadmeadows, 3047, VIC, Australia
Tel.: (61) 3 9358 2000
Web Site: http://www.rotometrics.com
Machine Tool Distr
N.A.I.C.S.: 423840
Cain Harper (Gen Mgr-Australia & New Zealand)

RotoMetrics China Ltd. (2)
Room 1701 17/F Lee Wei Commercial Building 1-3 Hart Avenue, Tsimshatsui, Kowloon, China (Hong Kong)
Tel.: (852) 2721 9854
Web Site: http://www.rotometrics.com
Machine Tool Distr
N.A.I.C.S.: 423840

RotoMetrics International A/S (2)
Smedeholm 19 - 21, 2730, Herlev, Denmark
Tel.: (45) 32 47 7 100
Sales Range: $50-74.9 Million
Emp.: 20
Printing Cutting Tools Mfr
N.A.I.C.S.: 333515
Kenny Hechmann (Mng Dir)

RotoMetrics International Ltd (2)
Walsall Road, Aldridge, WS9 0SW, West Midlands, United Kingdom
Tel.: (44) 1922 610000
Web Site: http://www.rotometrics.com
Machine Tool Distr
N.A.I.C.S.: 423840

RotoMetrics Italia Srl (2)
Via Europa 41, 20010, Pogliano Milanese, Italy
Tel.: (39) 02 93540115
Web Site: http://www.rotometrics.com
Machine Tool Distr
N.A.I.C.S.: 423840

RotoMetrics Rotationswerkzeuge GmbH (2)
Peter-Sander-Strasse 7, 55252, Wiesbaden, MZ-Kastel, Germany
Tel.: (49) 6134 72 62 0
Web Site: http://www.rotometrics.de
Emp.: 15
Machine Tool Distr
N.A.I.C.S.: 423840
Peter Smith (Gen Mgr)

Rotometrics Canada Inc. (2)
7615 Danbro Crescent, Mississauga, L5N 6P9, ON, Canada
Tel.: (905) 858-3800
Machine Tool Distr
N.A.I.C.S.: 423840

Webster Industries Inc. (1)
325 Hall St, Tiffin, OH 44883-1419
Tel.: (419) 447-8232
Web Site: http://www.websterchain.com
Sales Range: $25-49.9 Million
Emp.: 275
Conveying & Engineering Chain & Malleable Iron Casting Mfr

MPE PARTNERS, LLC

MPE Partners, LLC—(Continued)
N.A.I.C.S.: 333922
Dean E. Bogner *(Chief Comml Officer & Exec VP)*
Andrew J. Felter *(Pres & CEO)*
Nicholas D. Spurck *(VP-Ops)*
Steven Hickey *(CFO)*
Deb Anderson *(VP-Tech & Innovation)*

Division (Domestic):

Portland Chain Manufacturing Co. (2)
9630 SW Herman Rd, Tualatin, OR 97062-8080 **(100%)**
Tel.: (503) 692-4818
Web Site: http://www.websterchain.com
Sales Range: $10-24.9 Million
Emp.: 3
Mfr of Welded Steel Chains
N.A.I.C.S.: 332111

Subsidiary (Domestic):

Stacy Equipment Co. (2)
325 Hall St, Tiffin, OH 44883-1419 **(100%)**
Tel.: (419) 447-6903
Sales Range: $10-24.9 Million
Emp.: 2
Distr of Power Transmission Equipment
N.A.I.C.S.: 333922

Division (Domestic):

Webster Manufacturing Co. (2)
325 Hall St, Tiffin, OH 44883-1419 **(100%)**
Tel.: (419) 447-8232
Web Site: http://www.websterchain.com
Sales Range: $25-49.9 Million
Emp.: 250
Conveyors, Elevators & Components, Material Handling Equipment
N.A.I.C.S.: 333922
Dean Bogner *(VP-Sls)*
Andrew Felter *(Pres)*

Subsidiary (Domestic):

Webster-Portalloy Chains, Inc. (2)
PO Box 1747, Meridian, MS 39302-1747 **(100%)**
Tel.: (601) 482-0183
Web Site: http://www.websterchain.com
Sales Range: $25-49.9 Million
Emp.: 13
Malleable & Welded Steel Chain
N.A.I.C.S.: 332618

MPEG LA LLC
6312 S Fiddlers Green Ste 400 E, Greenwood Village, CO 80111
Tel.: (303) 331-1880 DE
Web Site: http://www.mpegla.com
Year Founded: 1996
Sales Range: $10-24.9 Million
Emp.: 20
Provider of Patent Owner & Lessor Services
N.A.I.C.S.: 533110
Lawrence A. Horn *(Pres & CEO)*
Daniel Abraham *(VP-Science & Bus Strategy)*
Brodie Philpott *(Mgr-Royalty Svcs)*
J. Gascon *(CFO)*

MPG LOGISTICS, INC.
1675 N Wayneport Rd, Macedon, NY 14502
Tel.: (315) 986-1172
Web Site: http://www.mpglogistics.net
Year Founded: 2005
Sales Range: $1-9.9 Million
Emp.: 4
Transportation & Logistics Services
N.A.I.C.S.: 481112
James Klimasewski *(Pres)*

MPH HOTELS, INC.
100 2nd Ave S, Saint Petersburg, FL 33701
Tel.: (727) 289-3844
Web Site: http://www.mphhotels.com
Year Founded: 2003
Sales Range: $10-24.9 Million
Emp.: 12
Hotel Development & Management
N.A.I.C.S.: 721110
Michael P. Holtz *(Pres)*

MPI HOLDINGS, INC.
3311 S State Rd 19, Peru, IN 46970-7476
Tel.: (765) 473-4673
Year Founded: 1989
Sales Range: $10-24.9 Million
Emp.: 220
Meat Packing Services
N.A.I.C.S.: 311611
John A. Marburger *(Pres & Treas)*

MPK EQUITY PARTNERS
3000 Turtle Creek Blvd, Dallas, TX 75219
Tel.: (214) 238-5800
Web Site:
http://www.mpkequitypartners.com
Equity Investment Firm
N.A.I.C.S.: 523999
Douglas L. Kennealey *(Mng Partner)*
Patrick K. McGee *(Mng Partner)*
Nick Huerta *(VP)*

MPLT HEALTHCARE, LLC
3701 FAU Blvd Ste 300, Boca Raton, FL 33431
Tel.: (954) 507-4838
Web Site:
http://www.mplthealthcare.com
Year Founded: 2012
Sales Range: $25-49.9 Million
Emp.: 65
Health Care Srvices
N.A.I.C.S.: 621999
Jay Mays *(Founder & CEO)*
Liz Hale *(Sr VP-Ops)*
Gregg Straus *(CFO & Exec VP)*
Melissa Beam *(Dir-Project Mgmt)*
Alex Garcia *(Dir-HR)*

MPM CAPITAL LLC
The John Hancock Tower 200 Clarendon St 54th Fl, Boston, MA 02116
Tel.: (617) 425-9200 DE
Web Site:
http://www.mpmcapital.com
Year Founded: 1997
Rev: $2,500,000,000
Emp.: 30
Life Science Equity Investment Firm
N.A.I.C.S.: 523999
Daniel J. Hicklin *(Mng Dir)*
Elizabeth Stoner *(Mng Dir)*
Todd Foley *(Mng Dir)*
Ansbert K. Gadicke *(Mng Dir)*
Kazumi Shiosaki *(Mng Dir)*
John W. Vander Vort *(Mng Dir, COO & Chief Compliance Officer)*
Owen Patrick Hughes Jr. *(Mng Dir)*
Lauren Cauley *(CFO)*
Gregory Sieczkiewicz *(Mng Dir)*
Briggs W. Morrison *(Mng Dir)*
Sarah Reed *(COO & Gen Counsel)*
Dan Hicklin *(Mng Dir)*
Hans-Peter Gerber *(Chief Scientific Officer)*
Kristen Laguerre *(Mng Dir-Fin)*
Laura Brass *(Mng Dir)*
Mitchell F. Finer *(Mng Dir)*
Patrick A. Baeuerle *(Mng Dir)*
Matthew Roden *(Partner)*
Vaughn M. Kailian *(Mng Dir)*

Subsidiaries:

MPM Capital - San Francisco (1)
601 Gateway Blvd Ste 350, South San Francisco, CA 94080
Tel.: (650) 553-3300
Web Site: http://www.mpmcapital.com
Life Science Equity Investment Firm
N.A.I.C.S.: 523999

Luke Evnin *(Mng Dir)*
James Paul Scopa *(Mng Dir)*
William Greene *(Partner-Venture)*
Ansbert K. Gadicke *(Founder & Mng Dir)*
Edward M. Hurwitz *(Mng Dir)*
Pablo J. Cagnoni *(Mng Dir-San Francisco)*
Lauren Cauley *(CFO)*
Sarah Reed *(COO & Gen Counsel)*
Gary Patou *(Mng Dir)*

MPOWER, INC.
11810 Grand Park Ave Ste 500 N, Bethesda, MD 20852
Tel.: (301) 788-2420
Web Site: http://www.mpower-inc.com
Year Founded: 2011
Sales Range: $1-9.9 Million
Metal Machinery Distr
N.A.I.C.S.: 423830
Mary Affeldt *(CEO)*

MPW INDUSTRIAL SERVICES GROUP, INC.
9711 Lancaster Rd SE, Hebron, OH 43025
Tel.: (740) 927-8790 OH
Web Site:
http://www.mpwservices.com
Year Founded: 1997
Sales Range: $100-124.9 Million
Emp.: 1,500
Building Maintenance Services
N.A.I.C.S.: 561790
Monte R. Black *(Founder, Chm & CEO)*
Derek Asseff *(Mgr-Tax)*
John Kujawa *(Mgr-IT)*
Shawn Notestone *(Controller)*
Joshua Nye *(Engr-Applications)*
Kathleen Price *(Dir-Medical)*
Matthew Morgan *(Engr-Applications)*
Justin Pierce *(Dir-Engrg & Mfg)*
Jim Tyznik *(Dir-HR)*
Jared Black *(Pres)*
Jim Neville *(Exec VP-Sls & Mktg)*

Subsidiaries:

Aquatech Environmental, Inc. (1)
25105 Brest, Taylor, MI 48180-6849
Tel.: (734) 946-4464
Rev.: $9,500,000
Emp.: 136
Building Maintenance Services
N.A.I.C.S.: 561720

MPW Container Management Corp. (1)
9711 Lancaster Rd SE, Hebron, OH 43025
Tel.: (800) 827-8790
Web Site: http://www.mpwservices.com
Sales Range: $1-9.9 Million
Repair & Maintenance Services
N.A.I.C.S.: 811210
Curtis Pray *(Mgr-Ops)*

MPW Industrial Cleaning Corp. (1)
9711 Lancaster Rd SE Rte 37, Hebron, OH 43025
Tel.: (740) 927-8790
Web Site: http://www.mpwservices.com
Sales Range: $100-124.9 Million
Emp.: 300
Provider of Industrial Cleaning Services
N.A.I.C.S.: 561720
Monte R. Black *(CEO)*

MPW Industrial Services Group (1)
4848 W 130th St, Cleveland, OH 44135-5163
Tel.: (216) 362-8400
Rev.: $5,000,000
Emp.: 50
Building Maintenance Services
N.A.I.C.S.: 561720
Mike Byington *(Gen Mgr)*

MPW Industrial Services Group (1)
907 Belden Ave SE, Canton, OH 44707-2613
Tel.: (330) 454-1898
Web Site: http://www.mpwservice.com
Rev.: $5,000,000

U.S. PRIVATE

Emp.: 85
Industrial Maintenance Services
N.A.I.C.S.: 561720

MPW Industrial Services of Indiana, LLC (1)
95 E 200 N, Rockport, IN 47635
Tel.: (812) 649-2908
Provider of Building Maintenance Services
N.A.I.C.S.: 811310
Moni Bowak *(Owner)*

MPW Industrial Services, Ltd. (1)
490 Montrose Ave Unit 1, Toronto, M6G 3H1, ON, Canada **(100%)**
Tel.: (416) 536-7258
Web Site: http://www.mpwservices.com
Sales Range: $10-24.9 Million
Emp.: 70
Provider of Repair Services; Water Blasting; Cryogenics
N.A.I.C.S.: 811310

MPW Industrial Water Services, Inc. (1)
150 S 29th St, Newark, OH 43055
Tel.: (740) 345-2431
Web Site:
http://www.mpwindustrialservices.com
Sales Range: $10-24.9 Million
Emp.: 25
Water Transportation Services
N.A.I.C.S.: 488390
Tim Dondero *(Gen Mgr)*

MQ MEDICAL TECHNOLOGIES CORPORATION
9454 Wilshire Blvd Ste 612, Beverly Hills, CA 90212
Tel.: (310) 888-1870 DE
Year Founded: 2015
Investment Services
N.A.I.C.S.: 523999
James Cassidy *(Pres & Sec)*
James McKillop *(VP)*

MQ&C ADVERTISING & MARKETING
1611 West Ave, Austin, TX 78701-1531
Tel.: (512) 499-0660
Web Site: http://www.mq-c.com
Year Founded: 1981
Sales Range: $10-24.9 Million
Emp.: 6
Automotive, Entertainment, Government/Political/Public Affairs, Real Estate, Restaurant, Retail
N.A.I.C.S.: 541810
Cindy C. K. Carman *(Owner)*
Ben Morris *(Owner)*
Ilaria Bonalumi *(Media Dir-Radio)*
Linda Sanchez *(Sr Acct Exec)*
Juli Sarich *(Sr TV Buyer)*
Manasseh Sarpong *(CFO)*

MR. AMAZING LOANS CORPORATION
3960 Howard Hughes Parkway Ste 490, Las Vegas, NV 89169
Tel.: (702) 227-5626 FL
Web Site:
http://www.mramazingloans.com
Year Founded: 2010
Rev.: $1,356,962
Assets: $3,642,842
Liabilities: $2,387
Net Worth: $3,640,455
Earnings: ($2,363,375)
Emp.: 3
Fiscal Year-end: 12/31/18
Online Consumer Loan Services
N.A.I.C.S.: 522310
Paul Mathieson *(Pres, CEO & CFO)*

MR. CHRISTMAS INC.
5841 E Shelby Dr, Memphis, TN 38141

COMPANIES

MR. CHRISTMAS (implied)
Tel.: (901) 365-6040 — NY
Web Site: http://www.mrchristmas.com
Year Founded: 1933
Sales Range: $75-99.9 Million
Emp.: 38
Mechanical & Musical Decorations Creator Designer Mfrr & Whslr
N.A.I.C.S.: 424990
Terry Hermanson *(Chm)*

Subsidiaries:

Mr. Christmas Limited (1)
39 Chatham Road South Suite 901, Kowloon, China (Hong Kong) (70%)
Tel.: (852) 23690082
Web Site: http://www.mrchristmas.com
Sales Range: $10-24.9 Million
Emp.: 20
Distr of Mechanical Collectible Christmas Decorations
N.A.I.C.S.: 423220
Terry Hermanson *(Chm)*

MR. FORMAL INC.
1205 SE Grand Ave, Portland, OR 97214
Tel.: (503) 238-7216
Web Site: http://www.mrformaltuxedos.com
Rev.: $13,870,000
Emp.: 320
Tuxedo Rental
N.A.I.C.S.: 532281
Pam VanWinkle *(Reg Mgr)*
Micah Haley *(Asst Dir-Mktg)*
Edwin Honeycutt III *(Pres)*

MR. GASKET COMPANY
10601 Memphis Ave Bldg 12, Brooklyn, OH 44144
Tel.: (216) 688-8300
Web Site: http://www.mrgasket.com
Sales Range: $10-24.9 Million
Emp.: 200
Automotive Parts & Accessories Mfr
N.A.I.C.S.: 336390
Bob Bruegging *(VP-Sls Dev)*

Subsidiaries:

Mr. Gasket Inc. (1)
10601 Memphis Ave Ste 12, Brooklyn, OH 44144-2043
Tel.: (216) 688-8300
Web Site: http://www.mrgasket.com
Mfr of Automotive Accessories
N.A.I.C.S.: 336390
Bob Bruegging *(VP-Sls)*

Division (Domestic):

Mr. Gasket Mallory Products Division (2)
10601 Memphis Ave Ste 12, Cleveland, OH 44144-2058 (100%)
Tel.: (775) 882-1622
Web Site: http://www.mrgasket.com
Sales Range: $10-24.9 Million
Emp.: 80
Mfr of Automotive High Performance Ignition Products
N.A.I.C.S.: 336320

MR. PAPERBACK
1135 Hammond St, Bangor, ME 04401
Tel.: (207) 990-4107
Web Site: http://www.mrpaperback.com
Sales Range: $10-24.9 Million
Emp.: 125
Book Stores
N.A.I.C.S.: 459210
Tim William *(Pres)*
Nancy Burnham *(Mgr)*

MR. ROOF HOLDING COMPANY LLC.
3511 E Ellsworth Rd, Ann Arbor, MI 48864
Tel.: (734) 668-4970
Web Site: http://www.mrroof.com
Rev.: $12,600,000
Emp.: 30
Residential Remodeler
N.A.I.C.S.: 236118
Fred Belshaw *(Gen Mgr)*
Matthew Young *(Project Mgr)*

MR. SHOWER DOOR INC.
260 Hathaway Dr, Stratford, CT 06615
Tel.: (203) 838-3667
Web Site: http://www.mrshowerdoor.com
Sales Range: $1-9.9 Million
Emp.: 21
Shower Door Mfr
N.A.I.C.S.: 327211
Tom Whitaker *(Owner & Pres)*
Thomas Locurto *(Controller)*

MR. SPECIAL SUPERMARKETS INC.
620 Santa Teresa Journet Ave, Mayaguez, PR 00682
Tel.: (787) 834-2695 — PR
Web Site: http://www.mrspecialpr.com
Year Founded: 1966
Sales Range: $200-249.9 Million
Emp.: 990
Grocery Stores
N.A.I.C.S.: 445110
Edwin Alonso *(VP-Fin)*
Santos Alonso Jr. *(VP-Ops)*
Santos Alonso-Maldonado Sr. *(Pres)*

MR/DD BOARD, INC.
22644 Highway 59 S, Robertsdale, AL 36567
Tel.: (251) 947-5608
Web Site: http://www.themrddboardinc.com
Sales Range: $10-24.9 Million
Emp.: 17
Disability Care Board Operator
N.A.I.C.S.: 813920
Cindy Haber *(Exec Dir)*
Mike Larrimore *(VP)*
Norma Giles *(Treas)*
Peggy Vanover *(Pres)*

MR2 GROUP, INC.
101 Convention Ctr Dr Plz 124, Las Vegas, NV 89109
Tel.: (702) 483-4000 — NV
Web Site: http://www.mr2group.com
Year Founded: 2017
Sales Range: $10-24.9 Million
Emp.: 36
Marketing Research & Public Opinion Polling
N.A.I.C.S.: 541910
James T. Medick *(Chm & Pres)*
Bruce H. Baum *(CFO & COO)*
Gary E. Stein *(Gen Counsel, Sec & Exec VP)*
Alexander J. Medick *(Chief Mktg Officer)*

MRA INTERNATIONAL, INC.
3979 S Tamiami Trl, Sarasota, FL 34231
Tel.: (941) 921-4016
Web Site: http://www.diamondvaultjewelers.com
Year Founded: 1978
Sales Range: $1-9.9 Million
Jewelry & Diamond Retailer
N.A.I.C.S.: 458310
Ali Chokr *(Co-Founder & Co-Owner)*
LaRue Chokr *(Co-Founder & Co-Owner)*
Michael Chokr *(Co-Owner)*
Rachad Chokr *(Co-Owner)*
Amir Chokr *(Co-Owner)*

MRA-THE MANAGEMENT ASSOCIATION, INC.
N19W24400 Riverwood Dr, Waukesha, WI 53188
Tel.: (262) 696-3327 — WI
Web Site: http://www.mranet.org
Year Founded: 1901
Sales Range: $10-24.9 Million
Emp.: 271
Business Assistance Services
N.A.I.C.S.: 813910
Amy Wangerin *(Dir-HR Trng)*
Kimberly Kent-Slattery *(Mgr-Roundtables)*
Deidre Garrett *(Dir-HR Svcs)*
Cedar Duerkop *(Dir-Org Dev)*
Julie McBride *(Mgr-Member Rels-Northern Illinois)*

MRC MEDICAL COMMUNICATIONS
12 Lincoln Blvd Ste 201, Emerson, NJ 07630
Tel.: (201) 986-0251
Web Site: http://www.mrcmedical.net
Year Founded: 1978
Sales Range: $10-24.9 Million
Emp.: 10
N.A.I.C.S.: 541810
David J. Rector *(Founder & Pres)*
Susan Rector *(Dir-New Bus Dev)*

MRC POLYMERS, INC.
3307 S Lawndale Ave, Chicago, IL 60623-5034
Tel.: (773) 890-9000
Web Site: http://www.mrcpolymers.com
Rev.: $20,000,000
Emp.: 100
Mfr of Polycarbonate Resins & Other Thermoplastic Compounds
N.A.I.C.S.: 325211
Gerald Galazin *(Dir-Quality)*
Colleen Farrell *(Mgr-Accts Payable)*
David Brodsky *(Mgr-Pur)*
Paul Binks *(Pres & CEO)*

MRE CONSULTING, INC.
3800 Buffalo Speedway Ste 200, Houston, TX 77098
Tel.: (713) 844-6400
Web Site: http://www.mreconsulting.com
Year Founded: 1994
Sales Range: $10-24.9 Million
Emp.: 145
Technical & Business Consulting Services
N.A.I.C.S.: 541611
Mike Short *(Pres)*
Shane Merz *(VP)*
Dru Neikirk *(VP)*
Huan Bui *(Controller)*
Bill Bucy *(Partner)*
Doug Ashmore *(Partner)*
Bjorn Haggelman *(Partner)*
Michael D. Burger *(Mng Dir-Trading-Risk Management)*

MRESULT CORP.
5 Shaws Cove Ste 208, New London, CT 06320
Tel.: (860) 439-0038
Web Site: http://www.mresult.com
Year Founded: 2002
Sales Range: $10-24.9 Million
Emp.: 15
Computer System Design Services
N.A.I.C.S.: 541512
Bob Moore *(VP-Project Mgmt)*

MRIGLOBAL
425 Volker Blvd, Kansas City, MO 64110-2241
Tel.: (816) 753-7600 — MO
Web Site: http://www.mriglobal.org
Year Founded: 1943
Sales Range: $125-149.9 Million
Emp.: 690
Research & Development Services
N.A.I.C.S.: 541720
R. Thomas Fleener *(CFO, Treas & Exec VP)*
Reachel Beichley *(Gen Counsel & VP)*
Thomas M. Sack *(Pres & CEO)*
Robert Conklin *(VP-Defense & Infrastructure)*
Roger Harris *(VP-Sls & Mktg)*
Steve Phillips *(VP-Sls & Mktg)*

MRM CONSTRUCTION SERVICES, INC.
4806 S 16th St, Phoenix, AZ 85040
Tel.: (602) 340-0378 — AZ
Web Site: http://www.mrmcs.net
Year Founded: 2002
Sales Range: $10-24.9 Million
Emp.: 50
Construction Services
N.A.I.C.S.: 236210
Marie Torres *(Owner)*
Michelle McNeal *(Asst Controller)*

MRM PROPERTY & LIABILITY TRUST
2591 Wexford-Bayne Rd Ste 301, Sewickley, PA 15143-8676
Tel.: (724) 934-9797 — PA
Year Founded: 2002
Sales Range: $10-24.9 Million
Property & Casualty Insurance Services
N.A.I.C.S.: 524126
Matthew R. Mathews *(CEO)*
James Reid *(Vice Chm)*
Wiliam Poston *(Chm)*
Pete Poninsky Sr. *(Treas)*

MRO HOLDINGS LP
5215 N O'Connor Blvd Ste 1820, Irving, TX 75039
Tel.: (469) 357-3616
Web Site: http://www.mroholdings.com
Holding Company; Aviation Maintenance & Repair Facilities
N.A.I.C.S.: 551112
Greg Colgan *(CEO)*
Doug Dalbey *(Chief Compliance Officer)*
Alfredo Sol *(CFO)*
Rob Cords *(COO)*
Trucker Morrison *(Chief Comml Officer)*
Jess Losada *(CEO-TechOps Mexico)*
Alejandro Echeverria *(CEO-Aeroman)*

Subsidiaries:

Flightstar Aircraft Services, LLC (1)
6025 Flightline Dr, Jacksonville, FL 32221
Tel.: (904) 741-0300
Web Site: http://www.flightstarjax.com
Emp.: 1,000
Aircraft & Airport Services
N.A.I.C.S.: 488190
Jerry Hernandez *(Pres & CEO)*
Tucker Morrison *(COO)*
Mark Shuman *(CFO)*
Dan Hasert *(Dir-Maintenance)*
Christopher Long *(VP-Operational Support)*
Joseph Ng *(VP-Safety & Quality)*
Mike James *(Dir-Matl)*
Robert Tarpley *(Dir-Continous Improvement)*
Chris Dahlman *(Dir-Production Control)*
Jose Gonzalez *(Dir-Maintenance)*
Michelle Rodriguez *(Dir-HR)*
Sam Jackson *(VP-Maintenance)*
Charlie Boschung III *(Dir-Quality)*

MRS BAIRD'S BAKERIES BUSINESS TRUST — U.S. PRIVATE

MRO Holdings LP—(Continued)

MRS BAIRD'S BAKERIES BUSINESS TRUST
PO Box 937, Fort Worth, TX 76101
Tel.: (817) 615-3100
Sales Range: $300-349.9 Million
Emp.: 3,400
Bakery Products Mfr
N.A.I.C.S.: 311812
Victor Vargas *(Mgr-Mfg)*
John Foley *(VP-Sls)*
Paulette Jones *(Dir-Fin)*
Juan Mulduon *(Pres)*
Johnnie Turner *(Project Mgr)*
Linden Blackmon *(Dir-Environment)*

MRS. CLARK'S FOODS L.C.
740 SE Dalbey Dr, Ankeny, IA 50021-3908
Tel.: (515) 964-8100
Web Site: http://www.mrsclarks.com
Year Founded: 1926
Fruit & Vegetable Juices, Sauces, Marinades, Salad Dressings & Mayonnaise Mfr
N.A.I.C.S.: 311941
Julie Southwick *(Sls Mgr)*

MRS. GERRY'S KITCHEN, INC.
2110 Yh Hanson Ave, Albert Lea, MN 56007
Tel.: (507) 373-6384
Web Site: http://www.mrsgerrys.com
Year Founded: 1973
Sales Range: $10-24.9 Million
Emp.: 95
Salad Production Services
N.A.I.C.S.: 311991
Gerry Vogt *(Pres)*
Betty Nienoord *(VP-Mfg & Engrg)*
Brenda Donahe *(Mgr-Mktg & Dir-Sls & Mktg)*
Donna Kluczny *(Sr Engr-Mechanical)*
Diane Simon *(Mgr-HR)*

MS BUBBLES INC.
2731 S Alemeda St, Los Angeles, CA 90058
Tel.: (323) 544-0300
Web Site: http://www.msbubbles.com
Rev.: $24,000,000
Emp.: 50
Mfr of Women's & Children's Clothing
N.A.I.C.S.: 424350
Aneeta Chopra *(Pres)*
Rajeshwar Chopra *(Owner)*

MS CARVER LUMBER CO.
8700 North University St, Peoria, IL 61615
Tel.: (309) 692-2000
Web Site: http://www.carverlumber.com
Rev.: $13,856,237
Emp.: 40
Lumber & Other Building Materials
N.A.I.C.S.: 423310
Mark Booth *(Pres)*

MS DISTRIBUTORS OF TOLEDO
5809 Angola Rd, Toledo, OH 43615
Tel.: (419) 865-8231
Web Site: http://www.msdis.com
Sales Range: $10-24.9 Million
Emp.: 15
Fireplace Equipment & Accessories
N.A.I.C.S.: 423220
Trent Scholler *(Pres)*
David David Visel *(Mgr-Sls)*

MS INTERNATIONAL INC.
2095 N Batavia St, Orange, CA 92865
Tel.: (714) 685-7500
Web Site: http://www.msistone.com
Sales Range: $10-24.9 Million
Emp.: 90
Granite Building Stone
N.A.I.C.S.: 423320
Sohil Chodhari *(Engr-Sys)*
Renuka Doshi *(Coord-Payroll)*
Kunjal Khant *(Mgr-Software Dev)*
Neha Mehta *(Controller)*
Sanjay Sanghvi *(Sr VP)*
Andy Shah *(Mgr-IT)*
Glenda Valdez *(Dir-Import Logistics)*
Nitin Vyas *(Project Mgr-RFID)*

MS TECHNOLOGY, INC.
137 Union Valley Rd, Oak Ridge, TN 37830-8097
Tel.: (865) 483-0895
Web Site: http://www.mstechnology.com
Engineeering Services
N.A.I.C.S.: 541330
Michael J. Smith *(CIO)*
John E. Razor *(VP-Bus Dev)*
Paul D. Steneck *(VP-Engineered Equipment)*
J. Soni Davidson *(Sr Mgr-Project)*
Sarah Henderson *(CFO)*
Randy Inklebarger *(Pres)*

Subsidiaries:

MillenniTEK LLC (1)
631 Barbrow Ln, Knoxville, TN 37932-3249
Tel.: (865) 966-2170
Web Site: http://www.millennitek.com
Sales Range: $10-24.9 Million
Emp.: 15
Nuclear Reactor Component Mfr
N.A.I.C.S.: 333248

MSA ADVERTISING & PUBLIC RELATIONS
475 Park Ave S 6th Fl, New York, NY 10016
Tel.: (212) 532-5151 NY
Web Site: http://www.msanewyork.com
Year Founded: 1951
Rev.: $30,000,000
Emp.: 30
Fiscal Year-end: 12/31/04
N.A.I.C.S.: 541810
Keith Klein *(Exec VP)*
Sam Ash *(Sr Dir-Creative)*
Paul Greenberg *(Sr VP-Bus Dev & Acct Svcs)*
Bob Mangini *(VP-Opers)*
Sherman Yee *(Sr Dir-Art)*
Ron Spivak *(Sr Dir-Art)*

MSA PROFESSIONAL SERVICES, INC.
1230 S Blvd., Baraboo, WI 53913
Tel.: (608) 356-2771
Web Site: http://www.msa-ps.com
Year Founded: 1962
Geophysical Surveying & Mapping Services
N.A.I.C.S.: 541360

MSA: THE THINK AGENCY
2530 Meridian Pkwy Ste 200, Durham, NC 27713
Tel.: (919) 463-9680 NC
Web Site: http://www.marketsmart.net
Year Founded: 1991
Rev.: $12,000,000
Emp.: 55
Full Service
N.A.I.C.S.: 541810
Lewis Finch *(Pres)*
Gerry Jacobs *(Sr Acct Mgr)*
Dennis Wipper *(VP & Dir-Creative)*
Jan Johnson *(CEO)*
Stuart Westland *(Acct Dir)*
Beth Clough *(Dir-Media)*
Paul Blade *(Dir-Creative)*
Patrick Harrell *(Mgr-Production)*
Cindi August *(Mgr-Project)*
Mark Worrell *(Mgr-Print Production)*
Mike Inscoe *(Graphic Designer)*

MSB MUTUAL HOLDING COMPANY
2221 Landmark Pl, Manasquan, NJ 08736
Tel.: (732) 292-8400 NJ
Web Site: http://www.manasquanbank.com
Year Founded: 1997
Sales Range: $10-24.9 Million
Emp.: 160
Bank Holding Company
N.A.I.C.S.: 551111
Catherine Franzoni *(CFO & Exec VP)*

Subsidiaries:

Manasquan Savings Bank (1)
2221 Landmark Pl, Manasquan, NJ 08736
Tel.: (732) 292-8400
Web Site: http://www.manasquanbank.com
Sales Range: $10-24.9 Million
Emp.: 115
Retail & Commercial Banking
N.A.I.C.S.: 522180
Catherine Franzoni *(CFO & Exec VP)*
Jeffrey P. Casten *(VP-Comml Lending)*
Joan C. Konopka *(VP-HR)*
James S. Vaccaro *(Chm, Pres & CEO)*
Mark Beriault *(Chief Lending Officer & Exec VP)*
Luke Caverly *(Sr VP-Comml Lending)*
Beth Culos *(VP-Comml Lending)*
Robert Hart *(Sr VP-Residential Lending)*
William Horvath *(Sr VP-Comml Lending)*
Bruce Oswald *(Chief Retail Officer & Sr VP)*
Ann Slavick *(VP-Deposit Ops)*
Mary Anne Whittemore *(Sr VP-Comml Lending)*
Steve Yarosz *(VP-Facilities)*

MSC DISTRIBUTING INC.
3939 W Washington, Phoenix, AZ 85003
Tel.: (602) 258-0122
Web Site: http://www.mscdist.com
Sales Range: $10-24.9 Million
Emp.: 26
Petroleum Products
N.A.I.C.S.: 424720
Scott MacEwan *(CFO)*
Lee Atwater *(Chm)*
Ron Van De Pol *(Pres)*
Jon Rosman *(VP-Branded Fuels)*
Curtis Thornhill *(VP-Comml Sls)*

MSCO INC.
200 E Appleton Ave, Sheffield, AL 35660
Tel.: (256) 383-3131
Web Site: http://www.mscoinc.com
Rev.: $34,300,000
Emp.: 220
Industrial Supplies Merchant Whslr
N.A.I.C.S.: 423840
Bill Redding *(Mgr-Div)*
Edith Martin Ruggles *(Chm)*
Darell Heaton *(Mgr-Birmingham)*
Chris Williams *(Gen Mgr-Fasteners)*

Subsidiaries:

Martin Fastening Solutions (1)
200 Appleton Ave, Sheffield, AL 35680
Tel.: (800) 935-1392
Web Site: http://www.martinsupply.com
Emp.: 300
Industrial Component Distr
N.A.I.C.S.: 423840
Kenny Price *(Mgr-Implementation)*

Martin Industrial Supply (1)
200 Appleton Ave, Sheffield, AL 35660
Tel.: (256) 383-3131
Web Site: http://www.mscoinc.com
Industrial Supply Distr
N.A.I.C.S.: 423840
David Ruggles *(Pres)*
Bill Redding *(VP-Sls & Mktg)*

Subsidiary (Domestic):

Ziegler Tools Inc. (2)
6215 Fulton Industrial Blvd, Atlanta, GA 30336
Tel.: (404) 346-2141
Web Site: http://www.zieglertools.com
Rev.: $12,300,000
Emp.: 75
Industrial Supplies Distr
N.A.I.C.S.: 423840

Martin Plant Services (1)
200 Appleton Ave, Sheffield, AL 35660
Tel.: (800) 828-8116
Mfr Support Services
N.A.I.C.S.: 561210
Glenn Johnson *(Dir-Ops)*

Martin Safety Solutions (1)
3088 Lakeview Rd, Memphis, TN 38116
Tel.: (800) 828-8116
Safety Equipment Distr
N.A.I.C.S.: 423490
Bill Redding *(VP-Sls & Mktg)*

Townsend Door & Hardware (1)
148 Conalco Dr, Jackson, TN 38302
Tel.: (731) 935-8643
Emp.: 12
Hardware Distr
N.A.I.C.S.: 423710
Norman McMaster *(Mgr)*

Townsend Systems (1)
148 N Conalco Dr, Jackson, TN 38301
Tel.: (731) 935-8757
Sales Range: $25-49.9 Million
Emp.: 23
Electrical Equipment Distribution & Installation Services
N.A.I.C.S.: 238210
Dennis Cooper *(Gen Mgr)*
Carolyn McCauley *(Office Mgr)*
David Burngasser *(Project Mgr)*
Michelle Knight *(Mgr-Warehouse)*

MSD ACQUISITION CORP.
645 5th Ave 21st Fl, New York, NY 10022
Tel.: (213) 303-1650 Ky
Web Site: https://www.msdacquisitioncorp.com
Year Founded: 2021
MSDA—(NASDAQ)
Rev.: $8,294,282
Assets: $583,479,441
Liabilities: $606,075,352
Net Worth: -$22,595,911
Earnings: $30,489,899
Emp.: 2
Fiscal Year-end: 12/31/22
Investment Services
N.A.I.C.S.: 523999
Gregg Lemkau *(CEO)*
John Cardoso *(CFO)*
John Phelan *(Chm)*

MSD CAPITAL, L.P.
645 5th Ave 21st Fl, New York, NY 10022
Tel.: (212) 303-1650 DE
Web Site: http://www.msdcapital.com
Year Founded: 1998
Privater Equity Firm
N.A.I.C.S.: 523999
Barry A. Sholem *(Partner)*
Glenn Fuhrman *(Co-Founder & Co-Mng Partner)*
John C. Phelan *(Co-Founder & Co-Mng Partner)*
Marc R. Lisker *(Partner)*
Robert M. Platek *(Partner)*
Douglas Londal *(Partner)*
Alisa M. Mall *(Chief Investment Officer)*
Brendan Rogers *(Partner)*
Chris Workman *(Partner)*
Coburn Packard *(Partner)*
Marcello Liguori *(Partner)*

Subsidiaries:

MSD Partners, L.P. (1)

645 5th Ave 21st Fl, New York, NY 10022-5910
Tel.: (212) 303-1650
Web Site: http://www.msdpartners.com
Investment Advisory & Management Services
N.A.I.C.S.: 523940
Robert Platek *(Partner & Co-Mgr-Special Opportunities Portfolio)*
Barry A. Sholem *(Co-Founder-Real Estate & Partner-Real Estate)*
Kevin D. Brown *(Co-Head)*
Christopher F. Bertrand *(Mng Dir)*
Glenn Fuhrman *(Co-Founder & Co-Mng Partner)*
John Phelan *(Co-Founder & Co-Mng Partner)*
Doug Amacher *(Mng Dir)*
John Cardoso *(Mng Dir)*
Jenny Killeen *(Mng Dir)*
Marcello Liguori *(Partner)*
Robert Simonds *(Mng Dir)*
Marc Lisker *(Partner)*
Douglas Londal *(Partner)*
Brendan Rogers *(Partner)*
Barry Sholem *(Partner)*
Chris Workman *(Partner)*
Kevin Brown *(Sr Mng Partner)*
Simon Crocker *(Mng Dir)*
Christopher G. Gleysteen *(Principal)*

Holding (Domestic):

Endries International, Inc. (2)
714 W Ryan St, Brillion, WI 54110-0069
Tel.: (920) 756-5381
Web Site: http://www.endries.com
Sales Range: $300-349.9 Million
Industrial Equipment, Machinery & Other Related Components Mfr & Distr
N.A.I.C.S.: 339993
Steve Endries *(Pres & CEO)*

Subsidiary (Domestic):

Branam Fastening Systems Inc. (3)
7864 Root Rd, North Ridgeville, OH 44039-4084
Tel.: (440) 327-3200
Web Site: http://www.branamfastening.com
Fasteners & Studs Supplier
N.A.I.C.S.: 423710

Joint Venture (Domestic):

Hayward Industries, Inc. (2)
620 Division St, Elizabeth, NJ 07201
Tel.: (908) 351-5400
Web Site: http://www.hayward-pool.com
Holding Company; Swimming Pool Equipment & Parts Mfr
N.A.I.C.S.: 551112
Kevin P. Holleran *(Pres & CEO)*
Dave MacNair *(VP-Mktg)*
Eifion Jones *(CFQ & Sr VP)*

Subsidiary (Domestic):

Goldline Controls, Inc. (3)
61 Whitecap Dr, North Kingstown, RI 02852
Tel.: (401) 583-1100
Web Site: http://www.hayward.com
Sales Range: $10-24.9 Million
Emp.: 122
Electronic Pool Controls Mfr
N.A.I.C.S.: 334519
Laurie Roberto *(Dir-HR)*

Hayward Industrial Products, Inc. (3)
1 Hayward Industrial Dr, Clemmons, NC 27012
Tel.: (336) 712-9900
Web Site: http://www.haywardindustrial.com
Sales Range: $50-74.9 Million
Emp.: 600
Sales of Industrial Plastic Valves
N.A.I.C.S.: 333310

Hayward Pool Products, Inc. (3)
620 Division St, Elizabeth, NJ 07201-2012
Tel.: (908) 351-5400
Web Site: http://www.haywardnet.com
Sales Range: $25-49.9 Million
Emp.: 85
Mfr Of Service Machines
N.A.I.C.S.: 459999
Robert Davis *(Pres & CEO)*

Subsidiary (Non-US):

Hayward Pool Europe (4)

P.I. Plaine de l'ain, Allee des Chenes, 01150, Saint-Vulbas, France
Tel.: (33) 825000549
Web Site: http://www.haywardnet.com
Sales Range: $25-49.9 Million
Emp.: 50
N.A.I.C.S.: 459110

Hayward Pool Products Canada, Inc. (4)
2880 Plymouth Drive, Oakville, L6H 5R4, ON, Canada
Tel.: (905) 829-2880
Web Site: https://www.hayward-pool.ca
Sales Range: $10-24.9 Million
Emp.: 75
Pool Equipment Mfr
N.A.I.C.S.: 333414

Branch (Domestic):

Hayward Pool Products, Inc. (4)
1 Hayward Industrial Dr, Clemmons, NC 27102
Tel.: (908) 355-7995
Web Site: http://www.haywardpool.com
Sales Range: $50-74.9 Million
Pool Products Mfr
N.A.I.C.S.: 459999
Clarke Hale *(Pres)*

Unit (Domestic):

Hayward/IMG (3)
2875 Pomona Blvd, Pomona, CA 91768
Tel.: (909) 594-0082
Web Site: http://www.haywardpoolproducts.com
Sales Range: $10-24.9 Million
Emp.: 15
Pool Products
N.A.I.C.S.: 423910
Robert De Martini *(Gen Mgr)*
Gloria Ward *(Controller)*
Diego Gutierrez *(Mgr-Comml Technical Sls-Midwest)*
Paul Hammond *(Mgr-Comml Technical Sls-Northeast)*
Chad Norton *(Mgr-Comml Technical Sls-West & Southwest)*

Holding (Domestic):

Ring Container Technologies Inc. (2)
1 Industrial Park Rd, Oakland, TN 38060-4048
Tel.: (901) 465-3607
Web Site: http://www.ringcontainer.com
Plastic Food, Chemical & Household Good Container Mfr
N.A.I.C.S.: 326160
Brian Smith *(Pres & COO)*
Jason Hamblen *(VP-Plant Ops)*

Subsidiary (Domestic):

Rapac Inc. (3)
65 Industrial Park, Oakland, TN 38060
Tel.: (901) 465-3607
Web Site: http://www.rapac.com
Rev.: $24,444,125
Emp.: 80
Polystyrene Packaging Material Mfr
N.A.I.C.S.: 325211

MSD INVESTMENT CORP.
1 Vanderbilt Ave 26th Fl, New York, NY 10017
Tel.: (212) 303-4728 MD
Year Founded: 2021
Rev.: $80,568,000
Assets: $1,047,077,000
Liabilities: $565,231,000
Net Worth: $481,846,000
Earnings: $39,352,000
Fiscal Year-end: 12/31/22
Investment Management Service
N.A.I.C.S.: 523999
Robert Platek *(Chm, Pres & CEO)*
Brian S. Williams *(CFO)*

MSG DISTRIBUTORS, INC.
10 Dubon St Ste 2, Farmingdale, NY 11735
Tel.: (631) 801-1041 NY
Web Site: https://boxed.com

Consumables & Household Essentials Distr
N.A.I.C.S.: 445298
Mark Gadayev *(Pres)*

Subsidiaries:

Boxed, Inc. (1)
61 Broadway Fl 30, New York, NY 10006
Tel.: (646) 586-5599
Web Site: https://boxed.com
Rev.: $177,266,677
Assets: $231,604,850
Liabilities: $233,180,563
Net Worth: ($1,575,713)
Earnings: ($69,222,605)
Fiscal Year-end: 12/31/2021
Investment Services
N.A.I.C.S.: 523999
David S. Harris *(COO)*
Chieh Huang *(CEO)*

MSI BUILDING SUPPLIES INC.
3814 Crown Bay No 8, Charlotte Amalie, VI 00802
Tel.: (340) 776-8800
Web Site: http://www.msiinteriors.com
Sales Range: $10-24.9 Million
Emp.: 50
Rough, Dressed & Finished Lumber
N.A.I.C.S.: 423310
Kristine Brunt *(Treas)*
Thomas Brunt III *(CEO)*

MSI CAPITAL PARTNERS LLC
555 Michelle Ln, Trappe, PA 19426
Tel.: (610) 308-4778 PA
Web Site: http://www.mgmtserv.com
Privater Equity Firm
N.A.I.C.S.: 523999
Bill Wilkins *(Mng Principal)*

Subsidiaries:

Green Diamond Sand Products Inc. (1)
Cnr 6th & E St, Riddle, OR 97469-7469
Tel.: (541) 874-3111
Web Site: http://www.greendiamondsand.com
Construction & Industrial Sand Mining, Processing & Sales
N.A.I.C.S.: 212321
Brian Rebuck Jr. *(Gen Mgr-Ops)*

MSI COMPUTER CORP.
901 Canada Ct, City of Industry, CA 91748
Tel.: (626) 913-0828
Web Site: http://www.msicomputer.com
Sales Range: $100-124.9 Million
Emp.: 100
Computer & Computer Peripheral Equipment & Software Merchant Whslr
N.A.I.C.S.: 423430
Joseph Hsu *(Pres)*

MSI CREDIT SOLUTIONS
2811 Internet Blvd Ste 250, Frisco, TX 75034
Tel.: (866) 217-9841
Web Site: http://www.msicredit.com
Year Founded: 2006
Sales Range: $1-9.9 Million
Emp.: 50
Credit Repair & Restoration Services
N.A.I.C.S.: 522390
Ricardo Mendiola *(Pres & Founder)*

MSI GENERAL CORPORATION
W 215 E Wisconsin Ave, Oconomowoc, WI 53066
Tel.: (262) 367-3661
Web Site: http://www.msigeneral.com
Rev.: $41,222,496
Emp.: 36
Industrial Buildings, New Construction
N.A.I.C.S.: 236210

Dirk J. Debbink *(Chm & CEO)*
Susan C. Butler *(CFO & Exec VP)*
Ken Krahe *(VP-Ops)*
Jim Olson *(VP & Dir-Design)*
Tim Melan *(VP & Dir-Construction)*
Jeffrey Packee *(COO)*
Eric Neumann *(VP)*
Tim Knepprath *(VP)*
Julie Mitchell *(VP & Dir-Select Projects)*
Lori Wittkopp *(Project Coord-Ops)*
Duncan C. Delhey *(Mng Partner)*
Don McNeeley *(Pres)*

MSI SSL
622 Banyan Trl Ste 200, Boca Raton, FL 33431
Tel.: (561) 962-2413
Web Site: http://www.msissl.com
Year Founded: 2004
Sales Range: $10-24.9 Million
Emp.: 12
LED Lighting
N.A.I.C.S.: 335139
Howard Haimsohn *(Pres)*

MSIGHTS INC.
10800 Sikes Pl, Charlotte, NC 28277
Tel.: (704) 246-6283
Web Site: http://www.msights.com
Year Founded: 2004
Sales Range: $1-9.9 Million
Emp.: 30
Cloud Based Reporting
N.A.I.C.S.: 541618
Scott A. East *(Co-Founder, Pres & CEO)*
Laura Stevenson *(VP-Client Engagement)*
James Groo *(Mng Dir-EMEA & APAC)*
Ivan Aguilar *(Co-Founder & CTO)*

MSL PROPERTY MANAGEMENT
5401 N University Dr Ste 103, Coral Springs, FL 33067-4636
Tel.: (954) 491-4511
Web Site: http://www.mslmgt.com
Sales Range: $10-24.9 Million
Emp.: 50
Real Estate Managers
N.A.I.C.S.: 531210
Murray Liebowitz *(Pres)*
Richard Pasey *(Controller)*
Sheldon Leibowitz *(VP)*
Beth Frost *(Sec)*

Subsidiaries:

Harbor Inn of CS Associates (1)
801 Harbor Inn Dr, Coral Springs, FL 33071
Tel.: (954) 344-9116
Web Site: http://www.m-s-l.com
Rev.: $2,736,733
Emp.: 6
Subdividers & Developers
N.A.I.C.S.: 237210
Maria Eeluca *(Mgr)*
Lucy Gonzalez *(Mgr)*

MSM PROTEIN TECHNOLOGIES, INC.
10 Roessler Rd Ste A, Woburn, MA 01801
Tel.: (781) 321-3322 MA
Web Site: http://www.msmprotein.com
Sales Range: $1-9.9 Million
Emp.: 10
Pharmaceutical Developer & Mfr
N.A.I.C.S.: 325412
Davis Farmer *(Founder & Chm)*
David Kreimer *(Founder, Pres & COO)*
Eldar Kim *(Founder & Chief Scientific Officer)*

MSMC RESIDENTIAL REALTY LLC

MSMC Residential Realty LLC—(Continued)

MSMC RESIDENTIAL REALTY LLC
1425 Madison Ave, New York, NY 10029
Tel.: (212) 731-3083   NY
Year Founded: 2003
Sales Range: $25-49.9 Million
Real Estate Manangement Services
N.A.I.C.S.: 531390
Michael Pastier *(VP)*

MSNW GROUP, LLC
2257 Northgate Spur, Ferndale, WA 98248
Tel.: (360) 366-4600
Web Site: http://www.msnwgroup.com
Year Founded: 1995
Sales Range: $10-24.9 Million
Emp.: 467
Building Maintenance Services
N.A.I.C.S.: 236220
Janelle Bruland *(Founder & CEO)*
Terell Weg *(Pres)*
Kristina Thayer *(Dir-Bus Dev)*
Scott Nally *(Dir-HR)*
Byron Cooper *(Gen Mgr-Facility Svcs)*

MSOUTH EQUITY PARTNERS, LLC
2 Buckhead Plaza 3050 Peachtree Rd NW Ste 550, Atlanta, GA 30305
Tel.: (404) 816-3255   DE
Web Site: http://www.msouth.com
Year Founded: 2007
Rev.: $1,300,000,000
Investment Management Service
N.A.I.C.S.: 523940
Michael D. Long *(Partner)*
Bart A. McLean *(Partner)*
Wanda R. Morgan *(CFO)*
Peter S. Pettit *(Partner)*
Barry L. Boniface *(Partner)*
Dan Campbell *(Partner-Fund IV)*
Charles J. Stubbs *(Partner)*
Anthony M. Hauser *(Principal)*
Mark Lawrence Feidler *(Partner)*

Subsidiaries:

Big Language Solutions LLC (1)
Two Buckhead Plaza 3050 Peachtree Rd NW Ste 550, Atlanta, GA 30305
Tel.: (404) 401-5828
Web Site: http://www.biglanguage.com
Language Services
N.A.I.C.S.: 611630
Jeff Brink *(CEO)*

Subsidiary (Domestic):

ProTranslating, Inc. (2)
2850 Douglas Rd, Coral Gables, FL 33134
Tel.: (305) 371-7887
Web Site: http://www.protranslating.com
Translation Services
N.A.I.C.S.: 541930
Colin Klevan *(VP-Ops)*
Carlos Estefani *(VP-Client Svcs)*
Nestor Urquiza *(VP-Tech)*
Luis R. De La Vega *(CEO)*

Nth Degree Inc. (1)
2675 Breckinridge Blvd Ste 200, Duluth, GA 30096-8953
Tel.: (770) 934-2550
Web Site: http://www.nthdegree.com
Sales Range: $25-49.9 Million
Emp.: 275
Global Event Management
N.A.I.C.S.: 561920
Elise Simons *(Dir-Mktg Comm)*
John Yohe *(Pres & CEO)*
Gary Critelli *(CFO)*
Scott Bennett *(Exec VP)*
Shannon Scherer *(VP & Gen Mgr)*
Robert Lowe *(Pres-Events)*
David Smith *(Dir-IT Svcs)*
Rich Ennis *(CEO-Atlanta)*

John Newcomb *(VP-Event Architecture & Client Dev-Southern California)*
John Hense *(Co-CFO)*

Subsidiary (Domestic):

Fern Exposition Services LLC (2)
645 Linn St, Cincinnati, OH 45203
Tel.: (513) 333-7060
Web Site: http://www.fernexpo.com
Sales Range: $25-49.9 Million
Emp.: 200
Exposition & Event Planning Management Services
N.A.I.C.S.: 541890
Michael Cox *(Exec VP)*
Scott Stallings *(Sr VP-Natl Sls)*
Sheila Pannell *(VP-Natl Sls)*
Steven Detrick *(Dir-Exhibiter Sls & Svc)*
Jim Kelley *(VP-Mktg & Indus Rels)*
Steve Larsen *(COO)*
Neil McMullin *(Sr VP)*

Subsidiary (Non-US):

Nth Degree EMEA (2)
56 Marsh Wall, London, E14 9TP, United Kingdom
Tel.: (44) 2075373151
Global Event Management
N.A.I.C.S.: 561920
Francis Mugford *(Dir-Europe)*
Anthony Lacey *(Acct Dir)*
Scott Bennett *(Exec VP-Client Svcs)*

Nth Degree Germany (2)
Kolner Str 69, 41363, Juchen, Germany
Tel.: (49) 2165872700
Web Site: http://www.nthdegree.com
Global Event Management
N.A.I.C.S.: 561920

Safemark Inc. (1)
2101 Park Ctr Dr Ste 125, Orlando, FL 32835
Tel.: (407) 299-0044
Web Site: http://www.safemark.com
Holding Company; Commercial Secure Storage & Guest Amenity Products Mfr & Services
N.A.I.C.S.: 551112
George H. Oelschlig *(Chm & CEO)*
Steven G. Sapp *(CFO)*

Signal Outdoor Advertising LLC (1)
101 Sunnytown Rd Ste 312, Casselberry, FL 32707
Tel.: (407) 856-7079
Web Site: http://www.signaloutdoor.com
Emp.: 6
Outdoor Advertising Agency
N.A.I.C.S.: 541850
Rick Newcomer *(VP-Sls & Mktg)*

Branch (Domestic):

Signal Outdoor Advertising (2)
68 Southfield Ave Bldg 2 Ste 100, Stamford, CT 06902
Tel.: (203) 328-3763
Web Site: http://www.signaloutdoor.com
Outdoor Advertising Agency
N.A.I.C.S.: 541850
Eric Gomperts *(Mgr-Mktg)*

Signal Outdoor Advertising (2)
100 J E Jefryn Blvd, Deer Park, NY 11729
Tel.: (631) 667-9800
Web Site: http://www.signaloutdoor.com
Emp.: 50
Outdoor Advertising Agency
N.A.I.C.S.: 541850
John Savey *(Pres & CEO)*

Signal Outdoor Advertising (2)
10800 Hanna St Ste R, Beltsville, MD 20707
Tel.: (301) 317-6714
Web Site: http://www.signaloutdoor.com
Emp.: 15
Outdoor Advertising Agency
N.A.I.C.S.: 541850

Signal Outdoor Advertising (2)
1835 NW 112th Ave Ste 161, Miami, FL 33172
Tel.: (305) 969-6100
Web Site: http://www.signaloutdoor.com
Emp.: 7
Outdoor Advertising Agency
N.A.I.C.S.: 541850

Mtchel Green *(Gen Mgr)*
Signal Outdoor Advertising (2)
1901 E Linden Ave Unit 9, Linden, NJ 07036
Tel.: (908) 862-7000
Web Site: http://www.signaloutdoor.com
Emp.: 5
Outdoor Advertising Agency
N.A.I.C.S.: 541850
Nick Persad *(Mgr-Mktg)*

Signal Outdoor Advertising (2)
6011 Benjamin Rd Ste 104, Tampa, FL 33634
Tel.: (813) 249-6309
Web Site: http://www.signaloutdoor.com
Sales Range: $10-24.9 Million
Emp.: 9
Outdoor Advertising Agency
N.A.I.C.S.: 541850
Katie Nickerson *(Gen Mgr)*

Vectorply Corporation (1)
3400 S Railroad St, Phenix City, AL 36867   (100%)
Tel.: (334) 291-7704
Web Site: http://www.vectorply.com
Sales Range: $25-49.9 Million
Reinforcing Fabrics For The Composite Industry Mfr
N.A.I.C.S.: 522130
Trey Sawtelle *(Co-Pres)*
Trevor Humphrey *(Co-Pres & Interim CEO)*
Tamir Levy *(VP-Sls)*
Darwin Sears *(Dir-Mfg)*
Trevor Gundberg *(Dir-Composites Engrg)*
Mike Ditzler *(Engr-Field)*
Pam Freeman *(Mgr-Logistics)*
Jennifer Gaylor *(Controller)*

MSP CAPITAL MANAGEMENT, L.L.C.
3953 Maple Ave Ste 350, Dallas, TX 75219
Tel.: (214) 545-5573
Web Site: http://www.montgomerystreetpartners.com
Year Founded: 2013
Real Estate Investment Services
N.A.I.C.S.: 531210
Murray McCabe *(Founder & Mng Partner)*
Max Lamont *(Partner)*
Luke Pak *(Principal)*
Boris Marinov *(VP)*
Erin O'Grady *(VP)*
Amy Villarreal *(Controller)*

MSPACE
10400 Yellow Cir Dr Ste 500, Minnetonka, MN 55343
Tel.: (612) 332-0122
Web Site: http://www.yourmspace.com
Sales Range: $10-24.9 Million
Emp.: 35
Video Conferencing & Audiovisual Integration Services
N.A.I.C.S.: 561499
Patricia Gilbert *(Mgr-Fin & Accts)*
Griggs Nichols *(Engr-AV Sys)*
Don Hauff *(CFO)*
Julie Weispfenning *(Dir-Ops)*
Nathan Pesch *(Dir-Sls)*
Jay Nelson *(Gen Mgr)*
Mike Goodell *(Mgr-Field Svcs)*
Sam Van Moer *(Project Mgr)*
Emily Kallberg *(Supvr-Acct)*
Julia Kinnich *(Supvr-Acct)*
Wayne Lusthoff II *(Mgr-Bus Dev)*

MSR PUBLIC POWER AGENCY
1231 11th St, Modesto, CA 95354-0701
Tel.: (209) 526-7450   CA
Web Site: http://www.msrpower.org
Year Founded: 1980
Sales Range: $25-49.9 Million

U.S. PRIVATE

Emp.: 4
Electric Services
N.A.I.C.S.: 221118
Martin Hopper *(Gen Mgr)*

MSS TECHNOLOGIES INC.
1555 E Orangewood Ave, Phoenix, AZ 85020
Tel.: (602) 387-2100
Web Site: http://www.msstech.com
Sales Range: $10-24.9 Million
Emp.: 60
Computer Related Consulting Services
N.A.I.C.S.: 541512
Michael Hawksworth *(Pres)*
Nadine Davies *(Mgr-Consultant)*

MST CONSTRUCTORS INC.
128 Park 35 Cove S, Buda, TX 78610
Tel.: (512) 312-2088
Web Site: http://www.mstconstructors.com
Sales Range: $10-24.9 Million
Emp.: 8
Commercial Contractor for Industrial Buildings & Warehouses
N.A.I.C.S.: 236220
Debbie Bratton *(Sec)*

MT PACKAGING INC.
1276 50th St, Brooklyn, NY 11219
Tel.: (718) 853-5620
Web Site: http://www.mtpackaging.com
Sales Range: $10-24.9 Million
Emp.: 120
Provider of Shipping Supplies
N.A.I.C.S.: 424130
Steven Wallerstein *(Pres)*
Jack Elesant *(Controller)*

MT. GRAHAM REGIONAL MEDICAL CENTER
1600 S 20th Ave, Safford, AZ 85546
Tel.: (928) 348-4000   AZ
Web Site: http://www.mtgraham.org
Year Founded: 1970
Sales Range: $10-24.9 Million
Emp.: 530
Health Care Srvices
N.A.I.C.S.: 622110
Mark E. Marchetti *(Pres & CEO)*
Caro Gaetje *(Chm)*
Cindy Bryce *(Treas & Sec)*
Bruce Stanfield *(Vice Chm)*

MTC DIRECT
17837 Rowland St, City of Industry, CA 91748
Tel.: (626) 839-6800
Web Site: http://www.mtcdirect.com
Sales Range: $10-24.9 Million
Emp.: 40
Computer & Computer Peripheral Equipment & Software Merchant Wholesalers
N.A.I.C.S.: 423430
Roy Han *(CEO)*

MTC DISTRIBUTING
4900 Stoddard Rd, Modesto, CA 95356
Tel.: (209) 523-6449
Web Site: http://www.mtc-dist.com
Sales Range: $125-149.9 Million
Emp.: 160
Tobacco & Tobacco Products
N.A.I.C.S.: 424940
Tom Aiken *(Pres)*
Dave Eakin *(Dir-Fundraising)*

MTC ENGINEERING, LLC
428 Shearer Blvd, Cocoa, FL 32922
Tel.: (321) 636-9480   FL
Web Site: http://www.mtceng.com

COMPANIES

Year Founded: 1996
Designs Develops & Mfg Motorcycle Engine Parts
N.A.I.C.S.: 336310
Eric Hochstetler (Pres)

MTC INC.
800 Dolorosa Ste 204, San Antonio, TX 78207
Tel.: (210) 225-3955
Rev.: $14,100,000
Emp.: 150
Mexican Restaurant
N.A.I.C.S.: 722511
Cruz Cortez (Chm)
Tony Aguirre (Dir-Beverage)

MTC KENWORTH INC.
239-77 Bergen Tpke, Ridgefield Park, NJ 07660
Tel.: (201) 641-4440
Web Site: http://www.mtckw.net
Year Founded: 1989
Sales Range: $25-49.9 Million
Emp.: 50
Sales of New Trucks
N.A.I.C.S.: 441110
Frank Casagrande (Pres)
Jim D'arcy (Controller)

MTC TRANSFORMERS, INC.
823 Fairview Rd, Wytheville, VA 24382
Tel.: (276) 228-7943
Web Site: http://www.mtctransformers.com
Year Founded: 1985
Sales Range: $10-24.9 Million
Emp.: 117
Electrical Apparatus & Equipment Whslr
N.A.I.C.S.: 423610
Thomas M. Hough (CEO)
Dan Day (Gen Mgr-Sls & Mktg)

MTD MICRO MOLDING
15 Trolley Crossing Rd, Charlton, MA 01507
Tel.: (508) 248-0111
Web Site: http://www.mtdmicromolding.com
Year Founded: 1972
Sales Range: $1-9.9 Million
Emp.: 19
Microscopic Components Mfr
N.A.I.C.S.: 333514
Kim Goodwin (Dir-Quality)
Gary Hulecki (Exec VP)
Dennis Tully (Pres)
Lindsay Mann (Project Mgr)
Brian Matachun (Dir-Technical Sls-Eastern Reg)

MTD TECHNOLOGIES INC.
911 Chestnut St, Clearwater, FL 33756-5643
Tel.: (727) 546-2446
Rev.: $22,000,000
Emp.: 215
Automotive Stampings
N.A.I.C.S.: 336370
Dennis Ruppel (Pres)

MTHINK LLC
55 New Montgomery St Ste 617, San Francisco, CA 94105
Tel.: (415) 371-8800
Web Site: http://www.mthink.com
Sales Range: $10-24.9 Million
Emp.: 15
Magazine & Book Publisher
N.A.I.C.S.: 513120
Chris Trayhorn (Founder & CEO)

Subsidiaries:

Montgomery Media International, LLC (1)
300 Montgomery St Ste 1135, San Francisco, CA 94104
Tel.: (415) 397-2400
Magazine Publisher
N.A.I.C.S.: 513120

Division (Domestic):

Revenue (2)
55 New Montgomery St Ste 617, San Francisco, CA 94105
Tel.: (415) 371-8800
Web Site: http://mthink.com
Magazine
N.A.I.C.S.: 513120
Tobias Siegel (Dir-Sls)

MTI ENTERPRISES INC.
421 W 54th St 2nd Fl, New York, NY 10019
Tel.: (212) 541-4684
Web Site: http://www.mtishows.com
Sales Range: $10-24.9 Million
Emp.: 25
Music Licensing & Royalties
N.A.I.C.S.: 533110
Fredric B. Gershon (CEO)
Carroll Edelson (Sr VP)
Koji Aoshika (VP-Asia-Pacific)
Dominique Chicoye (Mgr-Customer Acct)
Andre Correia (Asst Controller)
Drew Cohen (Pres)
Brian O'Sullivan (Dir-Amateur Licensing)
Richard Salfas (VP-Licensing & Concert Presentations-Intl)
Stephen Schiano (Controller)
Tralen Doler (Coord-Mktg & Promotions)
Wes Urish (Coord-Mktg & Promotions)
Marcus Woollen (Dir-Digital Strategy)
Deb Hartnett (Dir-Legal & Bus Affairs)
Jason Cocovinis (Dir-Mktg)
E. Karl Gallmeyer (Dir-Music Library)
Matt Boethin (Dir-Pro Licensing)
Sal Shera (Office Mgr)

MTI HOME VIDEO
14216 SW 136th St, Miami, FL 33186
Tel.: (305) 255-8684
Web Site: http://www.mtivideo.com
Year Founded: 1984
Sales Range: $10-24.9 Million
Emp.: 12
Movie Videos Distr
N.A.I.C.S.: 512120
Larry Brahms (Pres & CEO)
Jay Grossman (VP-Sls & Acq)
Claudia Brahms (VP)
Mark Dresner (Mgr-Natl Acct)
Alice de Buhr (Mgr-Natl Acct)

MTI SYSTEMS INC.
59 Interstate Dr, West Springfield, MA 01089
Tel.: (413) 733-1972   MA
Web Site: http://www.mtisystems.com
Year Founded: 1982
Sales Range: $75-99.9 Million
Emp.: 20
Cost Estimating Computer Software Publisher
N.A.I.C.S.: 513210
Thomas Charkiewicz (CTO)
Rene Laviolette (COO)

MTL INSURANCE COMPANY
1200 Jorie Blvd, Oak Brook, IL 60523
Tel.: (630) 990-1000
Web Site: http://www.mutualtrust.com
Rev.: $193,383,645
Emp.: 130
Life Insurance
N.A.I.C.S.: 524113

MTM RECOGNITION CORPORATION
3405 SE 29th St, Del City, OK 73115-1609
Tel.: (405) 670-4545   OK
Web Site: http://mtmrecognition.com
Year Founded: 1971
Sales Range: $25-49.9 Million
Emp.: 550
Trophies Mfr
N.A.I.C.S.: 315120
David R. Smith (Founder & Owner)
Roger Mashore (CEO)
Mike Ketcherside (VP-Bus Dev)
Molly Martin (Legal Counsel)

MTM TECHNOLOGIES, INC.
1200 High Ridge Rd, Stamford, CT 06905
Tel.: (203) 975-3700   NY
Web Site: http://www.mtm.com
Year Founded: 1986
Sales Range: $150-199.9 Million
Emp.: 425
Systems Consultants & Technical Specialists Services
N.A.I.C.S.: 541512
Yvonne Gluck (Sr VP-Strategic Initiatives)
Jason Bernstein (Sr VP-Ops Fin)
Brian Coffey (Sr VP-Sls)
Rosemarie Milano (Sr VP-Fin)
Jason Crist (Chm)
Marcus Holloway (Pres & CEO)
Bill Kleyman (CTO)
Chris Chrobocinski (Sr VP-Cloud & Managed Svcs)
Gregory J. Turner (CIO & Sr VP-Innovation Svcs)
Lance Kirk (CFO & Chief Admin Officer)
Souzana Dandoura-Ketonis (Head-HR)

Subsidiaries:

MTM Technologies Inc. (1)
13610 Barrett Ofice Dr, Ballwin, MO 63021
Tel.: (314) 966-5688
Sales Range: $200-249.9 Million
Local Area Network (Lan) Systems Integrator
N.A.I.C.S.: 423430

MTN CAPITAL PARTNERS LLC
489 5th Ave 24th Fl, New York, NY 10017
Tel.: (212) 400-2667
Web Site: http://www.mtncapital.com
Privater Equity Firm
N.A.I.C.S.: 523999
Olivier Trouveroy (Founder)
Dan Negrea (Mng Partner)
Ivan L. Lustig (Mng Dir)
Terrance Kennedy (Dir-Bus Dev)

Subsidiaries:

Kings Super Markets, Inc. (1)
700 Lanidex Plz, Parsippany, NJ 07054
Tel.: (973) 463-3200
Web Site: http://www.kingswebsite.com
Supermarket Operator
N.A.I.C.S.: 445110
Judith A. Spires (Pres & CEO)

MTONE WIRELESS CORPORATION
3080 Olcott St Ste 100-A, Santa Clara, CA 95054
Tel.: (408) 986-8988   DE
Web Site: http://www.mtone.com
Year Founded: 1994
Sales Range: $10-24.9 Million
Emp.: 322
Mobile Phone Services
N.A.I.C.S.: 517112

Peng Qiao (COO)

Subsidiaries:

Mtone Wireless Telecommunications (Shanghai) Co., Ltd. (1)
Rm 1106 The Yongding Mansion, 3388 Gong He Xin Rd, Shanghai, 200436, China
Tel.: (86) 2161485222
Web Site: http://www.mtone.com.cn
Sales Range: $10-24.9 Million
Emp.: 120
Provider of Value-Added Services to Mobile Phone Users Throughout China
N.A.I.C.S.: 517112

MTPCS, LLC
1170 Devon Park Dr Ste 104, Wayne, PA 19087
Tel.: (610) 535-6338   DE
Web Site: http://www.cellularone.com
Emp.: 80
Holding Company; Cellular Telecommunications Services
N.A.I.C.S.: 551112
Jonathan D. Foxman (Pres & CEO)
Jungmok Han (Supvr-Fin Reporting)
Kevin Marshall (Dir-Bus Sys)
Jesse Martinez (Engr-Transport)

Subsidiaries:

Broadpoint, LLC (1)
1211 NW Bypass, Great Falls, MT 59404
Tel.: (800) 233-8372
Web Site: http://www.broadpointinc.com
Cellular Communications Services
N.A.I.C.S.: 517112

MTS HEALTH PARTNERS, L.P.
623 5th Ave 14th Fl, New York, NY 10022
Tel.: (212) 887-2100   DE
Web Site: http://www.mtspartners.com
Year Founded: 2000
Sales Range: $75-99.9 Million
Emp.: 40
Healthcare Industry Strategic Advisory, Capital Raising & Investment Services
N.A.I.C.S.: 523940
Curtis S. Lane (Sr Mng Dir)
Mark E. Epstein (Partner)
Oliver T. Moses (Sr Mng Dir)
Jay A. Shiland (Partner)
Andrew J. Weisenfeld (Mng Partner)
Lucy Darita-Oppenheim (Chief Compliance Officer)
Peter J. Collum (Partner)
Andrew B. Fineberg (Partner)
Sooin Kwon (Partner)
David M. Pontius (Principal)
David N. Low Jr. (Partner)
Dennis Conroy (Mng Dir, CFO & COO)
Safeta Pejcinovic (Mgr-Acctg)
Kristin R. Dilmore (VP-HR)
Michael A. Ludwig (VP)
William W. Stitt (Partner)
Evan R. Bernstein (VP)
Darryl J. Bolden (VP)
Gaurav Goel (VP)
Christopher C. Petrini (VP)
Anamaria Sudarov (VP)
Tony Tran (VP)
Alex Tzoukas (VP)
Kazuki Kusaka (Partner)
David Low (Partner)
Ravi Mehrotra (Partner)

Subsidiaries:

WindRose Health Investors, LLC (1)
623 5th Ave 16th Fl, New York, NY 10022
Tel.: (212) 887-2105
Web Site: http://www.windrose.com
Healthcare Industry Private Equity Firm
N.A.I.C.S.: 523999
Curtis S. Lane (Sr Mng Dir)
Oliver T. Moses (Sr Mng Dir)

MTS HEALTH PARTNERS, L.P.

MTS Health Partners, L.P.—(Continued)

Alexander Buzik *(Principal)*
Christopher J. Burnes *(VP)*
Lucy Darita-Oppenheim *(Chief Compliance Officer)*
David M. Pontius *(Principal)*
Sean S. Reilly *(CFO)*
Renee R. Simms *(Dir-Investor Rels)*

Holding (Domestic):

Veristat LLC (2)
118 Tpke Rd, Southborough, MA 01772
Tel.: (508) 429-7340
Web Site: http://www.veristat.com
Sales Range: $10-24.9 Million
Emp.: 187
Medical Research & Development Services
N.A.I.C.S.: 541715
Barbara Balser *(Chief Scientific Officer & Exec VP)*
John P. Balser *(Pres)*
Brenda Baxter *(Dir-Clinical Monitoring)*
Patrick Flanagan *(CEO)*
Erin Gaffney *(Dir-Data Mgmt)*
Faith Haines Kolb *(VP-Biometrics)*
Mark Chang *(Sr VP-Strategic Statistical Consulting)*
Colleen Pelton *(Chief Talent Officer)*
Lauren L. Brennan *(VP-Mktg)*
Elizabeth R. Madichie *(Exec VP-Global Regulatory Affairs)*

Woodbury Products, Inc. (2)
15 Verbena Ave, Floral Park, NY 11001
Tel.: (516) 594-8100
Web Site:
http://www.woodburyproducts.com
Health & Personal Care Stores
N.A.I.C.S.: 456199
Brian Darling *(Exec VP)*
Seth Segel *(Pres & CEO)*
John Holtz *(Sr VP-Ops)*

MTS3 INC.
12500 Fair Lakes Cir, Fairfax, VA 22033-3804
Tel.: (703) 227-0900
Web Site: http://www.mts3inc.com
Year Founded: 1994
Sales Range: $50-74.9 Million
Emp.: 65
Engineeering Services
N.A.I.C.S.: 541330
Randall Scott *(Chm & CEO)*

Subsidiaries:

Mandex Inc. (1)
12500 Fair Lks Cir, Fairfax, VA
22033-3804 (100%)
Tel.: (703) 227-0900
Web Site: http://www.mandex.com
Sales Range: $10-24.9 Million
Emp.: 150
Management Consulting Services
N.A.I.C.S.: 541612
Randall Scott *(CEO)*
Sherry Brown *(Mgr-Pur)*
Dale Beard *(VP-Ops)*
Doug Jimenez *(Exec VP)*
Cathy Pettis *(Mgr-Acctg)*
John Robison *(Controller)*
Rebecca Warwick *(Mgr-HR)*

MUD PIE LLC.
4893 Lewis Rd Ste A, Stone Mountain, GA 30083
Tel.: (678) 397-0170
Web Site: http://www.mud-pie.com
Year Founded: 1988
Sales Range: $50-74.9 Million
Emp.: 94
Electronic Shopping Services
N.A.I.C.S.: 458110
Fred Pannek *(Pres)*
Betsey Eastman *(Mgr-Independent Channel Sls & Mktg)*
Zander Brekke *(Gen Counsel & Dir-HR)*
Marcia Miller *(Founder & CEO)*
Steve Bulla *(VP-Distr)*

MUDD ADVERTISING
915 Technology Pkwy, Cedar Falls, IA 50613
Tel.: (319) 277-2003
Web Site: http://www.mudd.com
Sales Range: $50-74.9 Million
Emp.: 144
Automotive
N.A.I.C.S.: 541810
Rob Mudd *(Pres-Hypercasting)*
Chris Mudd *(Pres-Direct Mktg)*
Chad Wauters *(VP-Sls)*
Gary Kroeger *(Assoc Dir-Creative)*
Kathy Lenius *(Dir-Media)*
Jim Sartorius *(CIO)*
Mark Thuringer *(Dir-Ops)*
Frank Seng *(CFO)*
Wendy Jermier *(Mgr-HR)*
Jim Mudd Sr. *(Chief Spiritual Officer)*
Jim Mudd Jr. *(CEO)*

Subsidiaries:

Mudd Advertising (1)
211 W Wacker Dr 2nd Fl, Chicago, IL 60606
Tel.: (312) 781-0176
Web Site: http://www.mudd.com
N.A.I.C.S.: 541810

MUDD-LYMAN SALES & SERVICES CORPORATION
5135 Golf Rd Ste 203, Skokie, IL 60077-1200
Tel.: (847) 679-3600
Web Site: http://www.mudd-lyman.com
Sales Range: $10-24.9 Million
Emp.: 85
Hardware Distr
N.A.I.C.S.: 423710
Donald Mudd *(Pres)*
Robert Lyman *(Sec)*

MUDRICK CAPITAL MANAGEMENT L.P.
527 Madison Ave 6th Fl, New York, NY 10022
Tel.: (646) 747-9500
Web Site:
http://www.mudrickcapital.com
Year Founded: 2009
Investment Services
N.A.I.C.S.: 523940
Victor Danh *(Mng Dir)*
Janet Joyce Arzt *(Pres)*
Glenn Springer *(CFO)*
Jonathan Villoslada *(Controller)*
Elizabeth Kalvoda *(Office Mgr)*
John O'Callaghan *(Chief Compliance Officer & Gen Counsel)*
Jason B. Mudrick *(Founder, CEO & Chief Investment Officer)*
David Kirsch *(Mng Dir)*

MUELLER CORPORATION
530 Spring St, East Bridgewater, MA 02333
Tel.: (508) 583-2800
Web Site:
http://www.muellercorp.com
Sales Range: $50-74.9 Million
Emp.: 100
Plating & Polishing Services
N.A.I.C.S.: 332813
Glenn Mueller *(VP-Sls & Mktg)*
Mark Svizzero *(Pres & Gen Mgr)*
Kathleen M. Anderson *(Treas)*

MUELLER ELECTRIC COMPANY
2850 Gilchrist Rd Bldg 5A, Akron, OH 44305
Tel.: (216) 771-5225
Web Site:
http://www.muellerelectric.com
Year Founded: 1908
Sales Range: $10-24.9 Million
Emp.: 55
Harness Wiring Sets, Internal Combustion Engines
N.A.I.C.S.: 336320
Joelle Davis *(Dir-Fin)*
Cliff Prosek *(Pres)*

Subsidiaries:

Elcor Inc. (1)
640 Sugar Ln, Elyria, OH 44035
Tel.: (440) 365-5941
Web Site: http://www.elcorincorporated.com
Sales Range: $1-9.9 Million
Emp.: 23
Cable Assemblies, Power Cords, Wiring Harnesses & Other Related Products Mfr
N.A.I.C.S.: 423610
Glen Hersteck *(VP)*
Eddie Williams *(Gen Mgr)*

MUELLER FIELD OPERATIONS, INC.
1600 W Phelp St, Springfield, MO 65802
Tel.: (417) 831-3000 MO
Web Site: http://www.muel.com
Year Founded: 1998
Sales Range: $125-149.9 Million
Emp.: 350
Stainless Steel Products Mfr & Distr
N.A.I.C.S.: 332710

MUELLER GRAPHIC SUPPLY INC.
11475 W Theodore Trecker Way, West Allis, WI 53214-1138
Tel.: (414) 475-0990 WI
Web Site:
http://www.muellergraphics.com
Year Founded: 1982
Sales Range: $25-49.9 Million
Emp.: 15
Graphics Art Distr
N.A.I.C.S.: 423830
Marilyn J. Mueller *(Owner, Chm & CEO)*
Candace Leathers *(Pres & COO)*
Gerald Walsh *(VP-Sys Admin)*

MUELLER INC.
1915 Hutchins Ave, Ballinger, TX 76821
Tel.: (325) 365-3555 TX
Web Site: http://www.muellerinc.com
Emp.: 750
Metal Roofing & Steel Building Products Mfr
N.A.I.C.S.: 332311
Harold Browning *(Mgr-BMC Mfg)*
Michael Hoten *(Mgr-ICT Ops)*
Bill Brown *(Branch Mgr)*

Subsidiaries:

The Burly Corporation of North America, Inc. (1)
754 N Burleson Blvd, Burleson, TX 76028-2902
Tel.: (817) 295-1128
Web Site: http://www.burlycorp.com
Sales Range: $10-24.9 Million
Emp.: 45
Miscellaneous Fabricated Wire Products Mfr
N.A.I.C.S.: 332618

MUELLER METALS INC.
2152 Schwartz Rd, San Angelo, TX 76904
Tel.: (325) 651-9558
Web Site:
http://www.muellermetals.com
Rev.: $23,315,887
Emp.: 4
Steel Products Mfr & Distr
N.A.I.C.S.: 423510
Fred H. Mueller *(Pres)*

MUELLER ROOFING DISTRIBUTORS INC.
327 E Wyoming Ave, Cincinnati, OH 45215-3047
Tel.: (513) 821-7909 OH
Web Site:
http://www.muellerroofing.com
Year Founded: 1875
Sales Range: $25-49.9 Million
Emp.: 200
Roofing, Siding, Window & Hardware Distribution Sales
N.A.I.C.S.: 423330
Herbert J. Mueller *(CEO)*
Hugh Hillix *(VP-Sls & Mktg)*
Jeff West *(Mgr-Ops)*
Randy Bauer *(VP-Comml Sls)*
Steve Thomas *(Mgr-Store-Retail)*
Scott Fritsch *(Pres)*
Mike O'Connor *(CFO)*

MUELLER SERVICES, INC.
63 Main St, Tonawanda, NY 14150
Tel.: (716) 691-4344
Web Site: http://www.mueller-inc.com
Year Founded: 1980
Sales Range: $200-249.9 Million
Emp.: 1,100
Insurance Services
N.A.I.C.S.: 524298
John Noe *(Pres & Principal)*
Daniel Noe *(VP)*
Leo Noe *(Founder & Principal)*

MUELLER SPORTS MEDICINE, INC.
1 Quench Dr, Prairie Du Sac, WI 53578-2100
Tel.: (608) 643-8530 WI
Web Site:
http://www.muellersportsmed.com
Year Founded: 1961
Sales Range: $25-49.9 Million
Emp.: 90
Pharmaceuticals for Athletes Mfr
N.A.I.C.S.: 325412
Brett Mueller *(Pres)*
Brian Mulcahy *(Mgr-Sls-South Europe & North Africa)*
Chris Luebcke *(Mgr-Sls-Europe)*
Gertrude Lim *(Dir-Sls-Asia)*
Ken Wasylik *(Mgr-Sls-Gulf States)*
Michael Lauenstein *(Dir-Sls-Canada)*
Richard Walker *(Dir-Sls-UK, Ireland, France, South Africa & Scandinavia)*
Tim Jahnke *(Mgr-Natl Sls-Sporting Goods Retail)*
Josh Buckley *(Mgr-Sls-Latin America & Caribbean)*

Subsidiaries:

Mueller Japan (1)
Daiwa-Zisho 74-1 Yamashita-cho, Naka-ku, Yokohama, 231-0023, Japan
Tel.: (81) 45 651 7800
Web Site: http://www.muellerjapan.com
Sales Range: $10-24.9 Million
Emp.: 10
Sporting Goods Mfr & Distr
N.A.I.C.S.: 339920
Hiroshi Tsubawara *(Pres)*

MUENCH-KREUZER CANDLE COMPANY
617 E Hiawaatha, Syracuse, NY 13221-4969
Tel.: (315) 471-4515 DE
Year Founded: 1925
Sales Range: $50-74.9 Million
Emp.: 100
Mfr & Distr of Church Products
N.A.I.C.S.: 339999
John P. Brogan *(Chm)*
Roland Devore *(Pres & Mgr-Mktg)*

COMPANIES

MUFFLER MAN SUPPLY CO
4129 Holiday Dr, Flint, MI 48507
Tel.: (810) 234-1640
Sales Range: $10-24.9 Million
Emp.: 18
Exhaust Systems Mfr
N.A.I.C.S.: 423120
James Christiansen *(Owner)*
Robert Bernhoft *(Pres)*

MUHLENBERG COMMUNITY HOSPITAL
440 Hopkinsville St, Greenville, KY 42345
Tel.: (270) 338-8000   KY
Web Site: http://www.mchky.org
Year Founded: 1938
Sales Range: $75-99.9 Million
Emp.: 591
Health Care Srvices
N.A.I.C.S.: 622110
Kathleen Mitchell *(Chief Nursing Officer)*

MUHLENBERG GREENE ARCHITECTS LTD.
The Madison Bldg Ste 1000 400 Washington St, Reading, PA 19601
Tel.: (610) 376-4927
Web Site: http://www.mgarchitects-ltd.com
Year Founded: 1920
Sales Range: $1-9.9 Million
Emp.: 20
Architectural Design Services
N.A.I.C.S.: 541310
Dennis W. Rex *(Pres)*

MUIR ENTERPRISES INC
3575 W 900 S, Salt Lake City, UT 84101
Tel.: (801) 363-7695
Web Site:
  http://www.coppercanyonfarms.com
Sales Range: $10-24.9 Million
Emp.: 12
Packing Goods for Shipping Distr
N.A.I.C.S.: 424480
Phillip R. Muir *(Pres & CEO)*
Chuck Madsen *(CFO & VP-Admin)*
Murray Harris *(Mgr-Sls)*

MULBERRY METAL PRODUCTS, INC.
2199 Stanley Ter, Union, NJ 07083-4300
Tel.: (908) 688-8850   NJ
Web Site:
  http://www.mulberrymetal.com
Year Founded: 1926
Rev.: $35,000,000
Emp.: 100
Metal Wall Plates, Wiring Devices, Outlet Boxes & Covers & Installation Accessories Mfr
N.A.I.C.S.: 335932
Richard E. Mueller *(Exec VP)*
Kristina Horn *(VP)*
Bob Walker *(Mgr-Natl Sls)*

MULBERRY MOTOR PARTS INC.
160 S Broadway Ave, Bartow, FL 33830
Tel.: (863) 533-0788
Sales Range: $10-24.9 Million
Emp.: 15
Automotive Supplies & Parts
N.A.I.C.S.: 423120
William A. Read *(Pres)*

MULBERRYS, LLC
2587 Fairview Ave N, Roseville, MN 55113
Tel.: (866) 473-0798
Web Site:
  http://www.mulberryscleaners.com
Garment Care Services
N.A.I.C.S.: 812320
Dan Miller *(CEO)*
Subsidiaries:
Laundry Locker Inc.   (1)
1530 Custer Ave, San Francisco, CA 94124
Tel.: (415) 255-7500
Web Site: http://www.laundrylocker.com
Drycleaning & Laundry Services (except Coin-Operated)
N.A.I.C.S.: 812320
Julia Chan *(Mgr-Sr Demand Generation Mktg)*

MULDER HEALTH CARE FACILITY, INC.
713 N Leonard St, West Salem, WI 54669
Tel.: (608) 786-1600   WI
Web Site:
  https://atriumlivingcenters.com
Year Founded: 1963
Rev.: $2,000,000
Emp.: 120
Fiscal Year-end: 12/31/09
Continuing Care Retirement Communities
N.A.I.C.S.: 623311

MULHEARN REALTORS INC.
18000 Studebaker Rd Ste 600, Cerritos, CA 90703
Tel.: (562) 860-2625
Rev.: $19,121,000
Emp.: 800
Real Estate Brokers & Agents
N.A.I.C.S.: 531210
Bruce Mulhearn *(Pres)*
Bonnie Murray *(Mgr-Admin)*
Tim Rush *(Dir-Mktg)*

MULHERIN LUMBER CO
705 Industrial Dr, Evans, GA 30809
Tel.: (706) 863-6070
Web Site:
  http://www.mulherinlumber.com
Sales Range: $10-24.9 Million
Emp.: 30
Lumber Rough Dressed & Finished
N.A.I.C.S.: 423310
Louis Mulherin *(CEO)*
Sean Grady *(VP)*

MULHERN BELTING, INC.
148 Bauer Dr, Oakland, NJ 07436-3105
Tel.: (201) 337-5700   NJ
Web Site:
  http://www.mulhernbelting.com
Year Founded: 1932
Sales Range: $50-74.9 Million
Emp.: 110
Industrial Conveyor Belting Mfr
N.A.I.C.S.: 326220
Mike Mulhern *(Owner)*
Jean Bouley *(Mgr-Acctg)*

MULL INDUSTRIES INC.
1025 Main St, Wheeling, WV 26003
Tel.: (304) 233-3369
Web Site:
  http://www.mullindustries.com
Rev.: $13,000,000
Emp.: 4
Structural Shapes; Iron Or Steel
N.A.I.C.S.: 423510
W. Quay Mull II *(Pres)*

MULLANE MOTORS
6200 S Transit Rd, Lockport, NY 14094
Tel.: (716) 625-9191
Web Site: http://www.mullane.com
Year Founded: 1945
Sales Range: $10-24.9 Million
Emp.: 40
Car Dealer
N.A.I.C.S.: 441110
Paul Mullane *(Owner)*
Ben MacDonald *(Gen Mgr)*

MULLANEY CORPORATION
36 School St, Leominster, MA 01453
Tel.: (978) 537-8900
Rev.: $30,215,493
Emp.: 36
Industrial Buildings, New Construction
N.A.I.C.S.: 236210
Barbara Connelly *(Office Mgr)*

MULLEN ADVERTISING & PUBLIC RELATIONS, INC.
3636 N Central Ave Ste 1000, Phoenix, AZ 85012-1940
Tel.: (602) 222-4300
Web Site: http://www.mullenadv.com
Year Founded: 1965
Sales Range: $25-49.9 Million
Emp.: 20
Advertising Agencies
N.A.I.C.S.: 541810
Carter K. Mullen *(Owner)*

MULLEN MOTORS INC.
E Main St, Southold, NY 11971
Tel.: (631) 765-3564
Web Site:
  http://www.mullenmotorsnewyork.com
Sales Range: $10-24.9 Million
Emp.: 30
Car Whslr
N.A.I.C.S.: 441110
Richard Mullen *(Owner)*

MULLER BRESSLER BROWN
4739 Belleview Ave Ste 100, Kansas City, MO 64112-1316
Tel.: (816) 531-1992
Web Site:
  http://www.mbbagency.com
Year Founded: 1982
Sales Range: $100-124.9 Million
Emp.: 33
Advetising Agency
N.A.I.C.S.: 541810
John Muller *(Creative Exec Officer)*
Jennifer Nugent *(Dir-Media)*
Phil Bressler *(Partner & Chief Client Svcs Officer)*
Jim Brown *(Coord-Design)*
Denny Meier *(Partner & CFO)*
Shan Neely *(Dir-Creative)*
Chad Milam *(Dir-Interactive)*
Francine Garcia *(Dir-Creative Svcs)*
Andrea Hayob *(Dir-PR & Consumer Engagement)*
Danielle Larson *(Project Mgr)*
Leah Mountain *(Acct Dir)*
Richard Cherra *(Exec Dir-Plng & Dev)*
Bob Waddell *(Acct Supvr)*
Tate Vobach *(Coord-Earned Media)*
Leslie Godlewski *(Dir-Earned Media)*

MULLER CONSTRUCTION SUPPLY
1230 Yard Ct, San Jose, CA 95133
Tel.: (408) 279-7050
Web Site:
  http://www.mullerconstructionsupply.com
Sales Range: $25-49.9 Million
Emp.: 40
Hardware Distr
N.A.I.C.S.: 423710
Peter Muller *(Pres)*
John Diaz *(Exec VP)*
Brian McGovern *(VP)*
Mark Logan *(Mgr-Warehouse)*

MULLER INC.
2800 Grant Ave, Philadelphia, PA 19114-2302
Tel.: (215) 676-7575   PA
Web Site: http://www.mullerbev.com
Year Founded: 1954
Sales Range: $25-49.9 Million
Emp.: 150
Beer & Ale Whslr
N.A.I.C.S.: 424810
Joel Shafer *(CFO)*
Tim Jones *(Area Mgr-Sls)*
Marty Farrell *(VP-Sls & Mktg)*
Larry Beebe *(Area Mgr-Sls)*

MULLIGAN CONSTRUCTORS INC.
3601 Vineland Rd Ste 14, Orlando, FL 32811-7231
Tel.: (407) 654-6523
Web Site:
  http://www.mulliganconstructors.com
Sales Range: $10-24.9 Million
Commercial & Institutional Building Construction
N.A.I.C.S.: 236220
Jason E. Mulligan *(Pres)*
Richard Mulligan *(CEO)*

MULLIGAN LTD.
1351 Sepulveda Blvd, Torrance, CA 90501
Tel.: (310) 325-9806
Web Site:
  http://www.mulliganfun.com
Sales Range: $10-24.9 Million
Emp.: 80
Amusement Park
N.A.I.C.S.: 713110
Robert Araiza *(Dir-Sls & Mktg)*

MULLIGAN TECHNOLOGIES, INC.
8654 Orf Rd, Lake Saint Louis, MO 63367
Tel.: (636) 698-6001
Web Site:
  http://www.mulligantechnologies.com
Year Founded: 2004
Sales Range: $10-24.9 Million
Emp.: 3
Computer Systems Design
N.A.I.C.S.: 541512
Stephen Petro *(VP)*
Teresa Petro *(Pres)*
Mike Peroutka *(Sr Acct Exec)*

MULLIN/ASHLEY ASSOCIATES, INC.
306 Canon St, Chestertown, MD 21620
Tel.: (410) 778-2184
Web Site:
  http://www.mullinashley.com
Year Founded: 1978
Sales Range: Less than $1 Million
Emp.: 15
Business-to-Business Health Care Services
N.A.I.C.S.: 541810
Marlayn D. King *(Creative Dir)*
Phillip L. Nones *(Pres & Client Svcs Dir)*
L. Stephen Patrick *(Production Mgr)*
Stephanie Anne Robbins Edwards *(Mng Partner)*
Trena K. Williamson *(Acct Exec)*

MULLINS & ASSOCIATES INC.

MULLINS & ASSOCIATES INC.

Mullins & Associates Inc.—(Continued)
522 S Northwest Hwy, Barrington, IL 60010-4616
Tel.: (847) 382-1800
Year Founded: 1964
Sales Range: $25-49.9 Million
Emp.: 189
Provider of Management Consulting Services
N.A.I.C.S.: 541612
Willard Mullins (Pres)
Bill Mullins (Controller)

Subsidiaries:
Systems & Software Service Inc. (1)
522 S NW Hwy, Barrington, IL 60010-4616
Tel.: (847) 382-1800
Web Site: http://www.1sssi.com
Sales Range: $10-24.9 Million
Emp.: 126
Provider of Software Engineering Services
N.A.I.C.S.: 541330

MULLINS FOOD PRODUCTS INC.
2200 S 25th Ave, Broadview, IL 60155
Tel.: (708) 344-3224
Web Site: http://www.mullinsfood.com
Year Founded: 1934
Sales Range: $100-124.9 Million
Emp.: 350
Sauce & Beverage Mfr & Distr
N.A.I.C.S.: 311941
Joan P. Mullins (Sec)
Susan Baltrus (Mgr-HR)
Michael Mullins (COO)
Mike Ratini (Mgr-Procurement)
Jeanne P. Gannon (Pres)

MULTI CAPITAL GROUP I, LLC
44 Wall St, New York, NY 10005
Tel.: (212) 742-0707
Web Site: http://www.multigroups.com
Year Founded: 2003
Real Estate Credit
N.A.I.C.S.: 522292
Eli Verschleiser (CEO)

MULTI CHEVROLET INC.
2675 Rte 22 W, Union, NJ 07083
Tel.: (908) 686-2800
Web Site: http://www.multiautomall.com
Year Founded: 1969
Rev.: $42,000,000
Emp.: 120
Owner & Operator of Car Dealerships
N.A.I.C.S.: 441110
Valerie Tino (VP)
James V. Tino Sr. (Pres)
James Tino Jr. (VP)

MULTI IMAGE GROUP INC.
1701 Clint Moore Rd, Boca Raton, FL 33487
Tel.: (561) 994-3515
Web Site: http://www.multiimagegroup.com
Rev.: $22,200,000
Emp.: 120
Motion Picture & Video Production
N.A.I.C.S.: 512110
Arlene Sclafani (CEO)
James V. Sclafani (Pres)
John Reitzes (CFO)

MULTI MEDIA CHANNELS, LLC
310 W Walnut, Fourth Fl, Green Bay, WI 54303
Tel.: (715) 258-3207
Web Site: https://www.mmclocal.com
Newspaper Publishers
N.A.I.C.S.: 513110

Subsidiaries:
Peshtigo Times Printers & Publishers (1)
841 Maple St, Peshtigo, WI 54157-1341
Tel.: (715) 582-4541
Web Site: https://peshtigotimes.com
Internet Publishing & Broadcasting & Web Search Portals
N.A.I.C.S.: 516210
Mary Ann Gardon (Owner)

MULTI MEDIA SERVICES CORP.
915 King St Fl 2nd, Alexandria, VA 22314
Tel.: (703) 739-2160 VA
Web Site: http://www.multi-media-services.com
Year Founded: 1983
Sales Range: $1-9.9 Million
Emp.: 4
Media Buying Services
N.A.I.C.S.: 541830
Anthony M. Fabrizio (Chm & Treas)
Dwight Sterling (Pres)
Lyssa Seward (Dir-Media)

MULTI PACKAGING SOLUTIONS, INC. - ALLEGAN
504 Eastern Ave, Allegan, MI 49010
Tel.: (269) 686-8744
Web Site: http://www.multipkg.com
Emp.: 130
Tradebinding & Related Work
N.A.I.C.S.: 323120

MULTI SERVICE CENTER
1200 S 336th St, Federal Way, WA 98003
Tel.: (253) 835-7678
Web Site: http://www.mschelps.org
Rev.: $12,100,000
Emp.: 65
Individual & Family Services
N.A.I.C.S.: 624190
Bob Wrablewski (Sec)
Robin Corak (CEO)

MULTI-AD, INC.
1720 W Detweiller Dr, Peoria, IL 61615-1612
Tel.: (309) 692-1530
Web Site: http://www.multi-ad.com
Year Founded: 1945
Sales Range: $25-49.9 Million
Emp.: 160
Retail Advertising Materials & Programs Mfr; Contract Printing
N.A.I.C.S.: 513199
John F. Kocher (Pres)
Shelby Vaughan (CFO)
Jill Addy Wright (Sr VP)
Mike Coughlon (VP-Pre-Media)

Subsidiaries:
Multi-Ad Recas (1)
1720 W Detweiller Dr, Peoria, IL 61615-1612
Tel.: (309) 692-1530
Web Site: http://www.multiad.com
Sales Range: $25-49.9 Million
Emp.: 150
Web Hosting Services
N.A.I.C.S.: 513199
Rachel McMenimen (VP)

MULTI-BANK SERVICES LTD.
1000 Town Ctr Ste 2300, Southfield, MI 48075
Tel.: (248) 291-1100
Web Site: http://www.mbssecurities.com
Year Founded: 1988
Sales Range: $25-49.9 Million
Emp.: 100
Bond Brokers
N.A.I.C.S.: 523150

David Maccagnone (Chm & CEO)
Michael Drews (Vice Chm)
Jeff Maccagnone (Pres)
Michael Karsner (CFO)

MULTI-HEALTH SYSTEMS, INC.
60 Industrial Pkwy Ste 706, Cheektowaga, NY 14227
Tel.: (416) 492-2627
Web Site: http://www.mhs.com
Publishing Services
N.A.I.C.S.: 513199
Hazel Wheldon (Pres & CEO)

Subsidiaries:
Discovery Learning Inc. (1)
431 Spring Garden St, Greensboro, NC 27401-6564
Tel.: (336) 272-9530
Web Site: http://www.discoverylearning.com
Management Consulting Services
N.A.I.C.S.: 541618
Chris Musselwhite (Pres & CEO)

MULTI-MEDIA DISTRIBUTION CORP.
15232 US Hwy 19 North Ste B, Clearwater, FL 34683-5471
Tel.: (727) 447-4147
Web Site: http://www.dva.com
Rev.: $11,000,000
Emp.: 15
Video Tape Production
N.A.I.C.S.: 423990
Brad Kugler (Pres)

MULTI-METALS
715 E Gray St, Louisville, KY 40202
Tel.: (502) 589-3781
Web Site: http://www.multi-metals.com
Year Founded: 1955
Sales Range: $75-99.9 Million
Emp.: 100
Mfr of Tungsten Carbide Tool Bits, Blanks & Wear Parts
N.A.I.C.S.: 333515
Shawn Teague (VP-Sls & Mktg)
Lenny Wiseman (VP-Fin & Admin)
Franc Koljaka (VP-Ops & Engrg)

MULTI-NET MARKETING, INC.
224 E Monument St, Colorado Springs, CO 80903
Tel.: (719) 444-0371
Web Site: http://www.multinetmarketing.com
Year Founded: 1995
Sales Range: $10-24.9 Million
Emp.: 8
Media Buying Services
N.A.I.C.S.: 541830
Betsy Thairgen (Media Buyer)
Jane E. Price (COO)
Alana King (Dir-Traffic)

MULTI-PLASTICS, INC.
7770 N Central Dr, Lewis Center, OH 43035-9404
Tel.: (740) 548-4894 OH
Web Site: http://www.multi-plastics.com
Year Founded: 1979
Sales Range: $25-49.9 Million
Emp.: 140
Thin-Gauged Plastic Film Distr
N.A.I.C.S.: 424610
John R. Parsio Sr. (Founder)

Subsidiaries:
Multi-Plastics Europe Ltd. (1)
Columbus House 30 Manchester Rd, Northwich, CW9 5ND, Cheshire, United Kingdom (100%)
Tel.: (44) 1606330011
Web Site: http://www.multiplastics.co.uk

Sales Range: $10-24.9 Million
Emp.: 50
N.A.I.C.S.: 425120
Paul Frich (Mng Dir)

Multi-Plastics Extrusions, Inc. (1)
600 Dietrich Ave, Hazleton, PA 18201-0658
Tel.: (570) 455-1931
Web Site: http://www.multi-plastics.com
Sales Range: $25-49.9 Million
Extruded Plastic Sheet & Film Mfr
N.A.I.C.S.: 326113

Multi-Plastics, Inc. (1)
1125 Dividend Ct, Peachtree City, GA 30269-1926
Tel.: (770) 486-6828
Web Site: http://www.multi-plastics.com
Sales Range: $10-24.9 Million
Emp.: 25
Mfr & Distr of Thin Gauge Plastic Films for the Envelope, Carton, Label & Printing Industries
N.A.I.C.S.: 326113
Chad Grossman (Plant Mgr)

Multi-Plastics, Inc. (1)
11625 Los Nietos Rd, Santa Fe Springs, CA 90670-2009
Tel.: (562) 692-1202
Web Site: http://www.multiplastics.com
Sales Range: $10-24.9 Million
Emp.: 15
N.A.I.C.S.: 425120
Rafael Enriquez (Plant Mgr)

Multi-Plastics, Inc. (1)
1253 Naperville Dr, Romeoville, IL 60446-1041
Tel.: (630) 226-0580
Sales Range: $10-24.9 Million
Emp.: 30
N.A.I.C.S.: 425120

Multi-Plastics, Inc. (1)
210 Commodore Dr, Swedesboro, NJ 08085-1292
Tel.: (856) 241-9014
Sales Range: $10-24.9 Million
Emp.: 50
N.A.I.C.S.: 425120
Mike Budd (Mgr-Global Mktg)

Multi-Plastics, Inc. (1)
55 Moore Ct, Whitby, L1N 9Z8, ON, Canada (100%)
Tel.: (905) 430-7511
Web Site: https://www.multi-plastics.com
Sales Range: $10-24.9 Million
Emp.: 35
Distr Of Plastic Products
N.A.I.C.S.: 326199

MULTICARE HEALTH SYSTEM
PO Box 5299, Tacoma, WA 98415-0299
Tel.: (253) 403-1000 WA
Web Site: http://www.multicare.org
Year Founded: 1987
Sales Range: $1-4.9 Billion
Emp.: 10,818
Health Care Srvices
N.A.I.C.S.: 622110
William G. Robertson (Pres & CEO)
Florence Chang (COO & Exec VP)
Lois I. Bernstein (Sr VP-Community Svcs)
Theresa M. Boyle (Sr VP-Strategy & Bus Dev)
Mark Gary (Sr VP & Gen Counsel)
Anna Loomis (CFO)
Claire Spain-Remy (Chief Physician Officer)

MULTICULTURAL COMMUNITY SERVICES OF THE PIONEER VALLEY, INC.
1000 Wilbraham Rd, Springfield, MA 01109
Tel.: (413) 782-2500 MA
Web Site: http://www.mcsnet.org
Year Founded: 1979
Sales Range: $10-24.9 Million
Emp.: 569

Mentally Disabled People Housing Services
N.A.I.C.S.: 624229
Bernard Cohen (Pres)
Paul Conlon (Exec Dir)

MULTIGRAINS, INC.
117 Water St, Lawrence, MA 01841
Tel.: (978) 691-6100
Web Site:
http://www.multigrainsbakeries.com
Year Founded: 1976
Sales Range: $25-49.9 Million
Emp.: 205
Commercial Bakery Services
N.A.I.C.S.: 311812
Joseph A. Faro (Pres & CEO)
Darren Gaiero (Dir-Pur)
Chuck Brandano (Exec VP & Dir-R&D)

MULTILINE TECHNOLOGY INC.
400 Broadhollow Rd, Farmingdale, NY 11735
Tel.: (631) 249-8300
Web Site: http://www.multiline.com
Sales Range: $10-24.9 Million
Emp.: 60
Equipment for the PCB Industries Mfr
N.A.I.C.S.: 333248
Michael Angelo (Pres)
David Angelo (Dir-Pur)
John Karcher (CFO)
John Kidd (Engr-Sls)
Scott Dolecek (Mgr-Tech Svc)

Subsidiaries:

Multiline Technology, Inc., Printed Circuit Board Division (1)
75 Roebling Ct, Ronkonkoma, NY 11779-9202
Tel.: (631) 249-8300
Web Site: http://www.multiline.com
Sales Range: $10-24.9 Million
Emp.: 30
Provider of Equipment & Accessories for the Precise Registration of Multilayer Circuit Boards
N.A.I.C.S.: 333248
Michael Angelo (Co-Pres)
David Angelo (Co-Pres)
Ronn Ferina (Dir-Engrg)
Scott Dolecek (Mgr-Technical Svc)
Mary Endres (Mgr-Sls-Parts & Accessories)

Multiline Technology, Inc., Printing Products Division (1)
400 Broadhollow Rd, Farmingdale, NY 11735
Tel.: (631) 249-8300
Web Site: http://www.multiline.com
Sales Range: $10-24.9 Million
Emp.: 40
Provider of Registration Systems & Products for Flexographic & Lithographic Systems
N.A.I.C.S.: 333248

MULTIMEDIA PLUS, INC.
853 Broadway Ste 1605, New York, NY 10003
Tel.: (212) 982-3229 NY
Web Site:
http://www.multimediaplus.com
Year Founded: 1997
Sales Range: $1-9.9 Million
Emp.: 14
Production of Video & Interactive Multimedia Training for Retail Clients
N.A.I.C.S.: 512110
David Harouche (Founder & CEO, CTO)
Jodi Harouche (Principal)
Anthony DeLuca (CFO)
Greg Orsi (Dir-Interactive Dev)
Robert Guadalupe (Sr VP-Sls & Mktg)

MULTIPLE CONCRETE ACCESSORIES
20284 N Rand Rd, Palatine, IL 60074
Tel.: (847) 438-2000
Web Site:
http://www.multipleconcrete.com
Year Founded: 1976
Sales Range: $10-24.9 Million
Emp.: 40
Concrete Materials
N.A.I.C.S.: 423320
Michael Longfield (Pres)
Kathy Eigel (VP)

MULTIPLE ORGANICS, INC.
200 Linus Pauling Dr, Hercules, CA 94547
Tel.: (415) 482-9800
Web Site:
http://www.multipleorganics.com
Sales Range: $10-24.9 Million
Emp.: 11
Natural & Organic Foods Distr
N.A.I.C.S.: 456191
Dave Lanstein (Founder & CEO)

MULTIPLEX COMPANY INC.
2100 Future Dr, Sellersburg, IN 47172-1874
Tel.: (812) 256-7777 MO
Web Site: http://www.multiplex-beverage.com
Year Founded: 1979
Sales Range: $10-24.9 Million
Emp.: 200
Provider of Refrigeration & Heating Equipment Services
N.A.I.C.S.: 333415
Edwin Verhulst (Mng Dir)

Subsidiaries:

Multiplex International Sales Corp. (1)
2100 Future Dr, Sellersburg, IN 47172
Tel.: (812) 256-7777
Sales Range: $10-24.9 Million
Emp.: 2
Provider of Refrigeration Equipment & Supply Services
N.A.I.C.S.: 423740

MULTISEAL INC.
4320 Hitch Peters Rd, Evansville, IN 47711
Tel.: (812) 428-3422
Web Site: http://www.multiseal-usa.com
Sales Range: $10-24.9 Million
Emp.: 50
Sealants
N.A.I.C.S.: 325520
Gary M. Rust (Pres & CEO)
Scott Wire (Mgr-Production)

MULTISTACK, LLC
1065 Maple Ave, Sparta, WI 54656-2379
Tel.: (608) 366-2400
Web Site: http://www.multistack.com
Year Founded: 1989
Air-Conditioning, Warm Air Heating Equipment & Commercial & Industrial Refrigeration Equipment Mfr
N.A.I.C.S.: 333415
Dick Campbell (Co-Founder)
Charles Kenyon (Pres & CEO)
Bill Bast (Co-Founder)
Monte Holman (Co-Founder)

Subsidiaries:

Desert Aire Corp. (1)
N120 W18485 Freistadt Rd, Germantown, WI 53022-3022
Tel.: (262) 946-7400
Web Site: http://www.desert-aire.com
Other Commercial & Service Industry Machinery Mfr
N.A.I.C.S.: 333310
Hal Sindelar (Product Mgr-Engrg)

MULTISYSTEMS RESTAURANTS INC.
801 Ponce de Leon Ave, San Juan, PR 00907
Tel.: (787) 273-3180
Sales Range: $10-24.9 Million
Emp.: 25
Steak & Barbecue Restaurants
N.A.I.C.S.: 722511
Jorge Colon Nevarez (Chm)

MULTIVISON INC.
1220 Iroquois Ave, Naperville, IL 60563
Tel.: (630) 579-4000
Web Site: http://www.multivision-inc.com
Rev.: $14,000,000
Emp.: 170
Computer System Design Services
N.A.I.C.S.: 541512
Ganesh Kasilingam (VP)

MULTNOMAH ATHLETIC CLUB
1849 SW Salmon St, Portland, OR 97205
Tel.: (503) 223-6251
Web Site: http://www.themac.com
Sales Range: $10-24.9 Million
Emp.: 500
Private Athletic Membership Club
N.A.I.C.S.: 713940
Lisa Bendt (Exec Dir)
Norm Rich (Gen Mgr)

MULTRI PRECISION, LLC
115 Main St, Oakville, CT 06779
Tel.: (860) 274-2536 CT
Year Founded: 1985
Precision Machined Components Mfr
N.A.I.C.S.: 332999
Mark James Procopio (Chm)

MULVANE COOPERATIVE UNION INC.
220 Poplar St, Mulvane, KS 67110
Tel.: (316) 777-1121
Web Site:
http://www.mulvanecoop.com
Sales Range: $10-24.9 Million
Emp.: 17
Grains
N.A.I.C.S.: 424510

MUMMES INC.
120 Hwy 173 N, Hondo, TX 78861
Tel.: (830) 426-3313
Web Site:
http://www.mummesinc.com
Sales Range: $10-24.9 Million
Emp.: 50
Farm Supplies
N.A.I.C.S.: 424910
Eric Meyer (Mgr)
Jamie Perez (Mgr-Retail)

MUNA FEDERAL CREDIT UNION
4400 Hwy 39 N, Meridian, MS 39301
Tel.: (601) 693-8563
Web Site:
https://www.munafederal.com
Year Founded: 1962
Credit Union
N.A.I.C.S.: 522130

MUNAFO INC.
9145 Cincinnati Columbus, West Chester, OH 45069
Tel.: (513) 777-3006
Web Site:
http://www.spiritandpartystore.com
Rev.: $14,200,000

Emp.: 40
Supermarket
N.A.I.C.S.: 445110
Chris Munafo (Pres)

MUNCHKIN, INC.
7835 Gloria Ave, Van Nuys, CA 91406
Tel.: (818) 893-5000
Web Site: http://www.munchkin.com
Year Founded: 1991
Sales Range: $10-24.9 Million
Emp.: 50
Designer, Mfr & Distr of Infant & Toddler Products
N.A.I.C.S.: 326160
Andrew Keimach (Pres)
Steven B. Dunn (Founder & CEO)
Marc Hayes (VP-Sls)
Jeffrey Kaltreider (VP-Mktg)
Petty Rader (Gen Counsel)
Katie Harrington (Sr Mgr-PR & Social Media)
Tom Emrey (CFO & COO)
Diana Barnes (Chief Brand Officer & Dir-Creative)
Alan Wizemann (Chief Digital Officer)
Shannon Robbins (Dir-Social Media & PR)

MUNCIE AVIATION CO.
5201 N Walnut St, Muncie, IN 47303
Tel.: (765) 289-7141
Web Site:
http://www.muncieaviation.com
Rev.: $5,454,000
Emp.: 54
Other Airport Operations
N.A.I.C.S.: 488119
Martin Ingram (Pres & Mgr-Sls)
Rick Manes (VP-Property & Fuel Sls)

Subsidiaries:

Des Moines Flying Service, Inc. (1)
5304 Fleur Dr, Des Moines, IA 50321
Tel.: (515) 256-5300
Web Site: http://www.dmfs.com
Rev.: $3,636,000
Emp.: 36
Other Airport Operations
N.A.I.C.S.: 488119
Steve Thompson (Pres)
Martin Ingram (Chm)

MUNGER TOLLES & OLSON LLP
350 S Grand Ave 35th Fl, Los Angeles, CA 90071
Tel.: (213) 683-9100
Web Site: http://www.mto.com
Year Founded: 1962
Sales Range: $200-249.9 Million
Emp.: 201
Legal Advisory Services
N.A.I.C.S.: 541110
Ronald L. Olson (Partner)
Martin D. Bern (Partner-San Francisco)

MUNICIBID.COM LLC
1608 Walnut St 12th Fl, Philadelphia, PA 19103
Web Site: http://www.municibid.com
Year Founded: 2006
Sales Range: $10-24.9 Million
Management Consulting Services
N.A.I.C.S.: 541618
Greg Berry (CEO)

MUNICIPAL AUTHORITY OF WESTMORELAND COUNTY
124 Park & Pool Rd, New Stanton, PA 15672
Tel.: (724) 834-6500
Web Site: http://www.mawc.org
Rev.: $38,932,892
Emp.: 115

Municipal Authority of Westmoreland County—(Continued)
Water Supply
N.A.I.C.S.: 221310
Randy Roadman (Chm)
Bruce Robinson (Vice Chm)
Jawdat Nikuola (Vice Chm)
Vicki Vittone (Sec & Asst Treas)

MUNICIPAL ELECTRIC AUTHORITY OF GEORGIA
1470 Riveredge Pkwy, Atlanta, GA 30328-4686
Tel.: (770) 563-0300 GA
Web Site: http://www.meagpower.org
Year Founded: 1975
Sales Range: $800-899.9 Million
Emp.: 100
Public Power Joint Action Agency
N.A.I.C.S.: 926130
Mary G. Jackson (Chief Acctg Officer & VP)
James E. Fuller (Pres & CEO)
Steven M. Jackson (VP-Power Supply)
Paul Warfel (Reg Mgr)
Edward Easterlin (CFO)

MUNICIPAL IMPROVEMENT CORPORATION OF LOS ANGELES
200 N Main St City Hall E, Los Angeles, CA 90012
Tel.: (213) 473-7526 CA
Year Founded: 1984
Sales Range: $75-99.9 Million
City Development Services
N.A.I.C.S.: 541320
Royce A. Menkus (Treas)
Lily Y. Lee (VP)
Maurice Weiner (Pres)
Faye Washington (Sec)

MUNICIPAL SUPPLY INC.
1550 NE 51st Ave, Des Moines, IA 50313
Tel.: (515) 262-1300 IA
Web Site: http://www.municipalsupplyinc.com
Sales Range: $10-24.9 Million
Emp.: 25
Whslr of Contractors' Materials
N.A.I.C.S.: 423810
Sandy Daton (Office Mgr)

MUNICIPAL TRUST & SAVINGS BANK
720 Main St NW, Bourbonnais, IL 60914
Tel.: (815) 935-8000
Web Site: http://www.municipalbank.com
Sales Range: $10-24.9 Million
Emp.: 51
State Savings Banks, Not Federally Chartered
N.A.I.C.S.: 522180
Merlin Karlock (CEO)
Catherine Boicken (Exec VP)
Sheryl Trudeau (VP)

MUNIE OUTDOOR SERVICES, INC.
1000 Milburn School Rd, Caseyville, IL 62232
Tel.: (618) 632-5296
Web Site: http://www.muniegreencare.com
Year Founded: 1989
Sales Range: $10-24.9 Million
Emp.: 100
Irrigation Sprinkler System Installation & Commercial Maintenance
N.A.I.C.S.: 561730

Joseph Munie (Pres)
Joseph Munie (Pres)
Subsidiaries:

Munie Greencare (1)
1000 Milburn School Rd, Caseyville, IL 62232
Tel.: (618) 632-5296
Web Site: http://www.munieoutdoor.com
Rev.: $1,172,716
Emp.: 20
Lawn & Garden Services
N.A.I.C.S.: 561730
Joseph Munie (Pres)

Outdoor Construction Inc. (1)
1000 Milburn School Rd, Caseyville, IL 62232
Tel.: (618) 632-5296
Web Site: http://www.muniegreencare.com
Rev.: $1,300,000
Emp.: 20
Irrigation Sprinkler System Installation
N.A.I.C.S.: 238220
Joseph Munie (Founder & Pres)

MUNN RABOT LLC
33 W 17th St Fl 3, New York, NY 10011-5511
Tel.: (212) 727-3900
Web Site: http://www.munnrabot.com
Year Founded: 1995
Rev.: $20,000,000
Emp.: 15
Advetising Agency
N.A.I.C.S.: 541810
Orson Munn (CEO & Partner)
Peter Rabot (Partner & Chief Creative Officer)
Virginia Stewart (Controller & Dir-HR)
Val Junker (Dir-MIS)
Rachel Manis (VP-Ops)
Robin Peskin (Assoc Dir-Media)
Kate Roderick (Acct Supvr)
Clarisa Garcia (Media Planner)

MUNNELL & SHERRILL INC.
1163 Northeast 63rd Ave, Portland, OR 97213
Tel.: (503) 281-0021 OR
Web Site: http://www.munnell-sherrill.com
Year Founded: 1915
Sales Range: $10-24.9 Million
Emp.: 52
Provider of Mill Supplies
N.A.I.C.S.: 423840
Mike Posekany (Mgr)
Gary Butts (Pres)

MUNRO & COMPANY, INC.
3770 Malvern Rd, Hot Springs, AR 71902
Tel.: (501) 262-6000 AR
Web Site: http://www.munroshoes.com
Year Founded: 1972
Sales Range: $150-199.9 Million
Emp.: 400
Footwear Mfr
N.A.I.C.S.: 316210
Donald Munro (Founder)
Subsidiaries:

Jumping-Jacks Shoes Div (1)
3770 Malevrn Rd, Hot Springs National Park, AR 71901
Tel.: (501) 262-6000
Web Site: http://www.munroshoe.com
Sales Range: $25-49.9 Million
Emp.: 150
Children's Shoes Mfr
N.A.I.C.S.: 316210
Mollie Munro (Exec VP)

Lake Catherine (1)
190 Elmwood Dr, Hot Springs National Park, AR 71901-6735
Tel.: (501) 262-6000

Sales Range: $25-49.9 Million
Emp.: 80
Mfr of Private Label & Military Shoes
N.A.I.C.S.: 316210
Donald Munro (Chm)

MUNRO COMPANIES, INC.
955 3rd Ave, Grand Junction, CO 81501
Tel.: (800) 942-4270
Web Site: http://www.munropump.com
Pumps & Pump Accesories Mfr
N.A.I.C.S.: 333996
Guy Collins (Natl Dir-Sls)
Subsidiaries:

Green Industry Solutions Inc. (1)
2193 Overlook Ct, Grand Junction, CO 81507-3506
Tel.: (970) 024-7631
Architectural Services
N.A.I.C.S.: 541310
Richard Edwards (Pres)

MUNROE CREATIVE PARTNERS
1435 Walnut St Ste 600, Philadelphia, PA 19102-3219
Tel.: (215) 563-8080 PA
Web Site: http://www.munroe.com
Year Founded: 1989
Rev.: $10,000,000
Emp.: 28
Collateral, Full Service, Graphic Design, Interactive Agencies, Production
N.A.I.C.S.: 541810
Judy Munroe (Founder & Pres)
Michael Cavallaro (Sr Dir-Art)
Earl Gansky (CFO & Partner)
Michael Licata (Partner & Sr Art Dir)
Frank V. Pileggi (Partner & Chief Creative Officer)
Jami Slotnick (Partner & Sr Project Mgr)
Harry Volpe (Sr Mgr-Production)
Jennifer Long (Accountant)
Sharmika Ferguson (Project Coord)
Melisa Malchoff (Dir-Art)
Lauren Ciallella (Mgr-Creative)
Katelyn Joyce (Project Coord)
Subsidiaries:

Munroe Creative Partners (1)
711 3rd Ave 16th Fl, New York, NY 10017
Tel.: (212) 284-7683
Web Site: http://www.munroe.com
Sales Range: $10-24.9 Million
Emp.: 15
N.A.I.C.S.: 541810
Marisa Noble (Coord-Project)
Judy Munroe (CEO)

MUNSON LAKES NUTRITION LLC
917 6th St, Howard Lake, MN 55349
Tel.: (320) 543-2561
Web Site: http://www.munsonlakes.com
Year Founded: 1951
Sales Range: $10-24.9 Million
Emp.: 30
Providers of Feed Production
N.A.I.C.S.: 459910
Wade Serfling (Mgr-Retail Store)

MURAD SKIN RESEARCH LABS INC.
2121 Rosecrans Ave, El Segundo, CA 90245
Tel.: (310) 726-0600
Web Site: http://www.murad.com
Rev.: $61,200,000
Emp.: 160
Cosmetics
N.A.I.C.S.: 456120
Howard Murad (Pres)

MURDOCK COMPANIES INC.
1111 E 1st St, Wichita, KS 67214
Tel.: (316) 262-0401
Web Site: http://www.mcos.com
Sales Range: $10-24.9 Million
Emp.: 30
Industrial Supplies
N.A.I.C.S.: 423840
Brenda Blazer (Pres)

MURDOCK HOLDINGS, LLC
10900 Wilshire Blvd Ste 1600, Los Angeles, CA 90024
Tel.: (310) 208-3636 DE
Holding Company
N.A.I.C.S.: 551112
David Howard Murdock (Chm & CEO)
Subsidiaries:

Castle & Cooke, Inc. (1)
10900 Wilshire Blvd, Los Angeles, CA 90024-6501
Tel.: (310) 208-3636
Web Site: http://www.castlecooke.net
Sales Range: $25-49.9 Million
Emp.: 40
Real Estate Investment, Development, Brokerage & Management Services
N.A.I.C.S.: 531390
David Howard Murdock (Chm & CEO)
Gary Wong (Pres, CFO & Treas)
Dean Pillion (VP-Tax)
Chris Ervin (Dir-Bus Dev-North Carolina)
Mark Spitzer (VP-Ops-North Carolina)
Ryan S. Gores (Gen Counsel, Sec & VP)
Charlene Mims (VP-HR)

Subsidiary (Domestic):

Castle & Cooke Properties, Inc. (2)
680 Iwilei Rd 5th Fl Ste 510, Honolulu, HI 96817-5390
Tel.: (808) 548-4811
Web Site: http://www.castlecookehawaii.com
Real Estate Investment, Development, Brokerage & Management Services
N.A.I.C.S.: 531390
Harry A. Saunders (Pres)
W. Bruce Barrett (Exec VP-Residential Ops)
Richard Mirikitani (Gen Counsel, Sec & Sr VP)
Susan Harada (VP-Retail Ops)

Holding (Domestic):

Flexi-Van Leasing, Inc. (2)
251 Monroe Ave, Kenilworth, NJ 07033-1106
Tel.: (908) 276-8000
Web Site: http://www.flexivan.com
Sales Range: $75-99.9 Million
Emp.: 100
Van & Truck Leasing Services
N.A.I.C.S.: 532490
Charlie Wellins (Pres & COO)

Unit (Domestic):

Keene's Pointe Realty (2)
527 Main St, Windermere, FL 34786
Tel.: (407) 876-8879
Web Site: http://www.cc-keenespointe.com
Sales Range: $1-9.9 Million
Emp.: 13
Residential Real Estate Agency
N.A.I.C.S.: 531210
Bruce Freeman (Pres)

Holding (Domestic):

Pacific Clay Products, Inc. (2)
14741 Lake St, Lake Elsinore, CA 92530-1610
Tel.: (951) 674-2131
Web Site: http://www.pacificclay.com
Sales Range: $50-74.9 Million
Clay Brick & Tile Mfr & Distr
N.A.I.C.S.: 327120
David Hollingsworth (Pres)
Clint Kramer (Dir-Bus Dev)

Division (Domestic):

Yankee Hill Brick & Tile (3)
3705 S Coddington Ave, Lincoln, NE 68522

Tel.: (402) 477-6663
Web Site: http://www.yankeehillbrick.com
Sales Range: $10-24.9 Million
Emp.: 75
Clay Brick & Tile Mfr & Distr
N.A.I.C.S.: 327120

Plant (Domestic):

Yankee Hill Brick & Tile - Omaha Brick Yard (4)
13840 C Plz, Omaha, NE 68144
Tel.: (402) 330-2751
Web Site: http://www.yankeehillbrick.com
Clay Brick Mfr & Distr
N.A.I.C.S.: 327120

Subsidiary (Domestic):

Sherwood Development Company (2)
2300 Norfield Ct, Thousand Oaks, CA 91361
Tel.: (805) 496-1833
Web Site: http://www.sherwoodcountryclub.com
Sales Range: $50-74.9 Million
Emp.: 7
Residential Real Estate Development & Brokerage Services
N.A.I.C.S.: 237210
Milan Georgeff (Dir-Client Svcs)
Mike McMullen (Dir-Construction & Ops)
Nathan Stockmeir (VP-Sls, Ops, Product & Land Dev)

MURDOCK WEBBING COMPANY INCORPORATED
27 Foundry St, Central Falls, RI 02863
Tel.: (401) 724-3000
Web Site: http://www.mrdkweb.com
Rev: $20,000,000
Emp.: 130
Webbing, Woven
N.A.I.C.S.: 313220
Don A. Deangelis (Pres)

MUREX PROPERTIES, LLC
12629 New Brittany Blvd Bldg Ste 16, Fort Myers, FL 33907
Tel.: (239) 790-0004
Web Site: http://www.murexproperties.com
Year Founded: 2004
Sales Range: $25-49.9 Million
Emp.: 75
Manufactured Housing Communities Owner & Manager
N.A.I.C.S.: 531311
Steven P. Adler (Owner & Pres)
Wes B. Perry (CFO)

MURFIN DRILLING COMPANY INC.
250 N Water St Ste 300, Wichita, KS 67202-1216
Tel.: (316) 267-3241   KS
Web Site: http://www.murfininc.com
Year Founded: 1991
Sales Range: $25-49.9 Million
Emp.: 300
Oil Drilling & Gas Well Services
N.A.I.C.S.: 213111
Robert D. Young (CFO)
David L. Murfin (Pres)
George E. Hansen III (Executives)

MURFREESBORO PURE MILK COMPANY
2450 Southgate Blvd, Murfreesboro, TN 37128
Tel.: (615) 893-3810
Sales Range: $10-24.9 Million
Emp.: 64
Dairy Products
N.A.I.C.S.: 424430
Davis Young (VP)
Herbert D. Young Jr. (Pres)

MURNANE BUILDING CONTRACTORS INC
104 Sharron Ave, Plattsburgh, NY 12901
Tel.: (518) 561-4010
Web Site: http://www.murnanebuilding.com
Rev: $27,900,000
Emp.: 50
Commercial & Office Building Contractors
N.A.I.C.S.: 236220
Patrick T. Murnane (Co-Pres)
Corey A. Kosmoski (Project Mgr)
Michael Cowden (VP)
Andrew P. Kantor (Project Mgr)
James R. Hogel (VP)
Ann Marie Jones (Sr Project Mgr & Dir-Construction Mgmt Svcs)
Roger Bramer (Project Mgr)
Stephen C. Welch (Project Mgr)
Peter J. Shanahan (Sr Project Mgr)
Christopher K. Murnane (Project Mgr)
Peggy Demers (Office Mgr)
Shawn Murphy (Project Mgr)
Mike Siskavich (Project Mgr)
Jeremy Williams (Project Mgr)
Pat Murnane (Pres)

MURNANE PACKAGING CORPORATION
607 Northwest Ave, Northlake, IL 60164
Tel.: (708) 449-1200   IL
Web Site: http://www.murnanecompanies.com
Year Founded: 1919
Emp.: 55
Folding Paperboard Box & Other Packaging Products Mfr
N.A.I.C.S.: 322212
Thomas Hanson (VP-Ops)
Patrick J. Murnane (Exec VP)
Frank J. Murnane Jr. (Pres & CEO)

MURNANE PAPER COMPANY
345 W Fischer Farm Rd, Elmhurst, IL 60126
Tel.: (630) 530-8222   IL
Web Site: http://www.murnanepaper.com
Year Founded: 1982
Printing Paper Distr
N.A.I.C.S.: 424110
Robert Hunt Jr. (Pres)

MURPHCO OF FLORIDA INC.
6802 Commonwealth Ave, Jacksonville, FL 32254
Tel.: (904) 781-6008
Web Site: http://www.murphcofl.com
Year Founded: 1972
Sales Range: $10-24.9 Million
Emp.: 80
Motel, Franchised
N.A.I.C.S.: 721110
Josh Harrison (VP)

MURPHEY TAYLOR AND ELLIS INC.
3095 Vineville Ave, Macon, GA 31204
Tel.: (478) 743-2671
Rev: $25,000,000
Emp.: 15
Nonresidential Building Operators
N.A.I.C.S.: 531110
Henry P. Persons III (Pres)

MURPHREE VENTURE PARTNERS
1221 Lamar Ste 1136, Houston, TX 77010
Tel.: (713) 655-8500
Web Site: http://www.murphreeventures.com
Privater Equity Firm

N.A.I.C.S.: 523999
Patrick E. Murphree (Partner)

MURPHY & DURIEU
120 Broadway Fl 17, New York, NY 10271
Tel.: (212) 618-0900
Web Site: http://www.murphy.com
Rev: $14,400,000
Emp.: 130
Dealers, Security
N.A.I.C.S.: 523150
Richard J. Murphy (Gen Partner)

MURPHY & NOLAN INC.
340 Peat St, Syracuse, NY 13217
Tel.: (315) 474-8203
Web Site: http://www.murphynolan.com
Sales Range: $10-24.9 Million
Emp.: 60
Metals Service Centers & Offices
N.A.I.C.S.: 423510
William Michael Murphy (Pres & CEO)
Stephen C. Polito (Mgr-Acct)
Patrick R. Murphy (Co-COO & VP)
John J. Murphy IV (Chm & Treas)
John J. Murphy III (COO & VP)

MURPHY BED CO., INC.
42 Central Ave, Farmingdale, NY 11735-6906
Tel.: (631) 420-4330
Web Site: http://www.murphybedcompany.com
Year Founded: 1900
Sales Range: Less than $1 Million
Emp.: 8
Steel Beds Mfr
N.A.I.C.S.: 337126
Kathy Red (Mgr-Internet Svcs)

MURPHY BROTHERS INC.
3812 E Broadway Ave, Spokane, WA 99202
Tel.: (509) 535-1591
Sales Range: $10-24.9 Million
Emp.: 20
Sewer Line Construction
N.A.I.C.S.: 237110
William O. Murphy (Chm)
Chuck Murphy (Treas)
Donald E. Murphy (Partner)

MURPHY BUSINESS & FINANCIAL CORPORATION
513 N Belcher Rd, Clearwater, FL 33765
Tel.: (727) 725-7090   FL
Web Site: http://www.murphybusiness.com
Year Founded: 1994
Sales Range: $1-9.9 Million
Emp.: 100
Business Services & Franchisor
N.A.I.C.S.: 561499
Jim Sinclair (VP)
John McElaney (Dir-Tech)
Sandee Devine (VP-Franchise Dev)
Tom Coba (CEO)

MURPHY COMPANY
2350 Prairie Rd, Eugene, OR 97402-9742
Tel.: (541) 461-4545   OR
Web Site: http://www.murphyplywood.com
Sales Range: $50-74.9 Million
Emp.: 300
Lumber & Wood Products Mfr & Retailer
N.A.I.C.S.: 321212
Mark Gryziec (Mgr-Softwood Plywood Sls)

Bob Sauter (Mgr-Sls-Northwest & Rocky Mountain)
Mike Vidan (Mgr-Territory Sls)
Dan Semsak (Dir-Engineered Wood Products)

Subsidiaries:

Murphy Plywood (1)
2350 Prairie Rd, Eugene, OR 97402-9742   (100%)
Tel.: (541) 461-4545
Web Site: http://www.murphyplywood.com
Sales Range: $25-49.9 Million
Emp.: 200
Softwood Plywood, Veneered Hardwood Plywood & Panels
N.A.I.C.S.: 321211
Chan Manda (CEO)

MURPHY COMPANY MECHANICAL CONTRACTORS & ENGINEERS INC.
1233 N Price Rd, Saint Louis, MO 63132-2303
Tel.: (314) 997-6600   MO
Web Site: http://www.murphynet.com
Year Founded: 1907
Sales Range: $100-124.9 Million
Emp.: 200
Plumbing, Heating & Air-Conditioning
N.A.I.C.S.: 238220
Mark L. Bengard (Sr VP-Sls & Pre-Construction)
Chris Carter (VP-Svc)
Asif Kadiani (Sr Engr-Design Build)
Tim Barton (VP-Indus Bus Dev)
Nick Zahner (Engr-Safety)
Dan Blanton (Sr Project Mgr-Institutional)
Kevin Suiter (VP-Estimating)
Robert Koester (CFO & Exec VP)
Thomas C. Skaggs (COO)
Robert N. Mathisen (Sr VP & Gen Mgr-Colorado Office)
Patrick J. Murphy Jr. (Pres & CEO)

Subsidiaries:

Murphy Company Mechanical Contractors & Engineering Inc. (1)
3790 Wheeling St, Denver, CO 80239   (100%)
Tel.: (303) 371-6600
Web Site: http://www.murphynet.com
Sales Range: $25-49.9 Million
Emp.: 180
Mechanical Contractor
N.A.I.C.S.: 238220

MURPHY DOOR, INC.
2380 S 1900 W, Ogden, UT 84401
Web Site: http://www.murphydoor.com
Year Founded: 2014
Sales Range: $1-9.9 Million
Emp.: 38
Residential Interior Door Mfr
N.A.I.C.S.: 321911
Jeremy G. Barker (CEO)

MURPHY O'BRIEN, INC.
11444 W Olympic Blvd Ste 600, Los Angeles, CA 90064
Tel.: (310) 453-2539   CA
Web Site: http://www.murphyobrien.com
Year Founded: 1989
Sales Range: $10-24.9 Million
Emp.: 50
Public Relations Agency
N.A.I.C.S.: 541820
Karen Murphy O'Brien (Chm & CEO)
Brett O'Brien (Mng Dir)
Allyson Rener (Mng Dir)
L. D. Reyer (CFO)
Stacy Lewis (Exec VP)
Rachel Esserman (VP)
Kimi Ozawa (Sr VP)
Laura Millet (VP)

MURPHY O'BRIEN, INC.

Murphy O'Brien, Inc.—(Continued)
Lisa Goldstein (VP)
Wendi Shapiro (Sr VP)
Michael Altneu (VP-Real Estate)

MURPHY TRACTOR & EQUIPMENT CO., INC.
1800 S W St PO Box 17366, Wichita, KS 67217-0366
Tel.: (316) 945-1015
Web Site:
http://www.murphytractor.com
Year Founded: 1991
Sales Range: $10-24.9 Million
Emp.: 36
Construction & Mining Machinery Services
N.A.I.C.S.: 423810
Tom Udland (Pres)
Bill Buckles (VP-Sls)
Rodney Young (CFO)
Jim Romesburg (Mgr-Parts)
Rich Fawson (Gen Mgr-Product Support)
Adam Karsten (Gen Mgr-Compact Equipment)
Terry Stefan (Mgr-Bridgeport)
Mike Slinger (Mgr-Midwest)
Candace Jindra (Mgr-Mktg)
Jesse Pantoja (Mgr-Svc-Columbus)
Max Miller (VP-Used Equipment)

MURPHY TRANSPORTATION INC.
49 Kanes Ln, Middletown, NJ 07748
Tel.: (732) 741-4600
Sales Range: $10-24.9 Million
Emp.: 100
Local & Suburban Transit
N.A.I.C.S.: 485119
John J. Murphy (Pres)

MURPHY WAREHOUSE COMPANY
701 24th Ave SE, Minneapolis, MN 55414
Tel.: (612) 623-1200
Web Site:
http://www.murphywarehouse.com
Sales Range: $10-24.9 Million
Emp.: 195
General Warehousing
N.A.I.C.S.: 493110
Tom Griep (VP-Fin)
Andy Welna (Mgr-Ops)
Richard T. Murphy Jr. (Pres & CEO)

MURPHY-HOFFMAN COMPANY
4501 College Blvd Ste 190, Leawood, KS 66211
Tel.: (816) 483-6444
Web Site: http://www.mhc.com
Year Founded: 1975
Sales Range: $500-549.9 Million
Emp.: 2,300
Truck Sales
N.A.I.C.S.: 423110
Timothy R. Murphy (Exec Chm)

Subsidiaries:

Arkansas Kenworth Inc. (1)
1524 N Corrington Ave, Kansas City, MO 64120
Tel.: (816) 483-7035
Web Site: http://www.mhctruck.com
Sales Range: $10-24.9 Million
Emp.: 4
Truck Tractors
N.A.I.C.S.: 423110
Timothy R. Murphy (Pres)

Colorado Kenworth Inc. (1)
7007 Sandown Rd, Denver, CO 80216
Tel.: (720) 941-0833
Web Site: http://www.mhctruck.com
Rev: $99,500,000

Emp.: 250
Truck Sales
N.A.I.C.S.: 423110
Timothy R. Murphy (Pres)
Ken Hoffman (Exec VP-Sls)

MHC Financial Services (1)
1644 N Corrington Ave, Kansas City, MO 64120
Tel.: (816) 483-0441
Web Site: http://www.mhctruck.com
Sales Range: $10-24.9 Million
Emp.: 13
Truck Finance Leasing
N.A.I.C.S.: 423110

MHC Ford (1)
3331 One Pl, Memphis, TN 38116
Tel.: (901) 332-8990
Web Site: http://www.mhcfordmemphis.com
Sales Range: $10-24.9 Million
Emp.: 20
Heavy Truck Sales & Leasing Business
N.A.I.C.S.: 441110
Timothy R. Murphy (Pres)

MHC Kenworth Co. Inc. (1)
3068 Millbranch, Memphis, TN 38116
Tel.: (816) 483-6444
Web Site: http://www.mhctruck.com
Rev: $55,800,000
Emp.: 4
Pickups, New & Used
N.A.I.C.S.: 441110
Timothy R. Murphy (Pres)

MHC Kenworth-Oklahoma City (1)
7200 W I-40 Service Rd, Oklahoma City, OK 73128
Tel.: (405) 717-4500
Web Site: http://www.mhctruck.com
Sales Range: $50-74.9 Million
Emp.: 82
Full Service Transport Refrigeration Leasing & Rental Operations
N.A.I.C.S.: 493120
Timothy R. Murphy (Pres)

MHC Truck Leasing Inc. (1)
1600 N Corrington Ave, Kansas City, MO 64120
Tel.: (816) 841-1800
Web Site: http://www.mhctruck.com
Rev: $30,000,000
Emp.: 20
Truck Leasing, Without Drivers
N.A.I.C.S.: 532120

MHC Truck Source Inc. (1)
3501 Manchester Traffic Way, Kansas City, MO 64129
Tel.: (816) 921-8600
Rev: $26,600,000
Emp.: 7
Trucks, Tractors & Trailers; Used
N.A.I.C.S.: 441120
Bryan Haupt (VP & Gen Mgr-Used Truck)

Midamerican Truck Maintenance (1)
1524 N Corrington Ave, Kansas City, MO 64120
Tel.: (816) 483-7035
Web Site: http://www.mhctruck.com
Rev: $15,000,000
Emp.: 300
General Truck Repair
N.A.I.C.S.: 811111

Ozark Kenworth Inc. (1)
1524 N Corrington Ave, Kansas City, MO 64120
Tel.: (816) 483-7035
Web Site: http://www.mhctruck.com
Rev: $157,100,000
Emp.: 250
Truck Tractors
N.A.I.C.S.: 423110
Timothy R. Murphy (Pres)

MURRAY A. GOLDENBERG TEXTILES
10795 Harry Hines Blvd, Dallas, TX 75220
Tel.: (214) 351-6651
Web Site: http://www.goldendor.com
Rev: $21,205,943
Emp.: 125
Piece Goods & Other Fabrics
N.A.I.C.S.: 424310

Ted Butler (Pres & CFO)
Murray Goldenberg (COO)
Cheryllynn Sylvia (Mgr-Accts Payable)
Ana Berkley (Mgr-Ops)

MURRAY COMPANY
12215 Fern Ridge Pkwy Ste 213, Saint Louis, MO 63141
Tel.: (314) 576-2818
Web Site: http://www.murray-company.com
Sales Range: $25-49.9 Million
Emp.: 26
General Contractor Of Radio Stations; Hospitals
N.A.I.C.S.: 236220
John O'Hara (Pres)

MURRAY COMPANY
18414 S Santa Fe Ave, Rancho Dominguez, CA 90221
Tel.: (310) 637-1500
Web Site:
http://www.murraycompany.com
Year Founded: 1913
Plumbing, Heating & Air-Conditioning Services
N.A.I.C.S.: 238220
Andy Johnson (Dir-Design Build)
Jim DeFlavio (Pres & CEO)
Alvin Aeschlimann (CFO)
Don Odom (VP-Bus Dev)
Greg Huff (VP-Advanced Technologies)
John Vanderelst (VP)
Shaabini Alford (VP-Project Mgmt & Design Build)
Terry James (Gen Mgr)

MURRAY FABRICS, INC.
837 E 79th Str, Cleveland, OH 44103-1817
Tel.: (216) 881-4041
Web Site:
http://www.murrayfabrics.com
Sales Range: $10-24.9 Million
Emp.: 20
Carpet & Rug Mfr
N.A.I.C.S.: 314110
Joyce Senney (Sec)
Walter Senney (Pres)

MURRAY FEISS IMPORT CORP
125 Rose Feiss Blvd, Bronx, NY 10454
Tel.: (718) 292-2024
Web Site: http://www.feiss.com
Sales Range: $75-99.9 Million
Emp.: 220
Lighting Fixtures
N.A.I.C.S.: 423610
Greg Vandia (Pres)

MURRAY GUARD, INC.
58 Murray Guard Dr, Jackson, TN 38305-3609
Tel.: (731) 668-3400
Web Site:
http://www.murrayguard.com
Year Founded: 1967
Sales Range: $25-49.9 Million
Emp.: 2,500
Security & Armored Car Services
N.A.I.C.S.: 561612
David Harris (VP & Controller)
James L. Exum (Co-Founder-TotalREACH)
Roger G. Murray Jr. (Chm & CEO)
Gerald P. Ferguson Jr. (Pres)

MURRAY RESOURCES, LTD.
800 Gessner Rd Ste 170, Houston, TX 77024
Tel.: (713) 935-0009

Web Site:
http://www.murrayresources.com
Year Founded: 1988
Sales Range: $1-9.9 Million
Emp.: 17
Recruiting & Staffing Services
N.A.I.C.S.: 561311
Marsha Murray (Founder & Pres)
Keith Wolf (Mng Dir)
Kara DiCarlo (Sr Dir-Bus Dev)
Lauren Labauve (Assoc Dir-Bus Dev)
Carol Watkins (Mgr-Kingwood Office)

Subsidiaries:

Kingwood Personnel (1)
600 Rockmead Dr Ste 101, Kingwood, TX 77339
Tel.: (281) 358-2018
Web Site:
http://www.kingwoodpersonnel.com
Employment Placement Agencies
N.A.I.C.S.: 561311
Carol McCord (Founder)

MURRAYS FORD INC.
3007 Blinker Pkwy, Du Bois, PA 15801
Tel.: (814) 371-6600
Web Site:
http://www.murraysdubois.com
Sales Range: $75-99.9 Million
Emp.: 130
Retailer of Commercial Trucks
N.A.I.C.S.: 423110
Harv Murray (Founder)
Blake Sechman (Gen Mgr-Sls)
Mark Trunzo (Mgr-Sls)
Jim Nestlerode (Mgr-Sls)
Rich Keller (Mgr-Fleet)
Dennis Clark (Bus Mgr)
Tim Parsons (Gen Mgr)

MURRY'S, INC.
7852 Walker Dr Ste 420, Greenbelt, MD 20770
Tel.: (301) 420-6400   DE
Web Site: http://www.murrys.com
Year Founded: 1948
Sales Range: $100-124.9 Million
Emp.: 250
Food Products, Specializing in Meat, Frozen & Packaged Goods
N.A.I.C.S.: 424420
Ira Mendelson (CEO)
Stuart Mendelson (Sr VP)
Gary Gold (Sr VP)
Brad Holland (CFO)

MURSIX CORPORATION
2401 N Executive Park Dr, Yorktown, IN 47396-9806
Tel.: (765) 282-2221
Web Site: http://www.mursix.com
Sales Range: $10-24.9 Million
Emp.: 300
Metal Stamping
N.A.I.C.S.: 332119
Todd Murray (Pres)
Randy Cremeans (Dir-Sls & Engrg)
Susan Carlock (VP-Bus Dev & Corp Rels)
Hassan Hashem (Dir-Ops-Mfg Facility)

Subsidiaries:

Aul Brothers Tool & Die Inc. (1)
9609 W Jackson St, Muncie, IN 47304
Tel.: (765) 759-5124
Rev: $2,595,000
Emp.: 15
Metal Stamping
N.A.I.C.S.: 332119

Dakota Engineering, Inc. (1)
2851 N Webster Ave, Indianapolis, IN 46219-1012
Tel.: (317) 546-8460
Web Site:
http://www.dakotaengineering.com

COMPANIES

Sales Range: $1-9.9 Million
Emp.: 35
Distr of Cold Headed Fasteners & Wireform Products
N.A.I.C.S.: 339993
Shannon Smoot (Mgr-Quality)

MURTECH CONSULTING
4700 Rockside Rd Ste 250, Independence, OH 44131
Tel.: (216) 328-8580
Web Site: http://www.murtechconsulting.com
Year Founded: 2000
Rev.: $9,500,000
Emp.: 250
Administrative Management & General Management Consulting Services
N.A.I.C.S.: 541611
Ailish Murphy (Owner & Pres)
Jennifer Banish (Coord-Ops)

MURTHY LAW FIRM
10451 Mill Run Cir, Owings Mills, MD 21117
Tel.: (410) 356-5440
Web Site: http://www.murthy.com
Year Founded: 1994
Sales Range: $10-24.9 Million
Emp.: 80
Law firm
N.A.I.C.S.: 541110
Sheela Murthy (Founder)
Pamela Genise (Atty)
Timothy Sachse (Atty)
Christopher Drinan (Atty)
Aron Finkelstein (Atty)
Joel Yanovich (Atty)
Adam Rosen (Atty)
Alissa Klein (Atty)
Anu Parameshwaran (Atty)
Brian Green (Atty)
Dana Delott (Atty)
James McLaughlin (Atty)
Jessica Beaver (Atty)
Aaron Fuccello (Jr Atty)
Zachary Haugen (Jr Atty)

MUSCATINE POWER & WATER
3205 Cedar St, Muscatine, IA 52761
Tel.: (563) 263-2631
Web Site: http://www.mpw.org
Year Founded: 1900
Rev.: $116,463,566
Assets: $228,639,974
Liabilities: $62,950,058
Net Worth: $165,689,916
Earnings: ($2,272,442)
Emp.: 350
Fiscal Year-end: 12/31/18
Electronic Services
N.A.I.C.S.: 221118
Gage Huston (Gen Mgr)
Erika Cox (Dir-Customer & Tech Experience)
Brandy Olson (Dir-Legal, Regulatory & People Svcs)
Ryan Streck (Dir-Utility Svc Delivery)
Doug White (Dir-Power Production & Supply)
Mark Roberts (Dir-Fin & Admin Svcs)

MUSCO CORPORATION
100 1st Ave W, Oskaloosa, IA 52577
Tel.: (641) 673-0411
Web Site: http://www.musco.com
Sales Range: $25-49.9 Million
Emp.: 1,000
Area & Sports Luminaries
N.A.I.C.S.: 335139
Joe Crookham (CEO)
Brett Paulsen (Project Mgr)
Frank Hansen (Gen Mgr)
Karen Keep (Controller)

MUSCO FAMILY OLIVE COMPANY
17950 Via Nicolo, Tracy, CA 95377-9767
Tel.: (209) 836-4600   CA
Web Site: http://www.olives.com
Year Founded: 1942
Sales Range: $100-124.9 Million
Emp.: 300
Processing of Olives, Peppers & Onions
N.A.I.C.S.: 311421
Nicholas Musco (Founder)
Felix Musco (Pres)

MUSCULAR MOVING MEN, LLC
2950 E Mohawk Ln Ste100, Phoenix, AZ 85050
Web Site: http://www.muscularmovingmen.com
Year Founded: 2008
Sales Range: $1-9.9 Million
Emp.: 75
Freight Transportation Services
N.A.I.C.S.: 488510
Justin Hodge (Co-Founder)
Josh Jurhill (Co-Founder)

MUSCULOSKELETAL TRANSPLANT FOUNDATION
125 May St, Edison, NJ 08837
Tel.: (732) 661-0202   DC
Web Site: http://www.mtf.org
Year Founded: 1987
Sales Range: $25-49.9 Million
Emp.: 1,297
Tissue Transplantation Services
N.A.I.C.S.: 621991
Joe Yaccarino (Pres & CEO)
Michael Schuler (VP-New Bus Dev)
Michael J. Kawas (CFO & Exec VP)
Martha Anderson (Exec VP-Donor Svcs)
Mark Spilker (Exec VP-R&D)
Matthew J. Kuehnert (Dir-Medical)

MUSEGLOBAL, INC.
1 Embarcadero Ste 500, San Francisco, CA 94111
Tel.: (415) 896-6873   DE
Web Site: http://www.museglobal.com
Year Founded: 2001
Software Publisher
N.A.I.C.S.: 513210
Kate Noerr (Co-Founder)
Peter Noerr (Co-Founder)

MUSEUM HACK, LLC
27 W 10th St Ste 5, New York, NY 10011
Web Site: http://www.museumhack.com
Year Founded: 2013
Sales Range: $1-9.9 Million
Emp.: 50
Tour Operator
N.A.I.C.S.: 561520
Carly Hill (Mktg Mgr)
Bryce Weinert (Ops Mgr)
Marielle Howell (Sls Mgr)
Nick Gray (Founder)
Tasia Duske (CEO)

MUSEUM OF AMERICAN FINANCE
48 Wall St, New York, NY 10005
Tel.: (212) 908-4110
Web Site: http://www.moaf.org
Emp.: 115
Finance History Museum
N.A.I.C.S.: 712110
Jeanne Baker Driscoll (Dir-Dev)
Kristin Aguilera (Deputy Dir)
David J. Cowen (Pres & CEO)

MUSEUM OF FINE ARTS OF ST. PETERSBURG FLORIDA INC.
255 Beach Dr NE, Saint Petersburg, FL 33701
Tel.: (727) 896-2667
Web Site: http://www.mfastpete.org
Sales Range: $10-24.9 Million
Emp.: 30
Art Museum
N.A.I.C.S.: 712110
David Connelly (Dir-PR)

MUSEUM OF FLIGHT FOUNDATION
9404 E Marginal Way S, Seattle, WA 98108-4097
Tel.: (206) 764-5700   WA
Web Site: http://www.museumofflight.org
Year Founded: 1965
Sales Range: $10-24.9 Million
Emp.: 236
Aviation Museum
N.A.I.C.S.: 712110
Trip Switzer (VP-Dev)
Matt Hayes (CFO)
Laurie Haag (COO)
Douglas R. King (Pres & CEO)

MUSEUM OF HISTORY & INDUSTRY
860 Terry Ave N, Seattle, WA 98109
Tel.: (206) 324-1126   WA
Web Site: http://www.mohai.org
Year Founded: 1914
Sales Range: $1-9.9 Million
Emp.: 69
Museums
N.A.I.C.S.: 712110
Donna DiFiore (CFO & COO)
Jackie Durbin (Dir-Mktg & Comm)
Chad Richardson (Treas)
Chuck Nordhoff (Pres)
Leonard Garfield (Exec Dir)
Maureen Frisch (VP)
Mike Repass (Sec)

MUSEUM OF NEW MEXICO FOUNDATION
1411 Paseo de Peralta, Santa Fe, NM 87501
Tel.: (505) 982-6366
Web Site: https://www.museumfoundation.org
Year Founded: 1962
Museum Exhibition Services
N.A.I.C.S.: 711510

MUSEUM OF SCIENCE & HISTORY OF JACKSONVILLE, INC.
1025 Museum Cir, Jacksonville, FL 32207
Tel.: (904) 396-6674   FL
Web Site: https://www.themosh.org
Year Founded: 1941
Rev.: $2,200,000
Emp.: 57
Fiscal Year-end: 12/31/06
Museums And Art Galleries, Nsk
N.A.I.C.S.: 712110

MUSEUM OF SCIENCE AND INDUSTRY
57th St and Lk Shore Dr, Chicago, IL 60637
Tel.: (773) 684-1414
Web Site: http://www.msichicago.org
Year Founded: 1933
Sales Range: $125-149.9 Million
Emp.: 400
Science & Technology Museum
N.A.I.C.S.: 712110

Kurt E. Haunfelner (VP-Exhibits & Collections)
Christopher M. Crane (Chm)
Julian Mackenzie (Pres & CEO)
Anthony Vitagliano (VP-Exhibitions & Engagement)

MUSEUM QUALITY DISCOUNT FRAMING
1964 4th Ave S, Seattle, WA 98134
Tel.: (206) 624-1057
Web Site: http://www.mqf.com
Rev.: $15,800,000
Emp.: 40
Frames For Artists' Canvases
N.A.I.C.S.: 339940
Adrian Hanauer (Owner)

MUSGROVE MILLS, INC.
150 Hamrick Str, Gaffney, SC 29340
Tel.: (864) 489-4731
Web Site: http://www.hamrickmills.com
Sales Range: $10-24.9 Million
Emp.: 210
Apparels Mfr
N.A.I.C.S.: 315990
Carlisle Hamrick (Pres)

MUSIC CENTER, INC.
135 N Grand Ave, Los Angeles, CA 90012
Tel.: (415) 863-7327   CA
Web Site: http://www.haight-ashbury-music.com
Year Founded: 1980
Sales Range: $1-9.9 Million
Emp.: 30
Musical Instrument & Supplies Stores
N.A.I.C.S.: 459140
Massoud Badakhshan (Pres)
Lisa Specht (Chm)

MUSIC SALES CORPORATION
180 Madison Ave, New York, NY 10016
Tel.: (212) 254-2100   NY
Web Site: http://www.musicsales.com
Year Founded: 1935
Sales Range: $75-99.9 Million
Emp.: 80
Music Publishing
N.A.I.C.S.: 512230
Barrie Wise (Pres)
Kalen Rogers (Sec)
Denise Maurin (VP-Ops)
Tomas Wise (Dir-Digital Publ)
G. Schirmer (VP)
Philip Black (Mgr-Pro)
Karen Kloack (VP-Film & TV)
Bob Knight (VP-Film)

Subsidiaries:

Associated Music Publishers   (1)
180 Madison Ave, New York, NY 10016   (100%)
Tel.: (212) 254-2100
Web Site: http://www.musicsalesclassical.com
Sales Range: $25-49.9 Million
Emp.: 30
Music Publishers
N.A.I.C.S.: 512230
Thomas Wise (Pres)

Bosworth GmbH   (1)
Dorotheenstrasse 3, Berlin, 10117, Germany   (100%)
Tel.: (49) 302232200
Web Site: http://www.bosworth.de
Sales Range: $10-24.9 Million
Emp.: 12
Music Publishers
N.A.I.C.S.: 512230
Michael Ohst (Mng Dir)
Susanne Muller (Dir-Mktg)

Chester Music   (1)
14-15 Berners St, London, W1T 3LJ, United Kingdom   (100%)

MUSIC SALES CORPORATION — U.S. PRIVATE

Music Sales Corporation—(Continued)
Tel.: (44) 2076127400
Web Site: http://www.chesternovello.com
Sales Range: $10-24.9 Million
Music Publishers
N.A.I.C.S.: 512230
James Rushton (Mng Dir)

Chester Musice France (1)
10 Rue De La Grange Bateliere, 75009, Paris, France **(100%)**
Tel.: (33) 153246852
Web Site:
http://www.musicsalesclassical.com
Sales Range: $10-24.9 Million
Emp.: 12
Music Publisher Services
N.A.I.C.S.: 512230
Claude Duvuvier (Mng Dir)

Edition Wilhelm Hansen (1)
Bornhomsgade 1A, Copenhagen, 1266, Denmark **(100%)**
Tel.: (45) 33117888
Web Site: http://www.ewh.dk
Sales Range: $10-24.9 Million
Emp.: 15
Music Publishers
N.A.I.C.S.: 512230
Loui Tornqvist (Mng Dir)

G. Schirmer, Inc. (1)
180 Madison Ave 24th Fl, New York, NY 10016 **(100%)**
Tel.: (212) 254-2100
Web Site: http://www.schirmer.com
Sales Range: $25-49.9 Million
Emp.: 30
Music Publishers
N.A.I.C.S.: 512230
Peggy Monastra (Dir-Promo)
Ed Matthew (Sr Mgr-Promo)

Music Sales Limited (1)
14-15 Berners Street, London, W1T 3LJ, United Kingdom **(100%)**
Tel.: (44) 2076127400
Web Site: http://www.musicsales.co.uk
Sales Range: $10-24.9 Million
Emp.: 70
Music Publishers
N.A.I.C.S.: 512230
Robert Wise (Owner)
David Holley (Grp Mng Dir)

Music Sales Pty. Limited (1)
Level 4 30-32 Carrington St, Sydney, 2000, NSW, Australia **(100%)**
Tel.: (61) 292998877
Web Site: http://www.wr.com.au
Sales Range: $10-24.9 Million
Emp.: 10
Music Publishers
N.A.I.C.S.: 512230

Music Sales West (1)
1247 6th St, Santa Monica, CA 90401 **(100%)**
Tel.: (310) 458-9861
Web Site: http://www.musicsales.com
Sales Range: $10-24.9 Million
Emp.: 10
Music Publishers
N.A.I.C.S.: 512191
Chelsea Davenport (Office Mgr)

Novello & Co. Ltd. (1)
14-15 Berners Street, London, W1T 3LJ, United Kingdom **(100%)**
Tel.: (44) 2076127400
Web Site: http://www.chesternovello.com
Sales Range: $50-74.9 Million
Emp.: 10
Music Publishers
N.A.I.C.S.: 512230
James Rushton (Mng Dir)
Gill Graham (Dir-European Promo)
Kate Johnson (Mgr-Promo)
John Boughtwood (Head-Media & TV)
Steve Francis (Head-Copyright)

Omnibus Press (1)
257 Park Ave S Fl 20, New York, NY 10010-7304
Tel.: (212) 254-2100
Web Site: http://www.omnibuspress.com
Sales Range: $10-24.9 Million
Emp.: 20
Music Publishers

N.A.I.C.S.: 424350

Union Musical Ediciones SL (1)
Marques de la Ensenada 4 Piso 3, Madrid, 28004, Spain **(100%)**
Tel.: (34) 913084040
Web Site: http://www.musicsales.com
Sales Range: $10-24.9 Million
Emp.: 6
Music Publishers
N.A.I.C.S.: 512230

MUSICAL ARTS ASSOCIATION
11001 Euclid Ave, Cleveland, OH 44106
Tel.: (216) 231-7300
Web Site:
https://www.clevelandorchestra.com
Year Founded: 1915
Sales Range: $10-24.9 Million
Emp.: 200
Symphony Orchestra
N.A.I.C.S.: 711130
Joe Short (Mgr-Stage)
Binne Ross (CMO)
Justin Holden (Dir-PR)
Abby Mitchell (Chief Dev Officer)
Andre Gremillet (Pres & CEO)
Rich Kramer (Vice Chm)
Hewitt B. Shaw (Sec)
Beth E. Mooney (Treas)

MUSICAL HERITAGE SOCIETY INC.
1710 State Route 35, Oakhurst, NJ 07755-2910
Tel.: (732) 531-7000
Web Site:
http://www.musicalheritage.org
Year Founded: 1989
Sales Range: $10-24.9 Million
Emp.: 60
Music Mail Order
N.A.I.C.S.: 512230
Donald Nissim (VP)
Kelly McWilliams (Mgr-Production)

Subsidiaries:

The Jazz Store (1)
1710 Hwy 35, Oakhurst, NJ 07755
Tel.: (732) 531-7000
Direct Marketing Services for Jazz Merchandise
N.A.I.C.S.: 459420

MUSICNOTES, INC.
8020 Excelsior Dr Ste 201, Madison, WI 53717
Tel.: (608) 662-1680
Web Site:
http://www.musicnotes.com
Sales Range: $10-24.9 Million
Emp.: 35
Online Digital Sheet Music Retailer & Downloading Services
N.A.I.C.S.: 459140
Tim Reiland (Chm & CFO)

MUSICTODAY II, LLC
5391 Three Notch'd Rd, Crozet, VA 22932
Tel.: (434) 205-7049 VA
Web Site: https://musictoday.com
Year Founded: 2017
ECommerce Marketing Agency
N.A.I.C.S.: 541830
Del Wood (CEO)
Eric Borgersen (Dir-IT)
Jason Coyner (Dir-Transportation)
Dan Buckman (Dir-Client Svcs)
Dan Garner (Dir-Ops)
Joey Porterfield (Dir-Mktg)
Sarah Saunders (Dir-HR)

MUSKA ELECTRIC COMPANY
1985 Oakcrest Ave, Roseville, MN 55113
Tel.: (651) 636-5820 MN

Web Site:
http://www.muskaelectric.com
Year Founded: 1919
Sales Range: $75-99.9 Million
Emp.: 200
Provider of Electrical Contracting Services
N.A.I.C.S.: 238210
Ron Von Bank (Pres)
Jeffrey Marko (Owner)
Erik Hampton (Project Mgr)

MUSKEGON CASTINGS CORP
1985 East Laketon Ave, Muskegon, MI 49442
Tel.: (231) 773-4491
Web Site:
http://www.portcitygroup.com
Sales Range: $10-24.9 Million
Emp.: 107
Aluminum Die-Castings
N.A.I.C.S.: 331523
John Essex (CEO)

MUSKINGUM VALLEY HEALTH CENTERS
716 Adair Ave, Zanesville, OH 43701
Tel.: (740) 891-9000 OH
Web Site:
http://www.mvhealthcenters.org
Year Founded: 2007
Sales Range: $10-24.9 Million
Emp.: 199
Health Care Srvices
N.A.I.C.S.: 622110
David Klein (Chief Medical Officer)
Dan Atkinson (CEO)

MUSS DEVELOPMENT CO
11835 Queens Blvd, Forest Hills, NY 11375
Tel.: (718) 263-3800
Web Site: http://www.muss.com
Sales Range: $10-24.9 Million
Emp.: 50
Multi-Family Dwellings, New Construction
N.A.I.C.S.: 236116
Joshua Muss (Pres & CEO)
Jeffrey Kay (COO & Sr VP-Pub Affairs)

MUSSELMAN & HALL CONTRACTORS LLC.
4922 E Blue Banks, Kansas City, MO 64130
Tel.: (816) 861-1234
Web Site: http://www.mandh.net
Rev.: $25,000,000
Emp.: 40
Highway Street & Bridge Construction
N.A.I.C.S.: 237310
Douglas Hall (CEO)
Michael Morris (Pres)
Dexter Phillips (Exec VP-Bituminous Ops)
Mark Weese (CFO)
Dan Kroesen (VP & Mgr-Architectural Concrete)
Kyle Van Slyke (VP-Concrete Ops)
Tim Moulis (Mgr-Asphalt Div)
Adam Turley (Mgr-Bus Dev-Railroad Div)
Butch Schloemann (Project Mgr)
Jason Fleck (VP-Railroad Div)
Jason Gardner (Mgr-Railroad Ops)

MUSSELMAN BROTHERS INC.
2912 Eastpoint Pkwy, Louisville, KY 40223
Tel.: (502) 451-2300
Sales Range: $10-24.9 Million
Emp.: 2
Hotel
N.A.I.C.S.: 721110

William Musselman (VP & Dir)
Thomas Musselman Sr. (Pres & Dir)

MUSSELMAN'S DODGE INC.
5717 Baltimore National Pike, Catonsville, MD 21228-1785
Tel.: (410) 744-7400
Web Site:
http://www.musselmansdodge.net
Sales Range: $10-24.9 Million
Emp.: 55
Car Whslr
N.A.I.C.S.: 441110
J. D. McDaniels (Dir-Svc)
Debbie Pierce (Controller)
Tim Wilson (Pres)

MUSSER FORESTS, INC.
Rte 119 N, Indiana, PA 15701
Tel.: (724) 465-5686 PA
Web Site:
http://www.musserforests.com
Year Founded: 1928
Sales Range: $1-9.9 Million
Emp.: 180
Nursery Stock Whslr & Retail Mail Order
N.A.I.C.S.: 111421
Fred Musser (Pres)

MUSSER MOTORS INC.
1212 W Moore Ave, Terrell, TX 75160
Tel.: (972) 563-2663
Web Site:
http://www.mussermotors.com
Sales Range: $10-24.9 Million
Emp.: 35
Sales, Service, Parts & Bodyshop For New & Used Automobiles
N.A.I.C.S.: 441110
Wylie G. Musser (Owner)
Gabe Musser (VP)
Alice Craig (Controller)

MUSSER-DAVIS LAND COMPANY
4600 Madison Ave Ste 600, Kansas City, MO 64112
Tel.: (816) 410-4600 MO
Year Founded: 1916
Sales Range: $10-24.9 Million
Emp.: 9
Land Company
N.A.I.C.S.: 531390
Dennis R. Austin (Asst Treas)
Douglas M. Young (Chm & Pres)
Terry L. Jobnson (Treas)
Douglas K. True (VP)
James R. Mueller (Sec)

MUSSERS INC.
35 Friendly Dr, Quarryville, PA 17566
Tel.: (717) 284-4147 PA
Web Site:
http://www.mussersmarket.com
Year Founded: 1976
Sales Range: $10-24.9 Million
Emp.: 104
Operator of Independent Supermarket
N.A.I.C.S.: 445110
Michael J. Musser (Pres)
Greg Musser (Treas)

MUSSON BROS., INC.
909 Boyce Dr, Rhinelander, WI 54501-3836
Tel.: (715) 365-8700 WI
Web Site:
http://www.mussonbrothersinc.com
Year Founded: 1945
Sales Range: $25-49.9 Million
Emp.: 170
Ready-Mixed Concrete, Asphalt Paving, Excavation & Material Trucking Services

N.A.I.C.S.: 237310
Jim Musson (Pres)

Subsidiaries:

Musson Bros., Inc. - Brookfield Office (1)
2415 N 124th St, Brookfield, WI 53005
Tel.: (262) 790-5060
Web Site: http://www.mussonbrothers.com
Sales Range: $25-49.9 Million
Emp.: 10
Ready-Mixed Concrete, Asphalt Paving, Excavation & Material Trucking Services
N.A.I.C.S.: 237310
Mike Sikma (Mgr)

MUSSON-PATOUT AUTOMOTIVE GROUP INC.
214 W Hwy 90 Frontage Rd, New Iberia, LA 70560
Tel.: (337) 443-4511
Web Site: http://www.mussonpatout.com
Sales Range: $25-49.9 Million
New & Used Car Dealers
N.A.I.C.S.: 441110
Diane Musson (Co-Owner)
Kelly Patout-Romero (Co-Owner)
Bart Romero (VP)
Nathan Hebert (Gen Mgr)
Benjamin Richard (Sls Mgr-Buick GMC)
BJ Girouard (Sls Mgr-Used Car)
Chett Peliter (Sls Mgr-Toyota)
Tra Dupuis (Owner)
Russell Lewis Jr. (Mgr-Used Car)

MUSTANG ALLIANCES, INC.
410 Park Ave 15th Fl, New York, NY 10022   NV
Year Founded: 2007
Anti-Lock Braking Systems Distr
N.A.I.C.S.: 423120
Leonard Sternheim (CEO)
Lawrence Harris Wolfe (CFO)

MUSTANG DYNAMOMETER
2300 Pinnacle Pkwy, Twinsburg, OH 44087
Tel.: (330) 963-5400
Web Site: http://www.mustangdyne.com
Year Founded: 1975
Sales Range: $10-24.9 Million
Emp.: 50
Automotive Related Machinery Mfr
N.A.I.C.S.: 333248
Eser Manav (VP-Ops)

Subsidiaries:

Mustang Dynamometer, China (1)
A 1915 Freetown No 58 Southern, Dongsanhuan Rd, Beijing, 100022, Chaoyang, China
Tel.: (86) 1058673571
Web Site: http://www.mustangdynecn.com
Sales Range: $10-24.9 Million
Emp.: 3
Mfr of Automotive Parts
N.A.I.C.S.: 336390

Mustang Dynamometer, Los Angeles (1)
5 Lancewood Way, Irvine, CA 92612-2108
Tel.: (949) 786-3966
Mfr of Automotive Machinery
N.A.I.C.S.: 333310

Mustang Vacuum Systems Inc. (1)
7135 16th St E, Sarasota, FL 34243
Tel.: (941) 377-1440
Web Site: http://www.mustangvac.com
Emp.: 45
Vacuum Equipment Mfr & Distr
N.A.I.C.S.: 333310
Richard Greenwell (Co-Founder & Pres)
Dean Ganzhorn (Co-Founder & CEO)
Josh Mangum (Mgr-Applications)
Robert Choquette (VP-Tech)
Donald Ganzhorn Jr. (Co-Founder)

MUSTANG FUEL CORPORATION
9800 N Oklahoma Ave, Oklahoma City, OK 73114
Tel.: (405) 748-9400
Web Site: http://www.mustangfuel.com
Year Founded: 1949
Rev.: $131,619,818
Emp.: 80
Crude Petroleum Production
N.A.I.C.S.: 211120
E. Carey Joullian IV (Chm, Pres & CEO)
M. Scott Chapline (CFO, Treas & Sr VP)

Subsidiaries:

Eagle Gas Marketing Company (1)
13439 Brdwy Ext, Oklahoma City, OK 73114
Tel.: (405) 748-9400
Web Site: http://www.mustangfuel.com
Rev.: $106,844,600
Emp.: 72
Gas Power Marketers
N.A.I.C.S.: 221210
E. Carey Joullian IV (Chm, Pres & CEO)

MUSTANG GAS PRODUCTS LLC
9800 N Oklahoma Ave, Oklahoma City, OK 73114
Tel.: (405) 748-9400
Web Site: http://www.mustangfuel.com
Sales Range: $25-49.9 Million
Emp.: 100
Natural Gas Producer
N.A.I.C.S.: 221210
E. Carey Joullian IV (Chm, Pres & CEO)

Subsidiaries:

Mustang Gas Products (1)
RR 3 Box 124M, Hennessey, OK 73742-9573
Tel.: (405) 853-4374
Sales Range: $25-49.9 Million
Emp.: 12
Crude Petroleum Production
N.A.I.C.S.: 211120

MUSTANG TRACTOR & EQUIPMENT COMPANY
12800 Northwest Fwy, Houston, TX 77040-6302
Tel.: (713) 460-2000
Web Site: http://www.mustangcatused.com
Year Founded: 1952
Sales Range: $10-24.9 Million
Emp.: 750
Distr of Diesel & Natural Gas Engines; Material Handling & Heavy Equipment
N.A.I.C.S.: 423810
Brad Tucker (Pres)

Subsidiaries:

Mustang Power Systems (1)
12800 NW Fwy, Houston, TX 77040 (100%)
Tel.: (713) 460-2000
Web Site: http://www.mustangcat.com
New Engine Sales
N.A.I.C.S.: 423810
Brad Tucker (Pres)

Mustang Rental Services Inc. (1)
12800 NW Fwy US 290, Houston, TX 77040
Tel.: (713) 460-2000
Web Site: http://www.mustangcat.com
Rev.: $15,000,000
Emp.: 4
Heavy Construction Equipment Rental
N.A.I.C.S.: 532412
Brad Tucker (Pres)
Todd Fisk (Exec VP & Gen Mgr)

MUSTARD SEED HEALTH FOOD MARKET
3885 W Market St, Akron, OH 44333
Tel.: (330) 666-7333   OH
Web Site: http://www.mustardseedmarket.com
Year Founded: 1981
Sales Range: $10-24.9 Million
Emp.: 150
Provider of Health Foods
N.A.I.C.S.: 456191
Margaret Kanfer-Nabors (Founder & Co-Owner)
Phillip Nabors (Owner)

MUTO COMMUNICATIONS, LLC
PO Box 537, Port Jefferson, NY 11777
Tel.: (631) 849-4301
Web Site: http://www.mutocomm.com
Year Founded: 2000
Sales Range: $1-9.9 Million
Emp.: 5
Public Relations & Advertising Campaigns
N.A.I.C.S.: 541820
Paul Muto (Pres & COO)

MUTUAL BANCORP
1500 Iyannough Rd, Hyannis, MA 02601
Tel.: (888) 225-4636
Web Site: https://www.mutualbancorpmhc.com
Emp.: 100
Bank Holding Company
N.A.I.C.S.: 551111

Subsidiaries:

Cape Cod Five Cents Savings Bank (1)
97 Cranberry Hwy, Orleans, MA 02653
Tel.: (508) 240-0500
Web Site: http://www.capecodfive.com
Rev.: $144,963,000
Assets: $3,423,898,000
Liabilities: $3,103,292,000
Net Worth: $320,606,000
Earnings: $24,531,000
Emp.: 523
Fiscal Year-end: 12/31/2018
Banking Services
N.A.I.C.S.: 522180
Dorothy A. Savarese (Chm & CEO)
Robert A. Talerman (Pres)
Ellen C. Covell (Officer-Comml Loan & VP)
Alison B. Czuchra (Chief Fiduciary Officer & VP)
James O. Eldredge (Officer-Govt Banking & VP)
Patricia B. Piva (Asst VP-Sandwich & Mgr-Banking Center Plymouth)
Garret Smith (Officer-Treasury Mgmt)
John DeVito (Officer-Comml Loan & Asst VP)
Andrew Foss (Officer-Comml Loan & VP)

Fidelity Mutual Holding Company (1)
675 Main St, Fitchburg, MA 01420
Tel.: (978) 345-4331
Web Site: http://www.fidelitybankonline.com
Sales Range: $25-49.9 Million
Mutual Bank Holding Company
N.A.I.C.S.: 551111
Christopher W. McCarthy (Pres & COO)
Sherri Pitcher (Chief Life Design Officer & Sr VP)
Edward F. Manzi Jr. (Chm & CEO)

Subsidiary (Domestic):

Fidelity Co-Operative Bank (2)
675 Main St, Fitchburg, MA 01420
Tel.: (978) 345-4331
Web Site: http://www.fidelitybankonline.com
Sales Range: $25-49.9 Million
Emp.: 143
Federal Savings Bank
N.A.I.C.S.: 522180
Barry D. Bliss (Chief Comml Banking Officer & Sr VP)

Laurie Benson (Sr VP & Head-Retail Banking)
Edward F. Manzi Jr. (Chm & CEO)

MUTUAL BENEFICIAL ASSOCIATION, INC.
1301 Lancaster Ave Ste 102, Berwyn, PA 19312-1290
Tel.: (610) 722-0253   DE
Web Site: http://www.mutualbeneficial.com
Year Founded: 1913
Sales Range: $10-24.9 Million
Fire Insurance Services
N.A.I.C.S.: 524113
Stephen M. Santarlasci (Pres)
Mary L. Gibney (Treas & Sec)
Richard O. Dietrich (VP)

MUTUAL BENEFIT ASSOCIATION HAWAII
819 S Beretania Ste 200, Honolulu, HI 96813
Tel.: (808) 539-1600
Web Site: http://www.royalstate.com
Rev.: $13,900,000
Emp.: 4
Mutual Benefit Associations
N.A.I.C.S.: 522291
Ron Sufugu (Pres)

Subsidiaries:

Royal Insurance Agency Inc. (1)
819 S Beretania St, Honolulu, HI 96813
Tel.: (808) 539-1700
Web Site: http://www.rsg-tria.com
Insurance Agents
N.A.I.C.S.: 524210

Royal State Insurance (1)
819 S Beretania St, Honolulu, HI 96813
Tel.: (808) 539-1600
Web Site: http://www.royalstate.com
Sales Range: Less than $1 Million
Emp.: 30
Life Insurance
N.A.I.C.S.: 524113
Blaise Liu (Chief Admin Officer & VP)

MUTUAL BENEFIT INSURANCE COMPANY
409 Penn St, Huntingdon, PA 16652
Tel.: (814) 643-3000   PA
Web Site: http://www.mutualbenefitgroup.com
Year Founded: 1908
Fire, Marine & Casualty Insurance Provider
N.A.I.C.S.: 524126
Joe Sloan (Treas)
Steven C. Silver (Pres & CEO)

MUTUAL CAPITAL GROUP, INC.
41908 Route 6, Wyalusing, PA 18853
Tel.: (484) 901-9861   PA
Web Site: https://mutualcapitalgrp.com
Holding Company; Insurance Services
N.A.I.C.S.: 551112

Subsidiaries:

Mutual Capital Holdings, Inc. (1)
41908 Route 6, Wyalusing, PA 18853
Tel.: (484) 901-9861
Insurance Services
N.A.I.C.S.: 524298
Reiner R. Mauer (Pres & CEO)

Subsidiary (Domestic):

Tuscarora Wayne Insurance Co. (2)
601 State St, Wyalusing, PA 18853
Tel.: (570) 746-1515
Web Site: https://www.twmic.com
Rev.: $4,000,000
Emp.: 30
Insurance Related Services
N.A.I.C.S.: 524298

MUTUAL CAPITAL GROUP, INC.

Mutual Capital Group, Inc.—(Continued)
Isaac Graham (Mgr)
Jay Chadwick (Pres)
Aaron C. Welles (Gen Mgr-Keystone National Insurance Company)
Brian F. Bolinger (CFO, Treas & Sr VP)
Daniel J. Borges (CIO & VP)
Shelby W. Napoli (Chief Corp Rels Officer, Sec & VP)
Todd E. Salsman (COO & Sr VP)
David J. Schweitzer (Chief Claims Officer & VP)

MUTUAL INDUSTRIES NORTH INC.
707 W Grange Ave, Philadelphia, PA 19120
Tel.: (215) 927-6000   DE
Web Site:
http://www.mutualindustries.com
Year Founded: 1910
Sales Range: $25-49.9 Million
Emp.: 150
Mfr & Distributor of Broadwoven Fabric Mills
N.A.I.C.S.: 313210
Edmund Dunn (Chm & CEO)
Andrew Dunn (VP)
Stuart Levin (CFO)
Mary Brown (Sec)

MUTUAL LIQUID GAS & EQUIPMENT CO., INC.
17117 S Broadway St, Gardena, CA 90248
Tel.: (323) 321-3771
Web Site:
http://www.mutualpropane.com
Sales Range: $10-24.9 Million
Emp.: 45
Propane Conversion Equipment
N.A.I.C.S.: 423830
Tom Boerum (VP & Gen Mgr)

MUTUAL MATERIALS COMPANY
605 119th Ave NE, Bellevue, WA 98005
Tel.: (425) 452-2300
Web Site:
http://www.mutualmaterials.com
Rev.: $27,100,000
Emp.: 100
Brick & Structural Clay Tile
N.A.I.C.S.: 327120
Kendall Anderegg (Pres & COO)

MUTUAL OF AMERICA LIFE INSURANCE COMPANY
320 Park Ave, New York, NY 10022-6839
Tel.: (212) 224-1600   NY
Web Site:
http://www.mutualofamerica.com
Year Founded: 1945
Rev.: $3,010,724,249
Assets: $23,665,667,673
Liabilities: $22,828,255,592
Net Worth: $837,412,081
Earnings: ($19,645,524)
Emp.: 1,000
Fiscal Year-end: 12/31/19
Group & Individual Variable Annuities & Pensions & Retirement Services
N.A.I.C.S.: 524113
John Richard Greed (Chm, Pres & CEO)
James J. Roth (Gen Counsel & Sr Exec VP)
Rosaly Urbaez (Mgr-Svc)
Thomas V. Donato (Head-Reg)
Tara Favors (Chief HR Officer & Exec VP)

Subsidiaries:

Mutual of America Capital Management Corporation   (1)
320 Park Ave, New York, NY 10022-6839
Tel.: (212) 224-1900
Web Site:
http://www.capitalmanagementcorp.com
Investment Management Service
N.A.I.C.S.: 523940
Kevin M. Walsh (CMO & Sr VP)
Nancy C. McAvey (Sr VP-Client Svc)
Patrick J. Sullivan (VP-Mktg & Sls)
Paul E. Travers (Sr VP & Dir-Client Svc & Admin)
Susan J. Ferber (Sr VP-Client Svc)

MUTUAL OF ENUMCLAW INSURANCE CO. INC.
1460 Wells St, Enumclaw, WA 98022-3003
Tel.: (360) 825-2591   WA
Web Site:
http://www.mutualofenumclaw.com
Year Founded: 1898
Sales Range: $100-124.9 Million
Emp.: 500
Insurance Services
N.A.I.C.S.: 524126
Eric Nelson (Pres)
Rich Hawkins (VP-Mktg)
Heather Caffoe (Product Mgr-Comml)
Rena Bilodeau (VP-HR)

MUTUAL OF OMAHA INSURANCE COMPANY
Mutual of Omaha Plz 3300, Omaha, NE 68175
Tel.: (402) 351-8026   NE
Web Site:
http://www.mutualofomaha.com
Year Founded: 1909
Rev.: $3,500,015,621
Assets: $8,084,019,676
Liabilities: $4,911,301,789
Net Worth: $3,172,717,887
Earnings: ($157,418,781)
Emp.: 4,620
Fiscal Year-end: 12/31/18
Holding Company; Life Insurance, Annuities, Reinsurance & Other Financial Products & Services
N.A.I.C.S.: 551112
James T. Blackledge (Chm & CEO)

Subsidiaries:

Companion Life Insurance Co.   (1)
888 Veterans Hwy Ste 515, Hauppauge, NY 11788-2934   (100%)
Tel.: (516) 561-4580
Sales Range: $25-49.9 Million
Emp.: 4
Insurance Company
N.A.I.C.S.: 524113

East Campus Realty, LLC   (1)
Mutual Of Omaha PLZ, Omaha, NE 68175
Tel.: (402) 342-7600
Real Estate Development Services
N.A.I.C.S.: 531390

Mutual of Omaha Investor Services, Inc.   (1)
3300 Mutual Of Omaha Plz, Omaha, NE 68175-0001   (100%)
Tel.: (402) 351-5770
Web Site: http://www.mutualofomaha.com
Sales Range: $50-74.9 Million
Emp.: 28
Mutual Fund
N.A.I.C.S.: 524113
Richard A. Witt (Chief Investment Officer & Exec VP)

United World Life Insurance Company   (1)
Mutual of Omaha Plz, Omaha, NE 68175
Tel.: (402) 342-7600
Web Site: http://www.mutualomaha.com
Sales Range: $50-74.9 Million
Emp.: 75
Fire Insurance Services
N.A.I.C.S.: 524113

United of Omaha Life Insurance Company   (1)
Mutual of Omaha Plz, Omaha, NE 68175
Tel.: (402) 342-7600
Web Site: http://www.mutualofomaha.com
Sales Range: $50-74.9 Million
Emp.: 100
Life Insurance Products & Services
N.A.I.C.S.: 524113

MUTUAL REINSURANCE BUREAU
1780 S Bell School Rd, Cherry Valley, IL 61016
Tel.: (815) 332-3155
Web Site: http://www.mutualre.com
Sales Range: $10-24.9 Million
Emp.: 28
Reinsurance Carriers, Accident & Health
N.A.I.C.S.: 524130
Kenneth L. Hense (Asst VP-Claims)
Lisa K. Ebbers (Asst VP-Underwriting Svcs)
Scott A. Johannsen (Controller & Asst VP)
Dorothy Henderson (Asst VP)
Dave Grant (Mgr-Intl Underwriting)
Timothy M. Dorr (Pres & CEO)
Michael J. Guevara (Sr VP)
Steven J. South (VP-DP)
Richard W. Hall (VP-Underwriting Svcs)

MUTUAL SAVINGS CREDIT UNION INC.
2040 Valleydale Rd, Birmingham, AL 35244
Tel.: (205) 682-1100
Web Site:
http://www.mutualsavings.org
Rev.: $10,300,000
Emp.: 105
Credit Union
N.A.I.C.S.: 522130
Kendall Speed (Pres & CEO)
Douglas Key (Sr VP-Strategic Plng)

MUTUAL SECURITY CREDIT UNION, INC.
12 Progress Dr, Shelton, CT 06484-1489
Tel.: (203) 402-7400   CT
Web Site: http://www.mscu.net
Year Founded: 2001
Sales Range: $10-24.9 Million
Emp.: 99
Credit Union
N.A.I.C.S.: 522130
Larry F. Holderman (Pres & CEO)
Karen Levasseur (CFO)
Jeffrey Levesque (VP-IT)

MUTUAL SHAREHOLDER SERVICES, LLC (MSS)
8000 Town Centre Dr Ste 400, Broadview Heights, OH 44147
Tel.: (440) 922-0066
Web Site: http://www.mutualss.com
Year Founded: 1999
Sales Range: $1-9.9 Million
Emp.: 28
Transfer Agent & Accounting Services
N.A.I.C.S.: 541219
Gregory B. Getts (Pres)

MUTUAL WELDING CO., LTD.
2846 Ualena St Ste 5, Honolulu, HI 96819-1943
Tel.: (808) 839-5111   HI
Year Founded: 1949
Sales Range: $75-99.9 Million
Structural Steel Fabrication, Erection & Construction Services
N.A.I.C.S.: 238120
Kawicka Chun (VP)

MUTUAL WHEEL COMPANY INC.

U.S. PRIVATE

2345 4th Ave, Moline, IL 61265
Tel.: (309) 757-1200
Web Site:
http://www.mutualwheel.com
Sales Range: $10-24.9 Million
Emp.: 74
Automotive Supplies & Parts Truck Parts & Accessories & Service
N.A.I.C.S.: 423120
Dave Engstrom (Co-Pres)
Rich Engstrom (Co-Pres)
Bob Engstrom (Co-Pres)

MUTUAL WHOLESALE LIQUOR INC.
4510 S Boyle Ave, Los Angeles, CA 90058
Tel.: (323) 587-7641
Web Site:
http://mutualwholesaleliquor.com
Sales Range: $10-24.9 Million
Emp.: 40
Liquor Sales
N.A.I.C.S.: 424820
Homer DeJesus (Mgr-Acctg Dept)
Steve Lukacs (Dir-Sls-Natl)
Fiel Aranda (Asst Mgr-Credit)
Harvey Monastirsky (Owner & Pres)
Manuel Ramirez (Mgr-Warehouse)
Marjorie Kenton (Mgr-Credit)
Sollie Vitente (Mgr-HR & Sr Accountant)

MUTUALONE BANK
160 Cochituate Rd, Framingham, MA 01701
Tel.: (508) 820-4000   MA
Web Site: http://www.mutualone.com
Year Founded: 1889
Sales Range: $300-349.9 Million
Emp.: 70
Banking Services
N.A.I.C.S.: 522110
Mark Haranas (Pres & CEO)
Brady M. Connors (Sr VP-Comm Lending)
Brian Ledwith (Exec VP)
Jeffery D. Ryan (VP-Comml Lending)
David Flynn (VP-Comml Lending)
Andrew E. Zelman (Sr VP)

MUTZ MOTORS L.P.
1430 W Memorial Blvd, Lakeland, FL 33815
Tel.: (863) 682-1100
Web Site:
http://www.lakelandautomall.com
Sales Range: $75-99.9 Million
Emp.: 150
Automobiles, New & Used
N.A.I.C.S.: 441110
Greg Balasco (Gen Mgr)
Robert Aguinaga (Mgr-Sls)

MUV, INC.
15770 Dallas Pkwy Ste 1100, Dallas, TX 75248
Tel.: (214) 348-9898   TX
Web Site: http://www.muvpeople.com
Year Founded: 2001
Sales Range: $1-9.9 Million
Emp.: 52
Chauffeured Transportation Services
N.A.I.C.S.: 485320
Arthur Veytsman (Co-Founder)

MUV-ALL TRAILER COMPANY
320 W St, Saint Martin, MN 56376
Tel.: (320) 548-2111   MN
Web Site:
http://www.muvalltrailer.com
Truck Trailer Mfr
N.A.I.C.S.: 336212
John Harding (VP)

MUZI MOTORS INC.

557 Highland Ave, Needham Heights, MA 02494
Tel.: (781) 444-5300 MA
Web Site: http://www.muzimotors.com
Year Founded: 1932
Sales Range: $25-49.9 Million
Emp.: 160
Sales of New & Used Automobiles
N.A.I.C.S.: 441110
Fred Muzi *(Pres)*
Neal Cammarano *(CEO)*
Dean Schulte *(Mgr-Facilities)*

MUZINICH & CO., INC.
450 Park Ave Ste 1804, New York, NY 10022
Tel.: (212) 888-3413 NY
Web Site: http://www.muzinich.com
Year Founded: 1988
Sales Range: $10-24.9 Million
Emp.: 30
Security Brokers
N.A.I.C.S.: 523150
George Muzinich *(Founder & CEO)*
David A. Bowen *(Portfolio Mgr)*
Warren Hyland *(Mgr-Debt Portfolio-London)*
Howard Mahon *(Dir-Pan Europe Private Debt-Dublin)*
Tom Douie *(Head-Distr-Global)*
Peter Andersson *(Head-Nordics-London)*

MUZINICH BDC, INC.
450 Park Ave, New York, NY 10022
Tel.: (212) 888-3413 DE
Year Founded: 2019
Rev.: $11,061,998
Assets: $153,727,680
Liabilities: $52,014,593
Net Worth: $101,713,087
Earnings: $8,711,748
Fiscal Year-end: 12/31/22
Investment Services
N.A.I.C.S.: 523999
Jeffrey Youle *(Pres & CEO)*
Cheryl Rivkin *(Chief Admin Officer, Sec & Dir-Compliance)*
Paul Fehre *(Chm, CFO & Treas)*

MV EQUIPMENT LLC
17777 US Hwy 385, Burlington, CO 80807
Tel.: (719) 346-8213 CO
Farm & Garden Machinery & Equipment Merchant Whslr
N.A.I.C.S.: 423820
Allen Troester *(VP-Parts & Svc)*

Subsidiaries:

MV Equipment (1)
704 E 8th Ave, Yuma, CO 80759
Tel.: (970) 848-5482
Web Site: http://www.mvequipment.com
Farm Equipment & Supplies Whslr
N.A.I.C.S.: 423820

MV MARKETING INC.
1133 N Tustin Ave, Anaheim, CA 92807
Tel.: (714) 630-0700
Web Site: http://www.corvettemike.com
Rev.: $13,023,104
Emp.: 50
Used Automobiles
N.A.I.C.S.: 441110
Michael Vietro *(Owner)*

MV PORTFOLIOS, INC.
10752 Deerwood Park Blvd Ste 100, Jacksonville, FL 32256
Tel.: (904) 903-4504 NV
Web Site: http://www.mvportfolios.com
Year Founded: 2004

Assets: $566,740
Liabilities: $1,600,789
Net Worth: ($1,034,049)
Earnings: ($1,886,804)
Emp.: 3
Fiscal Year-end: 06/30/17
Investment Services
N.A.I.C.S.: 523999
Scott Fletcher *(Chm, Pres & CEO)*

MV TRANSPORTATION INC.
4620 Westamerica Dr, Fairfield, CA 94534
Tel.: (707) 863-8980
Web Site: http://www.mvtransit.com
Year Founded: 1975
Sales Range: $150-199.9 Million
Emp.: 45
Transportation Services
N.A.I.C.S.: 485119
Alexis Lodde *(Co-Founder & Co-Owner)*
John Michel *(Chief Strategy & Innovation Officer & Pres-Intl)*
Beth Prunier *(Chief Sls Officer-Shuttle, School Bus & Events)*
Gary Coles *(Chief Sls Officer-Core Bus)*
Ted Navitskas *(Gen Counsel)*
Chris Burls *(VP-Strategy & Transformation)*
Jeff Womack *(CMO)*
Emily Somerville *(VP & Assoc Gen Counsel)*
Feysan Lodde *(Co-Founder & Co-Owner)*
Debra Wilson *(Chief Procurement Officer)*
Dorina Hertner *(Chief Risk Officer)*
Erin Niewinski *(CFO)*
Jarrett Andrews *(Chief HR Officer)*
John Calame *(Sr VP-Fleet & Facilities)*
Scott Sosnowski *(Chief Sls Officer)*
Thomas A. Egan *(CEO)*
Mark Collins *(Pres & COO)*
Kevin M. Jones *(CEO)*

Subsidiaries:

MVT Canadian Bus, Inc. (1)
17535 55 B Avenue, Surrey, V3S 5V2, BC, Canada
Tel.: (604) 575-6610
Web Site: http://www.mvtcanada.com
Passenger Transportation Services
N.A.I.C.S.: 485999
Edna Craig *(Gen Mgr)*

MVC ACQUISITION CORP.
287 Bowman Ave, Purchase, NY 10577
Tel.: (914) 701-0310 DE
Web Site: http://www.mvccapital.com
Year Founded: 2007
Sales Range: $10-24.9 Million
Emp.: 15
Investment Services
N.A.I.C.S.: 523999
Michael Theodore Tokarz *(Chm)*

MVC HOLDINGS LLC
27087 Gratiot Ave Fl 2, Roseville, MI 48066-2985
Tel.: (248) 641-4700
Web Site: http://www.mvcusa.com
Holding Company
N.A.I.C.S.: 551112
Michael Torakis *(Chm)*

Subsidiaries:

McKechnie Vehicle Components (1)
27087 Gratiot Ave, Roseville, MI 48066
Tel.: (586) 491-2600
Web Site: http://www.mvcusa.com
Sales Range: $25-49.9 Million
Emp.: 30
Automotive Components Mfr

N.A.I.C.S.: 336390
Michael Torakis *(CEO)*
Linda Torakis *(Pres)*
Jeffrey E. Palazzolo *(CFO)*
Randy Sorensen *(Exec VP-Mfg)*
Tim Coots *(Dir-Mfg)*

Subsidiary (Domestic):

McKechnie Tooling & Engineering (2)
501 Prairie Ave NW, Staples, MN 56479
Tel.: (218) 894-1218
Web Site: http://www.mcktool.com
Sales Range: $25-49.9 Million
Emp.: 18
Mould For Plastic Injection Moulding Mfr
N.A.I.C.S.: 326199
Ron Meyer *(Gen Mgr)*

MVD COMMUNICATIONS, LLC.
5188 Cox Smith Rd, Mason, OH 45040
Tel.: (513) 683-4711
Web Site: http://www.mvdcommunications.com
Year Founded: 1992
Sales Range: $10-24.9 Million
Emp.: 110
Wired Telecommunication Services
N.A.I.C.S.: 517111
Jeffrey L. Black *(Pres)*

MVD EXPRESS
10200 Menaul NE, Albuquerque, NM 87114
Tel.: (505) 323-0408
Web Site: http://www.mvdwebexpress.com
Year Founded: 1998
Sales Range: $1-9.9 Million
Emp.: 89
Transportation Program & Administration Services
N.A.I.C.S.: 926120
Melissa Stock *(COO)*
Diane Lacen *(Dir-HR)*
Candido Alarid *(Dir-IT & Mgr-Ops)*

MVL GROUP, INC.
1061 E Indiantown Rd Ste 300, Jupiter, FL 33477
Tel.: (561) 748-0931
Web Site: http://www.quicktest.com
Year Founded: 1998
Holding Company
N.A.I.C.S.: 551112
Adam L. Rodgers *(Pres & CEO)*
Edward W. Dean *(CFO)*

Subsidiaries:

Quick Test/Heakin (1)
1061 E Indiantown Rd Ste 300, Jupiter, FL 33477-5143
Tel.: (561) 748-0931
Web Site: http://www.quicktest.com
Sales Range: $25-49.9 Million
Emp.: 1,400
Global Information Retrieval & Data Collection Services
N.A.I.C.S.: 541910
Lori Weingarten *(Sr VP)*
Adam L. Rodgers *(Pres)*
Edward Dean *(CFO)*
Scott Sherman *(Controller)*
Christy Crossan *(Dir-Acct Mgmt)*

MVM, INC.
44620 Guilford Dr Ste 150, Ashburn, VA 20147
Tel.: (571) 223-4500 VA
Web Site: http://www.mvminc.com
Year Founded: 1979
Sales Range: $200-249.9 Million
Emp.: 3,500
Government Security, Translation & Related Services
N.A.I.C.S.: 561613

Dario O. Marquez *(Founder & Chm)*
Louie McKinney *(Sr VP-Govt Affairs)*
Kevin P. Marquez *(Pres & CEO)*
Maria Campos *(Sr VP)*

MVNP
999 Bishop St 21th Fl, Honolulu, HI 96813-4429
Tel.: (808) 536-0881 HI
Web Site: http://www.mvnp.com
Year Founded: 1946
Rev.: $28,000,000
Emp.: 92
Advertising Agencies, Advertising Specialties, Full Service
N.A.I.C.S.: 541810
Nick Ng Pack *(Owner)*
Lori Kimura *(Media Dir)*
Bob Soares *(Print Production Dir)*
Jenni Katinszky *(Brdcst Dir)*
Patricia Eng *(CFO)*
Markus Staib *(COO)*
Dave Daniels *(Assoc Dir-Creative)*
Lynn Yoshida *(Controller)*
Mike Wagner *(Assoc Dir-Creative)*
Susan E. Moss *(Dir-HR)*
Vince Soliven *(Dir-Creative)*
Kris Tanahara *(Dir-Comm)*

MVP GROUP INTERNATIONAL, INC.
1031 Le Grand Blvd, Charleston, SC 29492 KY
Web Site: http://www.mvpgroupint.com
Private Label & Branded Candles & Home Fragrance Product Designs, Mfr & Marketer
N.A.I.C.S.: 459420
Darrell L. McNair *(Pres & CEO)*

Subsidiaries:

CBK Ltd. (1)
600 E Sherwood Dr, Union City, TN 38261
Tel.: (731) 885-7836
Web Site: http://www.mwcbk.com
Sales Range: $100-124.9 Million
Emp.: 165
Decorative Products Whslr
N.A.I.C.S.: 424990

MVP HEALTH CARE INC.
625 State St, Schenectady, NY 12301-2207
Tel.: (518) 370-4793 NY
Web Site: http://www.mvphealthcare.com
Year Founded: 1982
Sales Range: $75-99.9 Million
Emp.: 1,700
Managed Health Care
N.A.I.C.S.: 621491
Ellen B. Sax *(VP-Community Engagement)*
Carole Montepare *(VP-Mgmt Sls & Acct)*
Christopher Del Vecchio *(Pres & COO)*
Cupid Gascon *(VP-Clinical Transformation)*
Kelly Smith *(VP-Sls)*
Monice Barbero *(Gen Counsel)*
Denise V. Gonick *(Pres & CEO)*
James H. Poole III *(Chief Security Officer)*

Subsidiaries:

MVP Health Care Inc. (1)
625 State St PO Box 2207, Schenectady, NY 12301-2207 (100%)
Tel.: (518) 370-4793
Web Site: http://www.mvphealthcare.com
Sales Range: $25-49.9 Million
Emp.: 9
Managed Health Care
N.A.I.C.S.: 524210
Doug Urbanski *(Product Mgr)*
Robin Messick *(Acct Mgr)*

MVP HEALTH CARE INC.   U.S. PRIVATE

MVP Health Care Inc.—(Continued)
Chris Brino (Mgr-Contracts & Pro Rels-East Reg)
Gayle Churchill (Mgr-Reinsurance-ASO)
Bradley Colacino (Mgr-Bus Process Quality & User Acceptance Testing)
Cori Olsen (Suprv-Fin Plng & Analysis)
Carla Renders (Project Mgr-Network Strategy & Payment Reform)
Denise Stasik (VP-Quality & Advocacy)

MVP Health Care Inc. (1)
66 Knight Ln Ste 10, Williston, VT 05495-9300 (100%)
Tel.: (802) 264-6500
Web Site: http://www.mvphealthcare.com
Sales Range: $10-24.9 Million
Emp.: 30
Provider of Managed Health Care Insurance
N.A.I.C.S.: 621491
Bill Little (VP)

MVP Health Care Inc. (1)
4947 Commercial Dr Ste 3, Yorkville, NY 13495-1120 (100%)
Tel.: (315) 736-1625
Web Site: http://www.mvphealthcare.com
Provider of Managed Health Care
N.A.I.C.S.: 524210

MVP Health Care Inc. (1)
620 Erie Blvd W Ste 201, Syracuse, NY 13204
Tel.: (315) 426-3700
Web Site: http://www.mvphealthcare.com
Rev.: $4,300,000
Emp.: 50
Provider of Managed Health Care
N.A.I.C.S.: 928110
Vandana Govindan (Mgr-HR)

MVP NISSAN OF EXTON
200 W Lincoln Hwy, Exton, PA 19341
Tel.: (610) 594-7400
Sales Range: $50-74.9 Million
Emp.: 70
Car Whslr
N.A.I.C.S.: 441110
Joseph Bush (Exec Dir)

MVTRAC, LLC
260 E Helen Rd, Palatine, IL 60067
Tel.: (847) 485-2300
Web Site: http://www.mvtrac.com
Software Development Services
N.A.I.C.S.: 541511
Luke K. Smith (Pres)
Brad J. Davis (COO)
Garry W. Jackson (Exec VP-Investigations)

MW INDUSTRIES, INC.
3426 Toringdon Way Ste 100, Charlotte, NC 28277
Tel.: (704) 837-0331
Web Site: https://www.mwcomponents.com
Emp.: 100
Industrial Machinery Mfr
N.A.I.C.S.: 333248

Subsidiaries:

MW Components (1)
3426 Toringdon Way Ste 100, Charlotte, NC 28277
Tel.: (704) 837-0331
Web Site: https://www.mwcomponents.com
Industrial Machinery Mfr
N.A.I.C.S.: 333248
Simon J. Newman (Chm)
Simon Newman (CEO)

Subsidiary (Domestic):

Elgin Fastener Group (2)
PO Box 785, Versailles, IN 47042
Tel.: (812) 689-8917
Web Site: http://www.elginfasteners.com
Industrial Fasteners
N.A.I.C.S.: 332722

Subsidiary (Domestic):

Chandler Products (3)

1491 Chardon Rd, Cleveland, OH 44117-1510
Tel.: (216) 481-4400
Web Site: http://www.chandlerproducts.com
Sales Range: $25-49.9 Million
Emp.: 60
Cold Headed Fasteners Mfr
N.A.I.C.S.: 332722

MW MARKETING GROUP
7831 Meadowood Dr, Hudsonville, MI 49426
Tel.: (616) 308-1572
Web Site: http://www.mw-mg.com
Year Founded: 2003
Sales Range: Less than $1 Million
Emp.: 4
N.A.I.C.S.: 541810
Mark Weber (Owner)

MW UNIVERSAL INC.
2008 Cypress St Ste 120, Paris, KY 40361
Tel.: (859) 987-8110
Year Founded: 2006
Metal Products Manufacturing & Assembly Services
N.A.I.C.S.: 332111
George Hofmeister (Pres & Sec)
Pete Peterson (COO)
Tom Weaver (CFO)
Rick Wolf (VP-Admin)
Dave Holm (VP-Pur)

Subsidiaries:

Cerion, LLC (1)
2424 John Daly Rd, Inkster, MI 48141
Tel.: (313) 785-5956
Holding Company
N.A.I.C.S.: 551112

LC Manufacturing LLC (1)
4150 N Wolcott Rd, Lake City, MI 49651
Tel.: (231) 839-7102
Web Site: http://www.lcmanufacturingllc.com
Mfr of Closed-Die Steel Forgings
N.A.I.C.S.: 333514

MPI International, Inc. (1)
21177 Hilltop St, Southfield, MI 48033
Tel.: (248) 351-1030
Web Site: http://www.mpi-int.com
Sales Range: $150-199.9 Million
Emp.: 1,000
Fineblanking Mfr
N.A.I.C.S.: 336370

Metavation, LLC (1)
21177 Hilltop St, Southfield, MI 48033-4912
Tel.: (313) 278-5956
Sales Range: $100-124.9 Million
Emp.: 40
Automotive Components Mfr
N.A.I.C.S.: 336390
Gary Veselica (Mgr-Rubber Dev)

Western Forge Corporation (1)
4607 Forge Rd, Colorado Springs, CO 80907
Tel.: (719) 598-5070
Web Site: http://www.westernforge.com
Sales Range: $75-99.9 Million
Emp.: 540
Metal Hand Tool Mfr
N.A.I.C.S.: 332216
Fred Radtke (VP-Brand & Product Mgmt)

MWH PRESERVATION LTD. PARTNER
RR 302, Bretton Woods, NH 03575
Tel.: (603) 278-1000
Web Site: http://www.omnihotels.com
Sales Range: $25-49.9 Million
Emp.: 1,000
Resort Hotel
N.A.I.C.S.: 721110
Bretton Woods (Dir-Sls)
Craig Clemmer (Asst Dir-Sls)

MWI CORPORATION
33 NW 2nd St, Deerfield Beach, FL 33441
Tel.: (954) 426-1500
Web Site: http://www.mwicorp.com
Sales Range: $25-49.9 Million
Emp.: 160
Pumps & Pumping Equipment
N.A.I.C.S.: 333914
Edward Saurazas (Engr-Electrical)
Danielle Londeree (Engr-Environmental)
Dario Puche (Mgr-Reg Sls)
Thomas Hyde (Mgr-Sls Repair)
Tom Roegiers (VP-Fin & Admin)

MWM DEXTER INC.
107 S Washington Ave, Aurora, MO 65605
Tel.: (417) 887-6299
Web Site: http://www.mwmdexter.com
Year Founded: 1922
Sales Range: $10-24.9 Million
Emp.: 140
Provider of Commercial Printing Services
N.A.I.C.S.: 323111
John Weldy (VP & Controller)
John W. Burkhart (Chm)

MWS ENTERPRISES INC.
5701 Transit Rd, East Amherst, NY 14051
Tel.: (716) 689-0600
Web Site: http://www.mwsenterprises.com
Rev.: $12,645,242
Emp.: 5
Convenience Store
N.A.I.C.S.: 445131
Mark W. Sidebottom (Owner & Pres)
Patti Sidebottom (Treas & Sec)

MWW GROUP LLC
1 Meadowlands Plz, East Rutherford, NJ 07073
Tel.: (201) 507-9500   DE
Web Site: http://www.mww.com
Year Founded: 1986
Emp.: 100
Public Relations Agency
N.A.I.C.S.: 541820
Michael W. Kempner (Pres & CEO)
Carreen Winters (Chm & Chief Strategy Officer)
William P. Murray (Exec VP-Pub Affairs)
Patrick Herridge (Mng Dir-UK)
Stephen Macias (Sr VP-Diversity & Inclusion)
Carl Sorvino (Sr VP & Exec Dir-Creative)
Tara Naughton (Exec VP & Dir-Mgmt)
Gareth Davies (VP-Digital Strategy-London)
Bret Werner (Pres)
Parker Ray (Exec VP)
Gina Cherwin (Chief People Officer & Exec VP)
Michelle Gordon (Sr VP-Res & Insights)
Will Starace (CFO)
John Digles (Exec VP & Gen Mgr-Midwest)
Joe Flores (Exec VP-Sports & Entertainment)
Shimon Sandler (Sr VP-Search Mktg)
Eli Feldblum (Sr VP-Search Mktg)

Subsidiaries:

MWW Group (1)
1 Meadowlands Plz, East Rutherford, NJ 07073
Tel.: (201) 507-9500
Sales Range: Less than $1 Million
Emp.: 10
Advertising Agencies Services
N.A.I.C.S.: 541810

Gina Ormand Cherwin (Chief People Officer & Exec VP)
Cecilia Coakley (Sr VP-Corp Reputation)
John Digles (Exec VP & Gen Mgr-Midwest)
Eli Feldblum (Sr VP-Search Mktg)
Joe Flores (Exec VP-Sports & Entertainment)
Michelle Gordon (Sr VP-Res & Insights)
Dawn Lauer (Mng Dir-B2B Comm & Exec VP)
Parker Ray (Exec VP)
Shimon Sandler (Sr VP-Search Mktg)
Will Starace (CFO)
Rich Tauberman (Exec VP-Corp Comm)
Bret Werner (Pres)

MWW Group (1)
660n S Figueroa St, Los Angeles, CA 90017
Tel.: (213) 486-6560
N.A.I.C.S.: 541810
Sheena Stephens (VP-Consumer Lifestyle Mktg)
Joe Keenan (VP-LGBT Practice)
Christina Stokes (Dir-Talent Acq)
Loren Waldron (VP-Bus Dev Svcs)

The MWW Group (1)
222 W State St Ste 306, Trenton, NJ 08608
Tel.: (609) 396-0067
Web Site: http://www.mww.com
Emp.: 10
Communications, Consumer Marketing, Government/Political/Public Affairs, Public Relations
N.A.I.C.S.: 541820
Lori Price Abrams (VP)

The MWW Group (1)
205 N Michigan Ave Ste 2010, Chicago, IL 60601
Tel.: (312) 853-3131
Web Site: http://www.mww.com
Emp.: 15
Communications, Consumer Marketing, Public Relations
N.A.I.C.S.: 541820
John Digles (Exec VP & Gen Mgr-Chicago)
Katie Myles (VP-Consumer Lifestyle Mktg)
Loren Waldron (VP-Bus Dev Svcs)
J. P. Schuerman (Pres-Western Reg)
Patrick Herridge (Mng Dir-UK)
Paul Tencher (Sr VP & Dir-Publ Affair-Natl)
William P. Murray (Exec VP)
Alissa J. Blate (Exec VP-Global Brand Mktg & Comm)
Brian Kempner (Gen Counsel & Exec VP)
Don McIver (Chief People & Admin Officer & Exec VP)
Bret Werner (Chief Client Officer & Exec VP)

The MWW Group (1)
660 S Figueroa St Ste 1400, Los Angeles, CA 90017
Tel.: (213) 486-6560
Web Site: http://www.mww.com
Emp.: 22
Communications, Consumer Marketing, Public Relations
N.A.I.C.S.: 541820

The MWW Group (1)
304 Pk Ave S, New York, NY 10010
Tel.: (212) 704-9727
Web Site: http://www.mww.com
Emp.: 200
Communications, Consumer Marketing, Public Relations
N.A.I.C.S.: 541820
Claire A. Koeneman (Pres-Fin Rels Bd & Gen Mgr-Midwest-Chicago)
Lauren Karasek (VP-Social Media Strategy)
Jess Seilheimer (Chief Strategy Officer)
Lori Robinson (Sr VP-Consumer Lifestyle Mktg Practice)
Nicole Bott (VP-Corp Comm)
Arthur Schwartz (Mng Dir-Corp Comm & Sr VP)

The MWW Group (1)
600 Battery St Fl 1, San Francisco, CA 94111-1820
Tel.: (415) 395-5900
Sales Range: Less than $1 Million
Emp.: 10
N.A.I.C.S.: 541820
Molly Mulloy (Exec VP & Gen Mgr)

MX CORPORATION

COMPANIES

705 W 28th St, Hialeah, FL 33010
Tel.: (305) 597-9881
Sales Range: $10-24.9 Million
Emp.: 5
Computer & Computer Peripheral Equipment & Software Merchant Wholesalers
N.A.I.C.S.: 423430
Simon Chew *(Pres)*

MXSECURE, INC.
17550 N Perimeter Dr Ste 250, Scottsdale, AZ 85255
Tel.: (480) 776-8900   AZ
Web Site: http://www.mxsecure.com
Year Founded: 2003
Sales Range: $10-24.9 Million
Emp.: 40
Medical Transcription Services
N.A.I.C.S.: 561499

MY ALARM CENTER LLC
3803 W Chester Pike Ste 100, Newtown Square, PA 19073
Tel.: (866) 484-4800
Web Site:
  http://www.myalarmcenter.com
Year Founded: 2000
Security System Monitoring Services
N.A.I.C.S.: 561621
Carole Dalton *(Chief HR Officer)*
Anastasia Bottos *(Pres & COO)*
Erik Mellon *(VP-Tech)*
James Harper *(VP-Sls-East)*
Darren Goodman *(Sr VP-Sls)*

MY AUTOGROUP
444 Auto Center Cir, Salinas, CA 93907
Tel.: (831) 444-4000
Web Site: http://www.mycars.com
New & Used Automobile Dealer
N.A.I.C.S.: 441110
Tino Montero *(Mgr-Fin)*

Subsidiaries:

MY Chevrolet (1)
444 Auto Center Cir, Salinas, CA 93907
Tel.: (831) 240-4855
Web Site: http://www.mychevrolet.org
Sales Range: $25-49.9 Million
Emp.: 50
New & Used Automobile Dealer
N.A.I.C.S.: 441110
Rhonda Good *(Office Mgr)*
Darrick Hoskins *(Pres)*

MY COMPUTER WORKS, INC
7975 N Hayden Rd Ste C320, Scottsdale, AZ 85258
Tel.: (602) 635-6150
Web Site:
  http://www.mycomputerworks.com
Year Founded: 2005
Sales Range: $1-9.9 Million
Emp.: 13
Personal Computer Support Services
N.A.I.C.S.: 541513
Luke M. Ford *(Founder & Pres)*

MY JOB MATCHER, INC.
108 Wild Basin Rd Ste 250, Austin, TX 78746
Web Site: http://www.job.com
Internet Publishing & Broadcasting & Web Search Portals
N.A.I.C.S.: 516210
Kristen Reed *(Dir-Mktg)*
Paul Sloyan *(Co-Founder & CEO)*
Arran Stewart *(Co-Founder & Chief Visionary Officer)*

Subsidiaries:

Hirevergence LLC (1)
9644 W Linebaugh Ave, Tampa, FL 33626-1805
Tel.: (813) 289-5502
Web Site: http://www.hirevergence.com

Employment Placement Agencies
N.A.I.C.S.: 561311
Mark J. Tuszynski *(Founder)*
Dave Gilden *(Founder)*
Julio Sanchez *(Founder)*

PrincetonOne LLC (1)
390 Amwell Rd Ste 504, 088544, Hillsborough, NJ
Tel.: (908) 281-6023
Web Site: http://www.princetonone.com
Staffing & Recruitment Services
N.A.I.C.S.: 541612
Dave Campeas *(Founder, Pres & CEO)*
Gary Suskin *(COO)*
Becky Gardner *(Sr Dir-Comm)*
Meghan Corso *(Mgr-Strategic Acct)*
Trish Ryan *(VP)*
Cathleen Anderson *(VP-Contract Staffing)*
Jon Bender *(VP-Pro Search)*
Mike Rocky *(VP-Resource Allocation & Bus Dev)*
Tara Britt *(Acct Mgr-Strategic)*

Subsidiary (Non-US):

PrincetonOne Asia (2)
23 Fl 3 106 Boai 2nd Rd, Kaohsiung, Taiwan
Tel.: (886) 919257007
Staffing & Recruiting Services
N.A.I.C.S.: 541612

endevis, LLC (1)
819 Kingsbury St Suite 100, Maumee, OH 43617
Tel.: (419) 482-4848
Web Site: http://www.endevis.com
Sales Range: $1-9.9 Million
Emp.: 25
Internet Based Recruitment Services
N.A.I.C.S.: 517810
Mick Fecko *(Co-Founder & Chief Admin Officer)*
Mark Melfi *(Co-Founder)*
Ron Walters *(Co-Founder)*
Wayne Voris *(Sr Mng Partner)*

MY NATURAL MARKET
12636 S 125 W Suite C, Draper, UT 84020
Web Site:
  http://www.mynaturalmarket.com
Year Founded: 2008
Sales Range: $1-9.9 Million
Emp.: 14
Vitamin & Mineral Supplements
N.A.I.C.S.: 456191
Gintar Grazhees *(Principal)*

MY NISSAN - KIA
222 Auto Center Cir, Salinas, CA 93907
Tel.: (831) 759-8888
Sales Range: $10-24.9 Million
Emp.: 60
Car Whslr
N.A.I.C.S.: 441110
Brian Verdin *(Gen Mgr-Sls)*

MY OWN MEALS, INC.
400 Lake Cook Rd, Deerfield, IL 60015
Tel.: (847) 948-1118   DE
Web Site:
  http://www.myownmeals.com
Year Founded: 1986
Sales Range: $75-99.9 Million
Emp.: 130
Mfr of Refrigeration-Free Ethnic Food Products, Kosher & Halal Meals & Military Rations
N.A.I.C.S.: 311999
Elizabeth Doyle *(VP)*

Subsidiaries:

J&M Food Products Company (1)
400 Lake Cook Rd Ste 107, Deerfield, IL 60015-4929   (100%)
Tel.: (847) 948-1290
Web Site: http://www.halalcertified.com
Sales Range: $10-24.9 Million
Emp.: 20

Halal Certified Refrigeration Free Meals & Military Rations
N.A.I.C.S.: 311999
Mary Anne Jackson *(VP)*

MY PET CHICKEN LLC
483 Monroe Tpke Ste 322, Monroe, CT 06468
Tel.: (908) 795-1007
Web Site:
  http://www.mypetchicken.com
Year Founded: 2005
Sales Range: $1-9.9 Million
Emp.: 15
Online Shopping Services
N.A.I.C.S.: 459210
Traci Torres *(Owner)*

MY PLUMBER INC.
6897 Gateway Ct, Manassas, VA 20109
Tel.: (703) 273-4400
Web Site: http://www.myplumber.com
Rev.: $11,980,000
Emp.: 200
Plumbing Contractor
N.A.I.C.S.: 238220
R. Wendell Presgrave *(Founder & CEO)*
Mark W. Presgrave *(VP)*

MY RECEPTIONIST, INC.
Bldg D02 Ste 410 800 Wisconsin St Mailbox 109, Eau Claire, WI 54703
Web Site:
  http://www.myreceptionist.com
Year Founded: 1996
Sales Range: $1-9.9 Million
Emp.: 75
Business Products & Services
N.A.I.C.S.: 513199
Jeff Noe *(Pres & CEO)*

MY SIGNATURE LIVING, LLC
6528 S Tamiami Trl, Sarasota, FL 34231
Tel.: (941) 894-6692
Web Site:
  http://www.mysignatureliving.com
Sales Range: $1-9.9 Million
Kitchen & Bathroom Remodelers
N.A.I.C.S.: 236118
Michael O'Connor *(Co-Owner)*
Nichole O'Connor *(Co-Owner)*

MY SPORTS DREAMS
258 Rte 117 Bypass Rd, Bedford Hills, NY 10507
Tel.: (914) 241-0204
Web Site:
  http://www.mysportsdreams.com
Year Founded: 2004
Sales Range: $1-9.9 Million
Emp.: 22
Fitness & Recreational Sports Centers
N.A.I.C.S.: 713940
Anya Praino *(Dir-Graphics)*

MY-D HAN-D MFG. INC.
10881 McArtor Rd, Dodge City, KS 67801-6763
Tel.: (620) 225-0263   KS
Web Site:
  http://www.mydhandsales.com
Year Founded: 1961
Sales Range: $10-24.9 Million
Emp.: 18
Farm Machinery & Equipment Mfr
N.A.I.C.S.: 333111
Kevin Tieben *(Pres)*
Patricia Tieben *(Treas & Sec)*
Steven Tieben *(VP)*

MY-VILLAGES, INC.
11450 SE Dixie Hwy Ste 201, Hobe Sound, FL 33455

Tel.: (914) 400-4376
Web Site: http://myvillages.com
Year Founded: 2011
Marine Mobile Technology
N.A.I.C.S.: 513210
Kevin Hutchinson *(Founder & CEO)*

MY1STOP LLC
3200 Liberty Bell Rd Ste 300, Fort Scott, KS 66701
Tel.: (316) 554-9700
Web Site: http://www.my1stop.com
Year Founded: 2005
Sales Range: $1-9.9 Million
Emp.: 12
Online Printing Supplies Retailer
N.A.I.C.S.: 424120
Johnny Bellmyer *(Pres)*
Rita Schroeder *(Office Mgr)*

MYCLIKS INC.
23548 Calabasas Rd Ste 106, Calabasas, CA 91302
Tel.: (818) 436-6410   CA
Web Site: http://www.mycliks.com
Year Founded: 2017
Emp.: 3
Consumer Products Distr
N.A.I.C.S.: 519290
Danial Marnokaran Abdullah *(Pres & CEO)*
Thaewendran Marnokaran *(CFO)*
Rajiv Pushpanathan *(Sec)*

MYCO MEDICAL
158 Towerview Ct, Cary, NC 27513
Tel.: (919) 460-2535
Web Site:
  http://www.mycomedical.com
Year Founded: 1993
Sales Range: $10-24.9 Million
Emp.: 23
Medical & Dental Equipment
N.A.I.C.S.: 423450
Sam Kumar *(Pres & CEO)*
Christine Simpson *(Mgr-Mktg)*
Tim Krotchko *(Mgr-Quality)*
Tammy Lee *(Coord-Customer Care)*
Jackie Flynn *(Mgr-Ops)*
Raniel Saludo *(Controller)*
Molly Pendse *(Mgr-HR)*

MYCOMPUTERCAREER INC.
5511 Capital Center Dr Ste 500, Raleigh, NC 27606
Web Site:
  http://www.mycomputercareer.edu
Year Founded: 2007
Sales Range: $50-74.9 Million
Emp.: 450
Educational Support Services
N.A.I.C.S.: 611710
Tony Galati *(Founder & CEO)*

MYCON GENERAL CONTRACTORS INC.
17311 Dallas Pkwy Ste 300, Dallas, TX 75248
Tel.: (972) 529-2444
Web Site: http://www.mycon.com
Year Founded: 1987
Sales Range: $25-49.9 Million
Emp.: 35
Provider of Commercial & Office Building Construction Services
N.A.I.C.S.: 236220
Charles R. Myers *(Founder & CEO)*
Doug Talley *(Pres)*
Bill Brady *(VP-Estimating)*
Shawn Pyatt *(CFO)*
Justin Jeffus *(Sr VP)*
Alexis Semach *(Dir-Bus Dev)*
Roger Pavlovich *(VP)*
Tim Keys *(VP-Ops)*
Wesley Weaver *(VP)*

MYCONE DENTAL SUPPLY CO. INC. U.S. PRIVATE

Mycon General Contractors Inc.—(Continued)

MYCONE DENTAL SUPPLY CO. INC.
616 Hollywood Ave, Cherry Hill, NJ 08002
Tel.: (856) 663-4700 DE
Web Site:
  http://www.keystoneind.com
Year Founded: 1908
Sales Range: $25-49.9 Million
Emp.: 100
Distr of Dental Equipment & Supplies
N.A.I.C.S.: 423450
Gloria Berger (Exec VP)
Miguel Perez (VP)

MYCROFT INC.
369 Lexington Ave 5th Fl, New York, NY 10017
Tel.: (212) 983-2656 NY
Web Site: http://www.mycroftinc.com
Year Founded: 1988
Sales Range: $25-49.9 Million
Emp.: 290
Computer System Design Services
N.A.I.C.S.: 541512
Sam Tang (CTO)
Rich Palacios (Dir-Inside Sls)

MYDIGITALOFFICE HOLDINGS INC.
Bethesda Twrs 4350 E W Hwy Ste 401, Bethesda, MD 20814
Tel.: (206) 438-9957
Web Site: https://mydigitaloffice.com
Year Founded: 2015
Holding Company
N.A.I.C.S.: 551112
Ali Moloo (CEO & Founder)
Subsidiaries:

myDigitalOffice.com, LLC (1)
Bethesda Twrs 4350 E W Hwy Ste 401, Bethesda, MD 20814
Tel.: (206) 438-9957
Web Site: https://mydigitaloffice.com
Emp.: 100
Hotel Data Platform
N.A.I.C.S.: 541511
Ali Moloo (Founder & CEO)

Subsidiary (Domestic):

Datavision Technologies Inc. (2)
1806 N Flamingo Rd Ste 200, Pembroke Pines, FL 33028-1030
Tel.: (954) 433-3633
Web Site: http://www.datavisiontech.com
Electronics Stores
N.A.I.C.S.: 449210
Shery Marek (Pres)
Sudharshan Chary (Founder & CEO)

MYDX, INC.
4225 Executive Sq Ste 600, La Jolla, CA 92037 NV
Web Site: https://www.mydxlife.com
Year Founded: 2012
MYDX—(OTCBB)
Sales Range: Less than $1 Million
Emp.: 1
Science & Technology Services
N.A.I.C.S.: 541715
Daniel Rida Yazbeck (Chm, CEO-Interim & CFO-Interim)
Subsidiaries:

CDx, Inc. (1)
6335 Ferris Sq Ste B, San Diego, CA 92121
Tel.: (858) 434-0705
Web Site: http://www.mydxlife.com
Research & Development Services
N.A.I.C.S.: 541715
Nicholas Hadler (Co-Founder & VP-Ops)
Robert Vigil (VP-Software Engrg)
Daniel Yazbeck (Co-Founder, Chm & CEO)

MYECHECK, INC.
2600 E Bidwell St Ste 190, Folsom, CA 95630 DE
Web Site: http://www.myecheck.com
Year Founded: 2004
Rev.: $730,777
Assets: $3,034,065
Liabilities: $3,003,412
Net Worth: $30,653
Earnings: ($5,114,181)
Emp.: 6
Fiscal Year-end: 12/31/15
Electronic Check Services
N.A.I.C.S.: 522320
Edward R. Starrs (Chm, Pres & CEO)
Robert Steven Blandford (CTO)
Joe Creamer (Gen Counsel)
Jim Wojtak (Mgr-Nalt Sls)
Christine Cowan (Dir-Fin)

MYEDGE LLC
1360 Blair Dr Ste L, Odenton, MD 21113
Tel.: (714) 322-3097
Web Site:
  http://www.medgestore.com
Year Founded: 2006
Sales Range: $25-49.9 Million
Emp.: 56
Protective Cases for Tablets & Cell Phones
N.A.I.C.S.: 334210
Patrick Mish (Principal)
Devon Mish (VP-Mktg)

MYELIN HEALTH COMMUNICATIONS, INC.
23 Drydock Ave Ste 810 W, Boston, MA 02210
Tel.: (617) 330-9393 DE
Web Site:
  http://www.mergeworld.com
Marketing & Communication Services
N.A.I.C.S.: 541613
Ron Bess (CEO)
Chris Tussing (CMO)
Kellie Bliss (Pres/Mng Dir-Chicago)
Kevin Houlihan (Pres/Chief Creative Officer-Chicago)
Lauren Tucker (Chief Strategy Officer)
Riley Sheehan (CTO)
Troy Mastin (CFO)
Kerry Griffin (Chief Talent Officer)
Bob Bernstein (Exec VP & Dir-Media)
Lauren Sheehan (Exec VP & Head-Design)
Subsidiaries:

Dodge Communications, Inc. (1)
11675 Rainwater Dr Ste 300, Alpharetta, GA 30009
Tel.: (770) 998-0500
Web Site:
  http://www.dodgecommunications.com
Public Relations Agency
N.A.I.C.S.: 541820
Brad Dodge (Founder & Pres)
Cathi Hilpert (Dir-Strategic Svcs)
Jenny Orr (Dir-Creative)
Jerold Cooper (CFO)
Chowning Johnson (Exec VP-Acct Mgmt)
Elisabeth Deckon (Sr VP-Ops)
Ted Keim (VP-Bus Dev)
Kat Mcdavitt (VP-Strategic Svcs)
Kelcie Chambers (Acct Dir)
Jill Gardner (Dir-Copywriting)
Laura Larsen (VP)
Michelle Morris (Acct Dir)
Erin Peitso (Acct Dir)
Nicole Wojno (Dir-Mktg)
Suzanne Bedell (Head-Mktg & Active Health Mgmt)
Katelyn Lewis (Assoc Acct Mgr)
Wyatt Avison (Assoc Acct Mgr)

HY Connect (1)
142 E Ontario St Ste 13, Chicago, IL 60611
Tel.: (312) 787-2330
Web Site: http://www.hyc.com
Advetising Agency

N.A.I.C.S.: 541810
Tony Bonilla (VP & Creative Dir)
Michael A. Smith (Exec VP-Ops & Client Svcs)
Carie Pflug (Dir-Bus Dev)
Ron Bess (Pres & CEO)
Kerry Griffin (Chief Talent Officer)

MYERCONNEX
7609 A Airpark Rd, Gaithersburg, MD 20879
Tel.: (240) 888-4300
Web Site:
  http://www.myerconnex.com
Sales Range: $10-24.9 Million
Emp.: 11
High Fidelity Stereo Equipment Sales & Services
N.A.I.C.S.: 449210
Jon Myer (CEO)

MYERS CONTAINER, LLC
8435 NE Killingsworth, Portland, OR 97220
Tel.: (503) 501-5830
Web Site:
  http://www.myerscontainer.com
Metal Container Mfr
N.A.I.C.S.: 332439
Kyle Stavig (CEO)
Subsidiaries:

General Steel Drum LLC (1)
4500 S Blvd, Charlotte, NC 28209
Tel.: (800) 796-4226
Metal Container Mfr
N.A.I.C.S.: 332439

Subsidiary (Domestic):

North Coast Container Corp. (2)
8806 Crane Ave, Cleveland, OH 44105-1622
Tel.: (216) 441-6214
Web Site: http://www.ncc-corp.com
Mfr of Metal Barrels, Drums & Pails
N.A.I.C.S.: 332439
James E. Beardsley (VP)
Earnest C. Beardsley (Chm & CEO)
William C. Syvuk (VP-Ops)

Subsidiary (Domestic):

STC Transporation Inc. (3)
8806 Crane Ave, Cleveland, OH 44105-1622
Tel.: (216) 441-6214
Web Site: http://www.ncc-corp.com
Sales Range: $10-24.9 Million
Emp.: 14
Trucking Service
N.A.I.C.S.: 484121

MYERS DIESEL & EQUIPMENT
1900 Hartzok Rd, Chambersburg, PA 17202
Tel.: (717) 263-2000 PA
Year Founded: 1981
Sales Range: $10-24.9 Million
Emp.: 3
Repairing Services for Automobiles & Heavy Motor Equipment
N.A.I.C.S.: 423110
John Myers (Owner)

MYERS FAMILY LP
4746 Ohana Ln, Clinton, WA 98236
Tel.: (360) 321-5693
Rev.: $23,300,000
Emp.: 6
Grocery Stores
N.A.I.C.S.: 457120
Kent Myers (Partner)
Sandy Wright (Office Mgr)
David Martin (Controller)

MYERS PARK COUNTRY CLUB
2415 Roswell Ave, Charlotte, NC 28209
Tel.: (704) 376-0741 NC

Web Site:
  http://www.myersparkcc.com
Year Founded: 1921
Sales Range: $10-24.9 Million
Emp.: 268
Country Club
N.A.I.C.S.: 713910
Kamal Sakakini (Gen Mgr)
Rhonda Kennedy (Controller)
Leslie Evans (Sec-Membership)
Franco Farroch (Mgr-Clubhouse)

MYERS POWER PRODUCTS, INC.
2950 E Philadelphia St, Ontario, CA 91761
Tel.: (951) 520-1900
Web Site:
  http://www.myerspowerproducts.com
Emp.: 300
Power & Emergency Lighting Products Mfr
N.A.I.C.S.: 335139
Diana Grootonk (Pres & CEO)
Greg Odion (Sr VP-Special Ops)
George Hodous (Mgr-HR)
Jon Waggener (VP-Sls & Mktg)
Rick Sanchez (VP-Ops)
Tony Williams (VP-Ops)
Sandeep Zope (Mgr-Engrg)
Nancy Gordon-Brooks (Dir-Mktg)
Robert Sellons (Mgr-LV Sls Application)
Subsidiaries:

Myers Power Products (1)
2201 N Central Expy Ste 135, Richardson, TX 75080-2778
Tel.: (214) 446-9200
Sales Range: $10-24.9 Million
Emp.: 2
DC Power Solutions & Telecommunication Services
N.A.I.C.S.: 517810

Myers Power Products, Inc. (1)
44 S Commerce Way, Bethlehem, PA 18017
Tel.: (610) 868-3500
Web Site:
  http://www.myerspowerproducts.com
Sales Range: $25-49.9 Million
Emp.: 120
Uninterruptible Power Supplies, Inverters, Emergency Lighting Equipment & Energy Efficient Retrofit Kits
N.A.I.C.S.: 335999

MYERS-COX CO
8797 Kapp Dr, Peosta, IA 52068
Tel.: (563) 583-8200
Web Site: http://www.myerscox.com
Year Founded: 1922
Sales Range: $25-49.9 Million
Emp.: 54
Mfr of Tobacco & Tobacco Products
N.A.I.C.S.: 424940
Mary Carew (Pres)

MYERS-HOLUM, INC.
666 5th Ave Ste 421, New York, NY 10103
Tel.: (212) 873-7873
Web Site:
  http://www.MyersHolum.com
Year Founded: 1981
Rev.: $9,900,000
Emp.: 40
Develops & Installs Data-Storage & Business-Intelligence Systems
N.A.I.C.S.: 541611
Knute Holum (Exec VP)
Mark Myers (CEO)

MYERS-STEVENS & CO. INC.
625 Market St, San Francisco, CA 94105
Tel.: (415) 543-4040

Web Site:
http://www.myersstevens.com
Sales Range: $10-24.9 Million
Emp.: 13
Insurance Brokers
N.A.I.C.S.: 524210

MYGO GAMES HOLDING CO.
12708 Riata Vista Cir Ste B-140, Austin, TX 78727
Tel.: (832) 900-9366 FL
Year Founded: 2009
Sales Range: Less than $1 Million
Emp.: 4
Investment Services
N.A.I.C.S.: 523999
Paul Chandler Watson *(Pres & CMO)*
G. Jonathan Pina *(CEO, CFO, Treas & Sec)*

MYGRANT GLASS COMPANY INC.
3271 Arden Rd, Hayward, CA 94545
Tel.: (510) 786-1425
Web Site:
http://www.mygrantglass.com
Sales Range: $25-49.9 Million
Emp.: 500
Automobile Glass
N.A.I.C.S.: 423120
Michael R. Mygrant *(Pres)*

MYGREENBUILDINGS, LLC
205 N Orange Ave Ste 1 SE, Sarasota, FL 34236
Tel.: (941) 366-7280
Web Site: http://www.mgbbuilt.com
Year Founded: 2006
Sales Range: $1-9.9 Million
Emp.: 10
Building Construction Services
N.A.I.C.S.: 236210
Steve Ellis *(Founder)*
Mark Dail *(Mgr-Residential Project)*

MYHOME LLC
353 W 48th St, New York, NY 10036
Tel.: (212) 666-2888
Web Site: http://www.myhomeus.com
Year Founded: 2001
Sales Range: $10-24.9 Million
Emp.: 12
Homes & Apartment Renovation & Remoding
N.A.I.C.S.: 236118
Yoel Piotraut *(Founder & Mng Partner)*
Oshri Elbaz *(Partner & Mng Dir)*
Noam Hanuka *(CEO)*

MYLES F. KELLY INC.
4357 Harrison Ave, Harrison, NJ 07029
Tel.: (973) 481-0600
Web Site: http://www.mylesfkelly.com
Rev.: $15,400,000
Emp.: 26
Roofing & Siding Materials
N.A.I.C.S.: 423330
Jeffrey Kelly *(Pres)*
Kevin Keller *(Gen Mgr)*
Kyle Tomasello *(Mgr)*
Michele Mulrenan *(Sec)*
Sara Neal *(Mgr-Inside Sls)*

MYLIFE.COM, INC.
914 Westwood Blvd 517, Los Angeles, CA 90024
Tel.: (310) 571-3144
Web Site: http://www.mylife.com
Year Founded: 2002
Sales Range: $10-24.9 Million
Emp.: 70
Online Social Networking Directory
N.A.I.C.S.: 513140
Jeffrey Tinsley *(Founder & CEO)*

MYMIC LLC
1040 University Blvd Ste 100, Portsmouth, VA 23703
Tel.: (757) 391-9200
Web Site: http://www.mymic.net
Year Founded: 2000
Sales Range: $10-24.9 Million
Emp.: 85
Software Development Services
N.A.I.C.S.: 541511
Thomas W. Mastaglio *(Co-Chm)*
Bradford J. Carpenter *(CFO & COO)*
Bernie Jacques *(VP-Bus Ops)*
William L. Younger Jr. *(Co-Chm)*

MYND PROPERTY MANAGEMENT, INC.
1611 Telegraph Ave Ste 1200, Oakland, CA 94612
Tel.: (510) 616-9522
Web Site: http://www.mynd.co
Property Management Services
N.A.I.C.S.: 531110
Doug Brien *(Founder & CEO)*

Subsidiaries:

Jevons Properties, LLC (1)
303 W Martin Luther King Jr Blvd, Yakima, WA 98902
Tel.: (509) 895-7777
Web Site: http://www.jevonsproperties.com
Offices of Real Estate Agents & Brokers
N.A.I.C.S.: 531210
Enrique Jevons *(Mgr-Reg Property)*

MYOFFICE, INC.
6060 Nancy Ridge Dr Ste 100, San Diego, CA 92121
Tel.: (858) 800-2114
Web Site: http://www.4myoffice.com
Year Founded: 1986
Sales Range: $10-24.9 Million
Emp.: 110
Packing & Crating Services
N.A.I.C.S.: 488991
Shaun T. Alger *(CEO & COO)*

MYOFFICEPRODUCTS LLC
22 Century Blvd Ste 420, Nashville, TN 37214
Tel.: (615) 507-3900
Web Site:
http://www.myofficeproducts.com
Year Founded: 2002
Rev.: $92,200,000
Emp.: 350
Business Products & Services
N.A.I.C.S.: 459410
John Frisk *(Pres)*

Subsidiaries:

MyOfficeProducts LLC (1)
121 Kelsey Ln Ste F, Tampa, FL 33619
Tel.: (877) 696-7266
Web Site: http://www.myofficeproducts.com
Sales Range: $1-9.9 Million
Emp.: 20
Office Furniture Dealer
N.A.I.C.S.: 423210

MYONEX, LLC
100 Progress Dr, Horsham, PA 19044
Tel.: (610) 477-3168
Web Site: https://www.myonex.com
Year Founded: 1987
Pharmaceutical Manufacturing
N.A.I.C.S.: 325412
Michael Cohen *(Exec Chm)*
James Lovett *(CEO)*
Mary Ann Walsh *(Chief HR Officer)*

Subsidiaries:

SaveWay Compounding Pharmacy, LLC (1)
31 Albe Dr Unit 1, Newark, DE 19702
Tel.: (302) 369-5520
Web Site:
http://www.savewaypharmacy.com

Sales Range: $1-9.9 Million
Emp.: 10
Pharmaceutical Product Whslr
N.A.I.C.S.: 424210
Calvin A. Freedman *(Pres)*
Brenda L. Pavlic *(VP)*

MYOTCSTORE.COM
19-35 Hazen St, East Elmhurst, NY 11370
Tel.: (718) 204-6966
Web Site: http://www.myotcstore.com
Year Founded: 2007
Sales Range: $10-24.9 Million
Emp.: 20
Health & Beauty Products
N.A.I.C.S.: 456191
Yamini Vellampalli *(Owner)*

MYREX INDUSTRIES
9119 Weedy Ln, Houston, TX 77093
Tel.: (713) 691-5200
Web Site: http://www.myrex.com
Sales Range: $100-124.9 Million
Emp.: 65
Fabricated Structural Metal
N.A.I.C.S.: 332312
Jim Moffa *(Pres)*
Kelly Boze *(VP-Sls)*
Charles Weimer *(Mgr-Quality Assurance)*
Judith Grimm *(Mgr-Acctg)*

MYRIAD DEVELOPMENT, INC.
8601 RR 2222 Ste 3-250, Austin, TX 78730
Tel.: (512) 302-3262
Web Site: http://www.myriad-development.com
Year Founded: 1997
Sales Range: $10-24.9 Million
Emp.: 25
Underwriting Services to Property & Casualty Insurance & Mortgage Industries
N.A.I.C.S.: 524298
Chris Roussel *(CEO)*
Mike Whittington *(Pres & CIO)*
Richard Brooks *(Sr VP-Sls & Mktg)*

MYRIAD MOBILE LLC
503 7th St N, Fargo, ND 58102
Tel.: (701) 369-0633
Web Site:
http://www.myriadmobile.com
Year Founded: 2011
Sales Range: $1-9.9 Million
Mobile Application Development Services
N.A.I.C.S.: 513210
Jake Joraanstad *(Co-Founder & CEO)*
Ryan Raguse *(Co-Founder & Chm)*
Jeremy Johnson *(Partner & Dir-Sls-Natl)*
Eston Taylor *(COO & Dir-Ops)*
Mark Hempel *(Pres)*
Adam Wendorf *(VP-Fin)*
Camille Weber Grade *(VP-Sls & Mktg)*

Subsidiaries:

iNet Solutions Group, Inc. (1)
13215 Birch Dr Ste 201, Omaha, NE 68164
Tel.: (402) 330-0636
Web Site: http://www.farmcentric.com
Software Solutions for Agriculture Industry
N.A.I.C.S.: 513210
Dan Kuyper *(VP)*

MYRIAD RESTAURANT GROUP
249 W Broadway, New York, NY 10013
Tel.: (212) 219-9500

Web Site:
http://www.myriadrestaurantgroup.com
Year Founded: 1985
Sales Range: $50-74.9 Million
Emp.: 15
Full Service Restaurant Operator
N.A.I.C.S.: 722511
Tracy J. Nieporent *(Partner & Dir-Mktg)*
Drew Nieporent *(Owner)*
Martin Shapiro *(Mng Partner)*
Agnes Chiao *(CFO & Partner)*

Subsidiaries:

Batard (1)
239 W Broadway, New York, NY 10013
Tel.: (212) 219-2777
Web Site:
http://www.myriadrestaurantgroup.com
Restaurant Services
N.A.I.C.S.: 722511
John Winterman *(Mng Partner)*

Centrico (1)
211 W Broadway, New York, NY 10013
Tel.: (212) 431-0700
Restaurant Services
N.A.I.C.S.: 722511
Drew Nieporent *(Owner)*

Nobu Fifty Seven (1)
40 W 57th St, New York, NY 10019
Tel.: (212) 757-3000
Sales Range: $10-24.9 Million
Restaurant Services
N.A.I.C.S.: 722511

Nobu London (1)
Metropolitan Hotel 19 Old Pk Ln, London, W1K 1LB, United Kingdom
Tel.: (44) 2074474747
Web Site: http://www.noburestaurants.com
Restaurant Services
N.A.I.C.S.: 722511

Nobu New York (1)
105 Hudson St, New York, NY 10013
Tel.: (212) 219-0500
Sales Range: $10-24.9 Million
Restaurant Services
N.A.I.C.S.: 722511
Richard Notar *(Mng Partner)*
Robert De Niro *(Co-Owner)*
Drew Nieporent *(Co-Owner)*
Nobu Matsuhisa *(Co-Owner & CEO)*

Nobu Next Door (1)
105 Hudson St, New York, NY 10013
Tel.: (212) 334-4445
Sales Range: $10-24.9 Million
Restaurant Services
N.A.I.C.S.: 722511
David Gordon *(Dir-Wine)*
Nobu Matsuhisa *(Owner)*

Pulse (1)
45 Rockefeller Plz 3rd Fl, New York, NY 10111
Tel.: (212) 218-8666
Web Site: http://www.pulse-restaurant.com
Restaurant Services
N.A.I.C.S.: 722511

Rubicon (1)
2415 Dowling Pl, Berkeley, CA 94705-2011
Tel.: (415) 434-4100
Restaurant Services
N.A.I.C.S.: 722511
Drew Nieporent *(Owner)*

Tribeca Grill (1)
375 Greenwich St, New York, NY 10013
Tel.: (212) 941-3900
Web Site:
http://www.myriadrestaurantgroup.com
Sales Range: $10-24.9 Million
Restaurant Services
N.A.I.C.S.: 722511
David Gordon *(Dir-Wine)*
Tracy J. Nieporent *(Partner & Dir-Mktg)*
Martin Shapiro *(Mng Partner)*
Drew Nieporent *(Owner)*

MYRIAD SUPPLY COMPANY, LLC
22 W 19th St 4th Fl, New York, NY 10011
Tel.: (212) 366-6996

MYRIAD SUPPLY COMPANY, LLC — U.S. PRIVATE

Myriad Supply Company, LLC—(Continued)
Web Site:
  http://www.myriadsupply.com
Year Founded: 2003
Sales Range: $10-24.9 Million
Emp.: 70
Computer & Software Stores
N.A.I.C.S.: 459510
Mark Hosny (CFO)
John Murtha (Acct Exec)
Ryan Swanson (Sr Acct Exec)

MYRIAD360, LLC
199 Water St 34th Fl, New York, NY 10038
Web Site: http://www.myriad360.com
Year Founded: 2003
Sales Range: $150-199.9 Million
Emp.: 93
IT Management Services
N.A.I.C.S.: 541618
Andrew Fisher (Founder & CEO)
David Brady-Gossage (Exec VP-Rels)
Ernesto Vasconcellos (VP-Logistics)
Hilary De Courcey (Exec VP-People Ops)
Michael Sloan (Exec VP-Revenue)

MYRICK CONSTRUCTION INC.
101 Shady Oak Dr, Biscoe, NC 27209-9590
Tel.: (910) 428-2106   NC
Web Site:
  http://www.myrickconstruction.com
Year Founded: 1968
Sales Range: $25-49.9 Million
Emp.: 210
Provider of Construction & Contracting Services
N.A.I.C.S.: 236220
Bobby H. Myrick (Treas)
Teena Myrick (Dir-Mktg)
Bobby Harold Myrick Jr. (Pres)

MYRICK GUROSKY & ASSOCIATES
4 Riverchase Rdg, Birmingham, AL 35244
Tel.: (205) 313-3020   AL
Web Site:
  http://www.mgandassociates.com
Year Founded: 1993
Rev.: $35,000,000
Emp.: 15
Commercial & Office Building, New Construction
N.A.I.C.S.: 236220
Wayne Myrick (CEO)
Paul Head (CFO & Treas)
Wayne Myrick (CEO)
Alan Dobbins (Dir-Project Dev)
Scott Gurosky (Pres)
Mike Evans (Dir-Pre-Construction Svcs)

MYRON BOWLING AUCTIONEERS INC.
3901 Kraus Ln, Hamilton, OH 45014
Tel.: (513) 738-3311
Web Site:
  http://www.myronbowling.com
Sales Range: $10-24.9 Million
Emp.: 30
Industrial Auctioneers
N.A.I.C.S.: 561990
Myron C. Bowling (Pres)
Bill Oliver (Mgr-Ops)
Joe Oliver (Mng Partner)
Greg Hengehold (Mng Partner)
Doug Reiter (Dir-Mktg)
Julie Endres (Controller)
Linda Kendall (Coord-Adv)
Christopher Lee (Dir-Bus Dev)

MYRON EVENSON'S CARDS & GIFTS
4653 Chatsworth St N, Shoreview, MN 55126
Tel.: (651) 482-8511
Rev.: $13,000,000
Emp.: 12
Greeting Cards
N.A.I.C.S.: 459420

MYRON F. STEVES & COMPANY
3131 Eastside Ste 600, Houston, TX 77098
Tel.: (713) 522-1100
Web Site:
  http://www.myronsteves.com
Year Founded: 1955
Sales Range: $25-49.9 Million
Emp.: 200
Holding Company; Provider of Healthcare, Property & Casualty Insurance
N.A.I.C.S.: 524210
Teresa Steves Skinner (Mng Dir-Educators Pro Liability)
Frederick B. Steves (Chm & Partner)
Myron F. Steves Jr. (Vice Chm, Partner & Exec Dir-Healthcare)
Subsidiaries:
Myron F. Steves & Company   (1)
1120 Captiol Of Texas Bldg 3 Ste 120, Austin, TX 78746
Tel.: (512) 328-4300
Web site: http://www.myronsteves.com
Sales Range: $25-49.9 Million
Emp.: 8
Provider of Insurance Agents & Brokers
N.A.I.C.S.: 524210

MYRON MANUFACTURING CORPORATION
205 Maywood Ave, Maywood, NJ 07607-1007
Tel.: (201) 843-6464   NJ
Web Site: http://www.myron.com
Year Founded: 1949
Sales Range: $100-124.9 Million
Emp.: 218
Mfr of Vinyl Covered Calendars & Advertising Specialties, Business Gifts & Sales Aids
N.A.I.C.S.: 326199
Mike Adler (Founder & Chm)
James Adler (CEO)
William Byrne (CFO)

MYRTLE HILLIARD DAVIS COMPREHENSIVE HEALTH CENTERS, INC.
5471 Dr Martin Luther King Dr, Saint Louis, MO 63112
Tel.: (314) 367-5820   MO
Web Site: http://www.mhdchc.org
Year Founded: 1969
Sales Range: $10-24.9 Million
Emp.: 286
Health Care Srvices
N.A.I.C.S.: 621610
Angela Clabon (CEO)
Leslie R. McCrary-Etuk (Chief Medical Officer)
Carol Henley (Chief Dental Officer)
Renee Brooks (CIO)
James Paine Jr. (COO)

MYSTIC SCENIC STUDIOS INC.
293 Lenox St, Norwood, MA 02062-3462
Tel.: (781) 329-9006
Web Site:
  http://www.mysticscenic.com
Sales Range: $10-24.9 Million
Emp.: 110
Theatrical Scenery
N.A.I.C.S.: 339999
Jim Ray (Pres)
Richard Dugdale (Project Mgr)
Steve Brown (Engr-Architectural)
John Botke (Project Mgr)
Mark Howes (Project Mgr)

MYSTIC SEAPORT
75 Greenmanville Ave, Mystic, CT 06355
Tel.: (860) 572-0711   CT
Web Site:
  http://www.mysticseaport.org
Year Founded: 1929
Sales Range: $10-24.9 Million
Seaport Museum Operator
N.A.I.C.S.: 713990
Stephen C. White (Pres)
Michael S. Hudner (Sec)

MYSTIC STAMP COMPANY
9700 Mill St, Camden, NY 13316-9101
Tel.: (315) 245-2690   NY
Web Site:
  http://www.mysticstamp.com
Year Founded: 1923
Sales Range: $25-49.9 Million
Emp.: 140
Mail Order Stamps for Collectors
N.A.I.C.S.: 459999
Mark Fox (Gen Mgr)
David Sundman (Pres)
Don Arsenault (Mgr-IT)

MYSTIC VALLEY ELDER SERVICES, INC.
300 Commercial St Ste 19, Malden, MA 02148
Tel.: (781) 324-7705   MA
Web Site: http://www.mves.org
Year Founded: 1975
Sales Range: $25-49.9 Million
Emp.: 229
Elderly People Assistance Services
N.A.I.C.S.: 624120
Sandy Fall (Dir-Quality Improvement)
Sharon Ferraguto (Dir-HR)
Angie Fitzgerald (Dir-Nutrition)
Sean Hubacz (Dir-Fin)
Deb Pelletier (Office Mgr)
Janice T. Houghton (Pres)
Joanne Solazzo (Dir-Client Svcs)
Kathleen M. Beaulieu (VP)
Lisa Gurgone (CEO)

MYSTIC VALLEY WHEEL WORKS INCORPORATED
480 Trapelo Rd, Belmont, MA 02478
Tel.: (617) 489-3577
Web Site:
  http://www.wheelworks.com
Year Founded: 1977
Sales Range: $10-24.9 Million
Emp.: 50
Bicycle & Bicycle Parts
N.A.I.C.S.: 459110
Clinton Paige (Pres)

MYSUPPLYCHAINGROUP (MSCG)
1500 First Ave N Suite A111, Birmingham, AL 35203
Tel.: (205) 706-4300
Web Site: http://www.mysupplychaingroup.com
Year Founded: 2009
Sales Range: $1-9.9 Million
Emp.: 12
Supply Chain Process Reengineering & Application Implementation Services
N.A.I.C.S.: 541614
Omar Zuberi (Founder & Mng Partner)

MYTEK NETWORK SOLUTIONS
2225 W Whispering Wind Dr Ste 105, Phoenix, AZ 85085
Web Site: http://mytek.net
Year Founded: 2008
Sales Range: $1-9.9 Million
Emp.: 27
IT Support
N.A.I.C.S.: 541690
Brian Blakley (Pres)
Katharine Blakley (Controller)

MYTICKETIN.COM
2100 W Loop Ste 205, Houston, TX 77027
Tel.: (713) 429-1560
Web Site: http://www.myticketin.com
Year Founded: 2006
Sales Range: $1-9.9 Million
Emp.: 5
Sports & Entertainment Ticket Brokerage
N.A.I.C.S.: 713990
Malcom Robinson (CEO)

MYWEDDING.COM LLC
4700 Castleton Way Ste 210, Castle Rock, CO 80109
Web Site:
  http://www.mywedding.com
Year Founded: 2002
Sales Range: $1-9.9 Million
Emp.: 17
Online Wedding Guide Publisher
N.A.I.C.S.: 812990
James McGarvey (Pres)

MZD ADVERTISING
120 Vermont St Ste 100, Indianapolis, IN 46204-1831
Tel.: (317) 924-6271
Year Founded: 1950
Rev.: $22,000,000
Emp.: 30
Advetising Agency
N.A.I.C.S.: 541810
Tom Conrad (Sr Controller)
Darla Shields (New Bus Dir & Acct Exec)
David Ayers (Dir-Pub Rels)
Allan Zuckerman (Chm & CEO)
Rich Lunseth (Creative Dir)
Blair Englehart (Sr VP)
T.J. Gipson (Dir-Multicultural)
Rick Doyle (Media Dir)
Kiley Kellermeyer (Acct Exec-PR)
Ashlie Hartgraves (Art Dir)
Matt Kiefer (Specialist-Multimedia)
Michelle Dunlap (Asst Controller-HR)
Pam Christian (Office Mgr-Acctg)
Ray Volpe (Sr Acct Exec)
Jill Baker (Media Buyer)

MZINGA, INC.
20 Burlington Mall Rd Ste 420, Burlington, MA 01803
Tel.: (781) 577-8900   DE
Web Site: http://www.mzinga.com
Sales Range: $10-24.9 Million
Emp.: 100
Online Training Program Software Publisher
N.A.I.C.S.: 513210
Barry Libert (Founder & Chm)
Subsidiaries:
Mzinga   (1)
5095 Ritter Rd Ste 112, Mechanicsburg, PA 17055
Tel.: (717) 790-0400
Online Employee Education & Training Software
N.A.I.C.S.: 513210

N&A ENTERPRISES INC.

7261 Lampson Ave, Garden Grove, CA 92841
Tel.: (714) 894-2443
Web Site: http://www.bigdfloorcovering.com
Sales Range: $10-24.9 Million
Emp.: 50
Floor Coverings
N.A.I.C.S.: 238330
Dody Brennan (CFO)
Steven E. Kleinhans Sr. (CEO)

N&M COOL TODAY, INC.
6143 Clark Center Ave, Sarasota, FL 34238
Tel.: (941) 921-5581
Web Site: http://www.cooltoday.com
Sales Range: $10-24.9 Million
Emp.: 100
Air Conditioning, Heating & Plumbing Contractor
N.A.I.C.S.: 238220
Jaime DiDomenico (Owner & Pres)
Charles Blum (Mgr-Indoor Air Quality & Energy)
Bryant Ray (Mgr-Ops)

N&M TRANSFER CO., INC.
630 Muttart Rd, Neenah, WI 54956-9752
Tel.: (920) 722-7760
Web Site: http://www.nmtransfer.com
Year Founded: 1981
Sales Range: $25-49.9 Million
Emp.: 800
Provider of Local Trucking Services
N.A.I.C.S.: 484110
Kevin Pawlacyk (Pres)
Thomas Pawlacyk (CEO)
Dave Williams (VP-Fin)

N&S TRACTOR CO. INC.
600 S Hwy 59, Merced, CA 95340
Tel.: (209) 383-5888
Web Site: http://www.nstractor.com
Rev.: $16,716,639
Emp.: 67
Agricultural Machinery & Equipment
N.A.I.C.S.: 423820
Arthur Nutcher (Pres)

N-LINK CORPORATION
4040 Wheaton Way Ste 112, Bremerton, WA 98310
Tel.: (360) 415-5600
Web Site: http://www.n-link.net
Year Founded: 1995
Sales Range: $10-24.9 Million
Emp.: 144
Information Technology Services
N.A.I.C.S.: 541519
Sandra Green (Founder & CEO)
Chris Bauer (Pres-Washington DC)
Dayna Ebersole (Pres-Bremerton WA)

N-TARA, INC.
2214 E Fairview Ave, Johnson City, TN 37601
Tel.: (423) 926-8272
Web Site: http://www.ntara.com
Year Founded: 1999
Sales Range: $10-24.9 Million
Emp.: 20
Advertising Agencies
N.A.I.C.S.: 541810
Neil Owen (Founder & Chief Strategy Officer)
Jeff Morris (Founder, Pres & CEO)
Shane McCown (VP-Engrg)

N-TECH SOLUTIONS INC.
9256 Bendix Rd Ste 208, Columbia, MD 21045
Tel.: (877) 683-2448
Web Site: http://www.ntechsol.com
Year Founded: 2005
Sales Range: $1-9.9 Million
Emp.: 10
IT & Business Process Consulting
N.A.I.C.S.: 541618
Kenn Raatjes (VP-Sls & Mktg)

N-TIER SOLUTIONS INC.
2596 Landmark Dr, Winston Salem, NC 27103
Tel.: (336) 765-3500
Web Site: http://www.n-tiersolutions.com
Year Founded: 1999
Sales Range: $10-24.9 Million
Emp.: 91
It Consulting
N.A.I.C.S.: 541690
Richard Stroud (Pres)

N-TIERACTIVE INCORPORATED
137 National Plz Ste 300, Oxon Hill, MD 20745
Tel.: (240) 273-3355
Web Site: http://www.n-tieractive.com
Year Founded: 2001
Sales Range: $1-9.9 Million
Emp.: 23
Information Technology Services
N.A.I.C.S.: 541512
Marty Spain (Pres & CEO)
Jill Moon Corcoran (CFO & VP)

N. ARMSTRONG ADVERTISING
2103 64th St, Lubbock, TX 79412
Tel.: (806) 745-9004
Year Founded: 1974
Sales Range: Less than $1 Million
Emp.: 1
N.A.I.C.S.: 541810
Nelda Armstrong (Owner)

N. GINSBURG & SON INCORPORATED
10709 Gilroy Rd Ste 150, Hunt Valley, MD 21031
Tel.: (410) 329-9680
Web Site: http://www.floors-etc.com
Year Founded: 1899
Sales Range: $10-24.9 Million
Emp.: 45
Retailer of Commercial Floor Coverings
N.A.I.C.S.: 449121
Stanley Ginsburg (Owner & Pres)

N. GLANTZ & SON
2501 Constant Comment Pl, Louisville, KY 40299
Tel.: (502) 426-4473
Web Site: http://www.nglantz.com
Sales Range: $25-49.9 Million
Emp.: 200
Sign Supply Distr
N.A.I.C.S.: 423440
Joe Hartman (Co-Chm & CEO)
Michael Kelley (Pres & COO)
Davey Glantz (Co-Chm & CEO)
Beth Wolf (Dir-Mktg)
Jim Shaw (Dir-Pur)
Scott Clinton (Mgr-Inventory Control)

N. JONAS & COMPANY, INC.
1301 Adams Rd, Bensalem, PA 19020
Tel.: (215) 639-8071
Web Site: http://www.njonas.com
Sales Range: $10-24.9 Million
Emp.: 20
Swimming Pool & Spa Chemicals Wholesale to Trade
N.A.I.C.S.: 424690
Ed Wexler (VP-Sls)

N. MERFISH PLUMBING SUPPLY CO.
1211 Kress St, Houston, TX 77020
Tel.: (713) 869-5731
Web Site: http://www.merfish.com
Sales Range: $25-49.9 Million
Emp.: 90
Pipe & Tubing, Steel
N.A.I.C.S.: 423510

N.A. DEGERSTROM INC.
3303 N Sullivan Rd, Spokane, WA 99216
Tel.: (509) 928-3333
Web Site: http://www.nadinc.com
Rev.: $12,170,951
Emp.: 72
Open Pit Gold Mining
N.A.I.C.S.: 212220
Chris Myers (Pres)
Nancy Rodriguez (Asst Controller)

N.A. MANS SONS INC.
3300 W Jefferson Ave, Trenton, MI 48183
Tel.: (734) 676-3000
Web Site: http://www.manslumber.com
Sales Range: $25-49.9 Million
Emp.: 75
Provider of Retail Lumber & Other Building Materials
N.A.I.C.S.: 423310
Michael A. Mans (Pres)
Anna Motschall (CFO)

N.B. FAIRCLOUGH & SONS INC.
800 E 27th St, Paterson, NJ 07513
Tel.: (973) 742-6412
Web Site: http://www.faircloughfuel.com
Rev.: $10,212,039
Emp.: 25
Fuel Oil Dealers
N.A.I.C.S.: 457210
John H. Fairclough (Pres)

N.B. GOODWYN & SONS INC.
2510 Bellwood Rd, Richmond, VA 23237
Tel.: (804) 545-4663
Web Site: http://www.nbgoodwynlumber.net
Sales Range: $10-24.9 Million
Emp.: 30
Lumber Products
N.A.I.C.S.: 444110
David Beck (VP)
Russ R. Beck III (Pres)

N.B. HANDY COMPANY
65 10th St, Lynchburg, VA 24504
Tel.: (434) 847-4495
Web Site: http://www.nbhandy.com
Sales Range: $250-299.9 Million
Emp.: 350
Wholesale Distributor Of Sheets, Galvanized Or Other Coated
N.A.I.C.S.: 423610
Tom Millis (CFO)
Bruce Christean (Vice Chm)
Geneva Jackson (Controller)

N.B. LIEBMAN & CO. INC.
4705 Carlisle Pk, Mechanicsburg, PA 17050
Tel.: (717) 761-4550
Web Site: http://www.nbliebman.com
Year Founded: 1919
Sales Range: $10-24.9 Million
Emp.: 50
Retailer of Household Furniture
N.A.I.C.S.: 449110
Charles B. Liebman (Pres)
Carol Liebman (VP)

N.B. WEST CONTRACTING COMPANY
2780 Mary Ave, Saint Louis, MO 63144
Tel.: (314) 962-3145
Web Site: http://www.nbwest.com
Sales Range: $10-24.9 Million
Emp.: 80
Highway & Street Paving Contractor
N.A.I.C.S.: 237310
Larry West (Pres)

N.B.M. CORPORATION
201 E Carl Albert Pkwy, McAlester, OK 74501
Tel.: (918) 423-2265
Web Site: http://www.thebankna.com
Year Founded: 1927
Sales Range: $125-149.9 Million
Emp.: 105
Commercial Banking Services
N.A.I.C.S.: 551111
Mike McGowan (Chm)
Subsidiaries:
The Bank, National Association (1)
201 E Carl Albert Pkwy, McAlester, OK 74501
Tel.: (918) 423-2265
Banking Services
N.A.I.C.S.: 522110
Lisa Johnson (Mgr-HR)

N.C. FARM BUREAU MUTUAL INSURANCE CO. INC.
5301 Glenwood Ave, Raleigh, NC 27612-3244
Tel.: (919) 782-1705
Web Site: http://www.ncfbins.com
Year Founded: 1953
Sales Range: $800-899.9 Million
Emp.: 1,200
Fire, Marine & Casualty Insurance
N.A.I.C.S.: 524126
Perry Crutchfield (Treas)
Dwayne Graham (Mgr-Agency)
Roger Gardner (Mgr-Info Sys Div)

N.E. FINCH CO.
1925 S Darst St, Peoria, IL 61607
Tel.: (309) 671-1433
Web Site: http://www.nefinch.com
Sales Range: $25-49.9 Million
Emp.: 10
Commercial & Office Building Contractors
N.A.I.C.S.: 236220
Tom Finch (Pres)
Doug Wilson (Gen Mgr-Ops)
Ronald Witt (Project Mgr)

N.E.W. CUSTOMER SERVICES COMPANIES, INC.
22894 Pacific Blvd, Sterling, VA 20166-9543
Tel.: (703) 318-7700
Web Site: http://www.newcorp.com
Year Founded: 1983
Sales Range: $75-99.9 Million
Emp.: 6,000
Third Party Administrator of Extended Service Plans
N.A.I.C.S.: 561499
David Bosserman (CFO, COO & Sr VP)
Danny Hourigan (Pres-Intl)
Raymond J. Zukowski (Sr VP-Customer Experience)
Dan Hulkower (VP & Gen Mgr-Client Svcs)
Joe Romano (Sr VP-Client Svcs & Bus Dev)
Steven Voss (Sr VP-Fin & Treas)
Terri Feely (Sr VP-HR)
Barry Danoff (Sr VP-IT)

N.E.W. CUSTOMER SERVICES COMPANIES, INC.

N.E.W. Customer Services Companies, Inc.—(Continued)
Christina DeRosa (Sr VP-Product & Mktg)
Kevin Porter (Sr VP-Strategy & Corp Dev)
Sean Skelley (Sr VP-Svc Solutions)
Chuck Stewart (Sr VP-Client Svcs & Bus Dev)
Rodney Brown (VP & Controller)
Jamie Farver (VP-Program Mgmt)
Matt Frankel (Pres-NEW Customer Protection Co)
Simrun Gialleonardo (VP & Asst Gen Counsel)
Tim Copp (Gen Mgr-Client Svcs & VP)
Rob DiRocco (VP-Client Svcs & Bus Dev)
Steve Gusa (VP-Sls Dev & Trng)
Kim Reinecke (VP-Client Support & Integration)
Robert Siegel (VP & Gen Mgr-Client Svcs)
Glenn Gibney (VP & Gen Mgr-Client Svcs)
Brian David (VP & Gen Mgr-Internet Svcs)
Aaron Vance (VP-Intl Sls & Mktg)
Fred Schaufeld (Founder & Chm)

N.E.W. PLASTICS CORP.
112 4th St, Luxemburg, WI 54217
Tel.: (920) 845-2326
Web Site: http://www.newplastics.com
Year Founded: 1968
Sales Range: $10-24.9 Million
Emp.: 200
Mfr of Plastic Bottles, Jars & Lumber for the Food, Chemical, Cosmetic, Agricultural, Pharmaceutical & Nutraceutical Industries
N.A.I.C.S.: 326113
Mike Rekitzke (Pres)
Jean Lange (Mgr)
Subsidiaries:

Fulcrum Container LLC (1)
3180 Spruce St, Saint Paul, MN 55117
Tel.: (651) 481-8601
Web Site: http://www.fulcruminc.com
Sales Range: $1-9.9 Million
Emp.: 23
Plastics Bottle Mfr
N.A.I.C.S.: 326160
Samir Mehta (Pres)

N.F. SHELDON INC.
914 Southbridge St, Auburn, MA 01501
Tel.: (508) 721-9876
Web Site: http://www.sheldons.com
Sales Range: $10-24.9 Million
Emp.: 20
Motorcycles
N.A.I.C.S.: 441227
Orville Sheldon (Pres)
Ed Stevens (Gen Mgr)
Dustin Papierski (Mgr-Rental)

N.F. SMITH & ASSOCIATES, LP
5306 Hollister St, Houston, TX 77040
Tel.: (713) 430-3000   TX
Web Site: http://www.smithweb.com
Year Founded: 1984
Sales Range: $750-799.9 Million
Emp.: 400
Semiconductors, Electronic Components & Computer Products Distr
N.A.I.C.S.: 423690
Robert G. Ackerley (Co-Founder)
Lee C. Ackerley (Co-Founder & Exec VP)
Marc Barnhill (Chief Trading Officer)

Mark Bollinger (Chief Globalization Officer)
Sean Trinh (VP-Fin)
Choon Byun (Chm-Asia Pacific)
Matthew H. Hartzell (Chief Admin Officer)
Phyllis Tsu (CIO)
Kirk Wehby (COO)
Thuy Tran (Gen Counsel)
Art Figueroa (VP-Global Ops)
Margo Evans (VP-Mktg)
Layla Wright (VP-Pur-Global)
Cleat Kimbrough (VP-Europe, Middle East & Africa)
Nick Bedford (CFO)
Phoebe Chan (Gen Mgr-Beijing)
Gordon Qiu (VP-China)
Jovial Zhang (Dir-Pur-Asia)
Rocky Xu (VP-Global Pur)
Subsidiaries:

Ontility LLC (1)
5306 Hollister St, Houston, TX 77040
Tel.: (281) 854-1400
Web Site: http://www.ontility.com
Solar Product Distr
N.A.I.C.S.: 423690
Alexandra Harrison (Exec VP-Sls & Procurement)
Lindsey Garland (VP-Acctg)

N.H. BRAGG & SONS
92 Perry Rd, Bangor, ME 04401
Tel.: (207) 947-8611
Web Site: http://www.nhbragg.com
Rev.: $22,658,522
Emp.: 100
Industrial Supplies
N.A.I.C.S.: 423840
Dan Clark (Gen Mgr)

N.H. SCHEPPERS DISTRIBUTING CO
2300 St Marys Blvd, Jefferson City, MO 65109-1145
Tel.: (573) 636-4831
Web Site: http://www.nhscheppers.com
Sales Range: $10-24.9 Million
Emp.: 25
Beer & Other Fermented Malt Liquors
N.A.I.C.S.: 424810
Lacy Priesmeyer (Coord-Graphic Design)

N.H. STONE INC.
853 S Hwy 11, Sharpsburg, KY 40374
Tel.: (606) 247-2311
Sales Range: $10-24.9 Million
Emp.: 60
Provider of Guardrail & Highway Construction Services
N.A.I.C.S.: 237310
Olivia K. Stone (Pres)
Vicky Curry (Office Mgr)

N.H. YATES & CO., INC.
117 Church Ln C, Cockeysville, MD 21030-4903
Tel.: (410) 667-6300   MD
Web Site: http://www.nhyates.com
Year Founded: 1949
Sales Range: $10-24.9 Million
Emp.: 50
Provider of Plumbing Services
N.A.I.C.S.: 423720
James H. Yates (Pres)
Jim Winemiller (Controller)
John Thomas (CEO)

N.J. MALIN & ASSOCIATES, LP
15870 Midway Rd, Addison, TX 75001-4279
Tel.: (915) 592-2680   TX
Web Site: http://www.malinusa.com

Year Founded: 1971
Sales Range: $50-74.9 Million
Emp.: 360
Material Handling Equipment Mfr
N.A.I.C.S.: 423830
John Creme (Pres)

N.K. HURST CO., INC.
230 W McCarty St, Indianapolis, IN 46225-1234
Tel.: (317) 634-6425   IN
Web Site: http://www.hurstbeans.com
Year Founded: 1938
Sales Range: $25-49.9 Million
Emp.: 45
Packagers of Dried Bean Products
N.A.I.C.S.: 424510
Rick Hurst (Pres)
Nancy Maschmeyer (Mgr-Distr Div)

N.K.S. DISTRIBUTORS, INC.
399 New Churchmans Rd, New Castle, DE 19720
Tel.: (302) 322-1811
Web Site: http://www.nksdistributors.com
Year Founded: 1949
Emp.: 104
Beverage Distr
N.A.I.C.S.: 424820
Chris Devlin (Dir-Off Premise Sls)
George Briggs (VP-Sls & Mktg)
Jim Brown (Dir-On-Premise Sls)
Joanne Peake (VP-HR & Admin)
Kathy Willes (VP-Fin)

N.O. SIMMONS & ASSOCIATES INCORPORATED
167 E Price Rd, Brownsville, TX 78521
Tel.: (956) 546-2216
Rev.: $12,701,207
Emp.: 10
Land Subdividers & Developers, Residential
N.A.I.C.S.: 237210
Raymond Corkill (Pres)
Lorudes Carrasel (VP)

N.P. CONSTRUCTION OF NORTH FLORIDA, INC.
6510 Columbia Park Dr Unit 206, Jacksonville, FL 32258
Tel.: (904) 262-8830
Web Site: http://www.npconst.com
Year Founded: 1998
Rev.: $3,200,000
Emp.: 6
Nonresidential Construction
N.A.I.C.S.: 236220
Nelson E. Peraza (Founder & Pres)

N.R. INVESTMENTS INC.
1111 Park Centre Blvd Ste 450, Miami, FL 33169
Tel.: (305) 625-0949
Web Site: http://www.nrinvestments.com
Year Founded: 2001
Emp.: 68
Real Estate Investment Management Services
N.A.I.C.S.: 523999
Ron Gottesmann (Co-Founder & Principal)
Nir Shoshani (Co-Founder & Principal)
Terry Wellons (COO)
Natalie Bailey (Mgr-Acctg & HR)
Carlos Frost (Mgr-Premier Property Mgmt)
Roey Binshtok (Reg Mgr-Construction)
Rodney Levi (Gen Mgr-NR Peru)

U.S. PRIVATE

Subsidiaries:

N.R. Investments, Inc. (1)
Av Manuel Olguin 373 Stgo de Surco, Lima, Peru
Tel.: (51) 1 434 1808
Real Estate Investment Management Services
N.A.I.C.S.: 523999

N.S. FARRINGTON & CO.
1335 Bridgeport Dr, Kernersville, NC 27284
Tel.: (336) 788-7705
Web Site: http://www.nsfarrington.com
Year Founded: 1951
Sales Range: $1-9.9 Million
Emp.: 38
Industrial Laundry & Dry Cleaning Supply Distr
N.A.I.C.S.: 423850
Micheal Ross (Pres)

N.S. PACKAGING LLC
PO Box 240007, Charlotte, NC 28224-0007
Tel.: (704) 889-0402
Year Founded: 1997
Rev.: $45,000,000
Emp.: 405
Coated & Laminated Packaging Paper Mfr
N.A.I.C.S.: 322220
W. Battle Wall III (CEO)

N.V. HEATHORN INC.
1155 Beecher St, San Leandro, CA 94577
Tel.: (510) 569-9100   CA
Web Site: http://www.nvheathorn.com
Year Founded: 1932
Sales Range: $25-49.9 Million
Emp.: 500
Provider of Warm Air Heating & Air Conditioning Contracts
N.A.I.C.S.: 238220
Edward W. Heathorn (Sec)
David A. Heathorn (CFO)
Dave Wenner (Pres)

N.W. WHITE & COMPANY
100 Independence Blvd, Columbia, SC 29210
Tel.: (803) 216-7000
Web Site: http://www.nw-white.com
Sales Range: $1-9.9 Million
Emp.: 55
Hauling & Transportation
N.A.I.C.S.: 484220
Charles R. Jackson (Owner)
Dustin Hoffman (Gen Mgr-Columbia & Special Svcs)
Art Youngblood (Gen Mgr-Greenwood Div)
Fran Gregory (Gen Mgr-Greer Div)
Stan James (Gen Mgr-Anderson Div)
David Jacques (Gen Mgr-Special Svcs)
Steven Jackson (Gen Mgr-Charleston Div)

N2 ACQUISITION HOLDINGS CORP.
500 S Pointe Dr Ste 240, Miami Beach, FL 33139
Tel.: (786) 482-6333   DE
Year Founded: 2021
Investment Services
N.A.I.C.S.: 523999
Noam Gottesman (Co-Chm)
Martin E. Franklin (Co-Chm)
Guy Weltsch (Pres & CEO)
Robert A. E. Franklin (COO & VP)
Desiree DeStefano (CFO & Asst Sec)
Alejandro San Miguel (VP & Sec)

COMPANIES | NACE INTERNATIONAL

N2 SOLUTIONS LLC
113 Liberty Ave., Lafayette, LA 70508
Tel.: (866) 940-2450
Web Site: https://n2-solutions.com
Year Founded: 2016
Oil & Gas Distr
N.A.I.C.S.: 221210
Subsidiaries:

Pipe Freezing Services, Inc. (1)
41 Morriston Rd, Petal, MS 39465
Tel.: (601) 544-5775
Web Site: http://www.pfsn2services.com
Rev.: $1,837,000
Emp.: 11
Wood Container & Pallet Mfr
N.A.I.C.S.: 321920
Ted Vise (Owner)

NA HOKU, INC.
2005 Kalia Rd, Honolulu, HI 96815
Tel.: (808) 837-1200
Web Site: http://www.nahoku.com
Year Founded: 1924
Rev.: $86,700,000
Emp.: 539
Jewelry Stores
N.A.I.C.S.: 458310
Steven Bookatz (COO)
Edward D. Sultan III (CEO)
Edward D. Sultan Jr. (Chm)

NA ORION INTERNATIONAL CONSULTING GROUP, INC.
400 Regency Forst Dr St 310, Raleigh, NC 27518
Tel.: (919) 851-3309
Web Site:
http://www.orioninternational.com
Sales Range: $10-24.9 Million
Emp.: 100
Placement Agencies
N.A.I.C.S.: 561311
Mike Starich (Pres)

NA SALES COMPANY INC.
301 E Grand Ave, South San Francisco, CA 94080
Tel.: (650) 827-2020
Web Site: http://www.nasales.com
Sales Range: $75-99.9 Million
Emp.: 75
Groceries & Related Products
N.A.I.C.S.: 424490
Tetsuo Mochizuki (Pres)

NAB CONSTRUCTION CORP.
11220 14th Ave, College Point, NY 11356-1408
Tel.: (718) 762-0001 NY
Web Site:
http://www.nabconstruction.com
Year Founded: 1954
Sales Range: $10-24.9 Million
Emp.: 110
Industrial Buildings & Warehouses
N.A.I.C.S.: 236220
Kevin Donahue (Controller)
Gary Simpson (Pres)
Don Callahan (Superintendent)

NABCO ELECTRIC
2800 2nd Ave, Chattanooga, TN 37407
Tel.: (423) 622-8463
Web Site:
http://www.nabcoelectric.com
Sales Range: $10-24.9 Million
Emp.: 95
Electrical Wiring Services
N.A.I.C.S.: 238210
Greg Bowman (Pres)
Wes Bowman (VP)
Nancy Malone (Sec)
Virginia Miller (Mgr-Admin)

NABCO, INC.
1001 Corporate Dr Ste 205, Canonsburg, PA 15317
Tel.: (724) 746-9617
Web Site: http://www.nabcoinc.com
Year Founded: 1980
Sales Range: $10-24.9 Million
Emp.: 25
Total Explosive Containment Vessel (TCV) Mfr
N.A.I.C.S.: 561621
William Presutti (CFO)
Kim King (Dir-Engrg)

NABEEL'S CAFE & MARKET
1706 Oxmoor Rd, Birmingham, AL 35209
Tel.: (205) 879-9292
Web Site: https://www.nabeels.com
Year Founded: 1992
Sales Range: $10-24.9 Million
Emp.: 16
Food Service
N.A.I.C.S.: 722513
John Krontiras (Gen Mgr)
Anthony Krontiras (Product Mgr-Engrg)

NABER CHRYSLER DODGE JEEP RAM
45 Naber Dr, Shallotte, NC 28470
Tel.: (910) 754-2811
Web Site:
http://www.naberchryslerdodgejeep.com
Sales Range: $10-24.9 Million
Emp.: 44
Car Whslr
N.A.I.C.S.: 441110
Bryan Cheers (Principal)
Matt Gerrald (Sec)

NABHOLZ CONSTRUCTION CORP.
612 Garland St, Conway, AR 72032-4418
Tel.: (501) 505-5800 AR
Web Site: http://www.nabholz.com
Year Founded: 1949
Sales Range: $200-249.9 Million
Emp.: 800
Provider of Contracting Services
N.A.I.C.S.: 236220
Greg Williams (CEO)
Brad Hegeman (Co-COO)
Don Greenland (Officer-Strategic Growth)
Bill Hannah (Chm)
Gregg Scholtens (Exec VP-Ops)
Brandon Wall (Mgr-Svc-Fort Smith)
Steven Rosch (Asst Project Mgr)
Chris Goevert (Superintendent)
Jake Nabholz (Pres-South)
Shane Fernandez (Pres-Southwest)
Greg Fogle (Co-COO)
Steve Clouten (Pres-Central)
Bryan Bruich (CFO)
Michael Parker (Pres-Energy & Environmental)
Jon Pahl (Pres-Midwest)
Andrea Woods (Corp Counsel & Exec VP)
Ben Montgomery (Pres-Indus Svcs)
Andrew Adlong (Exec VP-Ops)
Brian Cunneen (Exec VP-Ops)
Jim Spotts (Pres-Civil)
Chris Kauffman (Exec VP-Ops)
Phil Moffitt (Exec VP-Ops)
Doyle Phillips (Exec VP-Preconstruction)
David Nabholz (Exec VP-Ops)
Mike Meadors (Exec VP-Preconstruction Svcs Conway)
Rob Dodd (Exec VP-Ops)
Mike Mackey (VP-Ops-Kansas)

Subsidiaries:

Nabholz Construction Corp. - Ozark Division (1)
3301 N 2nd St, Rogers, AR 72756
Tel.: (479) 636-5380
Web Site: http://www.nabholz.com
Sales Range: $25-49.9 Million
Emp.: 300
Provider of Construction Services
N.A.I.C.S.: 236220
Clay Gordon (VP-Mktg)
David Petty (Mgr-Specialty Svcs)

Nabholz Construction Corp. - Tulsa Division (1)
10319 E 54th St, Tulsa, OK 74146
Tel.: (918) 632-7200
Web Site: http://www.nabholz.com
Sales Range: $25-49.9 Million
Emp.: 60
Construction Services
N.A.I.C.S.: 236220
Shane Fernadez (Pres)

NABRO ABLE LLC
8350 E Evans Rd Ste C-4, Scottsdale, AZ 85260
Tel.: (480) 403-8300 AZ
Web Site: http://www.orban.com
Year Founded: 2005
Sales Range: $25-49.9 Million
Emp.: 40
Holding Company; Broadcast Transmission Audio Processing Equipment Developer & Mfr
N.A.I.C.S.: 551112
Charles Jayson Brentlinger (Pres & Mgr)

Subsidiaries:

Orban (1)
7209 Browning Rd, Pennsauken, NJ 08109
Tel.: (856) 719-9900
Web Site: http://www.orban.com
Sales Range: $100-124.9 Million
Emp.: 20
Broadcast Transmission Audio Processing Equipment Developer & Mfr
N.A.I.C.S.: 334220
Robert Orban (Chief Engr)

NABROS INC
4320 Winfield Rd Ste 200, Warrenville, IL 60555
Tel.: (630) 836-8765
Web Site: http://www.nabros.com
Year Founded: 2002
Sales Range: $1-9.9 Million
Emp.: 55
Technical Consulting
N.A.I.C.S.: 541990
Abhinandan Rajmane (Pres)

NAC GROUP INC.
10001 16 St N, Saint Petersburg, FL 33716
Tel.: (727) 576-0550
Web Site: http://www.nacsemi.com
Rev.: $30,000,000
Emp.: 100
Electronic Parts & Equipment Merchant Whslr
N.A.I.C.S.: 423690
John Connolly (VP)
Joes Sandrs (VP)
Jonathan Stanton (Pres & CEO)
Scott Garnett (Mgr-Sls)

NAC, INC.
2025 1st Ave Ste 300, Seattle, WA 98121-3131
Tel.: (206) 441-4522
Web Site:
http://www.nacarchitecture.com
Sales Range: $10-24.9 Million
Emp.: 180
Architectural Services
N.A.I.C.S.: 541310
Thomas J. Stroeher (CFO & Principal)
Dana Harbaugh (Pres & CEO)
John C. Eckert (Assoc Principal)
Jack Schneider (Assoc Principal)
Brian Love (Assoc Principal)
Timothy A. Ballard (Principal)
Trish E. Buzan (Principal & Dir-IT)
Michael J. Cole (Principal)
Keith M. Comes (Mng Principal)
Brent S. Compton (Assoc Principal)
Kevin P. Flanagan (Mng Principal)
Mark J. Gifford (Assoc Principal)
Thomas E. Golden (Principal)
Brent G. Harding (Principal)
Douglas G. Heyamoto (Assoc Principal)
Daniel C. Jardine (Principal)
Helena L. Jubany (Principal)
Dan A. Kurtz (Principal)
Melissa A. McFadgen (Principal)
Mark A. McMicheal (Principal)
Pierce McVey (Principal)
Jeani Natwick (Principal)
Leticia Ochoa (Assoc Principal)
Michael R. O'Malley (Principal)
Ryan D. Palmquist (Assoc Principal)
Michael Pinto (Principal)
William W. Rash (Assoc Principal)
Philip Riedel (Principal)
Matthew W. Rumbaugh (Principal)
Chad S. Schmidt (Assoc Principal)

Subsidiaries:

Trinity Health Group, Ltd. (1)
827 Yard St, Columbus, OH 43212
Tel.: (614) 899-4830
Web Site: http://www.trinitynac.com
Architectural Services
N.A.I.C.S.: 541310
John M. Chory (Principal)
Sara Herridge (Project Mgr)

NACA LOGISTICS (USA), INC.
5000 Airport Plz Dr, Long Beach, CA 90805
Tel.: (562) 432-4430 CA
Web Site:
http://www.nacalogistics.com
Year Founded: 1978
Sales Range: $150-199.9 Million
Emp.: 750
Holding Company; Provider of Freight Transportation Arrangement Services
N.A.I.C.S.: 488510
Bruce Ericson (VP-Import Sls)
Vince Argenzio (VP)
Irene Wu (Controller-United States)
Michael Sinclair (Dir-Global Sls)

Subsidiaries:

Vanguard Logistics Services (1)
2665 E Del Amo Blvd, Rancho Dominguez, CA 90221-9550
Tel.: (310) 835-8900
Web Site: http://www.vanguardlogistics.com
Freight Forwarding & General Warehousing Services
N.A.I.C.S.: 488510
Onno Meij (CEO)

NACE INTERNATIONAL
1440 S Creek Dr, Houston, TX 77084-4906
Tel.: (281) 228-6223 TX
Web Site: http://www.nace.org
Year Founded: 1943
Sales Range: $25-49.9 Million
Emp.: 122
Corrosion Protection Services
N.A.I.C.S.: 541620
Jody Bradel (Mgr-Relationship)
Linda Goldberg (Head-Intl Bus Dev)
Gretchen Jacobson (Dir-Content Dev)
Melissa Mishler (Acct Mgr-Interiors)
Matt Miller (Acct Exec-Channel)
Bob Chalker (CEO)

NACE INTERNATIONAL — U.S. PRIVATE

NACE International—(Continued)

David Barnes (Vice Chm)
Cynthia O'Malley (Chief Integration Officer)
Helena Seelinger (Exec Dir)

NACEL OPEN DOOR, INC.
380 Jackson St Ste 200, Saint Paul, MN 55101
Tel.: (651) 686-0080   ND
Web Site: http://www.nacelopendoor.org
Year Founded: 1997
Sales Range: $10-24.9 Million
Emp.: 167
Educational Support Services
N.A.I.C.S.: 611710
Tom Kalinowski (Dir-Academic Year Program Network)
Shannon Rausch (Dir-Mktg & Comm)
Roy Nilsson (CFO)
Rich Banasikowski (VP-Ops)
Rae Lenway (Dir-Ops)
Frank Tarsitano (Pres & CEO)
Peggy Spurgeon (Dir-Curriculum & Instruction)
Sandy Morgan (Dir-Academic Year Program Student Advising)
Kim Devlin (Dir-Natl Recruitment)
Luke Wonjoong Lee (Dir-Asian Ops & Fin)
Jennifer Tarsitano (Dir-Strategic Dev)

NACHI MACHINING TECHNOLOGY CO.
715 Pushville Rd, Greenwood, IN 46143-9782
Tel.: (586) 263-0100
Year Founded: 1929
Sales Range: $25-49.9 Million
Emp.: 100
Machine & Tools: Shaving, Honing, Grinding, Gaging, Sound Testing, Hobbing, Shaping, Deburring, Tooth Pointing, Chamfering, Precision Ball Screws, Contract Heat Treatment
N.A.I.C.S.: 333517
Francis Wisner (Pres)
Dave Petrimoulx (Reg Mgr)
Rodney Soenen (Product Mgr)

NACHON ENTERPRISES INC.
2477 W 4th Ave, Hialeah, FL 33010
Tel.: (305) 888-5236
Web Site: http://www.nachonenterprises.com
Rev: $15,900,000
Emp.: 115
Hardware Stores
N.A.I.C.S.: 444140
Carlos Nachon Jr. (Pres)

NACKARD BOTTLING COMPANY
4980 E Railhead Ave, Flagstaff, AZ 86004
Tel.: (928) 526-2229
Sales Range: $25-49.9 Million
Emp.: 300
Soft Drinks: Packaged In Cans, Bottles
N.A.I.C.S.: 312111
Patrick M. Nackard (Pres)

NADEAU CORP.
1633 Stanford St, Santa Monica, CA 90404
Tel.: (310) 453-8385
Web Site: http://www.furniturewithasoul.com
Sales Range: $10-24.9 Million
Emp.: 40
Furniture
N.A.I.C.S.: 423210
Tom Nadeau (CEO)

NADEL & GUSSMAN LLC
15 E 5th St Ste 3200, Tulsa, OK 74103
Tel.: (918) 583-3333
Rev.: $13,600,000
Emp.: 117
Crude Petroleum Production
N.A.I.C.S.: 211120
Wayne Hamilton (CFO)
Jim Adelson (Mgr)

NADEL ARCHITECTS, INC.
1990 S Bundy Dr Ste 400, Los Angeles, CA 90025
Tel.: (310) 826-2100   CA
Web Site: http://www.nadelarc.com
Year Founded: 1974
Sales Range: $75-99.9 Million
Emp.: 100
Architectural Services
N.A.I.C.S.: 541310
Herbert Nadel (CEO)
Andrew Simmons (Dir-Hospitality Studio)
David Anderson (Owner, Principal & Dir-Retail Studio)
Greg Lyon (Owner, Principal & Dir-Design)
Mark Mikelson (Owner, Principal & Dir-Retail Studio)
Greg Palaski (Owner & Principal)
Tina Tayag (Owner, CFO, Principal & Controller)
Patrick Winters (Owner, Principal & Dir-Design)
David Jacobson (Exec VP & Dir-Office Sector Studio)
Stella Debibi (Mng Dir-Bus Dev)

NADEL PHELAN, INC.
269 Mt Hermon Rd Ste 107, Scotts Valley, CA 95066
Tel.: (831) 439-5570
Web Site: http://www.nadelphelan.com
Year Founded: 1993
Sales Range: $10-24.9 Million
Emp.: 20
Branding & Research, Strategic Technology Communications & Public Relations
N.A.I.C.S.: 541820
Paula Phelan (Pres & CEO)
Fred Nadel (COO & VP-Market Res)
Cara Sloman (VP)
Lisa Christensen (Mgr-Ops)

NADER WHOLESALE GROCERS INC.
3636 W 83rd Pl, Chicago, IL 60652
Tel.: (773) 582-1000
Sales Range: $10-24.9 Million
Emp.: 8
Groceries; General Line
N.A.I.C.S.: 424410
Equab Ali (Pres)

NADIA INC.
12021 Harper Ave, Detroit, MI 48213
Tel.: (313) 527-0050
Sales Range: $1-9.9 Million
Emp.: 28
Groceries; General Line
N.A.I.C.S.: 424410
Alia Al-Naimi (Pres)

NADLER MODULAR STRUCTURES
11 Harmony Ste F, Spring Valley, NY 10977
Web Site: http://www.nadlermodular.com
Year Founded: 2002
Rev.: $5,600,000
Emp.: 6
Supplier Quality Modular Buildings, Classrooms, Sales Trailers & Mobile Offices
N.A.I.C.S.: 321991
Jeff Neeman (Pres)
Steven Muller (VP)

NADY SYSTEMS, INC.
6701 Shellmound St, Emeryville, CA 94608-1023
Tel.: (510) 652-2411   CA
Web Site: http://www.nady.com
Year Founded: 1976
Sales Range: $75-99.9 Million
Emp.: 60
Mfr of Wireless Microphones & Communicators
N.A.I.C.S.: 334290
John Nady (Founder, Pres & CEO)
Fred Shrag (Gen Counsel)

NAECO LLC
100 Naeco Way, Peachtree City, GA 30269
Tel.: (770) 487-6006
Web Site: http://www.naeco.net
Year Founded: 1999
Sales Range: $10-24.9 Million
Emp.: 23
Electrical Contacts & Assemblies
N.A.I.C.S.: 335999
David Bergmann (Pres)

NAFSA
1307 New York Ave NW 8th Fl, Washington, DC 20005-4701
Tel.: (202) 737-3699   DC
Web Site: http://www.nafsa.org
Year Founded: 1948
Rev.: $20,896,754
Assets: $23,228,239
Liabilities: $7,241,936
Net Worth: $15,986,303
Earnings: ($618,246)
Emp.: 113
Fiscal Year-end: 12/31/18
Educational Association
N.A.I.C.S.: 813920
James Mahoney (Sr Dir-Mktg)
Robin Little (Dir-Production & Mktg Svcs)
Elaine Meyer-Lee (Asst VP-Learning-Global)
Fanta Aw (Chm & Pres)
Stephen Ferst (VP-Pub Policy & Practice)
Allison Cash Spiro (Assoc Dir-Education Abroad Outreach & Regulatory Practice)
Caroline Donovan White (Sr Dir-Education Abroad Svcs)
David Fosnocht (Dir-Immigration Practice Resources)
Dina Gillespy (Assoc Dir-Organizational Advancement)
Dorothea Antonio (Deputy Exec Dir)
Gail Hochhauser (Sr Dir-Organizational Advancement)
Heather MacCleoud (Dir-Academic Affairs)
Jane Hoffman (CFO & Deputy Exec Dir)
Joanne Kuriyan (Dir-Exhibits)
Joann Ng Hartmann (Sr Dir-IEM-ISS Svcs & Volunteer Engagement)
Kyle Contrata (Dir-Data Science & Event Tech)
Lauren Newton (Assoc Dir-Professional Learning Svcs)
Leslie Murray (Dir-Meeting Plng & Svcs)
Mark Farmer (Dir-Higher Education & Pub Policy)
Meredith Bell (Editor-Digital Content)
Meredith Brodbeck (Assoc Dir-Web Comm)
Pete Mason (Dir-Digital Experience)
Rebecca Morgan (Sr Dir-Media Comm & Advocacy)
Steve Springer (Dir-Regulatory Practice Liaison)
Tanith Fowler Corsi (Asst Dir-Graduate Admissions)
Esther Brimmer (CEO)

NAGEL FARM SERVICE INC.
6202 Nagel Rd, Preston, MD 21655
Tel.: (410) 673-7123
Web Site: http://www.nagelgrain.com
Rev.: $22,000,000
Emp.: 28
Whslr of Grains
N.A.I.C.S.: 424510
David Nagel (Pres & CEO)
Chat Nagel (VP)

NAGLE PAVING COMPANY
39525 W 13 Mile Rd Ste 300, Novi, MI 48377-2303
Tel.: (248) 553-0600
Web Site: http://www.naglepaving.com
Sales Range: $50-74.9 Million
Emp.: 11
Paving Company (Residential & Commercial)
N.A.I.C.S.: 237310
Larry Brennan (Pres)

NAGLER GROUP
5 Bedford Farms Dr Ste 304, Bedford, NH 03110
Tel.: (603) 637-1492
Web Site: http://www.naglergroup.com
Year Founded: 2008
Sales Range: $1-9.9 Million
Emp.: 20
Administrative & HR Staffing Services
N.A.I.C.S.: 561311
Matt Nagler (Mng Partner)
Jason Kroll (Mng Partner)
Paul Becker (Mng Partner)
Gary Wing (Mng Partner)
Jason Alexander (Mng Partner)
Maura Mann (VP)
Elizabeth Eastman (Dir-Admin & HR)
Salina McIntire (Dir-Mktg)
Tammy Vigliotti (Dir-Mktg & Comm)
Alyssa Lavoie (Dir-Project Mgmt)
Chip Fierimonte (Dir-Recruiting)
Dawn Jesmer (Dir-Recruiting)
Jillian Vaillancourt (Dir-Recruiting)

NAI MID-MICHIGAN
2149 Jolly Rd Ste 200, Okemos, MI 48864
Tel.: (517) 487-9222
Web Site: http://www.naimidmichigan.com
Commercial Real Estate Services
N.A.I.C.S.: 531390
Tim Miller (CEO)

NAI SOUTHWEST FLORIDA, INC.
13120 Westlinks Terrace Blvd Ste 2, Fort Myers, FL 33913
Tel.: (239) 437-3330
Web Site: http://www.naiswfl.com
Year Founded: 2001
Sales Range: $25-49.9 Million
Emp.: 10
Real Estate Brokerage, Investment & Consulting Services
N.A.I.C.S.: 531210
Kevin N. Fitzgerald (Pres & Principal)
Lana J. Fitzgerald (CFO & Exec VP)
Brett A. Rosenthal (Mng Dir-Corp & Investment Svcs)

NAI TALCOR

COMPANIES

1018 Thomasville Rd Ste 200A, Tallahassee, FL 32303
Tel.: (850) 224-2300
Web Site: http://www.naitalcor.com
Sales Range: $1-9.9 Million
Emp.: 50
Real Estate Brokerage
N.A.I.C.S.: 531210
Rebecca Adams *(Comptroller & Mgr-HR)*
Kristy Bennett *(Dir-Acctg)*
Beverly Hayes *(Mgr-Property)*
Don Gowdy *(Mgr-Property)*
Frank Langston *(Principal & Bus Mgr)*
Jimmy Nystrom *(Dir-Leasing)*
Whitney VanLandingham *(Dir-Mktg)*
Rick Smith *(COO)*
Debbie Weber *(Mgr-Property)*
Butch Gaddis *(Dir-Property Mgmt)*
E. Edward Murray Jr. *(Pres)*

NAIAD MARITIME GROUP, INC.
50 Parrott Dr, Shelton, CT 06484
Tel.: (203) 929-6355
Web Site: http://www.naiad.com
Sales Range: $10-24.9 Million
Emp.: 50
Ship Mfr
N.A.I.C.S.: 336611
John Venables *(Pres)*

Subsidiaries:

Naiad Dynamics Holland, BV (1)
Sleperweg 10, 6222 NK, Maastricht, Netherlands
Tel.: (31) 436049200
Web Site: http://www.naiad.com
Sales Range: $10-24.9 Million
Emp.: 8
Ship Stabilization Systems Mfr
N.A.I.C.S.: 336611
John Venables *(Mng Dir)*

Naiad Dynamics UK, Ltd. (1)
Hamilton Rd, Cosham, Portsmouth, PO6 4PX, Hampshire, United Kingdom (100%)
Tel.: (44) 2392539750
Web Site: http://www.naiad.com
Sales Range: $10-24.9 Million
Emp.: 20
Ship Mfr
N.A.I.C.S.: 336611

Naiad Dynamics US, Inc. (1)
23620 3 Notch Rd, Hollywood, MD 20636 (100%)
Tel.: (301) 690-2010
Web Site: http://www.naiad.com
Sales Range: $10-24.9 Million
Emp.: 25
Metal Fabricated Mfr
N.A.I.C.S.: 541320
Chris Pappas *(Dir-Engrg)*

NAICS ASSOCIATION, LLC
129 Lakeshore Dr, Rockaway, NJ 07866
Tel.: (973) 625-5626
Web Site: http://www.naics.com
Year Founded: 1993
Sales Range: $1-9.9 Million
Emp.: 10
Business Information Publisher & List Marketer
N.A.I.C.S.: 513130
Mitch Feldman *(Pres)*

NAIL COMMUNICATIONS
63 Eddy St, Providence, RI 02903
Tel.: (401) 331-6245
Web Site: http://www.nail.cc
Year Founded: 1998
Rev.: $20,000,000
Emp.: 22
Advetising Agency
N.A.I.C.S.: 541810
Brian Gross *(Partner-Creative)*
Alec Beckett *(Partner-Creative)*
Jeremy Crisp *(Mng Partner)*
Laura Crigler *(Dir-Art-Awesomeness)*
Kaitlyn Vicinte *(Mgr-Community)*
Rebecca Donovan *(Acct Mgr)*
Niki Brazier *(Project Coord)*

NAIL MEDIA GROUP
700 Canal St 2nd Fl, Stamford, CT 06902
Tel.: (212) 686-9710
Web Site: http://www.nailmediagroup.com
Sales Range: $25-49.9 Million
Emp.: 10
Media Buying Services
N.A.I.C.S.: 541830
Jack Nail *(CEO)*
Cindy Seebeck *(Dir-Media)*
Bob Mauser *(Mng Dir)*

NAILOR INDUSTRIES
4714 Winfield Rd, Houston, TX 77039
Tel.: (281) 590-1172
Web Site: http://www.nailor.com
Year Founded: 1971
Sales Range: $125-149.9 Million
Emp.: 230
HVAC Products & Systems
N.A.I.C.S.: 333415

Subsidiaries:

Thermal Corporation (1)
4637 Winfield Rd, Houston, TX 77039
Tel.: (281) 590-1172
Web Site: http://www.thermal-corp.com
Sales Range: $25-49.9 Million
Industrial Heating Products
N.A.I.C.S.: 333415

NAIMOR, INC.
2025 Masonry Way, Bellingham, WA 98226-8011
Tel.: (360) 756-9700
Web Site: http://www.naimormetal.com
Fabricated Metal Products Mfr
N.A.I.C.S.: 332710
Shahrokh A. Naieni *(Co-Owner & Pres)*
Mojdeh Naieni *(Co-Owner & Plant Mgr)*

Subsidiaries:

Automated Metal Technologies, Inc. (1)
15340 NE 92nd St Ste C, Redmond, WA 98052
Tel.: (425) 895-9733
Web Site: http://www.naimormetalfabrication.com
Sales Range: $1-9.9 Million
Emp.: 20
Fabricated Metal Products Mfr
N.A.I.C.S.: 332710
Shahrokh A. Naieni *(Co-Owner & Pres)*
Mojdeh Naieni *(Co-Owner & Plant Mgr)*

NAJAFI COMPANIES, LLC
The Esplanade 2525 E Camelback Rd Ste 850, Phoenix, AZ 85016
Tel.: (602) 476-0600 AZ
Web Site: http://www.najafi.com
Year Founded: 2003
Privater Equity Firm
N.A.I.C.S.: 523999
Jahm Najafi *(CEO)*

Subsidiaries:

Author Solutions, LLC (1)
1663 Liberty Dr Ste 200, Bloomington, IN 47403
Tel.: (812) 339-6000
Web Site: http://www.authorsolutions.com
Self-Publishing Authors Services
N.A.I.C.S.: 513199
Bill Becher *(COO)*
Joe Steinbach *(CIO)*
Bill Elliott *(Pres)*
Derrick Purvis *(Chief Revenue Officer)*
Melissa Bauer *(Gen Counsel)*
Merrell Rio *(Assoc VP-Ops & Gen Mgr)*

Subsidiary (Domestic):

iUniverse, LLC (2)
1663 Liberty Dr Ste 200, Bloomington, IN 47403
Tel.: (844) 349-9409
Web Site: http://www.iuniverse.com
Printed & Online Self Publishing Services
N.A.I.C.S.: 513199

NAJARIAN FURNITURE COMPANY
17560 E Rowland St, City of Industry, CA 91748
Tel.: (626) 839-8700
Web Site: http://www.najarianfurniture.com
Year Founded: 1988
Sales Range: $25-49.9 Million
Emp.: 40
Household Furniture Mfr & Distr
N.A.I.C.S.: 337121
Michael Lawrence *(Exec VP-Ops)*
Carlos Dominguez *(VP-Sls-Natl)*
Michael Najarian *(Pres)*

NAKA'S, INC.
3097 Oihana St, Lihue, HI 96766-1400
Tel.: (808) 246-4886
Rev.: $4,500,000
Emp.: 20
Holding Company
N.A.I.C.S.: 424130
Ross Nakashima *(Pres)*
Patricia Nakashima *(VP)*

Subsidiaries:

Ventures Associates, Inc. (1)
3097 Oihana St, Lihue, HI 96766-1400
Tel.: (808) 246-4886
Web Site: http://www.ventureskauai.com
Distr of Industrial & Personal Service Paper
N.A.I.C.S.: 424130
Ross Nakashima *(Owner)*

NAKED RESTAURANTS, INC.
440 Totten Pond Rd Ste 4, Waltham, MA 02451-2031
Tel.: (781) 609-2242
Web Site: http://www.nakedfish.com
Sales Range: $10-24.9 Million
Emp.: 800
Restaurant Services
N.A.I.C.S.: 722511
Cathy Tsoukalas *(CFO)*
Jill Laboissiere *(Mgr-HR)*
Joey Crugnale *(Pres)*

NAKOMA GROUP
4000 Barranca Pkwy Ste 250, Irvine, CA 92604
Tel.: (949) 262-3298
Web Site: http://www.nakomagroup.com
Sales Range: $10-24.9 Million
Emp.: 15
Information Technology Services
N.A.I.C.S.: 541512
Ronald E. English *(Pres & CEO)*
Edward N. Myers *(Chm)*

Subsidiaries:

Nakoma Group (1)
4000 Barranca Pkwy Ste 250, Irvine, CA 92604-1713
Tel.: (480) 496-5701
Computer Management & Consulting Services
N.A.I.C.S.: 541611

Nakoma Group Enterprise Solutions (1)
9800 Mount Pyramid Ct Ste 400, Englewood, CO 80112
Tel.: (877) 643-7463

Enterprise Solutions
N.A.I.C.S.: 561499

NAME BRANDS INC.

NALCO DISTRIBUTING, INC.
1000 Labore Industrial Ct, Saint Paul, MN 55110
Tel.: (651) 636-8124
Sales Range: $10-24.9 Million
Emp.: 60
Industrial Product Distr
N.A.I.C.S.: 423840
Ken Kruger *(CEO)*

NAMASTE SOLAR ELECTRIC, INC.
4571 Broadway St, Boulder, CO 80304
Tel.: (303) 447-0300
Web Site: http://www.namastesolar.com
Year Founded: 2004
Sales Range: $10-24.9 Million
Emp.: 100
Electrical Work
N.A.I.C.S.: 238210
Blake Jones *(Co-Founder & Co-Owner)*
Heath Mackay *(Co-Owner & Mgr-Project Dev-SouthWest Reg)*
Teri Lema *(Co-Owner)*
Steven Carroll *(Dir-Svc)*
Jason Sharpe *(Co-Owner & CEO)*
Eric Meyer *(Co-Owner & Mgr-IT)*
Jessica Hodge *(Co-Owner & Mgr-HR)*
Tom Zwahlen *(Co-Owner & Dir-Fin)*
Kristin Eiler *(Co-Owner & Coord-HR)*
Jason Brown *(Co-Owner)*
Tim Milliano *(Co-Owner)*
Walt Schilling *(Co-Owner)*
Angela Burke *(Co-Owner & Mgr-Residential Design Grp)*
Arthur Hicks *(Co-Owner & Designer-CAD)*
Jon Wedel *(Co-Owner & Dir-Ops-Comml Utility)*
Ryan Dulaney *(Co-Owner)*
Sean Hawkins *(Co-Owner)*
Matt Griffiths *(Co-Owner & Mgr-Comml Svc)*
Cynthia Christensen *(Co-Owner & Dir-Sls Comml Utility)*
Martin Beggs *(Co-Owner & Designer-Comml Front End)*
Nick Williamson *(Co-Owner & Mgr-Preconstruction)*
Sam Mason *(Co-Owner)*
Aaron Friedlander *(Co-Owner & Designer-Comml Technical)*
Justin Huff *(Co-Owner)*
Rick Coen *(Co-Owner & Designer-Comml Technical)*

NAMBE MILLS INC.
2891 Cooks Rd, Santa Fe, NM 87507
Tel.: (505) 471-2912
Web Site: http://www.nambe.com
Rev.: $23,200,000
Emp.: 250
Novelties & Giftware, Including Trophies
N.A.I.C.S.: 332999
Shannon Brown *(Dir-Sls-Specialty, Gift & Intl)*
Bill Robedee *(Pres & CEO)*
Theresa Clemmer *(Dir-Sls-Corp, Hospitality & Special Markets)*

NAME BRANDS INC.
7215 S Memorial Dr, Tulsa, OK 74133
Tel.: (918) 307-0284
Web Site: http://www.halfofhalf.com
Sales Range: $10-24.9 Million
Emp.: 400
Retailer of Women's & Children's Clothing

NAME BRANDS INC.

Name Brands Inc.—(Continued)
N.A.I.C.S.: 458110
Paul Venamon (Controller)

NAMELY, INC.
Western Union Telegraph Bldg 195 Broadway, New York, NY 10007
Tel.: (855) 626-3591
Web Site: http://www.namely.com
Emp.: 40
Human Resources Software Developer
N.A.I.C.S.: 513210
Matt Straz (Founder & CEO)
Debra Squyres (VP-Client Svcs)
Judson Griffin (Reg VP-Sls)
Amy Roy (Chief People Officer)

NAMEMEDIA, INC.
225 Wyman St, Waltham, MA 02451
Tel.: (781) 839-2800
Web Site:
    http://www.namemedia.com
Sales Range: $50-74.9 Million
Emp.: 150
Domain Name Registration Services
N.A.I.C.S.: 541519
Brian D. Lucy (CFO)
Jason Miner (COO)

NAMIFY LLC
280 W 900 N, Springville, UT 84663
Tel.: (801) 491-8068
Web Site: http://www.namify.com
Year Founded: 2001
Sales Range: $10-24.9 Million
Emp.: 105
Customizable Promotional Items
N.A.I.C.S.: 315990
Brad Gasaway (VP-Mktg)
Scott Bishop (VP-Ops)
Chris Jensen (CEO)
Kristina Kayda (Mgr-Customer Svc)
Vanessa Alldredge (VP-Sls)
Bryan L. Welton Jr. (Chm)

NAMTEK CORP
124 Bedford Ctr Rd, Bedford, NH 03110
Tel.: (603) 488-6600
Web Site: http://www.namtek.com
Year Founded: 2006
Sales Range: $10-24.9 Million
Emp.: 60
Computer System Design Services
N.A.I.C.S.: 541512
Keith Turgeon (Pres)

NAMTRA BUSINESS SOLUTIONS, INC.
11800 Sunrise Valley Dr Ste 317, Reston, VA 20191
Tel.: (703) 391-7071
Web Site: http://www.nbsit.com
Year Founded: 1997
Rev.: $8,100,000
Emp.: 89
Computer System Design Services
N.A.I.C.S.: 541512
Ayesha Khalid (Pres & CEO)
Jerry Myers (Dir-Bus Dev)

NAN, INC.
1938 Hau St, Honolulu, HI 96819
Tel.: (808) 842-4929
Web Site: http://www.nanhawaii.com
Year Founded: 2003
Sales Range: $1-9.9 Million
Emp.: 12
Commercial & Institutional Building Construction
N.A.I.C.S.: 236220
Fooney Freestone (Pres)
Frank Okimoto (VP)
Ryan Nakaima (VP)
Nan Chul Shin (Founder & Owner)

Subsidiaries:

Grace Pacific LLC (1)
949 Kamokila Blvd Ste 200, Kapolei, HI 96707
Tel.: (808) 674-8383
Web Site: http://www.gracepacific.com
Sales Range: $200-249.9 Million
Roadway Construction Services
N.A.I.C.S.: 237310
Myles Mizokami (Interim Pres)

Subsidiary (Domestic):

GP Roadway Solutions, Inc. (2)
660 Mapunapuna St, Honolulu, HI 96819-2031
Tel.: (808) 833-2502
Web Site:
    https://www.gproadwaysolutions.com
Sales Range: $1-9.9 Million
Road Safety Solutions
N.A.I.C.S.: 238990

NANA REGIONAL CORPORATION, INC.
PO Box 49, Kotzebue, AK 99752
Tel.: (907) 442-3301 AK
Web Site: http://www.nana.com
Year Founded: 1972
Sales Range: $1-4.9 Billion
Emp.: 11,576
Oil Field Services
N.A.I.C.S.: 213112
William Iggiagruk Hensley (Founder)
Donald G. Sheldon (Vice Chm)
Lance Miller (VP-Natural Resources)
Linda Lee (Chm)
Mary F. Sage (Sec)
Wayne Westlake (Pres & CEO)
Liz Cravalho (VP-External & Govt Affairs)
Kimberly Cunningham (CFO & Sr VP)
Gia Hanna (VP-Shareholder Rels)
Lori Henry (COO & VP)
John Hendrix (Pres-Comml Grp)

Subsidiaries:

Nana Development Corporation (1)
909 W 9th Ave, Anchorage, AK 99501
Tel.: (907) 265-4100
Web Site: http://www.nana-dev.com
Sales Range: $100-124.9 Million
Emp.: 15,000
Development Opportunities
N.A.I.C.S.: 925120

Subsidiary (Domestic):

Akima, LLC (2)
13873 Park Center Rd Ste 400N, Herndon, VA 20171
Tel.: (571) 323-5200
Web Site: http://www.akima.com
Emp.: 5,700
Information Technology Consulting Services
N.A.I.C.S.: 541512
Bill Monet (Pres & CEO)
Larry Mechner (CFO)
David Turner (VP-Corp Dev)
Juvy McCarthy (Pres-Tech Solutions & Products Grp)
Barry Smallwood (CTO & CIO)
Lou Seijido (Pres-Construction Grp)
Rick Craig (Pres-Facilities Solutions Grp)
Chris Jenkins (VP-Ops)
John Lanzillotta (VP-Compliance & SBA Strategy)
Richard Valentine (VP-Bus Dev)
Douglas S. Dudley (Dir-Air Force Cyber Programs-Tech Solutions & Products Grp)
Duncan Greene (Pres-Mission Sys, Engrg & Tech Grp)
Barbara Doherty (VP-Contracts & Procurement)
Jean-Francois Blanc (Chief Growth Officer)
Candy Curtin (Chief HR Officer)
Mike Alvarado (Chief Growth Officer)
Robin Dewar (VP-Bus Dev)

Subsidiary (Domestic):

Akima Construction Services, LLC (3)

U.S. PRIVATE

7901 Sandy Spring Rd Ste 510, Laurel, MD 20707
Tel.: (301) 617-8723
Web Site: http://www.akimaconstruction.com
Emp.: 10
Construction Management Services
N.A.I.C.S.: 236220
Paul Karmazinski (Pres & Gen Mgr)

Akima Facilities Management, LLC (3)
13873 Park Center Rd Ste 400N, Herndon, VA 20171
Tel.: (512) 263-1848
Web Site: http://www.akimafacmgmt.com
Facility Support & Management Consulting Services
N.A.I.C.S.: 561210
Rick Craig (Pres)

Akima Global Services, LLC (3)
13873 Park Center Rd Ste 400N, Herndon, VA 20171
Tel.: (703) 766-6837
Web Site:
    http://www.akimaglobalservices.com
Information Technology Consulting Services
N.A.I.C.S.: 541512

Akima Infrastructure Services, LLC (3)
2 Eaton S Ste 900, Hampton, VA 23669
Tel.: (757) 265-9570
Web Site: http://www.akimainfrasvcs.com
Management Consulting Services
N.A.I.C.S.: 541618

Akima Intra-Data, LLC (3)
13873 Park Center Rd Ste 400N, Herndon, VA 20171
Tel.: (706) 221-8471
Web Site: http://www.akimaintradata.com
Administrative Support Services
N.A.I.C.S.: 561110
Rick Craig (Pres)
LeRoy Hinton (Dir-Ops)

Akima Logistics Services, LLC (3)
13873 Park Center Rd Ste 400N, Herndon, VA 20171
Tel.: (610) 574-4579
Web Site: http://www.akimalogistics.com
Logistics Management Consulting Services
N.A.I.C.S.: 541614
Jeff Crist (VP & Gen Mgr)

Akima Technical Solutions, LLC (3)
11405 N Community House Rd Ste 400, Charlotte, NC 28277
Tel.: (704) 970-1200
Web Site:
    http://www.akimatechsolutions.com
Aviation Support Services
N.A.I.C.S.: 488190

Cazador, LLC (3)
13873 Park Center Rd Ste 400N, Herndon, VA 20171
Tel.: (719) 387-7450
Web Site: http://www.cazador.biz
Professional Services
N.A.I.C.S.: 813920
David Hoy (Gen Mgr)
Barbara Isaacs (Mgr-Bus Dev)
Mark Dias (Dir-Ops)
Miles Harrison (Dir-Field Ops)

Kisaq, LLC (3)
13873 Park Ctr Rd Ste 400N, Herndon, VA 20171
Tel.: (907) 751-8400
Web Site: http://www.kisaq.com
Industrial Building Construction Services
N.A.I.C.S.: 236210

Nakuuruq Solutions, LLC (3)
13873 Park Center Rd Ste 300N, Herndon, VA 20171
Tel.: (703) 766-6750
Web Site: http://www.nakuuruq.com
Engineering Consulting Services
N.A.I.C.S.: 541330

Pegasus Aviation Services, LLC (3)
3901 Old International Airport Rd, Anchorage, AK 99502
Tel.: (907) 245-0357
Web Site: http://www.pegasusanc.com
Aviation Maintenance & Support Services
N.A.I.C.S.: 488119

Carlos Nelson (Pres & Dir-Strategy Dev)
Joe Zerck (VP-Ops & Gen Mgr)

Pinnacle Solutions, Inc. (3)
8 Parade St NW Ste 301, Huntsville, AL 35806
Tel.: (256) 327-4181
Web Site:
    http://www.pinnaclesolutionsinc.com
Sales Range: $1-9.9 Million
Emp.: 66
Engineering & Training Services
N.A.I.C.S.: 541330
Mike Durant (Founder)
Tina Tucker (Pres & CEO)

Portico Services, LLC (3)
10126 Residency Rd, Manassas, VA 20110
Tel.: (571) 323-5975
Web Site: http://www.porticoservices.com
Sales Range: $25-49.9 Million
Emp.: 50
Industrial Building Construction Services
N.A.I.C.S.: 236210
Doug Krause (Pres)

SAVA, LLC (3)
13873 Park Center Rd Ste 400N, Herndon, VA 20171
Tel.: (703) 766-6772
Web Site: http://www.savasolutions.com
Sales Range: $50-74.9 Million
Emp.: 450
Facility Support & Management Consulting Services
N.A.I.C.S.: 561210
Christopher L. Jenkins (Pres)
Lou Ronca (Dir-Bus Dev)
Scott Yamashita (Dir-Program Mgmt Office)
Chris Purvis (Program Mgr)

Synteras, LLC (3)
13873 Park Center Rd Ste 300N, Herndon, VA 20171
Tel.: (703) 766-6757
Web Site: http://www.synteras.com
Sales Range: $10-24.9 Million
Emp.: 37
Management Consulting Services
N.A.I.C.S.: 541611
Jay Jayamohan (Mng Dir)
Steve Chiodini (Dir-Ops)

Truestone, LLC (3)
13873 Park Center Rd Ste 300N, Herndon, VA 22171
Tel.: (703) 766-6900
Web Site: http://www.truestonefed.com
Information Technology Consulting Services
N.A.I.C.S.: 541512
Kim Cook (Dir-Bus Dev)
Bob Strong (Dir-Bus Ops)
Rich Witherspoon (Mgr-DOD Programs)
Julie Gordon (Mgr-IT Program)
Donald E. Atwell (Pres)
Rob Nicholson (Mgr-Program-Maritime Ops)

Subsidiary (Domestic):

Grand Isle Shipyard Inc. (2)
18838 Hwy 3235, Galliano, LA 70354
Tel.: (985) 475-5238
Web Site: http://www.gisy.com
Sales Range: $25-49.9 Million
Emp.: 15
Oilfield Maintenance Services
N.A.I.C.S.: 213112

Plant (Domestic):

Grand Isle Shipyard Inc. - Fabrication Facility (3)
18838 Hwy 3235, Galliano, LA 70354
Tel.: (985) 839-9331
Web Site: http://www.gisy.com
Construction Engineering Services
N.A.I.C.S.: 541330

Subsidiary (Domestic):

NMS (2)
5600 B St, Anchorage, AK 99518
Tel.: (907) 273-2400
Web Site: http://www.nmsusa.com
Facility Management Services
N.A.I.C.S.: 561210
Craig Clemens (VP-Health, Safety, Security & Environment)
Derrell Webb (VP-Ops, Food & Facilities Mgmt)

Eric Fox (VP-Ops & Security)
Dawn Kimberlin (VP-Mktg & Comm)
Bill Tandeske (VP-Security)
Sandy West (Chief HR Officer-Comml Sector)
Matthew Daggett (Pres)
Sandy Halliwill (CIO-Comml Sector)

Paa River Construction, LLC (2)
6250 S Airpark Pl, Anchorage, AK 99502
Tel.: (907) 562-5303
Emp.: 15
Civil & Mining Engineering Services
N.A.I.C.S.: 541330
Shelly Schwenn (Gen Mgr)

Piksik, LLC (2)
7941 Sandlewood Pl, Anchorage, AK 99507
Tel.: (907) 563-3456
Web Site: http://www.piksik.com
Sales Range: $25-49.9 Million
Emp.: 4
Film & Digital Production Services
N.A.I.C.S.: 512110
Bob Crockett (Gen Mgr)
Robin Kornfield (Pres)
Deborah Schildt (Mgr-Production)
Brice Habeger (Mgr-Video Production)

NANCY MARSHALL COMMUNICATIONS
151 Capitol St Ste 1, Augusta, ME 04330
Tel.: (207) 623-4177
Web Site: http://www.marshallpr.com
Sales Range: $1-9.9 Million
Emp.: 14
Public Relations Agency
N.A.I.C.S.: 541820
Charlene Williams (Pres)
Nancy Marshall (Founder & CEO)
Anna McDermott (Acct Exec)
Juli B. Settlemire (Bus Mgr)
Greg Glynn (Acct Exec)
Jessica Donahue (Acct Supvr)
Whitney Moreau (Acct Exec)
Alisa Meggison (Mgr-Digital Mktg)
Liz LeClair (Coord-Acct)

NANCY MYERS BEAUTY SHOP
1198 N 10th St, Noblesville, IN 46060
Tel.: (317) 773-5080
Web Site: http://www.nancymyerssalonandspa.com
Sales Range: $10-24.9 Million
Emp.: 12
Toilet Preparation Mfr
N.A.I.C.S.: 325620
Nancy Myers (Co-Founder)
Terry Myers (Co-Founder)

NANCY PHANEUF COMMERCIAL REALTY & DEVELOPMENT
283 E Davis Blvd Ste 207, Tampa, FL 33606
Tel.: (813) 259-1519
Web Site: http://nprdevelopment.com
Sales Range: $1-9.9 Million
Commercial Real Estate Broker & Developer
N.A.I.C.S.: 531210
Nancy Phaneuf (Pres)

NANDORF INC.
4301 Midlothian Tpke, Midlothian, IL 60445-3924
Tel.: (708) 371-4245 WA
Web Site: http://www.uniquethriftstore.com
Year Founded: 1969
Sales Range: $25-49.9 Million
Emp.: 550
Provider of Retail Services
N.A.I.C.S.: 459510
Dave Legler (Mgr-IT)

NANETTE LEPORE
225 W 35th St, New York, NY 10001
Tel.: (212) 594-0012
Web Site: http://www.nanettelepore.com
Rev.: $46,700,000
Emp.: 50
Womens & Girls Cut & Sew Other Outerwear Mfr
N.A.I.C.S.: 315250
Nanette Lepore (Owner)
Robert Savage (Pres)

NANIGANS, INC.
60 State St 12th Fl, Boston, MA 02109
Tel.: (888) 507-4456
Web Site: http://www.nanigans.com
Emp.: 160
Advertising Software Publisher
N.A.I.C.S.: 513210
Ric Calvillo (Co-Founder, Pres & CEO)
Claude Denton (Co-Founder & CTO)

NANITAS INC.
4041 Ambassador Caffery Pkwy, Lafayette, LA 70503
Tel.: (337) 988-6534
Web Site: http://www.gabrielsfinejewelry.com
Year Founded: 1979
Sales Range: $75-99.9 Million
Emp.: 9
Jewelry Store Owner & Operator
N.A.I.C.S.: 458310
Gabriel A. Shaik (Pres)

NANOLAB TECHNOLOGIES, INC.
1708 McCarthy Blvd, Milpitas, CA 95035
Tel.: (408) 433-3320
Web Site: http://www.nanolabtechnologies.com
Year Founded: 2011
Failure Analysis, Analytical Microscopy, Surface Analysis & FIB Circuit Edit Services
N.A.I.C.S.: 541380
John P. Traub (Pres & CEO)

NANOSAVE TECHNOLOGIES, INC.
444 Seabreeze Blvd Ste 705, Daytona Beach, FL 32118
Tel.: (386) 310-4994
Lubricant Mfr & Distr
N.A.I.C.S.: 324191
Gregory E. Lykiardopoulos (Chm, Pres, CEO & CFO)

NANOTHERAPEUTICS, INC.
13859 Progress Blvd Ste 300, Alachua, FL 32615
Tel.: (386) 462-9663 FL
Web Site: http://www.nanotherapeutics.com
Year Founded: 1999
Sales Range: $1-9.9 Million
Emp.: 50
Biopharmaceutical Researcher & Developer
N.A.I.C.S.: 541715
James D. Talton (Co-Founder)
Barbel Eppler (Chief Quality Officer)
Dennis Tomisaka (Dir-BD Special Projects)
James F. Kirk (VP-Engrg)
Ron Cobb (Chief Scientific Officer)
Weaver H. Gaines (Gen Counsel)
Gary A. Ascani (VP-Bus Dev)
Robert J. Hennessey (Chm)
James M. Matthew (CFO)
Carl N. Kraus (Chief Medical Officer)
Peter H. Khoury (Pres & CEO)

NANOTOX, INC.
4111 Todd Ln, Austin, TX 78744
Tel.: (512) 804-2800 TX
Web Site: http://www.nanotox.com
Year Founded: 2005
Sales Range: $1-9.9 Million
Emp.: 9
Nanoparticle Risk Assessment Services
N.A.I.C.S.: 541690
Harry C. Bushong (Pres)
William Stahl (CFO)
John Denson (Gen Counsel)

NANT CAPITAL, LLC
9922 Jefferson Blvd, Culver City, CA 90232
Tel.: (310) 836-6400
Investment Services
N.A.I.C.S.: 523999

NANTAHALA OUTDOOR CENTER
13077 Hwy 19 W, Bryson City, NC 28713
Tel.: (828) 488-2175
Web Site: http://www.noc.com
Year Founded: 1972
Sales Range: $25-49.9 Million
Emp.: 600
Outdoor Center Recreational Camps
N.A.I.C.S.: 721214
Charles Conner (Dir-Mktg)
Donna Campbell (CFO)
Melissa Humble (Mgr)
Charles Laws (Mgr-Guide & Retail)
Kelly Hebrank (Mgr-Talent & Leadership Dev)
Andrew Tobey (Coord-Invoice)

NANTERO, INC.
25 Olympia Ave Ste B, Woburn, MA 01801
Tel.: (978) 569-0177
Web Site: http://www.nantero.com
Sales Range: $10-24.9 Million
Emp.: 30
Semiconductor Related Devices
N.A.I.C.S.: 334413
Greg Schmergel (Co-Founder, Chm & CEO)
Thomas Rueckes (Co-Founder & CTO)
Sohrab Kianian (VP-Licensing & Bus Dev)
Robert O. Lindefjeld (Gen Counsel)
Jim Handy (Dir-Objective Analysis)
Lee Cleveland (VP-Design)

NANTUCKET DREAMLAND FOUNDATION
17 S Water St, Nantucket, MA 02554
Tel.: (508) 332-4822 MA
Web Site: http://www.nantucketdreamland.org
Year Founded: 2007
Sales Range: $10-24.9 Million
Emp.: 43
Art & Cultural Center Operator
N.A.I.C.S.: 711310
Traci Finnerty (Dir-Fin & Admin)
Bill Liddle (Pres)
Charles Ryan (Treas)
Kathy Penske (Sec)
James Pallotta (VP)

NANTUCKET HARVEST CO., INC.
1 West St, Fall River, MA 02720
Tel.: (508) 324-9800
Web Site: http://www.stirrings.com
Sales Range: $25-49.9 Million
Dehydrated Food Mfr
N.A.I.C.S.: 311423

Subsidiaries:

Stirrings (1)
One W St, Fall River, MA 02720
Tel.: (508) 324-9800
Web Site: http://www.stirrings.com
Sales Range: $25-49.9 Million
Emp.: 39
All-Natural Cocktail Mixers
N.A.I.C.S.: 312111
Bill Creelman (Founder)

NANTWORKS, LLC
9920 Jefferson Blvd, Culver City, CA 90232
Tel.: (310) 883-1300 DE
Web Site: http://www.nantworks.com
Year Founded: 2010
Holding Company; Information & Communication Technologies & Services
N.A.I.C.S.: 551112
Patrick Soon-Shiong (Founder)

Subsidiaries:

Altor BioScience, LLC (1)
2810 N Commerce Pkwy, Miramar, FL 33025-3958
Tel.: (954) 443-8600
Web Site: http://www.altorbioscience.com
Biopharmaceutical Mfr, Researcher & Developer
N.A.I.C.S.: 541715
Peter Rhode (VP-R&D)
John H. Lee (Sr VP-Adult Medical Affairs)
Amy Rock (VP-Clinical Dev & Regulatory Affairs)
Jin-an Jiao (VP-Protein Therapeutics Purification & Dev)

ImmunityBio, Inc. (1)
3530 John Hopkins Ct, San Diego, CA 92121
Tel.: (858) 696-5235
Web Site: https://www.immunitybio.com
Rev.: $240,000
Assets: $362,356,000
Liabilities: $812,176,000
Net Worth: ($449,820,000)
Earnings: ($416,567,000)
Emp.: 725
Fiscal Year-end: 12/31/2022
Cell & Immunotherapy Products Mfr
N.A.I.C.S.: 325412
Patrick Soon-Shiong (Chm & Chief Scientific & Medical Officer-Global)
Fabio M. Benedetti (Chief Strategy Officer)
David C. Sachs (CFO)
Regan J. Lauer (Chief Acctg Officer)
Sandeep Reddy (Chief Medical Officer)
Jason Liljestrom (Gen Counsel)
Regan J. Lauer (Chief Acctg Officer)
Sarah Singleton (Chief Comm Officer & Head-Patient Advocacy)
Manju Saxena (Sr VP-Product Development & VP)
Elizabeth Gabitzsch (Sr VP-Product Development & Vaccine Programs & VP)
Rich Adcock (Pres & CEO)
Hans Klingemann (Chief Science Officer)
Enrique Dilone (CTO)
Barry J. Simon (Chief Admin Officer & Chief Corp Affairs Officer)

Subsidiary (Domestic):

NantCell, Inc. (2)
9920 Jefferson Blvd, Culver City, CA 90232
Tel.: (310) 883-1300
Immuno-oncological Cellular Treatment Research & Development
N.A.I.C.S.: 325414

Subsidiary (Domestic):

Etubics Corporation (3)
410 W Harrison St Ste 100, Seattle, WA 98119-4007
Tel.: (206) 838-5110
Web Site: http://www.etubics.com
Chemicals Mfr
N.A.I.C.S.: 325412
Elizabeth S. Gabitzsch (VP-Res)

GlobeImmune, Inc. (3)
1450 Infinite Dr, Louisville, CO 80027
Tel.: (720) 667-2300

NANTWORKS, LLC

NantWorks, LLC—(Continued)
Web Site: https://globeimmune.com
Sales Range: $1-9.9 Million
Biopharmaceutical Researcher & Developer
N.A.I.C.S.: 325412

NantHealth, Inc. (1)
760 W Fire Twr Rd Ste 107, Winterville, NC 28590
Tel.: (310) 883-1300
Web Site: https://www.nanthealth.com
Rev.: $67,002,000
Assets: $159,551,000
Liabilities: $384,944,000
Net Worth: ($225,393,000)
Earnings: ($67,779,000)
Emp.: 380
Fiscal Year-end: 12/31/2022
Healthcare Industry Information Technology Products & Services
N.A.I.C.S.: 541512
Patrick Soon-Shiong (Chm & CEO)
Bob Petrou (CFO)
Charles Hunt (VP-User Experience)
R. Haris Naseem (CEO)
Lauren Schiegg (COO)
Scott Maratea (Chief Revenue Officer)
Laura Harrison (CIO & Chief Information Security Officer)
Megan Salmon-Gardell (Chief Nursing Officer)
Arlyn Small (Chief People Officer)
Sean Henson (Sr VP & Gen Mgr)
Alan Brown (Sr VP & Gen Mgr)
Marc L. Harrison (Chief Legal Officer)

Subsidiary (Domestic):

NaviNet, Inc. (2)
179 Lincoln St, Boston, MA 02111-2425
Tel.: (617) 715-6000
Web Site: http://www.navinet.net
Healthcare Data Hosting Services
N.A.I.C.S.: 518210

NANTZE SPRINGS INC.
156 W Carroll St, Dothan, AL 36302
Tel.: (334) 794-4218
Web Site:
http://www.nantzesprings.com
Rev.: $28,400,000
Emp.: 150
Other Grocery & Related Products Merchant Whslr
N.A.I.C.S.: 424490
Ben Garrett (Treas & Sec)
Fred Garrett (Chm)
Malone Garrett (Pres)

NAO, INC.
1284 E Sedgley Ave, Philadelphia, PA 19134
Tel.: (215) 743-5300
Web Site: http://www.nao.com
Year Founded: 1912
Sales Range: $50-74.9 Million
Emp.: 50
Mfr of Industrial Oil & Gas Burners, Furnace Equipment & Flare Burners for Anti-Pollution
N.A.I.C.S.: 334513
Cor N. Knook (Mgr-Sls)
Drew Tryens (Controller)
Kim Miller (Supvr-Sls)
Nancy Tryens (Dir-HR)
John Anderson (Mgr-UL Control Panel Shop)
John F. Straitz III (Pres)

Subsidiaries:

NAO Texas (1)
9973 County Rd 302, Plantersville, TX 77363-1215 (100%)
Tel.: (936) 894-2867
Web Site: http://www.nao.com
Sales Range: $10-24.9 Million
Emp.: 6
Storage & Test Site
N.A.I.C.S.: 611710

NAOC HOLDINGS

5900 Wilshire Blvd Ste 2612, Los Angeles, CA 90036
Tel.: (323) 330-0590
Equity Investment Firm
N.A.I.C.S.: 523999

NAPA VALLEY PETROLEUM INC.
257 S Kelly Rd, Vallejo, CA 94503
Tel.: (707) 252-6888
Web Site:
http://www.napavalleypetroleum.com
Rev.: $18,300,000
Emp.: 9
Gasoline
N.A.I.C.S.: 424720
Tim Cardoza (Plant Mgr)
Dave Massey (Mgr-Ops)

NAPCO STEEL INC.
1800 Arthur Dr, West Chicago, IL 60185
Tel.: (630) 293-1900
Web Site: http://www.napcosteel.com
Year Founded: 1976
Sales Range: $10-24.9 Million
Emp.: 50
Steel
N.A.I.C.S.: 423510
Jack Napoli (Pres)
Jeffrey Jourdan (Controller)

NAPCO, INC.
120 Trojan Ave, Sparta, NC 28675
Tel.: (336) 372-5214
Web Site: http://www.napcousa.com
Year Founded: 1977
Specialty Packaging Products Mfr
N.A.I.C.S.: 322212
Rocky Proffit (Founder & CEO)
Shannon Lawrence (Mgr-Matls)
Dan Duncan (Dir-New Product Dev)
Jerry Pearce (Exec VP)
Rick Proffit (VP-Ops)
Debbie Bare (Mgr-Cust Svc)
Dan Edwards Jr. (Mgr-Production Plng)

Subsidiaries:

Vulcan Information Packaging (1)
1 Looseleaf Ln, Vincent, AL 35178
Tel.: (800) 633-4526
Binders & Custom Packaging Products Mfr
N.A.I.C.S.: 323111
Laurel Pate (Acct Mgr)
Daphne Garrett (Sls Mgr-Acct)
Debra Hollis (Sls Mgr-Acct)
Tom Harmon (VP & Gen Mgr)

NAPERVILLE PARK DISTRICT
320 W Jackson Ave, Naperville, IL 60540
Tel.: (630) 848-5000
Web Site:
http://www.napervilleparks.org
Year Founded: 1966
Rev.: $15,559,962
Emp.: 300
Provider of Recreational Services; Operator of Parks & Golf Courses
N.A.I.C.S.: 713990
Katie Sepe (Dir-HR)
Ed Provow (Dir-Golf)
Brad Wilson (Dir-Recreation)
Eric Shutes (Dir-Plng)
Sameera Luthman (Dir-Mktg & Comm)
Ray McGury (Exec Dir)
Kevin Finnegan (Dir-Parks)
Sue Stanish (Dir-Fin)
Debbie Kretzmann (Mgr-Community Rels)
Omar Sandoval (Mgr-IT)
Sara Cass (Mgr-Program)
Drew Hogue (Mgr-Trades)

Jessica Burgdorf (Project Mgr)
Peggy Pelkonen (Project Mgr)
Mike Piszynski (Project Mgr)

NAPLES BEACH HOTEL & GOLF CLUB
851 Gulf Shore Blvd N, Naples, FL 34102
Tel.: (239) 261-2222
Web Site:
http://www.naplesbeachhotel.com
Sales Range: $25-49.9 Million
Emp.: 360
Hotel & Golf Club
N.A.I.C.S.: 721110
Michael E. Watkins (Owner & Pres)
Jason Parsons (Gen Mgr)
Sarah Cardenas (Grp Mgr-Sls)

NAPLES CHILDREN & EDUCATION FOUNDATION
4305 Exchange Ave, Naples, FL 34104
Tel.: (239) 514-2239
Web Site:
http://www.napleswinefestival.com
Year Founded: 2000
Sales Range: $10-24.9 Million
Emp.: 7
Educational Support Services
N.A.I.C.S.: 611710
Bob Clifford (Chm)
Jerry Starkey (Treas & Sec)
Dave Gibbons (Vice Chm)

NAPLES DODGE INC.
6381 Airport Rd N, Naples, FL 34109
Tel.: (239) 594-2100
Web Site:
http://www.naplesdodge.com
Sales Range: $10-24.9 Million
Emp.: 66
New & Used Car Dealers
N.A.I.C.S.: 441110
Tom Myers (Co-Owner)
Jon Myers (Co-Owner)

NAPLES LUMBER & SUPPLY INC.
3828 Radio Rd, Naples, FL 34104
Tel.: (239) 643-7000
Web Site:
http://www.napleslumber.com
Year Founded: 1971
Sales Range: $10-24.9 Million
Emp.: 80
Lumber & Building Materials Retailer
N.A.I.C.S.: 423310
Ron Labbe (Owner)

NAPLES NISSAN
3640 Pine Ridge Rd, Naples, FL 34109
Tel.: (239) 643-3800
Web Site:
http://www.naplesnissan.com
Year Founded: 2008
Sales Range: $75-99.9 Million
Emp.: 80
Car Dealership
N.A.I.C.S.: 441110
James Pool (Exec Mgr)
Jimmy Goodwin (Mgr-Fin)
Abraham Rodriguez (Mgr-Fin)
John Heisler (Mgr-Sls)
Josh Blackburn (Mgr-Parts)
Robert Sneed (Mgr-Svc)
Tracy Lee Bournazian (Mgr-Sls)
Scott Stone (Mgr-Sls)

NAPLES REALTY SERVICES INC.
4980 Tamiami Trl N Ste 200, Naples, FL 34103
Tel.: (239) 262-4333

Web Site:
http://www.naplesrealtyservices.com
Rev.: $15,685,930
Emp.: 230
Real Estate Brokers & Agents
N.A.I.C.S.: 531210
John A. Steinwand (Pres & Principal)

NAPLES REDEVELOPMENT INC.
400 5th Ave S Ste 204, Naples, FL 34102
Tel.: (239) 331-7940
Web Site:
http://www.naplesredevelopment.com
Sales Range: $1-9.9 Million
Single Family Construction Services
N.A.I.C.S.: 236115
Adam Smith (Principal)

NAPLES SHUTTER, INC.
1025 Power St, Naples, FL 34104
Tel.: (239) 566-8161
Web Site:
http://www.naplesshutter.com
Sales Range: $1-9.9 Million
Emp.: 20
Shutters & Other Hurricane Protection Products Mfr
N.A.I.C.S.: 321918
Brian Trecek (VP)
Jonathan Leach (Pres & CEO)

NAPLETON AUTO WERKS
6600 E Riverside Blvd, Loves Park, IL 61111-4426
Tel.: (815) 636-6600
Web Site:
http://www.shopnapleton.com
Year Founded: 1981
Sales Range: $10-24.9 Million
Emp.: 100
Car Whslr
N.A.I.C.S.: 441110
William Napleton (Pres)
Paul Napleton (VP)
Sue Adkins (Controller)

NAPLETON BUICK GMC
100 W Golf Rd, Schaumburg, IL 60195-3604
Tel.: (847) 884-1300
Web Site:
http://www.napletonbuickgmc.com
Year Founded: 2001
Sales Range: $10-24.9 Million
Emp.: 35
New Car Whslr
N.A.I.C.S.: 441110
Steve Napleton (Chm)
Chuck Weck (Pres)
Bryan Hess (Gen Mgr)

NAPLETON NISSAN
1301 Indianapolis Blvd, Schererville, IN 46375-1313
Tel.: (219) 865-3800
Sales Range: $10-24.9 Million
Emp.: 50
New Car Whslr
N.A.I.C.S.: 441110
Bill Napleton (Pres)

NAPLETON RIVER OAKS CHRYSLER JEEP DODGE
17225 Torrence Ave, Lansing, IL 60438-1016
Tel.: (708) 636-5800
Web Site: http://www.napleton.com
Year Founded: 2009
Sales Range: $10-24.9 Million
Emp.: 65
Car Whslr
N.A.I.C.S.: 441110

Raymond Czarnik (Pres)
Ed Napleton (Owner)
Barbara Riordan (Controller)

NAPOLI FOODS, INC.
10 Knotter Dr, Cheshire, CT 06410
Tel.: (860) 276-4000
Web Site:
http://www.napolifoodsinc.com
Sales Range: $10-24.9 Million
Emp.: 65
Grocery Products Retailer
N.A.I.C.S.: 424490
Mark Cipriano (Pres)
Michael Cipriano (VP)
David Kelly (Mgr)

NAPP-GRECCO COMPANY
1500 McCarter Hwy, Newark, NJ 07104
Tel.: (973) 482-3500
Web Site: http://www.napp-grecco.com
Sales Range: $10-24.9 Million
Emp.: 90
Crude Petroleum Pipelines
N.A.I.C.S.: 486110
Joseph Napp (Pres)

NAPPEN & ASSOCIATES
171 Corp Dr, Montgomeryville, PA 18936
Tel.: (215) 643-4848
Web Site: http://www.nappen-associates.com
Sales Range: $10-24.9 Million
Emp.: 11
Land Subdividers & Developers, Commercial
N.A.I.C.S.: 237210
Connie Riegler (Exec VP)
Lisa Novotny (Mgr-Leasing & Property)
Scott Henderson (Sr VP-Real Estate Ops)
David Barnhart (VP)

NARCO FREEDOM, INC.
250 Grand Concourse, Bronx, NY 10451
Tel.: (718) 292-2240   NY
Web Site:
http://www.drugtreatmentny.com
Year Founded: 1971
Sales Range: $25-49.9 Million
Emp.: 501
Drug & Alcohol Addiction Rehabilitation Services
N.A.I.C.S.: 623220
J. R. Denis (Dir-Medical)
Alan Brand (CEO)

NARDELLO & CO. LLC
1212 Ave of the Americas, New York, NY 10036
Tel.: (212) 537-5300   NY
Web Site:
https://www.nardelloandco.com
Year Founded: 2004
Investigative Services
N.A.I.C.S.: 561611
Daniel Anthony Nardello (Founder, Chm & CEO)
Sabina Menschel (Pres, Partner & COO)
Tara MacMillan (Partner, Chief Professional Officer & Head-Americas Reg)
Warren Feldman (Partner & Chief Legal Officer)
Jeff Boose (Partner & CFO)
Michael J. Ramos (Partner, Chief Compliance Officer & Chief Risk Officer)
Thomas F. Feeney (Partner)

Elizabeth Anscombe (CMO & Chief Bus Dev Officer)
Wendy Bellus (Chief People Officer)

NARRAGANSETT BREWING CO
60 Ship St, Providence, RI 02903
Tel.: (401) 437-8970
Web Site:
http://www.narragansettbeer.com
Year Founded: 1888
Sales Range: $1-9.9 Million
Emp.: 13
Brewery
N.A.I.C.S.: 312120
Mark Hellendrung (CEO)
Brent Parker (Mgr-Sls)

NARRAGANSETT FINANCIAL CORP.
330 Swansea Mall Dr, Swansea, MA 02777
Tel.: (508) 678-7641
Web Site:
http://www.baycoastbank.com
Sales Range: $25-49.9 Million
Emp.: 250
Bank Holding Company
N.A.I.C.S.: 551111
Nicholas M. Christ (Pres & CEO)

Subsidiaries:

BayCoast Bank (1)
330 Swansea Mall Dr, Swansea, MA 02777
Tel.: (508) 678-7641
Web Site: http://www.baycoastbank.com
Rev.: $47,865,000
Emp.: 322
Fiscal Year-end: 12/31/2013
Banking Services
N.A.I.C.S.: 522110
Nicholas M. Christ (Pres & CEO)
Carl W. Taber (Chief Lending Officer & Exec VP)
June Goguen (Officer-Comml Lending & First VP)
Elizabeth Ferreira (Asst VP & Asst Controller)
Maria Rego (Asst VP)
Terri Lorri Ferreira (Asst VP)
Julie Ramos Gagliardi (VP-Corp Giving & Community Rels)
Kevin M. Braga (First VP-Risk Mgmt)
David Herzfeld (Sr VP-Merchant Program)

Subsidiary (Domestic):

Partners Insurance Group LLC (2)
1 Crandall Rd, Tiverton, RI 02878-2608
Tel.: (401) 162-9936
Web Site:
http://www.citizensunioninsurance.com
Insurance Agencies & Brokerages
N.A.I.C.S.: 524210
Leslie Hudson (VP)

Subsidiary (Domestic):

Hadley Insurit Group Insurance, Inc. (3)
246 Durfee St, Fall River, MA 02720
Tel.: (508) 676-5949
Web Site: http://www.hadleyinsurit.com
Insurance Agencies & Brokerages
N.A.I.C.S.: 524210
Christopher Hadley (Sec)

NARRAGANSETT IMPROVEMENT CO
223 Allens Ave, Providence, RI 02903
Tel.: (401) 331-7420
Web Site: http://www.nicori.com
Sales Range: $50-74.9 Million
Emp.: 100
Subdividers & Developers
N.A.I.C.S.: 237210
John E. Everson (Pres)
Christopher Beauchamps (Superintendent)
Mark Beauchamp (Superintendent)

NARROW FABRIC AMERICA CORPORATION
830 Boylston St Ste 209, Chestnut Hill, MA 02467
Tel.: (617) 232-6060
Sales Range: $100-124.9 Million
Emp.: 1,000
Narrow Fabric Mills
N.A.I.C.S.: 313220
Emil Bernstein (CFO)

NASH CHEVROLET CO., INC.
630 Scenic Hwy, Lawrenceville, GA 30046-6363
Tel.: (678) 317-2797   GA
Web Site: http://www.nashchevy.com
Year Founded: 1955
Sales Range: $50-74.9 Million
Emp.: 150
Automobile Dealership
N.A.I.C.S.: 441110
Tommy Nash (Pres)
Todd Nash (VP)
Mark Nash (VP)
Ed Hopcraft (Treas & Sec)

NASH HEALTH CARE SYSTEMS INC.
2460 Curtis Ellis Dr, Rocky Mount, NC 27804-2237
Tel.: (252) 962-8000   NC
Web Site:
http://www.nashunchealthcare.org
Year Founded: 1971
Sales Range: $75-99.9 Million
Emp.: 1,800
Hospitals, Clinics & Rehabilitation Facilities Owner
N.A.I.C.S.: 622110
Brad Weisner (COO & Exec VP)
Meera Kelley (Chief Medical Officer)
Michelle Cosimeno (Chief Nursing Officer & VP)
Stacy Sumner Jesso (Chief Dev Officer & VP)
John A. Barker (Treas)
L. Lee Isley (Pres & CEO)
Shawn Hartley (CFO & Sr VP)
Crystal Hayden (Chief Nursing Officer & Sr VP)

Subsidiaries:

MSO Nash Inc. (1)
2301 Medpark Dr, Rocky Mount, NC 27804-1400
Tel.: (252) 443-8000
Web Site: http://www.nhcs.com
Sales Range: $10-24.9 Million
Emp.: 14
Provider of Specialty Outpatient Clinic Services
N.A.I.C.S.: 622210

NASH HOLDINGS LLC
1150 15th St NW, Washington, DC 20071
Tel.: (202) 334-6000   DE
Year Founded: 2013
Holding Company; Newspaper Publisher
N.A.I.C.S.: 551112
Jeffrey Bezos (Mng Partner)

Subsidiaries:

El Tiempo Latino LLC (1)
1150 15th St NW, Washington, DC 20071
Tel.: (202) 334-9100
Web Site: http://www.eltiempolatino.com
Newspaper Publishing Services
N.A.I.C.S.: 513110

Greater Washington Publishing, LLC (1)
1919 Gallows Rd Ste 200, Vienna, VA 22182
Tel.: (703) 992-1100
Web Site: http://www.gwpi.net
Rev.: $1,100,000
Emp.: 60
Publishing Services
N.A.I.C.S.: 513110
Becky Loker (Pres & CEO)

Post-Newsweek Media, LLC (1)
9030 Comprint Ct, Gaithersburg, MD 20877-4102
Tel.: (301) 948-3120
Web Site: http://www.gazette.net
Sales Range: $125-149.9 Million
Emp.: 100
Newspaper Publishers
N.A.I.C.S.: 513110
Karen Acton (CEO)

Subsidiary (Domestic):

Comprint Military Publications (2)
9030 Comprint Ct, Gaithersburg, MD 20877-1307
Tel.: (301) 921-2800
Web Site: http://www.dcmilitary.com
Sales Range: $10-24.9 Million
Emp.: 50
Military Publications
N.A.I.C.S.: 513199
John Rives (Publr)

Unit (Domestic):

Mount Airy Gazette (2)
218 S Main St, Mount Airy, MD 21771
Tel.: (301) 831-0047
Web Site: http://www.gazette.net
Sales Range: Less than $1 Million
Emp.: 5
Newspaper Publishers
N.A.I.C.S.: 513110

Subsidiary (Domestic):

Southern Maryland Newspapers (2)
23125 Camden Way, California, MD 20619
Tel.: (301) 862-2111
Web Site: http://www.gazette.net
Sales Range: $10-24.9 Million
Emp.: 35
Newspaper Publishing
N.A.I.C.S.: 513110

Robinson Terminal Warehouse LLC (1)
7201 Wimsatt Rd, Springfield, VA 22150 (100%)
Tel.: (703) 836-8300
Web Site: http://www.robinsonterminal.com
Sales Range: $25-49.9 Million
Emp.: 10
Warehousing Services
N.A.I.C.S.: 493110
Richard Clutter (Gen Mgr)

WP Company LLC (1)
1301 K St NW, Washington, DC 20071 (100%)
Tel.: (202) 334-6000
Web Site: https://www.washingtonpost.com
Sales Range: $450-499.9 Million
Emp.: 3,000
Newspaper Publishers
N.A.I.C.S.: 513110
Stephen P. Hills (Pres & Gen Mgr)
Gerald Rosberg (Sr VP-Plng & Dev)
Marc H. Rosenberg (Sr Mgr-Sls-Adv)
Ann L. McDaniel (Sr VP)
Steve Stup (VP & Gen Mgr-Adv Products & Strategy)
Wes Tyeryar (Reg VP)
Martin Baron (Exec Editor)
Peter Wallsten (Deputy Natl Editor-Political)
Adam Kushner (Editor-Digital Opinion & Analysis)
Carlos Lozada (Editor-Outlook)
Wallace Cooney (VP-Fin & Chief Acctg Officer)
Emilio Garcia-Ruiz (Mng Editor)
Stephen P. Gibson (CFO)
Beth Diaz (VP-Audience Dev)
Kristine Coratti (VP-Comm)
Mike Madden (Deputy Editor-Outlook & Post Everything)
David Swerdlick (Asst Editor-Outlook & Post Everything)
Alex Treadway (VP-Leadership Sls)
Paul Tsigrikes (VP-Mktg)
Micah Gelman (Dir-Editorial Video)
Scott Wilson (Natl Editor)
Miki King (Pres-Arc XP)
Megan H. Chan (Dir-Digital Ops)

NASH HOLDINGS LLC

U.S. PRIVATE

Nash Holdings LLC—(Continued)
Cameron Barr *(Mng Editor)*
Scot Gillespie *(CTO)*
Shailesh Prakash *(CIO & VP-Digital Product Dev)*
Richard Just *(Editor-Magazine)*
Liz Seymour *(Exec Editor-Features)*
Mitch Rubin *(Deputy Editor-Features)*
David Malitz *(Deputy Editor-Features)*
Tracy Grant *(Mng Editor)*
Elias Lopez *(Sr Dir-Opinions-Intl)*
Allison Michaels *(Editor-Audio-Politics-Audio Dept)*
Joy Robins *(Chief Revenue Officer-Global)*
Krissah Thompson *(Mng Editor-Diversity & Inclusion)*
Elite Truong *(Dir-Strategic Initiatives)*
Scott Weisenthal *(Head-Creative Grp)*
Jenna Pirog *(Deputy Editor-Strategic Initiatives)*
Courtney Beesch *(Editor-Social Media-Instagram Team)*
Matea Gold *(Interim Deputy Editor-Natl)*
David Shipley *(Editor-Opinion)*
Renae Merle *(Editor-America Desk)*
Ruth Marcus *(Assoc Editor)*
Kathy Baird *(Chief Comm Officer)*
Frederick J. Ryan Jr. *(CEO & Publr)*

Unit (Domestic):

The Washington Post News Service & Syndicate (2)
1301 K St NW, Washington, DC 20071-0001
Tel.: (202) 334-7666
Web Site: http://www.washingtonpost.com
Emp.: 30
News Syndicate & Publisher Services
N.A.I.C.S.: 516210
Alan Shearer *(CEO & Dir-Editorial)*
Maria Gatti *(Dir-Sls & Mktg)*
Karen Greene *(Mgr-Ops)*
James Hill *(Sr Editor)*
Kay Coyte *(Mng Editor)*
Manuel Canales *(Editor-Graphics-Assignment)*
Emily M. Eng *(Editor-Assignment-Graphics)*
Katie Zezima *(Editor-Climate & Environment-Dept)*
Lisa Bonos *(Editor-Asst Tech)*
Mary Duenwald *(Sr Editor-Opinion Section)*
Sara Abdulla *(Editor-Opinions)*
Stuart Leavenworth *(Editor-Policy, Politics & Power-Climate & Environment Dept)*
Zachary Goldfarb *(Editor-Climate & Environment)*
Douglas Jehl *(Editor-Foreign)*
Kendra Nichols *(Editor-Global Breaking News-Seoul)*
Joyce Lau *(Editor-Breaking News-Seoul)*
Lori Montgomery *(Editor-Fin)*
Christina Passariello *(Editor-Tech)*
Maite Fernandez Simon *(Editor-Audience Strategy-Bus)*

Washingtonpost.Newsweek Interactive Company, LLC (2)
401 Courthouse Rd, Alexandria, VA 22216
Tel.: (703) 518-4419
Web Site: http://www.washingtonpost.com
Sales Range: $75-99.9 Million
Emp.: 250
Online News Publication
N.A.I.C.S.: 513140
Katharine B. Weymouth *(Dir-Advertising Sls & Asst Gen Counsel)*
Jennifer Moyer *(VP-Fin)*
Mark Whitaker *(VP & Editor-in-Chief)*

NASH JOHNSON & SONS FARMS INC.
Hwy 117 N, Rose Hill, NC 28458
Tel.: (910) 289-3113 NC
Year Founded: 1950
Sales Range: $100-124.9 Million
Emp.: 1,806
Provider of Poultry Slaughtering & Processing Services
N.A.I.C.S.: 311615
Chuck Cashwell *(Controller)*
Debbie Blackburn *(Supvr-Flock Acctg-AR)*
Subsidiaries:

Columbia Farms Inc. (1)
125 N Lee St, Leesville, SC 29070-8099
Tel.: (803) 532-4488
Sales Range: $10-24.9 Million
Emp.: 120
Provider of Poultry Slaughtering & Processing Services
N.A.I.C.S.: 311615
Robert C. Johnson *(CEO)*

NASH OIL COMPANY INC.
3989 Highmarket St, Georgetown, SC 29440
Tel.: (843) 546-6666
Web Site: http://www.nashoil.com
Year Founded: 1995
Sales Range: $25-49.9 Million
Emp.: 30
Distr of Petroleum Products
N.A.I.C.S.: 424710
Mark Nash *(Pres & CEO)*

NASH PRODUCE, LLC.
6160 S Nc 58, Nashville, NC 27856
Tel.: (252) 443-6011
Web Site:
http://www.nashproduce.com
Sales Range: $25-49.9 Million
Emp.: 50
Postharvest Crop Activity Services
N.A.I.C.S.: 115114
Thomas Joyner *(Pres)*
Richard Joyner *(VP)*

NASHOBA VALLEY SPIRITS, LTD.
100 Wattaquadock Hill Rd, Bolton, MA 01740
Tel.: (978) 779-5521
Web Site:
http://www.nashobawinery.com
Sales Range: $25-49.9 Million
Emp.: 40
Alcoholic Beverages Mfr
N.A.I.C.S.: 312120
Richard Pelletier *(Pres)*
Annie Parrow *(Mgr-Restaurant)*

NASHUA HOMES OF IDAHO INC.
5200 S Federal Way, Boise, ID 83716-9638
Tel.: (208) 345-0222 ID
Web Site:
http://www.nashuahomesofidaho.com
Year Founded: 1989
Sales Range: $25-49.9 Million
Emp.: 150
Mfr of Mobile Homes
N.A.I.C.S.: 321991
Ron Yanke *(Owner & Pres)*
Kenneth Nash *(Mgr-Engrg)*
Donald Kiehl *(Mgr-Sls)*

NASHVILLE CARES
633 Thompson Ln, Nashville, TN 37204
Tel.: (615) 259-4866 TN
Web Site:
http://www.nashvillecares.org
Year Founded: 1985
Sales Range: $10-24.9 Million
HIV Prevention & Awareness Services
N.A.I.C.S.: 813212
David Frederick *(Pres)*
Jim Creason *(Treas)*
Joseph Interrante *(CEO)*
Anne C. Martin *(VP)*
Charles Fields Jr. *(Sec)*

NASHVILLE DENTAL INC.
1229 Northgate Bus Pkwy, Madison, TN 37115-2475
Tel.: (615) 868-3911
Web Site:
http://www.nashvilledental.com
Sales Range: $10-24.9 Million
Emp.: 30
Dental Equipment & Supplies
N.A.I.C.S.: 423450
Michael V. Brown *(Pres)*
Susan Brock *(Treas)*

NASHVILLE ELECTRIC SERVICE
1214 Church St, Nashville, TN 37246
Tel.: (615) 747-3981
Web Site: http://www.nespower.com
Year Founded: 1939
Sales Range: $1-4.9 Billion
Emp.: 966
Electric Power Distr
N.A.I.C.S.: 221122
Irma Paz-Bernstein *(Chm)*
Robert Campbell Jr. *(Vice Chm)*

NASHVILLE MACHINE COMPANY, INC.
530 Woodycrest Ave, Nashville, TN 37210-4323
Tel.: (615) 244-2030 TN
Web Site:
http://www.nashvillemachine.com
Year Founded: 1887
Sales Range: $200-249.9 Million
Emp.: 450
Provider of Mechanical Construction Services
N.A.I.C.S.: 238220
J. Lynn Wilson *(CFO, Treas & Sec)*
Rick Richards *(Plant Mgr)*
Adam Crews *(Project Mgr)*
Jennifer Cox *(Acct Mgr)*
Sam Chitty *(Gen Mgr)*
Tim Towle *(Mgr-Field Ops)*

NASHVILLE PREDATORS, LLC
501 Bdwy, Nashville, TN 37203-3932
Tel.: (615) 770-2355 DE
Web Site:
http://www.predators.nhl.com
Year Founded: 1998
Sales Range: $75-99.9 Million
Emp.: 510
Professional Hockey Franchise
N.A.I.C.S.: 551112
David Poile *(Pres-Hockey Ops & Gen Mgr)*
Gerry Helper *(Sr VP)*
Nat Harden *(Sr VP-Ticket Sls & Youth Hockey)*
Chris Junghans *(Chief Revenue Officer & Exec VP)*
Allison Simms *(Sr VP-HR)*
Brandon Walker *(Mgr-Hockey Ops)*
Brian Poile *(Dir-Hockey Ops)*
David Kells *(Sr VP-Booking)*
Kevin Wilson *(Dir-Comm)*
Scott Nichol *(Dir-Player Dev)*
Sean Henry *(Pres & CEO)*
Wade Redden *(Asst Dir-Player Dev)*
Herb Fritch *(Chm)*

NASHVILLE READY MIX INC.
605 Cowan St, Nashville, TN 37207
Tel.: (615) 256-2071
Web Site:
http://www.nashvillereadymix.net
Sales Range: $10-24.9 Million
Emp.: 35
Producer of Ready Mixed Concrete
N.A.I.C.S.: 327320
Steve Meadows *(Pres)*
Jimmy Dickey *(Mgr-Sls)*

NASHVILLE RUBBER & GASKET COMPANY, INC.
1900 Elm Tree Dr, Nashville, TN 37210
Tel.: (615) 883-0030
Web Site:
http://www.nashvillerubber.com
Year Founded: 1966
Sales Range: $10-24.9 Million
Emp.: 40
Gaskets Whslr
N.A.I.C.S.: 423840
Don Garner *(Co-Pres)*
Kevin Baggett *(Mgr-Sls)*
Eddie Jones *(Office Mgr)*

NASHVILLE STATIONERY CO. INC.
1621 Church St, Nashville, TN 37203
Tel.: (615) 329-1811
Web Site: http://www.noifurniture.com
Sales Range: $10-24.9 Million
Emp.: 50
Office Furniture
N.A.I.C.S.: 449110
Hershel W. Peppers *(Pres)*
Rick Peppers *(Vp)*
Pat Wright *(Treas)*

NASHVILLE STEEL CORP.
7211 Centennial Blvd, Nashville, TN 37209
Tel.: (615) 350-7933 TN
Web Site:
http://www.nashvillesteel.com
Year Founded: 1960
Sales Range: $75-99.9 Million
Emp.: 30
Steel Service Warehouse
N.A.I.C.S.: 423510
Laura Johnson *(Chief Acctg Officer)*
Okey Johnson III *(Pres & CEO)*
Subsidiaries:

White Star Steel (1)
2200 Harbor Blvd, Houston, TX 77020-7506
Tel.: (713) 675-6501
Web Site: http://www.whitestarsteel.com
Sales Range: $10-24.9 Million
Emp.: 25
Steel Service Center
N.A.I.C.S.: 423510
Okey B. Johnson *(Pres & CEO)*
Marcella Cox *(Mgr-Control)*
Joe Pharr *(Mgr-Quality)*
Greg Johnson *(VP-Ops)*

NASHVILLE SYMPHONY ASSOCIATION
1 Symphony Pl, Nashville, TN 37201
Tel.: (615) 687-6500 TN
Web Site:
http://www.nashvillesymphony.org
Year Founded: 1920
Sales Range: $10-24.9 Million
Emp.: 100
Symphony Orchestra
N.A.I.C.S.: 711130
Alan D. Valentine *(Pres & CEO)*
Jonathan Marx *(VP-Comm)*
Chad Boyd *(CFO)*
Emily Shannon *(Dir-Ticket Svcs)*
Walter Bitner *(Dir-Education & Community Engagement)*
Jennifer Puryear *(Sec)*
Jeff Walraven *(Treas)*
Marye Walker Lewis *(Co-CFO)*
Tonya McBride Robles *(COO)*
Alison Bolton *(VP-Artistic Admin)*
Giancarlo Guerrero *(Dir-Music)*

NASHVILLE WIRE PRODUCTS, INC.
199 Polk Ave, Nashville, TN 37210
Tel.: (615) 743-2500 TN
Web Site:
http://www.nashvillewire.com
Year Founded: 1934
Sales Range: $150-199.9 Million
Emp.: 500
Marketer of Wire Containers; Wire Pallets; Wire Baskets; Conveyor Guards; Point of Purchase Display Racks; Oven Racks; Refrigerator Racks; Fan Guard Mfr

N.A.I.C.S.: 332618
Mathew Hendon (Mgr-Sls)
Steve Johnson (VP-Sls)
Subsidiaries:

Nashville Wire Products, Inc. - Material Handling - Bordeaux Facility (1)
1604 County Hospital Rd, Nashville, TN 37218
Tel.: (615) 743-2600
Sales Range: $25-49.9 Million
Emp.: 300
Wire Product Mfr
N.A.I.C.S.: 332618
Robert Rollins (VP-Material Handling)

Nashville Wire Products, Inc. - Material Handling - Frankfort Facility (1)
616 Industrial Rd Frankfort Industrial Park, Frankfort, KY 40601
Tel.: (502) 783-5800
Wire Product Mfr
N.A.I.C.S.: 332618

Nashville Wire Products, Inc. - Nashville Display - Dover Facility (1)
720 Natcor Dr, Dover, TN 37058
Tel.: (615) 743-2680
Sales Range: $25-49.9 Million
Emp.: 70
Wire Product Whslr
N.A.I.C.S.: 332618
John Gingrich (Plant Mgr)

Nashville Wire Products, Inc. - Nashville Display - Lebanon Facility (1)
306 Hartman Dr, Lebanon, TN 37087
Tel.: (615) 743-2970
Web Site: http://www.nashvillewire.com
Wire Product Mfr & Supplier
N.A.I.C.S.: 332618

Nashville Wire Products, Inc. - OEM Parts - Auburn Facility (1)
1955 McMillian St, Auburn, AL 36832
Tel.: (334) 887-6200
Wire Product Mfr
N.A.I.C.S.: 332618

Nashville Wire Products, Inc. - OEM Parts - Juarez Facility (1)
Blvd Juan Pablo II No 2650, Cd Juarez, Chihuahua, 32575, Mexico
Tel.: (52) 656 257 1319
Fabricated Wire Product Mfr
N.A.I.C.S.: 332618

Nashville Wire Products, Inc. - OEM Parts - White Bluff Facility (1)
4586 Highway 70 E, White Bluff, TN 37187
Tel.: (615) 743-2700
Wire Product Mfr
N.A.I.C.S.: 332618

NASHVILLE ZOO AT GRASSMERE
3777 Nolensville Pike, Nashville, TN 37211
Tel.: (615) 833-1534 TN
Web Site: http://www.nashvillezoo.org
Year Founded: 1989
Sales Range: $10-24.9 Million
Emp.: 217
Zoo Conservation Services
N.A.I.C.S.: 712130
Andy Tillman (COO)
Suzanne Iler (Chief Dev Officer)
Rick Schwartz (Pres)
Robin Patton (Chm)
Sheryl Rogers (Sec)

NASON CONSTRUCTION, INC.
3411 Silverside Rd Tatnall Bldg Ste 200, Wilmington, DE 19810-3642
Tel.: (302) 529-2800 PA
Web Site: http://www.nasonconstruction.com
Year Founded: 1922
General Construction Company & Construction Management
N.A.I.C.S.: 236220

Julie Topkis Nason (Pres-Bus Dev & Mktg)
Matt Mangat (Dir-Preconstruction)
Thomas W. Nason II (CEO)

NASON, YEAGER, GERSON, HARRIS & FUMERO P.A.
Sabadell United Bank Tower 1645 Palm Beach Lakes Blvd Ste 1200, West Palm Beach, FL 33401
Tel.: (561) 686-3307
Web Site: http://www.nasonyeager.com
Year Founded: 1960
Emp.: 19
Law Firm
N.A.I.C.S.: 541110
George E. Harding (Atty)
Gary N. Gerson (Pres)
Michael D. Harris (Atty)
Brian C. Hickey (Atty)
Richard Levenstein (Atty)
Abby Spears (Atty)
Phil DiComo (Shareholder Atty)
Alan I. Armour II (Atty)
Subsidiaries:

Haile Shaw & Pfaffenberger, P.A. (1)
660 US Hwy 1 3rd Fl, North Palm Beach, FL 33408
Tel.: (561) 627-8100
Web Site: http://www.haileshaw.com
Law Firm
N.A.I.C.S.: 541110
Gerald L. Principe (Atty)
Terry E. Resk (Atty)
David M. Shaw (Atty)
William J. Pfaffenberger (Atty)
Brad Jankowski (Atty)
Robert G. Haile Jr. (Atty)

NASSAU CANDY DISTRIBUTORS INC.
530 W John St, Hicksville, NY 11801
Tel.: (516) 433-7100 NY
Web Site: http://www.nassaucandy.com
Year Founded: 1984
Candy Distr
N.A.I.C.S.: 424450
Les Stier (Pres)
Joe Vanella (CFO)
Subsidiaries:

Island Natural, Inc. (1)
4207 20th Ave, Long Island City, NY 11105
Tel.: (718) 721-8000
Web Site: http://www.islandnatural.com
Other Grocery & Related Products Merchant Whslr
N.A.I.C.S.: 424490
Paul Burstyn (Founder & Pres)
Peter Berelson (Mgr-Pur)
Dave Berke (Mgr-Ops)
Susie Soric (Office Mgr)

The Warrell Corp. (1)
1250 Slate Hill Rd, Camp Hill, PA 17011
Tel.: (717) 761-5440
Web Site: http://www.pwarrellcorp.com
Candy & Other Confectionary Products
N.A.I.C.S.: 424450
Lincoln A. Warrell (Chm)
Richard Warrell (Exec VP-Sls & Mktg)
Kevin Silva (Pres & CEO)

NASSAU FARMERS ELEVATOR CO.
301 1st Ave, Nassau, MN 56257
Tel.: (320) 668-2323 MN
Year Founded: 1899
Sales Range: $10-24.9 Million
Emp.: 16
Automotive Tires, Oil, Fertilizer & Feed Distr
N.A.I.C.S.: 424510
Jay J. Hansen (Mgr-Grain)
Rick Barrett (Mgr-Agronomy)
Lisa Bornhorst (Office Mgr)

NASSAU HOLDING CORP.
3636 N Causeway Blvd Ste 300, Metairie, LA 70002
Tel.: (504) 837-5766
Rev.: $15,000,000
Emp.: 20
Provider of Oil & Gas Well Drilling Servcies
N.A.I.C.S.: 213111
William A. Hines (Chm)
William M. Hines (VP)
Linda Poche (Controller)

NASSAU LENS CO., INC.
160 LeGrand Ave, Northvale, NJ 07647
Tel.: (201) 767-8033
Web Site: http://www.nassau247.com
Sales Range: $25-49.9 Million
Emp.: 150
Lens Mfr
N.A.I.C.S.: 423460
Ozanian Diana (Mgr-Credit & Collection)
Ralph Dalo (Dir-Sourcing)
Ziva Bloch (Supvr-Customer Svc)

NASSAU PARADISE ISLAND PROMOTION BOARD
1200 S Pine Island Rd Ste 700, Plantation, FL 33324
Web Site: http://www.nassauparadiseisland.com
Year Founded: 1977
Sales Range: $10-24.9 Million
Tour Operator
N.A.I.C.S.: 561591
Frederick Lounsberry (CEO)
George Myers (Chm)
Michael Reckley (Sec)
Wililam Naughton (Treas)
George Markantonis (Vice Chm)

NASSAU POOLS CONSTRUCTION, INC.
3420 Westview Dr, Naples, FL 34104
Tel.: (239) 643-0990 FL
Web Site: http://www.nassaupools.com
Year Founded: 1968
Sales Range: $1-9.9 Million
Emp.: 50
Swimming Pool Construction
N.A.I.C.S.: 238990
Tom L. Threlkeld (Pres)

NASSAU REGIONAL OFF-TRACK BETTING
220 Fulton Ave, Hempstead, NY 11550
Tel.: (516) 572-2800
Web Site: http://www.nassauotb.com
Sales Range: $25-49.9 Million
Emp.: 350
Off-Track Betting
N.A.I.C.S.: 713290
John Fabio (Exec VP)
Margaret Feis (Mgr)
Joseph Cairo (Pres)

NASSAU SUFFOLK LUMBER & SUPPLY CORPORATION
3800 Veterans Memorial Hwy, Bohemia, NY 11716
Tel.: (631) 467-2020
Web Site: http://www.nassausuffolklumber.com
Year Founded: 1971
Rev.: $44,436,011
Emp.: 150
Lumber, Plywood & Millwork
N.A.I.C.S.: 423310

William H. Van Tuyl (Chm)
Brian Mooney (Mgr-Wood Truss Div)
Dorothy Cunningham (Mgr-Sls)
James Iannotti (Branch Mgr)

NASSCO, INC.
5365 S Moorland Rd, New Berlin, WI 53151
Tel.: (414) 422-9960
Web Site: http://nasscoinc.com
Year Founded: 1955
Emp.: 150
Janitorial & Packaging Supplies Distr
N.A.I.C.S.: 423440
Mark Melzer (Pres)
Katti Pudleiner (Coord-Sls & Mktg)
Kurt Melzer (VP-Ops)
Paul Melzer (Project Mgr)
Subsidiaries:

Messner Inc. (1)
1326 E Washington Ave, Madison, WI 53703
Tel.: (608) 256-7784
Web Site: http://www.nascoinc.com
Janitorial & Building Maintenance Supplies Distr
N.A.I.C.S.: 423440
Mark Melver (Owner)

NASSER COMPANY INC.
22720 Savi Ranch Pkwy, Yorba Linda, CA 92887
Tel.: (714) 279-2100
Web Site: http://www.nasserco.com
Year Founded: 1984
Rev.: $36,000,000
Emp.: 100
Bond Brokers
N.A.I.C.S.: 424410
Burhan Nasser (Pres)

NASSIMI CORPORATION
370 7th Ave Fl 16, New York, NY 10001
Tel.: (212) 643-8080
Web Site: http://www.nassimi.com
Rev.: $10,933,910
Emp.: 50
Piece Goods & Other Fabrics
N.A.I.C.S.: 424310
Edward Nassimi (Pres)

NASTOS CONSTRUCTION INC.
1421 Kenilworth Ave NE, Washington, DC 20019
Tel.: (202) 398-5500
Web Site: http://www.nastos.com
Rev.: $10,201,880
Emp.: 7
Commercial & Office Buildings, Renovation & Repair
N.A.I.C.S.: 236220
Lilian Romero (Mgr-Tech Svcs)

NASTYGOAT CORPORATION
3102 Oak Lawn Ave Ste 900, Dallas, TX 75219
Tel.: (972) 707-8530
Web Site: http://www.rewardstyle.com
Year Founded: 2011
Sales Range: $50-74.9 Million
Emp.: 225
Business Consulting Services
N.A.I.C.S.: 541613
Amber Venz Box (Co-Founder & Pres)
Baxter Box (Co-Founder & CEO)
Bill Bodin (CTO)
Jeff Dawson (CFO & Gen Mgr-Intl)
Kacy Cole (Sr VP-Mktg)

NAT SHERMAN INC.
12 E 42nd St, New York, NY 10017-0002
Tel.: (212) 764-4175

NAT SHERMAN INC.

U.S. PRIVATE

Nat Sherman Inc.,—(Continued)
Web Site:
http://www.natsherman.com
Year Founded: 1930
Sales Range: $10-24.9 Million
Emp.: 100
Mfr, Distributor & Retailer of Cigars, Cigarettes & Gifts
N.A.I.C.S.: 424940
Joel Sherman (Pres & CEO)
Nashad Juman (Mgr-Mktg & Strategic Plng)
Albert Dettore (Chief People Officer)
Lionel Legry (CIO)
Michael Herklots (VP-Retail & Brand Dev)
Cristina Becerra (Mgr-HR)
Eileen Ravalico (Reg Mgr-Sls)
Larry Sherman (Exec VP-Intl)

NATARE CORPORATION
5905 W 74th St, Indianapolis, IN 46278
Tel.: (317) 290-8828
Web Site: http://www.natare.com
Year Founded: 1992
Water Sports Equipment
N.A.I.C.S.: 339920
Michael T. Walsh (Pres & CEO)
Jon Breiner (VP)

NATCHEZ TRACE ELECTRIC POWER ASSOCIATION
555 E Madison St, Houston, MS 38851
Tel.: (662) 456-3037
Web Site: http://www.ntepa.com
Sales Range: $10-24.9 Million
Emp.: 35
Electronic Services
N.A.I.C.S.: 221118
Norma Kilgore (Gen Mgr)

NATCO PRODUCTS CORPORATION
155 Brookside Ave, West Warwick, RI 02893-3802
Tel.: (401) 828-0300
Web Site: http://www.natcohome.com
Year Founded: 1917
Sales Range: $25-49.9 Million
Emp.: 360
Mfr of Carpets, Rugs & Window Curtains
N.A.I.C.S.: 326199
Robert T. Galkin (Chm)
Michael Litner (Pres)
Steven Buke (CFO)

Subsidiaries:

Corona Curtain Manufacturing Co. Inc. (1)
401 Neponset St, Canton, MA 02021
Tel.: (617) 350-6970
Rev.: $45,000,000
Emp.: 4
Curtains, Window: Made From Purchased Materials
N.A.I.C.S.: 339999

NPC South Inc. (1)
1101 Riverbend Rd, Dalton, GA 30721
Tel.: (706) 278-5911
Rev.: $27,000,000
Emp.: 180
Wholesale of Carpets & Rugs
N.A.I.C.S.: 314110
Kerry Kinoman (Plant Mgr)

NATCOM BANCSHARES, INC.
1127 Tower Ave, Superior, WI 54880
Tel.: (715) 394-5531
Web Site: http://www.nbofc.com
Year Founded: 1998
Sales Range: $25-49.9 Million
Emp.: 100
Bank Holding Company
N.A.I.C.S.: 551211

Subsidiaries:

National Bank of Commerce (1)
1127 Twr Ave, Superior, WI 54880
Tel.: (715) 394-5531
Web Site: http://www.nbofc.com
Sales Range: $25-49.9 Million
Emp.: 50
Provider of Banking Services
N.A.I.C.S.: 522110
Steven R. Burgess (CEO)
Valerie Blanchenay (VP & Dir-Mktg)
Bobbie Dumonsau (Sr VP & Dir-Deposit Ops)
Jeremy Egnash (CFO & Exec VP)
Linda Emmert (Asst VP-Fin)
Diane Foss-Engstrom (VP-Internal Audit)
John Matthews (Sr VP & Dir-Community Banking)
Sandy Mattson (VP-Compliance & Dir-Loan Review)
Lonnie Swartz (Chief Credit Officer & Exec VP)
Bruce Thompson (Exec VP)

NATCOM MARKETING
80 SW 8th St Ste 2230, Miami, FL 33130
Tel.: (786) 425-0028   FL
Year Founded: 1982
Rev.: $15,200,000
Emp.: 10
Advetising Agency
N.A.I.C.S.: 541810
Robert J. Rodriguez (Pres)
Gigi Pastrawa (CFO)
Bob Bauer (Sr VP)
Giselle Mas (Acct Mgr)
Las Hernandez (VP-Mktg Svcs)

NATE WADE SUBARU
1207 S Main St, Salt Lake City, UT 84111-4492
Tel.: (801) 355-7571
Web Site: http://www.natewade.com
Year Founded: 1958
Sales Range: $25-49.9 Million
Emp.: 80
Car Whslr
N.A.I.C.S.: 441110
Kirk Schneider (Mgr)

NATEL ENGINEERING COMPANY, INC.
9340 Owensmouth Ave, Chatsworth, CA 91311
Tel.: (818) 734-6500   CA
Web Site: http://www.natelengr.com
Year Founded: 1975
Rev.: $24,069,000
Emp.: 200
Hybrid Integrated Circuits
N.A.I.C.S.: 334413
Sudesh Arora (Pres & CEO)
James A. Angeloni (COO-Aerospace & Defense Ops)
Will Bolinger (VP-Quality)
Kunal Sharma (COO)
Laura L. Siegal (CFO)

Subsidiaries:

EPIC Technologies, LLC (1)
200 E Bluegrass Dr, Norwalk, OH 44857
Tel.: (419) 668-2891
Web Site: http://www.epictech.com
Sales Range: $50-74.9 Million
Emp.: 164
Electronic Manufacturing Services to OEMs
N.A.I.C.S.: 334418
Steven C. Fries (CFO)
Joe Rogers (Sr VP-Global Ops)

Hytek Microsystems, Inc. (1)
400 Hot Springs Rd, Carson City, NV 89706
Tel.: (775) 883-0820
Sales Range: $10-24.9 Million
Emp.: 35
Mfr of Microelectronic Circuits
N.A.I.C.S.: 334413

Natel Engineering Co., Inc. - Agave Plant (1)
Blvd Independencia #1450 Int 99 Col Patria II, Ciudad Juarez, CP 32790, Chihuahua, Mexico
Tel.: (52) 915 791 5300
Web Site: http://www.natelems.com
Semiconductor Manufacturing Operations
N.A.I.C.S.: 334111
Steve Fraser (VP-Ops)

NATERRA INTERNATIONAL INC.
1250 Freeport Pkwy, Coppell, TX 75019
Tel.: (972) 616-6100
Web Site: http://www.naterra.us
Year Founded: 1922
Sales Range: $10-24.9 Million
Emp.: 55
Perfumes, Cosmetics & Other Toilet Preparations Mfr
N.A.I.C.S.: 325620
Jin K. Song (CEO)

NATERRA LAND
43 Main St Southeast Ste 506, Minneapolis, MN 55414
Tel.: (612) 331-6929
Sales Range: $25-49.9 Million
Emp.: 14
Subdividers & Developers
N.A.I.C.S.: 237210

Subsidiaries:

Naterra Land (1)
34076 conuty Rd 3, Crosslake, MN 56442
Tel.: (218) 967-0666
Real Estate Agents & Managers
N.A.I.C.S.: 531210

Naterra Land Tennessee LLC (1)
3637 Wears Vly Rd, Sevierville, TN 37862
Tel.: (865) 429-1203
Sales Range: $10-24.9 Million
Emp.: 2
Real Estate Agents & Managers
N.A.I.C.S.: 531210

NATFRESH BEVERAGES CORP.
2800 Post Oak Blvd Ste 4100, Houston, TX 77056
Tel.: (832) 390-2235   NV
Web Site:
http://www.natfreshbeverages.com
Year Founded: 2012
Natural Spring Water
N.A.I.C.S.: 312112
Oliver Yi Lung Lin (Pres, CEO, CFO, Chief Acctg Officer, Treas & Sec)

NATH COMPANIES INCORPORATED
900 American Blvd E Ste 300, Bloomington, MN 55420
Tel.: (952) 853-1400   MN
Web Site:
http://www.nathcompanies.com
Year Founded: 1980
Sales Range: $100-124.9 Million
Emp.: 50
Restaurant, Hotel & Real Estate Management Services
N.A.I.C.S.: 722513
Mahendra Nath (Co-Owner, Pres & CEO)
Asha Nath (Co-Owner, Sec & VP)
Deepak Nath (Project Mgr)
Shalini Nath-Walia (Treas)
Dave S. Walia (Project Mgr)

Subsidiaries:

Nath Florida Franchise Group (1)
900 American Blvd E, Minneapolis, MN 55420
Tel.: (952) 288-2300
Web Site: http://www.nathcompanies.com
Rev.: $2,000,000
Emp.: 3
Fast-Food Restaurant, Chain
N.A.I.C.S.: 722513

Nath Management Inc (1)
900 E American Blvd Ste 300, Bloomington, MN 55420
Tel.: (952) 853-1400
Web Site: http://www.nathcompanies.com
Sales Range: Less than $1 Million
Emp.: 25
Apartment Building Operator
N.A.I.C.S.: 531110
Asha Nath (Treas, Sec & VP)
Mahendra Nath (Owner, Pres & CEO)

Nath Minnesota Franchise Group (1)
900 E American Blvd Ste 300, Minneapolis, MN 55420
Tel.: (952) 853-1400
Web Site: http://www.nathcompanies.com
Fast-Food Restaurant, Chain
N.A.I.C.S.: 722513
Mahendra Nath (Pres & CEO)

NATHAN & LEWIS SECURITIES INC
119 W 40th St, New York, NY 10018
Tel.: (212) 354-8800
Year Founded: 1976
Rev.: $115,000,000
Emp.: 130
Investment Securities Services
N.A.I.C.S.: 523150
Jay Lewis (Pres)

NATHAN ASSOCIATES INC.
1777 N Kent St Ste 1400, Arlington, VA 22209
Tel.: (703) 516-7700   DE
Web Site: http://www.nathaninc.com
Professional, Scientific & Technical Services
N.A.I.C.S.: 541990
Sue Chodakewitz (Pres & CEO)
Stephen E. Sellick (Sr VP)
Paul W. Moore (Sr VP)
Jeffrey Singer (Sr VP)
Edward H. Bersoff (Chm)
Eamon Cassidy (Mng Dir)
Jennifer Feinleib (VP-Global HR)

Subsidiaries:

Gnarus Advisors LLC (1)
1777 N Kent St Ste 1400, Arlington, VA 22209
Tel.: (571) 384-2444
Web Site: http://www.gnarusllc.com
Business Management Consulting Services
N.A.I.C.S.: 541611
Bret C. Cohen (Gen Counsel & VP)
Kerri H. Grant (Principal)
Eric T. Kirschner (Principal)
Stephen E. Sellick (Founder & Mng Dir)
Jorge E. Sirgo (Principal)
Daniel Maloney (Principal)
Brandon Kivler (Principal)
Blair Hubbard (Principal)
Marc Scoppettone (Principal)
Brian Henthorn (Principal)

NATHAN LITTAUER HOSPITAL & NURSING HOME
99 E State St, Gloversville, NY 12078
Tel.: (518) 725-8621   NY
Web Site: http://www.nlh.org
Year Founded: 1894
Sales Range: $75-99.9 Million
Emp.: 1,086
Health Care Srvices
N.A.I.C.S.: 622110
Michael D. Ostrander (CFO & VP)
Leslie Beadle (VP-Admin)
Martin Brown (CIO & VP-Info Svcs)
Cheryl G. McGrattan (VP-Mktg, PR & Community Rels)
Lana E. Wydra (VP-HR)
Geoff Peck (VP-Exec Dir)
Laurence Kelly (Pres & CEO)

COMPANIES

Frederick Goldberg (CMO & VP-Medical Affairs)
Patrice McMahon (Vp-Primary Care Svcs)

NATHANTABOR.COM
390 Peters Creek Pkwy, Winston Salem, NC 27101
Tel.: (336) 416-7117
Web Site: http://www.nathantabor.com
Year Founded: 2005
Sales Range: $1-9.9 Million
Emp.: 47
Real Estate
N.A.I.C.S.: 531390
Nathan Tabor (Owner)

NATION PIZZA AND FOODS, LLC
601 E Algonquin Rd, Schaumburg, IL 60173-3803
Tel.: (847) 397-3320
Web Site: http://www.nationpizza.com
Year Founded: 1947
Sales Range: $50-74.9 Million
Emp.: 800
Pizza Ingredients
N.A.I.C.S.: 424490
Marshall Bauer (CEO)
Joe Giglio (CFO)
Bruce Waid (Dir-IT)

NATION'S BEST HOLDINGS, LLC
223 Elk Ave 202 B, Crested Butte, CO 81224
Tel.: (409) 553-1386   DE
Web Site: http://nationsbest.net
Year Founded: 2019
Holding Company; Home Improvement Services
N.A.I.C.S.: 551112
Chris Miller (Founder, Pres & CEO)
Robert Debs (VP-Fin & IR)
Summer Loveland (CFO)

Subsidiaries:

Bridgeport Building Centers   (1)
1002 10th St, Bridgeport, TX 76426
Tel.: (940) 683-5144
Web Site: http://www.buildingcenters.net
Sales Range: $10-24.9 Million
Emp.: 25
Construction Materials Whslr
N.A.I.C.S.: 423390
Ronnie Hess (Pres)

NATIONAL ACADEMY OF SCIENCES
2101 Constitution Ave NW, Washington, DC 20418-0007
Tel.: (202) 334-2000   DC
Web Site: http://www.nas.edu
Year Founded: 1863
Sales Range: $75-99.9 Million
Emp.: 1,200
Provides Independent Advice to the Government on Issues of Science, Technology & Public Health
N.A.I.C.S.: 541715
John Brauman (Sec-Home)
Marcia McNutt (Pres)

NATIONAL AIR CARGO INC.
350 Windward Dr, Orchard Park, NY 14127
Tel.: (716) 631-0011
Web Site: http://www.nationalaircargo.com
Rev.: $20,000,000
Emp.: 35
Air Freight Forwarder
N.A.I.C.S.: 481212
Robert Schlager (Mgr-Ops-Americas)
Jim Richeal (Mgr-Svc)

NATIONAL ALARM & PROTECTION
6510 Southcenter Blvd # 2, Tukwila, WA 98188
Tel.: (206) 248-6070
Rev.: $10,600,000
Emp.: 35
Safety & Security Specialization
N.A.I.C.S.: 561621

NATIONAL ALLIANCE ON MENTAL ILLNESS
3803 N Fairfax Dr Ste 100, Arlington, VA 22203
Tel.: (703) 524-7600   MO
Web Site: http://www.nami.org
Year Founded: 1979
Sales Range: $10-24.9 Million
Emp.: 88
Behavioral Healthcare Services
N.A.I.C.S.: 621420
David Levy (CFO)
Ronald S. Honberg (Dir-Policy & Legal Affairs)
Steve Pitman (Pres)
Lacey Berumen (First VP)
Bob Spada (Treas)
Victoria Gonzalez (Second VP)
Cheri Villa (COO)
Charles R. Harman (Chief Dev Officer)
Susan Gaffney (Natl Dir-Field Capacity & Governance)
Katrina Gay (Dir-Strategic Partnerships-Natl)
Valerie Hunter (Natl Dir-Org Dev & Talent Mgmt)
Angela Kimball (Natl Dir-Advocacy & Public Policy)
James Stewart (CIO)
Ken Duckworth (Dir-Medical)
Ellen Ritz (Chm)
Kerry Graves (Exec Dir-NAMI Metropolitan Baltimore)
Cheryl Davis (Assoc Provost-Res & Creative Activity)
Christine Reasoner (Exec Dir)
Daniel H. Gillison Jr. (CEO)

NATIONAL AMERICAN INSURANCE COMPANY
1010 Manvel Ave, Chandler, OK 74834
Tel.: (405) 258-0804
Web Site: http://www.naico.com
Year Founded: 1987
Insurance Brokerage
N.A.I.C.S.: 524210
W. Brent LaGere (CEO)
Lance A. LaGere (PreS & COO)
Malinda Laird (Exec VP)

NATIONAL AMUSEMENTS, INC.
846 University Ave, Norwood, MA 02062
Tel.: (781) 461-1600
Web Site: http://www.showcasecinemas.com
Holding Company for Television & Motion Picture Companies, Cable Systems, Television & Radio Stations & Multiplex Cinemas
N.A.I.C.S.: 551112
Shari E. Redstone (Chm, Pres & CEO)
William LeClair (Sr VP-Food & Beverage)
Joseph Mollo (CIO & Sr VP-IT)
Richard Sherman (CFO & Sr VP)
Mark Walukevich (Sr VP-Intl Film)
Kevin Barry (VP-Construction)
Patricia Reeser (Sr VP)
Paula Keough (Gen Counsel)

Subsidiaries:

Paramount Global   (1)
1515 Broadway, New York, NY 10036   (77.4%)
Tel.: (212) 258-6000
Web Site: https://www.paramount.com
Rev.: $29,652,000,000
Assets: $53,543,000,000
Liabilities: $30,493,000,000
Net Worth: $23,050,000,000
Earnings: ($608,000,000)
Emp.: 21,900
Fiscal Year-end: 12/31/2023
Media Streaming Distribution Services
N.A.I.C.S.: 516120
Richard M. Jones (Chief Veteran Officer, Gen Counsel-Tax & Exec VP)
George Cheeks (Pres & CEO-CBS)
Ray Hopkins (Pres-Networks Distr-U.S.)
John Halley (Pres-Adv)
Jo Ann Ross (Chm-Adv)
Brian Robbins (CEO)
Christa A. D'Alimonte (Gen Counsel, Sec & Exec VP)
Katherine Gill-Charest (Chief Acctg Officer, Exec VP & Controller)
Doretha Lea (Exec VP-Public Policy & Govt Rels-Global)
Julia Phelps (Chief Comm & Corp Mktg Officer & Exec VP)
Nancy R. Phillips (Chief People Officer & Exec VP)
Marva Smalls (Exec VP-Public Affairs-Kids & Family Entertainment & Head-Inclus)
Chris McCarthy (Pres, CEO-Media Networks, Showtime, and MTV Entertainment Studios & Interim Principal Executive Officer)
Naveen K. Chopra (CFO & Exec VP)
Phil Wiser (CTO & Exec VP)
Lee Sears (Exec VP & Head-Intl Adv Sls & Integrated Mktg)
Dan Cohen (Chief Content Licensing Officer)
Jonathan Karp (Pres)
Scott M. Mills (CEO)
Colleen Fahey Rush (Chief Res Officer)
Tom Ryan (Pres)
Kristin Southey (Exec VP)
Pamela O. Kaufman (Pres/CEO-Intl Markets, Global Consumer Products, and Experiences)

Subsidiary (Domestic):

BET Holdings LLC   (2)
1 BET Plz 1235 W St NE, Washington, DC 20018-1211
Tel.: (202) 608-2000
Web Site: http://www.bet.com
Sales Range: $1-4.9 Billion
Emp.: 685
Holding Company; Cable Television Network & Other Media Products & Services
N.A.I.C.S.: 551112
Quinton Bowman (Sr VP-HR)
Raymond Goulbourne (Exec VP-Brdcst Media Sls)
Jeanine Liburd (Chief Mktg & Comm Officer)
Cybelle Brown (VP-Sls & Bus Dev-Digital & Event Productions)
Michael D. Armstrong (Gen Mgr)
Essie Chambers (Sr VP-Original Programming-Centric)
Tom Gorke (Exec VP-Sls & Bus Dev)
Zola Mashariki (Exec VP & Head-Original Programming-Los Angeles)
Scott M. Mills (Pres & CEO)
Donna Blackman (Sr VP-Bus Ops)

Subsidiary (Domestic):

Black Entertainment Television, LLC   (3)
1235 W St NE, Washington, DC 20018-1211   (100%)
Tel.: (202) 608-2000
Web Site: http://www.bet.com
Sales Range: $50-74.9 Million
Emp.: 400
Cable Television Network
N.A.I.C.S.: 516210
Robert Louis Johnson (Founder)
Stephen G. Hill (Exec VP-Entertainment & Music Programming)

Subsidiary (Domestic):

BET Interactive, LLC   (4)
1235 W St NE, Washington, DC 20018   (100%)
Tel.: (202) 608-2000
Web Site: http://www.bet.com
Sales Range: $50-74.9 Million
Emp.: 20
Internet Publishing Services
N.A.I.C.S.: 516210

BET Services, Inc.   (4)
1331 Us Highway 80 E Ste 1, Mesquite, TX 75150-5712
Tel.: (972) 288-1374
Video Production & Taping Services
N.A.I.C.S.: 512110

Subsidiary (Non-US):

Bahamas Underwriters Services Limited   (2)
Lex Hse George St, Nassau, Bahamas
Tel.: (242) 2423258184
Auditing Services
N.A.I.C.S.: 541211

Subsidiary (Domestic):

Bellator Sport Worldwide LLC   (2)
5000 Birch St Ste 7100, Newport Beach, CA 92660
Tel.: (949) 222-3400
Web Site: http://www.bellator.com
Mixed Martial Arts Promotional Services
N.A.I.C.S.: 711310

Big Ticket Pictures Inc.   (2)
5842 W Sunset Blvd, Hollywood, CA 90028
Tel.: (323) 860-0200
Video Production Services
N.A.I.C.S.: 512199
Jane Davis (Product Mgr)

Big Ticket Productions Inc.   (2)
1438 N Gower St, Los Angeles, CA 90028
Tel.: (650) 269-8757
Web Site: http://www.thebigs.ca
Emp.: 65
Motion Picture & Video Production Services
N.A.I.C.S.: 512110

Subsidiary (Non-US):

Brainpool TV GmbH   (2)
Schanzenstrasse 22, 51063, Cologne, Germany
Tel.: (49) 22165090
Web Site: http://www.brainpool.de
Sales Range: $25-49.9 Million
Emp.: 200
Television Program Producers
N.A.I.C.S.: 512110
Jorg Grabosch (CEO)

Subsidiary (Domestic):

Branded Productions, Inc.   (2)
1101 S Broad St Ste 200, Lansdale, PA 19446
Tel.: (215) 694-1889
Web Site: http://www.brandedvideo.com
Video Production Services
N.A.I.C.S.: 512110

CBS Broadcasting Inc.   (2)
51 W 52nd St, New York, NY 10019
Tel.: (212) 975-4321
Web Site: http://www.cbs.com
Sales Range: $800-899.9 Million
Emp.: 8,000
Television & Radio Broadcasting Services
N.A.I.C.S.: 516120
Radha Subramanyam (Chief Res & Analytics Officer & Exec VP)
Susan Zirinsky (Pres-News)
Neeraj Khemlani (Co-Pres & Co-Head)
Wendy McMahon (Co-Pres & Co-Head)
Chris Ender (Exec VP-Comm)

Division (Domestic):

CBS Entertainment Division   (3)
51 W 52nd St, New York, NY 10019
Tel.: (212) 975-4321
Web Site: http://www.cbscorporation.com
Entertainment Programming Schedule Creator
N.A.I.C.S.: 516120
George Cheeks (Pres & CEO)

NATIONAL AMUSEMENTS, INC.   U.S. PRIVATE

National Amusements, Inc.—(Continued)

Thom Sherman *(Sr Exec VP-Programming)*
Bryon Rubin *(CFO & COO)*

CBS News (3)
51 W 52nd St, New York, NY 10019
Web Site: https://www.cbsnews.com
Sales Range: $900-999.9 Million
News & Public Affairs Producer
N.A.I.C.S.: 516120
Steve Friedman *(Sr VP-CBS News)*
Ingrid Ciprian-Matthews *(Exec VP)*
Tim Gaughan *(VP-News Gathering)*
Christa Robinson *(Sr VP-Comm)*
Rick Jefferson *(VP-News Ops)*
Susan Zirinsky *(Pres-Troubled News Div)*
Lance Frank *(VP-Comm)*

CBS Sports Division (3)
51 W 52nd St, New York, NY 10019
Tel.: (212) 975-4321
Web Site: http://www.sportsline.com
Sales Range: $25-49.9 Million
Emp.: 150
Sports Programming Producer
N.A.I.C.S.: 516120
Michael L. Aresco *(Exec VP-Programming)*
Sean McManus *(Pres-Sports)*
John Bogusz *(Exec VP)*
Ken Aagaard *(Exec VP-Ops, Engrg & Production Svcs)*
Rob Correa *(Exec VP-Programming)*
Harold Bryant *(VP-Production)*
Clark C. Kellogg Jr. *(Executives)*

CBS Television Distribution (3)
2450 Colorado Ave Ste 500E, Santa Monica, CA 90404
Tel.: (310) 264-3300
Web Site: http://www.cbstvd.com
Sales Range: $100-124.9 Million
Emp.: 500
Production, Marketing & Distribution Services to Broadcast, Cable, Home Video, In-Flight & Emerging Media
N.A.I.C.S.: 541613
Leslie Ryan *(Sr VP-Comm)*
Joe Ferullo *(Exec VP-Current Programming)*
Steven A. LoCascio *(CFO & COO)*
Dawn Abel *(Exec VP-Res)*
Cassie Thomas *(Sr VP-HR)*
Scott Trupchak *(Exec VP-Media Sls)*
Jonathan Bingaman *(Exec VP-Domestic Licensing & Distr)*

Subsidiary (Domestic):

King World Productions, Inc. (4)
2401 Colorado Ave Ste 110, Santa Monica, CA 90404
Tel.: (310) 264-3300
Web Site: http://www.kingworld.com
Feature Films & Television Production Distr
N.A.I.C.S.: 512120

Subsidiary (Domestic):

CSTV Networks, Inc. (3)
85 10th Ave 3rd Fl, New York, NY 10011
Tel.: (212) 342-8700
Web Site: http://www.cstv.com
Sales Range: $25-49.9 Million
Emp.: 230
College Sports Cable Television Services
N.A.I.C.S.: 516210
Eric Krasnoo *(VP-Sls)*
Dan Sabreen *(Mgr-Sports Publicity)*

Subsidiary (Non-US):

CBS Canada Co. (2)
26 Queen Street, PO Box 186, Saint Catharines, L2R 6S7, ON, Canada
Tel.: (905) 688-9855
Web Site: https://www.cbscanada.com
Sales Range: $10-24.9 Million
Emp.: 1
Storage Services
N.A.I.C.S.: 493110

Subsidiary (Domestic):

CBS Collegiate Sports Properties Inc. (2)
N 111 Vista Rd Ste 3A, Spokane, WA 99212
Tel.: (509) 324-3365
Web Site: http://www.cbscsp.com
Sales Range: $25-49.9 Million
Emp.: 21
Sports Marketing Services
N.A.I.C.S.: 541613

CBS Films Inc. (2)
1100 Glendon Ave Ste 1100, Los Angeles, CA 90024
Tel.: (310) 575-7560
Web Site: http://www.cbsfilms.com
Emp.: 50
Motion Picture & Video Production Services
N.A.I.C.S.: 512110
Terry Press *(Pres)*
Steven Friedlander *(Exec VP-Theatrical Distr)*
Reid Sullivan *(CFO)*
Rik Toulon *(Gen Counsel & Exec VP)*
Scott Shooman *(Exec VP-Acquisitions & Co-Productions)*

CBS Interactive Inc. (2)
235 2nd St, San Francisco, CA 94105
Tel.: (415) 344-2000
Web Site: http://www.cbsinteractive.com
Sales Range: $400-449.9 Million
Emp.: 3,500
Online Media Publisher
N.A.I.C.S.: 516210
Laura Summers *(VP-Sls-Global)*
Ashley Esqueda *(Sr Editor)*
Susan Lundgren *(Sr VP-Comm)*
Darin Bassin *(Gen Counsel)*
Renee Budig *(CFO & Exec VP)*

Branch (Domestic):

CBS Interactive Inc. (3)
28 E 28th St 10th Fl, New York, NY 10016
Tel.: (646) 472-4000
Web Site: http://www.cbsinteractive.com
Emp.: 120
Online Media Publisher
N.A.I.C.S.: 516210
Dale Durrett *(VP-Natl Sls-BtoB)*

Subsidiary (Non-US):

CBS Interactive Japan K.K. (3)
Sumitomofudosan Hitosubashi Building 2F 3-9-1Kanda-Jinbocho, Chiyoda-ku, Tokyo, 101-0051, Japan
Tel.: (81) 3 3238 0704
Online Media Publisher
N.A.I.C.S.: 516210

CBS Interactive Limited (3)
207 211 Old St Warehouse, The Bower, London, EC1V9NR, United Kingdom
Tel.: (44) 207 021 1000
Web Site: http://www.cbsinteractive.co.uk
Emp.: 150
Online Media Publisher
N.A.I.C.S.: 516210
Steve Wing *(Head-Consumer)*

CBS Interactive Pte. Ltd. (3)
18 Robinson Road 10-01, Centrepoint, Singapore, Singapore
Tel.: (65) 6506 6688
Web Site: http://www.cbsinteractive.com
Online Media Publisher
N.A.I.C.S.: 516210

Subsidiary (Domestic):

CBS SportsLine.com, Inc. (3)
1401 W Cypress Creek Rd, Fort Lauderdale, FL 33309-1825
Tel.: (954) 351-2120
Web Site: http://www.cbssports.com
Sales Range: $25-49.9 Million
Emp.: 275
Internet-Based Sports Media Services
N.A.I.C.S.: 516210
Jason Kint *(CEO)*

TechTracker, Inc. (3)
55 SW Yamhill St 3rd Fl, Portland, OR 97204-3312
Tel.: (503) 227-2571
Web Site: http://www.techtracker.com
Sales Range: $10-24.9 Million
Emp.: 25
Software Information & Services
N.A.I.C.S.: 513210
Anshu Ahluwalia *(Mgr-Circulation)*

Subsidiary (Non-US):

CBS Interactive Pty. Ltd. (2)
Level: 10 201 Elizabeth Street, Sydney, 2000, NSW, Australia
Tel.: (61) 285149999
Web Site: http://www.cbsinteractive.com.au
Advertising Consulting Services
N.A.I.C.S.: 541810

CBS International Holdings B.V. (2)
H J E Wenckebachweg 80, Amsterdam, 1096 AR, Noord-Holland, Netherlands
Tel.: (31) 207154080
Entertainment Services
N.A.I.C.S.: 541840

CBS International Sales Holdings B.V. (2)
Singel 540 5 th Floor, 1017 AZ, Amsterdam, Noord-Holland, Netherlands
Tel.: (31) 207167330
Media & Entertainment Broadcasting Services
N.A.I.C.S.: 516120
Gielijn Hilarius *(Gen Mgr)*

CBS International Television Australia Pty Limited (2)
L 4 27-31 Macquarie Pl, Sydney, 2000, NSW, Australia
Tel.: (61) 282744444
Web Site: http://www.cbs.com
Emp.: 4
Motion Picture & Video Distribution Services
N.A.I.C.S.: 512120

Subsidiary (Domestic):

CBS MaxPreps Inc. (2)
4080 Plz Goldorado Cir Ste A, Cameron Park, CA 95682
Tel.: (800) 329-7324
Web Site: http://www.maxpreps.com
Sports Website Services
N.A.I.C.S.: 711219
Andy Beal *(Founder & Pres)*

CBS Outernet Inc. (2)
140 Sherman St, Fairfield, CT 06824
Tel.: (203) 255-7860
Web Site: http://www.signstorey.com
Sales Range: $25-49.9 Million
Emp.: 12
Interactive Marketing & Merchandising Systems
N.A.I.C.S.: 516120

CBS Overseas Inc. (2)
51 W 52nd St Bsmt 1, New York, NY 10019-6100
Tel.: (212) 975-4321
Web Site: http://www.cbs.com
Television Broadcasting Station
N.A.I.C.S.: 516120

CBS Studios Inc. (2)
26030 Ave Hall, Santa Clarita, CA 91355-3479
Tel.: (661) 702-9102
Motion Picture & Video Production Services
N.A.I.C.S.: 512110
Kristen Hall *(Exec VP-Comm)*

CBS Television Stations Inc. (2)
51 W 52nd St, New York, NY 10019
Tel.: (212) 975-4321
Web Site: http://www.cbslocal.com
Television Broadcasting Services
N.A.I.C.S.: 516120
Peter Dunn *(Pres)*
Mike Wittman *(Sr VP & Controller)*
Kevin Walsh *(Pres/Gen Mgr-San Francisco Bay Area Properties)*
Lauren Crane *(Sr VP-Multiplatform Sls)*
Julio Marenghi *(Pres-Sls)*

Unit (Domestic):

KCBS-TV (3)
4200 Radford Ave, Studio City, CA 91604
Tel.: (818) 655-2000
Web Site: http://www.cbsla.com
Sales Range: $10-24.9 Million
Emp.: 100
Television Broadcasting Services
N.A.I.C.S.: 516120
Steve Mauldin *(Pres & Gen Mgr)*
Bill Dallman *(VP & Dir-News)*

KCNC-TV (3)
1044 Lincoln St, Denver, CO 80203 (100%)
Tel.: (303) 861-4444

Web Site: http://www.cbs4denver.com
Rev.: $22,900,000
Emp.: 215
Television Broadcasting Station
N.A.I.C.S.: 516120
Tim Wieland *(Dir-News)*
Kristine Strain *(Asst Dir-News)*
John Montgomery *(Mgr-News Ops)*

KOVR-TV (3)
2713 Kovr Dr, Sacramento, CA 95605
Tel.: (916) 374-1313
Web Site: http://www.cbs13.com
Sales Range: $25-49.9 Million
Emp.: 220
Television Broadcasting Services
N.A.I.C.S.: 516120
Tim Calderhead *(Dir-HR)*
Ben Wong *(Engr-Brdcst Maintenance)*

KPIX-TV (3)
855 Battery St, San Francisco, CA 94111-1597
Tel.: (415) 362-5550
Web Site: http://www.cbs5.com
Sales Range: $10-24.9 Million
Emp.: 65
Television Broadcasting Services
N.A.I.C.S.: 516120
Ross Chan *(Acct Exec-Sls)*

KTVT Broadcasting Company LP (3)
10111 N Central Expy, Dallas, TX 75231
Tel.: (817) 451-1111
Web Site: http://www.cbs11tv.com
Sales Range: $25-49.9 Million
Emp.: 300
Television Broadcasting Station
N.A.I.C.S.: 516120
Laurie Passman *(Asst Dir-News)*
C. J. Hoyt *(Mng Editor)*
Sim Kolliner *(Dir-Programming)*

KYW-TV (3)
1555 Hamilton St, Philadelphia, PA 19130
Tel.: (215) 977-5300
Web Site: http://www.cbs3.com
Sales Range: $25-49.9 Million
Emp.: 225
Television Broadcasting Services
N.A.I.C.S.: 516120
Susan Schiller *(VP & Dir-News)*
Sara Cisomirski *(Dir-Mktg)*
Shelley Hoffman *(Mgr-Pub Affairs)*
Marc Lustig *(Controller)*
Brien Kennedy *(Pres & Gen Mgr)*

Los Angeles Television Station KCAL LLC (3)
4200 Radford Ave, Studio City, CA 91604
Tel.: (818) 655-2000
Web Site: http://www.losangeles.cbslocal.com
Sales Range: $25-49.9 Million
Emp.: 500
Television Broadcasting Services
N.A.I.C.S.: 516120
Steve Mauldin *(Pres & Gen Mgr)*

WBBM-TV (3)
22 W Washington, Chicago, IL 60602
Tel.: (312) 899-2222
Web Site: http://www.cbs2chicago.com
Sales Range: $25-49.9 Million
Emp.: 500
Television Broadcasting Services
N.A.I.C.S.: 516120
Derek Dalton *(Pres & Gen Mgr)*

WBZ-TV (3)
1170 Soldiers Field Rd, Boston, MA 02134
Tel.: (617) 787-7000
Web Site: http://www.wbztv.com
Sales Range: $25-49.9 Million
Emp.: 300
Television Broadcasting Services
N.A.I.C.S.: 516120
Theresa Rooney *(Mgr-Ops)*
Sean Barnacoat *(Mgr-News Promos)*
Gary LaPlante *(Dir-News)*
Avry Sandler *(Dir-Content Dev & Comml Ops)*

WCBS-TV (3)
524 W 57th St, New York, NY 10019
Tel.: (212) 975-4321
Web Site: http://www.cbsnewyork.com
Television Broadcasting Services
N.A.I.C.S.: 516120
Rich Paleski *(Dir-Brdcst Ops & Engrg)*
Robbie Sosa *(Editor-Assignment)*

COMPANIES

NATIONAL AMUSEMENTS, INC.

Vince McCarthy *(Mgr-Local Sls)*
Dan Forman *(Mng Editor-News Dept)*

WCCO-TV (3)
90 S. 11th St, Minneapolis, MN 55403-2414
Tel.: (612) 339-4444
Web Site: http://www.wcco.com
Sales Range: $25-49.9 Million
Emp.: 165
Television Broadcasting Services
N.A.I.C.S.: 516120
Mike Max *(Dir-Sports)*

WFOR-TV (3)
8900 NW 18th Ter, Miami, FL 33172
Tel.: (305) 591-4444
Web Site: http://www.miami.cbslocal.com
Sales Range: $25-49.9 Million
Emp.: 400
Television Broadcasting Services
N.A.I.C.S.: 516120

WJZ-TV (3)
3725 Malden Ave, Baltimore, MD 21211
Tel.: (410) 466-0013
Web Site: http://www.baltimore.cbslocal.com
Sales Range: $25-49.9 Million
Emp.: 165
Television Broadcasting Services
N.A.I.C.S.: 516120
Jay B. Newman *(VP & Gen Mgr)*
Bob Imhoff *(Controller)*
Brenda Comfort *(Asst Controller)*
K. C. Robertson *(Dir-Creative Svcs)*

Subsidiary (Non-US):

CBS Worldwide Netherlands B.V. (2)
Singel 540-5hg, 1017 AZ, Amsterdam, North Holland, Netherlands
Tel.: (31) 20 715 4082
Media & Entertainment Broadcasting Services
N.A.I.C.S.: 516120

CBS-CSI International B.V. (2)
Singel 540-5th floor, Amsterdam, 1017 AZ, Netherlands
Tel.: (31) 207167330
Motion Picture & Video Production Services
N.A.I.C.S.: 512110

Subsidiary (Domestic):

Championship Productions Inc. (2)
2730 Graham St, Ames, IA 50010
Tel.: (515) 232-3687
Web Site: http://www.championshipproductions.com
Sales Range: $10-24.9 Million
Emp.: 20
Sports Service
N.A.I.C.S.: 711211

Subsidiary (Non-US):

Channel 5 Broadcasting Ltd. (2)
10 Lower Thames Street, London, EC3R 6EN, United Kingdom
Tel.: (44) 20 8612 7000
Web Site: http://www.channel5.com
Television Broadcasting Station
N.A.I.C.S.: 516120
Ben Frow *(Dir-Programming)*

Subsidiary (Domestic):

Charter Media Company (2)
1204 Avenue B, Scottsbluff, NE 69361
Tel.: (906) 635-9848
Web Site: http://www.chartermedia.com
Television Broadcasting Services
N.A.I.C.S.: 516120

Detroit Television Station WKBD Inc. (2)
26905 W Eleven Mile Rd, Southfield, MI 48033
Tel.: (248) 355-7000
Television & Radio Stations
N.A.I.C.S.: 327910

Eagle Direct, Inc. (2)
311 Wilson Farm Rd, Gastonia, NC 28056-9528
Tel.: (704) 869-8944
Media & Advertising Services
N.A.I.C.S.: 541840

Subsidiary (Non-US):

Famous Players Investments B.V. (2)
Singel 540-5th Floor, Amsterdam, 1017 AZ, North Holland, Netherlands
Tel.: (31) 207154080
Investment Management Service
N.A.I.C.S.: 523940

Giraudy Viacom Outdoor S.A. (2)
17 Rue de Marignan, 75008, Paris, France
Tel.: (33) 155005300
Web Site: http://www.giraudy.fr
Sales Range: $50-74.9 Million
Emp.: 935
Public Relations Services
N.A.I.C.S.: 541820

Gravity Productions Inc. (2)
45 Mitton Pl, Kitchener, N2R 1B3, ON, Canada
Tel.: (519) 571-9112
Web Site: http://www.gravityproductions.ca
Motion Picture & Video Production
N.A.I.C.S.: 512110

Subsidiary (Domestic):

Inside Edition Inc. (2)
51 & 52 St, New York, NY 10019
Tel.: (212) 817-5555
Web Site: http://www.insideedition.com
Magazine Publishing Services
N.A.I.C.S.: 513120
Robert Read *(Mng Editor)*
Tony Coghlan *(Mng Editor)*

Subsidiary (Non-US):

King & Maxwell Productions Inc. (2)
10/210 555 Brooksbank Ave, North Vancouver, V7J 3S5, BC, Canada
Tel.: (604) 983-5588
Motion Picture & Video Production Services
N.A.I.C.S.: 512110

Subsidiary (Domestic):

MTV Networks Company (2)
1515 Broadway, New York, NY 10036
Tel.: (212) 258-8000
Web Site: http://www.mtv.com
Sales Range: $5-14.9 Billion
Cable Television Programming Services
N.A.I.C.S.: 513210
Alexis Rodriguez *(VP-Integrated Mktg)*
Liza Burnett Fefferman *(Sr VP-Comm)*
Abhishek K. Rao *(Sr Dir-MTV Brand-Southeast Asia)*
Paras Sharma *(Head-Digital Media-Asia)*
Simon Bates *(VP & Head-Asia Pacific)*
Nina L. Diaz *(Co-Pres)*
Chris McCarthy *(Co-Pres)*

Subsidiary (Domestic):

Atom Entertainment Inc. (3)
Fl 12 225 Bush St, San Francisco, CA 94104-4254
Tel.: (415) 503-2400
Sales Range: $25-49.9 Million
Emp.: 85
Licenser & Distributor of Short Films, Animations & Digital Media Via Television, Airlines, Theaters, Home Video & DVD, the Internet & Broadband Services
N.A.I.C.S.: 449210

Comedy Partners (3)
345 Hudson St, New York, NY 10014
Tel.: (212) 767-8600
Web Site: http://www.comedycentral.com
Sales Range: $25-49.9 Million
Emp.: 209
All Comedy Network Owner & Operator
N.A.I.C.S.: 516210
Kent Alterman *(Pres)*
Jill Offman *(Mng Dir-UK & Exec VP-Intl)*
Louise Holmes *(VP & Gen Mgr-UK, Northern & Eastern Europe)*
Steve Elliott *(VP-Branded Entertainment Dev)*
Tanya Giles *(Gen Mgr)*
Lucy Robinson *(VP-Original Programming-London)*
Jennifer Danielson *(Sr VP-Digital-SoHo)*
Josh Line *(Exec VP-Mktg & Creative)*
Erika Soto Lamb *(VP-Social Impact Strategy)*

Country Music Television, Inc. (3)
330 Commerce St, Nashville, TN 37201 (100%)
Tel.: (615) 335-8400
Web Site: http://www.cmt.com
Sales Range: $10-24.9 Million
Emp.: 200
Country Music Cable Network
N.A.I.C.S.: 516210
Lewis Bogach *(VP-Program Dev & Production)*
Neil Holt *(Sr VP-Natl Adv Sls)*
Cindy McLean Finke *(VP-Program Publicity & Comm)*
Stephanie Molina *(VP-Program Publicity-West Coast)*
Rory Levine *(VP-Consumer Mktg)*
Tessa Jordan *(VP-Program Plng)*
Heather DeVaney Graffagnino *(VP-Production Mgmt)*
Quinn Brown *(VP-Production)*
Shaleen Desai *(VP-Scripted Programming-Los Angeles)*

Country Services Inc. (3)
14925 219th Ave NW, Elk River, MN 55330
Tel.: (763) 263-7207
Management Consulting Services
N.A.I.C.S.: 541611

Daza Productions Inc. (3)
224 S 200 W Ste 250, Salt Lake City, UT 84101
Tel.: (801) 983-6415
Web Site: http://www.daz3d.com
Software Development Services
N.A.I.C.S.: 541511

Subsidiary (Non-US):

Game One SAS (3)
22 Rue Jacques Dulud, Neuilly-sur-Seine, 92200, France
Tel.: (33) 170949494
Web Site: http://www.gameone.net
Television Broadcasting Station
N.A.I.C.S.: 516120
Thierry Cammas *(Gen Mgr)*

Subsidiary (Domestic):

Harmonix Music Systems, Inc. (3)
675 Massachusetts Ave 6th Fl, Cambridge, MA 02139
Tel.: (617) 491-6144
Web Site: http://www.harmonixmusic.com
Sales Range: $25-49.9 Million
Emp.: 225
Developer of Music Based Videogames
N.A.I.C.S.: 541490
Alex Rigopulos *(Co-Founder, Chm & CEO)*
Steve Janiak *(CEO)*
Chris Rigopulos *(COO)*
Walter Somol *(VP-Publ)*
Mike Verrette *(VP-Dev)*

Subsidiary (Non-US):

Invisions Holding B.V. (3)
Naritaweg 207, Amsterdam, 1043 CB, Netherlands
Tel.: (31) 2017667047
Holding Company
N.A.I.C.S.: 551112

Subsidiary (Domestic):

LOGO (3)
1515 Broadway, New York, NY 10036
Tel.: (212) 258-8000
Web Site: http://www.logoonline.com
Gay & Lesbian Cable Network Services
N.A.I.C.S.: 516210
Liza Burnett Fefferman *(Sr VP-Comm)*
Chris McCarthy *(Pres)*

Subsidiary (Non-US):

MTV Channel Espana S.L.U. (3)
Paseo de Recoletos 33 2 planta, Madrid, 28004, Spain
Tel.: (34) 917818432
Web Site: http://www.mtvmusica.es
Video Production & Taping Services
N.A.I.C.S.: 512110

MTV Hong Kong Limited (3)
Suite 3607 36/F Tower 6 The Gateway 9 Canton Road Harbour City, Kowloon, China (Hong Kong)
Tel.: (852) 23120555
Television Broadcasting Services
N.A.I.C.S.: 516120

MTV Networks Africa (Pty) Limited (3)
Block B Ground Fl, Johannesburg, 2196, South Africa
Tel.: (27) 114282900
Emp.: 90
Motion Picture Distribution Services
N.A.I.C.S.: 512120
Alex Okosi *(Gen Mgr)*

MTV Networks Australia Pty Ltd (3)
Groud Fl 4 16 Yurong St, Sydney, 2018, NSW, Australia
Tel.: (61) 299210200
Web Site: http://www.mtv.com.au
Emp.: 7
Television Broadcasting Services
N.A.I.C.S.: 516120
Hanan Alexander *(Gen Mgr)*

MTV Networks B.V. (3)
TT Neveritaweg 6, Postbus 10001, Amsterdam, 1001 CB, Netherlands
Tel.: (31) 204937000
Web Site: http://www.mtvnetworks.nl
Sales Range: $25-49.9 Million
Emp.: 150
Motion Picture Distribution Services
N.A.I.C.S.: 512120

MTV Networks Belgium BvbA (3)
Ankerrui 2, Antwerp, 2000, Belgium
Tel.: (32) 34003820
Web Site: http://www.viacom.com
Emp.: 11
Television Broadcasting Services
N.A.I.C.S.: 516120
Rainer Muller *(Gen Mgr)*

MTV Networks Germany GmbH (3)
Stralauer Allee 6, Berlin, 10245, Germany
Tel.: (49) 307001000
Web Site: http://www.mtvnetworks.com
Sales Range: $50-74.9 Million
Emp.: 150
Television Broadcasting Services
N.A.I.C.S.: 516120
Mark Stecht *(Gen Mgr)*

MTV Networks Japan K.K. (3)
2-8-2 Jingumae, Shibuya, Tokyo, 150-0001, Japan
Tel.: (81) 364343148
Web Site: http://www.mtvjapan.com
Television Broadcasting Services
N.A.I.C.S.: 516120

Subsidiary (Domestic):

MTV Networks Latin America Inc. (3)
1111 Lincoln Rd 6th Fl, Miami Beach, FL 33139
Tel.: (305) 535-3700
Web Site: http://www.mtvla.com
Emp.: 200
Television Broadcasting Services
N.A.I.C.S.: 516120
Pierluigi Gazzolo *(Pres)*
Juan Carlos Acosta *(COO)*

Subsidiary (Non-US):

MTV Networks Ltda (3)
Av Lusiada 1500-392 Lisboa, Lisbon, 1500392, Portugal
Tel.: (351) 211206600
Web Site: http://www.mtv.pt
Television Broadcasting Services
N.A.I.C.S.: 516120
Victor Mourao *(Gen Mgr)*

Subsidiary (Domestic):

MTV Networks On Campus Inc. (3)
1515 Broadway, New York, NY 10036
Tel.: (212) 654-7048
Web Site: http://www.mtvu.com
Television Broadcasting Services
N.A.I.C.S.: 516120
Chris McCarthy *(Exec VP)*
Sophia Cranshaw *(VP)*
Stephen Friedman *(Exec VP)*

Subsidiary (Non-US):

MTV Networks Polska B.V. (3)
NDSM-plein 6, Amsterdam, 1033 WC, Netherlands
Tel.: (31) 204937000

NATIONAL AMUSEMENTS, INC.   U.S. PRIVATE

National Amusements, Inc.—(Continued)
Sales Range: $25-49.9 Million
Emp.: 150
Television Broadcasting Services
N.A.I.C.S.: 516120

MTV Networks Schweiz AG (3)
Rutistrasse 14, Schlieren, 8952, ZH, Switzerland
Tel.: (41) 445565656
Television Broadcasting Services
N.A.I.C.S.: 516120

MTV Ownership (Portugal), LDA (3)
Avenida Das ForCas Armadas 125 4 C, Lisbon, 1600-079, Portugal
Tel.: (351) 211206600
Sales Range: $10-24.9 Million
Emp.: 80
Motion Picture Distribution Services
N.A.I.C.S.: 512120
Victor Mourao *(Gen Mgr)*

MTV Pubblicita S.r.l. (3)
Corso Europa 5, Milan, 20122, Italy
Tel.: (39) 027621171
Television Advertising Services
N.A.I.C.S.: 541890

Subsidiary (Domestic):

MTVN Video Hits Inc. (3)
1515 Broadway, New York, NY 10036-8901
Tel.: (212) 258-7800
Web Site: http://www.vh1.com
Sales Range: $25-49.9 Million
Emp.: 210
Cable Television Broadcasting Services
N.A.I.C.S.: 516210
Tony Carbone *(VP-Digital Content & Programming)*
Stacy Alexander *(Sr VP-Talent & Casting)*
Bill Flanagan *(Exec VP & Editorial Dir-MTVN)*
Stephen K. Friedman *(Pres-MTV)*
Fernando Mills *(VP-Production & Programming)*
Lily Neumeyer *(Sr VP-Dev)*
Chris McCarthy *(Pres)*
Paul Ricci *(Sr VP & Head-Alternative Programming & Dev)*
Dara Cook *(VP-Strategic Dev)*

Subsidiary (Non-US):

Milano Design Studio S.r.l. (3)
Corso Europa 5, Milan, 20122, MI, Italy
Tel.: (39) 027621171
Web Site: http://www.milanodesign.com.my
Television Broadcasting Services
N.A.I.C.S.: 516120

Subsidiary (Domestic):

Nickelodeon Direct Inc. (3)
1515 Broadway 44th Fl, New York, NY 10036-8901
Tel.: (212) 258-6003
Web Site: http://www.nickpress.com
Sales Range: $125-149.9 Million
Emp.: 2,000
Cable Television Programming & Distribution Services
N.A.I.C.S.: 516210
Russell Hicks *(Chief Creative Officer & Pres-Content Dev & Production)*
James Stephenson *(Sr VP-Animation & Games)*
Chris Viscardi *(Sr VP-Content Dev-Franchise Properties)*
Dion Vlachos *(Exec VP-Retail Sls, Mktg & Publ)*
Shelly Sumpter Gillyard *(Exec VP-Talent, Music & Events)*

Subsidiary (Domestic):

Nick at Nite's TV Land Retromercials Inc. (4)
1515 Broadway Lobby, New York, NY 10036-8901
Tel.: (212) 258-8000
Entertainment Services
N.A.I.C.S.: 711190

Subsidiary (Non-US):

Nickelodeon Australia (4)
Grnd Fl 4 16 Yurong St, Darlinghurst, 2010, NSW, Australia
Tel.: (61) 298136200
Web Site: http://www.nickelodeon.com.au
Emp.: 120
Cable & Other Pay Television Services
N.A.I.C.S.: 516210
Brian Robbins *(Pres & CEO)*
Jordana Kirby *(Mgr-Mktg)*
Ramsey Naito *(Exec VP-Animation)*
Paul DeBenedittis *(Exec VP-Programming & Content Strategy)*
Kari Kim *(VP-Animal Dev-Burbank)*
Eryk Casemiro *(Sr VP-Nickelodeon Preschool-Burbank)*
Angelique Yen *(Sr VP-Physical Production-Burbank)*
Eddie Gamarra *(VP-Studio Bus Dev-Burbank)*
Sabrina Caluori *(Exec VP & Head-Mktg & Brand Strategy)*

Subsidiary (Domestic):

Nickelodeon Global Network Ventures Inc. (4)
1515 Broadway 39th Fl, New York, NY 10036
Tel.: (212) 258-7500
Television Broadcasting Services
N.A.I.C.S.: 516120

Subsidiary (Non-US):

Nickelodeon India Pvt. Ltd. (4)
36 B Dr R K Shirodkar Marg Parel East, Mumbai, 400012, India
Tel.: (91) 2243412424
Video Production & Taping Services
N.A.I.C.S.: 512110

Nickelodeon International Limited (4)
1729 Hawley Crescent, London, NW1 8TT, United Kingdom
Tel.: (44) 2074785200
Web Site: http://www.nickelodeon.co.uk
Television Stations & Broadcasting Services
N.A.I.C.S.: 516120
Dan Frugtniet *(VP-Licensing & Consumer Products Bus Dev)*
Alison Bakunowich *(Sr VP & Gen Mgr)*
Chris Rose *(VP-Intl Animation Production & Dev)*
Nina Hahn *(Sr VP-Intl Production & Dev)*

Subsidiary (Domestic):

Open Door Productions Inc. (3)
10131 National Blvd Ste A, Los Angeles, CA 90034-3804
Tel.: (310) 559-2001
Web Site: http://www.opendoorprod.net
Television Broadcasting Services
N.A.I.C.S.: 512110

Subsidiary (Non-US):

Paramount Comedy Channel Espana S.L. (3)
Paseo Recoletos 33 Plt 2, Madrid, 28004, Spain
Tel.: (34) 917818400
Web Site: http://www.paramountcomedy.es
Video Production & Taping Service
N.A.I.C.S.: 512110

Subsidiary (Domestic):

Peppercorn Productions, Inc. (3)
94 N 100 E, Smithfield, UT 84335-1539
Tel.: (435) 563-9045
Advertising Services
N.A.I.C.S.: 541810

Subsidiary (Non-US):

Viacom International Media Networks (3)
Kungsbro Strand 31, 112 26, Stockholm, Sweden
Tel.: (46) 850678000
Web Site: http://www.mtv.se
Emp.: 65
Music Oriented Programming Services
N.A.I.C.S.: 711130
David Lynn *(Pres & CEO)*
Daniel Munoz *(Sr Dir-Affiliates, Digital & Res-Iberian)*
Raquel Lopez *(Dir-Res-Portugal & Spain)*
Peter Flamman *(Sr VP-Youth & Music & Kids & Family Brands)*
Raffaele Annecchino *(Pres/Mng Dir-SWEMEA)*
Jill Offman *(Exec VP)*
James Currell *(Mng Dir-UKNEE)*
Alex Okosi *(Exec VP/Mng Dir-Africa)*
Asif Ali *(Dir-Affiliate Sls-Southeast Asia)*
Paras Sharma *(Sr VP/Gen Mgr-Southeast Asia)*
Melody Tan *(COO)*
Louise Bucknole *(VP-Programming-Kids)*
Alison Bakunowich *(Sr VP/Gen Mgr-Milkshake)*
Paul Dunthorne *(COO-UK, Northern & Eastern Europe)*
Ed Taylor *(Creative Dir)*
Simone Fenu *(Sr Dir-Licensing & Consumer Products-Italy & Greece)*
Felix Ruoff *(VP-Retail Sls & Consumer Products-South & West-Europe)*
Maria Kyriacou *(Pres-UK & North & East Europe)*

Subsidiary (Domestic):

iFILM Corp. (3)
1024 N Orange Dr, Hollywood, CA 90038-2318
Tel.: (323) 308-3400
Web Site: http://www.ifilm.com
Sales Range: $10-24.9 Million
Emp.: 60
Streaming Video Content Provider
N.A.I.C.S.: 517810
Jame Gumb *(Mng Editor)*

Subsidiary (Domestic):

North Shore Productions Inc. (2)
205 Se Grand Ave Ste 203, Portland, OR 97214
Tel.: (503) 225-0919
Web Site: http://www.northshorepro.com
Motion Picture & Video Production Services
N.A.I.C.S.: 512110

Paramount Pictures Corporation (2)
5555 Melrose Ave, Los Angeles, CA 90038
Tel.: (323) 956-5000
Web Site: http://www.paramount.com
Sales Range: $150-199.9 Million
Emp.: 1,700
Motion Picture Production Services
N.A.I.C.S.: 512110
Brian Robbins *(Pres & CEO)*
Mark Badagliacca *(CFO & Exec VP)*
Amy Powell *(Pres-Paramount Television & Digital Entertainment)*
Bob Buchi *(Pres-Worldwide Home Media Distr)*
Tara Yin *(Gen Mgr-China)*
Shannon Petranoff *(Sr VP-Interactive Mktg)*
Christine Benitez *(VP-Multicultural Mktg)*
Rebecca Mall *(Co-Pres-Domestic Mktg)*
Peter Giannascoli *(Co-Pres-Domestic Mktg)*
Mo Rhim *(Sr VP-Intl Digital Mktg)*
Kath Skerry *(VP-Digital Mktg)*
Brandon Nichols *(VP-Digital Mktg)*
Vivianne Waisman *(VP-Licensing)*
Natalie Bowman *(Dir-Creative Adv)*
Nav Kaur *(Dir-Mktg Partnerships)*
Andrew Gumpert *(COO)*
Jim Gianopulos *(Chm & CEO)*
Peter McPartlin *(Exec VP-Strategic Plng & Bus Ops)*
Dan Cohen *(Pres-Worldwide Home Entertainment & Television Distr)*
Chris Petrikin *(Exec VP-Comm & Corp Branding-Global)*
Mireille Soria *(Pres-Paramount Animation)*
David Miercort *(Exec VP)*
Stephen Plum *(Sr Exec VP & Head-Motion Picture Bus & Legal Affairs)*
Mary Daily *(Co-Pres-Worldwide Mktg & Distr)*
Mia Ammer *(VP-Corp Comm)*
Liz West *(Exec VP-Mktg Comm-Intl Theatrical Mktg & Worldwide Home)*
Ramsey Naito *(Exec VP-Paramount Animation)*
Michael D. Armstrong *(Exec VP-Television Licensing & Ops-Worldwide)*
Danielle Kupchak *(Exec VP-Global Creative Content)*
Len Iannelli *(Sr VP-Special Projects & Events)*
Marc Weinstock *(Co-Pres-Worldwide Mktg & Distr)*
Danielle De Palma *(Exec VP-Domestic Mktg)*
Tamar Teifeld *(Sr VP-Digital Mktg)*
Chris Aronson *(Pres-Domestic Theatrical Distr)*
Emma Watts *(Pres-Motion Picture Grp)*
Jeremy Kramer *(Pres-Paramount Players)*
Ashley Brucks *(Sr Exec VP-Production-Paramount Players)*

Subsidiary (Domestic):

BN Productions Inc. (3)
395c Ipswich Rd, Boxford, MA 01921-1507
Tel.: (978) 352-4730
Web Site: http://www.bnproductions.com
Emp.: 3
Rigging Curtains Production Services
N.A.I.C.S.: 541921
Anna Barbieri *(Pres)*

Blackout Productions Inc. (3)
15742 63rd Pl N, Loxahatchee, FL 33470-3460
Tel.: (561) 793-9424
Web Site: http://www.blackoutproductions.com
Motion Picture Production Services
N.A.I.C.S.: 512120
Royceanne Hazera *(Office Mgr-Sls)*

Subsidiary (Non-US):

Cinematic Arts B.V. (3)
Hoogoorddreef 5, Amsterdam, 1101 BA, Noord Holland, Netherlands
Tel.: (31) 203422830
Video Production & Taping Service
N.A.I.C.S.: 512110

Subsidiary (Domestic):

Columbus Circle Films LLC (3)
5700 Wilshire Blvd Ste 700, Los Angeles, CA 90036
Tel.: (323) 956-5381
Motion Picture & Video Production Services
N.A.I.C.S.: 512110

DIGICO Inc. (3)
6609 White Post Rd, Centreville, VA 20121
Tel.: (703) 222-9494
Emp.: 15
Business Services
N.A.I.C.S.: 561990

DreamWorks LLC (3)
100 Universal Plaza Bldg 5121, Universal City, CA 91608
Tel.: (818) 733-7000
Web Site: http://www.dreamworksstudios.com
Sales Range: $100-124.9 Million
Emp.: 1,500
Motion Picture & Television Program Production Services
N.A.I.C.S.: 512110
David Geffen *(Co-Founder & Co-Chm)*
Steven Spielberg *(Co-Founder & Co-Chm)*
Lyndsay Harding *(CFO)*

Subsidiary (Domestic):

DW Distribution L.L.C. (4)
3316 W Puetz Rd, Franklin, WI 53132
Tel.: (414) 761-1897
Trucking Service
N.A.I.C.S.: 484110

DW Films L.L.C. (4)
3315 Corinth Ave, Los Angeles, CA 90066
Tel.: (310) 391-3382
Motion Picture & Video Production Services
N.A.I.C.S.: 512110

DW Studios Productions L.L.C. (4)
100 Universal City Plz, Universal City, CA 91608
Tel.: (818) 733-9631
Motion Picture & Video Production Services
N.A.I.C.S.: 512110

DW Television L.L.C. (4)
88 Naples Rd Ste 1, Brookline, MA 02446
Tel.: (508) 647-2292
Television Broadcasting Services
N.A.I.C.S.: 516120

Subsidiary (Non-US):

Films Paramount S.A. (3)
1 Rue Meyerbeer, 75009, Paris, France   (100%)
Tel.: (33) 147423500

Web Site: http://www.paramount.fr
Sales Range: $10-24.9 Million
Emp.: 40
Motion Picture Producer
N.A.I.C.S.: 512110

Futa B.V. (3)
Hoogoorddreef 5, Amsterdam, 1101 BA, North Holland, Netherlands
Tel.: (31) 203422830
Motion Picture & Video Production Services
N.A.I.C.S.: 512110

Subsidiary (Domestic):

GC Productions Inc. (3)
43 Round House Rd, Bedford, NY 10506
Tel.: (914) 234-7515
Motion Picture & Video Distribution Services
N.A.I.C.S.: 512120

Grace Productions LLC (3)
1106 Lancaster Rd, Takoma Park, MD 20912-6914
Tel.: (301) 445-6771
Motion Picture Production Services
N.A.I.C.S.: 512120

Paramount Advertiser Services Inc. (3)
1633 Broadway Fl 11, New York, NY 10003
Tel.: (212) 654-6900
Web Site: http://www.paramount.com
Sales Range: $10-24.9 Million
Emp.: 45
Television & Radio Time Seller
N.A.I.C.S.: 541840

Subsidiary (Non-US):

Paramount British Pictures Limited (3)
Bldg 5 Chiswick Park 566 Chiswick High Rd, London, United Kingdom
Tel.: (44) 2075345200
Web Site: http://www.paramountpictures.com
Motion Picture Production Services
N.A.I.C.S.: 512110

Paramount Home Entertainment (Australasia) Pty. Limited (3)
L 21 Tower A 821 Pacific Hwy, Chatswood, 2067, NSW, Australia
Tel.: (61) 290878900
Emp.: 4
Durable Goods Whslr
N.A.I.C.S.: 423990
Kjell Kleppe (Mng Dir)
Amy Reinhard (Pres-Worldwide Television & Home Media Acq-Media Distr)

Paramount Home Entertainment (Brazil) Limitada (3)
Al Rio Negro 585, Barueri, 06454-000, SP, Brazil
Tel.: (55) 1141662282
Web Site: http://www.paramountbrasil.com.br
Sales Range: $25-49.9 Million
Emp.: 17
Motion Picture Distribution Services
N.A.I.C.S.: 512120

Paramount Home Entertainment (Denmark) I/S (3)
Sylows Alle 1, Frederiksberg, 2000, Denmark
Tel.: (45) 38320270
Durable Goods Whslr
N.A.I.C.S.: 423990

Paramount Home Entertainment (Finland) Oy (3)
Yrjonkatu 11c 14, 120, Helsinki, Finland
Tel.: (358) 96981300
Sales Range: $25-49.9 Million
Emp.: 4
Home Entertainment Services
N.A.I.C.S.: 512110

Paramount Home Entertainment (Germany) GmbH (3)
Beta Str 10c, Unterfohring, 85774, Germany
Tel.: (49) 892060640
Motion Picture Distribution Services
N.A.I.C.S.: 512120

Paramount Home Entertainment (Mexico) S. de R.L. de C.V. (3)
Torre Optima 3 Av Paseo de las Palmas No 425-11, Col Lomas de Chapultepec, 11000, Mexico, Mexico
Tel.: (52) 5585251700
Web Site: http://www.paramountvideo.com.mx
Emp.: 19
Motion Picture Production & Distribution Services
N.A.I.C.S.: 512110
Raul Bravo Cabrera (Dir Gen)

Paramount Home Entertainment (Norway) ANS (3)
Rosen Krantz Gate 4, Oslo, 159, Norway
Tel.: (47) 22034970
Oil Distr
N.A.I.C.S.: 424990

Paramount Home Entertainment (Sweden) AB (3)
Lilla Bommen 1Gothenburg, Gothenburg, 411 04, Sweden
Tel.: (46) 317712450
Web Site: http://www.paramount.se
Sales Range: $25-49.9 Million
Emp.: 20
Motion Picture Distribution Services
N.A.I.C.S.: 512120

Paramount Home Entertainment International Limited (3)
Building 5 Chiswick Park, London, W4 5YF, United Kingdom
Tel.: (44) 2031842300
Web Site: http://www.paramountpictures.co.uk
Emp.: 15
Durable Goods Whslr
N.A.I.C.S.: 423990

Paramount International Netherlands B.V. (3)
Postbus 59600, Amsterdam, 1040 LC, Netherlands
Tel.: (31) 206175888
Web Site: http://www.paramount.com
Motion Pictures & Video Distr
N.A.I.C.S.: 512120

Paramount Pictures Australia Pty. (3)
Level 1 65 Pirrama Rd, Pyrmont, 2009, NSW, Australia
Tel.: (61) 292647444
Web Site: http://www.paramountpicturesaustralia.com.au
Sales Range: $25-49.9 Million
Emp.: 20
Motion Picture Distribution Services
N.A.I.C.S.: 512120
Michael Selwyn (Mng Dir)
Greg Taylor (Office Mgr)

Paramount Pictures Entertainment Canada Inc. (3)
40 University Ave Ste 900, Toronto, M5J 1T1, ON, Canada
Tel.: (416) 969-9901
Video Recorders & Players Mfr
N.A.I.C.S.: 334310

Paramount Pictures France Sarl (3)
1 Rue Meyerbeer, 75009, Paris, France
Tel.: (33) 140073838
Motion Picture Distribution Services
N.A.I.C.S.: 512120

Paramount Pictures International Limited (3)
Building 5 Chiswick Park 566 Chiswick High Road, London, W4 5YF, United Kingdom
Tel.: (44) 2031842100
Web Site: http://www.paramount.com
Motion Picture Distribution Services
N.A.I.C.S.: 512120

Paramount Pictures Mexico S. de R.L. de C.V. (3)
Torre Optima 3 Av Paseo de las Palmas No 425-9, Col Lomas de Chapultepec, 11000, Mexico, Mexico
Tel.: (52) 5552016300
Web Site: http://www.paramountpictures.com
Emp.: 30
Motion Picture & Video Distribution Services
N.A.I.C.S.: 512120

Brian Pritchett (Pres)
Ricardo Cortes (Pres)

Paramount Pictures NZ (3)
303 Parnell Road, Auckland, 1151, New Zealand
Tel.: (64) 93796269
Web Site: http://www.paramountpictures.co.nz
Sales Range: $25-49.9 Million
Emp.: 11
Motion Picture Distribution Services
N.A.I.C.S.: 512120
Peter Garner (Gen Mgr)

Subsidiary (Domestic):

Paramount Production Support Inc. (3)
5-33 54th Ave Long Island City, Astoria, NY 11101-2521
Tel.: (718) 729-6525
Web Site: http://www.paramountpictures.com
Sales Range: $10-24.9 Million
Emp.: 15
Motion Picture & Video Production Services
N.A.I.C.S.: 512110

Subsidiary (Non-US):

Paramount Production Support Inc. (3)
8015 N Fraser Way, Burnaby, V5j 5M8, BC, Canada (100%)
Tel.: (604) 294-9660
Web Site: http://www.paramount.com
Sales Range: $10-24.9 Million
Emp.: 50
Motion Picture Services
N.A.I.C.S.: 512199
Nav Degun (Dir-Sls)

Paramount Spain S.L. (3)
Calle Albacete 3 10, Madrid, 28027, Spain
Tel.: (34) 913225800
Web Site: http://www.paramount.com
Sales Range: $25-49.9 Million
Emp.: 50
Motion Picture Distribution Services
N.A.I.C.S.: 512120
Montserrat Gil (Gen Mgr)

Subsidiary (Domestic):

Paramount Worldwide Productions Inc. (3)
100 Bull St Fl 4, Savannah, GA 31401
Tel.: (912) 200-5221
Motion Picture Theater Operating Services
N.A.I.C.S.: 512131

Superstar Productions USA Inc. (3)
4974 SW 186 Tiki Way, Miramar, FL 33029
Tel.: (954) 389-1137
Web Site: http://www.floridasuperstarproductions.com
Motion Picture Production Services
N.A.I.C.S.: 512120
Robert Duerra (Owner)

Joint Venture (Non-US):

United International Pictures (3)
Bldg 5 Chiswick Park 566 Chiswick High Road, London, W4 5YF, United Kingdom (33%)
Tel.: (44) 20 3184 2500
Web Site: http://www.uip.com
International Movie & Video Distr & Marketer
N.A.I.C.S.: 512120
Kristy Grant-Hart (Chief Compliance Officer)

Subsidiary (Domestic):

Radford Studio Center Inc. (2)
4024 Radford Ave, Studio City, CA 91604-2101
Tel.: (818) 655-5837
Television Broadcasting Services
N.A.I.C.S.: 516120

Sacramento Television Stations Inc. (2)
2713 Kovr Dr, West Sacramento, CA 95605
Tel.: (916) 374-1313
Television Broadcasting Services
N.A.I.C.S.: 516120

NATIONAL AMUSEMENTS, INC.

Subsidiary (Non-US):

Servicios Administrativos America S. de RL de C.V. (2)
Manuel Avila Camacho 76 Lomas De Chapultepec, Mexico, 11000, Mexico
Tel.: (52) 5554221200
Emp.: 11
Management Consulting Services
N.A.I.C.S.: 541611

Subsidiary (Domestic):

Showtime Networks Inc. (2)
1633 Brdwy, New York, NY 10019-6708
Tel.: (212) 708-1600
Web Site: http://www.sho.com
Sales Range: $50-74.9 Million
Emp.: 500
Premium Cable Television Services
N.A.I.C.S.: 516210
David Nevins (Chm & CEO)
Donald Buckley (CMO)
Amy Israel (Exec VP-Scripted Programming-West Coast)
Gary Levine (Co-Pres-Entertainment)
Stephen Espinoza (Pres-Sports & Event Programming)
Vinnie Malhotra (Exec VP-Non Fiction Programming-West Coast)
Jana Winograde (Co-Pres-Entertainment)
Jessie Dicovitsky (VP-Original Programming)
Virginia Lazalde-McPherson (Exec VP-Bus Affairs)
Erin Calhoun (Exec VP-Comm-Los Angeles)

Subsidiary (Domestic):

Showtime Marketing Inc. (3)
6604 Tiara Ct, Clinton, MD 20735
Tel.: (301) 218-4474
Emp.: 2
Marketing Consulting Services
N.A.I.C.S.: 541613

Showtime Networks Inc. (UK) (3)
1633 Broadway, New York, NY 10019-6708
Tel.: (212) 708-1600
Web Site: http://www.showtimeonline.com
Sales Range: $50-74.9 Million
Emp.: 500
Premium Cable Television Services
N.A.I.C.S.: 516210

Showtime Satellite Networks, Inc. (3)
1633 Broadway, New York, NY 10019-6708 (100%)
Tel.: (212) 708-1600
Web Site: http://www.showtime.com
Cable Satellite Services
N.A.I.C.S.: 516210

The Movie Channel (3)
1633 Broadway, New York, NY 10019 (100%)
Tel.: (212) 708-1600
Web Site: http://www.sho.com
Premium Cable Television Services
N.A.I.C.S.: 516210
Matthew C. Blank (Chm & CEO)

Subsidiary (Non-US):

Simon & Schuster (UK) Limited (2)
1st Floor 222 Gray s Inn Road, London, WC1X 8HB, United Kingdom
Tel.: (44) 2073161900
Web Site: http://www.simonandschuster.co.uk
Emp.: 105
Books Publishing Services
N.A.I.C.S.: 513130
Gill Richardson (Grp Dir-Sls)
Laura Hough (Dir-Sls-Mass Market, Special Sls & Children's)
Dominic Brendon (Dir-Sls-Bookshops, On-line & Digital)
Sara-Jade Virtue (Dir-Special Sls & Brand-Comml Women's Fiction)

Subsidiary (Domestic):

Stat Crew Software, Inc. (2)
230 Northland Blvd 234, Cincinnati, OH 45253-1520
Tel.: (513) 771-4192
Web Site: http://www.statcrew.com

NATIONAL AMUSEMENTS, INC.

U.S. PRIVATE

National Amusements, Inc.—(Continued)
Computer & Software Stores
N.A.I.C.S.: 449210

TSM Services Inc. (2)
5067 Van Buren Rd, Delray Beach, FL 33484-4255
Tel.: (561) 417-6737
Web Site: http://www.tsmadvantage.com
Television Broadcasting Services
N.A.I.C.S.: 516120

TV Guide Online Holdings LLC (2)
11 W 42nd St 16th Fl, New York, NY 10036
Tel.: (212) 852-7500
Holding Company
N.A.I.C.S.: 551112

Subsidiary (Non-US):

Ten Network Holdings Limited (2)
1 Saunders Street, Pyrmont, 2009, NSW, Australia
Tel.: (61) 296501010
Web Site: http://www.network10.com.au
Holding Company; Television Station Operator; Display Advertising Services
N.A.I.C.S.: 551112
Paul Anderson (CEO)

Subsidiary (Domestic):

Network Ten Pty. Limited (3)
1 Saunders St, Pyrmont, 2009, NSW, Australia (100%)
Tel.: (61) 296501010
Web Site: http://www.10play.com.au
Television Station Operator; Display Advertising Services
N.A.I.C.S.: 516120
Paul Anderson (CEO)
Rod Prosser (Chief Sls Officer)
Beverley McGarvey (Chief Content Officer & Exec VP-ViacomCBS Australia & New Zealand)
Carla Webb-Sear (CFO)
Rachel Day (Gen Mgr-HR)
Stuart Thoms (Gen Counsel & Sec)

Subsidiary (Domestic):

Network Ten (Adelaide) Pty Limited (4)
80 Hutt Street, Adelaide, 5000, SA, Australia
Tel.: (61) 8 8225 1010
Web Site: http://www.10play.com.au
Television Broadcasting Services
N.A.I.C.S.: 516120
Frank Filosi (Gen Mgr)

Network Ten (Brisbane) Pty Limited (4)
Sir Samuel Griffith Drive, Mount Coot-tha, Brisbane, 4066, QLD, Australia
Tel.: (61) 7 3214 1010
Web Site: http://www.10play.com.au
Television Broadcasting Services
N.A.I.C.S.: 516120
Linus Bagley (Mgr-Ops)
Angela Neville (Gen Mgr)

Network Ten (Melbourne) Pty Limited (4)
Como Centre Level 4 620 Chapel Street, PO Box 5000, South Yarra, 3141, VIC, Australia
Tel.: (61) 3 9275 1010
Web Site: http://www.10play.com.au
Television Broadcasting Services
N.A.I.C.S.: 516120

Network Ten (Perth) Pty Limited (4)
Level 4 502 Hay Street, Subiaco, Perth, 6062, WA, Australia
Tel.: (61) 8 9380 1010
Web Site: http://www.10play.com.au
Television Broadcasting Services
N.A.I.C.S.: 516120

Subsidiary (Domestic):

The Audio House, Inc. (2)
500 Treasure Coast Plz, Vero Beach, FL 32960
Tel.: (772) 562-3767
Web Site: http://www.audiohouseinc.com
Electronic Design & Installation Services
N.A.I.C.S.: 423620

Subsidiary (Non-US):

VIMN Belgium BVBA (2)
Ankerrui 2B, 2000, Antwerp, Belgium
Tel.: (32) 3 400 38 20
Sales Range: $25-49.9 Million
Emp.: 10
Television Broadcasting Services
N.A.I.C.S.: 516120

VIMN Germany GmbH (2)
Stralauer Allee 6, 10245, Berlin, Germany
Tel.: (49) 30 700100 0
Web Site: http://www.vimn.com
Sales Range: $25-49.9 Million
Emp.: 220
Television Broadcasting Services
N.A.I.C.S.: 516120

VIMN Netherlands B.V. (2)
TT Neveritaweg 6, 1033 WC, Amsterdam, Netherlands
Tel.: (31) 204937000
Web Site: http://www.vimn.nl
Television Broadcasting Services
N.A.I.C.S.: 516120
Jaco Peeringa (Dir-PR-Comedy & Entertainment)
Danielle Boersma (Mgr-PR-Comedy & Entertainment)
Maurice Hols (Sr VP)

VIMN Nordic AB (2)
Kumgsbro Strand 31, Stockholm, 11226, Sweden
Tel.: (46) 8 506 780 00
Web Site: http://www.mtvnetworks.se
Sales Range: $25-49.9 Million
Emp.: 35
Television Broadcasting Services
N.A.I.C.S.: 516120
Andrea Sahlgren (Sr VP & Gen Mgr)

VIMN Poland sp. z o.o. (2)
Trinity Park III ul Domaniewska 49, 02-672, Warsaw, Poland
Tel.: (48) 224772000
Television Broadcasting Services
N.A.I.C.S.: 516120
Monika Wysocka (Dir-Adv & Brand Solutions)
Daniel Reszka (VP-Program Content, Entertainment Channels, Mktg & Product)
Dariusz Janczewski (Gen Mgr)

VIMN Polska B.V. (2)
Tt Neveritaweg 6, Amsterdam, 1033 WC, Noord-Holland, Netherlands
Tel.: (31) 204937000
Television Broadcasting Services
N.A.I.C.S.: 516120

Subsidiary (Domestic):

VJK Inc. (2)
811 E Stone Ct, Addison, IL 60101
Tel.: (630) 833-4899
Emp.: 2
Industrial Machinery & Equipment Whslr
N.A.I.C.S.: 423830

Subsidiary (Non-US):

Vendor Publicidad Exterior S de RL de CV (2)
Profesor Mendoza No 138-B, Villahermosa, 86020, Tabasco, Mexico
Tel.: (52) 9937223439
Web Site: http://mexico.cbsoutdoor.com
Outdoor Advertising Services
N.A.I.C.S.: 541850

Joint Venture (Non-US):

Viacom 18 Media Pvt. Ltd. (2)
36 B Dr RK Shirodkar Marg Parel East, Mumbai, 400012, India
Tel.: (91) 22 4341 2424
Web Site: http://www.viacom18.com
Media Distr
N.A.I.C.S.: 516120
Ajit Andhare (COO-Viacom 18 Motion Pictures)
Ferzad Palia (Head-Youth, Music & English Entertainment)
Namrata Tata (Head-Ad Sls, Youth, Music & English Entertainment)
Nikhil Sane (Head-Bus-Viacom 18 Motion Pictures)
Ravish Kumar (Head-Reg TV Network)
Deepak Rajyadhakshya (Head-Colors Marathi)
Raj Kannan (Head-Programming-Colors Tamil)
Radha Ramamurthy (Head-Ideation-Colors Tamil)
Aratrika Bhaumik (Head-Ideation-Colors Bangla)
Biswarup Das (Head-Mktg-Colors Bangla & Colors Odia)
Abhaya Simha (Head-Digital-Kannada Entertainment)
Darshil Bhatt (Head-Programming-Gujarati Entertainment)
Mahesh Shetty (Head-Network Sls)

Subsidiary (Domestic):

Star India Private Limited (3)
Star House Urmi Estate 95 Ganpatrao Kadam Marg Lower Parel West, Mumbai, 400 013, India
Tel.: (91) 2266305555
Web Site: http://www.startv.com
Television Broadcasting Services
N.A.I.C.S.: 516120
K. Madhavan (Mng Dir)
Kevin Vaz (CEO-South Bus)
Sanjay Jain (Co-Pres & CFO)
Amita Maheshwari (Pres/Head-HR)
Deepak Jacob (Co-Pres & Gen Counsel)
Gaurav Banerjee (Pres/Head-Hindi & English Entertainment)
Gurjeev Singh Kapoor (Pres-Distr)
Nitin Bawankule (Head-Ad Sls)
Sunil Rayan (Pres/Head-Disney & Hotstar India)

Subsidiary (Non-US):

Network Digital Distribution Services FZ-LLC (4)
Boutique Office #9, PO Box 502197, Media City, Dubai, United Arab Emirates
Tel.: (971) 4 391 2333
Web Site: http://www.startv.com
Television Broadcasting Services
N.A.I.C.S.: 516120

Star Middle East FZ-LLC (4)
Boutique Office #9, PO Box 502197, Dubai Media City, Dubai, United Arab Emirates
Tel.: (971) 43912333
Web Site: http://www.startv.com
Television Broadcasting Services
N.A.I.C.S.: 516120

Subsidiary (Domestic):

Star Sports India Private Limited (4)
Star House Urmi Estate 95 Ganpatrao Kadam Marg Lower Parel West, Mumbai, 400 013, India
Tel.: (91) 2266305555
Web Site: http://www.startv.com
Television Broadcasting Services
N.A.I.C.S.: 516120
Gautam Thakar (CEO)

Subsidiary (Non-US):

Starvision Hong Kong Limited (4)
Suite 3104 31/f Eight Commercial Tower 8 Sun Yip Street, Chai Wan, China (Hong Kong)
Tel.: (852) 28970975
Web Site: https://www.starvision.com.hk
Media & Entertainment Services
N.A.I.C.S.: 512199

Subsidiary (Domestic):

Vijay Television Private Limited (4)
Star House Urmi Estate 95 Ganpatrao Kadam Marg, Lower Parel West, Mumbai, 400013, India
Tel.: (91) 222 6100084
Web Site: http://www.startv.com
Television Broadcasting Services
N.A.I.C.S.: 516120

Subsidiary (Non-US):

Viacom A.G. (2)
Alpenstrasse 12, CH-6300, Zug, Switzerland (100%)
Tel.: (41) 417298220
Web Site: http://www.viacom.com
Motion Picture & Tape Distr
N.A.I.C.S.: 512120

Viacom Brand Solutions Limited (2)
17 29 Hawley Crescent, London, NW1 8TT, United Kingdom
Tel.: (44) 2072847777
Web Site: http://www.mtv.co.uk
Emp.: 50
Advertising Services
N.A.I.C.S.: 541890

Subsidiary (Domestic):

Viacom Consumer Products Inc. (2)
5555 Melrose Ave, Los Angeles, CA 90038
Tel.: (323) 956-5000
Web Site: http://www.viacom.com
Entertainment Licensing Services
N.A.I.C.S.: 926150

Subsidiary (Non-US):

Viacom Global Hungary Kft. (2)
Bocskai Ut 134-146, 1113, Budapest, Hungary
Tel.: (36) 18771500
Web Site: http://www.viacom.com
Emp.: 35
Motion Picture Production & Distribution Services
N.A.I.C.S.: 512110

Subsidiary (Domestic):

Viacom Global Services Inc. (2)
1515 Broadway, New York, NY 10036
Tel.: (212) 258-6000
Telecommunication Servicesb
N.A.I.C.S.: 517111

Subsidiary (Non-US):

Viacom International Pty. Limited (2)
7 Grosvenor Pl, Brookvale, 2119, NSW, Australia (100%)
Tel.: (61) 299075651
Web Site: http://www.viacom.com
Motion Picture & Video Distr
N.A.I.C.S.: 512120

Subsidiary (Domestic):

Viacom International Services Inc. (2)
1515 Broadway, New York, NY 10036
Tel.: (212) 258-6000
Subscription Television Services
N.A.I.C.S.: 516210

Subsidiary (Non-US):

Viacom Networks Brasil Programacao Televisiva E Publicidade Ltda. (2)
Francisco Matarazzo 1400, 05001-903, Sao Paulo, Brazil
Tel.: (55) 1138661730
Web Site: http://www.viacombrasil.com.br
Television Broadcasting Services
N.A.I.C.S.: 516120
Raul Costa (Mng Dir)

Subsidiary (Domestic):

Visions Productions, Inc. (2)
7 Ruth Ave, Pontiac, MI 48341
Tel.: (248) 332-5610
Web Site: http://www.visionproduction.com
Advertising Services
N.A.I.C.S.: 541890

Subsidiary (Non-US):

WVI Films B.V. (2)
Singel 540-5th Floor, Amsterdam, 1017 AZ, Netherlands
Tel.: (31) 207167330
Television Broadcasting Services
N.A.I.C.S.: 516120

Subsidiary (Domestic):

WhoSay, Inc. (2)
1515 Broadway, New York, NY 12526
Tel.: (518) 537-5795
Web Site: http://www.whosay.com
Software Publisher
N.A.I.C.S.: 513210

NATIONAL APARTMENT ASSOCIATION
4300 Wilson Blvd Ste 400, Arlington, VA 22203

COMPANIES

Tel.: (703) 518-6141 VA
Web Site: http://www.naahq.org
Year Founded: 1939
Sales Range: $10-24.9 Million
Emp.: 71
Rental Housing Support Services
N.A.I.C.S.: 813910
Doug Culkin *(Pres & CEO)*
Robert Pinnegar *(COO & Exec VP)*
Gregory Brown *(Sr VP-Govt Affairs)*
Rebecca M. Sullivan *(VP-Comm & Mktg)*
Jeremy Figoten *(Sr VP-Meetings, Comm & Business Dev)*

NATIONAL AQUARIUM IN BALTIMORE INC.
501 E Pratt St, Baltimore, MD 21202
Tel.: (410) 576-3800
Web Site: http://www.aqua.org
Sales Range: $25-49.9 Million
Emp.: 400
Aquarium
N.A.I.C.S.: 712130
John C. Racanelli *(Pres & CEO)*
Dale Schmidt *(COO & Exec VP)*
Margot Amelia *(CMO & Sr VP)*
Scott Douglas Melton *(Chief Philanthropy Officer & Sr VP)*
Stephanie Chall *(Dir-Corp Membership & Sponsorship)*
Candace Osunsade *(Chief Admin Officer & Sr VP)*
Kris Hoellen *(Chief Conservation Officer & Sr VP)*
Holly Bourbon *(Dir-Dive Programs)*
Liz Evans *(Mgr-Behavioral Husbandry & Animal Programs)*
Andrew Pulver *(Dir-Husbandry)*
Ashleigh Clews *(Mgr-Animal Care Center)*
Thomas E. Robinson *(Chm)*
Jane W. I. Droppa *(Vice Chm)*
Tamika Langley Tremaglio *(Vice Chm)*
Victor Restrepo *(VP)*
Sean Beattie *(VP-Institutional Giving)*

NATIONAL ASSET RECOVERY SERVICES
16253 Swingley Ridge Rd Ste 300, Chesterfield, MO 63017
Tel.: (636) 530-7985
Web Site: http://www.narsnet.com
Year Founded: 1993
Sales Range: $50-74.9 Million
Emp.: 3,200
Management Consulting Services
N.A.I.C.S.: 541618
Gregory A. Cappa *(COO)*
Christopher H. Buehrle *(Pres & CEO)*
David Kreisman *(Sec)*
Michael V. Juniewicz *(CFO & Sr VP)*
David Owenby *(VP-Ops)*
Vincent Ko *(VP-Client Svc)*
Dirk Menzel *(VP-IT)*

NATIONAL ASSOCIATION FOR COLLEGE ADMISSION COUNSELING
1050 N Highland St Ste 400, Arlington, VA 22201
Tel.: (703) 836-2222 DE
Web Site: http://www.nacacnet.org
Year Founded: 2007
Sales Range: $10-24.9 Million
Emp.: 66
Educational Professional Association
N.A.I.C.S.: 813920
Michelle Lucas *(Dir-Information Systems)*
Shanda T. Ivory *(Dir-Comm, Publ & Tech)*
Joan B. Burdette *(Dir-Fin & Admin)*
David Burge *(VP)*

NATIONAL ASSOCIATION FOR STOCK CAR AUTO RACING, INC.
1 Daytona Blvd, Daytona Beach, FL 32114-1243
Tel.: (386) 253-0611 FL
Web Site: http://www.nascar.com
Year Founded: 1947
Sales Range: $1-4.9 Billion
Emp.: 850
Professional Stock Car Racing Organization
N.A.I.C.S.: 813910
Steve O'Donnell *(Chief Racing Dev Officer & Exec VP)*
Steve Phelps *(Pres)*
Chad Seigler *(VP-Bus Dev-Intl)*
Brad Moran *(Dir-Canadian Tire Series)*
Brandon Igdalsky *(Mng Dir-Event Mktg & Promotion)*
Scott Warfield *(Mng Dir-Digital & Social Content)*
Evan Parker *(Mng Dir-Content Strategy)*
Jeff Wohlschlaeger *(Mng Dir-Series Mktg)*
George Silbermann *(Mng Dir)*
Daryl Wolfe *(Chief Sls & Partnership Officer)*
Jim Cassidy *(Chief Intl Officer)*
Ben Kennedy *(Gen Mgr-Camping World Truck Series)*
Jay Fabian *(Mng Dir-Cup Series)*
Scott Miller *(Sr VP-Competition)*
John Ferguson *(Chief HR Officer & Sr VP)*

Subsidiaries:

International Speedway Corporation (1)
1 Daytona Blvd, Daytona Beach, FL 32114
Tel.: (386) 254-2700
Web Site: http://www.internationalspeedwaycorporation.com
Rev.: $675,036,000
Assets: $2,249,360,000
Liabilities: $613,402,000
Net Worth: $1,635,958,000
Earnings: $225,284,000
Fiscal Year-end: 11/30/2018
Holding Company: Motorsports Racetrack Owner, Operator & Events Promoter
N.A.I.C.S.: 551112
W. Garrett Crotty *(Chief Admin Officer & Exec VP)*
Daryl Q. Wolfe *(Chief Mktg Officer & Exec VP)*
John R. Saunders *(Pres)*
Craig A. Neeb *(Chief Innovation & Dev Officer & Exec VP)*
Frank Kelleher *(VP-Sls & Mktg)*
Laura E. Jackson *(Chief HR Officer & Sr VP-Corp Svcs)*
Gregory S. Motto *(CFO, Treas & Exec VP)*
Derek Muldowney *(Pres-Design & Dev & VP)*
Jeff Boerger *(Pres-Kansas Speedway Dev Corp & VP-Corp Dev)*
Benjamin Odom *(VP & Deputy Gen Counsel)*
Lesa France Kennedy *(Vice Chm & CEO)*

Subsidiary (Domestic):

Americrown Service Corporation (2)
1801 W International Speedway Blvd, Daytona Beach, FL 32114 (100%)
Tel.: (386) 947-3800
Web Site: http://www.americrown.com
Sales Range: $75-99.9 Million
Food & Beverage Concessions, Merchandise & Catering Services
N.A.I.C.S.: 561499

Auto Club Speedway (2)
9300 Cherry Ave, Fontana, CA 92335
Tel.: (909) 429-5000
Web Site: http://www.autoclubspeedway.com
Motorsports Racetrack Operator
N.A.I.C.S.: 711212
Brian Geye *(Sr Dir-Ops)*
Dave Allen *(Pres)*
Ray Wilkings *(VP-Ops)*
David Alley *(Dir-Comm)*
Art Avila *(Dir-Acctg)*
Chris Carlson *(Sr Dir-Corp Sls & mktg)*
Deanna Ingram *(Dir-Ticketing)*
Josh Avila *(Sr Dir-Consumer Mktg)*
Sandy Carnes *(Dir-Emergency Medical Svcs)*
Mike Carnes *(Dir-Fire Safety)*
Debbie Bervel *(Dir-Medical)*

Darlington Raceway of South Carolina, LLC (2)
1301 Harry Byrd Hwy, Darlington, SC 29532 (100%)
Tel.: (843) 395-8900
Web Site: http://www.darlingtonraceway.com
Sales Range: $25-49.9 Million
Emp.: 15
Motorsports Racetrack Operator
N.A.I.C.S.: 711212
Kerry Tharp *(Pres-Track)*

Daytona International Speedway, LLC (2)
1801 W International Speedway Blvd, Daytona Beach, FL 32114 (100%)
Tel.: (386) 254-2700
Web Site: http://www.daytonainternationalspeedway.com
Sales Range: $25-49.9 Million
Motorsports Racetrack Operator
N.A.I.C.S.: 711212

Event Equipment Leasing, LLC (2)
1801 West International Speedway Blvd, Daytona Beach, FL 32114
Tel.: (904) 947-6446
Commercial Event Equipment Leasing Services
N.A.I.C.S.: 532490
W. Garrett Crotty *(Exec Dir)*

Event Support Corporation (2)
1 Daytona Blvd, Daytona Beach, FL 32114 (100%)
Tel.: (386) 254-2700
Web Site: http://www.iscmotorsports.com
Sales Range: $250-299.9 Million
Race Track Operations
N.A.I.C.S.: 551112

Homestead-Miami Speedway, LLC (2)
1 Ralph Sanchez Speedway Blvd, Homestead, FL 33035-1501
Tel.: (305) 230-5000
Web Site: http://www.homesteadmiamispeedway.com
Motorsports Racetrack Operator
N.A.I.C.S.: 711212
Albert Garcia *(VP-Ops)*
William Donnay *(Dir-Facility Ops)*
Matthew Becherer *(Pres-Track)*
Hope Mees *(Dir-Event Ops)*
Shawn McGee *(VP-Sls & Mktg)*
Edwin Gonzalez *(Dir-Acctg & Fin)*
Ali Bradshaw *(Sr Dir-Sls)*
Neal Gulkis *(Sr Dir-Comm & Mktg)*
Jay Fraioli *(Dir-Security & Access)*
Fernando Fernandez *(Dir-Emergency Svcs)*

ISC Publications, Inc. (2)
1801 W Intl Speedway Blvd, Daytona Beach, FL 32114-1215 (100%)
Tel.: (386) 254-2700
Web Site: http://www.iscmotorsports.com
Sales Range: $10-24.9 Million
Emp.: 34
Race Track Operations
N.A.I.C.S.: 711212

ISC.com, LLC (2)
1 Daytona Blvd, Daytona Beach, FL 32114 (100%)
Tel.: (386) 254-2700
Web Site: http://www.internationalmotorsport.com
Sales Range: $1-9.9 Million
Emp.: 10
Race Track Operations
N.A.I.C.S.: 711212
Brian France *(CEO)*

ISM Raceway (2)
125 S Avondale Blvd Ste 200, Avondale, AZ 85323
Tel.: (623) 463-5400
Web Site: http://www.ismraceway.com
Motorsports Racetrack Operator
N.A.I.C.S.: 711212
James Hamilton *(Dir-Govt Affairs)*
Scott Rovn *(VP-Sls)*
Greg Fresquez *(Mgr-Comm)*
Brett Adams *(Sr Dir-Ops)*
Bill Hindman *(Sr Mgr-Security & Ops)*
Gale Powers *(Dir-Venue Experience & Guest Svcs)*
Jonathan Stone *(Sr Dir-Corp Sls)*
Kaleb Hancock *(Dir-Ticket Sls & Svcs)*
Terrie Ball *(Sr Mgr-Ops & Acctg)*
Terry Overbey *(Mgr-Facility Ops)*
Rodney Scearce *(Dir-Comm)*
Julie Giese *(Pres)*

Kansas Speedway Corporation (2)
400 Speedway Blvd, Kansas City, KS 66111 (100%)
Tel.: (913) 328-3300
Web Site: http://www.kansasspeedway.com
Sales Range: $10-24.9 Million
Emp.: 20
Racetrack Operator
N.A.I.C.S.: 711212
Ryan Hogue *(Sr Dir-Comm & Consumer Mktg)*
Darren Cook *(VP-Ops)*
Kelly Hale *(Dir-PR)*
Patrick Warren *(Pres)*
Joe Fowler *(VP-Sls & Mktg)*
Greg Scott *(Sr Mgr-Event Ops & Logistics)*
Eric Peterson *(Dir-Corp Sls & Mktg)*
Connie Boring *(Office Mgr-Ops, Credentials & Admin)*
Greg Franke *(Dir-Acctg & Bus Admin)*
Andrew Seaman *(Coord-HR)*
Josh Roehr *(Mgr-Consumer Mktg)*
Ally Piatt *(Mgr-Digital Mktg & Social Media)*
David Tregemba *(Dir-Ticket Sls)*
Clayton Lovekamp *(Mgr-Sls)*
Torey Rhoads *(Mgr-Bus Dev)*
Sarah Kay Broeker *(Mgr-Bus Dev)*
Kym Singmaster *(Supvr-Ticket Svcs)*
Braden McDaniel *(Mgr-Acct-Ticket Sls)*
Gary Lee *(Mgr-Facility Ops)*
Amber Shobe *(Mgr-Special Events)*
Jorge Arita *(Supvr-Grounds)*
Bryan Scott *(Coord-Security Field)*
Shelia Palmer *(Coord-Security)*
Sandy Moon *(Sr Mgr-Ticket Ops & Fin Analysis)*
Dawn Watkins *(Coord-Camping)*
Heather Nichols *(Dir-Food & Beverage)*
Kyle Burns *(Mgr-Premium Svcs)*
Allen Kirchner Jr. *(Acct Exec-Ticket Sls)*

Kansas Speedway Development Corp. (2)
1801 W International Speedway Blvd, Daytona Beach, FL 32114 (100%)
Tel.: (913) 328-3300
Web Site: http://www.kansasspeedway.com
Sales Range: $25-49.9 Million
Racetrack & Casino Land Development & Construction Operations
N.A.I.C.S.: 237210

Martinsville International, Inc. (2)
340 Speedway Rd, Martinsville, VA 24112
Web Site: http://www.martinsvillespeedway.com
Motorsports Racetrack Operator
N.A.I.C.S.: 711212
Clay Campbell *(Pres)*
Karen Parker *(VP-Sls & Mktg)*
Gordon Wilson *(Dir-Facility Ops)*
Matt Brannock *(VP-Ops)*
Billy Moore *(Superintendent-Track)*
Ashley Oakes *(Sr Mgr-Sls)*
Tracie Slack *(Dir-Ticket Ops)*
Brooks Taylor *(Dir-PR)*
Heather Motley *(Mgr-Ticketing Svcs)*
Blake Collins *(Sr Mgr-Bus Dev)*
Russ Fulcher *(Dir-Acctg)*
Ginger Agee *(Pres & Exec VP)*
Harrison Hamlet *(Mgr-Comm)*

Michigan International Speedway, Inc. (2)
12626 US Hwy 12, Brooklyn, MI 49230-9068 (100%)
Tel.: (517) 592-6666
Web Site: http://www.mispeedway.com

NATIONAL ASSOCIATION FOR STOCK CAR AUTO RACING, INC.   U.S. PRIVATE

National Association for Stock Car Auto Racing, Inc.—(Continued)
Sales Range: $10-24.9 Million
Emp.: 50
Motorsports Racetrack Operator
N.A.I.C.S.: 711212
Tim Booth (Dir-Guest Svcs)
Brad Kuhbander (Mgr-Media Rels)
Rick Brenner (Pres)
C. Ryan Shelton (VP-Bus Ops)
Rob Hemmig (Sr Mgr-Corp Partnerships)
Jason Lucas (Dir-Mktg & Comm)

Motor Racing Network, Inc. (2)
555 MRN Dr, Concord, NC 28027 (100%)
Tel.: (704) 262-6700
Web Site: http://www.mrn.com
Sales Range: $10-24.9 Million
Emp.: 37
Racing Sports Radio Network
N.A.I.C.S.: 519290
David Hyatt (Pres)

Motorsports Acceptance Corporation (2)
1 Daytona Blvd, Daytona Beach, FL 32114 (100%)
Tel.: (386) 254-2700
Web Site: http://www.iscmotorsports.com
Sales Range: $50-74.9 Million
Emp.: 20
Race Track Operations
N.A.I.C.S.: 711212
Susanne Thompson (Sec)
Wendy Mavrinac (Sec)

North American Testing Company, Inc. (2)
1801 W International Speedway Blvd, Daytona Beach, FL 32114 (100%)
Tel.: (904) 947-6446
Web Site: http://www.internationalspeedwaycorporation.com
Sales Range: $75-99.9 Million
Race Track Operations
N.A.I.C.S.: 541380
Kelly Mellichampe (Dir-HR)

Raceway Associates, LLC (2)
500 Speedway Blvd, Joliet, IL 60433
Tel.: (815) 722-5500
Web Site: http://www.chicagolandspeedway.com
Sales Range: $25-49.9 Million
Motorsports Racetrack Operator
N.A.I.C.S.: 711212

RacingOne Multimedia, LLC (2)
1 Daytona Blvd, Daytona Beach, FL 32114-1252
Tel.: (386) 253-2863
Telecommunication Servicesb
N.A.I.C.S.: 517810

Richmond International Raceway, Inc. (2)
600 E Laburnum Ave, Richmond, VA 23222 (100%)
Tel.: (804) 228-7500
Web Site: http://www.richmondraceway.com
Sales Range: $10-24.9 Million
Emp.: 47
Motorsports Racetrack Operator
N.A.I.C.S.: 711212
Jeff Hedrick (Sr Dir-Ops)
Louis Gilmore (Sr Dir-Bus Dev)
Linwood Burrow (Dir-Track Ops)
Dennis Bickmeier (Pres)
April Matanoski (Sr Mgr-Creative Svcs)
Justin Johnson (Mgr-Ticketing & Guest Svcs)
Michael Storti (Dir-Acctg)
Brandon Brown (Sr Mgr-Digital Strategy)
Courtney Brockwell (Mgr-PR)
Vaughan Crittenden (Mgr-Comm)
Brent S. Gambill (Sr Dir-Comm & Digital)
Michael Evranian (Dir-Bus Dev)
Nicolle Guinan (Sr Mgr-Corp Partnerships)
Mark Clements (Sr Mgr-Bus Dev)
Megan Hazzard (Dir-Events)
Chris Alberta (Mgr-Security)
Laura Ivey (Coord-Event)
Jimmy Hays (Supvr-Event Ops)
Tommy Johnson (Mgr-Maintenance)
Ray Smith (Sr Mgr-Mktg & Fan Dev)
James Hall (Sr Dir-Ticket Sls & Consumer Mktg)
Hilary Adams (Mgr-Mktg & Fan Engagement)
Danielle Lockemy (Coord-Ticket Ops & Guest Svcs)
Nathan Davis (Sr Acct Exec-Ticket Sls)
Nick Meeson (Sr Acct Exec-Ticket Sls)
Zach Curtis (Coord-Mktg)
Rob Garella (Acct Exec-Ticket Sls)
Bill Menefee (Acct Exec-Ticket Sls)
Steven Bales (Dir-Food & Beverage)

Route 66 Raceway, LLC (2)
500 Speedway Blvd, Joliet, IL 60433
Tel.: (815) 727-7223
Web Site: http://www.route66raceway.com
Sales Range: $25-49.9 Million
Motorsports Racetrack Operator
N.A.I.C.S.: 711212

Southeastern Hay & Nursery, LLC (2)
1801 West Intl Speedway Blvd, Daytona Beach, FL 32114 (100%)
Tel.: (386) 254-2700
Web Site: http://www.daytonainternationalspeedway.com
Tree Nursery
N.A.I.C.S.: 111421

Talladega Superspeedway, LLC (2)
3366 Speedway Blvd, Talladega, AL 35160 (100%)
Tel.: (256) 362-2261
Web Site: http://www.talladegasuperspeedway.com
Sales Range: $150-199.9 Million
Emp.: 40
Motorsports Racetrack Operator
N.A.I.C.S.: 711212

Watkins Glen International, Inc. (2)
2790 County Route 16, Watkins Glen, NY 14891 (100%)
Tel.: (607) 535-2486
Web Site: http://www.theglen.com
Sales Range: $25-49.9 Million
Motorsports Racetrack Operator
N.A.I.C.S.: 711212
Michael Printup (Pres)
Andrew Smith (VP-Sls & Mktg)
Chris Cornett (VP-Facilities & Ops)
Chris Banker (Dir-PR)
Joe Green (Dir-Event Ops)
Tyler Hoke (Sr Mgr-Mktg & Community Rels)
Mike Gardner (Mgr-PR)
Rob Roessel (Sr Mgr-Corp Sls)
Cindy Lewis-Black (Dir-Partnership Mgmt)
Deserai Diffenderfer (Acct Exec-Partnership Mgmt)
Tina Simpson (Dir-Ticketing)
Jose Cervantes (Sr Mgr-Corp Sls)
Natalie Costello (Coord-Ticket Sls)
Rebecca Mitchell (Mgr-Sls)
Greg Walerski (Dir-Acctg)
George Hall (Mgr-Acctg)
Marianne Marts (Dir-Guest & Special Svcs)
Alan Wendlandt (Sr Mgr-Projects & Maintenance)
Craig Gallow (Mgr-Security)
Luke Schock (Mgr-Concession)
Jessica Cramer (Office Mgr)
Sarah Yarrington (Mgr-Retail)
Larry Mosher (Supvr-Maintenance & Landscaping)
Chuck Bianco (Supvr-Buildings & Grounds)

NATIONAL ASSOCIATION FOR THE SELF-EMPLOYED, INC.
7701 Las Colinas Rdg Ste 120, Irving, TX 75063
Tel.: (817) 251-6273   TX
Web Site: http://www.nase.org
Year Founded: 1981
Sales Range: $10-24.9 Million
Emp.: 18
Entrepreneurial Business Support Services
N.A.I.C.S.: 561499
John K. Hearrell (VP-Membership & Affiliate Programs)
Katie Vlietstra (VP-Govt Rels & Pub Affairs)
Melissa Alford (Controller)
Thom Childers (Dir-Software Dev)
Scott P. Stryker (Sr Mgr-Membership & Comm)
Keith R. Hall (Pres & CEO)

NATIONAL ASSOCIATION OF CHARTER SCHOOL AUTHORIZERS
105 W Adams St Ste 1900, Chicago, IL 60603
Tel.: (312) 376-2300   CO
Web Site: http://www.qualitycharters.org
Year Founded: 2000
Sales Range: $1-9.9 Million
Emp.: 39
School Authorizer Association
N.A.I.C.S.: 813910
William Haft (VP-Authorizer Dev)
Katie Holland Fishel (Mgr-Contract Admin)
Katie Piehl (Dir-Authorizer Dev)
Michael R. Cernauskas (CFO)
Mary Zawaski (Mgr-Fin & Admin)
Kristin Rennels (Dir-Dev)
Corrie Leech (Dir-Media Rels)
Amanda Fenton (Dir-State & Federal Policy)
Greg Richmond (Pres & CEO)
Karega Rausch (VP-Res & Evaluation)
Whitney Spalding Spencer (Dir-Authorizer Dev)
Sean Conlan (Dir-Res & Evaluation)
Jobi Cates (VP-Comm & Dev)
Kasey Miller (VP-Talent & Engagement)

NATIONAL ASSOCIATION OF CHRONIC DISEASE DIRECTORS
2200 Century Pkwy Ste 250, Atlanta, GA 30345
Tel.: (770) 458-7400   GA
Web Site: http://www.chronicdisease.org
Year Founded: 1988
Sales Range: $10-24.9 Million
Chronic Disease Prevention Services
N.A.I.C.S.: 813212
John Robitscher (CEO)
Todd Bruce (Sr Dir-Ops)

NATIONAL ASSOCIATION OF COLLEGE AND UNIVERSITY BUSINESS OFFICERS
1110 Vermont Ave NW Ste 800, Washington, DC 20005
Tel.: (202) 861-2500   IL
Web Site: http://www.nacubo.org
Year Founded: 1956
Sales Range: $10-24.9 Million
Educational Support Services
N.A.I.C.S.: 611710
Sue Menditto (Dir-Acctg Policy)
Anne Gross (VP-Regulatory Affairs)
Maryann Terrana (Dir-Constituent Programs & Member Engagement)
Randall G. Gentzler (Chm)
Mary Lou Merkt (Vice Chm)
Lynn Valenter (Sec)
Mary Bachinger (Dir-Tax Policy)
Sally Grans Korsh (Dir-Facilities Mgmt & Environmental Policy)
Susan Whealler Johnston (Pres & CEO)

NATIONAL ASSOCIATION OF COLLEGE STORES, INC.
500 E Lorain St, Oberlin, OH 44074
Tel.: (440) 775-7777   OH
Web Site: http://www.nacs.org
Year Founded: 1951
Sales Range: $10-24.9 Million
Emp.: 200
College Book Stores Association
N.A.I.C.S.: 813910
Ed Schlichenmayer (COO)
Lynn Kovach (Dir-Member Concrete Svcs)
Jane Nizza (Dir-Fin)
Ben Ryba (Sr Dir-Facilities & Logistics)
Mary Adler-Kozak (Dir-Expositions)
Rich Hershman (VP-Govt Rels)
Kaye Oswald (Dir-Art)
Valerie Ringel (Dir-Creative Svcs)
Daniel Bell (CTO)
Robert A. Walton (CEO)

Subsidiaries:

Connect2One (1)
4350 Glendale Milford Rd, Cincinnati, OH 45242
Tel.: (513) 754-0111
Web Site: http://www.connect2one.com
Sales Range: $1-9.9 Million
Emp.: 7
Fiscal Year-end: 03/31/2015
College Bookstore Purchasing & Marketing Services
N.A.I.C.S.: 561499
Michelle Johnson (Program Dir)
Paula Haerr (VP)
Jeff Pavic (VP-Retail Dev)
Rob Faust (Program Mgr)

NATIONAL ASSOCIATION OF COMMUNITY HEALTH CENTERS
7501 Wisconsin Ave Ste 1100W, Bethesda, MD 20814
Tel.: (301) 347-0400   DC
Web Site: http://www.nachc.org
Year Founded: 1972
Sales Range: $25-49.9 Million
Emp.: 99
Hospital Association
N.A.I.C.S.: 813910
Darline DeMott (Exec Mgr)
Tom Van Coverden (Pres & CEO)
Dave Taylor (COO)
Ricardo Guzman (Chm)
Lathran Woodard (Sec)
Michael Holmes (Treas)

NATIONAL ASSOCIATION OF COUNTY AND CITY HEALTH OFFICIALS
1100 17th St NW 7th Fl, Washington, DC 20036
Tel.: (202) 783-5550   DC
Web Site: http://www.naccho.org
Year Founded: 1985
Sales Range: $25-49.9 Million
Emp.: 151
Community Care Services
N.A.I.C.S.: 624190
Jennifer Li (Dir-Environmental Health & Health & Disability)
Richard Hofrichter (Sr Dir-Health Equity)
Adriane Casalotti (Head-Govt & Pub Affairs Dept)

NATIONAL ASSOCIATION OF FEDERAL CREDIT UNIONS
3138 10th St N, Arlington, VA 22201-2149
Tel.: (703) 842-2831   CA
Web Site: http://www.nafcu.org
Year Founded: 1967
Rev.: $19,086,993
Assets: $26,503,213
Liabilities: $12,513,547
Net Worth: $13,989,666
Earnings: $946,388
Emp.: 75
Fiscal Year-end: 12/31/18
Credit Union Operator
N.A.I.C.S.: 522130

Anthony W. Demangone (COO & Exec VP)
Eric Miller (VP-IT)
Greg Johns (VP-Fin)
Catherine Safady (VP-Membership & Sls)
Carrie Hunt (Gen Counsel & Exec VP-Govt Affairs)
Devon Lyon (Dir-Education)
Curt Long (VP-Res)
Bradford Thaler (VP-Legislative Affairs)
Paul Timm (VP-Mktg)

NATIONAL ASSOCIATION OF HOME BUILDERS
1201 15th St NW, Washington, DC 20005
Tel.: (202) 266-8200
Web Site: http://www.nahb.org
Year Founded: 1942
Sales Range: $25-49.9 Million
Emp.: 750
Business Associations
N.A.I.C.S.: 813910
Geoff Cassidy (Sr VP-Exhibitions & Meetings)
Sheila Miller (VP-Multifamily & 55+ Housing)
Greg Ugalde (Chm)

NATIONAL ASSOCIATION OF INDEPENDENT SCHOOLS, INC.
1129 20th St NW Ste 800, Washington, DC 20036-3425
Tel.: (202) 973-9700 MA
Web Site: http://www.nais.org
Year Founded: 1959
Sales Range: $10-24.9 Million
Emp.: 68
Educational Support Services
N.A.I.C.S.: 611710
Amy Ahart (Sr Dir-Annual Conference)
Efrem Abate (Accountant)
Janyce Bryant (Dir-Admin & Facilities)
Caroline Blackwell (VP-Equity & Justice)

NATIONAL ASSOCIATION OF INSURANCE AND FINANCIAL ADVISORS
2901 Telestar Ct 6th Fl, Falls Church, VA 22042-1205
Tel.: (703) 770-8100 DC
Web Site: http://www.naifa.org
Year Founded: 1921
Sales Range: $10-24.9 Million
Emp.: 76
Financial Support Services
N.A.I.C.S.: 524298
Diane Boyle (VP-Federal Govt Rels)
Paul C. Wessel (VP-Fin & Facilities)
Juli McNeely (Pres)
Kevin M. Mayeux (CEO)

NATIONAL ASSOCIATION OF PROFESSIONAL BASEBALL LEAGUES, INC.
9550 16th St N, Saint Petersburg, FL 33716
Tel.: (727) 822-6937
Web Site: http://web.minorleaguebaseball.com
Year Founded: 1901
Rev.: $2,500,000
Emp.: 40
Governing Body of Minor League Baseball Teams
N.A.I.C.S.: 813990
Stan Brand (VP)
Pat O'Conner (Pres & CEO)
Scott Poley (Sr VP-Legal Affairs)

Rob Colamarino (Dir-IT)
Tim Brunswick (VP-Baseball Ops)
Brian Earle (VP-Bus Svcs)
Rod Meadows (VP-Sls & Mktg)
Heather Raburn (Sr Acct Mgr)
Mary Marandi (Mgr-Team Relations)
Tim Purpura (COO & Exec VP)
Katie Davison (Sr VP-Digital Strategy & Bus Dev)
Tara Thornton (Mgr-HR)
Will Kent (Mgr-Partnership Mktg)
Brad Friedman (Coord-Social Media Mktg)
Stefanie Loncarich (Dir-Special Events)
Courtney Nehls (Asst Dir-Community Engagement)
Mark Labban (Sr Mgr-Special Events & Affiliate Programming)
Gerald Jones (VP-Bus Dev & Media)
Mallory Roberts (Sr Mgr-Digital Mktg & Comm)
Melissa Giesler-Hassell (Coord-Trademarks & Intellectual Property)
Jessica Nori (Coord-Events & Partnerships)
Vincent Pierson (Dir-Diversity & Inclusion)
Jess Schneider (Mgr-Umpire Ops)
Meghan Madson (Coord-Mktg)

NATIONAL ASSOCIATION OF REALTORS
430 N Michigan Ave, Chicago, IL 60611-4087
Web Site: http://www.realtor.org
Year Founded: 1908
Sales Range: $75-99.9 Million
Emp.: 300
Trade Association Services
N.A.I.C.S.: 813910
Bob Goldberg (CEO)
Mark Birschbach (VP-Innovation, Tech, and Strategic Bus)
Leslie Rouda Smith (VP)
Wendy Cole (Mng Dir & Editor)
Victoria Gillespie (Chief Mktg & Comm Officer)
Shannon McGahn (Chief Advocacy Officer)
Elizabeth Mendenhall (Co-Pres)
John Smaby (Co-Pres)
Vince Malta (Co-Pres)
Sumanth Reddy Arani (Pres-Natl)
Nancy Lane (Treas)
Andrea Moore (VP-Diversity, Inclusion & Talent Opportunity)
Donna Gland (Sr VP-Talent Dev & Resources)
Kevin M. Sears (VP)

Subsidiaries:

DotHome, LLC. (1)
3029 Prospect Ave, Cleveland, OH 44115
Tel.: (216) 361-1000
Real Estate Manangement Services
N.A.I.C.S.: 531190

Institute of Real Estate Management (1)
430 N Michigan Ave, Chicago, IL 60611-4011
Tel.: (312) 329-6000
Web Site: http://www.irem.org
Sales Range: $25-49.9 Million
Emp.: 60
Not-for-Profit Certified Property Management Association
N.A.I.C.S.: 813910
Mary W. Wilken (Pres)

NATIONAL ASSOCIATION OF SECONDARY SCHOOL PRINCIPALS
1904 Association Dr, Reston, VA 20191-1537
Tel.: (703) 860-0200 VA

Web Site: http://www.principals.org
Year Founded: 1916
Sales Range: $10-24.9 Million
Emp.: 111
Educational Support Services
N.A.I.C.S.: 611710
Nancy Riviere (Dir-Event Svcs)
Amanda Karhuse (Dir-Govt Rels)
Michael Allison (Co-Pres)
Daniel P. Kelley (Co-Pres)
Ralph Funk (Treas)

NATIONAL AUDUBON SOCIETY, INC.
225 Varick St, New York, NY 10014
Tel.: (212) 979-3196
Web Site: https://www.audubon.org
Year Founded: 1905
Rev.: $116,692,000
Emp.: 400
Fiscal Year-end: 06/30/18
Conservation & Education Society
N.A.I.C.S.: 813410
George S. Golumbeski (Treas)
Joseph Ellis (Sec)
Mark Jannot (VP-Content)
Gary Langham (VP)
Susan Lunden (COO)
Lorraine Sciarra (Gen Counsel & VP)
Peter Vincent (VP-HR)
Susan Bell (Chm)
David B. Hartwell (Co-Vice Chm)
David J. Roux (Co-Vice Chm)
Jose Carbonell (CMO)
Claire Douglass (Dir-Natl Campaigns)
David O'Neill (Chief Conservation Officer)
David J. Ringer (Chief Network Officer)
Brian Trusty (VP-Central Flyway)
Sarah Greenberger (VP-Conservation Policy)
Doug Meffert (VP-Gulf Coast & Mississippi Flyway)
Stephen Meyer (COO)
Sean O'Connor (Chief Dev Officer)
Elizabeth Gray (CEO)

Subsidiaries:

Audubon Magazine (1)
225 Varick St 7 Fl, New York, NY 10014-9536
Tel.: (212) 979-3102
Web Site: http://www.audubon.org
Emp.: 235
National Audubon Society Publisher
N.A.I.C.S.: 513120
Susan Bell (Sec)
Joseph Ellis (Asst Sec)
David B. Ford (Chm)
David Hartwell (Vice Chm)
David Roux (Vice Chm)
Margaret Walker (Vice Chm)
Matt Anderson (VP-Climate Change & Strategic Initiatives)
John Beavers (VP-Intl Alliances Program)
Jose Carbonell (CMO)
Mike Daulton (VP-Policy & Strategy)
Mary Beth Henson (CFO & VP)
Anne Lieberman (Chief Dev Officer)
Susan Lunden (COO)
Andy Roos (CIO & VP)
Lorraine Sciarra (Gen Counsel & VP)
Peter Vincent (VP-HR)

NATIONAL AUTO PARTS WAREHOUSE, LLC
11150 NW 32nd Ave, Miami, FL 33167
Tel.: (305) 953-7270 FL
Web Site: http://www.npwcompanies.com
Year Founded: 1969
Motor Vehicle Supplies & New Parts Merchant Whslr
N.A.I.C.S.: 423120
Larry Pacey (Pres & CEO)
Chris Pacey (Exec VP)
Carl Luque (VP-Ops)

Rick Kovalick (Sr VP-Pur & Mktg)
Bill Melone (Mgr-Traditional Parts Category)
Jeff Nagle (Gen Mgr-Boaz)

Subsidiaries:

Engine & Performance Warehouse, Inc. (1)
955 Decatur St Unit D, Denver, CO 80204
Tel.: (303) 572-8844
Web Site: http://www.epwi.net
Sales Range: $10-24.9 Million
Emp.: 50
Automotive Supplies & Parts Mfr
N.A.I.C.S.: 423120
Paul Van Woensel (Pres)
Duane Zook (Gen Mgr-South)

Felt Auto Parts Company (1)
2581 Lincoln Ave, Ogden, UT 84401
Tel.: (801) 394-7778
Rev.: $1,366,900
Emp.: 6
Automotive Parts Wholesaler
N.A.I.C.S.: 441330
Steven R. Hoellein (Pres)

Performance Warehouse Company, Inc. (1)
9440 N Whitaker Rd, Portland, OR 97217
Tel.: (503) 417-5302
Web Site: http://www.performancewarehouse.com
Sales Range: $100-124.9 Million
Emp.: 250
Automotive Part Whslr
N.A.I.C.S.: 423120
Ray Baxter Jr. (VP)

Subsidiary (Domestic):

Performance Warehouse (2)
5950 N 9th St, Tacoma, WA 98409-7601
Tel.: (253) 597-6050 (100%)
Sales Range: $10-24.9 Million
Emp.: 41
Automotive Replacement Parts
N.A.I.C.S.: 423120
Ron Brown (Product Mgr-Mktg)

NATIONAL AUTOMOBILE CLUB, INC.
1151 E Hillsdale Blvd, Foster City, CA 94404
Tel.: (650) 294-7000 CA
Web Site: http://www.nationalautoclub.com
Year Founded: 1924
Sales Range: $1-9.9 Million
Emp.: 75
Travel Arrangement & Reservation Services
N.A.I.C.S.: 561599
Arthur Hedges (Pres)

NATIONAL AVIATION ACADEMY
6225 Ulmerton Rd, Clearwater, FL 33760
Tel.: (727) 531-2080
Web Site: http://www.naa.edu
Sales Range: $10-24.9 Million
Emp.: 80
Aviation Training & Education
N.A.I.C.S.: 611519
Mike Wisniewski (Pres)
Laurie Conners (Exec VP)
Mac Elliott (Owner & CEO)
George Nelson (Pres)
John Okenfus (Dir-Admissions)
Douglas Ecks (Dir-Education)

NATIONAL BAND & TAG CO.
721 York St, Newport, KY 41072-0430
Tel.: (859) 261-2035 KY
Web Site: http://www.nationalband.com
Year Founded: 1902
Sales Range: $25-49.9 Million

NATIONAL BAND & TAG CO.   U.S. PRIVATE

National Band & Tag Co.—(Continued)
Emp.: 38
Poultry & Turkey Leg Bands, Wing Bands, Cage & Nest Markers, Terminal Tags, Tool Checks, Dog License & Rabies Vaccination Tags, Swim Pool Tags & Advertising Specialty Tags Mfr
N.A.I.C.S.: 332119
Faye Haas Wendel *(Treas, Sec & VP-Personnel)*
Kevin A. Haas *(VP-Laser & R&D)*

NATIONAL BANK TRUST CO. OF SYCAMORE
230 W State St, Sycamore, IL 60178
Tel.: (815) 895-2125
Web Site: http://www.banknbt.com
Rev.: $28,161,000
Emp.: 160
National Commercial Banks
N.A.I.C.S.: 522110
Michael Cullen *(Pres)*
David McCoy *(Controller)*

NATIONAL BANKCARD SYSTEMS, INC.
6528 N Lamar Blvd, Austin, TX 78752
Tel.: (512) 494-9200
Web Site: http://www.enbs.com
Year Founded: 1997
Sales Range: $25-49.9 Million
Emp.: 31
Provider of Credit Card Processing & Check Cashing Verification Products & Services.
N.A.I.C.S.: 522320
Penny Baker *(Pres & CEO)*
Pete Estep *(COO)*

NATIONAL BANNER COMPANY, INC.
11938 Harry Hines Blvd, Dallas, TX 75234-5919
Tel.: (972) 241-2131   TX
Web Site:
  http://www.nationalbanner.com
Year Founded: 1952
Sales Range: $75-99.9 Million
Emp.: 185
Mfr of Banners, Pennants, Flags & Decals
N.A.I.C.S.: 339950
Don Girard *(Treas)*
Abraham Goldfarb *(Chm & Pres)*

NATIONAL BASKETBALL ASSOCIATION
Olympic Twr 645 5th Ave, New York, NY 10022
Tel.: (212) 407-8000   NY
Web Site: http://www.nba.com
Year Founded: 1946
Sales Range: $150-199.9 Million
Emp.: 800
Professional Basketball Organization
N.A.I.C.S.: 813990
Kathleen Behrens *(Exec VP-Social Responsibility & Player Programs)*
Sal Larocca *(Sr VP-Global Mdsg Grp)*
Paul E. Jacobs *(Owner & Vice Chm-Sacramento Kings)*
Robert Criqui *(Pres-Admin)*
Adam Silver *(Commissioner)*
Steven M. Angel *(Sr VP-League Ops & Officiating)*
Ski Austin *(Exec VP-Events & Attractions)*
Michael Bass *(Sr VP-Mktg Comm)*
Chris Brennan *(Sr VP-Retail Dev)*
Peter Farnsworth *(Sr VP-Bus Dev)*
Christopher Granger *(Exec VP-Team Mktg & Bus Ops)*
Daniel Meiseles *(Exec VP & Exec Producer-Production, Programming & Brdcst)*
Vicky Picca *(Sr VP-Licensing & Bus Affairs)*
Christopher J. Russo *(Sr VP-Facilities & Admin)*
Kenny Payne *(Sr VP-Events & Attractions)*
Thomas A. Carelli *(Sr VP-Brdcst)*
Linda Choong *(Sr VP-Retail Grp)*
Paul Hirschheimer *(Sr VP-Multimedia Production)*
Darrell McLennan-Fordyce *(Sr Dir-Comm)*
Joe Dumars *(Exec VP & Head-Basketball Ops)*
Byron O. Spruell *(Pres-League Ops)*
Aaron Ryan *(Sr VP-Mktg Solutions & Basketball-United States)*
Andrew Lustgarten *(Sr VP-Global Strategy)*
Ayala Deutsch *(Deputy Gen Counsel & Sr VP)*
Bill Koenig *(Pres-Global Media Distr)*
Bob Lanier *(VP)*
Brendan Donohue *(Sr VP-Team Mktg & Bus Ops)*
Charles L. Rosenzweig *(Sr VP-Entertainment & Player Mktg)*
Dan Rossomondo *(Sr VP-Global Media)*
Daniel S. Rube *(Deputy Gen Counsel & Sr VP)*
David Denenberg *(Sr VP-Global Media Distr & Bus Affairs)*
David Dongwei Yang *(Sr VP-Bus Affairs-China)*
Ella Wong *(Gen Counsel-China & Sr VP)*
Emilio Collins *(Exec VP-Global Mktg Partnerships)*
George Land *(Sr VP-Programming & Production-NBA China)*
Greg Taylor *(Sr VP-Player Dev)*
Jace Provo *(Sr VP-Events & Head-Medical Affairs)*
Jarad Franzreb *(Sr VP-Production)*
Kelly Flatow *(Sr VP-Mktg)*
Kerry A. Tatlock *(Sr VP-Global Mktg Partnerships)*
Kiki Van De Weghe *(Sr VP-Basketball Ops)*
Kim Bohuny *(Sr VP-Intl Basketball Ops)*
Mark Aronson *(Sr VP-Events)*
Matt Brabants *(Sr VP-Global Media Distr & Bus Ops)*
Matt Winick *(Sr VP-Scheduling & Game Ops)*
Melissa Rosenthal Brenner *(Sr VP-Digital Media)*
Michael T. Allen *(Sr VP-Digital Products & Emerging Tech)*
Myles C. Pistorius *(Sr VP-Events)*
Peter Fink *(Sr VP-Events)*
Rachel Jacobson *(Sr VP-Bus Dev)*
Raymond Tao *(Sr VP-Global Mktg Partnerships-China)*
Richard W. Buchanan *(Chief Compliance Officer, Gen Counsel & Exec VP)*
Robert Friedrich *(Sr VP-Bus, Fin & Legal Affairs)*
Robert W. Millman *(Sr VP-Intl Licensing & Bus Dev)*
Rod Thorn *(Pres-Basketball Ops)*
Scott Levy *(Mng Dir-Asia & India & Sr VP)*
Shirin Malkani *(Sr VP-Global Media Distr & Bus Affairs)*
Stephen M. Hellmuth *(Exec VP-Ops & Tech)*
Stephen O. Richard *(Sr VP-Bus Dev & Ops)*
Tim Frank *(Sr VP-Basketball Comm)*
Todd Jacobson *(Sr VP-Social Responsibility)*
Gin Chao *(VP-Corp Dev-China)*
Malcolm Turner *(Pres-G League)*
Arnon de Mello *(VP & Mng Dir-Latin America)*
Jeff Geels *(Sr Dir-Global Media Distr)*
Scott Flemming *(Sr Dir-Basketball Ops-India)*
Monty McCutchen *(VP & Head-Referee Dev & Trng)*
Michelle D. Johnson *(Sr VP & Head-Referee Ops)*
Shareef Abdur-Rahim *(Pres-G League)*
Diane Gotua *(VP-Global Bus Ops)*
Rajesh Sethi *(Mng Dir-India)*
Kelly L. Loeffler *(Owner/Chm-Atlanta Dream)*
Amy Brooks *(Chief Innovation Officer & Pres-Team Mktg & Bus Ops)*
Malik Rose *(VP-Basketball Ops)*
Victor Williams *(CEO-Africa)*
Oris R. Stuart *(Chief People & Inclusion Officer)*
Tammy Henault *(CMO)*
Mark A. Tatum *(Deputy Commissioner & COO)*

Subsidiaries:

Hardwood Funding LLC   (1)
100 Pl Dr, Secaucus, NJ 07094
Tel.: (201) 865-1500
Financial Service Provider
N.A.I.C.S.: 525990

NBA China   (1)
19th Floor Office Tower 2 China Central Place, No. 79 Jianguo Road Chaoyang District, Beijing, 100025, China
Tel.: (86) 10 5200 8200
Web Site: http://china.nba.com
Professional Basketball Organization
N.A.I.C.S.: 813990
Michael Ma *(CEO)*

NBA Digital   (1)
1050 Techwood Dr, Atlanta, GA 30318
Tel.: (404) 827-1700
Video Online Streaming
N.A.I.C.S.: 516210
Shayna Stewart *(Dir-Strategic Bus Dev)*

NBA Properties, Inc.   (1)
100 Plz Dr, Secaucus, NJ 07094-3766
Tel.: (201) 865-1500
Web Site: http://www.nba.com
Sales Range: $10-24.9 Million
Emp.: 25
Marketing & Licensing for the NBA
N.A.I.C.S.: 711320
Alaya Deutsch *(Sr VP & Chief Intellectual Property Counsel)*

WNBA Enterprises, LLC   (1)
645 5th Ave, New York, NY 10022-5910
Tel.: (212) 688-9622
Web Site: http://www.wnba.com
Sales Range: $10-24.9 Million
Emp.: 25
Administrators for the Women's National Basketball Association
N.A.I.C.S.: 711211
Jamin S. Dershowitz *(Gen Counsel)*
Kelley Hardwick *(Dir-Security)*
Christine Godleski *(COO)*
Todd Harris *(VP-Brdcst)*
Patrick Mulrenin *(Dir-Digital Media)*
Michael Whitehead *(Sr VP-Fin)*

YinzCam, Inc.   (1)
5541 Walnut St, Pittsburgh, PA 15232
Tel.: (412) 600-1165
Web Site: http://www.yinzcam.com
Software And Mobile Applications Mfr
N.A.I.C.S.: 513210
Priya Narasimhan *(CEO & Founder)*

NATIONAL BASKETBALL PLAYERS ASSOCIATION
133 Ave of the Americas 5th Fl, New York, NY 10036
Tel.: (212) 655-0880   NY
Web Site: http://www.nbpa.com
Year Founded: 1954
Sales Range: $10-24.9 Million
Emp.: 422
Basket Ball Association
N.A.I.C.S.: 813990
Michele A. Roberts *(Exec Dir)*
W. Gary Kohlman *(Gen Counsel)*
Anthony Tolliver *(Treas & Sec)*
David N. Lafleur *(Chief Admin Officer)*
Erica McKinley *(COO)*
Gary Arrick *(CFO)*
Jordan Schlachter *(CMO)*
Kyle Korver *(VP)*
Shelia Thompson *(Mgr-Acctg)*
Steve Blake *(VP)*
Dan Gladstone *(Sr VP-Grassroots Basketball & Bus Dev)*
Chris Paul *(Pres)*
Chrysa Chin *(Exec VP-Strategy & Dev)*
C. J. McCollum *(VP)*
Andre Iguodala *(First VP)*
Pau Gasol *(VP)*
Garrett Temple *(VP)*
William D. Parham *(Dir-Mental Health & Wellness)*
Jaylen Brown *(VP)*
Malcolm Brogdon *(VP)*
Bismack Biyombo *(VP)*

NATIONAL BEER WHOLESALERS ASSOCIATION
1101 King St Ste 600, Alexandria, VA 22314-2944
Tel.: (703) 683-4300   VA
Web Site: http://www.nbwa.org
Year Founded: 1938
Sales Range: $10-24.9 Million
Emp.: 27
Beer Wholesaler Association
N.A.I.C.S.: 813910
Craig Purser *(Pres & CEO)*
Kimberly McKinnish *(CFO)*
Patti Rouzie *(VP-Membership & Meetings)*
Paul Pisano *(Sr VP-Indus Affairs & General Counsel)*
Brittaney Meierling *(Dir-Legislative Affairs)*
Margaret Cos Manner *(Dir-Info Sys)*
Marcia Jonas *(Dir-Art)*
Pamela Yereb *(Sr VP-Admin & Fin)*
Tracey Anderson *(Dir-Meetings)*
Laurie Knight *(VP-Govt Affairs)*
Eric Bunning *(Dir-Federal Affairs)*

NATIONAL BLUES MUSEUM
615 Washington Ave, Saint Louis, MO 63101
Tel.: (314) 231-0400   MO
Web Site:
  http://www.nationalbluesmuseum.org
Year Founded: 2010
Sales Range: $1-9.9 Million
Art & Education Museum
N.A.I.C.S.: 712110
Dion Brown *(Founder)*
Robert Endicott *(Chm)*
Bernie Hayes *(Interim Exec Dir)*

NATIONAL BOARD FOR CERTIFICATION IN OCCUPATIONAL THERAPY, INC.
12 S Summit Ave Ste 100, Gaithersburg, MD 20877
Tel.: (301) 990-7979   MD
Web Site: http://www.nbcot.org
Year Founded: 1988
Sales Range: $10-24.9 Million
Emp.: 39
Occupational Therapy Services
N.A.I.C.S.: 621340
Dennis Tobin *(Chm)*
Debra Ammondson *(Vice Chm)*

COMPANIES / NATIONAL CAPITAL INDUSTRIES

NATIONAL BOARD FOR PROFESSIONAL TEACHING STANDARDS
1525 Wilson Blvd Ste 700, Arlington, VA 22209
Tel.: (703) 465-2700   DE
Web Site: http://www.nbpts.org
Year Founded: 1987
Sales Range: $25-49.9 Million
Emp.: 102
Professional Standard Review Organization
N.A.I.C.S.: 813920
Trey Clifton *(VP-Assessment)*
Loveen Bains *(Sr Mgr-Strategic Projects)*
Laura Benedetto *(Mgr-Strategic Projects)*
Lisa Clarke *(Dir-Policy & Partnerships)*
Jeff Derrick *(Dir-Fin)*
Michelle Accardi *(Dir-Policy & Partnerships)*
Michael DiConti *(CFO)*
Marc D'Anjou *(Sec)*
Amber Parker *(Sr VP-Outreach & Engagement)*
Stephen Helgeson *(VP-New Products & Svcs)*
Nancy Schwartz *(VP-Outreach & Engagement)*

NATIONAL BOARD OF MEDICAL EXAMINERS
3750 Market St, Philadelphia, PA 19104-3102
Tel.: (215) 590-9500   DC
Web Site: http://www.nbme.org
Year Founded: 1915
Sales Range: $150-199.9 Million
Emp.: 590
Health Care Srvices
N.A.I.C.S.: 621491
Suzanne T. Anderson *(Chm)*
Alfred F. Tallia *(Treas)*

NATIONAL BOARD OF OSTEOPATHIC MEDICAL EXAMINERS, INC.
8765 W Higgins Rd Ste 200, Chicago, IL 60631-4174
Tel.: (773) 714-0622   IN
Web Site: http://www.nbome.org
Year Founded: 1996
Sales Range: $10-24.9 Million
Emp.: 195
Health Care Srvices
N.A.I.C.S.: 622110
John R. Gimpel *(Pres & CEO)*
Wayne R. Carlsen *(Chm)*

NATIONAL BOILER SERVICE INC.
176 N Industrial Blvd, Trenton, GA 30752
Tel.: (706) 657-6200
Web Site: http://www.nationalboiler.com
Rev.: $20,000,000
Emp.: 35
Boiler Maintenance Contractor
N.A.I.C.S.: 238220
Robert Hunter *(Pres)*
Geno Patterson *(Co-Superintendent)*
Steve Nelms *(Co-Superintendent)*

NATIONAL BRANDS, INC.
4633 W Polk St, Phoenix, AZ 85043-2902
Tel.: (602) 269-3201   AZ
Web Site: http://www.nationalbrands.com
Year Founded: 1975
Sales Range: $75-99.9 Million
Emp.: 9
Retailer & Distributor of Home Furnishings & Electrical Appliances, Parts & Equipment
N.A.I.C.S.: 423620
Terry Thomas *(Chm)*
Richard Hollenbeck *(Pres)*

NATIONAL BREAST CANCER FOUNDATION, INC.
2600 Network Blvd Ste 300, Frisco, TX 75034
Tel.: (972) 248-9200   TX
Web Site: http://www.nationalbreastcancer.org
Year Founded: 1991
Sales Range: $10-24.9 Million
Emp.: 37
Breast Cancer Patient Wellness Services
N.A.I.C.S.: 813212
Kevin Hail *(COO)*
Douglas Feil *(VP-Programs)*
Camilla Payne *(VP-Mktg)*
John Reece *(CFO & Chief Strategy Officer)*
Lindsay Griffin *(Dir-HR & Acctg)*
Janelle Hail *(Chm & CEO)*
Laura Gaspard *(Dir-Fundraising)*
Mark Gomez *(Sr Dir-Creative)*
Ronald Brooks *(Treas)*
Rebecca Buell *(Sr Dir-Fin)*
Danae Johnson *(Dir-Dev)*

NATIONAL BROKERAGE SERVICES, INC.
6225 N Meeker Pl Ste 100, Boise, ID 83713-1579
Tel.: (208) 472-3437
Web Site: http://www.natbrokers.com
Year Founded: 1996
Sales Range: $25-49.9 Million
Emp.: 74
Insurance Services
N.A.I.C.S.: 524298
Todd Ruplinger *(Pres)*

NATIONAL BUILDING MAINTENANCE, INC.
5005 N Hesperides St, Tampa, FL 33614
Tel.: (813) 877-7467   FL
Web Site: http://www.nbnfla.com
Year Founded: 1962
Sales Range: $1-9.9 Million
Emp.: 95
Janitorial Services
N.A.I.C.S.: 561720
Ursula Page *(Pres)*

NATIONAL BULK EQUIPMENT, INC.
12838 Stainless Dr, Holland, MI 49424-8218
Tel.: (616) 399-2220
Web Site: http://www.nbe-inc.com
Bulk Bag Handling, Mixing, Storage, Conveying, Dumping & Dry Bulk Material Equipment
N.A.I.C.S.: 333998
C. Todd Reed *(Pres)*
Dave Denhof *(Gen Mgr)*
Ellen Kaines *(VP-Fin)*

NATIONAL BUSINESS AVIATION ASSOCIATION, INC.
1200 G St NW Ste 1100, Washington, DC 20005
Tel.: (202) 783-9000   DC
Web Site: http://www.nbaa.org
Year Founded: 1947
Sales Range: $25-49.9 Million
Emp.: 84
General Aviation Industry Association
N.A.I.C.S.: 813319
Dick Doubrava *(VP-Govt Affairs)*
Holly Clark *(Chief People Officer)*
Marc Freeman *(CFO)*
Todd Wormington *(Dir-IT)*
Paul Anderson *(Chm)*
Benjamin Schwalen *(Sec)*
Edward M. Bolen *(Pres & CEO)*
Llyod Newton *(Vice Chm & Treas)*
Cheryl Padilla *(VP-Conventions & Forums Admin Affairs)*
Chris Strong *(Sr VP-Conventions & Membership)*
Dan Hubbard *(Sr VP-Comm)*
Mike Nichols *(VP-Operational Excellence & Pro Dev)*
Doug Carr *(VP-Regulatory & Intl Affairs)*
Christa Lucas *(VP-Govt Affairs & Outreach)*

NATIONAL BUSINESS INSTITUTE
1218 McCann Dr, Altoona, WI 54720
Tel.: (715) 835-8525   WI
Web Site: http://www.nbi-sems.com
Year Founded: 1995
Sales Range: $10-24.9 Million
Emp.: 115
Legal Educational Support Services
N.A.I.C.S.: 541199
Tia Embke *(Dir-Mktg)*

NATIONAL BUSINESS SUPPLY INC.
2595 Bellingham, Troy, MI 48083
Tel.: (248) 823-5400   MI
Web Site: http://www.navbus.com
Year Founded: 1948
Sales Range: $10-24.9 Million
Emp.: 100
Office & Business Interior Design & Company Branding Solutions
N.A.I.C.S.: 541410
Richard Schwabauer *(Owner & Pres)*
Pam Smith *(Reg VP-Sls)*
Kristin Gula *(CFO)*
Ed Kleiss *(Dir-Ops & Svc Solutions)*
Heather Lanier *(COO)*
Tami Reynolds *(Dir-Client Experience)*
Greg Quante *(Dir-Comml Cleaning Solutions)*
Jill Burton *(Dir-Creative)*
Jim Thompson *(Dir-Sls & Corp Team)*
Scott Telder *(Gen Mgr)*
Jon Devin *(Gen Mgr-Audiovisual Solutions)*
Lance Rice *(Gen Mgr-Lansing)*
Ingrid Ams *(VP-Sls)*
Lori Powe *(VP-Sls)*
Mark Sawchuk *(VP-Sls & Healthcare & Education)*

Subsidiaries:

NBS-Bay City   (1)
701 Salzburg Rd, Bay City, MI 48706
Tel.: (989) 895-8574
Web Site: http://www.navbus.com
Office & Business Interior Design & Company Branding Solutions
N.A.I.C.S.: 541410

NBS-Toledo   (1)
4 N Saint Clair St, Toledo, OH 43604
Tel.: (419) 662-2040
Web Site: http://www.yournbs.com
Emp.: 12
Office & Business Interior Design & Company Branding Solutions
N.A.I.C.S.: 541410

NATIONAL CAMERA EXCHANGE INC.
9300 Hwy 55, Golden Valley, MN 55427-4758
Tel.: (763) 546-6831
Web Site: http://www.nationalcamera.com
Year Founded: 1914
Sales Range: $25-49.9 Million
Emp.: 185
Sales of Camera & Photographic Supplies
N.A.I.C.S.: 449210
Kelly Pittman *(Mgr-Adv)*
Matt Ogden *(Mgr)*
Kathleen Radice *(Mgr-Photo Lab)*
Mark Christman *(Mgr-Store)*
Mike Lamotte *(VP)*

NATIONAL CAPITAL BANK OF WASHINGTON
316 Pennsylvania Ave SE, Washington, DC 20003
Tel.: (202) 546-8232
Web Site: http://www.nationalcapitalbank.com
Year Founded: 1889
Rev.: $19,381,272
Assets: $466,589,497
Liabilities: $422,851,448
Net Worth: $43,738,049
Earnings: $2,646,807
Fiscal Year-end: 12/31/18
Banking Services
N.A.I.C.S.: 522110
David M. Glaser *(Sr VP & Dir-eClient & Treasury Svcs)*
James M. Didden *(Sr Mgr-Rels)*
William T. Pedas *(VP-Circle Mgmt)*
Debra A. Keats *(Chief Retail Admin Officer & Exec VP)*
Juan J. Elias *(VP & Mgr-Wire Transfer)*
Robin P. Anderson *(Officer-Banking)*
Carmella G. Elliott *(Officer-Banking)*
Fatima P. Fonseca *(Asst VP & Mgr-Branch)*
Sherri A. Waid *(Officer-Banking)*
Joseph Marchese *(Chief Credit Officer & Exec VP)*
Ryan W. McKinley *(Officer-Comml Loan & Sr VP)*
Amy M. Woodward *(VP & Dir-HR)*
Keith B. Arnold *(VP-Credit Admin)*
Sharon T. Peters *(VP & Mgr-Loan Admin)*
Daniel S. Solomonraj *(Asst VP & Mgr-Branch)*
Christopher S. Reddick *(VP & Dir-Mortgage Sls)*
Robin Robertson *(Sr VP, Mktg Dir & Dir-Retail Banking)*
Kathryn Speakman *(Officer-Comml Loan & VP)*
Richard M. Sobonya *(Sr VP & Dir-Construction Lending)*
Patricia M. Ostrander *(Chief Admin & Compliance Officer & Exec VP)*
Elaine B. Rial *(Sr VP & Dir-Loan Ops & Admin)*
Renee C. Aldrich *(Chief Comml Loan Officer & Exec VP)*
Francina Jones *(Sr VP & Controller)*
Paul T. Yeloushan *(CIO & Exec VP)*
Robert G. Byrer *(Compliance Officer & VP)*
Randal J. Rabe *(CFO & Exec VP)*
William Bauder *(VP & Fin Dir)*
James Olevson *(Pres & CEO)*
Bradley J. Duncan *(Sr VP & Dir-Construction Lending)*
Sean A. Biehl *(Officer-Comml Loan & VP)*
Matthew W. Santmyer *(Sr VP & Dir-Strategic Projects)*
R. Andrew Didden Jr. *(Chief Investment Svcs Officer & Exec VP)*
James H. Thompson III *(Treas & Sr VP)*
William G. DuBose II *(Officer-Mortgage Loan & VP)*

NATIONAL CAPITAL INDUSTRIES

NATIONAL CAPITAL INDUSTRIES

National Capital Industries—(Continued)
3420 Kenilworth Ave, Bladensburg, MD 20710
Tel.: (301) 864-4150
Web Site: http://www.natcap.com
Sales Range: $10-24.9 Million
Emp.: 36
General Construction Machinery & Equipment
N.A.I.C.S.: 423810
C. Richard Johnson *(Chm & CEO)*
Helen L. Johnson *(Vice Chm)*
Steve Malley *(CFO & VP)*
Diane Arch *(Mgr-Credit)*

NATIONAL CAPITOL CONTRACTING
8255 Greensboro Dr Ste C 100, Mclean, VA 22203
Tel.: (703) 243-9696
Web Site: http://www.nccsite.com
Year Founded: 2002
Sales Range: $1-9.9 Million
Emp.: 51
Video Production & Taping Services
N.A.I.C.S.: 512290
Chris Marquez *(Pres & CEO)*
Lorene Eberhardt *(VP-Ops)*

NATIONAL CAPTIONING INSTITUTE
3725 Concorde Pkwy Ste 100, Chantilly, VA 20151
Tel.: (703) 917-7600
Web Site: http://www.ncicap.org
Rev.: $16,690,081
Emp.: 175
Film Processing, Editing & Titling; Motion Picture
N.A.I.C.S.: 512191
Gene Chao *(Chm, Pres & CEO)*
Juan Mario Agudelo *(Dir-Sls & Mktg-Natl)*

NATIONAL CAR RENTAL OF PHOENIX
1805 E Sky Harbor Cir, Phoenix, AZ 85034
Tel.: (602) 275-4771
Web Site: http://www.nationalcar.com
Sales Range: $75-99.9 Million
Emp.: 400
Car Rental Services
N.A.I.C.S.: 532111
Charles J. Aton *(Pres)*

NATIONAL CASEIN CO. INC.
601 W 80th St, Chicago, IL 60620
Tel.: (773) 846-7300
Web Site: http://www.nationalcasein.com
Sales Range: $25-49.9 Million
Emp.: 110
Glue
N.A.I.C.S.: 325520
Hope T. Cook *(Pres)*
Charles Cook *(VP)*

NATIONAL CAUCUS & CENTER ON BLACK AGING, INC.
1220 L St NW Ste 800, Washington, DC 20005
Tel.: (202) 637-8400 DC
Web Site: http://www.ncba-aged.org
Year Founded: 1980
Sales Range: $10-24.9 Million
Emp.: 2,411
Social Advocacy Organization
N.A.I.C.S.: 813319
Angie Boddie *(Dir-Health Programs)*
Rosalind Brooks *(Dir-Senior Environmental Employment Program)*
Karyne Jones *(Pres & CEO)*
Elias Hussein *(Exec VP)*
Debra Carter *(Dir-Senior Community Svcs Employment Program)*
Lucia R. Riddle *(Treas)*

NATIONAL CENTER FOR MANUFACTURING SCIENCES INC.
3025 Boardwalk Ste 250, Ann Arbor, MI 48108-3230
Tel.: (734) 995-0300 DE
Web Site: http://www.ncms.org
Year Founded: 1987
Sales Range: $10-24.9 Million
Emp.: 34
Provider of Commercial Physical Research Services
N.A.I.C.S.: 541715
Rebecca Taylor *(Sr VP)*
Beth Bolog *(Sec)*
Courtney Hill *(Gen Mgr-Mfg-Quality Tech)*
Jon Riley *(Sr VP-Tech)*
Lisa Strama *(Pres & CEO)*
Pam Hurt *(Dir-Comm)*

Subsidiaries:

Technologies Research Corporation (1)
3025 Boardwalk St Ste 250, Ann Arbor, MI 48108-3230
Tel.: (734) 995-0300
Sales Range: $10-24.9 Million
Emp.: 3
Provider of Commercial Physical Research Services
N.A.I.C.S.: 541715

NATIONAL CENTER FOR MISSING & EXPLOITED CHILDREN
699 Prince St, Alexandria, VA 22314-3175
Tel.: (703) 224-2150 DC
Web Site: http://www.missingkids.com
Year Founded: 1984
Sales Range: $25-49.9 Million
Emp.: 401
Child Care Services
N.A.I.C.S.: 622210
Manus Cooney *(Chm)*
Karen Tandy *(Vice Chm)*
Colleen Nick *(Sec)*
John F. Clark *(Pres & CEO)*
Michelle C. Delaune *(COO & Sr VP)*
Susan Herbert Peacock *(VP-HR)*
Gavin Portnoy *(VP-Strategic Advancement & Partnerships)*
Yiota G. Souras *(Gen Counsel & Sr VP)*
Michael Spence *(CFO & VP)*

NATIONAL CENTER FOR STATE COURTS
300 Newport Ave, Williamsburg, VA 23185
Tel.: (757) 259-1565 DC
Web Site: http://www.ncsc.org
Year Founded: 1971
Sales Range: $25-49.9 Million
Emp.: 369
Court Improvement Organization
N.A.I.C.S.: 561492
Gwen Williams *(CFO & VP-Fin & Admin)*
Paul Embley *(CIO)*
Robert Baldwin *(Gen Counsel & Exec VP)*
Thomas Clarke *(VP-Res & Tech)*
Daniel Hall *(VP-Court Consulting Svcs)*
Jacquie Ring *(Program Mgr)*
Mark Cady *(Chm)*

NATIONAL CHARITY SERVICES
1905 Brentwood Rd, Washington, DC 20018
Tel.: (800) 506-0172
Web Site: http://www.nationalcharityservices.com
Year Founded: 2006
Sales Range: $1-9.9 Million
Emp.: 15
Logistical & Managerial Support to Nonprofits in All Fundraising Projects
N.A.I.C.S.: 541618
Jeremy Silverstein *(Mng Dir)*

NATIONAL CHILDREN'S CENTER, INC.
6200 2nd St NW, Washington, DC 20011
Tel.: (202) 722-2300 DC
Web Site: http://www.nccinc.org
Year Founded: 1958
Rev.: $25,039,528
Emp.: 476
Child Care & Development Services
N.A.I.C.S.: 624110
Steven Dale *(Sr Dir-Adult Svcs)*
Craig Dewing *(Dir-IT & Mgt Info Systems)*
Beth Jarrett *(Dir-Quality Improvement)*
Patricia Browne *(CEO)*

NATIONAL CHRISTIAN CHARITABLE FOUNDATION, INC.
11625 Rainwater Dr Ste 500, Alpharetta, GA 30009
Tel.: (404) 252-0100 GA
Web Site: http://www.nationalchristian.com
Year Founded: 1982
Sales Range: $800-899.9 Million
Emp.: 103
Christian Ministry Services
N.A.I.C.S.: 813110
Dave Johnson *(CFO & Chief Investment Officer)*
Bill Williams *(Co-CEO)*
David Wills *(Pres)*
Dan Brown *(CIO)*
Steve Chapman *(Chief Creative Officer)*
Jay Bennett *(Chm)*
Phil Drake *(Vice Chm)*
Terry Parker *(Co-Founder)*
Ron Blue *(Co-Founder)*
Kevin Arner *(Chief Strategy Officer)*
Chris Holdorf *(Co-CEO)*
Randy Thrasher *(COO)*
Tim Townsend *(Gen Counsel)*

NATIONAL CHURCH RESIDENCES
2335 N Bank Dr, Columbus, OH 43220-5499
Tel.: (614) 451-2151
Web Site: http://www.ncr.org
Year Founded: 1961
Sales Range: $10-24.9 Million
Emp.: 1,300
Real Estate Managers
N.A.I.C.S.: 531210
Mark Ricketts *(Pres & CEO)*
Jacci Nickell *(COO-Sr Living & Sr VP)*
Tanya Hahn *(CFO)*
George Tabit *(VP-Construction & Dev Svcs)*
Susan DiMickele *(Gen Counsel & Sr VP)*
Heather Widney *(Exec Dir-Lincoln Village)*
Megan Kelley *(VP-Pub Policy & Govt Rels)*
Kelli Meyung *(VP-Healthcare Ops)*
Danielle Willis *(Chief Diversity Officer & Sr VP-Employee Engagement)*
Julie Fox *(VP-Engagement & Leadership Dev)*

NATIONAL CIGAR CORPORATION
407 N Main St, Frankfort, IN 46041-1729
Tel.: (765) 659-3326 IN
Web Site: http://www.broadleafcigars.com
Year Founded: 1943
Sales Range: $1-9.9 Million
Emp.: 40
Mfr of Cigars & Tobacco
N.A.I.C.S.: 111910
James K. Pogue *(Pres)*
Kenneth J. Wolf *(VP-Sls & Mktg)*
Jerry E. Green *(VP-HR)*
Carl Berger Jr. *(Chm)*

NATIONAL CITY VOLKSWAGEN
3131 National City Blvd, National City, CA 91950
Tel.: (619) 336-4030
Web Site: https://www.nationalcityvolkswagen.com
Sales Range: $10-24.9 Million
New Car Dealers
N.A.I.C.S.: 441110
Manny Sedano *(Principal)*

NATIONAL COATINGS & SUPPLIES, INC.
4900 Falls of Neuse Rd Ste 150, Raleigh, NC 27609
Tel.: (866) 529-1682 NC
Web Site: http://www.ncs-coatings.com
Year Founded: 2009
Paint & Coatings Mfr
N.A.I.C.S.: 424950
Wayne Lavrack *(Pres)*
Curtis Beeson *(VP-Acctg Ops)*
Bernie Blickenstaff *(VP-Corp Client Support Grp)*
Dean Worley *(CEO)*
Randy Butler *(Mgr-Ops)*
Michael Smith *(Mgr-Ops)*
Sung Pek *(Mgr-District-Ops)*
Aaron Rickels *(Mgr-District-Ops)*

NATIONAL COLLEGIATE ATHLETIC ASSOCIATION
1802 Alonzo Watford Sr Dr, Indianapolis, IN 46202
Tel.: (317) 917-6222
Web Site: http://www.ncaa.org
Sales Range: $25-49.9 Million
Emp.: 400
Collegiate Athletic Program Governing Organization
N.A.I.C.S.: 711211
Durenka Robie *(Coord-Corp Brdcst & Alliances)*
Stacey Osburn *(Dir-Pub & Media Rels)*
Charlie Baker *(Pres)*
Charles D. Baker Jr. *(Pres)*

NATIONAL COLLEGIATE SCOUTING ASSOCIATION
1415 N Dayton St 4th Floor, Chicago, IL 60642
Tel.: (866) 495-5172
Web Site: http://www.ncsasports.org
Year Founded: 2000
Sales Range: $25-49.9 Million
Emp.: 317
Collegiate Recruiting Services
N.A.I.C.S.: 541612

COMPANIES
NATIONAL CORPORATE HOUSING

Christopher Krause *(Founder & CEO)*
Lisa Strasman *(Pres & COO)*
Izell Reese *(Exec VP)*

NATIONAL COMMITTEE FOR QUALITY ASSURANCE
1100O 13L St NW Ste1000, Washington, DC 20005-4938
Tel.: (202) 955-3500 — DC
Web Site: http://www.ncqa.org
Year Founded: 1991
Sales Range: $10-24.9 Million
Emp.: 300
Measures the Performance of Managed Health Care Systems
N.A.I.C.S.: 813910
Margaret E. O'Kane *(Pres)*
Victoria Street *(Dir-NCQA Education)*
Mary Barton *(VP-Performance Measurement)*
Stephen Easterday *(VP-Quality Solutions Grp)*
Scott Hartranft *(CFO)*
Rick Moore *(CIO)*

NATIONAL COMMUNITY REINVESTMENT COALITION, INC.
740 15th St NW Ste 400, Washington, DC 20002
Tel.: (202) 628-8866 — DC
Web Site: http://www.ncrc.org
Year Founded: 1990
Sales Range: $10-24.9 Million
Emp.: 63
Community Development Services
N.A.I.C.S.: 624190
Anneliese Lederer *(Mgr-Compliance)*
Cypriana Hicklen *(Accountant-Grant)*
Dica Adotevi *(CFO)*
Eric Hersey *(Dir-Comm)*

NATIONAL COMPREHENSIVE CANCER NETWORK
275 Commerce Dr, Ste 300, Fort Washington, PA 19034
N.A.I.C.S.:

Subsidiaries:

NCCN Foundation (1)
3025 Chemical Rd Ste 100, Plymouth Meeting, PA 19462
Tel.: (215) 690-0300
Web Site: https://www.nccn.org
Health Care Srvices
N.A.I.C.S.: 621610

NATIONAL COMPUTER SERVICES
1941 Citrona Dr, Fernandina Beach, FL 32034
Tel.: (904) 321-0050
Web Site: http://www.ncsjobs.com
Sales Range: $25-49.9 Million
Emp.: 250
Custom Computer Programming Services
N.A.I.C.S.: 541511
Charles Hughes *(Owner)*

NATIONAL CONCRETE PRODUCTS COMPANY
939 S Mill St, Plymouth, MI 48170-4320
Tel.: (734) 453-8448 — MI
Year Founded: 1959
Sales Range: $50-74.9 Million
Emp.: 3
Mfr of Sewer Pipe, Manhole Covers & Underground Systems
N.A.I.C.S.: 327332
Jack E. Cook *(Pres)*
James J. Manson *(Sec & VP)*
Robert Terwin *(Treas & VP)*

NATIONAL CONEY ISLAND INC.
27947 Groesbeck Hwy, Roseville, MI 48066
Tel.: (586) 771-7744
Web Site: http://www.nationalconeyisland.com
Sales Range: $10-24.9 Million
Emp.: 2,000
Fast Food Restaurants & Stands
N.A.I.C.S.: 722513
Tom Giftos *(Founder & Pres)*
Dan Roma *(CFO)*

NATIONAL CONGRESS OF PARENTS AND TEACHERS
1250 N Pitt St, Alexandria, VA 22314
Tel.: (703) 518-1200 — IL
Web Site: http://www.pta.org
Year Founded: 1897
Sales Range: $10-24.9 Million
Emp.: 67
Family & Child Care Services
N.A.I.C.S.: 624190
Heidi May Wilson *(Sr Mgr-Media Rels-Comm Dept)*
Suzan Yungner *(Dir-Field Svcs & Trng)*
LaWanda Toney *(Dir-Strategic Comm)*
Wayne Bauman *(Treas & Sec)*
Laura Bay *(Pres)*
Shannon Sevier *(VP-Advocacy)*
Debra Strauss *(VP-Membership)*
Nathan R. Monell *(Exec Dir)*
Andrea Kost *(Pres-South Dakota)*
Sheila McGuire *(Pres-Wyoming)*
Tanya Robinson *(Pres-South Carolina)*
James Thomasell *(CFO-Fin Dept)*

NATIONAL CONSORTIUM OF BREAST CENTERS INC.
PO Box 1334, Warsaw, IN 46581-1334
Tel.: (574) 267-8058 — IN
Web Site: http://www.breastcare.org
Year Founded: 1991
Sales Range: $1-9.9 Million
Emp.: 9
Breast Health Care Services
N.A.I.C.S.: 622110
Jennifer Cobb Hayes *(Mgr-Certifications)*
Kimberly Samuels *(Exec Dir)*

NATIONAL CONSTRUCTION ENTERPRISES INC.
1001 W 11th St, Mishawaka, IN 46544-4818
Tel.: (574) 259-8581
Web Site: http://www.gibson-lewis.com
Year Founded: 1978
Sales Range: $100-124.9 Million
Emp.: 50
Provider of Construction Services
N.A.I.C.S.: 238310
Robert Lingenfelter *(Pres)*

Subsidiaries:

Ann Arbor Ceiling & Partition Co. (1)
5075 Carpenter Rd, Ypsilanti, MI 48197-9601
Tel.: (734) 434-1600
Web Site: http://annarborceiling.com
Sales Range: $10-24.9 Million
Emp.: 12
Provider of Construction Services
N.A.I.C.S.: 238310
Rob Walrich *(Pres)*

Commercial Building Materials LLC (1)
5075 Carpenter Rd, Ypsilanti, MI 48197-9601
Tel.: (734) 434-4600
Sales Range: $10-24.9 Million
Emp.: 28
Provider of Construction Supplies
N.A.I.C.S.: 423320

Flagship Construction Co., LLC (1)
4052 Dean Martin Dr, Las Vegas, NV 89103
Tel.: (702) 739-1722
Web Site: http://www.flagship-construction.com
Construction Engineering Services
N.A.I.C.S.: 541330

Gibson-Lewis of Indianapolis, LLC (1)
5366 Rock Hampton Ct, Indianapolis, IN 46268-1028 (100%)
Tel.: (317) 876-7054
Web Site: http://www.gibson-lewisofindianapolis.com
Sales Range: $25-49.9 Million
Emp.: 12
Construction Services
N.A.I.C.S.: 238310
Mark Masenthin *(Mgr-Contract)*
Douglas Harrison *(Pres)*

Gibson-Lewis, LLC (1)
1001 W 11th St, Mishawaka, IN 46544
Tel.: (574) 259-8581
Web Site: http://www.gibson-lewis.com
Plaster Contracting Services
N.A.I.C.S.: 238310
Rob Lingenfelter *(Pres)*

Huron Valley Glass Company LLC (1)
5075 Carpenter Rd, Ypsilanti, MI 48197-9601
Tel.: (734) 434-1160
Web Site: http://www.diamondvogel.com
Sales Range: $10-24.9 Million
Emp.: 40
Provider of Glass Services
N.A.I.C.S.: 238150

Micco LLC (1)
715 Auburn Rd, Pontiac, MI 48342-3306
Tel.: (248) 334-7753
Web Site: http://www.miccoconstruction.com
Sales Range: $10-24.9 Million
Construction Services
N.A.I.C.S.: 236220

Subsidiary (Domestic):

Micco Construction LLC. (2)
715 Auburn Rd, Pontiac, MI 48342
Tel.: (248) 334-7753
Web Site: http://www.miccoconstruction.com
Commercial Building Contracting Services
N.A.I.C.S.: 236220
Jeff Wojcehowicz *(Project Mgr)*

National Door Systems, LLC (1)
715 Auburn Rd, Pontiac, MI 48342
Tel.: (248) 332-0255
Web Site: http://www.nationaldoorsystems.com
Door & Window Whslr
N.A.I.C.S.: 423310
David Boehmer *(VP)*

National Enclosure Company (1)
715 Auburn Rd, Pontiac, MI 48342
Tel.: (248) 332-4250
Web Site: http://www.nationalenclosure.com
Commercial Building Contracting Services
N.A.I.C.S.: 236220
Bill Lincoln *(VP-Sls)*
David Sauld *(Pres)*
Paul Becks *(Exec VP)*

National Maintenance Services, LLC (1)
715 Auburn Rd, Pontiac, MI 48342
Tel.: (248) 334-1977
Web Site: http://www.nationalmaintenanceservices.com
Building Construction Services
N.A.I.C.S.: 236220

Pontiac Ceiling & Partition Co. LLC (1)
715 Auburn Rd, Pontiac, MI 48343-3306
Tel.: (248) 332-0252
Web Site: http://www.pcp-nce.com
Sales Range: $25-49.9 Million
Provider of Construction Services
N.A.I.C.S.: 238310
Ronnie Crescenti *(Mgr-HR)*

Wal-Mark Contracting Group Inc. (1)
5203 N Howard Ave, Tampa, FL 33603-1419
Tel.: (813) 348-4711
Web Site: http://www.walmarkcontracting.com
Sales Range: $10-24.9 Million
Emp.: 15
Provider of Construction Services
N.A.I.C.S.: 238310
Kevin Barnhart *(Pres)*

NATIONAL CONSTRUCTORS INC.
11820 Miramar Pkwy, Miramar, FL 33025
Tel.: (954) 443-3060
Web Site: http://www.nationalconstructors.com
Sales Range: $10-24.9 Million
Emp.: 18
Commercial & Office Building, New Construction
N.A.I.C.S.: 236220

NATIONAL CONSUMER LAW CENTER, INC.
7 Winthrop Sq, Boston, MA 02110-1245
Tel.: (617) 542-8010 — MA
Web Site: http://www.nclc.org
Year Founded: 1969
Sales Range: $10-24.9 Million
Emp.: 59
Law firm
N.A.I.C.S.: 541199
Margaret Kohler *(CFO)*
Donna Wong *(Dir-Pub Ops)*
Svetlana Ladan *(Dir-Ops & IT)*
Olga Shmatkova *(Accountant)*
Donna Daley *(Vice Chm)*
Michael Ferry *(Chm)*
Richard Dubois *(Exec Dir)*
Stuart Rossman *(Dir-Litigation)*
Lauren Saunders *(Assoc Dir)*
Debbie Parziale *(Office Mgr)*
Jan Kruse *(Dir-Comm)*
Steve Hurley *(Chief Dev Officer)*
SarahEmily Lekberg *(Mgr-Conference & Trng)*
Tashia Graham *(Mgr-HR)*
Shannon Halbrook *(Coord-Digital Publications)*
Denise Lisio *(Dir-Editing & Production)*
James Lynch *(Mgr-Mktg & Sls)*

NATIONAL COOPERATIVE BUSINESS ASSOCIATION CLUSA INTERNATIONAL
1775 Eye St NW, Washington, DC 20006
Tel.: (202) 638-6222 — DC
Web Site: http://www.ncba.coop
Year Founded: 1916
Sales Range: $25-49.9 Million
Emp.: 96
Business Associations
N.A.I.C.S.: 813910
Andrew Jacob *(Chm)*
Helen Godfrey-Smith *(Treas)*
Debbie Trocha *(Sec)*

NATIONAL CORPORATE HOUSING
365 Herndon Pkwy Ste 111, Herndon, VA 20170
Tel.: (703) 464-5700
Web Site: http://www.nationalcorporatehousing.com
Year Founded: 1999
Sales Range: $75-99.9 Million
Emp.: 122
Temporary Housing
N.A.I.C.S.: 624229

NATIONAL CORPORATE HOUSING

National Corporate Housing—(Continued)
Tom Atchison *(CEO)*
Kregg Anderson *(CFO & CIO)*
Cindy Hancock *(Reg VP)*
Vicki Johnson *(Gen Mgr-Columbus)*
Hillary Hunt-Boster *(Asst Gen Mgr-Columbus)*
Irina Keen *(Acct Mgr-Global)*
Misty Gregarek *(Chief Talent Officer)*

NATIONAL CORSET SUPPLY HOUSE
3240 E 26th St, Vernon, CA 90058
Tel.: (323) 261-0265 CA
Web Site: http://www.shirleyofhollywood.com
Year Founded: 1948
Sales Range: $10-24.9 Million
Emp.: 180
Mfr & Distributor of Women's Chemises, Camisoles, Teddies & Corset Bustiers
N.A.I.C.S.: 315250
Roy Schlobohm *(Pres)*

Subsidiaries:

Finebrand Division (1)
3720 S Santa Fe Ave, Los Angeles, CA 90058
Tel.: (323) 588-3220
Emp.: 5
Mfr & Distributor of Corsets; Women's & Children's Accessories
N.A.I.C.S.: 315250
Kim Zeder *(Mng Dir)*

NATIONAL COUNCIL FOR AIR AND STREAM IMPROVEMENT, INC.
1513 Wallnut St 200, Cary, NC 27511
Tel.: (919) 941-6400
Web Site: http://www.ncasi.org
Sales Range: $10-24.9 Million
Emp.: 13
Environmental Research
N.A.I.C.S.: 541720
Dirk Kroskop *(Pres)*

NATIONAL COUNCIL FOR BEHAVIORAL HEALTH
1701 K St NW Ste 400, Washington, DC 20006
Tel.: (202) 684-7457 DC
Web Site: http://www.thenationalcouncil.org
Year Founded: 1980
Sales Range: $50-74.9 Million
Emp.: 48
Behavioral Healthcare Services
N.A.I.C.S.: 623220
Jeannie Campbell *(COO & Exec VP)*
Betsy Schwartz *(VP-Pub Education & Strategic Initiatives)*
Donald Miskowiec *(Chm)*
Chuck Ingoglia *(Pres & CEO)*

NATIONAL COUNCIL OF JUVENILE & FAMILY COURT JUDGES
PO Box 8970, Reno, NV 89507
Tel.: (775) 784-6012 NV
Web Site: http://www.ncjfcj.org
Year Founded: 1975
Sales Range: $10-24.9 Million
Emp.: 117
Legal Aid Services
N.A.I.C.S.: 541199
Anthony Capizzi *(Pres)*
John J. Romero Jr. *(Pres)*

NATIONAL COUNCIL OF STATE BOARDS OF NURSING
111 E Wacker Dr Ste 2900, Chicago, IL 60601-4277
Tel.: (312) 525-3600 PA
Web Site: http://www.ncsbn.org
Year Founded: 1978
Sales Range: $75-99.9 Million
Emp.: 112
Nursing Care Services
N.A.I.C.S.: 611519
Debra Scott *(Exec Dir)*
Joseph Dudzik *(Dir-HR)*
Alicia Byrd *(Dir-Member Rels)*
Dawn Kappel *(Dir-Mktg & Comm)*
Robert Clayborne *(CFO)*
Gloria Damgaard *(Treas)*
Katherine Thomas *(Pres)*
David Benton *(CEO)*

NATIONAL COUNCIL OF TEACHERS OF MATHEMATICS
1906 Association Dr, Reston, VA 20191-1502
Tel.: (703) 620-9840 IL
Web Site: http://www.nctm.org
Year Founded: 1920
Sales Range: $10-24.9 Million
Emp.: 96
Educational Professional Association
N.A.I.C.S.: 813920
Ken Krehbiel *(Assoc Exec Dir-Comm)*
Joanne Hodges *(Sr Dir-Publications)*

NATIONAL COUNCIL YMCA OF THE USA
101 N Wacker Dr Ste 1600, Chicago, IL 60606
Tel.: (312) 977-0031
Web Site: http://www.ymca.net
Sales Range: $75-99.9 Million
Emp.: 250
Membership Sports & Recreation Clubs
N.A.I.C.S.: 713940
Neal Nicoll *(Pres & CEO)*
Diane Hurles *(Mgr-Donor Rels)*
Kate Markin *(CMO & Sr VP)*
Jim Mellor *(CFO)*

NATIONAL COURT APPOINTED SPECIAL ADVOCATE ASSOCIATION
100 W Harrison N Tower Ste 500, Seattle, WA 98119
Tel.: (206) 270-0072 WA
Web Site: http://www.casaforchildren.org
Year Founded: 1984
Sales Range: $10-24.9 Million
Emp.: 42
Business Associations
N.A.I.C.S.: 813910
Adam J. Liff *(Treas)*
Britt Banks *(Sec)*
Patricia Bresee *(Vice Chm)*
William R. Collins *(Chm)*
Tara Perry *(CEO)*

NATIONAL CROP INSURANCE SERVICES INC.
8900 Indian Creek Pkwy Ste 600, Overland Park, KS 66210
Tel.: (913) 685-2767 KS
Web Site: http://www.ag-risk.org
Year Founded: 1989
Sales Range: $10-24.9 Million
Emp.: 46
Crop Insurer Association
N.A.I.C.S.: 524126
Sherri Scharff *(VP-Membership Svcs)*
Laurie Langstraat *(VP-PR)*
Jim Crist *(CFO & COO)*
Linda Kovelan *(Exec Dir-Svcs)*
Laurence Crane *(VP-Program Outreach & Risk Mgmt Education)*
Thomas P. Zacharias *(Pres)*

NATIONAL CUSTOMER ENGINEERING, INC.
1866 Friendship Dr Ste B, El Cajon, CA 92020
Tel.: (619) 212-3000
Web Site: http://www.ncegroup.com
Year Founded: 1981
Sales Range: $10-24.9 Million
Emp.: 125
Data Management Services
N.A.I.C.S.: 423430
Jim Raven *(Pres, CEO & COO)*

NATIONAL CUTTING HORSE ASSOCIATION
260 Bailey Ave, Fort Worth, TX 76107
Tel.: (817) 244-6188 TX
Web Site: http://www.nchacutting.com
Year Founded: 1946
Sales Range: $10-24.9 Million
Emp.: 44
Cutting Horse Association
N.A.I.C.S.: 813990
Sandy Brandt *(Accountant)*
Shana Veale *(Controller)*
Mike Franklin *(Accountant)*

NATIONAL DEFENSE INDUSTRIAL ASSOCIATION
2111 Wilson Blvd Ste 400, Arlington, VA 22201-3061
Tel.: (703) 522-1820 DC
Web Site: http://www.ndia.org
Year Founded: 1919
Sales Range: $25-49.9 Million
Emp.: 80
Defense Industry Association
N.A.I.C.S.: 813910
Peter Steffes *(VP-Govt Policy)*
Rene Carbone Bardorf *(Chief Comm Officer)*
Craig McKinley *(Pres & CEO)*
Arnold Punaro *(Chm)*
Ashley Bunce *(Exec Dir-Women In Defense)*
Wes Hallman *(Sr VP-Policy)*
Michael Bayer *(Vice Chm)*

NATIONAL DELIVERY SYSTEMS
8700 Robert Fulton Dr Ste 600, Columbia, MD 21046-2660
Tel.: (410) 312-4770
Web Site: http://www.national-delivery.com
Year Founded: 2007
Sales Range: $10-24.9 Million
Emp.: 10
General Freight Trucking Services
N.A.I.C.S.: 484110
Ken Buck *(Pres)*

NATIONAL DESIGN & TRADE NETWORK
522 S 400 W, Salt Lake City, UT 84101
Tel.: (801) 531-7538
Web Site: http://www.interiorsolutions.net
Rev.: $12,400,000
Emp.: 85
Office Furniture
N.A.I.C.S.: 541410
Peter Harris *(Owner & Pres)*
Larry Bonner *(Co-Owner & Controller)*

NATIONAL DEVELOPMENT
2310 Washington St, Newton Lower Falls, MA 02462
Tel.: (617) 527-9800
Web Site: http://www.natdev.com
Sales Range: $10-24.9 Million
Emp.: 80
Provider of Land Development Services
N.A.I.C.S.: 237210
Theodore R. Tye *(Mng Partner)*
Diane Breed *(VP-HR)*
Thomas M. Alperin *(Pres)*
Richard Schwartz *(Gen Counsel & Sr VP)*
Andrew Gallinaro *(Partner & Dir-Asset Mgmt)*
Stephen A. Kinsella *(Partner & CFO)*
David Bracken *(Sr VP)*
Tony Salvucci *(Sr VP-Construction)*
Douglas Straus *(Sr VP & Dir-Residential Dev)*
John J. O'Neil III *(Mng Partner)*
Edward L. Marsteiner II *(Partner & Dir-Acquisitions)*

Subsidiaries:

Cranshaw Construction (1)
2310 Washington St, Newton, MA 02462
Tel.: (617) 964-1533
Web Site: http://www.cranshaw.com
Industrial Buildings & Warehouses
N.A.I.C.S.: 236220
Tony Salvucci *(Sr VP-Pre Construction & Estimating)*
Steve Kinsella *(CFO)*
Robert Lyons *(Pres)*
Karen Hardy *(Comp-Mktg)*
Christine Georgoudis *(VP-Acctg)*
Frank Lucey *(VP-Field Ops)*
Kathy McMahon *(VP-Mktg & Comm)*

NATIONAL DEVELOPMENT & RESEARCH INSTITUTES, INC.
71 W 23rd St 4th Fl, New York, NY 10010
Tel.: (212) 845-4400 NY
Web Site: http://www.ndri.org
Year Founded: 1961
Sales Range: $10-24.9 Million
Emp.: 100
Biomedical Research & Development Services
N.A.I.C.S.: 541715
Harlan Matusow *(Project Dir)*

NATIONAL DISTRIBUTION CENTERS
1515 BurntMill Rd, Cherry Hill, NJ 08003
Tel.: (856) 691-7000
Web Site: http://www.nfi.com
Sales Range: $250-299.9 Million
Emp.: 6,000
Warehousing, Self Storage
N.A.I.C.S.: 531130
Sidney R. Brown *(Owner)*
Jeff Brown *(Pres)*
Dawn Kreiner *(Dir-Customer Svs)*

NATIONAL DISTRIBUTORS INC.
1517 Avco Blvd, Sellersburg, IN 47172
Tel.: (812) 246-6306
Rev.: $39,825,328
Emp.: 140
Trucking Except Local
N.A.I.C.S.: 484121
Jeff Kaps *(VP-Safety & HR)*
Eric Vaughn *(Owner & COO)*

NATIONAL DIVERSIFIED SALES INC.
851 N Harvard Ave, Lindsay, CA 93247-1714
Tel.: (559) 562-9888 CA
Web Site: http://www.ndspro.com
Year Founded: 1977
Sales Range: $25-49.9 Million
Emp.: 200
Provider of Plastic Products
N.A.I.C.S.: 326199
Mike Gummeson *(Pres & CEO)*

NATIONAL DME, L.C.

7757 Allen St, Midvale, UT 84047-7227
Tel.: (801) 262-3236
Web Site: http://www.nationaldme.net
Year Founded: 1998
Sales Range: $10-24.9 Million
Emp.: 200
Miscellaneous Product Whslr
N.A.I.C.S.: 456120
Joseph Cottis (*Principal*)

NATIONAL ELECTRIC COIL
800 King Ave, Columbus, OH 43212-2644
Tel.: (614) 488-1151   OH
Web Site: http://www.national-electric-coil.com
Year Founded: 1934
Sales Range: $150-199.9 Million
Emp.: 900
Repair of Large Electrical Rotating Equipment
N.A.I.C.S.: 334416
Robert Barton (*Pres & CEO*)
Thomas Steuber (*CFO*)
Stephen Jeney (*VP-Sls & Mktg*)

NATIONAL ELECTRICAL MANUFACTURERS ASSOCIATION
1300 N 17th St Ste 900, Arlington, VA 22209-3801
Tel.: (703) 841-3200   DE
Web Site: http://www.nema.org
Year Founded: 1926
Sales Range: $10-24.9 Million
Emp.: 100
Trade Association; Standards, Statistics, Government Affairs
N.A.I.C.S.: 813910
Patrick Hughes (*Mgr-Govt*)
Kyle Pitsor (*VP*)
Ken Ayres (*Mgr*)
Lucius Kahng (*Mgr-Info Sys*)
Rich Stinson (*Chm*)
John Caskey (*VP-Ops*)
Andy Dhokai (*Dir-Federal Rels*)
Steve Wilcox (*Dir-Market Res*)
Megan Hayes (*Dir-Regulatory & Standards Strategy*)
Laurie Miller (*Dir-Statistical Ops*)
Clark Silcox (*Gen Counsel*)
Philip Squair (*VP-Govt Rels*)
Brett Brenner (*Pres-ESFI*)
Debra Phillips (*Pres & CEO*)

Subsidiaries:

National Electrical Manufacturers Association - Medical Imaging and Technology Alliance Division   (1)
1300 N 17th St Ste 900, Arlington, VA 22209
Tel.: (703) 841-3200
Web Site: http://www.medicalimaging.org
Medical Imaging Equipment Mfr
N.A.I.C.S.: 334510
Stephen Vastagh (*Sec-DICOM*)
Andy Dhokai (*Dir-Federal Rels*)
Cheryl Kreider Carey (*Dir-Ops & Admin*)
Cassandra Ricci (*Mgr-Govt Rels*)
Luiza Kowalczyk (*Mgr-DICOM Ops*)
Megan Hayes (*Dir-Regularity & Standards Strategy*)
Patrick Hope (*Exec Dir*)
Peter Weems (*Dir-Policy & Strategy*)

NATIONAL ELECTRONIC ALLOYS
3 Fir Ct, Oakland, NJ 07436
Tel.: (201) 337-9400
Web Site: http://www.nealloys.com
Rev.: $20,000,000
Emp.: 21
Metals Service Centers & Offices
N.A.I.C.S.: 423510
Richard Geoffrion (*Pres*)

NATIONAL ELECTROSTATICS CORPORATION
7540 Graber Rd, Middleton, WI 53562
Tel.: (608) 831-7600
Web Site: http://www.pelletron.com
Sales Range: $50-74.9 Million
Emp.: 104
Miscellaneous Electrical Equipment & Component Mfr
N.A.I.C.S.: 335999
Robert Daniel (*COO & Exec VP*)
George Klody (*VP*)
Greg Norton (*VP-Mktg*)
James B. Schroeder (*Sr VP*)
James A. Ferry (*Pres & CEO*)
Mark Sundquist (*Sr VP*)

NATIONAL ENERGY & LIGHT, LLC
14 Celina Ave Ste 9, Nashua, NH 03063
Tel.: (603) 821-9954
Web Site: http://www.nelcompany.com
Year Founded: 2013
Sales Range: $25-49.9 Million
Emp.: 37
Lighting Product & Equipment Mfr
N.A.I.C.S.: 335139
Jim Schmidt (*Pres*)

NATIONAL ENERGY SERVICES, INC.
8965 S Eastern Ave Ste 120E, Las Vegas, NV 89123
Tel.: (877) 871-6400   NV
Web Site: http://www.nationalenergysvcs.com
Year Founded: 1997
Sales Range: $10-24.9 Million
Emp.: 3
Holding Company; Specialized Automation Control Systems & Machinery
N.A.I.C.S.: 551112
Robert W. Chance (*Pres & CEO*)
Jeremy Wayne Briggs (*CFO, Chief Acctg Officer & VP*)

Subsidiaries:

JD Field Services, Inc.   (1)
2080 S 1500 E, Vernal, UT 84078
Tel.: (435) 781-1242
Web Site: http://www.jdfieldservices.com
Sales Range: $10-24.9 Million
Oilfield Equipment Services
N.A.I.C.S.: 213112
Susan Holmes (*Dir-HR & Safety*)

NATIONAL ENTERTAINMENT COLLECTIBLES ASSOCIATION, INC
603 Sweetland Ave, Hillside, NJ 07205
Tel.: (908) 686-3300
Web Site: http://www.necaonline.com
Toy Mfr & Distr
N.A.I.C.S.: 339930
Joel Weinshanker (*COO*)

Subsidiaries:

Kidrobot Inc.   (1)
1420 Pearl St Ste 200, Boulder, CO 80302
Tel.: (303) 217-9400
Web Site: http://www.kidrobot.com
Emp.: 200
Limited Edition Toy Mfr
N.A.I.C.S.: 339930
Bob Africa (*Pres*)
Frank Kozik (*Creative Dir*)

NATIONAL ENTERTAINMENT NETWORK, INC.
325 Interlocken Pkwy B, Broomfield, CO 80021
Tel.: (866) 902-0595
Web Site: http://www.nen-inc.com

Vending Machine Operators
N.A.I.C.S.: 445132
Jim Sevalt (*Pres*)
Randy Chilton (*CMO*)
Nicholas Miceli (*Dir-Fin & Bus Intelegence*)
Heather DeLuca (*VP-Sls*)
Jennifer McNeill (*Sr Dir-Product & Mktg*)
Meredith Clinton (*VP-Sls*)
Brad Garrison (*Sr Dir-Natl Accts*)
Wallis Finger (*Gen Counsel*)

NATIONAL ENZYME COMPANY
15366 US Hwy 160, Forsyth, MO 65653
Tel.: (417) 546-4796
Web Site: http://www.nationalenzyme.com
Year Founded: 1932
Sales Range: $10-24.9 Million
Emp.: 110
Mfr of Food Enzyme Products
N.A.I.C.S.: 325199
Anthony Collier (*Owner*)
Jennifer Wilson (*Dir-Sls*)
Charlie Amidon (*COO*)
Naeem Shaikh (*VP-Res & Innovation*)
David Lermy (*Dir-Gift of Hope*)
Jim Astemborski (*Dir-Ops*)
Nick Bruns (*Pres & CEO*)

NATIONAL EQUIPMENT CORP.
801 E 141st St, Bronx, NY 10454
Tel.: (718) 585-0200
Web Site: http://www.unionmachinery.com
Sales Range: $10-24.9 Million
Emp.: 80
Food Products Machinery
N.A.I.C.S.: 333241
Arthur Greenberg (*Exec VP*)
John S. Greenberg (*VP & Gen Mgr*)

NATIONAL EQUITY TITLE AGENCY
75 Lemont Rd Ste 305, Woodridge, IL 60517
Tel.: (312) 782-4290   IL
Web Site: http://www.netcotitle.com
Year Founded: 1980
Sales Range: $25-49.9 Million
Emp.: 5
Providers of Real Estate Title Insurance
N.A.I.C.S.: 524127
John Baumgart (*Pres & CEO*)

NATIONAL EWP, INC.
630 Lincoln Ave, Woodland, CA 95695
Tel.: (530) 668-4080
Sales Range: $25-49.9 Million
Emp.: 100
Metal Mining Services
N.A.I.C.S.: 238910
Jeffrey Morgan (*Owner & CEO*)

NATIONAL EXPERT WITNESS NETWORK
3960 Howard Hughes Pkwy Ste 500, Las Vegas, NV 89169
Tel.: (530) 872-8100
Web Site: http://www.newnexperts.com
Year Founded: 2002
Sales Range: $1-9.9 Million
Emp.: 7
Business Products & Services
N.A.I.C.S.: 561499
David McDonald (*Pres & CEO*)
Justin Gabb (*Mgr-Case*)
Paul Bissett (*Mgr-Case*)

NATIONAL FAMILY CARE LIFE INSURANCE
13530 Inwood Rd, Dallas, TX 75244
Tel.: (972) 387-8553
Sales Range: $10-24.9 Million
Emp.: 20
Accident Insurance Carriers
N.A.I.C.S.: 524113
Sandra Lee Erwin (*Chm*)
Clyde Pullis (*Pres*)

NATIONAL FEDERATION OF INDEPENDENT BUSINESS
53 Century Blvd Ste 250, Nashville, TN 37214-4618
Tel.: (615) 872-5800   TN
Web Site: http://www.nfib.com
Year Founded: 1943
Sales Range: $25-49.9 Million
Emp.: 800
Small Business Association
N.A.I.C.S.: 813910
Todd Pack (*Sr Mgr-Media*)
Juanita Duggan (*Pres & CEO*)
Shawn Lewis (*Dir-State Comm*)
Gordon Denlinger (*Dir-Pennsylvania*)
Thor Stacey (*Dir-Alaska*)

NATIONAL FEDERATION OF THE BLIND
200 E Wells St at Jernigan Pl, Baltimore, MD 21230
Tel.: (410) 659-9314   DC
Web Site: http://www.nfb.org
Year Founded: 1949
Sales Range: $1-9.9 Million
Emp.: 83
Disability Assistance Services
N.A.I.C.S.: 624120
John Berggren (*Exec Dir-Ops*)
Mark Riccobono (*Pres*)
Pam Allen (*Chm & First VP*)
Ron Brown (*Second VP*)
James Gashel (*Sec*)
Jeannie Massay (*Treas*)
Anil Lewis (*Exec Dir*)

NATIONAL FFA FOUNDATION
6060 FFA Dr, Indianapolis, IN 46278
Web Site: https://www.ffa.org
Year Founded: 1928
Educational Support Services
N.A.I.C.S.: 611710

NATIONAL FIBER SUPPLY LLC
303 W Madison St Ste 1650, Chicago, IL 60606-3328
Tel.: (312) 346-4800   IL
Web Site: http://www.natfbr.com
Year Founded: 1977
Sales Range: $10-24.9 Million
Emp.: 27
Supplier of Fiber for Paper
N.A.I.C.S.: 423930
Kathy Launski (*Mgr-HR*)

NATIONAL FIBER, INC.
50 Depot St, Belchertown, MA 01007-9619
Tel.: (413) 283-2462
Web Site: http://www.nationalfiber.com
Emp.: 35
Cellulose Products Mfr
N.A.I.C.S.: 238310
Chris Hoch (*Owner & Pres*)

NATIONAL FIRE PROTECTION ASSOCIATION
1 Batterymarch Pk, Quincy, MA 02169-7454
Tel.: (617) 770-3000   MA
Web Site: https://www.nfpa.org
Year Founded: 1896
Emp.: 300

NATIONAL FIRE PROTECTION ASSOCIATION

National Fire Protection Association—(Continued)
Standards Development, Publishing & Educational Organization; Fire Prevention & Safety Program
N.A.I.C.S.: 813920
Bruce H. Mullen (CFO & Sr VP)
Jim Pauley (Pres & CEO)
Thomas A. Lawson (Treas)
Russell B. Leavitt (Vice Chm)

NATIONAL FIRE PROTECTION INC.
515 Dover Rd Ste 2600, Rockville, MD 20850
Tel.: (301) 340-6500
Web Site: http://www.natlfire.com
Sales Range: $10-24.9 Million
Emp.: 130
Provider of Sprinkler Contracting Services
N.A.I.C.S.: 238220
George Buell (Pres)

NATIONAL FISHERIES INSTITUTE INC.
7918 Jones Branch Dr Ste 700, McLean, VA 22102
Tel.: (703) 752-8880
Web Site: http://www.aboutseafood.com
Sales Range: Less than $1 Million
Emp.: 12
Advocacy Organization for the Seafood Industry
N.A.I.C.S.: 813319
Kayla Bennett (Comm Mgr)
Lisa Wallenda Picard (Pres & CEO)

NATIONAL FLEET MANAGEMENT, INC.
1061 Boulder Rd, Greensboro, NC 27409
Web Site: http://www.nationalfleetmgt.com
Year Founded: 2008
Sales Range: $1-9.9 Million
Emp.: 200
Fleet Management Services
N.A.I.C.S.: 484121
Larry Newsome (Gen Mgr)

NATIONAL FLORAL SUPPLY OF MARYLAND
3825 Leonard Town Rd Ste 4, Waldorf, MD 20602
Tel.: (301) 932-7600
Web Site: http://www.flowersonbase.com
Sales Range: $10-24.9 Million
Emp.: 8
Florists
N.A.I.C.S.: 459310
Katherine O'Bryan (Treas & Sec)
Rose Ouellett (Gen Mgr)

NATIONAL FOOD GROUP
46820 Magellan Dr Ste A, Novi, MI 48377
Web Site: http://www.nationalfoodgroup.com
Year Founded: 1990
Sales Range: $25-49.9 Million
Emp.: 50
Wholesale Distributor of Food Products
N.A.I.C.S.: 424490
Scott Kamen (CFO)
Bud Zecman (Founder)
Sean Zecman (Pres & CEO)

NATIONAL FOOD STORES, INC.
76 National Rd, Edison, NJ 08817-2809
Tel.: (732) 287-2800   NJ
Year Founded: 1909
Rev.: $110,000,000
Emp.: 35
Convenience Stores Owner & Operator
N.A.I.C.S.: 445131
Harry Shah (Pres)
Rosemarie Shah (VP)

NATIONAL FOOTBALL LEAGUE
345 Park Ave, New York, NY 10154
Tel.: (212) 450-2000   NY
Web Site: http://www.nfl.com
Year Founded: 1920
Sales Range: $1-4.9 Billion
Emp.: 450
Professional Football Organization
N.A.I.C.S.: 813990
Roger Goodell (Commissioner)
Ron Hill (Asst Dir-Football Ops)
Peter O'Reilly (Sr VP-Events)
Eric P. Grubman (Exec VP)
Alberto Riveron (Sr VP-Officiating)
Matt Birk (Dir-Football Dev)
Anna Isaacson (Sr VP-Social Responsibility)
Cathy Lanier (Head-Security)
Paul D. Ballew (Chief Data & Analytics Officer)
Michelle Micone (Sr VP-Consumer Products)
Jonathan Nabavi (VP-Pub Policy & Govt Affairs)
Woody Johnson (Owner)
Dasha Smith (Chief Admin Officer, Chief People Officer & Exec VP)
Marissa M. Solis (Sr VP-Global Brand & Consumer Mktg)

Subsidiaries:

NFL Films, Inc.   (1)
1 NFL Plz, Mount Laurel, NJ 08054-1201
Tel.: (856) 222-3500
Web Site: http://www.nflfilms.com
Sales Range: $25-49.9 Million
Emp.: 262
Mfr, Promote & Distribute Films about the National Football League
N.A.I.C.S.: 512110

NFL Management Council   (1)
345 Park Ave, New York, NY 10154
Tel.: (212) 450-2000
Web Site: http://www.nfl.com
Sales Range: $10-24.9 Million
Emp.: 305
N.A.I.C.S.: 711211
Chris Cooper (Mgr-Labor Ops)

NFL Ventures, Inc.   (1)
345 Park Ave, New York, NY 10154
Tel.: (212) 450-2000
Sport Event Organizer
N.A.I.C.S.: 711310

NATIONAL FOOTBALL LEAGUE PLAYERS ASSOCIATION
1133 20th St NW, Washington, DC 20036
Tel.: (202) 463-2200   DC
Web Site: http://www.nflpa.com
Year Founded: 1956
Sales Range: $75-99.9 Million
Emp.: 150
Professional Football Players' Business Association & Labor Union
N.A.I.C.S.: 813910
Carl Francis (Dir-Comm)
Richard Berthelsen (Gen Counsel)
Dana Hammonds Shuler (Sr Dir-Player Affairs)
Charles Ross (Dir-Fin & Asset Mgmt)
Erin Douglas (Controller)
Miki Yaras-Davis (Sr Dir-Benefits)
Adora Williams (Sr Mgr-Benefits)
Bethany Marshall (Dir-Benefits)
Mark Levin (Dir-Salary Cap & Agent Admin)
Athelia Doggette (Asst Dir-Salary Cap & Agent Admin)
Doug Finniff (Sr Mgr-Salary Cap & Agent Admin)
Richard Persons (Dir-Info Sys)
John Persons (Mgr-Info Sys)
Thomas DePaso (Gen Counsel)
Ira Fishman (Mng Dir)
Iva Lamanna (Asst Controller)
Andre Collins (Exec Dir-Former Player Svcs)
Tyrone Allen (Dir-Professional Athletes Foundation)
Heather McPhee (Assoc Gen Counsel)
Timothy Christine (Dir-Security)
Kerry Cosover (Sr Mgr-Travel & Events)
Doug Whaley (Dir-College Scouting)
J. C. Tretter (Pres)

Subsidiaries:

National Football League Players Incorporated   (1)
1133 20th St NW, Washington, DC 20036   (100%)
Tel.: (202) 463-2200
Web Site: http://www.nflplayers.com
Sales Range: $10-24.9 Million
Emp.: 100
Professional Football Player Licensing & Marketing Services
N.A.I.C.S.: 533110
DeMaurice Smith (Exec Dir)
George Hegamin (Dir-Scholastic Outreach)
Gina Scott (VP-Partner Svcs)

NATIONAL FOOTBALL MUSEUM, INC.
2121 George Halas Dr NW, Canton, OH 44708-2630
Tel.: (330) 456-8207
Web Site: http://www.profootballhof.com
Year Founded: 1963
Sales Range: $1-9.9 Million
Emp.: 90
Professional Sports Museum
N.A.I.C.S.: 712110
Joe Horrigan (Exec Dir)
Pete Fierle (VP-Comm)
Kevin Shiplett (VP-Ops & Facilities)
Dennis Nash (Vice Chm)
Joseph Halter (Sec)
Roger A. Bettis (Treas)
Steve Strawbridge (Chief Admin Officer)
Michael Munoz (VP-Character Dev)
Anne Graffice (VP-Dev & Strategic Adventures)
Brock Richards (VP-Sls & Mktg)

NATIONAL FORENSIC SCIENCE TECHNOLOGY CENTER, INC.
8285 Bryan Dairy Rd Ste 125, Largo, FL 33777
Tel.: (727) 395-2511   FL
Web Site: http://www.nfstc.org
Year Founded: 1995
Sales Range: $10-24.9 Million
Testing Laboratory & Forensic Services
N.A.I.C.S.: 541380
Kevin Lothridge (CEO)
Mitchell R. Morrissey (Pres)
James J. Cali (Treas)
Dave Sylvester (Chief Projects Officer)
Liz Yourkievitz (Dir-HR Svcs)
David Touchton (Officer-Facility Security)
Dennis Thureson (Dir-Fin)
Chris Vivian (Dir-Comm)
Becky Carter (Dir-Art)
Veronica Bowles (Mgr-Project Svcs)

U.S. PRIVATE

NATIONAL FOREST FOUNDATION
Bldg 27 Ste 3 Fort Missoula Rd, Missoula, MT 59804
Tel.: (406) 542-2805   DC
Web Site: http://www.nationalforests.org
Year Founded: 1993
Sales Range: $10-24.9 Million
Emp.: 43
Environmental Conservation Services
N.A.I.C.S.: 813312
Karen DiBari (Dir-Conservation Connect)
Ray A. Foote (Exec VP-Dev & Comm)
Sheree Bombard (Dir-Admin)
Mary Mitsos (Pres & CEO)
Lee Fromson (Treas)
Timothy Proctor Schieffelin (Sec)
Robin Hill (Controller)
Adam Liljeblad (Dir-Conservation Awards)
Luba Mullen (Assoc Dir-Dev)
Marcus Selig (VP-Field Programs)
Wes Swaffar (Dir-Ecosystem Svcs)
Deborah Snyder (Mgr-Dev Svcs)
Emily Struss (Coord-Event)
Lee Quick (Accountant)
Marlee Ostheimer (Coord-Philanthropy & Partnerships)
Zia Maumenee (Officer-Conservation Programs)
Craig R. Barrett (Chm)

NATIONAL FOUNDATION FOR CANCER RESEARCH
4600 EW Hwy Ste 525, Bethesda, MD 20814
Tel.: (301) 654-1250   MA
Web Site: http://www.nfcr.org
Year Founded: 1973
Sales Range: $10-24.9 Million
Emp.: 27
Disease Research Fundraising Services
N.A.I.C.S.: 813212
Franklin C. Salisbury Jr. (Pres)
Michael Wang (Chief Strategy Officer)
David Bjork (VP-Dev)
Kwok Leung (CFO & Sec)
Sujuan Ba (Pres & COO)
Padmakumar Kaimal (VP-Tech Alliance & Bus Dev)
Brian R. Leyland-Jones (VP-Molecular & Experimental Medicine)
Peter Vogt (Chief Science Officer & Exec VP)

NATIONAL FOUNDATION FOR CREDIT COUNSELING
2000 M St NW, Washington, DC 20036-3307
Tel.: (202) 677-4300
Web Site: http://www.nfcc.org
Year Founded: 1951
Sales Range: $10-24.9 Million
Emp.: 15
Nonprofit Credit Counseling Services
N.A.I.C.S.: 813910
Paul Weiss (CFO & Chief of Staff)
William Binzel (Sr VP)
Jeff Faulkner (Acting Pres & Acting CEO)
Nelson A. Diaz (Chm)

NATIONAL FROZEN FOODS CORPORATION
1600 Fairview Ave E, Seattle, WA 98102-3749
Tel.: (206) 322-8900   WA
Web Site: http://www.nationalfrozenfoods.com
Year Founded: 1912
Sales Range: $200-249.9 Million

Emp.: 800
Processor of Frozen Vegetables
N.A.I.C.S.: 311411
R.H. Grader *(Pres)*
Mark von Hagel *(Treas & VP-Fin)*

Subsidiaries:

National Frozen Foods Corporation - Albany (1)
745 30th Ave SW, Albany, OR 97322-3543 **(100%)**
Tel.: (541) 928-3306
Web Site:
http://www.nationalfrozenfoods.com
Sales Range: $50-74.9 Million
Emp.: 250
Mfr of Frozen Foods
N.A.I.C.S.: 311411
Armando Nunez *(Gen Mgr)*

National Frozen Foods Corporation - Chehalis (1)
PO Box 479, Chehalis, WA 98532-0479
Tel.: (360) 748-4403
Web Site:
http://www.nationalfrozenfoods.com
Sales Range: $25-49.9 Million
Emp.: 150
Seller of Frozen Foods
N.A.I.C.S.: 311411
Dick Grader *(Pres)*

National Frozen Foods Corporation - Moses Lake (1)
14406 Rd 3 NE, Moses Lake, WA 98837
Tel.: (509) 766-0793
Web Site:
http://www.nationalfrozenfoods.com
Sales Range: $25-49.9 Million
Emp.: 200
Frozen Food Mfr
N.A.I.C.S.: 311411
Gary Ash *(Gen Mgr)*

National Frozen Foods Corporation - Quincy Division (1)
10504 Hwy 28 W, Quincy, WA 98848
Tel.: (509) 787-1585
Frozen Food Mfr
N.A.I.C.S.: 311412

NATIONAL FRUIT PRODUCT COMPANY, INC.
701 Fairmont Ave, Winchester, VA 22601-4987
Tel.: (540) 665-4677 VA
Web Site:
http://www.whitehousefoods.com
Year Founded: 1908
Apple Related Products Distr
N.A.I.C.S.: 311421

Subsidiaries:

National Fruit Product Company, Inc. - Brand Retail Division (1)
701 Fairmont Ave, Winchester, VA 22601
Tel.: (540) 432-0408
Fruit & Vegetable Whslr
N.A.I.C.S.: 424480

National Fruit Product Company, Inc. - Food Services Division (1)
701 Fairmont Ave, Winchester, VA 22601
Tel.: (540) 662-3401
Fruit & Vegetable Whslr
N.A.I.C.S.: 424480

National Fruit Product Company, Inc. - Private Label Retail Division (1)
701 Fairmont Ave, Winchester, VA 22601
Tel.: (540) 974-6869
Fruit & Vegetable Whslr
N.A.I.C.S.: 424480

NATIONAL FUEL OIL INC.
175 Orange St, Newark, NJ 07103
Tel.: (973) 621-8866
Web Site:
http://www.nationalfueloil.com
Sales Range: $10-24.9 Million
Emp.: 22
Fuel Oil Dealers
N.A.I.C.S.: 457210

Robert Ayars *(Pres)*

NATIONAL FUNDING INC.
9530 Towne Ctr Dr, San Diego, CA 92121
Web Site:
http://www.nationalfunding.com
Year Founded: 1999
Sales Range: $10-24.9 Million
Emp.: 85
Financing Services to Small Businesses
N.A.I.C.S.: 525990
Dave Gilbert *(Founder & CEO)*
Justin Thompson *(Chief Revenue Officer)*
Rob Rosenblatt *(Pres-Business Loan Center)*
Joseph Gaudio *(Pres)*

Subsidiaries:

Quick Bridge Funding, LLC (1)
410 Exchange Ste 150, Irvine, CA 92602
Tel.: (888) 233-9085
Web Site:
http://www.quickbridgefunding.com
Small Business Lending Services
N.A.I.C.S.: 522291

NATIONAL GARDEN WHOLESALE
5408 NE 88th St Bldg A, Vancouver, WA 98665
Tel.: (360) 883-8846
Web Site:
http://www.sunlightsupply.com
Rev.: $59,500,000
Emp.: 150
Horticultural Lighting Fixture Mfr
N.A.I.C.S.: 423610
Craig Ryan Hargreaves *(Pres)*

NATIONAL GEOGRAPHIC SOCIETY
1145 17th St NW, Washington, DC 20036-4701
Tel.: (202) 857-7000 DC
Web Site:
http://www.nationalgeographic.com
Year Founded: 1888
Sales Range: $400-449.9 Million
Emp.: 1,300
Social Awareness & Media Organization; Book, Magazine & Video Publisher, Distr & Online Retailer
N.A.I.C.S.: 813410
Terry Adamson *(Exec VP-NGS)*
Terry D. Garcia *(Exec VP-Mission Programs)*
Elizabeth J. Hudson *(Exec VP)*
Bryan Kinkade *(Mgr-Travel)*
Charlie Attenborough *(Mng Dir-Intl)*
Declan Moore *(Chief Media Officer)*
Brooke Runnette *(Chief Program & Impact Officer & Exec VP)*
Mike Ulica *(CFO, COO & Exec VP)*
Leora Hanser *(Sr VP-Partnerships)*
Tara Bunch *(Chief Admin Officer)*
Tracy R. Wolstencroft *(Pres & CEO)*
Mara Dell *(Chief HR Officer)*
Whitney Johnson *(VP & Dir-Visual & Immersive Experiences)*
Crystal Brown *(Chief Comm Officer)*

Subsidiaries:

NGHT, LLC (1)
1145 17th St NW, Washington, DC 20036
Tel.: (202) 857-7708
Web Site:
http://www.nationalgeographic.com
National Geographic Digital Media Services
N.A.I.C.S.: 516120
Gary Knell *(CEO)*

National Geographic Books Group (1)
1145 17th St NW, Washington, DC 20036-4701

Tel.: (202) 857-7000
Web Site:
http://www.nationalgeographic.com
Book Publishing
N.A.I.C.S.: 513130
Nina D. Hoffman *(Pres)*
Holly Saunders *(Mgr-Mktg)*
Melina Gerosa Bellows *(Chief Education Officer)*
Hector Sierra *(Sr VP & Gen Mgr)*
Janet Goldstein *(Sr VP & Dir-Editorial)*
Nancy Feresten *(Sr VP-Education & Children's Media)*
Jennifer Emmett *(VP-Content, Education & Children's Media)*

National Geographic Magazine Group (1)
1145 17th St NW, Washington, DC 20036-4688
Tel.: (202) 857-7000
Web Site:
http://www.nationalgeographic.com
Sales Range: $125-149.9 Million
Emp.: 1,000
Periodical Publishers
N.A.I.C.S.: 513120
Nathan Lump *(Editor-in-Chief)*
David Miller *(Exec VP & Gen Mgr)*

NATIONAL GRAPE CO-OP ASSOCIATION, INC.
2 S Portage St, Westfield, NY 14787-1400
Tel.: (716) 326-5200 NY
Web Site:
http://www.nationalgrape.com
Year Founded: 1945
Sales Range: $75-99.9 Million
Emp.: 20
Cooperative Marketing of Grape Products
N.A.I.C.S.: 311421
Joseph C. Falcone *(Pres)*
Brent Roggie *(COO & Gen Mgr)*

Subsidiaries:

Welch Foods Inc. (1)
3 Concord Farms 575 Virginia Rd, Concord, MA 01742-9101 **(100%)**
Tel.: (978) 371-1000
Web Site: http://www.welchs.com
Sales Range: $100-124.9 Million
Grape, Cranberry & Tomato Juices; Concentrates; Light Juice Cocktails; Grape Jelly & Jam; Squeezable Jelly, Jam & Preserves; Fruit Spreads Mfr
N.A.I.C.S.: 311421
Thomas Wilkinson *(Chm)*
David Eisen *(CMO)*

Division (Domestic):

Welch's International (2)
300 Baker Ave Ste 101, Concord, MA 01742 **(100%)**
Tel.: (978) 371-1000
Web Site: http://www.welchs.com
Sales Range: $50-74.9 Million
Retailer & Marketer of Frozen Fruit Juices & Vegetables
N.A.I.C.S.: 311421
Dennis Rak *(Chm)*
Christine Kinahan *(Chief People Officer)*
TJ Gordon *(CFO)*
Trevor Bynum *(Pres & CEO)*

NATIONAL GUARDIAN LIFE INSURANCE COMPANY
2 E Gilman St, Madison, WI 53703-1479
Tel.: (608) 257-5611 WI
Web Site: http://www.nglic.com
Year Founded: 1909
Sales Range: $200-249.9 Million
Emp.: 240
Provider of Life Insurance & Retirement Annuities
N.A.I.C.S.: 524113
John D. Larson *(Pres & CEO)*
Walter R. Lethem *(Asst VP & Dir-Info Tech)*
Mark L. Solverud *(VP)*
Dave Anderson *(COO & Exec VP)*

Subsidiaries:

NGL Holdings Inc. (1)
2 E Gilman St, Madison, WI 53703-1479 **(100%)**
Tel.: (608) 257-5611
Web Site: http://www.nglic.com
Sales Range: $300-349.9 Million
Emp.: 170
Holding Company
N.A.I.C.S.: 524113
Sherri A. Kliczak *(Sec & VP)*
Katherine A. Johnson *(VP & Dir-HR)*
Mark Solverud *(CEO)*

Subsidiary (Domestic):

NGL American Life (2)
2 E Gilman St, Madison, WI 53703 **(100%)**
Tel.: (608) 257-5611
Web Site: http://www.nglic.com
Sales Range: $50-74.9 Million
Life Insurance
N.A.I.C.S.: 524113
John D. Larson *(Co-Chm, Pres & CEO)*
Mark L. Solverud *(COO & Exec VP)*
Brian Hogan *(CFO & VP)*

NGL Investment Services Inc. (2)
2 E Gilman St, Madison, WI 53703-1479 **(100%)**
Tel.: (608) 257-5611
Web Site: http://www.nglic.com
Sales Range: $100-124.9 Million
Investment Management Service
N.A.I.C.S.: 524113
John D. Larson *(Chm, Pres & CEO)*

Preneed Reinsurance Company of America (1)
2 E Gilman St, Madison, WI 53701
Tel.: (608) 257-5611
Insurance
N.A.I.C.S.: 524210

Settlers Life Insurance Company (1)
1969 Lee Hwy, Bristol, VA 24201-1636 **(100%)**
Tel.: (276) 645-4300
Web Site: http://www.settlerslife.com
Sales Range: $50-74.9 Million
Emp.: 67
Life Insurance
N.A.I.C.S.: 524113
John D. Larson *(CEO)*
Mark L. Solverud *(Chief Actuary & VP)*
Charles L. Carty *(VP-Info Tech)*
Joyce Geiger *(Sec & VP-HR)*
Michael Lowe *(Pres)*
Eddie Grills *(Reg Dir-Mktg)*
Amy Smith *(Dir-Mktg)*
Josh Dixon *(Dir-Telesales Ops)*
Steve Bontell *(CMO)*
Evan Monahan *(Mgr-Agent Performance)*
Shawn Rose *(VP-Ops)*

NATIONAL HANOVER PRESS LTD
30-02 48th Ave, Long Island City, NY 11101
Tel.: (212) 924-1763
Web Site:
http://www.nationalhanover.com
Sales Range: $25-49.9 Million
Emp.: 30
Commercial Printing, Lithographic
N.A.I.C.S.: 323111
William Canfield *(Pres)*

NATIONAL HEALTH CORPORATION
1901 N State Hwy 360, Grand Prairie, TX 75050
Tel.: (817) 640-1900
Rev.: $169,164,000
Emp.: 315
Accident & Health Insurance Carriers
N.A.I.C.S.: 524114

Subsidiaries:

Capitol Life Insurance Company (1)
1658 Cole Blvd Ste 208, Golden, CO 80401
Tel.: (303) 237-9303

NATIONAL HEALTH CORPORATION

U.S. PRIVATE

National Health Corporation—(Continued)
Sales Range: $25-49.9 Million
Emp.: 2
Life Insurance
N.A.I.C.S.: 524113

National Health Insurance Co (1)
1901 N State Hwy 360, Grand Prairie, TX 75050
Tel.: (817) 640-1900
Rev.: $18,474,566
Emp.: 250
Accident & Health Insurance Carriers
N.A.I.C.S.: 524114

US Health Advisors Inc (1)
1901 N Hwy 360, Grand Prairie, TX 75050
Tel.: (888) 551-5571
Web Site: http://www.nhccare.com
Rev.: $4,509,727
Emp.: 1
Marketing Services
N.A.I.C.S.: 541613

NATIONAL HEALTH PARTNERS, INC.
120 Gibraltar Rd Ste 107, Horsham, PA 19044
Tel.: (215) 682-7114 IN
Web Site: http://www.carexpresshealth.com
Year Founded: 1989
Sales Range: $1-9.9 Million
Emp.: 8
Healthcare Membership Organization
N.A.I.C.S.: 524114
Patricia S. Bathurst (VP-Mktg)

NATIONAL HEALTHCARE DISTRIBUTION, INC.
8251 Mayfield Rd Ste 101, Chesterland, OH 44026
Tel.: (216) 292-6029
Web Site: http://www.nhd.net
Year Founded: 1994
Sales Range: $75-99.9 Million
Emp.: 925
Holding Company; Imaging Equipment Distr
N.A.I.C.S.: 551112
George Walker (Chm)

Subsidiaries:

CMX Medical Imaging (1)
6601 S Glacier St, Tukwila, WA 98188
Tel.: (425) 656-1269
Web Site: http://www.cmximaging.com
Sales Range: $10-24.9 Million
Emp.: 45
Medical Imaging Distr & Services
N.A.I.C.S.: 423450
Tim Beyer (Mgr-Svc)
Brian Van Valey (VP & Controller)
Dave Petrie (Dir-Pur & Mgr-Warehouse)
Fred Prenner (VP-Imaging Equipment)

NATIONAL HEALTHCARE RESEARCH & EDUCATION FINANCE CORPORATION
1445 Ross Ave Ste 3800, Dallas, TX 75202-2711
Tel.: (216) 636-7389 TX
Year Founded: 2000
Sales Range: $1-9.9 Million
Medical Research Services
N.A.I.C.S.: 541715
David Rowan (Sec)
Michael Harrington (Treas)
Steven C. Glass (Pres)
Kristina Raspe (VP)
Howard Feuerstein (Vice Chm)

NATIONAL HEALTHCARE REVIEW INC.
22144 Clarendon St Ste 270, Woodland Hills, CA 91367
Tel.: (818) 704-6144
Web Site: http://www.nhri.com
Sales Range: $10-24.9 Million

Emp.: 45
Auditing Services
N.A.I.C.S.: 541211
George Kasparek (Pres & CEO)
Jerry Nielsen (CFO)
Scott Booher (Mgr-HR)
Judy Derby (Mgr-Reporting Support)

NATIONAL HEAT & POWER CORP
7631 Austin Ave, Skokie, IL 60077
Tel.: (847) 965-3900
Web Site: http://www.nhpcorp.net
Sales Range: $10-24.9 Million
Emp.: 20
Plumbing Contractor
N.A.I.C.S.: 238220
Harold Hurvitz (CEO)
Bruce Hurvitz (Pres)
Michael Hurvitz (VP)
Michael Russ (Treas)

NATIONAL HERITAGE ACADEMIES, INC.
3850 Broadmoor Ave SE Ste 201, Grand Rapids, MI 49512
Tel.: (877) 223-6402 MI
Web Site: http://www.nhaschools.com
Year Founded: 1995
Sales Range: $75-99.9 Million
Emp.: 1,512
Public School Administrative Services
N.A.I.C.S.: 923110
J. C. Huizenga (Founder)
Tari Reinink (CMO)
Angelia Coleman (Principal-Timberland Charter Academy)
Todd McKee (Chief Academic Officer)
Aric Dershem (VP-Admin)
Nick Paradiso (VP-Govt Rels & Partner Svcs)
Nick Sheltrown (VP-Analytics & Accountability)
Steve Conley (CFO)
Thea Reigler (VP-People Svcs)
Brian Britton (Pres & CEO)

NATIONAL HERITAGE FOUNDATION, INC.
6201 Leesburg Pike Ste 405, Falls Church, VA 22044
Tel.: (703) 536-8708
Web Site: http://www.nhf.org
Sales Range: $25-49.9 Million
Emp.: 15
Fund Raising Charities
N.A.I.C.S.: 561990
Julie Houk (VP-Dev)
Janet H. Ridgely (VP)
John T. Houk III (Pres & CEO)

NATIONAL HOCKEY LEAGUE
1185 Avenue of the Americas 15th Fl, New York, NY 10036-1104
Tel.: (212) 789-2000
Web Site: http://www.nhl.com
Year Founded: 1900
Sales Range: $75-99.9 Million
Emp.: 300
Professional Hockey Organization
N.A.I.C.S.: 813990
Steve Mayer (Chief Content Officer-Events & Entertainment & Exec VP)
Stephen McArdle (Exec VP-Digital Media & Strategy Plng)
David Proper (Exec VP-Media & Intl Strategy)
George Parros (Head-Player Safety)
Kim Davis (Exec VP-Social Impact, Growth Initiatives & Legislative Affairs)
Tod Leiweke (CEO-Seattle)
Jonathan J. Ledecky (Co-Owner-New York)

NATIONAL HOME COMMUNITIES LLC
6991 E Camelback Rd Ste B310, Scottsdale, AZ 85251
Tel.: (480) 423-5700
Rev.: $16,200,000
Emp.: 300
Mobile Home Site Operators
N.A.I.C.S.: 459930
Colin Edward (Pres)

Subsidiaries:

Silver Dollar Golf & Trap CLB (1)
12515 Silver Dollar Dr, Odessa, FL 33556
Tel.: (813) 920-4185
Web Site: http://www.rvonthego.com
Rev.: $2,900,000
Emp.: 50
Gun Club, Membership
N.A.I.C.S.: 721214

NATIONAL HVAC SERVICE LTD.
101 Bradford Rd, Wexford, PA 15090
Tel.: (724) 935-9390
Web Site: http://www.nationalhvacservice.com
Rev.: $20,000,000
Emp.: 3
Plumbing, Heating, Air-Conditioning
N.A.I.C.S.: 238220
Jay W. Noel (Pres & CEO)
Vicky Hack (Controller)

NATIONAL INDUSTRIAL LUMBER CO (NILCO)
1 Chicago Ave, Elizabeth, PA 15037
Tel.: (412) 384-3900 DE
Web Site: http://www.nilco.net
Year Founded: 1909
Forest Products Distr
N.A.I.C.S.: 423310
Mike Hoag (CEO)

NATIONAL INFORMATION SOLUTIONS COOPERATIVE (NISC)
1 Innovation Circle, Lake Saint Louis, MO 63367
Tel.: (636) 922-9158
Web Site: http://www.nisc.cc
Year Founded: 2000
Sales Range: $25-49.9 Million
Emp.: 527
IT Solutions for Consumer & Subscriber Billing, Accounting, Engineering & Business Operations
N.A.I.C.S.: 518210
Vern Dosch (Pres & CEO)
Tracy Porter (CFO & VP-Corp Svcs)
Dan Wilbanks (COO & VP-R&D & Quality)
Doug Rembolt (VP-Utility & Shared Svcs)
Ed Wolff (VP-Professional Svcs)
David Bonnett (VP-Mktg)
Todd Eisenhauer (VP-Strategy & Ops Solutions)
John Smith (Chm)

NATIONAL INSTITUTE OF AEROSPACE
100 Exploration Way, Hampton, VA 23666
Tel.: (757) 325-6700 VA
Web Site: http://www.nianet.org
Year Founded: 2002
Sales Range: $25-49.9 Million
Emp.: 122
Aerospace Research & Development Services
N.A.I.C.S.: 541715
Kerry L. Christian (CFO & Treas)
Karl L. Drews (Sec & VP-Ops)
Douglas O. Stanley (Pres & Exec Dir)
Bo Walkley (VP-Res & Program Dev)

Carly Bosco (Dir-NASA Langley Programs)
Jan Griffen (Dir-Contracts)
David Throckmorton (VP-Res)

NATIONAL INSTRUMENTS CORPORATION
11500 N MoPac Expy, Austin, TX 78759-3504
Tel.: (804) 119-0000 DE
Web Site: https://www.ni.com
Year Founded: 1976
NATI—(NASDAQ)
Rev.: $1,656,975,000
Assets: $2,358,538,000
Liabilities: $1,202,414,000
Net Worth: $1,156,124,000
Earnings: $139,644,000
Emp.: 7,000
Fiscal Year-end: 12/31/22
Supplier of Computer-Based Instrumentation Software & Hardware Products & Solutions
N.A.I.C.S.: 334513
R. Eddie Dixon Jr. (Chief Legal Officer & Sr VP)

Subsidiaries:

AWR Japan KK (1)
Level 5 711 Building 7-11-18, Nishi-Shinjuku, Tokyo, 160-0023, Japan
Tel.: (81) 359374803
Software Development Services
N.A.I.C.S.: 541511
Norihiko Tadokoro (Area Mgr-East)

AWR-APLAC Oy (1)
Lars Sonckin Kaari 10, 02600, Espoo, Finland
Tel.: (358) 108345900
Web Site: http://www.awcorp.com
Software Development Services
N.A.I.C.S.: 541511
Miia Lamberg (Office Mgr)

BEEcube, Inc. (1)
4600 Patrick Henry Dr, Santa Clara, CA 95054 (100%)
Tel.: (408) 610-6900
Web Site: http://www.beecube.com
Computer Hardware & Software Consulting Services
N.A.I.C.S.: 541512
Kevin Camera (Founder & Sr VP-Engrg)

Measurement Computing Corporation (1)
10 Commerce Way, Norton, MA 02766
Tel.: (508) 946-5100
Web Site: https://www.mccdaq.com
Data Acquisition Hardware Mfr
N.A.I.C.S.: 334118

Subsidiary (Domestic):

Data Translation, Inc. (2)
100 Locke Dr, Marlborough, MA 01752
Tel.: (508) 481-3700
Web Site: http://www.datatranslation.com
Designer & Mfr of Data Acquisition Solutions for Test & Measurement Marketplace
N.A.I.C.S.: 334118

Subsidiary (Non-US):

Data Translation GmbH (3)
Im Weilerlen 10, 74321, Bietigheim-Bissingen, Germany
Tel.: (49) 714295310
Web Site: http://www.datatranslation.eu
Emp.: 10
Data Acquisition Solutions for Test & Measurement Marketplace
N.A.I.C.S.: 423430

Micropross SAS (1)
11 and 21 Rue Hubble Parc De La Haute Borne, 59650, Villeneuve d'Ascq, France

Tel.: (33) 320746630
Web Site: http://www.micropross.com
Electronic Component & Device Mfr
N.A.I.C.S.: 334419

NI Hungary Kft. (1)
Neumann Janos utca 1/E 2 em, 1117, Budapest, Hungary
Tel.: (36) 14811400
Web Site: http://www.ni.com
Emp.: 1,000
Hardware Product Mfr
N.A.I.C.S.: 332510

NI Solutions (Proprietary) Limited (1)
G3 Midview Building Thandanani Office Park Invicta Road, Vorna Valley, Midrand, 1685, Gauteng, South Africa
Tel.: (27) 118058197
Web Site: http://www.ni.com
Emp.: 12
Software Publisher
N.A.I.C.S.: 513210

NI Southeast Asia Sdn. Bhd. (1)
Wisma Kemajuan Jalan 19/1 Suite L 2-1 Level 2, Petaling Jaya, 46300, Selangor Darul Ehsan, Malaysia
Tel.: (60) 379482000
Web Site: http://malaysia.ni.com
Graphic System Design Services
N.A.I.C.S.: 541512

NI Taiwan Corporation (1)
12F No 216 Sec 2 Dunhua S Rd, Taipei, 106, Taiwan
Tel.: (886) 223772222
Web Site: http://www.ni.com
Software Development Services
N.A.I.C.S.: 541511

National Instruments (Thailand) Co., Ltd. (1)
123 Suntowers Building B 30th Floor Unit Number 3001, Vibhavadi Rangsit Road Chomphon Chatuchak, Bangkok, 10900, Thailand
Tel.: (66) 22786777
Web Site: http://www.thailand.ni.com
Graphical System Design Services
N.A.I.C.S.: 541430

National Instruments AM LLC (1)
123 Hovsep Emin Str EIF Entrance, Yerevan, 0051, Armenia
Tel.: (374) 10219710
Software Development Services
N.A.I.C.S.: 541511

National Instruments Asia Minor Olcum Cihazlari Ticaret Limited Sirketi (1)
Zincirlikuyu Mah Korean War Cad Yonca Apt, Block No 1 Floor 2 Apartment 7 Zinciliku the Sisli, 34394, Istanbul, Turkiye
Tel.: (90) 2122793031
Web Site: http://turkey.ni.com
Automotive Testing Equipment Mfr
N.A.I.C.S.: 334519

National Instruments Australia Corporation (1)
PO Box 382, North Ryde, 1670, NSW, Australia
Tel.: (61) 1800300800
Web Site: http://www.ni.com
Sales Range: $10-24.9 Million
Emp.: 25
Prepackaged Software Publishers
N.A.I.C.S.: 513210

National Instruments Belgium N.V. (1)
Ikaroslaan 79, 1930, Zaventem, Belgium
Tel.: (32) 27570020
Web Site: http://www.ni.com
Software Publisher
N.A.I.C.S.: 513210

National Instruments Brazil Ltda. (1)
Av Paulista 509 21 andar - Cerqueira Cesar, 01311-910, Sao Paulo, SP, Brazil
Tel.: (55) 1131493149
Web Site: http://www.brasil.ni.com
Software Development Services
N.A.I.C.S.: 541511

National Instruments Chile Spa. (1)
Cerro El Plomo 5680 Of 304 Piso 3 Edificio De Las Artes Torre 6, Las Condes, Chile
Tel.: (56) 224375340
Web Site: http://www.chile.ni.com
Emp.: 10
Software Development Services
N.A.I.C.S.: 541511

National Instruments China Corporation (1)
Building 45 No 1387 ZhangDong Road, Pudong District, Shanghai, 201203, Pudon, China
Tel.: (86) 2150509800
Web Site: http://www.ni.com
Supplier of Computer-Based Instrumentation Software & Hardware Products & Solutions
N.A.I.C.S.: 334610

National Instruments Colombia SAS (1)
Avenida Kra 45 97-50 Of 1104, Bogota, Colombia
Tel.: (57) 8005181773
Web Site: http://www.colombia.ni.com
Software Development Services
N.A.I.C.S.: 541511

National Instruments Corporation (UK) Limited (1)
Measurement House Newbury Business Park London Road, Newbury, RG14 2PZ, Berkshire, United Kingdom
Tel.: (44) 1635523545
Web Site: http://www.ni.com
Sales Range: $25-49.9 Million
Emp.: 100
Supplier of Computer-Based Instrumentation Software & Hardware Products & Solutionss
N.A.I.C.S.: 334610

National Instruments Corporation Denmark (1)
Agern Alle 11, 2970, Horsholm, Denmark
Tel.: (45) 45762600
Web Site: http://www.digital.ni.com
Sales Range: $1-9.9 Million
Emp.: 10
Supplier of Computer-Based Instrumentation Software & Hardware Products & Solutions
N.A.I.C.S.: 334610
Robert Morton (VP)

National Instruments Corporation France (1)
9-11 rue du Debarcadere, 92700, Colombes, France
Tel.: (33) 157662424
Web Site: http://www.ni.com
Sales Range: $100-124.9 Million
Emp.: 80
Supplier of Computer-Based Instrumentation Software & Hardware Products & Solutions
N.A.I.C.S.: 334610

National Instruments Corporation Germany (1)
Ganghofer Strasse 70B, 80339, Munich, Germany
Tel.: (49) 897413130
Web Site: http://www.ni.com
Sales Range: $50-74.9 Million
Emp.: 200
Supplier of Computer-Based Instrumentation Software & Hardware Products & Solutions
N.A.I.C.S.: 334610

National Instruments Corporation Italy (1)
Palazzo U4 Via Del Bosco Rinnovato 8, Assago, 20090, Milan, 20080, Italy
Tel.: (39) 02413091
Web Site: http://www.digital.ni.com
Sales Range: $100-124.9 Million
Emp.: 50
Supplier of Computer-Based Instrumentation Software & Hardware Products & Solutions
N.A.I.C.S.: 334610

National Instruments Corporation Japan (1)
Nomura real Estate Development Shiba-Daimon Bldg, 9F 1-9-9 Shiba Daimon, Tokyo, 105-0012, Japan
Tel.: (81) 354722970
Web Site: http://www.ni.com
Sales Range: $25-49.9 Million
Emp.: 100
Supplier of Computer-Based Instrumentation Software & Hardware Products & Solutions
N.A.I.C.S.: 334610

National Instruments Corporation Singapore (1)
Westgate Tower 1 Gateway Drive, Singapore, 608531, Singapore
Tel.: (65) 62265886
Web Site: http://digital.ni.com
Sales Range: $10-24.9 Million
Emp.: 80
Supplier of Computer-Based Instrumentation Software & Hardware Products & Solutionss
N.A.I.C.S.: 334610

National Instruments Corporation Spain (1)
C/Playa de Lencres 2 Europa Empresarial Edificio Londres, 1a plta Oficina 7, 28290, Madrid, Spain
Tel.: (34) 916400085
Web Site: http://www.digital.ni.com
Sales Range: $10-24.9 Million
Emp.: 20
Supplier of Computer-Based Instrumentation Software & Hardware Products & Solutions
N.A.I.C.S.: 334610

National Instruments Denmark ApS (1)
Agern Alle 11, 2970, Horsholm, Denmark
Tel.: (45) 45762600
Web Site: http://www.denmark.ni.com
Software Development Services
N.A.I.C.S.: 541511

National Instruments Dresden GmbH (1)
Am Waldschlobchen 2, 1099, Dresden, Germany
Tel.: (49) 3512069310
Web Site: http://www.signalion.com
Semiconductor & Related Device Mfr
N.A.I.C.S.: 334413

National Instruments Egypt LLC (1)
290 North Side Second Sector 6th Floor A, 5th District, New Cairo, Egypt
Tel.: (20) 1121900002
Web Site: http://www.ni.com
Emp.: 10
Software Development Services
N.A.I.C.S.: 541511

National Instruments France SAS (1)
11 rue du Debarcadere, 92700, Colombes, France
Tel.: (33) 15 766 2424
Web Site: http://www.france.ni.com
Software Development Services
N.A.I.C.S.: 541511

National Instruments Germany GmbH (1)
Ganghoferstrasse 70 b, 80339, Munich, Germany
Tel.: (49) 897413130
Web Site: http://www.germany.ni.com
Graphical System Design Services
N.A.I.C.S.: 541430

National Instruments Hungary Kft. (1)
Neumann Janos utca 1/E 2 em, 1117, Budapest, Hungary
Tel.: (36) 14811400
Web Site: http://www.hungary.ni.com
Emp.: 78
Hardware Product Mfr
N.A.I.C.S.: 332510

National Instruments Instrumentacija, avtomatizacija in upravljanje procesov d.o.o. (1)
Kosovelova ulica 15, 3000, Celje, Slovenia
Tel.: (386) 34254270
Web Site: http://slovenia.ni.com
Sales Range: $10-24.9 Million
Emp.: 4
Computer Application Software Publisher
N.A.I.C.S.: 513210

National Instruments Italy s.r.l. (1)
Palazzo U4 Via Del Bosco Rinnovato 8, Centro Direzionale Milanofiori Nord, 20090, Assago, MI, Italy
Tel.: (39) 0241 3091
Web Site: http://www.italy.ni.com
Software Development Services
N.A.I.C.S.: 541511

National Instruments Japan KK (1)
Shiba Daimon 1-9-9 Nomura Real Estate Shibadaimon building 8F, Minato-ku, Tokyo, 105-0012, Japan
Tel.: (81) 120527196
Software Development Services
N.A.I.C.S.: 541511

National Instruments Lebanon SARL (1)
Bechara El Khoury Avenue Bachoura Sector, Berytech Beirut Digital District Bldg 5th floor, Beirut, Lebanon
Tel.: (961) 1646111
Software Development Services
N.A.I.C.S.: 541511

National Instruments Poland Sp. Z.o.o. (1)
International Business Center IBCII ul Polna 11, 00-633, Warsaw, Poland
Tel.: (48) 223289010
Web Site: http://www.poland.ni.com
Graphical Application Software Development Services
N.A.I.C.S.: 541511

National Instruments Portugal Unipessoal Lda. (1)
Avenida D Joao II 50 Edificio Mar Vermelho, parish of Parque das Nacoes, Lisbon, 2740-122, Portugal
Tel.: (351) 210311210
Web Site: http://www.portugal.ni.com
Sales Range: $25-49.9 Million
Emp.: 3
Application Software Development Services
N.A.I.C.S.: 541511

National Instruments RUS LLC (1)
Ozernaya Street 42 office 1101, Moscow, 119361, Russia
Tel.: (7) 4957836851
Web Site: http://www.russia.ni.com
Software Development Services
N.A.I.C.S.: 541511

National Instruments Saudi Arabia, LLC (1)
King AbdulAziz Road Port Gate Building - Office 37, PO Box 7511, Al Khaldiya, 31472, Dammam, Saudi Arabia
Tel.: (966) 38143838
Software Development Services
N.A.I.C.S.: 541511

National Instruments Singapore (PTE) Ltd. (1)
29 International Business Park Acer Building TowerB 0-02, Singapore, 609923, Singapore
Tel.: (65) 62265886
Web Site: http://www.singapore.ni.com
Graphical System Design Services
N.A.I.C.S.: 541430

National Instruments Spain, S.L. (1)
C/Playa de Lencres 2 Europa Empresarial, Edificio Londres - 1a plta Oficina 7 Las Rozas, 28290, Madrid, Spain
Tel.: (34) 916400085
Web Site: http://www.spain.ni.com
Software Development Services
N.A.I.C.S.: 541511

National Instruments Switzerland Corporation (1)
Sonnenbergstrasse 53, Ennetbaden, Baden, 5408, Switzerland
Tel.: (41) 562005151
Web Site: http://switzerland.ni.com
Software Publisher
N.A.I.C.S.: 513210

National Instruments Taiwan Corporation (1)
12F No 216 Sec 2 Dunhua S Rd, Daan District, Taipei, 106, Taiwan
Tel.: (886) 223772222
Web Site: http://www.ni.com

NATIONAL INSTRUMENTS CORPORATION
U.S. PRIVATE

National Instruments Corporation—(Continued)
Supplier of Computer-Based Instrumentation Software & Hardware Products & Solutions
N.A.I.C.S.: 334610

Optimal Plus Ltd. (1)
26 Ha'Rokmim Street Building A - 2nd Floor, Holon, 5885800, Israel
Tel.: (972) 89308800
Web Site: http://www.optimalplus.com
Semiconductor Distr
N.A.I.C.S.: 423690

PT. National Instruments Indonesia (1)
16th Floor Suite E23 Jl Asia Afrika No 8 Gelora Bung Karno, Senayan, Jakarta, 10270, Indonesia
Tel.: (62) 2129241991
Web Site: http://www.indonesia.ni.com
Graphical System Design Services
N.A.I.C.S.: 541430

Phase Matrix, Inc. (1)
4600 Patrick Henry Dr, Santa Clara, CA 95054
Tel.: (408) 610-6810
Web Site: http://www.phasematrix.com
Sales Range: $25-49.9 Million
Emp.: 50
Radio Frequency Instruments
N.A.I.C.S.: 334515
Pete Pragastis *(Founder)*

NATIONAL INSURANCE COMPANY
510 Ave Munoz Rivera, San Juan, PR 00918
Tel.: (787) 758-8080   PR
Web Site:
  http://www.multinationalpr.com
Year Founded: 1961
Sales Range: $25-49.9 Million
Emp.: 300
Life Insurance
N.A.I.C.S.: 524113
Edgar Rodriguez *(Sr VP-Ops)*
Carlos M. Benitez Jr. *(Pres)*

NATIONAL INSURANCE SERVICES, INC.
250 S Executive Dr, Brookfield, WI 53005
Tel.: (262) 785-9995
Web Site: http://www.nisbenefits.com
Rev.: $17,000,000
Emp.: 104
Insurance Agencies & Brokerages
N.A.I.C.S.: 524210
Bruce Miller *(Pres & CEO)*
Alex J. Legrand *(Dir-IT)*
Stephanie Laudon *(Reg VP)*
Bill Enright *(Dir-Consulting Svcs)*
Aaron A. Casper *(Dir-Market Dev)*
Steve Ott *(Reg VP)*
Mark Williams *(Reg VP)*
David Norton *(VP-Fin & Admin)*

NATIONAL INVESTMENT SERVICES, INC.
777 E Wisconsin Ave Ste 2350, Milwaukee, WI 53202
Tel.: (414) 765-1980   WI
Web Site: http://www.nisi.net
Year Founded: 1968
Sales Range: $50-74.9 Million
Emp.: 15
Investment Advisory & Asset Management Services
N.A.I.C.S.: 523940
Larry Harold Haslee *(Chief Compliance Officer)*
Robert P. Brooks *(CEO)*
Kent J. White *(Chief Investment Officer)*
Barbara A. Schalla *(Portfolio Mgr-Corp Bonds)*
Jason C. Berrie *(Co-Chief Investment Officer & Portfolio Mgr)*
Mark R. Anderson *(Chief Strategy Officer & Portfolio Mgr)*
Scott O. Van Lith *(Controller)*
James S. Kaplan *(Portfolio Mgr-Lead & Structured Products)*
Norman E. Sidler *(Mng Partner & Principal)*
Andrew J. Gruebling *(VP-Consultant Rels)*
Lesly M. Barnes *(Portfolio Mgr-Structured Products)*
Ray Caprio *(Dir-Institutional Sls)*
John P. Fremgen *(Mng Partner & Principal)*
Dawn M. Giannini *(Dir-Tech Svcs)*
Jonathan B. Hoenecke *(CFO)*
Bartlett J. McCartin III *(Mng Partner & Principal)*

NATIONAL JOURNAL GROUP
600 New Hampshire Ave NW Fl 4, Washington, DC 20037-2403
Tel.: (202) 739-8400   DE
Web Site:
  http://www.nationaljournal.com
Year Founded: 1969
Sales Range: $150-199.9 Million
Emp.: 350
Magazines, Newsletters, Books & Directories Publisher Concerning Government Policy & Politics
N.A.I.C.S.: 513120
Josh Kraushaar *(Editor-Political)*
Michael D. Gottlieb *(Exec Dir-Policy Brands Roundtable)*
Stephen Smith *(Editor-in-Chief)*
Ben Pershing *(Mng Editor)*
Jeff Dufour *(Editor-Real Time News)*
Afzal Bari *(VP-Strategy & Ops)*
Kevin Turpin *(Exec Dir-Strategy & Ops)*
Molly Broemmelsiek *(Sr Dir-Bus Dev)*
Katherine Collins *(Chief Bus Dev Officer)*

Subsidiaries:

The Atlantic Monthly Group, Inc. (1)
600 New Hampshire Ave NW, Washington, DC 20037
Tel.: (202) 266-7000
Web Site: http://www.theatlantic.com
Sales Range: $10-24.9 Million
Emp.: 55
Magazine Publishing Services
N.A.I.C.S.: 513120
Vernon Loeb *(Editor-Politics)*
Jeffrey Goldberg *(Editor-in-Chief)*
Adrienne LaFrance *(Exec Editor)*
Lauren N. Williams *(Sr Editor)*
Bob Cohn *(Pres-The Atlantic)*
Hayley Romer *(Chief Revenue Officer & Publr)*
Alex Hardiman *(Chief Bus Officer & Chief Product Officer)*
Kimberly Lau *(Exec VP-Strategy & Ops)*
Sam Rosen *(Sr VP-Growth)*
Peter Lattman *(Vice Chm)*
Nick Thompson *(CEO)*
Andrea Valdez *(Mng Editor-Newsroom-The Atlantic)*

Affiliate (Domestic):

The Atlantic Advertising Sales (2)
286 Madison Ave 8th Fl, New York, NY 10017
Tel.: (212) 284-7647
Web Site: http://www.theatlantic.com
News, Foreign Affairs & Cultural Trends Publisher
N.A.I.C.S.: 513110

NATIONAL JUVENILE DEFENDER CENTER
1350 Connecticut Ave NW St 304, Washington, DC 20036
Tel.: (202) 452-0010   DC
Web Site: http://www.njdc.info
Year Founded: 2002
Sales Range: $1-9.9 Million
Emp.: 14
Legal Aid Services
N.A.I.C.S.: 541199
Sonia Slone *(Dir-Ops)*
Kim Dvorchak *(Exec Dir)*
Bridgett Ortega *(Pres)*
Kenneth Schmetterer *(VP)*
Jacqueline Baillargeon *(Treas)*
Ryan Myers *(Sec)*

NATIONAL LADDER & SCAFFOLD COMPANY, INC.
29350 John R Rd, Madison Heights, MI 48095
Tel.: (248) 399-0984   MI
Web Site:
  http://www.nationalladder.com
Year Founded: 1969
Sales Range: $10-24.9 Million
Emp.: 30
Hardware Stores
N.A.I.C.S.: 444140
Leo E. Corradi *(Pres)*

NATIONAL LAND REALTY, LLC
7001 Pelham Rd Ste M, Greenville, SC 29615
Tel.: (855) 384-5263
Web Site:
  http://www.nationalland.com
Year Founded: 2007
Real Estate Brokerage Services
N.A.I.C.S.: 531210
Jason Walter *(Founder & CEO)*
Aaron Graham *(Pres)*
Ann Gaffigan *(CTO)*
Susan Floyd *(COO)*
Jason Burbage *(Exec VP)*

Subsidiaries:

Crosby & Associates, Inc. (1)
141 5th St NW Ste 202, Winter Haven, FL 33881
Tel.: (863) 293-5600
Web Site: http://www.crosbyresidential.com
Offices of Real Estate Agents & Brokers
N.A.I.C.S.: 531210
Rick Gonzalez *(Exec Dir)*

NATIONAL LAW ENFORCEMENT OFFICERS MEMORIAL FUND
901 E St NW Ste 100, Washington, DC 20004-2025
Tel.: (202) 737-3400   DC
Web Site: http://www.nleomf.com
Year Founded: 1984
Sales Range: $10-24.9 Million
Emp.: 42
Civic & Social Organization
N.A.I.C.S.: 813410
Krista Humphrey *(Dir-Direct Mktg)*
Desiree Luongo *(Officer-Safety & Wellness Initiative & Sr Project Mgr)*
Ray Hord *(Chief Dev Officer)*
Steve Groeninger *(Sr Dir-Comm & Mktg)*
John Ashcroft *(Chm)*
Craig W. Floyd *(Founder)*
Suzie Sawyer *(Sec)*
James Osgood *(Treas)*
Jon Adler *(Vice Chm)*
Patrick P. Montuore *(Chief Law Enforcement Rels & Memorial Officer)*
David L. Brant *(COO & Exec Dir-Museum)*

NATIONAL LEAGUE FOR NURSING
2600 Virginia Avenue NW 8th Fl, Washington, DC 20037
Tel.: (800) 669-1656   DC
Web Site: http://www.nln.org
Year Founded: 1952
Sales Range: $10-24.9 Million
Emp.: 93
Nursing Care Services
N.A.I.C.S.: 623110
Janice Brewington *(Co-Chief Program Officer)*
Linda Christensen *(Chief Admin Officer)*
Mike Kristek *(Deputy Chief Admin Officer)*
Beverly Malone *(CEO)*
Anne R. Bavier *(Co-Pres)*
Patricia Yoder-Wise *(Co-Treas)*
G. Rumay Alexander *(Co-Pres)*
Teresa Shellenbarger *(Sec)*
Stephen Cerame *(CFO)*
Cathleen Shultz *(Chm)*
M. Elaine Tagliareni *(Co-Chief Program Officer)*
Patricia Castaldi *(Co-Treas)*
Michael Keaton *(Dir-Comm)*

NATIONAL LIFE INSURANCE COMPANY
1 National Life Dr, Montpelier, VT 05604
Tel.: (802) 229-3333   VT
Web Site:
  http://www.nationallifegroup.com
Year Founded: 1848
Sales Range: $1-4.9 Billion
Emp.: 900
Life Insurance, Annuities, Variable Annuities, Mutual Funds & Outside Investment Programs
N.A.I.C.S.: 524113
Bob Cotton *(COO)*
Mehran Assadi *(Chief People Officer & Sr VP)*
Thomas Hyde Brownell *(Pres/CEO-Sentinel Asset Management, Inc)*
Gregory Donald Woodworth *(Gen Counsel & Sr VP)*
Jason Doiron *(Chief Investment Officer)*
Tom Anfuso *(CIO & Sr VP)*
Achim Schwetlick *(Sr VP & Head-Bus Innovation Grp)*
Vesta Bovair *(Sr VP & Head-Customer Innovation Grp)*

Subsidiaries:

Equity Services, Inc. (1)
1 National Life Dr, Montpelier, VT 05604
Tel.: (800) 344-7437
Web Site: http://www.nationallifegroup.com
Broker & Dealer in Mutual Fund Shares & Other Securities
N.A.I.C.S.: 523150
Jean Smith *(Dir-Securities Ops)*
Robert Franklin *(Chief Compliance Officer)*
Ata Azarshahi *(Pres & CEO)*

Life Insurance Companies of the Southwest (1)
15455 Dallas Pkwy Ste 800, Addison, TX 75001-6496   (100%)
Tel.: (214) 638-7100
Web Site: http://www.lifeofsouthwest.com
Sales Range: $50-74.9 Million
Emp.: 130
Life Insurance & Annuity Company
N.A.I.C.S.: 524113
Ross Sneyd *(Dir-Corp & Community Rels)*

Sentinel Administrative Services, Inc. (1)
1 National Life Dr, Montpelier, VT 05604-0001   (100%)
Tel.: (802) 229-3333
Web Site: www.sentinelfunds.com
Sales Range: $50-74.9 Million
Emp.: 65
Administrator of Insurance Plans
N.A.I.C.S.: 524210

Sentinel Advisors Co. (1)
1 National Life Dr, Montpelier, VT 05604-1000   (100%)
Tel.: (802) 223-9300
Web Site:
  http://www.sentinelinvestments.com

Investment Advisor to Sentinel Funds
N.A.I.C.S.: 523940

Sentinel Asset Management, Inc. (1)
1 National Life Dr, Montpelier, VT 05604
Tel.: (800) 282-3863
Web Site:
   http://www.sentinelinvestments.com
Asset Management Services
N.A.I.C.S.: 541618

NATIONAL LUMBER CO.
24595 Groesbeck Hwy, Warren, MI 48089-2145
Tel.: (586) 775-8200   MI
Sales Range: $100-124.9 Million
Emp.: 250
Whslr & Retailer of Lumber; Manufacturer of Rough Lumber & Trusses
N.A.I.C.S.: 423310
James Rosenthal *(Pres & CEO)*
Allen Strickstein *(VP)*

NATIONAL MACHINE COMPANY
4880 Hudson Dr, Stow, OH 44224
Tel.: (330) 688-6494
Web Site:
   http://www.nationalmachinecompany.com
Year Founded: 1967
Sales Range: $10-24.9 Million
Emp.: 250
Mfr of Pneumatic & Hydraulic Aircraft Valves
N.A.I.C.S.: 332710
Jeff Bissell *(CFO)*

NATIONAL MAGNETICS GROUP, INC.
1210 Win Dr, Bethlehem, PA 18017-7061
Tel.: (610) 867-7600
Web Site:
   http://www.magneticsgroup.com
Sales Range: $10-24.9 Million
Emp.: 80
Magnetic Material Mfr
N.A.I.C.S.: 327110
Paul B. Oberbeck *(Pres)*
Bernard Riccardo *(Supvr-Production)*
Mark Northrup *(VP)*
Sandy Gaito *(Mgr-Acctg)*

Subsidiaries:

TCI Ceramics (1)
1210 Win Dr, Bethlehem, PA 18017-7061
Tel.: (610) 867-7600
Sales Range: $10-24.9 Million
Emp.: 20
Microwave Ceramics Mfr
N.A.I.C.S.: 334419

NATIONAL MARKETING SOLUTIONS (NMS)
117 S 9th Ave Ste 1, Caldwell, ID 83605
Tel.: (855) 350-2555
Web Site:
   http://www.natlmarketingsolutions.com
Year Founded: 2005
Sales Range: $1-9.9 Million
Emp.: 23
Lead Generation, Telemarketing & Appointment Setting for Companies
N.A.I.C.S.: 541613
Ryan Hart *(Pres)*
Bernise Nunez *(Mgr-Production)*

NATIONAL MARROW DONOR PROGRAM, INC.
500 N 5th St, Minneapolis, MN 55401
Tel.: (612) 627-5800
Web Site: https://www.nmdp.org
Year Founded: 1987
Emp.: 700

Health Care Srvices
N.A.I.C.S.: 621610
Patricia L. Jones *(Sr VP-HR)*
Dennis L. Confer *(Chief Medical Officer)*
Michael Boo *(Chief Strategy Officer)*
Amy Ronneberg *(CFO)*
Ann R. Berkey *(Vice Chm)*
William G. Pomeroy *(Sec)*
Brian Lindberg *(Chief Legal Officer & Gen Counsel)*
Karen Dodson *(COO)*
Mike McCullough *(CIO)*
Tracy Schmidt *(Sr VP-HR)*
Jeffrey W. Chell *(CEO)*

NATIONAL MECHANICAL SERVICES, LLC
100 Leuning St, South Hackensack, NJ 07606
Tel.: (201) 488-5151
Web Site: http://www.national-mechanical.com
Sales Range: $10-24.9 Million
Emp.: 60
Provider of Plumbing, Heating & Air Conditioning Contracting Services
N.A.I.C.S.: 238220
Richard Mortman *(Pres)*

NATIONAL MEDICAL SERVICES, INC.
3701 Welsh Rd, Willow Grove, PA 19090
Tel.: (215) 657-4900   PA
Web Site: http://www.nmslab.com
Sales Range: $10-24.9 Million
Emp.: 300
Clinical Toxicology & Forensic Testing Laboratories
N.A.I.C.S.: 541380
Robert A. Middleberg *(VP-Quality Assurance & Dir-Laboratory)*
James G. Murphy *(CFO)*
Ron Fazio *(VP-Bus Dev-Integrated Forensic Svcs)*
Pierre G. Cassigneul *(Pres & CEO)*
Maria Rieders *(Sec)*
Marlow Hicks *(VP-Ops)*
Jennifer N. Furness *(VP-Sls & Mktg)*
David Delia *(Co-CFO)*
Barry K. Logan *(Sr VP-Forensic Science Initiatives)*
Steven A. Noel *(VP-Laboratory Ops)*
Frederick G. Strathmann *(VP-Quality Assurance)*
William S. Hough Jr. *(VP-HR)*

NATIONAL MERIT SCHOLARSHIP CORP.
1560 Sherman Ave Ste 200, Evanston, IL 60201-4897
Tel.: (847) 866-5100
Web Site:
   https://www.nationalmerit.org
Year Founded: 1955
Educational Support Services
N.A.I.C.S.: 611710
Larry D. Brady II *(Vice Chm)*

NATIONAL MICRO RENTAL
28 Abeel Rd, Monroe, NJ 08831
Tel.: (609) 395-0550
Web Site: http://www.nmrrents.com
Sales Range: $50-74.9 Million
Emp.: 100
Computer Rental & Leasing
N.A.I.C.S.: 532420
Michael J. Meduri *(Pres & CEO)*
Jason Newman *(Dir-Tech Svcs)*
Donna Tobia *(Dir-Creative Svcs)*

NATIONAL MILK PRODUCERS FEDERATION

2101 Wilson Blvd Ste 400, Arlington, VA 22201
Tel.: (703) 243-6111   VA
Web Site: http://www.nmpf.org
Year Founded: 1916
Sales Range: $25-49.9 Million
Emp.: 19
Dairy Product Promoter
N.A.I.C.S.: 541810
Tom Balmer *(Exec VP)*
Jim Mulhern *(Pres & CEO)*
Paul Bleiberg *(Sr Dir-Govt Rels)*

NATIONAL MILL INDUSTRY, INC.
500 Commerce Rd, Linden, NJ 07036-2427
Tel.: (908) 862-8400   NY
Web Site:
   http://www.carnivalbras.com
Year Founded: 1947
Sales Range: $10-24.9 Million
Emp.: 15
Brassieres, Corsets & Lingerie Mfr & Whslr
N.A.I.C.S.: 315250
Victor Shacalo *(Chm & CEO)*
Joseph Cohen *(VP)*

NATIONAL MOLDING CORPORATION
5 Dubon Ct, Farmingdale, NY 11735-1007
Tel.: (631) 293-8696   NY
Web Site:
   http://www.nationalmolding.com
Year Founded: 1965
Sales Range: $10-24.9 Million
Emp.: 80
Molded Plastic Products & Assemblies Mfr
N.A.I.C.S.: 326199
Mel Menkuta *(Controller)*

Subsidiaries:

NMC Shanghai, Ltd. (1)
No 16 Lane 269 Huazhe Road Songjiang Export Processing Zone-Section A, Shanghai, 201613, China
Tel.: (86) 21 3783 7755
Web Site: http://www.nationalmolding.com
Emp.: 100
Plastic Mold Mfr
N.A.I.C.S.: 333511
Lillian Wang *(Mgr-HR)*

Security Plastics Division/NMC LLC (1)
14427 NW 60th Ave, Miami Lakes, FL 33014-2806
Tel.: (305) 823-5440
Web Site: http://www.nationalmolding.com
Custom Injection Molder of Engineered Component Thermoplastic Component & Mechanical & Decorative Secondary Ops Supplied to the E/E Automotive & Telecommunications Market Mfr
N.A.I.C.S.: 326199
Thomas Linton *(Pres & CEO)*

Subsidiary (Non-US):

Fawn de Mexico (2)
Ave Impulso No 3001 Parque Industrial Impulso, Chihuahua, Mexico   (100%)
Tel.: (52) 6144420742
Web Site: http://www.fawnplastics.com
Mold Component Mfr
N.A.I.C.S.: 333511

NATIONAL MORTGAGE & FINANCE CO. LTD.
1165 Bethel St Ste 2, Honolulu, HI 96813
Tel.: (808) 539-9777
Web Site:
   http://www.hawaiianprop.com
Year Founded: 1929
Sales Range: $100-124.9 Million
Emp.: 400

Provider of Financial Services
N.A.I.C.S.: 524210

Subsidiaries:

National Securities & Investments Inc. (1)
1022 Bethel St, Honolulu, HI 96813-4302
Tel.: (808) 531-1311
Web Site: http://www.highlineinsurance.com
Sales Range: $50-74.9 Million
Emp.: 380
Provider of Investment Services
N.A.I.C.S.: 531210

NATIONAL MUSIC PUBLISHERS' ASSOCIATION
975 F St NW Ste 375, Washington, DC 20004
Tel.: (202) 393-6672
Web Site: http://www.nmpa.org
Year Founded: 1917
Emp.: 10
Music Business Association
N.A.I.C.S.: 813910
David Israelite *(Pres & CEO)*
Irwin Z. Robinson *(Chm)*
Danielle Malito Aguirre *(Gen Counsel & Exec VP)*
Charlotte Sellmyer *(Sr VP-External Affairs)*
Jonathan Cohen *(VP)*
Shannon Sorensen *(VP-Govt Affairs)*
Katharine McClenny *(Dir-Comm & Gold & Platinum Program)*
Chris Cylke *(Sr VP-Govt Affairs)*
Amelia Wang *(VP-Govt Affairs & Industry Rels)*

NATIONAL MUTUAL BENEFIT
6522 Grand Teton Plz, Madison, WI 53719
Tel.: (608) 833-1936
Web Site: http://www.nmblife.org
Year Founded: 1902
Sales Range: $25-49.9 Million
Emp.: 57
Fraternal Life Insurance Organization
N.A.I.C.S.: 524113

NATIONAL NAIL CORP.
2964 Clydon Ave SW, Grand Rapids, MI 49519
Tel.: (616) 538-8000
Web Site:
   http://www.nationalnail.com
Year Founded: 1962
Sales Range: $50-74.9 Million
Emp.: 200
Distr & Sales of Nails, Screws & Other Building Products
N.A.I.C.S.: 423510
W. Scott Baker *(Pres & CEO)*
Greg Hartmann *(Gen Mgr-Bus-Northeast)*
Kevin Brockmyre *(Gen Mgr-Market Dev-New England)*
Steve Graff *(Dir-Distr)*

NATIONAL NETWORK DIGITAL SCHOOLS
294 Massachusetts Ave, Rochester, PA 15074
Tel.: (724) 764-7200   PA
Web Site: http://www.nndsonline.org
Year Founded: 2005
Sales Range: $25-49.9 Million
Emp.: 383
Educational Support Services
N.A.I.C.S.: 611710
Stephanie Pennington *(Pres)*

NATIONAL NEWS BUREAU AGENCY
PO Box 43039, Philadelphia, PA 19129-3039
Tel.: (215) 849-9016
Web Site:
   http://www.nationalnewsbureau.com
Year Founded: 1980

National News Bureau Agency—(Continued)
Sales Range: $1-9.9 Million
Emp.: 12
Promotions & Advertising
N.A.I.C.S.: 541810
Harry Jay Katz (Exec Dir)
Andy Edelman (Editor-Features)
Frank Stallone (Editor-Intl Boxing)

NATIONAL NONWOVENS
180 Pleasant St, Easthampton, MA 01027
Tel.: (413) 527-3445
Web Site:
 http://www.nationalnonwovens.com
Rev.: $13,200,000
Emp.: 75
Felts, Woven: Wool, Mohair, Or Similar Fibers
N.A.I.C.S.: 313210
Charles Kunce (Mgr-Mgmt Info Sys)

NATIONAL NOODLE INC.
1122 State Rte 3, National Stock Yards, IL 62071
Tel.: (618) 271-1122
Sales Range: $10-24.9 Million
Emp.: 80
Mfr of Dry Noodles
N.A.I.C.S.: 311824

NATIONAL OAK DISTRIBUTORS INC.
6529 Southern Blvd, West Palm Beach, FL 33413
Tel.: (561) 478-2711
Web Site:
 http://www.nationaloak.com
Sales Range: $10-24.9 Million
Emp.: 25
Automotive Supplies & Parts
N.A.I.C.S.: 423120
Karen Fielden (Mgr-Acctg)
Thomas Fogarty (Dir-Sls)
Marc Noland (CFO & VP-Supply Chain)
Samy Pineda (Mgr-Ops)

NATIONAL OLDER WORKER CAREER CENTER
3811 N Fairfax Dr Ste 900, Arlington, VA 22203
Tel.: (703) 558-4200   DC
Web Site: http://www.nowcc.org
Year Founded: 1997
Sales Range: $10-24.9 Million
Emp.: 26
Employment Placement Services
N.A.I.C.S.: 561311
Gregory A. Merrill (Pres & CEO)
Linda Holiman (Controller)
Cito Vanegas (CFO)
Caroline Espree (Dir-HR)
Yvonne Bolton (Mgr-Payroll)
Barbara Bronislawska (Mgr-ACES Program)
Al Ressler (Sr Dir-Field Ops)
Bridget Farley (Mgr-SEE Program)
Cynthia A. Langley (Chm)
Frank K. Hurd (Vice Chm)
Ellen Tunstall (Treas & Sec)
Tammie Reynolds (Coord-Field)

NATIONAL OPINION RESEARCH CENTER COLORADO
3852 N Avers Ave, Chicago, IL 60618-4002
Tel.: (773) 256-6000
Web Site: http://www.norc.org
Rev.: $46,136,448
Emp.: 250
Research Services, Except Laboratory
N.A.I.C.S.: 541910
Julia Lane (Principal)
Dan Gaylin (Pres & CEO)

Ellen Beatty (CFO & Exec VP-Fin & Admin)
Tenia Davis (Chief HR Officer & Sr VP)

NATIONAL OPTRONICS INC.
100 Avon St, Charlottesville, VA 22902
Tel.: (434) 295-9126
Web Site:
 http://www.nationaloptronics.com
Sales Range: $10-24.9 Million
Emp.: 150
Ophthalmic Goods
N.A.I.C.S.: 339115
Andy Huthoefer (CEO)
Christy Habony (Dir-HR)
Martin Bergeron (Gen Mgr)

NATIONAL PACKAGING SERVICES
1000 New County Rd Bldg 3, Secaucus, NJ 07094
Tel.: (201) 488-6700
Web Site: http://www.natpack.com
Rev.: $21,000,000
Emp.: 20
Sales of Industrial Supplies
N.A.I.C.S.: 423840
Bob Strasser (Pres)

NATIONAL PACKAGING SERVICES CORPORATION
3303 Spirit Way, Green Bay, WI 54304
Tel.: (920) 983-9223   WI
Web Site: http://www.npscorp.com
Year Founded: 1996
Sales Range: $10-24.9 Million
Towels, Tissues & Spill Control Products Mfr
N.A.I.C.S.: 322291
Andrew Francis Hetzel Jr. (Pres & CEO)
Paul Rudzinski (Acct Mgr-Natl)
Brian Rathsack (Mgr-Raw Matl Pur)

Subsidiaries:

Evolution Sorbent Products, LLC (1)
1149 Howard Dr, West Chicago, IL 60185-1621
Tel.: (630) 293-8055
Web Site: http://www.espsorbents.com
Absorbent Fabric Products Mfr
N.A.I.C.S.: 313230
Bryan Sims (CEO)
Larry Wolf (CFO)

NPS Worldwide--UK Limited (1)
Unit 4 Wellington Park, Hedge End, Southampton, SO30 2QU, Hants, United Kingdom
Tel.: (44) 23 8027 4123
Web Site: http://www.lubetech.co.uk
Absorbent & Spill Control Products Developer & Distr
N.A.I.C.S.: 423840
Neil Barron (Mng Dir)

NATIONAL PACKAGING SPECIALISTS, INC.
200 Central Ave, Mountainside, NJ 07092
Tel.: (908) 233-7489
Sales Range: $10-24.9 Million
Emp.: 11
Manufacturers' Representative for Plastic Packaging Materials
N.A.I.C.S.: 424990

NATIONAL PARTS DEPOT
900 SW 38th Ave, Ocala, FL 34474
Tel.: (352) 861-8701
Web Site: http://www.npdlink.com
Sales Range: $25-49.9 Million
Emp.: 200
Auto & Truck Equipment & Parts
N.A.I.C.S.: 441330

James A. Schmidt (Pres)
Allen Baer (Controller)
Kirk Hansen (Dir-Mktg & Project Mgr)

NATIONAL PARTS SUPPLY COMPANY INC.
535 Milltown Rd, North Brunswick, NJ 08902
Tel.: (732) 247-5171
Web Site:
 http://www.nationalpartssupply.net
Sales Range: $10-24.9 Million
Emp.: 120
Supplier of Automotive Parts & Accessories
N.A.I.C.S.: 441330
Susan Viscomi (CFO)
John Warren (Mgr-Sls)

NATIONAL PATIENT SERVICES CORPORATION
9096 E Bahia Dr Ste 103, Scottsdale, AZ 85260
Tel.: (480) 385-5786   AZ
Web Site:
 http://www.nationalpatientservices.com
Year Founded: 2002
Sales Range: $75-99.9 Million
Emp.: 8
Pharmaceutical Product Fulfillment & Marketing Services
N.A.I.C.S.: 541613
Rick Randall (Pres)
Omar Sayed (Founder & CEO)

NATIONAL PERSONNEL ASSOCIATES COOPERATIVE, INC.
1680 Viewpond Dr SE, Grand Rapids, MI 49508-4907
Tel.: (616) 455-6555
Web Site:
 http://www.npaworldwide.com
Sales Range: $10-24.9 Million
Emp.: 7
Network of Personnel Placement Professionals
N.A.I.C.S.: 541612
Dave Nerz (Pres)

NATIONAL PETROLEUM INC.
6621 39th Ave, Kenosha, WI 53142-7123
Tel.: (262) 652-4100   WI
Web Site:
 http://www.nationalpetroleum.net
Year Founded: 1991
Sales Range: $10-24.9 Million
Emp.: 95
Petroleum Bulk Stations & Terminals
N.A.I.C.S.: 424710

NATIONAL PIPE HANGER CO. CORP
200 Campus Dr RR 30, Mount Holly, NJ 08060
Tel.: (609) 261-5353
Web Site:
 http://www.nationalpipehanger.com
Sales Range: $10-24.9 Million
Emp.: 50
Sales of Pipe & Tubing
N.A.I.C.S.: 423510
Bill McCabe (Pres)

NATIONAL PLASTICS COLOR INC.
2600 W 77th St, Valley Center, KS 67147
Tel.: (316) 755-1273
Web Site:
 http://www.nationalplasticscolor.com
Rev.: $23,300,000
Emp.: 111

Cyclic Crudes & Intermediates
N.A.I.C.S.: 325199
Bill Sutherland (Pres)
Donyail Williams (Mgr-HR)

NATIONAL POOL CONSTRUCTION
1220 US Hwy 130, Robbinsville, NJ 08691
Tel.: (609) 448-3366   NJ
Web Site:
 http://www.nationalpoolsandspas.com
Year Founded: 2001
Rev.: $13,600,000
Emp.: 20
Swimming Pool Construction
N.A.I.C.S.: 238990
Kathy Adams (Controller)
Ron Burrell (Pres)

NATIONAL PORK BOARD
1776 NW 114th St, Des Moines, IA 50325
Tel.: (515) 223-2600
Web Site: http://www.pork.org
Year Founded: 1969
Sales Range: $50-74.9 Million
Emp.: 70
Pork Industry Business Association
N.A.I.C.S.: 813910
Patrick Fleming (Dir-Mktg Intelligence, Innovation & Social Responsibility)
Kathy Codner (Dir-Meeting Svcs)
Pamela Johnson (Dir-Consumer Comm)
Ernie Barnes (Dir-Industry Svcs, Producer & Industry Rels)
Stephen Gerike (Dir-Foodservice Mktg)
Steve Larsen (Dir-Pork Safety)
Allan Stokes (Dir-Environmental Programs)
Patrick Webb (Dir-Swine Health Programs)
Calvin VandeKrol (VP-Fin)
Lisa Becton (Dir-Science & Tech & Swine Health Info & Res)
Cynthia Cunningham (Asst VP-Comm)
Kevin Waetke (VP-Strategic Comm)
Terry O'Neel (Pres)
David Pyburn (Sr VP-Science & Tech)
David Bottagaro (Mgr-Foodservice Mktg & Domestic Mktg)
Robert Christine (Mgr-Reg Relationship, Midwest, Producer & Indus Rels)
Jose de Jesus (Dir-Consumer Mktg & Comm)
Chris Hostetler (Dir-Animal Svc & Science & Tech)
Adria Huseth (Mgr-Nutrition Comm, Res, Science & Tech)
Claire Masker (Dir-PR & Comm)
James Murray (Mgr-Foodservice Mktg & Domestic Mktg)
Becca Nepple (VP-Intl Mtkg)
Dinah Peebles (Mgr-Certification Program & IR)
Sharlotte Peterson (Mgr-Outreach Projects & IR)
David Newman (VP)
Michael Skahill (Treas)
Jerry Flint (VP-Engagement & Outreach)
Bill Even (CEO)
Bryan Humphreys (VP-Producer, State & Indus Rels)
Jacque Matsen (VP-Strategic Comm)
Jamie Burr (Chief Sustainability Officer)
Jason Menke (Dir-Consumer PR)

NATIONAL POSITIONS

COMPANIES
NATIONAL RELIGIOUS BROADCASTERS

5012 Chesebro Rd Ste 200, Agoura Hills, CA 91301
Tel.: (818) 676-9819
Web Site:
http://www.nationalpositions.com
Year Founded: 2004
Sales Range: $10-24.9 Million
Emp.: 725
Internet Marketing & Advertising
N.A.I.C.S.: 541613
Bernard May *(Pres)*
Gary Puterman *(Co-Founder)*
Annette Victor Hall *(Controller)*
Marc Levy *(CFO)*
Sachin Shah *(CTO)*

NATIONAL PREMIUM, INC.
N26 W23315 Paul Rd, Pewaukee, WI 53072
Tel.: (262) 513-2400
Web Site:
http://www.nationalpremium.com
Rev.: $23,000,000
Emp.: 68
Services Related Advertising
N.A.I.C.S.: 541890
Daniel Golla *(Mgr-Program)*
Sandi Rinka *(Controller)*
Richard Schmidt *(Pres & Treas)*
Melissa Smith *(Acct Mgr)*
Matt Hatcher *(Acct Exec)*
Evalyn Martin *(Acct Exec)*
Kimberly Busboom *(VP)*

NATIONAL PRODUCT SALES INC.
1600 Empire Rd, Salt Lake City, UT 84104
Tel.: (801) 972-4132
Web Site: http://www.npsstore.com
Rev.: $25,000,000
Emp.: 350
Owner & Operator Surplus & Salvage Stores
N.A.I.C.S.: 455219
Kelly N. Farmer *(Founder & Pres)*

NATIONAL PRODUCT SERVICES
1234 Tech Blvd, Tampa, FL 33619
Tel.: (972) 373-9484
Web Site: http://www.npsinet.com
Sales Range: $50-74.9 Million
Emp.: 5,000
Merchandising Services
N.A.I.C.S.: 561499
Rich D'Amico *(Pres & CEO)*
Scott Murphy *(Exec VP-Sls & Mktg)*
Ken Southerland *(Dir-IT)*
Rich Mitchell *(Gen Counsel)*
Tom Fleissner *(Dir-Special Projects)*
Jen Reno *(Dir-HR)*

Subsidiaries:

Impact Resources, LLC (1)
2987 Claremont Rd Ste 200, Atlanta, GA 30329
Tel.: (404) 233-7658
Merchandising Services
N.A.I.C.S.: 561499

NATIONAL PROPERTY ANALYSTS
230 S Broad St Mezzanine Level, Philadelphia, PA 19102
Tel.: (215) 790-4700
Sales Range: $10-24.9 Million
Emp.: 18
Real Estate Agents & Managers
N.A.I.C.S.: 531210
Edward B. Lipkin *(Pres & CEO)*
Howard M. Levy *(Dir-Leasing)*
Michael Fedak *(Dir-Ops)*
David A. Simon *(VP)*

NATIONAL PURCHASING CORP
1 Ada Ste 150, Irvine, CA 92618
Tel.: (949) 250-4774
Web Site: http://www.hpsionline.com
Sales Range: $10-24.9 Million
Emp.: 75
Purchasing Service
N.A.I.C.S.: 561499
Kirk Lindahl *(VP)*
David Lindahl *(Chm)*

NATIONAL QUALITY FORUM
1030 15th St NW Ste 800, Washington, DC 20005
Tel.: (202) 783-1300 DC
Web Site: http://www.qualityforum.org
Year Founded: 1999
Sales Range: $25-49.9 Million
Emp.: 137
Medical Quality Improvement Organization
N.A.I.C.S.: 813920
Neal Comstock *(VP-Member Rels)*
Bruce Siegel *(Chm)*
Helen Burstin *(Chief Scientific Officer)*
James Chase *(Vice Chm)*
Lawrence M. Becker *(Treas)*
Marc Charon *(CFO)*
Nicole Silverman *(COO)*
Kathleen Giblin *(Sr VP-Quality Innovation)*
Marcia Wilson *(Sr VP-Quality Measurement)*
Patricia Green *(VP-Comm)*
Jason Johnson *(VP-IT)*
Elisa Munthali *(VP-Quality Measurement)*

NATIONAL RAILROAD PASSENGER CORPORATION
1 Massachusetts Ave NW, Washington, DC 20001
Tel.: (215) 856-7924 DC
Web Site: http://www.amtrak.com
Year Founded: 1971
Sales Range: $1-4.9 Billion
Emp.: 20,156
National Inter-City Rail Passenger System
N.A.I.C.S.: 482111
Tracie A. Winbigler *(CFO & Exec VP)*
William J. Flynn *(Pres & CEO)*
Eleanor D. Acheson *(Chief Legal Officer, Gen Counsel, Sec & Exec VP)*
D. J. Stadtler *(Exec VP-Admin)*
Anthony R. Coscia *(Chm)*
Jeffrey R. Moreland *(Vice Chm)*
Stephen J. Gardner *(Chief Operating & Comml Officer)*
J. Timothy Griffin *(CMO & Exec VP)*
Christian Zacariassen *(CIO)*
Scot Naparstek *(Exec VP-Ops)*
Steve Predmore *(Chief Safety Officer & Exec VP)*

Subsidiaries:

Chicago Union Station Company (1)
525 W Vanburen Str, Chicago, IL 60606-5701 (100%)
Tel.: (202) 906-3000
Web Site:
http://www.chicagounionstation.com
Railroad Passenger Terminal
N.A.I.C.S.: 488210

Washington Terminal Company (1)
3222 M St NW, Washington, DC 20007-3621
Tel.: (202) 906-3000
Web Site: http://www.amtrakexpress.com
Railroad Passenger Terminal
N.A.I.C.S.: 488210

NATIONAL RAILWAY EQUIPMENT COMPANY
908 Shawnee St, Mount Vernon, IL 62864
Tel.: (618) 241-9270
Web Site:
http://www.nationalrailway.com
Year Founded: 1984
Sales Range: $25-49.9 Million
Emp.: 80
Railroad Equipment & Parts Repair, Sales & Distr
N.A.I.C.S.: 336510
Kirby Roseveare *(Dir-International Sls)*
Peter Umbriana *(Project Mgr)*
Steven Beal *(Pres)*

Subsidiaries:

NRE Power Systems, Inc. (1)
5222 Highway 311, Houma, LA 70360
Tel.: (985) 872-5480
Web Site: http://www.nrecps.com
Locomotive Product Whslr
N.A.I.C.S.: 423860
Bryan Chaisson *(VP-Ops & Sls)*

NRE Wheel Works Inc. (1)
5300A N 33rd St, Milwaukee, WI 53209
Tel.: (414) 462-8244
Web Site: http://www.nre.com
Emp.: 15
Locomotive Product Whslr
N.A.I.C.S.: 423860
Ed Werner *(Gen Mgr)*

VMV Paducahbilt (1)
1300 Kentucky Ave, Paducah, KY 42003-1961
Tel.: (270) 444-4555
Web Site: http://www.paducahbilt.com
Sales Range: $25-49.9 Million
Railroad Equipment Sales
N.A.I.C.S.: 336510
Robert A. Pedersen *(VP & Gen Mgr)*

NATIONAL RAILWAY HISTORICAL SOCIETY.
100 N 20th St Ste 400, Philadelphia, PA 19103
Tel.: (215) 557-6606 MD
Web Site: http://www.nrhs.com
Year Founded: 1935
Sales Range: $1-9.9 Million
Railway Heritage Resource Preservation Services
N.A.I.C.S.: 712110
Barry Smith *(Editor)*
Joe Maloney *(VP)*
Bradley F. Bender *(Sec & Editor)*

NATIONAL RAILWAY SUPPLY INC.
37 W Fairmont Ave Ste 322, Savannah, GA 31406
Tel.: (912) 920-4575
Web Site: http://www.nrsga.com
Sales Range: $10-24.9 Million
Emp.: 10
Railroad Equipment & Supplies Sells To Class One Railroads & Transit Companies & Shortline Railroads,
N.A.I.C.S.: 423860
J.D. Beck *(CFO)*

NATIONAL REAL ESTATE INFORMATION SERVICES INC.
100 Beecham Dr, Pittsburgh, PA 15205-4601
Tel.: (412) 921-7400 PA
Year Founded: 1990
Sales Range: $25-49.9 Million
Emp.: 160
Provider of Real Estate Information Services
N.A.I.C.S.: 531320
Michael E. Forgas *(Pres)*
Jo Murin *(Pres)*
Jeff Horrell *(Sr VP)*

NATIONAL REALTY & DEVELOPMENT CORP.
3 Manhattanville Rd Ste 202, Purchase, NY 10577-2117
Tel.: (914) 694-4444
Web Site: http://www.nrdc.com
Year Founded: 1960
Sales Range: $25-49.9 Million
Emp.: 75
Commercial Real Estate Development & Management Services
N.A.I.C.S.: 531210
Richard A. Baker *(Chm)*
Robert C. Baker *(Chm & CEO)*
John G. Orrico *(Pres)*
Jerrold G. Bermingham *(Exec VP-Dev & Acq)*
Brian F. Sekel *(Exec VP-Real Estate)*
Noel T. Mannion *(Exec VP-Property Ops)*
Mark E. Silverman *(Dir-Billing & Collections)*
Charles Bryant *(Dir-Maintenance Svcs)*
Richard A. Kaufman *(Gen Counsel & Exec VP)*
John L. Scala *(CFO & Exec VP)*
Robert Scuderi *(Controller)*
Dawn V. Dunckley *(Dir-Tax)*
Dovid M. Spector *(Sr VP-Leasing)*
Melissa Biolchini *(Asst Dir-Billing)*
Donna Justo *(Dir-Mktg)*
Jose Navarro *(Project Mgr)*
Maria McCann *(Mgr-Property)*
Nick Hrvatin *(VP-Leasing)*

Subsidiaries:

NRDC Real Estate Advisors (1)
3 Manhattanville Rd, Purchase, NY 10577-2117 (100%)
Tel.: (914) 272-8080
Sales Range: $25-49.9 Million
Emp.: 50
Real Estate Research & Strategic Planning Services
N.A.I.C.S.: 531390
Lee S. Neibart *(Founder)*

Regional Construction Corp. (1)
3 Manhattanville Rd, Purchase, NY 10577-2117
Tel.: (914) 272-8062
Web Site: http://www.nrdc.com
Sales Range: $10-24.9 Million
Emp.: 4
Commercial Building Construction
N.A.I.C.S.: 236220
Thomas M. Marciniec *(Pres)*
Alex Thompson *(VP-Tenant Construction)*

NATIONAL RECOVERY AGENCY
2491 Paxton St, Harrisburg, PA 17111
Tel.: (717) 540-5605
Web Site:
http://www.nationalrecovery.com
Year Founded: 1976
Rev.: $32,000,000
Emp.: 180
Collection Agencies
N.A.I.C.S.: 561440
Arthur A. Kusic *(CEO)*
Steve Kusic *(Pres)*
Kimberly Summerlot *(Mgr-Bus Dev)*
Ashley Johnson *(Mgr-Client Svc & Compliance)*
Bradley Huffman *(Dir-IT)*
Craig Andrus *(Mgr-Trng)*
Michael West *(Mgr-Trng)*
Rocco Bruno *(Mgr-Bus Dev)*
Yvonne Cooper *(Asst Mgr-Trng)*

NATIONAL RELIGIOUS BROADCASTERS
9510 Technology Dr, Manassas, VA 20110
Tel.: (703) 330-7000 DC
Web Site: http://www.nrb.org
Year Founded: 1944

NATIONAL RELIGIOUS BROADCASTERS

National Religious Broadcasters—(Continued)
Sales Range: $1-9.9 Million
Emp.: 40
Christian Ministry Services
N.A.I.C.S.: 813110
Beth Wakefield *(Dir-Conventions & Expositions)*
Steve Cross *(Dir-Mktg)*
Melissa Sturgis *(Dir-Membership)*
Aaron Mercer *(VP-Govt Rels)*
Kenneth Chan *(Dir-Comm)*
Michael D. Little *(Chm)*
Mike Kisha *(VP-Fin)*
Troy Miller *(COO & Exec VP)*

NATIONAL REPROGRAPHICS INC.
44 W 18th St Fl 3, New York, NY 10011
Tel.: (212) 366-7000
Web Site: http://www.nrinet.com
Sales Range: $10-24.9 Million
Emp.: 200
Photocopying & Duplicating Services
N.A.I.C.S.: 323111
Doug Magid *(Pres)*
Rick Sciorra *(Dir-IS)*
Daniel Gabrich *(VP-Ops)*
Ronald Amato *(Office Mgr)*
Nathan Schultz *(Mgr-Floor)*
Lawrence Seamon *(Acct Exec)*
Lori DeHart *(Mgr-HR)*
Alan Sussman *(CFO & VP-Fin)*
Ellen Feuer *(Chm)*

NATIONAL RESTAURANT ASSOCIATION
2055 L St NW Suite 700, Washington, DC 20036
Tel.: (202) 331-5900
Web Site: http://www.restaurant.org
Emp.: 150
Promote Entrepreneurship & Hospitality in the Restaurant Industry
N.A.I.C.S.: 813910
Joe Kadow *(Chm)*
Jeff Davis *(Vice Chm)*
Jay Stieber *(Treas)*
Marv Irby *(CFO)*
Deb Billow *(Exec VP-Mktg & Membership)*
Terry J. Erdle *(Chief Revenue Officer)*
Yvonne Wolf *(Exec VP-HR)*
Tom Bene *(Pres & CEO)*

NATIONAL RESTAURANT DEVELOPMENT, INC.
625 DeKalb Industrial Way Ste 100, Decatur, GA 30033
Tel.: (404) 499-1960 GA
Web Site: http://www.nrdiusa.com
Year Founded: 1996
Sales Range: $150-199.9 Million
Emp.: 1,200
Holding Company; Franchise Fast-Food Restaurants Owner & Operator
N.A.I.C.S.: 551112
Aziz Hashim *(Pres & CEO)*
Anwar Bhayani *(CFO)*
Shana Gonzales *(COO)*

Subsidiaries:

NRD Holdings, LLC (1)
625 DeKalb Industrial Way Ste 100, Decatur, GA 30033
Tel.: (404) 499-1960
Web Site: http://www.nrdiusa.com
Franchise Fast-Food Restaurants Operator
N.A.I.C.S.: 722513
Aziz Hashim *(Pres & CEO)*
Anwar Bhayani *(CFO)*
Akber Rahim *(Dir-IT)*

NATIONAL RESTAURANT SUPPLY COMPANY
7125 Indus Ave, El Paso, TX 79915
Tel.: (915) 544-2121 TX
Web Site: http://www.nrsupply.com
Year Founded: 1947
Sales Range: $75-99.9 Million
Emp.: 100
Wholesale Distributor of Restaurant Equipment & Supplies; Industrial & Personal Service Paper, Janitorial Supplies
N.A.I.C.S.: 423440
Bruce Gulbas *(Pres)*

NATIONAL RESTORATION SYSTEMS
1500 Hicks Rd Ste 200, Rolling Meadows, IL 60008
Tel.: (847) 483-7700
Web Site: http://www.nrsys.com
Sales Range: $10-24.9 Million
Emp.: 50
Concrete Repair
N.A.I.C.S.: 238110
Frank Reagan *(Exec VP)*
Maureen Dell *(Office Mgr)*

NATIONAL RETAIL CORPORATION
4939 Big Island Dr, Jacksonville, FL 32246-7405
Tel.: (904) 292-2855
Sales Range: $10-24.9 Million
Emp.: 16
Furniture Retailer
N.A.I.C.S.: 449110
Alexander G. Chatkewitz *(Pres)*
Frank Watson *(Chm)*

NATIONAL RETAIL SYSTEMS, INC.
2820 16th St, North Bergen, NJ 07047
Tel.: (201) 330-1900 NJ
Web Site: http://www.nrsonline.com
Year Founded: 1953
Sales Range: $75-99.9 Million
Emp.: 600
Logistic Services
N.A.I.C.S.: 551112
Raymond Wisniewski *(COO)*
Frank Walsh *(Pres)*

Subsidiaries:

Keystone Freight Corp. (1)
2820 16th St, North Bergen, NJ 07047
Tel.: (201) 330-1900
Web Site: http://www.nrsonline.com
Sales Range: $25-49.9 Million
Emp.: 400
Truckload, Private Fleets & Lane-Specific Line Haul Services
N.A.I.C.S.: 484110

National Retail Transportation (1)
2820 16th St, North Bergen, NJ 07047
Tel.: (201) 863-3200
Web Site: http://www.nrsonline.com
Rev: $42,900,000
Emp.: 500
Local & Regional Trucking Services
N.A.I.C.S.: 484121
Raymond Wisniewski *(Pres)*

NATIONAL REVIEW, INC.
215 Lexington Ave, New York, NY 10016-6023
Tel.: (212) 679-7330 NY
Web Site: http://www.nationalreview.com
Year Founded: 1955
Sales Range: $50-74.9 Million
Emp.: 40
Political Opinion Magazine Publisher
N.A.I.C.S.: 513120
James X. Kilbridge *(CFO)*
Richard Lowry *(Editor-Magazine & Website-Washington)*
Scott Budd *(Publr)*
Benny Johnson *(Dir-Social Media)*

NATIONAL RIGHT TO WORK COMMITTEE
8001 Braddock Rd Ste 500, Springfield, VA 22160
Tel.: (703) 321-9820 VA
Web Site: http://www.nrtwc.org
Year Founded: 1975
Sales Range: $10-24.9 Million
Emp.: 550
Employee Welfare Services
N.A.I.C.S.: 813930
Matthew M. Leen *(VP)*
Greg W. Mourad *(VP)*
Mary J. King *(VP)*
Anne M. Coulter *(Sec)*

NATIONAL RIVET & MANUFACTURING CO.
21 E Jefferson St, Waupun, WI 53963-1942
Tel.: (920) 324-5511 WI
Web Site: http://www.nationalrivet.com
Rivets & Automatic Rivet Setting Machines Mfr
N.A.I.C.S.: 332722
J. Bur Zeratsky *(Owner)*

NATIONAL ROOFING CO. INC.
4011 Roland Ave, Baltimore, MD 21211
Tel.: (410) 235-5827 MD
Web Site: http://www.nationalroofingusa.com
Year Founded: 1930
Sales Range: $10-24.9 Million
Emp.: 250
Roofing Contractors
N.A.I.C.S.: 238160
Debbie Zapora *(CFO & Sr VP)*
Rob Hughes *(Dir-Estimating & Contracts)*
Kendall Thrasher *(Mgr-Acctg Dept)*
Maribel Munoz *(Head-Estimating & Contracts)*
Francine Campos *(Dir-HR)*

NATIONAL RURAL TELECOMMUNICATIONS COOPERATIVE
2121 Cooperative Way Ste 600, Herndon, VA 20171
Tel.: (703) 787-0874
Web Site: http://www.nrtc.coop
Year Founded: 1986
Emp.: 100
Telecommunications Services Including Internet, Wireless & Cable
N.A.I.C.S.: 517810
Terry Gilmore *(CFO)*
Greg Santoro *(Chief Mktg & Strategy Officer & Sr VP)*
Jeff Wilson *(Chm)*
Shannon Clark *(Vice Chm)*
Tim Mergen *(Treas & Sec)*
Chuck Divone *(Gen Counsel)*
James DaBramo *(Pres-Broadband Solutions Division)*
J. Timothy Bryan *(CEO)*

Subsidiaries:

NeoNova Network Services Inc. (1)
1201 Edwards Mill Rd Ste 102, Raleigh, NC 27607
Tel.: (919) 460-3330
Web Site: http://www.neonova.net
Sales Range: $25-49.9 Million
Emp.: 80
Internet & Voice Telecommunications Systems
N.A.I.C.S.: 517810
Chris Beatson *(CTO)*
Ray Carey *(CEO)*
Mike DeFrancesco *(CFO)*
Jason McGinnis *(Pres)*

SecurityCoverage Inc. (1)
6060 Huntington Ct NE, Cedar Rapids, IA 52402
Tel.: (319) 298-4700
Web Site: http://www.securitycoverage.com
Security System Services
N.A.I.C.S.: 561621

NATIONAL SAFE PLACE
2429 Crittenden Dr, Louisville, KY 40217
Tel.: (502) 635-3660 KY
Web Site: http://www.nationalsafeplace.org
Year Founded: 2006
Sales Range: $1-9.9 Million
Youth Welfare Services
N.A.I.C.S.: 624110
Laurie Jackson *(Pres & CEO)*
Susan Harmon *(Dir-Sls Place Natl Ops)*
Michael Fitz *(Chm)*

NATIONAL SAFETY ASSOCIATES
140 Cresent Dr, Collierville, TN 38017
Tel.: (901) 850-3000 TN
Web Site: http://www.nsaonline.com
Year Founded: 1970
Sales Range: $125-149.9 Million
Emp.: 160
Mfr of Household Water Filters & Air Filters
N.A.I.C.S.: 423720
Jay Martin *(Founder & Chm)*
Stan Turk *(CFO)*
George Poteet *(VP-Mfg)*
Travis Garza *(CEO-Global)*

NATIONAL SAFETY COMMISSION (NSC)
PO Box 3359, Ponte Vedra Beach, FL 32004-3359
Tel.: (904) 688-2284
Web Site: http://www.lowestpricetrafficschool.com
Year Founded: 2002
Sales Range: $10-24.9 Million
Emp.: 60
Safety Training
N.A.I.C.S.: 922190
Ken Underwood *(Founder, Pres & CEO)*

NATIONAL SAFETY COUNCIL
1121 Spring Lake Dr, Itasca, IL 60143-3201
Tel.: (630) 285-1121
Web Site: https://www.nsc.org
Year Founded: 1913
Safety Services
N.A.I.C.S.: 813319

NATIONAL SCHOOL BOARDS ASSOCIATION
1680 Duke St, Alexandria, VA 22314
Tel.: (703) 838-6722 IL
Web Site: http://www.nsba.org
Year Founded: 1949
Sales Range: $10-24.9 Million
Emp.: 125
Educational Support Services
N.A.I.C.S.: 611710
Kanisha Williams-Jones *(Mng Dir & Dir-Leadership Svcs)*
Deborah Rigsby *(Dir-Federal Legislation)*
Beth Branham *(Treas & Sec)*
Kevin E. Ciak *(Pres)*
Thomas J. Gentzel *(CEO)*
Heather Eggleston *(Dir-Conferences & Meetings)*
Pamela Saunders *(Dir-HR)*
Ronald Skinner *(Chief Member Svcs Officer)*
Kelly Pollitt *(Chief Advocacy Officer-Washington)*

Rory Davenport *(Chief Comm Officer)*
Heather Dean *(COO)*
John A. Reeb *(Mng Dir)*

NATIONAL SCIENCE TEACHERS ASSOCIATION
1840 Wilson Blvd, Arlington, VA 22201
Tel.: (703) 243-7100 DC
Web Site: http://www.nsta.org
Year Founded: 1960
Sales Range: $25-49.9 Million
Emp.: 121
Scientific Research Services
N.A.I.C.S.: 541715
David L. Evans *(Sec)*
Natacia Campbell *(Dir-Multicultural & Equity in Science Education)*
Doug Hodum *(Dir-District II)*
Mary L. Loesing *(Dir-District IV)*
Shannon Hudson *(Dir-District X)*
Dennis Schatz *(Dir-Informal Science)*
Kenneth L. Huff *(Dir-Middle Level Science Teaching)*
Jennifer S. Thompson *(Dir-Preschool & Elementary)*
Eric Brunsell *(Dir-Prof Dev)*
Mary Gromko *(Pres)*
Aimee Kennedy *(VP-Education)*

NATIONAL SCOUTING REPORT INC.
128 Total Solutions Way, Alabaster, AL 35007
Tel.: (205) 216-0080
Web Site: http://www.nsr-inc.com
Sales Range: $10-24.9 Million
Emp.: 15
Sports Services
N.A.I.C.S.: 713940
Robert Rigney *(Pres)*

NATIONAL SECURITY SYSTEMS INC.
511 Manhasset Woods Rd, Manhasset, NY 11030-1663
Tel.: (516) 627-2222 NY
Year Founded: 1958
Sales Range: $25-49.9 Million
Emp.: 27
Electrical Equipment & Supplies
N.A.I.C.S.: 335999
Jay Barron *(Pres)*

NATIONAL SEPTEMBER 11 MEMORIAL & MUSEUM
200 Liberty St 16th Fl, New York, NY 10281
Tel.: (212) 312-8800 NY
Web Site: http://www.911memorial.org
Year Founded: 2003
Sales Range: $75-99.9 Million
Emp.: 305
Memorial & Museum
N.A.I.C.S.: 812220
Michael Rubens Bloomberg *(Chm)*
Noelle Lilien *(Gen Counsel & Sec)*
Allison Blais *(Exec VP & Deputy Dir-Strategy & Advancement)*
Michael R. Bloomberg *(Chm)*
Ernie Blundell *(Exec VP & Deputy Dir-Ops)*
Clifford Chanin *(Exec VP & Deputy Dir-Museum Programs)*
George E. Pataki *(Chm)*
Shelby Prichard *(Exec VP & Deputy Dir-Admin)*

NATIONAL SERVICES GROUP INC.
1682 Langley Ave, Irvine, CA 92614-5620
Tel.: (714) 564-7900
Web Site: http://www.nationalservicesgroup.com
Sales Range: $25-49.9 Million
Emp.: 650
Painting & Paper Hanging
N.A.I.C.S.: 238320
Matt Stewart *(Exec Officer)*
Jeff Gunhus *(Exec Officer)*

Subsidiaries:

CWPNC Inc. (1)
1682 Langley Ave, Irvine, CA 92614
Tel.: (714) 564-7904
Web Site: http://www.nationalservicesgroup.com
Sales Range: $10-24.9 Million
Emp.: 50
Painting & Paper Hanging
N.A.I.C.S.: 238320
Matthew K. Stewart *(CEO)*

College Works Painting Inc. (1)
1682 Langley Ave, Irvine, CA 92614
Tel.: (714) 564-7900
Web Site: http://www.collegeworks.com
Residential Painting
N.A.I.C.S.: 238320
Spencer Pepe *(Exec Officer)*
Marc Blumenthal *(Chief Bus Dev Officer)*
Chris Heerdegen *(Pres)*
Rob Lovato *(VP-Virginia)*
Sean Phelps *(VP-Great Plains & Arizona)*
Rob Sprong *(VP-California)*
Kyle Lindsey *(Exec VP)*
Tom Ackmann *(Exec VP)*

NATIONAL SLEEP THERAPY
53 Regional Dr Ste 201, Concord, NH 03301
Web Site: http://www.nstherapy.com
Year Founded: 2008
Sales Range: $1-9.9 Million
Emp.: 22
Sleep Therapy Services & Equipment
N.A.I.C.S.: 423450
Eric Cohen *(Co-Founder & Pres)*
Peter Falkson *(Co-Founder & CEO)*

NATIONAL SLOVAK SOCIETY
351 Valley Brook Rd, McMurray, PA 15317-3337
Tel.: (724) 731-0094 PA
Web Site: http://www.nsslife.org
Year Founded: 1890
Sales Range: $125-149.9 Million
Emp.: 25
Family Welfare Services
N.A.I.C.S.: 624190
David G. Blazek *(Pres & CEO)*
Linda M. Strom *(CFO, Treas & Sec)*
Joseph Stefka Jr. *(Chm)*

NATIONAL SOCIETY DAUGHTERS OF THE AMERICAN REVOLUTION
1776 D St NW, Washington, DC 20006-5303
Tel.: (202) 628-1776 DC
Web Site: http://www.dar.org
Year Founded: 1896
Sales Range: $10-24.9 Million
Emp.: 176
Historical Preservation Services
N.A.I.C.S.: 541720
Ann Turner Dillon *(Pres)*
Martha Gee Barnhart *(Treas)*

NATIONAL SOCIETY OF BLACK ENGINEERS
205 Daingerfield Rd, Alexandria, VA 22314
Tel.: (703) 549-2207 TX
Web Site: http://www.nsbe.org
Year Founded: 1976
Sales Range: $10-24.9 Million
Emp.: 27
African-American Engineers Association
N.A.I.C.S.: 813920

Sossena Wood *(Chm)*
Victoria Hills *(Vice Chm-Exec Bd)*
Janeen Uzzell *(CEO)*
Charles Thompson III *(Chief Dev & Mktg Officer)*

NATIONAL SPECIALTY ALLOYS
18250 Kieth Harrow, Houston, TX 77084
Tel.: (281) 345-2115
Web Site: http://www.nsalloys.com
Emp.: 150
Steel
N.A.I.C.S.: 423510
Brad Poole *(VP-Natl Sls)*
Harold Vance *(Asst VP-Information Svcs-Houston)*
Anthony Kosler *(VP-Specialty Products)*
Steve DeCelles *(Reg Mgr-Sls)*
Ron Haynie *(VP-Reg Sls)*
Eileen Casiraghi *(VP-Ops)*
Mark Russ *(Pres & CEO)*

NATIONAL SPINNING COMPANY, INC.
1212 Avenue Of The Americas Ste 1901, New York, NY 10036
Tel.: (212) 382-6400 NY
Web Site: http://www.natspin.com
Year Founded: 1921
Sales Range: $450-499.9 Million
Emp.: 700
Mfr & Importer of Spun Yarns for Knitting, Weaving & Home Crafts
N.A.I.C.S.: 313110
Jim Chesnutt *(Chm)*
Robert Gordon *(Mgr-Sls-NY)*
Ed Atkins *(Dir-Mfg)*
Sandy Berger *(Mgr-Credit-NY)*
Linda Fanton *(CFO)*
Jim Booterbaugh *(CEO)*
David Swaim *(CFO)*

Subsidiaries:

Carolina Nonwovens Corporation (1)
1884 Kawai Rd, Lincolnton, NC 28092
Tel.: (704) 735-5600
Web Site: http://www.carolinanonwovens.com
Emp.: 50
Mattress & Construction Product Mfr
N.A.I.C.S.: 321219
Ed Hull *(Bus Mgr)*

Caron International (1)
1481 W 2nd St, Washington, NC 27889-4157
Tel.: (252) 975-7111
Web Site: http://www.caron.com
Sales Range: $50-74.9 Million
Emp.: 400
Mfr of Consumer Yarns & Craft Kits
N.A.I.C.S.: 313110

National Spinning Co. (1)
240 Spinning Rd, Whiteville, NC 28472
Tel.: (910) 642-4181
Web Site: http://www.nationalspinning.com
Sales Range: $50-74.9 Million
Emp.: 250
Yarn Textile Mfr
N.A.I.C.S.: 313110
Rudy Ballance *(Plant Mgr)*
H. Robert Miller *(Vice Chm)*

National Spinning Company, Inc - ALAMANCE DYE PLANT (1)
226 Glen Raven Rd, Burlington, NC 27215
Tel.: (336) 226-0141
Spun Yarn Mfr
N.A.I.C.S.: 313110
Ed Atkins *(Plant Mgr)*

National Spinning Company, Inc - BEULAVILLE SPINNING PLANT (1)
326 Lyman Rd, Beulaville, NC 28518
Tel.: (910) 298-3131
Yarn Mfr
N.A.I.C.S.: 313110

NATIONAL STEEL RULE CO. INC.
750 Commerce Rd Ste 750, Linden, NJ 07036
Tel.: (908) 862-3366
Web Site: http://www.steelrule.com
Sales Range: $25-49.9 Million
Emp.: 95
Mfr of Steel Rules
N.A.I.C.S.: 332216
Edmund Mucci *(Pres)*

NATIONAL STORES, INC.
15001 S Figueroa St, Gardena, CA 90248
Tel.: (310) 324-9962
Web Site: http://www.fallasparedes.com
Rev.: $30,000,000
Emp.: 400
Owner & Operator of Family Clothing Stores
N.A.I.C.S.: 458110
Jimmy Zhang *(Sr Mgr-Inventory Control)*
Lisa Schwartz *(VP-Allocation)*
Donna Durr *(Mgr)*
Jane Bartlett *(Mgr-Store)*
Patricia Alvarez *(Mgr-Store)*
Brenda Mendoza *(Supvr-Sls Audit)*
Sandra Bouquet *(Coord-Benefits)*
Chris Nichols *(Exec VP-Ops)*
Jamal Juma *(Reg Mgr-Loss Prevention)*

NATIONAL STRATEGIES PUBLIC RELATIONS, LLC
3030 N Rocky Point Dr W Ste 150, Tampa, FL 33607
Tel.: (813) 865-3093
Web Site: http://www.nspublicrelations.com
Emp.: 10
Public Relations
N.A.I.C.S.: 541820
Jennifer Vickery *(CEO)*
Lan Pratt *(COO & VP)*

NATIONAL STUDENT CLEARINGHOUSE
2300 Dulles Station Blvd Ste 300, Herndon, VA 20171
Tel.: (703) 742-4200 VA
Web Site: http://www.studentclearinghouse.org
Year Founded: 1993
Sales Range: $25-49.9 Million
Emp.: 210
Educational Support Services
N.A.I.C.S.: 611710
Ricardo D. Torres *(Pres & CEO)*
Doug Falk *(CIO)*
Mike Ketcham *(CFO)*
George Levathes *(VP-Compliance & Education Fin Industry Rels)*
Jonell Sanchez *(VP-Education Svcs)*
Bridget Sedlock *(Mng Dir-Corp Svcs)*
John Ramsey *(Chief Info Security Officer)*
Mary Chapin *(Chief Legal Officer)*
Larry Hatch *(VP-Industry & Workforce Svcs)*

NATIONAL SYSTEMS CONSULTING L.P.
5945 Dallas Pkwy Ste 100, Plano, TX 75093
Tel.: (972) 212-7433 TX
Web Site: http://www.nsiamerica.com
Year Founded: 1996
Sales Range: $10-24.9 Million
Emp.: 175
Computer System Design Services
N.A.I.C.S.: 541512

NATIONAL SYSTEMS CONSULTING L.P.

National Systems Consulting L.P.—(Continued)
Hari Patro (Mng Partner)
Seelam Reddy (Mng Partner)
Mukesh Shah (Mng Partner)

NATIONAL THOROUGHBRED RACING ASSOCIATION
2525 Harrodsburg Rd Ste 510, Lexington, KY 40504-3359
Tel.: (859) 245-6872
Web Site: http://www.ntra.com
Year Founded: 1998
Sales Range: $10-24.9 Million
Emp.: 25
Governing Body of Thoroughbred Horse Racing
N.A.I.C.S.: 711219
Keith Chamblin (COO)
Alex Waldrop (Pres & CEO)
Steve Koch (Exec Dir-Safety & Integrity Alliance)
Jeffrey Burch (Sr VP-NTRA Advantage)
Holly Short (Mgr-Digital Mktg)

NATIONAL TICKET COMPANY
5562 Snydertown Rd, Paxinos, PA 17860
Tel.: (570) 672-2900
Web Site: http://www.nationalticket.com
Year Founded: 1907
Sales Range: $10-24.9 Million
Emp.: 200
Providers of Ticketing to the Mass Entertainment & Amusement Industries
N.A.I.C.S.: 323111
Edward Ludes (VP-Production)
Gary Chabot (Acct Mgr)

NATIONAL TOOL & MANUFACTURING COMPANY
581 Wheeling Rd, Wheeling, IL 60090
Tel.: (847) 806-9800
Web Site: http://www.ntm.com
Year Founded: 1933
Sales Range: $50-74.9 Million
Emp.: 55
Mfr of Standard & Special Mold Sets & Components for Plastic Molds
N.A.I.C.S.: 333511

NATIONAL TRADE SUPPLY, LLC
2011 Southtech Dr Ste 100, Greenwood, IN 46143
Tel.: (317) 536-7445
Web Site: http://www.ntsupply.com
Sales Range: $10-24.9 Million
Emp.: 17
Online Sales of HVAC & Energy Saver Equipment
N.A.I.C.S.: 333415
Todd Anthony (Co-Founder & CEO)
Tyler Dishman (Co-Founder & Pres)
Jon Coppedge (Dir-Sls & Customer Svc)

NATIONAL TRANSPORTATION & LOGISTICS, INC.
20992 S Ferguson Rd, Oregon City, OR 97045
Tel.: (503) 632-5071
Sales Range: $10-24.9 Million
Emp.: 55
Air Cargo Services
N.A.I.C.S.: 488510
Richard A. Trute (Pres)
Mary P. Trute (Sec)

NATIONAL TRAVELERS INC.
3205 Cimarron Dr, Conway, AR 72032
Tel.: (501) 764-4678
Web Site: http://www.nationaltraveIersrv.com
Year Founded: 1967
Sales Range: $10-24.9 Million
Emp.: 12
Retailer of Recreational Vehicles
N.A.I.C.S.: 441210
Chris Block (Pres)
Gene Lunday (Mgr-Svc)

NATIONAL TRUST FOR HISTORIC PRESERVATION
600 14th St NW Ste 500, Washington, DC 20005
Tel.: (202) 588-6000
Web Site: https://savingplaces.org
Year Founded: 1949
Emp.: 150
Society for Historic Preservation
N.A.I.C.S.: 712120
David A. Brown (Chief Preservation Officer)
Paul W. Edmondson (Chief Legal Officer)
Stephanie K. Meeks (Pres & CEO)
Andy Grabel (Assoc Dir-Pub Affairs)
Erica Stewart (Mgr-Pub Affairs)
Germonique R. Ulmer (VP-Pub Affairs)
Jessica Pumphrey (Mgr-Pub Affairs)
Robin Scullin (Dir-Pub Affairs)
Sarah Heffern (Assoc Dir-Social Media Strategy)
Tim Mikulski (Mgr-Pub Affairs)
Virgil McDill (Assoc Dir-Pub Affairs)
Valerie Balint (Mgr-Historic Artists' Homes & Studios-Chesterwood)
Donna Hassler (Exec Dir-Chesterwood)
Jon Kevin Gossett (Chief Advancement Officer)

NATIONAL TUBE HOLDING COMPANY INC.
303 Massey Bldg, Birmingham, AL 35203
Tel.: (205) 322-8816
Web Site: http://www.nationaltube.com
Year Founded: 1990
Sales Range: $25-49.9 Million
Emp.: 475
Provider of Copper Rolling & Drawing Services
N.A.I.C.S.: 331420

Subsidiaries:

American Tubing Inc. (1)
2191 Ford Ave, Springdale, AR 72764 (100%)
Tel.: (479) 756-1291
Web Site: http://www.americantubing.com
Sales Range: $10-24.9 Million
Emp.: 150
Fabrication Of Copper Cubical Components
N.A.I.C.S.: 331420
Chuck Lewis (Pres)
Eddie Carmean (Superintendent-Production)

National Copper & Smelting Company Inc. (1)
3333 Stanwood Blvd NE, Huntsville, AL 35811-8505
Tel.: (256) 859-4510
Web Site: http://www.nationaltube.com
Sales Range: $25-49.9 Million
Emp.: 150
Copper Rolling & Drawing Services
N.A.I.C.S.: 331420

Prairie Ronde Realty Company, Inc. (1)
415 E Prairie Ronde St, Dowagiac, MI 49047-1348
Tel.: (269) 782-2141
Sales Range: $10-24.9 Million
Emp.: 2
Provider of Real Estate Agency Services
N.A.I.C.S.: 531210
Tom Fox (Pres)

NATIONAL URBAN LEAGUE
80 Pine St 9th Fl, New York, NY 10005
Tel.: (212) 558-5300
Web Site: https://www.nul.org
Year Founded: 1910
Social Organization Services
N.A.I.C.S.: 813920

NATIONAL UTILITY SERVICE, INC.
1 Maynard Dr, Park Ridge, NJ 07656-0712
Tel.: (201) 391-4300   NJ
Web Site: http://www.nusconsulting.com
Year Founded: 1934
Rev.: $63,000,000
Emp.: 750
Business Consultancy Services
N.A.I.C.S.: 541618
Gary J. Soultanian (Co-Pres)
Richard D. Soultanian (Co-Pres)
Robert A. Heinrich (VP & Gen Mgr)

Subsidiaries:

NUS Consulting Group (1)
1 Fatsbursgatan, 10462, Stockholm, Sweden (100%)
Tel.: (46) 87020045
Web Site: http://www.nusconsulting.se
Sales Range: $25-49.9 Million
Emp.: 11
Energy Management Solutions
N.A.I.C.S.: 541613
Richard Soultanian (Gen Mgr)

NUS Deutschland GmbH (1)
Peter-Muller-Str 10, 40684, Dusseldorf, Germany (100%)
Tel.: (49) 211862290
Sales Range: $25-49.9 Million
Emp.: 45
Energy Management Solutions
N.A.I.C.S.: 561110

NUS International Pty. Ltd. (1)
Level 5 77 Pacific Hwy, PO Box 1140, Sydney, 2060, NSW, Australia (100%)
Tel.: (61) 299227676
Web Site: http://www.nusconsulting.com.au
Sales Range: $25-49.9 Million
Emp.: 25
Energy Management Solutions
N.A.I.C.S.: 561110
Tony Hake (Mng Dir)

NUS Italia, s.r.l. (1)
Via M.Gioie 168, 20125, Milan, Italy
Tel.: (39) 02671591
Web Site: http://www.nusconsulting.com
Sales Range: $25-49.9 Million
Emp.: 25
Energy Management Solutions
N.A.I.C.S.: 561110
Claudio Enriquez (Mng Dir)

NUS-South Africa (1)
1st Floor Moorgate Dunkeld Park, 6 North Road Dunkeld West, Johannesburg, 2196, South Africa (100%)
Tel.: (27) 0112684500
Web Site: http://www.nusconsulting.com
Sales Range: $50-74.9 Million
Emp.: 40
Energy & Telecommunications Consulting Services
N.A.I.C.S.: 541611

National Utility Service (Canada) Ltd. (1)
111 Gordon Baker Road Suite 500, North York, M2H 3R2, ON, Canada (100%)
Tel.: (416) 490-9922
Web Site: http://www.nusconsulting.ca
Sales Range: $25-49.9 Million
Emp.: 36
Business Consultants For Communications
N.A.I.C.S.: 541611
Wally Khalil (Gen Mgr)

National Utility Service, S.A. (1)
Ikaroslaan 37, 1930, Zaventem, Belgium
Tel.: (32) 26499754
Web Site: http://www.nusconsulting.com
Sales Range: $25-49.9 Million
Emp.: 8
Energy Management Solutions
N.A.I.C.S.: 561110
Allin Rieke (Gen Mgr)

National Utility Service, S.A. (1)
4 rue Louis Bleroit, 92502, Rueil-Malmaison, Cedex, France
Tel.: (33) 155477000
Web Site: http://www.nusconsulting.fr
Sales Range: $25-49.9 Million
Emp.: 50
Energy Management Solutions
N.A.I.C.S.: 561110

Nus Consulting Group Pty Limited (1)
Level 5 77 Pacific Highway, North Sydney, 2060, NSW, Australia
Tel.: (61) 2 9922 7676
Web Site: http://www.nusconsulting.com.au
Sales Range: $10-24.9 Million
Emp.: 40
Management Consulting Services
N.A.I.C.S.: 541611
Tony Hake (Gen Mgr)
Dennis Schaefer (VP-Sls)

Viking Energy Management LLC (1)
15720 John J Delaney Dr 300, Charlotte, NC 28277
Tel.: (704) 540-9089
Web Site: http://www.vikingem.com
Energy Management Consulting Services
N.A.I.C.S.: 541690

NATIONAL VAN LINES, INC.
2800 W Roosevelt Rd, Broadview, IL 60155-3756
Tel.: (708) 450-2900   IL
Web Site: http://www.nationalvanlines.com
Year Founded: 1934
Sales Range: $75-99.9 Million
Emp.: 130
Household Goods Moving Services
N.A.I.C.S.: 484210
Maureen Beal (Chm & CEO)
Jorja Colter (VP-Customer Experience & Quality)
Gerry Mundt (VP-Fin)
Tim Helenthal (Pres & COO)

NATIONAL VENDOR, INC.
26249 Enterprise Ct, Lake Forest, CA 92630
Tel.: (949) 305-4500
Web Site: http://www.nationalvendor.com
Year Founded: 1997
Sales Range: $10-24.9 Million
Emp.: 65
Oversettlement Mitigation Service
N.A.I.C.S.: 524291
Kelly D. Henry (VP-Mktg)

NATIONAL VITAMIN CO. INC.
1145 W Gila Bend Hwy, Casa Grande, AZ 85122
Tel.: (520) 426-3100   AZ
Web Site: http://www.nationalvitamin.com
Year Founded: 1974
Vitamin Preparations
N.A.I.C.S.: 325412
Earl Courtney (Partner-VP-Sls)

NATIONAL WHOLESALE COMPANY INC.
400 National Blvd, Lexington, NC 27292
Tel.: (336) 248-5904
Web Site: http://www.shopnational.com
Sales Range: $25-49.9 Million
Emp.: 140
Women's Apparel, Mail Order

COMPANIES

N.A.I.C.S.: 424350
Lynda Smith Swann (Pres)
Betty McMahan (VP-Adv)
David Lyttle (Mgr-IT)

NATIONAL WHOLESALE LIQUIDATORS INC.
111 Hempstead Tpke, West Hempstead, NY 11552
Tel.: (516) 489-3300
Web Site: http://www.nationalwholesaleliquidators.com
Rev.: $10,800,000
Emp.: 1
Purchasing Service
N.A.I.C.S.: 541611
Guillermo Paredes (Mgr)

NATIONAL WILD TURKEY FEDERATION
770 Augusta Rd, Edgefield, SC 29824-0530
Tel.: (803) 637-3106   SC
Web Site: https://www.nwtf.org
Year Founded: 1973
Sales Range: $25-49.9 Million
Emp.: 120
Wildlife Conservation Services
N.A.I.C.S.: 813312
Becky Humphries (CEO)
Doug Saunders (Chief Mktg & Strategy Officer)
Dave Mahlke (Sr VP-Field Ops & Volunteer Rels)
Vern Ross (Chm)
Marvin Hartley (Pres)
Vincent M. Rosdahl (VP)
Robert Higginbotham (Sec)
Harlan Starr (Treas)
Karen Lee (VP-Comm)
Matt Fenoff (VP-Dev)
Ellen M. Lintal (CFO)

NATIONAL WILDLIFE FEDERATION
11100 Wildlife Cente Dr, Reston, VA 20190-5362
Tel.: (703) 438-6000
Web Site: http://www.nwf.org
Year Founded: 1936
Sales Range: $100-124.9 Million
Emp.: 275
Wildlife, Wild Places & the Environment Protection Services; Magazine Publisher
N.A.I.C.S.: 813312
Kevin J. Coyle (VP-Education & Trng)
Miles Grant (Dir-Comm-Natl Advocacy Center)
Jordan Lubetkin (Sr Mgr-Comm-Great Lakes)
Jeremy Symons (Sr VP)
Maureen P. Smith (CMO)
Collin O'Mara (Pres & CEO)
Lisa Moore (Dir-Editorial-Magazine)
Dirk Sellers (VP-Philanthropy)
Brandi Colander (Assoc VP-Natural Resources & Energy)
Barbara Bramble (VP-Intl Wildlife Conservation & Corp Strategies)
Andy Buschbaum (VP-One Federation)
Hilary Harp Falk (VP-Reg Conservation)
Cindy Golos (VP-Strategic Bus Ops)
Benjamin Kota (Gen Counsel)
Aaron Kindle (Sr Mgr-Western Sporting Campaigns)
Marcia Brownlee (Mgr-Sportswoman's Initiative-Artemis)
Tracy Stone-Manning (Assoc VP-Public Lands Program)

Subsidiaries:

Your Big Backyard   (1)
11100 Wildlife Ctr Dr, Reston, VA 20190
Tel.: (703) 438-6000
Web Site: http://www.nwf.org
Magazine
N.A.I.C.S.: 513120
Susan McElhinney (Editor-Photo)

NATIONAL WINE & SPIRITS, INC.
700 W Morris St, Indianapolis, IN 46206
Tel.: (317) 636-6092   IN
Web Site: http://www.nwscorp.com
Year Founded: 1934
Sales Range: $700-749.9 Million
Emp.: 1,725
Beverages, Liquors, Wines & Spirits Whslr
N.A.I.C.S.: 424810
James E. Lacrosse (Chm, Pres, CEO & CFO)
John J. Baker (COO, Sec & Exec VP)
Dwight Deming (VP-Info Sys)
Patrick A. Trefun (Treas & Controller)

Subsidiaries:

Consolidated Distilled Products   (1)
PO Box1602, Indianapolis, IN 46206   (100%)
Tel.: (773) 254-9000
Web Site: http://www.nwscorp.com
Sales Range: $50-74.9 Million
Emp.: 700
Distr of Beverages
N.A.I.C.S.: 424820

NATIONAL WOOD PRODUCTS, INC.
2705 S 600 W, Salt Lake City, UT 84115
Tel.: (801) 977-1171   UT
Web Site: http://www.nationalwood.com
Sales Range: $100-124.9 Million
Emp.: 150
Lumber: Rough; Dressed & Finished
N.A.I.C.S.: 423310
Vivian Fisher (Controller)
Kurt Mitek (VP)
John Bernard (Mgr-Flooring Div)

NATIONAL YOUTH ADVOCATE PROGRAM
1801 Watermark Dr Ste 200, Columbus, OH 43215
Tel.: (614) 487-8758   OH
Web Site: http://www.nyap.org
Year Founded: 1983
Sales Range: $25-49.9 Million
Emp.: 534
Youth & Family Support Services
N.A.I.C.S.: 624190
F. Edward Sparks (Exec VP)
Joyette Smith-Ross (Dir-HR)
Renee Ellenberger (Dir-Foster Care)
Michelle Corry (Dir-Clinical Svcs)
Mary Ramseyer (Chm)
Marvena Twigg (Pres & CEO)
Jackie Rowand (Sec)
David Gemmill (Treas)
Delois McKinley-Eldridge (Vice Chm)

NATIONAL-GENERAL SUPPLY, INC.
PO Box 2288, Great Falls, MT 59401
Tel.: (406) 761-6861
Year Founded: 1979
Sales Range: $10-24.9 Million
Emp.: 31
Hardware Whslr
N.A.I.C.S.: 423710
Aaron Weissman (CEO & Gen Mgr)

NATIONALLINK, INC.
2235 Auto Center Dr, Glendora, CA 91740
Tel.: (909) 447-7970
Web Site: http://www.nationallink.com
Sales Range: $10-24.9 Million
Emp.: 35
Turnkey Solutions for ATM Industry
N.A.I.C.S.: 333310
Sam Kandah (Pres & CEO)

NATIONAWIDE SCREENING SERVICES, INC.
324 S Services Rd, Ste 102 Melville, NY 11747
Tel.: (877) 696-5700
Web Site: http://nsshire.com
Security & Investigation Services
N.A.I.C.S.: 561611
Robert Santoro (Mng Dir)

NATIONS RELIABLE LENDING, LLC
2506 W St S Ste 400, Houston, TX 77098
Tel.: (713) 275-1300
Web Site: http://www.nrlmtg.com
Year Founded: 2007
Sales Range: $1-9.9 Million
Emp.: 104
Mortgage Lender
N.A.I.C.S.: 522310
Matthew Hyde (Branch Mgr)
Zach Ron (Pres)

NATIONWIDE APPRAISAL NETWORK (NAN)
250 Pine Ave N Suite A, Oldsmar, FL 34677
Tel.: (888) 760-8899
Web Site: http://www.nationwide-appraisal.com
Year Founded: 2008
Sales Range: $10-24.9 Million
Emp.: 30
Appraisal & Valuation Services to Lenders, Bankers & Mortgage Companies
N.A.I.C.S.: 531320
Cari Burris (Co-Founder & Dir-Ops)
Joni Pilgrim (Co-Founder & Chief Bus Dev Officer)
Cristy Conolly (Dir-Quality Assurance & Compliance)
Cindy Bechtel (Mgr-Vendor Rels-Northern Reg)
Jennifer Falzarano (Mgr-Client Rels)
Marilyn Fullwood (Mgr-Vendor Rels-Southern Reg)
Jennifer Graham (Dir-Admin)
Kevin Johnson (Sr VP-Sls)
Gwen Goodman (Mgr-Acctg)
Amy Fuhrer (Mgr-Client Rels)
Natasha Skinner (Mgr-Client Rels)
Nathan West (Mgr-Client Rels)
Ryan Retaleato (Sr VP-Sls)
Mario Dumitrescu (Supvr-Acct)
Theresa Marshall (Supvr-Acct)
Kayla McDonald (Supvr-Acct)
Wayne Simmons (Supvr-Acct)
Monica Bankus (VP-Ops)

NATIONWIDE ARGOSY SOLUTIONS, LLC
2500 W Loop S Ste 500, Houston, TX 77027
Tel.: (713) 961-4700   TX
Web Site: http://www.nwas-llc.com
Year Founded: 1998
Sales Range: $700-749.9 Million
Emp.: 1,200
Holding Company
N.A.I.C.S.: 551112
Kim Cosco (VP-Mktg & Sls)
Todd Bone (VP-Enterprise Solutions)

Subsidiaries:

Cerqa Copyright   (1)

NATIONWIDE FOODS INC.

1309 Rutherford Ln, Austin, TX 78753   (100%)
Tel.: (512) 439-1281
Web Site: http://www.cerqa.com
Sales Range: $10-24.9 Million
Emp.: 45
Commercial Printing
N.A.I.C.S.: 323111
Donna Andruk (Mgr-Supply Chain & Distr)

Franklin-Dodd Communications LLC   (1)
950 SE 8th St, Hialeah, FL 33010
Tel.: (305) 885-8707
Web Site: http://www.franklindodd.com
Emp.: 60
Commercial Printing, Marketing & Order Fulfillment Services
N.A.I.C.S.: 323111
George Aguioar (VP)

Graphics West, Inc.   (1)
3901 Graphic Ctr Dr, Las Vegas, NV 89118-1765
Tel.: (702) 798-9444
Web Site: http://www.graphicswest.com
Sales Range: $10-24.9 Million
Emp.: 110
Commercial Printing
N.A.I.C.S.: 323111

Jones Company   (1)
1907 Crutchfield St, Chattanooga, TN 37406
Tel.: (423) 624-3355
Web Site: http://www.jonesprinting.com
Emp.: 50
Commercial Printing Services
N.A.I.C.S.: 323111

Sutherland Printing, Inc.   (1)
525 N Front St, Montezuma, IA 50171
Tel.: (641) 623-5115
Web Site: http://www.sutherlandprinting.com
Commercial Printing Services
N.A.I.C.S.: 323111

NATIONWIDE COURT SERVICES, INC.
761 Koehler Ave Ste A, Ronkonkoma, NY 11779
Tel.: (631) 981-4400   NY
Web Site: http://www.nationwidecourtservice.com
Year Founded: 1993
Sales Range: $1-9.9 Million
Emp.: 30
Media Buying Services
N.A.I.C.S.: 541199
Arlene Nelson (Pres & CEO)
Alex Carlomagno (Gen Counsel)
George V. Nelson Jr. (VP)

Subsidiaries:

Nationwide Court Services, Inc.   (1)
20 Vesey St Rear Lobby, New York, NY 10007
Tel.: (212) 349-3776
Web Site: http://www.nationwidecourtservices.com
Emp.: 15
Law firm
N.A.I.C.S.: 541810
Arlene Nelson (Pres & CEO)
Jonathan Tatun (Gen Counsel)
George V. Nelson Jr. (VP)

NATIONWIDE CREDIT, INC.
PO Box 14581, Des Moines, IA 50306-3581
Tel.: (800) 456-4729
Web Site: http://www.ncirm.com
Year Founded: 1947
Debt Collection & Accounts Receivable Management
N.A.I.C.S.: 561440
Sumit Bahadur (COO)
Joseph Spicer (VP-Secured Collections)
Odran Hickey (Gen Counsel)
Maurice Rico (Dir-Compliance)

NATIONWIDE FOODS INC.
700 E 107th St, Chicago, IL 60628-3806

NATIONWIDE FOODS INC.

Nationwide Foods Inc.—(Continued)
Tel.: (773) 787-4900
Sales Range: $125-149.9 Million
Emp.: 500
Processed Meat Mfr
N.A.I.C.S.: 311612
Patrick Keeble (Acct Dir-Fin)
Frank Swan (Chm, Pres & CEO)

NATIONWIDE GROUP
3435 N Cicero Ave, Chicago, IL 60641
Tel.: (773) 777-7600
Web Site: http://www.nac-loans.com
Sales Range: $50-74.9 Million
Emp.: 200
Life Insurance
N.A.I.C.S.: 522291
Martin Less (CEO)

Subsidiaries:

Founders Insurance Co. (1)
1645 E Birchwood Ave, Des Plaines, IL 60018
Tel.: (847) 768-0040
Web Site: http://www.foundersinsurance.com
Rev.: $62,601,476
Emp.: 155
Non-Standard Personal Automobile Insurance
N.A.I.C.S.: 524210

Nationwide Acceptance Corporation (1)
3435 N Cicero Ave, Chicago, IL 60641
Tel.: (773) 777-7600
Web Site: http://www.nac-loans.com
Rev.: $23,300,000
Consumer Finance Companies
N.A.I.C.S.: 522291

NATIONWIDE LIFT TRUCKS INC.
3900 N 28th Ter, Hollywood, FL 33020
Tel.: (954) 922-4645
Web Site: http://www.toyotanlt.com
Sales Range: $10-24.9 Million
Emp.: 70
Retailer of Forklift Parts
N.A.I.C.S.: 441110
Arthur R. Conte (Pres)
Thomas Conte (VP)
Frank Koneski (VP & Controller)

NATIONWIDE MAGAZINE & BOOK DISTRIBUTORS
3000 E Grauwyler Rd, Irving, TX 75061
Tel.: (972) 438-2123
Web Site: http://www.nationwideirving.com
Rev.: $11,991,389
Emp.: 100
Trucking Except Local
N.A.I.C.S.: 484121
Ben Madill (Pres)
Barb McDaniel (Mgr-Ops)

NATIONWIDE MORTGAGE BANKERS, INC.
68 S Service Rd Ste 340, Melville, NY 11747
Web Site: http://www.nmbnow.com
Year Founded: 2011
Sales Range: $25-49.9 Million
Emp.: 400
Mortgage Banking Services
N.A.I.C.S.: 522292
Richard M. Steinberg (Founder & Chm)
Nate Hernandez (COO)
Jodi Hall (Pres)
Jarrett Stanley (Exec VP-Mktg)

NATIONWIDE MOTOR SALES CORP
2085 York Rd, Lutherville Timonium, MD 21093
Tel.: (410) 252-8000
Web Site: http://www.nationwideauto.com
Year Founded: 1955
Sales Range: $75-99.9 Million
Emp.: 70
Sales of New & Used Automobiles
N.A.I.C.S.: 441110
Theresa Crouse (Dir-HR)
David Snyder (Dir-E-Commerce)
William H. Schaefer Jr. (Pres)

NATIONWIDE NEWSPAPERS ADVERTISING, LLC
5955 Masters Blvd, Orlando, FL 32819
Tel.: (407) 909-1644
Web Site: http://www.nationwideadvertising.com
Year Founded: 1999
Sales Range: $10-24.9 Million
Emp.: 6
Advertising, Magazines, Newspaper
N.A.I.C.S.: 541810

NATIONWIDE PAYMENT SOLUTIONS, LLC
400 Techn Way, Scarborough, ME 04074
Tel.: (207) 883-3859
Year Founded: 2002
Rev.: $15,000,000
Emp.: 59
Office Administrative Services
N.A.I.C.S.: 561110
Jamie Nonni (CEO)

NATIONWIDE SECURITY & BUILDING SERVICES
21720 S Vermington Ave, Downey, CA 90810
Tel.: (562) 862-1782
Web Site: http://www.nsbs.net
Rev.: $10,869,564
Emp.: 44
Locksmith Shop
N.A.I.C.S.: 561622
Rhonda Blanchard (Pres & CEO)
Dawn Railey (VP-HR)
Jennifer Tinson (Acct Mgr-Natl)

NATIONWIDE SECURITY SOLUTIONS INC.
7200 NE 41st St Ste 101, Vancouver, WA 98662
Tel.: (360) 718-2213
Web Site: http://www.trustnationwide.com
Year Founded: 2006
Sales Range: $1-9.9 Million
Emp.: 43
Security Systems
N.A.I.C.S.: 561621
Adam Wise (Dir-Mktg)
Roy Merwin (Controller)
Billie Hard (VP)

NATIONWIDE SOUTHEAST INC.
1000 S River Industrial Blvd, Atlanta, GA 30315
Tel.: (404) 624-0011
Web Site: http://www.nwlog.com
Year Founded: 1956
Sales Range: $10-24.9 Million
Emp.: 100
Provider of Transportation Services
N.A.I.C.S.: 484121
Roger Heath (Dir-Safety, Recruiting & Driver Qualifications)
Edsel Cleveland (Pres)

NATIONWIDE STUDIOS, INC.
400 N Belvedere Dr, Gallatin, TN 37066
Tel.: (615) 452-8353
Web Site: http://www.teddybearportraits.com
Rev.: $15,000,000
Emp.: 102
Provider of Photographic Portrait Services
N.A.I.C.S.: 541921
Amanda Maddox (Mgr-Sls Field)
Phillip B. Rooney Jr. (Chm)

NATIONWIDE TARPS INC.
50 Willow St, Amsterdam, NY 12010
Tel.: (518) 843-1545
Web Site: http://www.ntiglobal.com
Sales Range: $10-24.9 Million
Emp.: 25
Polyethylene Film
N.A.I.C.S.: 326113
Steve Raeburn (Pres)

NATIONWIDE TRUCK BROKERS INC.
4203 Roger B Chaffee Memorial Dr SE Ste 2, Wyoming, MI 49548-3476
Tel.: (616) 878-5554
Web Site: http://www.ntbtrk.com
Rev.: $37,220,000
Emp.: 30
Trucking Except Local
N.A.I.C.S.: 484121
Henry Schwarz (Pres)

NATIVE AMERICAN ENERGY GROUP, INC.
61-43 186th St Ste 507, Fresh Meadows, NY 11365
Tel.: (718) 408-2323
Web Site: http://www.nativeamericanenergy.com
Year Founded: 2005
Sales Range: Less than $1 Million
Emp.: 5
Oil & Gas Exploration Services
N.A.I.C.S.: 213112
Joseph G. D'Arrigo (Co-Founder & CEO)
Raj S. Nanvaan (Co-Founder, CFO & COO)
Richard Ross (Chief Comm Officer)
Linda C. Chontos (Officer-Admin Ops)

NATIVE AMERICAN HEALTH CENTER
1151 Harbor Bay Pkwy, Alameda, CA 94502
Tel.: (510) 747-3030
Web Site: http://www.nativehealth.org
Year Founded: 1972
Sales Range: $10-24.9 Million
Emp.: 307
Community Health Care Services
N.A.I.C.S.: 621498
Cindi Adams (Chm)
Robert Little Cloud (Sec)
Carmen Foghorn (Treas)
Lee Davenport (Vice Chm)
Martin Waukazoo (CEO)

NATIVE AMERICAN HERITAGE ASSOCIATION
830-F John Marshall Hwy, Front Royal, VA 22630
Tel.: (540) 636-1020
Web Site: http://www.naha-inc.org
Year Founded: 1998
Sales Range: $25-49.9 Million
Emp.: 10
Social Welfare Services
N.A.I.C.S.: 813319
Erin K. Hibbs (Sec)
Pamela J. Myers (Chm & Pres)

U.S. PRIVATE

NATIVE ENVIRONMENTAL, LLC
2435 E University, Phoenix, AZ 85034
Tel.: (602) 254-0122
Web Site: http://www.nativeaz.com
Year Founded: 2001
Sales Range: $10-24.9 Million
Emp.: 60
Environmental Consulting Services
N.A.I.C.S.: 541620
Jon W. Riggs (Pres)

NATIVE LAND DESIGN, LLC
301 Brushy Creek Rd, Cedar Park, TX 78613
Tel.: (512) 918-2270
Web Site: http://www.nativelanddesign.com
Year Founded: 2001
Sales Range: $1-9.9 Million
Emp.: 130
Landscape Design
N.A.I.C.S.: 541320
Ben Collinsworth (CEO)
Stan Johnson (Principal)

NATIVE PATHS LLC
527 Broadway Ave, Sonoma, CA 95476
Web Site: http://www.nativepath.com
Year Founded: 2013
Sales Range: $25-49.9 Million
Emp.: 14
Nutrition Product Distr
N.A.I.C.S.: 456199
Chad Walding (Co-Founder)
Chris Clark (Co-Founder)

NATOLI ENGINEERING CO. INC.
28 Research Park Cir, Saint Charles, MO 63304
Tel.: (636) 926-8900
Web Site: http://www.natoli.com
Year Founded: 1973
Sales Range: $10-24.9 Million
Emp.: 150
Pharmaceutical Machinery
N.A.I.C.S.: 333248
Dale Natoli (Pres)

NATRAN LLC
12460 Nw Freeway, Houston, TX 77092
Tel.: (281) 402-9852
Web Site: http://www.natran.com
Year Founded: 2006
Sales Range: $1-9.9 Million
Emp.: 20
Pest Management Services
N.A.I.C.S.: 561710
Gordon Doran (CEO)

NATREL COMMUNICATIONS
119 cherry Hill Rd, Parsippany, NJ 07054
Tel.: (973) 292-8400
Year Founded: 1999
Sales Range: $25-49.9 Million
Emp.: 40
N.A.I.C.S.: 541810
Allan Trent (Founding Partner)
David Nakamura (Founding Partner)
Susan Mayer Roher (Assoc Dir-Creative)
Nicole Hyland (Sr VP & Dir-Client Svcs)
Tracey Baker (Production Mgr)
Jessica Benos (Acct Exec)
Carol Flynn (Sr Editor)
Laura Wisniewski (Acct Supvr)
Ed Shankman (Chief Creative Officer & Sr VP)
Heather Cunningham (VP & Acct Grp Supvr)

Olivia Ganguzza *(Acct Grp Supvr)*
Trudy Chiavelli *(Sr Acct Exec)*
Gianna Esposito *(Acct Exec)*

NATSOURCE LLC
100 William St Ste 2005, New York, NY 10038
Tel.: (212) 232-5300
Web Site: http://www.natsource.com
Sales Range: $25-49.9 Million
Emp.: 27
Asset Management Services in Global Emissions & Renewable Energy Markets
N.A.I.C.S.: 523999
Mike Intrator *(Mng Dir, Principal & Portfolio Mgr-Asset Mgmt Svcs)*

NATURAL CAPITALISM SOLUTIONS
11823 N 75th St, Longmont, CO 80503
Tel.: (720) 684-6580   CO
Web Site: http://www.natcapsolutions.org
Year Founded: 2004
Sales Range: $1-9.9 Million
Emp.: 7
Professional & Management Development Training Services
N.A.I.C.S.: 611430
L. Hunter Lovins *(Pres)*
Nancy Johnston *(Treas & Sec)*

NATURAL CHEMISTRY, INC.
40 Richards Ave 30, Norwalk, CT 06854
Tel.: (800) 753-1233
Web Site: http://www.naturalchemistry.com
Polish & Other Sanitation Good Mfr
N.A.I.C.S.: 325612
Mark Munford *(CEO)*

NATURAL DECORATIONS, INC.
777 Industrial Park Dr, Brewton, AL 36426
Tel.: (251) 867-7077   AL
Web Site: http://www.ndi.com
Year Founded: 1992
Sales Range: $10-24.9 Million
Emp.: 110
Artificial Trees & Flowers
N.A.I.C.S.: 339999
Carol Faris Gordy *(Owner & CEO)*
Tammy Kervin *(Controller)*

NATURAL DESIGNS LANDSCAPING INC.
PO Box 1678, Lutz, FL 33548
Tel.: (813) 949-4933
Web Site: http://www.ndlllc.com
Year Founded: 1978
Sales Range: $1-9.9 Million
Landscaping Services
N.A.I.C.S.: 561730
Phillip Petresky *(Pres)*

NATURAL GAS PROCESSING COMPANY
101 Division, Worland, WY 82401
Tel.: (307) 347-8221
Sales Range: $50-74.9 Million
Emp.: 50
Natural Gas Distribution
N.A.I.C.S.: 221210
David L. Hamilton *(Pres)*

NATURAL LANDS TRUST, INC.
1031 Palmers Mill Rd, Media, PA 19063
Tel.: (610) 353-5587   PA
Web Site: http://www.natlands.org
Year Founded: 1960
Sales Range: $10-24.9 Million
Emp.: 50
Land Conservation Services
N.A.I.C.S.: 712190
William G. Warden IV *(Vice Chm)*
John A. Terrill II *(Chm)*

NATURAL ORGANICS, INC.
548 Broadhollow Rd, Melville, NY 11747
Tel.: (631) 293-0030
Web Site: http://www.naturesplus.com
Sales Range: $25-49.9 Million
Emp.: 355
Vitamin Products Development
N.A.I.C.S.: 325412
James Gibbons *(Pres)*
Roseann Marinelli *(Dir-Fin)*
Susan Lange *(Dir-HR)*

NATURAL RESOURCE GOVERNANCE INSTITUTE
80 Broad St Ste 1801, New York, NY 10004
Tel.: (646) 929-9750   DC
Web Site: http://www.resourcegovernance.org
Year Founded: 2006
Sales Range: $10-24.9 Million
Philanthropic Services
N.A.I.C.S.: 813211
Daniel Kaufmann *(Pres & CEO)*
Lucy Berkowitz *(Chief Fin & Admin Officer)*
Lee Bailey *(Dir-Comm)*
Jim Cust *(Dir-Res & Data)*
Alexandra Gillies *(Dir-Governance Programs)*

NATURAL RESOURCES CONSULTING, INC.
209 Commerce Pkwy, Cottage Grove, WI 53527
Tel.: (608) 839-1998   WI
Web Site: http://www.nrcdifference.com
Year Founded: 1998
Sales Range: $1-9.9 Million
Emp.: 48
Environmental Consulting
N.A.I.C.S.: 541620
Thomas Girman *(Project Mgr)*

NATURAL RETREATS US LLC
675 Peter Jefferson Pkwy Ste 250, Charlottesville, VA 22901
Tel.: (877) 805-7794   DE
Web Site: http://www.naturalretreats.com
Year Founded: 2006
Luxury Vacation Rental Management Company
N.A.I.C.S.: 721214
Ashley Horsley *(Sr VP)*
Chris Holden *(CEO)*

Subsidiaries:

360 Blue, LLC   (1)
2048 W County Hwy 30A Ste 107, Santa Rosa Beach, FL 32459
Web Site: http://www.360blueproperties.com
Real Estate Investment Services
N.A.I.C.S.: 531210
Basia Cohen *(Partner-Talent, Quality & Improvement)*

NATURAL SEASONING COMPANY
7400 S Narragansett Ave, Chicago, IL 60638-6022
Tel.: (708) 458-4118
Sales Range: $10-24.9 Million
Emp.: 175
Spice & Extract Mfr
N.A.I.C.S.: 311942
Peter Garvy *(Pres)*

NATURAL SPROUT COMPANY, LLC
3524 S Culpepper Circle Suite C, Springfield, MO 65804
Tel.: (417) 882-9604
Web Site: http://www.natsprout.com
Year Founded: 1995
Emp.: 100
Ingredient Supplier to Health Food Manufacturers
N.A.I.C.S.: 456191
William Pfeifer *(Owner)*

NATURAL STONE CONCEPTS LLC
3906 Enterprise Ave, Naples, FL 34104
Tel.: (239) 263-1930
Web Site: http://www.naturalstoneconcepts.com
Year Founded: 2002
Rev.: $14,980,000
Emp.: 35
Granite & Marble Fabrication Services
N.A.I.C.S.: 327991
Eli Magilewski *(CFO)*
Edward J. Angell *(Pres)*
Carlos Magilewski *(Founder & CEO)*

NATURAL SUPPLEMENT ASSOCIATION INC.
3300 Stelzer Rd, Columbus, OH 43219-3034
Tel.: (303) 384-0080
Web Site: http://www.eas.com
Sales Range: $50-74.9 Million
Emp.: 220
Vitamins & Minerals
N.A.I.C.S.: 424210
Chris Scoggins *(VP-EAS Brands)*

NATURAL WAY, INC.
2481 Brown Rd, Lake Orion, MI 48359
Tel.: (248) 239-4000   MI
Web Site: http://www.naturalwaylawn.com
Year Founded: 1991
Sales Range: $1-9.9 Million
Emp.: 55
Lawn & Garden Services
N.A.I.C.S.: 561730
Keith Fetzner *(Founder & Pres)*
Jessica Firment *(Office Mgr)*

NATURALIFE ECO VITE LABS
20433 Earl St, Torrance, CA 90503
Tel.: (310) 370-1563
Web Site: http://www.paragonlabsusa.com
Rev.: $20,300,000
Emp.: 90
Vitamins & Minerals
N.A.I.C.S.: 424210
Jay Kaufman *(Pres)*

NATURE PURE LLC.
26586 State Rd 739, Raymond, OH 43067
Tel.: (937) 358-2364
Web Site: http://www.naturepure.us
Sales Range: $10-24.9 Million
Emp.: 32
Egg Producing Services
N.A.I.C.S.: 112330
Scott Colwell *(VP)*
Kurt Lausecker *(Pres)*

NATURE'S FOOTPRINT, INC.
3324 E Smith Rd, Bellingham, WA 98226
Tel.: (360) 592-4285
Web Site: http://www.naturesfootprint.com
Year Founded: 2003
Eco-Friendly Garden Products, Recycling & Waste Minimization Products
N.A.I.C.S.: 811411
Ralph Rhoads *(Pres)*

Subsidiaries:

Cascade Sales   (1)
3316 E Smith Rd, Bellingham, WA 98226
Tel.: (360) 592-5970
Web Site: http://www.cascadesales.com
Specialty Product Sales for Homes & Gardens
N.A.I.C.S.: 444110
Ralph Rhoads *(Pres)*

NATURE'S VALUE, INC.
468 Mill Rd, Coram, NY 11727
Tel.: (631) 846-2500
Web Site: http://www.naturesvalue.com
Year Founded: 1992
Sales Range: $50-74.9 Million
Emp.: 265
Pharmaceutical Preparation Mfr
N.A.I.C.S.: 325412
Oscar Ramjeet *(Pres)*
Brandon Thompson *(Supvr-Shipping)*

NATUREBRIDGE
28 Geary St Ste 650, San Francisco, CA 94108
Tel.: (415) 992-4700   CA
Web Site: http://www.naturebridge.org
Year Founded: 1971
Sales Range: $10-24.9 Million
Emp.: 260
Environmental Literacy Support Services
N.A.I.C.S.: 813312
Leigh Westerlund *(VP-Ops)*
Tracy Thompson *(Sec)*
Carroll C. Yandell *(Vice Chm)*
Ian Yolles *(Chm)*
Aaron Rich *(Dir-Golden Gate)*
Jen Kidder *(Dir-Education)*
Jennie Pardi *(Dir-Education)*
Kim Hanson *(Dir-Education)*
Kristina Rylands *(Dir-Yosemite)*
Meg Jakubowski *(Dir-Education)*
Melissa Johnson *(Dir-Southern California)*
Phillip Kilbridge *(Pres & CEO)*
Randall E. Reynoso *(Treas)*
Reed Schneider *(Dir-Education)*
Stephen Streufert *(VP-Education & Dir-Pacific Northwest)*
Galen Quaring *(CFO)*
Zack MacDonald *(Chief Dev Officer)*

NATUREPLEX LLC
11085 Airport Rd, Olive Branch, MS 38654
Tel.: (662) 874-1370
Web Site: http://www.natureplex.com
Pharmaceuticals Product Mfr
N.A.I.C.S.: 325412
Victor Santos *(Owner)*

NATURERIPE FARMS LLC
9450 Corkscrew Palms Cir Ste 202, Estero, FL 33928-6422
Tel.: (239) 591-1664
Web Site: http://www.natureripefarmstrade.com
Berry Grower, Importer & Distr
N.A.I.C.S.: 424480
Brian Bocock *(VP-Sls)*

NATURES INNOVATION, INC.
5317 Palmero Ct, Buford, GA 30518
Tel.: (770) 904-2499
Web Site: http://www.naturesinnovation.com
Year Founded: 2004
Sales Range: $1-9.9 Million
Emp.: 17

NATURES INNOVATION, INC.

Natures Innovation, Inc.—(Continued)
Natural Health & Skin Care Product Distr
N.A.I.C.S.: 424990
Bill Carlson *(Founder & CEO)*
Jody Sachse *(CTO)*

NATURESTAR BIO-TEC INC.
1770 S Vineyard Ave 1270 E Acacia, Ontario, CA 91761
Tel.: (909) 930-1878
Web Site:
http://www.naturestarusa.com
Sales Range: $1-9.9 Million
Emp.: 15
Health Supplements Mfr
N.A.I.C.S.: 325412
Liquiong Fei *(Pres)*

NATURIPE BERRY GROWERS INC.
PO Box 4280, Salinas, CA 93912
Tel.: (831) 722-2430   CA
Web Site:
http://www.naturipeberrygrowers.com
Year Founded: 1917
Sales Range: $100-124.9 Million
Emp.: 40
Crop Preparation Services for Market
N.A.I.C.S.: 111339
Connie Dimas *(Coord-Production)*
Sonny Pulido *(Dir-Product Integrity)*

NATURWOOD HOME FURNISHINGS, INC.
2711 Mercantile Dr, Rancho Cordova, CA 95742
Tel.: (916) 638-2424
Web Site: http://www.naturwood.com
Rev.: $23,030,918
Emp.: 65
Furniture Retailer
N.A.I.C.S.: 449110
Lisa Keyes *(Pres)*

NAU HOLDING COMPANY
7333 Sunwood Dr NW, Anoka, MN 55303-5119
Tel.: (763) 427-3770
Web Site: http://www.naucountry.com
Sales Range: $10-24.9 Million
Emp.: 15
Holding Agents for Insurance Companies
N.A.I.C.S.: 524126

Subsidiaries:

NAU Ca Crop Ins   (1)
120 Main St Ste I, Woodland, CA 95776
Tel.: (530) 662-7466
Web Site: http://www.naucountry.com
Property & Casualty Insurance Agent
N.A.I.C.S.: 524128

NAU Country Insurance Company   (1)
7333 Sunwood Dr, Ramsey, MN 55303
Tel.: (763) 427-3770
Web Site: http://www.naucountry.com
Sales Range: $1-9.9 Million
Fire, Marine & Casualty Insurance & Carriers
N.A.I.C.S.: 524126
James R. Korin *(Pres)*
Michael Deal *(Chief Mktg Tech Officer)*
Mark Mossman *(Sr VP-Claims)*
Doug Jakway *(Gen Counsel & Sr VP-Compliance)*
Bill Wilson *(Sr VP-Underwriting)*
Larry Heitman *(Sr VP)*
Bill Lorimer *(Sr VP-Branch Ops)*
Ken Janicek *(Sr VP-Branch Ops)*
Jay Domer *(Sr VP-Branch Ops)*
John Wienstroer *(Sr VP-Branch Ops)*
Marv Goergen *(CFO & Sr VP)*
Carolyn Scobie *(Sec)*

NAU Insurance Company   (1)
1020 36th St SW, Fargo, ND 58103

Property & Casualty Insurance Agent
N.A.I.C.S.: 524126

NAUGHTON ENERGY CORPORATION
PO Box 709, Pocono Pines, PA 18350
Tel.: (570) 646-0422
Web Site:
http://www.naughtonenergy.com
Year Founded: 1976
Sales Range: $10-24.9 Million
Emp.: 7
Coal, Petroleum, Natural Gas & Lubricant Supplier
N.A.I.C.S.: 423520
Mariette Naughton *(Pres)*

NAUGHTON'S PLUMBING SALES CO., INC.
1140 W Prince Rd, Tucson, AZ 85705-3111
Tel.: (520) 293-2220
Web Site: http://www.naughtons.com
Year Founded: 1951
Sales Range: $10-24.9 Million
Emp.: 70
Air Conditioning Equipment Whslr
N.A.I.C.S.: 423730
Frank W. Naughton *(Pres)*

NAULTS ENTERPRISES INC.
420 2nd St, Manchester, NH 03102
Tel.: (603) 669-7220
Web Site: http://www.naults.com
Year Founded: 1961
Sales Range: $25-49.9 Million
Emp.: 25
New & Used Motorcycles & ATV'S
N.A.I.C.S.: 441227
Richard M. Nault *(Pres)*

NAUMANN GROUP REAL ESTATE INC.
2050 Capital Cir NE, Tallahassee, FL 32308
Tel.: (850) 325-1681
Web Site:
http://www.naumanngroup.com
Sales Range: $1-9.9 Million
Emp.: 5
Real Estate Brokerage
N.A.I.C.S.: 531210
Jason Naumann *(Owner)*

NAUMES INC.
2 Barnett Rd, Medford, OR 97501-3666
Tel.: (541) 772-6268   OR
Web Site: http://www.naumesinc.com
Year Founded: 1946
Sales Range: $25-49.9 Million
Emp.: 300
Grower & Processor of Fruit
N.A.I.C.S.: 111339
Michael D. Naumes *(Pres & CEO)*
Robert Boggess *(Gen Counsel & Mgr-Real Estate)*
Annie Eadie *(CFO & Controller)*

Subsidiaries:

Growers Refrigerating Company, Inc.   (1)
2 W Barnett St, Medford, OR 97501-3666
Tel.: (541) 772-6268
Sales Range: $10-24.9 Million
Emp.: 6
Provider of Refrigerated Warehousing & Storage Services
N.A.I.C.S.: 111339

NAUTIC PARTNERS, LLC
50 Kennedy Plz 12th Fl, Providence, RI 02903-2393
Tel.: (401) 278-6770   RI
Web Site: http://www.nautic.com
Year Founded: 1986

Privater Equity Firm
N.A.I.C.S.: 551112
Habib Y. Gorgi *(Mng Dir)*
Bernie Buonanno *(Mng Dir)*
Scott Hilinski *(Mng Dir)*
Chris Crosby *(Mng Dir)*
Jim Beakey *(Mng Dir-Bus Dev)*
Mark C. Perlberg *(Mng Dir)*
Charles R. Bartolini *(CFO & Chief Compliance Officer)*
Christopher F. Corey *(Mng Dir)*
Keith H. Farrow *(VP)*
Daniel P. Killeen *(VP)*
Allan M. B. Petersen *(Mng Dir & VP)*
Christopher A. Pierce *(Mng Dir)*
Edward J. Sohn *(VP)*

Subsidiaries:

1105 Media, Inc.   (1)
9201 Oakdale Ave Ste 101, Chatsworth, CA 91311
Tel.: (818) 814-5200
Web Site: http://www.1105media.com
Sales Range: $50-74.9 Million
Emp.: 300
Online & Print Business-to-Business Information Product Services
N.A.I.C.S.: 513120
Michael J. Valenti *(Exec VP)*
Anne A. Armstrong *(Chief Content Officer & Chief Alliances Officer)*
Karen Cavallo *(Publr-Home Medical Equipment Editorial Grp)*
Kevin O'Grady *(Pres & Publr)*
Rajeev Kapur *(CEO)*
Irene Fincher *(Dir-Audience Dev-Enterprise Computing Grp)*
Becky Nagel *(VP-Digital Strategy)*
Brent Sutton *(VP-Events)*
Erik A. Lindgren *(CTO)*
Sanjay Tanwani *(CFO)*

Subsidiary (Domestic):

1105 Media Government Information Group   (2)
3141 Fairview Park Dr Ste 777, Falls Church, VA 22042
Tel.: (703) 876-5100
Web Site: http://www.1105govinfo.com
Government Media & Publishing Services
N.A.I.C.S.: 513110
Anne Armstrong *(Pres)*

Aerostar Aerospace Manufacturing, Inc.   (1)
2688 E Rose Garden Ln, Phoenix, AZ 85050
Tel.: (602) 861-1145
Web Site:
http://www.aerostaraerospace.com
Precision Machined Components & Assemblies Mfr & Marketer
N.A.I.C.S.: 423830
Jeff Hailey *(Gen Mgr)*

Aurora Plastics, LLC   (1)
9280 Jefferson St, Streetsboro, OH 44241
Tel.: (330) 422-0700
Web Site: http://www.auroraplastics.com
Sales Range: $1-9.9 Million
Emp.: 12
Pellet & Foam PVC Powder Compound Mfr & Distr
N.A.I.C.S.: 326150
Steve Harrigan *(VP-Sls)*
Matt McDonald *(CFO)*
Jeff Conard *(Sr VP-Ops)*
Luc Tremblay *(Pres-Canadian Ops)*
Darrell K. Hughes *(Pres & CEO)*

Curtis Industries, LLC   (1)
70 Hartwell St, West Boylston, MA 01583
Tel.: (508) 853-2200
Web Site: http://www.curtisindustries.net
Sales Range: $10-24.9 Million
Compact Tractor Mfr
N.A.I.C.S.: 333924

Davidson Hotel Company LLC   (1)
1 Ravinia Dr Ste 1600, Atlanta, GA 30346
Tel.: (678) 349-0909
Web Site: http://www.davidsonhotels.com
Sales Range: $10-24.9 Million
Holding Company; Hotel & Resort Owner & Operator

U.S. PRIVATE

N.A.I.C.S.: 551112
Kathy Hood *(VP-Sls, Mktg & Revenue Mgmt)*
John Belden *(Chm)*
Steven Margol *(Chief Investment Officer)*
Stephen Kilroy *(VP-Food & Beverage)*
Ted Arps *(Sr VP-Bus Dev)*
Phillip Miller *(VP-Design & Construction)*
Barry E. Wabler *(CFO & Exec VP)*
Crystal Beasley *(Gen Counsel & Sr VP)*
Thom Geshay *(Pres & CEO)*
Bernie Murphy *(Sr VP-Bus Dev)*
Dan Engle *(VP-Field Sls)*
Kyle Bowman *(VP-Investment Mgmt)*
Mary Powers *(VP-HR)*
Ben Fulwider *(Pres)*
Jason Rabidoux *(VP-Bus Dev-West Coast)*
Lew Lemon *(Reg VP-Ops)*
Marisa Serrano *(Reg VP-Ops)*
Rodger Sellers *(Dir-Recruiting)*
Tim Debruin *(Dir-Catering & Convention Svcs)*
Tom Rybski *(Sr Dir-Projects)*
Chris Lopilato *(Sr Dir-Corp Acctg)*
Hank Artime *(Treas & VP-Fin)*
Holly Lawson *(Dir-People & Culture-Lifestyle & Luxury Div-Pivot Hotels & Resort)*
Albert Smith *(Sr VP)*
Michele Smith *(VP-Hotel Acctg)*
Rob Morgan *(Sr VP-Transitions & Ops Strategy)*
Linda Schumann *(Sr VP-HR)*
Carl Meyers *(Dir-Training & Org Dev)*

Innovative Renal Care LLC   (1)
3102 W End Ave Ste 1100, Nashville, TN 37203
Tel.: (615) 515-9880
Web Site: http://irc.health
Dialysis & Kidney Care Services
N.A.I.C.S.: 621492

Subsidiary (Domestic):

American Renal Associates Holdings, Inc.   (2)
500 Cummings Ctr Ste 6550, Beverly, MA 01915
Tel.: (978) 922-3080
Web Site: http://www.americanrenal.com
Rev.: $822,522,000
Assets: $1,086,791,000
Liabilities: $1,002,252,000
Net Worth: $84,539,000
Earnings: ($13,790,000)
Emp.: 4,977
Fiscal Year-end: 12/31/2019
Dialysis Services
N.A.I.C.S.: 621492
Joseph A. Carlucci *(Chm & CEO)*
Syed T. Kamal *(Pres)*
Toshiya Roberts *(VP-Technical Svcs)*
Karen Bowman *(VP-Divisional)*
Shari K. Cousins *(Sr VP-Clinical & Regulatory Svcs)*
James M. Dilts *(VP-Divisional)*
Richard E. Fishpaw *(Reg VP-Ops)*
Ashwin Patel *(VP-Divisional)*
Craig Smith *(VP-Clinical Admin)*
Don E. Williamson *(COO & Exec VP)*
Charles Betts *(Dir-Govt Affairs)*
Kathleen Cardenas *(Reg VP-Ops)*
Bernadette Johnson *(Reg VP-Ops)*
Darren Lehrich *(Sr VP-Strategy & IR)*
Fariba Rafieha *(Reg VP-Ops)*
Neal Minahan *(Chief Compliance Officer & VP)*
Richard Pacheco *(VP-Admin)*
Rosalynn Handler *(Reg VP-Ops)*
Angie Howe *(Reg VP-Ops)*
Stan Langhofer *(VP-Texas)*
Ann Mooney *(VP-Clinical Res)*
Donna Steinert *(Reg VP-Ops)*
Thomas Vander Ploeg *(VP-Project Mgmt)*
Jessica Whitten *(VP-Internal Audit)*
Mark Herbers *(Interim CFO & Interim Chief Acctg Officer)*
Nicholas Carlucci *(VP-Financial Ops)*
Mark Paglierani *(VP-Financial Plng & Analysis)*
Victoria Labriola *(Acting Gen Counsel)*

Subsidiary (Domestic):

ARA - Ludlow Dialysis, LLC   (3)
14 Chestnut Pl Ste B, Ludlow, MA 01056
Tel.: (413) 583-7983
Dialysis Clinic Services
N.A.I.C.S.: 621492

COMPANIES

ARA Dialysis Unit at Ohio Valley Hospital, LLC (3)
27 Heckel Rd Ste 113, McKees Rocks, PA 15136
Tel.: (412) 331-2423
Dialysis Clinic Services
N.A.I.C.S.: 621492

ARA-ADELPHI LLC (3)
1801 Metzerott Rd, Adelphi, MD 20783
Tel.: (301) 434-1884
Kidney Dialysis Center Services
N.A.I.C.S.: 621492

ARA-Augusta Clinic LLC (3)
1000 Telfair St, Augusta, GA 30901-2208
Tel.: (706) 774-0130
Kidney Dialysis Center Services
N.A.I.C.S.: 621492

ARA-Aventura LLC (3)
19056 Ne 29th Ave, Aventura, FL 33180-2802
Tel.: (305) 692-9006
Kidney Dialysis Center Services
N.A.I.C.S.: 621492

ARA-Boca Raton Dialysis LLC (3)
1905 Clint Moore Rd Ste 211, Boca Raton, FL 33496
Tel.: (561) 893-6878
Dialysis Clinic Services
N.A.I.C.S.: 621492

ARA-Daytona Beach Dialysis LLC (3)
720 N Clyde Morris Blvd, Daytona Beach, FL 32114
Tel.: (386) 947-9872
Kidney Dialysis Clinic Services
N.A.I.C.S.: 621492

ARA-Johnston Dialysis LLC (3)
1526 Atwood Ave, Johnston, RI 02919
Tel.: (401) 521-0400
Renal Dialysis Clinic Services
N.A.I.C.S.: 621492

ARA-Naples Dialysis Center LLC (3)
4529 Executive Dr Ste 103, Naples, FL 34119
Tel.: (239) 566-7180
Dialysis Clinic Services
N.A.I.C.S.: 621492

ARA-Naples South Dialysis Center LLC (3)
4270 Tamiami Trl E Ste 1, Naples, FL 34112
Tel.: (239) 774-7523
Dialysis Clinic Services
N.A.I.C.S.: 621492

ARA-Orange Park LLC (3)
2141 Loch Rane Blvd Ste 115, Orange Park, FL 32073-4239
Tel.: (904) 272-7331
Kidney Dialysis Services
N.A.I.C.S.: 621492

ARA-Providence Dialysis LLC (3)
9 Plenty St, Providence, RI 02907
Tel.: (401) 273-4898
Renal Dialysis Clinic Services
N.A.I.C.S.: 621492

ARA-Rhode Island Dialysis II LLC (3)
318 Waterman Ave, East Providence, RI 02914-3525
Tel.: (401) 435-5200
Dialysis Clinic Services
N.A.I.C.S.: 621492

ARA-South Laburnum Dialysis LLC (3)
4817 S Laburnum Ave, Richmond, VA 23231
Tel.: (804) 222-7718
Emp.: 11
Kidney Dialysis Services
N.A.I.C.S.: 621492

ARA-Titusville Dialysis LLC (3)
801 Garden St, Titusville, FL 32796-3408
Tel.: (321) 567-0122
Emp.: 12
Kidney Dialysis Center Services
N.A.I.C.S.: 621492

ARA-Tiverton Dialysis LLC (3)
22 Hurst Ln, Tiverton, RI 02878
Tel.: (401) 624-4403
Renal Dialysis Clinic Services
N.A.I.C.S.: 621492

ARA-West Jacksonville LLC (3)
425 N Lee St Ste 103, Jacksonville, FL 32204
Tel.: (904) 598-2711
Kidney Dialysis Center Services
N.A.I.C.S.: 621492

ARA-Yuba City Dialysis LLC (3)
2115 E Onstott Rd, Yuba City, CA 95991-1556
Tel.: (530) 673-6656
Dialysis Clinic Services
N.A.I.C.S.: 621492

Ameri-Tech Kidney Center- Arlington, LLC (3)
1138 S Bowen Rd, Arlington, TX 76013
Tel.: (817) 265-7115
Kidney Dialysis Clinic Services
N.A.I.C.S.: 621492

Ameri-Tech Kidney Center- Bedford, LLC (3)
1600 Central Dr Ste 130, Bedford, TX 76022
Tel.: (817) 545-2044
Kidney Dialysis Center Services
N.A.I.C.S.: 621492

American Renal Texas, L.P. (3)
66 Cherry Hill Dr, Beverly, MA 01915
Tel.: (978) 922-3080
Dialysis Center Operator
N.A.I.C.S.: 621492

American Universal-Hockessin, LLC (3)
5936 Limestone Rd Ste 101, Hockessin, DE 19707-8930
Tel.: (302) 239-4106
Kidney Dialysis Clinic Services
N.A.I.C.S.: 621492

Arlington Dialysis Center, LLC (3)
7645 Merrill Rd, Jacksonville, FL 32277
Tel.: (904) 744-6130
Dialysis Clinic Services
N.A.I.C.S.: 621492

Bay City Dialysis Center, LLP (3)
200 Medical Ctr Ct Ste 200, Bay City, TX 77414
Tel.: (979) 323-0818
Dialysis Clinic Services
N.A.I.C.S.: 621492

Beaumont-ARA Dialysis LLP (3)
1085 S 23Rd St, Beaumont, TX 77707-4201
Tel.: (409) 840-2020
Dialysis Clinic Services
N.A.I.C.S.: 621492

Belle Glade Dialysis Center, LLC (3)
933 Se 1St St, Belle Glade, FL 33430-4305
Tel.: (561) 996-0602
Dialysis Clinic Services
N.A.I.C.S.: 621492

Big Lake Kidney Center LLC (3)
3240 Hwy 441 S, Okeechobee, FL 34974
Tel.: (863) 824-0225
Kidney Dialysis Clinic Services
N.A.I.C.S.: 621492

Boardman Dialysis Center LLC (3)
7153 Tiffany Blvd, Boardman, OH 44514
Tel.: (330) 729-1355
Kidney Dialysis Center Services
N.A.I.C.S.: 621492

Bradenton Dialysis Center LLC (3)
5837 W 21st Av, Bradenton, FL 34209
Tel.: (941) 792-7800
Kidney Dialysis Center Services
N.A.I.C.S.: 621492

Brockton Dialysis Center, LLC (3)
375 Westgate Dr, Brockton, MA 02301
Tel.: (508) 586-2791
Kidney Dialysis Center Services
N.A.I.C.S.: 621492

Brockton Healthcare Clinic, LLC (3)
76 Campanelli Industrial Dr, Brockton, MA 02301
Tel.: (508) 427-5329

Kidney Dialysis Clinic Services

Butler-ARA, LLC (3)
111 Woody Dr, Butler, PA 16001
Tel.: (724) 431-2241
Kidney Dialysis Center Services
N.A.I.C.S.: 621492

Cape Coral Kidney Center, LLC (3)
2735 Santa Barbra Blvd, Cape Coral, FL 33941
Tel.: (239) 772-2988
Kidney Dialysis Services
N.A.I.C.S.: 621492

Carolina Dialysis LLC (3)
115 Interstate Park, Spartanburg, SC 29303
Tel.: (864) 576-9999
Kidney Dialysis Center Services
N.A.I.C.S.: 621492

Carrollton Regional Dialysis Center, LLC (3)
1128 N I-35E, Carrollton, TX 75006
Tel.: (972) 242-7648
Kidney Dialysis Services
N.A.I.C.S.: 621492
Michael E. Nurenberg (Dir-Medical)
Carla Cancel (Mgr-Clinic)

Central Columbia Kidney Center, LLC (3)
3511 Medical Dr, Columbia, SC 29203
Tel.: (803) 771-0518
Emp.: 8
Kidney Dialysis Center Services
N.A.I.C.S.: 621492

Central Kittanning Dialysis Center LLC (3)
One Nolte Dr 700 Medical Arts Ste 720, Kittanning, PA 16201
Tel.: (724) 543-3151
Kidney Dialysis Center Services
N.A.I.C.S.: 621492

Champion Dialysis Center, LLC (3)
4554 Mahoning Ave NW, Warren, OH 44483
Tel.: (330) 847-0189
Kidney Dialysis Center Services
N.A.I.C.S.: 621492

Clarion Dialysis Center, LLC (3)
825 E Main St, Clarion, PA 16214
Tel.: (814) 223-4655
Kidney Dialysis Clinic Services
N.A.I.C.S.: 621492

Clermont Dialysis Center LLC (3)
1625 Hancock Rd, Clermont, FL 34711-7667
Tel.: (352) 243-2083
Kidney Dialysis Center Services
N.A.I.C.S.: 621492

Clewiston Dialysis Center, LLC (3)
851 W Ventura Ave, Clewiston, FL 33440-3409
Tel.: (863) 983-8855
Dialysis Clinic Services
N.A.I.C.S.: 621492

Clifton Dialysis Center, LLC (3)
51 Clifton Ave Unit A, Clifton, NJ 07011
Tel.: (973) 546-3750
Kidney Dialysis Center Services
N.A.I.C.S.: 621492

Clinton Dialysis Clinic, LLC (3)
103 Ab Jacks Rd, Clinton, SC 29325-2112
Tel.: (864) 833-0150
Dialysis Clinic Services
N.A.I.C.S.: 621492

Columbia Northeast Kidney Center, LLC (3)
7499 ParkLn Rd Ste 136, Columbia, SC 29203
Tel.: (803) 865-0554
Kidney Dialysis Clinic Services
N.A.I.C.S.: 621492

Complete Dialysis Care, LLC (3)
607 E 7th St, Odessa, TX 79761
Tel.: (432) 558-0497
Web Site: http://www.completedialysiscare.com
Kidney Dialysis Center Services
N.A.I.C.S.: 621492

NAUTIC PARTNERS, LLC

Dearborn Kidney Center, LLC (3)
5111 Auto Club Dr Bldg B Ste 120, Dearborn, MI 48126
Tel.: (313) 982-9788
Kidney Dialysis Center Services
N.A.I.C.S.: 621492

Delano Kidney Center, LLC (3)
1980 Cecil Av, Delano, CA 93215-1513
Tel.: (661) 721-2830
Kidney Dialysis Center Services
N.A.I.C.S.: 621492

Delray Beach Dialysis Center LLC (3)
5130 Linton Blvd Ste G4, Delray Beach, FL 33484
Tel.: (561) 498-5959
Kidney Dialysis Center Services
N.A.I.C.S.: 621492

Dentsville Kidney Center, LLC (3)
201 Columbia Mall Blvd Ste 141, Columbia, SC 29223
Tel.: (803) 865-1068
Emp.: 8
Kidney Dialysis Clinic Services
N.A.I.C.S.: 621492

Desoto Regional Dialysis Center LLC (3)
2651 Bolton Boone Dr Bldg B, DeSoto, TX 75115
Tel.: (972) 780-5991
Kidney Dialysis Services
N.A.I.C.S.: 621492
Richard Fuquay (Dir-Medical)
Elizabeth Gomez (Mgr-Clinic)

Dialysis Care Center of Palm Coast LLC (3)
515 Palm Coast Pkwy SW Units 2 3 4, Palm Coast, FL 32137-5700
Tel.: (386) 447-4477
Dialysis Clinic Services
N.A.I.C.S.: 621492

Dialysis Center of Milledgeville, LLC (3)
1520 N Columbia St Ste 100, Milledgeville, GA 31061-2474
Tel.: (478) 414-0123
Kidney Dialysis Clinic Services
N.A.I.C.S.: 621492

Dialysis Center of Wakefield LLC (3)
10 High St Ste C D & E, Wakefield, RI 02879-3176
Tel.: (401) 792-3450
Kidney Dialysis Clinic Services
N.A.I.C.S.: 621492

Dialysis Center of West Orange LLC (3)
101 Old Short Hills Rd, West Orange, NJ 07052
Tel.: (973) 736-8300
Dialysis Clinic Services
N.A.I.C.S.: 621492

Dialysis Center of West Warwick LLC (3)
1775 Bald Hill Rd, Warwick, RI 02886
Tel.: (401) 823-8420
Kidney Dialysis Center Services
N.A.I.C.S.: 621492

Dialysis Center of Westerly LLC (3)
1 Rhody Dr, Westerly, RI 02891
Tel.: (401) 596-0368
Renal Dialysis Clinic Services
N.A.I.C.S.: 621492

Dialysis Center of Western Massachusetts LLC (3)
601 Memorial Dr, Chicopee, MA 01020
Tel.: (413) 593-3078
Kidney Dialysis Clinic Services
N.A.I.C.S.: 621492

Dialysis Center of Woonsocket LLC (3)
2100 Diamond Hill Rd, Woonsocket, RI 02895
Tel.: (401) 765-4995
Renal Dialysis Clinic Services
N.A.I.C.S.: 621492

Dialysis Services of London, LLC (3)
306 S Plz, London, KY 40741

NAUTIC PARTNERS, LLC

U.S. PRIVATE

Nautic Partners, LLC—(Continued)
Tel.: (606) 862-0110
Dialysis Clinic Services
N.A.I.C.S.: 621492

Dialysis Services of Pineville, LLC (3)
12904 Robert L Madon Byp, Pineville, KY 40977
Tel.: (606) 337-1110
Dialysis Clinic Services
N.A.I.C.S.: 621492

Dublin Dialysis Center, LLC (3)
2400 Bellevue Rd Ste 29A, Dublin, GA 31021
Tel.: (478) 304-1501
Web Site: http://www.dublindialysiscenter.com
Kidney Dialysis Center Services
N.A.I.C.S.: 621492

El Paso Health, LLC (3)
1145 Westmoreland Dr, El Paso, TX 79925-5615
Tel.: (915) 532-3778
Web Site: http://www.elpasohealth.com
Medical Care Management Services
N.A.I.C.S.: 621492
Frank J. Dominguez *(Pres & CEO)*
Janel Lujan *(COO)*
Sharon Perkins *(CIO & Officer-HIPAA Security)*
Rocio Chavez *(Chief Compliance Officer)*
David M. Palafox *(Dir-Medical)*

Ellicott Kidney Center, LLC (3)
3000 N Rdg Rd Ste A, Ellicott City, MD 21043
Tel.: (410) 465-0273
Emp.: 13
Kidney Dialysis Center Services
N.A.I.C.S.: 621492

Estrella Mountain Dialysis, LLC (3)
9250 W Thomas Rd, Phoenix, AZ 85037
Tel.: (623) 772-7363
Emp.: 7
Kidney Dialysis Center Services
N.A.I.C.S.: 621492

Fall River Kidney Center, LLC (3)
48 Weaver St, Fall River, MA 02720
Tel.: (508) 677-4911
Kidney Dialysis Center Services
N.A.I.C.S.: 621492

Florida Dialysis Center of Celebration, LLC (3)
5051 W Irlo Bronson Memorial Hwy, Kissimmee, FL 34746
Tel.: (407) 397-2588
Dialysis Clinic Services
N.A.I.C.S.: 621492

Florida Dialysis Center of Orlando, LLC (3)
1711 35th St Ste109, Orlando, FL 32839
Tel.: (407) 648-9722
Kidney Dialysis Center Services
N.A.I.C.S.: 621492

Fort Myers Kidney Center, LLC (3)
14181 S Tamiami Trl Ste 120, Fort Myers, FL 33912-1939
Tel.: (239) 415-1062
Kidney Dialysis Clinic Services
N.A.I.C.S.: 621492

Fort Valley Dialysis Center, LLC (3)
135 Avera Dr, Fort Valley, GA 31030-5007
Tel.: (478) 827-0776
Dialysis Clinic Services
N.A.I.C.S.: 621492

Grand Prairie Dialysis Center, LLC (3)
550 S Carrier Pkwy Ste 450, Grand Prairie, TX 75051-1500
Tel.: (972) 237-2400
Kidney Dialysis Clinic Services
N.A.I.C.S.: 621492

Great Falls Dialysis, LLC (3)
498 E 30th St, Paterson, NJ 07504
Tel.: (973) 569-0500
Renal Dialysis Clinic Services
N.A.I.C.S.: 621492

Greenacres Dialysis Center, LLC (3)
5702 Lk Worth Rd Ste 1, Greenacres City, FL 33463
Tel.: (561) 357-9547
Kidney Dialysis Clinic Services
N.A.I.C.S.: 621492

Greenville Dialysis Clinic, LLC (3)
220 A Howe St, Greenville, SC 29601
Tel.: (864) 271-2002
Kidney Dialysis Center Services
N.A.I.C.S.: 621492

Hammond Dialysis Clinic, LLC (3)
42286 Veterans Ave, Hammond, LA 70403
Tel.: (985) 345-8855
Kidney Dialysis Center Services
N.A.I.C.S.: 621492

Hawthorn Kidney Center, LLC (3)
537 Faunce Corner Rd, Dartmouth, MA 02747-1242
Tel.: (508) 994-9692
Kidney Dialysis Clinic Services
N.A.I.C.S.: 621492

Herald Square Dialysis, LLC (3)
1 Herald Sq Ste 100, New Britain, CT 06051
Tel.: (860) 223-4963
Web Site: http://www.heraldsquaredialysis.com
Kidney Dialysis Center Services
N.A.I.C.S.: 621492

Heritage Dialysis Center LLC (3)
67 Cooper St, Agawam, MA 01001
Tel.: (413) 786-2022
Kidney Dialysis Center Services
N.A.I.C.S.: 621492

Howard University Dialysis Center, LLC (3)
2041 Georgia Ave NW, Washington, DC 20060
Tel.: (202) 865-7365
Emp.: 28
Kidney Dialysis Center Services
N.A.I.C.S.: 621492

Hunt County Regional Dialysis Center LLC (3)
3301 Ridgecrest Rd Ste 1, Greenville, TX 75402
Tel.: (903) 455-0579
Kidney Dialysis Services
N.A.I.C.S.: 621492
Steven Gieser *(Dir-Medical)*
Stanley Mathew *(Mgr-Clinic)*

Jasper-ARA Dialysis L.L.P. (3)
930 Marvin Hancock Dr, Jasper, TX 75951-4752
Tel.: (409) 384-4200
Dialysis Clinic Services
N.A.I.C.S.: 621492

Jupiter Kidney Center LLC (3)
1701 Military Trail Ste140, Jupiter, FL 33458
Tel.: (561) 744-4661
Kidney Dialysis Center Services
N.A.I.C.S.: 621492

Kerman Dialysis Center, LLC (3)
14945 W Whitesbridge Ave, Kerman, CA 93630-1111
Tel.: (559) 846-0023
Dialysis Clinic Services
N.A.I.C.S.: 621492

Kidney Care Centers of Cambridge Ohio, LLC (3)
6901 Glenn Hwy Ste A, Cambridge, OH 43725-8685
Tel.: (740) 439-1431
Kidney Dialysis Clinic Services
N.A.I.C.S.: 621492

Kidney Care Centers of Coshocton Ohio, LLC (3)
23649 Airport Rd, Coshocton, OH 43812
Tel.: (740) 291-8030
Kidney Dialysis Clinic Services
N.A.I.C.S.: 621492

Kidney Center of Arvada LLC (3)
5265 Vance St Ste 100, Arvada, CO 80002
Tel.: (303) 403-1127
Emp.: 10
Kidney Dialysis Center Services
N.A.I.C.S.: 621492

Kidney Center of Bear Creek, LLC (3)
11058 W Jewell Ave, Lakewood, CO 80232
Tel.: (303) 233-4204
Emp.: 7
Kidney Dialysis Center Services
N.A.I.C.S.: 621492

Kidney Center of Bexley, LLC (3)
1151 College Ave, Columbus, OH 43209-2827
Tel.: (614) 231-2200
Kidney Dialysis Clinic Services
N.A.I.C.S.: 621492

Kidney Center of Lafayette LLC (3)
2655 Crescent Dr Ste C, Lafayette, CO 80026
Tel.: (720) 890-4661
Emp.: 15
Kidney Dialysis Center Services
N.A.I.C.S.: 621492

Kidney Center of Lakewood LLC (3)
6166 W Alameda Ave, Lakewood, CO 80226-3539
Tel.: (303) 922-6371
Kidney Dialysis Clinic Services
N.A.I.C.S.: 621492

Kidney Center of Longmont LLC (3)
1960 Ken Pratt Blvd Ste A, Longmont, CO 80501
Tel.: (303) 485-7100
Renal Dialysis Clinic Services
N.A.I.C.S.: 621492
Peter J. Boseman *(Dir-Medical)*

Kidney Center of North Denver, LLC (3)
6920 W 38th Ave, Wheat Ridge, CO 80033-4966
Tel.: (303) 463-3041
Kidney Dialysis Clinic Services
N.A.I.C.S.: 621492

Kidney Center of Westminster LLC (3)
8410 Decatur St, Westminster, CO 80031
Tel.: (303) 430-6518
Kidney Dialysis Center Services
N.A.I.C.S.: 621492

Lake Gray Dialysis Center LLC (3)
6196 Lk Gray Blvd Ste 112, Jacksonville, FL 32244
Tel.: (904) 772-0933
Kidney Dialysis Clinic Services
N.A.I.C.S.: 621492

Langhorne Dialysis LLC (3)
880 Town Ctr Dr, Langhorne, PA 19047
Tel.: (215) 757-4115
Kidney Dialysis Center Services
N.A.I.C.S.: 621492

Lawton Dialysis Center, LLC (3)
5110 W Gore Blvd, Lawton, OK 73505-5909
Tel.: (580) 248-3733
Kidney Dialysis Clinic Services
N.A.I.C.S.: 621492

Lehigh Acres Dialysis Center, LLC (3)
3227 Lee Blvd Unit A, Lehigh Acres, FL 33971
Tel.: (239) 303-1724
Kidney Dialysis Center Services
N.A.I.C.S.: 621492

Lewis-Clark Kidney Center, LLC (3)
2116 12th Ave, Lewiston, ID 83501
Tel.: (208) 743-0662
Kidney Dialysis Center Services
N.A.I.C.S.: 621492

Lexington Kidney Center, LLC (3)
2831 Augusta Rd, West Columbia, SC 29170
Tel.: (803) 796-8785
Web Site: http://www.aracolumbia.com
Kidney Dialysis Services
N.A.I.C.S.: 621492
Muhammad Islam *(Pres)*

Lincoln Park Kidney Center, LLC (3)
1491 Southfield Rd, Lincoln Park, MI 48146
Tel.: (313) 928-4560
Kidney Dialysis Services
N.A.I.C.S.: 621492

MOHAWK VALLEY DIALYSIS CENTER, INC. (3)
115 Town Sq Dr, Amsterdam, NY 12010
Tel.: (518) 627-0280
Kidney Dialysis Center Services
N.A.I.C.S.: 621492

Madera Kidney Center, LLC (3)
1560 Country Club Dr, Madera, CA 93638
Tel.: (559) 673-5259
Kidney Dialysis Center Services
N.A.I.C.S.: 621492

Metro St. Louis Dialysis - Florissant, LLC (3)
10160 W Florissant Ave, Saint Louis, MO 63136-2104
Tel.: (314) 869-4978
Kidney Dialysis Clinic Services
N.A.I.C.S.: 621492

Miami Regional Dialysis Center West, LLC (3)
900 Park Ctr Blvd Ste 400, Miami Gardens, FL 33169
Tel.: (305) 625-7125
Kidney Dialysis Center Services
N.A.I.C.S.: 621492

Miami-ARA LLC (3)
100 NW 170Th St Ste 106, North Miami Beach, FL 33169-5513
Tel.: (305) 650-8822
Kidney Dialysis Center Services
N.A.I.C.S.: 621492

Nephrology Center of Detroit, LLC (3)
20001 Livernois Ave, Detroit, MI 48221
Tel.: (313) 861-0340
Kidney Dialysis Services
N.A.I.C.S.: 621492

North Main Kidney Center, LLC (3)
3900 N Main St, Columbia, SC 29203
Tel.: (803) 779-1201
Kidney Dialysis Center Services
N.A.I.C.S.: 621492

Northeast Philadelphia Dialysis Center, LLC (3)
9815 Roosevelt Blvd Ste 1A, Philadelphia, PA 19114
Tel.: (215) 330-0494
Kidney Dialysis Services
N.A.I.C.S.: 621492
Zubin P. Kolangaden *(Dir-Medical)*

Oil City Dialysis Center, LLC (3)
6945 Us 322 Ste 640, Cranberry, PA 16319
Tel.: (814) 677-7034
Kidney Dialysis Center Services
N.A.I.C.S.: 621492

Parker Kidney Center, LLC (3)
18320 Cottonwood Dr Ste C, Parker, CO 80138
Tel.: (303) 625-7508
Web Site: http://www.parkerkidneycenter.com
Kidney Dialysis Services
N.A.I.C.S.: 621492

Pickaway Dialysis Center LLC (3)
1180 N Ct St Ste E, Circleville, OH 43113-1397
Tel.: (740) 477-2072
Kidney Dialysis Center Services
N.A.I.C.S.: 621492

Regional Dialysis Center of Lancaster LLC (3)
2500 W Pleasant Run Rd Ste 100, Lancaster, TX 75146
Tel.: (972) 274-0192
Kidney Dialysis Services
N.A.I.C.S.: 621492
Venkata Yalamanchili *(Dir-Medical)*
Kasandra Thomas *(Mgr-Clinic)*

Regional Dialysis Center of Mesquite LLC (3)
1650 Republic Pkwy Ste 100, Mesquite, TX 75150
Tel.: (972) 613-4715
Renal Dialysis Clinic Services
N.A.I.C.S.: 621492
Enrique Carino *(Dir-Medical)*
Stanley Mathew *(Mgr-Clinic)*

COMPANIES

NAUTIC PARTNERS, LLC

Richmond Regional Dialysis, LLC (3)
3384 Creighton Rd, Richmond, VA 23223-2618
Tel.: (804) 644-0489
Dialysis Clinic Services
N.A.I.C.S.: 621492

Seneca Dialysis Center, LLC (3)
685 S Oak St, Seneca, SC 29678-3827
Tel.: (864) 885-0273
Kidney Dialysis Center Services
N.A.I.C.S.: 621492

South Arlington Dialysis Center, LLC (3)
3415 S Cooper St Ste 118, Arlington, TX 76015-3434
Tel.: (817) 465-8585
Kidney Dialysis Clinic Services
N.A.I.C.S.: 621492

South Augusta Dialysis Clinic, LLC (3)
3206 Peach Orchard Rd, Augusta, GA 30906-3540
Tel.: (706) 798-5774
Hemodialysis Center Services
N.A.I.C.S.: 621492

Southwest Jacksonville Dialysis Center LLC (3)
1584 Normandy Vlg Pkwy Ste 29, Jacksonville, FL 32221
Tel.: (904) 781-7272
Kidney Dialysis Services
N.A.I.C.S.: 621492

Space City Dialysis Center, LLC (3)
6518 Memorial Dr, Texas City, TX 77591
Tel.: (409) 965-0318
Kidney Dialysis Center Services
N.A.I.C.S.: 621492

Spartanburg Dialysis, LLC (3)
128 Dillon Dr, Spartanburg, SC 29307
Tel.: (864) 587-1507
Kidney Dialysis Center Services
N.A.I.C.S.: 621492

St. Petersburg Kidney Care South, LLC (3)
4050 34th St S, Saint Petersburg, FL 33711
Tel.: (727) 867-1279
Kidney Dialysis Clinic Services
N.A.I.C.S.: 621492

Swainsboro Dialysis Clinic, LLC (3)
3 Medical Ctr Dr, Swainsboro, GA 30401-5777
Tel.: (478) 237-8186
Kidney Dialysis Center Services
N.A.I.C.S.: 621492

Taunton Healthcare Clinic, LLC (3)
1 Washington St Ste 9, Taunton, MA 02780-3960
Tel.: (508) 828-5986
Kidney Dialysis Center Services
N.A.I.C.S.: 621492

The Dialysis Center of Attleboro, LLC (3)
Attleboro Crossing 217 S Main St Store 7, Attleboro, MA 02702
Tel.: (508) 236-6041
Kidney Dialysis Services
N.A.I.C.S.: 621492

The Dialysis Center of Gary - Merrillville, LLC (3)
6059 BRdway, Merrillville, IN 46410-2619
Tel.: (219) 980-1090
Kidney Dialysis Center Services
N.A.I.C.S.: 621492

The Dialysis Center of Hammond, LLC (3)
7 Sibley St, Hammond, IN 46320
Tel.: (219) 937-2819
Kidney Dialysis Center Services
N.A.I.C.S.: 621492

The Dialysis Center of North Philadelphia, LLC (3)
1300 W Lehigh Ave Ste 106, Philadelphia, PA 19132
Tel.: (215) 223-1018
Renal Dialysis Clinic Services
N.A.I.C.S.: 621492

Steven G. Dimitriou *(Dir-Medical)*

The Dialysis Center of Portage, LLC (3)
5615 Us Hwy 6, Portage, IN 46368
Tel.: (219) 762-4848
Kidney Dialysis Center Services
N.A.I.C.S.: 621492

The Dialysis Center of Schererville, LLC (3)
1534 US Hwy 41, Schererville, IN 46375
Tel.: (219) 322-5448
Kidney Dialysis Services
N.A.I.C.S.: 621492

The Dialysis Unit of Center City Philadelphia, LLC (3)
230 N Broad St 12th Fl Bobst Bldg, Philadelphia, PA 19102-1121
Tel.: (215) 563-9383
Renal Dialysis Clinic Services
N.A.I.C.S.: 621492
Larry E. Krevolin *(Dir-Medical)*

The Kidney Center of South Philadelphia, LLC (3)
1930 S Broad St Unit 7, Philadelphia, PA 19145
Tel.: (215) 463-3120
Kidney Dialysis Services
N.A.I.C.S.: 621492

The Kidney Center on Main, LLC (3)
2144 N Main St Ste 2, Longmont, CO 80501
Tel.: (303) 485-8911
Renal Dialysis Clinic Services
N.A.I.C.S.: 621492
Richard K. Halterman *(Dir-Medical)*

Thornton Kidney Center, LLC (3)
8451 Pearl St, Thornton, CO 80229
Tel.: (303) 227-9981
Kidney Dialysis Center Services
N.A.I.C.S.: 621492

Universal Dialysis Center, LLC (3)
3804 Bladensburg Rd, Cottage City, MD 20722-1613
Tel.: (301) 277-2704
Kidney Dialysis Clinic Services
N.A.I.C.S.: 621492

University Kidney Center Bluegrass, LLC (3)
1935 Bluegrass Ave Ste 100, Louisville, KY 40215-1191
Tel.: (502) 368-5843
Kidney Dialysis Center Services
N.A.I.C.S.: 621492

Wallingford Dialysis Care, LLC (3)
720 N Main St Ext Ste 3, Wallingford, CT 06492
Tel.: (203) 265-0667
Kidney Dialysis Center Services
N.A.I.C.S.: 621492

Waltham Dialysis LLC (3)
135 Beaver St Ste 310, Waltham, MA 02452
Tel.: (781) 642-0331
Kidney Dialysis Services
N.A.I.C.S.: 621492

Warren Dialysis Center LLC (3)
8720 E Market St Ste 1A, Warren, OH 44484-2364
Tel.: (330) 609-5502
Kidney Dialysis Services
N.A.I.C.S.: 621492

Wellesley Dialysis LLC (3)
195 Worcester St, Wellesley, MA 02481-5568
Tel.: (781) 431-1414
Kidney Dialysis Services
N.A.I.C.S.: 621492

Western Community Dialysis Center, LLC (3)
11301 Okeechobee Blvd, Royal Palm Beach, FL 33411
Tel.: (561) 791-2252
Kidney Dialysis Center Services
N.A.I.C.S.: 621492

Westhampton Regional Dialysis, LLC (3)
500 E Laburnum Ave, Richmond, VA 23222

Tel.: (804) 228-3682
Web Site: http://www.nephspec.com
Emp.: 7
Kidney Dialysis Clinic Services
N.A.I.C.S.: 621492

Wharton Dialysis Care, L.L.P. (3)
205 N Alabama Rd, Wharton, TX 77488
Tel.: (979) 532-0012
Dialysis Clinic Services
N.A.I.C.S.: 621492

Woodhaven Dialysis Center, LLC (3)
1336 Bristol Pike Ste 110, Bensalem, PA 19020
Tel.: (215) 639-1070
Kidney Dialysis Center Services
N.A.I.C.S.: 621492

Woodland Park Dialysis Center, LLC (3)
1225 Mcbride Ave, Woodland Park, NJ 07424
Tel.: (973) 890-2394
Kidney Dialysis Clinic Services
N.A.I.C.S.: 621492

Youngstown-Warren Home Dialysis, LLC (3)
4531 Belmont Ave, Youngstown, OH 44505
Tel.: (330) 759-3807
Kidney Dialysis Center Services
N.A.I.C.S.: 621492

Lindstrom Metric, LLC (1)
2950 100th Ct NE, Blaine, MN 55449
Tel.: (763) 780-4200
Web Site: http://www.lindfastgrp.com
Metric Fastener Mfr & Distr
N.A.I.C.S.: 339993
Virgil W. Lindstrom *(Founder)*
Neil Yeargin *(CEO)*

Subsidiary (Domestic):

Hodell-Natco Industries Inc. (2)
7825 Hub Pkwy, Cleveland, OH 44125
Tel.: (800) 321-4862
Web Site: http://www.hodell-natco.com
Sales Range: $10-24.9 Million
Bolts Mfr
N.A.I.C.S.: 423710
Otto Reidl *(CEO)*
Brandon Liebhard *(VP-West Reg & Gen Mgr-Reno)*
Sean Liebhard *(Mgr-IT)*
Matt Tolley *(Gen Mgr-Orlando)*
John Pratte *(Dir-Ops)*
Jeff Weese *(Mgr-Quality)*
Susan Specker *(Controller)*
Kevin Reidl *(Pres)*
Dan Reidl *(Exec VP)*
Ryan Causey *(Gen Mgr-Colombia)*
Mike Johnstone *(Gen Mgr-St Louis)*
Dave Crowl *(Gen Mgr-Houston)*
Laurel Zurawick *(Dir-HR)*

Stelfast, Inc. (2)
22979 Stelfast Pkwy, Strongsville, OH 44149
Tel.: (440) 879-0077
Web Site: http://www.stelfast.com
Bolt, Nut, Screw, Rivet & Washer Mfr
N.A.I.C.S.: 332722
Dan Kulik *(Branch Mgr)*
Simmi Sakhuja *(Owner & Pres)*

Titan Fastener Products, Inc. (2)
2627 Sidney Lanier Dr, Brunswick, GA 31525-6812
Tel.: (912) 262-6400
Web Site: http://www.titanfasteners.com
Industrial Supplies Whslr
N.A.I.C.S.: 423840

Magnolia Creek (1)
645 Crenshaw Rd, Columbiana, AL 35051-3277
Tel.: (205) 678-4373
Web Site: http://www.magnolia-creek.com
General Medical & Surgical Hospitals
N.A.I.C.S.: 622110
Jim Palmer *(CEO)*

PEP Industries LLC (1)
110 Frank Mossberg Dr, Attleboro, MA 02703
Tel.: (508) 226-5600
Web Site: http://www.pep-corp.com
Holding Company; Precision Engineered Products Mfr

N.A.I.C.S.: 551112
John Manzi *(Pres & COO)*

Pantherx Specialty, LLC (1)
24 Summit Park Dr, Pittsburgh, PA 15275
Tel.: (412) 547-3483
Web Site: https://www.pantherxrare.com
Sales Range: $25-49.9 Million
Pharmaceuticals Product Mfr
N.A.I.C.S.: 325412
Timothy Davis *(Sr VP-Special Project)*
Austin Russian *(VP-Program Management)*
Robert Snyder *(Pres)*

Qantum Communications Corporation (1)
1201 Story Ave Ste 123, Louisville, KY 40206
Tel.: (502) 568-6633
Radio Broadcasting Services
N.A.I.C.S.: 516110
Linda Schufter *(Pres)*

SurfacePrep Mobile LLC (1)
9000 Byron Commerce Dr SW, Byron, MI 49315
Tel.: (617) 275-5992
Web Site: https://surfaceprep.com
Industrial Machinery Mfr
N.A.I.C.S.: 333248
Mike Currie *(CEO)*

Subsidiary (Domestic):

Diamond Tool and Abrasives Inc. (2)
39w207 Highland Ave, Elgin, IL 60123-4209
Tel.: (847) 888-8850
Web Site: http://www.dtabrasives.com
Hobby, Toy & Game Stores
N.A.I.C.S.: 459120
John Thietje *(Mgr)*

Tabula Rasa HealthCare, Inc. (1)
228 Strawbridge Dr Ste 100, Moorestown, NJ 08057
Web Site: https://www.tabularasahealthcare.com
Rev.: $299,516,000
Assets: $384,149,000
Liabilities: $441,180,000
Net Worth: ($57,031,000)
Earnings: ($147,510,000)
Emp.: 1,027
Fiscal Year-end: 12/31/2022
Healtcare Services
N.A.I.C.S.: 621491
Christopher F. Corey *(Dir)*
John Figueroa *(Dir)*
Joseph Anderson *(Dir)*

Subsidiary (Domestic):

CareKinesis, Inc. (2)
228 Strawbridge Dr, Moorestown, NJ 08057
Web Site: http://www.carekinesis.com
Health Care Management Services
N.A.I.C.S.: 621610
Calvin H. Knowlton *(Founder & Chm)*
Orsula V. Knowlton *(Pres)*
Robert L. Alesiani *(Chief Pharmacotherapy Officer)*
Michael S. Awadalla *(Sr VP-Clinical Svcs & Medication Safety)*

DoseMe LLC (2)
228 Strawbridge Dr, Moorestown, NJ 08057
Tel.: (832) 358-3308
Web Site: https://doseme-rx.com
Software Development Services
N.A.I.C.S.: 541511
Nicola Hunter *(Dir-Mktg & Comm)*
Michael Dorkhom *(Head-Tech)*

Medliance, LLC (2)
1839 S Alma School Rd Ste 230, Mesa, AZ 85210
Tel.: (480) 784-6335
Web Site: https://medliance.com
Health Care Management Services
N.A.I.C.S.: 621610
Candy Rebstock *(Sr VP)*
Diane Mitrevski *(Dir-Information Sys)*

PersonifilRx, LLC (2)
225 Metro Ctr Blvd Bldg 2, Warwick, RI 02886
Tel.: (401) 593-0500
Web Site: https://www.personifil.com
Health Care Srvices
N.A.I.C.S.: 621999

NAUTIC PARTNERS, LLC

U.S. PRIVATE

Nautic Partners, LLC—(Continued)

eClusive LLC (2)
7700 Equitable Dr Ste 100, Eden Prairie, MN 55344
Tel.: (952) 400-7600
Web Site: http://www.eclusive.com
Healthcare Information Solution & Services Provider
N.A.I.C.S.: 621999

Vallen Distribution Inc. (1)
1460 Tobias Gadson Blvd, Charleston, SC 29407
Tel.: (843) 745-2465
Web Site: http://www.vallen.com
Electrical Materials & Safety Products
N.A.I.C.S.: 423610
Lisa A. Mitchell (Pres)
Melanie Hardy (Mgr-Sustainable Dev)
Pamela Midden Sullivan (Dir-Trng & Staffing)
Bruce Lodge (Mgr-Corp Pur)
Scott Moore (VP-Contracts)

Subsidiary (Domestic):

Bryant Electric Supply Company Inc. (2)
825 Groves St, Lowell, NC 28098-1706
Tel.: (704) 866-6000
Web Site: http://www.bryantelec.com
Sales Range: $25-49.9 Million
Emp.: 250
Electrical, Industrial, Power Transmission & Electronics Supplies & Controls
N.A.I.C.S.: 423610

Subsidiary (Domestic):

Bryant Electric Supply Company Inc. (3)
222 22nd St SW, Hickory, NC 28602
Tel.: (828) 328-2295
Web Site:
http://www.bryantsupplydirect.com
Rev.: $27,258,121
Emp.: 15
Electrical Supplies
N.A.I.C.S.: 423610
Tim Wingler (Mgr-Ops)

Subsidiary (Domestic):

Encon Safety Products (2)
6825 W Sam Houston Pkwy N, Houston, TX 77041-4026
Tel.: (843) 745-2400
Web Site: http://www.enconsafety.com
Rev.: $19,925,000
Emp.: 160
Safety & Protective Equipment
N.A.I.C.S.: 423840
Jim Johnson (Gen Mgr)
Shannon Harper (Product Mgr-Emergency Shower & Eye Wash)
Jenna Villarreal (Mgr-Mktg)
Linda Baltus (Mgr-PPE Bus Unit)

Subsidiary (Non-US):

Hagemeyer Canada (2)
Eastgate Industrial Estate 4810 92 Avenue, 4810-92 Avenue, Edmonton, T6B 2X4, AB, Canada
Tel.: (780) 468-3366
Web Site: http://www.centuryvallen.com
Sales Range: $125-149.9 Million
Emp.: 350
Industrial Supplies Whslr
N.A.I.C.S.: 423840
Guy Mersereau (Pres & COO)
Kelly Meyers (Dir-Natl Accts)

Subsidiary (Domestic):

Hagemeyer North America (2)
2730 Edmonds Ln, Lewisville, TX 75067
Tel.: (972) 304-7200
Web Site: http://www.hagemeyerna.com
Rev.: $150,000,000
Emp.: 30
Electrical & Industrial Supplies & Tools
N.A.I.C.S.: 423610
Lisa Michelle (Pres)

Hagemeyer North America (2)
7920 14th St W, Rock Island, IL 61201-7423
Tel.: (309) 787-8160
Web Site: http://www.hagemeyerna.com

Sales Range: $5-14.9 Billion
Electrical & Industrial Supplies & Tools
N.A.I.C.S.: 423840
Lisa A. Mitchell (Pres)

Division (Domestic):

Hagemeyer North America (3)
5660 S Westridge Dr, New Berlin, WI 53151-7950
Tel.: (262) 814-0263
Sales Range: $25-49.9 Million
Emp.: 15
Electrical & Industrial Supplies & Tools
N.A.I.C.S.: 423840
Vince Carriveau (Mgr-Ops)
Gregory Graetz (Project Coord)

Hagemeyer North America (3)
710 College Ave, Borger, TX 79007
Tel.: (806) 273-3680
Web Site: http://www.hagemeyerna.com
Rev.: $264,928,000
Emp.: 5
Industrial Supply Distribution
N.A.I.C.S.: 423830

Subsidiary (Non-US):

Proveedora De Seguridad Industrial Del Golfo S.A. De C.V. (2)
Blvd Adolfo Lopez Mateos 4000, Tampico, 89339, Tamaulipas, Mexico
Tel.: (52) 8332301700
Web Site:
http://www.vallenproveedora.com.mx
Sales Range: $50-74.9 Million
Emp.: 200
Industrial Supplies Whslr
N.A.I.C.S.: 423840

Subsidiary (Domestic):

WESCO Integrated Supply, Inc. (2)
225 W Station Square Dr Ste 700, Pittsburgh, PA 15219
Tel.: (516) 484-6070
Web Site: https://www.vallenis.com
Electrical Materials
N.A.I.C.S.: 423610

Vantage Mobility International, LLC (1)
5202 S 28th Pl, Phoenix, AZ 85040
Tel.: (602) 348-8267
Web Site: http://www.vantagemobility.com
Vehicle Accessibility Products Mfr
N.A.I.C.S.: 441330
Tim Barone (Chm)
Mark Shaughnessy (Pres & CEO)

NAUTICAL MARINE INC.
109 Tarnava St, Port Isabel, TX 78578
Tel.: (956) 943-5481
Sales Range: $10-24.9 Million
Emp.: 1
Seafood Distr
N.A.I.C.S.: 424460
Jeffrey Zimmerman (VP)

NAUTILUS ENVIRONMENTAL, LLC.
4340 Vandever Ave, San Diego, CA 92120
Tel.: (858) 587-7333
Web Site:
http://www.nautilusenvironmental.com
Year Founded: 2004
Sales Range: $1-9.9 Million
Emp.: 37
Environmental Consulting & Testing
N.A.I.C.S.: 541620
Marilyn O'Neill (Founder & CEO)
Peter Arth (Dir-Laboratory)
Katie Payne (Mgr-Quality Assurance & Compliance)
Adrienne Cibor (Sr Mgr-Project)
Kasey Skrivseth (Project Mgr-Sediments)

NAVAJO AGRICULTURAL PRODUCTS INDUSTRY INC.
PO Drawer 1318, Farmington, NM 87499
Tel.: (505) 566-2600 NM
Web Site:
http://www.navajopride.com
Year Founded: 1976
Sales Range: $300-349.9 Million
Emp.: 410
Provider of Farming Services
N.A.I.C.S.: 921140
Tsosie Lewis (CEO)
Beulah John (Dir-HR)
Mike Freeman (Engr-Civil)

NAVAJO SHIPPERS INC.
1400 W 64th Ave, Denver, CO 80221-2430
Tel.: (303) 287-3800 CO
Web Site: http://www.navajo.com
Year Founded: 1981
Sales Range: $25-49.9 Million
Emp.: 700
Trucking Service
N.A.I.C.S.: 484230
Donald R. Digby (Owner & Pres)
Brenda Schaack (Controller)

Subsidiaries:

Navajo Express Inc. (1)
1400 West 64th Avenue, Denver, CO 80221-2430
Tel.: (303) 287-3800
Web Site: http://www.vajo.com
Sales Range: $100-124.9 Million
Emp.: 50
Provider of Trucking Services
N.A.I.C.S.: 484230
Donald R. Digby (Pres)
Derek Smith (Dir-Logistics)
Tina Martinez (Mgr-Claims)

NAVAJO TRACTOR SALES INC.
221 N Hwy 491, Gallup, NM 87301
Tel.: (505) 863-3806
Web Site:
http://www.navajotractor.com
Sales Range: $10-24.9 Million
Emp.: 35
Farm Machinery,
N.A.I.C.S.: 459999

NAVAJO TRIBAL UTILITY AUTHORITY
Hwy 12 N, Fort Defiance, AZ 86504
Tel.: (928) 729-5721 AZ
Web Site: http://www.ntua.com
Year Founded: 1965
Sales Range: $50-74.9 Million
Emp.: 540
Combination Utilities; Multi Utility Services
N.A.I.C.S.: 221118
Walter W. Haase (Gen Mgr)
Thomas Nelson (CFO)
Paul Bemore (Mgr-HR)
Clyde Casciato (Gen Mgr-Choice NTUA Wireless)

NAVAL CONTINUING CARE RETIREMENT FOUNDATION, INC.
1 Fleet Landing Blvd, Atlantic Beach, FL 32233
Tel.: (904) 246-9900 FL
Web Site:
http://www.fleetlanding.com
Year Founded: 1985
Sales Range: $25-49.9 Million
Emp.: 399
Lifecare Retirement Community Operator
N.A.I.C.S.: 623311
Cynthia Hack (Controller)
Olivia Bush (Dir-Charitable Gift Plng)
Tamara Schwarz (Sr Dir-HR)
Elizabeth Sholar (Sr Dir-Health Care Svcs)

NAVARRE CHEVROLET INC.
1310 E College St, Lake Charles, LA 70605
Tel.: (337) 474-1999
Web Site:
http://www.billynavarreauto.com
Sales Range: $10-24.9 Million
Emp.: 300
Automobiles, New & Used
N.A.I.C.S.: 441110
Billy Navarre (Owner)

NAVARRO COUNTY ELECTRIC COOPERATIVE, INC.
3800 W Hwy 22, Corsicana, TX 75151-0616
Tel.: (903) 874-7411 TX
Web Site: http://www.navarroec.com
Year Founded: 1937
Sales Range: $25-49.9 Million
Emp.: 47
Electric Power Transmission Services
N.A.I.C.S.: 221122
George Smith (Treas & Sec)
Ron Buckley (Pres)
Kent Sheffield (VP)

NAVARRO RESEARCH & ENGINEERING, INC.
669 Emory Valley Rd, Oak Ridge, TN 37830
Tel.: (865) 220-9650
Web Site:
http://www.navresearch.com
Sales Range: $10-24.9 Million
Emp.: 160
Provider of Business Consulting & Engineering Services
N.A.I.C.S.: 561210
Susana Navarro-Valenti (Pres)
Harold Lawrence (Coord-HR)
Randy Trusley (VP-Bus Ops)

NAVASOTA VALLEY ELECTRIC COOPERATIVE
PO Box 848, Franklin, TX 77856
Tel.: (979) 828-3232
Web Site:
http://www.navasotavalley.com
Year Founded: 1941
Sales Range: $25-49.9 Million
Emp.: 50
Distr of Electric Power
N.A.I.C.S.: 221122
James Calhoun (Gen Mgr)
Billie Sue Corry (Pres)
John Perry (Treas & Sec)
Jerry Robertson (VP)

NAVICUS
951 Broken Sound Pkwy Ste 190, Boca Raton, FL 33487
Tel.: (561) 826-8000
Web Site: http://www.navicus.com
Year Founded: 2002
Sales Range: $25-49.9 Million
Emp.: 20
Health & Allied Services
N.A.I.C.S.: 621999
Kirk Watts (CIO)
Jesse Berger (CEO)
Marie Falconer (VP-Acctg)

NAVIGA BUSINESS SERVICES, LLC
109 N Brush St Ste 400, Tampa, FL 33602
Tel.: (813) 837-2220
Web Site:
http://www.navigaservices.com
Year Founded: 2002
Sales Range: $1-9.9 Million
Emp.: 10
Recruitment Services
N.A.I.C.S.: 561311

COMPANIES

Kathleen Steffey *(Founder & CEO)*
Angela O'Neal *(Coord-Recruiting-Natl)*
Kevin Steffey *(Pres)*
John Iannarelli Jr. *(Coord-Res Support)*

NAVIGANT CREDIT UNION
1005 Douglas Pike, Smithfield, RI 02917-1206
Tel.: (401) 233-4700 RI
Web Site: http://www.navigantcu.org
Year Founded: 1915
Emp.: 297
Credit Union Operator
N.A.I.C.S.: 522130
Frederick Reinhardt *(Chief Lending Officer & Sr VP)*
Kathleen Orovitz *(Sr VP-Retail Banking)*
Kenneth Senus *(Sr VP-IT)*
H. Chris Der Vartanian *(Chief Risk Officer & Sr VP)*
Donald Osley *(Mgr-Relationship)*
Ester Barros *(Mgr-Bus Svcs)*
Steve A. Loprochio *(Asst VP & Mgr-Relationship-Comml Lending)*
Pamela S. LaBreche *(Asst VP & Mgr-Relationship-Comml Lending)*
Gary E. Furtado *(Pres & CEO)*
Roland R. Lachapelle *(Vice Chm)*
Joseph R. Beretta *(Chm)*
Ann M. Kashmanian *(Sec)*
Lisa G. Dandeneau *(COO & Exec VP)*
Jason M. Jolin *(CFO & Sr VP)*

NAVIGATE AFFORDABLE HOUSING PARTNERS, INC.
500 Office Park Dr, Birmingham, AL 35223
Tel.: (888) 466-5572 AL
Web Site: http://www.navigatehousing.com
Year Founded: 1980
Sales Range: $450-499.9 Million
Emp.: 55
Community Housing Services
N.A.I.C.S.: 624229
Eric Q. Strong *(CEO)*
Natoya Witherspoon *(Mgr-Relationship)*
Julie L. Reynolds *(COO)*
Charlie Wade *(Mgr-Relationship)*
Linda Eaton *(Mgr-Relationship)*
Nate Greathree *(Coord-Contract Admin)*
Tim Shearer *(Coord-Contract Admin)*
Vernell Callahan *(Coord-Contract Admin)*
Dale Marcus *(Dir-HR)*
Lisa McCarroll *(Dir-Contract Admin)*
Tom Gerundo *(Coord-Contract Admin)*
Yolanda Clark *(Mgr-Relationship)*

NAVIGATE CORPORATION
1200 Liberty Ridge Dr Ste 125, Wayne, PA 19087
Tel.: (484) 383-0606 PA
Web Site: http://www.navigatecorp.com
Year Founded: 1994
Emp.: 55
Management Consulting Services
N.A.I.C.S.: 541618
Jerry Goldberg *(Partner)*
Brian Lee *(Partner)*
David Crossed *(Partner)*
Robert Kathol *(Founder & Mng Partner)*
John Hutton *(Principal)*
Christopher Jacobs *(Sr Mgr)*
Cyndi Stains *(CFO)*
Ian Waxman *(Principal)*
Adam Taicher *(Principal)*
Kip Wetzel *(Principal)*

NAVIGATION CAPITAL PARTNERS, INC.
1175 Peachtree St NE 10th Fl, Atlanta, GA 30361
Tel.: (404) 264-9180 DE
Web Site: http://www.navigationcapital.com
Privater Equity Firm
N.A.I.C.S.: 523999
Lawrence Mock *(Co-Founder & Mng Partner)*
Mark E. Downs *(Co-Founder & Partner)*
John D. Richardson *(Co-Founder & Mng Partner)*
Eerik Giles *(Co-Founder & Partner)*
Craig Kirsch *(Operating Partner)*
O. G. Greene *(Operating Partner)*
Darlene Clott *(CFO & Chief Compliance Officer)*
Kevin Keough *(Mng Dir-Ops)*
Lawrence E. Mock Jr. *(Founder & Mng Partner)*

Subsidiaries:

Brightwell Payments, Inc. (1)
4401 Northside Pkwy NW, Atlanta, GA 30327
Tel.: (404) 855-2462
Web Site: http://www.brightwell.com
Emp.: 60
Prepaid Debit Card Issuer
N.A.I.C.S.: 522210
Lynn Cherry *(Chief Compliance Officer)*
Hal Ramakers *(Sr VP-Solution-Global)*
Mike Gaburo *(CEO)*
Konstantinos Machairas *(VP-Sls-South Europe)*
Audrey Hall *(Sr VP-Mktg)*
John Markendorf *(Sr VP-Client Svcs)*
John McEwan *(CFO)*
Larry Hipp *(COO)*
Scot Brands *(Sr VP-Fin)*

James Brown Contracting Inc. (1)
6908 Chapman Rd, Lithonia, GA 30058
Tel.: (770) 482-6521
Web Site: http://www.browntrucking.com
Freight Trucking Services
N.A.I.C.S.: 484121
Kevin Slaughter *(VP)*

Pecora Corporation (1)
165 Wambold Rd, Harleysville, PA 19438
Tel.: (215) 723-6051
Web Site: http://www.pecora.com
Sales Range: $25-49.9 Million
Emp.: 120
Sealants, Adhesives & Repellent Mfr & Sales
N.A.I.C.S.: 325520
Joe Virdone *(Pres & CEO)*

NAVIGATOR CREDIT UNION
PO Box 1647, Pascagoula, MS 39568-1647
Tel.: (228) 762-3542 MS
Web Site: http://www.navigatorcu.org
Year Founded: 1939
Sales Range: $1-9.9 Million
Emp.: 126
Credit Union
N.A.I.C.S.: 522130
Bill McCoy *(CFO)*
Robert A. Fertitta *(Pres & CEO)*
Dennis A. Sumrall *(Chief Risk Officer)*
Josh Duncan *(Chief Lending Officer)*
Patrice Mims *(COO)*
Ashley Harmon *(CIO)*
C. L. Ates *(Vice Chm)*
Kathy Scarbrough *(Chief Comm Officer)*
Tony Taylor *(Sec)*
Walter L. Moore *(Chief HR Officer)*
Joseph V. Krebs Jr. *(Chm)*

NAVIS
389 SW Scalehouse Ct Ste 100, Bend, OR 97702
Web Site: http://www.naviscrm.com
Year Founded: 1987
Reservation Sales Systems & Call Management Services for Lodging Industry
N.A.I.C.S.: 518210
Kyle Buehner *(CEO)*
Matt Juarez *(VP-Ops)*
Kishore Bhattacharjee *(VP-Engrg)*
Kelsie Skinner *(Sr Mgr-Mktg)*
Gary Lawrence *(CFO)*
Brooke Hue *(VP-People & Culture)*
Bryan Turner *(VP-Product Solutions)*

NAVITAS BUSINESS CONSULTING INC
44365 Premier Plaza Ste 220, Ashburn, VA 20147
Tel.: (571) 222-4646
Web Site: http://www.navitas-tech.com
Year Founded: 2000
Sales Range: $1-9.9 Million
Emp.: 50
It Consulting
N.A.I.C.S.: 541690
Sandhya Bayireddy *(Pres)*

NAVLETS GARDEN CENTERS INC.
360 Civic Dr Ste D, Pleasant Hill, CA 94523
Tel.: (925) 689-7940
Web Site: http://www.navletsgardens.com
Rev.: $10,100,000
Emp.: 80
Retail Nurseries & Garden Stores
N.A.I.C.S.: 444240
Patricia Gray *(Pres)*

NAVOPACHE ELECTRIC CO-OPERATIVE INC.
1878 W White Mtn Blvd, Lakeside, AZ 85929
Tel.: (928) 368-5118 AZ
Web Site: http://www.navopache.org
Year Founded: 1946
Sales Range: $50-74.9 Million
Emp.: 110
Electronic Services
N.A.I.C.S.: 221122
Paul O'dair *(Mgr-Fin)*
David Plumb *(CEO)*

NAVOS MENTAL HEALTH SOLUTIONS
2600 SW Holden St, Seattle, WA 98126
Tel.: (206) 933-7000 WA
Web Site: http://www.navos.org
Year Founded: 1963
Sales Range: $50-74.9 Million
Emp.: 725
Mental Health Care Services
N.A.I.C.S.: 621420
David M. Johnson *(CEO)*
Cassie Undlin *(COO)*
Alice Braverman *(VP-Dev & Community Rels)*
Don Gillmore *(Pres)*
Patti Neuberger *(Treas)*
Mary Sellers *(CIO)*
Megan M. Kelly *(Chief Clinical Officer)*

NAVVIS HEALTHCARE, LLC
555 Maryville University Dr Ste 240, Saint Louis, MO 63141
Tel.: (636) 536-9443
Web Site: http://www.navvishealthcare.com
Healthcare Management Consulting Services
N.A.I.C.S.: 541611
Michael R. Farris *(Chm & CEO)*
Tim Elliott *(Gen Counsel & Exec VP)*
Robert Bauer *(Exec VP)*
Kristi Short *(Sr VP-Post-Acute Care)*
Randy Combs *(CFO)*
Marc Grossman *(CIO)*
Chuck Eberl *(CMO)*
Lee Angus *(Sr VP)*
Po Chou *(Sr VP)*
Michael Connolly *(Sr VP)*
Holly Firestine *(VP)*
Nicole Amling *(VP-HR)*
Linda Morrison *(VP-Ops)*
Tom Spradling *(VP)*
Kathy Hardesty *(VP)*
Kathy Gibala *(VP)*
Bruce Henderson *(Pres)*
Mandy Mangat *(Chief Medical Officer)*
Jeff Garibaldi *(Chief Product Officer)*
Sheila Fuse *(Sr VP-Policy & Payment Models)*
Robin Hug *(Sr VP)*
Nicole Bradberry *(Pres-Florida Market)*
Miles Snowden *(COO)*

NAVY ARMY COMMUNITY CREDIT UNION
5725 Spohn Dr, Corpus Christi, TX 78414-4117
Tel.: (361) 986-4500 TX
Web Site: http://www.navyarmyccu.com
Year Founded: 1955
Sales Range: $100-124.9 Million
Emp.: 305
Credit Union Operator
N.A.I.C.S.: 522130
Sarah O'Brien *(Pres)*
Pete Rivera *(Chm)*
John Jackson *(Sec)*

NAVY FEDERAL CREDIT UNION
820 Follin Ln SE, Vienna, VA 22180
Tel.: (888) 842-6328 VA
Web Site: http://www.navyfederal.org
Year Founded: 1933
Sales Range: $1-4.9 Billion
Credit Union
N.A.I.C.S.: 522130
John A. Lockhard *(Chm)*
Kenneth R. Burns *(Sec)*
Mary McDuffie *(Pres & CEO)*
Tony Gallardy *(CIO)*
Sovan Shatpathy *(CTO)*
Holly C. Kortright *(Chief HR Officer)*
Edward R. Cochrane Jr. *(Second Vice Chm)*

NAVY MUTUAL AID ASSOCIATION
29 Carpenter Rd, Arlington, VA 22212
Tel.: (703) 945-1440 VA
Web Site: http://www.navymutual.org
Year Founded: 1879
Sales Range: $250-299.9 Million
Emp.: 106
Veteran Family Support Services
N.A.I.C.S.: 813410
David Fridell *(CFO)*
Stephen R. Pietropaoli *(COO)*
Lauren M. Bloom *(Gen Counsel & VP-Govt Affairs)*
David Bragg *(VP-IT)*
Michelle L. Brickwedde *(VP-HR)*

NAVY SEAL FOUNDATION, INC.
1619 D St, Virginia Beach, VA 23459
Tel.: (757) 363-7490 VA

NAVY SEAL FOUNDATION, INC.

Navy SEAL Foundation, Inc.—(Continued)
Web Site:
http://www.navysealfoundation.org
Year Founded: 2000
Sales Range: $10-24.9 Million
Emp.: 9
Naval Warfare Support Services
N.A.I.C.S.: 561990
Jennifer Bragaw (Dir-Dev & Events)
Michael Baumer (Treas)
Marcela Szymanski (Vice Chm)
Scott Burke (CFO)
Ted Muhlner (Sec)
Robin King (CEO)
Garry Bonelli (Chm)

NAVY-MARINE CORPS RELIEF SOCIETY
875 N Randolph St Ste 225, Arlington, VA 22203
Tel.: (703) 696-4904
Web Site: http://www.nmcrs.org
Year Founded: 1904
Sales Range: $25-49.9 Million
Emp.: 248
Navy & Marine Personnel Assistance Services
N.A.I.C.S.: 813410
Peter B. Collins (COO & Exec VP)
Willie L. Williams (CIO & VP)
Shelley S. Marshall (Chief Dev & Comm Officer & VP)
Robert B. Neller (Chm)
Kathy Estes (Chief Admin Officer & VP)
Wesley H. Schmidt Jr. (CFO & VP)

NAYA VENTURES LLC
222 W Las Colinas Blvd Ste 755E, Irving, TX 75039
Tel.: (214) 630-1480 TX
Web Site:
http://www.nayaventures.com
Venture Capital & Private Equity Firm
N.A.I.C.S.: 523999
Dayakar Puskoor (Mng Partner)

NAYAMODE, INC.
2481 152nd Ave Ne, Redmond, WA 98052
Tel.: (425) 296-1940
Web Site: http://www.nayamode.com
Year Founded: 2005
Sales Range: $10-24.9 Million
Emp.: 45
Advertising Agency Services
N.A.I.C.S.: 541810
Srivats Srinivasan (Founder & CEO)

NAYLOR & BREEN BUILDERS, INC.
2335 Franklin St, Brandon, VT 05733
Tel.: (802) 247-6527
Web Site:
http://www.naylorbreen.com
Year Founded: 1978
Sales Range: $10-24.9 Million
Emp.: 60
Nonresidential Construction Services
N.A.I.C.S.: 236220
Robert Naylor (Pres & Mgr-Risk)

NAYLOR COMMERCIAL INTERIORS, INC.
2765 W Kingsley Rd, Garland, TX 75041-2406
Tel.: (972) 278-2620
Sales Range: $10-24.9 Million
Emp.: 100
Civil Engineering Services
N.A.I.C.S.: 236220
Justin Neal (Project Mgr)
Paula Naylor (Pres)

NAYLOR PIPE COMPANY
1230 E 92nd St, Chicago, IL 60619-7991
Tel.: (773) 721-9400 IL
Web Site: http://www.naylorpipe.com
Year Founded: 1925
Sales Range: $10-24.9 Million
Emp.: 100
Steel Pole Mfr
N.A.I.C.S.: 331210
John J. Czulno (Pres)

NAZARENE PUBLISHING HOUSE
2923 Troost Ave, Kansas City, MO 64109
Tel.: (816) 931-1900
Web Site: http://www.nph.com
Sales Range: $10-24.9 Million
Emp.: 250
Pamphlets: Publishing & Printing
N.A.I.C.S.: 513130
Mark Brown (VP)
Merritt Nielson (Chief Editor)

NAZARETH LIVING CENTER
2 Nazareth Ln, Saint Louis, MO 63129
Tel.: (314) 487-3950 MO
Web Site:
http://www.nazarethlivingcenter.com
Year Founded: 1987
Sales Range: $10-24.9 Million
Emp.: 270
Retirement Community Operator
N.A.I.C.S.: 623311
Ron Mantia (CEO)
Daniel J. Sinclair (Chm)
Kevin Rymanowski (Treas)
Elaine S. Moore (Vice Chm)
Mary Kay Hadican (Sec)

NAZARETH VOLUNTEER AMBULANCE CORPS
PO Box 326, Nazareth, PA 18064
Tel.: (610) 759-5422 PA
Web Site:
http://www.nazarethems.com
Year Founded: 1980
Sales Range: $1-9.9 Million
Emp.: 37
Ambulance Service
N.A.I.C.S.: 621910
Paul Kokolus (Treas)
Alfred Pierce (Sec)

NAZTEC INTERNATIONAL GROUP, LLC
8983 Okeechobee Blvd Ste 202-125, West Palm Beach, FL 33411
Tel.: (561) 802-4110 FL
Web Site:
http://www.naztecgroup.com
Year Founded: 2003
Sales Range: $1-9.9 Million
Emp.: 23
IT Consulting & Election Products Mfr & Distr
N.A.I.C.S.: 541618
Sal Pazhoor (Pres & CEO)

NB VENTURES, INC.
100 Walnut Ave, Clark, NJ 07066
Tel.: (732) 382-6565
Web Site: http://www.gep.com
Year Founded: 1999
Sales Range: $10-24.9 Million
Emp.: 85
Supply Chain Technology & Consulting Firm
N.A.I.C.S.: 541690
Subhash Makhija (Co-Founder & CEO)
Jagadish Turimella (Co-Founder & COO)
Roopa Gandhi (Co-Founder & Pres)
Neha Desai Shah (Co-Founder & Exec VP-Bus Dev)
Santosh Katakol (VP-Tech)
Stephen Bucalo (VP-Consulting)
Binayak Shrestha (VP-Consulting)
Abhishek Pandey (VP-Bus Dev)
Tunir Chatterjee (VP-Delivery-Global)
Wayne R. Clark (VP-Global Delivery)
Suresh Visvanathan (VP-Sls-Global)
Al Girardi (VP-Mktg & Analyst Rels)
Ramachander Raja (VP-Fin)
Mita Gupta (VP-Bus Dev)
Badri Narayanan (VP-Global)
B. Braun (VP-Strategic Procurement)
Subsidiaries:
Enporion, Inc. (1)
2 Harbour Pl 302 Knights Run Ave Ste 1050, Tampa, FL 33602
Tel.: (813) 864-8200
Web Site: http://www.enporion.com
Sales Range: $1-9.9 Million
Emp.: 40
Business-to-Business E-Commerce Software & Solutions
N.A.I.C.S.: 513210
George M. Gordon (Chm & CEO)

NBBJ GROUP
223 Yale Ave N, Seattle, WA 98109
Tel.: (206) 223-5555 WA
Web Site: http://www.nbbj.com
Year Founded: 1948
Sales Range: $750-799.9 Million
Emp.: 750
Architectural Services
N.A.I.C.S.: 541310
Paul Audsley (CIO & Principal)
Edwin Beltran (Principal)
Steve McConnell (Mng Partner)
Jonathan Ward (Partner-Design)
Kelly Griffin (Principal)
Juli Cook (COO & Partner)
Jane Loura (Principal)
Sam Stubblefield (Principal)
Carl Tully (Principal)
Dale Alberda (Principal)
Hassan Gardezi (Principal)
Juli Faris Bruce (Principal)
Kieran Breen (Principal)
Laurie Chambers (Principal)
Meghan Novak (Principal & Dir-Mktg)
Richard Dallam (Mng Partner)
Rick Poulos (Principal & Dir-Comml Markets-Los Angeles)
John Hendry (Principal)
Stacey Hooper (Principal)
Mark Lippi (Principal)
Laurie McCoy (Principal)
Jane McElroy (Principal)
Jose Sama (Principal)
Jonathan Wall (Principal)
A. J. Montero (Partner)
Alex Krieger (Principal)
Anne Cunningham (Principal)
Brenda Clark (CFO)
Bryan Langlands (Principal)
Chuck Kolb (Principal)
Daniel Ayars (Principal-Design)
David Lewis (Partner)
Eric Levine (Principal)
Janet Dugan (Principal)
Josie Briggs (Principal)
Marco Belcastro (Principal)
Mitzi D'Amico (Principal)
Phu Duong (Principal)
Robert Mankin (Partner)
Rodney Crumrine (Principal)
Ross Leventhal (Principal)
Steve Kopf (Principal)
Susan Bower (Principal)
Suzanne Carlson (Principal)
Tim Johnson (Partner)
Subsidiaries:
NBBJ (1)
250 S High St, Columbus, OH 43215
Tel.: (614) 224-7145
Web Site: http://www.nbbj.com
Sales Range: $25-49.9 Million
Emp.: 200
Architectural Services Interior Design Management And Planning Services Project And Cost Management
N.A.I.C.S.: 541310
Doug Tarris (Partner)
Edwin Beltran (Principal)
Dale Alberda (Principal-Seattle)
Paul Audsley (Principal & Dir-Digital Practice-Columbus)
Daniel Ayars (Principal-Design-Columbus)
Shivani Bhattacharya (Mgr-BIM-India)
Susan Bower (Principal-Columbus)
Dennis A. Brandon (Principal-Columbus)
Christian Carlson (Principal-Consulting-Seattle)
Laurie Chambers (Principal-San Francisco)
Juli Cook (COO-Seattle)
William Bain Jr. (Partner-Consulting-Seattle)

NBC CORP. OF OKLAHOMA
13401 N Pennsylvania, Oklahoma City, OK 73120
Tel.: (405) 748-9100 OK
Web Site: http://www.nbc.bank
Year Founded: 1931
Sales Range: $10-24.9 Million
Emp.: 122
Bank Holding Company
N.A.I.C.S.: 551111
Jeff Greenlee (Pres)
Subsidiaries:
NBC Oklahoma (1)
13401 N Pennsylvania, Oklahoma City, OK 73120
Tel.: (405) 748-9100
Web Site: http://www.nbc.bank
Emp.: 45
Commericial Banking
N.A.I.C.S.: 522110
C. Kendric Fergeson (Chm)
Christy Sanford (Sr VP-Treasury Svcs)
H. K. Hatcher (Pres & CEO)
James E. Talkington (Vice Chm)
Jerry Krittenbrink (CFO & Exec VP)
Leigh-Anne Taylor (COO & Exec VP)
Michelle Griffin (Officer-Loan & Sr VP)
Toni Nance (Officer-Loan & Sr VP)
Jay Smith (Officer-Loan & Sr VP)
Glenn Floresca (Pres-OKC Market)
Sheila Heim (Officer-Comml Lending & Sr VP)
Doug Shultz (Officer-Loan & Sr VP)

NBC TELEVISION AFFILIATES ASSOCIATION
13974 Travois Trl, Parker, CO 80138-8635
Tel.: (303) 841-6624 DC
Year Founded: 1985
Sales Range: $1-9.9 Million
Television Professional Association
N.A.I.C.S.: 813920
Brian Lawlor (Co-Chm)
Vince Sadusky (Treas)
Dave Lougee (Vice Chm)
Jordan Wertlieb (Co-Chm & Pres)
Jim Conschafter (Sec)
Ralph Oakley (Vice Chm-Govt Affairs)

NBC TRUCK EQUIPMENT INC.
28130 Groesbeck Hwy, Roseville, MI 48066
Tel.: (586) 774-4900
Web Site:
http://www.nbctruckequip.com
Rev.: $12,759,660
Emp.: 60
Truck Parts & Accessories
N.A.I.C.S.: 423120
Christopher Utykanski (Controller)
Donna Nielsen (Sec)
Ronald Kreiter (Mgr-Svc)
E. William Roland Jr. (Pres)

NBE BANCSHARES, INC.
137 S Main St, Earlville, IL 60518

Tel.: (815) 246-8411 DE
Web Site:
http://www.pioneerstatebank.com
Year Founded: 1982
Sales Range: $1-9.9 Million
Bank Holding Company
N.A.I.C.S.: 551111
Michael R. Stevens *(CEO-Pioneer State Bank)*
James R. Bann *(Chm, Pres & CEO)*
Quint T. Harmon *(Pres-Pioneer State Bank)*

Subsidiaries:

Pioneer State Bank (1)
137 S Main St, Earlville, IL 60518
Tel.: (815) 246-8411
Web Site: http://www.pioneerstatebank.com
Sales Range: $1-9.9 Million
Emp.: 27
Commericial Banking
N.A.I.C.S.: 522110
Michael R. Stevens *(CEO)*
Sarah A. Cansino *(VP)*
James R. Bann *(Chm)*
Quint T. Harmon *(Pres & Chief Lending Officer)*
Suli Gazafer *(VP)*
Stacia Little *(Sr VP)*

NBI, INC.
2707 W Eisenhower Blvd Ste 4, Loveland, CO 80537-3141
Tel.: (303) 684-2700 DE
Year Founded: 1975
Sales Range: $10-24.9 Million
Emp.: 166
Holding Company; Glass Manufacturing & Hotels & Other Properties
N.A.I.C.S.: 327212
Jay H. Lustig *(Chm, Pres & CEO)*

NBO SYSTEMS, INC.
3676 W California Ave Bldg D, Salt Lake City, UT 84104
Tel.: (801) 746-8000
Year Founded: 1994
Rev.: $11,601,000
Emp.: 52
Mfr & Supplier Gift Cards
N.A.I.C.S.: 459420
Keith A. Guevara *(Founder)*
Christopher Foley *(CFO)*
John J. Arego *(Acting COO)*
D. Kent Jasperson *(Controller)*

NC ELITE VOLLEYBALL CLUB
5317 N Hills Dr, Raleigh, NC 27612
Tel.: (919) 264-7492
Web Site: http://www.ncelitevb.org
Rev.: $1,023,393
Assets: $209,488
Liabilities: $24,225
Net Worth: $185,263
Earnings: $26,987
Emp.: 3
Fiscal Year-end: 07/31/14
Volleyball Club
N.A.I.C.S.: 711211
Gary DeJames *(Founder & Exec Dir)*
Micholene Schumacher *(Dir-Ops)*
John Dillinger *(Treas & Dir-Admin)*
Sandra Merkel-DeJames *(Dir-Admin)*

NC2 MEDIA, LLC
230 Franklin Rd Bldg 2B, Franklin, TN 37064-2292
Tel.: (800) 275-8555 TN
Web Site: http://nc2media.com
Year Founded: 2012
Digital Content Publisher
N.A.I.C.S.: 516210
Matthew Sterling *(Dir-Post-Production)*

Subsidiaries:

Lonely Planet Publications Pty. Limited (1)
90 Maribyrnong Street, Footscray, 3011, VIC, Australia
Tel.: (61) 3 8379 8000
Web Site: http://www.lonelyplanet.com
Sales Range: $75-99.9 Million
Emp.: 300
Travel Guidebook Publisher; Online Travel Reservation Services
N.A.I.C.S.: 513130
Maureen Wheeler *(Co-Founder)*
Tony Wheeler *(Co-Founder)*
Gus Balbontin *(CTO)*
Chris Zeiher *(Dir-Sls & Mktg-Asia Pacific)*
Luis Cabrera *(Pres & CEO)*

Subsidiary (Non-US):

Lonely Planet Publications Limited (2)
Media Centre 201 Wood Lane, London, W12 7TQ, United Kingdom
Tel.: (44) 20 8433 1333
Web Site: http://www.lonelyplanet.com
Travel Guidebook Publisher; Online Travel Reservation Services
N.A.I.C.S.: 513130
Peter Grunert *(Editor-Traveller)*
Shona Gold *(Gen Mgr-EMEA)*
Denise Cavanagh *(Mgr-Online & HR-EMEA)*
Nikki Emmans *(Head-Online Mktg)*

NCA PARTNERS, INC.
1200 Westlake Ave N Ste 600, Seattle, WA 98109
Tel.: (206) 689-5615
Web Site: http://www.nwcap.com
Year Founded: 1992
Privater Equity Firm
N.A.I.C.S.: 523999
Bradford Creswell *(Co-Founder & Partner)*
John Jacobs *(Partner)*

NCALA, LLC
1400 Greenleaf Ave, Elk Grove Village, IL 60007-5523
Tel.: (847) 593-3364
Web Site:
http://www.ganebrothers.com
Year Founded: 1846
Box & Book Board Products Mfr
N.A.I.C.S.: 322212
John McLoraine *(VP)*

NCCI HOLDINGS INC.
901 Peninsula Corporate Cir, Boca Raton, FL 33487
Tel.: (561) 893-1000
Web Site: http://www.ncci.com
Year Founded: 1922
Sales Range: $150-199.9 Million
Emp.: 900
Compensation Insurance Services
N.A.I.C.S.: 524126
Alfredo T. Guerra *(CFO)*
Bradley Kitchens *(Chief HR Officer)*
Mark Mileusnic *(Chief Customer Ops Officer)*
Tracy A. Ryan *(Chm)*
Michael B. Spears *(CIO & Chief Data Officer)*
Susan Donegan *(Chief Regulatory Officer)*
Elisa Glazer *(Exec Dir-Talent Dev)*

NCH CORPORATION
2727 Chemsearch Blvd, Irving, TX 75062-6454
Tel.: (972) 438-0211 DE
Web Site: http://www.nch.com
Year Founded: 1919
Sales Range: $1-4.9 Billion
Emp.: 8,500
Chemical & Maintenance Specialties, Water Treatment & Remediation, Plumbing Supplies & Specialty Industrial Supplies
N.A.I.C.S.: 325612

Walter Levy *(Co-Pres & CEO)*
Irena Kildisas *(Treas & VP)*

Subsidiaries:

Advantage Systems Inc. (1)
2727 Chemsearch Blvd, Irving, TX 75062-6454
Tel.: (972) 438-0211
Sales Range: $25-49.9 Million
Emp.: 100
Plumbing & Hydronic Heating Supplies
N.A.I.C.S.: 444180

Bramton Company Inc. (1)
2727 Chemsearch Blvd, Irving, TX 75062-6454 (100%)
Tel.: (972) 438-0397
Web Site: http://www.bramton.com
Rev.: $2,600,000
Emp.: 50
Enzyme & Isoenzyme Diagnostic Agents
N.A.I.C.S.: 325412

Certified Laboratories (1)
2727 Chemsearch Blvd, Irving, TX 75062-6454
Tel.: (972) 438-0211
Web Site: http://www.nch.com
Sales Range: $25-49.9 Million
Emp.: 200
Industrial Chemicals
N.A.I.C.S.: 325998

Chemsearch (1)
2727 Chemsearch Blvd, Irving, TX 75062-6454
Tel.: (972) 438-0211
Sales Range: $10-24.9 Million
Emp.: 15
Industrial Chemicals
N.A.I.C.S.: 325612
Walter Levy *(Co-Pres & Co-CEO-NCH)*
Jim Bird *(CEO-NAC)*
Craig Cain *(Sr VP-Supply Chain & Ops)*
Mark Cohen *(Dir-Labeling)*
Robin King *(Mgr-Customer Relationship Mgmt & Inside Sls Ops)*
Danielle Merriman *(Mgr-Mktg-Oil & Gas)*
Alesia Romero *(Acct Mgr-Mktg)*

LSP Products Group Inc. (1)
3689 Arrowhead Dr, Carson City, NV 89706
Tel.: (775) 884-4242
Web Site: http://www.lspproducts.com
Rev.: $18,300,000
Emp.: 175
Plumbing Hardware Mfr
N.A.I.C.S.: 326199
Scott Clark *(VP-Sls & Mktg)*
Tony Frank *(Mgr-Territory Sls-West)*
Joe Kuklis *(Mgr-Sls-Eastern Reg)*

Mantek (1)
2727 Chemsearch Blvd, Irving, TX 75062-6454
Tel.: (972) 438-0211
Sales Range: $125-149.9 Million
Emp.: 500
Industrial Chemicals
N.A.I.C.S.: 335314
Russ Price *(Mgr)*

Mohawk Laboratories Division (1)
2730 Carl Rd, Irving, TX 75062-6405
Tel.: (972) 438-0551
Sales Range: $50-74.9 Million
Emp.: 110
Industrial Chemicals
N.A.I.C.S.: 325998
Paul Mckowen *(Plant Mgr)*

NCH (UK) Ltd. (1)
NCH House, Springvale Avenue, Bilston, WV14 0QL, West Midlands, United Kingdom
Tel.: (44) 1902 510202
Web Site: http://www.nch.com
Chemical Specialties, Fasteners, Welding Alloys & Plumbing Parts Mfr & Marketer
N.A.I.C.S.: 424690

NCH - Hungary Kft. (1)
Konyves K krt 12-14 Lurdy haz III em, 1097, Budapest, Hungary
Tel.: (36) 1 456 2100
Sales Range: $10-24.9 Million
Emp.: 25
Industrial Maintenance Solution Provider
N.A.I.C.S.: 333998

Georgina Beier *(Mng Dir)*

NCH AG (1)
Lindenstrasse 10, CH 6340, Baar, Switzerland
Tel.: (41) 41 711 20 84
Web Site: http://www.nch.com
Chemical Specialties, Fasteners, Welding Alloys & Plumbing Parts Marketer
N.A.I.C.S.: 424690

NCH Belgium Inc (1)
Sphere Business Park Unit 9 Z3 Doornveld 160-162, 1731, Zellik, Belgium
Tel.: (32) 2 255 94 45
Industrial Cleaning & Maintenance Services
N.A.I.C.S.: 561720

NCH Chile S.A. (1)
La Concepcion 56 Of 802, Providencia, Santiago, Chile
Tel.: (56) 2 235 5549
Web Site: http://www.nchchile.com
Industrial Cleaning & Maintenance Services
N.A.I.C.S.: 561720

NCH Colombia, S.A. (1)
Transversal 93 No 61-02 Int 19/20, Santa Fe De Bogota, Bogota, Colombia
Tel.: (57) 1 434 3603
Industrial Maintenance Solution Provider
N.A.I.C.S.: 811310

NCH Corporation Korea (1)
Woojin Bldg 8th Fl 76-4 Jamwon Dong, Seocho Gu, Seoul, 137-909, Korea (South)
Tel.: (82) 234820204
Web Site: http://www.nch.com
Sales Range: $25-49.9 Million
Emp.: 100
Mfr of Chemicals
N.A.I.C.S.: 325998
Dongeun Kim *(Mgr)*

NCH Corporation Puerto Rico (1)
PO Box 1166, Carolina, PR 00986-1166
Tel.: (787) 769-9900
Web Site: http://www.nchsafe.com
Sales Range: $10-24.9 Million
Emp.: 27
Maintenance, Repair & Operating Products Mfr
N.A.I.C.S.: 325612
Irvin L. Levy *(VP)*
Joseph H. Cleveland *(Sec)*

NCH Croatia d.o.o. (1)
Nodilova 7, Zagreb, 10000, Croatia
Tel.: (385) 1 4622 213
Web Site: http://www.ncheurope.com
Sales Range: $10-24.9 Million
Emp.: 3
Industrial Cleaning & Maintenance Services
N.A.I.C.S.: 561720
Georgina Breier *(Mgr-Ops)*

NCH Czechoslovakia spol s.r.o. (1)
Nadrazni 203, Mesice, 250 64, Prague, Czech Republic
Tel.: (420) 2 8398 1567
Web Site: http://www.nch.com
Emp.: 150
Chemical Specialties, Fasteners, Welding Alloys & Plumbing Parts Mfr & Marketer
N.A.I.C.S.: 325998
Dan Pazeirek *(Gen Mgr)*

NCH Ecuador S A. (1)
Calle Juan Molineros Iote 30 y Avenida Eloy Alfaro, Quito, Ecuador
Tel.: (593) 346 4840
Industrial Cleaning & Maintenance Product Mfr
N.A.I.C.S.: 811310

NCH Espanola S.A. (1)
Isla de Java 12, Madrid, 28034, Spain
Tel.: (34) 917 285900
Web Site: http://www.nch.com
Emp.: 100
Industrial Maintenance Solution Provider
N.A.I.C.S.: 333998
Jesse Ronquillo *(Gen Mgr)*

NCH GmbH (1)
Dreieichstrasse 6, 64546, Morfelden, Germany
Tel.: (49) 6105 2010
Web Site: http://www.nch.com
Emp.: 20

NCH CORPORATION

NCH Corporation—(Continued)
Chemical Specialties, Fasteners, Welding Alloys & Plumbing Parts Mfr & Marketer
N.A.I.C.S.: 424690
Andreas Lode (Mgr-Sls)

NCH Ireland Ltd. (1)
Unit 10 Brookville Business Park, Ardee Road, Dundalk, County Louth, Ireland
Tel.: (353) 42 393 5500
Web Site: http://www.nch.com
Chemical Specialty Fastener Welding Alloy & Plumbing Part Mfr
N.A.I.C.S.: 424690

NCH Italia Srl (1)
Viale Europa 30c5, Cusago, 20090, Milan, Italy
Tel.: (39) 02 90 331 461
Web Site: http://www.nch.com
Sales Range: $10-24.9 Million
Emp.: 50
Industrial Maintenance Solution Provider
N.A.I.C.S.: 811310
Alfredo Gilardi (Mng Dir)

NCH Korea Ltd (1)
8th Floor Woojin Bldg 306 Banpo-Daero Seocho-Gu, Seoul, 137909, Korea (South)
Tel.: (82) 2 3482 2581
Web Site: http://www.nch.co.kr
Sales Range: $10-24.9 Million
Emp.: 100
Industrial Cleaning & Maintenance Services
N.A.I.C.S.: 561720
Dong Eun Kim (Country Mgr)

NCH Norge AS (1)
Trygve Nilsens Vei 8, PO Box 68, Oslo, 1061, Norway
Tel.: (47) 22 78 72 00
Emp.: 61
Industrial Maintenance Solution Provider
N.A.I.C.S.: 333998
Eivene Pedersen (Office Mgr)

NCH Peru, S.A. (1)
Av Eucaliptos Mza E-Lote 7 Sector Santa Genoveva Distritio de, Lurin, Lima, Peru
Tel.: (51) 1 614 3500
Web Site: http://www.nchperu.com
Industrial Maintenance Solution Services
N.A.I.C.S.: 811310

NCH ROMANIA Produse de Intretinere SRL (1)
Dimitrie Pompei Nr 5-7 Sector 2, Bucharest, 023817, Romania
Tel.: (40) 21 529 51 00
Emp.: 20
Industrial Book Publisher
N.A.I.C.S.: 513130
Andrea Irimia (Mgr-Ops)

NCH SLOVAKIA s. r. o. (1)
Drieoova 34, 821 02, Bratislava, Slovakia
Tel.: (421) 2 4341 4387
Web Site: http://www.ncheurope.com
Sales Range: $10-24.9 Million
Emp.: 12
Industrial Maintenance Solution Provider
N.A.I.C.S.: 811310
Igor Tarina (Mng Dir)

National Chemsearch of Canada Ltd. (1)
247 Orenda Road, Brampton, L6T 1E6, ON, Canada (100%)
Tel.: (905) 457-5220
Web Site: http://www.nch.com
Sales Range: $25-49.9 Million
Emp.: 25
Specialty Chemicals Mfr
N.A.I.C.S.: 325998

Division (US):

Chem-Aqua, Inc., (2)
PO Box 152170, Irving, TX 75015
Tel.: (972) 438-0232
Web Site: http://www.ChemAqua.com
Sales Range: $50-74.9 Million
Custom Designed Water Treatment Programs
N.A.I.C.S.: 221310
Allan Browning (Mgr-Tech Mktg)

Subsidiary (Domestic):

Anderson Chemical Company Inc. (3)
1840 Waterville Rd, Macon, GA 31206
Tel.: (478) 803-6100
Web Site: http://www.andersonchemical.com
Sales Range: $10-24.9 Million
Chemical Preparations
N.A.I.C.S.: 325998

Nch d.o.o. Ljubljana (1)
Parmova 53, Ljubljana, 1000, Slovenia
Tel.: (386) 1 436 1572
Web Site: http://www.nch.com
Sales Range: $10-24.9 Million
Emp.: 2
Industrial Maintenance Solution Provider
N.A.I.C.S.: 811310

Out International Inc. (1)
2727 Chemsearch Blvd, Irving, TX 75062-6454
Tel.: (972) 438-0157
Web Site: http://www.outinternational.com
Rev.: $810,000
Emp.: 15
Pet Supplies
N.A.I.C.S.: 339999

NCH HEALTHCARE SYSTEM, INC.
350 7th St N, Naples, FL 34102
Tel.: (239) 513-7000
Web Site: http://www.nchmd.org
Sales Range: Less than $1 Million
Emp.: 4,000
Health Care Srvices
N.A.I.C.S.: 561110
Phillip Dutcher (Interim CEO & COO)
Aurora Estevez (Co-Chief Medical Officer)
Beth Martin (Asst Sec)
Jim Martin (Chief Dev Officer)
Gary Parsons (Co-Chief Medical Officer)
Michael Riley (Chief Strategy Officer)
Michele Thoman (Chief Nursing Officer & Interim COO-NHH Campus)
Thomas J. Gazdic (Treas & Sec)
Mariann MacDonald (First Vice Chm)
Zachary Bostock (Chief Admin Officer)

NCK CAPITAL LLC
4514 Cole Ave Ste 325, Dallas, TX 75205
Tel.: (800) 519-5606
Web Site: http://www.nckcapital.com
Privater Equity Firm
N.A.I.C.S.: 523999
Michael Kornman (Mng Partner)

Subsidiaries:

Tricoci University of Beauty Culture (1)
6625 N Avondale, Chicago, IL 60631
Tel.: (630) 528-3330
Web Site: http://www.tricociuniversity.edu
Cosmetology & Barber Schools
N.A.I.C.S.: 611511

NCL GRAPHIC SPECIALTIES, INC.
N29 W22960 Marjean Ln, Waukesha, WI 53186
Tel.: (262) 832-6100
Web Site: http://www.nclgraphicspecialties.com
Sales Range: $25-49.9 Million
Emp.: 200
Commercial Lithographic Printing
N.A.I.C.S.: 323111
Kirn Hermberg (Dir-Ops)

NCM ASSOCIATES, INC.
10551 Barkley Ste 200, Overland Park, KS 66212
Tel.: (913) 649-7830
Web Site: http://www.ncm20.com
Year Founded: 1945
Emp.: 100
Business & Management Consulting Services
N.A.I.C.S.: 541618
Paul Faletti (Pres & CEO)
Gerald Kuehl (CFO & VP)
Jill Hobbie (VP-HR & Ops)
Skye Nguyen (Dir-Mktg & Comm)

Subsidiaries:

Kain Automotive, Inc. (1)
380 S Mill St Ste 204, Lexington, KY 40508-2560
Tel.: (859) 269-8302
Web Site: http://www.kainautomotive.com
Emp.: 100
General Automotive Repair
N.A.I.C.S.: 811111
David Kain (Owner)

NCM FINANCIAL, INC.
Roosevelt Ct 2101 Cedar Springs Rd Ste 1050, Dallas, TX 75201
Tel.: (800) 686-3259   TX
Web Site: http://www.ncmfinancial.com
Year Founded: 2006
Investment Research & Financial Software
N.A.I.C.S.: 513210
Michael A. Noel (Chm & CEO)

NCMIC GROUP INC.
14001 University Ave, Clive, IA 50325-8258
Tel.: (515) 313-4500
Web Site: http://www.ncmicgroup.com
Year Founded: 1946
Rev.: $66,485,398
Emp.: 170
Financial Services
N.A.I.C.S.: 551112
Louis Sportelli (Pres)
Eric Madcharo (CIO)
Bruce Beal (VP-Claims)
Jacqueline Anderson (Sec)
Cindy Pearce-Karrick (CMO & Sr VP)
Mike McCoy (CEO)
Rich Johnson (Sr Acct Exec)

Subsidiaries:

NCMIC Insurance Co. (1)
14001 University Ave, Clive, IA 50325-8258
Tel.: (515) 313-4500
Web Site: http://www.ncmic.com
Sales Range: $50-74.9 Million
Emp.: 200
Insurance Agents, Brokers & Service
N.A.I.C.S.: 524210
Louis Sportelli (Pres)

Subsidiary (Domestic):

Managed Chiropractics Inc. (2)
PO Box 905, Plainville, CT 06062-0905
Tel.: (303) 322-7272
Rev.: $630,000
Emp.: 8
Management Consulting Services
N.A.I.C.S.: 485999

NCP COATINGS INC.
225 Fort St, Niles, MI 49120
Tel.: (269) 683-3377
Web Site: http://www.ncpcoatings.com
Rev.: $15,771,051
Emp.: 100
Paints & Allied Products
N.A.I.C.S.: 325510
Diane Williams (Supvr-Customer Svc)
Rob Holzapfel (Mgr-Quality)

NCT VENTURES LLC
1 Marconi Pl 274 Marconi Blvd Ste 400, Columbus, OH 43215
Tel.: (614) 794-2732   OH
Web Site: http://www.nctventures.com
Venture Capital Firm
N.A.I.C.S.: 523999
Richard Langdale (Founder & CEO)
Michael Butler (Venture Partner)
Lindsay Karas (Corp Counsel)

NDC CONSTRUCTION COMPANY
1001 3rd Ave W Ste 600, Bradenton, FL 34205
Tel.: (941) 747-1062
Web Site: http://www.ndcconstruction.com
Year Founded: 1968
Sales Range: $1-9.9 Million
Emp.: 35
Residential Remodeler
N.A.I.C.S.: 236118
Ronald J. Allen (Pres)
Gary L. Huggins (Exec VP)
Gary P. Esporrin (CFO & Sr VP)
Charles J. Scott (Sr VP)
Adam W. Phillips (VP)

NDI CONSTRUCTION
1212 S Bellevue Blvd, Memphis, TN 38106
Tel.: (901) 774-8150
Sales Range: $10-24.9 Million
Emp.: 30
Drywall
N.A.I.C.S.: 238310
Mike Hardy (Pres)

NDI RECOGNITION SYSTEMS
105 E State Rd 434, Winter Springs, FL 32708
Tel.: (321) 441-1800
Web Site: http://www.ndi-rs.com
Year Founded: 1997
Sales Range: $1-9.9 Million
Emp.: 22
License Plate Recognition Technologies for Law Enforcement
N.A.I.C.S.: 561621
Keith Yahn (Pres)

NDP, LLC
1909 26th St Ste 1E, Boulder, CO 80302
Tel.: (303) 339-0853
Web Site: http://www.ndpgroup.com
Year Founded: 2005
Computer Network System Design & Engineering Services
N.A.I.C.S.: 541519
German Nunez (Co-Founder & Pres)

Subsidiaries:

Advanced Radar Corporation (1)
PO Box 19225, Boulder, CO 80308
Tel.: (720) 565-0300
Web Site: http://www.advancedradarcorp.com
Weather Radar Equipment & Realated Products Developer & Services
N.A.I.C.S.: 334511
Roelof T. Bruintjes (Founder)
Kim Weaver (Chief Engr)

NDT SYSTEMS, INC.
5542 Buckingham Dr., Huntington Beach, CA 92649-1182
Tel.: (714) 893-2438   CA
Web Site: http://www.ndtsystems.com
Year Founded: 1974
Sales Range: $50-74.9 Million
Emp.: 30
Mfr of Ultrasonic Measuring & Controlling Instruments, Transducers & Probes
N.A.I.C.S.: 334519
Steve Pastore (Engr-Design)
Steven Rawnsley (Engr-Quality)

NE MEDIA GROUP, INC.

135 Morrissey Blvd, Boston, MA 02125-3310
Tel.: (617) 929-2000   MA
Web Site: http://www.boston.com
Year Founded: 1998
Sales Range: $50-74.9 Million
Holding Company; Newspaper Publisher
N.A.I.C.S.: 551112
John W. Henry (Owner)

Subsidiaries:

Boston Globe Electronic Publishing LLC   (1)
135 Congress St, Boston, MA 02210
Tel.: (617) 929-7900
Web Site: http://www.bostonglobe.com
Sales Range: $25-49.9 Million
Emp.: 90
Electronic Newspaper Publisher
N.A.I.C.S.: 513110

Globe Specialty Products, Inc.   (1)
9 Latti Farm Rd, Millbury, MA 01527-2132
Tel.: (508) 871-1900
Web Site: http://www.globedirectmail.com
Sales Range: $25-49.9 Million
Emp.: 100
Advertising & Marketing Services
N.A.I.C.S.: 541860
Daniel Dickerson (Mgr-Production)

GlobeDirect, LLC   (1)
300 Constitution Dr, Taunton, MA 02780-7359
Tel.: (508) 871-1900
Web Site: http://www.globedirectmail.com
Direct Mail Marketing Services
N.A.I.C.S.: 541860
Amy Morrison (Mgr-Client Svcs)
Dawn Paradis (Mgr-Data & Distr)
Daniel Dickerson (Mgr-Production)

Retail Sales, LLC   (1)
75 York Ave Ste A, Randolph, MA 02368-1841   (100%)
Tel.: (781) 963-8169
Sales Range: $10-24.9 Million
Emp.: 15
Retail Services
N.A.I.C.S.: 513110

The Boston Globe   (1)
135 William T Morrissey Blvd, Boston, MA 02125-3310
Tel.: (617) 929-2000
Web Site: http://www.bostonglobe.com
Newspaper Publishing
N.A.I.C.S.: 513110
Marjorie Pritchard (Editor-Op-Ed Page)
Maria Tack (Coord-Sls)
Peter Doucette (VP-Consumer Sls & Mktg)
Wade Sendall (VP-IT)
Janice Page (Deputy Mng Editor-Features)
Bill Greene (Dir-Photography)
Catherine Aldrich (Asst Dir-Design)
Greg Klee (Sr Supvr-Design)
Jane Martin (Asst Dir-Design)
Kim Chapin (Deputy Dir-Photography)
Michael Workman (Dir-Digital Design)
Shira T. Center (Editor-Political)
Veronica Chao (Editor-Sunday Magazine)
Omar Vega (Asst Dir-Design)
Tonia Cowan (Dir-Graphics)
Scott LaPierre (Editor-Multimedia)
Lisa Tuite (Head-Library)
Vinay Mehra (Pres & CFO)
Linda Pizzuti Henry (CEO)
Dale Carpenter (Sr VP-Print Ops)
Dan Krockmalnic (Gen Counsel)
Shirley Leung (Interim Editor-Editorial Page)

NEACE VENTURES

110 W Main St 2nd Floor, Louisville, KY 40202
Tel.: (502) 379-6130
Web Site: http://www.neaceventures.com
Privater Equity Firm
N.A.I.C.S.: 551112
John Neace (Chm)
Brad Estes (Pres)
Craig Nance (Mng Dir-Fin)
Maria Triplett (Dir-HR)
Rusty Fazio (Dir-IT)

Tim Anderson (Controller)
Barry Geswein (Controller)
Dalton Shell (Office Mgr)
Katie Uttich (Dir-Mktg)

Subsidiaries:

Falls City Brewing Company   (1)
116 S 10th St, Louisville, KY 47710
Tel.: (502) 257-7147
Web Site: http://www.fallscitybeer.com
Breweries
N.A.I.C.S.: 312120
Shane Uttich (Pres)

Tin Man Brewing Co.   (1)
1430 W Franklin St, Evansville, IN 47710
Tel.: (812) 618-3227
Web Site: http://www.tinmanbrewing.com
Breweries
N.A.I.C.S.: 312120
Nick Davidson (Founder & Pres)

NEAD ORGANIZATION INC.

187 E Union Ave, East Rutherford, NJ 07073
Tel.: (201) 460-5200
Web Site: http://www.neadelectric.com
Rev.: $87,657,314
Emp.: 33
Electrical Work
N.A.I.C.S.: 238210
Robert Marziotte (Pres)

Subsidiaries:

Nead Electric Inc   (1)
187 E Union Ave, East Rutherford, NJ 07073
Tel.: (201) 460-5200
Web Site: http://www.neadelectric.com
General Electrical Contractor
N.A.I.C.S.: 238210
Robert Marziotto (CEO)

NEAL H. KNAPP, LLC

1020 NE Pine Island Rd Ste 205, Cape Coral, FL 33909
Tel.: (239) 458-4776
Web Site: http://www.nealhknapp.com
Sales Range: $1-9.9 Million
Emp.: 15
Brewing & Distilling Equipment Distr
N.A.I.C.S.: 423830
Neal H. Knapp (Pres)

Subsidiaries:

Brew-Bev   (1)
1020 NE Pine Is Rd Ste 205, Cape Coral, FL 33909
Tel.: (239) 458-4776
Web Site: http://nealhknapp.com
Emp.: 4
Brewing & Distilling Consulting & Equipment Sales
N.A.I.C.S.: 541618
Neal H. Knapp (Pres)

NEANY INC.

44010 Commerce Ave Ste A, Hollywood, MD 20636
Tel.: (301) 373-8700
Web Site: http://www.neanyinc.com
Sales Range: $10-24.9 Million
Emp.: 65
Tactical Surveillance Aeronautical Solutions
N.A.I.C.S.: 334511
Steven Steptoe (Pres & CEO)
Cheri Phelan (Mgr-Pur)
Chris Curtis (Engr-Aeronautical)
James Hunter (Mgr-Ops)

NEAPCO HOLDINGS, LLC

6735 Haggerty Rd, Belleville, MI 48111
Tel.: (734) 447-1380   DE
Web Site: http://www.neapco.com
Year Founded: 2008
Emp.: 400

Holding Company; Motor Vehicle Driveshaft, Propshaft & Other Components Mfr & Distr
N.A.I.C.S.: 551112
Gerald E. Coster (COO)
Arvind Srinivasan (VP-Engrg & R&D-Global)
Erik Leenders (VP-Sls, Mktg & Strategy)
Kenneth L. Hopkins (Pres & CEO)
Greg Anderson (CFO)

Subsidiaries:

Neapco Components, LLC   (1)
501 Sargent St, Beatrice, NE 68310
Tel.: (402) 228-4288
Web Site: http://www.neapcocomponents.com
Sales Range: $25-49.9 Million
Emp.: 300
Motor Vehicle Driveshaft Propshaft & Other Component Mfr
N.A.I.C.S.: 336350

Neapco Drivelines (Shanghai) Co., Ltd.   (1)
555 West Nanjing Road Suite 407 Pacheer Commercial Center, Jing'an District, Shanghai, 200041, China
Tel.: (86) 21 6135 9661
Web Site: http://www.neapco.com
Motor Vehicle Driveshaft, Propshaft & Other Components Distr
N.A.I.C.S.: 423120

Neapco Drivelines, LLC   (1)
6735 Haggerty Rd, Belleville, MI 48111
Tel.: (734) 447-1380
Web Site: http://www.neapco.com
Emp.: 1,000
Motor Vehicle Driveshaft & Propshaft Mfr & Distr
N.A.I.C.S.: 336350
Paulette Caylor (Mgr-HR)
Renee Ellison (Controller)
Bryan Wolff (Mgr-Pur)
Michael Kinsella (Mgr-Product Dev)
Kellie Lukasavitz (Mgr-Product Dev)

Neapco Europe GmbH   (1)
Henry-Ford-Str 1, 52351, Duren, Germany
Tel.: (49) 2421 226 000
Web Site: http://www.neapco.com
Motor Vehicle Driveshaft, Propshaft & Other Components Mfr & Distr
N.A.I.C.S.: 336350
Chris Traidl (CEO)

Neapco Europe Sp. z o.o.   (1)
Ul Kaliska 72, 46-320, Praszka, Poland
Tel.: (48) 34 3500 000
Web Site: http://www.neapco.com
Emp.: 80
Motor Vehicle Driveshaft, Propshaft & Other Components Mfr & Distr
N.A.I.C.S.: 336350
Jacek Swierczak (Mgr-Sls)
Edmund Majtyka (Bus Mgr)

NEAR EARTH AUTONOMY, INC.

5001 Baum Blvd Ste 750, Pittsburgh, PA 15213-1856
Tel.: (412) 254-3542
Web Site: http://www.nearearthautonomy.com
Research & Development in the Physical, Engineering & Life Sciences
N.A.I.C.S.: 541715
Lorri Ziegler-Robinson (Controller)

NEAR NORTH NATIONAL TITLE, LLC

222 N LaSalle S Ste 600, Chicago, IL 60601
Tel.: (312) 419-3900
Web Site: https://nntg.com
Emp.: 100
Title Insurance & Real Estate Settlement Services
N.A.I.C.S.: 541191
Dan Fowler (CEO)

Subsidiaries:

O'Connor Title Services, Inc.   (1)
162 W Hubbard St, Chicago, IL 60610
Tel.: (312) 527-4700
Web Site: http://www.oconnortitle.com
Insurance Agency & Brokerage Services
N.A.I.C.S.: 524210
John R. O'Connor (CEO)

NEARON ENTERPRISES

101 Ygnacio Valley Rd Ste 450, Walnut Creek, CA 94596
Tel.: (925) 743-3300
Web Site: http://www.nearon.com
Year Founded: 1945
Sales Range: $1-9.9 Million
Emp.: 20
Real Estate Development & Investment
N.A.I.C.S.: 531390
Heather White (Mgr-Investments)
Tony Perino (Pres)
Irene Nomura (Sr VP-Acctg & Controller)
Nick Rini (VP)
Blaine Emmons (CFO)
Chang Soo Lee (VP)

Subsidiaries:

Nearon Enterprises - Property Management Division   (1)
PO Box 550, Danville, CA 94526-3881
Tel.: (925) 208-8080
Web Site: http://www.nearon.com
Property Management
N.A.I.C.S.: 531312
Gail Burke (VP-Property Mgmt)

NEARSHORE TECHNOLOGY COMPANY, LLC

1353 Riverstone Pkwy Ste 120-335, Canton, GA 30114   DE
Web Site: http://www.nearshoretechnology.com
Year Founded: 2013
Sales Range: $10-24.9 Million
Emp.: 240
Software Development Services
N.A.I.C.S.: 541511
Gabriel J. Apodaca (CEO)
Mark T. Crandal (Pres)
Yancy W. Riddle (COO)
Brian M. Peterson (CTO)
Sheri S. Apodaca (Chief Admin Officer)

NEARU SERVICES

2101 Sardis Rd N, Charlotte, NC 28227
Tel.: (212) 341-7561
Web Site: http://www.nearu-services.com
Year Founded: 2019
HVAC, Plumbing & Electrical Services
N.A.I.C.S.: 238220
Jay Darfler (CEO)
Ashish Achlerkar (Founder & Chm)
Doug Wilson (Vice Chm)

Subsidiaries:

2nd Wind Heating & Air Conditioning, Inc.   (1)
6130 Shakespeare Rd, Columbia, SC 29223
Tel.: (803) 786-7433
Web Site: http://www.2ndwindhvac.com
Plumbing, Heating & Air-Conditioning Contractors
N.A.I.C.S.: 238220
Mickey Lawler (Pres & CEO)

Energy Savers of Georgia, Inc.   (1)
1409 17th St, Columbus, GA 31901
Tel.: (706) 890-4959
Web Site: http://www.energysaversair.com
Site Preparation Contractor
N.A.I.C.S.: 238910

NEARU SERVICES

NearU Services—(Continued)

Hwayne Bell (Founder)

Grogg's Heating & Air Conditioning Inc. (1)
5349 Dupont Rd, Parkersburg, WV 26101
Tel.: (304) 355-9421
Web Site: http://www.groggs.com
Site Preparation Contractor
N.A.I.C.S.: 238910

NEATHAWK DUBUQUE & PACKETT
1 E Cary St, Richmond, VA 23219-3732
Tel.: (804) 783-8140
Year Founded: 1984
Rev.: $47,000,000
Emp.: 43
Advetising Agency
N.A.I.C.S.: 541810
Roger D. Neathawk (Chm)
Susan E. Dubuque (Pres)
Charles B. Miller (Sr VP & Dir-Media)
John Bedor (Sr VP)
Morris Davis (VP-Creative)
Jamie McGovern (Dir-Art)
Robert J. Reid (Assoc Dir-Media)
Danny Fell (CEO)
Todd Foutz (Exec VP)
Mary Alice Czerwonka (Sr VP)
Lois Ayers (VP & Mgr-Accts)

Subsidiaries:

Neathawk Dubuque & Packett (1)
417 Market St, Chattanooga, TN 37402
Tel.: (423) 752-4687
Emp.: 14
N.A.I.C.S.: 541810
Daniel Fell (Exec VP)
Douglas Cook (Dir-Creative)
Todd Foutz (Exec VP)
Mary Alice Czerwonka (Sr VP)

Neathawk Dubuque & Packett (1)
410 S Jefferson St, Roanoke, VA 24011
Tel.: (540) 345-5403
Web Site: http://www.ndp-agency.com
Sales Range: Less than $1 Million
Emp.: 10
Communications, Education, Financial, Health Care, Travel & Tourism
N.A.I.C.S.: 541810
Todd Foutz (Exec VP)
John Griessmayer (Chief Creative Officer & Sr VP)
Kym Davis (Dir-Art)

NEB CORPORATION
130 S Main St, Fond Du Lac, WI 54935
Tel.: (920) 921-7700 WI
Web Site: http://www.nebat.com
Year Founded: 1974
Sales Range: $75-99.9 Million
Emp.: 333
Bank Holding Company
N.A.I.C.S.: 551111
Peter E. Stone (Chm)
Eric P. Stone (Vice Chm & CEO)

Subsidiaries:

National Exchange Bank & Trust (1)
130 S Main St, Fond Du Lac, WI 54935
Tel.: (920) 921-7700
Web Site: http://www.nebat.com
Sales Range: $75-99.9 Million
Commericial Banking
N.A.I.C.S.: 522110
Peter E. Stone (Chm)
David G. Kramer (Controller)
David R. Moody (Sr VP-Loans)
S. Adam Stone (Sr VP)
Eric P. Stone (Vice Chm & CEO)
Lisa Karst (Asst VP)
Mitch Greenfield (Asst VP-Beaver Dam)
Tami Christian (Sr VP)
James R. Chatterton (Pres & COO)

NEBCO INC.
1815 Y St, Lincoln, NE 68508
Tel.: (402) 434-1212
Web Site: http://www.nebcoinc.com
Year Founded: 1908
Sales Range: $75-99.9 Million
Emp.: 55
Ready Mixed Concrete
N.A.I.C.S.: 524210
James P. Abel (CEO)

Subsidiaries:

Beatrice Concrete Company Inc. (1)
400 Scott St, Beatrice, NE 68310
Tel.: (402) 223-4289
Web Site: http://www.beatriceconcretecompany.com
Ready-Mixed Concrete Products & Services
N.A.I.C.S.: 327320
Jamie Renshaw (CEO)
Rick Dorn (Controller)
Todd Krieger (Mgr-Plant)
Joe Armstrong (Mgr-Plant)
Bob Boardman (Mgr-Plant)
Jason Easter (Mgr-Plant)
Lynn Henrichs (Mgr-Fleet)
Paul Kostal (Coord-Ready Mix)
Terry Meyer (Mgr-Mine)
Jerry Meyer (VP)
Ray Wagner (VP-Ready Mix Ops)
Lloyd Warren (Mgr-Mine)
Mike Sturm (Plant Supvr)
Terry Howell (Asst Mgr-Plant)

NEBO AGENCY LLC
1000 Marietta St NW, Atlanta, GA 30318
Tel.: (404) 885-1201
Web Site: http://www.neboagency.com
Year Founded: 2004
Sales Range: $1-9.9 Million
Emp.: 35
Advertising & Marketing
N.A.I.C.S.: 541810
Brian Easter (CEO)
Adam Harrell (Founder)
Kimm Lincoln (Pres)
Cael Olsen (Dir-User Experience)
Todd Slutzky (Dir-Strategic Opportunities)

NEBRASKA ALUMINUM CASTINGS, INC.
4280 E Hadco Rd, Hastings, NE 68902
Tel.: (402) 462-5139
Web Site: http://www.nealuminum.com
Year Founded: 1975
Sales Range: $10-24.9 Million
Emp.: 70
Metal Die-Casting Services
N.A.I.C.S.: 331523
Elisabeth Hasley (VP)
George E. Hasley (Pres)
Ray Marsh (Gen Mgr)
Mark Jasperson (Mgr-Ops)
Jesse Wright (Mgr-Quality Assurance)
Dale Brown (Controller)
John Uhrich (Dir-Safety & Mgr-Pur)
Patty McKimmey (Mgr-HR)
Greg Henderson (Mgr-Quality Assurance)

NEBRASKA BANKSHARES, INC.
222 Main St, Farnam, NE 69029
Tel.: (308) 569-2311 NE
Year Founded: 1967
Bank Holding Company
N.A.I.C.S.: 551111
Karl J. Randecker Sr. (Pres & CEO)

Subsidiaries:

Community Bank (1)
1108 W 7th St, Alma, NE 68920
Tel.: (308) 928-2929
Web Site: http://www.acommunitybank.com
Commericial Banking
N.A.I.C.S.: 522110

Jared Baker (VP)

First State Bank (1)
914 Lake Ave, Gothenburg, NE 69138
Tel.: (308) 537-3684
Web Site: http://www.1ststatebank.com
Sales Range: $1-9.9 Million
Emp.: 22
Commericial Banking
N.A.I.C.S.: 522110
Linda Rodine (VP)

First State Bank (1)
222 Main St, Farnam, NE 69029
Tel.: (308) 569-2311
Web Site: http://www.1ststatebank4me.com
Sales Range: $1-9.9 Million
Emp.: 17
Commericial Banking
N.A.I.C.S.: 522110

NEBRASKA DEPARTMENT OF CORRECTIONAL SERVICES
801 W Prospector Pl, Lincoln, NE 68522
Tel.: (402) 471-2654
Web Site: http://www.corrections.nebraska.gov
State Corrections Organization Housing
N.A.I.C.S.: 922140
Scott Frakes (Dir)
Diane Sabatka-Rine (Chief Operations Officers)
Robert Madsen (Deputy Dir-Prison)
Erinn Criner (Dir-Human Talent)

Subsidiaries:

Community Correctional Center of Lincoln (1)
2270 W Van Dorn St, Lincoln, NE 68522
Tel.: (402) 471-6272
Web Site: http://www.corrections.nebraska.gov
Facilities Services
N.A.I.C.S.: 561210
Jeff Miller (Religious Coord)

NEBRASKA ELECTRIC GENERATION & TRANSMISSION COOPERATIVE, INC.
2472 18th Ave, Columbus, NE 68601
Tel.: (402) 564-8142
Web Site: http://www.negt.coop
Year Founded: 1956
Sales Range: $200-249.9 Million
Emp.: 4
Electric Power Distr
N.A.I.C.S.: 221122
Darin Bloomquist (Asst Gen Mgr)
Bruce A. Pontow (Gen Mgr)

NEBRASKA FAMILIES COLLABORATIVE
2110 Papillion Pkwy, Omaha, NE 68164
Tel.: (402) 492-2500 NE
Web Site: http://www.nebraskafc.org
Year Founded: 2009
Sales Range: $50-74.9 Million
Emp.: 375
Family Care Services
N.A.I.C.S.: 624190
Donna Rozell (COO)
Jaimie Anderson-Hoyt (Dir-Grant Dev)
Stacy Giebler (Dir-Acctg)
Lynn Castrianno (Dir-Continuous Quality Improvement & Data Mgmt)
John Jeanetta (Sec)
Kathy Bigsby-Moore (Chm)
Peg Harriott (Vice Chm)
Judy Rasmussen (Treas)
Viv Ewing (VP-HR & Community Rels)

NEBRASKA INVESTMENT FINANCE AUTHORITY INC.
1230 O St Ste 200, Lincoln, NE 68508-1402
Tel.: (402) 434-3900 NE
Web Site: http://www.nifa.org
Year Founded: 1978
Sales Range: $25-49.9 Million
Emp.: 25
Issuer of Housing Bonds
N.A.I.C.S.: 522292
Tim Kenny (Exec Dir)
Steve Clements (COO)
Christie Weston (Deputy Dir-Fin)
Jacki Young (Mgr-Program)
Judy Krasomil (Treas)
Ted Simpson (Dir-Dev)
Robin Ambroz-Hollman (Deputy Dir-Programs)
Cindy Trautman (Asst Mgr-Homeownership)
Elizabeth Fimbres (Mgr-Outreach Program)
Teresa Kile (Mgr-Program-LIHTC)

NEBRASKA MACHINERY COMPANY INC.
11002 Sapp Brothers Dr, Omaha, NE 68138
Tel.: (402) 891-8600 NE
Web Site: http://www.nebraska-machinery.com
Year Founded: 1953
Sales Range: $150-199.9 Million
Emp.: 550
Construction & Mining Machinery
N.A.I.C.S.: 423810
John Swanson (Chm & Exec VP)
Joleen Schauer (Mgr-Parts)
Rich Swanson (Pres & CEO)

Subsidiaries:

NMC Cat (1)
2800 Nebraska Ave, Council Bluffs, IA 51501
Tel.: (712) 352-0435
Industrial Parts & Equipment Whslr
N.A.I.C.S.: 423690

NMC Material Handling Inc. (1)
1210 S 3600 W, Salt Lake City, UT 84104
Tel.: (801) 977-0700
Industrial Machinery & Equipment Whslr
N.A.I.C.S.: 423830

NMC Technologies (1)
10501 S US Hwy 281, Doniphan, NE 68832
Tel.: (402) 845-6503
Equipment Repair & Maintenance Services
N.A.I.C.S.: 811310

NEBRASKA METHODIST HEALTH SYSTEM INC.
825 S 169th St, Omaha, NE 68118
Tel.: (402) 354-4800 NE
Web Site: http://www.bestcare.org
Year Founded: 1981
Emp.: 768
Health Care Services Organization
N.A.I.C.S.: 813920
Peggy Helget (Chief Nursing Officer & VP-Patient Svcs)
Steve Goeser (Pres & CEO)
Jeff Francis (CFO & VP)
Gregory Hutteger (Chief Medical Information Officer)

Subsidiaries:

Shared Service Systems Inc. (1)
1725 S 20th St, Omaha, NE 68108-3889
Tel.: (402) 536-5300
Web Site: http://www.sharedomaha.com
Sales Range: $25-49.9 Million
Emp.: 157
Wholesale Distributor of Medical & Hospital Equipment
N.A.I.C.S.: 423450
David Koraleski (Pres)

NEBRASKA PLASTICS, INC.
700 W Hwy 30, Cozad, NE 69130

Tel.: (308) 784-2500
Web Site:
http://www.countryestate.com
Year Founded: 1945
Plastic Tank Mfr
N.A.I.C.S.: 326122
Paul German (Pres)
Lois German (Sec)

NEBRASKA PUBLIC POWER DISTRICT
1414 15th St, Columbus, NE 68601-5226
Tel.: (402) 564-8561
Web Site: http://www.nppd.com
Year Founded: 1970
Sales Range: $1-4.9 Billion
Emp.: 2,003
Electric Utility Company
N.A.I.C.S.: 221118
John McClure (VP-Govt Affairs)
Jeanne Schieffer (Mgr-Corp Comm & PR)
Traci Bender (CFO & VP)
Ken Kunze (Chm)
Jerry L. Chlopek (Sec)
Ken Curry (VP-Customer & Corp Svcs)
Thomas Kent (Pres & CEO)
Alan Dostal (Dir-Res)
Timothy Arlt (Gen Mgr-Retail)
Chris Overman (Dir-Safety & Human Performance)
Conrad Saltzgaber (Chief Audit & Ethics Officer)
Larry Arens (Mgr-Acct)
Stan Clouse (Mgr-Acct)
Chris Hegert (Mgr-Acct)
Chad Podolak (Mgr-Acct)
Terry Rajewich (Mgr-Acct)
Brian Vasa (Mgr-Acct)
Craig Vincent (Mgr-Acct)

NEBRASKA SOYBEAN BOARD
3815 Touzalin Ave Ste 101, Lincoln, NE 68507
Tel.: (402) 441-3240
Web Site:
http://www.nebraskasoybeans.org
Year Founded: 1995
Sales Range: $10-24.9 Million
Emp.: 6
Soybean & Soybean Product Promoter
N.A.I.C.S.: 541715
Victor Bohuslavsky (Exec Dir)
Terry Horky (Sec)
Teri Zimmerman (Mgr-Education & Outreach)
Tony Johanson (Chm)
Aryel Smith (Coord-Comm)
Cale Buhr (Coord-Market Dev)

NEBRASKA TITLE COMPANY
14680 W Dodge Rd Ste 1, Omaha, NE 68154
Tel.: (402) 861-9220
Web Site: http://www.nebtitleco.com
Direct Title Insurance Carriers
N.A.I.C.S.: 524127
Jane Bartlett (Dir-Branch Ops)
Jennifer Strand (Pres & Gen Counsel)
Vickie Williamson (Dir-Residential Title Scvs)
Subsidiaries:

Barney Abstract & Title Co. (1)
2222 2nd Ave, Kearney, NE 68847
Tel.: (308) 234-5548
Web Site: http://www.nebtitleco.com
Title Abstract & Settlement Offices
N.A.I.C.S.: 541191
Andi Moritz (Office Mgr)

NEBRASKA TRANSPORT CO. INC.
1225 Country Club Rd, Gering, NE 69341
Tel.: (308) 635-1214
Web Site: http://www.nebt.com
Sales Range: $10-24.9 Million
Emp.: 230
Provider of Overnight Transportation Services
N.A.I.C.S.: 484122
Brent Holliday (CEO)
Tony Lacy (COO)
Barb Shaw (Mgr-Terminal)
Chad Cranston (Mgr-Terminal)
Danny Tompkins (Dir-HR)
John Rooker (Mgr-Terminal)
Marcus Henman (Controller)
Monte Myers (Dir-Truckload)
Peggy Robinson (Dir-Safety)
Perry Delzer (Mgr-IT)
Rick Smith (Mgr-Maintenance)
Shawna Payne (Mgr-Claims)

NEBRASKA TRUCK CENTER, INC.
4747 Juergen Rd, Grand Island, NE 68801
Tel.: (308) 384-0130
Web Site:
http://www.nebraskatruck.com
Year Founded: 1969
Sales Range: $25-49.9 Million
Emp.: 100
Retailer of New & Used Trucks
N.A.I.C.S.: 441110
Lloyd Brown (Chm)
Kent Brown (Pres)
Kurt Brown (VP & Mgr-Sls)
Jeffrey Hoefer (Dir-Parts & Svc)
Greg Paulson (Mgr-Svc-Grand Island)
Rodney Stagemeyer (Gen Mgr-Sls)
Tracy Olson (Mgr-Parts-North Platte)
Scott Moses (Mgr-Svc-North Platte)
Jeremy Clark (Mgr-Body Shop)

NEBRASKA-IOWA SUPPLY COMPANY
1160 Lincoln St, Blair, NE 68008
Tel.: (402) 426-2171
Web Site: http://www.neiasupply.com
Rev.: $47,306,331
Emp.: 10
Gasoline
N.A.I.C.S.: 424720
Thomas J. Lippincott (Chm)
Mark Lippincott (Pres)

NEBRASKALAND
355 Food Center Dr Bldg G, Bronx, NY 10474
Tel.: (718) 842-0700
Web Site:
http://www.nebraskaland.com
Year Founded: 1989
Sales Range: $25-49.9 Million
Emp.: 200
Processed Meat & Sea Food Mfr & Distr
N.A.I.C.S.: 311611
Daniel Romanoff (Exec VP)
Jeff Spradlin (VP)
Richard Romanoff (Mgr-Mktg Res)
Barbara Sarner (Dir-Sls)

NEBRASKALAND TIRE COMPANY
S 283 I 80, Lexington, NE 68850
Tel.: (308) 324-2338
Web Site: http://www.thetirestore.com
Rev.: $30,879,673
Emp.: 18
Automotive Tires
N.A.I.C.S.: 441340
Gary Wright (Pres)

NEBULA, INC.
215 Castro St 3rd Fl, Mountain View, CA 94041
Tel.: (650) 539-9900
Web Site: http://www.nebula.com
Sales Range: $1-9.9 Million
Emp.: 60
Computer Hardware Mfr
N.A.I.C.S.: 334118
Chris C. Kemp (Co-Founder)
Devin Carlen (Co-Founder)
Gordon L. Stitt (CEO)
Herb Schneider (Sr VP-Engrg)
Huy Nguyen (VP-Product Mgmt & Mktg)

NECC TELECOM, INC.
1607 E Big Beaver Rd Ste 300, Troy, MI 48083
Tel.: (954) 374-6286
Web Site: http://www.necc.us
Rev.: $40,500,000
Emp.: 52
Telecommunications Resellers
N.A.I.C.S.: 517121

NECCO
503A Darby Creek Rd, Lexington, KY 40509
Tel.: (859) 264-8796
Web Site: http://www.necco.org
Year Founded: 1999
Sales Range: $25-49.9 Million
Emp.: 434
Family Support Services
N.A.I.C.S.: 624190
Stephen O. Mullins (Chief Tech Innovation Officer)
Edward D. Necco (CEO)
Amy Kennedy-Rickman (Exec Dir-West Virginia)
Bob Carpenter (COO)
Greg Thompson (Exec Dir-Ohio)
Kelly Adkins-Conley (Exec Dir-Kentucky)
Pamela Priddy (Chief Clinical Officer)
Ron Aceto (Dir-Business Analytics)
J. P. Montgomery (Chief Strategy Officer)
Mark Davis (CFO)
Mavis Williamson (Exec Dir-Georgia)
Rob Goodwin (Chief People Officer)

NED BARD & SON CO.
120-132 S Maple Ave 6, Leola, PA 17540
Tel.: (717) 656-2931
Web Site: http://www.nedbard.com
Sales Range: $10-24.9 Million
Emp.: 100
Trucking
N.A.I.C.S.: 484121

NED CORP.
18 Grafton St, Worcester, MA 01604-4934
Tel.: (508) 798-8546
Web Site: http://www.nedcorp.com
Year Founded: 1964
Sales Range: $50-74.9 Million
Emp.: 6
Diamond Cutting Tools For Cutting Concrete & Stone Products
N.A.I.C.S.: 333515

NEDCO ELECTRICAL SUPPLY, INC.
4200 Spring Mountain Rd, Las Vegas, NV 89102
Tel.: (702) 367-0400
Web Site: http://www.nedco.com
Sales Range: $50-74.9 Million
Emp.: 85
Electrical Fittings & Construction Materials
N.A.I.C.S.: 423610

Paul Winard (Founder & Chm)
Ed Haffen (Mgr-Ops)
Mark Winard (Pres & Principal)

NEDCO ELECTRONICS INCORPORATED
1520 E Edinger Ave Ste A, Santa Ana, CA 92705
Tel.: (714) 821-1516
Web Site:
http://www.nedcoelectronics.com
Year Founded: 1955
Sales Range: $10-24.9 Million
Emp.: 20
Distr of Electronic Components
N.A.I.C.S.: 423690
Mike Costello (Mgr-Ops)
Brad Dinkel (CEO-Utah)
Tom DeLand (Gen Mgr)
Josh Heathcote (Gen Mgr)
Dominic Laudando (Gen Mgr)
Randy Sitowski (Gen Mgr)

NEDELCO INC.
1001 12th St, Aurora, NE 68818
Tel.: (402) 694-5101
Rev.: $23,777,766
Emp.: 125
Local Telephone Communications
N.A.I.C.S.: 517121
Phillip C. Nelson (Pres)
Subsidiaries:

Hamilton Telecommunications (1)
1001 12th St, Aurora, NE 68818
Tel.: (402) 694-5101
Web Site: http://www.hamiltontel.com
Rev.: $4,900,000
Emp.: 50
Long Distance Telephone Communications
N.A.I.C.S.: 516210
Phillip C. Nelson (Pres & CEO)
Cindy Blase (Asst Mgr-HR)
Dan Molliconi (COO-Telecom & Tech)
John Nelson (Pres & CEO)
Pat Shaw (Gen Mgr-Mid-State Community TV)

Hamilton Telecommunications (1)
509 N Dewey St, North Platte, NE 69101
Tel.: (308) 534-4341
Web Site: http://www.nque.com
Rev.: $390,000
Emp.: 6
Information Retrieval Services
N.A.I.C.S.: 517810

NEEB CORPORATION
336 E Butler St, Bad Axe, MI 48413-1267
Tel.: (989) 269-6481
Year Founded: 1919
Sales Range: $75-99.9 Million
Emp.: 45
Petroleum & Petroleum Products Whslr; Gasoline & Retail Convenience Store Operators
N.A.I.C.S.: 445131

NEEDHAM & COMPANY INC.
445 Pk Ave Fl 3, New York, NY 10022-2606
Tel.: (212) 371-8300
Web Site:
http://www.needhamco.com
Year Founded: 1985
Sales Range: $50-74.9 Million
Emp.: 195
Security Brokers & Dealers
N.A.I.C.S.: 523150
George A. Needham (Co-Founder)
Chad Keck (Vice Chm)
Sean Dwyer (Mng Dir & Head-Sls Trading)
John Lazo (Mng Dir & Head-Trading)
Bernard H. Lirola (Mng Dir)
Colleen Holmes (Principal)
Jim Apostolides (Mng Dir)
Andrew J. Malik (Chm)

NEEDHAM & COMPANY INC.   U.S. PRIVATE

Needham & Company Inc.—(Continued)
David Townes (Co-Founder)
Jack Higgins (Mng Dir)
James King (Mng Dir)
Pooyan Mehdizadeh (Mng Dir)
Brian J. Perrault (Mng Dir)
Thomas Maloney (Mng Dir & Dir-Equity Res)
Philip Ianniello (Mng Dir & Head-Boston Office Investment Banking)
Jeffrey J. Posner (Mng Dir & Head-Institutional Sls-Natl)
Gunjeet Baweja (Mng Dir & Head-West Coast Mergers & Acq)

NEEDHAM COOPERATIVE BANK INC.
1063 Great Plain Ave, Needham, MA 02492
Tel.: (781) 444-2100
Web Site: http://www.needhambank.com
Sales Range: $25-49.9 Million
Emp.: 58
State Commercial Banks
N.A.I.C.S.: 522110
Jack W. McGeorge (Chm)
Stephanie Maiona (VP-Lending)
Joseph P. Campanelli (CEO)

NEEDLEMAN DROSSMAN & PARTNERS
902 Broadway 15th Fl, New York, NY 10010
Tel.: (212) 506-0770
Web Site: http://www.needlemandrossman.com
Sales Range: $10-24.9 Million
Emp.: 40
N.A.I.C.S.: 541810
Neil Drossman (Chm & Co-Creative Dir)

NEEKO-SUAVE, INC.
1101 Fort Crook Rd N, Bellevue, NE 68005
Tel.: (402) 341-6422
Web Site: http://www.centuryconverting.com
Year Founded: 1998
Sales Range: $10-24.9 Million
Emp.: 15
Converted Paper Product Mfr
N.A.I.C.S.: 322299
Timothy J. Odorisio (Pres)

NEENAN COMPANY
5701 Blue Pkwy, Kansas City, MO 64130
Tel.: (816) 923-1300
Web Site: http://www.neenco.com
Sales Range: $25-49.9 Million
Emp.: 50
Plumbing & Hydronic Heating Supplies
N.A.I.C.S.: 423720
Michael Neenan (Pres)
Joseph Neenan (VP)
Linda Neenan (Sec)
Robert Kuhnlein (Gen Mgr)
Andrew Neenan (Mgr-Sls)
Kevin Neenan (Dir-Branch Ops)
Jeff Ivey (Controller)
Tim Storey (Mgr-Pur)
Erica Oatman (Mgr-Acct Receivable)
Connie Heitman (Mgr-Acct Payable)
Dennis Creech (Mgr-Southwest Reg)
Pat Storey (Mgr-Lenexa & Olathe)
Joe Yunghans (Mgr-Lawrence & Emporia)

NEENAN COMPANY
3325 S Timberline Rd Ste 100, Fort Collins, CO 80525
Tel.: (970) 493-8747
Web Site: http://www.neenan.com
Sales Range: $150-199.9 Million
Emp.: 100
General Contractor; Provider of Real Estate Services
N.A.I.C.S.: 236220
Randy Meyers (CEO)
Shawn Sullivan (VP-Bus Dev-Comml Projects)
David Shigekane (Pres)
Jennifer Slupe (Coord-Client Svcs)

NEESSEN CHEVROLET INC.
2007 S Hwy 77 Bypass, Kingsville, TX 78363
Tel.: (361) 592-2668
Web Site: http://www.neessenautomotive.com
Sales Range: $25-49.9 Million
Emp.: 45
Automobiles, New & Used
N.A.I.C.S.: 441110
Phillip Neessen (Pres)

NEFCO CORP.
411 Burnham St, East Hartford, CT 06108
Tel.: (860) 289-0285
Web Site: http://www.gonefco.com
Sales Range: $10-24.9 Million
Emp.: 80
Industrial Supplies Whslr
N.A.I.C.S.: 423840
David Gelles (Pres)
Gerald Gelles (Chm)
Skip Maxfield (VP)
Subsidiaries:
Edge Construction Supply, LLC (1)
1503 E Riverside Ave, Spokane, WA 99202
Tel.: (509) 535-9841
Web Site: https://www.edgecs.com
Sales Range: $10-24.9 Million
Emp.: 90
Supplier of Heavy Construction Equipment
N.A.I.C.S.: 532412
Nancy Othmer (VP-Admin)
Newman Associates, Inc (1)
80 Hudson Rd, Canton, MA 02021
Tel.: (781) 329-4000
Web Site: http://www.newmanassoc.com
Rev: $7,500,000
Emp.: 30
Plumbing & Heating Equipment & Supplies, Hydronics, Merchant Whslr
N.A.I.C.S.: 423720
Richard Tamulionis (Pres)
Laura Condon (Controller)
Butch Tamulionis (VP-Bus Dev)

NEFF + ASSOCIATES, INC.
The Novelty Bldg 15 S Third St 4th Fl, Philadelphia, PA 19106
Tel.: (215) 627-4747   PA
Web Site: http://www.neffassociates.com
Year Founded: 1984
Sales Range: $10-24.9 Million
Emp.: 12
Advertising Agencies
N.A.I.C.S.: 541810
Adam Englehart (Dir-Art)

NEFF CO.
112 N Main St, Avon, IL 61415
Tel.: (309) 465-3184
Web Site: http://www.neffcoag.com
Rev: $15,749,164
Emp.: 20
Farm Implements
N.A.I.C.S.: 423820
William Maloney (Owner)
Sharon Coates (Controller)

NEFF ENGINEERING COMPANY, INC.
7114 Innovation Blvd, Fort Wayne, IN 46818-1373
Tel.: (260) 489-6007   IN
Web Site: http://www.neffengineering.com
Year Founded: 1987
Sales Range: $10-24.9 Million
Emp.: 100
Industrial Machinery & Equipment Distr
N.A.I.C.S.: 423830
Clay Neuenschwander (Controller)
Dan Neff (CEO)

NEFF MOTIVATION INC.
645 Pine St, Greenville, OH 45331
Tel.: (937) 548-3194
Web Site: http://www.neffco.com
Sales Range: $25-49.9 Million
Emp.: 600
Manufactures Emblems, Badges & Insignia: From Purchased Materials
N.A.I.C.S.: 314999
Michael Less (Dir-Sls)
James Monroe (Dir-Athletic)
Subsidiaries:
Rock Creek Athletics, Inc. (1)
91 6th Ave W, Grinnell, IA 50112
Tel.: (641) 236-9115
Men's Clothing Stores
N.A.I.C.S.: 458110

NEFF PACKAGING SOLUTIONS INC.
10 Kingbrook Pkwy, Simpsonville, KY 40067
Tel.: (513) 204-3433
Web Site: http://www.neffpackaging.com
Sales Range: $10-24.9 Million
Emp.: 100
Folding Paperboard Boxes
N.A.I.C.S.: 322212
Robert Neff (Pres & CEO)

NEFF-PERKINS COMPANY INC.
2950 Indus Pk Dr, Austinburg, OH 44010-9763
Tel.: (440) 275-1009   OH
Web Site: http://www.neffp.com
Year Founded: 1946
Sales Range: $10-24.9 Million
Emp.: 262
Fabricated Rubber Products
N.A.I.C.S.: 326299
Robert A. Elly (Owner)
Brian Elly (Sls Acct Mgr)

NEGRI ELECTRONICS
6255 S Sandhill Rd Ste 600, Las Vegas, NV 89120
Web Site: http://www.negrielectronics.com
Year Founded: 2006
Sales Range: $1-9.9 Million
Emp.: 14
Electronic Accessories
N.A.I.C.S.: 449210
Ryan J. Negri (Founder)

NEGWER MATERIALS INCORPORATED
49 Airport Rd, Saint Louis, MO 63135
Tel.: (314) 522-0579
Web Site: http://www.negwer.com
Sales Range: $25-49.9 Million
Emp.: 160
Building Materials, Interior
N.A.I.C.S.: 423310
Tom Bredel (Mgr-Product Sls)

NEHEMIAH CORPORATION OF AMERICA
640 Bercut Dr, Sacramento, CA 95811
Tel.: (916) 231-1999
Web Site: http://www.nehemiahcorp.org
Sales Range: $125-149.9 Million
Emp.: 45
Land Subdividers & Developers, Residential
N.A.I.C.S.: 237210
Darrell Teat (Pres)
Nicole Learned (VP-Ops)
Erik Grotte (CFO)

NEHEMIAH HOUSING DEVELOPMENT FUND
551 Vandalia Ave 1st Fl, Brooklyn, NY 11239
Tel.: (718) 642-2330   NY
Year Founded: 1995
Sales Range: $10-24.9 Million
Emp.: 4
Housing Assistance Services
N.A.I.C.S.: 624229
Ronald Waters (Gen Mgr)

NEHER ELECTRIC SUPPLY INC.
3629 N Teutonia Ave, Milwaukee, WI 53206
Tel.: (414) 871-5700
Web Site: http://www.neherelectric.com
Sales Range: $10-24.9 Million
Emp.: 17
Electrical Supplies
N.A.I.C.S.: 423610
Richard Steggeman (Pres)
Don Bullock (VP)
Troy Nettesheim (Mgr-Sls & Pur)

NEHMEN-KODNER
431 N Polo Dr, Saint Louis, MO 63105
Tel.: (314) 721-1404
Web Site: http://www.n-kcreative.com
Year Founded: 1987
Sales Range: Less than $1 Million
Emp.: 2
Advetising Agency
N.A.I.C.S.: 541810
Gary A. Kodner (VP & Gen Mgr)
Peggy S. Nehmen (Owner, Dir-Art & Graphic Designer)

NEHOC INC.
7013 Orchard Lake Rd Ste 115, West Bloomfield, MI 48322-3692
Tel.: (248) 737-0100
Web Site: http://www.barrycohen.com
Year Founded: 1984
Sales Range: Less than $1 Million
Emp.: 4
Consulting, Travel & Tourism
N.A.I.C.S.: 541810
Larry Howard (Art Dir)
Lisa Cohen (Brdcst Production Dir)
Barney Cohen (HR Dir)
Larry Cohen (Sls Promo Dir)
Carole Sue Gold (Controller)
Rebecca Smith (Media Dir)
Eric Bryen (Gen Counsel)
Lisa Urist (Sec, Mktg Dir & Media)

NEIDIGER TUCKER BRUNER INC.
9540 Maroon Circle Ste 250, Englewood, CO 80112
Tel.: (303) 825-1825
Web Site: http://www.ntbinc.com
Rev: $11,969,561
Emp.: 40
Brokers Security
N.A.I.C.S.: 523150
Eugene L. Neidiger (Founder & Chm)
Anthony B. Petrelli (Pres & Mng Dir)

Michael Morgan *(Mng Dir & Exec VP)*
Robert Parrish *(Mng Dir)*
Regina Roesener *(Exec VP & Mng Dir-Corp Fin)*

NEIGHBOR INSURANCE SERVICES
1240 8th Ave, Marion, IA 52302
Tel.: (319) 373-4307
Web Site: http://www.neighborinsurance.com
Sales Range: $10-24.9 Million
Emp.: 25
Insurance Agents
N.A.I.C.S.: 524210
Eldon Neighbor *(Co-Owner)*
Mark Neighbor *(Co-Owner)*

Subsidiaries:

Farmers State Bank (1)
1240 8th Ave, Marion, IA 52302
Tel.: (319) 377-4891
Web Site: http://www.myfsbonline.com
Rev.: $28,593,395
Emp.: 114
Commercial Banking Services
N.A.I.C.S.: 522110
Gene Neighbor *(Pres & CEO)*

NEIGHBORCARE HEALTH
1200 12th Ave S Ste 901, Seattle, WA 98144
Tel.: (206) 461-6935
Web Site: http://www.neighborcare.org
Year Founded: 1969
Sales Range: $25-49.9 Million
Emp.: 570
Community Health Care Services
N.A.I.C.S.: 621498
Marcus Rempel *(Chief Medical Officer)*
Janine Childs *(CFO)*
Barbara Shickich *(Chm)*
Andrea M. P. Dahl *(Sec)*
Rick Rubin *(Vice Chm)*
Joseph Sparacio *(Chief Dev Officer)*
Sarah Vander Beek *(Chief Dental Officer)*
Rashad A. Collins *(CEO)*

NEIGHBORHOOD ASSISTANCE CORPORATION OF AMERICA
225 Centre St, Boston, MA 02119
Tel.: (617) 250-6244
Web Site: http://www.naca.com
Year Founded: 1994
Sales Range: $50-74.9 Million
Emp.: 801
Homeownership Organization
N.A.I.C.S.: 813990
Martin White *(VP)*
Kent Whitney *(VP-Real Estate)*
George Weber *(Gen Counsel)*
Detria Austin *(COO)*

NEIGHBORHOOD CREDIT UNION
13651 Montfort Dr, Dallas, TX 75380-3476
Tel.: (214) 748-9393
Web Site: http://www.myncu.com
Year Founded: 1930
Sales Range: $10-24.9 Million
Emp.: 161
Credit Union
N.A.I.C.S.: 522130
Chet Kimmell *(Pres & CEO)*
James Frankeberger *(CFO)*
Carolyn Jordan *(Sr VP)*
Mike Roark *(Sr VP-Lending & Collections)*
Dwayne Boozer *(Chm)*
Dwain Woodard *(Treas & Sec)*
John Logan *(Vice Chm)*

NEIGHBORHOOD HEALTH CENTER CORPORATION
1700-58 Myrtle Ave, Plainfield, NJ 07063
Tel.: (908) 753-6401
Web Site: http://www.phcmednet.org
Year Founded: 1969
Sales Range: $10-24.9 Million
Emp.: 224
Health Care Srvices
N.A.I.C.S.: 622110
Derrick C. Williams *(COO & Acting VP)*
Rudine Smith *(Pres & CEO)*
Christopher Biondolillo *(Dir-Medical)*
Stacy Dean *(Chief Clinical Officer)*

NEIGHBORHOOD HEALTH CLINICS
1717 S Calhoun St, Fort Wayne, IN 46802
Tel.: (260) 458-2641
Web Site: http://www.nhci.org
Year Founded: 1994
Sales Range: $10-24.9 Million
Emp.: 168
Health Care Srvices
N.A.I.C.S.: 622110
Scott Jackson *(Treas)*
Terry Broberg-Swangin *(Chm)*
Holli Seabury *(Vice Chm)*
Dollye Carlisle *(Sec)*
Melissa Bradberry *(Treas)*

NEIGHBORHOOD HEALTH PLAN INC.
253 Summer St 5th Fl, Boston, MA 02110-1114
Tel.: (617) 772-5500
Web Site: http://www.nhp.org
Year Founded: 1986
Sales Range: $100-124.9 Million
Emp.: 400
Medical & Health Care Plans
N.A.I.C.S.: 524114
Matthew Fishman *(Chm)*
Anton B. Dodek *(Chief Medical Officer)*
Carole Bradford *(VP-HR)*
Dana Rashti *(Chief Mktg Officer & Chief Strategy Officer)*
David Segal *(Pres & CEO)*
Joseph C. Capezza *(CFO)*
Katie Catlender *(Chief Comml Officer)*
Mark McCormick *(COO-Interim)*
Paulette Shaw Querner *(Chief Medicaid Officer)*

NEIGHBORHOOD HEALTH PLAN OF RHODE ISLAND, INC.
299 Promenade St, Providence, RI 02908
Tel.: (401) 459-6000
Web Site: http://www.nhpri.org
Year Founded: 1986
Sales Range: $125-149.9 Million
Emp.: 150
Insurance Brokerage Services
N.A.I.C.S.: 524210
Deborah Enos *(Pres)*
Peter M. Marino *(CEO)*
Merrill Thomas *(Chm)*
Marylou Buyse *(Chief Medical Officer & Sr VP)*
Ronald Pearsall *(CIO)*
Joanne Roux *(VP-Fin)*

NEIGHBORHOOD HOUSING SERVICES OF CHICAGO INC.
1279 N Milwaukee Ave Fl 4, Chicago, IL 60622
Tel.: (773) 329-4010
Web Site: http://www.nhschicago.org
Year Founded: 1975
Sales Range: $50-74.9 Million
Emp.: 85
Low-Cost Housing
N.A.I.C.S.: 522291
Ella Casey *(Dir-Org Dev & HR)*
Kristin Faust *(Pres)*
Anjanette Brown *(CFO)*
Linda Greene *(Dir-Redevelopment Corp)*
Donna Clarke *(COO)*
Don Meyer *(Exec VP)*
Matthew Roth *(Treas)*
Dane Cleven *(Chm & Pres)*
Ed Wehmer *(CEO)*

NEIGHBORHOOD HOUSING SERVICES OF SOUTH FLORIDA
300 NW 12th Ave, Miami, FL 33128
Tel.: (305) 751-5511
Web Site: http://www.nhssf.org
Year Founded: 1978
Sales Range: $25-49.9 Million
Emp.: 48
Community Housing Assistance Services
N.A.I.C.S.: 624229
Mia Batlle *(Chief Dev Officer)*
Willie L. Duckworth *(Vice Chm)*
Dennis Rodrigues *(Treas)*
Patricia Algaze *(Chm)*
Maedell Brown *(Vice Chm)*
Mary MacNamara *(Officer-CRA, Sec-Total Bank & Sr VP-Compliance)*
Paul Petrella *(Mgr-Tech & Data)*
Rosa Franco Ortiz *(Office Mgr)*
Kimberly T. Henderson *(Pres & CEO)*

NEIGHBORHOOD LEGAL SERVICES OF LOS ANGELES COUNTY
1102 E Chevy Chase Dr, Glendale, CA 91205
Tel.: (818) 291-1760
Web Site: http://www.nlsla.org
Year Founded: 1965
Sales Range: $10-24.9 Million
Emp.: 128
Legal Assistance Services
N.A.I.C.S.: 541199
Neal S. Dudovitz *(Exec Dir)*
Lynne M. Hiortdahl *(CFO & COO)*
Sharon Bashan *(Dir-Pro Bono & Ops)*
Mandy Wu *(Sec)*
Richard S. Tom *(Pres)*

NEIGHBORHOOD LOANS
55 W 22nd St Ste 130, Lombard, IL 60148
Tel.: (800) 207-8595
Web Site: http://www.neighborhoodloans.com
Year Founded: 2005
Sales Range: $1-9.9 Million
Emp.: 40
Mortgage Loans to Consumers for Purchasing & Refinancing Homes
N.A.I.C.S.: 522310
Reno Manuele *(Pres)*
Anthony Ameti *(CFO & VP)*
Brandon Poulos *(VP-Lending)*

NEIGHBORHOOD NETWORKS PUBLISHING
3311 Merchant Ct, Wilmington, NC 28405
Tel.: (910) 202-0917
Web Site: http://www.n2pub.com
Year Founded: 2004
Sales Range: $1-9.9 Million
Emp.: 30
Specialty Magazine & Newsletter Publisher
N.A.I.C.S.: 513120

Duane Hixon *(Co-Founder & CEO)*
Earl Seals *(Co-Founder & Pres)*
Marty Fukuda *(COO)*
Brad LaLuzerne *(CFO)*

NEIGHBORHOOD RESTAURANTS INC.
601 Main St Ste 102, Hazard, KY 41701-1382
Tel.: (606) 436-0736
Web Site: http://www.neighborhoodrestaurants.com
Rev.: $80,000,000
Emp.: 20
Fast-Food Restaurant, Chain
N.A.I.C.S.: 722511
Theresa Johnson *(Pres)*

NEIGHBORHOOD VISITING NURSE ASSOCIATION
795 E Marshall St Ste 204, West Chester, PA 19380
Tel.: (610) 696-6511
Year Founded: 1975
Sales Range: $10-24.9 Million
Emp.: 255
Community Welfare Services
N.A.I.C.S.: 624190
Gina Petersen *(Dir-MIS)*
Mary Ellen Josephs *(Vice Chm)*
Steven D. Hobman *(Treas)*
Janet S. Hickman *(Sec)*
Andrea Devoti *(Pres & CEO)*
Charles Barr *(Dir-Medical)*
Keith D. Coughey *(Chm)*

NEIGHBORIMPACT
2303 SW 1st St, Redmond, OR 97756
Tel.: (541) 548-2380
Web Site: http://www.neighborimpact.org
Year Founded: 1985
Sales Range: $10-24.9 Million
Emp.: 242
Community Support Services
N.A.I.C.S.: 624190
Susan Bailey *(Pres)*
Linda Walker *(Treas & Sec)*
Andrus Soper *(VP)*
Scott Cooper *(Exec Dir)*
Kim Lonien *(CEO)*

NEIGHBORLY CARE NETWORK
13945 Evergreen Ave, Clearwater, FL 33762-4525
Tel.: (727) 573-9444
Web Site: http://www.neighborly.org
Sales Range: $1-9.9 Million
Emp.: 115
Health & Wellness Programs for Seniors & Their Families
N.A.I.C.S.: 923120
Debra Shade *(Pres & CEO)*
David Lind *(Dir-IT)*
Sheri Gruden *(Coord-Intake & Mktg)*
Cathy Christmas *(Supvr-Route)*

NEIGHBORS CONSTRUCTION CO. INC.
9800 Legler Rd, Lenexa, KS 66219
Tel.: (913) 422-5555
Web Site: http://www.neighborsconstruction.com
Sales Range: $25-49.9 Million
Emp.: 50
Residential Construction
N.A.I.C.S.: 236115
Roger H. Neighbors *(Pres)*
Nancy L. Neighbors *(Treas, Sec & VP)*

NEIGHBORS IN NEED OF SERVICES, INC.

NEIGHBORS IN NEED OF SERVICES, INC.

Neighbors In Need Of Services, Inc.—(Continued)
402 W Robertson St, San Benito, TX 78586
Tel.: (956) 399-9944
Web Site: http://www.ninosinc.org
Year Founded: 1990
Sales Range: $10-24.9 Million
Emp.: 667
Community Care Center
N.A.I.C.S.: 624190
Erie Tejada (Dir-Children Svcs)
Manuela Rendon (Exec Dir-Head Start)
David Kowalski (Dir-MIS)
Lusila Ortega (Asst Dir-Head Start)
Tracy Torres (Fin Dir)
Stephanie Cantu (Officer-Personnel)
Raul Garza III (Dir-Childrens Health & Safety)

NEIL HUFFMAN NISSAN INC.
4136 Shelbyville Rd, Louisville, KY 40207-3234
Tel.: (502) 897-3151
Web Site: http://www.neilhuffmannissan.com
Year Founded: 1979
Sales Range: $100-124.9 Million
Emp.: 60
Retailer of New & Used Automobiles
N.A.I.C.S.: 441110
Neil Huffman (Pres & COO)

Subsidiaries:

Neil Huffman Volkswagen Mazda Suburu (1)
4926 Dixie Hwy, Louisville, KY 40216-2540
Tel.: (502) 426-8048
Web Site: http://www.neilhuffman.com
Sales Range: $25-49.9 Million
Automobile Dealership
N.A.I.C.S.: 441110
Neil Huffman (Pres)

NEIL INTERNATIONAL INC.
450 E Bunker CT, Vernon Hills, IL 60061
Tel.: (847) 549-7627
Web Site: http://www.neilenterprises.com
Year Founded: 1961
Sales Range: $10-24.9 Million
Emp.: 5
Injection Molded Finished Plastics Product Mfr
N.A.I.C.S.: 326199
Neil Fine (Pres)

Subsidiaries:

Illini Inc. (1)
450 E Bunker Ct, Vernon Hills, IL 60061
Tel.: (847) 549-7627
Web Site: http://www.illiniline.com
Emp.: 50
Signs & Advertising Specialties
N.A.I.C.S.: 339950
Neil Fine (Pres)

Neil Enterprises Inc (1)
450 E Bunker Ct, Vernon Hills, IL 60061
Tel.: (847) 549-7627
Web Site: http://www.neilenterprises.com
Photo Novelty Products
N.A.I.C.S.: 423410
Jerry Fine (Founder)
Neil Fine (Pres)

NEIL KELLY CO. INC.
804 N Alberta St, Portland, OR 97217
Tel.: (503) 288-7461
Web Site: http://www.neilkelly.com
Rev.: $18,000,000
Emp.: 200
General Remodeling, Single-Family Houses
N.A.I.C.S.: 236118

Tom Kelly (Pres)
Julia Spence (VP-Comm)
Don Scharff (Mgr-Corp Mktg)
Dan Watson (CFO)

NEILL AIRCRAFT COMPANY
1260 W 15th St, Long Beach, CA 90813
Tel.: (562) 432-7981
Web Site: http://www.neillaircraft.com
Rev.: $22,000,000
Emp.: 135
Aircraft Parts & Auxiliary Equipment Mfr
N.A.I.C.S.: 336413
Brad Barnette (Gen Mgr)
Victor Paquini (Mgr-Ops)
Anne Schmidt (Controller)

NEILL CORPORATION
303 S Pine St, Hammond, LA 70403-4133
Tel.: (985) 345-1085
Web Site: http://www.neill.net
Year Founded: 1968
Rev.: $30,122,940
Emp.: 300
Distr of Service Establishment Equipment
N.A.I.C.S.: 423850
Michael Baker (Dir-Creative)
Candice Hoz (Exec Dir-Sls)
Jim Petrillo (Principal)
Tom Petrillo (Principal)

NEILL-LAVIELLE SUPPLY CO.
1711 S Floyd St, Louisville, KY 40208-2740
Tel.: (502) 637-5401
Web Site: http://www.neill-lavielle.com
Year Founded: 1881
Sales Range: $100-124.9 Million
Emp.: 200
Distr of Mill Supplies, Machine Tools, Ball & Roller Bearings & Steel Fabrications
N.A.I.C.S.: 423840
Robert G. Pfeiffer (Pres & CEO)
Kevin Harbeson (Sr VP & Controller)
George Pfeiffer (COO)

Subsidiaries:

Bearings of Kentucky (1)
1711 S Floyd St, Louisville, KY 40208
Tel.: (502) 637-1444
Industrial Supplies Whslr
N.A.I.C.S.: 423840

NEISEN BANCSHARES, INC.
170 Meeker Ave N, Watkins, MN 55389
Tel.: (320) 764-2600
Web Site: http://www.fsbwatkins.com
Bank Holding Company
N.A.I.C.S.: 551111

Subsidiaries:

Farmers State Bank of Watkins (1)
170 Meeker Ave N, Watkins, MN 55389 (100%)
Tel.: (320) 764-2600
Web Site: http://www.fsbwatkins.com
Sales Range: $1-9.9 Million
Emp.: 10
State Commercial Banks
N.A.I.C.S.: 522110
Dave Neisen (Pres)

NEISEWANDER ENTERPRISES INC.
1101 E River Rd, Dixon, IL 61021-0448
Tel.: (815) 288-1431
Web Site: http://www.raynor.com
Year Founded: 1974
Sales Range: $125-149.9 Million
Emp.: 700
Metal Doors & Related Products Mfr
N.A.I.C.S.: 332321

Subsidiaries:

Raynor Garage Doors (1)
1101 E River Rd, Dixon, IL 61021-3252
Tel.: (815) 288-1431
Web Site: http://www.raynor.com
Sales Range: $25-49.9 Million
Emp.: 755
Overhead & Garage Doors Mfr
N.A.I.C.S.: 332321
Ray H. Neisewander III (Pres & CEO)
Mike Dean (Dir-Mfg & Tech Skills)

Division (Domestic):

Raynor Distribution Center (2)
550 Ryerson Rd, Lincoln Park, NJ 07035-2049
Tel.: (973) 696-7550
Web Site: http://www.raynor.com
Garage Door Mfr
N.A.I.C.S.: 332321

Raynor Distribution Center (2)
5160 Havana St Unit G, Denver, CO 80239
Tel.: (303) 371-1690
Sales Range: $25-49.9 Million
Emp.: 6
Commercial & Residential Garage Doors Distr
N.A.I.C.S.: 423310

Raynor Manufacturing. Co., Inc. (1)
1101 E River Rd, Dixon, IL 61021-3252 (100%)
Tel.: (815) 288-1431
Web Site: http://www.raynor.com
Sales Range: $25-49.9 Million
Emp.: 500
Mfr of Metal Doors
N.A.I.C.S.: 332321

NEJ, INC.
170 Pinesbridge Rd, Beacon Falls, CT 06403
Tel.: (203) 463-3300
Web Site: http://www.nejinc.com
Year Founded: 1990
Excess Inventory Management Services Private Label Apparel Mfr & Retailer Services
N.A.I.C.S.: 561990
Ed Mascolo (Founder & Pres)
Tony Melaragno (Controller & Mgr-Inventory Control)
Bob Allegrini (COO)
Brendan Lynch (CFO)

Subsidiaries:

Bills Khakis (1)
170 Pinesbridge Rd, Beacon Falls, CT 06403
Tel.: (203) 463-2300
Web Site: http://www.billskhakis.com
Men's & Boys' Apparel Mfr, Whslr & Online Retailer
N.A.I.C.S.: 315250
Mary Jo Dever (VP-Sls)

NEL GROUP, INC.
655 Fairfield Ct, Ann Arbor, MI 48108
Tel.: (734) 730-9164
Web Site:
Holding Company
N.A.I.C.S.: 551112
Daryl R. Kipke (Pres & CEO)

Subsidiaries:

NeuroNexus Technologies, Inc. (1)
655 Fairfield Ct Ste 100, Ann Arbor, MI 48108
Tel.: (734) 913-8858
Web Site: http://www.neuronexus.com
Biotechnology Research & Development Services
N.A.I.C.S.: 541714
Daryl R. Kipke (Pres)
Jamille Hetke (Engr)
Rio Vetter (Dir-R&D)
Kc Kong (Dir-Sls & Mktg)

NELCO PRODUCTS INC.
22 Riverside Dr, Pembroke, MA 02359
Tel.: (781) 826-3010
Web Site: http://www.nelcoproducts.com
Sales Range: $10-24.9 Million
Emp.: 29
Electrical Apparatus & Equipment
N.A.I.C.S.: 423610
Charles W. Nelson (Co-Founder & Pres)
Maureen Meech (Controller)
Michelle Abbondanzio (Sr Acct Exec)
Andrew Moss (Sr Acct Exec)

NELLIS MANAGEMENT CORPORATION
2940 104th St, Urbandale, IA 50322-2800
Tel.: (515) 252-1742
Web Site: http://www.nellismanagement.com
Year Founded: 1964
Sales Range: $25-49.9 Million
Emp.: 600
Restaurant Management Services
N.A.I.C.S.: 541611
Mark Levitt (Pres)
John Wilson (Mgr-IT)
Alexa Suhr (Mgr-Payroll)

NELLYMOSER, INC.
11 Water St, Arlington, MA 02476
Tel.: (781) 645-1515
Web Site: http://www.nellymoser.com
Sales Range: $25-49.9 Million
Emp.: 35
Wired Telecommunications Resellers
N.A.I.C.S.: 517121
John Puterbaugh (Founder & CEO)
Epiphany Vera (VP-Engrg & Ops)
Todd Griffith (VP-Creative & Client Svcs)

NELS GUNDERSON CHEVROLET, INC.
I 94 & Hwy 10, Osseo, WI 54758
Tel.: (715) 597-3180
Web Site: http://www.osseoauto.com
Year Founded: 1995
Sales Range: $10-24.9 Million
Emp.: 25
Car Whslr
N.A.I.C.S.: 441110
Nels Gunderson (Pres)

NELSEN STEEL & WIRE CO.
9400 Belmont Ave, Franklin Park, IL 60131
Tel.: (847) 671-9700
Web Site: http://www.nelsensteel.com
Year Founded: 1939
Sales Range: $50-74.9 Million
Emp.: 100
Mfr of Cold-Drawn Steel Bars & Wire
N.A.I.C.S.: 331221
Bill Geary (CFO)
Jim Sarwark (Dir-Sls-Mktg)
C. Davis Nelsen II (Chm, Pres & CEO)

NELSON & GILMORE
1604 Aviation Blvd, Redondo Beach, CA 90278
Tel.: (310) 376-0296
Web Site: http://www.nelsongilmore.com
Year Founded: 1978
Sales Range: $10-24.9 Million
Emp.: 11
Advertising Agencies
N.A.I.C.S.: 541810
Wayne Nelson (CEO)

COMPANIES

NELSON & SCHMIDT, INC.
600 E Wisconsin Ave, Milwaukee, WI 53202
Tel.: (414) 224-0210 WI
Web Site:
   http://www.nelsonschmidt.com
Year Founded: 1971
Sales Range: $1-9.9 Million
Emp.: 50
Advetising Agency
N.A.I.C.S.: 541810
Cody Pearce (COO)
Chris Vitrano (Chief Mktg Officer)
Mike Fredrick (Chief Creative Officer)
Lynne Chamberlain (Dir-HR)
Spencer Allen (Dir-IT)
Becky Davidson (Dir-Acct Plng & Mgmt)
Brooke Etzel (Mgr-Project)
Jeff Ericksen (Dir-Grp Creative)
Jason Gantner (Dir-Production)
Maria Halverson (Mgr-Media)
Laura Hinrichsen (Dir-Media Svcs)
James Jelak (Dir-Acct Plng & Mgmt)
Sabrina Karani (Dir-UX Design)
Clay Konnor (Dir-Grp Creative)
Scott Lawson (Dir-Creative)
Sarah Lockwood (Mgr-Project)
Amy Nunnemacher (Dir-PR)
Jason Petersen (Dir-Creative)
Cristy Schuenke (Controller)
Amanda Seed (Coord-Acct)
Sarah Duchemin (Acct Supvr)
Nicole Koremenos (Acct Supvr-PR)
Alex Wehrley (Acct Supvr-PR)
Daniel H. Nelson Sr. (Chm)
Daniel H. Nelson Jr. (Pres & CEO)

NELSON & SMALL INC.
212 Canco Rd, Portland, ME 04103-4221
Tel.: (207) 775-5666 ME
Web Site:
   http://www.nelsonsmall.com
Year Founded: 1936
Sales Range: $75-99.9 Million
Emp.: 50
Whslr of Residential Appliances; Commercial Laundry Products; Vented Heating Products
N.A.I.C.S.: 423620
Kenneth M. Nelson (Pres, CEO & Co-Owner)
David L. Small (COO & Co-Owner)
Peter W. LaRose (Sr VP & Gen Mgr-Sls)
Joan Pelletier (Controller)
Steven Smith (Mgr-IT)

NELSON ADVERTISING SOLUTIONS
19080 Lomita Ave, Sonoma, CA 95476-1546
Tel.: (707) 935-6113
Web Site: http://www.nelsonhr.com
Year Founded: 1970
Sales Range: $300-349.9 Million
Emp.: 250
N.A.I.C.S.: 541810
Gary D. Nelson (Founder)
Anthony Bartenetti (Pres-Nelson Staffing & COO)
Lisa Marie Johnson (Dir-HR)

NELSON AIR DEVICE CORP
4628 54th Ave, Maspeth, NY 11378
Tel.: (718) 729-3801
Web Site:
   http://www.nelsonairdevice.com
Rev.: $10,400,000
Emp.: 100
Heating & Air Conditioning Contractors
N.A.I.C.S.: 238220
Mark Steele (Dir-Ops)
Nelson Blitz (Owner & Pres)
Michael Doff (VP)

NELSON BROTHERS INC.
820 Shades Creek Pkwy, Birmingham, AL 35209
Tel.: (205) 414-2900
Web Site:
   http://www.oricaminingservices.com
Rev.: $26,000,000
Emp.: 35
Amatols (Explosive)
N.A.I.C.S.: 325920
Jason Baker (Dir-Fin)
Bill Kemp (Mgr-Aviation Dept)
Terry Newton (Dir-Safety, Compliance & HR)
Larry M. Sparks (Dir-IT)
Mell Ellison (Sr Acct Mgr)
William H. Nelson III (CEO)

NELSON CHEESE FACTORY INC.
S237 State Rd 35, Nelson, WI 54756
Tel.: (715) 673-4725
Web Site:
   http://www.nelsoncheese.com
Rev.: $11,700,000
Emp.: 15
Cheese; Natural & Processed
N.A.I.C.S.: 311513
Edward Greenheck (Owner)
Stacy Pretzer (Mgr)

NELSON DISTRIBUTING INC.
1125 80th St SW, Everett, WA 98203
Tel.: (425) 353-9701
Web Site:
   http://www.nelsonpetroleum.com
Sales Range: $200-249.9 Million
Emp.: 60
Petroleum Bulk Stations
N.A.I.C.S.: 424710
Mark Nelson (Pres)

NELSON ELECTRIC CO.
618 14th Ave SW, Cedar Rapids, IA 52404
Tel.: (319) 366-6257
Web Site:
   http://www.nelsonelectric.com
Sales Range: $10-24.9 Million
Emp.: 100
General Electrical Contractor
N.A.I.C.S.: 238210
John Negro (Pres)
Jerry Nelson (Owner)
Stan Pfoff (Project Mgr)

NELSON ELECTRIC SUPPLY CO. INC.
926 State St, Racine, WI 53404
Tel.: (262) 637-7661
Web Site: http://www.nelson-electric.com
Sales Range: $10-24.9 Million
Emp.: 42
Electrical Apparatus & Equipment
N.A.I.C.S.: 423610
Thomas R. Leuenberger (Pres & Gen Mgr)
Peter Landgraf (VP-Engrg)

NELSON FORD MAZDA
201 Commonwealth Blvd, Martinsville, VA 24112
Tel.: (276) 638-2331 VA
Web Site:
   http://www.autosbynelson.com
Year Founded: 1975
Sales Range: $25-49.9 Million
Emp.: 138
New & Used Car Dealers
N.A.I.C.S.: 441120
G. R. Nelson (Pres)
Barry L. Nelson (VP)
Joann M. Nelson (Treas & Sec)
Tawni Hundley (Controller)

NELSON FORD-LINCOLN-MERCURY, INC.
2228 College Way, Fergus Falls, MN 56537
Tel.: (218) 998-8878
Web Site: http://www.nelsonford.com
Sales Range: $25-49.9 Million
Emp.: 60
Car Dealership Owner & Operator
N.A.I.C.S.: 423110
David Johnson (Mgr-Sls)

NELSON HALL CHEVROLET, INC.
1811 S Frontage Rd, Meridian, MS 39301
Tel.: (601) 693-4411
Web Site:
   http://www.nelsonhallchevrolet.com
Year Founded: 1970
Sales Range: $25-49.9 Million
Emp.: 48
Car Whslr
N.A.I.C.S.: 441110
W. Nelson Hall (Pres)

NELSON HOMES, INC.
7309 Merchant Ct, Sarasota, FL 34240
Tel.: (941) 907-2292
Sales Range: $10-24.9 Million
Emp.: 20
Residential Construction
N.A.I.C.S.: 236115
Derek Nelson (Pres)

NELSON IRRIGATION CORPORATION
848 Airport Rd, Walla Walla, WA 99362
Tel.: (509) 525-7660
Web Site:
   http://www.nelsonirrigation.com
Rev.: $15,600,000
Emp.: 150
Sprinkler Systems, Field
N.A.I.C.S.: 332919
John Rowley (Mgr-Rotator Product)

NELSON LEASING INC.
2700 Hwy 12 SE, Willmar, MN 56201
Tel.: (320) 235-2770
Web Site:
   http://www.nelsonleasing.com
Sales Range: $25-49.9 Million
Emp.: 125
Trucks, Commercial
N.A.I.C.S.: 423110
Dale Nelson (Pres)
Ryan Nelson (VP)

NELSON MILL & AGRI-CENTER
217 N Center Ave, Viroqua, WI 54665
Tel.: (608) 637-2192
Web Site: http://www.nelsonmill.com
Rev.: $24,100,000
Emp.: 65
Feed
N.A.I.C.S.: 424910
Roy G. Kanis (Treas)
Cheryl Day (Sec)

NELSON MULLINS RILEY & SCARBOROUGH LLP
Meridian 17th Fl 1320 Main St, Columbia, SC 29201
Tel.: (803) 799-2000
Web Site:
   http://www.nelsonmullins.com
Year Founded: 1897
Sales Range: $200-249.9 Million
Emp.: 414
Legal Advisory Services
N.A.I.C.S.: 541110
Amanda S. Kitts (Partner)
Jody A. Bedenbaugh (Partner)
A. Mattison Bogan (Partner)
Thomas A. Brumgardt (Partner)
James H. Burns (Partner)
Glen P. Caulk (Partner)
Dell P. Chappell (Partner)
Paul T. Collins (Partner)
Matt Abee (Partner)
Weston Adams III (Partner)
Bradley D. Barringer (Partner)
Heyward D. Bonyata (Partner)
Sally H. Caver (Partner)
Jarrett Coco (Partner)
Lucile H. Cohen (Partner)
Brian P. Crotty (Partner)
Bart Daniel (Partner)
Christopher J. Daniels (Partner)
Travis Dayhuff (Partner)
Gus M. Dixon (Partner)
Dwight F. Drake (Partner)
David E. Dukes (Partner)
Mark C. Dukes (Partner)
Debbie Whittle Durban (Partner)
Sarah T. Eibling (Partner)
Julie A. Flaming (Partner)
Joseph E. Fornadel III (Partner)
Daniel J. Fritze (Partner)
Christopher C. Genovese (Partner)
Sean C. Hastings (Partner)
Bernard F. Hawkins Jr. (Partner)
Rachel Atkin Hedley (Partner)

NELSON NISSAN
800 W Queens St, Broken Arrow, OK 74012-1741
Tel.: (918) 258-6581
Web Site:
   http://www.nelsonnissan.com
Year Founded: 1982
Sales Range: $10-24.9 Million
Emp.: 47
New Car Whslr
N.A.I.C.S.: 441110
Craig Grotts (Comptroller)
Lyndsey Toscano (Mgr)

NELSON PIPING COMPANY
1417 22nd St, Rockford, IL 61108-3546
Tel.: (815) 398-1910
Sales Range: $10-24.9 Million
Emp.: 100
Plumbing Services
N.A.I.C.S.: 238220
Lenny Hill (Pres)

NELSON TREE SERVICE INC.
3300 Office Pk Dr, Dayton, OH 45439-2212
Tel.: (937) 294-1313 OH
Web Site: http://www.nelsontree.com
Year Founded: 1971
Sales Range: $50-74.9 Million
Emp.: 2,800
Ornamental Shrub & Tree Services; Line Clearance Company
N.A.I.C.S.: 561730
Jeff Jones (Exec VP)

NELSON TRUCK EQUIPMENT CO. INC.
20063 84th Ave S, Kent, WA 98032
Tel.: (253) 395-3825 WA
Web Site:
   http://www.nelsontruck.com
Year Founded: 1949
Sales Range: $10-24.9 Million
Emp.: 43
Provider of Truck Parts & Accessories
N.A.I.C.S.: 423120
Roy W. Nelson (Pres)

NELSON WESTERBERG, INC.
1500 Arthur Ave Ste 200W, Elk Grove Village, IL 60007-5726

NELSON WESTERBERG, INC.

U.S. PRIVATE

Nelson Westerberg, Inc.—(Continued)
Tel.: (847) 437-2080 IL
Web Site:
http://www.nelsonwesterberg.com
Year Founded: 1904
Sales Range: $150-199.9 Million
Emp.: 435
Mfr & Distributor of Household Goods
N.A.I.C.S.: 484210
Kenneth O. Curry *(Co-Pres & COO-Intl Svcs)*
Greg Koehlinger *(Exec VP)*
David Green *(Sr VP-Ops)*
Stephen Westerberg *(VP)*

Subsidiaries:

Commercial Record Center (1)
1500 Arthur Ave Unit B, Elk Grove Village, IL 60007-5744
Tel.: (847) 437-7744
Sales Range: $10-24.9 Million
Emp.: 6
Record & Data Storage
N.A.I.C.S.: 484210

Nelson Westerberg Atlas (1)
6701 Discovery Blvd, Mableton, GA 30126-4647 (100%)
Tel.: (404) 344-1547
Sales Range: $10-24.9 Million
Emp.: 50
Mfr & Distributor of Household Goods
N.A.I.C.S.: 484110
John R. Westerberg *(Chm & CEO)*

Nelson Westerberg Atlas (1)
3214 Commander Dr, Carrollton, TX 75006-2507 (100%)
Tel.: (972) 447-0040
Web Site: http://www.nelsonwesterberg.com
Sales Range: $10-24.9 Million
Emp.: 13
Mfr & Distributor of Household Goods
N.A.I.C.S.: 484110
John R. Westerberg *(Owner)*
Alan S. Mileski *(Pres & COO)*
Edward J. Pionke *(Pres & COO-Domestic Svcs)*
Robert Akers *(VP & Gen Mgr)*

Nelson Westerberg International Inc. (1)
1500 Arthur Ave Ste 100, Elk Grove Village, IL 60007-5726 (100%)
Tel.: (847) 437-2080
Web Site: http://www.nelsonwesterberg.com
Sales Range: $10-24.9 Million
Emp.: 8
International Relocation
N.A.I.C.S.: 488510
John R. Westerberg *(Chm & CEO)*

Nelson Westerberg of Illinois (1)
1201 Arthur Ave, Elk Grove Village, IL 60007-5705 (100%)
Tel.: (847) 437-7050
Web Site: http://www.nelsonwesterberg.com
Sales Range: $50-74.9 Million
Emp.: 40
Household Goods Transport & Warehousing
N.A.I.C.S.: 484110

Nelson Westerberg/Atlas Van Lines (1)
180 Meister Ave, Somerville, NJ 08876-3465 (100%)
Tel.: (908) 725-3800
Web Site: http://www.nelsonwesterberg.com
Sales Range: $10-24.9 Million
Emp.: 35
Moving & Storage Services
N.A.I.C.S.: 493190
John R. Westerberg *(Founder & Chm)*
Greg Koehlinger *(Exec VP)*
Tom Philbin *(Sr VP-Sls & Bus Dev)*
Stephen Westerberg *(CEO)*
Terry C. Young *(CFO)*

NELSON WHITE SYSTEMS, INC.
8725 A Loch Raven Blvd, Baltimore, MD 21286
Tel.: (410) 668-9628
Web Site:
http://www.nelsonwhite.com
Rev.: $7,400,000

Emp.: 70
Audio Visual Systems Solutions
N.A.I.C.S.: 459999
Bill Young *(Engr)*
Arlene Wilder *(Owner)*
Tom Wilder *(Pres)*
Ken Rosier *(Gen Mgr)*

NELSON-JAMESON INC.
2400 E 5th St, Marshfield, WI 54449-4627
Tel.: (715) 387-1151 WI
Web Site:
http://www.nelsonjameson.com
Year Founded: 1947
Sales Range: $50-74.9 Million
Emp.: 120
Mfr of Industrial Machinery & Equipment
N.A.I.C.S.: 423830
John E. Nelson *(Chm)*
Jerry Lippert *(Pres)*
Murray Smith *(Dir-Sls & Mktg)*

NELSON-MILLER, INC.
2800 Casitas Ave, Los Angeles, CA 90039-2942
Tel.: (866) 979-9931
Web Site: http://www.nelson-miller.com
Year Founded: 1937
Plastic Injection Molding, Mold Decorating & Backlighting Solutions for Switchgear & Electrical Equipment
N.A.I.C.S.: 335313
Jim Kaldem *(Pres)*

Subsidiaries:

Wilson-Hurd Manufacturing Co., Inc. (1)
311 Winton St, Wausau, WI 54403
Tel.: (715) 845-9221
Web Site: http://www.wilsonhurd.com
Custom Decorative Name Plates Mfr; Panels; Dials; Electronic Control Products
N.A.I.C.S.: 339950
Peter Dehne *(VP-Ops)*

NELSON-YOUNG LUMBER CO.
11 S Catlin St, Edgerton, WI 53534
Tel.: (608) 884-3316 WI
Web Site: http://www.nylumber.com
Year Founded: 1913
Lumber & Other Building Materials
N.A.I.C.S.: 423310
John Nelson *(VP)*
Tracy Tronnes *(Controller)*

NELSONS OIL & GAS INCORPORATED
146 N 6th Ave, Edgemont, SD 57735
Tel.: (605) 662-7500
Web Site: http://www.gwtc.net
Sales Range: $10-24.9 Million
Emp.: 20
Convenience Stores, Independent
N.A.I.C.S.: 445131
Virginia Nelson *(Owner)*
Brian Nelson *(Owner)*

NEMAHA COUNTY COOPERATIVE ASSOCIATION
223 E Main St, Seneca, KS 66538
Tel.: (785) 336-6153
Web Site: http://www.ncca.com
Sales Range: $25-49.9 Million
Emp.: 33
Grains Distributions
N.A.I.C.S.: 424510

NEMCO, INC.
301 Meuse Argonne St, Hicksville, OH 43526-1143
Tel.: (419) 542-7751

Web Site:
http://www.nemcofoodequip.com
Sales Range: $10-24.9 Million
Emp.: 70
Foodservice Equipment Solution Operator
N.A.I.C.S.: 423440
Joe Ciecierski *(Mgr-Sls)*

NEMER CHRYSLER PLYMOUTH DODGE
728 Quaker Rd, Queensbury, NY 12804
Tel.: (518) 793-2571
Year Founded: 1989
Sales Range: $10-24.9 Million
Emp.: 40
Car Whslr
N.A.I.C.S.: 441110
Robert Nemer *(VP)*

NEMER FIEGER
6250 Excelsior Blvd Ste 203, Minneapolis, MN 55416-2735
Tel.: (952) 925-4848 MN
Web Site:
http://www.nemerfieger.com
Year Founded: 1957
Rev.: $24,000,000
Emp.: 30
Advetising Agency
N.A.I.C.S.: 541810
Jim Fieger *(CEO)*
Jon Woestehoff *(CMO)*
Eric Loeffler *(VP-Mktg Comm)*
Allen Jorgensen *(Sr Acct Exec)*
Janice Sandhoefner *(Mgr-Office)*
J. Marie Fieger *(Pres)*
Juliann Heath *(Dir-Media)*
Chad Olson *(VP-Entertainment Mktg)*
Amy Severson *(Sr Acct Exec)*
Kristin Laursen *(Media Buyer)*
Kyle Gustafson *(Graphic Designer)*
Peggy Hayes *(Mgr-Fin Svcs)*
Tom Messina *(Dir-Mktg & Training)*
Paul Spicer *(Controller)*
Scott Tretter *(Graphic Designer)*
Tom Whelan *(COO & Exec VP)*
Molly Mulvehill Steinke *(Sr Acct Exec)*
Samantha Graf *(Acct Exec)*
Jan Crownover *(Acct Supvr)*
Danielle Smith *(Acct Exec)*
Megan Swenson *(Acct Exec)*
Carly Borak *(Acct Coord)*
David Fieger *(Dir-New Bus Engagement)*
Zoa Ryan *(Production Artist)*
Tim Gogolin *(Sr Acct Exec)*
Malley Chapman *(Acct Coord)*
Mike White *(Dir-Creative)*
Barbara Hamilton-Sustad *(Acct Dir)*
Ben Aldritt *(Acct Exec)*
Alyssa Kringen *(Acct Coord)*
Amanda Van Nevel *(Acct Coord)*
Tracy Skogland *(Assoc Mgr-St. Louis Park)*

NEMET MOTORS
15312 Hillside Ave, Jamaica, NY 11432
Tel.: (718) 523-5858
Web Site:
http://www.nemetmotors.com
Rev.: $31,700,000
Emp.: 170
Automobiles, New & Used
N.A.I.C.S.: 441110
Tom Nemet *(Pres)*
Igal Stark *(Mgr-Sls)*
Mitchell Rolnick *(Mgr-Sls)*
Orvil Russel Brown *(Mgr)*
Sharen McAvoy *(Mgr-Sls)*

NEMITH MOTOR CORP.
962 Loudon Rd, Latham, NY 12110

Tel.: (518) 785-8531
Web Site: http://www.nemith.com
Sales Range: $10-24.9 Million
Emp.: 75
Car Whslr
N.A.I.C.S.: 441110
Mike Orcutt *(Gen Mgr)*

NEMO
1875 SE Belmont St, Portland, OR 97214
Tel.: (503) 872-9631
Web Site:
http://www.nemodesign.com
Year Founded: 1999
Rev.: $60,000,000
Emp.: 40
Advetising Agency
N.A.I.C.S.: 541810
Trevor Graves *(Founder, Principal & Dir-Bus Dev)*
Andy Westhusing *(Dir-Art)*
Anna Stark *(Designer-Graphic)*
Brian McWhorter *(Project Dir)*
Carey Garland *(Office Mgr & Coord-Event)*
Cassandra Powell *(Sr Project Mgr)*
Curt Allan *(Dir-Ops)*
Eugene Good *(Dir-Art)*
Mark Lewman *(Principal & Dir-Creative)*

NEMO MOTORS CORP.
303 Twin Dolphin Dr, Redwood City, CA 94065
Tel.: (650) 632-4392
Electric Vehicle Mfr & Distr
N.A.I.C.S.: 336110
Jean-Francois Amyot *(VP-Bus Affairs)*

NEMONT TELEPHONE COOPERATIVE
61 Hwy 13 S, Scobey, MT 59263
Tel.: (406) 783-2200
Web Site: http://www.nemont.net
Rev.: $12,000,000
Emp.: 70
Local Telephone Communications
N.A.I.C.S.: 517121
Ben Boreson *(Pres)*
Mike Kilgore *(CEO)*

NEOCARTA VENTURES, INC.
204 E 2nd Ave Ste 428, San Mateo, CA 94401
Tel.: (415) 277-0230
Web Site: http://www.neocarta.com
Year Founded: 1999
Venture Capital Investment Firm
N.A.I.C.S.: 523999
Lee R. Pantuso *(Mng Dir)*
Tony J. Pantuso *(Mng Dir)*

Subsidiaries:

Neocarta Ventures, Inc. - Boston (1)
801 Boylston St, Boston, MA 02116
Tel.: (617) 266-3770
Web Site: http://www.neocarta.com
Rev.: $3,738,000
Emp.: 6
Venture Capital Investment Firm
N.A.I.C.S.: 523999

NEOGOV
222 N Sepulveda Blvd Ste 2000, El Segundo, CA 90245
Tel.: (310) 631-9990 CA
Web Site:
http://www.governmentjobs.com
Year Founded: 2000
Sales Range: $1-9.9 Million
Emp.: 53
On-Demand Workforce Management Services
N.A.I.C.S.: 541618

Ed Cavazos (VP-Biz Dev)
Joseph Valens (Engr-Database)
Ralf Fowler (Sr VP)
Amit Bansal (VP-Res & Dev)
Santa Monica (Dir-Mgmt Info Sys)

NEON ONE LLC
1801 W Warner Ave Ste 201, Chicago, IL 60613
Tel.: (888) 860-6366
Web Site: http://www.neoncrm.com
Software Publisher
N.A.I.C.S.: 513210
Jeff Gordy (Pres)
Michael Farb (CEO)
Robert Wechsler (Chm)

Subsidiaries:

CiviCore, LLC (1)
1580 Lincoln St Ste 1120, Denver, CO 80203-1513
Tel.: (303) 477-0900
Web Site: http://www.civicore.com
Software Development Services
N.A.I.C.S.: 513210
Charles Naumer (Founder & CEO)

NEOPAL LLC
5100 Cross Continents Dr, Houston, TX 77032
Tel.: (281) 219-9600   TX
Web Site: http://www.neopal.com
Year Founded: 1999
Sales Range: $10-24.9 Million
Emp.: 70
Wood Container & Pallet Mfr
N.A.I.C.S.: 321920
Jeff Krug (Pres)

NEOSYSTEMS CORP.
1861 International Dr Ste 200, Tysons Corner, VA 22102
Tel.: (571) 234-4940
Web Site:
   http://www.neosystemscorp.com
Year Founded: 2000
Sales Range: $10-24.9 Million
Emp.: 97
Management Consulting Services
N.A.I.C.S.: 541611
Michael Tinsley (Co-Founder & CEO)
Rob Wilson (Co-Founder & CTO)
Sandra Fox (VP-Client Svcs)
Jerry Falvey (Sr VP-Client Svcs)
Richard Wilkinson (VP-Client Svcs)
Mike Dunn (CFO)
Pamela Potts (VP-Human Capital Svcs)
Randy Cole (Sr VP-Consulting Svcs & Product Sls)
Andy Hoskins (VP-Managed IT Svcs)
Ross Robinson (VP-Nonprofit Client Svcs)
Matthew Fogo (Sr VP-Sls)
Kendra Leser (VP-Bus Sys Solutions)

NEOTEK CORPORATION INC.
11474 Gulfstream Rd, Arlington, TN 38002
Tel.: (615) 793-5900
Web Site: http://www.neotekauto.com
Sales Range: $10-24.9 Million
Emp.: 6
Automotive Supplies & Parts
N.A.I.C.S.: 423120
Larry Wu (Pres)

NEOTROPE
4332 W 230th St, Torrance, CA 90505-3411
Tel.: (310) 373-4856
Web Site: http://www.neotrope.com
Year Founded: 1983
Rev.: $1,000,000
Emp.: 10
Fiscal Year-end: 12/31/15
Brand Identity, Advertising, Multimedia, Web Development & Public Relations Services
N.A.I.C.S.: 541820
Christopher Laird Simmons (Founder & CEO)

NEP ELECTRONICS INC.
805 Mittel Dr, Wood Dale, IL 60191
Tel.: (630) 595-8500
Web Site:
   http://www.nepelectronics.com
Sales Range: $10-24.9 Million
Emp.: 80
Electronic Wholesale Distribution
N.A.I.C.S.: 423690
Thomas Lotus (Pres)
Jim Brander (Gen Mgr)
Denise Chiuccariello (Mgr-Mktg)
Dave Molter (Mgr-IT)
James Neff (Mgr-Production)
Robert Schmidt (Supvr-Production)
Rob Luciano (Engr-Sls)
John Marshall (Mgr-Pur)

NEPHI RUBBER PRODUCTS
255 W 1100 N, Nephi, UT 84648
Tel.: (435) 623-1740
Web Site: http://www.nrpjones.com
Year Founded: 1985
Sales Range: $10-24.9 Million
Emp.: 140
Mfr of Hose, Beltings & Fitting Products
N.A.I.C.S.: 326220
Shauna Winter (Controller)

NEPHROLOGY FOUNDATION OF BROOKLYN
1845 McDonald Ave, Brooklyn, NY 11223
Tel.: (718) 336-9700   NY
Year Founded: 1979
Sales Range: $10-24.9 Million
Emp.: 119
Renal Care Services
N.A.I.C.S.: 621492
Allen I. Herman (Pres & CEO)

NEPHRON PHARMACEUTICALS CORPORATION
4121 SW 34th St, Orlando, FL 32811
Tel.: (407) 999-2225
Web Site:
   http://www.nephronpharm.com
Year Founded: 1937
Sales Range: $25-49.9 Million
Emp.: 500
Pharmaceuticals Mfr
N.A.I.C.S.: 325412
Lou Kennedy (Owner & CEO)
Barbara Lee (CFO)
Julie Rameas (Chief Procurement Officer)

NEPSIS INC.
8692 Eagle Creek Cir, Minneapolis, MN 55378
Tel.: (952) 746-2003
Web Site: https://www.nepsisinc.com
Year Founded: 1994
Sales Range: $1-9.9 Million
Emp.: 15
Asset Management
N.A.I.C.S.: 523940
Mark Pearson (Founder, CEO & Chief Investment Officer)
Chuck Etzweiler (Dir-Res)
Alyssa Pearson (Mgr-Mktg)
Matt Pearson (Pres)

Subsidiaries:

Sevenich Butler Gerlach Brazil, Ltd. (1)
2221 Ford Pkwy Ste 300, Saint Paul, MN 55116
Tel.: (651) 690-1040
Web Site: http://www.sbgb.com
Offices of Certified Public Accountants
N.A.I.C.S.: 541211

NEPTUNE MARKETING TECHNOLOGIES
101 Fayette St, Perth Amboy, NJ 08861
Tel.: (732) 293-0099
Rev.: $13,172,498
Emp.: 15
Telephone Communications
N.A.I.C.S.: 517121
John D. DiDomenico (Pres & CEO)

NEPTUNE SOCIETY INC.
1250 S Pine Island Rd Ste 500, Plantation, FL 33324
Tel.: (954) 556-9400
Web Site:
   http://www.neptunesociety.com
Rev.: $20,800,000
Emp.: 117
Cremation Services
N.A.I.C.S.: 812210
Marco Markin (CEO)
James L. Rea (Mgr-Svc-Detroit)

NER CONSTRUCTION MANAGEMENT, INC.
867 Woburn St, Wilmington, MA 01887
Tel.: (978) 988-1111
Web Site:
   http://www.nerconstruction.com
Sales Range: $25-49.9 Million
Emp.: 450
Provider of Masonry & Other Stonework Services
N.A.I.C.S.: 238140
Richard W. Sylvester (CEO)
Frank Loconte (Pres)
Paulette Condell (Dir-Pre-Construction & Sls)
Joe Kennedy (Mgr-Facilities)

NER HOLDINGS INC.
307 S Delsea Dr, Glassboro, NJ 08028-2608
Tel.: (856) 881-5524
Web Site: http://www.nerdata.com
Year Founded: 1971
Sales Range: $75-99.9 Million
Emp.: 50
Holding Company; Computer Peripheral Equipment Mfr
N.A.I.C.S.: 551112
Francis C. Oatway (Chm & CEO)
Stephen Oatway (Pres & COO)
Chris Oatway (CFO & CIO)
Greg Stover (Sr VP-Sls)
Scott Steele (Sr VP-Bus Dev & Mktg)
Tom Bergamo (Mgr-Credit & Collections)
Rob Huttemann (VP & Gen Mgr)
Ron Celli (Dir-Media Mgmt)
Eric Austin (VP-Ops)

Subsidiaries:

NER Data Products, Inc. (1)
307 S Delsea Dr, Glassboro, NJ 08028-2608 (100%)
Tel.: (856) 881-5524
Web Site: http://www.nerdata.com
Sales Range: $10-24.9 Million
Emp.: 45
Mfr of Storage Products for Tape Cartridges & Computer Printer Supplies
N.A.I.C.S.: 334118
Stephen Oatway (Pres)

NER Holdings Inc. - Toronto Facility (1)
95 Mural Street Suite 600, Richmond Hill, L4B 3G2, ON, Canada
Tel.: (856) 881-5524
Information Technology Consulting Services
N.A.I.C.S.: 541512

NERCON ENGINEERING & MANUFACTURING INC.
3972 S US Hwy 45, Oshkosh, WI 54902
Tel.: (920) 233-3268
Web Site: http://www.nercon.com
Year Founded: 1976
Sales Range: $10-24.9 Million
Emp.: 50
Design & Build Packaging Machinery
N.A.I.C.S.: 333993
James L. Nerenhausen Sr. (Founder)

NERDS ON CALL
1355 Churn Creek Rd, Redding, CA 96003
Tel.: (530) 242-9200
Web Site: http://www.callnerds.com
Year Founded: 2004
Rev.: $2,400,000
Emp.: 200
Computer Repair & Maintenance
N.A.I.C.S.: 811210
Andrea Eldridge (Founder & Pres)
Evan Brown (Supvr-Customer Svc)

NERESON AUTOMOTIVE INC.
923 Hwy 10 E, Detroit Lakes, MN 56501-4217
Tel.: (218) 847-5688
Web Site:
   http://www.neresonautomotive.com
Sales Range: $10-24.9 Million
Emp.: 55
Car Whslr
N.A.I.C.S.: 441110
Brad Richard (Pres)

NES FINANCIAL
50 W San Fernando St Ste 300, San Jose, CA 95113
Web Site: http://nesfinancial.com
Year Founded: 2005
Sales Range: $10-24.9 Million
Emp.: 42
Financial Services
N.A.I.C.S.: 522320
Michael Halloran (Founder & CEO)
Dan Yoder (Gen Mgr-Private Equity Fund Admin)
Reid Thomas (Exec VP & Gen Mgr)
Kelly Alton (Gen Counsel)
Izak Joubert (CTO)
Christian Lyndes (Sr VP-Sls)
Justin Flanagan (Mng Dir-New York)
Tom Steipp (Pres & COO)
Adam Kaufman (Sr VP-Mktg)
Will Lopez (VP-Engagement Mgmt)
Scott Ramsey (Sr VP-Product Mktg)
Dawn Shuster (Sr VP-Client Svcs)
Kristen West (Sr VP-Fin)
Laura Kelly (VP-Mktg)
Lou Van Dyk (VP-IT)
Michael Richards (Sr VP-Fund Acctg)
John Hart (CFO)

NES HOLDINGS, INC.
3724 National Dr Ste 105, Raleigh, NC 27612-4878
Tel.: (919) 510-5500   IL
Web Site:
   http://www.nesholdings.com
Year Founded: 1975
Sales Range: $125-149.9 Million
Emp.: 190
Provider of Physician Staffing for Emergency Rooms
N.A.I.C.S.: 561320
Janice Hill (Controller)

NESBITT INVESTMENT COMPANY
100 S Price Rd, Tempe, AZ 85281
Tel.: (480) 423-7600
Web Site: http://www.nesbitts.com

NESBITT INVESTMENT COMPANY — U.S. PRIVATE

Nesbitt Investment Company—(Continued)

Year Founded: 1955
Rev.: $28,200,000
Emp.: 150
Highway Construction Services
N.A.I.C.S.: 551112

Subsidiaries:

Arizona Pavement Profiling (1)
100 S Price Rd, Tempe, AZ 85281
Tel.: (480) 423-7600
Web Site: http://www.nesbitt.com
Rev.: $720,000
Emp.: 7
Surfacing & Paving Services
N.A.I.C.S.: 237310
James L. Nesbitt (Pres)
Ken Damgaard (Engr-Recycling)

Century Materials Inc (1)
100 S Price Rd, Tempe, AZ 85281
Tel.: (480) 894-2831
Sales Range: $10-24.9 Million
Emp.: 100
Equipment Mfr
N.A.I.C.S.: 336999

Nesbitt Contracting Co Inc (1)
100 S Price Rd, Tempe, AZ 85281
Tel.: (480) 423-7600
Web Site: http://www.nesbitts.com
Rev.: $17,900,000
Emp.: 120
Highway & Street Paving Contractor
N.A.I.C.S.: 237310

NESCO, INC.

6140 Parkland Blvd, Cleveland, OH 44124-4187
Tel.: (440) 461-6000 DE
Web Site:
  http://www.nescoresource.com
Year Founded: 1956
Sales Range: $1-4.9 Billion
Emp.: 14
Holding Company; Utility Vehicles & Products Rental, Retail & Distr
N.A.I.C.S.: 551112
Robert J. Tomsich (Chm & CEO)

Subsidiaries:

Barth Industries, Co. LP (1)
12650 Brookpark Rd, Cleveland, OH 44130-1154
Tel.: (216) 267-1950
Web Site: http://www.barth-landis.com
Sales Range: $10-24.9 Million
Builder of Special Production Machinery & Production Parts
N.A.I.C.S.: 333517

Division (Domestic):

Landis Machine (2)
12650 Brookpark Rd, Cleveland, OH 44130-1154
Tel.: (216) 267-1964
Web Site: http://www.barthindustries.com
Mfr & Builder of Special Production Machinery
N.A.I.C.S.: 333517
Rich Legan (Exec VP)

NESHKIN CONSTRUCTION COMPANY INCORPORATED

24204 Aurora Rd, Bedford Heights, OH 44146
Tel.: (216) 241-3397
Web Site: http://www.neshkin.com
Sales Range: $25-49.9 Million
Emp.: 10
Commercial & Office Building, New Construction
N.A.I.C.S.: 236220
Terry Muth (Pres)

NESMITH CHEVROLET BUICK PONTIAC GMC

7334 Hwy 280 W, Claxton, GA 30417
Tel.: (912) 739-1744
Web Site:
  http://www.nesmithnow.com
Rev.: $36,113,298
Emp.: 50
Automobiles, New & Used
N.A.I.C.S.: 441110
Martin W. Nesmith (Pres)
Demere Nesmith (Gen Mgr)
Star Harris (Head-HR)

NEST FEATHERINGS INC.

6425 W Sahara Ave, Las Vegas, NV 89146
Tel.: (702) 362-6707
Web Site: http://www.nest-featherings.com
Sales Range: $10-24.9 Million
Emp.: 12
Painting & Paper Hanging
N.A.I.C.S.: 449110
Lorraine Sorenson (Pres)

NEST INTERNATIONAL

550 Crescent Blvd, Gloucester City, NJ 08030
Web Site: http://www.enternest.com
Year Founded: 1994
Sales Range: $25-49.9 Million
Emp.: 85
Construction Services
N.A.I.C.S.: 236220
Bob Almond (Chm & CEO)
Kellie D'Andrea (Pres)
Rob Almond (VP-Ops)
Frank Allison (Controller)

NEST SEEKERS LLC

415 Madison Ave 20th Fl, New York, NY 10017
Tel.: (212) 252-8772
Web Site:
  http://www.nestseekers.com
Year Founded: 2001
Real Estate Agents & Brokers
N.A.I.C.S.: 531210
Eddie Shapiro (Pres & CEO)

NESTOR PARTNERS

55 W 46th ST 31st Fl, New York, NY 10036
Tel.: (212) 332-7300 NJ
Year Founded: 1976
Rev.: $1,752,284
Assets: $136,464,322
Liabilities: $4,418,249
Net Worth: $132,046,073
Earnings: $22,088,878
Fiscal Year-end: 12/31/22
Diversified Portfolio Services
N.A.I.C.S.: 523160
Harvey Beker (Chm)

NESTUCCA RIDGE STORAGE

9005 Nestucca Rdg Rd, Pacific City, OR 97135
Tel.: (503) 965-7779
Web Site:
  http://www.nestuccaridge.com
Rev.: $13,500,000
Emp.: 7
Subdividers & Developers
N.A.I.C.S.: 237210
Mary J. Jones (Pres)

NET 2 TECHNOLOGY GROUP INC.

680 Louis Dr, Warminster, PA 18974
Tel.: (215) 328-9000
Web Site: http://www.net2tg.com
Rev.: $17,500,000
Emp.: 11
System Integration Services
N.A.I.C.S.: 541512
Gregory Paladino (Pres & CEO)

NET ATLANTIC, INC.

10 Federal St Ste 26, Salem, MA 01970
Tel.: (978) 219-1900
Web Site: http://www.netatlantic.com
Year Founded: 1995
Sales Range: $1-9.9 Million
Emp.: 50
Email Marketing Software
N.A.I.C.S.: 513210
Andrew Lutts (Founder & CEO)
Wesley Owen (VP-Tech Ops)
R. J. Phipps (VP-Customer Success)
David Cloyd (Pres)

NET DIRECT MERCHANTS

217 N Seminary St, Florence, AL 35630
Tel.: (256) 765-2171
Web Site:
  http://www.netdirectmerchants.com
Year Founded: 2002
Sales Range: $1-9.9 Million
Emp.: 8
Online Retailer of Hearth & Home Products
N.A.I.C.S.: 455219
Richard D. Morse Jr. (Founder)

NET MATRIX SOLUTIONS

10235 W Little York Rd Ste 435, Houston, TX 77040
Tel.: (281) 598-2600
Web Site:
  http://www.netmatrixsolutions.com
Year Founded: 2001
Rev.: $24,400,000
Emp.: 150
Computer Related Services
N.A.I.C.S.: 541512
Nikhil Jain (Pres)
Pankaj Maheshwari (Founder & CEO)
Jennifer Patrick (Dir-Creative)

NET SAVINGS LINK, INC.

4740-20 Nesconset Hwy, Port Jefferson, NY 11776
Tel.: (516) 246-6435 NV
Web Site:
  http://www.netsavingslink.com
Year Founded: 2007
Sales Range: Less than $1 Million
Wellness Products Distr
N.A.I.C.S.: 424490
Steven Baritz (Pres, CEO, CFO, Principal Acctg Officer, Treas & Sec)

NET SYSTEMS

1 Peters Canyon Rd Ste 100, Irvine, CA 92606-1400
Tel.: (949) 752-5100 CA
Web Site: http://www.net-systems.com
Sales Range: $10-24.9 Million
Emp.: 10
Resells Computers & Electronics
N.A.I.C.S.: 517121
Fares Koudsi (CEO)

NET XPERTS LLC

1500 Ardmore Blvd Ste 206, Pittsburgh, PA 15221
Tel.: (412) 244-6389
Web Site:
  http://www.thenetxperts.com
Year Founded: 2002
Sales Range: $1-9.9 Million
Emp.: 25
Computer System Design Services
N.A.I.C.S.: 541512
Marc Sachs (Pres)
Megan Pinkosky (Coord-Mktg)
Angela Desiderato (VP-Managed Svcs)
Michael Green (Dir-Sls)
Ryan Connelly (Engr-Tech Bus)

NET-INSPECT

25 Central Way Ste 300, Kirkland, WA 98053
Tel.: (425) 233-6176
Web Site: http://www.net-inspect.com
Year Founded: 2001
Sales Range: $1-9.9 Million
Emp.: 7
Software Development Services
N.A.I.C.S.: 541511
Mike Dunlop (CEO)
Ron Trout (VP & Gen Mgr)

NET2EZ INC.

1801 Ave of the Stars Ste 1011, Los Angeles, CA 90067
Tel.: (310) 426-9933
Web Site: http://www.net2ez.com
Sales Range: $10-24.9 Million
Emp.: 150
Network Integration Services
N.A.I.C.S.: 541511
Pervez Delawalla (CEO)
Jamie Daquino (Pres & COO)
Daniel Faubel (Dir-Network Engrg)
Sean Aubert (VP-Sls)

NET@WORK, INC.

575 8th Ave, New York, NY 10018
Tel.: (212) 997-5200
Web Site: http://www.netatwork.com
Year Founded: 1996
Emp.: 100
Information Technology Services & Solutions
N.A.I.C.S.: 541512
Vera Margarita (Chief People Officer)
Valentin Domange (Dir-Bus Dev)
Marc Mandelbaum (Dir-Mktg)
Uri Weis (CTO)
Alex Solomon (Founder & Co-Pres)
Edward Solomon (Founder & Co-Pres)
Seth Ellertson (VP-Sls)
Jeffrey Goldberg (Dir-IT Svcs)
Karen Field (Dir-Sls Ops)
Kelly Hummel (Dir-Sage 300 Practice)
Kyle Conquy (Dir-Enterprise Solutions)
Rocco Passafuime (Dir-Infrastructure Sls)
Tom Miller (Dir-Partner Alliance Program)
Paul Frydman (COO)
Igal Rabinovich (Dir-Partner Success)
Jennifer Lin (Mng Dir-Compliance)
Lucy Maresco (Chief HR Officer)
Drew Macbeth (Dir-NetSuite Practice)

Subsidiaries:

Dresser & Associates, Inc. (1)
243 US Route 1, Scarborough, ME 04074
Tel.: (207) 885-0809
Web Site: http://www.dresserassociates.com
Human Resources Management Software Solutions
N.A.I.C.S.: 513200
Mark F. Dresser (Pres & Dir)

NexVue Information Systems, Inc. (1)
65 Broad St 2, Stamford, CT 06901
Tel.: (203) 327-0800
Web Site: http://www.nexvue.com
Rev.: $6,660,000
Emp.: 20
Office Supplies & Stationery Stores
N.A.I.C.S.: 459410

Pixafy, Inc. (1)
315 W 36th St 3rd Fl, New York, NY 10018
Tel.: (212) 596-7404
Web Site: http://www.pixafy.com
Sales Range: Less than $1 Million
Emp.: 45
Software Development Services
N.A.I.C.S.: 541511

COMPANIES

Joshua O'Connell (VP-Client Svcs)
Eric DiPalma (Dir-Project Mgmt)
Jason Riemer (Mgr-Bus Dev)

Southeast Computer Solutions, Inc. (1)
15165 NW 77th Ave Ste 2009, Miami, FL 33014
Tel.: (305) 556-4697
Web Site:
  http://www.southeastcomputers.com
Software Solutions
N.A.I.C.S.: 513210
Ralph Ceccarelli (VP)

NETAFIM IRRIGATION INC.
5470 E Home Ave, Fresno, CA 93727
Tel.: (559) 453-6800
Web Site: http://www.netafimusa.com
Sales Range: $10-24.9 Million
Emp.: 100
Irrigation Equipment Self-Propelled
N.A.I.C.S.: 333111
Dennis Hannaford (Product Mgr)

NETBASE SOLUTIONS, INC.
2087 Landings Dr, Mountain View, CA 94043
Tel.: (650) 810-2100
Web Site: http://www.netbase.com
Sales Range: $1-9.9 Million
Emp.: 20
Social Media Analytics Solution & Services
N.A.I.C.S.: 513210
Peter Caswell (CEO)
Bob Pape (VP-Svcs & Customer Success)
Bob Ciccone (COO & Exec VP-Products, Engrg & Ops)

NETBRIEFINGS, INC.
421 Wabasha St N 2nd Fl, Saint Paul, MN 55102
Tel.: (651) 225-1532
Web Site:
  http://www.netbriefings.com
Sales Range: $1-9.9 Million
Emp.: 21
Webcasting Software
N.A.I.C.S.: 513210
Roger Anderson (CTO)
Jeanneane Kloss (Dir-Mktg)
Charles Peters (Pres)

NETCARE ACCESS
199 S Central Ave, Columbus, OH 43223
Tel.: (614) 276-2273   OH
Web Site:
  http://www.netcareaccess.org
Year Founded: 1972
Sales Range: $10-24.9 Million
Emp.: 369
Mental Health Care & Substance Abuse Rehabilitation Services
N.A.I.C.S.: 621420
A. King Stumpp (Pres & CEO)
Carrie Wirick (Dir-Community & Residential Svcs)
Kimberly Reynolds (Dir-Dev & PR)
Pablo Hernandez (Dir-Forensic Medical)
Allan Brown (Dir-HR)
Joseph Trocchio (Chm)
Merrill Lynch (VP)

NETCOM LEARNING
519 8th Ave 2nd Fl, New York, NY 10018
Tel.: (212) 629-7265
Web Site:
  http://www.netcomlearning.com
Sales Range: $10-24.9 Million
Emp.: 64
Online Training Services
N.A.I.C.S.: 513199

Russell Sarder (Chm & CEO)
David Fremed (CFO)
Tuan Yang (CMO)
Mudit Mittal (COO)
Adam Chng (CIO & CTO)
Titu Sarder (Pres)
Daniel Yun (VP-Learning)

NETCOM TECHNOLOGIES, INC.
7616 Standish Pl, Rockville, MD 20855
Tel.: (301) 670-0486
Web Site: http://www.netcomtec.com
Year Founded: 1988
Sales Range: $10-24.9 Million
Emp.: 25
Contractor of Voice, Data & Video Wiring
N.A.I.C.S.: 238210
Eric Joplin (Project Mgr)

NETCOM3 INC.
30025 Alicia Pkwy, Laguna Niguel, CA 92677
Tel.: (310) 595-4326
Web Site:
  http://www.netcom3global.com
Year Founded: 2001
Sales Range: $1-9.9 Million
Emp.: 15
Antivirus Software
N.A.I.C.S.: 513210
Cashier Myricks (Pres)

NETDIRECTOR
10951 Countryway Blvd Ste 102, Tampa, FL 33626
Tel.: (813) 749-7131
Web Site: http://www.netdirector.biz
Year Founded: 2005
Sales Range: $1-9.9 Million
Emp.: 15
SaaS-Based Data & Document Exchange Services
N.A.I.C.S.: 513210
Harry Beisswenger (CEO)
Darren Meiggs (VP-Ops)
Trudy Hunter (VP-IT)

NETE
8280 Greensboro Dr Ste 200, McLean, VA 22102
Tel.: (703) 893-6383
Web Site: http://www.nete.com
Year Founded: 1999
Sales Range: $1-9.9 Million
Emp.: 50
Computer Related Services
N.A.I.C.S.: 541519
Sandeep Somaiya (Mng Dir)
Jolly Vasani (Founder & Pres)

NETFORTIS, INC.
455 Market St Ste 620, San Francisco, CA 94105
Tel.: (888) 469-5100
Web Site: http://www.netfortris.com
Year Founded: 1994
Internet Protocol Services; Voice & Data, Communications, Applications & Security
N.A.I.C.S.: 518210
Grant Evans (CEO)
Bryan Koehler (CFO)
Thomas Swayze (CTO)
Swapan Nandi (Sr VP-Products & Svcs)
Kelli Tejada (Sr VP-Mktg)
Daniel Miller (Sr VP-Ops)

NETGAIN TECHNOLOGY INC.
720 W Saint Germain St, Saint Cloud, MN 56301-3501
Tel.: (320) 251-4700

Web Site:
  http://www.netgainhosting.com
Year Founded: 2000
Sales Range: $1-9.9 Million
Emp.: 57
Custom Computer Programming Services
N.A.I.C.S.: 541511
Scott Baynes (VP-Tech)
Franco Cusipag (VP-Fin)
Matt Riley (VP-Ops)
Scott Warzecha (Founder, Chm & CEO)
Kevin Lynch (CEO)

NETH & SON INC.
146 Taylor Dr, Depew, NY 14043
Tel.: (716) 685-3539
Web Site:
  http://www.nethandson.com
Year Founded: 1973
Sales Range: $10-24.9 Million
Emp.: 70
Roofing Contractors
N.A.I.C.S.: 238160
Thomas Neth (Pres)

NETH & SONS INC.
364 E Landstreet Rd, Orlando, FL 32824
Tel.: (407) 447-2270
Sales Range: $10-24.9 Million
Emp.: 60
Roofing Installation Services
N.A.I.C.S.: 238390
Thomas Neth (Owner)

NETLINK
999 Tech Row, Madison Heights, MI 48071
Tel.: (248) 204-8800
Web Site: http://netlink.com
Year Founded: 1998
Emp.: 7,000
Information Technology Services
N.A.I.C.S.: 541512
Dilip Dubey (Co-Founder, Co-Owner, Chm & CEO)
Anurag Shrivastava (Co-Founder, Co-Owner, Vice Chm, Pres-Global & CEO-EMEA)
Greg Hacias (VP-Bus Dev & HR)

NETMARK.COM
1930 N Woodruff Ave, Idaho Falls, ID 83401
Tel.: (800) 935-5133
Web Site: http://www.netmark.com
Year Founded: 2007
Sales Range: $1-9.9 Million
Emp.: 65
Increased Sales Through Internet Marketing
N.A.I.C.S.: 541613
Chad Heath (Founder & Pres)
Anita Ogden (Controller)
John Broadbent (CEO)

NETPACE, INC.
5000 Executive Pkwy Ste 530, San Ramon, CA 94583
Tel.: (925) 543-7760   CA
Web Site: http://www.netpace.com
Year Founded: 1997
Sales Range: $10-24.9 Million
Emp.: 60
Computer System Design Services
N.A.I.C.S.: 541512
Omar Khan (CEO)

NETPLUS MARKETING, INC.
625 Ridge Pike Bldg E Ste 200, Conshohocken, PA 19428
Tel.: (610) 897-2380
Web Site:
  http://www.netplusmarketing.com

NETRIX LLC

Year Founded: 1996
Rev.: $10,000,000
Emp.: 37
Advetising Agency
N.A.I.C.S.: 541810
Robin Neifield (Co-Founder, CEO-Strategist)
Denise E. Zimmerman (Pres & Chief Strategy Officer)
David Larkins (VP-Mktg)
Sarah Miller (Dir-Integrated Media)
Richard Clifford (VP-Client Svc)
John Shanley (Dir-Creative)

NETPR, INC.
PO Box 1790, Santa Rosa Beach, FL 32459
Tel.: (850) 259-1231
Web Site: http://www.netpr.net
Sales Range: Less than $1 Million
Emp.: 2
Exhibit/Trade Shows, Game Integration, Internet/Web Design, Magazines, Public Relations, Publicity/Promotions, Publishing, Real Estate
N.A.I.C.S.: 541820
Kimberly Maxwell (Founder, Pres & CEO)

NETPRPRO, INC.
6101 Long Prairie Rd Ste 744-114, Flower Mound, TX 75028
Tel.: (972) 239-3655
Web Site: http://www.netprpro.com
Sales Range: $1-9.9 Million
Emp.: 5
Interactive Advertising Agency
N.A.I.C.S.: 541810
Don Lokke (Co-Owner)
Ross Jones (Co-Owner & Dir-Natl Sls)

NETREO, INC.
7171 Warner Ave Ste B787, Huntington Beach, CA 92647
Tel.: (949) 221-0790
Web Site: http://www.netreo.net
Year Founded: 2000
Sales Range: $1-9.9 Million
Emp.: 10
Computer System Design Services
N.A.I.C.S.: 541512
Brandy Sleeth (Mgr-Network Ops Center)
Matt Watson (CTO)
Jasmin Young (CEO)

Subsidiaries:

Stackify, LLC   (1)
8900 Stateline Rd Ste100, Leawood, KS 66206
Tel.: (816) 888-5055
Web Site: http://www.stackify.com
Software Development Services
N.A.I.C.S.: 541511
Matt Watson (Founder)
Craig Ferril (COO)
Alexandra Altvater (Mktg Dir)
Megan Amos (Dir-Customer Success)
Chris Nickols (Product Dir)

NETRIX LLC
2801 Lakeside Dr, Bannockburn, IL 60015
Tel.: (847) 283-7300
Web Site: http://www.netrixllc.com
Year Founded: 1989
Sales Range: $25-49.9 Million
Emp.: 80
IT Services & Support
N.A.I.C.S.: 541690
Don Penland (VP-Corp Dev)
Rob Dang (CEO)
Brian Hurley (Mgr-Bus Dev)
Marc Castiglione (Mgr-Bus Dev)
Jouni Churchill (Mgr-Bus Dev)

NETRIX LLC

Netrix LLC—(Continued)
Michael Smith *(Mgr-Bus Dev)*
Neil Parekh *(Partner & Dir-Sls Engrg)*
Connor Shank *(Assoc Dir-Southeast)*
Eric Edmonds *(Dir-Mktg)*
Greg P. Richards *(CFO)*
Sharon Shlimoun *(Sr Mgr-PR & Comm)*
Mike Gribble *(Sr VP-Sls)*
Chris Jones *(Sr VP-Mktg)*
Rick Parham *(Partner)*
Michael Reiss *(Partner)*

Subsidiaries:

PSC Group, LLC (1)
1051 Perimeter Dr Ste 500, Schaumburg, IL 60173
Tel.: (847) 517-7200
Web Site: http://www.psclistens.com
Information Technology Consulting Services
N.A.I.C.S.: 541512
Jeff Ney *(Co-Partner)*
Rick Parham *(Co-Partner)*
John Quirk *(Co-Partner)*
Michael Reiss *(Co-Partner)*
Tony Fremarek *(Co-Partner)*

Subsidiary (Domestic):

Thermoplastic Services Inc. (2)
1700 W 4th St, Dequincy, LA 70633-4329
Tel.: (337) 786-7022
Web Site:
http://www.thermoplasticservices.com
Plastics Material & Resin Mfr
N.A.I.C.S.: 325211
W. P. Fisher *(Plant Mgr)*

NETROADSHOW, INC.
3475 Piedmont Rd Ste 450, Atlanta, GA 30305
Tel.: (404) 504-7160
Web Site:
http://www.netroadshow.com
Year Founded: 1997
U.S. Securities & Exchange Commission Compliant Online Communication Tools & Services
N.A.I.C.S.: 519290
Daniel Taylor *(Project Mgr)*
Jonathan Young *(Mgr-Ops)*

NETRONOME, INC.
5201 Great America Pkwy Ste 419, Santa Clara, CA 95054
Tel.: (408) 496-0022
Web Site: http://www.netronome.com
Year Founded: 2003
Sales Range: $25-49.9 Million
Emp.: 150
Semiconductor Product Mfr
N.A.I.C.S.: 334413
Niel Viljoen *(Co-Founder & CEO)*
Perry J. Grace *(CFO & VP-Admin)*
Jim Finnegan *(COO)*
Mike Benson *(Sr VP-Platform Engrg & Ops)*
Gavin Stark *(CTO)*
Johann Tonsing *(Co-Founder & Sr VP-Software Engrg)*
Sujal Das *(VP & Gen Mgr-Strategy & Data Center Bus)*
Jennifer Mendola *(Mgr-Mktg Comm)*

NETSERTIVE, INC.
2400 Perimeter Park Dr Ste 100 Research Triangle Region, Morrisville, NC 27560
Web Site: http://www.netsertive.com
Year Founded: 2009
Sales Range: $1-9.9 Million
Emp.: 73
Local Digital Marketing & Channel Marketing Technology Services
N.A.I.C.S.: 541613
Brendan Morrissey *(Co-Founder & CEO)*
Bill Nagel *(Co-Founder & CMO)*

Bob Bradley *(VP-Sls & Bus Dev)*
Kevin Fitzgerald *(COO)*
Paul Bock *(CTO)*
David Logan *(Sr VP-Products)*
Debbie Edmondson *(VP-Team Dev)*
Chris Perkins *(Dir-Comml Sls)*
Jason Sayen *(Dir-Residential Sls)*
Jim Doherty *(Exec VP-Sls & Mktg)*
Steve Leonard *(Pres)*
Sean Witty *(CFO)*
Peter Durand *(Chief Revenue Officer)*

Subsidiaries:

Mixpo, Inc. (1)
520 Pike St Ste 1600, Seattle, WA 98101
Web Site: http://www.mixpo.com
Sales Range: $10-24.9 Million
Emp.: 89
Advertising Services
N.A.I.C.S.: 541810
Charlie Tillinghast *(Pres & CEO)*
Salim Hemdani *(VP-Software Dev)*
Kate Reinmiller *(VP-Client Svcs & Product Mgmt)*
Matt Bartholomew *(VP-Engrg)*
Erin Martin *(VP-Customer Success & Ops)*
Adam Noble *(VP-Mktg)*

NETSHELTER, INC.
128 King St 3rd Fl, San Francisco, CA 94107
Tel.: (415) 365-4950
Web Site: http://www.netshelter.net
Sales Range: $10-24.9 Million
Technology Media Network
N.A.I.C.S.: 541810
Peyman Nilforoush *(Co-Founder & CEO)*
Pirouz Nilforoush *(Co-Founder & Pres)*
Michele Sweeney *(Chief Sls & Mktg Officer)*
Jeff Stephens *(Sr VP-Fin)*
Michele Slack *(Sr VP-Bus Ops)*
Colleen Daly *(Sr VP-Sls)*
Suzie Ewing *(VP-People & Culture)*

NETSKOPE, INC.
4984 El Camino Real Ste 102, Los Altos, CA 94022 DE
Web Site: http://www.netskope.com
Emp.: 100
Data Cloud Storage & Security Services
N.A.I.C.S.: 518210
Sanjay Beri *(Founder & CEO)*
Rajneesh Chopra *(VP-Product Mgmt)*
Chris Andrews *(Sr VP-Worldwide Sls)*
Rick Holden *(VP-Bus Dev & Alliances)*
Bob Gilbert *(Sr Dir-Product Mktg)*
Michael See *(Dir-Sls Engrg)*
Bobby Shoker *(VP)*
Alok Kothari *(Mng Dir-India)*
Gary Ochs *(VP-Channels)*
Abhay Kulkarni *(VP-Engrg)*
Jamie Barnett *(VP-Ops)*
Eduard Meelhuysen *(VP-Sls)*
Lebin Cheng *(VP-App Engrg)*
Hesham Eassa *(VP-Cloud Ops-Global)*
Amol Kabe *(VP-Product Mgmt)*
Mario Puras *(VP-Sls Engrg)*
James Sung *(VP-Customer Success & Support)*
Jason Clark *(Chief Strategy Officer)*
Ilona Simpson *(CIO-Europe, Middle East & Africa)*
Mike Anderson *(Chief Digital & Info Officer)*

NETSOFT HOLDINGS, LLC
11650 Olio Rd Ste 1000-193, Fishers, IN 46037
Web Site: http://www.hubstaff.com
Year Founded: 2012
Sales Range: $1-9.9 Million

Emp.: 45
Software Development Services
N.A.I.C.S.: 541511
David Nevogt *(Founder)*

NETSOURCE TECHNOLOGY INC.
951 Calle Negocio, San Clemente, CA 92673
Tel.: (949) 713-0800
Web Site:
http://www.nstechnology.com
Rev.: $31,394,747
Emp.: 30
Electronic Parts & Equipment Mfr & Distr
N.A.I.C.S.: 423690
G. B. Munoz *(Pres)*

NETSTAR-1, INC.
9713 Key W Ave Ste 400, Rockville, MD 20850
Tel.: (240) 425-4200
Sales Range: $100-124.9 Million
Emp.: 250
Information Technology Design, Installation & Support Services
N.A.I.C.S.: 541513

NETSTEPS
1250 E 200 S Ste 3C, Lehi, UT 84043
Tel.: (801) 642-3750
Web Site: http://www.netsteps.com
Year Founded: 2004
Sales Range: $1-9.9 Million
Emp.: 34
Technology Services to Direct Sales Companies
N.A.I.C.S.: 334610
Kevin Vitale *(CEO)*
Cannon Holbrook *(CFO)*

NETSTRATEGIES
4031 University Dr Ste 100, Fairfax, VA 22030
Tel.: (703) 739-6750
Web Site:
http://www.netstrategies.com
Year Founded: 2002
Sales Range: $1-9.9 Million
Internet Marketing Services
N.A.I.C.S.: 541613
John Schultz *(Pres & CEO)*
Karl Boehm *(Dir-E-Marketing Strategy)*
Joshua Watson *(Dir-Search Engine Optimization)*
Scott Vollmer *(Mgr-Web Project)*

NETSWORK INC.
7485 N Palm Ave Ste 100, Fresno, CA 93711
Tel.: (559) 440-4400
Sales Range: $10-24.9 Million
Emp.: 46
Computer Consulting Services
N.A.I.C.S.: 423430

NETT SOLUTIONS INC.
65 Enterprise, Aliso Viejo, CA 92656
Tel.: (949) 330-7060
Web Site:
http://www.nettsolutions.com
Year Founded: 2003
Sales Range: $10-24.9 Million
Emp.: 47
Advertising & Marketing
N.A.I.C.S.: 541890
Carl Hagmier *(CEO)*
Brian Bartlett *(Acct Exec)*

NETUNO USA INC.
18501 Pines Blvd Ste 206, Pembroke Pines, FL 33029
Tel.: (305) 513-0904

U.S. PRIVATE

Web Site: http://www.netunousa.com
Year Founded: 1989
Sales Range: Less than $1 Million
Emp.: 9
Fish & Shellfish Products Importer
N.A.I.C.S.: 424460
Luciano Bonaldo *(Pres)*

NETVISION RESOURCES, INC.
2201 Cooperative Way Ste 600, Herndon, VA 20171
Tel.: (703) 342-4282
Web Site:
http://www.netvisionresources.com
Year Founded: 1999
Computer System Design Services
N.A.I.C.S.: 541512
Vishnu Seri *(VP-Bus Dev)*
Srinivas Mankala *(Pres & CEO)*
John Long *(Chief Strategy Officer)*
Srinivas Tata *(VP-IT Solutions)*
Sandeep Maram *(Dir-Business & IT Ops)*
Sunny Nangia *(Dir-Resource Mgmt)*
Vasu Mankala *(Mgr-Recruitment)*
Aparna Jha *(Mgr-HR)*

NETWEAVE SOCIAL NETWORKING LLC
7222 49th Pl E, Palmetto, FL 34221
Tel.: (941) 567-1727
Web Site:
http://www.netweaveonline.com
Sales Range: $1-9.9 Million
Emp.: 8
Social Media Management
N.A.I.C.S.: 541611
Kevin McNulty *(Pres & CEO)*
Pamela Harper *(COO & Sr VP)*
Erin McNulty *(VP-Quality Assurance)*
Andrew Jackson *(Mgr-Community)*

NETWORK ADJUSTERS INC.
850 Fulton St, Farmdale, NY 11735
Tel.: (516) 747-6400
Web Site:
http://www.networkadjusters.com
Year Founded: 1958
Rev.: $17,000,000
Emp.: 69
Insurance Claim Adjusters, Not Employed By Insurance Company
N.A.I.C.S.: 524291
Mark J. Ahern *(Pres)*
Thomas Daffron *(Asst VP-IT)*
Paul Nastro *(CFO)*
J. Mayer *(VP-Claims)*
Annette Barbera *(Dir-Claim)*
April Fay *(Dir-Claim)*

NETWORK AFFILIATES INC.
940 Wadsworth Blvd Ste 300, Lakewood, CO 80214
Tel.: (303) 232-2707
Web Site: http://www.netaff.com
Rev.: $28,943,916
Emp.: 40
Commercials, Television: Tape Or Film
N.A.I.C.S.: 512110
Norton C. Frickey *(Pres & CEO)*
Brian Hutchin *(Mgr-Acct)*
Jeff Buenz *(Mgr-Acct)*
Tammy Kehe *(VP)*
Nancy Stroud *(Mgr-Traffic)*

NETWORK CABLING SERVICES, INC.
12626 Fuqua St, Houston, TX 77034-4629
Tel.: (281) 484-1777
Web Site:
http://www.networkcablingser vices.com
Year Founded: 1999
Sales Range: $10-24.9 Million

Emp.: 130
Electronic Cable Installation Services
N.A.I.C.S.: 541519
Lori Veltri (Pres)
Mark Veltri (COO)
Greg Brittain (VP)
Shane Whatley (Mgr-Ops)
Robert Apgar (Chm)
Jeff Jandron (VP-Sls)
Jesse Mendez (Mgr-Corpus Christi Branch)

NETWORK CAPITAL FUNDING CORP.
5 Park Plz Ste 800, Irvine, CA 92614
Tel.: (949) 442-0060 NV
Web Site:
http://www.networkcapital.net
Year Founded: 2002
Sales Range: $10-24.9 Million
Emp.: 400
Mortgage Banker
N.A.I.C.S.: 522310
Tri Nguyen (CEO)
Bryon Kungl (Mgr-Credit)
Eric Tran (Mgr-Mortgage Sls)
Michael Morgan (Mgr-Credit)
Andrea Espinosa (Mgr-Licensing)

NETWORK COMMERCIAL SERVICE, INC.
6355 Topanga Canyon Blvd Ste 255, Woodland Hills, CA 91367
Tel.: (818) 360-6697 CA
Web Site: http://www.ncsiweb.com
Year Founded: 1952
Collection Agency
N.A.I.C.S.: 561440
Brandi Roschko (Atty)
Edwin B. Siegel (Atty)
Stephen F. Moss (Mgr-Agency)

NETWORK CONSULTING SERVICES, INC.
585 W 500 S, Bountiful, UT 84010
Tel.: (801) 295-7555
Web Site: http://www.ncsi.us
Year Founded: 2002
Sales Range: $10-24.9 Million
Emp.: 20
Business Consulting Services
N.A.I.C.S.: 541618
Bryan Boam (Pres)
Janalee Boam (VP)

NETWORK COURIER SERVICES INC.
21061 S Western Ave 3rd Fl, Torrance, CA 90501
Tel.: (310) 410-7777 CA
Web Site: http://www.nglog.com
Year Founded: 1971
Rev.: $120,000,000
Emp.: 400
Air Courier Services
N.A.I.C.S.: 492110
Ed Petrone (CFO)

NETWORK DATA SYSTEMS INC.
50 Commerce Dr Ste 120, Schaumburg, IL 60173-5308
Tel.: (847) 385-6700
Web Site: http://www.network-data.com
Sales Range: $10-24.9 Million
Emp.: 140
Provider of Computer System Services
N.A.I.C.S.: 541512
Al Siders (Pres & CEO)
Carl Larson (VP-Sls)

NETWORK ENHANCED TELECOM LLP
119 W Tyler St Ste 100, Longview, TX 75601
Tel.: (903) 323-4900
Web Site: http://www.networkip.net
Year Founded: 1998
Sales Range: $1-9.9 Million
Emp.: 30
Telephone Communications
N.A.I.C.S.: 517121
Peter R. Pattullo (CEO)
Toni Van Burkleo (CFO)
Mike Truemner (VP-Network Ops & Tandem Svcs)
Brian Kirk (VP-Bus Dev)
Nichole Janner (Sr VP-Product Dev)
Stephan Broquie (COO & CTO)

NETWORK FOR GOOD, INC.
1140 Connecticut Ave NW Ste 700, Washington, DC 20036
Tel.: (888) 284-7978 DE
Web Site:
http://www.networkforgood.org
Year Founded: 2001
Sales Range: $125-149.9 Million
Emp.: 47
Fundraising Services
N.A.I.C.S.: 561499
Bob Deily (Co-CFO)
Bill Strathmann (CEO)
Susan Kearney (COO)
Vince Talbert (Chm)
Maria Canfora (Co-CFO)
Sean Zito (CTO)

NETWORK FOR TEACHING ENTREPRENEURSHIP
120 Wall St 18th Fl, New York, NY 10005
Tel.: (212) 232-3333 NY
Web Site: http://www.nfte.com
Year Founded: 1986
Sales Range: $10-24.9 Million
Emp.: 92
Educational Support Services
N.A.I.C.S.: 611710
Dan Delany (Sr VP-Strategy & Mgmt)
Kim Smith (Sr VP-Programs & Res)
Ben Rodriguez (COO)
Matthew J. Audette (CFO)
Ronald E. Garrow (Vice Chm)
Sanford Krieger (Gen Counsel)
Troy Carter (Founder)
J. D. LaRock (Pres & CEO)

NETWORK HARDWARE RESALE, LLC
6500 Hollister Ave, Santa Barbara, CA 93117
Tel.: (805) 964-9975
Web Site:
http://www.networkhardware.com
Year Founded: 1985
Sales Range: $25-49.9 Million
Emp.: 500
Used Networking Equipment Whslr
N.A.I.C.S.: 423430
Chuck Sheldon (Chm)
Mike Sheldon (Pres & CEO)
Michael W. Lodato (VP-Mktg & Bus Dev)
Mark V. Kelly (VP-IT)
Todd Mitchell (VP-HR)
Angelique Davis (Mgr-Mktg & PR)
Jeff Zanardi (Dir-Svcs)

NETWORK IMAGING SOLUTIONS INC.
242 E 90th St, Davenport, IA 52806
Tel.: (563) 285-6123
Web Site: http://www.nisia.com
Rev.: $25,200,000
Emp.: 200
Computer Peripheral Equipment Mfr
N.A.I.C.S.: 334118

Kimberly Payne (Mgr-Procurement)
Shawn Sparks (Mgr-Matls)
Todd Jackson (Mgr-Quality)

NETWORK OUTSOURCE, INC.
135 Denton Ave, New Hyde Park, NY 11040
Tel.: (516) 488-5888
Web Site:
http://www.networkoutsource.com
Year Founded: 2001
Sales Range: $1-9.9 Million
Emp.: 52
Business & Educational Technology Solutions
N.A.I.C.S.: 541512
Adam Mahoney (CEO)
Vasco Browne (Engr-Remote Svcs)
Steve Battiste (Dir-ITSM)

NETWORK SERVICES COMPANY
1100 E Woodfield Rd Ste 200, Schaumburg, IL 60173
Tel.: (847) 803-4888 DE
Web Site:
http://www.networkdistributors.com
Sales Range: $75-99.9 Million
Emp.: 130
Branded Paper & Plastic Products & Cleaning Materials Mfr
N.A.I.C.S.: 424130
Warren Noble (Dir-Supplier Program)
Chris Adams (Exec Dir-Value Chain Svcs)
Keith Marcoe (COO)

NETWORK SOLUTIONS PROVIDER (NSP)
400 Continental Blvd 6th Fl, El Segundo, CA 90245
Tel.: (805) 248-7992
Web Site:
http://www.networksolutionsprovider.com
Year Founded: 2005
Sales Range: $1-9.9 Million
Emp.: 24
Offers VoIP, DS3, Ethernet, Wireless, Colocation & Telephone Systems Services
N.A.I.C.S.: 517111
Pooja Chakravarti (Mgr-Media)

NETWORK SYSTEMS INTERNATIONAL, INC.
3859 Battleground Ave Suite 301, Greensboro, NC 27401
Tel.: (336) 271-8400 NV
Web Site: http://www.nesi.net
Year Founded: 1974
Sales Range: $10-24.9 Million
Emp.: 15
Develops & Markets Enterprise Resource Planning & Supply Chain Management Software Solutions
N.A.I.C.S.: 513210
Robbie M. Efird (CEO)
Aitan Zacharin (CMO & CIO)
Jeanne Hebert (VP-Mktg & Clinical Res)

NETWORK9, LLC
8200 Memorial Ste A, Dublin, OH 43064
Tel.: (614) 340-9885 OH
Web Site: http://www.network9.com
Year Founded: 2004
Sales Range: $10-24.9 Million
Emp.: 22
Telecommunications
N.A.I.C.S.: 238210
Dave Blakely (Engr-Applications)

NETWORKERS FUNDING, LLC
2200 S Main St, West Bend, WI 53095-0614
Tel.: (262) 334-6000
Web Site:
http://www.networkersfunding.com
Year Founded: 2001
Sales Range: $1-9.9 Million
Emp.: 30
Administrative & Payroll Fund Management Services
N.A.I.C.S.: 541611
Joyce Dieck (Pres)

NETWORKING TECHNOLOGIES & SUPPORT, INC.
14421 Justice Rd, Midlothian, VA 23113
Tel.: (804) 379-1800
Web Site:
http://www.networkingtech.com
Year Founded: 1997
Sales Range: $1-9.9 Million
Emp.: 150
System Integration Services
N.A.I.C.S.: 541512
Bernard Robinson (Founder & Pres)

NETWORKOMNI
3835 E Thousand Oaks Blvd Ste R, Westlake Village, CA 91362-6622
Web Site:
http://www.networkomni.com
Rev.: $20,000,000
Emp.: 55
Translation Services
N.A.I.C.S.: 541930
George Ulmer (Chm & CEO)
Laura Raville (CFO)

NETWORKS UNLIMITED, INC.
2526 Patterson Rd Ste 201, Grand Junction, CO 81505
Tel.: (970) 243-3311
Web Site:
http://www.itsaboutaction.com
Year Founded: 2001
Rev.: $2,200,000
Emp.: 15
Computer System Design Services
N.A.I.C.S.: 541512
Mark Swain (Pres)

NETWORLD ALLIANCE, LLC
13100 Eastpoint Park Blvd, Louisville, KY 40223-4163
Tel.: (502) 241-7545
Web Site:
http://www.networldmediagroup.com
Year Founded: 2000
Book Publishers
N.A.I.C.S.: 513130
Liz Matney (Sr Mgr-Bus Dev)
Tom Harper (CEO)
Kathy Doyle (Pres)

Subsidiaries:

Vending Times Inc. (1)
1375 Broadway, New York, NY 10018
Tel.: (212) 302-4700
Web Site: http://www.vendingtimes.com
Rev.: $1,300,000
Emp.: 11
Periodical Publishers
N.A.I.C.S.: 513120
Alicia Lavay (Pres & Publr)
Carl Brands (Exec VP)
Randy Cesco (Mgr-Sls-Natl)
Erin B. James (Mng Editor)

NETWOVEN INC.
3837 Stone Pointe Way, Pleasanton, CA 94588
Tel.: (925) 931-9390
Web Site: http://www.netwoven.com
Year Founded: 2001
Rev.: $4,200,000
Emp.: 25

NETWOVEN INC.

Netwoven Inc.—(Continued)
Computer Related Consulting Services
N.A.I.C.S.: 541512
Viraj Bais *(Founder & CTO)*
Sushant Agarwal *(CTO-India)*
Debabrata Dutta *(VP-Engrg-India)*

NETXPOSURE, INC.
735 SW First Ave Third Fl, Portland, OR 97204
Tel.: (503) 499-4342
Web Site: http://www.netex.net
Year Founded: 1995
Digital Asset Management Software Developer
N.A.I.C.S.: 541511
Jason Wheling *(Pres, CEO & CTO)*

Subsidiaries:

ASL Acquisition, Inc. (1)
4633 Old Ironsides Dr, Santa Clara, CA 95054
Tel.: (408) 330-8700
Web Site: http://www.chuckwalla.com
Sales Range: $1-9.9 Million
Emp.: 20
Prepackaged Software
N.A.I.C.S.: 513210
Ashwin Shah *(Founder, Pres & CTO)*

NEU'S BUILDING CENTER, INC.
N95 W16915 Richfield Way, Menomonee Falls, WI 53051
Tel.: (262) 251-6550
Web Site: http://www.toolme.com
Year Founded: 1945
Sales Range: $10-24.9 Million
Emp.: 50
Hardware Whslr
N.A.I.C.S.: 423710
Harvey Neu *(CEO)*
Michael Karch *(Pres & COO)*
Cindy Neu *(VP)*

NEUBERGER BERMAN GROUP LLC
1290 Avenue of the Americas, New York, NY 10104
Tel.: (212) 476-9000 DE
Web Site: https://www.nb.com
Year Founded: 1939
Rev.: $427,000,000,000
Holding Company; Investment Management Services
N.A.I.C.S.: 551112
Joseph V. Amato *(Pres & CIO-Equities)*
George H. Walker *(Chm & CEO)*
Erik L. Knutzen *(Mng Dir & Chief Investment Officer-Multi Asset)*
Dik van Lomwel *(Head-EMEA & Latin America)*
Clay Khan *(Head-Bus-Canada)*
Kent Chen *(Mng Dir-Asia Pacific)*
Matthew Malloy *(Mng Dir, Head-Insurance Solutions & Head-Institutional Client Group-Global)*
Alberto Salato *(Head-Southern Europe)*
Alan Yip *(Mng Dir & Head-Portfolio Solutions-Asia Pacific)*
Keita Kubota *(Mng Dir/Sr Portfolio Mgr-Japan)*
J. Douglas Kramer *(Head-Institutional Equity & Multi Asset Class)*
Maarten Nederlof *(Mng Dir & Head-Portfolio Solutions-Americas)*
Alexander Samuelson *(Mng Dir & Head-Media Relations-Global)*
Jonathan Bailey *(Mng Dir & Head-Environment, Social & Governance, and Impact Investing-Global)*
Gilles Drukier *(Mng Dir & Head-Insurance Solutions-Europe, Middle East, Africa)*
Samuel Porat *(Mng Dir & Head-Alternative Yield Strategies)*
Zachary Sigel *(Mng Dir)*
Niall O'Sullivan *(Mng Dir & Chief Investment Officer-Multi Asset Strategies-EMEA)*
Matthew Thompson *(Mng Dir & Head-Intermediary Distr-Australia)*
Oliver Little *(Sr VP & Head-Insurance Solutions-UK)*

Subsidiaries:

Almanac Realty Investors, LLC (1)
1251 Ave of Americas, New York, NY 10020
Tel.: (814) 278-7206
Web Site: http://www.almanacrealty.com
Nonresidential Property Managers
N.A.I.C.S.: 531312
David Haltiner *(VP)*

IOU Financial Inc. (1)
1 Place Ville-Marie Suite 1670, Montreal, H3B 2B6, QC, Canada
Tel.: (514) 789-0694
Web Site: https://www.ioufinancial.com
Rev.: $17,804,622
Assets: $48,847,420
Liabilities: $38,784,224
Net Worth: $10,063,195
Earnings: $1,165,697
Emp.: 51
Fiscal Year-end: 12/31/2019
Loan Services
N.A.I.C.S.: 522310
Philippe Marleau *(Founder)*
Evan Price *(Chm)*
Joshua Zickefoose *(VP-Sls & Strategy)*
Kimberley Haffey *(VP-Sls)*
Carl Brabander *(Exec VP-Strategy)*
Rosey Painter *(VP)*
Thomas Crevier *(VP)*
Lori Haygood *(VP)*
Jason Stevens *(VP)*

Subsidiary (US):

IOU CENTRAL INC. (2)
1255 Roberts Blvd Ste 116, Kennesaw, GA 30188
Web Site: http://www.ioucentral.com
Sales Range: $75-99.9 Million
Emp.: 4
Internet Loan Marketplace
N.A.I.C.S.: 522310

NB Alternatives Advisers LLC (1)
325 N Saint Paul St Ste 4900, Dallas, TX 75201
Tel.: (214) 647-9593
Investment Management Service
N.A.I.C.S.: 523940
Anthony D. Tutrone *(Mng Dir & Head-NB Alternatives-Global)*
John P. Buser *(Mng Dir & Head-Private Investment Portfolios-Global)*
Brien P. Smith *(Mng Dir-Dallas)*
Peter J. Von Lehe *(Mng Dir-New York)*
David S. Stonberg *(Mng Dir-New York)*
Jonathan D. Shofet *(Mng Dir-New York)*
Patricia Miller Zollar *(Mng Dir-New York)*

NB Renaissance Partners (1)
Via San Damiano 7, 20121, Milan, Italy
Tel.: (39) 0276415811
Web Site: https://www.nb.com
Privater Equity Firm
N.A.I.C.S.: 523999

Joint Venture (Domestic):

Biolchim S.p.A. (2)
Via San Carlo 2130, 40059, Medicina, Bologna, Italy
Tel.: (39) 051 6971811
Web Site: http://www.biolchim.it
Sales Range: $50-74.9 Million
Specialty Fertilizers & Biostimulants Mfr & Distr
N.A.I.C.S.: 325314
Leonardo Valenti *(Mng Dir)*

Neuberger Berman LLC (1)
1290 6th Ave, New York, NY 10104
Tel.: (212) 476-9000
Web Site: http://www.nb.com
Investment Management Service
N.A.I.C.S.: 523940

Joseph V. Amato *(Pres & Chief Investment Officer-Equity)*
Sam Petrucci *(Head-Advice, Plng & Fiduciary Svcs-NB Private Wealth)*
Jonathan Bailey *(Head-Environmental, Social & Governance Investing)*
Shannon Saccocia *(Chief Investment Officer-NB Private Wealth)*
Stephanie Luedke *(Head-NB Private Wealth)*
Gregory Khost *(Head-Bus Dev-NB Private Wealth)*
Julia Chu *(Head-Philanthropy & Family Governance Advisory-NB Private Wealth)*

Affiliate (Domestic):

Neuberger Berman Energy Infrastructure and Income Fund Inc. (2)
1290 Ave of the Americas, New York, NY 10104
Tel.: (212) 476-8800
Sales Range: $10-24.9 Million
Closed-End Investment Fund
N.A.I.C.S.: 525990

OveriIT S.p.A. (1)
Via Bassi 81, Fiume Veneto, 33080, Pordenone, Italy
Tel.: (39) 0434562911
Web Site: http://www.overit.it
Software & IT Services
N.A.I.C.S.: 541511
Marco Zanuttini *(Mng Dir)*
Luca Turco *(Mgr-IT Svcs)*
Andrea Zamarian *(Dir)*
Paolo Bergamo *(Chm & CEO)*

NEUGER COMMUNICATIONS GROUP, INC.
25 Bridge Sq, Northfield, MN 55057
Tel.: (507) 664-0700
Web Site: http://www.neuger.com
Professional, Scientific & Technical Services
N.A.I.C.S.: 541990
David L. Neuger *(Pres & CEO)*
Richard E. Esse *(VP)*
Joanne B. Henry *(Exec VP)*
Carol M. O'Neill *(Office Mgr)*

Subsidiaries:

Engage Print, Inc. (1)
1000 5th St W, Northfield, MN 55057
Tel.: (507) 645-4421
Web Site: http://www.engageprint.com
Sales Range: $1-9.9 Million
Emp.: 25
Commercial Printing
N.A.I.C.S.: 323111
Carla Hansen *(Acct Exec)*

NEUHAUS & COMPANY INC.
2000 E Expy 83, Weslaco, TX 78596
Tel.: (956) 968-7502
Web Site: http://www.barbeeneuhaus.com
Rev.: $38,476,544
Emp.: 52
Tractors, Agricultural
N.A.I.C.S.: 423820
Earl Neuhaus *(Owner)*

NEUMANN BROTHERS INC.
1435 Ohio St, Des Moines, IA 50314-3423
Tel.: (515) 243-0156 IA
Web Site: http://www.neumannbros.com
Year Founded: 1912
Sales Range: $50-74.9 Million
Emp.: 300
Nonresidential Construction
N.A.I.C.S.: 236220
Michael G. Simpson *(CFO & Exec VP)*

NEUMANN ENTERPRISES, INC.
W 330 N 6233 Hasslinger Dr, Nashotah, WI 53058
Tel.: (262) 966-1001

Sales Range: $10-24.9 Million
Emp.: 1
Preserves Open & Green Spaces in Southern Wisconsin
N.A.I.C.S.: 321114
Kelly Odonnell *(Mgr)*

NEUMANN FAMILY SERVICES
5547 N Ravenswood Ave, Chicago, IL 60640
Tel.: (773) 769-4313 IL
Web Site: http://www.neumannfamilyservices.org
Year Founded: 1949
Sales Range: $10-24.9 Million
Emp.: 517
Family Support Services
N.A.I.C.S.: 624190
Jolie Horen *(Pres)*
Mark Jak *(Co-Vice Chm)*
Stella Black *(Co-Vice Chm)*
Paul Naye *(CFO)*
Paul Selden *(Pres & CEO)*

NEUMANN SYSTEMS GROUP, INC.
890 Elkton Dr Ste 101, Colorado Springs, CO 80907
Tel.: (719) 593-7848
Web Site: http://www.neumannsystemsgroup.com
Sales Range: $10-24.9 Million
Emp.: 57
Emission Control System Mfr
N.A.I.C.S.: 334519
David K. Neumann *(CEO)*
Michael D. Neumann *(CFO)*
Jay Brasseur *(CTO)*
George Luke *(VP-Bus Ops)*

NEURODIMENSION, INC.
3701 NW 40th Ter Ste 1, Gainesville, FL 32606
Tel.: (352) 377-5144 FL
Web Site: http://www.nd.com
Year Founded: 1991
Sales Range: $1-9.9 Million
Emp.: 13
Medical Software Products
N.A.I.C.S.: 513210
Gary Geniesse *(Pres)*
Gary Lynn *(CEO)*
Steve Thompson *(Engr-Tech Support)*

NEUROSIGMA, INC.
10960 Wilshire Blvd Ste 1910, Los Angeles, CA 90024
Tel.: (310) 479-3100 DE
Web Site: http://www.neurosigma.com
Year Founded: 2008
Bioelectronic Products Mfr
N.A.I.C.S.: 334510
David Hayes *(Chief Admin Officer, Gen Counsel, Sr VP & Sec)*
Ian A. Cook *(Chief Medical Officer & Sr VP)*
Colin P. Kealey *(VP-Advanced Dev & Medical Affairs)*
Lodwick M. Cook *(Chm)*
Sam Wild *(CFO)*
Charles W. Winkler *(VP-Fin Plng)*
Phil Oseas *(VP-Fin & Ops)*
A. David Johnson *(Dir-Advanced Materials)*
Vikas Gupta *(Dir-Engrg)*
Patrick Miller *(Ops Mgr)*
Charles W. Winckler *(VP-Fin Plng)*

NEUTECH PACKAGING SYSTEMS, LLC
2049 Mercer Rd, Lexington, KY 40511-1018
Tel.: (859) 223-0938

Web Site:
http://www.neutechpackaging.com
Year Founded: 2003
Sales Range: $50-74.9 Million
Emp.: 5
Packaging Solutions
N.A.I.C.S.: 561910
Dave Neuer (Owner & Pres)

NEUTRAL POSTURE, INC.
3904 N Texas Ave, Bryan, TX 77803-0555
Tel.: (979) 778-0502 TX
Web Site:
http://www.neutralposture.com
Year Founded: 1989
Sales Range: $10-24.9 Million
Emp.: 100
Mfr, Marketer & Distr of Ergonomic Chairs
N.A.I.C.S.: 337214
Rebecca Boenigk (Chm & CEO)
Brian Rutherford (Chief Acctg Officer & VP)

NEUTRON INTERACTIVE
224 S 200 W Suite 100, Salt Lake City, UT 84101
Tel.: (801) 327-9090
Web Site:
http://www.neutroninteractive.com
Year Founded: 2005
Sales Range: $10-24.9 Million
Emp.: 40
Online Marketing Performance-Based Company
N.A.I.C.S.: 541613
Dan Caffee (CEO)
Shaun Ritchie (Founder)
Felicia Romney (Dir-Client Rels)
Adam Fullmer (Acct Mgr)
Michael Jonaitis (Dir-Tech)
Ryan Kempema (Dir-Partner Rels)

NEUVILLE CHRYSLER-DODGE-JEEP LLC.
1407 Royalton St, Waupaca, WI 54981
Tel.: (715) 258-3232
Web Site:
http://www.neuvillechryslerdodgejeep.com
Year Founded: 2007
Sales Range: $10-24.9 Million
Emp.: 20
Car Whslr
N.A.I.C.S.: 441110
Todd Peterson (Gen Mgr)

NEVA ONE LLC
1300 Buckeye Rd Ste A, Minden, NV 89423
Tel.: (775) 782-7275
Year Founded: 2013
Holding Company
N.A.I.C.S.: 551112
David Park (Principal)
Jon Park (Principal)

NEVADA BEVERAGE CO.
3940 W Tropicana Ave, Las Vegas, NV 89103-5516
Tel.: (702) 739-9474 NV
Web Site: http://www.patclarklv.com
Year Founded: 1943
Sales Range: $25-49.9 Million
Emp.: 280
Distr of Beer & Ale
N.A.I.C.S.: 424810
Pat Clark (Pres)
Jim Dobrynski (Dir-Draught & Special Events)
Andrew Flood (Brand Mgr-Monster Energy)
Mark Lawson (Brand Mgr-Craft)
Rob Nelson (Dir-On-Premise)
Scott Grossardt (Mgr-Off-Premise Sls)

NEVADA CLASSIC THOROUGHBREDS, INC.
4604 E Contessa St, Mesa, AZ 85205
Tel.: (480) 241-8668 NV
Web Site: http://www.nctfarm.com
Year Founded: 2000
Assets: $24,012
Net Worth: $24,012
Earnings: ($1,121)
Fiscal Year-end: 06/30/24
Animal Breeding Services
N.A.I.C.S.: 115210
Brad Brimhall (Chm, Pres, CEO, Acting CFO & Chief Acctg Officer)

NEVADA CLASSICS, INC.
2150 W NW Hwy Ste 114-1015, Grapevine, TX 76051
Tel.: (702) 785-0090
Web Site:
http://www.nevadaclassics.com
Sales Range: $10-24.9 Million
Emp.: 4
Classic Car Restoration & Retailer
N.A.I.C.S.: 811121
Mark Logan (Pres)

NEVADA CORPORATE HEADQUARTERS, INC.
101 Convention Ctr Dr 7th Fl, Las Vegas, NV 89109
Tel.: (702) 873-3488
Web Site: http://www.nchinc.com
Year Founded: 1992
Sales Range: $10-24.9 Million
Emp.: 63
Business Management Consulting Services
N.A.I.C.S.: 541618
Cort W. Christie (Co-Founder & Pres)
Derek Rowley (Co-Founder)
Trevor Rowley (Exec VP)

NEVADA GENERAL INSURANCE COMPANY
5685 Spring Mtn Rd, Las Vegas, NV 89146
Tel.: (702) 367-9616
Web Site: http://www.nvgeneral.com
Sales Range: $25-49.9 Million
Emp.: 35
Providers of Automobile Insurance
N.A.I.C.S.: 524126
Jim Schallert (Pres)

Subsidiaries:

AIC America (1)
5685 Spring Mtn Rd, Las Vegas, NV 89146
Tel.: (702) 367-6722
Web Site:
http://www.autoinsuranceamerica.com
Rev.: $2,793,969
Emp.: 9
Insurance Agents & Brokers
N.A.I.C.S.: 524210

Nevada General Insurance Co (1)
5685 W Spring Mtn Rd, Las Vegas, NV 89146
Tel.: (702) 367-9616
Sales Range: $10-24.9 Million
Emp.: 32
Automobile Insurance
N.A.I.C.S.: 524126
James Schallert (Pres)

NEVADA IRRIGATION DISTRICT
1036 W Main St, Grass Valley, CA 95945
Tel.: (530) 273-6185
Web Site: http://www.nidwater.com
Year Founded: 1921
Sales Range: $25-49.9 Million
Emp.: 170
Supplier of Water
N.A.I.C.S.: 221310
Timothy Crough (Asst Gen Mgr)
Lisa Tassone (Sec)
Gary King (Chief Engrg Officer)
Greg Jones (Interim Gen Mgr)

NEVADA PF LLC
339 Ctr Green Dr, Las Vegas, NV 89148
Tel.: (702) 483-1865
Web Site: https://www.prairiefire.com
Handgun Safety Training Programs & Services
N.A.I.C.S.: 922190
Sal Siino (Chm)
Lanny Barnes (Chief Experience Officer)

Subsidiaries:

Front Sight Management LLC (1)
1 Front Sight Rd, Pahrump, NV 89061
Tel.: (702) 837-7433
Web Site: http://www.frontsight.com
Sporting Goods Retailer
N.A.I.C.S.: 459110

NEVADA STATE CORPORATE NETWORK, INC.
777 N Rainbow Blvd Ste 250, Las Vegas, NV 89107
Tel.: (702) 838-8599 NV
Web Site: http://www.nscn.com
Year Founded: 2001
Sales Range: $1-9.9 Million
Emp.: 60
Incorporating Services, Business Credit & Professional Services to New Companies
N.A.I.C.S.: 561499
Laura Davidson (Mgr-Social Media)

NEVADA TRIO INC.
140 S Prado Rd, El Paso, TX 79907
Tel.: (915) 860-4480 NV
Web Site:
http://www.candrdistributing.com
Year Founded: 1994
Sales Range: $25-49.9 Million
Emp.: 220
Producer of Petroleum Products
N.A.I.C.S.: 424720
James A. Cardwell Sr. (Pres)

Subsidiaries:

C&R Distributing Inc. (1)
140 S Prado Rd, El Paso, TX 79907-6136
Tel.: (915) 860-4480
Web Site: http://www.candrdistributing.com
Sales Range: $10-24.9 Million
Emp.: 45
Producer of Petroleum Products
N.A.I.C.S.: 424720
Adrian Amaya (Coord-Fuel Pricing & Logistics)

NEVE YERUSHALAYIM INC.
25 Broadway, New York, NY 10004
Tel.: (212) 422-1110 NY
Web Site: http://www.nevey.org
Year Founded: 1970
Sales Range: $1-9.9 Million
Emp.: 9
Educational Support Services
N.A.I.C.S.: 611710
Dovid Refson (Pres)
Raphael Butler (VP)

NEVILLE CENTER AT FRESH POND
640 Concord Ave, Cambridge, MA 02138
Tel.: (617) 497-0600 MA
Web Site:
http://www.nevillecenter.org
Year Founded: 1999
Sales Range: $10-24.9 Million
Emp.: 231
Nursing Care Services
N.A.I.C.S.: 623110
Sabine Charles (Dir-Nursing)
Jeanne Lawson (Dir-MDS & PPS)
Jamie Cohen (Dir-Rehabilitation)

NEVILLE CHEMICAL COMPANY
2800 Neville Rd, Pittsburgh, PA 15225-1408
Tel.: (412) 331-4200 DE
Web Site: http://www.nevchem.com
Year Founded: 1925
Sales Range: $100-124.9 Million
Emp.: 250
Mfr of Synthetic Hydrocarbon Resins & Coumarone-Indene Resins
N.A.I.C.S.: 325211
Thomas F. McKnight (Pres & CEO)
Jack Ferguson (VP-Mfg & Plant Mgr)
Randi Dauler (Chm)
Richard E. Radi (CFO & Treas)

Subsidiaries:

NEVCO, Inc. (1)
2800 Neville Rd, Pittsburgh, PA 15225-1408
Tel.: (412) 331-4200
Industrial Inorganic Chemical Mfr
N.A.I.C.S.: 325180

Vitae Investment Co., Inc. (1)
801 W St Fl 2, Wilmington, DE 19801-1607
Tel.: (302) 656-8985
Provider of Security Brokerage Services
N.A.I.C.S.: 523150

NEVINS FAMILY OF SERVICES
10 Ingalls Ct, Methuen, MA 01844
Tel.: (978) 682-7611 MA
Web Site: http://www.nevinsfamily.org
Year Founded: 1979
Sales Range: $10-24.9 Million
Emp.: 315
Individual & Family Support Services
N.A.I.C.S.: 624190
Cynthia Ashton (Dir-External Rels)
Lisa Shea (Dir-Community Dev)
Joyce Shannon (Pres & CEO)
Sharon Walsh (Dir-Bus Ops)
Kris Fleming (Dir-HR)
William Pitocchelli (Dir-Admissions)
Barbara Strzykalski (Dir-Rehabilitation Svcs)
Leslie Cafiero (Dir-Social Svcs)
Alan Shafer (Treas)
Patricia Demers (Chm)

NEVINS-ADAMS-LEWBEL-SCHELL PROPERTIES INC
920 Garden St Ste A, Santa Barbara, CA 93101
Tel.: (805) 963-2884
Web Site: http://www.nals.com
Sales Range: $10-24.9 Million
Emp.: 480
Commercial & Industrial Building Operation
N.A.I.C.S.: 531120
Jay Stryker (Reg VP)
Jorge Jimenez (Controller)

NEVO ENERGY, INC.
20400 Stevens Creek Blvd Ste 740, Cupertino, CA 95014
Tel.: (408) 418-2424
Web Site:
https://www.nevoenergy.com
Emp.: 1
Eletric Power Generation Services
N.A.I.C.S.: 221111
Adam McAfee (Pres, CEO, CFO, Treas & Sec)

NEW & IMPROVED MEDIA

New & Improved Media—(Continued)

NEW & IMPROVED MEDIA
550 N Continental Blvd Ste 120, El Segundo, CA 90245
Tel.: (310) 578-2300
Web Site: http://www.newandimprovedmedia.com
Year Founded: 1988
Sales Range: $50-74.9 Million
Emp.: 15
Media Buying Services
N.A.I.C.S.: 541830
Don Terrell *(Pres)*
Keith Fisher *(CEO)*
Chris Yokogawa *(Media Dir)*
Danna Prosser *(Dir-Fin-Ops)*

NEW AGE COMPUTER SOLUTIONS
1176 Teakwood Dr, Greenville, NC 27834
Tel.: (252) 321-8622
Rev.: $15,000,000
Emp.: 15
Personal Computers
N.A.I.C.S.: 449210

NEW AGE INVESTMENTS INC.
9440 Autoplex Dr, Montclair, CA 91763
Tel.: (800) 970-0431
Web Site: http://www.metronissan.com
Emp.: 150
New & Used Car Dealer
N.A.I.C.S.: 441110

Subsidiaries:

Ontario Nissan Inc. (1)
9440 Autoplex St, Montclair, CA 91763
Tel.: (909) 625-5575
Web Site: http://www.metronissan.com
Rev.: $32,000,000
Emp.: 138
Automobiles, New & Used
N.A.I.C.S.: 441110
Dave Marvin *(Pres)*

NEW AGE MEDIA VENTURES LLC
5790 Fayetteville Rd Ste 200, Durham, NC 27713
Web Site: http://www.aaehq.com
Year Founded: 2002
Sales Range: $25-49.9 Million
Emp.: 50
Event Management Services
N.A.I.C.S.: 711310
Greg Friedlander *(Pres & CEO)*
Margo Sarlo *(COO)*
Jill Landers *(VP-Bus Affairs)*
Richard Michelli *(CTO)*
Marly Black *(Dir-Mktg)*

NEW ALBANY MOTOR CO. INC.
1801 Broadway St, Clarksville, IN 47150
Tel.: (812) 948-7711
Web Site: http://www.coyledeals.com
Rev.: $20,000,000
Emp.: 60
Sales of New & Used Automobiles
N.A.I.C.S.: 441110
Michael Coyle *(Pres)*

NEW ANGLE MEDIA LLC
2601 E Thomas Rd Ste 235, Phoenix, AZ 85016
Tel.: (602) 840-5530
Web Site: http://www.newanglemedia.com
Year Founded: 2003
Sales Range: $1-9.9 Million
Emp.: 10

Internet Marketing Services
N.A.I.C.S.: 541613
Steve Roberts *(Co-Founder & CEO)*
Kris Brandt *(Co-Founder & Pres)*
Mike Finazzo *(Sr VP)*
Andrew Tamala *(Dir-Creative)*
Shaun Roberts *(Dir-Software)*

NEW AVENUES TO INDEPENDENCE, INC.
17608 Euclid Ave, Cleveland, OH 44112
Tel.: (216) 481-1907   OH
Web Site: http://www.newavenues.net
Year Founded: 1952
Sales Range: $10-24.9 Million
Emp.: 628
Disability Assistance Services
N.A.I.C.S.: 624120
Thomas Lewins *(Exec Dir)*
Karen Knavel *(Dir-Community Rels)*
Bridget Bernhard *(Dir-Clinical Svcs)*
Jonathan Good *(Chm)*
Adam Fletcher *(Sec)*
Robert Angart *(Treas)*

NEW BALANCE ATHLETIC SHOE, INC.
100 Guest St, Boston, MA 02135-2040
Tel.: (617) 783-4000   MA
Web Site: https://www.newbalance.com
Year Founded: 1906
Sales Range: $1-4.9 Billion
Emp.: 5,500
Footwear Manufacturing
N.A.I.C.S.: 316210
James S. Davis *(Chm)*
Anne Davis *(Vice Chm & Exec VP-Admin)*
John Wilson *(Exec VP-Mfg)*
Edward Haddad *(VP-Intellectual Property & Licensed Products)*
John Withee *(CFO & Exec VP)*
Alan Rosen *(Treas & VP)*
Carol O'Donnell *(VP-Corp HR)*
Peter Zappala *(VP-Specialty Sls)*
Stephanie Smith *(VP-Retail)*
Edith Harmon *(VP-R & D-Kids & Wellness)*
Jim Connors *(VP-Global Design & Dev)*
Bill Hayden *(VP-Fin)*
Christine Madigan *(VP-Responsible Leadership)*
Romina Bongiovanni *(Dir-Intl Mktg-Global)*

Subsidiaries:

Brine, Inc. (1)
32125 Hollingsworth Ave, Warren, MI 48092-3804
Tel.: (508) 478-3250
Web Site: http://www.brine.com
Sales Range: $10-24.9 Million
Emp.: 100
Sporting Goods Mfr & Distr
N.A.I.C.S.: 339920

New Balance Canada, Inc. (1)
5-2905 Argentia Rd, Mississauga, L5N 8G6, ON, Canada   (100%)
Tel.: (905) 949-1100
Web Site: https://www.newbalance.ca
Sales Range: $10-24.9 Million
Emp.: 30
Marketer of Athletic Shoes
N.A.I.C.S.: 458210

NEW BEDFORD PANORAMEX CORPORATION
1480 N Claremont Blvd, Claremont, CA 91711-3538
Tel.: (909) 982-9806   CA
Web Site: http://www.nbpcorp.com
Year Founded: 1966

Sales Range: $50-74.9 Million
Emp.: 42
Airport Lighting Systems
N.A.I.C.S.: 334220
Bryce Nielsen *(Controller)*
Steven Ozuna *(Pres)*
Kenneth Gauthier *(Mgr-Matl)*

NEW BERLIN PLASTICS INC.
5725 S Westridge Dr, New Berlin, WI 53151
Tel.: (262) 784-3120
Web Site: http://www.nbplastics.com
Sales Range: $10-24.9 Million
Emp.: 120
Injection Molding Of Plastics
N.A.I.C.S.: 326199
Jeff Held *(CEO)*
Mark Siewert *(VP)*
Mandy Kiefer *(Mgr-HR)*
James Schneberger *(Pres)*
Michelle Mihaljevich Swank *(Mgr-Acct)*
Joy Hertlein *(CFO)*
Mike Tippery *(Dir-Mfg)*
Mike Moore *(Mgr-Demand)*
Dan Manning *(Mgr-Engrg)*
Joseph Mechery *(VP-Sls)*
Rich Musselman *(Supvr-Toolroom)*

NEW BOSTON FUND, INC.
75 State St Ste 1410, Boston, MA 02109
Tel.: (617) 723-7760
Web Site: http://www.newbostonfund.com
Year Founded: 1993
Rev.: $15,800,000
Emp.: 135
Real Estate Investment Management Services
N.A.I.C.S.: 237210
Eric VanDusen *(Sr VP-Capital Markets-Dev)*
Kirk A. Sykes *(Sr VP)*
Timothy J. Medlock *(Pres & COO)*
James P. Kelleher *(CIO)*
Jonathan D. Gillman *(Sr VP-Asset Mgmt)*
Michael J. Doherty *(CFO & Sr VP)*

Subsidiaries:

New Boston Management Services Inc. (1)
75 State St Ste 1500, Boston, MA 02109
Tel.: (617) 723-7760
Web Site: http://www.newbostonfund.com
Rev.: $12,400,000
Emp.: 80
Land Subividers & Developers, Residential
N.A.I.C.S.: 237210
Michael J. Buckley *(Sr VP-Fin)*
Michael J. Doherty *(Sr VP-Strategy)*
Rocky Hill *(Sr VP-Fin)*
Timothy J. Medlock *(COO & Sr VP)*
Jonathan D. Gillman *(Sr VP-Asset Mgmt)*
James P. Kelleher *(Chief Investment Officer)*
John D. Jarrett *(Sr VP)*

NEW BRAUNFELS UTILITIES
263 Main Plz, New Braunfels, TX 78130-5135
Tel.: (830) 629-8400
Web Site: http://www.nbutexas.com
Year Founded: 1942
Sales Range: $50-74.9 Million
Emp.: 200
Electronic Services
N.A.I.C.S.: 221122
Paula DiFonzo *(CEO)*
Gretchen Reuwer *(Mgr-Comm)*
Al Kaufmann *(Exec Dir-Electric Svcs)*
Roger Biggers *(Exec Dir-Water Svcs)*

NEW BRIGHTON FORD, INC.
1100 Silver Lake Rd, New Brighton, MN 55112

Tel.: (877) 821-1509   MN
Web Site: http://www.newbrightonford.com
Sales Range: $200-249.9 Million
New & Used Automobiles Retailer
N.A.I.C.S.: 441110
Bill Jansen *(Gen Mgr)*

NEW BRUNSWICK DEVELOPMENT CORPORATION
120 Albany St 7th Fl Tower 1, New Brunswick, NJ 08901
Tel.: (732) 249-2220   NJ
Web Site: http://www.devco.org
Year Founded: 1976
Sales Range: $10-24.9 Million
Emp.: 23
Real Estate Development Services
N.A.I.C.S.: 531390
George R. Zoffinger *(Chm)*
Sarah F. Clarke *(Exec VP)*
Allison V. Brown *(VP)*
Merissa A. Buczny *(VP)*
Jean A. Holtz *(VP)*
Vito R. Nardelli *(Vice Chm)*
Michael Dombrowski *(Sec)*
Randall L. Currier *(VP)*
John M. Halliday *(Controller)*
Christopher J. Paladino *(Pres)*

NEW BRUNSWICK PLATING INC.
1010 Jersey Ave, New Brunswick, NJ 08901
Tel.: (732) 545-6522
Web Site: http://www.nbplating.com
Rev.: $15,644,035
Emp.: 50
Electroplating Of Metals
N.A.I.C.S.: 332813
Anthony Melchione *(Pres)*
Bobbi Sica *(Controller)*
Michael Sica *(Mgr-Pur)*
Bobbi Gumbinger *(CFO)*
Rohan Seepersaud *(Mgr-Quality)*

NEW BUFFALO CORPORATION
950 Hoff Rd, Saint Louis, MO 63366
Tel.: (636) 532-9888
Web Site: http://www.buffalotools.com
Year Founded: 1964
Rev.: $45,900,000
Emp.: 100
Whslr of Tools & Home Products
N.A.I.C.S.: 423220
Randy Smith *(Pres)*
Martin Ahrens *(VP)*

NEW CAPITAL PARTNERS
2101 Highland Ave S Ste 700, Birmingham, AL 35205
Tel.: (205) 939-8400
Web Site: http://www.newcapitalpartners.com
Privater Equity Firm
N.A.I.C.S.: 523999
Jim Little *(Mng Partner)*
James Outland *(Mng Partner)*
Adam Cranford *(Partner)*
John Cline *(Mng Dir)*
Stan Lewis *(Mng Dir)*
Paul Pless *(Principal)*
Trey Miller *(Principal)*
Howard Glenn *(VP-Talent)*
Dana Levering *(Chief Compliance Officer & VP)*
Carter Karras *(VP-Fin)*
Nicole Burchfield *(Office Mgr)*

Subsidiaries:

Collect RX Inc. (1)
6720 Rockledge Dr Tower B Ste 600, Bethesda, MD 20817
Tel.: (301) 230-2440
Web Site: http://www.collectrx.com

Medical, Dental & Hospital Equipment & Supplies Merchant Whslr
N.A.I.C.S.: 423450
Josh Keller (Gen Mgr-Svc Solutions)
Ira Brenner (Pres)
Joe Esparraguera (CFO)
Pat O'Connor (Chief Revenue Officer)
Kristina Donahue (VP-Revenue Cycle Solutions)
Patricia Dixon (VP-Claim Optimization)
Lisa Stovall (VP-Bill Resolution)

NEW CARS INC.
7304 El Cajon Blvd, San Diego, CA 92115
Tel.: (619) 697-2886
Web Site: http://www.newcarsinc.com
Year Founded: 1986
Sales Range: $10-24.9 Million
Emp.: 25
Sales of Automobiles, New & Used
N.A.I.C.S.: 441110
Kevin J. Watkins (Pres & CEO)
Dave Almond (Mgr-Sls)
Terri Nielson (Bus Mgr)

NEW CASTLE HOTELS, LLC
2 Corp Dr Ste 154, Shelton, CT 06484-6246
Tel.: (203) 925-8370   CT
Web Site: http://www.newcastlehotels.com
Year Founded: 1994
Sales Range: $150-199.9 Million
Emp.: 4,200
Hotels & Motels
N.A.I.C.S.: 721110
David Buffam (CEO)
Bryan Woodhouse (VP & Controller)
Gerald Chase (Pres & COO)
Don Urbahn (VP-Sls & Revenue Mgmt-US & Canda)
Julian Buffam (Dir-Bus Dev-Acq & Dev)
Judi Scofield (CFO & VP)
Matthew Mackenzie (Gen Mgr-Westin Nova Scotian)

NEW CENTURY FARM SERVICE INC.
1017 Ogan Ave, Grinnell, IA 50112
Tel.: (641) 236-3117   IA
Web Site: http://www.newcenturyfs.com
Year Founded: 2001
Sales Range: $10-24.9 Million
Emp.: 15
Mfr of Grain & Fertilizer
N.A.I.C.S.: 444240
Jake Jacobs (Gen Mgr)
Randy Beichley (Treas & Sec)
Shelly Kruse (Pres)

NEW CHARLOTTE CORPORATION
600 E 4th St, Charlotte, NC 28202-2848
Tel.: (704) 336-3992   NC
Year Founded: 1990
Sales Range: $25-49.9 Million
Community Welfare Services
N.A.I.C.S.: 624190
Robert Campbell (Sec & VP)
Gregory C. Gaskins (Pres)
Scott Greer (Treas & VP)

NEW CITY MOVING LLC
2929 N Campbell Ave, Chicago, IL 60618
Tel.: (773) 489-0600
Web Site: http://www.newcitymovers.com
Year Founded: 2009
Sales Range: $10-24.9 Million
Emp.: 74
Logistic Services
N.A.I.C.S.: 541614

Brian Slater (Founder & Pres)

NEW CONTEXT SERVICES, INC.
717 Market St Ste 100, San Francisco, CA 94103-2105
Web Site: http://www.newcontext.com
Data Processing, Hosting & Related Services
N.A.I.C.S.: 518210
Daniel Riedel (CEO)
Herb Kelsey (CTO)
Azadeh Ghiasvand (VP-Engrg)
Lisa Garland (CFO)
Alexandra Shapiro (CMO)
Yvette Turner Stephens (VP-Pro Svcs)
Dustin Payne (VP-Sls)

NEW COOPERATIVE, INC.
2626 1st Ave S, Fort Dodge, IA 50501
Tel.: (515) 955-2040   IA
Web Site: http://www.newcoop.com
Year Founded: 1973
Sales Range: $200-249.9 Million
Emp.: 400
Grain & Farm Supplies Storage & Wholesale Distr
N.A.I.C.S.: 493130
Mark Walter (Mgr-Grain)
Shan Jaeschke (Mgr-Agronomy)
Lynn Dreyer (Mgr-HR)
Dennis Knight (Dir-Safety)
Kent Nolting (Mgr-Feed Dep)
Keith Jensen (CFO)
Michael Nelson (Mgr-Blairsburg Location)
Doug Yetmar (Mgr-Reg 2)
Arthur Free (Mgr-Lanesboro Location)
Tyler Toyne (Mgr-Lanyon Location)
Frank Huseman (Mgr-Ops)
Gary Devereaux (Mgr-Palmer Location)
Brian Wagner (Pres)

NEW COUNTRY LEXUS OF WESTPORT
1317 Post Rd E, Westport, CT 06880
Tel.: (203) 255-1531
Web Site: http://www.newcountrylexusofwestport.com
Rev.: $26,000,000
Emp.: 24
Automobile Dealership
N.A.I.C.S.: 441110
Chris Frillici (Mgr-Body Shop)

NEW COUNTRY MOTOR CAR GROUP INC.
358 Broadway Ste 403, Saratoga Springs, NY 12866
Tel.: (518) 584-7700   NY
Web Site: http://www.newcountry.com
Sales Range: $150-199.9 Million
Emp.: 925
New & Used Automobiles Retailer
N.A.I.C.S.: 561110
Michael Cantanucci (Pres)
Carl Leuchton (CFO)
Chris Mackey (VP)
Timothy Parker (Reg VP)

NEW CREATURE
2003 Horsebarn Rd Ste 4, Rogers, AR 72758
Tel.: (479) 273-7377
Web Site: http://www.new-creature.com
Year Founded: 1999
Sales Range: $25-49.9 Million
Emp.: 25
Setup Paperboard Box Mfr

N.A.I.C.S.: 322219
Joe March (CFO)

NEW CREDIT AMERICA, LLC
PO Box 9125, Portland, OR 97207-9125
Web Site: http://www.newcreditamerica.com
Year Founded: 2014
Sales Range: $10-24.9 Million
Emp.: 42
Consumer Lending Services
N.A.I.C.S.: 522291
Todd Rice (Founder & CEO)

NEW DAY DIAGNOSTICS LLC
138 NW 16th St, Boca Raton, FL 33432
Tel.: (561) 705-0452
Medical Equipment Mfr
N.A.I.C.S.: 339112
Navroze Mehta (Founder & CEO)

NEW DAY MARKETING, LTD.
923 Olive St, Santa Barbara, CA 93101
Tel.: (805) 965-7833
Web Site: http://www.newdaymarketing.com
Year Founded: 1987
Sales Range: $50-74.9 Million
Emp.: 20
Media Buying Services
N.A.I.C.S.: 541810
Robert Hunt (Pres)
Jeff Thomson (VP)

NEW DEAL MERCANTILE INC.
7130 Gateway Blvd E, El Paso, TX 79915
Tel.: (915) 778-9230
Web Site: http://www.newdealsfurniture.com
Rev.: $12,640,536
Emp.: 50
Furniture Retailer
N.A.I.C.S.: 449110
John Falbey (Pres)
Juanita Falbey (Owner)

NEW DESSERTS
550 85th Ave, Oakland, CA 94621
Tel.: (510) 567-2900
Web Site: http://www.justdesserts.com
Year Founded: 1974
Rev.: $14,000,000
Emp.: 120
Retail Bakeries
N.A.I.C.S.: 311821
Susan Caldwell (Controller)
Mani Niall (Exec Chef)

NEW DIMENSIONS INC.
10687 Daskins Way, Manassas, VA 20109
Tel.: (703) 361-1605
Web Site: http://www.newdimensionsinc.com
Year Founded: 1988
Rev.: $20,000,000
Emp.: 20
New Construction, Single-Family Houses
N.A.I.C.S.: 236115
Scott Alderson (Owner & CEO)
Vincent Charlton (Project Mgr)

NEW DIXIE OIL CORPORATION
1501 Marshall St, Roanoke Rapids, NC 27870
Tel.: (252) 537-4118
Web Site: http://www.newdixieoil.com
Sales Range: $25-49.9 Million
Emp.: 225
Kerosene

N.A.I.C.S.: 424720
Scott Aman (Pres)
John Elam (Mgr-Ops)

NEW DOMINION PACKAGING COMPANY INC.
186 Dillard Rd, Madison Heights, VA 24572-2530
Tel.: (434) 929-6701
Year Founded: 2002
Sales Range: $10-24.9 Million
Emp.: 100
Folding Carton Mfr & Distr
N.A.I.C.S.: 322212
Tom Scott (Owner)

NEW EARTH LIFE SCIENCES, INC.
565 Century Ct, Klamath Falls, OR 97601
Tel.: (541) 882-5406   DE
Web Site: http://www.newearth.com
Sales Range: $10-24.9 Million
Emp.: 100
Nutritional Supplements Mfr & Distr
N.A.I.C.S.: 325412
Jerry Anderson (Pres)
Doug Jackson (VP-Ops)
Ann Wilson (Dir-Customer Svc)
Jean Gleason (CFO)
Bilal Ruknuddeen (CEO)
Kevin Larson (VP-Sls & Field Dev)

NEW EDITIONS CONSULTING, INC.
6858 Old Dominion Dr Ste 230, McLean, VA 22101
Tel.: (703) 356-8035
Web Site: http://www.neweditions.net
Year Founded: 1987
Rev.: $7,000,000
Emp.: 41
Administrative Management & General Management Consulting Services
N.A.I.C.S.: 541611
Shelia S. Newman (Founder, Owner & Pres)
Cindy Ryan (VP)
Christine Domzal (Sr Mgr-Res)
Kathryn Becker (Dir-Creative)
Tracy Turner (Dir-Bus)
Tracy Mills (CFO)
Stephanie Mensh (Dir-Project)
Nicholas Truesdell (Mgr-Programmer & IT)
Catherine Savino (Program Dir)
Anna Lenhart (Project Mgr)
Tyler Matney (Project Mgr)
Jayme Pendergraft (Project Mgr)
Cherie Takemoto (Project Mgr)
Jane Rath (VP)

NEW ENERGY SYSTEMS GROUP
116 W 23rd St 5th Fl, New York, NY 10011
Tel.: (917) 573-0302   NV
Web Site: http://www.newenergysystemsgroup.com
Year Founded: 2001
Sales Range: $50-74.9 Million
Emp.: 428
Battery Mfr
N.A.I.C.S.: 335910
Junfeng Chen (CFO & Sec)
Weihe Yu (Chm & CEO)

NEW ENGLAND AIR SYSTEMS INC.
43 Krupp Dr, Williston, VT 05495
Tel.: (802) 864-3800
Web Site: http://www.neair.com
Year Founded: 1972
Sales Range: $10-24.9 Million
Emp.: 125

NEW ENGLAND AIR SYSTEMS INC.

New England Air Systems Inc.—(Continued)
Mechanical Contractor
N.A.I.C.S.: 238220
Stephen Bartlett (Pres)
Jason Noel (Project Mgr)

NEW ENGLAND AQUARIUM
Central Wharf, Boston, MA 02110-3399
Tel.: (617) 973-5200 MA
Web Site: http://www.neaq.org
Year Founded: 1957
Sales Range: $25-49.9 Million
Emp.: 435
Aquarium Operator
N.A.I.C.S.: 712130
Donna K. Hazard (Chm)
Daniel S. Evans (Sec)
Vikki Spruill (Pres & CEO)
Lauren Hunter-Dyson (VP-Talent & Culture)

NEW ENGLAND CAPITAL PARTNERS, INC.
One Gateway Center Ste 405, Newton, MA 02458
Tel.: (617) 964-7300 DE
Web Site: http://www.necapitalpartners.com
Emp.: 3
Privater Equity Firm
N.A.I.C.S.: 523999
Kevin M. McCafferty (Chm)

NEW ENGLAND COUNTRY PIES, INC.
736 Milford Rd, Merrimack, NH 03054
Tel.: (603) 883-7111 NH
Year Founded: 1984
Sales Range: $1-9.9 Million
Emp.: 25
Freshly Baked Fruit & Cream Pies, Soups & Sandwiches
N.A.I.C.S.: 311812
Joseph Lannan (CEO & Owner)

NEW ENGLAND DEVELOPMENT CORPORATION
75 Park Plz Ste 3, Boston, MA 02116
Tel.: (617) 965-8700
Web Site: http://www.nedevelopment.com
Year Founded: 1978
Sales Range: $1-9.9 Million
Emp.: 150
Land Subdivision
N.A.I.C.S.: 237210
Stephen R. Karp (Founder, Chm & CEO)
Steven S. Fischman (Pres)
Bruce M. Herman (Exec VP & Controller)
Armen D. Aftandilian (Exec VP-Dev)
Carol F. Carbonaro (Exec VP-Leasing)
Kenneth A. Leibowitz (Exec VP-Acq & Fin)
Paul O. McGinn (Pres-MarketPlace Dev)
James A. Fischer (Sr VP-Plng, Design & Construction)
Issie Shait (Sr VP-Property Mgmt)
Diane C. Retzky (VP-HR)
T J Just (Gen Mgr-Outlets-Des Moines)

NEW ENGLAND FARM WORKERS COUNCIL INC.
11-13 Hampden St, Springfield, MA 01103
Tel.: (413) 781-2145 CT
Year Founded: 1971
Sales Range: $50-74.9 Million
Emp.: 664

Humane Welfare Services
N.A.I.C.S.: 624190
Vanessa Otero (Treas)
Joseph Greene (VP)
Heriberto Flores (Chm & Pres)
John Motto (CFO)

NEW ENGLAND FOUNDATION CO. INC.
1 Westinghouse Plz Ste D, Hyde Park, MA 02136
Tel.: (617) 689-0550
Web Site: http://www.nefco.com
Year Founded: 1913
Rev.: $15,000,000
Emp.: 66
Foundation & Footing Contractor
N.A.I.C.S.: 238110
Anne McMahon (Controller)

NEW ENGLAND INVESTMENT & RETIREMENT GROUP, INC.
231 Sutton St Ste 2A & 2B, North Andover, MA 01845
Tel.: (978) 975-2559
Web Site: http://www.neinv.com
Year Founded: 1995
Sales Range: $1-9.9 Million
Emp.: 13
Investment Advisory Services
N.A.I.C.S.: 523940
Nick Giacoumakis (Founder & Co-Pres)
Laura Giacoumakis (Co-Pres)
Les Satlow (Dir-Res & Sr Portfolio Mgr)
Patrick Sheppard (COO & Chief Compliance Officer)

NEW ENGLAND LAW BOSTON
154 Stuart St, Boston, MA 02116
Tel.: (617) 451-0010 MA
Web Site: http://www.nesl.edu
Year Founded: 1908
Sales Range: $25-49.9 Million
Emp.: 316
Law Firm
N.A.I.C.S.: 541110
Casey Hoskins (Pres)

NEW ENGLAND LEAD BURNING CO.
2 Burlington Woods Ste 300, Burlington, MA 01803-4543
Tel.: (781) 933-1940
Web Site: http://www.nelco-usa.com
Sales Range: $25-49.9 Million
Emp.: 100
Decontamination Services
N.A.I.C.S.: 334413
Richard Le Blanc (Pres & CEO)

NEW ENGLAND LIFE CARE INC.
600 Southborough Dr, South Portland, ME 04106
Tel.: (207) 321-6352
Web Site: http://www.nelifecare.org
Sales Range: $10-24.9 Million
Emp.: 25
Home Infusion Therapy/Specialty Pharmacy
N.A.I.C.S.: 456199
Tom Sahrmann (CFO)
Andrew Heindl (VP-Partnership Dev)

NEW ENGLAND LIFE FLIGHT, INC.
Robins St Hngr 1727 Hanscom Air Force Base, Bedford, MA 01730
Tel.: (781) 863-2213
Web Site: http://www.bostonmedflight.org
Year Founded: 1985
Rev.: $13,010,118
Emp.: 120

Critical Care Transport Service
N.A.I.C.S.: 481219
Charles Blathras (Mgr-Program)
Andrew Farkas (COO)
Maura Hughes (CFO)

NEW ENGLAND LOW VISION & BLINDNESS
799 W Boylston St Ste 140, Worcester, MA 01606
Tel.: (508) 853-8200
Web Site: http://www.nelowvision.com
Year Founded: 1992
Emp.: 112
Visual Impairment Products, Sales & Assessments
N.A.I.C.S.: 333310
Kelly Krug (Mgr-Fin)
Scott V. Krug (Pres)
David Keeler (Gen Mgr)
Michelle Perkins (Specialist-Assistive Tech)

Subsidiaries:

Vision Dynamics, LLC (1)
470 W Main St, Cheshire, CT 06410-2450 (100%)
Tel.: (203) 271-1944
Web Site: http://www.visiondynamics.com
Low Vision & Blindness Aids, Products & Assessments
N.A.I.C.S.: 456130
Charles J. Collins (CEO)
Randolph Kinkade (Chief Medical Officer)

NEW ENGLAND MEDICAL TRANSCRIPTION
375 George Wright Rd, Woolwich, ME 04579
Tel.: (207) 443-6919
Web Site: http://www.nemtinc.com
Year Founded: 1990
Rev.: $3,800,000
Emp.: 4
Medical Transcription
N.A.I.C.S.: 621511
Linda Sullivan (Principal)
Richard P. Sullivan (VP)
Holly Lagner (Mgr-HR)

NEW ENGLAND MOBILE BOOK FAIR
8284 Needham St, Newton, MA 02461
Tel.: (617) 527-5817
Web Site: http://www.nebookfair.com
Sales Range: $10-24.9 Million
Emp.: 40
Whslr of Books
N.A.I.C.S.: 424920
Tom Lyons (Owner)

NEW ENGLAND MOTOR FREIGHT, INC.
1-71 N Ave E, Elizabeth, NJ 07201-2936
Tel.: (908) 965-0100 NJ
Web Site: http://www.nemf.com
Year Founded: 1918
Sales Range: $400-449.9 Million
Emp.: 2,165
Trucking & Logistics
N.A.I.C.S.: 484122
Craig Eisenberg (CFO)
Myron P. Shevell (Chm)

Subsidiaries:

Carrier Industries (1)
212 Black Horse Ln, North Brunswick, NJ 08902-4319
Tel.: (732) 287-7930
Web Site: http://www.carrierindustries.com
Rev.: $40,000,000
Emp.: 200
Freight Transportation Arrangement
N.A.I.C.S.: 484122

U.S. PRIVATE

NEW ENGLAND OFFICE SUPPLY INC.
135 Lundquist Dr, Braintree, MA 02184
Tel.: (781) 794-8800
Web Site: http://www.neosusa.com
Rev.: $15,300,000
Emp.: 80
Stationery & Office Supplies
N.A.I.C.S.: 424120
Indira Patel (Pres & CEO)
Dennis McCarthy (VP-Ops)
Daniel Hooley (Mgr-Print Production)
Jamie Boutilier (Sr Acct Exec)

NEW ENGLAND ORGAN BANK
60 1st Ave, Waltham, MA 02451-1106
Tel.: (617) 558-6653
Web Site: http://www.neob.org
Rev.: $23,873,301
Emp.: 127
Organ Procurement Services
N.A.I.C.S.: 621991
Francis L. Delmonico (Dir-Medical)
Richard S. Luskin (Pres & CEO)
Briana Torrey (Coord-Donation)
Denise Batchelder (Coord-Donation)

NEW ENGLAND PLASTICS CORP
310 Salem St, Woburn, MA 01801
Tel.: (781) 933-6004
Web Site: http://www.newenglandplastics.com
Sales Range: $10-24.9 Million
Emp.: 85
Thermoformed Finished Plastics Products
N.A.I.C.S.: 326113
Robert Kearin (Pres)
Michael Famiglietti (Treas)
Rick Morin (Engr)

NEW ENGLAND PRESS SERVICE
370 Common St, Dedham, MA 02026
Tel.: (781) 320-8050
Web Site: http://www.nenpa.com
Year Founded: 1950
Sales Range: Less than $1 Million
Emp.: 4
Newspapers
N.A.I.C.S.: 541810
Linda Conway (Dir-Bus Dev)
Latifa Sanchez (Adv Network Manager)
Lindsay Ford (Mgr-Adv Ops)

NEW ENGLAND SYSTEMS, INC.
102 Great Hill Rd, Naugatuck, CT 06770
Tel.: (203) 723-4431
Web Site: http://www.nsiserve.com
Year Founded: 1985
Computer & Data Processing Equipment Repair & Sale
N.A.I.C.S.: 811210
Thomas McDonald (Pres)

NEW ENGLAND TECHNOLOGY GROUP, INC.
1 Davenport St, Cambridge, MA 02140-1402
Tel.: (617) 864-5551 MA
Web Site: http://www.netgworld.com
Year Founded: 1981
Sales Range: $50-74.9 Million
Emp.: 10
Producer of Interactive Programs
N.A.I.C.S.: 334118

NEW ENGLAND TRADING GLOBAL, INC.

389 W Elm St, Pembroke, MA 02359
Tel.: (781) 826-7143
Web Site:
http://www.netglobalboston.com
Year Founded: 2004
Sales Range: $10-24.9 Million
Emp.: 7
Metal Mining Services
N.A.I.C.S.: 213114
Skip Aluisy *(Pres)*
Susan Edwards *(VP-Fin)*
Steven Aluisy *(VP-Sls)*
Joan Brigham *(Mgr-Sls-Eastern Reg)*

NEW ENGLAND TRUCK SALES & SERVICES INC.
15 E Industrial Rd, Branford, CT 06405
Tel.: (203) 481-0373   CT
Web Site: http://www.netruck.com
Year Founded: 1942
Rev.: $31,000,000
Emp.: 55
Sales of New & Used Commercial Trucks
N.A.I.C.S.: 423110
Gerald Beauton Jr. *(Pres)*

NEW ENGLAND WOODEN WARE CORP.
205 School St, Gardner, MA 01440
Tel.: (978) 632-3600
Web Site:
http://www.newoodenware.com
Rev.: $25,000,000
Emp.: 140
Mfr of Corrugated Boxes
N.A.I.C.S.: 322211
Nancy White *(Mgr-HR)*

NEW ENTERPRISE ASSOCIATES, LLC
1954 Greenspring Dr Ste 600, Timonium, MD 21093-4135
Tel.: (410) 842-4000   DE
Web Site: http://www.nea.com
Sales Range: $25-49.9 Million
Emp.: 100
Investment Services
N.A.I.C.S.: 523999
Louis Citron *(Chief Admin Officer & Chief Legal Officer)*
Forest Baskett *(Gen Partner-Menlo Park)*
Anthony Florence *(Gen Partner & Head-Tech Investing)*
Tim Schaller *(CFO & COO)*
Peter J. Barris *(Chm & Gen Partner-Washington)*
Peter Sonsini *(Gen Partner)*
Justin Klein *(Partner)*
Carmen Chang *(Gen Partner)*
Jon Sakoda *(Gen Partner-Menlo Park)*
Josh Makower *(Gen Partner)*
Sara Nayeem *(Partner)*
Amit Mukherjee *(Partner)*
Vanessa Larco *(Partner-Bay Area)*
Mohamad Makhzoumi *(Gen Partner & Head-Healthcare Svcs & Healthcare IT Investing)*
Albert Lee *(Partner-Design)*
Holly Rose Faith *(Partner-Talent)*
Stephen N. Oesterle *(Venture Partner)*
Andrew Schoen *(Principal-New York)*
Blake Wu *(Partner-Healthcare Investing Team)*
Ben Narasin *(Partner)*
Aaron Jacobson *(Partner)*
Kavita Patel *(Venture Partner-Healthcare)*
Richard C. Kramlich *(Co-Founder & Chm)*
Jonathan Golden *(Partner-Menlo Park & San Francisco)*
Matthew McAviney *(Principal-Healthcare Team-Menlo Park & San Francisco)*
Tak Cheung *(Principal-Healthcare Team-Menlo Park & San Francisco)*
Crystal Huang *(Principal)*
Ed Matherg *(Gen Partner)*
Rick Yang *(Gen Partner & Head-Consumer Tech Investing)*
Danielle Lay *(Principal)*
Luke Pappas *(Principal)*
Jai Sajnani *(Principal)*
Tony Florence *(Gen Partner & Head-Tech Investing)*
Scott R. Gottlieb *(Partner)*
Liza Landsman *(Gen Partner)*
Elliott Sigal *(Partner-Venture)*
Kavita K. Patel *(Venture Partner)*
Philip Chopin *(Partner)*
Liza K. Landsman *(Gen Partner)*
Dayna B. Grayson *(Partner-Washington)*
Jeffrey R. Immelt *(Venture Partner)*
Hilarie Koplow-McAdams *(Venture Partner)*
Paul S. Walker *(Gen Partner)*
Carol G. Gallagher *(Partner-Menlo Park)*
Ali Behbahani *(Gen Partner)*
Frank A. Bonsal III *(Founder)*
Scott D. Sandell *(Mng Gen Partner)*
Edward T. Mathers *(Partner)*
Subsidiaries:

Everside Health, LLC   (1)
1400 Wewatta St., Ste. 350, Denver, CO 80202
Tel.: (866) 808-6005
Web Site: https://www.eversidehealth.com
Sales Range: $10-24.9 Million
Emp.: 5
Health Care Srvices
N.A.I.C.S.: 622110
Allison Velez *(Chief People Officer)*
Chris Miller *(CEO)*
Heather Dixon *(CFO)*
Adam Johnson *(Chief Growth & Strategy Officer)*
Heather Dixon *(CFO)*

Subsidiary (Domestic):

Healthstat, Inc.   (2)
4601 Charlotte Park Dr Ste 390, Charlotte, NC 28217-1900
Tel.: (704) 529-6161
Web Site: http://www.healthstatinc.com
Ambulatory Health Care Services
N.A.I.C.S.: 621999
Melissa Parks *(Dir-Recruiting)*
Phillip Franklin *(Chief Medical Officer)*

NEW ENTERPRISE STONE & LIME CO., INC.
3912 Brumbaugh Rd, New Enterprise, PA 16664
Tel.: (814) 766-2211
Web Site: http://www.nesl.com
Year Founded: 1924
Sales Range: $600-649.9 Million
Emp.: 2,415
Crushed & Broken Limestone Services
N.A.I.C.S.: 212312
Donald L. Detwiler *(Vice Chm)*
Daryl Black *(Chief Acctg Officer & Controller)*
Robert J. Schmidt *(COO & Exec VP)*
Paul I. Detwiler III *(Pres & CEO)*
Paul I. Detwiler Jr. *(Chm)*
Subsidiaries:

ABC Paving Co. Inc.   (1)
500 Como Park Blvd, Cheektowaga, NY 14227
Tel.: (716) 826-7310
Sales Range: $10-24.9 Million
Contractor of Highway & Street Paving
N.A.I.C.S.: 237310
Steve Detwiler *(CEO)*

ASTI Transportation Systems Inc.   (1)
18 Blevins Dr, New Castle, DE 19720-4152
Tel.: (302) 328-3220
Web Site: http://www.asti-trans.com
Sales Range: $10-24.9 Million
Emp.: 12
HIghway Information Systems
N.A.I.C.S.: 334290

Buffalo Crushed Stone, Inc.   (1)
2544 Clinton St, West Seneca, NY 14224
Tel.: (716) 823-6745
Web Site:
http://www.buffalocrushedstone.com
Sales Range: $1-9.9 Million
Emp.: 15
Ground or Treated Mineral & Earth Mfr
N.A.I.C.S.: 327992

Plant (Domestic):

Buffalo Crushed Stone, Inc. - Alfred Sand and Gravel Plant   (2)
638 State Route 244, Alfred, NY 14803-0038
Tel.: (607) 587-8102
Web Site: http://www.nesl.com
Stone Product Mfr
N.A.I.C.S.: 327991
Jamie Hypnarowski *(Pres)*

Buffalo Crushed Stone, Inc. - Barton Road Blacktop Plant   (2)
91 Barton Rd, Clarence, NY 14031
Tel.: (716) 631-7500
Concrete Products Mfr
N.A.I.C.S.: 327390

Buffalo Crushed Stone, Inc. - Como Park Blacktop Plant   (2)
500 Como Park Blvd, Cheektowaga, NY 14227
Tel.: (716) 683-3700
Hot Mix Asphalt Mfr
N.A.I.C.S.: 327390

Buffalo Crushed Stone, Inc. - Franklinville Sand and Gravel Plant   (2)
Route 16 N Route 98, Franklinville, NY 14737-0106
Tel.: (716) 566-9636
Web Site:
http://www.buffalocrushedstone.com
Emp.: 13
Stone Product Mfr
N.A.I.C.S.: 327991
Bridget Fox *(Gen Mgr)*

Buffalo Crushed Stone, Inc. - Olean Blacktop Plant   (2)
Constitution Ave, Olean, NY 14760
Tel.: (716) 372-8900
Emp.: 5
Hot Mix Asphalt Mfr
N.A.I.C.S.: 327390
Tim Fox *(Gen Mgr)*

EJB Paving & Materials Co.   (1)
1119 Snyder Rd, West Lawn, PA 19609
Tel.: (610) 678-1913
Web Site: http://www.ejbreneman.com
Highway & Street Construction Services
N.A.I.C.S.: 237310
Phil Wagner *(Partner)*

Eastern Industries, Inc.   (1)
4401 Camp Meeting Rd, Center Valley, PA 18034-9467
Tel.: (610) 866-0932
Web Site: http://www.eastern-ind.com
Sales Range: $25-49.9 Million
Emp.: 70
Building Material Supplier
N.A.I.C.S.: 423320
Dave Resh *(Mgr-Pur)*
John Pruzinsky *(Gen Mgr-Sls)*
Lucy Schlottman *(Supvr-Billing)*
Dave Seaman *(Mgr-Heavy Equipment)*

Plant (Domestic):

Eastern Industries, Inc. - Bethlehem Plant   (2)
1010 E Market St, Bethlehem, PA 18017
Tel.: (610) 759-3334
Hot Mix Asphalt Mfr
N.A.I.C.S.: 327390

Gateway Trade Center, Inc.   (1)
2544 Clinton St, Buffalo, NY 14224
Tel.: (716) 826-7310
Web Site: http://www.portofbuffalo.com
Port Operator
N.A.I.C.S.: 488310
Steven B. Detwiler *(Pres)*
Jim Pfohl *(Dir-Port)*
Joseph S. Laraiso *(Exec VP)*

Precision Solar Controls Inc.   (1)
2985 Market St, Garland, TX 75041-2429
Tel.: (972) 278-0553
Web Site:
http://www.precisionsolarcontrols.com
Sales Range: $25-49.9 Million
Emp.: 78
Traffic Signal & Message Boards Mfr
N.A.I.C.S.: 335139

Valley Quarries Inc.   (1)
297 Quarry Rd, Chambersburg, PA 17202
Tel.: (717) 267-2244
Web Site: http://www.valleyquarries.com
Sales Range: $10-24.9 Million
Emp.: 13
Producer of Central Mixed Concrete
N.A.I.C.S.: 327320
Paul Detweiler *(Pres)*
Joseph Zimmerman *(Exec VP)*

Plant (Domestic):

Valley Quarries Inc. - Chambersburg Plant   (2)
2921 Stone Quarry Rd, Chambersburg, PA 17202
Tel.: (717) 264-5811
Stone Product Mfr
N.A.I.C.S.: 327991

Valley Quarries Inc. - Gettysburg Plant   (2)
1575 Baltimore Pike, Gettysburg, PA 17325
Tel.: (717) 334-3831
Stone Product Mfr
N.A.I.C.S.: 327991

Valley Quarries Inc. - Mt. Cydonia Plant I   (2)
1071 Mount Cydonia Rd, Fayetteville, PA 17222
Tel.: (717) 352-3588
Sand Quarrying Services
N.A.I.C.S.: 212321

Valley Quarries Inc. - Mt. Cydonia Plant II   (2)
243 Black Gap Rd, Fayetteville, PA 17222
Tel.: (717) 352-7081
Sand Quarrying Services
N.A.I.C.S.: 212321

Valley Quarries Inc. - Shippensburg Plant   (2)
472 Newville Rd, Shippensburg, PA 17257
Tel.: (717) 532-4161
Concrete Products Mfr
N.A.I.C.S.: 327390

NEW ERA BUILDERS
36445 Biltmore Pl Ste A, Willoughby, OH 44094-8228
Tel.: (440) 942-4900
Web Site: http://www.new-era-builders.com
Year Founded: 1989
Sales Range: $10-24.9 Million
Emp.: 21
Commercial & Industrial Construction Services
N.A.I.C.S.: 236220
Joe Lopez *(Founder & Pres)*

NEW ERA LIFE INSURANCE COMPANY OF THE MIDWEST
200 W Lk Pk Blvd Ste 1200, Houston, TX 77079
Tel.: (281) 368-7200
Web Site: http://www.neweralife.com
Sales Range: $50-74.9 Million
Emp.: 200
Life Insurance Agency
N.A.I.C.S.: 524210
Bill Chen *(Pres & CEO)*

NEW ERA LIFE INSURANCE COMPANY OF THE MIDWEST — U.S. PRIVATE

New Era Life Insurance Company of the Midwest—(Continued)

Subsidiaries:

Philadelphia American Life Insurance (1)
200 Westlake Park Blvd Ste 1200, Houston, TX 77079
Tel.: (281) 368-7200
Web Site: http://www.neweralife.com
Sales Range: $50-74.9 Million
Emp.: 170
Life Insurance
N.A.I.C.S.: 524113

NEW ERA PORTFOLIO
2101 E St Elmo Rd Ste 110, Austin, TX 78744
Tel.: (512) 928-3200
Web Site: http://www.newerahd.com
Year Founded: 2000
Sales Range: $10-24.9 Million
Emp.: 75
Limited Edition Prints
N.A.I.C.S.: 323111
Joseph Garcia (Founder & CEO)
Amy Johnson (Mgr-Customer Experience)
Elizabeth Watson (Mgr-Customer Experience)
Sean Evans (Sr Mgr-Ops)
Candice Benge (Mgr-Studio)
Don Hickson (Mgr-Shipping)
Darron Green (VP-Bus Ops)

NEW ERA TECHNOLOGY
1155 Phoenixville Pike Ste 114-115, West Chester, PA 19380
Tel.: (877) 696-7720
Web Site: https://www.neweratech.com
Year Founded: 1988
Rev.: $1,100,000
Emp.: 150
Power & Communication Line & Related Structures Construction
N.A.I.C.S.: 237130
Kevin Flounders (Owner)
David Johnson (Pres)

NEW ERA TECHNOLOGY, INC.
1370 Ave of the Americas 10th Fl, New York, NY 10019
Tel.: (617) 367-7474
Web Site: http://www.neweratech.com
Information Technology Services
N.A.I.C.S.: 519290
Maureen Gochenauer (Mgr-Pur)
Joe Ewart (CEO)
Marina Gregory (COO)
Punit Dewan (CFO)
Mike Harmon (Chief Sls Officer)
Jaie Solis (Pres-Enterprise Solutions Group)
Sean Doherty (Pres-Technology Solution Group)
Nick Grogan (Pres-Midmarket Solution Group)

Subsidiaries:

Cameo Solutions (1)
9078 Union Ctr Blvd Ste 200, West Chester Township, OH 45069
Tel.: (513) 645-4220
Information Services
N.A.I.C.S.: 519290

NEW EVOLUTION VENTURES, LLC
3595 Mt Diablo Blvd Ste 300, Lafayette, CA 94549
Tel.: (925) 297-6360 DE
Web Site: http://www.nev.com
Venture Capital Firm
N.A.I.C.S.: 523999

Jim Rowley (Co-Founder & CEO)
Mike Feeney (Exec VP)
Mark Mastrov (Co-Founder)

NEW FLIGHT CHARTERS
525 Ponderosa Dr, Jackson, WY 83001
Tel.: (307) 734-7750
Web Site: http://www.newflightcharters.com
Year Founded: 2003
Rev.: $7,100,000
Emp.: 9
Logistics & Transportation Services
N.A.I.C.S.: 481219
Nanette Poorman (Mgr-Charter)
Blake Smith (Mgr-Charter)
Michelle Murphy (Mgr-Charter)
Richard Colson (Pres)
Mark Baroni (Mgr-Charter)

NEW GARDEN LANDSCAPING & NURSERY INC.
5577 Garden Village Way, Greensboro, NC 27410
Tel.: (336) 665-0291
Web Site: http://www.newgarden.com
Sales Range: $10-24.9 Million
Emp.: 150
Landscape Contractors & Retail Nursery
N.A.I.C.S.: 561730
Morris Newlin (Owner)
Conrad Hayter (Pres)

NEW GLARUS BREWING COMPANY
2400 State Hwy 69, New Glarus, WI 53574
Tel.: (608) 527-5850 WI
Web Site: http://www.newglarusbrewing.com
Year Founded: 1993
Sales Range: $25-49.9 Million
Emp.: 70
Malt Beverage Mfr
N.A.I.C.S.: 312120
Dan Carey (Co-Owner)
Deborah Carey (Founder & Pres)

NEW GOLD DISCOVERIES, INC.
31878 Del Obispo St Ste 118-331, San Juan Capistrano, CA 92675 WY
Year Founded: 2015
Emp.: 1
Gold Mining Services
N.A.I.C.S.: 212220
Jerome Banks (CEO & Sec)

NEW HAMPSHIRE ELECTRIC COOPERATIVE INC.
579 Tenney Mtn Hwy, Plymouth, NH 03264-3154
Tel.: (603) 536-1800
Web Site: http://www.nhec.com
Year Founded: 1939
Sales Range: $25-49.9 Million
Emp.: 200
Electronic Services
N.A.I.C.S.: 221122
Brenda Inman (Mgr-Fin Svcs)
Lisa Work (Supvr-Credit)
Steven Camerino (Pres & CEO)

NEW HAMPSHIRE HOUSING FINANCE AUTHORITY
32 Constitution Dr, Bedford, NH 03110-6000
Tel.: (603) 472-8623 NH
Web Site: http://www.nhhfa.org
Year Founded: 1975
Sales Range: $100-124.9 Million
Emp.: 110
Real Estate Agents & Managers
N.A.I.C.S.: 925110

Dean Christon (Exec Dir)
Christopher R. Miller (Mng Dir-Mgmt & Dev)
Patricia Donahue (Mng Dir-HR & Admin)
Andrew Boyle (Dir-Asset Mgmt)
Ronald Gaudio (Mgr-Mortgage Servicing)
David Hebert (Mng Dir-IT)
Sandra Kenney (Controller)
Dee Ann Pouliot (Dir-Assisted Housing Div)
David B. Sargent (Mng Dir-Fin & CFO)
James Menihane (Dir-Housing Dev)
William Ray (Dir-Plng & Policy)
Lynn Greenleaf Lippitt (Dir-Housing Svcs)
Deborah Granfield (Dir-Rental Assistance)
Brenda Southmayd Mahoney (Dir-Bus Dev)
Chris McNally (Dir-Sys Admin)
Ignatius MacLellan (Mng Dir-Homeownership)
Rob Dapice (Mng Dir-Mgmt & Dev)

NEW HAMPSHIRE INDUSTRIES INC.
35 Connecticut Riverbend Pl, Claremont, NH 03743
Tel.: (603) 448-1090
Web Site: http://www.nhi-mfg.com
Rev.: $12,000,000
Emp.: 150
Pulleys, Metal
N.A.I.C.S.: 332510
John Batten (Pres)
John Seaver (CFO)

NEW HAMPSHIRE PLASTICS INC.
1 Bouchard St, Manchester, NH 03103
Tel.: (603) 669-8523
Year Founded: 1971
Sales Range: $10-24.9 Million
Emp.: 100
Plastic Films & Sheets Mfr
N.A.I.C.S.: 326113
Kevin Dale (Mgr-Sls)

NEW HANOVER COUNTY ABC BOARD
523 S 17th St, Wilmington, NC 28401
Tel.: (910) 762-7611
Web Site: http://www.ncabc.com
Year Founded: 1935
Sales Range: $25-49.9 Million
Emp.: 40
Retailer of Liquor Stores
N.A.I.C.S.: 445320
Cedric A. Dickerson (Vice Chm)
Michael Herring (Chief Admin Officer)

NEW HARBOR CAPITAL MANAGEMENT LLC
500 W Madison Ste 2830, Chicago, IL 60661
Tel.: (312) 876-8605
Web Site: http://www.newharborcap.com
Private Equity Firm
N.A.I.C.S.: 523999
Tom Formolo (Partner)
Ed Lhee (Partner)
Jocelyn Stanley (Partner)
Nicki Lambropoulos (VP-Portfolio Fin)
John Roselli (Partner-Operating)
Kevin Bochenek (VP-Fin & Admin)
Michelle Montgomery (Mgr-Acctg)
Hayley Formolo (Mgr-Mktg)

Subsidiaries:

Certica Solutions, Inc. (1)
301 Edgewater Pl, Wakefield, MA 01880
Tel.: (781) 245-4515
Web Site: http://www.certicasolutions.com
Rev.: $1,200,000
Emp.: 14
Data Processing, Hosting & Related Services
N.A.I.C.S.: 518210
Jeffrey Averick (CTO)
Mark Rankovic (Pres)
Sarah Bassett (VP-Client Svcs)
Rodney Green (VP-Sls & Mktg)
Linda Bradshaw (VP-Education Content Products)
Ken Hale (CFO)
Peter Tweed (VP-Software Products)

NEW HAVEN CITY PARKING AUTHORITY
50 Union Ave, New Haven, CT 06519
Tel.: (203) 946-8930
Web Site: http://www.nhparking.com
Sales Range: $10-24.9 Million
Emp.: 115
Provider of Parking Services
N.A.I.C.S.: 812930
Paul Wydra (Dir-Fin)

NEW HERITAGE CAPITAL LLC
Prudential Tower 800 Boylston St Ste 2200, Boston, MA 02199
Tel.: (617) 439-0688
Web Site: http://www.newheritagecapital.com
Year Founded: 2006
Privater Equity Firm
N.A.I.C.S.: 523999
Nickie Norris (Sr Partner, COO & Chief Comml Officer)
Mark Jrolf (Sr Mng Partner)
Tristan Velez (Sr VP-Fin)
Mark Jrolf (Sr Mng Partner)
Melissa Barry (Partner)
Judson Samuels (Partner)
Kyle Veatch (Principal)
Ryan Popper (VP)
Bret Kuchenbecker (VP)
Greg Katz (VP-Bus Dev)
Charles K. Gifford Jr. (Sr Partner)

Subsidiaries:

Continental Services Inc. (1)
700 Stephenson Hwy, Troy, MI 48083
Tel.: (248) 414-1700
Web Site: https://www.continentalserves.com
Catering Services
N.A.I.C.S.: 722320
Matt Hubbard (CEO)
Chris Antoniotti (Dir-Innovative Dining Solutions)
Jennifer Schoenbart (Ops Mgr-Reg)
Jason Olinik (Dir-Dining Ops)
Paul Bardy (VP-Mdsg & Data Science)
Ferris Anthony (Dir-Ops)

DeWinter Holdings, LLC. (1)
1919 S. Bascom Ave Ste 250, Campbell, CA 95008
Tel.: (408) 297-7500
Web Site: https://www.dewintergroup.com
Emp.: 342
Business Services: Staffing
N.A.I.C.S.: 561330
Shane Oberg (CEO & Partner)

Subsidiary (Domestic):

Syrinx Consulting Corporation (2)
160 Gould St 3160, Waltham, MA 02492
Tel.: (781) 487-7800
Web Site: http://www.syrinx.com
Sales Range: $1-9.9 Million
Emp.: 36
Custom Software Applications Mfr
N.A.I.C.S.: 334610
Andrew Gelina (Pres & CEO)
Colin Reposa (VP-Resource Mgmt)
Tony Mastroianni (VP-Dev Svcs)

FMS Solutions Holdings, LLC (1)
800 Corporate Dr Ste 350, Fort Lauderdale, FL 33334
Tel.: (443) 604-7536
Web Site: https://www.fmssolutions.com

COMPANIES — NEW JERSEY LIFE & HEALTH INSURANCE GUARANTY ASSOCIATION

Accounting & Consulting Services
N.A.I.C.S.: 541214
Robert Graybill *(CEO)*

Subsidiary (Domestic):

Retail Financial Services (2)
2800 Campus Dr Ste 44, Minneapolis, MN 55441
Tel.: (763) 545-1033
Web Site: http://www.retailfinancial.net
Other Accounting Services
N.A.I.C.S.: 541219
Julie Lenner *(Owner)*

NEW HILL MANAGEMENT, LLC
225 Franklin St, Boston, MA 02110
Tel.: (617) 217-2770
Web Site: http://www.newhillmgt.com
Investment Management Service
N.A.I.C.S.: 523999
Jeffrey S. Garner *(Mng Partner)*
James Nimmo *(Partner)*
Kenneth E. Freeman *(VP)*

NEW HOLLAND MOTOR COMPANY, INC.
508 W Main St, New Holland, PA 17557
Tel.: (717) 354-4901 PA
Web Site: http://www.newhollandauto.com
Year Founded: 1981
New & Used Car Dealerships Owner & Operator
N.A.I.C.S.: 441110
Charlie Whiteman *(Gen Mgr-Sls)*
Robert Lehman *(Gen Sls Mgr-Toyota)*
Mike Connors *(Dir-Fin & Insurance)*
Jeff Dietrich *(Mgr-Fin & Insurance)*
Bryan Bogin *(Mgr-Sls)*
Jake Spatz *(Dir-Used Car)*
Gregg Kennedy *(Mgr-Sls)*
Rich Christman *(Mgr-Toyota Sls)*
Karen Kase *(Controller)*
Kevin Locke *(Dir-Parts)*
Brent Kerchner *(Mgr-Recon)*
Travis Buzzard *(Mgr-Govt & Comml Sls)*
John Good *(Mgr-Parts-Columbus)*
Mike Bargmann *(Mgr-Toyota Sls)*
Sheri Hackman *(Mgr)*
Carl Crone *(Mgr-Svc)*
Geoff Penske *(Pres)*

NEW HOPE COMMUNITY, INC.
5 New Hope Community Dr, Loch Sheldrake, NY 12759
Tel.: (845) 434-8300 NY
Web Site: http://www.newhopecommunity.org
Year Founded: 1975
Sales Range: $25-49.9 Million
Emp.: 593
Developmental Disability Assistance Services
N.A.I.C.S.: 624190
Tariq Iqbal *(CFO)*
Arthur Moretti *(Exec Dir)*

NEW HORIZON COMMUNICATIONS GROUP
200 Baker Ave Ste 300, Concord, MA 01742
Tel.: (781) 290-4600
Web Site: http://www.nhcgrp.com
Year Founded: 2002
Sales Range: $25-49.9 Million
Emp.: 39
Telecommunications
N.A.I.C.S.: 517810
Robert Fabbricatore *(CEO)*
Stephen Gibbs *(Pres & COO)*

NEW HORIZON COUNSELING CENTER, INC.
108-19 Rockaway Blvd, Ozone Park, NY 11420
Tel.: (718) 845-2620 NY
Web Site: http://www.nhcc.us
Year Founded: 1981
Nonprofit Mental Health Counselor
N.A.I.C.S.: 621420
Flora Bienstock *(Dir-Clinical & Program)*
Herrick Lipton *(Dir-Admin & Fin)*
Isac Bechor *(VP & Exec Dir)*
Sigal Mashall *(Dir-HR)*
Gary Goldstein *(Chm)*
Herrick Lipton *(CEO & Dir-Admin & Fin)*
Flora Bienstock *(Chief Clinical Officer & Dir-Clinical & Program)*
Sigal Mashall *(Chief Admin Officer & Dir-HR)*

NEW HORIZON EQUITY GROUP, INC.
980 9th St 16th Fl, Sacramento, CA 95814
Tel.: (844) 300-5500 CA
Year Founded: 2013
Business Consulting & Support Services
N.A.I.C.S.: 541611
Tracy Smith *(Chm, Pres, CEO, CFO, Treas & Sec)*

NEW HORIZON F S INC.
50071 Highway 64, Miles, IA 52064
Tel.: (563) 886-1600
Sales Range: $10-24.9 Million
Emp.: 120
Farm Supplies
N.A.I.C.S.: 424910
Galen Bronson *(Gen Mgr)*

Subsidiaries:

New Horizon Farm Service (1)
625 First St PO Box 137, De Witt, IA 52742-1901
Tel.: (563) 659-5155
Sales Range: $10-24.9 Million
Emp.: 7
Farm Supplies
N.A.I.C.S.: 457210

NEW HORIZON KIDS QUEST, INC.
3405 Annapolis Ln N Ste 100, Minneapolis, MN 55447-5343
Tel.: (763) 557-1111 MN
Web Site: http://www.kidsquest.com
Sales Range: $50-74.9 Million
Emp.: 500
Developer, Owner & Operator of Supervised Children's Entertainment Facilities
N.A.I.C.S.: 624410
William M. Dunkley *(Chm & CEO)*
Susan K. Dunkley *(Pres)*

NEW HORIZON SUPPLY CO-OPERATIVE
1775 4th St, Fennimore, WI 53809
Tel.: (608) 822-3217
Web Site: http://www.newhorizonsco-op.com
Rev.: $20,035,762
Emp.: 20
Feed
N.A.I.C.S.: 457120

NEW HORIZONS BAKING COMPANY
211 Woodlawn Ave, Norwalk, OH 44857
Tel.: (419) 663-6432
Web Site: http://www.newhorizonsbaking.com
Year Founded: 1973
Rev.: $35,443,412
Emp.: 100
Mfr of Bakery Products
N.A.I.C.S.: 311812
Tilmon F. Brown *(CEO)*

Subsidiaries:

Coalescence, LLC. (1)
3455 Millennium Ct, Columbus, OH 43219
Tel.: (614) 861-3639
Web Site: http://www.coalescencellc.com
Sales Range: $10-24.9 Million
Emp.: 42
Flavor Extract Mfr
N.A.I.C.S.: 311942
Angela N. Cauley *(Co-Founder & CEO)*
Ian Blount *(COO & Sr VP)*
Larry E. Lee *(CFO)*

Graffiti Foods, Ltd. (1)
333 Outerbelt St, Columbus, OH 43213
Tel.: (614) 759-1921
Web Site: http://www.graffitifoods.com
Prepared Sauces Mfr
N.A.I.C.S.: 311941
Lisa Hughes *(Bus Mgr)*

NEW HORIZONS CREDIT UNION
622 Azalea Rd, Mobile, AL 36609
Tel.: (251) 316-3240 AL
Web Site: http://www.newhcu.org
Year Founded: 1950
Sales Range: $10-24.9 Million
Emp.: 82
Financial Management Services
N.A.I.C.S.: 522130
Helen A. Sylvester *(Mgr-Acctg)*
Linda Brown *(Chm)*
Lisa Corvo *(Pres & CEO)*
Edith Franklin *(Controller)*
Ralph Altice *(Vice Chm)*

NEW HORIZONS HEALTH SYSTEMS, INC.
330 Roland Ave, Owenton, KY 40359
Tel.: (502) 484-3663 KY
Web Site: http://www.nhhsonline.com
Year Founded: 2000
Sales Range: $10-24.9 Million
Emp.: 121
Health Care Srvices
N.A.I.C.S.: 622110
Bernard Poe *(Chm & CEO)*
Judy Poe *(Sec)*
Janet Wright *(Vice Chm & Asst CEO)*
Doug Smalara *(Dir-Medical)*
Eric Baumann *(Asst Dir-Medical)*

NEW HORIZONS INCORPORATED
37 Bliss Rd, Unionville, CT 06085
Tel.: (860) 675-4711
Web Site: http://www.newhorizonsvillage.com
Sales Range: $10-24.9 Million
Emp.: 70
Subdividers & Developers
N.A.I.C.S.: 237210
Robert Maher *(CFO)*
Linda Iovanna *(Mgr-HR)*

NEW HORIZONS OF THE TREASURE COAST AND OKEECHOBEE
4500 Midway Rd, Fort Pierce, FL 34981
Tel.: (772) 468-5600 FL
Web Site: http://www.nhtcinc.org
Year Founded: 1958
Sales Range: $10-24.9 Million
Emp.: 447
Behavioral Healthcare Services
N.A.I.C.S.: 623220
John Wolsiefer *(Chm)*
John Romano *(Pres & CEO)*
Robert Zomok *(Treas)*
Garry Wilson *(Vice Chm)*

NEW HORIZONS PICTURE CORP.
11600 San Vicente Blvd, Los Angeles, CA 90049-5102
Tel.: (310) 820-6733 CA
Web Site: http://www.newhorizonspictures.com
Year Founded: 1983
Sales Range: $25-49.9 Million
Emp.: 250
Motion Picture & Video Production Services
N.A.I.C.S.: 512110
Roger Corman *(Co-Founder & Pres)*
Julie Corman *(Co-Founder & VP)*
Germaine Simiens *(VP-Legal Affairs)*
Tom Krentzin *(CFO)*

NEW HORIZONS REHABILITATION SERVICES, INC.
1814 Pond Run, Auburn Hills, MI 48326-2768
Tel.: (248) 340-0559 MI
Web Site: http://www.newhorizonsrehab.org
Year Founded: 1964
Sales Range: $10-24.9 Million
Emp.: 1,224
Disability Assistance Services
N.A.I.C.S.: 624120
Jason Kaszubski *(Dir-HR)*
Stan A. Gramke *(Pres & CEO)*
Tim Hatfield *(VP-Rehabilitation)*
Beth Alberti *(Sec)*
David Lubin *(Vice Chm)*
Leo Kujawa *(Chm)*
Marvin Keller *(Treas)*
David Stoker *(Dir-Mfg)*
Dawn Caracallo *(Dir-PR)*
Angela Rainge *(Dir-Fin)*

NEW ISRAEL FUND
6 E 39 St Ste 301, New York, NY 10016
Tel.: (212) 613-4400 CA
Web Site: http://www.nif.org
Year Founded: 1979
Sales Range: $25-49.9 Million
Emp.: 45
Grantmaking Services
N.A.I.C.S.: 813211
Thomas J. Cole *(Controller)*
Tatyana Leifman *(Mgr-Database)*
Jimmy Taber *(Assoc Dir-Dev)*
Clive Sheldon *(Chm-UK)*
Jennifer Gorovitz *(VP-Ops & Admin)*
Daniel Sokatch *(CEO)*
David Myers *(Pres)*

NEW JERSEY BUSINESS FORMS MANUFACTURING CORPORATION
55 W Sheffield Ave, Englewood, NJ 07631
Tel.: (201) 569-4500
Web Site: http://www.njbf.com
Rev.: $14,000,000
Emp.: 70
Mfr of Manifold Business Forms
N.A.I.C.S.: 323111
John Harnett *(Pres)*
Andrew Harnett *(CFO)*
David Harnett *(VP-Sls)*

NEW JERSEY LIFE & HEALTH INSURANCE GUARANTY ASSOCIATION
11 Wharf Ave Ste 1, Red Bank, NJ 07701
Tel.: (732) 345-5200 NJ
Web Site: http://www.njlifega.org
Year Founded: 1991
Sales Range: Less than $1 Million
Emp.: 2

NEW JERSEY LIFE & HEALTH INSURANCE GUARANTY ASSOCIATION

New Jersey Life & Health Insurance Guaranty Association—(Continued)

Life & Health Insurance Guaranty Association
N.A.I.C.S.: 813910
J. M. Lenaghan (Exec Dir)

NEW JERSEY MANUFACTURERS INSURANCE COMPANY
301 Sullivan Way, West Trenton, NJ 08628
Tel.: (609) 883-1300
Web Site: http://www.njm.com
Year Founded: 1913
Sales Range: $1-4.9 Billion
Emp.: 2,500
Property & Casualty Insurance
N.A.I.C.S.: 524126
Bernard M. Flynn (Pres & CEO)
Diane T. Brendley (Asst VP)

Subsidiaries:

NJM Bank FSB (1)
301 Sullivan Way, West Trenton, NJ 08628
Tel.: (609) 538-8729
Web Site: http://www.njmbank.com
Sales Range: $50-74.9 Million
Emp.: 30
Provider of Banking Services
N.A.I.C.S.: 522110

NEW JERSEY MONTHLY
55 Park Pl, Morristown, NJ 07963
Tel.: (973) 539-8230
Web Site: http://www.njmonthly.com
Year Founded: 1976
Sales Range: $1-9.9 Million
Emp.: 50
News & Information on New Jersey Publisher
N.A.I.C.S.: 513120
Kate S. Tomlinson (Owner)
Deborah Jay Cortelyou (Dir-Production Ops)
Beth Bressman (Dir-Promotions)
Amanda Staab (Assoc Editor)
Michael Livesey (CFO)
Laura Baer (Creative Dir)

NEW JERSEY PERFORMING ARTS CENTER
1 Center St, Newark, NJ 07102
Tel.: (973) 642-8989   NJ
Web Site: http://www.njpac.org
Year Founded: 1988
Sales Range: $10-24.9 Million
Emp.: 504
Art Event Organizer
N.A.I.C.S.: 711310
Warren Tranquada (COO & Exec VP)
Lisa Hayward (CFO & VP)

NEW JERSEY SPORTS & EXPOSITION AUTHORITY
50 State Route 120, East Rutherford, NJ 07073
Tel.: (201) 935-8500
Web Site: http://www.njsea.com
Sales Range: $100-124.9 Million
Emp.: 2,700
Horse Race Track Operation
N.A.I.C.S.: 711212
Derek Lashine (Supvr-Box Office Computer Ops)
Joe Abramo (Dir-Parking & Traffic)
Lou Terminello (Dir-Sls)
Vincent Prieto (Pres & CEO)

NEW JERSEY TURNPIKE AUTHORITY INC.
518 Main St, Woodbridge, NJ 07095
Tel.: (732) 750-5300   NJ
Web Site: http://www.state.nj.us
Year Founded: 1951
Sales Range: $1-4.9 Billion
Emp.: 2,395

Inspection & Fixed Facilities
N.A.I.C.S.: 488490
Ronald Gravino (Vice Chm)
James Carone (Dir-Internal Audit)
Mary Elizabeth Garrity (Dir-HR)
Donna Manuelli (CFO)
Robert B. Quirk (Dir-Tolls)
Andrea Ward (Dir-Procurement & Matls Mgmt)
Chris Christie (Governor)
Joseph W. Mrozek (Exec Dir)
Henry Eibel (Dir-Ops)
Richard Hammer (Chm)
Kenneth Mcgoldrick (Dir-Maintenance)
Jose Dios (CIO)
Ernest Whelan (Sec)

NEW JIGU TRADING CORP.
5608 37th Ave, Woodside, NY 11377
Tel.: (718) 205-5959
Web Site: http://www.harlem125.com
Sales Range: $10-24.9 Million
Emp.: 20
Beauty Salon & Barber Shop Equipment & Supplies
N.A.I.C.S.: 423850
Jong Chul Hong (Pres)

NEW KING INC.
874 Silas Deane Hwy, Wethersfield, CT 06109
Tel.: (860) 257-9000
Rev.: $11,000,000
Emp.: 40
Fast-Food Restaurant, Chain
N.A.I.C.S.: 722513
Lynn Kayser (Office Mgr)

NEW LEAF COMMUNITY MARKETS INC.
1101 Pacific Ave Ste 333, Santa Cruz, CA 95060
Tel.: (831) 466-9060
Web Site: http://www.newleaf.com
Sales Range: $10-24.9 Million
Emp.: 500
Grocery Stores
N.A.I.C.S.: 445110
Wendy Collie (Pres & CEO)
Loaura Ramsey (Mgr-HR)

NEW LEAF PAPER, LLC
510 16th St Ste 520, Oakland, CA 94612
Tel.: (415) 291-9210
Web Site: http://www.newleafpaper.com
Sales Range: $10-24.9 Million
Emp.: 8
Recycled Paper Products Retailer
N.A.I.C.S.: 541990
Jeff Mendelsohn (Founder & Chm)
Staci Laskar (Mgr-Supply Chain)

NEW LEGEND, INC.
PO Box 712, Yuba City, CA 95992
Tel.: (530) 674-3100
Web Site: http://www.newlegendinc.com
Sales Range: $10-24.9 Million
Emp.: 200
Long-Distance & Truckload Freight Trucking Services
N.A.I.C.S.: 484121
Sherry Ayuyu (Mgr-Payroll)
Jonathon Fulmer (Mgr-Safety)
Erika Lopez (Mgr-CSR)

NEW LIFE HIKING SPA, INC.
PO Box 395, Killington, VT 05751
Tel.: (802) 353-2954
Web Site: http://www.newlifehikingspa.com
Sales Range: $10-24.9 Million
Emp.: 20

Wellness Resort & Spa
N.A.I.C.S.: 721110
James LeSage (Co-Owner & Pres)
Kathleen LeSage (Co-Owner & VP)

NEW LIFE SOLUTION, INC.
260 Franklin St Ste 1010, Boston, MA 02110
Tel.: (617) 916-1262
Web Site: http://www.mequilibrium.com
Year Founded: 2011
Sales Range: $1-9.9 Million
Emp.: 50
Human Resource Requirement Services
N.A.I.C.S.: 541612
Jan Janesse Bruce (Co-Founder & CEO)
Adam Perlman (Co-Founder & Chief Medical Officer)
Andrew Shatte (Co-Founder & Chief Science Officer)
Pam Boiros (CMO)
Tom Brennan (CFO)

NEW LIMECO, LLC.
25251 SW 139th Ave, Homestead, FL 33032-5505
Tel.: (305) 258-1611
Web Site: http://www.newlimeco.com
Rev.: $8,700,000
Emp.: 50
Fresh Fruit & Vegetable Merchant Whslr
N.A.I.C.S.: 424480
Don Edger (Mgr-Ops)
Eddie Caram (Gen Mgr)

NEW LONDON COMMUNICATIONS, LLC
343 Curie Dr, Alpharetta, GA 30005
Tel.: (770) 442-1363   DE
Web Site: http://www.mynewlondon.com
Year Founded: 1986
Sales Range: $10-24.9 Million
Emp.: 50
Advertising Agency; Commercial Printing Services
N.A.I.C.S.: 541810
Eric Rountree (CEO)
Larry Ballew (VP-Sls)
Tim Bennett (Plant Mgr)
Lori Cooper (VP-Fin)
Donnie Halcomb (Mgr-Estimating)

NEW LONDON COUNTY MUTUAL INSURANCE COMPANY, INC.
101 High St, Norwich, CT 06360-5605
Tel.: (860) 887-3553
Web Site: http://www.nlcinsurance.com
Year Founded: 1840
Sales Range: $25-49.9 Million
Emp.: 100
Provider of Fire, Marine & Casualty Insurance Services
N.A.I.C.S.: 524126
Steve Chezalier (Pres & CEO)

NEW LONDON FARMERS CO-OPERATIVE
400 North Chestnut St, New London, IA 52645
Tel.: (319) 367-2236
Year Founded: 1960
Sales Range: $10-24.9 Million
Emp.: 12
Marketer of Grains
N.A.I.C.S.: 424510

NEW MAC ELECTRIC COOPERATIVE
12105 E Hwy 86, Neosho, MO 64850
Tel.: (417) 451-1515
Web Site: http://www.newmac.com
Rev.: $11,700,000
Emp.: 70
Distribution, Electric Power
N.A.I.C.S.: 221122
Mitch McCumber (CEO & Gen Mgr)
Mary Hatfield (Mgr-Admin)
Mark K. Rakes (Mgr-Mktg-Customer Svcs)

NEW MEXICO EDUCATIONAL ASSISTANCE FOUNDATION
7400 Tiburon NE, Albuquerque, NM 87109
Tel.: (505) 345-3371   NM
Web Site: http://www.nmeaf.org
Year Founded: 1981
Sales Range: $50-74.9 Million
Emp.: 140
Grantmaking Services
N.A.I.C.S.: 813211
Grace Tackman (Asst VP-HR)
Elwood Farber (Pres)
Brad Allpass (VP-Fin)

NEW MEXICO MUTUAL CASUALTY COMPANY
3900 Singer Blvd NE, Albuquerque, NM 87109
Tel.: (505) 345-7260
Web Site: http://www.nmmcc.com
Sales Range: $25-49.9 Million
Emp.: 115
Workers' Compensation Insurance Services
N.A.I.C.S.: 524126
Lou Volk (VP)
Susan Kittredge (Dir-Mktg)
Alec Grandon (Mgr-Risk & Safety)
Dianne Ledesma (Dir-Provider Network, Rels & Quality)
Kristen Carey (Dir-Underwriting)
Dan Stock (Dir-Policyholder Svcs)
Dustin King (Mgr-Underwriting)
Cynthia Mohler (VP-HR & Admin)
Gina Hickman (CFO & VP)
Claudia Sanchez (Dir-Mktg & Policyholder Svcs)

Subsidiaries:

Foundation Reserve Insurance Co. (1)
3900 Singer NE, Albuquerque, NM 87109
Tel.: (505) 345-7260
Web Site: http://www.newmexicomutual.com
Sales Range: $50-74.9 Million
Emp.: 105
Fire, Marine & Casualty Insurance Services
N.A.I.C.S.: 524126
Ryan Inzenga (Mgr-Underwriting-Workers' Compensation)
Susan Wilson (VP-Bus Dev)
Tim Thackaberry (Dir-IT)
Karen Schroeder (Mgr-IT Application)

Keenan & Associates Inc. (1)
2355 Crenshaw Blvd Ste 200, Torrance, CA 90501-3329
Tel.: (310) 212-3344
Web Site: http://www.keenan.com
Sales Range: $100-124.9 Million
Insurance Services
N.A.I.C.S.: 524210
Sean K. Smith (Pres & CEO)
Suzanne Miles Smith (Sr VP-Human Capital)
David Seres (COO)
Tara Schilling (Sr VP)
Dan Keenan (Sr VP)
John Scatterday (Sr VP)
John Stephens (Sr VP)

NEW MEXICO SPACEPORT AUTHORITY

COMPANIES

NEW MOUNTAIN CAPITAL, LLC

901 E University Ave Ste 965L, Las Cruces, NM 88001
Tel.: (575) 373-6110
Web Site: http://www.spaceportamerica.com
Year Founded: 2006
Sales Range: $25-49.9 Million
Emp.: 500
Space Research & Technology
N.A.I.C.S.: 927110
Richard Holdridge *(Chm)*
Tammara Anderton *(Dir-Sls & Mktg)*
Ryan Noble *(Chief Procurement Officer & Gen Counsel)*
Aaron Prescott *(Dir-Bus Dev)*
Chris Lopez *(Dir-Site Ops)*
Dan Hicks *(CEO)*
Melissa Kemper Force *(Gen Counsel)*

NEW MOTORS INC.

8670 Peach St, Erie, PA 16509
Tel.: (814) 868-4805
Web Site: http://www.newmotors.com
Sales Range: $10-24.9 Million
Emp.: 65
New & Used Car Dealer
N.A.I.C.S.: 441110
Larry New *(Owner)*
Jim Vollant *(Gen Mgr)*
Keith Wright *(Dir-Parts & Svcs)*
Gabe Pulvino *(Mgr-Sls-BMW/VW)*
Joe Armbruster *(Dir-Internet)*
Nicole Ditullio *(Mgr-Fin)*
Allen Yingling *(Mgr-Fin)*

NEW MOUNTAIN CAPITAL, LLC

1633 Broadway Fl 48, New York, NY 10019
Tel.: (212) 720-0300 DE
Web Site: http://www.newmountaincapital.com
Year Founded: 1999
Private Equity & Investment Management Firm
N.A.I.C.S.: 523999
Robert R. Grusky *(Co-Founder)*
Matthew S. Holt *(Mng Dir & Pres-Private Equity)*
Daniel P. Riley *(Mng Dir)*
James T. Lavallee *(Dir-Ops)*
Andre V. Moura *(Mng Dir)*
Peter Masucci *(Mng Dir)*
John R. Kline *(Mng Dir)*
David C. Coquillette *(Mng Dir)*
Albert A. Notini *(Operating Partner-Group & Mng Dir)*
Teddy Kaplan *(Mng Dir)*
A. Joe Delgado *(Mng Dir & Deputy Head-Strategic Equity)*
Ignacio Sarria *(Mng Dir)*
Brian Murphy *(Dir)*
Joy Y. Xu *(Dir)*
Laura C. Holson *(Mng Dir & COO-Credit Platform)*
Kyle B. Peterson *(Executives)*
Jack Qian *(Mng Dir)*
Prasad Chintamaneni *(Mng Dir)*
Dirk Bontridder *(CEO)*
Joe Walker *(Mng Dir)*
Albert A. Notini *(Mng Dir)*
Robert A. Hamwee *(Mng Dir)*
Adam B. Weinstein *(CFO & COO)*
Joseph Hartswell *(Mng Dir & Chief Compliance Officer)*
Steven Bruce Klinsky *(Co-Founder & CEO)*

Subsidiaries:

Accolite, Inc. (1)
1801 Gateway Blvd Ste 209, Richardson, TX 75080
Tel.: (972) 586-7778
Web Site: http://www.accolite.com
Custom Computer Programming Services
N.A.I.C.S.: 541511

Derrick Ryskamp *(Mgr-Bus Dev)*

Aegion Corporation (1)
17988 Edison Ave, Chesterfield, MO 63005-1195
Tel.: (636) 530-8000
Web Site: http://www.aegion.com
Rev.: $807,764,000
Assets: $901,447,000
Liabilities: $493,082,000
Net Worth: $408,365,000
Earnings: ($31,861,000)
Emp.: 4,138
Fiscal Year-end: 12/31/2020
Infrastructure & Pipeline Protection Products & Services
N.A.I.C.S.: 811310
David F. Morris *(CFO & Exec VP)*
Mark A. Menghini *(Gen Counsel, Sec & Sr VP)*
Rick Laurent *(Pres-Energy Svcs)*
Katie Cason *(Sr VP-Strategy & Comm)*
John L. Heggemann *(Chief Acctg Officer, Sr VP & Controller)*
Kevin Rippee *(Sr VP-Ops & Energy Svcs)*
Leanne Romesburg *(VP-HR-Energy Svcs)*
Michael Wolf *(Sr VP-Sls, Mktg, Strategic Plng & Energy Svcs)*
Enrique Zarate *(VP-Health, Safety, Security & Environmental)*
Robert M. Tullman *(Pres & CEO)*

Subsidiary (Domestic):

Aegion Holding Company, LLC (2)
17988 Edison Ave, Chesterfield, MO 63005
Tel.: (636) 530-8000
Web Site: http://www.aegion.com
Emp.: 250
Holding Company
N.A.I.C.S.: 551114

Brinderson Constructors, Inc. (2)
3070 Bay Vista Ct Ste E, Benicia, CA 94510
Tel.: (707) 752-8000
Industrial Maintenance Services
N.A.I.C.S.: 561499

Brinderson L.P. (2)
18841 S Broadwick St Ste 200, Rancho Dominguez, CA 90220
Tel.: (714) 466-7100
Web Site: http://www.brinderson.com
Sales Range: $50-74.9 Million
Emp.: 500
Pipeline Construction Services
N.A.I.C.S.: 237120

Brinderson Services, LLC (2)
3330 Harbor Blvd, Costa Mesa, CA 92626-1502
Tel.: (714) 466-7100
Web Site: http://www.brinderson.com
Building Construction Services
N.A.I.C.S.: 541330

Subsidiary (Non-US):

Building Chemical Supplies Limited (2)
Unit 6E 33 Kaiwaharwhara Road, PO Box 27-397, Wellington, New Zealand
Tel.: (64) 44737894
Web Site: http://www.buildingchemicalsupplies.co.nz
Chemical Product Whslr
N.A.I.C.S.: 424690

Subsidiary (Domestic):

C & L Water Solutions, Inc. (2)
12249 N Mead Way, Littleton, CO 80125
Tel.: (303) 791-2521
Web Site: https://www.clwsi.com
Rev.: $2,839,000
Emp.: 17
Wood Container & Pallet Mfr
N.A.I.C.S.: 321920
Danny Braning *(Project Mgr)*
Christopher Larson *(VP-Bus Dev & Production)*
Tracy Stenger *(Asst Project Mgr)*
Jeff Maier *(Dir-Engrg)*

Commercial Coating Services International, LLC (2)
10655 Jefferson Chemical Rd, Conroe, TX 77301
Tel.: (936) 539-3294

Web Site: http://www.commercialcoating.com
Field Joint Coating & Custom Coating Services
N.A.I.C.S.: 332812

Subsidiary (Non-US):

Concrete Solutions Limited (2)
30 Crummer Road Grey Lynn, 1021, Auckland, New Zealand
Tel.: (64) 93020027
Web Site: http://www.concretesolutions.co.nz
Commercial Concrete Services
N.A.I.C.S.: 238110

Subsidiary (Domestic):

Culy Contracting, LLC (2)
5 Industrial Park Dr, Winchester, IN 47394
Tel.: (765) 584-8509
Web Site: http://www.culycontracting.com
Sales Range: $10-24.9 Million
Emp.: 90
Sewer Line & Related Structure Construction Services
N.A.I.C.S.: 237110
Aaron Anderson *(Project Mgr)*
Mark Schildmeier *(Project Mgr)*
Mark Ramsey *(Project Mgr)*
Bruce Culy *(Ops Mgr)*

Subsidiary (Non-US):

Environmental Techniques Limited (2)
1 Flush Park Knockmore Road, Lisburn, BT28 2DX, United Kingdom
Tel.: (44) 2892677500
Web Site: http://www.environmentaltechniques.com
Engineeering Services
N.A.I.C.S.: 541330

Fibrwrap Construction (M) Sdn Bhd (2)
No 4-3 Jalan 11/116B Kuchai Entrepreneurs Park Off Jalan Kuchai Lama, Off Jalan Kuchai Lama, Kuala Lumpur, 58200, Malaysia
Tel.: (60) 379873177
Web Site: http://www.fibrwrap.com
Emp.: 15
Pipeline Construction Services
N.A.I.C.S.: 237120

Fibrwrap Construction Pte Ltd (2)
10 Toh Guan Rd 03-10 TT International Tradepark, Singapore, 608838, Singapore
Tel.: (65) 68985248
Web Site: http://www.fibrwrap.sg
Pipeline Construction Services
N.A.I.C.S.: 237120

Fibrwrap Construction Services Ltd. (2)
110A 81 Golden Drive, Coquitlam, V3K 6R2, BC, Canada
Tel.: (604) 945-5429
Pipeline Construction Services
N.A.I.C.S.: 237120

Subsidiary (Domestic):

Fibrwrap Construction Services, Inc. (2)
1979 Wiesbrook Dr Unit C, Oswego, IL 60543
Tel.: (630) 906-9800
Web Site: http://www.fclp.com
Emp.: 60
Pipeline Construction Services
N.A.I.C.S.: 237120
Mark Brand *(Gen Mgr)*

Subsidiary (Non-US):

Fyfe (Hong Kong) Limited (2)
Unit 5 22th Floor Metropole Square, Sha Tin, China (Hong Kong)
Tel.: (852) 35795588
Web Site: http://www.aegion.com
Emp.: 40
Pipeline Construction Services
N.A.I.C.S.: 237120

Fyfe Asia Pte. Ltd. (2)
6 Clementi Loop Unit 02-20, Singapore, 129814, Singapore
Tel.: (65) 68985248

Web Site: http://www.fyfeasia.com
Emp.: 30
Pipeline Construction Services
N.A.I.C.S.: 237120

Fyfe Borneo Sdn Bhd (2)
Unit 20 2nd Floor Block B Bangunan Ben Kassim and Hjh Zaliha, Spg 440 Kg Sg Tilong Jln Muara, Bandar Seri Begawan, BC2115, Brunei Darussalam
Tel.: (673) 2341625
Pipeline Construction Services
N.A.I.C.S.: 237120
Rodney Cheong *(Dir-Bus Dev)*

Subsidiary (Domestic):

Fyfe Co. LLC (2)
4995 Murphy Canyon Rd Ste 110, San Diego, CA 92123
Tel.: (858) 642-0694
Web Site: http://www.fyfeco.com
Sales Range: $25-49.9 Million
Emp.: 40
Pipeline Construction Services
N.A.I.C.S.: 237120

Subsidiary (Non-US):

Fyfe Japan Co. Ltd. (2)
The SOHO 1210 2-7-4 Aoumi, Koutou-ku, Tokyo, 135-0064, Japan
Tel.: (81) 364571910
Pipeline Construction Services
N.A.I.C.S.: 237120
Basem Abdullah *(Mgr)*

Hockway Middle East FZE (2)
Liu 22 Silicon Oasis, PO Box 440136, Dubai, United Arab Emirates
Tel.: (971) 43263120
Web Site: http://www.hockway.com
Sales Range: $25-49.9 Million
Emp.: 25
Oil & Gas Construction Services
N.A.I.C.S.: 237120

Insitu Envirotech (S.E. Asia) Pte. Ltd. (2)
8 Tuas Avenue 20, Singapore, 638821, Singapore
Tel.: (65) 65474994
Sales Range: $25-49.9 Million
Emp.: 30
Pipeline Construction Services
N.A.I.C.S.: 237120

Insituform A/S (2)
Drejergangen 13, 2690, Karlslunde, Denmark
Tel.: (45) 70214224
Infrastructure & Pipeline Protection Product & Services
N.A.I.C.S.: 811310

Insituform Asia Limited (2)
DD 77 Lot 1552A/1A Ping Che Village Ta Ku Ling, Fanling, China (Hong Kong)
Tel.: (852) 26590156
Web Site: http://www.insituform.com
Pipeline Construction Services
N.A.I.C.S.: 237120

Insituform Linings Limited (2)
12-20 Brunel Close Park Farm Industrial Estate, Wellingborough, NN8 6QX, United Kingdom
Tel.: (44) 1933678266
Web Site: http://www.aegion.com
Emp.: 30
Pipeline Construction Services
N.A.I.C.S.: 237120

Insituform Rioolrenovatietechnieken B.V. (2)
Chroomstraat 91, Zoetermeer, 2718 RT, Netherlands
Tel.: (31) 880403600
Web Site: http://www.insituform.nl
Sales Range: $25-49.9 Million
Emp.: 90
Water & Sewer Pipeline Construction Services
N.A.I.C.S.: 237110

Insituform Technologies Iberica S.A. (2)
Avda de La Cruz 16, 28343, Valdemoro, Madrid, Spain
Tel.: (34) 918955040

NEW MOUNTAIN CAPITAL, LLC

New Mountain Capital, LLC—(Continued)
Web Site: http://www.insituform.es
Sales Range: $25-49.9 Million
Emp.: 28
Pipeline Construction Services
N.A.I.C.S.: 237120

Insituform Technologies Limited (2)
5743 - 68 Avenue, Edmonton, T6B 3P8, AB, Canada
Tel.: (780) 413-0200
Sales Range: $50-74.9 Million
Emp.: 100
Pipeline Construction Services
N.A.I.C.S.: 237120
Kenneth Foster *(Pres)*

Insituform Technologies Limited (2)
4-8 Brunel Close Park Farm Industrial Estate, Wellingborough, NN8 6QX, Northamptonshire, United Kingdom
Tel.: (44) 1933 670500
Web Site: http://www.insituform.co.uk
Pipeline Construction Services
N.A.I.C.S.: 237120

Holding (Domestic):

Insituform Technologies, LLC
17988 Edison Ave, Saint Louis, MO 63005
Tel.: (800) 234-2992
Web Site: http://www.insituform.com
Emp.: 200
Pipeline Protection & Maintenance Services
N.A.I.C.S.: 237990

Subsidiary (Domestic):

CRTS, Inc. (3)
1807 N 170th E Ave, Tulsa, OK 74116
Tel.: (918) 877-5210
Web Site: http://www.crtsinc.com
Sales Range: $10-24.9 Million
Emp.: 60
Specialty Trade Contractor Services
N.A.I.C.S.: 238990

Division (Domestic):

Corrpro Companies, Inc. (3)
7000 A Hollister Ste 300, Houston, TX 77040
Tel.: (713) 460-6000
Web Site: http://www.corrpro.com
Sales Range: $150-199.9 Million
Emp.: 100
Pipeline Construction Services
N.A.I.C.S.: 237120

Subsidiary (Non-US):

Corrpro Canada Inc. (4)
West 250 2 St SW tower 18th floor, Calgary, T2P 0B4, AB, Canada
Tel.: (403) 235-6400
Web Site: http://www.corrpro.ca
Sales Range: $75-99.9 Million
Emp.: 30
Pipeline Construction Services
N.A.I.C.S.: 237120
Jeff McFarlane *(VP & Gen Mgr)*

Corrpro Companies Europe Ltd. (4)
Adam Street, Bowesfield Lane Cleveland, Stockton-on-Tees, TS18 3HQ, United Kingdom
Tel.: (44) 1642614106
Web Site: http://www.corrpro.co.uk
Sales Range: $75-99.9 Million
Emp.: 50
Pipeline Construction Services
N.A.I.C.S.: 237120
Mark Davies *(Mng Dir)*

Subsidiary (Domestic):

Ocean City Research Corporation (4)
50 Tennessee Ave, Ocean City, NJ 08226
Tel.: (609) 399-2417
Web Site: http://www.corrpro.com
Sales Range: $75-99.9 Million
Emp.: 7
Engineeering Services
N.A.I.C.S.: 541330

Division (Domestic):

Insituform (3)
7333 Monroe Rd, Houston, TX 77061

Tel.: (636) 530-8000
Web Site: http://www.insituform.com
Sales Range: $75-99.9 Million
Emp.: 650
Utility Line & Highway Maintenance Services
N.A.I.C.S.: 237110

Insituform Tech, Inc. (3)
17220 Bel Ray Pl, Belton, MO 64012
Tel.: (816) 318-8477
Web Site: http://www.insituform.com
Sales Range: $1-9.9 Million
Emp.: 20
Pipeline Protection & Maintenance Services
N.A.I.C.S.: 237990

Insituform Technologies USA, Inc. (3)
17988 Edison Ave, Chesterfield, MO 63005 (100%)
Tel.: (636) 530-8000
Web Site: http://www.insituform.com
Sales Range: $250-299.9 Million
Emp.: 200
Pipeline Construction Services
N.A.I.C.S.: 237120

Insituform of New England, Inc (3)
253b Worcester Rd, Charlton, MA 01507
Tel.: (508) 248-1700
Emp.: 45
Pipeline Protection & Maintenance Services
N.A.I.C.S.: 237990

Subsidiary (Non-US):

United Sistema de Tuberias Ltda. (3)
Puerta del Sol No 55 Piso 11 Oficina 111, Las Condes, Santiago, 6761294, Chile (60%)
Tel.: (56) 22074966
Web Site: http://www.unitedchile.cl
Sales Range: $1-9.9 Million
Emp.: 15
Pipeline Construction Services
N.A.I.C.S.: 237120

Subsidiary (Domestic):

Manufactured Technologies Corporation (2)
17988 Edison Ave, Chesterfield, MO 63005
Tel.: (844) 593-6946
Real Estate Services
N.A.I.C.S.: 531390

Subsidiary (Non-US):

PT Fyfe Fibrwrap Indonesia (2)
Ruko Pinangsia Blok I 26, Lippo Karawaci, Tangerang, 15811, Banten, Indonesia
Tel.: (62) 2155763933
Web Site: http://www.fyfeindonesia.com
Emp.: 30
Construction Machinery Mfr
N.A.I.C.S.: 333120

Subsidiary (Domestic):

Pacific Coast Field Services, Inc. (2)
21711 103rd Avenue Ct E C304, Graham, WA 98338
Tel.: (253) 381-7791
Web Site: http://www.pcfsconstruction.com
Artist Support Services
N.A.I.C.S.: 711510

Portland Utilities Construction Company, LLC (2)
117 Demase St, Portland, TN 37148
Tel.: (615) 325-3374
Web Site: http://www.pucc.org
Rev: $10,409,625
Emp.: 108
Underground Utilities Contractor
N.A.I.C.S.: 237110
Ernie Woodcock *(Pres)*
Michael Woodcock *(VP)*
John Keck *(Controller)*

Schultz Industrial Services, Inc. (2)
18841 S Broadwick St, Rancho Dominguez, CA 90220
Tel.: (661) 440-2503
Real Estate Services
N.A.I.C.S.: 531390

Subsidiary (Non-US):

Technologie & Art Pte. Ltd. (2)

8 Boon Lay Road 10-03 Tradehub 21, Singapore, 609964, Singapore
Tel.: (65) 68985248
Building Construction Services
N.A.I.C.S.: 236118

Subsidiary (Domestic):

Underground Solutions, Inc. (2)
13135 Danielson St Ste 201, Poway, CA 92064
Tel.: (858) 679-9551
Web Site: http://www.undergroundsolutions.com
Emp.: 100
Pipeline Construction Services
N.A.I.C.S.: 237120
Patrick Laidlaw *(Sls Mgr)*
Steve Austin *(Mgr-Sls-Rocky Mountain)*
Brett Fornelli *(Sls Mgr)*
Dan Christensen *(VP-Sls-Western Reg)*
John Kosiur *(VP-Sls-Eastern Reg)*
Robert Tatum *(Sls Mgr)*
Chad Andrews *(Sls Mgr)*
Geoffrey Burdick *(Sls Mgr)*
Ed Lobello *(Sls Mgr)*
David Reuter *(VP & Gen Mgr)*

Subsidiary (Domestic):

Process Solutions, Inc. (3)
1077 Dell Ave Ste A, Campbell, CA 95008
Tel.: (408) 370-6540
Web Site: http://www.4psi.net
Industrial Process Variable Instrument & Related Product Mfr
N.A.I.C.S.: 334513
Gunnar Thordarson *(VP & Reg Mgr-Sls)*
Jeff Rhodes *(Reg Mgr-Sls)*
Kevin Sanner *(Reg Mgr-Sls)*
Pete Kyrkos *(Reg Mgr-Sls)*
John Koch *(Reg Mgr-Sls)*
Ethan Brooke *(Reg Mgr-Sls)*
Tom Caulfield *(Reg Mgr-Sls)*

Subsidiary (Domestic):

United Pipeline Systems, Inc. (2)
135 Turner Dr, Durango, CO 81303
Tel.: (970) 259-0354
Web Site: http://www.unitedpipeline.com
Emp.: 25
Pipeline Construction Services
N.A.I.C.S.: 237120

Subsidiary (Non-US):

United Special Technical Services LLC (2)
Al-Harthy Complex, PO Box 307, Muscat, 118, Oman
Tel.: (968) 94306096
Pipeline Construction Services
N.A.I.C.S.: 237120

Video Injection-Insituform SAS (2)
ZA du Pont Rouge, Tremuson, 22440, France
Tel.: (33) 296948842
Web Site: http://www.insituform.fr
Sales Range: $25-49.9 Million
Emp.: 44
Waste Material Recycling & Recovery Services
N.A.I.C.S.: 562920

Apixio Inc. (1)
1850 Gateway Dr 3rd Fl, San Mateo, CA 94404
Tel.: (650) 227-4962
Web Site: http://www.apixio.com
Professional, Scientific & Technical Services
N.A.I.C.S.: 541990
Mark Scott *(CMO)*
Sachin Patel *(CEO)*
John Schneider *(CTO)*
Alan Sun *(VP-Product)*
Tom Magnotta *(Pres & COO)*

Apttis, Inc. (1)
4800 Westfields Blvd, Chantilly, VA 20151
Tel.: (703) 745-6016
Web Site: http://www.apttis.com
Sales Range: $750-799.9 Million
Governmental & Industrial Sector Information Technology Integration Services
N.A.I.C.S.: 541512
James Tip Underwood *(VP-IT Strategy & Deputy Gen Mgr-Sys Engrg & Info Solutions Grp)*

Broadcast Music Inc. (1)
10 Music Sq E, Nashville, TN 37203-4321
Tel.: (615) 401-2000
Web Site: http://www.bmi.com
Sales Range: $900-999.9 Million
Emp.: 600
Patent Owner & Lessor Services
N.A.I.C.S.: 533110
Bruce A. Esworthy *(CFO & Sr VP-Fin & Admin)*
Phillip R. Graham *(Sr VP-Publr Rels)*
Michael O'Neill *(Pres & CEO)*
Delia Orjuela *(VP)*
Stuart Rosen *(Gen Counsel & Sr VP)*
Ann Sweeney *(Sr VP-Global Policy)*
Alison Smith *(Sr VP-Ops, Distr & Admin)*
Barbara Cane *(VP-Creative-Worldwide)*
Catherine Brewton *(VP)*
Charles S. Feldman *(VP)*
Doreen Ringer Ross *(VP)*
Jody Williams *(VP)*
Michael Steinberg *(Exec VP-Creative & Licensing)*
Samantha Cox *(VP-Creative-New York)*
Tracie Verlinde *(VP-Creative-Los Angeles)*
Mason Hunter *(Asst VP-Creative-Nashville)*
Wardell Malloy *(Asst VP-Creative-Los Angeles)*
David F. Bills *(Exec VP)*
Antonella DiSaverio *(Sec)*
Porfirio Pina *(Sr VP)*
Gary Cannizzo *(Treas)*
Richard Garza *(VP)*
Randall McMillan *(VP-Bus Affairs, Creative & Licensing-New York)*
Alex Flores *(Sr VP-Creative)*
Michael Collins *(VP-Govt Rels)*
Clay Bradley *(VP-Creative)*

Cytel Inc. (1)
675 Massachusetts Ave, Cambridge, MA 02139
Tel.: (617) 661-2011
Web Site: http://www.cytel.com
Software Development Services
N.A.I.C.S.: 541511
Matthew S. Holt *(Bd of Dirs, Executives)*
Nitin Patel *(Co-Founder, Chm & CTO)*
Bryan Gleason *(CFO)*
Steve Herbert *(Sr VP-Sls & Bus Dev)*
Cyrus Mehta *(Co-Founder & Pres)*
Joshua Schultz *(CEO)*

Subsidiary (Domestic):

AXIO Research, LLC (2)
2601 4th Ave Ste 200, Seattle, WA 98121-1254
Tel.: (206) 547-2829
Web Site: http://www.axioresearch.com
All Other Personal Services
N.A.I.C.S.: 812990
Lee Hooks *(CEO)*
Kent Koprowicz *(COO)*
Michael Antinore *(Dir-Bus Dev)*
Benjamin Page *(Dir-Fin)*
Mark Rosettie *(Dir-HR)*
Joshua Sanders *(Dir-Quality Assurance)*
Brian Ingersoll *(Dir-IT)*

DRB Systems, Inc. (1)
3245 Pickle Rd, Akron, OH 44312
Tel.: (330) 645-3299
Web Site: http://www.drbsystems.com
Automated Management Systems, POS Terminals, Hand-Held Portable Touchscreen Terminals, Self-Pay Stations & Promotion Tools
N.A.I.C.S.: 541512

Subsidiary (Domestic):

Unitec LLC (2)
7125 Troy Hill Dr, Elkridge, MD 21075
Tel.: (443) 561-1200
Web Site: http://www.startwithunitec.com
Automatic Payment Stations Mfr
N.A.I.C.S.: 333310
Craig Goodwin *(Dir-Sls-Western Reg)*
Pam Piro *(Pres & CEO)*
Jeff Taylor *(Sls Mgr-Western Reg)*
Bob Rossini *(Sls Mgr-Eastern Reg)*

Datavant, Inc. (1)
925 N Point Pkwy Ste 350, Alpharetta, GA 30005
Tel.: (800) 367-1500
Web Site: http://www.cioxhealth.com
Medical Office Practice Management & Document Management Software & Information Services

COMPANIES

NEW MOUNTAIN CAPITAL, LLC

N.A.I.C.S.: 513210
Matthew S. Holt (Bd of Dirs, Executives)
Matt Holt (Chm)
Hoil Kim (Chief Legal Officer & Gen Counsel)
Mike Connolly (Pres-Clinical Data Acq & Insights)
Amir Keren (CTO-Retrieval Solutions)
Dan O'Connor (Chief Strategy Officer)
Derek Frame (CIO)
Florian Quarre (Chief Digital Officer)
Jeff Gartland (Pres-Clinical Revenue Integrity Solutions)
Leke Adesida (Chief Compliance Officer)
Lori Reel (Chief Acctg Officer)
Patty Sheridan (Sr VP-Clinical Data Svcs)
Pete McCabe (CEO)
Shannon West (Chief Innovation Officer)

Unit (Domestic):

ArroHealth (2)
49 Wireless Blvd Ste 140, Hauppauge, NY 11788
Tel.: (631) 780-5000
Web Site: http://www.arrohealth.com
Health Insurance Services
N.A.I.C.S.: 524114
Joseph Driscoll (Exec Chm)

Branch (Domestic):

Ciox Health, LLC - Green Bay (2)
1030 Ontario Rd, Green Bay, WI 54311
Tel.: (800) 236-3355
Web Site: http://www.cioxhealth.com
Health Information Management Services
N.A.I.C.S.: 518210
Elisa Logan (VP-Mktg)
George Abatjoglou (Pres-Provider Solutions)
Brian Simons (COO-Provider Solutions)
Bob Donnelly (Sr VP-Sales-Provider Solutions)

Digital Insurance, LLC (1)
200 Galleria Pkwy SE, Atlanta, GA 30339
Tel.: (770) 250-2900
Web Site: http://www.onedigital.com
Emp.: 85,000
Employee Benefits Administration & Consulting Services
N.A.I.C.S.: 524292
Chuck Ristau (CFO)
Adam Bruckman (Pres & CEO)
Mike Sullivan (Chief Growth Officer)
Julie Cape (Exec VP-Client Svcs & SMB Markets)
Elizabeth Chrane (Chief People Officer)
Jeff Fallick (Reg Mng Principal-Pacicfic Region)

Subsidiary (Domestic):

Beneflex Insurance Services, Inc. (2)
101 W Anapamu St 3rd Fl, Santa Barbara, CA 93101
Tel.: (805) 684-5100
Web Site: http://www.beneflexsb.com
Insurance Brokerage Services
N.A.I.C.S.: 524210
Daniel G. Cattaneo (Founder & CEO)
Lesa Caputo (Principal)
Suzanne Robertson (COO, CFO & Principal)

C.T. Hellmuth & Associates, LLC (2)
8401 Connecticut Ave Ste 501, Chevy Chase, MD 20815-5800
Tel.: (301) 986-6500
Web Site: http://www.cthellmuth.com
Emp.: 50
Employee Benefits Administration & Consulting Services
N.A.I.C.S.: 524292
James R. Hellmuth (Pres)

Cherry Creek Benefits (2)
9781 S Meridian Blvd Ste 110, Englewood, CO 80112
Tel.: (303) 771-2221
Direct Insurance Carriers
N.A.I.C.S.: 524128

Compass Consulting Group, LLC (2)
4348 Southpoint Blvd Ste 400, Jacksonville, FL 32216-0903
Tel.: (904) 281-2222
Web Site: http://www.compassconsultinginc.com
Insurance & Employee Benefit Consulting Services
N.A.I.C.S.: 524298
T. Eric Foster (COO, Principal & Exec VP)
Toni L. O'Brien (Sr VP-Ops)
W. H. Chip Dempsey (VP)
Leigh A. Mills (VP)
Scott C. Snyder (Pres & Principal)

Crum-Halsted Agency, Inc. (2)
2350 Bethany Rd, Sycamore, IL 60178
Tel.: (815) 756-2906
Web Site: http://www.crumhalsted.com
Direct Title Insurance Carriers
N.A.I.C.S.: 524127
Patrick Fagan (VP)
Ted Rosenow (Pres)

East Coast Benefit Plans, Inc. (2)
2 Commercial St Ste 101, Sharon, MA 02067
Tel.: (781) 461-8070
Web Site: http://www.ecbp.com
Insurance Brokerage Services
N.A.I.C.S.: 524210

Fulcrum Partners, LLC (2)
216 Clatter Bridge Rd, Ponte Vedra Beach, FL 32081
Tel.: (904) 296-2563
Web Site: http://www.fulcrumpartersllc.com
Insurance Agencies & Brokerages
N.A.I.C.S.: 524210
Bruce Brownell (Mng Dir & Partner)

Houska Insurance Services Inc. (2)
10990 Wilshire Blvd Ste 1220, Los Angeles, CA 90024
Tel.: (310) 297-2700
Web Site: http://www.houskainsurance.com
Insurance Agencies & Brokerages
N.A.I.C.S.: 524210

Insight Performance, Inc. (2)
150 Royall St Ste 207, Canton, MA 02021
Tel.: (781) 326-8201
Web Site: http://www.insightperformance.com
Administrative Management & General Management Consulting Service
N.A.I.C.S.: 541611
Nancy Mobley (Founder, CEO & Mng Principal)
Rebecca Blake (Principal-HR Consulting Svcs)
Sheila Scott (Dir-Client Rels)
Amy Scannell (VP-HR Consulting Scvs)
Darren J. Ambler (Principal-Mng Consultant)
Jane O'Connor (Dir-Bus Dev)
Julie Mele (Mgr-HR Project Specialist)
Michael D. Ward (Pres & mng Principal)
Molly B. Lee (Controller)
Adam Brodeur (Mgr-Benefits Consultant)
Jeanine Mackinaw (Partner-HR Bus)
Carol Salloway (Sr Partner-HR Bus)
Danielle Danilov (Partner-HR Bus)
Diane Tremblay (Coord-Recruiting)
Reilly Billian (Partner-HR bus)
Ed Bleiler (Mgr-Sr Benefits Consultant-Large Grp Practice)
Kerry Smith (Sr Partner-HR Bus-Beverly)
Erin Stewart (Partner-HR Bus-Beverly)

Kistler Tiffany Benefits Co. (2)
1605 N Cedar Crest Blvd Ste 410, Allentown, PA 18104
Tel.: (610) 437-3606
Web Site: http://www.ktbenefits.com
Sales Range: $1-9.9 Million
Emp.: 46
Employee Benefits Consulting
N.A.I.C.S.: 524298
Stewart T. Anmuth (VP)
Debra A. Labant (Dir-Ops)
Brian E. Daggett (CFO)
Shawn N. Orenstein (Pres)
Joseph Dowd (VP)
T. Ryan Schaible (Principal)
Deborah Hartnett (Mgr-Client Rels)
John Zurbach (Dir-Sls)
Scott Wham (Dir-Compliance Svcs)
Wilmer R. Schultz (Dir-HR)
William O. Daggett Jr. (CEO)

Lyons HR, Inc. (2)
1941 Florence Blvd, Florence, AL 35630
Tel.: (256) 767-5900
Web Site: http://www.lyonshr.com
Payroll Services
N.A.I.C.S.: 541214
Liz Agee (Exec Dir)
Catherine Glaze (VP-Corp HR)
Alan Ridgway (Sr VP-Strategic Dev)
Bruce Cornutt (Pres-HRO Outsourcing)
Scott McAlister (Pres-IT Div)
Wade Krett (CFO)

Subsidiary (Domestic):

Aabakus, Inc. (3)
750 Old Hickory Blvd Ste 275, Brentwood, TN 37027
Tel.: (615) 377-3900
Web Site: http://www.aabakus.com
Emp.: 171
Human Resource Management Services
N.A.I.C.S.: 923130
Susan G. Goyer (Pres & CEO)

Acline HR (3)
25074 Olympia Ave Ste 100, Punta Gorda, FL 33950-3926
Tel.: (941) 347-8625
Web Site: http://www.aclinehr.com
Payroll Services
N.A.I.C.S.: 541214
Richard Schaub (Pres)

Subsidiary (Domestic):

Mann & Watters, Inc. (2)
1017 Ashes Dr Ste 100, Wilmington, NC 28405
Tel.: (910) 509-2966
Web Site: http://www.mannandwatters.com
Employee Benefits Administration & Consulting Services
N.A.I.C.S.: 524292
Thomas F. Mann (Founder & Pres)
Devon Cullen (Acct Mgr)

Marder Benefits, Inc. (2)
20202 Hwy 59, Humble, TX 77338-2419
Tel.: (281) 446-0950
Human Resource Consulting Services
N.A.I.C.S.: 541612

Division (Domestic):

OneDigital Health & Benefits (2)
200 Galleria Pkwy Ste 1950, Atlanta, GA 30339
Tel.: (770) 250-2900
Benefit Advisory Services, Analytics, Compliance Support, Human Resources Management Tools & Comprehensive Insurance Services
N.A.I.C.S.: 524298
Adam Bruckman (Pres & CEO)

Subsidiary (Domestic):

OneDigital Investment Advisors LLC (2)
11101 Switzer Rd, Overland Park, KS 66210
Tel.: (877) 742-2021
Investment Advice Services
N.A.I.C.S.: 523940

Subsidiary (Domestic):

Triad Financial Advisors Inc. (3)
3623 N Elm St Ste 102, Greensboro, NC 27455
Tel.: (336) 230-0071
Web Site: https://www.triadfa.com
Investment Advice
N.A.I.C.S.: 523940
Nathaniel Carswell (VP)

WealthSource Partners, LLC (3)
735 Tank Farm Rd Ste 240, San Luis Obispo, CA 93401
Web Site: http://www.wealthsource.com
Sales Range: $1-9.9 Million
Emp.: 50
Financial Services
N.A.I.C.S.: 523999
Bryan Sullivan (CEO)
Martin Martorana (Dir-Private Client)
Sara White (Mgr-Client Relationship)
Tricia Mulay (Dir-HR)
David Ito (Chief Compliance Officer)
Eric Patton (CFO)
Jon Dubravac (Chief Bus Dev Officer)

Subsidiary (Domestic):

Paradigm Group, LLC (2)
1600 Division St Ste 220, Nashville, TN 37203
Tel.: (615) 515-3308
Web Site: http://www.paradigmgroup.net
Human Resouce Services
N.A.I.C.S.: 923130
Bob Dugan (Principal)
Heather Eshagpour (Dir-Client Svcs)

Resourceful HR LLC (2)
93 S Jackson St Ste 60321, Seattle, WA 98104-2818
Tel.: (206) 463-3110
Web Site: http://www.resourcefulhr.com
Human Resource Consulting Services
N.A.I.C.S.: 541612
Stephanie Tauscher (Mgr-Recruiting & Temporary HR Staffing Services)
Fae Alexander (Acct Mgr-HR Temporary Staffing Svcs)
Jennifer Olsen (CEO & Principal)

The Providence Insurance Group, Inc. (2)
4180 Providence Rd Ste 200, Marietta, GA 30062
Tel.: (678) 239-0495
Web Site: http://www.pg-ins.com
Insurance Agencies & Brokerages
N.A.I.C.S.: 524210

The Reaves Agency, LLC (2)
851 International Pkwy Ste 120, Richardson, TX 75081
Tel.: (972) 669-2435
Web Site: http://www.reavesagency.com
Insurance Agencies & Brokerages
N.A.I.C.S.: 524210

Veritas Risk Services, LLC (2)
3025 Highland Pkwy Ste 650, Downers Grove, IL 60515
Tel.: (630) 734-3500
Web Site: http://www.veritasrs.com
Emp.: 5,000
Insurance Agencies & Brokerages
N.A.I.C.S.: 524210
Doug Truax (Mng Partner)

Diversified Foodservice Supply, Inc. (1)
607 W Dempster St, Mount Prospect, IL 60056
Tel.: (847) 966-9700
Web Site: http://www.dfsupply.com
Holding Company; Foodservice Industry Equipment, Replacement Parts & Accessories Distr, Maintenance & Repair Services
N.A.I.C.S.: 551112
Mike Cate (Pres & CEO)
Ken Gradman (CFO)
Raeann Fracek (Controller)
John DeBord (Sr VP-Sls)

Subsidiary (Domestic):

AllPoints Foodservice Parts & Supplies, Inc. (2)
607 W Dempster St, Mount Prospect, IL 60056
Tel.: (847) 966-9700
Web Site: http://www.allpointsfps.com
Foodservice Industry Equipment, Replacement Parts & Accessories Distr, Maintenance & Repair Services
N.A.I.C.S.: 423440
Phil Wisehart (VP)
Robert Piotrowski (Dir-Sls Ops)
Azie Khan (Mng Dir)
John McDermott (Mgr-Product Dev)
Eric Trelstad (Dir-Sls)

Franklin Machine Products, Inc. (2)
101 Mount Holly Bypass, Lumberton, NJ 08048
Tel.: (609) 267-3700
Web Site: http://www.fmponline.com
Sales Range: $10-24.9 Million
Emp.: 130
Foodservice Industry Equipment, Replacement Parts & Accessories Distr, Maintenance & Repair Services
N.A.I.C.S.: 423440
Joe Grato (Chm)
Bill Brower (Dir-Sls)
Michael A. Conte Sr. (Pres)

Mill Hardware & Food Service, Inc. (2)
4855 E 345th St, Willoughby, OH 44094

NEW MOUNTAIN CAPITAL, LLC

New Mountain Capital, LLC—(Continued)
Tel.: (440) 946-9444
Web Site: http://www.millhardware.com
Emp.: 20
Foodservice Industry Equipment, Replacement Parts & Accessories Distr, Maintenance & Repair Services
N.A.I.C.S.: 423440
Jeffrey Davis (Pres)

Tundra Restaurant Supply, Inc. (2)
3825 Walnut St Unit E, Boulder, CO 80301
Tel.: (303) 440-4142
Web Site: http://www.etundra.com
Sales Range: $10-24.9 Million
Emp.: 85
Foodservice Industry Equipment, Replacement Parts & Accessories Distr, Maintenance & Repair Services
N.A.I.C.S.: 423440
Connie Werth (Mgr-Acctg)
Robyn Marlow (Mgr-HR)

Equian, LLC (1)
5975 Castle Creek Pkwy Ste 100, Indianapolis, IN 46250
Tel.: (800) 962-6831
Web Site: http://www.equian.com
Health Insurance Payment Services
N.A.I.C.S.: 524298

Subsidiary (Domestic):

First Recovery Group, LLC (2)
26555 Evergreen Rd Ste 200, Southfield, MI 48076
Tel.: (248) 443-4800
Web Site: http://www.firstrecoverygroup.com
Healthcare Cost Management Services
N.A.I.C.S.: 561440
Michelle Gaggini (Pres)

Nurse Audit, LLC (2)
134 Pleasant St, Portsmouth, NH 03801
Tel.: (603) 436-6200
Web Site: http://www.nurseaudit.com
Sales Range: $1-9.9 Million
Emp.: 15
Healthcare Business Consulting
N.A.I.C.S.: 541618
Sharon Weston (CEO)

Flexan, LLC (1)
500 Bond St, Lincolnshire, IL 60069
Tel.: (224) 543-0003
Web Site: http://www.flexan.com
Molded Rubber Products
N.A.I.C.S.: 326299
Jim Fitzgerald (CEO)
Tony Orsini (COO)
Mike Huiras (VP-Sls & Mktg)
Jon Wacks (VP-Quality)
Amy Shepley (VP-HR)
David Milner (CFO)

Subsidiary (Domestic):

Medron, LLC (2)
4752 W California Ave, Salt Lake City, UT 84104
Tel.: (801) 214-3053
Web Site: http://flexan.com
Surgical & Medical Instrument Mfr
N.A.I.C.S.: 339112
Jim Fitzgerald (CEO)

HealthComp LLC (1)
621 Santa Fe Ave, Fresno, CA 93721
Tel.: (559) 499-2450
Web Site: http://www.healthcomp.com
Rev.: $16,100,000
Emp.: 165
Medical Insurance Claim Processing, Contract Or Fee Basis
N.A.I.C.S.: 524292
Phillip Musson (CEO)
Serena Watkins (Mgr)
Valerie Vanzandt (Acct Mgr-Mktg)

Horizon Services, LLC (1)
320 Century Blvd, Wilmington, DE 19808
Tel.: (410) 267-4623
Web Site: http://www.horizonservices.com
Site Preparation Contractor
N.A.I.C.S.: 238910
David Geiger (Founder & CEO)

Subsidiary (Domestic):

Casteel Heating And Cooling, Inc. (2)
305 Petty Road Lawrenceville, Marietta, GA 30043
Tel.: (777) 766-1657
Web Site: http://www.casteelair.com
Site Preparation Contractor
N.A.I.C.S.: 238910
Robert Casteel (Pres)
John Hillis (VP)

Subsidiary (Domestic):

Accutemp Heating-Cooling, Inc. (3)
869 Pickens Industrial Dr, Marietta, GA 30062
Tel.: (770) 795-1061
Web Site: http://www.accutempair.com
Rev.: $1,900,000
Emp.: 16
Site Preparation Contractor
N.A.I.C.S.: 238910
Jerry D. McAnally (Pres)

Subsidiary (Domestic):

Gold Medal Plumbing Heating Cooling Electric, Inc. (2)
11 Cotters Ln, East Brunswick, NJ 08816
Tel.: (732) 707-2870
Web Site: http://www.goldmedalservice.com
Plumbing, Heating & Air-Conditioning Services
N.A.I.C.S.: 238220

Subsidiary (Domestic):

Gold Medal Service, LLC (3)
20 Booker St, Westwood, NJ 07675
Tel.: (201) 664-4343
Web Site: http://www.goldmedalservice.com
Plumbing, Heating & Air-Conditioning Services
N.A.I.C.S.: 238220

ILC Dover LP (1)
1 Moonwalker Rd, Frederica, DE 19946-2080
Tel.: (302) 335-3911
Web Site: http://www.ilcdover.com
Plastic Device for Pharmaceutical & Military & Space Application Mfr
N.A.I.C.S.: 326199
Doug Durney (Dir-Bus Dev & Mktg)
Paul Guglielmi (Dir-Sls-PPE Div)
Fran DiNuzzo (Pres)

JDA Software Group, Inc. (1)
14400 N 87th St, Scottsdale, AZ 85260-3649
Tel.: (480) 308-3000
Web Site: http://www.jda.com
Holding Company; Supply Chain Management Software & Support Services
N.A.I.C.S.: 551112
Salil Joshi (Exec VP-Cloud & Customer Success)
Kevin Iaquinto (CMO & Exec VP)
Martin Felli (Chief Compliance Officer, Chief Legal Officer & Sec)
Jolene Peixoto (Dir-Corp Comm)
Lloyd G. Waterhouse (Vice Chm)
Mark Morgan (Chief Revenue Officer & Exec VP)
David Rye (Sr VP-Strategy & Corp Dev)
Girish Rishi (CEO)
Niranjan Thirumale (Sr VP & Mng Dir-Centers of Excellence-India, Mexico & Poland)
Kevin Moriarty (CFO & Exec VP)
Nathalie Carruthers (Chief HR Officer & Exec VP)
Michael Capellas (Chm)
Desikan Madhavanur (Chief Dev Officer & Exec VP)
Sharon Mills (Chief Customer Officer)

Subsidiary (Non-US):

Beijing JDA Technologies Company Ltd. (2)
Zhongguancun Metropolis Tower 7/F Metropolis Tower No 2 Dongsan Str, Zhongguancun Xi Zone, Haidian District, Beijing, 100080, China
Tel.: (86) 10 6260 2200
Software Solutions & Services
N.A.I.C.S.: 541511

JDA Chile S.A. (2)
Avda Vitacura 2736 Office 503 5th Floor, Las Condes, Santiago, Chile
Tel.: (56) 22310700
Sales Range: $10-24.9 Million
Emp.: 20
Supply Chain Management Software Development Services
N.A.I.C.S.: 541511

JDA International Ltd. (2)
3 The Arena, Downshire Way, Bracknell, RG12 1PU, Berks, United Kingdom
Tel.: (44) 1344354500
Web Site: http://www.jda.com
Sales Range: $50-74.9 Million
Software Solutions
N.A.I.C.S.: 541511

JDA Software (Taiwan), Inc. (2)
Room 1172 11/F Walsin Xinyi Building 1 Songzhi Road, Taipei, 11047, Taiwan
Tel.: (886) 2 8729 2181
Supply Chain Management Software Services
N.A.I.C.S.: 541511
Abaw Juan (Country Mgr)
Richard Hsiao (VP-Svcs)

JDA Software Asia Pte. Ltd. (2)
5 Temasek Boulevard 15-02, Suntec Tower 5, Singapore, 038985, Singapore
Tel.: (65) 6305 4350
Software Solutions
N.A.I.C.S.: 513210
Henning Bruns (VP-Global Consulting PMO)

JDA Software Australia Pty. Ltd. (2)
Level 9 53 Walker Street, North Sydney, 2060, NSW, Australia
Tel.: (61) 2 8923 6272
Software Solutions
N.A.I.C.S.: 541511
Patrick Viney (Sr Dir-Retail Industry Strategies)

JDA Software Belgium (2)
Zaventem on Belgicastraat 17, 1930, Brussels, Belgium
Tel.: (32) 2 431 25 00
Software Development Services
N.A.I.C.S.: 541511

JDA Software Canada Ltd. (2)
80 Tiverton Court, Markham, L3R 0G4, ON, Canada
Tel.: (905) 752-4000
Software Solutions & Services
N.A.I.C.S.: 541511

JDA Software France S.A. (2)
70 Boulevard de Courcelles, 75017, Paris, France (100%)
Tel.: (33) 156792700
Web Site: http://www.jda.com
Sales Range: $10-24.9 Million
Emp.: 45
Software Solutions
N.A.I.C.S.: 541511
Nicolas Cuzin (Mgr-Global Support)

JDA Software India Private Limited (2)
9th-11th Floors Meenakshi Infrastructures, Survey No 39P Gachibowli, Hyderabad, 500 032, Andhra Pradesh, India
Tel.: (91) 4066961000
Web Site: http://www.jda.com
Sales Range: $50-74.9 Million
Supply Chain Management Software
N.A.I.C.S.: 541511

JDA Software Italy S.r.l. (2)
Building 03 7/a Parco Tecnologico Energy Park, Via Monza, 20871, Vimercate, MB, Italy (100%)
Tel.: (39) 039 6382 1
Web Site: http://www.jda.com
Emp.: 20
Software Solutions & Services
N.A.I.C.S.: 334610
Stefania Sainaghi (Office Mgr)

JDA Software Japan Co., Ltd. (2)
Nakameguro GT Tower 19F 2-1-1 Kamimeguro, Meguro-ku, Tokyo, 153 0051, Japan
Tel.: (81) 3 4461 1000
Web Site: http://www.jda.com
Emp.: 60
Software Solutions & Services
N.A.I.C.S.: 541511
Isao Obasawa (Gen Mgr)

JDA Software Korea, Ltd. (2)
7 Fl GFC 152 Teheran-ro, Seocho-gu, Seoul, 135 984, Korea (South)
Tel.: (82) 230160700
Web Site: http://www.jda.com
Supply Chain Management Software
N.A.I.C.S.: 541511
Ayako Sudo (Mgr-HR)

JDA Software Netherlands B.V. (2)
Beemdstraat 50, 5652 AB, Eindhoven, Netherlands
Tel.: (31) 40 2302500
Software Solutions
N.A.I.C.S.: 541511

JDA Software Nordic AB (2)
8th Floor Vasagatan 23, 111 20, Stockholm, Sweden (100%)
Tel.: (46) 8 473 40 00
Web Site: http://www.jda.com
Sales Range: $1-9.9 Million
Emp.: 10
Software Development Services
N.A.I.C.S.: 513210

JDA Software Russia Holdings, Inc. (2)
Kosmodamianskaya Nab 52 Building 3 9th Floor, Riverside Towers BC, 115035, Moscow, Russia
Tel.: (7) 495 642 8730
Web Site: http://www.jda.com
Sales Range: $10-24.9 Million
Supply Chain Management Software Services
N.A.I.C.S.: 541511

JDA Software Shanghai Co. Ltd. (2)
Unit 06 29th Floor Raffles City 268 Xizang Middle Road, Shanghai, 200001, China
Tel.: (86) 2123279400
Web Site: http://www.jda.com
Sales Range: $10-24.9 Million
Emp.: 40
Supply Chain Management Software
N.A.I.C.S.: 541511

Subsidiary (Domestic):

JDA Software, Inc. (2)
14400 N 87th St, Scottsdale, AZ 85260-3649
Tel.: (480) 308-3000
Web Site: http://www.jda.com
Supply Chain Management Software & Support Services
N.A.I.C.S.: 513210
Todd Johnson (Chief Customer Officer)
Nathalie Carruthers (Chief HR Officer & Exec VP)

Branch (Domestic):

JDA Software, Inc. - Akron (3)
308 N Cleveland-Massillon Rd, Akron, OH 44333
Tel.: (330) 665-2120
Web Site: http://www.jda.com
Sales Range: $25-49.9 Million
Emp.: 35
Develops Software for Retail Stores
N.A.I.C.S.: 513210

JDA Software, Inc. - Rockville (3)
9713 Key W Ave Ste 200, Rockville, MD 20850
Tel.: (301) 255-5000
Web Site: http://www.jda.com
Sales Range: $150-199.9 Million
Computer Software & Services
N.A.I.C.S.: 513210
Paula Natoli (VP-Product Mgmt)

JDA Software, Inc. - West Des Moines (3)
3737 Woodland Ave Ste 310, West Des Moines, IA 50266 (100%)
Tel.: (515) 327-9300
Software Designer
N.A.I.C.S.: 513210

JDA Software, Inc. - Westlake Village (3)
2801 Townsgate Rd, Westlake Village, CA 91361
Tel.: (818) 737-7625
Web Site: http://www.jda.com
Sales Range: $25-49.9 Million
Computer MRPII Software & Services
N.A.I.C.S.: 513210

NEW MOUNTAIN CAPITAL, LLC

Subsidiary (Non-US):

JDA Solutions do Brasil Ltda. (2)
Av Paulista 1337 19 andar conj 192, Bela Vista, 01311 200, SP, Brazil
Tel.: (55) 1135499800
Web Site: http://www.jda.com
Sales Range: $10-24.9 Million
Emp.: 17
Software Solutions & Services
N.A.I.C.S.: 541511
Paulo Vita Da Silva *(Mgr-Sls)*
Antonio Faoro *(Grp VP-Latin America Svcs)*
Affonso Leme *(Dir-Mfg Bus Dev)*

JDA Technologies Finland Oy Ltd. (2)
Peltotie 41, 28400, Ulvila, Finland
Tel.: (358) 25317700
Sales Range: $10-24.9 Million
Emp.: 25
Supply Chain Management Software
N.A.I.C.S.: 541511
Sami Lahti *(Gen Mgr)*

JDA Technologies, GmbH (2)
Erika-Mann-Strasse 7, 80636, Munich, Germany
Tel.: (49) 89 462377 0
Web Site: http://www.jda.com
Emp.: 25
Supply Chain Software
N.A.I.C.S.: 541511

Jarrow Formulas, Inc. (1)
1824 S Robertson Blvd, Los Angeles, CA 90035
Tel.: (310) 204-6936
Web Site: http://www.jarrow.com
Rev.: $7,500,000
Emp.: 34
Drugs & Druggists' Sundries Merchant Whslr
N.A.I.C.S.: 424210
Clay DuBose *(Treas)*
Ben Khowong *(CEO)*

National HME, Inc. (1)
7451 Airport Frwy, Richland Hills, TX 76118
Tel.: (817) 332-4433
Web Site: http://www.nationalhme.com
Hospice Health Care Equipment Distr
N.A.I.C.S.: 423450
Michael Miller *(CFO)*
Joshua Robertson *(Founder & Chief Dev Officer)*
Carrie Jo Howard *(VP-Ops-Hospice Cloud)*
Jeffrey Waldman *(Chm & CEO)*

Subsidiary (Domestic):

Hospice Source LLC (2)
3440 Sojourn Dr Ste 150, Carrollton, TX 75006
Tel.: (214) 572-0520
Web Site: http://www.hospicesource.net
Medical Equipment Distr
N.A.I.C.S.: 423450
Jeff West *(CEO)*
Tamera V-Black *(VP-Sls)*
Anthony Rosich *(CFO)*
Mike Marino *(COO)*
Troy Gourdin *(Exec VP-Ops)*
Marlee Leblanc *(VP-HR)*
Darren Tewes *(VP-Pro Svcs)*
Clay Hooten *(Dir-Mktg & Comms)*

Subsidiary (Domestic):

Respiratory Therapy Home Care (3)
9142 Sonrisa St, Bellflower, CA 90706
Tel.: (562) 529-8690
Home Health Equipment Rental
N.A.I.C.S.: 532283
John Morris *(Principal)*
Tim Hansen *(Pres)*

Specialized Medical Services, Inc. (3)
5343 N 118th Ct, Milwaukee, WI 53225
Tel.: (414) 476-1112
Web Site: http://www.specializedmed.com
Oxygen Supplier & Respiratory Services & Health Care Consulting
N.A.I.C.S.: 334510
Steve Marshall *(CEO)*
Debbie Griffith *(Chief Clinical Officer & VP)*
Eddie Long *(CFO)*
Greg Reppar *(COO)*

Subsidiary (Domestic):

Premier Medical Corporation (4)
5055 E 48th Ave, Denver, CO 80216
Tel.: (303) 650-4400
Web Site: http://www.premiermedicalcorp.com
Oxygen Supplier, Respiratory Equipment & Therapy
N.A.I.C.S.: 334510
Kim Davis *(Ops Mgr)*
Brian Ford *(Reg Mgr-Ops-West Colorado)*
Aron Garcia *(Mgr-Warehouse)*
MacArthur Lundquist *(Reg Mgr-Ops-Loveland)*
Ryan Woinarowicz *(Reg Mgr-Ops-Wyoming)*
Sam Bruner III *(VP-Natl)*
Sam Bruner Jr *(Mgr-Purchasing)*

Specialized Medical Services, Inc. (4)
16535 Southpark Dr, Westfield, IN 46074
Tel.: (317) 706-7379
Web Site: http://www.specializedmed.com
Medical Equipment Rental Services
N.A.I.C.S.: 532283

Subsidiary (Domestic):

Therapy Support, Inc. (2)
2803 N Oak Grove Ave, Springfield, MO 65803
Tel.: (417) 887-5873
Web Site: http://www.therapysupport.com
Emp.: 500
Medical Equipment & Supplies Whslr
N.A.I.C.S.: 423450
Brian Pavlin *(Co-Founder)*
David Pavlin *(Co-Founder & CEO)*
Cindi Peterson *(Dir-Compliance)*

New Mountain Finance Corporation (1)
1633 Broadway 48th Fl, New York, NY 10019
Tel.: (212) 720-0300
Web Site: https://www.newmountainfinance.com
Rev.: $294,630,000
Assets: $3,354,927,000
Liabilities: $2,028,736,000
Net Worth: $1,326,191,000
Earnings: $119,604,000
Fiscal Year-end: 12/31/2022
Investment Services
N.A.I.C.S.: 523999
John R. Kline *(Pres & CEO)*
Laura C. Holson *(COO & COO-Credit bus)*
Robert A. Hamwee *(Vice Chm)*
Adam B. Weinstein *(Chief Admin Officer & Exec VP)*
Joseph Hartswell *(Chief Compliance Officer & Sec)*
Steven Bruce Klinsky *(Chm)*
Linda Chiu *(Dir-Tax)*
James Lavallee *(Dir-Ops)*
Ivo Turkedjiev *(Mng Dir)*
Vivian Ko *(Mgr-Tax)*
Matthew Miller *(Mgr)*
Cyrus Moshiri *(Dir)*
William Murphy *(Dir)*
Jag Buddhavarapu *(VP)*
Stephen Tully *(VP)*
Kris Corbett *(CFO & Treas)*
Diana Thomas *(Controller & Dir)*
Alec Freeman *(Ops Mgr & Mgr)*
Parrie Italiano *(Ops Mgr & Mgr)*
Meredith McAneny *(Deputy Chief Compliance Officer & Mgr)*
Joshua Porter *(Mng Dir & Head-Credit Special Situations)*
Joy Xu *(Mng Dir)*
Peter Calabro *(Mng Dir)*
Catherine Dunn *(Head-Capital Markets & Dir)*
Tushar Bindal *(VP)*
Kevin Schneider *(VP)*
Stephanie Slaven *(VP)*
Kaitlyn Grigoleit *(VP & Controller-Credit Asst)*
Michael Doyle *(Mgr-Accounting)*
Kaitlin Johnsen *(Mgr-Accounting)*
Evelyn Wang *(Mgr-Accounting)*
James W. Stone III *(Mng Dir)*

Joint Venture (Domestic):

UniTek Global Services, Inc. (2)
1817 Crane Ridge Dr Ste 500, 39216, Jackson, MS
Tel.: (601) 320-0443
Web Site: http://www.unitekglobalservices.com
Wireless Telecommunication Services
N.A.I.C.S.: 517112

Subsidiary (Domestic):

FTS USA, LLC (3)
Gywnedd Hall Ste 302 1777 Sentry Pkwy W, Blue Bell, PA 19422
Tel.: (615) 515-5399
Web Site: http://www.unitekglobalservices.com
Cable Installation & Maintenance Services
N.A.I.C.S.: 335921

Southern Diversified Technologies, Inc. (3)
130 N 2nd St, Brookhaven, MS 39601
Tel.: (770) 554-4011
Web Site: http://www.sdt-1.com
Engineeering Services
N.A.I.C.S.: 541330

Subsidiary (Non-US):

Wirecomm Systems, Inc. (3)
107 Corstate Ave, Concord, L4K-4Y2, ON, Canada
Tel.: (905) 405-8018
Web Site: http://www.unitekglobalservices.com
Cable Installation & Maintenance Services
N.A.I.C.S.: 517112
Domenic Sorbara *(Pres)*

NuSil Technology LLC (1)
1050 Cindy Ln, Carpinteria, CA 93013
Tel.: (805) 684-8780
Web Site: http://www.nusil.com
Sales Range: $25-49.9 Million
Silicone Compounds Formulator & Mfr
N.A.I.C.S.: 325211
Matthew M. Bennett *(Co-CEO)*
James Smith *(COO)*

Ontario Systems, LLC (1)
1150 W Kilgore Ave, Muncie, IN 47305-1588
Tel.: (765) 751-7000
Web Site: http://www.ontariosystems.com
Accounts Receivable Management Solutions
N.A.I.C.S.: 513210
Matthew S. Holt *(Bd of Dirs, Executives)*
Ron Fauquher *(Co-Founder)*
Mike Meyer *(VP & Gen Mgr-Outsource Group Bus)*
Casey Stanley *(VP-Bus Dev & Mktg)*
Jason Harrington *(CEO)*
Ben Kolb *(Engr-Lead Software)*
Jim Adamson *(VP)*
Rozanne Andersen *(Chief Compliance Officer & VP)*
Alex Forman *(Gen Counsel & VP)*
Dave Hahn *(VP & Controller)*
Jill Lehman *(Chief People Officer & VP-Admin)*
Jay Moorman *(VP-Client Svcs)*
Melissa Norcross *(VP-Strategy & Fin)*
Michael Wolfe *(CTO & VP)*
Steve Scibetta *(VP & Gen Mgr-Healthcare Bus Unit)*
Roger Carney *(VP-Ops)*
Wilbur R. Davis *(Co-Founder)*

Qualus Power Services Corp. (1)
4040 Rev Dr, Cincinnati, OH 45232
Tel.: (800) 434-0415
Web Site: http://qualuspowerservices.com
Holding Company
N.A.I.C.S.: 551112
Paul Cody *(CEO)*

Subsidiary (Domestic):

CE Power Solutions, LLC (2)
4040 Rev Dr, Cincinnati, OH 45232
Tel.: (513) 563-6150
Web Site: http://www.cepower.net
Electronic & Precision Equipment Repair & Maintenance Services
N.A.I.C.S.: 811210
Rhonda Harris *(VP-HR)*
Chris Campbell *(Pres)*
Jim Cialdea *(Chief Technical Officer)*

Subsidiary (Domestic):

CE Power Engineered Services, LLC (3)
4040 Rev Dr, Cincinnati, OH 45232
Tel.: (800) 434-0415
Web Site: http://www.cepower.net
Engineeering Services
N.A.I.C.S.: 541330

Subsidiary (Domestic):

Utilities Plus Energy Services (4)
1260 Industrial Park, Eveleth, MN 28658-9507
Tel.: (218) 744-4200
Appliance Repair & Maintenance
N.A.I.C.S.: 811412

Subsidiary (Domestic):

Patterson Power Engineers LLC (2)
1413 Chestnut St, Chattanooga, TN 37402-4420
Tel.: (423) 702-9981
Web Site: http://www.pattersonpowerengineers.com
Engineeering Services
N.A.I.C.S.: 541330
Russ Patterson *(Owner)*

Power Grid Engineering, LLC (2)
100 Colonial Ctr Pkwy Ste 400, Lake Mary, FL 32746
Tel.: (321) 244-0170
Web Site: http://www.powergridengineering.com
Power Systems Engineering & Consulting Services
N.A.I.C.S.: 237990
Michael J. Wright *(Pres)*
Andre Uribe *(VP-Bus Dev)*
William Glenn Durie *(VP-Technical Svcs)*
Petter Fiskerud *(VP-Ops)*
Kristy Swegheimer *(Dir-HR)*
Nabil May *(CFO & VP-Support Svcs)*
Victor Laird *(VP-Client Mgmt)*

Sparta Systems, Inc. (1)
2000 Waterview Dr Ste 300, Hamilton, NJ 08691
Tel.: (609) 807-5100
Web Site: http://www.spartasystems.com
Emp.: 250
Management Software Developer
N.A.I.C.S.: 513210
Sharon Marnien *(Chief HR Officer)*
Vinit Doshi *(COO)*
Jeffrey Longoria *(Chief Revenue Officer)*
Stan Gonsalves *(CTO)*
Bob Robinson *(VP & Gen Counsel)*
Hari Subramanian *(VP-Prod Mgmt)*
Lesley Harris *(VP-Global Svc Delivery & Support)*
Dana S. Jones *(CEO)*

Strategic Partners, Inc. (1)
9800 De Soto Ave, Chatsworth, CA 91311
Tel.: (818) 671-2100
Web Site: http://www.strategicpartners.net
Work Uniforms & Footwear Mfr & Distr
N.A.I.C.S.: 315250
Philip Suarez *(VP-Ops)*
Julie Tockgo *(Mgr-Licensing)*
Bill Bosch *(VP-Sls & Mdsg)*

Tinuiti Inc. (1)
111 West 33rd Street, Suite 1510, New York, NY 10120
Tel.: (833) 846-8484
Web Site: http://www.tinuiti.com
Online Marketing & Advertising Services
N.A.I.C.S.: 541613
Matthew S. Holt *(Chm)*
Dalton Dorne *(CMO)*
Jesse Eisenberg *(Chief Comml Officer & Sr VP-Bus Dev)*
Nii A. Ahene *(Chief Strategy Officer)*
Diana DiGuido *(Chief Client Officer)*

W2O Group (1)
60 Francisco St, San Francisco, CA 94133
Tel.: (415) 362-5018
Web Site: http://www.w2ogroup.com
Emp.: 300
Corporate Communications, Corporate Identity, Crisis Communications, Integrated Marketing, Media Relations
N.A.I.C.S.: 541820

NEW MOUNTAIN CAPITAL, LLC

New Mountain Capital, LLC—(Continued)

Jim Weiss *(Founder)*
Angela Gillespie *(Chief Strategy Officer-Global MedTech Practice)*
Paulo Simas *(Mng Partner & Chief Creative Officer)*
Laura Levitan *(Chief Networking Officer)*
Dorinda Marticorena *(Mng Dir-Entertainment Practice)*
Jennifer Gottlieb *(Pres)*
Anita Bose *(Head-Client Dev-Chicago)*
Jennifer Labus *(Mng Dir-Integrated Mktg-New York)*
Richard Neave *(CFO)*
Mary Corcoran *(Pres-Twist-EMEA)*
Dominic Viola *(Mng Dir-Client Svcs-Sentient)*
Donna Duncan *(Dir-Healthcare Grp)*
Chuck Hemann *(Mng Dir-Analytics)*
Adam Cossman *(Chief Digital Officer)*
Debra Dowd *(Chief Mktg Officer & Sr VP)*
Seth Duncan *(Chief Analytics Officer)*
Bryan Specht *(Grp Pres-Transformation, Consumer Activation & Mktg)*
Matt Titus *(Exec VP-Sls & Customer Experience)*
Marcos Mendell *(Exec VP-Health Platform Innovation)*
Stephanie Garcia *(Chief People Officer)*
Andy Johnson *(CIO)*
Shankar Narayanan *(CEO)*
Wendy Carhart *(Chief Comm, Culture & Purpose Officer)*

Subsidiary (Domestic):

Discern, LLC (2)
1120 N Charles St Ste 200, Baltimore, MD 21201
Tel.: (410) 542-4470
Web Site: http://www.discernconsulting.com
General Management Consulting Services
N.A.I.C.S.: 541611
Peggy Oehlmann *(Project Dir)*
Guy D'Andrea *(Founder & Mng Partner)*

Marketeching Solutions, LLC. (2)
30 W Bridge St Ste 4, New Hope, PA 18938
Tel.: (908) 892-5435
Web Site: http://www.Marketeching.com
Sales Range: $1-9.9 Million
Emp.: 6
Marketing Consulting Services
N.A.I.C.S.: 541613
Kevin M. Johnson *(Pres)*

Branch (Domestic):

WCG (2)
199 Water St Ste 14, New York, NY 10038
Tel.: (212) 301-7200
Web Site: http://www.wcpglobal.com
Emp.: 25
Communications & Public Relations
N.A.I.C.S.: 541820
Nancy Fitzsimmons *(Mng Dir-Healthcare)*
Lauren Hougas *(Sr Mgr-Analytics)*
Aaron Strout *(Pres-Silicon Valley)*

Western Dental Services Inc. (1)
530 S Main St, Orange, CA 92868-4506
Tel.: (714) 480-3000
Web Site: http://www.westerndental.com
Sales Range: $250-299.9 Million
Dental Services
N.A.I.C.S.: 621210
Jeffrey Miller *(Pres & Chief Legal Officer)*
John Luther *(Chief Dental Officer)*
Daniel D. Crowley *(Chm & CEO)*
Lisa Dawe *(Chief Strategy Officer & Exec VP)*
Preet M. Takkar *(CIO)*
Robert A. Eisen *(Chief HR Officer)*
Jennifer Mallon *(VP-Bus Dev)*
Leslie Gibbs *(CMO)*
Zhi Meng *(Sr VP-Speciality)*
Maria Zenaida Jones *(VP-Supply Chain Mgmt)*
Lane Harter *(VP-Procurement)*
Keith Kooman *(VP-Fin Plng & Analysis)*
Eric M. Royal *(Chief Compliance Officer)*
Vivek Kumar *(Chief Credit Officer)*
Paul A. Holt *(CFO & Exec VP)*

Subsidiary (Domestic):

Mid-Atlantic Dental Service Holdings LLC (2)
630 W Germantown Pike Ste 120, Plymouth Meeting, PA 19462
Tel.: (484) 455-4550
Web Site: http://www.mid-atlanticdental.com
Dental Services
N.A.I.C.S.: 621210
C. Mitchell Golman *(CEO)*
Leigh Feenburg *(COO)*
Sean Porrini *(CFO)*
Richard Rush *(Dir-Quality Assurance & Compliance)*
Michael S. Ayes *(Dir-Bus Dev)*
Suzanne Baals *(Dir-Ops)*
Jared Ayes *(Dir-Integrations)*
Jeanne Kenworthy *(Office Mgr)*

Subsidiary (Domestic):

Birner Dental Management Services, Inc. (3)
1777 S Harrison St Ste 1400, Denver, CO 80210
Tel.: (303) 691-0680
Web Site: http://www.perfectteeth.com
Sales Range: $50-74.9 Million
Dental Practice Management Services
N.A.I.C.S.: 621210
Mitchell Goldman *(Pres, CEO, Treas & Sec)*

Zep Inc. (1)
1310 Seaboard Industrial Blvd NW, Atlanta, GA 30318
Tel.: (404) 352-1680
Web Site: http://www.zepinc.com
Sales Range: $650-699.9 Million
Emp.: 2,000
Holding Company; Commercial, Industrial & Institutional Cleaning & Maintenance Chemical Products Mfr & Marketer
N.A.I.C.S.: 551112
Matthew S. Holt *(Bd of Dirs, Executives)*
Edward F. Lonergan *(Exec Chm)*
Darrin Baum *(VP & Gen Mgr-Vehicle Care)*
William Moody *(Pres-Sls & Svc)*
John Callahan *(VP-Mktg & Sls)*
William Reitz *(Chief Procurement Officer & Sr VP)*
Richard Guida *(VP-Plng & Logistics)*
Dan Smytka *(CEO)*

Subsidiary (Domestic):

Amrep, Inc. (2)
1310 Seaboard Industrial Blvd, Atlanta, GA 30318
Tel.: (770) 422-2071
Specialty Automotive Aftermarket, Janitorial & Industrial Chemical & Sanitation Products Mfr & Marketer
N.A.I.C.S.: 325612

New Wave Industries, Ltd. (2)
3315 Orange Grove Ave, North Highlands, CA 95660 **(100%)**
Tel.: (916) 978-9990
Web Site: http://www.purclean.com
Sales Range: $1-9.9 Million
Emp.: 18
Water Treatment Solutions for the Vehicle Washing Industry
N.A.I.C.S.: 811192
Charles Borchard *(VP-Ops)*
Gary Hirsh *(Pres)*
Dave Sharma *(Controller)*

Subsidiary (Non-US):

Zep Europe B.V. (2)
Vierlinghweg 30, 4612 PN, Bergen-op-Zoom, Netherlands
Tel.: (31) 164 250100
Web Site: http://www.zepindustries.eu
Emp.: 5
Holding Company; Regional Managing Office; Sanitation & Industrial Cleaning Products Mfr
N.A.I.C.S.: 551112
Alessandro Brighenti *(Gen Mgr)*

Subsidiary (Domestic):

Zep Industries B.V. (3)
Vierlinghweg 30, 4612 PN, Bergen-op-Zoom, Netherlands
Tel.: (31) 164250100
Web Site: http://www.zepindustries.eu
Industrial Cleaning Chemical Product Mfr
N.A.I.C.S.: 325612

Subsidiary (Non-US):

Zep Industries N.V. (3)
Frankrijklei 33, 2000, Antwerp, Belgium
Tel.: (32) 3470117
Web Site: http://www.zepindustries.be
Industrial Cleaning Products
N.A.I.C.S.: 532490

Zep Italia S.r.l. (3)
Via Nettunense KM 25000, 4011, Aprilia, LT, Italy
Tel.: (39) 06926691
Web Site: http://www.zep.it
Emp.: 190
Industrial Cleaning Products
N.A.I.C.S.: 532490

Zep UK Limited (3)
Tanhouse Lane, Widnes, WA8 0RR, Cheshire, United Kingdom
Tel.: (44) 151 422 1000
Web Site: http://zepcommercial.co.uk
Commercial, Industrial & Institutional Cleaning & Sanitation Products Mfr & Marketer
N.A.I.C.S.: 325612
Max Burnham *(Dir-Sls & Mktg)*

Unit (Domestic):

Zep Inc. - Enforcer Products (2)
1310 Seaboard Ind Blvd, Atlanta, GA 30318
Tel.: (888) 805-4357
Web Site: http://www.enforcer.com
Emp.: 1,000
Pesticides, Herbicides & Specialty Plumbing Chemicals Mfr
N.A.I.C.S.: 325320
Bill Redmond *(CEO)*

Division (Domestic):

Zep Inc. - Niagara National Division (2)
2135-A Hills Ave NW, Atlanta, GA 30318
Tel.: (404) 350-2600
Web Site: http://www.niagaranationalcorp.com
Emp.: 20
Commercial Motor Vehicle Washing Systems Developer, Mfr & Distr
N.A.I.C.S.: 333310
Paul Barnett *(Gen Mgr)*

mCare Solutions, LLC (1)
6900 N Dallas Pkwy Ste 300, Plano, TX 75024
Tel.: (484) 840-1984
Web Site: http://www.revintsolutions.com
Healthcare Revenue Recovery & Auditing Services
N.A.I.C.S.: 525990
Frank Forte *(Chief Revenue Officer)*
Sowri Krishnan *(CTO)*
Chris Jones *(Chief HR Officer)*
Lee Rivas *(CEO)*
Kyle Hicock *(Pres & Gen Mgr)*
Kristina Bourke *(COO)*

Subsidiary (Domestic):

Revint Solutions (2)
7300 Lone Star Dr Ste C200, Plano, TX 75024
Tel.: (484) 840-1984
Healthcare Provider Services
N.A.I.C.S.: 621610
Lee Rivas *(CEO)*
Jennifer Williams *(CFO)*

NEW OMNI BANK, N.A.
1235 S Garfield Ave, Alhambra, CA 91801-5037
Tel.: (626) 284-5555
Web Site: http://www.newomnibank.com
Year Founded: 1979
National Trust Companies With Deposits, Commercial
N.A.I.C.S.: 522110
Chien Keng Huang *(Chm & CEO)*
David Wang *(COO & Sr VP)*

NEW ORLEANS JAZZ AND HERITAGE FOUNDATION
1205 N Rampart St, New Orleans, LA 70116
Tel.: (504) 558-6100
Web Site: http://www.jazzandheritage.org

Year Founded: 1970
Emp.: 125
Provider of Festival Operation & Foundation Services
N.A.I.C.S.: 713990
Marsha A. Boudy *(Chief Admin Officer)*
Don Marshall *(Exec Dir)*
Donna Santiago *(First VP)*
Kathleen Turner *(Second VP)*
Jeffrey Goldring *(Third VP)*
David Francis *(Sec)*
Sarita Carriere *(Dir-Fin & HR)*

NEW ORLEANS METROPOLITAN CONVENTION & VISITORS BUREAU
2020 Saint Charles Ave, New Orleans, LA 70130
Tel.: (504) 566-5011
Web Site:
http://www.neworleansinfo.com
Sales Range: $10-24.9 Million
Emp.: 85
Tourist Information Bureau
N.A.I.C.S.: 561591
Stephen Perry *(Pres & CEO)*
Kristian Sonnier *(VP-Comm & PR)*

NEW ORLEANS MUSEUM OF ART
1 Collins Diboll Cir City Park, New Orleans, LA 70124
Tel.: (504) 658-4100
Web Site: http://www.noma.org
Year Founded: 1911
Sales Range: $10-24.9 Million
Emp.: 80
Art Museum
N.A.I.C.S.: 712110
Christina Carr *(Mgr-Grants)*
Sesthasak Boonchai *(Mgr-Digital Asset)*
Brad J. Caldwell *(Mgr-Pub Programs)*
Donna Dunn *(Mgr-HR)*
Jennifer Ickes *(Mgr-Exhibitions)*
Molly Cobb *(Mgr-Dev & Membership Ops)*
Raleigh P. Cooper *(Mgr-Private Events)*
Kristen Jochem *(Mgr-Donor Rels & Events)*
Mary Degnan *(Mgr-Creative Designs)*
Pamela Buckman *(Mgr-Sculpture Garden)*
Steve Lewis *(Mgr-Building)*

NEW ORLEANS PELICANS NBA, LLC
1250 Poydras St 19th Fl, New Orleans, LA 70113
Tel.: (504) 593-4700
Web Site: http://www.pelicans.com
Year Founded: 1988
Sales Range: $10-24.9 Million
Emp.: 200
Professional Basketball Team
N.A.I.C.S.: 711211
Edward F. Lang *(CFO & Sr VP)*
Danny Ferry *(Interim Gen Mgr)*

NEW ORLEANS SAINTS L.P.
5800 Airline Dr, Metairie, LA 70003-3876
Tel.: (504) 733-0255
Web Site:
http://www.neworleanssaints.com
Year Founded: 1966
Sales Range: $10-24.9 Million
Emp.: 130
Professional Football Franchise
N.A.I.C.S.: 711211
Edward F. Lang *(CFO & Sr VP)*
Tom Benson *(Owner)*

COMPANIES

NEW RITE AID, LLC

Greg Bensel (*Sr VP-Comm*)
Dennis Lauscha (*Pres*)
Mickey Loomis (*Exec VP & Gen Mgr*)
Terry Ashburn (*Dir-Facilities*)
Jeff Huffman (*Dir-IT*)
Jody Barbier (*Sr Mgr-Network & Support*)
Jason Trosclair (*Dir-Youth Programs*)
Elicia Broussard-Sheridan (*Dir-Community Affairs*)
Cindy Hart (*Sr Dir-Corp Sls Acct*)
Michael Stanfield (*Sr VP-Sls*)
Ben Hales (*VP-Mktg & Bus Dev*)
Ian Tigchelaar (*Sr Dir-Bus & Mktg Ops*)
Vicky Neumeyer (*Gen Counsel & Sr VP*)
Justin Macione (*Mgr-Football Comm*)
Dave Desposito (*Dir-Video*)
Fred McAfee (*Dir-Player Dev*)
Khai Harley (*VP-Football Admin*)
James Nagaoka (*Dir-Ops*)
John Baumgartner (*Mgr-Equipment*)
Danny Lawless (*Dir-Secretariat*)
Derrick James (*Mgr-Box Office*)
Jay Romig (*Dir-Admin*)
E. D. Lang (*CFO & Sr VP*)

NEW PENDULUM CORPORATION
1100 N Market St 4th Fl, Wilmington, DE 19890
Tel.: (211) 8146862219
Web Site: https://newpendulum.com
Holding Company
N.A.I.C.S.: 551112
Clark Stapelfeld (*Pres & CEO*)

Subsidiaries:

New Pig Corporation (1)
1 Pork Ave, Tipton, PA 16684
Tel.: (814) 684-0101
Web Site: http://www.newpig.com
Sales Range: $75-99.9 Million
Emp.: 300
Provider of Absorbent Products for Plant Safety & Cleanliness
N.A.I.C.S.: 325612
Nino F. Vella (*Pres & CEO*)
Carl DeCaspers (*Dir-PR*)
James Kerlin (*Controller*)
Ben Stapelfeld (*Chm*)

Subsidiary (Domestic):

Spilltech Environmental Inc (2)
1627 Odonoghue St, Mobile, AL 36615
Tel.: (251) 694-0102
Web Site: http://www.spilltech.com
Rev.: $22,600,000
Emp.: 80
Absorbant Mfr
N.A.I.C.S.: 325211
Susan Naser (*VP-Sls*)

Rhino Research Industries, LLC (1)
580 Vlg Blvd Ste 330, West Palm Beach, FL 33409-1953
Web Site: http://www.masonways.com
Commercial Equipment Merchant Whslr
N.A.I.C.S.: 423440
Judd Ettinger (*Exec VP*)

NEW POINT STONE CO.
992 S County Rd 800 E, Greensburg, IN 47240
Tel.: (812) 663-2021
Web Site: http://www.newpointstone.com
Rev.: $11,137,277
Emp.: 17
Crushed & Broken Limestone
N.A.I.C.S.: 212312
Kenneth T. Wanstrath (*Pres*)
Steve Wanstrath (*VP*)

NEW PORT AUTO CENTER, INC.
4625 US Hwy 19, New Port Richey, FL 34652-4943
Tel.: (727) 849-6699
Year Founded: 1979
Sales Range: $10-24.9 Million
Emp.: 90
Car Whslr
N.A.I.C.S.: 441110
Dennis L. (*Pres*)
Gene Nigro (*Gen Mgr*)

NEW PROCESS STEEL LP
5800 Westview Dr, Houston, TX 77055
Tel.: (713) 686-9631
Web Site: http://www.nps.cc
Rev.: $360,000,000
Emp.: 800
Steel Mfrs
N.A.I.C.S.: 423510
Richard Fant (*CEO*)
Bert Campanelli (*Dir-Corp Credit*)

NEW REGENCY PRODUCTIONS INC.
10201 W Pico Blvd Bldg 12, Los Angeles, CA 90035
Tel.: (310) 369-8300
Web Site: http://www.newregency.com
Year Founded: 1991
Rev.: $15,300,000
Emp.: 50
Motion Picture & Video Production
N.A.I.C.S.: 512110
Arnon Milchan (*Founder*)
Yariv Milchan (*Chm*)

NEW RESOURCES COMPANIES
1000 N Water St Suite 950, Milwaukee, WI 53202-6669
Tel.: (414) 289-7960
Web Site: http://www.gonrc.com
Year Founded: 1992
Sales Range: $10-24.9 Million
Emp.: 76
Holding Company: Consulting Services
N.A.I.C.S.: 551112
Nathan Christenson (*Head-Mktg*)

Subsidiaries:

New Resources Consulting (1)
1821 Walden Office Square, Schaumburg, IL 60173 (100%)
Tel.: (800) 320-0702
Web Site: http://www.nrconsults.com
Business & IT Consulting Services
N.A.I.C.S.: 541618
Suzanne Faase (*Dir-Recruiting*)

NEW RESOURCES CONSULTING, LLC
1000 N Water St Ste 250, Milwaukee, WI 53202
Tel.: (414) 289-7960
Web Site: http://www.nrconsults.com
Year Founded: 1992
Sales Range: $10-24.9 Million
Emp.: 110
Management Consulting Services
N.A.I.C.S.: 541611
Brian Birchbauer (*VP-Mgmt Consulting Practice*)
Leah Osiecki (*Mgr-Relationship*)
Don Weber (*VP-Client Rels & Gen Mgr*)
Chris Bailey (*Dir-Ops*)
Jill Means (*Dir-Mktg*)
Lorne Tappa (*VP-Fin & Admin*)
Mark Grosskopf (*Pres & CEO*)
Heather Potokar (*Dir-Recruiting*)

NEW RITE AID, LLC
1200 Intrepid Ave 2nd Fl, Philadelphia, PA 19112
Tel.: (717) 761-2633   DE
Year Founded: 2022
Holding Company
N.A.I.C.S.: 551112
Matthew C. Schroeder (*Interim CEO*)

Subsidiaries:

Rite Aid Corporation (1)
1200 Intrepid Ave 2nd Fl, Philadelphia, PA 19112
Tel.: (717) 761-2633
Web Site: https://www.riteaid.com
Rev.: $24,091,899,000
Assets: $7,527,362,000
Liabilities: $8,169,138,000
Net Worth: ($641,776,000)
Earnings: $749,936,000
Emp.: 47,000
Fiscal Year-end: 03/04/2023
Retail Drug Store Operator
N.A.I.C.S.: 456110
Matthew C. Schroeder (*CFO & Exec VP*)
Karen Staniforth (*Chief Pharmacy Officer & Sr VP*)
Jessica Kazmaier (*Chief HR Officer & Exec VP*)
Eric Sira (*Sr Mgr-Asset Protection & Supply Chain*)
Jeff Olson (*VP-Corp Comm*)
Byron Purcell (*Treas*)
Trent Kruse (*Sr VP-IR & Treasury*)
Texanna Reeves (*VP-Diversity, Equity & Inclusion*)
Thomas Sabatino (*Chief Legal Officer & Exec VP*)
Bruce G. Bodaken (*Chm*)

Subsidiary (Domestic):

Eagle Managed Care Corp. (2)
30 Hunter Ln, Camp Hill, PA 17011
Tel.: (717) 761-2633
Employee Benefit Pension Services
N.A.I.C.S.: 525110

Elixir Insurance Company (2)
7835 Freedom Ave NW, North Canton, OH 44720
Web Site: https://www.elixirinsurance.com
Health Insurance Services
N.A.I.C.S.: 524114

Envision Insurance Company (2)
7835 Freedom Ave NW, North Canton, OH 44720
Tel.: (330) 405-8089
Web Site: https://www.elixirinsurance.com
Insurance Agency & Brokerage Services
N.A.I.C.S.: 524210

Envision Medical Solutions, LLC (2)
7835 Freedom Ave NW, North Canton, OH 44720
Tel.: (813) 514-8235
Web Site: https://www.emsmed.com
Health Care Srvices
N.A.I.C.S.: 621610

Envision Pharmaceutical Services, LLC (2)
7835 Freedom Ave NW, North Canton, OH 44720
Tel.: (330) 405-8080
Web Site: https://www.elixirsolutions.com
Pharmaceutical Benefit Management Support Services
N.A.I.C.S.: 518210

Subsidiary (Domestic):

MedTrak Services, LLC (3)
10895 Lowell Ave Ste 100, Overland Park, KS 66210
Tel.: (913) 262-6851
Web Site: http://www.medtrakrx.com
Emp.: 125
Prescription Benefit Management Services
N.A.I.C.S.: 524292
Mark Fendler (*Chm*)

Subsidiary (Domestic):

GDF, Inc. (2)
1404 Wiltwyck Rd, Baltimore, MD 21209
Tel.: (202) 270-0151
Business Support Services
N.A.I.C.S.: 561499

Harco, Inc. (2)
7308 Grade Ln, Louisville, KY 40219
Tel.: (502) 366-4596
Web Site: https://www.harcoinc.com

Emp.: 12
Drug Retailer
N.A.I.C.S.: 456110

Health Dialog Services Corp. (2)
1 Financial Ctr 675 Atlantic Ave 21st Fl, Boston, MA 02111
Tel.: (617) 406-5200
Web Site: https://www.healthdialog.com
Sales Range: $75-99.9 Million
Emp.: 150
Health Care Management Programs
N.A.I.C.S.: 541611
Peter Goldbach (*Chief Medical Officer*)

Subsidiary (Domestic):

Health Dialog Analytic Solutions Corp. (3)
2 Monument Sq, Portland, ME 04101
Tel.: (207) 822-3700
Web Site: http://www.healthdialog.com
Sales Range: $25-49.9 Million
Emp.: 150
Medical Analytical Solutions
N.A.I.C.S.: 541715

Subsidiary (Domestic):

Hunter Lane, LLC (2)
315 Bridge St, South Hamilton, MA 01982
Tel.: (978) 468-9503
Business Support Services
N.A.I.C.S.: 561990

K&B Mississippi Corporation (2)
1220 Jerry Clower Blvd, Yazoo City, MS 39194-3077
Tel.: (662) 746-9926
Emp.: 20
Drug Stores Proprietary Stores
N.A.I.C.S.: 456110
James Sharp (*Gen Mgr*)

Maxi Drug South, L.P. (2)
21 Kingstown Rd, Wyoming, RI 02898
Tel.: (401) 539-6001
Emp.: 4
Drug Retailer
N.A.I.C.S.: 456110

RediClinic LLC (2)
9 E Greenway Plz Ste 2950, Houston, TX 77046
Tel.: (713) 935-0333
Web Site: https://www.rediclinic.com
Healtcare Services
N.A.I.C.S.: 622110
Shannon Blair (*COO*)
Molly Smith (*VP-Clinical Svcs*)
Michelle Bubel (*Sr Dir-HR & Recruiting*)
Keith Lott (*Dir-Field Ops*)

Rite Aid Drug Palace, Inc. (2)
6410 Platt Ave, West Hills, CA 91307-3216
Tel.: (818) 348-4850
Pharmaceuticals Mfr
N.A.I.C.S.: 325412

Rite Aid Lease Management Company (2)
30 Hunter Ln, Camp Hill, PA 17011
Tel.: (717) 761-2633
Healtcare Services
N.A.I.C.S.: 622110

Rite Aid of Alabama, Inc. (2)
10390 Technology Dr, Cottondale, AL 35453-3040
Tel.: (205) 633-1217
Pharmaceuticals Mfr
N.A.I.C.S.: 325412

Rite Aid of Connecticut, Inc. (2)
404 Main St, Ansonia, CT 06401
Tel.: (203) 734-3152
Medical Insurance Services
N.A.I.C.S.: 524114

Rite Aid of Delaware, Inc. (2)
40 Georgetown Plz, Georgetown, DE 19947-2300
Tel.: (302) 856-2015
Medical Equipment Distr
N.A.I.C.S.: 423450

Rite Aid of Illinois, Inc. (2)
3200 Market St, Camp Hill, PA 17011
Tel.: (717) 763-1181
Web Site: http://www.riteaid.com
Pharmaceutical Retailer

NEW RITE AID, LLC

New Rite Aid, LLC—(Continued)
N.A.I.C.S.: 456110

Rite Aid of Maine, Inc. (2)
464 Main St, Springvale, ME 04083-1818
Tel.: (207) 324-1222
Medical Equipment Distr
N.A.I.C.S.: 423450

Rite Aid of Maryland, Inc. (2)
8601 Baltimore National Pike, Ellicott City, MD 21043
Tel.: (410) 480-1377
Drug Retailer
N.A.I.C.S.: 456110

Rite Aid of New Hampshire, Inc. (2)
50 Storrs St, Concord, NH 03301
Tel.: (603) 228-0968
Pharmaceutical Retailer
N.A.I.C.S.: 456110

Rite Aid of South Carolina, Inc. (2)
515 S Hampton St, Kershaw, SC 29067-1834
Tel.: (803) 475-7370
Web Site: http://www.riteaid.com
Sales Range: $25-49.9 Million
Emp.: 12
Pharmaceuticals Product Mfr
N.A.I.C.S.: 325412

Rite Aid of Virginia, Inc. (2)
2260A Hunters Woods Plz, Reston, VA 20191
Tel.: (703) 860-0300
Web Site: http://www.riteaid.com
Drug Retailer
N.A.I.C.S.: 456110

Rite Aid of Washington, D.C., Inc. (2)
30 Hunter Ln, Camp Hill, PA 17011
Tel.: (717) 763-1181
Drug Stores Proprietary Stores
N.A.I.C.S.: 456110

Rx Options, LLC (2)
2181 E Aurora Rd Ste 101, Twinsburg, OH 44087
Tel.: (330) 405-8080
Emp.: 75
Management Consulting Services
N.A.I.C.S.: 541611

The Bartell Drug Company (2)
4025 Delridge Way SW Ste 400, Seattle, WA 98106
Tel.: (206) 767-1345
Web Site: http://www.bartelldrugs.com
Sales Range: $500-549.9 Million
Emp.: 1,600
Drug Store Operator
N.A.I.C.S.: 456110
George D. Bartell (Chm)
Kathi Lentzsch (Pres & CEO)

Thrifty PayLess, Inc. (2)
650 Walnut Ave, Greenfield, CA 93927-4928
Tel.: (831) 674-5565
Web Site: http://www.riteaid.com
Pharmacy
N.A.I.C.S.: 339112

NEW RIVER COMMUNICATIONS, INC.
1819 SE 17th St, Fort Lauderdale, FL 33316
Tel.: (954) 535-0644
Web Site: http://www.newrivercommunications.com
Year Founded: 2000
Sales Range: $10-24.9 Million
Emp.: 7
N.A.I.C.S.: 541810
Rod Taylor (Pres)
Shaun Petersen (Acct Supvr)
Laura Brill (Dir-Art)
Larry Montali (Owner)

NEW RIVER ELECTRICAL CORPORATION
15 Cloverdale Pl, Cloverdale, VA 24077-0070
Tel.: (540) 966-1650 VA
Web Site: http://www.newriverelectrical.com
Year Founded: 1984
Sales Range: $25-49.9 Million
Emp.: 500
Electrical Work
N.A.I.C.S.: 238210
Carolena Trammell (Controller)
Thomas M. Wolden (Pres & CEO)

NEW RIVER INDUSTRIES INC.
6540 Viscoe Rd, Radford, VA 24143
Tel.: (540) 731-8000
Sales Range: $25-49.9 Million
Emp.: 150
Acetate Polyester Rayon Broadwoven Fabrics
N.A.I.C.S.: 313210

NEW RIVER VALLEY BENEFITS CONSORTIUM
PO Box 785, Lexington, VA 24450
Tel.: (540) 463-3566 VA
Year Founded: 2003
Sales Range: Less than $1 Million
Self Insurance Services
N.A.I.C.S.: 525190
Jerry Higgins (Chm)
Alan Cummins (Vice Chm)

NEW ROCHELLE TOYOTA
47 Cedar St, New Rochelle, NY 10801
Tel.: (914) 576-8000
Web Site: http://www.newrochelletoyota.com
Sales Range: $10-24.9 Million
Emp.: 70
Car Whslr
N.A.I.C.S.: 441110
Donny Lia (Gen Mgr)

NEW SAGAYA
2525 Blueberry Rd Ste 106, Anchorage, AK 99503-2647
Tel.: (907) 563-0220
Web Site: http://www.newsagaya.com
Year Founded: 1985
Sales Range: $10-24.9 Million
Emp.: 6
Specialty Seafood Mfr & Distr
N.A.I.C.S.: 445110
Paul Reid (Mgr)

NEW SCHOOL PROPERTIES, INC.
5646 Milton St Ste 888, Dallas, TX 75206
Tel.: (214) 234-0696 TX
Web Site: http://www.newschoolprop.com
Year Founded: 2010
Sales Range: $25-49.9 Million
Emp.: 3
Real Estate Investment Services
N.A.I.C.S.: 525990
Thomas N. Herbelin (Chm, Pres, CEO & CFO)

NEW SENSOR CORPORATION
55-01 2nd St, Long Island City, NY 11101
Tel.: (718) 937-8300
Web Site: http://www.newsensor.com
Sales Range: $25-49.9 Million
Emp.: 60
Mfr & Sales Electronic Parts & Equipment
N.A.I.C.S.: 423690
Michael Matthews (Pres)
Ralph Trimarchi (Mgr-Sls)

NEW SOURCE ENERGY CORPORATION
914 N Broadway Ste 230, Oklahoma City, OK 73102
Tel.: (405) 272-3028 DE
Web Site: http://www.newsource.com
Sales Range: $25-49.9 Million
Emp.: 8
Oil & Gas Exploration Services
N.A.I.C.S.: 211120
Kristian B. Kos (Pres & CEO)
Richard D. Finley (CFO & Treas)

NEW SOUTH BANCSHARES INC.
210 Automation Way, Birmingham, AL 35210
Tel.: (205) 951-1000 AL
Web Site: http://www.newsouthfederal.com
Year Founded: 1989
Sales Range: $100-124.9 Million
Emp.: 5
Bank Holding Company
N.A.I.C.S.: 551111
Roger Dale Murphree (Exec VP)

Subsidiaries:

New South Federal Savings Bank (1)
6000 Legacy Dr, Plano, TX 75024-3601
Tel.: (205) 951-1000
Web Site: http://www.newsouthfederal.com
Rev.: $81,718,000
Emp.: 600
Federal Savings Bank
N.A.I.C.S.: 522310

NEW SOUTH EQUIPMENT MATS
281 Old Jackson Rd, Madison, MS 39110
Tel.: (601) 859-7472
Web Site: http://www.newsouthmat.com
Year Founded: 2007
Sales Range: $10-24.9 Million
Emp.: 34
Mfr of Eco-Friendly, Heavy-Duty Mats & Runners for Construction, Environmental Remediation & Energy Exploration
N.A.I.C.S.: 336999
Drew St. John (CEO)
Scott Poole (VP-Ops)

NEW SOUTH FORD, INC.
1200 N Frontage Rd, Meridian, MS 39301
Tel.: (601) 693-6821
Web Site: http://www.newsouthford.net
Year Founded: 1977
Sales Range: $10-24.9 Million
Emp.: 68
Car Whslr
N.A.I.C.S.: 441110
Milburn Vanveckhoven (Pres)

NEW SOUTH RESTORATIONS INC.
2377 John Glenn Dr Ste 106, Chamblee, GA 30341 DE
Year Founded: 1994
Sales Range: $10-24.9 Million
Drywall & Insulation Contractors
N.A.I.C.S.: 238310
Elise Stephens (Sec)
Charles Moncrief Jr. (Pres, CEO & CFO)

NEW SOUTH SUPPLY LLC
951 Harbor Dr, West Columbia, SC 29169
Tel.: (803) 791-8700
Web Site: http://www.newsouthsupply.com
Year Founded: 1981
Sales Range: $10-24.9 Million

Emp.: 40
Concrete Building Products
N.A.I.C.S.: 423320
Jim Sobeck (Pres)
Jon Black (Mgr-Sls)

NEW SOUTHWEST BAKING COMPANY
600 Phil Gramm Boulevard, Bryan, TX 77807
Tel.: (979) 778-6600
Year Founded: 1996
Sales Range: $25-49.9 Million
Emp.: 250
Bakery Products Mfr
N.A.I.C.S.: 311812
Fred Bower (CEO)
John Paterakis (Partner)
Buddy King (Mgr-Production)
Terry Stone (Dir-HR)
Myla Aguilar (Mgr)
Trey Elliott (VP-Fin)
Steve Warden (VP-Bakery Ops)

NEW STANDARD CORPORATION
74 Commerce Way, York, PA 17406
Tel.: (717) 757-9450 PA
Web Site: http://www.newstandard.com
Year Founded: 1940
Sales Range: $50-74.9 Million
Emp.: 400
Mfr of Metal Stampings, Assemblies & Automotive Stampings
N.A.I.C.S.: 332119
Robert Traup (Mgr-Pur)
Morton F. Zifferer Jr. (Chm & CEO)

Subsidiaries:

New Standard Corporation - Rocky Mount Plant (1)
3883 S Church St, Rocky Mount, NC 27801
Tel.: (252) 446-5481
Fabricated Structural Metal Mfr
N.A.I.C.S.: 332312
Joe Garner (Dir-Ops)
Scott Saiers (Engr-Mfg)

NEW STATE CAPITAL PARTNERS LLC
2001 Palmer Ave Ste 205, Larchmont, NY 10538
Tel.: (212) 675-1600 DE
Web Site: http://www.newstatecp.com
Year Founded: 2013
Privater Equity Firm
N.A.I.C.S.: 523999
David Blechner (Sr Principal)
John Beauclair (Sr Principal)
John Kim (Sr Principal)
James Michael Laisure (Operating Partner)
Wake Smith (Partner-Operating)
Paul Block (Partner)
Charles Entrekin (Partner)
Jim Farr (Partner)
Erika Jung (Partner)
Robert McPherson (Partner)
Frank Muehleman (Partner)
Jordan Reber (Partner)
Andrew Sekel (Partner)
Maureen Spivack (Partner)
Frank Lazaran (Partner-Operating)

Subsidiaries:

Agility Recovery Solutions, Inc. (1)
2221 Northmont Pkwy Ste 300, Duluth, GA 30096
Tel.: (704) 927-7933
Web Site: http://www.agilityrecovery.com
Business Continuity Services
N.A.I.C.S.: 541513
Mark San Fratello (CEO)

Computer Data Source, Inc. (1)

COMPANIES

275 Industrial Way W, Eatontown, NJ 07724
Tel.: (732) 542-7300
Web Site: http://www.cds.net
Computer & Office Machine Repair & Maintenance
N.A.I.C.S.: 811210
Jim McDivitt *(CTO)*
Dan Newton *(CEO)*
Chuck Cwirka *(COO)*
Joe Nuzzolo *(CFO)*
Brian Reagan *(CMO)*

Patuxent Roofing & Contracting, LLC (1)
8684 Veterans Hwy Ste 101, Millersville, MD 21108
Tel.: (855) 729-7510
Web Site: https://paxservicesgroup.com
Roofing Contractors
N.A.I.C.S.: 238160

Subsidiary (Domestic):

Cram Roofing Company Inc (2)
111 Soledad St, San Antonio, TX 78205
Tel.: (210) 694-7815
Web Site: http://www.cramroofing.com
Rev.: $8,600,000
Emp.: 75
Other Building Finishing Contractors
N.A.I.C.S.: 238390
Gary Cram *(Pres)*
Scott D. Voyles *(Mgr-Ops)*
Mark R. Eichelbaum *(COO)*

The Expo Group, Inc. (1)
5931 W Campus Cr Dr, Irving, TX 75063
Tel.: (972) 580-9000
Web Site: http://www.theexpogroup.com
Rev.: $22,000,000
Emp.: 160
Convention & Show Services
N.A.I.C.S.: 561920
Randy Pekowski *(Pres & COO)*
Dana Freker Doody *(VP-Comm & Strategic Client Solutions)*
Corey Kelley *(Chief Tech & Experience Officer)*
Millie Garcia *(Acct Mgr-Chicago)*
Shannon McDaniel *(VP-Sls Dev)*
Ken Dec *(Exec VP-Mktg & Client Strategies)*
Chad Chappell *(Dir-Sls-Natl)*
Toby Purdy *(Chief Sls Officer)*
Michael Preston *(Exec VP-Natl Accounts Level 5)*
Tim Boobar *(CFO)*

Subsidiary (Domestic):

Allied Convention Service, Inc. (2)
2502 Lk Orange Dr, Orlando, FL 32837-7802
Tel.: (407) 851-0261
Web Site: http://www.bredeallied.com
Convention & Trade Show Organizers
N.A.I.C.S.: 561920
Charles T. Premone *(Pres)*

NEW TANGRAM, LLC
9200 Sorensen Ave, Santa Fe Springs, CA 90670
Tel.: (562) 365-5000 CA
Web Site: http://www.tangraminteriors.com
Sales Range: $25-49.9 Million
Emp.: 300
Office Furniture Sales & Distr
N.A.I.C.S.: 423210
Charlotte Wiederholt *(Pres-Tangram Studio)*
Dave Teper *(Gen Mgr-Flooring & Light Construction)*
David Morgan *(VP-Sls)*
Denyse Sharp *(VP-Design & Customer Svc)*
Dirk Manning *(Dir-Sls-Orange County)*
Kathy MacIntosh *(Dir-Ops)*
Kellie Reed *(Gen Mgr-Fresno)*
Mitchel Zelinger *(VP-Bus Dev)*
Nick Meter *(Dir-Sls-Los Angeles)*
Paul Smith *(Chief Mktg Officer)*
Sheila O'Flynn *(Dir-Sls-Los Angeles)*
Amber Jones *(Dir-Sls-Education)*

Subsidiaries:

New Tangram, LLC - Newport Beach (1)
1375 Dove St Ste 300, Newport Beach, CA 92660
Tel.: (949) 955-6700
Web Site: http://www.tangraminteriors.com
Office Furniture Distr
N.A.I.C.S.: 449110
David Morgan *(VP)*

NEW TEACHER CENTER
110 Cooper St 500, Santa Cruz, CA 95060
Tel.: (831) 600-2228 CA
Web Site: http://www.newteachercenter.org
Year Founded: 2008
Sales Range: $25-49.9 Million
Emp.: 228
Educational Support Services
N.A.I.C.S.: 611710
Angela Covert *(Vice Chm)*
Ellen Moir *(Founder)*
Lynn Kepp *(Sr VP-Strategic Partnerships)*
Shruti Sehra *(Chm)*
Kitty Dixon *(Sr VP-Innovation)*
Cindy Brunswick *(Sr VP-Program Strategy & Delivery)*
Sandar Riina *(VP-HR)*
Ali Picucci *(VP-Impact & Improvement)*
Kamilah Jones *(VP-Mktg & External Affairs)*
Tommy Chang *(CEO)*
Arthur Mills IV *(COO)*
Atyani Howard *(Chief Program Officer)*

NEW TECH GLOBAL VENTURES, LLC
1030 Regional Park Dr, Houston, TX 77060
Tel.: (281) 951-4330
Web Site: http://www.ntglobal.com
Sales Range: $150-199.9 Million
Emp.: 550
Project Management & Consulting Services
N.A.I.C.S.: 541618
Larry A. Cress *(Pres)*
Jeffrey R. Cummins *(VP)*
Daniel R. Lockwood *(VP)*

NEW THERMOSERV, LTD.
3901 Pipestone Rd, Dallas, TX 75212
Tel.: (800) 635-5559
Web Site: http://www.ntl-brands.com
Sales Range: $10-24.9 Million
Emp.: 200
Plastics Product Mfr
N.A.I.C.S.: 326199
Sendy Tran *(Dir-Sls)*

Subsidiaries:

Gessner Products Company, Inc. (1)
241 N Main St, Ambler, PA 19002
Tel.: (215) 646-7667
Web Site: http://www.gessnerproducts.com
All Other Plastics Product Mfr
N.A.I.C.S.: 326199

NEW URBAN WEST INC.
2001 Wilshire Blvd Ste 401, Santa Monica, CA 90403
Tel.: (310) 566-6390
Web Site: http://www.newurbanwest.com
Rev.: $95,677,288
Emp.: 10
Speculative Builder, Single-Family Houses
N.A.I.C.S.: 236115
Adam Browning *(CEO)*
Jason Han *(COO)*

NEW VALUE CAPITAL LLC
1389 Center Dr #200, Park City, UT 84098
Tel.: (435) 252-0545
Web Site: http://www.newvaluecapital.com
Privater Equity Firm
N.A.I.C.S.: 523999
Paul Lehman *(Partner)*
Adam Raper *(Partner)*

Subsidiaries:

Dynojet Research, Inc. (1)
2191 Mendenhall Dr Ste 105, North Las Vegas, NV 89081
Tel.: (702) 399-1423
Web Site: http://www.dynojet.com
Emp.: 160
Dynamometer Instruments Mfr
N.A.I.C.S.: 334519
David Winiarczyk *(CFO)*
Danny Hourigan *(Sr VP)*

NEW VENTURE FUND
1201 Connecticut Ave NW Ste 300, Washington, DC 20036
Tel.: (202) 595-1061 DC
Web Site: http://www.newventurefund.org
Year Founded: 2006
Sales Range: $100-124.9 Million
Emp.: 98
Fundraising Services
N.A.I.C.S.: 813211
Andrew Schulz *(Gen Counsel)*
Lee Bodner *(Co-Pres)*

NEW VENTURE PARTNERS LLC
430 Mountain Ave, New Providence, NJ 07974
Tel.: (908) 464-0900
Web Site: http://www.nvpllc.com
Holding Company
N.A.I.C.S.: 551112
Andrew Garman *(Mng Partner)*
Tom Uhlman *(Mng Partner)*
Marc Rappoport *(CFO & Partner)*

NEW VISION CO-OP
101 9th St, Heron Lake, MN 56137
Tel.: (507) 793-2301
Web Site: http://www.newvision.coop
Sales Range: $250-299.9 Million
Emp.: 120
Grain Elevators
N.A.I.C.S.: 424510
Frank McDowell *(Gen Mgr)*
Kevin Doppenberg *(Div Mgr)*
Dennis Weber *(Mgr-Ops)*
Cheryl Westerman *(Controller)*

NEW VISION DISPLAY, INC.
1430 Blue Oaks Blvd Ste 100, Roseville, CA 95747-5156
Tel.: (916) 786-8111 CA
Web Site: http://www.newvisiondisplay.com
Year Founded: 2012
Emp.: 3,000
Custom Display, Touch Panel & Cover Lens Products Mfr
N.A.I.C.S.: 334419
Jeff Olyniec *(CEO & COO)*
Alan M. Lefko *(CFO)*
David Kruse *(Chief Sls Officer & Pres-Sls & Mktg-Worldwide)*
Matthias Pfeiffer *(CTO-Display Solutions)*
Farouk Zabel *(CTO-Touch Solutions)*
Bill Moore *(Pres-EMEA)*
Steve Gerisch *(VP-Sls-Americas)*
Shahna Kothapally *(Dir-Product Engrg)*

Subsidiaries:

One Stop Displays, LLC (1)
135 W Central Blvd, Orlando, FL 32801
Tel.: (407) 480-5800
Web Site: http://www.osddisplays.com
Monitor & Display Mfr
N.A.I.C.S.: 334118
Khaled Khuda *(Founder)*

NEW VISION USA, INC.
8322 E Hartford Dr, Scottsdale, AZ 85255-5466
Tel.: (480) 927-8999
Web Site: http://www.newvision.com
Year Founded: 1995
Sales Range: $25-49.9 Million
Emp.: 150
Pharmaceutical Preparation Mfr
N.A.I.C.S.: 325412
B. K. Boreyko *(Founder)*
Lauren Boreyko *(Founder)*
Karen Boreyko *(Founder)*

NEW VISIONS FOR PUBLIC SCHOOLS
205 E 42nd St, New York, NY 10017
Tel.: (212) 645-5110 NY
Web Site: http://www.newvisions.org
Year Founded: 1989
Sales Range: $10-24.9 Million
Emp.: 116
Educational Support Services
N.A.I.C.S.: 611710
Mark Dunetz *(Pres)*
Beverly Donohue *(VP-Policy & Res)*
Cynthia Rietfcha *(COO)*
Shannon Curran *(Chief Schools Officer)*
Gary L. Ginsberg *(Chm)*

NEW WASHINGTON STATE BANK INC.
402 E Main St, New Washington, IN 47162
Tel.: (812) 293-3321 WA
Web Site: http://www.newwashbank.com
Year Founded: 1972
Sales Range: $10-24.9 Million
Emp.: 80
Provider of Banking Services
N.A.I.C.S.: 522110
Patrick Glotzbach *(Pres)*
Scott Benner *(Controller)*
Jessica Carroll *(CEO)*
Stephanie Pruitt *(Mgr-Sellersburg)*
Tim Rigrish *(VP)*
Lea Ann Lumpkins *(Branch Mgr-Jeffersonville)*
Lee Thomas *(VP)*
Amanda Matheny *(VP)*

NEW WATER CAPITAL, L.P.
2424 N Federal Hwy Ste 418, Boca Raton, FL 33431
Tel.: (561) 235-7310 DE
Web Site: http://www.newwatercap.com
Privater Equity Firm
N.A.I.C.S.: 523999
Brian McGee *(Mng Partner)*
Jason Neimark *(Mng Partner)*
Anuj Singh *(Principal)*
Brian Pawlowski *(CFO)*
Eric Bitel *(VP-Ops)*
Nick LaRosa *(VP)*

Subsidiaries:

BLI Legacy, Inc. (1)
1013 Tamarac Dr, Carpentersville, IL 60110
Tel.: (847) 428-6059
Web Site: http://www.bulklift.com
Chemicals Mfr
N.A.I.C.S.: 325998
Brian M. Kelly *(Pres & CEO)*

Custom Corned Beef, Inc. (1)
3575 Logan Court, Denver, CO 80216
Tel.: (303) 296-8686

NEW WATER CAPITAL, L.P.

New Water Capital, L.P.—(Continued)
Web Site:
http://www.customcornedbeef.com
Rev.: $1,000,000
Emp.: 5
Meat & Meat Related Products Whslr
N.A.I.C.S.: 424470
John Jewsbury (Pres)

Klosterman Baking Company, Inc. (1)
4760 Paddock Rd, Cincinnati, OH 45229-1004
Tel.: (513) 242-1004
Web Site: http://www.klostermanbakery.com
Baked Goods Mfr
N.A.I.C.S.: 311812
Dennis Wiltshire (Exec VP)

Myotek Industries Inc. (1)
1176 Main St Ste B, Irvine, CA 92614
Tel.: (949) 502-3776
Web Site: http://www.myotek.com
Automotive Parts & Accessories Mfr
N.A.I.C.S.: 441380

Subsidiary (Domestic):

Amptech, Inc. (2)
201 Glocheski Dr, Manistee, MI 49660
Tel.: (231) 299-1230
Web Site: http://www.amptechinc.com
Printed Circuit Assembly Mfr
N.A.I.C.S.: 334418
Eric Carlin (Ops Mgr)

Sea Link International IRB, Inc. (1)
13151 66th St N, Largo, FL 33773
Tel.: (727) 523-8660
Web Site: http://www.sealinkinternational.com
High Precision Automotive Lighting Components Mfr
N.A.I.C.S.: 336320

Subsidiary (Domestic):

Hicks Plastics Company, Inc. (2)
51308 Industrial Dr, Macomb, MI 48042
Tel.: (586) 786-5640
Web Site: http://www.hicksplastics.com
Plastics Product Mfr
N.A.I.C.S.: 326199

Worth Collection Ltd. (1)
520 8th Ave #2301, New York, NY 10018
Tel.: (212) 268-0312
Web Site: http://www.worthny.com
Womens Clothing
N.A.I.C.S.: 315250
Fran Della Badia (CEO)
Cindy Hall (Gen Mgr-Mdse)
John Disa (Chm)

NEW WATER STREET CORP.
55 Water St, New York, NY 10041
Tel.: (212) 747-9120 DE
Web Site: http://www.55water.com
Year Founded: 1986
Sales Range: $125-149.9 Million
Emp.: 63
Office Space Provider
N.A.I.C.S.: 531120
Frank Magnani (VP-Special Projects)
William H. Pupplo (VP-Construction)
George Acero (VP-Building Sys)

NEW WAVE YACHTS
17 Ashland Ave, Manchester, MA 01944
Tel.: (978) 526-9996
Web Site:
http://www.newwaveyachts.com
Sales Range: $10-24.9 Million
Emp.: 12
Dealers of Boats & Yachts
N.A.I.C.S.: 441222
Bob Wilcox (Pres)

Subsidiaries:

New Wave Yachts, Dealership (1)
6 1/2 Bridge St, Dartmouth, MA 02748
Tel.: (508) 993-9100
Web Site: http://www.newwaveyachts.com

Sales Range: $10-24.9 Million
Emp.: 7
Dealers of Boats & Yachts
N.A.I.C.S.: 541990

NEW WAY AIR BEARINGS
50 McDonald Blvd, Aston, PA 19014
Tel.: (610) 494-6700
Web Site:
http://www.newwayairbearings.com
Year Founded: 1994
Sales Range: $10-24.9 Million
Emp.: 50
Plastics Product Mfr
N.A.I.C.S.: 326199
Drew Devitt (Founder, CEO & CTO)
Nick Sotiropoulos (Chief Engr)
Nick Hackett (Pres & CEO)
Shawn Garrison (VP-Fin & Ops)

NEW WEST DISTRIBUTING, INC.
127 Woodland Ave, Reno, NV 89523
Tel.: (775) 355-5500
Web Site:
http://www.newwestdistributing.com
Sales Range: $10-24.9 Million
Emp.: 60
Alcoholic Beverages Whslr
N.A.I.C.S.: 424810
Steve Pierce (Area Mgr-Bus)

NEW WEST NEWSPAPERS INC.
2533 N Carson St Ste 4239, Carson City, NV 89706
Tel.: (775) 841-9417
Rev.: $12,000,000
Emp.: 2
Newspapers, Publishing & Printing
N.A.I.C.S.: 513110

Subsidiaries:

Jackson County Newspapers Inc. (1)
410 Race St, Ravenswood, WV 26164-1702
Tel.: (304) 273-2424
Sales Range: $10-24.9 Million
Emp.: 20
Commercial Printing, Lithographic
N.A.I.C.S.: 323111
Frank Atkins (Mgr)

NEW WEST REALTY DEVELOPMENT CORP.
928 S Bishop Ste 2, Chicago, IL 60607
Tel.: (312) 829-2100
Web Site:
http://www.newwestrealty.com
Sales Range: $25-49.9 Million
Emp.: 3
Commercial Real Estate & Related Services
N.A.I.C.S.: 531390
Frank Mauro (Mgr-Property)

NEW WEST, LLC
9630 Ormsby Station Rd, Louisville, KY 40223
Tel.: (502) 891-2500 KY
Web Site:
http://www.newwestagency.com
Year Founded: 1971
Sales Range: $10-24.9 Million
Emp.: 20
Advetising Agency
N.A.I.C.S.: 541810

Subsidiaries:

Mo' Better Marketing, LLC (1)
950 Breckenridge Ln Ste 140, Louisville, KY 40207
Tel.: (502) 891-2541
Web Site: http://www.mobetter.com
Full Service Advertising Agency
N.A.I.C.S.: 541810

Carl Brazley (Founder, Pres & CEO)

NEW WESTERN ENERGY CORPORATION
1140 Spectrum, Irvine, CA 92618
Tel.: (949) 435-0977 NV
Web Site:
http://newwesternenergy.com
Year Founded: 2008
Sales Range: Less than $1 Million
Emp.: 4
Oil & Gas Exploration
N.A.I.C.S.: 211120

NEW WINDSOR VOLUNTEER AMBULANCE CORPS INC.
PO Box 4334, New Windsor, NY 12553
Tel.: (845) 563-3111 NY
Web Site:
http://www.newwindsorems.org
Year Founded: 1957
Sales Range: $1-9.9 Million
Emp.: 25
Ambulance Service
N.A.I.C.S.: 621910
Dawn Marshall (Pres)
Joseph Micheletti (Chm)
Courtney Polkowski (Sec)
Elizabeth Nolcox (VP)
Marie Matthews (Treas)

NEW WORLD CAR NISSAN, INC.
12908 IH 35 N, San Antonio, TX 78233
Tel.: (210) 599-5931
Web Site:
http://www.worldcarnissan.net
Sales Range: $10-24.9 Million
Emp.: 75
New Car Dealers
N.A.I.C.S.: 441110
Leon Reid (Gen Mgr-Sls)
Tracy Young (Mgr-Fin)

NEW WORLD IMPORTS INC.
180 West 80th St Ste 206, New York, NY 10024
Tel.: (212) 947-2202
Rev.: $30,000,000
Emp.: 15
Men's & Boys' Clothing
N.A.I.C.S.: 424350
Peter Oswald (VP)

NEW WORLD TECHNOLOGIES, INC.
1363 Veterans Memorial Hwy Ste 22, Hauppauge, NY 11788 DE
Web Site:
http://www.newworldtek.com
Year Founded: 2018
Assets: $787,469
Liabilities: $4,395,631
Net Worth: ($3,608,162)
Earnings: ($3,354,512)
Emp.: 3
Fiscal Year-end: 10/31/21
Medical Device Mfr & Distr
N.A.I.C.S.: 334510
Hank Tucker (Chm, Pres, CEO & Sec)
Andrew Fitzpatrick (COO)
Richard Gonsalves (CFO)

NEW WORQ, LLC
3625 N Hall St Ste 615, Dallas, TX 75219
Tel.: (972) 379-8183
Web Site: http://www.newworq.com
Business Consulting Services
N.A.I.C.S.: 541611
Brenda Bazan (Mng Partner)
Shaunna Black (Mng Partner)

U.S. PRIVATE

NEW YORK ATHLETIC CLUB
180 Central Park S, New York, NY 10019-1562
Tel.: (212) 247-5100 NY
Web Site: http://www.nyac.org
Year Founded: 1868
Rev.: $34,543,656
Emp.: 408
Physical Fitness Facilities
N.A.I.C.S.: 713940
Roger Simon (Gen Mgr)
Daniel Perez (Asst Gen Mgr)
Carolyn Gleason (Dir-Mktg)
Andrew Alfred (Dir-HR)

NEW YORK BITUMINOUS PRODUCTS CORP.
1297 Craigville Rd, Chester, NY 10918
Tel.: (845) 782-7231
Web Site: http://www.nybit.com
Rev.: $18,500,000
Emp.: 90
Industrial Supplies Merchant Whslr
N.A.I.C.S.: 423840
Anthony Santoro (Reg Mgr-Sls)
Shawn Thom (Mgr-Quality Control)

NEW YORK BLOOD CENTER, INC.
310 E 67th St, New York, NY 10065
Tel.: (212) 570-3000
Web Site:
http://www.nybloodcenter.org
Sales Range: $250-299.9 Million
Emp.: 1,400
Blood Collection, Distribution & Services
N.A.I.C.S.: 621991
Robert Purvis (VP-Customer Svc)

NEW YORK CAROLINA EXPRESS
1314 Conklin Rd, Conklin, NY 13748
Tel.: (607) 723-7977
Rev.: $13,511,913
Emp.: 35
Trucking
N.A.I.C.S.: 484121
Jeffrey P. Bump (CEO)
Todd Bushnell (VP-Fin)

NEW YORK CENTER FOR CHILD DEVELOPMENT
159 W 127th St, New York, NY 10027
Tel.: (212) 752-7575 NY
Web Site: http://www.nyccd.org
Sales Range: $10-24.9 Million
Emp.: 155
Child Care & Development Services
N.A.I.C.S.: 624110
Judith Wolff Kimberg (VP)
Rena Gordon (Asst Sec)

NEW YORK CENTRAL ART SUPPLY, INC.
62 3rd Ave, New York, NY 10003-5534
Tel.: (212) 477-0400 DE
Web Site:
http://www.nycentralart.com
Year Founded: 1907
Sales Range: $10-24.9 Million
Emp.: 24
Artist Materials Retailer
N.A.I.C.S.: 459999
Steven Steinberg (Pres & CEO)

NEW YORK CENTRAL MUTUAL FIRE INSURANCE COMPANY INC.
1899 Central Plz E, Edmeston, NY 13335-1828
Tel.: (607) 965-8321 NY
Web Site: http://www.nycm.com

Year Founded: 1899
Sales Range: $200-249.9 Million
Emp.: 1,100
Fire, Marine, Property & Casualty Insurance
N.A.I.C.S.: 524126
Vanness Daniel Robinson (Pres & CEO)
Albert Pylinski (CFO)

NEW YORK CITY BALLET
20 Lincoln Ctr Plz, New York, NY 10023
Tel.: (212) 870-5677
Web Site: http://www.nycballet.com
Sales Range: $25-49.9 Million
Emp.: 400
Ballet Producer
N.A.I.C.S.: 711110
Brooks Parsons (Sr Dir-Ops)
Katherine E. Brown (Exec Dir)
Katharina Plumb (Assoc Dir-Comm)
Shelby Schroeder (Deputy Dir-Special Events)
Susanna Organic (Asst Dir-Volunteer Programmatic Svcs)
Jill Jefferson (Dir-Acquisition Mktg)
Ann Harrell (Dir-Capital Campaign)
Marc Happel (Dir-Costumes)
Ricky Kim (Dir-Creative Svcs)
Michaela Drapes (Dir-Digital Content & Dev)
Stephan Czarnomski (Dir-IT)
Penny Jacobus (Dir-Lighting)
Douglas James Hamilton (Dir-Membership)
Dustin Brauneck (Dir-Mktg)
Marguerite Mehler (Dir-Production)
Thomas A. Lemanski (Dir-Rehearsal Admin)
Perry Silvey (Dir-Technical)
Kristin Kennedy Clark (Sec)
Gordon B. Pattee (Treas)
Jonathan Stafford (Dir-Artistic)
Robert I. Lipp (Pres)

NEW YORK CITY CRIMINAL JUSTICE AGENCY, INC.
52 Duane St 3rd Fl, New York, NY 10007
Tel.: (646) 213-2500 NY
Web Site: http://www.nycja.org
Year Founded: 1977
Sales Range: $10-24.9 Million
Emp.: 264
Law firm
N.A.I.C.S.: 541199
Michael Jacobson (Chm)
Jerome E. McElroy (Exec Dir)
Geraldine Ferrara (Sec)

NEW YORK CITY HOUSING DEVELOPMENT CORPORATION
110 William St, New York, NY 10038
Tel.: (212) 227-5500
Web Site: http://www.nychdc.com
Rev.: $167,426,000
Emp.: 90
Investor
N.A.I.C.S.: 523999
Richard Froehlich (Pres-Acting)
Eric Enderlin (Pres)
Louise Carroll (Chm)

Subsidiaries:

Housing New York Corporation (1)
110 William St 10th Fl, New York, NY 10038
Tel.: (212) 227-5500
Web Site: http://www.nychdc.com
Sales Range: $50-74.9 Million
Housing Programs, Planning & Development: Government
N.A.I.C.S.: 524210

New York City Housing Development Corp (1)
110 William St Fl 10, New York, NY 10038
Tel.: (212) 227-9745
Web Site: http://www.nychdc.com
Sales Range: $50-74.9 Million
Emp.: 200
Housing Programs, Planning & Development: Government
N.A.I.C.S.: 523940
Eric Enderlin (Pres)

NEW YORK CITY OFF-TRACK BETTING CORPORATION
1501 Broadway Times Sq, New York, NY 10036-5601
Tel.: (212) 221-5200 NY
Year Founded: 1970
Sales Range: $800-899.9 Million
Emp.: 2,700
Horse Racing Services
N.A.I.C.S.: 713290
Ron Ceisler (Sr VP-Mktg)
Ray Casey (Pres)

NEW YORK CITY OPERA INC.
75 Broad St, New York, NY 10004
Tel.: (212) 870-5600
Web Site: http://www.nycopera.com
Sales Range: $25-49.9 Million
Emp.: 600
Producer of Opera
N.A.I.C.S.: 711110
Joseph Gasperec (Asst Dir-Tech)
Bill Updegraff (Dir-Mktg)
Albert Sherman (Dir-Stage)
Frances O'Connell (Mgr-Database)

NEW YORK COMMUNITY TRUST
909 3rd Ave, New York, NY 10022
Tel.: (212) 686-0010 NY
Web Site: http://www.nycommunitytrust.org
Year Founded: 1923
Sales Range: $350-399.9 Million
Emp.: 50
Trusts For Religious Organization
N.A.I.C.S.: 813211
Lorie A. Slutsky (Pres)
Jane L. Wilton (Gen Counsel)
Robert V. Edgar (VP)
Heidi Hotzler (Controller)
Mercedes M. Leon (VP-Admin)
Patricia Jenny (VP-Grants)
Gay Young (Dir-Donor Svcs)
Kerry McCarthy (Program Dir)
Carolyn M. Weiss (CFO)
Wen Weng (Controller)
Eileen P. Casey (Dir-Investment Reporting)
Ayanna Russell (Dir-Office Ops)
Laura Rossi (Exec Dir)
Roderick V. Jenkins (Officer-Youth & Families Program)
Amy Wolf (Officer-Comm)

NEW YORK COMPENSATION INSURANCE RATING BOARD
733 3rd Ave, New York, NY 10017
Tel.: (212) 697-3535 NY
Web Site: http://www.nycirb.org
Year Founded: 1914
Sales Range: $10-24.9 Million
Emp.: 150
General Insurance Services
N.A.I.C.S.: 524298
George Vega (VP)
Lucy Decaro (VP)
Philip Reda (VP-Underwriting)

NEW YORK COUNTY HEALTH SERVICES REVIEW ORGANIZATION
199 Water St 27th Fl, New York, NY 10038
Tel.: (212) 897-6000 NY
Web Site: http://www.medreview.us
Year Founded: 1974
Sales Range: $10-24.9 Million
Emp.: 87
Medical Review Services
N.A.I.C.S.: 813920
Joseph B. Stamm (Pres & CEO)
Seth Lewin (Chief Medical Officer & VP)
Juanita A. Evereteze (Dir-Medical)
Robert A. Rosenbloom (VP-Legal Affairs & City Contracts)
Harriet Starr (VP-Govt Contracts)
Norman B. Medow (Chm)

NEW YORK CRUISE LINES INC.
42nd St and the W Side Hwy, New York, NY 10036
Tel.: (212) 563-3200
Web Site: http://www.circleline.com
Sales Range: $25-49.9 Million
Emp.: 250
Yacht Brokers
N.A.I.C.S.: 541990
Craig Kanarick (CEO)
John Banks (Chm)

NEW YORK DISASTER INTERFAITH SERVICES
4 W 43rd St Ste 407, New York, NY 10036
Tel.: (212) 669-6100 NY
Web Site: http://www.nydis.org
Year Founded: 2003
Sales Range: $1-9.9 Million
Emp.: 11
Disaster Readiness, Response & Recovery Services
N.A.I.C.S.: 624230
Matt O'Connell (Dir-Ops & Client Data)
Peter Cavadini (Dir-Volunteer Group Housing Program)
Ronald Drews (Pres)
Ruth Yoder Wenger (Exec VP)
Elder Betty C. Jones (VP)
Altaj Ilyas (Treas)
Judy Chen (Sec)
Peter B. Gudaitis (CEO)
Cecilia Aranzamendez (VP)

NEW YORK EHEALTH COLLABORATIVE, INC.
40 Worth St 5th Fl, New York, NY 10013
Tel.: (646) 619-6400 NY
Web Site: http://www.nyehealth.org
Year Founded: 2006
Sales Range: $50-74.9 Million
Emp.: 124
Health Care Srvices
N.A.I.C.S.: 622110
Paul Wilder (CIO)
Anuj Desai (VP-Market Dev)
Bruno Pettoni (CFO)
Inez Sieben (COO)
Alexandra Cohen (VP-Product Mgmt)
Cem Weiss (Mgr-Data Center Team)
Darryl Hollar (Dir-Product Mgmt)
Fabianni Builes (Dir-Project Mgmt)
Jesse Giuliani (Mgr-Bus Dev)
Brett Johnson (VP-Healthcare Advisory Professional Svcs)
Cynthia Sutliff (Dir-Policy)
David Whitlinger (Exec Dir)
Dennis Whalen (Sec)

NEW YORK FOOTBALL GIANTS, INC.
1925 Ctr 1925 Giant Dr Ste G, East Rutherford, NJ 07073
Tel.: (201) 935-8111 NY
Web Site: http://www.giants.com
Year Founded: 1925
Sales Range: $125-149.9 Million
Emp.: 140
Professional Football Team
N.A.I.C.S.: 711211
John K. Mara (Pres & CEO)
Rusty Hawley (VP-Mktg)
Pat Hanlon (Sr VP-Comm)
Christine Procops (CFO & Sr VP)
Steve Hamrahi (VP-Fin)
Doug Murphy (Dir-Creative Svcs)
Mike Stevens (CMO & Sr VP)
Ronnie Barnes (VP-Medical Svcs)
Steve Tisch (Chm & Exec VP)
Chris Mara (Sr VP-Player Personnel)
Don Sperling (VP-Giants Entertainment)
Dan Lynch (VP-Media & Partnerships)
Jim Phelan (VP-Team Ops)
Marc Ross (VP-Player Evaluation)
David Tyree (Dir-Player Dev)
Joe Shoen (Gen Mgr)
Jonathan M. Tisch (Treas)

NEW YORK FRAGRANCE INC.
162 Port Richmond Ave, Staten Island, NY 10302
Tel.: (718) 816-1112
Web Site: http://www.americanfragrances.com
Year Founded: 1973
Sales Range: $10-24.9 Million
Emp.: 4
Perfumes
N.A.I.C.S.: 424210
Rama Krishna Cherukuri (Pres)

Subsidiaries:

American International Management (1)
162 Port Richmond Ave, Staten Island, NY 10302
Tel.: (718) 818-0119
Web Site: http://www.americanfragrances.com
Fragrances
N.A.I.C.S.: 541511

NEW YORK HALL OF SCIENCE
4701 11th St, Corona, NY 11368
Tel.: (718) 699-0005
Web Site: http://www.nyhalsci.org
Sales Range: $10-24.9 Million
Emp.: 150
Science Museum
N.A.I.C.S.: 712110
Mary Record (Dir-Comm)
Margaret Honey (Pres & CEO)

NEW YORK HEALTH CARE, INC.
20 E Sunrise Hwy Ste 201, Valley Stream, NY 11581
Tel.: (718) 375-6700 NY
Web Site: http://www.nyhc.com
Sales Range: $25-49.9 Million
Emp.: 1,460
Women Healthcare Services
N.A.I.C.S.: 621610
Murry Englard (CEO)

NEW YORK HEALTH CLUB INC.
18 E 50th St 4th Fl, New York, NY 10022
Tel.: (212) 797-1500
Web Site: http://www.hrcbest.com
Rev.: $12,100,000
Emp.: 20
Athletic Club & Gymnasiums, Membership
N.A.I.C.S.: 713940
Howard Brodsky (Pres & CEO)

NEW YORK INSTITUTE OF TECHNOLOGY

New York Health Club Inc.—(Continued)

NEW YORK INSTITUTE OF TECHNOLOGY
1855 Broadway, New York, NY 10023-7692
Tel.: (212) 261-1500
Web Site: http://www.nyit.edu
Year Founded: 1955
Colleges & Universities
N.A.I.C.S.: 611310
Niyazi Bodur *(VP-IT & Infrastructure)*
Kim Margan *(Assoc Dir-Publ & Adv)*
Nancy Donner *(VP-Comm & Mktg)*
Diego Rios *(Dir-Art)*
Jerry Balentine *(VP-Medical Affairs & Global Health)*
Patrick Love *(VP-Student Affairs)*
Alex Wang *(Dir-Mktg & Promotions)*
Julie Godsoe *(Dir-Editorial)*
Libby Sullivan *(Dir-Media Rels)*
Paula Giraldo *(Assoc Dir-Art)*
Henry C. Foley *(Pres)*
Dan Velez *(Dir-Athletics & Recreation)*
Catherine R. Flickinger *(Gen Counsel)*
Mark C. Hampton *(VP-Plng, Analytics & Decision Support)*
Patrick Minson *(VP-Dev & Alumni Rels)*
Junius J. Gonzales *(VP-Academic Affairs & Provost)*
Nada Marie Anid *(VP-Strategic Comm & External Affairs)*

NEW YORK ISLANDERS HOCKEY CLUB, L.P.
200 Merrick Ave, East Meadow, NY 11554
Tel.: (516) 501-6700 NY
Web Site: http://www.newyorkislanders.com
Year Founded: 1972
Sales Range: $50-74.9 Million
Emp.: 100
Professional Hockey Franchise
N.A.I.C.S.: 711211
Arthur Maccarthy *(CFO & Sr VP)*
Paul Lancey *(Sr VP-Sls & Mktg)*
Ken Morrow *(Dir-Pro Scouting)*
Garth Snow *(Gen Mgr)*
Lou Lamoriello *(Pres-Hockey Ops)*
Scott Malkin *(Co-Owner)*
Chris Lamoriello *(Asst Gen Mgr)*

NEW YORK JETS FOOTBALL CLUB, INC.
1 Jets Dr, Florham Park, NJ 07932-1215
Tel.: (973) 549-4800 NY
Web Site: http://www.newyorkjets.com
Year Founded: 1963
Sales Range: $50-74.9 Million
Emp.: 130
Professional Football Franchise
N.A.I.C.S.: 711211
Clay Hampton *(Sr Dir-Ops)*
Tim Tubito *(Dir-Multimedia & Gameday Experiential Production)*
Mike Maccagnan *(Gen Mgr)*
Brian Heimerdinger *(Dir-Player Personnel)*

NEW YORK KIDS CLUB
W 89th/91st St 601/644 Amsterdam Ave, New York, NY 10024
Tel.: (212) 721-4400
Web Site: http://www.nykidsclub.com
Year Founded: 2001
Sales Range: $10-24.9 Million
Emp.: 104
Educational Enrichment Programs, Theme Camps & Special Events for Children Eight Weeks to Ten Years Old

N.A.I.C.S.: 923110
Pam Wolf *(Founder)*

NEW YORK LEGAL ASSISTANCE GROUP
7 Hanover Sq 18th Fl, New York, NY 10004
Tel.: (212) 613-5000 NY
Web Site: http://www.nylag.org
Year Founded: 1990
Sales Range: $10-24.9 Million
Emp.: 140
Law firm
N.A.I.C.S.: 541110
Merritt Birnbaum *(Dir-Dev)*
Isaak Melamud *(Dir-IT)*
Rick Rand *(Dir-HR)*

NEW YORK LIFE INSURANCE COMPANY
51 Madison Ave, New York, NY 10010
Tel.: (212) 576-7000 NY
Web Site: http://www.newyorklife.com
Year Founded: 1845
Rev.: $34,499,000,000
Assets: $371,648,000,000
Liabilities: $324,130,000,000
Net Worth: $47,518,000,000
Earnings: $2,728,000,000
Fiscal Year-end: 12/31/19
Life Insurance; Financial Services & Annuities
N.A.I.C.S.: 524113
Theodore A. Mathas *(Chm & CEO)*
Sheila K. Davidson *(Chief Legal Officer & Exec VP)*
Craig L. DeSanto *(Pres)*
Anthony R. Malloy *(Chief Investment Officer & Exec VP)*
Mark J. Madgett *(Exec VP & Head-Agency)*
Alain M. Karaoglan *(Sr VP)*
Aaron Ball *(Sr VP & Head-Insurance Solutions)*
Alexander I. Cook *(Sr VP & Head-Strategic Capabilities)*
Carla T. Rutigliano *(Sr VP & Head-HR & Corp Affairs)*
Bill Cassidy *(CIO)*
George Nichols III *(Executives)*

Subsidiaries:

Cornerstone Capital Management Holdings LLC (1)
3600 Minnesota Dr Ste 70, Minneapolis, MN 55435
Tel.: (952) 229-8100
Web Site: http://www.cornerstonecapital.com
Investment Management Service
N.A.I.C.S.: 523940
Andrew D. Ver Planck *(Chief Investment Officer, Sr VP & Mgr-Lead Portfolio)*
Andrew S. Wyatt *(CEO)*
Thomas G. Kamp *(Pres, Chief Investment Officer & Mgr-Lead Portfolio)*
Loren R. Kix *(Chief Admin Officer & Sr VP)*
Francis J. Ok *(Sr VP & Head-Trading)*
Edward Ramos *(Chief Investment Officer, Sr VP & Mgr-Lead Portfolio)*
James Wylie *(Sr VP & Global Head-Distribution)*
Herman A. Abdul *(CFO & Sr VP)*
Melissa M. Carty *(VP-Institutional Bus Dev)*
Bryan G. Sandvig *(VP-Institutional Bus Dev)*
John Strohman *(VP-Institutional Bus Dev)*

Credit Value Partners, LP (1)
49 W Putnam Ave, Greenwich, CT 06830
Tel.: (203) 893-4700
Web Site: http://www.cvp7.com
Investment Advisory & Asset Management Services
N.A.I.C.S.: 523940
Donald Pollard *(Mng Partner & Portfolio Mgr-Opportunistic & Distressed Credit)*
Adolfo Waisburg *(Sr VP-Opportunistic & Distressed Credit)*

Joseph Matteo *(Partner & Portfolio Mgr-CLO)*
Neel Doshi *(Sr VP-CLO)*
Howard Sullivan *(Partner & COO)*
Joseph Cambareri *(CFO & Sr VP)*
Geoff Gribling *(Sr VP)*
Ray Colleran *(Sr VP)*

GoldPoint Partners LLC (1)
51 Madison Ave Ste 1600, New York, NY 10010
Tel.: (212) 576-6500
Web Site: http://www.goldpointpartners.com
Sales Range: $25-49.9 Million
Emp.: 40
Investment Management Service
N.A.I.C.S.: 523940
John Schumacher *(Founder)*
Thomas Haubenstricker *(CEO)*
Charles Cocuzza *(Principal)*
Scott Iorio *(Principal)*
Lorne Smith *(Gen Counsel)*
Michael Kho *(Principal)*
Vijay Palkar *(Principal)*
Robert M. Barrack *(COO)*
Sean Gelb *(CFO)*
Scott Higbee *(Head-Bus Dev & Sr Mng Principal)*
Robert Bailey *(CFO)*
Patrick Noonan *(Dir-Consultant Rels & Mktg)*
Amanda Parness *(Principal)*
Binayak Mishra *(Principal)*
Henry Lehmann *(Principal & Head-Fund Admin)*
Matthew Cashion *(Principal)*
Michael Wirth *(Sr VP-Acctg & Reporting Grp)*
Quint Barker *(Principal)*
Vishal Garg *(Sr VP & Head-Fin Plng & Analysis)*
Vivian Lin *(Sr VP-Acctg & Reporting Grp)*

NYLIFE Distributors LLC (1)
169 Lackawanna Ave, Parsippany, NJ 07054
Tel.: (973) 394-2844
Investment Management Service
N.A.I.C.S.: 523940

NYLIFE Insurance Company of Arizona (1)
51 Madison Ave, New York, NY 10010
Tel.: (212) 576-7000
Fire Insurance Services
N.A.I.C.S.: 524210

New York Life & Health Insurance Company Inc. (1)
390 Berry St Fl 4, Brooklyn, NY 11249
Tel.: (718) 486-4600
Web Site: http://www.express-scripts.com
Sales Range: $50-74.9 Million
Emp.: 70
Insurance Agents
N.A.I.C.S.: 524113
David Hoory *(Gen Mgr)*

New York Life Annuity Inc (1)
51 Madison Ave, New York, NY 10010-1603 (100%)
Tel.: (212) 576-7000
Web Site: http://www.newyorklife.com
Oil & Gas Limited Partnerships
N.A.I.C.S.: 524128
Theodore Mathas *(Pres)*

New York Life Foundation (1)
51 Madison Ave, New York, NY 10010-1603
Tel.: (212) 576-7000
Web Site: http://www.newyorklifeannuities.com
Sales Range: $50-74.9 Million
Emp.: 25
Non-Profit Corporation
N.A.I.C.S.: 524113

New York Life Inc. (1)
51 Madison Ave, New York, NY 10010-1603
Tel.: (212) 576-7000
Web Site: http://www.newyorklife.com
Sales Range: $1-4.9 Billion
Emp.: 5,000
Hospital & Medical Service Plans
N.A.I.C.S.: 524128
Ted Mathas *(Chm & CEO)*
Kevin Heine *(Head-Corp Comm)*

New York Life Insurance & Annuity Corporation (1)

51 Madison Ave, New York, NY 10010-1603 (100%)
Tel.: (212) 576-7000
Sales Range: $1-4.9 Billion
Emp.: 4,000
Insurance Services
N.A.I.C.S.: 524128

New York Life Insurance Company (1)
200 Continental Dr Ste 306, Newark, DE 19713-4336 (100%)
Tel.: (302) 369-7351
Web Site: http://www.newyorklife.com
Sales Range: $25-49.9 Million
Emp.: 14
Group Life & Health Insurance
N.A.I.C.S.: 524113
Theodore A. Mathas *(Chm & CEO)*

New York Life Insurance Company (1)
4505 Las Virgenes Rd Ste 200, Calabasas, CA 91302-1956
Tel.: (818) 880-4164
Web Site: http://www.michaeldixon.com
Investment Advice
N.A.I.C.S.: 523940
Michael Dixon *(Owner)*

New York Life Insurance Ltd. (1)
11th Floor Shin Young Bldg, 68 5 Cheong Tam Tong, Gang Nam Gu, Seoul, 135-100, Korea (South) (100%)
Tel.: (82) 221074600
Web Site: http://www.nyli.co.kr
Insurance & Financing
N.A.I.C.S.: 522299

New York Life International Inc. (1)
51 Madison Ave, New York, NY 10010-1603 (100%)
Tel.: (212) 576-7000
Web Site: http://www.newyorklife.com
Life Insurance
N.A.I.C.S.: 524113
Eric B. Campbell *(Exec VP & Chief Distr Officer)*
Susan Cartledge *(Sr VP-HR)*
Vikram Sawhney *(Sr VP-Bus Dev)*
William Beaty *(Vice Chm)*

Subsidiary (Non-US):

Seguros Monterrey New York Life, S.A. (2)
Paseo de la Reforma No 342 Col Juarez Delegacion, Bosques De Chapultepec, 11580, Cuauhtemoc, Mexico (100%)
Tel.: (52) 5553269000
Web Site: http://www.monterrey-newyorklife.com.mx
Sales Range: $150-199.9 Million
Emp.: 600
Insurance Company
N.A.I.C.S.: 524298
Gary Bennett *(CEO)*

New York Life International Investment (1)
51 Madison Ave, New York, NY 10010-1603
Tel.: (212) 576-7000
Sales Range: $150-199.9 Million
Emp.: 2,000
Holding Company For Worldwide Investments
N.A.I.C.S.: 551112

New York Life Investment Management LLC (1)
51 Madison Ave, New York, NY 10010-1603
Tel.: (212) 576-7000
Web Site: http://www.nylim.com
Sales Range: $250-299.9 Million
Emp.: 1,000
Insurance Agents, Brokers & Service
N.A.I.C.S.: 524113
Yie-Hsin Hung *(CEO)*
David G. Bedard *(CFO)*
Anthony Malloy *(Exec VP)*
Stephen Fisher *(Pres)*
Jae Yoon *(Chief Investment Officer)*
John A. McLean *(Sr Mng Dir)*
Kirk Lehneis *(COO)*
Jac McLean *(Head-Distr-US)*
Jean-Pierre Gerard *(Head-Bus Intelligence & Data Analytics)*
John Pavese *(Head-Relationship Mgmt-Global)*

COMPANIES

Subsidiary (Non-US):

CANDRIAM Investors Group (2)
136 route d'Arlon, 1150, Luxembourg, Luxembourg (100%)
Tel.: (352) 27 9751 29
Web Site: http://www.candriam.com
Sales Range: $50-74.9 Million
Emp.: 60
Open-End Multi-Specialist Asset Manager Investments
N.A.I.C.S.: 525910
Jean-Yves Maldague (Mng Dir)
Emmanuel Simon (Mgr-Client)
Christian Sibella (Mgr- Acctg)
Elena Guanter Ros (Head-Client Rels & Dev-Iberia & Latin America)
Renato Guerriero (Head-Distr-Global)

Subsidiary (Non-US):

CANDRIAM Investors Group-Belgium (3)
Avenue des Arts 58, 1000, Brussels, Belgium (99%)
Tel.: (32) 2 509 60 00
Provides Asset Management & Financial Analysis
N.A.I.C.S.: 531390
Naim Aboujaoude (Chm)

CANDRIAM Investors Group-France (3)
40 Rue Washington, 75408, Paris, Cedex 08, France (100%)
Tel.: (33) 153934000
Sales Range: $75-99.9 Million
Emp.: 170
Security Brokerage & Dealers
N.A.I.C.S.: 523150
Naim Abou-Jaoude (Gen Mgr)

CANDRIAM Investors Group-Germany (3)
Gruneburgweg 58-62, 60422, Frankfurt, Germany
Tel.: (49) 69 7593 8823
Sales Range: $50-74.9 Million
Emp.: 4
Asset Management Services
N.A.I.C.S.: 523940

CANDRIAM Investors Group-Italy (3)
Via Dei Bossi 4, 20121, Milan, Italy
Tel.: (39) 02 31 82 83 60
Emp.: 5
Asset Management Services
N.A.I.C.S.: 523940
Johan Oberg (Gen Mgr)

CANDRIAM Investors Group-Spain (3)
Paseo Castellana 141 Planta 18, 28046, Madrid, Spain
Tel.: (34) 91 360 94 75
Sales Range: $50-74.9 Million
Emp.: 6
Asset Management Services
N.A.I.C.S.: 523940
Javier Ruiz (Gen Mgr)

CANDRIAM Investors Group-Switzerland (3)
Rue du 31 Decembre 40-42, 1207, Geneva, Switzerland
Tel.: (41) 22 707 90 00
Sales Range: $50-74.9 Million
Emp.: 5
Asset Management Services
N.A.I.C.S.: 523940
Bernard de Halleux (Mng Dir)

CANDRIAM Investors Group-The Netherlands (3)
Lichtenauerlaan 102-120, 3062 ME, Rotterdam, Netherlands
Tel.: (31) 10 204 56 51
Sales Range: $50-74.9 Million
Emp.: 3
Asset Management Services
N.A.I.C.S.: 523940
Stefaan Coosemans (Mgr)

Subsidiary (Domestic):

MacKay Shields LLC (2)
1345 Avenue of the Americas, New York, NY 10105
Tel.: (212) 303-6360
Web Site: http://www.mackayshields.com
Emp.: 150
Investment Management Service
N.A.I.C.S.: 523940
Jeffrey S. Phlegar (Chm & CEO)
John W. Akkerman (Exec Mng Dir & Head-Distr-Global)
James Farrell (Mng Dir)
Christopher Roberti (Mng Dir)
Janelle Woodward (Pres)

Division (Domestic):

New York Life Investment Management Guaranteed Products (2)
169 Lackawanna Ave, Parsippany, NJ 07054
Tel.: (973) 394-3000
Web Site: http://www.nylinvestments.com
Sales Range: $150-199.9 Million
Emp.: 650
Insurance Agents, Brokers & Service
N.A.I.C.S.: 551112
John Yong Kim (Pres & Chief Investment Officer)
Jae Yoon (Sr Mng Dir & Co-Chief Investment Officer)

New York Life Long Term Care Insurance (1)
6200 Bridgepoint Pkwy, Austin, TX 78730 (100%)
Tel.: (512) 703-5555
Sales Range: $50-74.9 Million
Emp.: 100
Long Term Insurance Supplier
N.A.I.C.S.: 524128

New York Life Securities Inc. (1)
51 Madison Ave, New York, NY 10010-1603 (100%)
Tel.: (212) 576-7000
Web Site: http://www.nylaarp.com
Registered Broker-Dealer Securities
N.A.I.C.S.: 524210

New York Life Structured Asset Management Company Ltd. (1)
51 Madison Ave, New York, NY 10010-1603
Tel.: (212) 576-7000
Web Site: http://www.newyorklife.com
Sales Range: $25-49.9 Million
Emp.: 2
Management Services
N.A.I.C.S.: 524113

Windsor Life Assurance Ltd. (1)
Windsor House Telford Ctr, Telford, TF3 4NB, United Kingdom (100%)
Tel.: (44) 188733333
Web Site: http://www.windsor-life.com
Sales Range: $200-249.9 Million
Emp.: 500
Life Insurance
N.A.I.C.S.: 524128

NEW YORK MEDIA, LLC
75 Varick St 4th Fl, New York, NY 10013
Tel.: (212) 508-0772 DE
Web Site: http://www.mediakit.nymag.com
Sales Range: $10-24.9 Million
Emp.: 200
Magazine Holding Company
N.A.I.C.S.: 513120
Michael Silberman (Gen Mgr-Digital)
Pamela Wasserstein (CEO)
Lauren Starke (Dir-Comm)
Aude White (Mgr-Comm)
Jacqueline Cinguina (Head-Sls & Mktg)
Kate Solinsky (Head-Sls)

Subsidiaries:

New York Magazine (1)
75 Varick St, New York, NY 10013
Tel.: (212) 508-0700
Web Site: http://www.nymag.com
Sales Range: $10-24.9 Million
Emp.: 100
Magazine Publisher
N.A.I.C.S.: 513120
Lawrence C. Burstein (Publr)
Sona Hacherian Hofstede (Exec Dir-Creative & Mktg Svcs)
Ron Stokes (Exec Dir-Online Sls & Mktg)
Gabriel Sherman (Editor-Natl Affairs)
Lauren Starke (Dir-PR)
Michelle Imbrogno Miller (Exec Dir-Print & Integrated Sls)
Matt Johnston (Exec Producer-Video)
David Haskell (Editor-in-Chief)
Hanna Rosin (Dir-Editorial-Audio)
Sukjong Hong (Editor-Curbed)

NEW YORK MUNICIPAL POWER AGENCY
6652 Hammersmith Dr, East Syracuse, NY 13057
Tel.: (315) 453-1761 NY
Web Site: http://www.nympa.org
Year Founded: 1996
Sales Range: $50-74.9 Million
Emp.: 2
Insurance Services
N.A.I.C.S.: 524298
Anthony Modafferi (Gen Mgr)

NEW YORK ORGAN DONOR NETWORK, INC.
460 W 34th St 15th Fl, New York, NY 10001-3406
Tel.: (646) 291-4444 NY
Web Site: http://www.donatelifeny.org
Year Founded: 1978
Sales Range: $25-49.9 Million
Emp.: 198
Organ & Tissue Donation Awareness Services
N.A.I.C.S.: 813212
Jim Aranda (CFO & VP-Admin)
Amy L. Friedman (Dir-Medical)
James Pardes (VP-Mktg & Comm)
Lloyd E. Ratner (Chm)
Helen M. Irving (Pres & CEO)
Robert S. Kurtz (Sec)
Lee H. Perlman (Treas)
Sander S. Florman (Vice Chm)

NEW YORK PAVING INC.
3718 Railroad Ave, Long Island City, NY 11101-2033
Tel.: (718) 482-0780 NY
Year Founded: 1976
Sales Range: $25-49.9 Million
Emp.: 300
Highway & Street Construction
N.A.I.C.S.: 237310
Anthony Bartone (Pres)
Robert J. Coletti Jr. (Gen Counsel)

NEW YORK POWER AUTHORITY, INC.
123 Main St Ste 1600, White Plains, NY 10601
Tel.: (518) 433-6700 NY
Web Site: http://www.nypa.gov
Year Founded: 1931
Sales Range: $50-74.9 Million
Emp.: 1,500
Electronic Services
N.A.I.C.S.: 921190
Robert P. Lurie (CFO)
Justin E. Driscoll (Gen Counsel & Exec VP)
Gil C. Quiniones (Pres & CEO)
John R. Koelmel (Chm)
Jill C. Anderson (Chief Comml Officer & Exec VP)
Kristine Pizzo (Sr VP-HR & Shared Svcs)
Eugene L. Nicandri (Vice Chm)
Genevieve Fabela (Treas)
Joseph Kessler (COO & Exec VP)
Ken Lee (CIO & Sr VP)
Jennifer Sutton (Sr VP-Internal Audit)
Bryant Bullard (Mgr-Northern New York)
Philip Toia (Sr VP-Power Supply)

NEW YORK PUBLIC RADIO

NEW YORK PRIVATE BANK & TRUST CORPORATION
6 E 43rd St, New York, NY 10017
Tel.: (212) 850-4085 DE
Web Site: http://www.nypbt.com
Year Founded: 1850
Emp.: 100
Bank Holding Company
N.A.I.C.S.: 551111
George J. Dickson (Exec VP)
James A. Berger (Mng Dir)
David Marcus (Mng Partner-Emigrant Partners)
William M. Folberth III (Mng Dir)

Subsidiaries:

Emigrant Bank (1)
5 E 42nd St, New York, NY 10017
Tel.: (212) 850-4000
Web Site: http://www.emigrant.com
Federal Savings Bank
N.A.I.C.S.: 522180
Howard P. Milstein (Chm & CEO)
Harriet Edelman (Vice Chm)

Subsidiary (Domestic):

Emigrant Capital Corp. (2)
6 E 43rd St 20th Fl, New York, NY 10017-4609
Tel.: (212) 850-4460
Web Site: http://www.emigrantcapital.com
Sales Range: $50-74.9 Million
Emp.: 8
Investment Banking
N.A.I.C.S.: 525920
Christopher Staudt (Partner)
Rafael Romero (Principal)
William Staudt (Partner)
Robert L. Nardelli (Partner)

Emigrant Funding Corporation (2)
6 E 43rd St 10th Fl, New York, NY 10017-4609
Tel.: (212) 850-4880
Web Site: http://www.emigrant.com
Sales Range: $50-74.9 Million
Emp.: 40
Commericial Loan
N.A.I.C.S.: 525920
Peter Hollnsteiner (Sr VP)

Emigrant Mortgage Company, Inc. (2)
7 Westchester Plz Ste 229, Elmsford, NY 10523
Tel.: (914) 785-1139
Web Site: http://www.emigrantmortgage.com
Sales Range: $10-24.9 Million
Emp.: 60
Mortgage Lending
N.A.I.C.S.: 522292

NEW YORK PUBLIC RADIO
160 Varick St, New York, NY 10013
Tel.: (646) 829-4000
Web Site: http://www.wnyc.org
Radio Station Operator
N.A.I.C.S.: 516110
Michele Rusnak (CFO & VP-Fin, Admin & Bus Affairs)
Thomas Hjelm (Chief Digital Officer & Exec VP)
Tom Bartunek (VP-Plng & Special Projects)
Elizabeth Culp (Sr Dir-Major Gifts & Legacy Giving)
Jennifer Houlihan Roussel (Sr Dir-Publicity)
Hal Trencher (VP-Sponsorship)
May Stuntz (Chm)
Goli Sheikholeslami (Pres & CEO)
Ayesha Ahmad (CMO)
Josefa Velasquez (Editor-Economics & Equity)
Stephanie Clary (Deputy Editor-in-Chief)

Subsidiaries:

WQXR FM (1)
160 Varick St, New York, NY 10013

NEW YORK PUBLIC RADIO — U.S. PRIVATE

New York Public Radio—(Continued)
Tel.: (212) 633-7600
Web Site: http://www.wqxr.com
Sales Range: $10-24.9 Million
Emp.: 20
Classical Music Radio Station
N.A.I.C.S.: 516110
Thomas Bartunek (VP-Plng & Special Projects)

NEW YORK RACING ASSOCIATION, INC.
PO Box 90, Ozone Park, NY 11417
Tel.: (718) 641-4700   NY
Web Site: http://www.nyra.com
Year Founded: 1955
Sales Range: $250-299.9 Million
Emp.: 1,223
Racetracks Owner & Operator
N.A.I.C.S.: 711212
Carmen Barrera (Dir-Horsemen's Rels)
Glen Kozak (VP-Facilities & Racing Surfaces)
David O'Rourke (Interim CEO)
Stephen Travers (Sr Dir-Hospitality & Guest Svcs)
Jelena Alonso (VP & Comptroller)
Ross Didia (Treas)
Bruce Johnstone (Mgr-Ops-Racing)
Lynn LaRocca (Chief Experience Officer & Sr VP)
Joseph Lambert (Chief Admin Officer, Gen Counsel, Sec & Sr VP)
Martin Panza (Sr VP-Ops-Racing)
Bob J. Hughes (CIO & VP)
Darran Miner (Dir-Mktg)
James Ranton (Chief HR Officer & VP)
Gordon Lavalette (CFO & Sr VP)
Matt Salvato (Sec-Racing)
Tony Allevato (Pres-NYRA Bets)
Michael J. Del Giudice (Chm)

NEW YORK RAVIOLI & PASTA CO.
12 S Denton Ave, New Hyde Park, NY 11040
Tel.: (516) 741-7287
Web Site: http://www.nyravioli.com
Sales Range: $10-24.9 Million
Emp.: 30
Pasta Mfr
N.A.I.C.S.: 311991
David Creo (Pres)
Paul Moncada (Owner)
Tricia Nacewicz (Office Mgr)

NEW YORK REPLACEMENT PARTS CORP.
19 School St, Yonkers, NY 10701
Tel.: (914) 965-0122
Web Site: http://www.nyrpcorp.com
Year Founded: 1972
Sales Range: $10-24.9 Million
Emp.: 15
Plumbing Fittings & Supplies
N.A.I.C.S.: 423720
John Green (Gen Mgr)
Rick Green (Gen Mgr-Manhattan)
Vicky Giacchetti (Mgr-Acctg)

NEW YORK SHIPPING ASSOCIATION, INC.
333 Thornall St Ste 3A, Edison, NJ 08837
Tel.: (732) 452-7800   NY
Web Site: http://www.nysanet.org
Year Founded: 1955
Sales Range: $250-299.9 Million
Emp.: 32
Shipping Association
N.A.I.C.S.: 813910
Stephen Ahearn (Mgr-Production Control)
Susan Winfree (Officer-Workforce Dev & Corp Diversity & VP)
Barbara Blanton (Dir-Trng & Safety)
Steven M. Pessel (Dir-IT)
John Nardi (Pres)
Eugenia Rozenberg (Dir-Fin Svcs)
Charles Darrell (COO & Exec VP)
Daniel Massaro (CFO)
Jennifer Brendt (Sec)
James H. Cobb Jr. (Dir-Govt Affairs)

NEW YORK STATE BAR ASSOCIATION
1 Elk St, Albany, NY 12207
Tel.: (518) 463-3200   NY
Web Site: http://www.nysba.org
Year Founded: 1877
Sales Range: $25-49.9 Million
Emp.: 149
Law firm
N.A.I.C.S.: 541199
Kathleen R. Baxter (Gen Counsel)
Daniel J. McMahon (Dir-Publications)
David R. Watson (Exec Dir)
Brandon Vogel (Mgr-Social Media & Web Content)
Kim Francis (Mgr-Program)
Robert Millman (Coord-Digital Media)
Don Gardinier (Mgr-Print Shop)
Jeffrey Ordon (Mgr-IT Ops)
Lucian Uveges (Mgr-Application Dev)
Tirsa Kennedy (Coord-HR)
Claire P. Gutekunst (Pres)
Mark Wilson (Mgr-Bar Svcs)
Kristin M. O'Brien (Sr Dir-Fin)
Richard Rifkin (Sr Dir-Govt Rels)
Ronald Kennedy (Sr Dir-Govt Rels)
Paula Doyle (Sr Dir-HR)

NEW YORK STATE BRIDGE AUTHORITY
PO Box 1010, Highland, NY 12528
Tel.: (845) 691-7245
Web Site: http://www.nysba.state.ny.us
Year Founded: 1932
Sales Range: $25-49.9 Million
Emp.: 250
Toll Bridge Inspection & Maintenance Services
N.A.I.C.S.: 488490
Bob Russo (Dir-Admin Svcs)
Gregory J. Herd (Dir-IT)
George Fong (Mgr-Contract Maintenance)
Peter Bielawski (Mgr-Application Dev)
Francine Byrne (Mgr-PC Svcs)
Frank Mazzella (Mgr-Electronic Toll Sys & Technical Svcs)
Tara Sullivan (Deputy Exec Dir)

NEW YORK STATE CORRECTIONAL OFFICERS & POLICE BENEVOLENT ASSOCIATION, INC.
102 Hackett Blvd, Albany, NY 12209
Tel.: (518) 427-1551   NY
Web Site: http://www.nyscopba.org
Year Founded: 1998
Sales Range: $10-24.9 Million
Employee Benefit Services
N.A.I.C.S.: 525120
Michael Mazzella (VP-Correction Mid-Hudson)
Michael B. Powers (Pres)
Clarence Fisher (VP)
Joe Miano (VP-Correction West)
Tammy Sawchuk (Exec VP)
Mike Dildine (Sec-Recording)
James Miller (Dir-Public Rels)
John Harmon Jr. (VP-Law Enforcement)

NEW YORK STATE ENERGY RESEARCH & DEVELOPMENT AUTHORITY
17 Columbia Cir, Albany, NY 12203-6339
Tel.: (518) 862-1090   NY
Web Site: http://www.nyserda.org
Year Founded: 1975
Sales Range: $10-24.9 Million
Emp.: 300
Commercial Physical Research-Energy Analysis
N.A.I.C.S.: 541715
Kate Muller (Dir-Comm & Crop Mktg)
Kelly Tyler (Dir-Communities & Local Govt)
Mark Mitchell (Dir-Internal Audit)
Susan Moyer (Dir-Corp Mktg)
Tom Lynch (Dir-Govt Affairs)
Alicia Barton (Pres & CEO)
Richard L. Kauffman (Chm)

NEW YORK STATE NURSES ASSOCIATION
131 W 33rd St 4th Fl, New York, NY 10001
Tel.: (212) 785-0157   NY
Web Site: https://www.nysna.org
Year Founded: 1902
Sales Range: $25-49.9 Million
Emp.: 214
Trained Nurse Association
N.A.I.C.S.: 813920
Judy Sheridan-Gonzalez (Pres)
Jill Furillo (Exec Dir)

NEW YORK STATE THRUWAY AUTHORITY
200 Southern Blvd, Albany, NY 12209
Tel.: (518) 436-2700   NY
Web Site: http://www.nysthruway.gov
Year Founded: 1950
Sales Range: $550-599.9 Million
Emp.: 3,500
Toll Road & Operating Canal
N.A.I.C.S.: 488490
Dan Weiller (Dir-Pub Affairs)
Peter Sanderson (Mgr-Tappan Zee Bridge Replacement Project)

Subsidiaries:

New York State Canal Corporation (1)
200 Southern Blvd, Albany, NY 12209-2018
Tel.: (518) 436-2700
Web Site: http://www.ny.gov
Sales Range: $50-74.9 Million
Emp.: 820
Water Transportation Services
N.A.I.C.S.: 488390

NEW YORK TRANSIT INC.
24610 Indus Blvd, Hayward, CA 94545
Tel.: (510) 576-1100   NY
Year Founded: 1983
Rev.: $37,018,223
Emp.: 50
Footwear; Womens Shoes
N.A.I.C.S.: 424340
William Tai (Pres)
Doug Younce (CFO)
Lisa Martinez (Mgr-Ops)
Yoni Feliciano (Office Mgr)
Alejandro Martinez (Coord-Shipping)

NEW YORK YANKEES PARTNERSHIP
1 E 161st St, Bronx, NY 10451
Tel.: (718) 293-4300   OH
Web Site: http://newyork.yankees.mlb.com
Holding Company; Professional Baseball Club
N.A.I.C.S.: 551112
Harold Z. Steinbrenner (Mng Gen Partner)
Henry G. Steinbrenner (Gen Partner)
Jessica Steinbrenner (Gen Partner)
Jennifer Steinbrenner Swindal (Gen Partner)

Subsidiaries:

New York Yankees (1)
Yankee Stadium 1 E 161st St & River Ave, Bronx, NY 10451
Tel.: (718) 293-6000
Web Site: http://www.yankees.com
Sales Range: $300-349.9 Million
Emp.: 120
Professional Baseball Club
N.A.I.C.S.: 711211
Jessica Steinbrenner (Chm)
Deborah A. Tymon (Sr VP-Mktg)
Randy Levine (Pres)
Brian Cashman (Sr VP & Gen Mgr)
Jean Afterman (Sr VP & Asst Gen Mgr)
Lonn A. Trost (COO & Gen Counsel)
Brian Smith (Sr VP-Corp & Community Rels)
Sonny Hight (Chief Security Officer & Sr VP)
Michael J. Tusiani (Sr VP-Partnerships)
Jennifer Steinbrenner Swindal (Vice Chm & Gen Partner)
Joan Steinbrenner (Vice Chm)
Robert Brown (Co-CFO & VP-Acctg)
Marty Greenspun (Sr VP-Strategic Ventures)
Alan Chang (VP-Legal Affairs & Deputy Gen Counsel)
Scott Krug (Co-CFO & Sr VP-Fin Ops)
Anthony Bruno (Sr VP)
Derrick Baio (Controller)
Irfan Kirimca (Sr Dir-Ticket Ops)
Doug Behar (Sr VP-Stadium Ops)
Mike Lane (CIO & Sr VP-Tech & Brdcst)
Kevin Dart (VP-Ticket Sls, Svc & Ops)
Kara Mooney (Sr Dir-Creative Svcs)
Manuel Garcia (Exec Dir-Florida Counsel)
Jason Zillo (VP-Comm & Media Rels)
Emily Hamel (VP-Non-Baseball Events)
Todd Letcher (Exec Dir-Stadium & Event Security)
Alfred Santasiere III (Sr Dir-Publ)

SWB Yankees, LLC (1)
235 Montage Mountain Rd, Moosic, PA 18507 (50%)
Tel.: (570) 969-2255
Web Site: http://www.swbrailriders.com
Sales Range: $10-24.9 Million
Professional Baseball Club
N.A.I.C.S.: 711211
Kristina Knight (Dir-Corp Svcs & Special Events)
Karen Luciano (Mgr-Corp Svcs)
Rob Galdieri (Ops Mgr)
Curt Camoni (VP-Stadium Ops)
William Steiner (Dir-Gameday Ops)
Steve Horne (Dir-Field Ops)
Seth Atkinson (Dir-Ticket Ops)
Jeremy Ruby (Exec VP-Ops)
Joe Villano (Dir-Ballpark Ops)
Paul Chilek (Exec VP-Bus Ops)
Katie Beekman (VP-Mktg & Corp Svcs)
Mike Trudnak (VP-Sls)
Rob Crain (Pres & Gen Mgr)
John Sadak (Dir-Media Rels & Brdcst)

Yankees Entertainment & Sports Network, LLC (1)
805 3rd Ave 30th Fl, New York, NY 10022
Tel.: (646) 487-3600
Web Site: http://www.yesnetwork.com
Sports & Entertainment Programming Network
N.A.I.C.S.: 516210
Howard Levinson (Sr VP-Adv Sls)
John Filippelli (Pres-Production & Programming)
Jon Litner (CEO)

NEW YORK-PRESBYTERIAN HEALTHCARE SYSTEM, INC.
525 E 68th St, New York, NY 10065
Tel.: (212) 746-5454   NY
Web Site: http://www.nyp.org
Year Founded: 1993
Sales Range: $1-4.9 Billion

Emp.: 19,376
Hospital Operator
N.A.I.C.S.: 622110
Anne Dinneen (Chief Investment Officer & Sr VP)

Subsidiaries:

Palisades Medical Center (1)
7600 River Rd, North Bergen, NJ 07047-6217
Tel.: (201) 854-5000
Web Site: http://www.palisadesmedical.org
Sales Range: $150-199.9 Million
Emp.: 1,000
Hospital Operator
N.A.I.C.S.: 622110
Bruce Markowitz (Pres & CEO)
David Berkowitz (COO & VP-Admin)
Reuben D. Fernandez (VP-Patient Care Svcs)
Theresa De Leon (Chm)
Andrew Horowitz (Vice Chm)
Leonard Lauricella (Treas)
Kevin O'Connor (Sec)

Subsidiary (Domestic):

Palisades Child Care Center Inc. (2)
115 River Rd Ste 7, Edgewater, NJ 07020-1009
Tel.: (201) 945-1447
Web Site:
    http://www.palisadeschildcarecenter.org
Rev.: $450,000
Emp.: 25
Child Day Care Services
N.A.I.C.S.: 624410

NEW YUNG WAH TRADING LLC
311 Richardson St, Brooklyn, NY 11222
Tel.: (718) 388-3322
Web Site: http://www.nywtc.com
Year Founded: 1993
Sales Range: $100-124.9 Million
Emp.: 30
Groceries, General Line
N.A.I.C.S.: 424410
Juan Qing Lin (Pres)

Subsidiaries:

NYW Trading LLC (1)
5700 Lewis Rd, Sandston, VA 23150
Tel.: (804) 226-6200
Web Site: http://www.nywtc.com
Grocery General Line Distr
N.A.I.C.S.: 424410

NYWP Enterprise LLC. (1)
1300 Island Ave, McKees Rocks, PA 15136
Tel.: (412) 778-0128
Grocery Product Distr
N.A.I.C.S.: 424490

NEW ZEALAND LAMB COOPERATIVE, INC.
20 Westport Rd Ste 372, Wilton, CT 06897-4522
Tel.: (203) 529-9100   NJ
Web Site: http://www.nzlamb.com
Year Founded: 1962
Sales Range: $50-74.9 Million
Emp.: 75
Lamb Importer & Whslr
N.A.I.C.S.: 424470
Shane O'Hara (Pres)
Peter M. Gilligan (VP-Sls & Mktg)
Marybeth Laleman (Mgr-Eastern Region Sls)
Christopher Thompson (Dir-Culinary Dev)
Clay Nicholson (Dir-Retail Sls)
Kathleen Diaz (Mgr-Western Reg Sls)
David Grieshop (Coord-Sls)

Subsidiaries:

New Zealand Lamb Company (1)
10 Shorncliffe Road Unit 1, Etobicoke, M9B 3S3, ON, Canada   (100%)
Tel.: (416) 231-5162

Web Site: http://www.thelambcompany.com
Sales Range: $10-24.9 Million
Emp.: 20
Meat Processing & Storage
N.A.I.C.S.: 311613
Anthony A. Ruffo (Pres-Canada)

NEW-COM INC.
412 E Gowan Rd, North Las Vegas, NV 89032
Tel.: (702) 642-3331
Web Site: http://www.nclasvegas.com
Year Founded: 1984
Sales Range: $25-49.9 Million
Emp.: 600
Provider of Administrative Services for Heavy Construction Equipment Rental Companies
N.A.I.C.S.: 532412
Greg Paulk (Pres)
Donald Cunningham (Controller)
Tory Rambur (VP)
Brady Stevens (Principal)
Mark Urban (Project Mgr)

Subsidiaries:

Biodiesel of Las Vegas Inc. (1)
5233 E El Campo Grande Ave, North Las Vegas, NV 89115
Tel.: (702) 942-4395
Web Site:
    http://www.biodieseloflasvegas.com
Biodiesel Mfr
N.A.I.C.S.: 324110
Nanette Miller (Mgr-Acctg)

MMC Inc. (1)
408 E Gowan Rd, North Las Vegas, NV 89032
Tel.: (702) 642-3332
Rev.: $5,800,000
Emp.: 75
Water Main Construction
N.A.I.C.S.: 237110

Tab Contractors Inc. (1)
412 E Gowan Rd, North Las Vegas, NV 89032-8040
Tel.: (702) 642-3033
Web Site: http://www.nclasvegas.com
Rev.: $40,000,000
Emp.: 30
Water & Sewer Line Construction
N.A.I.C.S.: 237110
Greg J. Paulk (Pres)

NEW-YORK HISTORICAL SOCIETY
170 Central Park W 77th St, New York, NY 10024
Tel.: (212) 873-3400   NY
Web Site: http://www.nyhistory.org
Year Founded: 1809
Sales Range: $25-49.9 Million
Emp.: 381
Historical Preservation Services
N.A.I.C.S.: 541720
Andrew Buonpastore (VP-Ops)
Richard Shein (CFO & Asst Treas)
Mia Nagawiecki (Dir-Education)
Pam B. Schafler (Chm)
Margaret K. Hofer (VP & Dir-Museum)
Louise Mirrer (Pres & CEO)

NEWAGE INDUSTRIES, INC.
145 James Way, Southampton, PA 18966-3817
Tel.: (215) 526-2300   NY
Web Site:
    http://www.newageindustries.com
Year Founded: 1954
Sales Range: $10-24.9 Million
Emp.: 70
Holding Company; Manufacturer of Plastic Tubing & Hoses
N.A.I.C.S.: 326199
Kenneth D. Baker (CEO)
Robert Volk (Exec Dir-Ops)

Stephen Kuhns (Mgr-Sls)
Mary Marcus (Exec Dir-Quality)
Stephen McDevitt (Mgr-Inside Sls)

Subsidiaries:

Colex International, Ltd. (1)
Unit G1 Valley Way Welland Business Park, Market Harborough, LE16 7PS, Leicestershire, United Kingdom
Tel.: (44) 1858461100
Web Site: http://www.colexint.com
Sales Range: $1-9.9 Million
Emp.: 50
Hose & Tibe Mfr
N.A.I.C.S.: 332722
David Dix (Mgr-Export Sls)
Britt Hitchcock (Mgr-Quality Control)
Martyn Fischer (Mgr-Sls)

NewAge Industries, Inc. - Advanta-Pure Division (1)
145 James Way, Southampton, PA 18966
Tel.: (215) 526-2151
Web Site: http://www.advantapure.com
Emp.: 130
Hose Fitting & Tubing Mfr
N.A.I.C.S.: 332912
David Schwass (Dir-Sls)
Michael Allard (Dir-Sls & Mktg)
Stephen McDevitt (Mgr-Inside Sls)
Lawrence Morano III (Mgr-Sls-Global)

NEWAGESYS, INC.
231 Clarksville Rd Ste 200, Princeton Junction, NJ 08550
Tel.: (609) 919-9800
Web Site: http://www.newagesys.com
Year Founded: 1994
Sales Range: $10-24.9 Million
Emp.: 180
IT Consulting Firm
N.A.I.C.S.: 541511
Limy John (Pres & CEO)
Danielle Jennings (Mgr-Bus Dev)

NEWARK COMMUNITY HEALTH CENTERS, INC.
741 Broadway, Newark, NJ 07104
Tel.: (973) 483-1300   NJ
Web Site: http://www.nchcfqhc.org
Year Founded: 1986
Sales Range: $10-24.9 Million
Emp.: 299
Community Health Care Services
N.A.I.C.S.: 621498
Pamela Clarke (Pres & CEO)
Denise C. Fyffe (Chm)
Obed Prinvil (Treas)
Michael L. Moor (Sec)
James N. Clarke (Vice Chm)

NEWARK TOBACCO & CANDY CO. INC.
137 Freeway Dr E, East Orange, NJ 07018
Tel.: (973) 678-1406
Rev.: $24,900,000
Emp.: 5
Smoking Tobacco
N.A.I.C.S.: 424940

NEWARK TOYOTA WORLD
1344 Marrows Rd, Newark, DE 19711
Tel.: (302) 368-6262
Web Site:
    http://www.newarktoyotaworld.com
Rev.: $22,900,000
Emp.: 60
Automobiles, New & Used
N.A.I.C.S.: 441110
Warren A. Price (Pres)
Maryann Franks (Controller)
Eric Mosely (Mgr-Direct Sls)

NEWARK WIRE CLOTH CO.
160 Fornelius Ave, Clifton, NJ 07013
Tel.: (973) 778-4478

Web Site:
    http://www.newarkwire.com
Year Founded: 1911
Sales Range: $10-24.9 Million
Emp.: 35
Fabricated Wire Products: Wire Cloth, Filtration Equipment, Strainers & Screens Mfr
N.A.I.C.S.: 332618
Richard W. Campbell (Pres)
Robert D. Lucki (VP)

NEWAVA TECHNOLOGY, INC.
1323 9th Ave SW, Watertown, SD 57201
Tel.: (605) 886-0264   SD
Web Site: http://www.newava.com
Year Founded: 1994
Power Distr & Specialty Transformer Mfr
N.A.I.C.S.: 335311
Keith Muhl (Pres & Dir-Engrg)

Subsidiaries:

NASCENTechnology Manufacturing, Inc. (1)
1404 9th Ave Sw, Watertown, SD 57201
Tel.: (605) 882-8513
Web Site: http://www.nascentechnology.com
Electronic Components Mfr
N.A.I.C.S.: 334419

NEWAX, INC.
700 W Irving Park Rd Ste A-1, Chicago, IL 60613
Tel.: (773) 935-0710
Year Founded: 1960
Electronic Parts Distr
N.A.I.C.S.: 423690
John A. Loring (Chm, Pres & CEO)

NEWAY PACKAGING CORP.
1973 East Via Arado, Rancho Dominguez, CA 90220
Tel.: (310) 898-3400
Web Site: http://www.newaypkg.com
Sales Range: $10-24.9 Million
Emp.: 40
Shipping Supplies
N.A.I.C.S.: 561910
Russ Freebury (Owner)
Carole Schmittauer (Asst Gen Mgr)
Joe Garcia (Dir-IT Svcs)
Brady Facer (Mgr-Bus Dev)
Jeff Moser (Mgr-Sls)

NEWAYS INC.
2089 Neways Dr, Springville, UT 84663
Tel.: (801) 423-2800
Web Site: http://www.neways.com
Year Founded: 1992
Sales Range: $400-449.9 Million
Emp.: 600
Direct Retailer of Herbal Supplements & Aromatherapy & Fitness Products
N.A.I.C.S.: 325411
Robert S. Conlee (Chm & CEO)
Thomas Mower Jr. (Pres)

NEWBATH
4360 Washington Ave, New Orleans, LA 70125
Tel.: (504) 218-4198
Web Site:
    http://www.newbathnow.com
Year Founded: 2003
Rev.: $3,400,000
Emp.: 18
Specialty Trade Contractors
N.A.I.C.S.: 238990
Lawrence Closs (CEO)

NEWBRIDGE FINANCIAL, INC.
1451 W Cypress Creek Rd, Fort Lauderdale, FL 33309
Tel.: (954) 334-3450

NEWBRIDGE FINANCIAL, INC.

Newbridge Financial, Inc.—(Continued)
Web Site:
http://www.newbridgefinancial.com
Rev.: $30,000,000
Emp.: 4
Financial Advisory & Brokerage Services
N.A.I.C.S.: 523160
Guy Amico (Owner)

NEWBRIDGE SERVICES INC.
7 Industrial Rd, Pequannock, NJ 07440
Tel.: (973) 839-2520
Web Site: http://www.newbridge.org
Year Founded: 1963
Sales Range: $10-24.9 Million
Emp.: 225
Behavioral Healthcare Services
N.A.I.C.S.: 623220
Andrea Wasser-Malmud (Chief Pro Officer)
L. Michelle Borden (COO)
David R. Lacouture (Chief Admin Officer)
Robert L. Parker (CEO)
Melody Federico (Chief Real Estate Officer)

NEWBURY BUILDERS, LLC.
169 S Liberty St, Powell, OH 43065
Tel.: (614) 785-1414
Sales Range: $10-24.9 Million
Emp.: 14
Residential Construction Services
N.A.I.C.S.: 236118
Scott Newcomb (Principal)

NEWBURY COMICS INC.
5 Guest St, Brighton, MA 02135-2016
Tel.: (617) 254-1666
Web Site:
http://www.newburycomics.com
Year Founded: 1978
Sales Range: $50-74.9 Million
Emp.: 400
Record & Prerecorded Tape Stores
N.A.I.C.S.: 449210
Michael Dreese (Co-Founder & CEO)
Elizabeth D. Bierbower (Executives)
John Brusger (Co-Founder)

NEWBURYPORT FIVE CENTS SAVINGS BANK
63 State St, Newburyport, MA 01950
Tel.: (978) 462-3136
Web Site:
http://www.newburyportbank.com
Rev.: $12,821,307
Emp.: 80
State Savings Banks, Not Federally Chartered
N.A.I.C.S.: 522180
Scott Eaton (Sr VP)
Marc A. MacBurnie (Exec VP)
Loretta Laplante (Mgr-Customer Svc)
John Burcke (VP)
Jerry A. Bazata (VP-Comml Lending)
Lloyd Hamm Jr. (Pres & CEO)

NEWBY BUICK-OLDSMBILE-PONTIAC-GMC
1629 S Convention Ctr, Saint George, UT 84790
Tel.: (435) 673-1100
Web Site:
http://www.newbybuick.com
Rev.: $33,572,593
Emp.: 65
Automobiles, New & Used
N.A.I.C.S.: 441110
Kenneth B. Newby (Pres)
Russ Newby (VP & Gen Mgr)

NEWCASTLE CONSTRUCTION, INC.
3978 Parkwood Rd SE, Bessemer, AL 35022
Tel.: (205) 426-2307
Web Site: http://www.newcastle-homes.com
Year Founded: 1997
Sales Range: $10-24.9 Million
Emp.: 15
Residential Construction
N.A.I.C.S.: 236115
Glenn Siddle (Founder, Pres & CEO)
Michael Anderson (VP-Ops)

NEWCASTLE LIMITED
150 N Michigan Ave, Chicago, IL 60601
Tel.: (312) 252-1400
Web Site:
http://www.newcastlelimited.com
Rev.: $1,500,000
Emp.: 15
Land Subdivision
N.A.I.C.S.: 237210
Michael R. Haney (Founder, Pres & CEO)
Kristen L. Martin (Dir-Retail Leasing)
Jack Potts (CFO)
Dan Thalheimer (VP-Acq)

Subsidiaries:

Newcastle Advisors LLC (1)
150 N Michigan Ave Ste 3610, Chicago, IL 60601-7569
Tel.: (312) 252-1400
Web Site: http://www.newcastlelimited.com
Land Subdividing Services
N.A.I.C.S.: 237210

NEWCASTLE PARTNERS LLC
140 Greenwich Ave, Greenwich, CT 06830
Tel.: (203) 863-9892
Web Site: http://www.newcastle-partners.com
Year Founded: 1985
Emp.: 5
Private Investment Firm
N.A.I.C.S.: 523999
John R. Lowden (Founder, Pres & Chief Investment Officer)

NEWCASTLE PARTNERS LP
200 Crescent Ct Ste 1400, Dallas, TX 75201
Tel.: (214) 661-7474
Rev.: $32,200,000
Emp.: 10
Private Equity Investment Firm
N.A.I.C.S.: 523999
Mark E. Schwarz (Gen Partner)

Subsidiaries:

Pinnacle Frames and Accents, Inc. (1)
2606 Hwy 67 S, Pocahontas, AR 72455
Tel.: (870) 892-5227
Web Site:
http://www.nielsenbainbridgegroup.com
Sales Range: $50-74.9 Million
Frames & Framed Art Mfr & Sales
N.A.I.C.S.: 314120
Scott Slater (Pres)

Division (Domestic):

Pinnacle Frames & Accents, Inc. (2)
2606 US Hwy 67 S, Pocahontas, AR 72455 (100%)
Tel.: (870) 892-5227
Web Site: http://www.pinnacleframe.com
Sales Range: $50-74.9 Million
Mfr & Wholesale of Wood Picture Frames
N.A.I.C.S.: 314120
Tim Charon (Sr VP-Sls & Mktg)
Scott Slater (Pres & CEO)

NEWCO INC.
619 6th Ave, Greeley, CO 80631
Tel.: (970) 352-5024
Web Site: http://www.newco-inc.com
Year Founded: 1964
Electrical Equipment Whslr
N.A.I.C.S.: 423610
Clayton Richard (Pres)
Larry Richard (Sr VP)
Mark Daviet (CEO & Mgr-Credit)
Doug May (Mgr-Colorado)

NEWCO METALS INC.
7268 S State Rd 13, Pendleton, IN 46064
Tel.: (317) 485-7721
Web Site:
http://www.newcometals.com
Year Founded: 1986
Sales Range: $50-74.9 Million
Emp.: 37
Nonferrous Metals Scrap
N.A.I.C.S.: 423930
Kipp Barber (CEO)
Steve Craver (Sr VP)
Rich Hogan (Mgr-Production)
Mike Rasmussen (Co-Owner)

NEWCO VALVES LP
13127 Trinity Dr, Houston, TX 77477
Tel.: (281) 302-4900
Web Site:
http://www.newmansvalve.com
Year Founded: 1936
Rev.: $109,600,000
Emp.: 650
Industrial Supply Merchant Whslr
N.A.I.C.S.: 423840
Ginger Restovic (Partner)

NEWCOMB SPRING CORP.
5408 Panola Industrial Bl, Decatur, GA 30035
Tel.: (770) 981-2803
Web Site:
http://www.newcombspring.com
Rev.: $21,700,000
Emp.: 75
Wire Springs
N.A.I.C.S.: 332613
Robert Jacobson (Pres)
G. Donald Jacobson (Chm & CEO)
Jason Bingham (Mgr-Ops)

NEWDAY COMMUNICATIONS INC.
50 Water St, Norwalk, CT 06854
Tel.: (203) 851-5700
Web Site:
http://www.newdaycom.com
Year Founded: 1995
Sales Range: $1-9.9 Million
Advetising Agency
N.A.I.C.S.: 541810
Peter S. Varco (CEO)
Michael Varco (Acct Mgr)
George Blystone (Acct Mgr)
Julie Murray (Acct Mgr)
Greg Jontos (Sr Dir-Art)

NEWELL FUEL SERVICE INC.
108 S Memorial Hwy, Trucksville, PA 18708
Tel.: (570) 696-3838
Web Site: http://www.newellfuel.com
Year Founded: 1978
Rev.: $13,400,000
Emp.: 20
Providers of Heating Service & Premium Petroleum Products to Commercial & Residential Customers
N.A.I.C.S.: 424710

NEWELL MACHINERY COMPANY INC.
1405 Mitchell Dr, Hiawatha, IA 52233-2102
Tel.: (319) 393-1610
Web Site:
http://www.newellmachinery.com

Sales Range: $10-24.9 Million
Emp.: 100
Building Equipment Installation Services
N.A.I.C.S.: 238290
Tim Grissel Jr. (Pres)

NEWELL RECYCLING SOUTHEAST, LLC
1359 Central Ave, East Point, GA 30344
Tel.: (404) 766-1621
Web Site:
http://www.newellrecycling.com
Scrap Metal Recycling
N.A.I.C.S.: 423930
Sharon Newell Shirley (CEO)
Chip Shirley (Pres & COO)
Bobby Triesch (VP-Ops)
Frank Goulding (VP-Mktg)

Subsidiaries:

Blaze Recycling & Metals LLC (1)
1882 Mitchell Rd, Norcross, GA 30071
Tel.: (770) 447-0175
Web Site: http://www.blazerecycling.com
Sales Range: $10-24.9 Million
Emp.: 50
Scrap Metal Recycling Services
N.A.I.C.S.: 423930
Jerry Bernier (Controller)

Newell Recycling of Atlanta, LLC (1)
1359 Central Ave, Atlanta, GA 30344
Tel.: (404) 766-1621
Web Site: http://www.newellrecycling.com
Sales Range: $10-24.9 Million
Emp.: 115
Providers of Recycling, Waste Materials
N.A.I.C.S.: 562920
Sharon Newell Shirley (CEO)
Joe Carrico (VP-HR & Safety)
Chip Shirley (Pres & COO)
Bobby Triesch (VP-Ops)
Bob Ward (CFO)

NEWFIELD BANCORP INC.
18 S West Blvd, Newfield, NJ 08344-9558
Tel.: (856) 692-3440
Web Site:
http://www.newfieldbank.com
Year Founded: 1934
Sales Range: $500-549.9 Million
Emp.: 150
Bank Holding Company
N.A.I.C.S.: 551111
Joanne Barsuglla (Controller & Sr VP)
John Borelli Jr. (Pres & CEO)

Subsidiaries:

Newfield National Bank (1)
18 S W Blvd, Newfield, NJ 08344-9558
Tel.: (856) 692-3440
Commericial Banking
N.A.I.C.S.: 522110
Rob Tola (Chief Lending Officer & Sr VP)
Dainis Basens (Chief Credit Officer & Sr VP)
John Borelli Jr. (Pres & CEO)

NEWFIELD CONSTRUCTION, INC.
225 Newfield Ave, Hartford, CT 06106
Tel.: (860) 953-1477
Web Site:
http://www.newfieldconstruction.com
Year Founded: 1969
Sales Range: $75-99.9 Million
Emp.: 50
Civil Engineering Services
N.A.I.C.S.: 237310
Damien T. Davis (Pres)
Peter Etzel (VP-Ops)

NEWFRONT INSURANCE, INC.

55 2nd St Fl 18, San Francisco, CA 94105
Tel.: (415) 754-3635
Web Site: http://www.newfront.com
Year Founded: 2017
Insurance Brokerage
N.A.I.C.S.: 524210
Spike Lipkin *(CEO)*
Gordon Wintrob *(CTO)*
Raphael Parker *(Chief Growth Officer)*
David Juelfs *(Principal)*
Michelle Landver *(Principal)*
Keith Brown *(Principal)*
Brian Hetherington *(Pres)*
Jonathan Naranjo *(Sr VP)*
John Meister *(Principal)*
Jane Paolucci *(Sr VP-Mktg)*
Linde Hotchkiss *(Exec VP)*
Adam Johnson *(Sr VP)*
DeWayne Anderson *(Program Mgr-Diversity, Equity & Inclusion)*
Paige Maisonet *(Head-People)*
Traci Johnson *(Dir-Comm)*
Cole Wagner *(Exec VP)*
Matthew Summers *(Reg Mng Dir-Texas)*

NEWGARD DEVELOPMENT GROUP INC.
1300 Brickell Ave Ste 400, Miami, FL 33131
Tel.: (305) 938-5707
Web Site: http://www.newgardgroup.com
Sales Range: $50-74.9 Million
Emp.: 10
Real Estate Development, Construction, Investment & Management
N.A.I.C.S.: 237610
Harvey Hernandez *(Founder, Chm & CEO)*
Luis E. Riquezes *(VP-Construction)*
Rudy Anez *(Sr Project Mgr)*
Esther Marquez *(Mgr-Mktg)*
Juan Pedro San Martin *(VP-Dev)*

NEWGROUND RESOURCES
15450 S Outer Forty Dr Ste 300, Chesterfield, MO 63017-2062
Tel.: (636) 898-8100   IL
Web Site: http://www.newground.com
Year Founded: 1913
Rev.: $80,000,000
Emp.: 150
Consultants, Designers & General Contractors Specific to the Financial Industry
N.A.I.C.S.: 236220
Kevin J. Blair *(Pres & CEO)*
Thomas D. Auer *(Sr VP-Design)*
Steve Clark *(Reg VP-Bus Dev)*
Mike Neff *(Dir-Production)*
Tom White *(Reg VP)*
Skip Zaegel *(CFO & Exec VP)*
Greg Ward *(Pres)*
Chip Nix *(Sr VP-Build Ops)*
Jeff Winter *(Sr VP-Bus Dev)*
Subsidiaries:

Adrenaline, Inc.   (1)
112 Hammond Dr, Atlanta, GA 30328
Tel.: (404) 252-9995
Web Site: http://www.adrenalineshot.com
Sales Range: $10-24.9 Million
Emp.: 10
Advertising Agencies
N.A.I.C.S.: 541810
Douglas E. Strickler *(Founder & CEO)*
Teri Mez *(Dir-Digital Art)*
Nancy Auclair *(VP & Dir-Strategic Sourcing)*
Allyson Bowers *(Dir-Studio-Portsmouth)*
Rebecca Doepke *(Dir-Culture)*
Ryan Drasher *(Dir-Construction & Renovations)*
Scott Florini *(Dir-Consulting)*
Tex Grubbs *(Dir-Art)*
Laura Harvey *(Dir-Art)*

Scott Hilton *(VP & Dir-Program)*
Greg McCabe *(Dir-Retail Design)*
Becky Ocampos *(Dir-Studio-Atlanta)*

Digital Financial Network Inc.   (1)
15450 S Outer 40 Dr, Chesterfield, MO 63017
Tel.: (636) 898-8100
Web Site: http://www.newground.com
Rev.: $370,000
Emp.: 8
Marketing Consulting Services
N.A.I.C.S.: 541613
Jim Kueneke *(Pres)*
Charles Zaegel *(CFO & Exec VP)*
John Ungashick *(VP & Controller)*
Kevin Blair *(Pres & CEO)*

NewGround Consulting   (1)
15450 S Outer Forty Dr Ste 300, Chesterfield, MO 63017
Tel.: (636) 898-8100
Web Site: http://www.newground.com
Sales Range: $25-49.9 Million
Emp.: 60
Consulting Services
N.A.I.C.S.: 236220
John T. Golitz *(Owner)*
Tom Auer *(VP-Archecture & Engr)*
Ted Golitz *(Chm)*

NewGround Resources   (1)
415 W Golf Rd Ste 19, Arlington Heights, IL 60005
Tel.: (847) 228-1800
Web Site: http://www.newground.com
Sales Range: $50-74.9 Million
Emp.: 5
Bank Building Construction & Design
N.A.I.C.S.: 236220
Cody Kelly *(VP-Bus Dev)*

NEWHERE, INC.
19851 Nordhoff Pl Ste 105, Chatsworth, CA 91311
Web Site: http://www.cbdfx.com
Year Founded: 2012
Sales Range: $10-24.9 Million
Emp.: 65
Cannabidiol Product Retailer
N.A.I.C.S.: 459999
Ali Esmaili *(Co-Founder & CEO)*
Jameson Rodgers *(Co-Founder & Chief Commi Officer)*

NEWHOLD ENTERPRISES LLC
52 Vanderbilt Ave Ste 2005, New York, NY 10017
Tel.: (212) 653-0153
Web Site: https://newhold.com
Year Founded: 2017
Holding Company
N.A.I.C.S.: 551112
Charlie Baynes-Reid *(Mng Dir)*
Subsidiaries:

PRIME AE Group, Inc.   (1)
551 Research Dr Ste 300, Baltimore, MD 21228
Tel.: (410) 654-3790
Web Site: http://www.primeeng.com
Emp.: 400
Privater Equity Firm
N.A.I.C.S.: 523940
Pamela Butziger *(Chief People Officer)*
Kurt Bergman *(Pres & CEO)*

Holding (Domestic):

Integrated Engineering, PLLC   (2)
519 E Babcock St, Bozeman, MT 59715-4713
Tel.: (406) 586-8988
Web Site: http://www.iesweb.com
Electronics Stores
N.A.I.C.S.: 449210
Dan Vanluchene *(Owner)*

Subsidiary (Domestic):

Jacobi, Toombs & Lanz, Inc.   (2)
1829 E Spring St Ste 201, New Albany, IN 47150
Tel.: (502) 583-5994
Web Site: http://www.jtleng.com
Engineeering Services

N.A.I.C.S.: 541330
Mike Harris *(Pres)*

NEWK'S FRANCHISE COMPANY
2660 Ridgewood Dr Ste 100, Jackson, MS 39216
Tel.: (601) 982-1160
Web Site: http://www.newkscafe.com
Year Founded: 2004
Rev.: $11,700,000
Emp.: 249
Food & Beverage
N.A.I.C.S.: 722310
Chris Newcomb *(Founder & CEO)*
Adam Karveller *(Dir-IT)*
Rachael Myrick *(Project Mgr-Building & Design)*
Alan Wright *(CMO)*
Kevin Anderson *(VP-Company Ops)*
Scott Stanford *(VP-HR)*
Michael Clock *(Pres & CFO)*

NEWKIRK ELECTRIC ASSOCIATES
1875 Roberts St, Muskegon, MI 49442
Tel.: (231) 722-1691
Web Site: http://www.newkirk-electric.com
Year Founded: 1961
Sales Range: $50-74.9 Million
Emp.: 600
Providers of Electrical Services
N.A.I.C.S.: 238210
Ted Anton *(Pres)*
Nate Leenhouts *(Project Mgr)*
Todd Knight *(Project Mgr)*

NEWKIRK, DENNIS & BUCKLES, INC.
304 N Penn Ave, Independence, KS 67301
Tel.: (620) 331-3700
Web Site: http://www.ndb-insurance.com
Year Founded: 1989
Sales Range: $10-24.9 Million
Emp.: 15
Provider of Insurance Services; Agents & Brokers
N.A.I.C.S.: 524210
Doug Buckles *(Pres)*
Maura Samora *(Dir-Ops)*

NEWLEADS, INC.
400 E Esplanade Dr Ste 200, Oxnard, CA 93036
Tel.: (805) 604-4444
Web Site: http://www.newleads.com
Year Founded: 1996
Sales Range: $1-9.9 Million
Emp.: 14
Exhibit Lead Management Software
N.A.I.C.S.: 513210
John Hasbrouck *(Pres & CEO)*
Karl Becker *(COO)*

NEWLIFE BIKES, INC.
6411 Boykin Spaniel Rd, Charlotte, NC 28277
Tel.: (704) 846-8709   NV
Year Founded: 2012
Cycling Information & Support Services
N.A.I.C.S.: 519290
J. Stephen Keller *(Pres, CEO, Treas & Sec)*

NEWLY WEDS FOODS, INC.
1106 S Bridge St, Yorkville, IL 60560
Tel.: (773) 489-7000   IL
Web Site: https://www.newlywedsfoods.com
Year Founded: 1932
Sales Range: $400-449.9 Million

Emp.: 5,300
Dry Pasta, Dough & Flour Mixes Manufacturing from Purchased Flour
N.A.I.C.S.: 311824
Charles T. Angell *(Pres)*
Mike Hopp *(VP-Mfg)*
Brian Johnson *(CFO)*
Subsidiaries:

Newly Weds Foods Asia Pacific   (1)
32 Davis Rd, Wetherill Park, Sydney, 2164, NSW, Australia
Tel.: (61) 294269300
Web Site: http://www.nwfap.com
Sales Range: $50-74.9 Million
Emp.: 170
Custom Blended Spice Seasoning & Batter Mfr
N.A.I.C.S.: 335999
Kelvin Boyle *(Gen Mgr)*

Newly Weds Foods, Inc.   (1)
70 Grove St Ste 80, Watertown, MA 02472-2829   (100%)
Tel.: (617) 926-7600
Sales Range: $25-49.9 Million
Emp.: 85
Processes Batter Mixes & Bread Crumbs
N.A.I.C.S.: 311812
John Lincoln *(Gen Mgr)*

Newly Weds Foods, Inc.   (1)
1111 Angell Dr, Springdale, AR 72764-7916   (100%)
Tel.: (479) 756-7300
Web Site: http://www.newlywedsfood.com
Sales Range: $25-49.9 Million
Emp.: 130
Mfr of Food Coatings
N.A.I.C.S.: 311999
Karen Horton *(Gen Mgr)*

Newly Weds Foods, Inc.   (1)
412 W Flottman Rd, Gerald, MO 63037
Tel.: (573) 764-3396
Sales Range: $25-49.9 Million
Emp.: 50
Processes Seasoning Blends; Cleans, Grinds Spices
N.A.I.C.S.: 311942

Newly Weds Foods, Inc.   (1)
187 Industrial Ln SW, Cleveland, TN 37311-8293
Tel.: (423) 559-0909
Sales Range: $25-49.9 Million
Emp.: 225
Mfr Stuffing & Breading, Food Coatings
N.A.I.C.S.: 311824
Charles Angell *(Owner)*

Newly Weds Foods, Ltd.   (1)
Owl Ln, Ossett, WF5 9AX, West Yorkshire, United Kingdom
Tel.: (44) 924280444
Web Site: http://www.newlywedsfoods.co.uk
Sales Range: $25-49.9 Million
Emp.: 50
Marketing & Sales Office
N.A.I.C.S.: 445298

NEWMAN & KENG PAVING COMPANY
1480 FM 141, Giddings, TX 78942
Tel.: (979) 542-2558
Rev.: $10,616,830
Emp.: 20
Highway & Street Paving Services
N.A.I.C.S.: 237310
Jamie Manning *(Comptroller)*

NEWMAN & ULLMAN, INC.
2312 Lakeshore Dr, Pekin, IL 61554
Tel.: (309) 676-0538   IL
Web Site: http://www.newman-ullman.com
Year Founded: 1859
Sales Range: $25-49.9 Million
Emp.: 30
Wholesale Trade Distr
N.A.I.C.S.: 425120
Bill Parker *(Pres & Gen Mgr)*

NEWMAN LUMBER CO., INC.

NEWMAN LUMBER CO., INC.   U.S. PRIVATE

Newman Lumber Co., Inc.—(Continued)
11367 Reichold Rd, Gulfport, MS 39503-4127
Tel.: (228) 832-1899   MS
Web Site: http://www.newmanlumber.com
Year Founded: 1947
Sales Range: $10-24.9 Million
Emp.: 20
Wholesale of Mahogany Products
N.A.I.C.S.: 423310
Doug Newman (Pres)
Janette Robbins (Sec)

NEWMAN'S OWN, INC.
1 Morningside Dr N, Westport, CT 06880
Tel.: (203) 222-0136   DE
Web Site: http://www.newmansown.com
Year Founded: 1982
Sales Range: $125-149.9 Million
Emp.: 28
Spaghetti Sauce, Popcorn, Salad Dressing & Lemonade Mfr & Distr
N.A.I.C.S.: 311941
Thomas Indoe (Pres & COO)
David Best (VP-Mktg)
Lori DiBiase (VP-Supply Chain)
Ellen Marram (Chm)

NEWMAN/HAAS RACING, LLC
500 Tower Pkwy, Lincolnshire, IL 60069
Tel.: (847) 634-8210   IL
Web Site: http://www.newman-haas.com
Year Founded: 2005
Professional Open-Wheel Racing Team
N.A.I.C.S.: 711211
Carl A. Haas (Owner)

NEWMARK ADVERTISING, INC.
15821 Ventura Blvd Ste 570, Encino, CA 91436-2947
Tel.: (818) 461-0300   CA
Web Site: http://www.newmarkad.com
Year Founded: 1968
Sales Range: $10-24.9 Million
Emp.: 30
Advetising Agency
N.A.I.C.S.: 541810
David Newmark (Chm & CEO)
Patty Newmark (Pres & COO)

NEWMARK ASSOCIATES, INC.
7 E Frederick Pl Ste 500, Cedar Knolls, NJ 07927
Tel.: (973) 884-4444   NJ
Web Site: http://www.newmarkrealestate.com
Year Founded: 1987
Sales Range: $10-24.9 Million
Emp.: 28
Commercial Real Estate Brokerage & Advisory Services
N.A.I.C.S.: 531210
Susanne Newmark (Pres & CEO)
Judith Tell Feldman (Mng Dir & Assoc Dir-Sls-Healthcare Div)
Nancy Glick (COO)
Deborah Myers (Mng Dir)
Meryl Ehrenkranz (Sr VP)
David Bieber (Exec Acct Dir)
Bill Cunningham (VP)
Nancy Stanton-Tuckman (VP)
Peter Caraballo (VP)
Helene Elbaum (VP)
Marcelo Adinolfi (VP)
Patricia Cunningham (VP-Sls)

NEWPORT APPAREL CORPORATION
1215 W Walnut St, Compton, CA 90220-5009
Tel.: (310) 605-1900   CA
Web Site: http://www.newporting.com
Year Founded: 1988
Sales Range: $25-49.9 Million
Emp.: 75
Women's Lines
N.A.I.C.S.: 424350
James Kim (Pres)
Kimberly Kim (CFO)
Joyce Cho (Fin Officer)

NEWPORT AUTO CENTER INC.
1030 N Coast Hwy, Newport, OR 97365
Tel.: (541) 265-8547   OR
Web Site: http://www.sunwesthonda.com
Year Founded: 1989
Sales Range: $10-24.9 Million
Emp.: 26
New & Used Car Dealers
N.A.I.C.S.: 441110
Gary Nicholson (Pres)

NEWPORT DIVERSIFIED INC.
19200 Von Karman Ave Ste 1000, Irvine, CA 92612
Tel.: (949) 851-1355
Web Site: http://www.nd-inc.com
Year Founded: 1984
Sales Range: $10-24.9 Million
Emp.: 10
Retailer of Flea Markets
N.A.I.C.S.: 561990
Luanne Tacey (Asst Mgr)

NEWPORT GLOBAL ADVISORS, L.P.
21 Waterway Ave Ste 150, The Woodlands, TX 77380
Tel.: (713) 559-7400
Web Site: http://www.newportglobaladvisors.com
Year Founded: 2005
Investment Management Service
N.A.I.C.S.: 523999
Timothy T. Janszen (CEO)
Tony Longi (Mng Dir, COO & Chief Compliance Officer)
Ryan L. Langdon (Co-Founder & Sr Mng Dir)

NEWPORT INTERNATIONAL OF TIERRA VERDE, INC.
675 30th Ave N Ste 102, Saint Petersburg, FL 33704
Tel.: (727) 894-1188
Web Site: http://www.newportintl.com
Year Founded: 1964
Sales Range: $1-9.9 Million
Emp.: 20
Fish & Seafood Mfr & Merchant Whslr
N.A.I.C.S.: 424460
Anjan Tharakan (Pres)

NEWPORT NEWS GENERAL AND NON SECTARIAN HOSPITAL ASSOCIATION INC.
608 Denbigh Blvd Ste 800, Newport News, VA 23608-4487
Tel.: (757) 875-7838   VA
Year Founded: 1982
Sales Range: $10-24.9 Million
Real Estate Support Services
N.A.I.C.S.: 531120
William B. Downey (Pres & CEO)
Wade Dudley Broughman (CFO, Treas & Exec VP)

NEWPORT PARTNERS, LLC
3760 Tanglewood Ln, Davidsonville, MD 21035
Tel.: (301) 889-0017
Web Site: http://www.newportpartnersllc.com
Year Founded: 2002
Sales Range: $1-9.9 Million
Emp.: 6
Construction Consulting
N.A.I.C.S.: 541690
Liza Bowles (Gen Mgr)

NEWPORT SALES INC.
1 Newport Plz, Freeport, NY 11520
Tel.: (516) 771-4444
Rev.: $17,827,667
Emp.: 15
Cosmetics
N.A.I.C.S.: 424210
Carl M. Klein (Pres)

NEWPORT SAND & GRAVEL CO. INC.
8 Reeds Mill Rd, Newport, NH 03773
Tel.: (603) 863-1000
Web Site: http://www.carrollconcrete.com
Year Founded: 1959
Sales Range: $10-24.9 Million
Emp.: 30
Ready Mixed Concrete
N.A.I.C.S.: 327320
Shaun Carroll Sr. (Pres)

NEWPORT UTILITIES BOARD INC.
170 Cope Blvd, Newport, TN 37821-2870
Tel.: (423) 625-2800   TN
Web Site: http://www.newportutilities.com
Year Founded: 1939
Sales Range: $25-49.9 Million
Emp.: 91
Electronic Services
N.A.I.C.S.: 221118
Glenn Ray (Gen Mgr)
Carmen Lichty (Mgr-Customer Svc)
Jimmy Robertson (Mgr-Electric-CPSv)
Connie Frisbee (Mgr-HR, PHR & UHR)

NEWPRO, INC.
26 Cedar St, Woburn, MA 01801
Tel.: (781) 933-4100   MA
Web Site: http://www.newpro.com
Year Founded: 1950
Sales Range: $10-24.9 Million
Emp.: 70
Provider of Replacement Windows & Doors
N.A.I.C.S.: 444110
Tom Foxon (Mgr-Installation)
Ricci Tarlowski (Dir-HR)
Jenny Christensen (VP-Mfg)

NEWRY CORP
14725 Detroit Ave Ste 210, Lakewood, OH 44107
Tel.: (440) 808-3839
Web Site: http://www.newrycorp.com
Year Founded: 1987
Rev.: $4,000,000
Emp.: 23
Business Support Services
N.A.I.C.S.: 561499
Mark M. Clusky (Pres)
Chris McCarthy (VP-Ops & Admin)
Ellen Young (VP)

NEWS COMMUNICATIONS, INC.
2 Park Ave Ste 1405, New York, NY 10016
Tel.: (212) 689-2500   NV
Sales Range: $10-24.9 Million
Emp.: 92
Newspaper Publisher & Distr
N.A.I.C.S.: 513110
James A. Finkelstein (Pres & CEO)
E. Paul Leishman (CFO & Sec)

NEWS GAZETTE INC.
15 E Main St, Champaign, IL 61820
Tel.: (217) 351-5252
Web Site: http://www.news-gazette.com
Sales Range: $10-24.9 Million
Emp.: 400
Newspapers, Publishing & Printing
N.A.I.C.S.: 513110
John Foreman (Pres & Publr)
John Reed (Publr)
Bob Shelton (Dir-Ops)

NEWS MEDIA CORPORATION
211 Hwy 38 E, Rochelle, IL 61068
Tel.: (815) 562-4171
Web Site: http://www.newsmediacorporation.com
Year Founded: 1975
Sales Range: $25-49.9 Million
Emp.: 650
Newspapers
N.A.I.C.S.: 513110
John C. Tompkins (Owner & Chm)
John Shank (COO & Grp Publr-Illinois)
Jennifer Simmons (Editor)
Patrick Duffy (Dir-Adv)
Lori Laye (Chief Admin Officer)
J. J. Tompkins (Chief Revenue Officer)

Subsidiaries:

Alamosa Newspapers Inc.   (1)
2205 State Ave, Alamosa, CO 81101
Tel.: (719) 589-2553
Web Site: http://www.alamosanews.com
Sales Range: $10-24.9 Million
Emp.: 30
Newspaper Publishers
N.A.I.C.S.: 513110
Keith R. Cerny (Publr)
Shasta Quintana (Mgr-Circulation)

Brookings Newspapers LLC   (1)
312 5th St, Brookings, SD 57006
Tel.: (605) 692-6271
Web Site: http://www.brookingsregister.com
Rev.: $1,800,000
Emp.: 20
Job Printing & Newspaper Publishing Combined
N.A.I.C.S.: 513110
William N. McMacken (Publr)

Cottage Grove Sentinel   (1)
116 N 6th St, Cottage Grove, OR 97424-0002
Tel.: (541) 942-3325
Web Site: http://www.cgsentinel.com
Sales Range: $10-24.9 Million
Emp.: 8
Newspaper Publishers
N.A.I.C.S.: 513110
Gary Manly (Gen Mgr)

Huron Newspapers LLC   (1)
49 3rd St SE, Huron, SD 57350
Tel.: (605) 352-6401
Web Site: http://www.plainsman.com
Rev.: $2,500,000
Emp.: 60
Newspapers, Publishing & Printing
N.A.I.C.S.: 513110

Mendota Publishing Corporation   (1)
703 Illinois Ave, Mendota, IL 61342
Tel.: (815) 539-9396
Web Site: http://www.mendotareporter.com
Rev.: $560,000
Emp.: 6
Newspapers, Publishing & Printing
N.A.I.C.S.: 513110

Newport News Times   (1)
831 NE Avery St, Newport, OR 97365-0075

Tel.: (541) 265-8571
Web Site:
   http://www.newportnewstimes.com
Sales Range: $50-74.9 Million
Emp.: 20
Newspaper Publishers
N.A.I.C.S.: 513110
Lee Breedlove (Mgr-Press Ops)

News Media Corporation (1)
49 3rd St SE, Huron, SD 57350
Tel.: (605) 352-3313
Rev.: $290,000
Emp.: 30
Offset Printing
N.A.I.C.S.: 323111
Mark Davis (Pres)

Wyoming Newspapers Inc. (1)
849 Front St, Evanston, WY 82930
Tel.: (307) 789-6560
Web Site: http://www.uintacountyherald.com
Media Production & Newspaper Publisher
N.A.I.C.S.: 513110
Mark Tesoro (Publr)

Wyoming Newspapers Inc. (1)
2025 Main St, Torrington, WY 82240
Tel.: (307) 532-2184
Web Site:
   http://www.torringtontelegram.com
Sales Range: $1-9.9 Million
Emp.: 20
Newspaper Publishers
N.A.I.C.S.: 513110
Rob Mortimore (Publr)

NEWS TRIBUNE CO.
210 Monroe St, Jefferson City, MO 65101
Tel.: (573) 636-3131
Web Site:
   http://www.newstribune.com
Rev.: $10,000,000
Emp.: 120
Newspapers, Publishing & Printing
N.A.I.C.S.: 513110
Jane Haslag (Mgr-Adv)

NEWS-JOURNAL CORPORATION
901 6th St, Daytona Beach, FL 32117
Tel.: (386) 252-1511
Web Site: http://www.news-journalonline.com
Sales Range: $50-74.9 Million
Emp.: 900
Newspapers
N.A.I.C.S.: 513110
Michael Redding (CEO)

NEWS-PRESS & GAZETTE COMPANY
825 Edmond St, Saint Joseph, MO 64501-2737
Tel.: (816) 271-8500   MO
Web Site: http://www.npgco.com
Year Founded: 1845
Sales Range: $100-124.9 Million
Media Holding Company; Newspaper Publishing, Television Broadcasting & Commercial Printing Services
N.A.I.C.S.: 551112
Lee Sawyer (Exec VP-Berks Grp)
Brian Bradley (Pres)
Bill Severn (Chief Org Effectiveness Officer & Exec VP)
Jennifer Wright (Mgr-Corp Personnel)
Tim Hannan (CFO & Exec VP)
Laura Clark (Chief People Officer)
Mike Meara (Pres-Brdcst)
Stacey Hill (COO & Exec VP)
David R. Bradley Jr. (Chm & CEO)

Subsidiaries:

Berks Group (1)
825 Edmond St, Saint Joseph, MO 64501
Tel.: (816) 236-6214
Web Site: http://www.berksgroup.com
Private Equity Fund
N.A.I.C.S.: 551112

Jay C. Longbottom (Partner-Operating)
Doug Krebs (Partner-Operating)

Subsidiary (Domestic):

Swiss-Tech, LLC (2)
1441 Wisconsin St, Delavan, WI 53115
Tel.: (262) 728-6363
Web Site: http://www.swisstechllc.com
Precision Component Mfr
N.A.I.C.S.: 332721
Kenneth Bliss (Chm)
Carl Bardenwerper (CFO)
Frank Meiland (Pres & CEO)
Karen Ozanich (Dir-Mfr & Logistics)
Matt Bills (Mgr-Quality & Compliance)
Jason Price (Dir-Engrg & Support Tech)

NPG Printing Co. (1)
1301 S 58th St, Saint Joseph, MO 64507
Tel.: (816) 236-6200
Web Site: http://www.npgprinting.com
Sales Range: $10-24.9 Million
Emp.: 85
Printing Services
N.A.I.C.S.: 323111
Kevin Smith (Plant Mgr)

NPG of Oregon, Inc. (1)
62990 O B Riley Rd, Bend, OR 97701
Tel.: (541) 383-2121
Web Site: http://www.ktvz.com
Sales Range: $10-24.9 Million
Emp.: 60
Television Broadcasting Station
N.A.I.C.S.: 516120
Jim DeChant (Dir-Technical Ops)
Danette Schlapfer (Mgr-HR)
Kara McGinn (Mgr-Promos)

Unit (Domestic):

KFXO-TV (2)
62990 OB Riley Rd, Bend, OR 97701
Tel.: (541) 382-7220
Web Site: http://www.ktvz.com
Emp.: 60
Mfr of Heating Systems & Components
N.A.I.C.S.: 333414
Lee Anderson (Dir-News)
Bob Singer (Gen Mgr)

News-Press Digital (1)
825 Edmond St, Saint Joseph, MO 64501
Tel.: (816) 271-8688
Digital Marketing Services
N.A.I.C.S.: 541613

Pikes Peak Television, Inc. (1)
399 S 8th St, Colorado Springs, CO 80905-1803
Tel.: (719) 632-1515
Web Site: http://www.krdo.com
Sales Range: $25-49.9 Million
Emp.: 100
Television Broadcasting Station
N.A.I.C.S.: 516120
Jerry Killion (Dir-Ops)
Timothy A. Larson (Gen Mgr-KRDO-TV)
Mike Lewis (Dir-Radio Program)

NEWSBANK, INC.
5801 Pelican Bay Blvd Ste 600, Naples, FL 34108-2734
Tel.: (802) 875-2910
Web Site: http://www.newsbank.com
Sales Range: $10-24.9 Million
Emp.: 250
Press Clipping Service
N.A.I.C.S.: 424920
Daniel S. Jones (Pres)

Subsidiaries:

Readex (1)
5801 Pelican Bay Blvd Ste 600, Naples, FL 34108
Tel.: (239) 263-6004
Web Site: http://www.readex.com
Emp.: 60
Academic Materials Publisher
N.A.I.C.S.: 513120
David Braden (Pres)

NEWSGATOR TECHNOLOGIES, INC.
950 17th St Ste 2500, Denver, CO 80202

Tel.: (800) 608-4597
Web Site: http://www.newsgator.com
Year Founded: 2004
Sales Range: $10-24.9 Million
Emp.: 85
Software Developer
N.A.I.C.S.: 513210
Daniel Kraft (Pres & CEO)

Subsidiaries:

NewsGator Technologies (1)
Amstel Business Park Joop Geesinkweg 901-999, 1096 AZ, Amsterdam, Netherlands
Tel.: (31) 20 561 7038
Software Developer
N.A.I.C.S.: 513210

NewsGator Technologies (1)
La Grande Arche Paroi Nord, La Defense, 92044, Paris, France
Tel.: (33) 1 40 90 34 29
Software Developer
N.A.I.C.S.: 513210
Andre Bonvanie (Gen Mgr-EMEA)

NewsGator Technologies (1)
1 Jalan Kembangan, Singapore, 419154, Singapore
Tel.: (65) 9736 4447
Software Publisher
N.A.I.C.S.: 513210

NewsGator Technologies (1)
Suite 1017 Level 1 22-36 Mountain Street, Ultimo, 2007, NSW, Australia
Tel.: (61) 2 8006 6632
Software Developer
N.A.I.C.S.: 513210

Sitrion ONE (1)
29th Floor 1 Canada Square, Canary Wharf, London, E14 5DY, United Kingdom
Tel.: (44) 207 7121783
Web Site: http://www.sitrion.com
Software Developer
N.A.I.C.S.: 513210
Andre Bonvanie (Gen Mgr-EMEA)
Onno Hektor (VP-Sls-EMEA)

NEWSLINK GROUP, LLC.
6910 NW 12th St, Miami, FL 33126
Tel.: (305) 594-5754
Web Site:
   http://www.newslinkgroup.net
Year Founded: 2004
Sales Range: $25-49.9 Million
Emp.: 250
Book Distributing Services
N.A.I.C.S.: 459210
Christopher G. Korge (Chm)
Ziad El-Assad (Dir-Dev)
Raymond Kayal Jr. (CEO)

NEWSMAX MEDIA, INC.
750 Park of Commerce Dr, Boca Raton, FL 33487
Tel.: (561) 686-1165   NV
Web Site: http://www.newsmax.com
Year Founded: 1998
Rev.: $11,000,000
Emp.: 215
Online News & Information; Financial & Health Newsletters, Nationally Distributed Magazine
N.A.I.C.S.: 513199
Christopher Ruddy (CEO)
David Patten (Mng Editor)
Walter Raps (Sr VP-Brdcst Ops & Engrg-TV)
Ric Grenell (VP-Dev-Intl)

NEWSPAPER ASSOCIATION OF AMERICA
4401 Wilson Blvd Ste 900, Arlington, VA 22203
Tel.: (571) 366-1000   VA
Web Site: http://www.naa.org
Year Founded: 1992
Sales Range: $25-49.9 Million
Emp.: 25
Newpaper Association
N.A.I.C.S.: 813910

Paul Boyle (Sr VP-Pub Policy)
John Murray (VP-Audience Dev)
Danielle Coffey (VP-Pub Policy)
David Chavern (Pres & CEO)
Michael MaLoon (VP-Innovation)
Tony W. Hunter (Chm)
Terry Kroeger (Vice Chm)
Mark E. Aldam (Sec)
Sarah Burkman (VP-HR & Ops)
Michelle Harris (VP-Membership & Dev)
Robert Walden (CFO)

NEWSPRING CAPITAL LLC
Radnor Financial Center 555 E Lancaster Ave 3rd Fl, Radnor, PA 19087
Tel.: (610) 567-2380
Web Site:
   http://www.newspringcapital.com
Sales Range: $25-49.9 Million
Emp.: 40
Equity Investment Firm Services
N.A.I.C.S.: 523999
Michael A. DiPiano (Founder & Mng Gen Partner)
Marc R. Lederman (Gen Partner)
Glenn T. Rieger (Gen Partner)
Jonathan S. Schwartz (Pres & COO)
Brian G. Murphy (Gen Partner)
Christopher W. Bodine (Venture Partner)
Steven Hobman (Gen Partner)
Skip Maner (Gen Partner)
Andrew Panzo (Gen Partner)
Gregory Barger (Gen Partner)
Michael Dimartile (Dir-IR)
Adam Veverka (Mng Dir-Bus Dev)
Kapila Ratnam (Gen Partner)
Anne Vasquez (Partner)
Hart Callahan (Principal)
Lee Garber (Principal)
Brian Kim (Partner)
Kristin Lee (Principal)
Justin Nadile (Principal)
Mark Pacala (Partner)
Satya Ponnuru (Partner)
Bob Valvano (Principal)

Subsidiaries:

Bridge Core LLC (1)
1775 Tysons Blvd 5th fl, McLean, VA 22102
Tel.: (814) 644-7853
Web Site: https://bcore.com
Software Publisher
N.A.I.C.S.: 513210

Subsidiary (Domestic):

teKnoluxion Consulting LLC (2)
1143 5th St NW Ste 1, Washington, DC 20001-3610
Tel.: (504) 606-6441
Web Site: http://www.teknoluxion.com
Computer System Design Services
N.A.I.C.S.: 541512
Jimmy Gardner (Owner)

Financeware, LLC (1)
1065 Andrew Dr., West Chester, PA 19380
Tel.: (888) 701-4206
Web Site:
   https://www.financewaregroup.com
Financial Services
N.A.I.C.S.: 523999
Bob Ward (CEO)

Subsidiary (Domestic):

QUODD Financial Information Services, Inc (2)
30 Montgomery St, Ste 600, Jersey City, NJ 07302
Tel.: (866) 537-5518
Web Site: https://quodd.com
Financial Services
N.A.I.C.S.: 523999
Bob Ward (CEO)

Subsidiary (Domestic):

Xignite, Inc. (3)

NEWSPRING CAPITAL LLC U.S. PRIVATE

NewSpring Capital LLC—(Continued)
1825 S Grant St Ste 100, San Mateo, CA 94402
Tel.: (650) 655-3700
Web Site: http://www.xignite.com
Sales Range: $1-9.9 Million
Emp.: 10
Financial Software
N.A.I.C.S.: 513210
Stephane Dubois *(Founder & CEO)*
Al Chang *(CTO)*
Peter Caswell *(Chm)*
Kerry Langstaff *(CMO)*
Mark Rowe *(CFO)*

Magna5 LLC (1)
1000 Cliff Mine Rd Ste 520, Pennsylvania, PA
Tel.: (844) 624-6255
Web Site: https://www.magna5global.com
Cloud, Security & Managed Services
N.A.I.C.S.: 541511
Bob Farina *(CEO)*

Subsidiary (Domestic):

Interphase Systems, Inc. (2)
2 Valley Sq Ste 110, 19422, Blue Bell, PA
Tel.: (610) 276-5500
Web Site:
  http://www.interphasesystems.com
Data Processing, Hosting & Related Services
N.A.I.C.S.: 518210
John Biglin *(CEO)*
Ray Bouknight *(Dir-Validation & Compliance)*
Lew Smith *(Dir-Client Svcs)*
Michael J. Walsh *(Dir-Managed Svcs)*
Denise Biglin *(Pres)*
Joe Kniffen *(Dir-Application Dev & Project Mgmt)*
Jon Prange *(Dir-Enterprise Architecture)*
Anthony Severino *(VP-Sls & Mktg)*
Thomas Dahlgren *(Dir-IT Infrastructure & Security Eviti)*

The Sentinel Company (1)
8618 Westwood Ctr Dr Ste 240, Vienna, VA 22182
Tel.: (703) 663-8725
Web Site: http://www.e3federal.com
Holding Company
N.A.I.C.S.: 523999
Andrew Maner *(Chm)*

Subsidiary (Domestic):

E3 Federal Solutions, LLC (2)
2011 Crystal Dr Ste 400, Arlington, VA 22202
Tel.: (703) 682-6925
Web Site: http://www.e3federal.com
Management Consulting Services
N.A.I.C.S.: 541611
Everett S. Johnson *(Pres)*
Missy Barber *(Project Mgr-Performance)*
Tony Bonanno *(Mgr)*
Christopher Mangune *(Coord-Trng)*
Alex Porfirenko *(Project Mgr)*
Donald Paine *(CFO)*
Cameron Hogan *(Chief Strategy Officer)*
Carrie Kramer *(Dir-Civilian Acct)*
Deirdre Pender *(Dir-Contracts)*
Richard Schult *(Dir-DoD Acct)*
Andy Maner *(CEO)*
Mehdi Cherqaoui *(COO)*

Operational Intelligence LLC (2)
4567 Mackenzie Ct, Warrenton, VA 20187
Tel.: (703) 639-7369
Web Site: http://www.oi-llc.com
Sales Range: $10-24.9 Million
Emp.: 70
Intelligence Services
N.A.I.C.S.: 541330
Amy Lewin *(CEO)*

US Pack Logistics LLC (1)
Chrysler Bldg 405 Lexington Ave Ste 4901, New York, NY 10174
Tel.: (212) 631-0233
Web Site: http://www.gouspack.com
Logistic Services
N.A.I.C.S.: 541614
Peter Glazman *(Owner)*

Subsidiary (Domestic):

Best Courier & Delivery Service (2)

223 Peterson Rd, Libertyville, IL 60048
Tel.: (847) 816-6229
Web Site: http://www.bestcourier.com
Rev.: $5,640,000
General Freight Trucking, Local
N.A.I.C.S.: 484110

Capital Delivery System Inc. (2)
25 Utley Dr Ste 700, Camp Hill, PA 17011-8039
Tel.: (717) 561-7782
Web Site: http://www.capitaldelivery.com
General Freight Trucking, Local
N.A.I.C.S.: 484110
Jim Stubbs *(Pres)*

Utilipath, LLC (1)
136 Corporate Park Dr Ste G, Mooresville, NC 28117
Tel.: (704) 948-1005
Web Site: http://www.utilipath.com
Sales Range: $25-49.9 Million
Construction & Engineering Services
N.A.I.C.S.: 237130
Joaquin A. Luna *(CEO)*
Baxter Hayes *(COO)*
Jack C. Roberts *(CMO)*
Pedro Ferreira *(Chief Bus Dev Officer)*
Angelia Ryan *(Controller)*
Eric Plott *(Pres)*
Terry Metze *(Exec VP-Ops)*

Verisma Systems, Inc. (1)
1421 Prince St. Ste 250, Alexandria, VA 22314
Tel.: (866) 390-7404
Web Site: https://verisma.com
Health Information Technology Provider
N.A.I.C.S.: 513210
Marty McKenna *(CEO)*

Subsidiary (Domestic):

Scanstat Technologies, LLC (2)
288 S Main St Ste 600, Alpharetta, GA 30009-1983
Tel.: (770) 569-2445
Web Site: http://www.scanstat.com
Printing
N.A.I.C.S.: 323111
Matt Rohs *(Chief of Staff)*
Glenn Andrews *(CEO)*

Vertical Management Systems, Inc. (1)
15440 Laguna Canyon Rd Ste 160, Irvine, CA 92618
Web Site: http://www.vmsholdings.com
Sales Range: $1-9.9 Million
Emp.: 45
Custom Computer Programming Services
N.A.I.C.S.: 541511
Rose Thomas *(Gen Counsel & Sr VP)*
Bob Ward *(Chief Revenue Officer)*
Cort Williams *(Sr VP-Global Product & Strategy)*
Justin DuBrueler *(CFO)*
Marguerite Peters *(Pres)*

X5 Solutions (1)
1008 Western Ave Ste 400, Seattle, WA 98104
Tel.: (206) 973-5800
Web Site: http://www.x5solutions.com
Telecommunication Servicesb
N.A.I.C.S.: 517810
Nathan Bledsoe *(CTO)*
Rick Hirsh *(Chm)*
Greg Forrest *(CEO)*
Dan Horton *(CIO)*
Barbara Meyer *(Controller)*
Shawn Kearney *(CFO)*
Frank William *(VP & Gen Mgr-Oregon)*

Subsidiary (Domestic):

Cornerstone Telephone Co. LLC (2)
2 3rd St Ste 303, Troy, NY 12180
Tel.: (518) 272-1018
Web Site:
  http://www.cornerstonetelephone.com
Telecommunications Resellers
N.A.I.C.S.: 517121
Dan Yamin *(Co-Founder & CEO)*
Donald Walsh *(Co-Founder & CTO)*
Richard Drake *(CFO)*
Ron Cole *(Chief Revenue Officer)*

NEWSTONE CAPITAL PARTNERS, LLC

300 Crescent Ct Ste 1600, Dallas, TX 75201
Tel.: (310) 689-1710
Web Site: http://www.newstone.com
Emp.: 15
Financial Investment Services
N.A.I.C.S.: 523999
Timothy P. Costello *(Co-Founder & Mng Dir)*
John C. Rocchio *(Co-Founder & Mng Dir)*

NEWSWAYS DISTRIBUTORS

1324 Cypress Ave, Los Angeles, CA 90065
Tel.: (323) 258-6000
Web Site: http://www.newsways.com
Year Founded: 1985
Sales Range: $50-74.9 Million
Emp.: 180
Book, Periodical & Newspaper Merchant Whslr
N.A.I.C.S.: 424920
Ofelia Dammeier *(Dir-HR)*
Scott Wheeler *(Mgr-Ops)*
John L. Dorman *(Pres)*

NEWTEX INDUSTRIES INC.

8050 Victor Mendon Rd, Victor, NY 14564
Tel.: (585) 924-9135
Web Site: http://www.newtex.com
Year Founded: 1978
Sales Range: $10-24.9 Million
Emp.: 50
Mfr of Fiberglass Fabrics
N.A.I.C.S.: 313210
Bal Dixit *(Founder & Chm)*
Jerry Joliet *(CEO)*

NEWTON CONSULTING, LLC

4632 State Rte 40 Ste 200, Claysville, PA 15323
Tel.: (724) 663-5827
Web Site:
  http://www.newtonconsulting.com
Sales Range: $10-24.9 Million
Emp.: 63
Healthcare Software Consulting Services
N.A.I.C.S.: 541512
Bill Boehner *(VP-Tech Consulting)*
Toni Kellar *(Dir-Mktg & Corp Comm)*
Rick Newton *(Founder & Pres)*
Chris Hafner *(VP-Strategy & Dir-Ops-Europe)*
Shari Kienzle *(Dir-HR)*
Chris Malarky *(Dir-Fin)*

NEWTON HEALTHCARE CORPORATION

600 Medical Center Dr, Newton, KS 67114
Tel.: (316) 283-2700
Web Site:
  http://www.newtonmedicalcenter.com
Year Founded: 1988
Sales Range: $50-74.9 Million
Emp.: 723
Health Care Srvices
N.A.I.C.S.: 622110
Todd Kasitz *(CFO & VP-Fin)*
Mike Keller *(COO & VP-Ops)*
Vallerie Gleason *(VP-Physician Svcs)*
Todd Tangeman *(VP-HR)*

NEWTON INSTRUMENT COMPANY

111 E A St, Butner, NC 27509
Tel.: (919) 575-6426
Web Site: http://www.enewton.com
Year Founded: 1949
Sales Range: $10-24.9 Million
Emp.: 170
Mfr of Medical Instruments

N.A.I.C.S.: 334210
Walter L. Newton *(Pres)*
Stephen Bigelowe *(Controller)*

NEWTON MEDIA ASSOCIATES, INC.

824 Greenbrier Pkwy Ste 200, Chesapeake, VA 23320
Tel.: (757) 547-5400
Web Site:
  http://www.newtonmedia.com
Year Founded: 1995
Sales Range: $10-24.9 Million
Emp.: 10
Fiscal Year-end: 12/31/15
Media Buying Services
N.A.I.C.S.: 541830
Steve Newton *(Pres & CEO)*
Janet Burke *(Dir-Media)*

NEWTON NISSAN OF GALLATIN, INC.

1461 Nashville Pike, Gallatin, TN 37066-3149
Tel.: (615) 451-6827
Web Site:
  http://www.newtonnissan.com
Sales Range: $10-24.9 Million
Emp.: 16
Used Car Whslr
N.A.I.C.S.: 441120
Mike Abbondanza *(Owner & Gen Mgr)*
Tad Drusky *(Bus Mgr)*
Dave Daniels *(Dir-Parts & Svc)*

NEWTON OIL COMPANY, INC.

3150 S 460 E, Lafayette, IN 47905
Tel.: (765) 742-4001
Web Site: http://www.newtonoil.com
Sales Range: $10-24.9 Million
Emp.: 13
Whslr of Petroleum Products
N.A.I.C.S.: 424710
Charles Newton *(Pres & Co-Owner)*
Jim Newton *(VP & Co-Owner)*

NEWTON WALL COMPANY

1600 N Harrison Ave, Shawnee, OK 74804
Tel.: (405) 275-1582
Web Site:
  http://www.wallvargaincenter.com
Rev.: $24,290,052
Emp.: 75
Variety Stores
N.A.I.C.S.: 455219
Liz Wall *(Pres)*

NEWTON-DAVIS INC.

2503 N Wood Ave, Florence, AL 35630
Tel.: (256) 766-0456
Sales Range: $10-24.9 Million
Emp.: 80
Supermarkets, Chain
N.A.I.C.S.: 445110
Eric Davis *(Pres)*

NEWTOWN SAVINGS BANK

39 Main St, Newtown, CT 06470
Tel.: (203) 426-2563
Web Site: http://www.nsbonline.com
Rev.: $29,905,000
Emp.: 200
Savings & Loan Associations, Not Federally Charter
N.A.I.C.S.: 522180
John Trentacosta *(Pres & CEO)*
Dan Long *(Sr VP-Mktg & Mgr-Ops)*
Michelle Dias *(Mgr-Southford & Asst Treas)*
Frank Yaworowski *(Mgr-Monroe & Asst Treas)*

NEXBANK CAPITAL, INC.

2515 McKinney Ave Ste 1100, Dallas, TX 75201
Tel.: (972) 934-4700
Web Site: http://www.nexbank.com
Bank Holding Company
N.A.I.C.S.: 551111
John L. Holt Jr. *(Vice Chm)*
Rhett Miller *(Chief Banking Officer)*
Stacy Hodges *(CFO)*
Matthew Siekielski *(Pres & CEO)*

Subsidiaries:

NexBank, SSB (1)
2515 McKinney Ave Ste 1100, Dallas, TX 75201
Tel.: (972) 934-4700
Web Site: http://www.nexbank.com
Sales Range: $250-299.9 Million
Emp.: 85
Federal Savings Bank
N.A.I.C.S.: 522180
John L. Holt Jr. *(Chm, Pres & CEO)*
Rhett Miller *(Chief Banking Officer)*
John L. Holt Jr. *(Chm, Pres & CEO)*
Matthew Siekielski *(COO & Exec VP)*
Dierk Hohman *(Gen Counsel)*
Rhett Miller *(Chief Credit Officer & Exec VP)*
Stacy Hodges *(CFO & Exec VP)*

NEXCESS.NET LLC
21700 Melrose Ave, Southfield, MI 48075
Tel.: (866) 639-2377
Web Site: http://www.nexcess.net
Year Founded: 2000
Sales Range: $1-9.9 Million
Emp.: 80
Web Hosting Solutions from Shared Hosting & Virtual Private Servers
N.A.I.C.S.: 518210
Jay Al-Qalyuby *(Dir-Customer Svc)*
Chris Wells *(Pres)*

NEXCOM GROUP
1225 Harding Pl, Charlotte, NC 28204
Tel.: (704) 940-1864
Web Site:
http://www.nexcomgroup.com
Year Founded: 2001
Rev.: $5,400,000
Emp.: 53
Information Technology Services
N.A.I.C.S.: 449210
Michelle Breneman *(Dir-Expense Mgmt)*

NEXE BLOCKCHAIN, INC.
3709 Promontory Point Dr Ste 129, Austin, TX 78744
Tel.: (512) 717-7769 DE
Year Founded: 2017
Investment Services
N.A.I.C.S.: 523999
Victor Wong *(CEO)*

NEXEN GROUP INC.
560 Oak Grove Pkwy, Vadnais Heights, MN 55127
Tel.: (651) 484-5900
Web Site:
http://www.nexengroup.com
Sales Range: $10-24.9 Million
Emp.: 50
Clutches, Except Vehicular
N.A.I.C.S.: 333613
Jim Hasart *(COO)*
Dave Amundson *(Dir-Bus Ops)*

NEXGEN BUILDING SUPPLY
1099 Greenleaf Ave, Elk Grove Village, IL 60007
Tel.: (847) 303-9800
Web Site:
http://www.nexgenbuildingsupply.com
Year Founded: 1920

Construction Equipment & Materials Mfr
N.A.I.C.S.: 423390
Rachel Quintilian *(Reg Mgr-Pur)*

Subsidiaries:

NexGen Building Supply (1)
164 Trade St, Lexington, KY 40511
Tel.: (859) 231-6150
Web Site:
http://www.nexgenbuildingsupply.com
Building Materials Distr
N.A.I.C.S.: 423310
Dave Woolums *(Office Mgr)*

NEXGEN MEDIA WORLDWIDE, INC.
331 W 57th St Suite 128, New York, NY 10019
Tel.: (212) 957-7660
Web Site:
http://www.nexgenmedia.com
Year Founded: 1979
Sales Range: $50-74.9 Million
Emp.: 10
Media Buying Services
N.A.I.C.S.: 541830
Neil Faber *(Chm & CEO)*
Amy Hochberg *(Pres)*

NEXGEN METALS, INC.
1560 W Artesia Sq Ste A, Gardena, CA 90248
Tel.: (310) 944-9300
Web Site:
http://www.nexgenworld.com
Sales Range: $10-24.9 Million
Emp.: 3
Steel Distr
N.A.I.C.S.: 423510
Andrew Kim *(Mgr)*

NEXGENIX, INC.
2 Peters Canyon Ste 200, Irvine, CA 92606
Tel.: (714) 665-6240
Web Site: http://nexvisionix.com
Rev.: $34,400,000
Emp.: 441
Software Publisher
N.A.I.C.S.: 513210
Rick Dutta *(Founder, Chm & CEO)*
Martin Onofrio *(Sr VP-Sls-Mktg)*

NEXION HEALTH, INC.
6937 Warfield Ave, Sykesville, MD 21784
Tel.: (410) 552-4800
Web Site: http://www.nexion-health.com
Emp.: 4,000
Nursing Home Operator
N.A.I.C.S.: 623110
Fran Kirley *(Pres & CEO)*
Meera Riner *(COO)*
Brian Lee *(Gen Counsel)*
Keith Mutschler *(Treas)*
Susan Ways *(Dir-HR)*

NEXIUS SOLUTIONS INC.
11951 Freedom Dr 13th Fl, Reston, VA 20190
Tel.: (703) 650-7777
Web Site: http://www.nexius.com
Year Founded: 2001
Sales Range: $25-49.9 Million
Emp.: 285
Computer Related Services
N.A.I.C.S.: 541512
Mark Baysinger *(Pres)*
Joe Baeumel *(VP-Pro Svcs)*
Paul Andre *(VP-Tech)*

NEXLOGIC TECHNOLOGIES INC.
2085 Zanker Rd, San Jose, CA 95131

Tel.: (408) 436-8150
Web Site: http://www.nexlogic.com
Sales Range: $10-24.9 Million
Emp.: 65
Bare Printed Circuit Board Mfr
N.A.I.C.S.: 334412
Zulki Khan *(Founder & Pres)*
Yaseen Haroon *(Controller)*

NEXLUBE TAMPA LLC
777 S Harbour Island Blvd Ste 250, Tampa, FL 33602
Tel.: (813) 228-7260
Web Site: http://www.nexlube.com
Sales Range: $25-49.9 Million
Emp.: 75
Petroleum Recycling & Mfr
N.A.I.C.S.: 324199
Enzio D'Angelo *(COO)*
Monte Bell *(Pres)*
Alberto Mendoza *(VP-Bus Dev & Mktg)*
Malone Mitchell III *(Chm)*

NEXPRISE, INC.
5950 La Pl Ct Ste 200, Carlsbad, CA 92008
Tel.: (760) 804-1333
Year Founded: 1997
Software Development Services
N.A.I.C.S.: 541511
Kendra Drysdale *(Pres)*

NEXSAN CORPORATION
1287 Anvilwood Ave, Sunnyvale, CA 94089
Tel.: (760) 690-1111 DE
Web Site: http://www.nexsan.com
Year Founded: 2000
Holding Company; Computer Storage Technologies Mfr & Whslr
N.A.I.C.S.: 551112
Gregg Pugmire *(Sr VP-Sls & Mktg)*
Gary Watson *(CTO)*
Danny Zheng *(CEO)*
David Bartizal *(VP-Global Svc & Support)*

Subsidiaries:

Nexsan Technologies Canada Inc (1)
3001405 Trans Canada Hwy, Dorval, H9P 2V9, QC, Canada
Tel.: (514) 683-1020
Blank Magnetic & Optical Recording Media Mfr
N.A.I.C.S.: 334610

Nexsan Technologies Incorporated (1)
1287 Anvilwood Ave, Sunnyvale, CA 94089
Tel.: (760) 690-1111
Web Site: http://www.nexsan.com
Blank Magnetic & Optical Recording Media Mfr
N.A.I.C.S.: 334610

Nexsan Technologies Limited (1)
Units 3335 Parker Centre Mansfield Road, Derby, DE21 4SZ, United Kingdom
Tel.: (44) 1332597168
Blank Magnetic & Optical Recording Media Mfr
N.A.I.C.S.: 334610

NEXT CENTURY CORPORATION
2701 Technology Dr Annapolis Jct, Columbia, MD 20701
Tel.: (443) 545-3100
Web Site:
http://www.nextcentury.com
Year Founded: 2002
Sales Range: $10-24.9 Million
Emp.: 130
Custom Computer Programming Services
N.A.I.C.S.: 541511

Paul Butterfield *(Co-Founder & VP)*
Mark Allen *(VP-Bus Dev)*
Marco de Palma *(VP-Ops)*
John T. McBeth *(CEO)*
John Beakes *(Co-Founder & Chm)*
Candace Krug *(VP-Admin)*
Jim Long *(Exec VP)*
Charlie Butterfield *(Co-Founder)*
Sarah Otchet *(CFO)*
James Weyant *(VP)*

NEXT CENTURY TECHNOLOGIES, INC.
1555 Coomber Ct, Herndon, VA 20170
Tel.: (703) 629-6406
Holding Company
N.A.I.C.S.: 551112
Ronald D. Wright *(Pres & CEO)*

NEXT DAY BLINDS CORPORATION
8251 Preston Ct, Jessup, MD 20794
Tel.: (240) 568-8800
Web Site:
http://www.nextdayblinds.com
Rev.: $30,292,086
Emp.: 350
Drapery Hardware & Window Blinds & Shades
N.A.I.C.S.: 337920
Fred Alladin *(VP)*
David Miller *(Asst Mgr)*
Steve Freishtat *(CEO)*
Sydney Engle *(Mgr-Field)*
Allison Siegel *(Pres)*

NEXT DAY FLYERS
18711 S Broadwick St, Rancho Dominguez, CA 90220
Tel.: (310) 747-3800
Web Site:
http://www.nextdayflyers.com
Sales Range: $25-49.9 Million
Quick Printing, Mailing & Finishing Services
N.A.I.C.S.: 541860
David Handmaker *(Founder & CEO)*

NEXT FUEL, INC.
821 Frank St, Sheridan, WY 82801
Tel.: (307) 674-2145 NV
Web Site: http://www.next-fuel.com
Year Founded: 2007
Sales Range: Less than $1 Million
Emp.: 4
Hydrogen Technology Developer
N.A.I.C.S.: 541715
Jeff Harris *(Pres & CTO)*

NEXT GALAXY CORP.
1680 Michigan Ave Ste 700, Miami Beach, FL 33139
Year Founded: 2009
Software Development Services
N.A.I.C.S.: 541511
Michel St-Pierre *(Pres & CFO)*

NEXT GENERATION FILMS, INC.
215 Industrial Dr, Mansfield, OH 44904
Tel.: (419) 884-8150 OH
Year Founded: 1994
Sales Range: $25-49.9 Million
Emp.: 250
Fiscal Year-end: 12/31/11
Unsupported Plastics Packaging Film & Sheet Mfr
N.A.I.C.S.: 326112

NEXT GENERATION FUNDRAISING, INC.
1235 Westlakes Dr Ste 130, Berwyn, PA 19312
Tel.: (610) 640-1555 PA

NEXT GENERATION FUNDRAISING, INC.

Next Generation Fundraising, Inc.—(Continued)
Web Site: http://www.nextgenfr.com
Fundraising Services
N.A.I.C.S.: 561499
Tim O'Leary *(Principal & CEO)*
Carol Leister *(Principal & COO)*

Subsidiaries:

Drakes Bay Fundraising, Inc. (1)
1100 Larkspur Landing Cir, Larkspur, CA 94939
Tel.: (415) 461-6202
Web Site: http://www.drakesbaynet.com
Sales Range: $1-9.9 Million
Emp.: 16
Fundraising Services
N.A.I.C.S.: 561499
Cindy Germain *(Dir-Fundraising Svcs)*

NEXT GENERATION WIRELESS INC.
215 1 2 Main St, Cedar Falls, IA 50613
Tel.: (319) 266-5070
Web Site: http://www.ngwtoday.net
Year Founded: 2001
Sales Range: $10-24.9 Million
Emp.: 80
Cell Phone Retailer
N.A.I.C.S.: 517112
Bill Bradford *(Owner & Pres)*
Bethany Benner *(VP-Sls & Mktg)*
James Rozendaal *(CFO)*
Jennie Tranbarger *(Mgr-Bus)*
Sadie Foertsch *(Mgr-Mktg)*

NEXT INSURANCE, INC.
409 Sherman Ave, Palo Alto, CA 94306
Tel.: (855) 222-5919
Web Site: http://www.nextinsurance.com
Year Founded: 2016
Insurance Services
N.A.I.C.S.: 524210
Guy Goldstein *(CEO & Founder)*
Eran Liron *(Chief Strategy Officer)*
Chris Rhodes *(Chief Insurance Officer)*

NEXT LEVEL BURGER COMPANY, INC.
70 SW Century Dr Ste 1070, Bend, OR 97702
Tel.: (458) 600-3990
Web Site: https://www.nextlevelburger.com
Emp.: 100
Restaurant Operators
N.A.I.C.S.: 722511
Matt de Gruyter *(CEO & Founding Partner)*

Subsidiaries:

Veggie Grill, Inc. (1)
5855 Green Vly Cir Ste 208, Culver City, CA 90230
Tel.: (310) 745-5228
Web Site: https://veggiegrill.com
Emp.: 100
Restaurant Operators
N.A.I.C.S.: 722511

NEXT LEVEL CHURCH, INC.
12400 Plantation Rd, Fort Myers, FL 33966
Tel.: (239) 274-3755
Web Site: http://www.nextlevelchurch.com
Year Founded: 2002
Sales Range: $1-9.9 Million
Emp.: 25
Religious Organizations
N.A.I.C.S.: 813110

Sarah Keller *(Exec Dir)*
Karen Murano *(Dir-Maintenance)*
Jennifer Jackson *(Dir-Experience)*
Craig Davis *(Dir-Bus Dev)*

NEXT MANAGEMENT, LLC
15 Watts St 6th Fl, New York, NY 10013
Tel.: (212) 925-5100
Web Site: http://www.nextmanagement.com
Year Founded: 1989
Sales Range: $1-9.9 Million
Emp.: 40
Modeling Agency
N.A.I.C.S.: 711410
Faith Kates *(Co-CEO)*
Kyle Hagler *(Div Pres)*
Joel Wilkenfeld *(Co-CEO)*

NEXT MARKETING
2820 Paterson, Norcross, GA 30071
Tel.: (770) 225-2200
Web Site: http://www.nextmarketing.com
Year Founded: 1993
Marketing Consulting Services
N.A.I.C.S.: 541613
Henry J. Rischitelli *(Pres & CEO)*
Paul Duffy *(Exec VP-Client Svcs & Agency Ops)*
Tim Leaumont *(Exec VP-Fin & Bus Ops)*
Linda Trocano *(Sr VP-Channel Svcs)*
Seth Ferguson *(Sr VP-Events & Ops)*
Michael Hernandez *(VP-Bus Dev)*

NEXT PAGE, INC.
8300 NE Underground Dr Pillar 122, Kansas City, MO 64161
Tel.: (816) 459-8404
Web Site: http://www.gonextpage.com
Year Founded: 1990
Sales Range: $1-9.9 Million
Emp.: 70
Digital Printing Services
N.A.I.C.S.: 323111
Eric C. Danner *(Pres)*
Dan Vogt *(VP-Production)*
Gina M. Danner *(VP & Sec)*

Subsidiaries:

Digigraph Xpress LLC (1)
8300 NE Underground Dr Pillar 119B, Kansas City, MO 64161
Tel.: (816) 471-4700
Web Site: http://www.printbig.com
Printing Services
N.A.I.C.S.: 323111
B. Joseph Duffy *(Pres)*

NEXT POINT BEARING GROUP, LLC
28364 Avenue Crocker, Valencia, CA 91355
Tel.: (818) 988-1880
Web Site: http://www.nextpointbearing.com
Rev.: $15,000,000
Emp.: 30
Bearings & Component Parts Mfr & Distr
N.A.I.C.S.: 332991
Mark Mickelson *(Chm)*

NEXT STAR COMMUNICATIONS, INC.
6600 Sugarloaf Pkwy, Duluth, GA 30097
Tel.: (770) 814-9095
Web Site: http://www.nxtstr.com
Year Founded: 2000
Sales Range: $10-24.9 Million
Cellular Phone Retailer
N.A.I.C.S.: 449210
Robert K. Moeck *(Owner)*

NEXT STEP DOMESTIC VIOLENCE PROJECT
733 Bangor Rd PO Box 1466, Ellsworth, ME 04605-1466
Tel.: (207) 667-0176
Web Site: http://www.nextstepdvproject.org
Year Founded: 1993
Sales Range: $1-9.9 Million
Emp.: 14
Crisis Counseling Services
N.A.I.C.S.: 624230
Rebecca Hobbs *(Exec Dir)*
Arlyn Whitelaw *(Sec)*
Cynthia Shoppe *(Treas)*
Starie Seay *(Pres)*
Robert Tracy *(VP)*

NEXT STEP EDUCATION GROUP, INC.
2 W Main Ste 200, Victor, NY 14564
Tel.: (585) 742-1260
Web Site: http://www.nextstepu.com
Year Founded: 1995
Sales Range: $1-9.9 Million
Emp.: 11
Magazine Publisher
N.A.I.C.S.: 513120
David Mammano *(Founder & CEO)*
Diana Fisher *(Dir-Mktg & Brand)*
Renee Bates *(Mgr-Fin & HR)*
Laura Sestito *(Coord-Production & Editorial)*
Katie Barry *(Dir-Curriculum)*
Theresa Santa *(Dir-Sls-Southeast)*

NEXT STEP LEARNING INC.
3655 N Point Pkwy Ste 600, Alpharetta, GA 30005
Tel.: (770) 521-1135
Web Site: http://www.nextsteplearning.com
Year Founded: 1998
Sales Range: $10-24.9 Million
Emp.: 70
Corporate Training
N.A.I.C.S.: 611430
Dawn Weiss *(Coord-Trng)*

NEXT STEP LIVING, INC.
21 Drydock Ave #2, Boston, MA 02210
Tel.: (866) 867-8729
Web Site: http://nextstepliving.com
Year Founded: 2008
Sales Range: $25-49.9 Million
Emp.: 800
Home Energy Efficiency & Environmental Impact Evaluations
N.A.I.C.S.: 541620
Geoff Chapin *(Founder & CEO)*
Brian Greenfield *(COO)*

NEXT TIER CONCEPTS, INC.
1945 Old Gallows Rd Ste 400, Vienna, VA 22182
Tel.: (703) 288-0010
Web Site: http://www.ntconcepts.com
Year Founded: 1998
Sales Range: $10-24.9 Million
Emp.: 100
Geospatial Technology Consulting, Custom Application Development, eLearning, Multimedia & Technical Services
N.A.I.C.S.: 541690
Christopher J. Cusano *(Exec VP)*
Elizabeth Meola *(Mgr-Bus Dev)*
Michele A. Bolos *(Founder & CEO)*
Debbie Pearson *(Mgr-HR)*
Darin L. Powers *(Pres & COO)*
Brandon Ginsburg *(Chief Growth Officer & Sr VP)*

NEXT WORLD CAPITAL PARTNERS LLC

U.S. PRIVATE

836 Montgomery St, San Francisco, CA 94133
Tel.: (415) 202-5450
Web Site: http://www.nextworldgroup.com
Emp.: 20
Private Equity & Capital Investment Firm
N.A.I.C.S.: 523999
Sebastien Lepinard *(Founder-San Francisco Office)*
Jerome Theot *(COO-Brussels Office)*
Tom Rikert *(Partner)*

Subsidiaries:

Next World Capital LLC (1)
836 Montgomery St, San Francisco, CA 94133
Tel.: (415) 202-5450
Web Site: http://www.nextworldcap.com
Privater Equity Firm
N.A.I.C.S.: 523999
Sebastien Lepinard *(Gen Partner)*
Craig Hanson *(Partner)*
Ben Fu *(Partner)*
Frederic Halley *(Partner-Operating)*
Tom Rikert *(Partner)*

NEXTCARE HOLDINGS, INC.
1138 N Alma School Rd Ste 120, Mesa, AZ 85201
Tel.: (480) 924-8382
Web Site: http://www.nextcare.com
Year Founded: 1993
Holding Company; Urgent Care & Occupational Medicine Centers Owner & Operator
N.A.I.C.S.: 551112
John Julian *(Pres & CEO)*
Rex T. Clevenger *(CFO)*
Laura Becker *(Chief Compliance Officer)*
Jeffrey R. Gerlach *(Chief Growth Officer)*
Joleen Haxton *(VP-Ancillary Svcs)*
Hector G. Barragan *(Sr VP-Ops)*
Keith Marple *(Sr VP-Reimbursement Svc)*

Subsidiaries:

NextCare, Inc. (1)
1138 N Alma School Rd Ste 120, Mesa, AZ 85201
Tel.: (480) 924-8382
Web Site: http://www.nextcare.com
Urgent Care & Occupational Medicine Centers Operator
N.A.I.C.S.: 621399
John Julian *(Pres & CEO)*
Ken Walsh *(Chief Admin Officer)*
Laura Becker *(Chief Compliance Officer)*
Jeffrey R. Gerlach *(Sr VP-Bus Dev & Strategic Growth)*
Joleen Haxton *(VP-Ancillary Svcs)*
Keith Marple *(Sr VP-Reimbursement Svcs)*
Michael A. Kaplan *(Dir-Medical-Natl)*
Rex T. Clevenger *(CFO)*
Larry Crist Jr. *(COO)*

NEXTDOCS CORPORATION
500 N Gulph Rd Ste 240, King of Prussia, PA 19406
Tel.: (610) 265-9474
Web Site: http://www.nextdocs.com
Year Founded: 2006
Sales Range: $1-9.9 Million
Emp.: 50
Software Solutions
N.A.I.C.S.: 334610
Zikria Syed *(Co-Founder & CEO)*
Matt Walz *(Co-Founder & CTO)*
Erik Smith *(VP-Sls)*
Nitin Bhatia *(VP-Global Svcs)*

NEXTERA MEDIA, LLC
7851 W 185th St, Tinley Park, IL 60477
Tel.: (708) 478-4500

COMPANIES

Web Site:
http://www.nexteramedia.com
Sales Range: Less than $1 Million
Online Media & Advertising Services
N.A.I.C.S.: 519290
Jaffer Ali *(Co-Founder & CEO)*
Anisa Ali *(Co-Founder & COO)*
Tom Zegar *(Co-Founder & VP-Media)*
Jeanie Davis *(VP-SIs)*
Mary Kolacki *(Dir-Comm)*
Jim Bosco *(Gen Counsel)*
Michele Chojnowski *(Mgr-E-Commerce)*
Kris Skora *(Mgr-e-Commerce)*
Andy Meyers *(Dir-Tech)*
Erin Chambers *(Dir-Creative Svcs)*
Karen LePretre *(Mgr-Fulfillment)*
Tammy Heath *(Dir-Customer Svc)*

Subsidiaries:

GopherCentral.com (1)
7851 W 185th St Ste 106, Tinley Park, IL 60477
Tel.: (708) 478-4500
Web Site: http://www.gophercentral.com
Emp.: 30
Newlsetter Site
N.A.I.C.S.: 541611
Jaffer Ali *(Pres)*

NEXTGEN CONSULTING INC.

1420 N Capitol St NW, Washington, DC 20002
Tel.: (202) 527-9595
Web Site: http://www.ngciglobal.com
Year Founded: 2006
Sales Range: $1-9.9 Million
Emp.: 35
Business Management Consulting Services
N.A.I.C.S.: 541618
Saif Rehman *(CEO)*

NEXTGEN INFORMATION SERVICES, INC.

3660 S Geyer Rd Ste 300, Saint Louis, MO 63127
Tel.: (314) 588-1212   MO
Web Site: http://www.nextgen-is.com
Year Founded: 1997
Sales Range: $25-49.9 Million
Emp.: 694
Information Technology Staffing Services
N.A.I.C.S.: 541511
Maria del Carmen Jacob *(CEO)*
Steve Martak *(Dir-Client Svcs)*
Lori Eaton *(Pres)*
Robert Feldman *(Dir-Diversity & Strategic Partnerships)*
Steve Kaufmann *(Dir-Client & Govt Svcs)*

NEXTGEN REPORTING LLC

999 Old Eagle School Rd Ste 118, Wayne, PA 19087-2556
Web Site:
http://www.nextgenreporting.com
Court Reporting & Stenotype Services
N.A.I.C.S.: 561492
David Noteware *(CEO)*

Subsidiaries:

Wilcox & Fetzer Ltd. (1)
1330 N King St, Wilmington, DE 19801-3220
Tel.: (302) 655-0477
Web Site: http://www.wilfet.com
Emp.: 15
Court Reporting & Stenotype Services
N.A.I.C.S.: 561492
David Noteware *(Pres)*

NEXTGLASS TECHNOLOGIES CORPORATION

9454 Wilshire Blvd Ste 610, Beverly Hills, CA 90210
Tel.: (949) 673-4510   DE
Year Founded: 2015
Glass Product Production & Distribution
N.A.I.C.S.: 327215
Low Koon Poh *(Pres, CFO, Treas & Sec)*
John Ki Park *(CEO)*

NEXTIER, INC.

222 Market St, Kittanning, PA 16201
Tel.: (724) 543-1125   PA
Web Site:
http://www.nextierbank.com
Year Founded: 1980
Sales Range: $150-199.9 Million
Emp.: 240
Bank Holding Company
N.A.I.C.S.: 551111
Clem Rosenberger *(Pres & CEO)*

Subsidiaries:

Mars Bancorp, Inc. (1)
145 Grand Ave, Mars, PA 16046
Tel.: (724) 625-1555
Web Site: https://investors.marsbank.com
Rev.: $15,163,637
Assets: $505,152,276
Liabilities: $466,404,345
Net Worth: $38,747,931
Earnings: $2,113,598
Fiscal Year-end: 12/31/2021
Bank Holding Company
N.A.I.C.S.: 551111
James Victor Dionise *(Pres & CEO)*
Michael J. Kirk *(CFO, Treas, Sec & Exec VP)*
Janet L. van Buskirk Balentine *(Chm)*
J. Jay Thier *(Vice Chm)*
Tracie L. Williams *(Chief HR Officer & Sr VP)*
Travis Squyres *(Chief Risk Officer & Sr VP)*
Lisa M. Kooker *(Chief Credit Officer & Sr VP)*
Stephanie A. Embry *(Chief Retail Banking Officer & Sr VP)*
Stephen L. Eckert *(CMO & Sr VP)*
Mark D. Drenchko *(Chief Comml Banking Officer & Sr VP)*

Subsidiary (Domestic):

Mars Bank (2)
145 Grand Ave, Mars, PA 16046
Tel.: (724) 625-1555
Web Site: http://www.marsbank.com
Sales Range: $10-24.9 Million
Emp.: 100
Fiscal Year-end: 12/31/2012
National Commercial Banks
N.A.I.C.S.: 522110
Michael J. Kirk *(CFO & Sr VP)*
Lisa M. Kooker *(Chief Credit Officer & Sr VP)*
Jim Dionise *(Pres & CEO)*
Jennifer Crofutt *(Mgr-Cranberry)*
Stephanie Elder *(Mgr-Richland)*
Jeannette Muhl *(VP-Comml Lending)*
Greg Homrock *(Mgr-Retail Banking)*
Tod Novak *(VP-Mortgage Lending)*
Greg Vallecorsa *(VP-Comml Banking)*
Andrew Chiapusio *(VP-Comml Banking)*
James Hein *(Sr VP-Fin)*
Nicolina Shetler *(Asst VP-Mortgage Lending)*

NexTier Bank, N.A. (1)
222 Market St, Kittanning, PA 16201
Tel.: (724) 543-1125
Web Site: http://www.nextierbank.com
Rev.: $15,561,000
Assets: $422,362,000
Liabilities: $377,213,000
Net Worth: $45,149,000
Earnings: $4,662,000
Emp.: 83
Fiscal Year-end: 12/31/2013
Federal Savings Bank
N.A.I.C.S.: 522180
Clem Rosenberger *(Pres & CEO)*
Maria Smathers *(CMO)*

Daniel Baronick *(Sr VP & Mgr-North Central Pennsylvania Market)*
John Havas *(Sr VP & Mgr-Central Pennsylvania Market)*

NEXTLOT, INC

7780 Brier Creek Pkwy Ste 310, Raleigh, NC 27617
Tel.: (919) 361-1111
Web Site: http://www.nextlot.com
Year Founded: 2007
Sales Range: $1-9.9 Million
Emp.: 20
Online Auction Software Development Services
N.A.I.C.S.: 541511
Scott Finkelstein *(CEO)*
Norman Finkelstein *(Pres)*
Matt Henderson *(VP-Auction Ops & Tech)*
Dan Levine *(Chm)*

NEXTRAN CORPORATION

1986 W Beaver St, Jacksonville, FL 32209
Tel.: (904) 354-3721   FL
Web Site: http://www.nextranusa.com
Year Founded: 1992
Sales Range: $200-249.9 Million
Emp.: 500
Medium & Heavy-Duty Trucks Dealer, Parts Retailer & Maintenance Services
N.A.I.C.S.: 441227
Jon W. Pritchett *(Pres & CEO)*
Don Cox *(VP/Gen Mgr-Florida)*
Francisco Blanco *(VP & Gen Mgr)*
Nick Abatecola *(Gen Mgr-Florida)*
David Bennett *(Gen Mgr-Georgia)*
Todd Brown *(VP & Gen Mgr)*

Subsidiaries:

Westfall GMC Truck Inc. (1)
3915 NE Randolph Rd, Kansas City, MO 64161-9383
Tel.: (816) 455-7262
Web Site: http://www.westfallgmc.com
Retailer of New & Used Trucks
N.A.I.C.S.: 423110
Randy O'Dell *(Mgr-Svc)*
Kelly Mayfield *(Mgr-Parts)*
Stephen Crowley *(Asst Mgr-Parts)*

NEXTRIO, LLC

4803 E 5th St, Tucson, AZ 85711
Tel.: (520) 545-7100
Web Site: http://www.nextrio.com
Year Founded: 2002
Sales Range: $1-9.9 Million
Emp.: 30
Data Processing, Hosting & Related Services
N.A.I.C.S.: 518210
Eric Behling *(CFO)*
Cristie Street *(Co-Founder, CEO & Mng Partner)*
Bill Street *(Co-Founder & CTO)*
Oscar Fowler *(Co-Founder & Chief Architect)*
Cathryn Murrow *(Mgr-Ops)*
Jennie Smith *(Dir-Technical Accounts)*
Megan Robertson *(Dir-Mktg)*

NEXTTRIP HOLDINGS, INC.

1560 Sawgrass Corporate Prkwy Ste 130, Sunrise, FL 33323
Tel.: (888) 444-5555
Web Site: https://nexttrip.com
Holding Company
N.A.I.C.S.: 551112

Subsidiaries:

NextTrip, Inc. (1)
3900 Paseo del Sol, Santa Fe, NM 87507
Tel.: (954) 526-9688
Rev.: $458,752
Assets: $5,088,842

NEXTWORTH SOLUTIONS, INC.

Liabilities: $1,960,813
Net Worth: $3,128,029
Earnings: ($6,656,837)
Emp.: 14
Fiscal Year-end: 02/29/2024
Industrial 3D Software Mfr
N.A.I.C.S.: 513210
Frank D. Orzechowski *(CFO, Principal Acctg Officer, Treas & Sec)*
Jacob Brunsberg *(Pres & CEO)*

NEXTWORLD, LLC

8200 E Maplewood Ave, Greenwood Village, CO 80111
Tel.: (303) 903-3345
Web Site: http://www.nextworld.net
Year Founded: 2016
Computer Software Services
N.A.I.C.S.: 541511
Kylee McVaney *(CEO)*

Subsidiaries:

Data Systems International, Inc. (1)
1201 Walnut Ste 1100, Kansas City, MO 64106
Tel.: (816) 416-5000
Web Site: http://www.dsiglobal.com
Computer Programming Services
N.A.I.C.S.: 541511
Matt McGraw *(Founder & Chm)*
Mark Baldwin *(CFO & Gen Counsel)*
Mark Goode *(Pres & CEO)*
Gary Delancy *(CTO)*

Subsidiary (Non-US):

DSI Asia/Pacific (2)
380 382 Canterbury Rd, PO Box 42, Surry Hills, 3127, VIC, Australia (100%)
Tel.: (61) 398350600
Web Site: http://www.dsionline.com.au
Sales Range: $10-24.9 Million
Emp.: 15
Provider of Custom Computer Programming Services
N.A.I.C.S.: 541511

DSI EMEA Ltd. (2)
3000 Cathedral Hill, Guildford, GU27YB, Surrey, United Kingdom (100%)
Tel.: (44) 483243560
Sales Range: $10-24.9 Million
Emp.: 80
Provider of Custom Computer Programming Services
N.A.I.C.S.: 541511

Subsidiary (Domestic):

Unibar, Inc. (2)
7801 W 110th St Ste 201, Overland Park, KS 66210
Tel.: (913) 696-4090
Software Development Services
N.A.I.C.S.: 541511

eNSYNC Solutions, Inc. (2)
Corporate Woods 9300 W 110th St Ste 620, Overland Park, KS 66210 (100%)
Tel.: (913) 647-8640
Web Site: http://www.ensyncsolutions.com
Professional Software Consulting & Technical Services & IFS Implementations
N.A.I.C.S.: 541690
Roger Resley *(Pres & CEO)*
Mark Baldwin *(Sr VP-Admin & Gen Counsel)*

NEXTWORTH SOLUTIONS, INC.

900 Technology Park Dr Ste 200, Billerica, MA 01821-4134
Tel.: (978) 374-6398
Web Site: http://www.nextworth.com
Year Founded: 2005
Sales Range: $10-24.9 Million
Emp.: 30
Online Shopping Services
N.A.I.C.S.: 449210
David Chen *(Pres & CEO)*
Bill Fitzgerald *(VP-Retail Accts)*
Brett Thomas *(Product Mgr)*
Robert Joseph *(Mgr-Ops)*

NEXTWORTH SOLUTIONS, INC.

NextWorth Solutions, Inc.—(Continued)
Crystal Kase (Product Mgr-Pricing)
Ron Cuthbertson (Pres-Global Ops)
Kimberly Henning (VP-Bus Dev & Mktg)

NEXUM INC.
190 S LaSalle St Ste 1450, Chicago, IL 60603
Tel.: (312) 726-6900   IL
Web Site: http://www.nexuminc.com
Year Founded: 2002
Sales Range: $25-49.9 Million
Emp.: 75
Resells Data-Security Products & Handles Installation, Maintenance & Training
N.A.I.C.S.: 611430
David Lesser (Pres & CEO)
J. D. Butt (VP-Solutions)
Mike Scher (Gen Counsel & VP)

NEXUS
505 Highway 169 N Ste 500, Plymouth, MN 55441-6447
Tel.: (763) 551-8640   MN
Web Site: http://www.nexustreatment.org
Year Founded: 1981
Sales Range: $25-49.9 Million
Emp.: 1,500
Behavioral Healthcare Services
N.A.I.C.S.: 623220
Laureen Carlson (Sec)
Jennifer McIntosh (VP-HR)
Natalie McGrady (Chm)
Michelle K. Murray (Pres & CEO)
Margaret Vimont (VP-Strategy & Svc Dev)
Scott McGuire (CFO)

NEXUS CAPITAL MANAGEMENT LP
11100 Santa Monica Blvd Ste 250, Los Angeles, CA 90025
Tel.: (424) 330-8820
Web Site: http://www.nexuslp.com
Privater Equity Firm
N.A.I.C.S.: 523999
Damian J. Giangiacomo (Co-Founder, Co-CIO & Partner)
Michael S. Cohen (Co-Founder, Co-CIO & Partner)
Daniel E. Flesh (Co-Founder, Co-CIO & Partner)
Benjamin Fader-Rattner (Mng Dir)

Subsidiaries:

FTD Group, Inc. (1)
3113 Woodcreek Dr, Downers Grove, IL 60515
Tel.: (630) 719-7800
Holding Company
N.A.I.C.S.: 551112
Jeff Clarke (Chm)

HDT GLOBAL, Inc. (1)
30500 Aurora Rd Ste 100, Solon, OH 44139
Tel.: (216) 438-6111
Web Site: https://www.hdtglobal.com
Shelters, Generators, Heaters, Air Filtration Devices & Other Engineered Solutions
N.A.I.C.S.: 333414
Kevin J. McSweeney (Pres & CEO)
Vincent Buffa (Chm)
John Conway (VP-Strategic Capture Mgmt)

Subsidiary (Domestic):

Aviation Ground Equipment Corp. (2)
53 Hanse Ave, Freeport, NY 11520
Tel.: (516) 546-0003
Web Site: http://www.aviationgroundequip.com
Rev.: $1,780,000
Emp.: 10
Other Airport Operations
N.A.I.C.S.: 488119

Barry Spilka (Pres & CEO)

MAV Beauty Brands, Inc. (1)
100 New Park Place Suite 810, Vaughan, L4K 0H9, ON, Canada
Tel.: (416) 347-8954
Rev.: $116,543,000
Assets: $426,433,000
Liabilities: $190,982,000
Net Worth: $235,451,000
Earnings: $6,506,000
Emp.: 93
Fiscal Year-end: 12/31/2020
Beauty Product Distr
N.A.I.C.S.: 456120
Laurel MacKay-Lee (CFO)
Serge Jureidini (Pres & CEO)

Subsidiary (Domestic):

Marc Anthony Cosmetics Ltd. (2)
100 New Park Place Suite 810, Vaughan, L4K 0H9, ON, Canada
Web Site: http://www.marcanthony.com
Hair Styling Product Distr
N.A.I.C.S.: 456120

NEXUS DIRECT
101 W Main St Ste 400, Virginia Beach, VA 23510
Tel.: (757) 340-5960
Web Site: http://www.nexusdirect.com
Year Founded: 2004
Sales Range: $10-24.9 Million
Emp.: 30
Advetising Agency
N.A.I.C.S.: 541810
Suzanne Cole Nowers (Founder & CEO)
Ashley Gundlach (Assoc VP-Client Svcs)
Kara Stolpinski (Mgr-Mktg-Interactive)
Susan Mann (Pres)
Meg Dawes (VP-Strategic Svcs)
Kristi Rinck (Assoc VP-Production & Data Svcs)
Amanda McCrowell (Mgr-Mktg)
Jeannie Escobar (Acct Mgr)
Neill McIvor (Acct Dir)
Shelly Hanna (Mgr-Bus Dev)

NEXUS DISTRIBUTION CORPORATION
6558 W 73rd St, Chicago, IL 60638-6003
Tel.: (708) 458-2489   IL
Web Site: http://www.nexusdistribution.com
Year Founded: 1980
Rev.: $30,076,819
Emp.: 300
Trucking Except Local
N.A.I.C.S.: 484121
Dean W. Hansen (Chm, Pres & CEO)
William D. Hansen (Exec VP)
Debra Barrett (Dir-Acctg)
Michael Gicewicz (Mgr-Transportation Svcs)

NEXUS PHARMACEUTICALS, INC.
400 Knightsbridge Pkwy, Lincolnshire, IL 60069
Tel.: (847) 996-3790
Web Site: http://www.nexuspharma.net
Year Founded: 2003
Sales Range: $75-99.9 Million
Emp.: 41
Pharmaceutical Product Mfr & Distr
N.A.I.C.S.: 325412
Mariam S. Darsot (CEO)
Ayesha Ahmed (Gen Counsel & VP-HR)
Matt Cohen (VP-Tech Svcs)
Vince LoPiccolo (VP-Sls & Mktg)
John Cook (VP-Ops)

NEXUS PLASTICS, INC.
1 Loretto Ave, Hawthorne, NJ 07506-1303
Tel.: (973) 427-3311   NJ
Web Site: http://www.nexusplastics.com
Year Founded: 1982
Sales Range: $75-99.9 Million
Emp.: 110
Specialty Extruded Films & Bags Mfr
N.A.I.C.S.: 326113
Marwan Sholakh (Pres)
Wayne Dzierzanowski (Mgr-Quality Control)
Kariman Sholakh (Mgr-HR)

NEXXAR GROUP INC.
140 E Ridgewood Ave, Paramus, NJ 07652
Tel.: (201) 477-6045
Sales Range: $100-124.9 Million
Emp.: 900
Financial Services Focusing on Money Transfers
N.A.I.C.S.: 522320
Michael Solomon (Controller)
Jack Elrod (Mng Dir-HR)

Subsidiaries:

Omnex Group, Inc. (1)
580 Sylvan Ave Ste MA, Englewood Cliffs, NJ 07632
Tel.: (201) 568-5239
Web Site: http://www.omnexgroup.com
Money Transfer Services
N.A.I.C.S.: 525990
Darren Manelski (Pres & CEO)
Gerald Popovsky (Chief Compliance Officer & Gen Counsel)

Subsidiary (Domestic):

Giromex Inc. (2)
580 Sylvan Ave, Englewood Cliffs, NJ 07632
Tel.: (201) 568-5209
Web Site: http://www.giromex.com
Sales Range: $10-24.9 Million
Emp.: 146
Money Transfer Services
N.A.I.C.S.: 522390

NEXXTWORKS, INC.
30798 US Hwy 19 N, Palm Harbor, FL 34684
Tel.: (727) 725-0400
Web Site: http://www.nexxtworks.com
Year Founded: 1997
Sales Range: $10-24.9 Million
Emp.: 50
Voice & Data Full Service Communications
N.A.I.C.S.: 517121
Richard A. Cartagena (Pres & CEO)
James Gilliand (Mgr-Svc)
Shane Reynolds (Sr Project Mgr)

NEXXUS VENTURES
820A Kifer Rd, Sunnyvale, CA 94086
Tel.: (408) 499-3695
Web Site: http://nexusventures.com
Venture Capital Investment Firm
N.A.I.C.S.: 523999
Tsuyoshi Taira (Co-Founder & Mng Dir-Investments)
Mo Khan (Co-Founder & Mng Dir-Investments)
Mukesh Ahuja (Co-Founder & Mng Dir-Accelerator)
Guillermo Sohnlein (Venture Partner)

NEY OIL COMPANY
145 S Water St, Ney, OH 43549
Tel.: (419) 658-2324
Web Site: http://www.neyoil.com
Sales Range: $25-49.9 Million
Emp.: 100
Petroleum Bulk Stations
N.A.I.C.S.: 424710
Danny Knott (Pres)

NEYER MANAGEMENT
3927 Brotherton Rd Ste 200, Cincinnati, OH 45209
Tel.: (513) 618-6000
Web Site: http://www.neyermanagement.com
Year Founded: 1998
Rev.: $5,000,000
Emp.: 41
Real Estate Agents & Managers
N.A.I.C.S.: 531210
John E. Neyer (CEO)
Richard Beasley (Mgr-Property)

NFCO INC.
2121 Brooks St, Neenah, WI 54956
Tel.: (920) 725-7000
Web Site: http://www.nfco.com
Sales Range: $300-349.9 Million
Emp.: 1,000
Investment Holding Companies, Except Banks
N.A.I.C.S.: 551112
Tom Riordan (CEO)

NFF, INC.
1023 15th St Nw Ste 500, Washington, DC 20005
Tel.: (202) 783-9011
Web Site: http://www.nffinc.com
Year Founded: 1996
Sales Range: $10-24.9 Million
Emp.: 47
Scientific & Technical Consulting Services
N.A.I.C.S.: 541690
Patricia Digangi (Office Mgr)
Hess Fatemi (CEO)

NFFS INC.
9210 Cypress Green Dr, Jacksonville, FL 32256
Tel.: (904) 683-8054
Web Site: http://www.nffsinc.com
Year Founded: 2007
Sales Range: $10-24.9 Million
Emp.: 14
Construction Engineering Services
N.A.I.C.S.: 238160
Steven Kelly (Gen Mgr)

NFG DISTRIBUTION CORP NYD VEBA FOR COLLECTIVELY BARGAINED EES
6363 Main St, Williamsville, NY 14221-5887
Tel.: (716) 857-7771   MI
Year Founded: 1991
Sales Range: $25-49.9 Million
Health & Welfare Benefit Services
N.A.I.C.S.: 525120
Anna Marie Cellino (Chm)

NFI INDUSTRIES, INC.
1515 Burnt Mill Rd, Cherry Hill, NJ 08003   NJ
Web Site: https://www.nfiindustries.com
Year Founded: 1932
Sales Range: $1-4.9 Billion
Emp.: 17,000
General Freight Trucking, Long-Distance, Truckload
N.A.I.C.S.: 484121
Jeffrey S. Brown (Vice Chm)
Scott Benton (CIO)
Craig Bollinger (Sr VP-Risk Mgmt)
Rob Barron (Exec VP)
William Bliem (VP-Maintenance)
Scott Brucker (Sr VP & Gen Counsel)
Bill Long (VP-Sls)
Bill Mahoney (Sr VP-Sls)
James Shafer (Sr VP-Solutions Design & Engrg)
Mike Greco (Sr VP-Logistics-Global)

COMPANIES

NGP ENERGY CAPITAL MANAGEMENT, LLC

Sashi Wishart *(Sr VP-Ops-Integrated Logistics Solutions)*
David Broering *(Pres-Integrated Logistics Solutions)*
Sidney R. Brown *(Pres & CEO)*
Subsidiaries:

G&P Trucking Company, Inc. (1)
126 Access Rd, Gaston, SC 29053-9501
Tel.: (803) 791-5500
Web Site: http://www.gptruck.com
Sales Range: $125-149.9 Million
Emp.: 500
Provider of Trucking Services
N.A.I.C.S.: 484121
G. Clifton Parker *(Pres & Gen Mgr)*
Billy Lynch *(CFO & VP)*
Richard Strobel *(Sr VP)*
Steve McCourt *(Sr VP-Sls & Ops)*
Mike George *(Dir-IT)*
Dennis Stanley *(Dir-Revenue)*
Martha Landreth *(Dir-HR)*
Stan Nutt *(Dir-Intermodal)*
Steve Jordan *(Mgr-Greer Corp Parts)*
John Billingsley *(Dir-Safety)*
Rick Drennan *(Dir-Security)*
William Kohl *(Dir-Pricing-Traffic)*
David Shaw *(Asst Mgr-Fin Reporting)*
Louis Burch *(Mgr-Fleet)*
James Reynolds *(Mgr-Fleet)*
Steve Farris *(Mgr-Intermodal Fleet)*
George Kanski *(Mgr-Intermodal Equipment)*
Sara Watson *(Mgr-Intermodal Fleet)*
Al Sellers *(Dir-G&P Logistics)*
Michael Smith *(Mgr-Fleet-Logistics)*
Wendy Williams *(Coord-Logistics)*
Aaron Banker *(Mgr-Fleet)*
Greg Gaskins *(Coord-Safety)*
Jay Craft *(Acct Mgr)*
Jennifer Davis *(Acct Mgr)*
Toby Guidry *(Mgr-Fleet)*
Travis McPherson *(Dir-Ops)*
Vanessa Williamson *(Mgr-Fleet)*

Interactive Logistics Inc. (1)
1515 Burnt Mill Rd, Vineland, NJ 08003
Tel.: (856) 857-1324
Web Site: http://www.nfiindustries.com
Rev.: $81,000,000
Emp.: 70
Transportation Agents & Brokers
N.A.I.C.S.: 488510

NFI Canada (1)
2800 Skymark Ave #501, Mississauga, L4W 5A6, ON, Canada
Tel.: (877) 312-1243
Web Site: http://www.nficanada.com
Transportation Logistics & Warehousing
N.A.I.C.S.: 541614

NFI Logistics (1)
1515 Burnt Mill Rd, Cherry Hill, NJ 08003
Tel.: (856) 857-1324
Sales Range: $50-74.9 Million
Emp.: 600
Logistic Services
N.A.I.C.S.: 488510
Joe Roeder *(Pres)*

NFI Warehousing & Distribution (1)
1515 Burnt Mill Rd, Cherry Hill, NJ 08003
Tel.: (856) 857-1324
Web Site: http://www.nfiindustries.com
Emp.: 500
Warehousing & Distribution Services
N.A.I.C.S.: 493110
Joe Roeder *(Pres)*

Plant (Domestic):

NFI Warehousing & Distribution Division - Arlington Facility (2)
3000 E Pioneer Pkwy, Arlington, TX 76010
Tel.: (909) 393-3172
Logistics Consulting Servies
N.A.I.C.S.: 541614

NFI Warehousing & Distribution Division - Bensenville Facility (2)
600 Eagle Rd, Bensenville, IL 60106
Tel.: (909) 393-3172
Logistics Consulting Servies
N.A.I.C.S.: 541614

Plant (Non-US):

NFI Warehousing & Distribution Division - Brampton Facility (2)
25 Cottrelle Blvd, Brampton, L6S 6L2, ON, Canada
Tel.: (909) 393-3172
Logistics Consulting Servies
N.A.I.C.S.: 541614

Plant (Domestic):

NFI Warehousing & Distribution Division - Champlain Facility (2)
2002 Ridge Rd, Champlain, NY 12919
Tel.: (866) 219-7450
Logistics Consulting Servies
N.A.I.C.S.: 541614

NFI Warehousing & Distribution Division - Chino Facility (2)
16047 Mountain Ave, Chino, CA 91708
Tel.: (909) 393-3172
Logistics Consulting Servies
N.A.I.C.S.: 541614

NFI Warehousing & Distribution Division - Dayton Facility (2)
270 Heller Park Ct, Dayton, NJ 08810
Tel.: (856) 470-2008
Logistics Consulting Servies
N.A.I.C.S.: 541614

NFI Warehousing & Distribution Division - Hebron Facility (2)
3680 Langley Dr, Hebron, KY 41048
Tel.: (866) 219-7450
Logistics Consulting Servies
N.A.I.C.S.: 541614

NFI Warehousing & Distribution Division - Logan Township Facility (2)
1150 Commerce Blvd, Logan Township, NJ 08085
Tel.: (856) 470-2008
Logistics Consulting Servies
N.A.I.C.S.: 541614

NFI Warehousing & Distribution Division - Ontario Facility (2)
1991 S Cucamonga Ave, Ontario, CA 91761
Tel.: (866) 219-7450
Logistics Consulting Servies
N.A.I.C.S.: 541614

NFI Warehousing & Distribution Division - Orlando Facility (2)
901 W Landstreet Rd, Orlando, FL 32824
Tel.: (856) 470-2008
Logistics Consulting Servies
N.A.I.C.S.: 541614

NFI Warehousing & Distribution Division - Pennsauken Facility (2)
3905 River Rd, Pennsauken, NJ 08110
Tel.: (866) 219-7450
Logistics Consulting Servies
N.A.I.C.S.: 541614

Subsidiary (Domestic):

World Warehouse & Distribution Inc. (2)
5 Coton Ln, Champlain, NY 12919-5327
Tel.: (518) 298-4748
Web Site: http://www.worldwarehouse.com
Sales Range: $10-24.9 Million
Emp.: 250
Transportation & Warehousing Services
N.A.I.C.S.: 484110

SCR Air Services, Inc. (1)
PO Box 68671, Seattle, WA 98168
Tel.: (206) 241-2083
Web Site: http://www.scrair.com
Support Activities for Air Transportation
N.A.I.C.S.: 488190

United Express Service, Inc. (1)
1000 Elm St, Rocky Hill, CT 06067
Tel.: (860) 529-7737
Web Site: http://united7737.homestead.com
Sales Range: $1-9.9 Million
Emp.: 36
Freight Brokerage Transportation Services
N.A.I.C.S.: 488510
Brian Reich *(Pres)*

NFINITY ATHLETIC CORPORATION
530 Permalume Pl, Atlanta, GA 30318
Tel.: (404) 478-7873
Web Site: http://www.nfinity.com
Year Founded: 2003
Sales Range: $1-9.9 Million
Emp.: 30
Women's Footwear & Apparel Stores
N.A.I.C.S.: 458210
Tate Chalk *(CEO)*
Nadine Baxter *(VP-Mktg)*

NFM GROUP INC.
200 1st Ave 4th FL, Pittsburgh, PA 15222
Tel.: (412) 394-6400   PA
Web Site: http://www.nfmgroup.com
Advetising Agency
N.A.I.C.S.: 541810
Preston Ciranni *(Pres)*

Subsidiaries:

Dymun + Company, Inc. (1)
200 1st Ave, Pittsburgh, PA 15222-1512
Tel.: (412) 325-6400
Web Site: http://nfmdymun.com
Advetising Agency
N.A.I.C.S.: 541810
Terrie Rembish *(Dir-Media)*
Val Peterson *(Art Dir)*
Christine Beregi *(Acct Mgr)*
Joe Winkler *(Designer-Graphic)*
Dick Robert *(Dir-Comm)*
Alex Oleynik *(Dir-Digital)*
Jeremie Musyt *(Creative Dir)*
Mitchell Watts *(Dir-Design)*
Preston Ciranni *(Pres & CEO)*
Tammy Kundla *(Controller)*
Victor Kimmel *(Acct Dir)*

NFM/WELDING ENGINEERS, INC.
577 Oberlin Rd, Massillon, OH 44647-7899
Tel.: (330) 837-3868
Web Site: http://www.nfm.net
Year Founded: 1973
Sales Range: $10-24.9 Million
Emp.: 150
Machine Shop, Jobbing & Repair
N.A.I.C.S.: 332710
Phillip Roberson *(Pres)*

Subsidiaries:

NFM (Dalian) Machinery Co., Ltd. (1)
Room 2802 Youhao Mansion 158 Youhao Road, Zhongshan District, Dalian, China
Tel.: (86) 411 8281 6991
Plastic & Rubber Machine Mfr
N.A.I.C.S.: 333248

NFM IDDON Ltd. (1)
Quin Street, Leyland, PR25 2TB, Lancashire, United Kingdom
Tel.: (44) 1772 421258
Web Site: http://www.nfmiddon.co.uk
Industrial Machinery Mfr
N.A.I.C.S.: 333248

NFS HOLDINGS INC.
10971 E Airport Service Rd, Swanton, OH 43558
Tel.: (419) 865-2311
Web Site: http://www.nationalflight.com
Sales Range: $10-24.9 Million
Aircraft Maintenance & Repair Services
N.A.I.C.S.: 488190
Thomas J. Wiles *(Pres)*

Subsidiaries:

National Flight Services Inc (1)
10971 E Airport Service R, Swanton, OH 43558
Tel.: (419) 865-2311
Web Site: http://www.nationalflight.com
Sales Range: $10-24.9 Million
Emp.: 75
Aircraft Maintenance & Repair Services
N.A.I.C.S.: 488190
Thomas J. Wiles *(Owner & Pres)*
Jeff Cousin *(Dir-Quality)*

Subsidiary (Domestic):

Propulsion Controls Company (2)
10737 NW Ambassador Dr, Kansas City, MO 64153
Tel.: (816) 891-9093
Web Site: http://www.propulsioncontrolsco.com
Aviation Support Services
N.A.I.C.S.: 488119

NFUSION GROUP, LLC
5000 Plz on the Lake Ste 200, Austin, TX 78746
Tel.: (512) 716-7000
Web Site: http://www.nfusion.com
Sales Range: $10-24.9 Million
Emp.: 54
Advetising Agency
N.A.I.C.S.: 541810
John Ellett *(Founder & CEO)*
Jay Watson *(VP-Connections Plng & Media)*
Bill Parkes *(Chief Digital Officer & Exec VP)*
Steven Callahan *(VP-Experience Strategy & Design)*
Ellen Kolsto *(VP-Insights & Plng)*
Scott Stater *(Dir-Client Success)*
Gray Hall *(Chm, Pres & CEO)*
Matt Huser *(Mng Dir)*

NG&G FACILITY SERVICES INTERNATIONAL
263 Jenckes Hill Rd, Lincoln, RI 02865
Tel.: (401) 333-4800
Web Site: http://www.nggservices.com
Rev.: $20,000,000
Emp.: 70
Fence Construction
N.A.I.C.S.: 238150
Charles Vachon *(Pres)*
Alan Riendeau *(COO)*

NGA HOLDCO, LLC
21 Waterway Ave Ste 150, The Woodlands, TX 77380
Tel.: (713) 559-7400   NV
Year Founded: 2007
Sales Range: $1-9.9 Million
Financial Investment Services
N.A.I.C.S.: 523999
Timothy T. Janszen *(Operating Mgr)*
Ryan L. Langdon *(Mgr)*
Roger A. May *(CFO & Mgr)*

NGP ENERGY CAPITAL MANAGEMENT, LLC
5221 N O'Connor Blvd Ste 1100, Irving, TX 75039
Tel.: (972) 432-1440
Web Site: http://www.ngpenergycapital.com
Energy Private Equity Investment Firm
N.A.I.C.S.: 523999
Kenneth A. Hersh *(CEO)*
Tony R. Weber *(COO & Mng Partner)*
Craig S. Glick *(Partner & Sr Mng Dir)*
Christopher D. Ray *(Sr Mng Dir)*
Christopher G. Carter *(Mng Partner)*
Robert A. Edwards *(Exec VP-Corp Dev)*
Jeffrey A. Zlotky *(Partner)*
Jill W. Lampert *(Chief Fin & Admin Officer)*
Philip J. Deutch *(Partner)*
Brian Patterson *(Partner-IR)*
Carolyn Flinchum *(Dir-Mktg)*
James Wallis *(Partner-Houston)*

Subsidiaries:

Bicent Power LLC (1)

NGP ENERGY CAPITAL MANAGEMENT, LLC U.S. PRIVATE

NGP Energy Capital Management, LLC—(Continued)

100 North West St, Easton, MD 21601
Tel.: (410) 770-9500
Electric Power Services
N.A.I.C.S.: 221122
Paul Prager *(Chm & CEO)*
Douglas Halliday *(COO & Exec VP)*
Nazar Khan *(Sr VP-Dev & Acq)*

Subsidiary (Domestic):

Centennial Power, Inc. (2)
1930 Burntboat Dr, Bismarck, ND 58503
Tel.: (701) 222-7989
Power Company
N.A.I.C.S.: 221118

Colorado Energy Management, LLC (2)
2575 Park Ln Ste 200, Lafayette, CO 80026
Tel.: (303) 442-5112
Web Site: http://www.coloradoenergy.com
Emp.: 17
Electrical Power Plant
N.A.I.C.S.: 221118
Elizabeth Strothman *(Gen Mgr-Ledger)*

Quatro Resources Inc. (1)
801 Sixth Avenue Southwest Suite 2100, Calgary, T2P 3W2, AB, Canada
Tel.: (403) 221-7700
Web Site: http://www.quatroresources.ca
Sales Range: $1-9.9 Million
Emp.: 16
Oil & Gas Exploration, Drilling & Production
N.A.I.C.S.: 211120

NGP VAN, INC.
1101 15th St NW Ste 500, Washington, DC 20005
Tel.: (202) 686-9330
Web Site: http://www.ngpvan.com
Year Founded: 1997
Sales Range: $1-9.9 Million
Emp.: 44
Computer & Software Services
N.A.I.C.S.: 513210
Stuart Trevelyan *(CEO)*
Louis Levine *(Gen Mgr-Fundraising & Compliance)*
John Lee *(CTO)*
Michelle Stephenson *(Chief Revenue Officer)*

NH3 SERVICE COMPANY
945 Johnson Ave, Salinas, CA 93901
Tel.: (831) 424-5716
Web Site: http://www.nh3service.com
Sales Range: $250-299.9 Million
Emp.: 30
Fertilizer & Fertilizer Materials Distributors
N.A.I.C.S.: 424910
Jim Lipe *(Pres)*

NHR, LLC
6500 Hollister Ave, Santa Barbara, CA 93117
Tel.: (805) 964-9975
Web Site: http://www.curvature.com
Sales Range: $200-249.9 Million
Emp.: 500
Computer Network Hardware Distr
N.A.I.C.S.: 423710
Mike Sheldon *(Pres & CEO)*
Glenn Fassett *(Gen Mgr-Intl)*
Mark Kelly *(VP-IT)*
Michael Lodato *(Sr VP-Sls & Mktg)*
Jeff Zanardi *(VP-Bus Dev & Product Mktg)*

NHS HUMAN SERVICES, INC.
620 E Germantown Pike, Lafayette Hill, PA 19444
Tel.: (610) 238-4403 PA
Web Site: http://www.nhsonline.org
Year Founded: 1986
Sales Range: $25-49.9 Million
Emp.: 330

Individual & Family Support Services
N.A.I.C.S.: 624190
Karen Markle *(VP-Childrens Svcs)*
Derrick Yacovelli *(CFO)*
Leah Pason *(Exec VP-Corp Admin)*
Kate Williams *(Asst Gen Counsel)*
Patricia Pisauro *(VP-Mktg & Comm)*
Suzanne Campbell *(VP-Admin & Behavioral Health Svcs)*
Joseph S. Martz *(CEO)*
Malcolm Musgrove *(VP-Children's Svcs)*
Rich Yanoski *(VP-Bus Dev)*

NHS MANAGEMENT, LLC.
931 Fairfax Park, Tuscaloosa, AL 35406
Tel.: (205) 391-3600
Web Site: http://www.nhsmanagement.com
Year Founded: 1981
Sales Range: $250-299.9 Million
Emp.: 5,000
Intermediation Services
N.A.I.C.S.: 523910
Keith Benton *(Controller)*
Frederick Huff *(Office Mgr)*
J. Norman Estes *(Pres)*
Claude Lee *(VP-Fin)*

NI WELDING SUPPLY, L.L.C.
1315 Hwy 90 E, New Iberia, LA 70560
Tel.: (337) 364-5747
Year Founded: 1984
Rev.: $39,804,477
Emp.: 55
Welding Equipment & Services
N.A.I.C.S.: 333992
Bobby Templet *(Pres)*
Chickley Thibodeaux *(Gen Mgr)*

NIAGARA CONSERVATION CORPORATION
45 Horsehill Rd Hanover Technical Center Ste 102, Cedar Knolls, NJ 07927
Tel.: (973) 829-0800 NJ
Web Site: http://www.niagaraconservation.com
Year Founded: 1977
Rev.: $62,600,000
Emp.: 72
Industrial Machinery & Equipment Merchant Whslr
N.A.I.C.S.: 423830
William Cutler *(Founder & Pres)*

NIAGARA CUTTER, INC.
200 John James Audubon Pkwy, Amherst, NY 14228-1120
Tel.: (716) 689-8400 NY
Web Site: http://www.niagaracutter.com
Year Founded: 1954
Sales Range: $100-124.9 Million
Emp.: 240
Mfr of Metal Cutting Tools
N.A.I.C.S.: 333515
Sherwood Bollier *(Pres)*
Jerry Covert *(Mgr-ITS Dept)*
Mark Slimko *(Controller)*

NIAGARA FALLS MEMORIAL MEDICAL CENTER
621 10th St, Niagara Falls, NY 14302
Tel.: (716) 278-4000 NY
Web Site: http://www.nfmmc.org
Year Founded: 1895
Sales Range: $75-99.9 Million
Emp.: 1,075
Health Care Srvices
N.A.I.C.S.: 622110
Raj Mehta *(CFO)*
Sanjay Chadha *(Sr VP-Svc Line Ops)*
Sheila K. Kee *(COO & VP)*

Julie Zito Clark *(Dir-Mktg, Specials Events & Projects)*
Cheryl Quarantello *(Dir-Health Info Mgmt)*
Judy Krupa *(Mgr-Emergency Dept Care Transitions)*
Jacquelyn Bixler *(Dir-HR)*
Peggy Grandinetti *(VP-Info Sys & Tech)*
Joseph A. Ruffolo *(Pres & CEO)*
JoAnn Pellegrino *(Chief Nursing Officer & VP)*
Vijay Bojedla *(Chief Medical Officer & VP)*
Vicki Landes *(VP-Foundation & Community Rels)*
Judith Nolan Powell *(VP-Foundation & Community Rels)*
Ankush Chander *(Asst Dir-Medical Laboratories)*

NIAGARA FRONTIER TRANSPORTATION AUTHORITY
181 Ellicott St, Buffalo, NY 14203
Tel.: (716) 855-7300
Web Site: http://www.nfta.com
Year Founded: 1967
Sales Range: $350-399.9 Million
Emp.: 1,300
Transportation Administration Services
N.A.I.C.S.: 926120
Patrick Dalton *(Dir-Internal Auditing & Corp Compliance)*
William Vanecek *(Dir-Aviation)*
John Cox *(CFO)*
Helen Tederous *(Dir-Pub Affairs)*
Steven Duquette *(CIO)*
Kimberley A. Minkel *(Pres & Exec Dir)*
David J. State *(Gen Counsel)*

Subsidiaries:

Niagara Frontier Transit & Metro System (1)
181 Ellicott St, Buffalo, NY 14203-2221
Tel.: (716) 855-7300
Web Site: http://www.nfta.com
Sales Range: $100-124.9 Million
Emp.: 1,100
Transportation
N.A.I.C.S.: 485113
Karen Novo *(Dir-HR)*
James Jones *(Supvr-Vehicle Maintenance)*
Michael Bykowski *(Dir-Engrg)*
Timothy P. Carvana *(Dir-HSEQ)*
John Cox *(CFO)*
Patrick Dalton *(Dir-Internal Audit & Corp Compliance)*
C. Douglas Hartmayer *(Dir-Pub Affairs)*
Kimberley A. Minkel *(Exec Dir)*
John A. Oborn *(CIO)*
Linda Seay *(Dir-Diversity Dev & EEO)*
David J. State *(Gen Counsel)*
William Vanecek *(Dir-Aviation)*

NIAGARA TRANSFORMER CORP.
1747 Dale Rd, Buffalo, NY 14225
Tel.: (716) 896-6500
Web Site: http://www.niagaratransformer.com
Year Founded: 1938
Sales Range: $75-99.9 Million
Emp.: 100
Power, Lighting & Distribution Transformers Mfr
N.A.I.C.S.: 335311
John F. Darby *(Pres)*
William Hanavan *(Mgr-Indus Sls)*
Sheldon P. Kennedy *(VP-Engrg)*
William L. Mangum *(Mgr-Sls Utility)*

NIANTIC, INC.
2 Bryant Ste 220, San Francisco, CA 94105
Tel.: (415) 570-8871
Web Site: http://www.nianticlabs.com

Year Founded: 2011
Augmented Reality Game Designer & Developer
N.A.I.C.S.: 513210
John Hanke *(Founder & CEO)*
Megan Quinn *(COO)*

NIBBI BROTHERS
1433 17th St, San Francisco, CA 94107-2400
Tel.: (415) 863-1820
Web Site: http://www.nibbi.com
Sales Range: $100-124.9 Million
Emp.: 150
Residential Construction Services
N.A.I.C.S.: 236118
Larry Nibbi *(Owner)*

NIBCO INC.
1516 Middlebury St, Elkhart, IN 46516-1167
Tel.: (574) 295-3000 IN
Web Site: http://www.nibco.com
Year Founded: 1904
Sales Range: $400-449.9 Million
Emp.: 2,788
Plumbing Fittings & Valves Mfr
N.A.I.C.S.: 332919
Rex R. Martin *(Chm)*
Alice A. Martin *(Vice Chm & Chief Revenue Officer)*
Steven Malm *(Pres & CEO)*
David Goodling *(Sr VP-Supply Chain)*
Cody Huffines *(CIO & VP)*
Chris Mason *(VP-Supply Chain Svcs)*
Todd A. Nowicki *(VP-Supply Chain Svcs)*

Subsidiaries:

Matco-Norca, LLC (1)
1944 Route 22, Brewster, NY 10509
Tel.: (845) 278-7570
Web Site: http://www.matco-norca.com
Sales Range: $10-24.9 Million
Emp.: 75
Plumbing Fixtures, Equipment, Supplies, Valves & Fittings Distr
N.A.I.C.S.: 423720
Russell Stern *(Chm)*
Lynn McVay *(Pres)*
John Grasso *(VP-Ops)*

NIBCO Inc. - Lebanon Plant (1)
2800 Henkle Dr, Lebanon, OH 45036
Tel.: (513) 933-9929
Web Site: http://www.nibco.com
Plastics Plumbing Fixture Mfr
N.A.I.C.S.: 326191
Ashley Martin *(Gen Mgr)*

NIBCO Sp. z o.o. (1)
ul Polskich Kolei Panstwowych 6, 92-402, Lodz, Poland
Tel.: (48) 42 677 56 00
Sales Range: $10-24.9 Million
Emp.: 30
Valve & Fitting Mfr & Distr
N.A.I.C.S.: 332919

NIBLOCK DEVELOPMENT CORP.
300 McGill Ave NW, Concord, NC 28027-6150
Tel.: (704) 788-4818 NC
Web Site: http://www.niblockhomes.com
Year Founded: 1974
Sales Range: $10-24.9 Million
Emp.: 35
Single-Family Housing Construction
N.A.I.C.S.: 236115
Mark Michaud *(CFO)*
Mark Niblock *(VP)*
William Niblock *(Pres)*

NIBLOCK EXCAVATING INC.
906 Maple St, Bristol, IN 46507
Tel.: (574) 848-4437
Rev.: $18,100,000
Emp.: 96

Asphalt & Asphaltic Paving Mixtures (Not From Refineries)
N.A.I.C.S.: 324121
Gary Niblock *(Pres)*
Marcus King *(Project Mgr)*

NIC GLOBAL MANUFACTURING SOLUTIONS, INC.
23518 63rd Ave SE, Woodinville, WA 98072
Tel.: (425) 489-4300
Web Site: http://www.nicmfg.com
Rev.: $31,000,000
Emp.: 500
Sheet Metal Fabrication & Assembly Services
N.A.I.C.S.: 238390
Garth Troyer *(Mgr-Sls-Gallatin)*
Greg Raymer *(Dir-Materials-Midwest Div)*
Troy Wood *(VP-Midwest Div)*
Bridget Brewer *(Pres)*

NIC HOLDING CORPORATION
225 Broad Hollow Rd, Melville, NY 11747-0398
Tel.: (631) 293-4700
Web Site: http://www.northville.com
Sales Range: $75-99.9 Million
Emp.: 90
Petroleum Services
N.A.I.C.S.: 424710

Subsidiaries:

Northville Natural Gas, LLC   (1)
25 Melville Park Rd, Melville, NY 11747-0398
Tel.: (631) 293-4700
Web Site: http://www.northvillenaturalgas.com
Natural Gas Distribution Services
N.A.I.C.S.: 221210

NICE SHOES, LLC
352 Park Ave S 16th Fl, New York, NY 10010
Tel.: (212) 683-1704
Web Site: http://www.niceshoes.com
Year Founded: 1996
Rev.: $1,400,000
Emp.: 13
Fiscal Year-end: 12/31/06
Video Post Production
N.A.I.C.S.: 512110
Dominic Pandolfino *(CEO)*
Mike Donovan *(Head-Production)*
Travis Taylor *(VP-Sls & Mktg)*
Lucien Yang *(Dir-Art)*
Lenny Mastrandrea *(Head-Color)*

NICE-PAK PRODUCTS, INC.
2 Nice Pak Pk, Orangeburg, NY 10962-1317
Tel.: (845) 365-1700   NY
Web Site: http://www.nicepak.com
Year Founded: 1957
Sales Range: $400-449.9 Million
Emp.: 1,000
Folded Moist Towelettes; Contract Packagers of Unit Packets to the Drug, Cosmetic & Pharmaceutical Industry
N.A.I.C.S.: 322120
Dawn Rubel *(VP-Quality)*
Shawn Smith *(Gen Counsel & Exec VP)*

Subsidiaries:

Nice Pak International Ltd.   (1)
Aber Park, Flint, CH6 5EX, United Kingdom
Tel.: (44) 1352 736 700
Web Site: http://www.nice-pak.co.uk
Sales Range: $25-49.9 Million
Emp.: 500
Wet Wipe Mfr & Distr
N.A.I.C.S.: 322291

Professional Disposables International, Inc.   (1)
400 Chestnut Rdg Rd, Woodcliff Lake, NJ 07677
Web Site: http://www.wearepdi.com
Sales Range: $75-99.9 Million
Sanitary Paper Product Mfr
N.A.I.C.S.: 322291
Robert P. Julius *(Founder & Chm)*
Esperanza Carrion *(VP & Gen Mgr-Sani Pro)*
Zachary T. Julius *(CEO)*
Kent Davies *(Pres & COO)*
Sean Gallimore *(Sr VP & Gen Mgr-PDI Healthcare)*
Shawn Smith *(Chief Compliance Officer, Gen Counsel & Exec VP)*
Jonathan Kupperman *(Exec VP-Dev-Global)*
Mariano Balaguer *(CFO)*
David Eberson *(Chief HR Officer)*
Tony Cerasuolo *(Sr VP-Fin)*
Keyne Monson *(Chief Comml Officer)*
Firas Abulaban *(VP-Quality)*

NICHE RETAIL, LLC
2240 Greer Blvd, Sylvan Lake, MI 48320
Tel.: (248) 738-6200
Year Founded: 2001
Rev.: $11,600,000
Emp.: 37
Retail Operations
N.A.I.C.S.: 459999
Chris Frye *(Mgr-Wholesale)*

NICHOLAS CONSOLIDATED INC.
10779 N Milgard Way, Surprise, AZ 85379
Tel.: (602) 269-6994
Web Site: http://www.canyonpipe.com
Rev.: $23,800,000
Emp.: 50
Air Conditioning Equipment
N.A.I.C.S.: 423730
Ed Condrat *(Controller)*

Subsidiaries:

Canyon Pipe & Supply, Inc.   (1)
10779 N Solar Canyon Way, Surprise, AZ 85379
Tel.: (623) 544-5200
Web Site: http://www.canyonpipe.com
Plumbing Product Mfr & Distr
N.A.I.C.S.: 332999
Mike Lengyel *(Gen Mgr)*
Sherri McKinstray *(Mgr-Acctg)*

NICHOLAS HOMES INC.
15990 N Green Way Hayden Loop Ste 600, Scottsdale, AZ 85260
Tel.: (480) 860-2500
Rev.: $125,000,000
Emp.: 100
Provider of Carpentry Services
N.A.I.C.S.: 238130
Michael G. Nicholas *(Pres)*
Harry Griffith *(CFO & Controller)*

NICHOLAS MARKETS INC.
195 Brownton Rd, Haledon, NJ 07508-1553
Tel.: (973) 595-5080
Web Site: http://nicholasmarkets.com
Year Founded: 1943
Sales Range: $50-74.9 Million
Emp.: 425
Grocery Stores
N.A.I.C.S.: 445110
Patricia O'Shea *(Controller)*
Robert Greenway *(Dir-Store)*

NICHOLS AGRISERVICE, LLC.
1783 Davis Ave, Nichols, IA 52766
Tel.: (319) 723-4221
Web Site: http://www.nicholsag.com
Sales Range: $10-24.9 Million
Emp.: 32
Grain & Field Bean Merchant Whslr

N.A.I.C.S.: 424510
Josh Otoole *(Owner)*
Jamie Phillips *(Office Mgr)*

NICHOLS BROSCH WURTE WOLFE & ASSOCIATES, INC.
161 Almeria Ave, Coral Gables, FL 33134
Tel.: (305) 443-5206   FL
Web Site: http://www.nbww.com
Year Founded: 1968
Sales Range: $1-9.9 Million
Emp.: 60
Architectural Services
N.A.I.C.S.: 541310
Bruce F. Brosch *(Pres)*
John R. Nichols *(CEO)*
James P. Wurst *(VP)*
Donald F. Wolfe *(VP)*

NICHOLS BROTHERS BOAT BUILDERS
5400 S Cameron Rd, Freeland, WA 98249
Tel.: (360) 331-5500
Web Site: http://www.nicholsboats.com
Year Founded: 1964
Sales Range: $10-24.9 Million
Emp.: 150
Commercial Cargo Ships, Building & Repairing
N.A.I.C.S.: 336611
Charlotte Whitaker *(Office Mgr)*
Gavin Higgins *(CEO)*

NICHOLS MOTORCYCLE SUPPLY INC.
4141 W 126th St, Chicago, IL 60803
Tel.: (708) 597-3340
Web Site: http://www.nicholsmotorcycle.com
Sales Range: $10-24.9 Million
Emp.: 50
Motorcycle Parts
N.A.I.C.S.: 423120

NICHOLS TEAM, INC.
75 Highpower Rd, Rochester, NY 14623
Tel.: (585) 427-9480
Web Site: http://www.nicholsteam.com
Year Founded: 1983
Sales Range: $10-24.9 Million
Emp.: 25
Provider of Land Subdivider & Developer Services
N.A.I.C.S.: 236210
John Nichols *(Founder, Pres, CEO & Partner)*
J. Barclay Carpenter *(CFO & VP-Fin)*
Jim Burm *(Partner & VP-Project Mgmt)*
Ric Carley *(Partner, COO &, Officer-Team Safety)*
Clay Carpenter *(Partner & CFO)*
John Nichols *(Founder, Pres, CEO & Partner)*

NICHOLSON & HALL CORPORATION
41 Columbia St, Buffalo, NY 14204
Tel.: (716) 854-8100   NY
Web Site: http://www.nicholson-hall.com
Year Founded: 1988
Sales Range: $10-24.9 Million
Emp.: 200
Insulation Of Pipes & Boilers
N.A.I.C.S.: 238990
Michael Madia *(Pres)*
Don Mason *(VP)*
Donald Mason *(VP)*
Russel Ward *(Treas)*
William Cole *(Project Mgr)*

NICHOLSON INDUSTRIES INC.
200 S Orcas St, Seattle, WA 98108
Tel.: (206) 682-2752
Web Site: http://www.nicholsonmanufacturing.com
Rev.: $10,900,000
Emp.: 160
Sawmill & Woodworking Machinery Mfr
N.A.I.C.S.: 333243
Scott Howell *(CEO)*

NICK CHEVROLET & PONTIAC
22 W 7th Ave, Tarentum, PA 15084
Tel.: (724) 224-2700
Web Site: http://www.nickchevrolet.com
Year Founded: 1955
Sales Range: $10-24.9 Million
Emp.: 51
Car Whslr
N.A.I.C.S.: 441110
John Petrishen *(Principal)*

NICK CORSELLO CHEVROLET INC.
500 Lincoln Ave, Bellevue, PA 15202
Tel.: (412) 734-5000
Web Site: http://www.pittsburghchevrolet.net
Year Founded: 1952
Sales Range: $10-24.9 Million
Emp.: 50
Car Dealership
N.A.I.C.S.: 441110
Lee V. Corsello *(Pres & CEO)*

NICK MAYER LINCOLN-MERCURY, INC.
24400 Center Ridge Rd, Westlake, OH 44145
Tel.: (440) 835-3700
Web Site: http://www.nickmayer.com
Sales Range: $10-24.9 Million
Emp.: 40
New Car Dealers
N.A.I.C.S.: 441110
Dale Kieffer *(Mgr-Svc)*
Chad Mayer *(Gen Mgr)*

NICK NICHOLAS FORD, INC.
2901 Hwy 44 W, Inverness, FL 34453
Tel.: (352) 726-1231
Web Site: http://www.nicknicholasford.com
Sales Range: $25-49.9 Million
Emp.: 70
Car Whslr
N.A.I.C.S.: 441110
Shane T. Bryant *(Sec)*
Dora F. Hunt *(CFO)*
Lynda Nicholas *(Dir-Ops)*
Nick Nicholas *(Pres)*

NICK STRIMBU INC.
3500 Pkwy Dr, Brookfield, OH 44403
Tel.: (330) 448-4071
Web Site: http://www.nickstrimbu.com
Sales Range: $10-24.9 Million
Emp.: 130
Trucking Except Local
N.A.I.C.S.: 484121
William J. Strimbu *(Pres)*
Thomas L. Nesbit *(VP-Ops)*
Goerge Siefert *(Dir-HR)*

NICKEL CARS OF ABILENE, INC.
3906 Brooks St, Missoula, MT 59804
Tel.: (406) 251-5904
Sales Range: $10-24.9 Million
Emp.: 20
Used Car Whslr
N.A.I.C.S.: 441120

Nickel Cars of Abilene, Inc.—(Continued)

Milton Nickel (Principal)

NICKELS & DIMES INC.
1844 N Preston Rd, Celina, TX 75009
Tel.: (972) 939-4200
Web Site: http://www.tilt.com
Rev.: $35,200,000
Emp.: 250
Video Game Arcade
N.A.I.C.S.: 713120
Ron Kostelny (Pres)
Kevin Jordan (Sr VP-Ops)
Shirley Ballard (Dir-Lease Admin)

NICKERSON BUSINESS SYSTEMS, INC.
2525 Drane Field Rd Ste 10, Lakeland, FL 33811
Tel.: (863) 644-1120
Web Site: http://www.pt-solutions.com
Year Founded: 1988
Sales Range: $1-9.9 Million
Emp.: 20
Computer & Office Machine Repair, Maintenance & Distribution
N.A.I.C.S.: 811210
Connie Nickerson (Pres & CEO)
Anthony Burts (Mgr-Learning Center)
Rodney Nickerson (VP)

NICKERSON LUMBER COMPANY
15 Main St, Orleans, MA 02653-2442
Tel.: (508) 255-0200 MA
Web Site: http://www.midcape.net
Year Founded: 1895
Sales Range: $100-124.9 Million
Emp.: 250
Sawmill Products, Structural Lumber, Prefabricated Homes, Kitchen & Bath Appliances Sales
N.A.I.C.S.: 423310
Joshua A. Nickerson (Chm)

NICKLAS SUPPLY INC.
1237 Freedom Rd, Cranberry Township, PA 16066
Tel.: (724) 772-5700
Web Site: http://www.nicklassupply.com
Sales Range: $10-24.9 Million
Emp.: 25
Plumbing & Hydronic Heating Supplies
N.A.I.C.S.: 423720
Mark Nicklas (VP)

NICKLAUS COMPANIES, LLC
11780 US Hwy 1 Ste 500, North Palm Beach, FL 33408
Tel.: (561) 227-0300 DE
Web Site: http://www.nicklaus.com
Year Founded: 2007
Holding Company; Golf Course Designer; Golf Clubs & Accessories Mfr & Whslr
N.A.I.C.S.: 551112
Jack William Nicklaus (Founder)
Howard Milstein (Chm)
John Reese (CEO)
Jack W. Nicklaus II (Pres-Nicklaus Design)
Subsidiaries:

Nicklaus Design, LLC (1)
11780 US Hwy 1 Ste 500, North Palm Beach, FL 33408
Tel.: (561) 227-0300
Web Site: http://www.nicklaus.com
Sales Range: $10-24.9 Million
Emp.: 50
Golf Course Designer
N.A.I.C.S.: 541320

Paul Stringer (VP)
Nicklaus Golf Equipment Company, L.C. (1)
11780 US Hwy 1 Ste 500, North Palm Beach, FL 33408-3336
Tel.: (561) 881-7981
Web Site: http://www.nicklausgolf.com
Sales Range: $25-49.9 Million
Emp.: 25
Golf Clubs & Related Accessories Mfr, Whslr & Online Retailer
N.A.I.C.S.: 339920
Jack William Nicklaus (Founder & Chm)

NICKLAUS OF FLORIDA, INC.
5300 Gulf Blvd, Saint Pete Beach, FL 33706
Tel.: (727) 363-5100 FL
Web Site: http://www.sirata.com
Year Founded: 1962
Sales Range: $10-24.9 Million
Emp.: 300
Hotels Owner & Operator
N.A.I.C.S.: 721110
Deborah Nicklaus (Owner)
Gregg Nicklaus (Pres)
Tim Coultas (Gen Mgr)

NICOLAS VILLALBA WHOLESALERS
3435 Northwest 60th St, Miami, FL 33055
Tel.: (305) 638-4550
Web Site: http://www.northandsouthwholesalers.com
Year Founded: 1993
Sales Range: $10-24.9 Million
Emp.: 55
Wholesale Distributor of Pharmaceuticals
N.A.I.C.S.: 424210
Nicolas Villalba (Pres)

NICOLAZZO & ASSOCIATES INC.
101 Federal St Ste 710, Boston, MA 02110
Tel.: (617) 951-0000 MA
Web Site: http://www.nicolazzo.com
Year Founded: 1975
Sales Range: $1-9.9 Million
Emp.: 4
Public Relations Agency
N.A.I.C.S.: 541820
Richard E. Nicolazzo (Mng Partner)
Joseph M. Grillo (Partner)

NICOLET CAPITAL PARTNERS, LLC
1603 Orrington Ave Ste 815, Evanston, IL 60201
Tel.: (847) 563-5377
Web Site: http://www.nicoletcap.com
Privater Equity Firm
N.A.I.C.S.: 523999
Brett A. Snyder (Pres)
Subsidiaries:

InterFlex Acquisition Company, LLC (1)
3200 N Carolina Hwy 268 W, Wilkesboro, NC 28697
Tel.: (336) 921-3505
Web Site: http://www.interflexgroup.com
Sales Range: $25-49.9 Million
Emp.: 1,500
Provider of Commercial Printing; Lithographic
N.A.I.C.S.: 323111
Monica Murray (VP-IT & Sys)

Subsidiary (Domestic):

Star Packaging Corp. (2)
453 Eighty Five Cir, College Park, GA 30349
Tel.: (404) 763-2800

Sales Range: $10-24.9 Million
Emp.: 100
Plastic & Laminated Bags Mfr
N.A.I.C.S.: 326111
Brian Votaw (Mgr-Sls & Bus Dev)

Transilwrap Company, Inc. (1)
9201 W Belmont Ave, Franklin Park, IL 60131
Tel.: (847) 678-1800
Web Site: http://www.transilwrap.com
Sales Range: $75-99.9 Million
Emp.: 500
Mfr, Coater & Converter of Plastics in Lamination, Print, Packaging & Industrial Markets
N.A.I.C.S.: 326113
Andy J. Brewer (Pres & CEO)

Subsidiary (Domestic):

Interfilm Holdings Inc. (2)
127 Turningstone Ct, Greenville, SC 29611
Tel.: (864) 269-4690
Web Site: http://www.interfilm-usa.com
Sales Range: $25-49.9 Million
Emp.: 150
Unsupported Plastics Film & Sheet
N.A.I.C.S.: 326113
Dan Ezelle (Acct Mgr-Southeast Reg)
Rod Nelson (Acct Mgr-South Midwest Reg)
Mark Shoban (Acct Mgr-Southwest Reg)
Paul Sweeney (Acct Mgr-Northwest Reg)

Division (Domestic):

Brushfoil (3)
1 Shoreline Dr Ste 6, Guilford, CT 06437
Tel.: (203) 453-7403
Web Site: http://www.brushfoil.com
Mfr of Graphic Brushed Label Facestocks, Laminating Films & Paper Stocks
N.A.I.C.S.: 322220
Jeff Freaney (Supvr-Production)

Division (Domestic):

Transilwrap Company, Inc. (2)
9000 9th St Ste 140, Rancho Cucamonga, CA 91730 (100%)
Tel.: (909) 944-9981
Web Site: http://www.transilwrap.com
Sales Range: $25-49.9 Million
Emp.: 29
Plastics & Film Sheets Mfr
N.A.I.C.S.: 424610
Ever Garcia (Plant Mgr)

Plant (Domestic):

Transilwrap Company, Inc. - Hebron Plant (2)
3700 Hebron Rd, Hebron, OH 43025
Tel.: (740) 929-5100
Emp.: 105
Polystyrene & Cast Co-Extruded Plastic Materials Mfr
N.A.I.C.S.: 326113

Division (Domestic):

Transilwrap Company, Inc. - Lamination/ID Securities Division (2)
9201 W Belmont Ave, Franklin Park, IL 60131-2842 (100%)
Tel.: (847) 678-1800
Web Site: http://www.transilwrap.com
Sales Range: $25-49.9 Million
Emp.: 125
Plastics & Film Sheets Mfr
N.A.I.C.S.: 326113

Transilwrap Company, Inc. - Northeast Division (2)
14 N Commerce Way, Bethlehem, PA 18017-8614 (100%)
Tel.: (610) 954-9999
Web Site: http://www.transilwrap.com
Sales Range: $25-49.9 Million
Emp.: 26
Plastics & Film Sheets Mfr
N.A.I.C.S.: 326113
Richard Rushatz (Plant Mgr)

Transilwrap Company, Inc. - Printable Plastics Division (2)
22889 Lunn Rd, Strongsville, OH 44149 (100%)
Tel.: (440) 638-2000
Web Site: http://www.transilwrap.com

Sales Range: $25-49.9 Million
Emp.: 100
Plastics & Film Sheets Mfr
N.A.I.C.S.: 326113

Transilwrap Company, Inc. - Specialty & Industrial Films Division (2)
1420 Valwood Pkwy Ste 200, Dallas, TX 75006-6892
Tel.: (972) 484-3211
Web Site: http://www.transilwrap.com
Sales Range: $25-49.9 Million
Emp.: 60
Plastics & Film Sheets Mfr
N.A.I.C.S.: 326113

NICOLET PLASTICS, INC.
16685 State Rd 32, Mountain, WI 54149
Tel.: (715) 276-4200 WI
Web Site: http://www.nicoletplastics.com
Year Founded: 1986
Sales Range: $1-9.9 Million
Emp.: 90
Plastics Components for OEMs Mfr
N.A.I.C.S.: 326199
Robert MacIntosh (Chm)
Bob Gafvert (Mgr-Bus Dev)
John Ogorek (Pres & CEO)
JoAnn Esser (Sr Acct Mgr)
Doug Baril (VP-Engrg)

NICOLIA READY-MIX INC.
36 Kroemer Ave, Riverhead, NY 11901
Tel.: (631) 669-7000
Web Site: http://www.nicoliareadymix.com
Rev.: $13,346,708
Emp.: 50
Ready-Mixed Concrete Products
N.A.I.C.S.: 238110
Michael R. Fletcher (Gen Mgr-Sls)

NICOLLET CATTLE COMPANY, INC.
3348 Sherman Ct Ste 103, Saint Paul, MN 55121
Tel.: (651) 209-6770
Sales Range: $200-249.9 Million
Emp.: 4
Meat Packing Services
N.A.I.C.S.: 311611
Gary Goldberger (Pres & CEO)
Larry Aust (Mgr-Sls)
Jay Goldberger (VP)
Paul Thoemke (Controller)

NIECO EQUIPMENT CORPORATION
7950 Cameron Dr, Windsor, CA 95492
Tel.: (707) 284-7100 CA
Web Site: http://www.nieco.com
Sales Range: $50-74.9 Million
Emp.: 70
Mfr of Commercial Broilers for Restaurants & Fast Food Chains
N.A.I.C.S.: 333310
Debbie Losgren (Controller)

NIEDERAUER INC.
1976 W San Carlos St, San Jose, CA 95128
Tel.: (408) 297-2440
Web Site: http://www.westernappliance.com
Rev.: $19,000,000
Emp.: 50
Electric Household Appliances
N.A.I.C.S.: 449210
Phil Zimmerman (Controller)

NIEHAUS COMPANIES INC.
1422 E Elkhorn Rd, Vincennes, IN 47591
Tel.: (812) 886-4412 IN

Web Site: http://www.niehausinc.com
Year Founded: 1933
Sales Range: $10-24.9 Million
Emp.: 30
Kitchen & Bath Design Services & Rental Home Centers
N.A.I.C.S.: 423310
David Niehaus *(VP-Sls)*

NIELLO VOLVO OF SACRAMENTO
4609 Madison Ave, Sacramento, CA 95841
Tel.: (916) 488-2400
Web Site: http://volvo.niello.com
New Car Dealers
N.A.I.C.S.: 441110
Kathie Jordan *(Office Mgr)*
Roger Martin *(Mgr-Parts)*
Keith Fradenburg *(Gen Mgr)*
Reza Farid *(Mgr-Used Car)*
Ken Hernandez *(Mgr-Svc)*
T. J. Upton *(Sls Mgr)*
Jamie Reynolds *(Fin Mgr)*

NIELSEN BROTHERS, INC.
100 Pine St Ste 301, Bellingham, WA 98225
Tel.: (360) 671-9078
Web Site:
  http://www.nielsenbrothers.net
Year Founded: 1990
Sales Range: $10-24.9 Million
Emp.: 65
Lumber, Plywood, Millwork & Wood Panel Whslr
N.A.I.C.S.: 423310
Robert Nielsen *(Pres)*
Bill Foulds *(Gen Mgr)*
Tom Jessup *(Controller)*

NIELSEN KELLERMAN INC.
21 Creek Cir, Boothwyn, PA 19061
Tel.: (610) 447-1555
Web Site: http://www.nkhome.com
Sales Range: $10-24.9 Million
Emp.: 80
Waterproof Electronic Equipment Mfr
N.A.I.C.S.: 334419
Ben Churchill *(Mgr-Sls)*
Katie Godfrey *(Sr Acct Exec-Global)*
Michael Naughton *(VP-Bus Dev)*
Paula Whittaker *(Dir-HR)*
Doris Ward *(Mgr-Matls)*
Tim Godrey *(Mgr-Facilities)*
Tim Phelps *(Mgr-Production)*
Alix James *(CEO)*
Brad Griste *(Controller)*
Nils Steffenson *(Dir-Engrg)*
Carrie Capili *(Dir-Mktg, Branding & ECommerce)*
Chuck Arkell *(Dir-Sls)*
Madeline Delaney *(Product Mgr)*
Austin Wilcox *(Product Mgr)*

NIELSON & COMPANY INCORPORATED
8000 Governors Sq Blvd Ste 101, Miami Lakes, FL 33016
Tel.: (305) 722-2663
Web Site:
  http://www.nielsonbonds.com
Rev.: $10,200,000
Emp.: 37
Direct Property & Casualty Insurance Carriers
N.A.I.C.S.: 524126
Olga Neilson *(VP)*
Charles J. Nielson *(Pres & Treas)*
David Hoover *(COO)*

NIELSON CONSTRUCTION
825 N Loop Rd, Huntington, UT 84528
Tel.: (435) 687-2494

Web Site:
  http://www.nielsonconstruction.com
Sales Range: $25-49.9 Million
Emp.: 280
Highway & Street Construction Services
N.A.I.C.S.: 237310
Wayne L. Nielson *(Pres)*

NIEMANN FOODS INC.
1501 N 12th St, Quincy, IL 62301
Tel.: (217) 221-5600   DE
Web Site:
  http://www.mycountymarket.com
Year Founded: 1917
Sales Range: $10-24.9 Million
Emp.: 75
Provider of Grocery Services
N.A.I.C.S.: 445110
Chris Niemann *(CFO & Exec VP)*
Jeff Miller *(Controller)*
Ron Cook *(VP & Dir-Mktg)*

NIGHT VISION ENTERTAINMENT
9944 S Santa Monica Blvd, Los Angeles, CA 90212
Tel.: (323) 512-8400
Web Site:
  http://www.NightVisionEnt.com
Year Founded: 2005
Sales Range: $1-9.9 Million
Emp.: 11
Marketing Company
N.A.I.C.S.: 541613
Brett Hyman *(Pres)*

NIGHTINGALE-CONANT CORPORATION
6245 W Howard St, Niles, IL 60714-3403   DE
Web Site: http://www.nightingale.com
Year Founded: 1960
Sales Range: $75-99.9 Million
Emp.: 145
Audio & Video Training; Self-Development Programs
N.A.I.C.S.: 611710
Vic Conant *(Chm)*
Gary Chappell *(CEO)*

Subsidiaries:

Nightingale-Conant Recording & Tape Duplicating Division   (1)
1400 S Wolf Rd Ste 103, Wheeling, IL 60090
Tel.: (847) 647-0300
Web Site: http://www.nightingale.com
Sales Range: $25-49.9 Million
Emp.: 70
Making Of CDs And Cassettes
N.A.I.C.S.: 512110
Vick Conant *(Chm)*

NIHAKI SYSTEMS, INC.
50 Cragwood Rd Ste 216, South Plainfield, NJ 07080
Tel.: (732) 438-1906
Web Site: http://www.nihaki.com
Year Founded: 1997
Sales Range: $10-24.9 Million
Emp.: 110
It Consulting
N.A.I.C.S.: 541511
Mahender Musuku *(Dir-Admin)*
Amar Musku *(Mgr-HR)*

NII HOLDINGS, INC.
12110 Sunset Hills Rd Ste 600, Reston, VA 20190
Tel.: (703) 390-5100   DE
Web Site: http://www.nii.com
Year Founded: 1995
Rev.: $620,697,000
Assets: $1,059,830,000
Liabilities: $1,241,399,000
Net Worth: ($181,569,000)

Earnings: ($143,080,000)
Emp.: 2,640
Fiscal Year-end: 12/31/18
Digital Wireless Communication Services
N.A.I.C.S.: 517112
Daniel E. Freiman *(Acting Principal Exec Officer, CFO & Sr VP)*
Timothy M. Mulieri *(VP & Controller)*

NIKA TECHNOLOGIES, INC.
2000 Tower Oaks Blvd 6th Fl, Rockville, MD 20852
Tel.: (301) 770-3520
Web Site:
  http://www.nikatechnologies.com
Year Founded: 1998
Sales Range: $25-49.9 Million
Emp.: 42
Engineering & Construction Management Services
N.A.I.C.S.: 541330
Kabir Chaudhary *(Pres & CEO)*
Usman Shakir *(CFO & Exec VP)*
Mark Smith *(Sr VP)*
Lorenza Peterson *(Sr VP-Facilities Ops Mgmt)*

NIKAIA, INC.
7962 Old Georgetown Rd 3C, Bethesda, MD 20814
Tel.: (301) 530-8170
Web Site: http://www.nikaia.com
Year Founded: 1998
Sales Range: Less than $1 Million
Emp.: 14
Importer & Distr of European Fashion Accessories for Women
N.A.I.C.S.: 424990
Nathalie Duncan *(Pres)*

NIKE COMMUNICATIONS, INC.
75 Broad St Ste 510, New York, NY 10004
Tel.: (212) 529-3400
Web Site: http://www.nikecomm.com
Year Founded: 1984
Sales Range: $10-24.9 Million
Emp.: 30
Public Relations Agency
N.A.I.C.S.: 541820
Nina Kaminer *(Pres)*
Stefanie Altman *(VP)*

NIKKEL & ASSOCIATES INC.
728 E Lincoln Way, Ames, IA 50010
Tel.: (515) 232-8606
Web Site: http://www.nai-ames.com
Year Founded: 1985
Rev.: $12,609,825
Emp.: 130
Contractor of Electrical Work: General Contractor
N.A.I.C.S.: 238210
Dennis Tiernan *(Pres)*

NIKSOFT SYSTEMS CORPORATION
1984 Isaac Newton Sq W Ste 306A, Reston, VA 20190
Tel.: (703) 435-2260
Web Site: http://www.niksoft.com
Year Founded: 1998
Sales Range: $10-24.9 Million
Emp.: 70
Custom Computer Programming Services
N.A.I.C.S.: 541511
Manesh Gupta *(Pres & CEO)*
Jon Cassady *(Dir-Contracts)*

NILES IRON & METAL CO. INC.
700 S Main St, Niles, OH 44446-1372
Tel.: (330) 652-2262   OH

Web Site: http://www.nilesiron.com
Year Founded: 1947
Sales Range: $25-49.9 Million
Emp.: 55
Scrap & Waste Materials
N.A.I.C.S.: 423930
Gary Clayman *(Pres)*
Michael Clayman *(VP)*

NILODOR, INC.
10966 Industrial Pkwy NW, Bolivar, OH 44612-8991
Tel.: (330) 874-1017   OH
Web Site: http://www.nilodor.com
Year Founded: 1954
Sales Range: $50-74.9 Million
Emp.: 30
Deodorizers & Cleaners; Carpet Care Services
N.A.I.C.S.: 325612
Les W. Mitson *(Pres)*
Kurt Peterson *(VP-Sls)*
Todd Sauser *(Dir-Mktg)*

NILOY INC.
5875 Peachtree Indus Blvd Ste 340, Norcross, GA 30092
Tel.: (770) 734-4311
Web Site: http://www.dctsystems.net
Sales Range: $25-49.9 Million
Emp.: 95
Computers, Software & Hardware Services
N.A.I.C.S.: 423430
Chuck Thakkar *(Pres)*

NILSEN FEED & GRAIN COMPANY
502 Broadway St, Eureka, CA 95501
Tel.: (707) 442-3741
Web Site:
  http://www.nilsencompany.com
Sales Range: $10-24.9 Million
Emp.: 30
Farm Equipment Parts & Supplies
N.A.I.C.S.: 423820
Dennis A. Nilsen *(Pres)*

NILSON AND COMPANY INC.
5617 S 1475 E, Ogden, UT 84403
Tel.: (801) 392-8100
Web Site:
  http://www.nilsonhomes.com
Rev.: $14,000,000
Emp.: 40
Single-Family Houses New Construction
N.A.I.C.S.: 236115
Bruce L. Nilson *(Owner & CEO)*
David Lowry *(CFO)*

NILSON VAN & STORAGE INC.
6821 N Main St, Columbia, SC 29203
Tel.: (803) 786-1090
Web Site: http://www.nilsonvan.com
Sales Range: $10-24.9 Million
Emp.: 100
Household Goods Transport
N.A.I.C.S.: 484210
Phyllis Nilson *(Pres)*

NIMBUSNOW, LLC
601 Cleveland St Ste 501, Clearwater, FL 33755
Tel.: (727) 330-3200
Web Site: http://www.nimbusnow.com
Sales Range: $1-9.9 Million
Emp.: 35
IT Consulting & Software Solutions
N.A.I.C.S.: 541519
Jennifer Alonso *(CEO)*
Kathy Meriwether *(Controller)*

NIMITZ PARTNERS, INC. BEST WESTERN PLAZA HOTEL

Nimitz Partners, Inc. Best Western Plaza Hotel—(Continued)
3253 N Nimitz Hwy Ste 400, Honolulu, HI 96819
Tel.: (808) 836-3636
Sales Range: $10-24.9 Million
Emp.: 300
Hotel & Motel Operating Services
N.A.I.C.S.: 721110
Randy Ahlo (Gen Mgr)

NIMLOK COMPANY
111 Rawls Rd, Des Plaines, IL 60018
Tel.: (847) 647-1012
Web Site: http://www.nimlok.com
Sales Range: $10-24.9 Million
Emp.: 125
Displays & Cutouts Window & Lobby
N.A.I.C.S.: 339950
Gerald Perutz (Chm)
Simon Perutz (Pres)
Deborah Venable (Pres-Chicago)
Timothy Perutz (Sec)
Michael Benson (Gen Mgr-Chicago)

NIMNICHT CHEVROLET COMPANY
1550 Cassat Ave, Jacksonville, FL 32210
Tel.: (904) 387-4041
Web Site: http://www.nimnichtchevy.com
Sales Range: $75-99.9 Million
Emp.: 200
New & Used Car Dealers
N.A.I.C.S.: 441110
Scott Maier (Mgr-Svcs)
Billie Nugent Nimnicht III (Pres)

NINA FOOTWEAR CORP.
200 Park Ave S, New York, NY 10003
Tel.: (212) 399-2323
Web Site: http://www.ninashoes.com
Year Founded: 1955
Sales Range: $10-24.9 Million
Emp.: 100
Mfr of Footwear
N.A.I.C.S.: 424340
Alan Johnson (Pres)
Ezra Dabah (CEO)
Jason Yagoda (Chief Strategic Officer)
Stanley Silverstein I (Chm)

NINA MIA, INC.
826 Enterprise Way, Fullerton, CA 92831
Tel.: (714) 773-5588
Web Site: http://www.pastamia.com
Year Founded: 1984
Sales Range: $10-24.9 Million
Emp.: 100
Pasta Product Mfr
N.A.I.C.S.: 311991
Diego Mazza (Founder)
Robert Casella (CFO)

NINA PLASTICS, INC.
1903 Cypress Lake Dr, Orlando, FL 32837
Tel.: (407) 851-6620
Web Site: http://www.niaflex.com
Year Founded: 1979
Rev.: $31,800,000
Emp.: 121
World Wide Expansion & Uncompromising Service
N.A.I.C.S.: 315250

NINER BIKES
3904 Del Amo Blvd Ste 802, Torrance, CA 90503
Tel.: (877) 646-3792
Web Site: http://www.ninerbikes.com
Year Founded: 2005
Sales Range: $1-9.9 Million
Emp.: 30
Mfr & Sales of Mountain Bikes with 29-Inch Diameter Wheels Offering Greater Stability & Control
N.A.I.C.S.: 336991
Brett Rosenbauer (Mgr-Global Sls)
Thomas Connelly (CFO)
Chris Sugai (Owner & Pres)
Mike Gann (Pres)
Kenneth Gensel (VP-Fin)
Linda Travis (Mgr-Inside Sls)

NINFA'S HOLDINGS, L.P.
2704 Navigation Blvd, Houston, TX 77003
Tel.: (713) 228-1175
Web Site: http://www.ninfas.com
Year Founded: 1973
Rev.: $19,500,000
Emp.: 900
Eating Place
N.A.I.C.S.: 722511

NINJA JUMP INC.
3221 N San Fernando Rd, Los Angeles, CA 90065
Tel.: (323) 255-5418
Web Site: http://www.ninjajump.com
Year Founded: 1993
Sales Range: $1-9.9 Million
Emp.: 75
Children's Inflatable Jumping Rooms Mfr
N.A.I.C.S.: 339930
Rouben Gourchounian (Pres)

NINNESCAH RURAL ELECTRIC COOPERATIVE ASSOCIATION, INC.
20112 W Hwy 54, Pratt, KS 67124-0967
Tel.: (620) 672-5538
Web Site: http://www.ninnescah.com
Year Founded: 1939
Sales Range: $10-24.9 Million
Emp.: 17
Electric Power Distr
N.A.I.C.S.: 221122
Teresa Miller (Gen Mgr)
Paul W. Unruh (Sec)
Glen Honeman (Vice Chm)
Ronald R. Schultz (Chm)
Edwin D. Lenkner (Treas)

NINTH DISTRICT OPPORTUNITY, INC.
PO Drawer L, Gainesville, GA 30503
Tel.: (770) 532-3191
Web Site: http://www.ndo.org
Year Founded: 1967
Sales Range: $25-49.9 Million
Emp.: 751
Family Support Services
N.A.I.C.S.: 624190
Linda Highsmith (CFO)
Janice A. Riley (Exec Dir)
Karen Laws (Dir-Head Start)

NIP GROUP, INC.
900 Route 9 N Ste 503, Woodbridge, NJ 07095-1003
Tel.: (800) 446-7647
Web Site: http://www.nipgroup.com
Insurance & Risk Management Services
N.A.I.C.S.: 524210
Richard Augustyn (Founder & CEO)
David Springer (Pres)
Tracy A. Wehringer (CMO)
Anthony Mignone (CIO)
Conrad G. Cyriax (Gen Counsel)
Donna R. Jantzen (Pres-NIP Programs)
Dean Mortilla (Pres-Specialty Brokerage)
Lyn W. Winters (Pres-Conventus Inter-Insurance Exchange)
Jonathan Hall (Pres-NIP Mgmt Svcs)
John Bertoli (Sr VP-Mktg)
Maria Hurley (Sr VP-People)
Roseanne Laudisio (Chief Info Officer)
Lawrence J. Dunn III (CFO)

Subsidiaries:

Marquis Agency (1)
900 Route 9 N Ste 503, Woodbridge, NJ 07095
Tel.: (800) 272-6771
Web Site: http://www.marquisagency.com
Insurance Services
N.A.I.C.S.: 524210
Richard Augustyn (CEO)
Gregory DerAsadourian (Pres)
Keith Fitschen (VP)
Debra Christen (VP)
Lawrence J. Dunn III (CFO)

NIPPON INDUSTRIES, INC.
2430 S Watney Way, Fairfield, CA 94533-6730
Tel.: (707) 427-3127
Web Site: http://www.nipponindustries.com
Sales Range: $10-24.9 Million
Emp.: 31
Frozen Specialty Food Mfr
N.A.I.C.S.: 311412
Eric D. Wong (Pres)

NIRAM, INC.
4 E Frederick Pl, Cedar Knolls, NJ 07927
Tel.: (973) 299-4455
Web Site: http://www.niram.com
Sales Range: $10-24.9 Million
Emp.: 25
Civil Engineering Services
N.A.I.C.S.: 236220
Ana Monterlo (Mgr)
Chongtae Kim (Mgr)

NIRVANA, INC.
1 Nirvana Plz, Forestport, NY 13338
Tel.: (315) 942-4900
Web Site: http://www.nirvanawater.com
Year Founded: 1995
Sales Range: $25-49.9 Million
Emp.: 160
Natural Spring Water Mfr & Distr
N.A.I.C.S.: 312112
Mo Rafizadeh (VP)
Mansur Rafizadeh (VP)
Ed Wiehl (VP)
Michael Sciarra (Plant Mgr)

NIRVANIX, INC.
9191 Towne Center Dr Ste 500, San Diego, CA 92122
Tel.: (619) 764-5650
Web Site: http://www.nirvanix.com
Sales Range: $1-9.9 Million
Cloud Storage Services
N.A.I.C.S.: 513210
Debra Chrapaty (Chm & CEO)
Dru Borden (Sr VP-Products & Strategy)
Dave Barr (VP-Engrg)
Randall S. Hollis (VP-Ops)

NISA INVESTMENT ADVISORS LLC
150 N Meramec Ave Ste 640, Saint Louis, MO 63105
Tel.: (314) 721-1900
Web Site: http://www.nisaia.com
Sales Range: $25-49.9 Million
Emp.: 50
Management Investment, Open-End
N.A.I.C.S.: 525910
Jess B. Yawitz (Co-Founder & Chm)
William J. Marshall (Co-Founder)
Robert C. Krebs (Dir-Client Svcs & Defined Contribution Solutions)
Ken Lester (Mng Dir-Portfolio Mgmt)
Gregory J. Yess (COO & Mng Dir-Client Svcs)
Mark Fortier (Dir-Defined Contribution Product Design & Implementation)
Mark A. Folkins (Chief Admin Officer)
Marianne O'Doherty (Chief Compliance Officer)
David J. Kon (Chief Data Officer)
Matt D. Kaplan (Chief Risk Officer)
Bella L. F. Sanevich (Gen Counsel)
David G. Eichhorn (CEO)
Anthony R. Pope (Mng Dir-Portfolio Mgmt)

NISBET OIL COMPANY
1818 Baxter St, Charlotte, NC 28204
Tel.: (704) 332-7755
Web Site: http://www.nisbetoil.com
Rev.: $11,700,000
Emp.: 24
Diesel Fuel
N.A.I.C.S.: 424720
William S. Johns (CFO)
James J. White III (Chm)

NISSAN BONDESEN-HARDY INC.
950 N Tomoka Farms Rd, Daytona Beach, FL 32124
Tel.: (386) 255-2441
Web Site: http://www.daytonanissan.com
Sales Range: $10-24.9 Million
Emp.: 50
Car Dealership
N.A.I.C.S.: 441110
Gary Yeomans (VP)
Nancy Giverson (CFO)
Fred Smith (Gen Mgr-Sls)
Michael Shaw (Mgr-Svc)

NISSAN KIA WORLD
3057 Route 10, Denville, NJ 07834
Tel.: (973) 442-0500
Web Site: http://www.denvillenissan.com
Sales Range: $10-24.9 Million
Emp.: 40
Car Whslr
N.A.I.C.S.: 441110
Chris Preziosi (Pres)

NISSAN LYNNES CITY INC.
318 Bloomfield Ave, Bloomfield, NJ 07003
Tel.: (973) 743-2111
Web Site: http://www.lynnesnissan.com
Sales Range: $10-24.9 Million
Emp.: 35
Automobiles, New & Used
N.A.I.C.S.: 441110
Dominick Tozzo (Owner)
Julie Tozzo (VP)

NISSAN OF BAKERSFIELD
2800 Bacheco Rd, Bakersfield, CA 93313-2604
Tel.: (661) 835-8600
Web Site: http://www.nissanofbakersfield.com
Year Founded: 1997
Rev.: $47,700,000
Emp.: 128
New & Used Car Dealers
N.A.I.C.S.: 441110
Fernando Juarez (Mgr-Used Car)
Jeremy Watt (Mgr-Parts)

NISSAN OF BERGENFIELD INC.

318 S Washington Ave, Bergenfield, NJ 07621
Tel.: (201) 385-3600
Web Site:
http://www.nissanofbergenfield.com
Rev.: $30,000,000
Emp.: 17
New Car Dealers
N.A.I.C.S.: 441110
John Stefanidis *(Owner)*

NISSAN OF BOURNE
60 MacArthur Blvd, Bourne, MA 02532
Tel.: (508) 759-4400
Web Site:
http://www.nissanofbourne.com
Sales Range: $10-24.9 Million
Emp.: 35
New & Used Automobiles
N.A.I.C.S.: 441110
Tony Provost *(Owner)*
Laura Tormey *(Mgr-Fin)*
Chris Calverley *(Controller)*

NISSAN OF COOL SPRINGS LLC
212 Comtide Ct, Franklin, TN 37067
Tel.: (615) 790-2500   TN
Web Site:
http://www.nissanofcoolsprings.com
Year Founded: 1985
Sales Range: $25-49.9 Million
Emp.: 100
Car Dealership Owner & Operator
N.A.I.C.S.: 441110
Mack Allen *(Mgr-Fleet & Comml)*
Tom Murray *(Dir-Pre-Owned Sls)*
Craig St. Amour *(Mgr-Parts)*
Jason Stacy *(Owner & Exec Mgr)*
David Webb *(Asst Mgr-Parts)*
Jason Buckner *(Dir-Bus Dev)*
Rob King *(Dir-Fin)*
Garreth Collins *(Dir-Parts)*
Art Perry *(Mgr-Detail & Lot Porter)*
Marty Lang *(Mgr-Fin)*
Kyle Stewart *(Mgr-Internet Sls)*
Brad Davis *(Mgr-Parts-Columbus)*
Riley Groves *(Mgr-Sls)*
John Barbarotto *(Mgr-Wholesale Parts)*

NISSAN OF HAWTHORNE
1060 Goffle Rd, Hawthorne, NJ 07506
Tel.: (973) 427-0200
Web Site:
http://www.nissanofhawthorne.com
Sales Range: $25-49.9 Million
Emp.: 25
Automobiles, New & Used
N.A.I.C.S.: 441110
John Stefanidis *(Owner)*
Rosana Batista *(Mgr-BDC)*
Melvin Blount *(Mgr-Parts)*

NISSAN OF HUNTINGTON
850 E Jericho Tpke, Huntington Station, NY 11746
Tel.: (631) 439-7000
Web Site:
http://www.nissanofhuntington.com
Sales Range: $10-24.9 Million
Emp.: 88
Car Whslr
N.A.I.C.S.: 441110
Mark Farouq *(Gen Mgr)*

NISSAN OF MANHATTAN
662 11th Ave, New York, NY 10036
Tel.: (212) 459-1500
Web Site:
http://www.nissanofmanhattan.net
Automobiles, New & Used
N.A.I.C.S.: 441110

Bin Lou *(Mgr-Sls)*
Angelo Tranquellino *(Mgr-Sls)*
James Pang *(Mgr-Fin)*
Carmelo Giuffre *(Chm & Pres)*

NISSAN OF MELBOURNE
440 S Harbor City Blvd, Melbourne, FL 32901
Tel.: (321) 723-2941
Web Site:
http://www.nissanofmelbourne.com
Year Founded: 1991
Sales Range: $10-24.9 Million
Emp.: 50
Car Whslr
N.A.I.C.S.: 441110
Paul Fusillo *(Pres)*

NISSAN OF NORWICH
691 W Thames St, Norwich, CT 06360
Tel.: (860) 892-6000
Web Site:
http://www.nissanofnorwich.com
Rev.: $12,600,000
Emp.: 40
New Car Dealers
N.A.I.C.S.: 441110
Sam Ismail *(Gen Mgr-Sls)*

NISSAN OF RENO
865 Kietzke Ln, Reno, NV 89502-2015
Tel.: (775) 322-3700
Web Site:
http://www.nissanofreno.com
Sales Range: $10-24.9 Million
Emp.: 50
Car Whslr
N.A.I.C.S.: 441110
Taylor J. Wondries *(Gen Mgr)*
Paul C. Wondries *(Pres)*
S. Roberta Zamora *(Sec)*

NISSAN OF ROANOKE RAPIDS
407 Premier Blvd, Roanoke Rapids, NC 27870
Tel.: (252) 537-1041
Web Site: http://www.nissanofrr.com
Sales Range: $10-24.9 Million
Emp.: 30
New & Used Automobiles
N.A.I.C.S.: 441110
Hubert Vester *(Owner & Pres)*

NISSAN SOUTH
6889 Jonesboro Rd, Morrow, GA 30260-2902
Tel.: (770) 968-1360
Web Site:
http://www.nissansouthmorrow.com
Year Founded: 1992
Sales Range: $10-24.9 Million
Emp.: 75
Car Whslr
N.A.I.C.S.: 441110
Scott Smith *(Owner)*
Chris White *(Gen Mgr)*

NISSCO RESTAURANT DEALER GROUP, INC.
28200 Old 41 Rd Ste 208, Bonita Springs, FL 34135
Tel.: (239) 390-0950
Web Site: http://www.nisscorest.com
Year Founded: 1985
Sales Range: $1-9.9 Million
Emp.: 8
Restaurant Equipment Dealer Organization
N.A.I.C.S.: 813920
Scott Hunter *(Pres)*

NITCO HOLDING CORPORATION

205 N Washington St, Hebron, IN 46341
Tel.: (219) 996-2981   IN
Web Site: http://www.nitco.com
Year Founded: 1904
Sales Range: $10-24.9 Million
Emp.: 200
Local & Long Distance Telephone Services
N.A.I.C.S.: 517121
Rhys G. Mussman *(CEO)*

NITEL, INC.
1101 W Lk St 6th Fl, Chicago, IL 60607
Tel.: (773) 529-6300
Web Site: http://www.nitelusa.com
Sales Range: $25-49.9 Million
Emp.: 80
Telecommunications & Internet Services
N.A.I.C.S.: 517810
Milan Saric *(CFO)*
Rick Stern *(CEO)*
Ron Grason *(COO)*
Jim McCabe *(VP-Ops)*
Linda Leone *(Dir-Pricing)*
Clay Hulen *(Dir-Alternate Channel Sls)*
Jason Borkowicz *(Dir-Mktg)*
Bill Hager *(Dir-Carrier Sls)*
Gabe Rosalis *(Dir-Enterprise Sls)*
Paul Rios *(Gen Counsel)*
Lawrence Edmond *(VP-Network Engrg)*
Kevin Weber *(VP-Sls)*
Jason Dishon *(Exec VP-Sls & Mktg)*
Nate James *(VP-Acct Mgmt)*
Michael R. Cote *(Exec Chm)*

NITRAM METAL FABRICATORS INC.
135 Joey Dr, Elk Grove Village, IL 60007
Tel.: (847) 956-8470
Year Founded: 1974
Sales Range: $10-24.9 Million
Emp.: 28
Forming Machine Work, Sheet Metal
N.A.I.C.S.: 332322
Edward Suerth *(Mgr-Pur)*

NITRAM, LLC
322 N Military Rd, Fond Du Lac, WI 54935-2266
Tel.: (920) 929-0667
Year Founded: 2003
Gun Sights Mfr
N.A.I.C.S.: 332999
Todd R. Martin *(CEO)*

Subsidiaries:

Poly-Choke   (1)
322 N Military Rd, Fond Du Lac, WI 54935
Tel.: (920) 929-0667
Web Site: http://www.poly-choke.com
Sales Range: $10-24.9 Million
Emp.: 2
Adjustable Shotgun Chokes & Accessories Mfr
N.A.I.C.S.: 332999
Todd R. Martin *(CEO)*

NITRIDE SOLUTIONS INC.
3333 W Pawnee St, Wichita, KS 67213-1829
Tel.: (316) 260-5228
Web Site:
http://www.nitridesolutions.com
Semiconductor & Related Device Mfr
N.A.I.C.S.: 334413
Jeremy Jones *(Founder)*

NITRO MOBILE SOLUTIONS LLC
10210 Highland Manor Dr Ste 325, Tampa, FL 33610

Tel.: (888) 970-6660
Web Site:
http://www.nitromobilesolutions.com
Year Founded: 2009
Sales Range: $1-9.9 Million
Mobile Applications
N.A.I.C.S.: 513210
Pete Slade *(Founder & CEO)*
Cathy Pettis *(VP-Fin Svcs)*

NITRO RIGGING, LLC.
2585 E Lake Dr, Deland, FL 32724-3208
Tel.: (570) 332-8964
Web Site: http://www.nitrorigging.com
Sales Range: $1-9.9 Million
Emp.: 50
Textile Products Mfr
N.A.I.C.S.: 314999
Nick Rugai *(Owner)*

NITRO SOFTWARE, INC.
225 Bush St Ste 700, San Francisco, CA 94104
Tel.: (415) 651-4700
Web Site: http://www.nitropdf.com
Year Founded: 1997
Sales Range: $1-9.9 Million
Emp.: 30
Software & Creative Innovation Digital Services
N.A.I.C.S.: 513210
Sam Chandler *(Founder)*
Gina O'Reilly *(COO-Global Sls & Mktg)*
Richard Wenzel *(VP-Strategic Ops)*
Candice O'Meara *(VP-Fin)*
Steve Bower *(VP-Customer Success & Solutions)*
Cormac Whelan *(CEO)*

NITTANY BUILDING SPECIALTIES, INC.
105 E Plank Rd, Port Matilda, PA 16870
Tel.: (814) 692-5533
Web Site:
http://www.nittanybuilding.com
Rev.: $10,700,000
Emp.: 25
Glass
N.A.I.C.S.: 444180
Terry Deaven *(Pres)*
Jackie Hook *(Sec-Fin)*

Subsidiaries:

Nittany Building Specialites, Inc., Flooring Division   (1)
105 W Plank Rd, Port Matilda, PA 16870
Tel.: (814) 692-5533
Web Site: http://www.nittanybuilding.com
Sales Range: $25-49.9 Million
Flooring
N.A.I.C.S.: 444180
Terry Deaven *(Founder)*
Rob Musselman *(VP)*
Joel Deaven *(VP)*
Jacquelynn Hook *(Pres)*

Nittany Building Specialties, Inc., Glass Division   (1)
105 W Plank Rd, Port Matilda, PA 16870
Tel.: (814) 692-5533
Web Site: http://www.nittanybuilding.com
Sales Range: $25-49.9 Million
Glass
N.A.I.C.S.: 444180
Jacquline Hook *(Pres)*

NITTANY OIL COMPANY INC.
1540 Martin St, State College, PA 16803-3058
Tel.: (814) 237-4859   PA
Web Site:
http://www.nittanyenergy.com
Year Founded: 1958
Sales Range: $10-24.9 Million
Emp.: 105

NITTANY OIL COMPANY INC.

Nittany Oil Company Inc.—(Continued)
Petroleum Bulk Station & Terminal Services
N.A.I.C.S.: 424710
James O. Martin *(Pres)*
John Martin *(Controller)*

Subsidiaries:

Hill Top Oil Company Inc. (1)
4313 William Penn Hwy Ste 1, Mifflintown, PA 17059
Tel.: (717) 436-2647
Rev.: $12,000,000
Emp.: 5
Whslr of Gasoline & Fuel Oil
N.A.I.C.S.: 424720
Tim Under Martin *(Pres)*

NITTERHOUSE CONCRETE PRODUCTS INC.
2655 Molly Pitcher Hwy, Chambersburg, PA 17201-9203
Tel.: (717) 267-4505 PA
Web Site: http://www.nitterhouse.com
Year Founded: 1923
Rev.: $25,000,000
Emp.: 200
Concrete Products
N.A.I.C.S.: 327390
William K. Nitterhouse *(Partner)*
Gary Meyers *(CFO, Treas & Sec)*
Clifford Miles *(VP-Field Svcs)*
Edward Luke *(Mgr-Quality Control)*
Mark T. Taylor *(Pres)*
Daryl Wenger *(Mgr-Sls)*
John M. Jones *(VP-Bus Dev)*
John H. Gorrell Jr. *(VP-Admin & Safety)*

NITYO INFOTECH CORPORATION
2652 Hidden Valley Dr #102, Pittsburgh, PA 15241
Tel.: (724) 941-1067
Web Site: http://www.nityo.com
Year Founded: 2005
Sales Range: $10-24.9 Million
Emp.: 558
Information Technology Services, Management Consulting & Outsourcing Services
N.A.I.C.S.: 541512
Baskar Nathan *(CFO)*
Naveen Kumar *(Founder & CEO)*
Linda Villa *(VP-Global HR)*
Akash Tiwari *(Mng Dir-Americas)*

Subsidiaries:

Nityo Infotech (Thailand) Ltd (1)
4th Floor T Shinawatra Building 94 Sukhumvit Soi 23, Bangkok, 10110, Thailand
Tel.: (66) 26642068
Management Consulting, Information Technology & Outsourcing Services
N.A.I.C.S.: 541618

Nityo Infotech Inc. (1)
Rm 208 2nd Floor Vicente Madrigal Building, 6793 Ayala Avenue, Makati, 1226, Philippines
Tel.: (63) 27531079
Web Site: http://www.nityo.com
Management Consulting, Information Technology & Outsourcing Services
N.A.I.C.S.: 541618

Nityo Infotech Limited (1)
Albany House, Market St, Maidenhead, SL6 8BE, Berkshire, United Kingdom
Tel.: (44) 1628421500
Web Site: http://www.nityo.com
Management Consulting, Information Technology & Outsourcing Services
N.A.I.C.S.: 541618

Nityo Infotech Services Pte Ltd. (1)
260 Tanjong Pagar Road #08-02, Singapore, 088542, Singapore
Tel.: (65) 63277230
Web Site: http://www.nityo.com
Management Consulting, Information Technology & Outsourcing Services
N.A.I.C.S.: 541618

Nityo Infotech Services Pvt. Ltd. (1)
30/304 Eco House Vishweshwar Nagar First Cross Road off Aarey Road, New Link Road Andheri, Mumbai, 400063, India
Tel.: (91) 2265739444
Web Site: http://www.nityo.com
Management Consulting, Information Technology & Outsourcing Services
N.A.I.C.S.: 541618
Subodh Hegde *(Mng Dir)*

Nityo Infotech Services Sdn Bhd (1)
A-9-1 Northpoint Office Midvalley City No 1, Medan Syed Putra Utara, Kuala Lumpur, 59200, Malaysia
Tel.: (60) 322820600
Management Consulting, Information Technology & Outsourcing Services
N.A.I.C.S.: 541618

NIVEN FAMILY WINE ESTATES
5828 Orcutt Rd, San Luis Obispo, CA 93401
Tel.: (805) 269-8200
Web Site: http://www.nivenfamilywines.com
Year Founded: 1973
Wine Mfr
N.A.I.C.S.: 312130
Rob Takigawa *(Dir-Winemaking)*

NIVIS LLC
Ste 300 1000 Cir 75 Pkwy SE, Atlanta, GA 30339-6051
Tel.: (678) 202-6800
Web Site: http://www.nivis.com
Year Founded: 1989
Sales Range: $10-24.9 Million
Emp.: 40
Computer Integrated Systems Design
N.A.I.C.S.: 541512
Doug Johns *(Chm & CEO)*

NIXON PEABODY LLP
100 Summer St, Boston, MA 02110-2131
Tel.: (617) 345-1000
Web Site: http://www.nixonpeabody.com
Year Founded: 1875
Sales Range: $400-449.9 Million
Emp.: 1,001
Law firm
N.A.I.C.S.: 541110
David A. Vicinanzo *(Partner)*
Philip B. Taub *(Partner)*
Richard M. Stein *(Partner)*
George J. Skelly *(Partner)*
Ruth H. Silman *(Partner)*
Andrew L. Share *(Partner)*
Mark D. Seltzer *(Partner)*
Jeffrey W. Sacks *(Partner)*
Jonathan Sablone *(Partner)*
David S. Rosenthal *(Partner)*
Jay D. Rosenbaum *(Partner)*
Lauri Walker *(COO)*
Andrew I. Glincher *(Partner)*
James E. Vallee *(Partner)*
Nathan Bernard *(Partner)*
Rebecca Simone *(Partner)*
Kristin Jamberdino *(Partner)*
Thomas Gaynor *(Mng Partner-San Francisco)*
Maria S. Swiatek *(Partner)*
Tina Sciocchetti *(Partner)*
Jennifer Hayes *(Partner)*
Jinjian Huang *(Partner)*
Carlo Porreca *(Dir-NP Capital Connector)*
Ashley E. Champion *(Partner)*
Catherine Ng *(Partner)*
Dan Deane *(Partner)*
Elizabeth Baio *(Partner)*
Richa Naujoks *(Partner)*
Stephanie T. Seiffert *(Partner)*
Theodore Ghorra *(Partner)*
Tyler Savage *(Partner-Rochester)*
Adam Gwaltney *(Partner)*
Graham Beck *(Partner)*
Andrew Potts *(Partner-Washington)*
Darren Miller *(Partner)*
Jared C. Lusk *(Mng Partner-Rochester)*
Charles S. Gaziano *(Mng Dir)*
Christopher L. Melvin *(Mng Dir)*
Keri McWilliams *(Partner)*
Matthew Mullen *(Partner)*
Kendal Tyre *(Partner-Washington)*
Lior Zorea *(Partner-Corp Practice-Natl)*
Adam Tarosky *(Partner-Washington)*
Michael J. Summerhill *(Partner-Complex Comml Disputes Practice)*

NIXON STATE BANK
200 N Nixon Ave, Nixon, TX 78140
Tel.: (830) 582-1511
Web Site: http://www.nixonstatebank.com
Banking Services
N.A.I.C.S.: 522110
Brad S. Akin *(Pres & CEO)*

NIXON UNIFORM SERVICE INC.
500 Centerpoint Blvd, New Castle, DE 19720
Tel.: (302) 764-7550
Web Site: http://www.nixonmedical.com
Rev.: $15,163,202
Emp.: 175
Uniform Supply
N.A.I.C.S.: 812331
Jason Berstein *(Pres)*

NIXON-EGLI EQUIPMENT CO.
2044 S Vineyard Ave, Ontario, CA 91761-7748
Tel.: (909) 930-1822
Web Site: http://www.nixon-egli.com
Sales Range: $25-49.9 Million
Emp.: 48
General Construction Machinery & Equipment
N.A.I.C.S.: 423810
Steve Nixon *(CEO)*
Carl Bahnsen *(VP-Municipal Sls)*
Randy Davis *(Mgr-Parts)*
James Nixon *(Mgr-Sls)*

NIXSOL INC.
53 Knightsbridge Rd Ste Ste 216, Piscataway, NJ 08854
Tel.: (732) 649-1565
Web Site: http://www.nixsol.com
Year Founded: 2004
Rev.: $2,100,000
Emp.: 22
Computer System Design Services
N.A.I.C.S.: 541512
Praveen Kari *(Pres)*
Annu Rao *(Office Mgr)*
Himaja Pogula *(Engr-Software)*

NJ LENDERS CORP.
219 Paterson Ave, Little Falls, NJ 07424-1657
Tel.: (973) 890-0005 NJ
Web Site: http://www.njlenders.com
Year Founded: 1991
Rev.: $300,000,000
Emp.: 50
Mortgage Bankers & Correspondents
N.A.I.C.S.: 522292
Donald Maita *(CEO)*
Charles Shulman *(VP)*
Steven Grossman *(Mgr)*

NJ SHARING NETWORK
691 Central Ave, New Providence, NJ 07974
Tel.: (908) 516-5400 NJ
Web Site: http://www.njsharingnetwork.org
Year Founded: 1987
Sales Range: $25-49.9 Million
Emp.: 196
Organ, Tissue Donation & Transplantation Services
N.A.I.C.S.: 621991
Joseph S. Roth *(Pres & CEO)*
Joyce Jardot *(Dir-HR)*
Jorge Kalil *(CIO)*
Barry Newman *(CFO & VP-Fin)*
Prakash Rao *(VP-Diagnostics & Res Ops & Dir-Transplant Laboratory)*
Carolyn Welsh *(Dir-Organ Donation Svcs)*
Elisse E. Glennon *(Chief Admin Officer, VP & Exec Dir)*
Alene Stewart *(Dir-Quality Sys & Tissue Donation Svcs)*

NJ TRANSIT CORPORATION
1 Penn Plz E, Newark, NJ 07105-2245
Tel.: (973) 491-7000 NJ
Web Site: http://www.njtransit.com
Year Founded: 1979
Sales Range: $1-4.9 Billion
Emp.: 11,500
Public Transportation Services
N.A.I.C.S.: 926120
Dennis J. Martin *(VP & Gen Mgr-Bus Ops)*
Kevin Corbett *(Pres & CEO)*

Subsidiaries:

ARH III Insurance Co., Inc. (1)
151 Meeting St Ste 301, Charleston, SC 29401
Tel.: (843) 577-1030
Insurance Brokerage Services
N.A.I.C.S.: 524210

NJ TRANSIT Mercer, Inc. (1)
600 Sloan Ave, Trenton, NJ 08619
Tel.: (609) 689-1702
Transport & Logistic Services
N.A.I.C.S.: 561110

New Jersey Transit Bus Operations (1)
1 Penn Plz E, Newark, NJ 07105
Tel.: (973) 491-7000
Web Site: http://www.njtransit.com
Rev.: $209,062,000
Bus Public Transportation Services
N.A.I.C.S.: 485210

New Jersey Transit Rail Operations (1)
1 Penn Plz E, Newark, NJ 07105-2245
Tel.: (973) 491-7912
Web Site: http://www.nj.com
Sales Range: $350-399.9 Million
Emp.: 3,500
Rail Public Transportation Service
N.A.I.C.S.: 485210
Robert Lavell *(VP & Gen Mgr)*

NJD SPECIALTY RETAIL, INC.
2101 Production Dr, Louisville, KY 40299
Tel.: (502) 634-3097
Web Site: http://www.buyhappyfeet.com
Sales Range: $1-9.9 Million
Emp.: 20
Online Slippers Retailer
N.A.I.C.S.: 424340
Patrick Yates *(Owner & Pres)*

NJEVITY, INC.
9250 E Costilla Ave Ste 325, Greenwood Village, CO 80112-3648
Tel.: (720) 870-9700
Web Site: http://www.njevity.com
Year Founded: 2001

COMPANIES

Custom Computer Programming Services
N.A.I.C.S.: 541511
Chris Dobkins *(Pres & CEO)*
Melissa Sandrovich *(Dir-Cust Success)*
Tudor Coleman *(Dir-Cloud Technology & Compliance)*
Pam Misialek *(Dir-Cloud Applications)*
Mike McPhilomy *(Dir-Sls)*

NJM-CLI PACKAGING SYSTEMS INTERNATIONAL
77 Bank St, Lebanon, NH 03766
Tel.: (603) 448-0300
Web Site:
http://www.njmpackaging.com
Sales Range: $10-24.9 Million
Emp.: 80
Labeling Machines, Industrial
N.A.I.C.S.: 333993
Michel Lapierre *(Pres & CEO)*
Jim Moretti *(CFO)*
Andre Caumartin *(VP-Fin & Ops)*
Dan Lapierre *(VP)*
Mark LaRoche *(VP-Sls)*

NJOY ELECTRONIC CIGARETTE
15455 N Greenway Hayden Loop Rd Ste C-15, Scottsdale, AZ 85260
Tel.: (480) 305-7950
Web Site: http://www.njoy.com
Year Founded: 2006
Sales Range: $25-49.9 Million
Emp.: 16
Electronic Cigarette Shopping Services
N.A.I.C.S.: 449210
Roy Anise *(Exec VP)*
Elie Wurtman *(Chm)*
Bill Barba *(VP-Fin & Ops)*
Drew Beaver *(CMO)*
Mark Scatterday *(Sr VP-Mfg & Dev)*
John Bax *(CFO)*
David Graham *(Sr VP-Intl Regulatory Affairs)*

NLETS, INC.
1918 W Whispering Wind Dr, Phoenix, AZ 85085
Tel.: (623) 308-3500   DE
Web Site: http://www.nlets.org
Year Founded: 1974
Sales Range: $10-24.9 Million
Emp.: 34
Telecommunication Servicesb
N.A.I.C.S.: 517810
Keith Meyers *(Fin Dir & Dir-Admin)*
Bonnie Locke *(Dir-Bus Dev)*
Kurt Anzelmo *(Dir-Ops)*
Steve Correll *(Exec Dir)*

NLM INC.
14320 Joy Rd, Detroit, MI 48228
Tel.: (313) 272-4050
Sales Range: $50-74.9 Million
Emp.: 35
Freight Transportation Arrangement
N.A.I.C.S.: 488510
Greg Hughs *(Pres)*

Subsidiaries:

Artisan Container Service Llc   (1)
14320 Joy Rd, Detroit, MI 48228
Tel.: (313) 272-4050
Transportation Agents & Brokers
N.A.I.C.S.: 488510

NLOGIC
4901 Corporate Dr Ste H, Huntsville, AL 35805
Tel.: (256) 704-2525
Web Site: http://www.nlogic.com
Year Founded: 2005
Sales Range: $1-9.9 Million

Emp.: 55
Aerospace Engineering Services
N.A.I.C.S.: 541330
Tim Thornton *(Pres & CEO)*
Ron Davis *(CTO)*
Bob Faulkner *(Program Dir)*
Kevin Langjahr *(VP)*
Neil Miller *(Mgr-Program)*

NLP LOGIX, LLC
4215 Southpoint Blvd Ste 230, Jacksonville, FL 32216
Tel.: (904) 437-4040
Web Site: http://www.nlplogix.com
Sales Range: $1-9.9 Million
Software Developer
N.A.I.C.S.: 513210
Ted Willich *(CEO)*
Robert Marsh *(CTO)*
Matthew Berseth *(Chief Scientist)*

NLR, INC.
250 Main St, East Windsor, CT 06088
Tel.: (860) 292-1992
Web Site: http://www.nlr-green.com
Year Founded: 1993
Rev.: $4,200,000
Emp.: 25
Refuse System
N.A.I.C.S.: 562920
Steve Rorick *(Reg Mgr-Sls)*
Raymond Graczyk *(Pres)*

NLYTE SOFTWARE AMERICAS LIMITED
2800 Campus Dr Ste 135, San Mateo, CA 94403-2554
Tel.: (650) 642-2700
Web Site: http://www.nlyte.com
Year Founded: 2004
Emp.: 200
Data Center Service Management (DCSM) Solutions
N.A.I.C.S.: 513210
Robert Neave *(Co-Founder, CTO & VP-Product Mgmt)*
Doug Sabella *(Pres & CEO)*
Mark Gaydos *(CMO)*
Owen Nisbett *(CFO)*
Sandra Denton *(VP-Channels & Alliances)*
Niraj Desai *(VP-Field Engrg)*
Phil Kelly *(VP-Engrg)*
David Provance *(VP-Worldwide Sls)*
John Moreton *(Co-Founder)*
Moshe Benjo *(VP-Sls-EMEA)*
Andy Redfern *(CIO)*
Enzo Greco *(Chief Strategy Officer)*
Robert Gene Bearden Jr. *(Chm)*

Subsidiaries:

FieldView Solutions, Inc.   (1)
275 Raritan Ctr. Pkwy, Edison, NJ 08837
Tel.: (732) 395-6920
Web Site: http://www.fieldviewsolutions.com
Emp.: 150
Infrastructure Management Software Solutions
N.A.I.C.S.: 513210
Russ Webb *(COO)*
Tom Edwards *(CFO)*
Sev Onyshkevych *(CMO)*
Tim Regovich *(CTO)*
Rita Lindsay-Sonatore *(Creative Dir)*
Owen Nisbett *(CFO)*

NM MARKETING COMMUNICATIONS, INC.
706 Waukegan Rd, Glenview, IL 60025
Tel.: (847) 657-6011
Web Site:
http://www.nmmarketingbiz.com
Year Founded: 1999
Sales Range: $1-9.9 Million
Emp.: 6

Public Relations Agency
N.A.I.C.S.: 541820
Norwin A. Merens *(Mng Dir)*
Jeff Wessman *(Dir-Design)*
Elaine Fiedler *(Editor)*
Paul Lloyd *(Project Mgr)*

NMC METALS INC.
310 N Pleasant Ave, Niles, OH 44446
Tel.: (330) 652-2501   OH
Web Site:
http://www.nilesexpandedmetal.com
Emp.: 52
Metal & Plastic Mesh & Composite Products Mfr & Whslr
N.A.I.C.S.: 332618
Claudine Cioffi *(Dir-Sls & Mktg)*
William E. Phillips Sr. *(Chm & CEO)*
William E. Phillips Jr. *(Pres & COO)*

Subsidiaries:

MetalSpand, Inc.   (1)
1000 E G Ave, Waurika, OK 73573
Tel.: (580) 228-2393
Metal Mesh Fencing Products Mfr & Whslr
N.A.I.C.S.: 332618

Niles Fence & Security Products, LLC   (1)
310 N Pleasant Ave, Niles, OH 44446-1173
Tel.: (330) 652-0743
Web Site: http://www.nilesfence.com
Metal Wire & Mesh Fence & Security Products Mfr & Whslr
N.A.I.C.S.: 332618
Stacey Hoover *(Gen Mgr)*

NMC/WOLLARD COMPANY
2021 Truax Blvd, Eau Claire, WI 54703
Tel.: (715) 835-3151
Web Site: http://www.nmc-wollard.com
Sales Range: $25-49.9 Million
Emp.: 75
Provider of Ground Support Equipment Services
N.A.I.C.S.: 333924
Barry Lubs *(Mgr-Mfg & Coord-Lean)*

NMI HEALTH, INC.
50 W Liberty St Ste 880, Reno, NV 89501
Tel.: (914) 760-7857   NV
Web Site: http://www.nmihealth.com
Year Founded: 1991
Sales Range: Less than $1 Million
Emp.: 3
Healthcare Product Developer & Distr
N.A.I.C.S.: 339999
Edward J. Suydam *(CEO)*

NMR CONSULTING
201 Defense Hwy Ste 200, Annapolis, MD 21401
Tel.: (410) 573-0080
Web Site:
http://www.nmrconsulting.com
Year Founded: 1996
Rev.: $14,500,000
Emp.: 98
Computer Systems Design & Related Services
N.A.I.C.S.: 541511
David Jones *(VP)*

NMS - IMAGING
12501 Prosperity Dr 205, Silver Spring, MD 20904
Tel.: (301) 622-4300
Web Site:
http://www.nmsimaging.com
Sales Range: $10-24.9 Million
Emp.: 20
Micrographic Equipment
N.A.I.C.S.: 423420
Steve Dring *(Pres)*
Mike Morrison *(VP)*

NMS CAPITAL SERVICES, LLC

NMS CAPITAL SERVICES, LLC
32 Old Slip Ste 32D, New York, NY 10005
Tel.: (212) 422-7099   DE
Web Site: http://www.nms-capital.com
Year Founded: 2010
Privater Equity Firm
N.A.I.C.S.: 523940
Martin E. Chavez *(Co-Founder & Mng Partner)*
Kevin M. Jordan *(Co-Founder & Mng Partner)*
James G. Wilson *(Partner & CFO)*
Luis A. Gonzalez *(Partner)*
David M. Peterson *(Mng Dir)*
Noel Jeon *(Mng Dir)*

Subsidiaries:

Anne Arundel Dermatology P.A.   (1)
101 Ridgely Ave Ste 10, Annapolis, MD 21401
Tel.: (443) 351-3376
Web Site: http://www.aadermatology.com
Offices of All Other Miscellaneous Health Practitioners
N.A.I.C.S.: 621399
Felicia Francis *(Dir-HR)*

CORDENTAL Group Management, LLC   (1)
8016 Plainfield Rd, Cincinnati, OH 45236
Tel.: (855) 876-4532
Web Site: http://cordentalgroup.com
Dental Services
N.A.I.C.S.: 622110
Steven Jones *(Co-Founder & Chief Development Officer)*
Dana Soper *(Co-Founder & CEO)*

Subsidiary (Domestic):

AppleWhite Dental LLC   (2)
40 Main St Ste 103, Dubuque, IA 52001
Tel.: (563) 582-1448
Web Site:
http://applewhitedentalpartners.com
Dental Services
N.A.I.C.S.: 621210
Thomas McCoy *(Owner, Pres & CEO)*
Jeff Mentzer *(CFO)*

DirectMed Parts & Service LLC   (1)
12525 Stowe Dr., Poway, CA 92064
Tel.: (858) 251-8752
Web Site: https://directmedparts.com
Emp.: 100
Healthcare Services
N.A.I.C.S.: 621610

Subsidiary (Domestic):

Technical Prospects LLC   (2)
1000 S County Rd Cb, Appleton, WI 54914-8614
Web Site:
http://www.technicalprospects.com
Medical, Dental & Hospital Equipment & Supplies Merchant Whslr
N.A.I.C.S.: 423450
Jeremy Probst *(Pres & CEO)*

Omni Ophthalmic Management Consultants LLC   (1)
485 Rte 1 S Bldg A, Iselin, NJ 08830
Tel.: (732) 750-0400
Web Site: https://oomc.com
Ophthalmic Management Services
N.A.I.C.S.: 561990
Christopher Quinn *(CEO)*
John L. Henry *(CMO)*
Regina F. Gurvich *(Chief Compliance Officer & VP)*
Matt Sobierralski *(VP-Bus Dev)*
Carl W. Desch Jr. *(Chief Admin Officer)*

Subsidiary (Domestic):

Ludwick Eye Center Ltd.   (2)
825 5th Ave Ste 102, Chambersburg, PA 17201
Tel.: (717) 262-9700
Web Site: https://oomc.com
Health Practitioners
N.A.I.C.S.: 621399
Robin Samuelson *(Supvr-Billing)*

NMS CAPITAL SERVICES, LLC

NMS Capital Services, LLC—(Continued)

US Foot & Ankle Specialists, LLC (1)
1621 Quail Run, Charlottesville, VA 22911
Tel.: (434) 975-5433
Web Site: http://www.footandankle-usa.com
Podiatric Services
N.A.I.C.S.: 621999

Subsidiary (Domestic):

Foot & Ankle Associates of Southwest Virginia, P.C. (2)
222 Walnut Ave SW, Roanoke, VA 24016-4723
Tel.: (540) 344-3668
Web Site: http://www.drzelen.com
Offices of Podiatrists
N.A.I.C.S.: 621391

NNRF, INC.
8221 3rd Ave Ste 204, Downey, CA 90241
Coal & Other Mineral Ore Services
N.A.I.C.S.: 423520
Bernard S. Mayfield (Pres & CEO)

NO FRILLS SUPERMARKETS INC.
7401 F St, Omaha, NE 68127
Tel.: (402) 399-9244
Web Site: http://www.nofrillssupermarket.com
Rev.: $119,100,000
Emp.: 20
Supermarket
N.A.I.C.S.: 445110
Dennis Edison (Pres)

NO/AIDS TASK FORCE
2601 Tulane Ave Ste 500, New Orleans, LA 70119
Tel.: (504) 821-2601 LA
Web Site: http://www.noaidstaskforce.org
Year Founded: 1983
Sales Range: $10-24.9 Million
Emp.: 216
Medical Care Services
N.A.I.C.S.: 621610
Noel Twilbeck Jr. (CEO & Exec Dir)

NOAH TECHNOLOGIES CORPORATION
1 Noah Park, San Antonio, TX 78249-3419
Tel.: (210) 691-2000 TX
Web Site: http://www.noahtech.com
Year Founded: 1978
Sales Range: $10-24.9 Million
Emp.: 100
High Purity Inorganic Chemicals Mfr
N.A.I.C.S.: 325180
Sonya Blumenthal (Pres)
Bob Blumenthal (VP)
Diane Milner (Mgr-Mktg)
Jamie Hong (CEO)

NOAH W. KREIDER & SON
1461 Lancaster Rd, Manheim, PA 17545-9768
Tel.: (717) 665-4415 PA
Web Site: http://www.kreiderfarms.com
Year Founded: 1955
Rev.: $30,000,000
Emp.: 325
Chicken Eggs
N.A.I.C.S.: 112310
Charles A. Paul (Controller)
Dave Andrews (VP-Sls & Mktg)

NOARUS AUTO GROUP
6701 Ctr Dr W Ste 925, Los Angeles, CA 90045-1535
Tel.: (310) 258-0920
Web Site: http://www.noarus.com
Rev.: $66,800,000
Emp.: 12
Provider of New & Used Automobiles
N.A.I.C.S.: 441110
Williams Hurst (Pres)
Gary Allwood (CFO & VP)
Norris J. Bishton Jr. (Pres & CEO)

Subsidiaries:

Airport Marina Ford (1)
5880 W Centinela Ave, Los Angeles, CA 90045
Tel.: (310) 256-4961
Web Site: http://www.airportmarinaford.com
Sales Range: $25-49.9 Million
Provider of New & Used Automobiles
N.A.I.C.S.: 441110
Dan Theroux (Gen Mgr)
Scott Greenwald (Dir-Fin)

NOBEL LIMITED COMPANY
5759 Fleet St Ste 210, Carlsbad, CA 92008
Tel.: (760) 405-0105
Web Site: http://www.nobelglobe.com
Year Founded: 1998
Sales Range: $25-49.9 Million
Emp.: 194
Online Pre-Paid Phone Card Distributor
N.A.I.C.S.: 517121
Thomas Knobel (Founder, Chm & CEO)

NOBILIS HEALTH CORP.
11700 Katy Fwy Ste 300, Houston, TX 77079
Tel.: (713) 355-8614
Web Site: http://www.nobilishealth.com
Year Founded: 2007
Outpatient Surgery Centers Owner & Operator
N.A.I.C.S.: 622110
Neil Badlani (Chief Medical Officer)

Subsidiaries:

Athas Health, LLC (1)
10740 N Central Expy Ste 275, Dallas, TX 75231
Tel.: (214) 261-3600
Web Site: http://www.athas-health.com
Emp.: 75
Health Care Srvices
N.A.I.C.S.: 622110
Steve Ganss (CFO)

Bellaire Surgical Hospital Holdings, LLC (1)
4801 Bissonnet St, Bellaire, TX 77401-4028
Tel.: (713) 275-1111
Health Care Srvices
N.A.I.C.S.: 622110

Central Medical Solutions, LLC (1)
PO Box 13618, Oklahoma City, OK 73113
Tel.: (405) 715-3610
Web Site: http://www.centralmedicalsolutions.com
Financial Management & Consulting Services
N.A.I.C.S.: 541611
Stacey Rawls (Pres)

DeRosa Medical PC (1)
9377 E Bell Rd Ste 143, Scottsdale, AZ 85260
Tel.: (480) 619-4097
Web Site: http://www.derosamedical.com
Health Practitioners
N.A.I.C.S.: 621399
Angela DeRosa (Pres)

Elite Surgical Affiliates (1)
2100 W Loop S Ste 1200, Houston, TX 77027
Tel.: (713) 877-0600
Web Site: http://www.elitesurgicalaffiliates.com
Family Planning Centers
N.A.I.C.S.: 621410
Lori Ramirez (Co-Pres & CEO)
Abigail Berkman (Chief Dev Officer)
Boyd Yarbrough (Pres)

Chuck Bell (CIO)
Patrick Kinder (COO)
Suzanne Dixon (Chief Legal Officer)
Meggan Bushee (Chief Compliance Officer)

Hermann Drive Surgical Hospital, LP (1)
2001 Hermann Dr, Houston, TX 77004
Tel.: (713) 285-5500
Web Site: http://www.hermanndrivesurgicalhospital.com
Health Care Srvices
N.A.I.C.S.: 622110
Michael Torn (CEO)

Houston Metro Ortho and Spine Surgery Center, LLC (1)
4219 Richmond Ste 200, Houston, TX 77027
Tel.: (713) 487-0001
Web Site: http://www.houstonmetrosurgery.com
Health Care Srvices
N.A.I.C.S.: 622110

NH Clinical Services, PLLC (1)
10740 N Central Expy, Dallas, TX 75231-2161
Tel.: (214) 378-4656
Health Care Srvices
N.A.I.C.S.: 622110

Perimeter Road Surgical Hospital, LLC (1)
17500 N Perimeter Dr, Scottsdale, AZ 85257-7808
Tel.: (480) 586-2300
Web Site: http://www.scottsdalelibertyhospital.com
Health Care Srvices
N.A.I.C.S.: 622110
Steven M. Siwek (CEO)

Phoenix Surgery Center, LLC (1)
3320 N 2nd St, Phoenix, AZ 85012
Tel.: (602) 200-8288
Web Site: http://www.akdhc.com
Health Care Srvices
N.A.I.C.S.: 622110

Southwest Freeway Surgery Center Management, LLC (1)
4120 SW Fwy 200, Houston, TX 77027-7339
Tel.: (713) 355-8600
Health Care Srvices
N.A.I.C.S.: 622110

NOBILIS INC.
3689 Comml Ave, Northbrook, IL 60062
Tel.: (847) 714-9714 IL
Web Site: http://www.nobilisgroup.com
Sales Range: Less than $1 Million
Emp.: 3
Desks, Smoking Accessories, Clock Encasements & Golf Accessories Mfr
N.A.I.C.S.: 424120
Paul Singh (Pres)

NOBLE CAPITAL MARKETS
150 E Palmetto Park Rd Ste 110, Boca Raton, FL 33431
Tel.: (561) 994-1191 FL
Web Site: http://www.noblecapitalmarkets.com
Year Founded: 1984
Merchant & Investment Banking
N.A.I.C.S.: 523150
Nico P. Cronk (Pres & CEO)

NOBLE FORD
2406 N Jefferson Way, Indianola, IA 50125-9456
Tel.: (515) 961-8151
Web Site: http://www.nobleford.com
Year Founded: 1988
Sales Range: $25-49.9 Million
Emp.: 100
New Car Whslr
N.A.I.C.S.: 441110
Yodi Ollom (Owner)

NOBLE HOUSE HOTELS & RESORTS, LTD.
600 6th St S, Kirkland, WA 98033
Tel.: (425) 827-8737 WA
Web Site: http://www.noblehousehotels.com
Sales Range: $100-124.9 Million
Emp.: 2,000
Motels & Resorts
N.A.I.C.S.: 721110
Michael Benecke (Pres)
Patrick R. Colee (Founder & Chm)
Liz Johnson (Dir-Travel Indus & Sls)
John M. Donoghue (CEO)
James P. Colee (Pres-Dev)
Sean Mullen (Pres-Acq)
Steve Sanborn (VP-Fin & Bus Dev)
Kevin Falk (Controller)
John Valis (VP-Engrg)
Karen Ranker (VP-HR)
Scott Colee (Chief Creative Officer)
Thomas Haas (VP-Food & Beverage)
Chris Schaefer (Corp Dir-Restaurants)
Janette Ament-Pierce (Chief Acctg Officer)
Jason Moll (Dir-Rooms)
Jay Robinson (Dir-MIS)
Jaz Jeanne (Dir-Great People)
Julie Chavarria (Dir-Travel Indus Sls)
Matt Trahan (Mng Dir-South Florida & VP)
Michelle Sehulster (Dir-Travel Indus Sls)
Veronica Kistner (VP-Sls)
Chad Bustos (Sr VP-Sls & Mktg)

Subsidiaries:

Little Palm Island Associates, Ltd. (1)
28500 Overseas Hwy, Little Torch Key, FL 33042
Tel.: (305) 872-2524
Web Site: http://www.littlepalmisland.com
Sales Range: $1-9.9 Million
Emp.: 100
Hotel & Spa
N.A.I.C.S.: 721110
Matt Trahan (Gen Mgr)

Napa Valley Wine Train, Inc. (1)
1275 McKinstry St, Napa, CA 94559
Tel.: (707) 253-2111
Web Site: http://www.winetrain.com
Wine & Dining Train Ride Operator
N.A.I.C.S.: 487110
Anthony Giaccio (CEO & CFO)
Andrea Guzman (Dir-Sls & Partnerships)

Ocean Key Resort & Spa (1)
0 Duval St, Key West, FL 33040
Tel.: (305) 296-7701
Web Site: http://www.oceankey.com
Emp.: 250
Hotel & Spa
N.A.I.C.S.: 721110
Matt Trahan (Gen Mgr)
Rodger Levering (Dir-Food & Beverage)

WaterColor Inn & Resort (1)
34 Goldenrod Cir, Santa Rosa Beach, FL 32459
Tel.: (850) 534-5000
Web Site: http://www.watercolorresort.com
Hotel
N.A.I.C.S.: 721110

NOBLE INVESTMENT GROUP, LLC
2000 Monarch Tower 3424 Peachtree Rd NE, Atlanta, GA 30326
Tel.: (404) 419-1000 GA
Web Site: http://www.nobleinvestment.com
Year Founded: 1993
Real Estate Private Equity Fund Manager & Hotel Operator, Purchaser & Developer
N.A.I.C.S.: 531390
Steven Nicholas (Principal & Exec VP-Asset Mgmt)

Mark Rafuse *(Chief Admin Officer)*
Benjamin Brunt *(Principal & Exec VP-Acquisition & Dev)*
Aditya Bhoopathy *(Principal)*
Rodney S. Williams *(Chief Investment Officer & Mng Principal)*
Kevin Grass *(Principal)*
Roy Croop *(Sr VP)*
Michael Quinlan *(Sr VP)*
Emily Feeney *(Sr Dir-Capital Market)*
Mitesh B. Shah *(CEO)*
Denise Kauble *(Dir-Asset Mgmt)*
Dan Konzelmann *(VP-Investment)*
Emily Feeney *(Sr Dir-Capital Market)*
Jeff Pennington *(Sr Dir-Fin)*
James Conley Jr. *(CFO)*

Subsidiaries:

New Haven Hotel LLC (1)
229 George St, New Haven, CT 06510
Tel.: (203) 498-3100
Web Site: http://www.newhavenhotel.com
Hotel & Event Services
N.A.I.C.S.: 721110

NOBLE LUMBER INC.
160 Camellia Ct, Beavercreek, OR 97045
Tel.: (503) 632-2030
Sales Range: $10-24.9 Million
Emp.: 4
Lumber: Rough, Dressed & Finished
N.A.I.C.S.: 423310
Charles Noble Jr. *(Pres)*

NOBLE MARKETING INC.
121 S Orange Ave Suite 1070 N, Orlando, FL 32801
Tel.: (888) 933-5646
Web Site: http://www.gonoble.com
Year Founded: 1994
Sales Range: $10-24.9 Million
Emp.: 22
Multisensory Product Development for Pharmaceutical & Biotechnology Brands
N.A.I.C.S.: 541613
Jeff Baker *(Co-Founder, Pres & CEO)*
Paul van der Pol *(Dir-R&D)*
Joe Jensen *(Dir-Comm)*
Craig Baker *(Exec VP)*
Hayley Baker *(Co-Founder)*
Dawn Kleinsmith *(Dir-Fin)*
Michael Siemer *(Dir-Engrg)*
Tom Wilmoth *(COO)*
Dennis Paller *(Dir-Production)*

NOBLE OIL SERVICES, INC.
5617 Clyde Rhyne Dr, Sanford, NC 27330
Tel.: (919) 774-8180
Web Site: http://www.nobleoil.com
Year Founded: 1986
Sales Range: $75-99.9 Million
Emp.: 153
Re-refining & Resale of Used Oil
N.A.I.C.S.: 238990
Yoke P. Chung *(Mgr-Environmental, Health & Safety)*

NOBLE RESTAURANT GROUP INC.
18010 Sky Park Cir # 275, Irvine, CA 92614
Tel.: (949) 477-6080
Sales Range: $10-24.9 Million
Emp.: 5
American Restaurant
N.A.I.C.S.: 722511
Gregg Diganci *(Pres)*

NOBLE VENTURES CORP.
4867 Palm Coast Pkwy Unit 4, Palm Coast, FL 32137 FL
Web Site: http://www.nobleventures.com
Year Founded: 1993
Sales Range: $1-9.9 Million
Emp.: 15
Direct Mail Advertising Services
N.A.I.C.S.: 541860
Robin Lahiri *(Pres & CEO)*
Sabrina Robles *(Mgr-Client Svc)*
Nirav Patel *(Mgr-Tech)*
Obed Dorceus *(Gen Counsel)*

NOBLES COOPERATIVE ELECTRIC
22636 US Hwy 59, Worthington, MN 56187
Tel.: (507) 372-7331 MN
Web Site: http://www.noblesce.coop
Year Founded: 1936
Sales Range: $10-24.9 Million
Emp.: 22
Electric Power Distr
N.A.I.C.S.: 221122
Ronald J. Schwartau *(Chm)*
David D. Clarke *(Treas & Sec)*
Lee A. York *(Vice Chm)*
Adam Tromblay *(Gen Mgr)*
Tracey Haberman *(Mgr-Member Svcs)*

NOBOX MARKETING GROUP, INC.
180 NE 39Th St Ste 225, Miami, FL 33137
Tel.: (305) 571-2008
Web Site: http://www.nobox.com
Sales Range: $10-24.9 Million
Emp.: 12
N.A.I.C.S.: 541810
Carlos M. Garcia *(Partner & Chief Strategist)*
Margarita Irriszary *(Partner)*

NOCO ENERGY CORP.
2440 Sheridan Dr Ste 301, Tonawanda, NY 14150
Tel.: (716) 874-6200
Web Site: http://www.noco.com
Sales Range: $200-249.9 Million
Emp.: 550
Petroleum Products
N.A.I.C.S.: 424720
James D. Newman *(Pres)*
Michael F. Newman *(Exec VP)*
Michael Bradley *(CFO)*
R. J. Stapell *(Chm)*
Jim DeFilippis *(VP & Gen Mgr-Express)*

NODAK ELECTRIC COOPERATIVE, INC.
4000 32nd Ave S, Grand Forks, ND 58201-5944
Tel.: (701) 746-4461 ND
Web Site: http://www.nodakelectric.com
Year Founded: 1940
Sales Range: $150-199.9 Million
Emp.: 75
Provider of Electrical Power Distribution Services
N.A.I.C.S.: 221122
Tom A. Edwards *(Mgr-Acctg & Fin)*
Blaine Rekken *(Mgr-Energy Svcs & Customer)*
Mylo Einarson *(Pres & CEO)*

NODAK INSURANCE COMPANY
1101 1st Ave N, Fargo, ND 58102
Tel.: (701) 298-4200 ND
Web Site: http://www.nodakins.com
Year Founded: 1946
Sales Range: $50-74.9 Million
Emp.: 136
Property & Casualty Providing Services
N.A.I.C.S.: 524126
Jim Alexander *(Pres & CEO)*
Brian Doom *(CFO)*
Patrick Duncan *(VP-Shared Svcs)*
William R. Devlin *(Vice Chm)*

Subsidiaries:

American West Insurance Company (1)
1101 1st Ave N, Fargo, ND 58102
Tel.: (701) 298-4200
Web Site: http://www.yourawi.com
Emp.: 90
General Insurance Services
N.A.I.C.S.: 524210
Jim Alexander *(Gen Mgr)*

Battle Creek Mutual Insurance Company (1)
603 S Preece St, Battle Creek, NE 68715-0340
Tel.: (402) 347-0470
Web Site: http://www.bcmutual.com
Sales Range: $1-9.9 Million
Emp.: 14
Property Insurance Services
N.A.I.C.S.: 524126
Becky Ridder *(Asst Treas)*
Tom Chambers *(Dir-Claims & Ops)*

NODAWAY VALLEY BANK
304 N Main St, Maryville, MO 64468
Tel.: (660) 562-3232
Web Site: http://www.nodawayvalleybank.com
Sales Range: $10-24.9 Million
Emp.: 150
State Commercial Banks
N.A.I.C.S.: 522110
Jim Davis *(CFO)*
Bob Hall *(Sr VP-Bus Dev)*
R. Cort Hegarty *(Pres & COO)*

NOEL CANNING CORPORATION
1001 S 1st St, Yakima, WA 98901-3403
Tel.: (509) 248-4545 WA
Web Site: http://www.noelcorp.com
Year Founded: 1940
Sales Range: $50-74.9 Million
Emp.: 320
Provider of Soft Drink Canning Services
N.A.I.C.S.: 312111
Rodger Noel *(Pres)*
Sam Brackely *(Plant Mgr)*
Cindy Zimmerman *(CFO & VP)*

NOEL FURNITURE INC.
2727 SW Fwy, Houston, TX 77098
Tel.: (713) 874-5200
Web Site: http://www.noelfurniture.com
Sales Range: $50-74.9 Million
Emp.: 70
Furniture Retailer
N.A.I.C.S.: 449110
J. Tod Noel *(Owner)*
Brian Courtright *(Bus Mgr)*

NOEL GROUP, LLC
501 NMC Dr, Zebulon, NC 27597
Tel.: (919) 570-0178 NC
Web Site: http://www.noelgroup.net
Year Founded: 1996
Investment Holding Company; Engineered Synthetic Materials Products Mfr
N.A.I.C.S.: 551112
Marc Noel *(CEO)*

Subsidiaries:

Nomaco, Inc. (1)
501 NMC Dr, Zebulon, NC 27597-2762
Tel.: (919) 269-6500
Web Site: http://www.nomaco.com
Sales Range: $100-124.9 Million
Emp.: 300
Polyethelene Foam Mfr

N.A.I.C.S.: 326199
Marc Noel *(Chm)*
Kathryn Taylor *(Sec)*
Julian Young *(Pres-Nomaco Home Furnishings)*
Claude Demby *(CEO)*

Nomacorc, LLC (1)
400 Vintage Park Dr, Zebulon, NC 27597 (50%)
Tel.: (919) 460-2200
Web Site: http://www.nomacorc.com
Extruded Synthetic Wine Closures Mfr & Whslr
N.A.I.C.S.: 339999
Malcolm Thompson *(VP-Strategy & Innovation)*
Jay Cummins *(VP-Global Sls)*
John Wojcik *(VP-Ops-North America)*
Lars von Kantzow *(Pres & CEO)*
Heino Freudenberg *(CEO)*
Marc Noel *(Chm)*

NOFZIGER DOOR SALES, INC.
8280 Estates Pkwy, Plain City, OH 43064
Tel.: (614) 873-3905
Web Site: http://www.dublinohiogaragedoors.com
Year Founded: 1940
Sales Range: $10-24.9 Million
Emp.: 10
Lumber & Building Material Whslr
N.A.I.C.S.: 444110
Jon Nofziger *(Principal)*

NOGAMA CONSTRUCTION CORP.
Metro Office Park Ste 310, Guaynabo, PR 00968
Tel.: (787) 273-7633
Web Site: http://www.nogama.com
Sales Range: $25-49.9 Million
Emp.: 175
Construction Engineering Services
N.A.I.C.S.: 237310
Warren Gonzalez *(Treas)*

NOGGINLABS, INC.
4621 N Ravenswood Ave Ste 303, Chicago, IL 60640
Tel.: (773) 878-9011
Web Site: http://www.nogginlabs.com
Year Founded: 1997
Rev.: $5,100,000
Emp.: 52
Educational Support Services
N.A.I.C.S.: 611710
Brian Knudson *(Co-Owner & CEO)*
Samantha Weber *(Dir-Sls & Mktg)*
Traci Knudson *(Co-Owner & CFO)*

NOL-TEC SYSTEMS INC.
425 Apollo Dr, Circle Pines, MN 55014
Tel.: (651) 237-7962
Web Site: http://www.nol-tec.com
Emp.: 62
Conveyors & Conveying Equipment Mfr
N.A.I.C.S.: 333922
Jerry VanDerWerff *(Reg Mgr-Sls)*
Lynn Joachim *(Treas & Sec)*

Subsidiaries:

Nol-Tec Europe, S.r.l. (1)
Via Milano 4, 20064, Gorgonzola, Italy
Tel.: (39) 02 95 16 875
Web Site: http://www.nol-teceurope.com
Industrial Machinery Mfr
N.A.I.C.S.: 333248

Nol-Tec Systems (Asia) Pte. Ltd. (1)
No 10 Admiralty Street 02-14 Northlink Building, Singapore, 757695, Singapore
Tel.: (65) 6753 5535
Web Site: http://www.nol-tecasia.com.sg
Industrial Machinery Mfr
N.A.I.C.S.: 333248

NOLAN CAPITAL, INC.

Nol-Tec Systems Inc.—(Continued)

NOLAN CAPITAL, INC.
58 11th St, Hermosa Beach, CA 90254
Tel.: (424) 675-7605
Web Site: https://nolancap.com
Year Founded: 2014
Holding Company
N.A.I.C.S.: 551112
James Shin (CFO)
Peter J. Nolan (Founder)

Subsidiaries:

Coastal Farm & Home Supply, LLC (1)
1355 Goldfish Farm Rd SE, Albany, OR 97322
Tel.: (541) 967-3450
Web Site: https://www.coastalcountry.com
Rev.: $16,600,000
Emp.: 300
Feed & Farm Supply
N.A.I.C.S.: 459999
Bruce Wheeler (Pres)

Water Engineering, Inc. (1)
1574 County Rd 10, Mead, NE 68041
Tel.: (402) 624-2286
Sales Range: $1-9.9 Million
Emp.: 16
Basic Inorganic Chemical Mfr
N.A.I.C.S.: 325180
John Gallagher (Mgr-Sls)
Vickie Push (Controller)
Bill Flagle (Production Mgr)
David Wagenfuhr (CEO)

Subsidiary (Domestic):

American Water Treatment, Inc. (2)
6324 Bartmer Ave, Saint Louis, MO 63130
Tel.: (314) 721-0470
Web Site: http://www.americanwatertreatment.com
Electronic & Precision Equipment Repair & Maintenance
N.A.I.C.S.: 811210
Eric Wilson (VP)

Delta Chemical Corp. (2)
757 Central Ave, Jefferson, LA 70121
Tel.: (504) 733-0630
Web Site: https://www.deltachemicalcorp.com
Rev.: $4,410,000
Emp.: 14
Power Boiler & Heat Exchanger Mfr
N.A.I.C.S.: 332410
Jack Felde (Mgr)

Earthwise Environmental, Inc. (2)
1290 Mark St, Bensenville, IL 60106
Tel.: (630) 475-3070
Web Site: http://www.earthwiseenvironmental.com
Sales Range: $1-9.9 Million
Emp.: 9
Commercial & Service Industry Machine Mfr
N.A.I.C.S.: 333310
Robert S. Miller (Founder & Pres)

Scientific Boiler Water Conditioning Co, Inc. (2)
515 Pennsylvania Ave, Linden, NJ 07036
Tel.: (908) 486-2000
Web Site: http://www.sci-water.com
Sales Range: $1-9.9 Million
Emp.: 10
Miscellaneous Chemical Product & Preparation Mfr
N.A.I.C.S.: 325998

NOLAN'S RV CENTER INC.
6935 Federal Blvd, Denver, CO 80221
Tel.: (303) 429-6114
Web Site: http://www.nolansrv.com
Rev.: $17,000,000
Emp.: 65
Recreational Vehicle Dealers
N.A.I.C.S.: 441210
Jerry C. Nolan (Pres)
Jack Nolan (VP)
Linda Pasco (Controller)

NOLAND HEALTH SERVICES, INC.
600 Corporate Pkwy Ste 100, Birmingham, AL 35242
Tel.: (205) 783-8440
Web Site: http://www.nolandhealth.com
Year Founded: 1913
Rehabilitation & Healthcare Services
N.A.I.C.S.: 621999
Carol Knight (VP-Senior Living Div)
John Heffner (VP-Hospital Div)
Gary M. Glasscock (Pres & CEO)
R. Gary Goff (CFO & Exec VP)
Melody Banks (VP-HR)

NOLAND SALES CORP.
815 Mittel Dr, Wood Dale, IL 60191
Tel.: (630) 787-9500
Web Site: http://www.nolandsales.com
Sales Range: $10-24.9 Million
Emp.: 60
Carpet Distr
N.A.I.C.S.: 423220
Jeffrey Chassee (Pres)
Erika McCormick (Project Mgr)
Mike Ryan (VP-Ops)

NOLIN RURAL ELECTRIC COOPERATIVE CORPORATION
411 Ring Rd, Elizabethtown, KY 42701
Tel.: (270) 765-6153
Web Site: http://www.nolinrecc.com
Rev.: $32,648,287
Emp.: 96
Distribution, Electric Power
N.A.I.C.S.: 221122
Michael L. Miller (Pres)
Cheryl Thomas (VP-Office Svcs)

NOLL HUMAN RESOURCE SERVICE
12905 W Dodge Rd, Omaha, NE 68154
Tel.: (402) 391-7736
Web Site: http://www.nolljobs.com
Year Founded: 1976
Sales Range: $10-24.9 Million
Emp.: 20
Provider of Human Resource Services
N.A.I.C.S.: 561311
Peggy Noll (Exec VP)
Laura Gano (Mgr-Ops)

NON-METALLIC COMPONENTS INC.
650 Northern Ct, Poynette, WI 53955
Tel.: (608) 635-7366
Web Site: http://www.nonmetallic.com
Sales Range: $10-24.9 Million
Emp.: 90
Sales of Plastic Injection Molders
N.A.I.C.S.: 326199
Stuart Varner (Pres)

NONANTUM CAPITAL PARTNERS LLC
888 Boylston St Ste 1100, Boston, MA 02199
Tel.: (617) 245-8050
Web Site: http://nonantumcapital.com
Privater Equity Firm
N.A.I.C.S.: 523999
Ronald M. De Feo (Co-Founder & Partner)
Jon Biotti (Mng Partner)

Subsidiaries:

Ross-Simons Inc. (1)
9 Ross Simons Dr, Cranston, RI 02920-4475
Tel.: (401) 463-3100
Web Site: http://www.ross-simons.com
Sales Range: $50-74.9 Million
Emp.: 400
Catalog & Mail-Order Services
N.A.I.C.S.: 458310
Darrell S. Ross (CEO)

NONBOX
5307 S 92nd St, Hales Corners, WI 53130-1677
Tel.: (414) 425-8800
Year Founded: 1959
Sales Range: $10-24.9 Million
Emp.: 25
Brand Development, Strategic Planning
N.A.I.C.S.: 541810
Bill Eisner (Owner)

Subsidiaries:

Nonbox (1)
319 SW Washington St Mezzanine Level, Portland, OR 97204
Tel.: (503) 227-1638
Sales Range: $10-24.9 Million
Emp.: 12
N.A.I.C.S.: 541810
Steve Karakas (Partner)
Dave Parmley (Partner)
Ian Hamilton (Dir-Sports Mktg)
Steve Flood (Partner)
Katie Williams (Acct Coord)

Nonbox (1)
1970 E OSCEOLA Pkwy Ste 47, Orlando, FL 34743
Tel.: (321) 287-4919
Emp.: 10
N.A.I.C.S.: 541810
Scott Jeffery (Partner)

NONINVASIVE MEDICAL TECHNOLOGIES, INC.
6412 S Arville St, Las Vegas, NV 89118
Tel.: (702) 614-3360
Web Site: http://www.nmtinc.org
Sales Range: Less than $1 Million
Emp.: 18
Medical Device Developer, Mfr & Marketer
N.A.I.C.S.: 339112
Ronald McCaughan (Chm & CEO)

NONPAREIL CORPORATION
40 N 400 W, Blackfoot, ID 83221-5632
Tel.: (208) 785-5880
Year Founded: 1950
Sales Range: $25-49.9 Million
Emp.: 200
Mfr of Fresh Potatoes & Provider of Dehydrated Fruits, Vegetables & Soups
N.A.I.C.S.: 311423
Christopher T. Abend (Pres)
Jace Katseanes (Controller & Mgr-Benefits)
Brett Suthers (Mgr-Engrg & Environmental)
Carlos Mercado (Mgr-HR)
Dee Bjarenson (Mgr-Process Quality & Food Safety)
Mark Gabrylczyk (Mgr-Natl Food Svc)
Tim Thie (Mgr-Sls)
Patti Callison (Mgr-Logistics)
Rulon Robinson (Mgr-Traffic)

Subsidiaries:

Idaho Potato Packers Corporation (1)
40 N 400 W, Blackfoot, ID 83221-5632 (100%)
Tel.: (208) 785-5880
Sales Range: $50-74.9 Million
Emp.: 150
Provider of Fresh Fruits & Vegetables
N.A.I.C.S.: 424480
Christopher T. Abend (Pres)

NONPROFIT VOTE
2464 Massachusetts Ave Ste 210, Cambridge, MA 02140
Tel.: (617) 357-8683
Web Site: http://www.nonprofitvote.org
Year Founded: 2006
Sales Range: $1-9.9 Million
Emp.: 4
Vote Right Protection Services
N.A.I.C.S.: 561990
Brian Miller (Exec Dir)
Amy Kreines (Office Mgr)
Julian Johannesen (Dir-Res & Trng)
Michael Weekes (Chm)
Martina Bouey (Treas)

NONPROFITEASY, INC.
1300 Valley House Dr Ste 100-41, Rohnert Park, CA 94928
Tel.: (707) 929-3563
Web Site: http://www.nonprofiteasy.com
Software Developer
N.A.I.C.S.: 513210
Lomesh Shah (Founder & CEO)

Subsidiaries:

Fundly Inc. (1)
2390 El Camino Real, Palo Alto, CA 94306
Tel.: (650) 493-5886
Web Site: http://www.fundly.com
Software Publisher
N.A.I.C.S.: 513210
Mike Nobil (VP-Ops)
Dennis Hu (CEO)

NOODLES BY LEONARDO INC.
1702 Schwan Ave NW, Devils Lake, ND 58301
Tel.: (701) 662-8300
Year Founded: 1978
Sales Range: $25-49.9 Million
Emp.: 100
Macaroni & Spaghetti
N.A.I.C.S.: 311824
Leonard Gasparre (Pres)
Ken Auni (Controller)

NOOK INDUSTRIES INC.
4950 E 49th St, Cleveland, OH 44125
Tel.: (216) 271-7900
Web Site: http://www.nookindustries.com
Year Founded: 1969
Sales Range: $25-49.9 Million
Emp.: 200
Screw Machine Products
N.A.I.C.S.: 332721
Ron Doneck (Pres)
Greg Burkhart (Dir-HR)
Jim Mangan (VP-Sls)
David Semanik (Mgr-IT)

NOOKA INC.
16 W 36th St Ste 1302, New York, NY 10018
Tel.: (212) 216-0056
Web Site: http://www.nooka.com
Year Founded: 2004
Sales Range: $1-9.9 Million
Emp.: 20
Watches & Other Fashion Accessories
N.A.I.C.S.: 334519
Matthew Waldman (Founder)

NOON HOUR FOOD PRODUCTS, INC.
215 N Des Plaines St, Chicago, IL 60661-1140
Tel.: (312) 382-1177
Web Site: http://www.noonhourfoods.com

Year Founded: 1876
Sales Range: $25-49.9 Million
Emp.: 75
Herring, Cheese & Specialty Pancakes Producer
N.A.I.C.S.: 424490
Paul A. Buhl *(Pres)*
Pat Freeman *(Treas)*

NOON IMPORT-EXPORT SALES, INC.
5506 6th Ave S Ste 101, Seattle, WA 98108
Tel.: (206) 283-8400   CA
Web Site: http://www.noon-intl.com
Year Founded: 1977
Sales Range: $10-24.9 Million
Emp.: 16
General Line Groceries
N.A.I.C.S.: 424410
Veronica Brown *(Controller)*

NOON TURF CARE
582 Main St, Hudson, MA 01749
Tel.: (978) 562-1707
Web Site:
   http://www.noonturfcare.com
Year Founded: 2001
Sales Range: $1-9.9 Million
Emp.: 40
Lawn Fertilization & Insect Control
N.A.I.C.S.: 561710
Jerry Fuller *(Mgr-Comml Sls)*
Sabrina Uhlman *(Mgr-Customer Loyalty)*
Kevin Schofield *(Reg Mgr-Sls)*
Allison Radzewicz *(Dir-HR)*

NOONAN BROTHERS PETROLEUM PRODUCTS
415 W St, West Bridgewater, MA 02379
Tel.: (508) 588-8026
Web Site: http://www.jpnoonan.com
Rev.: $33,021,080
Emp.: 50
Petroleum Products
N.A.I.C.S.: 424720
J. Peter Noonan Sr. *(Pres)*

NOONAN ENERGY CORPORATION
86 Robbins Rd, Springfield, MA 01104
Tel.: (413) 734-7396   MA
Web Site:
   http://www.noonanenergy.com
Year Founded: 1890
Rev.: $21,400,000
Emp.: 55
Fuel Oil Dealers
N.A.I.C.S.: 457210
Edward J. Noonan *(Chm)*
Ted Noonan *(Pres & CEO)*

NOOR, INC.
12 W 37th St Ste 501, New York, NY 10018
Tel.: (212) 812-3390
Web Site: http://www.noorinc.com
Staffing Agency
N.A.I.C.S.: 561311
Habib Noor *(Owner)*

Subsidiaries:

The Legal Group Inc.   (1)
1560 Sawgrass Corporate Pkwy 4th Fl, Fort Lauderdale, FL 33323
Tel.: (954) 331-1077
Web Site: http://www.thelegalgroup.net
Law firm
N.A.I.C.S.: 541110
Amy Levin *(CEO)*
Laura Joy Pedowitz *(Dir-Client Dev)*
Ayleen Gonzalez *(COO)*
Charline Ramon *(Dir-Legal Recruitment)*

NOOSH INC.
1300 Island Dr Ste 201, Redwood City, CA 94065
Tel.: (650) 637-6000
Web Site: http://www.noosh.com
Rev.: $17,200,000
Emp.: 40
Custom Computer Programming Services
N.A.I.C.S.: 541511
Dave Hannebrink *(COO)*
Jerome Marcus *(Mng Dir)*

NOPETRO, LLC
3848 killearn Ct, Tallahassee, FL 32309
Tel.: (850) 224-4516
Web Site: http://www.nopetro.com
Year Founded: 2007
Sales Range: $1-9.9 Million
Emp.: 7
Compressed & Liquefied Natural Gas Fueling Stations Construction & Supply Services
N.A.I.C.S.: 237120
Jorge A. Herrera *(Co-Founder & CEO)*
Jonathan Locke *(Co-Founder, Pres & COO)*
Walter Bussells *(CFO)*
Andre Salcines *(VP-Construction)*
Jose David Santizo *(Mgr-Maintenence & Supvr-Station Ops)*
Christopher Pina *(Dir-Mktg)*
Mayra Urbano *(Controller)*
R. Edward Hart *(Dir-Natural Gas Supply Chain Mgmt)*

NOR-CAL BEVERAGE CO., INC.
2286 Stone Blvd, West Sacramento, CA 95691-4050
Tel.: (916) 372-0600   CA
Web Site: http://www.ncbev.com
Year Founded: 1937
Sales Range: $100-124.9 Million
Emp.: 620
Bottler & Whslr of Soft Drinks, Fruit Juices & Beer; Full Line Vending Operations, Food Service & Trucking
N.A.I.C.S.: 312111
Donald R. Deary *(Chm)*
Shelly Ingrim *(VP-Sls & Mktg)*
Mike Matroni *(COO)*
Diane Carlin *(Mgr-Benefits)*
Shannon Deary-Bell *(Pres & CEO)*

NOR-CAL FOODS, INC.
3421 Tully Rd, Modesto, CA 95350-0839
Tel.: (209) 521-9201
Web Site: http://www.deltaco.com
Year Founded: 2001
Sales Range: $10-24.9 Million
Emp.: 202
Restaurant Operating Services
N.A.I.C.S.: 722513
Roberto Martinez *(Pres)*

NOR-CAL MOVING SERVICES
2001 Marina Blvd, San Leandro, CA 94577-3204
Tel.: (510) 357-7111   CA
Web Site: http://www.nor-calmoving.com
Year Founded: 1982
Sales Range: $50-74.9 Million
Emp.: 300
Local Trucking with Storage
N.A.I.C.S.: 484210
Peter Mazzetti *(Pres)*
Bev Klein *(VP)*
Dave Konecny *(VP)*
Anthony Vukovic *(VP)*

NOR-COTE INTERNATIONAL INC.
506 Lafayette Ave, Crawfordsville, IN 47933
Tel.: (765) 362-9180
Web Site: http://www.norcote.com
Year Founded: 1976
Rev.: $17,000,000
Emp.: 60
Mfr & Sales of Printing Ink
N.A.I.C.S.: 325910
Ray Siebrase *(Dir-Mfg)*

NOR-MAR INC.
6550 Gunpark Dr, Boulder, CO 80301
Tel.: (303) 581-0300
Year Founded: 1968
Sales Range: $75-99.9 Million
Emp.: 500
Holding Company; Fast Food Restaurants Owner & Operator
N.A.I.C.S.: 551112
Joe Lukas *(Pres)*
John Kay *(Controller)*

NORAC COMPANY INC.
405 S Motor Ave, Azusa, CA 91702
Tel.: (626) 334-2908
Web Site: http://www.norac.com
Sales Range: $25-49.9 Million
Emp.: 60
Industrial Organic Chemicals
N.A.I.C.S.: 325199
Wallace McCloskey *(Pres)*
Frank Parish *(Controller)*

NORAIR ENGINEERING CORPORATION
337 Brightseat Rd Ste 200, Landover, MD 20785
Tel.: (301) 499-2202
Web Site: http://www.norair.com
Sales Range: $25-49.9 Million
Emp.: 100
Industrial Plant Construction
N.A.I.C.S.: 237990
Dragan Sdoganovic *(VP)*
Susan Peck *(Controller & Office Mgr)*
Richard H. Norair Jr. *(Pres)*

NORAM INTERNATIONAL PARTNERS LLC
61 Spit Brool Ste 407, Nashua, NH 03060
Tel.: (978) 857-7451
Web Site:
   http://www.norampartners.com
Year Founded: 2006
Sales Range: $10-24.9 Million
Emp.: 45
Buys & Resells Overstock Items & Customer Returns
N.A.I.C.S.: 561499
Michael DuGally *(Co-Founder & COO)*
Kellie DuGally *(Co-Founder, Pres & CEO)*

NORBELLA INC.
46 Plympton St, Boston, MA 02118
Tel.: (617) 542-1040
Rev.: $40,000,000
N.A.I.C.S.: 541810
Stephanie Noris *(Pres)*
Greg Angland *(Dir-Media)*
Alice Campbell *(Dir-Bus Dev)*

NORBERT E. MITCHELL CO. INC.
7 Federal Rd, Danbury, CT 06810
Tel.: (203) 744-0600   CT
Web Site: http://www.nemitchell.com
Year Founded: 1987
Sales Range: $25-49.9 Million
Emp.: 120
Provider of Petroleum Products & Services
N.A.I.C.S.: 457210
Mike Moffa *(Controller)*
Ginamarie Defreitas *(Coord-Delivery)*
Todd Rossi *(Mgr)*
Norbert Mitchell Jr. *(Pres)*

NORBEST, INC.
PO Box 890, Moroni, UT 84646   UT
Web Site: http://www.norbest.com
Year Founded: 1930
Sales Range: $1-9.9 Million
Emp.: 1,200
Mfr of Fresh & Frozen Turkeys & Poultry Products
N.A.I.C.S.: 424440
Robert Wangerien *(Sr VP-Sls & Mktg)*
Hank Huang *(Dir-R&D)*

NORBY DISTRIBUTING CO.
5700 Saratoga Rd, Dubuque, IA 52002
Tel.: (563) 556-8972
Web Site:
   http://www.norbysfarmfleet.com
Rev.: $17,400,000
Emp.: 99
Distr of Hardware
N.A.I.C.S.: 423710
Gregory W. Norby *(Pres)*
Paula Norby *(VP)*

NORCAL GOLD, INC.
5200 Sunrise Blvd Ste 5, Fair Oaks, CA 95628
Tel.: (916) 536-7600   CA
Web Site: http://www.remaxgold.com
Year Founded: 1994
Emp.: 100
Real Estate Agency
N.A.I.C.S.: 531210
James O'Bryon *(Pres)*

Subsidiaries:

Norcal Gold, Inc. - Fair Oaks   (1)
5252 Sunrise Blvd Ste 6, Fair Oaks, CA 95628
Tel.: (916) 537-2400
Web Site: http://www.remaxgold.com
Sales Range: $1-9.9 Million
Emp.: 75
Real Estate Agency
N.A.I.C.S.: 531210
Monica Francis *(Mgr-Employee Svcs)*

Norcal Gold, Inc. - Lodi   (1)
1217 W Tokay St Ste A, Lodi, CA 95240
Tel.: (209) 368-5311
Web Site: http://www.remaxgold.com
Sales Range: $1-9.9 Million
Emp.: 25
Real Estate Agency
N.A.I.C.S.: 531210
Jennie Alvarez *(Coord-Transaction)*

Norcal Gold, Inc. - Sacramento   (1)
3620 Fair Oaks Blvd Ste 300, Sacramento, CA 95864
Tel.: (916) 609-2800
Web Site: http://www.remaxgold.com
Sales Range: $1-9.9 Million
Real Estate Agency Services
N.A.I.C.S.: 531390

NORCAL RENTAL GROUP LLC
800 E Airway Blvd, Livermore, CA 94550
Tel.: (925) 456-9750
Web Site: http://www.crescorent.com
Sales Range: $10-24.9 Million
Emp.: 150
Provider of Heavy Construction Equipment Rental Services
N.A.I.C.S.: 532412
Chris Smith *(Pres)*

NORCO DELIVERY SERVICES

NORCO DELIVERY SERVICES

Norco Delivery Services—(Continued)
851 E Cerritos Ave, Anaheim, CA 92805
Tel.: (714) 520-8600
Web Site:
  http://www.norcodelivery.com
Rev.: $14,300,000
Emp.: 258
General Freight Trucking, Local
N.A.I.C.S.: 484110
Mark Nakaihara *(VP-Sls)*
David Rich *(VP)*
Tom Hoskins *(CEO)*

NORCO INDUSTRIES, INC.
365 W Victoria St, Compton, CA 90220-6062
Tel.: (310) 639-4000
Web Site:
  http://www.norcoindustries.com
Year Founded: 1964
Sales Range: $10-24.9 Million
Emp.: 120
General Industrial Machinery
N.A.I.C.S.: 333998
David Miller *(VP-Ops)*

NORCO, INC.
1125 W Amity Rd, Boise, ID 83705-5412
Tel.: (208) 336-1643 ID
Web Site: http://www.norco-inc.com
Year Founded: 1948
Sales Range: $50-74.9 Million
Emp.: 1,200
Industrial Machinery & Equipment
N.A.I.C.S.: 423830
Jim Kissler *(CEO)*
Ned Pontious *(Pres)*
Brent Seward *(VP-Medical)*
Troy Johnson *(VP-Central Zone)*
George Douzenis *(VP-Eastern Zone)*
Mike Calcaterra *(VP-Northern Zone)*
Larry Booth *(Mgr-Welding Products)*
Jason Whitehead *(Mgr-Bulk Gas)*
Keith Partch *(Mgr-Specialty Gas)*
Robert Mohr Gerry *(VP-Indus)*
Elias Margonis *(Pres)*
Mike Sabin *(CFO)*

Subsidiaries:

Norco Inc. - Ephrata Fill Gas Plant (1)
276 Enterprise St, Ephrata, WA 98823
Tel.: (509) 754-3518
Industrial Machinery & Equipment Mfr
N.A.I.C.S.: 333310
Chris Voss *(Mgr)*

Norco Inc. - Lewiston Fill Gas Plant (1)
1102 Snake River Ave, Lewiston, ID 83501
Tel.: (208) 746-0508
Industrial Machinery & Equipment Mfr
N.A.I.C.S.: 333310
Doug Dvorak *(Mgr)*

Norco Inc. - Moses Lake A.S.U. Plant (1)
2757 Road N NE, Moses Lake, WA 98837
Tel.: (509) 764-5032
Industrial Machinery & Equipment Mfr
N.A.I.C.S.: 333310
Sean Welch *(Mgr)*

Norco Inc. - Nampa A.S.U. Plant (1)
16205 Norco Way, Nampa, ID 83687
Tel.: (208) 461-9324
Industrial Machinery & Equipment Mfr
N.A.I.C.S.: 333310
Steve Reinhart *(Mgr)*

NORCOM INC.
200 Wilson Rd, Griffin, GA 30223
Tel.: (770) 447-5525
Web Site: http://www.norcominc.com
Year Founded: 1978
Sales Range: $25-49.9 Million
Emp.: 135

Notebooks: Made From Purchased Paper
N.A.I.C.S.: 322230
Kathy Maddox *(Mgr-Accts)*
Hal Rahn *(Pres & CEO)*
Joe Zelazny *(CFO)*

NORCON INC.
661 W Ohio St, Chicago, IL 60654-5516
Tel.: (312) 715-9200
Web Site: http://www.norconinc.com
Year Founded: 2000
Sales Range: $50-74.9 Million
Emp.: 47
Nonresidential Construction Services
N.A.I.C.S.: 236220
Charles Norwesh *(Pres)*

NORCON INDUSTRIES INC.
5412 E Calle Cerrito, Tempe, AZ 85283
Tel.: (480) 839-2324
Web Site:
  http://www.norconindustries.net
Year Founded: 1974
Sales Range: $10-24.9 Million
Emp.: 48
Mfr of Floor Coverings
N.A.I.C.S.: 423220
Nicole Hahn *(Office Mgr)*

NORCOR TECHNOLOGIES CORPORATION
338 S Sharon Amity Rd, Charlotte, NC 28211
Tel.: (704) 309-4101 FL
Web Site:
  http://www.norcortechnologies.com
Technology, Energy & Construction Products
N.A.I.C.S.: 334419
Mark Clayton *(Pres & Treas)*
Marquis Bey *(Sec)*
Robert Warner *(VP)*
Wellesley K. Clayton Sr. *(CEO)*

NORCOSTCO, INC.
825 Rhode Is Ave S, Minneapolis, MN 55426-1611
Tel.: (763) 544-0601 MN
Web Site: http://www.norcostco.com
Year Founded: 1884
Sales Range: $50-74.9 Million
Emp.: 50
Provider of Retail & Rental of Formal Wear; Mens, Boys & Womens Clothing; Theatrical Supplies & Costumes
N.A.I.C.S.: 423490
Erik Schindler *(Pres)*
Rob Koontz *(Project Mgr)*

NORCROSS COMPANY
900 Spring St, Petoskey, MI 49770
Tel.: (231) 347-2501
Web Site:
  http://www.prestonfeather.com
Year Founded: 1979
Sales Range: $10-24.9 Million
Emp.: 115
Retailer of Lumber & Other Building Materials
N.A.I.C.S.: 423310
William N. Norcross *(Pres)*

NORDER SUPPLY, INC (NSI)
136 E Main St, Bruning, NE 68322-0010
Tel.: (402) 353-6175
Web Site:
  http://www.nordersupply.com
Sales Range: $10-24.9 Million
Emp.: 12
Crop Protection, Seed, Fertilizer, Grain, Custom Applications & Agronomic Consultations & Services

N.A.I.C.S.: 424910
Tim Norder *(Pres)*

NORDIC AVIATION CAPITAL INC.
401 E Las Olas Blvd Ste 1700, Fort Lauderdale, FL 33301
Tel.: (954) 763-4737
Web Site: http://www.nac.dk
Year Founded: 1990
Aircraft Leasing, Management & Technical Support to General & Corporate Customers
N.A.I.C.S.: 522220
Neville Taylor *(Head-Mktg)*
Elaine Kirby *(Chief Contract Officer)*
Morten Mikkelsen *(CFO-Billund)*
Gareth Halpin *(Chief Funding Officer-Limerick)*
Mike Jones *(Exec VP-Global Mktg)*
David Farrell *(Chief Risk Officer & ExecVP)*
Colin Joyce *(Exec VP-Mktg Ops)*
Ross McKeand *(Sr VP-Specialty Markets & Fleet Plng)*
Norman C. T. Liu *(Pres & CEO)*
Eva Ferguson *(VP-Mktg & Comm)*
Brian Power *(Exec VP-Fleet Ops)*

NORDIC COLD STORAGE, LLC
4300 Pleasantdale Rd, Atlanta, GA 30340-3526
Tel.: (770) 448-7400 DE
Web Site: http://www.nordiccold.com
Sales Range: $150-199.9 Million
Public Storage Warehousing
N.A.I.C.S.: 493120
Don Schoenl *(Pres & CEO)*
Peter S. Wareing *(Vice Chm)*
Tracy Matthews *(VP-Sls)*

NORDIC CONTRACTING COMPANY, INCORPORATED
111 Howard Blvd, Ledgewood, NJ 07852
Tel.: (973) 584-2000
Web Site:
  http://www.nordiccontractinginc.com
Year Founded: 1993
Sales Range: $50-74.9 Million
Emp.: 200
Remodeling Services
N.A.I.C.S.: 236118
John Jacobsen *(Pres)*
Ken Jacobsen *(Pres)*
Ted Vitcusky *(VP)*
Jody Larson *(Project Mgr)*
John Hanright *(Project Mgr)*
Janet Jacobsen *(Mgr-Payroll)*
Lisa Miller *(Mgr-Contract)*
Bob Tiefenbacher *(Controller)*
Linda White *(Office Mgr)*
Gil Wright *(Project Mgr)*
Warren Burgher *(Project Mgr)*
Wally Peer III *(Project Mgr)*

NORDIC ENERGY SERVICES, LLC
1 Tower Ln Ste 300, Oakbrook Terrace, IL 60181
Tel.: (630) 321-0888
Web Site: http://www.nordicenergy-us.com
Year Founded: 2004
Sales Range: $25-49.9 Million
Emp.: 20
Alternative Retail Electric & Natural Gas Services
N.A.I.C.S.: 221122
James C. Deering *(CEO)*
Michael Stein *(VP-Fin)*
Blake Birch *(Dir-Regulatory Affairs)*
Adam Bashe *(Chief Sls Officer)*

NORDIC GROUP OF COMPANIES, LTD.
715 Lynn Ave Ste 100, Baraboo, WI 53913-2488
Tel.: (608) 356-0136 WI
Web Site:
  http://www.nordicgroup.com
Year Founded: 1947
Sales Range: $200-249.9 Million
Emp.: 2,000
Holding Company for Manufacturing & Marketing Companies
N.A.I.C.S.: 541611
William R. Sauey *(Chm)*

Subsidiaries:

Columbia ParCar Corp. (1)
1115 Commercial Ave, Reedsburg, WI 53959-2133
Tel.: (608) 524-4600
Web Site: http://www.parcar.com
Rev.: $12,000,000
Emp.: 85
Mfr of Golf Cars, Passenger, Commercial & Utility Vehicles
N.A.I.C.S.: 336999
Todd Sauey *(Chm & CEO)*
Scott Breckley *(COO & Exec VP)*
Jim Dorman *(VP-Bus Dev)*

Flambeau, Inc. (1)
801 Lynn Ave, Baraboo, WI 53913
Tel.: (608) 355-6500
Web Site: http://www.flambeau.com
Injection & Blow Molded Components Mfr
N.A.I.C.S.: 326199
Jason Sauey *(Pres & CEO)*
Dennis Cook *(VP-Medical Markets Grp)*
Troy Deppey *(VP-North America)*

Division (Domestic):

Duncan Toys Company (2)
15981 Valplast St, Middlefield, OH 44062-0005 (100%)
Tel.: (440) 632-1631
Web Site: http://www.yo-yo.com
Sales Range: $25-49.9 Million
Emp.: 20
Toy Mfr
N.A.I.C.S.: 459120

Subsidiary (Non-US):

Flambeau Europlast, Ltd. (2)
Manston Road, Ramsgate, CT12 6HW, Kent, United Kingdom
Tel.: (44) 1843 854000
Plastics Product Mfr
N.A.I.C.S.: 322219
Neil Bizley *(Bus Mgr-Duncan)*
John Wingfield *(Mng Dir)*

Subsidiary (Domestic):

The Neat Nursery Co. (3)
Manston Road, Ramsgate, CT12 6HW, Kent, United Kingdom
Tel.: (44) 1843 854 000
Web Site: http://www.neatnursery.com
Molded Plastic Product Mfr
N.A.I.C.S.: 326199
John Wingfield *(Mng Dir)*

Branch (Domestic):

Flambeau Inc. (2)
15981 Valplast St, Middlefield, OH 44062-0097 (100%)
Tel.: (440) 632-1631
Web Site: http://www.flambeau.com
Sales Range: $150-199.9 Million
Emp.: 1,500
Toy Mfr
N.A.I.C.S.: 339930
Heather Gifford *(Coord-Pur & Production)*
Carolyn Corley *(Mgr-Ops-Middlefield)*
Dave Jamison *(Product Dir-New Dev)*
Jason Sauey *(Pres)*

Division (Domestic):

Flambeau Plastics Co. (2)
801 Lynn Ave, Baraboo, WI 53913-2746 (100%)
Tel.: (608) 356-5551
Web Site: http://www.flambeau.com

Sales Range: $75-99.9 Million
Emp.: 400
Mfr of Engineered Plastic Products for Original Equipment
N.A.I.C.S.: 326199
Chris Gurreri (CEO)

Branch (Domestic):

Flambeau Products-Columbus (2)
4325 Middle Rd, Columbus, IN 47203-1830
Tel.: (812) 372-4899
Web Site: http://www.flambeau.com
Sales Range: $50-74.9 Million
Emp.: 200
Mfr of Hardware Boxes & Cabinets & Toolboxes
N.A.I.C.S.: 326199

Division (Domestic):

Flambeau Southeast Co. (2)
1330 Atlanta Hwy, Madison, GA 30650-2068 (100%)
Tel.: (706) 342-8300
Web Site: http://www.flamcorp.com
Sales Range: $25-49.9 Million
Emp.: 150
Mfr of Engineered Plastic Product & Fluid Systems (Cap, Tanks, Fittings)
N.A.I.C.S.: 326199

Flambeau Technologies (2)
801 Lynn Ave, Baraboo, WI 53913-2746
Tel.: (608) 356-5551
Web Site: http://www.flambeau.com
Sales Range: $75-99.9 Million
Emp.: 500
Plastics Product Mfr
N.A.I.C.S.: 326199

Plant (Domestic):

Flambeau, Inc. - ArtBin Division (2)
15981 Valplast Rd, Middlefield, OH 44062
Tel.: (800) 232-3474
Web Site: http://www.artbin.com
Emp.: 200
Plastic Product Whslr
N.A.I.C.S.: 424610
Neil Bizley (Bus Mgr)

Flambeau, Inc. - Flambeau Blow Molding Facility (2)
715 Lynn Ave, Baraboo, WI 53913
Tel.: (608) 356-5551
Plastics Product Mfr
N.A.I.C.S.: 326199

Flambeau, Inc. - Flambeau Columbus Facility (2)
4325 Middle Rd, Columbus, IN 47203
Tel.: (812) 372-4899
Plastics Product Mfr
N.A.I.C.S.: 326199
Mark Shirley (Plant Mgr)

Division (Domestic):

Flambeau, Inc. - Flambeau Fluid Systems Division (2)
801 Lynn Ave, Baraboo, WI 53913
Tel.: (608) 355-6558
Web Site: http://www.flambeaufluids.com
Plastics Product Mfr
N.A.I.C.S.: 326199

Flambeau, Inc. - Flambeau Hardware Products Division (2)
15981 Valplast Rd, Middlefield, OH 44062
Tel.: (800) 457-5252
Web Site: http://www.flambeauhardware.com
Plastics Product Mfr
N.A.I.C.S.: 326199

Plant (Domestic):

Flambeau, Inc. - Flambeau Injection Molding Facility (2)
801 Lynn Ave, Baraboo, WI 53913
Tel.: (608) 356-5551
Web Site: http://www.flambeau.com
Emp.: 500
Plastics Product Mfr
N.A.I.C.S.: 326199

Flambeau, Inc. - Flambeau Madison Facility (2)
1330 Atlanta Hwy, Madison, GA 30650

Tel.: (706) 342-8300
Plastics Product Mfr
N.A.I.C.S.: 326199

Flambeau, Inc. - Flambeau Middlefield Facility (2)
15981 Valplast Rd, Middlefield, OH 44062-0097
Tel.: (440) 632-1631
Web Site: http://www.flambeau.com
Plastics Product Mfr
N.A.I.C.S.: 326199
Jason Sauey (CEO)

Division (Domestic):

Flambeau, Inc. - Flambeau Outdoors Division (2)
15981 Valplast Rd, Middlefield, OH 44062
Tel.: (800) 232-3474
Web Site: http://www.flambeauoutdoors.com
Emp.: 200
Hunting & Fishing Product Mfr
N.A.I.C.S.: 339920
Chris Gurreri (Gen Mgr)

Plant (Domestic):

Flambeau, Inc. - Flambeau Phoenix Facility (2)
3301 W Vernon Ave, Phoenix, AZ 85009
Tel.: (602) 484-4520
Web Site: http://www.flambeau.com
Thermoplastic Components Mfr
N.A.I.C.S.: 326199

Flambeau, Inc. - Flambeau Sharon Center Facility (2)
1468 Wolf Creek Trl, Sharon Center, OH 44274-0247
Tel.: (330) 239-0202
Web Site: http://www.flambeau.com
Plastics Product Mfr
N.A.I.C.S.: 326199

Flambeau, Inc. - Flambeau Weldon Facility (2)
100 Grace Dr, Weldon, NC 27890
Tel.: (252) 536-2171
Plastics Product Mfr
N.A.I.C.S.: 326199
David Faulkner (Gen Mgr)

Plant (Non-US):

Flambeau, Inc. - Plasticos Flambeau Facility (2)
Calle 17 No 3692 Ampliacion Morelos, 25217, Saltillo, Coahuila, Mexico
Tel.: (52) 844 411 9760
Web Site: http://www.flambeau.co.uk
Plastics Product Mfr
N.A.I.C.S.: 326199
Edward Tremor (CEO)

PACJETS Financial Ltd. (1)
PO Box 342, Baraboo, WI 53913
Tel.: (608) 356-7303
Web Site: http://www.pacjets.com
Automobile Leasing Services
N.A.I.C.S.: 532112
Lori Halvorson (Office Mgr)

Seats Incorporated (1)
1515 Industrial St, Reedsburg, WI 53959
Tel.: (608) 524-8261
Web Site: http://www.seatsinc.com
Rev.: $28,000,000
Emp.: 826
Mfr of Industrial, Recreational & Transportational Seating
N.A.I.C.S.: 337127
Gerald L. Ward (VP-Ops)

NORDIC INDUSTRIES INC.
1437 Furneaux Rd, Olivehurst, CA 95961
Tel.: (530) 742-7124   NV
Web Site: http://www.nordicind.com
Year Founded: 1990
Sales Range: $10-24.9 Million
Emp.: 60
Heavy Construction
N.A.I.C.S.: 236210
Dale Martin (Controller)
Mark Warner (Dir-Special Projects)

NORDIC NATURALS, INC.
111 Jennings Dr, Watsonville, CA 95076
Tel.: (831) 724-6200
Web Site: http://www.nordicnaturals.com
Sales Range: $1-9.9 Million
Emp.: 115
Health Supplements Mfr
N.A.I.C.S.: 325412
Joar Opheim (Pres)
Alexandra Vansandt (Supvr-Retail Sls)
Marci Van der Meulen (Mgr-Sls-Retail Div-Natl)
Meredith Greiner (Mgr-Mktg)

NORDIC TUGS INC.
11367 Higgins Airport Way, Burlington, WA 98233
Tel.: (360) 757-8847
Web Site: http://www.nordictugsinc.com
Sales Range: $10-24.9 Million
Emp.: 100
Tugboats Building & Repairing
N.A.I.C.S.: 336611
Dave Allen (Dir-Customer Svcs)

NORDIS DIRECT, INC.
4401 NW 124th Ave, Coral Springs, FL 33065
Tel.: (954) 323-5500
Web Site: http://www.nordisdirect.com
Year Founded: 1989
Sales Range: $10-24.9 Million
Emp.: 78
Marketing Consulting Services
N.A.I.C.S.: 541613
Ronnie Selinger (Founder, Pres & CEO)
Ira Turetsky (VP-Fin)
Deborah Risch (VP-Client Svcs & Installation)
Richard O'Rourke (Sr VP-Bus Dev)
Mike Rosini (VP-Ops)
Jane Ricketts (Dir-Client Svcs)
Julie Troum (Dir-Expresso Implementation)
Shelley Dolan (Dir-Mktg Comm)

NORDLIE INC.
25300 Guenther Rd, Warren, MI 48091-3759
Tel.: (586) 755-4200
Web Site: http://www.nordlie.com
Year Founded: 1928
Sales Range: $25-49.9 Million
Emp.: 180
Flowers & Florists Supplies Mfr & Whslr
N.A.I.C.S.: 424930
Jim Nordlie (Pres)
Thomas Addison (VP)
Tom Figueroa (VP-Michigan)

NORDON INC
691 Exch St, Rochester, NY 14608
Tel.: (585) 546-6200
Web Site: http://www.nordon.com
Sales Range: $10-24.9 Million
Emp.: 90
Injection Molding Of Plastics
N.A.I.C.S.: 326199
Terry J. Donovan (Pres)
Paul Reed (Bus Mgr)
John Buck (Engr-Sls)

NOREEN HERON & ASSOCIATES
1528 W Fullerton Ave, Chicago, IL 60614
Tel.: (773) 477-7666
Web Site: http://www.heronpr.com
Year Founded: 2000
Sales Range: $10-24.9 Million

Emp.: 7
Public Relations Agency
N.A.I.C.S.: 541820
Noreen Heron Zautcke (Pres)

NORFIELD INDUSTRIES
725 Entler Ave, Chico, CA 95928
Tel.: (530) 879-3137
Web Site: http://www.norfield.com
Year Founded: 1959
Sales Range: $10-24.9 Million
Emp.: 120
Mfr & Distributor of Doors
N.A.I.C.S.: 423840
Bruce Norlie (Pres)

NORFOLK DREDGING COMPANY
110 Centerville Tpke N, Chesapeake, VA 23320
Tel.: (757) 547-9391
Web Site: http://www.norfolkdredging.com
Year Founded: 1899
Sales Range: $25-49.9 Million
Emp.: 179
Dredging Contractor
N.A.I.C.S.: 236210

NORFOLK IRON & METAL CO. INC.
3001 N Victory Rd, Norfolk, NE 68702
Tel.: (402) 371-1810   NE
Web Site: http://www.norfolkiron.com
Year Founded: 1908
Sales Range: $125-149.9 Million
Emp.: 400
Metals Service Centers & Offices
N.A.I.C.S.: 423510
Richard A. Robinson (Pres)
Steve Ball (CFO)

NORFOLK TRUCK CENTER INCORPORATED
736 Tidewater Dr, Norfolk, VA 23504
Tel.: (757) 622-3246
Web Site: http://www.norfolktruckcenter.com
Sales Range: $10-24.9 Million
Emp.: 35
Retailer of Trucks & Truck Parts
N.A.I.C.S.: 441110
David Harlow (VP)
Bruce Harlow (Treas, Sec & VP)
John Harlow Sr. (Pres)

NORGE BUILDERS INC.
595 Union Blvd, Totowa, NJ 07512
Tel.: (800) 541-2198
Web Site: http://www.alliedbuilding.com
Sales Range: $10-24.9 Million
Emp.: 3,000
Roofing & Siding Materials
N.A.I.C.S.: 423330
Bob Feury Jr. (CEO)

NORGLEN CORPORATION
629 Broadway, Long Branch, NJ 07740
Tel.: (732) 222-3833
Sales Range: $1-9.9 Million
Emp.: 25
Automotive Supplies & Parts
N.A.I.C.S.: 423120
Robert Scheer (Pres)

NORIDIAN MUTUAL INSURANCE COMPANY
4510 13th Ave S, Fargo, ND 58121-0001
Tel.: (701) 282-1100   ND
Web Site: http://www.bcbsnd.com
Year Founded: 1940
Sales Range: $200-249.9 Million

NORIDIAN MUTUAL INSURANCE COMPANY

Noridian Mutual Insurance Company—(Continued)
Emp.: 1,300
Hospital & Medical Service Plans
N.A.I.C.S.: 524114
Tim Huckle (Pres & CEO)
Pam Gulleson (VP-Pub Affairs)
Greg C. Glasner (Vice Chm)
David Sprynczynatyk (Chm)
Daniel Conrad (Co-Chief Legal Officer & Exec VP)
Dave Breuer (CFO & Exec VP)
Stacie Heiden (Exec VP-Strategic Dev & Health Delivery)
Jon Bogenreif (Sr VP-Ops)
Joan McCusker (Sr VP-HR & Enterprise Risk Mgmt)
Pat Bellmore (CMO & Sr VP-Mktg)
Don Campbell (Co-Chief Legal Officer & Sr VP)

Subsidiaries:

Noridian Healthcare Solutions, LLC (1)
900 42nd St S, Fargo, ND 58103
Tel.: (877) 657-6474
Web Site: http://www.noridiansolutions.com
Health Care Srvces
N.A.I.C.S.: 321999
Kevin Erickson (Sr VP-Medicaid & State Ops)
Rich Haugen (CFO)
Jeanne Narum (VP-Compliance & Audit)
Fran Ask (Project Mgr-Admin)
Joe Williamson (Dir-Govt Affairs)
Jon Bogenreif (Pres & CEO)
Tiff Dschaak (VP-Product & Bid Mgmt)
Robert Barela (Chief Growth Officer & Sr VP)
Ranga Nutakki (Gen Counsel, Sec & Sr VP)
Jennifer Sandell (Sr VP-Strategy & Enterprise Risk Mgmt)
Laura Werk (CFO & Sr VP)
Cathy Benoit (Sr VP-Govt Contracts)
Cailin Shovkoplyas (Comm Mgr)

NORKOL CONVERTING CORPORATION
11650 W Grand Ave, Melrose Park, IL 60164-1300
Tel.: (708) 531-1000
Web Site: http://www.norkol.com
Year Founded: 1968
Sales Range: $25-49.9 Million
Emp.: 200
Paper Mills; Paper Converter
N.A.I.C.S.: 322120
Lawrence Kolinski (Pres)

NORKUS ENTERPRISES INC.
505 Richmond Ave, Point Pleasant Beach, NJ 08742
Tel.: (732) 899-4040
Year Founded: 1935
Sales Range: $50-74.9 Million
Emp.: 1,000
Operators of Supermarkets
N.A.I.C.S.: 445110
Gerard K. Norkus (Pres)
Jane Lemonde (Controller)
Ericson T. Tendencia (Mgr-Liquor Store)
Marylou Pederson (Mgr-Payroll)

NORLAINE INC.
15650 Salt Lake Ave, City of Industry, CA 91745
Tel.: (626) 961-2471
Web Site: http://www.patinav.com
Year Founded: 1908
Sales Range: $75-99.9 Million
Emp.: 120
Mfr of Mannequins & Display Merchandise
N.A.I.C.S.: 339999

Subsidiaries:

Patina-V (1)
15650 Salt Lake Ave, City of Industry, CA 91745 (100%)
Tel.: (626) 961-2471
Web Site: http://www.patinav.com
Sales Range: $25-49.9 Million
Mannequins & Display Merchandise Mfr
N.A.I.C.S.: 339999

NORLIFT OF OREGON, INC.
7373 SE Milwaukie Expy, Portland, OR 97222
Tel.: (503) 659-5438
Web Site: http://www.norliftor.com
Sales Range: $10-24.9 Million
Emp.: 55
Industrial Machinery & Equipment Whslr
N.A.I.C.S.: 423830
Tom Leslie (Pres)
Mike Leslie (Mgr-Parts)
Kevin Blow (Mgr-Rental & Used Equipment)
Dean Walker (Mgr-Sls)
David Millette (Mgr-Warehouse Product Territory)
Tim Pryse (Asst Mgr-Parts)
Greg Jonas (Mgr-Svc-Columbus)

NORLUX
1225 Bowes Rd, Elgin, IL 60123
Tel.: (630) 784-7500
Web Site: http://www.norluxcorp.com
Year Founded: 2000
Sales Range: $10-24.9 Million
Emp.: 59
LED Light Assemblies Manufacturing
N.A.I.C.S.: 335139
Bruce Rhodes (Dir-Engrg)

NORMAC INCORPORATED
10 Loop Rd, Arden, NC 28704
Tel.: (828) 209-9000
Web Site: http://www.normac.com
Year Founded: 1968
Sales Range: $10-24.9 Million
Emp.: 40
Grinding Machines, Metalworking
N.A.I.C.S.: 333517
Douglas Slowik (VP-Res)
Chuck McDonald (Engr-R&D)

NORMAN & COMPANY, INC.
106 State St E, Oldsmar, FL 34677
Tel.: (813) 855-8300
Web Site: http://www.classictrak.com
Year Founded: 1984
Sales Range: $1-9.9 Million
Third Party Administrator
N.A.I.C.S.: 524292
Norman J. Ferenz (Pres & Principal)
Gerald E. Davis (VP & Principal)
Jerry Davids (COO & Principal)

NORMAN EQUIPMENT COMPANY
9850 Indus Dr, Bridgeview, IL 60455
Tel.: (708) 233-5521
Web Site: http://www.normanfilters.com
Rev.: $33,000,000
Emp.: 40
Hydraulic Systems Equipment & Supplies
N.A.I.C.S.: 423830
Phillip J. Netznik (Pres)
Brad Bennett (VP-Mtls Mgmt)

NORMAN LOVE CONFECTIONS
11380 Lindbergh Blvd, Fort Myers, FL 33913
Tel.: (239) 561-7215
Web Site: http://www.normanloveconfections.com
Year Founded: 2001
Sales Range: $1-9.9 Million
Emp.: 60
Chocolate Mfr & Retailer
N.A.I.C.S.: 311352
Norman Love (Founder & Pres)

NORMAN NOBLE INCORPORATED
5507 Avion Park Dr, Cleveland, OH 44143-1921
Tel.: (216) 761-2133
Web Site: http://www.normannoble.net
Rev.: $16,800,000
Emp.: 450
Machine Shop, Jobbing & Repair
N.A.I.C.S.: 332710
John Kujanek (Mgr-Acct & Engr-Technical Sls)
Nancy Shepard (Mgr-Acct & Engr-Technical Sls)
Tom Kavanaugh (Acct Mgr-Technical Sls-Northeast Territory)
Brian Hrouda (Dir-Sls & Mktg)
Janet Menke (Supvr-Acct)

NORMAN REGIONAL HEALTH SYSTEM
901 N Porter Ave, Norman, OK 73071
Tel.: (405) 307-1000
Web Site: http://www.normanregional.com
Year Founded: 1946
Health & Wellness Services
N.A.I.C.S.: 621399
Danny Kelley (CIO)

NORMAN S. WRIGHT & CO.
2121 E Magnolia St, Phoenix, AZ 85031
Tel.: (602) 275-4467
Web Site: http://nswhvacaz.com
Sales Range: $10-24.9 Million
Emp.: 25
Air Conditioning Equipment Distr
N.A.I.C.S.: 423730
Diane Langmade (CEO)
Jess Knoth (Sr VP)

NORMAN SUPPLY COMPANY
825 SW 5th St, Oklahoma City, OK 73109
Tel.: (405) 235-9511
Web Site: http://www.normansupply.com
Sales Range: $10-24.9 Million
Emp.: 44
Plumbing & Hydronic Heating Supplies
N.A.I.C.S.: 423720
Evelyn N. Kunkel (Pres)
Joe Sher (Treas & Sec)
Greg Barrow (Gen Mgr)

NORMAN W. FRIES INC.
Hwy 301 N, Claxton, GA 30417
Tel.: (912) 739-3181
Web Site: http://www.claxtonpoultry.com
Year Founded: 1949
Sales Range: $100-124.9 Million
Emp.: 1,600
Poultry Boiler, Producer & Sales
N.A.I.C.S.: 311615
Norman W. Fries (Owner)

NORMAN WRIGHT MECHANICAL EQUIPMENT CORP.
99A S Hill Dr, Brisbane, CA 94005
Tel.: (415) 467-7600
Web Site: http://www.norman-wright.com
Sales Range: $10-24.9 Million
Emp.: 150
Warm Air Heating Equipment & Supplies
N.A.I.C.S.: 423730
Richard Leoa (Pres)

NORMAN'S NURSERY
8665 E Duarte Rd, San Gabriel, CA 91775
Tel.: (626) 285-9795
Web Site: http://www.nngrower.com
Rev.: $57,500,000
Emp.: 620
Nurseries Whslr
N.A.I.C.S.: 111421
Nancy Webb (COO)
Theodore P. Norman (CEO)
Charles R. Norman (Pres)

NORMAN-SPENCER AGENCY, INC.
8075 Washington Vlg Dr, Dayton, OH 45458
Tel.: (937) 435-1316
Web Site: http://www.norman-spencer.com
Year Founded: 1988
Sales Range: $25-49.9 Million
Emp.: 160
Property & Casualty Insurance Underwriting Agency
N.A.I.C.S.: 524210
Brian Norman (Pres)
Patrick Malone (CFO)

Subsidiaries:

Northern Star Management, Inc. (1)
92 E Main St Ste 409, Somerville, NJ 08876
Tel.: (908) 253-9484
Web Site: http://www.northernstarins.com
Sales Range: $1-9.9 Million
Property & Casualty Insurance Underwriting Management Services
N.A.I.C.S.: 524298
George Karlis (Pres)

Thorn Valley Enterprises (1)
8498 W Fall Creek Dr, Pendleton, IN 46064
Tel.: (317) 485-6114
Web Site: http://www.thornvalleyent.net
Automotive Repair & Maintenance
N.A.I.C.S.: 811198
Natalie Beckler (Office Mgr)
Walt Guntharp (Pres)
Tom Flaten (VP-Ops & Mktg)

NORMANDEAU ASSOCIATES, INC.
25 Nashua Rd, Bedford, NH 03110-5527
Tel.: (603) 472-5191
Web Site: http://www.normandeau.com
Year Founded: 1970
Sales Range: $100-124.9 Million
Emp.: 175
Environmental Consulting Services
N.A.I.C.S.: 541690
Pamela Hall (Chm & CEO)
Paul Geoghegan (VP)
Robert Varney (Pres)
Curtis Thalken (COO & Sr VP)
Rick Simmons (Sr VP)

NORMANDY CONSTRUCTION CO. INC.
440 E Ogden Ave Ste 2, Hinsdale, IL 60521
Tel.: (630) 455-5600
Web Site: http://www.normandybuilders.com
Rev.: $12,000,000
Emp.: 50
Single-Family Home Remodeling, Additions & Repairs
N.A.I.C.S.: 236118
Reginald Marzec (Pres & Principal)
Andrew Wells (Gen Mgr & VP)

NORMANDY INDUSTRIES INC.

1150 Freeport Rd, Pittsburgh, PA 15238
Tel.: (412) 826-1825
Web Site: http://www.normandyproducts.com
Sales Range: $10-24.9 Million
Emp.: 8
Fittings For Pipe, Plastics
N.A.I.C.S.: 326122
Robert L. Americus (Pres)

NORMS RESTAURANTS
17904 Lakewood Blvd, Bellflower, CA 90706
Tel.: (562) 804-4485
Web Site: http://www.normsrestaurants.com
Year Founded: 1949
Sales Range: $10-24.9 Million
Emp.: 1,500
Owner & Operator of Restaurants
N.A.I.C.S.: 722511
Amir Durrani (Dir-Trng)
Cindy Varela (Dir-Svcs)
Genevieve Thompson (Dir-Svcs)

NORPAC FOODS, INC.
3225 25th St SE, Salem, OR 97302-0458
Tel.: (503) 769-2101   OR
Web Site: http://www.norpac.com
Year Founded: 1924
Sales Range: $75-99.9 Million
Emp.: 1,200
Processor of Frozen & Canned Fruits & Vegetables
N.A.I.C.S.: 311411
Randy Berning (Controller)
Steven Becic (Dir-Foodservice)
Richard Munekiyo (CFO)
Sean Campbell (Pres & CEO)

Subsidiaries:

Hermiston Foods, LLC   (1)
2250 S Hwy 395, Hermiston, OR 97838-9466   (100%)
Tel.: (541) 567-8448
Sales Range: $25-49.9 Million
Providing Food Processing Services
N.A.I.C.S.: 311411
Roy Stephen (Gen Mgr)
Cyd Bothum (Office Mgr)

Norpac Foods, Inc. - Brooks Plant   (1)
4755 Brooklake Rd NE, Salem, OR 97305
Tel.: (503) 393-4221
Web Site: http://www.norpac.com
Canned & Frozen Fruit & Vegetable Mfr
N.A.I.C.S.: 311421
Stan Baggett (Plant Mgr)

Norpac Foods, Inc. - Plant 6   (1)
2210 Madrona Ave SE, Salem, OR 97302
Tel.: (503) 581-8260
Canned & Frozen Fruit & Vegetable Mfr
N.A.I.C.S.: 311421

Norpac Foods, Inc. - Plant 7   (1)
2325 Madrona Ave SE, Salem, OR 97302
Tel.: (503) 581-1426
Frozen Fruit, Juice & Vegetable Mfr
N.A.I.C.S.: 311411
Mike Lane (Gen Mgr)

NORQUIST SALVAGE CORPORATION
2151 Professional Dr Ste 200, Roseville, CA 95661-3761
Tel.: (916) 787-1070   CA
Web Site: http://www.thrifttown.com
Year Founded: 1972
Sales Range: $25-49.9 Million
Emp.: 12
Used Merchandise Stores
N.A.I.C.S.: 459510
Wendy Steinmetz (VP-Mktg)
Lane Steinmetz (Pres & CFO)
Doona Doglione (Dir-HR)

NORRENBERNS FOODS
95 Mascoutah Plz Dr, Mascoutah, IL 62258
Tel.: (618) 566-7010
Web Site: http://www.jamesandsons.com
Sales Range: $10-24.9 Million
Emp.: 40
Grocery Stores
N.A.I.C.S.: 445110
Donald T. Norrenberns (Pres)
Robert Hill (Asst Mgr)
Kevin Spring (Mgr-Store)
Brandon Voss (Mgr-Store)

NORRIS ACURA WEST
8559 Baltimore National Pike, Ellicott City, MD 21043-4202
Tel.: (410) 461-7000
Web Site: http://www.norrisacurawest.com
Year Founded: 2006
Sales Range: $50-74.9 Million
Emp.: 231
Car Whslr
N.A.I.C.S.: 441110
Andrew Zimmer (Mgr-Svc)
Brian Marshall (Dir-Sls)
Irv Silverman (Mgr-Sls)
Nwokili G. Nushann (Mgr-Fin)
Ron Speert (Mgr-Fin)

NORRIS AGGREGATE PAVING CO.
14242 Terminal Ave, Ottumwa, IA 52501
Tel.: (641) 682-3427
Web Site: http://www.norrisasphalt.com
Year Founded: 1992
Sales Range: $10-24.9 Million
Emp.: 135
Highway & Street Paving Contractor
N.A.I.C.S.: 237310
Brady Meldrem (Pres)

NORRIS AUTOMOTIVE GROUP
925 Merritt Blvd, Baltimore, MD 21222
Tel.: (410) 285-0600
Web Site: http://www.norrisautogroup.com
Year Founded: 1917
Sales Range: $200-249.9 Million
Emp.: 400
Automotive Dealership in New & Used Cars & Trucks Sales
N.A.I.C.S.: 441110
Andrew Franklin (CEO)

NORRIS BEGGS & SIMPSON NORTHWEST LIMITED PARTNERSHIP
121 SW Morrison St Ste 200, Portland, OR 97204
Tel.: (503) 223-7181
Web Site: http://www.nbsrealtors.com
Year Founded: 1932
Sales Range: $10-24.9 Million
Emp.: 40
Commercial Real Estate
N.A.I.C.S.: 531210
J. Clayton Hering (Chm)
Jan Robertson (Pres)
Sean Turley (VP)
MaryKay West (VP)

NORRIS ELECTRIC COOPERATIVE
8543 N State Hwy 130, Newton, IL 62448
Tel.: (618) 783-8765
Web Site: http://www.norriselectric.com
Year Founded: 1938
Sales Range: $25-49.9 Million
Emp.: 69
Eletric Power Generation Services
N.A.I.C.S.: 221118

NORRIS FURNITURE INC.
14125 S Tamiami Trl, Fort Myers, FL 33912
Tel.: (239) 690-9844
Web Site: http://www.norrishomefurnishings.com
Sales Range: $1-9.9 Million
Emp.: 70
Household Furniture Retailer
N.A.I.C.S.: 449110
Larry Norris (Owner)

NORRIS PUBLIC POWER DISTRICT
606 Irving St, Beatrice, NE 68310
Tel.: (402) 223-4038
Web Site: http://www.norrisppd.com
Sales Range: $25-49.9 Million
Emp.: 81
Transmission, Electric Power
N.A.I.C.S.: 221121
Jerry Enns (Mgr-Engrg)
Randy Evans (Mgr-Ops)
Michelle Junker (Mgr-Corp Svcs)
Bruce A. Vitosh (CEO & Gen Mgr)

NORRIS SALES ASSOCIATES INC.
19111 Detroit Rd Ste 202, Cleveland, OH 44116-1740
Tel.: (440) 333-4030   OH
Web Site: http://www.norris-sales.com
Year Founded: 1973
Sales Range: $25-49.9 Million
Emp.: 6
Metal Injection Molding
N.A.I.C.S.: 423510
John Norris (Pres)

NORSOUTH CONSTRUCTS
25 Chatham Ctr S Ste 100, Savannah, GA 31405
Tel.: (912) 354-6096
Web Site: http://www.nsconstructs.com
Year Founded: 1986
Apartment Building Construction
N.A.I.C.S.: 236117
Michael Creeden (CEO)
Colin Edelstein (Pres-Atlanta)
Patrick Johnston (COO)
Marly Shuman (VP-Construction)

NORSTAR INC.
203 SE Alder St Ste 202, Portland, OR 97214
Tel.: (503) 239-4266
Sales Range: $10-24.9 Million
Emp.: 20
Pet Supply Mfr & Distr
N.A.I.C.S.: 424990

NORSTRA ENERGY INC.
414 Manor Rd, Laredo, TX 78041 NV
Web Site: http://www.norstraenergy.com
Year Founded: 2010
Emp.: 2
Oil & Gas Exploration
N.A.I.C.S.: 211120
Glen Landry (Pres, CEO, Treas & Sec)

NORTEX COMMUNICATIONS COMPANY
205 N Walnut St, Muenster, TX 76252
Tel.: (940) 759-2251
Web Site: http://www.nortex.com
Year Founded: 1909
Sales Range: $10-24.9 Million
Emp.: 46
Provider of Telephone Communication Services
N.A.I.C.S.: 517121
Alvin M. Fuhrman (Pres & CEO)
Joey Anderson (VP-Ops)
Chris McNamara (Mgr-IT Network)
Eileene Newland (Supvr-Svc Support)
Debbie Bishop (Mgr-Retail Sls)

NORTH
1515 NW 19th Ave, Portland, OR 97209
Tel.: (503) 222-4117   OR
Web Site: http://www.north.com
Year Founded: 1991
Rev.: $20,000,000
Emp.: 24
Full Service
N.A.I.C.S.: 541810
Jim Carey (Dir-Creative)
Mark Ray (Pres & Exec Dir-Creative)
Rebecca Armstrong (Mng Partner)
Lori Jones (Creative Dir)
Steve Rauner (Exec Producer)
Nathan Plowman (Dir-Strategic)
Dave Allen (Dir-Digital Media)
Ashod Simonian (Mgr-Projects)

NORTH 6TH AGENCY, INC.
18 Harrison St, New York, NY 10013
Tel.: (914) 907-8553
Web Site: http://www.n6a.com
Scientific & Technical Consulting Services
N.A.I.C.S.: 541690
Bill McCue (Sr VP)
Carli Griffin (Acct Exec-Ikuzo Grp)
Jason Abrams (Acct Dir-Haraka Grp)
Matt Rizzetta (Founder & Chm)
Daniela Mancinelli (CEO)
Amy Rosen (Sr VP)
Lori Ruggiero (Sr VP)
John Hannaway (COO)
Nina Velasquez (Sr VP-Talent Dev)
Karen Mateo (Sr VP)
Jordan Cohen (CMO)
Patrick Brady (Chief Revenue Officer)

Subsidiaries:

Atlas Communications, Inc.   (1)
140 Broadway Fl 46, New York, NY 10005
Tel.: (212) 858-7640
Computer Integrated Systems Design, Nsk
N.A.I.C.S.: 541512

NORTH ALABAMA FABRICATING CO.
4632 Richard Arrington Blvd N, Birmingham, AL 35212
Tel.: (205) 591-5554
Web Site: http://www.nafcofab.com
Rev.: $15,000,000
Emp.: 23
Building Components, Structural Steel
N.A.I.C.S.: 332312
John R. Parrish (Founder & Pres)
Mike Miller (Project Mgr)

NORTH AMERICA FIRE EQUIPMENT COMPANY
1515 Moulton St W, Decatur, AL 35601
Tel.: (256) 353-7100
Web Site: http://www.nafeco.com
Sales Range: $10-24.9 Million
Emp.: 70
Distr of Firefighting Equipment
N.A.I.C.S.: 423850
Jerrell David Oaks (Pres)
Brian Oaks (Office Mgr)
Ronald Woodall (VP)

NORTH AMERICA FOOD & BEVERAGE INC.

NORTH AMERICA FOOD & BEVERAGE INC.

U.S. PRIVATE

North America Food & Beverage Inc.—(Continued)
PO Box 6753, Chesterfield, MO 63006
Tel.: (314) 275-9059
Sales Range: $10-24.9 Million
Emp.: 5
Food & Beverage Product Mfr
N.A.I.C.S.: 311999
Rick Clatt (Pres)

NORTH AMERICAN AUTOMOTIVE SERVICES, INC.
1 Oakbrook Terrace Ste 600, Oakbrook Terrace, IL 60181
Tel.: (630) 530-3955
Web Site: http://www.ednapleton.com
New & Used Automobile Dealerships
N.A.I.C.S.: 441110
Edward F. Napleton (Pres)
Bruce Etheridge (CFO & COO)
Katherine R. Napleton (Sec)
Tracy Cook (Dir-HR)

Subsidiaries:

Napleton Schaumburg Motors, Inc. (1)
110 W Golf Rd, Schaumburg, IL 60195
Tel.: (847) 285-5311
Web Site:
http://www.schaumburgmazda.com
Sales Range: $50-74.9 Million
Emp.: 100
New & Used Car Dealer
N.A.I.C.S.: 441110
Stephen Napleton (Chm)
Charles Weck (Pres)
Danny Napleton (Gen Mgr)

Village Chevrolet Co. (1)
16100 Wayzata Blvd, Wayzata, MN 55391
Tel.: (952) 476-6111
Web Site:
http://www.villageautomotivegroup.com
Emp.: 400
Holding Company; New & Used Cars Dealer
N.A.I.C.S.: 551112
Stephanie Smith (Mgr-Corp Mktg)
Steve Bloomer (Pres & CEO)
Steve Bennett (Partner, COO & VP)

Subsidiary (Domestic):

Lexus of Maplewood (2)
3000 Hwy 61, Saint Paul, MN 55109
Tel.: (651) 483-6111
Web Site:
http://www.lexusofmaplewood.com
Sales Range: $1-9.9 Million
Emp.: 30
New Car Dealers
N.A.I.C.S.: 441110
Joseph Petrusa (Mgr-Vehicle Sls)

Village Chevrolet Company - Wayzata Auto Center (2)
1755 Wayzata Blvd, Wayzata, MN 55391
Tel.: (952) 473-5444
Web Site: http://www.villagechev.com
Sales Range: $25-49.9 Million
Emp.: 138
Car Whlsr
N.A.I.C.S.: 441110
Steve Bloomer (Pres)
Grant Osgood (Gen Mgr)
Bill Dunne (Gen Mgr-Sls)
Cal Lenz (Mgr-Parts)
Dave Popp (Mgr-Svc)
Jeremiah Silbernick (Mgr-Comml Bus Elite)
John Watters (Mgr-Internet Bus)
Kevin McDonough (Bus Mgr)
Kit Bolton (Mgr-Sls)
Matt Dahl (Mgr-Parts Svc)
Nick Brabeck (Mgr-Sls)
Paul Berens (Mgr-Inventory)

Village Luxury Imports Inc. (2)
16100 Wayzata Blvd, Wayzata, MN 55391
Tel.: (952) 476-6111
Web Site: http://www.lexusofwayzata.com
Sales Range: $25-49.9 Million
Emp.: 100
Automobiles, New & Used
N.A.I.C.S.: 441110

Robert Katz (Gen Mgr)
Scott Houghland (Mgr-Bus)
Michael G. Dalton (Gen Mgr)
Wayne Koosman (Mgr-Customer Svc)

NORTH AMERICAN BANCARD, LLC
250 Stephenson Hwy, Troy, MI 48083
Tel.: (248) 269-6000   DE
Web Site: http://www.nabancard.com
Year Founded: 1991
Business Services
N.A.I.C.S.: 522320
Terri Harwood (COO)
Kirk Haggarty (CFO)
Jim Parkinson (CIO)

Subsidiaries:

Electronic Payment Exchange, Inc. (1)
1201 N Market St Ste 701, Wilmington, DE 19801
Tel.: (302) 288-0600
Web Site: http://www.epx.com
Back Office Electronic Payment Exchange Processing
N.A.I.C.S.: 423690
Raymond Moyer (Pres & CEO)
Tim Oneacre (Sr VP & Gen Mgr)

NORTH AMERICAN BISON COOPERATIVE
1658 Hwy 281, New Rockford, ND 58356
Tel.: (701) 947-2505
Web Site: http://www.nabison.com
Sales Range: $10-24.9 Million
Emp.: 30
Meat Packing Plants
N.A.I.C.S.: 311611
Dieter L. Pape (Pres & CEO)

Subsidiaries:

North American Provisioner Inc. (1)
1658 Hwy 281, New Rockford, ND 58356
Tel.: (701) 947-2505
Web Site: http://www.nabison.com
Sales Range: $10-24.9 Million
Meats & Meat Products
N.A.I.C.S.: 424470

NORTH AMERICAN BOLT & SCREW CO. INC.
3039 40th Ave Nw, Rochester, MN 55901-1759
Tel.: (212) 966-3310   NY
Year Founded: 1948
Sales Range: $10-24.9 Million
Emp.: 20
Bolts, Nuts, Rivets & Washers, Labels
N.A.I.C.S.: 332721
Jack Laufer (VP)
Sam Laufer (VP)

NORTH AMERICAN COATINGS, INC.
8450 W 191st St Unit 19, Mokena, IL 60448
Tel.: (815) 464-3053   MI
Web Site:
http://www.saswaygroup.com
Year Founded: 1982
Sales Range: $25-49.9 Million
Emp.: 212
Painting & Fireproofing Coatings Application Service
N.A.I.C.S.: 238990
Chris Murphy (VP-Fin)

Subsidiaries:

CL Coatings, LLC (1)
8450 W 191st St Unit 19, Mokena, IL 60448
Tel.: (863) 709-1809
Web Site: http://www.nacoatings.com
Industrial Painting, Fireproofing & Specialty Coating Services
N.A.I.C.S.: 238990

Industrial Coatings & Fireproofing (1)
1398 E 29th St, Signal Hill, CA 90755
Tel.: (562) 426-7105
Web Site: http://www.nacoatings.com
Industrial Coatings & Fireproofing Application Services
N.A.I.C.S.: 238990

SEI Coatings, LLC (1)
8450 W 191st St Unit 19, Mokena, IL 60448
Tel.: (815) 464-3053
Web Site: http://www.nacoatings.com
Sales Range: $10-24.9 Million
Emp.: 15
Industrial Coating Application Services
N.A.I.C.S.: 238990
Spiro Poulos (Pres)

NORTH AMERICAN COMMUNICATIONS INC.
7 Edgemont Rd, Katonah, NY 10536
Tel.: (914) 273-8620   DE
Web Site: http://www.nacmail.com
Year Founded: 1979
Sales Range: $10-24.9 Million
Emp.: 2,000
Fully Integrated Direct Mail Mfr & Fulfillment Company
N.A.I.C.S.: 561431
Nicholas Robinson (Pres & CEO)
Chet Williams (Sr VP-Sls)

Subsidiaries:

North American Communications, Inc. (NAC) (1)
141 NAC Dr, Duncansville, PA 16635   (100%)
Tel.: (814) 696-3553
Web Site: http://www.nacmail.com
Direct Mail Mfr & Distr
N.A.I.C.S.: 561431
Robert Herman (Pres & COO)
Tera Herman (VP)
George Reed (Exec VP)
Nick Robinson (CEO)
Chet Williams (Sr VP-Sls)

NORTH AMERICAN COMPANY
312 S E 17th St Ste 300, Fort Lauderdale, FL 33316
Tel.: (954) 463-0681   FL
Web Site:
http://www.northamericanfund.com
Year Founded: 1939
Sales Range: $75-99.9 Million
Emp.: 2
Venture Capital Investments; Real Estate Development
N.A.I.C.S.: 523910
R. David Bergonia (Mng Partner)
Charles L. Palmer (Co-Founder, Chm, Pres, CEO & Mng Partner)

Subsidiaries:

Valley Meats LLC (1)
2302 1st St, Coal Valley, IL 61240
Tel.: (309) 799-7341
Web Site: http://www.valleymeatsllc.com
Processed Meat Product Mfr
N.A.I.C.S.: 311612
Jeff Jobe (Pres)
Randy Ehrlich (Reg Mgr-Sls)
Gary Mitchell (Reg Mgr-Sls)
Adam Jobe (Reg Mgr-Sls)

NORTH AMERICAN CORP.
2101 Claire Ct, Glenview, IL 60025-7634
Tel.: (847) 832-4000
Web Site:
http://www.nacorporation.com
Sales Range: $10-24.9 Million
Emp.: 350
Janitorial & Office Supplies Mfr & Whlsr
N.A.I.C.S.: 456120
Rosemarie Egan (CFO)
Mark Gaggiano (Dir-IT)
John A. Miller (Pres & CEO)

NORTH AMERICAN DEVELOPMENT GROUP
400 Clematis St Ste 201, West Palm Beach, FL 33401
Tel.: (561) 578-8700
Web Site: http://www.nadg.com
Year Founded: 1977
Sales Range: $50-74.9 Million
Emp.: 150
Real Estate Investment & Management Services
N.A.I.C.S.: 531390
John W. S. Preston (Chm)

Subsidiaries:

Centrecorp Management Services Ltd. (1)
2851 John St Suite 1, Markham, L3R 5R7, ON, Canada
Tel.: (905) 477-9200
Web Site: http://www.centrecorp.com
Sales Range: $25-49.9 Million
Emp.: 100
Property Management & Other Real Estate Services
N.A.I.C.S.: 531312
Brett Glanfield (Sr VP-Property Mgmt)
Simon Smith (Sr VP-Leasing)
Tony Fazari (Sr VP-Specialty Leasing)
Tracy Butler-Schembri (Exec VP)
Anthony McKee (VP)
Jennifer O'Leary (VP)
Spence Mueller (VP)
Sherene Pickering (VP)

NORTH AMERICAN EQUIPMENT UPFITTERS, INC.
6 Sutton Cir, Hooksett, NH 03106
Tel.: (603) 624-6288
Web Site: http://www.naeuinc.com
Year Founded: 1999
Rev.: $9,500,000
Emp.: 60
Industrial Machinery & Equipment Merchant Whlslr
N.A.I.C.S.: 423830
Jacqui Delude (Controller)
Jay Bornstein (Gen Mgr)
Jay Jorgensen (Mgr-Parts)
Janet Dunican (Pres)
Michael Dunican (VP)
Chris McKay (Mgr-Svc-Columbus)
Sean Stanton (Office Mgr)

NORTH AMERICAN FILTER CORPORATION
200 W Shore Blvd, Newark, NY 14513
Tel.: (315) 331-7000   NY
Year Founded: 1989
Sales Range: $10-24.9 Million
Emp.: 75
Manufacture Filters, General Line For Industrial Use
N.A.I.C.S.: 333998
Steve Taylor (Pres)
Glenn Sanders (VP-Sls & Mktg)
Steve Taylor (Pres)

NORTH AMERICAN GOLD & MINERALS FUND
848 N Rainbow Blvd 3003, Las Vegas, NV 89107
Tel.: (702) 951-9303   NV
Web Site: http://www.nagoldfund.com
Year Founded: 2007
Emp.: 1
Metal Mining & Exploration Services
N.A.I.C.S.: 212290
Ronald Yadin Lowenthal (Chm, Treas & Sec)

NORTH AMERICAN HYDRAULICS INC.
11549 Sun Belt Ct, Baton Rouge, LA 70809
Tel.: (225) 751-0500   LA

Web Site: http://www.nahi.com
Year Founded: 1977
Sales Range: $25-49.9 Million
Emp.: 160
Supplier of Hydraulic Systems Equipment & Supplies
N.A.I.C.S.: 423830
Kevin Brown (Pres)

NORTH AMERICAN MARKETING CORPORATION
100 Sanrico Dr, Manchester, CT 06040-9010
Tel.: (860) 649-3666   PA
Web Site: http://www.namcopool.com
Year Founded: 1962
Sales Range: $25-49.9 Million
Emp.: 500
Retailer of Swimming Pools, Products & Accessories
N.A.I.C.S.: 459999
Mark Scott (Pres & CEO)

NORTH AMERICAN OIL & GAS CORP.
701 E Santa Clara St, Ventura, CA 93001
Tel.: (805) 665-6308   NV
Web Site: http://www.namoag.com
Year Founded: 2010
Sales Range: $1-9.9 Million
Emp.: 2
Oil & Natural Gas Exploration Services
N.A.I.C.S.: 211120
Robert John Rosenthal (Chm, Pres, CEO & Sec)
Cosimo Damiano (CFO)

NORTH AMERICAN PACKAGING LLC
535 Route 6 & 209, Milford, PA 18337
Tel.: (570) 296-0350
Web Site: http://www.econo-pak.com
Packaging & Display Assembly Services
N.A.I.C.S.: 561910
PJ Wiebel (CEO)

NORTH AMERICAN PARTNERS IN ANESTHESIA LLP
1305 Walt Whitman Rd Ste 300, Melville, NY 11747
Tel.: (516) 945-3000
Web Site:
   http://www.napaanesthesia.com
Year Founded: 1986
Sales Range: $1-9.9 Million
Anesthesia Management Services
N.A.I.C.S.: 541611
Timothy J. Dowd (Mng Partner)
Lloyd Straus (Pres)
Ken Miles (CFO & Exec VP)
John Bugos (CFO)
Jill Hoenigmann (Mgr-Mktg)
John Kalix (COO)
Michael Lemonds (Pres-ProCare Pain Solutions)
Rafael Cartagena (CEO)

NORTH AMERICAN PROPERTIES INC.
212 E 3rd St Ste 300, Cincinnati, OH 45202
Tel.: (513) 721-2744
Web Site:
   http://www.naproperties.com
Year Founded: 1954
Sales Range: $75-99.9 Million
Emp.: 400
Real Estate Development, Investment & Leasing Services
N.A.I.C.S.: 531390
Joe Williams (Chm)
Tom Williams (Pres & CEO)

Anthony Hobson (Mng Partner)
Kevin Riley (COO & Partner)
Maggie Dillman (Dir-Tax)
Ellen Mayleben (Dir-Asset Mgmt)
Nick Rabin (Mgr-Assets-Multifamily)
Sandra Winkle (Dir-HR)
Donel Autin (CFO)
Tim Perry (Chief Investment Officer)
Dale Hafele (Mng Partner)
Justin Long (VP-Dev-North American Properties)
Shawn McIntyre (Mng Partner)
Richard Munger (Partner & VP-Dev-North American Properties)
Mike Pacillio (Mng Partner)
Mark Toro (Mng Partner)

NORTH AMERICAN ROOFING SYSTEMS, INC.
14025 Riveredge Dr Ste 600, Tampa, FL 33637
Tel.: (866) 567-2064
Web Site: http://www.naroofing.com
Year Founded: 1979
Roofing Contractors
N.A.I.C.S.: 238160
Dwight A. Marwede (Dir-Technical)
Michelle Youngblood (Interim CFO)
Jeff Brummett (Sr Dir-Sls & Mktg)
Darin Blackwell (Sr Dir-Production)
Jill Tackett (Dir-Svc)
Alex Lissenden (Mgr-Sls)
Tony Dover (Dir-Quality and Safety)
Kyle Shelton (Dir-Estimating)
Ryan Cripe (Mng Dir-Production)
Mary Kasunick (Dir-HR)
Mary Michael (Dir-Training)

NORTH AMERICAN SIGNS INC.
3601 Lathrop St, South Bend, IN 46628
Tel.: (574) 234-5252
Web Site:
   http://www.northamericansigns.com
Sales Range: $10-24.9 Million
Emp.: 92
Signs & Advertising Specialties
N.A.I.C.S.: 339950
Noel H. Yarger (Chm)
John Maurice Yarger (Pres & CEO)
Derek Tobolski (Project Mgr)

NORTH AMERICAN SPINE SOCIETY
7075 Veterans Blvd, Burr Ridge, IL 60527
Tel.: (630) 230-3600   IL
Web Site: http://www.spine.org
Year Founded: 1995
Sales Range: $10-24.9 Million
Emp.: 51
Spine Care Services
N.A.I.C.S.: 813212
Eric Muehlbauer (Exec Dir)
F. Todd Wetzel (Pres)

NORTH AMERICAN TECHNOLOGIES GROUP, INC. (NAMC)
429 S Memory Lane, Marshall, TX 75670
Tel.: (903) 923-7200   DE
Web Site: http://www.tietek.com
Year Founded: 1986
Sales Range: $25-49.9 Million
Emp.: 131
Composite Ties Mfr
N.A.I.C.S.: 336510
Joe B. Dorman (Gen Counsel)
Joseph W. Christian (Dir-HR & Special Projects)
D. Patrick Long (Chm & CEO)
Holly Lowry (Controller)
Dale Ramthun (Mgr-Ops)

Subsidiaries:

TieTek, Inc.   (1)
14315 W Hardy Rd, Houston, TX 77060   (100%)
Tel.: (281) 847-0029
Web Site: http://www.tietek.com
Sales Range: $1-9.9 Million
Emp.: 72
Mfr of Composite Railroad Ties
N.A.I.C.S.: 332322

NORTH AMERICAN TRADING, LLC.
7380 W Sand Lk Rd Ste 400, Orlando, FL 32819
Tel.: (407) 352-7006
Year Founded: 2000
Sales Range: $10-24.9 Million
Emp.: 1,200
Textile Products Distr
N.A.I.C.S.: 424310
Xavier Haddad (Pres)

NORTH AMERICAN TRAILER LLC
2896 W 2100 S, Salt Lake City, UT 84119
Web Site:
   http://www.northamericantrailer.com
Trailer Retailer
N.A.I.C.S.: 441227

NORTH AMERICAN TRANSPORT CONCEPTS
2261 Brookhollow Plaza Dr Ste 209, Arlington, TX 76006-7431
Tel.: (817) 472-6988
Web Site:
   http://www.natcotransport.com
Sales Range: $10-24.9 Million
Emp.: 95
Transportation Agents & Brokers
N.A.I.C.S.: 488510
Sharon Porter (Coord-Freight)

NORTH AMERICAN TRUCK & TRAILER, INC.
4500 N Cliff Ave, Sioux Falls, SD 57104-0553
Tel.: (605) 332-7112   SD
Web Site:
   http://www.northamericantrucktrailer.com
Year Founded: 1989
Sales Range: $50-74.9 Million
Emp.: 500
Distr of Trucks & Trailers
N.A.I.C.S.: 423110
William Rush (Pres, Treas & Sec)

Subsidiaries:

Black Hills Truck & Trailer Inc.   (1)
2910 E Mall Dr, Rapid City, SD 57701-8510   (100%)
Tel.: (605) 348-3019
Web Site:
   http://www.blackhillstrucktrailer.com
Sales Range: $10-24.9 Million
Emp.: 60
Automobiles & other Motor Vehicles
N.A.I.C.S.: 423110
Tom Helland (Gen Mgr)

Colorado Brake & Supply Inc.   (1)
5001 E 52nd Ave, Commerce City, CO 80022
Tel.: (303) 289-1011
Web Site: http://www.brake.com
Emp.: 20
Motor Vehicle Parts Distr
N.A.I.C.S.: 423120
Dave Ford (Gen Mgr)
John Blaise (Gen Mgr)

Colorado Truck Equipment & Parts Inc   (1)
5001 E 52nd Ave, Commerce City, CO 80022

Tel.: (303) 289-6240
Rev.: $2,300,000
Emp.: 12
Motor Vehicle Supplies, New Parts, Service & Sales
N.A.I.C.S.: 488510

Custom Leasing of Iowa Inc   (1)
5430 Harbor Dr, Sioux City, IA 51111
Tel.: (712) 252-2278
Emp.: 5
Truck Leasing Services
N.A.I.C.S.: 532120
Ken Schulte (Mgr)

Custom Truck & Equipment, LLC   (1)
1800 E Benson St, Sioux Falls, SD 57104
Tel.: (605) 336-1727
Web Site:
   http://www.northamericantrucktrailer.com
Emp.: 15
Truck Leasing Services
N.A.I.C.S.: 532120
Bryan Rush (Gen Mgr)

Custom Truck Leasing, Inc.   (1)
4500 N Cliff Ave, Sioux Falls, SD 57104
Tel.: (855) 365-4966
Web Site:
   http://www.customtruckleasing.com
Emp.: 12
Truck Leasing Services
N.A.I.C.S.: 532120

Sioux City Truck & Trailer   (1)
4535 Harbor Dr, Sioux City, IA 51111
Tel.: (712) 258-2444
Web Site: http://www.siouxcitykenworth.com
Rev.: $18,200,000
Emp.: 55
Truck Tractors
N.A.I.C.S.: 423110
Darla Christensen (Controller)

Sioux Falls Truck & Trailer, Inc.   (1)
4500 N Cliff Ave, Sioux Falls, SD 57104-0553   (100%)
Tel.: (605) 332-7112
Web Site: http://www.nattinc.com
Sales Range: $25-49.9 Million
Emp.: 75
Automotive Distr
N.A.I.C.S.: 441110
William Rush (Pres)

Volvo Trucks of Omaha Inc.   (1)
11351 S 153rd St, Omaha, NE 68138
Web Site:
   http://www.northamericantrucktrailer.com
Emp.: 50
Truck Rental Services
N.A.I.C.S.: 532120
Steve Christensen (Gen Mgr)

Watertown Truck & Trailer Inc.   (1)
3925 9th Ave SE, Watertown, SD 57201
Tel.: (855) 259-2082
New & Used Truck Dealer
N.A.I.C.S.: 441110
Mike Laurenz (Mgr)

West Point Chevrolet, Inc.   (1)
1212 N Lincoln, West Point, NE 68788
Web Site: http://www.westpointchevy.com
Emp.: 20
Truck Leasing Services
N.A.I.C.S.: 532120
Karen Breitkreutz (Mgr-Sls)

NORTH AMERICAN VIDEO CORPORATION
1041 North Pacific Enter, Anaheim, CA 92806-1965
Tel.: (714) 779-7499   DE
Web Site: http://www.navco.com
Year Founded: 1971
Sales Range: $25-49.9 Million
Emp.: 190
Sales of Electronic Parts & Equipment
N.A.I.C.S.: 423690
Bill Gross (Pres)

Subsidiaries:

American Cabling & Communications Inc.   (1)
4430 E Miraloma Ave Unit D, Anaheim, CA 92807-1965   (100%)
Tel.: (714) 693-3303
Web Site: http://www.accinc.com

NORTH AMERICAN VIDEO CORPORATION — U.S. PRIVATE

North American Video Corporation—(Continued)
Sales Range: $10-24.9 Million
Emp.: 11
Cabling & Network Services Distr
N.A.I.C.S.: 423690
Eric Handors *(Gen Mgr)*

NORTH ARKANSAS ELECTRIC COOPERATIVE, INC.
225 S Main St, Salem, AR 72576-9419
Tel.: (870) 670-5600 AR
Web Site: http://www.naeci.com
Year Founded: 1939
Sales Range: $25-49.9 Million
Emp.: 121
Electronic Services
N.A.I.C.S.: 221118
Mel Coleman *(CEO)*

NORTH ATLANTIC COMPONENTS, INC.
711-1 Koehler Ave, Ronkonkoma, NY 11779
Tel.: (631) 467-6300
Web Site: http://www.northatlantic.com
Sales Range: $10-24.9 Million
Emp.: 25
Distr of Electronic Parts
N.A.I.C.S.: 423690
Chris Lovito *(Pres)*
Elena Hueley *(VP)*

NORTH ATLANTIC INDUSTRIES INC.
110 Wilbur Pl, Bohemia, NY 11716
Tel.: (631) 567-1100
Web Site: http://www.naii.com
Rev.: $10,000,000
Emp.: 110
Instruments to Measure Electricity & Testing Equiment
N.A.I.C.S.: 334515
William Forman *(Pres & CEO)*

Subsidiaries:

Apex Signal Corporation (1)
110 Wilbur Pl, Bohemia, NY 11716
Tel.: (631) 981-1100
Web Site: http://www.naii.com
Sales Range: $1-9.9 Million
Emp.: 24
Traffic Signals, Electric
N.A.I.C.S.: 334290

Astrosystems Automation (1)
110 Wilbur Pl, Bohemia, NY 11716
Tel.: (631) 567-1100
Rev.: $530,000
Emp.: 4
Transducers & Coders Mfr
N.A.I.C.S.: 333613

Logitek Inc. (1)
110 Wilbur Pl, Bohemia, NY 11716
Tel.: (631) 567-1100
Web Site: http://www.naii.com
Electronic Circuits
N.A.I.C.S.: 334419
William Forman *(CEO)*

NORTH ATLANTIC STATES REGIONAL COUNCIL OF CARPENTERS
750 Dorchester Ave, Boston, MA 02125
Tel.: (617) 268-3400
Web Site: https://www.nasrcc.org
Year Founded: 1996
Residential Contractor Services
N.A.I.C.S.: 236116

NORTH ATLANTIC TRADING COMPANY, INC.
777 Post Rd Ste 304, Darien, CT 06820-4721
Tel.: (203) 202-9547
Web Site: http://www.natcinc.net
Sales Range: $100-124.9 Million
Emp.: 230
Holding Company
N.A.I.C.S.: 551112

Subsidiaries:

National Tobacco Company LP (1)
5201 Interchange Way, Louisville, KY 40229-2184
Tel.: (502) 778-4421
Sales Range: $25-49.9 Million
Emp.: 180
Mfr of Chewing Tobacco
N.A.I.C.S.: 312230
Larry Wexler *(CEO)*
Thomas Helms Jr. *(Owner)*

NORTH BAY CADILLAC CO. INC.
720 Northern Blvd, Great Neck, NY 11021
Tel.: (516) 466-6200
Web Site: http://www.northbaycadillac.com
Rev.: $18,400,000
Emp.: 35
Automobiles, New & Used
N.A.I.C.S.: 441110
Hugh Weidinger *(Pres)*

NORTH BAY FORD LINCOLN MERCURY
1999 Soquel Ave, Santa Cruz, CA 95062
Tel.: (831) 457-5858
Web Site: http://www.northbayford.com
Sales Range: $25-49.9 Million
Emp.: 56
Automobiles, New & Used
N.A.I.C.S.: 441110
William R. Winterhalder *(Pres)*
Carmen Tinoco *(Mgr-Svc)*

NORTH BAY IMPORTS, INC.
81 C South Main St, East Windsor, CT 06088
Tel.: (860) 627-0710
Web Site: http://www.northbayimports.com
Year Founded: 2003
Sales Range: $10-24.9 Million
Emp.: 12
Used Car Whslr
N.A.I.C.S.: 441120
David J. Mason Jr. *(Owner)*

NORTH BAY JOBS WITH JUSTICE
55 Ridgway Ave, Santa Rosa, CA 95402
Tel.: (707) 582-5634
Web Site: https://www.northbayjobswithjustice.org
Year Founded: 2007
Emp.: 30
Labor Organization Services
N.A.I.C.S.: 813930

NORTH BAY PRODUCE, INC.
1771 N US 31 S, Traverse City, MI 49684
Tel.: (231) 946-1941
Web Site: http://www.northbayproduce.com
Year Founded: 1984
Sales Range: $75-99.9 Million
Emp.: 25
Fruit & Vegetable Whslr
N.A.I.C.S.: 424480
Mark Girardin *(Pres)*

NORTH BAY REGIONAL CENTER
600 Air Park Rd, Napa, CA 94558-6267
Tel.: (707) 256-1100
Web Site: http://www.nbrc.net
Year Founded: 1972
Rev.: $56,096,308
Emp.: 150
Developmental & Rehabilitation Services
N.A.I.C.S.: 624310
Michi Gates *(Dir-Client Svcs)*
Angel Giroux-Greber *(VP)*

NORTH BAY REHABILITATION SERVICES
649 Martin Ave, Rohnert Park, CA 94928
Tel.: (707) 585-1991
Web Site: http://www.nbrs.org
Rev.: $11,507,570
Emp.: 50
Employment, Housing & Non-vocational Programs & Services
N.A.I.C.S.: 561311
Robert Hutt *(Pres & CEO)*

NORTH BAY RESOURCES INC.
3995 Yerkes Rd, Collegeville, PA 19426
Tel.: (215) 661-1100 DE
Web Site: http://www.northbayresources.com
Year Founded: 2004
Sales Range: Less than $1 Million
Emp.: 1
Gold, Silver, Platinum, Palladium, Copper, Zinc, Lead & Molybdenum Mining Services
N.A.I.C.S.: 212220
Perry Leopold *(Chm, Pres & CEO)*

Subsidiaries:

Ruby Gold, Inc. (1)
571-C Searls Ave, Nevada City, CA 95959 (100%)
Tel.: (530) 470-9230
Rev.: $381
Assets: $2,593,777
Liabilities: $3,910,482
Net Worth: ($1,316,705)
Earnings: ($1,286,873)
Fiscal Year-end: 12/31/2013
Gold Mining
N.A.I.C.S.: 212220
Perry Leopold *(Chm, CEO, CFO & Principal Acctg Officer)*
William S. Watters *(COO)*

NORTH BERGEN MUNICIPAL UTILITY AUTHORITY
6200 Tonnelle Ave, North Bergen, NJ 07047
Tel.: (201) 422-0100
Web Site: http://www.northbergen.org
Rev.: $24,000,000
Emp.: 130
Wastewater Treatment Plants Operation
N.A.I.C.S.: 237110
Frank Pestana *(Exec Dir)*
Patricia Bartoli *(CFO)*

NORTH BRANCH CAPITAL, LLC
Drake Oak Brook Plaza, 2215 York Rd, Ste 420, Oak Brook, IL 60523
Tel.: (630) 526-3220
Web Site: http://www.northbranchcap.com
Year Founded: 2014
Privater Equity Firm
N.A.I.C.S.: 523999
Jon Leiman *(Partner)*
Dan Bauman *(Partner)*
Bill Huber *(Partner)*

NORTH BRIDGE VENTURE MANAGEMENT COMPANY, INC.
60 William St Ste 350, Wellesley, MA 02481
Tel.: (781) 290-0004 DE
Web Site: http://www.northbridge.com
Year Founded: 1994
Rev.: $3,200,000,000
Emp.: 40
Privater Equity Firm
N.A.I.C.S.: 523999
Richard A. D'Amore *(Founder & Gen Partner)*
James A. Goldstein *(Partner)*
Carmichael S. Roberts *(Gen Partner)*
Paul A. Santinelli *(Partner)*
Holly Maloney *(Principal)*
Russ Pyle *(Partner)*
Roshen Menon *(Gen Partner)*
Chris Cavanagh *(Principal)*
Brendan Gibney *(VP)*
Won Park *(Principal)*

Subsidiaries:

Zettics, Inc. (1)
5 Liberty Way, Westford, MA 01886
Tel.: (978) 254-5329
Data Analytic Services
N.A.I.C.S.: 518210
Sterling Wilson *(Pres & CEO)*
Asa Kalavade *(CTO & Sr VP)*
Tal Kedar *(CFO)*
John Gillespie *(Sr VP-Sls)*
Ian Herbert-Jones *(Sr VP)*
Joe Levy *(VP-Customer Strategy & Mktg)*
Andrew Gibbs *(VP-Product Mgmt)*
Prasasth Palnati *(VP-Engrg)*
Stephen Douglas *(VP-Tech)*
John Thomas *(Dir-Res)*
Adam Guy *(VP-Monetization)*

Subsidiary (Domestic):

Velocent Systems, Inc. (2)
1250 E Diehl Rd, Naperville, IL 60563
Tel.: (630) 799-3800
Web Site: http://www.velocent.com
Emp.: 15
Data Processing Services
N.A.I.C.S.: 423430
Ian Herbert Jones *(CEO)*
Stephen Douglas *(CTO)*
Tom Smith *(COO)*
Jagadeesh Dantuluri *(VP-Mktg)*
Randy Johnson *(VP-Engrg)*
Eric Hong *(Co-Founder)*
Philip Stevens *(Sr VP-Sls)*
Larry Border *(Dir-Fin)*

NORTH BROS. FORD
33300 Ford Rd, Westland, MI 48185
Tel.: (734) 421-1300
Web Site: http://www.northbrothersford.net
Year Founded: 1936
Sales Range: $10-24.9 Million
Emp.: 100
New Car Dealers
N.A.I.C.S.: 441110
Nathan Quenby *(Mgr-New Vehicle Sls)*
Matt McCutcheon *(Mgr-Fin)*
Gary Bratt *(Mgr-Parts)*
Bill Carcone *(Mgr-Collision Center)*
Joel Coiner *(Mgr-Quick Lane)*
Jackie Marcaccini *(Mgr-Customer Care)*
Kenneth Pretko *(Mgr-Special Fin)*
Jim Bigelow *(Asst Mgr-Parts)*
Ray Harbin *(Mgr-Gen Sls)*
Adam King *(Mgr-Sls-New Vehicle)*
Rick Burczyk *(Mgr-Sls-Used Vehicle)*
Randy Woodward *(Mgr-Svc-Columbus)*

NORTH CAMBRIA FUEL CO.
175 McKnight Rd, Blairsville, PA 15717-7961
Tel.: (724) 459-3714 PA
Year Founded: 1946
Sales Range: $25-49.9 Million

Emp.: 10
Bituminous Coal & Lignite-Surface
N.A.I.C.S.: 212114
Ron Little (Gen Mgr)
Kathy Albright (Controller)

NORTH CAROLINA ELECTRIC MEMBERSHIP CORPORATION
3400 Sumner Blvd, Raleigh, NC 27616
Tel.: (919) 872-0800
Web Site: http://www.ncemcs.com
Sales Range: $25-49.9 Million
Emp.: 150
Electric Power Supplier
N.A.I.C.S.: 221122
Jane Pritchard (Dir-Corp Comm)
Tim Bennett (VP-Wholesale Rates, Billing & Settlement)
Gerry Moore (Mgr-Acctg)
Rochelle Gilliam (Supvr-Association Svcs)

NORTH CAROLINA GRANITE CORP.
151 Granite Quarry Trl, Mount Airy, NC 27030
Tel.: (336) 786-5141
Web Site: http://www.ncgranite.com
Sales Range: $10-24.9 Million
Emp.: 120
Building Stone Products
N.A.I.C.S.: 327991
Kenny Moles (CFO & VP)
William Swift (Pres & CEO)
Donald Shelton (Pres)

NORTH CAROLINA JOINT UNDERWRITING ASSOCIATION
5520 Dillard Dr, Cary, NC 27518
Tel.: (919) 821-1299   NC
Web Site: http://www.ncjua-nciua.org
Year Founded: 1969
Sales Range: $10-24.9 Million
Emp.: 65
Insurance Underwriting Association
N.A.I.C.S.: 524113
Aaron Scurlock (Mgr-IT)
Alvin Ashworth (CFO)
Bob Eades (Dir-Claims Ops & Mgr-Claims)
Lee Dunn (Asst Gen Mgr)
Tekeela Barnes (Mgr)
Vita Wooten (Mgr)

NORTH CAROLINA LUMBER COMPANY
6676 High Pine Church Rd, Asheboro, NC 27205
Tel.: (336) 498-6600
Web Site: http://www.eastfurniture.com
Rev.: $18,593,505
Emp.: 200
Lumber, Hardwood Dimension
N.A.I.C.S.: 321912
Steve Hunsucker (Controller)
Bruce Hughes (Owner)

NORTH CAROLINA MUTUAL LIFE INSURANCE COMPANY
411 W Chapel Hill St, Durham, NC 27701-3616
Tel.: (919) 682-9201   NC
Web Site: http://www.ncmutuallife.com
Year Founded: 1898
Sales Range: $200-249.9 Million
Emp.: 80
Fire Insurance Services
N.A.I.C.S.: 524113
Michael L. Lawrence (Pres)
Jacqueline Britt (Treas, VP & Controller)
James Herbert Speed Jr. (Bd of Dirs, Executives)

Subsidiaries:
The Signature Group, LLC   (1)
950 Franklin Ave, Garden City, NY 11530
Tel.: (516) 764-1100
Web Site: http://www.signatureinsurance.com
Financial Management Services
N.A.I.C.S.: 523940
Carole N. Shulman (Dir-Admin)
Kenneth W. Fressle (Mgr-Real Estate Program)
Diana L. Johanson (Co-Mgr-Personal Insurance Underwriting)
Melissa Price (Controller)

NORTH CAROLINA MUTUAL WHOLESALE DRUG COMPANY
816 Ellis Rd, Durham, NC 27703-6019
Tel.: (919) 596-2151   NC
Web Site: http://www.mutualdrug.com
Sales Range: $400-449.9 Million
Emp.: 135
Drugs, Sundries & Health & Beauty Aids Whslr
N.A.I.C.S.: 424210
Thomas Davis (Pres)
Mike Bromme (CFO)
David Moody (CEO)

NORTH CAROLINA OPERA
612 Wade Ave Ste 100, Raleigh, NC 27605
Tel.: (919) 792-3850   NC
Web Site: http://www.ncopera.org
Year Founded: 2010
Sales Range: $1-9.9 Million
Emp.: 2
Operatic Productions
N.A.I.C.S.: 711130
Eric Mitchko (Gen Dir)
Julie Williams (Mgr)
Linda T. Carlson (Mgr-Production)
Kristin Hartzell (Mgr-Community Rels)
C. Thomas Kunz (Pres)
John Lunsford (Treas)
Sterling Perkinson (Sec)
Francis Acquaviva (VP)

NORTH CAROLINA RATE BUREAU
2910 Sumner Blvd, Raleigh, NC 27616
Tel.: (919) 582-1056
Web Site: http://www.ncrb.org
Year Founded: 1977
Sales Range: $10-24.9 Million
Emp.: 69
General Insurance Services
N.A.I.C.S.: 525190
David Sink (CFO)
Ray Evans (Gen Mgr)
Rebecca Williams (Mgr-Data Analysis)
Delisa Fairley (Mgr-Insurance Data Ops)
Joanna Biliouris (COO)
Tim Lucas (Mgr-Personal Lines)
Karen Byrd (Mgr-Assigned Risk & Ops Support)
Betty Hurst (Mgr-Workers Compensation)
Shelley Chandler (CIO)
Vicki Godbold (Chief Admin Officer)

NORTH CAROLINA RURAL ECONOMIC DEVELOPMENT CENTER, INC.
4021 Carya Dr, Raleigh, NC 27610
Tel.: (919) 250-4314   NC
Web Site: http://www.ncruralcenter.org
Year Founded: 1987
Sales Range: $10-24.9 Million
Emp.: 30

Rural Community Development Services
N.A.I.C.S.: 925120
Mary Kay Clifford (Controller)
Patty Eller (Office Mgr)

NORTH CAROLINA SYMPHONY
3700 Gleenwood Ave 130, Raleigh, NC 27612
Tel.: (919) 733-2750
Web Site: http://www.ncsymphony.org
Sales Range: $10-24.9 Million
Emp.: 85
Symphony Orchestra
N.A.I.C.S.: 711130
Brenda Knight (Mgr-Fin)
Jeannie Mellinger (Dir-Comm)
Sandi Macdonald (Pres & CEO)
Glenda Hughes (Controller)

NORTH CASCADE BUILDING MATERIALS
3001 Smith Ave, Everett, WA 98201
Tel.: (425) 258-2588   WA
Web Site: http://www.northcascade.net
Year Founded: 1969
Sales Range: $10-24.9 Million
Emp.: 25
Lumber; Plywood & Millwork Whslr
N.A.I.C.S.: 423310
Willie Weyers (Pres, Treas & Sec)

NORTH CASTLE PARTNERS, LLC
183 E Putnam Ave, Greenwich, CT 06830
Tel.: (203) 862-3200   DE
Web Site: http://www.northcastlepartners.com
Year Founded: 1997
Sales Range: $1-4.9 Billion
Emp.: 20
Privater Equity Firm
N.A.I.C.S.: 523999
Alyse Skidmore (CFO & Chief Compliance Officer)
Jonathan Canarick (Mng Dir)
Alison Minter (Mng Dir)
David Weston (Principal)
Erin O'Brien Edwards (Principal)
Jay Galluzzo (Mng Dir)
Hemanshu Patel (Principal)
Charles F. Baird Jr. (Founder & CEO)

Subsidiaries:
Healthy Holdings, Inc.   (1)
1422 Woodland Dr, Saline, MI 48176
Tel.: (734) 944-5445
Web Site: http://www.flatoutbread.com
Sales Range: $1-9.9 Million
Retail Bakery; Flatbreads, Wraps & Snack Crisps
N.A.I.C.S.: 445291
Michael Marsh (Sec & VP)
Stacey Marsh (CEO)

SmartyPants, Inc.   (1)
4056 Del Rey Ave Ste A, Venice, CA 90292
Web Site: http://www.smartypantsvitamins.com
Sales Range: $1-9.9 Million
Emp.: 25
Nutrition Product Distr
N.A.I.C.S.: 456191
Courtney Nichols Gould (Co-Founder & Co-CEO)
Gordon Gould (Co-Founder & Co-CEO)

NORTH CENTRAL CO-OP INC.
PO Box 299, Wabash, IN 46992-0299
Tel.: (260) 563-8381   IN
Web Site: http://www.ncc.coop
Year Founded: 1927
Sales Range: $50-74.9 Million

Emp.: 175
Distribution of Fertilizers & Agricultural Products
N.A.I.C.S.: 424910
Doug Bible (CFO)
Mark Tullis (Pres & CEO)
Jason Verhaeghe (Mgr-Ops)

NORTH CENTRAL EQUITY LLC
60 S 6th St Ste 2535, Minneapolis, MN 55402
Tel.: (612) 465-0260
Web Site: http://www.ncequity.net
Year Founded: 2004
Sales Range: $25-49.9 Million
Emp.: 500
Privater Equity Firm
N.A.I.C.S.: 523999
Elam Baer (CEO)
Laura Conradi Carlson (VP-Fin)
Peter M. Jacobson (VP-Fin Analysis)
Drew S. Backstrand (Gen Counsel)
Gregory L. Wilmes (Dir-Acq)
Daniel L. Hogan (CFO)
Bernie Coyle (VP-Mfg)
Deanna Keefe (Dir-HR)
Ron Jost (VP & Dir-Banking)

Subsidiaries:
First Communications LLC   (1)
9530 Padgett St Ste 101, San Diego, CA 92126
Tel.: (858) 547-5700
Sales Range: $10-24.9 Million
Emp.: 5
Communication Service
N.A.I.C.S.: 517111

Mereen-Johnson Machine Company   (1)
575 SE 9th St Ste 200, Minneapolis, MN 55414
Tel.: (612) 529-7791
Web Site: http://www.mereen-johnson.com
Sales Range: $10-24.9 Million
Woodworking Machinery Mfr
N.A.I.C.S.: 333243
Timothy Brown (Mgr-Mktg)
John Branch (Mgr-Sls-New Machinery)
Brooke Ripley (Office Mgr)
Dave Olson (Mgr-Technical Support)
Andy Asp (VP-Engrg)
David Joslyn (Mgr-Product Line)
Paul Wilmes (CEO)

Sunrise Fiberglass LLC.   (1)
5175 260th St, Wyoming, MN 55092
Tel.: (651) 462-5313
Web Site: http://www.sunrisefiberglass.com
Sales Range: $1-9.9 Million
Emp.: 42
Fiberglass Components & Assembly Mfr
N.A.I.C.S.: 326130
Ray Pixley (Pres & CEO)
Liz Marihart (Office Mgr)

NORTH CENTRAL FARMERS ELEVATOR, INC.
125th Ave, Ipswich, SD 57451
Tel.: (605) 426-6021   SD
Web Site: http://www.ncfe.coop
Year Founded: 1915
Sales Range: $10-24.9 Million
Emp.: 100
Grain & Field Beans
N.A.I.C.S.: 424510
Joe Zikmund (Controller)
Subrena Green (Dir-Comm)
David Dohman (Dir-Ops-Grain)
Deanne Hoyle (Mgr-HR)
Mike Nicholas (Gen Mgr)
Richard Osterday (Pres)
Jim Kanable (Dir-Agronomy Ops)

NORTH CENTRAL GRAIN COOPERATIVE, INC.
Railroad Right Of Way, Bisbee, ND 58317

NORTH CENTRAL GRAIN COOPERATIVE, INC. U.S. PRIVATE

North Central Grain Cooperative, Inc.—(Continued)
Tel.: (701) 656-3263 ND
Web Site: http://www.ncgrain.com
Year Founded: 1984
Sales Range: $10-24.9 Million
Emp.: 35
Grain & Field Beans
N.A.I.C.S.: 424510
Larry Swalheim (Gen Mgr)

NORTH CENTRAL KANSAS COOP
508 N Main St, Hope, KS 67451
Tel.: (785) 366-7213
Web Site: http://www.nckcoop.com
Sales Range: $10-24.9 Million
Emp.: 32
Grain Elevators
N.A.I.C.S.: 424510
Dave Baier (Chm)
Terry Reiff (Vice Chm)

NORTH CENTRAL MISSOURI ELECTRIC COOPERATIVE, INC.
Hwy E West, Milan, MO 63556
Tel.: (660) 265-4404 MO
Web Site: http://www.ncmec.coop
Year Founded: 1940
Sales Range: $10-24.9 Million
Emp.: 32
Electric Transmission Services
N.A.I.C.S.: 221122
Melvin Scott (Pres)
Lowell Tucker (VP)
Neil Guyer (Sec)
Roger Casady (Treas)

NORTH CENTRAL TELEPHONE COOPERATIVE
872 Hwy 52 By Pass E, Lafayette, TN 37083
Tel.: (615) 666-2151
Web Site: http://www.nctc.com
Rev.: $18,438,898
Emp.: 84
Local Telephone Communications
N.A.I.C.S.: 517121
Flo Agee (Supvr-Customer Svc)
Johnny McClanahan (Acting Pres & Acting CEO)

NORTH CHARLESTON SEWER DISTRICT
7225 Stall Rd, North Charleston, SC 29419
Tel.: (843) 764-3072
Web Site: http://www.ncsd-sc.com
Sales Range: $10-24.9 Million
Emp.: 125
Sewage Treatment Services
N.A.I.C.S.: 221320
Gary N. Alford (Asst District Mgr-Ops)
Jarred Jones (Dir-Capital Projects)

NORTH COAST COOPERATIVE INC.
811 I St, Arcata, CA 95521
Tel.: (707) 822-5947
Web Site: http://www.northcoastcoop.com
Sales Range: $10-24.9 Million
Emp.: 200
Cooperative Food Store
N.A.I.C.S.: 445110
Ron Sharp (Controller)

NORTH COAST MEDIA, LLC
IMG Center 1360 E 9th St 10th Fl, Cleveland, OH 44114
Tel.: (216) 706-3740
Web Site: http://www.northcoastmedia.net
Sales Range: $10-24.9 Million
Emp.: 35
Periodical Publishers
N.A.I.C.S.: 513120
Kevin Stoltman (Pres)

NORTH COAST MERCANTILE CO.
1115 W Del Norte St, Eureka, CA 95501
Tel.: (707) 445-4910
Web Site: http://www.ncmercantile.com
Sales Range: $10-24.9 Million
Emp.: 40
Beer & Other Fermented Malt Liquors
N.A.I.C.S.: 424810
Robert Hansen (Pres & Gen Mgr)

NORTH COAST OPPORTUNITIES, INC.
413 N State St, Ukiah, CA 95482
Tel.: (707) 462-1954 CA
Web Site: http://www.ncoinc.org
Year Founded: 1968
Sales Range: $10-24.9 Million
Emp.: 267
Community Welfare Services
N.A.I.C.S.: 624190
Jeff Tyrrell (Chm)
Ross Walker (Vice Chm)
John Goldsmith (Treas & Sec)
Patty Bruder (Exec Dir)

NORTH COAST TECHNOLOGY INVESTORS, L.P.
206 S Fifth Ave Ste 550, Ann Arbor, MI 48104
Tel.: (734) 662-7667
Web Site: http://www.northcoastvc.com
Investment Services
N.A.I.C.S.: 523999
Lindsay Aspergren (Co-Founder/Gen Partner)
Hugo Braun (Co-Founder/Partner)
Stephanie Schumacher (Mgr-Admin & Controller)

NORTH COUNTRY BUSINESS PRODUCTS
1112 RailRd St SE, Bemidji, MN 56601
Tel.: (218) 751-4140
Web Site: http://www.ncbpinc.com
Rev.: $14,883,594
Emp.: 50
Office Equipment
N.A.I.C.S.: 423420
Dean Crotty (Chm)
Curt Crotty (VP-Svcs)
Jim Freed (Pres & CEO)

NORTH COUNTRY HOSPITAL
189 Prouty Dr, Newport, VT 05855
Tel.: (802) 334-7331 VT
Web Site: http://www.nchsi.org
Year Founded: 1919
Sales Range: $75-99.9 Million
Emp.: 651
Health Care Srvices
N.A.I.C.S.: 622110
Gary Gillespie (Vice Chm-Fin)
Kathryn Austin (Co-Chm)
Melissa Pettersson (Sec)
Alan Wing (Co-Chm)

NORTH COUNTRY INSURANCE CO.
21170 New York St Rte 232, Watertown, NY 13601
Tel.: (315) 788-4730 NY
Web Site: http://www.ncins.com
Year Founded: 1877
Sales Range: $10-24.9 Million
Emp.: 25
Provider of Property & Casualty Insurance & Services
N.A.I.C.S.: 524210
Stephen J. Duflo (CFO & Treas)
Marc Ladouceur (Pres & CEO)
Cora Donahue (Sec)

NORTH COUNTRY MARKETING LTD.
4114 Hoffman Rd, Saint Paul, MN 55110-3708
Tel.: (651) 433-4600
Web Site: http://www.northcountrymktg.com
Sales Range: $25-49.9 Million
Emp.: 10
Sporting & Recreation Goods
N.A.I.C.S.: 423910
Michael Schuett (Pres)

NORTH COUNTRY WINDOWS & DOORS, LLC
4840 Doris Bair Cir, Lincoln, NE 68504
Tel.: (402) 474-4880
Web Site: http://www.northcountrywindowsanddoors.com
Rev.: $11,000,000
Emp.: 30
Vinyl Windows
N.A.I.C.S.: 444110
Tina Denton (Mgr-Fin)

NORTH COUNTY FORD INC.
450 W Vista Way, Vista, CA 92083
Tel.: (760) 945-9900
Web Site: http://www.northcountyford.com
Rev.: $137,035,875
Emp.: 213
New & Used Car Dealers
N.A.I.C.S.: 441110
Scott Crowley (Gen Mgr)

NORTH COUNTY HEALTH PROJECT, LNC.
150 Valpreda Rd, San Marcos, CA 92069
Tel.: (760) 736-6700 CA
Web Site: http://www.nchs-health.org
Year Founded: 1973
Sales Range: $25-49.9 Million
Emp.: 636
Health Care Srvices
N.A.I.C.S.: 622110
Deizel Sarte (COO)
Patrick A. Tellez (Chief Medical Officer)
Irma Cota (Pres & CEO)
Andrew S. Rinde (Sec)
Shelia Brown (Chm)
Carl Pinkard (Treas)

NORTH COVE PARTNERS
17 State St 22nd Fl, New York, NY 10004
Tel.: (212) 440-5700 DE
Web Site: http://www.northcovepartners.com
Year Founded: 1993
Sales Range: $25-49.9 Million
Emp.: 15
Private Equity & Mezzanine Investment Firm
N.A.I.C.S.: 523999
Christopher J. Birosak (Mng Dir)
Jaideep Hebbar (Principal)
Brian Gorczynski (Mng Dir)
Paul Schilpp (Principal)
Akshay Singh (Principal)
William Woo (Principal)
Ling Ivy Lee (VP)

Subsidiaries:

Atrium Corporation (1)
3890 W NW Hwy Ste 500, Dallas, TX 75220
Tel.: (214) 630-5757
Web Site: http://www.atrium.com
Sales Range: $50-74.9 Million
Emp.: 100
Holding Company; Window & Door Mfr
N.A.I.C.S.: 551112
Gregory T. Faherty (Pres)
Chris Reilly (VP-Mktg-Retail & Distr)
Steven Monks (Sr VP-Ops)

Subsidiary (Domestic):

Atrium Companies, Inc. (2)
3890 W NW Hwy Ste 500, Dallas, TX 75220
Tel.: (214) 630-5757
Web Site: http://www.atrium.com
Doors & Windows Mfr & Distr
N.A.I.C.S.: 332321

Subsidiary (Domestic):

Aluminum Screen Manufacturing Co. (3)
610 N Wildwood Dr, Irving, TX 75061
Tel.: (972) 579-4951
Sales Range: $10-24.9 Million
Solar Window Screen Mfr
N.A.I.C.S.: 332321

Atrium Door & Window Co. (3)
3890 NW Hwy Ste 500, Dallas, TX 75220
Tel.: (214) 630-5757
Web Site: http://www.atrium.com
Sales Range: $100-124.9 Million
Mfr of Aluminum Windows & Doors
N.A.I.C.S.: 332321

Atrium Windows & Doors, Inc. (3)
9001 Ambassador Row, Dallas, TX 75247-4509
Tel.: (904) 355-1476
Web Site: http://www.atriumcomp.com
Design & Installation of Household Windows & Doors
N.A.I.C.S.: 821911
Donna Manchester (VP-HR)

Superior Engineered Products Corp. (3)
1650 S Archibald Ave, Ontario, CA 91761-7604
Tel.: (909) 930-1800
Sales Range: $100-124.9 Million
Door & Window Mfr
N.A.I.C.S.: 332321

Thermal Industries, Inc. (3)
5450 2nd Ave, Pittsburgh, PA 15207
Tel.: (412) 244-6400
Web Site: http://www.thermalindustries.com
Sales Range: $75-99.9 Million
Mfr of Vinyl Windows, Patio Doors & Enclosures, Decks, Docks & Railing Systems
N.A.I.C.S.: 332321
Scott Jeffreys (VP-Sls)

Cricut, Inc. (1)
10855 S River Front Pkwy, South Jordan, UT 84095
Tel.: (385) 351-0633
Web Site: https://www.cricut.com
Rev.: $886,296,000
Assets: $949,627,000
Liabilities: $276,892,000
Net Worth: $672,735,000
Earnings: $60,666,000
Emp.: 775
Fiscal Year-end: 12/31/2022
Toys, Hobby Goods & Supplies Mfr
N.A.I.C.S.: 423920
Ashish Arora (Pres & CEO)
Ryan Harmer (VP-Acctg & Controller)
Jennia Parkin (VP-Product Mgmt-Global)
Jeremy Crystal (VP-Hardware Engrg)
Kimball Shill (CFO)
David Henry (Exec VP-Product & Member Care)
Jean-Claude Etter (VP-Ops Asia)
Matt Tuttle (VP-Business Development)
Michelle Fishberg (VP-Global Product Mgmt)
Noelle Sieradzki (VP-Materials)
Richard Murphy (VP-Operations)
Sanjay Dhar (VP-IT Platforms & Security)
Shane Bertola (VP-Subscriptions & DTC Monetization)
Siva Tharmarajah (VP-Quality Assurance)
Sriram Alagappa (VP-Software Engrg)
Tara McElroy (VP-Sales)

Vincent Young *(VP-Channel Mktg & Business Development-Americas)*
Vivek Jayaraman *(Exec VP-Platform)*
Jim Suva *(Sr VP-Finance, Treasurer, and Investor Relations)*
Frank Iarusci *(Exec VP-Sls & Channel Mktg)*
Randy Wood *(VP & Assoc Gen Counsel)*
Jason Makler *(Chm)*
Don Olsen *(Gen Counsel-Human Resources & Exec VP)*
Gaurav Jindal *(VP-Data)*
Miranda Oliver *(VP-People)*
Patrick Chrobak *(VP & Dir-Consumer Platform)*
Tom Wailes *(VP-User Experience)*
Ariel Fischer *(Exec VP-Direct-to,Consumer,Consumables)*
Josh Mecham *(VP-E-commerce,Analytics)*

NORTH DAKOTA MILL & ELEVATOR ASSOCIATION
1823 Mill Rd, Grand Forks, ND 58203-1535
Tel.: (701) 795-7000 ND
Web Site: http://www.ndmill.com
Year Founded: 1922
Sales Range: $75-99.9 Million
Emp.: 120
Flour Mfr; Terminal Elevator & Packaging Warehouse
N.A.I.C.S.: 311211
Chris Lemoine *(Mgr-Production Ops)*
Steve Sannes *(Mgr-Sls)*
Mike Jones *(Mgr-Transportation & Logistics)*
Bob Sombke *(Mgr-Quality Assurance & Technical Svc)*
Vance Taylor *(Pres & Gen Mgr)*
Bruce Burman *(Mgr-IT Software)*
Jeff Bertsch *(Mgr-Grain Procurement)*
Kevin Robinson *(Mgr-IT Hardware)*
Tamra Srnsky *(Mgr-HR)*
James Storie *(Mgr-IT Programming)*

NORTH DALLAS MOVING & STORAGE COMPANY CO., INC.
1804 Trinity Vly Dr, Carrollton, TX 75006-6509
Tel.: (972) 241-1562
Web Site: http://www.ndms.com
Year Founded: 1966
Sales Range: $10-24.9 Million
Emp.: 25
General Freight Trucking Services
N.A.I.C.S.: 484121
Brandon Morris *(Pres)*

NORTH EAST HEAT & LIGHT CO.
10700 W Main Rd, North East, PA 16428
Tel.: (814) 725-4302
Web Site: http://www.northeastborough.com
Year Founded: 1886
Sales Range: $1-9.9 Million
Natural Gas Distribution
N.A.I.C.S.: 221210
Samuel S. Miller *(Pres)*

NORTH EAST MISSISSIPPI ELECTRIC POWER ASSOCIATION
PO Box 1076, Oxford, MS 38655
Tel.: (662) 234-6331 MS
Web Site: http://www.northeastpower.org
Year Founded: 1937
Sales Range: $10-24.9 Million
Emp.: 65
Electric Power Distr
N.A.I.C.S.: 221122
Jim McClure *(Dir-Safety & Substation Maintenance)*
Keith Hayward *(CEO & Gen Mgr)*
Larry Little *(Atty)*

Margaret Callahan *(Mgr-Acctg)*
Ray Gallagher *(Treas & Sec)*
James Downs *(Pres)*
Pam Helton *(Mgr-Office Svcs)*
Randall Abel *(Mgr-Engrg & Ops)*
John Davis *(VP)*
Jason Long *(Engr-Ops)*
Marlin Williams *(Mgr-Member Svcs)*
Linda Liggins *(Supvr-Accts Receivable)*
Tracie Russell *(Mgr-Billing)*

NORTH ELECTRIC SUPPLY, INC.
1290 N Opdyke Rd, Auburn Hills, MI 48326
Tel.: (248) 373-1070 MI
Web Site: http://www.northelectric.com
Year Founded: 1972
Sales Range: $10-24.9 Million
Emp.: 13
Supplier of Electrical Construction Materials
N.A.I.C.S.: 423610
Frank Nutt *(Pres)*

NORTH FLORIDA MOTOR COMPANY
4620 Southside Blvd, Jacksonville, FL 32216
Tel.: (904) 642-4100
Web Site: http://www.nflm.com
Sales Range: $25-49.9 Million
Emp.: 75
Automobiles, New & Used
N.A.I.C.S.: 441110
Bill Lynch *(Pres)*
Tom Lynch *(Gen Mgr)*

NORTH FLORIDA SALES
3601 Regent Blvd, Jacksonville, FL 32224-6500
Tel.: (904) 645-0283 KY
Web Site: http://www.abwholesaler.com
Year Founded: 1995
Sales Range: $25-49.9 Million
Emp.: 200
Distr of Beer & Ale
N.A.I.C.S.: 424810
Greg Flowers *(Gen Mgr)*
Virgil Pelham *(Pres)*
Maggie Lombardi *(Mgr-HR)*
Bracy Taylor *(Mgr-Key Acct)*

NORTH FLORIDA SHIPYARDS INC.
2060 E Adams St, Jacksonville, FL 32202
Tel.: (904) 354-3278 FL
Web Site: http://www.northfloridashipyard.com
Year Founded: 1970
Sales Range: $10-24.9 Million
Emp.: 250
Repair Services
N.A.I.C.S.: 811310
Matthew Self *(Pres)*
Robert Wilson *(CFO & VP)*
Anna Dunn *(Sec)*

Subsidiaries:

North Florida Shipyards Inc. - Mayport Facility (1)
Bldg 1933 Bailey Rd, Jacksonville, FL 32228
Tel.: (904) 249-7266
Web Site: http://www.northfloridashipyard.com
Ship Building & Maintenance Services
N.A.I.C.S.: 336611
Matt Self *(CEO)*

NORTH GEORGIA BRICK COMPANY INC.
2405 Oak Ste W, Cumming, GA 30041-6456
Tel.: (770) 886-6555 GA
Web Site: http://www.northgeorgiabrick.com
Year Founded: 1982
Sales Range: $25-49.9 Million
Emp.: 150
Brick, Stone & Related Material
N.A.I.C.S.: 423320
Larry Tarver *(VP-Sls)*
John Alvord *(Pres)*
Dave Mayton *(Acct Mgr)*
Jason Hammonds *(Acct Mgr)*

NORTH GEORGIA ELECTRIC MEMBERSHIP CORPORATION
1850 Cleveland Hwy, Dalton, GA 30722
Tel.: (706) 259-9441 GA
Web Site: http://www.ngemc.com
Year Founded: 1936
Sales Range: $25-49.9 Million
Emp.: 170
Electronic Services
N.A.I.C.S.: 221122
Ron Hutchins *(Pres & CEO)*
Laura Sparks *(Dir-Mktg)*
Jeff Brown *(VP-Ops)*

NORTH HAVEN PRIVATE INCOME FUND LLC
1585 Broadway, New York, NY 10036
Tel.: (212) 761-4000 DE
Web Site: https://www.northhavenprivateincomefund.com
Finance Services
N.A.I.C.S.: 525990
Jeff Levin *(Pres & CEO)*
Orit Mizrachi *(COO)*

Subsidiaries:

SL Investment Corp. (1)
1585 Broadway, New York, NY 10036
Tel.: (212) 761-4000
Rev.: $83,441,000
Assets: $1,135,857,000
Liabilities: $619,625,000
Net Worth: $516,232,000
Earnings: $52,004,000
Fiscal Year-end: 12/31/2022
Investment Services
N.A.I.C.S.: 523940
David Pessah *(CFO)*
Thomas P. Torrisi *(Interim Chief Compliance Officer)*
Jeffrey S. Levin *(Pres & CEO)*

NORTH HILL NEEDHAM, INC.
865 Central Ave, Needham, MA 02492
Tel.: (781) 444-9910 MA
Web Site: http://www.northhill.org
Year Founded: 1979
Sales Range: $25-49.9 Million
Emp.: 372
Senior Care Services
N.A.I.C.S.: 624120
Anne Orens *(Dir-Bus Dev)*
Darren Roy *(CFO & Treas)*
David J. Maw *(VP-Ops & Exec Dir)*
Ted Owens *(Chm)*
Eddie Brown *(Dir-HR)*
Patricia A. Paulin *(Dir-Fin, Plng & Admin)*
Harold Goodale Jr. *(Dir-Facilities)*

NORTH IOWA COOPERATIVE
105 S 1st St, Thornton, IA 50479
Tel.: (641) 998-2711
Web Site: http://www.nicoop.com
Grain & Field Bean Merchant Whslr
N.A.I.C.S.: 424510
Creighton Nelson *(Mgr-Agronomy Div)*
Chuck Schafer *(Gen Mgr)*

Craig Backhaus *(Grain Mgr)*
Ed Paulus *(Reg Mgr)*
Kevin Weiss *(Location Mgr-Clear Lake)*

NORTH KANSAS CITY BEVERAGE CO.
203 E 11th Ave, Kansas City, MO 64116
Tel.: (816) 471-4895
Web Site: http://www.nkcbev.com
Rev.: $21,486,345
Emp.: 50
Beer & Other Fermented Malt Liquors
N.A.I.C.S.: 424810
Curt Borland *(Pres)*
Chad Curtis *(Dir-Sls)*

NORTH LOS ANGELES COUNTY REGIONAL CENTER INC.
15400 Sherman Way Ste 170, Van Nuys, CA 91406-4272
Tel.: (818) 778-1900
Web Site: http://www.nlacrc.org
Year Founded: 1974
Sales Range: $10-24.9 Million
Emp.: 300
Provider of Business Consulting Services
N.A.I.C.S.: 611710
Ellen Stein *(CFO)*

NORTH LOUISIANA ROOFING SUPPLY
1802 Southern Ave, Shreveport, LA 71101
Tel.: (318) 674-8780
Web Site: http://www.roofingsupplygroup.com
Sales Range: $10-24.9 Million
Emp.: 12
Roofing Distributors
N.A.I.C.S.: 423330
Robert McCalman *(Gen Mgr)*

NORTH METRO COMMUNITY SERVICES, INC.
1001 W 124th Ave, Westminster, CO 80234
Tel.: (303) 457-1001 CO
Web Site: http://www.nmetro.org
Year Founded: 1965
Sales Range: $25-49.9 Million
Emp.: 667
Developmental Disability Assistance Services
N.A.I.C.S.: 624120
Carrie Morris *(Dir-Support Svcs)*
Jennifer O'Shea *(Dir-HR)*
Ryan Grygiel *(Dir-Residential Svcs)*
George Montoya *(CFO & Exec Dir)*
Randy Brodersen *(Exec Dir)*
Bill Hawthorne *(VP)*
Doug Shepherd *(Treas)*
Edward Bertagnolli *(Pres)*
Pauline Burton *(Sec)*
Robert Hunter *(Dir-Day Program)*

NORTH METRO MEDICAL CENTER
1400 Braden St, Jacksonville, AR 72076
Tel.: (501) 985-7000
Web Site: http://www.northmetromed.com
Year Founded: 1962
General Medical Services
N.A.I.C.S.: 622110
James Ballangee *(CEO)*
Knaudia Bridges *(Dir-Support Svcs)*
Tonya Brownfield *(Dir-Inpatient Svcs)*
Polly DuLaney *(Dir-Lab)*
James Jordan *(Dir-Nutritional & Environmental Svcs)*

NORTH METRO MEDICAL CENTER

North Metro Medical Center—(Continued)

Paige Ballard (Dir-Pharmacy)
Michelle Blocker (Mgr-Sleep Center)
Kerry Ward (Dir-Perioperative Svcs)
Van Davis (Dir-Therapy Svcs)
Tiffany Kagebein (Transition Dir)
Lauren Garland (Mgr-Cardiopulmonary)
Christine Thompson (Dir-Emergency Dept)
Beau Bridges Jr. (Program Dir)

NORTH MIDDLESEX SAVINGS BANK
7 Main St, Ayer, MA 01432
Tel.: (978) 772-3306   MA
Web Site: http://www.nmsb.com
Year Founded: 1885
Sales Range: $125-149.9 Million
Emp.: 190
Provider of Savings Institutions
N.A.I.C.S.: 522180
Paul D. Bresnahan (Chm)
John J. Spinello (VP & Controller)
Andrew Witherbee (VP-Mktg)
William Keyles (VP & Dir-Learning & Dev)
Michael J. Duval (Officer-Comml Loan & Asst VP)
Richard Bennet (CEO)
Walter J. Dwyer IV (Pres)

NORTH MISSOURI TIRE, INC
615 E 3rd St, Milan, MO 63556
Tel.: (660) 265-4223
Automobile & Other Motor Vehicle Merchant Whslr
N.A.I.C.S.: 423110
Marty Campbell (Pres)

NORTH PACIFIC CORPORATION
5612 Lk Washington Blvd NE Ste 102, Kirkland, WA 98033-7352
Tel.: (425) 822-1001
Web Site: http://www.npc-usa.com
Year Founded: 1993
Fish & Seafood Frozen, Unpackaged
N.A.I.C.S.: 424460
Valeri Shegnagaev (Owner)

NORTH PALM HYUNDAI, LLC.
3703 Northlake Blvd, Lake Park, FL 33403-1629
Tel.: (561) 721-3800
Web Site: http://www.northpalmhyundai.com
Year Founded: 2006
Sales Range: $25-49.9 Million
Emp.: 100
New Car Whslr
N.A.I.C.S.: 441110
Edward F. Napleton (Pres)
Kristen Napleton (VP)
Jim Priegel (Principal)

NORTH PARK LINCOLN MERCURY INC.
9207 San Pedro Ave, San Antonio, TX 78216
Tel.: (210) 341-8841   TX
Web Site: http://www.nplm.com
Year Founded: 1973
Sales Range: $125-149.9 Million
Emp.: 250
Retailer of New & Used Automobiles
N.A.I.C.S.: 441110
Clarence J. Kahlig (Owner & Pres)
Billy Vaughn (VP)
David Hoyer (Controller)

NORTH PARK TRANSPORTATION CO. INC.
5150 Columbine St, Denver, CO 80216
Tel.: (303) 295-0300   CO
Web Site: http://www.nopk.com
Year Founded: 1957
Sales Range: $25-49.9 Million
Emp.: 325
Trucking Except Local
N.A.I.C.S.: 484121
Peter B. Kooi (Pres & Treas)
Greg Walkup (Reg Mgr)

NORTH PENN WATER AUTHORITY
300 Forty Foot Rd, Lansdale, PA 19446
Tel.: (215) 855-3617
Web Site: http://www.northpennwater.org
Sales Range: $10-24.9 Million
Emp.: 60
Supplier of Water
N.A.I.C.S.: 221310
Anthony Bellitto (Exec Dir)
Dale Reichenbach (Dir-Fin & Acctg)
Lorraine Girone (Supvr-Acctg)

NORTH RANCH COUNTRY CLUB
4761 Vly Spring Dr, Westlake Village, CA 91362-4357
Tel.: (805) 496-1995   CA
Web Site: http://www.northranchcc.org
Year Founded: 1976
Sales Range: $10-24.9 Million
Emp.: 181
Country Club Operator
N.A.I.C.S.: 713910
Rachel Stull (Dir-Membership)
Jenelle Kagay (Dir-Catering)
Kate Papa (Mgr-Catering Sales Event)
Mark Wilson (Dir-Golf)
Scott Miller (Head-Golf Pro)

NORTH RIVER CAPITAL LLC
5642 Coventry Ln, Fort Wayne, IN 46804
Tel.: (260) 432-2233
Web Site: http://www.northrivercapital.net
Year Founded: 2008
Emp.: 25
Privater Equity Firm
N.A.I.C.S.: 523999
Daniel M. Rifkin (Partner)
Richard S. Rifkin (Partner)
Martin S. Rifkin (Partner)
Gary E. Rohrs (Partner)
Grant A. Schultz (Partner)
Jennifer L. Wilson (Partner)
Paul Everett (Partner)

Subsidiaries:

Auburn Gear, Inc.   (1)
400 E Auburn Dr, Auburn, IN 46706-3499
Tel.: (260) 925-3200
Web Site: http://www.auburngear.com
Sales Range: $50-74.9 Million
Emp.: 170
Motor Vehicle Gear Mfr & Whslr
N.A.I.C.S.: 336350
Greg Henderson (Dir-Mktg & Sls)
Martin Palmer (Pres)
Todd Webb (Mgr-Matls)
Michael Lashure (Dir-Engrg & Quality Assurance)

NORTH SAN DIEGO COUNTY TRANSIT
810 Mission Ave, Oceanside, CA 92054
Tel.: (760) 966-6500
Web Site: http://www.gonctd.com
Rev.: $19,776,487
Emp.: 32
Local & Suburban Transit
N.A.I.C.S.: 485119

Mathew Tucker (Exec Dir)

NORTH SEA PARTNERS LLC
45 Rockefeller Plz Ste 2000, New York, NY 10111
Tel.: (212) 235-2477
Web Site: http://www.nspartnersllc.com
Investment Banking Services
N.A.I.C.S.: 523150
Jonathan D. Calder (Mng Partner)
Adrian W. Doherty (Mng Partner)
David B. Miller (CEO)

NORTH SEATTLE COMMUNITY COLLEGE FOUNDATION
9600 College Way N, Seattle, WA 98103
Tel.: (206) 527-3604
Web Site: http://www.northseattle.edu
Student Scholarship & Financial Aid
N.A.I.C.S.: 611710
Mark Mitsui (Pres)
Roy Flores (VP-Student Svcs)

Subsidiaries:

American Financial Solutions   (1)
2815 2nd Ave Ste 280, Seattle, WA 98121
Tel.: (360) 377-9000
Web Site: http://www.myfinancialgoals.org
Sales Range: $10-24.9 Million
Emp.: 50
Student Scholarship & Financial Aid
N.A.I.C.S.: 561499
Cindy Seremek (Exec Dir)

NORTH SHORE BANCORP
248 Andover St, Peabody, MA 01960
Tel.: (978) 573-1300
Web Site: http://www.northshore-bank.com
Year Founded: 1998
Sales Range: $25-49.9 Million
Emp.: 207
Bank Holding Company
N.A.I.C.S.: 551111
Kevin M. Tierney Sr. (CEO)

NORTH SHORE BANK, FSB
15700 W Bluemound Rd, Brookfield, WI 53005
Tel.: (262) 797-3858   WI
Web Site: http://www.northshorebank.com
Year Founded: 1923
Rev.: $97,257,000
Assets: $2,044,746,000
Liabilities: $1,789,306,000
Net Worth: $255,440,000
Earnings: $12,769,000
Emp.: 500
Fiscal Year-end: 09/30/19
Federal Savings Bank
N.A.I.C.S.: 522180
Audrey Sellers (VP-Comml Banking)

NORTH SHORE COMMUNITY HEALTH CENTER, INC.
47 Congress St Ste 504, Salem, MA 01970
Tel.: (978) 744-8388   MA
Web Site: http://www.nschi.org
Year Founded: 1977
Sales Range: $10-24.9 Million
Emp.: 130
Community Health Care Services
N.A.I.C.S.: 621498
Kathryn Hollett (Dir-Quality Improvement)
Gabrielle DeMille (Dir-Dental)
Marion Winfrey (Pres)
Rosario Ubiera-Minaya (Dir-Outreach & Enrollment)
Kiame Mahaniah (Chief Medical Officer)
Margaret A. Brennan (CEO)
Damian Archer (Assoc Dir-Medical)

Ellen Reece (Assoc Dir-Medical-Gloucester)
Jose Morell (Dir-Behavioral Health)
Paula Ricci (Chief HR Officer)

NORTH SHORE FINANCIAL CORPORATION
131 W Superior St, Duluth, MN 55802
Tel.: (218) 722-4784   MN
Year Founded: 1985
Sales Range: $10-24.9 Million
Bank Holding Company
N.A.I.C.S.: 551111
Fred Lewis (Pres)

Subsidiaries:

North Shore Bank of Commerce   (1)
131 W Superior St, Duluth, MN 55802
Tel.: (218) 722-4784
Web Site: http://www.banknorthshore.com
Commericial Banking
N.A.I.C.S.: 522110
Brian Murphy (Chief Lending Officer)
Brenda Brannan (Chief Wealth Mgmt Officer)
Jena M. Hart (Mgr-Private Banking)
Ken Johnson (Pres & CEO)
Doug Lewis (Chm)

NORTH SHORE INFINITI INC.
1225 Northern Blvd, Manhasset, NY 11030
Tel.: (516) 773-1000
Web Site: http://www.infinitiofmanhasset.com
Rev.: $33,000,000
Emp.: 60
New & Used Car Dealers
N.A.I.C.S.: 441110
David Sine (Exec Mgr)

NORTH SHORE LIJ HEALTH SYSTEMS
1979 Marcus Ave Ste E 124, New Hyde Park, NY 11042
Tel.: (516) 396-6410
Web Site: http://www.northshorelij.com
Sales Range: $1-9.9 Million
Emp.: 30
Miscellaneous Ambulatory Health Care Services
N.A.I.C.S.: 621999
Janet Schaetzle (Office Mgr)
Laura S. Peabody (Chief Legal Officer & Sr VP-Legal Affairs-Great Neck)
Andrew Schulz (Gen Counsel & VP-Legal Affairs-Great Neck)

Subsidiaries:

Melville Surgery Center, LLC   (1)
1895 Walt Whitman Rd, Melville, NY 11747
Tel.: (631) 293-9700
Web Site: http://www.melvillesurgerycenter.com
Professional, Scientific & Technical Services
N.A.I.C.S.: 541990
David Benisch (Partner)

NORTH SHORE MORTGAGE INCORPORATED
10620 N College Ave, Indianapolis, IN 46280
Tel.: (317) 844-7211
Web Site: http://www.northshoremort.com
Sales Range: $25-49.9 Million
Emp.: 10
Mortgage Services
N.A.I.C.S.: 522310
Steven P. Bond (Pres & CEO)
Bruce P. Bond (CFO)

NORTH SHORE MOVERS, INC.
912 E Park Ave, Libertyville, IL 60048

Tel.: (847) 498-6560 IL
Web Site:
   http://www.northshoremovers.com
Year Founded: 1968
Sales Range: $75-99.9 Million
Emp.: 75
Local & Long Distance Moving & Storage
N.A.I.C.S.: 484110

NORTH SHORE OIL COMPANY INC.
5114 Hwy 61, Silver Bay, MN 55614
Tel.: (218) 226-3241
Web Site: http://www.nsop.biz
Sales Range: $10-24.9 Million
Emp.: 25
Petroleum Bulk Stations
N.A.I.C.S.: 424710
Wade LeBlanc (Gen Mgr)

NORTH SHORE PEDIATRIC THERAPY
1308 Waukegan Rd Ste 103, Glenview, IL 60025
Tel.: (847) 486-4140
Web Site: http://www.nspt4kids.com
Year Founded: 1999
Rev.: $2,500,000
Emp.: 100
Physical, Occupational, Speech Therapists & Audiologists
N.A.I.C.S.: 621340
Deborah Michael (Pres)

NORTH SHORE REALTY GROUP
12363 Shermer Rd, Northbrook, IL 60062
Tel.: (847) 657-7700
Web Site:
   http://www.northshorelimited.com
Rev.: $10,000,000
Emp.: 18
Real Estate Brokers & Agents
N.A.I.C.S.: 531210
Joseph Licari (Pres)

NORTH SHORE REFRIGERATION CO. INC.
880 Cambridge Dr, Elk Grove Village, IL 60007-2437
Tel.: (847) 677-7100
Rev.: $24,500,000
Emp.: 30
Refrigeration & Installation Services
N.A.I.C.S.: 811412

NORTH SHORE SANITARY DISTRICT
William Koepsel Dr, Gurnee, IL 60031
Tel.: (847) 623-6060
Web Site:
   http://www.northshorewrd.org
Year Founded: 1914
Sales Range: $25-49.9 Million
Emp.: 100
Water Treatment of Sewage Systems
N.A.I.C.S.: 221320
Tom Lentz (Superintendent)
Daniel Pierce (Pres)
Preston Carter (Treas)
Stephen Drew (VP)

NORTH SHORE SUPPLY COMPANY INC.
1566 Miles St, Houston, TX 77015-6319
Tel.: (713) 453-3533
Web Site: http://www.nssco.com
Year Founded: 1955
Sales Range: $100-124.9 Million
Emp.: 230
Metals Service Centers & Offices
N.A.I.C.S.: 423510
William K. Nemzin (Chm)
Buzzy Bluestone (CEO)
Byron Cooper (Pres & COO)

Subsidiaries:

Ford Steel Company (1)
2475 Rock Island Blvd, Saint Louis, MO 63043-3520
Tel.: (314) 567-4680
Web Site: http://www.fordsteel.com
Sales Range: $10-24.9 Million
Emp.: 35
Iron & Steel Products Mfr
N.A.I.C.S.: 423510
Tom Ford (VP)
Tony Morrison (Pres)
Georgianne Rhone (Mgr-Acctg)
Bob Midyett (Gen Mgr)
Josie Chappell (Office Mgr)
Joe Skalas (Mgr-Fabrication Inquiries RFQ)
Tom Johnson (Controller)
Terry Craghead (Mgr-Trafffic, Inquiries & RFQ)
Dick Dennis (Mng Dir)
Christopher Roylance (Mng Dir)

Subsidiary (Non-US):

Ford Steel Chile Industrial SA (2)
Augusto Leguia Sur 79 Oficina 405, Las Condes, Santiago, Chile
Tel.: (56) 2 4811818
Fabricated Structural Metal Mfr
N.A.I.C.S.: 332312

NORTH SHORE TRUST AND SAVINGS
700 S Lewis Ave, Waukegan, IL 60085
Tel.: (847) 336-4430
Web Site:
   http://www.northshoretrust.com
Year Founded: 1921
Emp.: 120
Savings & Loan Associations
N.A.I.C.S.: 522180
Stephen G. Lear (Chm)
Alain H. Oller (Sr Officer-Loans)
Nathan E. Walker (CEO)

NORTH SIDE BANK & TRUST CO.
4125 Hamilton Ave, Cincinnati, OH 45223
Tel.: (513) 542-7800
Web Site:
   http://www.northsidebankandtrust.com
Sales Range: $25-49.9 Million
Emp.: 100
Banking Services
N.A.I.C.S.: 522110
Clifford Coors (Chm)
Jack Coors (Pres)
Stan Boehmer (CFO)

NORTH SIDE FORD
12300 San Pedro Ave, San Antonio, TX 78216
Tel.: (210) 525-9800
Web Site: http://www.nsford.com
Sales Range: $50-74.9 Million
Emp.: 192
Automobiles, New & Used
N.A.I.C.S.: 441110
Brenda Gresham (Mgr-Special Fin)
Cindee Kirk (Mgr-Bus Dev)
Don Bartholomew (Mgr-Fin)
Eric McCaig (Dir-New Vehicle)
John Novak (Dir-New Car)
Robert Strom (Mgr-Collision)
Randy Butler (Mgr-Sls)
Ron Sutton (Mgr-Used Car)
Tommy Cude (Mgr-Comml Sls)
David Starnes (Mgr-Sls)
Jerry Valdez (Mgr-Fin)
Marcelo Canlas (Mgr-Fin)
Tracy L. Ingram (Mgr-Inventory)

NORTH SIDE IMPORTS INC.
3650 W Pratt Ave, Lincolnwood, IL 60712-3724
Tel.: (847) 674-5550
Web Site:
   http://www.northsideimports.com
Sales Range: $10-24.9 Million
Emp.: 300
Automotive Supplies & Parts
N.A.I.C.S.: 423120
Zoya Ghiasi (Dir-HR)
Moe Jalil (Mgr-Sls)

NORTH SNOHOMISH ENTERPRISES
13619 Mukilteo Speedway, Lynnwood, WA 98037
Tel.: (425) 771-1266
Sales Range: $10-24.9 Million
Emp.: 77
Grocery Stores, Independent
N.A.I.C.S.: 445110
Maurey Olson (Pres)

NORTH SOUTH SUPPLY INC.
686 3rd Pl, Vero Beach, FL 32962
Tel.: (772) 569-3810
Web Site: http://www.northsouth.net
Rev.: $17,000,000
Emp.: 19
Plumbing & Hydronic Heating Supplies
N.A.I.C.S.: 423720
Bobby J. Hiers (Founder & Pres)
Shellie Jiannotti (VP)
John Almeda (Dir-Info Mgmt Sys)
Shelly Gianotti (VP)
Ken Kelley (Gen Mgr)

NORTH STAR AUTOMOTIVE GROUP
22426 Perry Hwy, Zelienople, PA 16063
Tel.: (724) 716-4092
Web Site:
   http://www.northstarmotors.com
New & Used Car Dealer
N.A.I.C.S.: 441110
Ron Dakan (Pres)

Subsidiaries:

North Star Chevrolet, Inc. (1)
5854 University Blvd, Moon Township, PA 15108
Tel.: (412) 264-3325
Web Site:
   http://www.northstarmotorgroup.com
Sales Range: $25-49.9 Million
Emp.: 55
New & Used Car Dealer
N.A.I.C.S.: 441110
Ron Dakan (Pres)

North Star Pontiac, GMC, Oldsmobile, Inc. (1)
22426 Perry Hwy, Zelienople, PA 16063
Tel.: (724) 716-4092
Web Site: http://www.northstarpontiac.net
Sales Range: $25-49.9 Million
Emp.: 30
New & Used Car Dealer
N.A.I.C.S.: 441110
Ron Casella (Gen Mgr)
Harry Haser (Mgr-Used Cars)

NORTH STAR CONSTRUCTION MANAGEMENT
2 City Center 645 W Hamilton St Ste 208, Allentown, PA 18101
Tel.: (610) 395-7005
Web Site:
   http://www.northstarcm.com
Year Founded: 1986
Sales Range: $1-9.9 Million
Emp.: 37
Construction Management, Project Development & Design
N.A.I.C.S.: 236210
Jessica Gentile (Project Dir-Dev)
James Gentile (Pres)
Brian Weiss (Superintendent)

NORTH STAR CONTRACTORS INC.
29501 Mayo Trail Rd, Catlettsburg, KY 41129
Tel.: (606) 739-8415
Rev.: $18,500,000
Emp.: 15
Bituminous Coal Underground Mining
N.A.I.C.S.: 212115
Pam Taylor (Sec)
Carl Kirk Sr. (Pres)

NORTH STAR DESTINATION STRATEGIES LLC
209 Danyacrest Dr, Nashville, TN 37214
Tel.: (615) 232-2103
Web Site:
   http://www.northstarideas.com
Year Founded: 2000
Sales Range: $10-24.9 Million
Emp.: 10
Advetising Agency
N.A.I.C.S.: 541810
Don McEachern (Pres & CEO)

NORTH STAR GROUP, LLC.
600 Maryland Ave SW Ste 860E, Washington, DC 20024
Tel.: (202) 715-0030
Web Site:
   http://www.northstargroupllc.com
Year Founded: 2006
Sales Range: $1-9.9 Million
Emp.: 36
Consulting, Outsourcing & Training Services
N.A.I.C.S.: 541618
Robert Olsen (Co-Founder & CEO)
Michael Shveda (Chief Strategy Officer)
Everett Zillinger (VP-Corp Comm)
Raymond Orie (VP-Pro Svcs)
Linda Wang (Mgr-Fin Analysis)
Julie O'Toole (VP-Bus Ops)
Steve Morrill (Dir-IT)
Sandra Anderson (Mgr-Comm Program)
Brian Heun (Partner & Mgr-Sls & Relationship)

NORTH STAR ICE EQUIPMENT CORPORATION
8151 Occidental Ave S, Seattle, WA 98108
Tel.: (206) 763-7300 WA
Web Site:
   http://www.northstarice.com
Year Founded: 1950
Rev.: $10,000,000
Emp.: 40
Mfr of Continuous Flake Ice Makers & Mechanical Ice Dispensing Systems
N.A.I.C.S.: 333415
Lee Shepardson (Chm)
Chuck Pfeiffer (Reg Mgr-Sls)
Cecil Ugarte (Reg Mgr-Sls)

NORTH STAR MUTUAL INSURANCE CO.
269 Barstad Rd S, Cottonwood, MN 56229
Tel.: (507) 423-6262 MN
Web Site:
   http://www.northstarmutual.com
Year Founded: 1920
Sales Range: $150-199.9 Million
Emp.: 200
Fire, Marine & Casualty Insurance Services
N.A.I.C.S.: 524126

NORTH STAR MUTUAL INSURANCE CO.

North Star Mutual Insurance Co.—(Continued)
Larry Johnson *(VP-Agency & Support Svcs)*
Joe E. Hoff *(COO, Sec & Exec VP)*
Marvin J. Mohn *(VP-Corp Svcs)*
Michael Flugum *(Sr VP)*

NORTH STAR TERMINAL & STEVEDORE COMPANY, LLC
790 Ocean Dock Rd, Anchorage, AK 99501
Tel.: (907) 272-7537
Web Site: http://www.northstarak.com
Sales Range: $10-24.9 Million
Emp.: 20
Provider of Stevedoring Services
N.A.I.C.S.: 488320
Steve Post *(VP)*
Wayne Barrowcliff *(Office Mgr-Homer)*
Jeffrey A. Bentz *(Pres)*

NORTH STATE BANCORP
6204 Falls of Neuse Rd, Raleigh, NC 27609
Tel.: (919) 719-9400 NC
Web Site: http://www.northstatebank.com
Year Founded: 2002
Sales Range: $25-49.9 Million
Emp.: 139
Bank Holding Company
N.A.I.C.S.: 551111
Larry D. Barbour *(Pres & CEO)*
Kirk A. Whorf *(CFO & Exec VP)*
Amanda M. Lloyd *(Chief People Officer & Exec VP)*
Jonathan N. Krieps *(COO, Chief Banking Officer & Exec VP)*
Brian S. Hedges *(Chief Credit Officer & Exec VP)*
Fred J. Smith Jr. *(Chm)*

NORTH STATE GROCERY INC.
20803 Front St, Cottonwood, CA 96022
Tel.: (530) 347-4621 CA
Web Site: http://www.shophqf.com
Year Founded: 1988
Sales Range: $125-149.9 Million
Emp.: 1,400
Provider of Grocery Store Services
N.A.I.C.S.: 445110
Richard E. Morgan Jr. *(Pres & CEO)*
Michael Weaver *(Mgr-Inventory Control)*
Michel Leclerc *(CFO)*
Mike Bible *(VP-Pur & Mktg)*
Steve Kasper *(Dir-IT)*
Eric Schmidt *(Dir-Loss Prevention)*
Harry Avila *(Dir-Maintenance)*
Brad Askeland *(VP-Holiday Market)*
Subsidiaries:
Holiday Quality Foods, Inc. (1)
20803 Front St, PO Box 439, Cottonwood, CA 96022
Tel.: (530) 347-4621
Web Site: http://www.holidayqualityfoods.com
Sales Range: $125-149.9 Million
Emp.: 1,000
Provider of Grocery Store Services
N.A.I.C.S.: 445110

NORTH STATE STEEL INC.
1010 W Gum Rd, Greenville, NC 27834
Tel.: (252) 830-8884
Web Site: http://www.northstatesteel.com
Sales Range: $10-24.9 Million
Emp.: 30
Fabricated Structural Metal
N.A.I.C.S.: 332312
Tom Trevathan *(Pres)*
Kathy Allsbrook *(Office Mgr)*

NORTH STATES INDUSTRIES INC.
5455 Highway 169 N, Plymouth, MN 55442
Tel.: (763) 486-1756
Web Site: http://www.northstatesind.com
Sales Range: $10-24.9 Million
Emp.: 18
Injection Molding Of Plastics
N.A.I.C.S.: 326199
Sheila Schmidt *(Mgr-Payroll & Accts Payable)*
Jim Phillips *(Sr Mgr-Sls)*
Julie Yager Grad *(VP-Sls & Mktg)*

NORTH TERRACE PM LLC
4344 Belleview Ave, Kansas City, MO 64111
Tel.: (816) 561-7368
Web Site: http://www.northterrace.com
Year Founded: 2005
Sales Range: $1-9.9 Million
Emp.: 20
Real Estate Services
N.A.I.C.S.: 531390
Brandon Laughridge *(Pres)*

NORTH TEXAS ENERGY, INC.
5057 Keller Springs Rd Ste 300, Addison, TX 75001
Tel.: (469) 718-5572 NV
Web Site: http://www.northtexasenergy.net
Year Founded: 2011
Sales Range: Less than $1 Million
Emp.: 1
Crude Oil & Natural Gas Production
N.A.I.C.S.: 325194
Kevin Jones *(Chm & CEO)*
Sanah Marah *(CFO)*

NORTH TEXAS FOOD BANK
3677 Mapleshade Ln, Plano, TX 75075
Tel.: (214) 330-1396
Web Site: https://www.ntfb.org
Year Founded: 1982
Nutritional Food Distr
N.A.I.C.S.: 456191

NORTH TEXAS MUNICIPAL WATER DISTRICT
501 E Brown St, Wylie, TX 75098-4406
Tel.: (972) 442-5405
Web Site: http://www.ntmwd.com
Year Founded: 1954
Sales Range: $100-124.9 Million
Emp.: 600
Water & Waste Water Treatment
N.A.I.C.S.: 221310
Joe Joplin *(Pres)*
Robert Thurmond *(Sec)*
Terry Sam Anderson *(VP)*

NORTH TEXAS PUBLIC BROADCASTING
3000 Harry Hines Blvd, Dallas, TX 75201
Tel.: (214) 871-1390 TX
Web Site: http://www.kera.org
Year Founded: 1985
Rev.: $26,576,982
Assets: $58,939,437
Liabilities: $16,220,829
Net Worth: $42,718,608
Emp.: 98
Fiscal Year-end: 06/30/18
Television Broadcasting Services
N.A.I.C.S.: 516120
Deborah Johnson *(Exec VP-Dev & Mktg)*
William S. Leftwich *(CFO)*
Mary Anne Alhadeff *(Pres & CEO)*
Sylvia Komatsu *(Chief Content Officer & Exec VP)*
Don Glendenning *(Sec)*
Janie McGarr *(Chm)*
Levi Hamilton Davis *(Vice Chm)*
Mary Pat Higgins *(Treas)*
Melissa Fetter *(Chm)*
Tim Crouch *(Vice Chm)*
Yolette Garcia *(Sec)*
William R. Young *(VP-Television Programming)*
Glenn Fisher *(COO)*
Richard Holter Jr. *(VP-News)*

NORTH TEXAS STATE SOCCER ASSOCIATION, INC.
3803 Parkwood Blvd Ste 200, Frisco, TX 75034
Tel.: (214) 297-5022 TX
Web Site: http://www.ntxsoccer.org
Year Founded: 1964
Sales Range: $10-24.9 Million
Emp.: 59
Soccer Association
N.A.I.C.S.: 711211
Gary Williamson *(Dir-Coaching & Player Dev)*
David Messersmith *(Exec Dir)*
Lisa Skiles *(Office Mgr)*
Billy Babcock *(Pres)*
Carlos Quinones *(VP-Appeals & Disciplinary)*
Dick Metivier *(Treas)*

NORTH TOWNE GRILL & SEAFOOD
2093 Eagle Landing Blvd, North Charleston, SC 29406
Tel.: (843) 863-1001
Web Site: http://www.northtownegrill.com
Year Founded: 1972
Sales Range: $10-24.9 Million
Emp.: 20
Sea Food Services
N.A.I.C.S.: 722511
Athan Fokas *(Pres & Sec)*
Maki Nikatos *(VP & Treas)*

NORTH VALLEY HOSPITAL
1600 Hospital Way, Whitefish, MT 59937
Tel.: (406) 863-3500 MT
Web Site: http://www.nvhosp.org
Year Founded: 1955
Sales Range: $25-49.9 Million
Emp.: 386
Health Care Srvices
N.A.I.C.S.: 622110
Catherine Todd *(Dir-Mktg & Community Rels)*
Traci Waugh *(Dir-Compliance)*
Maura Fields *(Chief Clinical Officer)*
Mike Barnes *(Dir-Info Sys)*
Ken Archer *(CEO)*
John McReynolds *(Interim CEO)*
Jan Gonzales *(Dir-HR)*

NORTH WEST RURAL ELECTRIC COOPERATIVE
1505 Albany Pl SE, Orange City, IA 51041
Tel.: (712) 707-4935
Web Site: http://www.nwrec.com
Year Founded: 1935
Sales Range: $50-74.9 Million
Emp.: 40
Electric Power Distr
N.A.I.C.S.: 221118
Curtis Ahrenholz *(Dir-Fin & Svc)*
Derald Philips *(Dir-Safety & Loss Control)*
Lyle D. Korver *(CEO & Gen Mgr)*
Del Beyer *(VP)*
Tom Wagner *(Treas)*
Doug Becker *(Asst Treas & Asst Sec)*
Douglas Alons *(Dir-Ops)*
Derrick Haak *(Asst Dir-Ops)*
Rob Driesen *(Dir-Member Svcs)*
Jeffrey Allen Rehder *(Pres)*

NORTH WOODS ADVERTISING
15 Bldg Ste 1201 15 S 5th St, Minneapolis, MN 55402
Tel.: (612) 340-9999
Web Site: http://www.northwoodsadvertising.com
Sales Range: Less than $1 Million
Emp.: 10
Food Service,
Government/Political/Public Affairs
N.A.I.C.S.: 541810
Bill Hillsman *(Founder)*
Jill Harrison *(Mgr-Bus & Dir-Fin)*
Linda Fisher *(Dir-Bus Dev)*
Vaughn Juares *(Dir-Creative)*

NORTHAMPTON COMMUNITY COLLEGE
3835 Green Pond Rd, Bethlehem, PA 18020
Tel.: (610) 861-5300
Web Site: http://www.northampton.edu
Year Founded: 1967
Sales Range: $1-9.9 Million
Emp.: 70
College
N.A.I.C.S.: 611310
Mark Erickson *(Pres)*

NORTHAMPTON GROWERS PRODUCE SALES, INC.
21471 S Bayside Rd, Cheriton, VA 23316
Tel.: (757) 331-3200 VA
Web Site: http://www.northamptongrowers.com
Year Founded: 1959
Fresh Fruits & Vegetables Distr
N.A.I.C.S.: 424480
Steve McCready *(Co-Owner & Controller)*
Calvert Cullen *(Co-Owner & Pres)*

NORTHBAY HEALTHCARE
4500 Business Center Dr, Fairfield, CA 94534
Tel.: (707) 646-3110 CA
Web Site: http://www.northbay.org
Year Founded: 1984
Sales Range: $50-74.9 Million
Emp.: 362
Health Care Srvices
N.A.I.C.S.: 622110
Kathy Richerson *(Chief Nursing Officer & VP)*
Ken McCollum *(VP-HR)*
Steve Huddleston *(VP-Pub Affairs)*
Arthur E. DeNio *(CFO & VP)*
Christopher T. Timbers *(CIO & VP-Information Sys)*
Mary Mancini *(Treas & Sec)*
Stephen Power *(Vice Chm)*
B. Konard Jones *(Pres & CEO)*
Mark Sievers *(Chm)*

NORTHCENTRAL MISSISSIPPI ELECTRIC POWER ASSOCIATION
4600 Northcentral Way, Olive Branch, MS 38654
Tel.: (662) 838-2151 MS
Web Site: http://www.northcentralepa.com
Year Founded: 1950
Sales Range: $10-24.9 Million
Emp.: 85
Distribution, Electric Power
N.A.I.C.S.: 221122

COMPANIES — NORTHEAST CONTROLS INC.

Kevin Doddridge *(Gen Mgr)*
Jerry Nichols *(VP)*
W. T. Woods *(Treas & Sec)*
Pat Woods *(Pres)*
James E. Woods *(Atty)*
Kevin Doddridge *(Gen Mgr)*
Mark Nichols *(Dir-Admin)*
Darin Farley *(Dir-Construction)*
J. D. Cox *(Dir-Safety & Loss Control)*

NORTHCENTRAL TELCOM INC.
4450 Englund Rd, Prentice, WI 54556
Tel.: (715) 428-2175
Web Site: http://www.northcentraltelcom.com
Sales Range: $10-24.9 Million
Emp.: 70
Telephone & Telephone Equipment Installation
N.A.I.C.S.: 238210
James Carlson *(VP)*
Mary Jean Peterson *(Mgr-Quality Assurance & Materials)*

NORTHCOTT HOSPITALITY INTERNATIONAL, LLC
250 Lk Dr E, Chanhassen, MN 55317-9364
Tel.: (952) 294-5000
Web Site: http://www.northcotthospitality.com
Year Founded: 1994
Sales Range: $25-49.9 Million
Emp.: 50
Restaurants & Motels Owner & Operator
N.A.I.C.S.: 722511
Brian Schwen *(CFO)*
Paul Kirwin *(Pres & CEO)*
Tina Paulsen *(Office Mgr)*

Subsidiaries:

Wheatstone Restaurant Group LLC (1)
250 Lake Dr E, Chanhassen, MN 55317-9364
Tel.: (952) 294-5100
Sales Range: $10-24.9 Million
Restaurant Services
N.A.I.C.S.: 722511
Tina Paulsen *(Office Mgr)*
Paul Kirwin *(Pres & CEO)*
Julie Roetger *(Sr VP-Ops)*

NORTHCREST MEDICAL CENTER
100 Northcrest Dr, Springfield, TN 37172
Tel.: (615) 384-2411
Web Site: http://www.northcrest.com
Year Founded: 1987
Sales Range: $75-99.9 Million
Emp.: 774
Health Care Srvices
N.A.I.C.S.: 622110
Randy Davis *(Pres & CEO)*
Kim Pridgen *(CFO & VP)*
Angie Beard *(Chief Nursing Officer & VP)*
David Bellar *(Chm)*

NORTHCURRENT PARTNERS, LLC
401 Park Ave S 9th Fl, New York, NY 10016
Web Site: http://www.northcurrentpartner.com
Year Founded: 2019
Venture Capital & Private Equity
N.A.I.C.S.: 523910
Alex Z. Brown *(Mng Partner)*
Buck Marshall *(Mng Partner)*
Jason Wall *(Operating Partner)*

Subsidiaries:

Belle Air Inc. (1)
3464 Avalon Park E Blvd Ste 4, Orlando, FL 32828-4808
Tel.: (407) 410-7296
Plumbing, Heating & Air-Conditioning Contractors
N.A.I.C.S.: 238220
Louis Burbano *(Co-Founder)*
Jason Wall *(Pres)*
Maritza Burbano *(Co-Founder)*

NORTHCUTT CHEVROLET-BUICK CO.
3201 W Owen K Garriott Rd, Enid, OK 73703
Tel.: (580) 234-5171
Web Site: http://www.northcuttauto.com
Sales Range: $25-49.9 Million
Emp.: 100
New & Used Car Dealers
N.A.I.C.S.: 441110
Leonard Northcutt *(Pres)*
Yolanda Doffer *(CFO)*

NORTHCUTT INC.
5055 N Broadway St, Wichita, KS 67219
Tel.: (316) 838-1477
Web Site: http://www.northcutt.org
Sales Range: $10-24.9 Million
Emp.: 37
Sales & Service Trailer Repair
N.A.I.C.S.: 811114
Larry Allen *(VP & Mgr-Svcs)*
Bill Q. Johnston Jr. *(Pres)*

NORTHDALE OIL INC.
448 Main Ave, Neche, ND 58265
Tel.: (701) 886-7533
Web Site: http://www.northdaleoil.com
Sales Range: $10-24.9 Million
Emp.: 18
Whslr of Petroleum Products
N.A.I.C.S.: 513110
Scott Reck *(Pres)*
Missy Reck *(VP)*

NORTHEAST BEHAVIORAL HEALTH CORPORATION
199 Rosewood Dr Ste 250, Danvers, MA 01923
Tel.: (978) 968-1700 MA
Web Site: http://www.nebhealth.org
Year Founded: 1970
Sales Range: $50-74.9 Million
Emp.: 1,845
Mental & Emotional Disordered People Assistance Services
N.A.I.C.S.: 623220
Aine Greaney *(Dir-Comm)*
Hilary Jacobs *(VP-Addiction Treatment Svcs)*
Howard R. Grant *(Pres)*

NORTHEAST BLUEPRINT & SUPPLY CO., INC.
1230 E 286th St, Cleveland, OH 44132
Tel.: (216) 261-7500
Web Site: http://www.northeastblueprint.com
Year Founded: 1957
Sales Range: Less than $1 Million
Emp.: 7
Reprographic Services
N.A.I.C.S.: 561439
Michael Rogazione *(Mgr-Tech Svc)*
Tim Yurick *(Pres)*
Jim Yurick *(CEO)*

NORTHEAST BUILDERS SUPPLY HOME CENTER LLC
1460 Barnum Ave, Bridgeport, CT 06610
Tel.: (203) 366-4757
Web Site: http://www.nbslumber.com
Year Founded: 1868
Sales Range: $10-24.9 Million
Emp.: 121
Supplier of Building Materials & Contracts
N.A.I.C.S.: 423310
Jan Cohen *(Pres)*

NORTHEAST CAPITAL & ADVISORY INC
7 Airport Park Blvd, Latham, NY 12110
Tel.: (518) 426-0100
Web Site: http://www.northeastcapital.net
Year Founded: 1992
Sales Range: $10-24.9 Million
Emp.: 5
Investment Banking & Consulting Services
N.A.I.C.S.: 523150
Arthur L. Loomis II *(Pres)*
Thomas F. Collins III *(Mng Dir)*

NORTHEAST COMMUNICATIONS INC.
244 E Union Tpke, Wharton, NJ 07885
Tel.: (973) 328-4000
Web Site: http://www.northeastcommunications.com
Sales Range: $10-24.9 Million
Emp.: 20
Radio & Television Equipment & Parts
N.A.I.C.S.: 423690
John Davieau *(Pres)*

Subsidiaries:

WPNH (1)
110 Babbitt Rd, Franklin, NH 03235
Tel.: (603) 536-2500
Web Site: http://www.wpnhfm.com
Radio Stations
N.A.I.C.S.: 516110
Fred Caruso *(Dir-Ops)*

NORTHEAST COMMUNICATIONS OF WISCONSIN INCORPORATED
450 Security Blvd, Green Bay, WI 54313
Tel.: (920) 617-7000
Web Site: http://www.nsighttel.com
Year Founded: 1982
Sales Range: $100-124.9 Million
Emp.: 500
Telecommunication Servicesb
N.A.I.C.S.: 517112
Patrick D. Riordan *(Pres & CEO)*
James W. Lienau *(Co-CTO & VP-Technical Svcs)*
Todd Whitenack *(CIO & VP-IT)*
Brighid Riordan *(Dir-Pub Affairs)*
Lee E. Thibaudeau *(Co-CTO)*

Subsidiaries:

New Cell, Inc. (1)
1580 Mid Valley Dr, De Pere, WI 54115
Tel.: (920) 339-4000
Web Site: http://www.cellcom.com
Wireless Communication Services
N.A.I.C.S.: 517112
Dan Fabry *(COO & VP)*

Nsight Teleservices (1)
1580 Mid Valley Dr, De Pere, WI 54115
Tel.: (920) 617-7050
Web Site: http://www.nsighttel.com
Sales Range: $10-24.9 Million
Emp.: 5
Internet Service Provider
N.A.I.C.S.: 517810

Mark M. Naze *(CEO)*
Patrick D. Riordan *(Chm, Pres & Chief Strategy Officer)*
Daniel S. Fabry *(COO)*
Brighid A. Riordan *(Chief Innovation Officer & VP-Emerging Svcs & Pub Affairs)*
Lee E. Thibaudeau *(CTO)*
Ronald J. Van Nuland *(CFO & Treas)*

Nsight Telservices (1)
122 S Saint Augustine St, Pulaski, WI 54162
Tel.: (920) 822-8121
Web Site: http://www.nsighttel.com
Sales Range: $10-24.9 Million
Emp.: 15
Cable & Other Pay Television Services
N.A.I.C.S.: 516210
Todd Whitenack *(CIO)*
Bill Dumke *(Engr-RF)*
Jim Paulos *(Mgr)*
Bonnie Cayemberg *(Mgr-Community Rels)*
Dan S. Fabry *(COO & VP-Mobile Svcs)*
James W. Lienau *(CTO & VP-Corp Technical Svcs)*
Mark M. Naze *(CFO & Treas)*
Susan A. Powers *(VP-HR)*
Robert H. Riordan *(Exec VP & Dir-Corp Dev)*
Patrick D. Riordan *(Pres & CEO)*
Robert M. Webb *(VP-Fixed Ops & Technical Projects)*

Nsight Telservices (1)
122 S St Augustine St, Pulaski, WI 54162
Tel.: (920) 865-7000
Web Site: http://www.nsighttel.com
Sales Range: $25-49.9 Million
Emp.: 300
Communication Service
N.A.I.C.S.: 517810
Patrick D. Riordan *(Chm, Pres & Chief Strategy Officer)*
Dan S. Fabry *(COO)*
Ron Van Nuland *(CFO & Treas)*

St. Paul Tower, L.L.C. (1)
1046 Gray Ct, Green Bay, WI 54303-3718
Tel.: (920) 617-7100
Sales Range: $10-24.9 Million
Emp.: 12
Provider of Water Sewer & Utility Lines Setting Services
N.A.I.C.S.: 237130

NORTHEAST CONTRACTORS INC.
100 Moody St, Ludlow, MA 01056
Tel.: (413) 589-7201
Web Site: http://www.northeastcontractors.com
Rev.: $21,571,253
Emp.: 30
Excavation Work
N.A.I.C.S.: 238910
John Rodegher *(VP-Engrg)*
Nelson Rodrigues *(Superintendent)*
Jason Sergentanis *(Pres)*

NORTHEAST CONTROLS INC.
3 Enterprise Ave, Clifton Park, NY 12065
Tel.: (518) 664-6600
Web Site: http://www.northeastcontrols.com
Year Founded: 1967
Sales Range: $25-49.9 Million
Emp.: 50
Controlling Instruments & Accessories
N.A.I.C.S.: 423830
Susan M. Johnson *(CFO & Treas)*
Eric Sanborn *(Mgr-Valves & Regulators Acct)*
Gerard Monast *(Mgr-Valves & Regulators Acct)*
David F. Pellington *(Mgr-Svcs)*
David J. Rizzo *(Pres)*
Daniel Shea *(VP-Sls)*
Greg Frederick *(Engr-Sys)*
Daniel Hagen *(Engr-Inside Sls)*
Paul Pechulis *(Engr-Sys)*
Todd Rice *(Mgr-Valves & Regulators Acct)*

NORTHEAST CONTROLS INC.   U.S. PRIVATE

Northeast Controls Inc.—(Continued)
Dave Zoladz *(Mgr-Valves & Regulators Acct)*
Holly Robinson *(Accountant)*
Joy Mitchell *(Accountant)*
Liz Parker *(Project Mgr)*
Wayne Blaauboer *(Supvr-Field Svc)*

NORTHEAST DONUT SHOP MANAGEMENT
5201 11 Darrah St, Philadelphia, PA 19124
Tel.: (215) 288-3407
Web Site: http://www.dunkindonuts.com
Sales Range: $10-24.9 Million
Emp.: 50
Doughnuts
N.A.I.C.S.: 445291
Billy Hong *(Pres)*

NORTHEAST DRINKS GROUP LLC
1321 Exchange St, Middlebury, VT 05753
Web Site: http://www.ne-dg.com
Beverages Mfr
N.A.I.C.S.: 424500
David Mandler *(Partner)*

Subsidiaries:

Vermont Hard Cider Company, LLC   (1)
1321 Exchange St, Middlebury, VT 05753
Tel.: (802) 398-2090
Web Site: http://www.woodchuck.com
Sales Range: $1-9.9 Million
Emp.: 35
Hard Cider Mfr & Distr
N.A.I.C.S.: 312120

NORTHEAST FOODS, INC.
601 Caroline St, Baltimore, MD 21231-2812
Tel.: (410) 276-7254   MD
Web Site: http://www.nefoods.com
Year Founded: 1965
Sales Range: $25-49.9 Million
Emp.: 850
Producers of Bread, Cake & Related Products
N.A.I.C.S.: 311812
William Paterakis *(Pres)*

NORTHEAST GEORGIA HEALTH SYSTEM INC.
743 Spring St NE, Gainesville, GA 30501-3741
Tel.: (770) 219-9000   DE
Web Site: http://www.nghs.com
Year Founded: 1951
Hospital & Health Care Services
N.A.I.C.S.: 622110
Pranav Kumar Jain *(Chief Medical Information Officer & VP)*

Subsidiaries:

Winder HMA, LLC   (1)
316 N Broad St, Winder, GA 30680
Tel.: (770) 867-3400
Web Site: http://www.nghs.com
Health Care Srvices
N.A.I.C.S.: 622110
Cassie Ball *(CFO)*

NORTHEAST GROCERY, INC.
461 Nott St, Schenectady, NY 12308
Web Site: https://www.northeastgrocery.com
Year Founded: 1932
Emp.: 16,000
Grocery Retailer
N.A.I.C.S.: 445110
Frank Curci *(CEO)*

NORTHEAST GROUP

700 Perry Hill Rd, Coventry, RI 02816
Tel.: (401) 392-8400
Web Site: http://www.neastgroup.com
Year Founded: 1978
Sales Range: $1-9.9 Million
Emp.: 11
Marketing Consulting & Sales Promotion
N.A.I.C.S.: 541810
Fran Mays *(Exec VP & Acct Exec)*
Barbara Gerstenblatt *(Acct Exec)*
Margaret Potter *(Acct Exec)*
W. C. S. Mays III *(Pres & Treas)*

NORTHEAST GUIDANCE CENTER
2900 Conner Bldg A, Detroit, MI 48215
Tel.: (313) 308-1400   MI
Web Site: http://www.neguidance.org
Year Founded: 1963
Sales Range: $10-24.9 Million
Emp.: 118
Behavioral Healthcare Services
N.A.I.C.S.: 621420
Sherry Ellen McRill *(CEO)*
Philip D. Whitfield *(CFO & Mgr-IT)*

NORTHEAST HEALTH SERVICES, LLC
30 Taunton Green Ste 5, Taunton, MA 02780
Tel.: (508) 880-6666
Web Site: http://www.northeasthealthservices.com
Year Founded: 1998
Sales Range: $1-9.9 Million
Emp.: 20
General Health Services
N.A.I.C.S.: 621420
Donna Brennan *(Dir-Clinical)*
Michael Schneider *(Pres-Pennsylvania)*
Brian Wheelan *(CEO)*

Subsidiaries:

Columbia Associates Psychiatry P.C.   (1)
2501 N Glebe Rd Ste 303, Arlington, VA 22207-3558
Tel.: (703) 841-1290
Web Site: http://www.columbiapsychiatry-dc.com
Offices of Physicians (except Mental Health Specialists)
N.A.I.C.S.: 621111
Anita Snow *(Office Mgr)*
Gary Spivack *(Founder Partner & Dir-Medical)*

New Directions Counseling Services, LLC   (1)
117 VIP Dr Ste 310, Wexford, PA 15090
Tel.: (724) 934-3905
Web Site: http://www.newdirectionspgh.com
Individual & Family Services
N.A.I.C.S.: 624190

NORTHEAST HOSPITAL CORPORATION
85 Herrick St, Beverly, MA 01915
Tel.: (978) 922-3000   MA
Year Founded: 1893
Sales Range: $300-349.9 Million
Emp.: 2,892
Health Care Srvices
N.A.I.C.S.: 622110
Cynthia C. Donaldson *(VP-Ancillary Svcs)*
Elizabeth Conrad *(VP-HR)*

NORTHEAST HOT-FILL CO-OP, INC.
25 Copeland Dr, Ayer, MA 01432-1790
Tel.: (978) 772-9287

Sales Range: $50-74.9 Million
Emp.: 45
Soft Drinks Mfr
N.A.I.C.S.: 312111
John H. Webster *(Pres)*
Robert Rauh *(Sec)*

NORTHEAST KANSAS COMMUNITY ACTION PROGRAM, INC.
1260 220th St, Hiawatha, KS 66434
Tel.: (785) 742-2222   KS
Web Site: http://www.nekcap.org
Year Founded: 1965
Rev.: $8,037,584
Assets: $2,026,943
Liabilities: $700,873
Net Worth: $1,326,070
Earnings: $13,287
Emp.: 130
Fiscal Year-end: 03/31/19
Providing Education & Social Services
N.A.I.C.S.: 813410
James T. Scherer *(Pres)*
Brad Lippert *(Treas)*
Joy Padgett *(First VP)*
Jody Allen *(Sec)*
Eric Noll *(Second VP)*

NORTHEAST LOUISIANA POWER COOP
1411 Landis St, Winnsboro, LA 71295
Tel.: (318) 435-4523
Web Site: http://www.nelpco.coop
Sales Range: $10-24.9 Million
Emp.: 60
Distribution, Electric Power
N.A.I.C.S.: 221122
Richard T. Strong *(Treas & Sec)*
Jeff Churchwell *(Mgr)*
Ronald G. Uptigrove *(Mgr-Bastrop Branch)*
Thad H. Waters Jr. *(Pres)*
Alton L. Welch Jr. *(VP)*
Joe Acreman Jr. *(Mgr-Oak Grove Branch)*

NORTHEAST MICHIGAN COMMUNITY SERVICE AGENCY, INC.
2375 Gordon Rd, Alpena, MI 49707
Tel.: (989) 356-3474   MI
Web Site: http://www.nemcsa.org
Year Founded: 1968
Sales Range: $25-49.9 Million
Emp.: 742
Community Action Services
N.A.I.C.S.: 624190
Pete Hennard *(Chm)*
Kenneth Glasser *(Treas)*
Dorothy Pintar *(Dir-School Success Partnership)*
Patricia Rondeau *(Vice Chm)*

NORTHEAST MONTANA HEALTH SERVICES
315 Knapp St, Wolf Point, MT 59201
Tel.: (406) 653-6500   MT
Web Site: http://www.nemontanahealthservices.homestead.com
Year Founded: 1948
Sales Range: $10-24.9 Million
Emp.: 504
Healtcare Services
N.A.I.C.S.: 622110
Myrna Kampen *(Dir-Lab)*

NORTHEAST OHIO NEIGHBORHOOD HEALTH SERVICES, INC.
8300 Hough Ave, Cleveland, OH 44103
Tel.: (216) 231-7700   OH

Web Site: http://www.neonhealth.org
Year Founded: 1967
Sales Range: $10-24.9 Million
Emp.: 368
Health Care Srvices
N.A.I.C.S.: 622110
Lynn Johnson *(Dir-Ops)*
Billy Foster *(Dir-Dental)*
Al Barker *(CIO)*
Karen K. Butler *(COO)*

NORTHEAST OHIO REGIONAL SEWER DISTRICT
3900 Euclid Ave, Cleveland, OH 44115-2504
Tel.: (216) 641-6000
Web Site: http://www.neorsd.org
Year Founded: 1972
Sales Range: $25-49.9 Million
Emp.: 400
Providers of Sanitary Services
N.A.I.C.S.: 562998
Frank Greenland *(Dir-Watershed Programs)*
Constance Haqq *(Dir-Admin & External Affairs)*
Kyle Dreyfuss-Wells *(CEO)*
Darnell Brown *(Pres)*
James Bunsey *(COO)*
Eric Luckage *(Chief Legal Officer)*
Kenneth Duplay *(CFO)*
Ronald D. Sulik *(VP)*
Tim DeGeeter *(Sec)*

Subsidiaries:

Northeast Ohio Regional Sewer District - Easterly Wastewater Treatment Plant   (1)
14021 Lakeshore Blvd, Cleveland, OH 44110
Tel.: (216) 531-4892
Waste Water Treatment Services
N.A.I.C.S.: 221320

Northeast Ohio Regional Sewer District - Southerly Wastewater Treatment Plant   (1)
6000 Canal Rd, Cuyahoga Heights, OH 44125
Tel.: (216) 641-3200
Web Site: http://www.neorsd.org
Waste Water Treatment Services
N.A.I.C.S.: 221320

Northeast Ohio Regional Sewer District - Westerly Wastewater Treatment Plant   (1)
5800 Cleveland Memorial Shoreway, Cleveland, OH 44102
Tel.: (216) 961-2187
Waste Water Treatment Services
N.A.I.C.S.: 221320

NORTHEAST OKLAHOMA ELECTRIC COOPERATIVE INC.
443857 Hwy 60 E, Vinita, OK 74301
Tel.: (918) 256-6405   OK
Web Site: http://www.neelectric.com
Year Founded: 1938
Sales Range: $25-49.9 Million
Emp.: 214
Provider of Electric Services
N.A.I.C.S.: 221122
Cindy Hefner *(Mgr-PR)*
David Cusick *(Mgr-NRS Right-of-Way)*
Susanne Frost *(Mgr-Office Svcs)*
Sheila Allgood *(Mgr-RECTEC)*
Rick Shurtz *(Mgr-Ops)*
Anthony Due *(Gen Mgr)*

Subsidiaries:

Northeast Rural Services Inc.   (1)
27039 S 4440 Rd PO Box 399, Vinita, OK 74301-0399
Tel.: (918) 256-6405
Web Site: http://www.neelectric.com
Sales Range: $25-49.9 Million
Emp.: 109

Provider of Radio, Television & Electronic Services
N.A.I.C.S.: 449210

RECtec Technology & Communication (1)
212S Main St, Grove, OK 74344
Tel.: (918) 787-9316
Web Site: http://www.rectec.net
Emp.: 10
Communication Equipment Mfr
N.A.I.C.S.: 334220
Ricky Hignite *(Gen Mgr)*

NORTHEAST OKLAHOMA PUBLIC FACILITIES AUTHORITY
103 N College Ave, Tahlequah, OK 74464
Tel.: (918) 456-6268
Sales Range: $10-24.9 Million
Emp.: 33
Gas Transmission & Distribution
N.A.I.C.S.: 221210
Jim Reagan *(Gen Mgr)*

NORTHEAST PARENT & CHILD SOCIETY, INC.
530 Franklin St, Schenectady, NY 12305
Tel.: (518) 346-1284　　NY
Web Site: http://www.neparentchild.org
Year Founded: 1888
Sales Range: $25-49.9 Million
Emp.: 581
Child & Family Care Services
N.A.I.C.S.: 624190
Jennifer Lawrence *(VP-Career Svcs)*
John E. Henley *(Pres & CEO)*
Kevin Walsh *(VP-Community Living Svcs)*
Christopher Burky *(Dir-Medical)*
Anne Blaauboer *(Dir-Seneca Young Women's Program)*

NORTHEAST REMSCO CONSTRUCTION, INC.
1433 Hwy 34 S B1, Farmingdale, NJ 07727
Tel.: (732) 557-6100　　NJ
Web Site: http://www.northeastconstruction.org
Year Founded: 1991
Sales Range: $100-124.9 Million
Emp.: 288
Public-Works Contractor, Microtunnel & Submarine Cable Specialists
N.A.I.C.S.: 237110

Subsidiaries:

Caldwell Marine International, LLC (CMI) (1)
1433 Highway 34 S B1, Farmingdale, NJ 07727
Tel.: (732) 557-6100
Web Site: http://www.caldwellmarine.com
Emp.: 50
Marine Contractor Specializing in Submarine Cable Installation & Heavy Marine Construction
N.A.I.C.S.: 237990
Rolando E. Acosta *(Pres & CEO)*
James B. Yulle *(VP)*
Al Perez *(Project Mgr)*

NORTHEAST SALES DISTRIBUTING INC.
840 Ronald Wood Rd, Winder, GA 30680
Tel.: (678) 963-7700　　DE
Web Site: http://www.nesdist.com
Year Founded: 1957
Sales Range: $25-49.9 Million
Emp.: 200
Beer & Ale
N.A.I.C.S.: 424810

Dave Black *(CEO)*
Andre Green *(Asst Mgr-Warehouse)*
Jason Coffey *(Supvr-Fleet)*
Morgan Klein *(Gen Mgr-Sls)*

Subsidiaries:

Skyland Distributing Co., Inc. (1)
1 Overland Industrial Blvd, Asheville, NC 28806
Tel.: (828) 670-6600
Web Site: http://www.sdcwnc.com
Alcoholic Beverage Distr
N.A.I.C.S.: 424820
Carl Marvin *(Mgr-Trade Dev)*

NORTHEAST SECURITIES INC.
333 Earle Ovington Blvd, Mitchel Field, NY 11553-3645
Tel.: (516) 396-1600　　NY
Web Site: http://www.nesec.com
Year Founded: 1989
Sales Range: $10-24.9 Million
Emp.: 110
Securities Broker
N.A.I.C.S.: 523150
Stephen J. Perrone *(CEO)*
Paul Duffy *(Pres)*
Dan Nicholas *(COO)*

NORTHEAST SENIOR HEALTH CORPORATION
85 Herrick St, Beverly, MA 01915
Tel.: (978) 922-3000　　NH
Year Founded: 1981
Sales Range: $10-24.9 Million
Emp.: 207
Elderly Housing Assitance Services
N.A.I.C.S.: 624100
Jennifer Gizmunt *(VP-Admin)*
David Spackman *(Sec)*
Maryellen Lear *(Asst Sec)*
Edmund Soucy *(Dir-NESH Bud)*
Darcey Adams *(VP-Community Programs)*
Nancy Moore *(Exec Dir-HH)*
Timothy O'Connor *(Treas)*
James D. Dunne *(CEO)*
Howard R. Grant *(Pres)*

NORTHEAST SOLITE CORPORATION
962 Kings Hwy, Saugerties, NY 12477
Tel.: (845) 246-2177
Web Site: http://www.nesolite.com
Year Founded: 1947
Sales Range: $1-9.9 Million
Emp.: 85
Producer of Minerals
N.A.I.C.S.: 327992
John W. Roberts *(Chm & Treas)*
Philip Nesmith *(CEO)*
Jessica Eng *(Sr VP-Sales)*
Philip Nesmith *(Pres)*
Ken Scaplehorn *(Controller)*

NORTHEAST TEXAS FARMERS CO-OP
428 Jackson St N, Sulphur Springs, TX 75482-2651
Tel.: (903) 885-3143　　TX
Web Site: http://www.netfc.com
Year Founded: 1939
Sales Range: $75-99.9 Million
Emp.: 84
Retailer of Feed & Farm Supplies
N.A.I.C.S.: 424910
Harold Bryant *(Pres)*
Bradley R. Johnson *(Gen Mgr)*
Anita Stapleton *(Controller)*
Jim Ratzlaff *(Mgr-Credit & Retail Farm Supply)*
Donny Peters *(Mgr-Store)*

NORTHEAST TREATERS INC.
201 Springfield Rd, Belchertown, MA 01007
Tel.: (413) 323-7811
Web Site: http://www.netreaters.com
Year Founded: 1985
Sales Range: $50-74.9 Million
Emp.: 40
Producer & Seller of Pressure Treated Products
N.A.I.C.S.: 321114
David Reed *(Pres)*
David Yankee *(Mgr-Traffic & Coord-Production)*

NORTHEAST VALLEY HEALTH CORPORATION
1172 N Maclay Ave, San Fernando, CA 91340
Tel.: (818) 898-1388　　CA
Web Site: http://www.nevhc.org
Year Founded: 1971
Sales Range: $50-74.9 Million
Emp.: 855
Community Health Care Services
N.A.I.C.S.: 621498
Stephen Gutierrez *(CIO)*
Theresa Nitescu *(COO)*
Kimberly Wyard *(CEO)*
Christine Park *(Chief Medical Officer)*

NORTHEAST WINDOW & DOOR ASSOCIATION
S5460 Maelou Dr, Hamburg, NY 14075-3737
Tel.: (202) 367-1173
Web Site: http://www.nwda.net
Home Center Operator
N.A.I.C.S.: 444110
Jeff Alles *(Owner)*

Subsidiaries:

Window & Door Manufacturers Association (1)
330 N Wabash Ave Ste 2000, Chicago, IL 60611
Tel.: (312) 321-6802
Web Site: http://www.wdma.com
Window & Door Mfr
N.A.I.C.S.: 321911
Michael O'Brien *(Pres & CEO)*

NORTHEASTERN ENVELOPE COMPANY
2 Maxson Dr, Old Forge, PA 18518
Tel.: (570) 451-3320
Web Site: http://www.northeasternenvelope.com
Rev.: $10,737,667
Emp.: 100
Envelopes
N.A.I.C.S.: 322230
Terry Burks *(Pres & CEO)*
Eileen Burke *(Controller)*
James F. Ferrario Jr. *(VP)*

NORTHEASTERN RURAL ELECTRIC MEMBERSHIP CORPORATION
4901 E Park 30 Dr, Columbia City, IN 46725
Tel.: (260) 244-6111　　IN
Web Site: http://www.nremc.com
Year Founded: 1935
Sales Range: $100-124.9 Million
Emp.: 62
Electric Power Distr
N.A.I.C.S.: 221122
Jim Eitsert *(VP-Distr Svcs)*
Kevin Quickery *(VP-Corp Svcs)*
Gregg Kless *(Pres & CEO)*
Doug Ferrell *(VP-Member Svcs)*

NORTHEASTERN SUPPLY INC.
8323 Pulaski Hwy, Baltimore, MD 21237-2941
Tel.: (410) 574-0010　　MD
Web Site: http://www.northeastern.com
Year Founded: 1971
Sales Range: $25-49.9 Million
Emp.: 136
Plumbing Fixtures, Equipment & Supplies
N.A.I.C.S.: 423720
Steve Cook *(Chm, Pres & CEO)*
Mike Cornbrooks *(VP-Ops)*
Steve Coppage *(VP-Bus Dev)*
Mike Tagliaferri *(VP-Comml Plumbing & Water Sys Sls)*
Frank Collacchi *(Dir-IT)*
Alan Cowan *(VP-Residential Plumbing)*
R. J. Kline *(Reg Mgr-Sls)*
Rick Foxwell *(Reg Mgr-Sls)*
Russ Everson *(VP-HVAC)*

NORTHERN AG SERVICE INC.
105 Armour St, West Union, IA 52175
Tel.: (563) 422-6281
Web Site: http://www.northernagservice.com
Sales Range: $10-24.9 Million
Emp.: 14
Grain Elevators
N.A.I.C.S.: 459999
Randy Osmundson *(Pres)*

NORTHERN AIR CARGO INC.
3900 Old Intl Airport Rd, Anchorage, AK 99502-1009
Tel.: (907) 243-3331　　AK
Web Site: http://www.nac.aero
Year Founded: 1956
Sales Range: $25-49.9 Million
Emp.: 250
Air Transportation, Scheduled
N.A.I.C.S.: 481112
Ann Campbell *(VP-Govt Svcs & Contracting)*
Blake Arrington *(Mgr-Mktg & Comm)*
Christina Coursey *(Dir-Employee Svcs & Trng)*
Frank Asay *(Mgr-Store)*
Grant Perry *(Supvr-Svcs Desk)*
Hope Bindley *(Mgr-Station)*
Stephanie Holthaus *(VP-Cargo)*
Elizabeth Russell *(Mgr-Admin)*
Eric Robinson *(Superintendent-Maintenance)*
Margaret Hailey *(Supvr-Customer Svc)*
Marina Carey Jarvis *(Project Mgr)*
Mike Stevens *(Mgr-Sls)*
Rhea Landrum *(Mgr-Tech Publ)*
Gideon Garcia *(Gen Mgr)*

NORTHERN ARIZONA HEALTHCARE CORPORATION
1200 N Beaver St, Flagstaff, AZ 86001
Tel.: (928) 779-3366　　AZ
Web Site: http://www.nahealth.com
Year Founded: 1985
Sales Range: $50-74.9 Million
Emp.: 3,404
Health Care Srvices
N.A.I.C.S.: 622110
Wayne Fox *(Treas)*
Alice Gagnaire *(Chm)*
Florence L. Spyrow *(Pres & CEO)*

NORTHERN ARIZONA BEHAVIORAL HEALTH AUTHORITY, INC.
1300 S Yale St, Flagstaff, AZ 86001
Tel.: (928) 774-7128　　AZ
Web Site: http://www.narbha.org
Year Founded: 1967
Sales Range: $125-149.9 Million

NORTHERN ARIZONA BEHAVIORAL HEALTH AUTHORITY, INC.   U.S. PRIVATE

Northern Arizona Behavioral Health Authority, Inc.—(Continued)

Emp.: 119
Behavioral Healthcare Services
N.A.I.C.S.: 623220
Michael Kuzmin (CFO)
Teresa Bertsch (Chief Medical Officer)
Mary Jo Gregory (Pres & CEO)
Lindsay Miller (CIO & Chief Bus Officer)
Lina Wallen (Treas)
Barbara Bartell (Sec)
James Wurgler (Chm)

NORTHERN AUTOMOTIVE, INC.
8600 N High St, Worthington, OH 43085
Tel.: (614) 436-2001   OH
Web Site: http://www.columbusmitsu.com
Sales Range: $10-24.9 Million
Emp.: 50
New & Used Car Dealer
N.A.I.C.S.: 441110
Thomas Carpenter (Pres)
Darrell Patterson (CFO)

NORTHERN BANK & TRUST COMPANY
275 Mishawum Rd, Woburn, MA 01801
Tel.: (781) 937-5400
Web Site: http://www.nbtc.com
Rev.: $18,759,000
Emp.: 40
State Trust Companies Accepting Deposits, Commercial
N.A.I.C.S.: 522110
Dawn C. Ferrari (VP-HR)
Donald P. Queenin (Exec VP)
Darren R. Sawicki (VP-Ops)
Janet E. Hill (VP-Deposit Ops)
David Hanafin (VP-Wealth Mgmt)
J. Lawrence Mawn (VP)
Nisha Jakhu (Asst VP & Mgr-Woburn)
Frank Vozzella (Asst VP & Mgr-Burlington)
Jay Dilorio (Sr VP-Comml Lending)
Anthony Rizzo (Sr VP-Residential Lending)
Christine Downey (Chief Risk Officer)
Brent Boucher (VP-Residential Lending)
Marianne Cacciola (VP & Mgr-Liquidity)
Warren Brown (VP-Emerging Markets)
Raymond Clark (Exec VP)
Michael Kosicki (VP)
James J. Mawn Jr. (Pres & CEO)
Joseph Saling III (VP-IT)

NORTHERN BERKSHIRE EMS, INC.
PO Box 1045, North Adams, MA 01247
Tel.: (413) 664-6680   MA
Web Site: http://www.northadamsambulance.com
Year Founded: 1978
Ambulance Service
N.A.I.C.S.: 621910
Edward Nimmons (Treas)
Elizabeth Milanesi (Sec)
Paul Ethier (Pres)

Subsidiaries:
Village Ambulance Service, Inc.   (1)
30 Water St, Williamstown, MA 01267
Tel.: (413) 458-4889
Web Site: http://www.villageambulance.com
Ambulance Service
N.A.I.C.S.: 621910

Erwin Stuebner (Pres)
David Rempell (VP)
Joan Zegras (Sec)
Matthew Sheehy (Treas)
Mike Noyes (VP)

NORTHERN BOILER & MECHANICAL CONTRACTORS
2025 Latimer Dr, Muskegon, MI 49442
Tel.: (231) 777-2525
Sales Range: $1-9.9 Million
Emp.: 15
Mechanical Contractor
N.A.I.C.S.: 238220
R. James Federighe (Pres)
Tom Carlson (Project Mgr)
Adam Gillis (Project Mgr)

NORTHERN BUILDING PRODUCTS
111 Central Ave, Teterboro, NJ 07608
Tel.: (201) 943-6400
Web Site: http://www.northernbuildingproducts.com
Year Founded: 1956
Sales Range: $25-49.9 Million
Emp.: 155
Metal Doors, Sash & Trim Mfg
N.A.I.C.S.: 332321
Robert Pecorella (Pres)
Kinnari Patel (Project Mgr)

NORTHERN BUSINESS MACHINES INC
24 Terry Ave, Burlington, MA 01803
Tel.: (781) 272-2034
Web Site: http://www.nbminc.com
Year Founded: 1985
Rev.: $18,000,000
Emp.: 81
Business Machines & Equipment Whslr
N.A.I.C.S.: 459999
William Tracia (Founder & Principal)
Rob Basler (Mgr-Sls)
Jack Enos (Reg Mgr-Sls)
Vern Hydorn (VP-Sls)
Steve Burges (Controller)

NORTHERN CALIFORNIA CONGREGATIONAL RETIREMENT HOMES, INC.
8545 Carmel Valley Rd, Carmel, CA 93923
Tel.: (831) 624-1281   CA
Year Founded: 1960
Sales Range: $10-24.9 Million
Emp.: 196
Elder Care Services
N.A.I.C.S.: 623312
Roger D. Bolgard (Chm)
R. B. Busch III (Vice Chm)

NORTHERN CALIFORNIA INSTITUTE FOR RESEARCH AND EDUCATION
4150 Clement St 151NC, San Francisco, CA 94121-1545
Tel.: (415) 750-6954   CA
Web Site: http://www.ncire.org
Year Founded: 1988
Sales Range: $25-49.9 Million
Emp.: 409
Medical Research Services
N.A.I.C.S.: 541715
Stephen Morange (CFO)
Judy Yee (Vice Chm)

NORTHERN CALIFORNIA POWER AGENCY
651 Commerce Dr, Roseville, CA 95678-6420
Tel.: (916) 781-3636   CA
Web Site: http://www.ncpa.com

Year Founded: 1968
Sales Range: $400-449.9 Million
Emp.: 149
Electric Power Distribution
N.A.I.C.S.: 221121
Jane Cirrincione (Asst Gen Mgr-Legislative & Regulatory Affairs)
Murray Grande (Mgr-Geothermal Facilities)
Donna I. Stevener (CFO & Asst Gen Mgr-Fin & Admin Svcs)
Ken Speer (Asst Gen Mgr-Generation Svcs)
David Dockham (Asst Gen Mgr-Power Mgmt)
Randy S. Howard (Gen Mgr)
Vicki L. Cichocki (Mgr-HR)

NORTHERN CATV SALES INC.
185 Ainsley Dr, Syracuse, NY 13210-4202
Tel.: (315) 422-1230
Web Site: http://www.arcomlabs.com
Year Founded: 1976
Sales Range: $25-49.9 Million
Emp.: 70
Sales of Electronic Parts & Equipment
N.A.I.C.S.: 423690
Basil Dillon-Malone (Reg VP)
Gabriel Larios (Reg VP)
Roman Pierzchanowski (Reg VP-Europe)

Subsidiaries:
Arrow-Communication Labs Inc.   (1)
185 Ainsley Dr, Syracuse, NY 13210-4202
Tel.: (315) 422-1230
Web Site: http://www.arcomdigital.com
Sales Range: $25-49.9 Million
Emp.: 100
Provider of Radio & TV Communications Services
N.A.I.C.S.: 334220
Gregory Tresness (Pres-Arcom Digital)
Katy Frisch (Pres)

NORTHERN CHILDRENS SERVICES
5301 Ridge Ave, Philadelphia, PA 19128
Tel.: (215) 482-1423   PA
Web Site: http://www.northernchildren.org
Year Founded: 1853
Sales Range: $10-24.9 Million
Emp.: 322
Child Care & Development Services
N.A.I.C.S.: 624110
Renata Coobs-Fletcher (Pres & CEO)
Paul C. Rovner (Treas)
Mary Stitt (Vice Chm)

NORTHERN COCHISE COMMUNITY HOSPITAL, INC.
901 W Rex Allen Dr, Willcox, AZ 85643
Tel.: (520) 384-3541   AZ
Web Site: http://www.ncch.net
Year Founded: 1966
Sales Range: $10-24.9 Million
Emp.: 255
Healtcare Services
N.A.I.C.S.: 622110
Roland Knox (CEO)

NORTHERN CONTOURS HOLDING CORP.
1355 Mendota Heights Rd Ste 100, Saint Paul, MN 55120
Tel.: (651) 695-1698   DE
Web Site: http://www.northerncontours.com
Emp.: 400
Holding Company; Wood, Veneer & Thermofoil Cabinet Door Mfr
N.A.I.C.S.: 551112

John Goebel (Chm, Pres & CEO)

Subsidiaries:
Northern Contours Inc.   (1)
409 S Robert St, Fergus Falls, MN 56537
Tel.: (218) 736-2973
Web Site: http://www.northerncontours.com
Sales Range: $25-49.9 Million
Emp.: 150
Wood, Veneer & Thermofoil Cabinet Door Mfr
N.A.I.C.S.: 337110

NORTHERN EMPIRE PIZZA INCORPORATED
4141 38th St SW, Fargo, ND 58104
Tel.: (701) 282-3484
Sales Range: $1-9.9 Million
Emp.: 7
Pizzeria Chain
N.A.I.C.S.: 722513
Terry Nordenstrom (Pres)
Kim Young (Sec & Dir-HR)

NORTHERN ENERGY INC.
231 S Indiana Ave, Gaylord, MI 49735
Tel.: (989) 732-5495
Web Site: http://www.northern-energy.com
Sales Range: $10-24.9 Million
Emp.: 13
Fuel Oil Dealers
N.A.I.C.S.: 457210
David Miller (Pres)

NORTHERN ENGINE & SUPPLY CO.
2929 W Superior St, Duluth, MN 55806
Tel.: (218) 628-2836
Web Site: http://www.northernengine.com
Rev.: $10,081,814
Emp.: 47
General Construction Machinery & Equipment
N.A.I.C.S.: 333120
Gordon W. Seitz (Gen Mgr)
Sharon Jarols (Office Mgr)

NORTHERN ENGRAVING CORPORATION
803 S Black River St, Sparta, WI 54656
Tel.: (608) 269-6911   WI
Web Site: http://www.norcorp.com
Year Founded: 1928
Sales Range: $200-249.9 Million
Emp.: 1,200
Mfr of Metal Stampings
N.A.I.C.S.: 332119
Bob Meyer (Reg Mgr-Sls)
Dan Myhre (Mgr-R&D)
Judith Webber (Coord-Sample)
Ken Schmidt (Program Mgr & Engr-Mfg)
Mike Mulvaney (Mgr-Engrg)
Sandra Cavadini (Mgr-HR)
Jerry Hoerres (Mgr-Graphic Arts)
Carrie Jensen (Mgr-Customer Svc)
John Bainter (Plant Mgr)
Brad VanKirk (Dir-IT)

NORTHERN FACTORY SALES INC.
2701 4th Ave SW, Willmar, MN 56201
Tel.: (320) 235-2288
Web Site: http://www.northernfactory.com
Year Founded: 1972
Sales Range: $10-24.9 Million
Emp.: 90
Automotive Supplies & Parts
N.A.I.C.S.: 423120
Roger Gauquie (CEO)

NORTHERN FEED & BEAN OF LUCERN
33278 Hwy 85, Lucerne, CO 80646
Tel.: (970) 352-7875
Web Site:
http://www.northernfeedandbean.com
Sales Range: $10-24.9 Million
Emp.: 12
Grains
N.A.I.C.S.: 424510
Robert Brunner (Exec Dir)

NORTHERN FRUIT COMPANY, INC.
220 2nd St NE, East Wenatchee, WA 98802
Tel.: (509) 884-3575
Web Site:
http://www.northernfruit.com
Rev.: $64,900,000
Emp.: 30
Postharvest Crop Activities
N.A.I.C.S.: 115114
Doug Pauly (Pres)

NORTHERN HOLDINGS INC.
1984 Old Mssion Dr Ste A7, Solvang, CA 93463
Tel.: (805) 688-6878
Sales Range: $10-24.9 Million
Emp.: 10
Grocery Stores, Chain
N.A.I.C.S.: 445110
Jonathan King (Pres)

Subsidiaries:

New Frontiers Holdings (1)
1984 Old Mssion Dr Ste A7, Solvang, CA 93463
Tel.: (805) 688-6878
Emp.: 70
Grocery Stores, Chain
N.A.I.C.S.: 445110
Patricia Decatado (Pres)

New Frontiers Natural Foods V (1)
1420 W Hwy 89A, Sedona, AZ 86336
Tel.: (928) 282-6311
Health Foods
N.A.I.C.S.: 456191

NORTHERN IMPORTS, INC.
2239 E Division St, Arlington, TX 76011
Tel.: (817) 640-2299 TX
Web Site:
http://www.workwearboots.com
Year Founded: 1980
Sales Range: $1-9.9 Million
Emp.: 60
Shoe Stores
N.A.I.C.S.: 458210
Allen Watterson (Gen Mgr)

Subsidiaries:

My Boot Store, Inc. (1)
726 S Grandview Ave, Odessa, TX 79761-7157
Tel.: (432) 580-8997
Web Site: http://www.western-wear-store.com
Shoe Stores
N.A.I.C.S.: 458210
Alan Rochat (Owner)

NORTHERN INDIANA PAINT SUPPLY, INC.
500 Leiter Dr, Warsaw, IN 46580-2482
Tel.: (574) 269-4241 IN
Web Site: http://www.painters-supply.com
Year Founded: 1982
Motor Vehicle Supplies & New Parts Merchant Whslr
N.A.I.C.S.: 423120

NORTHERN INDUSTRIAL INC.
200 S Orcas St, Seattle, WA 98108
Tel.: (206) 682-2752
Rev.: $29,300,000
Emp.: 250
Sawmills
N.A.I.C.S.: 321113
Scott Howell (CEO)
Scott Nicholson (Pres)
Steven Smith (CFO)

NORTHERN IRON OF ST. PAUL, LLC
867 Forest St N, Saint Paul, MN 55106-3886
Tel.: (651) 778-3300 MN
Web Site: http://www.northernim.com
Year Founded: 1986
Sales Range: $10-24.9 Million
Emp.: 60
Machine Shop, Jobbing & Repair Services; Iron Foundry
N.A.I.C.S.: 332710
Scott Hamlett (Pres & CEO)

NORTHERN KENTUCKY AREA DEVELOPMENT DISTRICT
22 Spiral Dr, Florence, KY 41042
Tel.: (859) 283-1885 KY
Web Site: http://www.nkadd.org
Year Founded: 1971
Sales Range: $10-24.9 Million
Emp.: 998
Community Development Services
N.A.I.C.S.: 813410
Lewis Diaz (Vice Chm)
Kris Knochelmann (Treas & Sec)
Harold Shorty Tomlinson (Chm)

NORTHERN KENTUCKY WATER DISTRICT
2835 Crescent Spring Rd, Erlanger, KY 41018
Tel.: (859) 578-9898
Web Site: http://www.nkywater.org
Sales Range: $25-49.9 Million
Emp.: 140
Produce Water & Sell
N.A.I.C.S.: 221310
Jack Bragg (VP-Fin)
Richard Harrison (VP)

NORTHERN LAKES COOPERATIVE
15877 Hwy 63, Hayward, WI 54843
Tel.: (715) 634-3211
Web Site: http://www.nlcoop.com
Sales Range: $25-49.9 Million
Emp.: 160
Grocery Stores
N.A.I.C.S.: 445110
Mike Cavellie (Gen Mgr)

NORTHERN LIGHTS INC.
421 Chevy St, Sagle, ID 83860
Tel.: (208) 263-5141
Web Site: http://www.norlight.org
Sales Range: $10-24.9 Million
Emp.: 70
Electronic Services
N.A.I.C.S.: 221118
Elissa Glassman (Dir-Comm)
Annie Terracciano (Controller)

NORTHERN MACHINING & REPAIR, INC.
1701 N 26th St, Escanaba, MI 49829
Tel.: (906) 786-0566 MI
Web Site:
http://www.northernmachining.com
Year Founded: 1984
Sales Range: $10-24.9 Million
Emp.: 27
Industrial Machinery
N.A.I.C.S.: 332710
Jon Liss (Pres)

Subsidiaries:

Mechanical Supply (1)
1701 N 26th St, Escanaba, MI 49829
Tel.: (906) 789-0355
Web Site:
http://www.northernmachining.com
Industrial Supplies Merchant Whslr
N.A.I.C.S.: 423840
Tim McCarthy (Mgr-Sls)
Melissa Johnson (Mng Dir)

NORTHERN MAINE MEDICAL CENTER
194 E Main St, Fort Kent, ME 04743
Tel.: (207) 834-3155 ME
Web Site: http://www.nmmc.org
Year Founded: 1948
Sales Range: $25-49.9 Million
Emp.: 397
Mental Health Services
N.A.I.C.S.: 621420
Alain Bois (COO)
James Thibodeau (Sec)
John Ezzy (VP)
Peter J. Sirois (CEO)

NORTHERN MANOR MULTI-CARE CENTER
199 N Middletown Rd, Nanuet, NY 10954
Tel.: (845) 623-3904 NY
Web Site:
http://www.northernmanor.com
Year Founded: 1991
Sales Range: $25-49.9 Million
Emp.: 415
Residential Health Care Services
N.A.I.C.S.: 623990
Morris Klein (Exec Dir)
Gedalia Klein (COO)

NORTHERN MANUFACTURING CO, INC.
132 N RailRd St, Oak Harbor, OH 43449
Tel.: (419) 898-2821
Web Site:
http://www.northernmfg.com
Year Founded: 1951
Sales Range: $25-49.9 Million
Emp.: 156
Stainless Steel Products Mfr
N.A.I.C.S.: 331513
Nichole Magnone (Mgr-Acctg)

NORTHERN MICHIGAN SUBSTANCE ABUSE SERVICES INC.
2136 W M-32, Gaylord, MI 49735
Tel.: (989) 732-1791 MI
Web Site: http://www.nmsas.net
Year Founded: 1976
Sales Range: $10-24.9 Million
Emp.: 21
Substance Abuse Rehabilitation Services
N.A.I.C.S.: 621420
Sue Winter (Exec Dir)
Susan Latuszek (Mgr-Fin & HR)

NORTHERN MISSOURI BANCSHARES, INC.
1604 Main St, Unionville, MO 63565
Tel.: (123) 456-7890 MO
Web Site:
http://www.onlinefarmersbank.com
Year Founded: 1987
Bank Holding Company
N.A.I.C.S.: 551111
David Tribble (Pres & CEO)

Subsidiaries:

Exchange Bank of Missouri (1)
101 S Church, Fayette, MO 65248
Tel.: (660) 248-3388
Web Site: http://www.ebmo.com
Sales Range: $1-9.9 Million
Emp.: 42
Commercial Banking Services
N.A.I.C.S.: 522110
Don L. Brown (Pres & CEO)

Farmers Bank of Northern Missouri (1)
1604 Main St, Unionville, MO 63565
Tel.: (660) 947-2474
Web Site:
http://www.onlinefarmersbank.com
Sales Range: $50-74.9 Million
Emp.: 88
State Commercial Banks
N.A.I.C.S.: 522110

NORTHERN MONTANA HEALTH CARE
30-13th St, Havre, MT 59501
Tel.: (406) 265-2211 MT
Web Site: http://www.nmhcare.org
Year Founded: 1921
Sales Range: $50-74.9 Million
Emp.: 726
Health Care Srvices
N.A.I.C.S.: 622110
Karen Pollington (VP)
Kim Lucke (VP-Fin)

NORTHERN MOTOR COMPANY
1419 Ludington St, Escanaba, MI 49829-2836
Tel.: (906) 786-1130 MI
Web Site:
http://www.northernmotor.com
Sales Range: $10-24.9 Million
Emp.: 25
Retailer of New & Used Cars
N.A.I.C.S.: 441110
Marilyn Henderson (Office Mgr)
John Arball (Gen Mgr-Sls)
Ashley Clarke (Bus Mgr)
Mike McAuley (Mgr-Sls)
Steve Davidson (Mgr-Parts)

NORTHERN NEW YORK COMMUNITY FOUNDATION, INC.
120 Washington St Ste 400, Watertown, NY 13601
Tel.: (315) 782-7110 NY
Web Site: http://www.nnycf.org
Year Founded: 1929
Sales Range: $10-24.9 Million
Emp.: 4
Grantmaking Services
N.A.I.C.S.: 813211
Rande S. Richardson (Exec Dir)

NORTHERN OFFSHORE LTD.
Energy Ctr II 575 N Dairy Ashford Ste 200, Houston, TX 77079
Tel.: (281) 649-2600
Web Site:
http://www.northernoffshore.com
Year Founded: 2000
Emp.: 200
Contract Drilling Equipment; Drilling Support Services
N.A.I.C.S.: 532412
Gary L. Bauer (Sr VP-Worldwide Ops)
Bruce Kain (VP-QHSET & Risk Mgmt)
John Monks (Sr VP & Mgr-Europe & Africa)
H. Gary Sullivan (Chief Acctg Officer & VP)
R. Bradley Forth (CFO & Sr VP)
Yuanhui Sun (Chm & Interim Pres & CEO)
Edward E. Hare (Sr VP-Corp Strategy & Plng)
Anthony Beebe (VP-Technical & Projects)
G. Campbell Austin (VP-Global Human Resources)

NORTHERN OFFSHORE LTD.   U.S. PRIVATE

Northern Offshore Ltd.—(Continued)

Peter Cunnion (*VP-Asia Pacific & Middle East*)
Clay Coan (*VP-Mktg & Contracts-Middle East & Asia Pacific*)
Gordon Donald (*VP-Mktg & Contracts-Europe & Africa*)
Paul Ravesies III (*Sr VP-Mktg, Bus Dev & IR*)

NORTHERN PACIFIC GROUP
15 East Lake St Ste 301, Wayzata, MN 55391
Tel.: (952) 456-5302
Web Site: http://www.northernpacificgroup.com
Private Equity Investment Firm
N.A.I.C.S.: 523999
Marcy Haymaker (*Principal*)
Scott M. Honour (*Mng Partner*)

Subsidiaries:

Solar Spectrum Holdings LLC (1)
150 Linden St, Oakland, CA 94607
Tel.: (844) 777-6527
Web Site: http://www.solarspectrum.com
Holding Company
N.A.I.C.S.: 551112
William B. Nettles Jr. (*Pres & COO*)

Subsidiary (Domestic):

Solar Spectrum LLC (2)
150 Linden St, Oakland, CA 94607
Tel.: (844) 777-6527
Web Site: http://www.solarspectrum.com
Solar Technology Services
N.A.I.C.S.: 221114
William B. Nettles Jr. (*Pres & COO*)
Patrick McGivern (*CEO*)

Sungevity, Inc. (2)
66 Franklin St Ste 310, Oakland, CA 94607
Tel.: (510) 496-5500
Web Site: https://www.sungevity.com
Solar Technology Services
N.A.I.C.S.: 221114
David White (*CFO*)

Subsidiary (Domestic):

Hawaii Energy Connection (3)
99-1350 Koaha Placa, Aiea, HI 96701
Tel.: (808) 524-7336
Web Site: https://www.kumukit.com
Commercial & Residential Sustainable Energy Services Including Grid-Tied Photovoltaic Systems
N.A.I.C.S.: 221114

NORTHERN PARTNERS CO-OPERATIVE
1000 6th Ave, Mendota, IL 61342-1766
Tel.: (815) 539-6772
Web Site: http://www.northernpartners.net
Year Founded: 2009
Grain, Crop & Feed Production
N.A.I.C.S.: 424510
Alan Zehr (*CFO*)
Eric Anderson (*CEO*)
Jim Meyer (*Dir-Ops*)
Mark Corrigan (*Dir-Agronomy Procurement*)
Steve Villegas (*Dir-Energy*)
Tyler Meloy (*Dir-Mktg & Grain Org*)
Jay Marshall (*Dir-Grain Mdse*)
Randi Halbmaier (*Dir-HR*)
Cory Biers (*Sec & Treas*)

NORTHERN PLAINS ELECTRIC COOPERATIVE
1515 Main St, Carrington, ND 58421
Tel.: (701) 652-3156
Web Site: http://www.nplains.com
Sales Range: $10-24.9 Million
Emp.: 50
Distribution, Electric Power
N.A.I.C.S.: 221122

Bruce Garber (*Bus Mgr*)
Scott Buchholtz (*Mgr-IT*)
Jay Jacobson (*Mgr-Alliance*)
Craig Rysavy (*Mgr-Ops*)
Seth Syverson (*Mgr-Engrg*)
Tracy Boe (*Pres*)

NORTHERN PLANET LLC
9725 SW Beaverton Hillsdale Hwy Ste 210A, Beaverton, OR 97005
Tel.: (909) 992-0502
Web Site: http://www.partybell.com
Year Founded: 2005
Sales Range: $1-9.9 Million
Party Supplier Online Retailer
N.A.I.C.S.: 459420
Ankush Aggarwal (*CEO*)

NORTHERN POWER SYSTEMS CORP.
29 Pitman Rd, Barre, VT 05641
Tel.: (802) 461-2955   BC
Web Site: http://www.northernpower.com
Year Founded: 2012
Sales Range: $25-49.9 Million
Emp.: 72
Wind Turbine Mfr
N.A.I.C.S.: 333611

NORTHERN REFRIGERATED TRANSPORTATION INC.
2700 W Main St, Turlock, CA 95380
Tel.: (209) 664-3800
Web Site: http://www.northernrefrigerated.com
Year Founded: 1947
Rev.: $17,500,000
Emp.: 110
Refrigerated Products Transport
N.A.I.C.S.: 484230
Richard Mello (*Pres*)
Dan Watson (*Controller*)
John Doidge (*VP*)

NORTHERN RESOURCES CO-OPERATIVE
PO Box 420, Roseau, MN 56751
Tel.: (218) 463-1805
Sales Range: $10-24.9 Million
Emp.: 50
Fertilizer & Fertilizer Materials
N.A.I.C.S.: 424910
Kelly Christianson (*Gen Mgr*)

NORTHERN SALES COMPANY OF ALASKA, INC.
2260 Industrial Blvd, Juneau, AK 99801-8533
Tel.: (907) 586-3945   AK
Web Site: http://www.nsales.com
Year Founded: 1975
Sales Range: $10-24.9 Million
Emp.: 130
Tobacco & Tobacco Products
N.A.I.C.S.: 424130
Lance Crosby (*Pres*)

NORTHERN STAMPING INC.
6600 Chapek Pkwy, Cuyahoga Heights, OH 44125
Tel.: (216) 883-8888
Web Site: http://www.northernstamping.com
Year Founded: 1989
Sales Range: $25-49.9 Million
Emp.: 500
Mfr of Automotive Stampings
N.A.I.C.S.: 336370
Matthew S. Friedman (*Pres & CEO*)
Jerry Smith (*Mgr-Engrg*)
Ronald G. Campbell (*COO & VP-Fin*)
Scott Sheffield (*VP-Ops*)

NORTHERN STAR COOPERATIVE
105 Main Ave W, Deer River, MN 56636
Tel.: (218) 246-8660
Web Site: http://www.northernstarcoop.com
Year Founded: 1932
Rev.: $12,800,000
Emp.: 59
Operators of Petroleum Bulk Stations & Terminals
N.A.I.C.S.: 424710
Dave Delawyer (*Gen Mgr*)
Brad Box (*Asst Mgr-Energy*)
Jim Daigle (*Mgr-C-Store & Car Wash*)
Patti Oelkers (*Mgr-Credit*)
Nikki Osse (*Office Mgr*)

NORTHERN STAR INDUSTRIES INC.
130 N Industrial Dr, Iron Mountain, MI 49801
Tel.: (906) 776-3480
Web Site: http://www.northernstarind.com
Sales Range: $25-49.9 Million
Emp.: 500
General Electrical Contractor
N.A.I.C.S.: 333120
David J. Brule Sr. (*Pres*)

NORTHERN STATES METALS CORP.
51 N Main St, West Hartford, CT 06107
Tel.: (860) 521-6001
Web Site: http://www.extrusions.com
Year Founded: 1973
Sales Range: $10-24.9 Million
Emp.: 80
Supplier of Aluminum Bars, Rods, Ingots, Sheets, Pipes & Plates: Extrusion, Fabrication, Finishing, Assembly & Packaging
N.A.I.C.S.: 423510
Kenneth A. Mack (*Pres & CEO*)

NORTHERN STEEL CASTINGS INC.
80 Oliver St, Wisconsin Rapids, WI 54494
Tel.: (715) 423-8040
Rev.: $22,300,000
Emp.: 100
Metal Service Centers & Other Metal Merchant Whslr
N.A.I.C.S.: 423510
Randy Hetzel (*Supvr-Maint*)
Glenn Greg (*Pres*)

NORTHERN STEEL TRANSPORT CO.
6041 Benore Rd, Toledo, OH 43612
Tel.: (419) 729-3867
Web Site: http://www.nsttransport.com
Rev.: $20,134,361
Emp.: 200
Contract Haulers
N.A.I.C.S.: 484121
James A. Clair (*Pres*)

NORTHERN TECHNOLOGIES GROUP INC.
5425 Beaumont Ctr Blvd Ste 900, Tampa, FL 33634
Tel.: (813) 885-7500
Web Site: http://www.ntgit.com
Year Founded: 2002
Sales Range: $1-9.9 Million
Emp.: 30
IT Consulting Services
N.A.I.C.S.: 541690

Wendy Hafner (*Pres*)
David Morris (*COO & VP*)
John Hafner (*CTO & VP-Federal Solutions*)

NORTHERN TOOL & EQUIPMENT COMPANY, INC.
2800 Southcross Dr W, Burnsville, MN 55306-6936
Tel.: (952) 894-9510   MN
Web Site: http://www.northerntool.com
Year Founded: 1980
Sales Range: $650-699.9 Million
Emp.: 400
Mfr of Automotive Stampings
N.A.I.C.S.: 444140
Donald L. Kotula (*Founder*)
Suresh Krishna (*Pres & CEO*)

Subsidiaries:

Northern Tool & Equipment Co. Ltd. (1)
Unit 2 Interchange Park, Portsmouth, PO3 5QD, Hamp, United Kingdom
Tel.: (44) 2392657600
Web Site: http://www.northerntooluk.com
Sales Range: $10-24.9 Million
Emp.: 50
Tools & Equipment Mail-Order Catalog
N.A.I.C.S.: 444140

The Golf Warehouse, Inc. (1)
8833 E 34th St N, Wichita, KS 67226
Tel.: (316) 838-5551
Web Site: http://www.tgw.com
Sales Range: $10-24.9 Million
Emp.: 160
Online Sports Equipment, Apparel & Accessories Retailer
N.A.I.C.S.: 459110
Aaron Paul (*Dir-HR*)
Ronnie Eskridge (*Dir-Customer Rels*)

The Sportsman's Guide, Inc. (1)
411 Farwell Ave, South Saint Paul, MN 55075-0239
Tel.: (651) 451-3030
Web Site: http://www.sportsmansguide.com
Sales Range: $25-49.9 Million
Mail-Order & Online Hunting, Outdoor Living & Truck Accessories & Apparel Retailer
N.A.I.C.S.: 458110
Matt Sullivan (*VP-Mktg*)
Douglas E. Johnson (*Sr VP-Mktg*)
Jay Berlin (*CEO*)
Tim Arland (*Sr VP-E-Commerce*)
Todd Wermerson (*CIO & Sr VP-IT*)
Kelly Dietrich (*Sr Dir-Sys, Networking & Data Center*)
Brandon Thompson (*Sr Dir-Web Dev*)
Mike Weise (*Sr Dir-Customer Experience Mktg*)
Kevin Bergerson (*Sr Dir-New Customer Mktg*)

Subsidiary (Domestic):

The Sportsman's Guide Outlet, Inc. (2)
490 Hardman Ave, South Saint Paul, MN 55075
Tel.: (651) 552-5248
Web Site: http://www.sportsmansguide.com
Discount Sporting Goods Retail Store Operator
N.A.I.C.S.: 459110
Terri Kenyon (*Mgr*)

NORTHERN VIRGINIA ELECTRIC COOPERATIVE INC.
10323 Lomond Dr, Manassas, VA 20109-3173
Tel.: (703) 335-0500   VA
Web Site: http://www.novec.com
Year Founded: 1983
Sales Range: $50-74.9 Million
Emp.: 300
Provider of Electric Services
N.A.I.C.S.: 221122
Stan C. Feuerberg (*Pres & CEO*)
J. Manley Garber (*Dir*)

COMPANIES

NORTHERN VIRGINIA HOMES
11480 Sunset Hill Rd Ste 120 E, Reston, VA 22190
Tel.: (703) 255-2900
Web Site: http://www.northernvahomes.com
Sales Range: $150-199.9 Million
Emp.: 20
Real Estate Brokers & Agents
N.A.I.C.S.: 531210
Richard R. Rager *(Pres)*

NORTHERN VIRGINIA MEDIA SERVICES
19 N King St, Leesburg, VA 20176
Tel.: (703) 771-8800
Web Site: http://www.insidenova.com
Newspaper Publishing
N.A.I.C.S.: 513110
Bruce Potter *(COO)*
Nicky Marshok *(Reg Dir-Production)*
Katie Barchas *(Coord-Mktg & Events)*
Colleen McGrew *(Mgr-Mktg)*
Tonya Fields *(Mgr-Classified Sls)*
Kari Pugh *(Sr Editor)*
Connie Fields *(Reg Mgr-Adv)*

Subsidiaries:

Families Magazines, Inc. (1)
11260 Roger Bacon Dr Ste 20, Reston, VA 20190
Tel.: (703) 318-1385
Web Site: http://www.washingtonfamily.com
Emp.: 20
Magazine Publisher
N.A.I.C.S.: 513120
Brenda Hyde *(Founder & Publr)*

NORTHERN WIND INC.
16 Hassey St, New Bedford, MA 02740
Tel.: (508) 997-0727
Web Site: http://www.northernwind.com
Sales Range: $50-74.9 Million
Emp.: 80
Seafoods
N.A.I.C.S.: 424460
Michael Fernandes *(Pres)*
Doreen Wotton *(Office Mgr)*
Ken Melanson *(Founder & Chm)*
Christina Rocha *(Mgr-Intl Traffic)*
George Kouri *(CEO)*
Ken Loud *(VP-New Product Dev)*
Adam Taylor *(VP-Retail Sls)*
James Dwyer *(Chief Comml Officer)*

NORTHFIELD SAVINGS BANK INC.
33 S Main St, Northfield, VT 05663-6703
Tel.: (802) 476-2400   DE
Web Site: http://www.nsbvt.com
Year Founded: 1867
Sales Range: $50-74.9 Million
Emp.: 150
State Commercial Banks
N.A.I.C.S.: 522110
Cory B. Richardson *(CFO & Sr VP)*
Donna M. Bohonnon *(Officer-Community Banking-Bethel)*
Tracy Davis *(Officer-Community Banking-Williston Road)*
Wendy Kellett *(Officer-Community Banking-Waterbury)*
Cheryl A. LaFrance *(COO & Sr VP)*
Alfred J. Flory *(Chief Lending Officer & Sr VP)*
Janet R. Kinney *(Sec)*
Thomas Leavitt *(Pres & CEO)*
Charlotte E. Magurn *(Asst Sec)*
Edward T. Sulva *(VP & Controller)*
Joel E. Dube *(VP-Comml Banking)*
John P. Ravaschiere *(VP-Comml Banking)*
Marsha Wimble *(VP-Comml Banking)*
Megan L. Cicio *(VP-Comml Svcs)*
Peter W. Goodell *(VP-Consumer Credit)*
Deb Kerin *(VP-Community Banking-Central)*

NORTHGATE ELECTRIC CORP.
63 Depot Rd, Huntington Station, NY 11746
Tel.: (631) 271-2242
Web Site: http://www.northgateelectriccorp.com
Rev.: $19,000,000
Emp.: 20
Provider of Electrical Contracting Services
N.A.I.C.S.: 238210
Dina Dunn *(Pres)*

NORTHGATE GONZALEZ INC.
1201 N Magnolia Ave, Anaheim, CA 92801
Tel.: (714) 778-3784
Web Site: http://www.northgatemarkets.com
Year Founded: 1992
Sales Range: $25-49.9 Million
Emp.: 80
Operator of Grocery Stores
N.A.I.C.S.: 445110
Miguel Gonzalez Jr. *(Pres)*

NORTHGATE PETROLEUM COMPANY
2549 Scott Ave, Chico, CA 95928
Tel.: (530) 342-6504
Web Site: http://www.northgatepetroleum.com
Rev.: $25,000,000
Emp.: 17
Engine Fuels & Oils
N.A.I.C.S.: 424720
Bud Caldwell *(Pres)*

NORTHLAND ALUMINUM PRODUCTS INC.
5005 County Rd 25, Minneapolis, MN 55416-2274
Tel.: (952) 920-2888   MN
Web Site: http://www.nordicware.com
Year Founded: 1946
Rev.: $17,000,000
Emp.: 200
Cookware, Bakeware, Barbecue & Microwave Accessories Mfr
N.A.I.C.S.: 326199
Reed Winter *(Mgr-New Products Dev)*
H. David Dalquist Jr. *(Pres & CEO)*

Subsidiaries:

Northland Aluminum Products Inc.-Nordic Ware Division (1)
5005 County Rd 25, Minneapolis, MN 55416-2274
Tel.: (952) 920-2888
Web Site: http://www.nordicware.com
Sales Range: $25-49.9 Million
Emp.: 150
Kitchenware Mfr
N.A.I.C.S.: 333241
David Dalquist *(Pres)*

NORTHLAND ASSOCIATES, INC.
4701 Buckley Rd, Liverpool, NY 13088
Tel.: (315) 451-3722
Web Site: http://www.northlandassoc.com
Year Founded: 1982
Rev.: $50,000,000
Emp.: 125
Public Utility Construction Services
N.A.I.C.S.: 238160

James Tyler *(Pres)*
Scott Johnson *(Mgr-Safety)*

NORTHLAND BUILDINGS INC.
2894 58th St, Eau Claire, WI 54703
Tel.: (715) 874-4200
Web Site: http://www.northlandbuildings.com
Sales Range: $10-24.9 Million
Emp.: 30
Building Contractors
N.A.I.C.S.: 236220
Aaron Constantine *(Mgr-Pur)*
Pete Marsnik *(CEO)*

NORTHLAND COLD STORAGE, INC.
2490 S Broadway, Green Bay, WI 54304
Tel.: (920) 431-4601
Web Site: http://www.ncold.com
Rev.: $12,000,000
Emp.: 20
Refrigerated Warehousing & Storage
N.A.I.C.S.: 493120
Kathleen Pokel *(Pres & Mgr-Northland Freight Svcs)*
David Pokel *(Gen Mgr-Warehouse Ops)*
Martin Demeny *(Mgr-Maintenance & Refrigeration)*
Ben Bergeron *(Mgr-IT)*

NORTHLAND CORPORATION
2600 E Hwy 146, La Grange, KY 40031
Tel.: (502) 222-1441
Web Site: http://www.northlandcorp.com
Sales Range: $10-24.9 Million
Emp.: 70
Hardwood Lumber
N.A.I.C.S.: 423310
Orn E. Gudmundsson *(Pres & CEO)*
Tim Girardi *(VP-Sls)*
Marlene Hughes *(VP-Admin)*

NORTHLAND FARMS, LLC
11161 120th Ave, West Olive, MI 49460-9629
Tel.: (616) 846-1477   MI
Web Site: http://www.northlandfarmsllc.com
Sales Range: $1-9.9 Million
Emp.: 180
Wholesale Growing & Distribution of Trees & Ornamental Plants
N.A.I.C.S.: 424930
Rich Bramer *(Gen Mgr)*
Greg Helsen *(Mgr-Sls)*

NORTHLAND FOREST PRODUCTS INC.
16 Church St, Kingston, NH 03848-3062
Tel.: (603) 642-3665   NH
Web Site: http://www.northlandforest.com
Year Founded: 1970
Sales Range: $75-99.9 Million
Emp.: 80
Lumber, Plywood & Millwork
N.A.I.C.S.: 423310
Jameson S. French *(Pres & CEO)*
Mark Alden *(Mgr-Sls)*
John Lenane *(Asst Mgr-Ops)*

NORTHLAND HOLDINGS INC.
PO Box 24527, Seattle, WA 98124
Tel.: (206) 763-3000
Web Site: http://www.northlandservices.com
Rev.: $187,000,000
Emp.: 150
Deep Sea Freight Transportation Services
N.A.I.C.S.: 483113
Larry Stauffer *(Pres)*

NORTHLAND INVESTMENT CORPORATION
2150 Washington St, Newton, MA 02462
Tel.: (617) 965-7100
Web Site: http://www.northland.com
Year Founded: 1970
Sales Range: $100-124.9 Million
Emp.: 400
Real Estate Investment Services
N.A.I.C.S.: 523999
Lawrence R. Gottesdiener *(Chm)*
Suzanne D. Abair *(COO)*
Beth H. Kinsley *(Gen Counsel)*
Steven P. Rosenthal *(Pres & CEO)*
Gina Montanaro *(VP-Multifamily)*
Ami Fatula *(CFO)*
Devin Evangelista *(VP-Asset Mgmt)*
Jay Babbitt *(Dir-HR)*
Matthew Gottesdiener *(Sr VP-Acq & Corp)*
Pauline Lucido *(Dir-Fin)*
Rachel Greene *(Dir-Mktg)*
Rita Tyszka *(VP-Comml)*
Kent Gonzales *(VP-Dev)*
Roman Stephens *(Sr VP-Multifamily)*
Peter M. Standish Jr. *(Sr VP-Acq, Dev & Comml Mgmt)*

NORTHLAND LAWN SPORT & EQUIPMENT
14 US-41, Negaunee, MI 49866
Tel.: (906) 401-0708
Web Site: http://www.mynorthland.com
Year Founded: 2016
Farm & Garden Machinery & Equipment Wholesaler
N.A.I.C.S.: 423820

Subsidiaries:

Moose Lake Implement & Sport (1)
504 Industrial Rd, Moose Lake, MN 55767
Tel.: (218) 485-4486
Web Site: http://www.mooselakeimplement.com
Sales Range: $1-9.9 Million
Emp.: 12
Ret Snowmobiles Lawn & Garden Equipment And Boats & Motors
N.A.I.C.S.: 441227
Ida Gassert *(Pres & Treas)*

NORTHLAND TELEPHONE SYSTEMS, LTD.
258 Genesee St, Utica, NY 13502
Tel.: (315) 624-2000
Web Site: http://www.northlandtel.com
Year Founded: 1982
Rev.: $21,500,000
Emp.: 200
Communications Services Provider
N.A.I.C.S.: 517111
Jeremiah O. McCarthy *(Pres)*
Brenda Grosso *(Mgr-HR)*

NORTHLAND TRUCKING INC.
1515 S 22nd Ave, Phoenix, AZ 85009
Tel.: (800) 214-5564
Web Site: http://www.northlandtrucking.com
Sales Range: $10-24.9 Million
Emp.: 150
Trucking Except Local
N.A.I.C.S.: 532120
Norman Skoog *(Pres & Gen Mgr)*

NORTHLANE CAPITAL PARTNERS, LLC
2 Bethesda Metro Ctr Ste 1510, Bethesda, MD 20814
Tel.: (301) 272-9990
Web Site: http://www.northlanecapital.com
Year Founded: 2017
Privater Equity Firm

NORTHLANE CAPITAL PARTNERS, LLC

Northlane Capital Partners, LLC—(Continued)
N.A.I.C.S.: 523999
Justin DuFour (Partner)
Sean Eagle (Partner)
Eugene Krichevsky (Partner)
David Steinglass (Partner)
Brian Foist (CFO & Chief Compliance Officer)
Claudia Evans (Office Mgr)
Scott Kauffman (Partner)

Subsidiaries:

Choice Financial Holdings, Inc. (1)
4501 23rd Ave S, Fargo, ND 58104
Tel.: (701) 356-9700
Web Site:
    http://www.choicefinancialgroup.com
Bank Holding Company
N.A.I.C.S.: 551111
Brian L. Johnson (Pres & CEO)
Jeff Kram (CFO)
Brian P. Johnson (COO)

Subsidiary (Domestic):

Choice Financial Group (2)
4501 23rd Ave S, Fargo, ND 58104
Tel.: (701) 356-9700
Web Site:
    http://www.choicefinancialgroup.com
Sales Range: $50-74.9 Million
Emp.: 230
Commericial Banking
N.A.I.C.S.: 522110
Brent Zavalney (Dir-Facilities & Related Svcs)
Lisa Artz (Exec Dir-Corp Rels)
Cheryl Feltman (Coord-Event & Specialist-Culture Dev)
Samantha Berg (Dir-Employee Dev & Recruiting)
Brian L. Johnson (Pres & CEO)
Jeff Kram (CFO)
Brian P. Johnson (COO)
Tim Heilman (CIO)
Greg Goodman (Chief Credit Officer)
Paul Bakkum (Chief Risk Officer)
Mike Boub (Chief Strategy Officer)
Mike Bindas (Dir-Wealth Mgmt)
Coralee Demers (VP-Ops)
Tara Field (VP-Compliance)
Greg Schwab (Sr VP-Lending Ops)
Sharon Karsky (Sr VP-Frontline Ops)
Tim Karsky (Mng Dir-Bus Dev)
Chuck Klabo (Mgr-Insurance)
Tom Jasper (COO-Choice Bank & Exec VP-Choice Bank)

Subsidiary (Domestic):

K.P.R., Inc. (3)
1015 C Eden Way N, Chesapeake, VA 23320-2787
Tel.: (757) 547-5118
Web Site:
    http://www.parkerreigleinsurance.com
Insurance Related Activities
N.A.I.C.S.: 524298
Billy R. Davis Jr. (VP)

Schlather Insurance Agency Inc. (3)
900 E Broad St, Elyria, OH 44035
Tel.: (440) 647-3313
Web Site:
    http://www.schlatherinsurance.com
Insurance Related Activities
N.A.I.C.S.: 524298
David Schlather (VP)

Potpourri Group Inc. (1)
101 Billerica Ave Bldg 2 N, Billerica, MA 01862
Tel.: (978) 256-4100
Web Site: http://www.potpourrigroup.com
Multi-title Catalog Publisher
N.A.I.C.S.: 484121
Jack Rosenfeld (Chm)
Jonathon Fleischmann (Pres & CEO)

SAI-Med Partners LLC (1)
4970 Demoss Rd #300, Reading, PA 19606
Tel.: (610) 685-4200
Web Site: https://www.sai-med.com
Business Consulting & Services
N.A.I.C.S.: 561499

Subsidiary (Domestic):

PharmaForce International Inc. (2)
2645 Perkiomen Ave, Reading, PA 19606
Tel.: (610) 370-5640
Web Site: http://www.pharmaforce.biz
Rev.: $1,500,000
Emp.: 25
Agents & Managers for Artists, Athletes, Entertainers & Other Public Figures
N.A.I.C.S.: 711410
Tom Nordhoy (Pres)

SMG Network, Inc. (1)
300 Conshohocken State Rd Ste 450, West Conshohocken, PA 19428
Tel.: (610) 729-7900
Web Site: http://www.smgworld.com
Venue Management, Marketing & Development Services
N.A.I.C.S.: 711320
Wes Westley (Pres & CEO)
John Burns (CFO & Exec VP)
Joe Daly (VP-Fin)
Maureen Ginty (Exec VP-Mktg Svcs & HR)
Bob Cavalieri (Reg VP-Stadiums & Arenas)
Bob McClintock (COO-Convention Centers & Sr VP)
John Adams (Reg VP-Convention Centers)
Doug Thornton (Exec VP-Stadiums & Arenas)
Harry Cann (Reg VP-Stadiums & Arenas)
David Causton (Reg VP-Convention Center)
Jim McCue (Sr VP-Entertainment)
Shaun Beard (Sr VP-SAVOR)
Thom Connors (Reg VP-Convention Centers)
Michael Codoy (Reg VP-Ops)
Michael Krouse (Reg VP-Convention Centers)
Craig Liston (Reg VP-Convention Centers)
Lon Rosenberg (Reg VP-Stadiums & Arenas)
Tracey Short (Reg VP-Convention Centers)
Steve Tadlock (Reg VP-Stadiums & Arenas)
John Bolton (VP-Live Entertainment)
Bruce Hanson (Corp Counsel & VP)
Pat Lamboy (VP-Sls)
Matt Longo (VP-Fin)
Bob Papke (VP-Live Entertainment Theaters)
Kurt Sinclair (VP-IT)
Leonard Bonacci (Reg VP-Stadiums & Arenas)
Lewis Dawley III (Sr VP-Convention Ctr)

Division (Non-US):

SMG Europe (2)
Manchester Arena Victoria Station, Manchester, M3 1AR, United Kingdom
Tel.: (44) 1619505000
Web Site: http://www.smg-europe.com
Venue Management, Marketing & Development Services
N.A.I.C.S.: 711320
Mike Cowley (Dir-Facilities Svcs)
John Sharkey (Exec VP-Ops)
Richard Still (Sr VP-Fin & Admin)
Tom Lynch (Dir-Bus Dev)
Darran Coulson (VP-Food & Beverage)

Division (Domestic):

SMG Food & Beverage, LLC (2)
300 Conshohocken State Rd, West Conshohocken, PA 19428
Tel.: (610) 729-7900
Web Site: http://www.savorsmg.com
Sales Range: $1-9.9 Million
Emp.: 40
Food Service Contractors
N.A.I.C.S.: 722310
Jamie Parks (Reg Dir-Food & Beverage-SAVOR)

SmartWave Technologies Corp. (1)
1 Marmac Dr, Toronto, M9W 1E7, ON, Canada
Tel.: (416) 679-5050
Electrical & Electronic Mfr
N.A.I.C.S.: 334419
Jack Vresics (CEO)

Subsidiary (US):

Multi-Tech Systems Inc. (2)
2205 Woodale Dr, Mounds View, MN 55112-4909
Tel.: (763) 785-3500
Web Site: http://www.multitech.com
Telephony, Internet, Remote Access & Device Networking Products Mfr
N.A.I.C.S.: 334210
Patricia Sharma (Chm)
Del Palacheck (COO)
Bruce Richardson (CFO)
Stefan Lindvall (CEO)
Mike Fahrion (CTO)
David Chu (VP-Channel Sls)

Value Management Group LLC (1)
3100 W End Ave Ste 940, Nashville, TN 37203-1377
Tel.: (615) 777-7300
Web Site: http://www.vmghealth.com
Professional, Scientific & Technical Services
N.A.I.C.S.: 541990
Don Barbo (Mng Dir-Bus Valuation Practice-Dallas)
Greg Koonsman (CEO)
Jason Ruchaber (Mng Dir-Bus Valuation-Denver)
Ben Ulrich (Mng Dir-Compensation Dir)
Cordell Mack (Mng Dir)

Subsidiary (Domestic):

Health Care Futures, L.P. (2)
300 Park Blvd, Itasca, IL 60143
Tel.: (630) 467-1700
Web Site: http://www.healthcarefutures.com
Management Consulting Services
N.A.I.C.S.: 541618
Robert Kaufman (Owner)

Winmo, LLC (1)
3098 Piedmont Rd NE Ste 200, Atlanta, GA 30305-2600
Tel.: (404) 350-0600
Web Site: https://www.winmo.com
Sales Range: $1-9.9 Million
Emp.: 37
Direct Advertising & Marketing Consulting Services
N.A.I.C.S.: 541860
Dave Currie (CEO)

NORTHLICH

Sawyer Point Bldg 720 Pete Rose Way, Cincinnati, OH 45202
Tel.: (513) 421-8840   OH
Web Site: http://www.northlich.com
Year Founded: 1949
Emp.: 100
Advetising Agency
N.A.I.C.S.: 541810
Kathy Selker (Pres & CEO)
Brian Newberry (Chief Strategy Officer)
Mark Willis (Chief Conversation Officer)
Kerry Broderick (VP & Dir-Ideation Digital Tech)
Kristin Margolin (Acct Exec)
Preeti Thakar (Acct Supvr)
Brian Nelson (Art Dir)
Dan Rapp (VP & Dir-Ideation)
Linda Burchett (Sr Media Planner & Buyer)
Shaun Ethier (VP & Dir-Engagement)
Carey McGuire (Dir-Creative)
Tammy Monroe (VP & Dir-PR)
Jason Ruebel (Chief Integration Officer)
Stephanie Kirschner (VP & Controller)
Amie Becker (VP & Dir-Connection Plng)
Frank Moricca (VP & Gen Mgr-Columbus)
Troy Walker (Dir-Growth Strategy)
Nichole Rhenisch (Sr Acct Mgr)
Ashley Davis (Sr Acct Mgr)
Terry Dillon (Assoc Dir-Creative)
Rob Lunsford (Dir-Strategic Mktg)
Tim McCort (COO)
Megan Damcevski (Asst Acct Mgr)
Cassie Bredensteiner (Acct Mgr)
Brian LeCount (VP & Acct Dir)
Stacey Swift (Acct Mgr)
Liz Phillips (Chief Client & Strategy Officer)
Lindsay Gilbert (Sr Art Dir)

U.S. PRIVATE

Pat Pujolas (Exec Creative Dir)
Teresa Martinez (VP-Client Strategy)
Lauren Mongelluzzo (Acct Mgr)

Subsidiaries:

Northlich (1)
580 N 4th St Ste 660, Columbus, OH 43215
Tel.: (614) 220-4370
N.A.I.C.S.: 541810
Frank Moricca (VP & Gen Mgr)
Maria Riethman (Acct Mgr)

Northlich (1)
815 Superior Ave Ste 1 13th Fl, Cleveland, OH 44114
Tel.: (216) 803-1230
N.A.I.C.S.: 541810
Mark Willis (Chief Conversation Officer)
Jeffrey Warman (Exec Creative Dir)

Northlich Public Relations (1)
720 E Pete Rose Way Ste 120, Cincinnati, OH 45202-3579
Tel.: (513) 421-8840
Web Site: http://www.northlich.com
Rev.: $5,400,000
Emp.: 25
Public Relations Agency
N.A.I.C.S.: 541820
Kathy Selker (Pres & CEO)
Jeffery Warman (Exec Creative Dir)
Andi Crawford (Acct Supvr)
Lindsy Breese (Sr Acct Mgr-Pub Rel)
Brian Newburry (Chief Strategy Officer)
Frank Moricca (VP & Gen Mgr-Columbus)
Shaun Ethier (VP & Dir-Engagement)
Tammy Monroe (VP & Dir-PR-APR)

Branch (Domestic):

Northlich-Columbus (2)
580 N 4th St Ste 660, Columbus, OH 43215
Tel.: (614) 573-0910
Web Site: http://www.northlich.com
Emp.: 10
N.A.I.C.S.: 541810
Mark J. Willis (Chief Conversation Officer)
Kathy Selker (Pres & CEO)
Jeffrey Warman (Exec Creative Dir)
Frank Moricca (VP & Gen Mgr)
Amie Becker (VP & Dir-Connection Plng)

NORTHLIGHT FINANCIAL LLC

1 Grand Central 60 E 42nd St Ste 2800, New York, NY 10165
Tel.: (212) 247-0330   DE
Web Site:
    http://www.northlightfinancial.com
Year Founded: 2002
Investment Management Service
N.A.I.C.S.: 523940
Michael Jahrmarkt (Co-Founder)
Robert Woods (Co-Founder, Mng Partner & Co-Chief Investment Officer)
Mark Hirschhorn (Co-Founder, Mng Partner & Chief Legal Officer)
Christopher Jahrmarkt (Partner & Co-Chief Investment Officer)
Robert Moorhead (Dir-Portfolio Mgmt)

Subsidiaries:

PDS Gaming Corporation (1)
6280 Annie Oakley Dr, Las Vegas, NV 89120-4409
Tel.: (702) 736-0700
Web Site: http://www.pdsgaming.com
Slot Machine & Other Electronic Gaming Equipment Sales & Leasing Services
N.A.I.C.S.: 522220
Johan P. Finley (Founder)
Peter D. Cleary (Pres, CFO & Treas)
Lona M. B. Finley (Sec & Exec VP)
Rick Laman (VP-Casino Sls)
Simon Burgess (Sr VP-Domestic Bus Dev)
John Tipton (Gen Counsel)
Gina Garner-Ball (VP-Fin & Controller)
Alex Dungan (CEO)

NORTHPOINT COMMUNICATIONS GROUP, INC.

303 2nd St S Tower, San Francisco, CA 94107
Tel.: (415) 403-4003
Year Founded: 1999
Data Network Services
N.A.I.C.S.: 517810
Herman Bluestein (Chief Dev Officer)

NORTHPOINT SOLUTIONS LLC.
130 W 42nd St, New York, NY 10036
Tel.: (212) 819-1700
Web Site: http://www.northps.com
Year Founded: 2003
Sales Range: $10-24.9 Million
Emp.: 107
Business Management Consulting Services
N.A.I.C.S.: 541618
Richard Cooley (Mng Partner)
Joseph Amarante (Founder & Partner)
Apurva Patel (Sr VP)
Johan Glozman (Sr VP)
Dileep Bhat (Sr VP)
Nikolay Kojuharov (Sr VP)
Craig Fitzpatrick (Head-Bus Dev)

NORTHPORT NETWORK SYSTEMS, INC.
Ste 4200 601 Union St, Seattle, WA 98101
Tel.: (206) 652-3451
Information Technology Services
N.A.I.C.S.: 541512
Yan Zhao (Chm, Pres & CEO)

NORTHRIDGE ACADEMY, LLC
3631 N Ridge Rd, Wichita, KS 67205
Tel.: (316) 729-0830
Web Site:
   http://www.northridgeacademyllc.com
Year Founded: 2006
Sales Range: $1-9.9 Million
Emp.: 50
Child Care Services
N.A.I.C.S.: 624410
Lori Tos (Owner)

NORTHRIDGE CORP.
5535 Bull Creek Rd, Tarentum, PA 15084
Tel.: (412) 455-5299   PA
Year Founded: 2019
Investment Services
N.A.I.C.S.: 523999
Christopher Netelkos (CEO)

NORTHSHORE UNIVERSITY HEALTHSYSTEM
2650 Ridge Ave Ste 1420, Evanston, IL 60201
Tel.: (847) 570-2000   IL
Web Site: http://www.northshore.org
Year Founded: 1891
Emp.: 10,596
Health Care Services Organization
N.A.I.C.S.: 813910
Gary E. Weiss (CFO, Treas & Exec VP)
J. P. Gallagher (Pres & CEO)
Steven Smith (CIO)
Thomas H. Hodges (Chief Investment Officer)
Harry Jones (Chief Compliance Officer)
William R. Luehrs (Chief HR Officer)
Mary Keegan (Chief Nursing Officer)
Subsidiaries:

Evanston Hospital   (1)
2650 Ridge Ave, Evanston, IL 60201
Tel.: (847) 570-2000
Web Site: http://www.northshore.org
Hospital Operator
N.A.I.C.S.: 622110
Douglas M. Silverstein (Pres)

Glenbrook Hospital   (1)
2100 Pfingsten Rd, Glenview, IL 60026
Tel.: (847) 657-5800
Web Site: http://www.northshore.org
Hospital Operator
N.A.I.C.S.: 622110
Sean O'Grady (Pres)

Highland Park Hospital   (1)
777 Park Ave W, Highland Park, IL 60035
Tel.: (847) 432-8000
Web Site: http://www.northshore.org
Hospital Operator
N.A.I.C.S.: 622110
Jesse Peterson Hall (Pres)

Northwest Community Healthcare Corporation   (1)
800 W Central Rd, Arlington Heights, IL 60005-2349
Tel.: (847) 618-4968
Web Site: http://www.nch.org
Sales Range: $125-149.9 Million
Emp.: 3,000
Hospital & Medical Center Operator
N.A.I.C.S.: 622110
Glen Malan (CIO & VP)
Steve Scogna (Pres & CEO)
Ann Patrick (VP-HR)
Michael Hartke (COO)

NORTHSHORE UTILITY DISTRICT
6830 NE 185th St, Kenmore, WA 98028
Tel.: (425) 398-4400
Web Site: http://www.nud.net
Sales Range: $10-24.9 Million
Emp.: 53
Water Supply
N.A.I.C.S.: 221310
Fanny Yee (Gen Mgr)

NORTHSIDE CENTER FOR CHILD DEVELOPMENT
1301 5th Ave, New York, NY 10029
Tel.: (212) 426-3400   NY
Web Site:
   http://www.northsidecenter.org
Year Founded: 1947
Sales Range: $10-24.9 Million
Emp.: 312
Child Care & Development Services
N.A.I.C.S.: 624110
Susane Berg (Dir-Admin & Ops)
Jean Holland (Dir-Clinic)
Sandra Scott (Dir-Quality Mgmt)
Thelma Dye (Exec Dir)

NORTHSIDE ENGINEERING SERVICES, INC.
300 S Belcher Rd, Clearwater, FL 33765
Tel.: (727) 443-2869
Web Site:
   http://www.northsideengineeringincorporated.com
Year Founded: 1989
Sales Range: $1-9.9 Million
Emp.: 10
Civil Engineering Services
N.A.I.C.S.: 237990
Housh Ghovaee (Owner & CEO)

NORTHSIDE HOSPITAL
1000 Johnson Ferry Rd NE, Atlanta, GA 30342-1606
Tel.: (404) 851-8000
Web Site: http://www.northside.com
Year Founded: 1970
Sales Range: $500-549.9 Million
Emp.: 10,000
Operator of Medical Hospital
N.A.I.C.S.: 622110
Jon Strasser (Coord-Ops)
Katherine Bledsoe (Mgr-Health Info Svs)
Kathleen Gamblin (Coord-Oncology Navigation)
Kathy James (Mgr-Clinical Supply Chain)
Kathy Miles (Mgr-Ops)
Kristen Moody (Mgr-Budgets & Performance Analytics)
Lisa Gilman (Mgr-Radiology)
Lisa Modglin (Coord-Data Warehouse)
Megan Freeman (Mgr-Clinical Pharmacy Svcs)
Hugh Roberts (Mgr-Patient Fin Svcs)
Julie Ballantine (Dir-Strategic Plng)
Jorge Hernandez (Chief Compliance Officer)
Catherine Butler (Dir-Legal Svcs)
Cindy Gambon (Mgr-Nurse Ops)
Doug MacDonald (VP-Plng)
Frank Watson (Mgr)
Chris Munn (Dir-Emergency Svcs)
Diane Clancy (Mgr-Mktg & PR)
Deidre Dixon (Dir-Radiology Svcs & Radiation Therapy)
Dwight Hill (VP)
Aljeanette Eaddy (Coord-Clinical Nurse & Cardica Rehab Wellstar Cobb)
Amy Yost (Mgr-Cardiology Svcs)
Beth Allen (Mgr-Outpatient Svcs For Women)
Bridget Green (Dir-HR)
Bradley Holt (Dir-Patient Fin Svcs)
Steve Aslinger (Dir-Facilities Plng)
Sharal Buchanan (Mgr-Clinical)
Patrick Gilligan (Mgr-Radiology)
Patty McGregor (Coord-Lactation)
Teresa Dawson-Collier (Mgr-Employee Rels)
Trella Greene (Mgr-Ops)
Skip Putnam (VP)
Stephanie Walton (Coord-HR Admin & Physician Practices)
Jack Chen (Dir-Cardiology)
Kim E. Sharif (Coord-Ops)
Ernie Fuller (Mgr)
Katrina Denson (Mgr-Clinical)
Jacob Collins (Mgr-PFS)
Randy Cosby (Mgr-Tech Svcs)
James Waldrop (Project Mgr)
Julie Eaton (Project Mgr-Ops)
Barbara Rutt (Coord-Clinical Pharmaceutical)
Melissa Sugg (Mgr)
Angela Austin (Mgr-Physician Practice)
Maria Montgomery (Supvr-Clinical)
Mamie Maier (Supvr-Clinical Nurse)
Helena Walo (Chief Nursing Officer)
Kristy Redd-Hachey (CFO)
Valerie Powell-Stafford (CEO)
Carrie Johnson (Dir-PR & Comm)

NORTHSIDE SERVICES, INC.
10701 N Nebraska Ave, Tampa, FL 33612
Tel.: (813) 962-8815
Web Site:
   http://www.northsideac.com
Rev.: $2,640,000
Emp.: 20
Electrical Contractor
N.A.I.C.S.: 238210
Brian Harre (Owner)
Subsidiaries:

Palm Harbor Heating & Air Conditioning, Inc.   (1)
1040 Kapp Dr, Clearwater, FL 33765-2148
Tel.: (727) 786-3276
Web Site: http://www.phhvac.com
Appliance Repair & Maintenance Services
N.A.I.C.S.: 811412
Peter J. Tremblay (Pres)
Deborah M. Tremblay (VP)

NORTHSIDE TRUCKS
6221 NE Columbia Blvd, Portland, OR 97218
Tel.: (503) 282-7777
Web Site:
   http://www.northsidetrucks.com
Rev.: $48,000,000
Emp.: 65
Automotive Retailer
N.A.I.C.S.: 441120
Monte Eby (Mgr-Ford Svc)
Tiffany Meade (Mgr-Fin)
Rod Bergquist (Mgr-Fleet Sls)
Don Beezley (Mgr-Comml Sls)
Jim McDonough (Pres)

NORTHSTAR CAPITAL, LLC
2310 Plz 7 45 S 7th St, Minneapolis, MN 55402
Tel.: (612) 371-5700
Web Site:
   http://www.northstarcapital.com
Year Founded: 1993
Equity Investment Firm
N.A.I.C.S.: 523999
Douglas E. Mark (Mng Partner)
Brian J. Schneider (Mng Partner)
Christopher J. Kocourek (Partner & Portfolio Mgr-Investment)
David A. Shuler (Partner)
Timothy S. Duffy (CFO & Chief Compliance Officer)
Daniel E. Kleineman (Principal)
Ethan C. Eid (VP)
Kyle P. Sexton (Controller)

NORTHSTAR COOPERATIVE INC.
4200 Forest Rd Bldg A, Lansing, MI 48910
Tel.: (517) 351-3180
Web Site:
   http://www.northstarcooperative.com
Sales Range: $10-24.9 Million
Emp.: 210
Bovine Artificial Insemination Services & Solutions
N.A.I.C.S.: 115210

NORTHSTAR COUNSELORS INC.
101 Lake St W Ste 210, Wayzata, MN 55391
Tel.: (952) 475-9000   MN
Web Site:
   http://www.northstarcounselors.com
Year Founded: 1971
Sales Range: $1-9.9 Million
Emp.: 20
Public Relations Agency
N.A.I.C.S.: 541820
Joseph M. McCarthy (Pres & CEO)
Lynn McCarthy (VP)
Patrick M. Mccarthy (Dir)
John Katsantonis (Sr VP-Tech)

NORTHSTAR EDUCATION FINANCE, INC.
930 Blue Gentian Rd Ste 100, Eagan, MN 55121-1678
Tel.: (608) 327-1968   DE
Web Site: http://www.northstar.org
Year Founded: 2000
Rev.: $103,367,000
Assets: $2,126,920,000
Liabilities: $1,958,294,000
Net Worth: $168,626,000
Earnings: ($4,645,000)
Fiscal Year-end: 09/30/19
Educational Loan Provider
N.A.I.C.S.: 611710

NORTHSTAR FIRE PROTECTION OF TEXAS, INC.
4616-2 Howard Ln Ste 400, Austin, TX 78728
Tel.: (512) 833-0800

NORTHSTAR FIRE PROTECTION OF TEXAS, INC.

Northstar Fire Protection of Texas, Inc.—(Continued)

Web Site:
http://www.northstarfire.com
Year Founded: 1985
Sales Range: $25-49.9 Million
Emp.: 50
Provider of Fire Sprinkler System Installation Services
N.A.I.C.S.: 238220
Jason McKeown (Mgr)
Jesse Klups (Project Mgr)

NORTHSTAR INDUSTRIES INC.
126 Merrimack St, Methuen, MA 01844
Tel.: (978) 975-5500
Web Site:
http://www.northstarind.com
Sales Range: $50-74.9 Million
Emp.: 40
Buildings, Portable: Prefabricated Metal
N.A.I.C.S.: 332311
Tom Quine (Pres & VP-Tech Svcs)
Jim Hunt (VP)
Jim Austan (CFO)
Jim Smilikas (VP)

NORTHSTAR MACHINE & TOOL CO., INC.
4212 Enterprise Cir, Duluth, MN 55811
Tel.: (218) 720-2920
Web Site:
http://www.northstaraerospace.com
Sales Range: $1-9.9 Million
Emp.: 50
Manufactures Parts for Personal, Business & Instructional Airplanes
N.A.I.C.S.: 336413
Gary J. Corradi (Pres & CEO)

NORTHSTAR MEMORIAL GROUP, LLC
1900 St James Place Ste 300, Houston, TX 77056
Tel.: (832) 308-2790
Web Site: http://www.nsmg.com
Year Founded: 2004
Sales Range: $25-49.9 Million
Emp.: 550
Funeral Services
N.A.I.C.S.: 812210
Mark Hamilton (Pres & CEO)
Brian Sullivan (COO & Exec VP)
Mark Shinder (CFO & Exec VP)
Mike Zislis (CIO)

Subsidiaries:

Page Theus Funeral Home (1)
914 W Main St, Leesburg, FL 34748
Tel.: (352) 504-0120
Web Site:
http://www.pagetheusfuneralhome.com
Emp.: 6
Funeral Services
N.A.I.C.S.: 812210
Jim Semesco (VP)
Laura Brown (Office Mgr)
William C. Ward III (Gen Mgr)

NORTHSTAR MOVING CORP.
9120 Mason Ave, Chatsworth, CA 91311
Tel.: (818) 727-0128   CA
Web Site:
http://www.northstarmoving.com
Year Founded: 1994
Sales Range: $1-9.9 Million
Emp.: 40
Moving & Storage Services
N.A.I.C.S.: 493110
Ram Katalan (Pres)

NORTHSTAR RECYCLING GROUP
94 Maple St, East Longmeadow, MA 01028
Tel.: (413) 263-6010
Web Site: http://www.nsrecycle.com
Year Founded: 1898
Sales Range: $100-124.9 Million
Emp.: 50
Recycling Services
N.A.I.C.S.: 562998
Noah Goodman (Co-Owner)
Aaron Furman (Gen Mgr)
Annette Maruca (Acct Mgr)
Amy Shepherd (Acct Mgr)
Amanda Zawtocki (Dir-Acct Mgmt)
Emily Wilson (Sr Mgr-Mktg)
Lisa Hughes (Acct Mgr)
Rebekah Guzek (Acct Mgr)
Tina Brown (Accountant)
Shawna Duling-Laczko (Dir-Strategic Initiatives)

NORTHSTAR RESTORATION SERVICES, LLC
4900 Stewart Ave, Wausau, WI 54401
Tel.: (715) 227-3231
Web Site:
http://www.northstarrestorationservices.com
Year Founded: 2011
Sales Range: $1-9.9 Million
Emp.: 31
Residential & Commercial Restoration Services
N.A.I.C.S.: 236118
Jay Cricks (Dir-Sls & Mktg)

NORTHSTAR RISK MANAGEMENT & INSURANCE SERVICES INC.
1777 Botelho Dr Ste 360, Walnut Creek, CA 94596-5084
Tel.: (925) 975-5900
Web Site: http://www.northstar-ins.com
Year Founded: 1993
Sales Range: $10-24.9 Million
Emp.: 15
Insurance Brokerage Services
N.A.I.C.S.: 524210
Charles Bates (Pres & CEO)
Chris Thorndike (Exec VP)
Michael P. Martin (Exec VP)

NORTHSTAR SOLUTIONS GROUP
2669 Shillington Rd Ste 187, Reading, PA 19608
Tel.: (610) 568-4996
Web Site: http://www.northstarsg.com
Year Founded: 2004
Sales Range: $1-9.9 Million
Emp.: 25
It Consulting
N.A.I.C.S.: 541690
Chris Collins (Pres)
Bill Fox (Dir-Ops)

NORTHSTAR STEEL & ALUMINUM
205 Bouchard St, Manchester, NH 03103
Tel.: (603) 668-3600
Web Site:
http://www.nstarmetals.com
Rev.: $20,000,000
Emp.: 30
Mfr of Steel
N.A.I.C.S.: 423510
James MacVane (Pres)

NORTHSTAR.IO, INC.
809 N Racine Ste 300, Chicago, IL 60642
Tel.: (312) 421-3270
Web Site: http://www.conventus-sei.com
Year Founded: 2006
Sales Range: $1-9.9 Million
Emp.: 31
Information Technology Consulting Services
N.A.I.C.S.: 541512
Andrew Shea (VP-Bus Dev)
Steve Opfer (VP-Ops)
Jodi Glenn Fox (Project Mgr-Consulting Ops)

NORTHSTAR/RXR NEW YORK METRO REAL ESTATE, INC.
590 Madison Ave 34th Fl, New York, NY 10022
Tel.: (212) 547-2600   MD
Web Site:
http://www.northstarrxrreit.com
Year Founded: 2014
Sales Range: $1-9.9 Million
Real Estate Investment Services
N.A.I.C.S.: 525990
Scott H. Rechler (Chm)
David Schwarz (Pres & CEO)
Frank V. Saracino (CFO & Treas)
Ann B. Harrington (Gen Counsel & Sec)

NORTHTOWN AUTOMOTIVE CO., INC.
1135 Millersport Hwy, Amherst, NY 14226
Tel.: (716) 836-4600
Web Site:
http://www.northtownauto.com
Year Founded: 1970
Sales Range: $50-74.9 Million
Emp.: 500
Retailer of Automobiles
N.A.I.C.S.: 441110
Norman Schreiber (Co-Owner)
Joseph Calabrese (Co-Owner)
Lawrence Schreiber (Co-Owner)
Craig Schreiber (VP)
Harold Erbacher (CFO)

NORTHTOWN FORD MERCURY
415 Cedar Ave W, Menomonie, WI 54751
Tel.: (715) 232-6353
Web Site:
http://www.northtownford.com
Sales Range: $10-24.9 Million
Emp.: 55
Car Whslr
N.A.I.C.S.: 441110
Eric Mickelson (Gen Mgr)

NORTHVIEW ENTERPRISES
120 Webster St, Louisville, KY 40206
Tel.: (502) 228-7908
Sales Range: $10-24.9 Million
Emp.: 23
Operative Builder Services
N.A.I.C.S.: 236117
Mark Held (Pres)

NORTHWELL HEALTH, INC.
2000 Marcus Ave, New Hyde Park, NY 11042
Tel.: (516) 321-6100   NY
Web Site: https://www.northwell.edu
Year Founded: 1997
Emp.: 69,000
Health Care Services Organization
N.A.I.C.S.: 813920
Maureen White (Chief Nursing Officer & Exec VP)
Mark Solazzo (COO & Exec VP)
Terry Lynam (Chief PR Officer & Sr VP)
David Battinelli (Chief Medical Officer & Sr VP)
Michael J. Dowling (Pres & CEO)
Margaret M. Crotty (Chm)
Stephen Bello (Exec Dir-East)
John Flanagan (VP-Govt Affairs-Suffolk & Eastern Nassau Counties)
Maxine Carrington (Chief HR Officer & Sr VP)
Ramon Soto (Chief Mktg & Comm Officer & Sr VP)
Joseph Leston (Deputy CMO)
Margaret Crotty (Chm)

Subsidiaries:

Formativ Health (1)
4875 Belfort Rd, Jacksonville, FL 32256
Tel.: (844) 818-1020
Web Site: http://www.formativhealth.com
Patient Engagement Services
N.A.I.C.S.: 621999
Nick Stefanizzi (CEO-Interim)

Subsidiary (Domestic):

Etransmedia Technology Inc. (2)
385 Jordan Rd Rensselaer Technology Pk, Troy, NY 12180
Tel.: (518) 283-5418
Online Records Management Services
N.A.I.C.S.: 561440

Subsidiary (Domestic):

Associated Billing Services, Inc. (3)
13430 N Black Canyon Hwy Ste 100, Phoenix, AZ 85029-1310
Tel.: (602) 943-9200
Accounting Services
N.A.I.C.S.: 541219

NORTHWEST ADMINISTRATORS INC.
2323 Eastlake Ave E, Seattle, WA 98102-3305
Tel.: (206) 329-4900   WA
Web Site: http://www.nwadmin.com
Year Founded: 1956
Sales Range: $100-124.9 Million
Emp.: 330
Pension, Health & Welfare Funds
N.A.I.C.S.: 525120
Chuck Geyer (VP-IS)
Michael Sander (VP)
Norbert Embreus (Mgr-Ops & IS)
Ruth McDonagh (Mgr-HR)
Bob Gies (Exec VP)
Nathan Hartman (VP-Ops)

NORTHWEST ALABAMA GAS DISTRICT
310 2nd St SW, Hamilton, AL 35570
Tel.: (205) 921-3106
Web Site: http://www.nwagd.com
Sales Range: $10-24.9 Million
Emp.: 51
Natural Gas Distr
N.A.I.C.S.: 221210
Heath Reed (Gen Mgr)

NORTHWEST ALUMINUM SPECIALTIES, INC.
2929 W 2nd St, The Dalles, OR 97058
Tel.: (541) 296-6161   OR
Web Site:
http://www.nwaluminum.com
Aluminum Casting, Cutting, Machining, Deburring & Homogenization Services
N.A.I.C.S.: 331523
William R. Reid (Pres)

NORTHWEST ARKANSAS PAPER CO., INC.
2400 Cantrell Rd Ste 116, Little Rock, AR 72202-2133
Tel.: (501) 374-5884   AR
Web Site: http://www.napcolr.net

Year Founded: 1967
Sales Range: $10-24.9 Million
Emp.: 5
Mfr of Uncoated Paper & Multiwall
N.A.I.C.S.: 424130
David Boyle (Controller)

NORTHWEST BANCORPORATION OF ILLINOIS, INC.
300 E NW Hwy, Palatine, IL 60067
Tel.: (847) 358-6262
Web Site:
  http://www.firstbankillinois.com
Year Founded: 1977
Sales Range: $50-74.9 Million
Emp.: 40
Holding Company; Banking Services
N.A.I.C.S.: 522110
Ken Eiserman (VP & Cashier-Investments & HR)
Alan Reasoner (CEO & Pres)

Subsidiaries:

First Bank & Trust Company of Illinois Inc. (1)
300 E Northwest Hwy, Palatine, IL 60067-8117 (100%)
Tel.: (847) 358-6262
Web Site: http://www.firstbankillinois.com
Sales Range: $300-349.9 Million
Emp.: 35
Provider of Banking Services
N.A.I.C.S.: 522110
Alan Reasoner (Pres & CEO)
Emad Murrar (Chief Lending Officer & Sr VP)
Meaghan Harmon (COO)

NORTHWEST BANK & TRUST COMPANY
1454 W Locust St, Davenport, IA 52806
Tel.: (563) 388-2511
Web Site:
  http://www.northwestbank.com
Sales Range: $10-24.9 Million
Emp.: 85
State Commercial Banks
N.A.I.C.S.: 523999
Joe Slavens (Pres & CEO)
Barbara Dettlaff (Sr VP-Ops & HR)
Patricia Vaccaro (VP-IT & Loan Servicing)
Donna Connors (Controller)
James DeBoeuf (COO)
Karen Goodall (VP)
Margaret Rich (Officer-Comml Investment & VP)
John Crowe (VP)
Chris Heller (Sr VP)
Tracy Schwind (Sr VP-Mktg)
Keith Bonjour (VP & Portfolio Mgr)
Todd Schirmer (VP & Mgr-Rochester)
Shane E. Oschman (VP & Mgr-Bradford)
Julie Marasco (Pres-Northwest Pennsylvania)

NORTHWEST BEDDING CO.
6102 S Hayford Rd, Spokane, WA 99224
Tel.: (509) 244-3000
Web Site: http://www.nwbedding.com
Sales Range: $10-24.9 Million
Emp.: 47
Mattress Mfr
N.A.I.C.S.: 337910
Robert L. Evanson (Pres)
Lee M. Kvalheim (Treas & Sec)
Tracy Dedeaux (Plant Mgr)

NORTHWEST BROADCASTING, INC.
2111 University Park Dr Ste 650, Okemos, MI 48864
Tel.: (517) 347-4141   DE
Sales Range: $25-49.9 Million

Emp.: 500
Holding Company; Television Broadcasting Stations Owner & Operator
N.A.I.C.S.: 551112
Brian W. Brady (Pres & CEO)

Subsidiaries:

Blackhawk Broadcasting LLC (1)
1965 S 3rd Ave, Yuma, AZ 85364
Tel.: (928) 782-1111
Emp.: 70
Television Broadcasting Station
N.A.I.C.S.: 516120
Paul Heebink (Gen Mgr)

Unit (Domestic):

Blackhawk Broadcasting LLC - KSWT-DT (2)
1301 S 3rd Ave, Yuma, AZ 85364
Tel.: (928) 782-5113
Web Site: http://www.kswt.com
Television Broadcasting Station
N.A.I.C.S.: 516120
Yesi Rios Carlos (Bus Mgr-HR & Acctg)
Gail Chango (Mgr-Programming & Traffic)
Michael Ochoa (Mgr-Creative Svcs)
Fred McCarty (Mgr-Promos)

Blackhawk Broadcasting LLC - KYMA-DT (2)
1385 S Pacific Ave, Yuma, AZ 85365-1725
Tel.: (928) 782-1111
Web Site: http://www.kyma.com
Emp.: 55
Television Broadcasting Station Services
N.A.I.C.S.: 516120
Ernesto Romero (Dir-News)
Yesi Rios Carlos (Mgr-Bus & Acctg)
Brian W. Brady (Pres & CEO)

Broadcasting Communications, LLC (1)
820 Crater Lake Ave Ste 105, Medford, OR 97504
Tel.: (541) 772-2600
Web Site: http://www.fox26medford.com
Rev.: $1,400,000
Emp.: 20
Television Broadcasting Station
N.A.I.C.S.: 516120
Dave Olmsted (Gen Mgr)

Mountain Broadcasting, LLC (1)
4600 S Regal St, Spokane, WA 99223
Tel.: (509) 448-2828
Web Site: http://www.myfoxspokane.com
Sales Range: $10-24.9 Million
Emp.: 40
Television Broadcasting Station
N.A.I.C.S.: 516120
Doug Holroyd (Gen Mgr)
Ron Sweatte (Dir-Engrg)

Stainless Broadcasting, LLC (1)
4600 Vestal Pkwy E, Vestal, NY 13850
Tel.: (607) 770-4040
Web Site: http://www.wicz.com
Emp.: 30
Television Broadcasting Station
N.A.I.C.S.: 516120
John Leet (Gen Mgr)
Rosemary Gaeta (Bus Mgr)
Vernon Rowlands (Program Dir)
Wayne Gordon (Gen Sls Mgr & Sls Mgr-Natl)

NORTHWEST BUILDING MATERIALS & SUPPLY CO.
31 W Diehl Rd, Naperville, IL 60563
Tel.: (630) 416-1010
Web Site:
  http://www.northwestbuildingmaterial.com
Rev.: $16,200,000
Emp.: 20
Supplier of Building Materials
N.A.I.C.S.: 423310
Kathy Henry (Controller)
Charles R. Hansen Sr. (CEO)

NORTHWEST CASCADE INC.
10412 John Bananola Way E, Puyallup, WA 98373
Tel.: (253) 848-2371   WA

Web Site: http://www.nwcascade.com
Year Founded: 1985
Rev.: $31,945,702
Emp.: 300
Water, Sewer & Utility Lines
N.A.I.C.S.: 237110
Eric Wright (Dir-Safety)
Clint Myers (VP-Construction)
Carl Liliequist (Pres)
Greg Potts (CFO)

NORTHWEST CENTER
7272 W Marginal Way S, Seattle, WA 98108
Tel.: (206) 285-9140   WA
Web Site: http://www.nwcenter.org
Year Founded: 1966
Sales Range: $25-49.9 Million
Emp.: 1,295
Child Disability Assistance Services
N.A.I.C.S.: 624120
Mike Quinn (VP-Bus Dev)
Ty Taylor (CEO & COO)
Robin Krueger (CFO)
Mike Gano (Chm)
Jeff Roush (Vice Chm)
Marti Louther (Sec)
Brian Volkert (Treas)
Tracy Squillace (Chief Mktg Officer)
Emily Miller (Chief People Officer)
Laura Kneedler (Chief Mission Officer)
Volker Wellmann (Sr VP-Integrated Facility Svcs)
Jenn Ramirez Robson (VP-Employment Svcs)

NORTHWEST COMMUNITY ACTION PROGRAMS OF WYOMING INC.
500 15 Mile Rd, Worland, WY 82401
Tel.: (307) 347-6185
Web Site: http://www.nowcap.com
Sales Range: $75-99.9 Million
Emp.: 250
Social Advocacy Organization
N.A.I.C.S.: 813319
E. J. Stolns (Pres)

NORTHWEST COMMUNITY BANK
86 Main St, Winsted, CT 06098
Tel.: (860) 379-7561
Web Site:
  http://www.nwcommunitybank.com
Rev.: $17,339,000
Emp.: 84
Federal Savings Institutions
N.A.I.C.S.: 522180
Linda F. Milkowski (CFO, Treas & Sr VP)
Monica Diulio (Asst VP-Torrington Branch)
Gayle Moraski (VP)
Daniel J. Sullivan (VP)
Gregori P. Tonon (VP)
Steven J. Zarrella (Chief Lending Officer & Sr VP)

NORTHWEST COMMUNITY CARE NETWORK
2000 W 1st St Ste 704, Winston Salem, NC 27104
Tel.: (336) 716-2698   NC
Web Site:
  http://www.nwcommunitycare.org
Year Founded: 2006
Sales Range: $10-24.9 Million
Emp.: 75
Healtcare Services
N.A.I.C.S.: 622110
Akelo Harris (Project Mgr)
Kelly Garrison (Mgr-Quality Improvement)
Linda Michalski (Mgr-Ops)
Michael Cottingham (Mgr-Comm)

NORTHWEST COMMUNITY CREDIT UNION
PO Box 70225, Springfield, OR 97475-0145
Tel.: (800) 452-9515   OR
Web Site: http://www.nwcu.com
Year Founded: 1949
Sales Range: $25-49.9 Million
Emp.: 302
Financial Support Services
N.A.I.C.S.: 523999
Barb Blackmore (Chm)

NORTHWEST CONTAINER SERVICES INC.
11920 N Burgard Rd, Portland, OR 97203
Tel.: (503) 286-4873
Web Site:
  http://www.nwcontainer.com
Sales Range: $25-49.9 Million
Emp.: 80
Container Transportation Services
N.A.I.C.S.: 484121
Gary Cardwell (VP)
Carlee Service (Mgr-Accts Payable)
Paul Keeth (Mgr-Portland)

NORTHWEST CRANE SERVICE, LLC.
1125 40th St Ste B, Woodward, OK 73801
Tel.: (580) 254-8070
Web Site:
  http://www.northwestcraneservice.com
Year Founded: 2001
Rev.: $31,900,000
Emp.: 71
Support Services
N.A.I.C.S.: 561990
Juana Tackett (Mgr-HR)

NORTHWEST DAIRY ASSOCIATION
PO Box 34377, Seattle, WA 98124
Tel.: (877) 632-6455
Web Site: http://www.nwdairy.coop
Sales Range: $1-4.9 Billion
Dairy Co-op
N.A.I.C.S.: 112120
Steven Rowe (Gen Counsel & Sr VP)
Stan Ryan (Pres & CEO)
Allan Huttema (Chm)

Subsidiaries:

Darigold, Inc. (1)
PO Box 34377, Seattle, WA 98124-1377
Tel.: (206) 284-7220
Web Site: http://www.darigold.com
Sales Range: $1-4.9 Billion
Emp.: 1,160
Dairy Products Mfr & Marketer
N.A.I.C.S.: 112120
Dermot Carey (Sr VP-Ingredients Div)
Nathan Davis (Sr VP-Fin)
Stan Ryan (Pres)
Richard Scheitler (CIO)
Monica Johnson (Gen Counsel)
Kristi Kangas (COO)
Joe Coote (CEO)
Duane Naluai (Chief Customer Officer)

NORTHWEST DOOR INC.
19000 Canyon Rd E, Puyallup, WA 98446
Tel.: (253) 375-0700   WA
Web Site: http://www.nwdusa.com
Year Founded: 1969
Sales Range: $10-24.9 Million
Emp.: 220
Metal Doors, Sash & Trim
N.A.I.C.S.: 332321
Brian Miller (Mgr-Nampa)

NORTHWEST ELECTRICAL SUPPLY CO. INC.

NORTHWEST ELECTRICAL SUPPLY CO. INC. U.S. PRIVATE

NorthWest Electrical Supply Co. Inc.—(Continued)
600 E Rand Rd, Mount Prospect, IL 60056
Tel.: (847) 255-3700
Web Site: http://www.nwelectrical.com
Year Founded: 1956
Sales Range: $10-24.9 Million
Lighting & Electrical Equipment Whslr & Distr
N.A.I.C.S.: 423610
Thomas Reindl (Pres)

NORTHWEST ENERGY EFFICIENCY ALLIANCE
421 SW 6th Ave Ste 600, Portland, OR 97204
Tel.: (503) 688-5400   OR
Web Site: http://www.neea.org
Year Founded: 1996
Sales Range: $25-49.9 Million
Emp.: 82
Energy Efficiency Utility Service Provider
N.A.I.C.S.: 541350
Stacy Blumberg (Sr Mgr-Mktg)
Suelynn Callahan (Dir-Bus Admin)
Debbie Driscoll (Mgr-Strategic Market)
Kevin J. Christie (Sec)
John Francisco (Chm)
Robert Curry (Sr Project Mgr)
Andrew Grassell (Treas)
Cory Scott (Vice Chm)
Christopher Kroeker (Sr Mgr-Product)
Emily Moore (Sr Mgr-Strategic Markets)
Harvey Mathews (Sr Mgr-Market Intelligence)
Jeff Mitchell (Sr Mgr-Residential)
Jeremy Litow (Dir-Stakeholder Engagement & Comm)
Julia Harper (Dir-Market Execution)
Mark Roller (Sr Mgr-IT)
Stephanie Rider (Sr Mgr-Market Plng)
Susan Hermenet (Dir-Tech, Plng & Evaluation)
Susan Stratton (Exec Dir)
Virginia Mersereau (Mgr-Comm)

NORTHWEST ENTERPRISES INC.
1078 S Metcalf St, Lima, OH 45804
Tel.: (419) 224-8045
Web Site: http://www.northwestoil.com
Rev.: $17,000,000
Emp.: 19
Petroleum Bulk Stations & Terminals
N.A.I.C.S.: 424710
Harold Jackson Jr. (Pres)

NORTHWEST EQUIPMENT SALES INC.
2405 Janeen St, Boise, ID 83709
Tel.: (208) 362-3400
Web Site: http://www.nwesales.com
Rev.: $14,190,527
Emp.: 50
Trailers For Trucks, New & Used
N.A.I.C.S.: 423110
James Hibler (Founder & Pres)

NORTHWEST FARM CREDIT SERVICES ACA
1700 S Assembly St, Spokane, WA 99224-2121
Tel.: (509) 340-5600
Web Site: http://www.farm-credit.com
Year Founded: 1985
Rev.: $77,496,000
Emp.: 420
Federal & Federally Sponsored Credit
N.A.I.C.S.: 522299
Adam Teichert (Mgr-American Falls)
Allan Bafus (Mgr-Spokane)
Andy Lundquist (Mgr-Dillon)
Andy VanderPlaat (Mgr-Pendleton)
Bill Lickley (Mgr-Twin Falls)
Brooke Kmetz (Mgr-Miles City)
Candace Powell (Mgr-Beaverton)
Christina Withers (Mgr-Central Point)
Craig Shindler (Mgr-Sunnyside)

NORTHWEST FIBER LLC
Tel.: (866) 947-5988
Web Site: https://ziplyfiber.com
Emp.: 100
Telecommunications Resellers
N.A.I.C.S.: 517121
Subsidiaries:
Tylite Holdings, Inc.   (1)
24001 E Mission Ave Ste 50, Liberty Lake, WA 99019-2500
Tel.: (509) 927-7837
Web Site: http://www.ptera.net
Data Processing, Hosting & Related Services
N.A.I.C.S.: 518210

NORTHWEST FINANCIAL CORP.
431 202nd St, Arnolds Park, IA 51331
Tel.: (712) 580-4153   IA
Web Site: http://www.bank-northwest.com
Year Founded: 1988
Sales Range: $100-124.9 Million
Emp.: 390
Bank Holding Company
N.A.I.C.S.: 551111
Jeff Plagge (Pres & CEO)
Dwight K. Conover (Chm)
Brent Johnson (CFO)
Alex Oponski (Chief People Officer)
Julie A. Black (Pres-IT Svcs)
Sandra Marcus Lindgren (Chief Risk & Audit Officer)
Lee Schoenewe (Sr Officer-Credit Risk)
Ted Wallinger (VP-Fin)
Dave Ward (Chief Credit Officer)
Subsidiaries:
Northwest Bank   (1)
705 Grand Ave, Spencer, IA 51301-0080
Tel.: (712) 262-2202
Web Site: http://www.bank-northwest.com
Sales Range: $50-74.9 Million
Emp.: 315
Commericial Banking
N.A.I.C.S.: 522110
Greg Post (Pres & CEO)
Clay Baker (Sr VP & Mgr-Bus Banking-Omaha)
Doug Benjamin (Pres-Spencer)
Doug Berte (Pres-Humboldt)
Patricia Berte (Pres-Algona)
Troy Boelman (Pres-Ankeny)
John Bothof (Pres-Omaha)
Joe Conover (Exec VP & Dir-Charter Strategies-Arnolds Park)
Dan DeBoest (Pres-Sioux City)
Kevin R. Eekhoff (Pres-Le Mars)
Jed Jensen (Pres-Spirit Lake)
Donald Nickerson (Pres-West Des Moines)
Paul Pick (Sr VP-West Des Moines)
John Taets (Pres-Fort Dodge)
Eric Walhof (Pres-Sioux Center)

Northwest Commercial Credit Corp.   (1)
14320 Arbor St, Omaha, NE 68144
Tel.: (402) 334-1481
Commercial Banking Services
N.A.I.C.S.: 522110
Donald M. Shiu (Pres)

Northwest Wealth Management, LLC   (1)
705 Grand Ave, Spencer, IA 51301
Tel.: (712) 580-4145
Web Site: http://www.invest-northwest.com
Emp.: 6
Investment Advisory & Wealth Management Services
N.A.I.C.S.: 523940

The First National Bank in Creston   (1)
101 W Adams St, Creston, IA 50801-3104
Tel.: (641) 782-2195
Web Site: http://www.fnbcreston.com
Sales Range: $10-24.9 Million
Emp.: 66
Federal Savings Bank
N.A.I.C.S.: 522180
Sharon Higgins (VP-Mktg)
Steve Crittenden (Sr VP)
Randy Huewe (Pres & CEO)
Julie Black (Pres-Clinical Dept)
Staci Heaberlin (Asst VP)
Syd Hudek (Asst VP)
Ruth Leiser (Officer-Compliance)
Randy Ringsdorf (Asst VP)

NORTHWEST FIRESTOP
6419 Monroe St, Sylvania, OH 43560
Tel.: (419) 517-4777
Web Site: http://www.northwestfirestop.com
Year Founded: 2002
Sales Range: $1-9.9 Million
Emp.: 2
Construction Services
N.A.I.C.S.: 238990
James House (Pres)

NORTHWEST FLORIDA COMMUNITY HOSPITAL
1360 Brickyard Rd, Chipley, FL 32428
Tel.: (850) 638-1610
Web Site: http://www.nfch.org
Year Founded: 1951
Sales Range: $50-74.9 Million
Emp.: 212
Critical Access Hospital & Long-Term Care Facility
N.A.I.C.S.: 622110
Gabriel E. Berry (Sec & Treas)
Michael Kozar (CEO)

NORTHWEST FRAMING
1964 4th Ave S, Seattle, WA 98134
Tel.: (206) 624-1057
Web Site: http://www.nwframing.com
Year Founded: 1974
Rev.: $10,000,000
Emp.: 15
Picture Framing
N.A.I.C.S.: 339940
Steve L. Dodd (Pres)
Shannon Haley (Mgr)
Rocky Martinez (Dir-Ops)

NORTHWEST FUEL INJECTION SERVICE, INC.
330 N High St, Columbus Grove, OH 45830
Tel.: (419) 659-2124
Web Site: http://www.diesels-r-us.com
Year Founded: 1962
Sales Range: $1-9.9 Million
Emp.: 50
Fuel Injection Systems
N.A.I.C.S.: 811114
Ralph Anderson (Pres)
Subsidiaries:
Northwest Fuel Injection Service of Indiana, L.L.C.   (1)
PO Box 617 114 S Morgan St, Mentone, IN 46539   (100%)
Tel.: (574) 353-7781
Web Site: http://www.diesels-r-us.com
Repairer of Fuel Injection Systems
N.A.I.C.S.: 811114

Northwest Fuel Injection Service of Michigan, LLC   (1)
211 N Jipson St, Blissfield, MI 49228-1167   (100%)
Tel.: (517) 486-4324
Web Site: http://www.diesels-r-us.com
Repairer of Fuel Injection Systems
N.A.I.C.S.: 811114

Lynnette Layman (Office Mgr)

NORTHWEST GEORGIA ONCOLOGY SUPPLY
340 Kennestone Hospital Blvd Ste 200, Marietta, GA 30060-1173
Tel.: (770) 281-5100
Web Site: http://www.ngoc.com
Rev.: $10,000,000
Emp.: 50
Medical & Hospital Equipment
N.A.I.C.S.: 423450
Robert C. Hermann (Pres)
Scott Parker (CFO)

NORTHWEST GRAIN GROWERS, INC.
850 N 4th Ave, Walla Walla, WA 99362-0210
Tel.: (509) 525-6510   WA
Web Site: http://www.nwgrgr.com
Sales Range: Less than $1 Million
Emp.: 28
Agricultural Services
N.A.I.C.S.: 424510
Chris Peha (Gen Mgr)

NORTHWEST HANDLING SYSTEMS, INC.
1100 SW 7th St, Renton, WA 98057
Tel.: (425) 255-0500   WA
Web Site: http://www.nwhs.com
Year Founded: 1971
Sales Range: $25-49.9 Million
Emp.: 200
Industrial Machinery & Equipment Distr
N.A.I.C.S.: 423830
James J. Frank (Pres)
Clark Kosty (VP-Fin & Controller)
Brad Marr (Mgr-Dock Field Svc)
Curtis Orr (Mgr-Field Svc)
Jeremy Kipfer (Mgr-Field Svc)
Wayne Puccinelli (Mgr-Field Svc)

NORTHWEST HEALTH CAREERS, LLC
7398 Smoke Ranch Rd, Las Vegas, NV 89128
Tel.: (702) 389-7269   NV
Web Site: http://www.northwestcareercollege.edu
Year Founded: 1997
Sales Range: $10-24.9 Million
Emp.: 100
Educational Support Services
N.A.I.C.S.: 611710
John Kenny (Founder)

NORTHWEST INC.
27016 Knickerbocker Rd, Cleveland, OH 44140
Tel.: (440) 871-2780
Sales Range: $10-24.9 Million
Emp.: 5
Whslr of Lumber & Wood Products
N.A.I.C.S.: 423310
John Gaskell (Pres)

NORTHWEST INSULATION CO. INC.
204 E Wilson St, Borger, TX 79007
Tel.: (806) 274-7324
Web Site: http://www.nwinsulation.com
Sales Range: $10-24.9 Million
Emp.: 50
Insulation Of Pipes & Boilers
N.A.I.C.S.: 238990
John D. Kaplan (Pres)

NORTHWEST IOWA POWER COOPERATIVE
31002 C38, Le Mars, IA 51031
Tel.: (712) 546-4141   IA

Web Site: http://www.nipco.coop
Year Founded: 1949
Sales Range: $75-99.9 Million
Emp.: 47
Electric Power Distr
N.A.I.C.S.: 221121
Steven J. Ver Mulm (VP-Engrg & Ops)
Matthew R. Washburn (Exec VP & Gen Mgr)
Jane Scheitler (CFO)

NORTHWEST IOWA SYMPHONY ORCHESTRA
498 4th Ave NW, Sioux Center, IA 51250
Tel.: (712) 722-6230
Sales Range: Less than $1 Million
Emp.: 50
Symphony Orchestra
N.A.I.C.S.: 813990
James Koldenhoven (Gen Mgr)
Bernie Weitenaar (Pres)

NORTHWEST JUSTICE PROJECT
401 2nd Ave S Ste 407, Seattle, WA 98104
Tel.: (206) 464-1519   WA
Web Site: http://www.nwjustice.org
Year Founded: 1995
Sales Range: $10-24.9 Million
Emp.: 235
Law firm
N.A.I.C.S.: 541199
Deborah Perluss (Gen Counsel & Dir-Advocacy)
Joan Kleinberg (Dir-Strategic Initiatives)
Steve Pelletier (Dir-Fin)
Susan Encherman (Dir-Admin)
Vicente Omar Barraza (Vice Chm)
Diana Bob (Treas)
Carolyn Estrada (Sec)
Karen Holland (Dir-HR)
Bryan Baker (Dir-Dev)

NORTHWEST KIDNEY CENTERS
700 Broadway, Seattle, WA 98122
Tel.: (206) 292-2707   WA
Web Site: http://www.nwkidney.org
Year Founded: 1962
Sales Range: $75-99.9 Million
Emp.: 620
Health Care Srvices
N.A.I.C.S.: 622110
Connie Anderson (VP-Clinical Ops)
Betsy Mickel (VP-HR)
Austin T. Ross (VP-Plng)
Suzanne Watnick (Chief Medical Officer)
Paramita Mukherjee (Dir-Medical-Auburn Dialysis Center)
Frank Fung (Dir-Medical-Renton Dialysis Center)
Chris Matala (Dir-Supply Chain)
Heather Johnson (Dir-Clinical)
Jayson Hood (Dir-Clinical)
Bob Peck (VP-HR)
Jane Pryor (VP-Dev & PR)

NORTHWEST LOGISTICS INC.
1125 40th St Ste B, Woodward, OK 73801
Tel.: (580) 254-5441
Web Site: http://www.nwlogistics.com
Year Founded: 1968
Sales Range: $10-24.9 Million
Emp.: 75
Logistics & Transportation
N.A.I.C.S.: 488510
Andy Hodges (Owner)

NORTHWEST NEW JERSEY

COMMUNITY ACTION PROGRAM
350 Marshall St, Phillipsburg, NJ 08865
Tel.: (908) 454-7000   NJ
Web Site: http://www.norwescap.org
Year Founded: 1965
Sales Range: $10-24.9 Million
Community Action Services
N.A.I.C.S.: 624190
Terry Newhard (CEO)
MaryLou Schnurr (Chm)
Elycia Lerman (Vice Chm & Sec)
James Buehler (Deputy Treas)
Patrick Grogan (Assoc Dir)
Thomas Pepe (Treas)
Maritza Baakman (Sec)
Cornelio Montejo (Chief Fiscal Officer)
Terry Nerhardt (CEO)

NORTHWEST NEWS CO., INC.
1701 Rankin St, Missoula, MT 59808-1629
Tel.: (406) 721-7801   MT
Web Site: http://www.bngmsla.com
Year Founded: 1971
Books, Periodicals & Newspapers Distr
N.A.I.C.S.: 424920
Peter Bintz (Marketing Director)
Jim Sanborn (Dir-Book Ops)

NORTHWEST OIL & GAS TRADING COMPANY, INC.
4650 Wedekind Rd Ste 2, Sparks, NV 89431
Tel.: (775) 882-7549   NV
Web Site: http://www.nwoil.org
Year Founded: 2017
Assets: $1,020
Liabilities: $323,926
Net Worth: ($322,906)
Earnings: ($305,364)
Emp.: 2
Fiscal Year-end: 05/31/19
Oil & Gas Exploration Services
N.A.I.C.S.: 213112
Joachim Haas (Pres & CEO)
Thomas Hoeder (CFO)

NORTHWEST OIL COMPANY INC
210 N Elliott Ave, Aurora, MO 65605
Tel.: (417) 678-2604   AR
Sales Range: $10-24.9 Million
Emp.: 3
Petroleum Products
N.A.I.C.S.: 424710
Butch Roberson (Owner)

NORTHWEST PACKAGING INC.
1996 Univ Ave W, Saint Paul, MN 55104
Tel.: (651) 649-1040
Web Site: http://www.nwpkg.com
Sales Range: $10-24.9 Million
Emp.: 55
Mfr of Corrugated Boxes Made From Purchased Materials
N.A.I.C.S.: 322211
Karen Gerr (Office Mgr)

NORTHWEST PACKING COMPANY INC.
1701 W 16th St, Vancouver, WA 98660
Tel.: (360) 696-4356   OR
Web Site: http://www.neiljonesfoodcompanies.com
Year Founded: 1980
Sales Range: $25-49.9 Million
Emp.: 152

Canned Fruits & Specialties
N.A.I.C.S.: 311421
Mark Mahoney (Mgr-Sls-East)
Bernie Cook (Mgr-Sls-Central)
Bahman Dejbod (Dir-Intl Bus)
Renata Muller (Dir-Retail Sls)
Ed Astley (Mgr-Natl Accts-East)

NORTHWEST PET PRODUCTS INC.
350 N Pekin Rd, Woodland, WA 98674
Tel.: (360) 225-8855
Rev.: $43,033,153
Emp.: 45
Dog Food
N.A.I.C.S.: 311111

NORTHWEST PIPE FITTINGS, INC.
33 S 8th St W, Billings, MT 59102-5840
Tel.: (406) 252-0142   DE
Web Site: http://www.northwestpipe.net
Year Founded: 1957
Sales Range: $75-99.9 Million
Emp.: 140
Mfr of Plumbing & Heating Supplies
N.A.I.C.S.: 423720
Randy Bentley (Pres-Belgrade)
Greg Peterson (CFO)

NORTHWEST PLAN SERVICES, INC.
5446 California Ave SW Ste 200, Seattle, WA 98136
Tel.: (206) 933-1500   WA
Web Site: http://www.nwp401k.com
Year Founded: 1994
Retirement Plan Administration Services
N.A.I.C.S.: 524292
Rick Howell (Principal)
Tim Wulfekuhle (Pres & CEO)
Tom O'Brien (VP)
Rob Dent (VP-Client Svcs)
Jennifer Clark (VP-Participant Svcs)
Jim Overton (VP-Large Plan Ops)
Erich von Bereghy (Dir-Southeast)
Rolf Trautmann (Principal)
Sean Powell (Dir-Mid-Atlantic & NE)
Shanley Johndrow (VP-Client Svcs-Mill Creek)

Subsidiaries:

CDM Retirement Consultants, Inc.   (1)
300 E Joppa Rd Ste 601, Towson, MD 21286
Tel.: (410) 823-3788
Web Site: http://www.cdmretirement.com
Emp.: 30
Retirement Plan Administration Services
N.A.I.C.S.: 524292
Virginia McGinnis (Co-Owner)
Jim Keenehan (Dir-Bus Dev)

Kaufmann & Goble Associates, Inc.   (1)
160 W Santa Clara St Ste 1550, San Jose, CA 95113
Tel.: (408) 298-1170
Human Resources, Employee Benefits Consultancy & Recordkeeping Services
N.A.I.C.S.: 541612
Sid Kaufmann (Founder)

Trautmann, Maher & Associates, Inc.   (1)
15130 Main St Ste 300, Mill Creek, WA 98012   (100%)
Tel.: (425) 742-0177
Web Site: http://www.trautmannmaher.com
Sales Range: $1-9.9 Million
Emp.: 30
Retirement Plan Consulting & Administration Services
N.A.I.C.S.: 524298

Dennis Maher (VP)
Rolf Trautmann (VP)

Venuti & Associates   (1)
1975 W El Camino Real Ste 206, Mountain View, CA 94040
Tel.: (650) 960-5700
Web Site: http://www.venutiassociates.com
Actuarial Consulting Services
N.A.I.C.S.: 541612
David Venuti (Pres)

NORTHWEST RESTAURANTS
18815 139th Ave Ne Ste C, Woodinville, WA 98072-3565
Tel.: (425) 486-6336
Sales Range: $25-49.9 Million
Emp.: 900
Fast-Food Restaurant Holdings
N.A.I.C.S.: 722513
Sam Sibert (Owner)
Dawn Edwards (Controller)

NORTHWEST SENIOR & DISABILITY SERVICES
3410 Cherry Ave NE, Salem, OR 97309
Tel.: (503) 304-3400
Web Site: http://www.nwsds.org
Year Founded: 1982
Rev.: $15,476,379
Emp.: 250
Aging & Disability Services
N.A.I.C.S.: 923130
Mike Propes (Vice Chm)
Kathy George (Chm)

NORTHWEST STAFFING RESOURCES INC.
700 SW Taylor St Ste 200, Portland, OR 97205-2133
Tel.: (503) 323-9190   OR
Web Site: http://www.nwstaffing.com
Year Founded: 1985
Sales Range: $25-49.9 Million
Emp.: 70
Help Supply Services
N.A.I.C.S.: 561320
Kristen McConnell (Mgr-Portland)
Amy Marconi (Mgr-Beaverton)
Jennie Taylor (Gen Mgr)

NORTHWEST STEEL & PIPE INC.
4802 S Park St, Tacoma, WA 98409
Tel.: (253) 473-8888
Web Site: http://www.nwsteel.net
Rev.: $11,600,000
Emp.: 45
Metal Service Centers & Other Metal Merchant Whslr
N.A.I.C.S.: 423510
Brian Wax (Treas)
Jeff Wax (Sec)
Michael C. Wax (Pres)

NORTHWEST STRATEGIES
441 W 5th Ave Ste 500, Anchorage, AK 99501
Tel.: (907) 563-4881   AK
Web Site: http://www.nwstrat.com
Year Founded: 1987
Sales Range: $1-9.9 Million
Emp.: 25
Public Relations Agency
N.A.I.C.S.: 541820
Tim Woolston (Owner & CEO)
Amanda Combs (Acct Exec)
Tiffany Tutiakoff (Pres)

NORTHWEST SUPPLY COMPANY INC.
4006 McFarland Blvd, Northport, AL 35476
Tel.: (205) 339-2892
Rev.: $11,000,000
Emp.: 35
Plumbing & Hydronic Heating Supplies
N.A.I.C.S.: 423830

NORTHWEST SUPPLY COMPANY INC.

Northwest Supply Company Inc.—(Continued)
Leon Kemp (Pres)

NORTHWEST TERRITORIAL MINT, LLC.
80 E Airpark Vista Blvd, Dayton, NV 89403
Tel.: (775) 246-6000
Web Site: http://www.nwtmint.com
Year Founded: 1984
Sales Range: $200-249.9 Million
Emp.: 230
Fabricated Metal Products Mfr
N.A.I.C.S.: 332999
Ross Hansen (Founder)

NORTHWEST TIRE & SERVICE INC.
3425 W Pierson Rd Ste 1, Flint, MI 48504
Tel.: (810) 785-1633
Web Site: http://www.northwesttire.com
Rev.: $12,812,026
Emp.: 10
Automotive Tires
N.A.I.C.S.: 441340
A.J Faught (Owner)
Jack Schrader (Controller)

NORTHWEST TOBACCO & CANDY CO.
612 W Cener St, Fayetteville, AR 72701-5028
Tel.: (479) 442-6546   AR
Year Founded: 1960
Sales Range: $1-9.9 Million
Emp.: 11
Wholesale Distributor of Tobacco, Tobacco Products & Candy
N.A.I.C.S.: 424940
Mike Stockburger (Gen Mgr)

NORTHWEST WATER HEATER INC.
3909 196th St SW, Lynnwood, WA 98036
Tel.: (206) 282-4700   WA
Web Site: http://www.washingtonenergy.com
Year Founded: 1980
Sales Range: $25-49.9 Million
Emp.: 295
Provider of Plumbing, Heating & Air-Conditioning Services
N.A.I.C.S.: 238220
Craig Olson (CEO)
Tamara Davis (Mgr-Ops)

Subsidiaries:

Washington Energy Services Company Inc.   (1)
3909 196th St SW, Lynnwood, WA 98036
Tel.: (206) 282-4700
Web Site: http://www.wyeth.com
Sales Range: $50-74.9 Million
Emp.: 250
Mfr of Plumbing Fixtures & Equipment
N.A.I.C.S.: 423720
Craig Olson (Pres & CEO)

NORTHWEST WEB CO.
3453 Cascade Ter, West Linn, OR 97068-9269
Tel.: (541) 345-0552
Web Site: http://www.northwestweb.net
Sales Range: $10-24.9 Million
Emp.: 60
Offset Printing
N.A.I.C.S.: 323111
Mark Marth (CEO)
Chad Greene (Mgr-Data)
John Morgan (Mgr-Prepress)
Tim Crocker (Pres)
Jack Anderson (Mgr-Shipping)

NORTHWEST WHOLESALE INC.
1567 N Wenatchee Ave, Wenatchee, WA 98801-1156
Tel.: (509) 662-2141   WA
Web Site: http://www.nwwinc.com
Year Founded: 1937
Sales Range: $10-24.9 Million
Emp.: 48
Farm Supplies
N.A.I.C.S.: 424910
Ken Knappert (Gen Mgr)
Chuck Rix (Mgr-Pkg Sls)

NORTHWESTERN BANCSHARES, INC.
4 N Main St, Dilworth, MN 56529
Tel.: (218) 287-2311   MN
Web Site: http://www.nwbanks.com
Year Founded: 1941
Sales Range: $1-9.9 Million
Emp.: 43
Bank Holding Company
N.A.I.C.S.: 551111
John Satrom (Pres & CEO)
Ladd Lyngaas (Exec VP-Bus Banking)

Subsidiaries:

Northwestern Bank, N.A.   (1)
4 N Main St, Dilworth, MN 56529
Tel.: (218) 287-2311
Web Site: http://www.nwbanks.com
Emp.: 15
Federal Savings Bank
N.A.I.C.S.: 522180
John Satrom (Pres & CEO)
Ladd Lyngaas (Exec VP-Bus Banking)
Jodie Schimek (Officer-Bus Banking)

NORTHWESTERN BANK
202 N Brige St, Chippewa Falls, WI 54729
Tel.: (715) 723-4461   WI
Web Site: http://www.northwesternbank.com
Year Founded: 1904
Sales Range: $10-24.9 Million
Emp.: 95
Banking Services
N.A.I.C.S.: 522110
Gerald Jacobson (Pres)
Jerry Kuehl (Sr VP)

NORTHWESTERN COUNSELING & SUPPORT SERVICES, INC.
107 Fisher Pond Rd, Saint Albans, VT 05478
Tel.: (802) 524-6554   VT
Web Site: http://www.ncssinc.org
Year Founded: 1958
Sales Range: $25-49.9 Million
Emp.: 530
Behavioral Healthcare Services
N.A.I.C.S.: 621420
Ted Mable (Exec Dir)
Amy Putnam (Dir-Fin & Admin)
Tony Treanor (Dir-HR)
Joe Halko (Dir-Community Rels)
Kim McClellan (COO & Dir-Ops)
Tim Gallagan (CFO & Dir-Fin)
Kathleen Brown (Dir-Dev Svcs)
Steve Broer (Dir-Behavioral Health Svcs)

NORTHWESTERN ELECTRIC COOPERATIVE, INC.
2925 Williams Ave, Woodward, OK 73801
Tel.: (580) 256-7425
Web Site: http://www.nwecok.coop
Sales Range: $10-24.9 Million
Emp.: 50
Distribution, Electric Power
N.A.I.C.S.: 221122

Curt Cloyd (Mgr-IT)
Jonna Hensley (Coord-Member Svcs & Comm)

NORTHWESTERN ENGINEERING COMPANY
314 Founders Pk Dr, Rapid City, SD 57701
Tel.: (605) 394-3310   SD
Web Site: http://www.nwemanagement.com
Year Founded: 1927
Sales Range: $10-24.9 Million
Holding Company Real Estate Management & Development Services
N.A.I.C.S.: 551112
Patrick A. Tlustos (Pres)
David Crabb (CFO)
James D. Adelstein (Exec VP)

Subsidiaries:

Hills Products Group, Inc.   (1)
4025 E Colorado Blvd, Spearfish, SD 57783
(100%)
Tel.: (605) 394-3310
Web Site: http://www.hillsproductsgroup.com
Sales Range: $10-24.9 Million
Emp.: 100
Producer of Building Materials & Related Products
N.A.I.C.S.: 321113
Stanford M. Adelstein (Chm)
Mark Balding (Gen Mgr)

NWE Management Company   (1)
PO Box 2624, Rapid City, SD 57709
(100%)
Tel.: (605) 394-3310
Web Site: http://www.nwemanagement.com
Sales Range: Less than $1 Million
Emp.: 20
Real Estate Management
N.A.I.C.S.: 532412
Stanford Adelstein (Pres)
Pat Thustos (CEO)
David Crabb (CFO)
Steve Colgan (Mng Dir)
Brad Hammerback (COO)

NORTHWESTERN MEAT, INC.
2100 NW 23rd St, Miami, FL 33142-8454
Tel.: (305) 633-8112   FL
Web Site: http://www.numeat.com
Year Founded: 1961
Sales Range: $75-99.9 Million
Emp.: 145
Wholesaler, Importer & Exporter of Meat, Poultry & Seafood
N.A.I.C.S.: 424470
Elpidio Nunez Ojeda (Founder & CEO)
Olga M. Nunez (Pres & Mgr-Pur & Sls)

Subsidiaries:

Northwestern Selecta, Inc.   (1)
599 Calle 15 NW, San Juan, PR 00920
Tel.: (787) 781-1950
Web Site: http://www.northwesternselecta.com
Sales Range: $50-74.9 Million
Emp.: 400
Meat Product Whslr
N.A.I.C.S.: 424420

NORTHWESTERN MEDICAL CENTER, INC.
133 Fairfield St, Saint Albans, VT 05478
Tel.: (802) 524-5911   VT
Web Site: http://www.northwesternmedicalcenter.org
Year Founded: 1977
Sales Range: $75-99.9 Million
Emp.: 687
Health Care Srvices
N.A.I.C.S.: 622110

Jonathan Billings (VP-Plng & Community Rels)
Jane Catton (COO & Sr VP)
Joel Benware (VP-Info Sys & Compliance)
Lowrey Sullivan (Chief Medical Officer)
Jill Berry Bowen (CEO)
Bill O'Connor (Sec)
Kevin Manahan (Treas)

NORTHWESTERN MEMORIAL HEALTHCARE
251 E Huron St, Chicago, IL 60611-2908
Tel.: (312) 926-6363
Web Site: http://www.nmh.org
Sales Range: $25-49.9 Million
Emp.: 6,464
Hospital & Health Care Operations
N.A.I.C.S.: 622110
Megan McCann (Mgr-Media Rels)
John A. Orsini (CFO & Sr VP)
Firas Wehbe (Chief Res Informatics Officer-Feinberg School of Medicine)

Subsidiaries:

CDH-Delnor Health System, Inc.   (1)
25 N Winfield Rd, Winfield, IL 60190
Tel.: (630) 315-8000
Web Site: http://www.cadencehealth.org
Hospital & Health Care Management Services; Hospital & Specialty Outpatient Clinic Operations
N.A.I.C.S.: 622110
Michael Vivoda (Pres-Western Reg)
Debra O'Donnell (VP & Chief Nursing Officer)
Drew Palumbo (VP-Ambulatory & Physician Svcs)

Unit (Domestic):

Behavioral Health Services   (2)
27 W 350 High Lake Rd, Winfield, IL 60190-1262
(100%)
Tel.: (630) 933-4000
Web Site: http://www.cdh.org
Sales Range: $10-24.9 Million
Emp.: 100
Outpatient Alcohol/Mental Health Treatment Services
N.A.I.C.S.: 621498

Subsidiary (Domestic):

Central DuPage Hospital Association   (2)
25 N Winfield Rd, Winfield, IL 60190-1227
(100%)
Tel.: (630) 213-9600
Web Site: http://www.nm.org
General In-Patient Hospital Services
N.A.I.C.S.: 622110
Kevin P. Most (Chief Medical Officer & VP-Medical Affairs)
Brian Lemon (Pres)
Julia Nelson (Sr Dir-Diagnostic & Interventional Imaging)

Delnor-Community Hospital   (2)
300 Randall Rd, Geneva, IL 60134
Tel.: (630) 208-3000
Web Site: http://www.cadencehealth.org
Hospital
N.A.I.C.S.: 622110
Maureen Bryant (Pres)
Danna Baer (Mgr-Gift Shop)

Joint Venture (Domestic):

HealthTrack Sports & Wellness, LLC   (2)
875 Roosevelt Rd, Glen Ellyn, IL 60137-6168
Tel.: (630) 942-9600
Web Site: http://www.htsw.net
Fitness & Wellness Facility
N.A.I.C.S.: 713940
Cris Castillo (Gen Mgr)
Jill Feitl (Mgr-Web Site Dev & Internet Mktg)
Sue Kamphuis (Dir-Sls & Mktg)
Peggy Hayley (Dir-Programs)

COMPANIES

Northwestern Medical Faculty Foundation, Inc. (1)
680 N Lake Shore Dr Ste 1118, Chicago, IL 60611
Tel.: (312) 695-1920
Web Site: http://www.nmff.org
Sales Range: $10-24.9 Million
Emp.: 200
Medical Education Services
N.A.I.C.S.: 611310
James L. Schroeder (Pres & CEO)

Northwestern Memorial Foundation (1)
251 E Huron Ste 3-200 Galter Pavilion, Chicago, IL 60611
Tel.: (312) 926-2033
Web Site: http://foundation.nmh.org
Sales Range: $10-24.9 Million
Emp.: 75
Medical Foundation
N.A.I.C.S.: 813211
Aurora Calzolaio (Dir-Prospect Res)
Holly Gibout (VP)
Jean Kostelansky (Dir-Clinical Affairs)
Kathryn Michael (Dir-Annual Giving)
Ann E. Murray (Dir-Philanthropy)
Emma Partridge (Coord-Philanthropy)
Leslie Post-Weissinger (Dir-Philanthropy)
David Sack (VP)
Sean Sullivan (Coord-Benefactor Rels)
Betty Sweetland (Dir-Ops)

Northwestern Memorial Home Health Care (1)
680 N Lk Shore Dr Ste 1316, Chicago, IL 60611
Tel.: (312) 926-2000
Web Site: http://www.nm.org
Emp.: 2,100
Women Healthcare Services
N.A.I.C.S.: 621610
Dean M. Harrison (Pres & CEO)
Mary Golf (Coord-Pharmacy Practice)
Jean Kostelansky (Dir-Clinical Affairs)
Mariquita Sumague (Head-Res)
Nicole Willis (Mgr-Adult Respiratory Care & Blood Gas Svcs)
Theresa Falcon (Mgr-Performance)
Peter McCanna (COO & Exec VP)

Northwestern Memorial Hospital (1)
251 E Huron, Chicago, IL 60611
Tel.: (312) 926-2000
Web Site: http://www.nmh.org
Emp.: 6,000
Hospital
N.A.I.C.S.: 622110
Peter McCanna (COO & Exec VP)
Larry D. Richman (Chm)

Northwestern Memorial Physicians Group (1)
201 E Huron 12th Fl Ste 105, Chicago, IL 60611
Tel.: (312) 926-3627
Web Site: http://www.nm.org
Physicians Office
N.A.I.C.S.: 621111
Daniel M. Derman (Pres)

NORTHWESTERN REGION EMPLOYEE BENEFIT TRUST
252 Waterford St, Edinboro, PA 16412
Tel.: (814) 734-5610   PA
Web Site: http://www.norebt.org
Year Founded: 1993
Sales Range: $50-74.9 Million
Health & Welfare Benefits Services
N.A.I.C.S.: 525120
Barbara DeJesus (Treas)
Susan Fisher (Vice Chm)
Laura Urban (Chm)

NORTHWESTERN WISCONSIN ELECTRIC CO.
104 S Pine St, Grantsburg, WI 54840
Tel.: (715) 463-5371
Web Site: http://www.nweco.com
Sales Range: $10-24.9 Million
Emp.: 46
Electric Power Distr
N.A.I.C.S.: 221122
David Dahlberg (Pres)

NORTHWIND INVESTMENTS INC.
109 E Broadway St, Mount Pleasant, MI 48858
Tel.: (989) 772-2600
Sales Range: $25-49.9 Million
Emp.: 5
Fast-Food Restaurant, Independent
N.A.I.C.S.: 722513
Kevin Egnatuk (Pres & CEO)
Marcia Cronk (Dir-HR)
Greg Johnroe (Controller)

NORTHWOOD AUTO PLAZA INC.
212 7th St, Eureka, CA 95501
Tel.: (707) 443-4861
Web Site: http://www.northwoodchevy.com
Sales Range: $10-24.9 Million
Emp.: 25
Automobiles, New & Used
N.A.I.C.S.: 441120
Lenore J. Dias (CFO)
Mark Dias (Pres)
Tammy Stemwedel (Controller)

NORTHWOOD EQUITY ELEVATOR CO.
600 Lander Ave, Northwood, ND 58267
Tel.: (701) 587-5291
Web Site: http://www.northwoodequity.com
Sales Range: $10-24.9 Million
Emp.: 25
Grain Elevators
N.A.I.C.S.: 424510
Scott Ostlie (Mgr)

NORTHWOOD FOODS INC.
1105 8th St N, Northwood, IA 50459
Tel.: (641) 324-1466
Web Site: http://www.northwoodfoods.net
Rev.: $50,000,000
Emp.: 90
Animal Slaughtering
N.A.I.C.S.: 311611
Brian Burkard (Pres)
Kristy Meyer (Coord-Freight)
Michele Schaefer (Office Mgr)

NORTHWOOD HEALTH SYSTEMS
111 19th St, Wheeling, WV 26003
Tel.: (304) 843-7860   WV
Web Site: http://www.northwoodhealth.com
Year Founded: 1967
Sales Range: $10-24.9 Million
Emp.: 565
Behavioral Healthcare Services
N.A.I.C.S.: 621420
Tom Dzmura (Dir-IT)
Steve Corder (Dir-Medical)
Richard D. Stockley (CFO)
Tina Derksen (Controller)

NORTHWOOD INVESTMENT CORPORATION
59948 Downs Rd, La Grande, OR 97850
Tel.: (541) 962-6274
Web Site: http://www.northwoodmfg.com
Year Founded: 1990
Sales Range: $10-24.9 Million
Emp.: 200
Provider of Travel Trailers & Campers
N.A.I.C.S.: 336214
Craig Orton (Pres & CEO)

Subsidiaries:

Northwood Homes Incorporated (1)
59948 Downs Rd, La Grande, OR 97850-8453
Tel.: (541) 962-6274
Web Site: http://www.northwoodmfg.com
Sales Range: $10-24.9 Million
Emp.: 5
Provider of Mobile Home Dealer Services
N.A.I.C.S.: 336214
Ron Nash (Pres)

Northwood Manufacturing, Inc. (1)
59948 Downs Rd, La Grande, OR 97850
Tel.: (541) 962-6274
Web Site: http://www.northwoodmfg.com
Travel Trailers & Camper Mfr
N.A.I.C.S.: 336214

NORTHWOOD INVESTORS, LLC
575 Fifth Ave 23rd Fl, New York, NY 10017
Tel.: (212) 573-0800
Web Site: http://www.northwoodinvestors.com
Emp.: 50
N.A.I.C.S.:
John Z. Kukral (Pres & CEO)
Erwin K. Aulis (COO)
Khaled W. Kudsi (Sr Mng Dir)
Jerome Anselme (Mng Dir)
Ross M. Cowan (Sr Mng Dir)
Michael M. O'Shaughnessy (Mng Dir)
Brady A. Thurman (Mng Dir)
Brian Crittendon (Mng Dir)
James E. Rehlaender (CEO)
Wendi Clarke (Dir-HR)
Cheryl Dallos (Dir-HR)
Bryan Barbieri (VP-PR)
Steve Gordon (Sr VP-ECommerce)
Nicole Spillane (Sr VP-Mktg)
Nizar Adeeb (VP-Sls)
Heather Paduck (CFO)
Thomas McGrath (Chief Compliance Officer)
Brent Reid (Exec VP-Fin)
Bob Frost (Exec VP-HR)
Jordan Kornberg (Mng Dir)
Marshall W. Nevins (Mng Dir)
Shiva Viswanathan (Mng Dir)
Kelvin Zen Tak Cheng (Sr VP)
Kuan Cheung Sin (Sr VP)
Maarten van den Brink (Sr VP)
Yvo Timmermans (Sr VP)
Gabir Boyer (Sr VP-Fin & Asset Mgmt)
Andrew Smith (VP)
Daniel M. Palmieri (VP)
James W. Geskey (VP)
Jennifer Davis (VP)
Jenny Buttrick (VP)
Nick Turner (VP)
Olivier Marguin (VP)
Richard Pellatt (VP)
Richard Strachan (VP)
Scott Barnaik (VP-Hotel Acctg Svcs)

Subsidiaries:

Vitura (1)
42 rue de Bassano, 75008, Paris, France
Tel.: (33) 142257642
Web Site: https://vitura.fr
Rev.: $58,328,297
Assets: $1,752,867,472
Liabilities: $937,587,956
Net Worth: $815,279,517
Earnings: ($4,514,354)
Emp.: 3
Fiscal Year-end: 12/31/2022
Property Investment Services
N.A.I.C.S.: 523940
Jerome Anselme (CEO)
Sophie Kramer (Mgr-Asset)
Olivier Marguin (Head-Asset Mgmt)
Charlotte de Laroche (Fin Mgr)
John Z. Kukral (Chm)

NORTON CONSTRUCTION CO.
6055 Rockside Woods Blvd, Cleveland, OH 44131
Tel.: (216) 447-0070
Sales Range: $10-24.9 Million
Emp.: 10
Land Preparation Construction
N.A.I.C.S.: 236210
Steven Viny (Partner)
Lane Lisy (Sec)
Wynn Gerber (Controller)
Joseph Balog (Pres)

NORTON HEALTHCARE, INC.
234 E Gray St Ste 450, Louisville, KY 40202
Tel.: (502) 629-8060   KY
Web Site: http://www.nortonhealthcare.com
Year Founded: 1886
Rev.: $2,370,778,000
Assets: $3,163,248,000
Liabilities: $617,620,000
Net Worth: $2,545,628,000
Earnings: $251,932,000
Fiscal Year-end: 12/31/18
Hospital Owner & Operator
N.A.I.C.S.: 622110
Russell F. Cox (Pres & CEO)
Michael W. Gough (COO & Exec VP)
Steven T. Hester (Chief Medical Officer & Pres-Provider Ops & Sys)
Tracy E. Williams (Chief Nursing Dev & Learning Officer & Sr VP)
Steve L. Ready (CIO & Sr VP)
Dana Allen (Chief Mktg & Comm Officer & Sr VP)
Robert B. Azar (Chief Legal Officer & Sr VP)
Mary Jo Bean (Sr VP-Plng & Bus Analysis)
Thomas W. Johnson (Chief Comm Officer & VP-PR)
Edie Nixon (Vice Chm)
Douglas A. Winkelhake (Pres-Hospital Ops)
Charlotte Ipsan (Chief Admin Officer-Norton Women's & Children Hospital)
Scott Watkins (Sr VP-Ops)
Lynnie Meyer (Chief Dev Officer & Sr VP)
Ronald C. Oliver (Sr VP-Mission & Outreach)
Matthew P. Ayers (Chief Admin Officer-Norton Hospital)
Riggs Lewis (VP-Sys-Health Policy)
Andrew Strausbaugh (Chief Admin Officer-Brownsboro Hospital)
Joseph M. Flynn (Chief Admin Officer-Norton Medical Grp)
Mureena Turnquest Wells (Mng Dir)
Brian Posnansky (Mng Dir)
Angela Cox (Mng Dir)
Amanda W. Carter (Mng Dir)
Nabil Dada (Mng Dir)
Sarah Hargrave (Mng Dir)
Jennifer Howard Tasman (Mng Dir)
Handel Jones (Mng Dir)
George Calvert (Mng Dir)
Antony Hazel (Mng Dir)
Libby Mims (Mng Dir)
Jill Blandford (Mng Dir)
Arpit Agrawal (Mng Dir)
Kristine Holthouser (Mng Dir)
Kimberly A. Case (Mng Dir)
Sarah Price (Mng Dir)
David Bercovici (Mng Dir)
Laura Chandler (VP-Sys-Admin & Governance)
Kari J. Zahorik (Mng Dir)
Edward Dunn (Mng Dir)
Crystal Narcisse (Mng Dir)
Benjamin Lerner (Mng Dir)
Allegra Saving (Mng Dir)
Shaun Madahar (Mng Dir)
Marcella D. Perez (Mng Dir)
Emmett C. Ramser (Chief Admin Officer)
Kelly McCants (Exec Dir-Healthcare Institute-Health Equity & Dir-Medical)

NORTON HEALTHCARE, INC.

U.S. PRIVATE

Norton Healthcare, Inc.—(Continued)
Gladys Lopez *(Chief HR Officer & Sr VP)*
Adam D. Kempf *(CFO & Sr VP)*
Steve Heilman *(Chief Health Innovation Officer & Sr VP)*
Randy Hamilton *(Chief Admin Officer-Audubon Hospital)*
Vanessa L. Garrett *(Officer-Compliance, Audit & Sys Privacy)*

NORTON INDUSTRIES
20670 Corsair Blvd, Hayward, CA 94545
Tel.: (510) 786-3638   CA
Web Site: http://www.nortonpackaging.com
Year Founded: 1966
Plastic Pail Mfr
N.A.I.C.S.: 326199
Howard C. Norton *(Pres)*

NORTON LILLY INTERNATIONAL INC.
1 Saint Louis Ctr Ste 5000, Mobile, AL 36602
Tel.: (251) 431-6335
Web Site: http://www.nortonlilly.com
Year Founded: 1841
Sales Range: $10-24.9 Million
Emp.: 300
Shipping Services
N.A.I.C.S.: 488510
Dwain Denniston *(Exec VP)*
Alejandro Barthold *(Pres & CEO)*
Flemming Buhl *(Chief Comml Officer)*
Andreas Ebensperger *(Exec VP)*
Paul Carlton *(Exec VP)*
Steve Haverstock *(Exec VP)*
Patricio Garcia *(CFO)*
H. Winchester Thurber III *(Chm)*

NORTON PACKAGING INC.
20670 Corsair Blvd, Hayward, CA 94545-1008
Tel.: (510) 786-3445   CA
Web Site: http://www.nortonpackaging.com
Year Founded: 1972
Sales Range: $10-24.9 Million
Emp.: 200
Supplier of Plastic Products
N.A.I.C.S.: 332510
Scott Norton *(Co-Pres)*
Alan Fraley *(Controller)*

NORTON SOUND ECONOMIC DEVELOPMENT CORPORATION
2701 Gambell St Ste 400, Anchorage, AK 99503
Tel.: (907) 274-2248
Web Site: http://www.nsedc.com
Year Founded: 1997
Sales Range: $10-24.9 Million
Emp.: 70
Promote & Provide Economic Development in Western Alaska
N.A.I.C.S.: 311710
Janis Ivanoff *(Pres & CEO)*
Dan Harrelson *(Vice Chm)*
Josh Osborne *(Plant Mgr)*
Orville Toolie *(Plant Mgr)*
Tyler Rhodes *(COO)*
Katie Peterson *(Gen Counsel)*
Karl Erickson *(Mgr-Vessel)*
Frank Doty *(Plant Mgr)*
Simon Kinneen *(VP-Quota & Mgr-Acq)*

Subsidiaries:

Norton Sound Seafood Products   (1)
201 Belmont Point, Nome, AK 99762
Tel.: (907) 274-2248

Web Site: http://www.nortonsoundseafood.com
Sales Range: $10-24.9 Million
Cured Canned Seafood Mfr
N.A.I.C.S.: 311710

NORVANCO INTERNATIONAL, INC.
4301 W Vly Hwy E, Sumner, WA 98390
Tel.: (253) 987-4000
Web Site: http://www.norvanco.com
Year Founded: 1976
Sales Range: $75-99.9 Million
Emp.: 100
Customhouse Brokers
N.A.I.C.S.: 488510
Robert Juranich *(Owner)*
Rick Fogle *(Dir-Ops)*
Marcus Moore *(VP-Sls)*

NORWALK AUTO AUCTION
12405 Rosecrans Ave, Norwalk, CA 90650
Tel.: (562) 864-7464
Web Site: http://www.norwalkautoauction.com
Rev.: $37,000,000
Emp.: 125
Automobile & Other Motor Vehicle Merchant Whslr
N.A.I.C.S.: 423110
Ismael Orta *(Mgr-Gen Sls)*
Kelly Gugliuzza *(Mgr-Special Acct)*
Judy Torres *(Mgr-Titles Dept)*
Conrad Dozier *(Mgr)*
Charlie Gonzales *(Mgr)*
Lou Rudich *(COO & Exec VP)*
David Aker *(Controller)*
Gonzalo Rodriguez *(Mgr-Inventory)*

NORWALK COMPRESSOR COMPANY, INC.
1650 Stratford Ave, Stratford, CT 06615-6419
Tel.: (203) 386-1234   CT
Web Site: http://www.norwalkcompressor.com
Year Founded: 1864
Sales Range: $50-74.9 Million
Emp.: 50
Mfr of High & Low Pressure Air & Gas Compressors
N.A.I.C.S.: 333912
Arthur McCauley *(Pres & CEO)*
Mario Perrotta *(Dir-Sls & Mktg)*
Andrew Kremnev *(Dir-Engrg)*

NORWALK CUSTOM ORDER FURNITURE
100 Furniture Pkwy, Norwalk, OH 44857-9587
Tel.: (419) 744-3200   OH
Web Site: http://www.norwalkfurniture.com
Year Founded: 1902
Upholstered Livingroom Furniture & Tables Mfr
N.A.I.C.S.: 337121

NORWALK POWDERED METALS, INC.
1100 Boston Ave Bldg 3, Bridgeport, CT 06610-2654
Tel.: (203) 338-8000   CT
Web Site: http://www.norwalkpm.com
Year Founded: 1958
Rev.: $20,000,000
Emp.: 100
Powdered Metals & Engineered Components Mfr
N.A.I.C.S.: 331221
Thomas A. Blumenthal *(Pres)*
Richard Webb *(VP-Ops)*
Ann Blumenthal *(COO)*

NORWALK READY-MIXED CONCRETE, INC.
1535 N Ave, Norwalk, IA 50211
Tel.: (515) 981-0631   IA
Web Site: http://www.norwalkreadymix.com
Sales Range: $10-24.9 Million
Emp.: 60
Ready Mixed Concrete
N.A.I.C.S.: 327320
Jack D. Bohlender *(Pres)*

NORWAY BANCORP, INC.
261 Main St, Norway, ME 04268
Tel.: (207) 743-7986
Web Site: http://www.norwaysavingsbank.com
Year Founded: 1866
Sales Range: $10-24.9 Million
Emp.: 280
Bank Holding Company
N.A.I.C.S.: 551111
Patricia Weigel *(Pres/CEO-Norway Savings Bank)*

Subsidiaries:

Norway Savings Bank   (1)
261 Main St, Norway, ME 04268
Tel.: (207) 743-7986
Web Site: http://www.norwaysavingsbank.com
Sales Range: $50-74.9 Million
Savings Bank
N.A.I.C.S.: 522180
Ann Brett *(CTO & Sr VP)*
Ian T. Pullen *(Asst VP-Comm)*
Patrica Weigel *(Pres & CEO)*
Scott Smith *(VP & Mgr-Bethel)*
Amanda Dyer *(Mgr-Freeport)*
Gary Bellegarde *(VP-Comml Lending)*

NORWAY HOUSE
913 E Franklin Ave, Minneapolis, MN 55404
Tel.: (612) 871-2211   MN
Web Site: http://www.norwayhouse.org
Year Founded: 2004
Rev.: $1,018,276
Assets: $4,064,296
Liabilities: $2,402,820
Net Worth: $1,661,476
Fiscal Year-end: 12/31/17
Cultural & Art Event Operator
N.A.I.C.S.: 711310
Brian Osberg *(Sec)*
Chelsea Hall *(Office Mgr)*
David Distad *(VP)*
Jeff Mueller *(Dir-Ops)*

NORWELL MANUFACTURING CO., INC.
82 Stevens St, East Taunton, MA 02718-1314
Tel.: (508) 822-5854
Web Site: http://www.norwellinc.com
Rev.: $5,000,000
Emp.: 50
Mfr of Lighting Fixtures
N.A.I.C.S.: 335131
Alan Indursky *(Pres)*
Sharon Evanichko *(Controller)*
Kathy Moniz *(Mgr-Accts Payable)*

NORWEST VENTURE PARTNERS
525 University Ave Ste 800, Palo Alto, CA 94301
Tel.: (650) 321-8000
Web Site: http://www.nvp.com
Rev.: $3,700,000,000
Privater Equity Firm
N.A.I.C.S.: 523999
Sergio Monsalve *(Partner)*
Venkat A. Mohan *(Gen Partner)*
Jon Kossow *(Mng Partner)*
Matthew Howard *(Mng Partner)*
Promod Haque *(Sr Mng Partner)*

Joshua Goldman *(Gen Partner)*
Vab Goel *(Gen Partner)*
Kurt Betcher *(CFO & Partner)*
Robert Abbott *(Gen Partner)*
Sonya Brown *(Gen Partner)*
Ran Ding *(Principal)*
Ed Yip *(VP)*
Parker Barrile *(Partner)*
Lisa Wu *(Partner-Venture Capital)*
Rob Arditi *(Gen Partner)*
Stew Campbell *(Principal)*
Sean Jacobsohn *(Partner)*
Tiba Aynechi *(Gen Partner)*

NORWOOD CO-OPERATIVE BANK
11 Central St, Norwood, MA 02062
Tel.: (781) 762-1800
Web Site: http://www.norwoodbank.com
Year Founded: 1889
Rev.: $16,825,000
Emp.: 58
Commercial Banking Services
N.A.I.C.S.: 522110
Christopher B. Dixon *(Pres & CEO)*
Susan A. Alves *(VP & Mgr-Data Ops)*
Jose DaCunha *(VP & Mgr-Info Sys)*
Karen Goggin *(Treas & VP)*
Carol Berezin *(Branch Mgr)*
Tracey A. Robbins *(VP & Mgr-Residential Lending)*
Philip C. Swan *(VP)*
John Galvani *(Sr VP)*
Carrie Keough *(Sr VP & Mgr-Retail)*
Stephen Mandozzi *(Sr VP-Ops)*
Nancy Folan *(VP-HR & Admin)*

NORWOOD COMMERCIAL CONTRACTORS INC.
214 Park St, Bensenville, IL 60106-2565
Tel.: (630) 595-6200
Web Site: http://norwoodcommercial.com
Sales Range: $10-24.9 Million
Emp.: 15
Civil Engineering Services
N.A.I.C.S.: 237310
Douglas Hudson *(Pres)*

NORWOOD MEDICAL
2122 Winners Cir, Dayton, OH 45404
Tel.: (937) 228-4101
Web Site: http://www.norwoodmedical.com
Sales Range: $10-24.9 Million
Emp.: 220
Metal Medical Device Mfr
N.A.I.C.S.: 339112
Charlie Yoss *(Controller)*
Kenneth J. Hemmelgarn Sr. *(Pres)*

NORWOOD SASH & DOOR MANUFACTURING CO.
4953 Section Ave, Cincinnati, OH 45212
Tel.: (513) 531-5700
Sales Range: $10-24.9 Million
Emp.: 30
Lumber & Other Building Materials
N.A.I.C.S.: 423310

NOS COMMUNICATIONS INC.
250 Pilot Rd Ste 300, Las Vegas, NV 89119-3514
Tel.: (702) 547-8000   MD
Web Site: http://www.nos.com
Year Founded: 1992
Rev.: $195,000,000
Emp.: 400
Provider of Telephone Communications Services
N.A.I.C.S.: 517121
Joe Koppy *(CEO)*

COMPANIES

NOSHOK INC.
1010 W Bagley Rd, Berea, OH 44017
Tel.: (440) 243-0888
Web Site: http://www.noshok.com
Year Founded: 1967
Sales Range: $10-24.9 Million
Emp.: 45
Process Control Instruments Mfr & Distr
N.A.I.C.S.: 334513
Jeff N. Scott (Pres)
Christian F. L. Cole (VP)
Corbin Schmitt (Mgr-Core Accts & Customer Support)
Michael F. Lancaster (Mgr-Engrg)
Michael D. Walker (Mgr-Sls-Western Reg)
Stanley A. Wright (Mgr-Sls-Southwest Reg)
Jeffery C. Dillen (Mgr-Sls-Midwest)
Jeffrey S. Mendrala (CFO)
Sheryl A. Pritt (Mgr-Mktg)
Barry C. Rowley (Mgr-Quality Assurance)
Jason A. Reust (Mgr-Sls-Great Lakes)
Mark Duckworth (Mgr-Sls-Northeast Reg)
Scott A. Mullendore (Mgr-Sls-Southeast)
Gerald M. Hafichuk (Mgr-Sls-Western Canadian)

NOSTALGIA FAMILY BRANDS, INC.
20 Pape Dr, Atlantic Highlands, NJ 07716
Tel.: (732) 291-3661   DE
Year Founded: 2010
Assets: $9,300
Liabilities: $122,633
Net Worth: ($113,333)
Earnings: ($23,661)
Fiscal Year-end: 12/31/18
Discontinued Consumer Brands Retailer
N.A.I.C.S.: 423990
William P. McDermitt (Pres & CEO)
Edward O'Donnell (CFO, Sec & VP)

NOSTALGIC IMAGES INC.
26012 Nostalgic Rd, Defiance, OH 43512
Tel.: (419) 784-1728
Web Site: http://www.nostalgicimages.com
Year Founded: 1985
Sales Range: $10-24.9 Million
Emp.: 10
Fabricated Metal Products Mfr
N.A.I.C.S.: 332999
Jason Westrick (Gen Mgr)

NOTHERN CAPITAL INC.
7200 Corporate Ctr Dr Ste 505, Miami, FL 33126
Year Founded: 2004
Sales Range: $75-99.9 Million
Emp.: 79
Homeowner & Business Insurance
N.A.I.C.S.: 524210
Alex Anthony (Chm & CEO)
Albert Fernandez (Vice Chm & COO)
Wayne Fletcher (Pres)
J. C. Miguelez (VP-Ops & Regulatory Affairs)
Maria DiGiorgio (Gen Counsel & Sec)
Kevin Walton (CFO)

NOTOCO INDUSTRIES LLC
10380 Airline Hwy, Baton Rouge, LA 70816
Tel.: (225) 292-1303
Web Site: http://www.notocoindustries.com
Sales Range: $10-24.9 Million
Emp.: 55
Lighting Fixtures
N.A.I.C.S.: 423610
Norman Born (CFO)
Jeremie Hartzog (Mgr-Credit)

NOTRE DAME FEDERAL CREDIT UNION
6757 Cascade Rd SE Box #210, Grand Rapids, MI
Web Site: httpss://www.notredamefcu.com
Emp.: 200
Financial Services
N.A.I.C.S.: 522130
Thomas Gryp (Pres & CEO)

Subsidiaries:

Mission Management & Trust, Co.   (1)
3567 E Sunrise Dr Ste 235, Tucson, AZ 85718
Tel.: (520) 577-5559
Web Site: http://www.missiontrust.com
Sales Range: $1-9.9 Million
Emp.: 19
Trust, Fiduciary & Custody Activities
N.A.I.C.S.: 523991
Laurel Olson (Pres)
Cynthia Sprague (VP & Dir-Trust Ops)
Rhonda Perez (Controller)

NOTRE DAME HEALTH CARE CENTER, INC.
555-559 Plantation St, Worcester, MA 01605
Tel.: (508) 852-3011   MA
Web Site: http://www.notredamehealthcare.org
Year Founded: 1990
Sales Range: $10-24.9 Million
Emp.: 420
Health Care Srvices
N.A.I.C.S.: 622110
Elizabeth McLaughlin (Treas)
Karen Rizzo (Dir-Hospice)
Margaret Coffin (Exec Dir)
Ellen Agritelley (Chm)
Karen M. Laganelli (CEO)

NOTT COMPANY
4480 Round Lk Rd W, Saint Paul, MN 55112-1961
Tel.: (651) 415-3400   MN
Web Site: http://www.nottco.com
Year Founded: 1939
Sales Range: $25-49.9 Million
Emp.: 150
Distr of Industrial Supplies
N.A.I.C.S.: 423840
Edward Davis (Pres & CEO)
Christy Clark (Chief Admin Officer)
Darrell Babcock (CFO)

NOURIA ENERGY CORP.
326 Clark St, Worcester, MA 01606-1214
Tel.: (508) 762-3700
Web Site: http://www.nouriaenergy.com
Year Founded: 1989
Gasoline Stations & Convenience Stores
N.A.I.C.S.: 457110
Tony El-Nemr (Pres & CEO)
Fouad El-Nemr (Exec VP)
Rich Fusco (CFO)
Joe Hamza (COO)
Tom Healey (VP-Tech Svcs)
Natalya Fater (VP-HR)
Dorothy Fleishman (VP-Real Estate & Bus Dev)
Richard Smith (VP-Carwash Ops)

Subsidiaries:

H. A. Mapes, Inc.   (1)
152 Pleasant St, Springvale, ME 04083
Tel.: (207) 490-2963
Web Site: http://www.hamapes.com
Rev.: $6,100,000
Emp.: 20
Petroleum & Petroleum Products Merchant Wholesalers, except Bulk Stations & Terminals
N.A.I.C.S.: 424720
H. A. Mapes (Pres)

NOURISON RUG CORP.
5 Sampson St, Saddle Brook, NJ 07663-5911
Tel.: (201) 368-6900
Web Site: http://www.nourison.com
Year Founded: 1979
Sales Range: $75-99.9 Million
Emp.: 225
Mfr of Area Rugs
N.A.I.C.S.: 423220
Ron Giampiccolo (VP-E-Commerce)
Jack Nakeshian (Exec Dir-Natl Acct)
Paquette Paula (VP-Soft Home)
Julie Rosenblum (Exec Dir-Licensing)
Gerard O'Keefe (Sr VP-Sls & Production)
Mary Earhart (Acct Exec-North Carolina & South Carolina)
Steven Brandon (Mng Dir-Hospitality-Calhoun)
Giovanni Marra (Dir-Mktg & Digital Strategy)
Jonny Peykar (VP-Hospitality)
Peter Lipkin (VP-Hospitality Sls)
Robert Tucci (Dir-Sls-Natl)

NOVA BIOMEDICAL CORPORATION
200 Prospect St, Waltham, MA 02453-3465
Tel.: (781) 894-0800
Web Site: http://www.novabio.us
Year Founded: 1976
Sales Range: $50-74.9 Million
Emp.: 1,200
Diagnostic Hematology, Electrolytes, Blood Gas Instruments & Supplies Mfr
N.A.I.C.S.: 334516
Ronald Newby (Dir-Mktg)

Subsidiaries:

Nova Biomedical Canada, Ltd.   (1)
17-2900 Argentia Road, Mississauga, L5N 7X9, ON, Canada
Tel.: (905) 567-7700
Web Site: http://www.novabio.us
Medical & Hospital Equipment Whslr
N.A.I.C.S.: 423450

Nova Biomedical GmbH   (1)
Heffring Str Bldg G, 64546, Morfelden-Walldorf, Germany
Tel.: (49) 6074 8448 0
Web Site: http://www.novabiomedical.de
Sales Range: $10-24.9 Million
Emp.: 30
Blood Testing Analyzer Distr
N.A.I.C.S.: 423450
Anne Deutsch (Gen Mgr)

Nova Biomedical K.K.   (1)
Mita 43MT Building-7F 13-16 Mita 3-chome, Minato-ku, Tokyo, 108-0073, Japan
Tel.: (81) 3 5418 4141
Blood Testing Analyzer Mfr
N.A.I.C.S.: 334510

Nova Biomedical U.K.   (1)
Aston Lane South, Runcorn, WA7 3FY, Cheshire, United Kingdom
Tel.: (44) 1928 704040
Web Site: http://www.novabio.us
Sales Range: $10-24.9 Million
Emp.: 28
Medical & Hospital Equipment Whslr
N.A.I.C.S.: 423450
Elisabeth Wagster (Gen Mgr)

NOVA FINANCIAL HOLDINGS, INC.
1420 Locust St, Philadelphia, PA 19102-3728
Tel.: (215) 545-6500
Rev.: $4,400,000
Emp.: 26
Bank Holding Company
N.A.I.C.S.: 522110
Edward J. DiMarcantonio (Chm)
Barbara Gibbs (Mgr)

Subsidiaries:

NOVA Savings Bank   (1)
1420 Locust St, Philadelphia, PA 19102
Tel.: (215) 545-6500
Sales Range: $75-99.9 Million
Provider of State Savings Banks
N.A.I.C.S.: 522180

NOVA HOTEL RENOVATION & CONSTRUCTION LLC
601 S Lincoln Ave, Clearwater, FL 33756
Tel.: (727) 447-2800
Web Site: http://www.novahrc.com
Sales Range: $25-49.9 Million
Emp.: 40
Renovation & Construction Services
N.A.I.C.S.: 236220
Chip Hardy (Pres)
Simone Azzam (Exec VP)

NOVA INFRASTRUCTURE MANAGEMENT, LLC
400 Madison Ave Ste 11B, New York, NY 10017
Tel.: (646) 889-8100   DE
Web Site: https://www.novainfrastructure.com
Year Founded: 2017
Privater Equity Firm
N.A.I.C.S.: 523999
Doug Turtz (CEO)
Chris Beall (Founder & Mng Partner)

Subsidiaries:

A&R Bulk-Pak, Inc.   (1)
452 York St, Elizabeth, NJ 07201
Tel.: (908) 558-7440
Web Site: http://www.arbulkpak.com
General Warehousing & Storage
N.A.I.C.S.: 493110
Avi Ron (Mgr-Ops)

Ats Logistics, Inc.   (1)
4033 W Montague Ave., Charleston, SC 29418
Tel.: (843) 308-6555
Web Site: http://www.atsinc.net
Sales Range: $1-9.9 Million
Emp.: 60
General Warehouse/Storage Freight Transportation Arrangement
N.A.I.C.S.: 493110
James A. Gianoukos (Pres & CEO)

UGE International Ltd.   (1)
417 5th Ave Ste 803, New York, NY 10016
Tel.: (917) 720-5685
Web Site: https://www.ugei.com
Rev.: $1,407,438
Assets: $6,190,975
Liabilities: $10,471,506
Net Worth: ($4,280,531)
Earnings: ($991,907)
Emp.: 35
Fiscal Year-end: 12/31/2020
Investment Services
N.A.I.C.S.: 523999
Nicolas Blitterswyk (CEO)
Mateo Chaskel (Mng Dir)
Robert van Duynhoven (COO)
Eddy Ji (Dir-Procurement)
Tyler Adkins (Chief Revenue Officer)
Stephanie Bird (CFO)
Pam Gica (Reg Dir)
Edgar Lim (Mng Dir)

Xchange Telecom Corp.   (1)
PO Box 190433, Brooklyn, NY 11219-0433
Tel.: (718) 853-3999
Web Site: http://www.xchangetele.com
Sales Range: $10-24.9 Million
Emp.: 54

NOVA INFRASTRUCTURE MANAGEMENT, LLC U.S. PRIVATE

Nova Infrastructure Management, LLC—(Continued)
Long Distance Telephone Communications Service
N.A.I.C.S.: 517121
Darren Feder (Pres)
Rudy Morando (CEO)

NOVA MARKETING SERVICES LLC
11522 Rock Island Ct, Maryland Heights, MO 63043
Tel.: (314) 993-3525
Web Site: http://www.novamktg.com
Year Founded: 1992
Inventory & Data Management Solutions
N.A.I.C.S.: 323111
Kathy Abbett (Dir-Customer Solutions)
Amy Spomer (Gen Mgr)
Rocky Abett (VP-Sls)

NOVA PRESSROOM PRODUCTS, LLC
1663 N McDuff Ave, Jacksonville, FL 32254
Tel.: (904) 292-2554
Web Site:
   http://www.novapressroom.com
Year Founded: 2007
Sales Range: $10-24.9 Million
Emp.: 25
Printing Press Chemicals & Other Products Mfr
N.A.I.C.S.: 325998
Ron Rose (Pres)
Ray Brady (VP-Tech Svcs)
Don Tartt (VP-Ops)
Dan Roll (VP-Product Dev)
Greg Rose (VP-Sls)
John Hart (CFO & VP)
Watsie Petree (Mgr-Dealer Svcs)
Brian Liberato (Mgr-Technical-Coatings)
Richard Day (Mgr-Environ Health & Safety)
Regina Pannell (Mgr-Technical-UV Products)
Mark J. Nuzzaco (Dir-Govt Affairs)

NOVA SALON SYSTEMS
501 Vandell Way, Campbell, CA 95008
Tel.: (408) 866-1191
Web Site:
   http://www.novasalonsystems.com
Year Founded: 1984
Sales Range: $10-24.9 Million
Emp.: 100
Whslr of Hair & Skin Care Products
N.A.I.C.S.: 423850
Ken Mammini (Pres)

NOVA SMART SOLUTIONS, INC.
2885 Sanford Ave SW 36883, Grandville, MI 49418
Tel.: (786) 220-3322   FL
Web Site:
   http://www.novasmartsolutions.com
Year Founded: 2015
Aerial Vehicle Mfr
N.A.I.C.S.: 336411
Sergio Camarero Blanco (Pres, CEO, Treas & Sec)
Jesus Emilio Hoyos Quintero (CFO)

NOVA SOLUTIONS INC.
421 W Indus Ave, Effingham, IL 62401
Tel.: (217) 342-7070
Web Site: http://www.novadesk.com
Year Founded: 1988
Sales Range: $10-24.9 Million
Emp.: 100
Wood Office Furniture

N.A.I.C.S.: 337211
Jerry Doll (Dir-Mktg)
Cindy Fulk (Mgr-Customer Svc)

NOVA STAR INNOVATIONS, INC.
2157 S Lincoln St, Salt Lake City, UT 84106
Tel.: (801) 323-2395   WY
Year Founded: 1986
Assets: $265
Liabilities: $427,853
Net Worth: ($427,588)
Earnings: ($34,417)
Emp.: 250
Fiscal Year-end: 12/31/22
Semiconductor Equipment Mfr
N.A.I.C.S.: 333242
Mark S. Clayton (Pres, Treas & Sec)

NOVA VENTURES GROUP CORP.
600 Unicorn Park Dr, Woburn, MA 01801
Tel.: (781) 897-1200   DE
Web Site: http://www.novavg.com
Year Founded: 2006
Emp.: 10
Holding Company; Electrochemistry Analytical Instruments Mfr
N.A.I.C.S.: 551112
Jim Barbookles (Chm & CEO)
Michael Larkin (CFO)
Tom Paquette (Exec VP-Mktg)
Janet Barbookles (VP & Gen Counsel)
Randall Crowder (Founder & Mng Partner)

Subsidiaries:

Roctest Ltd.   (1)
680 Avenue Birch, Saint-Lambert, J4P 2N3, QC, Canada
Tel.: (450) 465-1113
Web Site: https://www.roctest.com
Sales Range: $10-24.9 Million
Measuring Instruments Mfr
N.A.I.C.S.: 334515

Subsidiary (Non-US):

EN OM FRA, S.A.   (2)
6-8 avenue Eiffel, 77220, Gretz, France   (100%)
Tel.: (33) 164064776
Web Site: http://www.enomfra.fr
Sales Range: $10-24.9 Million
Vibrating Wire Technology & Field Instrumentation Services
N.A.I.C.S.: 334513
Jean Vaseux (Dir Gen)

Subsidiary (Domestic):

FISO Technologies, Inc.   (2)
500 St-Jean-Baptiste Suite 195, PO Box 195, Quebec, G2E 5R9, QC, Canada   (100%)
Tel.: (418) 688-8065
Web Site: http://www.fiso.com
Emp.: 150
Developer, Mfr & Marketer of Fiber Optic Sensors & Measuring Instruments
N.A.I.C.S.: 334516
Maxim Vachon-Savary (Dir-Sls & Mktg)

Subsidiary (US):

Roctest Inc.   (2)
PO Box 3568, Champlain, NY 12919-3568   (100%)
Tel.: (518) 561-3300
Web Site: http://www.roctest.com
Mfr & Designer Measuring Instruments
N.A.I.C.S.: 423490
Christina Gage (Dir-Sls Dept)

Subsidiary (Non-US):

SMARTEC sa   (2)
Via Pobiette 11, CH 6928, Manno, Switzerland
Tel.: (41) 916101800

Web Site: http://www.smartec.ch
Developer, Mfr & Distr of Structural Health Monitoring Systems for Geotechnical, Civil & Structural Engineering
N.A.I.C.S.: 334513

Telemac, S.A.   (2)
10 avenue Eiffel, 77220, Gretz, Armainvilliers, France   (100%)
Tel.: (33) 164064080
Web Site: http://www.telemac.fr
Sales Range: $10-24.9 Million
Emp.: 5
Vibrating Wire Technology & Field Instrumentation Services
N.A.I.C.S.: 334513
Borsne Frederec (Gen Mgr)

NOVA-TECH INTERNATIONAL, INC.
800 Rockmead Dr Ste 102, Kingwood, TX 77339-2496
Tel.: (281) 359-8538
Web Site: http://www.novatech-usa.com
Year Founded: 1995
Sales Range: $1-9.9 Million
Emp.: 9
Pumps & Pumping Equipment Mfr
N.A.I.C.S.: 333914
Kent Anderson (VP)

NOVACES, LLC
Poydras Ctr 650 Poydras St Ste 2320, New Orleans, LA 70130
Tel.: (504) 544-6888
Web Site: http://www.novaces.com
Year Founded: 2004
Sales Range: $1-9.9 Million
Emp.: 32
Information Technology Services
N.A.I.C.S.: 518210
Bahadir Inozu (CEO)
Ivan Radovic (Pres)
Brian MacClaren (COO)

NOVACOAST, INC.
1505 Chapala St, Santa Barbara, CA 93101
Tel.: (805) 568-0171   CA
Web Site: http://www.novacoast.com
Year Founded: 1996
Sales Range: $10-24.9 Million
Emp.: 75
Information Technology Services
N.A.I.C.S.: 541512
Darin Sanders (Mgr-Sls-Natl)
Eron Howard (Chief Delivery Officer)
Geoff Gilbert (VP-Engrg)
Janice Newlon (COO)
Paul Anderson (Founder & CEO)
Gabe Laughlin (CFO)
Katie McAuliff (VP)
Kelley Damore (VP & Dir-Editorial)
Emmy Savenelli (Corp Counsel)
Adam L. Gray (CTO)

Subsidiaries:

Network Design & Integration, Inc.   (1)
2900 Wilcrest Dr Ste 370, Houston, TX 77042
Tel.: (713) 626-7900
Sales Range: $10-24.9 Million
Emp.: 10
IT Services
N.A.I.C.S.: 541512
Paul Anderson (Pres)

NOVAK BIDDLE VENTURE PARTNERS, LP
7501 Wisconsin Ave E Tower Ste 1380, Bethesda, MD 20814
Tel.: (240) 497-1910
Web Site:
   http://www.novakbiddle.com
Year Founded: 1997
Sales Range: $25-49.9 Million
Emp.: 15

Privater Equity Firm
N.A.I.C.S.: 523999
Joy E. Binford (CFO)
Melanie Ness (Controller)
Tina Anderson (Mgr-Ops)
Annie Lurth (Mgr-Acctg)
Prashanth V. Boccasam (Gen Partner)
Simita Bose (Partner)
E. Rogers Novak Jr. (Gen Partner)
A. G. W. Biddle III (Gen Partner)
Philip L. Bronner (Gen Partner)

NOVAK FORNEY & ASSOCIATES, LLC
6105 Memorial Hwy Ste A14, Tampa, FL 33615
Tel.: (813) 490-7477
Web Site:
   http://www.novakforney.com
Sales Range: $1-9.9 Million
Commercial Real Estate Broker
N.A.I.C.S.: 531210
Mark Forney (Principal)
Mike Novak (Principal)

NOVAK GROUP LLC
22374 Fossil Ridge, San Antonio, TX 78261-3015
Tel.: (210) 325-4853
Web Site:
   http://www.novakgroupllc.com
Energy Efficiency & Construction Management Solutions
N.A.I.C.S.: 541690
Mike Novak (Founder & CEO)

Subsidiaries:

San Marcos Air Conditioning, Inc.   (1)
3500 Hwy 123, San Marcos, TX 78666
Tel.: (512) 353-2511
Web Site:
   http://www.sanmarcosairconditioning.com
Sales Range: $10-24.9 Million
Emp.: 35
Heating, Ventilation & Air-Conditioning Services
N.A.I.C.S.: 238220
Lucas Novak (Owner)

NOVAMEX ENERGY, INC.
1610 Woodstead Ct Ste 330, Woodlands, TX 77380-3403
Tel.: (214) 953-9358
Year Founded: 2006
Oil & Gas Exploration Services
N.A.I.C.S.: 213112
Coleman Payne (Sec)

NOVAMEX, INC.
500 W Overland Ave, El Paso, TX 79901
Tel.: (915) 594-1618
Web Site: http://www.novamex.com
Rev.: $60,610,646
Emp.: 86
Soft Drink Mfr & Distr
N.A.I.C.S.: 312111
Ramon Carrasco (Pres)
Louis Fernandez (CEO)
Jesus Tarango (Controller & Mgr-Acctg)
Liberato Aguilar (Mgr-Grocery Div)
Rigoberto Espinoza (Mgr-HR)
Tomas de Leon (CFO)
Lupe Nieves (Coord-Acctg)
Sanford Gross (Exec VP)
Jazhen Gonzalez (Mgr)
Bill Dunmead (Mgr-Logistics)
Jose Manzanedo (Mgr-Mktg)
Donna Sanchez (Sr Mgr-HR)

NOVANT HEALTH, INC.
2085 Frontis Plz Blvd, Winston Salem, NC 27103-3013
Tel.: (336) 718-5000   NC

Web Site:
http://www.novanthealth.org
Year Founded: 1997
Sales Range: $1-4.9 Billion
Emp.: 20,000
Health Care Srvices
N.A.I.C.S.: 561110
Carl S. Armato *(Pres & CEO)*
Sallye Liner *(Chief Clinical Officer)*
Jesse Cureton *(Chief Consumer Officer & Exec VP)*
Stephen J. Motew *(Pres-Market & Sr VP-Novant Health Forsyth Medical Center)*
Thomas N. Zweng *(Chief Medical Officer & Exec VP)*
Jeffery T. Lindsay *(COO & Exec VP-Ops Performance & Strategic Growth-Health Sys)*
G. Patrick Phillips *(Chm)*
Angela Yochem *(Chief Digital Officer & Exec VP)*
Robert M. Barr *(Vice Chm)*
Denise Mihal *(Chief Nursing & Clinical Ops Officer & Exec VP)*
Eric Eskioglu *(Chief Medical Officer & Exec VP)*
Fred Hargett *(CFO & Exec VP)*
Pam Oliver *(Pres & Exec VP-Physician Network)*
Tanya Blackmon *(Chief Diversity & Inclusion Officer & Exec VP)*
Sophie Karzis *(Sec)*
Mark J. King *(VP-Res & Innovation)*
Carmen Canales *(Chief HR Officer & Sr VP)*
Frank Edward Emory Jr. *(Chief Admin Officer & Exec VP)*

Subsidiaries:

Prince William Health Systems Inc. (1)
8650 Sudley Rd Ste 411, Manassas, VA 20110-4416
Tel.: (703) 369-8270
Web Site: http://www.pwhs.org
Sales Range: $75-99.9 Million
Emp.: 1,500
Wealth Management Services
N.A.I.C.S.: 621491

Subsidiary (Domestic):

MRI & Imaging of Georgia (2)
3480 Preston Rdg Rd Ste 600, Alpharetta, GA 30005
Tel.: (678) 992-7200
Web Site: http://www.georgiamri.com
Sales Range: $50-74.9 Million
Emp.: 100
Magnetic Resonance Imaging & Computer Tomography Center
N.A.I.C.S.: 621498
Melissa Geralds *(Gen Mgr)*

PWH Foundation Inc. (2)
8609 Sudley Rd Ste 301, Manassas, VA 20110-4416
Tel.: (703) 369-8201
Web Site: http://www.pwhs.org
Sales Range: $10-24.9 Million
Emp.: 3
Provider of Social Services
N.A.I.C.S.: 621111

NOVAQUEST CAPITAL MANAGEMENT, LLC
4208 Six Forks Rd Ste 920, Raleigh, NC 27609
Tel.: (919) 459-8620   DE
Web Site: http://www.novaquest.com
Year Founded: 2000
Healthcare Industry-Focused Investment & Asset Management Firm
N.A.I.C.S.: 523999
Jeffrey Edwards *(Partner)*
Vern Davenport *(Partner)*
Ron Wooten *(Chief Investment Officer & Mng Partner)*
John Bradley *(Co-Founder, COO & Partner)*
Jonathan Tunnicliffe *(Co-Founder & Partner)*
Robert Hester *(CFO)*
Michael Bologna *(Partner)*
Matt Bullard *(Partner)*
Bryan Mills *(Chief Admin Officer)*

Subsidiaries:

Azurity Pharmaceuticals, Inc. (1)
8 Cabot Rd Ste 2000, Woburn, MA 01801
Tel.: (978) 867-1010
Web Site: http://www.azurity.com
Pharmaceutical Preparation Mfr
N.A.I.C.S.: 325412

Subsidiary (Domestic):

Arbor Pharmaceuticals LLC (2)
Six Concourse Pkwy Ste 1800, Atlanta, GA 30328
Tel.: (678) 334-2420
Web Site: http://www.arborpharma.com
Pharmaceuticals Product Mfr
N.A.I.C.S.: 325412
Brian Adams *(VP-Bus Dev)*
Steven Caras *(VP-Clinical Dev)*
Mary Lou Freathy *(VP-Regulatory Affairs, Quality & Mfg)*
Jason McCarthy *(CFO)*
Thom Rowland *(VP-Comml Ops)*
Leslie Zacks *(VP, Gen Counsel & Chief Compliance Officer)*
Jason Wild *(Chm)*
Edward J. Schutter *(Pres & CEO)*

Silvergate Pharmaceuticals Inc. (2)
6251 Greenwood Plz Blvd Ste 101, Greenwood Village, CO 80111-4809
Tel.: (855) 379-0382
Web Site: http://www.silvergatepharma.com
Chemicals Mfr
N.A.I.C.S.: 325412
Frank Segrave *(CEO)*

Catalyst Clinical Research LLC (1)
4039 Masonboro Loop Rd Ste 1-G, Wilmington, NC 28409
Tel.: (919) 443-9241
Web Site: http://catalystcr.com
Clinical Research Services
N.A.I.C.S.: 541714
Nick Dyer *(CEO)*

Subsidiary (Domestic):

CE3, Inc. (2)
246 Goose Ln Ste 202, Guilford, CT 06437
Tel.: (203) 404-7500
Web Site: http://www.ce3inc.com
Scientific & Technical Consulting Services
N.A.I.C.S.: 541690
Susan Albert *(Project Mgr)*
Holly Coulter *(Co-Founder)*
Tim Garrelts *(Co-Founder)*

CoreRX, Inc. (1)
14205 Myerlake Cir, Clearwater, FL 33760
Tel.: (727) 259-6950
Web Site: http://www.corerxpharma.com
Sales Range: $1-9.9 Million
Emp.: 50
Pharmaceuticals Mfr
N.A.I.C.S.: 325412
Todd R. Daviau *(Pres)*
Bill Reid *(Dir-Project Mgmt & Logistics)*
Tim Hudson *(CFO)*
Kyle Brinkman *(Dir-Quality Assurance)*
Janice Cacace *(Sr Dir-Formulation Dev)*
Ajay Damani *(CEO)*
Dan Dobry *(Chief Strategy Officer)*

Subsidiary (Domestic):

Societal CDMO, Inc. (2)
1 E Uwchlan Ave Ste 112, Exton, PA 19341
Tel.: (770) 534-8239
Web Site: https://www.societalcdmo.com
Rev.: $90,214,000
Assets: $157,443,000
Liabilities: $97,584,000
Net Worth: $59,859,000
Earnings: ($19,881,000)
Emp.: 275
Fiscal Year-end: 12/31/2022
Pharmaceuticals Mfr
N.A.I.C.S.: 325412
Richard Sidwell *(Chief Scientific Officer, Sr VP & VP)*

Subsidiary (Domestic):

Recro Gainesville LLC (3)
1300 Gould Dr, Gainesville, GA 30504
Tel.: (770) 531-8100
Web Site: https://www.societalcdmo.com
Pharmaceuticals Product Mfr
N.A.I.C.S.: 325412

Mycovia Pharmaceuticals, Inc. (1)
4505 Emperor Blvd Ste 300, Durham, NC 27703
Tel.: (919) 467-8539
Web Site: https://mycovia.com
Pharmaceutical Drugs Research, Development & Mfr
N.A.I.C.S.: 325412
Neil Moore *(VP-Ops)*
Patrick Jordan *(CEO)*
James Gordon Still *(Chief Medical Officer)*
Stephen Brand *(Sr VP-Clinical Dev)*
Thorsten Degenhaardt *(Sr VP-Global Ops)*
Rachel Gee *(Sr Dir-Regulatory Affairs)*
Kristen Oberg *(Dir-Ops)*
Caroline Carr *(Dir-Fin)*
Tiffany Ahlers *(Sr VP-Commercialization)*

NOVASPECT INC.
1124 Tower Rd, Schaumburg, IL 60173
Tel.: (847) 956-8020   DE
Web Site: http://www.novaspect.com
Year Founded: 1936
Process Management Solutions; Control Valves & Regulators Mfr
N.A.I.C.S.: 423830
Jayme Bojicic *(VP-Ops)*
Joe Simchak *(Pres)*
Mike Franz *(CFO)*
Kelly Mutuc *(VP-HR)*

NOVASTAR DEVELOPMENT INC.
18215 72nd Ave S, Kent, WA 98032
Tel.: (425) 251-6110
Web Site:
http://www.barghausen.com
Sales Range: $10-24.9 Million
Emp.: 130
Land Subdividing Services
N.A.I.C.S.: 237210
Tom Barghausen *(Pres)*
Cindy Schafer *(Principal)*

NOVATAE RISK GROUP, LLC
12700 Park Central Dr Ste 510, Dallas, TX 75251
Tel.: (888) 810-2770
Web Site: https://novatae.com
Insurance Services
N.A.I.C.S.: 524210
Richard Kerr *(CEO)*
Jim Siddall *(CFO)*
Von Breaux *(COO)*
Jean Wiskowski *(CMO)*

Subsidiaries:

American Management Corporation (1)
824 Frnt St, Conway, AR 72032-5438
Tel.: (501) 932-5799
Web Site: http://www.amcinsurance.com
Direct Property & Causality Insurance Carriers
N.A.I.C.S.: 524126
Stephen Robertson *(Mgr)*

NOVATEC INC.
222 Thomas Ave, Baltimore, MD 21225-3327
Tel.: (410) 789-4811   MD
Web Site: http://www.novatec.com
Year Founded: 1972
Sales Range: $10-24.9 Million
Emp.: 100
Industrial Furnaces & Ovens
N.A.I.C.S.: 333994
Conrad Bessemer *(Pres)*
Charles Slater *(Project Mgr)*
Douglas Arndt *(Engr-Energy & Drying Sys)*
Brown Bush *(Mgr-Lab)*

NOVATECH, LLC
1720 Molasses Way, Quakertown, PA 18951
Tel.: (484) 812-6000   KS
Web Site:
http://www.novatechweb.com
Automation Products Designer & Mfr
N.A.I.C.S.: 333248
Volker Oakey *(Chm & CEO)*
Aubrey Zey *(Founder & Dir-Technical Advisory)*
Jean Bandy *(VP & Gen Mgr-Process Ops)*
Alan Staatz *(VP & Gen Mgr-Substation Automation)*
Frank Wendt *(VP-Mfg, Procurement & LEAN)*
Scott Pickering *(Dir-Bus Dev)*
Joan Mann *(Dir-Org Effectiveness)*
Rod Ray *(Dir-Strategy & Tech)*
Jeff Lindtner *(Sr VP-Sls & Mktg)*
Ramesh Nuggihali *(COO)*

Subsidiaries:

NovaTech, LLC - Orion Utility Automation Division (1)
13555 W 107th St, Lenexa, KS 66215
Tel.: (913) 451-1880
Web Site: http://www.novatechweb.com
Emp.: 70
Industrial Process Automation Equipment Mfr & Software Publisher
N.A.I.C.S.: 334118

NOVATION HOLDINGS, INC.
1800 NW Corporate Blvd Ste 201, Boca Raton, FL 33431
Tel.: (321) 452-9091   FL
Web Site: http://www.allezoe.com
Year Founded: 1998
Sales Range: Less than $1 Million
Emp.: 4
Investment Services
N.A.I.C.S.: 523999
Michael J. Gelmon *(Chm, Pres & CEO)*

NOVATION INDUSTRIES
5151 Bolger Ct, McHenry, IL 60050
Tel.: (815) 578-8888
Web Site:
http://www.novationindustries.com
Year Founded: 1967
Sales Range: $10-24.9 Million
Emp.: 15
Plastics Product Mfr
N.A.I.C.S.: 326199
Chris Metz *(CEO)*
Scott Baxter *(Pres)*
Pete Martel *(Controller)*
Brian Johannsen *(Plant Mgr)*

NOVEDA TECHNOLOGIES, INC.
1200 US Hwy 22 E Ste 2000, Bridgewater, NJ 08807
Tel.: (908) 534-8855
Web Site: http://www.noveda.com
Year Founded: 2006
Software Publisher
N.A.I.C.S.: 513210
Govi Rao *(Pres & CEO)*

NOVEL IRON WORKS INC.
250 Ocean Rd, Greenland, NH 03840-2442
Tel.: (603) 436-7950   MA
Web Site: http://www.noveliron.com
Year Founded: 1956
Sales Range: $10-24.9 Million
Emp.: 110

NOVEL IRON WORKS INC.   U.S. PRIVATE

Novel Iron Works Inc.—(Continued)

Fabricated Structural Metal
N.A.I.C.S.: 332312
Thomas Heaney *(Exec VP)*
Leo A. Moreau *(Pres)*
Keith Moreau *(VP-Sls)*

NOVELAIRE TECHNOLOGIES
10132 Mammoth Ave, Baton Rouge, LA 70814-4420
Tel.: (225) 924-0427   GA
Web Site: http://www.novelaire.com
Year Founded: 1998
Sales Range: $50-74.9 Million
Emp.: 40
Mfr & Marketers of Energy Conservation, Dehumidification & Desiccant Wheels & Cassettes
N.A.I.C.S.: 333413
Neil Stephansson *(Pres)*
Carl Nayden *(Treas & VP)*
Bryan Toler *(Supvr)*

NOVELART MANUFACTURING COMPANY
2121 Section Rd, Cincinnati, OH 45237
Tel.: (513) 351-1900
Web Site: http://www.topiczinc.com
Rev.: $16,300,000
Emp.: 90
Corrugated Boxes, Partitions, Display Items, Sheets & Pad
N.A.I.C.S.: 322211
Barb Milius *(Mgr-Sls)*

NOVELTEX MIAMI, INC.
151 E 10th Ave, Hialeah, FL 33010-5191
Tel.: (305) 887-8191   FL
Gifts & Souvenirs Mfr
N.A.I.C.S.: 459420
Anton Maratos *(Owner, VP - Mktg & New Product Dev)*

NOVICA UNITED, INC.
3250 Ocean Park Blvd Ste 300, Santa Monica, CA 90405
Tel.: (310) 479-6685
Web Site: http://www.novica.com
Year Founded: 1998
Sales Range: $10-24.9 Million
Emp.: 50
Online Retailer of Art Merchandise
N.A.I.C.S.: 459920
Robert Milk *(CEO)*

NOVIDAM CAPITAL LLC
1501 Broadway 12th Fl, New York, NY 10036
Tel.: (212) 380-6862   DE
Web Site: http://novidam.com
Emp.: 100
Privater Equity Firm
N.A.I.C.S.: 523999

NOVINGER GROUP, INC.
1400 N Cameron St Ste 100, Harrisburg, PA 17103-1012
Tel.: (717) 930-0400   PA
Web Site: http://www.novingergroup.com
Year Founded: 1987
Sales Range: $1-9.9 Million
Emp.: 300
Plastering, Drywall & Insulation Services
N.A.I.C.S.: 238310
James David Novinger *(Pres)*
Steven Powers *(Dir-Construction)*
Susan Janesko *(Project Mgr)*
Brian Duncan *(Mgr-Warehouse)*
Laura Lehman-Salada *(Mgr-Info Sys)*

Subsidiaries:

Ciesco Inc.   (1)
109 Miller Ln, Harrisburg, PA 17110-1728
Tel.: (717) 232-5825
Web Site: http://www.ciescoinc.com
Sale of Brick, Stone & Related Materials
N.A.I.C.S.: 423320

Kelly Systems Inc.   (1)
1441 Stoneridge Dr, Middletown, PA 17057   (100%)
Tel.: (717) 930-0500
Web Site: http://www.novingergroup.com
Plastering, Drywall & Insulation Services
N.A.I.C.S.: 238310
George Irwin *(Dir-Constructions)*

Novinger's Inc.   (1)
1441 Stoneridge Dr, Middletown, PA 17057-5977
Tel.: (717) 930-0300
Web Site: http://www.novingergroup.com
Plastering, Drywall & Insulation Services
N.A.I.C.S.: 238310
James David Novinger *(Pres)*
Craig Cox *(Dir-Panel Sls)*
Laura Lehman-Salada *(Mgr-Info Sys)*

NOVO 1, INC.
4301 Cambridge Rd, Fort Worth, TX 76155
Tel.: (817) 355-8200   DE
Web Site: http://www.dialog-direct.com
Year Founded: 1987
Telemarketing Services
N.A.I.C.S.: 561422
Mary Murcott *(CEO)*
Eric Rothert *(COO)*
Mitchell Swindell *(CTO)*
Jack Wilkie *(CMO)*
Rosemary Bennett *(Sr VP-Sls)*
Matthew Cocks *(VP-Dev)*
Tim Collopy *(VP-Dev)*
Jeffrey Bauernschmidt *(VP-Dev)*
Leila Lassetter *(Dir-Site)*
Michelle Levy *(Dir-Site)*
Mike Satterlee *(Dir-Site)*

NOVOLINK COMMUNICATIONS, INC.
699 S Friendswood Dr, Friendswood, TX 77546
Tel.: (281) 652-4800   TX
Web Site: http://www.novolink.com
Year Founded: 2000
Sales Range: $1-9.9 Million
Emp.: 65
Telecommunications Resellers
N.A.I.C.S.: 517121
Ignatius Leonards *(Pres & CEO)*
Nathan Skuse *(VP-Sls & Bus Dev)*
Sharon Brown *(VP-Fin & Admin)*
Alexey Pogodin *(VP-Software Dev)*

NOVOLOGIX INC.
10400 Viking Dr Ste 200, Eden Prairie, MN 55344
Tel.: (952) 826-2500
Web Site: http://www.novologix.net
Year Founded: 1995
Sales Range: $450-499.9 Million
Emp.: 38
Ancillary Healthcare Management Services
N.A.I.C.S.: 541611
David J. McLean *(CEO)*

NOVU, INC.
5401 Gamble Dr Ste 300, Minneapolis, MN 55416
Web Site: http://www.novu.com
Year Founded: 2011
Sales Range: $25-49.9 Million
Emp.: 200
Health Care Srvices
N.A.I.C.S.: 621999
Tom Wicka *(Co-Founder & CEO)*
Jeff Harmsen *(CFO)*
John Wicka *(Co-Founder)*
Steve Smerz *(Exec VP-Tech)*
Meg Koepke *(VP-Strategy)*

NOVUM MEDICAL PRODUCTS, INC.
80 Creekside Dr, Amherst, NY 14228
Tel.: (800) 274-2742   NY
Web Site: http://novummed.com
Year Founded: 1985
Mfg Metal Household Furniture Mfg Furniture/Fixtures
N.A.I.C.S.: 337126
Tom Afzal *(CEO)*

NOVUS INC.
655 Calle Cubitas, Guaynabo, PR 00969-2802
Tel.: (787) 272-4546   PR
Web Site: http://www.novushoes.com
Year Founded: 1973
Sales Range: $50-74.9 Million
Emp.: 825
Shoes, Bags & Accesories Retailer
N.A.I.C.S.: 458210
Sandra Castellon Fernandez *(Dir-Mktg)*

Subsidiaries:

La Favorita Inc.   (1)
655 Calle Cubitas, Guaynabo, PR 00969-2802
Tel.: (787) 272-4546
Web Site: http://www.novushoes.com
Sales Range: $10-24.9 Million
Emp.: 12
Shoe Stores
N.A.I.C.S.: 458210

NOVUS MEDICAL DETOX CENTER OF PASCO COUNTY, LLC
9270 Royal Palm Ave, New Port Richey, FL 34654
Tel.: (866) 596-7313
Web Site: http://www.novusdetox.com
Year Founded: 2007
Sales Range: $1-9.9 Million
Emp.: 27
Prescription Drug Detox & Treatment Programs
N.A.I.C.S.: 621491
Brent Agin *(Medical Dir)*
Kent Runyon *(VP-Community Rels)*
Joy Augustine *(Dir-Nursing Staff)*
Manuel Correa *(Clinical Supvr)*

NOVUS WOOD GROUP, LP
5900 Haynesworth Ln, Houston, TX 77034
Tel.: (281) 922-1000
Web Site: http://www.novuswoodgroup.com
Year Founded: 1985
Rev.: $67,700,000
Emp.: 30
Solid Waste Management & Recycling Services
N.A.I.C.S.: 423930
Ronald H. Blackwelder *(Mgr-Forest Products)*
Billy R. Holt *(Mgr-Bus Dev & IT)*
Scott C. Mactier *(Mng Partner)*
Roger D. Oldigs *(VP-Ops)*
Steve M. Ghormley *(VP-Bus Dev)*
James L. Goodyear *(CFO)*
William H. Winters *(Pres & CEO)*

NOVUSTERRA INC.
7135 Collins Ave 1234, Miami, FL 33141
Tel.: (786) 473-6233   FL
Web Site: https://www.novusterrainc.com
Year Founded: 2020
Emp.: 1

Chemicals Mfr
N.A.I.C.S.: 325998
Andrew Weeraratne *(CEO)*
Gerardine Botte *(CTO)*
Mark C. Jensen *(Chm)*

NOW COMMUNICATIONS
4816 S Ash Ave Ste 101, Tempe, AZ 85282
Web Site: http://www.workwithnow.com
Year Founded: 2009
Sales Range: $1-9.9 Million
Emp.: 110
Television, Internet & Phone Products & Services
N.A.I.C.S.: 517121
Jon Shields *(Pres-Sls)*

NOW COURIER INC.
111 E McCarty St, Indianapolis, IN 46225
Tel.: (317) 638-7071
Web Site: http://www.nowcourier.com
Sales Range: $10-24.9 Million
Emp.: 40
Provider of Courier Services
N.A.I.C.S.: 561499
Bob Welch *(Dir-Compliance & Safety)*
Dallas Harris *(Dir-Ops)*
Ron Ping *(Reg Mgr-Ops)*
Ryan Jacob *(CFO)*
Ryan Schwalbach *(CEO)*

NOW ELECTRONICS, INC.
48 Elm St, Huntington, NY 11743
Tel.: (631) 351-8300   NY
Web Site: http://www.nowelectro.com
Year Founded: 1981
Sales Range: $1-9.9 Million
Electronic Parts & Equipment Distr
N.A.I.C.S.: 423690
Aaron Goodridge *(Pres & CEO)*

Subsidiaries:

Twilight Now, LLC   (1)
325 N Shepard St, Anaheim, CA 92806
Tel.: (714) 257-2257
Semiconductor Mfr & Whslr
N.A.I.C.S.: 334413
Randy Greene *(Co-CEO)*
Aaron Goodridge *(Co-CEO)*

NOW HEALTH GROUP, INC.
395 Glen Ellyn Rd, Bloomingdale, IL 60108-2176
Tel.: (630) 545-9098   IL
Web Site: http://www.nowfoods.com
Year Founded: 1963
Sales Range: $25-49.9 Million
Emp.: 1,000
Vitamins & Supplements Mfr
N.A.I.C.S.: 311514
Elwood Richard *(Founder)*
Michael Lelah *(Dir-Tech)*
Dan Richard *(VP-Sls & Mktg-Global)*
Jim Ritcheske *(Mgr-Mktg)*
Jim Emme *(CEO)*
Michelle Canada *(VP-HR)*
Aaron Secrist *(VP-Quality & Regulatory Affairs)*
Joe Fulco *(Pres-Fruitful Yield Retail Div)*

NOWAK CONSTRUCTION CO. INC.
200 S Goddard Rd, Goddard, KS 67052
Tel.: (316) 794-8898
Web Site: http://www.nowakconstruction.com
Sales Range: $100-124.9 Million
Emp.: 85
Utility & Water Main Construction
N.A.I.C.S.: 237110
Joseph B. Nowak *(Pres)*
John Nowak *(VP)*

NOWCOM CORPORATION
4751 Wilshire Blvd Ste 115, Los Angeles, CA 90010
Tel.: (323) 692-4040
Web Site: http://www.nowcom.com
Year Founded: 1988
Sales Range: $150-199.9 Million
Emp.: 728
Computer System Design Services
N.A.I.C.S.: 541512
Vimal Kumar *(CTO)*
Jay Kamdar *(Pres)*
Don Rufus Hankey *(Chm)*
Matt Mee-Lee *(Sr VP-Ops-Southeast Asia)*

NOZONE, INC.
350 E Cermak Rd Ste 240, Chicago, IL 60616-1568
Tel.: (312) 602-2689
Web Site: http://www.steadfast.net
Sales Range: $1-9.9 Million
Emp.: 10
Web Hosting & Server Services
N.A.I.C.S.: 518210
Karl A. Zimmerman *(Founder)*
David J. Carter *(CFO)*
Kevin M. Stange *(CTO)*

NPC CREATIVE SERVICES, LLC
5014 Gunn Hwy, Tampa, FL 33624
Tel.: (813) 960-5092
Web Site: http://www.npccs.com
Year Founded: 2005
Sales Range: $1-9.9 Million
Public Relations
N.A.I.C.S.: 541820
Elizabeth Roop *(Pres)*

NPC RESTAURANT HOLDINGS, LLC
7300 W 129th St, Overland Park, KS 66213
Tel.: (913) 327-5555   DE
Web Site: http://www.npcinternational.com
Sales Range: $1-4.9 Billion
Emp.: 29,000
Restaurant Management Services
N.A.I.C.S.: 722511
Troy D. Cook *(CFO, Sec & Exec VP-Fin)*
Linda L. Sheedy *(Sr VP-Mktg)*
Vonnie K. Walbert *(Sr VP-People Leadership)*
Michael J. Woods *(VP-IT)*
Kirby W. Mynier *(VP-East)*
Tracy A. Armentrout *(VP-West)*
Thomas D. White *(VP-South)*
Randy Adams *(VP-Ops-Wendy's)*
James K. Schwartz *(Chm, Pres & CEO)*
James K. Schwartz *(Chm, Pres & CEO)*

NPC, INC.
13710 Dunnings Hwy, Claysburg, PA 16625
Tel.: (814) 239-8787   PA
Web Site: http://www.npcweb.com
Year Founded: 1931
Sales Range: $25-49.9 Million
Emp.: 450
Commercial Printing Services
N.A.I.C.S.: 323111
Mark Barnhart *(Owner & CEO)*
Tim McCarthy *(CFO & Exec VP)*
Chip Gallaher *(Chief Bus Dev Officer & Exec VP)*
Sherri Steward *(Dir-HR)*
Mark Kelly *(Pres)*
Bob Latoche *(COO & Exec VP)*
Ed Detwiler *(Sr VP-Government Solutions)*
Larissa Crum *(Sr VP-Strategic Sls)*

NPE, LLC
4767 New Broad St, Orlando, FL 32814
Tel.: (888) 866-4998
Web Site: http://www.mynpecoaching.com
Year Founded: 2006
Sales Range: $1-9.9 Million
Emp.: 10
Fitness Consultants
N.A.I.C.S.: 713940
Sean Greeley *(Founder & CEO)*
Brad Tucker *(COO)*

NPG HEALTH LLC
445 S St Ste 305, Morristown, NJ 07960
Tel.: (973) 845-9970
Web Site: https://npghealth.com
Health Platform & Solution-focused Agency
N.A.I.C.S.: 541511

Subsidiaries:

Managed Market Resources LLC (1)
500 International Dr Ste 355, Budd Lake, NJ 07828-1300
Tel.: (973) 426-6500
Web Site: http://www.m2res.com
Marketing Consulting Services
N.A.I.C.S.: 541613
Randy Ross *(Sr VP)*

NRC ELECTRONICS, INC.
6600 Park of Commerce Blvd, Boca Raton, FL 33487
Tel.: (561) 241-8600
Web Site: http://www.nrcelectronics.com
Year Founded: 1974
Sales Range: $10-24.9 Million
Emp.: 65
Electronics Distr
N.A.I.C.S.: 423690
Dennis Eiden *(Pres)*
Eric Eisen *(VP)*
Tina Giumenta *(Mgr-Southeastern Reg)*
Audrey Engel *(Product Mgr)*
Paulette Pelletier *(Acct Mgr)*
Scott Lamey *(Mgr-Global Acct)*

NRD CAPITAL MANAGEMENT, LLC
4170 Ashford Dunwoody Rd Ste 390, Atlanta, GA 30319
Tel.: (404) 499-1960   DE
Web Site: http://www.nrdcapital.com
Year Founded: 2014
Privater Equity Firm
N.A.I.C.S.: 523999
Susan E. Beth *(COO)*
Aziz Hashim *(Founder & Mng Partner)*
Harrison Price *(Principal)*

Subsidiaries:

Frisch's Restaurants, Inc. (1)
2800 Gilbert Ave, Cincinnati, OH 45206
Tel.: (513) 961-2660
Web Site: http://www.frischs.com
Rev.: $211,893,000
Assets: $129,011,000
Liabilities: $29,001,000
Net Worth: $100,010,000
Earnings: $9,955,000
Emp.: 2,200
Fiscal Year-end: 06/02/2015
Holding Company; Restaurants Developer, Franchisor, Owner & Operator
N.A.I.C.S.: 551112
Michael R. Everett *(VP-Info Sys)*
Aziz Hashim *(Pres, CEO & Sec)*

Subsidiary (Domestic):

Frisch Indiana LLC (2)
2800 Gilbert Ave, Cincinnati, OH 45206-1206   (100%)
Tel.: (513) 961-2660
Web Site: http://www.frischs.com
Restaurant Operators
N.A.I.C.S.: 722511

Frisch Kentucky LLC (2)
2800 Gilbert Ave, Cincinnati, OH 45206-1206   (100%)
Tel.: (513) 961-2660
Web Site: http://www.frischs.com
Restaurant Operators
N.A.I.C.S.: 722511

Frisch Ohio LLC (2)
2800 Gilbert Ave, Cincinnati, OH 45206-1206   (100%)
Tel.: (513) 961-2660
Web Site: http://www.frischs.com
Restaurant Operators
N.A.I.C.S.: 722511

Ruby Tuesday, Inc. (1)
333 E Broadway Ave, Maryville, TN 37804
Tel.: (865) 379-5700
Web Site: http://www.rubytuesday.com
Sales Range: $900-999.9 Million
Casual Dining Restaurant Franchiser, Owner & Operator
Jennifer Harmon *(CMO)*

Subsidiary (Domestic):

Ruby Tuesday of Anderson, Inc. (2)
5530 Scatterfield Rd, Anderson, IN 46013-3141
Tel.: (765) 643-2496
Restaurant Operating Services
N.A.I.C.S.: 722511

Ruby Tuesday of Arvada, Inc. (2)
5525 Wadsworth Bypass, Arvada, CO 80002-3105
Tel.: (303) 940-0441
Web Site: http://www.rubytuesday.com
Restaurant Operating Services
N.A.I.C.S.: 722511

Ruby Tuesday of Columbia, Inc. (2)
827 S James Campbell Blvd, Columbia, TN 38401
Tel.: (931) 381-7089
Web Site: http://www.rubytuesday.com
Restaurant Operating Services
N.A.I.C.S.: 722511
Jill Gillun *(Mng Partner)*

Ruby Tuesday of Deerwood, Inc. (2)
12075 SW 152nd St, Miami, FL 33177-1607
Tel.: (305) 238-6036
Restaurant Operating Services
N.A.I.C.S.: 722511

Ruby Tuesday of Frederick, Inc. (2)
7385 Guilford Dr, Frederick, MD 21703
Tel.: (240) 379-6415
Web Site: http://www.rubytuesday.com
Restaurant Operating Services
N.A.I.C.S.: 722511

Ruby Tuesday of Linthicum, Inc. (2)
950 International Dr, Linthicum, MD 21090
Tel.: (410) 694-0031
Web Site: http://www.rubytuesday.com
Restaurant Operating Services
N.A.I.C.S.: 722511
Glenn Smith *(Mng Partner)*

Ruby Tuesday of Marley Station, Inc. (2)
7900 Governor Ritchie Hwy, Glen Burnie, MD 21061
Tel.: (410) 766-4446
Restaurant Operating Services
N.A.I.C.S.: 722511

Ruby Tuesday of Pocomoke City, Inc. (2)
145 Newtown Blvd, Pocomoke City, MD 21851
Tel.: (410) 957-0249
Restaurant Operating Services
N.A.I.C.S.: 722511

Ruby Tuesday of Russellville, Inc. (2)
115 E Harrell Dr, Russellville, AR 72802
Tel.: (479) 858-7151
Restaurant Operating Services
N.A.I.C.S.: 722511

Ruby Tuesday of Salisbury, Inc. (2)
2300 N Salisbury Blvd Ste H101, Salisbury, MD 21801
Tel.: (410) 546-5049
Web Site: http://www.rubytuesday.com
Restaurant Operating Services
N.A.I.C.S.: 722511

Ruby Tuesday of Southcase, Inc. (2)
13145 S Orange Blossom Trl, Orlando, FL 32837-6599
Tel.: (407) 854-8308
Restaurant Operating Services
N.A.I.C.S.: 722511

NRG MEDIA, LLC
2875 Mount Vernon Rd SE, Cedar Rapids, IA 52403
Tel.: (319) 862-0300
Web Site: http://www.nrgmedia.com
Year Founded: 2005
Sales Range: $200-249.9 Million
Emp.: 452
Operator of AM & FM Radio Stations
N.A.I.C.S.: 516110
Mary K. Quass *(Pres & CEO)*
Jo Ann Carstensen *(Mgr-Corp Bus)*
Chuck DuCoty *(COO)*
Erica Dreyer *(Dir-Integrated Media)*
Shane Sparks *(Gen Mgr)*
Jim Smith *(CFO)*
George Nicholas *(Dir-Engrg)*
Jeff Winfield *(Dir-Programming)*
Cynthia Lohman *(Gen Counsel & Dir-HR)*
Allyson Hillman *(Mgr-Market)*

NRI INC.
1015 18th St NW Ste 710, Washington, DC 20036-5206
Tel.: (202) 466-4670
Web Site: http://www.nri-staffing.com
Year Founded: 1967
Sales Range: $10-24.9 Million
Emp.: 20
Temporary Help Service
N.A.I.C.S.: 561320
Robert Mulberger *(Pres & CEO)*
Bob McClimans *(Exec VP)*

NRI REAL ESTATE INVESTMENT & TECHNOLOGY, INC.
1340 S Dixie Hwy Ste 612, Coral Gables, FL 33146
Tel.: (305) 529-9928   MD
Year Founded: 2021
Rev.: $37,084,303
Assets: $199,231,389
Liabilities: $149,151,363
Net Worth: $50,080,026
Earnings: ($10,986,189)
Fiscal Year-end: 12/31/22
Real Estate Investment Services
N.A.I.C.S.: 531190
Brent Reynolds *(Pres)*
Charles D. Nolan Jr. *(Chm)*

NRI USA LLC
13200 S Bdwy, Los Angeles, CA 90061
Tel.: (323) 345-6456
Web Site: http://www.nri-distribution.com
Year Founded: 2011
Sales Range: $25-49.9 Million
Emp.: 350
Business Management Services
N.A.I.C.S.: 561499
Chris Maydaniuk *(Pres)*
Peter Mckenna *(CEO)*
Will Jordan *(Dir-Operational Support & Strategy)*
Ray Dale-Johnson *(Acct Dir)*
Sunny Bagri *(Dir-IT)*

NRT TECHNOLOGIES INC.
3525 E Post Rd Ste 120, Las Vegas, NV 89120
Tel.: (702) 851-4747

NRT TECHNOLOGIES INC.

NRT Technologies Inc.—(Continued)
Web Site: http://www.nrttech.com
Year Founded: 1993
Human Resource Consulting Services
N.A.I.C.S.: 541612
John Dominelli *(Founder & CEO)*
Michael Dominelli *(CMO & Exec VP)*
Aron Ezra *(Chief Digital Officer)*
Diran Kludjian *(Exec VP-Sls)*
Rosa Laricchia *(Exec VP-Client Rels)*
Joe Coady *(Sr VP-Sys & Dev)*
Gary Lindsay *(Sr VP-Svcs & Ops)*

Subsidiaries:

VisuaLimits, LLC (1)
2505 Anthem Vlg Dr Ste E-430, Henderson, NV 89052
Tel.: (702) 498-0986
Web Site: http://www.visualimits.com
Electronic Parts & Equipment Merchant Whslr
N.A.I.C.S.: 423690
Perry Stasi *(Pres & CEO)*

NSC TECHNOLOGIES, INC.
500 Crawford St Ste401, Portsmouth, VA 23707-2019
Tel.: (866) 672-2677
Web Site: http://www.nsc-tech.com
Year Founded: 2000
Staffing & Recruiting Services
N.A.I.C.S.: 561311
Paul J. Rodriguez *(CEO)*

Subsidiaries:

Staff Matters Inc. (1)
2251 E Grant Rd, Tucson, AZ 85719-3414
Tel.: (520) 647-9100
Web Site: http://www.staffmattersinc.com
Employment Placement Agencies
N.A.I.C.S.: 561311
Garrett Kowalewski *(CEO)*

Superior Resource Group, Inc. (1)
126 N Madison St, Green Bay, WI 54301
Tel.: (920) 432-5400
Web Site: http://www.superior-rg.com
Engineeering Services
N.A.I.C.S.: 541330
Brian Michaud *(Branch Mgr)*

NSGDATACOM, INC.
5112 Pegasus Ct Ste X, Frederick, MD 21704
Tel.: (301) 662-5926
Web Site: http://www.nsgdata.com
Year Founded: 1991
Software & Hardware Engineering & Development
N.A.I.C.S.: 334210
Graham King *(Founder & Pres)*
Richard Yalen *(CEO)*
Dave Parker *(Dir-Intl Sls & Ops)*

NSI INSURANCE GROUP
8181 NW 154th St Ste 230, Miami Lakes, FL 33016-5882
Tel.: (305) 556-1488
Web Site: http://www.nsigroup.org
Insurance Agencies & Brokerages
N.A.I.C.S.: 524210
Josette Toussaint Rigaud *(Acct Mgr)*

Subsidiaries:

Insure-Link, Inc. (1)
14050 NW 14th St Ste 170, Sunrise, FL 33323
Tel.: (954) 308-1348
Web Site: http://www.preferredlinkins.com
Emp.: 40
Insurance Agencies & Brokerage Services
N.A.I.C.S.: 524210
Shelly-Ann Bryce *(Pres)*

NSI LAB SOLUTIONS, INC.
7212 Acc Blvd, Raleigh, NC 27617
Tel.: (919) 789-3000
Web Site: http://www.nsi-es.com

Year Founded: 1982
Food Microbiology Proficiency Testing Program
N.A.I.C.S.: 325998
Mark Hammersla *(Pres)*
Cheryl Russell *(Mgr-Logistics)*
Mike Birckhead *(Mgr-Lab)*

NSK & ASSOCIATES, INC.
2 Liberty Sq 7th Fl, Boston, MA 02109
Tel.: (617) 303-0480   MA
Web Site: http://www.nskinc.com
Year Founded: 1997
Sales Range: $1-9.9 Million
Emp.: 50
Information Technology Consulting & Outsourcing Services
N.A.I.C.S.: 541519
Ryan Hickey *(VP-Pro Svcs)*
Nancy Swan Keddy *(Founder & Sr Partner)*
Timothy Lasonde *(Pres)*
Ahmed Fadili *(VP-Managed IT Svcs)*

NSPHERE INC.
100 Franklin St 5th Fl, Boston, MA 02110
Tel.: (617) 933-7500
Web Site: http://www.directorym.com
Year Founded: 2002
Rev.: $17,000,000
Emp.: 100
Electronic Media, Internet/Web Design, Web (Banner Ads, Pop-ups, etc.), Yellow Pages Advertising
N.A.I.C.S.: 541810
Panos Bethanis *(Co-Founder & CEO)*
Jim Woodroffe *(Co-Founder & CTO)*
Jean-Eric Penicaud *(COO)*
Michael Powers *(VP-Strategic Dev)*
Imad Qawi *(Chief Architect)*
Steve Burr *(Chief Revenue Officer)*
Chris Williams *(VP-Ops & Legal Affairs)*
Ruy Cuadra *(VP-Ops)*
William Pasos *(VP-Strategic Partnerships)*

NSPIRE HEALTH, INC.
1830 Lefthand Cir, Longmont, CO 80501
Tel.: (303) 666-5555
Web Site: http://www.nspirehealth.com
Year Founded: 1990
Sales Range: $10-24.9 Million
Emp.: 75
Surgical & Medical Instruments Mfr
N.A.I.C.S.: 339112
Michael Sims *(Pres)*
Dan Calore *(Mgr-Natl Svs)*

Subsidiaries:

nSpire Health GmbH (1)
Schlimpfhofer Strasse 14, 97723, Bad Kissingen, Germany
Tel.: (49) 973681810
Web Site: http://de.nspirehealth.com
Surgical & Medical Instruments Mfr
N.A.I.C.S.: 339112

nSpire Health Ltd. (1)
Unit 10 Harforde Court, John Tate Road, Hertford, SG13 7NW, United Kingdom
Tel.: (44) 1992526300
Web Site: http://www.nspirehealth.com
Sales Range: $10-24.9 Million
Emp.: 20
Surgical & Medical Instruments Mfr
N.A.I.C.S.: 339112

NSR SOLUTIONS INC.
702 Russell Ave Ste 305, Gaithersburg, MD 20877
Tel.: (301) 299-4508
Web Site: http://www.nsrsolutions.com

Year Founded: 2003
Sales Range: $10-24.9 Million
Emp.: 136
Information Technology Consulting Services
N.A.I.C.S.: 541512
Ali Rassoulpour *(CFO)*

NSS ENTERPRISES, INC.
3115 Frenchmens Rd, Toledo, OH 43607-2918
Tel.: (419) 531-2121   OH
Web Site: http://www.nss.com
Year Founded: 1911
Sales Range: $25-49.9 Million
Emp.: 170
Floor & Carpet Cleaning Equipment Mfr
N.A.I.C.S.: 333310
Ronald P. Tonies *(CEO & CFO)*
Ruben Arreguin *(Mgr)*

Subsidiaries:

NSS Enterprises, Inc. - NSS European Division (1)
Unit 7 55 Nottingham Rd Pinfold Business Park, Stapleford, NG9 8AD, Nottingham, United Kingdom
Tel.: (44) 115 939 1568
Web Site: http://www.nssinc.co.uk
Floor Care Equipment Mfr
N.A.I.C.S.: 333310

NTA GRAPHICS INC.
501 Republic Cir, Birmingham, AL 35214
Tel.: (205) 798-2123
Web Site: http://www.northtoledographics.com
Year Founded: 1948
Sales Range: $10-24.9 Million
Offset Printing Services
N.A.I.C.S.: 323111

Subsidiaries:

NTA Graphics South, Inc. (1)
501 Republic Cir, Birmingham, AL 35214
Tel.: (205) 798-2123
Web Site: http://www.ntagraphics.com
Sales Range: $1-9.9 Million
Offset Printing Services
N.A.I.C.S.: 323111
Rodney Parker *(VP)*

NTC GROUP
3 Pickwick Plz, Greenwich, CT 06830-5538
Tel.: (203) 862-2800   DE
Web Site: http://www.ntcgroupinc.com
Year Founded: 1985
Sales Range: $50-74.9 Million
Emp.: 2
Provider of Investment Services
N.A.I.C.S.: 541611
Thomas C. Foley *(Chm)*
Susan Ogden *(Mgr-Acctg)*
Christene Jones *(Pres & CEO)*

NTC MAZZUCA CONTRACTING
10907 Guilford Rd Ste A, Annapolis Junction, MD 20701
Tel.: (410) 964-0101
Web Site: http://www.ntcmd.com
Year Founded: 2001
Sales Range: $25-49.9 Million
Emp.: 27
Commercial & Institutional Building Construction
N.A.I.C.S.: 236220
Jennifer Gunther *(Mgr-Acctg)*
David Mazzuca *(Pres)*
Matt Klaff *(VP-Bus Dev)*
Ed Dolson *(Exec VP)*
Leonard Auchincloss *(VP)*

U.S. PRIVATE

NTE SOLUTIONS
24 Cathedral Place Ste 300, Saint Augustine, FL 32084
Tel.: (904) 687-1857
Web Site: http://www.nteenergy.com
Year Founded: 2009
Sales Range: $1-9.9 Million
Emp.: 20
Infrastructure Services
N.A.I.C.S.: 541330
Seth Shortlidge *(Pres & CEO)*
Tim Eves *(Principal)*
Michael Green *(Principal)*
Chris Rega *(Principal)*
Stephanie Clarkson *(CFO)*

NTELICOR, LP
302 N Market St Ste 250, Dallas, TX 75202
Tel.: (214) 655-2600   TX
Web Site: http://www.ntelicor.com
Year Founded: 1998
Sales Range: $10-24.9 Million
Emp.: 100
IT Staffing & Consulting
N.A.I.C.S.: 561311
Mark Cohen *(Pres)*
Deanna Rivera *(Mgr-HR)*

NTELX, INC.
1945 Old Gallows Rd Ste 700, Vienna, VA 22182
Tel.: (703) 356-5050
Web Site: http://www.ntelx.com
Year Founded: 1999
Sales Range: $1-9.9 Million
Emp.: 1,075
Software Publisher
N.A.I.C.S.: 513210
Rob Quartel *(Chm & CEO)*
Robert Rosenberg *(CFO & Mng Dir-Pub Sector Solutions)*
Dhiren Patel *(Pres)*

NTH CONSULTANTS, LTD.
480 Ford Field 2000 Brush St, Detroit, MI 48226
Tel.: (313) 237-3900   MI
Web Site: http://www.nthconsultants.com
Year Founded: 1968
Sales Range: $100-124.9 Million
Emp.: 250
Engineering Consulting & Environmental Services
N.A.I.C.S.: 541330
Keith M. Swaffar *(Chm)*
Kevin B. Hoppe *(Pres & CEO)*
Jeffrey P. Jaros *(Sr VP)*

Subsidiaries:

NTH Consultants, Ltd. (1)
480 Ford Field Gate G 2000 Brush St, Detroit, MI 48226
Tel.: (313) 237-3900
Web Site: http://www.nthconsultants.com
Sales Range: $10-24.9 Million
Emp.: 50
Engineering Consulting
N.A.I.C.S.: 541380
Keith Swaffar *(COO & VP)*
April Williams *(Coord-Billing)*
Jim Parsons *(Dir-Ops-Laboratory)*
Rick Burns *(Sr VP)*

NTH Consultants, Ltd. (1)
444 Creamery Way Ste 100, Exton, PA 19341-2847
Tel.: (610) 524-2300
Web Site: http://www.nthconsultants.com
Sales Range: $25-49.9 Million
Emp.: 230
Geotechnical & Environmental Engineering
N.A.I.C.S.: 541330
Kevin B. Hoppe *(Pres & CEO)*

NTH Consultants, Ltd. (1)
1430 Munroe Ave NW Ste 180, Grand Rapids, MI 49505 (100%)
Tel.: (616) 957-3690

COMPANIES

Web Site: http://www.nthconsultants.com
Sales Range: $10-24.9 Million
Emp.: 20
Environmental & Structural Engineering Consultation
N.A.I.C.S.: 541690

NTH Consultants, Ltd. (1)
608 S Washington Ave, Lansing, MI 48933-2304
Tel.: (517) 484-6900
Web Site: http://www.nthconsultants.com
Sales Range: $10-24.9 Million
Emp.: 30
Geotechnical & Environmental Engineering
N.A.I.C.S.: 541330
Jeffrey P. Jaros *(COO & Exec VP)*

NTH Consultants, Ltd. (1)
41780 Six Mile Rd, Northville, MI 48168
Tel.: (248) 553-6300
Web Site: http://www.nthconsultants.com
Sales Range: $10-24.9 Million
Emp.: 130
Engineering Consulting & Environmental Services
N.A.I.C.S.: 541330

NTH GENERATION COMPUTING, INCORPORATED
17055 Camino San Bernardo, San Diego, CA 92127
Tel.: (858) 451-2383
Web Site: http://www.nth.com
Year Founded: 1991
Sales Range: $10-24.9 Million
Emp.: 50
Computer Integration Services
N.A.I.C.S.: 541512
Richard Baldwin *(Chief Strategy Officer)*
Jan Baldwin *(Founder & CEO)*
Jim Russ *(VP-Enterprise Tech)*
Dan Molina *(CTO)*
Todd Burkhardt *(VP-Tech Svcs)*
Dwayne Gilliam *(Sr VP-Sls)*
Joyce Russell *(CFO & Exec VP)*

NTI CORPORATION
9999 Muirlands Blvd, Irvine, CA 92618
Tel.: (949) 421-0720
Web Site: http://www.nticorp.com
Rev.: $5,600,000
Emp.: 40
Developer of Easy-to-Use Software for Digital Media & Storage Management
N.A.I.C.S.: 334112
William Yao *(Pres & CEO)*
David Yao *(Exec VP)*

NTS CORPORATION
600 N Hurstbourne Pkwy Ste 300, Louisville, KY 40222
Tel.: (502) 426-4800
Web Site:
    http://www.ntsdevelopment.com
Year Founded: 1985
Sales Range: $50-74.9 Million
Holding Company; Real Estate Investment & Development
N.A.I.C.S.: 551112
Jack Dale Nichols *(Chm)*
Brian F. Lavin *(Pres & CEO)*
Gregory A. Wells *(CFO & Exec VP)*
David B. Pitchford *(Treas & Sr VP)*
Rosann D. Tafel *(Gen Counsel & Sr VP)*

Subsidiaries:

NTS Development Company (1)
600 N Hurstbourne Pkwy Ste 300, Louisville, KY 40222
Tel.: (502) 426-4800
Web Site: http://www.ntsdevelopment.com
Sales Range: $50-74.9 Million
Emp.: 350
Residential & Commercial Real Estate Development & Property Management Services

N.A.I.C.S.: 237210
Jack Dale Nichols *(Chm)*
Brian F. Lavin *(Pres & CEO)*
Gregory A. Wells *(CFO & Exec VP)*
David B. Pitchford *(Treas & Sr VP)*
Rosann D. Tafel *(Gen Counsel & Sr VP)*
Ellen Lamb *(Dir-Corp Mktg)*
Neil Mitchell *(Sr VP)*
Lewis Borders *(Sr VP-Leasing)*
Michelle Jarboe *(Sr VP-Healthcare Properties)*

Subsidiary (Domestic):

NTS Residential Management Company (2)
600 N Hurstbourne Pkwy Ste 300, Louisville, KY 40222
Tel.: (502) 426-4800
Emp.: 45
Residential Property Management Services
N.A.I.C.S.: 531311
Jack Dale Nichols *(Chm)*
Brian F. Lavin *(Pres & CEO)*
Ellen Lam *(Dir-Mktg)*

NTS Residential Properties, Inc. (2)
600 N Hurstbourne Pkwy Ste 300, Louisville, KY 40222
Tel.: (502) 426-4800
Emp.: 200
Residential Real Estate Development Services
N.A.I.C.S.: 237210
Jack Dale Nichols *(Chm)*
Brian F. Lavin *(Pres & CEO)*

NTS Realty Capital, Inc. (1)
600 N Hurstbourne Pkwy Ste 300, Louisville, KY 40222
Tel.: (502) 426-4800
Web Site: http://www.ntsdevelopment.com
Real Estate Investment Financing Services
N.A.I.C.S.: 522299
Jack Dale Nichols *(Chm)*
Brian F. Lavin *(Pres & CEO)*
David B. Pitchford *(Treas & Sr VP)*

NTS Realty Partners, LLC (1)
600 N Hurstbourne Pkwy Ste 300, Louisville, KY 40222
Tel.: (502) 426-4800
Real Estate Investment Firm
N.A.I.C.S.: 531390
Jack Dale Nichols *(Chm)*
Brian F. Lavin *(Pres & CEO)*
David B. Pitchford *(Treas & Sr VP)*

NTVB MEDIA, INC.
209 Park Dr, Troy, MI 48083
Tel.: (248) 583-4190
Web Site: http://www.ntvbmedia.com
Year Founded: 1981
Sales Range: $1-9.9 Million
Emp.: 50
Commercial Lithographic Printing
N.A.I.C.S.: 323111
Andrew DeAngelis *(Pres)*

Subsidiaries:

TV Guide (1)
3221 W Big Beaver Rd, Troy, MI 48084
Tel.: (248) 458-0120
Web Site: http://www.tvguide.com
TV & Entertainment News, Scoops & Live Event Coverage
N.A.I.C.S.: 513120

NTY FRANCHISE COMPANY
4350 Baker Rd Ste 350, Minnetonka, MN 55343
Tel.: (952) 923-1223
Web Site:
    http://www.ntyfranchise.com
Year Founded: 2007
Resale Retail Franchises
N.A.I.C.S.: 458110
Ron Olson *(Founder & Pres)*

NU CAL FOODS INC.
720 S Stockton Ave, Ripon, CA 95366
Tel.: (209) 254-2200
Web Site: http://www.nucalfoods.com

Year Founded: 1996
Sales Range: $10-24.9 Million
Emp.: 35
Provider of Poultry Products
N.A.I.C.S.: 424410
David Crockett *(Pres)*
Lupe Gutierrez *(Mgr-Customer Svc)*
Mark Powell *(Coord-Quality Assurance)*

NU FLOW AMERICA INC.
7710 Kenamar Ct, San Diego, CA 92121
Tel.: (619) 275-9130
Web Site: http://www.nuflowtech.com
Year Founded: 2005
Sales Range: $10-24.9 Million
Emp.: 111
Plumbing Services
N.A.I.C.S.: 238220
Cameron Sean Manners *(Pres & CEO)*
Bill Turner *(Reg Mgr)*
Dennis Warwick Persaud *(VP-Ops)*
Dee Baker *(Mgr-Contract)*

NU IMAGE FABRICS, INC.
110 W 49th St Ste 901, New York, NY 10018
Tel.: (212) 382-1170
Sales Range: $10-24.9 Million
Emp.: 8
Mfr of Textile Converters
N.A.I.C.S.: 314999
Fred Wunderlich *(Pres)*
Stephanie Earl *(Owner & Mgr-Ops)*

NU IMAGE, INC.
6423 Wilshire Blvd, Los Angeles, CA 90048
Tel.: (310) 388-6900
Web Site: http://www.nuimage.net
Year Founded: 1992
Sales Range: $100-124.9 Million
Emp.: 50
Motion Picture & Video Producer & Distr
N.A.I.C.S.: 512110
Trevor Short *(CFO)*
Avi Lerner *(Founder)*

Subsidiaries:

First Look Holdings, LLC (1)
2000 Ave of the Stars Ste 410, Los Angeles, CA 90067
Tel.: (424) 202-5000
Web Site: http://www.firstlookmedia.com
Sales Range: $75-99.9 Million
Emp.: 500
Holding Company
N.A.I.C.S.: 551112

Subsidiary (Domestic):

First Look Studios, Inc. (2)
5900 Wilshire Blvd Ste 1800, Los Angeles, CA 90036-5018
Tel.: (424) 202-5000
Sales Range: $50-74.9 Million
Motion Picture, Video & Television Program Producer & Distr
N.A.I.C.S.: 512110

Millennium Films, Inc. (1)
6423 Wilshire Blvd, Los Angeles, CA 90048
Tel.: (310) 388-6900
Web Site: http://www.millenniumfilms.com
Sales Range: $25-49.9 Million
Motion Picture Producer
N.A.I.C.S.: 512110
Trevor Short *(Co-Founder & CFO)*
Avi Lerner *(Co-Founder & Chm)*
Boaz Davidson *(Head-Dev & Creative Affairs)*
Lonnie Ramati *(Exec VP-Bus & Legal Affairs)*
Jeffrey Greenstein *(Pres)*

NU VAN TECHNOLOGY INC.
2155 Hwy 1187 PO Box 2293, Mansfield, TX 76063

NU-WA INDUSTRIES, INC.

Tel.: (817) 225-0250
Sales Range: $10-24.9 Million
Emp.: 130
Sales of Semitrailers for Truck Tractors
N.A.I.C.S.: 336212
Greg Geltmeier *(Controller)*
Gavin Worthy *(Co-Owner)*
Richard Worthy *(Co-Owner)*
Jenny Riddle *(Mgr-HR)*

NU-CALGON WHOLESALER INC.
2008 Altom Ct, Saint Louis, MO 63146
Tel.: (314) 523-4429
Web Site: http://www.nucalgon.com
Sales Range: $50-74.9 Million
Emp.: 50
Chemical & Allied Products Merchant Whslr
N.A.I.C.S.: 424690
Robert F. Pierce *(Pres)*
Al Butler *(CEO)*

NU-SASH OF INDIANAPOLIS INCORPORATED
1333 Sadlier Circle West Dr, Indianapolis, IN 46239
Tel.: (317) 874-2780
Web Site:
    http://www.nusashofindianapolis.com
Year Founded: 1975
Sales Range: $10-24.9 Million
Emp.: 85
Mfr of Door & Window Products & Sunrooms
N.A.I.C.S.: 444110
Ron McKee *(Pres)*

NU-SONS ELECTRIC INC.
3630 Shaw Blvd, Naples, FL 34117
Tel.: (239) 435-1990
Web Site:
    http://www.nusonselectric.com
Sales Range: $1-9.9 Million
Emp.: 30
Electrical Contractor
N.A.I.C.S.: 238210
Douglas Nusz *(Pres)*
Brett Withrow *(Project Mgr)*
Cheryl Nusz *(Mgr-Ops)*

NU-TEC ROOFING CONTRACTORS LLC
5025 Emco Dr, Indianapolis, IN 46220-4846
Tel.: (317) 255-4464
Web Site:
    http://www.nutecroofing.com
Year Founded: 1984
Rev.: $27,800,000
Emp.: 340
Roofing, Siding & Sheetmetal Work
N.A.I.C.S.: 238160
Otis Burdine *(Gen Mgr)*
Bruce Bubenzer *(Pres & CEO)*
Mark Wheatley *(Controller)*
Edward Chowning *(CFO)*

NU-WA INDUSTRIES, INC.
3701 Johnson Rd, Chanute, KS 66720-4003
Tel.: (620) 431-2088
Web Site: http://www.nuwa.com
Year Founded: 1969
Sales Range: $10-24.9 Million
Emp.: 300
RVs Mfr
N.A.I.C.S.: 336214
Neil Ford *(Pres)*
Michael Mitchell *(CEO)*
Jan Crawford *(CFO)*

NU-WAY CONCRETE FORMS INC.

Nu-Way Concrete Forms Inc.—(Continued)

NU-WAY CONCRETE FORMS INC.
4190 Hoffmeister Ave, Saint Louis, MO 63125-2205
Tel.: (314) 544-1214
Web Site: http://www.nuwayinc.com
Year Founded: 1955
Sales Range: $25-49.9 Million
Emp.: 204
Mfr of Concrete Forms, Equipment & Accessories
N.A.I.C.S.: 423320
Daphne Rhomberg *(Mgr-Mktg & Sls)*
Pat Shocklee *(Mgr-Svc)*
Justin Finley *(Coord-Rental)*
Kevin Krus *(Mgr-Warehouse)*
Pat Shocklee *(Mgr-Svcs & Mgr-Svc)*

NU-WAY INDUSTRIES, INC.
555 Howard Ave, Des Plaines, IL 60018
Tel.: (847) 298-7710
Web Site: http://www.nuwayindustries.com
Sales Range: $25-49.9 Million
Emp.: 250
Mfr of Sheet Metal
N.A.I.C.S.: 332322
Steven Southwell *(Pres)*
Mary Howard *(Exec VP)*
Donald J. Ziemba *(Controller)*
Eric Petty *(Dir-Bus Dev)*

NU-WAY SPEAKER PRODUCTS INC.
945 Anita Ave, Antioch, IL 60002
Tel.: (847) 395-5141
Sales Range: $10-24.9 Million
Emp.: 35
Electronic Loads & Power Supplies
N.A.I.C.S.: 334419
Claude D. Smith *(CEO)*
Bob Tate *(Mgr-Matls)*
Steve Loberger *(Mgr-Sls)*
Maureen Emmrich *(Office Mgr)*
Jim Smith *(VP)*
Jim Smith *(VP)*

NU-WAY SUPPLY COMPANY INC.
5227 Auburn Rd, Utica, MI 48317-4113
Tel.: (586) 731-4000
Web Site: http://www.nuwaysupply.com
Year Founded: 1945
Sales Range: $10-24.9 Million
Emp.: 104
Distr of Plumbing Fixtures, Equipment & Supplies
N.A.I.C.S.: 423720
Wince Ranelli *(Chm)*

NUCCI BROS INC.
145 Oval Dr, Islandia, NY 11749
Tel.: (631) 234-6300
Web Site: http://www.nuccibros.com
Rev.: $25,281,264
Emp.: 20
Swimming Pools, Equipment & Supplies
N.A.I.C.S.: 423910
Robert Higgins *(Gen Mgr)*
Pat Dolan *(Mgr-Office-Pur)*

NUCKLES OIL COMPANY INC.
1020 Bloomington Ave, Bloomington, CA 92316
Tel.: (909) 877-2651
Web Site: http://www.meritoil.com
Sales Range: $50-74.9 Million
Emp.: 40
Petroleum Products
N.A.I.C.S.: 424720

Ronald Nuckles *(Pres)*

NUCLEAR MEDICINE PROFESSIONALS, INC.
4566 NW 5th Blvd Ste K, Gainesville, FL 32609
Tel.: (352) 327-1000
Web Site: http://www.mobilenuclear.com
Year Founded: 2001
Rev.: $2,600,000
Emp.: 11
Medical & Hospital Equipment Whslr
N.A.I.C.S.: 423450
Traci Millett *(CFO)*
John Millett *(Founder)*
Matthew Hart *(Treas)*

NUCLEUS BIOLOGICS LLC
10929 Technology Pl, San Diego, CA 92127
Tel.: (858) 251-2010
Web Site: http://nucleusbiologics.com
Year Founded: 2016
Biotechnology Research
N.A.I.C.S.: 541714
David Sheehan *(Pres & CEO)*
Will Ater *(CFO)*
Michael Morgan *(VP-Sls)*
Brad Taylor *(VP-Mktg)*

Subsidiaries:

Primorigen Biosciences Inc. (1)
510 Charmany Dr, Madison, WI 53719
Tel.: (608) 441-8332
Chemicals Mfr
N.A.I.C.S.: 325412

NUCOMPASS MOBILITY SERVICES INC.
6800 Koll Ctr Pkwy, Pleasanton, CA 94566
Tel.: (925) 734-3434 DE
Web Site: http://www.nucompassmobility.com
Year Founded: 1965
Relocation Management Services
N.A.I.C.S.: 541618
Frank Patitucci *(Chm)*
Elise Riordan *(CTO)*
Serena Torvik *(VP-Bus Process & Gen Counsel)*
Ron Whitmill *(CEO)*
Cara Skourtis *(VP-Corp Knowledge & Experience)*
Dave Marron *(VP-Sls & Mktg)*
Lesley DeHoney *(VP-Worldwide Ops)*
Paul Sorrentino *(VP-Corp Partnership)*

NUCOURSE DISTRIBUTION INC.
7465 Lampson Ave, Garden Grove, CA 92841
Tel.:
Web Site: http://www.resellers.nucourse.com
Year Founded: 2008
Sales Range: $25-49.9 Million
Emp.: 40
Wireless Product Accessories
N.A.I.C.S.: 334220
Nick Seedorf *(Pres)*

NUECES COUNTY MHMR COMMUNITY CENTER
1630 S Brownlee Blvd, Corpus Christi, TX 78404
Tel.: (361) 886-6900 TX
Web Site: http://www.bhcnc.org
Year Founded: 1972
Sales Range: $10-24.9 Million
Emp.: 489
Behavioral Healthcare Services
N.A.I.C.S.: 623220

Lorraine Moon *(Dir-Ops & Authority Svcs)*
Mike Davis *(CEO)*

NUECES FARM CENTER INC.
7510 Hwy 37, Corpus Christi, TX 78409
Tel.: (361) 387-1572
Web Site: http://www.nuecespower.com
Year Founded: 1989
Sales Range: $10-24.9 Million
Emp.: 80
Distr of Farm & Construction Equipment
N.A.I.C.S.: 423820
Clifton W. Bradshaw *(Pres)*
Will Shook *(Mgr-Product Svcs)*

NUESTRA CLINICA DEL VALLE, INC.
801 W 1st St, San Juan, TX 78589
Tel.: (956) 787-8915 TX
Web Site: http://www.nuestraclinicadelvalle.org
Year Founded: 1971
Sales Range: $10-24.9 Million
Emp.: 343
Health Care Srvices
N.A.I.C.S.: 622110
Carolyn Huff *(Chief Dental Officer)*
Orlando Lucio *(CFO)*
Lucy Ramirez *(CEO)*
Juanita Rangel *(Chm)*
Juan F. Garcia *(Treas)*
Viola Elizondo *(Vice Chm)*

NUETERRA CAPITAL MANAGEMENT, LLC
11221 Roe Ave Ste 320, Leawood, KS 66221
Tel.: (913) 387-0510
Web Site: http://www.nueterra.com
Privater Equity Firm
N.A.I.C.S.: 523999
Dan Tasset *(Chm & CEO)*
Dan Saale *(CFO)*

Subsidiaries:

Benefit Management Inc. (1)
2015 16th St, Great Bend, KS 67530
Web Site: http://www.benefitmanagementllc.com
Health Benefits Administration Services
N.A.I.C.S.: 524298
Heather Miessler *(Sr VP-Ops)*
Mike Minton *(Sr VP-Sls & Client Sevcs)*

Blue Chip Surgical Center Partners, LLC (1)
312 Walnut St Suite 1120, Cincinnati, OH 45202 (100%)
Tel.: (513) 723-2300
Web Site: http://www.bcvc.com
Ambulatory Surgical & Emergency Centers
N.A.I.C.S.: 621493
Jeff Leland *(Exec VP)*
Angie Fischer *(CFO)*
Jack Wyant *(Mng Dir)*

ValueHealth LLC (1)
11221 Roe Ave, Leawood, KS 66211
Tel.: (888) 887-2619
Web Site: http://www.valuehealth.com
Ambulatory Health Care Services
N.A.I.C.S.: 621999
Don Bisbee *(CEO)*

Subsidiary (Domestic):

Surgery Center of Lancaster, LLC (2)
810 Plz Blvd, Lancaster, PA 17601
Tel.: (717) 431-2368
Web Site: http://www.scoflancaster.com
Outpatient Surgical Services
N.A.I.C.S.: 622110
Jan Tucker *(Office Mgr)*

NUEVO ADVERTISING GROUP, INC.
1990 Main St Ste 750, Sarasota, FL 34236
Tel.: (941) 752-4433
Web Site: http://www.nuevoadvertising.com
Year Founded: 2004
Sales Range: $10-24.9 Million
Emp.: 6
Advertising Agencies
N.A.I.C.S.: 541810
Pedro Perez *(Co-Owner & VP-Media)*
Roseanne Avella-Perez *(Co-Owner)*

NUFFER SMITH TUCKER, INC.
4045 3rd Ave Ste 200, San Diego, CA 92103
Tel.: (619) 296-0605
Web Site: http://www.nstpr.com
Year Founded: 1974
Sales Range: $1-9.9 Million
Emp.: 20
Advetising Agency
N.A.I.C.S.: 541810
Bill Trumpfheller *(Pres)*
Teresa Siles *(Mng Dir & Sr VP)*
Sarah Czarnecki *(Acct Exec)*
Ventura Olvera *(Acct Coord)*

NUGEN HOLDINGS, INC.
44645 Guilford Dr Ste 201, Ashburn, VA 20147
Tel.: (703) 858-0036 DE
Web Site: http://www.ngmcorp.com
Year Founded: 2006
Sales Range: $1-9.9 Million
Emp.: 14
Magnet Electrical Motor Systems, Controllers, Vehicle Interface Modules Systems, Components & Software
N.A.I.C.S.: 335312
Eric Takamura *(Chm, Pres & CEO)*
John Salatino *(VP-Engrg & Programs)*
Henry Y.L. Toh *(Vice Chm & Exec VP)*
Marshall G. Webb *(CFO)*

NUGENT SAND COMPANY
1833 River Rd, Louisville, KY 40206
Tel.: (502) 584-0158
Web Site: http://www.nugentsand.com
Rev.: $18,000,000
Emp.: 87
Common Sand Mining
N.A.I.C.S.: 212321
Steve Showey *(VP)*
Robert L. Chandonnet *(Owner & Pes)*
Thomas C. Nugent III *(Co-Pres)*

NUGGET MARKET INC.
168 Ct St, Woodland, CA 95695
Tel.: (530) 669-3300
Web Site: http://www.nuggetmarket.com
Year Founded: 1926
Rev.: $100,167,614
Emp.: 1,151
Cooperative Food Store
N.A.I.C.S.: 445110
Eric Stille *(Pres & CEO)*
Dennis Lindsay *(CFO)*
Gene Stille *(Chm)*
Kate Stille *(Dir-Mktg)*

Subsidiaries:

Glen Ellen Village Market (1)
13751 Arnold Dr, Glen Ellen, CA 95442
Tel.: (707) 996-6728
Web Site: http://www.glenellenvillagemarket.org
Supermarket & Grocery Stores

N.A.I.C.S.: 445110
Leslie Crook (Dir-HR)

Sonoma Market Inc. (1)
500 W Napa St Ste 550, Sonoma, CA 95476
Tel.: (707) 996-3411
Web Site: http://sonomamarket.net
Supermarket & Grocery Stores
N.A.I.C.S.: 445110

NUJAK DEVELOPMENT, INC.
714 N Massachusetts Ave, Lakeland, FL 33801
Tel.: (863) 686-1565 FL
Web Site: http://www.nujak.com
Year Founded: 1992
Sales Range: $1-9.9 Million
Emp.: 20
Full-Service Construction & Commercial Real Estate Services
N.A.I.C.S.: 236220
Frank Kendrick (Pres & CEO)

NUKK-FREEMAN & CERRA, P.C.
26 Main St Ste 301, Chatham, NJ 07928
Tel.: (973) 564-9100
Web Site: http://www.nfclegal.com
Sales Range: $1-9.9 Million
Emp.: 26
Employment Law Consulting Services
N.A.I.C.S.: 922190
Suzanne M. Cerra (Partner)
Holly English (Partner)
Kerrie R. Heslin (Partner)
Katherin Nukk-Freeman (CEO)
Robin H. Rome (Partner)
Rachel G. Freedberg (Dir-HR & Org Dev)
Claudia E. Lechtman (Dir-Mktg)

NULAB, INC.
2161 Logan St, Clearwater, FL 33765
Tel.: (727) 446-1126
Web Site: http://www.nulabinc.com
Year Founded: 1992
Sales Range: $10-24.9 Million
Emp.: 80
Nutritional Supplements Mfr
N.A.I.C.S.: 325411
Marisol Defino (Dir-Product Dev)
Teresa Tinoco (Gen Mgr)

NULAID FOODS INC.
200 W 5th St, Ripon, CA 95366-2766
Tel.: (209) 599-2121 CA
Web Site: http://www.nulaid.com
Year Founded: 1963
Sales Range: $75-99.9 Million
Emp.: 50
Packaged Egg Products Mfr & Distributor
N.A.I.C.S.: 424440
David Crockett (Pres & CEO)
Dean Peters (VP-IT)

NUMA TOOL CO.
646 Thompson Rd, Thompson, CT 06277
Tel.: (860) 923-9551
Web Site: http://www.numahammers.com
Year Founded: 1985
Rev.: $12,000,000
Emp.: 72
Mfr; & Designer of Down Hole Hammers & Bits
N.A.I.C.S.: 333131
Ralph H. Leonard (Pres)

NUMARK CREDIT UNION
1654 Terry Dr Route 6, Joliet, IL 60434-2729
Tel.: (815) 729-3211 IL
Web Site: http://www.numarkcu.org
Year Founded: 1954
Sales Range: $10-24.9 Million
Credit Union Operator
N.A.I.C.S.: 522130
Kevin Quinn (CIO)
Debbie Reed (VP-Fin)
Linda Sachaschik (Mgr-HR)
Kari Endres (VP-Mktg)
Karen Wilson (VP-Lending)
Michelle Balog (Exec VP)
Jessica Mellen (VP-Ops)

NUMARK LABORATORIES, INC.
164 Northfield Ave, Edison, NJ 08837-3855
Tel.: (732) 417-1870 DE
Web Site: http://www.numarklabs.com
Year Founded: 1987
Sales Range: $10-24.9 Million
Emp.: 20
Marketer of Over-the-Counter & Prescription Products
N.A.I.C.S.: 424210
Robert C. Stites (Asst Dir-Product)
Patrick M. Lonergan (Pres & CEO)
Moaiz F. Daya (Co-Founder & VP-Mktg)
Benjamin M. Deavenport (VP-Fin)

NUMATIC ENGINEERING INC.
7915 Ajay Dr, Sun Valley, CA 91352
Tel.: (818) 768-1200
Web Site: http://www.numaticengineering.com
Year Founded: 1955
Sales Range: $10-24.9 Million
Emp.: 43
Distr of Pneumatic & Electrical Automation Control Components
N.A.I.C.S.: 423830
Steve Leach (Pres)
Dave Leach (CFO)
Janet Burton (Mgr-Customer Svc & HR)

NUMBERWORKS, LLC
203 S 13th St Ste 200, Minneapolis, MN 55403
Tel.: (612) 230-7100
Web Site: http://www.sallllc.com
Sales Range: $1-9.9 Million
Emp.: 115
Financial Staffing Services
N.A.I.C.S.: 561320
Jeff Donnay (Mgr-Sls)
Denise Doll-Kiefer (CFO)
Joan Foley (Mgr-Acctg)
Craig Dexheimer (Dir-Ops & Admin)
John Folkstead (Founder)
Amy Langer (Founder)
Nance Torrence (Mgr-Ops)

NUMECENT HOLDINGS LTD.
15635 Alton Pkwy Ste 100, Irvine, CA 92618
Tel.: (949) 833-2800
Web Site: http://www.numecent.com
Software Publisher
N.A.I.C.S.: 513210
Osman Kent (Co-Founder)
Arthur S. Hitomi (Co-Founder & CTO)
Ed Corrente (CFO)
Tom Lagatta (Pres & CEO)
Bernard Harguindeguy (Chm)
Doug Pfiffner (CTO)
Mark Khandjian (COO)
Steve Sickler (Sr VP-Sls)

Subsidiaries:

Approxy Inc. (1)
15635 Alton Pkwy Ste 100, Irvine, CA 92618
Tel.: (949) 833-9498
Web Site: http://www.approxy.com
Software & Technology Development Services

N.A.I.C.S.: 513210
Yavuz Ahiska (Co-Founder & Chm)

NUMERICA CORPORATION
4850 Hahns Peak Dr Ste 200, Loveland, CO 80538
Tel.: (970) 461-2000
Web Site: http://www.numerica.us
Year Founded: 1996
Sales Range: $1-9.9 Million
Emp.: 49
Scientific Research & Development Services
N.A.I.C.S.: 541715
Aubrey B. Poore (Founder & Chief Scientific Officer)
Jeff Poore (Pres)
Benjamin J. Slocumb (Program Dir)
Nick Coult (VP-Interactive Intelligence Sys)
Shawn Herman (Program Dir)
Brian Strock (Mgr-Bus)
Jeff Aristoff (Mgr-Program)
Philip Du Toit (Mgr-Program)
Nino Gadaleta (Mgr-Program)
Jason Johnson (Mgr-Program)
J. Nate Knight (Program Dir)
Deanna Hildenbrand (Asst VP-Mktg & Comm)
Don Wick (Dir-Ops)

NUMERICA CREDIT UNION
14610 E Sprague Ave, Spokane Valley, WA 99216
Tel.: (509) 535-7613
Web Site: http://www.numericacu.com
Rev.: $34,300,000
Emp.: 300
Credit Union
N.A.I.C.S.: 522130
Nancy Norbury-Harter (Chief Branding Officer)
Jennifer Lehn (COO)
Cindy Leaver (CFO)
Kelley Ferguson (CIO)
Nathan L. Vore (Program Mgr-Small Bus & Pro Svcs)
Kenneth Plank (Chief Lending Officer)
Chris Blotsky (Asst VP-Home Loan Center)
Greg Hansen (Sr VP-Bus Svcs)
Rob Stephens (Sr VP-Fin)
Dan Pearse (VP)
Curt Fuller (VP)

NUMERICAL CONCEPTS, INC.
Ft Harrison Indus Park 4040 1st Pkwy, Terre Haute, IN 47804-4235
Tel.: (812) 466-5261 IN
Web Site: http://www.numericalconcepts.com
Year Founded: 1973
Sales Range: $10-24.9 Million
Emp.: 40
Special Industrial Machinery Designer & Mfr
N.A.I.C.S.: 333248
Nancy S. Jones (Pres)

Subsidiaries:

McCain Bindery Systems, Inc. (1)
14545 W Edison Dr, New Lenox, IL 60451
Tel.: (815) 462-1129
Web Site: http://www.mccainbindery.com
Bookbinding, Magazine Binding & Newspaper Inserting Machinery Rebuilding & Relocating Services
N.A.I.C.S.: 423830

NUMINA GROUP, INCORPORATED
10331 Werch Dr, Woodridge, IL 60517
Tel.: (630) 343-2600 IL

Web Site: http://www.numinagroup.com
Year Founded: 1986
Emp.: 25
Industrial Automation & Conveyor Control Systems Designer & Mfr
N.A.I.C.S.: 333922
Daniel T. Hanrahan (Co-Founder)
Mark Woodworth (Co-Founder)

Subsidiaries:

INDEV Gauging Systems, Inc. (1)
6830 Forest Hills Rd, Loves Park, IL 61111-4367
Tel.: (815) 282-4463
Web Site: http://www.indevsystems.com
Emp.: 5
In-Line Measurement & Process Control Systems Mfr
N.A.I.C.S.: 334513
Bruce A. Johnson (Mgr-Sls)
Jim Wicker (Mgr-Sls & Bus Dev)

NUPATH, INC.
147 New Boston St, Woburn, MA 01801
Tel.: (781) 935-7057 MA
Web Site: http://www.nupathinc.org
Year Founded: 1968
Sales Range: $10-24.9 Million
Emp.: 453
Disabled People Assistance Services
N.A.I.C.S.: 624120
Daniel Harrison (Pres & CEO)
Ted Horn (VP-Quality & Trng)
Laure Porter (VP-HR)
Daniel Lannan (Sr VP-Program Ops)
Karen Sullivan (VP-Residential Ops)
Greg Morris (Sr VP-Admin Ops)
William Yetz (Sr VP-Fin)
Diann Sespico (Chm)
Beatriz Grayson (Sec-Recording)
Barbara Crystal (Treas)
Brett Reily (VP-Mktg & Comm)
John Rossi (Vice Chm)

NUPOWER, LLC
20 Marshall St Ste 300, Norwalk, CT 06854
Tel.: (203) 354-1529
Year Founded: 2003
Sales Range: $25-49.9 Million
Emp.: 2
Renewable Power Project Development
N.A.I.C.S.: 221118
Daniel J. Donovan (Mng Partner)
Scott Gilmartin (VP)

NURSE ON CALL HOME HEALTHCARE
1926 10th Ave N Ste 400, Lake Worth, FL 33461
Tel.: (561) 586-9148
Web Site: http://www.nurseoncallfl.com
Emp.: 2,000
Women Healthcare Services
N.A.I.C.S.: 621610
Dale Clift (CEO)

NUSENDA CREDIT UNION
4100 Pan American Fwy NE, Albuquerque, NM 87107
Tel.: (505) 889-7755
Web Site: https://www.nusenda.org
Year Founded: 1936
Emp.: 569
Financial Services
N.A.I.C.S.: 523999

Subsidiaries:

Western Heritage Bank (1)
230 S Alameda Blvd, Las Cruces, NM 88005-2619
Tel.: (575) 541-0058
Web Site: http://www.westernheritagebank.com

Nusenda Credit Union—(Continued)
Commericial Banking
N.A.I.C.S.: 522110
Cindy Bennett *(CEO)*
Teryl Beck *(Sr VP-Residential Mortgage Financing)*

NUSPIRE CORP
3155 Dallavo Ct, Commerce Township, MI 48390-1607
Tel.: (877) 435-1640
Web Site: http://www.nuspire.com
Network Security Services
N.A.I.C.S.: 518210
Saylor Frase *(Chm)*
Greg Yarrington *(COO)*
Ken Carson *(CFO)*
Matt Corney *(CTO)*
Joe Breen *(Chie Revenue Officer)*
Dan Hoban *(Chief Strategy Officer)*
Lewie Dunsworth *(CEO)*

NUSS TRUCK GROUP
6500 Hwy 63 S, Rochester, MN 55904
Tel.: (507) 288-9488
Web Site: http://www.nussgrp.com
Rev.: $55,600,000
Emp.: 200
Trucks; Tractors & Trailers: New & Used
N.A.I.C.S.: 441110
Scott Nelson *(Controller)*
Brad Nuss *(VP)*
Greg Nuss *(VP)*

NUSSER INDUSTRIES INC.
1 Howard Ave, Somerset, NJ 08873
Tel.: (732) 560-8111
Rev.: $14,700,000
Emp.: 120
Tubes, Seamless Steel
N.A.I.C.S.: 331210

Subsidiaries:

Acme/Romac Inc. (1)
1 Howard Ave, Somerset, NJ 08873
Tel.: (732) 560-8111
Steel Pipe & Tubes
N.A.I.C.S.: 331210

NUTECH SYSTEMS INC.
2675 Paces Ferry Rd Ste 215, Atlanta, GA 30339
Tel.: (770) 434-7063
Web Site: http://www.nutech-inc.com
Year Founded: 1995
Sales Range: $10-24.9 Million
Emp.: 35
Other Management Consulting Services
N.A.I.C.S.: 541618
Nachu Anbil *(Pres)*
Anil Kumar *(Acct Mgr)*

NUTIS PRESS INC.
3540 E Fulton St, Columbus, OH 43227
Tel.: (614) 237-8626
Web Site: http://www.nutispress.com
Sales Range: $10-24.9 Million
Emp.: 100
Offset Printing
N.A.I.C.S.: 323111
Tory Peterson *(Mgr-Sls)*

NUTIVA
213 West Cutting Blvd, Richmond, CA 94804
Web Site: http://www.nutiva.com
Year Founded: 1999
Sales Range: $10-24.9 Million
Emp.: 30
Natural Food Products
N.A.I.C.S.: 456191
John W. Roulac *(Founder & CEO)*

NUTLEY HEATING & COOLING SUPPLY CO.
156 Chestnut St, Nutley, NJ 07110
Tel.: (973) 667-6880
Web Site: http://www.nutleysupply.com
Rev.: $15,775,653
Emp.: 40
Plumbing & Hydronic Heating Supplies
N.A.I.C.S.: 423720

NUTMEG INTERNATIONAL TRUCKS INC.
130 Brainard Rd, Hartford, CT 06114
Tel.: (860) 249-8635
Web Site: http://www.nutmegtrucks.com
Rev.: $23,400,000
Emp.: 125
Pickups, New & Used
N.A.I.C.S.: 441110
Mike Scholla *(Controller)*
Brad Smith *(Mgr-Sls & Lease)*

NUTMEG UTILITY PRODUCTS INC.
1755 Highland Ave, Cheshire, CT 06410
Tel.: (203) 272-2291
Web Site: http://www.nutmegutility.com
Year Founded: 1975
Sales Range: $10-24.9 Million
Emp.: 35
Emergency Alarms
N.A.I.C.S.: 334290
Jeneane Lavallee *(CEO)*

NUTRAMAX LABORATORIES, INC.
2208 Lakeside Blvd, Edgewood, MD 21040
Tel.: (410) 776-4000
Web Site: http://www.nutramaxlabs.com
Year Founded: 1992
Sales Range: $25-49.9 Million
Emp.: 225
Mfr, Researcher, Developer & Marketer of Nutraceuticals & Pharmaceuticals
N.A.I.C.S.: 325412
Kerry Johnson *(Product Mgr-Consumer)*
Stacey Buzzell *(Product Mgr-Equine)*
Annie Colliflower *(Reg Mgr-Sls)*
Derek Hebert *(Supvr-QC)*
Pete Patras *(VP)*

NUTRAWISE CORPORATION
1111 Bell Ave, Tustin, CA 92780
Tel.: (714) 361-4660
Web Site: http://www.nutrawise.net
Year Founded: 2009
Sales Range: $25-49.9 Million
Emp.: 50
Pharmaceutical Preparation Mfr
N.A.I.C.S.: 325412
Darren Rude *(Founder & CEO)*

NUTRI-FORCE NUTRITION, INC.
14620 NW 60th Ave, Miami Lakes, FL 33014
Tel.: (305) 468-1600
Web Site: http://www.nutriforce.com
Year Founded: 2000
Sales Range: $25-49.9 Million
Emp.: 300
Contract Vitamin & Supplements Mfr
N.A.I.C.S.: 325412
Dan Alhadeff *(COO)*
Anthony Alfonso *(CEO)*
Michael James Beardall *(Pres)*

NUTRICAP LABS
70 Carolyn Blvd, Farmingdale, NY 11735
Web Site: http://www.NutricapLabs.com
Year Founded: 2003
Sales Range: $10-24.9 Million
Emp.: 25
Vitamin & Supplement Mfr
N.A.I.C.S.: 456191
Jason Provenzano *(Founder)*

NUTRICITY.COM LLC
9419 E San Salvador Dr Ste 102, Scottsdale, AZ 85258
Web Site: http://www.nutricity.com
Year Founded: 2006
Sales Range: $1-9.9 Million
Emp.: 18
Health & Nutrition Products
N.A.I.C.S.: 456191
Nathan Gisvold *(CEO)*

NUTRIENTS FOR LIFE FOUNDATION
425 3rd St SW Suite 950, Washington, DC 20024
Tel.: (202) 962-0490 DE
Web Site: http://www.nutrientsforlife.org
Year Founded: 2004
Sales Range: $1-9.9 Million
Emp.: 100
Agricultural Programs
N.A.I.C.S.: 813910
Harriet Wegmeyer *(Exec Dir)*
William J. Doyle *(Chm)*
Ford West *(Pres)*
Carol Dorrough *(Treas)*

NUTRIMIX FEED CO., INC.
PO Box 3464, Catano, PR 00693
Tel.: (787) 641-5175
Web Site: http://www.nutrimixpr.com
Sales Range: $10-24.9 Million
Emp.: 52
Farm Animal Food Product Mfr
N.A.I.C.S.: 311119
Damian Rivera *(VP & Mgr)*
Waldemar Gonzalez *(Pres)*
Federico Estremera *(Treas & Sec)*

NUTRIO.COM, INC.
2225 N Commerce Pkwy Ste 7, Weston, FL 33326
Tel.: (954) 385-4700
Web Site: http://www.nutrio.com
Year Founded: 1999
Sales Range: $10-24.9 Million
Emp.: 8
Healthy Living, Nutrition & Fitness Websites Licenser & Services
N.A.I.C.S.: 621399
Thomas E. Davis *(CTO)*
Kim Evenson *(Sr VP-Mktg)*

NUTRITION INC.
580 Wendel Rd Ste 100, Irwin, PA 15642
Tel.: (724) 978-2100
Web Site: http://www.thenutritiongroup.biz
Year Founded: 1975
Rev.: $35,000,000
Emp.: 1,800
Contract Food Services
N.A.I.C.S.: 722310
Edward Caswell *(CEO)*
Donald Baker *(Controller)*
Jerald Moore *(Pres)*
Ian O'Bryan *(Dir-HR)*

NUTRITIONAL HEALTH INSTITUTE LABORATORIES, LLC
2820 Remington Green Cir, Tallahassee, FL 32308

Tel.: (850) 597-7906
Web Site: http://www.nhil.tv
Medical Researcher Developer
N.A.I.C.S.: 621511
Mehran P. Ghazvini *(Partner)*
Rene M. Reed *(Partner)*
Konky Sotomayor *(Principal)*

Subsidiaries:

Global Green, Inc. (1)
2820 Remington Cir, Tallahassee, FL 32308 (89.13%)
Tel.: (850) 597-7906
Web Site: http://www.globalgreeninc.org
Assets: $15,292
Liabilities: $240,736
Net Worth: ($225,444)
Earnings: ($90,093)
Fiscal Year-end: 12/31/2014
Animal Medicine Researcher & Developer
N.A.I.C.S.: 621511
Mehran P. Ghazvini *(Chm & CEO)*
Rene M. Reed *(VP)*
Konky Sotomayor *(VP-R&D)*

NUTRITIONAL HOLDINGS, INC
210 S Beck Ave, Chandler, AZ 85226
Tel.: (480) 966-9630
Web Site: https://www.aznutritional.com
Year Founded: 1996
Sales Range: $25-49.9 Million
Emp.: 180
Nutritional Supplements Mfr
N.A.I.C.S.: 325412
Aaron Blunck *(Co-Founder)*
Jonathan Pinkus *(Co-Founder)*
Jacqueline Bish *(Exec VP-Fin & Acctg)*
Rebecca Vanderplaats *(Dir-Quality Assurance)*

NUTRITIONAL PRODUCTS INTERNATIONAL INC.
165 E Palmetto Park Rd Ste 320, Boca Raton, FL 33432
Tel.: (561) 544-0719
Web Site: http://www.nutricompany.com
Sales Range: $1-9.9 Million
Nutraceuticals, Sports Nutrition, Skin Care, Personal Care, Functional Food & Beverage Distr & Marketer
N.A.I.C.S.: 424490
Mitch Gould *(Founder & CEO)*
Brian Philip Gould *(VP-Retail Ops)*
Scott Gould *(VP-Bus Dev)*
Michael Myrthil *(Dir-Global Procurement)*
Jeff Fernandez *(Dir-Sls-Global)*
Stephanie Wilson *(Coord-Intl Sls)*
Loralei Timonere *(Coord-Sls)*
Julia Maxwell *(Dir-Bus Affairs-Intl)*
Wanderson Pereria *(Mgr-Logistics-Global)*
Irvin Garcia *(Sr Acct Mgr)*
Nick Santoriello *(VP-Global Procurement)*
Brian Dietz *(VP-Sls & Mktg)*
William Vanegas *(Acct Mgr-Natl)*
Rodica Lesan *(Dir-PR)*

NUTTER CUSTOM CONSTRUCTION, LLC
1 Fletcher Ave, Sarasota, FL 34237
Tel.: (941) 924-1868
Web Site: http://www.nuttercustomconstruction.com
Sales Range: $1-9.9 Million
Emp.: 6
Single Family Housing Construction & Remodeling Services
N.A.I.C.S.: 236115
T. J. Nutter *(Owner)*

NUVECTRA CORPORATION

5830 Granite Pkwy Ste 1100, Plano, TX 75024
Tel.: (214) 474-3103 DE
Web Site: http://www.nuvectramed.com
Year Founded: 2008
Rev.: $48,831,000
Assets: $158,012,000
Liabilities: $65,116,000
Net Worth: $92,896,000
Earnings: ($48,131,000)
Emp.: 197
Fiscal Year-end: 12/31/18
Neurostimulation Technology Developer & Mfr
N.A.I.C.S.: 541715
Melissa G. Beare *(Gen Counsel & Exec VP)*
Bernie Bosley *(Exec Dir-Regulatory & Clinical Affairs)*
Bonnie Schmidt *(Chief HR Officer & VP)*
Jennifer J. Kosharek *(CFO & Exec VP)*
Chuck Harvey *(CIO & VP)*
Ben Tranchina *(CTO)*

NUVEI TECHNOLOGIES
5000 Legacy Dr Ste 320, Plano, TX 75024-3112
Web Site: http://www.nuvei.com
Employment Placement Agencies
N.A.I.C.S.: 561311
Dreux Flaherty *(Sr VP-Global One Sls)*

Subsidiaries:

SafeCharge International Group Limited (1)
Ground Floor Dorey Court, Admiral Park, Saint Peter Port, GY1 2HT, Guernsey
Tel.: (44) 20 7861 3232
Web Site: http://www.safecharge.com
E-Commerce Payments Services
N.A.I.C.S.: 425120
Yuval Ziv *(Mng Dir-Safe Charge & Head-Global Acquiring)*
Philip Atherton *(Global Compliance Officer)*
Praful Morar *(Chief Strategy Officer)*
Philip Fayer *(Chm & CEO)*
Max Attias *(COO)*
David Schwartz *(CFO)*

NUVUS GRO CORP.
7703 N Lamar Blvd Ste 510, Austin, TX 78752-1055
Tel.: (512) 206-4205 NV
Web Site: http://www.buildingturbines.com
Wind Turbine Mfr
N.A.I.C.S.: 333611
Greg Miller *(Chief Bus Dev Officer)*
Paul Severin *(Pres & COO)*
John F. Graham Sr. *(Founder & CEO)*

Subsidiaries:

Pro Music Rights Inc. (1)
3811 Airport Pulling Rd, Naples, FL 34105
Web Site: http://www.promusicrights.com
Assets: $50,135
Liabilities: $95,491
Net Worth: ($45,356)
Earnings: ($443,586)
Fiscal Year-end: 12/31/2019
Music Licensing Services
N.A.I.C.S.: 512230
Jake P. Noch *(Founder, Chm, Pres, CEO, CFO & Sec)*

NUWAY COOPERATIVE INC.
Hwy 4 S, Trimont, MN 56176
Tel.: (507) 639-2311
Web Site: http://www.nuwaycoop.com
Year Founded: 1981
Sales Range: $25-49.9 Million
Emp.: 87
Distr of Agricultural Chemicals
N.A.I.C.S.: 445131

Kevin Jones *(CEO)*
Steve Sorenson *(CFO)*

NUWAY TOBACCO COMPANY INC.
200 Sullivan Ave, South Windsor, CT 06074-1944
Tel.: (860) 289-6414
Year Founded: 1988
Sales Range: $1-9.9 Million
Emp.: 45
Tobacco Processor
N.A.I.C.S.: 312230
Charles B. Shepard *(Pres)*
Ray Voorhes *(Exec VP)*
Lou Fitch *(Office Mgr)*

NVE BANK
76 Engle St, Englewood, NJ 07631-2905
Tel.: (201) 816-2800
Web Site: http://www.nvebank.com
Year Founded: 1880
Sales Range: $25-49.9 Million
Emp.: 80
Banking, Except Federal
N.A.I.C.S.: 522180
Robert Rey *(Pres & CEO)*

NVER ENTERPRISES INC.
19303 Hwy 99, Lynnwood, WA 98036
Tel.: (425) 774-1414
Web Site: http://www.westernrv.com
Year Founded: 1986
Sales Range: $25-49.9 Million
Emp.: 10
Dealer of Travel Trailers & Motor Homes
N.A.I.C.S.: 441210
Hrag Salibian *(Pres)*

NVEST, INC.
560 Davis St Ste 250, San Francisco, CA 94111 DE
Holding Company; Financial Investing & Wealth Management App Developer
N.A.I.C.S.: 551112
Michael T. Sha *(CEO)*
Meagher Evan *(CFO)*
Lisa Haugh *(Sec)*

Subsidiaries:

SigFig Wealth Management, LLC (1)
560 Davis St Ste 250, San Francisco, CA 94111
Tel.: (415) 558-9611
Web Site: http://www.sigfig.com
Financial Investing & Wealth Management App Developer
N.A.I.C.S.: 541511
Michael T. Sha *(Founder & CEO)*
Terry Banet *(Chief Investment Officer)*
Aaron Gubin *(Dir-Fin & Res)*

NVIS INC.
11495 Sunset Hills Rd Ste 106, Reston, VA 20190
Tel.: (703) 891-1130
Web Site: http://www.nvisinc.com
Year Founded: 2002
Rev.: $3,400,000
Emp.: 11
Electronic Computer Mfr
N.A.I.C.S.: 334111

NVISH SOLUTIONS INC.
39899 Balentine Dr Ste 200, Newark, CA 94560
Tel.: (805) 712-3704
Web Site: http://www.nvish.com
Year Founded: 2007
Sales Range: $1-9.9 Million
Emp.: 275
IT Consulting Services
N.A.I.C.S.: 541690

Neeraj Kahal *(Co-Founder & Mng Partner)*
Gurmail Singh *(Co-Founder & Mng Partner)*
Gaurav Gagneja *(Head-Digital Mktg & Bus Dev)*

NW HOLDING CO.
620 Doddridge St, Saint Louis, MO 63147
Tel.: (314) 383-6100
Sales Range: $10-24.9 Million
Emp.: 35
Provider of Petroleum Products
N.A.I.C.S.: 524210
Mariano Costello *(Pres)*
Delores Costello *(VP)*

Subsidiaries:

Fuel Man Inc. (1)
7450 Hall St, Saint Louis, MO 63147
Tel.: (314) 383-6100
Rev.: $1,600,000
Emp.: 10
Convenience Store
N.A.I.C.S.: 445131

Nu Way Service Station Inc. (1)
620 Doddridge St, Saint Louis, MO 63147
Tel.: (314) 383-6100
Sales Range: $10-24.9 Million
Emp.: 22
Truck Rental & Leasing, No Drivers
N.A.I.C.S.: 532120

NW SERVICES CORPORATION
5063 Alabama Hwy, Ringgold, GA 30736
Tel.: (706) 965-3000 GA
Web Site: http://www.nwgb.com
Year Founded: 1983
Sales Range: $10-24.9 Million
Emp.: 220
Bank Holding Company
N.A.I.C.S.: 551111
L. Wesley Smith *(Chm & CEO)*
Jeff Kovach *(CFO)*

Subsidiaries:

Northwest Georgia Bank (1)
5063 Alabama Hwy PO Box 789, Ringgold, GA 30737
Tel.: (706) 965-3000
Web Site: http://www.nwgb.com
Rev.: $28,790,662
Emp.: 100
Commericial Banking
N.A.I.C.S.: 522110
Stephen Bark *(Asst VP-Collections)*
Kerry Riley *(Exec VP)*
Taryn Hall-Roberts *(VP & Mgr-Fort Oglethorpe)*
Rich Balthrop *(VP-Retail & Sls)*
Alice Holsopple *(Asst VP)*

NW SIGN INDUSTRIES INC.
360 Crider Ave, Moorestown, NJ 08057
Tel.: (856) 802-1677
Web Site: http://www.nwsignindustries.com
Sales Range: $10-24.9 Million
Emp.: 76
Signs & Advertising Specialties
N.A.I.C.S.: 339950
Ronald Brodie *(Pres)*
Jeff Bolas *(Controller)*

NWJ COMPANIES, INC.
9 E 40th St, New York, NY 10016
Tel.: (212) 202-1461
Year Founded: 1991
Residential Real Estate Development Services
N.A.I.C.S.: 531311
Michael A. Greenzang *(VP-Stabilization)*
Brian M. Kroker *(VP-Asset Mgmt)*
David H. McLain *(Gen Counsel & VP-Acq)*

Jonathan Coffen *(VP-Lender Direct Div)*
Charles Rich *(VP-Fin)*
Steven J. Wissak *(Dir-Fin-Equity)*
Nick Moos *(Dir-Mgmt)*

NWS MICHIGAN INC.
17550 Allen Rd, Wyandotte, MI 48192
Tel.: (734) 324-3000
Web Site: http://www.nwscorp.com
Rev.: $25,000,000
Emp.: 200
Liquor
N.A.I.C.S.: 424820
George Ogorzaly *(Gen Mgr)*
Gibran Jabboori *(Portfolio Mgr)*
Dale Rennell *(Portfolio Mgr)*

NXC IMAGING
2118 4th Ave S, Minneapolis, MN 55404
Tel.: (612) 870-1561
Web Site: http://www.nxc-imaging.com
Sales Range: $50-74.9 Million
Emp.: 100
X-Ray Machine & Equipment Distr
N.A.I.C.S.: 423450
Michelle Johnson *(Coord-Sls & Mktg)*
Dan Lind *(Area Mgr-Svc)*
Bryon Walz *(Project Mgr)*

NXCHAIN, INC.
17702 Mitchell N, Irvine, CA 92614
Tel.: (408) 673-2464
Year Founded: 2011
Software Development Services
N.A.I.C.S.: 541511
Sean Tabatabai *(Pres, CEO, Treas & Sec)*

NXGEN PAYMENT SERVICES
940 Spokane Ave Ste 5, Whitefish, MT 59937
Tel.: (406) 871-4969
Web Site: http://www.nxgen.com
Year Founded: 1999
Sales Range: $1-9.9 Million
Emp.: 10
Payment Processing Services
N.A.I.C.S.: 522320
Tim Hinderman *(VP-Global Mktg & Sls)*
Giuseppe Caltabiano *(Pres)*
Tom Nitopi *(CEO)*

NXGN, INC.
116 W Jackson Blvd 225, Chicago, IL 60604
Tel.: (312) 971-9715
Web Site: http://www.nxgn.io
Year Founded: 2012
Sales Range: $1-9.9 Million
Emp.: 6
Network Security Services
N.A.I.C.S.: 513199
Jack Morawski *(Founder & Mng Partner)*

NXP CORP.
5195 Drnnigens Gade Ste 3, Saint Thomas, VI 00802
Tel.: (340) 777-4222
Web Site: http://www.littleswitzerland.com
Year Founded: 1991
Sales Range: $25-49.9 Million
Emp.: 200
Jewelry Store Operator
N.A.I.C.S.: 458310
Hal Tayler *(Pres)*

Subsidiaries:

Little Switzerland, Inc. (1)
354 Indusco Ct, Troy, MI 48083

NXP CORP.

NXP Corp.—(Continued)
Tel.: (248) 556-2910
Web Site: http://www.littleswitzerland.com
Duty-Free Luxury Product Retailer
N.A.I.C.S.: 458310

NXTBOOK MEDIA, LLC
480 New Holland Ave Ste 9000, Lancaster, PA 17602
Tel.: (717) 735-9740
Web Site:
  http://www.nxtbookmedia.com
Year Founded: 2003
Sales Range: $1-9.9 Million
Emp.: 52
Computer Software Publisher
N.A.I.C.S.: 518210
Eric Gervase (Dir-Sls)
Jacob Keeler (Dir-Agency Svcs)

NXTKEY CORPORATION
1712 Pioneer Ave Ste 415, Cheyenne, WY 82001
Tel.: (307) 333-0711
Web Site: http://www.nxtkey.com
Cloud Technology, Cyber Security Solutions & Enterprise Information Management Services
N.A.I.C.S.: 518210
Shivaji Sengupta (Founder & CEO)
Tonia Sengupta (Exec VP)
Baha Azimirad (VP)

Subsidiaries:

Magnus Management Group, LLC (1)
9157 Ogden Park Ct, Bristow, VA 20136-2159
Tel.: (703) 606-2002
Web Site:
  http://www.magnusmanagement.com
General Management Consulting Services
N.A.I.C.S.: 541611
Baha Azimirad (VP)

NXTLVL MARINE, LLC
1208 Branch Rd 620 S, Austin, TX 78734
Tel.: (512) 263-2811
Web Site:
  https://www.nxtlvlmarine.com
Boat Dealers
N.A.I.C.S.: 441222
Blake Flanagan (Pres)

Subsidiaries:

MarineMax TX, L.P. (1)
1490 N Stemmons Freeway, Lewisville, TX 75067
Tel.: (972) 436-9979
Web Site: http://www.marinemax.com
Sales Range: $100-124.9 Million
Emp.: 35
Recreational Boat Retailer
N.A.I.C.S.: 458110

Sail & Ski Inc. (1)
12971 Research Blvd, Austin, TX 78750
Tel.: (512) 258-0733
Web Site: http://www.sailandski.com
Motor Boat Dealers
N.A.I.C.S.: 441222

NXTSOFT LLC
850 Corporate Pkwy Ste 110-A, Birmingham, AL 35242
Tel.: (800) 915-3381
Web Site: http://www.nxtsoft.com
Software Publisher
N.A.I.C.S.: 513210
David Brasfield (Founder & CEO)
Andy McMakin (Pres)
Will Blackburn (CTO)
Christopher Parks (Sr VP-Implementation)
Chuck Diulus (Chief Revenue Officer)

NYCA
444 S Cedros Ave Ste 101, Solana Beach, CA 92075-1967
Tel.: (760) 231-0351
Web Site: http://www.nyca.com
Year Founded: 2002
Sales Range: $10-24.9 Million
Emp.: 50
Advetising Agency
N.A.I.C.S.: 541810
Michael Mark (CEO & Dir-Creative)
Lynne C. Roswall (VP & Dir-Production)
Dave Huerta (VP & Assoc Dir-Creative)
Travis Graham (VP & Assoc Dir-Creative)

NYCOM INC.
14200 Michaux Glen Dr, Midlothian, VA 23113
Tel.: (804) 794-3044
Web Site: http://www.nycominc.net
Sales Range: $25-49.9 Million
Emp.: 80
Laboratory Casework & Equipment Supplier
N.A.I.C.S.: 337127
Jonathan F. Nystrom (Pres)

NYDREE FLOORING
1191 Venture Dr, Forest, VA 24551
Tel.: (434) 525-5252
Web Site:
  http://www.nydreeflooring.com
Year Founded: 1967
Sales Range: $25-49.9 Million
Emp.: 200
Flooring Products Mfr
N.A.I.C.S.: 321918
Robin Richardson (Project Coord)
Jason Brubaker (VP-Sls & Mktg)
Cathy Mansour (Dir-Mktg)

NYHUS CHEVROLET & BUICK INC.
120 2nd Ave NE, Staples, MN 56479-2534
Tel.: (218) 894-1652
Web Site:
  http://www.nyhuschevbuick.com
Sales Range: $10-24.9 Million
Emp.: 31
Car Whslr
N.A.I.C.S.: 441110
Ron Biebighauser (Owner)

NYHUS COMMUNICATIONS LLC
720 3rd Ave Fl 12, Seattle, WA 98104
Tel.: (206) 323-3733
Web Site: http://www.nyhus.com
Year Founded: 2004
Rev.: $2,500,000
Emp.: 20
Public Relations Agencies
N.A.I.C.S.: 541820
Roger Nyhus (Pres & CEO)
Beth Hester (Dir-Pub Affairs & Ops)
Heidi De Laubenfels (VP-Ops)
Karen Johnson (Acct Mgr)

NYKO TECHNOLOGIES INC.
1990 Westwood Blvd, Los Angeles, CA 90025
Tel.: (310) 446-6602
Web Site: http://www.nyko.com
Sales Range: $25-49.9 Million
Emp.: 20
Video Games
N.A.I.C.S.: 423920
Herschel Naghi (CEO)
Chris Arbogast (Dir-Sls & Mktg)
Ronald Klingbeil (Controller)
Radu Popa (VP-Supply Chain)
Jeremy Bell (Mgr-IT)

NYLACARB CORPORATION
1725 98th Ave, Vero Beach, FL 32966
Tel.: (772) 569-5999
Web Site: http://www.nylacarb.com
Year Founded: 1988
Sales Range: $1-9.9 Million
Emp.: 35
All Other Plastics Product Mfr
N.A.I.C.S.: 326199
Frank Cooley (VP)
Scott Cooley (Pres)

NYLE CORPORATION
12 Stevens Rd Ste B, Brewer, ME 04412
Tel.: (207) 989-4335
Web Site: http://www.nyle.com
Year Founded: 1984
Sales Range: $10-24.9 Million
Emp.: 50
Mfr of Medical & Hospital Equipment
N.A.I.C.S.: 333415
Samuel Nyer (Chm)
Donald C. Lewis (Pres)
Julie Piper (Sec)

NYLO HOTELS LLC
5300 Marsh Ridge Rd Ste 110, Carrollton, TX 75010
Tel.: (972) 590-4450
Web Site: http://www.nylohotels.com
Hotel Owner & Operator
N.A.I.C.S.: 721110
Michael Mueller (Pres & CEO)
Patrick O'Neil (Exec VP-Ops)
Michael Landreneau (VP & Controller)
Tim Copella (VP-Pur)
Alexis Shreffler (Dir-Sls & Revenue Mgmt)
Maegan Smith (Mgr-Social Media)

Subsidiaries:

NYLO Dallas South Side (1)
1325 S Lamar St, Dallas, TX 75215
Tel.: (214) 421-1080
Web Site: http://www.nylohotels.com
Emp.: 67
Hotel Operations
N.A.I.C.S.: 721110
Trent Yoder (Gen Mgr)
Marisol Lopez (Dir-Sls)

NYLO Irving/Las Colinas (1)
1001 W Royal Ln, Irving, TX 75039
Tel.: (972) 373-8900
Web Site:
  http://www.tapestrycollection3.hilton.com
Hotel Operations
N.A.I.C.S.: 721110
Grace Nungesser (Dir-Sls)

NYLO New York City (1)
2178 Broadway at W 77th St, New York, NY 10024
Tel.: (212) 362-1100
Hotel Operations
N.A.I.C.S.: 721110
Michael Dwyer (Dir-Sls & Mktg)
Conny Wang (Gen Mgr)

NYLO Plano/Legacy (1)
8201 Preston Rd, Plano, TX 75024
Tel.: (972) 624-6990
Web Site: http://www.nylohotels.com
Emp.: 50
Hotel Operations
N.A.I.C.S.: 721110
Kelley Glasscock (Assoc Dir-Sls)
Maegan Smith (Mgr-Grp & Catering Sls)
Luis Aquilar (Gen Mgr)
Monte Greene (Dir-Sls)

NYLO Providence/Warwick (1)
400 Knight St, Warwick, RI 02886
Tel.: (401) 734-4460
Web Site: http://www.nylohotels.com
Emp.: 450
Hotel Operations
N.A.I.C.S.: 721110
Jackson Donoyan (Gen Mgr)
Randi Paola (Dir-Sls)

U.S. PRIVATE

NYLOK CORPORATION
15260 Hallmark Dr, Macomb, MI 48042
Tel.: (586) 786-0100
Web Site: http://www.nylok.com
Sales Range: $10-24.9 Million
Emp.: 300
Painting, Coating & Hot Dipping
N.A.I.C.S.: 332812
Tadashi Carney (Dir-New Bus Dev)

NYM WORLDGROUP, INC.
9551-1333 Broadway Ste 502, New York, NY 10018
Tel.: (212) 564-9550
Web Site:
  http://www.nymworldgroup.com
Year Founded: 1992
Sales Range: $50-74.9 Million
Emp.: 6
Media Buying Services
N.A.I.C.S.: 541810
Vilma Ella (Controller)
James E. Parker (Pres)
Mary Marengo (Acct Dir)
Nathaniel Martin (Acct Exec)

NYMAN CONSTRUCTION
23209 Miles Rd Fl 2, Cleveland, OH 44128
Tel.: (216) 475-7800
Web Site:
  http://www.nymanconstruct.com
Sales Range: $25-49.9 Million
Emp.: 30
Civil Engineering Services
N.A.I.C.S.: 237310
Dal Jaffray (Project Mgr)

NYMBUS, INC.
1000 5th St, Miami Beach, FL 33139
Web Site: http://www.nymbus.com
Business Website Development & Design
N.A.I.C.S.: 561499
David Mitchell (Pres)
Scott Killoh (Founder)
Harry Flood (CFO)
Dave Soli (CTO)
Scott Sharp (COO)
Anne Miela (COO-Banking)
Jan Frymyer (Sr VP-Client Svcs-Glastonbury)
Richard D. Lang (Gen Counsel-Glastonbury)
Joerg Richter (COO-Platforms)
Jeffery Kendall (Chm & CEO)
Trish North (Chief Customer Officer)
Michelle Prohaska (Chief Compliance Officer)
Crina Pupaza (Chief People Officer)

Subsidiaries:

R.C. Olmstead, Inc. (1)
9961 Brewster Ln Ste 100, Powell, OH 43065
Web Site: http://www.rcolmstead.com
Sales Range: $1-9.9 Million
Emp.: 38
Custom Computer Programming Services
N.A.I.C.S.: 541511
Robert Olmstead (Founder & Chm)

Sharp BancSystems, Inc. (1)
4009 Airport Fwy, Bedford, TX 76021 (100%)
Tel.: (817) 438-2200
Web Site:
  http://www.sharpbancsystems.com
Sales Range: $1-9.9 Million
Emp.: 50
Integrated Banking Software Solutions
N.A.I.C.S.: 541511
Scott Sharp (CEO & Pres)

NYP INC
113 E Walnut, Chilhowee, MO 64733
Tel.: (660) 678-5551

Web Site: http://www.nypcorp.com
Sales Range: $75-99.9 Million
Emp.: 5
Malt Mfr
N.A.I.C.S.: 311213
Mike Riley (Pres)

NYPROMOLD INC.
144 Pleasant St, Clinton, MA 01510-3416
Tel.: (978) 365-4547
Web Site: http://www.nypromold.com
Year Founded: 1987
Industrial Molds
N.A.I.C.S.: 333511
Brian DeRienze (Engr-Design)
Shelby Tole (Mgr-HR)
Nicholas Connor (Mgr-Acctg)

NYSTROM, INC.
9300 73rd Ave N, Minneapolis, MN 55428
Tel.: (763) 488-9200
Web Site: http://www.nystrom.com
Year Founded: 1948
Sales Range: $25-49.9 Million
Emp.: 177
Sheet Metal Work Mfg
N.A.I.C.S.: 332322
Sue Thomas (CEO)
Scott Bendix (VP-Sls & Mktg)
Gretchen Kelly (CFO)

NYTEF PLASTICS LTD.
633 Dunferry Rd, Bensalem, PA 19020
Tel.: (215) 638-0800
Web Site:
http://www.nytefplastics.com
Rev.: $24,500,000
Emp.: 40
Plastics Materials
N.A.I.C.S.: 424610
Susan Stefanic (Mgr-AR)
Richard Corda (Mgr-Tooling Maintenance)
Ken Huck (Mgr-Production)
Morton R. French Jr. (CEO)

Subsidiaries:

Nytef Plastics Corp. (1)
633 Dunksferry Rd, Bensalem, PA 19020
Tel.: (215) 638-0800
Web Site: http://www.nytef.com
Sales Range: $10-24.9 Million
Vulcanized Fiber Plates, Sheets, Rods, Or Tubes
N.A.I.C.S.: 326199
Morton R. French Jr. (Pres)

NYX INC.
36111 Schoolcraft Rd, Livonia, MI 48150-1216
Tel.: (734) 462-2385
Web Site: http://www.nyxinc.com
Year Founded: 1959
Sales Range: $75-99.9 Million
Emp.: 1,800
Automotive Interior & Under-Hood Products Mfr
N.A.I.C.S.: 333248
Chain S. Sandhu (Chm)
Vijay Kanakamedala (Pres)
Jatinder-Bir Sandhu (CEO)
Eddie Alam (Dir-Matls)

Subsidiaries:

Beach Mold & Tool Inc. (1)
999 Progress Blvd, New Albany, IN 47150-2258
Tel.: (812) 945-2688
Web Site: http://www.beachmold.com
Sales Range: $150-199.9 Million
Emp.: 985
Mfr of Plastic Injection Molds & Equipment
N.A.I.C.S.: 561990
William H. Beach (Founder)
Juanita Beach (Founder)

Subsidiary (Domestic):

Beach Mold & Tool Virginia, Inc. (2)
300 Industrial Pkwy, Emporia, VA 23847
Tel.: (434) 634-8810
Web Site: http://www.beachmold.com
Plastic Injection Molding Services
N.A.I.C.S.: 238350
Doug Batliner (Pres)

NYX Fort Wayne (1)
5727 Industrial Rd, Fort Wayne, IN 46825
Tel.: (260) 484-0595
Molding Primary Plastics
N.A.I.C.S.: 326199

NYXIO TECHNOLOGIES CORPORATION
1330 SW 3rd Ave, Portland, OR 97201   NV
Web Site: https://nyxio.com
Year Founded: 2006
Sales Range: Less than $1 Million
Emp.: 5
Consumer Electronics Developer & Mfr
N.A.I.C.S.: 334111

O S HOLDINGS, INC.
13320 NE Jarrett St, Portland, OR 97230-1093
Tel.: (503) 238-0664
Sales Range: $10-24.9 Million
Emp.: 41
Spice & Extract Mfr
N.A.I.C.S.: 311942
Lawrence Black (Chm)
Patricia Boday (Pres)

O&G INDUSTRIES, INC.
112 Wall St, Torrington, CT 06790
Tel.: (860) 489-9261   DE
Web Site: http://www.ogind.com
Year Founded: 1920
Sales Range: $300-349.9 Million
Emp.: 700
Nonresidential Construction
N.A.I.C.S.: 236220
Raymond R. Oneglia (Vice Chm)
David Oneglia (Pres)
John Baranoski (Dir-Fabrication & Distr Center)
Thomas D'Orvilliers (Project Engr-Masonry Div)

Subsidiaries:

O&G Industries, Inc. - Harwinton Concrete Plant (1)
255 Bogue Rd, Harwinton, CT 06791
Tel.: (860) 485-6600
Building Construction Services
N.A.I.C.S.: 236220

O&H DANISH BAKERY
1515 Rapids Dr, Racine, WI 53404
Tel.: (262) 554-1311
Web Site:
http://www.ohdanishbakery.com
Year Founded: 1949
Sales Range: $10-24.9 Million
Emp.: 83
Commercial Bakery Services
N.A.I.C.S.: 311812
Eric A. Olesen (Pres)
Peter Olesen (VP)
Frank Amodio (Dir-Sls)

O&K INC.
2121 E 37th St, Los Angeles, CA 90058-1416
Tel.: (323) 846-5700
Web Site:
http://www.oneclothing.com
Year Founded: 1989
Sales Range: $25-49.9 Million
Emp.: 250
Retail of Clothing for Children & Infants

N.A.I.C.S.: 424350
Alex Ok (Founder)

O&M INDUSTRIES INC.
5901 Ericson Way, Arcata, CA 95521
Tel.: (707) 822-8800
Web Site:
http://www.omindustries.com
Rev.: $12,550,978
Emp.: 55
Warm Air Heating & Air Conditioning Contractor
N.A.I.C.S.: 238220
John McBeth (Pres)
Rob McBeth (Owner & Pres)

O'BERRY CAVANAUGH
20 E Main St, Bozeman, MT 59715
Tel.: (406) 522-8075   MT
Web Site: http://www.ocbrand.com
Year Founded: 2004
Sales Range: $10-24.9 Million
Emp.: 9
Advetising Agency
N.A.I.C.S.: 541810
Cary Silberman (Dir-Creative)
Toni O'Berry (Owner & Founding Partner)
Diana Pailthorpe (Dir-Client Svcs)
Valerie Ross (Mgr-Ops & Acct)

O'BRIEN AUTO PARK
2850 Colonial Blvd, Fort Myers, FL 33966-1030
Tel.: (239) 277-1222
Web Site: http://www.obrieneasy.com
Year Founded: 1988
Sales Range: $25-49.9 Million
Emp.: 9
New Car Whslr
N.A.I.C.S.: 441110
Gary Matern (Principal)
Joseph D. O'Brien (Pres)

O'BRIEN AUTOMOTIVE TEAM
1111 O'Brien Dr, Urbana, IL 61801
Tel.: (217) 398-1222
Web Site: http://www.obrienteam.com
Rev.: $15,700,000
Emp.: 150
Automobile Sales
N.A.I.C.S.: 423110
Joseph D. O'Brien Jr. (Pres)

O'BRIEN GROUP
950 Tower Ln Ste 1250, Foster City, CA 94404
Tel.: (650) 377-0300
Web Site:
http://www.obriengroup.com
Sales Range: $125-149.9 Million
Emp.: 30
Land Subdividers & Developers, Residential
N.A.I.C.S.: 237210
Dennis O'Brien (Founder & Pres)
Caryn Kali (CFO)
Chuck Schoenberger (Partner & Sr VP-Ops)

O'BRIEN SOUTHERN TRENCHING, INC.
PO Box 849, Rural Hall, NC 27045
Tel.: (336) 969-0460
Sales Range: $10-24.9 Million
Emp.: 50
Utility Contracting Services
N.A.I.C.S.: 237110
Sandra H. O'Brien (Sec)
Tracy L. O'Brien (Pres)

O'BRYANT ELECTRIC, INC.
9314 Eton St, Chatsworth, CA 91311
Tel.: (818) 407-1986
Web Site:
http://www.obryantelectric.com

Year Founded: 1978
Sales Range: $25-49.9 Million
Emp.: 200
Electrical Construction Services
N.A.I.C.S.: 238210
Sean McKenna (VP-Project Mgmt)

O'CONNELL & GOLDBERG
450 N Park Rd Ste 600, Hollywood, FL 33021
Tel.: (954) 964-9098   FL
Web Site:
http://www.oconnellgoldberg.com
Year Founded: 1993
Sales Range: $1-9.9 Million
Emp.: 9
Public Relations Services
N.A.I.C.S.: 541820
Barbara W. Goldberg (CEO & Founding Partner)
Jeff Bray (Sr Editor & Acct Supvr)
Matt Levinson (COO)
Jillian Goltzman (Dir-Social Media)
Sasha Blaney (Sr Acct Exec)
Jen Milton (Sr Acct Exec)
Alyssa Wickham (Acct Exec)
Sofia Garcia (Sr Acct Exec)

O'CONNELL ELECTRIC COMPANY, INC.
830 Phillips Rd, Victor, NY 14564-9417
Tel.: (585) 924-2176
Web Site:
http://www.oconnellelectric.com
Year Founded: 1911
Sales Range: $50-74.9 Million
Emp.: 600
Providers of Electrical Work
N.A.I.C.S.: 238210
Walter T. Parkes (Chm)
Victor E. Salerno (CEO)
Joseph R. Pellerite (Exec VP-Ops)
Susan P. McNally (Sec)

Subsidiaries:

O'Connell Electric Company, Inc. (1)
301 Stoutenger St, East Syracuse, NY 13057-2831
Tel.: (315) 437-1453
Sales Range: $25-49.9 Million
Emp.: 225
General Electrical Contractor
N.A.I.C.S.: 238210
Donald Coon (Gen Mgr)

O'CONNELL LANDSCAPE MAINTENANCE
23091 Arroyo Vista, Rancho Santa Margarita, CA 92688
Tel.: (949) 589-2007
Web Site: http://www.oclm.com
Rev.: $13,687,851
Emp.: 1,000
Landscape Contractors
N.A.I.C.S.: 561730
George D. O'Connell (Owner)

O'CONNELL OIL ASSOCIATES INC.
545 Merrill Rd, Pittsfield, MA 01201
Tel.: (413) 499-4800
Web Site: http://www.oconnelloil.com
Sales Range: $125-149.9 Million
Emp.: 300
Fuel Oil
N.A.I.C.S.: 424720
Michael Sobon (Pres)

O'CONNOR & PARTNERS, INC.
2010 S 8th St, Saint Louis, MO 63104-4012
Tel.: (314) 772-0010   MO
Web Site: http://www.oconnor-partners.com
Year Founded: 1983

O'CONNOR & PARTNERS, INC.

O'Connor & Partners, Inc.—(Continued)
Sales Range: Less than $1 Million
Emp.: 12
Communications, Crisis Communications, Education, Entertainment, Environmental, Financial, Health Care, Nonprofit/Social Marketing, Real Estate, Retail, Travel & Tourism
N.A.I.C.S.: 541810
Ronald O'Connor (Principal)

O'CONNOR COMPANY
4909 N Lewis Ave, Sioux Falls, SD 57104
Tel.: (605) 336-0333
Web Site: http://www.oconnorco.com
Year Founded: 1970
Sales Range: $10-24.9 Million
Emp.: 75
HVAC, Heating & Air Conditioning
N.A.I.C.S.: 423730
Mike O'Connor (Pres-Sioux Falls)
Joel Porch (Co-Owner)

O'CONNOR COMPANY INC.
14851 W 99th St, Lenexa, KS 66215
Tel.: (913) 894-8788 KS
Web Site: http://www.oconnor-hvac.com
Year Founded: 1921
Sales Range: $10-24.9 Million
Emp.: 100
Distr of Warm Air Heating & Air Conditioning
N.A.I.C.S.: 423730
Bob Arnold (Mgr-Territory)
Dick McKinley (Mgr-Territory-American Standard)
Bob Meiners (Mgr-Credit)
Arnold Morgan (Mgr-Territory)
Bob Sampson (Mgr-Territory)
Scott Sayre (Mgr-Territory)
Mark Tindal (Mgr-Territory-American Standard)

O'CONNOR CONSTRUCTORS INC.
45 Industrial Dr, Canton, MA 02021
Tel.: (617) 364-9000
Web Site: http://www.oconnorcorp.com
Sales Range: $10-24.9 Million
Emp.: 50
Mechanical Contractor
N.A.I.C.S.: 238220
Christine McCarthy (Coord-Claims)
Ron Thomas (Project Mgr)

O'CONNOR GMC INC.
187 Riverside Dr, Augusta, ME 04330
Tel.: (207) 622-3191
Web Site: http://www.oconnorgmc.com
Sales Range: $75-99.9 Million
Emp.: 215
Sales of New & Used Pickups
N.A.I.C.S.: 441110
Paul McGuire (Gen Mgr)
Dan Doiron (Gen Mgr)

O'CONNOR OIL CORPORATION
555 N Pioneer Rd, Fond Du Lac, WI 54937
Tel.: (920) 921-8020
Rev.: $38,900,000
Emp.: 87
Gasoline Stations
N.A.I.C.S.: 457120
John Venturini (Pres & CEO)

O'CONNOR TELESERVICES INC.
640 Herman Rd Ste 3, Jackson, NJ 08527
Tel.: (732) 833-0600
Web Site: http://www.otstel.com
Rev.: $19,965,544
Emp.: 50
Communication Service
N.A.I.C.S.: 238210
James O'Connor (Pres & CEO)

O'DANIEL MOTORSALES INC.
5611 Illinois Rd, Fort Wayne, IN 46804
Tel.: (260) 435-5300 IN
Web Site: http://www.odanielauto.com
Year Founded: 1979
Sales Range: $50-74.9 Million
Emp.: 100
Sales of New & Used Cars
N.A.I.C.S.: 441110
Greg O'Daniel (Gen Mgr)

O'DAY EQUIPMENT, INC.
1301 40th St NW, Fargo, ND 58102
Tel.: (701) 282-9260
Web Site: http://www.odayequipment.com
Sales Range: $10-24.9 Million
Emp.: 40
Automobile Service Station Equipment
N.A.I.C.S.: 423120
Jim O'Day (CEO)
Wendy Simek (CFO)
Kim Blythe (Mgr-Customer Svc)

O'DONNELL LANDSCAPES, INC.
4291 Williams Rd, Estero, FL 33928
Tel.: (239) 992-8842
Web Site: http://www.odonnelllandscapes.com
Year Founded: 1981
Sales Range: $1-9.9 Million
Emp.: 130
Landscaping, Irrigation & Nursery Services
N.A.I.C.S.: 561730
Albert O'Donnell (Pres)

O'DONNELL STRATEGIC INDUSTRIAL REIT, INC.
3 San Joaquin Plz Ste 160, Newport Beach, CA 92660
Tel.: (949) 718-9898
Web Site: http://www.theindustrialREIT.com
Year Founded: 2011
Sales Range: Less than $1 Million
Real Estate Investment Services
N.A.I.C.S.: 525990
Douglas D. O'Donnell (Chm, Pres, CEO, CFO & Sec)

O'DONNELL'S TERMITE & PEST CONTROL, INC.
910 Hampshire, Quincy, IL 62301
Tel.: (217) 222-0049 IL
Web Site: https://www.odonnellspestcontrol.com
Year Founded: 2016
Exterminating & Pest Control Services
N.A.I.C.S.: 561710
Dustin R. Becks (Pres)

O'FALLON CASTING, LLC
600 Cannonball Ln, O'Fallon, MO 63366-0280
Tel.: (636) 272-6176
Web Site: http://www.ofalloncasting.com
Year Founded: 1969
Non-Ferrous Casting Mfr
N.A.I.C.S.: 331512
Bruce Willson (Sls Mgr)

O'GARA COACH COMPANY LLC
8833 W Olympic Blvd, Beverly Hills, CA 90211
Tel.: (310) 659-4050
Web Site: http://www.ogaracoach.com
Sales Range: $25-49.9 Million
Emp.: 35
New & Used Automobiles
N.A.I.C.S.: 441110
Chris Rogers (Mgr-Bus Dev)

O'HALLORAN ADVERTISING, INC.
270 Saugatuck Ave, Westport, CT 06880-6431
Tel.: (203) 341-9400
Web Site: http://www.ohalloranagency.com
Year Founded: 1971
Rev.: $20,000,000
Emp.: 28
Advertising Agencies, Advertising Specialties, Brand Development, Business-To-Business, Consumer Marketing, Direct Marketing, Yellow Pages Advertising
N.A.I.C.S.: 541810
Susan O'Halloran-Rocket (VP-Mktg & Client Svcs)
Kevin O'Halloran (Owner)

O'HALLORAN INTERNATIONAL INC.
3311 Adventureland Dr, Altoona, IA 50009
Tel.: (515) 967-3300
Web Site: http://www.ohallorans.com
Sales Range: $25-49.9 Million
Emp.: 90
Truck Tractors
N.A.I.C.S.: 423110
Todd Meyer (CFO)
James F. O'Halloran Sr. (Founder & Chm)
Jim O'Halloran Jr. (Pres)

O'HARA CHRYSLER DODGE JEEP RAM
1111 W Michigan Ave, Clinton, MI 49236-9686
Tel.: (517) 456-6555
Web Site: http://www.oharachryslerdodgejeepram.com
Sales Range: $10-24.9 Million
Emp.: 56
Car Whslr
N.A.I.C.S.: 441110
John Akens (Owner & Pres)
Tisha Mooneyham (Coord-Internet)

O'HARE-MIDWAY LIMOUSINE SERVICE INC.
3000 Dundee Rd Ste 106, Northbrook, IL 60062
Tel.: (847) 948-8768
Web Site: http://www.ohare-midway.com
Sales Range: $10-24.9 Million
Emp.: 50
Limousine Rental
N.A.I.C.S.: 485320
Dan Brennan (Mgr-Ops)

O'HARROW CONSTRUCTION COMPANY
4575 Ann Arbor Rd, Jackson, MI 49202
Tel.: (517) 764-4770
Web Site: http://www.oharrowconstruction.com
Rev.: $14,988,527

Industrial Building & Warehouse Operator
N.A.I.C.S.: 236210
George Kittle (Pres)

O'KEEFFE & CO.
921 King St, Alexandria, VA 22314
Tel.: (703) 883-9000
Web Site: http://www.okco.com
Year Founded: 1997
Sales Range: $10-24.9 Million
Emp.: 65
Public Relations Agency
N.A.I.C.S.: 541820
Steve O'Keeffe (Founder & Principal)
Gail Emery (Dir-Acct)
Mary Tobin (Dir-Acct)
Martin Nott (Dir-Acct)

Subsidiaries:

O'Keeffe & Co. (1)
837 Parkridge Dr, Media, PA 19063
Tel.: (610) 566-2909
Web Site: http://www.okco.com
Public Relations Agency
N.A.I.C.S.: 541820
Steve O'Keeffe (Founder & Principal)
Maureen O'Keeffe (Acct Dir)
Andrew LaVanway (VP)

O'Keeffe & Co. (1)
1430 Dresden Dr #335, Atlanta, GA 30319
Tel.: (404) 254-5881
Web Site: http://www.okco.com
Public Relations Agency
N.A.I.C.S.: 541820
Janice Hazen (Acct Dir)

O'Keeffe & Co. (1)
15783 Summit Rock Way, Clackamas, OR 97015
Tel.: (503) 658-7396
Web Site: http://www.okco.com
Public Relations Agency
N.A.I.C.S.: 541820

O'Keeffe & Co. (1)
99 San Gabriel Drive, Rochester, NY 14610
Tel.: (585) 271-1141
Web Site: http://www.okco.com
Emp.: 1
Public Relations Agency
N.A.I.C.S.: 541820
Steve O'Keeffe (VP)

O'KEEFFE'S, INC.
100 N Hill Dr Ste 12, Brisbane, CA 94005
Tel.: (415) 822-4222 CA
Web Site: http://www.okeeffes.com
Year Founded: 1946
Sales Range: $250-299.9 Million
Emp.: 75
Mfr of Custom & Standard Glass & Acrylic Skylights, Smoke Vents, Glass Fire Doors & Walls, Aluminum Ladders, Reglets & Roof Hatches
N.A.I.C.S.: 332323
William F. O'Keeffe (Pres & CEO)
Peter Cheung (Dir-Fin)

Subsidiaries:

Safety First (1)
100 N Hill Dr Ste 12, Brisbane, CA 94005 (100%)
Tel.: (415) 824-4900
Web Site: http://www.safti.com
Sales Range: $25-49.9 Million
Emp.: 20
Distr of Fire & Safety Rated Glass
N.A.I.C.S.: 444180
William F. O'Keeffe (Pres)

O'MALLEY HANSEN COMMUNICATIONS
180 N Wacker Dr Ste 400, Chicago, IL 60606
Tel.: (312) 377-0630
Web Site: http://www.omalleyhansen.com
Year Founded: 2006
Public Relations Agency
N.A.I.C.S.: 541820

COMPANIES

Kelly O'Malley *(Principal)*
Todd Hansen *(Principal)*
Noah Messel *(Supvr)*
Kristy Finch *(Dir-Media)*
Greg Avdoian *(Dir)*

O'MEARA FORD CENTER INC.
400 W 104th Ave, Northglenn, CO 80234
Tel.: (303) 254-5000
Web Site: http://www.omearaford.com
Sales Range: $25-49.9 Million
Emp.: 260
Automobiles, New & Used
N.A.I.C.S.: 441110
Brian O'Meara *(Owner)*
Jim Resler *(Controller)*
Chase Chantala *(Acct Mgr-Comml)*
Colin Cunningham *(Mgr-New Car Sls)*

O'MEARA-BROWN PUBLICATIONS, INC.
727 S Dearborn Ste 812, Chicago, IL 60605
Tel.: (312) 276-0610
Web Site: http://www.lakelandboating.com
Year Founded: 1942
Sales Range: $10-24.9 Million
Emp.: 10
Boating Magazine Publisher
N.A.I.C.S.: 513120
Kirsten Moxley *(Reg Mgr-Sls)*
Linda O'Meara *(VP-Mktg)*
Christy Bauhs *(Dir-Art)*

O'MELVENY & MYERS LLP
400 S Hope St, Los Angeles, CA 90071
Tel.: (213) 430-6000   CA
Web Site: http://www.omm.com
Year Founded: 1885
Sales Range: $800-899.9 Million
Emp.: 1,001
Legal Advisory Services
N.A.I.C.S.: 541110
Tad Allan *(Co-Partner)*
Thomas W. Baxter *(Co-Partner)*
Seth Aronson *(Co-Partner)*
Brian M. Berliner *(Co-Partner)*
Bradley J. Butwin *(Chm)*
Mark Samuels *(Partner)*
George C. Demos *(COO)*
Apalla U. Chopra *(Co-Partner)*
Matthew W. Close *(Co-Partner)*
David Deaton *(Co-Partner)*
Houman Ehsan *(Co-Partner)*
Marc Feinstein *(Co-Partner)*
Jeffrey Fowler *(Co-Partner)*
Richard Goetz *(Co-Partner)*
Courtney Dyer *(Co-Partner)*
Scott Elliott *(Partner & Head-Life Sciences Grp-San Francisco)*
Bimal Patel *(Partner)*
Einat Meisel *(Chm-Israel Practice-Silicon Valley & Partner-Mergers & Acq)*
Kiran Raj *(Partner-White Collar Defense & Corp Investigations Practice)*
Li Han *(Partner-Hong Kong)*
David P. White *(Executives)*

O'NEAL INC.
10 Falcon Crest Dr, Greenville, SC 29667
Tel.: (864) 298-2000
Web Site: http://www.onealinc.com
Year Founded: 1975
Sales Range: $200-249.9 Million
Emp.: 300
Consulting, Engineering & Architectural Services
N.A.I.C.S.: 541611

Judy Castleberry *(CFO)*
Jason Jones *(Dir-Virtual-Construction)*
Kevin Bean *(Pres & CEO)*

Subsidiaries:

DME Alliance, Inc.   (1)
7540 Windsor Dr Ste 311, Allentown, PA 18195
Tel.: (610) 366-1744
Web Site: http://www.dmeforlife.com
Sales Range: $1-9.9 Million
Emp.: 15
Engineering Consultants
N.A.I.C.S.: 541330
David M. Marks *(Pres)*

O'NEAL INDUSTRIES, INC.
2311 Highland Ave S Ste 200, Birmingham, AL 35205
Tel.: (205) 721-2880
Web Site: https://www.onealind.com
Year Founded: 1921
Sales Range: $1-4.9 Billion
Emp.: 3,000
Offices of Other Holding Companies
N.A.I.C.S.: 551112
Craft O'Neal *(Chm & CEO)*
Mike Rowland *(CFO)*
Troy Lugo *(VP & Controller)*
G. Ruffner Page Jr. *(Pres & COO)*

Subsidiaries:

O'Neal Steel, Inc.   (1)
744 41st St N, Birmingham, AL 35222-1124
Tel.: (205) 599-8000
Web Site: http://www.onealsteel.com
Sales Range: $1-4.9 Billion
Emp.: 3,750
Metals Mfr
N.A.I.C.S.: 423510
Craft O'Neal *(Chm)*
Eric Worley *(Mgr-Corp Safety & Security)*
Jim Davis *(Mgr-Corp Ops Svcs)*
Mike Symasek *(Controller)*
Jodi Parnell *(VP-Supply Chain Mgmt & Bus Dev)*
Stephen Armstrong *(Pres & CEO)*
Lauren Scott-Cumbie *(Mgr-Product Dev-South)*
Mitchell Harrison *(VP-Ops)*
Suzanne Lane *(CFO & VP)*
Tate Forrester *(VP-Sls & Mktg)*

Subsidiary (Domestic):

Aerodyne Alloys LLC   (2)
350 Pleasant Vly Rd, South Windsor, CT 06074
Tel.: (559) 275-1755
Web Site: http://www.aerodynealloys.com
Sales Range: $25-49.9 Million
Emp.: 60
Stainless Steel Products Mfr
N.A.I.C.S.: 423510
Greg Chase *(Pres)*
Mike Mills *(Mgr-Southeast)*

Leeco Steel, LLC   (2)
1011 Warrenville Rd Ste 500, Lisle, IL 60532
Tel.: (630) 427-2100
Web Site: http://www.leecosteel.com
Emp.: 40
Metals Service Center
N.A.I.C.S.: 423510
Denton Nordhues *(Pres & CEO)*
Chad Duffin *(VP-Sls)*
Jason Fredstrom *(Exec VP)*
Robert Bartley *(Reg Mgr)*
Rob Gallay *(Mgr-Sls-Wholesale Distr Div-Natl)*
Tim Quinlan *(Dir-Sls)*
Walt Quinlan *(Mgr-North Reg)*
Lacey Jackson *(Dir-Ops-North)*
Michael Delay *(Dir-Ops-South & Canada)*
Chad Schuh *(VP-Ops)*
Tom Barcelona Jr. *(Mgr-Southeast Reg)*

O'Neal Flat Rolled Metals, LLC   (2)
1229 S Fulton Ave, Brighton, CO 80601-6743   (100%)
Tel.: (303) 654-0300
Web Site: http://www.ofrmetals.com

Sales Range: $25-49.9 Million
Emp.: 250
Metals Distribution
N.A.I.C.S.: 423510
Phill Cavender *(VP-Sls-Western Reg)*
Bruce Pole *(CFO)*
Seth Wiener *(Gen Mgr-Southeastern Reg)*

Unit (Domestic):

O'Neal Flat Rolled Metals, LLC - Monroe   (3)
1 Fitzgerald Ave, Monroe Township, NJ 08831
Tel.: (609) 395-7007
Sales Range: $10-24.9 Million
Emp.: 50
Metal Product Distr
N.A.I.C.S.: 423510
Jeff Katz *(VP-Non-Ferrous)*

Division (Domestic):

O'Neal Manufacturing Services Division   (2)
744 41st St N, Birmingham, AL 35202
Tel.: (205) 599-8000
Web Site: http://www.onealsteel.com
Metal Service Centers; Fabricated Metal Products Mfr
N.A.I.C.S.: 332999
Steve McCracken *(Exec VP)*

Subsidiary (Domestic):

Iowa Laser Technology Inc.   (3)
7100 Chancellor Dr, Cedar Falls, IA 50613
Tel.: (319) 266-3561
Web Site: http://www.iowalaser.com
Rev.: $16,381,604
Emp.: 109
Fabricated Metal Assemblies & Components Mfr
N.A.I.C.S.: 332999
Joan Knock *(Mgr-HR)*
Dawn Bovy *(Supvr-Production Plng)*
Joe Barber *(Pres)*
Roger Blakesley *(Mgr-Sls)*

Subsidiary (Domestic):

Plus Ten Stainless, Inc.   (2)
2970 A Bay Vista Ct, Benicia, CA 94510
Tel.: (707) 745-4625
Web Site: http://www.plustenstainless.com
Sales Range: $25-49.9 Million
Emp.: 10
Stainless Steel Plate Distr
N.A.I.C.S.: 423510
Todd Rhodes *(Pres)*

TW Metals   (2)
The Arboretum Ste 204 760 Constitution Dr, Exton, PA 19341
Tel.: (610) 458-1300
Web Site: http://www.twmetals.com
Metals Service Center
N.A.I.C.S.: 423510
Jack Elrod *(Pres & CEO)*
Torian Keen *(Mgr-Wichita)*
Mary Ellen Eldridge *(Office Mgr)*
Norwin Lilly *(Mgr-Charleston & Cincinnati)*
Rosemary Smith *(Mgr-Commodity)*
Jon Veurink *(CFO & VP-Fin)*

United Performance Metals, Inc.   (2)
3475 Symmes Rd, Hamilton, OH 45015
Tel.: (513) 860-6500
Web Site: http://www.upmet.com
Sales Range: $25-49.9 Million
Emp.: 60
Specialty Stainless Steel & High Temperature Alloys Mfr
N.A.I.C.S.: 331110
Tom Kennard *(Pres)*
Kathy Esquerra *(Mgr-Inside Sls-California)*
Lauren Trebbien *(Coord-HR)*

O'NEAL, INC.
525 W William St, Ann Arbor, MI 48103-4998
Tel.: (734) 769-0770   MI
Web Site: http://www.onealconstruction.com
Year Founded: 1961
Sales Range: $10-24.9 Million
Emp.: 50

O'NEIL INDUSTRIES INC.

Provider of Commercial Construction Services
N.A.I.C.S.: 236220
Joe O'Neal *(Pres)*

Subsidiaries:

Kerrytown Shops of Ann Arbor Inc.   (1)
407 N 5th Ave, Ann Arbor, MI 48104-1107
Tel.: (734) 662-5008
Web Site: http://www.kerrytown.com
Rev.: $105,231
Emp.: 3
Provider of Subdivision & Development Services
N.A.I.C.S.: 237210
Karen Farmer *(Gen Mgr)*

O'Neal Construction Inc.   (1)
525 W William St, Ann Arbor, MI 48103-4943
Tel.: (734) 769-0770
Web Site: http://www.onealconstruction.com
Rev.: $37,427,466
Emp.: 30
Provider of Commercial Construction Services
N.A.I.C.S.: 236220
Joe O'Neal *(Pres)*
William Quinn *(VP)*

O'NEIL & ASSOCIATES INCORPORATED
495 Byers Rd, Miamisburg, OH 45342
Tel.: (937) 865-0800
Web Site: http://www.oneil.com
Rev.: $14,287,920
Emp.: 400
Technical Manuals; Publishing Only, Not Printed On Site
N.A.I.C.S.: 513199
Brian Pugh *(Engr-Application)*
Eric Nielsen *(Engr-Application II)*
Matthew Armstrong *(Mgr-Mktg & Proposal)*
Dave Stackhouse *(CIO & VP)*
Hernan Olivas *(Pres & CEO)*
Cindy Schneider *(Controller)*

O'NEIL BUICK - GMC INC.
869 W St Rd, Warminster, PA 18974
Tel.: (215) 672-0900
Web Site: http://www.oneilbuickgmc.com
Sales Range: $10-24.9 Million
Emp.: 38
Car Whslr
N.A.I.C.S.: 441110
Michael R. O'Neil *(Pres)*

O'NEIL INDUSTRIES INC.
1245 W Washington Blvd, Chicago, IL 60607
Tel.: (773) 755-1611   IL
Web Site: http://www.weoneil.com
Year Founded: 1925
Sales Range: $200-249.9 Million
Emp.: 450
General Contracting & Construction Management
N.A.I.C.S.: 236220
Pat McGowan *(Dir-HR)*
Kenneth A. McHugh *(Exec VP-Ops)*
Dan Feucht *(CFO)*

Subsidiaries:

W.E. O'Neil Construction   (1)
2601 N Fairview Ave, Tucson, AZ 85705
Tel.: (520) 792-0734
Web Site: http://www.weoneil.com
Sales Range: $10-24.9 Million
Emp.: 22
General Contractors
N.A.I.C.S.: 236210
John Hobbs *(Pres)*

W.E. O'Neil Construction Co. of California   (1)
909 N Sepulveda Ste 400, El Segundo, CA 90245-6903
Tel.: (310) 643-7900

O'NEIL INDUSTRIES INC.

U.S. PRIVATE

O'Neil Industries Inc.—(Continued)
Web Site: http://www.weoneil.com
Sales Range: $10-24.9 Million
Emp.: 30
Construction Contractor
N.A.I.C.S.: 236220
John Finn (Pres)
Marvin Wheat (VP-Northern California)
Rick Pomeroy (Project Dir-Northern California)

W.E. O'Neil Construction Co. of Colorado (1)
229 Vallejo St, Denver, CO 80223
Tel.: (303) 238-7900
Web Site: http://www.weoneil.com
Sales Range: $10-24.9 Million
Emp.: 15
Construction Contractor
N.A.I.C.S.: 236220

W.E. O'Neil Construction Company (1)
1245 W Washington Blvd, Chicago, IL 60607 **(90%)**
Tel.: (773) 755-1611
Web Site: http://www.weoneil.com
Sales Range: $25-49.9 Million
Emp.: 100
Construction Company
N.A.I.C.S.: 236220
D.J. Garlick (VP)
L.J. Reiner (Sr VP)
Brian Ramsay (Pres & CEO)
A. J. Jacobs (Mgr-Bus Dev)

W.E. O'Neil Construction Company of Arizona (1)
4511 E Kerby Ave, Phoenix, AZ 85040 **(83%)**
Tel.: (480) 921-8000
Sales Range: $10-24.9 Million
Emp.: 100
Construction Contractor
N.A.I.C.S.: 236220
Bryan Dunn (Pres-Phoenix & Tucson)

O'NEILL AUTOMOTIVE INC.
7979 Metcalf Ave, Overland Park, KS 66204
Tel.: (913) 648-5400
Web Site:
http://www.oneillhonda.com
Sales Range: $50-74.9 Million
Emp.: 130
New & Used Automobiles
N.A.I.C.S.: 441110
Richard S. O'Neill (Owner & Chm)
Sherri Bloesser (Controller)
Rick O'Neill Jr. (Pres)

O'NEILL ELECTRIC INC.
1101 NE 144th St Ste 101, Vancouver, WA 98685
Tel.: (503) 493-6045
Sales Range: $10-24.9 Million
Emp.: 50
Electrical Wiring Services
N.A.I.C.S.: 238210
Maurice Rahming (Owner)

O'NEILL INC.
1071 41st Ave, Santa Cruz, CA 95062-4400
Tel.: (831) 475-7500 CA
Web Site: http://www.oneill.com
Year Founded: 1952
Sales Range: $25-49.9 Million
Emp.: 231
Fabricated Rubber Product Mfr
N.A.I.C.S.: 326299
John Pope (COO)
Michelle Molfino (CFO)

O'NEILL PROPERTIES GROUP, LP
201 King of Prussia Rd, King Of Prussia, PA 19087
Tel.: (610) 239-6100
Web Site:
http://www.oneillproperties.com

Year Founded: 1988
Sales Range: $10-24.9 Million
Emp.: 100
Real Estate Developers
N.A.I.C.S.: 237210
J. Brian O'Neill (Chm & CEO)
Ahmed Rafik (Mgr-Mgmt Info Sys)
Guy Wolfington (Reg Dir)
Sharon Slusarski (Coord-HR)

O'NEILLS CHEVROLET & BUICK
5 W Main St, Avon, CT 06001
Tel.: (860) 677-1666
Web Site:
http://www.oneillschevybuick.com
Sales Range: $10-24.9 Million
Emp.: 35
Sales of New & Used Automobiles
N.A.I.C.S.: 441110
Lawrence Sullivan (Pres)
Sean Sullivan (Gen Mgr)

O'REILLY MEDIA, INC.
1005 Gravenstein Hwy N, Sebastopol, CA 95472-3858
Tel.: (707) 827-7000 CA
Web Site: http://www.oreilly.com
Year Founded: 1978
Sales Range: $25-49.9 Million
Emp.: 277
Technical Writing & Publishing Services
N.A.I.C.S.: 513130
Laura Baldwin (Pres)
Timothy B. O'Reilly (Founder, Chm & CEO)
Jeanne Cordisco (Chief People Officer)

Subsidiaries:

O'Reilly AlphaTech Ventures (1)
1 Lombard St Ste 303, San Francisco, CA 94111
Tel.: (415) 693-0200
Web Site: http://www.oatv.com
Investment Services
N.A.I.C.S.: 523999
Bryce Roberts (Mng Dir)
Mark Jacobsen (Mng Dir)
Tim O'Reilly (Founder & CEO)

O'Reilly China (1)
Suite 807 Building C Cheng Ming Mansion 2 Xizhimen South Street, Xicheng District, Beijing, 100035, China
Tel.: (86) 10 88097475
Web Site: http://www.oreilly.com.cn
Technical Writing & Publishing Services
N.A.I.C.S.: 513130

O'Reilly Japan (1)
Intelligent Plaza Building 1F 26 Banchi 27 Sakamachi, Shinjuku-ku, Tokyo, 160-0002, Japan
Tel.: (81) 3 3356 5227
Web Site: http://www.oreilly.co.jp
Emp.: 15
Technical Writing & Publishing Services
N.A.I.C.S.: 513130
Fumi Yamakawa (Gen Mgr)

O'Reilly UK (1)
5 St-Georges, Farnham, GU9 7LW, Surrey, United Kingdom
Tel.: (44) 1252 721284
Web Site: http://www.oreilly.com
Emp.: 8
Technical Writing & Publishing Services
N.A.I.C.S.: 513130
Graham Cameron (Mng Dir)

O'Reilly Verlag (1)
Balthasastr 81, 50670, Cologne, Germany
Tel.: (49) 2219731600
Web Site: http://www.oreilly.de
Technical Writing & Publishing Services
N.A.I.C.S.: 513130

Safari Books Online, LLC (1)
1003 Gravenstein Hwy N, Sebastopol, CA 95472 **(100%)**
Tel.: (707) 827-4100

Web Site: http://www.safaribooksonline.com
Sales Range: $1-9.9 Million
Emp.: 80
Online Book Publisher
N.A.I.C.S.: 513130
Andrew Savikas (CEO)

O'RIELLY MOTOR COMPANY
6100 E Broadway Blvd, Tucson, AZ 85711
Tel.: (520) 747-8000 AZ
Web Site: http://www.orielly.com
Year Founded: 1924
Rev.: $193,952,871
Emp.: 300
Holding Company; New & Used Car Dealership Owner & Operator
N.A.I.C.S.: 551112
Ann Edwards (Mgr-Cust Svcs)

Subsidiaries:

O'Rielly Chevrolet, Inc. (1)
6160 E Broadway Blvd, Tucson, AZ 85711-4023
Tel.: (520) 747-8000
Web Site: http://www.orielly.com
Sales Range: $50-74.9 Million
Emp.: 100
New & Used Car Dealer
N.A.I.C.S.: 441110
Chuck McCoy (Mgr-Svc)
Maria Brown (Mgr-HR)
Scott Vironet (Mgr-Svc)

O'ROURKE DIST. CO., INC.
223 McCarty St, Houston, TX 77029
Tel.: (713) 672-4500 TX
Web Site: http://www.orpp.com
Year Founded: 1932
Sales Range: $50-74.9 Million
Emp.: 80
Bulk & Retail Petroleum Products Distr
N.A.I.C.S.: 424710
Dennis O'Rourke (CEO)
Fred Blankenship (VP-Select Environmental)
Tony Garcia (VP-Specialty Fueling Svcs)

O'ROURKE MEDIA GROUP, LLC
281 N Main St, Saint Albans, VT 05478
Tel.: (802) 722-7902 VT
Web Site:
https://orourkemediagroup.com
Year Founded: 2018
Digital Agency & Internet Publishing
N.A.I.C.S.: 551112
Jim O'Rourke (CEO)

Subsidiaries:

Pagosa Springs SUN Publishing, Inc. (1)
466 Pagosa St, Pagosa Springs, CO 81147
Tel.: (970) 264-2100
Web Site: http://www.pagosasun.com
Rev.: $3,028,048
Emp.: 15
Other Commercial Printing
N.A.I.C.S.: 323111

Times Publishing Newspapers Inc. (1)
341 Rumpf Ave, Penndel, PA 19047-5523
Tel.: (215) 702-3405
Web Site: http://www.timespub.com
Newspaper Publishers
N.A.I.C.S.: 513110
Mary Helf (Sr VP & Atty)

O'ROURKE SALES COMPANY
3885 Elmore Ave Ste 100, Davenport, IA 52807
Tel.: (563) 823-1501 IA
Web Site:
http://www.orourkesales.com
Year Founded: 1965
Sales Range: $25-49.9 Million

Emp.: 180
Consumer Electronic Appliances & Equipment Distr
N.A.I.C.S.: 423610
Jeff O'Rourke (CEO)
Bill French (VP-Rent-To-Own-Sls)
Jay Nardone (VP-Computer & Phone Sls)

O'S COMPANIES INC.
301 S Market St, Wichita, KS 67202-3805
Tel.: (316) 265-5611 KS
Web Site: http://www.lario.net
Year Founded: 1985
Sales Range: $25-49.9 Million
Emp.: 96
Extraction of Crude Petroleum & Natural Gas
N.A.I.C.S.: 211120
Patrick E. O'Shaughnessy (Chm)
David Loger (CFO)

Subsidiaries:

Lario Oil & Gas Company (1)
301 S Market St, Wichita, KS 67202-3805 **(100%)**
Tel.: (316) 265-5611
Web Site: http://www.lario.net
Sales Range: $25-49.9 Million
Emp.: 40
Crude Petroleum & Natural Gas Production
N.A.I.C.S.: 211120
Mike O'Shaughnessy (Pres)

Division (Domestic):

Lario Oil & Gas Company - Denver Division (2)
1675 Larimer St, Denver, CO 80202
Tel.: (303) 595-8030
Emp.: 15
Oil & Gas Exploration Services
N.A.I.C.S.: 213112
David Thorpe (Mgr-Landman)

O'STEEL BUILDINGS, INC.
11780 S Carolina 90, Little River, SC 29566
Tel.: (704) 824-6061
Web Site:
http://www.osteelbuildings.com
Sales Range: $10-24.9 Million
Emp.: 15
Prefabricated Structures
N.A.I.C.S.: 423390
Beverly Lynn (Pres)

O'STEEN BROTHERS INC.
1006 SE 4th St, Gainesville, FL 32601
Tel.: (352) 376-1634
Web Site:
http://www.osteenbrothers.com
Sales Range: $10-24.9 Million
Emp.: 70
Site Work Construction
N.A.I.C.S.: 237310
William Bradley O'Steen (Co-Founder & Pres)
Lisa O'Steen (Treas)
Dexter O'Steen (Co-Founder & VP)

O'STEEN VOLVO
10863 Philips Hwy, Jacksonville, FL 32256
Tel.: (904) 396-5486
Web Site:
http://www.osteenvolvo.com
Year Founded: 1996
Sales Range: $10-24.9 Million
Emp.: 100
Car Whslr
N.A.I.C.S.: 441110
Bill Olive (Gen Mgr)
Mark O'Steen (Owner & Pres)
Tom O'Steen (Pres)

O'SULLIVAN COMMUNICATIONS
42 Davis Rd Ste 1, Acton, MA 01720
Tel.: (978) 264-0707
Web Site:
http://www.ocmarketing.com
Year Founded: 1991
Sales Range: Less than $1 Million
Emp.: 5
Full-Service Public Relations
N.A.I.C.S.: 541810
Meghan O'Sullivan (Pres)
Cheryl Allen (Dir-Creative)
Gabe D'Annunzio (VP)
Diane Hendrickson Winder (Exec VP-Healthcare-Biotech)
Cort Boulanger (Exec VP-Affairs & Crisis Comm)

O'TASTY FOODS, INC.
160 S Hacienda Blvd, City of Industry, CA 91745
Tel.: (626) 330-1229
Web Site:
http://www.otastyfoods.com
Year Founded: 1994
Sales Range: $10-24.9 Million
Emp.: 91
Frozen Specialty Food Mfr
N.A.I.C.S.: 311412
Ming Huang (Pres)
Maureen Hou (Office Mgr)
Ken Chen (VP)
Andy Huang (Gen Mgr)

O,R&L CONSTRUCTION CORP.
2 Summit Pl, Branford, CT 06405
Tel.: (203) 483-2040
Web Site:
http://www.orlconstruction.com
Sales Range: $10-24.9 Million
Emp.: 25
Industrial Buildings & Warehouses
N.A.I.C.S.: 236220
Franklin Todd Renz (Pres)
Tanya Cutolo (Dir-Design & Bus Dev)
Clifford Lennox (Project Mgr)
Subsidiaries:

O,R&L Commercial, LLC (1)
2 Summit Pl, Branford, CT 06405
Tel.: (203) 488-1555
Web Site: http://www.orlcommercial.com
Emp.: 8
Commercial Real Estate Services
N.A.I.C.S.: 531210
J. Richard Lee (Founder, Mng Dir & Dir-Comml)
Jay L. Morris (Mng Partner & Dir-Comml)

O,R&L Facility Services (1)
2 Summit Pl, Branford, CT 06405
Tel.: (203) 643-1001
Web Site: http://www.or-l.com
Facility & Maintenance Services
N.A.I.C.S.: 561210
Robert D. Owens (Pres)
Randall K. Ziegler (Exec VP & Dir-Bus Dev)
Louann Heft (Dir-Design & Pre-Construction)
J. Richard Lee (Dir-Comml)
Robert Johansmeyer (Exec VP-HR, Risk Mgmt & Corp Trng)

O. BERK COMPANY L.L.C.
3 Milltown Ct, Union, NJ 07083-8108
Tel.: (908) 851-9500 NJ
Web Site: http://www.oberk.com
Year Founded: 1910
Sales Range: $10-24.9 Million
Emp.: 90
Distr of Glass, Plastic & Metal Bottles & Containers
N.A.I.C.S.: 423840
Marc M. Gaelen (Pres & CEO)
Meryl Japha (Exec VP)
Subsidiaries:

AQL Decorating Co., Inc. (1)
215 Bergen Blvd, Fairview, NJ 07022
Tel.: (201) 941-1610
Web Site: http://www.aqldecorating.com
Packaging & Labeling Services
N.A.I.C.S.: 561910

Cosmetic Packaging Group (1)
3 Milltown Ct, Union, NJ 07083-8108
Tel.: (908) 851-9500
Distr of Glass, Plastic & Metal Bottles & Containers
N.A.I.C.S.: 423840

E.D. Luce Packaging (1)
13918 Equitable Rd, Cerritos, CA 90703-2315
Tel.: (562) 997-9777
Web Site: http://www.essentialsupplies.com
Rev.: $6,840,000
Emp.: 12
Industrial Supplies Merchant Whslr
N.A.I.C.S.: 423840
Zino Nakasuji (Pres)

KOLS Containers (1)
1408 Desoto Rd, Baltimore, MD 21230-1202 (100%)
Tel.: (410) 646-2300
Web Site: http://www.oberk.com
Sales Range: $10-24.9 Million
Emp.: 35
Distr of Glass, Plastic & Metal Bottles & Containers
N.A.I.C.S.: 423840

O. Berk Company - BottleStore Division (1)
3 Milltown Ct, Union, NJ 07083
Tel.: (908) 851-9500
Web Site: http://www.bottlestore.com
Plastics Bottle Mfr
N.A.I.C.S.: 326160

O. Berk Company of New England (1)
300 Callegari Dr, West Haven, CT 06516
Tel.: (203) 932-8000
Web Site: http://www.oberk.com
Distr of Glass, Plastic & Metal Bottles & Containers
N.A.I.C.S.: 423840
Mary Liversiete (Office Mgr)

VPI Packaging Inc. (1)
510 Franklin Ave Ste 4, Nutley, NJ 07110-1755
Tel.: (973) 235-9030
Web Site: http://www.vpipackaging.com
Packaging & Labeling Services
N.A.I.C.S.: 561910
Ronald Cataldo (Owner)

O. TREVINO CONSTRUCTION, LLC.
4501 N Hwy 377, Roanoke, TX 76262
Tel.: (817) 430-2410
Web Site: http://www.otconst.com
Sales Range: $10-24.9 Million
Emp.: 120
Structural Steel & Precast Concrete Contracting Services
N.A.I.C.S.: 238120
Vanessa Trevino Copeland (CFO)

O.A. NEWTON & SON CO
16356 Sussex Hwy, Bridgeville, DE 19933
Tel.: (302) 337-8211 DE
Web Site: http://www.oanewton.com
Year Founded: 1916
Sales Range: $10-24.9 Million
Emp.: 81
Materials Handling Systems; Agricultural Irrigation & Millwright Work Services
N.A.I.C.S.: 423830
Andrew Buman (Mgr-IT)
Robert F. Rider Jr. (CEO)

O.C. CLUSS LUMBER COMPANY
S Pennsylvania Ave, Uniontown, PA 15401-0696
Tel.: (724) 415-2100 PA
Web Site: http://www.occluss.com
Year Founded: 1918
Whslr & Retailer of Lumber & Building Materials
N.A.I.C.S.: 444110
Chris Cluss (Pres & CEO)
John Hill (CFO)
Michael Cluss (VP)
Reed Kneale (COO)
Jackie Nicholson (Dir-HR)
Paulette Schulze (Dir-Adv)

O.C. JONES & SONS INC.
1520 4th St, Berkeley, CA 94710
Tel.: (510) 526-3424
Web Site: http://www.ocjones.com
Rev.: $60,000,000
Emp.: 150
Grading
N.A.I.C.S.: 237310
Cam Yan (Asst Controller)
Lisa Larratt (Mgr-Risk)
Bret Berry (Project Mgr)
Greg Souder (Mgr-Estimating)
Rob Layne (Pres & CEO)
Beth Yoshida (CFO)
Mel Frisk (Mgr-Equipment)
Darren Hiatt (Mgr-Ops-Construction)
Kevin Goddard (Mgr-Ops-Engrg)

O.C. TANNER COMPANY INC.
1930 S State St, Salt Lake City, UT 84115-2311
Tel.: (801) 486-2430 UT
Web Site: http://www.octanner.com
Year Founded: 1927
Sales Range: $75-99.9 Million
Emp.: 1,600
Producer of Jewelry & Precious Metal
N.A.I.C.S.: 339910
David A. Petersen (CEO)
Harold Simons (Exec VP-Mfg)
Subsidiaries:

O.C. Tanner Manufacturing, Inc. (1)
1930 S State St, Salt Lake City, UT 84115-2311 (100%)
Tel.: (801) 486-2430
Web Site: http://www.octanner.com
Sales Range: $10-24.9 Million
Emp.: 15
Mfr of Jewelry & Precious Metal
N.A.I.C.S.: 423940

O.C. Tanner Recognition Company, Inc. (1)
1930 S State St, Salt Lake City, UT 84115-2311
Tel.: (801) 486-2430
Web Site: http://www.octanner.com
Sales Range: $100-124.9 Million
Mfr of Jewelry & Precious Stones
N.A.I.C.S.: 423940
Dave Patersen (CEO)

O.C. WELCH FORD LINCOLN INC.
4920 Independent Blvd, Hardeeville, SC 29927 SC
Web Site:
http://www.goseeocford.com
Sales Range: $100-124.9 Million
Emp.: 100
Car Dealership
N.A.I.C.S.: 441110
Chip Welch (VP)
Janey Welch (Treas & Sec)
O. C. Welch III (Pres)

O.D. SNIDER & SON INCORPARATED
13401 Vly Ave E, Sumner, WA 98390
Tel.: (253) 863-6341
Web Site:
http://www.pacificprideusa.com
Sales Range: $10-24.9 Million
Emp.: 20
Petroleum Bulk Stations
N.A.I.C.S.: 424710
Bryan Snider (Pres)

O.E. WHEELS, LLC
1916 72nd Dr E, Sarasota, FL 34243-3966
Tel.: (941) 921-0065
Web Site:
http://www.oewheelsllc.com
Year Founded: 2001
Sales Range: $25-49.9 Million
Emp.: 25
Wheels & Tires Whslr
N.A.I.C.S.: 423130
James Moore (Owner)

O.E.M. CONTROLS, INC.
10 Controls Dr, Shelton, CT 06484-6136
Tel.: (203) 929-8431
Web Site:
http://www.oemcontrols.com
Year Founded: 1986
Sales Range: $10-24.9 Million
Emp.: 192
Producer of Relays & Industrial Controls
N.A.I.C.S.: 335314
S. Brian Simons (CEO)
Rob Henry (Mgr-Sys & Production Support)

O.K. PETROLEUM DISTRIBUTION CORP.
185 Rte 109, West Babylon, NY 11704-6211
Tel.: (631) 321-0549
Web Site:
http://www.okpetroleum.com
Year Founded: 1977
Sales Range: $10-24.9 Million
Emp.: 25
Provider of Gasoline Services
N.A.I.C.S.: 457120
John Musacchia (Pres)

O2 AERO ACQUISITIONS LLC
12871 Trade Way Dr Ste 8, Bonita Springs, FL 34135
Tel.: (239) 405-6117
Investment Services
N.A.I.C.S.: 523999
Scott E. Ashton (Mng Dir)
Subsidiaries:

Aerox Aviation Oxygen Systems, LLC (1)
12871 Trade Way Dr Ste 8, Bonita Springs, FL 34135
Tel.: (239) 405-6117
Web Site: https://www.aerox.com
Aviation Oxygen Systems & Accessories Mfr
N.A.I.C.S.: 336413
Scott E. Ashton (Pres)

Fluid Power, Inc. (1)
1300 Hudson Gate Dr, Hudson, OH 44236
Tel.: (330) 653-5107
Web Site: http://www.fluidpowerohio.com
Sales Range: $1-9.9 Million
Emp.: 12
Aircraft Parts & Auxiliary Equipment Mfr
N.A.I.C.S.: 336413
Eugene Lamoreaux (Pres)

O2 FITNESS
135 E Martoin St Ste 201, Raleigh, NC 27601
Tel.: (919) 532-0702
Web Site:
http://www.o2fitnessclubs.com
Year Founded: 2003
Sales Range: $10-24.9 Million
Emp.: 400
Health & Fitness Clubs
N.A.I.C.S.: 713940

O2 FITNESS

O2 Fitness—(Continued)
Justin Mascho *(Gen Mgr)*
Jason Peters *(Gen Mgr)*
King Baldwin *(Gen Mgr)*
Marcus Hicks *(Gen Mgr)*
Matt Cody *(Gen Mgr)*
Matt Theders *(Gen Mgr)*
Melissa Griffin *(Gen Mgr)*
Tracy Gower *(Gen Mgr)*
Vic Victorino *(Gen Mgr)*

O2 INVESTMENT PARTNERS, LLC
40900 Woodward Ave Ste 200,
Bloomfield Hills, MI 48304
Tel.: (248) 554-4227
Web Site:
http://www.o2investment.com
Privater Equity Firm
N.A.I.C.S.: 523999
Jay J. Hansen *(Co-Founder, Pres & Mng Partner)*
Robert Harris Orley *(Principal)*
Todd Fink *(Co-Founder, CEO & Mng Partner)*
Gregg Orley *(Principal)*
Larry Lax *(Principal)*
Luke K. Plumpton *(Partner)*
Andrew Faubel *(VP)*
Sean Darin *(Principal)*

Subsidiaries:

4M Building Solutions, Inc. **(1)**
2827 Clark Ave, Saint Louis, MO 63103
Tel.: (314) 535-2100
Web Site: https://www.4-m.com
Janitorial & Related Facilities Services
N.A.I.C.S.: 561720
Tim M. Murch *(Chm & CEO)*
Steven Crain *(Pres & COO)*
Josh Hendricks *(VP-Central Div)*
Judy Botz *(CFO)*
Karina Villasenor *(VP-HR)*
Tom Covilli *(VP-Safety & Risk Mgmt)*
Dan Cline II *(Exec VP)*

Subsidiary (Domestic):

Capital Services, Inc. **(2)**
620 Taylor Sta Rd, Columbus, OH 43230
Tel.: (614) 224-0140
Web Site: http://www.capitalservicesinc.com
Sales Range: $1-9.9 Million
Emp.: 250
Janitorial Services
N.A.I.C.S.: 561720
John H. Schell *(Pres)*

Horizon Services Corporation
250 Governor St, East Hartford, CT 06108-2007
Janitorial Services
N.A.I.C.S.: 561720
Dave Hyun *(VP)*

Major Commercial Cleaning Inc. **(2)**
105 Haywood Ln, Nashville, TN 37211-2835
Tel.: (615) 983-8700
Janitorial & Related Facilities Services
N.A.I.C.S.: 561720
Robert Stewart *(Pres)*

Alpha Sintered Metals, Inc. **(1)**
95 Mason Run Rd, Ridgway, PA 15853
Tel.: (814) 773-3191
Web Site: http://www.alphasintered.com
Sales Range: $25-49.9 Million
Emp.: 250
Powdered Metal Product Mfr
N.A.I.C.S.: 332117
JoAnne Ryan *(Pres & CEO)*
Robert Hathorn *(CFO & VP)*
Dave Ryan *(VP-Ops)*
Larry Weis *(VP-Sls & Mktg)*
Mike O'Neill *(VP-Engrg)*
Steve Patrick *(Dir-Sls & Mktg)*
Michael Schloder *(Mgr-Mfg & Engrg)*
Janice Woelfel *(Dir-Pur)*
John Butterfuss *(Mgr-Resource)*
Amy Halpin *(Mgr-Quality Assurance)*
Corine Christoff *(VP-HR)*

Berlin Rosen Ltd. **(1)**
15 Maiden Ln Ste 1600, New York, NY 10038
Tel.: (646) 452-5637
Web Site: http://www.berlinrosen.com
Emp.: 462
Services Related to Advertising
N.A.I.C.S.: 541890
Daniel Massey *(VP)*
Kelly Vingelis *(VP-Digital Adv)*

Subsidiary (Domestic):

InkHouse **(2)**
260 Charles St Ste 200, Waltham, MA 02453
Tel.: (781) 966-4100
Web Site: http://www.inkhouse.com
Sales Range: $1-9.9 Million
Emp.: 80
Public Relation & Social Content Agency Services
N.A.I.C.S.: 541820
Tina Cassidy *(Chief Content Officer & Sr VP)*
Meg O'Leary *(Principal)*
Susan Elsbree *(VP)*
Ed Harrison *(Mng Dir)*
Dan O'Mahony *(Mng Dir)*
Brendan Monahan *(VP-Healthcare)*
Alison Morra *(COO)*
Beth Monaghan *(Founder & CEO)*
Tiffany Darmetko *(Exec VP-Client Svcs & Interim Gen Mgr-New York City)*
Tori Poole *(VP-Diversity, Equity & Inclusion)*
Laura Garofalo *(VP-Mktg)*
Anne Baker *(Gen Mgr-California)*
Samantha McGarry *(Exec VP-Story Crafting)*
Lisa van der Pool *(Exec VP-Media Strategy)*

Capital Construction Holdings **(1)**
501 W Travelers Trl, Burnsville, MN 55337
Tel.: (866) 989-6641
Web Site:
https://poweredbystronghouse.com
Roof Replacement & Repair Services
N.A.I.C.S.: 238160

Subsidiary (Domestic):

Infinity Roofing & Siding, Inc. **(2)**
18311 Clay Rd Ste B3, Houston, TX 77084
Tel.: (281) 855-2331
Web Site: http://www.infinityroofer.com
Sales Range: $10-24.9 Million
Emp.: 25
Roof Contract Services
N.A.I.C.S.: 238160
Derek Lindsey *(Founder & CEO)*
Mike Cannon *(Gen Mgr-Sls)*
Nicole Pate *(Mgr-Acctg)*
Chris Hubac *(Mgr-Production)*
Aubry Cluff *(Acct Mgr)*
Sarah Alexander *(Acct Mgr)*
Tasha Swindell *(Acct Mgr)*
Vanesa Martinez *(Acct Mgr)*

Civitas Public Affairs Group LLC **(1)**
409 7th St NW, Washington, DC 20004
Tel.: (202) 737-9700
Web Site:
http://www.civitaspublicaffairs.com
Services Related to Advertising
N.A.I.C.S.: 541890
Michelle Carroll *(Project Coord)*

Clio Holdings LLC **(1)**
845 McFarland Pkwy, Alpharetta, GA 30004
Tel.: (313) 647-5326
Web Site: http://www.clioholdings.com
Holding Company; Countertop Fabricator & Whslr
N.A.I.C.S.: 551112
Eric Tryon *(Co-Founder)*
Mike Varone *(Pres)*
Jeff Gallentine *(CFO & VP)*
Casey Jackson *(VP)*
Bryan Tolles *(Co-Founder & Exec Chm)*

Subsidiary (Domestic):

The Tryon Group Inc. **(2)**
845 Mcfarland Pkwy, Alpharetta, GA 30004
Tel.: (877) 363-8287
Web Site: http://www.premiersurfaces.com
Custom Countertop Installer & Stone Fabrication
N.A.I.C.S.: 423320
Mark Mosher *(VP & Gen Mgr)*

Top Master, Inc. **(2)**
2844 Roe Ln, Kansas City, KS 66103 **(100%)**
Tel.: (913) 492-3030
Web Site: http://www.top-master.com
Emp.: 400
Countertop Mfr & Whslr
N.A.I.C.S.: 337110
Corina Murguia *(Mgr-HR)*
Ashley Hunt *(Coord-Comml)*
Larry Wooldridge *(Mgr-Field Ops)*
Cassi Mayer *(Project Mgr)*
Mike Varone *(Pres)*

United States Marble, Inc. **(2)**
7839 Costabella Ave, Remus, MI 49340
Tel.: (989) 561-2293
Web Site: http://www.usmarble.com
Cut Stone & Stone Product Mfr
N.A.I.C.S.: 327991
David Mitchum *(Pres)*

Mantis Innovation Group, LLC **(1)**
11011 Richmond Ave Ste 500, Houston, TX 77042
Tel.: (877) 459-4728
Web Site: http://www.mantisinnovation.com
Holding Company; Energy Consulting & Facility Asset Management Services
N.A.I.C.S.: 551112
Daniel Marzuola *(CEO)*
Richard Rast *(Chief Strategy Officer)*
Rad Brannan *(CTO)*
Kevin McAlpin *(Gen Counsel)*
Kurt Keller *(CFO)*

Division (Domestic):

Bluefin, LLC **(2)**
6312 S Fiddlers Green Cir Ste 100E, Greenwood Village, CO 80111-0111
Tel.: (303) 809-6042
Web Site: http://www.bluefinllc.com
Engineering Services
N.A.I.C.S.: 541330
Kyle Shane *(Mgr-Strategic Accts)*
Jeremiah Dancy *(Pres)*
Vickie Crenshaw *(Sr VP)*

Subsidiary (Domestic):

Crenshaw Consulting Group, LLC **(3)**
7120 1-40 W Ste 210, Amarillo, TX 79106
Tel.: (505) 393-0073
Web Site:
http://www.crenshawconsultinggroup.vpweb.com
Sales Range: $1-9.9 Million
Emp.: 20
Business Consulting Services
N.A.I.C.S.: 541618
Vickie Crenshaw *(Owner)*

Division (Domestic):

EMEX LLC **(2)**
11011 Richmond Ave Ste 500, Houston, TX 77042-6007
Tel.: (713) 521-9797
Web Site:
http://www.energymarketexchange.com
Emp.: 100
General Management Consulting Services
N.A.I.C.S.: 541611
Kevin McAlpin *(Gen Counsel & VP)*
Dan Marzuola *(CEO)*
Kurt Keller *(CFO)*
Kris Hertel *(Pres)*
Rad Brannan *(CIO)*

Subsidiary (Domestic):

Texas Energy Aggregation **(3)**
712 Austin Ave, Waco, TX 76701-1742 **(100%)**
Tel.: (254) 751-0364
Web Site: http://www.texasenergyabc.com
Administrative Management & General Management Consulting Services
N.A.I.C.S.: 541611
T.J. Ermoian *(Pres)*
Kari McHam *(CFO)*

Mercury Manufacturing Company **(1)**
1212 Grove St, Wyandotte, MI 48192
Tel.: (734) 285-5150
Web Site: http://www.mercurymfg.com
Sales Range: $10-24.9 Million
Emp.: 63
Specialty Valves Mfr

U.S. PRIVATE

N.A.I.C.S.: 332911
Janice Wiegand *(Pres)*

O2 Auto Service Midco, LLC **(1)**
40900 Woodward Ave Ste 200, Bloomfield Hills, MI 48304
Tel.: (248) 988-3579
Web Site: https://gostraightaway.com
Automotive Repair Services
N.A.I.C.S.: 811111

Subsidiary (Domestic):

Maple Grove Auto Service, Inc. **(2)**
9225 Wellington Ln N, Maple Grove, MN 55369
Tel.: (763) 425-8575
Web Site: http://www.maplegroveauto.com
General Automotive Repair Services
N.A.I.C.S.: 811111

SIB Fixed Cost Reduction Company, LLC **(1)**
796 Meeting St, Charleston, SC 29403
Tel.: (843) 576-3606
Web Site: http://www.aboutsib.com
Emp.: 75
Management Cost Consulting
N.A.I.C.S.: 541618
Martin Skelly *(Pres)*
Matt Cauller *(COO)*
Dan O'Dea *(CFO)*
Richard Davis *(Chief People Officer)*
Kevin Flounders *(CEO)*

Subsidiary (Domestic):

Cost Control Associates, Inc. **(2)**
310 Bay Rd, Queensbury, NY 12804
Tel.: (518) 798-4437
Web Site:
http://www.costcontrolassociates.com
Sales Range: $1-9.9 Million
Emp.: 16
Business Consulting Services
N.A.I.C.S.: 541618
Keith Laake *(Founder & Pres)*
Allison Levin *(Dir-Analysis Team)*

Professional Waste Consulting, LLC **(2)**
71 Cavalier Blvd Ste 303, Florence, KY 41042
Tel.: (859) 746-2888
Web Site: http://www.prowastegroup.com
Waste & Recycling Consulting Service
N.A.I.C.S.: 541618
Jayson Aseere *(Owner)*

O2B KIDS
106 NW 33rd Ct Ste A, Gainesville, FL 32607
Tel.: (352) 338-9660
Web Site: http://www.o2bkids.com
Year Founded: 1998
Sales Range: $10-24.9 Million
Emp.: 300
Entertainment & Educational Programs for Children
N.A.I.C.S.: 611699
Danny Stevens *(Co-Founder & CEO)*
Kate Sherrard *(Dir-Special Events & Dir-Mktg)*
Ashley Peterson *(Mgr-Acctg)*
Andy Sherrard *(Co-Founder)*

O2IDEAS, INC.
505 20th St N Ste 1500, Birmingham, AL 35203
Tel.: (205) 949-9494
Web Site: http://www.o2ideas.com
Year Founded: 1967
Sales Range: $75-99.9 Million
Emp.: 65
Advertising Agency Services
N.A.I.C.S.: 541810
Shelley Stewart *(Founder)*

O2KL
10 W 18th St 6th Fl, New York, NY 10011
Tel.: (646) 829-6239
Web Site: http://www.o2kl.com
Year Founded: 2004

Sales Range: $10-24.9 Million
Emp.: 18
Advertising Agencies
N.A.I.C.S.: 541810
Danny Klein *(Dir-Creative)*
Jim Lurie *(Gen Mgr)*
John Kopilak *(Dir-Creative)*

O3 WORLD, LLC
1000 N Hancock St Ste 103, Philadelphia, PA 19123
Tel.: (215) 592-4739
Web Site: http://www.o3world.com
Year Founded: 2005
Sales Range: $100-124.9 Million
Emp.: 10
N.A.I.C.S.: 541810
Michael Gadsby *(Dir-Creative)*
Keith Scandone *(Dir-New Bus Dev)*
Barry Golombek *(Dir-Bus Dev)*

OAHU TRANSIT SERVICES INC.
811 Middle St, Honolulu, HI 96819-2316
Tel.: (808) 848-4400   HI
Web Site: http://www.thebus.org
Year Founded: 1991
Sales Range: $25-49.9 Million
Emp.: 1,800
Local & Suburban Transit Service; Non-Profit
N.A.I.C.S.: 485113
Kaina Awaa *(Mgr-HR)*
Lynnette Fukumoto *(Dir-Pur & Matls Mgmt)*
Guy Moriwaki *(Dir-IT)*
Romy Barut *(Asst Mgr-Maint)*
Ralph Faufata *(VP-Transportation)*
Tom Enomoto *(Mgr-Customer Svc)*
Eric Nakashima *(Dir-Safety & Security)*
Jerome Preese *(VP-Plng & Mktg)*

OAK CENTER HOMES PARTNERS, L.P.
1350 Columbia Ste 802, San Diego, CA 92101
Tel.: (619) 543-4200
Year Founded: 2011
Sales Range: $25-49.9 Million
Real Estate Development Services
N.A.I.C.S.: 531190
Barbara Stewart *(VP)*
Janice Starks *(Pres)*

OAK CONTRACTING, LLC.
1000 Cromwell Bridge Rd, Towson, MD 21286-3308
Tel.: (410) 828-1000
Web Site:
http://www.oakcontracting.com
Sales Range: $50-74.9 Million
Emp.: 35
Nonresidential Construction Services
N.A.I.C.S.: 236220
Douglas Eder *(Pres)*

OAK HALL INDUSTRIES LP
840 Union St, Salem, VA 24153
Tel.: (540) 387-0000
Web Site: http://www.oakhalli.com
Year Founded: 1889
Rev.: $15,500,000
Emp.: 130
Caps & Gowns (Academic Vestments)
N.A.I.C.S.: 458110
Peter Morrison *(Pres)*
Linda Peters *(Mgr-Pur)*

OAK HARBOR FREIGHT LINES, INC.
1339 W Valley Hwy N, Auburn, WA 98001
Tel.: (253) 288-8300   WA

Web Site: http://www.oakh.com
Year Founded: 1916
Sales Range: $75-99.9 Million
Emp.: 1,200
Provider of Transportation Services
N.A.I.C.S.: 484121
Edward H. Vander Pol *(Co-Owner & Co-Pres)*
David A. Vander Pol *(Co-Owner & Co-Pres)*
Ron Kieswether *(VP-Ops)*

Subsidiaries:

Oak Harbor Freight Lines   (1)
220 Katy Penman Rd, Bremerton, WA 98312-4301
Tel.: (360) 792-9644
Web Site: http://www.oakh.com
Sales Range: $10-24.9 Million
Emp.: 3
Trucking Except Local Distr
N.A.I.C.S.: 484121
David A. Vander Pol *(Co-Owner & Co-Pres)*
Edward H. Vander Pol *(Co-Owner & Co-Pres)*
Kevin Kellermann *(VP-Ops)*
Joel Spencer *(Mgr-Eastern Washington)*
Dan Vander Pol *(VP-Maintenance)*

OAK HARBOUR MARKETING LIMITED
1685 H St, Blaine, WA 98230
Tel.: (604) 421-9898
Web Site:
http://www.horizonseating.com
Rev.: $11,300,000
Emp.: 10
Furniture
N.A.I.C.S.: 423210
Patty Lee *(Pres)*
Kent Lee *(CEO)*

OAK HILL ADVISORS, L.P.
1 Vanderbilt 16th Fl, New York, NY 10017
Tel.: (212) 326-1500   DE
Web Site:
http://www.oakhilladvisors.com
Year Founded: 1996
Sales Range: $1-4.9 Billion
Emp.: 75
Investment Advisory & Portfolio Management Services
N.A.I.C.S.: 523940
Robert B. Okun *(Chief Investment Officer & Sr Partner)*
Adam B. Kertzner *(Partner & Mgr-Portfolio)*
Carl L. Wernicke *(Partner)*
Thomas S. Wong *(Partner & Portfolio Mgr-New York)*
Harpreet S. Anand *(Mng Dir-New York)*
Eitan Z. Arbeter *(Mng Dir & Portfolio Mgr)*
Nadav Braun *(Mng Dir)*
Jennifer Schultz Cohen *(Mng Dir-New York)*
Justin G. Tasso *(Mng Dir & Portfolio Mgr-New York)*
Alexis Attteslis *(Mng Dir & Portfolio Mgr-London)*
Lei Lei *(Mng Dir & Portfolio Mgr-London)*
Lucy Panter *(Mng Dir & Portfolio Mgr-London)*
Kent Usell *(Mng Dir)*
Fritz Thomas *(Partner)*
Christopher J. Cereghino *(Mng Dir-New York)*
Ohkee Peter Kwon *(Mng Dir-Hong Kong)*
Declan Tiernan *(Mng Dir)*
Michael Blumstein *(CFO)*
Raymond P. Murphy *(Chief Accounting Officer & Mng Dir)*
Walter Wright *(Mng Dir-Client Acctg & Head-Fort Worth Office)*

John Mack *(Mng Dir-Ops & Client Acctg-New York)*
Gregory S. Rubin *(Mng Dir & Gen Counsel-New York)*
Steven T. Wayne *(Mng Dir & Portfolio Mgr-New York)*
Adam Nankervis *(Principal)*
Colin Blackmore *(Mng Dir, Chief Compliance Officer & Gen Counsel-European)*
Jared Weisman *(Principal)*
John Convery *(Mng Dir)*
Kai Lee *(Mng Dir, Chief Compliance Officer & Assoc Gen Counsel)*
Natalie Harvard *(Mng Dir & Head-IR)*
Signe R. Brandt *(Principal)*
Steve Jones *(Mng Dir & COO-US Credit)*
Glenn R. August *(Founder & CEO)*
Glenn R. August *(CEO)*
William H. Bohnsack Jr. *(Pres & Sr Partner)*
Charles A. Irwin Jr. *(Principal)*
Glenn Russell August *(Co-Founder & CEO)*

OAK HILL PROPERTIES LLC
5305 Jefferson Pike C8, Frederick, MD 21703
Tel.: (301) 662-0435
Web Site:
http://www.oakhillproperties.com
Sales Range: $10-24.9 Million
Residential Construction
N.A.I.C.S.: 531120

OAK HILLS CARTON CO.
6310 Este Ave, Cincinnati, OH 45232-1450
Tel.: (513) 948-4200
Web Site:
http://www.oakhillscarton.com
Sales Range: $10-24.9 Million
Emp.: 25
Converted Paper Product Mfr
N.A.I.C.S.: 322299
Kimberly McCullah *(Mgr-Acctg)*

OAK INVESTMENT PARTNERS
195 Danbury Rd Bldg A Ste 220, Wilton, CT 06897
Tel.: (203) 226-8346
Web Site: https://www.oakvc.com
Year Founded: 1978
Emp.: 100
Private Equity Investment Firm
N.A.I.C.S.:
Scot B. Jarvis *(Venture Partner)*
Grace A. Ames *(Gen Partner & COO)*
David B. Black *(Partner-Tech)*
John Anthony Downer *(Partner-Venture)*
Tom Huseby *(Partner-Venture)*
Allan C. Y. Kwan *(Venture Partner)*
Ann Huntress Lamont *(Mng Partner)*
Angel Saad Gomez *(Venture Partner)*
Rob Majteles *(Partner-Operating-Internet,Consumer)*
Ann Lamont *(Mng Partner-Fin Svcs Tech)*
Dana Tavella *(Controller)*
Kathy Roland *(Partner-Venture-Retail,Restaurants)*
Steve Hafner *(Co-Founder & CEO)*
Sean Moriarty *(CEO)*

Subsidiaries:

XIOtech Corporation   (1)
9950 Federal Dr Ste 100, Colorado Springs, CO 80921
Tel.: (719) 388-5500
Web Site: http://www.xiostorage.com
Sales Range: $125-149.9 Million
Data Storage & Protection Products Mfr, Distr & Support Services
N.A.I.C.S.: 334112

Philip E. Soran *(Co-Founder)*
David Gustavsson *(CTO & Sr VP-Engrg)*
Blair Parkhill *(VP-Mktg)*
Gavin McLaughlin *(VP-OEM & Alliances)*
Bill Miller *(CEO)*
Mark Zeller *(VP-Sls-North America)*
Bill Alexander *(CFO)*
Steve Ashurst *(Gen Mgr-EMEA)*
John Grover *(VP-HR)*
Ellen Rome *(VP-Field Enablement & Demand Generation)*
Jeanie McIntyre *(Mgr-Comm & Event Mktg)*
Tim Cullen *(VP-Global Sls Ops)*

OAK LANE PARTNERS, LLC
4730 NW 2nd Ave Ste 100, Boca Raton, FL 33431
Tel.: (561) 465-4855
Web Site:
http://www.oaklanepartners.com
Private Equity Firm
N.A.I.C.S.: 523999
Bhavin Shah *(Chm)*
Mike Horne *(Sr Operating Partner)*
Chuck Connors *(Operating Partner-Transportation)*
Rick Okins *(CIO & Operating Partner)*
Neena Bohra *(Gen Counsel)*

Subsidiaries:

Maintech, Incorporated   (1)
14 Commerce Dr, Cranford, NJ 07016-3520
Tel.: (973) 330-3200
Web Site: http://www.maintech.com
Information Technology Consulting Services
N.A.I.C.S.: 541512
Frank W. D'Alessio *(Pres)*
Bob Coscia *(Exec VP)*
John Esposito *(VP-Strategic Sls)*
Dan DellaVentura *(Dir-Global Sls)*
William D'Alessio *(Sr VP-Svc Ops)*

OAK LAWN TOYOTA
4320 W 95th St, Oak Lawn, IL 60453
Tel.: (708) 423-5200
Web Site:
http://www.oaklawntoyota.com
Year Founded: 1971
Sales Range: $10-24.9 Million
Emp.: 50
Car Whslr
N.A.I.C.S.: 441110
Victoria Colosimo *(Mgr-Internet)*
Ronald Colosimo *(Pres)*

OAK LEAF MANAGEMENT INC.
9555 W Sam Eastern Pkwy S 250, Houston, TX 77099
Tel.: (713) 541-9724
Web Site:
http://www.oakleafmgmt.com
Sales Range: $25-49.9 Million
Emp.: 24
Commercial & Industrial Building Operation
N.A.I.C.S.: 531120
Patrick J. Tollett *(Pres)*

OAK LEAF PROPERTIES, LLC.
175 E Peacock Ave, Denton, NC 27239
Tel.: (336) 239-4107
Web Site:
http://www.oakleafproperties.com
Sales Range: $10-24.9 Million
Emp.: 10
Real Estate Agents & Brokerage Services
N.A.I.C.S.: 531210
Janet Petrozelle *(Owner)*

OAK PAPER PRODUCTS CO. INC.
3686 E Olympic Blvd, Los Angeles, CA 90023
Tel.: (323) 268-0507   CA

OAK PAPER PRODUCTS CO. INC.   U.S. PRIVATE

Oak Paper Products Co. Inc.—(Continued)

Web Site: http://www.acorn-paper.com
Year Founded: 1946
Custom & Stock Corrugated Boxes, Packaging products & Janitorial/Sanitary Supplies Mfr & Distr
N.A.I.C.S.: 322211
Max Weissberg (Pres)
David Weissberg (Owner)

Subsidiaries:

Acorn Paper Products Company (1)
3686 E Olympic Blvd, Los Angeles, CA 90023
Tel.: (323) 268-0507
Web Site: http://www.acorn-paper.com
Emp.: 250
Custom & Stock Corrugated Boxes, Packaging Products & Janitorial Supplies Mfr & Distr
N.A.I.C.S.: 322211
David Weissberg (CEO)
Max Weissberg (Pres)
Dick Seff (Chm)
Randy Seff (Exec VP)
Dave Karr (COO)
Debbie Allen (CFO)

OAK RIDGE CAPITAL GROUP, INC.
701 Xenia Ave S Ste 100, Golden Valley, MN 55416
Tel.: (763) 923-2200 NM
Web Site: http://www.oakridgefinancial.com
Year Founded: 1983
Sales Range: $25-49.9 Million
Emp.: 100
Real Estate Services
N.A.I.C.S.: 523940
Marc Kozberg (CEO)

OAK RIDGE UTILITY DISTRICT
120 S Jefferson Cir, Oak Ridge, TN 37830
Tel.: (865) 483-1377
Web Site: http://www.orud.org
Year Founded: 1951
Sales Range: $10-24.9 Million
Emp.: 42
Distr of Natural Gas
N.A.I.C.S.: 221210
Ben Andrews (Gen Mgr)
Alan Liby (Chm)
Robert DePriest (Controller)

OAK RIDGE WASTE & RECYCLING OF CT LLC
307 White St, Danbury, CT 06810
Tel.: (203) 743-0405
Web Site: https://oakridgewaste.com
Emp.: 100
Solid Waste Collection
N.A.I.C.S.: 562111
Kamil Bak (Controller)

OAK RIDGE, INC.
PO Box 1748, Leesburg, VA 20177
Tel.: (703) 777-5435
Web Site: http://www.oakridgecommunities.com
Year Founded: 1990
Sales Range: $10-24.9 Million
Emp.: 1
New Construction Builder
N.A.I.C.S.: 236115
Michael Gorman (Pres & CEO)
Beverly Gorman (VP)

OAK VIEW NATIONAL BANK
128 Broadview Ave, Warrenton, VA 20186
Tel.: (540) 359-7100

Web Site: http://www.oakviewbank.com
Year Founded: 2007
Sales Range: $1-9.9 Million
Emp.: 27
Banking Services
N.A.I.C.S.: 522110
Michael A. Ewing (CEO & Vice Chm)
Kevin A. Lee (Pres & Chief Credit Officer)
Earl H. Douple Jr. (Chm)

OAK-BARK CORPORATION
1224 Old Hwy 87 Rd, Riegelwood, NC 28456
Tel.: (910) 251-0234 NC
Web Site: http://www.oak-bark.com
Year Founded: 1959
Sales Range: $10-24.9 Million
Emp.: 140
Mfr of Industrial, Specialty & Fine Chemicals
N.A.I.C.S.: 325199
William Oakley (Chm)

OAKBROOK COMPANIES, INC.
142 W Station St, Barrington, IL 60010
Tel.: (630) 584-6580
Web Site: http://www.oakbrookco.com
Sales Range: $10-24.9 Million
Emp.: 8
Real Estate Development & Hotel Management
N.A.I.C.S.: 237210
David A. McArdle (CEO & Principal)
Philip J. Held (CFO & VP-Midwest Real Estate)
Joyce L. McArdle (Gen Counsel)
Rodney A. Welty (Sec & Controller)
Ned E. Dewhirst (Sr VP-Ops-Florida)

Subsidiaries:

Oakbrook Properties, Inc. (1)
24880 Burnt Pine Dr Ste 8, Bonita Springs, FL 34134
Tel.: (239) 992-5529
Web Site: http://www.oakbrookco.com
Emp.: 9
Construction Services
N.A.I.C.S.: 236220
Ned E. Dewhirst (Sr VP)

OAKBROOK HOMES INC.
30677 Old US 20, Elkhart, IN 46514
Tel.: (574) 674-9911
Web Site: http://www.oakbrookonline.com
Sales Range: $10-24.9 Million
Emp.: 57
New Construction, Single-Family Houses
N.A.I.C.S.: 236115
James Heinen (VP-Ops)

OAKES AGENCY INC.
234 Washington Ave, Grand Haven, MI 49417-1357
Tel.: (616) 842-3440 MI
Web Site: http://www.oakesagency.com
Year Founded: 1902
Sales Range: $1-9.9 Million
Emp.: 13
Insurance Agents, Brokers & Service
N.A.I.C.S.: 524210
Ken Terpstra (Pres)
Ralph Vanduyn (Controller)
Michael Wheelen (VP)

OAKHURST DAIRY
364 Forest Ave, Portland, ME 04101
Tel.: (207) 772-7468 ME
Web Site: http://www.oakhurstdairy.com
Year Founded: 1921

Sales Range: $75-99.9 Million
Emp.: 225
Milk Processing & Distr
N.A.I.C.S.: 311511
Joseph H. Hyatt (VP-HR & Safety)
Denise Bean (Mgr-Accts & Credit)
David Green (Mgr-Fleet & Facilities)
John H. Bennett (Pres)
James M. Lesser (VP-Sls & Mktg)
Michael Benar (Controller)
Patrick Raymond (Mgr-Maintenance)
Jeff Averill (Mgr-Quality Control Assurance)
Benjamin Chapman (Mgr-Shipping)
Colleen Thomas (Mgr-Sls Ops)
Stephen Rallis (Mgr-Sls-Alternative Channels)
Dwayne Dunn (Mgr-Sls-Chain Convenience Store)
James Carvalho (Mgr-Sls-Chain Grocery)
Andrew J. Russell (Mgr-Sls-Distributors & Food Svc)
Bradley C. Bowers (Plant Mgr)
Paul J. Connolly Jr. (CIO & VP-Sys)

OAKHURST INDUSTRIES
2050 S Tubeway Ave, Commerce, CA 90040
Tel.: (323) 724-3000
Rev.: $15,300,000
Emp.: 100
Bakery Products
N.A.I.C.S.: 311812
James D. Freund (Pres)

OAKHURST MEDICAL CENTERS, INC.
5582 Memorial Dr, Stone Mountain, GA 30083
Tel.: (404) 298-8998 GA
Web Site: http://www.oakmed.org
Year Founded: 1978
Sales Range: $10-24.9 Million
Emp.: 102
Health Care Srvices
N.A.I.C.S.: 622110
Jeff Taylor (CEO)
Charmaine Beckford-Willis (Dir-Nursing)
Clayton Knox (CFO)
Raulnina Uzzle (Chief Medical Officer)
Sam Donwell (Treas)
Brian Williams (Sec)
Frankie Barnes (Chm)

OAKLAND CONSULTING GROUP
9501 Sheridan St Ste 200, Lanham, MD 20706
Tel.: (301) 577-4111
Web Site: http://www.ocg-inc.com
Year Founded: 1997
Sales Range: $10-24.9 Million
Emp.: 67
Information Technology Consulting Services
N.A.I.C.S.: 541512
Cedric Nash (Pres & CEO)
Ken Arthur (VP-Ops)
Kathleen Jacobs (Mgr-Acctg & HR)
June Findlay (Mgr-Contracts)
Randy Randazzo (VP-Professional Svcs)
Rick Wheeler (VP-Bus Dev)

OAKLAND LIVINGSTON HUMAN SERVICE AGENCY
196 Cesar E Chavez Ave, Pontiac, MI 48343-0598
Tel.: (248) 209-2600 MI
Web Site: http://www.olhsa.org
Year Founded: 1964
Sales Range: $25-49.9 Million
Emp.: 596

Disabled & Elderly People Assistance Services
N.A.I.C.S.: 624120
Douglas Williams (Treas)
Deborah M. Majeski (Sec)
Cynthia Wells (Vice Chm)
Irene Onderchanin (Chm)
Janice Smith (Dir-Early Childhood Svcs)

OAKLAND MANAGEMENT CORP.
31731 Northwestern Hwy Ste 250 W, Farmington Hills, MI 48334
Tel.: (248) 855-5400 MI
Web Site: http://www.beztak.com
Year Founded: 1994
Sales Range: $1-9.9 Million
Emp.: 300
Real Estate Management & Investment
N.A.I.C.S.: 531390
Maurice Beznos (Pres)
Peter Odorico (VP-Acq & Dev)
Jason Kohler (Exec VP-Senior Living)

OAKLAND NURSERY INC.
1156 Oakland Park Ave, Columbus, OH 43224
Tel.: (614) 268-3511
Web Site: http://www.oaklandnursery.com
Rev.: $16,498,804
Emp.: 200
Nursery Stock, Seeds & Bulbs
N.A.I.C.S.: 444240
Paul Reiner (Pres)
Allison Miller (Office Mgr)

OAKLAND PACKAGING SUPPLY
871 Harbour Way S, Richmond, CA 94804
Tel.: (510) 307-4242
Web Site: http://www.oakpackaging.com
Rev.: $6,624,000
Emp.: 8
Industrial & Personal Service Paper Merchant Whslr
N.A.I.C.S.: 424130
Reina Miyamoto (Controller)

OAKLAND STANDARD CO., LLC
The Wabeek Bldg 280 W Maple St Ste 305, Birmingham, MI 48009
Tel.: (313) 647-5326 DE
Web Site: http://www.oaklandstandard.com
Year Founded: 2015
Privater Equity Firm
N.A.I.C.S.: 523999
Dan Bickersteth (Co-Founder & Mng Partner)
Bryan Tolles (Co-Founder & Mng Partner)
Joe Conroy (Partner)
Tim Flannery (Principal)

Subsidiaries:

Clio Holdings LLC (1)
845 McFarland Pkwy, Alpharetta, GA 30004
Tel.: (313) 647-5326
Web Site: http://www.clioholdings.com
Holding Company; Countertop Fabricator & Whslr
N.A.I.C.S.: 551112
Eric Tryon (Co-Founder)
Mike Varone (Pres)
Jeff Gallentine (CFO & VP)
Casey Jackson (VP)
Bryan Tolles (Co-Founder & Exec Chm)

Subsidiary (Domestic):

The Tryon Group Inc. (2)
845 Mcfarland Pkwy, Alpharetta, GA 30004
Tel.: (877) 363-8287
Web Site: http://premiersurfaces.com

COMPANIES

Custom Countertop Installer & Stone Fabrication
N.A.I.C.S.: 423320
Mark Mosher *(VP & Gen Mgr)*

Top Master, Inc. (2)
2844 Roe Ln, Kansas City, KS 66103 (100%)
Tel.: (913) 492-3030
Web Site: http://www.top-master.com
Emp.: 400
Countertop Mfr & Whslr
N.A.I.C.S.: 337110
Corina Murguia *(Mgr-HR)*
Ashley Hunt *(Coord-Comml)*
Larry Wooldridge *(Mgr-Field Ops)*
Cassi Mayer *(Project Mgr)*
Mike Varone *(Pres)*

United States Marble, Inc. (2)
7839 Costabella Ave, Remus, MI 49340
Tel.: (989) 561-2293
Web Site: http://www.usmarble.com
Cut Stone & Stone Product Mfr
N.A.I.C.S.: 327991
David Mitchum *(Pres)*

Motor City Industrial LLC (1)
1600 E 10 Mile Rd, Hazel Park, MI 48030
Tel.: (248) 399-2830
Web Site: http://www.motorcityindustrial.com
Fasteners & Related Products Distr
N.A.I.C.S.: 339993
Joe Stephens *(CEO)*

Subsidiary (Domestic):

Motor City Fastener, LLC (2)
1600 E 10 Mile Rd, Hazel Park, MI 48030
Tel.: (248) 399-2830
Web Site: http://www.motorcityfasteners.com
Hardware Distr
N.A.I.C.S.: 423710
Joe Stephens *(CEO)*

Quality Fasteners & Supply Co. (2)
3100 Adventure Ln, Oxford, MI 48371
Tel.: (248) 628-0892
Hardware Stores; Industrial Consumables & Ancillary Products Distr
N.A.I.C.S.: 444140
Jim Hiatt *(Gen Mgr)*
John Shepard *(Mgr-Warehouse)*

Smith Fastener Co., Inc. (2)
30 INDUSTRIAL WAY, PO BOX 8555, Charleston, WV 25303
Tel.: (304) 925-4787
Web Site: http://www.smithfastener.com
Industrial Supplies Merchant Whslr
N.A.I.C.S.: 423840

Oakland Industries Blocker Corp. (1)
709 James L Hart Pkwy, Ypsilanti, MI 48197
Tel.: (734) 961-3300
Web Site: http://www.oaklandind.com
Holding Company; Commercial & Industrial Equipment Mfr
N.A.I.C.S.: 551112
Dan Bickersteth *(Chm)*
Greg Harvey *(VP & Gen Mgr)*
Kristopher Morris *(Dir-Fin)*
Christopher Bommarito *(Dir-Bus Dev)*

Subsidiary (Domestic):

AutoTac, Inc. (2)
1235 Chicago Rd, Troy, MI 48083
Tel.: (248) 589-3350
Web Site: http://www.autotac.net
Blow Off Machines Mfr
N.A.I.C.S.: 333998
Steven Lipple *(Mgr-Engrg)*

InterClean Equipment, LLC (2)
709 James L Hart Pkwy, Ypsilanti, MI 48197 (100%)
Tel.: (734) 961-3300
Web Site: http://www.interclean.com
Large Vehicle Cleaning & Water Recycling Technologies Designer & Mfr
N.A.I.C.S.: 333310
Greg Harvey *(VP & Gen Mgr)*
Teresa Watson *(Controller)*
Claudia Springgay *(Sls Mgr)*
Scott Hessling *(Mgr-Pur)*

Oakland Automation, LLC (2)
25475 Trans X Rd, Odessa, WA 99159
Tel.: (509) 982-2661
Web Site: http://www.odessatrading.com
Sales Range: $1-9.9 Million
Grain Elevators
N.A.I.C.S.: 333248
Dan Bickersteth *(Acting CEO)*
Chris Beyersdorff *(Acting CFO)*

Plant (Domestic):

Oakland Automation, LLC - Novi Plant (3)
25475 Trans X Rd, Novi, MI 48375
Tel.: (734) 552-0212
Web Site: http://www.oaklandautomation.com
Industrial Robotics Equipment Designer, Mfr & Installation Services
N.A.I.C.S.: 333248
Ronald Matheson *(Grp Head-Gen Automation)*
Greg Pinkham *(Grp Head-Paint & Fluid Sys)*
Chris Muzzin *(Mgr-Engrg)*
Andrew DeNoon *(Project Mgr)*
Brandon Mahoney *(Sr Engr-Design)*

Temperform, LLC (1)
25425 Trans X Rd, Novi, MI 48375
Tel.: (248) 349-5230
Web Site: http://www.temperform.com
Sales Range: $1-9.9 Million
Emp.: 50
Steel Foundry
N.A.I.C.S.: 331513
A. J. Bartoletto *(Chm & CEO)*
Bruce Boettger *(Pres)*
Gloria Webber *(Mgr-Corp Sls)*

OAKLAWN JOCKEY CLUB, INC.
2705 Central Ave, Hot Springs, AR 71902
Tel.: (501) 623-4411
Web Site: http://www.oaklawn.com
Year Founded: 1904
Rev.: $15,000,000
Emp.: 450
Horse Racetrack & Casino Owner & Operator
N.A.I.C.S.: 711212
Charles J. Cella *(Pres)*

OAKLEAF SOFTWARE, INC.
65 Enterprise Ave, Aliso Viejo, CA 92656
Tel.: (949) 529-9272
Web Site: http://www.oakleafsolutions.co
Security Services Software
N.A.I.C.S.: 513210
Mark Heinrich *(CEO)*

Subsidiaries:

DPRA Inc. (1)
10215 Technology Dr, Knoxville, TN 37932
Tel.: (865) 777-3772
Web Site: http://www.dpra.com
Other Computer Related Services
N.A.I.C.S.: 541519
Ivan Eno *(Dir-Bus Dev)*
Mark Heinrich *(CEO)*
Greg Butler *(COO)*
Jason Forouhar *(VP-Customer Rels)*

OAKLEY CONSTRUCTION COMPANY, INC.
7815 S Claremont Ave, Chicago, IL 60620-5812
Tel.: (773) 434-1616
Web Site: http://www.oakleyconstruction.com
Sales Range: $10-24.9 Million
Emp.: 20
Civil Engineering Services
N.A.I.C.S.: 237310
Augustine Afriyie *(Pres)*

OAKLEY GROVES INC.
101 ABC Rd, Lake Wales, FL 33859-6844
Tel.: (863) 638-1435 FL
Web Site: http://www.oakleytransport.com
Year Founded: 1961
Rev.: $79,282,406
Emp.: 400
Process of Citrus Fruits
N.A.I.C.S.: 111320
Thomas E. Oakley *(Pres)*

Subsidiaries:

Oakley Transport, Inc. (1)
101 ABC Rd, Lake Wales, FL 33859-6844
Tel.: (863) 638-1435
Web Site: http://www.oakleytransport.com
Sales Range: $25-49.9 Million
Emp.: 200
Trucking & Transportation Services
N.A.I.C.S.: 484121
Thomas E. Oakley *(Pres)*

OAKLEY INDUSTRIES INC.
35166 Automation Dr, Clinton Township, MI 48035
Tel.: (586) 792-1261 MI
Web Site: http://www.oakley-ind.com
Year Founded: 1962
Sales Range: $25-49.9 Million
Emp.: 50
Mfr of Automotive Stampings
N.A.I.C.S.: 336370
Ronald Oakley *(CEO)*

OAKLEY INDUSTRIES INCORPORATED
3211 W Bear Creek Dr, Englewood, CO 80110
Tel.: (303) 761-1835
Rev.: $24,000,000
Emp.: 75
Tubes, Steel & Iron
N.A.I.C.S.: 331110
Gary A. Oakley *(Pres)*

OAKMONT CAPITAL RESOURCES, INC.
7321 Merchant Ct, Sarasota, FL 34240
Tel.: (941) 907-9008
Web Site: http://www.oakmont.net
Sales Range: $10-24.9 Million
Emp.: 10
Commercial Real Estate Management Services
N.A.I.C.S.: 531312
Rick Seyer *(Pres)*

OAKRIDGE BUILDERS INC.
1624 W 21 St, Tulsa, OK 74107-2708
Tel.: (918) 582-9333 OK
Web Site: http://www.oakbuild.com
Year Founded: 1985
Sales Range: $25-49.9 Million
Emp.: 450
Provider of Construction Services
N.A.I.C.S.: 236220
Missy Turley *(Dir-Mktg)*
Brian Smith *(Gen Mgr)*

OAKS CONSTRUCTION INC.
120 Preston Executive Dr Ste 101, Cary, NC 27513-8445
Tel.: (919) 469-3555
Rev.: $25,000,000
Emp.: 50
New Construction Commercial & Office Building
N.A.I.C.S.: 236220
Maxwell Oaks *(Chm)*
Greg Brock *(VP)*

OAKSTAR BANCSHARES, INC.
1020 E Battlefield Rd, Springfield, MO 68075
Tel.: (417) 877-2020
Web Site: http://www.oakstarbank.com
Bank Holding Company
N.A.I.C.S.: 551111
Randy Johnson *(Pres & CEO)*

Subsidiaries:

Oakstar Bank (1)
1020 E Battlefield St, Springfield, MO 65807
Tel.: (417) 877-2020
Web Site: http://www.oakstarbank.com
Sales Range: $1-9.9 Million
Emp.: 21
Commericial Banking
N.A.I.C.S.: 522110
Randy Johnson *(Pres & CEO)*
Mark A. Bybee *(Exec VP)*
James Coffer *(VP-Mortgage Banking)*
Kevin Dull *(VP-Mortgage Banking)*
Mike Lawson *(Chief Lending Officer & Sr Exec VP-OakStar Bank-Springfield-MO)*

OAKTREE ENTERPRISE SOLUTIONS, INC.
2201 Cooperative Way Ste 600, Herndon, VA 20171
Tel.: (571) 748-4070
Web Site: http://www.oaktreesolutions.com
Year Founded: 1999
Rev.: $7,200,000
Emp.: 45
IT Services
N.A.I.C.S.: 513210
David Ferguson *(CEO)*

OAKTREE GARDENS OLP, LLC
333 S Grand Ave 28th Fl, Los Angeles, CA 90071
Tel.: (213) 830-6300 DE
Year Founded: 2023
Rev.: $92,786,000
Assets: $787,073,000
Liabilities: $422,782,000
Net Worth: $364,291,000
Earnings: $25,924,000
Fiscal Year-end: 09/30/24
Investment Management Service
N.A.I.C.S.: 523999

OAKWOOD INDUSTRIES INC.
7250 Division St, Cleveland, OH 44146-5406
Tel.: (440) 232-8700 OH
Web Site: http://www.federalmetal.com
Year Founded: 1986
Sales Range: $10-24.9 Million
Emp.: 70
Mfr of Brass & Bronze Ingots
N.A.I.C.S.: 331492
David R. Nagusky *(Chm & CEO)*
Peter Nagusky *(Pres)*

Subsidiaries:

The Federal Metal Company (1)
7250 Division St, Cleveland, OH 44146-5406 (100%)
Tel.: (440) 232-8700
Web Site: http://www.federalmetal.com
Sales Range: $10-24.9 Million
Brass & Bronze Mfr
N.A.I.C.S.: 331492
David R. Nagusky *(Chm)*
Mike Buyarski *(COO)*
Rob Wittenberg *(CFO)*

OAKWOOD LUTHERAN HOMES ASSOCIATION, INC.
6205 Mineral Point Rd, Madison, WI 53705
Tel.: (608) 230-4699 WI
Web Site: http://www.oakwoodvillage.net
Year Founded: 1948
Sales Range: $10-24.9 Million
Emp.: 917
Elder Care Services
N.A.I.C.S.: 624120

OAKWOOD LUTHERAN HOMES ASSOCIATION, INC.

Oakwood Lutheran Homes Association, Inc.—(Continued)
Rick Bova (CEO)
Lori Van Dalen (VP-HR)
Keith E. VanLanduyt (VP-Mktg & Community Rels)
Paul Schmidt (Chm)
Roth Judd (Sec)
Sarah Kruger (Vice Chm)
Terry Hanson (Treas)

OAKWORKS INC.
923 E Wellspring Rd, New Freedom, PA 17349
Tel.: (717) 235-6807
Web Site: http://www.oakworks.com
Year Founded: 1978
Sales Range: $10-24.9 Million
Emp.: 130
Mfr of Portable Massage Tables & Therapeutic Equipment
N.A.I.C.S.: 423450
Jeff Riach (CEO)
Stephen McKinley (Dir-Quality & Compliance)
Richard Shuman (Pres)
Brian Emmer (VP-Sls & Bus Dev)
Bryan Griffiths (Mgr-Product Res & Dev)
Kim Spangle (Controller)

OASIS AVIATION INC.
5777 W Century Blvd Ste 1490, Los Angeles, CA 90045-7400
Tel.: (310) 670-7001   CA
Web Site: http://www.oasisaviation.com
Year Founded: 1978
Sales Range: $50-74.9 Million
Emp.: 70
Provider of Fuel Services to the Aviation & Commercial Industry
N.A.I.C.S.: 562211
Carl Burhanan (Owner & Pres)

Subsidiaries:

Oasis Nuclear Inc.   (1)
5777 W Century Blvd Ste 1490, Los Angeles, CA 90045-7400
Tel.: (310) 670-7001
Sales Range: $10-24.9 Million
Emp.: 6
Nuclear Waste Decontamination & Decommissioning Services
N.A.I.C.S.: 562211

OASIS LEGAL FINANCE LLC
9525 Bryn Mawr Ave, Rosemont, IL 60018
Tel.: (847) 521-4400
Web Site: http://www.oasisfinancial.com
Year Founded: 2002
Consumer Legal Funding Services
N.A.I.C.S.: 522299
Griffin Gordon (COO)
Robert Gallagher (CFO)
Phil Greenberg (Gen Counsel)
Greg Zeeman (CEO)

Subsidiaries:

Key Health Group Inc.   (1)
30699 Russell Ranch Rd Ste 175, Westlake Village, CA 91362-7374
Tel.: (877) 633-5436
Web Site: http://www.keyhealth.net
Lien Solutions Programs
N.A.I.C.S.: 522299

OASIS PIPE LINE COMPANY
12012 Wickchester Ln, Houston, TX 77079
Tel.: (713) 758-9800
Rev.: $24,729,000
Emp.: 14
Pipelines, Natural Gas
N.A.I.C.S.: 486210

Jim Labauve (Pres)

OASIS SALES CORP.
925C N Plum Grove Rd, Schaumburg, IL 60173-4704
Tel.: (847) 805-9500
Web Site: http://www.oasis-sales.com
Rev.: $83,000,000
Emp.: 15
Electronic Parts & Equipment
N.A.I.C.S.: 423690
Grant Grastorf (Mgr-Acct)
Fred Schlapman (VP & Mgr-WI)
Pat Murphy (VP-Distr Sls)

OASIS SYSTEMS, LLC
24 Hartwell Ave, Lexington, MA 02421-3103
Tel.: (781) 676-7333   MA
Web Site: http://www.oasissystems.com
Year Founded: 1997
Emp.: 1,000
Systems Engineering, Integration & Management
N.A.I.C.S.: 541512
Mike McElwain (Sr VP-Corp Bus Dev)
Maggie Wetzell (Sr VP-Contracts & Compliance)
Thomas J. Colatosti (Chm)
Greg Esses (VP-Eglin AFB Programs)
Pete Krawczyk (Pres-DoD Program Div)
Laura Evans (Sr VP-HR & Security)
David Markuson (Sr VP-Fin & Tech)
Tom Evans (VP-Cyber Security & IT)
John Schwanz (VP-Marine Ops & Facilities Mgmt)
Troy Rath (VP-Corp Dev & Growth Mgmt)
Brenda Boone (Pres-FAA & NASA Div)
Tim Nickerson (Pres-USAF ETASS II Div)
Kevin Veach (Pres-MAR Specialized Engrg Div)
Bob Sanguinet (VP-ETASS II HB Div)
Bruce Ward (VP-ETASS II HI)
Karen McMillan (Sr VP-Mission Support)
Dave Zolet (CEO)

Subsidiaries:

Human Solutions, Inc.   (1)
600 Maryland Ave SW Suite 800E, Washington, DC 20024
Tel.: (202) 808-3250
Web Site: http://www.humansolutionsinc.com
Human Resources & Executive Search Consulting Services
N.A.I.C.S.: 541612
Brenda Boone (Founder & Pres)
Bahar Sadjadi (Dir-Bus Dev)
Sanja Benak (Dir-HR)
Jay Maria (Dir-Contracts)
Karen McMillan (VP-Ops)
Melissa Williams (Dir-Mission Support)
Chuck Chamberlain (Dir-Ops)
Anetra Withers (Dir-Res & Nextgen Initiatives)
Dani Roach (Mgr-Recruiting)

OASYS MOBILE, INC.
8000 Regency Pkwy, Cary, NC 27518
Tel.: (919) 807-5600   DE
Web Site: http://www.oasysmobile.com
Sales Range: $1-9.9 Million
Emp.: 38
Mobile Media Services
N.A.I.C.S.: 541511
Doug Dyer (CEO)
Tracy Livers (VP-Publ)

OASYS, INC.
1575 Port Dr, Burlington, WA 98233
Tel.: (360) 428-3637   WA
Web Site: http://www.oasysinc.com
Year Founded: 1999
Copiers And Fax Machines
N.A.I.C.S.: 423420
Allen Grenz (CEO)

OATEY COMPANY
20600 Emerald Pkwy, Cleveland, OH 44135
Tel.: (216) 267-7100   OH
Web Site: http://www.oatey.com
Year Founded: 1916
Plumbing Products Mfr & Distr
N.A.I.C.S.: 332999
Neal Restivo (CEO)
John McMillan (Chm)
Michelle Newland (Chief Intl Bus Officer & Exec VP)
Daniel Mercier (Gen Mgr-Belanger UPT)
LaKisha Peterson (VP-Acctg)
Nicole Fournier (VP-Retail Bus)
Blake Oatey (VP-Intl Dev)
Jamie Clapper (VP-eCommerce)
Brian DiVincenzo (Chief Comml Officer & Exec VP)
Erin Drotleff (VP-Sourcing)
Scott Voisinet (Sr VP-Supply Chain)
Patrick Aquino (VP-Sls & Wholesale)
Christen Allen (Sls Mgr-Showroom & Tile Sls)
Logan Weiland (CFO & Sr VP)
Amanda Keiber (Dir-Corp Comm)
Patrick Hall (Sr VP-Retail)

Subsidiaries:

Oatey Supply Chain Services, Inc.   (1)
20600 Emerald Pkwy, Cleveland, OH 44135
Tel.: (216) 267-7100
Web Site: http://www.oatey.com
Plumbing & Hardware Products Distr
N.A.I.C.S.: 423720

OATS, INC.
2501 Maguire Blvd Ste 101, Columbia, MO 65201
Tel.: (573) 443-4516
Web Site: http://www.oatstransit.org
Sales Range: $10-24.9 Million
Emp.: 740
Local Passenger Transportation
N.A.I.C.S.: 485999
Cindi Tandy (Dir-Fin)
Kim Wood (Mgr-HR)
Christina Wadlow (Coord-Admin)

OBATA DESIGN, INC.
1610 Menard St, Saint Louis, MO 63104
Tel.: (314) 241-1710   MO
Web Site: http://www.obata.com
Year Founded: 1948
Sales Range: $10-24.9 Million
Emp.: 50
Communications Solutions for Businesses
N.A.I.C.S.: 541613
Chris Haller (Owner & Exec VP)
Carol Hosick (Sr Designer & Mgr-Accts)

OBEO, INC.
563 W 500 S Ste 130, Bountiful, UT 84010
Tel.: (800) 729-6236
Web Site: http://www.obeo.com
Year Founded: 1998
Emp.: 50
Online Marketing Solutions for Real Estate
N.A.I.C.S.: 541519
Richard Russell (Mgr-Cust Svc)

OBERBECK GRAIN CO.
700 Walnut St, Highland, IL 62249
Tel.: (618) 654-2387   IL
Web Site: http://www.oberbeckgrainco.com
Year Founded: 1958
Sales Range: $10-24.9 Million
Emp.: 8
Grain Whslr
N.A.I.C.S.: 424510
Robert J. Luitjohan (Pres)

OBERER DEVELOPMENT CO.
3475 Newmark Dr, Miamisburg, OH 45342
Tel.: (937) 278-0851
Web Site: http://www.oberer.com
Sales Range: $10-24.9 Million
Emp.: 100
Subdividers & Developers
N.A.I.C.S.: 237210
George R. Oberer Sr. (Founder & Chm)

OBERG INDUSTRIES CORP.
2301 Silverville Rd, Freeport, PA 16229-0315
Tel.: (724) 295-2121   PA
Web Site: http://www.oberg.com
Year Founded: 1948
Sales Range: $100-124.9 Million
Emp.: 650
Mfr of Carbide Stamping Dies, Ultra-Precision Components & Stampings
N.A.I.C.S.: 332119
David L. Bonvenuto (Pres & CEO)

Subsidiaries:

Oberg Arizona   (1)
1490 S Price Rd Ste 305, Chandler, AZ 85286
Tel.: (480) 940-2000
Web Site: http://www.oberg.com
Sales Range: $10-24.9 Million
Emp.: 9
Mfr
N.A.I.C.S.: 333514

Oberg Costa Rca, LTDA   (1)
Edificio D-2 Zona Franca Metropolitana, PO Box 168-3006, Barreal, Heredia, Costa Rica
Tel.: (506) 2239 8050
Web Site: http://www.oberg.com
Sales Range: $10-24.9 Million
Emp.: 106
Precision Product Mfr
N.A.I.C.S.: 332721
Robert Rebaz (Gen Mgr)

Oberg Industries   (1)
Silverville Rd, Freeport, PA 16229-0315
Tel.: (724) 295-2121
Web Site: http://www.oberg.com
Sales Range: $50-74.9 Million
Emp.: 600
Metal
N.A.I.C.S.: 332119
Rick Oberg (Chm)

Oberg Industries   (1)
604 Oberg Dr, Freeport, PA 16229
Tel.: (724) 295-2118
Web Site: http://www.oberg.com
Sales Range: $50-74.9 Million
Emp.: 600
Mfr of Carbide Parts
N.A.I.C.S.: 333514
Michael West (Engr-Dev)
Doug Mechling (Coord-Subcontract)
Dave Bonvenuto (Pres)

Oberg Industries Europe, GMBH   (1)
Zaunmullerweg 14, 82024, Taufkirchen, Germany
Tel.: (49) 89 614 9125
Precision Product Mfr & Whslr
N.A.I.C.S.: 332721

Oberg Industries, Inc.   (1)
Silverville Rd, Freeport, PA 16229
Tel.: (724) 295-5151
Sales Range: $10-24.9 Million
Emp.: 45
Mfr of Tool & Dye

N.A.I.C.S.: 333514
Dan Felack (Dir-Pur)

Oberg Medical (1)
2301 Silverville Rd, Freeport, PA 16229-0315
Tel.: (724) 295-2121
Sales Range: $25-49.9 Million
Medical Equipment Mfr
N.A.I.C.S.: 339112
Bill Broman (Project Mgr & Process Engr)

Oberg Mexico (1)
Calle Los Olivos 100 Modulo 1 y 2, Parque Industrial El Bajio, Tecate, 21430, Baja California, Mexico
Tel.: (52) 665 655 5239
Web Site: http://www.oberg.com
Sales Range: $10-24.9 Million
Emp.: 59
Precision Metal Stamping Mfr
N.A.I.C.S.: 332119

OBERLE & ASSOCIATES, INC.
700 NW 2nd St, Richmond, IN 47375-0398
Tel.: (765) 966-7715
Web Site: http://www.oberleinc.com
Year Founded: 1962
Sales Range: $10-24.9 Million
Emp.: 85
Commercial & Institutional Building Construction Services
N.A.I.C.S.: 236220
Ronald Oberle (Pres & CEO)
Rachel Hickey (Controller)
John Oberle (VP-Mktg)

OBERMAN TIVOLI MILLER PICKERT
500 S Sepulveda Blvd FL 4, Los Angeles, CA 90049
Tel.: (310) 471-9300
Web Site: http://www.media-services.com
Sales Range: $25-49.9 Million
Emp.: 45
Payroll Accounting Service
N.A.I.C.S.: 541512

Subsidiaries:

Film Payroll Services Inc. (1)
500 S Sepulveda Blvd, Los Angeles, CA 90049
Tel.: (310) 471-9300
Web Site: http://www.mediaservices.com
Data Processing Services
N.A.I.C.S.: 518210

OBERMILLER NELSON ENGINEERING, INC.
2201 12th St N Ste E, Fargo, ND 58102
Tel.: (701) 280-0500 ND
Web Site: http://www.obernel.com
Year Founded: 1992
Sales Range: $10-24.9 Million
Emp.: 125
Architectural & Engineering Services
N.A.I.C.S.: 541330
Paul Nelson (Dir-Ops-Minneapolis & Project Mgr-Mechanical)
Jeremiah Christenson (Mng Partner)
Jim Nelson (Co-Founder & Partner)
Dave Vig (Partner)
Brent Wavra (Partner)
Andrew Bartsch (Partner)
Ned Rector (Partner)
Eric Rieniets (Dir-Construction Admin)

OBERON MEDIA, INC.
100 Broadway 14th Fl, New York, NY 10005
Tel.: (646) 367-2020
Web Site: http://www.oberon-media.com
Year Founded: 2003
Multi-Platform Videogame Designer & Publisher
N.A.I.C.S.: 513210

Bob Hayes (Pres & COO)
Ginger Kraus (Sr VP-Sls)

OBERON SECURITIES, LLC
1412 Broadway Ste 2304, New York, NY 10018
Tel.: (212) 386-7080 NY
Web Site: http://www.oberonsecurities.com
Sales Range: $25-49.9 Million
Emp.: 20
Boutique Investment Banking & Customized Financial Solutions
N.A.I.C.S.: 523150
Adam Breslawsky (Mng Dir & Partner)
Elad Epstein (Co-Founder, Mng Dir & Partner)
Nicole Schmidt (Co-Founder, Mng Dir & Partner)
Youev Rekem (Mng Dir & Partner)
David Walsh (Mng Dir-Boston)
Scott L. Robinson (Mng Dir & Co-Head-Real Estate Investment Banking)

OBERWEIS DAIRY, INC.
951 Ice Cream Dr, North Aurora, IL 60542-8193
Tel.: (630) 897-6600 IL
Web Site: http://www.oberweis.com
Year Founded: 1927
Sales Range: $25-49.9 Million
Emp.: 427
Retail & Wholesale Milk, Ice Cream & Other Dairy Products
N.A.I.C.S.: 311511
Elizabeth Craig (VP-Retail Ops)
Joe Oberweis (Pres & CEO)
Dan Rosier (Dir-Brand Dev)

OBJECT CTALK INC.
1013 W 9th Ave, King of Prussia, PA 19406
Tel.: (610) 265-1278
Web Site: http://www.octalk.com
Year Founded: 1996
Sales Range: $1-9.9 Million
Emp.: 50
Systems Integration
N.A.I.C.S.: 541990
Atul Agrawal (CEO)

OBJECT SYSTEMS GROUP INC.
1333 Corporate Dr Ste 315, Irving, TX 75038
Tel.: (972) 650-2026
Web Site: http://www.osgcorp.com
Sales Range: $10-24.9 Million
Emp.: 20
Systems Software Transition Solutions
N.A.I.C.S.: 541511
Tony Gibson (Pres)
Michele Kemp (Controller)

OBJECT TECHNOLOGY SOLUTIONS, INC.
6363 College Blvd Ste 310, Overland Park, KS 66211
Tel.: (913) 345-9080
Web Site: http://www.otsi-usa.com
Year Founded: 1999
Rev.: $18,700,000
Emp.: 356
Computer Related Services
N.A.I.C.S.: 541519
Narasimha Gondi (Pres & CEO)

OBJECTIVE INTEGRITY, INC.
Liberty Sq Ste B-2 270 W Lancaster Ave, Malvern, PA 19355-1858
Tel.: (610) 644-2856
Web Site: http://www.softwarevalue.com

Year Founded: 1994
Emp.: 30
Software Value & Estimation Services
N.A.I.C.S.: 541519
Michael D. Harris (Owner & Pres)
Mark Richtermeyer (Exec VP & Head-Consulting)
Tom Cagley (VP-Consulting)
Tony Timbol (VP-Sls)
Anthony Manno III (VP-Outsourced Svcs)

OBJECTIVE MANAGEMENT GROUP, INC.
114 Tpke Rd Ste 102, Westborough, MA 01581
Tel.: (508) 366-6200
Web Site: http://www.objectivemanagement.com
Year Founded: 1990
Sales Range: $1-9.9 Million
Emp.: 8
Business Consulting Services
N.A.I.C.S.: 611710
Richard Cayer (Pres)
Dave Kurlan (CEO)
Matthew Hogan (Treas)

OBJECTIVITY INC.
3099 N 1st Str Ste 200, San Jose, CA 95134
Tel.: (408) 992-7100
Web Site: http://www.objectivity.com
Year Founded: 1988
Rev.: $11,823,638
Emp.: 40
Computer Software Development
N.A.I.C.S.: 541511
David I. Caplan (Chm)
John J. Jarrell (Dir, Pres, Pres, CEO & CEO)
Brian Clark (VP-Products)
Leon Guzenda (CTO)
Gary Lewis (CFO)
Ibrahim Sallam (VP-Field Svcs)

OBJECTSTREAM, INC.
7725 W Reno Ave Ste 307, Oklahoma City, OK 73127
Tel.: (405) 942-1052
Web Site: http://www.objectstream.com
Year Founded: 2005
Sales Range: $1-9.9 Million
Emp.: 59
Data Processing, Hosting & Related Services
N.A.I.C.S.: 518210

OBJECTWIN TECHNOLOGY, INC.
14800 Saint Marys Ln Ste 100, Houston, TX 77079-2936
Tel.: (713) 782-8200
Web Site: http://www.objectwin.com
Year Founded: 1997
Sales Range: $50-74.9 Million
Emp.: 600
Information Technology Solutions
N.A.I.C.S.: 541511
Shawn Karande (Founder & CEO)
Uma Chidambaram (VP-Bus Dev)

OBLONG FOOD CENTER INC.
E Main St, Oblong, IL 62449
Tel.: (618) 544-8681
Sales Range: $10-24.9 Million
Emp.: 121
Supermarkets, Chain
N.A.I.C.S.: 445110
Rick Rynke (Pres)

OBN HOLDINGS, INC.
8275 S Eastern Ave Ste 200, Las Vegas, NV 89123

Tel.: (702) 938-0467 NV
Web Site: http://www.obnholdings.com
Year Founded: 2002
Sales Range: $1-9.9 Million
Emp.: 8
Holding Company; Entertainment & Plastics
N.A.I.C.S.: 551112

OBRA CAPITAL, INC.
835 W. 6th St., Ste.1400, Austin, TX 78703
Tel.: (512) 961-8265
Web Site: https://www.obra.com
Emp.: 100
Financial Services
N.A.I.C.S.: 523999

Subsidiaries:

Unified Life Insurance Company (1)
7201 W 129th St Ste 300, Overland Park, KS 66213
Tel.: (913) 685-2233
Web Site: http://www.unifiedlife.com
Insurance Agencies & Brokerages
N.A.I.C.S.: 524210
Robert Eshleman (VP-Ops)

OBRIEN IMPORTS, INC.
1601 Fort Jesse Rd, Normal, IL 61761-2284
Tel.: (309) 454-1222
Web Site: http://www.obrienteam.com
Year Founded: 1987
Sales Range: $10-24.9 Million
Emp.: 39
Car Dealer
N.A.I.C.S.: 441110
Joseph D. O'Brien Jr. (Pres)

OBSCURA ANTIQUES & ODDITIES
207 Ave A, New York, NY 10009
Tel.: (212) 505-9251
Web Site: http://www.obscuraantiques.com
Emp.: 4
Obscure & Odd Antiques Dealer
N.A.I.C.S.: 459510
Mike Zohn (Co-Owner)
Evan Michelson (Co-Owner)

OBSERVANT LLC
1601 Trapelo Rd Ste 255 Ste 255, Waltham, MA 02451
Tel.: (781) 642-0644
Year Founded: 2003
Rev.: $8,700,000
Emp.: 21
Marketing Services
N.A.I.C.S.: 541910
John Hartman (VP)
Mike Feeha (Co-Founder, CEO & Mng Partner)
Erik Coats (Mng Partner & Exec VP)
Rich Durante (Co-Founder, Pres & Mng Partner)

OBSERVEPOINT LLC
251 W River Park Dr Ste 300, Provo, UT 84604
Web Site: http://www.observepoint.com
Year Founded: 2007
Sales Range: $10-24.9 Million
Emp.: 100
Software Development Services
N.A.I.C.S.: 541511
Robert Seolas (Founder)
John Pestana (CEO)

OBSERVER CAPITAL LLC
375 Hudson St, New York, NY 10014
Tel.: (212) 620-5700
Private Investment Firm
N.A.I.C.S.: 523999

OBSERVER CAPITAL LLC

Observer Capital LLC—(Continued)
Annie Cheung *(COO)*
Joseph Meyer *(Mng Partner)*

Subsidiaries:

Source Media LLC (1)
One State St Plaza 27th Fl, New York, NY 10004
Tel.: (212) 803-8200
Web Site: http://www.sourcemedia.com
Sales Range: $125-149.9 Million
Banking, Finance & Technology Information Services
N.A.I.C.S.: 519290
David Longobardi *(Chief Content Officer & Exec VP)*
Ying Wong *(Sr VP-HR & Office Mgmt)*
John Del Mauro *(Sr VP-Conferences & Events)*
Minna Rhee *(Chief Digital Officer)*
Harry Nikpour *(VP-Capital Markets)*
Michael Caruso *(CFO)*
AnnMarie Wills *(VP-Audience & Data)*
Dennis Strong *(Grp Publr-Banking)*
Rocco Impreveduto *(VP-Content Sls)*
Julian Orbon *(Sr VP-Custom Media)*
Melianthe Kines *(Dir-Audience Dev)*
Allison Adams *(Chief Subscription Officer)*
Gemma Postlethwaite *(CEO)*
Jeff Mancini *(Chief Strategy Officer)*
Christian Ward *(Chief Data Officer)*
David Evans *(Chief Content Officer)*
Lee Gavin *(Head-People & Culture)*
Dave Colford *(Chief Revenue Officer)*
Robyn Duda *(Head-Experiences & Networks)*
Fell Gray *(Head-Brand & Creative)*
Stacy Huggins *(Head-Mktg)*
Alan Kline *(Editor-in-Chief-American Banker)*

OBSERVER MEDIA GROUP, INC.
1970 Main St, Sarasota, FL 34236
Tel.: (941) 366-3468 FL
Web Site: http://www.youobserver.com
Year Founded: 1995
Sales Range: $10-24.9 Million
Emp.: 80
Newspaper Publishers
N.A.I.C.S.: 513110
David Beliles *(Chm)*
Matt Walsh *(CEO & Editor)*
Laura Keisacker *(CFO)*
Jill Raleigh *(Dir-Adv)*
Kathy Payne *(Dir-Creative Svcs & IT)*
Emily Walsh *(Publr)*
Kat Hughes *(Exec Editor)*
Kristen Boothroyd *(Dir-Legal Adv)*
Dan Entin *(VP-Product)*

Subsidiaries:

Business Observer (1)
1970 Main St, Sarasota, FL 34236
Tel.: (941) 362-4848
Web Site: http://www.businessoberverfl.com
Rev.: $1,350,000
Emp.: 10
Newspaper Publishers
N.A.I.C.S.: 513110
Matt Walsh *(Publr)*
Kat Hughes *(Mng Editor)*

OBSIDIAN ENTERPRISES, INC.
111 Monument Cir Ste 4800, Indianapolis, IN 46204
Tel.: (317) 237-4122 DE
Sales Range: $150-199.9 Million
Emp.: 450
Investment Holding Company; Truck Trailers, Recreational Vehicles & Rubber Mfr
N.A.I.C.S.: 551112
Jeffrey W. Osler *(Sr Exec VP)*

Subsidiaries:

Danzer Corporation (1)
17500 York Rd, Hagerstown, MD 21740-7599
Tel.: (301) 582-2000
Web Site: http://www.danzermorrison.com
Sales Range: $10-24.9 Million
Emp.: 125
Holding Company; Manufacture & Design of Truck Bodies & Accessories
N.A.I.C.S.: 336211

Subsidiary (Domestic):

Danzer Industries, Inc. (2)
17500 York Rd, Hagerstown, MD 21740-7599 (100%)
Tel.: (301) 582-2000
Mfr of Truck Bodies
N.A.I.C.S.: 336211

OBSIDIAN SOLUTIONS GROUP LLC
1320 Central Park Blvd Ste 304, Fredericksburg, VA 22401
Tel.: (877) 503-0222
Web Site: http://www.obsidiansg.com
Year Founded: 2010
Sales Range: $10-24.9 Million
Security & Investigation Services
N.A.I.C.S.: 561612
Tyrone Logan *(Founder & CEO)*

Subsidiaries:

Applied Rapid Technologies Corp. (1)
1130 International Pkwy Ste 127, Fredericksburg, VA 76106-4333
Tel.: (540) 371-1100
Web Site: http://www.hanksinc.com
Surgical Appliance & Supplies Mfr
N.A.I.C.S.: 339113
Bruce LeMaster *(Founder & Pres)*

OBVERSE CORPORATION
6856 Eastern Ave NW Ste 210, Washington, DC 20012
Tel.: (202) 291-0677
Web Site: http://www.obverse.net
Year Founded: 2002
Sales Range: $10-24.9 Million
Emp.: 40
Business Support Services
N.A.I.C.S.: 561499
James Detherage *(Pres & CEO)*
Timothy Thompson *(Exec VP)*

OBVIUS
20497 SW Teton Ave, Tualatin, OR 97062
Tel.: (503) 601-2099
Web Site: http://www.obvius.com
Year Founded: 2002
Sales Range: $25-49.9 Million
Emp.: 16
Electronic Computer Mfr
N.A.I.C.S.: 334111
Jim Lewis *(CEO)*
Allen Schatz *(CFO)*

OBXTEK INC.
8300 Boone Blvd Ste 800, Vienna, VA 22182
Tel.: (703) 373-3736
Web Site: http://www.obxtek.com
Year Founded: 2008
Sales Range: $1-9.9 Million
Emp.: 92
Information Technology Consulting Services
N.A.I.C.S.: 541512
Ed Jesson *(Pres & CEO)*
Timothy Pleus *(Project Mgr)*
Bill Phillips *(Exec VP-Ops)*
Sharon Harrington *(Chief HR Officer)*
Anthony Jimenez Jr. *(CTO)*

OCALA BREEDERS' SALES COMPANY
1701 SW 60th Ave, Ocala, FL 34474-1800
Tel.: (352) 237-2154
Web Site: http://www.obssales.com
Sales Range: $75-99.9 Million
Emp.: 40
Distr of Prepared Feeds
N.A.I.C.S.: 311119
Randy Edwards *(Controller & Mgr-Credit)*
Tom Ventura *(Pres)*
Lauren Marks *(Asst Dir-Sls)*
Tod Wojciechowski *(Dir-Sls)*

OCCASIONS CATERERS INC.
655 Taylor St NE, Washington, DC 20017
Tel.: (202) 546-7400
Web Site: http://www.occasionscaterers.com
Year Founded: 1986
Sales Range: $10-24.9 Million
Emp.: 35
Provider of Party Planning Services
N.A.I.C.S.: 812990
Eric Michael *(Co-Founder & Dir-Creative)*
John Mudd *(Controller)*

OCCI INC.
3200 County Rd 257, Fulton, MO 65251
Tel.: (573) 642-6087
Web Site: http://www.occimofab.com
Rev.: $12,000,000
Emp.: 70
Constructors of Dams: Heavy Construction
N.A.I.C.S.: 236210
Tom Smith *(Pres)*
Deborah Wynn *(Mgr-HR)*

OCCIDENTAL DEVELOPMENT GROUP, INC.
256 S Robertson Blvd, Beverly Hills, CA 90211
Tel.: (310) 358-3323 NV
Automation Technology for Single & Multi Unit New Construction & Existing Buildings
N.A.I.C.S.: 335999
Ian Gilbey *(Pres, Sec & Treas)*

Subsidiaries:

MCM Integrated Technologies, Ltd. (1)
221 2323 Quebec St, Vancouver, V5T 4S7, BC, Canada
Tel.: (604) 876-7494
Web Site: http://www.mcm-it.com
Computer Software Solutions Provider
N.A.I.C.S.: 541511
Murat F. Erbatur *(Pres)*

OCCIDENTAL INTERNATIONAL FOODS LLC
4 Middlebury Blvd Ste 3 Aspen Business Park, Randolph, NJ 07869
Tel.: (973) 970-9220
Web Site: http://www.occidentalfoods.com
Year Founded: 1998
Sales Range: $1-9.9 Million
Emp.: 5
Spices, Herbs & Seeds
N.A.I.C.S.: 311942
Scott P. Hall *(Pres)*

OCCIDENTAL MANAGEMENT INC.
8111 E 32nd St N Ste 101, Wichita, KS 67226
Tel.: (316) 262-3331
Web Site: http://www.occmgmt.com
Year Founded: 1997
Sales Range: $1-9.9 Million
Emp.: 9
Real Estate Services
N.A.I.C.S.: 531210

U.S. PRIVATE

Gary L. Oborny *(Founder, Chm & CEO)*
Chad Stafford *(Pres)*

OCCUPATIONAL HEALTH CENTERS OF CALIFORNIA, A MEDICAL, CORP.
3536 E Concours St Ste 350, Ontario, CA 91764
Tel.: (909) 481-7377
Year Founded: 1998
Sales Range: $1-9.9 Million
Emp.: 30
Offices of Physicians, Mental Health Specialists
N.A.I.C.S.: 621112
Joe Martinez *(Dir)*

OCCUPATIONAL TRAINING CENTER OF BURLINGTON COUNTY, INC.
2 Manhattan Dr, Burlington, NJ 08016
Tel.: (609) 267-6677 NJ
Web Site: http://www.otcbc.org
Year Founded: 1962
Sales Range: $25-49.9 Million
Emp.: 942
Disability Assistance Services
N.A.I.C.S.: 624120
Al Cascarina *(Pres)*
Darlene Barrington *(Sec)*
Robert Sobeck *(VP)*

OCEAN AIR INTERNATIONAL, INC.
490 Park Dr Ste 103, Weirton, WV 26062
Tel.: (304) 723-7272 PA
Web Site: http://www.oaiusa.com
Year Founded: 1970
Sales Range: $1-9.9 Million
Emp.: 13
Freight Transportation Arrangement
N.A.I.C.S.: 488510
Richard E. Starck *(Owner & CEO)*
Raymond Cowan *(Mgr-Network)*
Vince Sabatasse *(Mgr-Sys)*
Connie Sherensky *(Pres)*
Jim Paboucek *(Coord-Intl Traffic)*
Scott Montgomery *(Coord-Intl Traffic)*
Steve Marino *(CFO)*

OCEAN BANKSHARES, INC.
780 NW 42nd Ave, Miami, FL 33126
Tel.: (305) 569-5000 FL
Web Site: http://www.oceanbank.com
Year Founded: 1982
Sales Range: $75-99.9 Million
Bank Holding Company
N.A.I.C.S.: 551111
Sam Monti *(Chief Credit Officer & Exec VP)*
Yuni Navarro *(Chief Admin Officer & Exec VP)*
Ralph Gonzalez Jacobo *(Chief Lending Officer & Exec VP)*
Manuel M. Del Canal *(Exec VP-Wealth Mgmt)*
Cheryl Rees *(Sr VP & Dir-Mktg)*

Subsidiaries:

Ocean Bank (1)
780 NW 42nd Ave, Miami, FL 33126-5536
Tel.: (305) 569-5000
Web Site: http://www.oceanbank.com
Rev.: $124,695,000
Assets: $3,259,964,000
Liabilities: $2,888,158,000
Net Worth: $371,806,000
Earnings: $33,318,000
Emp.: 671
Fiscal Year-end: 12/31/2013
Personal & Commercial Banking Services
N.A.I.C.S.: 522110

COMPANIES

A. Alfonso Macedo *(Pres & CEO)*
Rogelio Villarreal *(Sr VP & Head-Comml Lending)*
Yuni Navarro *(Chief Admin Officer & Exec VP)*
Cheryl Rees *(Sr VP & Dir-Mktg)*
Sam Monti *(Chief Credit Officer & Exec VP)*
Stan Rubin *(CFO, Chief Risk Officer & Exec VP)*
Manuel M. Del Canal *(Exec VP & Head-Wealth Mgmt)*
Ralph Gonzalez-Jacobo *(Chief Lending Officer & Exec VP)*
Eddie Diaz *(Sr VP & Head-Corp Lending)*

OCEAN BEAUTY SEAFOODS, INC.
1100 W Ewing St, Seattle, WA 98119
Tel.: (206) 285-6800   WA
Web Site: http://www.oceanbeauty.com
Year Founded: 1910
Sales Range: $400-449.9 Million
Emp.: 1,300
Distr of Seafood
N.A.I.C.S.: 311710
Mark Palmer *(Pres & CEO)*
Tom Sunderland *(VP-Mktg & Comm)*

OCEAN BRIDGE GROUP
1714 16th St, Santa Monica, CA 90404
Tel.: (310) 392-3200
Web Site: http://www.oceanbridgegroup.com
Year Founded: 2002
Rev.: $265,000,000
Emp.: 20
Advetising Agency
N.A.I.C.S.: 541810
Cary Herrman *(Co-Founder & Pres)*
Ramie Ostrovsky *(Co-Founder & CEO)*

OCEAN CADILLAC INC.
1000 Kane Concourse, Miami, FL 33154
Tel.: (305) 864-2271
Web Site: http://www.cadillac.com
Sales Range: $25-49.9 Million
Emp.: 35
New & Used Automobiles
N.A.I.C.S.: 441110
Denise Rodriguez *(Controller)*

OCEAN COLONY PARTNERS
2450 S Cadrillo Hwy Ste 200, Half Moon Bay, CA 94019
Tel.: (650) 726-5764
Web Site: http://www.halfmoonbaygolf.com
Rev.: $19,400,000
Emp.: 100
Subdividers & Developers
N.A.I.C.S.: 237210
Mark Kenball *(Pres & Gen Partner)*

OCEAN CONSERVANCY
1300 19th St NW 8th Fl, Washington, DC 20036
Tel.: (202) 429-5609   DC
Web Site: http://www.oceanconservancy.org
Year Founded: 1972
Rev.: $37,275,306
Assets: $48,359,161
Liabilities: $2,260,644
Net Worth: $46,098,517
Earnings: $1,668,440
Emp.: 143
Fiscal Year-end: 06/30/18
Ocean Conservation Services
N.A.I.C.S.: 813312
Larry Amon *(CFO)*
Chris Dorsett *(VP-Conservation Policy & Programs)*
Janis Searles Jones *(CEO)*
Andreas Merkl *(Pres)*

Kenneth Donaldson *(VP-Fin)*
David C. Aldrich *(Treas)*
Thomas H. Allen *(Co-Chm)*
Kara Lankford *(Dir-Interim-Gulf Restoration Program)*

OCEAN COUNTY UTILITIES AUTHORITY
501 Hickory Ln, Bayville, NJ 08721-2157
Tel.: (732) 269-4500
Web Site: http://www.ocua.com
Rev.: $77,863,444
Assets: $370,627,489
Liabilities: $250,219,009
Net Worth: $120,408,480
Earnings: $2,665,644
Emp.: 260
Fiscal Year-end: 12/31/18
Sewerage Systems
N.A.I.C.S.: 221320
Daniel J. Hennessy *(Vice Chm)*
Frank F. Sadeghi *(Treas)*

OCEAN DRIVE ACQUISITION CORP.
311 S Wacker Dr Ste 6400, Chicago, IL 60606
Tel.: (312) 258-8300   DE
Year Founded: 2021
Investment Services
N.A.I.C.S.: 523999
Howard M. Lorber *(Chm)*
Steven Witkoff *(CEO)*
Kyle Asher *(Co-Pres)*
Aaron Peck *(Co-Pres)*
Scott Alper *(Chief Investment Officer)*
Peter Gruszka *(Chief Legal Officer)*
Scott Marienau *(CFO)*
Alex Witkoff *(VP)*

OCEAN DUNES RESORT & VILLAS
201 74th Ave N, Myrtle Beach, SC 29572-4201
Tel.: (843) 449-7441
Web Site: http://www.sandsresorts.com
Year Founded: 1981
Sales Range: $1-9.9 Million
Emp.: 5
Hotel & Motel Operating Services
N.A.I.C.S.: 721110

OCEAN EXPLORATION TRUST
PO Box 42, Old Lyme, CT 06371
Tel.: (860) 434-5808   CT
Web Site: http://www.oceanexplorationtrust.org
Year Founded: 2007
Sales Range: $10-24.9 Million
Emp.: 26
Scientific Research Services
N.A.I.C.S.: 541715
Kay McConagha *(Chief Admin Officer)*
Laurie Bradt *(VP-Bus Affairs)*
Allison Fundis *(VP-Education, Outreach & Comm)*
Nicole Raineault *(Dir-Science)*
Ethan Gold *(Dir-Software & Data Engrg)*

OCEAN GOLD SEAFOODS, INC.
1804 N Nyhus St, Westport, WA 98595
Tel.: (360) 268-2510
Web Site: http://www.oceangoldseafoods.com
Rev.: $15,900,000
Emp.: 900
Fresh & Frozen Seafood Processing
N.A.I.C.S.: 311710

Dennis Rydman *(Pres)*
Greg Shaughnessy *(Gen Mgr)*

OCEAN HARVEST WHOLESALE INC.
8751 Flagship Dr, Houston, TX 77029-4012
Tel.: (713) 224-3474
Web Site: http://www.ohwinc.com
Sales Range: $50-74.9 Million
Emp.: 90
Seafoods
N.A.I.C.S.: 424460
Eric Tran *(Pres & CEO)*

OCEAN MARINE GROUP INC.
5927 Washington Ave, Ocean Springs, MS 39564
Tel.: (228) 818-0200
Web Site: http://www.ocean-marine.com
Rev.: $11,000,000
Emp.: 20
Boats Repair Services & Transportation Equipment Whslr
N.A.I.C.S.: 441222
Michael K. King *(Owner & Pres)*
Chris Cason *(Gen Mgr)*

OCEAN MAZDA
9675 NW 12th St, Doral, FL 33172-2825
Tel.: (305) 460-7200
Web Site: http://www.oceanmazda.com
Year Founded: 1995
Sales Range: $25-49.9 Million
Emp.: 60
Car Whslr
N.A.I.C.S.: 441110
Serafin Garcia *(Pres)*

OCEAN MEDIA INC.
17011 Beach Blvd 15th Fl, Huntington Beach, CA 92647
Tel.: (714) 969-5244
Web Site: http://www.oceanmediainc.com
Year Founded: 1996
Sales Range: $200-249.9 Million
Emp.: 41
Media Buying Services
N.A.I.C.S.: 541830
Ron Louis Luebbert *(COO)*
Jay Langan *(Pres)*
Staci Larkin *(VP-Media)*

OCEAN MIST FARMS CORP.
10855 Ocean Mist Pkwy, Castroville, CA 95012
Tel.: (831) 633-2144   CA
Web Site: http://www.oceanmist.com
Year Founded: 1924
Sales Range: $50-74.9 Million
Emp.: 100
Grower, Packer & Shipper of Vegetables
N.A.I.C.S.: 115114
Edward Boutonnet *(Pres)*

OCEAN MOTORS, INC.
386 Rte 37 E, Toms River, NJ 08753
Tel.: (732) 244-8400   NJ
Web Site: http://www.tomsriverautomall.com
Year Founded: 1981
Sales Range: $100-124.9 Million
Emp.: 130
Retailer of New & Used Automobiles
N.A.I.C.S.: 441110
Mike Maffucci *(Gen Mgr)*
Bruce Winkler *(Controller)*

OCEAN PETROLEUM CO. INC.
PO Box 129, Newark, MD 21841
Tel.: (410) 632-0400

Web Site: http://www.oceanpetroleum.com
Rev.: $87,417,191
Emp.: 12
Gasoline
N.A.I.C.S.: 424720
Steve Ladd *(COO)*
Nancy Meredith *(Chief Admin Officer)*
Edward J. Ellis Jr. *(CEO)*

OCEAN PROPERTIES & MANAGEMENT, INC.
3500 S Atlantic Ave, New Smyrna Beach, FL 32169
Tel.: (386) 428-0513
Web Site: http://www.oceanprops.com
Sales Range: $1-9.9 Million
Emp.: 20
Real Estate Broker
N.A.I.C.S.: 531210
Kelley Desoto *(VP & Dir-Mktg)*
Carole Swan *(Mgr-Rental)*

OCEAN PROPERTIES, LTD.
1001 Atlantic Ave Ste 202, Delray Beach, FL 33483
Tel.: (561) 279-9900   FL
Web Site: http://www.oplhotels.com
Year Founded: 1969
Sales Range: $900-999.9 Million
Emp.: 5,500
Hotel Management & Commercial Land Development Services
N.A.I.C.S.: 721110
Michael Walsh *(Pres)*
Linda Haserot *(VP-Sls & Mktg)*
Steven Updike *(VP-Food & Beverage)*
Andy Berger *(VP-Ops)*

Subsidiaries:

Atlific Inc. (1)
250 Saint-Antoine Street West Suite 400, Montreal, H2Y 0A3, QC, Canada
Tel.: (514) 509-5500
Web Site: https://www.atlifichotels.com
Sales Range: $900-999.9 Million
Emp.: 3,000
Home Management Services
N.A.I.C.S.: 721110
Raymond St. Pierre *(VP-Ops-Eastern Canada)*
Christine Kennedy *(VP)*
Wendy Lamont *(Exec VP)*
Gordon Johnson *(VP)*
Bonnie Ng *(Treas)*

Jupiter Beach Resort & Spa (1)
5 N Hwy A1A, Jupiter, FL 33477-5145
Tel.: (561) 746-2511
Web Site: http://www.jupiterbeachresort.com
Hotel & Resort
N.A.I.C.S.: 721110
Diane D'Amico *(Dir-Sls & Mktg)*
Noelle Ricciardi *(Mgr-Sls)*
Justin Earle *(Gen Mgr)*

Longboat Key Club Moorings (1)
2630 Harbourside Dr, Longboat Key, FL 34228
Tel.: (941) 383-8383
Web Site: http://www.longboatkeymarina.com
Sales Range: $1-9.9 Million
Emp.: 15
Marinas
N.A.I.C.S.: 713930
Dennis Matthews *(Gen Mgr)*
David Leach *(Dir-Engrg)*

The Resort at Longboat Key Club (1)
442 Gulf of Mexico Dr, Longboat Key, FL 34228
Tel.: (941) 383-8821
Web Site: http://www.longboatkeyclub.com
Sales Range: $50-74.9 Million
Emp.: 500
Resort & Hotel
N.A.I.C.S.: 531210
Sandra Rios *(Dir-Mktg & Comm)*
Jonathan Lester *(Dir-Event Mgmt)*

OCEAN REEF CLUB INC.

OCEAN REEF CLUB INC.

U.S. PRIVATE

Ocean Reef Club Inc.—(Continued)

35 Ocean Reef Dr Ste 200, Key Largo, FL 33037-5263
Tel.: (305) 367-2611
Web Site: http://www.oceanreef.com
Year Founded: 1945
Sales Range: $50-74.9 Million
Emp.: 1,000
Beach Resort & Hotel
N.A.I.C.S.: 721110
Paul M. G. Astbury *(Pres)*
Peg Allman *(Suprv-Pur)*
Beth Davidson *(Mgr-Restaurant)*
Richard Weinstein *(VP-Sls & Mktg)*
Jenny Montas *(Asst Controller-F&B Cost)*
Chrisna Gilchrist *(Coord-HR)*
Rupert Rodriguez *(Dir-Catering)*
Shaun McKenna *(Mgr-Beverage Ops)*
Philippe Reynaud *(Sr Dir-Culinary Ops)*
Salima Aly *(Mgr-Banquets)*
Mark Kinney *(Mgr-Trng)*

OCEAN SHIPHOLDINGS, INC.
16211 Park Ten Pl, Houston, TX 77084
Tel.: (281) 579-3700
Web Site: http://www.oceanshipholdings.com
Year Founded: 1981
Rev.: $22,900,000
Emp.: 30
Tankers, Building & Repairing
N.A.I.C.S.: 336611
James P. McGregor *(Pres & COO)*
Robert Sheen *(VP-Ops)*
Joe F. Vaughn Jr. *(Chm & CEO)*

OCEAN SPRAY CRANBERRIES, INC.
1 Ocean Spray Dr, Lakeville, MA 02349
Tel.: (508) 946-1000   DE
Web Site: https://www.oceanspray.com
Year Founded: 1930
Sales Range: $1-4.9 Billion
Emp.: 500
Co-op Mfr & Marketer of Cranberry & Grapefruit Products
N.A.I.C.S.: 311421
Daniel Cunha *(CFO)*
Tom Hayes *(Pres & CEO)*
Sarah Evans *(Chief HR Officer)*
Monisha Dabek *(Chief Comml Officer-USA)*

Subsidiaries:

Ocean Spray Cranberries-Bordentown Plant   (1)
104 E Park St, Bordentown, NJ 08505-1424
Tel.: (609) 298-0905
Web Site: http://www.oceanspray.com
Sales Range: $50-74.9 Million
Emp.: 250
Mfr of Cranberry & Grapefruit Products
N.A.I.C.S.: 311421

Ocean Spray International Services (UK) Limited   (1)
Lily Hill House Lily Hill Road, Bracknell, RG12 2SJ, Berkshire, United Kingdom
Tel.: (44) 1932 575338
Frozen Food Product & Beverage Mfr
N.A.I.C.S.: 311421

Ocean Spray International Services, Inc.   (1)
1 Ocean Spray Dr, Lakeville, MA 02349-1000
Tel.: (508) 946-1000
Web Site: http://www.oceanspray.com
Sales Range: $25-49.9 Million
Emp.: 450
Mfr of Cranberry & Grapefruit Products
N.A.I.C.S.: 541618
Sandy Jones *(Mgr-Mktg-Special Markets)*
Bill Frantz *(Sr Mgr-Ag Economics & Govt Affairs)*
Margarita Gomez *(Sr Mgr-Quality)*
Beth Jordan *(Sr Mgr-Consumer Insights)*
Allen Modine *(Sr Mgr-Databases, Software & Digital Dev)*

OCEAN STATE COMMUNITY RESOURCES, INC.
310 Maple Ave Ste 102, Barrington, RI 02806
Tel.: (401) 245-7900   RI
Web Site: http://www.oscr.org
Year Founded: 1982
Sales Range: $10-24.9 Million
Emp.: 336
Developmental Disability Assistance Services
N.A.I.C.S.: 623210
David C. Reiss *(Exec Dir)*
Michelle C. Brodeur *(Dir-Fin)*
Wendy Davis *(Dir-Nursing)*
Lisa Rafferty *(Sec)*
Jennifer Fogel *(VP)*
James Campagna *(Chm)*
Anthony Dennis *(Treas)*

OCEAN STATE JOBBERS INC.
375 Commerce Pk Rd, North Kingstown, RI 02852-7739
Tel.: (401) 295-2672   RI
Web Site: http://www.oceanstatejoblot.com
Year Founded: 1977
Retailers Stores
N.A.I.C.S.: 455219
Marc Pearlman *(Pres)*
John Conforti *(CFO)*

OCEAN TECHNOLOGY INC.
796 Cromwell Park Dr Ste G, Glen Burnie, MD 21061
Tel.: (410) 761-2722
Web Site: http://www.oceantechnology.com
Sales Range: $10-24.9 Million
Emp.: 6
Seafoods
N.A.I.C.S.: 424460
Suzie Schwartz *(Controller)*

OCEAN WAY MOTORS INC.
500 SW Sublimity Blvd, Sublimity, OR 97385
Tel.: (503) 399-0123
Web Site: http://www.powerchevonline.com
Rev.: $144,906,323
Emp.: 60
Automobiles, New & Used
N.A.I.C.S.: 441110
Jim Church *(Mgr-Fleet)*
Phil Fitzner *(Mgr-Fleet)*
David Irey *(Mgr-Parts)*
Jaron Nygren *(Mgr-Sls)*
Randy Stewart *(Mgr-Svc)*

OCEANA, INC.
1350 Connecticut Ave NW 5th Fl, Washington, DC 20036
Tel.: (202) 833-3900   DC
Web Site: http://www.oceana.org
Year Founded: 2001
Sales Range: $25-49.9 Million
Emp.: 154
Ocean Conservation Services
N.A.I.C.S.: 813312
Ricardo Aguilar *(Dir-Projects & Res)*
Maribel Lopez *(Dir-Admin)*
Ulisses Lacava *(Dir-Comm)*
Alyssa Carnegie *(Dir-Comm)*
Simon Sidamon-Eristoff *(Chm)*
Dustin Cranor *(VP-Global Mktg & Comm)*
Jacqueline Savitz *(Chief Policy Officer)*
Andrew Sharpless *(CEO)*
Beth Lowell *(VP-Campaigns-US)*

OCEANAIR INC.
186A Lee Burbank Hwy, Revere, MA 02151
Tel.: (781) 286-2700
Web Site: http://www.oceanair.net
Sales Range: $25-49.9 Million
Emp.: 60
Customs Clearance Of Freight
N.A.I.C.S.: 488510
Jeff McLaren *(Mgr-Sls & Superyachts-West Coast)*
Tom Pickles *(Mgr-Superyacht Bus)*
Doanna Martis *(Controller)*
Timothy Dooner *(Dir-Bus Dev)*
Val Koen *(Acct Exec-Sls)*
Brenda Barnard *(Sr Dir-Export Compliance)*
Paul Rawate *(Mgr-Digital Mktg)*
Robert Sabelli *(Dir-Logistics)*

OCEANHOUSE MEDIA, INC.
PO Box 230928, Encinitas, CA 92023-0928
Tel.: (310) 910-5800
Web Site: http://www.oceanhousemedia.com
Year Founded: 2009
Sales Range: $1-9.9 Million
Emp.: 10
Publisher of Over 285 Mobile & Desktop Apps in Various Categories
N.A.I.C.S.: 513210
Michel Kripalani *(Founder & Pres)*
karen Kripalani *(Mgr-Media Mktg)*

OCEANIC EXPLORATION COMPANY
7800 E Dorado Pl Ste 250, Englewood, CO 80111
Tel.: (303) 220-8330   DE
OCEX—(OTCBB)
Natural Gas & Oil Exploration & Mining Services
N.A.I.C.S.: 211120

OCEANLAND SERVICE INC.
15241 Don Julian Rd, City of Industry, CA 91745-1002
Tel.: (626) 573-8429   CA
Web Site: http://www.oceanlandchb.com
Year Founded: 1981
Sales Range: $10-24.9 Million
Emp.: 50
Freight Transportation Arrangement
N.A.I.C.S.: 488510
Shirley Wood *(Owner & Controller)*

OCEANOS, INC.
892 Plain St Ste 208, Marshfield, MA 02050
Tel.: (781) 804-1010
Web Site: http://www.oceanosinc.com
Year Founded: 2001
Sales Range: $10-24.9 Million
Emp.: 10
Media Buying & Advertising Services
N.A.I.C.S.: 541830
Brian P. Hession *(Founder & Pres)*
Raghu Prabhu *(CTO)*
Artika Wadhwa *(Chief Legal Officer)*

OCEANS FUNDING COMPANY INC.
912 Drew St Ste 201, Clearwater, FL 33755
Tel.: (727) 441-2400
Sales Range: $10-24.9 Million
Emp.: 8
Mortgage Banker
N.A.I.C.S.: 522292

OCEANSIDE GLASSTILE COMPANY
5858 Edison Place, Carlsbad, CA 92008
Tel.: (760) 929-4000
Web Site: http://www.glasstile.com
Sales Range: $125-149.9 Million
Emp.: 220
Plastic Pipe & Pipe Fitting Mfr
N.A.I.C.S.: 326122
Sean Gildea *(Pres)*
Johnny Marckx *(Owner & Exec VP)*
Jeff Nibler *(VP-Sls)*
David Fatula *(Mgr-Technical Svcs)*

OCEANSIDE INSTITUTIONAL INDUSTRIES
2525 Long Beach Rd, Oceanside, NY 11572
Tel.: (516) 766-1461
Web Site: http://www.oceansidelaundry.com
Sales Range: $10-24.9 Million
Emp.: 350
Provider of Laundry Services
N.A.I.C.S.: 812331
Larry Amodio *(Dir-Sls & Svcs)*

OCEANSIDE PHOTO & TELESCOPE
918 Mission Ave, Oceanside, CA 92054
Tel.: (760) 722-3343
Web Site: http://www.optcorp.com
Year Founded: 1947
Sales Range: $10-24.9 Million
Emp.: 30
Astronomical & Photographic Equipment Retailer
N.A.I.C.S.: 449210
Eric Blackhurst *(Gen Mgr)*
Jason Farmer *(Mgr-Internet Sls Ops)*

OCEANSOUND PARTNERS, LP
320 Park Ave 8th Fl, New York, NY 10022
Tel.: (212) 433-3050
Web Site: http://www.oceansoundpartners.com
Privater Equity Firm
N.A.I.C.S.: 523999
Joe Benavides *(Mng Partner)*
David Stein *(Principal)*

Subsidiaries:

CFM   (1)
1232 E Baseline Rd., Unit 102, Tempe, AZ 85283
Web Site: https://whycfm.com
Emp.: 300
Information Technology Consulting Services
N.A.I.C.S.: 541512
J. C. Chen *(Dir-Software Dev)*

Subsidiary (Domestic):

Integrated Media Management, Inc.   (2)
2 City Hall Plz, Rahway, NJ 07065
Tel.: (908) 862-6600
Web Site: http://www.immonline.com
Sales Range: $1-9.9 Million
Emp.: 40
Stationery & Office Supplies Merchant Whslr
N.A.I.C.S.: 424120
Steve LaCarter *(VP-Bus Dev)*
Philip Elwyn *(Dir-Client Success)*
John Levy *(Exec VP)*
Nish Shah *(CTO)*

Digital Management, Inc.   (1)
1 Rock Spring Palza 6550 Rock Spring Dr 7th Fl, Bethesda, MD 20817
Tel.: (240) 223-4800
Web Site: http://www.dminc.com
Sales Range: $50-74.9 Million
Emp.: 1,500
Enterprise Information Management, Cybersecurity & Healthcare IT
N.A.I.C.S.: 541511

COMPANIES   OCEANSOUND PARTNERS, LP

Jay Sunny Bajaj (Founder, Chm & CEO)
John E. Welch (Chief Legal Officer & Exec VP)
Ken S. Bajaj (Pres)
Noah Asher (CFO)
Raj Paul (VP-IoT & Connected Svcs)
Scott B. Deutschman (Officer-Corp Dev)
Stacy Greine (CMO)

Subsidiary (Domestic):

Ambit Group LLC (2)
8607 Westwood Ctr Dr Ste 550, Vienna, VA 22182
Tel.: (703) 689-0881
Web Site: http://www.theambitgroup.com
IT Modernization, Business Transformation & Mission Support Services
N.A.I.C.S.: 561499
Kim Hayes (Founder & Co-CEO)
Ashequl Hoque (Co-CEO)
Sandra Peavy (CIO)
Qasim Hussain (Chief Innovation Officer)
Yasmeen Wynn (Chief Admin Officer)
LC Cook (Chief Growth Officer)
Eric Hansen (Sr VP-Delivery Ops)

Subsidiary (Domestic):

Greenzone Solutions, Inc. (3)
3507 Nutley St Ste 523, Fairfax, VA 22031
Tel.: (571) 933-8360
Web Site: http://www.greenzoneinc.com
General Management Consulting Services
N.A.I.C.S.: 541611
Wajid Hussain (Treas)

Subsidiary (Domestic):

The Pappas Group, Inc. (2)
4100 N Fairfax Sr Ste 400, Arlington, VA 22203
Tel.: (703) 349-7221
Web Site: http://www.pappasgroup.com
Sales Range: $10-24.9 Million
Emp.: 22
Advetising Agency
N.A.I.C.S.: 541810
Anthony Pappas (Founder & Pres)
Stefan Poulos (Exec Dir-Creative)
Mick Sutter (Dir-Creative-Copy & Content)

Gannett Fleming, Inc. (1)
207 Senate Ave, Camp Hill, PA 17011-2316
Tel.: (717) 763-7211
Web Site: http://www.gannettfleming.com
Municipal Construction & Engineering Services
N.A.I.C.S.: 541330
Judy L. Hricak (Chief Comm Officer & VP)
Robert M. Scaer (Chm, Pres & CEO)
Paul D. Nowicki (Pres & COO)
Jon Kessler (CFO & Exec VP)
John W. Kovacs (Exec VP, Exec VP & Dir-Earth Sciences)
Esther M. McGinnis (Exec VP)
Bryan Mulqueen (Exec VP & Dir-Transit & Rail)
Arthur Hoffmann Jr. (Chief Admin Officer & Exec VP)
George Campanella (Sr VP & Sr VP-Facilities)
Anthony Ferruccio (Sr VP & Dir-Construction Svcs Bus Line)
John Derr (Exec VP & Dir-Roadway)
Brendan Wesdock (Pres-GeoDecisions & Sr VP)

Subsidiary (Domestic):

Digioia, Gray & Associates, LLC (2)
570 Beatty Rd, Monroeville, PA 15146-1359
Tel.: (412) 372-4500
Web Site: http://www.digioiagray.com
Engineeering Services
N.A.I.C.S.: 541330
Mike Lively (Office Mgr)

Elgood-Mayo Corp. (2)
1817 Colonial Vlg Ln, Lancaster, PA 17601-6702   (100%)
Tel.: (717) 397-6201
Specialized Heavy Construction Equipment Designers, Fabricators & Suppliers
N.A.I.C.S.: 333131

Affiliate (Domestic):

Ganflec Architects & Engineers, Inc. (2)
209 Senate Ave, Camp Hill, PA 17011
Tel.: (717) 763-7220
Web Site: http://www.gannettflemingarchitects.com
Sales Range: $350-399.9 Million
Architectural Design & Engineering Services
N.A.I.C.S.: 541310
Charles H. Beauduy (Pres)
Robert Scaer (Pres)

Subsidiary (Domestic):

Gannett Fleming Project Development Corp. (2)
207 Senate Ave, Camp Hill, PA 17011-2325
Tel.: (717) 763-7270
Web Site: http://www.gfpdc.com
Sales Range: $10-24.9 Million
Emp.: 8
Industrial Building Construction Services
N.A.I.C.S.: 236210
Donald G. Morosky (Pres)
Judy Hricak (Mgr-Mktg)

Division (Non-US):

Gannett Fleming Transit & Rail Systems (2)
Transit & Rail Engineering Services

Subsidiary (Domestic):

Gannett Fleming Valuation & Rate Consultants, LLC (2)
209 Senate Ave Ste 630, Camp Hill, PA 17011
Tel.: (717) 763-7211
Web Site: http://www.gfvrc.com
Utility Valuation & Rate Consultancy Services
N.A.I.C.S.: 541611
John J. Spanos (VP-Depreciation Valuation)
William Stout (CEO)
C. Richard Clarke (Dir-Western US Svcs)
Constance E. Heppenstall (Project Mgr)
Larry E. Kennedy (VP)
John F. Wiedmayer (Project Mgr)
Harold Walker III (Mgr-Fin Studies)

Branch (Domestic):

Gannett Fleming, Inc. - Baltimore (2)
7133 Rutherford Road Rutherford Plaza Bldg Ste 300, Baltimore, MD 21244-2718
Tel.: (443) 348-2017
Web Site: http://www.gannettfleming.com
Engineeering Services
N.A.I.C.S.: 541330
William M. Stout (Chm & CEO)

Division (Domestic):

Gannett Fleming, Inc. - GANCOM Division (2)
207 Senate Ave, Camp Hill, PA 17011
Tel.: (717) 763-7387
Web Site: http://www.gancom.com
Construction Industry Reprographics, Graphic Design, Digital Printing & Information Technology Support Services
N.A.I.C.S.: 541430
Suzanne Beshore (Mgr-Production)
Jim Marshall (Mgr-Graphics)

Gannett Fleming, Inc. - GeoDecisions Division (2)
207 Senate Ave, Camp Hill, PA 17011
Tel.: (717) 763-7211
Web Site: http://www.geodecisions.com
Emp.: 700
Computerized Mapping & Database Management Services
N.A.I.C.S.: 541370
Brendan Wesdock (Co-Pres)
Tom Saltzer (Co-Pres)
Kevin Switala (VP)
Ricardo Duarte (Mgr-Mktg)
David Gilbert (Sr Project Mgr)
Robert Marsters (Dir-Intl Bus)
Brian Smith (VP-Comml Solution)

Branch (Domestic):

Gannett Fleming, Inc. - Roseville (2)
2251 Douglas Blvd STE 200, Roseville, CA 95661
Tel.: (916) 677-4800
Web Site: https://www.gannettfleming.com
Construction & Engineering Services
N.A.I.C.S.: 541330

Tom Sell (Principal-Office & VP)

Gannett Fleming, Inc. - Tampa (Corporate Lake Drive), FL (2)
Westlake Corp Center Ste 150 9119 Corporate Lake Dr, Tampa, FL 33634-6323
Tel.: (813) 882-4366
Web Site: http://www.gannettfleming.com
Emp.: 20
Engineeering Services
N.A.I.C.S.: 541330
Art Hoffmann (Chief Admin Officer & Exec VP)
Judy Hricak (Chief Comm Officer & VP)
Jon Kessler (CFO & Exec VP)
Paula Loht (Mgr-Corp Safety)
Esther McGinnis (Exec VP)
Paul Nowicki (Pres & CEO)

Subsidiary (Domestic):

Innovative Engineering, Inc. (2)
5410 Mount Pisgah Rd, York, PA 17406
Tel.: (717) 252-4730
Web Site: http://www.ietc-team.com
Sales Range: $10-24.9 Million
Emp.: 24
Electrical Design-Build Contractor
N.A.I.C.S.: 238210
John Emenheiser (VP-Field Svcs)
Jeff Limm (CFO)
Christina Price (Coord-Mktg)
William N. Luddy (Founder & Pres)
Bill Bleacher (Project Mgr)
George Whitcomb (VP-Engrg & Testing)

L.G. Hetager Drilling, Inc. (2)
1857 Woodland Ave Ext, Punxsutawney, PA 15767-2833
Tel.: (814) 938-7370
Web Site: http://www.hetager.com
Sales Range: $10-24.9 Million
Emp.: 35
Drilling Services Contractor
N.A.I.C.S.: 238990
Kathleen Benson (VP)
Paul Hale (Pres & CEO)

TerraSure Development, LLC (2)
207 Senate Ave, Camp Hill, PA 17011
Tel.: (717) 763-7211
Web Site: http://www.terrasure.net
Real Estate Remediation Services
N.A.I.C.S.: 531390
Chen-Yu Yen (Chm)
Donald G. Morosky (Sr VP)
John A. Buchheit (VP & Dir-Program)
Brent R. Chapman (Dir-Bus Dev-Eastern)
Claudia Rosen (Dir-Bus Dev-Western)

TranSystems Corp. (2)
2400 Pershing Rd Ste 400, Kansas City, MO 64108
Tel.: (800) 800-5261
Web Site: http://www.transystems.com
Engineering & Architectural Services
N.A.I.C.S.: 488999
Richard Morsches (CEO)
Kevin Chafin (Sr VP)

Division (Domestic):

BCE Engineers, Inc. (3)
6021 12th St E Ste 200, Tacoma, WA 98424
Tel.: (253) 922-0446
Web Site: http://www.bceengineers.com
Rev: $4,000,000
Emp.: 50
Fiscal Year-end: 12/31/2009
Engineeering Services
N.A.I.C.S.: 541330
Scott Zimbelman (Principal)
Dave Newkirk (Mgr-Mktg)
Jeff Hardwick (Sr Engr-Mechanical)

Subsidiary (Domestic):

L. Robert Kimball & Associates, Inc. (3)
615 W Highland Ave, Ebensburg, PA 15931-1048
Tel.: (814) 472-7700
Web Site: http://www.lrkimball.com
Engineering, Architecture & Communications Technology Services
N.A.I.C.S.: 541310

SEPI Engineering & Construction, Inc. (3)
1025 Wade Ave, Raleigh, NC 27605
Tel.: (919) 789-9977
Web Site: http://www.sepiengineering.com
Sales Range: $1-9.9 Million
Emp.: 63
Engineeering Services
N.A.I.C.S.: 541330
Steven Thomas (COO)
Sean Clark (Mgr-Environmental Dept)
Barry S. Moose (VP)
Robert Kirk (Asst VP-Transportation & Mgr-Charlotte-Transportation)
Ben Crawford (Mgr-Roadway Design Dept)
Wendee Smith (Dir-Environmental)
Jeff Westmoreland (Mgr-Land Plng Dept)
Rick Edwards (CFO)
Jerry Beckman (VP)
Danny Gardner (Sr Project Mgr-Roadway)
Imad Younis (Sr Project Mgr-Roadway)
Brad Eagy (VP-Bus Dev)
Jonathan Persson (Mgr-Ops & Maintenance Dept)
Jennifer Allen (Chief Strategy Officer)

Division (Domestic):

Vertical Transportation Excellence (2)
1801 Market St Fl 26 Ste 2600, Philadelphia, PA 19103
Tel.: (215) 561-4201
Web Site: http://www.vtexcellence.com
Emp.: 3
Elevator & Escalator Contractor
N.A.I.C.S.: 238290
Patrick J. Welch (Pres)
David P. Hansen (Sr VP)
Kenneth G. Hamby (VP-Elevator & Escalator Projects)
Anthony J. DeFrancesco (VP-Phoenix)
Robert C. Keller (VP-New York City)

RMA Group, Inc. (1)
12130 Santa Margarita Ct, Rancho Cucamonga, CA 91730
Tel.: (909) 989-1751
Web Site: https://rmacompanies.com
Sales Range: $1-9.9 Million
Emp.: 135
Engineeering Services
N.A.I.C.S.: 541330
Duane E. Lyon (Chm)
Slawek Dymerski (VP & Mgr-Southern California Reg)

Subsidiary (Domestic):

A. J. Edmond Company (2)
1530 W 16th St, Long Beach, CA 90813
Tel.: (562) 437-1802
Web Site: http://www.ajedmondco.com
Petroleum Refineries Analytical & Sampling Services
N.A.I.C.S.: 541910
Jeffery G. Rolle (Pres)
Wayne Rolle (VP)
Jignesh Panchal (Dir-Technical)
Robert Brooks (Mgr-Laboratory)
Mark Wyborney (Mgr-Laboratory)
Christopher Marsh (Mgr-Ops)
Gilbert Marquez (Dir-Lab Ops)

A3GEO, Inc. (2)
821 Bancroft Way, Berkeley, CA 94710
Tel.: (415) 425-0247
Web Site: http://www.a3geo.com
Testing Laboratories
N.A.I.C.S.: 541380
Dona Kelly (Pres)

Black Eagle Consulting, Inc. (2)
1345 Capital Blvd Ste A, Reno, NV 89502
Tel.: (775) 359-6600
Web Site: http://www.blackeagleconsulting.com
Sales Range: $1-9.9 Million
Emp.: 30
Engineering Services
N.A.I.C.S.: 541330
David Russell (Mgr-Construction Svcs Project)
Mitch Fink (Mgr-Construction Svcs Project)
Anna Dapra (Mgr-Laboratory)
Remo U. Osmetti (Treas & Sec)
Russell Bliss (Project Mgr)
Shane Cocking (Mgr-Quality Control Div)
Shaun A. Smith (Pres)
Vimal P. Vimalaraj (Mgr-Engrg Div)

Pri Asphalt Technologies, Inc. (2)

OCEANSOUND PARTNERS, LP

OceanSound Partners, LP—(Continued)

6408 Badger Dr, Tampa, FL 33610
Tel.: (813) 621-5777
Web Site: http://www.priasphalt.com
Sales Range: $1-9.9 Million
Emp.: 30
Business Services Testing Laboratory
N.A.I.C.S.: 541990
Kenneth Grzybowski (Pres)
Abdalla Al-Rawashdeh (Mgr-Lab)

Rone Engineering Services, LLC (2)
8908 Ambassador Row, Dallas, TX 75247
Tel.: (214) 630-9745
Web Site: http://www.roneengineers.com
Rev.: $1,760,000
Emp.: 10
Research & Development in Biotechnology
N.A.I.C.S.: 541714
Ken Riner (Mgr)

Smartronix, LLC (1)
44150 Smartronix Way, Hollywood, MD 20636
Tel.: (301) 373-6000
Web Site: http://www.smartronix.com
Sales Range: $10-24.9 Million
Emp.: 500
Computer Software Development
N.A.I.C.S.: 541715
Joe Gerczak (CFO & Exec VP)
Rick Kelley (Dir-Tech)
Sean McCarron (VP-Sls)
Spencer Colson (Dir-Sls)

Subsidiary (Domestic):

Datastrong, LLC (2)
8315 Lee Hwy Ste 300, Fairfax, VA 22031-2215
Tel.: (703) 992-9822
Web Site: http://www.datastrong.com
Computer System Design Services
N.A.I.C.S.: 541512
Christian Zax (CEO)

OCEANSTAR INTERNATIONAL INC.

3957 NW 126 Ave, Coral Springs, FL 33065
Tel.: (954) 753-4533
Web Site: http://www.osishipping.com
Year Founded: 2007
Sales Range: $1-9.9 Million
Emp.: 14
Freight Transportation
N.A.I.C.S.: 488510
Josh Morales (Pres & CEO)

OCENTURE LLC

6440 Southpoint Pkwy Ste 300, Jacksonville, FL 32216
Tel.: (904) 766-1600
Web Site: http://www.ocenture.com
Year Founded: 2000
Sales Range: $10-24.9 Million
Emp.: 20
Digital Security Solutions
N.A.I.C.S.: 541519

OCHIN, INC.

1881 SW Naito Pkwy, Portland, OR 97201
Tel.: (503) 943-2500   OR
Web Site: http://www.ochin.org
Year Founded: 2003
Sales Range: $25-49.9 Million
Emp.: 216
Health Care Srvices
N.A.I.C.S.: 622110
Abby Sears (CEO)
Kim Klupenger (VP-Partnerships & Relationships)
Paul Matthews (CTO)
Phil Lamb (Treas)
Denise Honzel (Chm)
Mario Gutierrez (Sec)
Josh Lemieux (VP-Dev & Foundation Engagement)
Sean Whiteley-Ross (CFO)
Yedda Trawick (COO)

Scott Fields (Chief Medical Officer & Chief Medical Informatics Officer)
Kevin Geoffroy (VP-Mktg)
Clayton Gillett (VP- Data Svcs & Integration)
Jennifer Stoll (VP-Govt & Pub Affairs)

OCHOA AG UNLIMITED FOODS, INC.

9660 W State St, Star, ID 83669
Tel.: (208) 343-6882   WA
Sales Range: $25-49.9 Million
Emp.: 210
Potato Farming; Frozen Potatoes Mfr
N.A.I.C.S.: 111211

OCHOCO LUMBER COMPANY

200 SE Coombs Flat Rd, Prineville, OR 97754-2549
Tel.: (541) 447-6296   OR
Web Site: http://www.ochocolumber.com
Year Founded: 1938
Sales Range: $75-99.9 Million
Emp.: 100
Lumber Mfr
N.A.I.C.S.: 321113
Bruce Daucsavage (Pres & CEO)
Donna Barnes (Mgr-Acctg)

Subsidiaries:

Deschutes Pine Sales, Inc. (1)
19810 Village Office Ct, Bend, OR 97702
Tel.: (541) 389-5000
Web Site: http://www.deschutespine.com
Wood Products Whslr
N.A.I.C.S.: 423310

Malheur Lumber Company (1)
60339 W Highway 26, John Day, OR 97845
Tel.: (541) 575-1148
Web Site: http://www.ochocolumber.com
Wood Products Mfr
N.A.I.C.S.: 321999

OCHS OIL COMPANY

1321 Distribution Way, Vista, CA 92081
Tel.: (760) 599-9572
Web Site: http://www.ochsoil.com
Sales Range: $10-24.9 Million
Emp.: 8
Service Station Supplies, Petroleum
N.A.I.C.S.: 424720
Travis Becktel (VP)

OCHSNER HEALTH SYSTEM

1514 Jefferson Hwy, New Orleans, LA 70121-2406
Tel.: (504) 842-3000
Web Site: http://www.ochsner.org
Sales Range: $500-549.9 Million
Emp.: 12,000
Wealth Management Services
N.A.I.C.S.: 622110
William McDade (Chief Academic Officer & Exec VP)
Robert I. Hart (Chief Medical Officer & Exec VP)
Pete November (Pres & CEO)
Andy Wisdom (Chm)

Subsidiaries:

Ochsner Medical Center-North Shore LLC (1)
100 Medical Ctr Dr, Slidell, LA 70461
Tel.: (985) 649-7070
Web Site: http://www.ochsner.org
Sales Range: $50-74.9 Million
Hospital
N.A.I.C.S.: 622110
Polly Davenport (CEO)

OCHSNER SYSTEM PROTECTION COMPANY

1514 Jefferson Hwy, New Orleans, LA 70121
Tel.: (504) 842-3400   LA

Web Site: http://www.ochsner.org
Year Founded: 2009
Sales Range: $1-9.9 Million
Insurer Association
N.A.I.C.S.: 813910
Warner L. Thomas (COO & VP)
Cristina R. Wheat (Sec)
Scott J. Posecai (CFO & VP)
Bobby C. Brannon (Treas & VP)

OCI INC.

2561 Memorial Blvd, Connellsville, PA 15425
Tel.: (724) 628-9580
Rev.: $23,000,000
Emp.: 10
Petroleum Bulk Stations
N.A.I.C.S.: 424710
Edward Franks (Pres)

OCKERLUND INDUSTRIES, INC.

1555 W Wrightwood Ct, Addison, IL 60101
Tel.: (630) 620-1269
Sales Range: $10-24.9 Million
Emp.: 45
Corrugated & Solid Fiber Box Mfr
N.A.I.C.S.: 322211
Stan Joray (Dir-Info Sys)
Guy Ockerlund (Owner)

OCMULGEE ELECTRIC MEMBERSHIP CORPORATION

5722 Eastman St, Eastman, GA 31023
Tel.: (478) 374-7001
Web Site: http://www.ocmulgeeemc.com
Year Founded: 1938
Sales Range: $10-24.9 Million
Electric Power Distr
N.A.I.C.S.: 221122
Barry H. Martin (Pres)
Charles M. Pittman (Treas & Sec)
John T. Woodard Jr. (VP)

OCMULGEE FIELDS INC.

131 Holiday Dr N, Macon, GA 31210
Tel.: (478) 471-2520
Web Site: http://www.ocmulgee.net
Sales Range: $25-49.9 Million
Emp.: 50
Subdividers & Developers
N.A.I.C.S.: 237210
Dwight Jones (Pres)
Pam Stewart (Office Mgr)

OCONEE ELECTRIC MEMBERSHIP

3445 Hwy 80 W, Dudley, GA 31022
Tel.: (478) 676-3191
Web Site: http://www.oconeeemc.com
Rev.: $17,059,050
Emp.: 50
Distribution, Electric Power
N.A.I.C.S.: 221122
Marty Smith (Pres & CEO)
Terri Howard (VP-Admin)
Robert Harrison (Dir-Pur & Safety)

OCONEE STATE BANK

35 N Main St, Watkinsville, GA 30677
Tel.: (706) 769-6611
Web Site: http://www.oconeestatebank.com
Sales Range: $10-24.9 Million
Emp.: 82
Provider of Banking Services
N.A.I.C.S.: 522110
John A. Hale (Vice Chm)
Virginia S. Wells (Vice Chm)
Neil Stevens (Pres & CEO)
Jim McLemore (CFO)

U.S. PRIVATE

OCONTO ELECTRIC COOPERATIVE

PO Box 168, Oconto Falls, WI 54154
Tel.: (920) 846-2816   WI
Web Site: http://www.ocontoelectric.com
Year Founded: 1936
Sales Range: $10-24.9 Million
Emp.: 41
Electric Energy Distribution Services
N.A.I.C.S.: 221122

OCP CONTRACTORS, INC.

1740 Commerce Rd, Holland, OH 43528
Tel.: (419) 865-7168
Web Site: http://www.ocp-contractors.com
Year Founded: 1968
Sales Range: $50-74.9 Million
Emp.: 347
Metal Stud Framing & Drywall Services
N.A.I.C.S.: 238310
Matthew Townsend (Pres)
Jeff Townsend (COO)
Ed Sellers (Pres)
Gerry Barr (Project Mgr)
Pamela Hepburn (VP)
Jeffrey Feller (Superintendent)
Sandy Webb (Mgr-Bus)
Jeff Whitey (Mgr-Warehouse)

OCTAGON HOLDINGS, LLC

267 5th Ave Ste 800, New York, NY 10016
Tel.: (212) 683-8811
Year Founded: 1997
Privater Equity Firm
N.A.I.C.S.: 523999

Subsidiaries:

Octagon Automotive, LLC (1)
25601 Hercules St Unit G, Valencia, CA 91355
Tel.: (323) 869-2299
Web Site: http://www.manik.com
Sales Range: $25-49.9 Million
Emp.: 200
Motor Vehicle Parts & Accessories Mfr
N.A.I.C.S.: 336390

OCTAGON RESOURCES INC.

2421 Wilcox Dr, Norman, OK 73069-3956
Tel.: (405) 366-0032
Web Site: http://www.octagonresources.com
Sales Range: $75-99.9 Million
Emp.: 6
Crude Petroleum & Natural Gas
N.A.I.C.S.: 211120
Brian Theriault (VP)

OCTANE ENERGY, LLC

310 W Wall St Ste 810, Midland, TX 79701
Tel.: (432) 685-7736
Web Site: http://www.octane-energy.com
Year Founded: 2013
Sales Range: $10-24.9 Million
Emp.: 75
Energy Consulting Services
N.A.I.C.S.: 541690
Jared Blong (Co-Founder, Pres & CEO)
Joe Cervantes (Co-Founder & Exec VP)
Deane Durham (VP-Ops)
Lori Merritt Blong (Co-Founder & Exec VP)

OCTAVUS GROUP LLC

37 Water St, Excelsior, MN 55331
Tel.: (952) 767-2920

Web Site:
http://www.octavusgroup.com
Investment Banking & Securities Dealing
N.A.I.C.S.: 523150
Jon C. Essen (COO)
Vukovich Thomas (Dir-Internal Sls)

Subsidiaries:

LoCorr Fund Management LLC (1)
687 Excelsior Blvd, Excelsior, MN 55331
Web Site: http://www.locorrfunds.com
Privater Equity Firm
N.A.I.C.S.: 523999
Kevin Kinzie (CEO)

OCTEX LLC
901 Sarasota Center Blvd, Sarasota, FL 34240
Tel.: (941) 371-6767   FL
Web Site: http://www.octex360.com
Year Founded: 1990
Sales Range: $10-24.9 Million
Emp.: 80
Precision Injection Molded Plastics Components
N.A.I.C.S.: 326199
Dan Mallon (Controller)
James Westman (Pres & CEO)
Steve Marquis (Mgr-Tooling)
Matt Mastromatteo (Engr-Sls)
Dorin Moon (Mgr-Quality & Regulatory Affairs)
Dave Dimmer (Mgr-Bus Dev)

OCTOPI BREWING, LLC
1131 Uniek Dr, Waunakee, WI 53597
Tel.: (608) 620-4705
Web Site:
http://www.octopibrewing.com
Year Founded: 2014
Sales Range: $1-9.9 Million
Emp.: 36
Beverage Product Mfr & Distr
N.A.I.C.S.: 312140
Isaac Showaki (Pres)

OCUSOFT, INC.
30444 SW Freeway, Rosenberg, TX 77471
Tel.: (281) 342-3350
Web Site: http://www.ocusoft.com
Year Founded: 1986
Sales Range: $10-24.9 Million
Emp.: 95
Soap & Detergent Mfr
N.A.I.C.S.: 325611
Cynthia L. Barratt (Co-Founder, Co-Chm & CEO)
Nat G. Adkins Jr. (Co-Founder & Co-Chm)

ODA PRIMARY HEALTH CARE NETWORK
14-16 Heyward St, Brooklyn, NY 11211
Tel.: (718) 260-4600   NY
Web Site: http://www.odahealth.org
Year Founded: 1974
Sales Range: $10-24.9 Million
Emp.: 230
Health Care Srvices
N.A.I.C.S.: 622110
Joel Kestenbaum (COO)
Joseph Deutsch (CEO)
Lennie Trainer (Dir-Fin)

ODD FELLOWS HOME OF PENNSYLVANIA
999 W Harrisburg Pike, Middletown, PA 17057
Tel.: (717) 944-3351   PA
Web Site:
http://www.middletownhome.org
Year Founded: 1875
Sales Range: $10-24.9 Million

Elder Care Services
N.A.I.C.S.: 623312
Lu Ann Ishaq (Dir-Fin)
Andrea Henney (Dir-Personal Care & Independent Living)
Patti A. Obenstine (Dir-Nutritional Svcs)
Sara Gigliotti (Dir-Clinical Resources)
Amanda L. McEvoy (Dir-Nursing)
Allison Slesser (Dir-Admissions & Medical Records)
Diana D. Oliver (Dir-HR)
Mary Ann Sluzis (Dir-Community Life)
Louis Vogel III (CEO)

ODDCAST, INC.
25 W 36th St 5th Fl, New York, NY 10018
Tel.: (212) 375-6290
Web Site: http://www.oddcast.com
Year Founded: 1999
Sales Range: $1-9.9 Million
Emp.: 20
Software Publisher
N.A.I.C.S.: 513210
Gil Sideman (CEO)

ODELL PUBLISHING INC
3200 Heartland Dr, Liberty, MO 64068
Tel.: (816) 781-2626
Web Site: http://www.odpub2.com
Rev.: $25,000,000
Emp.: 55
Offset Printing
N.A.I.C.S.: 323111
Dan Odell (Pres)
Jim Prodder (CFO)

ODEN MARKETING AND DESIGN
119 S Main St Ste 300, Memphis, TN 38103
Tel.: (901) 578-8055
Year Founded: 1971
Sales Range: $10-24.9 Million
Emp.: 60
N.A.I.C.S.: 541810
Bret A. Terwilleger (COO & Principal)
Tina Lazarini Niclosi (Principal & Exec VP)
Jeff Blankenship (VP & Assoc Dir-Creative)
Todd Strickland (CFO & VP)
Jamie Smith (Sr Acct Mgr)
Ashley Livingston (Sr Dir-Mktg-Digital)
Kate Stratman (Mgr-Stewardship Brand)
Colleen Wells (Dir-Writing)
Samantha Tweddell (Acct Mgr)
William F. Carkeet Jr. (CEO & Principal)

ODESSA UNION WAREHOUSE CO-OP
N2 Division St, Odessa, WA 99159
Tel.: (509) 982-2691
Web Site:
http://www.odessaunion.com
Sales Range: $10-24.9 Million
Emp.: 11
Grain Elevator, Storage Only
N.A.I.C.S.: 493130
Keith Bailey (Gen Mgr)

ODESUS INC.
11766 Wilshire Blvd Ste 400, Los Angeles, CA 90025-6551
Tel.: (310) 473-4600
Web Site: http://www.odesus.com
Year Founded: 2001
Sales Range: $10-24.9 Million
Emp.: 90
IT Staffing & Consulting Services
N.A.I.C.S.: 561311

Robert P. Michaels (Pres & CEO)

ODIN BREWING CO.
402 Baker Blvd, Tukwila, WA 98188
Tel.: (206) 241-1013
Web Site:
http://www.odinbrewing.wordpress.com
Brewery
N.A.I.C.S.: 312120
Daniel Lee (Owner)

Subsidiaries:

Hilliard's Beer (1)
1550 NW 49th St, Seattle, WA 98107-4731
Tel.: (206) 257-4486
Web Site: http://www.hilliardsbeer.com
Breweries
N.A.I.C.S.: 312120
Ryan Hilliard (Owner)

ODL INCORPORATED
215 E Roosevelt Ave, Zeeland, MI 49464-1239
Tel.: (616) 772-9111   MI
Web Site: http://www.odl.com
Year Founded: 1948
Sales Range: $150-199.9 Million
Emp.: 500
Building Product Mfr
N.A.I.C.S.: 321918
Scott Harder (VP-Sls & Mktg)
Jaclyn Harrison (Exec VP-HR)
David Klein (Pres & COO)

Subsidiaries:

ODL Europe Ltd. (1)
1 Brook Road, Bootle, L20 4XP, Liverpool, United Kingdom
Tel.: (44) 151 933 0299
Web Site: http://www.odleurope.com
Emp.: 37
Glass Products Mfr
N.A.I.C.S.: 327215
Nathan Barr (Gen Mgr)

ODNEY
1400 W Century Ave, Bismarck, ND 58503
Tel.: (701) 222-8721   ND
Web Site: http://www.odney.com
Year Founded: 1985
Rev.: $15,000,000
Emp.: 44
N.A.I.C.S.: 541810
Patrick Finken (Pres)
Michael Bruner (Dir-Creative-Corp)
Susan Moser (Dir-Ops)
Mike Pierce (Dir-Interactive)
Cindy Dupaul-Vogelsang (Dir-Media)
Marnie Piehl (Dir-Pub Relations)
Trish Helgeson (Dir-Acct Svcs)
Troy White (Gen Mgr-Fargo)
Brekka Kramer (Gen Mgr)

Subsidiaries:

Odney Advertising-Fargo (1)
102 Broadway, Fargo, ND 58102
Tel.: (701) 451-9028
Web Site: http://www.odney.com
Sales Range: $10-24.9 Million
N.A.I.C.S.: 541810
Kelly Heyer (Acct Exec)
Troy White (Gen Mgr & Acct Exec)

Odney Advertising-Minot (1)
7 3rd St SE Ste 101, Minot, ND 58701
Tel.: (701) 857-7205
Web Site: http://www.odney.com
Emp.: 10
N.A.I.C.S.: 541810
Brekka Kramer (Gen Mgr)
Dusty Zimmerman (Acct Exec)

ODOM CONSTRUCTION SERVICES, INC.
3601 Executive Blvd, Mesquite, TX 75149
Tel.: (972) 289-4447   TX

Year Founded: 1995
Sales Range: $10-24.9 Million
Emp.: 119
Commercial & Institutional Building Construction Services
N.A.I.C.S.: 236220
Veronica Odom (Pres)

ODW LOGISTICS INC.
400 W Nationwide Blvd Ste 200, Columbus, OH 43215
Tel.: (614) 549-5000
Web Site:
http://www.odwlogistics.com
Year Founded: 1972
Sales Range: $10-24.9 Million
Emp.: 400
General Warehousing Services
N.A.I.C.S.: 493110
Robert E. Ness (Founder)
Jon Petticrew (VP-Ops)
Jeff Clark (Exec VP)
David L. Hill (CFO)
John R. Ness (Pres & CEO)
Robin Lynch (VP-HR)
Todd Alloway (VP-Sls-ODW & Dist-Trans)
Ted Nikolai (Co-CFO)
John Guggenbiller (Pres)
Kerry Wilkinson (VP-HR)
Macy Bergoon (VP-IT)
Albert Campbell (Co-CFO)
Lee Kirk (COO)

ODYNE CORP.
89 Cabot Ct Ste L, Hauppauge, NY 11788
Tel.: (631) 750-1010
Propulsion System Mfr
N.A.I.C.S.: 336412
Alan Tannenbaum (CEO)

ODYSSEY DEVELOPMENT, INC.
227 W 1st St #650, Duluth, MN 55802
Tel.: (218) 728-8060   MN
Web Site:
http://www.odysseyresorts.com
Year Founded: 2003
Emp.: 320
Real Estate Developers
N.A.I.C.S.: 237210
Robert L. Ryan (CEO)

ODYSSEY ENTERPRISES, INC.
150 Nickerson St Ste 300, Seattle, WA 98109
Tel.: (206) 285-7445
Web Site:
http://www.odysseyseafood.com
Year Founded: 1981
Sales Range: $125-149.9 Million
Emp.: 220
Frozen Fish & Seafood Whslr
N.A.I.C.S.: 424420
Peter V. Cardone (Co-Founder & Partner)
Joel Skerlong (Partner)
Phil Crean (Partner)
R. Paul Adams (CFO & Partner)
Alexa Melendez (Plant Mgr)
Kathy Mills (Office Mgr & Coord-Production)
Barbara Earle Ballard (Pres)

Subsidiaries:

Northwest Seafood Processors, Inc. (1)
206 SW Michigan St, Seattle, WA 98106
Tel.: (206) 762-7256
Sales Range: $25-49.9 Million
Emp.: 150
Fresh & Frozen Seafood Processing
N.A.I.C.S.: 311710

ODYSSEY HOUSE

Odyssey House—(Continued)

ODYSSEY HOUSE
120 Wall St, New York, NY 10005
Tel.: (212) 361-1600 NY
Web Site:
http://www.odysseyhouseinc.org
Year Founded: 1967
Sales Range: $25-49.9 Million
Emp.: 398
Behavioral Healthcare Services
N.A.I.C.S.: 623220
Colleen Beagen *(VP & Dir-HR)*
Durga Vallabhaneni *(Chief Fin & Admin Officer & Sr VP)*
Justin Mitchell *(VP & Dir-Adult Residential Svcs)*
John Tavolacci *(COO & Exec VP)*

ODYSSEY INVESTMENT PARTNERS, LLC
590 Madison Ave 39th Fl, New York, NY 10022
Tel.: (212) 351-7900 NY
Web Site:
http://www.odysseyinvestment.com
Year Founded: 1997
Privater Equity Firm
N.A.I.C.S.: 523999
William F. Hopkins *(Co-Founder & Vice Chm)*
Brian Kwait *(Co-Founder & CEO)*
Doug Hitchner *(COO & Mng Principal)*
Stephen Berger *(Co-Founder & Chm)*
Jeffrey McKibben *(Sr Mng Principal)*
Craig Staub *(Sr Mng Principal)*
Dennis Moore *(Mng Principal)*
Jason Cowett *(Mng Principal)*
Brian Zaumeyer *(Mng Principal)*
Daniel Tiemann *(Mng Principal & Head-Portfolio Ops)*
Jeffrey Moffett *(Mng Principal)*
Jonathan Place *(Mng Principal)*
Matt Brown *(Principal)*
Vivian Hadis *(Chief Compliance Officer & Gen Counsel)*
Jennifer L. Rogg *(Mng Principal-Capital Raising & Head-IR)*
Henry Bendit *(Principal)*
Tom Cutting *(Principal)*
Jeff Chaney *(VP)*
Rob Denious *(Principal)*
David Napoletan *(VP)*
Bill Schwartz *(Principal)*
Teresa Paggi *(Controller)*

Subsidiaries:

Addison Professional Financial Search LLC (1)
125 S Wacker Dr, Chicago, IL 60606
Tel.: (312) 424-0300
Web Site: http://www.addisongroup.com
Staffing Services
N.A.I.C.S.: 541612
Thomas B. Moran *(CEO)*
Steve Wolfe *(Exec VP-Ops & Admin)*
Michael Samuels *(CFO)*
Allison Betancourt *(VP-People Strategy)*
Ed Kavanagh *(Pres-HR & Admin)*
Kelly Gorham *(Pres-Healthcare)*
Phil Gaddis *(Pres-Fin & Acctg Direct Hire)*
Jay Houston *(Pres-Fin & Acctg Contract)*
J. David Morgan *(Pres-IT & Engrng)*
Steve Levenkron *(CIO)*

Subsidiary (Domestic):

Bridgepoint Consulting LLC (2)
8310 N Capital of Texas Hwy Bldg 1 Ste 420, Austin, TX 78731
Tel.: (512) 437-7900
Web Site:
http://www.bridgepointconsulting.com
Emp.: 140
Management Consulting Services
N.A.I.C.S.: 541618
Robert Smith *(Co-Founder & Principal)*
Monica Gill *(Principal)*

Jeff Hiddemen *(Mng Dir-NetSuite Consulting)*
Gina Budd *(Mng Dir-Mktg)*
Kenneth Kase Conte *(Dir-Turnaround & Restructuring Practice-Dallas)*
Bill Patterson *(Principal & Head-Turnaround & Dispute)*
Karen Nicolaou *(Dir-Turnaround & Dispute Resolution Practice-Houston)*
Pete Pearson *(Dir-Startup Svcs Practice)*
Michael Johnson *(Mng Principal)*
Vince Trevino *(Principal)*
Manuel Azuara *(Mng Principal)*
David Roe *(Mng Dir-Risk Svcs)*
Karen Mellon *(Dir-Fin)*
Dawn Ragan *(Mng Dir)*
Vijay George *(Dir-Tech Consulting Practice)*
Ricky Berens *(Mgr-Bus Dev)*
Scott Gardner *(CFO)*

DLC Inc. (2)
21800 Oxnard St Ste 980, Woodland Hills, CA 91367
Tel.: (888) 957-3400
Web Site: http://www.dlcinc.com
Rev.: $28,800,000
Emp.: 164
Consulting Firm
N.A.I.C.S.: 541611
Thomas F. Sweeney *(CEO)*
Kerry Heiple *(Dir-Client Svcs-Chicago)*
Sonata Taman *(Dir-Client Svcs-Los Angeles)*
Sarina Kaye *(CFO)*
Sara Vigeland *(VP-Human Capital)*
Alexandra Von Tiergarten *(Sr VP)*

Harmony Healthcare, LLC (2)
2909 W Bay to Bay Blvd Ste 500, Tampa, FL 33629
Tel.: (813) 369-5159
Sales Range: $10-24.9 Million
Emp.: 312
Healthcare Staffing Services
N.A.I.C.S.: 541612
Christopher H. G. Brown *(Founder)*
Rita E. Cuellar *(Mgr-Fin Analysis & Plng)*
Cindy Kell *(Dir-Ops)*
Taylor Kolligs *(VP-Recruitment Solutions)*
John Bilello *(CFO)*
Brandon Martin *(VP-Client Solutions)*
Cyndi Thomas *(Chief Dev Officer)*
Bilal Mushtaq *(Chief Medical Officer)*
Randy Verdino *(CEO)*
Lisa Knowles *(Sr Dir-Client Solutions)*

HireStrategy, Inc. (2)
1875 Explorer St, Reston, VA 20190
Tel.: (703) 547-6700
Web Site: http://www.hirestrategy.com
Sales Range: $1-9.9 Million
Job Placement & Executive Recruitment Services
N.A.I.C.S.: 561320
Chris Vennitti *(Pres)*
Eric Klein *(Sr VP-IT Contract)*
Dan Connors *(Sr VP-Fin & Acctg Search)*
Jennifer Wright Simpson *(Sr VP-HR & Admin Staffing)*
Adam Lederer *(Sr VP-Fin & Acctg)*

HireSynergy, Inc. (2)
1001 McKinney Ste 1075, Houston, TX 77002
Tel.: (713) 222-7667
Web Site: http://www.addisongroup.com
Sales Range: $10-24.9 Million
Accounting, Finance & IT Personnel Recruitment Services
N.A.I.C.S.: 561311
Tom Moran *(CEO)*

Mondo (2)
102 Madison Ave 7th Fl, New York, NY 10016
Tel.: (212) 257-5111
Web Site: http://www.mondo.com
Sales Range: $25-49.9 Million
Emp.: 70
IT & Digital Staffing Agency
N.A.I.C.S.: 561311
Michael Kirven *(Founder & Chm)*
Tim Johnson *(CEO)*
Scott Zannini *(Mgr-Sls-Atlanta)*
Stephen Zafarino *(Mgr-Recruiting)*

Applied Technical Services, Inc. (1)
1190 Atlanta Industrial Dr, Marietta, GA 30066
Tel.: (770) 423-1400

Web Site: http://www.atsnetworks.com
Rev.: $4,700,000
Emp.: 175
Testing Laboratories
N.A.I.C.S.: 541380
Jim Hills *(Pres)*

Avtron Aerospace, Inc. (1)
7900 E Pleasant Valley Rd, Cleveland, OH 44131-5529
Tel.: (216) 750-5152
Web Site: http://www.avtronaero.com
Aerospace Testing Equipment Mfr
N.A.I.C.S.: 334515
Charles Gareis *(Aerospace Project Mgr)*

Barcodes, Inc (1)
200 W Monroe St, Chicago, IL 60606
Tel.: (312) 588-5960
Web Site: http://www.barcodesinc.com
Reseller of Automatic Identification & Data Capture Products, Including Mobile Computers, RFID Tags & Barcode Equipment
N.A.I.C.S.: 423440

Subsidiary (Domestic):

Alpha Card Systems, LLC (2)
17858 SW Uppr Boones Ferry Rd, Portland, OR 97224-7011
Tel.: (877) 740-9489
Web Site: http://www.alphacard.com
Photographic Equipment & Supplies Merchant Whslr
N.A.I.C.S.: 423410
Dusty Poole *(Dir-Ops, Customer Svc & Mgr-Tech)*

M S A Systems, Inc. (2)
1340 S De Anza Blvd Ste 103, San Jose, CA 95129-4644
Tel.: (714) 634-8700
Web Site: http://www.msasys.com
Sales Range: $1-9.9 Million
Emp.: 15
Custom Computer Programming Services
N.A.I.C.S.: 541511
Joe Wigton *(Mgr)*

Plasco, LLC (2)
5830 NW 163rd St, Miami Lakes, FL 33014
Tel.: (305) 625-4222
Web Site: http://www.plascoid.com
Emp.: 53
Identification & Card-Based Technology Solutions
N.A.I.C.S.: 541512
Alan D. Mendelson *(Pres & CEO)*

CPI International, Inc. (1)
811 Hansen Way, Palo Alto, CA 94304-1031
Tel.: (650) 846-2900
Web Site: http://www.cpii.com
Designs & Manufactures Satellite Communications Amplifiers & Medical X-Ray Generators
N.A.I.C.S.: 334220
Laura Kowalchik *(CFO)*
O. Joe Caldarelli *(Vice Chm)*
Robert A. Fickett *(CEO)*
Andrew C. Ivers *(Pres & COO)*

Division (Domestic):

CPI Malibu Division (2)
3760-A Calle Tecate, Camarillo, CA 93012-5060
Tel.: (805) 383-1829
Web Site: http://www.cpii.com
Designer & Mfr Antenna Systems (for Radar)
N.A.I.C.S.: 334290

Subsidiary (Domestic):

Communications & Power Industries LLC (2)
811 Hansen Way, Palo Alto, CA 94304-1031
Tel.: (650) 846-2900
Web Site: http://www.cpii.com
Communication Equipment Mfr
N.A.I.C.S.: 334220

Subsidiary (Domestic):

CPI ESSCO INC. (3)
90 Nemco Way Ste 1, Ayer, MA 01432
Tel.: (978) 568-5100
Web Site: https://www.cpii.com

U.S. PRIVATE

Ground-Based & Shipboard Radomes & Millimeter Wave Antenna Systems
N.A.I.C.S.: 517810

Subsidiary (Non-US):

L-3 Communications ESSCO Collins Ltd. (4)
Kilkishen, Shannon, Co Clare, Ireland
Tel.: (353) 61367244
Web Site: http://www.indigo.ie
Sales Range: $10-24.9 Million
Emp.: 30
Antenna Systems
N.A.I.C.S.: 334290
Jim Forde *(Mng Dir)*

Subsidiary (Domestic):

CPI Locus Microwave, Inc. (3)
176 Technology Dr Ste 200, Boalsburg, PA 16827
Tel.: (814) 466-6275
Web Site: http://www.cpi.com
Communication Equipment Mfr
N.A.I.C.S.: 334220
Dana Wilt *(Pres & Dir-Engrg)*

CPI Radant Technologies Division Inc. (3)
255 Hudson Rd, Stow, MA 01775-1446
Tel.: (978) 562-3866
Web Site: http://www.cpii.com
Communication Equipment Mfr
N.A.I.C.S.: 334220

Subsidiary (Domestic):

AdamWorks, LLC (4)
7367 S Revere Pkwy Bldg Unit 2, Centennial, CO 80112-6751
Tel.: (303) 200-6655
Web Site: http://www.adamworksinc.com
Plastics Product Mfr
N.A.I.C.S.: 326199

Subsidiary (Domestic):

CPI Satcom & Antenna Technologies Inc. (3)
4825 River Green Pkwy, Duluth, GA 30096
Tel.: (770) 497-8800
Wireless Communication Equipment Mfr
N.A.I.C.S.: 334220

Subsidiary (Non-US):

Communications & Power Industries Canada Inc. (3)
45 River Drive, Georgetown, L7G 2J4, ON, Canada
Tel.: (905) 877-0161
Web Site: http://www.cpii.com
Communication Equipment Mfr
N.A.I.C.S.: 334220

Division (Domestic):

Communications & Power Industries LLC - Beverly Microwave Division (3)
150 Sohier Rd, Beverly, MA 01915-5536
Tel.: (978) 922-6000
Web Site: http://www.cpii.com
Communication Equipment Mfr
N.A.I.C.S.: 334220

Division (Non-US):

Communications & Power Industries LLC - Communications & Medical Products Division (3)
45 River Drive, Georgetown, L7G 2J4, ON, Canada
Tel.: (905) 877-0161
Web Site: http://www.cpii.com
Communication Equipment Mfr
N.A.I.C.S.: 334220

Division (Domestic):

Communications & Power Industries LLC - Econco Division (3)
1318 Commerce Ave, Woodland, CA 95776-5908
Tel.: (530) 662-7553
Web Site: http://www.cpii.com
Communication Equipment Mfr
N.A.I.C.S.: 334220

COMPANIES — ODYSSEY INVESTMENT PARTNERS, LLC

Communications & Power Industries LLC - Microwave Power Products Division (3)
811 Hansen Way, Palo Alto, CA 94304-1015
Tel.: (650) 846-3900
Web Site: http://www.cpii.com
Communication Equipment Mfr
N.A.I.C.S.: 334220
Robert A. Fickett (Pres)

Division (Non-US):

Communications & Power Industries LLC - Satcom East Division (3)
45 River Drive, Georgetown, L7G 2J4, ON, Canada
Tel.: (905) 877-0161
Web Site: http://www.cpii.com
Communication Equipment Mfr
N.A.I.C.S.: 334220

Division (Domestic):

Communications & Power Industries LLC - Satcom West Division (3)
811 Hansen Way, Palo Alto, CA 94304-1031
Tel.: (650) 846-2801
Web Site: http://www.cpii.com
Communication Equipment Mfr
N.A.I.C.S.: 334220

Subsidiary (Domestic):

Orbital Systems, Ltd. (3)
3807 Carbon Rd, Irving, TX 75038-3415
Tel.: (972) 915-3669
Web Site: http://www.orbitalsystems.com
Communication Equipment Mfr
N.A.I.C.S.: 334290
Carl Schoeneberger (Pres)

Cross Country Infrastructure Services, Inc. (1)
2251 Rifle St, Aurora, CO 80011
Tel.: (303) 361-6797
Web Site: http://www.crosscountryis.com
Pipeline Construction Equipment, Tools & Supplies Whslr
N.A.I.C.S.: 423810
Steve Miner (Dir-Pipeline Equipment & Services)

Integrated Power Services LLC (1)
250 Executive Ctr Dr Ste 201, Greenville, SC 29615
Tel.: (864) 451-5600
Web Site: http://www.ips.us
Emp.: 25
Motor & Generator Repair Services
N.A.I.C.S.: 811310
John Zuleger (Pres & CEO)

Subsidiary (Domestic):

Precision Electric Motor Works, Inc. (2)
18 Sebago St, Clifton, NJ 07013
Tel.: (973) 471-2600
Web Site: http://www.precisionmotors.net
Sales Range: $1-9.9 Million
Emp.: 12
Electrical Repair Shops, Nsk
N.A.I.C.S.: 811210
Peter Zielonka (Pres)

Magna Legal Services (1)
1635 Market St Ste 800, Philadelphia, PA 19103-2206
Tel.: (312) 214-3110
Web Site: http://www.magnals.com
Law firm
N.A.I.C.S.: 541199
Lenny Levine (Partner)
Leonardo Duran (Gen Mgr-Foreign Language Svcs)
Erika Malady (Mgr-Bus Dev-Los Angeles)
Jennifer Janof (Mgr-Bus Dev)
Canby Wood (Mgr-Bus Dev-Washington)
Peter Hecht (Exec VP-Sls)
Mark Williams (CEO)
Bob Ackerman (Chm)
Jonathan Ackerman (Exec VP-Record Svcs)
Mark Calzaretta (Exec VP-Litigation Consulting)

Subsidiary (Domestic):

Regency-Brentano, Inc. (2)
13 Corporate Blvd Ne, Atlanta, GA 30329
Tel.: (404) 321-3333
Web Site: http://www.regencybrentano.com
Rev: $1,500,000
Emp.: 26
Court Reporting & Stenotype Services
N.A.I.C.S.: 561492
Brooke T. French (Pres)
Harvey Schulman (Mng Partner)

Trialgraphix Inc. (2)
103 W Broad St Ste 200, Falls Church, VA 22046
Tel.: (954) 885-1983
Web Site: http://www.trialgraphix.com
Rev: $23,000,000
Emp.: 240
Law firm
N.A.I.C.S.: 541199
David Stolberg (Sec)
Jorge Cadenas (Mgr-Trial Logistics Support)
Craig Gordon (Mgr-Database Production)
Michelle Howard (Dir-Staffing-Natl)

NSi Industries, LLC (1)
9730 Northcross Ctr Ct, Huntersville, NC 28078
Tel.: (704) 439-2420
Web Site: http://www.nsiindustries.com
Electrical Connectors, Wire Management Products & Related Electrical Components Mfr & Distr
N.A.I.C.S.: 334417
Tom Wallace (Exec VP-Sls)
G. R. Schrotenboer (CEO)
Dave Di Donato (COO)
Melissa McGinnis (Mgr-Customer Svcs)
Al Rzeczkowski (Sls Mgr-Great Lakes)
Brian Knoup (VP-Natl Accts)
Keith Babcock (Mgr-Natl Accts)

Subsidiary (Domestic):

Bridgeport Fittings, Inc. (2)
705 Lordship Blvd, Stratford, CT 06615
Tel.: (203) 377-5944
Web Site: http://www.bptfittings.com
Emp.: 200
Mfr of Electrical Fittings
N.A.I.C.S.: 335932
David Turk (VP-Sls & Mktg)
Delbert Auray (CEO)
Paul A. Suzio (Pres & COO)
Jay Pearson (Reg VP)
Larry Beach (Reg Dir-Sls)
Wayne Beach (Dir-Technical Sls)
Rick Taylor (VP-Mktg & Strategic Accts)
Chris DeCesare (Mgr-Mktg)

Lynn Electronics Corporation (2)
154 RailRd Dr, Warminster, PA 18974
Tel.: (215) 355-8200
Web Site: http://www.lynnelec.com
Sales Range: $10-24.9 Million
Emp.: 60
Harness Assemblies
N.A.I.C.S.: 334419
Michael Rosen (Pres)
Mike Boulanger (CEO)

Platinum Tools Inc. (2)
2450 Turquoise Cir, Newbury Park, CA 91320
Tel.: (805) 384-2777
Web Site: http://www.platinumtools.com
Datacom Products Mfr
N.A.I.C.S.: 334419

Polaris Sales, Co., Inc. (2)
11625 Prosperous Dr, Odessa, FL 33777
Tel.: (727) 372-1703
Web Site: http://www.polarisconnectors.com
Current-Carrying Wiring Device Mfr
N.A.I.C.S.: 335931

Painters Supply & Equipment Co. (1)
25195 Brest Rd, Taylor, MI 48180
Tel.: (734) 946-8119
Web Site: http://www.painters-supply.com
Rev: $27,500,000
Emp.: 40
Paints, Varnishes & Supplies
N.A.I.C.S.: 424950
Chester Taurence (Founder)
Brad June (VP-Ops)

Subsidiary (Domestic):

Interbay Coatings Inc. (2)
4027 S 50th St, Tampa, FL 33619-6727
Tel.: (813) 242-4100
Web Site: http://www.interbaycoatings.com
Paint, Varnish & Supplies Merchant Whslr
N.A.I.C.S.: 424950
Scott D. Lancaster (Pres)

Pexco LLC (1)
6470 E Johns Crossing Ste 430, Johns Creek, GA 30097
Tel.: (770) 777-8540
Web Site: http://www.pexco.com
Plastics Product Mfr
N.A.I.C.S.: 326199
Sam Patel (CEO)
Peter Speer (VP-Sls)
Femi Ogundimu (Mgr-IT)

Subsidiary (Domestic):

American Extruded Plastics, Inc. (2)
938 Reynolds Pl, Greensboro, NC 27403
Tel.: (336) 274-1131
Web Site: http://www.aeplastics.com
Rev: $2,333,333
Emp.: 25
Unsupported Plastics Profile Shape Mfr
N.A.I.C.S.: 326121

Enflo LLC (2)
315 Lake Ave, Bristol, CT 06010
Tel.: (860) 589-0014
Web Site: http://www.enflo.com
Rev: $4,000,000
Emp.: 40
All Other Plastics Product Mfr
N.A.I.C.S.: 326199
Myron A. Rudner (Pres)
Mark Lamoureaux (CEO)

Exlon Extrusion Inc (2)
3801 Northgate Dr, Greensboro, NC 27405
Tel.: (336) 621-1295
Rev: $1,900,000
Emp.: 9
All Other Plastics Product Mfr
N.A.I.C.S.: 326199
Dennis Swink (Pres)

Insultab, Inc. (2)
45 Industrial Pkwy, Woburn, MA 01801
Tel.: (781) 935-0800
Web Site: http://www.insultab.com
Tubing & Heat Shrinkable Tubing Products Mfr
N.A.I.C.S.: 331210
Gloria Cowen (VP-Mktg)

Performance Plastics, Ltd. (2)
4435 Brownway Ave, Cincinnati, OH 45209
Tel.: (513) 321-8404
Web Site: http://www.performanceplastics.com
Sales Range: $1-9.9 Million
Emp.: 40
Plastics Product Mfr
N.A.I.C.S.: 326199
Tom Mendel (CTO)
Chris Lawson (VP-Ops)
Anthony Malone (VP-Tech)

Plant (Non-US):

Pexco LLC - Monterrey (2)
Boulevard Interamerican #201, Parque Industrial Finsa, Apodaca, 66600, Nuevo Leon, Mexico
Tel.: (52) 81 8196 6700
Web Site: http://www.pexco.com
Plastics Product Mfr
N.A.I.C.S.: 326199

Plant (Domestic):

Pexco LLC - Morrisville (2)
16 Progress Dr, Morrisville, PA 19067-3702
Tel.: (215) 736-2553
Web Site: http://www.pexco.com
Plastics Product Mfr
N.A.I.C.S.: 326199

Pexco LLC - Tacoma (2)
3110 70th Ave E, Tacoma, WA 98424-3608
Tel.: (253) 284-8000
Web Site: http://www.pexco.com
Plastics Product Mfr
N.A.I.C.S.: 326199

Subsidiary (Domestic):

Scandia Plastics (2)
55 Westville Rd, Plaistow, NH 03865
Tel.: (603) 382-6533
Web Site: http://www.scandia-nh.com
Plastic Tank Mfr
N.A.I.C.S.: 325211

Plant (Domestic):

The Spectrum Plastics Group - Athol (2)
764 S Athol Rd, Athol, MA 01331
Tel.: (978) 249-5343
Web Site: http://www.spectrumplasticsgroup.com
Plastic Extrusions & Products Mfr
N.A.I.C.S.: 326199

Plant (Non-US):

The Spectrum Plastics Group - Mexicali Plant (2)
Circuito de las Misiones North #168, Parque Industrial Las Californias, Mexicali, 21394, BC, Mexico
Tel.: (52) 686 561 9924
Web Site: http://www.spectrumplasticsgroup.com
Plastic Materials Mfr
N.A.I.C.S.: 326199

Protective Industrial Products, Inc. (1)
968 Albany Shaker Rd, Latham, NY 12110
Tel.: (518) 861-0133
Web Site: http://www.pipusa.com
Mfr & Distributor of Gloves
N.A.I.C.S.: 423840
Robin Roberts (Sr VP-Sls)
Mike Brooks (Reg Mgr-Sls)
Sheila Schalk (Dir-Programmed Sls)
Thomas C. Fry (COO-Global)
Joe Milot Sr. (Pres/CEO-Global)

Service Champions, Inc. (1)
3150 E Birch St, Brea, CA 92821
Tel.: (714) 777-7777
Web Site: http://www.servicechampions.com
Heating & Air Conditioning, Plumbing & Electrical Services
N.A.I.C.S.: 238220
Leland Smith (CEO)
Frank DiMarco (COO)
Daniel Hamm (CFO)

Subsidiary (Domestic):

A.S.I. Hastings, Inc. (2)
4870 Viewridge Ave Ste 200, San Diego, CA 92123
Tel.: (858) 266-0456
Web Site: http://www.asiheatingandair.com
Sales Range: $1-9.9 Million
Emp.: 160
Plumbing, Heating & Air-Conditioning Contractors
N.A.I.C.S.: 238220
Kenneth Justo (Co-Owner)
Phil Justo (Co-Owner)

Adeedo! Drain, Plumbing, Heating, Air, & Electrical (2)
8599 Venice Blvd, Los Angeles, CA 90034
Tel.: (323) 296-8787
Web Site: http://www.adeedo.com
Plumbing, Heating & Air-Conditioning Contractors
N.A.I.C.S.: 238220
Jack Stephan (Pres)

Jet Services Inc. (2)
1553 Hymer Ave, Sparks, NV 89431
Tel.: (775) 331-3933
Rev: $3,800,000
Emp.: 25
Site Preparation Contractor
N.A.I.C.S.: 238910
James Walker (Owner)
Nanci Thomas (Treas)

Sierra Air, Inc. (2)
4875 Longley Ln, Reno, NV 89502
Tel.: (775) 800-5500
Web Site: http://www.sierraair.com
Sales Range: $1-9.9 Million
Plumbing, Heating & Air Conditioning Services
N.A.I.C.S.: 238220
Richard Lenzora (Principal)

Testek, LLC (1)
28320 Lakeview Dr, Wixom, MI 48393
Tel.: (734) 591-2271

ODYSSEY INVESTMENT PARTNERS, LLC

U.S. PRIVATE

Odyssey Investment Partners, LLC—(Continued)

Web Site: http://www.testek.com
Aerospace & Defense Test Equipment Mfr
N.A.I.C.S.: 334519

The Planet Group LLC (1)
800 Hillgrove Ave Ste 201, Western Springs, IL 60558
Tel.: (888) 845-2539
Web Site: http://www.theplanetgroup.com
Staffing & Recruiting Services
N.A.I.C.S.: 561311
Michael Stomberg (CEO)
Philip Monti (CFO)
Tim Bauwens (Founder)
Tim Simmerly (Pres)

Subsidiary (Domestic):

Future State Consulting LLC (2)
12525 SW Main St, Tigard, OR 97223
Tel.: (503) 567-8283
Web Site: http://www.futurepdx.com
Recruitment Consulting Services
N.A.I.C.S.: 541612
Dann Black (Co-Founder)
Harrison Bishop (Founder & Mng Dir)
Jan Paris (Controller)
Michelle Dieter (Specialist-Ops)

Interactive Business Systems, Inc. (2)
2625 Butterfield Rd, Oak Brook, IL 60523-1234
Tel.: (630) 571-9100
Web Site: http://www.ibs.com
Information Technology Solutions & Staffing
N.A.I.C.S.: 541512
Daniel Williams (Founder & CEO)
Frank Caroll (CFO)
Bob Kloss (VP-Chicago)
Jeff Jorgensen (Pres)
Karen Adkins (Dir-IBS Solutions)
Bob Turner (VP-Detroit)
Zach Katch (Branch Mgr-Milwaukee)
Ryan Sturgis (Branch Mgr-Downtown Chicago)

Winter, Wyman & Company, Inc. (2)
880 Winter St Ste 200, Waltham, MA 02451
Tel.: (781) 890-7000
Web Site: http://www.winterwyman.com
Sales Range: $50-74.9 Million
Emp.: 156
Employment Agencies
N.A.I.C.S.: 561311
Laurie Lopez (Partner & Sr Gen Mgr-Tech Contracting)
Ken Martin (Partner & Sr VP)
Jonathan Mazzocchi (Partner & Sr VP)
David Sanford (Exec VP-Client Rels)
Frank Dadah (Mng Dir)
David J. Melville (Founder & Chm)
Robert E. Boudreau Jr. (CEO)
Scott Ragusa (Pres)
William J. Diana (CFO)
Michelle D. Roccia (Exec VP-Corp Org Dev)
Elizabeth Spayne (Exec VP-Mktg)
Tracy A. Cashman (Partner & Sr VP)
Stuart Coleman (Partner & Sr Mng Dir)
Ben Hicks (Mng Dir & Partner-Software Tech-New England)
Beverly Morgan (Partner & Sr VP)
Glenn Freedman (Asst Mng Dir & Partner-Acctg & Fin-New England)
Robin Daman (Partner & Sr VP)
Peter Mulligan (Partner-Acctg, Fin & Admin-Staffing)
Jane Davis Long (Partner-Fin & Admin Div)
Brian Beaudry (Partner & Dir-Fin, HR & Admin Div)
Rae Sanders (Partner-Fin & Admin Div)
Tonya Salerno (Partner & Mgr-Fin & Admin Div)

TrialCard Incorporated (1)
2250 Perimeter Park Dr Ste 300, Morrisville, NC 27560
Tel.: (919) 415-4041
Web Site: http://www.trialcard.com
Pharmaceutical Product Access & Patient Support Services
N.A.I.C.S.: 812990
Mark Bogovich (CFO)
Scott Dulitz (Sr VP-New Products & Innovation)
Joseph Abdalla (Pres-TC Market Access)

Mark Droke (Sr VP-Patient Affordability & Virtual Engagement)
Mike Davis (Assoc VP-Sls)
Mark Bouck (Pres & CEO)
Michael Carlin (VP-Mktg)
Joe Stallings (Chief Culture & Talent Acq Officer)

Subsidiary (Domestic):

RxSolutions, Inc. (2)
3515 Harbor Blvd, Costa Mesa, CA 92626-1437
Tel.: (714) 226-3530
Web Site: http://www.rxsolutions.com
Online & Mail-Order Prescription Medicine Services
N.A.I.C.S.: 456110
Tom Heck (Pres)
Marc Brady (CFO)

ODYSSEY LOGISTICS & TECHNOLOGY CORP.
39 Old Ridgebury Rd, Danbury, CT 06810
Tel.: (203) 448-3900
Web Site: http://www.odysseylogistics.com
Sales Range: $25-49.9 Million
Emp.: 600
Hazardous Material Shipping Services
N.A.I.C.S.: 488510
Robert H. Shellman (Chm)
Raymond G. Maier (Chief Admin Officer, Gen Counsel & Exec VP)
Cosmo J. Alberico (Pres & COO)
John W. Nikolich (VP-Intl Transportation Mgmt)
Glenn E. Riggs (Sr VP-Corp Logistics Ops & Strategy)
Hans Stig Moller (CEO)
Maneet Singh (CIO)
Lori Davlos (Sr VP-Fin & Controller)
Mark Casiano (Sr VP-Sls & Mktg)

Subsidiaries:

ADS Logistics Co, LLC (1)
116 E 1100 N, Chesterton, IN 46304
Tel.: (219) 836-3900
Web Site: http://www.adslogistics.com
Emp.: 40
Metal Logistics & Supply Chain Management Services
N.A.I.C.S.: 488510
Matt Brinkley (VP-Ops)
William Ritter (Pres & CEO)
Jason Vavrik (CFO)
Jon Kelly (VP-Ops)
Denise Lagunas (Dir-Safety)
Becky Crum (Dir-Admin)

Capital Transportation Solutions LLC (1)
1915 Vaughn Rd, Kennesaw, GA 30144-5460
Tel.: (770) 690-8684
Web Site: http://www.shipwithcts.com
Sales Range: $10-24.9 Million
Emp.: 126
Logistics & Technology Services for Freight Transportation
N.A.I.C.S.: 541614
Keith A. Hancock (CEO)

Chemical Marketing Concepts LLC (1)
200 Pickett District Rd, New Milford, CT 06776-4416
Tel.: (860) 354-3997
Web Site: http://www.odysseylogistics.com
Fulfillment & Logistics Services, Including Storing, Packaging & Shipping Sample & Small Revenue Orders
N.A.I.C.S.: 541614

Interdom LLC (1)
11800 S 75th Ave Ste 2N, Palos Heights, IL 60463-1033
Tel.: (708) 671-2110
Web Site: http://www.interdompartners.com
Sales Range: $25-49.9 Million
Emp.: 50
Railway Intermodal Services
N.A.I.C.S.: 488510

Mike Popo (Controller)
Deb Feie (Mgr-Ops-Domestic)
Mike O'Brien (VP-Mktg-Intermodal-New York)
Steve Novak (VP-Mktg-Intermodal)
Sherri Jackson (VP-Mktg-Intermodal)

International Forwarders, Inc. (1)
1350 Ashley River Rd Ste A, Charleston, SC 29407
Tel.: (843) 769-7030
Web Site: http://www.ifichs.com
Sales Range: $10-24.9 Million
Emp.: 55
Freight Forwarding Services
N.A.I.C.S.: 488510
Donna Sharp (Branch Mgr)
Wallace Hester (VP & Gen Mgr)
Elaine Benton (CFO)
Kay Winnett (CEO)
Teresa Hart (Mgr-Gen Admin)
T. Michael Morris (VP-Export)
Kathie Warren (Sr Mgr-Export)

OL&T International (Shanghai) Company Ltd. (1)
Suite A 21/F Tower A Yueda International Plaza, 1118 Changshou Road, Shanghai, 200042, China
Tel.: (86) 21 611 787 21
Web Site: http://www.otysseylogistics.com
Emp.: 26
Freight Transportation & Logistics Services
N.A.I.C.S.: 488510
Lawrence Hu (Pres)

Odyssey International LLC (1)
39 Old Ridgebury Rd, Danbury, CT 06810 (100%)
Tel.: (203) 448-3900
Web Site: http://www.odysseylogistics.com
Emp.: 50
Export Freight Forwarder
N.A.I.C.S.: 488510
Robert H. Shellman (Pres)

Odyssey Logistics Europe BVBA (1)
Roderveldlaan 4, 2600, Berchem, Belgium
Tel.: (32) 3 200 2999
Web Site: http://www.odysseylogistics.com
Freight Transportation & Logistics Services
N.A.I.C.S.: 488510
Toine Matthijssen (Mng Dir)

Odyssey Overland, LLC (1)
4235 S Stream Blvd - Ste 300, Charlotte, NC 28217
Tel.: (704) 529-2618
Web Site: http://www.odysseylogistics.com
Emp.: 140
Freight Transportation Management Services
N.A.I.C.S.: 488510
Lou Trillo (Pres-North American Transportation)

Optimodal, Inc. (1)
Optimodal Bldg 119 N High St, West Chester, PA 19380 (100%)
Tel.: (610) 918-8232
Web Site: http://www.odysseylogistics.com
Multi-Modal Transportation of Tank Containers & Related Services
N.A.I.C.S.: 484220
Greg Snyder (Pres)
Gina Marrero (VP-Admin)
Barb Slawter (VP-Ops)
John Chieppa (Acct Mgr)
Frank Palazzolo (Acct Mgr)

ODYSSEY MANUFACTURING CO.
1484 Massaro Blvd, Tampa, FL 33619
Tel.: (813) 635-0339 DE
Web Site:
http://www.odysseymanufacturing.com
Year Founded: 2000
Sales Range: $25-49.9 Million
Emp.: 50
Polishes & Sanitation Products
N.A.I.C.S.: 325612
Marvin Rakes (Pres)
Patrick Allman (Gen Mgr)

ODYSSEY PICTURES CORPORATION
2321 Coit Rd Ste E, Plano, TX 75075
Tel.: (972) 867-0055
Web Site: http://www.odysseypix.com
Year Founded: 1989
Sales Range: $1-9.9 Million
Motion Picture Distr
N.A.I.C.S.: 512120
John W. Foster (Chm & CEO)

ODYSSEY SYSTEMS
201 Edgewater Dr Ste 270, Wakefield, MA 01880
Tel.: (781) 245-0111
Web Site:
http://www.odysseyconsult.com
Year Founded: 1997
Sales Range: $100-124.9 Million
Emp.: 175
Technical & Management Consulting Services
N.A.I.C.S.: 541690
Theresa Ceci (Dir-HR)

ODYSSEY TECHNICAL SOLUTIONS, LLC
3916 Gattis School Rd Ste 108, Round Rock, TX 78664
Tel.: (512) 989-7007 TX
Web Site: http://www.odysseyrf.com
Year Founded: 2000
Sales Range: $1-9.9 Million
Emp.: 65
Technical Solutions
N.A.I.C.S.: 541519
Jim Plourde (Pres)
David Durkee (Engr-Electrical-II)

ODYSSEY TELECOMMUNICATIONS, INC.
5811 South Park, Hamburg, NY 14075
Tel.: (877) 486-4704
Web Site: http://www.otelinc.com
Year Founded: 2008
Sales Range: $1-9.9 Million
Emp.: 6
VoIP Phone Systems
N.A.I.C.S.: 517810
Justin Wekenmann (Co-Founder & Exec VP)
Robert Blizniak (Co-Founder & Pres)

Subsidiaries:

AAVOIP (eXpress) (1)
5811 South Park, Hamburg, NY 14075 (100%)
Tel.: (877) 486-4704
Web Site: http://www.aavoip.com
VoIP Phone Systems for Individuals & Small Businesses
N.A.I.C.S.: 517810
Justin Wekenmann (Co-Founder & Exec VP)
Robert Blizniak (Co-Founder & Pres)

VoIP Gorilla (1)
5811 South Park, Hamburg, NY 14075 (100%)
Tel.: (877) 630-1992
Web Site: http://www.voipgorilla.com
VoIP Products & Telecommunications Services
N.A.I.C.S.: 517810
Justin Wekenmann (Co-Founder & Exec VP)
Robert Blizniak (Co-Founder & Pres)

OE MEYER CO.
3303 Tiffin Ave, Sandusky, OH 44870
Tel.: (419) 625-3054
Web Site: http://www.oemeyer.com
Sales Range: $25-49.9 Million
Emp.: 135
Welding Machinery & Equipment
N.A.I.C.S.: 423830
David Belden (Pres-Healthcare)
Hal Freehling (VP-Support Svcs)

COMPANIES / OEP CAPITAL ADVISORS, L.P.

OEC BUSINESS INTERIORS, INC.
900 N Church Rd, Elmhurst, IL 60126-1014
Tel.: (630) 589-5500   IL
Web Site: http://www.oecbusinessinteriors.com
Sales Range: $75-99.9 Million
Emp.: 120
Wholesale Distributor of Office Furniture
N.A.I.C.S.: 423210
Frances Riha *(Chm, Treas & Sec)*
Tom O'Mally *(CFO)*
Raymond R. Riha Sr. *(Pres)*
Raymond R Riha Jr. *(VP)*

OEC GROUP INC.
1 Cross Island Plz Ste 306 133-33 Brookville Blvd, Rosedale, NY 11422
Tel.: (562) 926-7186
Web Site: http://www.oecgroup.com
Rev.: $7,000,000
Emp.: 50
Freight Transportation Arrangement
N.A.I.C.S.: 488510
Robert Han *(CFO)*
Roy Chan *(VP-Ops & Customer Svc-Southwest Reg)*

OEM FABRICATORS, INC.
300 Mcmillan Rd, Woodville, WI 54028
Tel.: (715) 698-2111
Web Site: http://www.oemfab.com
Year Founded: 1986
Sales Range: $75-99.9 Million
Emp.: 489
Building Component Mfr
N.A.I.C.S.: 332311
Tom Aaby *(Sr VP-Bus Dev)*
S. Mark Tyler *(Co-Founder)*
Jim Hauschild *(Co-Founder)*

OEM GROUP, INC.
2120 W Guadalupe Rd, Gilbert, AZ 85233
Tel.: (480) 558-9200
Web Site: http://www.oemgroupinc.com
Year Founded: 1999
Sales Range: $10-24.9 Million
Emp.: 250
Semiconductor Capital Equipment Mfr & Distr
N.A.I.C.S.: 333242
Mike Lombardi *(COO)*
Mariah Gray *(Mgr-HR)*
Frank Su *(Dir-Sls-Asia Reg)*

Subsidiaries:

OEM Group Austria (1)
Karolingerstrasse 7C, A-5020, Salzburg, Austria   **(100%)**
Tel.: (43) 66222120
Web Site: http://www.oemgroupinc.com
Precision Semiconductor Tool Sales & Service
N.A.I.C.S.: 334413

OEM Group East (1)
416 S 4th St, Coopersburg, PA 18036-2039   **(100%)**
Tel.: (610) 282-0105
Web Site: http://www.oemgroupinc.com
Sales Range: $10-24.9 Million
Emp.: 50
Semiconductor Production Tools Mfr
N.A.I.C.S.: 333242

OEM Group Japan Co., Ltd.
2-39-15 Hazawaminami, Kanagawa-ku, Yokohama, 221 0866, Japan
Tel.: (81) 45 370 3523
Semiconductor Equipment Mfr, Sales & Service
N.A.I.C.S.: 334413

Rite Track Equipment Services, LLC (1)
8655 Rite Track Way, West Chester, OH 45069
Tel.: (513) 881-7820
Web Site: http://www.ritetrack.com
Electrical Equipment & Supplies
N.A.I.C.S.: 333242
Timothy Hayden *(Pres & CEO)*
John Noyes *(CTO & Dir-Product Mktg)*
Rick Balt *(VP-Sls)*
Rick Baldasare *(Mgr-Sls)*

SHELLBACK Semiconductor Technology (1)
416 S 4th St, Coopersburg, PA 18036
Tel.: (480) 609-8565
Web Site: http://shellbacksemi.com
Semiconductor Mfr
N.A.I.C.S.: 334413
Wayne Jeveli *(Pres & CEO)*

OEM PRESS SYSTEMS, INC.
311 S Highland Ave, Fullerton, CA 92832
Tel.: (714) 449-7500
Web Site: http://www.oempresssystems.com
Year Founded: 1969
Sales Range: $1-9.9 Million
Emp.: 23
Industrial Machinery Mfr
N.A.I.C.S.: 332710
John Copp *(Founder & Pres)*

Subsidiaries:

OEM Press Systems (Shenzhen) Co., Ltd. (1)
Suite 1323 Jinwei Building 4051 Jiabin Road, Luohu District, Shenzhen, 518001, China
Tel.: (86) 755 61628170
Industrial Machinery Mfr
N.A.I.C.S.: 332710

OEP CAPITAL ADVISORS, L.P.
510 Madison Ave 19th Fl, New York, NY 10022
Tel.: (212) 277-1500   DE
Web Site: http://www.oneequity.com
Year Founded: 2001
Emp.: 6,001
Privater Equity Firm
N.A.I.C.S.: 523940
Jamie W. Koven *(Sr Mng Dir)*
David Han *(Sr Mng Dir)*
Joerg Zirener *(Sr Mng Dir)*
JB Cherry *(Sr Mng Dir)*
Andrew Dunn *(Mng Dir)*
Chris Enger *(Dir-Fin)*
Inna Etinberg *(Principal)*
Joseph Huffsmith *(Mng Dir)*
Ante Kusurin *(Principal)*
Marc Lindhorst *(Principal)*
David Lippin *(Mng Dir & Head-IR)*
Jessica Marion *(CFO)*
Dunja Mauser *(Head-Ops & Dir)*
Chip Schorr *(Sr Mng Dir)*
Johann-Melchior von Peter *(Sr Mng Dir)*
Ori Birnboim *(Mng Dir)*
Charlie Cole *(Principal)*
Matthew Hughes *(Mng Dir)*
Steven Lunau *(Mng Dir)*
Vittorio Palladino *(VP)*
Philipp von Meurers *(Mng Dir)*
Steve Rappaport *(Dir-Research)*
Norma C. Corio *(Sr Mng Dir)*

Subsidiaries:

Acteon Group Ltd. (1)
Ferryside Ferry Rd, Norfolk, NR1 1SW, United Kingdom
Tel.: (44) 1603227019
Web Site: https://www.acteon.com
Offshore Oil & Gas Engineering & Drilling Services
N.A.I.C.S.: 213112
David Drysdale *(Exec VP-Infrastructure)*
Mel Zuydam *(CFO)*
Barry Parsons *(Chief Comml Officer)*
Rolf Althen *(Exec VP)*

Subsidiary (Domestic):

2H Offshore Engineering Ltd. (2)
Hollywood House Church St E, Woking, GU21 6HJ, Surrey, United Kingdom
Tel.: (44) 1483774900
Web Site: https://www.2hoffshore.com
Sales Range: $25-49.9 Million
Marine Riser System Design, Construction & Maintenance Services
N.A.I.C.S.: 237120
Yann Helle *(Mng Dir-London)*

Subsidiary (Non-US):

CAPE Group Pte. Ltd. (2)
10 Anson Road 12-14 International Plaza, Singapore, 079903, Singapore
Tel.: (65) 62622282
Web Site: https://capegroupglobal.com
Sales Range: $25-49.9 Million
Emp.: 20
Holding Company
N.A.I.C.S.: 551112
Yogaprakash Mahalingam *(Gen Mgr)*

Subsidiary (Domestic):

Claxton Engineering Services Ltd (2)
Bureside House North River Road Great Yarmouth, Norfolk, NR30 1TE, United Kingdom
Tel.: (44) 1493744500
Web Site: http://www.claxtonengineering.com
Sales Range: $75-99.9 Million
Emp.: 100
Oil & Natural Gas Well Engineering & Consulting Services
N.A.I.C.S.: 213112
Laura Claxton *(COO)*
Nick Wood *(Pres & Co-CEO)*
Nick Marriott *(Gen Mgr-Norway)*
Jason Moyles *(VP-Ops)*
Derrick Heskins *(Mgr-Sls)*
Sam Hanton *(Co-CEO)*
Geoff Morrison *(CFO)*
Nathan Darnell *(Head-QHSEE)*
Jon Cross *(VP-Bus Dev)*
Dave Macwilliam *(VP-Tech Solutions)*
Mark Stephen *(VP-Global Resources)*
Dannie Claxton *(Dir-Technical)*
Dawn Nichols *(Controller-Grp Fin)*
Tony Theriot *(Mgr-Bus Dev)*

Subsidiary (Non-US):

Fluke Engenharia Ltda. (2)
Avenida Das Americas 3434 Bloco 2-Sala 201-Barra Da Tijuca, Rio de Janeiro, 22640-102, Brazil
Tel.: (55) 2134313899
Offshore Oil & Natural Gas Well Mooring System Developer & Mfr
N.A.I.C.S.: 213112

Subsidiary (US):

InterAct PMTI, Inc. (2)
260 Maple Ct Ste 210, Ventura, CA 93003
Tel.: (805) 658-5600
Web Site: http://www.interactprojects.com
Sales Range: $100-124.9 Million
Oil & Gas Production Engineering, Project Management & Consulting Services
N.A.I.C.S.: 213112

Subsidiary (Domestic):

InterMoor (2)
Tern Place House Tern Place Bridge of Don, Aberdeen, AB23 8JX, United Kingdom
Tel.: (44) 1224701830
Web Site: https://acteon.com
Sales Range: $50-74.9 Million
Emp.: 20
Oil & Natural Gas Well Mooring & Anchoring System Mfr
N.A.I.C.S.: 213112
Alan Duncan *(Mng Dir)*

Subsidiary (Non-US):

InterMoor Pte. Ltd. (3)
25 Loyang Crescent Block 103 06-02, Mailbox No 5078, Tops Avenue 1, Singapore, 508988, Singapore
Tel.: (65) 65465928
Web Site: http://www.intermoor.com
Emp.: 22
Oil & Natural Gas Well Mooring & Anchoring System Mfr
N.A.I.C.S.: 213112
Alan Duncan *(Mng Dir-UK)*
David Smith *(Mng Dir-A/S)*

Subsidiary (Domestic):

Viking SeaTech Ltd. (3)
Peterseat Drive Peterseat Park, London, AB12 3HT, Altens, United Kingdom
Tel.: (44) 1224516516
Web Site: http://www.vikingseatech.com
Marine Equipment Distr
N.A.I.C.S.: 423910

Subsidiary (US):

InterMoor Inc. (2)
101 Youngswood Rd, Morgan City, LA 70380
Tel.: (985) 385-3083
Web Site: http://www.intermoor.com
Sales Range: $50-74.9 Million
Integrated Mooring Systems Mfr for the Offshore Oil & Gas Industries
N.A.I.C.S.: 237120

Subsidiary (Non-US):

Menck GmbH (2)
Industrial Area Moorkarten, Am Springmoor 5A, Kaltenkirchen, 24568, Germany
Tel.: (49) 41919110
Web Site: http://www.menck.com
Sales Range: $50-74.9 Million
Oil & Gas Well Engineering, Construction & Consulting Services
N.A.I.C.S.: 333132
Fabian Hippe *(Mng Dir)*
Bernhard Bruggaier *(Mng Dir)*

Subsidiary (Domestic):

Seatronics Ltd. (2)
Acteon House Peregrine Road, Aberdeenshire, Westhill, AB32 6JL, United Kingdom
Tel.: (44) 1224853100
Web Site: https://acteon.com
Sales Range: $25-49.9 Million
Emp.: 50
Subsea Electronic Equipment Supplier
N.A.I.C.S.: 423690
Derek Donaldson *(Mng Dir-Grp)*
Kevin Strachan *(Dir-Fin)*
Akram Ali *(Mgr-Reg-UAE)*
Scott Gray *(Mgr-Reg-Europe & Africa)*
Joanne Keilloh *(Mgr-Grp QHSE)*
Dale Townend *(Dir-Engrg)*
Jamie Neilson *(Supvr-ROV Engrg & Ops)*
David Owen *(Mgr-Technical-ROV Products)*
Innes Murray *(Engr-Trainee Survey Sys)*

Subsidiary (US):

Seatronics, Inc. (3)
1319 W Sam Houston Pkwy N Ste 150, Houston, TX 77043
Tel.: (713) 464-3311
Web Site: http://www.seatronics-group.com
Sales Range: $25-49.9 Million
Emp.: 20
Subsea Electronic Equipment Supplier
N.A.I.C.S.: 423690
Jenell Pence *(Pres)*

Subsidiary (Domestic):

TEAM Energy Resources Ltd. (2)
Ferryside Ferry Road, Norwich, NR1 1SW, United Kingdom
Tel.: (44) 1603767439
Web Site: https://www.team-energy.co.uk
Sales Range: $75-99.9 Million
Emp.: 25
Oil & Gas Well Engineering & Consulting Services
N.A.I.C.S.: 213112

Alltub BV (1)
Keizersgracht 62-64, 1015, Bondoufle, France   **(100%)**
Tel.: (33) 1 74056200
Web Site: http://www.alltub.com
Aluminum Tubing Mfr
N.A.I.C.S.: 331318

Subsidiary (Non-US):

Alltub Central Europe A.S. (2)

OEP CAPITAL ADVISORS, L.P.   U.S. PRIVATE

OEP Capital Advisors, L.P.—(Continued)
Zengerova 82, 280 62, Kolin, Czech Republic
Tel.: (420) 321 721 821
Sales Range: $25-49.9 Million
Aluminum Tubing Mfr
N.A.I.C.S.: 331318

Alltub Deutschland GmbH (2)
Suedwestpark 37-41, Nuremberg, 90449, Germany
Tel.: (49) 911 3092010
Aluminum Tubing Mfr
N.A.I.C.S.: 331318

Alltub Italia Srl (2)
Viale Rimembranze 23, 24050, Cividate al Piano, BG, Italy
Tel.: (39) 0363946011
Sales Range: $25-49.9 Million
Emp.: 26
Aluminum Tubing Mfr
N.A.I.C.S.: 331318

Alltub UK Limited (2)
Suite 12 Manor Crown Business Centre, Bourne, PE10 0BP, Lincolnshire, United Kingdom
Tel.: (44) 1778 420859
Web Site: http://www.alltub.com
Emp.: 1
Aluminum Tubing Sales
N.A.I.C.S.: 423510
David Keith Tooze (Sls Mgr)

Subsidiary (US):

Alltub USA, LLC (2)
515 Valley St Ste 190, Maplewood, NJ 07040
Tel.: (973) 761-1870
Aluminum Tubing Sales
N.A.I.C.S.: 423510

American Equipment Company, Inc. (1)
2106 Anderson Rd, Greenville, SC 29611
Tel.: (864) 295-7800
Web Site: http://www.ameco.com
Sales Range: $400-449.9 Million
Emp.: 1,300
Heavy Machinery & Equipment, Rental & Leasing; Construction Equipment Repair
N.A.I.C.S.: 532490
Tracey Cook (Pres)
Dean Smith (Dir-Execution Support Svcs)
Chris Arnold (Dir-Intl Ops & Strategic Projects)

Subsidiary (Domestic):

AMECO Holdings, Inc. (2)
2106 Anderson Rd, Greenville, SC 29611
Tel.: (864) 295-7800
Web Site: https://www.ameco.com
Sales Range: $50-74.9 Million
Emp.: 140
Holding Company
N.A.I.C.S.: 551112

Subsidiary (Non-US):

AMECO Mexico Administracion y Servicios S de RL/CV
Autopista Mexico Queretaro Ste 3065A Col Industrial Tlaxcolpan, Tlalnepantla, 54040, Tlaxcolpan, Mexico
Tel.: (52) 5585033500
Web Site: http://www.ameco.com.mx
Construction & Maintenance Services
N.A.I.C.S.: 532412

AMECO Services S de RL de CV (3)
Calzada Gonzalez Gallo No 2712, Col El Rosario, 44890, Guadalajara, Jalisco, Mexico
Tel.: (52) 13350003000
Web Site: http://www.ameco.com
Sales Range: $1-9.9 Million
Emp.: 2
Construction & Maintenance Services
N.A.I.C.S.: 532412

AMECO Services srl (3)
Carretera Monterrey-Saltillo Km 67 No 1200 Colonia Zimix, 66357, Santa Catarina, Mexico
Tel.: (52) 8110017700
Web Site: http://www.ameco.com.mx
Sales Range: $10-24.9 Million
Emp.: 15
Construction & Maintenance Services
N.A.I.C.S.: 532412

AMECO Services srl (3)
Blvd Adolfo Lopez Mateos No 1000 Col Universidad, Poniente, 89138, Tampico, Mexico
Tel.: (52) 8332103890
Web Site: http://www.ameco.com.mx
Sales Range: $100-124.9 Million
Emp.: 24
Construction & Maintenance Services
N.A.I.C.S.: 532412

AMECO Services srl (3)
Autopista Mexico-Queretaro No 3065-A, Col Industrial Tlaxcolpan, Mexico, 54040, Tlalnepantla, Mexico
Tel.: (52) 5585033500
Web Site: http://www.ameco.com.mx
Construction & Maintenance Services
N.A.I.C.S.: 532412

AMECO Services srl (3)
Km 117 Col Parque Empresarial Cuautlancingo, Lateral de la Autopista Mexico, Puebla, Mexico
Tel.: (52) 2223729300
Web Site: http://www.ameco.com
Sales Range: $10-24.9 Million
Emp.: 15
Construction & Maintenance Services
N.A.I.C.S.: 532412

AMECO Services srl (3)
Veracruz-Jalapa Km 99, 91693, Veracruz, Mexico
Tel.: (52) 2299209762
Construction & Maintenance Services
N.A.I.C.S.: 532412

AMECO Services srl (3)
Riveras De Atoyac No 1978 No A, Col Tde Viguera Oaxaca, 68120, Oaxaca, Mexico
Tel.: (52) 9515491941
Web Site: http://www.ameco.com
Sales Range: $10-24.9 Million
Emp.: 16
Construction & Maintenance Services
N.A.I.C.S.: 532412

AMECO Services srl (3)
Super Manzana 301 Mza 5 Lote 4 Km 17, Carretera Cancun-Aeropuerto, 77500, Cancun, Quintana Roo, Mexico
Tel.: (52) 9988862270
Web Site: http://www.ameco.com.mx
Sales Range: $10-24.9 Million
Emp.: 20
Construction & Maintenance Services
N.A.I.C.S.: 532412

AMECO Services, Inc. (3)
6909-42 Street Leduc, Edmonton, T9E 0W1, AB, Canada (100%)
Tel.: (587) 743-0651
Web Site: http://www.ameco.com
Sales Range: $10-24.9 Million
Emp.: 15
Equipment Rental & Leasing Nec
N.A.I.C.S.: 532490

AMECO Services, S. DE R.L. DE C.V. (3)
Autopista Mexico Queretaro No 3065-A, Fracc Industrial Tlaxcolpan, Tlalnepantla, 54040, Mexico
Tel.: (52) 55 8503 3500
Web Site: http://www.ameco.com.mx
Construction, Industrial & Mining Machinery & Equipment Distr & Rental Services
N.A.I.C.S.: 532412

Maquinaria Ameco Guatemala, Limitada (3)
Calz Aguilar Batres 48-95 Zona 12 Col Monte Maria, Villa Nueva, Guatemala, Guatemala
Tel.: (502) 24852145
Sales Range: $25-49.9 Million
Emp.: 5
Engineeering Services
N.A.I.C.S.: 541330

Subsidiary (Domestic):

AMECO Services, Inc. (2)
5200 Old Galveston Rd, Houston, TX 77017
Tel.: (713) 948-5515
Web Site: http://www.ameco.com
Sales Range: $100-124.9 Million
Emp.: 30
Construction & Maintenance Services
N.A.I.C.S.: 532412

AMECO Services, Inc. (2)
635 E NE Loop 323, Tyler, TX 75706
Tel.: (903) 593-7592
Web Site: http://www.ameco.com
Sales Range: $10-24.9 Million
Emp.: 45
Construction & Maintenance Services
N.A.I.C.S.: 532412

F&M Mafco Inc. (2)
9149 Dry Fork Rd, Harrison, OH 45030-1901
Tel.: (513) 367-2151
Web Site: http://www.fmmafco.com
Sales Range: $100-124.9 Million
Emp.: 250
Hardware
N.A.I.C.S.: 532412
Daniel McKenna (Pres)
Bill McKenna (VP-Ops)
Jim Zeisler (CFO)
Timothy Fries (VP-Sls & Mktg)

Associated Spring Corporation (1)
18 Main St, Bristol, CT 06010
Tel.: (860) 582-9581
Web Site: http://www.asbg.com
Rev.: $204,000,000
Emp.: 80
Custom Springs Mfr
N.A.I.C.S.: 332613

Plant (Domestic):

Associated Spring (2)
1445 Barnes Ct, Saline, MI 48176-9589 (100%)
Tel.: (734) 429-2022
Web Site: http://www.asbg.com
Sales Range: $100-124.9 Million
Custom Springs Mfr
N.A.I.C.S.: 332613

Associated Spring (2)
226 S Center St, Corry, PA 16407-1935 (100%)
Tel.: (814) 664-9646
Web Site: http://www.associatedspring.com
Sales Range: $75-99.9 Million
Custom Springs Mfr
N.A.I.C.S.: 332613

Subsidiary (Non-US):

Associated Spring (U.K.) Ltd. (2)
Unit 4 Grosvenor Business Centre, Vale Park, Evesham, WR11 1GS, Worcestershire, United Kingdom (100%)
Tel.: (44) 1386443366
Web Site: https://www.assocspring.co.uk
Sales Range: $10-24.9 Million
Emp.: 18
Springs & Spring Washers Mfr
N.A.I.C.S.: 334519

Associated Spring Mexico, S.A. (2)
Av Concordia No 4601-A Col Apodaca Centro, Apodaca, 66600, Nuevo Leon, Mexico (100%)
Tel.: (52) 8181450680
Web Site: http://www.asbg.com
Sales Range: $50-74.9 Million
Emp.: 114
Close-Tolerance Springs Mfr
N.A.I.C.S.: 334519

Unit (Domestic):

Associated Spring Raymond (2)
370 W Dussel Dr Ste A, Maumee, OH 43537-1604
Tel.: (419) 891-9292
Web Site: http://www.asraymond.com
Sales Range: $50-74.9 Million
Emp.: 45
Hardware Distr Services
N.A.I.C.S.: 423840

Subsidiary (Non-US):

Associated Spring Raymond (Shanghai) Co., Ltd. (2)
5th Floor North No 4 Building No 825 Ningqiao Road, Pudong New District, Shanghai, 201206, China
Tel.: (86) 2151348111
Web Site: http://www.raymondasia.com
Sales Range: $10-24.9 Million
Emp.: 12
Investment Management Service
N.A.I.C.S.: 333611

Associated Spring-Asia Pte. Ltd. (2)
28 Tuas Ave 2, Singapore, 639459, Singapore (100%)
Tel.: (65) 68635636
Web Site: http://www.asbg.com
Sales Range: $25-49.9 Million
Close-Tolerance Springs Mfr
N.A.I.C.S.: 334519

Joint Venture (Domestic):

NHK-Associated Spring Suspension Components Inc. (2)
3251 Nashville Rd, Bowling Green, KY 42101
Tel.: (270) 842-4006
Web Site: http://www.nascospg.com
Sales Range: $25-49.9 Million
Emp.: 350
Suspension Spring Components Mfr
N.A.I.C.S.: 332613

Subsidiary (Non-US):

Raymond Distribution-Mexico, S.A. de C.V.
Av Concordia No 4601-A Col Apodaca Centro, 66600, Apodaca, Nuevo Leon, Mexico
Tel.: (52) 8181450680
Web Site: http://www.asraymond.com.mx
Sales Range: $25-49.9 Million
Industrial Machinery Distr
N.A.I.C.S.: 423830

Brush Electrical Machines Ltd. (1)
Falcon Works, Nottingham Road, Loughborough, LE11 1EX, United Kingdom
Tel.: (44) 1509611511
Web Site: http://www.brush.eu
Sales Range: $200-249.9 Million
Emp.: 650
Motor & Generator Mfr
N.A.I.C.S.: 335312
Martyn Vaughan (Mng Dir)

Clayens NP Group (1)
10 Rue Jean Rostand, 69740, Genas, France
Tel.: (33) 478401152
Web Site: http://www.clayens-np.com
Sales Range: $250-299.9 Million
Emp.: 2,500
Plastics Product Mfr
N.A.I.C.S.: 326130
Eric Pisani (CEO)

Constantia Packaging AG (1)
Opernring 17, A-1010, Vienna, Austria
Tel.: (43) 588550
Web Site: http://www.constantia-packaging.com
Sales Range: $1-4.9 Billion
Emp.: 7,828
Packaging Products Mfr
N.A.I.C.S.: 561910

Dailycer S.A. (1)
Le Technoparc 34 rue CE Jeanneret, 78306, Poissy, Cedex, France
Tel.: (33) 139118181
Web Site: http://www.dailycer.fr
Sales Range: $75-99.9 Million
Emp.: 400
Mfr of Breakfast Cereals
N.A.I.C.S.: 311230

Subsidiary (Non-US):

Dailycer BV (2)
Zevenheuvelenweg 53 -55, 5048AN, Tilburg, Netherlands (100%)
Tel.: (31) 0134625525
Web Site: http://www.dalicia.nl
Sales Range: $50-74.9 Million
Emp.: 150
Cheese Manufacturing
N.A.I.C.S.: 311513
Ben Postma (Gen Mgr)

Dailycer Nederland B.V., Tilburg (2)
Zevenheuvelenweg 53 55, 5048 AN, Tilburg, Netherlands

Tel.: (31) 0134625525
Web Site: http://www.dailycer.nl
Sales Range: $25-49.9 Million
Emp.: 150
Cheese Products Mfr
N.A.I.C.S.: 311513

Dwk Life Sciences GmbH (1)
Otto-Schott-Strasse 21, 97877, Wertheim, Germany
Tel.: (49) 93428020
Web Site: https://www.dwk.com
Emp.: 1,900
Laboratory Glass Equipment Mfr
N.A.I.C.S.: 327213
Armin Reiche *(Mng Dir)*
Bernhard Scherer *(Mng Dir)*

Subsidiary (US):

Assem-Pak, Inc. (2)
1649 Castpa Pl, Vineland, NJ 08360
Tel.: (856) 692-3355
Web Site: http://www.assempak.com
Sales Range: $1-9.9 Million
Emp.: 75
Rubber Products Mfr
N.A.I.C.S.: 326299
Don Bayer *(Pres)*
Barbara George *(Supvr-Production)*

Kimble Chase Life Science & Research Products LLC (2)
1022 Spruce St, Vineland, NJ 08362 (51%)
Tel.: (856) 692-8500
Web Site: http://www.kimble-chase.com
Holding Company; Scientific Glass Products Mfr
N.A.I.C.S.: 551112
Randy Baughman *(CFO)*

Plant (Domestic):

Kimble Chase Life Science & Research Products LLC - Rochester Plant (3)
140 Bennington Dr, Rochester, NY 14616
Tel.: (585) 865-1290
Web Site: http://www.kimble-chase.com
Emp.: 900
Pharmaceutical & Cosmetic Bottles Mfr
N.A.I.C.S.: 327213

Kimble Chase Life Science & Research Products LLC - Rockwood Plant (3)
234 Cardiff Valley Rd, Rockwood, TN 37854
Tel.: (800) 451-3151
Web Site: http://www.kimble-chase.com
Scientific Glass Products Mfr
N.A.I.C.S.: 327215

Subsidiary (Non-US):

SciLabware Ltd. (2)
Unit4 Riverside2 Campbell Road, Stoke-on-Trent, ST4 4RJ, Staffordshire, United Kingdom
Tel.: (44) 1782 444406
Web Site: http://www.scilabware.com
Laboratory Glassware Products Mfr
N.A.I.C.S.: 334516
Edward Wynn *(Dir-Bus Dev)*

Subsidiary (US):

Wheaton Industries, Inc. (2)
1501 N 10th St, Millville, NJ 08332-2038
Tel.: (856) 825-1100
Web Site: http://www.wheaton.com
Laboratory Instruments & Equipments Mfr & Marketer
N.A.I.C.S.: 334516
Wayne L. Brinster *(CEO)*
Gregory W. Bianco *(VP-Quality Mgmt Sys)*
Stefan Baechle *(CFO)*
Tracy Neri-Luciano *(Dir-Mktg-Global)*
Jeff Schempp *(VP-Ops)*
Tonya M. Verna *(VP-Info Tech)*
Brian Seibert *(Dir-Strategic Pricing & Data Analysis)*
Steve Smith *(Mgr-Technical Svc)*
David Koi *(Pres)*
Rhonda Bright *(Mgr-Strategic Markets)*
Brian M. Cawley *(Territory Mgr)*
Ann Handy *(Territory Mgr)*
Megha Mamgain *(Territory Mgr)*
Joe Barbera *(Territory Mgr)*

Michael Flora *(Territory Mgr)*
Kyle DeBoer *(Reg Mgr)*
Doug Harris *(VP-Sls & Mktg)*

GKN Walterscheid GmbH (1)
Hauptstrasse 150, 53797, Lohmar, Germany (98.5%)
Tel.: (49) 2246120
Web Site: http://www.walterscheid.com
Sales Range: $200-249.9 Million
Emp.: 650
Mfr of Agri-Technical Driveline Systems & Gearboxes
N.A.I.C.S.: 336340

Subsidiary (US):

GKN Walterscheid Inc. (2)
2715 Davey Rd, Woodridge, IL 60517 (98.5%)
Tel.: (630) 972-9300
Web Site: http://www.gkn-walterscheid.com
Sales Range: $25-49.9 Million
Emp.: 100
Agricultural Driveline Systems Mfr
N.A.I.C.S.: 336350

Gordian Medical, Inc. (1)
17595 Cartwright Rd, Irvine, CA 92614-6680
Tel.: (949) 553-0103
Web Site: http://www.amtwoundcare.com
Offices of Physicians (except Mental Health Specialists)
N.A.I.C.S.: 621111
Kathy Clark *(Office Mgr)*

Heinz Hanggi GmbH (1)
Unterer Einschlag 9, Bettlach, 2544, Switzerland
Tel.: (41) 326443311
Web Site: http://www.hanggi.com
Sales Range: $100-124.9 Million
Emp.: 100
Stamped Insudrial Part Mfr
N.A.I.C.S.: 332119
Boris Wrobel *(Mgr-Div)*
Christian Candussi *(Head-Sls)*
Rolf Ingold *(Sls Mgr)*
Felix Quasniczka *(Mgr-NAFTA)*
Mirko Parravicini *(Mgr-Program)*
Bjorn Herbst *(Project Mgr)*
Melanie Kolatzki *(Sys Engr-Sales-Automotive)*

MSQ Partners Group Ltd. (1)
90 Tottenham Court Road, London, W1T 4TJ, United Kingdom
Tel.: (44) 2030266000
Web Site: http://www.msqpartners.com
Advertising Services
N.A.I.C.S.: 541810
Peter Reid *(CEO)*
Charles Courtier *(Chm)*
Kate Howe *(Exec Dir)*
Robert Goodwin *(Chief Data Officer)*
Ben Rudman *(Exec Dir)*

Subsidiary (Domestic):

Be Heard Group PLC (2)
53 Frith Street, London, W1D 4SN, United Kingdom
Tel.: (44) 2038286269
Web Site: http://www.beheardpartnership.com
Rev.: $73,238,432
Assets: $55,240,657
Liabilities: $35,990,304
Net Worth: $19,250,353
Earnings: ($9,005,446)
Emp.: 335
Fiscal Year-end: 12/31/2019
Advertising & Marketing Services
N.A.I.C.S.: 541810

Momentum Manufacturing Group, LLC (1)
23 National Ave, Georgetown, MA 01833
Tel.: (978) 659-6960
Web Site: http://www.mmg1982.com
Sheet Metal Work Mfg
N.A.I.C.S.: 332322
Steven Gore *(Chief Comml Officer)*
Matthew Smith *(Pres-Indus)*
James Moroney *(CEO)*
Thomas W. Mungovan *(CFO)*
John Brocke *(Pres-Technology)*
Andrew Curland *(Pres-Engineered Extrusions)*
Darci Ruggles *(Dir-Quality Systems)*

Subsidiary (Domestic):

H & M Metals, LLC (2)
9A Columbia Dr, Amherst, NH 03031
Tel.: (603) 889-8438
Web Site: http://www.hmmetals.net
Fabricated Structural Metal Mfr
N.A.I.C.S.: 332312
Dan Deveau *(Mgr-HR)*

Little Enterprises, Inc. (2)
31 Locust St, Ipswich, MA 01938
Tel.: (978) 356-7422
Web Site: http://www.littleent.com
All Other Miscellaneous Fabricated Metal Product Mfr
N.A.I.C.S.: 332999
Scott Little *(Pres)*

Vitex Extrusion, LLC (2)
43 Industrial Park Dr, Franklin, NH 03235
Tel.: (603) 934-5275
Web Site: http://www.vitexextrusions.com
Aluminum Extruded Product Mfr
N.A.I.C.S.: 331318
Andrew Curland *(Pres & CEO)*
Bob Tanner *(Dir-Ops-Value Added Production)*
Steve Jackson *(Dir-Bus Dev)*

Mythics Inc. (1)
1439 N Great Neck Rd Ste 201, Virginia Beach, VA 23454
Tel.: (757) 412-4362
Web Site: http://www.mythics.com
Sales Range: $100-124.9 Million
Emp.: 100
Computer Software
N.A.I.C.S.: 423430
Sloan Frey *(VP-Federal Infrastructure Sls)*
Shane Smutz *(Exec VP-Mythics Consulting)*
Doug Altamura *(Pres-Digital Transformation)*
Rick Welborn *(CFO)*
Chris Richards *(VP-Mktg)*
Gary Newman *(Pres)*
Al Wergley *(Gen Counsel)*
Brent Seaman *(VP-Cloud Solutions)*
Dale Darr *(VP-Contracts & Compliance)*
Dave Miller *(VP-Engineered Sys)*
Scott Tesnow *(VP-Federal Consulting)*
Sheri Mullin *(VP-HR)*
Nick Psimas *(VP-State & Local Infrastructure Sls)*
Randy Hardee *(VP-Tech)*
Robert Jones *(VP-Technical Svcs)*
Nicole Peternel *(Sr VP & Dir-Comm & PR)*
Aaron Cornfeld *(CTO)*

One Equity Partners Europe GmbH (1)
Neue Mainzer Str 84, Frankfurt am Main, 60311, Germany
Tel.: (49) 6950607470
Web Site: http://www.oneequity.com
Sales Range: $50-74.9 Million
Emp.: 10
Investment Management Service
N.A.I.C.S.: 523940
Joerg Zirener *(Mng Dir)*
Christoph Giulini *(Sr Mng Dir)*
Philipp von Meurers *(Mng Dir)*
Johann-Melchior von Peter *(Mng Dir)*
Dora Stojka *(Chief Admin Officer & Chief Compliance Officer)*
Chip Schorr *(Sr Mng Dir)*
Carlo Padovano *(Mng Dir)*

Orion Systems Integrators, Inc. (1)
333 Thornall St 7th Fl, Edison, NJ 08837
Tel.: (732) 422-9922
Web Site: http://www.orioninc.com
Sales Range: $25-49.9 Million
Emp.: 450
Custom Computer Programming Services
N.A.I.C.S.: 541511
Narendra Kumar *(Dir-Ops-India)*
Sunil Mehta *(Founder)*
Chetan Naik *(Exec VP)*
Jeffrey Robinson *(CFO)*
Raj Patil *(Pres & CEO)*
Pradeep Menon *(Exec VP & Head-Delivery)*
Mimi Young *(Exec VP-Digital Design)*
Satish Kumar *(Exec VP-Sls)*
Ramanan Seshadri *(Sr VP-Client Svcs)*
V. Balasubramanian *(Sr VP-Pharma & Life Sciences)*

Subsidiary (Domestic):

Tekmark Global Solutions LLC (2)
100 Metroplex Dr Ste 102, Edison, NJ 08817
Tel.: (732) 572-5400
Web Site: http://www.tekmarkinc.com
Rev.: $53,300,000
Emp.: 700
Computer Related Consulting Services
N.A.I.C.S.: 541512
Guy Del Grande *(CEO)*
Joshua Speicher *(Chief Information Security Officer)*
Tracey DelGrande *(COO)*
Jean Marie Sapounas *(Exec VP-Acctg, Bus Ops & HR)*
Jeff Cortley *(VP-Engrg Svcs & Solutions)*

PGW Auto Glass, LLC (1)
51 Dutilh Rd Ste 310, Cranberry Township, PA 16066
Tel.: (412) 995-6500
Web Site: http://www.buypgwautoglass.com
Sales Range: $100-124.9 Million
Automotive Glass Replacement Distr
N.A.I.C.S.: 811122

PS Holdco LLC (1)
PO BOX 8250, Birmingham, AL 35218
Tel.: (205) 788-4000
Web Site: http://www.pslogistics.com
Full-Service Logistics Company
N.A.I.C.S.: 541614
Scott Smith *(CEO)*
Houston Vaughn *(Pres & COO)*

Subsidiary (Domestic):

Buddy Moore Trucking, Inc. (2)
925 34th St N, Birmingham, AL 35222
Tel.: (205) 254-3682
Web Site: https://www.buddymooretrucking.com
General Freight Trucking, Long-Distance, Truckload
N.A.I.C.S.: 484121
E. H. Moore Jr. *(Pres)*

Diamond State Trucking, Inc. (2)
7659 Highway 270, Malvern, AR 72104
Tel.: (501) 332-5494
Web Site: http://www.diamondstatetrucking.com
General Freight Trucking, Long-Distance, Truckload
N.A.I.C.S.: 484121
Rodney Allen *(Pres)*

Jason Jones Trucking, Inc. (2)
7874 US 50, Shoals, IN 47581
Tel.: (812) 247-2954
Web Site: http://www.jasonjonestrucking.com
Specialized Freight Trucking
N.A.I.C.S.: 484230
Jeff Williams *(Mgr-Shop)*

Loudon County Trucking, LLC (2)
199 Commercial Park Dr, Loudon, TN 37774
Tel.: (865) 408-9062
Web Site: http://www.loudontrucking.com
Emp.: 50
Trucking Company
N.A.I.C.S.: 484110
Larry Jameson *(VP-Ops)*

Riechmann Transport Inc. (2)
3328 W Chain of Rocks Rd, Granite City, IL 62040
Tel.: (618) 797-6700
Transportation, Trucking & Railroad Company
N.A.I.C.S.: 484230

Southeast Logistics, Inc. (2)
5800 21st St, Tuscaloosa, AL 35401
Tel.: (205) 464-4745
Web Site: http://www.southeastlogistics.com
General Freight Trucking Services
N.A.I.C.S.: 484110
Rick McLain *(CFO)*
Beau Wicks *(Pres)*
Ricky Wilson *(Dir-Orientation)*
Bryan Golden *(Mgr-Shop & Maintenance)*
Shell Ann Golden *(Mgr-Payroll)*
Marty Hamner *(VP-HR & Recruiting)*

Prime Time Healthcare LLC (1)
15380 Weir St, 68137, Omaha, NE
Tel.: (402) 933-6700
Web Site: http://www.primetimehealthcare.com
Staffing & Recruitment Services

OEP CAPITAL ADVISORS, L.P.

U.S. PRIVATE

OEP Capital Advisors, L.P.—(Continued)
N.A.I.C.S.: 561311
David Dries *(Co-Founder & Mng Partner)*
Shawn Roeber *(CEO)*

Schoeller Arca Systems Group B.V. (1)
Hemzelaan 320, 8017, Zwolle, Netherlands
Tel.: (31) 384670700
Web Site:
http://www.schoellerarcasystems.com
Sales Range: $650-699.9 Million
Emp.: 1,300
Plastic Packaging Products Mfr
N.A.I.C.S.: 333993
Anselmo Garcia *(Reg Dir-Spain & Portugal)*
Witold Orlowski *(Reg Dir-Asia & Pacific)*
Michael Rinderle *(Mng Dir-Intl)*
Maciej Zietek *(Reg Dir-Central East Europe)*

Subsidiary (Non-US):

Schoeller Allibert (2)
176 avenue Charles de Gaulle, 92200, Neuilly-sur-Seine, France
Tel.: (33) 141200990
Web Site: http://www.schoellerallibert.com
Plastic Containers & Material Handling Products Mfr & Distr
N.A.I.C.S.: 326199
Ludo Gielen *(CEO)*
Martin Schoeller *(Co-Chm-Supervisory Bd)*
Christoph Schoeller *(Co-Chm-Supervisory Bd)*

Subsidiary (Non-US):

Logtek Limited (3)
Sir Stanley Clarke House 17 Ridgeway Quinton Business Park, Quinton, Birmingham, B32 1AF, United Kingdom
Tel.: (44) 1215060118
Web Site: http://www.logtek.com
Sales Range: $25-49.9 Million
Emp.: 20
Supply Chain Asset Management, Equipment Rental & Repair Services
N.A.I.C.S.: 561499

Schoeller Allibert Limited (3)
Road One Winsford Industrial Estate, Quinton, Winsford, CW7 3RA, United Kingdom
Tel.: (44) 1606561900
Web Site: http://www.schoellerallibert.com
Plastic Packaging Product. Mfr & Distr
N.A.I.C.S.: 326199

Subsidiary (Non-US):

Schoeller Allibert AB (2)
Hassleholmsvagen 10, PO Box 82, Perstorp, SE-28422, Sweden
Tel.: (46) 435777000
Web Site: http://www.schoellerallibert.com
Emp.: 15
Plastic Packaging & Shipping Products Mfr
N.A.I.C.S.: 326199
Jari Vaisanen *(Dir-Ops)*

Subsidiary (Domestic):

Schoeller Arca Systems BV (2)
Bruchterweg 88, 7772 BJ, Hardenberg, Netherlands
Tel.: (31) 523288900
Web Site:
http://www.schoellerarcasystems.nl
Sales Range: $25-49.9 Million
Emp.: 60
Plastic Packaging & Shipping Products Mfr
N.A.I.C.S.: 326199

Subsidiary (Non-US):

Schoeller Arca Systems GmbH (2)
Sacktannen 30, 19057, Schwerin, Germany
Tel.: (49) 38564520
Web Site:
http://www.schoellerarcasystems.de
Sales Range: $50-74.9 Million
Emp.: 170
Plastic Materials Mfr.
N.A.I.C.S.: 326199
Hans-Joachim Wiedmann *(Mng Dir)*
Bernhard Steidl *(CFO)*
Marcus Wille *(Dir-Sls-Matl Handling)*
Frank Reininghaus *(Mgr-Sls-Beverage)*

Schoeller Arca Systems GmbH (2)
Johannes Gutenberg Strasse 4, AT 2700, Wiener Neustadt, Austria
Tel.: (43) 262220656
Web Site:
http://www.schoellerarcasystems.at
Sales Range: $10-24.9 Million
Emp.: 10
Plastics Product Mfr
N.A.I.C.S.: 326199

Subsidiary (US):

Schoeller Arca Systems Inc. (2)
5202 Old Orchard Rd Ste 220, Skokie, IL 60077-1039
Tel.: (248) 355-3000
Sales Range: $10-24.9 Million
Emp.: 15
Plastics Product Mfr
N.A.I.C.S.: 326199

Subsidiary (Non-US):

Schoeller Arca Systems Limited (2)
17 Ridgeway Quinton Business Park, Birmingham, GB-32 1AF, West Midlands, United Kingdom
Tel.: (44) 121 506 0100
Web Site: http://www.schoellerallibert.com
Sales Range: $10-24.9 Million
Emp.: 550
Plastic Packaging Solutions for Materials Handling
N.A.I.C.S.: 326199

Schoeller Arca Systems Oy (2)
Askonkatu 9, 15100, Lahti, Finland
Tel.: (358) 3848211
Web Site:
http://www.schoellerarcasystems.fl
Rev.: $16,355,209
Emp.: 10
Plastics Product Mfr
Jari Vaisainen *(Mng Dir)*

Schoeller Arca Systems S.A. (2)
BP 69, F 01460, Nurieux, France
Tel.: (33) 474767947
Web Site:
http://www.schoellerarcasystems.fr
Sales Range: $75-99.9 Million
Emp.: 180
Plastics Product Mfr
N.A.I.C.S.: 326199

Schoeller Arca Systems S.L. (2)
Carretera Nacional 301 Km 377, Lorqui, 30564, Murcia, Spain
Tel.: (34) 968687519
Web Site: http://www.schoellerallibart.es
Sales Range: $25-49.9 Million
Emp.: 100
Plastics Product Mfr
N.A.I.C.S.: 326199
Anselmo Garcia *(Mng Dir)*

Schoeller Arca Systems ZAO (2)
Russkiy Diessel office 7507, Vsevolozhsk Kirpichniy Zavod, 188640, Saint Petersburg, Leningrad, Russia
Tel.: (7) 8123266520
Web Site: http://www.schoellerallibert.com
Rev.: $301,942
Emp.: 6
Plastics Product Mfr
N.A.I.C.S.: 326199
Dmitriy Timoshuk *(Gen Mgr)*

Schoeller Arca Systems, spol s.r.o. (2)
Pri Starej Pracharni 14, SK 831 04, Bratislava, Slovakia
Tel.: (421) 255565940
Web Site:
http://www.schoellerarcasystems.sk
Sales Range: $10-24.9 Million
Emp.: 13
Plastics Product Mfr
N.A.I.C.S.: 326199
Roman Galuszka *(Sls Mgr)*

Spartronics LLC (1)
2920 Kelly Ave, Watertown, SD 57201
Tel.: (605) 886-2519
Electronic & Electromechanical Devices Mfr
N.A.I.C.S.: 334419
Jeffrey T. Schlarbaum *(CEO)*
Todd Bradley *(Exec Chm)*
Michael R. Schlehr *(CFO)*

Subsidiary (Domestic):

Primus Technologies Corp. (2)
2333 Reach Rd, Williamsport, PA 17701-5579
Tel.: (570) 321-6264
Web Site: http://www.primus-tech.com
Printed Circuit Assembly Mfr
N.A.I.C.S.: 334418
Mitchell McCracken *(Engr-Mfg)*
Stephen Stone *(Pres)*
Chris Sullivan *(Chm & CEO)*
Frank G. Pellegrino *(Founder)*
Paul Cary *(VP-Ops)*

The Results Companies LLC (1)
100 NE 3rd Ave Ste 200, Fort Lauderdale, FL 33301-3301
Tel.: (954) 921-2400
Web Site:
http://www.theresultscompanies.com
Telephone Answering Services
N.A.I.C.S.: 561421
Alec Brecker *(Pres & CEO)*
Lori Brown *(Chief Experience Officer)*
Aaron Fender *(COO)*
Angelo Gencarelli *(CFO)*
Robert Rapp *(Founder & Chm)*

Tri-W Group, Inc. (1)
835 W Goodale Blvd, Columbus, OH 43212
Tel.: (614) 228-5000
Web Site: http://www.wwwilliams.com
Sales Range: $350-399.9 Million
Emp.: 700
Industrial Parts Distribution & Repair Services
N.A.I.C.S.: 423830
Richard Murch *(Treas & Controller)*
Alan Gatlin *(Pres & CEO)*
Andy Gasser *(CFO)*
Ron Taylor *(Mgr-Sls-Marine)*
Jennifer Mayer *(Mgr-Parts)*
Wendy Ables *(Mgr-Mktg)*

Subsidiary (Domestic):

Auto Safety House (2)
2630 W Buckeye Rd, Phoenix, AZ 85009-5744
Tel.: (602) 269-9721
Web Site: http://www.autosafetyhouse.com
Sales Range: $100-124.9 Million
Emp.: 109
Retail Sales of School Buses & Heavy Equipment
N.A.I.C.S.: 441330
Lisa Causse *(Sr VP-Ops & Comml Sls)*
Kevin Berg *(Mgr-Acct)*

CP Company (2)
5100 E 58th Ave, Commerce City, CO 80022
Tel.: (303) 287-2653
Web Site: http://www.ctpower.com
Sales Range: $10-24.9 Million
Emp.: 100
Supplier of Refrigeration Units
N.A.I.C.S.: 423610
Thomas Fries *(Chm)*
Carrie Kudrna *(Controller)*
Spencer Dietrich *(Pres)*

Desert Fleet-Serv, Inc. (2)
3029 E Southern Ave, Phoenix, AZ 85040
Tel.: (602) 437-7231
Web Site: http://www.desertfleet-serv.com
Sales Range: $1-9.9 Million
Emp.: 25
Mobile Services for Onsite Maintenance & Repair of Trucks & Trailers
N.A.I.C.S.: 811111

thyssenkrupp Marine Systems GmbH (1)
Werftstrasse 112-114, 24143, Kiel, Germany
Tel.: (49) 4317000
Web Site: https://www.thyssenkrupp-marinesystems.com
Commercial Shipbuilding
N.A.I.C.S.: 336611

Subsidiary (Domestic):

MV Werften Wismar GmbH (2)
Wendorfer Weg 5, 23966, Wismar, Germany
Tel.: (49) 3841770
Web Site: http://www.mv-werften.com
Emp.: 2,948
Ship Building Services
N.A.I.C.S.: 336611

OERTHER FOODS, INC.
8150 President Dr, Orlando, FL 32809
Tel.: (407) 859-7123
Web Site: http://www.mcfun.com
Year Founded: 1973
Sales Range: $25-49.9 Million
Emp.: 1,000
Fast-Food Restaurant Franchise Chain Owner & Operator
N.A.I.C.S.: 722513
Gary Oerther *(Owner & Co-Chm)*
Jeff Watson *(Vice Chm & COO)*
Kenny Powenski *(Dir-HR)*
Georgette Lemieux *(VP-Ops)*
Gregg Oerther *(Owner & CEO)*
Jeanie Oerther *(Owner & Co-Chm)*
Jon Siegel *(Pres-Ops)*
Mark Sherbondy *(Dir-Ops & Facilities)*
Paul Espaillat *(Dir-Ops & Mktg)*

OFD FOODS, LLC
525 25th Ave SW, Albany, OR 97322
Tel.: (541) 926-6001 OR
Web Site: http://www.ofd.com
Year Founded: 1963
Sales Range: $100-124.9 Million
Emp.: 380
Freeze Dried Foods & Non-Food Ingredients Mfr
N.A.I.C.S.: 311612
Philip Unverzagt *(CFO)*

Subsidiaries:

Mountain House (1)
32136 Hooska Ave Bldg 62, Tangent, OR 97389
Web Site: http://www.mountainhouse.com
Frozen Food Product Mfr
N.A.I.C.S.: 311612
Jim Marryman *(Pres)*

OFF MADISON AVE, LLC
5555 E Van Buren St Ste 215, Phoenix, AZ 85008
Tel.: (480) 505-4500
Web Site:
http://www.offmadisonave.com
Year Founded: 1998
Advertising Services
N.A.I.C.S.: 541810
David Anderson *(Co-Founder & CEO)*
Roger Hurni *(Co-Founder)*
Jacqueline Keidel *(Sr Acct Exec-PR & Social Media)*
Sasha Howell *(Chief Strategy Officer & Gen Mgr)*
Lizzy Lowy *(Dir-Client Svcs)*

Subsidiaries:

CGPR LLC (1)
24 Prospect St, Marblehead, MA 01945
Tel.: (781) 639-4924
Web Site:
http://www.cgprpublicrelations.com
Emp.: 6
Public Relations Firm
N.A.I.C.S.: 541820
Chris Ann Goddard *(Pres)*
Eleanor Sachs *(Exec VP)*
Craig M. Davis *(COO)*
Kristen Bujold *(Sr Acct Exec)*
Nicole Kieser *(Sr VP)*

Fineman PR (1)
330 Townsend St Suite 119, San Francisco, CA 94107
Tel.: (415) 392-1000
Web Site: http://www.finemanpr.com
Sales Range: $10-24.9 Million
Emp.: 15
Full-Service Brand Public Relations & Crisis Communications
N.A.I.C.S.: 541820
Michael B. Fineman *(Pres-Agency & Dir-Creative)*
Lorna Bush *(Sr VP)*

COMPANIES

Karmina Zafiro (VP)
Serene Buckley (Sr Dir-Content Strategy)
Travis Taylor (Exec VP)

OFF MARKET DATA, INC.
1680 Michigan Ave Ste 700, Miami, FL 33139
Tel.: (347) 594-5695
Web Site: http://www.urbint.com
Custom Computer Programming Services
N.A.I.C.S.: 541511
Trent A. Peugh (Pres-Damage Prevention)
Corey Capasso (Founder & CEO)
Matt Crye (Chief Customer Officer)
Bill Dall (Sr VP-Product & Tech)

Subsidiaries:

Opvantek, Inc. (1)
385 Oxford Valley Rd Suite 322, Yardley, 19067, PA
Tel.: (215) 968-7790
Administrative Management & General Management Consulting Service
N.A.I.C.S.: 541611

OFF ROAD UNLIMITED
2636 N Ontario St, Burbank, CA 91504
Tel.: (877) 563-1208 CA
Web Site: http://www.offroadunlimited.com
Year Founded: 1989
Automotive & Off Road Parts & Installation Services
N.A.I.C.S.: 423120
Maurice Rozo (Owner)

OFF THE GRID PUBLIC RELATIONS
3218 E Colonial Dr, Orlando, FL 32803
Tel.: (321) 281-8378
Web Site: http://www.offthegrid-pr.com
Sales Range: Less than $1 Million
Emp.: 4
Media Relations, Digital Services & Public Relations
N.A.I.C.S.: 541820
Lisa Thorell (Principal)

OFFENBACHER AQUATICS INC.
10001 Aerospace Rd, Lanham, MD 20706
Tel.: (301) 794-8794
Web Site: http://www.offenbachers.com
Sales Range: $10-24.9 Million
Emp.: 10
Outdoor & Garden Furniture & Recreation Equipment
N.A.I.C.S.: 449110
Karl F. Offenbacher (Pres)

OFFENHAUSER COMPANY
2201 Telephone Rd, Houston, TX 77023
Tel.: (713) 928-2981
Web Site: http://www.offenhauser.com
Sales Range: $10-24.9 Million
Emp.: 100
Fabricated Plate Work (Boiler Shop)
N.A.I.C.S.: 332313
Robert H. Dillard (Pres & CEO)
Alton Tarkington (Mgr-Manufacturing)

OFFERLE COOPERATIVE GRAIN & SUPPLY COMPANY
222 E SantaFe, Offerle, KS 67563
Tel.: (620) 659-2165
Web Site: http://www.offerle.coop
Sales Range: $10-24.9 Million
Emp.: 25

Grains
N.A.I.C.S.: 424510
Duane Boyd (Gen Mgr)

OFFICE & FLOORING WORX INC.
5000 Tampa Rd, Oldsmar, FL 34677
Tel.: (813) 855-5844
Web Site: http://www.office-worx.com
Sales Range: $1-9.9 Million
Emp.: 10
Office Furniture Dealer
N.A.I.C.S.: 423210
Brian R. Clark (Co-Founder)
Jennifer P. Clark (Co-Founder)

OFFICE & PROFESSIONAL EMPLOYEES INTERNATIONAL UNION
Tel.: (212) 367-0902 DC
Web Site: https://www.opeiu.org
Year Founded: 1946
Sales Range: $10-24.9 Million
Employee Union
N.A.I.C.S.: 813930
Mary Mahoney (Treas & Sec)
Nicole E. Korkolis (Dir-Comm, Education & Res)
Greg Blackman (Pres-GSAF/OPEIU Local 100-Reg III)
Richard Lanigan (Co-Pres)
John Mattiacci (Pres-Guild 45-Reg II)
Suzanne Mode (Bus Mgr-Local 8-Reg VI)
Christine Page (Co-Pres, VP-Diversity & Bus Mgr-Local 174)
Tamara Rubyn (Co-Pres & Bus Mgr-Local 29-Reg V)
Aaron E. Sanders (Pres-Local 512-Reg VII)
Mary Short (Pres-Local 32 Reg II)
Dennis R. Arrington (Pres-ITPEU/OPEIU Local 4873-Reg III)
Sharon Taylor (Pres-Local 459-Reg II)

OFFICE BEACON LLC
409 N Pacific, Redondo Beach, CA 90277
Tel.: (310) 863-4343
Web Site: http://www.officebeacon.com
Year Founded: 2001
Rev.: $3,200,000
Emp.: 800
Graphic Design Services
N.A.I.C.S.: 541430
Pranav Dalal (Pres & CEO)
Walter Thurmond III (Dir-Sls)
Najee Goode (Dir-Sls)
Caroline Dalal (Officer-Strategic Partnerships)

OFFICE CONCEPTS INC.
1142 N North Branch St, Chicago, IL 60642
Tel.: (312) 942-1100
Web Site: http://www.officeconcepts.com
Year Founded: 1938
Sales Range: $25-49.9 Million
Emp.: 133
Mfr of Office Work Stations & Furniture
N.A.I.C.S.: 423210
Tom Worniak (Owner)
Jeanne Busse (Acct Mgr)
Jim Sheridan (Dir-Ops)

OFFICE ENVIRONMENTS INC.
1500 Grundys Ln, Bristol, PA 19007
Tel.: (267) 553-1000
Web Site: http://www.oeonline.net
Sales Range: $10-24.9 Million
Emp.: 25
Office Furniture

N.A.I.C.S.: 423210
Thomas Graham (Pres & CEO)
Brian Ink (Dir-Ops)

OFFICE EQUIPMENT & SUPPLY
3192 Ampere Ave, Bronx, NY 10465
Tel.: (718) 823-6623
Web Site: http://www.oescbronx.com
Rev.: $18,700,000
Emp.: 2
Office Forms & Supplies
N.A.I.C.S.: 459410
Michael Maglio (Pres)

OFFICE EQUIPMENT COMPANY OF MOBILE, INC.
104 E 65th Service Rd, Mobile, AL 36607
Tel.: (251) 471-3368
Web Site: http://www.oecez.com
Rev.: $10,115,951
Emp.: 47
Office Forms & Supplies
N.A.I.C.S.: 459410
Thomas M. Bramlett (Chm)

OFFICE FURNITURE & DESIGN CONCEPTS, INC.
11866 Metro Pkwy, Fort Myers, FL 33966
Tel.: (239) 337-1212
Web Site: http://www.officefurnituredesignconcepts.com
Year Founded: 1974
Sales Range: $10-24.9 Million
Emp.: 20
Office Furniture Retailer
N.A.I.C.S.: 449110
Joe Gammons (Pres)

OFFICE FURNITURE CENTER, INC.
2117 W Kennedy Blvd, Tampa, FL 33606
Tel.: (813) 254-7253 FL
Web Site: http://www.ofctampa.com
Year Founded: 1987
Sales Range: $1-9.9 Million
Emp.: 10
Office Furniture Stores
N.A.I.C.S.: 449110
Edwin Celeiro (Pres)

OFFICE FURNITURE PARTNERSHIP
67 E Park Pl, Morristown, NJ 07960
Tel.: (973) 267-6966
Web Site: http://www.officefurniturepartnership.com
Rev.: $18,000,000
Emp.: 26
Office Furniture Distr
N.A.I.C.S.: 423210
Warren Levy (Pres & CEO)
Cathryn Fracasso (Controller)
Robin Heike (Coord-Sls)
Robert E. Marks (Partner)

OFFICE FURNITURE RENTAL ALLIANCE LLC
PO Box 280897, East Hartford, CT 06128
Tel.: (860) 528-2000
Web Site: http://www.ofra.com
Sales Range: $10-24.9 Million
Emp.: 160
Home Appliance, Furniture & Entertainment Rental Services
N.A.I.C.S.: 561320
Ralph Chappano (Pres)
Lori Shaker (Controller)

OFFICE RESOURCES, INC.

OFFICE MANAGEMENT SYSTEMS INC.
5911 Greenwood Pkwy, Bessemer, AL 35022
Tel.: (205) 565-2200 MS
Web Site: http://www.logistasolutions.com
Year Founded: 1983
Sales Range: $25-49.9 Million
Emp.: 200
Sales of Computers & Software
N.A.I.C.S.: 423430
Ronald E. Harper (Pres)

OFFICE MASTER INC.
1110 S Mildred Ave, Ontario, CA 91761
Tel.: (909) 392-5678 CA
Web Site: http://www.officemaster.com
Year Founded: 1986
Sales Range: $25-49.9 Million
Emp.: 50
Mfr Office Furniture
N.A.I.C.S.: 337214
William Chow (CEO)

OFFICE MOVERS OF FLORIDA LLC
4515 Oakfair Blvd Ste 105, Tampa, FL 33610
Tel.: (813) 304-2273
Web Site: http://www.officemoversofflorida.com
Sales Range: $10-24.9 Million
Emp.: 20
Moving & Storage Services
N.A.I.C.S.: 493110
Trent Potner (Pres)

OFFICE REMEDIES, INC.
171 Elden St Ste 160, Herndon, VA 20170
Tel.: (703) 478-0910
Web Site: http://www.oriresults.com
Year Founded: 1988
Sales Range: $10-24.9 Million
Emp.: 400
Data Entry Services
N.A.I.C.S.: 518210
Kathleen Benson (Co-Founder & CEO)
Sue Lynd (Co-Founder & COQ)
Shannon Brown (Pres & Partner)
Robert Pick (VP-Pub Sector Practice)

OFFICE RESOURCES INC.
816 E Broadway, Louisville, KY 40204
Tel.: (502) 589-8400 KY
Web Site: http://www.oriusa.com
Year Founded: 1993
Office Furniture Whslr
N.A.I.C.S.: 423210
George Bell (Owner, Pres & CEO)
Pam R. Freeman (CFO)

OFFICE RESOURCES, INC.
374 Congress St Ste 1, Boston, MA 02210
Tel.: (617) 423-9100
Web Site: http://www.ori.com
Year Founded: 1996
Sales Range: $150-199.9 Million
Emp.: 150
Furniture & Related Product Distr
N.A.I.C.S.: 449110
Lisa M. Barton (Sr Project Mgr)
Paul Fraser (Co-Founder & Principal)
Kevin Barbary (Co-Founder & Principal)
Ed Baust (Exec VP)
Rob Tenaglia (Sr VP-Sls & Gen Mgr)
Doug Ellis (Sr VP)
Adam Bacall (Exec VP)
Tracy O'Rourke (VP-Project Svcs)

OFFICE RESOURCES, INC.

U.S. PRIVATE

Office Resources, Inc.—(Continued)
Zoey Zarkadas (VP-Customer Experience)
Katie Damon (VP-Sls)
Holyn Nickerson (Exec VP-Bus Dev & Mktg)

OFFICE SOLUTIONS BUSINESS PRODUCTS SERVICES
23303 La Palma Ave, Yorba Linda, CA 92887
Tel.: (714) 692-7412
Web Site: http://www.officesolutions.com
Rev.: $23,500,000
Emp.: 100
Stationery & Office Supplies
N.A.I.C.S.: 424120
Robert J. Mairena (Pres)

OFFICE SUITES PLUS
1999 Richmond Rd, Lexington, KY 40502
Tel.: (859) 514-2000
Web Site: http://officesuitesplus.com
Sales Range: $10-24.9 Million
Emp.: 126
Management Consulting
N.A.I.C.S.: 541611
Steven Michael Fry (Mgr-HR)

OFFICE THREE SIXTY, INC.
7301 Woodland Dr, Indianapolis, IN 46278
Tel.: (317) 632-1360
Web Site: http://www.office3sixty.com
Office Supplies Mfr & Dist
N.A.I.C.S.: 459410
Chris White (Mgr-HR)
Subsidiaries:
Cardinal Office360 (1)
576 E Main St, Frankfort, KY 40601
Tel.: (502) 875-3300
Web Site: http://www.cardinaloffice.com
Stationery & Office Supplies Merchant Whslr
N.A.I.C.S.: 424120

OFFICEMATE INTERNATIONAL CORPORATION
90 Newfield Ave, Edison, NJ 08837
Tel.: (732) 225-7422
Web Site: http://www.officemate.com
Year Founded: 1979
Sales Range: $100-124.9 Million
Emp.: 100
Office Supplies
N.A.I.C.S.: 424120
Shwu Chen (Pres)
Roger Ko (Controller)
Martin Yang (Sr VP-Sls & Mktg)
Edward Chuang (Mgr & Project Engr)
Hwang Howard (Mgr-Logistic)
Jeff Bittens (VP-Sls & Mktg)
David Brous (VP-Sls)
Sharon Kiefer (Mgr-Sls-Natl)

OFFICESCAPE, INC.
8910 Purdue Rd Ste 480, Indianapolis, IN 46268-1197
Tel.: (317) 616-2222 IN
Web Site: http://www.officescape.com
Year Founded: 2000
Sales Range: $1-9.9 Million
Emp.: 38
Office Services & Technology
N.A.I.C.S.: 531210
Tracy Bowles (Mgr-Sls)

OFFICESUPPLY.COM
302 Industrial Dr, Columbus, WI 53925
Tel.: (920) 623-9528
Web Site: http://www.officesupply.com
Year Founded: 2003
Emp.: 30
Office Supplies Retailer
N.A.I.C.S.: 459410
Joe Schaefer (VP-Sls & Mktg)
Tim Horton (Co-Founder & CEO)
Jim Horton (Co-Founder & Pres)

OFFICEWORKS LLC
12000 Ex 5 Pkwy, Fishers, IN 46037
Tel.: (317) 577-3510
Web Site: http://www.officeworks.net
Sales Range: $10-24.9 Million
Emp.: 47
Office Furniture
N.A.I.C.S.: 493110
Thomas M. O'Neil (Owner & Pres)
Jim Calder (Mgr-Installation)
Joyce Posson (VP-Mktg & HR)
Patty Clark (Dir-Workplace Svcs)

OFFICEWORKS, INC.
149 Middlesex Tpke, Burlington, MA 01803
Tel.: (781) 270-9000
Web Site: http://www.officeworksinc.com
Office Space Planning Services
N.A.I.C.S.: 541618
Mark Loughlin (CEO)
Subsidiaries:
General Office Interiors, Inc. (1)
50 Cardinal Dr Ste 101, Westfield, NJ 07083
Tel.: (908) 688-9400
Web Site: http://www.generalofficeinteriors.com
Rev.: $15,198,086
Emp.: 12
Office Furniture
N.A.I.C.S.: 423210
Peter DeBease (Pres)
Robin Duym (Acct Mgr)

OFFICEXPRESS INC.
7701 Alabama Ave, Canoga Park, CA 91304
Tel.: (818) 884-5737
Web Site: http://www.oxpros.com
Year Founded: 2003
Sales Range: $1-9.9 Million
Emp.: 20
Office Supplies & Stationery Stores
N.A.I.C.S.: 459410
Mike Bushman (Pres)

OFFICIA IMAGING INC
7323 Engineer Rd, San Diego, CA 92111
Tel.: (858) 348-0831 CA
Web Site: http://www.officia.com
Year Founded: 1975
Sales Range: $10-24.9 Million
Emp.: 50
Copiers & Copier Supplies
N.A.I.C.S.: 459410
Thomas Deverell (Pres & CEO)

OFFIT KURMAN
300 E Lombard St Ste 2010, Baltimore, MD 21202
Tel.: (443) 738-1500
Web Site: http://www.offitkurman.com
Year Founded: 1987
Sales Range: $25-49.9 Million
Emp.: 157
Law Office
N.A.I.C.S.: 541110
Maurice L. Offit (Co-Founder & Pres)
Howard K. Kurman (Principal)
Jesse D. Delanoy (Principal & Atty)
Rajiv K. Goel (Atty)
Scott V. Kamins (Principal & Atty)
Michael N. Mercurio (Chm-Bus Law & Transactions Practice Grp & Atty)
Glenn D. Solomon (Principal & Atty)
Seymour B. Stern (Principal & Atty)
Jason C. Berger (Principal & Atty)
Christopher M. Wachter (Atty)
Aaron Bukowitz (COO & Exec VP)
Bryan Lawson (Dir-Mktg)
Toni Hannon (Mgr-Billing Sys)
John Brunnett (Mgr-Practice Grp)
Jim Ries (Mgr-Practice Grp)
B. Marvin Potler (Principal & Atty)
Bryn Sherman (Principal)
Douglas R. Kay (Dir-Comml litigation Atty & Practice Grp)
Marjorie Just (Principal)
Timothy C. Lynch (Mng Principal-Legal Affairs & Atty)
Todd A. Kelting (Principal & Atty)
Tracie Clabaugh (Principal & Atty-Frederick)
Frances C. Wilburn (Principal & Atty-Bethesda)
Sandra A. Brooks (Principal & Atty-Bethesda)
Russell B. Berger (Dir-Practice Grp & Atty-Labor & Employment)
Linda Sorg Ostovitz (Dir-Practice Grp & Atty-Family Law)
Fred H. Silverstein (Principal & Atty-Columbia)
Theodore P. Stein (Principal & Atty-Bethesda)
Wayne Watkinson (Principal & Atty-Woodbridge)
Richard P. Gilly (Principal & Atty-Philadelphia)
Joyce A. Kuhns (Principal)
Shirley Keisler (Principal)
David S. Greber (Principal)
Nichole Galvin (Principal)
Herbert R. Fineburg (Atty)
John A. Kane (Principal)
Alyce Verville (Dir-HR)
Joe Crossney (Mgr-Practice Grp)
Lisa Shattuck (Mgr-Client Rels)
Robert Skinner (Dir-IT)
Shirelle Dixon (Controller)
Joseph Condo (Principal-Tysons Corner)
Laurie M. Wasserman (Principal)
Jerry Boden (Mgr-Central Maryland)
Jeanna Lam (Principal)
Steve Hyatt (Chief HR Officer)
Kim DePuy (Reg Mgr-Tysons)
Christopher Raimund (Principal-Intellectual Property Practice)
James Gillis (Atty-Estates & Trusts Practice Grp-Tysons)
Stephen Metz (Principal-Bankruptcy & Restructuring Practice Grp-Bethesda)
Jason Hardman (Atty)
Richard Gray (Atty)
Joseph Mathis (Atty)
James N. Gaither (Atty)
Bryan King (Principal)
Kelcie Longaker (Atty)
Gregory Grissett (Atty)
Megan Shannon (Atty-Insurance Recovery Grp)
Franklin Miller (Principal)
W. Martin Williams (Principal)
Christopher D'Angelo (Principal-New York)
Rawan Hmoud (Principal-New York City)
Jennifer Friend-Kelly (Atty-Bethesda)
Allison W. Rosenzweig (Atty-Bus Law & Transactions)
Edward A. Bloom (Dir-Real Estate Law & Bus Transactions Atty & Practice Grp)
Catherine H. McQueen (Chm-Family Law Practice Grp & Atty-Family Law)
Diane S. Kotkin (Chm-Estate Plng Practice Grp & Atty-Estate Plng)
Ian P. Bartman (Chm-Comml Litigation Practice Grp & Atty-Bus Litigation)
Nate Fox (Chm-Real Estate Practice Grp & Atty-Real Estate, Construction)
April Rancier (Atty-Labor & Employment Law)
Laura Mayes (Atty-Construction Law Practice Grp-Philadelphia)
Veronica K. Yu (Atty-Labor & Employment Practice Grp)
Rebecca Prosper (Atty-Insurance Recovery Practice Grp-Philadelphia)
Jordan Savitz (Atty-Maryland)
Jared Johnson (Principal-Philadelphia)
Bill Hamel (Principal-Charlotte)
Joseph T. Kelley III (Principal)
William P. Cannon III (Principal)
Thomas Hicks III (Atty)
James E. Fagan III (Principal)

OFFSHORE CLEANING SYSTEMS, LLC.
9525 US Hwy 167, Abbeville, LA 70510
Tel.: (337) 898-2104
Web Site: http://www.offshorecleaningsystems.com
Emp.: 75
Air Purification Equipment Mfr
N.A.I.C.S.: 333413
Kenny Desormeux (Pres & CEO)
Michael B. Hutchison (CFO)
Guy Bergeron (Mgr-Shop)

OFFSHORE CRANE & SERVICE COMPANY
1375 N Olive St, Ventura, CA 93001
Tel.: (805) 648-3348
Web Site: http://www.truckandcrane.com
Sales Range: $10-24.9 Million
Emp.: 100
Cranes & Aerial Lift Equipment, Rental Or Leasing
N.A.I.C.S.: 532412
Tim Holder (Pres)

OFFSHORE ENERGY SERVICES INC.
5900 Hwy 90 E, Broussard, LA 70518
Tel.: (337) 233-3442
Web Site: http://www.offshoreenergyservices.com
Year Founded: 1976
Sales Range: $25-49.9 Million
Emp.: 250
Oil Field Services
N.A.I.C.S.: 213112
Charles M. Garber Sr. (Pres)

OFFSHORE INLAND SERVICES INC.
3521 Brookdale Dr S, Mobile, AL 36618
Tel.: (251) 479-6081
Web Site: http://www.offshoreinland.com
Rev.: $17,000,000
Emp.: 155
Hydraulic Equipment Repair
N.A.I.C.S.: 811210
Mark White (Mgr-Reg Sls)
Mike Riley (Project Mgr)

OFFSHORE JOINT SERVICES, INC.
1621 Prime W Pkwy, Katy, TX 77449
Tel.: (281) 578-6523 TX
Web Site: http://www.ojs.com
Year Founded: 1986
Sales Range: $1-9.9 Million
Emp.: 50

Subsea Oil Pipeline Protective Coating Application Services
N.A.I.C.S.: 213112

Subsidiaries:

PT OJS Komplex (1)
Pergudangan Green Town No 5, Batam, 29432, Bengkong, Indonesia
Tel.: (62) 778450095
Subsea Oil Pipeline Protective Coating Application Services
N.A.I.C.S.: 213112

OFFSHORE PETROLEUM CORP.
110 E Broward Blvd Ste 1700, Fort Lauderdale, FL 33301   DE
Year Founded: 1999
Oil & Gas Exploration Services
N.A.I.C.S.: 211120
John Rainwater (Chm, Pres & CEO)
Mickey Wiesinger (CFO & Sec)

OFFSHORE SERVICE VESSELS, LLC.
16201 E Main St Cut Off, Cut Off, LA 70345
Tel.: (985) 601-4444
Web Site: http://www.chouest.com
Rev.: $67,700,000
Emp.: 1,000
Marine Cargo Handling
N.A.I.C.S.: 488320
Roger White (Sr VP)
Charles Comeaux (CFO)
Adrian Dannald (Controller)

OFFSPRING SOLUTIONS
4031 University Dr, Fairfax, VA 22030
Tel.: (703) 277-7752
Web Site: http://www.offspringsolutions.com
Year Founded: 2003
Sales Range: $1-9.9 Million
Emp.: 18
Business Application Software Development Services
N.A.I.C.S.: 541511
Denise Rottier (Mgr-Office Ops)

OFS INTERNATIONAL LLC
7735 Miller Rd Ste 3, Houston, TX 77049
Tel.: (281) 452-3036   DE
Web Site: http://www.ofsint.com
Year Founded: 2012
Oilfield Support Services
N.A.I.C.S.: 213112
David Green (COO)

Subsidiaries:

Threading & Precision Manufacturing LLC (1)
7735 Miller Rd Ste 3, Houston, TX 77049
Tel.: (281) 452-3036
Web Site: http://www.ofsint.com
Oilwell Pipe Threading Services
N.A.I.C.S.: 332996
David Green (COO)

OFSCAP LLC
1235 North Loop W Ste 500, Houston, TX 77008
Tel.: (713) 823-2900
Web Site: http://www.ofscap.com
Investment & Merchant Bank
N.A.I.C.S.: 523150
James C. Row (Mng Dir)

Subsidiaries:

Oil & Gas Asset Clearinghouse, LLC (1)
1235 N Loop W Ste 510, Houston, TX 77008
Tel.: (281) 873-4600
Web Site: http://www.ogclearinghouse.com
Oil & Gas Properties Auction
N.A.I.C.S.: 531390

Patrick M. DaPra (VP-Negotiated Transactions)
Deon Warner (Pres)
Bryan Rabon (COO)
Amanda Knox Novak (Mgr-Bus Dev)
Matthew DaPra (Mgr-Bus Dev)
Thomas Campbell (VP-Engrg)
Russell A. Bellow (Dir-Product Dev)
Karl Gehring (Dir-Creative Svcs)

OFTEDAL CONSTRUCTION INC.
434 MT 59 N, Miles City, MT 59301
Tel.: (406) 232-5911
Web Site: http://www.oftedalconstruction.com
Sales Range: $75-99.9 Million
Emp.: 250
Earthmoving & Civil Engineering Construction Services Contractor
N.A.I.C.S.: 238910
Jeff McDonald (Pres)
Bradley M. Olson (Project Mgr)
Greg Jackson (VP)
Shawn Coffin (Dir-HR)
Matt Otterby (Mgr-Ops)
Irene Pluhar (Mgr-Payroll)
Cam Lundby (Project Mgr)
Chris Audiss (Project Mgr)
Payton Zierolf (Dir-Safety)
George Hruska (Mgr-Bus Dev)
John Lampert (Mgr-Equipment)
Don Hembree (Mgr-Maintenance)
Aaron Elrod (Mgr-Shop)
Dennis Kirchheck (Mgr-Shop)
Terry Hause (Officer-Safety)

OGAN/DALLAL ASSOCIATES, INC.
530 7th Ave Ste 606, New York, NY 10018
Tel.: (212) 840-0888
Web Site: http://www.odapr.com
Year Founded: 1986
Sales Range: $10-24.9 Million
Emp.: 8
Public Relations Agency
N.A.I.C.S.: 541820
Evelyn Dallal (Pres)

OGDEN LINCOLN MERCURY INC.
50 W Ogden Ave, Westmont, IL 60559-1336
Tel.: (630) 968-5600
Web Site: http://www.ogdenavenuemotors.com
Sales Range: $10-24.9 Million
Emp.: 58
New & Used Automobiles
N.A.I.C.S.: 532112
Mark Iozzo (Owner, Pres & CEO)
Fred Iozzo Sr. (Chm)

OGLETHORPE POWER CORPORATION
2100 E Exchange Pl, Tucker, GA 30084-5336
Tel.: (770) 270-7600   GA
Web Site: https://www.opc.com
Year Founded: 1974
Rev.: $1,740,185,000
Assets: $16,524,851,000
Liabilities: $14,295,887,000
Net Worth: $2,228,964,000
Earnings: $65,790,000
Emp.: 337
Fiscal Year-end: 12/31/23
Power Generation
N.A.I.C.S.: 221111
Elizabeth Bush Higgins (CFO & Exec VP)
Jami G. Reusch (VP-HR)
William F. Ussery (Exec VP-Member & External Rels)
Kenneth G. Warren (VP & Controller)

Annalisa M. Bloodworth (Gen Counsel & Sr VP)
Heather H. Teilhet (Sr VP-External Affairs)
David W. Sorrick (COO & Exec VP)
Bobby C. Smith Jr. (Chm)
Michael L. Smith (Pres & CEO)

OGLETREE, DEAKINS, NASH, SMOAK & STEWART, P.C.
The Ogletree Bldg 300 N Main St, Greenville, SC 29601
Tel.: (864) 271-1300
Web Site: http://www.ogletreedeakins.com
Year Founded: 1977
Sales Range: $250-299.9 Million
Emp.: 543
Labor & Employment Lawyers
N.A.I.C.S.: 541110
C. Matthew Keen (Mng Dir)
Charles B. Baldwin (Mng Dir)

OGM, LTD.
2480 Jackson Pike, Columbus, OH 43223
Tel.: (614) 539-8238   OH
Web Site: http://www.cleanwaterltd.com
Year Founded: 1997
Sales Range: $1-9.9 Million
Emp.: 13
Environmental Services
N.A.I.C.S.: 541620
Brad Malatesta (Owner & Pres)

Subsidiaries:

Clean Water Ltd. (1)
300 Cherokee Dr, Dayton, OH 45417   (100%)
Tel.: (937) 268-6501
Web Site: http://www.cleanwaterltd.com
Emp.: 100
Hazardous & Non-Hazardous Waste Water Treatment, Solvent Recovery, Used Oil Recycling, Transportation & Analytical Services
N.A.I.C.S.: 562920
Troy Picarello (Mgr-Fleet)

OH MY CRAFTS, INC.
1489 West 105 N, Orem, UT 84057
Tel.: (801) 785-9091
Web Site: http://www.ohmycrafts.com
Year Founded: 2005
Sales Range: $1-9.9 Million
Emp.: 60
Online Retailer of Crafts & Scrapbooking Products
N.A.I.C.S.: 459999
Sandy Cottle (Owner & Creative Dir)
Lyn Timboe (Mgr-Ops)

OHI MAINE
25 Freedom Pkwy, Hermon, ME 04401
Tel.: (207) 848-5804   ME
Web Site: http://www.ohimaine.org
Year Founded: 1979
Sales Range: $10-24.9 Million
Emp.: 426
Disability Assistance Services
N.A.I.C.S.: 623210
Bonniejean Brooks (Pres & CEO)
Margaret F. Criner (Treas)
Diane Boone (Chm)
Karen Berry (Sec)
Martha Harris (Vice Chm)
Brenda S. Leavitt (Project Mgr)
Deborah Deb Smith (Dir-Intellectual Disability Svcs)
Margaret Longsworth (Dir-Mental Health & Clinical Svcs)

OHIGRO INC.
6720 Gillete Rd, Waldo, OH 43356
Tel.: (740) 726-2429   OH
Web Site: http://www.ohigro.com

Year Founded: 1965
Sales Range: $10-24.9 Million
Emp.: 35
Retailer of Agricultural Services & Products
N.A.I.C.S.: 444240
Jeffrey Ward (Controller)

OHIO ASSOCIATED ENTERPRISES
1382 W Jackson St, Painesville, OH 44077
Tel.: (440) 354-2106
Web Site: http://www.meritec.com
Year Founded: 1967
Sales Range: $10-24.9 Million
Emp.: 140
Electronic Connector Mfr
N.A.I.C.S.: 334417

Subsidiaries:

Meritec (1)
1359 W Jackson St, Painesville, OH 44077
Tel.: (440) 354-3148
Designer & Mfr of High Performance Electronic Interconnects
N.A.I.C.S.: 334417
Ken Braund (Mgr-Sls)
Zane Daggett (Dir-Sls)

OHIO AUTO KOLOR, INC.
2600 Fisher Rd, Columbus, OH 43204
Tel.: (614) 276-8700
Web Site: http://www.ohioautokolor.com
Year Founded: 1962
Sales Range: $10-24.9 Million
Emp.: 80
Paints
N.A.I.C.S.: 423120
Gary Bumgarner (Pres)
Tim Wilson (Mgr-Warehouse)
Curtis Bumgarner (VP)

OHIO AWNING & MANUFACTURING CO.
2658 Scranton Rd, Cleveland, OH 44113-5144
Tel.: (216) 861-2400
Web Site: http://www.ohioawning.com
Year Founded: 1865
Sales Range: $1-9.9 Million
Emp.: 40
Textile Bag & Canvas Mills
N.A.I.C.S.: 314910
Jeff Mitchell (Gen Mgr)
William R. Morse (VP)
Tom Lock (Mgr-Storage & Scheduling)
Andrew R. Morse (Pres)

Subsidiaries:

Akron Tent & Awning Co. (1)
2658 Scranton Rd., Cleveland, OH 44113
Tel.: (216) 851-5400
Mfr of Tents & Awnings
N.A.I.C.S.: 313310

Ohio Awning Company (1)
5777 Grant Ave, Cleveland, OH 44105
Tel.: (216) 861-2400
Web Site: http://www.ohioawning.com
Mfr of Tents & Awnings
N.A.I.C.S.: 313310
Andy Morne (Pres)
Andrew Morse (Owner)

OHIO BLOW PIPE COMPANY
446 E 131st St, Cleveland, OH 44108
Tel.: (216) 681-7379
Web Site: http://www.obpairsystems.com
Sales Range: $10-24.9 Million
Emp.: 48

Ohio Blow Pipe Company—(Continued)
Manufacture Conveyors & Conveying Equipment
N.A.I.C.S.: 333922
Edward Fakeris (Pres)
John Huber (Mgr-Sls)

OHIO BUILDING AUTHORITY
30 E Broad St Ste 4020, Columbus, OH 43215
Tel.: (614) 466-5959   OH
Web Site: http://oba.ohio.gov
Sales Range: $250-299.9 Million
Emp.: 32
Nonresidential Building Operators
N.A.I.C.S.: 531120

OHIO CAPITAL CORPORATION FOR HOUSING
88 E Broad St Ste 1800, Columbus, OH 43215
Tel.: (614) 224-8446   OH
Web Site: http://www.occh.org
Year Founded: 1989
Sales Range: $125-149.9 Million
Emp.: 62
Community Housing Services
N.A.I.C.S.: 624229
Lori McMillan (Dir-Underwriting)
Sue Ziegler (COO)
Doug Klingensmith (VP-Dev)
Hal Keller (Pres)
John Kircher (Sr VP-Dev)
Myia Batie (Coord-Policy & Programs)

OHIO CARPENTERS' HEALTH FUND
1909 Arlingate Ln, Columbus, OH 43228
Tel.: (614) 236-2440   OH
Year Founded: 2008
Sales Range: $100-124.9 Million
Employee Welfare Services
N.A.I.C.S.: 525120
Doug Reffitt (Chm)
Kevin Reilly (Sec)

OHIO CASHFLOW, LLC
2428 W Sylvania Ave, Toledo, OH 43613
Web Site:
  http://www.ohiocashflow.com
Year Founded: 2014
Sales Range: $1-9.9 Million
Emp.: 10
Real Estate Investment Services
N.A.I.C.S.: 531390
Engelo Rumora (Founder)

OHIO COUNTY HOSPITAL CORPORATION
1211 Old Main St, Hartford, KY 42347
Tel.: (270) 298-7411   KY
Web Site:
  http://www.ohiocountyhospital.com
Year Founded: 1984
Sales Range: $25-49.9 Million
Emp.: 427
Health Care Srvices
N.A.I.C.S.: 622110
Shellie Shouse (CEO)
Jim Duke (Pres)
CeCe Robinson (Dir-Community Rels)

OHIO DECORATIVE PRODUCTS INC.
220 S Elizabeth St, Spencerville, OH 45887
Tel.: (419) 647-4191
Web Site: http://flexiblefoam.com
Sales Range: $100-124.9 Million
Emp.: 150
Plastics Foam Products
N.A.I.C.S.: 326150
Charles L. Moeller (Chm)

OHIO DESK CO., INC.
1122 Prospect Ave E, Cleveland, OH 44115-1292
Tel.: (216) 623-0600   OH
Web Site: http://www.ohiodesk.com
Year Founded: 1908
Sales Range: $10-24.9 Million
Emp.: 100
Sales of Furniture
N.A.I.C.S.: 423210
David B. Humphrey (Pres)
Michael Stepanek (Controller)

OHIO EDUCATION ASSOCIATION
225 E Broad St, Columbus, OH 43215
Tel.: (614) 228-4526   OH
Web Site: http://www.ohea.org
Year Founded: 1859
Sales Range: $50-74.9 Million
Emp.: 231
Educational Support Services
N.A.I.C.S.: 611710
Larry E. Wicks (Exec Dir)

OHIO FARMERS INSURANCE COMPANY
1 Park Cir, Westfield Center, OH 44251-5001
Tel.: (330) 887-0101   OH
Web Site:
  http://www.westfieldinsurance.com
Sales Range: $1-4.9 Billion
Emp.: 2,500
Holding Company; Insurance, Investment & Banking Services
N.A.I.C.S.: 551112
Jon W. Park (Chm, Pres & CEO-Westfield Bank)
Edward Largent III (Pres-Westfield Insurance)
Frank Carrino (Gen Counsel & Sec)
Stuart Rosenberg (Head-HR, IT, Mktg & Admin)
Joe Kohmann (CFO & Treas)
James Clay (CEO)

Subsidiaries:

Westfield Bancorp, Inc. (1)
2 Park Cir, Westfield Center, OH 44251-5002
Tel.: (330) 887-8224
Web Site: http://www.westfield-bank.com
Assets: $575,000,000
Emp.: 59
Bank Holding Company
N.A.I.C.S.: 551111
Robert Berry (Sec)
Timothy Phillips (Pres)
Matthew Berthold (CFO & Exec VP)

Subsidiary (Domestic):

Westfield Bank, FSB (2)
2 Park Cir, Westfield Center, OH 44251-5002
Tel.: (330) 887-8224
Web Site: http://www.westfield-bank.com
Emp.: 150
Savings Loans Commercial & Investment Banking Services
N.A.I.C.S.: 522110
Jon W. Park (Chm, Pres & CEO)
Kevin P. Vonderau (Chief Lending Officer)
Matthew Berthold (COO)
Matt Sprang (Pres-Agency Banking)
Michael Toth (Pres)
Scott Oboy (CFO)

Westfield Insurance Company (1)
1 Park Cir, Westfield Center, OH 44251
Tel.: (330) 887-0101
Web Site:
  http://www.westfieldinsurance.com
Sales Range: $300-349.9 Million
Emp.: 1,700
Property & Casualty Insurance Carrier & Services
N.A.I.C.S.: 524126
Edward Largent III (Chm, Pres & CEO)
Jennifer Palmieri (Chief People Officer)
Robyn R. Hahn (Pres-Small Bus Div)
Jack Kuhn (Pres-Westfield Specialty)
Graham Evans (Exec VP-Westfield Specialty & Head-Insurance-Intl)

OHIO GAS COMPANY
200 W High St, Bryan, OH 43506-0528
Tel.: (419) 636-1117   OH
Web Site: http://www.ohiogas.com
Year Founded: 1914
Sales Range: $150-199.9 Million
Emp.: 85
Natural Gas Utility
N.A.I.C.S.: 221210
Richard P. Hallett (Pres)
Doug Saul (VP-Ops)
Robert Eyre (VP-Gas Supply & Indus Svcs)
Kim A. Watkins (Treas)
Doug Westhoven (Mgr-Adv)

OHIO GRATINGS, INC.
5299 Southway St SW, Canton, OH 44706
Tel.: (330) 477-6707
Web Site:
  http://www.ohiogratings.com
Year Founded: 1970
Emp.: 100
Aluminum & Steel Bar Mfr
N.A.I.C.S.: 331221
David Bartley (Chm)
John Bartley (CEO)

Subsidiaries:

Precision Component Industries, LLC (1)
5325 Southway St SW, Canton, OH 44706-1943
Tel.: (330) 477-6287
Web Site: http://www.precision-component.com
Precision Machining, Shear Blades, Metal Stamping Dies
N.A.I.C.S.: 332710
Patricia Gerak (CEO)
Tony Gerak (Pres)

OHIO HISTORY CONNECTION
800 E 17th Ave, Columbus, OH 43211
Tel.: (614) 297-2300   OH
Web Site: http://www.ohiohistory.org
Year Founded: 1885
Sales Range: $25-49.9 Million
Emp.: 227
Museum Operator
N.A.I.C.S.: 712110
Burt Logan (CEO & Exec Dir)
Jeff Ward (CFO)
Jackie Barton (Dir-Museum & Library Svcs)
Todd Kleismit (Dir-Community & Govt Rels)
Stacey Halfmoon (Dir-American Indian Rels)
Jamison Pack (CMO)
Stacia Kuceyeski (Dir-Outreach)
George Kane (Dir-Historic Sites & Facilities)
Amanda Schraner Terrell (Dir-State Historic Preservation Office)
John Strick (Chief Dev Officer)
Kimberlee Kiehl (Dir-Museum)

OHIO MACHINERY CO.
3993 E Royalton Rd, Cleveland, OH 44147-2929
Tel.: (440) 526-6200   OH
Web Site: http://www.ohiocat.com
Year Founded: 1946
Sales Range: Less than $1 Million
Emp.: 1,100
Construction Equipment & Engine Dealer
N.A.I.C.S.: 441227
Kenneth Taylor (Pres)
Paul Liesem (VP-Sls)
Rich Graziosi (Controller)

Subsidiaries:

Ohio CAT (1)
3993 E Royalton Rd, Broadview Heights, OH 44147-2923 (100%)
Tel.: (440) 526-6200
Web Site: http://www.ohiocat.com
Diesel & Natural Gas Engine Sale Distr
N.A.I.C.S.: 423810
Ken Taylor (Pres)
Dan Bonnes (Mgr-Rental & Used Equipment)
Paul Kenosky (Product Mgr-Support Dev)
Kelly Love (VP-Agri Bus Div)

Division (Domestic):

Ohio Ag Equipment Sales Co., Inc. (2)
1820 E Wyandot Ave, Upper Sandusky, OH 43351
Tel.: (419) 209-0783
Web Site: http://www.ohiocat.com
Agricultural machinery & farming equipment
N.A.I.C.S.: 423820

Ohio Machinery Co. - Mantsinen USA Division (1)
3993 E Royalton Rd, Broadview Heights, OH 44147
Tel.: (888) 595-8389
Web Site: http://www.mantsinenusa.com
Material Handling Equipment Mfr
N.A.I.C.S.: 333248

The Cat Rental Store (1)
7700 Medusa Rd, Bedford, OH 44146-5547 (100%)
Tel.: (440) 658-2000
Web Site: http://www.catrents.ca
Tool & Equipment Rental
N.A.I.C.S.: 532412
Gord McDougall (Gen Mgr)

OHIO MEDICAL TRANSPORTATION
2827 W Dublin Granville Rd, Columbus, OH 43235
Tel.: (614) 791-4400
Web Site: http://www.medflight.com
Sales Range: $50-74.9 Million
Emp.: 200
Air Ambulance Services
N.A.I.C.S.: 621910
Todd Bailey (Dir-Bus Dev)
Tom Allenstein (Pres & CEO)
Kelly Garcia (Mgr-Acctg)
Mike Perkins (Dir-Ops)

Subsidiaries:

Coshocton County EMS LLC (1)
513 Chestnut St, Coshocton, OH 43812
Tel.: (740) 622-4294
Sales Range: $1-9.9 Million
Emp.: 50
Ambulance Service
N.A.I.C.S.: 621910

MedCare Ambulance (1)
3699 Paragon Rd, Columbus, OH 43228
Tel.: (614) 751-6651
Web Site: http://www.medcareohio.org
Ambulance Service
N.A.I.C.S.: 621910
Phil Koster (VP-Ops)

OHIO METAL TECHNOLOGIES, INC.
470 John Alford Pkwy, Hebron, OH 43025
Tel.: (740) 928-8288
Web Site: http://www.ohiometal.net
Year Founded: 1996
Sales Range: $10-24.9 Million
Emp.: 80
Iron & Steel Forging Services

N.A.I.C.S.: 332111
Akira Nagata (Co-Pres)
Toshi Hara (Co-Pres)
Chuck Shearer (Gen Mgr & Mgr-HR)
Monica Mathews (Mgr-QA)
Mitsu Shinohara (Mgr-Engrg)
Manabu Matsunaga (Engr-CVJ Shaft Production)

OHIO MULCH SUPPLY INC.
1600 Universal Rd, Columbus, OH 43207
Tel.: (614) 445-4455
Web Site: http://www.ohiomulch.com
Sales Range: $10-24.9 Million
Emp.: 100
Fertilizers & Agricultural Soil
N.A.I.C.S.: 424910
Ron Frost (Dir-Sls)

OHIO MUTUAL INSURANCE GROUP
1725 Hopley Ave, Bucyrus, OH 44820
Tel.: (419) 562-3011
Web Site: http://www.omig.com
Year Founded: 1901
Sales Range: $75-99.9 Million
Emp.: 180
Provider of Insurance Services
N.A.I.C.S.: 561311
James J. Kennedy (Pres & CEO)
Michael Coleman (Mgr-Casualty Unit)
David Hendrix (CFO)
Chuck Easum (Controller)
Hannah Jacobs (Project Mgr)

OHIO PACKING COMPANY
1306 Harmon Ave, Columbus, OH 43223-3365
Tel.: (614) 239-1600
Web Site: http://www.ohiopacking.com
Rev.: $21,469,729
Emp.: 90
Meat Packing Plants
N.A.I.C.S.: 311611
Walter H. Wilke (Pres & CEO)
Jeff Kriebel (Supvr-Shipping)

OHIO POWER TOOL
999 Goodale Blvd, Columbus, OH 43212
Tel.: (614) 481-2111
Web Site: http://www.ohiopowertool.com
Year Founded: 1983
Rev.: $27,000,000
Emp.: 15
Hardware Merchant Whslr
N.A.I.C.S.: 423710
James Amstutz (Pres)

OHIO PRESBYTERIAN RETIREMENT SERVICE
1001 Kingsmill Pkwy, Columbus, OH 43229
Tel.: (614) 888-7800
Web Site: http://www.oprs.org
Year Founded: 1922
Sales Range: $125-149.9 Million
Emp.: 2,500
Apartment Building Operator
N.A.I.C.S.: 531110
Bob Stillman (CFO)
Laurence C. Gumina (CEO)
Nykole Brewer (Dir-Nursing)
Laura Naso (Dir-PR & Comm)
Connie Tostevin (VP-Nursing & Clinical Svcs)
Barbara E. Riley (Chm)
Edward S. Snelz (Vice Chm)
Thomas G. Hofmann (Chief Foundation Officer)
Dana Ullom-Vucelich (Chief HR & Ethics Officer)
Joyce Miller (CIO)
Daniel J. O'Connor (COO)

OHIO SECURITY SYSTEMS INC.
2592 Elm Rd NE, Warren, OH 44483
Tel.: (330) 372-2066   OH
Web Site: http://www.osscompanies.com
Year Founded: 1988
Sales Range: $650-699.9 Million
Emp.: 85
Operators of Security Guard Services
N.A.I.C.S.: 561612
James A. Payiavlas (Pres)
Anthony Payiavlas (Treas)

OHIO STATE HOME SERVICES INC.
365 Highland Rd E, Macedonia, OH 44056
Tel.: (330) 467-1055
Web Site: http://www.ohiostatewaterproofing.com
Year Founded: 1978
Sales Range: $25-49.9 Million
Emp.: 170
Waterproofing
N.A.I.C.S.: 238990
Nick Dicello (Pres)

OHIO STEEL INDUSTRIES, INC.
2575 Ferris Rd, Columbus, OH 43224-2540
Tel.: (614) 471-4800   DE
Web Site: http://www.ohiosteel.com
Year Founded: 1958
Sales Range: $10-24.9 Million
Emp.: 150
Lawn & Garden Equipment
N.A.I.C.S.: 333112
Robert Hays (Dir-Fin)

OHIO TOOL SYSTEMS, INC.
3863 Congress Pkwy, Richfield, OH 44286
Tel.: (330) 659-4181
Web Site: http://www.ohiotool.com
Year Founded: 1974
Sales Range: $10-24.9 Million
Emp.: 55
Industrial Machinery & Equipment Whslr
N.A.I.C.S.: 423830
Brian Cummins (CFO)

OHIO TRANSPORT CORPORATION
9426 Freeway Dr, Macedonia, OH 44056-1000
Tel.: (216) 741-8000
Web Site: http://www.ohiotransport.com
Year Founded: 1988
Sales Range: $25-49.9 Million
Emp.: 20
Local Trucking Services
N.A.I.C.S.: 484110
William Hill (Owner & Pres)

OHIO VALLEY BANCORP, INC.
140 N Main St, Henderson, KY 42420
Tel.: (270) 831-1500   KY
Web Site: http://www.ohiovalleyfg.com
Sales Range: $10-24.9 Million
Emp.: 80
Bank Holding Company
N.A.I.C.S.: 551111
David Santore (CFO)
Scott P. Davis (Pres & CEO)
Chris D. Melton (Pres-Bank & Corp VP)
Andrea G. Payne (Sec)
Jeffrey E. Smith (Chm)

Subsidiaries:
Ohio Valley Financial Group, Inc.   (1)
140 N Main St, Henderson, KY 42420
Tel.: (270) 831-1500
Web Site: http://www.ohiovalleyfg.com
Emp.: 75
Personal & Commercial Banking Services
N.A.I.C.S.: 522110
Chris D. Melton (Pres)

OHIO VALLEY ELECTRIC CORPORATION
3932 US Rte 23, Piketon, OH 45661
Tel.: (740) 289-7200   OH
Web Site: http://www.ovec.com
Year Founded: 1952
Sales Range: $75-99.9 Million
Emp.: 310
Electric Utility Services
N.A.I.C.S.: 221118

OHIO VALLEY GOODWILL
10600 Springfield Pike, Cincinnati, OH 45215
Tel.: (513) 771-4800
Web Site: http://www.cincinnatigoodwill.org
Rev.: $20,067,577
Emp.: 625
Second Hand Clothing
N.A.I.C.S.: 459510
Dennis J. Barron (Sec)
Tim Mooney (Treas)
Jim Armour (Vice Chm)

OHIO VALLEY HEALTH SERVICES AND EDUCATION
2000 Eoff St, Wheeling, WV 26003
Tel.: (304) 234-0123   WV
Year Founded: 1914
Sales Range: $10-24.9 Million
Emp.: 1,919
Health Care Srvices
N.A.I.C.S.: 622110
Michael Caruso (Pres & CEO)
John Nally (Asst Dir-Pharmacy)
Michelle Heath (Mgr-Pharmacy Informatics)
Rick Scherich (Controller)
Lisa Simon (CFO & Sr VP)

OHIO VALLEY MANUFACTURING INC.
1501 Harrington Memorial Rd, Mansfield, OH 44903
Tel.: (419) 522-5818
Web Site: http://www.ohiovalleymfg.com
Sales Range: $10-24.9 Million
Emp.: 100
Stamping Metal
N.A.I.C.S.: 332119
Kim Catron (Treas)

OHIO VALLEY RESOURCES INC.
29325 Chagrin Blvd, Cleveland, OH 44122-4600
Tel.: (216) 765-1240   OH
Web Site: http://www.ohiovalleycoal.com
Year Founded: 1988
Sales Range: $50-74.9 Million
Emp.: 400
Coal Mining Services
N.A.I.C.S.: 213113
Robert E. Murray (Chm, Pres & CEO)
Michael Loiacono (Treas)
B. J. Cornelius (VP-Mktg & Sls)
Linda Ventura (Sec)
Michael O. McKown (Sr VP, Gen Counsel & Sec)

Subsidiaries:
The Ohio Valley Coal Company   (1)
56854 Pleasant Rdg Rd, Alledonia, OH 43902-9716
Tel.: (740) 926-1351
Rev.: $100,000,000
Emp.: 395
Coal Mining Services
N.A.I.C.S.: 213113

OHIO VALLEY SUPERMARKET INC.
210 2nd Ave, Gallipolis, OH 45631
Tel.: (740) 446-9312
Sales Range: $25-49.9 Million
Emp.: 250
Supermarket
N.A.I.C.S.: 445110
Brent R. Eastman (Co-Owner & Pres)
Cookie Crowder (Controller)
Kevin Eastman (VP)

OHIO VALLEY SUPPLY COMPANY
3512 Spring Grove Ave, Cincinnati, OH 45223
Tel.: (513) 681-8300
Web Site: http://www.ovsco.com
Sales Range: $10-24.9 Million
Emp.: 25
Lumber, Plywood & Millwork
N.A.I.C.S.: 423310
Jim Brandt (Mgr-Customer Svc)
Dave Greening (VP-Sls)
Alicia Jones (Mgr-Mktg & Comm)

OHIOGUIDESTONE
202 E Bagley Rd, Berea, OH 44017
Tel.: (440) 234-2006   OH
Web Site: http://www.ohioguidestone.org
Year Founded: 1864
Sales Range: $25-49.9 Million
Emp.: 1,182
Child & Family Support Services
N.A.I.C.S.: 624190
Joe Ziegler (Asst VP-Facilities & Project Mgmt)
Donna Keegan (COO & Exec VP)
Ben Kearney (Chief Clinical Officer & Exec VP)
Eric R. Pelander (Chm)
James T. Sayler (Vice Chm)
Mary K. Greulich (Treas)
Susan C. Hastings (Sec)
Andy Cooper (VP-Community Counseling)
Christine Evangelista (CFO & VP)
Richard R. Frank (Pres & CEO)
Karen Herrmann (VP-HR)
Cindy Naegele (VP-Advancement & Comm)
Mary Stiles (Gen Counsel & VP)

OHM INTERNATIONAL CORPORATION
2900 Wilcrest Dr Ste 150, Houston, TX 77042
Tel.: (713) 917-0111
Web Site: http://www.ohminternational.com
Sales Range: $10-24.9 Million
Emp.: 20
Electrical Apparatus & Equipment
N.A.I.C.S.: 423610
John A. Lanier (CFO & Exec VP)
Joe Black (Mgr-Accts)
Michael Gandolfo (Mgr-Ops)

OHMITE MANUFACTURING COMPANY

OHMITE MANUFACTURING COMPANY

Ohmite Manufacturing Company—(Continued)
27501 Bella Vista Pkwy, Warrenville, IL 60555
Tel.: (847) 258-0300   IL
Web Site: http://www.ohmite.com
Year Founded: 1925
Resistors & Rheostats, Switches, Transformers, Ceramic Parts & Materials Mfr
N.A.I.C.S.: 335314
Kirk Schwiebert *(Dir-Product Dev)*
Judy Heyse *(Mgr-Customer Svc)*
Norma Redmond *(Acct Mgr)*

OHO INTERACTIVE
1100 Massachusetts Ave, Cambridge, MA 02138
Tel.: (617) 499-4900
Web Site: http://www.oho.com
Year Founded: 2000
Sales Range: $1-9.9 Million
Emp.: 22
Web Design Services
N.A.I.C.S.: 541512
Edwin Hastings *(Pres & Mng Dir)*
Jason Smith *(Chief Creative Officer & Mng Dir)*
Barry Gilbane *(VP-Bus Dev)*

OHSMAN & SONS COMPANY INC.
311 3rd Ave Ste 106, Cedar Rapids, IA 52401-1934
Tel.: (319) 365-7546   IA
Web Site: http://www.ohsman.com
Year Founded: 1891
Sales Range: $10-24.9 Million
Emp.: 5
Cattle Hide Whslr
N.A.I.C.S.: 424590
Mark Pooley *(VP)*

OHSU FACULTY PRACTICE PLAN
3181 SW Sam Jackson Park Rd, Portland, OR 97239-3098
Tel.: (503) 494-8311
Health Care Management Services
N.A.I.C.S.: 541611
Danny Jacobs *(Pres)*

OICCO ACQUISITION III, INC.
4412 8th St SW, Vero Beach, FL 32968
Tel.: (772) 584-3308   DE
Year Founded: 2010
Investment Services
N.A.I.C.S.: 523999
Ronald Davis *(Pres, CEO, Chief Acctg Officer, Treas & Sec)*

OIL & GAS EQUIPMENT CORP.
8 Road 350, Farmington, NM 87415
Tel.: (505) 327-9624
Web Site: http://www.ogequip.com
Sales Range: $10-24.9 Million
Emp.: 22
Oil Refining Machinery, Equipment & Supplies
N.A.I.C.S.: 423830
Michael J. Degner *(Owner & Pres)*
Oletta Degner *(Owner)*

OIL CENTER RESEARCH INTERNATIONAL, LLC
106 Montrose Ave, Lafayette, LA 70503
Tel.: (337) 993-3559
Web Site: http://www.oilcenter.com
Rev.: $17,600,000
Emp.: 75
Lubricating Oils & Greases
N.A.I.C.S.: 324191
Brenda Ahrabi *(Pres)*

OIL CHEM TECHNOLOGIES
12822 Park One Dr, Sugar Land, TX 77478
Tel.: (281) 240-0161
Web Site: http://www.oil-chem.com
Year Founded: 1986
Sales Range: $1-9.9 Million
Emp.: 10
Surfactants & Processes for Chemical Enhanced Oil Recovery
N.A.I.C.S.: 325998
Christie Lee *(Pres)*
Paul Berger *(VP)*

OIL PATCH FUEL & SUPPLY INC.
1905 Bayou Ct, Brownsville, TX 78526
Tel.: (956) 831-4839
Sales Range: $10-24.9 Million
Emp.: 50
Petroleum Products
N.A.I.C.S.: 424720

OIL PURIFICATION SYSTEMS, INC.
2176 Thomaston Ave, Waterbury, CT 06704-1013
Tel.: (203) 346-1800
Web Site: http://www.ops-1.com
Year Founded: 2002
Emp.: 100
Oil Purification Systems
N.A.I.C.S.: 333618
Thomas Bock *(VP)*
Aamir Mumtaz *(CEO)*
Art Canzonetti *(VP-Mfg & Ops)*

OIL WELL SERVICE CO.
10840 Norwalk Blvd, Santa Fe Springs, CA 90670
Tel.: (562) 595-4501
Sales Range: $10-24.9 Million
Emp.: 150
Oil Field Services, Nec
N.A.I.C.S.: 213112
Matt Hensley *(Office Mgr)*

OIL-AIR PRODUCTS INC.
295 Hwy 55, Hamel, MN 55340
Tel.: (763) 478-8744
Web Site: http://www.oilair.com
Sales Range: $10-24.9 Million
Emp.: 43
Hydraulic Systems Equipment & Supplies
N.A.I.C.S.: 423830
Jeffrey Olson *(Engr-Electrical)*

OILMEN'S EQUIPMENT CORP.
140 Cedar Springs Rd, Spartanburg, SC 29302
Tel.: (864) 573-9311
Web Site: http://www.oilmens.com
Year Founded: 1952
Sales Range: $250-299.9 Million
Emp.: 100
Pumps & Pumping Equipment
N.A.I.C.S.: 423830
John Faris *(Pres)*
Trey Hill *(VP)*
Bob Wilkerson *(Controller)*
Chris Conway *(Controller)*

OILWELL INC.
1156 S State St Ste 101, Orem, UT 84097
Tel.: (801) 224-4634
Rev.: $12,900,000
Emp.: 129
Lubrication Service, Automotive
N.A.I.C.S.: 811191
Taylor Mortenson *(Treas)*

OINTON INTERNATIONAL INC.
5475 Tulane Dr SW, Atlanta, GA 30336
Tel.: (404) 699-1937
Web Site: http://www.color-stone.com
Sales Range: $10-24.9 Million
Emp.: 15
Distr Marble Building Stone
N.A.I.C.S.: 423320
David C. Liu *(Pres)*

Subsidiaries:

Color Stone International Inc.   (1)
5465 Tulane Dr SW Ste B, Atlanta, GA 30336
Tel.: (404) 699-1937
Web Site: http://www.color-stone.com
Sales Range: $10-24.9 Million
Emp.: 10
Building Stone
N.A.I.C.S.: 423320
David Liu *(Pres)*

OJ INSULATION CO. INC.
600 S Vincent Ave, Azusa, CA 91702
Tel.: (626) 812-6070
Web Site: http://www.ojinc.com
Sales Range: $25-49.9 Million
Emp.: 10
Insulation, Buildings
N.A.I.C.S.: 238310
Griff Jenkins *(Gen Mgr)*

OJAI VALLEY INN & SPA
905 Country Club Rd, Ojai, CA 93023
Tel.: (805) 646-1111
Web Site: http://www.ojairesort.com
Sales Range: $25-49.9 Million
Emp.: 600
Resort, Spa & Golf Course
N.A.I.C.S.: 721110
Stephen Crown *(Owner)*
Mark Greenslit *(Dir-Golf)*
Matthew Gabos *(Asst Dir-Food & Beverage)*
Ben Kephart *(Mgr-Food & Beverage)*
Alex Kim *(Mng Dir)*
Brian J. Skaggs *(Dir-Engrg)*

OJS BUILDING SERVICES INC.
1008 Lincoln Way E, South Bend, IN 46601
Tel.: (574) 287-2936
Web Site: http://www.ojsbsi.com
Sales Range: $10-24.9 Million
Emp.: 20
Mechanical Contractor
N.A.I.C.S.: 238220
Steven Meyer *(Pres)*
Brian Sears *(Gen Mgr)*

OK CHEVROLET, INC
512 S Whitcomb Ave, Tonasket, WA 98855
Tel.: (509) 486-8400   WA
Web Site: http://www.okchevy.net
Year Founded: 1973
New Car Dealers
N.A.I.C.S.: 441110
Angie Gavin *(Sls & Fin-Specialist)*

OK INTERIORS CORP.
11100 Ashburn Rd, Cincinnati, OH 45240
Tel.: (513) 742-3278
Web Site: http://www.okinteriors.com
Sales Range: $25-49.9 Million
Emp.: 160
Plastering Services
N.A.I.C.S.: 238310
Loren Schramm *(Pres)*

OK TIRE STORE INC.
2224 Main Ave, Fargo, ND 58103
Tel.: (701) 237-6525
Web Site: http://www.oktireinc.com
Sales Range: $25-49.9 Million
Emp.: 160

U.S. PRIVATE

Automotive Tires
N.A.I.C.S.: 441340
James Ohnstad *(Owner & Pres)*

OK3 AIR
1980 Airport Rd Hngr A, Heber City, UT 84032
Tel.: (435) 654-3962
Web Site: http://www.ok3air.com
Sales Range: $1-9.9 Million
Emp.: 20
Aircraft Rental Services
N.A.I.C.S.: 532411
Nadim AbuHaidar *(Pres)*
Jeff Dowling *(Dir-Maintenance)*
Alan Robertson *(CFO)*

OKADA TRUCKING CO. LTD.
2065 S King St Ste 105, Honolulu, HI 96826
Tel.: (808) 946-4894   HI
Year Founded: 1931
Sales Range: $10-24.9 Million
Emp.: 120
Transportation Services
N.A.I.C.S.: 484110
Westley Nokamura *(VP)*

OKALOOSA GAS DISTRICT
364 Valparaiso Pkwy, Valparaiso, FL 32580
Tel.: (850) 729-4700
Web Site: http://www.okaloosagas.com
Year Founded: 1953
Sales Range: $25-49.9 Million
Emp.: 126
Natural Gas Distr
N.A.I.C.S.: 221210
Gordon King *(CEO)*
Anne Bauer *(VP-Acctg & Fin)*
Brent Haywood *(VP-Ops)*
Eddie Springle *(VP-Mktg)*

OKAPI VENTURE CAPITAL, LLC
1590 S Coast Hwy Ste 10, Laguna Beach, CA 92651
Tel.: (949) 715-5555   DE
Web Site: http://www.okapivc.com
Year Founded: 2005
Privater Equity Firm
N.A.I.C.S.: 523999
Marc Averitt *(Co-Founder & Mng Dir)*
John Waller *(Partner)*
Jeff Bocan *(Partner)*
Sharon Stevenson *(Co-Founder & Mng Dir)*
Lisa Riedmiller *(Controller)*
Matt McRae *(Partner-Venture)*

OKAW FARMERS COOPERATIVE, INC.
1545 Cr 1900 N Cadwell, Arthur, IL 61911
Tel.: (217) 543-2157
Web Site: http://www.okawcoop.com
Sales Range: $10-24.9 Million
Emp.: 6
Grain Elevators
N.A.I.C.S.: 424510
Rodney Kauffman *(Comptroller)*

OKAW PROPERTIES INC.
Hwy 133, Arthur, IL 61911
Tel.: (217) 543-3870   IL
Sales Range: $25-49.9 Million
Emp.: 6
Accounting Solutions
N.A.I.C.S.: 541219
Fred Helmuth *(Pres)*

OKEANUS SCIENCE & TECHNOLOGY, LLC
2261 Denley Rd, Houma, LA 70363
Tel.: (985) 346-4666

Web Site: http://www.okeanus.com
Scientific Research Equipment Provider
N.A.I.C.S.: 541990
Ted Brockett (CEO)
Brenton LeBlanc (Pres & Gen Mgr)

Subsidiaries:

Sound Ocean Systems, Inc. (1)
17455 NE 67th Ct Ste 120, Redmond, WA 98052
Tel.: (425) 869-1834
Web Site: http://www.soundocean.com
Sales Range: $1-9.9 Million
Emp.: 15
Search And Navigation Equipment, Nsk
N.A.I.C.S.: 334511
Ted Brockett (Founder & Pres)
Dave Armstrong (Mgr-Ops)

OKEE INDUSTRIES INC.
91 Shield St, West Hartford, CT 06110
Tel.: (860) 953-1234
Web Site: http://www.okee.net
Sales Range: $10-24.9 Million
Emp.: 50
Builders' Hardware,
N.A.I.C.S.: 423710
Sean A. O'Keefe (Pres)

OKEFENOKE RURAL ELECTRIC MEMBERSHIP CORPORATION
14384 E Cleveland St, Nahunta, GA 31553
Tel.: (912) 462-5131 GA
Web Site: http://www.oremc.com
Year Founded: 1939
Sales Range: $25-49.9 Million
Emp.: 100
Electronic Services
N.A.I.C.S.: 221122
Joyce Strickland (Mgr-Support Svcs)
John Middleton (Gen Mgr)
R. Wayne Combs (Chm & Pres)

OKI FURNITURE FAIR INC.
7200 Dixie Hwy, Fairfield, OH 45014
Tel.: (513) 874-5553
Web Site: http://www.furniturefair.net
Sales Range: $50-74.9 Million
Emp.: 100
Owner & Operator of Furniture Stores
N.A.I.C.S.: 449110
Richard Daniels (Pres & CEO)
Ed Hartman (Mgr-Mktg)

OKLAHOMA CENTRAL CREDIT UNION
4956 S Peoria Ave, Tulsa, OK 74105
Tel.: (918) 664-6000 OK
Web Site: http://www.oklahomacentral.org
Year Founded: 1941
Sales Range: $10-24.9 Million
Emp.: 163
Credit Union Operator
N.A.I.C.S.: 522130
Carolyn Toalson (CFO)
Brad Scheidt (VP-Fin)
Gina Wilson (CEO)
Pepper Weatherly (VP-Retail Sls)
Jon Gorman (Sr VP-Comm & Outreach)

OKLAHOMA CITY COMMUNITY FOUNDATION, INC.
1000 N Broadway, Oklahoma City, OK 73102
Tel.: (405) 235-5603 OK
Web Site: http://www.occf.org
Year Founded: 1969
Sales Range: $25-49.9 Million
Emp.: 34
Charity Services
N.A.I.C.S.: 813211

Liz Eickman (Dir-Kirkpatrick Family Fund)
Joe Carter (Dir-Dev)
Bond Payne (Chm)

OKLAHOMA CITY OTHER POST EMPLOYMENT BENEFITS
100 N Walker Ave Ste 400, Oklahoma City, OK 73102
Tel.: (405) 297-2506 OK
Year Founded: 2008
Sales Range: $25-49.9 Million
Retiree Health Care Benefit Services
N.A.I.C.S.: 525120
Craig Freeman (Chm)

OKLAHOMA CITY ZOOLOGICAL PARK
2000 Remington Pl, Oklahoma City, OK 73111-7106
Tel.: (405) 424-3344
Web Site: http://www.okczoo.com
Year Founded: 1904
Sales Range: $50-74.9 Million
Emp.: 160
Botanical Garden
N.A.I.C.S.: 712130
Jerry Webb (Mgr-Graphics)
Bob Mathew (CFO)

OKLAHOMA ELECTRICAL SUPPLY COMPANY, INC.
4901 N Sewell Ave, Oklahoma City, OK 73118-7822
Tel.: (405) 525-9001 OK
Web Site: http://www.oesco.com
Year Founded: 1909
Sales Range: $25-49.9 Million
Emp.: 250
Electrical Contractor
N.A.I.C.S.: 238210
Stephen F. Young (Chm & Pres)
David F. Walker (CFO)

OKLAHOMA FARM BUREAU MUTUAL INSURANCE CO.
2501 N Stiles Ave, Oklahoma City, OK 73105
Tel.: (405) 523-2300
Web Site: http://www.okfarminsurance.com
Sales Range: $25-49.9 Million
Emp.: 230
Fire, Marine & Casualty Insurance Carriers
N.A.I.C.S.: 524126
Greg Golden (VP)
Monica Wilke (Exec Dir)
Tom Buchanan (Pres)
Thad Doye (Interim Exec Dir)

OKLAHOMA FORGE INC.
PO Box 701500, Tulsa, OK 74170
Tel.: (918) 446-5553
Web Site: http://www.oklahomaforge.com
Year Founded: 1957
Sales Range: $25-49.9 Million
Emp.: 48
Metal Forging
N.A.I.C.S.: 332111
Steve Duenner (Pres)
Sonny Davis (Gen Mgr)
Bob Philips (Mgr-Production)
Whitney Upton (Mgr-Quality Control)

OKLAHOMA GENERAL AGENCY, INC.
630 NE 63rd St, Oklahoma City, OK 73105
Tel.: (405) 840-9393
Web Site: http://www.youroga.com
Emp.: 100
Insurance Agencies & Brokerages

N.A.I.C.S.: 524210
Michelle Stull (Dir-HR)

Subsidiaries:

Jaeger & Haines, Inc. (1)
4268 N Gabel Dr, Fayetteville, AR 72703
Tel.: (479) 521-2551
Web Site: https://jplush.com
Sales Range: $1-9.9 Million
Emp.: 100
Insurance Agencies & Brokerages
N.A.I.C.S.: 524210

OKLAHOMA INSTALLATION COMPANY
2900 East Apache St, Tulsa, OK 74110
Tel.: (918) 272-1899
Web Site: http://www.oicusa.com
Sales Range: $10-24.9 Million
Emp.: 500
Store Fixture Installation
N.A.I.C.S.: 238130

OKLAHOMA MAGIC LP
6516 E Olie Ave, Oklahoma City, OK 73116
Tel.: (405) 858-0500
Sales Range: $10-24.9 Million
Emp.: 600
Franchise Owner of Fast-Food Restaurants; Pizzeria Chain
N.A.I.C.S.: 722513
Howe McCoy (Pres)
Darla Welchel (Mgr-Mktg)

OKLAHOMA MUNICIPAL POWER AUTHORITY
2701 W I 35 Frontage Rd, Edmond, OK 73013
Tel.: (405) 340-5047 OK
Web Site: http://www.ompa.com
Year Founded: 1981
Sales Range: $150-199.9 Million
Electric Power Distr
N.A.I.C.S.: 221122
Charles Lamb (Chm)
Drake Rice (Dir-Member Svcs)
Robert Johnston (Vice Chm)
Homer Nicholson (Sec)
Dave Osburn (Gen Mgr)
Randy Elliott (Gen Counsel)
Michael Mushrush (Dir-Ops)
John Vansant (CFO & Dir-Corp Svcs)
Jim McAvoy (Mgr-Engrg Svcs)
Tom Willis (Engr-Energy Svcs)

OKLAHOMA PROPERTY & CASUALTY INSURANCE GUARANTY ASSOCIATION
2601 NW Expressway Ste 330 E, Oklahoma City, OK 73112
Tel.: (405) 843-5454 OK
Year Founded: 1980
Sales Range: $10-24.9 Million
Emp.: 9
Insurance Services Association
N.A.I.C.S.: 524126
Larry Fitch (Gen Mgr)

OKLAHOMA STATE FAIR, INC.
3001 General Pershing Blvd, Oklahoma City, OK 73107
Tel.: (405) 948-6700 OK
Web Site: http://www.okstatefair.com
Year Founded: 1907
Sales Range: $10-24.9 Million
Emp.: 572
County Fair Organizer
N.A.I.C.S.: 711310
Timothy J. O'Toole (Pres & CEO)
Angela Nemecek (VP-HR & Admin)
J. Scott Munz (VP-Mktg & PR)
Jason Eddy (VP-IT)
Cindy Rogers (CFO & VP-Fin)
Bert Benear (Asst VP)

David Vorwald (Mgr)
Gary Orosco (VP-Sponsorship & Bus Dev)
Jeff Tracy (Coord-ADA)
Kevin Rogers (Controller-Fin)
Bill Allen (VP-Jim Norick Arena & Equine Facilities)
Alexandra Alex Philbrick (Mgr-Comm Space Sales)
James Johnson (VP-Food & Beverage)
Katelyn Kelly (Mgr-Pub & Integrated Media)

OKLAHOMA STATE UNIVERSITY MEDICAL CENTER TRUST
744 W 9th St, Tulsa, OK 74127
Tel.: (918) 599-1000
Web Site: http://www.osumc.net
Year Founded: 2008
Trust
N.A.I.C.S.: 523991
Amy Watters (Coord-Scholarship)
Kathryn Gage (Exec Dir-Student Affairs)
Aaron Christensen (Mgr-Graduate Student Svcs Center)
Ron King (Mgr-IT Help Desk)

Subsidiaries:

Oklahoma State University Medical Center (1)
744 W 9th St, Tulsa, OK 74127-9028
Tel.: (918) 599-1000
Web Site: http://www.osumc.net
Sales Range: $150-199.9 Million
Emp.: 1,200
Hospital
N.A.I.C.S.: 622110

OKLAHOMA STEEL & WIRE CO. INC.
Hwy 70 S, Madill, OK 73446
Tel.: (580) 795-7311
Web Site: http://www.oklahomasteel.com
Sales Range: $200-249.9 Million
Emp.: 350
Fencing, Made From Purchased Wire
N.A.I.C.S.: 332618
Colleen Moore (Co-Owner)
Craig Moore (Co-Owner)

OKLAHOMA TRANSPORTATION AUTHORITY
3500 N Martin Luther King Ave, Oklahoma City, OK 73111-4221
Tel.: (405) 425-3600
Web Site: http://www.ota.state.ok.us
Year Founded: 1947
Sales Range: $100-124.9 Million
Emp.: 580
Highway Construction Services
N.A.I.C.S.: 488490
Alan Freeman (Dir-Gen Admin)

OKLAHOMA'S CREDIT UNION
3001 N Lincoln Blvd, Oklahoma City, OK 73105
Tel.: (405) 606-6528 OK
Web Site: http://www.okcu.org
Year Founded: 1954
Sales Range: $25-49.9 Million
Credit Union Operator
N.A.I.C.S.: 522130
Mike Patterson (Chm)
Eddie Foreman (Vice Chm)
Mandi Phillips (Sec & Treas)

OKLAHOMASTONE.COM INC.
9311 NW Expy, Oklahoma City, OK 73099
Tel.: (405) 721-6775
Web Site: http://www.oklahomastone.com

OKLAHOMASTONE.COM INC.   U.S. PRIVATE

OklahomaStone.com Inc.—(Continued)
Year Founded: 2001
Sales Range: $1-9.9 Million
Emp.: 15
Stone Mining & Quarrying Services
N.A.I.C.S.: 212311
Keith Hadlock (Owner)

OKLAND CONSTRUCTION COMPANY INC.
1978 SW Temple, Salt Lake City, UT 84115-7103
Tel.: (801) 486-0144   UT
Web Site: http://www.okland-const.com
Year Founded: 1926
Sales Range: $25-49.9 Million
Emp.: 255
Nonresidential Construction
N.A.I.C.S.: 236220
Oscar Salazar (Mgr-Estimating & Preconstruction)

OKOBOJI FINANCIAL SERVICES, INC.
1019 Hwy 71 S, Okoboji, IA 51355
Tel.: (712) 332-9765
Year Founded: 1988
Rev.: $4,800,000
Emp.: 26
Security Brokers & Dealers
N.A.I.C.S.: 523150
Ralph R. Schneider (Pres)

OKOBOJI GM
2720 17th St, Spirit Lake, IA 51360-1081
Tel.: (712) 336-1500
Web Site: http://www.okobojigmtoyota.com
Year Founded: 1995
Sales Range: $10-24.9 Million
Emp.: 35
New Car Whslr
N.A.I.C.S.: 441110
Loren Holub (Pres)

OLANDER MEDIA GROUP
1224 Ottawa Ave, Ottawa, IL 61350
Tel.: (815) 680-6500
Web Site: http://www.olandergroup.com
Year Founded: 2001
Sales Range: $1-9.9 Million
Emp.: 3
Media Buying Services
N.A.I.C.S.: 541830
Mike Olander (Founder)

OLATHE FORD SALES INC.
1845 E Santa Fe St, Olathe, KS 66062
Tel.: (913) 782-0881
Web Site: http://www.olatheford.com
Rev.: $171,000,000
Emp.: 250
New & Used Automobiles
N.A.I.C.S.: 441110
Michelle Byers (CFO & Controller)
Marc McEver (Owner)
Steve Gibbs (Mgr-Comml Sls)

OLD BRIDGE MUNICIPAL UTILITY AUTHORITY
1 Old Bridge Plz, Old Bridge, NJ 08857
Tel.: (732) 721-5600
Web Site: http://www.oldbridge.com
Sales Range: $10-24.9 Million
Emp.: 85
Water & Sewer Authority
N.A.I.C.S.: 221310
Arthur Haney (Exec Dir)
Stephen Florek (Controller)
Gregg Grieve (Dir)
Tom Sonmmerm (Mgr-IT)

OLD CASTLE COASTAL INC.
4550 Clark Rd, Sarasota, FL 34233
Tel.: (941) 927-1482
Web Site: http://oldcastlecoastal.com
Stone Masonry Products Mfr
N.A.I.C.S.: 327331
Doug Campbell (Reg Sls Mgr)

OLD COLONY - GMAC REAL ESTATE
1210 Kanawha Blvd E, Charleston, WV 25301
Tel.: (304) 343-5124
Web Site: http://www.oldcolony.com
Rev.: $11,049,898
Emp.: 13
Selling Agent, Real Estate
N.A.I.C.S.: 531210
R. Joseph Miller (Pres)

OLD COLONY ELDER SERVICES
144 Main St, Brockton, MA 02301
Tel.: (508) 584-1561   MA
Web Site: http://www.ocesma.org
Year Founded: 1974
Sales Range: $25-49.9 Million
Emp.: 196
Disabled & Elderly People Assistance Services
N.A.I.C.S.: 624120
Barbara J. Garvey (Sec)
Diana Digiorgi (COO & Exec Dir)
Julie Murphy (Pres)
Ted E. Lang (VP)
Brenda Carrens (Mgr-Volunteer Programs)
Nicole Long (CEO)
Madeline Smith (Mgr-Dev)

OLD COLORADO INN HOTEL
211 S Colorado Ave, Stuart, FL 34994
Tel.: (772) 215-3437
Web Site: http://www.oldcoloradoinn.com
Sales Range: $1-9.9 Million
Hotel Operations
N.A.I.C.S.: 721110
Steven Vitale (Owner)

OLD COUNTRY MILLWORK INC.
1212 E 58th Pl, Los Angeles, CA 90001
Tel.: (323) 234-2940
Web Site: http://www.e-ocm.com
Sales Range: $10-24.9 Million
Emp.: 40
Aluminum Painting & Coating Services
N.A.I.C.S.: 332812
Gerard Kilgallon (CEO)

OLD DOMINION ELECTRIC COOPERATIVE
4201 Dominion Blvd, Glen Allen, VA 23060
Tel.: (804) 747-0592   VA
Web Site: http://www.odec.com
Year Founded: 1948
Rev.: $1,005,917,000
Assets: $2,204,979,000
Liabilities: $700,434,000
Net Worth: $1,504,545,000
Earnings: $11,305,000
Emp.: 132
Fiscal Year-end: 12/31/22
Electric Power Distr
N.A.I.C.S.: 221111
John C. Lee Jr. (Pres & CEO)
Bryan S. Rogers (CFO & Sr VP)
Allyson B. Pittman (VP & Controller)

Kirk Johnson (Sr VP-Member Engagement)
Christopher F. Cosby (COO & Sr VP)
John M. Robb III (Chief Legal Officer & Sr VP)

OLD DOMINION LAND CONSERVANCY, INC.
621 W Main St, Purcellville, VA 20132
Tel.: (540) 338-0077   VA
Web Site: http://www.odlc.us
Year Founded: 1998
Sales Range: $10-24.9 Million
Land & Water Resource Conservation Services
N.A.I.C.S.: 813312
Henry Stribling (Exec Dir)

OLD DOMINION TOBACCO COMPANY INC.
5400 Virginia Beach Blvd, Virginia Beach, VA 23462-1724
Tel.: (757) 497-1001   VA
Web Site: http://www.atlanticdominion.com
Year Founded: 1875
Sales Range: $10-24.9 Million
Emp.: 120
Tobacco, Tobacco Products, Beer, Groceries & Candy Whslr
N.A.I.C.S.: 424940
Robin Davis Ray (Owner)

Subsidiaries:
Hoffman Beverage Co., Inc.   (1)
5464 Greenwich Rd, Virginia Beach, VA 23462-6512
Tel.: (757) 499-1234
Web Site: http://www.hoffmanbeverage.com
Beer, Ale & Alcoholic Beverages Distr
N.A.I.C.S.: 424810
Don Albee (VP-Mktg)
Chris Scott (VP-IT)
Queenie Hamilton (Mgr-HR)
Randy Tennien (Dir-Grocery Sls)
David Blake (VP-Sls)
Robert Perkins (Mgr-Inventory Programming)

Old Dominion Tobacco Company Inc. - Carolina Division   (1)
3641 Legion Rd, Hope Mills, NC 28348
Tel.: (910) 424-2292
Web Site: http://www.atlanticdominiondistributors.com
Emp.: 60
Tobacco Product Distr
N.A.I.C.S.: 424940
Mark Hines (Branch Mgr)

OLD DOMINION TRUCK LEASING INC.
300 Arboretum Pl Ste 600, North Chesterfield, VA 23236
Tel.: (804) 275-7832   NC
Web Site: http://www.odleasing.com
Year Founded: 1963
Sales Range: $10-24.9 Million
Emp.: 100
Provider of Truck Leasing Services
N.A.I.C.S.: 532120
David Winkelman (Sr VP-Sls)
Wayne Tyree (VP-Ops)
Whit Congdon (Controller)

OLD DOMINION UNIVERSITY
Tel.: (757) 683-3000
Web Site: https://www.odu.edu
Year Founded: 1930
Colleges & Universities
N.A.I.C.S.: 611310
John R. Broderick (Pres)
David Harnage (COO)
Carol Simpson (VP-Academic Affairs & Provost)
Bob Fenning (VP-Admin & Fin)
September Sanderlin (VP-HR)

Ted Alexander (Dir-Broadcasting)
Jackie Barrow (Dir-Community Rels)
Eric Bohannon (Assoc Dir-Comm)
Marty Bradley (Assoc Dir-Athletic-Sports Medicine)
April Brecht (Dir-Jacobson Athletic Academic Center)
Paul Briggs (Dir-Video Svcs)
Chrisie Brown (Dir-Creative Svcs)
Michael Castle (Asst Dir-Athletic Ticketing & Office Mgr-Box)
Jason Chandler (Asst Dir-Athletic-Mktg)
Daniel Cornier (Mgr & Head-Athletic Equipment)
Lanie Deppe (Asst Dir-Sports Performance)
Rick French (Assoc Dir-Athletic-Ops)
Lori Friel (Dir-Athletic Academic Advising)
Grant Gardner (Asst Dir-Athletic Comm)
Michael Gibbs (Coord-Academic & Compliance)
Jeff Gordon (Asst Mgr-Equipment)
Carmen E. Harris (Coord-Spirit Squad & Mascot)
Boyzie Hayes (Coord-Video Svcs)
Sarah Holmes (Asst Dir-Athletic Ticketing)
Carol Hudson (Asst Dir-Athletic-Comm)
Pam Huntley (Coord-Women's Basketball Video)
Joe Makovec (Asst Dir-Sports Performance)
Ryan Martin (Dir-Sports Performance)
Todd McKeating (Mgr-Sls-Global Spectrum)
Alex Parr (Assoc Dir-Sports Performance)
Eric Potter (Asst Dir-Sports Performance)
Tina Price (Asst Dir-Athletic-Creative Svcs)
Maggie Roy (Asst Dir-Athletic Comm)
Christopher Schaefer (Asst Dir-Ticketing)
Camden Wood Selig (Dir-Athletic)
Greg Smith (Asst Dir-Athletic-Facilities & Events)
Joshua Smith (Asst Dir-Compliance)
Deana K. Smith (Coord-Scholarship Insurance)
Bruce Stewart (Sr Assoc Dir-Athletic & Mgr-Event Facilities & Football)
Nicole Turner (Asst Dir-Athletic-Bus & Fin)

OLD DUTCH FOODS, INC.
2375 Terminal Rd, Roseville, MN 55113-2530
Tel.: (651) 633-8810   MN
Web Site: http://www.olddutchfoods.com
Year Founded: 1958
Sales Range: $200-249.9 Million
Emp.: 500
Potato Chips, Corn Chips, Nuts, Popcorn, Pretzels & Other Snack Foods
N.A.I.C.S.: 311919
Steve Aanenson (Pres & CEO)
Trace Benson (CFO)
Matt Colford (Dir-Product Mgmt & Mktg)

Subsidiaries:
Humpty Dumpty Snack Foods, Inc.   (1)
545 Deerhurst Dr, Brampton, L6T 5K3, ON, Canada
Tel.: (800) 387-2273
Web Site: http://www.humptydumpty.com
Sales Range: $100-124.9 Million
Emp.: 250
Potato Chips & Other Salty Snack Food Products Mfr & Distr
N.A.I.C.S.: 311919

COMPANIES

Ivan Shreenan *(VP & Gen Mgr-Atlantic Div)*
Steve Leaver *(Mgr-Ops)*

OLD EUROPE CHEESE, INC.
1330 E Empire Ave, Benton Harbor, MI 49022
Tel.: (269) 925-5003
Web Site: http://www.oldeuropecheese.com
Year Founded: 1987
Sales Range: $10-24.9 Million
Emp.: 90
Cheese Mfr
N.A.I.C.S.: 311513
Francious Capt *(Gen Mgr)*
Michael Balane *(Mgr-Natl Sls)*

OLD FASHION FOODS, INC.
5521 Collins Blvd, Austell, GA 30106-3653
Tel.: (770) 948-1177 GA
Web Site: http://www.oldfashfd.com
Year Founded: 1965
Sales Range: $75-99.9 Million
Emp.: 100
Variety Products Sales Through Vending Machines
N.A.I.C.S.: 445132
Jerry W. Seneker *(Exec VP)*
Joseph C. Hulsey *(Sr VP-Fin)*
Billy D. Varner *(Controller)*
Terry C. Coker *(VP-Mktg)*

OLD FASHIONED FOODS INC.
650 Furnace St, Mayville, WI 53050
Tel.: (920) 387-4444
Web Site: http://www.oldfash.com
Sales Range: $50-74.9 Million
Emp.: 70
Cheese; Natural & Processed
N.A.I.C.S.: 311513
Peggy Pride *(Mgr-Store)*

OLD FORGE SPRING HOUSE
700 N Bethlehem Pike, Ambler, PA 19002
Tel.: (215) 643-6030
Sales Range: $10-24.9 Million
Emp.: 40
Car Whslr
N.A.I.C.S.: 441110
Michael Gleason *(Gen Mgr)*

OLD HOME FOODS, INC.
550 County Rd D W Ste 17, Saint Paul, MN 55112-3517
Tel.: (651) 228-9035 MN
Web Site: http://www.oldhomefoods.com
Year Founded: 1925
Sales Range: $75-99.9 Million
Emp.: 13
Mfr & Distributor of Cultured Dairy Products
N.A.I.C.S.: 311511
John R. Bonifaci *(CFO)*
Geoff Murphy *(CEO)*
Al Haeg *(Dir-Sls)*

OLD LYME GOURMET COMPANY
4 Huntley Rd, Old Lyme, CT 06371
Tel.: (860) 434-7347
Web Site: http://www.deepriversnacks.com
Year Founded: 2001
Sales Range: $10-24.9 Million
Emp.: 16
Snack Food Mfr
N.A.I.C.S.: 311919
Jim Goldberg *(Pres)*

OLD MASTER PRODUCTS INC.
7751 Hayvenhurst Ave, Van Nuys, CA 91406
Tel.: (818) 785-8886
Web Site: http://www.oldmasterproducts.com
Rev.: $14,000,000
Emp.: 22
Lacquers
N.A.I.C.S.: 424950
Jim Hilaski *(Pres)*
John Hunt *(Mgr-Sls)*
Liz Palacios *(Mgr-Admin)*

OLD MILL MARKETING
Renovators Old Mill, Millers Falls, MA 01349
Tel.: (413) 423-3497 MA
Year Founded: 1978
Sales Range: $10-24.9 Million
Emp.: 30
N.A.I.C.S.: 541810
Claude Jeanloz *(Pres)*

OLD MISSION BANCORP, INC.
2701 I 75 Business Spur, Sault Sainte Marie, 49783, MI
Tel.: (906) 635-9910
Bank Holding Company
N.A.I.C.S.: 551111

OLD O'BRIEN BANC SHARES, INC.
109 W 2nd St, Sutherland, IA 51058
Tel.: (712) 446-3324 IA
Web Site: http://www.mysecuritystate.com
Year Founded: 1983
Bank Holding Company
N.A.I.C.S.: 551111
James J. Johnson *(Chm)*
Darin J. Johnson *(Pres & CEO)*

Subsidiaries:

Security State Bank (1)
109 W 2nd St, Sutherland, IA 51058
Tel.: (712) 446-3324
Web Site: http://mysecuritystate.com
Commericial Banking
N.A.I.C.S.: 522110

OLD PEORIA COMPANY INC.
7900 Chicago Ave S, Bloomington, MN 55420-1324
Tel.: (952) 854-8600 MN
Web Site: http://www.qwsco.com
Year Founded: 1904
Sales Range: $100-124.9 Million
Emp.: 190
Wine & Distilled Beverages Whlsr
N.A.I.C.S.: 424820
Paul Curley *(Controller)*
Tom Morgal *(Exec VP & Mgr)*
Douglas Ohama *(VP & Mgr-Quality)*
Wayne E. Chaplin *(CEO)*

Subsidiaries:

Quality Wine Company Inc. (1)
2001 De Wolf St, Des Moines, IA 50316-2761
Tel.: (515) 265-3700
Rev.: $11,500,000
Emp.: 48
Wine & Distilled Beverages Wholesaler
N.A.I.C.S.: 424820

OLD SALEM MUSEUMS & GARDENS
600 S Main St, Winston Salem, NC 27101
Tel.: (336) 721-7300 NC
Web Site: http://www.oldsalem.org
Year Founded: 1950
Sales Range: $10-24.9 Million
Emp.: 200
Owner & Operator of Gift Shop, Retail Bakery, Book Store & Museums; Tourist Attraction
N.A.I.C.S.: 459420
John Larson *(VP-Restoration)*
Paula Locklair *(VP-Education)*

Robert A. Leath *(VP-Collections & Res)*
Eric N. Hoyle *(CFO & VP-Admin)*
Anthony Slater *(CFO)*
Ann A. Johnston *(Vice Chm)*
Frances Beasley *(VP-Dev)*
Chris Minter-Dowd *(Chm)*
Betsy J. Annese *(Sec)*
Franklin Vagnone *(Pres & CEO)*
Nicole Blalock *(Mgr-HR)*
Hayes Wauford Jr. *(Treas)*

OLD TOWN COFFEE & TEA CO INC
1027 Hillen St, Baltimore, MD 21202-4132
Tel.: (410) 752-1229
Web Site: http://www.eaglecoffee.com
Year Founded: 1921
Sales Range: $10-24.9 Million
Emp.: 20
Roasted Coffee Mfr
N.A.I.C.S.: 311920
Jacqueline Parris *(VP)*
Tom Brooks *(Controller)*
Nicholas Constantinides *(Pres)*

OLD TOWN IT, LLC
625 N Washington St, Alexandria, VA 22314
Tel.: (703) 579-6930
Web Site: http://www.oldtownit.com
Year Founded: 2007
Sales Range: $1-9.9 Million
Emp.: 40
Information Technology Consulting Services
N.A.I.C.S.: 541512
Tim Ward *(Pres & CEO)*
Meg Schwind *(Chief Mktg & Ops Officer)*
Laura Silberman *(Dir-Client Svc)*

OLD TUCSON COMPANY
201 S Kinney Rd, Tucson, AZ 85735
Tel.: (520) 883-0100
Web Site: http://www.oldtucson.com
Rev.: $11,600,000
Emp.: 130
Amusement Park
N.A.I.C.S.: 333810
Terry Verhage *(Gen Mgr)*

OLD VETERAN CONSTRUCTION, INC.
10942 S Halsted St, Chicago, IL 60628
Tel.: (773) 821-9900
Web Site: http://www.ovcchicago.com
Year Founded: 2006
Sales Range: $10-24.9 Million
Emp.: 35
Masonry Contractors
N.A.I.C.S.: 238140
Jose Maldonado *(Owner, Pres & Partner)*
Jose Maldonado *(Partner)*
Alex Polanco *(VP)*

OLD VIRGINIA BRICK COMPANY INC.
2500 W Main St, Salem, VA 24153
Tel.: (540) 389-2357
Web Site: http://www.oldvirginiabrick.com
Rev.: $13,491,651
Emp.: 120
Bricks Mfr
N.A.I.C.S.: 423320
Core Redfer *(CEO)*

OLD WEST PROPERTIES LLC
7915 Kensington Ct, Brighton, MI 48116
Tel.: (248) 446-0100

Sales Range: $10-24.9 Million
Emp.: 12
Eating Place
N.A.I.C.S.: 722513
Peter Lyders-Petersen *(Dir-Ops)*

OLD WESTBURY GOLF & COUNTRY CLUB
270 Wheatley Rd, Old Westbury, NY 11568
Tel.: (516) 626-1810 NY
Web Site: http://www.owgolf.com
Year Founded: 1961
Sales Range: $10-24.9 Million
Emp.: 259
Golf Club Operator
N.A.I.C.S.: 713910
Michael D. Jackson *(Controller)*

OLD WORLD INDUSTRIES, LLC
4065 Commercial Ave, Northbrook, IL 60062-1828
Tel.: (847) 559-2000 IL
Web Site: http://www.oldworldind.com
Year Founded: 1968
Sales Range: $500-549.9 Million
Emp.: 200
Automotive & Industrial Chemicals & Accessories Mfr
N.A.I.C.S.: 325998
Tom J. Hurvis *(Co-Founder & Chm)*
Riaz Waraich *(Co-Founder)*
Kevin Reilly *(CIO)*
John Turney *(CTO)*
Rick Stevens *(Chief Legal Officer)*
Jon Erickson *(Exec VP-Intl)*
Greg Noethlich *(CEO)*
Andy Rusie *(CFO)*
Warren Morrow *(COO)*

OLDACRE MCDONALD, LLC
3841 Green Hills Vlg Dr Ste 400, Nashville, TN 37215-2691
Tel.: (615) 269-5444 TN
Web Site: http://www.oldacremcdonald.com
Year Founded: 1994
Sales Range: $25-49.9 Million
Emp.: 15
Real Estate Development Services
N.A.I.C.S.: 531390
Bill Oldacre *(Principal)*
Mark McDonald *(Principal)*

OLDCASTLE COASTAL, INC.
5603 Anderson Rd, Tampa, FL 33614
Tel.: (813) 886-7761
Web Site: http://www.oldcastlecoastal.com
Year Founded: 2003
Concrete Products Mfr
N.A.I.C.S.: 327390
Tim Ortman *(Pres & CEO)*

OLDENBURG GROUP, INC.
1717 W Civic Dr, Milwaukee, WI 53209-4433
Tel.: (414) 354-6600 WI
Web Site: http://www.oldenburggroup.com
Year Founded: 1954
Sales Range: $25-49.9 Million
Emp.: 35
Holding Company
N.A.I.C.S.: 551112
Joe Wouters *(CFO)*
Linda Seeger *(Sec)*

Subsidiaries:

Oldenburg Aviation Inc. (1)
1717 W Civic Dr, Glendale, WI 53209-4433
Tel.: (414) 357-8600

OLDENBURG GROUP, INC.

Oldenburg Group, Inc.—(Continued)
Sales Range: Less than $1 Million
Emp.: 5
Air Transportation
N.A.I.C.S.: 481219

Oldenburg Group, Inc. - Defense Division (1)
2141 Woodward Ave, Kingsford, MI 49802-5316
Tel.: (906) 774-1500
Web Site: http://www.oldenburggroup.com
Sales Range: $50-74.9 Million
Industrial Trucks & Tractors
N.A.I.C.S.: 333924

Visa Lighting Corporation (1)
1717 W Civic Dr, Glendale, WI 53209-4433
Tel.: (414) 354-6600
Web Site: http://www.visalighting.com
Mfr of Commercial Lighting Fixtures
N.A.I.C.S.: 333924
Lauren Roberts (Mgr-Healthcare Market Dev)
Cindy Vera RedDoor (VP-Sls & Mktg)
Scott Manning (Sls Mgr-Midwest)

OLDER & LUNDY
1000 W Cass St, Tampa, FL 33606
Tel.: (813) 254-8998
Web Site: http://www.olalaw.com
Year Founded: 2003
Sales Range: $1-9.9 Million
Law firm
N.A.I.C.S.: 541110
Benjamin Older (Founder & Partner)

OLDFIELD DAVIS, INC.
2910 N Hall St, Dallas, TX 75204
Tel.: (214) 745-4545
Web Site: http://www.oldfielddavis.com
Year Founded: 1980
Rev.: $11,300,000
Emp.: 3
Fiscal Year-end: 12/31/04
N.A.I.C.S.: 541810
Rachel Mostert Davis (Pres, CEO & Co-Founder)
Jeff Waite (Digital Production & Traffic Mgr)
Cindie Snyder (Mgr-Acct Svcs)
Isabel Campos (Art Dir)
Shane Larson (Acct Coord)

OLDHAM CHEMICALS COMPANY INC.
3701 New Getwell Rd, Memphis, TN 38118
Tel.: (901) 794-0084
Web Site: http://www.oldhamchem.com
Sales Range: $10-24.9 Million
Emp.: 20
Insecticides
N.A.I.C.S.: 424910
Millard L. Oldham (Founder & Pres)
Marsha Reeves (VP)
Tommy Reeves (VP)

OLDHAM LUMBER CO. INC.
8738 Forney Rd, Dallas, TX 75227
Tel.: (214) 821-5194
Sales Range: $10-24.9 Million
Emp.: 32
Rough, Dressed & Finished Lumber
N.A.I.C.S.: 423310
Maria Navarrete (Coord-Inside Sls)

OLDWEBSITES.COM, INC.
4804 Skycrest Park Cove, Salt Lake City, UT 84108
Tel.: (801) 531-0404 UT
Web Site: http://www.oldwebsites.com
Business Services
N.A.I.C.S.: 561499
James Paul Roszel (Chm & Pres)

OLE SOUTH PROPERTIES INC.
262 Robert Rose Dr Ste 300, Murfreesboro, TN 37129
Tel.: (615) 896-0019
Web Site: http://www.olesouth.com
Sales Range: $10-24.9 Million
Emp.: 22
New Construction, Single-Family Houses
N.A.I.C.S.: 236115
John D. Floyd (Owner & Pres)
Trudy Wells (VP-HR)

OLEDWORKS LLC
1645 Lyell Ave Ste 140, Rochester, NY 14606
Tel.: (585) 287-6817 NY
Web Site: http://www.oledworks.com
Sales Range: $10-24.9 Million
Lighting Components Mfr
N.A.I.C.S.: 335999
Giana M. Phelan (Dir-Bus Dev)
David DeJoy (Co-Founder & CEO)
John Hamer (Co-Founder & COO)
Michael Boroson (Co-Founder & CTO)

OLEKSA ENTERPRISES INCORPORATED
3214 Earl L Core Rd, Morgantown, WV 26508
Tel.: (304) 296-8214
Sales Range: $25-49.9 Million
Emp.: 50
Real Estate Developers
N.A.I.C.S.: 531390
Dennis Brock Oleksa (Pres)

OLEN PROPERTIES CORP.
7 Corp Plz, Newport Beach, CA 92660
Tel.: (949) 644-6536 FL
Web Site: http://www.olenproperties.com
Year Founded: 1973
Rev.: $192,000,000
Emp.: 450
Nonresidential Building Operators
N.A.I.C.S.: 531120
Igor M. Olenicoff (Pres)
Nicole Faus (Mgr-Property)

OLES ENVELOPE CORPORATION
532 E 25th St, Baltimore, MD 21218
Tel.: (410) 243-1520
Year Founded: 1912
Sales Range: $25-49.9 Million
Emp.: 165
Envelopes
N.A.I.C.S.: 322230
John R. Young (Chm)
Mark Jones (Mgr-Customer Svc)
Al Zimmermann (Dir-Sls-Mktg)

OLESON'S FOODS INC.
3860 N Long Lk Rd Ste A, Traverse City, MI 49684
Tel.: (231) 947-6091
Web Site: http://www.olesonsfoods.com
Sales Range: $25-49.9 Million
Emp.: 200
Owner & Operator of Grocery Stores
N.A.I.C.S.: 445110
Donald Olson (CEO)

OLGOONIK CORPORATION
518 Main St, Wainwright, AK 99782
Tel.: (907) 763-2613
Web Site: http://www.olgoonik.com
Year Founded: 1973
Sales Range: $25-49.9 Million
Emp.: 50
Holding Company
N.A.I.C.S.: 551112
Howard A. Patkotak (Chm)
Steve Segevan (Vice Chm)
June Childress (Pres)
Hugh G. Patkotak (VP)

Subsidiaries:

Olgoonik Development, LLC (1)
360 W Benson Blvd Ste 302, Anchorage, AK 99503-7228
Tel.: (907) 562-8728
Web Site: http://www.olgoonik.com
Holding Company; Management & Support Services
N.A.I.C.S.: 551112

Subsidiary (Domestic):

Olgoonik Management Services, LLC (2)
360 W Benson Blvd Ste 302, Anchorage, AK 99503
Tel.: (703) 312-0080
Web Site: http://www.olgoonik-management-services.com
Sales Range: $50-74.9 Million
Emp.: 450
Management Services
N.A.I.C.S.: 541611

OLHAUSEN BILLIARD MFG, INC.
1124 Vaughn Pkwy, Portland, TN 37148
Tel.: (615) 323-8522
Web Site: http://www.olhausenbilliards.com
Year Founded: 1972
Emp.: 95
Billiard Tables Mfr & Distr
N.A.I.C.S.: 339920
Donald Olhausen (Chm & Pres)
Brian Rosselli (VP-Ops)

OLIN OIL CO. INC.
N 3461 State Rd 104, Brodhead, WI 53520
Tel.: (608) 897-8601
Rev.: $10,900,000
Emp.: 60
Petroleum Bulk Stations
N.A.I.C.S.: 424710
Donald B. Olin (Pres)

OLINDE'S FURNITURE & APPLIANCES
9536 Airline Hwy, Baton Rouge, LA 70815-5501
Tel.: (225) 926-3380 LA
Web Site: http://www.olindes.com
Sales Range: $100-124.9 Million
Emp.: 100
Sales of Furniture & Appliances
N.A.I.C.S.: 449110
David Onolinde (Mgr)
Lisa Swindle (Mgr-Acctg)
Ty Whitley (Mgr-Adv)
Yvette Hurst (Mgr-Sys)

OLIVA TOBACCO COMPANY
3104 N Armenia Ave, Tampa, FL 33607-1658
Tel.: (813) 248-4921 FL
Web Site: http://www.olivatobacco.com
Year Founded: 1934
Sales Range: $25-49.9 Million
Emp.: 10
Whslr of Tobacco & Operates Tobacco Farm
N.A.I.C.S.: 424590
John Oliva (Pres)
Angel Oliva (VP)
John E. Oliva Jr. (Treas)
Angel Oliva III (Sec)

OLIVE
377 Park Ave S 2nd Fl, New York, NY 10016
Tel.: (212) 254-9155
Web Site: http://www.olivemedia.com
Year Founded: 1997
Sales Range: Less than $1 Million
Emp.: 10
Advetising Agency
N.A.I.C.S.: 541810
John Yarusi (Principal & Dir-Stategic Branding)
Anna Gildea (COO & Dir-Client Svcs)
Richard Smith (Dir-Creative)

OLIVE & BETTE'S
155 W 72nd St Ste 408, New York, NY 10023
Tel.: (212) 712-0473
Web Site: http://www.oliveandbettes.com
Year Founded: 1991
Sales Range: $10-24.9 Million
Emp.: 45
Women's Wear Whslr
N.A.I.C.S.: 458110
Stacey Pecor (Pres)
Mark Ryan (COO)

OLIVE INTERACTIVE DESIGN & MARKETING INC.
401 Congress Ave Ste 1540, Austin, TX 78701-3637
Tel.: (512) 225-6481 TX
Web Site: http://www.olivedesign.com
Year Founded: 1997
Rev.: $1,000,000
Emp.: 11
Fiscal Year-end: 12/31/02
N.A.I.C.S.: 541810
Kyla Kanz (Owner & Principal)
Morag Kierns (Mgr-Ops)
Cody Estes (Sr Developer)

OLIVE TREE ENERGY, LLC
15488 N Nebraska Ave, Lutz, FL 33549
Tel.: (813) 978-3733
Web Site: http://www.olivetreeenergy.com
Year Founded: 2009
Sales Range: $10-24.9 Million
Emp.: 12
Energy Efficient Products
N.A.I.C.S.: 333415
Jay Fechtel (Co-Founder, Pres & CEO)
Tom Hebert (Co-Founder & CTO)

OLIVER C. JOSEPH
3795 State Route 15, Belleville, IL 62226-3100
Tel.: (618) 233-8140
Web Site: http://www.oliverjoseph.com
Sales Range: $10-24.9 Million
Emp.: 50
Car Whslr
N.A.I.C.S.: 441110
Brad D. Joseph (Owner)

OLIVER CARR COMPANY
1455 Pennsylvania Ave Ste 200, Washington, DC 20004
Tel.: (202) 303-3060
Web Site: http://www.carrcap.com
Year Founded: 1994
Sales Range: $10-24.9 Million
Emp.: 16
Real Estate Managers
N.A.I.C.S.: 531210
Oliver T. Carr Jr. (Chm)
Oliver T. Carr III (Pres)

OLIVER EXTERMINATING CORP.
658 NW 99th St, Miami, FL 33150
Tel.: (305) 758-1811

COMPANIES

Web Site:
http://www.guaranteepest.com
Sales Range: $10-24.9 Million
Emp.: 70
Pest Control Services
N.A.I.C.S.: 561710
Burt Putterman (Pres)
Olivier Grinda (CEO)

OLIVER H. VAN HORN CO., LLC
4100 Euphrosine St, New Orleans, LA 70125
Tel.: (504) 821-4100
Web Site: http://www.ohvanhorn.com
Sales Range: $10-24.9 Million
Emp.: 30
Industrial Supplies
N.A.I.C.S.: 423840
Charlie Van Horn (Pres)

OLIVER INSTRUMENT COMPANY
1111 E Beecher St, Adrian, MI 49221-3902
Tel.: (517) 263-2132
Web Site:
http://www.oliverofadrian.com
Year Founded: 1913
Sales Range: Less than $1 Million
Emp.: 10
Manual Cutter & Tool Grinder Mfr
N.A.I.C.S.: 333517
Mary Smith (Sec)

OLIVER M. DEAN, INC.
125 Brooks St, Worcester, MA 01606
Tel.: (508) 856-9100
Web Site: http://www.omdean.com
Year Founded: 1919
Sales Range: $10-24.9 Million
Emp.: 21
Wholeseller of Dairy Machinery & Equipment
N.A.I.C.S.: 423820
Richard Eldon (Pres)

OLIVER MARKETING, INC.
49 37th St NW, Auburn, WA 98001
Tel.: (253) 859-9568 WA
Web Site:
http://www.olivermarketing.com
Marketing Consulting Services
N.A.I.C.S.: 541613
Robert M. Oliver (Founder & CEO)

OLIVER OIL COMPANY INC.
1811 E 5th St, Lumberton, NC 28358
Tel.: (910) 738-1401
Sales Range: $25-49.9 Million
Emp.: 100
Petroleum Bulk Stations
N.A.I.C.S.: 424710
Christopher L. Oliver (Pres)

OLIVER RUSSELL & ASSOCIATES LLC
217 S 11th St, Boise, ID 83702
Tel.: (208) 344-1734
Web Site:
http://www.oliverrussell.com
Year Founded: 1991
Sales Range: $1-9.9 Million
Emp.: 11
Advetising Agency
N.A.I.C.S.: 541810
Russ Stoddard (Founder & CEO)
Raylene Brent (Mgr-Bus)
Chad Rea (Creative Dir)
Rob Osler (Mng Dir)

OLIVERI ARCHITECTS INC.
32707 US Hwy 19 N, Palm Harbor, FL 34684
Tel.: (727) 781-7525

Web Site: http://www.oliveriarchitects.com
Year Founded: 1992
Sales Range: $1-9.9 Million
Emp.: 22
Architectural Services
N.A.I.C.S.: 541310
Joseph L. Oliveri (Owner & Pres)
Amir Yacoub (Project Mgr)
David Scott Herrmann (VP & Dir-Design)
Sean Harrison (Mgr-CAD)

OLM, LLC
4 Trefoil Dr, Trumbull, CT 06611-1330
Tel.: (203) 445-7700
Web Site: http://www.olm.net
Year Founded: 1996
Sales Range: $10-24.9 Million
Emp.: 100
Web Hosting & Custom Internet Software Services
N.A.I.C.S.: 517810
George D. DeVack (Founder & Pres)
James Stacy (Treas & VP)
Sandra Stephens (Supvr)
Subsidiaries:

Webaxxs.com (1)
4 Trefoil Dr, Trumbull, CT 06611-1330
Tel.: (203) 445-7700
Web Site: http://www.webaxxs.net
Solutions for Web-Hosting, E-Commerce & Portal Services
N.A.I.C.S.: 517810
George D. DeVack (CEO & CFO)
George Devak (CEO)

OLMOS EQUIPMENT INC.
440 Pinn Rd, San Antonio, TX 78227-1232
Tel.: (210) 675-2949
Web Site: http://www.olmosinc.com
Site Preparation Contractor
N.A.I.C.S.: 238910
Hunter Schuehle (Owner)

OLMSTED-KIRK PAPER COMPANY
1601 Vly View Ln, Dallas, TX 75234
Tel.: (214) 637-2220
Web Site: http://www.okpaper.com
Year Founded: 1905
Rev.: $108,700,000
Emp.: 300
Retailer of Printing & Writing Paper
N.A.I.C.S.: 424110
David Brown (VP-Sls)
Subsidiaries:

Olmsted-Kirk Company of Houston, Inc. (1)
9565 W Wingfoot, Houston, TX 77041
Tel.: (713) 868-1531
Rev.: $17,200,000
Emp.: 30
Retailer of Printing & Writing Paper
N.A.I.C.S.: 424110
Richard Wales (VP & Gen Mgr)

Olmsted-Kirk Equipment & Supply Co. (1)
1601 Valley View Ln, Dallas, TX 75234
Tel.: (214) 637-2220
Web Site: http://www.oksupplyco.com
Emp.: 30
Floor Cleaning Equipment Mfr
N.A.I.C.S.: 333310

OLNEY BANCSHARES OF TEXAS, INC.
307 W Main St, Olney, TX 76374
Tel.: (940) 564-5516 TX
Web Site:
http://www.interbankus.com
Year Founded: 1987
Sales Range: $75-99.9 Million
Emp.: 431
Bank Holding Company

N.A.I.C.S.: 551111
Pascal J. Hosch (Pres & CEO)
Subsidiaries:

InterBank (1)
4921 N May Ave, Oklahoma City, OK 73112-6041
Tel.: (405) 782-4200
Web Site: http://www.interbankus.com
Sales Range: $75-99.9 Million
Commericial Banking
N.A.I.C.S.: 522110
Pascal J. Hosch (Pres & CEO)

OLNEYA RESTORATION GROUP
1887 Craig Rd, Saint Louis, MO 63416
Tel.: (314) 432-6100
Web Site: http://www.olneya.com
Year Founded: 2007
Sales Range: $1-9.9 Million
Emp.: 17
Building Restoration Services
N.A.I.C.S.: 236118
Crystal Anderson (Owner)

OLOGIE
447 E Main St, Columbus, OH 43215
Tel.: (614) 221-1107
Web Site: http://www.ologie.com
Year Founded: 1987
Sales Range: $10-24.9 Million
Emp.: 55
N.A.I.C.S.: 541810
Beverly Bethge (Founder, Sr Partner & Chief Creative Officer)
William Faust (Sr Partner)
Timothy Straker (Sr Partner & COO)
Bill Litfin (Chief Digital Officer)
Kelly Ruoff (Partner, Mng Dir-Creative)
Janelle Asplund (Assoc Dir-Creative)
Mark Love (Assoc Dir-Creative)
Kim McCanney (Exec Asst & Office Mgr)
Brooke Hawkins (Project Mgr)
Hannah Magid (Acct Mgr)
Katie Dickens (Sr Acct Mgr)
Jennifer Fredritz (Dir-Creative)
Dan Stanek (Chief Strategy Officer)

OLOMANA LOOMIS ISC, INC.
900 Fort St Mall Ste 350 Pioneer Plz, Honolulu, HI 96813
Tel.: (808) 469-3250 HI
Web Site:
http://www.olomanaloomisisc.com
Sales Range: $10-24.9 Million
Emp.: 14
Advetising Agency
N.A.I.C.S.: 541810
Alan Tang (Chm, Pres & CEO)
Carole Tang (Chief Comm Officer & Exec VP)
Natalie Cook (COO & VP-Mktg)
Mika Keauli'i (Dir-Fin & Media)
Daniel Guthmiller (Coord-Mktg)
Kristine Sato (Project Mgr-Comm)
Lisa Ching (Dir-Media & Mktg)
Mika Keaulii (Dir-Fin & Dir-Fin & Media)

OLSEN THIELEN & CO. LTD.
2675 Long Lake Rd, Roseville, MN 55113
Tel.: (651) 483-4521
Web Site: http://www.otcpas.com
Sales Range: $10-24.9 Million
Emp.: 120
Certified Public Accountants
N.A.I.C.S.: 541211
Barb Graf (Coord-Mktg)
Patrick D. Powers (Pres)
Thomas Campbell (Principal-Telecom Mgmt Advisory Svcs)

Andrea Addo (Principal-Audit & Acctg)
Adam Hennen (Principal-Audit & Acctg)

OLSHAN FOUNDATION REPAIR
5902 W 34th St, Houston, TX 77040
Tel.: (281) 664-8400
Web Site:
http://www.olshanfoundation.com
Rev.: $33,900,000
Emp.: 130
Foundation & Footing Contractor
N.A.I.C.S.: 238110

OLSHAN LUMBER CO.
2600 Commerce St, Houston, TX 77003
Tel.: (713) 225-5551
Web Site:
http://www.olshanlumber.com
Year Founded: 1933
Sales Range: $10-24.9 Million
Emp.: 55
Other Building Material Retailer
N.A.I.C.S.: 444180
Marcus J. Fikac (VP-Pur & Sls)
Michael D. Fikac (VP-Ops)
Rusti Ledermann (CFO & VP)
Marvin R. Fikac (Pres)

OLSON & CO. STEEL
1941 Davis St, San Leandro, CA 94577
Tel.: (510) 567-2200 CA
Web Site: http://www.olsonsteel.com
Year Founded: 1983
Sales Range: $1-4.9 Billion
Emp.: 250
Fabricated Structural Metal
N.A.I.C.S.: 332312
Dylan Olson (Pres)
Kevin J. Cullen (CFO)
Thomas Fluehr (COO & Exec VP)

OLSON OIL CO. INC.
1425 W Lincoln Ave, Fergus Falls, MN 56537
Tel.: (218) 736-2786
Sales Range: $10-24.9 Million
Emp.: 25
Petroleum Products
N.A.I.C.S.: 424720
Steven Olson (Pres)

OLSON OIL CO. INC.
115 Old Skokie Rd, Waukegan, IL 60085
Tel.: (847) 662-7400
Web Site: http://www.olsonoil.com
Sales Range: $25-49.9 Million
Emp.: 4
Petroleum Products
N.A.I.C.S.: 424720
Maureen McGovern (Pres)
Mario Orlandi (Mgr-Ops)

OLSON PRECAST COMPANY
2750 Marion Dr, Las Vegas, NV 89115
Tel.: (702) 643-4371
Web Site:
http://www.olsonprecast.com
Rev.: $10,800,000
Emp.: 50
Concrete Drainage Products Mfr
N.A.I.C.S.: 327332
Michael Olson (Pres)

OLSON RUG COMPANY
832 S Central Ave, Chicago, IL 60644-5501
Tel.: (773) 921-1300 DE
Web Site: http://www.olsonrug.com
Year Founded: 1874

OLSON RUG COMPANY

Olson Rug Company—(Continued)
Sales Range: $100-124.9 Million
Emp.: 100
Retailer of Carpets & Rugs
N.A.I.C.S.: 449121
Andy Hader (Pres)

OLSON TECHNOLOGY INC.
24926 State Hwy 108, Mi Wuk Village, CA 95346
Tel.: (209) 586-1022
Web Site: http://www.olson-technology.com
Year Founded: 1985
Sales Range: $10-24.9 Million
Emp.: 45
Distr of Cable Television Equipment Mfr & Whslr
N.A.I.C.S.: 334220
Thomas A. Olson (Pres)
Janice Sue Olson (VP)

OLSSON ASSOCIATES, INC.
601 P St Ste 200, Lincoln, NE 68508
Tel.: (402) 474-6311
Web Site: http://www.olssonassociates.com
Year Founded: 1956
Engineering & Design Services
N.A.I.C.S.: 541330
John E. Olsson (Founder)
Brad Strittmatter (CEO)
Ryan Beckman (Pres)
Jeff Jenkins (CFO)

Subsidiaries:
Tri-State Engineering, Inc. (1)
702 S Main St, Joplin, MO 64801
Tel.: (417) 781-0643
Web Site: http://www.tristate-engineering.com
Sales Range: $1-9.9 Million
Emp.: 42
Civil Engineering & Land Surveying Services
N.A.I.C.S.: 541330
Jerald Norton (VP)

OLTMANS CONSTRUCTION COMPANY
10005 Mission Mill Rd, Whittier, CA 90601-1739
Tel.: (562) 948-4242   CA
Web Site: http://www.oltmans.com
Year Founded: 1932
Sales Range: $250-299.9 Million
Emp.: 120
Contracting & Construction Services
N.A.I.C.S.: 236210
John Gormly (Pres)
Daniel A. Schlothan (CFO & VP)
Charles Roy (VP-Real Estate Svcs)
Robert Larson (VP-Thousand Oaks Office)
James Woodside (VP-Production)
Greg Grupp (VP-Real Estate Svcs)
Tony Perez (VP-Estimating)
Chris Bell (Dir-Production Mgmt)
Jackson Miller (Dir-Special Projects)
Joe Pike (Dir-Field Ops)
Joseph O. Oltmans II (Chm-Mgmt Bd & CEO)

OLUMS OF BINGHAMTON INC.
3701 Vestal Pkwy E, Vestal, NY 13850
Tel.: (607) 729-5775
Web Site: http://www.olums.com
Rev.: $28,169,223
Emp.: 235
Major Electric Household Appliances
N.A.I.C.S.: 449210
Jamie Striley (Sr VP)
Jennifer Brown (Office Mgr)

OLYMPIA CHIMNEY SUPPLY HOLDINGS, LLC
505 Cuthbertson St, Monroe, NC 28110
Tel.: (508) 347-3313
Web Site: http://www.olympiachimney.com
Emp.: 100
Sheet Metal Work Mfg
N.A.I.C.S.: 332322
Harold Smith (Mgr-HR)

Subsidiaries:
Copperfield Chimney Supply, Inc. (1)
600 Sanders St, Scranton, PA 18505
Tel.: (570) 362-7464
Web Site: https://www.copperfield.com
Emp.: 100
Chimney Systems & Ventilation Products Mfr & Whslr
N.A.I.C.S.: 332322
Brian Yourdon (CEO)

Subsidiary (Domestic):
New Energy Distributing, Inc. (2)
601 6th Ave NW, Dyersville, IA 52040
Tel.: (563) 875-8704
Web Site: http://www.woodstoves-fireplaces.com
Rev.: $5,264,000
Emp.: 8
Electrical Apparatus & Equipment, Wiring Supplies & Related Equipment Merchant Whslr
N.A.I.C.S.: 423610
Rick Eudaley (Founder & CEO)

OLYMPIA FUEL INC.
3231 Mottman Rd SW, Tumwater, WA 98512
Tel.: (360) 357-4411
Web Site: http://www.pacificpride.us
Sales Range: $10-24.9 Million
Emp.: 6
Gasoline Distr
N.A.I.C.S.: 424720
Arthur J. Mell (Pres)

OLYMPIA SALES, INC.
215 Moody Rd, Enfield, CT 06082
Tel.: (860) 749-0751
Web Site: http://www.olympiasales.net
Year Founded: 1966
Rev.: $21,000,000
Emp.: 10
Whslr Greeting Cards, Stationery & Labels; Catalog Sales of Paper Products & Domestic & Imported Gift Items
N.A.I.C.S.: 424120
Tom O'Hara (Pres)
Alan Bolduc (Mgr-Production)
Anna Harding (Dir-Mktg)

OLYMPIA SPORTS INC.
155 W Erie Ave, Philadelphia, PA 19140
Tel.: (215) 423-7447
Web Site: http://www.myolympiasports.com
Sales Range: $125-149.9 Million
Emp.: 125
Athletic Footwear
N.A.I.C.S.: 458210
Dan Kim (VP)

OLYMPIC BANCORP
619 Bay St, Port Orchard, WA 98366
Tel.: (360) 876-7834
Web Site: http://www.kitsapbank.com
Sales Range: $25-49.9 Million
Emp.: 260
Bank Holding Company
N.A.I.C.S.: 551111
Helen Langer Smith (Vice Chm)
Anthony M. George (COO & Exec VP)
Steven L. Politakis (Pres & CEO)
Linda Smith (Exec VP)
Cydly Langer Smith (Chm)
Alan Crain (CFO & Exec VP)
Jim Davis (CEO)
Steven Maxwell (Chief Lending Officer & Exec VP)

Subsidiaries:
Kitsap Bank (1)
619 Bay St, Port Orchard, WA 98366
Tel.: (360) 876-7800
Web Site: http://www.kitsapbank.com
Sales Range: $50-74.9 Million
Emp.: 225
Commercial Banking Services
N.A.I.C.S.: 522110
Janet Silcott (VP & Mktg Dir)
Steven L. Politakis (CEO)
Anthony M. George (Pres & COO)
Alan Crain (CFO & Exec VP)
Steve Maxwell (Chief Lending Officer & Exec VP)
Tim McLaughlin (VP & Mgr-Comml Market)
Linda Smith (Exec VP)

OLYMPIC BRAKE SUPPLY
907 Thomas Ave SW, Renton, WA 98057
Tel.: (206) 575-8100
Web Site: http://www.olybrake.com
Rev.: $10,600,000
Emp.: 80
Motor Vehicle Supplies & New Parts Merchant Whslr
N.A.I.C.S.: 423120
Gary L. Nelson (Owner & Pres)
Jaime Rosenkranz (Mgr-Acctg)

OLYMPIC CLUB
524 Post St, San Francisco, CA 94102
Tel.: (415) 345-5100
Web Site: http://www.olyclub.com
Rev.: $21,016,858
Emp.: 200
Athletic Club
N.A.I.C.S.: 713910
William W. Humphrey (Owner)
Casey Mitchell (Asst Controller)
Phil Magsaysay (Mgr-Night Crew)

OLYMPIC COMPANIES INC.
2823 Hedberg Dr, Minnetonka, MN 55305
Tel.: (952) 546-8166
Web Site: http://www.olympiccompanies.com
Sales Range: $650-699.9 Million
Emp.: 700
Drywall Mfr
N.A.I.C.S.: 238310
Rick Mondry (Project Mgr)
Mary Jo Conroy Lecy (VP)
Jeff Schwartz (VP)
Pat Forliti (VP)

OLYMPIC FOUNDRY INC.
5200 Airport Way S, Seattle, WA 98108
Tel.: (206) 764-6200
Web Site: http://www.olympicfoundry.com
Sales Range: $25-49.9 Million
Emp.: 42
Metal Service Centers & Other Metal Merchant Whslr
N.A.I.C.S.: 423510
Russell Goodsell (Pres)
Scott McLaughlin (VP)

OLYMPIC IMPORTED PARTS CORP.
5174 Eisenhower Ave Ste 210, Alexandria, VA 22304
Tel.: (703) 370-0850
Web Site: http://www.olyonline.com
Rev.: $18,500,000
Emp.: 55
Automotive Supplies & Parts

N.A.I.C.S.: 423120
W. Michael Brown (Pres)

OLYMPIC SECURITY SERVICES, INC.
631 Strander Blvd Ste A, Tukwila, WA 98188
Tel.: (206) 575-8531
Web Site: http://www.olympiksecurity.com
Sales Range: $10-24.9 Million
Emp.: 400
Provider of Security Guard Services
N.A.I.C.S.: 561612
Mark E. Vinson (Pres)
Joy Vinson (VP)
Mustafa Darrar (Mgr)
Tinel Stefanescu (Mgr-NW)
Patrick Daly (Mgr-Security)

OLYMPIC STAFFING SERVICES
588 S Grand Ave, Covina, CA 91724
Tel.: (626) 447-3558
Web Site: http://www.olystaffing.com
Sales Range: $10-24.9 Million
Emp.: 25
Temporary Administrative & Professional Services
N.A.I.C.S.: 561320
Michael J. Lamp (Founder, Pres & CEO)
Lisa Escobedo (Mgr-Staffing)
Brian P. Lamp (VP & Gen Mgr)
Loretta Dela Torre (Mgr-Acctg Solutions)

OLYMPUS CAPITAL HOLDINGS ASIA
485 Madison Ave 18th Fl, New York, NY 10022
Tel.: (212) 201-8533
Web Site: http://www.olympuscap.com
Year Founded: 1997
Rev.: $1,200,000,000
Emp.: 80
Privater Equity Firm
N.A.I.C.S.: 523999
David Shen (Head-Asian Ops)
Ping Chen (VP)
Daniel Ng (Exec Dir)
Jeff Glat (CFO & Mng Dir)

Subsidiaries:
Asia Environmental Partners, L.P. (1)
One Exchange Square, Suite 3406, Hong Kong, China (Hong Kong)
Tel.: (852) 2140 0500
Web Site: http://www.olympuscap.com
Private Equity Firm Focused on Renewable Energy & Environmental Services in Asia
N.A.I.C.S.: 523999
Frederick J. Long (Founder & Mng Dir)

OLYMPUS GROUP
9000 W Heather Ave, Milwaukee, WI 53224
Tel.: (414) 355-2010   WI
Web Site: http://www.olympusgrp.com
Year Founded: 1893
Sales Range: Less than $1 Million
Emp.: 185
Custom Printing & Flag Makers
N.A.I.C.S.: 323120
Scott Coulthurst (VP-Ops)
Brian Adam (Pres)
Ryan Holzhauer (Dir-Sls & Mktg)

OLYMPUS HOLDINGS, LLC
67 Park Pl E, Morristown, NJ 07960
Tel.: (973) 889-9100   DE
Web Site: http://www.olympusholdingsllc.com
Emp.: 250

COMPANIES

Holding Company; Electric Power Generation, Entertainment Production & Financial Investment Services
N.A.I.C.S.: 551112
Anthony V. Harrington *(Mng Dir)*
Christopher W. Bodell *(Mng Dir)*
Cooper Schieffelin *(Mng Dir)*
Edward L. Tirrell *(Mng Dir)*
Richard G. Vicens *(Pres & CEO)*
Sean P. Lane *(Gen Counsel, Sec & Exec VP-Governmental Affairs)*

Subsidiaries:

JW Hulme Co. LLC (1)
867 Grand Ave, Saint Paul, MN 55105
Tel.: (651) 222-7359
Web Site: http://www.jwhulmeco.com
Leather Goods Mfr
N.A.I.C.S.: 316990
Tom Alberts *(Mgr-Plng & Pur)*

Olympus Capital Investments, LLC (1)
67 Park Pl E, Morristown, NJ 07960
Tel.: (973) 889-9100
Web Site: http://www.olympuscapinv.com
Emp.: 25
Privater Equity Firm
N.A.I.C.S.: 523999
Dean N. Vanech *(Chm & CEO)*
Christopher W. Bodell *(Dir-Investments)*

Olympus Power, LLC (1)
67 Park Pl E, Morristown, NJ 07960
Tel.: (973) 889-9100
Web Site: http://www.olympuspower.com
Holding Company; Electric Power Generation & Distribution Services
N.A.I.C.S.: 551112
Richard G. Vicens *(Pres)*
Sean P. Lane *(Gen Counsel, Sec & Exec VP-Governmental Affairs)*
Roy Ott *(VP-Fin)*
Dennis T. O'Donnell *(VP-Asset Mgmt)*
Robert Dixon *(Dir-IT)*
Anthony V. Harrington *(Mng Dir)*
Phillip McCartin *(Dir-Tax & Risk Mgmt)*
Tammy Mikalouskas *(Dir-HR)*
Cooper Schieffelin *(Mng Dir)*
Edward L. Tirrell *(Mng Dir)*
Richard F. Albosta *(Chm)*

Olympus Productions, LLC (1)
67 Park Pl E, Morristown, NJ 07960
Tel.: (973) 889-9100
Web Site: http://www.olympusprod.com
Holding Company; Motion Picture & Theatrical Production Services
N.A.I.C.S.: 551112

Subsidiary (Domestic):

Olympus Pictures, LLC (2)
2901 Ocean Park Blvd Ste 217, Santa Monica, CA 90405
Tel.: (310) 452-3335
Web Site: http://www.olympuspics.com
Sales Range: $25-49.9 Million
Emp.: 6
Motion Picture Production Services
N.A.I.C.S.: 512110
Christopher W. Bodell *(VP-Fin)*
Geoff Linville *(VP-Production)*
Riel Roch Decter *(Dir-Ops & Production)*

Olympus Theatricals, LLC (2)
1133 Avenue of the Americas Ste 1630, New York, NY 10036
Tel.: (212) 719-0007
Web Site: http://www.olympustheatricals.com
Emp.: 10
Theatrical Production Services
N.A.I.C.S.: 711110
Elizabeth Timperman *(Exec Dir)*

OLYMPUS HOMES INC.
52 Westerville Sq Ste 224, Westerville, OH 43081
Tel.: (614) 523-4900
Web Site: http://www.olympushomes.com
Rev.: $12,000,000
Emp.: 15
Residential Construction
N.A.I.C.S.: 236115

Tom Schwade *(VP-Dev)*

OLYMPUS PARTNERS
Metro Ctr 4th Fl, Stamford, CT 06902
Tel.: (203) 353-5900
Web Site: https://olympuspartners.com
Year Founded: 1988
Privater Equity Firm
N.A.I.C.S.: 523999
Robert S. Morris *(Chm & CEO)*
Louis J. Mischianti *(Mng Partner)*
Paul A. Rubin *(Partner)*
Evan J. Eason *(Partner)*
James A. Conroy *(Mng Partner)*
L. David Cardenas *(Partner)*
Manu Bettegowda *(Mng Partner)*
David Haddad *(Partner)*
Jason Miller *(Partner)*
Matt Boyd *(Partner & VP)*
Griffin Barstis *(Partner & VP)*
Sam Greenberg *(Principal)*
Jim Villa *(CFO & Chief Compliance Officer)*
Matt Bujor *(VP)*
Connor Wood *(VP)*
Sid Ahuja *(VP)*
George Swenson *(VP)*

Subsidiaries:

G.E.T. Enterprises, LLC (1)
7401 Security Way Ste 200, Jersey Village, TX 77040
Tel.: (713) 467-9394
Web Site: http://www.get-melamine.com
Emp.: 200
Melamine & Plastic Tableware Designer, Mfr & Whslr
N.A.I.C.S.: 423220
Iana Fatkhutdinova *(Dir-Mktg)*
Heidi Modaro *(CEO)*
Dimitra Rizzi *(Chief Customer Officer)*

MEI Rigging & Crating, LLC (1)
421 Water Ave NE Ste 4300, Albany, OR 97321
Tel.: (480) 917-3870
Web Site: http://www.meiriggingcrating.com
Building Equipment Contractors
N.A.I.C.S.: 238290
Katherine Cleland *(Mgr-Mktg)*
Dan Cappello *(Pres & CEO)*

Subsidiary (Domestic):

A&A Machinery Moving, Inc. (2)
201 Dean Sievers Pl, Morrisville, PA 19067
Tel.: (215) 428-1100
Web Site: http://www.aamachinery.com
General Freight Trucking, Local
N.A.I.C.S.: 484110
Albert Lykon *(Founder & Pres)*
Nick Lykon *(Gen Mgr)*

Adams Machinery Movers, Inc. (2)
5165 John G Glover Ind Ct, Ellenwood, GA 30294
Tel.: (404) 366-2511
Web Site: http://www.adamsmachinerymovers.com
Forklift Rental & Rigging Services
N.A.I.C.S.: 532120

Coast International Services, Inc. (2)
4512 Wilkinson Blvd, Charlotte, NC 28208
Tel.: (704) 391-9109
Rev.: $3,000,000
Emp.: 25
Specialized Freight, except Used Goods, Trucking, Local
N.A.I.C.S.: 484220
Bob Knosby *(VP)*
Amy Lloyd *(Office Mgr)*

Hanks Machinery Movers, Inc. (2)
650 Skyline Dr, Hutchins, TX 75141
Tel.: (972) 225-1811
Web Site: http://www.hanksmachinery.com
Rigging & Machinery Moving Services
N.A.I.C.S.: 238290

Harnum Industries, Ltd. (2)
28 Pelham Ave, Methuen, MA 01844
Tel.: (978) 685-7700

Web Site: http://www.therigger.com
Rev.: $1,300,000
Emp.: 12
General Freight Trucking, Long-Distance, Truckload
N.A.I.C.S.: 484121
Gail Bond *(Acct Mgr)*
Keith Harnum *(Pres)*

Houston Crating, Inc. (2)
18941 Aldine Westfield Rd, Houston, TX 77073
Tel.: (281) 443-3222
Web Site: http://www.houstoncrating.com
Sales Range: $1-9.9 Million
Emp.: 22
Crating & Export Packing Services
N.A.I.C.S.: 561910

Pro-Pac International, Inc. (2)
700 Westinghouse Blvd, Charlotte, NC 28273
Tel.: (704) 504-3003
Web Site: http://propacinternational.com
Rev.: $3,600,000
Emp.: 25
Packing & Crating
N.A.I.C.S.: 488991
Jim Jones *(Pres)*

NPC International, Inc. (1)
8319 W 135th St, Overland Park, KS 66223
Tel.: (913) 402-7280
Web Site: http://www.npcinternational.com
Restaurant Franchise Owner & Operator
N.A.I.C.S.: 722513
James K. Schwartz *(Chm, Pres & CEO)*
Troy D. Cook *(CFO, Sec & Exec VP-Fin)*
Linda L. Sheedy *(Sr VP-Mktg)*
Michael J. Woods *(CIO)*
Lavonne K. Walbert *(Sr VP-People Leadership)*

Soliant Health Inc. (1)
1979 Lakeside Pkwy Ste 800, Tucker, GA 30084-5856
Web Site: http://www.soliant.com
Temporary Help Service
N.A.I.C.S.: 561320
Chance Griffin *(Acct Exec)*

Tank Holding Corp. (1)
6940 O St Ste 100, Lincoln, NE 68510
Tel.: (402) 467-5221
Web Site: http://www.tankholding.com
Emp.: 680
Holding Company
N.A.I.C.S.: 551112
Thomas J. Smith *(Co-CEO)*
Thomas O'Connell *(Co-CEO)*

Subsidiary (Domestic):

Meese Inc. (2)
1745 Cragmont St, Madison, IN 47250
Tel.: (201) 796-4667
Web Site: http://www.meese-inc.com
Plastic Products Mfr
N.A.I.C.S.: 326199
Pat Berry *(Mgr)*

Norwesco, Inc. (2)
4365 Steiner St, Saint Bonifacius, MN 55375-0439
Tel.: (952) 446-1945
Web Site: http://www.norwesco.com
Sales Range: $75-99.9 Million
Emp.: 40
Molded Polyethylene Tank Product Mfr
N.A.I.C.S.: 326199
Paul F. Klaus *(CFO)*
Thomas J. Smith *(Pres & CEO)*

Unit (Domestic):

Norwesco, Inc. - Hanford (3)
13241 11th Ave, Hanford, CA 93230
Tel.: (559) 585-1668
Web Site: http://www.norwesco.com
Emp.: 15
Plastic Tank Mfr
N.A.I.C.S.: 326199

Subsidiary (Domestic):

Rotational Molding, Inc. (2)
17022 S Figueroa St, Gardena, CA 90248-3019
Tel.: (310) 327-5401
Web Site: http://www.rotationalmoldinginc.com

OLYMPUS PARTNERS

Plastics Product Mfr
N.A.I.C.S.: 326199
Mario Poma *(CEO)*

Snyder Industries, Inc. (2)
6940 O St Ste 100, Lincoln, NE 68510
Tel.: (402) 467-5221
Web Site: http://www.snydernet.com
Sales Range: $75-99.9 Million
Emp.: 225
Polyethylene & Steel Tank Mfr
N.A.I.C.S.: 332420
Connie Lintz *(Mgr-Mktg Svcs)*
Michael Spurrier *(VP-Sls & Mktg)*
Dana Janssen *(Mgr-Customer Svc)*
Troy Lauver *(Acct Mgr-Midwest Reg-Intermediate Bulk Container Div)*
Thomas O'Connell *(Pres & CEO)*

Plant (Domestic):

Snyder Industries, Inc. - Mancelona (3)
2594 Valley Rd, Mancelona, MI 49659
Tel.: (231) 587-5900
Sales Range: $25-49.9 Million
Emp.: 75
Steel Tank Mfr
N.A.I.C.S.: 332420

Snyder Industries, Inc. - Marked Tree (3)
602 Industrial St, Marked Tree, AR 72365-1909
Tel.: (870) 358-3400
Sales Range: $25-49.9 Million
Emp.: 50
Mfr of High Integrity Tanks & Containers
N.A.I.C.S.: 326199
Derek Batz *(Plant Mgr)*

Division (Domestic):

Snyder Industries, Inc. - Plastic Solutions Division (3)
5677 W 73rd St, Indianapolis, IN 46278
Tel.: (317) 328-8000
Web Site: http://www.snyderplasticsolutions.com
Rotational Molded Plastic Products Mfr
N.A.I.C.S.: 326199
Jay Skinner *(VP-Sls & Mktg)*

Subsidiary (Domestic):

Solar Plastics LLC (2)
860 Johnson Dr, Delano, MN 55328-8612
Tel.: (763) 972-5600
Web Site: http://www.solarplastics.com
Sales Range: $50-74.9 Million
Emp.: 250
Rotational Molded Plastic Parts Mfr & Distr
N.A.I.C.S.: 326199
Gary Engen *(VP-Engrg)*
Cindy Janke *(Mgr-Production Scheduling)*
Tina Krause *(Supvr-Shipping)*
Todd Roling *(Plant Mgr)*
Mark Osmanski *(CEO)*

Spin Products, Inc. (2)
13878 Yorba Ave, Chino, CA 91710
Tel.: (909) 590-7000
Web Site: http://www.spinproducts.com
Sales Range: $1-9.9 Million
Emp.: 24
Plastics Product Mfr
N.A.I.C.S.: 326199
Paul Burlingham *(Co-Founder & Pres)*
Carol Burlingham *(Co-Founder)*

Vaco, LLC (1)
5501 Virginia Way 120, Brentwood, TN 37027
Tel.: (615) 324-8226
Web Site: http://www.vaco.com
Consulting & Staffing Services
N.A.I.C.S.: 561311
Jay Hollomon *(Co-Founder)*
Brian Waller *(Co-Founder & CEO)*
Steve Kass *(Chief Revenue Officer)*

Subsidiary (Domestic):

Alluvion Staffing, Inc. (2)
4190 Belfort Rd Ste 160, Jacksonville, FL 32216
Tel.: (904) 296-0626
Web Site: http://www.alluvionstaffing.com

OLYMPUS PARTNERS

Olympus Partners—(Continued)
Contract & Full-Time Personnel Employment
N.A.I.C.S.: 561311
Amy Messner (Mgr-Ops)
David Reichard (Pres & CEO)

Focus Search Partners LLC (2)
5410 Maryland Wy Ste 400, Brentwood, TN 37027
Tel.: (615) 432-0500
Web Site:
http://www.focussearchpartners.com
Employment Services
N.A.I.C.S.: 561311
Paul Frankenberg (Founder & Mng Partner)
Connie Adair (Mng Partner)
Adam Charlson (Mng Partner)

Subsidiary (Domestic):

The Taylor-Winfield Corporation (3)
3200 Innovation Pl, Youngstown, OH 44509
Tel.: (330) 259-8500
Web Site: http://www.taylor-winfield.com
Metalworking Machinery Distr
N.A.I.C.S.: 333519

Subsidiary (Domestic):

Greythorn, Inc. (2)
40 Lake Bellevue Dr Ste 200, Bellevue, WA 98005
Tel.: (425) 635-0300
Web Site: http://www.vaco.com
Employment Placement Agencies
N.A.I.C.S.: 561311

Vaco San Antonio (2)
15600 San Pedro Ave, San Antonio, TX 78232
Tel.: (210) 745-4200
Web Site: https://www.vaco.com
Financial Advisory Services
N.A.I.C.S.: 523940
Donna McIlveen (Mng Dir)

OLYMPUS REAL ESTATE CORP.
5080 Spectrum Dr Ste 1050 E, Addison, TX 75001
Tel.: (214) 377-1740
Rev.: $67,300,000
Emp.: 40
Hotel
N.A.I.C.S.: 721110

Subsidiaries:

Milestone Management (1)
5429 LBJ Fwy Ste 800, Dallas, TX 75240
Tel.: (972) 788-0510
Web Site: http://www.milestone-mgt.com
Residential Property Management
N.A.I.C.S.: 531110

Oly/Metro New Mexico LP (1)
330 E Palace Ave, Santa Fe, NM 87501
Tel.: (505) 983-6351
Web Site:
http://www.laposadadesantafe.com
Hotel
N.A.I.C.S.: 721110

Phoenix At Avondale Apartments (1)
3106 Memorial Dr Southeast A1, Atlanta, GA 30317
Tel.: (404) 284-1570
Rev.: $440,000
Emp.: 3
Apartment Building Operator
N.A.I.C.S.: 531110

OLYMPUS WORLDWIDE CHAUFFEURED SERVICES
5825 Glenridge Dr Bldg 3 Ste 290, Atlanta, GA 30328
Tel.: (404) 524-8000
Web Site: http://www.1olympus.com
Year Founded: 2005
Sales Range: $1-9.9 Million
Emp.: 10
Limousine & Sedan Transportation Services
N.A.I.C.S.: 485999

Johan DeLeeuw (Pres)
Brandon Burr (Mgr-Dispatch)

OMAHA AIRPLANE SUPPLY CO.
1101 Ave H Ste G, Carter Lake, IA 51510
Tel.: (712) 347-6666
Web Site:
http://www.omahaairplanesupply.com
Sales Range: $10-24.9 Million
Emp.: 14
Aircraft Equipment & Supplies
N.A.I.C.S.: 423860
Harold Cheesman (VP)

OMAHA COMMUNITY FOUNDATION
302 S 36th St Ste100, Omaha, NE 68131
Tel.: (402) 342-3458 NE
Web Site:
http://www.omahafoundation.org
Year Founded: 1991
Sales Range: $50-74.9 Million
Community Foundation
N.A.I.C.S.: 813211
Sara Boyd (Pres & CEO)
Melisa Sunde (CFO)
Matt Darling (VP-Donor Svcs)
Diane Darrington (Mgr-Grants)
Kali Baker (VP-Community Rels)
Todd D. Simon (Chm)
Constance M. Ryan (Vice Chm)
Patrick J. Corrigan (Treas)
Emily Nguyen (Dir-Res & Evaluation)
John Lauber (Sec)

OMAHA CREATIVE GROUP
10909 John Galt Blvd, Omaha, NE 68103
Tel.: (402) 597-3000 NE
Web Site:
http://www.omahasteaks.com
Year Founded: 1917
Sales Range: $25-49.9 Million
Emp.: 1,500
Direct Marketing, Promotional & Brand Strategies
N.A.I.C.S.: 541810
Bruce Simon (Pres)
Alan Simon (Chm)
Todd Simon (Sr VP)

OMAHA HARDWOOD LUMBER CO.
8109 F St, Omaha, NE 68127
Tel.: (402) 342-4489
Web Site: http://www.oharco.com
Sales Range: $10-24.9 Million
Emp.: 25
Floor Coverings
N.A.I.C.S.: 423220
Cheryl Rau (Controller)
Tim Delger (Mgr-Territory)

OMAHA NEON SIGN CO. INC.
1120 N 18th St, Omaha, NE 68102
Tel.: (402) 341-6077
Web Site:
http://www.omahaneon.com
Year Founded: 1923
Sales Range: $10-24.9 Million
Emp.: 40
Signs & Advertising Specialties
N.A.I.C.S.: 339950
Samuel J. Marchese (Pres)

OMAHA PERFORMING ARTS
1200 Douglas St, Omaha, NE 68102
Tel.: (402) 345-0202
Web Site:
http://www.omahaperformingarts.org
Year Founded: 2000
Sales Range: $10-24.9 Million
Emp.: 60
Theatrical Producer & Services
N.A.I.C.S.: 711310
Arnold Reeves (CFO & Sr VP-Fin & Admin)
Ricardo Berry (Dir-Info Svcs)
Sabrina Weiss (VP-Dev)
John K. Boyer (Sec)
John Gottschalk (Chm)
Danyel Siler (VP-Mktg & Comm)
Laura Kendall (VP-Programming & Education)

OMAHA PUBLIC POWER DISTRICT
444 S 16th St Mall, Omaha, NE 68102-2247
Tel.: (402) 536-4131 NE
Web Site: http://www.oppd.com
Year Founded: 1946
Sales Range: $1-4.9 Billion
Emp.: 1,691
Electric Power Distribution
N.A.I.C.S.: 221122
Timothy J. Burke (Pres & CEO)
Jon T. Hansen (VP-Energy Production & Mktg)
Mohamad I. Doghman (Chief Compliance Officer & VP-Energy Delivery)
Michael A. Mines (Chm)
Tim Gay (Vice Chm)
Juli A. Comstock (VP-Customer Svc)
Lisa A. Olson (VP-Public Affairs)
Kate W. Brown (VP-IT)
Martha L. Sedky (VP-Human Capital & Asst Sec)
Tim O'Brien (Mgr-Economic Dev)
Devin Meisinger (Sr Coord-Economic Dev)
Jason Esser (Coord-Bus Retention & Expansion)
Javier Fernandez (CFO & VP)

OMAHA STATE BANK INC.
12100 W Center Rd, Omaha, NE 68144
Tel.: (402) 333-9100
Web Site: http://www.corebank.com
Year Founded: 1972
Sales Range: $10-24.9 Million
Emp.: 105
State Commercial Banks
N.A.I.C.S.: 522110
Michael L. Dahir (Chm & CEO)
Jim Flodine (Sr VP)
Ann Glinski (VP-Cash Mgmt)
Jim Suing (Exec VP)
Todd Clevenger (Sr VP)
Lindsay Borgeson (VP-Retail Banking)

OMAHA STEAKS INTERNATIONAL, INC.
10909 John Galt Blvd, Omaha, NE 68137
Tel.: (402) 331-1010 NE
Web Site:
http://www.omahasteaks.com
Year Founded: 1917
Sales Range: $300-349.9 Million
Emp.: 1,800
Steaks, Meat & Gourmet Foods Marketer, Distr & Retailer
N.A.I.C.S.: 311612
Alan D. Simon (Chm)
Bruce A. Simon (Pres)
Todd D. Simon (Owner & Sr VP)
Frederick Simon (Exec VP)

Subsidiaries:

Omaha Steaks, Inc. (1)
11030 O St, Omaha, NE
68137-2382 (100%)
Tel.: (402) 597-3000
Web Site: http://www.omahasteaks.com
Sales Range: $25-49.9 Million
Emp.: 120
Steaks, Meat & Gourmet Foods Marketer, Distr & Retailer
N.A.I.C.S.: 445240
Alan D. Simon (Chm)
Bruce A. Simon (Pres)
Kent Knoll (Dir-Compliance)

Omaha Steaks-Retail Stores (1)
10909 John Galt Blvd, Omaha, NE
68137-2382 (100%)
Tel.: (402) 391-1562
Web Site: http://www.omahasteaks.com
Steaks, Meat & Gourmet Foods Retailer
N.A.I.C.S.: 445240
Todd Simon (Sr VP)

OmahaSteaks.com, Inc. (1)
11030 O St, Omaha, NE
68137-2346 (100%)
Tel.: (402) 597-3000
Web Site: http://www.omahasteaks.com
Sales Range: $25-49.9 Million
Emp.: 40
Online Retailer of Steaks, Meat & Gourmet Foods
N.A.I.C.S.: 445240
Bruce Simon (Pres & CEO)

OMAHA TRUCK CENTER INC.
10550 I St, Omaha, NE 68127
Tel.: (402) 592-2440
Web Site:
http://www.omahatruck.com
Sales Range: $100-124.9 Million
Emp.: 400
Trucks, Tractors & Trailers: New & Used
N.A.I.C.S.: 441110
Trey Mytty (Pres & CEO)
Bruce Fox (Mgr-Ops)
Trish Manna (Mgr-Credit)
Carlen Deveraux (Mgr-Parts)
Kevin Short (Mgr-Parts)
Jason Capps (Mgr-Svcs)

Subsidiaries:

Harrison Truck Centers, Inc. (1)
101 Plaza Dr, Elk Run Heights, IA 50707
Tel.: (319) 234-4453
Web Site: http://www.htctrucks.com
Commercial Truck & Freightliner Sales, Parts & Service
N.A.I.C.S.: 423110
Brian Harrison (Co-Owner & CEO)

OMAHA ZOOLOGICAL SOCIETY
3701 S 10th St, Omaha, NE 68107
Tel.: (402) 733-8401
Web Site: http://www.omahazoo.com
Year Founded: 1952
Sales Range: $10-24.9 Million
Emp.: 300
Zoological Garden
N.A.I.C.S.: 712130
Lee Simmons (Chm)
Jeremy Eddie (Controller)

OMAN ENTERPRISES INC.
8355 S Wadsworth Blvd, Littleton, CO 80128
Tel.: (303) 972-0787
Web Site: http://www.kidslovelpl.com
Rev.: $10,100,000
Emp.: 160
Commercial & Industrial Building Operation
N.A.I.C.S.: 531120
Terry Oman (Pres)

OMAR MEDICAL SUPPLIES, INC.
500 Crossing Dr Unit A, University Park, IL 60484
Tel.: (708) 534-8200
Web Site: http://www.omarinc.com
Year Founded: 1997
Sales Range: $10-24.9 Million
Emp.: 10

Gloves, Can Liners, Protective Clothing, Towel & Tissue, First Aid Kits, Corrugated Boxes, Safety & Medical Supplies & Equipment Mfr, Distr & Importer
N.A.I.C.S.: 423450
Willie L. Wilson *(Founder & CEO)*

OMAX CORP.
21409 72nd Ave S, Kent, WA 98032
Tel.: (253) 872-2300
Web Site: http://www.omax.com
Year Founded: 1993
Sales Range: $100-124.9 Million
Emp.: 185
Mfr of Abrasive Waterjet Systems
N.A.I.C.S.: 333517
John Cheung *(CEO)*
John H. Olsen *(VP-Ops)*
Steve Ulmer *(VP-Intl Sls)*

OMDA OIL & GAS, INC.
707 E Tahquitz Canyon Way Ste 6, Palm Springs, CA 92262
Tel.: (760) 318-0700
Oil & Gas Exploration Services
N.A.I.C.S.: 211130
Monte Anderson *(Vice Chm, Pres & CEO)*

OMEDA COMMUNICATIONS, INC.
555 Huehl Rd, Northbrook, IL 60062
Tel.: (847) 564-8900
Web Site: http://www.omeda.com
Year Founded: 1980
Sales Range: $10-24.9 Million
Emp.: 150
Online & Interactive Marketing Software & Services
N.A.I.C.S.: 513210
Aaron Oberman *(Pres & CEO)*
Randy Renner *(VP-Sls & Mktg)*
James Capo *(Chief Revenue Officer)*
Tony Napoleone *(VP-Client Success)*

Subsidiaries:

Hallmark Data Systems, Inc.   (1)
7300 N Linder Ave, Skokie, IL 60077
Tel.: (847) 564-8900
Web Site: http://www.halldata.com
Business-To-Business Fulfillment & Data Management Services
N.A.I.C.S.: 518210
Steve Crowe *(Gen Mgr)*
Tim Hunnewell *(COO)*
Robert Kennedy *(Assoc Dir-Client Relationship Mgmt)*
Laura Hynes *(Sr Mgr-Client Relationship)*
Nicole Backaus *(Sr Mgr-Client Relationship)*
Kate Thomas *(Sr Mgr-Client Relationship)*
Neal Kahn *(Sr Mgr-Client Relationship)*

OMEGA ADVISORS, INC.
810 7th Ave 33rd Fl, New York, NY 10019
Tel.: (212) 495-5200   DE
Web Site: http://www.omega-advisors.com
Year Founded: 1991
Rev.: $5,400,000,000
Emp.: 30
Portfolio Management & Investment Advisory Services
N.A.I.C.S.: 523940
Leon G. Cooperman *(Founder)*
Cyrus Cooper *(CIO)*
Steven Einhorn *(Vice Chm)*
Susan Leong *(Chief Compliance Officer)*
Denis Wong *(COO)*

OMEGA BRANDS INC.
5005 Interbay Blvd, Tampa, FL 33611
Tel.: (813) 514-1839   NV
Year Founded: 2012
Beverage Mfr & Distr
N.A.I.C.S.: 312111

Richard D. Russell *(Pres & CEO)*

OMEGA ELECTRIC CONSTRUCTION CO.
25 Omega Dr Ste 201, Williston, VT 05495
Tel.: (802) 862-0517
Rev.: $12,000,000
Emp.: 100
General Electrical Contractor
N.A.I.C.S.: 238210
Cheryl L. Senecal *(VP)*
Alfred R. Senecal Jr. *(Pres)*

OMEGA ELECTRONICS MANUFACTURING SERVICES
5390 Hellyer Ave, San Jose, CA 95138
Tel.: (408) 206-4260
Web Site: http://www.omega-ems.com
Year Founded: 2015
Electrical & Electronic Products Mfr
N.A.I.C.S.: 334419
Chris Alessio *(Pres & CEO)*
Ian Grover *(VP-Engrg)*
Phil Aguiar *(VP-Ops)*
Hassan Malak *(VP-Sls)*

Subsidiaries:

Vitron Electronic Services, Inc.   (1)
5400 Hellyer Ave, San Jose, CA 95138
Tel.: (408) 251-1600
Web Site: http://www.vitronmfg.com
Sales Range: $1-9.9 Million
Emp.: 60
Electronic & Precision Equipment Repair & Maintenance
N.A.I.C.S.: 811210

OMEGA ENTERPRISES INC.
1215 Hyland Ave, Kaukauna, WI 54130-1441
Tel.: (920) 759-2500   WI
Web Site: http://www.bassettmechanical.com
Year Founded: 1936
Sales Range: Less than $1 Million
Emp.: 350
Holding Company; Refrigeration Equipment & Supplies Whslr
N.A.I.C.S.: 551112
Kim Bassett *(Pres & CEO)*

Subsidiaries:

Bassett Inc.   (1)
1215 Hyland Ave, Kaukauna, WI 54130-1441
Tel.: (920) 759-2500
Web Site: http://www.bassettmechanical.com
Refrigeration Equipment & Supplies Whslr
N.A.I.C.S.: 423740
Jay Sauter *(VP-Fin)*
William R. Bassett *(CEO & COO)*
Kim Bassett-Heitzmann *(Pres)*
Mark Huiting *(Mgr-Plumbing Dept)*

OMEGA INDUSTRIES INC.
1010 Rowe St, Elkhart, IN 46516
Tel.: (574) 295-5353
Web Site: http://www.omeganationalproducts.com
Sales Range: $10-24.9 Million
Emp.: 150
Wood Cabinet, Cabinet Accessories & RV Specialty Products
N.A.I.C.S.: 321999
Rod McNerney *(Pres & CEO)*

OMEGA LABORATORIES, INC.
400 N Cleveland Ave, Mogadore, OH 44260
Tel.: (330) 628-5748
Web Site: http://www.omegalabs.net
Year Founded: 1999
Drug Testing Services
N.A.I.C.S.: 541715

Jay Davis *(Co-Owner)*
John C. Vitullo *(Co-Owner)*
Bill Corl *(CEO)*

Subsidiaries:

Acumium LLC   (1)
5133 W Terrace Dr 300, Madison, WI 53718
Tel.: (608) 310-9700
Web Site: http://www.acumium.com
Custom Computer Programming Services
N.A.I.C.S.: 541511
Dan Costello *(Founder & CEO)*

OMEGA LEGAL SYSTEMS, INC.
7272 E Indian School Rd Ste 480, Scottsdale, AZ 85251
Tel.: (602) 952-5240   AZ
Web Site: http://www.omegalegal.com
Year Founded: 1974
Sales Range: $10-24.9 Million
Emp.: 45
Developer of Financial & Legal Practice Management Software
N.A.I.C.S.: 513210
Donald A. Gall *(Pres & CEO)*
Linda Brower *(VP-Admin)*
Cheryl Burton *(Mgr-Programming)*
Debi Young *(Mgr-Client Svcs)*

OMEGA MEATS INC.
7209 Cessna Dr, Greensboro, NC 27409
Tel.: (336) 662-0000
Rev.: $30,300,000
Emp.: 4
Meat Markets, Including Freezer Provisioners
N.A.I.C.S.: 445240
Thomas Cassano *(Owner & Pres)*

OMEGA OPTICAL CO. LP
13515 N Stemmons Fwy, Dallas, TX 75234
Tel.: (972) 241-4141
Web Site: http://www.omega-dallas.com
Rev.: $10,800,000
Emp.: 99
Eyeglasses, Lenses & Frames
N.A.I.C.S.: 339115

OMEGA PARTNERS III LLC
1667 Chesterfield Grove Rd Chesterfield Ste 200, Saint Louis, MO 63005
Tel.: (314) 744-3300
Web Site: http://www.omegapartnersllc.com
Professional, Scientific & Technical Services
N.A.I.C.S.: 541990
Larry Wright *(Mgr)*

Subsidiaries:

Omega Partners Joliet LLC   (1)
27100 S Frontage Rd Channahon, Joliet, IL 60410
Tel.: (815) 423-2700
Petroleum Product Distr
N.A.I.C.S.: 424710

OMEGA SPORTS INC.
120 S Walnut Cir, Greensboro, NC 27409
Tel.: (336) 854-0797   NC
Web Site: http://www.omegasports.com
Year Founded: 1978
Sporting Goods & Bicycle Shops
N.A.I.C.S.: 459110
Philip W. Bowman *(Pres)*
R. Craig Carlock *(CEO)*
Blair Spellicy *(Mgr-Accts Payable)*
Matthew Keenan *(Mgr-Store)*

OMEGA STEEL CO.
3460 Hollenberg Dr, Bridgeton, MO 63044
Tel.: (314) 209-0992
Web Site: http://www.omegasteel.com
Sales Range: $10-24.9 Million
Emp.: 45
Carbon Steel Pipe & Tubing Supplier
N.A.I.C.S.: 423510
Greg Semmel *(Founder & Pres)*
Skip Palazzolo *(Mgr-Sls)*
Mike Burke *(Asst Mgr-Sls)*

OMEGA WORLD TRAVEL, INC.
3102 Omega Office Park, Fairfax, VA 22031-2400
Tel.: (703) 359-0200   VA
Web Site: http://www.omegatravel.com
Year Founded: 1972
Sales Range: $1-4.9 Billion
Emp.: 1,100
Travel Services
N.A.I.C.S.: 561510
Gloria Bohan *(Pres & CEO)*
Betsy Amos *(VP & Exec Dir)*

Subsidiaries:

TravTech Inc.   (1)
3102 Omega Office Park, Fairfax, VA 22031
Tel.: (703) 272-0024
Software Development Services
N.A.I.C.S.: 541511

OMEGA/CINEMA PROPS INC.
5857 Santa Monica Blvd, Los Angeles, CA 90038
Tel.: (323) 466-8201
Web Site: http://www.omegacinemaprops.com
Sales Range: $10-24.9 Million
Emp.: 43
Rental of Equipment & Props for Motion Picture Production
N.A.I.C.S.: 532490
E. Jay Krause *(Pres)*
Cheryl Jordan *(Controller)*
Barry Pritchard *(VP)*

OMEGA3 INNOVATIONS COMPANY
727 Commerce Dr, Venice, FL 34292
Tel.: (941) 485-4400
Web Site: http://www.omega3innovations.com
Sales Range: $1-9.9 Million
Emp.: 10
Nutritional Foods
N.A.I.C.S.: 311999
Bo Martinsen *(Co-Founder)*
Anne-Marie Chalmers *(Co-Founder)*

OMELET
3780 Wilshire Blvd 5th Fl, Los Angeles, CA 90010
Tel.: (213) 427-6400
Web Site: http://www.omeletla.com
Sales Range: $10-24.9 Million
Emp.: 20
Advertising, Brand Development & Integration, Graphic Design, Production (Ad, Film, Broadcast), Production (Print)
N.A.I.C.S.: 541810
Steven Amato *(Co-Founder)*
Ryan Fey *(Co-Founder)*
Shervin Samari *(Co-Founder & Dir-Creative)*
Frank Lucero *(Dir-Creative)*
Grant Holland *(Chief Creative Officer)*
Shannon McGlothin *(Exec Dir-Creative)*
Thas Naseemuddeen *(Chief Strategy Officer)*

Omelet—(Continued)
Don Kurz *(Chm & CEO)*
Ricardo Diaz *(Exec Dir-Digital)*
Dena Gonzalez *(Partner & Head-Bus Plng & Delivery)*
Devin Desjarlais *(Dir-Comm)*

OMG NATIONAL
1801 Pine Island Rd, Plantation, FL 33322
Tel.: (954) 742-5520
Web Site: http://www.omgnational.com
Sales Range: $1-9.9 Million
Emp.: 51
Digital Marketing Consulting Services
N.A.I.C.S.: 541613
Jerry Davis *(VP)*
Kelly Simmons *(Coord-Caribbean Mktg)*
Lisa Blevins *(VP-Subscription Sls)*

OMH, INC.
7747 S 6th St, Oak Creek, WI 53154
Tel.: (414) 768-9090   WI
Web Site: http://www.omhinc.com
Year Founded: 1988
Sales Range: $1-9.9 Million
Emp.: 31
Hoists, Cranes, And Monorails
N.A.I.C.S.: 333923
Jeffrey Morden *(Sec & VP)*

OMI INDUSTRIES
1 Corporate Dr Ste 100, Long Grove, IL 60047
Tel.: (847) 304-9111
Web Site: http://www.omi-industries.com
Year Founded: 1989
Sales Range: $10-24.9 Million
Emp.: 67
Eco-Friendly Chemicals & Natural Odor Eliminators
N.A.I.C.S.: 325998
Philip M. Coffey *(CEO & Mng Dir)*
Lisa Arnold *(Coord-Sls)*
Barbie Chmieleski *(Coord-Event)*
Tom Kelly *(CFO)*
Amanda Daluga *(Mgr-Sls-Natl)*
Stephen Lattis *(Dir-Ops)*

OMICIA, INC.
1611 Telegraph Ave Ste 500, Oakland, CA 94612
Tel.: (510) 595-0800   DE
Web Site: http://www.omicia.com
Biotechnology Research & Development
N.A.I.C.S.: 541714
Matthew Tindall *(CEO)*
John Stuelpnagel *(Co-Founder & Chm)*
Martin G. Reese *(Co-Founder, Pres & Chief Scientific Officer)*
Edward S. Kiruluta *(Co-Founder & CTO)*
Paul Billings *(Co-Founder & Chief Medical Officer)*
Adam Grant *(COO)*
Charlene Son Rigby *(VP-Products & Strategy)*
Mathias Klozenbuecher *(VP-Bus Dev)*

OMICO INC.
2025 Ragu Dr, Owensboro, KY 42303
Tel.: (270) 926-9981
Web Site: http://www.omicoplastics.com
Sales Range: $200-249.9 Million
Emp.: 200
Molding Primary Plastics
N.A.I.C.S.: 326199

William K. Mounts *(VP-Ops & Pur)*
Roger Evans *(Pres)*
Sondra Campbell *(Controller)*

OMICRON CONSULTING, LLC
PO Box 1047, Bryn Mawr, PA 19010
Tel.: (610) 822-3100
Web Site: http://www.omicron.com
Year Founded: 1980
Sales Range: $25-49.9 Million
Emp.: 110
Computer Consulting Services
N.A.I.C.S.: 541519
Randy Pritzker *(Founder, Pres & CEO)*
Valerie DeRusso *(COO & VP)*

OMIMEX RESOURCES, INC.
7950 John T White Rd, Fort Worth, TX 76120-3608
Tel.: (817) 460-7777
Web Site: http://www.omimex.com
Year Founded: 1987
Exploration & Production of Oil & Natural Gas
N.A.I.C.S.: 211120
Clark Storms *(VP)*

OMNI BIO PHARMACEUTICAL, INC.
5350 S Roslyn Ste 430, Greenwood Village, CO 80111
Tel.: (303) 867-3415   CO
Web Site: http://www.omnibiopharma.com
Emp.: 1
Pharmaceutical Researcher & Mfr
N.A.I.C.S.: 325412
Charles A. Dinarello *(Chief Scientific Officer)*
Bruce E. Schneider *(Chm & CEO)*
Bruce D. Forrest *(Chief Dev Officer)*
Jack F. Riccardi *(CFO)*

OMNI CIRCUITS INTERNATIONAL LLC.
15261 Telcom Dr, Brooksville, FL 34604
Tel.: (352) 799-9997
Web Site: http://www.omnicircuits.com
Rev.: $10,000,000
Emp.: 35
Electronic Parts & Equipment Merchant Whslr
N.A.I.C.S.: 423690
James Mchugh *(Gen Mgr)*

OMNI CORPORATION
2725 Broadbent Pkwy NE, Albuquerque, NM 87107
Tel.: (505) 338-3223
Web Site: http://www.omnicorporation.com
Sales Range: $10-24.9 Million
Emp.: 10
Computer Facilities Management
N.A.I.C.S.: 449210

OMNI ENTERPRISES INC.
5326 A St Ste 1, Anchorage, AK 99518
Tel.: (509) 493-2900
Sales Range: $25-49.9 Million
Emp.: 180
Country General Stores
N.A.I.C.S.: 455219

OMNI FACILITY SERVICES, INC.
24300 Southfield Rd Ste 220, Southfield, MI 48075-2820
Tel.: (248) 483-3170
Web Site: http://www.ofs-na.com
Year Founded: 1998
Sales Range: $25-49.9 Million

Emp.: 850
Building Maintenance Services
N.A.I.C.S.: 561720
Sandra Gronua *(CFO)*
Subsidiaries:
Omni Facility Services   (1)
1050 Tower Ln, Bensenville, IL 60106-1031
Tel.: (630) 521-0084
Web Site: http://www.ofs-na.com
Sales Range: $50-74.9 Million
Emp.: 500
Building Maintenance Services
N.A.I.C.S.: 423850

OMNI GLASS AND PAINT INC.
3530 Omni Dr, Oshkosh, WI 54904
Tel.: (920) 233-3333
Web Site: http://www.omnigp.com
Sales Range: $25-49.9 Million
Emp.: 200
Provider of Painting & Paper Hanging Contracting Services
N.A.I.C.S.: 238320
Dave Miller *(Pres)*
Dave Vanderzandes *(VP)*
Kerry Johnson *(Controller)*

OMNI HEALTH, INC.
5966 W 16th Ave, Hialeah, FL 33012
Year Founded: 2014
Rev.: $213,686
Assets: $58,084
Liabilities: $190,258
Net Worth: ($132,174)
Earnings: ($534,032)
Fiscal Year-end: 04/30/16
Investment Services
N.A.I.C.S.: 523999
Subsidiaries:
Malecon Pharmacy, Inc.   (1)
5966 W 16th Ave, Hialeah, FL 33012-6814
Tel.: (800) 709-8972
Web Site: http://www.maleconpharmacy.com
Emp.: 10
Medical & Pharmaceutical Products Distr
N.A.I.C.S.: 424210
Andrey Soloviev *(CEO)*

OMNI HOLDING COMPANY
14012 Giles Rd, Omaha, NE 68138
Tel.: (402) 895-5160
Rev.: $17,800,000
Emp.: 15
Resurfacing Contractor
N.A.I.C.S.: 237310
Donald D. Graham *(Pres)*
Nancy Graham Cagle *(VP)*
Subsidiaries:
Omni Engineering Inc.   (1)
14012 Giles Rd, Omaha, NE 68138
Tel.: (402) 895-6666
Surfacing & Paving
N.A.I.C.S.: 237310
Thunderbird Trucking Inc.   (1)
14012 Giles Rd, Omaha, NE 68138
Tel.: (402) 895-3454
Local Trucking without Storage
N.A.I.C.S.: 484110
US Asphalt Co   (1)
14012 Giles Rd, Omaha, NE 68138
Tel.: (402) 895-6666
Resurfacing Contractor
N.A.I.C.S.: 237310
Kyle Timmer *(Pres)*

OMNI MANAGEMENT ACQUISITION CORP.
5955 De Soto Ave Ste 100, Woodland Hills, CA 91367
Tel.: (818) 906-8300   DE
Web Site: http://www.omnimgt.com
Year Founded: 1970
Bankruptcy Administration Services

N.A.I.C.S.: 541611
Brian Osborne *(Pres & CEO)*
Eric Schwarz *(CFO)*
Scott Ewing *(VP-Bus Ops & Controls)*
Paul Deutch *(Sr VP)*
Brian Gelinas *(Dir-IT)*
Katie Nownes *(VP-Corp Restructuring Svcs)*
Alison Miller *(Sr VP)*
Jeriad Paul *(VP-Securities Svcs & Solicitation)*

OMNI MANUFACTURING INC.
901 McKinley Rd, Saint Marys, OH 45885
Tel.: (419) 394-7424
Web Site: http://www.omnimfg.com
Rev.: $10,000,000
Emp.: 140
Metal Stamping Mfr
N.A.I.C.S.: 332119
Wayne L. Freewalt *(Pres)*

OMNI PARTNERS, LP
225 Broadhollow Rd, Melville, NY 11747
Tel.: (631) 694-6900
Sales Range: Less than $1 Million
Emp.: 5
Nonresidential Building Operators
N.A.I.C.S.: 531312
Muriel Klopsis *(Mgr)*

OMNI PRODUCTS, INC.
3911 Dayton St, McHenry, IL 60050
Tel.: (815) 344-3100   DE
Web Site: http://www.omnirail.com
Year Founded: 1983
Designer & Manufacturer of Highway Railroad Grade Crossing Products
N.A.I.C.S.: 326299
Bob Cigrang *(Mgr-Sls)*

OMNI STRUCTURES & MANAGEMENT INC.
8900 King Rd, Loomis, CA 95650
Tel.: (916) 660-9287
Sales Range: $10-24.9 Million
Emp.: 10
Nonresidential Construction Services
N.A.I.C.S.: 236220
Rod Thayer *(Pres)*

OMNI SYSTEMS INC.
24400 Highland Rd, Richmond Heights, OH 44143
Tel.: (216) 377-5160
Web Site: http://www.omnisystem.com
Year Founded: 1990
Sales Range: $25-49.9 Million
Emp.: 80
Pressure Sensitive Barcode Labels
N.A.I.C.S.: 561910
Adam DeFrancesco *(Founder & CEO)*
Andy Macek *(Pres)*
Chris Allen *(Mgr-Ops)*
Lee Lopez *(Mgr-Production)*
Mike Murton *(Gen Mgr)*

OMNI VALVE COMPANY, LLC.
4520 Chandler Rd, Muskogee, OK 74403
Tel.: (918) 687-6100
Web Site: http://www.omnivalve.com
Sales Range: $10-24.9 Million
Emp.: 13
Crude Oil, Natural Gas & Other Petroleum Product Mfr & Distr
N.A.I.C.S.: 211120
Michael A. Johnson *(Pres & CEO)*

OMNI VENTURES, INC.
637 S Clarence St, Los Angeles, CA 90023
Tel.: (323) 981-0205   KS

Year Founded: 2008
Sales Range: Less than $1 Million
Emp.: 2
Equity Funding For Commercial & Recreational Projects
N.A.I.C.S.: 523999
Christian Adam Wicks *(Interim Pres & CEO)*
Deepak Ramchandani *(CEO)*

OMNIBUILD CONSTRUCTION INC.
213 W 35th St 7th Fl, New York, NY 10001-0001
Tel.: (212) 419-1930
Web Site: http://www.omnibuild.com
Year Founded: 2007
Sales Range: $200-249.9 Million
Emp.: 100
Hospitality, Residential & Educational Building Construction
N.A.I.C.S.: 236116
Dionysios Neofitidis *(Project Mgr)*
Peter Serpico *(CEO)*
John Mingione *(COO)*

OMNIFAB LLC
1316 W Main St, Auburn, WA 98001
Tel.: (253) 931-5151   WA
Web Site: http://www.omnifabllc.com
Year Founded: 1998
Sales Range: $1-9.9 Million
Emp.: 53
Metal Fabrication
N.A.I.C.S.: 332313
Justin Everly *(Project Mgr-Engrg)*

OMNIFICS INC.
5845 Richmond Hwy, Alexandria, VA 22314
Tel.: (703) 548-4040
Web Site: http://www.omnifics.com
Sales Range: $10-24.9 Million
Emp.: 40
Office Furniture
N.A.I.C.S.: 423210
Doug Williams *(VP-Ops)*
Jack Dempsey *(Mgr-Distr)*

OMNILIFT INC.
1938 Stout Dr, Warminster, PA 18974
Tel.: (215) 443-9090
Web Site: http://www.omnilift-inc.com
Year Founded: 1976
Sales Range: $10-24.9 Million
Emp.: 60
Lift Trucks & Parts
N.A.I.C.S.: 423830
William J. Boyle *(Pres)*
Martina Oberst *(Mgr-Accts Payable)*
Mike Kirkpatrick *(VP-Ops)*
Gina Coyle *(VP-Fin)*

OMNIMAX HOLDINGS, INC.
303 Research Dr Ste 400, Norcross, GA 30092
Tel.: (770) 449-7066   DE
Web Site: http://www.euramax.com
Sales Range: $800-899.9 Million
Emp.: 1,700
Holding Company; Metal & Plastic Building Exterior Products Mfr & Whslr
N.A.I.C.S.: 551112
Mary Cullin *(CFO, Treas & Sr VP)*
Richard C. Brown *(Pres & CEO)*
John Blount *(Chief Admin Officer, Gen Counsel, Sec & Sr VP)*

Subsidiaries:

Omnimax International, Inc. (1)
303 Research Dr Ste 400, Norcross, GA 30092-2584
Tel.: (770) 449-7066
Web Site: http://www.euramax.com
Metal & Plastic Building Exterior Products Mfr & Whslr

N.A.I.C.S.: 423330
Mary Cullin *(CFO & Sr VP)*
Richard C. Brown *(Pres & CEO)*

Unit (Domestic):

Amerimax Home Products (2)
450 Richardson Dr, Lancaster, PA 17603-4036
Tel.: (717) 299-3711
Web Site: http://www.amerimax.com
Sales Range: $50-74.9 Million
Emp.: 400
Supplier Of Steel Aluminum & Vinyl Rain-carrying Systems
N.A.I.C.S.: 332321
Dudley Rowe *(Pres)*

Subsidiary (Domestic):

Berger Building Products, Inc. (2)
805 Pennsylvania Blvd, Feasterville Trevose, PA 19053-7813
Tel.: (215) 355-1200
Web Site: http://www.bergerbuildingproducts.com
Sales Range: $25-49.9 Million
Emp.: 200
Loose Plumming Mater
N.A.I.C.S.: 332322
Norman Copley *(Gen Mgr)*

Unit (Domestic):

Global Expanded Metals (2)
4455 River Green Pkwy, Duluth, GA 30096
Tel.: (770) 641-1052
Web Site: http://www.globalexpandedmetals.com
Sales Range: $10-24.9 Million
Emp.: 25
Expanded Metal Mesh Products Mfr
N.A.I.C.S.: 332999

Subsidiary (Domestic):

InvisaFlow, LLC (2)
1350 Bluegrass Lakes Pkwy, Alpharetta, GA 30004-3395
Tel.: (678) 942-1327
Web Site: http://www.invisaflow.com
Plastic Water Drainage Products Mfr & Whslr
N.A.I.C.S.: 326199
Jeff Smith *(VP-Ops)*

OMNIPOINT, INC.
3684 Tampa Rd Unit 2, Oldsmar, FL 34677
Tel.: (813) 774-8199
Web Site: http://www.omnipointinc.com
Sales Range: $50-74.9 Million
Emp.: 150
IT Staffing Services
N.A.I.C.S.: 561311
Glenn Myer *(Partner & COO)*
Keith Diego *(Partner)*
Alfredo Gonzalez *(Partner)*
Will Hardy *(Partner)*
Derek Shipes *(Partner & Chief People Officer)*
Keith Will *(Partner)*

OMNIPOTECH, LTD.
11422A Craighead Dr, Houston, TX 77025
Tel.: (281) 768-4800
Web Site: http://www.omnipotech.com
Sales Range: $1-9.9 Million
Emp.: 15
Data Processing, Hosting & Related Services
N.A.I.C.S.: 518210
Robert Kyslinger *(Founder)*
Rob Apodaca *(Mgr-Ops)*

OMNIPRINT INTERNATIONAL INC.
3505 Cadillac Ave Ste F3, Costa Mesa, CA 92626
Web Site: http://www.omniprintonline.com

Year Founded: 2004
Sales Range: $1-9.9 Million
Emp.: 30
Digital Printer Mfr
N.A.I.C.S.: 323111
Victor Pena *(Pres & CEO)*
Said Canales *(Head-Tech & R&D)*

OMNISPHERE CORP.
9950 SW 107th Ave Ste 100, Miami, FL 33176
Tel.: (305) 388-4075
Web Site: http://www.omnisphere.net
Year Founded: 1973
Sales Range: $10-24.9 Million
Emp.: 9
Pulpwood; Paper
N.A.I.C.S.: 423990
Alexander F. Valdes *(Pres)*
Maria McCarthy *(Controller)*

OMNISTUDIO, INC.
1140 19th St NW Ste 320, Washington, DC 20036
Tel.: (202) 785-9605
Web Site: http://www.omnistudio.com
Year Founded: 1977
Sales Range: $1-9.9 Million
Emp.: 20
Graphic Design Services
N.A.I.C.S.: 541430
Eileen Kessler *(Founder, Pres & CEO)*

OMNITEAM INC.
9300 Hall Rd, Downey, CA 90241-5309
Tel.: (562) 923-9660
Web Site: http://www.omniteaminc.com
Year Founded: 1987
Sales Range: $10-24.9 Million
Emp.: 125
Air Conditioning System Installation Services
N.A.I.C.S.: 238220
Hans Haasis *(Pres)*

OMNITI
11830 W Market Pl Ste F, Fulton, MD 20759
Tel.: (240) 646-0770
Web Site: http://www.omniti.com
Year Founded: 1997
Sales Range: $1-9.9 Million
Emp.: 45
Information Technology Consulting Services
N.A.I.C.S.: 541512
Robert Treat *(CEO)*
Leon Fayer *(VP-Bus Dev)*

OMNITRANS
1700 W 5th St, San Bernardino, CA 92411
Tel.: (909) 379-7100
Web Site: http://www.omnitrans.org
Sales Range: $25-49.9 Million
Emp.: 674
Bus Line Operations
N.A.I.C.S.: 485113
Wendy Williams *(Dir-Mktg)*
Maurice Mansion *(Treas & Mgr)*
Mary Patterson *(Mgr-HR)*
Jennifer Sims *(Dir-Procurement)*
Sam Spagnolo *(Chm)*
Erin Rogers *(Deputy Gen Mgr)*
P. Scott Graham *(CEO & Gen Mgr)*
Connie Raya *(Dir-Maintenance)*

OMNIVUE BUSINESS SOLUTIONS
1355 Windward Concourse Ste 200, Alpharetta, GA 30005
Tel.: (770) 587-0095
Web Site: http://www.omnivue.net

Year Founded: 2003
Rev.: $5,400,000
Emp.: 29
Business Consulting Services
N.A.I.C.S.: 541618
Jeff Pyden *(Owner & Mng Dir)*

OMNOVA SOLUTIONS INC.
25435 Harvard Rd, Beachwood, OH 44122-6201
Tel.: (216) 682-7000   OH
Web Site: http://www.omnova.com
Year Founded: 1999
Rev.: $736,200,000
Assets: $556,100,000
Liabilities: $535,200,000
Net Worth: $20,900,000
Earnings: $22,400,000
Emp.: 1,850
Fiscal Year-end: 11/30/19
Emulsion Polymers, Specialty Chemicals & Engineered Surfaces Mfr
N.A.I.C.S.: 325998
James C. LeMay *(Gen Counsel & Sr VP-Corp Dev)*
Michael A. Quinn *(Chief HR Officer & Sr VP)*
Donald B. McMillan *(Chief Acctg Officer & VP)*
Marshall D. Moore *(CTO & Sr VP-Ops)*
Kathy Vanderheyden *(VP-Safety, Health, Environment & Security)*
Sandra L. Kowaleski *(Gen Mgr-Functional Coatings & Mfg Ops)*
William R. Seelbach *(Chm)*

Subsidiaries:

New Fluid Solutions Inc. (1)
6161 Savoy Dr Ste 248, Houston, TX 77036
Tel.: (713) 780-3600
Web Site: http://www.newfluid.com
Sales Range: $1-9.9 Million
Oil & Water Based Drilling Fluid Products Mfr
N.A.I.C.S.: 324191
Mano Shaarpour *(Founder)*

OMNOVA Ningbo Co., Ltd. (1)
308 Jiangbin Road Xiaogang United Development Zone, Ningbo Economic and Technical Development Zone, Ningbo, 315803, China
Tel.: (86) 57486183719
Web Site: http://www.omnova.com
Chemical Products Mfr
N.A.I.C.S.: 325998

OMNOVA Performance Chemicals (UK) Ltd. (1)
74-78 Wood Lane End, Hemel Hempstead, HP2 4RF, Hertfordshire, United Kingdom
Tel.: (44) 1442883124
Performance Chemicals Mfr
N.A.I.C.S.: 325211
Nigel Savory *(Mng Dir)*

OMNOVA Solutions Portugal S.A. (1)
Rua Francisco Lyon de Castro 28, 2725-397, Mem Martins, Portugal
Tel.: (351) 219269700
Emulsion Polymer & Specialty Chemical Mfr
N.A.I.C.S.: 325998

OMNOVA Solutions SAS (1)
Z I du Havre Route du Noroit, 76430, Sandouville, France
Tel.: (33) 232792200
Web Site: http://www.omnova.com
Paint & Coating Products Mfr
N.A.I.C.S.: 325510

OMP INC.
760 Kilroy Airport Rd Wy Swt 500, Long Beach, CA 90806
Tel.: (562) 628-1007
Web Site: http://www.obagi.com
Rev.: $38,400,000
Emp.: 58

OMP INC. | **U.S. PRIVATE**

Omp Inc.—(Continued)
Drugs, Proprietaries & Sundries
N.A.I.C.S.: 424210

OMS MOTION, INC.
15201 NW Greenbrier Pkwy Ste B-1,
Beaverton, OR 97006-7362
Tel.: (503) 629-8081
Web Site:
 http://www.omsinmotion.com
Sales Range: $1-9.9 Million
Emp.: 10
Embedded Multi-Axis Motion Controller Designer Mfr
N.A.I.C.S.: 334513
Phillip S. Brown (Owner & Pres)

OMW CORPORATION
21 Pamaron Way Ste G, Novato, CA 94949
Tel.: (415) 382-1669
Web Site: http://www.omwcorp.com
Year Founded: 1996
Sales Range: $1-9.9 Million
Emp.: 20
Precision Machinery Distr
N.A.I.C.S.: 423830
Mary Heitman (Office Mgr)
Joe Osborn (Founder)
Michael Leeds (Mgr-Production)

ON A SHOESTRING, INC.
3633 Cortez Rd W, Bradenton, FL 34210
Tel.: (941) 782-7023
Web Site:
 http://www.onashoestringinc.com
Year Founded: 2006
Sales Range: $10-24.9 Million
Emp.: 11
Shoe Stores
N.A.I.C.S.: 458210
Sharon Litschauer (Pres)
Steve Litschauer (CEO)
Rae Ann E. Darling Reed (VP)
Jim Larsen (Gen Mgr)

ON BOARD ENTERTAINMENT, INC.
85 Liberty Ship Way Ste 114, Sausalito, CA 94965-3314
Tel.: (415) 331-4789   CA
Web Site: http://www.obexp.com
Year Founded: 1996
Sales Range: $10-24.9 Million
Emp.: 15
Event Marketing & Promotional Services
N.A.I.C.S.: 541613
John Sullivan (VP-Ops)
Annie Reid (Acct Dir)
Cheryl Finster (VP-Agency Resources)
Deb Lemon (Owner & Pres)
Emily Dolber (Acct Dir)
Emily Luckett (Sr Acct Dir)
Trish Costello (Dir-Creative)

ON DEMAND ICARS, INC.
Pier 50, San Francisco, CA 94158
Tel.: (800) 897-9742
Web Site: http://www.icars.cc
Automotive Mobile Application & Software Services
N.A.I.C.S.: 518210
Mike Remedios (Pres)

Subsidiaries:

Limos.com, Inc.   (1)
Pier 50, San Francisco, CA 94158
Tel.: (877) 404-0553
Web Site: http://www.limos.com
Online Limousine Rental & Ground Transportation Services
N.A.I.C.S.: 532111

ON IDEAS, INC.
6 E Bay St Ste 100, Jacksonville, FL 32202-5422
Tel.: (904) 354-2600   FL
Web Site: http://www.onideas.com
Year Founded: 1983
Sales Range: $25-49.9 Million
Emp.: 40
Advetising Agency
N.A.I.C.S.: 541810
Thomas J. Bolling (CEO & Partner)
Frank Costantini (Chief Creative Officer & Partner)
Deonna Carver (CFO)
Matthew Dezern (Mgr-Tech)
Denise Graham (VP)
Tiffany Biziewski (Sr Dir-Art)
West Herford (Pres & Partner)
David Bonner (Exec Dir-Creative)
Michael Woeppel (Dir-Digital Production)

ON Q FINANCIAL, INC.
4800 N Scottsdale Rd Ste 5500,
Scottsdale, AZ 85251
Tel.: (480) 444-7100
Web Site:
 http://www.onqfinancial.com
Year Founded: 2004
Sales Range: $10-24.9 Million
Emp.: 100
Investment Management Service
N.A.I.C.S.: 523940
John F. Bergman (Pres)
Shirley Boynton (Sr VP-Compliance)
Nelson DeLeon (COO & Sr VP)
Mike Downing (Sr VP-Sls & Bus Dev)
Lee Williamson (Sr VP-Bus Dev)
Scott Frommert (CFO)
Heidi Zebro (Mgr-Branch Relationship)
Benjamin Andrus (Mgr-Gilbert)

ON SITE GAS SYSTEMS, INC.
35 Budney Rd, Newington, CT 06111
Tel.: (860) 667-8888
Web Site: http://www.onsitegas.com
Sales Range: $10-24.9 Million
Emp.: 40
Nitrogen, Oxygen & Other Gas Generation & Filtration Systems Mfr
N.A.I.C.S.: 221210
Francis X. Hursey (Founder & Pres)
Guy Hatch (CEO)
Sanh Q. Phan (VP-R&D & Chief Engr)

ON SITE MANAGEMENT INC.
417 W Mendenhall St, Bozeman, MT 59715
Tel.: (406) 586-1500
Web Site:
 http://www.onsitemanagement.com
Year Founded: 1983
Sales Range: $10-24.9 Million
Emp.: 40
New Construction Services
N.A.I.C.S.: 236115
Robin Thomas (Controller)
Peter Belschwender (Gen Mgr)

ON TARGET HEALTH, LLC
3960 Southeastern Ave, Indianapolis, IN 46203
Tel.: (317) 264-2165
Web Site:
 http://www.ontargethealth.com
Year Founded: 2014
Sales Range: $1-9.9 Million
Health Care Srvices
N.A.I.C.S.: 621999
Todd Foushee (Founder & CEO)

ON TARGET PROFESSIONALS
14000 Sunfish Lake Blvd Ste C, Ramsey, MN 55303

Tel.: (763) 432-2130
Web Site:
 http://www.myprofreight.com
Year Founded: 2007
Sales Range: $1-9.9 Million
Emp.: 6
Freight Transportation
N.A.I.C.S.: 488510
Glen Frick (Owner, Pres & COO)

ON THE MOVE CORP.
15321 NW 60th Ave Ste 109, Miami Lakes, FL 33014
Tel.: (941) 347-7380   NV
Year Founded: 2014
Investment Services
N.A.I.C.S.: 523999
Richard Reitano (Chm & CEO)
Jay Seewald (Pres & COO)
Russell Parker (Chief Branding Officer, Sec & Exec VP)

ON THE SCENE
500 N Dearborn St Ste 550, Chicago, IL 60654
Tel.: (312) 661-1440
Web Site:
 http://www.onthescenechicago.com
Year Founded: 1969
Rev.: $4,500,000
Emp.: 6
Office Administrative Services
N.A.I.C.S.: 561110
John Stachnik (Mng Partner)
Jay Weidner (Mng Partner)
Barb Harris (Sr Program Mgr)
Christine Grant (Sr Program Mgr)
Wendy Berg (Mgr-Natl Transportation)

ON TOP OF THE WORLD INC.
2069 World Parkway Blvd, Clearwater, FL 33763-3649
Tel.: (727) 799-3417
Web Site:
 http://www.palmacrerealestate.com
Year Founded: 1947
Sales Range: $10-24.9 Million
Emp.: 100
Real Estate Services
N.A.I.C.S.: 236117

ON-COR FROZEN FOODS LLC
627 Landwehr Rd, Northbrook, IL 60062-2309
Tel.: (847) 205-1040   IL
Web Site: http://www.on-cor.com
Year Founded: 1946
Sales Range: $200-249.9 Million
Emp.: 500
Frozen Food Mfr
N.A.I.C.S.: 311412
Howard Leafstone (Sr VP)
Barney Baillie (Dir-Plant Ops)
Larry Kueck (Dir-QA & R&D)

Subsidiaries:

Redi-Serve Foods   (1)
1200 Industrial Dr, Fort Atkinson, WI 53538-2758   (100%)
Tel.: (920) 563-6391
Sales Range: $50-74.9 Million
Distr of Frozen Foods
N.A.I.C.S.: 311612

ON-DEMAND MAIL SERVICES, LLC
1125 N Perry St, Pontiac, MI 48340
Tel.: (888) 954-6245
Web Site:
 http://www.ondemandmailservices.com
Year Founded: 2007
Direct Mail Services
N.A.I.C.S.: 541860
Tim Laura (Pres)
Rob Quick (VP-Ops)

Mike Tickles (VP-Postal Info & Sys)
Jill Spalding (Dir-Quality, Planning & Client Engagement)
Pam Schill (Dir-Fin)
Pete Jackson (Dir-Intl Mail)
Mike Curran (VP-Sls-Hebron)
Norman Zatorski (Mgr-Sr Acct)
Sandy Kuhlmann (Acct Mgr-Detroit)
Scott Porter (Mgr-Ops)
Chris Dean (Mgr-Ops-NJ & Philadelphia)
Brent Terebinski (Mgr-Ops-Hebron)

ON-LINE COMPUTER PRODUCTS INC.
672 Pleasant St, Norwood, MA 02062
Tel.: (781) 255-9100
Web Site: http://www.online-computer.com
Sales Range: $25-49.9 Million
Emp.: 20
Retail Computers, Peripherals & Software
N.A.I.C.S.: 423430
Al Butters (Pres)
Barbara Butters (CEO)

ON-POINT GROUP, LLC
3235 Levis Commons Blvd, Perrysburg, OH 43551
Tel.: (567) 336-9764
Web Site: http://onpointgroup.com
Emp.: 1,700
Privater Equity Firm
N.A.I.C.S.: 523999
Tom Cox (CEO)
Chris Davanzo (CFO)
Kevin Snyder (CIO)

Subsidiaries:

The Miner Corporation   (1)
11827 Tech Com Rd Ste 115, San Antonio, TX 78233-6015
Tel.: (830) 627-8600
Web Site: http://www.minercorp.com
Sales Range: $10-24.9 Million
Facilities Support Services
N.A.I.C.S.: 561210
Phil Miner (Chm)
David Janssen (Pres & CEO)
Chris Galvan (VP)
Justin Steen (CIO)
Bob Flecken (VP-Svcs)
Colette Hay (Dir-HR)
Tra Tramonte (VP-Miner Equipment)
John Cadena (VP-South Central USA)
Kathryn Giles (Coord-Bus Dev-Louisville & Nashville)
Dave Wright (Pres)

Subsidiary (Domestic):

Able Rolling Steel Door, Inc.   (2)
9 Romanelli Ave, South Hackensack, NJ 07606-1331
Tel.: (201) 487-2253
Web Site: http://www.ablerollingdoor.com
Sales Range: $1-9.9 Million
Emp.: 10
Lumber, Plywood, Millwork & Wood Panel Whslr
N.A.I.C.S.: 423310
Chris Hoehn (Co-Owner)
Michael Perrucci (Co-Owner)

Bob's Overhead Door Repair & Service, Inc.   (2)
7110 Golden Ring Rd Ste 106, Baltimore, MD 21221
Tel.: (410) 288-3667
Web Site: http://www.bobsohd.com
Sales Range: $1-9.9 Million
Emp.: 14
Overhead Doors Whslr
N.A.I.C.S.: 238130
Erin Smith (Pres)
Rob Smith (VP)

Charles H. Hodges & Son, Inc.   (2)
9574 Deereco Rd, 21093, Timonium, MD

COMPANIES

Tel.: (410) 467-8910
Web Site: http://www.chhodges.com
Foundation, Structure & Building Exterior Contractors
N.A.I.C.S.: 238190
Jamie Hodges (Pres)

Miner Central Texas (2)
11827 Tech Com Ste 115, San Antonio, TX 78233-6015
Tel.: (210) 655-8600
Web Site: http://www.minercorp.com
Sales Range: $10-24.9 Million
Emp.: 10
Facilities Support Services
N.A.I.C.S.: 561210
Phil Miner (Chm)

Miner Dallas (2)
1225 Capital Dr Ste 170, Carrollton, TX 75006
Tel.: (972) 373-8700
Web Site: http://www.minercorp.com
Sales Range: $10-24.9 Million
Emp.: 8
Facility Support Services
N.A.I.C.S.: 561210

Miner El Paso (2)
8370 Burnham Ste 400, El Paso, TX 79907
Tel.: (915) 599-2311
Web Site: http://www.minercorp.com
Sales Range: $10-24.9 Million
Facilities Support Services
N.A.I.C.S.: 561210
Paul Anguiano (Pres)

Miner Fleet Management Group (2)
111 W 7 San Antonio St Ste 200, New Braunfels, TX 78130
Tel.: (210) 892-1001
Web Site: http://www.minercorp.com
Sales Range: $10-24.9 Million
Warehousing Equipment Maintenance Services
N.A.I.C.S.: 811310
Jeff Schmeck (Pres & CEO)
Robert Villegas (VP-Trng & Tech Support)

Miner Houston (2)
5969 S Loop E, Houston, TX 77033
Tel.: (713) 263-1000
Web Site: http://www.minercorp.com
Facilities Support Services
N.A.I.C.S.: 561210
John Cadena (Pres)

Miner Southwest, LLC (2)
2848 N Omaha St, Mesa, AZ 85215
Tel.: (602) 426-1200
Web Site: http://www.minercorp.com
Sales Range: $10-24.9 Million
Facilities Support Services
N.A.I.C.S.: 561210
Brad Wicks (Pres)

Pace Material Handling, Inc. (2)
3904 B St NW, Auburn, WA 98001
Tel.: (253) 872-9006
Web Site:
  http://www.pacematerialhandling.com
Sales Range: $1-9.9 Million
Emp.: 13
Industrial Machinery And Equipment
N.A.I.C.S.: 423830
Robert Oury (Pres)
Tony Olson (Project Mgr)

Vigor Group, LLC (2)
1421 Stoneridge Dr, Middletown, PA 17057
Tel.: (717) 232-1033
Web Site: https://csdoors.com
Residential & Commercial Door Installation & Repair Services
N.A.I.C.S.: 332321
Dan Boarman (Pres & CEO)

Subsidiary (Domestic):

Allison Door Sales, Inc. (3)
1262 Loop Rd, Lancaster, PA 17601
Tel.: (717) 393-6650
Web Site: http://www.allisondoorsales.com
Rev.: $2,000,000
Emp.: 18
Framing Contractors
N.A.I.C.S.: 238130
Dolores Allison (Pres)

ON-RAMP WIRELESS, INC.
10920 Via Frontera Ste 200, San Diego, CA 92127
Tel.: (858) 201-6000   DE
Web Site: http://www.ingenu.com
Sales Range: $1-9.9 Million
Wireless Communication Network Systems Developer
N.A.I.C.S.: 334290
Ted Myers (Co-Founder & CTO)
Robert Boesel (Co-Founder & Chief Network Officer)
John Horn (CEO)
Tom Gregor (Pres & Gen Mgr-Pub Networks)
Landon Garner (CMO)
James Seines (VP-Fin)
Jason Wilson (Sr VP-Bus Dev)
Dan Halvorson (CFO & Exec VP)

ON-SITE FUEL SERVICE
1089 Old Fannin Rd Ste A, Brandon, MS 39047
Tel.: (601) 353-4142
Web Site:
  http://www.onsitefuelservice.com
Year Founded: 1986
Sales Range: $150-199.9 Million
Emp.: 115
On-Site Gasoline Service
N.A.I.C.S.: 457120
Larry Rice (VP-Ops)
Kevin French (CEO)

ON-TARGET SUPPLIES & LOGISTICS
1133 S Madison Ave, Dallas, TX 75208
Tel.: (214) 941-4885
Web Site: http://www.otsl.com
Year Founded: 1982
Sales Range: $25-49.9 Million
Emp.: 145
Whslr of Computer & Photocopying Supplies
N.A.I.C.S.: 424120
Gwyneith N. Black (Exec Dir-OTSL Charities)
Lorene B. Smith (Officer-Compliance & Sr VP)
Scott Sessions (Gen Counsel & Sr VP)
Bryan Bartlett (Dir-IT)
Melvin Hider (Dir-Safety & Security)
Albert C. Black Jr. (Chm, Pres & CEO)

ONBEYOND LLC
237 Cascade Dr, Fairfax, CA 94930
Tel.: (415) 453-9369
Web Site: http://www.onbeyond.com
Year Founded: 2003
Sales Range: Less than $1 Million
Emp.: 2
Advertising, Communications, Consulting, Government/Political/Public Affairs, Nonprofit/Social Marketing, Strategic Planning/Research
N.A.I.C.S.: 541810
Jonathan Polansky (Owner)

ONCE AGAIN NUT BUTTER COLLECTIVE INC.
12 S State St, Nunda, NY 14517
Tel.: (585) 468-2535
Web Site:
  http://www.onceagainnutbutter.com
Year Founded: 1976
Sales Range: $10-24.9 Million
Emp.: 60
Peanut Butter Mfr
N.A.I.C.S.: 311911
Robert Gelser (Pres & Gen Mgr)
Roy Graham (Co-Owner)
Gael Orr (Mgr-Comm)
Larry Filipski (CFO)

Subsidiaries:

Big Tree Organic Farms, Inc. (1)
2801 Lassiter Ln, Turlock, CA 95380
Tel.: (209) 669-3678
Web Site: http://www.bigtreeorganic.com
Sales Range: $1-9.9 Million
Emp.: 12
Confectionery Merchant Whslr
N.A.I.C.S.: 424450
Bill Reichle (Pres)

ONCO360
410 Park Ave Ste 820, New York, NY 10022
Tel.: (646) 356-7700
Web Site: http://www.onco360.com
Year Founded: 2003
Sales Range: $100-124.9 Million
Emp.: 67
Pharmaceutical Management Services
N.A.I.C.S.: 541611
Burt Zweigenhaft (Vice Chm & Chief Strategy Officer)
Amvrosios Ioannidis (VP-Mktg & Product Mgmt)
Ron Bookman (Sr VP-Trade Channel Strategy Rels)
Pharmacy Fernandez (Sr Mgr-Fin Analysis & Support Svcs)
Paul E. Jardina (Pres & CEO)
Benito Fernandez (Dir-Fin)
Dan Lavrich (Dir-IT)
Kevin Ellsworth (CFO & VP)
Robert Thomson (VP-Sls)

ONCOLOGIX TECH, INC.
1604 W Pinhook Rd #200, Lafayette, LA 71360
Tel.: (616) 977-9933   NV
Web Site: http://www.oclghealth.com
Year Founded: 1995
Sales Range: $1-9.9 Million
Emp.: 170
Medical Device Mfr
N.A.I.C.S.: 339112
Michael A. Kramarz (Chm, CEO, CFO & Sec)
Harold Halman (COO)

ONCOLOGY ANALYTICS, INC.
8751 W Broward Blvd Ste 500, Plantation, FL 33324
Tel.: (888) 916-2616
Web Site:
  http://www.oncologyanalytics.com
Year Founded: 2009
Sales Range: $1-9.9 Million
Emp.: 20
Web-Based Oncology Clinical Support Information System for Doctors on Optimum Cancer Drugs Usage
N.A.I.C.S.: 325411
Marc Fishman (Founder & Chm)
Danielle Fishman (Sr Dir-Ops)
Robert M. Walton (COO)
Balbino Vazquez (CFO)
Anna Schorer (Chief Medical Informatics Officer)
Elizabeth Smallwood (VP-Provider Rels & Network Dev)
William Shimp (Assoc Dir-Medical)
Kenneth Wurtz (Assoc Dir-Medical)
Debra Rosamelia (Controller)
Jurgen Kogler (Dir-Medical)
Laura Bobolts (Dir-Oncology Pharmaceutical Affairs)
Rick Dean (CEO)
Marisela Medrano (Sr Dir-Mktg & Sls)
David Fusari (CTO)

ONCOLOGY NURSING SOCIETY
125 Enterprise Dr, Pittsburgh, PA 15275
Tel.: (412) 859-6100   IL

ONCOURSE STRATEGIES

Web Site: http://www.ons.org
Year Founded: 1975
Sales Range: $10-24.9 Million
Emp.: 163
Oncology Nursing Services
N.A.I.C.S.: 622310
Michele Galioto (Dir-Education)
Michele R. McCorkle Dietz (Exec Dir)
Brenda Marion Nevidjon (CEO)
Susan Schneider (Chm)
Kay Harse (Treas)

ONCORE AVIATION LLC
1205 Scottsville Rd, Rochester, NY 14624
Web Site:
  http://www.oncoreaviation.com
Year Founded: 2016
Flight Training Center
N.A.I.C.S.: 611512
Todd Cameron (Owner & Founder)

Subsidiaries:

Prior Aviation Service, Inc. (1)
50 N Airport Dr, Buffalo, NY 14225
Tel.: (716) 633-1000
Web Site: http://www.prioraviation.com
Oil Transportation Services
N.A.I.C.S.: 488190
Tim Tressel (Dir-Maintenance)
Dave Mittlefehldt (Pres & CEO)
Ryan Burlingame (Dir-Flight Ops)
Dave Bridon (Supvr-Ops)
Charlie Strang (Mgr-Ops)
Chad Kaczmarek (Supvr-Ops)
Jill Jones (Coord-Admin)
Joleen Bailey (Supvr-Ops)
Mike Casper (Controller)

ONCOURSE STRATEGIES
1001 S Capital of Texas Hwy Bldg M Ste 200, Austin, TX 78746
Tel.: (512) 347-1244
Web Site:
  http://www.oncoursestrategies.com
Sales Range: $25-49.9 Million
Emp.: 250
Golf Course Management
N.A.I.C.S.: 713910
J. Michael Ussery (Founder & Pres)
Tracey Snyder (Controller & Officer Mgr)

Subsidiaries:

Blackhawk Golf Club (1)
2714 Kelly Ln, Pflugerville, TX 78660
Tel.: (512) 251-9000
Web Site: http://www.blackhawkgolf.com
Emp.: 15
Golf Club
N.A.I.C.S.: 713910
Jonathan Ayers (Gen Mgr)

Forest Creek Golf Club (1)
99 Twin Ridge Pkwy, Round Rock, TX 78664
Tel.: (512) 388-2874
Web Site: http://www.forestcreek.com
Golf Club
N.A.I.C.S.: 713910
Jim Papa (Gen Mgr)

Kingwood Cove Golf Club (1)
805 Hamblen Rd, Kingwood, TX 77339
Tel.: (281) 358-1155
Web Site: http://www.kingwoodcove.com
Emp.: 15
Golf Club
N.A.I.C.S.: 713910
Rob Crawford (Gen Mgr)

Oak Hill Golf Range (1)
5243 Hwy 290 W, Austin, TX 78735
Tel.: (512) 892-5634
Web Site: http://www.oakhillgolfrange.com
Golf Course
N.A.I.C.S.: 713910
Kevin Tracey (Gen Mgr)

Oakhurst Golf Club (1)
20700 Mills Branch Dr, Porter, TX 77365
Tel.: (281) 354-4653
Web Site: http://www.oakhurstgolfclub.com

ONCOURSE STRATEGIES

OnCourse Strategies—(Continued)
Golf Club
N.A.I.C.S.: 713910
David Preisler (Gen Mgr)

Riverside Golf Course (1)
1020 Grove Blvd, Austin, TX 78741
Tel.: (512) 386-7077
Web Site: http://www.riverside-gc.com
Emp.: 30
Golf Course
N.A.I.C.S.: 713910
Michael Travis (Head-Golf Pro)

Serenoa Golf Club (1)
6733 Serenoa Dr, Sarasota, FL 34241
Tel.: (941) 925-2755
Web Site: http://www.serenoagc.com
Sales Range: $1-9.9 Million
Emp.: 30
Golf Club
N.A.I.C.S.: 713910
Kevin Paschall (Gen Mgr)

WindRose Golf Club (1)
6235 Pine Lakes Blvd, Spring, TX 77379
Tel.: (281) 370-8900
Web Site: http://www.windrosegolfclub.com
Golf Club
N.A.I.C.S.: 713910
Kelly Walker (Gen Mgr)

ONCUE MARKETING LLC
916 N Main St, Stillwater, OK 74075
Tel.: (405) 372-3579
Web Site:
http://www.oncueexpress.com
Sales Range: $75-99.9 Million
Emp.: 600
Holding Company; Petroleum Bulk Stations
N.A.I.C.S.: 424710
Barden Kellum (COO)
Rusty Shaw (Chm)
Jim Griffith (CEO)
Steve James (CFO)

ONDRA-HUYETT ASSOCIATES, INC.
7584 Morris Court Ste 210, Allentown, PA 18106
Tel.: (610) 366-1709
Web Site: http://www.ohainc.com
Year Founded: 1995
Sales Range: $1-9.9 Million
Emp.: 42
Construction Managers, Builders & Residential Remodelers
N.A.I.C.S.: 236118
Mike Ondra (CEO)
Terry Hodge (Pres)

ONE 3 TWO, INC.
17462 Von Karman Ave, Irvine, CA 92614
Tel.: (714) 429-1595 CA
Web Site:
http://www.obeyclothing.com
Year Founded: 2000
Sales Range: $1-9.9 Million
Emp.: 30
Women's, Children's & Infants' Clothing & Accessories Merchant Whslr
N.A.I.C.S.: 424350
Shepard Fairey (Founder)

ONE ACRE FUND
1954 1st St Ste 183, Highland Park, IL 60035
Tel.: (617) 840-7634 IL
Web Site:
http://www.oneacrefund.org
Year Founded: 2005
Sales Range: $10-24.9 Million
Emp.: 43
Hunger Relief Services
N.A.I.C.S.: 624210
Nancy Tomkowicz (Sr VP-Fin)
Stephanie Hanson (Dir-Policy & Outreach)
Barrett Prinz (Chief People Officer)
Charite Nirere (Dir-Field Rutsiro)
Claver Rugirangoga (Dir-Field Huye)
Jake Goldberg (Dir-Fin)
Jean-Pierre Kanyemera (Dir-Field Rusizi)
Judith Wekesa (Dir-Field)
Patrick Keya (Dir-Field Webuye)
Pauline Wanjala (Dir-Field Lugari)
Phoebe Siketi (Dir-Field Bungoma)
Protus Wanguche (Dir-Field Butere)
Jake Goldberg Calhoun (CFO & Gen Partner)

ONE AMERICAN CORP.
2785 Hwy 20, Vacherie, LA 70090
Tel.: (225) 265-2265
Web Site: http://www.fabt.com
Rev.: $33,352,000
Emp.: 50
Banking Services
N.A.I.C.S.: 522110
Frank Bourgoif (Pres)

Subsidiaries:

First American Bank & Trust (1)
2785 Hwy 20, Vacherie, LA 70090
Tel.: (225) 265-2265
Web Site: http://www.fabt.com
Sales Range: $25-49.9 Million
Emp.: 55
State Trust Companies Accepting Deposits, Commercial
N.A.I.C.S.: 522110
Callie Billiot (Officer-Loan)
Keith Falgoust (Officer-Loan)

ONE CALL CONCEPTS INCORPORATED
7223 Pkwy Dr Ste 210, Hanover, MD 21076
Tel.: (410) 712-0082
Web Site: http://www.occinc.com
Sales Range: $10-24.9 Million
Emp.: 400
Data Base Information Retrieval
N.A.I.C.S.: 517810
Dan Florenzo (Controller)
Tom Hoff (Pres & CEO)
David Catrambone (COO)
Brian Simmons (Gen Mgr)

ONE CLICK VENTURES
1300 Windhorst Way Ste A, Greenwood, IN 46143
Tel.: (317) 215-6610
Web Site:
http://www.oneclickventures.com
Year Founded: 2005
Sales Range: $1-9.9 Million
Emp.: 60
E-Commerce & Online Retail Marketing
N.A.I.C.S.: 459999
Randy Stocklin (Co-Founder & CEO)
Angie Stocklin (Co-Founder & COO)

ONE CYPRESS ENERGY LLC
10100 Reunion Pl, San Antonio, TX 78216
Tel.: (210) 340-5900
Web Site:
http://www.onecypressenergy.com
Petroleum Supply & Trading
N.A.I.C.S.: 424720
Bruce A. Smith (Pres & CEO)
Gregory A. Wright (CFO & Treas)
Scott R. Phipps (Sr VP)
Claiborne B. Gregory Jr. (Gen Counsel & Sec)

Subsidiaries:

Geer Tank Trucks Inc. (1)
1136 S Main St, Jacksboro, TX 76458
Tel.: (940) 567-2677
Sales Range: $50-74.9 Million
Emp.: 25
Crude Oil Distr
N.A.I.C.S.: 424720

ONE LOVE FOUNDATION
119 Pondfield Rd, Bronxville, NY 10708
Tel.: (844) 832-6168 MI
Web Site: http://www.joinonelove.org
Year Founded: 2010
Sales Range: $1-9.9 Million
Domestic Violence Prevention Services
N.A.I.C.S.: 813410
Won Young Giuriceo (Treas)
Olwen Modell (Sec)
Sharon Robinson (Vice Chm)
Alexis Love Hodges (Co-Founder)
Sharon Donnelly Love (Co-Founder & Chm)
Julie Myers (CEO)
Ojeda Hall (Pres)

ONE MODEL MANAGEMENT LLC
42 Bond St 2nd Fl, New York, NY 10012
Tel.: (212) 505-5545
Web Site:
http://www.1management.com
Sales Range: $1-9.9 Million
Emp.: 10
Modeling Agency
N.A.I.C.S.: 711410
Scott Lipps (Pres & CEO)

ONE ON ONE MARKETING INC.
3098 Executive Pkwy Ste 300, Lehi, UT 84043-4611
Tel.: (801) 642-0234
Web Site: http://www.1on1.com
Year Founded: 2002
Sales Range: $50-74.9 Million
Emp.: 150
Management Consulting Services
N.A.I.C.S.: 541613
Nick Greer (Pres)
Branden Neish (VP-Product)
Brett Flitton (Sr Mgr-Mktg)
Rachel Beckstead (Sr Mgr-Mktg)
Travis Jacobson (Mgr-Affiliate Mktg)
Vince King (Mgr-External Call Floor)
Christopher Tracy (CEO)
Jeff Morrin (CFO)

ONE PICA, INC
177 Huntington Ave 13th Fl, Boston, MA 02115
Tel.: (617) 695-9995
Web Site: http://www.onepica.com
Year Founded: 2002
Sales Range: $1-9.9 Million
Emp.: 16
Digital Commerce Services
N.A.I.C.S.: 813910
Greg A. Segall (Principal & Pres)
Alexandra Robbins (Mgr-Mktg)

ONE PLANET GROUP LLC
1820 Bonanza St, Walnut Creek, CA 94596
Tel.: (925) 983-2800 CA
Web Site:
https://www.oneplanetgroup.com
Year Founded: 2020
Emp.: 100
Internet Marketing Services
N.A.I.C.S.: 541810
Payam Zamani (Founder, Chm & CEO)

Subsidiaries:

AutoWeb, Inc. (1)
Tel.: (949) 225-4500
Web Site: https://www.autoweb.com
Rev.: $71,585,000
Assets: $35,132,000
Liabilities: $22,375,000
Net Worth: $12,757,000
Earnings: ($5,659,000)
Emp.: 162
Fiscal Year-end: 12/31/2021
Online Automotive Marketing Services
N.A.I.C.S.: 541512
Chan W. Galbato (Bd of Dirs, Executives)
Daniel R. Ingle (COO & Exec VP)
Carlton D. Hamer (CFO & Exec VP)
Joshua J. Barsetti (Principal Acctg Officer, VP & Controller)

Subsidiary (Domestic):

AutoWeb, Inc. (2)
3401 N Miami Ave Unit 205, Miami, FL 33127
Tel.: (305) 777-7898
Web Site: http://www.autoweb.com
Automobile Dealers
N.A.I.C.S.: 441227

Autobytel Dealer Services, Inc. (2)
18872 Macarthur Blvd Ste 200, Irvine, CA 92612
Tel.: (949) 225-4500
Automotive Consulting Services
N.A.I.C.S.: 541613

Autobytel Florida, Inc. (2)
12950 Race Track Rd Ste 220, Tampa, FL 33626-1307
Tel.: (813) 579-9523
Automotive Consulting Services
N.A.I.C.S.: 541613

Autoweb.com, Inc. (2)
18872 MacArthur Blvd, Irvine, CA 92612
Tel.: (949) 225-4500
Web Site: http://www.autoweb.com
Sales Range: $50-74.9 Million
Emp.: 75
Online Automotive Information that Helps Consumers Select New or Pre-Owned Vehicles from Member Dealers
N.A.I.C.S.: 513199

Dealix Corporation (2)
1850 Gateway Dr Ste 205, San Mateo, CA 94404
Tel.: (877) 852-7576
Web Site: http://www.dealix.com
Online Motor Vehicle Purchasing Solutions
N.A.I.C.S.: 519290
Gregory Baszucki (Founder)

ONE REEL INC.
100 S King St Ste 100, Seattle, WA 98104
Tel.: (206) 281-7788
Web Site: http://www.onereel.org
Rev.: $17,136,455
Emp.: 65
Festival Operation
N.A.I.C.S.: 713990
Nick Cail (Dir-Advancement)

ONE ROCK CAPITAL PARTNERS, LLC
30 Rockefeller Plaza 54th Fl, New York, NY 10112
Tel.: (212) 605-6000
Web Site:
http://www.onerockcapital.com
Year Founded: 2010
Privater Equity Firm
N.A.I.C.S.: 523999
Kurtis T. Barker (Operating Partner-Bus & Environmental Services vertical)
Tony W. Lee (Co-Founder & Mng Partner)
R. Scott Spielvogel (Co-Founder & Mng Partner)
Kimberly D. Reed (Partner)
Kurt H. Beyer (Partner)
Michael T. Koike (Partner)
Joshua D. Goldman (Partner)
Cyrus D. Heidary (Principal)
Robert F. Hsu (Principal)
Deepa Patil Madhani (Head-IR)
Jack L. Rosenberg (Principal)
Joseph A. Agresti (Operating Partner)
Kurtis T. Barker (Operating Partner)

COMPANIES

ONE ROCK CAPITAL PARTNERS, LLC

Eric C. Evans *(Operating Partner)*
Andrew S. Georges *(Operating Partner)*
John A. Georges *(Operating Partner)*
Mike Mayer *(Operating Partner)*
Mark Oakeson *(Operating Partner)*
Frank Orfanello *(Operating Partner)*
Gary L. Tapella *(Operating Partner)*

Subsidiaries:

BlueTriton Brands, Inc. (1)
900 Long Ridge Rd Bldg 2, Stamford, CT 06902-1138
Tel.: (203) 629-7802
Web Site: http://www.nestle-watersna.com
Emp.: 650
Mineral Water & Domestic Water Bottling Services
N.A.I.C.S.: 424490
Charlie Broll *(Gen Counsel, Sec & Exec VP)*
Tom Smith *(Pres-Customer Dev & Sls Ops)*
Tara Carraro *(Chief Corp Affairs Officer & Exec VP)*
Henrik Jelert *(Exec VP-ReadyRefresh)*
Bill Trackim *(Exec VP-Technical & Production, Supply Chain & Procurement)*
David Tulauskas *(Chief Sustainability Officer & VP)*
Lisa Walker *(Chief HR Officer & Exec VP)*
Dean Metropoulos *(Chm)*
Javier Idrovo *(CFO)*
Paul Norman *(Pres-Retail)*
Kheri Holland Tillman *(CMO)*

Subsidiary (Domestic):

Arrowhead Mountain Spring Water Company (2)
900 Long Ridge Rd Building 2, Stamford, CT 06902
Tel.: (203) 531-4100
Web Site: http://www.nestle-watersna.com
Sales Range: $125-149.9 Million
Emp.: 600
Water Purification Systems for Home & Office, Bottled Water Service, Drinking Cups, Electric Water Coolers
N.A.I.C.S.: 424490
Bill Pearson *(CFO)*

Arrowhead Mountain Spring Water Company (2)
5772 Jurupa St, Ontario, CA 91761-3643
Tel.: (909) 974-0600
Web Site: http://www.nestlewatersnorthamerica.com
Sales Range: $25-49.9 Million
Emp.: 100
Water Quality Monitoring & Control Systems
N.A.I.C.S.: 424490

Arrowhead Mountain Spring Water Company (2)
1566 E Washington Blvd, Los Angeles, CA 90021
Tel.: (213) 763-1383
Web Site: http://www.arrowheadwater.com
Sales Range: $50-74.9 Million
Emp.: 4
Mineral or Spring Water Bottling
N.A.I.C.S.: 424490

Arrowhead Mountain Spring Water Company (2)
130 Fogg St, Colton, CA 92324-3563
Tel.: (909) 825-8543
Web Site: http://www.arrowheadwater.com
Sales Range: $25-49.9 Million
Emp.: 50
Mfr of Distilled Mineral & Spring Water
N.A.I.C.S.: 445298

Arrowhead Water (2)
52 Julian St, Ventura, CA 93001-2506
Tel.: (805) 653-0253
Web Site: http://www.arrowheadwater.com
Sales Range: $25-49.9 Million
Emp.: 24
Mineral & Spring Water Distribution
N.A.I.C.S.: 424490

Arrowhead Water (2)
3230 E Imperial Hwy Ste 100, Brea, CA 92821
Tel.: (714) 792-2100
Web Site: http://www.arrowheadwater.com
Sales Range: $50-74.9 Million
Emp.: 40
Provider of Bottled Water
N.A.I.C.S.: 424490
Rick Croarkin *(CFO & VP)*

Ice Mountain Spring Water (2)
4231 C Leap Rd, Hilliard, OH 43026-1125
Tel.: (614) 876-0626
Web Site: http://www.nestlewatersnorthamerica.com
Sales Range: $25-49.9 Million
Emp.: 40
Bottled Water Delivery
N.A.I.C.S.: 445298

Division (Non-US):

Nestle Water Canada Ltd. (2)
3440 Francis Hughes Ave, Ville de Laval, H7L 5A9, QC, Canada
Tel.: (450) 629-8543
Sales Range: $25-49.9 Million
Emp.: 25
Groceries & Related Products
N.A.I.C.S.: 445110
Adam Graves *(Pres)*

Nestle Waters Canada Inc. (2)
101 Brock Rd South, Puslinch, N0B 2J0, ON, Canada
Tel.: (519) 763-9462
Web Site: https://bluetriton.ca
Sales Range: $25-49.9 Million
Emp.: 220
Bottled Waters Production & Distribution
N.A.I.C.S.: 312112

Nestle Waters Canada Inc. (2)
101 Brock Road South, Puslinch, N0B 2J0, ON, Canada
Tel.: (604) 860-4888
Web Site: http://www.nestle-waters.com
Sales Range: $25-49.9 Million
Emp.: 100
Distribution of Bottled & Canned Soft Drinks
N.A.I.C.S.: 312111

Subsidiary (Domestic):

Nestle Waters North America Holdings, Inc. (2)
900 Long Rdg Rd Bldg 2, Stamford, CT 06902
Tel.: (203) 531-4100
Web Site: http://www.nestle-watersna.com
Emp.: 8,000
Investment Management Service
N.A.I.C.S.: 523999

Plant (Domestic):

Nestle Waters North America Inc. - Brea (2)
3230 E Imperial Hwy, Brea, CA 92821
Tel.: (714) 792-2100
Web Site: http://www.arrowheadwater.com
Sales Range: $25-49.9 Million
Emp.: 40
Mineral or Spring Water Bottling
N.A.I.C.S.: 424490

Nestle Waters North America Inc. - Breinigsville (2)
405 Nestle Way, Breinigsville, PA 18031
Tel.: (610) 530-7301
Mfr of Bottled Water
N.A.I.C.S.: 424490

Nestle Waters North America Inc. - Coppell (2)
1322 Crestside Dr, Coppell, TX 75019
Tel.: (972) 462-3600
Web Site: http://www.nestle-waters.com
Sales Range: $25-49.9 Million
Emp.: 200
Coffee & Tea Mfr
N.A.I.C.S.: 311920

Nestle Waters North America Inc. - Dracut (2)
32 Commercial Dr, Dracut, MA 01826-2836
Tel.: (978) 970-5656
Sales Range: $25-49.9 Million
Emp.: 58
Mineral & Spring Water Bottling
N.A.I.C.S.: 424490

Nestle Waters North America Inc. - Fort Lauderdale (2)
10599 Northwest 67th St, Fort Lauderdale, FL 33321-6407
Tel.: (954) 597-7852
Web Site: http://www.perrier.com
Sales Range: $25-49.9 Million
Emp.: 100
Home & Office Water & Coffee Delivery
N.A.I.C.S.: 312112

Nestle Waters North America Inc. - Greenwich (2)
900 Long Ridge Rd, Stamford, CT 06902
Tel.: (203) 629-7802
Web Site: http://www.nestle-watersna.com
Sales Range: $125-149.9 Million
Emp.: 600
Mineral Water
N.A.I.C.S.: 424490
Susan Vinales *(Mgr-Facilities)*

Nestle Waters North America Inc. - Jacksonville (2)
7035 Davis Creek Rd, Jacksonville, FL 32256-3027
Tel.: (904) 268-5152
Web Site: http://www.zephyrhillswater.com
Sales Range: $25-49.9 Million
Emp.: 20
Bottled Water Distr
N.A.I.C.S.: 445298

Nestle Waters North America Inc. - Lanham (2)
9921 Business Pkwy, Lanham, MD 20706-1836
Tel.: (301) 731-3448
Sales Range: $25-49.9 Million
Emp.: 60
Distilled Mineral & Spring Water
N.A.I.C.S.: 312112

Nestle Waters North America Inc. - Northbrook (2)
310 Huehl Rd, Northbrook, IL 60062-1918
Tel.: (847) 400-3657
Sales Range: $25-49.9 Million
Emp.: 10
Water Bottling
N.A.I.C.S.: 312112

Nestle Waters North America Inc. - Raynham (2)
375 Paramount Dr, Raynham, MA 02767
Tel.: (508) 977-9696
Web Site: http://www.nestlewaters.com
Sales Range: $50-74.9 Million
Emp.: 175
Natural Water Packaged In Cans
N.A.I.C.S.: 424490

Nestle Waters North America Inc. - Rochester (2)
146 Halstead St, Rochester, NY 14610-1946
Tel.: (585) 288-7241
Web Site: http://www.perriergroup.com
Sales Range: $25-49.9 Million
Emp.: 17
Mineral or Spring Water Bottling
N.A.I.C.S.: 325998

Nestle Waters North America Inc. - Thousand Palms (2)
72242 Varner Rd, Thousand Palms, CA 92276-3341
Tel.: (760) 343-3125
Web Site: http://www.perriergroup.com
Sales Range: $50-74.9 Million
Emp.: 10
Mineral or Spring Water Bottling
N.A.I.C.S.: 424490

Nestle Waters North America Inc. - Woodridge (2)
10335 Argon Woods Dr Ste 200, Woodridge, IL 60517
Tel.: (630) 271-7300
Sales Range: $25-49.9 Million
Emp.: 15
Bottled Water
N.A.I.C.S.: 424490

Nestle Waters North America Inc. - Zephyrhills (2)
4330 20th St, Zephyrhills, FL 33540-6703
Tel.: (813) 783-1959
Web Site: http://www.nestlewatersna.com
Sales Range: $125-149.9 Million
Emp.: 300
Mfr of Water Bottling Services

N.A.I.C.S.: 424490

Subsidiary (Domestic):

Ozarka Water (2)
PO Box 628, Wilkes Barre, PA 18703
Sales Range: $25-49.9 Million
Emp.: 15
Water Distilled
N.A.I.C.S.: 312112

Ozarka Water (2)
9351 E Point Dr, Houston, TX 77054-3715
Tel.: (713) 799-1452
Web Site: http://www.ozarkawater.com
Sales Range: $50-74.9 Million
Emp.: 200
Groceries & Related Products
N.A.I.C.S.: 424490

Poland Spring Corporation (2)
900 Long Ridge Rd Buld-2, Stamford, CT 06902-5091
Tel.: (203) 531-4100
Web Site: http://www.nestle-watersna.com
Sales Range: $250-299.9 Million
Emp.: 700
Bottler of Spring Water
N.A.I.C.S.: 424490

Division (Domestic):

Poland Spring Bottling (3)
109 Poland Spring Dr, Poland Spring, ME 04274-5327
Tel.: (207) 998-4315
Web Site: http://www.polandspring.com
Sales Range: $125-149.9 Million
Emp.: 300
Storage Services for Bottled & Canned Soft Drinks
N.A.I.C.S.: 424490

Plant (Domestic):

Poland Spring Corporation (3)
111 Thomas Mcgovern Dr, Jersey City, NJ 07305-4620
Tel.: (201) 531-2044
Web Site: http://www.polandspring.com
Sales Range: $25-49.9 Million
Emp.: 85
Water Distilled
N.A.I.C.S.: 424490

Poland Spring Corporation (3)
109 Poland Spring Dr, Poland Spring, ME 04274-5327
Tel.: (207) 998-4315
Web Site: http://polandspring.com
Sales Range: $50-74.9 Million
Emp.: 300
Bottled Water Mfr
N.A.I.C.S.: 312112

Subsidiary (Domestic):

Saratoga Spring Water Company (2)
11 Geyser Rd, Saratoga Springs, NY 12866-9038
Tel.: (518) 584-6363
Web Site: http://www.saratogaspringwater.com
Bottler of Mineral & Spring Water
N.A.I.C.S.: 312112
Adam Madkour *(CEO)*

Zephyrhills Spring Water Company (2)
6403 Harney Rd, Tampa, FL 33610
Tel.: (813) 621-2025
Web Site: http://www.zephyrhillswater.com
Spring Water Producer
N.A.I.C.S.: 312112

Constantia Flexibles Group GmbH (1)
Rivergate Handelskai 92, 1200, Vienna, Austria
Tel.: (43) 1 888 5640
Web Site: http://www.cflex.com
Assets: $2,149,529,138
Liabilities: $1,301,134,390
Net Worth: $848,394,748
Earnings: $61,393,448
Emp.: 8,350
Fiscal Year-end: 12/31/2016
Thin & Flexible Plastic & Cellulose Films, Aluminum Foils & Papers Mfr & Distr
N.A.I.C.S.: 326112

ONE ROCK CAPITAL PARTNERS, LLC

U.S. PRIVATE

One Rock Capital Partners, LLC—(Continued)
Ulrich Kostlin (Vice Chm-Supervisory Bd)
Pierre-Henri Bruchon (Member-Exec Bd & Exec VP-Pharma)
Michael Muller (Exec VP-HR)
Gerald Hummer (Member-Exec Bd & Exec VP-Aluminum Div)
Axel Glade (Member-Exec Bd & Exec VP-Film Div)
Daniel Winkler (Member-Exec Bd & Exec VP-Film Div)
Pim Vervaat (CEO & Member-Exec Bd)
Richard Kelsey (CFO-Interim & Member-Mgmt Bd)

Subsidiary (Non-US):

Constantia Afripack (2)
75 Richard Carte Road, Mobeni, Durban, 4092, South Africa
Tel.: (27) 314521300
Web Site: https://www.cflex.com
Emp.: 400
Paper Sack Mfr
N.A.I.C.S.: 322220
Arnold Vermaak (Chm)

Subsidiary (Domestic):

Constantia Afripack Labels Pinetown (3)
6 Mahogany Road Mahogany Ridge, Pinetown, 3610, South Africa
Tel.: (27) 317928350
Web Site: http://www.cflex.com
Emp.: 172
Plastics Material & Resin Mfr
N.A.I.C.S.: 325211

EnviroServe, Inc. (1)
4600 Brookpark Rd, Cleveland, OH 44134
Web Site: http://www.enviroserve.com
Hazardous Waste Collection
N.A.I.C.S.: 562112
Nathan Savage (CEO)

Subsidiary (Domestic):

Chemical Transportation, Inc. (2)
11105 N Casa Grande Hwy, Rillito, AZ 85654
Tel.: (520) 624-2348
Web Site: http://www.cti-az.com
Material Transportation Services
N.A.I.C.S.: 484121
Brian Bennett (Pres)
Olivia Trujillo (Mgr-Billing)

Clark Environmental, Inc. (2)
755 Prairie Industrial Pkwy, Mulberry, FL 33860
Tel.: (863) 425-4884
Web Site: http://www.clarkenvironmental.com
Environmental Consulting Services
N.A.I.C.S.: 541620
Beth Clark (Pres)
Jim Clark (VP)
John Warren (Mgr-Ops)

FXI Holdings, Inc. (1)
100 Matsonford Rd 5 Radnor Corporate Ctr Ste 300, Radnor, PA 19087
Tel.: (610) 744-2300
Web Site: http://www.fxi.com
Finished Goods, Sub-Assemblies, Services & Raw Materials Fabricators & Retailers
N.A.I.C.S.: 326150
Harold J. Earley (Pres & CEO)
Dean Ackerman (Exec VP-Ops)
Lori Bush (CMO & Sr VP-mKTG)

Subsidiary (Domestic):

FXI, Inc. (2)
5 Radnor Corporate Ctr Fl 3 100 Matsonford Rd, Radnor, PA 19087
Web Site: http://www.fxi.com
Foam Products Mfr
N.A.I.C.S.: 326150

GDP Companies, Inc. (1)
1780 Hughes Landing Blvd Ste 100, The Woodlands, TX 77380
Tel.: (936) 242-0508
Holding Company
N.A.I.C.S.: 551112
Paul Tayler (CEO)

Subsidiary (Non-US):

Distrupol Limited (2)
Thames House Gogmore Lane, Chertsey, KT16 9AP, Surrey, United Kingdom
Tel.: (44) 1932566033
Web Site: http://www.distrupol.com
Chemical Product Whslr
N.A.I.C.S.: 424690
Richard Orme (Mng Dir)
Andrew Canning (Mng Dir)
James Stanton (Dir-Bus Sys & Ops)
Jamie King (Sls Mgr)
Derek Watts (Sls Mgr)
Simon Clegg (Mgr-Bus Dev)
Markus Olofsson (Sls Mgr)
Mike Bramwell (Acct Mgr-Key)
Steve Hyden (Acct Mgr-Key)
Anthony Newborough (Acct Mgr-Key)
Rodney Garfield (Acct Mgr-Key)
Liam Moloney (Acct Mgr-Key)
James Sewell (Acct Mgr-Key)
Ben Wakerly (Acct Mgr-Key)
Conor Keogh (Acct Mgr-Key)
Tom Waag (Sls Mgr)
Chris Cooper (Engr-Dev)
Carl-Johan Levert (Acct Mgr-Key)
Fredrik Snellman (Acct Mgr-Key)
Mads Meilvang (Acct Mgr-Key)
Karin Lagerholm (Acct Mgr-Key)
Bo Anderson (Acct Mgr-Key)
James Daly (Engr-Dev)

Subsidiary (Non-US):

Distrupol B.V. (3)
Schouwburgplein 30-34, PO Box 21407, 3001 AK, Rotterdam, Netherlands
Tel.: (31) 102757880
Chemical Product Whslr
N.A.I.C.S.: 424690
Annemarie Struik (Mgr-Customer Svc & Mktg)

Distrupol Ireland Limited
536 Grants Crescent Greenogue Business Park, Rathcoole, Dublin, Ireland
Tel.: (353) 14019808
Chemical Product Whslr
N.A.I.C.S.: 424690
John Wallace (Mng Dir)

Distrupol Nordic AB (3)
Kungsgatan 6, PO Box 4072, 211 49, Malmo, Sweden
Tel.: (46) 406353080
Chemical Product Whslr
N.A.I.C.S.: 424690
Sophie Dahlkvist (Mgr-Customer Svc)

Subsidiary (Domestic):

Nexeo Plastics, LLC
1780 Hughes Landing Blvd Ste 100, The Woodlands, TX 77380
Tel.: (936) 242-0508
Plastic Product Distr
N.A.I.C.S.: 424610
Paul Tayler (CEO)
Richard Orme (Bus Dir)
Andrew Canning (Bus Dir)

Innophos Holdings, Inc. (1)
259 Prospect Plains Rd Bldg A, Cranbury, NJ 08512-3706
Tel.: (609) 495-2495
Web Site: http://www.innophos.com
Holding Company; Specialty Phosphates Mfr & Distr
N.A.I.C.S.: 551112
Mark Feuerbach (Sr VP & Interim CFO)
Joshua Horenstein (Chief Legal & HR Officer, Sec & Sr VP)
Amy Hartzell (Sr VP-Supply Chain & Pur)
Sherry Duff (Chief Mktg & Tech Officer & Sr VP)
Mark Santangelo (Sr VP-Mfg, Engrg & EH&S)
William Dunworth (Chief Acctg Officer, VP & Controller)
Richard Hooper (CEO)
Chris Antal (Mktg Mgr-Strategic)

Subsidiary (Non-US):

Innophos Mexicana S.A. de C.V. (2)
Bosque de Ciruelos No 186 Piso 11A, Seccion Miguel Hidalgo, 11700, Mexico, Mexico
Tel.: (52) 5553224808
Web Site: http://www.innophos.com.mx
Sales Range: $150-199.9 Million
Emp.: 12
Phosphate Products Mfg
N.A.I.C.S.: 325180

Subsidiary (Domestic):

Innophos Nutrition, Inc. (2)
680 N 700 W, North Salt Lake, UT 84054
Tel.: (801) 299-1661
Web Site: http://www.innophosnutrition.com
Pharmaceutical Products Distr
N.A.I.C.S.: 424210

Kelatron Corporation (2)
680 N 700 W, North Salt Lake, UT 84054
Tel.: (801) 394-4558
Web Site: http://www.kelatron.com
Sales Range: $10-24.9 Million
Emp.: 60
Mineral & Other Nutritional Supplement Mfr
N.A.I.C.S.: 325411
Kristy Boatright (Mgr-Fin)

Novel Ingredient Services, LLC (2)
72 Deforest Ave, East Hanover, NJ 07936
Tel.: (973) 808-5900
Web Site: http://www.novelingredient.com
Botanical Ingredients Distr
N.A.I.C.S.: 424490

Subsidiary (Domestic):

Tradeworks Group Inc. (3)
167 Main St 208, Brattleboro, VT 05301
Tel.: (802) 257-2440
Emp.: 6
Chemical Mfr & Whslr
N.A.I.C.S.: 325199

Subsidiary (Domestic):

Triarco Industries, LLC (2)
400 Hamburg Tpke, Wayne, NJ 07470
Tel.: (973) 942-5100
Web Site: http://www.triarco.com
Pharmaceutical & Nutritional Supplement Ingredient Mfr
N.A.I.C.S.: 325411
Rodger Rohde Jr. (Pres)

Nexeo Solutions, LLC (1)
6000 Parkwood Pl, Dublin, OH 43016
Tel.: (614) 790-3333
Web Site: http://www.nexeosolutions.com
Sales Range: $1-4.9 Billion
Emp.: 2,000
Chemicals, Plastics & Composites Distr; Environmental Services
N.A.I.C.S.: 424690

Subsidiary (Domestic):

Archway Sales, LLC (2)
4155 Manchester Ave, Saint Louis, MO 63110-3823
Tel.: (314) 533-4662
Web Site: http://www.archwaysales.com
Sales Range: $10-24.9 Million
Emp.: 72
Chemicals & Allied Products Distr
N.A.I.C.S.: 424690

Chemical Specialists & Development, Inc. (2)
9733 Meadow Rd, Conroe, TX 77305
Tel.: (936) 228-0865
Web Site: http://www.startexchemicals.com
Sales Range: $25-49.9 Million
Emp.: 200
Specialty Chemicals Distr
N.A.I.C.S.: 424690

North Pacific Paper Company, LLC (1)
3001 Industrial Way, Longview, WA 98632-8191
Tel.: (360) 636-6400
Web Site: http://www.norpacpaper.com
Newsprint & Paper Mill Operator
N.A.I.C.S.: 322120
Craig Anneberg (CEO)
Tom Crowley (VP-Sls & Mktg)
Rob Buckingham (VP-Mfg)
Nick Karavolos (VP-Supply Chain & Distr)
Craig Montgomery (Mgr-Customer Satisfaction)
Vince Leary (Mgr-Customer Satisfaction)
Peter Ouellette (Mgr-Pkg Products)
Tom Brookreson (CFO)

Orion Food Systems, LLC (1)
2930 W Maple St, Sioux Falls, SD 57107
Tel.: (605) 336-6961
Web Site: https://olmfoods.com
Frozen Specialty Food Mfr
N.A.I.C.S.: 311412

Subsidiary (Domestic):

Land Mark Products, Inc. (2)
1007 Okoboji Ave, Milford, IA 51351
Tel.: (712) 338-2771
Pizza & Sandwich Mfr
N.A.I.C.S.: 311991

Prefere Resins Holding GmbH (1)
Dr Hans-Lebach-Str 7, 15537, Erkner, Germany
Tel.: (49) 3362 72 0
Web Site: http://www.prefere.com
Thermoset Resins & Products Mfr
N.A.I.C.S.: 325211

Subsidiary (Domestic):

INEOS Melamines GmbH (2)
Alt Fechenheim 34, 60386, Frankfurt, Germany
Tel.: (49) 6941092319
Chemical Products Mfr
N.A.I.C.S.: 325199
Ashley Reed (CEO)
Holger Mueller (COO)

INEOS Paraform GmbH & Co. KG (2)
Hauptstrasse 30, 55120, Mainz, Germany
Tel.: (49) 6131621113
Petrochemical Products Mfr
N.A.I.C.S.: 324110
Mario Renner (Mgr-Bus)

Subsidiary (Domestic):

INEOS Chlor Atlantik GmbH (3)
Inhausersieler Strasse 25, Wilhelmshaven, 26388, Germany
Tel.: (49) 4425982672
Web Site: http://www.ineos.com
Sales Range: $125-149.9 Million
Emp.: 380
Chlorine & Other Chlorine Derivatives Whslr
N.A.I.C.S.: 424690
Peter Prinz (Gen Mgr)

Subsidiary (Non-US):

INEOS ChlorVinyls Belgium NV (3)
Heilig Hartlaan 21, 3980, Tessenderlo, Belgium (100%)
Tel.: (32) 13 612300
Web Site: http://www.ineos.com
Sales Range: $125-149.9 Million
Emp.: 320
Monovinylchloride Mfr
N.A.I.C.S.: 325211
Luc Leunis (CEO & Mng Dir)

INEOS Films & Compounds (3)
Hawkslease Chapel Ln, Lyndhurst, SO43 7FG, Hampshire, United Kingdom
Tel.: (44) 2380287043
Web Site: http://www.ineos.com
Sales Range: $700-749.9 Million
Emp.: 1,800
Specialty Plastic Films & Polyvinyl Chloride Compounds Mfr
N.A.I.C.S.: 326199
Iain Hogan (CEO)

Subsidiary (Non-US):

INEOS Compounds France SAS (4)
Chemin De Baconnes, Mourmelon-Le-Petit, 51400, Chalons-en-Champagne, France
Tel.: (33) 326661579
Web Site: http://www.ineoscompounds.com
Polyvinyl Chloride Compounds Mfr
N.A.I.C.S.: 325211

INEOS Compounds Italia Srl (4)
Via Leonardo Da Vinci 5, 44011, Ferrara, Italy
Tel.: (39) 0532 315511
Web Site: http://www.ineos.com
Sales Range: $50-74.9 Million
Emp.: 200
Polyvinyl Chloride Compounds Mfr
N.A.I.C.S.: 325211

INEOS Compounds Sweden AB (4)

Gevarsgatan 4, PO Box 22035, 254 66, Helsingborg, Sweden
Tel.: (46) 42 250 200
Web Site: http://www.ineos.se
Sales Range: $25-49.9 Million
Emp.: 60
Polyvinyl Chloride Compounds Mfr
N.A.I.C.S.: 325211
Jim Nilsson (Mng Dir)

INEOS Compounds Switzerland AG (4)
Industriestrasse, 5643, Sins, Switzerland
Tel.: (41) 417898000
Web Site: http://www.ineoscompounds.com
Sales Range: $25-49.9 Million
Emp.: 40
Polyvinyl Chloride Compounds Mfr
N.A.I.C.S.: 325211
Thomas Gunther Breitwieser (Mng Dir)

Subsidiary (Domestic):

INEOS Compounds UK Ltd. (4)
School Aycliffe Lane, Newton Aycliffe, DL5 6EA, United Kingdom
Tel.: (44) 1325300555
Web Site: http://www.ineoscompounds.com
Polyvinyl Chloride Compounds Mfr
N.A.I.C.S.: 325211

Plant (Domestic):

INEOS Newton Aycliffe Limited (5)
School Aycliffe Ln, Newton Aycliffe, DL5 6EA, Durham, United Kingdom
Tel.: (44) 01325300555
Web Site: http://www.ineous.com
Sales Range: $75-99.9 Million
Emp.: 200
Monomer Chemicals & Polyvinyl Chloride Polymer Products Whslr
N.A.I.C.S.: 424610

Subsidiary (Non-US):

INEOS Norge AS (4)
Herreveien 801, N 3966, Stathelle, Norway (100%)
Tel.: (47) 35006000
Web Site: http://www.ineoschlor.com
Sales Range: $125-149.9 Million
Emp.: 350
Noretyl Ethylene Cracker Mfr
N.A.I.C.S.: 326199
Erik Ronningen (Mgr-IT)

Subsidiary (Non-US):

Ineos Enterprises Group Limited (3)
Enterpirse House, PO Box 9, South Parade, Runcorn, WA7 4JE, Chesire, United Kingdom
Tel.: (44) 928 561111
Web Site: http://www.ineosenterprises.com
Chemicals Mfr
N.A.I.C.S.: 325998
John Reece (Dir-Fin)

Subsidiary (US):

CRISTAL US, Inc. (4)
20 Wight Ave Ste 150, Hunt Valley, MD 21030
Tel.: (410) 229-4400
Web Site: http://www.cristal.com
Commodity, Industrial, Performance & Specialty Chemicals Mfr; Titanium Tetrachloride Whslr
N.A.I.C.S.: 212290
Amy N. Drusano (Mgr-Comm)

Subsidiary (Non-US):

CRISTAL Pigment UK Ltd. (5)
Laporte Road, Grimbsy NE, Stallingborough, DN40 2PR, Lincolnshire, United Kingdom
Tel.: (44) 1469571000
Web Site: http://www.cristalglobal.com
Sales Range: $250-299.9 Million
Emp.: 800
Chemicals Mfr
N.A.I.C.S.: 325199

Cristal Mining Australia Limited - Australind Plant (5)
Lot 350 Old Coast Road, Australind, 6233, WA, Australia
Tel.: (61) 897808333
Web Site: http://www.cristal.com

Chemicals Mfr
N.A.I.C.S.: 325180
Harley Ross (Controller-Fin)

Subsidiary (US):

INEOS Calabrian (4)
1521 Green Oak Place Ste 200, Kingwood, TX 77339
Tel.: (281) 348-2303
Web Site: http://www.calabriancorp.com
Industrial Inorganic Chemical Mfr
N.A.I.C.S.: 325180
Randy Owens (CEO)

INEOS Chlor Americas Inc. (4)
2036 Foulk Rd Ste 204, Wilmington, DE 19810
Tel.: (302) 529-9601
Chemical Products Distr
N.A.I.C.S.: 424690

Subsidiary (Non-US):

INEOS Chlor Quimica, SA (4)
Gran Via 680 7o4a, 08010, Barcelona, Spain
Tel.: (34) 932701886
Chemical Products Distr
N.A.I.C.S.: 424690

INEOS Chlor Sales International Limited (4)
Room 1407 Harcourt House 39 Gloucester Road, Wanchai, China (Hong Kong)
Tel.: (852) 2922 1072
Chemical Products Distr
N.A.I.C.S.: 424690

INEOS Italia srl (4)
Via Carlo POMA 1, 20129, Milan, Italy
Tel.: (39) 02 745369
Chemical Products Distr
N.A.I.C.S.: 424690

INEOS Solvents Germany GmbH (4)
Roemerstrasse 733, 47443, Moers, Germany
Tel.: (49) 2841 49 0
Web Site: http://www.ineos.com
Sales Range: $25-49.9 Million
Emp.: 6
Solvents Mfr
N.A.I.C.S.: 325998
Wolf Haenel (COO)

Plant (Domestic):

INREOS Solvents Germany GmbH (5)
Shamrockstrasse 88, 44623, Herne, Germany
Tel.: (49) 2323 1477 3000
Solvents Mfr
N.A.I.C.S.: 325998
Wolf Haenel (COO)

Subsidiary (Non-US):

Ineos Enterprises France Sas (4)
Z I Baleycourt, BP 10095, 55103, Paris, Cedex, France
Tel.: (33) 3 29 83 32 44
Chemical Products Distr
N.A.I.C.S.: 424690
Christophe Sussat (COO)

Process Solutions (1)
1303 Batesville Rd, Greer, SC 29650
Tel.: (864) 879-8100
Emp.: 1,800
Holding Company; Plastic, Zinc, Nylon & Monofilament Products Mfr & Whslr
N.A.I.C.S.: 551112
Chuck Villa (CEO)

Subsidiary (Domestic):

Alltrista Plastics LLC (2)
1303 S Batesville Rd, Greer, SC 29650-4807 (100%)
Tel.: (864) 879-8100
Web Site: http://www.jardenplastics.com
Sales Range: $25-49.9 Million
Emp.: 90
Consumer Plastic Products Mfr
N.A.I.C.S.: 326199

Shakespeare Company, LLC (2)

6111 Shakespeare Rd, Columbia, SC 29223
Tel.: (803) 754-7011
Web Site: http://www.shakespearenylons.com
Fishing Tackle & Antennas Mfr
N.A.I.C.S.: 339920

Subsidiary (Non-US):

Shakespeare (Australia) Pty. Ltd. (3)
15 Saggart Field Road, Minto, 2566, NSW, Australia
Tel.: (61) 298209600
Sales Range: $10-24.9 Million
Emp.: 50
Fishing Line Mfr
N.A.I.C.S.: 339920

Division (Domestic):

Shakespeare Co., LLC - Monofilament Division (3)
6111 Shakespeare Rd, Columbia, SC 29223
Tel.: (803) 754-7011
Web Site: http://www.shakespearemonofilaments.com
Technical Monofilaments, Sewing Thread & Grass Trimmer Line Mfr
N.A.I.C.S.: 339920
Peter J. Brissette (VP-R&D)

Subsidiary (Non-US):

Shakespeare Monofilament U.K. Ltd. (3)
Enterprise Way, Fleetwood, FY7 8RY, Lancs, United Kingdom
Tel.: (44) 253858787
Technical Monofilaments, Sewing Thread & Grass Trimmer Line Mfr
N.A.I.C.S.: 339920

Robertshaw Controls Company (1)
1222 Hamilton Pkwy, Itasca, IL 60143
Tel.: (630) 260-3400
Web Site: http://www.robertshaw.com
Emp.: 6,500
Temperature & Pressure Controls, Oven & Water Heater Thermostats, Building Control Systems, Industrial Controls Mfr
N.A.I.C.S.: 334512
Eapon Chacko (Exec VP-Transportation)
Nish Attassery (Mgr-Global Program-Transportation)
Dan Knapper (Sr Mgr-Automotive Sls)
Lukas Krasula (Acct Mgr-Transportation-EMEA)
Ben Durley (VP-Global Supply Chain)
DV Sriram (Dir-Strategic Sourcing)
Fred Lieb (Mgr-Global Commodity)
Gerardo Ramirez (Mgr-Supply Chain-Mexico)
Jorge De Alba (Mgr-Pur-Mexico)
Elio Padovan (Sr Mgr-Supply Chain)

Terracare Associates, LLC (1)
8201 Southpark Ln Ste 110, Littleton, CO 80120
Tel.: (855) 863-8503
Web Site: http://myterracare.com
Landscape Design & Management Services
N.A.I.C.S.: 541320
Dean Murphy (Pres)
Bruce Verdick (VP-Texas)
David Mortensen (Regl VP-Colorado)
Justin Stewert (VP-Public Infrastructure)
Jeff Rudolph (CFO)
Matt Rogers (Reg Mgr-Northern California, TCA)

Therm-O-Disc, Incorporated (1)
1320 S Main St, Mansfield, OH 44907-2516
Tel.: (419) 525-8300
Sales Range: $200-249.9 Million
Emp.: 870
Thermostat Mfr
N.A.I.C.S.: 334512

Division (Domestic):

Therm-O-Disc, Inc. - Northville (2)
21800 Haggerty Rd Ste 207, Northville, MI 48167-8981
Tel.: (248) 347-0800
Web Site: http://www.thermodisc.com
Sales Range: $10-24.9 Million
Emp.: 1
Electronic Components & Decoders

N.A.I.C.S.: 423830

ONE SOTHEBY'S INTERNATIONAL REALTY, INC.
1537 San Remo Ave, Coral Gables, FL 33146
Tel.: (305) 666-0562
Web Site: http://www.onesothebysrealty.com
Activities Related to Real Estate
N.A.I.C.S.: 531390
Daniel de la Veg (Pres)

Subsidiaries:

Decorus Realty LLC (1)
16850 Collins Ave Ste 105, Sunny Isles Beach, FL 33160-4238
Tel.: (305) 944-8181
Web Site: http://www.decorusfund.com
Offices of Real Estate Agents & Brokers
N.A.I.C.S.: 531210
Gabriel Markovich (Co-Mng Partner)
David Koster (Co-Mng Partner)

ONE SOURCE ASSOCIATES, INC.
9111 Guilford Rd, Columbia, MD 21046
Tel.: (410) 309-4900
Web Site: http://www.onesa.com
Year Founded: 1939
Commercial Electric Fixture Mfr
N.A.I.C.S.: 335132
John McLoughlin (Pres & Principal)
Jack S. Floyd (CEO & Principal)
Bill Tucker (Principal & Sr VP-Construction)
David Paolicelli (Pres-Construction Grp)
Michael Morris (Principal & Sr VP-Projects)

Subsidiaries:

Paolicelli & Associates, Inc. (1)
Gregg & Hammond St, Carnegie, PA 15106
Tel.: (412) 276-8816
Web Site: http://www.paolicelli.com
Emp.: 14
Electrical Equipment & Component Mfr
N.A.I.C.S.: 335999
Dave Paolicelli (Pres)

ONE SOURCE TALENT
2653 Industrial Row, Troy, MI 48084
Tel.: (248) 816-7900
Web Site: http://www.onesourcetalent.com
Year Founded: 2003
Rev.: $6,100,000
Emp.: 94
Management Consulting Services
N.A.I.C.S.: 541618
Anthony Toma (Owner)
Bree Win (Mgr-Casting)

ONE STONE ENERGY PARTNERS, L.P.
540 Madison Ave, New York, NY 10019
Tel.: (212) 702-8670   Ky
Web Site: http://www.1stone-llc.com
Privater Equity Firm
N.A.I.C.S.: 523999
Robert Israel (Mng Partner)
Vadim Gluzman (Mng Partner)

Subsidiaries:

Yoho Resources Inc. (1)
Suite 500 521 - Third Avenue SW, Calgary, T2P 3T3, AB, Canada
Tel.: (403) 537-1771
Web Site: https://www.yohoresources.ca
Oil & Gas Exploration Services
N.A.I.C.S.: 213112
Sean Darragh (CFO)

ONE STOP BUSINESS CENTERS INC.

One Stop Business Centers Inc.—(Continued)

35 B Cabot Rd, Woburn, MA 01801
Tel.: (781) 272-4560
Web Site: http://www.osbc.net
Sales Range: $10-24.9 Million
Emp.: 70
Business Machines & Equipment
N.A.I.C.S.: 459999
Mark Fitzgerald (Sr Acct Exec)
Corinne Smith (Coord-Lease)

ONE TECHNOLOGIES, LTD.
8144 Walnut Hill Ln Ste 510, Dallas, TX 75231
Tel.: (469) 916-1700
Web Site:
  http://www.onetechnologies.net
Year Founded: 2000
Sales Range: $10-24.9 Million
Emp.: 15
Online Advertising & Search Engine Optimization Services
N.A.I.C.S.: 541890
Alex Chang (Co-Founder)
Roger Chang (Co-Founder)
Pete Berkland (VP-Strategic Relationships)
Fred Loeber (Gen Counsel & Sr VP)
Mary Welsh (VP-Partnership Mktg)
Sanjay Baskaran (CEO)
Halim Kucur (Chief Product Officer)
Bhargav Shah (CTO & Sr VP)
Carlos Medina (VP-Strategic Bus Dev)

ONE UNITED BANK
133 Federal St, Boston, MA 02110
Tel.: (617) 457-4400
Web Site: http://www.oneunited.com
Rev: $11,762,000
Emp.: 17
Commercial Banking Services
N.A.I.C.S.: 522110
Kevin Cohee (Owner, Chm & CEO)
James Slocum (CIO & Sr VP)
Sherri Brewer (Chief Retail Officer & Sr VP)
Cecilia Isaac (Chief Lending Officer & Sr VP)
Terri Williams (Pres & COO)
Robert Patrick Cooper (Gen Counsel & Sr VP)
Kimmie Jackson (Sr VP-HR)
John Trotter (CFO & Sr VP)
John L. Sims (Vice Chm)
Subsidiaries:

OneUnited Bank (1)
3683 Crenshaw Blvd, Los Angeles, CA 90016-4849
Tel.: (323) 295-3381
Web Site: http://www.oneunited.com
Sales Range: $50-74.9 Million
Emp.: 72
Banking & Financial Services
N.A.I.C.S.: 522110
Kevin Cohee (Owner, Chm & CEO)
Teri Williams (Pres, Pres, COO & COO)
Sherri Brewer (Chief Retail Officer & Sr VP)
Robert Patrick Cooper (Gen Counsel & Sr VP)
Cecilia Isaac (Chief Lending Officer & Sr VP)
Kimmie Jackson (Sr VP-HR)
John Trotter (CFO & Sr VP)

ONE WAY FURNITURE, INC.
535 Broadhollow Rd Ste A7, Melville, NY 11747-3701
Tel.: (631) 249-4390
Web Site:
  http://www.onewayfurniture.com
Year Founded: 2001
Sales Range: $10-24.9 Million
Emp.: 20
Discount Home & Office Furniture Retailer
N.A.I.C.S.: 449110

Mitch Lieberman (CEO)

ONE WORKPLACE
1057 Montague Expy, Milpitas, CA 95035-6818
Tel.: (408) 263-1001
Web Site:
  http://www.oneworkplace.com
Year Founded: 1925
Sales Range: $25-49.9 Million
Emp.: 320
Provider of Business Facilities Management
N.A.I.C.S.: 423210
Mark Ferrari (CEO)
Dave Ferrari (Pres)
Julie Jarvis (Exec VP)
Rod Price (Dir-Strategic Accts)
Dave Bryant (VP-Sls)
Laura Harmon (Dir-HR)

ONE WORLD INC
200 Arizona Ave NE Ste 100, Atlanta, GA 30307
Tel.: (404) 371-1745
Web Site: http://www.one-world-inc.com
Year Founded: 2001
Sales Range: $1-9.9 Million
Emp.: 8
Health Care Consulting Services
N.A.I.C.S.: 541618
Michele Smith (VP-Ops)

ONE/X
6300 Wilshire Blvd Ste 1505, Los Angeles, CA 90048
Tel.: (310) 289-4422
Web Site: http://www.one-x.com
Sales Range: $10-24.9 Million
Emp.: 7
Advertising, Industrial
N.A.I.C.S.: 541810
Jason Wulfsohn (Dir)
Ben Tiernan (Partner & Principal)
Duffy Humbert (Dir-Acct Svc)

ONE2ONE LIVING CORPORATION
3585 N Courtenay Pkwy Ste 5, Merritt Island, FL 32953   NV
Year Founded: 2008
Sales Range: Less than $1 Million
Emp.: 1
Investment Services
N.A.I.C.S.: 523999
Sayomphu Srithonnang (Pres, Treas & Sec)

ONE80 INTERMEDIARIES LLC
160 Federal St 4th Fl, Boston, MA 02110
Tel.: (615) 330-5700
Web Site:
  http://www.one80intermediaries.com
Insurance Company
N.A.I.C.S.: 524298
Matthew F. Power (Pres)
Edward Lopes (COO)
Jonathan Legge (Sr Mng Dir-Private Equity & Transactional Liability)
Subsidiaries:

Brokers Risk Placement Service, Inc. (1)
155 North Wacker Dr Ste 3700, Chicago, IL 60661
Tel.: (312) 906-8111
Web Site: http://www.brps.com
Insurance Agencies & Brokerages
N.A.I.C.S.: 524210
Cheryl Sandner (COO & Gen Counsel)

C & M First Services, Inc. (1)
1501 Broadway Ste 1506, New York, NY 10036
Tel.: (212) 221-3753

Web Site: http://www.cmfirst.com
Sales Range: $1-9.9 Million
Emp.: 20
Insurance Agencies & Brokerages
N.A.I.C.S.: 524210

Edward E. Hall & Company (1)
99 Mill Dam Rd, Centerport, NY 11721
Tel.: (631) 547-6003
Web Site: http://www.edwardehall.com
Sales Range: $1-9.9 Million
Emp.: 10
Insurance Agencies & Brokerage Services
N.A.I.C.S.: 524210
Micahel Heagerty (Mng Dir)
Mary Heagerty (Mng Dir)

Equity Partners Insurance Services, Inc. (1)
302 N Garfield Ave Ste 6, Monterey Park, CA 91754-1773
Tel.: (626) 288-2222
Web Site: http://www.epinsurance.com
Insurance Agencies & Brokerages
N.A.I.C.S.: 524210
Brian Silva (Partner)

International Excess Programs Managers (1)
3700 Park E Dr Ste 250, Richmond Heights, OH 44122
Tel.: (216) 797-9700
Web Site:
  http://www.internationalexcess.com
Insurance Services
N.A.I.C.S.: 524210
Kenneth E. Kukral (VP)

Prosurance Group, Inc. (1)
2685 Marine Way Ste 1408, Mountain View, CA 94043
Tel.: (650) 428-0818
Web Site: http://www.prosurancegroup.com
Sales Range: $1-9.9 Million
Emp.: 13
Insurance Agent/Broker
N.A.I.C.S.: 524210
John V. Wagner (Chm, CEO & Mng Dir)
Dorothy Kent (VP-Fidelity Crime Div)
Kimberly Laird (VP-Large Grp Admin)

Seacoast Specialty Administrators, Inc. (1)
3771 Nesconset Hwy Ste 212, Centereach, NY 11720-1154
Tel.: (631) 444-0900
Web Site: http://www.seacoastspecialty.com
Insurance Related Activities
N.A.I.C.S.: 524298
Christian J. Mahlstedt (Owner)

Selman & Company (1)
1 Integrity Pkwy, Cleveland, OH 44143-1500
Tel.: (440) 646-9336
Web Site: http://www.selmanco.com
Rev.: $300,000,000
Insurance Administration Services
N.A.I.C.S.: 524298
David L. Selman (Pres & CEO)
Elizabeth M. Boettcher (VP-Customer Contact Svcs)
Bryan M. Shantery (CIO & VP)
James P. Baum (CFO)
John L. Selman (Chm)
Cheryl M. Ahmad (Chief Admin Officer)
Dyer M. Bell (VP-Sls)

Subsidiary (Domestic):

Government Employees Association (2)
6110 Parkland Blvd, Cleveland, OH 44124
Web Site: http://www.geausa.org
Government Employee Benefits Services
N.A.I.C.S.: 524292
David L. Selman (Exec Dir)

Superior Furniture Solutions, Inc. (1)
4035 Park E Ct SE Ste 300, Grand Rapids, MI 49546
Tel.: (800) 686-5559
Web Site: http://www.montagefs.com
Furniture & Home Furnishings Mfg & Protection Plan Services
N.A.I.C.S.: 423220
Alan Salmon (Pres)

ONEACCORD CAPITAL LLC

1018 Market St, Kirkland, WA 98033
Tel.: (425) 250-0883   WA
Web Site: http://www.oneaccord.co
Year Founded: 2005
Management Consulting Services
N.A.I.C.S.: 541611
Jeff Rogers (Chm)
Scott Smith (Pres & CEO)
Mark Hulak (Mng Dir)
John Kaminski (Mng Dir)
Richard Brune (Principal)
Gasper Gulotta (Principal)
Glenn Hansen (Partner)
Keith Hartlage (Principal)
Dean Kato (Partner)
Jim Kodjababian (Principal)
Darin Leonard (Sr Partner & Sr VP)
Carl Poteete (Principal)
John Solheim (Principal)
John Steckler (Principal)
Norm Thomas (Principal)
Chris Venti (Principal)
Randal Rick (Partner-Nonprofit)
Subsidiaries:

Bestworth-Rommel, Inc. (1)
19818 74th Ave NE, Arlington, WA 98223
Tel.: (360) 435-2927
Web Site: http://www.bestworth.com
Corporate Imaging Services
N.A.I.C.S.: 541420

ONEBLOOD, INC.
10100 Dr Martin Luther King Jr St N, Saint Petersburg, FL 33716
Tel.: (407) 248-5000   FL
Web Site: http://www.oneblood.org
Year Founded: 2012
Emp.: 2,000
Blood Bank
N.A.I.C.S.: 621991
Rita Reik (Chief Medical Officer)
Lance Reed (CIO & COO)
Andrea Levenson (Sr VP-HR)
Susan Forbes (Sr VP-Mktg & Comm)
William H. Bieberbach (Vice Chm)
John Windham (Chm)
George Scholl (Pres & CEO)
Christopher Stiles (Vice Chm & Sec)
Alicia Bellido Prichard (Sr VP-Biologics-Saint Petersburg)
Michael Rogers (Sr VP-Donor Ops)
Judy Smith (Sr VP-Quality & Regulatory Affairs)
Jeanne E. Dariotis (Sr VP-Laboratories & Reference-Tallahassee)
Jeremy P. Miller (Treas)
Carl Peers (Sr VP-HR & Trng)
John E. Murphy Jr. (Chief Fin & Admin Officer)
Subsidiaries:

Community Blood Center of the Carolinas, Inc. (1)
4447 S Blvd, Charlotte, NC 28209
Tel.: (704) 972-4700
Web Site: http://www.cbcc.us
Blood Donation Services
N.A.I.C.S.: 621991
Todd Davis (Chm)
Eric S. Jenkins (Treas)
Martin Grable (Pres & CEO)
Ned Lipford (Dir-Medical)
Anne Howell (Dir-Training & Dev)
Rita Tate (Mgr-New Processes & Tech)
Deanne Wells (Dir-Quality Assurance)
Khou Moua (Dir-Technical & Hospital Svcs)
Robert H. Hammer III (Sec)

ONECOAST NETWORK CORPORATION
230 Spring St Nw Ste 1800, Atlanta, GA 30303-1096
Tel.: (404) 836-8900   GA
Web Site: http://www.onecoast.com
Year Founded: 1997
Sales Range: $25-49.9 Million

Emp.: 600
Wholesale Marketing & Sales Services to Vendors & Retailers for Home Decor, Gift & Collegiate Products
N.A.I.C.S.: 423220
Richard Butera *(CFO)*
Joe Floriani *(VP-HR & Recruiting)*
John Keiser *(CEO)*
Don McCoy *(VP-Tech Svcs)*
Elisabeth Bond-Johnson *(Mgr-Sls Ops-Gift Div)*
Majda Rensberger *(Exec VP)*
Susan Sacca *(Reg Sls Mgr-Southeast)*
Terry Stewart *(Exec VP)*
John Staley *(Exec VP-Gift Div)*

ONEHOPE WINE
PO Box 1117, Newport Beach, CA 92659
Web Site:
http://www.onehopewine.com
Year Founded: 2007
Sales Range: $1-9.9 Million
Emp.: 22
Winery
N.A.I.C.S.: 312130
Jake Kloberdanz *(CEO)*
Tom Leahy *(Pres)*
Blake Petty *(COO)*

ONEIDA MOLDED PLASTICS, LLC
104 S Warner St, Oneida, NY 13421-1510
Tel.: (315) 363-7990
Web Site:
http://www.oneidamoldedplastics.com
Year Founded: 1964
Thermoplastic Custom Molding Products & Services
N.A.I.C.S.: 326199
Steve Thalmann *(Pres & CEO)*
Brian Simchik *(CFO)*
David Power *(VP-Outdoor Recreational Sls)*
Mitch Nichols *(VP-Bus Dev)*
Kevin McGreevy *(VP-Bus Dev)*
David McManmon *(Dir-Engrng)*
John Andrews *(Mgr-Engrng)*

ONEIDA RESEARCH SERVICES, INC.
8282 Halsey Rd, Whitesboro, NY 13492
Tel.: (315) 736-5480
Web Site: http://www.orslabs.com
Year Founded: 1977
Sales Range: $10-24.9 Million
Emp.: 30
Testing Laboratories
N.A.I.C.S.: 541715
Thomas J. Rossiter *(Pres)*
Denise Moller *(Mgr-Fin & HR)*

ONEIDA TOTAL INTEGRATED ENTERPRISES (OTIE)
1033 N Mayfair Rd Ste 200, Milwaukee, WI 53226
Tel.: (414) 257-4200
Web Site: http://www.otie.com
Rev.: $11,800,000
Emp.: 170
Engineeering Services
N.A.I.C.S.: 541330
Nick Ni *(Pres)*

ONELOGIN, INC.
848 Battery St, San Francisco, CA 94111
Tel.: (415) 645-6830
Web Site: http://www.onelogin.com
Year Founded: 2009
Identity Management Software Developer
N.A.I.C.S.: 513210
Thomas Pedersen *(Co-Founder & CTO)*
Christian Pedersen *(Co-Founder)*
Justin Calmus *(Chief Security Officer)*
Brad Brooks *(CEO)*
Maura Theriault *(VP-Enterprise Sls)*
Matt Hurley *(VP-Channels, Strategic Alliances & Pro Svcs-Global)*
Venkat Sathyamurthy *(Chief Product Officer)*
Courtney Harrison *(Chief HR Officer)*
Bernard Huger *(CFO)*
Kevin Biggs *(Chief Revenue Officer)*
Rick Barr *(COO)*
Natalia Wodecki *(Dir-Global Comm)*
Dayna Rothman *(CMO)*

ONEMAIN FINANCE CORPORATION
601 NW 2nd St, Evansville, IN 47708
Tel.: (812) 424-8031 IN
Web Site:
https://www.onemainfinancial.com
Year Founded: 1962
Rev.: $4,564,000,000
Assets: $24,289,000,000
Liabilities: $21,109,000,000
Net Worth: $3,180,000,000
Earnings: $641,000,000
Emp.: 9,100
Fiscal Year-end: 12/31/23
Investment Management Service
N.A.I.C.S.: 523999

ONEMARKETDATA, LLC
2 Hudson Pl Baker Waterfront Plz 6th Fl, Hoboken, NJ 07030
Tel.: (201) 710-5977
Market Data Management & Analytical Solutions for Financial Industry
N.A.I.C.S.: 519290
Leonid Frants *(Pres & CEO)*

ONEONTA TRADING CORPORATION
1 Oneonta Dr, Wenatchee, WA 98801
Tel.: (509) 663-2191 WA
Web Site: http://www.oneonta.com
Year Founded: 1934
Holding Company; Fruit Farmer, Packer & Whslr
N.A.I.C.S.: 551112
Brian Focht *(Gen Mgr)*
Dalton Thomas *(Pres)*
Eric J. Stepper *(Controller)*
Scott Marboe *(Dir-Mktg)*
Steve Reinholt *(Sls Mgr-Export)*
Brad Thomas *(VP)*

Subsidiaries:

Oneonta-Starr Ranch Growers LLC (1)
1 Oneonta Way, Wenatchee, WA 98801
Tel.: (509) 663-2191
Web Site: http://www.oneonta.com
Fruit Farmer, Packer & Whslr
N.A.I.C.S.: 111331
Brian Focht *(Gen Mgr)*

ONEPAK, INC.
56 Main St 2nd Fl, Orleans, MA 02653
Tel.: (508) 247-9200
Web Site: http://www.onepak.com
Sales Range: $1-9.9 Million
Emp.: 1
Electronic Waste Packaging & Transportation Services
N.A.I.C.S.: 561910
Horacio R. Marquez *(VP-Fin)*
Steven V. Andon *(CEO)*
Jerry R. Drisaldi *(Vice Chm)*

ONEPOWER SYSTEMS LTD.
7345 E Peakview Ave, Centennial, CO 80111
Tel.: (866) 209-3225 NV
Web Site:
http://www.onepowerfinance.com
Year Founded: 2009
Corporate Financial Advisory Services
N.A.I.C.S.: 523940
Soha Hamdan *(Pres, CEO & CFO)*

ONERAIN, INC.
1531 Skyway Dr Suite D, Longmont, CO 80504
Tel.: (303) 774-2033
Web Site: http://www.onerain.com
Year Founded: 1992
Sales Range: $1-9.9 Million
Emp.: 18
Offers Real-Time & Historical Rainfall-Related Data & Professional Services
N.A.I.C.S.: 334513
James Logan *(Pres & CEO)*
Mike Zucosky *(Dir-Ops)*
Pamela Chacon *(Office Mgr)*

Subsidiaries:

High Sierra Electronics, Inc. (1)
155 Spring Hill Dr Ste 106, Grass Valley, CA 95945 (100%)
Tel.: (530) 273-2080
Web Site:
http://www.highsierraelectronics.com
Sales Range: $1-9.9 Million
Emp.: 50
Environmental Monitoring & Analytical Laboratory Instrument Mfr
N.A.I.C.S.: 334516
Frank Gutierrez *(Reg Mgr-Sls)*

ONESHIELD, INC.
62 Forest St, Marlborough, MA 01752
Tel.: (508) 475-0300
Web Site: http://www.oneshield.com
Sales Range: $25-49.9 Million
Emp.: 168
Insurance Software Developer
N.A.I.C.S.: 513210
Glenn Anschutz *(Pres)*
Vivek Gujral *(CTO & Exec VP)*
Jeff Liotta *(VP-Engrg)*
John McManus *(Chief Admin Officer, Gen Counsel & Exec VP)*
Heather Peacock *(Exec VP-Client Delivery & Svcs)*
John Rikala *(VP-Dev)*
Liza Smith *(Sr VP-Global Sls & Mktg)*
Ron Turner *(VP-Pro Svcs)*
Rakesh Parikh *(VP-Product Engrg)*
Tracey Giglia *(VP-Sls & Client Svcs)*
Liza Petrie *(Chief Product Officer)*
Janice Merkley *(VP-Mktg)*
Cameron Parker *(CEO)*

ONESOURCE GENERAL CONTRACTING, INC.
101 Devant St Ste 404, Fayetteville, GA 30214
Tel.: (770) 461-9924
Web Site:
http://www.onesourcegc.com
Year Founded: 1999
Rev.: $6,900,000
Emp.: 10
Commercial & Institutional Building Construction
N.A.I.C.S.: 236220
Robert Morris *(VP)*
Katie Nixon *(Acct Mgr)*
John King *(Pres)*

ONESOURCE VIRTUAL
5601 N MacArthur Blvd Ste 100, Irving, TX 75038
Tel.: (972) 916-9847
Web Site:
http://www.onesourcevirtual.com
Year Founded: 2008
Sales Range: $10-24.9 Million
Emp.: 260
Information Technology Consulting Services
N.A.I.C.S.: 541512
Brian Williams *(Chm)*
Britt Wirt *(Co-Founder & Chief Scientific Officer)*
Mark Turner *(Chief Admin Officer)*
Michael Simpson *(Exec VP)*
Duncan Harwood *(VP-Pro Svcs & Strategy)*
John Levey *(Exec VP-Sls)*
Scott Ingulli *(VP-IT)*
Brad Everett *(CMO)*
Michael Walenciak *(Gen Counsel & VP)*
John D. Bax *(CFO)*
Trey Campbell *(CEO)*
Jane Huston *(Sr VP-HR)*

ONESPRING LLC
1050 Crown Pointe Pkwy, Atlanta, GA 30338
Web Site: http://www.onespring.net
Year Founded: 2005
Rev.: $2,800,000
Emp.: 25
Computer System Design Services
N.A.I.C.S.: 541512
Jason Moccia *(Mng Partner)*
Robert Grashuis *(Partner-Comml Sector)*

ONESTA
Chrysler Bldg 405 Lexington Ave 26th Fl, New York, NY 10174
Tel.: (212) 907-6600
Web Site:
http://www.onestagroup.com
Year Founded: 2006
Sales Range: $1-9.9 Million
Internet Consulting Services
N.A.I.C.S.: 541690
Scott Liewehr *(Principal)*
Despina Papadopoulos *(Principal)*

ONESTOP INTERNET, INC.
2332 E Pacifica Pl, Rancho Dominguez, CA 90220
Tel.: (310) 894-7700
Web Site: http://www.onestop.com
Year Founded: 2004
Sales Range: $10-24.9 Million
Emp.: 100
E-Commerce Software & Solutions
N.A.I.C.S.: 513210
Steve Tandberg *(Co-Founder & Chief Culture Officer)*
Adriana Pulido *(Dir-ECommerce)*
Ibeth De La Torre *(Mgr-Customer Svc)*
Michael Wang *(Pres & CEO)*
Gary Cooperman *(CFO)*
Brett Morrison *(Co-Founder)*
Renee Washburn *(Partner-Ops & VP)*
Anton Reut *(Sr VP & Gen Mgr-Product & Tech)*
Rick Egan *(Sr VP & Gen Mgr-Revenue Mgmt)*
Kunah Yoon *(Sr VP-Creative Svcs)*
Chad Tulloch *(VP-ECommerce Strategy)*
Danielle Ilan-Weber *(VP-Onboarding Svcs)*
Eric Burns *(VP-Sls)*

ONESTOPERGONOMICS.COM
2825 Duell Ave, Medford, OR 97501
Tel.: (541) 982-4005
Web Site:
http://www.onestopergonomics.com

ONESTOPERGONOMICS.COM

OneStopErgonomics.com—(Continued)
Year Founded: 1999
Rev.: $8,500,000
Emp.: 5
Ergonomic Office Furniture, LCD & Flat Panel Mounting Solutions
N.A.I.C.S.: 449110
Peter M. Scholom (Pres)
Steven Scholom (Specialist-Online Graphics)

ONETA COMPANY
1401 S Padre Island Dr, Corpus Christi, TX 78416
Tel.: (361) 853-0123
Web Site: http://www.onetacc.com
Year Founded: 1973
Sales Range: $10-24.9 Million
Emp.: 128
Beverages & Snacks Distr
N.A.I.C.S.: 424490
Karl Koch (Co-Owner)
Judy Koch (Co-Owner)

ONETRUST LLC
1200 Abernathy Rd NE Bldg 600, Atlanta, GA 30328
Tel.: (844) 847-7154
Web Site: http://www.onetrust.com
Year Founded: 2016
Software Publisher
N.A.I.C.S.: 513210
Kim M. Rivera (Chief Legal & Business Officer)
Kabir Barday (CEO)
Alan Dabbiere (Co-Chm)
John Marshall (Co-Chm)
Blake Brannon (CTO)
Andrew Clearwater (Chief Privacy Officer)
Guido Torrini (CFO)
Marcelo Modica (Chief People Officer)
Emily McEvilly (Chief Customer Officer)

Subsidiaries:

Convercent, Inc. (1)
3858 Walnut St Ste #255, Denver, CO 80205
Tel.: (303) 526-7600
Web Site: http://www.convercent.com
Professional, Scientific & Technical Services
N.A.I.C.S.: 541990
Patrick Quinlan (CEO)

OneTrust Technology Limited (1)
82 St John St, Farringdon, London, EC1M 4JN, United Kingdom
Tel.: (44) 8000119778
Web Site: http://www.onetrust.com
Software Publisher; IT Consultancy Services
N.A.I.C.S.: 513210
Kabir Barday (CEO)

ONEVOICE COMMUNICATIONS, INC.
45610 Woodland Rd Ste 250, Sterling, VA 20166
Tel.: (703) 880-2500
Web Site: http://www.onevoiceinc.com
Year Founded: 2000
Rev.: $5,100,000
Emp.: 11
Telecommunications
N.A.I.C.S.: 517111
Christopher Kane (VP-Sls)
Stephen Dize (Pres & CEO)
Jeff Shannon (Dir-Mktg)

ONEWATER MARINE HOLDINGS LLC
6275 Lanier Islands Pkwy, Buford, GA 30518
Tel.: (855) 208-4359
Web Site: http://www.onewatermarine.com
Holding Company; Marine Retail Dealerships
N.A.I.C.S.: 551112
Austin Singleton (CEO)
Jack Ezzell (CFO)
Anthony M. Aisquith (Pres & COO)
Mitchell W. Legler (Chm)
Scott Cunningham Sr. (Exec VP-Retail Ops)

Subsidiaries:

Captains Choice Marine, Inc. (1)
3216 Hwy 378, Leesville, SC 29070
Tel.: (803) 291-4771
Web Site: http://www.ccmarine.com
Sales Range: $1-9.9 Million
Emp.: 20
Boat Distr
N.A.I.C.S.: 441222
Billy Lake (Mgr-Svc)
Chance Taylor (Gen Mgr)
Gabe Coker (Mgr-Bus)

Lookout Marine Sales (1)
6590 S Hwy 27, Somerset, KY 42501-6076 (100%)
Tel.: (606) 561-5904
Web Site: http://www.lookoutmarine.com
Emp.: 10
Boat Dealers
N.A.I.C.S.: 441222
Jimmy Troxtel (Owner)
Jimbob Troxtell (Gen Mgr)
Betty Cornett (Office Mgr)

Rambo Marine, Inc. (1)
15904 Hwy 231 N, Hazel Green, AL 35750
Tel.: (256) 952-3241
Web Site: http://www.rambomarine.com
Sales Range: $1-9.9 Million
Emp.: 11
Boat Dealers
N.A.I.C.S.: 441222
Karl Rambo (Pres)
Bennett Rambo (Gen Mgr)

Sundance Marine North, Inc. (1)
3321 NE Indian River Dr, Jensen Beach, FL 34957
Tel.: (772) 675-1913
Web Site: http://www.sundancemarineusa.com
Boat Distr
N.A.I.C.S.: 441222
Mitchell Milesi (Pres)

The Slalom Shop (1)
2908 N Stemmons Freeway, Lewisville, TX 75077-1724
Tel.: (972) 734-1578
Web Site: http://www.slalomshop.com
Boat Dealers
N.A.I.C.S.: 441222
Darrell Wilson (Owner)

ONEWORLD COMMUNICATIONS, INC.
2001 Harrison St, San Francisco, CA 94110
Tel.: (415) 355-1935
Web Site: http://www.owcom.com
Year Founded: 1994
Sales Range: Less than $1 Million
Emp.: 20
Advetising Agency
N.A.I.C.S.: 541810
Jonathan Villet (Producer-Creative & Strategist)
Fiona McDougall (Dir-Creative Production)
Mark Allen (Sr Acct Mgr & Dir-Video)
Roger Burgner (Mgr-Graphics Production)
Amy Stonecipher (Acct Exec)
Denise Bostrom (Copywriter & Scriptwriter)
Cipriano Iguaran (Mgr-Cultural & Hispanic Media)
Tim Gillerlain (Interactive Media Producer)
Teresa Schnabel (Mgr-Mktg Res)
Paolo Vascia (Photographer)
Bobby Valenzuela (Accountant)
Yvonne Lee (Mgr-Asian-American Community Rels)
Tom Donald (Dir-Film & Video)
Norman Buten (Copywriter & Dir-Creative)
Marguerite Cueto (Strategist-Hispanic Mktg)
David Wren (Mgr-PR & Copywriter)

ONEX INC.
2225 Colonial Ave, Erie, PA 16506-1868
Tel.: (814) 838-9638
Web Site: http://www.onexnet.com
Sales Range: $10-24.9 Million
Emp.: 30
Refractory Material
N.A.I.C.S.: 423840
Eric V. Walters (Pres)
Michael Ducato (VP)

ONGWEOWEH CORP.
767 Warren Rd PO Box 3300, Ithaca, NY 14852-3300
Tel.: (607) 266-7070
Web Site: http://www.ongweoweh.com
Year Founded: 1978
Sales Range: $10-24.9 Million
Emp.: 40
Provider of Pallet & Container Management Services
N.A.I.C.S.: 423310
Chip Dauber (Acct Mgr)
Justin Bennett (Pres)

ONIN STAFFING
430 Greensprings Hwy Ste 12, Birmingham, AL 35209
Tel.: (205) 945-8996
Web Site: http://www.oninstaffing.com
Sales Range: $25-49.9 Million
Emp.: 20
Provider of Temporary Staffing Services
N.A.I.C.S.: 561320
Ryan Maynard (Mgr-Fin)

ONION, INC.
730 N Franklin 7th Fl, Chicago, IL 60654
Tel.: (312) 751-0503
Web Site: http://www.theonion.com
Year Founded: 1990
Satirical Newspaper Publisher
N.A.I.C.S.: 513110
Josh Modell (Sr VP & Dir-Editorial)
Mike McAvoy (Pres & CEO)
Jordan David (Dir-Content Mktg)
Katie Pontius (Chief Resource Officer)
Kurt Mueller (Chief Creative Officer)
Rick Hamann (Chief Creative Officer)
Chris Sprehe (Sr VP-Product & Tech)
George Zwierzynski (VP-Labs & Studio Production)
Cole Bolton (Editor-in-Chief)
Eric Ervine (Art Dir)
Ben Berkley (Mng Editor)
Marnie Shure (Deputy Mng Editor)
Joe Fullman (Mktg Dir)
Chad Nackers (Mng Editor)
Nick Moore (Editor)
Ryan Natoli (Editor)

ONLINE 401(K)
101 Green St 2nd Fl, San Francisco, CA 94111
Tel.: (415) 593-5868
Web Site: http://www.theonline401k.com
Year Founded: 1999
Sales Range: $1-9.9 Million
Emp.: 51
Web Based 401k Plans
N.A.I.C.S.: 523999
Chad Parks (Founder & Pres)

ONLINE COMMERCE GROUP, LLC
3180 Wetumpka Hwy, Montgomery, AL 36110
Tel.: (334) 558-0863
Web Site: http://www.onlinecommercegroup.com
Year Founded: 2004
Sales Range: $1-9.9 Million
Emp.: 22
Online Furniture Retailer
N.A.I.C.S.: 423210
Jerry Maccartney (Gen Mgr)
Melissa Whiddon (VP-Fin)
Emily A. Nelms (Dir-Mktg & Comm)
Scott McGlon (Pres & CEO)

ONLINE COMPUTER LIBRARY CENTER, INC.
6565 Kiogour Pl, Dublin, OH 43017
Tel.: (614) 764-6000
Web Site: http://www.oclc.org
Year Founded: 1967
Sales Range: $150-199.9 Million
Emp.: 1,200
On-Line Data Base Library Cooperative
N.A.I.C.S.: 519210
Lorcan Dempsey (VP-Membership & Res)
Cindy Hilsheimer (Vice Chm)
John R. Patrick (Pres)
John F. Szabo (Chm)
Skip Prichard (CEO)
Bart Murphy (CIO & CTO)
Bill Rozek (CFO & Treas)

Subsidiaries:

OCLC Asia Pacific (1)
6565 Kilgour Pl, Dublin, OH 43017-3395
Tel.: (614) 764-6000
Web Site: http://www.oclc.org
Library Support & Services
N.A.I.C.S.: 517810
Eric Van Lubeek (Mng Dir & VP)

OCLC B.V. (1)
Postbus 876, Leiden, 2300 AW, Netherlands (100%)
Tel.: (31) 71 524 65 00
Web Site: http://www.oclc.org
Sales Range: $25-49.9 Million
Emp.: 100
Shared Technology Services, Original Research & Community Programs for Library Professionals
N.A.I.C.S.: 519210
Eric Van Lubeek (Mng Dir)

Subsidiary (Domestic):

Huijsmans en Kuijpers Automatisering BV (2)
Groningerweg 13-C, 9765, Paterswolde, Netherlands
Tel.: (31) 504065010
Library Management Services
N.A.I.C.S.: 519210

Subsidiary (Non-US):

Sisis Informationssysteme GmbH (2)
Personalabteilung Grunwalder Weg 28 g, Oberhaching, Munich, Germany
Tel.: (49) 89 61308 300
Library Management Services
N.A.I.C.S.: 519210

OCLC Canada (1)
9955 rue Chateauneuf bureau 135, Brossard, J4Z 3V5, QC, Canada (100%)
Tel.: (450) 656-8955
Web Site: https://www.oclc.org
Sales Range: $10-24.9 Million
Emp.: 5
Online Information & Library Services
N.A.I.C.S.: 517810
Daniel Boivin (Exec Dir)

OCLC Forest Press (1)
6565 Kilgour Pl, Dublin, OH 43017 (100%)
Tel.: (614) 764-6000
Web Site: http://www.oclc.org
Book Publishers
N.A.I.C.S.: 517810
Rick Schwieterman *(CFO, Treas & Exec VP)*

OCLC GmbH (1)
Grunwalder Weg 28g, 82041, Oberhaching, Germany
Tel.: (49) 8961308300
Web Site: http://www.oclc.org
Library Management Services
N.A.I.C.S.: 519210

OCLC Latin America and the Caribbean (1)
6565 Frantz Rd, Dublin, OH 43017-3395 (100%)
Tel.: (614) 764-6301
Web Site: http://www.oclc.org
Sales Range: $10-24.9 Million
Emp.: 2
Library Support & Services
N.A.I.C.S.: 517810
Humberto Abed *(Dir-Mexico)*

OCLC PICA (1)
7th Fl Tricorn House, 51 53 Hagley Rd, Birmingham, B16 8TP, Biringham, United Kingdom (60%)
Tel.: (44) 214564656
Web Site: http://www.oclcpica.org
Sales Range: $10-24.9 Million
Emp.: 20
Information Retrieval Services for Library Professionals
N.A.I.C.S.: 517810

Preservation Resources (1)
9 S Commerce Way, Bethlehem, PA 18017-8916 (100%)
Tel.: (610) 758-8700
Sales Range: $10-24.9 Million
Emp.: 70
Document Preservation Services
N.A.I.C.S.: 561990

netLibrary, Inc. (1)
4888 Pearl E Cir, Boulder, CO 80301
Tel.: (303) 544-0076
Web Site: http://www.netlibrary.com
Sales Range: $10-24.9 Million
Emp.: 50
Electronic Book Service
N.A.I.C.S.: 519210

ONLINE CONSULTING, INC.
505 Carr Rd Ste 100, Wilmington, DE 19809-2800
Tel.: (302) 225-4470
Web Site: http://www.onlc.com
Year Founded: 1983
Sales Range: $10-24.9 Million
Emp.: 30
Information Technology Training Services
N.A.I.C.S.: 611420
Jim Palic *(Co-Founder & Pres)*
Andy Williamson *(Co-Founder & CEO)*

ONLINE REWARDS
3102 Maple Ave Ste 450, Dallas, TX 75201
Tel.: (888) 826-0783
Web Site: http://www.online-rewards.com
Year Founded: 2002
Incentive & Loyalty Marketing Programs & Services
N.A.I.C.S.: 541613
Michael Levy *(Co-Founder, Pres & CEO)*
Marc Slagle *(Co-Founder & CIO)*
John Knodel *(Co-Founder & Dir-Client Svcs)*

ONLINE STORES, INC.
1000 Westinghouse Dr Ste 1, New Stanton, PA 15672
Tel.: (724) 925-5600
Web Site: http://www.onlinestores.com
Year Founded: 2002
Rev.: $20,700,000
Emp.: 90
Miscellaneous Store Retailers
N.A.I.C.S.: 459999
Kevin Hickey *(Owner)*
Lisa Hickey *(Pres)*
John Gilkey *(VP)*
Mindy Richards *(Supvr-Custom Products)*

ONLINE TRANSPORT SYSTEM, INC.
6311 W Stoner Dr, Greenfield, IN 46140-7413
Tel.: (317) 894-2159
Web Site: http://www.onlinetransport.com
Year Founded: 2000
Sales Range: $25-49.9 Million
Emp.: 150
Interstate Trucking Services
N.A.I.C.S.: 484121
Dan Cook *(Pres)*

Subsidiaries:

Frontier Transport Corporation (1)
6311 W Stoner Dr, Greenfield, IN 46140-7413
Tel.: (317) 636-1641
Web Site: http://www.frontiertransport.com
Sales Range: $25-49.9 Million
Emp.: 50
Trucking Service
N.A.I.C.S.: 484121
Steve Cook *(VP)*
Dan Cook *(Pres)*

Unit (Domestic):

Frontier Temperature Control (2)
6311 Stoner Dr, Greenfield, IN 46140
Tel.: (317) 636-1641
Web Site: http://www.frontiertransport.com
Sales Range: $25-49.9 Million
Emp.: 50
Temperature Controlled Transport Services
N.A.I.C.S.: 484121
Steve Cook *(Pres)*

W.S. Thomas Transfer, Inc. (1)
1854 Morgantown Ave, Fairmont, WV 26554
Tel.: (304) 363-8050
Web Site: http://www.wsthomas.com
Sales Range: $1-9.9 Million
Emp.: 100
General Freight Trucking Services
N.A.I.C.S.: 484121
Mark Thompson *(VP & Gen Mgr)*

ONLINE-REDEFINED, INC.
1347 N Stanley Ave Ste 4, Los Angeles, CA 90046
Tel.: (203) 668-5029 DE
Year Founded: 2008
Sales Range: Less than $1 Million
Emp.: 1
Computer Consulting Services
N.A.I.C.S.: 541690
Dan Faiman *(Pres & CEO)*

ONLY THE BEST, INC.
99-969 Iwaena St, Aiea, HI 96701
Tel.: (808) 487-9919
Web Site: http://www.crazyshirts.com
Sales Range: $75-99.9 Million
Emp.: 320
Custom Printed T-Shirts
N.A.I.C.S.: 458110
Mark Hollander *(Pres)*

ONMOBILE SYSTEMS, INC.
34760 Campus Dr, Fremont, CA 94555
Tel.: (510) 742-3000 DE
Web Site: http://www.onmobile.com
Year Founded: 2000
Sales Range: $1-9.9 Million
Emp.: 15
Custom Computer Programming Services
N.A.I.C.S.: 541511
Amit Dey *(CTO)*
Rajesh Moorti *(CFO)*

ONO TRANSPORT SERVICES, INC.
10603 Allentown Blvd Box 74, Ono, PA 17077
Tel.: (717) 865-2148
Web Site: http://www.jpdonmoyer.com
Year Founded: 1934
Sales Range: $10-24.9 Million
Emp.: 5
Bulk & Truck-Load Freight & Logistical Services
N.A.I.C.S.: 484121
F. T. Silfies *(Owner)*

Subsidiaries:

J.P. Donmoyer, Inc. (1)
10603 Allentown Blvd, Ono, PA 17077
Tel.: (717) 865-2148
Web Site: http://www.fts-jpd.com
Emp.: 30
Bulk & Truck-Load Freight & Logistical Services
N.A.I.C.S.: 484220
Chris Silfies *(Pres & COO)*
Evan Wechsler *(CEO)*

ONONDAGA COUNTY RESOURCE RECOVERY AGENCY
100 Elwood Davis Rd, North Syracuse, NY 13212
Tel.: (315) 453-2866
Web Site: http://www.ocrra.org
Sales Range: $25-49.9 Million
Emp.: 67
Refuse System
N.A.I.C.S.: 562219
Andrew Radin *(Dir-Recycling & Waste Reduction)*
Dereth Glance *(Exec Dir)*
Mike Reilly *(Chm)*

ONONDAGA COUNTY WATER AUTHORITY
200 Northern Concourse, Syracuse, NY 13212
Tel.: (315) 455-7061
Web Site: http://www.ocwa.org
Year Founded: 1951
Rev.: $44,679,037
Assets: $295,544,070
Liabilities: $102,136,130
Net Worth: $193,407,940
Earnings: $8,943,228
Emp.: 139
Fiscal Year-end: 12/31/18
Water Supply
N.A.I.C.S.: 221310
Michael E. Hooker *(Exec Dir)*
John V. Bianchini *(Chm)*
Eileen D. Gilligan *(Sec)*
Laurie J. Khanzadian *(Mgr-HR & Insurance)*
Kenneth C. Gardiner *(Treas)*
Curtis R. Marvin *(CFO)*
Geoffrey G. Miller Jr. *(COO & Deputy Exec Dir)*

ONPOINT COMMUNITY CREDIT UNION
PO Box 3750, Portland, OR 97208
Tel.: (503) 228-7077 OR
Web Site: http://www.onpointcu.com
Year Founded: 1932
Sales Range: $125-149.9 Million
Emp.: 369
Credit Union Operator
N.A.I.C.S.: 522130
Tory McVay *(Chief Retail Officer & Sr VP)*
Jim Hunt *(CFO & Sr VP)*
Jim Armstrong *(CIO & Sr VP)*
Keith Morris *(Vice Chm)*
Robert A. Stuart *(Pres & CEO)*
Tom Tsuruta *(Chm)*
Cori Harms *(Sec)*
Melisa Lindsay *(Mgr-Wealth & Investment Svcs)*
Veronica Ervin *(Chief Compliance Officer & Sr VP)*
Cecile Milam *(Chief Lending Officer & Sr VP)*
Stephen Owen *(COO & Sr VP)*
Steve Leugers *(Chief Credit Officer & Sr VP)*
Jackie Dunckley *(Chief Talent Officer)*

ONPOINT WARRANTY SOLUTIONS, LLC
1400 Main St Ste 132, Clarksville, IN 47129
Tel.: (877) 668-4681
Web Site: https://www.onpointwarranty.com
Year Founded: 2015
Consumer Services
N.A.I.C.S.: 561499

Subsidiaries:

Guardian Protection Products, Inc. (1)
2220 Hwy 70 SE Ste 100, Hickory, NC 28602
Tel.: (828) 261-0325
Web Site: http://www.guardianproducts.com
Furniture & Mattress Pad Protection Products Mfr
N.A.I.C.S.: 325998

ONPR
720 SW Washington St Ste 600, Portland, OR 97205
Tel.: (503) 802-4400
Web Site: http://www.onpr.com
Sales Range: Less than $1 Million
Emp.: 10
Communications, Event Marketing, Exhibit/Trade Shows, High Technology, Investor Relations, New Product Development, Public Relations, Strategic Planning
N.A.I.C.S.: 541820
Jody Peake *(CEO)*
Dave Wilson *(CFO, COO & Principal)*
Jeff Fishburn *(Acct Mgr)*

Subsidiaries:

OnPR (1)
PO Box 50428, Bellevue, WA 98004-5580
Tel.: (425) 454-6840
Web Site: http://www.onpr.com
N.A.I.C.S.: 541810
Gaby Adam *(Sr VP)*

OnPR GmbH (1)
Grasserstrasse 10, 80339, Munich, Germany
Tel.: (49) 89 3090 51610
Web Site: http://www.onpr.de
N.A.I.C.S.: 541820
Simon Jones *(Mng Dir)*
Ulrike Meinhardt *(Acct Dir)*

ONQ SOLUTIONS, INC.
24540 Clawiter Rd, Hayward, CA 94545
Tel.: (650) 241-0215
Web Site: http://www.onqsolutions.com
Year Founded: 2004
Sales Range: $25-49.9 Million
Emp.: 47
Merchandise Product Retailer
N.A.I.C.S.: 455219
Paul Chapuis *(CEO)*
Dean McLeod *(Mgr-Offshore Production)*

ONQ SOLUTIONS, INC.

ONQ Solutions, Inc.—(Continued)
Matt Jones (Mgr-Shipping & Receiving)
Brian Imhoff (Production Mgr)
Mike Logan (Ops Mgr-West)

ONRAD, INC.
1770 Iowa Ave Ste 280, Riverside, CA 92507
Tel.: (951) 786-0801
Web Site: http://www.onradinc.com
Year Founded: 1998
Sales Range: $10-24.9 Million
Emp.: 80
Radiology Software Development Services
N.A.I.C.S.: 541511
David Willcutts (CEO)
Alix Vincent (Chief Medical Officer)
Daniel Brazell (VP-Ops)

ONSET VENTURES
2400 Sand Hill Rd Ste 150, Menlo Park, CA 94025-6985
Tel.: (650) 529-0700
Web Site: http://www.onset.com
Sales Range: $10-24.9 Million
Emp.: 25
Intermediation Services
N.A.I.C.S.: 523910
Jennifer Lewis (Office Mgr)

ONSITE OCCUPATIONAL HEALTH & SAFETY, INC.
101 N Hart St, Princeton, IN 47670
Tel.: (812) 770-4480
Web Site: http://www.onsiteohs.com
Year Founded: 2008
Sales Range: $10-24.9 Million
Emp.: 165
Healthcare Services
N.A.I.C.S.: 621999
Kyle G. Johnson (Pres & CEO)
Kraig R. Johnson (Mgr-Program)
Randy Rahman (Dir-Fin)
Jeff Devine (Dir-Human Capital)
Gregory Fuller (Dir-Medical)

ONSTREAM MEDIA CORPORATION
1291 SW 29th Ave, Pompano Beach, FL 33069
Tel.: (954) 917-6655 FL
Web Site: http://www.onstreammedia.com
Year Founded: 1993
Emp.: 75
Webcasting & Networking Solutions for Entertainment Industry & Marketing Solutions for Travel Industry
N.A.I.C.S.: 541512
Clifford Friedland (Sr VP-Bus Dev)
Randy S. Selman (Chm, Pres & CEO)
Alan M. Saperstein (COO & Treas)
David Glassman (CMO & Sr VP)

Subsidiaries:

Infinite Conferencing, Inc. (1)
100 Morris Ave Ste 302, Springfield, NJ 07081
Tel.: (973) 671-0040
Web Site: http://www.infiniteconferencing.com
Sales Range: $10-24.9 Million
Emp.: 35
Tele Conferencing Services
N.A.I.C.S.: 517810
Clifford Friedland (Pres)
Arlene J. Ross (Chief Admin Officer)
Michelle Barnes (VP-Ops)
Sabrina George (VP-Mktg)
Julie Glazer (VP-Sls)

Intella II, Inc. (1)
2188 San Diego Ave Ste P, San Diego, CA 92110
Tel.: (619) 308-3600

Web Site: http://www.intella2.com
Sales Range: $1-9.9 Million
Emp.: 31
Telecommunications Resellers
N.A.I.C.S.: 517121

ONTARIO REFRIGERATION SERVICE
635 S Mtn Ave, Ontario, CA 91762
Tel.: (909) 984-2771
Web Site: http://www.ontariorefrigeration.com
Year Founded: 1958
Sales Range: $10-24.9 Million
Emp.: 104
Provider of Heating & Air Conditioning Contracting Services
N.A.I.C.S.: 238220
Phillip Talleur (Chm)
Brian McWilliams (Sr Acct Mgr)
Scott Gray (Mgr-Ops)
Sergio Delatorre (Supvr-Svc)
Mike Prendeville (Coord-Svc)

ONTRAPORT
2040 Alameda Padre Serra Ste 220, Santa Barbara, CA 93103
Web Site: http://www.ontraport.com
Year Founded: 2006
Sales Range: $1-9.9 Million
Emp.: 32
Business Management Software
N.A.I.C.S.: 513210
Landon Ray (Founder & CEO)

ONWARD CAPITAL LLC
525 W Monroe Ste 22109, Chicago, IL 60061
Tel.: (312) 577-8018
Web Site: http://www.onwardcapllc.com
Year Founded: 2015
Privater Equity Firm
N.A.I.C.S.: 523999
Marcus J. George (Partner)
Laura Lester (Partner)

Subsidiaries:

Domaille Engineering, LLC (1)
7100 Dresser Dr NE, Rochester, MN 55906
Tel.: (507) 281-0275
Web Site: http://www.domailleengineering.com
Emp.: 200
Precision Engineering Solutions, Supply Chain Management & Manufacturing Services
N.A.I.C.S.: 332710
Timothy E. Kane (Pres)
Dean A. Krueger (VP-Bus Dev)

Subsidiary (Domestic):

Tech Manufacturing, LLC (2)
45 Cooperative Way, Wright City, MO 63390
Tel.: (636) 745-9477
Web Site: http://www.techmanufacturing.com
Aircraft Equipment Mfr
N.A.I.C.S.: 336413
Jerry Halley (Exec VP & Chief Engr)
Tony Delf (COO & Exec VP)
Charles Stout (Pres)
Frank Kimball (Sr VP-Sls)
Dan Bertschmann (Mgr-QA)

ONYX INFOSOFT
4485 Tench Rd Ste 620, Suwanee, GA 30024
Tel.: (770) 232-7141
Web Site: http://www.onyxinfosoft.com
Year Founded: 2003
Rev.: $2,900,000
Emp.: 35
Telecommunications
N.A.I.C.S.: 517810

Rajeev Maddur (VP)
Sri Raj (Mgr)
Savita Anil (Pres)
Sam Mahalingam (Sec)

ONYX SPECIALTY PAPERS, INC.
40 Willow St, South Lee, MA 01260
Tel.: (413) 243-1231 MA
Web Site: http://www.onyxpapers.com
Year Founded: 2009
Sales Range: $100-124.9 Million
Emp.: 140
Decorative Laminates, Overlays & Other Technical Papers Mfr
N.A.I.C.S.: 322120
Patricia C. Begrowicz (Co-Owner & Pres)
Christopher Mathews (Co-Owner & Exec VP)

OOBE, INC.
511 Rhett St Ste 3, Greenville, SC 29601
Tel.: (864) 220-6623 DE
Web Site: http://www.oobe.com
Year Founded: 1994
Sales Range: $1-9.9 Million
Emp.: 24
Uniforms Mfr
N.A.I.C.S.: 315250
Caroline Bladon (Dir-Programs)

OOMBA, INC.
9840 Irvine Ctr Dr, Irvine, CA 92618
Tel.: (949) 825-6150
Web Site: http://www.oomba.com
Year Founded: 2012
Emp.: 50
Social Media Company & Related Software Sevices
N.A.I.C.S.: 518210
Michael Williams (CEO)

OORAH, INC.
1805 Swarthmore Ave, Lakewood, NJ 08701
Tel.: (732) 730-1000 NJ
Web Site: http://www.oorah.org
Year Founded: 2000
Sales Range: $10-24.9 Million
Emp.: 85
Individual & Family Support Services
N.A.I.C.S.: 624190
Avi Gordon (COO)
R. Yehoshua Weinstein (Dir-Outreach Dev)
Rabbi Eliyohu Mintz (CEO)

OOT BROS. INC.
5912 N Burdick St, East Syracuse, NY 13057
Tel.: (315) 656-7251
Web Site: http://www.oothomes.com
Sales Range: $10-24.9 Million
Emp.: 140
Supplier of Operative Building Materials & Products
N.A.I.C.S.: 236117

OPAA FOOD MANAGEMENT INC.
100 Chesterfield Bus Pkwy Ste 310, Chesterfield, MO 63005
Tel.: (636) 812-0777 MO
Web Site: http://www.opaafood.com
Year Founded: 1978
Sales Range: $10-24.9 Million
Emp.: 1,500
Provider of Food Service Contracts
N.A.I.C.S.: 722310
Kevin Short (Pres)

OPAL ISLAND ACQUISITION CORPORATION

9454 Wilshire Blvd Ste 612, Beverly Hills, CA 90212
Tel.: (310) 888-1870 DE
Year Founded: 2016
Investment Services
N.A.I.C.S.: 523999
James Cassidy (Pres & Sec)
James McKillop (VP)

OPALSTAFF
303 Najoles Rd Ste 104, Millersville, MD 21108
Tel.: (410) 729-1100
Web Site: http://www.opalstaff.com
Sales Range: $1-9.9 Million
Emp.: 10
Human Resource Consulting Services
N.A.I.C.S.: 541612
Trevor Simm (Founder & Pres)
Lisa Neill (Mgr-HR)
John Ross (Engr-Software)
Shawen O'Meara (Controller)

OPECO INC.
601 SE 30th St, Oklahoma City, OK 73129
Tel.: (405) 634-8500 OK
Web Site: http://www.opecoinc.com
Year Founded: 1985
Sales Range: $1-9.9 Million
Oil & Gas Well Machinery & Equipment Whslr
N.A.I.C.S.: 423830
Mark Day (Co-Founder & VP)
Richard Dixon (Co-Founder & Pres)

OPELOUSAS GENERAL HEALTH SYSTEM
539 E Prudhomme St, Opelousas, LA 70570-6449
Tel.: (337) 948-3011
Web Site: http://www.opelousasgeneral.com
Year Founded: 1957
Emp.: 1,000
Healthcare System
N.A.I.C.S.: 923120
Gina Bradley Tuttle (Chm)

OPEN ACCESS TECHNOLOGY INTERNATIONAL, INC.
3660 Technology Dr NE, Minneapolis, MN 55418
Tel.: (763) 201-2000 MN
Web Site: http://www.oati.com
Year Founded: 1995
Sales Range: $50-74.9 Million
Emp.: 280
Custom Computer Programming Services
N.A.I.C.S.: 541511
Jerry Dempsey (VP-Sls & Mktg)
Sasan Mochtari (Pres & CEO)
Farrokh Rahimi (VP-Market Design & Consulting)
Faramarz Maghsoodlou (Dir-Emerging Tech)

OPEN AMERICA INC.
4742 N 24th St Ste 450, Phoenix, AZ 85016
Tel.: (602) 224-0440 AZ
Web Site: http://www.openworksweb.com
Year Founded: 1983
Janitorial Service, Contract Basis
N.A.I.C.S.: 561499
Eric Roudi (Founder & CEO)
David Bosley (Exec VP)
Julie McCollum (CFO)
J. Anthony Hobson (VP-Strategic Bus Ops)
Matthew Hamilton (Div VP-Southern Reg)
Steve Moore (Div VP-Northwest)

COMPANIES — OPEN SYSTEMS, INC.

Pat Tumilty (Div VP-Central Reg)
Katrina Hughes (Div VP-Colorado & Arizona Reg)
Jo Ann Miya (Reg Dir-California)
Cliff D'Amico (Div VP)
Zac Smilack (Sr Reg Dir-Atlanta)
Victoria Murray (Sr Reg Dir-Austin & Dir-Natl Dev-Acting)
Robert Jobe (Reg Dir-Dallas)
Kurt Domine (Reg Dir-San Francisco)
Erik Cokrlic (Reg Dir-San Diego)
Christin Myers (Sr Reg Dir-Seattle & Dir-Strategic Bus-Acting)
Nicholas Mohammadpour (Reg Dir-Miami)
Kylee Hoffman (Mgr-Mktg)
Sherrie Holloway (Mgr-Franchise)
Tobi Waller (Reg Dir-Phoenix)
Zach Earles (Reg Dir-Charlotte)
Steffani Azcona (Reg Dir-New York/New Jersey)
Quina Feldstein (Reg Dir-Denver)
Mike Jahrling (Reg Dir-Chicago)
Charlie Rodriguez (Reg Dir-Tampa)
Ariel Smith (Reg Dir-Washington)
Whitney Jones (Reg Dir-Austin)
Tracey Cartee (Reg Dir-Nashville)

OPEN ARMS CARE CORPORATION
6 Cadillac Dr Ste 350, Brentwood, TN 37027
Tel.: (615) 254-4006   GA
Web Site: http://www.openarmscare.org
Year Founded: 1986
Sales Range: $25-49.9 Million
Emp.: 1,150
Disability Assistance Services
N.A.I.C.S.: 623210
Roberta Anderson (Dir-Quality & Improvement)
Vicki Cox (Exec Dir)
Charles Schnell (Exec Dir)
Stephen Westbrook (CFO)
Freddie Vanderveer (Dir-Facilities)
Sue Cook (Exec Dir)
Lisa King (Exec Dir)

OPEN DENTAL SOFTWARE
3995 Fairview Industrial Dr SE Ste 110, Salem, OR 97302
Tel.: (503) 363-5432
Web Site: http://www.opendental.com
Year Founded: 2005
Sales Range: $1-9.9 Million
Emp.: 60
Dental Software Development Services
N.A.I.C.S.: 541511
Jordan S. Sparks (Pres)
Arna Meyer (Mgr-Ops)
Cameron Buchanan (Engr-Software)

OPEN DOOR FAMILY MEDICAL CENTER, INC.
165 Main St, Ossining, NY 10562
Tel.: (914) 941-1263   NY
Web Site: http://www.opendoormedical.org
Year Founded: 1975
Sales Range: $25-49.9 Million
Emp.: 387
Health Care Srvices
N.A.I.C.S.: 624120
Andres Valdespino (Vice Chm)
David K. Sherman (Treas)
Donna Wade (Chm)
Margoth Pilla (Treas)
Daren Wu (CMO)
Janet Bozzone (Dir-Dentistry)
Maria Mazzotta (CFO)
Lindsay C. Farrell (Pres & CEO)

OPEN HAND
181 Armour Dr NE, Atlanta, GA 30324
Tel.: (404) 872-8089   GA
Web Site: http://www.projectopenhand.org
Year Founded: 1988
Sales Range: $10-24.9 Million
Emp.: 165
Health Care Srvices
N.A.I.C.S.: 622110
Susan Anderson (COO)
Matt Pieper (Exec Dir)
Kent R. Lindner (Pres)
Suzanne Dansby (Sec)
Todd A. Tautfest (Treas)
Alyce Toonk (VP)

OPEN KITCHENS INC.
1161 W 21st St, Chicago, IL 60608
Tel.: (312) 666-5335
Web Site: http://www.openkitchens.com
Year Founded: 1969
Sales Range: $10-24.9 Million
Emp.: 125
Provider of Catering Services
N.A.I.C.S.: 722320
Terese Fiore (Pres)
Ricardo Fiore (VP-Fin)

OPEN LOOP ENERGY, INC.
1878 N Safford Bryce Rd, Safford, AZ 85546
Tel.: (928) 348-9200
Web Site: http://www.openloop.net
Year Founded: 1992
Sales Range: $10-24.9 Million
Emp.: 75
Machine Shop Operator
N.A.I.C.S.: 332710
Charles A. Hoisington (Pres)
Chase Fite (Gen Mgr)

OPEN MORTGAGE, LLC
14101 W Hwy 290 #1300, Austin, TX 78737
Tel.: (888) 602-6626
Web Site: http://www.openmortgage.com
Year Founded: 2003
Rev.: $1,393,000
Emp.: 375
Real Estate Credit
N.A.I.C.S.: 522292
Scott Gordon (Founder & CEO)
Lucas Allen (Sr VP-Ops)
Adam O'Daniel (Sr VP-Mktg)
Scott Harkless (Chief Revenue Officer)
Joe Stephenson (Pres)
Brenda Hedeen (CFO)
Anthony Nolte (Chief Legal Officer)

OPEN PANTRY FOOD MARTS OF WISCONSIN INC.
10505 Corp Dr Ste 101, Pleasant Prairie, WI 53158-1605
Tel.: (262) 857-1156   WI
Web Site: http://www.openpantry.com
Year Founded: 1966
Sales Range: $50-74.9 Million
Emp.: 49
Gasoline Service Stations
N.A.I.C.S.: 457120
Robert A. Buhler (Pres & CEO)

OPEN ROAD AUTO GROUP
731 US Hwy 1, Edison, NJ 08817-4550
Tel.: (732) 985-1057
Web Site: http://www.openroad.com
Sales Range: $250-299.9 Million
Emp.: 1,300
Holding Company; New & Used Car Dealerships Owner & Operator
N.A.I.C.S.: 551112
Robert Forcini (Sr VP)
Rod Ryan (Founder & CEO)
Michael Morais (Pres)
Martin Gross (CFO)
Andrew Paul (VP)
Lisa G. Cesaro (Dir-HR)
Kathryn Reynolds (VP-Acctg & Controller)
Fran Anolik (Controller)
Susan Piltz (Controller)
Jennifer Redfern (Controller)
Joseph Billotti (VP)
Rob Singh (VP)

Subsidiaries:

Open Road BMW, Inc.   (1)
540 US Hwy 1, Edison, NJ 08817
Tel.: (732) 339-9700
Web Site: http://www.bmwedison.com
Sales Range: $10-24.9 Million
Emp.: 40
New & Used Car Dealer
N.A.I.C.S.: 441110
Robert Forcini (Sr VP)

Open Road of Bridgewater, LLC   (1)
1250 Rte 22 E, Bridgewater, NJ 08807
Tel.: (908) 685-0800
Web Site: http://www.openroadmercedesbenz.com
Sales Range: $10-24.9 Million
Emp.: 50
New & Used Car Dealer
N.A.I.C.S.: 441110
Mike Tedesco (Gen Mgr)

OPEN SKY MEDIA INC.
1250 S Capital of Texas Hwy Bldg 3 Ste #395, Austin, TX 78746
Tel.: (512) 263-9133   DE
Web Site: http://www.austinmonthly.com
Emp.: 25
Magazine Publisher
N.A.I.C.S.: 513120
Todd P. Paul (CEO)
Stewart Ramser (Publisher)
Jason Heid (Editor-in-Chief)
Julie A. Kunkle (Assoc Publisher)
Ashley Burch (Dir-Design)
Sarah Thurmond (Exec Editor)
Gene Menez (Editor-Austin Home)
Hector Sanchez (Dir-Art)
Shaina Golay (Dir-Art)
Cory Rivademar (Dir-Photo)
Darcie Duttweiler (Mgr-Digital Media)
Misty Pennock (Sls Mgr-Digital)
Michael Krainz (Controller)
Cindy Kim (Mgr-Acctg)
Chrissy Dickerson (Coord-Event)

Subsidiaries:

Gulfshore Business   (1)
3560 Kraft Rd Ste 301, Naples, FL 34105
Tel.: (239) 594-9980
Web Site: http://www.gulfshorebusiness.com
Sales Range: $10-24.9 Million
Magazine Publisher
N.A.I.C.S.: 513120
Phil Borchmann (Editor)
Tessa Tilden-Smith (Dir-Creative)
Jesse Adams (Dir-Art)
Debbie Coolman (Acct Exec)
Jaimie Duthoy (Dir-Mktg & Events)
Martha Leavitt (Mgr-Production)
Kerri Nolan (Dir-Circulation)

Gulfshore Life   (1)
1421 Pine Ridge Rd Ste 100, Naples, FL 34109
Tel.: (239) 449-4111
Web Site: http://www.gulfshorelife.com
Sales Range: $10-24.9 Million
Magazine Publisher
N.A.I.C.S.: 513120
Diane Loveless (Assoc Publr)
Kerri Nolan (Dir-Audience Dev)
Tessa Tilden-Smith (Dir-Creative)
David Sandler (Editor-in-Chief)
Elizabeth Goodman (Mgr-Acct-Natl)
Heather Bartolotta (Dir-IT)
Jesse Adams (Assoc Dir-Art)
Beth Armstrong (Assoc Dir-Art)
Jaimie Duthoy (Dir-Mktg)
Marcia Jaquith (Mgr-Acctg)
Matthew Kritis (Assoc Dir-Art)
Martha Leavitt (Mgr-Production)
Diane Lebreck (Publr)
Valerie Roop (Mgr-Production Svcs)
Mindy Roosa (Acct Exec)
Wendy Tooley (Dir-Sls-Lee County)

OPEN SYSTEMS INTERNATIONAL, INC.
4101 Arrowhead Dr, Medina, MN 55340
Tel.: (763) 551-0559
Web Site: http://www.osii.com
Rev.: $10,694,194
Emp.: 1,000
Computer Software Development
N.A.I.C.S.: 541511
Bahman Hoveida (Pres & CEO)
Ingram Ron (VP)
John Becker (Engr-Software)
Ryan Tetzlaff (Mgr-IT)
Kyle Goerz (Engr-Sls)
Mike Wenzel (Mgr)
Randy Berry (VP-Utilities)

OPEN SYSTEMS OF CLEVELAND, INC.
22999 Forbes Rd Ste A, Cleveland, OH 44146
Tel.: (440) 439-2332
Web Site: http://www.osinc.com
Year Founded: 1998
Sales Range: $10-24.9 Million
Emp.: 12
Distr of Computer Hardware; Designer & Servicer of Computer Networks
N.A.I.C.S.: 423430
Matt Oddis (Pres)
Kevin Kistner (Acct Mgr)
Diane Kearney (Acct Mgr)

OPEN SYSTEMS TECHNOLOGIES, INC.
605 Seward NW Ste 101, Grand Rapids, MI 49504
Tel.: (616) 574-3500
Web Site: http://www.ostusa.com
Year Founded: 1997
Sales Range: $50-74.9 Million
Emp.: 112
IT Services
N.A.I.C.S.: 541512
Meredith Bronk (Pres)
Kathryn Felver (Mgr-Risk & Compliance)
David Gerrity (Exec Dir-ERP)
James VanderMey (Chief Innovation Officer)
Chris van Nieuwenhuyze (Mgr-Blade & Server Practice)
Scott Dare (Mgr-BMC Practice)
W. Scott Montgomery (Mgr-Security Practice)
Mike TenHarmsel (Mgr-CBS Practice)
John Vancil (Dir-Pro Svcs)
Brian Anderson (Mgr-Application Dev & Bus Dev)
Bill Herington (Dir-Fin Ops)
Michael Lomonaco (Dir-Mktg & Comm)
Dawn Simpson (Mgr-Bus Dev)
Beth VanSlyke (Mgr-Recruiting Solutions Practice)
John Thayer (VP-Sls & Strategic Bus Dev)
Bryan Bentz (Engr-Windows Server)

OPEN SYSTEMS, INC.
4301 Dean Lakes Blvd, Shakopee, MN 55379
Tel.: (952) 403-5700   MN
Web Site: http://www.osas.com

OPEN SYSTEMS, INC.

Open Systems, Inc.—(Continued)
Year Founded: 1976
Business Management Software Publisher
N.A.I.C.S.: 513210
Bernd-Michael Rumpf (Chm)
Geoff Haydon (CEO)
May Mitchell (CMO)

Subsidiaries:

Blaschko Computers, Inc. (1)
3290 33rd St S, Saint Cloud, MN 56301
Tel.: (320) 252-0234
Web Site: http://www.processpromfg.com
Sales Range: $1-9.9 Million
Process Manufacturing Software Publisher
N.A.I.C.S.: 513210
Joseph J. Blauert (CEO)
Molly E. Caron (VP-Ops)
Charles N. Rice (VP-Product Dev)
Jeff C. Hauser (Dir-Pro Svcs)
Daniel Erickson (Dir-Product Strategy)
Kate M. Orbeck (Mktg Mgr)

Southware Innovations, Inc. (1)
1922 Professional Cir, Auburn, AL 36830 (100%)
Tel.: (334) 821-1108
Web Site: http://www.southware.com
Sales Range: $1-9.9 Million
Emp.: 50
Developer of Business Management & Accounting Software for Front-Office & Back-Office Operations
N.A.I.C.S.: 513210
James F. Clemens (Pres)
Bonnie Streeter (Mgr-Support)
Tim Sanders (Exec VP)
Tony Jones (Coord-Dev)

OPENAI, INC.
3180 18th St, San Francisco, CA 94110
Tel.: (415) 516-4158 DE
Web Site: https://openai.com
Year Founded: 2015
Holding Company; Artificial Intelligence Research & Deployment Services
N.A.I.C.S.: 551112
Samuel H. Altman (CEO)
Greg Brockman (Founder, Chm & Pres)
Ilya Sutskever (Chief Scientist)

Subsidiaries:

OpenAI, L.L.C. (1)
3180 18th St, San Francisco, CA 94110
Tel.: (415) 516-4158
Web Site: https://openai.com
Artificial Intelligence Research & Deployment Services
N.A.I.C.S.: 541511
Samuel H. Altman (CEO)
Greg Brockman (Co-Founder)
Ilya Sutskever (Chief Scientist)

OPENCAPE CORPORATION
3195 Main St, Barnstable, MA 02630
Tel.: (508) 362-2224 MA
Web Site: http://www.opencape.com
Year Founded: 2007
Rev: $1,259,071
Assets: $32,776,305
Liabilities: $107,107
Net Worth: $32,669,198
Earnings: ($2,572,992)
Emp.: 4
Fiscal Year-end: 12/31/14
Engineering Support Services
N.A.I.C.S.: 541330
Art Gaylord (Chm)
John Campbell (Vice Chm)
Sean O'Brien (Treas)

OPENDEAL INC.
335 Madison Ave, New York, NY 10010
Tel.: (212) 401-6930
Web Site: https://republic.com

Financial Services
N.A.I.C.S.: 523999

OPENFIBER KENTUCKY CO. LLC
1700 Eastpoint Pkwy Ste 230, Louisville, KY 40223
Tel.: (888) 349-9933
Web Site: https://accelecom.net
Emp.: 100
Telecommunications
N.A.I.C.S.: 517810
David Flessas (CEO)

Subsidiaries:

Georgia Public Web (1)
1470 Riveredge Pkwy, Atlanta, GA 30328-4640
Tel.: (770) 563-0013
Web Site: http://www.gapublicweb.net
Data Processing, Hosting & Related Services
N.A.I.C.S.: 518210
David Muschamp (Owner)

OPENGATE CAPITAL MANAGEMENT, LLC
10250 Constellation Blvd 30th Fl, Los Angeles, CA 90067
Tel.: (310) 432-7000 DE
Web Site: http://www.opengatecapital.com
Year Founded: 2005
Privater Equity Firm
N.A.I.C.S.: 523999
Andrew Nikou (Founder & CEO)
Julien Lagreze (Partner-France)
Matthias Gundlach (Mng Dir)
Marc Veillas (Mng Dir-France)
Alanna Chaffin (Head-Comm & IR)
Joshua Adams (Mng Dir)
Fabien Marcantetti (Mng Dir-France)
Rob Young (Principal)
Shawn Haghighi (Chief Compliance Officer & Gen Counsel)
Paul Bridwell (Mng Dir & COO)
Heather Malloy (CFO)

Subsidiaries:

Duraco Specialty Tapes LLC (1)
7400 W Industrial Dr, Forest Park, IL 60130-2514
Tel.: (708) 488-1025
Web Site: http://www.essentraspecialtytapes.com
Adhesive Tapes Mfr & Distr
N.A.I.C.S.: 339999
Edward Byczynski (CEO)

Subsidiary (Non-US):

Moss Plastic Products Trading (Ningbo) Co., Ltd. (2)
99 Huanghai Road, Beilun Dist, Ningbo, 315800, Zhejiang, China
Tel.: (86) 57426863666
Web Site: http://www.mossplastics.cn
Sales Range: $25-49.9 Million
Emp.: 21
Adhesive Tape Distr
N.A.I.C.S.: 424690
Lola Chen (Mgr-Customer Svc)

Subsidiary (Domestic):

Rayven, Inc. (2)
431 Griggs St N, Saint Paul, MN 55104
Tel.: (651) 642-1112
Web Site: http://www.rayven.com
Unsupported Plastics Film & Sheet (except Packaging) Mfr
N.A.I.C.S.: 326113
Rick Mercado (VP-Sls)
Joe Rubbelke (Mgr-Acct Sls-Midwest)
Joe Heinemann (Pres)

Strata-Tac, Inc. (2)
3980 Swenson Ave, Saint Charles, IL 60174
Tel.: (630) 879-9388
Web Site: http://www.stratatac.cc
Rev: $1,600,000
Emp.: 17

Offices of Other Holding Companies
N.A.I.C.S.: 551112
Chuck Casagrande (Owner)

Fichet Security Solutions (1)
7 rue Paul Dautier, 78141, Velizy-Villacoublay, Cedex, France
Tel.: (33) 1 34 64 65 34
Web Site: http://www.fichetgroup.com
Bank Security & Cash Handling Services
N.A.I.C.S.: 561621
Veronique Goriatcheff (Mgr-Export)

Subsidiary (Non-US):

Fichet Security Solutions Belgium SA/NV (2)
WA Mozartlaan 6, 1070, Drogenbos, Belgium
Tel.: (32) 24641911
Web Site: https://www.fichetgroup.com
Bank Security & Cash Handling Services
N.A.I.C.S.: 561621

Subsidiary (Domestic):

Fichet Security Solutions France SAS (2)
15/17 Avenue Morane Saulnier, BP 11, 78141, Velizy-Villacoublay, France
Tel.: (33) 810000800
Web Site: https://www.fichetgroup.com
Bank Security & Cash Handling Services
N.A.I.C.S.: 561621
Beni Sri (Mgr-Mktg & Comm)

Fusion Paperboard US, Inc. (1)
2255 Global Way, Hebron, KY 41048
Tel.: (859) 586-1100
Web Site: http://www.fusionpaperboard.com
Sales Range: $100-124.9 Million
Emp.: 300
Paperboard Conversion
N.A.I.C.S.: 322219
Ghislain Levesque (COO)
Joshua Duhaime (CFO)
Sheila Greco (Dir-HR)

Plant (Domestic):

Fusion Paperboard - Paper Mill (2)
130 Inland Rd, Versailles, CT 06383
Tel.: (860) 823-3600
Web Site: http://www.fusionpaperboard.com
Paperboard Mills
N.A.I.C.S.: 322130

Getronics Columbia Ltda (1)
Calle 100 No 8A-55 WTC Torre C Of 414, Bogota, Colombia
Tel.: (57) 1 638 1800
Web Site: http://www.getronics-latam.com
Telecommunication Servicesb
N.A.I.C.S.: 517810

Hamilton Scientific LLC (1)
1716 Lawrence Dr Ste 1, De Pere, WI 54115
Tel.: (920) 793-1121
Web Site: http://www.hamiltonscientific.com
Sales Range: $150-199.9 Million
Emp.: 1,800
Laboratory Furniture & Fume Hoods Mfr
N.A.I.C.S.: 337127

Subsidiary (Domestic):

Epoxyn Products LLC (2)
500 E 16th St, Mountain Home, AR 72653-5522
Tel.: (870) 425-4321
Web Site: http://www.epoxyn.com
Sales Range: $25-49.9 Million
Laboratory Work Surface Products
N.A.I.C.S.: 337127
Peter Greco (Gen Mgr)

Hufcor Incorporated (1)
2101 Kennedy Rd, Janesville, WI 53545-0824
Tel.: (608) 756-1241
Web Site: http://www.hufcor.com
Folding Door & Partition Systems Mfr
N.A.I.C.S.: 337126
Frank Scott (CFO)
Kevin Flanagan (Pres & CEO)

InRule Technology Inc. (1)
651 W Washington Blvd, Chicago, IL 60661
Tel.: (312) 648-1800
Web Site: http://www.inrule.com

U.S. PRIVATE

Software Publisher
N.A.I.C.S.: 513210
Rik Chomko (Co-Founder & CEO)
Loren Goodman (Co-Founder & CTO)
Mark Lonsway (Sr VP-Integrations)
Michael Bonner (Chief Revenue Officer)
Beth Worthem (CFO)
Matt Cowell (Chief Product Officer)
Stephen Graff (VP-Pro Svcs)

Jotul AS (1)
Langoyveien, PO Box 1411, Fredrikstad, 1602, Norway (93%)
Tel.: (47) 69359000
Web Site: http://www.jotul.com
Fireplace & Stove Mfr
N.A.I.C.S.: 333414
Mette Olafsen (Mgr-Brand & Product)

Subsidiary (Non-US):

Jotul France S.A. (2)
3 chemin du Jubin, 69570, Dardilly, France
Tel.: (33) 4 72 52 22 40
Web Site: http://www.jotul.fr
Stove & Fireplace Distr
N.A.I.C.S.: 423720

Jotul Hispania, S.L. (2)
Poligono Industrial Ruisenores II Nave 9, 50011, Zaragoza, Spain
Tel.: (34) 976 786716
Web Site: http://www.jotul.com
Cast Iron Stove Mfr & Distr
N.A.I.C.S.: 333414

Jotul Italia Srl (2)
Via Concordia 5/C5, Sesto San Giovanni, Milan, Italy
Tel.: (39) 0292882050
Web Site: http://www.jotul.com
Cast Iron Stove Mfr & Distr
N.A.I.C.S.: 333414

Jotul Lithuania (2)
Dale Misiuniene ul Statybininku 5, Bernatoniai, 38300, Panevezys, Lithuania
Tel.: (370) 613 277 39
Cast Iron & Wood Stove Distr
N.A.I.C.S.: 423720

Subsidiary (US):

Jotul North America Inc. (2)
55 Hutcherson Dr, Gorham, ME 04038
Tel.: (207) 591-6601
Web Site: http://www.jotul.us
Gas Hearth Products; Wood & Gas Stoves Mfr
N.A.I.C.S.: 333414

Subsidiary (Non-US):

Jotul Polska Sp. z o.o. (2)
ul Building 65, Gdansk, 80298, Poland
Tel.: (48) 58 7620810
Web Site: http://www.jotul.com
Cast Iron Stove Mfr & Distr
N.A.I.C.S.: 333414

KEM ONE S.A.S. (1)
210 avenue Jean Jaures, 69007, Lyon, France
Tel.: (33) 4 69 67 72 00
Web Site: http://www.kemone.com
Sales Range: $1-4.9 Billion
Emp.: 1,200
Chlorochemicals & Vinyl Products Mfr
N.A.I.C.S.: 325211
Frederic Chalmin (Dir Gen)
Alain de Krassny (Pres)
Pierre Fauvarque (Dir-Pur & Supply Chain)
Patrick Morel (Dir-R&D)

Subsidiary (Non-US):

Akishima Chemical Industries Co., Ltd (2)
88-6 Shingo, Higashimatsuyama, Saitama, 355-0071, Japan
Tel.: (81) 493 24 2255
Sales Range: $10-24.9 Million
Chemical Products Distr
N.A.I.C.S.: 424690

Alphacan B.V. (2)
Taylorweg 4, 5466 AE, Veghel, Netherlands
Tel.: (31) 413 380 800
Web Site: http://www.alphacan.nl
Plastic Tube & Profile Mfr
N.A.I.C.S.: 326122

COMPANIES

Michiel Kemperman (Mgr-HSEQ)

Alphacan Omniplast GmbH (2)
Am Bahnhof, 35630, Ehringshausen, Germany
Tel.: (49) 644 390 0
Web Site: http://www.omniplast.de
Plastic Tank Mfr
N.A.I.C.S.: 326122
Werner Boysen (Mng Dir)

Alphacan S.p.A. (2)
Via Santa Caterina 60/C, 38062, Arco, Trentino, Italy
Tel.: (39) 0464 587 500
Web Site: http://www.alphacan.it
Plastic Tube & Profile Mfr
N.A.I.C.S.: 326122
Borut Sirca (Mgr-Export)

Alphacan d.o.o. (2)
Zagrebacka 93, 10291, Prigorje Brdovecko, Croatia
Tel.: (385) 13340666
Web Site: http://www.alphacan.hr
Sales Range: $25-49.9 Million
Emp.: 1,000
Plastic Tube & Profile Mfr
N.A.I.C.S.: 326122
Josip Klasic (Gen Mgr)

Plasgom S.A.U. (2)
Mar Carib 5 Pol Ind La Torre del Rector, 08130, Santa Perpetua de Mogoda, Barcelona, Spain
Tel.: (34) 935742467
Web Site: http://www.plasgom.com
Sales Range: $25-49.9 Million
Emp.: 3
Chemical Products Mfr
N.A.I.C.S.: 325199
Jose Ramon Fernandez (Gen Mgr)
Anna Coll (Mgr-HR)

RESILIA S.r.l. (2)
Via Milano 201, 21017, Samarate, Italy
Tel.: (39) 0331 226 111
Web Site: http://www.resilia.it
PVC Compound Mfr
N.A.I.C.S.: 325991
Andrea Zanichelli (VP-R&D)

RESITECH Germany GmbH (2)
Am Farberwerder 11, D 04838, Eilenburg, Germany
Tel.: (49) 3423 60 24 23
Plastic Mfr
N.A.I.C.S.: 326199
Dirk Pfefferkorn (Mgr-R&D)

Subsidiary (Domestic):

Resinoplast S.A. (2)
Chemin de Saint-Leonard, 51863, Reims, France
Tel.: (33) 3 26 85 75 00
Vinyl Compound Mfr
N.A.I.C.S.: 325991
Jeremy Dauchin (Product Mgr)

Mersive Technologies, Inc. (1)
2399 Blake St Ste 100, Denver, CO 80205
Tel.: (303) 291-3775
Web Site: http://www.mersive.com
Software Publishing Services
N.A.I.C.S.: 541511
Stephen Webb (Co-Founder & Chief Scientist)
Christopher Jaynes (Co-Founder)
Rob Balgley (CEO)
Jeff Meyer (Gen Mgr-Europe, The Middle East, & Africa)
Rosario Marseglia (Sls Mgr-Germany, Austria & Switzerland)
Cyril Mattar (Reg Sls Mgr)
Ramy Alam (Engr-Sls-Middle East & Africa)
Johan Cederberg (Sls Mgr-Nordics, Baltics & Netherlands)
Monika Lozano Cruz (Engr-Sls-Nordics, Baltics & Netherlands)

Player One Amusement Group Inc. (1)
6420 Viscount Road, Mississauga, L4V 1H3, ON, Canada
Tel.: (416) 251-2122
Web Site: https://www.winwithp1ag.com
Emp.: 550
Entertainment Providers
N.A.I.C.S.: 711410

Profialis N.V. (1)
Brugstraat 27, 8720, Oeselgem, West Flanders, Belgium
Tel.: (32) 9 388 95 71
Web Site: http://www.profialis.com
Sales Range: $75-99.9 Million
PVC Extrusion Mfr Including Windows, Doors & Patio Systems
N.A.I.C.S.: 326199
Jurgen Wybo (Dir-Fin)
Axel De Potter (Mgr-Supply Chain)
Tamara van der Schueren (Mgr-Logistics)
Marcel De Rouck (Dir-Sls-Benelux-Export)

Subsidiary (Non-US):

Profex S.A.S. (2)
Rue de Vimy ZI Les Quatorze, 62210, Avion, Pas-de-Calais, France
Tel.: (33) 321085720
PVC Windows Distr
N.A.I.C.S.: 424610

Profialis Clerval S.A.S. (2)
2 Route de Santoche, 25340, Clerval, France
Tel.: (33) 381991818
Web Site: http://www.profialis.com
Sales Range: $50-74.9 Million
PVC Pipes & Windows Mfr & Distr
N.A.I.C.S.: 326199
Camille Langenaken (Mng Dir)

Profialis Polska Sp.z.o.o. (2)
Gnieznienska 47, Wagrowiec, 6200, Poland
Tel.: (48) 672626246
Web Site: http://www.wymar.pl
Distr of PVC Building Products Including Windows, Doors, Patios & Sliding Door Systems
N.A.I.C.S.: 424610

SMAC SA (2)
143 Avenue de Verdun, CS 20170, 92442, Issy-Les-Moulineaux, France
Tel.: (33) 1 55 95 48 00
Web Site: http://www.smac-sa.com
Construction; Asphalt Products Mfr
N.A.I.C.S.: 324121

Subsidiary (Domestic):

Societe de la Raffinerie de Dunkerque (2)
Route de l'Ouvrage Ouest, BP 4519, Dunkirk, 59381, France
Tel.: (33) 3 28 29 50 00
Oil Refining Services
N.A.I.C.S.: 324110

Sargent & Greenleaf, Inc. (1)
1 Security Dr, Nicholasville, KY 40356-2159
Tel.: (859) 885-9411
Web Site: http://www.sargentandgreenleaf.com
Sales Range: $50-74.9 Million
Emp.: 130
Mechanical & Electronic Locks Mfr
N.A.I.C.S.: 332510
Steven Samaan (VP-Global Supply Chain & Logistics)
Mark LeMire (CEO)

Subsidiary (Non-US):

Sargent & Greenleaf S.A. (2)
9 Ch du Croset, 1024, Ecublens, Switzerland
Tel.: (41) 216943400
Sales Range: $25-49.9 Million
Emp.: 7
Security System Services
N.A.I.C.S.: 561621

TV Guide Magazine Group, Inc. (1)
11 W 42nd St, New York, NY 10036
Tel.: (212) 852-7500
Web Site: http://www.tvguide.com
Online & Print Entertainment Periodical Publisher
N.A.I.C.S.: 513120
Aaron Shapiro (Head-West Coast Digital Sls)
Doug Brod (Editor-in-Chief)
Joseph Clemente (CFO)
Nerina Rammairone (Dir-Editorial)
Rich Sands (Sr Exec Editor)
Adam Goldband (VP-Tech)
Sasha Zullo (VP-Bus Dev)

OPENMAIL LLC
1501 Main St, Venice, CA 90291
Tel.: (310) 256-4882
Web Site: http://www.openmail.com
Marketing Software Developer & Services
N.A.I.C.S.: 541511
Chuck Ursini (Co-Founder & CEO)
John Fries (Co-Founder & CTO)
Michael Blend (Co-Founder)
Sanjeev Rao (Chief Product Officer)
Nathan Janos (Chief Data Officer)
Antonio Magnaghi (Exec VP-Engrg)
Brian Coppola (VP-Product)

Subsidiaries:

Infospace Holdings LLC (1)
1501 Main St Ste 201, Venice, CA 90291
Tel.: (310) 256-4882
Web Site: http://www.infospace.com
Holding Company; Custom Search & Monetization Programming Solutions
N.A.I.C.S.: 551112

OPENSYMMETRY, INC.
9225 Bee Caves Rd Bldg A Ste 100, Austin, TX 78733
Web Site: http://www.OpenSymmetry.com
Year Founded: 2004
Sales Range: $10-24.9 Million
Emp.: 43
Sales Performance Management Consulting Services
N.A.I.C.S.: 541618
Anthony Hutchins (Sr VP-Professional Svcs)
Jon Gingell (Sr VP-Tech)
Lindsey Derynck (Gen Counsel)

Subsidiaries:

OpenSymmetry-Australia (1)
40 Mount Street Level 17, Sydney, 2060, NSW, Australia (100%)
Tel.: (61) 2 8415 9764
Web Site: http://www.opensymmetry.com
Sales Performance Management Consulting
N.A.I.C.S.: 541618
Anthony Hutchins (Mng Dir)

OpenSymmetry-Canada (1)
87 Strathaven Pvt, K1J 1K7, Ottawa, ON, Canada (100%)
Tel.: (613) 482-2556
Web Site: http://www.opensymmetry.com
Sales Performance Management Consulting
N.A.I.C.S.: 541618

OpenSymmetry-Malaysia (1)
No 1-3 Jalan Solaris 2 Solaris Mont Kiara, 50480, Kuala Lumpur, Malaysia (100%)
Tel.: (60) 3 6209 9710
Web Site: http://www.opensymmetry.com
Sales Performance Management Consulting
N.A.I.C.S.: 541618

OpenSymmetry-South Africa (1)
Ground & First Floor Palazzo Towers West Montecasino William Nicol Dr, Fourways, Johannesburg, South Africa (100%)
Tel.: (27) 11 024 6736
Web Site: http://www.opensymmetry.com
Sales Performance Management Consulting Services
N.A.I.C.S.: 541618
Mark Kemp (Mng Dir)
Andy Bass (VP-EMEA)

OpenSymmetry-UK (1)
Bridge House Station Approach Great Missenden, Great Missenden, HP16 9AZ, Buckinghamshire, United Kingdom (100%)
Tel.: (44) 800 756 6736
Web Site: http://www.opensymmetry.com
Sales Performance Management Consulting Services
N.A.I.C.S.: 541613
Chad Hewson (Mng Dir)

OPENTECH ALLIANCE, INC.
2501 W Dunlap Ave Ste 255, Phoenix, AZ 85021
Tel.: (602) 749-9370

Web Site: http://www.opentechalliance.com
Year Founded: 2003
Technology Systems for Self-Service Storage Industry
N.A.I.C.S.: 541519
Robert Chiti (Pres & CEO)
Mike Connolly (Exec VP-Corp Dev)
Davin K. Dameron (CTO)
Dan Scaman (VP-Strategic Plng & Analysis)
Suzi Ocello (Dir-Ops)
Michael Sawyer (Dir-Mktg)
Mark Stephens (Mgr-Call Center)
Megan Smith (Controller)

Subsidiaries:

Storage Treasures LLC (1)
6991 E Camelback Rd Ste C302, Scottsdale, AZ 85251
Tel.: (480) 397-6503
Web Site: http://www.storagetreasures.com
Software Publisher
N.A.I.C.S.: 513210
Lance Watkins (CEO)

OPENWORKS
4742 N 24th St Ste 450, Phoenix, AZ 85016
Tel.: (602) 224-0440
Web Site: http://www.openworksweb.com
Year Founded: 1983
Sales Range: $10-24.9 Million
Emp.: 80
Commercial Cleaning Services
N.A.I.C.S.: 561720
Eric Roudi (Founder & CEO)
David Bosley (Exec VP)
Steve Moore (VP-Northwest Div)
Julie McCollum (CFO)
J. Anthony Hobson (VP-Corp Ops)
Jodi Slotnick (Dir-HR)
Spencer Stevens (Dir-Arizona)
Matthew Hamilton (Dir-Texas)
Jo Ann Miya (Dir-California Reg)
Pat Tumilty (VP-Central Reg Div)
Nate Wilkens (Dir-Northern California Reg)
Katrina Hughes (VP-Colorado & Arizona Reg Div)
Dave Hicks (Dir-Facility Solutions)
Cliff D'Amico (Dir-Tampa Bay)
Koby O'Hara (Dir-Houston)
Claire Limon (Head-Recruitment & Dev)
Mike Morrow (Dir-Wealth & Platform)
Carrie Morris (Chief People Officer)
Liz Caracciolo (COO)
Ryan Waldron (Sr VP-Growth)
Corine Probert (VP-Sls)

OPERA SOLUTIONS, LLC
180 Maiden Ln 17th Fl, New York, NY 10038
Tel.: (646) 437-2100
Web Site: http://www.operasolutions.com
Year Founded: 2004
Sales Range: $50-74.9 Million
Emp.: 414
Data Analysis Solutions
N.A.I.C.S.: 541690
Arnab Gupta (Chm & CEO)
Farhan Baaqri (CTO)
Sridhar Ramasubbu (CFO)
Tali Rabin (Chief HR Officer)
Laks Srinivasan (Co-COO)
Yuansong Liao (Co-COO)
Bhavi Mehta (Exec VP-Advanced Solutions)
Shishir Kapoor (Gen Mgr-New Delhi)
Esmond Jeng (Gen Mgr-Shanghai)

OPERATION COMPASSION
114 Stuart Rd NE Ste 370, Cleveland, TN 37312

OPERATION COMPASSION

Operation Compassion—(Continued)
Tel.: (423) 728-3932 TN
Web Site:
http://www.operationcompassion.org
Year Founded: 1997
Sales Range: $100-124.9 Million
Emp.: 18
Christian Ministry Services
N.A.I.C.S.: 813110
David Lorency (Pres)
Dennis Watkins (Sec-Corp)
Donnie W. Smith (Chm & CEO)
Kelvin Page (Chm & CEO)

OPERATION PAR, INC.
6655 66th St N, Pinellas Park, FL 33781
Tel.: (727) 545-7564 FL
Web Site:
http://www.operationpar.org
Year Founded: 1970
Rev.: $32,587,192
Assets: $28,816,178
Liabilities: $3,445
Net Worth: $28,812,733
Emp.: 651
Fiscal Year-end: 06/30/18
Community Support Services
N.A.I.C.S.: 624190
Dianne Clarke (COO & Exec Dir)

OPERATION THRESHOLD
1535 Lafayette, Waterloo, IA 50704
Tel.: (319) 291-2065 IA
Web Site:
http://www.operationthreshold.org
Year Founded: 1965
Sales Range: $10-24.9 Million
Emp.: 95
Community Care Services
N.A.I.C.S.: 624190
Craig Boche (Dir-HR)
Barbara Grant (Exec Dir)
Clarissa Nicholson (Dir-Plng & Compliance)
Billie Allen-Williams (Dir-Community Resources)
Marla Betts (Accountant)

OPERATIONAL TECHNOLOGIES CORPORATION
4100 NW Loop 410 Ste 230, San Antonio, TX 78229-4253
Tel.: (210) 731-0000
Web Site: http://www.otcorp.com
Year Founded: 1986
Sales Range: $10-24.9 Million
Emp.: 60
Scientific & Technical Solutions
N.A.I.C.S.: 541990
Wayne Shore (Founder)

Subsidiaries:

Operational Technologies Corporation-Midwest Regional Office (1)
1370 N Fairfield Rd A, Dayton, OH 45432
Tel.: (937) 429-0022
Web Site: http://www.otcorp.com
Sales Range: $10-24.9 Million
Emp.: 11
Scientific & Technical Solutions
N.A.I.C.S.: 541990

OPERIO GROUP, LLC
6601 Will Rogers Blvd, Fort Worth, TX 76140
Tel.: (682) 312-0034
Web Site:
https://www.operiogroup.com
Emp.: 100
Holding Company
N.A.I.C.S.: 335220
Alastair Sanderson (CEO)
Deb Blackwell (Chief Revenue Officer)

Subsidiaries:

Compression Components & Service, LLC (1)
364 Vly Rd Unit 100, Warrington, PA 18976-2521
Tel.: (267) 387-2000
Web Site: http://www.ccstabletpress.com
Industrial Machinery Mfr
N.A.I.C.S.: 333248
Fran Mallee (Pres)

Elizabeth Carbide Die Co. Inc. (1)
601 Linden St, McKeesport, PA 15132
Tel.: (412) 751-3000
Web Site: https://www.eliz.com
Sales Range: $10-24.9 Million
Emp.: 127
Die Sets For Metal Stamping (Presses)
N.A.I.C.S.: 333514
Richard Pagliari (Chm & CEO)
Tony Doherty (CFO)
Kenneth Spiegel (Pres & COO)

Subsidiary (Domestic):

Elizabeth-Hata International (2)
14559 Route 30, North Huntingdon, PA 15642
Tel.: (412) 829-7700
Web Site: http://www.eliz.com
Rev.: $3,444,000
Emp.: 28
All Other Miscellaneous Fabricated Metal Product Mfr
N.A.I.C.S.: 332999
David A. Keefer (Pres)
Richard A. Pagliari (Chm & CEO)

LFA Machines Oxford Ltd. (1)
Unit 4b Rowood Estate Murdock Road, Bicester, OX26 4PP, Oxon, United Kingdom
Tel.: (44) 01869 250234
Web Site: https://www.lfamachines.com
Pharmaceutical Machine Mfr
N.A.I.C.S.: 333310

Subsidiary (US):

LFA Machines DFW, LLC (2)
6601 Will Rogers Blvd, Fort Worth, TX 76140
Tel.: (682) 312-0034
Web Site: https://www.lfamachines.com
Pharmaceutical Machine Mfr
N.A.I.C.S.: 333310

Subsidiary (Domestic):

Vivion Inc. (3)
929 Bransten Rd, San Carlos, CA 94070
Tel.: (650) 595-3600
Web Site: http://www.vivioninc.com
Sales Range: $10-24.9 Million
Emp.: 12
Chemicals & Allied Products
N.A.I.C.S.: 424690
Michael Poleselli (Pres)
Nicole Lynn (Office Mgr)

OPEX CORPORATION
305 Commerce Dr, Moorestown, NJ 08057-4215
Tel.: (856) 727-1100
Web Site: http://www.opex.com
Year Founded: 1973
Sales Range: $25-49.9 Million
Emp.: 550
Mailroom Automation Machines Mfr
N.A.I.C.S.: 333310
David Stevens (Pres & CEO)
Jeff Bowen (Pres-Incoming & Scanning)

OPHTHALMIC CONSULTANTS OF LONG ISLAND
4212 Hempstead Turnpike, Bethpage, NY 11714
Tel.: (516) 731-4800
Web Site: https://www.ocli.net
Year Founded: 1997
Medical Practice
N.A.I.C.S.: 621111

Subsidiaries:

Crossroads Eye Care Associates, Ltd. (1)
4160 Washington Rd, McMurray, PA 15317
Tel.: (724) 941-1466
Web Site:
http://www.crossroadseyecare.com
Offices of Physicians (except Mental Health Specialists)
N.A.I.C.S.: 621111
Shelley Butti (Mgr-Optical)

Fishman Center For Total Eye Care (1)
9229 Queens Blvd Ste 2I, Rego Park, NY 11374-1072
Tel.: (718) 261-7007
Offices of Physicians (except Mental Health Specialists)
N.A.I.C.S.: 621111
Allen Fishman (Pres)

Retina Consultants of WNY (1)
531 Farber Lakes Dr, Williamsville, NY 14221-5773
Tel.: (716) 632-1595
Web Site: http://www.wnyretina.com
Offices of Physicians (except Mental Health Specialists)
N.A.I.C.S.: 621111
Linda Simonsen (Mgr)

OPICI WINE GROUP INC.
25 De Boer Dr, Glen Rock, NJ 07452-3301
Tel.: (201) 689-1200 DE
Web Site: http://www.opici.com
Year Founded: 1899
Rev.: $150,000,000
Emp.: 166
Wine & Distilled Beverages Producer
N.A.I.C.S.: 424820
Linda Opici (CEO)
Dave Barna (VP-Sls-NJ)
Philip Ward (Brand Mgr)
Tom Hopper (Dir-Fin)

Subsidiaries:

Opici Wine Company of Connecticut (1)
210 Old Gate Ln, Milford, CT 06460
Tel.: (203) 876-2830
Web Site: http://www.opici.com
Emp.: 30
Wine Distr
N.A.I.C.S.: 424820
Brian Lewis (Gen Mgr)

Opici Wine Company of NJ - American BD (1)
25 DeBoer Dr, Glen Rock, NJ 07452-3301 (100%)
Tel.: (201) 689-1200
Web Site: http://www.opici.com
Sales Range: $10-24.9 Million
Emp.: 5
Wine & Distilled Beverages
N.A.I.C.S.: 424820
Dave Barna (VP-Sls)

Opici Wines (1)
25 DeBoer Dr, Glen Rock, NJ 07452
Tel.: (201) 689-3256
Web Site: http://www.opiciwines.com
Emp.: 100
Wine Distr
N.A.I.C.S.: 424820
Mike Bruntz (Dir-Fine Wine)

OPINION DYNAMICS CORPORATION
1000 Winter St, Waltham, MA 02451
Tel.: (617) 492-1400
Web Site:
http://www.opiniondynamics.com
Year Founded: 1987
Consulting Firm; Energy Evaluation, Social & Behavioral Research, Energy Advising & Market Research
N.A.I.C.S.: 541620
Brad Kates (CEO)
Sharyn Barata (Sr VP-Industry Engagement)
Olivia Patterson (SR VP)
Yvonne Abel (Head-People & Culture)
Megan Campbell (Sr VP)

U.S. PRIVATE

OPOLIS DESIGN
The Gotham Bldg 2240 N Interstate Ave Ste 200, Portland, OR 97227
Tel.: (503) 287-7722
Web Site:
http://www.opolisdesign.com
Sales Range: Less than $1 Million
Emp.: 8
N.A.I.C.S.: 541810
Michael Verdine (Partner)
Dan Richards (Principal)

OPORTUN, INC.
PO Box 4085, Menlo Park, CA 94026
Tel.: (256) 319-3600 AL
Web Site: http://oportun.com
Year Founded: 2013
Rev.: $600,148,000
Assets: $2,201,874,000
Liabilities: $1,713,108,000
Net Worth: $488,766,000
Earnings: $61,598,000
Fiscal Year-end: 12/31/19
Bank Holding Company
N.A.I.C.S.: 551111
Alicia Dagosta (VP)
Ben Armstrong (CMO)
Casey Mueller (Principal Acctg Officer, Sr VP & Controller)
Christine Martin (VP-Total Rewards & HR Information Sys)
Chuck Johnston (VP-Data & Bus Intelligence)
David Needham (CTO)
Denise Sterling (Sr VP-Fin)
Eric Cunningham (VP-Collections)
Ezra Garrett (Sr VP-Pub Affairs & Impact)
Gaurav Rana (Sr VP-Data & Analytics)
Gonzalo Palacio (VP-Credit Cards)
Heidi Barron (VP-Store Dev & Facilities)
John Foxgrover (Treas & Sr VP-Capital Markets)
Jonathan Coblentz (CFO)
Kate Layton (Sec & Sr VP)
Mandip Shah (VP-Data Science & Direct Mail & Fraud)
Marta Palacios (VP)
Matt Jenkins (COO)
Nicholas Lecuyer (Sr VP-Strategy & Corp Dev)
Nils Erdmann (VP-IR)
Patrick Kirscht (Chief Credit Officer)
Ram Ramaswamy (VP-Engrg & Application Architecture)
Robin Lykins (Chief People Officer)
Joan Aristei (Chief Risk Officer & Gen Counsel)

Subsidiaries:

Progress Bank & Trust (1)
201 Williams Ave, Huntsville, AL 35801
Tel.: (256) 319-3600
Web Site: http://www.myprogressbank.com
Sales Range: $25-49.9 Million
Commericial Banking
N.A.I.C.S.: 522110
David Nast (Pres & CEO)
Andy Mann (Pres-Shoals Market)
Dabsey Maxwell (CFO & COO)
J.E.P. Buchanan (Chief Credit Officer & Sr Lender)
Lee R. Hoekenschneider (Pres-Huntsville Market)
Beth B. Richardson (Pres-Madison Market)
Sean Johnson (Pres-Birmingham Market)
Bruce W. Pylant (Pres-Decatur Market)
Dewayne Youngblood (Pres-Okaloosa & Walton County Market)
Charlie Vaughn (Chm)
Larry C. Weaver (Vice Chm)
Bhavani Kakani (Sec)

OPP CONSTRUCTION LLC
3625 N Washington St, Grand Forks, ND 58203

Tel.: (701) 775-3322
Web Site:
  http://www.oppconstruction.com
Sales Range: $10-24.9 Million
Emp.: 120
Concrete Work
N.A.I.C.S.: 237310
Gregory Opp *(Pres)*

OPPEDISANO'S BOOTERY
12 N Main St, Honeoye Falls, NY 14472
Tel.: (585) 624-1707
Web Site: http://www.shoe-store.net
Year Founded: 1924
Sales Range: $1-9.9 Million
Emp.: 7
Shoe Stores
N.A.I.C.S.: 458210
Korey Buzzell *(Co-Owner)*
Esther Buzzell *(Co-Owner)*

OPPENHEIMER COMPANIES, INC.
877 W Main St Ste 700, Boise, ID 83702-5887
Tel.: (208) 343-4883   ID
Web Site: http://www.oppcos.com
Year Founded: 1957
Sales Range: $10-24.9 Million
Emp.: 85
Food Processing, Sales & Marketing of Food Products
N.A.I.C.S.: 424480
Skip Oppenheimer *(CEO)*
Larry Lipschultz *(CFO)*
Doug Oppenheimer *(Owner & Pres)*

Subsidiaries:

Golbon   (1)
877 W Main St Ste 700, Boise, ID 83702-5887   (100%)
Tel.: (208) 342-7771
Web Site: http://www.golbon.com
Sales Range: $10-24.9 Million
Emp.: 40
Food Service Purchasing & Marketing
N.A.I.C.S.: 424480
Larry Lipschultz *(CFO)*

Interstate Food Processing Corporation   (1)
877 W Main St Ste 700, Boise, ID 83702-5887
Tel.: (208) 343-2602
Web Site:
  http://www.oppenheimercompanies.com
Sales Range: $10-24.9 Million
Emp.: 3
Food Processing
N.A.I.C.S.: 311411
Skip Oppenheimer *(Pres)*

Interstate Potato Packers Corp.   (1)
877 W Main St Ste 700, Boise, ID 83702
Tel.: (208) 343-4883
Food Products Distr
N.A.I.C.S.: 424490

Oppenheimer Development Corporation   (1)
877 W Main St Ste 700, Boise, ID 83702
Tel.: (208) 343-4883
Web Site:
  http://www.oppenheimerdevelopment.com
Real Estate Development Services
N.A.I.C.S.: 531390
Arthur F. Oppenheimer *(Pres)*
Jeremy Malone *(VP)*
Angela Wickham *(Mgr-Property)*
Coby Barlow *(Mgr-Property & Ops)*
Danielle Taniguchi *(Mgr-Property & Fin)*

Pacific Western Training Company   (1)
877 W Main St Ste 700, Boise, ID 83702
Tel.: (208) 345-0203
Web Site:
  http://www.pacificwesterntraining.com
Administrative Management Consulting Services
N.A.I.C.S.: 541611
Sherry G. Dyer *(Mng Dir)*

OPPORTUNE LLP
711 Louisiana Ste 1700, Houston, TX 77002
Tel.: (713) 490-5050
Web Site: http://www.opportune.com
Year Founded: 2005
Sales Range: $10-24.9 Million
Emp.: 150
Energy Industry Consultant Offering Tax, Finance Outsourcing & Enterprise Risk Services & Solutions
N.A.I.C.S.: 541213
David C. Baggett *(Mng Partner)*
Matt Flanagan *(Partner)*
Josh L. Sherman *(Partner)*
John Vanderhider *(Partner-Fin)*
James E. Boney *(Partner)*
John B. Echols *(Partner)*
Kurt King *(Partner)*
Lynn Loden *(Mng Dir)*
Yanic Harel *(Mng Dir)*
Jeanna Kostak *(COO-Outsourcing)*
Sean Clements *(Partner)*
Tommy Mars *(Mng Dir-Opportune EMEA)*
Charlie Palmer *(Mng Dir)*
Shane Randolph *(Partner)*
Lynell Rogeri *(Mng Dir)*
Kip Shore *(Mng Dir)*
Drew Lockard *(Mng Dir)*
Denna K. Arias *(Chief Corp Dev Officer)*
Steven Bradford *(Mng Dir)*
Ralph E. Davis *(Pres)*
Wade Stubblefield *(Mng Dir)*
Carl Wimberley *(Partner)*
Shane Bayless *(Pres-Outsourcing Practice)*
Randy Osterberg *(Mng Dir)*
Jonathan Harms *(Mng Dir)*
Kent Landrum *(Partner)*
Josh Shermen *(Partner)*
Ryan T. Senter *(Partner)*
Daniel Kohl *(Mng Dir-Opportune Partners LLC & Co-Head-Opportune Partners LLC)*
John Harris *(Mng Dir)*
Daniel Rojo *(Mng Dir-Opportune Partners LLC & Co-Head-Opportune Partners LLC)*
Ryan Culpepper *(VP-Engrg-Opportune Partners LLC)*
Morgan Rosenberg *(VP-Geology-Opportune Partners LLC)*
James Hanson *(Mng Dir-Opportune Partners LLC-New York)*
Steve Kennedy *(Mng Dir)*
Matthew Childress *(Chief Strategy Officer)*

Subsidiaries:

Ralph E. Davis Associates LP   (1)
711 Louisiana St Ste 3100, Houston, TX 77002
Tel.: (713) 490-5050
Web Site: http://www.ralphedavis.com
Petroleum Engineering & Support Services
N.A.I.C.S.: 541690
Allen C. Barron *(Pres)*

OPPORTUNITIES INDUSTRIALIZATION CENTERS INTERNATIONAL
1500 Walnut St Ste 1304, Philadelphia, PA 19102
Tel.: (215) 842-0220   PA
Web Site: http://www.oici.org
Year Founded: 1970
Sales Range: $10-24.9 Million
Community Welfare Services
N.A.I.C.S.: 624190
Vanessa Kilcrest *(Mgr-HR)*
Crispian Kirk *(Pres & CEO)*
Guillaume Castel *(Sec)*
James Talton *(Vice Chm)*
Sharon Reed Walker *(Treas)*
Edmund D. Cooke Jr. *(Chm)*

OPPORTUNITIES, INC.
200 E Cramer St, Fort Atkinson, WI 53538
Tel.: (920) 563-6926
Web Site: http://www.oppinc.com
Rev.: $11,700,000
Emp.: 100
Personnel Services
N.A.I.C.S.: 561330
Jason Frye *(Mgr-Sls-Mktg Staff)*
Robin Kennedy *(Mgr)*
Sheryl Labonne *(VP)*
Gordon Rossow *(Pres)*
Judith Rossow *(Treas & Sec)*
Dan Switalski *(Dir-Mfg Staff)*

OPPORTUNITY ENTERPRISES, INC.
2801 Evans Ave, Valparaiso, IN 46383
Tel.: (219) 464-9621   IN
Web Site: http://www.oppent.org
Year Founded: 1967
Sales Range: $10-24.9 Million
Emp.: 722
Developmental Disability Assistance Services
N.A.I.C.S.: 623210
Mark Fisher *(CFO)*
Latosha Knight *(Dir-Outsource)*
Lori Moulton *(Chm)*
Michelle Gonzalez *(Treas)*
Richard AmRhein *(Sec)*
Ellen DeMartinis *(CEO)*
Neil Samahon *(Vice Chm)*
Kathy Jackson *(Chief HR Officer)*
Judy Woodrick *(Dir-Clean Team)*
Lisa Barrios *(Dir-Daily Living Skills)*
Eric Ashton *(Dir-IT)*
Linda Hazen *(Dir-Major Gifting)*
Peter Wilson *(COO)*
Marie Kubina *(Dir-Curriculum)*
Kevin Toth *(Dir-Maintenance)*
Valerie Thill *(Chief Program Officer)*

OPPORTUNITY FINANCE NETWORK
123 S Broad St Ste 1930, Philadelphia, PA 19109
Tel.: (202) 618-6100   PA
Web Site: http://www.ofn.org
Year Founded: 2006
Rev.: $9,966,010
Assets: $149,985,977
Liabilities: $89,143,982
Net Worth: $60,841,995
Earnings: $926,092
Emp.: 126
Fiscal Year-end: 12/31/18
Social Advocacy Organization
N.A.I.C.S.: 813319
Seth Julyan *(Exec VP-Membership)*
Laurie Curran *(VP-Acctg)*
Shakeyda Daniels *(VP-Loan Ops)*
Inez Long *(CEO-Black Bus Investment Fund Florida)*
Jennifer Vasiloff *(Chief External Affairs Officer)*
Andrew Givens *(COO)*
Lisa Mensah *(Pres & CEO)*
Lisa Wright *(Sr VP-Fin Svcs)*
Andrea Longton *(Sr VP-Fin Svcs)*

OPPORTUNITY INTERNATIONAL, INC.
2122 York Rd Ste 150, Oak Brook, IL 60523
Tel.: (630) 242-4100   IL
Web Site: http://www.opportunity.org
Year Founded: 1971
Sales Range: $125-149.9 Million
Emp.: 128
Community Development Services
N.A.I.C.S.: 624190
Steve Lavey *(CFO)*
Dennis Ripley *(Chief Program Officer)*

David Simms *(Pres & Chief Dev Officer-Global)*
Ron Gray *(Gen Counsel)*
Dana D. Rice *(Sr VP-Global External Rels & Donor Strategy)*
Audrey Williams-Lee *(Global Chief HR Officer)*
Cliff Hampton *(Treas)*
Terry Watson *(Chm)*
Atul Tandon *(CEO)*

OPPORTUNITY PARTNERS, INC.
5500 Opportunity Ct, Minnetonka, MN 55343
Tel.: (952) 938-5511   MN
Web Site:
  http://www.opportunities.org
Year Founded: 1953
Sales Range: $25-49.9 Million
Emp.: 2,028
Disability Assistance Services
N.A.I.C.S.: 623210
Alice L. Johnson *(CFO)*
Doug Annett *(VP-Residential & Community Living)*
Rick Hammergren *(VP-Pub Policy, Vocational & Habilitation Svcs)*
Brian Pederson *(VP-Ops & Bus Svcs)*
Katie Nelsen *(Chief Advancement Officer)*
Cynthia Lesher *(Chm)*
Gregory Keane *(Treas)*
Todd Schoolman *(VP-HR)*
Armando Camacho *(Pres & CEO)*
Don Flower *(VP-IT)*
Ed Spencer Jr. *(Vice Chm)*

OPPRTUNITY, INC.
222 Broadway 20th Fl, New York, NY 10007
Tel.: (347) 796-1677
Web Site: http://www.opprtunity.com
Sales Range: $1-9.9 Million
Professionals & Businesses Networking Services
N.A.I.C.S.: 513199
Janis Krums *(Co-Founder)*
Bill Jula *(Co-Founder)*

OPPSOURCE INC.
1171 Northland Dr, Saint Paul, MN 55120
Web Site: http://www.oppsource.com
Year Founded: 2008
Sales Range: $1-9.9 Million
Emp.: 29
Advertising & Marketing
N.A.I.C.S.: 541890
Dan Metzger *(Partner & CEO)*
Damon Lawson *(Partner & Sr VP)*

OPSCODE, INC.
1008 Western Ave Ste 600, Seattle, WA 98104
Tel.: (206) 508-4799
Web Site: http://www.getchef.com
Sales Range: $1-9.9 Million
Cloud Infrastructure Automation
N.A.I.C.S.: 513210
Carolyn Scurrell *(Dir-Fin)*

OPSCOMPASS, LLC
9300 Underwood Ave, Suite 300, Omaha, NE 68114
Tel.: (877) 970-6879
Web Site:
  http://www.opscompass.com
Year Founded: 2016
Cloud Security & Operarions
N.A.I.C.S.: 518210
Manny Quevedo *(Founder)*
Matt Linderman *(Dir-Cloud Advisory)*
Nathan Biggs *(CEO)*

OPSCOMPASS, LLC

OpsCompass, LLC—(Continued)

Subsidiaries:

House of Brick Technologies LLC (1)
9300 Underwood Ave Ste 300, Omaha, NE 68114-2685
Tel.: (402) 445-0764
Web Site: http://www.houseofbrick.com
Computer System Design Services
N.A.I.C.S.: 541512
Nathan Biggs (CEO)

OPSWAT, INC.
398 Kansas St, San Francisco, CA 94103
Tel.: (415) 590-7300 DE
Web Site: http://www.opswat.com
Software Publisher
N.A.I.C.S.: 513210
Benny Czarny (Founder, Chm & CEO)
Simon Ho (CFO)
Stephen Gorham (COO)
Eric Spindel (Gen Counsel & Sec)
Dar Yossinger (VP-HR-Global)

Subsidiaries:

Bayshore Networks, LLC (1)
42 Richmond Ter, Staten Island, NY 10301
Tel.: (212) 797-1529
Web Site: http://www.bayshorenetworks.com
Sales Range: $1-9.9 Million
Emp.: 15
Computer System Design Services
N.A.I.C.S.: 541512
Francis Cianfrocca (Founder)
Ram Boreda (VP-Product Mgmt)

OPTCONNECT, LLC
865 W 450 N Ste 1, Kaysville, UT 84037
Web Site: http://www.optconnect.com
Year Founded: 2009
Sales Range: $1-9.9 Million
Emp.: 200
Wireless Networking Services
N.A.I.C.S.: 238290
Chris Baird (Pres & CEO)
Christie Kent (CFO)
Kevin Dalton (Chief Experience Officer)
Steve Garrett (Chief Product Officer)
Todd Christensen (Chief Tech & Innovation Officer)

Subsidiaries:

Premier Components Distrbution Corp. (1)
1225 Pear Ave 100, Mountain View, CA 94043-1431
Tel.: (650) 230-2000
Web Site: http://www.pws.bz
Sales Range: $1-9.9 Million
Emp.: 10
Electronic Parts & Equipment Merchant Whslr
N.A.I.C.S.: 423690
Vince Giacomini (Founder & Pres-PWS Bus Unit)

OPTECH, LLC
3290 W Big Beaver Rd Ste 220, Troy, MI 48084
Tel.: (313) 962-9000 MI
Web Site: http://www.optechus.com
Year Founded: 1999
Sales Range: $10-24.9 Million
Emp.: 170
Computer Related Services
N.A.I.C.S.: 541512
Scott Goodwin (Sr VP-Govt Svcs)
Angelique Rodriguez-Edge (Dir-Ops)
Debra Blair (Dir-Recruiting Ops)
Mark Duane (Dir-Bus Dev, IT & Healthcare)
Mary Engelman (Dir-PR & Govt Affairs)
Ronia F. Kruse (Founder, Pres & CEO)

OPTIC NERVE STUDIOS, INC.
9818 Glenoaks Blvd, Sun Valley, CA 91352
Tel.: (818) 771-1007
Web Site: http://www.opticnervefx.com
Year Founded: 1989
Sales Range: $1-9.9 Million
Emp.: 5
Teleproduction & Other Postproduction Services
N.A.I.C.S.: 512191
Glenn A. Hetrick (Owner & Supvr-Production)

OPTICAL SWITCH CORPORATION
8201 Preston Rd Ste 750, Dallas, TX 75225
Tel.: (214) 750-4326
Web Site: http://www.opticalswitch.com
Rev.: $17,600,000
Emp.: 50
Electrical Apparatus & Equipment
N.A.I.C.S.: 423610

OPTICSPLANET, INC.
3150 Commercial Ave, Northbrook, IL 60062
Tel.: (847) 513-6201
Web Site: http://www.opticsplanet.com
Year Founded: 2000
Rev.: $51,200,000
Emp.: 140
Photographic Equipment & Supplies Merchant Whslr
N.A.I.C.S.: 423410
Mark Levitin (CEO)
Pavel Shvartsman (Pres)

OPTIFY, INC.
710 2nd Ave Ste 840, Seattle, WA 98104
Tel.: (206) 388-4234
Web Site: http://www.optify.net
Year Founded: 2008
Sales Range: $1-9.9 Million
Digital Marketing Software
N.A.I.C.S.: 513210
Rob Eleveld (CEO)
Doug Wheeler (CMO)
Chris Hundley (CTO)
Brian Goffman (Chm)

OPTIGENEX, INC.
51 Newark St Ste 501, Hoboken, NJ 07030
Tel.: (201) 653-5195
Personal Care Product Mfr
N.A.I.C.S.: 325411
Daniel Zwiren (Pres, CEO & CFO)

OPTILEAF, INC.
924 N Main St, Wichita, KS 67203 FL
Web Site: http://www.optileaf.com
Year Founded: 2014
Sales Range: Less than $1 Million
Emp.: 5
Cannabis Industry Software Services
N.A.I.C.S.: 513210
Thomas Tran (Pres, CEO, CTO, Treas & Sec)
Nick Nguyen (CFO & COO)

OPTILINE ENTERPRISES, LLC
157 Main Dunstable Rd Ste 102, Nashua, NH 03060
Tel.: (603) 402-1446
Web Site: http://www.optiline.co

Year Founded: 2006
Sales Range: $25-49.9 Million
Emp.: 180
Metal Framing Services
N.A.I.C.S.: 238310
Tommy Bolduc (Co-Owner)
Mick Bolduc (Co-Owner)

OPTIMA ASSET MANAGEMENT SERVICES
1600 Dove St Ste 480, Newport Beach, CA 92660
Tel.: (949) 852-0900
Web Site: http://www.optimaasset.com
Sales Range: $10-24.9 Million
Emp.: 18
Real Estate Managers
N.A.I.C.S.: 531210
Kem Braswell (VP-Property Mgmt)
Danny Molgaard (Mgr-Property)
Jessica Mensoza (Mgr-Property)
Mary Duran (Sr Mgr-Leasing)
Jessica Mendoza (Mgr-Property)

OPTIMA GROUP, INC.
2150 Post Rd, Fairfield, CT 06824
Tel.: (203) 255-1066 CT
Web Site: http://www.optimagroupinc.com
Sales Range: $1-9.9 Million
Market Research, Consulting & Creative Services
N.A.I.C.S.: 541611
Kenneth R. Hoffman (Pres & Mng Dir)
Dennis Dolego (Dir-Res)
Ellen H. McKay (Mng Dir)
Susan Schaller (Mktg Dir)
Tracy H. M. Hubbard (Creative Dir)

OPTIMA SPECIALTY STEEL, INC.
200 S Biscayne Blvd Ste 5500, Miami, FL 33131-2310
Tel.: (305) 375-7560 DE
Web Site: http://www.optimasteel.com
Holding Company; Specialty Steel Products Mfr
N.A.I.C.S.: 551112
Michael Salamon (Pres & COO)
Anthony J. Verkruyse (CFO, Treas & VP)
Mordechai Korf (Chm & CEO)
Thad Florence (Gen Counsel)
Mony Bistritzky (VP-Procurement & Integration)

Subsidiaries:

Michigan Seamless Tube LLC (1)
400 McMunn St, South Lyon, MI 48178
Tel.: (248) 486-0100
Web Site: http://www.mstube.com
Steel Tube Mfr
N.A.I.C.S.: 331210

Niagara LaSalle Corporation (1)
1412 150th St, Hammond, IN 46327-1743
Tel.: (219) 853-6000
Web Site: http://www.niagralasalle.com
Sales Range: $50-74.9 Million
Emp.: 400
Cold Finished & Specialty Steel Bar Products Mfr
N.A.I.C.S.: 331221
Michael Salamon (Pres & COO)
Anthony J. Verkruyse (CFO & Treas)

Subsidiary (Domestic):

Niagara LaSalle Corporation - Buffalo Plant (2)
110 Hopkins St, Buffalo, NY 14220-2131
Tel.: (716) 827-7010
Web Site: http://www.niagralasalle.com
Sales Range: $25-49.9 Million
Emp.: 160
Steel Company
N.A.I.C.S.: 331221

Terry Johnson (Mgr-IT Ops)
Jeffrey Smith (Mgr-Maintenance)
Dennis Zion (Mgr-Facilities)

Niagara LaSalle Corporation - Warren Plant (2)
22700 Nagel St, Warren, MI 48089
Tel.: (586) 755-5800
Web Site: http://www.niagaralasalle.com
Sales Range: $10-24.9 Million
Emp.: 100
Steel Bars Producer
N.A.I.C.S.: 331221

OPTIMAL IDM, LLC
3959 Van Dyke Rd Ste 190, Lutz, FL 33558
Tel.: (813) 425-6351
Web Site: http://www.optimalidm.com
Year Founded: 2005
Sales Range: $1-9.9 Million
Emp.: 20
Software Publisher
N.A.I.C.S.: 513210
Lawrence Aucoin (Mng Partner)
Michael Brengs (Mng Partner)
Nada Jumper (Chief Software Architect)
Chris Curcio (VP-Channel Sls)
Mark Foust (Dir-Worldwide Sls)

OPTIMAL OUTCOMES, LLC
435 5th Ave N Ste 200, Saint Petersburg, FL 33701
Tel.: (727) 895-8902
Web Site: http://www.optimal-outcomes.com
Sales Range: $1-9.9 Million
Emp.: 11
Outpatient Centers, Medical Office Buildings & Cancer Centers Construction & Development
N.A.I.C.S.: 236210
Patrick Marston (Principal)
Andy Boggini (Principal)

OPTIMAL STRATEGIX GROUP, INC.
140 Terry Dr Ste 118, Newtown, PA 18940
Tel.: (215) 867-1880
Web Site: http://www.optimalstrategix.com
Sales Range: $10-24.9 Million
Emp.: 100
Business Consulting Services
N.A.I.C.S.: 541618
R. Sukumar (Pres & CEO)

OPTIMAX SYSTEMS, INC.
6367 Dean Pkwy, Ontario, NY 14519
Tel.: (585) 265-1066
Web Site: http://www.optimaxsi.com
Year Founded: 1991
Rev.: $13,000,000
Emp.: 150
Optical Prototype Mfr & Distr
N.A.I.C.S.: 333310
Michael Mandina (Pres)
Rick Plympton (CEO)
Bob Wiederhold (Mgr-Ops)
Tom Kelly (Controller-Fin)

OPTIMO IT
240 Market St Ste 112, Bloomsburg, PA 17815
Tel.: (877) 564-8552
Web Site: http://www.optimo-it.com
Year Founded: 2008
Sales Range: $1-9.9 Million
Emp.: 65
IT Consulting, Digital & Mobile Forensics, eDiscovery, Staffing & Recruitment
N.A.I.C.S.: 541613

COMPANIES

Miguel Miguelez *(Pres & CEO)*
Steve Gilmartin *(Sr VP-Bus Dev)*
Scott McCarty *(Dir-IT)*
Heather S. Stenglein *(Dir-HR)*

OPTIMUM HEALTHCARE, INC.
5403 N Church Ave, Tampa, FL 33614
Tel.: (813) 506-6000   FL
Web Site:
http://www.youroptimumhealthcare.com
Year Founded: 2006
Sales Range: $150-199.9 Million
Emp.: 15
Accident & Health Insurance Carrier
N.A.I.C.S.: 524114
Rupesh R. Shah *(CEO)*

OPTIMUM OUTSOURCING LLC
1300 Quail St Ste 202, Newport Beach, CA 92660
Tel.: (949) 610-7981
Web Site:
http://www.optimumoutsourcing.net
Year Founded: 2005
Sales Range: $1-9.9 Million
Emp.: 10
Human Resources Outsourcing & Payroll Processing
N.A.I.C.S.: 541214
Stacy Linden *(Pres)*

OPTIMUM RE CORPORATION
1345 River Bend Dr Ste 100, Dallas, TX 75247
Tel.: (214) 528-2020
Web Site: http://www.optimumre.com
Year Founded: 1987
Rev.: $15,900,000
Emp.: 50
Accident & Health Insurance Carriers
N.A.I.C.S.: 524114
Sebastien Blondeau *(Pres & COO)*
Gary Bedwell *(VP-Sls & Mktg-Western & Southern)*
Gord Gibbins *(Chief Dev Officer & Exec VP)*
Sheila Matheson *(VP-Sls & Mktg-Critical Illness)*
Abdelnour Khoury *(Asst VP-Admin Svcs)*
Dalia Khoury *(Asst VP-Admin Svcs)*
Francois Duguay *(Chief Actuary & Sr VP)*
Glenn Beuschel *(Dir-Treaties)*
Jonathan Racine *(VP-Bus Dev)*
Monica Clink *(Asst VP-Claims)*
Yves Leclerc *(Sr VP-Ops)*

OPTIMUM SYSTEM PRODUCTS INC.
5061 Fwy Dr E, Columbus, OH 43229
Tel.: (614) 885-4464
Web Site:
http://www.optimumsystem.com
Sales Range: $10-24.9 Million
Emp.: 30
Sales of Business Related Forms
N.A.I.C.S.: 424120
John Martin *(Pres)*
Julie Talks *(VP-Acctg)*

OPTIMUM TECHNOLOGY SOLUTIONS INC.
95 White Bridge Rd Ste 111, Nashville, TN 37205
Tel.: (615) 292-3047
Web Site: http://www.optyinc.com
Year Founded: 2003
Rev.: $3,500,000
Emp.: 63
Computer System Design Services
N.A.I.C.S.: 541512

OPTIMUS CORPORATION
9713 Key West Ave Ste 400, Rockville, MD 20850-3995
Tel.: (301) 585-7075
Rev.: $11,762,104
Emp.: 3
Systems Engineering, Computer Related
N.A.I.C.S.: 541512

OPTIMUS HEALTH CARE
982 E Main St, Bridgeport, CT 06608-2409
Tel.: (203) 696-3260   CT
Web Site:
http://www.optimushealthcare.org
Year Founded: 1976
Sales Range: $25-49.9 Million
Emp.: 442
Health Care Srvices
N.A.I.C.S.: 622110
Patrick Schmincke *(Chm)*
Lydia Martinez *(Treas)*
Iris N. Molina *(Sec)*
Edgar Rodriguez *(Vice Chm)*

OPTIMUS STEEL, LLC
Old Hwy 90, Beaumont, TX 77704
Tel.: (409) 768-1211   TX
Web Site: http://www.optimus-steelusa.com
Year Founded: 2017
Holding Company; Steel Products Mfr
N.A.I.C.S.: 551112
Ricardo A. Anawate *(VP-Ops)*

Subsidiaries:

Optimus Steel, LLC - Beaumont Steel Mill (1)
Old Hwy 90, Beaumont, TX 77704
Tel.: (409) 768-1211
Web Site: http://www.optimus-steelusa.com
Steel Wire & Rebar Mfr
N.A.I.C.S.: 331222

OPTION SIX, INC.
320 W 8th St Ste 220, Bloomington, IN 47404
Tel.: (812) 330-0606
Web Site: http://www.optionsix.com
Sales Range: $1-9.9 Million
Emp.: 60
Designs & Develops Custom Employee Training Courses
N.A.I.C.S.: 923110
William West *(Founder & Pres)*
Matt Donovan *(VP-Bus Dev)*

OPTIONABLE, INC.
635 Beach 19th St, Far Rockaway, NY 11691
Tel.: (516) 807-1981
Web Site: http://www.optionable.com
Sales Range: Less than $1 Million
Financial Brokerage Services
N.A.I.C.S.: 523999
Matthew L. Katzeff *(CFO)*
Dov Rauchwerger *(CEO)*

OPTIONS FOR COMMUNITY LIVING, INC.
202 E Main St, Smithtown, NY 11787
Tel.: (631) 361-9020   NY
Web Site: http://www.optionscl.org
Year Founded: 1982
Sales Range: $10-24.9 Million
Emp.: 197
Community Care Services
N.A.I.C.S.: 624190
Karen Schwartz *(Controller)*
Lori Barraud *(Dir-HR)*
Susan Steinhardt *(Officer-Compliance & Dir-Quality Improvement)*
Georgia Mavromatis Kuhen *(Dir-Mental Health Residential Svcs)*
Allison Covino *(Dir-Access to Care Programs)*
Yolanda Robano-Gross *(Exec Dir)*

OPTIONS FOR LEARNING
885 S Village Oaks Dr, Covina, CA 91724
Tel.: (626) 967-7848   CA
Web Site:
http://www.optionsforlearning.org
Year Founded: 1981
Emp.: 950
Child Care & Development Services
N.A.I.C.S.: 624410
Amy Nih *(CFO)*
John Beck *(CIO)*
Cliff Marcussen *(CEO & Exec Dir)*
Dolores Meade *(COO & Deputy Exec Dir)*
Patricia Huffman *(Chm)*
David Wilbur *(Vice Chm)*
Melissa Takeda *(Dir-HR)*
Cesar Soto *(Dir-Facilities)*
Mildred Balderrama *(Dir-Head Start South El Monte)*
Tracy Lynch *(Dir-Enrichment Program)*
Ruby Sevilla *(Dir-Early Head Start)*
Denise McCullough *(Dir-Full-day Preschool)*
Rosemary Olachea-Heaslip *(Dir-Surround Care)*
Deborah Slobojan *(Dir-State Preschool)*
Kimberly Dobson Garcia *(Mgr-Special Projects)*

OPTIONS UNIVERSITY
925 S Federal Hwy Ste 510, Boca Raton, FL 33432
Tel.: (561) 200-3709
Web Site:
http://www.optionsuniversity.com
Year Founded: 2004
Rev.: $3,800,000
Emp.: 19
School & Educational Services
N.A.I.C.S.: 611699
Brett Fogle *(Pres & CEO)*
Sarah Kuehner *(Office Mgr)*
Matthew Buckley *(Chief Strategy Officer)*
Bill Johnson *(Dir-Education)*

OPTISCAN, INC.
3612 W Dunlap Ave Ste A, Phoenix, AZ 85051
Tel.: (602) 789-7800   AZ
Web Site: http://www.optiscan.net
Year Founded: 1991
Sales Range: $1-9.9 Million
Emp.: 55
Optical Scanning Services
N.A.I.C.S.: 518210
Al Hawkins *(Pres & CEO)*
Michael Hawkins *(Gen Mgr)*

OPTISURE RISK PARTNERS, LLC
40 Start St, Manchester, NH 03101
Tel.: (603) 665-0800
Web Site: http://optisure.com
Year Founded: 2015
Emp.: 60
Insurance Brokers
N.A.I.C.S.: 524210
Paul Robert Burke *(Co-Founder & Chm)*
Peter R. Milnes *(Co-Founder & CEO)*
Chuck Robinson *(Dir-Mktg)*
George Brome *(Dir-IT)*
Jodi Hoyt *(Dir-HR)*
Randy Eifert *(Sr VP-Private Client & Risk Mgmt)*
Brook Milnes *(Mgr-Digital Mktg)*
Beth Needham *(Mgr-Insurance Ops)*
Jim Sullivan *(VP-Fin & Admin)*
Wendy Bagley *(Acct Exec-Personal Lines & Private Client)*

Subsidiaries:

Sutton James Incorporated (1)
100 Lindbergh Dr Brainard Airport, Hartford, CT 06114
Tel.: (860) 249-8066
Web Site: http://www.suttonjames.com
Insurance Agencies & Brokerages
N.A.I.C.S.: 524210
Jonathan Doolittle *(Pres)*

OPTIV INC.
1125 17th St Ste 1700, Denver, CO 80202
Tel.: (303) 298-0600   DE
Web Site: http://www.optiv.com
Year Founded: 2014
Sales Range: $900-999.9 Million
Emp.: 1,700
Cyber Security Service Provider
N.A.I.C.S.: 541690
Daniel D. Burns *(Founder & CEO)*
John F. Cassidy *(Chm)*
Timothy J. Hoffman *(Exec VP-Worldwide Client Solutions)*
S. Paul Lehman *(CIO)*
David M. Roshak *(CFO & Exec VP)*
David Castignola *(Exec VP-Worldwide Sls)*
Nate Brady *(Chief Acctg Officer)*
Veena Bricker *(Chief HR Officer)*
Stu Solomon *(Sr VP-Security Solutions & Ops)*
John Trauth *(Gen Mgr-Info Security-Federal)*
David Martin *(Chief Svcs Officer & Exec VP)*
Nichoel Brooks *(Dir-Federal Svcs)*
William H. Crouteh *(Gen Counsel & Sr VP)*
William H. Crouteh *(Gen Counsel & Sr VP)*

OPTIZMO TECHNOLOGIES, LLC
401 Congress Ave Ste 1540, Austin, TX 78701
Tel.: (512) 687-6272
Web Site: http://www.optizmo.com
Year Founded: 2009
Sales Range: $1-9.9 Million
Emp.: 14
Software Development Services
N.A.I.C.S.: 541511
Khris Thayer *(Co-Founder & CEO)*
Grant Fern *(Co-Founder & CTO)*
Jake Dearstyne *(Chief Revenue Officer)*
Brian Culp *(Dir-Sls & Client Services)*
Dave Prickett *(Dir-Admin Ops)*
Tom Wozniak *(COO)*

OPTO 22
43044 Business Pk Dr, Temecula, CA 92590
Tel.: (951) 695-3000
Web Site: http://www.opto22.com
Rev.: $14,500,000
Emp.: 240
Electronic Switches
N.A.I.C.S.: 334419
Benson Hougland *(VP-Mktg)*
Bruce Campbell *(Mgr)*
Robert Sheffres *(VP)*
Bill Ludwig *(Mgr-Sls)*
Gerhard Kreiling *(Mgr-Bus Dev-Intl)*
Matt Newton *(Dir-Technical Mktg)*
Craig Wilke *(Mgr-Midwest Reg)*
David Hill *(Mgr-Mktg Comm)*
James Davis *(Mgr-Southwest)*
Brian Barrett *(Reg Mgr-Sls)*
Dave Engsberg *(Reg Mgr-Sls)*
Norma Rodriguez *(Dir-Trng)*

OPTOPLEX CORP.

Opto 22—(Continued)

OPTOPLEX CORP.
374 Gateway Blvd, Fremont, CA 94538
Tel.: (510) 490-9930 CA
Web Site: http://www.optoplex.com
Year Founded: 2000
Sales Range: $10-24.9 Million
Emp.: 70
Fiber Optic Product Designer & Mfr
N.A.I.C.S.: 334210
James Cheng-Jee Sha (CEO)
Steve Huang (Mgr)
Vincent Chien (VP-Production)

OPTOSIGMA CORP.
3210 S Croddy Way, Santa Ana, CA 92704-6348
Tel.: (949) 851-5881
Web Site: http://www.optosigma.com
Sales Range: $10-24.9 Million
Emp.: 20
Optics & Optomechanics Mfr & Distr
N.A.I.C.S.: 333310
Michelle Young (Mgr-Sls-Eastern)
Steve McNamee (VP & Gen Mgr)

OPTS IDEAS
455 W Main St, Boise, ID 83702-7244
Tel.: (415) 339-2020 CA
Year Founded: 1982
Rev.: $2,600,000
Emp.: 15
Fiscal Year-end: 12/31/06
Experiential Event Marketing Agency
N.A.I.C.S.: 541613
Michael Christman (CEO & Partner)
Lisa Holland (Pres & Partner)
Chris Fitzgerald (Partner)

OPTUMHEALTH ALLIES
PO Box 10340, Glendale, CA 91209
Web Site:
   http://www.optumhealthallies.com
Year Founded: 1999
Sales Range: $10-24.9 Million
Emp.: 100
Online Marketplace for Medical Services
N.A.I.C.S.: 541618

OPTUS INC.
3423 One Pl, Jonesboro, AR 72404
Tel.: (870) 974-7700
Web Site: http://www.optusinc.com
Sales Range: $25-49.9 Million
Emp.: 175
Communications Equipment
N.A.I.C.S.: 423690
Mark Duckworth (Founder & Pres)
Allan Lew (CEO)
Stuart Bird (Mng Dir-Wholesale & Satellite)

OPU INC.
1533 Jamestown Dr, Murray, UT 84121
Tel.: (801) 544-2633 NV
Year Founded: 2008
Sales Range: Less than $1 Million
Business Management Services
N.A.I.C.S.: 541618
J. William Kirch (Pres, CEO, CFO & Sec)

OPUS 3 ARTISTS LLC
470 Park Ave S 9th Fl, New York, NY 10016
Tel.: (212) 584-7500 DE
Web Site:
   http://www.opus3artists.com
Year Founded: 1976
Sales Range: $25-49.9 Million
Emp.: 50

Classical Music & Performing Arts Talent Agency
N.A.I.C.S.: 711410
David V. Foster (Pres & CEO)
Jonathan Brill (Exec VP)
Leslie Beatrice (Mgr-Mktg & Promo)
Bob Brewer (CFO)
Sophia Bentley (Chief Acctg Officer & Mgr-HR)
Neil Benson (Sr VP & Dir-Booking-Natl)
Patricia A. Winter (Sr VP)
Mary Pat Buerkle (Sr VP)
Leonard Stein (Sr VP & Dir-Touring)
Caroline Woodfield (Sr VP & Mgr-Artists)
Bruce Sanchez (Mgr-Facilities)
Marsha Clarke (Chief Acctg Officer & Mgr-HR)
Christina Baker (Mgr-Artists & Attractions)
Benjamin Maimin (VP)
Jeffrey Vanderveen (VP)

Subsidiaries:

Opus 3 Artists GmbH (1)
Pariser Str 62, Berlin, 10719, Germany
Tel.: (49) 30 889 101 50
Sales Range: $10-24.9 Million
Emp.: 7
Artist Management Services
N.A.I.C.S.: 711410
Katharina Ronnefeld (Founder)
Jonathan Brill (Mng Dir)
Adelaide Docx (Mgr-Artist)
Alexander Busche (Mgr-Artist)

Opus 3 Artists LLC - Los Angeles (1)
5670 Wilshire Blvd Ste 1790, Los Angeles, CA 90036
Tel.: (323) 954-1776
Web Site: http://www.opus3artists.com
Sales Range: $10-24.9 Million
Emp.: 2
Classical Music & Performing Arts Talent Agency
N.A.I.C.S.: 711410
Jenny Vogel (Exec VP & Mgr-Artists & Conductors)
Leslie Beatrice (Mgr-Mktg & Promo)
Bob Brewer (CFO)
Marsha Clarke (Chief Acctg Officer & Mgr-HR)
Adelaide Docx (Mgr-Artists & Attractions)
Sophia Grevesmuhl (Mgr-Artists & Attractions)
Derrick McBride (Mgr-Artists & Attractions)
Matthew Oberstein (Mgr-Artists & Attractions)
Bruce Sanchez (Mgr-Facilities)

OPUS CAPITAL LLC
2730 Sand Hill Rd Ste 150, Menlo Park, CA 94025
Tel.: (650) 543-2900
Web Site:
   http://www.opuscapital.com
Emp.: 10
Investment Services
N.A.I.C.S.: 523999
Gill Cogan (Gen Partner)
Dan Avida (Gen Partner)
Joseph Cutts (CFO)
Jakki Lynn Haussler (Bd of Dirs, Executives)

OPUS EVENTS AGENCY
9000 SW Nimbus Ave, Beaverton, OR 97008
Tel.: (971) 223-0777
Web Site:
   http://www.opuseventsagency.com
Year Founded: 1993
Sales Range: $10-24.9 Million
Emp.: 85
Marketing Consulting Services
N.A.I.C.S.: 541613
Dena Lowery (COO)
Deette Kapustka (CFO)

Holly Files (Exec VP-Tech)
Paula Grayson (Exec VP-Agency Customer Success)
Grant Hammersley (Vice Chm)
Kim Kopetz (Exec VP-Strategy)
David Lemke (Exec VP-Creative)
Kerrie Sheldon (Exec VP-Strategy & Production)
Kristin Waters (Exec VP-Accounts-Global)

OPUS HOLDING, LLC
10350 Bren Rd W, Minnetonka, MN 55343
Tel.: (952) 656-4444
Web Site: http://www.opus-group.com
Holding Company
N.A.I.C.S.: 551112
Tim Murnane (Pres & CEO)
Linda Gonzales (CIO)
Tom Hoben (Gen Counsel & VP)
Dennis Power (CFO)
Kim Noonan (VP-Mktg & Brand)
Joe Downs (VP)
Pat Matre (VP-Real Estate)
Jeff Smith (VP)
Doug Swain (VP)
Matt Rauenhorst (Exec VP & Gen Mgr)

Subsidiaries:

Opus AE Group, Inc. (1)
10350 Bren Rd W, Minnetonka, MN 55343
Tel.: (952) 656-4444
Web Site: http://www.opus-group.com
Architectural Services
N.A.I.C.S.: 541310
Ed Gschneidner (Pres)
Michale Lederle (VP)

Opus Design Build, L.L.C. (1)
10350 Bren Rd W, Minnetonka, MN 55343
Tel.: (952) 656-4444
Web Site: http://www.opus-group.com
Design & Construction Services
N.A.I.C.S.: 541310
Dave Bangasser (Pres & CEO)
Rich Kauffman (VP-Indianapolis)
Douglas J. Swain (VP & Gen Mgr)

Opus Development Corporation (1)
10350 Bren Rd W, Minnetonka, MN 55343
Tel.: (952) 656-4444
Web Site: http://www.opus-group.com
Real Estate Development & Construction
N.A.I.C.S.: 531390
Tom Shaver (Pres & CEO)
John Gelderman (Sr VP-Natl Retail Dev)
Tom Lund (VP-Real Estate Dev)
Dave Menke (Sr VP & Gen Mgr)
John Meyers (VP-Real Estate Dev)
Ryan Carlie (Mgr-Real Estate-St. Louis)
Phil Cattanach (Dir-Real Estate Dev)
Peter Conlon (Sr Dir-Capital Markets)

Branch (Domestic):

Opus Development Corporation (2)
9700 W Higgins Rd Ste 900, Rosemont, IL 60018-4713
Tel.: (847) 692-4444
Web Site: http://www.opus-group.com
Sales Range: $100-124.9 Million
Emp.: 40
Commercial & Residential Real Estate Development, Architectural & Construction Services
N.A.I.C.S.: 237210

OPUS SOLUTIONS, LLC
9000 SW Nimbus Ave, Beaverton, OR 97008
Tel.: (971) 223-0777 OR
Web Site:
   http://www.opusagency.com
Year Founded: 1993
Brand Events & Marketing Agency
N.A.I.C.S.: 541820
Dena Lowery (COO)
Kim Kopetz (Pres)

Kristen Clark (Chief HR Officer)
DeEtte Kapustka (CFO)
John Trinanes (Chief Creative Officer)

Subsidiaries:

Ten Cue Productions (1)
1250 Addison St Ste 110, Berkeley, CA 94702-1782
Tel.: (510) 841-3000
Web Site: http://www.tencue.com
Convention & Trade Show Organizers
N.A.I.C.S.: 561920
Jeff Wilk (Owner)

OPYS PHYSICIAN SERVICES, LLC
One Indiana Sq Ste 2060, Indianapolis, IN 46204
Web Site: http://www.opys.com
Year Founded: 2012
Sales Range: $1-9.9 Million
Physician Outsourcing Services
N.A.I.C.S.: 621112
Andre Creese (Pres & CEO)
Alicia Calloway (COO)
Lee A. Flannery (Sr VP-Revenue Cycle)
Whitney M. Dishman (Reg Mgr)
Jay Nettles (Exec Dir-Post Acute Care)

ORANGE & BLUE DISTRIBUTING CO. INC.
2902 Lager Dr, Champaign, IL 61822
Tel.: (217) 352-4794
Sales Range: $25-49.9 Million
Emp.: 60
Distributing Beer & Other Fermented Malt Liquors
N.A.I.C.S.: 424810
B. J. Stipes (Gen Mgr)

ORANGE CAPITAL VENTURES GP, LLC
401 Park Ave S 10th Fl, New York, NY 10016 DE
Privater Equity Firm
N.A.I.C.S.: 523999
Daniel Lewis (Founder & Mng Partner)
Ankur Dharia (Partner)
Rhea Persaud (Controller)

Subsidiaries:

Ascend Fundraising Solutions (1)
1 Yonge Street Suite 700, Toronto, M5E 1E5, ON, Canada
Tel.: (416) 479-3873
Web Site: http://www.ascendfs.com
Software Technology Company; Fundraising Solutions
N.A.I.C.S.: 513210
Blair McGibbon (CFO)
Daniel Lewis (CEO)
Ken Cook (Chief Revenue Officer)
Dan Libro (Chief Product Officer)
Jason Little (VP-Bus Dev)
Dan Tanenbaum (Chief Innovation Officer)
Rita Fieder (Pres)

ORANGE COAST TITLE COMPANY INC.
1551 N Tustin Ave Ste 300, Novi, MI 48375
Tel.: (734) 552-0212 CA
Web Site:
   http://www.oaklandautomation.com
Year Founded: 1974
Sales Range: $75-99.9 Million
Emp.: 750
Industrial Robotic Equipment Mfr
N.A.I.C.S.: 541191
Rich Macaluso (Pres)
Angela Ballard (Branch Mgr-Modesto)
Kent Schmeeckle (VP)

Subsidiaries:

California Title Company (1)

COMPANIES

2365 Northside Dr Ste 250, San Diego, CA 92108-2709
Tel.: (858) 437-0714
Web Site: http://www.caltitle.com
Sales Range: $1-9.9 Million
Emp.: 50
Real Estate Services
N.A.I.C.S.: 524127

Financial Processing Systems Corporation (1)
640 N Tustin Ave Ste 200, Santa Ana, CA 92705-4646
Tel.: (714) 953-8681
Web Site: http://www.fpsnet.com
Sales Range: $10-24.9 Million
Emp.: 10
Data Processing & Preparation
N.A.I.C.S.: 518210

Orange Coast Title Company (1)
1955 Hunts Ln Ste 100, San Bernardino, CA 92408-3344
Tel.: (909) 825-8800
Web Site: http://www.oct.com
Sales Range: $10-24.9 Million
Emp.: 70
Surety Insurance
N.A.I.C.S.: 541191

Orange Coast Title Company of Los Angeles (1)
640 N Tustin Ave Ste 106, Santa Ana, CA 92705
Tel.: (562) 356-4700
Web Site: http://directory.octitle.com
Sales Range: $50-74.9 Million
Emp.: 155
Title Insurance
N.A.I.C.S.: 524127

ORANGE COMMERICAL CREDIT, INC.
2108 Caton Way SW, Olympia, WA 98502
Tel.: (360) 956-1514
Web Site: http://www.occfactor.com
Sales Range: $10-24.9 Million
Emp.: 20
All Other Nondepository Credit Intermediation
N.A.I.C.S.: 522299
Anthony Kinninger (Owner)
Jarrett Pope (VP & Office Mgr)
Jim Tipton (Acct Exec)
Kevin Allen (Portfolio Mgr)
Phil Uyehara (Gen Mgr)
Bob Dilliplaine (Officer-Bus Dev)
Chuck Naab (Officer-Bus Dev)
Natalie Graves (Officer-Bus Dev)
Tina Cawthorn (Officer-Bus Dev)
Todd Waller (Officer-Natl Sls)

ORANGE COUNTY ADULT ACHIEVEMENT CENTER
225 W Carl Karcher Way, Anaheim, CA 92801
Tel.: (714) 744-5301 CA
Web Site: http://www.mydaycounts.org
Year Founded: 1951
Sales Range: $10-24.9 Million
Emp.: 173
Disability Assistance Services
N.A.I.C.S.: 624120
Michael Galliano (CEO)
Aaron Flores (CFO)
Karen Errington (Program Dir-Consumer Choice Day Activity)
Marie Aguilera (Asst VP-Family Connections)
Robert Tiezzi (Dir-Intake & Assessment)
Patricia Granger (Program Dir-Work Activity)

ORANGE COUNTY BUILDING MATERIALS INC.
365 Old Hwy 90 W, Vidor, TX 77662
Tel.: (409) 769-2419
Sales Range: $10-24.9 Million
Emp.: 120
Retailer of Lumber & Other Building Materials
N.A.I.C.S.: 423310
Don Lightfoot (Pres)
Jerry Lightfoot (VP)

ORANGE COUNTY HEAD START, INC.
2501 S Pullman St Ste 100, Santa Ana, CA 92705
Tel.: (714) 241-8920 CA
Web Site: http://www.ochsinc.org
Year Founded: 1979
Sales Range: $25-49.9 Million
Emp.: 400
Child & Family Care Services
N.A.I.C.S.: 624190
Michelle Ahmad (Dir-Program Svcs)
Natalie Sarle (Dir-Plng Dev & Quality Sys)
Colleen Versteeg (Exec Dir)
Loyal Sharp (Dir-Fin & Admin)
Valerie Padilla (Dir-Educational Svcs)
Margaret Macari (Chm)
Mandy Corrales (Vice Chm)

ORANGE COUNTY NATIONAL GOLF CENTER & LODGE
16301 Phil Ritson Way, Winter Garden, FL 34787
Tel.: (407) 656-2626
Web Site: http://www.ocngolf.com
Year Founded: 1994
Sales Range: $10-24.9 Million
Emp.: 150
Golf Course & Club Owner & Operator
N.A.I.C.S.: 713910
Bruce Gerlander (Gen Mgr)
Alan Walker (Dir-Golf)
Charles Kinard (Dir-Info Sys)
Jimmy Bell (Dir-Sls-Mktg)
Ben Tharp (Mgr)

ORANGE COUNTY REMC
7133 N State Rd 337, Orleans, IN 47452
Tel.: (812) 865-2229 IN
Web Site: http://www.orangecountyremc.org
Year Founded: 1937
Sales Range: $10-24.9 Million
Emp.: 27
Electric Power Distr
N.A.I.C.S.: 221122
Brian Hawkins (VP)
Eugene Roberts (Treas & Sec)
Ben Lindsey (Pres)

ORANGE COUNTY SCHOOL READINESS COALITION, INC.
1940 Traylor Blvd, Orlando, FL 32804
Tel.: (407) 841-6607 FL
Web Site: http://www.elcofororangecounty.org
Year Founded: 2000
Sales Range: $50-74.9 Million
Emp.: 62
Educational Support Services
N.A.I.C.S.: 611710
Cindy Jurie (Dir-Res & Special Projects)
Darlene Jones (Mgr-Provider Rels)
Karen Willis (CEO)
Leonardo Almanza (Chief Admin Officer)
Erika Cooper (Sec)
Kari Conley (Vice Chm)
Lois Smith (Dir-Provider Svcs)
Paul Roldan (Treas)
Stacey Reynolds-Carruth (Dir-Community Relations & Resource Dev)

ORANGE COUNTY SPEAKER, INC.
12141 Mariners Way, Garden Grove, CA 92843-4023
Tel.: (714) 554-8520 CA
Web Site: http://www.speakerrepair.com
Year Founded: 1968
Sales Range: $10-24.9 Million
Emp.: 5
Speaker Equipment Repair & Sales
N.A.I.C.S.: 811210
Bryan Sunda (Owner)
Sharon Sunda (Pres)

ORANGE COUNTY TRANSPORTATION AUTHORITY
550 S Main St, Orange, CA 92868
Tel.: (714) 560-6282
Web Site: http://www.octa.net
Year Founded: 1972
Sales Range: $75-99.9 Million
Emp.: 2,000
Provider of Local & Suburban Transit
N.A.I.C.S.: 485113
Michael Hennessey (Chm)
Lisa A. Bartlett (Vice Chm)

ORANGE COUNTY WATER DISTRICT
18700 Ward St, Fountain Valley, CA 92708-6921
Tel.: (714) 378-3200 CA
Web Site: http://www.ocwd.com
Year Founded: 1933
Sales Range: $25-49.9 Million
Emp.: 175
Ground Water Information Agency
N.A.I.C.S.: 221310
Denis R. Bilodeau (Pres)
Philip L. Anthony (First VP)
Mike Markus (Gen Mgr)
Shawn Dewane (Second VP)

ORANGE COUNTY'S CREDIT UNION
PO Box 11777, Santa Ana, CA 92711-1777
Tel.: (714) 755-5900 CA
Web Site: http://www.orangecountyscu.org
Year Founded: 1938
Sales Range: $25-49.9 Million
Credit Union
N.A.I.C.S.: 522130
Lynda Savoit (COO & Sr VP)
Avery Robinson (VP-Org Dev)
Jeff Harper (Chief Lending Officer & Sr VP)
Greg Krause (CFO & Sr VP)
Shruti S. Miyashiro (Pres & CEO)
Vikki Beatley (Chm)
Chris Chase (Treas)
Dan Dillon (Sec)
Walt Krause (Vice Chm)
Laura Thompson (CIO & Sr VP)
Steven Ritchie (VP-Enterprise Risk Mgmt)
Susan Huss (VP-Consumer Lending)
Carlos Miramontez (VP-Mortgage Lending)

ORANGE GROVE CO-OPERATIVE
Hwy 359, Orange Grove, TX 78372
Tel.: (361) 384-2766 TX
Web Site: http://www.orangegrovecoop.com
Sales Range: $1-9.9 Million
Emp.: 20
Provider Of Agricultural Services
N.A.I.C.S.: 424510
Matt Habelka (Gen Mgr)
Pat Garcia (Office Mgr)

ORANGE LABEL ART & ADVERTISING
2043 Westcliff Dr Ste 303, Newport Beach, CA 92660
Tel.: (949) 631-9900 CA
Web Site: http://www.orangelabeladvertising.com
Year Founded: 1972
Sales Range: $10-24.9 Million
Emp.: 15
Advertising Specialties, Business-To-Business, Co-op Advertising, Direct Marketing, Hispanic Marketing, Information Technology, Media Buying Services, Radio, Retail, Strategic Planning, Teen Market
N.A.I.C.S.: 541810
Wesley Phillips (CEO)
Ian Crockett (Pres)
Deborah Nagel (Dir-Fin)
Rochelle Reider (VP)
Colleen Haberman (Dir-Special Projects)
Dustin Phillips (Mgr-Production)
Julia Laboski (Acct Exec & Copywriter)
Alise Vultree (Acct Exec)
Kim Chow (Coord-Media, Acct & Res)
Mike Thompson (Acct Exec & Digital Media Specialist)

ORANGE MOTOR COMPANY INC.
799 Central Ave, Albany, NY 12206
Tel.: (518) 489-5414 NY
Web Site: http://www.orangemotors.com
Year Founded: 1916
Sales Range: $125-149.9 Million
Emp.: 138
Provider of New & Used Automobile Sales, Parts & Service
N.A.I.C.S.: 441110
Carl W. Keegan (VP)
Rich Bell (Mgr-Accts)
Brian Randio (Mgr-Mktg)
Vince Speciale (Gen Mgr-Sls)

ORANGE PEEL ENTERPRISES, INC.
2183 Ponce De Leon Cir, Vero Beach, FL 32960
Tel.: (772) 562-2766
Web Site: http://www.greensplus.com
Year Founded: 1990
Rev.: $9,000,000
Emp.: 26
Groceries & Health Food Whslr
N.A.I.C.S.: 424490
Lani Deauville (Treas & VP)

ORANGE TREE STAFFING, LLC
111 E Fairbanks Ave, Winter Park, FL 32789
Tel.: (407) 388-4010
Web Site: http://www.orangetreestaffing.com
Year Founded: 2010
Sales Range: $1-9.9 Million
Emp.: 7
Human Resource Consulting Services
N.A.I.C.S.: 541612
Mardly R. Perez-Smith (Founder, Owner & Pres)
Cris Clark (Mgr-Payroll)

ORANGE WATER & SEWER AUTHORITY
400 Jones Ferry Rd, Carrboro, NC 27510
Tel.: (919) 968-4421
Web Site: http://www.owasa.org

ORANGE WATER & SEWER AUTHORITY

Orange Water & Sewer Authority—(Continued)
Year Founded: 1977
Rev.: $36,185,840
Assets: $360,974,764
Liabilities: $90,985,202
Net Worth: $269,989,562
Earnings: $7,531,609
Emp.: 130
Fiscal Year-end: 06/30/19
Water & Sewer Utility
N.A.I.C.S.: 221310
Ed Kerwin (Exec Dir)
Ed Holland (Dir-Plng)
Dan Przybyl (Dir-Bus IT Svcs)

ORANGE WORLD INC.
5395 W Irlo Bronson Memorial Hwy, Kissimmee, FL 34746-4711
Tel.: (407) 239-6031
Web Site: http://www.orangeworld192.com
Fruit Sales
N.A.I.C.S.: 424480
Eli Sfassie (Owner)

ORANGEWOOD PARTNERS LLC
9 W 57th St 33rd Fl, New York, NY 10019
Tel.: (212) 324-5630   DE
Web Site: http://www.orangewoodpartner.com
Year Founded: 2015
Privater Equity Firm
N.A.I.C.S.: 523999
Alan Goldfarb (Founder & Mng Partner)
Niel Goldfarb (Mng Partner)
Zach Rosskamm (Principal)

ORANGUTAN HOME SERVICES
2922 S Roosevelt St, Tempe, AZ 85282
Tel.: (602) 906-0111
Web Site: http://www.oservice.com
Year Founded: 1993
Sales Range: $10-24.9 Million
Emp.: 300
Plumbing, Heating & Air-Conditioning Contracting Services
N.A.I.C.S.: 238220
Ron Schuman (Owner)

ORANJTEK CO.
3422 Old Capitol Trl Ste 700, Wilmington, DE 19808
Tel.: (302) 996-5819   DE
Year Founded: 2013
Umbrella Mfr
N.A.I.C.S.: 339999
Karen Travis (Pres, CEO, CFO & Principal Acctg Officer)
Don Bodnar (CTO)

ORASI SOFTWARE, INC.
114 TownPark Dr Ste 400, Kennesaw, GA 30144
Tel.: (678) 819-5300
Web Site: http://www.orasi.com
Year Founded: 2002
Sales Range: $50-74.9 Million
Emp.: 202
Software Testing Services
N.A.I.C.S.: 541511
Nicholas Kavadellas (Pres & CEO)
James Azar (CTO & Sr VP)
Karl Rubin (Sr VP-Ops)
Caleb Billingsley (Sr VP-Performance, Data & Delivery)
Mark Lewis (Sr VP-Sls & Mktg)
Hardik Parekh (Mgr-Mobile & Internet of Things Automation-Quality Mgmt Sys)
James Arnold Jr. (Sr VP-Strategic Accts)

ORBEL CORPORATION
2 Danforth Dr, Easton, PA 18045
Tel.: (610) 829-5000   NJ
Web Site: http://www.orbel.com
Year Founded: 1961
Sales Range: $50-74.9 Million
Emp.: 50
Photo Chemical Milling, Chemical Etching, Electroplating & Precision Metal Parts Mfr
N.A.I.C.S.: 332813
Kenneth Marino (Pres & CEO)
Jon Raseley (Mgr-Plant)

ORBIMED ADVISORS LLC
601 Lexington Ave at 53rd St 54th Fl, New York, NY 10022-4629
Tel.: (212) 739-6400   DE
Web Site: http://www.orbimed.com
Year Founded: 1989
Rev.: $11,000,000,000
Emp.: 50
Healthcare & Pharmaceutical Industry Equity Investment & Fund Management Services
N.A.I.C.S.: 523999
Peter A. Thompson (Partner)
Samuel D. Isaly (Founder)
Sven H. Borho (Mng Partner)
Jonathan Todd Silverstein (Mng Partner)
W. Carter Neild (Gen Partner)
Kerrie Swingle (Dir-Investor Svcs)
Chau Quang Khuong (Partner- & Principal)
Alexander M. Cooper (Gen Counsel)
William Price (Mng Dir)
Kirsten Kearns (Head-HR-Global)
Ryan Loggie (Dir-Acctg & Tax)
Doug Coon (Chief Compliance Officer)
Kevin P. Olsen (Dir-Trading Ops)
Daniel Rhee (CTO)
Geoffrey C. Hsu (Partner)
Evan Sotiriou (CFO)
Swati Bansal (VP-Public Equity-Asia)
Tal Zaks (Partner-Venture)
Andrew P. Kanarek (Chief Risk Officer)
David Wang (Sr Mng Dir-Asia)
Erez Chimovits (Sr Mng Dir-Israel)
Ken Tang (VP)
Mark R. Jelley (VP)
Patrick P. Lally (VP)
Sunny Sharma (Sr Mng Dir-Asia)
Michael Eggenberg (Mng Dir)
Matthew Rizzo (Gen Partner)
Scott Green (Partner)
Richard D. Klemm (Partner)
Trevor M. Polischuk (Partner)
William F. Sawyer (Partner)
C. Scotland Stevens (Gen Partner)
Badreddin Edris (VP)
Mona Ashiya (Principal)
David Bonita (Executive)
Anat Naschitz (Mng Dir-Israel)
Klaus R. Veitinger (Venture Partner)
Rishi Gupta (Partner)
David P. Bonita (Partner-Private Equity)
Carl L. Gordon (Founding Partner & Co-Head-Global Private Equity)

Subsidiaries:

Response Biomedical Corp.   (1)
1781 - 75th Avenue W, Vancouver, V6P 6P2, BC, Canada   (63.2%)
Tel.: (604) 456-6010
Web Site: https://www.responsebio.com
Sales Range: $10-24.9 Million
Emp.: 56
Diagnostic & Therapeutic Products Mfr
N.A.I.C.S.: 339112
Peter A. Thompson (Executives)
Barbara R. Kinnaird (CEO)
Lewis J. Shuster (Chm)
Eric Whitters (COO)

ORBIS CASCADE ALLIANCE
2288 Oakmont Way, Eugene, OR 97401
Tel.: (541) 246-2470   OR
Web Site: http://www.orbiscascade.org
Year Founded: 2010
Sales Range: $10-24.9 Million
Library Management Services
N.A.I.C.S.: 519210
Keith Folsom (Mgr-IT)
Greg Doyle (Mgr-Electronic Res Program)
Al Cornish (Mgr-Shared ILS Program)

ORBIS TECHNOLOGIES, INC.
180 Admiral Cochrane Dr Ste 305, Annapolis, MD 21041
Tel.: (443) 569-6701   DE
Web Site: http://www.orbistechnologies.com
Year Founded: 2006
Strategic Technology Consulting Services
N.A.I.C.S.: 541611
Matt Fernandez (CFO)
Steven Ploof (VP-Ops & Customer Care)
Siobhan O'Hare (VP-Content Mgmt)
Thuy Pisone (Exec VP-Global Svcs)
Brian Ippolito (Pres & CEO)

Subsidiaries:

Writing Assistance, Inc.   (1)
3140 Harbor Ln Ste 130, Plymouth, MN 55447
Tel.: (763) 551-9772
Web Site: http://www.writingassist.com
Sales Range: $1-9.9 Million
Emp.: 16
Employment Placement Services
N.A.I.C.S.: 561311
Scott Hartmann (Pres & CEO)

ORBISONIA COMMUNITY BANCORP INC.
761 Elliott St, Orbisonia, PA 17243
Tel.: (814) 447-5552
Web Site: http://www.csborbisonia.com
Sales Range: $100-124.9 Million
Emp.: 91
State Commercial Banks
N.A.I.C.S.: 522110
Trudy Everhart (Pres)
Jessica Tice (Chm)

ORBIT EXPORTS LTD.
835-B San Julian St, Los Angeles, CA 90014
Tel.: (213) 623-6007
Textile & Fabric Product Distr
N.A.I.C.S.: 424310

ORBIT MEDIA STUDIOS, INC.
4043 N Ravens Ste 316, Chicago, IL 60613
Tel.: (773) 348-4581
Web Site: http://www.orbitmedia.com
Sales Range: $1-9.9 Million
Emp.: 30
Interactive Marketing Services
N.A.I.C.S.: 518210
Rene Fiel (Project Mgr)
Ben Steinbuhler (Project Mgr-Technical)
Andy Crestodina (Co-Founder & Dir-Strategy)
Amanda Gant (Mgr-Mktg)
Barrett Lombardo (Co-Founder & COO)
Todd Gettelfinger (CEO)
Anand Shukla (Dir-Project Mgmt)
Joe Daleo (Mgr-Web Dev)
Kurt Cruse (Dir-Creative)
Shellie Argeanton (Designer-Lead Web)

ORBIT SYSTEMS, INC.
22981 Mill Creek Dr, Laguna Hills, CA 92653
Tel.: (949) 852-9999
Web Site: http://www.orbitdirect.net
Sales Range: $50-74.9 Million
Emp.: 400
Electronic Components Distr
N.A.I.C.S.: 423690
Omar Turbi (Pres)

ORBITA CORPORATION
1205 Culbreth Dr, Wilmington, NC 28405
Tel.: (910) 256-5300
Web Site: http://www.orbita.net
Sales Range: $10-24.9 Million
Emp.: 30
Watchwinders Mfr
N.A.I.C.S.: 334519
Evelyn Agnoff (Owner)

ORBITA, INC.
1 Seaport Sq 77 Sleeper St Fl 2, Boston, MA 02210
Tel.: (617) 804-5550
Web Site: https://orbita.ai
Year Founded: 2015
Software Publisher
N.A.I.C.S.: 513210
Patty Riskind (CEO)
James Donato (CTO)
Mark Cline (VP-Customer Success)
Bill Rogers (Chm)
Nathan Treloar (COO)
Elizabeth Glaser (CMO)

Subsidiaries:

Wellbe, Inc.   (1)
8040 Excelsior Dr Ste 402, Madison, WI 53717
Tel.: (800) 960-4118
Web Site: http://www.wellbe.me
Sales Range: $1-9.9 Million
Healtcare Services
N.A.I.C.S.: 621498
James Dias (Founder & CEO)
David Elderbrock (CTO)
Abraham Palmbach (Pres & COO)
Kathryne Auerback (Dir-Product Mktg)
Bill Andrae (Dir-Customer Success)
Cody Cry (Mgr-Implementation Success)
Mike Fulton (Mgr-Customer Success)
Vicki Gentz (Mgr-Customer Success)
Melanie Glick (Dir-CarePath Solutions)
C. H. Walter Janssen (Mgr-Program-CarePath)
Ben Kojis (Coord-Product Dev)
Katie Boyd McGlenn (Dir-Innovation Res)
Maeghan Nicholson (Dir-Mktg Ops)
Caleb Ray (Mgr-Implementation Success)
Debra Voss (VP-Svc Line Solutions)
Meaghan Watson (Mgr-Customer Success)
Joel Weirauch (Engr-DevOps)
David Yoerger (VP-Health Sys Solutions)

ORBITFORM GROUP, LLC
1600 Executive Dr, Jackson, MI 49203-3469
Tel.: (517) 787-9447   MI
Web Site: http://www.orbitform.com
Year Founded: 2001
Sales Range: $25-49.9 Million
Emp.: 70
Bolt, Screw & Rivet Mfr
N.A.I.C.S.: 332722
Mike Shirkey (Owner)
Sean Cumming (Mgr-Reg Sls)
John Price (Mgr-Bus Dev)
Kevin Haueter (Reg Mgr-Sls)

ORC INDUSTRIES, INC.

COMPANIES

2700 Commerce St, La Crosse, WI 54603
Tel.: (608) 781-7727   WI
Web Site: http://www.orcind.com
Year Founded: 1966
Sales Range: $25-49.9 Million
Developmental Disability Assistance Services
N.A.I.C.S.: 624120
Barbara Barnard *(Pres)*

ORC UTILITY & INFRASTRUCTURE LAND SERVICES, LLC
7005 Shannon Willow Rd Ste 100, Charlotte, NC 28226
Tel.: (704) 529-3115
Web Site: http://orcolan.com
Year Founded: 2010
Sales Range: $25-49.9 Million
Emp.: 120
Real Estate Services
N.A.I.C.S.: 531390
Catherine Colan Muth *(CEO)*
Karen Ammar *(Chm)*
Steve Toth *(Pres & COO)*
Carmen Johnson *(CFO & Chief Admin Officer)*
Richard McNally *(Exec VP-Utility Division)*

ORCAS POWER & LIGHT COOP
183 Mount Baker Rd, Eastsound, WA 98245
Tel.: (360) 376-3550
Web Site: http://www.opalco.com
Rev.: $12,003,628
Emp.: 50
Distribution, Electric Power
N.A.I.C.S.: 221122
Foster Hildreth *(Gen Mgr)*

ORCHARD CHRYSLER DODGE JEEP
64600 Van Dyke Rd, Washington, MI 48095
Tel.: (586) 336-0200
Web Site: http://www.orchardcdj.com
Year Founded: 1969
Sales Range: $10-24.9 Million
Emp.: 75
Car Whslr
N.A.I.C.S.: 441110
Robert Brent *(Pres)*

ORCHARD HOLDINGS GROUP LLC
8044 Montgomery Rd Ste 522, Cincinnati, OH 45236
Tel.: (513) 754-3500
Web Site: http://www.orchardholdings.com
Emp.: 8
Privater Equity Firm
N.A.I.C.S.: 523999
Phil Collins *(Co-Founder & Mng Dir)*
Pete Boylan *(Co-Founder & Mng Dir)*
Jason Roudabush *(VP)*

ORCHARD INC.
1110 Main St Ste 200, Cincinnati, OH 45202
Tel.: (513) 438-8504
Web Site: http://ww.growatorchard.com
Year Founded: 2016
Sales Range: $1-9.9 Million
Emp.: 50
Online Shopping Services
N.A.I.C.S.: 512250
Cliff Schwandner *(Pres)*
Richard Walker *(Co-Founder & COO)*
Matt McKeown *(Co-Founder & Dir-Data Analytics)*
Kara Schwandner *(Co-Founder)*

ORCHARD, HILTZ & MCCLIMENT INC.
34000 Plymouth Rd, Livonia, MI 48150
Tel.: (734) 522-6711
Web Site: http://www.ohm-advisors.com
Year Founded: 1962
Rev.: $18,031,202
Emp.: 300
Consulting & Engineering Services
N.A.I.C.S.: 541620
Daniel Fredendall *(VP-Corp Svcs)*
Patrick Wingate *(Dir-Transportation)*
Gary Sebach *(Dir-Architectural Design)*

ORCHID ISLAND JUICE COMPANY
330 N Us Hwy 1, Fort Pierce, FL 34950
Tel.: (772) 465-1122
Web Site: http://www.orchidislandjuice.com
Rev.: $12,000,000
Emp.: 85
Grocery & Related Products Merchant Whslr
N.A.I.C.S.: 424490
David Cortez *(Chief Bus Officer)*
Marygrace Sexton *(CEO)*
Christine Diaz *(CFO)*
Michael D'Amato *(Dir-Sls)*
Joseph Caddy *(Plant Mgr)*
Lance Conley *(Mgr-Sls)*
Frank Tranchilla *(COO)*
P. J. Roustan *(Dir-Mktg)*

ORCO BLOCK COMPANY INC.
11100 Beach Blvd, Stanton, CA 90680-3207
Tel.: (714) 527-2239   CA
Web Site: http://www.orco.com
Year Founded: 1944
Sales Range: $100-124.9 Million
Emp.: 200
Mfr of Concrete Blocks
N.A.I.C.S.: 327331
Richard Muth *(Pres & Owner)*
Barbara Conibear *(Mgr-Credit)*

Subsidiaries:

ORCO Blended Products, Inc.   (1)
27347 E 3rd St, Highland, CA 92346
Tel.: (909) 862-2480
Web Site: http://www.orcoblendedproducts.com
Readymix Concrete Mfr
N.A.I.C.S.: 327320
Luciano Lopez *(Gen Mgr)*

Orco Block Company Inc. - ORCO Pavingstones Division   (1)
4545 Rutile St, Riverside, CA 92509
Tel.: (951) 685-8498
Web Site: http://www.orco.com
Emp.: 50
Paving Block Mfr
N.A.I.C.S.: 327331
Tom Hancock *(Mgr-Ops)*

Plant (Domestic):

ORCO Pavingstones - COACHELLA / IMPERIAL PLANT   (2)
35-240 Dillon Rd, Indio, CA 92201
Tel.: (760) 347-4000
Paving Block Mfr
N.A.I.C.S.: 327331

ORCO Pavingstones - INLAND EMPIRE PLANT   (2)
4545 Rutile St, Riverside, CA 92509
Tel.: (951) 685-8498
Web Site: http://www.orco.com
Emp.: 25
Paving Block Mfr
N.A.I.C.S.: 327331

ORCO Pavingstones - ORANGE / LOS ANGELES PLANT   (2)
11100 Beach Blvd, Stanton, CA 90680
Tel.: (714) 527-2239
Paving Block Mfr
N.A.I.C.S.: 327331

ORCO Pavingstones - TEMECULA VALLEY PLANT   (2)
26380 Palomar Rd, Romoland, CA 92585
Tel.: (951) 928-3839
Web Site: http://www.orco.com
Emp.: 11
Paving Block Mfr
N.A.I.C.S.: 327331
Clint Russell *(Office Mgr)*

ORCON CORPORATION
1570 Atlantic St, Union City, CA 94587
Tel.: (510) 489-8100
Web Site: http://www.orcon.com
Sales Range: $25-49.9 Million
Emp.: 50
Spunbonded Fabrics
N.A.I.C.S.: 327120
Hollis H. Bascom *(Pres)*
Bob Zajdel *(Gen Mgr)*
Dennis Murray *(CEO)*
Tom Macedo *(Plant Mgr)*

ORCUS TECHNOLOGIES, INC
5014 Gary Ave Unite 6888, Lubbock, TX 79493
Tel.: (866) 684-7191
Web Site: https://timeforge.com
Year Founded: 2007
Software Devolopment
N.A.I.C.S.: 513210

Subsidiaries:

Surveyconnect Inc.   (1)
5480 Valmont Rd Ste 225, Boulder, CO 80301-9405
Tel.: (303) 449-2969
Web Site: http://www.surveyconnect.com
Software Publisher
N.A.I.C.S.: 513210
Margie Brown *(Dir-Sls)*

ORDERS CONSTRUCTION COMPANY, INC.
501 6th Ave, Saint Albans, WV 25177
Tel.: (304) 722-4237
Web Site: http://www.ordersconstruction.com
Year Founded: 1966
Sales Range: $250-299.9 Million
Emp.: 8,000
Provider of Bridge & Tunnel Construction Services
N.A.I.C.S.: 237310
Robert O. Orders *(Founder)*
Don Sparks *(Controller)*
Nate Orders *(Pres)*
John Persun *(VP)*
Robert O. Orders Jr. *(CEO)*

ORE PHARMACEUTICALS INC.
One Main St Ste 300, Cambridge, MA 02142
Tel.: (617) 649-2001   DE
Web Site: http://www.orepharma.com
Year Founded: 1994
Sales Range: $1-4.9 Billion
Emp.: 14
Drug Discovery & Development Genomic & Data Management Technologies
N.A.I.C.S.: 325412
J. Stark Thompson *(Chm)*
Mark J. Gabrielson *(Pres & CEO)*
Stephen R. Donahue *(Sr VP)*

ORE-CAL CORPORATION
634 Crocker St, Los Angeles, CA 90021
Tel.: (213) 680-9540

OREGON CASCADE PLUMBING & HEATING, INC.

Web Site: http://www.ore-cal.com
Rev.: $120,000,000
Emp.: 70
Frozen Fish, Meat & Poultry
N.A.I.C.S.: 424420
Jojo Favis *(Mgr-HR)*
Juan Trevino *(Mgr-Logistics)*
Toni Tuck *(Controller)*
Mark Shinbane *(Pres)*

OREG SITE WORK SERVICES, LLC
350-C Fortune Ter Ste 218, Potomac, MD 20854
Tel.: (301) 960-4419
Web Site: http://www.nextdaydumpsters.com
Year Founded: 2007
Sales Range: $10-24.9 Million
Emp.: 26
Roll Off Dumpster Rental Services
N.A.I.C.S.: 562212
Matt Owings *(CEO)*

OREGON AERO, INC.
34020 Skwy Dr, Scappoose, OR 97056
Tel.: (503) 543-7399
Web Site: http://www.oregonaero.com
Sales Range: $25-49.9 Million
Emp.: 70
Aircraft Seating Equipment, Padding & Tool Mfr
N.A.I.C.S.: 336413
Jude Dennis *(Owner)*
Mike Dennis *(Founder, Pres & CEO)*
Lisa Maxim *(Mgr-HR)*

OREGON AFFORDABLE HOUSING ASSISTANCE CORPORATION
725 Summer St NE Ste B, Salem, OR 97301-1266
Tel.: (503) 986-2000   OR
Web Site: http://www.oregon.gov
Year Founded: 2010
Sales Range: $25-49.9 Million
Community Housing Assistance Services
N.A.I.C.S.: 624229
Julie Cody *(Treas)*
Kim Freeman *(Sec)*

OREGON CANADIAN FOREST PRODUCTS INC.
31950 Comml St NW, North Plains, OR 97133
Tel.: (503) 647-5011   OR
Web Site: http://www.ocfp.com
Year Founded: 1977
Sales Range: $25-49.9 Million
Emp.: 120
Lumber Mill Mfr
N.A.I.C.S.: 321912
Mike Holm *(Pres)*
Dustin Houeland *(CFO)*

Subsidiaries:

Industrial Pine Products, Inc.   (1)
220 Park Ave, Newberry, SC 29108
Tel.: (803) 276-9118
Hardwood Products Mfr
N.A.I.C.S.: 321211

OREGON CASCADE PLUMBING & HEATING, INC.
1728 22nd St SE, Salem, OR 97302-1255
Tel.: (503) 588-0355
Web Site: http://www.oregoncascade.com
Sales Range: $10-24.9 Million
Emp.: 100
Plumbing Services
N.A.I.C.S.: 238220

OREGON CASCADE PLUMBING & HEATING, INC.   **U.S. PRIVATE**

Oregon Cascade Plumbing & Heating, Inc.—(Continued)
Josh Welborn (Mgr)

OREGON CHERRY GROWERS INC.
1520 Woodrow St NE, Salem, OR 97301
Tel.: (503) 364-8421   OR
Web Site: http://www.orcherry.com
Year Founded: 1932
Sales Range: $50-74.9 Million
Emp.: 250
Maraschino Cherries Process, Retailer & Whslr
N.A.I.C.S.: 115114
Steve Travis (VP-Ops)
Matthew Gillespie (Dir-Mktg)
Don Bachouros (Mgr-Natl Sls-Ingredients)
Steven Anderson (Sr VP)
Naomi Schefcik (Corp Controller)
Chantal Wright (VP-Sls & Bus Dev)

Subsidiaries:

Oregon Cherry Growers (1)
PO Box 1577, The Dalles, OR 97058-8004
Tel.: (541) 296-5487
Web Site: http://www.orcherry.com
Canned Cherry & Fruits Specialties
N.A.I.C.S.: 311421
Tim Ramsey (CEO & Pres)

Oregon Cherry Growers Inc. - THE DALLES PLANT (1)
1st & Madison, The Dalles, OR 97058
Tel.: (541) 296-5487
Frozen Fruit Mfr
N.A.I.C.S.: 311411

OREGON CHILD DEVELOPMENT COALITION, INC.
9140 SW Pioneer Ct Ste E, Wilsonville, OR 97070
Tel.: (503) 570-1110   OR
Web Site: http://www.ocdc.net
Year Founded: 1971
Sales Range: $25-49.9 Million
Emp.: 1,377
Child Development Services
N.A.I.C.S.: 624110
Donalda Dodson (Exec Dir)
Don Horeseman (Dir-Fiscal)
Brian Schmedinghoff (Dir-Resource Dev)
Walter Kalinowski (Dir-HR)
LaRue Williams (Program Dir)
Maria Mottaghian (Program Dir)
Martha Ibarra (Program Dir)
Nora Kramer (Program Dir)
Anedelia Vasquez (Program Dir)
Barbara Fuentez (Program Dir)
Jennifer Heredia (Program Dir)
Geoffrey Lowry (Program Dir)
Lori Clark (Program Dir)
Grant Baxter (Chm)

OREGON COFFEE ROASTER, INC.
PO Box 223, North Plains, OR 97133
Tel.: (503) 647-5102
Web Site: http://www.oregoncoffee.com
Year Founded: 1985
Sales Range: $10-24.9 Million
Emp.: 20
Roasted Coffee Mfr & Whslr
N.A.I.C.S.: 311920
John Turner (Pres)
Cindy Ertell (Co-Owner)
Janet Munkres (Co-Owner)
Bobi Turner (Sec)

OREGON COMMUNITY CREDIT UNION
2880 Chad Dr, Eugene, OR 97408
Tel.: (541) 687-2347   OR
Web Site: http://www.oregoncommunitycu.org
Year Founded: 1956
Sales Range: $50-74.9 Million
Emp.: 334
Credit Union
N.A.I.C.S.: 522130
Bev Anderson (Chm)
Tom Larson (Vice Chm)
Genevieve Parker (Sec)
Mandy Jones (CEO & Treas)
Stephenie Phelan-Higa (Coord-Investment Svcs Admin)

OREGON EDUCATION ASSOCIATION
6900 SW Atlanta St, Portland, OR 97223
Tel.: (503) 684-3300   OR
Web Site: http://www.oregoned.org
Year Founded: 1927
Sales Range: $10-24.9 Million
Emp.: 136
Educational Support Services
N.A.I.C.S.: 611710
Hanna Vaandering (Pres)
Tony Crawford (VP)
Richard Sanders (Exec Dir)

OREGON ELECTRIC GROUP
1709 SE 3rd Ave, Portland, OR 97214-2507
Tel.: (503) 234-9900
Web Site: http://www.oregon-electric.com
Year Founded: 1961
Sales Range: $50-74.9 Million
Emp.: 900
Providers of Electrical Work
N.A.I.C.S.: 238210
Todd Grafley (Exec VP)
Jeff Theide (CEO)
Rutherford Justin (Mgr-Svcs)
Rob Wernli (Project Mgr)

OREGON INTERNATIONAL AIR FREIGHT COMPANY INC.
2100 SW River Pkwy, Portland, OR 97201
Tel.: (503) 736-5900
Web Site: http://www.oiaglobal.com
Year Founded: 1988
Sales Range: $25-49.9 Million
Emp.: 300
Provider of Freight Transportation Arrangements
N.A.I.C.S.: 488510
Steve Akre (Chm)
Eric Okimoto (VP)
Tim Sether (CFO)
Daniel McMorris (VP-Strategic Initiative)
Daniel Fornari (VP)

OREGON MUTUAL INSURANCE COMPANY, INC.
400 NE Baker St, McMinnville, OR 97128
Tel.: (503) 472-2141   OR
Web Site: http://www.ormutual.com
Year Founded: 1894
Sales Range: $100-124.9 Million
Emp.: 235
Dental Insurance Carrier & Direct Services
N.A.I.C.S.: 524114
Chuck Katter (VP-Clients)
Steve Patterson (Pres)

Subsidiaries:

Western Protectors Insurance Company (1)
PO Box 808, McMinnville, OR 97128
Tel.: (503) 472-2141
Web Site: http://www.ormutual.com
Sales Range: $50-74.9 Million
Emp.: 175
Insurance Agents, Brokers & Service
N.A.I.C.S.: 524210

OREGON NEWSPAPER ADVERTISING CO.
7150 SW Hampton St Ste 111, Portland, OR 97223-8365
Tel.: (503) 624-6397
Web Site: http://www.orenews.com
Year Founded: 1935
Sales Range: $10-24.9 Million
Emp.: 8
Newspaper Advertising Services
N.A.I.C.S.: 541810
Laurie Hieb (Exec Dir)

OREGON PALLET REPAIR, INC.
1805 SE 22nd St, Salem, OR 97302
Tel.: (503) 585-9999
Web Site: http://www.oregonpallet.com
Year Founded: 1998
Sales Range: $10-24.9 Million
Emp.: 85
Wood Container & Pallet Mfr
N.A.I.C.S.: 321920
Bryce Taylor (Pres)

OREGON POTATO COMPANY
6610 W Ct St, Kennewick, WA 99301-2010
Tel.: (509) 545-4545   WA
Web Site: http://www.oregonpotato.com
Potato Products, Dried & Dehydrated
N.A.I.C.S.: 311423
Frank Tiegs (Pres)

Subsidiaries:

Rader Farms, Inc. (1)
1270 E Badger Rd, Lynden, WA 98264
Tel.: (360) 354-6574
Web Site: http://www.raderfarms.com
Berry Farming Services
N.A.I.C.S.: 111334

Willamette Valley Fruit Company (1)
2994 82nd Ave NE, Salem, OR 97305
Tel.: (503) 586-2200
Web Site: http://www.wvfco.com
Berry Farming Services
N.A.I.C.S.: 111333
Dave Dunn (Gen Mgr)
Scott Dunn (Mgr-Ops)
Brent Sinn (Mgr-Maintenance)
Derek Imig (Mgr-Inventory & Sls)
Randy Chittenden (Accountant-Frozen Div)
Chuck Cato (Supvr-Food Safety)

OREGON RESTAURANT SERVICES, INC.
2444 NW 24th Ave, Portland, OR 97210
Tel.: (503) 228-5058
Sales Range: $10-24.9 Million
Emp.: 6
Family Restaurant Operating Services
N.A.I.C.S.: 722511
Dan Fischer (Pres & Sec)

OREGON SHAKESPEARE FESTIVAL
15 S Pioneer St, Ashland, OR 97520
Tel.: (541) 482-2111   OR
Web Site: http://www.osfashland.org
Year Founded: 1935
Sales Range: $25-49.9 Million
Emp.: 605
Theater
N.A.I.C.S.: 711110
Alys E. Holden (Dir-Production)
David Carey (Dir-Resident Voice & Text)
Scott Kaiser (Dir-Dev)
Bill Rauch (Dir-Artistic)
Cynthia Rider (Exec Dir)
Joan Langley (Dir-Education)
Katherine Gosnell (Mgr-Outreach Programs)
Torrie Allen (Dir-Dev)

OREGON STATE UNIVERSITY BOOKSTORE
663 SW 26th St, Corvallis, OR 97339
Tel.: (541) 737-4323
Web Site: http://www.osubookstore.com
Rev.: $15,837,483
Emp.: 155
Book Stores
N.A.I.C.S.: 459210
Brian E. Davis (Supvr-Digital Production Unit)
Bill Boyce (Dir-SHS Pharmacy)
Joe Bernert (Mgr-GIS & Database)
Scott Nelson (Asst Dir-Athletic Dev)

OREGON TRAIL EQUIPMENT LLC
4815 West Hwy 6, Hastings, NE 68901
Tel.: (402) 463-1339
Web Site: http://www.oregontraileq.com
Sales Range: $10-24.9 Million
Emp.: 150
Farm Implements
N.A.I.C.S.: 423820
Rick Bennett (Owner)

OREGON TRANSFER CO.
5910 N Cutter Cir, Portland, OR 97217
Tel.: (503) 943-3500
Web Site: http://www.oregontransfer.com
Sales Range: $10-24.9 Million
Emp.: 80
General Warehousing
N.A.I.C.S.: 493110
Steven D. Giering (Pres)
Joseph Lilly (CFO)
Amy Frewing (Dir-Client Svcs)
Mike Delaney (Dir-Ops)
Seth Schmedemann (Mgr-Bus Dev)
Steve Jeffrey (Dir-IT)
Victoria Masengale (Dir-HR)

OREN INTERNATIONAL INC.
1995 Hollywood Ave, Pensacola, FL 32505
Tel.: (850) 433-9080
Web Site: http://www.oren-intl.com
Sales Range: $25-49.9 Million
Emp.: 23
Mfr of Printing & Writing Paper
N.A.I.C.S.: 424110
Alan Nesmith (Pres)
Mark Jones (VP-Sls)

ORENCO SYSTEMS INC.
814 Airway Ave, Sutherlin, OR 97479
Tel.: (541) 459-4449
Web Site: http://www.orenco.com
Rev.: $10,600,000
Emp.: 230
Pump Jacks & Other Pumping Equipment
N.A.I.C.S.: 333914
Hal Ball (Pres)
Terry Bounds (Exec VP)
Mary Heilner (Mgr-HR)

ORENDA INTERNATIONAL, LLC
1406 W 14th St Ste 101, Tempe, AZ 85281-1000
Tel.: (480) 889-1001
Web Site: http://www.orendainternational.com

Year Founded: 2002
Sales Range: $1-9.9 Million
Emp.: 10
Anti-Aging, Immune & Weight Loss Products Whslr & Distr
N.A.I.C.S.: 424210
Year Founded: 1977
William Doug Sandstedt *(VP-Ops)*
Robert W. Hall *(Co-Founder)*
George W. Hall *(Co-Founder)*
Alaine Sepulveda *(VP-Sls)*

OREPAC HOLDING COMPANY INC.
30170 SW Ore Pac Ave, Wilsonville, OR 97070
Tel.: (503) 682-5050 OR
Web Site: http://www.orepac.com
Year Founded: 1977
Lumber, Plywood & Millwork Whslr
N.A.I.C.S.: 423310
Brad Hart *(Pres & CEO)*

Subsidiaries:

Bridger Forest Products (1)
2267 Amsterdam Rd, Belgrade, MT 59714-8903
Tel.: (406) 388-3383
Web Site:
 http://www.bridgerforestproducts.com
Lumber, Plywood, Millwork & Wood Panel Merchant Whslr
N.A.I.C.S.: 423310
Mike Hull *(Co-Owner)*
Steve Comer *(Co-Owner)*
Lynn Alpers *(CFO)*

Oregon Pacific Building Products Exchange Inc. (1)
30160 SW Ore Pac Ave, Wilsonville, OR 97070-9794
Tel.: (503) 682-5050
Sales Range: $10-24.9 Million
Emp.: 46
Lumber, Plywood & Millwork
N.A.I.C.S.: 423310
Glenn Hart *(Founder)*

Oregon Pacific Building Products Idaho Inc. (1)
5500 Federal Way, Boise, ID 83716 (100%)
Tel.: (208) 345-0562
Web Site: http://www.orepac.com
Sales Range: $10-24.9 Million
Emp.: 40
Lumber, Plywood & Millwork
N.A.I.C.S.: 423310
Steve Calverley *(Gen Mgr)*

Oregon Pacific Building Products Maple Inc. (1)
30160 SW Ore Pac Ave, Wilsonville, OR 97070-9794
Tel.: (503) 682-5050
Web Site: http://www.orepac.com
Rev.: $784,220,000
Emp.: 100
Lumber, Plywood & Millwork
N.A.I.C.S.: 423310
Glenn Hart *(Pres)*

Oregon Pacific Building Products Wash. Inc. (1)
30160 SW Ore Pac Ave, Wilsonville, OR 97070-9794
Tel.: (503) 682-5050
Web Site: http://www.orepac.com
Sales Range: $10-24.9 Million
Emp.: 100
Lumber, Plywood & Millwork
N.A.I.C.S.: 423310

ORG CHEM GROUP, LLC
2406 Lynch Rd, Evansville, IN 47711
Tel.: (800) 489-2306
Web Site: https://chem-group.com
Chemical Product & Preparation Mfr
N.A.I.C.S.: 325998

Subsidiaries:

MPR Services, Inc.
2443 N Gordon St Ste K, Alvin, TX 77511
Tel.: (281) 337-7424
Web Site: https://mprservices.com
Contaminant Removal Services
N.A.I.C.S.: 221320

ORGAIN BUILDING SUPPLY COMPANY
65 Commerce St, Clarksville, TN 37040
Tel.: (931) 647-1567
Web Site:
 http://www.orgainbuildingsupply.com
Sales Range: $10-24.9 Million
Emp.: 100
Lumber, Plywood & Millwork
N.A.I.C.S.: 423310
William H. Orgain *(Co-Owner & Pres)*
Jeremy Robertson *(Plant Mgr)*
David Russell *(Owner)*

ORGAN PROCUREMENT AGENCY OF MICHIGAN
3861 Research Park Dr, Ann Arbor, MI 48108
Tel.: (734) 973-1577 MI
Web Site:
 http://www.giftoflifemichigan.org
Year Founded: 1971
Sales Range: $1-9.9 Million
Emp.: 198
Organ Donation Services
N.A.I.C.S.: 621991
Anne Kowalczyk *(Chief Admin Officer)*
Bruce Nicely *(Chief Clinical Officer)*

ORGAN WORLDWIDE LLC
1603 Orrington Ave Unit 900, Evanston, IL 60201-3841
Tel.: (847) 866-9600
Web Site:
 http://www.organworldwide.com
Internet & Business Marketing & Consulting Services
N.A.I.C.S.: 541613
Larry Organ *(Chm)*

ORGANIC DYES AND PIGMENTS, LLC
65 Vly St, East Providence, RI 02914
Tel.: (401) 406-4164 DE
Web Site: http://www.organicdye.com
Year Founded: 1949
Dyes, Pigments & Chemical Auxiliaries Supplier
N.A.I.C.S.: 325130
John D'Amelio *(Pres)*

ORGANIC PLANT HEALTH, INC.
7077 E Marilyn Rd Ste 140, Scottsdale, AZ 85254
Tel.: (480) 779-0046 NV
Web Site:
 http://www.organicplanthealth.com
Sales Range: Less than $1 Million
Emp.: 4
Organic-Based, Natural & Environmentally Responsible Products Mfr, Distr & Sales
N.A.I.C.S.: 325312
William G. Styles *(Chm, Pres & CEO)*
J. Alan Talbert *(Vice Chm, COO & VP)*

ORGANICALLY GROWN CO.
1800B Prairie Rd, Eugene, OR 97402
Tel.: (541) 689-5320
Web Site:
 http://www.organicgrown.com
Year Founded: 1982
Rev.: $56,300,000
Emp.: 135
Fruits Vegetables & Herbs Whslr
N.A.I.C.S.: 424480
Robbie Vasilinda *(Dir-Fin)*

ORGANIZATIONAL DEVELOPMENT INC.
5311 Lake Worth Rd, Lake Worth, FL 33463
Tel.: (561) 304-0041
Sales Range: $10-24.9 Million
Emp.: 20
All Other Support Services
N.A.I.C.S.: 561990
Robert Preston *(Pres)*
John Monteagudo *(Mgr-PBA)*

ORGANIZATIONAL DYNAMICS INC.
36 Center St 163, Wolfeboro, NH 03894
Tel.: (781) 224-7300 MA
Web Site:
 http://www.orgdynamics.com
Year Founded: 1970
Sales Range: $50-74.9 Million
Emp.: 3
Provider of Training & Consulting Services for Business Design & Implementation of Management Development Quality Improvement
N.A.I.C.S.: 541618
Jane Joyce *(Dir-Ops)*

ORGANIZE.COM, INC.
6727 Columbus St, Riverside, CA 92504-1107
Tel.: (951) 351-7031
Web Site: http://www.organize.com
Year Founded: 1998
Sales Range: $10-24.9 Million
Emp.: 40
Online Retailer of Organization & Storage Products
N.A.I.C.S.: 423990
Kim Malcolm *(VP)*
Terry Shearer *(Pres)*

ORGANIZING FOR ACTION
224 N Desplaines Str Ste 500, Chicago, IL 60661
Tel.: (312) 893-6437 DC
Web Site:
 http://www.barackobama.com
Year Founded: 2013
Sales Range: $25-49.9 Million
Emp.: 197
Social Welfare Organization
N.A.I.C.S.: 813410
Sara El-Amine *(Dir-Natl Organizing)*

ORGILL, INC.
4100 S Houston Levee Rd, Collierville, TN 38017
Tel.: (901) 754-8850 TN
Web Site: https://www.orgill.com
Year Founded: 1847
Sales Range: Less than $1 Million
Emp.: 6,650
Hardware Merchant Wholesalers
N.A.I.C.S.: 423710
Brett Hammers *(Exec VP-Sls & Supply Chain)*
Marc Hamer *(Chief Digital & Info Officer & Exec VP)*

ORI SERVICES CORPORATION
4565 Ruffner St Ste 201, San Diego, CA 92111-2259
Tel.: (858) 576-4422
Web Site: http://www.oriservices.com
Year Founded: 1987
Sales Range: $10-24.9 Million
Emp.: 125
Technical Contracting Services
N.A.I.C.S.: 541330
Tracey Walcott *(CEO)*
Michael Law *(CFO)*
Thomas J. Underwood *(Pres & COO)*

ORIENT BANCORPORATION INC.
233 Sansome St, San Francisco, CA 94104
Tel.: (415) 338-0668
Web Site: http://www.bankorient.com
Rev.: $30,802,997
Emp.: 30
Bank Holding Company
N.A.I.C.S.: 551111
Ernest Go *(Chm)*
John Ng *(CEO)*
Carl Anderson *(CFO)*

ORIGEN FINANCIAL, INC.
The American Ctr 27777 Franklin Rd Ste 1700, Southfield, MI 48034
Tel.: (248) 746-7000 DE
Web Site:
 http://www.origenfinancial.com
Year Founded: 2003
Sales Range: Less than $1 Million
Emp.: 27
Real Estate Investment Trust
N.A.I.C.S.: 525990
W. Anderson Geater *(CFO)*

ORIGEN GLOBAL
2875 Oak Ave, Miami, FL 33133
Tel.: (305) 476-3551
Year Founded: 2006
Sales Range: $10-24.9 Million
Advertising Agencies
N.A.I.C.S.: 541810
Roberto S. Schaps *(CEO)*

Subsidiaries:

Origen Argentina (1)
Marchi 253, Buenos Aires, Argentina
Tel.: (54) 11 4773 1015
Advertising Agencies
N.A.I.C.S.: 541810

Origen Brazil (1)
Alameda Gabrielle Montero Da Silva 487, Sao Paulo, CEP 01441000, SP, Brazil
Tel.: (55) 11 3082 2180
Advertising Agencies
N.A.I.C.S.: 541810

Origen Colombia (1)
CRA 5 N 67-01 Rd Ste, Bogota, Colombia
Tel.: (57) 805 11 27
Advertising Agencies
N.A.I.C.S.: 541810

Origen Costa Rica (1)
100m este y 100m sur del Sedundito, Centro Comercial Plaza Mayor, San Jose, 5284-1000, Costa Rica
Tel.: (506) 220 1032
Advertising Agencies
N.A.I.C.S.: 541810

Origen Ecuador (1)
Avenida Gonzalez Suarez N27-317 y San Ignacio Esquina, Quito, Ecuador
Tel.: (593) 2250 5555
Advertising Agencies
N.A.I.C.S.: 541810

Origen El Salvador (1)
Calle Apaneca #4C Aroos de Santa Elena, Antiguo Cuscatlan, La Libertad, El Salvador
Tel.: (503) 2289 1044
Advertising Agencies
N.A.I.C.S.: 541810

Origen Espana (1)
Avenida Brasil 30 Posterior, Madrid, 28020, Spain
Tel.: (34) 914 183 300
Advertising Agencies
N.A.I.C.S.: 541810

Origen Guatemala (1)
Edificio Geminis 10 Torre Norte 17 Nivel, 12 Calle 1-25 Zona 10, Guatemala, Guatemala
Tel.: (502) 2335 3346
Advertising Agencies
N.A.I.C.S.: 541810

Origen Honduras (1)
Avd Rep de Venezuela 2130 Colonia Palmira, Tegucigalpa, Honduras

ORIGEN GLOBAL

Origen Global—(Continued)
Tel.: (504) 238 2000
Advertising Agencies
N.A.I.C.S.: 541810

Origen Mexico (1)
Fuente de Blanca 5 Tecamachalco, Naucalpan de Juarez, Mexico, 53950, DF, Mexico
Tel.: (52) 55 9149 2450
Advertising Agencies
N.A.I.C.S.: 541810
Jose Miguel Jaime (Dir)

Origen Nicaragua (1)
Centro BAC 4 Piso, Managua, Nicaragua
Tel.: (505) 274 4141
Emp.: 13
Advertising Agencies
N.A.I.C.S.: 541810

Origen Panama (1)
Los Angeles Calle 63 #20A, Panama, Panama
Tel.: (507) 236 0755
Advertising Agencies
N.A.I.C.S.: 541810

ORIGENE TECHNOLOGIES, INC.
9620 Medical Center Dr Ste 200, Rockville, MD 20850
Tel.: (888) 267-4286 DE
Web Site: http://www.origene.com
Year Founded: 1995
Sales Range: $10-24.9 Million
Biological Research & Drug Development Services
N.A.I.C.S.: 541715
Tracy Xie (CFO)

Subsidiaries:

Biocheck, Inc. (1)
323 Vintage Park Dr, Foster City, CA 94404
Tel.: (650) 573-1968
Web Site: http://www.biocheckinc.com
Sales Range: $1-9.9 Million
Emp.: 25
Immunodiagnostics Mfr
N.A.I.C.S.: 339112
Anna Pao (Dir-Admin)
John Chen (Pres & CEO)

Subsidiary (Domestic):

DRG International, Inc. (2)
1167 US Hwy 22 E, Mountainside, NJ 07092
Tel.: (908) 233-0758
Web Site: http://www.drg-international.com
Professional Equipment & Supplies Merchant Whslr
N.A.I.C.S.: 423490
Cyril E. Geacintov (Pres & CEO)

OriGene WUXI (1)
WuXi Bio-Park Meilianglu, Binhu District, 214092, Wuxi, Jiangsu, China
Tel.: (86) 510 81830666
Web Site: http://www.origene.cn
Biopharmaceutical Developer & Mfr
N.A.I.C.S.: 325412

SDIX, LLC (1)
111 Pencader Dr, Newark, DE 19702
Tel.: (302) 456-6789
Web Site: http://www.sdix.com
Biopharmaceutical Developer & Mfr
N.A.I.C.S.: 325414
Brenda Staehle (Pres)
Francis M. DiNuzzo (CEO)

Subsidiary (Non-US):

SDI Europe Limited (2)
Barnes Wallis House 25 Barnes Wallis Rd, Segensworth East, Fareham, PO15 5TT, Hampshire, United Kingdom
Tel.: (44) 1489898640
Web Site: http://www.sdix.com
Sales Range: $25-49.9 Million
Emp.: 2
Antibody Products & Analytical Test Kits Developer for the Food Safety & Water Quality Markets
N.A.I.C.S.: 541715

ORIGINAL APPALACHIAN ARTWORKS, INC.
1721 Hwy 75 S, Cleveland, GA 30528
Tel.: (706) 865-2171
Web Site: http://www.cabbagepatchkids.com
Year Founded: 1978
Sales Range: $10-24.9 Million
Emp.: 100
Toy Mfr
N.A.I.C.S.: 339930
Xavier Roberts (Founder)
Margaret McLean (Dir-Corp Comm)

ORIGINAL AUSTIN'S GROCERY STORES
3823 S Webster Ave, Green Bay, WI 54301
Tel.: (920) 337-0299
Web Site: http://www.originalaustins.com
Rev.: $34,400,000
Emp.: 70
Supermarkets & Other Grocery Stores
N.A.I.C.S.: 445110
Robert Austin (Pres)
Steven Austin (Treas & Sec)

ORIGINAL BRADFORD SOAP WORKS, INC.
200 Providence St, West Warwick, RI 02893
Tel.: (401) 821-2141
Web Site: http://www.bradfordsoap.com
Sales Range: $50-74.9 Million
Emp.: 300
Soap Mfr
N.A.I.C.S.: 325611
John H. Howland (Chm)
Chris Buckley (Exec VP-Bus Dev)
Michael Krause (VP-Sls)
Bert Reigstad (VP-Supply Chain & Safety)
Linda Barrett (VP-Acctg & Admin)
Stuart Benton (Pres & CEO)

ORIGINAL CRISPY PIZZA CRUST OF BOSTON CO. INC.
13 Blackstone Vly Pl, Lincoln, RI 02865
Tel.: (401) 333-9558
Web Site: http://www.originalpizza.com
Sales Range: $10-24.9 Million
Emp.: 36
Whslr of Pizza Supplies
N.A.I.C.S.: 424490
Benedetto J. Anzaldi (Pres)

ORIGINAL SOURCE MUSIC, INC.
8547 E Arapahoe Rd Ste J453, Greenwood Village, CO 80112 NV
Year Founded: 2009
Liabilities: $38,862
Net Worth: ($38,862)
Earnings: ($10,983)
Fiscal Year-end: 12/31/19
Film & Music Licensing Services
N.A.I.C.S.: 512230
Ichikawa Hiroshi (Chm, CEO & CFO)
Tonobe Masatatsu (CMO)
Gunjishima Sayo (COO)

ORIGINATE LABS
1400 Fashion Island Blvd Ste 400, San Mateo, CA 94404-2003
Tel.: (650) 525-3901
Year Founded: 2002
Rev.: $2,500,000
Emp.: 30
Custom Computer Programming Services

N.A.I.C.S.: 541511
Ali Shahriyari (Dir-R&D-Los Angeles)
Rob Meadows (Pres, CEO & Partner)
Tyler Buck (Dir-Products & Svcs)
Wes Dasse (Dir-Fin)

ORIGO ACQUISITION CORPORATION
708 3rd Ave, New York, NY 10017
Tel.: (212) 634-4512 Ky
Year Founded: 2014
Sales Range: Less than $1 Million
Emp.: 2
Investment Services
N.A.I.C.S.: 523999
Edward J. Fred (Pres & CEO)
Jose M. Aldeanueva (CFO, Treas & Sec)

ORILLION CORPORATION
6925 Portwest Dr Ste 110, Houston, TX 77024
Tel.: (713) 880-2980
Sales Range: $25-49.9 Million
Emp.: 92
Computer & Software Stores
N.A.I.C.S.: 517121
Jerry R. Sellers (Chm & CEO)

Subsidiaries:

Orillion USA Inc. (1)
6925 Portwest Dr Ste 110, Houston, TX 77024
Tel.: (713) 880-2980
Web Site: http://www.orillion.com
Rev.: $18,600,000
Emp.: 23
Telephone Communication, Except Radio
N.A.I.C.S.: 517121

ORIN USA
1101 N Prospect Ave, Itasca, IL 60143
Tel.: (630) 980-4380
Web Site: http://www.orinusa.com
Year Founded: 2001
Sales Range: $10-24.9 Million
Emp.: 193
Management Consulting Services
N.A.I.C.S.: 541618
Vincent Camporeale (Pres)
Maria Pappas (Acct Mgr)
Christopher Quam (Gen Mgr)

ORION ADVISOR SOLUTIONS, LLC
17605 Wright St, Omaha, NE 68130-2095
Tel.: (408) 974-1053 DE
Web Site: http://www.orionadvisor.com
Emp.: 100
Investment Advice
N.A.I.C.S.: 523940
Charles G. Goldman (Exec Chm)
Eric Clarke (Founder)
Natalie Wolfsen (CEO)
Kelly Waltrich (CMO)
Evan Hatch (Dir-Premier Svcs)
Sean Hollingshead (VP-Managed Accts)
Ben Frantz (VP-Bus Dev)
Paul Wick (VP-Bus Dev)
Jina Horton (VP-Bus Dev)
Michele Steinmetz (Dir-Comm)

Subsidiaries:

Redtail Technology, Inc. (1)
11285 Pyrites Way Ste B, Gold River, CA 95670
Tel.: (916) 669-1802
Web Site: http://www.redtailtechnology.com
Sales Range: $1-9.9 Million
Emp.: 44
Custom Computer Programming Services
N.A.I.C.S.: 541511
Brian McLaughlin (CEO)

U.S. PRIVATE

ORION ASSOCIATES
9400 Golden Vly Rd, Golden Valley, MN 55427
Tel.: (763) 450-5000
Web Site: http://www.orionassoc.net
Year Founded: 2000
Sales Range: $25-49.9 Million
Emp.: 2,650
Business Management Consulting Services
N.A.I.C.S.: 541611
Toni Thulen (CFO)
Cheryl Vennerstrom (COO)
Stephen Hage (Chief Admin Officer)
Rebecca Hage Thomley (Pres & CEO)
Rachel Pitkanen (Coord-ISO)
Lara Trujillo (Coord-ISO)
Missy Schraut (Coord-ISO)
Zach Garcia (Coord-ISO)
Amara Penske (Coord-ISO)
Tommy Nixon (Coord-ISO)
Theresa Bluhm (Dir-Billing)
Kathy Muench (Coord-ISO)
Justin Dukowitz (Dir-Payroll)
Andrew Pass (Dir-Mktg Projects)
Cheryl Tellock (Dir-Payroll)
Jason Hoffrogge (Dir-Training)
David Lindberg (Dir-HR)

ORION BUILDING CORPORATION
9025 Overlook Blvd Ste 100, Brentwood, TN 37027
Tel.: (615) 321-4499 TN
Web Site: http://www.orionbldg.com
Year Founded: 1983
Sales Range: $10-24.9 Million
Emp.: 35
Construction Contracting
N.A.I.C.S.: 236220
C. Richard Daughrity (Chm & Pres)
Randall Gill (Pres-Field Ops & Exec VP)
Cynthia D. Thomas (Dir-Admin & Mktg)
J. Moseley (CFO)
Jason Larkins (Project Mgr)
Joshua T. Gill (VP & Project Mgr)
Kenney Breeden (Project Mgr)
Tina C. Hall (Asst Controller)

Subsidiaries:

Cumberland Architectural Millwork, Inc. (1)
603 Davidson St, Nashville, TN 37213-1428 (100%)
Tel.: (615) 254-1710
Web Site: http://www.cumberlandmillwork.com
Rev.: $3,210,238
Provider of Millwork Services
N.A.I.C.S.: 321918
Andrew J. Martin (Pres)
Marshall Ross (Project Mgr)

ORION CHEMICAL TECHNOLOGIES
200 River Pointe Dr, Conroe, TX 77304
Tel.: (936) 521-1040
Sales Range: $10-24.9 Million
Emp.: 35
Chemicals & Allied Products
N.A.I.C.S.: 424690

ORION ENTRANCE CONTROL, INC.
76A Lexington Dr, Laconia, NH 03246
Tel.: (603) 527-4187
Web Site: http://www.orioneci.com
Year Founded: 2009
Sales Range: $1-9.9 Million
Emp.: 38
Security Door Detection System Mfr
N.A.I.C.S.: 334290

Stephen Caroselli (Founder & CEO)
Tom Elliott (Dir-Global Bus Dev)
Jerry Waldron (Mgr-Customer Care)
Chuck Waldron (Ops Mgr)
Joe Scott (Mgr-Engrg)

ORION FINANCIAL CORP.
6385 Old Shady Oak Rd Ste 270, Minneapolis, MN 55344
Tel.: (952) 767-7123 MN
Web Site: http://www.orionfinancial.com
Year Founded: 1982
Privater Equity Firm
N.A.I.C.S.: 523999
Alan R. Geiwitz (Founder, Pres & CEO)

Subsidiaries:

TC/American Crane Company (1)
11110 Industrial Cir NW Ste A, Elk River, MN 55330
Tel.: (763) 497-7000
Web Site: http://www.tcamerican.com
Cranes & Monorail Systems Designer, Mfr & Whslr
N.A.I.C.S.: 333923
Jeff Palkovich (CEO)

ORION FUNDING CREDIT UNION
400 Monroe AVE, Memphis, TN 38103
Tel.: (901) 385-5200
Web Site: http://www.orionfcu.com
Year Founded: 1957
Rev.: $1,000,000,000
Credit Services
N.A.I.C.S.: 522130
Daniel Weickenand (CEO)
Ashley McAdams (CFO)

ORION GENOMICS, LLC
4041 Forest Park Ave, Saint Louis, MO 63108
Tel.: (314) 615-6977
Web Site: http://www.oriongenomics.com
Sales Range: $1-9.9 Million
Emp.: 12
Oncology Diagnostic Products for Cancer Screening & Therapy Selection Developer
N.A.I.C.S.: 325412
Nathan D. Lakey (Pres & CEO)
John Finney (Chm)

ORION GLOBAL CORP.
5612 Brooklyn Ave, Sarasota, FL 34231
Tel.: (818) 621-4642 FL
Year Founded: 2014
Self Storage Services
N.A.I.C.S.: 493110
Eric Negroni (Pres, CEO, CFO, Principal Acctg Officer, Treas & Sec)

ORION GLOBAL SOLUTIONS, LLC
1040 Avenue of the Americas 15th Fl Ste 15B, New York, NY 10018
Tel.: (646) 661-1333
Web Site: http://www.orion-gs.com
Year Founded: 2015
Sales Range: $1-9.9 Million
Information Technology Management Services
N.A.I.C.S.: 541512
Yacov Wrocherinsky (Founder & CEO)
Dan Farrugia (VP)
W. Ellen (Dir-Advisory Svcs)
D. Jen (Mgr-Engagement)
G. Vicki (Mgr-People & Culture)

ORION INVESTMENT & MAN-
AGEMENT LTD. CORP.
200 S Biscayne Blvd 6th Fl, Miami, FL 33131
Tel.: (305) 278-8400
Web Site: http://www.orionmiami.com
Year Founded: 1978
Sales Range: $1-9.9 Million
Emp.: 11
Real Estate Services
N.A.I.C.S.: 531390
Joseph A. Sanz (Pres)
Nancy Araujo (Comptroller)
Silvi Santovenia (Mgr-Property-Natl)
Norman J. Buhrmaster (Sr VP)
Kevin Sanz (VP)
Steven Borysewich (VP-Real Estate)
Duane Comprosky (VP-Real Estate)

ORION MEDIA ASSOCIATES, INC.
PO Box 690, Clinton, TN 37717
Tel.: (865) 463-0018
Year Founded: 1999
Sales Range: $10-24.9 Million
Emp.: 10
Advertising Agencies
N.A.I.C.S.: 541810
Alfred A. Clark (VP)
Patricia Bailey (Acct Supvr)
Adrian Serle (Dir-Comml)

ORION MOBILITY
4 Mountainview Terrace Ste 101, Danbury, CT 06810
Tel.: (203) 762-0365
Web Site: http://www.orionmobility.com
Sales Range: $10-24.9 Million
Emp.: 30
Provider of Relocation Tracking Software & Management Services
N.A.I.C.S.: 541611
Peter Fonseca (Pres)
Laura Guion (Mgr-Expense Processing)
Quentin Hormel (Mgr-Tax)

Subsidiaries:

Relocation Taxes, LLC (1)
88 Danbury Rd, Wilton, CT 06897
Tel.: (203) 762-5678
Web Site: http://www.relotax.com
Sales Range: $10-24.9 Million
Emp.: 25
Tax Preparation Services
N.A.I.C.S.: 541213
Debbie Gioiella (Dir-Ops & Sls)

ORION RESOURCE PARTNERS (USA) LP
1211 Ave of the Americas Ste 3000, New York, NY 10036
Tel.: (212) 596-3511 DE
Web Site: http://www.orionresourcepartners.com
Year Founded: 2004
Rev.: $6,000,000,000
Alternative Investment Management Firm
N.A.I.C.S.: 523940
Oskar Lewnowski (Chief Investment Officer)
Jonathan Lamb (Mgr-Portfolio)
Istvan Zollei (Mgr-Portfolio)

Subsidiaries:

Dalradian Resources Inc. (1)
Queen's Quay Terminal 207 Queen's Quay West Suite 416, Toronto, M5J 1A7, ON, Canada
Tel.: (416) 583-5500
Holding Company; Gold Exploration & Mining Development Services
N.A.I.C.S.: 551112
Patrick Fergus Neill Anderson (Pres & CEO)

Keith Douglas McKay (CFO)
Marla Gale (VP-Comm)
Eric Joseph Luc Tremblay (COO)

Subsidiary (Non-US):

Dalradian Gold Limited (2)
3 Killybrack Road, Killybrack Business Park, Omagh, BT79 7DG, Northern Ireland, United Kingdom
Tel.: (44) 2882 246289
Web Site: http://www.dalradian.com
Gold Exploration & Mining Development
N.A.I.C.S.: 213114
Brian Kelly (Mng Dir)

ORION SEAFOOD INTERNATIONAL, INC.
20 Ladd St 3rd Fl, Portsmouth, NH 03801
Tel.: (603) 433-2220 NH
Web Site: http://www.orionseafood.com
Year Founded: 1988
Sales Range: $250-299.9 Million
Emp.: 14
Seafoods
N.A.I.C.S.: 424460
Alexander Scourby (Pres)

ORION SOUTH INC.
2550 Belle Chasse Hwy, Gretna, LA 70053-6758
Tel.: (504) 368-9760 DE
Web Site: http://www.ragenpower.com
Year Founded: 1956
Sales Range: $50-74.9 Million
Emp.: 390
Holding Company
N.A.I.C.S.: 551112
Thomas N. Reagan (Pres & CEO)
Angela Magee (Controller)
John Farrell (VP-Fin)

ORION TRANSPORTATION SERVICES INC.
4141 Pinnacle St Ste 217, El Paso, TX 79902-1042
Tel.: (915) 544-4565 TX
Year Founded: 1993
Sales Range: $10-24.9 Million
Emp.: 12
Transportation & Logistics Services
N.A.I.C.S.: 488999
Elizabeth Velazquez (Mgr)

ORITZ CORPORATION
Oritz Bldg 1555 Bayshore Hwy Ste 400, Burlingame, CA 94010
Tel.: (650) 692-8000
Web Site: http://www.oritzcorp.com
Year Founded: 1975
Sales Range: $10-24.9 Million
Emp.: 20
Exporting Meat & Meat Related Products
N.A.I.C.S.: 424470
Vladimir R. Grave (Pres & CEO)

ORIZON, INC.
51 Monroe St Ste 1600, Rockville, MD 20850
Tel.: (301) 309-2300
Web Site: http://www.orizon-inc.com
Year Founded: 1998
Sales Range: $10-24.9 Million
Emp.: 100
IT Consulting Services
N.A.I.C.S.: 541690
Shari Lerner (Dir-Ops)
Romero Vanbochove (Pres & CEO)

ORLANDINI ENTERPRISES
6155 S Eastern Ave, Los Angeles, CA 90040
Tel.: (323) 725-1332
Web Site: http://www.pacdiecast.com

Sales Range: $10-24.9 Million
Emp.: 75
Machinery Castings, Exc. Die, Non-ferrous, Exc. Alu
N.A.I.C.S.: 331529
Jeff Orlandini (Pres)

ORLANDO BALLET, INC.
2201 McRae Ave, Orlando, FL 32803
Tel.: (407) 426-1733 FL
Web Site: http://www.orlandoballet.org
Year Founded: 1974
Sales Range: $1-9.9 Million
Emp.: 32
Dance Company & Dance School
N.A.I.C.S.: 711120
Robert Hill (Dir-Artistic)
Eddy Frank Fernandez (Dir-Costume)
Katherine S. Fabian (Mng Dir)
Shane Jewell (Exec Dir)

ORLANDO DODGE
4101 W Colonial Dr, Orlando, FL 32808-8122
Tel.: (407) 299-1120
Web Site: http://www.orlandododge.com
Sales Range: $10-24.9 Million
Emp.: 100
Car Whslr
N.A.I.C.S.: 441110
Steward Smith (Gen Mgr)
Mike Smith (Pres)
Charles Worrell (Mgr-Fin)
Bryan Menihan (Mgr-Svc)

ORLANDO HEALTH, INC.
1414 Kuhl Ave, Orlando, FL 32806-2008
Tel.: (321) 841-2335 FL
Web Site: https://www.orlandohealth.com
Year Founded: 1917
Sales Range: $1-4.9 Billion
Emp.: 25,000
Health Care Srvices
N.A.I.C.S.: 622110
Nancy Dinon (VP-HR)
David Huddleson (VP-Corp Integrity)
Rick Schooler (CIO)
Kathy Swanson (Sr VP)
John W. Bozard (Sr VP)
Anne Peach (VP-Patient Care & Chief Nursing Officer)
Mildred Beam (Sr VP-Legal Affairs)
Andy Gardiner (Sr VP-External Affairs & Community Rels)
Jamal Hakim (COO)
David Strong (Pres & CEO)
Erick Hawkins (Sr VP-Strategic Mgmt)
Bernadette Spong (CFO)
A. Mark Weber (Dir-Internal Audit)
Stephen Stallard (Officer-Information Security & Privacy & Dir-Compliance)
Sunil S. Desai (Pres-Medical Grp & Sr VP)
Chris Jordan (CTO)
Linda Zinkovich (COO)
Ken Kozielski (VP-Customer Experience)
Ryan Zika (Gen Counsel)
Greg P. Ohe (Sr VP-Ambulatory)
Andrew J. Snyder (Sr VP-Mktg & Comm)
Karen Frenier (Chief HR Officer & VP)
Novlet Mattis (CIO)
Michele Tynes Napier (Chief Revenue Officer)
Dianna F. Morgan (Chm)

Subsidiaries:

Bayfront Health St. Petersburg (1)
701 6th St S, Saint Petersburg, FL 33701

ORLANDO HEALTH, INC.

Orlando Health, Inc.—(Continued)
Tel.: (727) 823-1234
Web Site: http://www.bayfrontstpete.com
Hospitals & Medical Centers Operator
N.A.I.C.S.: 622110
Eric Smith (CFO)
John McLain (CEO)
Michael Brown (Chm)
Austin Brown (COO)
Trina Espinola (Chief Medical Officer)
Lorraine Parker (Chief Nursing Officer & Asst VP)
John Moore (Pres)

ORLANDO LUTHERAN TOWERS
300 E Church St, Orlando, FL 32801
Tel.: (407) 425-1033
Web Site: http://www.orlandoseniorhealth.com
Rev.: $15,267,757
Emp.: 500
Apartment Building Operator
N.A.I.C.S.: 531110
Alicia Lebreque (Exec Dir)
James Murphy (Asst Dir-Sls & Mktg)
Jean-Claude Lalanne (Dir-Maintenance)
Tara Lofgren (Coord-RN Admissions & Mgr-Restorative)

ORLANDO UTILITIES COMMISSION
Reliable Plz 100 W Anderson St, Orlando, FL 32801
Tel.: (407) 434-2727
Web Site: http://www.ouc.com
Year Founded: 1923
Sales Range: $800-899.9 Million
Emp.: 1,040
Electric & Water Generation, Transmission & Distr
N.A.I.C.S.: 221118
Ken Ksionek (CEO & Gen Mgr)
John E. Hearn (CFO & VP-Fin & Support Svcs)
Byron Knibbs (VP-Sustainable Svcs)
Gregory D. Lee (First VP)
Linda Ferrone (Pres)
Jan Aspuru (VP-Electric & Water Production)
Chris Browder (Gen Counsel & VP)
Clint Bullock (VP-Electric & Water Delivery)
Maggie Duque (VP-Customer Svc)
Roseann Harrington (VP-Mktg, Comm & Community Rels)
Chip Merriam (VP-Legislative, Regulatory & Compliance)
Jerry Sullivan (CIO & VP-Info Tech)

ORLEANS FURNITURE INC.
1481 N Main St, Columbia, MS 39429
Tel.: (601) 736-9002
Web Site: http://www.orleansfurniture.com
Sales Range: $25-49.9 Million
Emp.: 335
Distr Of Wood Household Furniture
N.A.I.C.S.: 337122
Charles H. Griner (Chm)
Ed Marshall (Pres & CEO)

ORLEANS HOMEBUILDERS, INC.
3333 Street Rd Ste 101, Bensalem, PA 19020-2051
Tel.: (215) 245-7500 DE
Web Site: http://www.orleanshomes.com
Year Founded: 1969
Sales Range: $500-549.9 Million
Emp.: 500
Holding Company Residential Real Estate Acquisition Development & Single-Family Housing Construction Service
N.A.I.C.S.: 551112

Subsidiaries:

Orleans Corporation (1)
3333 St Rd Ste 101, Bensalem, PA 19020-2051 (100%)
Tel.: (215) 245-7500
Web Site: http://www.orleanshomes.com
Residential Real Estate Acquisition, Development & Single-Family Housing Construction
N.A.I.C.S.: 236117
Linda Kelley (VP-Mktg)
Alan Laing (CEO)
John Evans (Pres-North)
Patricia Grayauskie (VP-HR)

Subsidiary (Domestic):

Orleans RH PA-IL, LP (2)
650 E Algonquin Rd Ste 100, Schaumburg, IL 60173
Tel.: (847) 925-1400
Sales Range: $50-74.9 Million
Emp.: 100
Residential Real Estate Acquisition, Development & Single-Family Housing Construction
N.A.I.C.S.: 236117

Parker & Orleans Homebuilders, Inc. (2)
8730 Stoney Point Pkwy Ste 201, Richmond, VA 23235
Tel.: (804) 323-3100
Residential Real Estate Acquisition, Development & Single-Family Housing Construction
N.A.I.C.S.: 236117

ORLEANS INTERNATIONAL, INC.
30600 Northwestern Hwy Ste 300, Farmington Hills, MI 48334-3172
Tel.: (248) 855-5556 MI
Web Site: http://www.orleansintl.com
Year Founded: 1936
Sales Range: $75-99.9 Million
Emp.: 35
Importer of Beef Product Distr
N.A.I.C.S.: 424420
Earl Tushman (Pres & CEO)
J. Lawrence Tushman (Sec & VP)
Steve Sanger (Sr VP)

Subsidiaries:

Century International Trading Inc. (1)
21 Yost Blvd Ste 501, Pittsburgh, PA 15221
Tel.: (412) 823-3400
Emp.: 4
Frozen Meat Distr
N.A.I.C.S.: 424470
Nick Butera (Pres)

ORLOR INC.
1194 N Colony Rd, Wallingford, CT 06492
Tel.: (866) 664-6093
Web Site: http://www.executivehonda.com
Sales Range: $25-49.9 Million
New & Used Automobiles Distr
N.A.I.C.S.: 441110
Jason Hocking (Gen Mgr)
Jamie Mastroni (Mgr-Sls)
Tom Mizerek (Mgr-Sls & Used Car)
Steve Guerin (Mgr-Fin)

ORLY INTERNATIONAL, INC.
7710 Haskell Ave, Los Angeles, CA 91406
Tel.: (818) 994-1001 CA
Web Site: http://www.orlybeauty.com
Year Founded: 1975
Sales Range: $50-74.9 Million
Emp.: 85
Nail Care & Hand, Foot & Body Products Mfr
N.A.I.C.S.: 325620
Jeff Pink (Founder & Chm)
Mindy Chun (Mgr)
Elyse Piwonka (Head-Product Dev)

ORMSBY TRUCKING INC.
888 W Railroad St, Uniondale, IN 46791
Tel.: (260) 543-2233
Year Founded: 1951
Sales Range: $10-24.9 Million
Emp.: 175
Provider of Trucking Services
N.A.I.C.S.: 484121
Reg Ormsby (Pres)

ORNAMENTAL PRODUCTS LLC
2214 Shore St, High Point, NC 27263
Tel.: (336) 431-1129
Web Site: http://www.ornaprod.com
Sales Range: $10-24.9 Million
Emp.: 90
Moldings, Wood: Unfinished & Prefinished
N.A.I.C.S.: 321918
Greg Clark (Gen Mgr)

ORNDORFF & SPAID, INC.
11722 Old Baltimore Pike, Beltsville, MD 20705
Tel.: (301) 937-5911
Web Site: http://www.osroofing.com
Year Founded: 1953
Sales Range: $10-24.9 Million
Emp.: 160
Roofing Contractors
N.A.I.C.S.: 238160
Mitchell G. Spaid (Pres)

ORODAY, INC.
2393 Teller Rd Ste 104, Newbury Park, CA 91320
Tel.: (805) 498-9344
Web Site: http://www.webdcs.com
Year Founded: 1994
Sales Range: $25-49.9 Million
Emp.: 55
IT Consulting Services
N.A.I.C.S.: 541690
Joel Oropesa (Pres & CEO)
Jeff Daymude (CFO & Exec VP)
Garry Noel (VP-Sls & Svcs)
Bernadette Guerrero (Mgr-Accts)
Sondra Nilson (Dir-Bus Dev)

ORR CORPORATION
PO Box 198029, Louisville, KY 40259
Tel.: (502) 774-6546
Web Site: http://www.orrcorporation.com
Miscellaneous Durable Goods Merchant Whslr
N.A.I.C.S.: 423990
Ray Aldridge (Pres)
Clark Orr Jr. (Chm)

ORR INC.
4502 St Michael Dr, Texarkana, TX 75503
Tel.: (903) 794-5500
Web Site: http://www.orrauto.com
Sales Range: $50-74.9 Million
Emp.: 70
New & Used Automobiles
N.A.I.C.S.: 441110
Keith Orr (Pres)

ORR TOYOTA
301 S Poplar St, Searcy, AR 72143-6015
Tel.: (501) 281-4620
Web Site: http://www.orrsearcytoyota.com
Year Founded: 2003
Sales Range: $25-49.9 Million
Emp.: 75
New Car Whslr
N.A.I.C.S.: 441110
Amanda Ainworth (Controller)

ORRICK, HERRINGTON & SUTCLIFFE LLP
405 Howard St, San Francisco, CA 94105
Tel.: (415) 773-5700
Web Site: http://www.orrick.com
Year Founded: 1863
Sales Range: $800-899.9 Million
Emp.: 1,025
Law firm
N.A.I.C.S.: 541110
Michael J. O'Donnell (Partner)
Robert S. Shwarts (Partner)
Darrin Glymph (Partner & Head-Pub Fin-Washington DC)
Andrew Thorpe (Partner)
John Knox (Partner)
McGregor W. Scott (Partner)
Lauri A. Damrell (Partner)
Amy M. Ross (Partner)
Jessica R. Perry (Partner)
Analea J. Patterson (Partner-Litigation Div)
Pamela Johnson (Chief Practice Officer-Global Litigation Bus Unit-San Francisco)
Barry Levin (Partner-Complex Litigation & Dispute Resolution)
Christopher Vejnoska (Partner)
Mark P. Weitzel (Partner & Head-Energy & Infrastructure Grp)
Christopher Wilkinson (Partner)
Robert Stern (Partner)
Arnauld Achard (Partner)
Christopher Austin (Partner)
Howard S. Altarescu (Partner)
John Ansbro (Partner)
Matthew R. Archer (Partner)
Pascal Agboyibor (Partner)
Stephen C. Ashley (Partner)
Shawn Atkinson (Partner-London)
William F. Alderman (Partner)
Barrie Vanbrackle (Partner-Washington)
Jim Tierney (Partner-Washington)
Charles W. Allen (Partner)
Justin Gagnon (Mng Dir)
Jolie Goldstein (Chief Comm Officer)
Siobhan Handley (Chief Talent Officer)
Larry Low (Chief Legal Officer)
Laura Saklad (COO)
Catherine Zinn (Chief Client Officer)
Rich Morvillo (Partner-Washington)
Andy Morris (Partner-Washington)
Dan Nathan (Partner-Washington)
Noreen Phelan (Partner)
Mel Bostwick (Partner)
Emily Tabatabai (Partner)
Scott Ward (Partner)
Xiang Wang (Mng Partner-Asia)
Ed Batts (Head-Merger & Acq-Global & Private Equity Practice)
Jinsong Zhang (Partner-Merger & Acq & Private Equity Practice)
Wilhelm Nolting-Hauff (Partner-Dusseldorf)
Christoph Brenner (Partner)
Fabian von Samson-Himmelstjerna (Partner)
Christine Kaniak (Partner-Munich)

ORRIN B HAYES INC.
543 W Michigan Ave, Kalamazoo, MI 49007
Tel.: (269) 345-0167 MI
Web Site: http://www.hayescars.com
Year Founded: 1920
Sales Range: $25-49.9 Million

Emp.: 40
New & Used Automobiles
N.A.I.C.S.: 441110
Bob Bolinger *(Dir-Parts & Svc)*
Amanda Woodruff *(Controller)*
Robert O. Hayes II *(Pres)*

ORRISON DISTRIBUTING LTD.
1111 Dunn Ave, Cheyenne, WY 82001
Tel.: (307) 632-5628
Sales Range: $10-24.9 Million
Emp.: 17
Beer & Other Fermented Malt Liquors
N.A.I.C.S.: 424810
Nancy Eberhardt *(Office Mgr)*

ORSCHELN GROUP
2000 Hwy 63 S, Moberly, MO 65270
Tel.: (660) 263-4377
Web Site: http://www.orscheln.com
Sales Range: $300-349.9 Million
Emp.: 2,700
Holding Company; Mfr of Automotive Parts, Retail Agriculture, Hardware, Real Estate Development
N.A.I.C.S.: 551112

Subsidiaries:

DeNovus L.L.C. (1)
1 Hunthausen Dr, Moberly, MO 64024
Tel.: (660) 269-3881
Sales Range: $10-24.9 Million
Emp.: 15
Non-automotive Products & Extrusions, Grease, Lubrications & Corrosion Protectants; Manufacturer of Architectural & Industrial Sealants & Adhesives
N.A.I.C.S.: 325520

Elisha Technologies Inc (1)
1177 North Morley St PO Box 280, Moberly, MO 65270
Tel.: (660) 263-4377
Sales Range: $25-49.9 Million
Emp.: 200
Designer & Builder of Coating Systems for Industrial Use
N.A.I.C.S.: 541715

Felsted Products LLC (1)
1177 N Morley St, Moberly, MO 65270
Tel.: (660) 263-4377
Sales Range: $10-24.9 Million
Emp.: 62
Designer & Manufacturer of Mechanical Cables & Controls
N.A.I.C.S.: 332618

Glendinning Marine Products, Inc. (1)
740 Century Cir, Conway, SC 29526
Tel.: (843) 399-6146
Web Site: http://www.glendinningprods.com
Marine Component Mfr
N.A.I.C.S.: 335314
John Glendinning *(Pres)*

Heritage Hills Golf Course (1)
3534 Hwy JJ, Moberly, MO 65270
Tel.: (660) 269-8659
Web Site: http://www.heritagehillsgolfcourse.com
Emp.: 12
Golf Course Operator
N.A.I.C.S.: 713910
Kit Tennyson *(Mgr-Golf Ops)*

Orscheln Europe ULC (1)
Unit 1 Pelham Road, Central Park, Rugby, CV23 0PB, United Kingdom
Tel.: (44) 1788 561400
Motor Vehicle Parts Whslr
N.A.I.C.S.: 423120
Peter Smith *(Gen Mgr)*

Orscheln Industries Plating Division (1)
1177 N Morley, Moberly, MO 65270
Tel.: (660) 269-3404
Sales Range: $10-24.9 Million
Emp.: 18
In-House Plating Capabilities & Coating Processes
N.A.I.C.S.: 424910

Orscheln Management Co. (1)
2000 US Hwy 63 S, Moberly, MO 65270
Tel.: (660) 263-4900
Web Site: http://www.orscheln.com
Sales Range: $10-24.9 Million
Emp.: 35
Mfr of Parts for Original Equipment Manufacturers Automotive Industries; Retail Agricultural & Hardware Sales
N.A.I.C.S.: 541611

Subsidiary (Domestic):

Orscheln Farm & Home LLC (2)
1800 Overcenter Dr, Moberly, MO 65270-1521 (100%)
Tel.: (660) 263-4335
Web Site: http://www.orscheln.com
Operators of Farm & Home Stores
N.A.I.C.S.: 424910
Barb Westhues *(Sr VP & Controller)*
William L. Onscheln *(Pres)*
Barry Orscheln *(Chm & CEO)*

Orscheln Products LLC (1)
1177 N Morley St, Moberly, MO 65270
Tel.: (660) 263-4377
Web Site: http://www.orscheln.com
Sales Range: $25-49.9 Million
Emp.: 400
Supplier of Parking Brake Systems, Cables, Tilt Cab Locks for Industrial, Transportation & Off-highway OEMs
N.A.I.C.S.: 332618
Kim Gittemeier *(Mgr-HR)*
Chrissy Dignan *(Coord-Adv)*

Orscheln Products Trading Co. LTD (1)
501 5/F Block 10 KIC Plaza 290 Songhu Road, Yangpu, Shanghai, 200065, China
Tel.: (86) 21 5228 3110
Motor Vehicle Parts Whslr
N.A.I.C.S.: 423120

Orscheln Properties Co. L.L.C. (1)
1313 Riley Industrial Dr PO Box 676, Moberly, MO 65270 (100%)
Tel.: (660) 263-1312
Web Site: http://www.orscheln.com
Sales Range: $10-24.9 Million
Emp.: 10
Real Estate Developer of Apartment Complexes, Shopping Centers, Office & Industrial Parks.
N.A.I.C.S.: 531210

Orscheln Technologies PVT Ltd (1)
Plot No 28 North Phase SIDCO Industrial Estate, Ambattur, Chennai, 600098, India
Tel.: (91) 44 42896850
Web Site: http://www.orschelnindia.co.in
Emp.: 23
Motion Control Systems Mfr
N.A.I.C.S.: 332912
Satyandra Kumar Singh *(Asst Mgr-Sls & Mktg)*
Arun Kumar *(Engr-Mfg)*

QuEST Rail LLC (1)
106 E Hwy 224, Wellington, MO 64097-8214
Tel.: (816) 240-8425
Web Site: http://www.questrail.com
Emp.: 35
Electric Equipment Mfr
N.A.I.C.S.: 334419
Bob Orscheln *(Pres)*
Matthew Rankin *(Dir-Fin & Ops)*
Neal Quackenbush *(Dir-Engrg & Sls)*

Qualico Precision Products, LLC (1)
1251 County Road 1217, Moberly, MO 65270
Tel.: (660) 263-6210
Sales Range: $1-9.9 Million
Motor Vehicle Parts Mfr
N.A.I.C.S.: 336390

ORSINI NURSING AGENCY, INC.
1111 Nicholas Blvd, Elk Grove Village, IL 60007
Tel.: (847) 734-7373   IL
Web Site: http://www.orsinihealthcare.com
Year Founded: 1987
Sales Range: $50-74.9 Million
Emp.: 140
In-Home Health Care Services
N.A.I.C.S.: 621610
Tony Orsini *(Founder & CEO)*
Michael Fieri *(Pres)*
Carla Sawa *(CFO)*
David Frobel *(VP-Specialty Pharmacy)*
Dave Anderson *(Dir-Diabetes Total Care)*
Ryan Chick *(Dir-Org Dev)*
Jeanne Penton *(Dir-Wellness)*
Matthew Swajkowski *(Dir-IT)*

ORT AMERICA, INC.
75 Maiden Ln 10th Fl, New York, NY 10038
Tel.: (212) 505-7700   NY
Web Site: http://www.ortamerica.org
Year Founded: 1969
Sales Range: $10-24.9 Million
Emp.: 100
Educational Support Services
N.A.I.C.S.: 611710
Jeffrey Cooper *(CFO)*
Tanea Hammond *(Dir-Outreach & Dev)*
Gary S. Desberg *(Pres-Northeast Ohio)*
Naomi Reinharz *(Dir-Major Gifts)*
Leah Siskin *(Dir-Advancement)*
Roni Wallace *(Dir-Dev)*
Lawrence Ludwig *(Dir-Mgmt Information Svcs)*
Traci Robinson-Greene *(Mgr-Creative Svcs & Web, Mktg & Comm)*
Martin Greenberg *(Exec Dir)*
Alyson J. Lev *(Dir-Florida)*
Marla Landis *(Chief Dev Officer)*
Howard Lanznar *(Dir-Mktg & Comm)*
Sari Berkovich *(Dir-Mktg & Comm)*
Barbara Birch *(Pres & CEO)*

ORT TOOL & DIE CORPORATION
6555 S Dixie Hwy, Erie, MI 48133-9691
Tel.: (734) 848-6845   MI
Web Site: http://www.orttool.com
Year Founded: 1958
Sales Range: $25-49.9 Million
Emp.: 200
Mfr of Dies, Tools & Fixtures
N.A.I.C.S.: 541330
Angelo Milano *(VP)*
Robert Milano *(Pres)*

ORTEGO OIL & SUPPLY CO. INC.
125 Country Ln, Opelousas, LA 70570
Tel.: (337) 942-2008
Rev.: $12,000,000
Emp.: 20
Gasoline
N.A.I.C.S.: 424720
Mike Ortego *(Pres)*

ORTHO DEVELOPMENT CORPORATION
12187 S Business Park Dr, Draper, UT 84020
Tel.: (801) 553-9991
Web Site: http://www.odev.com
Year Founded: 1994
Surgical Appliances & Supplies
N.A.I.C.S.: 339113
Brent Bartholomew *(Pres)*
Ross Chamberlain *(Sr VP-Sls)*
Greg Larson *(CFO)*
Stan Despres *(VP-Product Dev)*
Kevin Kinnersley *(Dir-Mktg)*
Mark Alley *(Dir-Ops)*
Drew Weaver *(Dir-Quality & Regulatory Affairs)*
Steve Phippen *(Dir-Corp Affairs)*
Russ Stout *(Dir-Bus Planning)*
Rich Gray *(Dir-Area Sls)*
Brian Hughes *(Dir-Area Sls)*

ORTHOBANC LLC
2146 Chapman Rd, Chattanooga, TN 37421
Tel.: (423) 242-2750
Web Site: http://www.orthobanc.com
Year Founded: 2001
Sales Range: $1-9.9 Million
Emp.: 30
Account Management for Dentists & Orthodontists
N.A.I.C.S.: 541219
Jayme Marro *(Asst Dir-Mktg)*
William J. Holt Jr. *(Pres)*

ORTHOMERICA PRODUCTS INC.
505 31st St, Newport Beach, CA 92663
Tel.: (949) 723-4500
Web Site: http://www.orthomerica.com
Sales Range: $10-24.9 Million
Emp.: 3
Orthopedic Appliances
N.A.I.C.S.: 334510
David C. Kerr *(CEO)*
Jack Walker *(Mgr-Sls-Natl)*

ORTHOPAEDIC HOSPITAL
403 W Adams Blvd, Los Angeles, CA 90007
Tel.: (213) 741-8330   CA
Web Site: http://www.ortho-institute.org
Year Founded: 1923
Sales Range: $25-49.9 Million
Emp.: 196
Health Care Srvices
N.A.I.C.S.: 622110
Mary Beth Perrine *(Sr Dir-Community Outreach)*
Lourdes N. Abcede *(CFO)*
Nicole Weaver-Goller *(Sr Dir-Advancement)*
Mauricio Silva *(Dir-Medical)*
Deborah Justice *(Sr Dir-Ops)*
Mark Brandreth *(CEO-Gobowen)*

ORTHOSYNETICS, INC.
3850 N Causeway Blvd Ste 800, Metairie, LA 70002   DE
Web Site: http://www.orthosynetics.com
Year Founded: 1985
Operational, Financial, Marketing & Administrative Services to Orthodontic Centers
N.A.I.C.S.: 621210
David J. Marks *(Pres & CEO)*
Daniel D. Crowley *(Chm)*

ORTON MOTORS INC.
Hwy 371 N, Walker, MN 56484
Tel.: (218) 547-1719
Web Site: http://www.ortonoilco.com
Sales Range: $50-74.9 Million
Emp.: 15
Petroleum Products
N.A.I.C.S.: 424720
Tim Orton *(Pres)*

ORU KAYAK INC.
PO Box 7775, San Francisco, CA 94104
Tel.: (510) 677-4567
Web Site: http://www.orukayak.com
Sales Range: $1-9.9 Million
Kayak Mfr
N.A.I.C.S.: 339920

ORU KAYAK INC. — U.S. PRIVATE

Oru Kayak Inc.—(Continued)
Anton Willis *(Co-Founder & CEO)*
Ardy Sobhani *(Co-Founder & COO)*
Roberto Gutierrez *(Co-Founder & Chief Comml Officer)*

ORW IMPORT PARTS & MACHINE
7915 Balboa Ave, San Diego, CA 92111
Tel.: (858) 565-7792
Web Site:
http://www.offroadwarehouse.com
Year Founded: 1973
Sales Range: $10-24.9 Million
Emp.: 60
Automotive Parts; Sales & Service
N.A.I.C.S.: 441330

ORYON TECHNOLOGIES, INC.
4251 Kellway Cir, Addison, TX 75001
Tel.: (214) 267-1321 NV
Web Site: http://www.oryontech.com
Year Founded: 2002
Sales Range: Less than $1 Million
Emp.: 2
Three Dimensional Electroluminescent Technology
N.A.I.C.S.: 335139
Thomas Patrick Schaeffer *(CEO)*

OS SUPPORT, INC.
112 N Curry St, Carson City, NV 89703
Tel.: (775) 321-8224 NV
Year Founded: 2015
Rev.: $105
Liabilities: $75,652
Net Worth: ($75,652)
Earnings: ($24,170)
Fiscal Year-end: 06/30/21
Online Shopping Services
N.A.I.C.S.: 541512
Paramjit Mann *(Chm, Pres, CEO, CFO, Principal Acctg Officer, Treas & Sec)*

OSAGE VALLEY ELECTRIC COOP ASSOCIATION
1321 N Orange St, Butler, MO 64730
Tel.: (660) 679-3131
Web Site:
http://www.osagevalley.com
Rev.: $14,246,830
Emp.: 50
Distribution, Electric Power
N.A.I.C.S.: 221122
P. D. Kircher *(Pres)*

OSAIR INC.
7001 Center St, Mentor, OH 44060
Tel.: (440) 974-6500 OH
Year Founded: 1947
Sales Range: $10-24.9 Million
Emp.: 9
Provider of Commercial Chemicals
N.A.I.C.S.: 325120
Richard M. Osborne *(Pres & CEO)*
Donald Whiteman *(Controller)*

OSAN PETROLEUM COMPANY INC.
1167 6th St, Macon, GA 31206-1108
Tel.: (478) 742-4534 GA
Year Founded: 1973
Sales Range: $10-24.9 Million
Emp.: 13
Petroleum Products
N.A.I.C.S.: 424720
Pam Garcia *(VP)*
Richard Stiles *(VP-Ops)*

OSBORN & BARR COMMUNICATIONS
Cupples Sta 914 Spruce St, Saint Louis, MO 63102
Tel.: (314) 726-5511 MO
Year Founded: 1988
Rev.: $68,000,000
Emp.: 140
Advetising Agency
N.A.I.C.S.: 541810
Stephen D. Barr *(Chm)*
Rhonda Ries-Aguilar *(Pres)*
Suzan Knese *(COO)*
Dustin Johansen *(VP)*
Karen Pfautch *(VP)*
Nicole Phillips *(VP & Dir-Acct Grp)*

Subsidiaries:

Osborn & Barr (1)
304 W 8th St, Kansas City, MO 64105-1513
Tel.: (816) 471-2255
Emp.: 20
Advetising Agency
N.A.I.C.S.: 541810
Colleen Church-McDowall *(VP & Dir-PR)*
Boo Larson *(Mng Dir)*
Jaime Jonesmith *(Acct Dir)*
Courtney Floresca *(Assoc Dir-Integrated Media)*
Lance Burditt *(Grp Dir)*
Steve Barr *(Founder & Chm)*
Michael Turley *(CEO)*
Rhonda Ries-Aguilar *(CFO)*
Karen Pfautch *(VP)*
Brian Deverman *(VP)*

Paramore The Digital Agency LLC (1)
500 Church St Ste 500, Nashville, TN 37203
Tel.: (615) 386-9012
Web Site: http://www.paramoredigital.com
Sales Range: $1-9.9 Million
Advetising Agency
N.A.I.C.S.: 541810
Lauren Haines *(Project Mgr)*
Rebecca Brown *(Project Mgr-Media)*

OSBORN TRANSPORTATION, INC.
1245 W Grand Ave, Rainbow City, AL 35906-8943
Tel.: (256) 442-2514 AL
Web Site:
http://www.osborntransportation.com
Year Founded: 1970
Sales Range: $25-49.9 Million
Emp.: 300
Trucking Service
N.A.I.C.S.: 484110
Paul Skelton *(Pres)*
Mark Skelton *(VP-Ops)*
Daen Nunnaley *(Dir-Safety)*

OSBORNE CONSTRUCTION COMPANY
10602 NE 38th Pl Ste 100, Kirkland, WA 98033-7909
Tel.: (425) 827-4221 WA
Web Site: http://www.osborne.cc
Year Founded: 1987
Sales Range: $50-74.9 Million
Emp.: 150
Nonresidential Construction
N.A.I.C.S.: 236220
George R. Osborne *(Pres & CEO)*
Dale Congert *(Chm)*
Daniel C. Jacobson *(Exec VP)*
David Klopp *(COO & VP-Ops)*

OSBORNE PROPERTIES CORP.
2172 Dupont Dr Ste 12, Irvine, CA 92612-1317
Tel.: (949) 271-5676
Web Site:
http://www.osborneprop.com
Offices of Real Estate Agents & Brokers
N.A.I.C.S.: 531210
Dennis L. Osborne *(Pres)*

OSBURN ASSOCIATES INC.
9383 Vanatta Rd, Logan, OH 43138
Tel.: (740) 385-5732
Web Site: http://www.osburns.com
Sales Range: $10-24.9 Million
Emp.: 16
Fittings For Pipe, Plastics
N.A.I.C.S.: 326122
Mike Grove *(Office Mgr)*

OSBURN BUICK PONTIAC GMC TRUCK
501 Liberty Blvd, Dubois, PA 15801
Tel.: (814) 371-4600
Sales Range: $10-24.9 Million
Emp.: 30
Car Whslr
N.A.I.C.S.: 441110
James S. Osburn III *(Pres)*

OSCAR DE LA RENTA LTD.
11 W 42nd St, New York, NY 10036
Tel.: (212) 282-0500
Web Site:
http://www.oscardelarenta.com
Sales Range: $650-699.9 Million
Emp.: 100
Men's & Women's Clothing Designer
N.A.I.C.S.: 315250
Alex Bolen *(CEO)*
Giuseppe Celio *(COO)*
Lisa Treiber *(VP-Ops & Production)*
Tara Maietta *(Dir-Global Bridal Sls)*

OSCAR G CARLSTEDT CO. INC.
2252 Dennis St, Jacksonville, FL 32204-1839
Tel.: (904) 354-8474
Sales Range: $10-24.9 Million
Emp.: 13
Flowers & Florists Supplies
N.A.I.C.S.: 424930
Alice Givens *(Pres)*

OSCAR GRUSS & SON INCORPORATED
292 Medison Ave 14Fl, New York, NY 10017
Tel.: (212) 514-2400
Web Site: http://www.oscargruss.com
Year Founded: 1918
Rev.: $35,000,000
Emp.: 50
Brokers Security
N.A.I.C.S.: 523150
Michael Shaoul *(Pres)*

OSCAR HEALTH AGENCY INC.
295 Lafayette St 6th Fl, New York, NY 10012
Tel.: (646) 403-3677
Web Site: http://www.hioscar.com
Year Founded: 2013
Emp.: 60
Health Insurance Services
N.A.I.C.S.: 524114
R. Scott Blackley *(CFO)*
Mario Schlosser *(Co-Founder & CEO)*
Joshua Kushner *(Co-Founder & Chm)*
Dave Henderson *(Pres-Insurance)*
Edward Segel *(VP-Product)*
Alan Warren *(CTO & Sr VP-Engrg)*
Dennis Weaver *(Chief Clinical Officer)*
R. Scott Blackley *(CFO)*

OSCAR HEYMAN & BROTHERS, INC.
501 Madison Ave 15th Fl, New York, NY 10022
Tel.: (212) 593-0400
Web Site:
http://www.oscarheyman.com
Year Founded: 1912
Rev.: $9,000,000
Emp.: 100
Jewelry Mfr
N.A.I.C.S.: 339910
Marvin Heyman *(Pres)*

OSCAR ORDUNO, INC.
4600 Fuller Dr Ste 375, Irving, TX 75038
Tel.: (972) 717-3070
Web Site:
http://www.oscardunoinc.com
Year Founded: 2014
Sales Range: $25-49.9 Million
Emp.: 200
Construction Services
N.A.I.C.S.: 236220
Oscar Orduno *(Pres)*

OSCAR RENDA CONTRACTING INC.
608 Henrietta Creek Rd, Roanoke, TX 76262
Tel.: (817) 491-2703 TX
Web Site:
http://www.oscarrendacontracting.com
Year Founded: 1974
Sales Range: $10-24.9 Million
Emp.: 100
Water, Sewer & Utility Lines
N.A.I.C.S.: 237110
Oscar Renda *(Pres)*
Dennis Bailey *(Project Mgr)*
Jason Bowen *(Project Mgr)*
Shanna Snyder *(Asst Controller)*
Will Johnson *(Mgr-Bus Dev)*
Janie Rodriguez *(Coord-Estimating)*
Daniel Frettinger *(Project Mgr)*
Joe Savage *(Project Mgr)*

OSCAR WINSKI CO. INC.
2407 N 9th St, Lafayette, IN 47903
Tel.: (765) 742-1102
Web Site:
http://www.oscarwinski.com
Year Founded: 1985
Sales Range: $25-49.9 Million
Emp.: 200
Provider of Metals Recycling
N.A.I.C.S.: 423510
Michael J. Bluestein *(Pres)*
John Gage *(CFO)*
Jim Bronchik *(VP-Admin)*

OSCEOLA CAPITAL MANAGEMENT, LLC
1715 N Westshore Blvd Ste 200, Tampa, FL 33607
Tel.: (813) 792-6559
Web Site: http://www.osceola.com
Private Equity Firm & Holding Company
N.A.I.C.S.: 551112
Michael Babb *(Mng Partner)*
Ben Moe *(Mng Partner)*
Patrick Watkins *(VP)*
Erik Sewell *(VP)*

Subsidiaries:

Avision Sales Group (1)
73 Cedar Ave, Hershey, PA 17033
Tel.: (888) 381-8892
Outsourced Sales & Marketing Services
N.A.I.C.S.: 541613
Joe Orednick *(CEO)*

Subsidiary (Domestic):

Apex Commercial Kitchen Co (2)
4218 Roanoke Rd, Kansas City, MO 64111
Tel.: (816) 753-7355
Rev.: $1,990,000
Emp.: 5
Other Commercial Equipment Merchant Whslr
N.A.I.C.S.: 423440
Mark Klosterman *(Principal)*

Utility Sales Associates, Inc. (2)
930 E Oak St, Lake in the Hills, IL 60156-6166
Tel.: (847) 658-8965
Web Site: http://www.utilitysales.net
Rev.: $1,100,000
Emp.: 15
Business Consulting Services
N.A.I.C.S.: 541618
Allan Stearns *(Pres)*
Curt Dukes *(Mgr-Telecom Sls)*
Steve Cohen *(Mng Partner-Sls)*

Central Medical Supply, Inc. (1)
240 US Hwy No 206, Flanders, NJ 07836
Tel.: (973) 927-3032
Web Site: https://centralmedsupply.com
Sales Range: $1-9.9 Million
Emp.: 20
Home Health Equipment Rental
N.A.I.C.S.: 532283
Elaine Wirtenberg *(Sec)*
Richard Rassi *(Dir-Client Svcs)*

Subsidiary (Domestic):

Consolidated Medical & Surgical Supply Co, Inc. (2)
145 Windsor Hay Ste 211, New Windsor, NY 12553
Tel.: (845) 565-5820
Web Site: http://www.consolidatedmedical.net
Sales Range: $1-9.9 Million
Emp.: 6
Home Health Equipment Rental
N.A.I.C.S.: 532283

Industry Services Co Inc. (1)
6565 Rangeline Dr, Theodore, AL 36582
Tel.: (251) 443-6900
Web Site: http://www.industrysci.com
Rev.: $4,680,000
Emp.: 13
Other Construction Material Merchant Whslr
N.A.I.C.S.: 423390
Marion Fincher *(Project Mgr)*
Shawn Hunter *(Pres)*

Subsidiary (Domestic):

OMI Refractories, LLC (2)
40B Sayreton Dr, Birmingham, AL 35207
Tel.: (205) 254-6111
Sales Range: $1-9.9 Million
Emp.: 40
Nondepository Credit Intermediation
N.A.I.C.S.: 522299
Jeff Debennedetto *(Principal)*

Oak Mountain Industries, Inc. (2)
730 Superior St, Carnegie, PA 15106
Tel.: (412) 278-1545
Rev.: $1,900,000
Emp.: 10
Industrial Supplies Merchant Whslr
N.A.I.C.S.: 423840
Larry Williams *(Pres)*

Quote.com (1)
3853 Northdale Boulevard Suite 373, Tampa, FL 33624
Tel.: (888) 690-2444
Web Site: https://www.quote.com
Tech-enabled digital media & Performance marketing platform
N.A.I.C.S.: 513210
Joel Ohman *(CEO)*

Subsidiary (Domestic):

Ring2 Media (2)
121 Post Rd W, Westport, CT 06880
Tel.: (203) 295-3472
Web Site: http://www.ring2media.com
Sales Range: $1-9.9 Million
Emp.: 10
Advetising Agency
N.A.I.C.S.: 541810
Mark Fidel *(CEO)*

Revelation Pharma Corporation LLC (1)
9777 Pyramid Ct Ste 230, Englewood, CO 80112
Tel.: (855) 434-6154
Web Site: https://revcustomrx.com
Pharmacies & Drug Stores
N.A.I.C.S.: 456110
Shawn Hodges *(CEO)*

Subsidiary (Domestic):

Lee-Silsby Compounding Pharmacy (2)
3216 Silsby Rd, Cleveland Heights, OH 44118
Tel.: (216) 321-4303
Web Site: http://www.leesilsby.com
Drugs & Druggists' Sundries Merchant Whslr
N.A.I.C.S.: 424210
Beverly Israel *(Founder)*

The Tendit Group, LLC (1)
7979 ETufts Ave Ste 1500, 80237, Denver, CO 80237
Tel.: (720) 641-7087
Web Site: https://www.tenditgroup.com
Exterior Facility Services
N.A.I.C.S.: 561210
Sam Pope *(VP-Merger & Acq)*

Subsidiary (Domestic):

Hartco, Inc. (2)
601 E 45th Ave, Denver, CO 80216
Tel.: (303) 295-2424
Web Site: https://camcolorado.com
Sales Range: $1-9.9 Million
Emp.: 45
Janitorial Services
N.A.I.C.S.: 561720
Chris Folz *(Acct Mgr)*
Marilyn Noska *(COO)*
Butch Hartman *(Founder)*

Top Gun Pressure Washing, Inc. (1)
500 W 67th St, Loveland, CO 80538
Tel.: (970) 203-1110
Web Site: http://www.topgunpressurewashing.com
Janitorial Services
N.A.I.C.S.: 561720
Stephanie White *(Mgr-Sls)*

Subsidiary (Domestic):

Bob Popp Building Services, Inc. (2)
2100 S Valentia St, Denver, CO 80231
Tel.: (303) 751-3113
Web Site: http://www.bobpoppbuildingservices.com
Window Cleaning Snowplowing & Sweeping Service Parking Lot Etc
N.A.I.C.S.: 561720
Robert Popp *(Pres)*

Emerald Isle Landscaping, Inc. (2)
6849 S Dawson Cir, Centennial, CO 80112
Tel.: (303) 693-3072
Web Site: http://www.emeraldislelandscaping.com
Sales Range: $1-9.9 Million
Emp.: 125
Landscape Maintenance Services
N.A.I.C.S.: 561720
Josh Cyboron *(Mgr-Denver South)*
Andrew Key *(Pres)*

OSCEOLA COUNTY EXPRESSWAY AUTHORITY
1 Courthouse Sq Ste 1100, Kissimmee, FL 34741
Tel.: (407) 742-0200
Web Site: http://www.osceola.org
Sales Range: $1-9.9 Million
Road Management & Construction
N.A.I.C.S.: 488490
Jeff Jones *(Dir-Strategic Initiatives)*
Alison Dube *(Mgr-Exemptions Dept)*
Bill Burchfield *(Dir-Land Records)*
David Tomek *(Dir-Community Dev)*
Donna Renberg *(Asst Mgr-County)*
Frank Raymond *(Dir-Pub Works)*
Fred Walters *(Dir-Info Sys)*
Jerry Williams *(Dir-Comml Valuations)*
Linda D. Penny *(Gen Counsel)*
Todd Hoover *(Dir-Residential Valuations)*
Tori Goodyear *(Mgr-Customer Svcs)*

OSCO INDUSTRIES INC.
734 11th St, Portsmouth, OH 45662
Tel.: (740) 354-3183 OH
Web Site: http://www.oscoind.com
Year Founded: 1872
Commercial Gray Iron Castings
N.A.I.C.S.: 331511
Tom Kayser *(Mgr-Sls & Mktg)*
Mike Burke *(Mgr-Acctg)*

OSCODA PLASTICS, INC.
5585 N Huron Ave, Oscoda, MI 48750
Tel.: (989) 739-6900
Web Site: http://www.oscodaplastics.com
Year Founded: 1993
Sales Range: $10-24.9 Million
Emp.: 65
Plastics Product Mfr
N.A.I.C.S.: 326199
Kathy L. Allen *(Sr VP)*
Jason Tunney *(Exec VP)*

OSCOR INC.
3816 DeSoto Blvd, Palm Harbor, FL 34683
Tel.: (727) 937-2511 FL
Web Site: http://www.oscor.com
Year Founded: 1982
Sales Range: $10-24.9 Million
Emp.: 400
Implantable Cardiac Pacing Leads, Venous Access Systems & Diagnostic Catheters Mfr
N.A.I.C.S.: 339112
Thomas Osypka *(Pres & CEO)*
Bethania Tavarez *(VP-Sls & Bus Dev)*
Brian Walguarnery *(Dir-Engrg)*
Zaida Torres *(Mgr-Intl Sls)*
Geoff Marinec *(Mgr-Molding, Silicone & Extrusion)*
Udo Wollmann *(Dir-Ops)*
Darryl Baker *(Dir-HR-Global)*
Luis Perez *(Sr Dir-Ops-Global)*
Eric Hoegstrom *(Mgr-Design Controls-R&D Engrg Team)*

OSF INTERNATIONAL, INC.
0715 SW Bancroft St, Portland, OR 97239
Tel.: (503) 225-0433 OR
Web Site: http://www.osf.com
Year Founded: 1969
Sales Range: $100-124.9 Million
Emp.: 4,750
Casual Restaurant Operator
N.A.I.C.S.: 722511
Chris Dussin *(Pres)*
Christopher Hein *(VP-Mktg)*
Kim Davidson *(Coord-Mktg)*

OSHMAN FAMILY JEWISH COMMUNITY CENTER
3921 Fabian Way, Palo Alto, CA 94303
Tel.: (650) 223-8700 CA
Web Site: http://www.paloaltojcc.org
Year Founded: 1960
Sales Range: $10-24.9 Million
Emp.: 244
Fiscal Year-end: 07/01/14
Community Action Services
N.A.I.C.S.: 813319
Zack Bodner *(CEO)*
Mimi Sells *(CMO)*
Craig Seidel *(Sec)*
Susan Steiner Saal *(First VP)*
Sharon Leslie *(Pres)*
Orli Rinat *(VP)*

OSI GROUP, LLC
1225 Corp Blvd, Aurora, IL 60505
Tel.: (630) 851-6600 DE
Web Site: https://www.osigroup.com
Year Founded: 1909
Sales Range: Less than $1 Million
Emp.: 20,000
All Other Miscellaneous Food Manufacturing
N.A.I.C.S.: 311999
Nicole Johnson-Hoffman *(Chief Sustainability Officer & Sr VP)*
David McDonald *(Pres & COO)*

Subsidiaries:

Park 100 Foods Inc. (1)
326 E Adams St, Tipton, IN 46072-2006
Tel.: (765) 763-6064
Web Site: http://www.park100foods.com
Sales Range: $25-49.9 Million
Emp.: 200
Custom Food Manufacturing Services
N.A.I.C.S.: 311999
Robert Orr *(Project Mgr)*
Gary Meade *(Pres)*
David Alves *(VP)*
Rick Mager *(Mng Dir)*

Rose Packing Company, Inc. (1)
65 S Barrington Rd, Barrington, IL 60010-9508
Tel.: (800) 323-7363
Web Site: http://www.rosepacking.com
Smoked Meat Products Whslr & Mfr
N.A.I.C.S.: 311612
Peter Rose *(VP-Production)*
Dwight Stiehl *(Pres & CEO)*
James O'Hara *(CFO)*
Tom Shaughnessy *(Acct Mgr)*
Jim Vandenbergh *(VP-Sls & Mktg)*
Bruce Shirmulis *(Mgr-Shipping)*
Maria Maris *(Dir-Lab)*
Sean R. Tuftedal *(Mgr-Quality Assurance)*

OSI, INC.
1 Wayside Rd, Burlington, MA 01803-4609
Tel.: (561) 575-5499
Sales Range: $1-9.9 Million
Emp.: 646
Transcription & Technology Solutions
N.A.I.C.S.: 518210
Andy Renfroe *(CEO & Mng Partner)*

OSIBODU & ASSOCIATES EXPORTING USA, LLC
1101 Channelside Dr, Tampa, FL 33602
Tel.: (813) 864-5600
Web Site: http://www.oaexportingusa.com
Sales Range: $1-9.9 Million
Construction Building Products & Fertilizer Exporter
N.A.I.C.S.: 425120
Josiah S. Osibodu *(Pres)*

OSISOFT, LLC
777 Davis St Ste 250, San Leandro, CA 94577
Tel.: (510) 297-5800
Web Site: http://www.osisoft.com
Year Founded: 1980
Rev.: $60,000,000
Emp.: 700
Application Computer Software
N.A.I.C.S.: 513210
J. Patrick Kennedy *(Founder & CEO)*
Richard Beeson *(Dir-Engrg)*
Michael Siemer *(Pres)*
Wolfgang Kuchen *(Sr VP-Sls & Mktg)*

OSKAR BLUES BREWING COMPANY
1800 Pike Rd Unit B, Longmont, CO 80501
Tel.: (303) 485-9400
Web Site: http://www.oskarblues.com
Sales Range: $10-24.9 Million
Emp.: 196
Beer Canning Services
N.A.I.C.S.: 311422
Dale Katechis *(Owner)*

OSKAR HUBER INC.
618 2nd St Pike, Southampton, PA 18966
Tel.: (215) 355-4800 PA

OSKAR HUBER INC.

U.S. PRIVATE

Oskar Huber Inc.—(Continued)
Web Site: http://www.oskarhuber.com
Year Founded: 1927
Sales Range: $10-24.9 Million
Emp.: 35
Homefurnishings
N.A.I.C.S.: 449110
O. Robert Huber *(Co-Pres)*
Ron Huber *(Co-Pres)*
Doris Huber *(Treas)*

OSL HOLDINGS INC.
1669 Edgewood Rd Ste 214, Yardley, PA 19067
Tel.: (845) 363-6776 — NV
Web Site: http://www.oslholdings.com
Year Founded: 2006
Sales Range: Less than $1 Million
Emp.: 3
Holding Company; Technology Services
N.A.I.C.S.: 551112
Steven Gormley *(Chief Corp Dev Officer)*
Thomas D'Orazio *(Chief Acctg Officer, VP & Controller)*
Jonathan D'Agostino *(Acting VP-Corp Dev)*
Robert H. Rothenberg Jr. *(Pres & CEO)*
Michael E. Fasci Sr. *(CFO)*

OSM WORLDWIDE
651 Supreme Dr, Bensenville, IL 60106-1157
Tel.: (866) 681-7867
Web Site: http://www.osmworldwide.com
Year Founded: 2003
Sales Range: $25-49.9 Million
Emp.: 50
Shipping Consolidator Services
N.A.I.C.S.: 561910
Gaston Curk *(CEO)*
Christine Kelley *(Dir-Mktg)*
James Kelley *(Pres)*

OSPRAIE MANAGEMENT, LLC
437 Madison Ave 28th Fl, New York, NY 10022
Tel.: (212) 602-5000 — DE
Web Site: http://www.ospraie.com
Year Founded: 1999
Sales Range: $5-14.9 Billion
Emp.: 32
Investment Management Firm
N.A.I.C.S.: 523940
Dwight W. Anderson *(Founder & CEO)*

OSPREY CAPITAL LLC
825 Green Bay Rd Ste 100, Wilmette, IL 60091
Tel.: (847) 512-3180 — IL
Web Site: http://www.ospreycapitalllc.com
Year Founded: 2002
Venture Capital & Private Equity Firm
N.A.I.C.S.: 523999
David H. Hoffmann *(Founder & Principal)*
Frank Silcox *(Mng Dir)*
Greg Hoffman *(COO & Principal)*

Subsidiaries:

Erik Kellar Photography (1)
7091 Barrington Cir 101, Naples, FL 34108
Tel.: (239) 253-8687
Web Site: http://www.erikkellar.com
Commercial Photography
N.A.I.C.S.: 541922
Erik Kellar *(Pres)*

Innofactor Plc (1)
Keilaranta 9, FI-02150, Espoo, Finland
Tel.: (358) 102729000

Web Site: https://www.innofactor.com
Rev.: $76,764,515
Assets: $60,236,348
Liabilities: $33,472,912
Net Worth: $26,763,436
Earnings: $3,582,992
Emp.: 564
Fiscal Year-end: 12/31/2022
Software, Digital Document, Business Process Management, Customer-Specific Integration & CRM Solutions
N.A.I.C.S.: 513210
Sami Ensio *(Pres, CEO & Mgr-Finland)*
Anna Linden *(Chm)*
Vesa Syrjakari *(Exec VP-Bus Dev & Operational Excellence)*
Jorn Ellefsen *(Mng Dir & Mgr-Norway & Denmark)*
Markku Puolanne *(CFO)*
Michaela Skrabb *(Gen Counsel)*
Marcus Hasselblad *(Mng Dir)*
Lasse Lautsuo *(CMO)*
Janne Heikkinen *(Exec VP-Products & Svcs)*

Affiliate (Non-US):

GAP AG (2)
Hospitalstrasse 6, D-99817, Eisenach, Germany (23%)
Tel.: (49) 3691886923
Web Site: http://www.gapag.de
Application Software Solutions
N.A.I.C.S.: 423430

Subsidiary (Domestic):

PlanMill Ltd. (2)
Hameentie 19, 00500, Helsinki, Finland
Tel.: (358) 10 322 9110
Web Site: https://www.planmill.com
Business Management Services
N.A.I.C.S.: 513210
Thomas Hood *(CEO & Partner)*

OSPREY MANAGEMENT, LLC
1640 Powers Ferry Rd Bldg 26 Ste 200, Marietta, GA 30067
Tel.: (770) 726-2556
Web Site: http://www.contractosprey.com
Year Founded: 2001
Sales Range: $1-9.9 Million
Emp.: 9
General Contractor Services
N.A.I.C.S.: 236210
Kelvin King *(Founder)*

OSPREY S.A. LIMITED
7600 Grand River Ave, Brighton, MI 48114
Tel.: (810) 225-9660
Web Site: http://www.ospreysa.com
Year Founded: 1998
Sales Range: $25-49.9 Million
Emp.: 25
Commercial & Residential Real Estate Investment & Management Services
N.A.I.C.S.: 531210
Michael G. Cottrell *(CFO)*
Michael A. Collins *(CEO & Mng Partner)*
Terrance J. Manning *(Mng Dir)*
Wesley D. Marchal *(Dir-Acq)*

Subsidiaries:

Osprey Real Estate Services, LLC (1)
360 Central Ave Ste 1570, Saint Petersburg, FL 33701
Tel.: (727) 894-2525
Web Site: http://www.ospreyres.com
Real Estate Brokerage & Management Services
N.A.I.C.S.: 531210
Wendy S. Giffin *(Pres)*

OSPREY'S DOMINION VINEYARDS LTD.
44075 Main Rd, Peconic, NY 11958
Tel.: (631) 765-6188

Web Site: http://www.ospreysdominion.com
Sales Range: $10-24.9 Million
Emp.: 20
Vineyard & Wine Mfr
N.A.I.C.S.: 111332
Bud Koehler *(Pres)*
Peter Carey *(Mgr)*

OST TRUCKING COMPANY INC.
1205 68th St, Baltimore, MD 21237
Tel.: (410) 866-7700
Web Site: http://www.osttrucking.com
Sales Range: $10-24.9 Million
Emp.: 70
Provider of Trucking Services
N.A.I.C.S.: 484121
Ed Peach *(Pres)*
Mark Pelovitz *(Controller)*

OSTEEN PUBLISHING COMPANY
36 W Liberty St, Sumter, SC 29150
Tel.: (803) 774-1200
Web Site: http://www.theitem.com
Year Founded: 1894
Sales Range: $1-9.9 Million
Emp.: 120
Newspaper Publishers
N.A.I.C.S.: 513110
Hubert D. Osteen *(Chm)*
Lori Rabon *(District Mgr)*
Micah Green *(Chief Digital Officer)*

Subsidiaries:

Gulf Coast Newspapers, LLC (1)
901 N Mc Kenzie St, Foley, AL 36535
Tel.: (251) 947-7712
Web Site: http://www.gulfcoastnewstoday.com
Sales Range: $1-9.9 Million
Emp.: 20
Newspaper Publishers
N.A.I.C.S.: 513110
Parks Rogers *(Publr)*

OSTER COMMUNICATIONS INC.
6355 Ward Rd Unit 301, Arvada, CO 80004-3823
Tel.: (319) 277-1271
Sales Range: $10-24.9 Million
Emp.: 20
Pamphlets: Publishing & Printing
N.A.I.C.S.: 111998
Merrill J. Oster *(Pres)*
Kelly Myer *(Controller)*

OSTERMAN & CO. INC.
726 S Main St, Cheshire, CT 06410
Tel.: (203) 272-2233 — DE
Web Site: http://www.osterman-co.com
Sales Range: $10-24.9 Million
Emp.: 90
Plastics Materials
N.A.I.C.S.: 424610
James O. Dwyer *(Pres)*

OSTERMANCRON, INC.
10830 Millington Ct, Cincinnati, OH 45242
Tel.: (513) 771-3377 — OH
Web Site: http://www.ostermancron.com
Year Founded: 1997
Sales Range: $10-24.9 Million
Emp.: 20
Office Furniture Retail & Interior Design Services
N.A.I.C.S.: 449110
Diane Bullock *(Dir-Ops)*
Joel Osterman *(Co-Founder & Partner)*
Keith Cron *(Co-Founder & Partner)*

Susan Haidet *(Mgr-Sls & Mktg)*
Becky van Leur *(Acct Exec)*
Diana Broughton *(Mgr-PM)*

OSTROW ELECTRICAL CO. INC.
9 Mason St, Worcester, MA 01609-1803
Tel.: (508) 754-2641 — MA
Year Founded: 1939
Sales Range: $1-9.9 Million
Emp.: 350
Electrical Work
N.A.I.C.S.: 238210
Jonathan J. Ostrow *(Pres)*
Philip Ostrow *(VP)*

OSWALD COMPANIES
1360 E 9th St Ste 600, Cleveland, OH 44114-1715
Tel.: (216) 367-8787
Web Site: http://www.oswaldcompanies.com
Sales Range: $10-24.9 Million
Emp.: 230
Insurance Agents
N.A.I.C.S.: 524210
Robert J. Klonk *(Chm & CEO)*
Kathleen K. Miller *(VP)*
Denise Tapp *(Controller)*
Neil Quinn *(VP)*
Jessica Jung *(Dir-Property & Casualty)*
Tim Walsh *(Sr VP)*
Joseph DuBois *(CFO)*
Erin Blevins *(Mgr-Client-Personal Insurance)*
Chuck White *(Mgr-Construction)*
Jennifer Morrissey *(CIO)*
Sara Jones *(VP-Risk Mgmt & Strategy)*

OSWEGO VALLEY INSURANCE AGENCIES LLC
166 W 1st St, Oswego, NY 13126
Tel.: (315) 343-6310 — NY
Web Site: http://www.insureit.com
Year Founded: 1997
Insurance Agents
N.A.I.C.S.: 524210
Jim Poindexter *(VP)*
Verner M. Drohan *(Pres & CEO)*

OTA BROADCASTING, LLC
3201 Jermantown Rd Ste 380, Fairfax, VA 22030
Tel.: (703) 364-5300 — DE
Web Site: http://www.otabroadcasting.com
Year Founded: 2011
Television Broadcasting Stations Operator
N.A.I.C.S.: 516120
Bill Tolpegin *(CEO)*

Subsidiaries:

KTLN-TV (1)
100 Pelican Way Ste E, San Rafael, CA 94901
Tel.: (415) 485-5856
Web Site: http://www.ktln.tv
Emp.: 3
Television Broadcasting Station
N.A.I.C.S.: 516120
Debra Fraser *(Gen Mgr)*

KVOS-TV (1)
3111 Newmarket St Ste 108, Bellingham, WA 98226
Tel.: (360) 671-1212
Web Site: http://www.kvos.com
Television Broadcasting Station
N.A.I.C.S.: 516120
Sabrina Hlebichuk *(Office Mgr)*

OTAK, INC.
808 SW 3 AVE, Lake Oswego, OR 97204

COMPANIES

Tel.: (503) 635-3618
Web Site: http://www.otak.com
Year Founded: 1981
Rev.: $40,599,776
Emp.: 250
Civil Engineering & Construction Management Services
N.A.I.C.S.: 237310
Jim Hamann (Pres & CEO)
Brian Fleener (VP & Dir-Architecture)
Charles Pierson (Mgr-Construction Project)
Ben Bortolazzo (Dir-Plng & Design)
David S. Johnson (CFO)
Ken Swindaman (Mgr-Survey Dept)
Doug Beyerlein (Sr Engr-Water Resource)
Benjamin Wanlass (Controller)
Krissy Ehlers (Sr Mgr-Compensation & Benefits)
Javier Moncada (Project Mgr-Construction)
Chad P. Weiser (Principal-Plng, Landscape Architecture & Urban Design)
Don Hanson (Principal & Dir-Plng, Architecture & Design)
Doug Sarkkinen (Principal & Engr-Structural)
Jack Carlson (Principal-Surveying & Mapping)
Mandi Roberts (Principal-Plng, Landscape Architecture & Urban Design)
Michael Peebles (Principal & Dir-Transportation & Infrastructure-Oregon)
Nico M. Vanderhorst (Principal & Dir-Transportation & Infrastructure-Washington)
Niels van Dijk (VP)
Russ Gaston (Principal & Dir-Water & Natural Resources)
Casey McKenna (Sr Project Mgr-Architecture)
Justin Monahan (Dir-Contracts & Risk Mgmt-Corp Grp)

OTC INTERNATIONAL, LTD.
31-00 47th Ave, Long Island City, NY 11101-3068
Tel.: (718) 391-7400   NY
Web Site:
  http://www.otcinternational.com
Jewelry & Precious Stones Retailer
N.A.I.C.S.: 423940
Marlenie Paredes (Asst VP-Sls & Mktg)

OTERO COUNTY ELECTRIC COOP
404 Burro Ave, Cloudcroft, NM 88317
Tel.: (575) 682-2521
Web Site: http://www.ocec-inc.com
Rev.: $11,710,274
Emp.: 52
Electronic Services
N.A.I.C.S.: 221118
Fred Hansen (Sec)
Terry Buttram (COO)
Julie Walker-Grinder (Mgr-Fin)
Linda Hamilton (Mgr-HR)
Billy Massie (Mgr-Member Svcs)
Kathy Davis (Suprv-Billing)
Ray Rush (Mgr-Ops)
Matt Flotte (VP)
Scott Shafer (Treas)
Denny Burnett (Co-Sec)

OTEY WHITE & ASSOCIATES
8146 One Calais Ave, Baton Rouge, LA 70808-3155
Tel.: (225) 201-0032
Web Site: http://www.oteywhite.com
Year Founded: 1981
Sales Range: $25-49.9 Million
Emp.: 6
N.A.I.C.S.: 541810

Jack K. White (Mgr-Brdcst Production)
Angela de Gravelles (Dir-PR)
Mary P.N. Wilson (Comptroller)
Erin Hains (Acct Exec & Media Buyer)
Kiesha Michaelson (Dir-Art)
Jeff English (Dir-Creative)
Tara Mason (Dir-Media)
Trent Bland (Copywriter & Dir-Res)
Otey L. White III (Pres)

OTG EXP, INC.
352 Park Ave S Fl 10, New York, NY 10010
Tel.: (212) 776-1478   DE
Web Site:
  http://www.anotgexperience.com
Year Founded: 1996
Airport Restaurant Operator
N.A.I.C.S.: 722511
Eric J. Blatstein (Founder, Chm & CEO)
Joseph G. Ozalas (CFO & Exec VP)
Christopher Redd (Gen Counsel, Sec & Exec VP)

OTHER WORLD COMPUTING
8 Galaxyway, Woodstock, IL 60098
Tel.: (815) 333-5023
Web Site: http://www.macsales.com
Sales Range: $10-24.9 Million
Emp.: 163
Computer Products Whslr
N.A.I.C.S.: 423430
Larry O'Connor (Founder & CEO)
Rick Van Dyne (Dir-Sls)

OTIS & AHEARN INC.
20 Park Plz Ste 1101, Boston, MA 02116
Tel.: (617) 267-3500
Web Site: http://www.otisahearn.com
Sales Range: $10-24.9 Million
Emp.: 20
Provider of Real Estate Broker & Agency Services
N.A.I.C.S.: 531210
Kevin Ahearn (Pres)
Bill Ahearn (Sr VP-Fin & Admin)
Fred Alibrandi (Sr VP)
Kristin Pomponi (Office Mgr)
Michael Moran (Mng Dir)

OTIS TECHNOLOGY, INC.
6987 Laura St, Lyons Falls, NY 13368
Tel.: (315) 348-4300
Web Site: http://www.otisgun.com
Year Founded: 2005
Sales Range: $50-74.9 Million
Emp.: 136
Mfr of Portable Gun Systems
N.A.I.C.S.: 332992
Len Nelson (VP-Sls & Mktg)
Aaron Smith (Mgr-Sls-Western Reg)
Larry Williams (CEO)

OTO DEVELOPMENT
100 Dunbar St Ste 402, Spartanburg, SC 29306
Tel.: (864) 596-8930
Web Site:
  http://www.otodevelopment.com
Year Founded: 2004
Sales Range: $125-149.9 Million
Emp.: 1,065
Real Estate Development Services
N.A.I.C.S.: 531390
Bruce Collins (Dir-Dev-East Reg)
Mike Gallen (Dir-Dev-West Reg)
Taylor Callaham (Sr Dir-Real Estate-Reg)
Lisa Giaimo (VP-Sls & Mktg)
Rob Oursler (Dir-Ops-Mid-Atlantic)
David Ward (COO)

Kelly Haager (Sr Dir-Sls-East)
Kevin DeMark (Dir-Facilities)
Aimee Cheek (Dir-ECommerce)
Jack Hancharick (Corp Dir-Food & Beverage)
Sonia Santana (VP-People Svcs & Culture)
Chris Lewis (Dir-Facilities)
Dennis Mitchell (Mgr-Dev)
Jami Johnson (Dir-Sls-Northwest)
Joe Vieira (Mgr-Dev)
Lara Stabell-Gibb (Dir-Revenue Mgmt)
Seema Bandukda (Dir-Ops-Southwest Reg)
Suzanne McClendon (Mgr-Compliance Leave & WC)
Stephen Daley (VP-Construction)
Jason Boehm (VP-Bus Dev)
Jason Lynch (Gen Counsel)
George Rutledge (VP-Pur & Tech)
Todd Turner (Co-Founder & VP-Real Estate)
Michael Rosen (VP-Food & Beverage)
George Dean Johnson Jr. (Co-Founder)

OTOMIX, INC.
747 S Glasgow Ave, Inglewood, CA 90301-3011
Tel.: (310) 215-6100
Web Site: http://www.otomix.com
Year Founded: 1988
Sales Range: $10-24.9 Million
Emp.: 30
Men & Women's Sportswear
N.A.I.C.S.: 424350
Mitchell Bobrow (Owner-Otomix Athletic Company)

OTR WHEEL ENGINEERING, INC.
6 Riverside Industrial Park, Rome, GA 30162
Tel.: (706) 235-9781
Web Site: http://www.otrwheel.com
Year Founded: 1987
Rev.: $53,600,000
Emp.: 100
Tire & Tube Merchant Whslr
N.A.I.C.S.: 423130
Fredrick B. Taylor (Chm & Pres)

Subsidiaries:

Blackstone/OTR, LLC   (1)
6 Riverside Industrial Park, Rome, GA 30161-7301
Tel.: (706) 235-9781
Tire & Tube Merchant Whslr
N.A.I.C.S.: 423130
Fredrick B. Taylor (Pres & CEO)
Jeff Williams (Dir-Sls)

OTSEGO MEMORIAL HOSPITAL ASSOCIATION
825 N Center Ave, Gaylord, MI 49735
Tel.: (989) 731-2100   MI
Web Site: http://www.myomh.org
Year Founded: 1946
Sales Range: $75-99.9 Million
Emp.: 748
Health Care Srvices
N.A.I.C.S.: 622110
Thomas Lemon (Pres & CEO)
Robert Courtois (CFO & VP-Fin)
Barbara Miller (VP-Physician Svcs)

OTT CONSULTING INC.
222 Main St, Emmaus, PA 18049
Tel.: (610) 928-4690
Web Site: http://www.otteng.com
Year Founded: 2003
Sales Range: $1-9.9 Million
Emp.: 17
Civil Engineers & Surveyors
N.A.I.C.S.: 237990

OTTERBEIN SENIOR LIFESTYLE CHOICES

Subsidiaries:

OTT Consulting Inc.   (1)
PO Box 266 366 Blue Valley Dr, Bangor, PA 18013   (100%)
Tel.: (610) 588-2411
Web Site: http://www.otteng.com
Civil Engineers & Surveyors Consulting Services
N.A.I.C.S.: 541370
Reynold E. Petrelli (Founder)

OTTAWA COOPERATIVE ASSOCIATION
302 N Main St, Ottawa, KS 66067
Tel.: (785) 242-5170
Web Site:
  http://www.ottawacoop.com
Rev.: $23,567,397
Emp.: 60
Feed
N.A.I.C.S.: 424910
Adrian Derousseau (Gen Mgr)
Calvin Pearson (Mgr-Ops)

OTTAWA RUBBER COMPANY
1600 Commerce Rd, Holland, OH 43528-0553
Tel.: (419) 865-1378
Web Site:
  http://www.ottawarubber.com
Sales Range: $10-24.9 Million
Emp.: 25
Rubber Products Mfr
N.A.I.C.S.: 326291
Mike Bugert (Pres)
Jeff Bretz (Engr-Sls)
Jennifer Ward (Dir-Customer Svc)

OTTENBERGS BAKERS INC.
3330 75th Ave, Hyattsville, MD 20785-1501
Tel.: (202) 529-5800
Web Site: http://www.ottenbergs.com
Sales Range: $25-49.9 Million
Emp.: 170
Food Service Bakery
N.A.I.C.S.: 311812
Ray Ottenberg (Pres)
Lee Ottenberg (CEO)

OTTERBASE TECHNICAL SERVICES, INC.
555 3 Mile Rd NW, Grand Rapids, MI 49544
Tel.: (616) 451-2775
Web Site: http://www.otterbase.com
Sales Range: $10-24.9 Million
Emp.: 600
Consulting Services
N.A.I.C.S.: 541612

OTTERBEIN SENIOR LIFESTYLE CHOICES
580 N State Route 741, Lebanon, OH 45036
Tel.: (513) 932-2020   OH
Web Site: http://www.otterbein.org
Year Founded: 1912
Sales Range: $25-49.9 Million
Emp.: 758
Lifecare Retirement Community Services
N.A.I.C.S.: 623311
J. Christopher Green (CFO & VP-Fin)
Gary Horning (VP-Mktg & Comm)
Jason E. Miller (VP-Otterbein Lifestyle Communities)
Lynn App (Chm)
William Brownson (Vice Chm)
Leroy Chambliss (Sec)
Jeff Eyrich (VP-Skilled Nursing & Rehab)
Lois Mills (VP-HR)
Emily Weikert (VP-Clinical Quality)
Jill Wilson (Pres & CEO)

OTTERBOX PRODUCTS LLC

OtterBox Products LLC—(Continued)

OTTERBOX PRODUCTS LLC
1 Old Town Sq Ste 303, Fort Collins, CO 80524
Tel.: (970) 493-8446
Web Site: http://www.otterbox.com
Year Founded: 1996
Sales Range: $550-599.9 Million
Emp.: 550
Handheld Device Protective Cover Mfr
N.A.I.C.S.: 423990
Curt Richardson *(Founder & Chm)*
Brian Thomas *(Pres & CEO)*
Peter Lindgren *(COO)*

OTTO
1611 Colley Ave Ste C, Norfolk, VA 23517
Tel.: (757) 622-4050
Web Site: http://www.thinkotto.com
Year Founded: 2000
Emp.: 30
Advertising Services
N.A.I.C.S.: 541810
Pete Leddy *(Pres)*
Mark Edward Atkinson *(VP & Creative Dir)*
Diane Lingoni *(Dir-Production)*
Joe Mishkofski *(Mgr-Studio)*
Jenna Lambert *(Acct Supvr)*
Sherri Priester *(Dir-Media)*
Kim Gudusky Wilson *(Acct Supvr)*
Hunter Spencer *(Assoc Dir-Creative)*
Janet Merlo *(Acct Supvr)*
Lauren Shoff *(Mgr-Digital & Social Media)*
Scott Mackey *(Dir-Creative)*

Subsidiaries:

Otto (1)
217 77th St, Virginia Beach, VA 23451
Tel.: (757) 622-4050
Web Site: http://www.thinkotto.com
Emp.: 17
Advertising Agencies
N.A.I.C.S.: 541810
Sherri Priester *(Dir-Media)*
Pete Leddy *(Pres & Partner)*
Mark Edward Atkinson *(VP & Dir-Creative)*
Diane Lingoni *(Mgr-Production)*
Sabrina Bryan *(Dir-Art)*
Kim Gudusky *(Supvr-Acct)*
Megan Kresse *(Coord-Acct)*
Jenna Lambert *(Supvr-Acct)*
Scott Mackey *(Dir-Creative)*
Cindy Mackey *(Dir-PR)*
Janet Merlo *(Supvr-Acct)*
Lauren Shoff *(Mgr-Digital & Social Media)*
Hunter Spencer *(Dir-Creative)*

OTTO BAUM COMPANY, INC.
866 N Main St, Morton, IL 61550-1602
Tel.: (309) 266-7114
Web Site: http://www.ottobaum.com
Year Founded: 1937
Sales Range: $25-49.9 Million
Emp.: 300
Full Service Contracting; Masonry & Other Stonework
N.A.I.C.S.: 238140
Kurt L. Baum *(VP-Ops)*
Craig R. Baum *(VP-Estimating)*
Terry L. Baum *(Pres)*

Subsidiaries:

Core Construction Inc. (1)
866 N Main St, Morton, IL 61550-1602
Tel.: (309) 266-9768
Web Site: http://www.coreconstruct.com
Sales Range: $10-24.9 Million
Emp.: 30
Commercial Construction
N.A.I.C.S.: 541618

Subsidiary (Domestic):

Walton Construction-A Core Company, LLC (2)
9300 Renner Blvd, Lenexa, KS 66219
Tel.: (913) 982-2545
Industrial Building
N.A.I.C.S.: 236210

OTTO INTERNATIONAL INC.
3550 A E Jurupa St, Ontario, CA 91761-2945
Tel.: (909) 937-1998
Web Site: http://www.ottocap.com
Year Founded: 1983
Sales Range: $10-24.9 Million
Emp.: 106
Mfr & Distributor of Baseball Caps
N.A.I.C.S.: 424350
Razgo Lee *(Pres & CEO)*
Frank Jou *(Controller)*

OUR CHILDREN OUR FUTURE
450 S San Rafael Ave, Pasadena, CA 91105
Tel.: (626) 795-5255   CA
Year Founded: 1995
Sales Range: Less than $1 Million
Fundraising Services
N.A.I.C.S.: 813211
Jonathan Fuhrman *(CFO)*
Stephen English *(Sec)*
Molly Munger *(Pres)*

OUR CITY READING
4500 Perkiomen Ave, Reading, PA 19606
Tel.: (610) 370-3762   PA
Web Site: http://www.ourcityreading.org
Year Founded: 2001
Sales Range: $1-9.9 Million
Community Development Services
N.A.I.C.S.: 624190
James Boscov *(Vice Chm)*
Dieter Czerny *(Treas)*
John Connelly *(VP)*
Michael Ehlerman *(Pres)*
Walt Woolwine *(Sec)*
Albert Boscov *(Chm)*

OUR DAILY BREAD MINISTRIES
3000 Kraft Ave SE, Grand Rapids, MI 49512
Tel.: (616) 974-2210   MI
Web Site: http://ourdailybread.org
Year Founded: 1938
Christian Based Literature, Radio & Television
N.A.I.C.S.: 512290
Rick Dehaan *(Pres)*

OUR HOSPICE OF SOUTH CENTRAL INDIANA, INC.
2626 E 17th St, Columbus, IN 47201
Tel.: (812) 314-8000   IN
Web Site: http://www.ourhospice.org
Year Founded: 1980
Sales Range: $10-24.9 Million
Emp.: 180
Elder Care Services
N.A.I.C.S.: 623312
Marlene Weatherwax *(Treas & Sec)*
Suzanne Wells *(Chm)*
Laura Hurt *(Pres)*

OUR KIDS OF MIAMI-DADE/MONROE, INC.
401 NW 2nd Ave 10th Fl S Tower, Miami, FL 33128-1740
Tel.: (305) 455-6000   FL
Web Site: http://www.ourkids.us
Year Founded: 2002
Sales Range: $75-99.9 Million
Emp.: 176
Child & Family Care Services
N.A.I.C.S.: 624190
George Sheldon *(CEO)*

OUR MAN IN HAVANA LLC
55 Washington St Ste 453, Brooklyn, NY 11201
Tel.: (212) 505-3533
Web Site: http://www.omihnyc.com
Year Founded: 2003
Sales Range: $1-9.9 Million
Emp.: 50
Advertising Services
N.A.I.C.S.: 541810
Andrew Golomb *(Founder & Creative Dir)*
Sylve Rosen-Bernstein *(Creative Dir)*
Aisling Bodkin *(Head-Production)*
Tyler Barbiaux *(Acct Mgr)*
Stephanie Hsieh *(Acct Mgr)*

OUR SUNDAY VISITOR, INC.
200 Noll Plz, Huntington, IN 46750-4310
Tel.: (260) 356-8400   IN
Web Site: http://www.osv.com
Year Founded: 1912
Sales Range: $100-124.9 Million
Emp.: 300
Religious Books & Materials Publisher
N.A.I.C.S.: 513120
Therese Calouette *(Mgr-Adv)*
Kevin C. Rhoades *(Chm)*
Emily Stimpson *(Editor-Contributing)*
Jackie Lindsey *(Editor-Acq)*
Bill Dodds *(Editor)*

Subsidiaries:

AmericanChurch, Inc. (1)
525 McClurg Rd, Youngstown, OH 44512   (100%)
Tel.: (330) 758-4545
Web Site: http://www.americanchurch.com
Sales Range: $25-49.9 Million
Mfr of Religious Products & Offering Envelopes
N.A.I.C.S.: 322230
Steve Hewitt *(Editor-in-Chief)*
Chuch Zech *(Dir-Villanova Center)*
Mark Mogilka *(Dir-Stewardship & Pastoral Svcs)*
James W. Klingler *(Assoc Dir)*
Carol Fowler *(Dir-Personnel Svcs)*

OUR TOWN AMERICA, INC.
3845 Gateway Centre Blvd Ste 300, Pinellas Park, FL 33782
Tel.: (800) 497-8360
Web Site: http://www.ourtownamerica.com
Sales Range: $1-9.9 Million
Emp.: 60
Direct Mail Marketing
N.A.I.C.S.: 541860
Michael L. Plummer Jr. *(Pres)*

OURAY SPORTSWEAR, LLC
1201 W Mansfield Ave, Englewood, CO 80110
Tel.: (303) 789-4035
Web Site: http://www.ouraysportswear.com
Year Founded: 2007
Sportswear Designer & Mfr
N.A.I.C.S.: 423910
Craig Dudley *(Pres)*

OURISMAN AUTOMOTIVE GROUP
4400 Branch Ave, Marlow Heights, MD 20748
Tel.: (301) 423-4028
Web Site: http://www.ourisman.com
Year Founded: 1921
Sales Range: $750-799.9 Million
Emp.: 1,050
Owner of Auto Dealerships & Supplier of Automobile Parts & Services
N.A.I.C.S.: 441110

Mandell J. Ourisman *(Chm)*
John Ourisman *(Pres)*
Mohamed Reshed *(CFO)*

Subsidiaries:

Ourisman Chevrolet Company, Inc. (1)
4400 Branch Ave, Marlow Heights, MD 20748
Tel.: (240) 455-3386
Web Site: http://www.ourismanchevrolet.com
Sales Range: $500-549.9 Million
New Car Dealers
N.A.I.C.S.: 441110
Kenny Powers *(Gen Mgr)*
Natasha Jones *(Mgr-BDC)*
Doug Beverley *(   )*
Dave Jordan *(Mgr-Sls)*
Joe Laney *(Dir-Internet Sls)*
Magnus Onyima *(Mgr-New Car Sls)*
Patrice Taylor *(Mgr-Aftermarket)*

Ourisman Chrysler Dodge Jeep Ram of Clarksville (1)
12430 Auto Dr, Clarksville, MD 21029
Tel.: (855) 872-5346
Web Site: http://www.ourismanchrysler.com
Emp.: 50
Car Dealer
N.A.I.C.S.: 441110
Levi Haslup *(VP & Gen Mgr)*
Jeff Borakove *(Gen Sls Mgr)*
Wayne McCormick *(Mgr-Used Car)*
Dina Marshalek *(Bus Dir)*
Justin Chenoweth *(Sls Mgr)*
Dana McGriff *(Fin Mgr)*
Mike Catron *(Dir-Svc)*
Sid Glover *(Mgr-Parts)*

Ourisman Dodge, Inc. (1)
5900 Richmond Hwy, Alexandria, VA 22303
Tel.: (703) 329-1600
Web Site: http://www.ourismanchryslerjeepdodgeofalexandria.com
Sales Range: $10-24.9 Million
Emp.: 60
New Car Dealers
N.A.I.C.S.: 441110
Roy Hippert *(Mgr-Internet Sls)*
Whitey Sickle *(Dir-Fin)*
Cecil Khan *(Mgr-Fin)*
Dennis Higgins *(Mgr-Parts)*
Dino Mino *(Mgr-Svc)*
Bernard Parker *(Dir-Sls Ops)*
Chris Morrison *(Dir-Svc)*
Rick Lawrenson *(Dir-Pre Owned)*
Si Faiqe *(Gen Mgr-Sls)*
Andy Heye *(Gen Mgr)*
Omar Shahid *(Mgr-Fin)*
Asher Sher *(Dir-Fin)*

Ourisman Mitsubishi (1)
4404 Branch Ave, Marlow Heights, MD 20748
Tel.: (301) 423-4400
Web Site: http://www.ourismanmitsubishi.com
Sales Range: $10-24.9 Million
Emp.: 34
New Car Dealers
N.A.I.C.S.: 441110
Kenny Powers *(Gen Mgr)*
Thomas Woodruff *(Mgr-New Car-Mitsubishi)*
Carlos Miller *(Mgr-Fin)*
Donna Bumgardner *(Mgr-Svc)*
Matt Cooper *(Mgr-Fin)*
Steve Everett *(Mgr-Body Shop)*
Joe Laney *(Mgr-Internet Sls)*
Ashley Hansborough *(Mgr-Customer Svc)*
Jerris Millington *(Mgr-Fin)*
Patrice Taylor *(Mgr-Aftermarket)*

OURNETT HOLDINGS, INC.
122 E 42nd St, New York, NY 10168
Tel.: (212) 986-1544   NV
Web Site: https://www.ournett.com
Year Founded: 2013
ORNT—(OTCBB)
Online Retailer of Discounted Products
N.A.I.C.S.: 459999
Fernando Koatz *(Mgr)*
David Vara *(Dir-Tech)*

OUT OF THE BOXTECHNOLOGY

COMPANIES

7150 SW Hampton St #200, Tigard, OR 97223
Tel.: (503) 885-0776
Web Site:
http://www.outoftheboxtechnology.com
Bookkeeping, Consulting, Training & Software Integration Services
N.A.I.C.S.: 541611
Denise Loter-Koch *(Co-Founder & CEO)*
Lisa McCarthy *(Co-Founder & COO)*
Andrew Abrams *(Co-Founder & CTO)*

Subsidiaries:

EBS Associates, Inc.   (1)
7150 SW Hampton St #200, Tigard, OR 97223
Tel.: (503) 885-0776
Web Site: http://ebsassociates.com
Computer & Computer Peripheral Equipment & Software Merchant Whslr
N.A.I.C.S.: 423430
Denise Ann Koch *(Founder & CEO)*

OUTAGAMIE CO-OP SERVICES
3011 W Wisconsin Ave, Appleton, WI 54914
Tel.: (920) 739-8411
Web Site: http://www.ocscoop.com
Sales Range: $10-24.9 Million
Emp.: 109
Convenience Store
N.A.I.C.S.: 445131
Dan Schumann *(Gen Mgr)*
John Gerhardt *(Controller)*

OUTDOOR CAP COMPANY INC.
1200 Melissa Dr, Bentonville, AR 72712-6654
Tel.: (479) 273-5870
Web Site: http://www.outdoorcap.com
Year Founded: 1976
Sales Range: $25-49.9 Million
Emp.: 250
Headwear
N.A.I.C.S.: 315990
Paul Mahan *(Founder & Chm)*
Jerry House *(Exec VP-Fin & Admin)*
Chris McConnell *(Exec VP-Non-Retail Sls & Mktg)*
Nicole Tillman *(VP-Sourcing)*
Jeanelle Harris *(CEO)*
Jermaine Oldham *(Head-Tech)*
Andi Pratt *(Head-Commerce)*
Rhonda Norvell *(Head-HR)*
Mallory Swan *(Coord-Safety & Wellness)*

OUTDOOR RESEARCH INCORPORATED
2203 1st Ave S, Seattle, WA 98134
Tel.: (206) 467-8197   WA
Web Site:
http://www.outdoorresearch.com
Sales Range: $10-24.9 Million
Emp.: 200
Outdoor Apparel Mfr & Distr
N.A.I.C.S.: 314910
Joseph Wadden *(Dir-Ops)*
Jason Duncan *(Product Mgr)*
Melanie Sirirot *(Product Mgr)*
Suzanne Vincent *(Mgr-HR-PHR)*
Alexander Rodero *(Supvr-Factory Plng)*

OUTDOOR RESORTS OF AMERICA
101 S California Ave, Beaumont, CA 92223-2823
Tel.: (760) 345-2046
Web Site: http://www.outdoor-resorts.com
Year Founded: 1969
Rev.: $11,000,000
Emp.: 50
Luxury Recreational Vehicle Resorts Developer
N.A.I.C.S.: 237210

Subsidiaries:

Triple D of Brevard Inc   (1)
214 Horizon Ln, Melbourne Beach, FL 32951
Tel.: (321) 724-2600
Web Site: http://www.outdoor-resorts.com
Rev.: $96,000
Emp.: 2
Recreational Vehicle Parks
N.A.I.C.S.: 721214
David Graham *(Pres)*

OUTDOOR VENTURE CORP.
2280 S Hwy 1651, Stearns, KY 42647
Tel.: (606) 376-5021   KY
Web Site:
http://www.outdoorventure.com
Year Founded: 1978
Sales Range: $25-49.9 Million
Emp.: 230
Provider of Military Tents & Canvas Products
N.A.I.C.S.: 314910
J. C. Egnew *(Chm & Pres)*
Joe Fields *(VP-Bus Dev)*

OUTDOOR WORLD INC.
2720 S Rodeo Gulch, Soquel, CA 95073
Tel.: (831) 476-0233
Web Site:
http://www.theoutdoorworld.com
Sales Range: $10-24.9 Million
Emp.: 65
Sporting Goods
N.A.I.C.S.: 459110
Chris Thomas *(Pres)*

OUTER BANKS BLUE REALTY SERVICES
3732 N Croatan Hwy, Kitty Hawk, NC 27949
Tel.: (252) 255-1220
Web Site:
http://www.outerbanksblue.com
Year Founded: 2005
Sales Range: $1-9.9 Million
Emp.: 150
Real Estate Agency
N.A.I.C.S.: 531210
Tim Cafferty *(Pres)*

OUTERSTUFF, LTD.
1412 Broadway 18th FL, New York, NY 10018-7204
Tel.: (212) 594-9700   NY
Web Site: http://www.outerstuff.com
Year Founded: 1985
Sales Range: $10-24.9 Million
Emp.: 40
Girls & Childrens Outerwear
N.A.I.C.S.: 315250
Eli Daum *(Dir-IT)*
Larry Dix *(Mgr-Production)*
Ted Feindt *(VP-Ops)*
Nathan Fleisig *(Mgr-Social Responsibility)*
Jeff Miller *(Dir-Sls & Mdsg)*
Bob Saunders *(VP)*
Gary Silver *(Mgr-Production)*
Prajna Solanki *(Coord-Logistics)*
Evelyn Rodriguez *(Mgr-Import)*
Nicole Wisner *(Sr Mgr-Sls)*
Lily Nuculovic *(Acct Mgr)*

OUTLOOK NEBRASKA, INC.
4125 S 72nd St, Omaha, NE 68127
Tel.: (402) 614-3331   NE
Web Site:
http://www.outlooknebraska.org
Year Founded: 2000
Sales Range: $10-24.9 Million
Emp.: 74
Visually Impaired Care Services
N.A.I.C.S.: 623990
John Wick *(Dir-Fund Dev)*
Eric Stueckrath *(CEO)*
Mark Plutschak *(Mgr-HR)*
Brad Hale *(Mgr-Warehouse & Logistics)*
Tim Hurley *(CFO)*
Patrick Mac Bride *(COO)*
Matthew Evans *(Chm)*
Jay B. McMartin *(Sec)*
Steven Knapp *(Treas)*

OUTPOST NATURAL FOODS COOP
205 W Highland Ave Ste 501, Milwaukee, WI 53203
Tel.: (414) 431-3377
Web Site:
http://www.outpostnaturalfoods.coop
Rev.: $15,118,639
Emp.: 300
Health Foods
N.A.I.C.S.: 456191
Pam Mehnert *(Gen Mgr)*

OUTRAGEOUS INC.
18805 80th Pl S # B, Kent, WA 98032-1016
Tel.: (206) 768-0701
Year Founded: 1985
Sales Range: $10-24.9 Million
Emp.: 4
Whslr of Men's & Boys Clothing
N.A.I.C.S.: 424350
Roger Larsen *(Pres)*

OUTRAGEOUS VENTURES, INC.
75 Charter Oak Ave, Hartford, CT 06106-1903
Tel.: (860) 761-7235
Year Founded: 2001
Rev.: $6,400,000
Emp.: 35
Miscellaneous Nondurable Goods Merchant Whslr
N.A.I.C.S.: 424990
Steve Wampold *(Pres & CEO)*
Sean Obrien *(Sls Mgr-Natl)*
Jason Nocera *(Creative Dir)*
Anita Vega *(Mgr-Customer Svcs)*
Lisa Perkins *(Mgr-Fin)*
Steve Marcaurele *(Software Engr-Sys)*

OUTREACH COMMUNITY HEALTH CENTERS, INC.
711 W Capitol Dr, Milwaukee, WI 53206
Tel.: (414) 374-2400   WI
Web Site: http://www.orchc-milw.org
Year Founded: 1980
Sales Range: $10-24.9 Million
Community Health Care Services
N.A.I.C.S.: 621498
Warner Jackson *(Chm)*
Carla Y. Cross *(Sec)*
William Jenkins *(CEO)*
Bonica Voss *(Dir-HR)*
Janet Malmon *(Dir-Quality)*
Brian Resch *(CFO)*
Angela C. Sanders *(Dir-Behavioral Health)*
Rodney Ivy *(Dir-Clinics & Provider Rels)*
Yvonne Bell Gooden *(Dir-Community Svcs)*
Deidra Edwards *(Dir-Mktg Bus Dev)*
Peter Barbian *(Chief Medical Officer)*

OUTSIDE THE LINES, INC

OUTREACH TECHNOLOGY LLC
4806 Southern Breeze Dr, Naples, FL 34114-9465
Tel.: (877) 532-6332
Web Site:
http://www.outreachtechnology.net
Year Founded: 2002
Sales Range: $1-9.9 Million
Emp.: 200
IT Managed Services & Deregulated Electric & Gas Utilities to Business Customers
N.A.I.C.S.: 519290
Pete Keane *(Pres & CEO)*

OUTRIGGER LODGING SERVICES LIMITED PARTNERSHIP
16000 Ventura Blvd Ste 1010, Encino, CA 91436
Tel.: (818) 905-8280   NV
Web Site: http://www.olshotels.com
Year Founded: 1988
Sales Range: $75-99.9 Million
Emp.: 2,045
Provider of Management Services
N.A.I.C.S.: 561110
Marty Mannoja *(COO & Exec VP)*
Rick Ball *(VP-Corp Support Svcs)*

OUTSELL, INC.
330 Primrose Rd Ste 510, Burlingame, CA 94010
Tel.: (650) 342-6060   CA
Web Site: http://www.outsellinc.com
Year Founded: 1994
Sales Range: $1-9.9 Million
Emp.: 35
Marketing Research & Public Opinion Polling
N.A.I.C.S.: 541910
Anthea C. Stratigos *(CEO)*
Chuck Richard *(VP-Lead Analyst)*
Greg Chagaris *(Founder)*
Rudy Lopez *(Dir-Fin)*
Kate Worlock *(VP)*

OUTSELL, LLC
225 S 6th St Ste 3200, Minneapolis, MN 55402
Tel.: (612) 236-1500
Web Site: http://www.outsell.com
Sales Range: $10-24.9 Million
Emp.: 70
Prepackaged Software Services
N.A.I.C.S.: 513210
Mike Wethington *(Co-Founder & CEO)*
Bryana Harwood *(Pres)*
Fred Senn *(Co-Founder & Partner)*
Steve Gill *(Chm)*
Guy Super *(VP-Sls)*
Jon Petron *(Dir-Ops)*
Litded Davis *(VP-Product & Program Mgmt)*
Chris Johnson *(VP-Dev)*
Jon Ochetti *(CFO)*

OUTSIDE INTERACTIVE, INC.
1600 Pearl St, Boulder, CO 80302
Tel.: (855) 688-0567
Web Site: https://www.outsideinc.com
Advertising Services
N.A.I.C.S.: 541850
Robin Thurston *(Founder & CEO)*

Subsidiaries:

MapMyFitness, Inc   (1)
610 W 5th St Ste 605, Austin, TX 78701
Tel.: (512) 360-8700
Web Site: http://www.mapmyfitness.com
Sales Range: $1-9.9 Million
Emp.: 53
Sporting Geophysical Mapping Services
N.A.I.C.S.: 541360

OUTSIDE THE LINES, INC
20331 Irvine Ave E7, Newport Beach, CA 92660

OUTSIDE THE LINES, INC

Outside the Lines, Inc—(Continued)

Tel.: (714) 637-4747
Web Site: http://www.otl-inc.com
Sales Range: $1-9.9 Million
Emp.: 15
Construction Services
N.A.I.C.S.: 236220
J. Wickham Zimmerman (CEO)
Jack Larsen (VP)

OUTSKIRTS PRESS INC.
10940 S Parker Rd Ste 515, Parker, CO 80134
Tel.: (303) 805-2788
Web Site: http://www.outskirtspress.com
Year Founded: 2002
Sales Range: $1-9.9 Million
Emp.: 100
Full Service Publishing
N.A.I.C.S.: 513130
Brent Sampson (Pres, CEO & CMO)
Lynn Sampson (CFO & CTO)
Kelly Schuknecht (VP)

OUTSOURCE CONSULTANTS, LLC
600 Hwy 169 S Ste 1690, Saint Louis Park, MN 55426
Web Site: http://www.outsource-consultants.com
Year Founded: 2013
Sales Range: $1-9.9 Million
Emp.: 12
Telecommunication Servicesb
N.A.I.C.S.: 517810
Corey Kotlarz (Founder & Pres)
Rick Monro (VP-Sls)
Dave LaBatt (VP-Global Sls)

OUTSOURCE INC.
397 W Wekiva Spring Rd Ste 117, Longwood, FL 32779
Tel.: (407) 774-1951
Web Site: http://www.outsource-inc.com
Year Founded: 1993
Rev.: $20,127,928
Emp.: 350
Temporary Help Service
N.A.I.C.S.: 561320
Joe Salyer (COO)
Lori Hudson (VP-Creative)
Gary R. Hudson (VP & Gen Mgr)
Linda Massey (Mgr-Accts Div)
Rod Medlin (Mgr-Mid Atlantic)
Sam Bevlin (Dir-Ops)

OUTSOURCE IT CORP
6810 Crain Hwy, La Plata, MD 20646
Tel.: (301) 539-0200
Web Site: http://www.outsourceitcorp.com
Year Founded: 2004
Sales Range: $10-24.9 Million
Emp.: 53
Information Technology Consulting Services
N.A.I.C.S.: 541512
Craig Guice (Co-Founder, Pres & CEO)
Mark Vliet (Co-Founder, CTO & Sr VP)

OUTSOURCE TECHNICAL
2 Corporate Plz Ste 125, Newport Beach, CA 92660
Tel.: (310) 640-8575
Web Site: http://www.ostechnical.com
Sales Range: $10-24.9 Million
Emp.: 11
Placement Agencies
N.A.I.C.S.: 561311
Keila Barahona (Pres & Dir-HR)
Don Hughes (CFO)
Tina Christiansen (Sr Acct Mgr)

OUTTEN CHEVROLET INC.
1701 W Tilghman St, Allentown, PA 18104
Tel.: (610) 434-4201
Web Site: http://www.outtencars.com
Rev.: $23,289,377
Emp.: 42
Automobiles, New & Used
N.A.I.C.S.: 441110
Willie Outten (Pres)

OV LOOP, INC.
400 W Cummings Park, Woburn, MA 01801
Tel.: (877) 737-7297
Web Site: http://www.ovloop.com
Year Founded: 2019
Payment Services
N.A.I.C.S.: 522320
Will Graylin (CEO)

Subsidiaries:

Push Pay, Inc. (1)
333 Las Olas Way, Fort Lauderdale, FL 33301
Tel.: (844) 604-8075
Web Site: http://www.pushpayments.com
Financial Transaction Services
N.A.I.C.S.: 522320
Travis Dulaney (Co-Founder & CEO)
Bob Chevlin (Co-Founder & Chief Innovation Officer)
Don Mileff (Dir-Tech)
Khuram Ahmad (Dir-Ops)
Patricia Hill (VP-Bus Dev)

OV SMITH & SONS INC.
Big Chimney St, Charleston, WV 25302
Tel.: (304) 965-3481
Sales Range: $10-24.9 Million
Emp.: 500
Provider of Convienent Shops
N.A.I.C.S.: 445110
Glenn W. Smith (Pres)

OVAL PARTNERS
335 Bryant St 2nd Fl, Palo Alto, CA 94301
Tel.: (650) 443-4401
Web Site: http://www.ovalpartners.com
Multi-family Office Investment Firm
N.A.I.C.S.: 551112
Jake Mizrahi (Co-Founder & Mng Dir)
John Knoll (Co-Founder & Mng Dir)
Dan Ruhl (Partner)
Kyle Robertson (Principal)

Subsidiaries:

FlexPrint, LLC (1)
2845 N Omaha St, Mesa, AZ 85215
Web Site: http://www.flexprintinc.com
Printer & Copier Sales
N.A.I.C.S.: 333310
Frank Gaspari (CEO)
Jeff Wilson (VP-Bus Dev)
Tom Callinan (Pres)
Mike Weetman (CFO)
Chase Cabanillas (CIO)

Subsidiary (Domestic):

Advance Business Systems & Supply Company (2)
10755 York Rd, Cockeysville, MD 21030
Tel.: (410) 252-4800
Web Site: https://www.advancestuff.com
Sales Range: $25-49.9 Million
Emp.: 210
Retailer of Office Equipment & Supplies
N.A.I.C.S.: 423420
Alan I. Elkin (Co-Founder & Pres)
Lois Elkin (Exec VP)
Jeff Elkin (COO)

Cannon IV Inc. (2)
6814 Hillsdale Ct, Indianapolis, IN 46250
Tel.: (800) 825-7779
Web Site: http://www.cannon4.com
MFPS & Printer Mfr
N.A.I.C.S.: 333248

David Sullivan (Dir-Sls)

Shamrock Office Solutions (2)
6908 Sierra Ct Ste A, Dublin, CA 94568-2625
Tel.: (925) 875-0480
Web Site: http://www.shamrockoffice.com
Office Technology, Document Management Software, Managed IT Services & Multi-Function Printers
N.A.I.C.S.: 423420
Brian Driscoll (Owner)

New Charter Technologies, LLC (1)
3801 E Florida Ave Ste 820, Denver, CO 80210
Tel.: (800) 345-9605
Web Site: https://www.newchartertech.com
IT Support, Cybersecurity & Cloud Computing Services
N.A.I.C.S.: 518210
Mitch Morgan (CEO)

Subsidiary (Domestic):

BIZ Technology Solutions, Inc. (2)
224 Rolling Hill Rd, Mooresville, NC 28117
Tel.: (704) 658-1707
Web Site: http://www.biztechnologysolutions.com
Rev.: $2,000,000
Emp.: 30
Software Publisher
N.A.I.C.S.: 513210
Mike Chouffani (Pres)

OVATION ENTERPRISES, INC.
17350 N Hartford Dr, Scottsdale, AZ 85255
Tel.: (480) 348-0100 AZ
Web Site: http://www.ccsprojects.com
Sales Range: $100-124.9 Million
Emp.: 145
Holding Company; Presentation Technology Equipment & Services
N.A.I.C.S.: 551112
John Godbout (Chm & CEO)
Beth Godbout (Pres)

OVATION HOLDINGS, INC.
3003 Tamiami Trl N Ste 100, Naples, FL 34103
Tel.: (239) 919-5888
Web Site: http://www.encorebank.com
Bank Holding Company
N.A.I.C.S.: 551111
Thomas Ray (Pres & CEO)
Brian Avril (CFO & Exec VP)

Subsidiaries:

Encore Bank, National Association (1)
2120 Kings Hwy, Port Charlotte, FL 33980
Tel.: (239) 919-5888
Web Site: http://www.encorenationalbank.com
Rev.: $10,618,000
Assets: $349,772,000
Liabilities: $316,155,000
Net Worth: $33,617,000
Earnings: $(149,000)
Emp.: 48
Fiscal Year-end: 12/31/2013
Banking Services
N.A.I.C.S.: 522110
Thomas Ray (Pres & CEO)
Theodore Etzel (Chm)
Richard Fain (Sr VP-Comml Lending-Lee County)
Brian Avril (CFO & Exec VP)
Sally Ricciardelli (Mgr-Bonita Springs)
Frances Fabbro (Mgr-Sun City)
William Blevins (Officer-Lending & Sr VP)
Dharmesh Patel (Sr VP & Head-Retail Banking)
Carol Woodward (Officer-Credit & Sr VP)
Janis Vargas (Sr VP-Comml & SBA Lending-Fort Myers)

OVATION MUSIC & STUDIOS, INC.
8194 Glades Rd, Boca Raton, FL 33434

Tel.: (561) 487-0451
Web Site: http://www.ovationmusicstudios.com
Private Music Lessons; Music Store Operations
N.A.I.C.S.: 713990

OVATIONS FOOD SERVICES LP
18228 US Hwy 41 N, Lutz, FL 33549
Tel.: (813) 948-6900
Web Site: http://www.ovationsfoodservices.com
Year Founded: 1997
Sales Range: $250-299.9 Million
Emp.: 7,500
Food, Beverage & Merchandise Management Services
N.A.I.C.S.: 722330
Kenneth J. Young (Co-Founder & Pres)
Charles Neary (Exec VP-West)
Nick Nicora (VP-Bus Dev-Western Reg)
Todd Wickner (Co-Founder)
Stephen Gregosky (Sr VP-Client Rels)
Mike Frost (Reg VP)
Doug Drewes (Exec VP-East)
John LaChance (Sr VP)
Tom Marchetto (Sr VP-Strategic Mktg)
Charles Lawrence (Sr VP-Bus Dev)
Karen Muros (Exec Dir-Employee & Labor Rels)
Adrienne Hanson (CFO)
Rachael Cagle (Controller)
Kristen Thompson (Dir-Mktg)
Max Van Rees (VP-Facilities Plng)
David Specht (VP-HR)
Jarrid Crews (Mgr-IT)
Kraig Pomrenke (Dir-Bus Dev)
Mark Healy (Sr VP)

OVERCASH ELECTRIC INC.
2106 Charlotte Hwy PO Box 359, Mooresville, NC 28117
Tel.: (704) 664-3113
Web Site: http://www.overcashelectric.com
Sales Range: $10-24.9 Million
Emp.: 120
General Electrical Contractor
N.A.I.C.S.: 238210
Jennifer Meadows (Corp Sec)
Kathy Neel (Sec)

OVERDRIVE INTERACTIVE
38 Everett St Ste 201, Boston, MA 02134
Tel.: (617) 254-5000
Web Site: http://www.ovrdrv.com
Year Founded: 2001
Sales Range: $10-24.9 Million
Emp.: 25
Advertising Agencies
N.A.I.C.S.: 541613
Harry J. Gold (Co-Founder & CEO)
Ty Velde (Co-Founder & Dir-Client Svcs)
Andrew Abrahams (Co-Founder & Dir-Interactive Svcs)

OVERGROUP CONSULTING LLC
630 E Government St, Pensacola, FL 32502
Tel.: (850) 470-5502
Web Site: http://www.overgroup.com
Year Founded: 2002
Sales Range: $1-9.9 Million
Emp.: 21
Web Based Back Office System for the Telecom Industry
N.A.I.C.S.: 541519

Brent Maropis *(CEO)*
J. Ross Overstreet *(Co-Founder & CTO)*
Bill White *(Co-Founder)*
Evan Rice *(VP-Sls & Mktg)*
Lauren Stern *(VP-Fin)*
Leslie Ingram *(VP-Implementation Svcs)*
Jena Overstreet *(VP-Client Svcs)*

OVERHEAD CONVEYOR CO.
1330 Hilton Rd, Ferndale, MI 48220-2837
Tel.: (248) 547-3800   MI
Web Site: http://www.occ-conveyor.com
Year Founded: 1945
Sales Range: $75-99.9 Million
Emp.: 72
Designer, Manufacturer & Installer of Conveyor Systems
N.A.I.C.S.: 333922
Thomas M. Woodbeck *(Pres)*

OVERIT MEDIA INC.
435 New Scotland Ave, Albany, NY 12208
Tel.: (518) 465-8829
Web Site: http://www.overit.com
Sales Range: $1-9.9 Million
Emp.: 35
Digital Advertising Agency
N.A.I.C.S.: 541810
Lisa Barone *(CMO)*
Anna Varney *(Acct Exec)*
Joe Arcuri *(Dir-Design-UK)*
Paul Fahey *(COO)*
Michelle Dinsmore *(VP)*
Richard Skiermont *(Creative Dir)*
JoAnne Latham *(Dir-Acct Mgmt)*
Leanne Ricchiuti *(Acct Exec-PR)*
Androniki Bossonis *(Dir-Mktg & Automation)*
David Parker *(Engr-Audio)*
Paul Turaew *(Dir-Project Mgmt)*
Corey Breda *(Sr Mgr-Acct)*

OVERLAKE HOSPITAL MEDICAL CENTER
1035 116th Ave NE, Bellevue, WA 98004
Tel.: (425) 688-5000   WA
Web Site: http://www.overlakehospital.org
Year Founded: 1953
Sales Range: $400-449.9 Million
Emp.: 2,978
Health Care Srvices
N.A.I.C.S.: 622110
Lisa Brock *(Chief Compliance Officer & Chief HR Officer)*
Julie Clayton *(Chief Nursing Officer)*
J. Michael Marsh *(Pres & CEO)*
Jason Thompson *(Treas)*
Andrew Tokar *(CFO-Interim)*
David Knoepfler *(Chief Medical Officer)*
Molly Stearns *(Chief Dev Officer)*
Tom DeBord *(COO)*
Caitlin Hillary *(Chief Strategy Officer)*

OVERLAND INC
2668 Laurens Rd, Greenville, SC 29607
Tel.: (864) 232-7493
Web Site: http://www.landrovercarolinas.com
Rev.: $16,000,000
Emp.: 27
Sell & Service Trucks, Tractors & Trailers: New & Used
N.A.I.C.S.: 811111
Kent Banks *(Gen Mgr)*

OVERLAND SHEEPSKIN CO. INC
2096 Nutmeg Ave, Fairfield, IA 52556
Tel.: (641) 472-8484
Web Site: http://www.overland.com
Year Founded: 1973
Sales Range: $10-24.9 Million
Emp.: 75
Leather Garments Retailer
N.A.I.C.S.: 458110
James Furey *(Mgr-Payroll & Benefits)*

OVERLAND STORAGE, INC.
9112 Spectrum Ctr Blvd, San Diego, CA 92123
Tel.: (858) 571-5555   CA
Web Site: http://www.overlandstorage.com
Year Founded: 1980
Sales Range: $50-74.9 Million
Data Storage, Backup & Recovery Technologies Developer & Mfr
N.A.I.C.S.: 334112
Eric L. Kelly *(Chm & CEO)*
Kurt L. Kalbfleisch *(CFO)*
Tony Evans *(VP-Bus Dev & Sls-North America)*
Leah Robinson-Leach *(Dir-Corp & Media Comm)*
Tina Rogers Brown *(COO)*

Subsidiaries:
Overland Storage (Europe) Ltd.   (1)
Pinewood Chineham Business Park Rockford Lane, Basingstoke, RG24 8AL, Hampshire, United Kingdom
Tel.: (44) 1189898000
3D Virtualization Services
N.A.I.C.S.: 327910

Overland Storage GmbH   (1)
Feldstrasse 81, 44141, Dortmund, Germany
Tel.: (49) 23154360
3D Virtualization Services
N.A.I.C.S.: 518210

Overland Storage SARL   (1)
13 Rue Jean Rostand, 91400, Orsay, France
Tel.: (33) 181 9173 40
Web Site: http://www.overlandstorage.com
Magnetic Tape Data Storage Mfr & Marketer
N.A.I.C.S.: 334112

OVERLAND WEST, INC.
2805 Washington Blvd, Ogden, UT 84401-4212
Tel.: (801) 621-5735   UT
Web Site: http://www.overlandwest.com
Year Founded: 1941
Sales Range: $10-24.9 Million
Emp.: 50
Passenger Car Rental Franchises Owner & Operator
N.A.I.C.S.: 532111
Jerry H. Petersen *(Pres & CEO)*
Morgan P. Keyes *(Officer-PR & Exec VP-HR)*
Trevor E. Steenblik *(CFO)*
Stephen R. Jones *(VP & Dir-Rental Ops)*
Barbara Lam-Hales *(Mgr-Rental Ops)*
Erik J. Petersen *(CFO & Exec VP)*
F. Lynn Petersen *(VP & Dir-Sls Ops)*
Lawson E. Burnett *(CIO)*

Subsidiaries:
Overland West, Inc. - Billings Office   (1)
Billings Logan Airport 1901 Terminal Cir, Billings, MT 59105
Tel.: (406) 248-9151
Web Site: http://www.overlandwest.com
Sales Range: $10-24.9 Million
Emp.: 12
Passenger Car Rental Franchises Operator
N.A.I.C.S.: 532111
Lucas Rutz *(Branch Mgr)*

OVERLY DOOR COMPANY
574 W Otterman St, Greensburg, PA 15601
Tel.: (724) 834-7300   PA
Web Site: http://www.overly.com
Year Founded: 1888
Sales Range: $10-24.9 Million
Emp.: 100
Mfr of Metal Sliding Doors
N.A.I.C.S.: 332321
Timothy T. Reese *(CEO)*
Sarah Watkins *(Mgr-Pur)*
Elmer Knopf *(CFO)*

Subsidiaries:
Overly Manufacturing Company   (1)
574 W Otterman St, Greensburg, PA 15601-2148
Tel.: (724) 834-7300
Web Site: http://www.overly.com
Sales Range: $10-24.9 Million
Emp.: 25
Supplier of Metal Cladding Systems & Architectural Product Engineering & Fabrication of Custom Hollow Metal Door & Window Assembly Mfr
N.A.I.C.S.: 332321
Bill Hughes *(Mgr-Mktg)*
Terry Reese *(CEO)*

OVERMYER & ASSOCIATES INC.
911 Ctr Rdg Ct, Brentwood, TN 37027
Tel.: (615) 661-5330
Rev.: $38,000,000
Emp.: 6
Automotive Brokers
N.A.I.C.S.: 423110

OVERSEAS DEVELOPMENT CORP.
953 Washington Blvd Ste 5, Stamford, CT 06901-2917
Tel.: (203) 964-0111
Web Site: http://www.overseasdevelopment.com
Sales Range: $10-24.9 Million
Emp.: 30
Iron & Steel (Ferrous) Products
N.A.I.C.S.: 423510
Attila Turkkan *(Founder & Pres)*

OVERSEAS HARDWOODS COMPANY
24 Tacon St, Mobile, AL 36607
Tel.: (251) 457-7616
Web Site: http://www.overseashardwoods.com
Rev.: $22,000,000
Emp.: 50
Developer & Provider of Lumber & Lumber Products
N.A.I.C.S.: 321918
T. Lee Robinson Jr. *(Pres & CEO)*

OVERSEAS MILITARY SALES CORPORATION
175 Crossways Park Dr W, Woodbury, NY 11797-2002
Tel.: (516) 921-2800   NY
Web Site: http://www.encs.com
Sales Range: $75-99.9 Million
Emp.: 16
Sales of New & Used Automobiles to Military Personnel
N.A.I.C.S.: 441110
Allan Nigro *(Controller)*
Joe Cerame *(VP-Info Sys)*
Gary Rubin *(Mgr)*
Steve Thake *(Supvr-e-Commerce Sls)*
James Black *(Gen Counsel)*

OVERSEAS SERVICE CORPORATION
1100 Northpoint Pkwy Ste 200, West Palm Beach, FL 33407-1937
Tel.: (561) 683-4090   MD
Web Site: http://www.overseaservice.com
Year Founded: 1947
Sales Range: $100-124.9 Million
Emp.: 200
Provider of Services to Military
N.A.I.C.S.: 424410
Frank J. Hogan *(Chm & CEO)*
Paul Hogan *(Pres & COO)*
Rebecca L. Thompson *(Controller)*

Subsidiaries:
Overseas Service Corporation-Exchange Div   (1)
12700 Park Central Dr Ste 1409, Dallas, TX 75251-1500
Tel.: (972) 991-9390
Web Site: http://www.overseasservice.com
Manufacturers Representative, Exchanges Only
N.A.I.C.S.: 423830

OVERSEE.NET
550 S Hope St Ste 200, Los Angeles, CA 90071
Tel.: (213) 408-0080   CA
Web Site: http://www.oversee.net
Year Founded: 2000
Sales Range: $150-199.9 Million
Emp.: 200
Domain Name Management Services
N.A.I.C.S.: 541613
Lawrence Ng *(Founder & Chm)*
Elizabeth Murray *(CFO & Exec VP)*
Debra S. Domeyer *(CEO)*
Joanna McFarland *(VP & Gen Mgr-Consumer Fin Grp)*

Subsidiaries:
Moniker Online Services, LLC   (1)
20 SW 27th Ave Ste 201, Pompano Beach, FL 33069
Tel.: (954) 861-3500
Web Site: http://www.moniker.com
Online Domain Name Registration, Management & Monetization Services
N.A.I.C.S.: 541519

OVERSTOCK ART, LLC.
1401 S Mosley St, Wichita, KS 67211
Tel.: (316) 631-3999
Web Site: http://www.overstockart.com
Year Founded: 2001
Sales Range: $1-9.9 Million
Emp.: 14
Online Original Paintings Retailers
N.A.I.C.S.: 459920
David Sasson *(Founder, Pres & CEO)*
Amit Yaari *(VP-Ops & Pur)*
Amitai Sasson *(VP-Tech & Mktg)*
Stacy Sasson *(Owner)*

OVERSTOCKDEALS LLC
9090 Ridgeline Blvd, Highlands Ranch, CO 80129
Tel.: (303) 791-3636
Web Site: http://www.overstockdeals.com
Year Founded: 2007
Sales Range: $10-24.9 Million
Emp.: 10
Kitchen & Bath Fixtures
N.A.I.C.S.: 459999
Dave Ems *(Owner)*

OVERSTREET PAVING COMPANY
17728 US Hwy 41, Spring Hill, FL 34610-7437
Tel.: (352) 796-1631   FL
Year Founded: 1969
Sales Range: $75-99.9 Million
Emp.: 72

OVERSTREET PAVING COMPANY — U.S. PRIVATE

Overstreet Paving Company—(Continued)
Provider of Asphalt Paving & Resurfacing
N.A.I.C.S.: 237310
Monica Kramer *(VP)*
Thomas E. Overstreet Sr. *(Chm & CEO)*

OVERTON ENTERPRISES, LLC
8201 E Riverside Dr, Austin, TX 78744
Tel.: (512) 394-6089
Web Site: http://www.spibelt.com
Sales Range: $1-9.9 Million
Emp.: 12
Fitness Products Mfr
N.A.I.C.S.: 713940
Kim Overton *(Founder & CEO)*
Kevin Mahon *(Sr Acct Mgr)*
Troy Bower *(Mgr-Ops)*

OVERTON FINANCIAL CORPORATION
115 E Henderson, Overton, TX 75684
Tel.: (903) 834-3161 TX
Year Founded: 1986
Bank Holding Company
N.A.I.C.S.: 551111
Rogers Pope Sr. *(Chm, Pres & CEO)*
Rogers Pope Jr. *(Vice Chm)*
Randy Bjork *(CFO & Controller)*

Subsidiaries:

Texas Bank & Trust Company (1)
300 E Whaley, Longview, TX 75601
Tel.: (903) 237-5500
Web Site:
   http://www.texasbankandtrust.com
Sales Range: $75-99.9 Million
Emp.: 386
Commericial Banking
N.A.I.C.S.: 522110
Rogers Pope Sr. *(Chm)*
Scott Dickerson *(Chief Risk Officer & Exec VP)*
Bart Aldridge *(Portfolio Mgr)*
Jannette Erts *(Sr VP-Frisco)*
Claude E. Henry *(Pres-Tyler Market)*

OVERTON MOORE PROPERTIES
19300 S Hamilton Ave Ste 200, Gardena, CA 90248-4337
Tel.: (310) 323-9100 CA
Web Site: http://www.omprop.com
Year Founded: 1973
Sales Range: $75-99.9 Million
Emp.: 16
Real Estate Developers
N.A.I.C.S.: 236117
Timur Tecimer *(Pres & COO)*
Jim Middlemas *(CFO)*

OVERTON POWER DISTRICT NO 5
615 Moapa Vly Blvd, Overton, NV 89040
Tel.: (702) 397-2512
Web Site: http://www.opd5.com
Year Founded: 1935
Sales Range: $25-49.9 Million
Emp.: 45
Distribution of Electric Power
N.A.I.C.S.: 221122
David Anderson *(Chm)*

OVERTURE PARTNERS, LLC.
57 Wells Ave Ste 22, Newton, MA 02459
Tel.: (617) 614-9260
Web Site:
   http://www.overturepartners.com
Year Founded: 2001
Sales Range: $10-24.9 Million
Emp.: 123
Computer Related Services
N.A.I.C.S.: 541512

Diana Crowell *(CEO)*
Marty Goober *(Exec VP)*
Sandy Kontos *(Dir-Bus Dev)*
Paul Chamberlain *(VP-Fin)*
Matt Gleckman *(Exec VP)*

OVERTURF MOTOR CO. INC.
1016 W Columbia Dr, Kennewick, WA 99336
Tel.: (509) 586-3185
Web Site:
   http://www.overturfmotors.com
Sales Range: $10-24.9 Million
Emp.: 32
Car Whslr
N.A.I.C.S.: 441110
Doug D. Overturf *(Owner)*

OWASCO BEVERAGE INC.
1886 Clark St Rd, Auburn, NY 13021
Tel.: (315) 252-6111 NY
Year Founded: 1888
Sales Range: $25-49.9 Million
Emp.: 137
Beer & Other Fermented Malt Liquors Distr
N.A.I.C.S.: 424810
Thomas Potter *(Pres)*

OWATONNA FORD CHRYSLER
1001 Hoffman Dr, Owatonna, MN 55060-1109
Tel.: (507) 451-0080
Sales Range: $10-24.9 Million
Emp.: 50
Car Whslr
N.A.I.C.S.: 441110
Kay Cassen *(Principal)*
Bill Zaharia *(Pres)*

OWEN AYRES & ASSOCIATES, INC.
3433 Oakwood Hills Pkwy, Eau Claire, WI 54701-7698
Tel.: (715) 834-3161 WI
Web Site:
   http://www.ayresassociates.com
Year Founded: 1965
Sales Range: $25-49.9 Million
Emp.: 350
Architectural & Engineering Services
N.A.I.C.S.: 541330
Rich Schoenthalerr *(CEO & Exec VP)*
Sue Leith *(Dir-Mktg)*
Bruce Ommen *(Exec VP)*
Jan Zander *(Exec VP)*
Thomas Pulse *(Pres)*

OWEN ELECTRIC COOPERATIVE INC.
8205 Hwy 127 N, Owenton, KY 40359-3036
Tel.: (502) 484-3471 KY
Web Site:
   http://www.owenelectric.com
Year Founded: 1937
Sales Range: $25-49.9 Million
Emp.: 117
Electronic Services
N.A.I.C.S.: 221122
Jude Canchola *(Mgr-Residential Svcs)*
Shawn West *(Mgr-Acctg Benefits)*

OWEN ELECTRIC SUPPLY INC.
850 Greens Pkwy Ste 200, Houston, TX 77067
Tel.: (713) 691-0909
Rev.: $10,000,000
Emp.: 50
Sales of Electrical Apparatus & Equipment
N.A.I.C.S.: 423610

Wayne C. Owen *(Pres)*
Ed Wrobliske *(VP)*
Randall Searles *(Controller)*

OWEN FINANCIAL CORPORATION
201 W Morgan St, Spencer, IN 47460
Tel.: (812) 829-4811 IN
Web Site: http://www.ocsbank.com
Year Founded: 1933
Sales Range: $10-24.9 Million
Emp.: 90
Bank Holding Company
N.A.I.C.S.: 551111
Gordon L. Wells *(Chm)*
Charles Hines *(Treas, Sec & VP)*
Robert Taylor *(Exec VP)*
Janet L. Burks *(Mgr-Bridgeport)*
Lisa Knapp *(Mgr-Bridgeport)*
Michelle DeFord *(Sec)*
Ruth A. Jones *(Sr VP)*

Subsidiaries:

Owen County State Bank (1)
201 W Morgan St, Spencer, IN 47460
Tel.: (812) 829-4811
Web Site: http://www.ocsbank.com
Sales Range: $50-74.9 Million
Emp.: 100
Personal & Commercial Banking Services
N.A.I.C.S.: 522110
Gordon L. Wells *(Chm & Pres)*
Ed Hines *(Treas, Sec & VP)*
Ruth Jones *(Exec VP)*
Jerry Hays *(Sr VP-Monroe & Lawrence)*
Steven K. Pedigo *(Vice Chm)*
Michelle DeFord *(Sec & Asst VP)*
Lisa Knapp *(Branch Mgr)*
Keith A. Knipstein *(CFO & Sr VP-Investments)*
Richard Morris *(Mgr-eBus)*
Judy Scott *(Branch Mgr)*
Robert E. Taylor *(Exec VP)*

OWEN INDUSTRIES, INC.
501 Ave H, Carter Lake, IA 51510-1513
Tel.: (712) 347-5500 IA
Web Site: http://www.owenind.com
Year Founded: 1885
Sales Range: $50-74.9 Million
Emp.: 400
Fabricated Structural Metal; Metal Service Center
N.A.I.C.S.: 423510
Brad Johnson *(VP-HR)*
Edward Korbel *(CFO & VP-Fin)*
Craig Bence *(CIO & VP)*
Keith Siebels *(Sr VP-Sls)*
Bob Jacobsen *(VP & Gen Mgr-Missouri Valley Steel)*
Mark Radtke *(VP & Gen Mgr-Northern Plains Steel)*

Subsidiaries:

Lincoln Structural Solutions LLC (1)
8930 S137 Cir, Omaha, NE 68138
Tel.: (402) 505-9771
Web Site: http://www.lincolnstructural.com
Industrial Supplies Distr
N.A.I.C.S.: 423840
Danielle Kottas *(CEO)*

Missouri Valley Steel Co. (1)
1300 Division St, Sioux City, IA 51105-2653 (100%)
Tel.: (712) 255-1616
Web Site: http://www.owenindustries.com
Sales Range: $25-49.9 Million
Emp.: 60
Steel Service Center & Structural Steel Fabricator
N.A.I.C.S.: 423510
Robert E. Owen *(Pres)*
Brad McKinney *(Dir-Pur)*

Northern Plains Steel Co. (1)
3801 15th Ave N, Fargo, ND 58102-2836 (100%)
Tel.: (701) 282-6465
Web Site: http://www.npsteel.com

Sales Range: $25-49.9 Million
Emp.: 62
Steel Service Center
N.A.I.C.S.: 423510
Edward G. Korbel *(CFO)*
Mark Radtke *(VP & Gen Mgr)*

Owen Industries, Inc. - Northern Plains Finishing Division (1)
15514 37th St SE, Casselton, ND 58012
Tel.: (701) 347-0210
Web Site: http://www.owenind.com
Powder Coating Services
N.A.I.C.S.: 332812

Paxton & Vierling Steel Company- A Div of Owen Industries Inc (1)
501 Ave H, Carter Lake, IA 51510 (100%)
Tel.: (712) 347-5500
Web Site: http://www.pvsteel.com
Sales Range: $25-49.9 Million
Emp.: 200
Machine Shops; Steel Service Center; Structural Steel Fabricator
N.A.I.C.S.: 423510
Mark Holland *(Chief Engr Officer)*
Ravi Nigam *(Mng Dir)*
Minal Talwar *(Officer-Compliance & Sec)*

OWEN PACIFIC
1236 Compton Ave, Los Angeles, CA 90021-2331
Tel.: (213) 747-7125 CA
Year Founded: 1916
Sales Range: $75-99.9 Million
Emp.: 120
Provider of Commercial & Industrial Roofing
N.A.I.C.S.: 238160

OWEN SECURITY SOLUTIONS INC.
209 S Wall St, Calhoun, GA 30701
Tel.: (706) 629-7398
Web Site:
   http://www.owensecurity.com
Rev.: $8,554,000
Emp.: 13
Home & Business Security Services
N.A.I.C.S.: 561621
Gary Owen *(Owner)*

Subsidiaries:

Davis Security Services Inc. (1)
7830 Hwy 92, Woodstock, GA 30189
Tel.: (770) 516-5999
Security Guards & Patrol Services
N.A.I.C.S.: 561612
Michael Davis *(CEO)*

OWEN-AMES-KIMBALL COMPANY
300 Ionia Ave NW, Grand Rapids, MI 49503-2507
Tel.: (616) 456-1521 MI
Web Site: http://www.owen-ames-kimball.com
Year Founded: 1891
Sales Range: $100-124.9 Million
Emp.: 175
Non-Residential Building Contractors
N.A.I.C.S.: 236220
John C. LaBarge *(CFO)*
Frank Stanek *(Pres & CEO)*
Josh Szymanski *(Chief Strategy Officer)*

Subsidiaries:

Owen-Ames-Kimball Company (1)
11941 Fairway Lakes Dr, Fort Myers, FL 33913-8338 (100%)
Tel.: (239) 561-4141
Web Site: http://www.owen-ames-kimball.com
Sales Range: $25-49.9 Million
Emp.: 40
General Contractors
N.A.I.C.S.: 236220
David J. Dale *(Pres)*
Abel Natali *(Project Mgr)*
Jan Conrad *(VP & Mgr-Acctg Svcs & HR)*

COMPANIES

Matthew Zwack *(Chief Safety Officer)*
Tom Stanek *(Dir-Kalamazoo Ops)*
Jan-Erik Hustrulid *(Coord-Bus Dev)*

Owen-Ames-Kimball Engineering, Inc. (1)
300 Ionia Ave NW, Grand Rapids, MI 49503-2507 (100%)
Tel.: (616) 456-1521
Web Site: http://www.owen-ames-kimball.com
Sales Range: $10-24.9 Million
Emp.: 25
General Contractors
N.A.I.C.S.: 541310
Frank Stanek *(Pres & CEO)*

OWENS COMPANIES, INC.
930 E 80th St, Minneapolis, MN 55420
Tel.: (952) 854-3800
Web Site: http://www.owensco.com
Year Founded: 1957
Sales Range: $25-49.9 Million
Emp.: 150
Provider of Heating & Air Conditioning Contracting Services
N.A.I.C.S.: 238220
John J. Owens *(Pres & CEO)*
Mandy Beech *(VP-HR)*
Lee Cohan *(Mgr-Admin)*
David Holmquist *(Mgr-Central Chillers)*
Susan Wilson Robinson *(Coord-Mktg)*

OWENS MORTGAGE INVESTMENT FUND, A CALIFORNIA LIMITED PARTNERSHIP
2221 Olympic Blvd, Walnut Creek, CA 94595
Tel.: (925) 935-3840   CA
Year Founded: 1984
Sales Range: $10-24.9 Million
Real Estate Investment Services
N.A.I.C.S.: 525990
William C. Owens *(Chm, Pres & CEO)*
Bryan H. Draper *(CFO, Treas & Sec)*

OWENSMORRIS COMMUNICATIONS, INC.
29 S Lasalle St Ste 1000, Chicago, IL 60603-1502
Tel.: (312) 701-0388
Year Founded: 2006
Sales Range: $10-24.9 Million
Emp.: 20
Marketing Research Service
N.A.I.C.S.: 541910
Hoyett Owens *(Chm)*

OWENSVILLE SUPPLY, INC.
330 E Main St, Owensville, OH 45160
Tel.: (513) 732-0350   OH
Year Founded: 1955
Rev.: $12,800,000
Emp.: 30
Lumber Yard & Hardware Stores
N.A.I.C.S.: 423310

OWL COMPANIES
2465 Campus Dr, Irvine, CA 92612-1502
Tel.: (949) 797-2000   CA
Web Site: http://www.owlcompanies.com
Year Founded: 1919
Sales Range: $100-124.9 Million
Emp.: 1,389
Youth Education & Training Services
N.A.I.C.S.: 611710
Gregory J. Burden *(Chm & CEO)*
Stephen Seastrom *(Controller)*
Eric J. Perea *(VP-Real Estate)*

Subsidiaries:

Career Systems Development Corporation (1)
75 Thruway Park Dr Ste 100, West Henrietta, NY 14586
Tel.: (585) 334-8080
Web Site: http://www.careersystems.com
Education & Job Training for Youth Services
N.A.I.C.S.: 923110

Owl Education & Training, Inc. (1)
2465 Campus Dr, Irvine, CA 92612
Tel.: (949) 797-2000
Education & Vocational Training
N.A.I.C.S.: 923110

Owl Energy Resources, Inc. (1)
2465 Campus Dr, Irvine, CA 92612-1502 (100%)
Tel.: (949) 797-2000
Sales Range: $25-49.9 Million
Emp.: 22
Development, Ownership, Engineering & Operation Services for Power Generation & Cogeneration Facilities
N.A.I.C.S.: 541330

Tecolote Resources, Inc. (1)
2465 Campus Dr, Irvine, CA 92612
Tel.: (949) 797-2000
Real Estate
N.A.I.C.S.: 531390

OWL OIL INC.
369 New Britain Rd Ste E, Kensington, CT 06037
Tel.: (860) 829-5888
Rev.: $11,000,000
Emp.: 19
Heating Equipment except Warm Air Furnaces Mfg
N.A.I.C.S.: 333414
Leonard Shaw *(Owner & Pres)*

OWL SERVICES, INC.
888 W Big Beaver Rd Ste 200, Troy, MI 48084
Tel.: (248) 620-0070
Web Site: https://owlservices.com
Emp.: 100
Fueling Systems Construction, Petroleum Products, Maintenance, Repair & EV Charging Services
N.A.I.C.S.: 424710

Subsidiaries:

Dark Horse Enterprise, LLC (1)
4125 W I St, Bremerton, WA 98312-3652
Tel.: (360) 286-8477
Web Site: http://www.dhvet.com
Industrial Building Construction
N.A.I.C.S.: 236210
Derek J. Goschke *(Mgr)*

OWLS HEAD TRANSPORTATION MUSEUM
117 Museum St, Owls Head, ME 04854
Tel.: (207) 594-4418   ME
Web Site: http://www.owlshead.org
Year Founded: 1974
Sales Range: $1-9.9 Million
Emp.: 23
Museums
N.A.I.C.S.: 712110
Steve Lang *(Co-Founder)*
Duncan W. Brown *(Chm)*
Thomas H. Rudder *(Vice Chm)*
Gary C. Dunton *(Treas)*
James S. Rockefeller Jr. *(Co-Founder)*
Thomas J. Watson Jr. *(Founder)*

OWNER RESOURCE GROUP, LLC
600 Congress Ave Ste 200, Austin, TX 78701
Tel.: (512) 505-4180   DE
Web Site: http://www.orgroup.com
Privater Equity Firm

N.A.I.C.S.: 523999
Mark Green *(Chm)*
Will Burnett *(Mng Dir)*
Jon Gormin *(Mng Dir)*

Subsidiaries:

Advantage Business Media LLC (1)
100 Enterprise Dr Ste 600, Rockaway, NJ 07866-0912
Tel.: (973) 920-7000
Web Site: http://www.advantagemedia.com
Sales Range: $10-24.9 Million
Emp.: 100
Trade Magazine & Website Publisher
N.A.I.C.S.: 513120
Jim Lonergan *(CEO)*
Terry Freeburg *(CFO & COO)*
Beth Campbell *(Chief Content Officer)*
Nick Pinto *(Gen Mgr-Design Grp)*
Susanne Foulds *(VP-HR)*
Todd Baker *(Gen Mgr-Mfg Grp)*
Tim Besecker *(VP-Digital Product Dev)*

Subsidiary (Domestic):

Vicon Business Media, Inc. (2)
199 RTe 101 Bldg 7, Amherst, NH 03031
Tel.: (973) 920-7000
Web Site: http://www.viconpublishing.com
Sales Range: $1-9.9 Million
Emp.: 50
Trade Magazine & Website Publisher
N.A.I.C.S.: 513120
Luann Kulbashian *(Assoc Publr)*

Optimation Technology, Inc. (1)
50 High Tech Dr, Rush, NY 14543-9746
Tel.: (585) 321-2300
Web Site: http://www.optimation.us
Sales Range: $25-49.9 Million
Emp.: 25
Engineering & Systems Integration Services
N.A.I.C.S.: 541519
William Pollock *(Founder, Pres & CEO)*
Wendy Smith *(COO-Klug Sys & VP-Engrg)*

Richardson Molding, Inc. (1)
5601 S Meridian St Ste B, Indianapolis, IN 46217
Tel.: (317) 787-9463
Web Site: http://www.richardsonmolding.com
Plastics Product Mfr
N.A.I.C.S.: 326199

Surestaff, LLC (1)
150 E Pierce Rd Ste 260, Itasca, IL 60143
Tel.: (630) 250-7333
Web Site: https://www.sure-staff.com
Employment Placement Agency
N.A.I.C.S.: 561311
Tim Faber *(CEO)*

Subsidiary (Domestic):

Cardinal Services Inc. (2)
1721 Indian Wood Cir A, Maumee, OH 43537
Tel.: (419) 893-5400
Web Site: http://www.cardinalstaffing.com
Sales Range: $10-24.9 Million
Emp.: 50
Job Placement Agency
N.A.I.C.S.: 561311
Joan E. Fought *(Pres)*
Thomas E. Fought *(CEO)*
Angel McGee *(Mgr-Reg Sls)*
Campbell Laura *(Mgr-HR)*
Kevin Planck *(Dir-Adult Svcs)*
Joe Young *(Sr VP-Sales Rhonda Clemons)*
Christina Ice *(VP-Ops & Bus Dev)*

OWNERSEDGE INC.
N16 W23217 Stone Rdg Dr Ste 250, Waukesha, WI 53188
Tel.: (262) 506-3290   WI
Web Site: http://www.ownersedgeinc.com
Year Founded: 2015
Holding Company
N.A.I.C.S.: 551112
Lisa Reardon *(Chm & CEO)*

Subsidiaries:

Baycom, Inc. (1)

OX PAPER TUBE & CORE, INC.

2040 Radisson St, Green Bay, WI 54302-5426
Tel.: (920) 468-5426
Web Site: http://www.baycominc.com
Wireless Voice & Data Communications Provider
N.A.I.C.S.: 517810
Robert Dillon *(Pres)*

Subsidiary (Domestic):

Infinity Wireless, Inc. (2)
9494 Hemlock Ln N, Maple Grove, MN 55369
Tel.: (763) 315-8691
Web Site: http://www.baycominc.com
Wireless Telephones Mfr
N.A.I.C.S.: 334310
Hali Thoe *(Bus Mgr)*

Rhino Communication Rentals, LLC (1)
9494 Hemlock Ln N, Maple Grove, MN 55369
Tel.: (763) 315-8692
Web Site: http://www.rhinorentals.com
Telecommunication Servicesb
N.A.I.C.S.: 517810

OWNIT MORTGAGE SOLUTIONS OAKMONT
4360 Park Ter Dr Ste 100, Westlake Village, CA 91361-4627
Tel.: (818) 595-0200
Web Site: http://www.ownitmortgage.com
Rev.: $17,610,413
Emp.: 76
Mortgage Bankers & Loan Correspondents
N.A.I.C.S.: 531210

OWNLOCAL, INC.
205 W 9th St, Austin, TX 78701
Tel.: (512) 501-6265
Web Site: http://www.ownlocal.com
Year Founded: 2010
Software Publishers for Digital Advertising
N.A.I.C.S.: 513210
Landon Morales *(Chief Revenue Officer)*
Lloyd W. Armbrust *(Founder & CEO)*

Subsidiaries:

Wanderful Media (1)
325 Broadway St, Chico, CA 95928
Tel.: (530) 343-6400
Web Site: http://www.wanderful.com
Sales Range: $25-49.9 Million
Emp.: 150
Online Marketing Services; Software Developer
N.A.I.C.S.: 513210
Bob Clark *(Gen Mgr)*

OWYHEE GROUP COMPANIES
1075 S Ancona Way, Eagle, ID 83616
Tel.: (208) 938-6086   ID
Web Site: http://www.initial-attack.com
Year Founded: 2000
Sales Range: $1-9.9 Million
Emp.: 60
Military Apparel & Safety Equipment
N.A.I.C.S.: 315990
Douglas Lodge *(CEO)*
Michael McLaughlin *(Pres)*
Zach Barnes *(Dir-Mktg)*

OX PAPER TUBE & CORE, INC.
331 Maple Ave, Hanover, PA 17331
Tel.: (717) 630-0230
Web Site: http://www.oxpapertube.com
Year Founded: 1996
Sales Range: $100-124.9 Million
Emp.: 300
Paperboard Tube & Core Mfr

OX PAPER TUBE & CORE, INC.

U.S. PRIVATE

Ox Paper Tube & Core, Inc.—(Continued)
N.A.I.C.S.: 322299
Kevin Hayward *(CEO)*
Mark Wallace *(Sr VP-Ops)*
Jeff Lyman *(VP-Mill Ops)*
Tim Michaels *(VP-Tube & Core Ops)*
Michael Raymond *(Gen Mgr-Constantine Mill)*

Subsidiaries:

COREX US LLC (1)
Wood St 2116, Stevens Point, WI 54481
Tel.: (715) 544-1414
Packaging Product Distr
N.A.I.C.S.: 423840

Carolina Paper Tubes Inc. (1)
3932 Old US 25 Hwy, Zirconia, NC 28790
Tel.: (828) 869-9686
Web Site:
  http://www.carolinapapertubes.com
Paper Tube Mfr
N.A.I.C.S.: 322219
Jerry Melton *(Pres)*
Terry Brandt *(Mgr-Sls)*

Ox Paperboard LLC (1)
164 Eyster Rd, Halltown, WV 25423-0010
Tel.: (304) 725-2076
Web Site: http://www.oxindustries.com
Sales Range: $10-24.9 Million
Emp.: 80
Paperboard Mfr
N.A.I.C.S.: 322130
Kevin J. Hayward *(Pres)*

OXAGILE LLC

77 Water St 8th Fl, New York, NY 10005
Web Site: http://www.oxagile.com
Year Founded: 2005
Sales Range: $1-9.9 Million
Emp.: 107
International Software Development
N.A.I.C.S.: 513210
Dmitry Karpovich *(Owner & CEO)*

Subsidiaries:

Oxagile LLC (1)
4 Myel'nikayte Street, 220004, Minsk, Belarus (100%)
Tel.: (375) 17 211 2011
Web Site: http://www.oxagile.com
Software Development & Maintenance Support
N.A.I.C.S.: 513210
Olga Tikhomirova *(Mgr-HR & Recruiter-IT)*
Pavel Gavrilenko *(Head-Sls)*
Mihail Romanovsky *(Head-Mktg)*

OXAMEDIA CORPORATION

55 SE 2nd Ave, Delray Beach, FL 33444
Tel.: (561) 921-1094 DE
Web Site: http://www.oxamedia.com
Year Founded: 2010
Digital Advertising Services
N.A.I.C.S.: 541890
Risto Bozharov *(CEO)*
Veronika Putova *(Principal Fin Officer & COO)*
Giovanna Colombo *(Chief-Sls)*

OXARC INC.

4003 E Broadway Ave, Spokane, WA 99202-4528
Tel.: (509) 535-7794 WA
Web Site: http://www.oxarc.com
Year Founded: 1955
Sales Range: $25-49.9 Million
Emp.: 300
Provider of Welding & Industrial Supplies; Industrial & Medical Gases
N.A.I.C.S.: 423830
Jerry T. Walmsley *(Chm)*
Gregory H. Walmsley *(Pres)*
J. Nelson *(Exec VP)*

OXBOW CORPORATION

1601 Forum Pl Ste 1400, West Palm Beach, FL 33401-8101
Tel.: (561) 907-5400 FL
Web Site: https://www.oxbow.com
Year Founded: 1984
Sales Range: $1-4.9 Billion
Emp.: 1,000
All Other Petroleum & Coal Products Manufacturing
N.A.I.C.S.: 324199
William I. Koch *(Founder, Chm, Pres & CEO)*
David W. Clark *(Gen Counsel & Sec)*
Roy J. Schorsch *(Exec VP)*
Gord McIntosh *(Exec VP)*
Craig J. Cynor *(Exec VP)*
James R. Freney *(Exec VP-Activated Carbon & Special Projects)*

Subsidiaries:

Oxbow Carbon & Minerals International GmbH (1)
Caves Villages Building 8 Office 1 West Bay Street, Nassau, Bahamas
Tel.: (242) 327 8160
Petroleum Product Mfr & Whslr
N.A.I.C.S.: 424720

Oxbow Carbon & Minerals LLC (1)
1601 Forum Pl Ste 1400, West Palm Beach, FL 33401
Tel.: (561) 907-5400
Web Site: http://www.oxbow.com
Sales Range: $1-4.9 Billion
Emp.: 200
Green Calcineable Coke, Coal, Metallurgical Coke, Steel, Gypsum & Other Bulk Materials Whslr
N.A.I.C.S.: 423520
Eric Johnson *(Pres)*
William I. Koch *(Founder & CEO)*
Richard P. Callahan *(Gen Counsel)*
Zachary K. Shipley *(Co-CFO)*
David W. Clark *(Gen Counsel & Sec)*
William D. Parmelee *(Co-CFO)*
Roy J. Schorsch *(Sr VP-Ops)*

Subsidiary (Domestic):

Oxbow Calcining LLC (2)
1450 Lake Robbins Dr Ste 500, The Woodlands, TX 77380
Tel.: (281) 907-9500
Web Site: http://www.oxbow.com
Sales Range: $25-49.9 Million
Calcined Petroleum Coke Products Mfr
N.A.I.C.S.: 324199
Eric Johnson *(Exec VP)*

Subsidiary (Non-US):

Copetro, S.A. (3)
Ave Leandro No Alem 822 Piso 11, C1001AAQ, Buenos Aires, Argentina
Tel.: (54) 1143131800
Web Site: http://www.oxbow.com.ar
Sales Range: $10-24.9 Million
Emp.: 100
Mfr of Calcined Petroleum Coke Products
N.A.I.C.S.: 324199
Marcelo Jaworski *(Gen Mgr)*

Subsidiary (Domestic):

Oxbow Midwest Calcining LLC (3)
12308 New Ave, Lemont, IL 60439-3686
Tel.: (630) 257-7751
Web Site: http://www.oxbow.com
Sales Range: $25-49.9 Million
Emp.: 75
Coke Petroleum Mfr
N.A.I.C.S.: 324110

Subsidiary (Non-US):

Oxbow Coal B.V. (2)
Rochussenstraat 125, PO Box 1006, 3000 BA, Rotterdam, Netherlands
Tel.: (31) 104419200
Sales Range: $25-49.9 Million
Emp.: 40
Coal, Petroleum Coke & Other Carbon Products Whslr
N.A.I.C.S.: 423520
Patrick Biuning *(Gen Mgr)*

Subsidiary (Domestic):

Superior Adsorbents, Inc. (2)
3539 Oneida Vly Rd, Emlenton, PA 16373
Tel.: (724) 791-2411
Sales Range: $1-9.9 Million
Emp.: 25
Chemical Products Mfr
N.A.I.C.S.: 325998
Murty Hari *(Co-Owner)*
John Giglio *(Co-Owner)*

Oxbow Carbon Baton Rouge (1)
2200 Brooklawn Dr, Baton Rouge, LA 70807
Tel.: (225) 358-2700
Petroleum Product Whslr
N.A.I.C.S.: 424720

Oxbow Coal B.V. (1)
Maastoren Wilhelminakade 93, 3072 AP, Rotterdam, Netherlands
Tel.: (31) 10 441 9200
Web Site: http://www.oxbow.com
Emp.: 50
Petroleum Product Distr
N.A.I.C.S.: 424720
Patrick Bruning *(Mng Dir)*

Oxbow Coal Ltd. (1)
Southern Way Immingham Dock North East Lincolnshire, Immingham, DN40 2NX, United Kingdom
Tel.: (44) 1469 577635
Web Site: http://www.oxbowcoal.com
Sales Range: $10-24.9 Million
Emp.: 8
Petroleum Product Whslr
N.A.I.C.S.: 423520

Oxbow Coal S.a.r.l. (1)
Energy Park 132-134 bd de Verdun Immeuble 7-5eme etage, Courbevoie, 92400, France
Tel.: (33) 1 4717 1305
Petroleum Product Mfr
N.A.I.C.S.: 324199

Oxbow GmbH (1)
Hafenstrasse 1 Rheinhafen Orsoy, 47495, Rheinberg, Germany
Tel.: (49) 2844 900762
Petroleum Product Mfr
N.A.I.C.S.: 324199

Oxbow Mining, LLC (1)
3737 Hwy 133, Somerset, CO 81434
Tel.: (970) 929-5122
Web Site: http://www.oxbow.com
Sales Range: $75-99.9 Million
Emp.: 350
Coal Mining
N.A.I.C.S.: 212115
Mike Ludlow *(Pres)*

Oxbow Sulphur & Fertiliser (Brazil) Ltda (1)
Rua Pedroso Alvarenga 58-CJ 61, Sao Paulo, 04531-000, Brazil
Tel.: (55) 11 3168 3488
Web Site: http://www.oxbow.com
Emp.: 5
Fertilizer Mfr
N.A.I.C.S.: 325312

Oxbow Sulphur & Fertiliser (Singapore) Pte Ltd (1)
545 Orchard Road Hex 14-03 Far East Shopping Centre, Singapore, 238882, Singapore
Tel.: (65) 6339 1896
Web Site: http://www.oxbow.com
Sales Range: $10-24.9 Million
Emp.: 10
Fertilizer Mfr
N.A.I.C.S.: 325312
Catherine Tan *(Office Mgr)*

Oxbow Sulphur & Fertiliser (UK) Limited (1)
Nova Scotia House 70 Goldsworth Road Woking, Woking, GU21 6LQ, Surrey, United Kingdom
Tel.: (44) 1483 729741
Sales Range: $10-24.9 Million
Emp.: 2
Fertilizer Mfr
N.A.I.C.S.: 325314

OXBOW MACHINE PRODUCTS INC.

12743 Merriman Rd, Livonia, MI 48150
Tel.: (734) 422-7730
Web Site: http://www.oxbow-machine.com
Sales Range: $10-24.9 Million
Emp.: 25
Special Dies, Tools, Jigs & Fixtures
N.A.I.C.S.: 333514
Michael J. Tiano *(VP)*

OXCYON, INC.

17520 Engle Lake Dr, Middleburg Heights, OH 44130
Tel.: (440) 239-8611 OH
Web Site: http://www.oxcyon.com
Year Founded: 2000
Sales Range: $1-9.9 Million
Emp.: 42
Content Management Services
N.A.I.C.S.: 513210
Samuel Keller *(Pres & CEO)*

OXEIA BIOPHARMACEUTICALS, INC.

361 Newbury St Ste 500, Boston, MA 02115
Tel.: (617) 991-9150 DE
Web Site:
  https://www.oxeiabiopharma.com
Year Founded: 2014
Assets: $85,000
Liabilities: $9,017,000
Net Worth: ($8,932,000)
Earnings: ($1,971,000)
Emp.: 2
Fiscal Year-end: 12/31/21
Biotechnology Research & Development Services
N.A.I.C.S.: 541714
Michael Wyand *(CEO)*
Kartik Shah *(Co-Founder)*
Julianne Averill *(CFO)*
Vishal Bansal *(Co-Founder & Chief Scientific Officer)*

OXENDALE CHRYSLER DODGE JEEP

920 E St Rte 89A, Cottonwood, AZ 86326
Tel.: (928) 634-3656 AZ
Web Site: http://www.oxendale.com
Emp.: 40
New & Used Automobiles
N.A.I.C.S.: 441110
Matthew Oxendale *(Owner & Pres)*

OXFORD BANK AND TRUST

1111 W 22nd St Ste 800, Oak Brook, IL 60523
Tel.: (630) 629-5000
Web Site: http://www.oxford.bank
Rev.: $17,132,000
Emp.: 45
Commercial Bank
N.A.I.C.S.: 522110
Bruce Glawe *(Pres & CEO)*

OXFORD COMMUNICATIONS, INC.

11 Music Mtn Blvd, Lambertville, NJ 08530
Tel.: (609) 397-4242 DE
Web Site:
  http://www.oxfordcommunications.com
Year Founded: 1986
Sales Range: $25-49.9 Million
Emp.: 40
Advertising Agencies
N.A.I.C.S.: 541810
Chris Ledford *(Sr VP-Integrated Client Svcs)*
John J. Martorana *(Pres)*
Lauren Spencer *(Mgr-Traffic)*
Ashley Kloczynski *(Asst Mgr-Acct)*

OXFORD CONSTRUCTION COMPANY
3200 Palmyra Rd, Albany, GA 31707
Tel.: (229) 883-3232
Web Site:
http://www.oxfordconstruction.com
Sales Range: $25-49.9 Million
Emp.: 300
Highway & Street Paving Contractor
N.A.I.C.S.: 237310
J. Bruce Melton *(Pres)*
Melvin Edwards *(VP)*
Keith Miller *(Controller)*

OXFORD CONSULTING GROUP, INC.
385 County Line Rd W Ste210, Westerville, OH 43082
Tel.: (614) 310-2700
Web Site: http://www.oxford-consulting.com
Year Founded: 1998
Sales Range: $10-24.9 Million
Emp.: 150
Computer Related Services
N.A.I.C.S.: 541512
Adam Heeter *(CEO)*
Michelle Kerr *(Chm & Pres)*
Chris Halvorson *(Dir-Bus Integration Svcs)*
Chad Mead *(Dir-IT Prof Svcs)*
Andrew Engelbert *(Dir-IT Risk Mgmt & CISO)*
Lorrie Young *(Mgr-Fin)*
Chad Hooker *(Sr Dir-Supply Chain Solutions)*
Chad Young *(Sr VP-Staffing & Strategic Initiatives)*

OXFORD DEVELOPMENT COMPANY
1 Oxford Ctr Ste 4500 301 Grant St, Pittsburgh, PA 15219-1489
Tel.: (412) 261-1500
Web Site:
http://www.oxforddevelopment.com
Sales Range: $10-24.9 Million
Emp.: 2,200
Commercial & Industrial Building Operation
N.A.I.C.S.: 531120
Mark E. Mason *(Founder & Vice Chm)*
David M. Matter *(Pres & CEO)*
R. Scott Pollock *(VP-Dev)*

Subsidiaries:

GVA Oxford (1)
1 Oxford Ctr Ste 400, Pittsburgh, PA 15219
Tel.: (412) 261-0200
Web Site: http://www.gvaoxford.com
Sales Range: $10-24.9 Million
Emp.: 25
Provider of Real Estate Leasing & Brokerage Services
N.A.I.C.S.: 531120

OXFORD FINANCIAL GROUP LTD.
11711 N Meridian St Ste 600, Carmel, IN 46032
Tel.: (317) 843-5678
Web Site: http://www.ofgltd.com
Investment Advisor
N.A.I.C.S.: 523999
Jeffrey H. Thomasson *(CEO & Mng dir)*

Subsidiaries:

Innovative Displayworks, Inc. (1)
8825 Boston Pl, Rancho Cucamonga, CA 91730
Tel.: (909) 447-8254
Web Site: http://www.idw.global
Custom Architectural Woodwork & Millwork Mfr
N.A.I.C.S.: 337212

Leo Wills *(Co-Founder, Pres & CEO)*
Nathan Linder *(Co-Founder, COO & VP)*

OXFORD HOLDINGS INC.
3063 NW 23rd Ter, Fort Lauderdale, FL 33311-1402
Tel.: (954) 731-2811 FL
Year Founded: 1983
Sales Range: $25-49.9 Million
Emp.: 500
Provider of Commercial Construction Services
N.A.I.C.S.: 236220
Steve J. Watkins *(Chm & Pres)*

Subsidiaries:

Aetna Construction, Inc. (1)
3061 NW 23rd Ter, Fort Lauderdale, FL 33311-1402
Tel.: (954) 731-2811
Sales Range: $10-24.9 Million
Emp.: 100
Nonresidential Construction
N.A.I.C.S.: 236220

OXFORD MINING COMPANY, LLC
544 Chestnut St, Coshocton, OH 43812-1209
Tel.: (740) 622-6302 OH
Web Site:
http://www.westmoreland.com
Year Founded: 1985
Emp.: 20
Bituminous Coal Surface Mining
N.A.I.C.S.: 212114
Gregory J. Honish *(Sr VP-Ops)*

Subsidiaries:

Harrison Resources, LLC (1)
544 Chestnut St, Coshocton, OH 43812
Tel.: (740) 623-0015
Management Consulting Services
N.A.I.C.S.: 541611

OXFORD NORTHEAST, LTD.
400 Rella Dr Ste 165, Suffern, NY 10901 NY
Year Founded: 2018
Assets: $451,361
Liabilities: $596,828
Net Worth: ($145,467)
Earnings: ($139,030)
Fiscal Year-end: 09/30/19
Application Software Development Services
N.A.I.C.S.: 541511
Samuel Eisenberg *(CEO & CFO)*
Abraham Miller *(Chm & Pres)*
Eliezer Raksin *(Sec)*

OXFORD PROPERTIES, LLC
3284 Northside Pkwy NW Ste 150, Atlanta, GA 30339
Tel.: (770) 818-4050
Web Site: http://www.oxford-properties.com
Sales Range: $1-9.9 Million
Emp.: 45
New Multifamily Housing Construction
N.A.I.C.S.: 236116
Greg Kotarba *(CFO)*
Keith Rothwell *(Sr VP)*
Brenda J. Brawner *(Dir-HR)*
Ellen Chiang *(Partner & Controller)*
Bill Hall *(Partner)*
Bill Hargett *(Partner)*
Marie Thomas *(Partner & Exec VP)*
W. Daniel Faulk Jr. *(Co-Founder & Mng Partner)*
Richard A. Denny III *(Partner)*

OXFORD REALTY FINANCIAL GROUP
7200 Wisconsin Ave Ste 1005, Bethesda, MD 20814-4893

Tel.: (301) 654-3100
Rev.: $95,100,000
Emp.: 8
Real Estate Managers
N.A.I.C.S.: 531110

OXFORD REALTY, INC.
4700 Millenia Blvd Ste 175, Orlando, FL 32839
Tel.: (407) 629-1222
Web Site:
http://www.oxfordrealty.com
Sales Range: $10-24.9 Million
Emp.: 35
Real Estate Services
N.A.I.C.S.: 531210
Carol Ann Hewitt *(Owner)*

OXIEM, LLC
PO Box 1441, Springfield, OH 45501
Tel.: (937) 424-8950 OH
Web Site: http://www.oxiem.com
Year Founded: 2004
Sales Range: $10-24.9 Million
Emp.: 50
Advertising & Public Relations Agency
N.A.I.C.S.: 541810
John Fimiani *(Partner & Dir-Brand/Strategy)*
Bill Sterzenbach *(Partner & Dir-Tech)*
Crystal Olig *(Dir-Interactive)*
Mary Garrick *(Mgr-PR & Content Mktg)*
Christopher Haag *(Mgr-Dev)*
David Kragel *(Mgr-Search Mktg)*
Dave Hafenbrack *(Founder)*
Frank Sulka *(VP-Bus Dev)*

Subsidiaries:

Hafenbrack Marketing & Public Relations, Inc. (1)
15 W 4th St Ste 410, Dayton, OH 45402
Tel.: (937) 424-8950
Web Site: http://www.hafenbrack.com
Emp.: 25
Advertising & Public Relations Agency
N.A.I.C.S.: 541810
David C. Hafenbrack *(Pres & Founder)*

OXMOOR FORD LINCOLN MERCURY, INC.
100 Oxmoor Ln, Louisville, KY 40222
Tel.: (502) 426-2500
Sales Range: $10-24.9 Million
Emp.: 80
Car Whslr
N.A.I.C.S.: 441110
Jean Brown *(Gen Counsel)*
Tracy Farmer *(Pres)*

OXMOOR TOYOTA
8003 Shelbyville Rd, Louisville, KY 40222
Tel.: (502) 426-1200
Web Site:
http://www.oxmoortoyota.com
Year Founded: 1989
Sales Range: $25-49.9 Million
Emp.: 142
Car Whslr
N.A.I.C.S.: 441110
Rusty Shofner *(Mgr-Parts)*
Carolyn Gilbert *(Mgr-Sls)*

OXYDE CHEMICALS, INC.
225 Pennbright Dr, Houston, TX 77090
Tel.: (281) 874-9100
Web Site: http://www.oxydeusa.com
Sales Range: $25-49.9 Million
Emp.: 10
Petrochemicals & Plastics Wholesale Trade Agency
N.A.I.C.S.: 425120

Fernando Rodriguez *(Mng Dir)*
Steve Stone *(CFO)*
Alfonso Velez *(Dir-Latin America)*

Subsidiaries:

Oxyde Belgium BVBA (1)
Entrepotkaai 9, 2000, Antwerp, Belgium
Tel.: (32) 3205 1659
Web Site: http://www.oxyde.eu
Petrochemicals & Plastics Wholesale Trade Agency
N.A.I.C.S.: 425120

OXYGEN ADVERTISING, INC.
226 N E Sanchez Ave, Ocala, FL 34470
Tel.: (352) 591-4115
Web Site:
http://www.o2advertising.com
Year Founded: 1998
Emp.: 5
Full-Services Marketing & Advertising Agency
N.A.I.C.S.: 541810
Tandra Rabold *(Owner & Creative Dir)*

OYER INC.
1440 S Breiel Blvd, Middletown, OH 45044
Tel.: (513) 424-2421
Web Site:
http://www.coldwellbankeroyer.com
Sales Range: $10-24.9 Million
Emp.: 40
Real Estate Brokers & Agents
N.A.I.C.S.: 237210
Michael Combs *(Pres)*
Glenn Cunningham *(Gen Mgr)*

OZANAM HALL OF QUEENS NURSING HOME
42-41 201st St, Bayside, NY 11361
Tel.: (718) 423-2000 NY
Web Site: http://www.ozanamhall.org
Year Founded: 1969
Sales Range: $50-74.9 Million
Emp.: 713
Nursing Care Services
N.A.I.C.S.: 623110
James M. Koniarski *(CFO)*
Margaret White *(Dir-Rehabilitation)*
Harry C. Itoka *(Controller)*
Ann M. Callaghan *(Dir-Nursing)*
Luigi Capobianco *(Dir-Medical)*

OZANNE CONSTRUCTION COMPANY
1635 E 25th St, Cleveland, OH 44114
Tel.: (216) 696-2876
Web Site: http://www.ozanne.com
Rev.: $12,600,000
Emp.: 15
Nonresidential Construction
N.A.I.C.S.: 236220
Dominic Ozanne *(Pres & CEO)*

OZARK BORDER ELECTRIC COOP ASSOCIATION
US Hwy 67, Poplar Bluff, MO 63901
Tel.: (573) 785-4631
Web Site: http://www.ozarkborder.org
Rev.: $18,300,000
Emp.: 80
Distribution of Electric Power
N.A.I.C.S.: 221122
Stanley Estes *(Gen Mgr)*
Ansel I. Moore *(Mgr)*
Mark Yarbro *(Pres)*

OZARK MOTOR LINES INC.
3934 Homewood Rd, Memphis, TN 38118
Tel.: (901) 251-9711 TN
Web Site: http://www.ozark.com
Year Founded: 1961
Sales Range: $150-199.9 Million

OZARK MOTOR LINES INC.   U.S. PRIVATE

Ozark Motor Lines Inc.—(Continued)
Emp.: 900
Provider of Trucking Services
N.A.I.C.S.: 484121
Tommy Higginbotham (VP)
Mike Gilmore (VP)

OZARK NEWS DISTRIBUTION INC.
1630 N Eldon Ave, Springfield, MO 65803
Tel.: (417) 862-9224
Web Site: http://www.ozarkmagazine.com
Sales Range: $10-24.9 Million
Emp.: 31
Magazines
N.A.I.C.S.: 424920
Danny Moore (Pres)
Rhonda Bratten (Mgr)

OZARK STRUCTURES INC.
5731 W Hwy 60, Brookline, MO 65619
Tel.: (417) 865-5517
Web Site: http://www.ozarkstructures.com
Rev.: $10,300,000
Emp.: 100
Engineering & Design Services
N.A.I.C.S.: 321215
Michael Burkhart (Pres)
James W. Datema (Chm & CEO)

OZARK SUPERMARKET INC.
604 E South St, Ozark, MO 65721
Tel.: (417) 581-3300
Rev.: $15,000,000
Emp.: 75
Independent Grocery Store
N.A.I.C.S.: 445110
Charles E. Murfin Sr. (Pres)
Charles Murfin Jr. (VP)

OZARK TRUCKING INC.
4916 Dudley Blvd, McClellan, CA 95652-2521
Tel.: (916) 561-5400
Web Site: http://www.ozarktruckinginc.com
Rev.: $35,000,000
Emp.: 250
Local Trucking without Storage
N.A.I.C.S.: 484110
Jeff Cummings (Pres)
Debbie Watney (Mgr-Payroll)
Terry Johnson (Coord-Dispatch)

OZARK WAFFLES LLC
Ste E4 5305 McClanahan Dr, North Little Rock, AR 72116-7076
Tel.: (501) 771-2063
Rev.: $18,400,000
Emp.: 3
Restaurant, Family: Chain
N.A.I.C.S.: 722511
Jeff Harrell (Pres)

OZARK WAREHOUSES, INC.
4700 Wheeler Ave, Fort Smith, AR 72906
Tel.: (479) 646-6225   AR
Web Site: http://www.corrugatedspecialties.net
Year Founded: 1989
Sales Range: $1-9.9 Million
Emp.: 53
Corrugated & Solid Fiber Box Mfr
N.A.I.C.S.: 322211
Paul Henson (Pres)

Subsidiaries:

Century Corrugated Container Inc.   (1)
2734 FM 1252 W, Kilgore, TX 75662-4824
Tel.: (903) 984-1261

Corrugated Box Mfr
N.A.I.C.S.: 322211
Tim O'Bryant (Pres)

OZARKS COCA COLA/DR PEPPER BOTTLING COMPANY
1777 N Packer Rd, Springfield, MO 65803
Tel.: (417) 865-9900
Web Site: http://www.cocacolaozarks.com
Rev.: $65,000,000
Emp.: 300
Bottled & Canned Carbonated Beverages
N.A.I.C.S.: 312111
Edwin C. Rice (Chm & CEO)
Martin Meyers (Controller)
John Schaefer (Pres)
Bruce Long (VP-Mktg & Bus Dev)

OZARKS ELECTRIC COOPERATIVE CORPORATION
3641 W Wedington Dr, Fayetteville, AR 72704-5742
Tel.: (479) 521-2900   AR
Web Site: http://www.ozarksecc.com
Year Founded: 1938
Sales Range: $10-24.9 Million
Emp.: 200
Electronic Services
N.A.I.C.S.: 221122
Mitchell Johnson (Pres & CEO)
Todd Townsend (CFO & VP-Corp Svcs)
Kristin Immel (Mgr-Fin & Acctg)
Robert Erickson (Engr-Structural & GIS)
Carl Thomas (VP-IT)

OZARKS FEDERAL SAVINGS & LOAN ASSOCIATION
2 E Columbia St, Farmington, MO 63640
Tel.: (573) 756-6622
Web Site: http://www.ozarksfederal.com
Rev.: $181,000,000
Emp.: 28
Savings Institutions
N.A.I.C.S.: 522180
Dennis McIntosh (CEO)
Michele King (Treas & Sr VP)

OZINGA BROS., INC.
19001 Old Lagrange Rd, Mokena, IL 60448-8350
Tel.: (708) 326-4200   IL
Web Site: http://www.ozinga.com
Year Founded: 1928
Ready-Mixed Concrete & Building Materials Mfr & Whslr
N.A.I.C.S.: 327320
Ken Clay (Project Mgr)
Marty Ozinga (Pres)
Tim Ozinga (Co-Owner & Exec VP)
Derek Terpstra (Mgr-Dispatch)
Jeffrey Ozinga (Exec VP)
Don Van Dyk (CFO)
Tom Allen (Dir-Infrastructure)
John Sikkenga (Mgr-Quality Control)

Subsidiaries:

Ozinga Chicago RMC, Inc.   (1)
2255 S Lumber St, Chicago, IL 60616-2198
Tel.: (312) 432-5700
Web Site: http://www.ozinga.com
Sales Range: $25-49.9 Million
Emp.: 180
Ready Mixed Concrete
N.A.I.C.S.: 327320

Ozinga South Suburban RMC, Inc.   (1)
19001 Old LaGrange Rd, Mokena, IL 60448
Tel.: (708) 479-3080
Web Site: http://www.ozinga.com

Sales Range: $50-74.9 Million
Emp.: 55
Central-Mixed Concrete
N.A.I.C.S.: 327320

OZZIE'S PIPELINE PADDER, INC.
7102 W Sherman St, Phoenix, AZ 85043-4203
Tel.: (480) 585-9400   AZ
Web Site: http://www.ozzies.com
Year Founded: 1979
Pipeline Padding & Filter Systems Mfr
N.A.I.C.S.: 332919
Robert Dunstan (Pres & CEO)
Christopher Argue (VP & COO)

P & D BUILDERS, LTD.
59 Greif Pkwy Ste 100, Delaware, OH 43015
Tel.: (740) 201-8079
Web Site: http://www.home-builders-columbus.com
Year Founded: 1963
Sales Range: $10-24.9 Million
Emp.: 16
Housing Construction Services
N.A.I.C.S.: 236117
Mac Roberts (Pres)

P & G CHEVROLET, INC.
PO Box 560826, Charlotte, NC 28256
Tel.: (704) 598-4000
Web Site: http://www.parkschevrolet.com
Sales Range: $10-24.9 Million
Emp.: 164
New Car Dealers
N.A.I.C.S.: 441110
Debora J. Parks (Pres)

P & L ENTERPRISES OF NAPLES, INC.
829 Airport Rd N, Naples, FL 34104
Tel.: (239) 643-2292   FL
Web Site: http://www.naplesboatmart.com
Sales Range: $10-24.9 Million
Emp.: 30
Sales of Boats
N.A.I.C.S.: 441222
Philip Osborn (Pres)

P & S MASONRY, INC.
401 E Main St, Hamilton, TX 76531
Tel.: (254) 386-8975
Web Site: http://www.pandsmasonry.com
Year Founded: 1987
Sales Range: $10-24.9 Million
Emp.: 150
Masonry Contractors
N.A.I.C.S.: 238140
Joe Campbell (Mgr-Ops)
Elizabeth Beber (Dir-Safety)
Susie Odom (Pres)
Paul Odom (VP)

P P D, INC.
1900 W Yale Ave, Englewood, CO 80110
Tel.: (303) 979-6085
Photofinishing Laboratories, except One-Hour
N.A.I.C.S.: 812921
Mike Pearce (Pres)

P&B FABRICS INC.
1580 Gilbreth Rd, Burlingame, CA 94010
Tel.: (650) 692-0422
Web Site: http://www.pbtex.com
Rev.: $11,000,000
Emp.: 18
Broadwoven Fabric Mills, Cotton
N.A.I.C.S.: 313210

Edward Odessa (Pres)

P&B HOLDINGS, INC.
3063 Philmont Ave, Huntingdon Valley, PA 19006-4243
Tel.: (215) 947-3333   DE
Web Site: http://www.jadecorp.com
Year Founded: 1996
Rev.: $60,000,000
Emp.: 200
Holding Company
N.A.I.C.S.: 333515
Brian T. Manley (CEO)
John K. Delp (Pres)

P&B PETROLEUM CO. INC.
33 Bell St, Cleveland, GA 30528
Tel.: (706) 865-5111
Rev.: $12,000,000
Emp.: 3
Gasoline
N.A.I.C.S.: 424720
C. Lamar Black (Pres)

P&C CONSTRUCTION INC.
2500 E 18th St, Chattanooga, TN 37404
Tel.: (423) 493-0051
Web Site: http://www.pc-const.com
Year Founded: 1993
Sales Range: $25-49.9 Million
Emp.: 50
Construction Management Services
N.A.I.C.S.: 541330
Royce Cornelison (Founder & Pres)
Nic Cornelison (VP)
Mike Brown (Project Mgr-LEED AP)
Mike Payne (Project Mgr)
Jeremy Babb (Project Mgr-LEED AP)
Chase Steele (Project Mgr)
Jordan Cornelison (Project Mgr)
Chris Brown (Treas)
David Williams (Mgr-HR & Safety)
Jeff Johnson (Project Mgr)
Dustin Sauer (Project Engr-Portland Health Care)

P&C DISTRIBUTORS INC.
1020 Bonaventure Dr, Elk Grove Village, IL 60007
Tel.: (847) 879-6400
Web Site: http://www.dpoe.com
Sales Range: $10-24.9 Million
Emp.: 50
Business Machines & Equipment
N.A.I.C.S.: 459999
Chip Miceli (Founder)
Victor Miceli (Founder)

P&C GROUP, INC.
40000 Grand River Ave Ste 110, Novi, MI 48375-2121
Tel.: (248) 442-6800   MI
Web Site: http://www.camacollc.com
Year Founded: 1996
Sales Range: $200-249.9 Million
Emp.: 21
Mfr of Automotive Seat Components
N.A.I.C.S.: 332999
Arvind Pradhan (Pres & CEO)

Subsidiaries:

Camaco LLC   (1)
37000 W 2mile Rd, Farmington Hills, MI 48375-2121
Tel.: (248) 442-6800
Web Site: http://www.camacollc.com
Sales Range: $10-24.9 Million
Fabricated Metal Products
N.A.I.C.S.: 332999
Arvind Pradhan (Pres)
Pam Cooper (Coord-Admin)
Thomas Rockwell (CFO)
Lee Spruit (Dir-Program Mgmt & Tech)

Camaco Lorain Manufacturing   (1)
3400 River Industrial Park Rd, Lorain, OH 44052-2900

Tel.: (440) 288-4444
Web Site: http://www.camaco.com
Sales Range: $25-49.9 Million
Fabricated Metal Products
N.A.I.C.S.: 332999
Karen Brezenay (Dir-HR)

Lorain County Automotive Systems Inc. (1)
7470 Industrial Pkwy Dr D, Lorain, OH 44053-2064
Tel.: (440) 960-7470
Web Site: http://www.camacollc.com
Sales Range: $10-24.9 Million
Motor Vehicle Parts & Accessories
N.A.I.C.S.: 336390
Kathy Auble (Mgr-HR)

P&J TEAM AMERICA INC.
295 Ward Rd, Midlothian, TX 76065
Tel.: (972) 775-5476
Rev.: $26,815,397
Emp.: 100
Shipping Brokers
N.A.I.C.S.: 488510
Pat Porritt (Pres)

P&K EQUIPMENT INC.
17759 US Highway, Kingfisher, OK 73750
Tel.: (405) 375-3111 OK
Web Site: http://www.pkequipment.com
Year Founded: 1985
Sales Range: $10-24.9 Million
Emp.: 70
Farm Implements
N.A.I.C.S.: 423820
Barry Pollard (Pres)
Roland Mulherin (Mgr-Parts)

P&L TRANSPORTATION, INC.
PO Box 4132, Port Wentworth, GA 31407-2287
Tel.: (912) 964-1511 GA
Sales Range: $150-199.9 Million
Emp.: 400
Trucking Service
N.A.I.C.S.: 484110
John Bagarley (Pres)

P&M SOLUTIONS, LLC
4260 Communications Dr, Norcross, GA 30093
Tel.: (770) 840-8831
Web Site: http://www.domyownpestcontrol.com
Year Founded: 2004
Sales Range: $1-9.9 Million
Emp.: 15
Online Retailer of Pest Control Products & Supplies
N.A.I.C.S.: 561710
Michael Gossling (Co-Owner & Pres)
Philip Gossling (Co-Owner & VP)

P&N COAL CO. INC.
240 W Mahoning St, Punxsutawney, PA 15767
Tel.: (814) 938-7660
Web Site: http://www.pnresources.com
Sales Range: $10-24.9 Million
Emp.: 6
Strip Mining
N.A.I.C.S.: 212114
George D. Prushnok (Chm)
Andy Nelson (Treas & Sec)
John Prushnok (Pres)
Ken Stossell (Controller)

P&R ENTERPRISES INC.
5681 Columbia Pike Ste 101, Falls Church, VA 22041
Tel.: (703) 931-1000
Web Site: http://www.p-and-r.com
Year Founded: 1968
Sales Range: $100-124.9 Million
Emp.: 1,550
Provider of Janitorial & Building Related Services
N.A.I.C.S.: 561720
Charles H. Solem (Chm)
Carlos Sanchez (Pres)
Marshall Gross (Controller)
Richard Thompson (Exec VP)

P&R FASTENERS INC.
325 Pierce St, Somerset, NJ 08873
Tel.: (732) 302-3600
Web Site: http://www.prfast.com
Rev.: $30,000,000
Emp.: 46
Mfr & Supplier of Specialty Component Parts
N.A.I.C.S.: 332722
Benjamin S. Margulies (Pres)
Doug Joyce (Controller)
Beth Mills (Mgr-Matls)
Brian Isaacson (VP)
Joe Flynn Schweitzer (Acct Mgr)
Phil Vesuvio (Gen Mgr)
William Kartner (Mgr-QA)

P&R INDUSTRIES INC.
1524 Clinton Ave N, Rochester, NY 14621
Tel.: (585) 266-6725
Web Site: http://www.pandrindustries.com
Sales Range: $10-24.9 Million
Emp.: 35
Machine Tools, Metal Cutting Type
N.A.I.C.S.: 333517
Lawrence F. Coyle (Pres)
Nick Natale (Mgr)
John F. Buscaglia (Supvr-CNC Mill Dept)
Chris Sheelar (Dir-Sls)

P&R METALS, INC.
4017 Richard Arrington Blvd N, Birmingham, AL 35212
Tel.: (205) 328-2290 AL
Web Site: http://www.prmetals.com
Year Founded: 1999
Sales Range: $1-9.9 Million
Emp.: 16
Industrial Flooring Products
N.A.I.C.S.: 238330
James Robinson (Pres)

P&S INVESTMENT COMPANY INC.
2100 Riverside Dr, Green Bay, WI 54301-2375
Tel.: (920) 431-3500 DE
Year Founded: 1980
Sales Range: $25-49.9 Million
Emp.: 350
Trucking Except Local
N.A.I.C.S.: 484121
Hans Schaupp (Pres & CFO)
Evan Miller (VP-Fin)

Subsidiaries:

HFCS Transport Inc. (1)
2100 Riverside Dr, Green Bay, WI 54301-2375
Tel.: (920) 431-3500
Rev.: $6,000,000
Emp.: 30
Trucking Except Local
N.A.I.C.S.: 484121
Robert J. Schaupp (Pres)
Hans Schaupp (Pres)

LCL Bulk Transport Inc. (1)
2100 Riverside Dr, Green Bay, WI 54307-3566
Tel.: (920) 431-3500
Web Site: http://www.lclbulk.com
Emp.: 30
Trucking
N.A.I.C.S.: 484121
Robert J. Schaupp (Chm)
Hans Schaupp (Pres)

LCL Transit Company (1)
2100 Riverside Dr, Green Bay, WI 54301-2375
Tel.: (920) 431-3500
Rev.: $15,000,000
Emp.: 25
Interstate Trucking Services
N.A.I.C.S.: 484121

Transco Leasing Inc. (1)
2100 Riverside Dr, Green Bay, WI 54301-2375
Tel.: (920) 431-3500
Sales Range: $25-49.9 Million
Emp.: 30
Truck Rental & Leasing, No Drivers
N.A.I.C.S.: 532120

P&S TRANSPORTATION, INC.
PO Box 2487, Birmingham, AL 35201
Tel.: (205) 788-4000 AL
Web Site: http://www.pstrans.com
Year Founded: 2004
Sales Range: $1-9.9 Million
Emp.: 100
General Freight Trucking
N.A.I.C.S.: 484121
Robert Pike (Principal)
Kevin Poe (Dir-Customer Svc)
Scott Smith (Owner)
Stephen Westbrook (Mgr-Payroll)

Subsidiaries:

Purdy Brothers Trucking Company (1)
199 Commercial Park Dr, Loudon, TN 37774
Tel.: (865) 458-4642
Web Site: http://www.purdybros.com
Trucking Service
N.A.I.C.S.: 484121
James P. Purdy (CEO)
Douglas Surrett (Pres)

TA Services, Inc. (1)
241 Regency Pkwy, Mansfield, TX 76063
Tel.: (817) 539-8500
Web Site: http://www.taservices.us
Emp.: 39
Freight Transportation Arrangement
N.A.I.C.S.: 488510
Scott Schell (Pres & CEO)
Charles Dismuke (CFO)
Meagan Halford (VP-Mansfield Ops)
Ken Cromwell (Sr VP-Ops)
Jackie Askelson (VP-Ops-Midlothan)
Richard Bishop (Gen Mgr-Ops)
Dale Hughes (VP-Mill Svcs)
Tom Webster (VP-Sls & Mktg)
Thomas Hosack (VP-Bus Dev)

Subsidiary (Domestic):

KPI Logistics, Inc. (2)
535 N Hwy 101, Solana Beach, CA 92075
Tel.: (858) 436-7958
Web Site: http://www.kpilogistics.com
Transportation & Logistics Services
N.A.I.C.S.: 541614
Marc Macier (Pres & CEO)

P&W EXCAVATING INC.
PO Box 712, McConnellsburg, PA 17233
Tel.: (717) 485-5141 PA
Sales Range: $10-24.9 Million
Emp.: 90
Provider of Excavating & Grading Services
N.A.I.C.S.: 238910
Frank C. Plessinger (Pres)
Frank E. Plessinger (Sec)

P&W FOREIGN CAR SERVICE INC.
4801 Baum Blvd, Pittsburgh, PA 15213
Tel.: (412) 682-0788
Web Site: http://www.pandw.com
Sales Range: $10-24.9 Million
Emp.: 70
Car Dealership
N.A.I.C.S.: 441110

Tracey Foster (Owner & Pres)

P'KOLINO LLC
7300 NW 35th Ave, Miami, FL 33147
Web Site: http://www.pkolino.com
Year Founded: 2004
Sales Range: $1-9.9 Million
Emp.: 21
Play Products Focused on Child Development
N.A.I.C.S.: 423920
J. B. Schneider (Co-Founder)
Antonio Turco-Rivas (Co-Founder)

P-FLEET INC.
6390 Greenwich Dr Ste 200, San Diego, CA 92122
Tel.: (858) 348-2587 CA
Web Site: http://www.pfleet.com
Year Founded: 1986
Sales Range: $100-124.9 Million
Emp.: 15
Fuel & Payment Solutions to Commercial & Industrial Fleets
N.A.I.C.S.: 457210
Jake Zuanich (Pres)

P-G INDUSTRIES INC.
7th E 13th St, Anniston, AL 36201
Tel.: (256) 237-1957
Web Site: http://www.pryorgiggey.com
Sales Range: $10-24.9 Million
Emp.: 37
Clay Refractory Mfr
N.A.I.C.S.: 327120
Bruce E. Herman (CEO)
Charles S. Sparks (Pres)
Preston Insley (CFO)

P-H INVESTMENTS INC.
6655 Rookin St, Houston, TX 77074
Tel.: (713) 777-0053
Sales Range: $10-24.9 Million
Emp.: 2
Commercial & Office Building, New Construction
N.A.I.C.S.: 236220

P-K TOOL & MANUFACTURING CO.
4700 W Lemoyne St, Chicago, IL 60651
Tel.: (773) 235-4700
Web Site: http://www.pktool.com
Sales Range: $10-24.9 Million
Emp.: 100
Stamping Metal For The Trade
N.A.I.C.S.: 332119
Mary Lee (Treas & Sec)
Phil Kaiser Jr. (Pres)

P. AGNES INC.
2101 Penrose Ave, Philadelphia, PA 19145
Tel.: (215) 755-6900 PA
Web Site: http://www.pagnes.com
Year Founded: 1918
Sales Range: $125-149.9 Million
Emp.: 45
Provider of Commercial Building Construction Services
N.A.I.C.S.: 236220
Patrick S. Pasquariello (CEO)
Glenn D. Manning (Principal & VP-Preconstruction Svcs)
John Salmieri (CFO & Treas)
Jessica Slack (Assoc VP-Strategic Dev)

P. FLANIGAN & SONS INC.
2444 Loch Raven Rd, Baltimore, MD 21218-5430
Tel.: (410) 467-5900 MD
Web Site: http://www.pflanigan.com
Year Founded: 1885

P. Flanigan & Sons Inc.—(Continued)
Sales Range: $25-49.9 Million
Emp.: 250
Highway & Street Construction
N.A.I.C.S.: 237310
Jeffrey Serio (Engr)
Glenn Hunt (Dir-Safety)
Pierce J. Flanigan IV (Pres)

P. GIOIOSO & SONS, INC.
50 Sprague St, Hyde Park, MA 02136
Tel.: (617) 364-5800
Web Site: http://www.pgioioso.com
Year Founded: 1962
Sales Range: $25-49.9 Million
Emp.: 150
Sewer Line & Related Structure Construction Services
N.A.I.C.S.: 237110
Luigi Gioioso (Co-Founder)
Francesco Gioioso (Co-Founder, CEO & Treas)
Joseph Gioioso (Pres)
Joseph Bettencourt (VP)
Marco A. Gioioso (Sec)
Mario Romania (Project Mgr)
Giuseppe Gioioso (Co-Founder)
Ferrante S. Gioioso (Co-Founder)
Pelino A. Gioioso (Co-Founder)

P. KAUFMANN INC.
3 Park Ave, New York, NY 10016-4640
Tel.: (212) 292-2352
Web Site: http://www.pkcontract.com
Year Founded: 1957
Sales Range: $25-49.9 Million
Emp.: 250
Provider of Dry Goods & Notions
N.A.I.C.S.: 424310
Curtis Breedlove (Pres)

Subsidiaries:

Folia Inc. (1)
3010 Westchester Ave, Purchase, NY 10577-2535
Tel.: (914) 253-6433
Web Site: http://customers.folia-fabrics.com
Sales Range: $10-24.9 Million
Emp.: 45
Provider of Paper Products
N.A.I.C.S.: 424310

P. KAY METAL SUPPLY INC.
2448 E 25th St, Los Angeles, CA 90058
Tel.: (323) 585-5058   CA
Web Site: http://www.pkaymetal.com
Year Founded: 1978
Sales Range: $10-24.9 Million
Emp.: 28
Global Mfr of Solders & Fluxes
N.A.I.C.S.: 423510
Larry Kay (Pres)

Subsidiaries:

Industrias P. Kay de Mexico (1)
Calle De La Brea 3, Meseta Del Chema, Tijuana, 22696, BC, Mexico **(100%)**
Tel.: (52) 66258365
Web Site: http://www.pkaymetal.com
Sales Range: $10-24.9 Million
Emp.: 15
Mfr of Solders & Fluxes
N.A.I.C.S.: 325998

P. SCHOENFELD ASSET MANAGEMENT LLC
1350 Avenue of the Americas 21st Fl, New York, NY 10019
Tel.: (212) 649-9500
Web Site: http://www.psamllc.com
Year Founded: 1986
Sales Range: $50-74.9 Million
Emp.: 100
Provider of Investment Services
N.A.I.C.S.: 525990

Peter Schoenfeld (Founder, CEO & CIO)
John McVeigh (Deputy Portfolio Mgr-Merger Arbitrage)

P.A. LANDERS INC.
351 Winter St, Hanover, MA 02339
Tel.: (781) 826-8818   MA
Web Site: http://www.palanders.com
Year Founded: 1978
Sales Range: $25-49.9 Million
Emp.: 300
Providers of Highway & Street Construction Services
N.A.I.C.S.: 237310
Joseph Timmons (Pres & CEO)
Marcy Kearns (Mgr-Payroll & Benefits)
Robert Frade (Mgr-Concrete)

P.A.G. CAPITAL PARTNERS, LLC
150 N Wacker Dr Ste 2500, Chicago, IL 60606
Tel.: (312) 275-5758
Web Site: http://www.pagcapital.com
Privater Equity Firm
N.A.I.C.S.: 523999
David L. Anderson (Partner)
Alex Fridman (Partner)
Jeff Temple (Partner)
Stephen Sleigh (Partner)
Tim Van Mieghem (Partner)

Subsidiaries:

Corporate Technology Solutions LLC (1)
1971 E 5th St Ste 111, Tempe, AZ 85281-2972
Tel.: (480) 377-0225
Web Site: http://www.ctscabling.com
Sales Range: $10-24.9 Million
Emp.: 18
Cable System Design & Installation Services
N.A.I.C.S.: 237130
Brian Rhynas (Pres)
Wes Dearbaugh (Chm & CEO)

P.B. GAST & SONS INCORPORATED
355 Cottage Grove, Grand Rapids, MI 49510
Tel.: (616) 245-0574
Web Site: http://www.pbgast.com
Sales Range: $10-24.9 Million
Emp.: 35
Cleaning & Maintenance Equipment & Supplies
N.A.I.C.S.: 423850
Peter B. Gast (Pres-Laundry Div & Gen Mgr)
Fritz Gast (CEO & Exec VP)

P.C. CAMPANA INC.
13 74 E 28th St, Lorain, OH 44055-1138
Tel.: (440) 246-6500   OH
Web Site: http://www.pccampana.com
Year Founded: 1993
Sales Range: $10-24.9 Million
Emp.: 125
Provider of Blast Furnaces & Steel Mill Services
N.A.I.C.S.: 331110
Mike Marsico (Gen Mgr)
Jack Yakovich (Mgr-Sls)
Patti Campana (Owner)

P.C. RICHARD & SON
150 Price Pkwy, Farmingdale, NY 11735
Tel.: (631) 843-4300   NY
Web Site: http://www.pcrichard.com
Year Founded: 1909
Sales Range: $550-599.9 Million

Emp.: 2,173
Appliance, Electronics & Home Office Retailer
N.A.I.C.S.: 449210

Subsidiaries:

P.C. Richard & Son Long Island Corp. (1)
150 Price Pkwy, Farmingdale, NY 11735-1315
Tel.: (631) 843-4300
Sales Range: $25-49.9 Million
Emp.: 300
Provider of Household Appliance Services
N.A.I.C.S.: 449210

P.E.L., INC.
1350 Old Skokie Rd Ste 203, Highland Park, IL 60035-3058
Tel.: (847) 831-1049
Web Site: http://www.winediscountcenter.com
Year Founded: 1984
Sales Range: $10-24.9 Million
Emp.: 50
Alcoholic Beverage Sales
N.A.I.C.S.: 445320
Greg Kelly (CFO)

P.I. COMPONENTS CORP.
1951 Hwy 290 W, Brenham, TX 77833
Tel.: (979) 830-5400   TX
Web Site: http://www.pic.com
Year Founded: 1987
Sales Range: $10-24.9 Million
Emp.: 110
Diaphragm Seals Mfr
N.A.I.C.S.: 326291
Jay Scheldorf (Product Mgr)

P.I. ROOF MAINTENANCE, INC.
6109 Remount Rd, North Little Rock, AR 72118
Tel.: (501) 687-6246
Web Site: http://www.piroof.com
Year Founded: 2001
Sales Range: $1-9.9 Million
Emp.: 12
Repair, Installation & Maintenance of Roofing Systems
N.A.I.C.S.: 238160
Joel T. Johnson (Pres)

P.J. DICK INCORPORATED
225 N Shore Dr, Pittsburgh, PA 15212
Tel.: (412) 807-2000   PA
Web Site: http://www.pjdick.com
Year Founded: 1979
Sales Range: $200-249.9 Million
Emp.: 4,000
Heavy Building Contractors
N.A.I.C.S.: 236220
Stephen M. Clark (Exec VP-Fin)
Clifford R. Rowe Jr. (CEO)
Bernie Kobosky (Mgr-Mktg)
Jeffrey D. Turconi (Pres)
Joseph J. Franceschini (VP-Safety)

Subsidiaries:

Innovative Construction Services (1)
225 North Shore Dr, Pittsburgh, PA 15212
Tel.: (412) 462-9300
Web Site: http://www.estimating.pjdick.com
Sales Range: $25-49.9 Million
Emp.: 250
Construction Services
N.A.I.C.S.: 236115

Lindy Paving, Inc. (1)
586 Northgate Cir, New Castle, PA 16105 **(100%)**
Tel.: (724) 652-9330
Web Site: http://www.lindypaving.com
Sales Range: $10-24.9 Million
Emp.: 30
Asphalt Paving Services

N.A.I.C.S.: 237310
Stephen M. Clark (Exec VP-Fin)
Clifford R. Rowe Jr. (CEO)
Vince P. Tutino (Pres)

P.J. Dick-Trumbull-Lindy - Homer City Plant (1)
1981 Route 119 Highway S, Homer City, PA 15748
Tel.: (724) 336-1492
Commercial Building Construction Services
N.A.I.C.S.: 236220

P.J. Dick-Trumbull-Lindy - Koppel Plant (1)
1811 Shenango Rd, New Galilee, PA 16141
Tel.: (724) 200-0009
Web Site: http://www.pjdick.com
Sales Range: $25-49.9 Million
Emp.: 5
Commercial Building Construction Services
N.A.I.C.S.: 236220
Paul Reiner (Gen Mgr)

P.J. Dick-Trumbull-Lindy - Neville Island Plant (1)
4500 Neville Rd, Pittsburgh, PA 15225
Tel.: (412) 264-6933
Commercial Building Construction Services
N.A.I.C.S.: 236220

P.J. Dick-Trumbull-Lindy - New Kensington Plant (1)
201 Industrial Blvd, New Kensington, PA 15068
Tel.: (724) 336-1491
Commercial Building Construction Services
N.A.I.C.S.: 236220

P.J. Dick-Trumbull-Lindy - Second Avenue Plant (1)
2340 2nd Ave, Pittsburgh, PA 15219
Tel.: (412) 281-4389
Emp.: 10
Commercial Building Construction Services
N.A.I.C.S.: 236220
Paul Reiner (Gen Mgr)

Trumball Corporation/P.J. Dick, Inc. (1)
87 Smiley Dr, Saint Albans, WV 25177-1532 **(100%)**
Tel.: (304) 755-6945
Web Site: http://www.trumbullcorp.com
Sales Range: $10-24.9 Million
Emp.: 5
Road Construction & Estimating
N.A.I.C.S.: 237310
Stephen M. Clark (Exec VP-Fin)
Clifford R. Rowe Jr. (CEO)
John P. Maffeo Jr. (Exec VP)

P.J. HAYES, INC.
5391 Lakewood Ranch Blvd N Ste 200, Sarasota, FL 34240
Tel.: (941) 954-1599
Web Site: http://www.tandemconstruction.com
Year Founded: 1980
Sales Range: $25-49.9 Million
Emp.: 20
Construction Management
N.A.I.C.S.: 236220
Peter J. Hayes (Founder & Pres)
Brian M. Leaver (Principal & Sr VP)
Nathan Renner (Sr Project Mgr)

P.J. HOERR, INC.
107 N Commerce Pl, Peoria, IL 61604-5285
Tel.: (309) 688-9567   DE
Web Site: http://www.pjhoerr.com
Year Founded: 1914
Sales Range: $75-99.9 Million
Emp.: 138
Commercial Building Construction Contractor
N.A.I.C.S.: 236220
Robert Hoerr (CEO)
John Moses (VP)
Mike Waibel (Project Mgr)
Susan Skinner (Controller)

P.P.C.

6176 E Molloy Rd, East Syracuse, NY 13057-1020
Tel.: (315) 431-7200 NY
Web Site: http://www.ppc-online.com
Year Founded: 1981
Sales Range: $75-99.9 Million
Emp.: 200
Mfr of Telecommunications Equipment
N.A.I.C.S.: 334220
John Mezzalingua (Chm & Pres)
Mike Stys (Controller)
Rick Haube (Dir-Mktg)
Hansns Sallur (VP-Mktg)

P.S. INTERNATIONAL INC
1414 Raleigh Rd Ste 205, Chapel Hill, NC 27517-8834
Tel.: (919) 933-7400 IN
Web Site: http://www.psinternational.net
Year Founded: 1971
Sales Range: $75-99.9 Million
Emp.: 60
International Trader of Agricultural Commodities
N.A.I.C.S.: 424490
Catherine M. Fields (Pres & Treas)
Melvin C. Fields (Chm & CEO)
Allan Waldron (Controller)
Jean-Christophe Scalia (VP-Sugar)

P.T. FERRO CONSTRUCTION CO.
700 Rowell Ave, Joliet, IL 60433-2562
Tel.: (815) 726-6284
Web Site: http://www.ptferro.com
Year Founded: 1991
Sales Range: $25-49.9 Million
Emp.: 75
Excavation Services
N.A.I.C.S.: 238910
John T. Ferro (Owner)

P.W. MINOR & SON, INC.
3 Treadeasy Ave, Batavia, NY 14020-3009
Tel.: (585) 343-1500 NY
Web Site: http://www.pwminor.com
Year Founded: 1921
Sales Range: $100-124.9 Million
Emp.: 150
Women's & Men's Therapeutic Footwear Mfr
N.A.I.C.S.: 316210
Wolcott Hinchey (CFO)
Maryl Bedenko (VP-Fin)
Henry H. Minor Jr. (Chm & CEO)

P/A INDUSTRIES, INC.
522 Cottage Grove Rd, Bloomfield, CT 06002-3111
Tel.: (860) 243-8306 CT
Web Site: http://www.pa.com
Year Founded: 1954
Sales Range: $50-74.9 Million
Emp.: 50
Coil-Handling Equipment Mfr
N.A.I.C.S.: 333519
Edward Morris (Pres)
Paul Werkheiher (Mgr-IT)
Wyman Jeanne (Coord-AR)
Jeanne Wyman (Coord-AR)

Subsidiaries:

P/A Bohemia s.r.o. (1)
Zapy 110, Brandys nad Labem, 250 01, Czech Republic
Tel.: (420) 326906122
Web Site: http://www.pabohemia.cz
Sales Range: $10-24.9 Million
Emp.: 2
Metal Forming Equipment Distr
N.A.I.C.S.: 423830
Jaroslav Simek (Mng Dir)

P/A Brasil Ltda (1)
Rua Katia 134-Pq Sao George, Cotia, 06708-130, Sao Paulo, Brazil
Tel.: (55) 1146175497
Automation Equipment Mfr
N.A.I.C.S.: 811310

P/A GmbH (1)
Morikestr 30/2, 71636, Ludwigsburg, Germany
Tel.: (49) 71419744780
Web Site: http://www.pa.com
Automobile Parts Mfr
N.A.I.C.S.: 336390

P/A Industries (1)
522 Cottage Grove Rd, Bloomfield, CT 06002-3111
Tel.: (860) 243-8306
Web Site: http://www.pa.com
Sales Range: $10-24.9 Million
Emp.: 35
Forging Equipment Mfr
N.A.I.C.S.: 333519
Jerome Finn (Pres)

P/A Industries-Metal Stamping Equipment (1)
522 Cottage Grove Rd, Bloomfield, CT 06002
Tel.: (860) 243-8306
Web Site: http://www.pa.com
Sales Range: $10-24.9 Million
Emp.: 30
Metal Forming Equipment Mfr
N.A.I.C.S.: 333519
Jerome E. Finn (Owner)

PROMAK PRES OTOMASYON MAK. San. Ve Tic. Ltd. (1)
Perpa Ticaret Merkezi B Blok K11 No 1987 Okmeydani, Istanbul, Turkiye
Tel.: (90) 2123208510
Web Site: http://www.promakmakina.com
Automation Equipment Mfr
N.A.I.C.S.: 336110

P1 GROUP, INC.
13605 W 96 Terrace, Lenexa, KS 66219
Tel.: (913) 529-5000
Web Site: http://www.p1group.com
Sales Range: $10-24.9 Million
Emp.: 1,000
Plumbing, Heating & Air-Conditioning Contractors
N.A.I.C.S.: 238220
Smitty Belcher (CEO)
Bruce Belcher (COO)
Mike Belcher (Co-Pres)
Kollin Knox (Co-Pres)
Gloria Keating (CFO)
Chris Champagne (Mgr-Ops)
Steve Smith (VP)

P2 CAPITAL PARTNERS, LLC
590 Madison Ave 25th Fl, New York, NY 10022
Tel.: (212) 508-5500 DE
Web Site: http://www.p2capital.com
Year Founded: 2006
Privater Equity Firm
N.A.I.C.S.: 523999
Alex Silver (Partner)
Kareem Hammad (Partner)

Subsidiaries:

Blackhawk Network Holdings, Inc. (1)
6220 Stoneridge Mall Rd, Pleasanton, CA 94582
Tel.: (925) 226-9990
Web Site: https://www.blackhawknetwork.com
Sales Range: $1-4.9 Billion
Emp.: 3,000
Other Financial Vehicles
N.A.I.C.S.: 525990
Stewart Rigby (VP-Asia Pacific)
David Tate (Sr VP-US Bus)
Joan Lockie (Chief Acctg Officer, VP & Controller)
Teri Llach (CMO)
Kirsten Richesson (Gen Counsel)
Talbott Roche (Pres & CEO)
Steve Dekker (Mng Dir-Canada & Latin America)
Owen Sagness (Gen Mgr-Achievers)
Patrick Cronin (VP-Fin Plng, Analysis & IR)
David Jones (Gen Mgr-Digital & Incentive Div)
Jonathan Kenny (Mng Dir-Europe West)
Christian Lindner (Mng Dir-Europe East)
Amie Miller (Grp VP-Ops)
Nick Samurkas (COO)
Nikhil Sathe (CTO)
Helena Mao (VP-Product Strategy-Global)
Leila Pourhashemi (CIO & VP-Tech Bus Ops)
Brett Narlinger (Head-Commerce-Global)
Cory Gaines (Chief Product Officer)
David McLaughlin (CFO)
Jay Jaffin (CMO)
Suzanne Kinner (VP-HR)

Subsidiary (Non-US):

Achievers Corp. (2)
99 Atlantic Ave Ste 700, Toronto, M6K 3J8, ON, Canada
Tel.: (888) 622-3343
Web Site: http://www.achievers.com
Electronic Financial Transaction Processing Services
N.A.I.C.S.: 522320
Jeff Cates (CEO)

Subsidiary (Domestic):

Achievers LLC (2)
PO Box 122869, Fort Worth, TX 76121
Tel.: (817) 900-9489
Emp.: 12
Electronic Financial Transaction Processing Services
N.A.I.C.S.: 522320

Subsidiary (Non-US):

Blackhawk Network (Australia) Pty Ltd. (2)
Suite 202 6a Glen Street, Milsons Point, Sydney, 2061, NSW, Australia
Tel.: (61) 294602346
Web Site: https://blackhawknetwork.com
Prepaid Payment Network Utilizing Proprietary Technology Offering Prepaid Gift, Telecom & Debit Cards In Physical & Electronic Forms
N.A.I.C.S.: 522320

Subsidiary (Domestic):

Blackhawk Network California, Inc. (2)
5918 Stoneridge Mall Rd, Pleasanton, CA 94588
Tel.: (925) 226-9990
Web Site: http://www.giftcardmall.com
Prepaid & Payments Gift Cards Network Products
N.A.I.C.S.: 522320

CashStar, Inc. (2)
25 Pearl St, Portland, ME 04101
Tel.: (207) 549-2200
Digital Gift Card Solutions
N.A.I.C.S.: 541519

DigitalGlue (2)
41601 Date St, Murrieta, CA 92562
Tel.: (949) 388-9078
Web Site: http://www.digitalglue.com
Electronic Equipment Services
N.A.I.C.S.: 423690
Tim Anderson (Co-Founder, CEO & CTO)
Sean Busby (Co-Founder & Pres)
Dave Gordon (VP-Engrg)
John McCluskey (Dir-Sls)
Jon Mott (Dir-Software Dev)
Mark Reynolds (Dir-Ops)

Subsidiary (Non-US):

GVS Gift Voucher Shop Limited (2)
Unit 2 Swords Business Park, PO Box 8942, Swords, Dublin, Ireland
Tel.: (353) 1 8708100
Web Site: http://www.giftvouchershop.com
Gift Voucher Distr
N.A.I.C.S.: 459420
Michael Dawson (Founder & CEO)

Hawk Incentives Holdings Limited (2)
Westside London Road Hemel, Hemel Hempstead, HP3 9TD, Herts, United Kingdom
Tel.: (44) 2074198100
Professional Services
N.A.I.C.S.: 561990

Subsidiary (Non-US):

Grass Roots SL (3)
Calle Alcala 54 3 Derecha, 28014, Madrid, Spain
Tel.: (34) 915218338
Web Site: http://www.grassroots.es
Employee & Customer Engagement Solutions
N.A.I.C.S.: 541910

Subsidiary (Domestic):

OmniCard, LLC (2)
680 Andersen Dr Ste 430, Pittsburgh, PA 15220
Tel.: (866) 353-4877
Electronic Financial Transaction Processing Services
N.A.I.C.S.: 522320

SVM, LP (2)
3727 Ventura Dr, Arlington Heights, IL 60004
Tel.: (877) 300-1786
Prepaid Gift Cards Distr
N.A.I.C.S.: 541611
Marshall Reavis (Founder & CEO)
Jim Speir (VP-Sls & Mktg)
Jim Leroux (Pres)

Blount International, Inc. (1)
4909 SE International Way, Portland, OR 97222-4679
Tel.: (503) 653-8881
Web Site: http://www.blount.com
Sales Range: $800-899.9 Million
Emp.: 1,200
Industrial & Outdoor Power Cutting Equipment Mfr
N.A.I.C.S.: 332994
David A. Willmott (Pres & COO)
Chad E. Paulson (Gen Counsel, Sec & VP)
Dave P. Gillrie (Sr VP-Global Sls & Mktg-FLAG Div)
David K. Parrish (Sr VP-Global Supply Chain)
Kevin M. Trepa (CIO & Sr VP-Global Plng & Logistics)
Valdir R. Viana (VP-FLAG Mfg Ops)
Todd H. Hall (Pres-Farm, Ranch & Agriculture Div-Woods Equipment)
Bob Hickson (CFO)
Paul Tonnesen (CEO)

Subsidiary (Domestic):

Blount, Inc. (2)
4909 SE International Way, Portland, OR 97222-4679
Tel.: (503) 653-8881
Web Site: http://www.oregonproducts.com
Emp.: 3,000
Outdoor Power Equipment & Tools Mfr & Marketer
N.A.I.C.S.: 333112

Subsidiary (Non-US):

Blount Europe, S.A. (3)
Rue Emile Francqui 5, 1435, Mont-Saint-Guibert, Belgium
Tel.: (32) 10301111
Web Site: http://www.oregonproducts.eu
Cutting Systems & Farm Equipment Mfr
N.A.I.C.S.: 333515

Blount GmbH (3)
Lise-Meitner-Strasse 4, 70736, Fellbach, Germany
Tel.: (49) 71130033400
Web Site: http://www.oregonproducts.de
Industrial Garden & Forestry Cutting Product Mfr
N.A.I.C.S.: 333515
Ralf Geiger (Mng Dir)
Jochen Weber (Mng Dir)

Blount Industrial Ltda. (3)
Rua Emilio Romani 1630 CIC, CEP 81460-020, Curitiba, Parana, Brazil
Tel.: (55) 4121695800
Web Site: http://www.oregonbrasil.com.br
Cutting Chains, Bars & Accessories Mfr

P2 CAPITAL PARTNERS, LLC

P2 Capital Partners, LLC—(Continued)
N.A.I.C.S.: 332216

Blount Japan, Inc. (3)
Queens Tower C 12F 2-3-5 Minatomirai, Nishi-Ku, Yokohama, 220-6212, Japan
Tel.: (81) 456824433
Web Site: http://www.oregonchain.jp
Cutting Chain, Bars & Machine Tool Acessories Mfr
N.A.I.C.S.: 333515
Junko Ito (Dir)

Blount UK Ltd. (3)
Unit 3 Formal Business Park Northway Lane, Tewkesbury, GL20 8GY, Gloucestershire, United Kingdom
Tel.: (44) 1684297600
Web Site: http://www.oregonproducts.co.uk
Industrial, Garden & Forestry Cutting Products Mfr
N.A.I.C.S.: 333515

Oregon Distribution Ltd (3)
505 Edinburgh Road North, Guelph, N1H 6L4, ON, Canada
Tel.: (519) 822-6870
Web Site: http://www.oregonproducts.com
Industrial Machinery & Equipment Mfr & Distr
N.A.I.C.S.: 333998

Subsidiary (Domestic):

Blount Canada Ltd. (4)
505 Edinburgh Road North, Guelph, N1H 6L4, ON, Canada
Tel.: (519) 822-6870
Web Site: http://www.oregonproducts.com
Cutting Chain Bar & Accessory Mfr
N.A.I.C.S.: 332216

Subsidiary (Non-US):

Svenska Blount AB (3)
PO Box 1104, 432 15, Varberg, Sweden
Tel.: (46) 340645480
Web Site: http://www.oregonproducts.se
Industrial Machinery & Equipment Distr
N.A.I.C.S.: 423830

Subsidiary (Domestic):

SpeeCo, Inc. (2)
2606 S Illinois Route 2, Oregon, IL 61061
Tel.: (800) 525-8322
Web Site: http://www.speeco.com
Farm Accessories & Equipment Mfr
N.A.I.C.S.: 333111

Woods Equipment Company (2)
2606 S Illinois Rte 2, Oregon, IL 61061
Tel.: (815) 732-2141
Web Site: http://www.woodsequipment.com
Emp.: 550
Agricultural & Construction Machinery Mfr
N.A.I.C.S.: 333111
Angela Kay Larson (VP-Mktg)

P2BINVESTOR INC.
1120 Lincoln St Ste 100, Denver, CO 80203
Tel.: (720) 361-1500
Web Site: http://www.p2bi.com
Year Founded: 2012
Sales Range: $10-24.9 Million
Emp.: 31
Financial Management Services
N.A.I.C.S.: 541611
Krista Morgan (CEO)
James Shehigian (Pres)
Catherine Stanton (COO & Gen Counsel)
Cyd Petre (Chief Credit Officer)
Jim Ray (VP-Engrg)

P2P STAFFING CORP.
5810 Coral Ridge Dr Ste 250, Coral Springs, FL 33076
Tel.: (954) 656-8600 FL
Web Site: http://www.tekpartners.com
Year Founded: 2002
Sales Range: $50-74.9 Million
Emp.: 105
Technology Recruiting & Staffing Services

N.A.I.C.S.: 561311
Harris Katz (Co-Founder & Co-CEO)
Vito Scutero (Co-Founder & Co-CEO)
Jay Bevilacqua (Exec VP)
Jerald Sowell (Exec VP)
Mario Muoio (VP-Fin & Ops)
Alex Garcia (Dir-HR)
Emily Prno (Dir-Corp Recruiting)
Milgrim Bello (Dir-Strategic Mktg)
Anthony Sammartino (Sr VP-Solutions)
James A. Barret II (Sr Dir-Talent & Process)

Subsidiaries:

TekPartners (1)
5810 Coral Ridge Dr Ste 250, Coral Springs, FL 33076
Tel.: (954) 656-8600
Web Site: http://www.tekpartners.com
Sales Range: $50-74.9 Million
Emp.: 50
Technology Recruiting & Staffing Services
N.A.I.C.S.: 561311
Harris Katz (Co-Founder & Co-CEO)
Vito Scutero (Co-Founder & Co-CEO)
Jay Bevilacqua (Exec VP)
Brian Scutero (Mgr-Market)
Daniel Fink (Dir-Delivery)
James A. Barrett (Sr Dir-Talent & Process Dev)
Milgrim Bello (Dir-Strategic Mktg)
Alex Garcia (Dir-HR)
Emily Prno (Sr Dir-Talent Acquisition & Dev)
Gregg Straus (CFO & Exec VP)

P3I INC.
77 Main St, Hopkinton, MA 01748
Tel.: (508) 435-7882
Web Site: http://www.p3i-inc.com
Year Founded: 2000
Sales Range: $10-24.9 Million
Emp.: 198
Management Consulting Services
N.A.I.C.S.: 541611
Jose G. Ramos (Dir-Tech)
Janice P. Guy (Founder, Pres & CEO)
Catherine A. Dowling (VP-Fin)
Patricia A. Thomas-Fuller (VP-Bus Dev)
Roger L. Goudreau (VP-Ops)
Kathryn M. Gallucci (Dir-Tech-Comml Team & Process Grp)
Barbara A. Gilroy (Dir-Tech-Langley Programs)
Michael G. Lademan (Dir-Tech-Sys Acq Grp)
John L. Picklesimer (Dir-Tech-Enterprise Sys Grp)
Catherine R. Hunter (Dir-Tech-Trng Grp)

P3S CORPORATION
13750 San Pedro Ste 640, San Antonio, TX 78232
Tel.: (210) 496-6934
Web Site: http://www.p3scorp.com
Year Founded: 2005
Sales Range: $10-24.9 Million
Emp.: 221
Government Services
N.A.I.C.S.: 921190
John Mabry (CIO)
Paul Doolittle (VP)
MaryEllen Londrie (Owner)

P4G CAPITAL MANAGEMENT, LLC
150 California St 21st Fl, San Francisco, CA 94111
Tel.: (415) 510-2160 DE
Web Site: http://www.p4gcap.com
Privater Equity Firm
N.A.I.C.S.: 523999
Rachel E. Lehman (Co-Founder & Mng Partner)

Hugh Browne (Co-Founder & Mng Dir)
Dawn Radel (Mng Dir-Fin & Compliance)
Lee Rowey (Mng Dir)
Zach Jackson (VP)
Nat Bacon (VP)
Mason Duke (VP)
DJ Marshall (VP)
Sonya Petroff (Mgr-Office)

Subsidiaries:

Aero Components, LLC (1)
5124 Kaltenbrun Rd, Fort Worth, TX 76119-6400
Tel.: (817) 572-3003
Web Site: http://www.aero-components.com
Aircraft Components & Parts Mfr
N.A.I.C.S.: 336412
Jon Williams (CEO)
Mike Andrews (Program Mgr)
Vecki Blake (Owner)

Fore Machine Company, Inc. (1)
5933 Eden Dr, Fort Worth, TX 76117
Tel.: (817) 834-6251
Web Site: http://www.foremachine.com
Machining, Assembly, Bonding & Metal Processing
N.A.I.C.S.: 332999

Unique Elevator Interiors, Inc. (1)
1930 N Loop Rd, Alameda, CA 94502
Tel.: (510) 777-9050
Web Site: http://www.uniqueelevator.com
Plumbing, Heating & Air-Conditioning Contractors
N.A.I.C.S.: 238220
Thomas Irion (Pres & CEO)
Tim Crawford (VP)

PA ACQUISITION CORP.
980 Atlantic Ave Ste 103, Alameda, CA 94501
Tel.: (510) 747-1800
Web Site: http://www.partyamerica.com
Rev.: $22,000,000
Emp.: 70
Party Supplies
N.A.I.C.S.: 459420
Marty Allen (Pres & CEO)
Alice Tang (VP)
Mark Mumm (Controller)

Subsidiaries:

New Paper LLC (1)
12810 Elm Creek Blvd, Maple Grove, MN 55369-9406
Tel.: (763) 494-0065
Sales Range: $10-24.9 Million
Emp.: 11
Gift, Novelty & Souvenir Shops
N.A.I.C.S.: 459420
Michael A. Anderson (Gen Mgr)

PA DISTRIBUTION LLC
4310 W 5th Ave, Eugene, OR 97402
Tel.: (541) 485-1406
Web Site: http://www.pa-dist.com
Year Founded: 1959
Crafting Items Distr
N.A.I.C.S.: 424120
Cynthia Morris (Owner)

PA INC.
6626 Gulf Fwy, Houston, TX 77087
Tel.: (713) 570-4900
Web Site: http://www.painc.com
Sales Range: $10-24.9 Million
Emp.: 24
Pipes Valves & Fittings
N.A.I.C.S.: 423830
Cathy Galloway (VP)

PA PUBS INC.
2433 Morgantown Rd Ste 202, Reading, PA 19607-9692
Tel.: (610) 372-3000
Rev.: $10,600,000
Emp.: 14

Bar (Drinking Places)
N.A.I.C.S.: 722410
Michael Moore (VP)
Joseph M. Eways II (Pres)

PA-TED SPRING CO. INC.
137 Vincent P Kelly Rd, Bristol, CT 06010
Tel.: (860) 582-6368
Web Site: http://www.pa-ted.com
Sales Range: $10-24.9 Million
Emp.: 70
Wire Springs
N.A.I.C.S.: 332613
Dominic Robero (Co-Pres)
Eric Tedesco (Co-Pres)

PAACO AUTOMOTIVE GROUP LP
3200 E Randol Mill Rd, Arlington, TX 76011-6838
Tel.: (877) 810-4555
Web Site: http://publicautotx.com
Year Founded: 1992
Used Car Dealership Owner & Operator
N.A.I.C.S.: 441120
Alvin Johnson (CFO)

PAAMCO PRISMA HOLDINGS, LLC
19540 Jamboree Rd Ste 400, Irvine, CA 92612
Tel.: (949) 261-4900 DE
Web Site: http://www.paamcoprisma.com
Holding Company
N.A.I.C.S.: 551112
Jane Melissa Buchan (Co-Founder & CEO)
Judith F. Posnikoff (Mgr)
Girish Reddy (Co-Founder)

Subsidiaries:

Pacific Alternative Asset Management Company, LLC (1)
19540 Jamboree Rd Ste 400, Irvine, CA 92612
Tel.: (949) 261-4900
Web Site: http://www.paamco.com
Limited-Service Restaurants
N.A.I.C.S.: 722513
Carrie McCabe (Mng Dir)

Prisma Capital Partners LP (1)
9 W 57th St Ste 2600, New York, NY 10119
Tel.: (212) 590-0800
Web Site:
  http://www.prisma.paamcoprisma.com
Emp.: 70
Investment Management Service
N.A.I.C.S.: 523940
Girish Reddy (CEO)

Subsidiary (Non-US):

Prisma Capital Management International LLP (2)
100 Pall Mall, London, SW1Y 5NQ, United Kingdom
Tel.: (44) 2075935388
Web Site: http://prisma.paamcoprisma.com
Investment Management Service
N.A.I.C.S.: 523940

PABCO FLUID POWER COMPANY
2301 Windsor Ct, Addison, IL 60101
Tel.: (630) 317-2700 OH
Web Site: http://www.sun-source.com
Year Founded: 1962
Sales Range: $25-49.9 Million
Emp.: 600
Mfr of Custom Hydraulic & Pneumatic Cylinders
N.A.I.C.S.: 423830
Justin Jacobi (CEO)

COMPANIES

Subsidiaries:

Ohio Valley Flooring (1)
5555 Murray Rd, Cincinnati, OH 45227-2707
Tel.: (513) 561-3399
Web Site: http://www.ovf.com
Sales Range: $25-49.9 Million
Emp.: 200
Wholesalers In Flooring
N.A.I.C.S.: 423220
Al Hurt *(Pres & CEO)*

PAC STRAPPING PRODUCTS INC.
307 National Rd, Exton, PA 19341
Tel.: (610) 363-8805
Web Site:
  http://www.strapsolutions.com
Year Founded: 1982
Sales Range: $10-24.9 Million
Emp.: 40
Mfr of Plastic & Steel Strapping Products
N.A.I.C.S.: 326199
Peter J. Silvester *(VP)*
Chrissy Poth *(Controller)*
Edwin A. Brownley Jr. *(Pres)*

PAC WORLDWIDE CORPORATION
15435 NE 92nd St, Redmond, WA 98052-3516
Tel.: (425) 885-9330 WA
Web Site: http://www.pac.com
Year Founded: 1975
Sales Range: $25-49.9 Million
Emp.: 500
Packaging Solutions For Air Carrier & E-Commerce Industries; Manufactures Envelopes, Plastic Padded Mailers & Paperboard Mailers
N.A.I.C.S.: 424990
Matthew Konyn *(COO)*
Steve Foster *(Pres)*

Subsidiaries:

PAC National Inc. (1)
15435 NE 92nd St, Redmond, WA 98052-3516
Tel.: (425) 885-9330
Web Site: http://www.pac.com
Sales Range: $25-49.9 Million
Emp.: 28
Packaging Solutions For Air Carrier & E-Commerce Industries; Manufactures Envelopes, Plastic Padded Mailers & Paperboard Mailers
N.A.I.C.S.: 322220
Phillip A. Boshaw *(Chm)*
James Boshaw *(VP-Ops)*

Subsidiary (Non-US):

PAC Worldwide Mexico, S. de R.L. de C.V. (2)
Av Fulton 13 Zona Industrial Valle de Oro, San Juan del Rio, 76802, Queretaro, Mexico
Tel.: (52) 4271019400
Web Site: http://mx.pac.com
Plastic & Cardboard Packaging Mfr & Distr
N.A.I.C.S.: 326112

PAC-12 CONFERENCE
360 3rd St 3rd Fl, San Francisco, CA 94107
Tel.: (415) 580-4200 CA
Web Site: http://www.pac-12.com
Year Founded: 1959
Sales Range: $300-349.9 Million
Emp.: 186
Athlete Support Services
N.A.I.C.S.: 813990
Will Hunter *(VP-Ops)*
Danette Leighton *(CMO)*
Jamie Zaninovich *(COO)*
Anna Roberts *(Sr Dir-HR)*
Dave Hirsch *(VP-Comm)*

Woodie Dixon *(Gen Counsel & Sr VP-Bus Affairs)*
Laura Hazlett *(CFO)*
Andrew Walker *(VP-Pub Affairs & Head-Comm)*
Mark Shuken *(Pres-Cable Networks)*

PAC-WEST TELECOMM, INC.
4210 Coronado Ave, Stockton, CA 95204
Tel.: (209) 926-3300 CA
Web Site: http://www.pacwest.com
Year Founded: 1980
Sales Range: $75-99.9 Million
Emp.: 296
Wholesale Communications Infrastructure Services
N.A.I.C.S.: 517111
Todd Wallace *(COO)*
Jennifer Eubanks *(CFO)*

PACAL LLC
2500 W County Rd B, Saint Paul, MN 55113
Tel.: (651) 631-1111 MN
Web Site: http://www.pacal.com
Year Founded: 1891
Sales Range: Less than $1 Million
Emp.: 100
Fabricator of Steel Parts & Sub Assemblies
N.A.I.C.S.: 333120
Ervin F. Kamm *(Pres & CEO)*
Chris Hefty *(Mgr-Pur)*

Subsidiaries:

PACAL Industries, LLC (1)
2500 County Rd B W, Roseville, MN 55113
Tel.: (651) 628-6331
Emp.: 20
Steel Fabrication Services
N.A.I.C.S.: 331110
Ervin F. Kamm *(CEO)*
Jim Hartmann *(Dir-Core Sls)*

PACCESS LLC
700 NE Multnomah Ste 1600, Portland, OR 97232
Tel.: (503) 230-4890 DE
Year Founded: 1995
Sales Range: $10-24.9 Million
Emp.: 60
Business Services
N.A.I.C.S.: 541990
Scott Melkerson *(VP-Global Pkg Solutions)*
Jim Toms *(VP-Strategic Accts)*
Nina Palludan *(VP-IT)*
Wendy Wang *(VP-Asia)*
John Davidson *(Pres & CEO)*

PACE COMMUNICATIONS INC.
1301 Carolina St, Greensboro, NC 27401-1090
Tel.: (336) 378-6065 NC
Web Site: http://www.paceco.com
Year Founded: 1973
Rev.: $75,000,000
Emp.: 250
Publisher of Periodicals
N.A.I.C.S.: 513120
Bonnie McElveen-Hunter *(Founder & CEO)*
Leigh Ann Klee *(CFO & COO)*
Kevin Briody *(Chief Strategy Officer & Sr VP)*
Jason Whiting *(Pres)*
Brian Bowen *(VP-Visual Innovation)*
Gordon Locke *(CMO & Exec VP)*
Nicole Martin *(VP-Strategy, Media & Analytics)*

Subsidiaries:

Legacy Publications Inc. (1)
1301 Carolina St, Greensboro, NC 27401-1090
Tel.: (336) 378-6065

Web Site:
  http://www.legacypublications.com
Sales Range: $10-24.9 Million
Emp.: 4
Book Publishing
N.A.I.C.S.: 513130
Bonnie McElveen Hunter *(Pres & CEO)*

PACE COMPUTER SOLUTIONS INC
10480 Little Patuxent Pkwy Ste 760, Columbia, MD 21044
Tel.: (443) 539-0290
Web Site: http://www.pace-solutionsinc.com
Year Founded: 2003
Sales Range: $10-24.9 Million
Emp.: 83
Computer & Software Stores
N.A.I.C.S.: 449210
Vasubabu Maddisetty *(CEO)*
Ravi Chitkara *(Engr-Software)*

PACE EDITIONS INC.
44 W 18th St Fl 5, New York, NY 10011
Tel.: (212) 219-8000
Web Site: http://www.paceprints.com
Sales Range: $25-49.9 Million
Emp.: 25
Publisher of Fine Art Limited Edition Prints; Operator of Art Gallery
N.A.I.C.S.: 323111
Richard Solomon *(Pres)*

PACE ELECTRONICS INC.
3582 Technology Dr NW, Rochester, MN 55901-7687
Tel.: (507) 288-1853
Web Site: http://www.pacemso.com
Year Founded: 1962
Sales Range: $10-24.9 Million
Emp.: 31
Electronic Parts
N.A.I.C.S.: 423690
Opie Williams *(Pres)*

PACE ENGINEERING INC.
4800 Beidler Rd, Willoughby, OH 44094
Tel.: (440) 942-1234
Web Site: http://www.paceparts.net
Year Founded: 1984
Sales Range: $10-24.9 Million
Emp.: 100
Mfr of Machined Components for Construction, Mining, Drilling, Paving & Logging OEM's
N.A.I.C.S.: 333320
Craig R. Wallace *(Chm)*

PACE ENGINEERS, INC.
11255 Kirkland Way Ste 300, Kirkland, 98033, WA
Tel.: (425) 827-2014
Web Site:
  https://www.paceengrs.com
Emp.: 100
Engineering Services
N.A.I.C.S.: 541330
Ken Nilsen *(Pres)*

Subsidiaries:

C E S N W Inc (1)
15573 Bangy Rd, Lake Oswego, OR 97035
Tel.: (503) 968-6655
Web Site: http://www.cesnw.com
Rev.: $1,600,000
Emp.: 15
Engineering Services
N.A.I.C.S.: 541330
Carl Jenson *(Pres)*

PACE INC.
255 Air Tool Dr, Southern Pines, NC 28387
Tel.: (301) 490-9860

Web Site:
  http://www.paceworldwide.com
Year Founded: 1958
Sales Range: $10-24.9 Million
Emp.: 150
Electrical Equipment & Supply Mfr
N.A.I.C.S.: 334419

Subsidiaries:

PACE Europe, Ltd. (1)
11 Holdom Avenue, Bletchley, Milton Keynes, MK1 1QU, United Kingdom (100%)
Tel.: (44) 1908277666
Web Site: http://www.paceworldwide.com
Sales Range: $10-24.9 Million
Emp.: 5
Electric Equipment Mfr
N.A.I.C.S.: 335999
Eric Siegel *(Pres)*

PACE INDUSTRIES INC.
2545 W Polk St, Chicago, IL 60612
Tel.: (312) 226-5500
Web Site:
  http://www.pacekitchens.com
Rev.: $28,000,000
Emp.: 120
Wood Bathroom Vanities
N.A.I.C.S.: 337110
James Palka *(Pres)*
Richard Bontkowski *(VP)*
David Mathews *(Controller)*

PACE MOTOR LINES INC.
1425 Honeyspot Road Ext, Stratford, CT 06615
Tel.: (203) 366-3881
Web Site: http://www.pacemotor.com
Rev.: $15,500,000
Emp.: 10
Trucking Except Local
N.A.I.C.S.: 484121
Patrick Pacelli *(Pres)*
John Mollica *(Mgr-Terminal)*

PACE ORGANIZATION OF RHODE ISLAND
225 Chapman St, Providence, RI 02905
Tel.: (401) 490-6566 RI
Web Site: http://www.pace-ri.org
Year Founded: 2004
Sales Range: $10-24.9 Million
Emp.: 93
Elder Care Services
N.A.I.C.S.: 624120
Cheryl A. Dexter *(VP-Quality & Compliance)*
Kelly A. Lee *(VP-Community Engagement & Enrollment)*
Lynda M. Gilbert *(CFO)*
Chris Woulfe *(Treas)*
Joan Kwiatkowski *(CEO)*
Meredith Eckel *(Sec)*
Diana Franchitto *(Vice Chm)*
Tsewang Gyurmey *(Chief Medical Officer)*

PACE POLYETHYLENE MFG. CO. INC.
46 Calbert St, Harrison, NY 10528
Tel.: (914) 381-3000 NY
Rev.: $11,600,000
Emp.: 20
Unsupported Plastics Film & Sheet
N.A.I.C.S.: 326113
Stan Nathanson *(Pres)*

PACE PRESS, INC.
1 Caesar Pl, Moonachie, NJ 07074-1702
Tel.: (201) 935-7711 NY
Web Site: http://www.pacepress.com
Year Founded: 1914
Sales Range: $75-99.9 Million
Emp.: 92

PACE PRESS, INC.

U.S. PRIVATE

Pace Press, Inc.—Continued
Provider of Lithographic Printing Services
N.A.I.C.S.: 323111
Norma Villalobos (Controller)
Charles Licata (Mgr-Production)

PACE RESOURCES, INC.
140 E Market St, York, PA 17401
Tel.: (717) 852-1300   PA
Web Site: http://www.pace-resources.com
Year Founded: 1946
Sales Range: $150-199.9 Million
Emp.: 506
Holding Company
N.A.I.C.S.: 541330
Scott Thomassy (CFO & VP)
Kristen Evans (VP-HR)
Silvia H. Dugan (Chm)

Subsidiaries:

Bucharth Horn Inc.   (1)
445 W Philadelphia St, York, PA
17401-3383   (100%)
Tel.: (717) 852-1400
Web Site: http://www.bucharthorn.com
Sales Range: $25-49.9 Million
Emp.: 250
Consulting Engineer Architect & Planner Services
N.A.I.C.S.: 541330
Charles L. Kinney (COO)
Jay Sabo (VP-Northern Transportation Ops)
Brian S. Funkhouser (Pres & CEO)
Scott E. Russell (Sr VP-Water Resources)

Division (Domestic):

Bucharth Horn Inc   (2)
445 W Philadelphia St, York, PA 17404-3340
Tel.: (717) 852-1350
Web Site: http://www.bh-ba.com
Rev.: $35,000,000
Emp.: 200
Commercial Printing, Lithographic
N.A.I.C.S.: 541330
Matthew Todaro (Asst Dir-Construction Svcs Div)
Alexis Isenberg (Dir-Client Svcs & Project Mgr)
Ed Dimond (Dir-Environmental)
Jeff Culton (Dir-Water Resources)
Dominic Fekete (Engr-Highway)
Bryan Ondrasik (Engr-Mechanical)
Phil DePoe (Engr-Pro)
Jeffrey Kaminski (Engr-Structural)
Stephanie Schaefer (Reg Mgr)
Charles Kinney (Sr VP)
Brian Funkhouser (Pres & CEO)

Print-O-Stat, Inc.   (1)
1011 W Market St, York, PA
17404-3411   (100%)
Tel.: (717) 854-7821
Web Site: http://www.printostat.com
Sales Range: $25-49.9 Million
Emp.: 115
Retail Engineering Supplies; Office Printing
N.A.I.C.S.: 423490
John Horn (VP-Mktg)
Silvia Dugan (Pres & CEO)
Randy Byrd (VP-Svcs & Sys Support)
Irene Shipe (VP-Sls Support & Admin)
Bill Hawthorne (Territory Mgr)
Ann Suit (Mgr-Ops)
Danielle Langhauser (Mgr-Ops)
Michelle Frey (Coord-Customer Rels)
Russ E. Horn III (Exec VP)

PACE SUBURBAN BUS
550 W Algonquin Rd, Arlington Heights, IL 60005-4412
Tel.: (847) 364-7223
Web Site: http://www.pacebus.com
Year Founded: 1984
Sales Range: $75-99.9 Million
Emp.: 1,300
Local & Suburban Transit Bus Services
N.A.I.C.S.: 485113

Richard Kwasneski (Chm)
Rocky Donahue (Interim Exec Dir)

PACE SUPPLY CORP.
3033 Dutton Ave, Santa Rosa, CA 95407-7888
Tel.: (707) 545-7101   CA
Web Site: http://www.pacesupply.com
Year Founded: 1994
Sales Range: $10-24.9 Million
Emp.: 97
Plumbing Fixtures, Equipment & Supplies
N.A.I.C.S.: 423720
Ted M. Green (CEO)
Kelly Hubley (VP-Ops)

PACE SYSTEMS, INC.
2040 Corporate Ln, Naperville, IL 60563
Tel.: (630) 395-2260
Web Site: http://www.pace-systems.com
Year Founded: 1983
Sales Range: $25-49.9 Million
Emp.: 50
Computer Systems Integration
N.A.I.C.S.: 541512
Wayne Liu (Pres & CEO)
Ephrain Brantley (Engr-AV)
Prorwicz Gene (Dir-Special Sys)
Frank Provenzano (Mgr-Svcs Delivery)
Punahele Tannehill (Engr-Sys)
Amy Anderson (Acct Mgr)
Debra Doody (Office Mgr)
Steve Mancione (VP-Special Projects Sls)
Mike Jacoby (Engr-Sys)
Thomas Hubbard Jr. (Dir-Ops)

PACELINE EQUITY PARTNERS LLC
3625 N Hall St Ste 900, Dallas, TX 75219
Tel.: (469) 405-0910
Web Site: http://www.pacelineequity.com
Year Founded: 2018
Private Equity Firm
N.A.I.C.S.: 523999
Samuel Loughlin (CEO)
Leigh Sansone (Chief Investment Officer)
Sterling Donnelly (Head-IR)

Subsidiaries:

AHF, LLC   (1)
3840 Hempland Rd, Mountville, PA 17554
Tel.: (717) 251-1060
Web Site: http://www.AHFProducts.com
Solid Wood, Engineered Wood & Flooring Products Mfr & Distr
N.A.I.C.S.: 321999
Brian Carson (CEO)

Subsidiary (Domestic):

Crossville, Inc.   (2)
349 Sweeney Dr, Crossville, TN 38555
Tel.: (931) 484-2110
Web Site: http://www.crossvilleinc.com
Sales Range: $25-49.9 Million
Emp.: 300
Tiles Mfr
N.A.I.C.S.: 327110
Sam Dryden (VP-Mfg)
Craig Miller (Dir-R&D)
Jane Franklin (Mgr-HR)
Greg Mather (Pres & CEO)
Tom Kettering (Dir-Sls-Midwest/East)
Anthony Coggins (Dir-Sls-West/Mountain)

Progress Rail Equipment Leasing Corporation   (1)
15173NRd, Fenton, MI 48430
Tel.: (810) 714-4626
Web Site: http://www.progressrail.com
Industrial Machinery & Equipment Leasing Services

N.A.I.C.S.: 532490
Randy Chubaty (Mgr-Sls-Natl)

PACELINE, INC.
10737 Independence Pointe Pkwy, Matthews, NC 28105
Tel.: (704) 290-5007
Web Site: http://paceline.com
Year Founded: 1985
Medical Fabric Mfr
N.A.I.C.S.: 314999
David Glontz (Dir-Sls)
Joe Davant (Owner, Pres & CEO)

PACEMAKER STEEL AND PIPING CO.
501 Main St, Utica, NY 13501
Tel.: (315) 797-2161
Web Site: http://www.pacemakersteel.com
Sales Range: $10-24.9 Million
Emp.: 38
Steel Distr
N.A.I.C.S.: 423510
F. Eugene Romano (Chm)
Rich Evans (VP)

PACER CORPORATION
7735 NW 146 St Ste 202, Miami Lakes, FL 33016
Tel.: (305) 828-7660
Web Site: http://www.pacerco.com
Year Founded: 2003
Sales Range: $50-74.9 Million
Emp.: 400
Acquisition & Management of Financially Distressed Companies
N.A.I.C.S.: 523999
Rainier Gonzalez (Chm & CEO)
John Chi (CFO)
Jennifer Heath (Dir-HR)
John Vincent (COO-Medical Div)

Subsidiaries:

Pacer Health Corporation   (1)
14100 Palmetto Frontage Rd Ste 108, Miami Lakes, FL 33016
Tel.: (305) 828-7660
Web Site: http://www.pacerco.com
Sales Range: $10-24.9 Million
Emp.: 6
Owns & Operates Medical Facilities
N.A.I.C.S.: 531312
John Vincent (COO)

PACER ELECTRONICS OF FLORIDA, INC.
1555 Apex Rd, Sarasota, FL 34240
Tel.: (941) 378-5774   FL
Web Site: http://www.pacergroup.net
Year Founded: 1979
Sales Range: $25-49.9 Million
Emp.: 60
Electrical Apparatus & Equipment, Wiring Supplies & Related Equipment Mfr & Merchant Whslr
N.A.I.C.S.: 423610
John M. Swiatkowski (Pres)
Joseph Swiatkowski (CEO)
Stella Slack (Controller)

PACERS BASKETBALL, LLC
125 S Pennsylvania St, Indianapolis, IN 46204-3610
Tel.: (317) 917-2500   IN
Web Site: http://www.nba.com
Year Founded: 1983
Professional Basketball Team & Entertainment Arena Operator
N.A.I.C.S.: 711211
Rick Fuson (Pres & COO)
Sonya Clutinger (Sr Dir-Basketball Ops)
David Benner (Dir-Media Rels-Indiana Pacers)
Greg Smith (Dir-Exec Protection)
Karen Atkeson (Dir-Player Dev)

Kelly Krauskopf (Asst Gen Mgr)
James T. Morris (Vice Chm)
Kevin Pritchard (Pres-Basketball Ops)
Herbert Simon (Co-Owner, Chm, CEO & NBA Governor)
Frank Pulice (Gen Counsel & Sr VP)
Chad Buchanan (Gen Mgr)
Peter Dinwiddie (Sr VP-Basketball Ops)
Stephen Simon (Co-Owner & Alternate NBA Governor)
Paula Maxwell (Mgr-Risk)
Nate McMillan (Head-Coach)
Josh Corbeil (Sr Dir-Medical Ops & Head-Athletic Trainer)
Ryan Carr (Dir-Player Personnel)
Shawn Windle (Dir-Sports Performance)
Hansen Wong (Dir-Basketball Information & Technology)
Krissy Myers (Assoc Dir-Indiana Pacers Media Relations)
Spencer Anderson (Mgr-Basketball Admin)
Ryan Renteria (Coord-Scouting)
Tim Dather (Coord-Video)
Josh Conder (Mgr-Equipment)
Tim Brown (Coord-Basketball Ops)
Aaron Weaver (Coord-Basketball Ops)
Carl Daniels (VP-Player Dev)
Tamika Catchings (Dir-Player Programs & Franchise Dev)
Carl Nicks (Mgr-Player Dev)
Michael Hornback (Coord-Player Dev)
Brent Rockwood (Sr VP-Corp Community & PR)
Ted Wu (VP-Basketball Ops)
Tracy Ellis-Ward (Sr VP-Diversity, Equity & Inclusion)

PACES, INC.
7840 Washington Avenue, Kansas City, KS 66102
Tel.: (913) 563-6500   KS
Web Site: http://www.paceswc.org
Year Founded: 2010
Sales Range: $10-24.9 Million
Child & Family Care Services
N.A.I.C.S.: 624190
Judi Rodman (Exec Dir)

PACESETTER CAPITAL GROUP
2435 N Central Expy 200, Richardson, TX 75080
Tel.: (972) 991-1597
Sales Range: $10-24.9 Million
Emp.: 17
Venture Capital Company
N.A.I.C.S.: 541611
Donald Ray Lawhorne (Pres & CEO)
Mary Barrera (VP & Controller)
Divakar R. Kamath (Partner & Exec VP)
Rahul Vaid (Partner & Sr VP)

Subsidiaries:

Florida Texas Restaurant Group   (1)
2435 N Central Expwy Ste 200, Richardson, TX 75080
Tel.: (972) 991-1597
Rev.: $5,400,000
Mexican Restaurant
N.A.I.C.S.: 722511

PACESETTER CLAIMS SERVICE
2871 N Hwy 167, Catoosa, OK 74015
Tel.: (918) 665-8887
Web Site: http://www.pacesetterclaims.com
Sales Range: $10-24.9 Million
Emp.: 30

COMPANIES
PACIFIC COAST BUILDING PRODUCTS, INC.

Insurance Claim Adjusters, Not Employed By Insurance Company
N.A.I.C.S.: 524291
Tom Durall *(Mgr)*
Paul Meyer *(Mgr-Ops)*
Jim Shrewsbury *(VP-Claims)*
Dale Brassfield *(COO)*

PACESETTER GRAPHIC SERVICE
2672 Hickory Grove Rd NW, Acworth, GA 30101
Tel.: (770) 974-0297
Web Site: http://www.pacesetterusa.com
Rev.: $12,000,000
Emp.: 90
Printers' Rolls & Blankets
N.A.I.C.S.: 326299
Robert L. Allen *(Pres)*
Greg Montgomery *(Mgr-Sls)*
Margi Atkinson *(Office Mgr)*
Bryan Boyd *(VP-Sls)*

PACESETTERS, INC
2511 Highway 111 N, Cookeville, TN 38506
Tel.: (931) 537-9100   TN
Web Site: http://www.pacesetterstn.com
Year Founded: 1971
Sales Range: $10-24.9 Million
Emp.: 524
Developmental Disability Assistance Services
N.A.I.C.S.: 624120
Michelle Hennessee *(Sec)*
Carolyn Whitaker *(Treas)*
Barbara Sorrell *(Pres)*

PACHECO RANCH WINERY
235 Alameda Del Prado Rd, Novato, CA 94949
Tel.: (415) 883-5583
Web Site: http://www.pachecoranchwinery.com
Year Founded: 1970
Sales Range: $25-49.9 Million
Emp.: 52
Vineyard & Wine Mfr
N.A.I.C.S.: 111332
Fredric L. Schulte *(Partner)*
Janice Schulte *(Partner)*
Deborah Rowlands *(Partner)*
T. J. Meves *(Partner)*
Herbert Rowland *(Partner)*

PACIFIC AG, LLC
2995 S 1st St, Hermiston, OR 97838
Tel.: (541) 567-3610
Web Site: http://www.pacificag.com
Hay & Crop Residue Harvest
N.A.I.C.S.: 115114
Bill Levy *(Pres & CEO)*
Steve Van Knowerik *(VP-Ops)*
Rod Phelan *(VP-Harvest Ops)*
Harrison Pettit *(VP-Mktg & Corp Dev)*
Alan Kessler *(Controller)*

Subsidiaries:

Calaway Trading, Inc.   (1)
2009 W Dolarway Rd, Ellensburg, WA 98926
Tel.: (509) 962-6767
Web Site: http://www.calagri.com
Emp.: 100
Agricultural Commodity Products Distr & Whslr
N.A.I.C.S.: 424910
Jeff Calaway *(Pres)*
Shin Sasaki *(VP-Sls)*
Steve Lin *(VP-Sls)*
Blaine Calaway *(VP-Bus Dev)*

PACIFIC AGRI-PRODUCTS INC.
477 Forbes Blvd 2764, South San Francisco, CA 94080
Tel.: (650) 873-0440
Web Site: http://www.pacagri.com
Sales Range: $75-99.9 Million
Emp.: 30
Packaged Frozen Poultry
N.A.I.C.S.: 424420
James Monfredini *(Pres)*

PACIFIC AMERICAN FISH CO., INC.
5525 S Santa Fe Ave, Vernon, CA 90058
Tel.: (323) 319-1515   CA
Web Site: http://www.pafco.net
Year Founded: 1977
Fish & Seafood Whslr
N.A.I.C.S.: 424460
Peter Huh *(Pres & CEO)*

PACIFIC AMERICAN GROUP, LLC
104 Caledonia St, Sausalito, CA 94965
Tel.: (415) 331-3838
Web Site: http://www.pacamgroup.com
Sales Range: $25-49.9 Million
Emp.: 10
Holding Company
N.A.I.C.S.: 551112
Linda Childs Hothem *(CEO)*
Francis Meynard *(CFO)*
Theron Bullman *(Mgr-Property)*

PACIFIC ASIAN CONSORTIUM IN EMPLOYMENT
1055 Wilshire Blvd Ste 1475, Los Angeles, CA 90017
Tel.: (213) 353-3982   CA
Web Site: http://www.pacela.org
Year Founded: 1976
Sales Range: $25-49.9 Million
Emp.: 484
Employment & Job Training Services
N.A.I.C.S.: 561311
Rachelle Pastor-Arizmendi *(COO & VP)*
Jon Mayeda *(Sec)*
Kerry N. Doi *(Pres & CEO)*
Neil Yoneji *(Chm)*

PACIFIC AUTO BODY
1621 E Orangethorpe Ave, Fullerton, CA 92831
Tel.: (714) 572-6000
Web Site: http://www.pacificcollision.com
Sales Range: $10-24.9 Million
Emp.: 123
Automotive Body Shop
N.A.I.C.S.: 811121
Henry Bohen *(Pres)*

PACIFIC AVENUE CAPITAL PARTNERS, LLC
2447 Pacific Coast Hwy, Ste 101, Hermosa Beach, CA 90254
Tel.: (424) 254-9774   DE
Web Site: http://www.pacificavenuecapital.com
Year Founded: 2017
Privater Equity Firm
N.A.I.C.S.: 523999
Jason Leach *(Mng Dir)*
Chris Sznewajs *(Founder & Mng Partner)*
Mike Shepard *(Principal)*
Jonathan Sinnott *(VP)*
Doug Brookman *(VP-Bus Dev)*
Greg Anderson *(Operating Partner-Healthcare Svcs)*
Harold C. Bevis *(Operating Partner-Diversified Indus)*
Tom Chieffe *(Operating Partner-Building Products)*
Charles Veniez *(Operating Partner-Bus Svcs)*

Subsidiaries:

Cameron Ashley Building Products, Inc.   (1)
979 Batesville Rd Ste A, Greer, SC 29651
Tel.: (864) 297-6101
Web Site: http://www.cameronashleybp.com
Lumber & Wood Building Materials Mfr
N.A.I.C.S.: 423330
Donald DeMarie *(Pres & CEO)*
Beth Brown *(VP-HR)*
Sara Eller *(Dir-Mktg)*

Subsidiary (Domestic):

Cornerstone Business Services, Inc.   (2)
200 S Washington St Ste 401, Green Bay, WI 54301
Tel.: (920) 436-9890
Web Site: http://www.cornerstone-business.com
Mergers & Acquisitions Consulting Services
N.A.I.C.S.: 541910
Scott Bushkie *(Founder & Mng Partner)*
Erica Gilson *(Partner & Dir-Ops)*
Brad Kirkpatrick *(Mng Dir-Iowa)*
Chris Lay *(Mng Dir)*
Leroy Matuszak *(Sr VP)*
Rodney Ott *(Sr VP)*
Jason Salisbury *(VP)*
Charles Dallas *(VP)*
Jeffrey Bartels *(VP)*
Tyler VanderGaast *(Dir-Valuations)*

GDP Silvercote Inc.   (2)
29200 Fountain Pkwy, Cleveland, OH 44139
Tel.: (440) 248-2500
Web Site: http://www.silvercote.com
Rev.: $10,000,000
Emp.: 50
Fiberglass Insulation Mfr
N.A.I.C.S.: 327993

J&R Products, Inc.   (2)
1955 W Lancaster St, Bluffton, IN 46714
Tel.: (260) 353-3600
Web Site: http://www.jrproductsinc.com
Drywall & Insulation Contractors
N.A.I.C.S.: 238310

Emerald Textiles, LLC   (1)
1725 Dornoch Ct Ste 101, San Diego, CA 92154-7206
Tel.: (619) 330-7077
Web Site: http://www.emeraldsd.com
Linen Supply
N.A.I.C.S.: 812331
Andy Kratky *(CEO)*

PACIFIC BEST INC.
10725 Rush St, South El Monte, CA 91733
Tel.: (626) 350-4224
Web Site: http://www.pacificbestinc.com
Rev.: $14,700,000
Emp.: 100
Auto Parts Distributor
N.A.I.C.S.: 423120
Yungtai A. Hsu *(Pres)*

PACIFIC BUILDING GROUP
9752 Aspen Creek Ct Ste 150, San Diego, CA 92126
Tel.: (858) 552-0600
Web Site: http://www.pacificbuildinggroup.com
Sales Range: $25-49.9 Million
Emp.: 160
Commercial & Institutional Building Construction Services
N.A.I.C.S.: 236220
Gregory Rogers *(CEO)*
Jim Roherty *(Pres)*
Lisa Hitt *(CFO)*
Allison Simpson *(Dir-Bus Dev)*
Hollis Gentry *(Dir-Medical Svcs)*
Eric Mudge *(Dir-Ops)*
Matt Baroni *(Dir-Field Ops)*

PACIFIC BUSINESS GROUP ON HEALTH
575 Market St Ste 600, San Francisco, CA 94105
Tel.: (415) 281-8660   CA
Web Site: http://www.pbgh.org
Year Founded: 1990
Sales Range: $10-24.9 Million
Emp.: 35
Health Care Srvices
N.A.I.C.S.: 622110
Bill Kramer *(Exec Dir)*
Michael Chung *(CIO)*
Israel Ghebretinsae *(Dir-Fin)*
Norma Pugh *(Accountant)*
David Lansky *(Pres & CEO)*

PACIFIC CHOICE BRANDS, INC.
4652 E Date Ave, Fresno, CA 93725-2101
Tel.: (559) 476-3581   CA
Web Site: http://www.pacificchoice.com
Year Founded: 1980
Sales Range: $25-49.9 Million
Emp.: 275
Process Pickle Sauce & Salad Dressing Mfr
N.A.I.C.S.: 311941
Faith Buller *(Controller)*
Karl Maculans *(Dir-Food Safety)*
Chris Rabago *(Plant Mgr)*
Luigi Allegra *(Sr Dir-Sls & Mktg)*
Villalobos Boni *(VP)*

Subsidiaries:

Millcrest Products Corporation   (1)
4667 E Date Ave, Fresno, CA 93725-2101
Tel.: (559) 445-1745
Web Site: http://www.pacificchoice.com
Rev.: $4,400,000
Emp.: 1
Process Pickles, Sauces & Salad Dressings
N.A.I.C.S.: 311941

PACIFIC COAST BUILDING PRODUCTS, INC.
10600 White Rock Rd Ste 100, Rancho Cordova, CA 95670-6032
Tel.: (916) 631-6500   CA
Web Site: http://www.paccoast.com
Year Founded: 1953
Sales Range: $1-4.9 Billion
Emp.: 3,200
Roofing & Drywall Insulation Contractor; Building Materials & Veneer Mfr & Whslr; Clay, Pipe, Floor & Roof Tile Mfr; Local Trucking Services
N.A.I.C.S.: 327420
David J. Lucchetti *(Pres & CEO)*
Darren Morris *(CFO)*
Megan Vincent *(Dir-Community Rels)*
David J. Lucchetti *(Exec Chm)*

Subsidiaries:

Alcal Specialty Contracting, Inc.   (1)
946 N Market Blvd, Sacramento, CA 95834
Tel.: (916) 929-3100
Web Site: http://www.alcal.com
Sales Range: $10-24.9 Million
Emp.: 30
Building Finishing Services
N.A.I.C.S.: 238390
Darren Morris *(Pres)*

Basalite Concrete Products, LLC   (1)
605 Industrial Way, Dixon, CA 95620-9779
Tel.: (707) 678-1901
Web Site: http://www.basalite.com
Concrete Masonry Product Mfr & Distr
N.A.I.C.S.: 327331
Ron Mulligan *(VP-Mfg)*

Interstate Brick Company   (1)

PACIFIC COAST BUILDING PRODUCTS, INC. — U.S. PRIVATE

Pacific Coast Building Products, Inc.—(Continued)

9780 S 5200 W, West Jordan, UT 84065-5625 **(100%)**
Tel.: (801) 280-5200
Web Site: http://www.interstatebrick.com
Sales Range: $25-49.9 Million
Emp.: 200
Mfr & Sale of Bricks
N.A.I.C.S.: 327120

PABCO Building Products, LLC - H.C. Muddox Division (1)
4875 Bradshaw Rd, Sacramento, CA 95827
Tel.: (916) 859-6320
Web Site: http://www.hcmuddox.com
Sales Range: $10-24.9 Million
Emp.: 5
Bricks Mfr
N.A.I.C.S.: 327331
Greg Morrison (Plant Mgr)
Jerry Dowd (Mgr-Sls)
Michael Kelley (Mgr-Customer Svc)

PABCO Building Products, LLC - Interstate Brick Division (1)
9780 S 5200 W, West Jordan, UT 84081
Tel.: (801) 280-5200
Web Site: http://www.interstatebrick.com
Sales Range: $25-49.9 Million
Emp.: 100
Bricks Mfr
N.A.I.C.S.: 327331
Bill Lippman (Mgr-Customer Svc)
Chet Preston (Mgr-Special Project & Pur)
Dennis Webber (Mgr-Transportation)
Allen Brisk (Mgr-Pur)
Gerry Gunning (Mgr-Ops)
Sunup Mathew (Mgr-Northwest)
Shannon Perry (Mgr-Sls-Eastern Reg)
Mary Pettingill (Coord-HR)

PABCO Building Products, LLC - PABCO Gypsum Division (1)
10600 White Rock Rd Bldg B Ste 100, Rancho Cordova, CA 95670
Tel.: (510) 792-9555
Web Site: http://www.pabcogypsum.com
Emp.: 6
Gypsum Board Mfr
N.A.I.C.S.: 327420
Mark Burkhammer (Mgr-Sls-Gypsum Board)

PABCO Building Products, LLC - PABCO Paper Division (1)
4460 Pacific Blvd, Vernon, CA 90058
Tel.: (323) 581-6113
Web Site: http://www.pabcopaper.com
Sales Range: $25-49.9 Million
Emp.: 100
Paper Mills
N.A.I.C.S.: 322120
Bill Fraser (Plant Mgr)

PABCO Building Products, LLC - PABCO Roofing Products Division (1)
1718 Thorne Rd, Tacoma, WA 98421-3207
Tel.: (253) 272-0374
Web Site: http://www.pabcoroofing.com
Asphalt Shingle Mfr
N.A.I.C.S.: 324122
Brian Hobdy (VP & Gen Mgr)
David Randolph (Dir-Mfg)

Pacific Coast Companies, Inc. (1)
10600 White Rock Rd Ste 100, Rancho Cordova, CA 95670
Tel.: (916) 631-6500
Sales Range: $10-24.9 Million
Emp.: 100
Business Support Services
N.A.I.C.S.: 561499

Pacific Coast Supply, LLC (1)
4290 Roseville Rd, North Highlands, CA 95660-5710
Tel.: (916) 481-2220
Building Materials Distr
N.A.I.C.S.: 444180
Dwight Isaac (Dir-Mfg)
Clint Summers (Reg Mgr)

Division (Domestic):

Pacific Coast Supply, LLC - Anderson Lumber Division (2)
4290 Roseville Rd, North Highlands, CA 95660-5710
Tel.: (916) 481-2220
Web Site: http://www.andersonlumber.paccoast.com
Lumber Product Distr
N.A.I.C.S.: 423310

Pacific Coast Supply, LLC - Diamond Pacific Division (2)
150 Forni Rd, Placerville, CA 95667
Tel.: (530) 622-2680
Web Site: http://www.paccoastsupply.com
Building Materials Distr
N.A.I.C.S.: 444180

Pacific Coast Supply, LLC - P.C. Wholesale Division (2)
4290 Roseville Rd, North Highlands, CA 95660-5710
Tel.: (916) 971-2370
Web Site: http://www.pcwholesale.paccoast.com
Lumber Product Distr
N.A.I.C.S.: 423310

Pacific Coast Supply, LLC - Pacific Supply Division (2)
4290 Roseville Rd, North Highlands, CA 95660-5710
Tel.: (916) 481-2220
Web Site: http://www.paccoastsupply.com
Building Materials Distr
N.A.I.C.S.: 444180

PACIFIC COAST CABLING INC.
20717 Prairie St, Chatsworth, CA 91311
Tel.: (818) 407-1911
Web Site: http://www.pccinc.com
Year Founded: 1985
Rev.: $19,637,589
Emp.: 20
Computer Installation
N.A.I.C.S.: 238210
David S. Burr (Pres & CEO)
Richard J. Harris (Partner & VP-Sls)
James A. Wilmington (COO & Partner)

PACIFIC COAST CAPITAL PARTNERS, LLC
10100 Santa Monica Blvd Ste 1000, Los Angeles, CA 90067
Tel.: (310) 414-7870
Web Site: http://www.pccpllc.com
Year Founded: 1998
Sales Range: $150-199.9 Million
Emp.: 200
Real Estate Investment Firm
N.A.I.C.S.: 522310
Donald H. Kuemmeler (Partner-San Francisco)
Aaron Giovara (Partner-Sacramento)
Bryan Thornton (Partner-San Francisco)
Brian J. Heafey (Partner-San Francisco)
Greg Eberhardt (Partner)
William R. Lindsay (Partner)
Jennifer R. Diaz (Mng Dir-Asset Mgmt)
Jed W. Lassere (Partner-Investments)
Karen Ruiz (Controller)
Steve Towle (Partner & CFO)
Norma Cabrera (Sr VP & Dir-Portfolio Svcs)
John W. Randall (Partner)
Kevin Chin (Sr VP)
Bryan Cebula (Sr VP)
Eric J. Lind (Sr VP)
Erik R. Flynn (Partner-San Francisco)
Henry Hwang (Sr VP)
James Nearon (Sr VP)
Jim Galovan (Partner-San Francisco)
K. C. Boback Kriegel (Sr VP)
Kristin Canon (Sr VP-IR)
Melanie Gangel (Sr VP)
Ronald Bonneau (Sr VP)
Shadi A. Swoish (Sr VP)
Yon Cho (Partner)

Subsidiaries:

The Culver Studios (1)
9336 W Washington Blvd, Culver City, CA 90232-2628
Tel.: (310) 202-1234
Web Site: http://www.theculverstudios.com
Motion Picture Studio
N.A.I.C.S.: 512199
Tracy Wilson (Co-Mgr-IT & Telecom)
Steve Auer (VP-Facilities & Ops)

PACIFIC COAST CHEMICALS CO.
2424 4th St, Berkeley, CA 94710
Tel.: (510) 549-3535
Web Site: http://www.pcchem.com
Sales Range: $10-24.9 Million
Emp.: 35
Chemicals & Allied Products
N.A.I.C.S.: 424690
Steve Shafer (VP-Sls & Mktg)
Dominic Stull (Pres)

PACIFIC COAST ENERGY COMPANY LP
1555 Orcutt Hill Rd, Orcutt, CA 93455
Tel.: (805) 937-2576
Web Site: http://www.pceclp.com
Year Founded: 2004
Oil & Gas Exploration
N.A.I.C.S.: 211120
Randall H. Breitenbach (Chm & CEO)
Philip Brown (Sr VP-Ops)
Peter A. Singh (CFO)

Subsidiaries:

Pacific Coast Oil Trust (1)
601 Travis St 16th Fl, Houston, TX 77002
Tel.: (512) 236-6555
Web Site: https://royt.q4web.com
Rev.: $15,121,000
Assets: $204,626,000
Net Worth: $204,626,000
Earnings: $12,619,000
Fiscal Year-end: 12/31/2018
Oil & Gas Investment Services
N.A.I.C.S.: 523999

PACIFIC COAST EVERGREEN INC
5158 Bethel Rd SE, Port Orchard, WA 98367
Tel.: (360) 876-2061
Web Site: http://www.pacificcoastevergreens.com
Sales Range: $10-24.9 Million
Emp.: 18
Florists' Supplies
N.A.I.C.S.: 424930
Richard Berg (Pres)
Becky Hoit (Office Mgr)

PACIFIC COAST GROUP INC.
8350 S Durango Dr Ste 210, Las Vegas, NV 89113-4473
Tel.: (702) 256-8203
Web Site: http://www.pacificcoastgroup.com
Sales Range: $10-24.9 Million
Emp.: 6
Aircraft Rental
N.A.I.C.S.: 532411
Lawrence W. Olson (Founder, Pres & CEO)
Robert N. Thompson (VP)

PACIFIC COAST LIGHTING INC.
20238 Plummer St, Chatsworth, CA 91311
Tel.: (818) 886-9751
Web Site: http://www.pacificcoastlighting.com
Year Founded: 1979
Sales Range: $25-49.9 Million
Emp.: 300
Sales of Lighting Equipment

N.A.I.C.S.: 335139
Clark Linstone (CFO)
Rick Spicer (VP-Sls & Mktg)

PACIFIC COAST PRODUCERS
631 N Cluff Ave, Lodi, CA 95240-0756
Tel.: (209) 367-8800   CA
Web Site: http://www.pacificcoastproducers.com
Year Founded: 1971
Sales Range: $200-249.9 Million
Emp.: 750
Canned Fruit & Tomato Mfr & Distr
N.A.I.C.S.: 311421
Peter Wtulich (CIO & VP-Info Sys)
Michael VanGundy (Plant Mgr-Lodi)
Andrew K. Russick (VP-Sls & Mktg)
Daniel Sroufe (VP-Ops)
Mona Shulman (Gen Counsel & VP)
Steve Freeman (VP-Field Ops)
Mark Vallee (Dir-Bus Dev)
Pete Hansen (Dir-Food Svc Sls)
Beau St. Germain (Dir-Retail Sls)
Robert Jeremic (Dir-Supply Chain & Distr)
Tami Iverson (Mgr-Mktg Comm)
David Zuzich (Dir-Customer Svc & Mgr-Sls-Natl)
Nate Romberger (Mgr-Sls-Natl)
Chris Ward (Dir-Ops)
Kathi J. Shull (Sec)
Ted Kontopoulos (Sr Dir-Food Svc Sls)
Zeb Rocha (Treas & Controller)
Daniel L. Vincent (Pres & CEO)

Subsidiaries:

Pacific Coast Producers - Lodi Plant (1)
741 S Stockton St, Lodi, CA 95241-0880
Tel.: (209) 334-3352
Canned Food Product Mfr & Distr
N.A.I.C.S.: 311421
Mike Van Gundy (Plant Mgr)
Dan Vincent (Pres & CEO)
Ernie Gibson (Mgr-IT Ops)

Pacific Coast Producers - Oroville Plant (1)
1601 Mitchell Ave, Oroville, CA 95965
Tel.: (530) 533-4311
Sales Range: $150-199.9 Million
Canned Food Product Mfr & Distr
N.A.I.C.S.: 311421
Paul Fairbanks (Gen Mgr)

Pacific Coast Producers - Woodland Plant (1)
1376 Lemen Ave, Woodland, CA 95776
Tel.: (530) 662-8661
Canned Food Product Whslr
N.A.I.C.S.: 311421
Chris Ward (Mgr)

PACIFIC COLUMNS, INC.
505 W Lambert Rd, Brea, CA 92821
Tel.: (714) 257-9600
Web Site: http://www.pacificcolumns.com
Year Founded: 1998
Sales Range: $10-24.9 Million
Emp.: 65
Interior & Exterior Architectural Columns, Wainscoting & Wood Trim Online Sales
N.A.I.C.S.: 337212
Robert Sellek (CEO)
Jonee Scott (Mgr-Customer Svc)

PACIFIC COMMUNICATIONS
575 Anton Blvd Ste 900, Costa Mesa, CA 92626-7665
Tel.: (714) 427-1900   DE
Web Site: http://www.pacific-com.com
Year Founded: 1992
Rev.: $18,000,000
Emp.: 130

Advetising Agency
N.A.I.C.S.: 541810
Ryan Abbate (Pres)
Larry Dennis (Sr Art Dir)
Mark Wagner (Art Suprv)
Diane Hall (Exec Mgr-Opers)
James Marlin (Exec Mgr-Agency Svcs)
Karen Melanson (Sr VP & Dir-Client Svcs)
Craig Sullivan (Exec VP & Dir-Mgmt)
Henry Lee (Sr VP & Dir-Client Svcs)
Kristal Babbs (VP & Supvr-Mgmt)
Judy Doo (VP & Mgmt Suprv)
Zena Alam (Sr Dir-Art)
Mark Gilmour (Sr Dir-Art)
Peter Siegel (Sr VP & Exec Dir-Creative)
Patrick Macke (Grp Dir-Creative)

PACIFIC CONSTRUCTION SYSTEMS INC.
2275 116th Ave NE Ste 100, Bellevue, WA 98004-3032
Tel.: (425) 455-3000 WA
Web Site: http://www.paconsys.com
Year Founded: 1960
Sales Range: $50-74.9 Million
Emp.: 500
Mfr of Plastering Drywall & Insulation Products
N.A.I.C.S.: 238310
Treacy Roach (Sr Project Mgr)
Jerry Jensen (Project Mgr)

PACIFIC CREST BANCORP, INC.
3500 188th St SW Ste 575, Lynnwood, WA 98037
Tel.: (425) 670-9600 WA
Web Site: http://www.paccrest.com
Year Founded: 1998
Rev.: $60,000,000
Emp.: 100
Bank Holding Company
N.A.I.C.S.: 551111
Sheryl J. Nilson (Vice Chm, Pres & CEO)
Wayne Bull Jr. (CFO & Exec VP-Pacific Crest Savings Bank)
Fred Safstrom (Chm)
Cindy Funaro (Chief Risk Officer & Exec VP)
Kevin Hogan (Sr VP-Client Svcs)
Gena Emerson (VP-Banking Ops)
Scott Gibson (Sr VP & Mgr-Portfolio, Income Property & Construction Lending)

Subsidiaries:

Pacific Crest Savings Bank (1)
3500 188th St SW Ste 575, Lynnwood, WA 98037-4757
Tel.: (425) 670-9600
Web Site: http://www.paccrest.com
Sales Range: $25-49.9 Million
Emp.: 35
Savings & Home Loans
N.A.I.C.S.: 522180
Sheryl J. Nilson (Vice Chm, Pres & CEO)
Wayne Bull Jr. (CFO & Exec VP)
Cindy Lee Funaro (Chief Risk Officer & Exec VP)
Kevin Hogan (Sr VP-Client Svcs)
Scott Gibson (Sr VP & Mgr-Lending)
Gena Emerson (VP-Banking Ops)

PACIFIC DENTAL SERVICES, INC.
17000 Red Hill Ave, Irvine, CA 92614
Tel.: (714) 508-3600
Web Site: http://www.pacificdentalservice.com
Year Founded: 1994
Sales Range: $200-249.9 Million
Emp.: 3,500
Dental Services
N.A.I.C.S.: 621210
Stephen Thorne (Founder & Pres)
Jon Thorne (Sr VP-Ops Support)
Brady Aase (CFO)
Dan Burke (Gen Counsel & Sr VP-Platform Strategy)
Joe Feldsien (Sr VP-Professional Partnerships)

PACIFIC DIGITAL USA CORPORATION, INC.
10300 W Charleston, Las Vegas, NV 89135
Tel.: (702) 322-1413 NV
Year Founded: 2011
Software Publisher
N.A.I.C.S.: 513210
Michael Scott (CEO, CFO, Treas & Sec)

PACIFIC EVENT PRODUCTIONS
6989 Corte Santa Fe, San Diego, CA 92121
Tel.: (858) 458-9908
Web Site: http://www.pacificevents.com
Year Founded: 1990
Sales Range: $1-9.9 Million
Emp.: 155
Convention & Show Planning Services
N.A.I.C.S.: 561920
George Duff (Co-Owner, Co-Pres & Co-CEO)
Joanne Mera (Co-Owner, Co-Pres & Co-CEO)
Amy Berner (VP-Mktg & Comm & Sr Producer-Events)
Jim Lennox (VP-Sls)

PACIFIC FIBRE PRODUCTS INC.
20 Fibre Way, Longview, WA 98632
Tel.: (360) 577-7112
Web Site: http://www.pacfibre.com
Sales Range: $25-49.9 Million
Emp.: 150
Cut Stock Resawing Lumber & Planing
N.A.I.C.S.: 321912
Larry Lemmons (VP)
James Bobst (Mgr-HR)
Don Lightfool (Controller)

PACIFIC FOOD IMPORTERS INC.
18620 80th Ct S Bldg F, Kent, WA 98032
Tel.: (206) 682-2740
Web Site: http://www.pacificfoodimporters.com
Sales Range: $10-24.9 Million
Emp.: 25
Groceries
N.A.I.C.S.: 424410
Mike Croce (Gen Mgr)

PACIFIC GLOBAL INC.
1013 Centre Rd Ste 403S, Wilmington, DE 19805
Tel.: (510) 870-0248
Web Site: http://www.pacificbpo.com
Year Founded: 2008
Sales Range: $10-24.9 Million
Emp.: 1,450
Business Process Outsourcing Services
N.A.I.C.S.: 561439
Kumar Shwetabh (CEO)
Vivek Gaur (Mng Dir)
Sanjay Drabu (Pres)
Brian Lichtlin (VP-Sls)
Vivek Bahri (Dir-Quality & Compliance)

PACIFIC GRAIN & FOODS
4067 W Shaw Ave Ste 116, Fresno, CA 93722
Tel.: (559) 276-2580
Web Site: http://www.pacificgrainandfood.com
Year Founded: 1982
Sales Range: $10-24.9 Million
Emp.: 33
Food Grain Whlslr
N.A.I.C.S.: 424510
Lee Perkins (Pres)

PACIFIC GROSERVICE, INC.
567 Cinnabar St, San Jose, CA 95110
Tel.: (408) 727-4826 CA
Web Site: http://www.pitcofoods.com
Year Founded: 1982
Sales Range: $25-49.9 Million
Emp.: 150
Whlslr of Groceries
N.A.I.C.S.: 424410
Pericles Navab (Chm)

PACIFIC HIDE & FUR DEPOT
1401 3rd St NW, Great Falls, MT 59404-1902
Tel.: (406) 727-6222 MT
Web Site: http://www.pacific-recycling.com
Sales Range: $200-249.9 Million
Emp.: 650
Steel Service Center & Scrap Metal Recycler Operator
N.A.I.C.S.: 423510
Tim Culliton (CFO)
Jeff Millhollin (Pres & CEO)
Pat Kons (VP-Scrap Ops)
Kenneth Hess (CIO)
Stacey Lamy (Dir-HR)
Stuart Boylan (VP-Bus Dev)
Ken Halko (VP-Ferrous Processing & Trading)

PACIFIC HOSPITALITY GROUP, INC.
2532 Dupont Dr, Irvine, CA 92612-1524
Tel.: (949) 474-7368 CA
Web Site: http://www.pacifichospitality.com
Year Founded: 1997
Rev.: $20,400,000
Emp.: 150
Hotel Developer, Owner & Operator
N.A.I.C.S.: 721110
Timothy Busch (Founder & CEO)
Kory Kramer (Chief Investment Officer)
Maria Patrick (Dir-HR)
Terri Reid (Dir-Mktg)
John Moody (VP-Fin)
Nate Tanner (Dir-Food & Beverage)
Sven Grunder (Reg Dir-Ops)
Scott Meldrum (Chief Mktg Officer)
Paul J. McCormick (Pres & COO)
Melanie Bucci (CFO)
Ajeet Anand (VP-Sls & Mktg)
Stephen Schackne (Reg Dir-Food & Beverage)

Subsidiaries:

The Balboa Bay Club & Resort (1)
1221 Coast Hwy, Newport Beach, CA 92663
Tel.: (949) 630-4120
Web Site: http://www.balboabayclub.com
Emp.: 500
Resort Hotel Services
N.A.I.C.S.: 721110
Sam El-Rabaa (Gen Mgr)
Leticia Rice (Mgr-Membership Sls)

The Newport Beach Country Club (1)
1 Clubhouse Dr, Newport Beach, CA 92660
Tel.: (949) 644-9550

Web Site: http://www.newportbeachcc.com
Emp.: 60
Golf Country Club
N.A.I.C.S.: 713910
Kevin Martin (CEO)

PACIFIC HOUSING GROUP, LLC
6801 Ave 304, Visalia, CA 93291
Tel.: (559) 651-1133
Web Site: http://www.pacifichomesales.com
Sales Range: $25-49.9 Million
Emp.: 60
Holding Company: Real Estate
N.A.I.C.S.: 551112
George Biavante Jr. (Pres)

Subsidiaries:

Pacific Home Sales Inc. (1)
6801 Ave 304, Visalia, CA 93291
Tel.: (559) 651-1133
Web Site: http://www.pacifichomesales.com
Rev.: $25,000,000
Emp.: 27
Mobile Home Retailer
N.A.I.C.S.: 459930

PACIFIC INCOME ADVISERS INC.
1299 Ocean Ave Ste 210, Santa Monica, CA 90401
Tel.: (310) 393-1424
Web Site: http://www.pacificincome.com
Rev.: $10,391,000
Emp.: 41
Investment Advisory Services
N.A.I.C.S.: 523940
Heather U. Baines (Chm)
Michael Yean (VP)
Joseph Lloyd McAdams (Pres, CEO & Chief Investment Officer)
Daniel F. Meyer (Mng Dir & Portfolio Mgr)
Timothy B. Tarpening (Mng Dir-Bus Dev-Western)
Evangelos Karagiannis (Mng Dir & Portfolio Mgr)
Austin W. Rutledge (VP)
Arlen Sookias (VP)
Rory L. Hargaden (VP)
Guy Torres (VP)

PACIFIC INDUSTRIES INC.
18200 SW Teton Ave, Tualatin, OR 97062
Tel.: (503) 692-6082
Web Site: http://www.pacificindustries.com
Sales Range: $10-24.9 Million
Emp.: 30
Mfr of Industrial Machine Parts
N.A.I.C.S.: 423830
Richard Mark (CFO)

PACIFIC INSTITUTE FOR RESEARCH & EVALUATION
11720 Beltsville Dr Ste 900, Calverton, MD 20705-3111
Tel.: (301) 755-2700 CA
Web Site: http://www.pire.org
Year Founded: 1974
Sales Range: $25-49.9 Million
Emp.: 273
Science Research & Educational Support Services
N.A.I.C.S.: 541720
Bernard E. Murphy (Pres & CEO)
Diane Williams (Sec & Dir-Svcs & Corp Comm)
Gary A. Klig (CFO & Chief Admin Officer)
Brian O'Neill (Chm)

PACIFIC INTEGRATED HANDLING INC.

PACIFIC INTEGRATED HANDLING INC. U.S. PRIVATE

Pacific Integrated Handling Inc.—(Continued)
10215 Portland Ave, Tacoma, WA 98445
Tel.: (253) 535-5888
Web Site:
http://www.pacificintegrated.com
Rev.: $11,100,000
Emp.: 45
Industrial Machinery & Equipment Merchant Whslr
N.A.I.C.S.: 423830
David R. Sidor (CEO)
Mike Sidor (Pres)
Jenece Brown (Mgr-Svc)

PACIFIC INTERNATIONAL MARKETING, INC.
740 Airport Blvd, Salinas, CA 93912
Tel.: (831) 755-1398 AZ
Web Site: http://www.pim4u.com
Year Founded: 1989
Sales Range: $10-24.9 Million
Emp.: 75
Holding Company; Fresh Fruits & Vegetables Supplier
N.A.I.C.S.: 551112
Dave Johnson (Pres)
David Black (VP)
Veronica Urzua (Dir-HR)
Bryan Searcy (Dir-IT)
Steve Tripp (Gen Counsel)

Subsidiaries:
Dynasty Farms, Inc. (1)
740 Airport Blvd, Salinas, CA 93912-3737
Tel.: (831) 755-1375
Web Site: http://www.pim4u.com
Sales Range: $10-24.9 Million
Emp.: 65
Fresh Fruits & Vegetables Whslr
N.A.I.C.S.: 424480
Tom Russell (Pres)
Dave Johnson (VP)
David Black (COO)

PACIFIC LOGISTICS CORP.
7255 Rosemead Blvd, Pico Rivera, CA 90660
Web Site: http://www.pacific-logistics.com
Year Founded: 1999
Sales Range: $50-74.9 Million
Emp.: 350
Building Logistics Services
N.A.I.C.S.: 488999
Paul Martins (VP-Sls & Mktg)
Timothy Hewey (COO)

PACIFIC LUMBER & SHIPPING CO.
1200 5th Ave, Seattle, WA 98101
Tel.: (206) 682-7262 WA
Web Site: http://www.pls-lumber.com
Year Founded: 1932
Sales Range: $75-99.9 Million
Emp.: 20
Provider of Lumber & Wood Products
N.A.I.C.S.: 321113
Donald Cox (Controller)

PACIFIC MARINE & SUPPLY CO. LTD. INC.
841 Bishop St Ste 1110, Honolulu, HI 96813-3908
Tel.: (808) 531-7001
Web Site: http://www.navatekltd.com
Year Founded: 1950
Sales Range: $25-49.9 Million
Emp.: 500
Deep Sea Passenger Transportation
N.A.I.C.S.: 483112
Steven Loui (Pres & CTO)
Michael Schmicker (VP-Mktg & Corp Comm)

Subsidiaries:
Cap Insurance Company Inc. (1)
PO Box 30989, Honolulu, HI 96820-0989
Tel.: (808) 531-7001
Rev.: $995,581
Emp.: 5
Insurance Agents, Brokers & Service
N.A.I.C.S.: 524210

Catamaran Express Inc. (1)
841 Bishop St Ste 1880, Honolulu, HI 96813-3908
Tel.: (808) 531-7001
Rev.: $110,000
Emp.: 3
Amusement & Recreation
N.A.I.C.S.: 713990

Navatek, Ltd. (1)
841 Bishop St Ste 1110, Honolulu, HI 96813
Tel.: (808) 695-6643
Emp.: 49
Marine Engineering Services
N.A.I.C.S.: 541330

Pacific Shipyards International, LLC (1)
Pier 41 Honolulu Harbor, Honolulu, HI 96820
Tel.: (808) 848-6211
Web Site: http://www.pacificshipyards.com
Sales Range: $1-9.9 Million
Marine Engineering Services
N.A.I.C.S.: 541330
Iain Wood (COO)
Ben Nakaoka (CFO)
John Miller (Mgr-Bus Dev & Coatings Sys)
Scott Fleming (Mgr-Production)
Marvin Miller (Mgr-Quality Assurance, Environmental Health & Safety)
Leilani Dimaya (Controller)

Unitek Insulation Inc. (1)
96-1367 Waihona St, Pearl City, HI 96819-4402
Tel.: (808) 831-3076
Web Site: http://www.unitekhawaii.com
Sales Range: $1-9.9 Million
Emp.: 70
Specialty Trade Contractors
N.A.I.C.S.: 562910

Unitek Technical LLC (1)
PO Box 29177, Honolulu, HI 96820
Tel.: (808) 831-3076
Sales Range: $10-24.9 Million
Emp.: 20
Plastering, Drywall & Insulation
N.A.I.C.S.: 238310
Frank Schumann (Pres)

PACIFIC MARINE CREDIT UNION
1278 Rocky Point Dr, Oceanside, CA 92056
Tel.: (760) 631-8700 CA
Web Site: http://www.pmcu.com
Year Founded: 1952
Sales Range: $25-49.9 Million
Credit Union Operator
N.A.I.C.S.: 522130
George Hoagland (Vice Pres)
Richard B. Rothwell (Chm)
Gary Greving (Treas)
James Cothran (Sec)
Bill Birnie (Pres & CEO)
Todd Kern (CMO)
Sarai Rodgers (Chief HR Officer)

PACIFIC MARKET INTERNATIONAL, LLC
2401 Elliott Ave 4th Fl, Seattle, WA 98121
Tel.: (206) 441-1400 WA
Web Site: http://www.pmi-worldwide.com
Sales Range: $10-24.9 Million
Emp.: 750
Insulated Food & Beverage Container Designer, Mfr & Marketer
N.A.I.C.S.: 332431
Robert M. Harris (Founder & CEO)
Cambria Schmidt (Controller)
Tammy Perkins (Chief People Officer)
Jonathan Spencer (VP-Global Fin)
Leanne LaVere (Dir-Acct Mgmt)
Deb Ryan (Program Dir-Mgmt-Starbucks)

Subsidiaries:
Formation Brands, LLC (1)
400 Oyster Point Blvd Ste 200, South San Francisco, CA 94080
Tel.: (650) 238-1009
Web Site: http://www.formationbrandsllc.com
Emp.: 75
Houseware & Novelty Gift Distr.
N.A.I.C.S.: 449129
Mark Towery (Pres)
Leslie Miller (Founder & Exec VP-Sls Mktg)

PACIFIC MARKETING
21135 Erwin St, Woodland Hills, CA 91367-2512
Tel.: (818) 992-4300
Year Founded: 1995
Rev.: $10,000,000
Emp.: 12
Entertainment, Media Buying Services, Print
N.A.I.C.S.: 541810
David Wood (Owner & Pres)
Marlene Duncan (Treas)
Tera Perez (Dir-Creative)

PACIFIC MATERIAL HOLDING SOLUTIONS, INC.
30361 Whipple Rd, Union City, CA 94587
Tel.: (510) 786-0215
Web Site: http://www.yalepacific.com
Year Founded: 1993
Rev.: $35,887,962
Emp.: 82
Industrial Machinery & Equipment
N.A.I.C.S.: 423830
Ralph Logan (Pres)

PACIFIC MECHANICAL SUPPLY
13705 Milroy Pl, Santa Fe Springs, CA 90670
Tel.: (562) 921-0575
Web Site: http://www.pacmech.com
Rev.: $12,500,000
Emp.: 35
Gaskets
N.A.I.C.S.: 423840
Roger Fowler (Pres)

PACIFIC MEDICAL CENTERS
1200 12th Ave S, Seattle, WA 98144
Tel.: (206) 621-4466 WA
Web Site: http://www.pacificmedicalcenter.org
Year Founded: 2003
Sales Range: $100-124.9 Million
Emp.: 1,004
Health Care Srvices
N.A.I.C.S.: 622110
Linda A. Marzano (CEO)
Greg Clark (Chief Admin Officer)

PACIFIC MICRO-TECH
43218 Business Park Dr Ste 106, Temecula, CA 92590
Tel.: (951) 587-8324
Web Site: http://www.pacificmt.com
Rev.: $900,000
Emp.: 8
Computer System Design Services
N.A.I.C.S.: 541512
Eric D. Gozlan (Pres)

PACIFIC MOBILE STRUCTURES INC.
1554 Bishop Rd, Chehalis, WA 98532
Tel.: (360) 748-0121
Web Site:
http://www.pacificmobile.com
Year Founded: 1983
Rev.: $10,000,000
Emp.: 100
Provider of Modular & Mobile Commercial Buildings
N.A.I.C.S.: 444180
Garth Haakenson (Pres & CEO)
Sean Butler (COO)
Casey Sullivan (CFO)
Sean Butler (COO)
Tom Coyle (Sr VP-Construction & Dev)

Subsidiaries:
Golden Office Trailers Inc. (1)
26414 Murrieta Rd, 92585, Menifee, CA
Tel.: (951) 678-2177
Web Site:
http://www.goldenofficetrailers.com
Manufactured Home Dealers
N.A.I.C.S.: 459930
Hal Woods (Pres)

Pacific Mobile Structures Inc. (1)
4375 Farm Supply Dr, Ceres, CA 95307
Tel.: (209) 524-9128
Web Site: http://www.pacificmobile.com
Sales Range: $10-24.9 Million
Emp.: 21
Equipment Rental & Leasing
N.A.I.C.S.: 532490
Garth Richard (Pres)

PACIFIC MUNICIPAL CONSULTANTS
2729 Prospect Park Dr Ste 220, Rancho Cordova, CA 95670
Tel.: (916) 361-8384 CA
Web Site: http://www.pmcworld.com
Year Founded: 1995
Sales Range: $1-9.9 Million
Emp.: 140
Planning, Environmental & Municipal Services
N.A.I.C.S.: 541620
Philip Carter (Pres)

PACIFIC MUTUAL HOLDING COMPANY
700 Newport Ctr Dr, Newport Beach, CA 92660-6397
Tel.: (949) 219-3011 NE
Web Site:
http://www.pacificmutual.com
Year Founded: 1997
Sales Range: $5-14.9 Billion
Mutual Insurance Holding Company
N.A.I.C.S.: 551112
James T. Morris (Pres & CEO)
Sharon A. Cheever (Gen Counsel & Sr VP)
Edward R. Byrd (Chief Acctg Officer & Sr VP)
Joseph E. Celentano (Chief Risk Officer & Sr VP-Enterprise Risk Mgmt)
Mary Ann Brown (Exec VP)
Kerry Williams (COO)

Subsidiaries:
Pacific LifeCorp (1)
700 Newport Ctr Dr, Newport Beach, CA 92660-6307 (100%)
Tel.: (949) 219-3011
Web Site: http://www.pacificlife.com
Holding Company; Life Insurance
N.A.I.C.S.: 551112
James T. Morris (Chm, Pres & CEO)
Edward R. Byrd (Chief Acctg Officer & Sr VP)
Joseph E. Celentano (Exec VP)
Jane Marie Guoi (Sec & VP)
Jay Orlandi (Gen Counsel & Exec VP)

Subsidiary (Domestic):
Pacific Life Insurance Company (2)
700 Newport Ctr Dr, Newport Beach, CA 92660
Tel.: (949) 219-3011

Web Site: http://www.pacificlife.com
Sales Range: $5-14.9 Billion
Life & Health Insurance Services
N.A.I.C.S.: 524113
Sharon A. Cheever *(Gen Counsel & Sr VP)*
Adrian S. Griggs *(COO & Exec VP)*
Joseph E. Celentano *(Exec VP & Head-Retirement Solutions Div)*
Jane Marie Guon *(Sec & VP)*
Dewey P. Bushaw *(Exec VP-Retirement Solutions)*
Tod Nasser *(Sr VP-Investment Mgmt)*
Howard T. Hirakawa *(Sr VP-Investment Advisor Ops & Portfolio Mgr)*
Frank Boynton *(VP-Ops-Retirement Solutions Div)*
Max Gokhman *(Asst VP & Mgr-Portfolio)*
Carol Sudbeck *(Chief Admin Officer & Exec VP)*
Greg Reber *(Chief Distr Officer/Sr VP-Life Insurance)*
Tim Shaheen *(Sr VP-Strategy, Innovation & IT-Life Insurance)*
Juan Martinez *(VP-Bus & Tech Svcs)*
T. Anthony Premer *(Sr VP-Real Estate Investments)*
Thomas Gibbons *(Sr VP-Corp Dev, Treasury & Tax)*
Mike Shadler *(CIO & Sr VP)*
Kim Cunningham *(Sr VP-HR)*
John Dieck *(Chief Risk Officer & Sr VP-Enterprise Risk Mgmt)*

Subsidiary (Domestic):

Cadence Capital Management LLC (3)
265 Franklin St 4th Fl, Boston, MA 02110
Tel.: (617) 624-3500
Web Site: http://www.cadencecapital.com
Emp.: 50
Equity Investment Firm
N.A.I.C.S.: 523999
Michael J. Skillman *(CEO)*
William B. Bannick *(Mng Dir & Portfolio Mgr)*
Robert L. Fitzpatrick *(Sr Portfolio Mgr)*
Stephen C. Demirjian *(Sr Portfolio Mgr)*
J. Paul Dokas *(Sr Portfolio Mgr)*
Robert E. Ginsberg *(Sr Portfolio Mgr)*
Joseph L. Cargile *(Head-Trader)*
Charles K. Koeniger *(Head-Bus Dev & Client Svc & Dir)*
Kimberly A. Voss *(Compliance Officer)*
Austin M. Kairnes III *(Portfolio Mgr)*

Pacific Life & Annuity Company (3)
700 Newport Center Dr, Newport Beach, CA 92660
Tel.: (949) 219-3011
Web Site: http://www.pacificlife.com
Emp.: 1,000
Life Insurance
N.A.I.C.S.: 524113
James T. Morris *(Chm & CEO)*

Pacific Life Fund Advisors LLC (3)
700 Newport Center Dr, Newport Beach, CA 92660-6397
Tel.: (949) 219-3852
Investment Management Service
N.A.I.C.S.: 523940

Subsidiary (Non-US):

Pacific Life Re Limited (3)
Tower Bridge House Saint Katharines Way, London, E1W 1BA, United Kingdom
Tel.: (44) 2077091700
Web Site: http://www.pacificlifere.com
Sales Range: $50-74.9 Million
Emp.: 50
Insurance, Annuity & Financial Services
N.A.I.C.S.: 524298
Dave Howell *(CEO)*
James Tait *(Head-Protection-Europe)*
Andy McAleese *(Head-Longevity)*
Darren Spriggs *(Mng Dir-Europe)*
Hamish Wilson *(Head-R&D-Europe)*
Andrew Murphy *(Head-Longevity-Europe)*
Phill Beach *(Head-Pricing-Europe)*
Andrew Gill *(Mng Dir-Australia & Asia)*
Duncan Hayward *(CFO)*
Paul Lewis *(Chief Pricing Officer)*
George Scott *(Chief Risk Officer & Gen Counsel)*
Toby Strauss *(Chm)*

Branch (Non-US):

Pacific Life Re Limited (4)
182 Cecil Street 07-01 02 Frasers Tower, Singapore, 069547, Singapore
Tel.: (65) 63115411
Web Site: http://www.pacificlifere.com
Sales Range: $75-99.9 Million
Emp.: 50
Annuity & Life Insurance Services
N.A.I.C.S.: 524298
Andrew Gill *(Mng Dir-Australia & Asia)*

Subsidiary (Non-US):

Pacific Services Canada Limited (4)
375 University Avenue Suite 600, Toronto, M5G 2J5, ON, Canada
Tel.: (416) 408-9900
General Insurance Services
N.A.I.C.S.: 524210

Subsidiary (Domestic):

Pacific Select Distributors, Inc. (3)
700 Newport Ctr Dr, Newport Beach, CA 92660-6307 (100%)
Tel.: (949) 219-3881
Web Site: http://www.pacificlife.com
Emp.: 2,000
Life Insurance & Pension Fund Administration Services
N.A.I.C.S.: 524292
James T. Morris *(CEO)*

United Planners' Financial Services of America (3)
7333 E Doubletree Ranch Rd Ste 120, Scottsdale, AZ 85258-2051
Tel.: (480) 991-0225
Web Site: http://www.unitedplanners.com
Sales Range: $50-74.9 Million
Emp.: 40
Broker & Dealer Limited Partnership
N.A.I.C.S.: 523150

PACIFIC NATIONAL GROUP
2392 S Bateman Ave, Irwindale, CA 91010-3312
Tel.: (626) 357-4400 CA
Web Site: http://www.pacnatgroup.com
Year Founded: 1954
Sales Range: $25-49.9 Million
Emp.: 38
Commercial Building Construction Contractor
N.A.I.C.S.: 236220
Arden L. Boren *(Pres & CFO)*
Ciaran Barry *(VP-Construction)*
Steve Mathison *(VP-Construction)*
Joseph F. Cheatham *(VP-Estimating)*

PACIFIC NISSAN INC.
94 1299 Ka Uka Blvd, Waipahu, HI 96797
Tel.: (808) 680-7150
Web Site: http://www.tonynissan.com
Sales Range: $25-49.9 Million
Emp.: 50
Sell New & Used Car & Service & Parts
N.A.I.C.S.: 441110
Tony Masamitsu *(Chm)*
Stan Masamitsu *(Pres)*
Mike Koga *(CFO & VP)*

PACIFIC NORTHERN ENVIRONMENTAL CORP
1121 Columbia Blvd, Longview, WA 98632
Tel.: (360) 423-2245
Web Site: http://www.pnecorp.com
Year Founded: 1989
Sales Range: $10-24.9 Million
Emp.: 50
Service Station Equipment Installation, Maintenance & Repair
N.A.I.C.S.: 238990
Spencer Partridge *(CEO)*
Christian E. Lund *(Chm)*
John Birrell *(CFO)*
Todd Partridge *(Exec VP)*
David Bristol *(Gen Counsel & VP)*

Subsidiaries:

Cowlitz Clean Sweep (1)
55 Intl Way, Longview, WA 98632
Tel.: (360) 423-6316
Web Site: http://www.pnecorp.com
Emp.: 200
Environmental Cleanup Services
N.A.I.C.S.: 562910
John Partridge *(Pres & CEO)*
Steve Jabusch *(Sr VP)*
Spencer Partridge *(Gen Mgr)*

PACIFIC NORTHWEST CAPITAL CORP..
1820 N. Midland Blvd., Nampa, ID 83651
Tel.: (208) 461-0555
Web Site: http://www.pacificnwcapital.com
Holding Company
N.A.I.C.S.: 523999
Rick Meyer *(Co-Chm)*
Travis Meyer *(Co-Chm, CEO & Pres)*
Mark Adrian Oliver *(Treas)*
Todd Boeve *(Sec)*

Subsidiaries:

Idens Detailing Inc (1)
PO Box 88594, Seattle, WA 98138-2594
Tel.: (425) 226-2805
Web Site: http://www.idensdealerservices.com
Sales Range: $1-9.9 Million
Emp.: 50
Automotive Body, Paint & Interior Repair & Maintenance Services
N.A.I.C.S.: 811121
Kevin Iden *(Pres)*
Kyle Ferguson *(Gen Mgr)*
Rob Zippro *(Mgr-Ops-South)*
Joe Bonogofsky *(Mgr-Ops-North)*
Amanda Eckert *(Office Mgr)*

PACIFIC NORTHWEST FARMERS COOPERATIVE
117 W Chestnut St, Genesee, ID 83832
Tel.: (208) 285-1141 ID
Web Site: http://www.pnw.coop
Grains Producer & Whlsr
N.A.I.C.S.: 424510
Jeff Hall *(Chm)*
Frank Wolf *(Vice Chm)*
Aaron Gfeller *(Sec)*

Subsidiaries:

Pacific Northwest Farmers Cooperative-Genesee (1)
117 W Chestnut, Genesee, ID 83832
Tel.: (208) 285-1141
Web Site: http://www.pnw.coop
Grain Producer & Whlsr
N.A.I.C.S.: 424510
Bill Newbry *(CEO)*

PACIFIC OFFICE AUTOMATION, INC.
14747 NW Greenbrier Pkwy, Beaverton, OR 97006
Tel.: (503) 601-2228 OR
Web Site: http://www.pacificoffice.com
Year Founded: 1976
Sales Range: $25-49.9 Million
Emp.: 325
Sale of Copy & Fax Machines
N.A.I.C.S.: 459999
Terry Newsom *(Pres)*
Gerry Romjue *(Controller)*
John Totah *(VP)*
Rob Murray *(Acct Mgr)*
Rich Frunk *(Mgr-Tech)*

Subsidiaries:

Fenton's Office Solutions, Inc. (1)
565 1st St, Idaho Falls, ID 83401
Tel.: (208) 523-1444
Web Site: http://fos1.biz
Office Equipment Merchant Whlsr
N.A.I.C.S.: 423420
Vernon Fenton *(Owner)*

Northwest Office Technologies Inc. (1)
6280 E Seltice Way Ste B, Post Falls, ID 83854-5055
Tel.: (208) 769-7572
Web Site: http://www.nwotech.com
Office Equipment Merchant Whlsr
N.A.I.C.S.: 423420
Rick Wickham *(Pres & CEO)*

PACIFIC OFFICE INTERIORS
5304 Derry Ave Ste U, Agoura Hills, CA 91301
Tel.: (818) 735-0333
Web Site: http://www.poi.bz
Year Founded: 1986
Sales Range: $10-24.9 Million
Emp.: 30
Interior Design Consulting Services
N.A.I.C.S.: 541410
Free Taylor *(Pres)*
Ward Smith *(Principal)*
Scott Haws *(Mgr-Ops)*

PACIFIC OIL COMPANY LLC
1325 W Foothill Blvd, Upland, CA 91786
Tel.: (909) 875-8757 CA
Year Founded: 1998
Sales Range: $100-124.9 Million
Emp.: 90
Gasoline Service Station & Carwash
N.A.I.C.S.: 457110
Mirshafiee Nasrolah *(Pres)*
Ahmed Dehbozorg *(CFO)*
Hossein Dehbozorg *(Sec)*

PACIFIC OUTDOOR LIVING
8309 Tujunga Ave Ste 201, Sun Valley, CA 91352
Tel.: (818) 293-2709
Web Site: http://pacificoutdoorliving.com
Landscaping Design & Construction Services
N.A.I.C.S.: 561730
Terry Morrill *(Owner & Founder)*

Subsidiaries:

Pacific Pavingstone (1)
8309 Tujunga Ave Ste 101, Sun Valley, CA 91352
Tel.: (818) 658-9370
Web Site: http://www.pacificpavingstone.com
Landscaping Design & Services, Masonry & Concrete
N.A.I.C.S.: 561730
Terry Morrill *(Owner)*

PACIFIC PACKAGING PRODUCTS, INC.
24 Industrial Way, Wilmington, MA 01887-3434
Tel.: (978) 657-9100 MA
Web Site: http://www.pacificpkg.com
Year Founded: 1952
Sales Range: $25-49.9 Million
Emp.: 140
Provider of Industrial Services
N.A.I.C.S.: 424130
Robert H. Goldstein *(Treas)*
Frank D. Goldstein *(Pres)*
David A. Varsano *(Chm & CEO)*

PACIFIC PARTS & CONTROLS INC.
6255 Prescott Ct, Chino, CA 91710
Tel.: (909) 465-1174
Web Site: http://www.pacificparts.com
Rev.: $15,100,000
Emp.: 15
Electrical Supplies, Nec
N.A.I.C.S.: 423610

PACIFIC PARTS & CONTROLS INC.

U.S. PRIVATE

Pacific Parts & Controls Inc.—(Continued)
Frank Renek *(Pres)*
Kevin Renek *(VP-Sls)*
Wayne Melanson *(VP & Gen Mgr)*

PACIFIC PAVINGSTONE, INC.
8309 Tujunga Ave Ste 201, Sun Valley, CA 91352
Tel.: (818) 244-4000
Web Site:
http://www.pacificpavingstone.com
Sales Range: $1-9.9 Million
Emp.: 150
Concrete Contractor
N.A.I.C.S.: 238110
Chad Morrill *(Owner)*

PACIFIC PIONEER INSURANCE GROUP INC.
6363 Katella Ave, Cypress, CA 90630
Tel.: (714) 228-7888 DE
Web Site: http://www.pacpioneer.com
Year Founded: 1989
Sales Range: $25-49.9 Million
Emp.: 60
Provider of Insurance Services
N.A.I.C.S.: 524210
Lin W. Lan *(Founder & Pres)*
Robert Lan *(Dir-Comml Underwriting Division)*
Ping Chen *(CFO)*

PACIFIC PLUMBING SUPPLY CO.
7115 W Marginal Way SW, Seattle, WA 98106-1911
Tel.: (206) 762-5920 WA
Web Site:
http://www.pacificplumbing.com
Year Founded: 1949
Sales Range: $10-24.9 Million
Emp.: 110
Mfr of Plumbing Fixtures & Equipment
N.A.I.C.S.: 423720
Larry Solomon *(Pres & CEO)*
Brad McDonald *(VP-Sls)*
Jon Stafford *(CFO, Treas, Sec & VP)*
Ron Abramson *(VP & Gen Mgr)*
Sherri Norton *(Mgr-Credit)*
Cathy Kirk *(Controller)*
Dave Sokoloski *(VP-Info Sys)*
David Richards *(Mgr-Freight & Logistics)*

PACIFIC POWER PRODUCTS COMPANY
600 S 56th Pl, Ridgefield, WA 98642
Tel.: (360) 887-7400
Web Site: http://www.pacificdda.com
Year Founded: 1984
Sales Range: $75-99.9 Million
Emp.: 350
Mfr of Industrial Machinery & Equipments
N.A.I.C.S.: 423830
Barry Ward *(Mgr-Parts)*
Tim Burkhart *(Mgr-Parts)*

Subsidiaries:

Pacific Truck Centers (1)
487 South 56th Pl, Ridgefield, WA 98642
Tel.: (360) 887-7400
Web Site: http://www.pac-truck.com
Truck Retailer
N.A.I.C.S.: 441120

PACIFIC POWER SOURCE, INC.
17692 Fitch, Irvine, CA 92614
Tel.: (949) 251-1800
Web Site:
http://www.pacificpower.com
Year Founded: 1971
Sales Range: $1-9.9 Million

Emp.: 35
Power Supplies
N.A.I.C.S.: 334419
Kevin Voelcker *(Pres)*
Mitchel Orr *(Mgr-Sls)*

PACIFIC PRECISION LABORATORIES, INC.
20447 Nordhoff St, Chatsworth, CA 91311-5808
Tel.: (818) 700-8977 CA
Web Site: http://www.ppli.com
Year Founded: 1985
Designs, Engineers & Manufactures Precision Metrology & Process Control Instruments for Computer Disk Drives
N.A.I.C.S.: 335314
Chandu Vanjani *(Pres & CEO)*
Chandu Vanjani *(Pres)*

PACIFIC PRECISION METALS, INC.
10850 Wilshire Blvd 6th Fl, Los Angeles, CA 90024
Tel.: (909) 390-6782 CA
Web Site: http://www.pacificpm.com
Year Founded: 1950
Sales Range: $50-74.9 Million
Emp.: 6
Metal Stamping
N.A.I.C.S.: 332119
John Wallace *(Pres)*

Subsidiaries:

Tubing Seal Cap (1)
601 S Vincent Ave, Azusa, CA 91702-5102 (100%)
Tel.: (626) 334-0361
N.A.I.C.S.: 332119

PACIFIC PRESS PUBLISHING ASSOCIATION
1350 N Kings Rd, Nampa, ID 83687
Tel.: (208) 465-2500
Web Site:
http://www.pacificpress.com
Rev.: $29,378,153
Emp.: 180
Periodicals, Publishing & Printing
N.A.I.C.S.: 513120
Dale Galusha *(Pres)*
Doug Church *(VP-Mktg & Sls)*

PACIFIC PRIDE SEAFOOD INC.
4520 107th St SW, Mukilteo, WA 98275
Tel.: (425) 347-7994
Web Site:
http://www.pacseafoods.com
Rev.: $20,600,000
Emp.: 100
Fish & Seafood Merchant Whslr
N.A.I.C.S.: 424460
Frank Dominic Dulcich *(Pres)*

PACIFIC PROPERTIES III
66 E Santa Clara St, San Jose, CA 95113
Tel.: (408) 298-8600
Sales Range: $25-49.9 Million
Emp.: 25
Real Estate Investors, Except Property Operators
N.A.I.C.S.: 523999
Elizabeth Groendike *(Controller)*

Subsidiaries:

Saratoga Capital Inc. (1)
485 Alberto Way, Los Gatos, CA 95032
Tel.: (408) 298-8600
Web Site: http://saratogacapitalapts.com
Mortgage Banker
N.A.I.C.S.: 522292

PACIFIC RAIL SERVICES LLC

1131 SW Klickitat Way, Seattle, WA 98134
Tel.: (206) 382-4462
Web Site:
http://www.pacificrailservices.com
Sales Range: $25-49.9 Million
Emp.: 70
Provider of Railroad Maintenance & Repair Services
N.A.I.C.S.: 488210
John Gray *(Mng Partner)*

PACIFIC REALTY ASSOCIATES, LP
15350 SW Sequoia Pkwy Ste 300, Portland, OR 97224-7175
Tel.: (503) 624-6300 DE
Web Site: http://www.pactrust.com
Year Founded: 1972
Sales Range: $25-49.9 Million
Emp.: 100
Real Estate Investment Trust; Property Owner, Developer & Manager
N.A.I.C.S.: 525990
Peter F. Bechen *(Pres & CEO)*
John C. Hart *(CFO)*
David W. Ramus *(COO)*

Subsidiaries:

M&T Partners (1)
15350 SW Sequoia Pkwy Ste 300, Portland, OR 97224-7172 (100%)
Tel.: (503) 624-6300
Web Site: http://www.pactrust.com
Sales Range: $25-49.9 Million
Emp.: 45
Real Estate Developers & Investment Property Owners
N.A.I.C.S.: 531210
Peter F. Bechen *(Pres & CEO)*
John C. Hart *(CFO)*
David W. Ramus *(COO)*

PAC/SIB L.L.C. (1)
15350 SW Sequoia Pkwy Ste 300, Portland, OR 97224
Tel.: (503) 624-6300
Real Estate Property Leasing Services
N.A.I.C.S.: 531190

PACIFIC RUBBER & PACKING, INC.
1160 Indus Rd Ste 3, San Carlos, CA 94070
Tel.: (650) 595-5888 CA
Web Site:
http://www.pacificrubber.com
Year Founded: 1973
Sales Range: $10-24.9 Million
Emp.: 25
Distr of Mechanical Rubber Products & Sealing Components
N.A.I.C.S.: 423840
Peter C. Burfield *(Founder)*
Ashley Burfield *(Pres)*

PACIFIC SANDS, INC.
4611 Green Bay Rd, Kenosha, WI 53144
Tel.: (262) 925-0123
Web Site:
http://www.pacificsandsinc.com
Household & Commercial Cleaning Product Mfr
N.A.I.C.S.: 325612
Michael D. Michie *(Pres & CEO)*

PACIFIC SERVICE CREDIT UNION
3000 Clayton Rd, Concord, CA 94519
Tel.: (925) 609-5000 CA
Web Site:
http://www.pacificservice.org
Year Founded: 1939
Sales Range: $25-49.9 Million
Emp.: 107
Credit Union
N.A.I.C.S.: 522130

Stephen Punch *(Pres & CEO)*
Nannette Cutliff *(VP)*
Kristin Dove *(VP)*
Virginia Lampson *(VP)*
Barbara Smith *(VP)*

PACIFIC SHIP REPAIR & FABRICATION
1625 Rigel St, San Diego, CA 92113
Tel.: (619) 232-3200
Web Site: http://www.pacship.com
Sales Range: $10-24.9 Million
Emp.: 200
Mfr & Repair of Ships
N.A.I.C.S.: 336611
John Figueroa *(Supvr)*
Gary Thomas *(Dir-Contracts)*

PACIFIC SHORE STONES
13148 Raymer St N, Hollywood, CA 91605
Tel.: (818) 765-7454
Web Site:
http://www.pacificshorestones.com
Year Founded: 2004
Sales Range: $25-49.9 Million
Emp.: 75
Importer & Whslr of Exotic Natural Stones
N.A.I.C.S.: 423320
Marcus Santos *(Gen Mgr)*

PACIFIC SOFTWARE PUBLISHING, INC.
1404 140th Pl NE, Bellevue, WA 98007
Tel.: (425) 957-0808 WA
Web Site: http://www.pspinc.com
Year Founded: 1987
Sales Range: $1-9.9 Million
Emp.: 45
Internet & Computer Services
N.A.I.C.S.: 541512
Ken Uchikura *(Founder & Chm)*
Mayumi Nakamura *(Pres & CEO)*

PACIFIC SOURCE INC.
20321 Broadway Ave, Snohomish, WA 98296
Tel.: (425) 483-5511
Web Site: http://www.pacsource.com
Year Founded: 1993
Sales Range: $25-49.9 Million
Emp.: 75
Building Materials
N.A.I.C.S.: 423310
Mark Mason *(Reg Gen Mgr)*
Rob Bruce *(Mgr-Oahu)*
Joshua Ladd *(Mgr-Ops)*

PACIFIC SOUTHWEST COMMUNITY DEVELOPMENT CORPORATION
16935 W Bernardo Dr Ste 238, San Diego, CA 92127
Tel.: (858) 675-0506 CA
Web Site: http://www.pswcdc.org
Year Founded: 1996
Sales Range: $1-9.9 Million
Emp.: 35
Community Development Services
N.A.I.C.S.: 624190
Robert W. Laing *(Pres & Exec Dir)*
Juan P. Arroyo *(Exec Dir-Svcs)*
Tony Reyes *(Treas & Sec)*

PACIFIC STAINLESS PRODUCTS
58500 McNulty Way, Saint Helens, OR 97051
Tel.: (503) 641-7060
Web Site:
http://www.pacificstainless.com
Sales Range: $10-24.9 Million
Emp.: 90

Fabricated Steel Plate Work (Boiler Shop)
N.A.I.C.S.: 332313
Jeff Kemp *(Pres & CEO)*
Darrell Schuh *(VP-Sls)*
Stewart Melanie *(Controller)*
Sven Christofferson *(Gen Mgr)*
Trevor Brooks *(Mgr-Acct)*
Trina Yungen *(Acct Mgr-Sls)*
Jason Burgess *(Mgr-Quality Control)*
Floyd Humphrey *(Mgr-Engrg)*
Bob Ruth *(Mgr-Exhaust Sys)*
Jasen Cox *(Mgr-Installation)*
Michael Deuker *(Mgr-Production)*
Josh Grabner *(Mgr-Shipping & Receiving)*
Dennis Sugihara *(Treas)*

PACIFIC STAR COMMUNICATIONS, INC.
15055 SW Sequoia Pkwy Ste 100, Portland, OR 97224
Tel.: (503) 403-3000
Web Site: http://www.pacstar.com
Year Founded: 2000
Sales Range: $25-49.9 Million
Encrypted Voice, Data, Security & Other Telecommunication Services
N.A.I.C.S.: 541512
George Stroemple *(Chm)*
Charlie Kawasaki *(CTO)*
Jeff Sinclair *(VP-Sls)*
Peggy Miller *(CEO, Treas & Sec)*
Ed Rissberger *(VP-Product Dev)*
Rodney Snell *(Dir-Software Dev)*
Noelle Martz *(Dir-HR)*

PACIFIC STATES INDUSTRIES INCORPORATED
2 W Santa Clara St Fl 9, San Jose, CA 95113-1824
Tel.: (408) 271-7900
Web Site: http://www.sierrafence.com
Year Founded: 1979
Sales Range: $50-74.9 Million
Emp.: 575
Holding Company For Lumber, Fencing & Decks Contracting
N.A.I.C.S.: 423310
Roger Burch *(Pres)*
Austin Vanderhoof *(CFO)*
Thomas Tuttle *(Controller)*

Subsidiaries:

Sierra Lumber & Fence   (1)
1711 Senter Rd, San Jose, CA 95112-2515
Tel.: (408) 286-6975
Web Site: http://www.sierrafence.com
Rev.: $23,600,000
Emp.: 125
Lumber, Fencing & Decks-Contracting
N.A.I.C.S.: 238990
Jim Mobled *(Gen Mgr)*

Sierra Lumber & Fence   (1)
2 W Santa Clara St Fl 9, San Jose, CA 95113-1824
Tel.: (916) 688-8489
Sales Range: $10-24.9 Million
Emp.: 50
Lumber, Fencing & Decks-Contracting
N.A.I.C.S.: 238990

PACIFIC STEEL CASTING COMPANY
1333 2nd St, Berkeley, CA 94710-1317
Tel.: (510) 525-9200   CA
Web Site: http://www.pacificsteel.com
Year Founded: 1934
Sales Range: $100-124.9 Million
Emp.: 400
Mfr of Steel Castings
N.A.I.C.S.: 331513
Chuck Bridges *(CFO)*
Freddy Rivera *(Gen Mgr-Mfg)*
Chris Garlieb *(VP-Mktg)*

PACIFIC SUPERMARKET INC.
1420 Southgate Ave, Daly City, CA 94015
Tel.: (650) 994-1688
Rev.: $14,100,000
Emp.: 52
Grocery Stores, Independent
N.A.I.C.S.: 445110
Ken Jones *(Mgr)*
Don Nhan *(Mgr)*

PACIFIC SUPPLY COMPANY
675 N Batavia St, Orange, CA 92868
Tel.: (714) 633-6330
Web Site: http://www.pacificsupply.com
Sales Range: $100-124.9 Million
Emp.: 140
Distr of Roofing, Asphalt & Sheet Metal
N.A.I.C.S.: 423330
Jason Tayler *(Gen Mgr)*

PACIFIC SYMPHONY
3631 S Harbor Blvd Ste 100, Santa Ana, CA 92704-8908
Tel.: (714) 755-5788   CA
Web Site: http://www.pacificsymphony.org
Year Founded: 1980
Sales Range: $10-24.9 Million
Emp.: 392
Orchestra & Band Operator
N.A.I.C.S.: 711510
Eileen Jeanette *(VP-Artistic & Orchestra Ops)*
Gregory Pierre Cox *(VP-Dev)*
Brandon Rueda *(Dir-Orchestra Ops)*
Alan Ball *(Assoc VP-Dev)*
Mike Kerr *(Chm)*
Sean Sutton *(COO & Exec VP)*
Susan Miller Kotses *(Dir-Education & Community Engagement)*
Frank Terraglio *(VP-Mktg & PR)*
Lorraine Caukin *(Dir-Sls)*
John E. Forsyte *(Pres)*
Susan Anderson *(Sec)*
Joann Leatherby *(Vice Chm-Dev)*
Christopher D. Tower *(Vice Chm-Dev)*
Mark Nielsen *(Vice Chm-Fin & Treas)*
Alison Levinson *(Dir-Community Arts Participation)*
Bella Staav *(Dir-Youth Ensembles)*
Jean Oelrich *(Dir-Mktg & Loyalty Programs)*
Jesse Hiser *(Dir-Fin)*
Kurt Mortensen *(Dir-Audience Engagement)*
Luisa Cariaga *(Dir-Institutional Giving)*
Mary Hawkes *(Dir-Community Engagement)*
Tania Batson *(Assoc Dir-Individual Giving)*

PACIFIC TOLL PROCESSING, INC.
24724 S Wilmington Ave, Carson, CA 90745
Tel.: (310) 952-4992
Web Site: http://www.pacifictoll.com
Year Founded: 2001
Rev.: $23,900,000
Emp.: 37
Service Centers for Steel Sheet, Coil Distribution & Toll Processing
N.A.I.C.S.: 561990
Mark Proner *(Exec VP)*
Conni Fields *(Gen Mgr)*
Antony Camasta *(Pres)*

PACIFIC TOMATO GROWERS LTD.
503 Tenth St W, Palmetto, FL 34221-3801
Tel.: (941) 722-3291   FL

Web Site: http://www.sunripeproduce.com
Year Founded: 1982
Sales Range: $100-124.9 Million
Emp.: 300
Fruits & Vegetables Grower
N.A.I.C.S.: 111219
Liz Esformes *(Mgr-Mktg)*
Joey Poklemba *(Mgr-Sls)*
Billy L. Heller Jr. *(CEO)*

PACIFIC TRANSPORTATION LINES, INC.
94-360 Ukee St Ste A, Waipahu, HI 96797
Tel.: (808) 834-2677   HI
Web Site: http://www.pftl.com
Year Founded: 1989
Freight Transportation Arrangement
N.A.I.C.S.: 488510
James E. T. Koshiba *(Pres)*

PACIFIC UNION INTERNATIONAL, INC.
1699 Van Ness Ave, San Francisco, CA 94109
Tel.: (415) 345-3000
Web Site: http://www.pacificunion.com
Year Founded: 1975
Real Estate Development Services
N.A.I.C.S.: 531390
Mark A. McLaughlin *(CEO)*
Selma Hepp *(VP-Bus Intelligence)*
John Wright *(Sr VP-Pacific Union Comml)*
Vic Borelli *(Sr VP/Reg Dir-Pacific Union Comml)*
Brent Thompson *(COO)*
Chatty Arrieta *(VP-Ops)*

Subsidiaries:

Empire Realty Associates, Inc.   (1)
380 Diablo Rd, Danville, CA 94526
Tel.: (925) 217-5000
Web Site: http://www.empirerealty.com
Sales Range: $1-9.9 Million
Emp.: 50
Real Estate Agency
N.A.I.C.S.: 531210
Judi Keenholtz *(CEO)*
Brian Moggan *(Gen Mgr)*

Gibson International   (1)
11538 San Vicente Blvd, Los Angeles, CA 90049   (55%)
Tel.: (310) 820-0195
Web Site: http://www.gibsonintl.com
Sales Range: $10-24.9 Million
Emp.: 125
Real Estate Manangement Services
N.A.I.C.S.: 531210
Pat Heller *(Exec VP & Mgr-Sls)*
Scott Gibson *(Pres & CEO)*

The Mark Company / Pacific Union International, Inc.   (1)
1699 Van Ness, San Francisco, CA 94109   (100%)
Tel.: (415) 615-6815
Web Site: http://www.themarkcompany.com
Sales Range: $1-9.9 Million
Emp.: 23
Urban Residential Marketing & Sales
N.A.I.C.S.: 531210
Alan P. Mark *(Pres)*
Andy Ardila *(VP-Sls)*
Krysen Heathwood *(Mng Principal & Exec VP)*
Maranda Blanton *(Dir-Dev)*
Doug Shaw *(Principal)*
Hans Treuenfels *(Principal)*

PACIFIC VALLEY FOODS INC.
2700 Richards Rd Ste 101, Bellevue, WA 98005
Tel.: (425) 643-1805
Web Site: http://www.pacificvalleyfoods.com
Sales Range: Less than $1 Million
Emp.: 7

General Line Grocery Merchant Whslr
N.A.I.C.S.: 424410
John Hannah *(Pres)*
Scott C. Hannah *(Co-Owner, Chm & CEO)*
Lynn M. Hannah *(Co-Owner)*

PACIFIC VALLEY INVESTORS INC.
1050 Ralston Ave, Belmont, CA 94002
Tel.: (650) 637-8865
Web Site: http://www.pvihotelgroup.com
Year Founded: 1979
Emp.: 12
Property & Asset Management Services
N.A.I.C.S.: 523940
Debra Hopkins *(Dir-HR)*
Gary R. Bruton *(VP-Ops)*

PACIFIC WESTERN AGENCIES, INC.
7700 2nd Ave S, Seattle, WA 98108
Tel.: (206) 763-1802
Web Site: http://www.pacwestern.com
Sales Range: $50-74.9 Million
Electrical Cables Mfr & Distr
N.A.I.C.S.: 423610
Gary L. Ginter *(Pres)*

PACIFIC WOOD LAMINATES INC.
885 Railroad Ave, Brookings, OR 97415
Tel.: (541) 469-4177   OR
Web Site: http://www.pacificwoodlaminate.com
Year Founded: 1995
Sales Range: $50-74.9 Million
Emp.: 300
Softwood, Veneer & Plywood
N.A.I.C.S.: 321212
Ronald T. Fallert *(CEO)*
Gordon M. Ball *(CFO)*
Tim Beckley *(Mgr-HR)*
James Bruggeman *(Gen Mgr)*
Kenneth Caylor *(Mgr-Sls)*
Jeff Groom *(Co-CFO)*

PACIFIC WOOD PRESERVING OF BAKERSFIELD, INC.
5601 District Blvd, Bakersfield, CA 93313
Tel.: (661) 617-6385   NV
Web Site: http://www.pacificwood.com
Year Founded: 1979
Sales Range: $10-24.9 Million
Emp.: 23
Wood Preservation Treatment Services
N.A.I.C.S.: 321114
Richard F. Jackson *(Pres & CEO)*

PACIFICA COMPANIES, LLC
1785 Hancock St Ste 200, San Diego, CA 92110
Tel.: (619) 296-9000   CA
Web Site: https://www.pacificacompanies.com
Year Founded: 1978
Emp.: 3,000
Real Estate & Hotel Operations Services
N.A.I.C.S.: 531390
Deepak Israni *(Pres & Mng Dir)*
Adam Metzger *(VP & Dir-Debt Acq)*
Allison Rolfe *(Dir-Plng)*
Scott Russell *(Dir-Acq & Dev)*
Naresh Kotwani *(Principal)*
John Phillips *(CFO)*

PACIFICA COMPANIES, LLC

Pacifica Companies, LLC—(Continued)
Tom Sayer (Gen Counsel)
Derek Jensen (Dir-Acq)
Matt Reams (Dir-Acq)
Subsidiaries:

California-Nevada Methodist Homes (1)
201 19th St Ste 100, Oakland, CA 94612
Tel.: (510) 893-8989
Web Site: http://www.cnmh.org
Sales Range: $10-24.9 Million
Emp.: 292
Continuing Care Retirement Community Services
N.A.I.C.S.: 623311

Pacifica Host Hotels (1)
1775 Hancock St Ste 200, San Diego, CA 92110
Tel.: (619) 296-9000
Web Site: http://corporate.pacificahost.com
Sales Range: $10-24.9 Million
Emp.: 50
Hotel Operator
N.A.I.C.S.: 721110
Ashok Israni (Chm & Pres)

PACIFICA REAL ESTATE GROUP, LLC
200 E Carrillo St Ste 100, Santa Barbara, CA 93101-2102
Tel.: (805) 899-2400 CA
Web Site:
  http://www.pacificarealestate.com
Year Founded: 1969
Sales Range: $75-99.9 Million
Emp.: 30
Commercial Real Estate Investment, Property Management & Leasing Services
N.A.I.C.S.: 531390
E. Russell Fraser (Principal)
Arlene M. Kostock (CFO & Exec VP)
Robert C. Gibbs (Principal)

PACIFICA SENIOR LIVING
5417 Wesleyan Dr, Virginia Beach, VA 23455-6922
Tel.: (757) 541-2186
Web Site: http://www.pacificavirginiabeach.com
Continuing Care Retirement Communities
N.A.I.C.S.: 623311
Marika Johnson (VP-Ops)
Subsidiaries:

Scottsdale Residential Care Investors (1)
2620 N 68th St, Scottsdale, AZ 85257-1202
Tel.: (480) 946-6571
Web Site:
  http://www.pacificaseniorliving.com
Senior Care Homes
N.A.I.C.S.: 623312

PACIFICA SERVICES, INC.
106 S Mentor Ave Ste 200, Pasadena, CA 91106-2931
Tel.: (626) 405-0131 CA
Web Site:
  http://www.pacificaservices.com
Year Founded: 1979
Sales Range: $75-99.9 Million
Emp.: 80
Provider of Civil Engineering, Electronic Equipment Repair & Business Consulting Services
N.A.I.C.S.: 541330
Ernest M. Camacho (Pres & CEO)
Stephen Caropino (Exec VP)
Desiree De La O (VP-Admin)

PACIFICO ENTERPRISES, INC.
6701 Essington Ave, Philadelphia, PA 19153-3407
Tel.: (215) 492-1700 PA
Web Site:
  http://www.pacificocars.com
Year Founded: 1923
Sales Range: $75-99.9 Million
Emp.: 170
New & Used Automobiles Retailer
N.A.I.C.S.: 441110
Kerry T. Pacifico (Partner & Mgr)
Joe David Pacifico (Owner)
Michael Pacifico (Treas & Sec)

PACIFICO FORD, INC.
6701 Essington Ave, Philadelphia, PA 19153
Tel.: (215) 492-1700
Web Site:
  http://www.pacificoford.com
Sales Range: $250-299.9 Million
Emp.: 170
Car Whslr
N.A.I.C.S.: 441110
Georgenia Wigand (Coord-Sls)

PACIFICSOURCE HEALTH PLANS
110 International Way, Springfield, OR 97477
Tel.: (541) 686-1242
Web Site:
  http://www.pacificsource.com
Year Founded: 1933
Sales Range: $100-124.9 Million
Emp.: 375
Accident & Health Insurance Carriers
N.A.I.C.S.: 524114
Ken Provencher (Pres & CEO)
Peter Davidson (CFO & Exec VP)
Erick Doolen (COO & Exec VP)
Troy Kirk (Sr VP-Grp Sls)
Tony Kopki (VP-Comml Programs)
Dan Stevens (Exec VP-Product Line Mgmt)
Sharon Thomson (Exec VP-Community Strategy & Mktg)
Kevin Corcoran (Sls Dir-Seattle)
Todd Lovshin (VP & Dir-Washington)

PACIFICWIDE BUSINESS GROUP, INC.
3005 Silver Creek Rd Ste 210-214, San Jose, CA 95121
Tel.: (408) 532-1278 CA
Web Site: http://www.pacificwide.com
Year Founded: 2009
Real Estate Brokerage Services
N.A.I.C.S.: 531210
Leon Lee (Founder & CEO)

PACIUGO FRANCHISING, LP
1215 Viceroy Dr, Dallas, TX 75247
Tel.: (214) 654-9501 TX
Web Site: http://www.paciugo.com
Year Founded: 2000
Sales Range: $10-24.9 Million
Emp.: 40
Ice Cream Mfr
N.A.I.C.S.: 311520
Cristiana Acerbi Ginatta (Founder)

PACKABLE HOLDINGS, LLC
1516 Motor Pkwy, Hauppauge, NY 11788
Tel.: (855) 797-2257
Web Site: http://www.packable.com
Year Founded: 2010
Holding Company
N.A.I.C.S.: 551112
Andrew Vagenas (CEO)
Andreas Schulmeyer (CFO)
Chris Pfeiffer (COO)
Adam Rodgers (Chief Growth Officer)
Ash Mehra (CIO)
Leanna Bautista (Chief People Officer)
Subsidiaries:

Pharmapacks, LLC (1)
110-25 14th Ave, College Point, NY 11356
Web Site: http://www.pharmapacks.com
Online Health & Beauty Products Retailer
N.A.I.C.S.: 456110
Bradley Tramunti (Co-Founder & CMO)
Andrew Vagenas (Co-Founder & CEO)
James Mastronardi (CFO & Co-Founder)
Jonathan Webb (Partner & Pres)
Adam J. Berkowitz (Partner & COO)
Merri Hakobyan (Mgr-Accounts, Mktg & Strategy)

PACKAGE MACHINERY COMPANY, INC.
380 Union St Ste 58, West Springfield, MA 01089-4123
Tel.: (413) 732-4000 MA
Web Site:
  http://www.packagemachinery.com
Year Founded: 1913
Rev.: $7,000,000
Emp.: 21
Mfr of Automatic Wrapping & Packaging Machines & Injection Molding Machinery
N.A.I.C.S.: 333993
Katherine E. Putnam (Pres)

PACKAGING CONCEPTS ASSOC., LLC
4925 Park Rdg Blvd, Boynton Beach, FL 33426
Tel.: (561) 364-0014
Web Site:
  http://www.packagingconcepts.com
Sales Range: $100-124.9 Million
Emp.: 100
Plastics Bottle Mfr
N.A.I.C.S.: 326160
Philip Meshberg (Founder)

PACKAGING CONCEPTS INC.
9832 Evergreen Industrial Dr, Saint Louis, MO 63123-7249
Tel.: (314) 329-9700 MO
Web Site:
  http://www.packagingconcepts.com
Year Founded: 1972
Rev.: $20,000,000
Emp.: 275
Packaging Paper & Related Products Mfr & Distr
N.A.I.C.S.: 322220
John J. Irace (CEO)
Joe Becher (CFO)
Michael Dean (Supvr-Printing)
Don Skelton (Mgr-Scheduling)
Barbara Sondermann (Mgr-Customer Svc)
Tony Parsons (Mgr-Printing)
Beau Bartoni (VP-Sls)

PACKAGING MACHINERY MANUFACTURERS INSTITUTE, INC.
11911 Freedom Dr Ste 600, Reston, VA 20190
Tel.: (571) 612-3200 DE
Web Site: http://www.pmmi.org
Year Founded: 1933
Sales Range: $25-49.9 Million
Emp.: 48
Packaging Machinery Manufacturer Association
N.A.I.C.S.: 813910
Caroline Abromavage (Dir-Ops)
Katie Bergmann (Sr VP)
Michele Bupp (Mgr-Mktg & Comm)
Fred Hayes (Dir-Technical Svcs)
Heather Harvey (Mgr-Membership Dev)
Jessica Lawshe (Mgr-Web & Digital Svcs)
Anna Hudson (Mgr-Events)

Dolores Valdovinos (Mgr-Customer Svc)
Glen Long (Sr VP)
Ivonne Rico (Coord-Commu & Mkg)
Jim Pittas (Pres & CEO)
Alejandra Aguirre Venegas (Mgr-Acctg)

PACKAGING PERSONIFIED, INC.
246 Kehoe Blvd, Carol Stream, IL 60188
Tel.: (630) 653-1655
Web Site:
  http://www.packagingpersonified.com
Year Founded: 1975
Sales Range: $25-49.9 Million
Emp.: 150
Plastic Packaging Materials Mfr
N.A.I.C.S.: 322220
Phyllis Muccianti (VP)
Steven Latakas (Mgr-Production)
Robert Hogan (Acct Mgr-Natl)
Joe Imburgia (Gen Mgr)
Subsidiaries:

Packaging Personified, Inc. (1)
122 S Aspen St, Sparta, MI 49345-1442
Tel.: (616) 887-8837
Web Site:
  http://www.packagingpersonified.com
Sales Range: $10-24.9 Million
Emp.: 120
Mfr of Plastic Bags
N.A.I.C.S.: 561910
James Wood (Gen Mgr)

PACKAGING RESOURCES, INC.
1023 W 55th St, Countryside, IL 60525
Tel.: (708) 447-7834
Web Site:
  http://www.pripackaging.com
Year Founded: 1998
Sales Range: $10-24.9 Million
Emp.: 20
Polybags, Films, Paper Bags, Containers & Paperboard Boxes Mfr
N.A.I.C.S.: 322220
Jeff Lucas (CEO)

PACKAGING SPECIALTIES INC.
1663 S Armstrong Ave, Fayetteville, AR 72701
Tel.: (479) 521-2580
Web Site: http://www.psi-ark.com
Rev.: $13,885,704
Emp.: 200
Flexographic Printing
N.A.I.C.S.: 323111
Dave Grulkey (VP-Sls)
Jeff Silva (Coord-Graphics)

PACKAGING SYSTEMS, LLC
170 Circle Dr N, Piscataway, NJ 08832
Tel.: (732) 802-2350
Web Site: http://www.psllc.com
Sales Range: $10-24.9 Million
Emp.: 150
Consumer Goods Packaging, Display, Filling & Distribution Services
N.A.I.C.S.: 561910
Sharon Liss (Dir-Admin)

PACKAGING TAPE INC.
8101 International Dr, Wausau, WI 54401
Tel.: (715) 845-7211
Web Site:
  http://www.packagingtapeinc.com
Rev.: $13,000,000
Emp.: 35

Pressure Sensitive Tape & Equipment Supplies
N.A.I.C.S.: 424130
Steve Menzner (VP-Admin)

PACKAGING UNLIMITED, LLC
1729 McCloskey Ave, Covington, KY 41014
Tel.: (502) 515-3900
Web Site: http://www.pkgunltd.com
Year Founded: 1975
Corrugated & Solid Fiber Box Mfr
N.A.I.C.S.: 322211

PACKARD MOTOR CAR CO. INC.
76 Monroe St, Boonton, NJ 07005
Tel.: (973) 334-2400
Web Site: http://www.packardmotorcar.com
Sales Range: $10-24.9 Million
Emp.: 65
Automotive Supplies & Parts
N.A.I.C.S.: 423120
Fred Kanter (Pres)
Dan Kanter (CFO & VP)

PACKARD TRANSPORT INC.
24021 S Municipal Dr, Channahon, IL 60410
Tel.: (815) 467-9260
Web Site: http://www.packardtransport.com
Sales Range: $25-49.9 Million
Emp.: 60
Trucking Except Local
N.A.I.C.S.: 484121
Joseph M. Crnkovic (Pres & CEO)
Rex D. Easton (Owner)

PACKER CITY INTERNATIONAL TRUCKS INC.
611 Hansen Rd, Green Bay, WI 54304-5319
Tel.: (920) 499-0879
Web Site: http://www.pcitrucks.com
Year Founded: 1982
Sales Range: $25-49.9 Million
Emp.: 125
Trucks & Other Parts
N.A.I.C.S.: 423110
Michelle Burt (CFO)
Alison Donarski (Mgr-HR)
Bob Renkens (Pres)

PACKET FUSION, INC.
4637 Chabot Dr Ste #350, Pleasanton, CA 94588
Tel.: (925) 701-2020 CA
Web Site: http://www.packetfusion.com
Year Founded: 2001
Scientific & Technical Consulting Services
N.A.I.C.S.: 541690
Matthew Pingatore (CEO)
Todd Peterson (Pres)
Sarah Ashley (Dir-Admin & Fin)
Kasey Nelson (Dir-Enterprise Sls)
William Holmes (Dir-Contact Center Solutions)
Craig Tetschlag (Dir-Major Accts)
Terry Tomasini (Dir-Client Svcs)

PACKETFABRIC, INC
9920 Jefferson Blvd, Culver City, CA 90232
Tel.: (424) 207-1300
Web Site: https://packetfabric.com
Year Founded: 2015
Internet Providers
N.A.I.C.S.: 517111
Bobby Rezaee (CFO)

PACKING MATERIAL COMPANY INC.
27280 Haggerty Rd Ste C16, Farmington Hills, MI 48331
Tel.: (248) 489-7000
Web Site: http://www.packingmaterial.com
Sales Range: $10-24.9 Million
Emp.: 15
Wood Pallets & Packing Materials Distr
N.A.I.C.S.: 321920
James B. Foster (Pres)
James Gross (Controller)

PACKLESS METAL HOSE INC.
8401 Imperial Dr, Waco, TX 76712
Tel.: (254) 666-7700
Web Site: http://www.packless.com
Year Founded: 1933
Sales Range: $10-24.9 Million
Emp.: 130
Supplier of Fluid Heat Transfer Parts & Other Special Assemblies to the Air Conditioning, Heating & Refrigeration Industries
N.A.I.C.S.: 332999
Scott Zifferer (Pres)
Doris Zifferer (Treas, Sec & VP)
Phil Midwood (Gen Mgr)

PACKRITE, LLC
1650 Packrite Ct, High Point, NC 27260
Tel.: (336) 884-0793
Web Site: http://www.packrite.net
Year Founded: 2008
Sales Range: $10-24.9 Million
Emp.: 55
Packing & Crating Services
N.A.I.C.S.: 488991
Mary Drummond (Owner)
Claire Hackbarth (Controller)
Kristina Smith (Mgr-Customer Svc)
Lavon Boone (VP-Fin)

PACKSIZE INTERNATIONAL, LLC
3760 W Smart Pack Way, Salt Lake City, UT 84104
Tel.: (801) 944-4814
Web Site: http://www.packsize.com
Year Founded: 2011
Sales Range: $50-74.9 Million
Emp.: 150
Packaging Machinery Mfr
N.A.I.C.S.: 333993
Hanko Kiessner (CEO)
Steve Saunders (VP-Bus Dev & Sls)
Horst Reinkensmeyer (Gen Mgr)
Brandon Brooks (VP-Mktg)
Jim Blee (COO)
Don Ralph (Sr VP-Supply Chain & Logistics)

PACO SPORT LTD. INC.
1385 Broadway Rm 1903, New York, NY 10018-6032
Tel.: (212) 575-9770 NY
Year Founded: 1989
Sales Range: $10-24.9 Million
Emp.: 30
Provider of Mens & Boys Clothing
N.A.I.C.S.: 424350
Bob Jebara (Pres)

PACO STEELE & ENGINEERING CORP.
19818 S Alameda St, Compton, CA 90221-6211
Tel.: (310) 537-6375
Web Site: http://www.pacosteel.com
Year Founded: 1974
Sales Range: $100-124.9 Million
Emp.: 30
Metals Service Centers & Offices
N.A.I.C.S.: 423510
Young Paik (CEO)

PACOR, INC.
333 Rising Sun Rd, Bordentown, NJ 08505
Tel.: (609) 324-1100 PA
Web Site: http://www.pacorinc.com
Year Founded: 1921
Sales Range: $100-124.9 Million
Emp.: 60
Fabricator of Thermal Insulation Products
N.A.I.C.S.: 423330
Joe D'Andrea (VP)
Ronald Latini (Pres & CEO)
Todd Hudson (Dir-Sls)
Subsidiaries:
Pacor, Inc. - Fabricating Division (1)
1924 Chespark Dr, Gastonia, NC 28052
Tel.: (704) 866-0895
Web Site: http://www.pacorinc.com
Emp.: 30
Ceramic Insulation Product Mfr
N.A.I.C.S.: 326140
Ed Jennigs (Gen Mgr)

PACPARTS INC.
1860 W Carson St Ste 102, Torrance, CA 90501
Tel.: (310) 515-0207
Web Site: http://www.pacparts.com
Sales Range: $1-9.9 Million
Emp.: 10
Distr of Electronic Parts & Equipment
N.A.I.C.S.: 423690
Paul J. O'Neil (Pres)

PACPIZZA LLC
220 Porter Dr Ste 100, San Ramon, CA 94583
Tel.: (925) 838-8567
Web Site: http://www.pacpizza.com
Sales Range: $75-99.9 Million
Emp.: 1,800
Pizzeria Franchisee
N.A.I.C.S.: 533110
Bruce McKinnon (Dir-Bus Ops)
Tina Meyer (Mgr-HR)
Lorena Timote (Gen Mgr-Restaurant)

PACS INDUSTRIES INC.
1211 Stewart Ave, Bethpage, NY 11714
Tel.: (516) 829-9060
Web Site: http://www.pacsindustries.com
Rev.: $16,818,042
Emp.: 23
Generator Control & Metering Panels
N.A.I.C.S.: 423610
Glen Ring (Controller)
Neil Minihane (CEO)
Niel Miele (Mgr-Engrg)

PACT
1828 L St NW Ste 300, Washington, DC 20036
Tel.: (202) 466-5666 DC
Web Site: http://www.pactworld.org
Year Founded: 1971
Sales Range: $150-199.9 Million
Emp.: 214
Community Support Services
N.A.I.C.S.: 624190
John Whalen (Pres)
Michelle Jones (Chief Human Capital Officer)

PACTIMO USA
6535 S Dayton St Ste 3005, Greenwood Village, CO 80111
Tel.: (303) 790-7807
Web Site: http://www.pactimo.com
Year Founded: 2005
Sales Range: $1-9.9 Million
Emp.: 100
Miscellaneous Apparel & Accessory Store
N.A.I.C.S.: 458110
Frank Kim (Principal)

PACWEST DISTRIBUTING, INC.
415 Boulder Ct Ste 600, Pleasanton, CA 94566
Tel.: (925) 224-9901
Web Site: http://www.pacwestdistributing.net
Year Founded: 2005
Sales Range: $1-9.9 Million
Emp.: 7
Transportation Services
N.A.I.C.S.: 488999
Tyson S. Lawrence (Pres & CEO)
Christopher Boenig (Exec VP-Full Truckload)
Bill Dodd (Exec VP-Truckload & Partial Shipments)
Myra Cervantes (Mgr-Accts Payable & Receivable)

PADDOCK CHEVROLET INC.
3232 Delaware Ave, Kenmore, NY 14217
Tel.: (716) 876-0945
Web Site: http://www.paddockchevrolet.com
Sales Range: $50-74.9 Million
Emp.: 90
New & Used Automobiles
N.A.I.C.S.: 441110
Darren Paddock (Dir-Fin)
Jeff Payne (Controller)
Bill Wertheim (Gen Mgr)
Rob Brostko (Mgr-Parts)

PADDOCK PUBLICATIONS, INC.
155 E Algonquin Rd, Arlington Heights, IL 60005
Tel.: (847) 427-4300 DE
Web Site: http://www.dailyherald.com
Year Founded: 1872
Sales Range: $100-124.9 Million
Emp.: 250
Publisher of Newspapers
N.A.I.C.S.: 513110
Kent L. Johnson (Treas & VP)
Douglas K. Ray (Chm, CEO & Publr)
James J. Galetano (VP-Circulation)
Robert Y. Paddock (Exec VP)
Colin O'Donnell (Sr VP & Dir-Content & Strategic Plng)
John Lampinen (Sr VP & Editor)
Scott T. Stone (Pres & COO)

PADGETT COMMUNICATIONS, INC.
4600 140th Ave N Ste 210, Clearwater, FL 33762 FL
Web Site: http://www.pcipro.com
Year Founded: 1995
Sales Range: $1-9.9 Million
Emp.: 18
Audience Response Systems Mfr
N.A.I.C.S.: 334290
Todd Padgett (Pres)

PADILLA SPEER BEARDSLEY INC.
1101 W River Pkwy Ste 400, Minneapolis, MN 55415-1241
Tel.: (612) 455-1700 MN
Web Site: http://www.padillacrt.com
Year Founded: 1961
Sales Range: $25-49.9 Million
Emp.: 120
Public Relations Agency
N.A.I.C.S.: 541820
Amy Fisher (VP-Tech Practice)
David Heinsch (Sr Dir-IR)
Thomas Jollie (Sr VP-Consumer Products)
Chris Higgins (Sr Dir-Mfg & Tech)

PADILLA SPEER BEARDSLEY INC.

Padilla Speer Beardsley Inc.—(Continued)

Matt Sullivan (VP-IR)
Kathy Burnham (Sr VP)
Danielle Engholm (VP-Mfg Practice)
Al Galgano (VP-IR)
Janet Stacey (VP-Health Care & Medical Devices)
Brian Prentice (VP-Creative Grp)
Carrie Young (VP-Creative Grp)
Bob McNaney (Sr VP-Crisis Consultancy)
Greg Tarmin (Sr VP)
Heath Rudduck (Chief Creative Officer)
Maureen Rehfuss (VP-HR & Admin)
Sean O'Brien (VP-Tech & Innovation)
Len Pollard (Acct Exec-Mfg Practice)
Kate Eissen (Acct Exec)
Amanda Abell (Acct Exec-Health Care Practice)
Heidi Wight (Sr Dir-Mfg Practice)
David Heinrich (Sr VP-Corp, Fin Svcs & IR)
Kris Patrow (Sr Dir-Corp Practice)

Subsidiaries:

PadillaCRT - Los Angeles (1)
617 W 7th St Ste 604, Los Angeles, CA 90017
Tel.: (310) 659-5380
Sales Range: $25-49.9 Million
Emp.: 70
Public Relations Agency
N.A.I.C.S.: 541820
Veronica Hunt (Acct Supvr)
Max Martens (VP)

PadillaCRT - New York (1)
320 W 13th St 7th Fl, New York, NY 10014
Tel.: (212) 229-0500
Rev.: $2,000,000
Emp.: 12
Public Relations Agency
N.A.I.C.S.: 541820
Joanne Tehrani (Sr Acct Exec)
Gregory Tarmin (Mng Dir-NY)
Fred Lake (Sr VP)

PadillaCRT - Norfolk (1)
2200 Colonial Ave Ste 10, Norfolk, VA 23517
Tel.: (757) 640-1982
Sales Range: $10-24.9 Million
Emp.: 15
Public Relations Agency
N.A.I.C.S.: 541820

PadillaCRT - Richmond (1)
101 W Commerce Rd, Richmond, VA 23224
Tel.: (804) 675-8100
Web Site: http://padillacrt.com
Emp.: 40
Public Relations Agency
N.A.I.C.S.: 541820
Lynn Casey (Chm)
Brian Ellis (Exec VP)
Mike Mulvihill (Exec VP)
Charlotte Evans (VP)
Michael Whitlow (Chief Growth Officer)
Jeff Wilson (Sr Dir-Bus Dev)
Kathryn Canning (Sr Acct Exec-Corp Practice)
Lauren Llewellyn (Sr Acct Exec-Corp Practice)
Rebecca Durkin (Assoc Dir-Creative)
Maria Briggs (Exec VP)
Dale Garton (CFO)
Matt Kucharski (Pres)
Heath Rudduck (Chief Creative Officer)
Greg Tarmin (Exec VP)
Chris Werle (Sr VP)

PADRES L.P.

100 Park Blvd, San Diego, CA 92101   DE
Tel.: (619) 795-5000
Web Site:
  http://www.sandiego.padres.mlb.com
Year Founded: 1968
Sales Range: $50-74.9 Million
Emp.: 150
Professional Baseball Club
N.A.I.C.S.: 711211

Brian Prilaman (Dir-Team Travel)
Ken Kawachi (Dir-Event Ops)
Jim Kiersnowski (Dir-Ticket Ops)
Ellen LoPresti (Sr Mgr-Ticket Sys)
Ronald Fowler (Chm)
Kameron Durham (Dir-Guest Svcs)
Sue Botos (VP-Community Rels)
Erik Meyer (Dir-Brdcst & Project Mgmt)
Gabriel Kunde (Sr Mgr-Ticket Ops)
Erik Greupner (Pres-Bus Ops)
Josh Stein (Asst Gen Mgr)
Todd Bollman (Dir-Acctg)
Devin Carr (Mgr-Acctg)
A. J. Preller (Exec VP & Gen Mgr)
Wayne Partello (CMO & Sr VP)
Ronda Sedillo (CFO & Sr VP)
Sam Geaney (Dir-Player Dev)
Nick Capo (Sr Dir-Ballpark Ops)
Pete DeYoung (Dir-Pro Scouting)
Scott Marshall (Chief Hospitality Officer & VP)
Peter Seidler (Mng Partner)
Tom Seidler (Sr VP-Community & Military Affairs)
Sergio del Prado (VP-Corp Partnerships)
Don Welke (VP-Scouting Ops)
Eric McKenzie (VP-Sls)
Fred Uhlman Jr. (VP & Asst Gen Mgr)

PADUCAH & LOUISVILLE RAILWAY, INC.

200 Clark St, Paducah, KY 42003
Tel.: (270) 444-4300
Web Site: http://www.palrr.biz
Year Founded: 1986
Railroad Operator
N.A.I.C.S.: 482111
Anthony V. Reck (Chm & CEO)
J. Thomas Garrett (Pres)
T. Greene (CFO, COO & VP)
Karen Tucker (Sr Dir-Corp Svcs)
Alayna Stinnett (Sr Mgr-Corp Svcs)
Thomas Clifton (Dir-Safety, Security & Training)
Patrick Reck (Mgr-Safety, Security & Training)
Sherri Goodwin (Mgr-Corp Svcs)

PADUCAH BANK SHARES, INC.

555 Jefferson St, Paducah, KY 42001
Tel.: (270) 575-5700
Web Site:
  http://www.paducahbank.com
Year Founded: 1984
Sales Range: $10-24.9 Million
Emp.: 135
Bank Holding Company; Commercial Banking, Trust & Investment Services
N.A.I.C.S.: 551111
Mardie Herndon (Pres)

Subsidiaries:

Paducah Bank & Trust Co., Inc. (1)
555 Jefferson St Ste 1, Paducah, KY 42001
Tel.: (270) 575-5700
Web Site: http://www.paducahbank.com
Rev.: $22,000,000
Emp.: 140
Commercial Banking, Trust & Investment Services
N.A.I.C.S.: 522110
Joseph H. Framptom (CEO)
Susan Guess (Dir-Mktg)
Mardie Herndon (Pres)

PAEDAE, INC.

360 E 2nd St Ste 350, Los Angeles, CA 90012   DE
Web Site: https://infillion.com
Mobile Marketing Software
N.A.I.C.S.: 541890

Rob Emrich (Founder & Chm)
Christa Carone (Pres)
Laurel Rossi (CMO)

Subsidiaries:

MediaMath, Inc. (1)
4 World Trade Ctr 150 Greenwich St 45 Fl, New York, NY 10007
Tel.: (646) 840-4200
Web Site: http://www.mediamath.com
Sales Range: $25-49.9 Million
Emp.: 750
Marketing Research Software & Services
N.A.I.C.S.: 541511
Neil H. Nguyen (CEO)
Joe Zawadzki (Co-Founder & CEO)
Ari Buchalter (Co-Founder & Pres-Tech)
David Reed (Mng Dir-Intl Bus Unit)
Erich Wasserman (Co-Founder & Global Head-Key Accts)
Greg Williams (Co-Founder & Sr VP-Open Partnerships)
Rahul Vasudev (Mng Dir-APAC)
Jesse Comart (VP & Head-Comm-Global)
Joanna O'Connell (CMO)
Viktor Zawadzki (Mgr-DACH-Nordics & Central/Eastern Europe)
Peter Piazza (Gen Counsel)
Wilfried Schobeiri (CTO)
Bob Scarperi (Global Head-Sls & Accts)
Jenna Griffith (Sr VP-Professional Svcs)
Dan Rosenberg (Sr VP-Corp Dev)
Jacob Ross (Gen Mgr-Audience)
Pranjal Desai (Mgr-India)
Zachary King (VP-Comml-Asia)
Elise James-Decruise (VP-New Mktg Institute)
Anna Grodecka-Grad (Chief Svcs Officer)
Stephen Steir (Sr VP-Engrg)
Franklin Rios (Chief Comml Officer & Head-Global Corp Dev)
Konrad Gerszke (Pres)
Eleni Nicholas (Chief Client Officer)
Sapna Kapur (CFO)

PAFF LANDSCAPE, INC.

6288 California St, Brooksville, FL 34604
Tel.: (352) 796-6654   FL
Web Site:
  http://www.pafflandscape.com
Year Founded: 1973
Sales Range: $1-9.9 Million
Emp.: 50
Landscaping Services
N.A.I.C.S.: 561730
J.N. Paff Jr. (Pres)

PAG DALY CITY LLC

6399 Mission St, Daly City, CA 94014
Web Site: http://www.citytoyota.com
Rev.: $29,600,000
Emp.: 45
Automobiles, New & Used
N.A.I.C.S.: 441110

PAGE BROS ENTERPRISES LTD.

360 Manchester Rd, Poughkeepsie, NY 12603
Tel.: (845) 452-7130
Web Site:
  http://www.pagehomecenter.com
Rev.: $18,500,000
Emp.: 58
Lumber & Other Building Materials
N.A.I.C.S.: 423310
William H. Page (Pres)

Subsidiaries:

H.G. Page & Sons Inc. (1)
360 Manchester Rd Rte 55, Poughkeepsie, NY 12603
Tel.: (845) 452-7130
Web Site: http://www.pagehomecenter.com
Rev.: $12,000,000
Home Center Operator
N.A.I.C.S.: 444110

H.G. Page Realty Corporation (1)
360 Manchester Rd, Poughkeepsie, NY 12603

U.S. PRIVATE

Tel.: (845) 452-7130
Web Site: http://www.pagehdc.com
Rev.: $170,000
Emp.: 3
Real Estate Brokers & Agents
N.A.I.C.S.: 444110
Jim Morrison (Gen Mgr)

PAGE MANAGEMENT CO., INC.

188 6th Ave A, New York, NY 10013
Tel.: (212) 219-3990
Real Estate Manangement Services
N.A.I.C.S.: 531390
Gabriel Brodsky (Owner)

Subsidiaries:

Thermal Dynamics International, Inc. (1)
12730 New Brittany Blvd, Fort Myers, FL 33907
Tel.: (239) 415-3601
Sales Range: $1-9.9 Million
Emp.: 12
Plumbing, Heating & Air-Conditioning Contractors
N.A.I.C.S.: 238220
John Meiser (VP)

PAGE ONE PR, LLC

2465 E Bayshore Rd Ste 348, Palo Alto, CA 94303
Tel.: (650) 565-9800   CA
Web Site: http://www.pageonepr.com
Year Founded: 2004
Rev.: $3,100,000
Emp.: 20
Fiscal Year-end: 12/31/06
Public Relations Services, Nsk
N.A.I.C.S.: 541820
Lonn Johnston (Founder & Pres-LEWIS Pulse)

PAGE SOUTHERLAND PAGE, INC.

400 W Cesar Chavez St Ste 500, Austin, TX 78701-3894
Tel.: (512) 472-6721
Web Site: http://www.pspaec.com
Year Founded: 1898
Sales Range: $10-24.9 Million
Emp.: 150
Business Services
N.A.I.C.S.: 541310
Peter M. Winters (Dir-Bus Dev-Dallas)

Subsidiaries:

Davis Brody Bond, Llp. (1)
315 Hudson St Fl 9, New York, NY 10013
Tel.: (212) 633-4700
Web Site: http://www.davisbrody.com
Sales Range: $1-9.9 Million
Emp.: 100
Architectural Services
N.A.I.C.S.: 541310
Steven M. Davis (Partner)
Mayine Lynn Yu (Assoc Partner)
John Henle (Assoc Partner)
Joseph Navarro (Assoc Partner)

PAGE STEEL, INC.

2040 Industrial Dr, Page, AZ 86040
Tel.: (928) 645-3166
Web Site: http://www.pagesteel.com
Rev.: $17,000,000
Emp.: 80
Fabricated Structural Metal
N.A.I.C.S.: 332312
Douglas Gardner (Pres)

PAGE TOYOTA, INC.

21262 Telegraph Rd, Southfield, MI 48034
Tel.: (248) 352-8580
Web Site: http://www.pagetoyota.com
Year Founded: 1970
Sales Range: $25-49.9 Million
Emp.: 107

Car Whslr
N.A.I.C.S.: 441110
Robert Vermeulen (Pres)

PAGE'S PRODUCE COMPANY
4601 Pacific Blvd, Vernon, CA 90058
Tel.: (323) 277-3660
Sales Range: $10-24.9 Million
Emp.: 55
Salsa Distr
N.A.I.C.S.: 311421
Jenny Woollett (Mgr-HR)
Mike Page (VP)
Craig Jaunzemis (Mgr-Sls)

PAGEFLEX INC.
200 Nickerson Rd, Marlborough, MA 01752-4695
Tel.: (617) 520-8600   DE
Web Site: http://www.pageflex.com
Year Founded: 2011
Sales Range: $1-9.9 Million
Emp.: 72
Software Publisher
N.A.I.C.S.: 513210
James P. Dore (CFO & Exec VP)
Costas Kitsos (VP-Engrg)
Dominic LeClaire (VP-Sls & Mktg)

PAGNOTTI ENTERPRISES INC.
46 Public Sq Ste 600, Wilkes Barre, PA 18701
Tel.: (570) 825-8700   PA
Year Founded: 1956
Sales Range: $25-49.9 Million
Emp.: 540
Holding Company: Compensation Insurance Services & Anthracite Coal Mining Preparation & Sales
N.A.I.C.S.: 551112
Michelene Kennedy (Pres)
Kenneth Weaver (CFO)

Subsidiaries:

Jeddo-Highland Coal Co. Inc.   (1)
46 Public Sq Ste 600, Wilkes Barre, PA 18701-2609   **(100%)**
Tel.: (570) 825-8700
Sales Range: $25-49.9 Million
Emp.: 9
Anthracite Mining
N.A.I.C.S.: 212115

PAI INDUSTRIES INC.
950 Northbrook Pkwy, Suwanee, GA 30024
Tel.: (770) 822-1000
Web Site: http://www.paiindustries.com
Rev.: $10,800,000
Emp.: 50
Motor Vehicle Parts & Accessories
N.A.I.C.S.: 336390
Habib Yavari (Owner)
Jerry Holton (Reg Mgr-Sls)
Amir Hummadi (VP)
Diana Burnell (Mgr-Acctg Dept)

PAI SERVICES LLC
840 N Lenola Rd Ste 6, Moorestown, NJ 08057
Tel.: (856) 231-4667
Sales Range: $25-49.9 Million
Payroll Software & Services
N.A.I.C.S.: 541214
Bill Scott (Chm)
Jeff Smith (CFO)
Curt Raffi (Exec VP-Corp Dev)
Robert Digby (CEO)
Phil McLaughlin (CIO)
Douglas Harrison (Pres-Svc Bureau Div)

PAIGE HENDRICKS PUBLIC RELATIONS INC
1255 W Magnolia Ave, Fort Worth, TX 76104
Tel.: (817) 924-2300
Web Site: http://www.phprinc.com
Sales Range: Less than $1 Million
Emp.: 8
N.A.I.C.S.: 541820
Susan Flyzik (Asst VP)
Marilyn Morris (Dir-Ops)

PAINE SCHWARTZ PARTNERS, LLC
1 Franklin Pkwy Bldg 910 Ste 120, San Mateo, CA 94403
Tel.: (650) 393-7100   DE
Web Site:
   http://www.paineschwartz.com
Year Founded: 2006
Privater Equity Firm
N.A.I.C.S.: 523999
Kevin Schwartz (CEO & Mng Partner)
Alexander Corbacho (Principal)
Angelos J. Dassios (Chief Investment Officer)
Robert M. Meyer (CFO)
John Anton (Dir-Operating)
David J. Buckeridge (Partner)
Stephen R. Padgette (Mng Dir)
Adam Fless (Mng Dir-Portfolio Excellence)
Gerald Adler (COO, Chief Compliance Officer & Gen Counsel)
Matthew Hershenson (Head-IR)
Steven Bierschenk (Mng Dir)
Spencer Swayze (Mng Dir)
Natasha Dossa (Principal)
Justin Kern (Principal)
Neha Singhania (Principal)
Renata Dinkelmann (Dir-Human Capital)
W. Dexter Paine III (Chm)

Subsidiaries:

AgroFresh Solutions, Inc.   (1)
1 Washington Sq 510-530 Walnut St Ste 1350, Philadelphia, PA 19106
Tel.: (267) 317-9139
Web Site: https://www.agrofresh.com
Rev.: $161,937,000
Assets: $697,710,000
Liabilities: $523,680,000
Net Worth: $174,030,000
Earnings: ($59,786,000)
Emp.: 300
Fiscal Year-end: 12/31/2022
Holding Company; Fresh Produce Preservation Products Developer, Mfr & Whslr
N.A.I.C.S.: 551112
Clinton A. Lewis Jr. (CEO)

Subsidiary (Non-US):

AgroFresh Comercial Peru S.A.C.   (2)
Panamericana Norte KM 1076 INT 05 Z I, Tambo Grande, Piura, Peru
Tel.: (51) 968090721
Web Site: http://www.agrofreshperu.com
Fresh Fruit & Vegetable Farming Services
N.A.I.C.S.: 115114

Subsidiary (Domestic):

AgroFresh Inc.   (2)
510-513 Walnut St Ste 1350, Philadelphia, PA 19106
Web Site: https://www.agrofresh.com
Fruit Management Services
N.A.I.C.S.: 325320

Subsidiary (Non-US):

AgroFresh Italia srl   (2)
Via Di Vittorio Giuseppe 18, 40013, Castel Maggiore, Italy
Tel.: (39) 051701398
Fresh Produce Preservation Product Services
N.A.I.C.S.: 551112

AgroFresh Polska Sp. Z.o.o.   (2)
Poznanska Str 98 MAG - Room 214 Bronisze Hall, 05-850, Ozarow Mazowiecki, Poland
Tel.: (48) 227215655
Web Site: http://agrofresh.pl
Fresh Fruit & Vegetable Distr
N.A.I.C.S.: 424480

AgroFresh Spain, S.L.   (2)
Avd Levante U D 28 esc A pta 17, 46025, Valencia, Spain
Tel.: (34) 963911591
Web Site: https://www.agrofresh.es
Fresh Fruit & Vegetable Distr
N.A.I.C.S.: 424480

Subsidiary (Domestic):

Pace International, LLC   (2)
5661 Branch Rd, Wapato, WA 98951
Web Site: http://www.paceint.com
Sales Range: $75-99.9 Million
Agricultural Chemical Products Mfr & Distr
N.A.I.C.S.: 325320
Michelle Smith (Sr Mgr-Sls & Field Svcs-South)

Capital Z Partners Management, LLC   (1)
142 W 57th St 4th Fl, New York, NY 10019
Tel.: (212) 965-2400
Web Site: http://www.capitalz.com
Sales Range: $75-99.9 Million
Emp.: 20
Private Equity Investment & Asset Management Services
N.A.I.C.S.: 523999
Roland V. Bernardon (CFO)
Lauri Testani (Controller)
Jonathan D. Kelly (Partner)
Chris Wolfe (Partner)
Trevor W. Pieri (Principal)
Robert A. Spass (Mng Partner)
Robert A. Spass (Mng Partner)
Bradley E. Cooper (Founder & Mng Partner)
Bradley E. Cooper (Founder & Mng Partner)
Robert A. Spass (Mng Partner)

Costa Group Holdings Limited   (1)
Tel.: (61) 383639000
Web Site: https://www.costagroup.com.au
Rev.: $885,150,942
Assets: $1,341,585,056
Liabilities: $809,824,607
Net Worth: $531,760,449
Earnings: $30,645,498
Emp.: 200
Fiscal Year-end: 01/01/2022
Holding Company
N.A.I.C.S.: 551112
David Thomas (Gen Counsel)
Kirsty Deglas (Chief Strategy Officer)
Wayne Johnston (CEO)

Fox Paine & Company, LLC   (1)
2105 Woodside Rd Ste D, Woodside, CA 94062-1153
Tel.: (650) 235-2075
Web Site: http://www.foxpaine.com
Rev.: $1,500,000,000
Emp.: 10
Private Equity Investment Company
N.A.I.C.S.: 523999
Saul A. Fox (CEO)
Jay Pulaski (CFO)

Holding (Domestic):

Global Indemnity Group, LLC   (2)
3 Bala Plz E Ste 300, Bala Cynwyd, PA 19004   **(80.5%)**
Tel.: (302) 691-6276
Web Site: https://www.gbli.com
Rev.: $628,534,000
Assets: $1,800,775,000
Liabilities: $1,174,546,000
Net Worth: $626,229,000
Earnings: ($850,000)
Emp.: 355
Fiscal Year-end: 12/31/2022
Holding Company; Property & Casualty Insurance & Reinsurance Products & Services
N.A.I.C.S.: 551112
Saul A. Fox (Chm)
Michael Loftus (Sr VP)
Brian Riley (CFO)
Bill Balderston (CMO)
David Elliott (Sr VP-Claims)
Alan Hirst (CIO)
Nicole Reilly (Sr VP-Human Resources)
Thomas Gibbons (Chief Actuary & Exec VP)
Stephen Ries (Sr VP & Head-Investor Relations)
Thomas M. McGeehan (CFO)

Subsidiary (Domestic):

Global Indemnity Group, Inc.   (3)
3 Bala Plz E Ste 300, Bala Cynwyd, PA 19004
Tel.: (610) 664-1500
Web Site: https://www.globalindemnity.ky
Holding Company; Property & Casualty Insurance & Reinsurance Products & Services
N.A.I.C.S.: 551112
Saul A. Fox (Chm)
Thomas Michael McGeehan (CFO & Exec VP-Fin & Ops)
Michael Loftus (VP)
Jonathan Oltman (Pres-Penn-Patriot)

Subsidiary (Domestic):

American Reliable Insurance Company   (4)
PO Box 6002, Scottsdale, AZ 85261
Tel.: (480) 483-8666
Web Site: http://www.americanreliable.com
Specialty Personal & Farm Owner Insurance Services
N.A.I.C.S.: 524126
Christina B. Cama (Sec & VP-HR & Admin)
Robert Hill (Pres)
Chad Ellwein (VP-Product Mgmt)
Nelson Allen (VP-IT Application Dev)
Stephen H. Graham (VP-Agriculture)
Valley Owens (VP-Underwriting & Ops)
Patricia Quint (VP-Claims)
Randall Gardner (Dir-Acctg)
Rose Larsen (Dir-Property Product Dev)
Jeff Labe (Mgr-Mktg)
Curt Mang (Mgr-Ops)
Mike Taber (Mgr-Ops MIS)

Collectibles Insurance Services, LLC   (4)
15 E Main St Ste 228, Westminster, MD 21157-5034
Web Site: http://www.collectinsure.com
Insurance Agents
N.A.I.C.S.: 524210
Dan Walker (Principal)

Diamond State Insurance Company   (4)
3 Bala Plz Ste 300, Bala Cynwyd, PA 19004-3481
Tel.: (610) 664-1500
Web Site:
   http://www.diamondstategroup.com
Commercial Property & Casualty Insurance
N.A.I.C.S.: 524126
Matthew B. Scott (Sr VP-Casualty Brokerage)

J.H. Ferguson & Associates, LLC   (4)
125 S Wacker Dr, Chicago, IL 60606
Tel.: (312) 705-4277
Web Site: http://www.jhferg.com
Rev.: $1,200,000
Emp.: 12
Property & Casualty Insurance
N.A.I.C.S.: 524126

Penn-America Group, Inc.   (4)
3 Bala Plz E Ste 300, Bala Cynwyd, PA 19004
Tel.: (610) 664-1500
Web Site: http://www.penn-america.com
Specialty Property & Casualty Insurance Products
N.A.I.C.S.: 524210

Subsidiary (Domestic):

Penn-America Insurance Company   (5)
3 Bala Plz E Ste 300, Bala Cynwyd, PA 19004
Tel.: (610) 664-1500
Web Site: http://www.penn-america.com
Property & Casualty Insurance Products & Services
N.A.I.C.S.: 524126
Richard W. Slomiany (VP-Claims)

Penn-Star Insurance Company   (5)

PAINE SCHWARTZ PARTNERS, LLC

Paine Schwartz Partners, LLC—(Continued)
3 Bala Plz E Ste 300, Bala Cynwyd, PA 19004
Tel.: (610) 664-1500
Property & Casualty Insurance Products & Services
N.A.I.C.S.: 524126

Subsidiary (Domestic):

U.S. Insurance Services, Inc. (4)
2000 Art Museum Dr Ste 4, Jacksonville, FL 32207-2504
Tel.: (904) 396-6646
Web Site: http://www.us-insurance.com
Insurance Brokerage Services
N.A.I.C.S.: 524210
Blair Fox (Natl Sls Mgr)

United National Group Ltd. (4)
3 Bala Plz E Ste 300, Bala Cynwyd, PA 19004-3481
Tel.: (610) 664-1500
Web Site: http://www.uai.ky
Insurance Services
N.A.I.C.S.: 524126

Subsidiary (Domestic):

United National Insurance Company (5)
3 Bala Plz E Ste 300, Bala Cynwyd, PA 19004-3481
Tel.: (610) 664-1500
Web Site: http://www.unitednat.com
Property & Casualty Insurance Products & Services
N.A.I.C.S.: 524126

Subsidiary (Non-US):

Wind River Reinsurance Company Ltd (3)
Burnaby Building 16 Burnaby Street, PO Box HM 716, Hamilton, HM CX, Bermuda
Tel.: (441) 292 6400
Web Site: http://www.windriver.bm
Specialty Property & Casualty Reinsurance
N.A.I.C.S.: 524130

Holding (Non-US):

L'Artisan Parfumeur S.A. (2)
12 place Vendome, F-75001, Paris, France
Tel.: (33) 140641564
Web Site: http://www.artisanparfumeur.com
Sales Range: $10-24.9 Million
Emp.: 10
Luxury Fragrance Mfr & Retailer
N.A.I.C.S.: 456120

Branch (US):

L'Artisan Parfumeur USA (3)
519 Broome St 3rd Fl, New York, NY 10013
Tel.: (212) 206-6577
Luxury Fragrance Mfr & Retailer
N.A.I.C.S.: 456120
Dana Kline (VP & Gen Mgr-Americas)

Holding (Non-US):

Penhaligon's Limited (2)
184-192 Drummond Street, London, NW1 3HP, United Kingdom
Tel.: (44) 2075906110
Web Site: http://www.penhaligons.com
Fragrances & Gifts Mfr & Distr
N.A.I.C.S.: 456120

Gerawan Farming Services, Inc. (1)
7108 N Fresno St Ste 450, Fresno, CA 93720
Tel.: (559) 787-8780
Web Site: http://www.prima.com
Sales Range: $1-9.9 Million
Emp.: 30
Postharvest Crop Activities (except Cotton Ginning)
N.A.I.C.S.: 115114

Registrar Corp (1)
144 Research Dr, Hampton, VA 23666
Tel.: (757) 224-0177
Web Site: http://www.registrarcorp.com
Administrative Management & General Management Consulting Service
N.A.I.C.S.: 541611

David Lennarz (Co-Founder & Pres)
Anna Benevente (Dir-Label & Ingredient Reviews)
Helen Anders (Mgr-Acctg)
Russell K. Statman (Exec Dir)
Mark Prinz (Dir-Import Alert Svcs)

PAINTER'S SUN COUNTRY MITSUBISHI
1600 S Hilton Dr, Saint George, UT 84770
Tel.: (435) 637-1600
Web Site: http://www.suncountryauto.com
Year Founded: 1980
Sales Range: $10-24.9 Million
Emp.: 35
New & Used Car Dealer
N.A.I.C.S.: 441110
James Painter (Owner)

PAINTERS ON DEMAND, LLC
3201 N Florida Ave, Tampa, FL 33603
Tel.: (855) 707-2468
Web Site: http://www.paintersondemand.net
Sales Range: $1-9.9 Million
Emp.: 35
Painting Contractor
N.A.I.C.S.: 238320
Chris Jimenez (Pres & CEO)
Frank Nieves (VP-Estimating & Sls)
Cameron Long (VP-Field Ops)

PAINTERS USA, INC.
570 Mitchell Rd, Glendale Heights, IL 60139
Tel.: (630) 653-8715
Web Site: https://www.paintersusa.com
Sales Range: $1-9.9 Million
Emp.: 40
Painting & Paper Hanging Services
N.A.I.C.S.: 238320
Meg Cook (Owner & Pres)

Subsidiaries:

Lakeside Painting, Inc. (1)
2892 Austin St, East Troy, WI 53120
Tel.: (262) 642-9445
Web Site: http://www.lakesidepainting.com
Sales Range: $1-9.9 Million
Emp.: 22
Painting & Wall Covering Contractors
N.A.I.C.S.: 238320

PAISANO PUBLICATIONS, LLC
28210 Dorothy Dr, Agoura Hills, CA 91301
Tel.: (818) 889-8740
Web Site: http://www.paisanopub.com
Sales Range: $25-49.9 Million
Emp.: 135
Magazine Publisher
N.A.I.C.S.: 513120
Joseph Teresi (Chm)
Tammy Porter (Pres & CEO)
Karen Johnson (Controller)

Subsidiaries:

Easyriders, LLC (1)
28210 Dorothy Dr, Agoura Hills, CA 91301-2605
Tel.: (818) 889-8740
Web Site: http://www.easyriders.com
Sales Range: $10-24.9 Million
Emp.: 25
Motorcycle, Special-Interest & Lifestyle Magazines Publisher
N.A.I.C.S.: 513120
Joe Teresi (Publr)
Gill Luna (Pres)

PAIZO PUBLISHING LLC
7120 185th Ave NE Ste 120, Redmond, WA 98052-0577

Tel.: (425) 250-0800
Web Site: http://www.paizo.com
Year Founded: 2002
Sales Range: $10-24.9 Million
Emp.: 55
Publisher of Fantasy Role Playing Games, Accessories, Novels & Pathfinder Series of Games
N.A.I.C.S.: 513199
Jeff Alvarez (COO)
Lisa Stevens (CEO)
Jenny Bendel (Dir-Mktg)
Pierce Watters (Dir-Sls)
Chris Self (Mgr-Fin)
James Jacobs (Editor-in-Chief)
Logan Bonner (Editor & Developer)
Vic Wertz (CTO)

PAK PETROLEUM MARKETING INC.
109 Higbee St, El Campo, TX 77437
Tel.: (979) 543-3922
Web Site: http://www.pakpetroleum.com
Sales Range: $25-49.9 Million
Emp.: 15
Petroleum Products
N.A.I.C.S.: 457210
Celina Shariff (Pres)

PAL GENERAL ENGINEERING INC.
5374 Eastgate Mall, San Diego, CA 92121
Tel.: (858) 638-7100
Web Site: http://www.palsd.com
Year Founded: 2008
Sales Range: $10-24.9 Million
Emp.: 36
Construction Engineering Services
N.A.I.C.S.: 541330
Marla Jahshan (Owner)
Raed Jashan (Project Mgr)
Ala Karaja (Superintendent)

PAL-DO COMPANY INC.
9701 S Tacoma Way, Lakewood, WA 98499
Tel.: (253) 581-7800
Sales Range: $10-24.9 Million
Emp.: 17
Specialty Food Items
N.A.I.C.S.: 424490
Bryant Park (Owner)

PALA GROUP, INC.
16347 Old Hammond Hwy, Baton Rouge, LA 70816
Tel.: (225) 272-5194   LA
Web Site: http://www.palagroup.com
Year Founded: 1986
Sales Range: $400-449.9 Million
Emp.: 800
Industrial Contractor
N.A.I.C.S.: 237990
George Tarajano (Pres)
Gay Young (Controller)

Subsidiaries:

Pala Interstate, LLC (1)
16347 Old Hammond Hwy, Baton Rouge, LA 70816-1730
Tel.: (225) 272-5194
Web Site: http://www.palagroup.com
Sales Range: $25-49.9 Million
Emp.: 78
Industrial Maintenance & Construction
N.A.I.C.S.: 236210
Michael Anthony (Coord-Corp Safety)
Scott Couper (Exec VP)
Brant Clayton (Mgr-Gen Construction-Texas)
Scott Barringer (Pres & COO)
Bill Roger (Reg Mgr-Safety)

PALA-INTERSTATE, INC.
16347 Old Hammond Hwy, Baton Rouge, LA 70816
Tel.: (225) 272-5194
Web Site: http://www.palagroup.com
Year Founded: 1973
Sales Range: $50-74.9 Million
Emp.: 700
Civil Engineering Services
N.A.I.C.S.: 237310
Jorge L. Tarajano (CEO)

PALACE LAUNDRY INC.
735 Lamont St NW, Washington, DC 20010-1526
Tel.: (202) 291-9200   DE
Web Site: http://www.linensoftheweek.com
Year Founded: 1951
Sales Range: $10-24.9 Million
Emp.: 30
Textile Rental Services
N.A.I.C.S.: 812331
Alan Bubes (CEO)
Ron Bubes (Pres)
Dominic Colombo (Gen Mgr)

PALADIN HEALTHCARE CAPITAL, LLC
222 N Sepulveda Blvd Ste 900, El Segundo, CA 90245
Tel.: (310) 414-2700   DE
Web Site: http://www.paladinhealthcare.com
Healthcare-Focused Private Equity Firm
N.A.I.C.S.: 523999
Joel Freedman (Founder, Chm, Pres & CEO)
Mike Rembis (Sr Mng Dir)
Brandon Garrett (Mng Dir-Bus Dev)

Subsidiaries:

Paladin Healthcare Management, LLC (1)
222 N Sepulveda Blvd Ste 900, El Segundo, CA 90245
Tel.: (310) 414-2700
Web Site: http://www.paladinhealthcare.com
Healthcare-Focused Investment Management Services
N.A.I.C.S.: 523940
Joel Freedman (Founder, Chm & CEO)
Barry A. Wolfman (Pres)
Steven Blake (CFO)
Ravi Sharma (COO)

Tenet HealthSystem Hahnemann, LLC (1)
230 N Broad St, Philadelphia, PA 19102
Tel.: (215) 762-7000
Web Site: http://www.hahnemannhospital.com
Medical Devices
N.A.I.C.S.: 622110

PALAGONIA BAKERY, INC.
508 Junius St, Brooklyn, NY 11212
Tel.: (718) 272-5400   NY
Year Founded: 1977
Sales Range: $100-124.9 Million
Emp.: 250
Mfr of Italian Bread & Kaiser Rolls
N.A.I.C.S.: 311812
Joseph P. Palagonia (Treas)
Chris Palagonia (Pres)
Anthony Palagonia (VP-Admin)

PALAU NATIONAL COMMUNICATIONS CORPORATION
PO Box 99, Koror, PW 96940
Tel.: (680) 587-9000   PW
Web Site: http://www.palaunet.com
Year Founded: 1982
Telecommunication Servicesb
N.A.I.C.S.: 517111
Todd Houseman (Gen Mgr)

PALECEK IMPORTS INC.

COMPANIES

601 Parr Blvd, Richmond, CA 94801
Tel.: (510) 236-7730
Web Site: http://www.palecek.com
Rev.: $35,000,000
Emp.: 55
Homefurnishings
N.A.I.C.S.: 423220
Allan Palecek *(CEO)*

PALISADE CAPITAL MANAGEMENT, LLC
1 Bridge Plz Ste 695, Fort Lee, NJ 07024
Tel.: (201) 585-7733 NJ
Web Site:
  http://www.palisadecapital.com
Year Founded: 1995
Private Equity, Wealth Management, Investment Advisory & Brokerage Services
N.A.I.C.S.: 523999
Martin L. Berman *(Co-Founder, Co-Chm & CEO)*
Jack Feiler *(Vice Chm)*
Steven E. Berman *(Vice Chm)*
Dennison T. Veru *(Co-Chm & Chief Investment Officer)*
Jeffrey D. Serkes *(Member-Mgmt Bd)*
Wendy S. Popowich *(Mng Dir-Private Wealth Mgmt)*
Mahendra Misir *(Mng Dir-Portfolio Admin)*
Bradley R. Goldman *(Mng Dir, Chief Compliance Officer & Gen Counsel)*
Bernard J. Picchi *(Mng Dir-Private Wealth Mgmt)*
Donna Szczupak *(VP & Controller)*
Frank Galdi *(Mng Dir & Chief Risk Officer)*
Marc Shapiro *(Mng Dir & Sr Portfolio Mgr)*
Dawn Brock *(Sr VP-Res)*
Bill Lee *(Mng Dir & Sr Portfolio Mgr)*
James J. McNeil *(Sr VP)*
Garo Norian *(Sr VP)*
William L. Potter *(Mng Dir & Sr Portfolio Mgr)*
Michael Feiler *(Mng Dir)*
Ray Lam *(Sr VP & Assoc Portfolio Mgr)*
Mitchell Leung *(Sr VP & Assoc Portfolio Mgr)*
Brian Deitelzweig *(Mng Dir-Trading)*
Kyle M. Kavanaugh *(Sr VP & Assoc Portfolio Mgr)*

PALISADES ASSOCIATES, INC.
9140 Vendome Dr, Bethesda, MD 20817
Tel.: (301) 469-7564
Web Site:
  http://www.palisadesassociates.com
Sales Range: $50-74.9 Million
Emp.: 1,000
Investment & Consulting Firm
N.A.I.C.S.: 523999
Richard Berger *(CFO)*

Subsidiaries:

Empire Kosher Poultry, Inc. (1)
Rte 5 PO Box 228, Mifflintown, PA 17059-9409
Tel.: (717) 436-5921
Web Site: http://www.empirekosher.com
Sales Range: $75-99.9 Million
Processor & Packer of Kosher Poultry
N.A.I.C.S.: 311615
Jeff Brown *(VP-Admin)*

PALISADES GROWTH CAPITAL, LLC
11726 San Vicente Blvd Ste 450, Los Angeles, CA 90049
Tel.: (310) 571-6214 DE
Web Site:
  http://www.palisadesgrowth.com
Equity Investment Firm
N.A.I.C.S.: 523999
Paul N. D'Addario *(Co-Founder & Partner)*
Anders Richardson *(Co-Founder & Partner)*
Jeff Anderson *(Partner)*
William Tomai *(CFO)*
Meshach Kisten *(Controller)*

PALISADES MEDIA GROUP, INC.
1620 26th St Ste 200 S, Santa Monica, CA 90404
Tel.: (310) 564-5400 CA
Web Site:
  http://www.palisadesmedia.com
Year Founded: 1996
Sales Range: $500-549.9 Million
Emp.: 75
Media Buying Services
N.A.I.C.S.: 541810
Roger A. Schaffner *(Owner & CEO)*
Laura Jean Bracken *(Pres & COO)*
Hwa Shih Lee *(VP-Digital Media)*
Erin Morgan *(Sr VP-Audio & Local Video)*
Casey Brathwaite *(VP & Dir-Strategy)*
Rhona Dass *(Sr VP & Dir-Strategic Plng)*
Matt Greenfield *(Sr VP-Client Svcs)*
Genevieve Wiersema *(VP & Grp Dir-Strategy)*

PALKAR INC.
3273 Claremont Way, Napa, CA 94558
Tel.: (707) 224-5468
Web Site: http://www.1alkar.com
Year Founded: 1985
Rev.: $12,000,000
Emp.: 16
Provider of Full Time or Temporary Staffing Agency Services
N.A.I.C.S.: 561320
Elizabeth Pridmore *(Pres)*
Jason Lewis *(Controller)*

PALLADIA, INC.
305 7th Ave10th Fl, New York, NY 10001
Tel.: (212) 633-6900 NY
Web Site: http://www.palladiainc.org
Year Founded: 1970
Sales Range: $25-49.9 Million
Emp.: 618
Community Action Services
N.A.I.C.S.: 624190
Sandra Stark *(Chm)*
Dianne LaBasse *(Vice Chm & Treas)*
Mary Beth C. Tully *(Sec)*

PALLADIAN CAPITAL PARTNERS LLC
420 Lexington Ave, New York, NY 10170
Tel.: (212) 880-2400
Web Site:
  http://www.palladiancap.com
Sales Range: $25-49.9 Million
Emp.: 5
Privater Equity Firm
N.A.I.C.S.: 523999
Jon A. Gordon *(Co-Founder)*
Carl D. Glaeser *(Co-Founder)*
B. Andrew Spence *(Mng Dir)*

Subsidiaries:

Equisearch Services Inc. (1)
555 Taxter Rd, Elmsford, NY 10523
Tel.: (914) 686-8000
Sales Range: $25-49.9 Million
Lost Account Holder Search Services; Unclaimed Asset Recovery Services
N.A.I.C.S.: 561611

PALLADIN CONSUMER RETAIL PARTNERS, LLC
John Hancock Twr 200 Clarendon St 26th Fl, Boston, MA 02116
Tel.: (617) 585-3800 DE
Web Site: http://www.pcrp.com
Emp.: 8
Privater Equity Firm
N.A.I.C.S.: 523999
Mark Schwartz *(CEO)*
Tom Casey *(Operating Partner)*
Caryn Lerner *(Operating Partner)*
R. Shawn Neville *(Chm)*
Anders Petersen *(Mng Dir)*

Subsidiaries:

Aerogroup International LLC (1)
201 Meadow Rd, Edison, NJ 08817-6002
Tel.: (732) 985-0495
Web Site: http://www.aerosoles.com
Sales Range: $150-199.9 Million
Emp.: 1,000
Women's Footwear Designer, Distr & Retailer
N.A.I.C.S.: 424340
Tom Reeve *(VP-Tech & Bus Solutions)*

Southeast Mechanical, LLC (1)
5142 N Causeway Dr., Winston-Salem, NC 27106
Tel.: (828) 432-0025
Web Site: https://www.southeast-mechanical.com
Electrical & Plumbing Services
N.A.I.C.S.: 238220

Subsidiary (Domestic):

Gentry Air Inc. (2)
3511 Associate Dr, Greensboro, NC 27405
Tel.: (336) 621-1070
Web Site: http://www.gentryair.com
Rev.: $5,640,000
Emp.: 30
Site Preparation Contractor
N.A.I.C.S.: 238910
Jennifer Gill *(Pres-HR & Insurance)*
Greg Gill *(VP-Superintendent & Sls)*

PALLADIUM EQUITY PARTNERS, LLC
Rockefeller Ctr 1270 Ave of the Americas 31st Fl, New York, NY 10020
Tel.: (212) 218-5150 DE
Web Site:
  https://www.palladiumequity.com
Year Founded: 1997
Privater Equity Firm
N.A.I.C.S.: 523999
Marcos A. Rodriguez *(Chm & CEO)*
Susan L. Lyons *(Partner)*
Kevin L. Reymond *(Vice Chm)*
Daniel Ilundain *(Partner)*
Justin R. Green *(Partner)*
Adam Shebitz *(Partner)*
Caleb Clark *(Partner)*
Leon Brujis *(Partner)*
Louisa M. Dalton *(Principal & Controller)*
Chris Allen *(Partner)*
Suzanne Wong *(CFO)*
Deborah Gallegos *(Co-Head-Sustainability)*

Subsidiaries:

Accupac, Inc. (1)
1501 Industrial Blvd, Mainland, PA 19451-0200
Tel.: (215) 256-7000
Web Site: http://www.accupac.com
Liquids, Creams, Gels & Other Pharmaceutical Compounds Mfr
N.A.I.C.S.: 561910
Mark Hinkel *(VP-Sls)*
Andrew Zelez *(Reg Dir-Sls)*

American Gilsonite Co. (1)
350 Cambridge Ave Ste 350, Palo Alto, CA 94306
Tel.: (650) 233-7166
Web Site: http://www.americangilsonite.com
Sales Range: $50-74.9 Million
Mining, Processing & Marketing of Gilsonite Hydrocarbon-Based Resin
N.A.I.C.S.: 212390
Bill Britton *(VP-Sls & Mktg)*
David G. Gallagher *(Pres & CEO)*
Willson Ropp *(Chm)*
Gail Brannan *(Coord-Domestic Sls)*
Craig Mueller *(Chief Comml Officer & VP)*

Unit (Domestic):

American Gilsonite Co.-Bonanza Mine (2)
29950 Bonanza Hwy, Bonanza, UT 84008
Tel.: (435) 789-1921
Web Site: http://www.americangilsonite.com
Emp.: 90
Gilsonite Mining & Processing
N.A.I.C.S.: 212390

Carpio Solutions Inc. (1)
140 Bradford Dr Ste C, West Berlin, NJ 08091-9216
Tel.: (919) 654-4574
Corporate Financial Management Software Developer
N.A.I.C.S.: 513210

Celeritas Management, Inc. (1)
East 4th St Studio 56, Richmond, VA 23224
Tel.: (804) 230-4235
Investment Portfolio Management
N.A.I.C.S.: 523940

DolEx Dollar Express, Inc. (1)
700 Highlander Blvd Ste 450, Arlington, TX 76015
Tel.: (817) 548-4700
Sales Range: $400-449.9 Million
Electronic Money Transfer Services
N.A.I.C.S.: 522320
George Zelinski *(Pres-North American Money Transfer)*

Subsidiary (Non-US):

Dolex Envios, S.A. de C.V. (2)
Perifercico Sur 3343 5 Piso Sand Jeronimo, Lidice, Mexico, 10200, Mexico
Tel.: (52) 5554909012
Sales Range: $125-149.9 Million
Electronic Money Transfer Services
N.A.I.C.S.: 522320
Salvador Velazquec *(Gen Mgr)*

United Europhil, S.A. (2)
Calle Alfonso XII, 58 Bajo, 28014, Madrid, Spain
Tel.: (34) 902 200 666
Web Site: http://www.europhil.com
Sales Range: $10-24.9 Million
Electronic Money Transfer Services
N.A.I.C.S.: 522320

Kar Nut Products Company (1)
1200 E 14 Mile Rd, Madison Heights, MI 48071-1421
Tel.: (248) 588-1903
Web Site: http://www.karsnuts.com
Trail Mixes & Nut Products Mfr & Whslr
N.A.I.C.S.: 311919
Nick Nicolay *(Pres)*
Scott McKinnon *(VP-Sls)*
Dan Bailey *(Dir-Ops)*
Jason Gearhart *(Sls Mgr-Natl)*

Subsidiary (Domestic):

Morley Candy Makers, LLC (2)
23770 Hall Rd, Clinton Township, MI 48036
Tel.: (586) 468-4300
Web Site: http://www.sanderscandy.com
Sales Range: $10-24.9 Million
Emp.: 200
Candy & Other Confectionery Products
N.A.I.C.S.: 311340
Mike Koch *(Gen Mgr)*

Kymera International (1)
2601 Weck Dr Research Triangle, Durham, NC 27709
Tel.: (919) 544-8090
Web Site:
  http://www.kymerainternational.com
Specialty Materials, Powders, Pastes & Granules Mfr
N.A.I.C.S.: 331318
Barton White *(CEO)*

PALLADIUM EQUITY PARTNERS, LLC

Palladium Equity Partners, LLC—(Continued)

Subsidiary (Domestic):

Acupowder International LLC (2)
901 Lehigh Ave, Union, NJ 07083
Tel.: (908) 851-4500
Web Site: http://www.acupowder.com
Sales Range: $10-24.9 Million
Emp.: 133
Mfr of Primary Metal Products
N.A.I.C.S.: 331221
Denise Gomez (Mgr-HR)

Subsidiary (Domestic):

Acupowder Tennessee LLC (3)
6621 Hwy 411 S, Greenback, TN 37742-2158 **(100%)**
Tel.: (865) 856-3021
Web Site: http://www.acupowder.com
Sales Range: $10-24.9 Million
Emp.: 35
Metal Powders
N.A.I.C.S.: 331221

Subsidiary (Non-US):

ECKA Granules Germany GmbH (2)
Frankenstrasse 12, D-90762, Furth, Germany
Tel.: (49) 9119747208
Web Site: http://www.ecka-granules.com
Rev.: $362,193,000
Alloying, Metal-Powders & Application Technology
N.A.I.C.S.: 212313
Eva Monica Kalawski (Bus Mgr)

Holding (Non-US):

Bahrain Atomisers International BSC (3)
Building 200 HWY 96 EAST Riffa, PO Box 5328, Manama, 5328, Bahrain
Tel.: (973) 17 830 008
Emp.: 50
Aluminum & Copper Alloy Mfr
N.A.I.C.S.: 331313
Tim McLaughlin (Gen Mgr)

Subsidiary (Non-US):

ECKA Granules Australia Pty. Ltd. (3)
4523 E Tamar Hwy, Bell Bay, 7253, TAS, Australia
Tel.: (61) 363828444
Web Site: http://www.ecka.com.au
Sales Range: $25-49.9 Million
Emp.: 50
Mineral Products Mfr
N.A.I.C.S.: 327999
David Williams (Mng Dir)

Unit (Domestic):

ECKA Granules Germany GmbH - Essen Bearing Technologies
Heinz-Backer-Str 26, 45356, Essen, Germany
Tel.: (49) 201861780
Sales Range: $25-49.9 Million
Emp.: 175
Metals Service Center
N.A.I.C.S.: 423510
Rolf Koring (Mng Dir)

Subsidiary (Non-US):

ECKA Granules Intl, Trading (Shanghai) Co. Ltd. (3)
Room C1106, Orient International Plaza, 85 Lou Shan Guan Road, Shanghai, 200336, China
Tel.: (86) 2162370710
Web Site: http://www.ecka-granules.com
Sales Range: $10-24.9 Million
Emp.: 2
Powder Metallurgy Part Mfr
N.A.I.C.S.: 332117
Jenny Gao (Country Mgr)

ECKA Granules Italia Srl (3)
Via A Moro 58, Mirano-Venezia, 30035, Vicenza, Italy **(100%)**
Tel.: (39) 0415701986
Sales Range: $25-49.9 Million
Emp.: 1
Metals Service Center
N.A.I.C.S.: 423510
Antonio Gandin (Gen Mgr)

ECKA Granules Japan Co. Ltd. (3)
4th Floor Dai 4 Sun Bridge Kudan Building, Kudankita 1-10-5 Chyoda-ku, 102-0073, Tokyo, Japan
Tel.: (81) 335122581
Web Site: http://www.ecka-granula.com
Sales Range: $25-49.9 Million
Emp.: 15
Metals Service Center
N.A.I.C.S.: 423510

ECKA Granules Metal Powders Ltd. (3)
Unit 23-26 Prothero Indus Est Bilport Line, Wednesbury, WS10 0NT, W Midlands, United Kingdom
Tel.: (44) 1215673350
Web Site: http://www.ecka-granules.com
Sales Range: $10-24.9 Million
Emp.: 25
Fabricated Metal Products Mfr
N.A.I.C.S.: 332999

Subsidiary (US):

ECKA Granules of America L.P. (3)
500 Prosperity Dr, Orangeburg, SC 29115
Tel.: (803) 536-0215
Web Site: http://www.ecka-granules.com
Metals Service Center
N.A.I.C.S.: 423510
Julie Waymouth (Gen Mgr)

Holding (Non-US):

Mepura Metallpulvergesellschaft m. b. H. (3)
Lachforst 2, 5282, Ranshofen, Austria
Tel.: (43) 7722 62216 0
Sales Range: $25-49.9 Million
Emp.: 50
Aluminum & Copper Alloy Mfr
N.A.I.C.S.: 331313

non ferrum Kranj d.o.o. (3)
Struzevo 66, 4000, Kranj, Slovenia
Tel.: (386) 42577550
Web Site: http://www.ecka-granules.com
Sales Range: $25-49.9 Million
Emp.: 15
Aluminum & Copper Alloy Mfr
N.A.I.C.S.: 331313
Mirko Tepina (Mgr)

Subsidiary (Domestic):

Global Titanium Inc. (2)
19300 Filer St, Detroit, MI 48234-2808
Tel.: (313) 366-5300
Web Site: http://www.globaltitanium.com
Sales Range: $10-24.9 Million
Emp.: 100
Titanium Metallurgical Products Mfr
N.A.I.C.S.: 331110
Bob Swenson (Pres-Sls, Pur & Product Inquiries)
Matthew Schmink (VP-Sls, Pur & Product Inquiries)
Adam Perry (VP-Ops)
Jim Dippel (VP-Product Dev, Sls, Pur & Product Inquiries)
Dennis McCarthy (CFO & VP)
Keith Berger (Mgr-Safety)

Kdf Fluid Treatment Inc. (2)
1500 Kdf Dr, Three Rivers, MI 49093
Tel.: (269) 273-3300
Web Site: http://www.kdfft.com
Rev.: $1,100,000
Emp.: 10
All Other Miscellaneous General Purpose Machinery Mfr
N.A.I.C.S.: 333998

Reading Alloys, Inc. (2)
220 Old West Penn Ave, Robesonia, PA 19551
Tel.: (610) 693-5822
Web Site: http://www.readingalloys.com
Emp.: 100
Electronic Instruments & Electromechanical Components Mfr
N.A.I.C.S.: 334514

SCM Metal Products, Inc. (2)
2601 Weck Dr, Research Triangle Park, NC 27709
Tel.: (919) 544-8090
Web Site: http://www.scmmetals.com
Sales Range: $50-74.9 Million
Emp.: 75
Metal Powder & Paste Mfr
N.A.I.C.S.: 325998
Wayne Daye (Mgr-Tech)

Thermal Spray Solutions, Inc. (2)
1105 International Plz Ste B, Chesapeake, VA 23323-1530
Tel.: (757) 673-2468
Web Site: http://www.thermalsprayusa.com
Metal Coating, Engraving & Allied Services to Manufacturers
N.A.I.C.S.: 332812
Scott E. Spruce (VP)

Q'Max Solutions Inc. (1)
1700 407 2nd Street SW, Calgary, T1X 0L8, AB, Canada
Tel.: (403) 513-6012
Web Site: http://www.qmax.com
Drilling Fluids & Environmental Services
N.A.I.C.S.: 213112

Subsidiary (US):

Anchor Drilling Fluids USA, LLC (2)
11700 Katy Freeway Ste 250, Houston, TX 77079
Tel.: (832) 672-4459
Web Site: http://www.anchorusa.com
Drilling Fluids Mfr
N.A.I.C.S.: 213112

Subsidiary (Non-US):

International Drilling Fluids and Engineering Services (IDEC) Ltd (2)
Office 802 Reef Tower JLT, Dubai, United Arab Emirates
Tel.: (971) 44518052
Web Site: http://www.idecint.com
Oil Field Drilling Services
N.A.I.C.S.: 213111
A. Seedat (Pres)

Quirch Foods, LLC (1)
7600 NW 82nd Pl, Miami, FL 33166
Tel.: (305) 691-3535
Web Site: https://www.quirchfoods.com
Sales Range: $700-749.9 Million
Emp.: 2,000
Meat & Meat Product Merchant Wholesalers
N.A.I.C.S.: 424470
Teresita del Calvo (Controller)
Carmen M. Sabater (CFO)
Bill Quirch (Exec VP)
John Rattigan Jr. (Chief Growth, Strategy & M&A Officer)
Charles M. Herington (Chm)

Subsidiary (Domestic):

Butts Foods Inc. (2)
432 N Royal St, Jackson, TN 38301
Tel.: (731) 423-3456
Web Site: http://www.buttsfoods.com
Sales Range: $25-49.9 Million
Emp.: 60
Meats, Fresh, Frozen
N.A.I.C.S.: 424470

Colorado Boxed Beef Co. (2)
302 Progress Rd, Auburndale, FL 33823-2711
Tel.: (863) 967-0636
Web Site: http://www.coloradoboxedbeef.com
Sales Range: $550-599.9 Million
Emp.: 410
Wholesale Distributor of Meat
N.A.I.C.S.: 424470
John J. Rattigan (Pres)

Subsidiary (Domestic):

ATG Transportation LLC (3)
302 Progress Rd, Auburndale, FL 33823
Tel.: (800) 432-3604
Web Site: http://www.atgtransport.com
Transportation Services
N.A.I.C.S.: 488999

Plant (Domestic):

Colorado Boxed Beef Co. - Atlanta Facility (3)
6150 Xavier Dr SW, Atlanta GA 30336
Tel.: (404) 799-0099
Web Site: http://www.coloradoboxedbeef.com
Food Products Distr
N.A.I.C.S.: 424420
Paula Karkover (Office Mgr)

Division (Domestic):

Colorado Boxed Beef Co. - CBBC International Division (3)
302 Progress Rd, Auburndale, FL 33823-2711
Tel.: (954) 764-1781
Web Site: http://www.coloradoboxedbeef.com
Emp.: 100
Food Products Distr
N.A.I.C.S.: 424420
John Rattigan (CEO)

Subsidiary (Domestic):

Prefco Distribution, LLC (3)
1190 W Loop N, Houston, TX 77055-7218
Tel.: (713) 880-0880
Food Product Whslr
N.A.I.C.S.: 424420
Barry Glauben (Pres)

The Great Fish Company (3)
5955 Pkwy N Blvd Ste A, Cumming, GA 30040
Tel.: (678) 455-8201
Web Site: http://www.greatfishco.com
Seafood Distr
N.A.I.C.S.: 424420

Remesas Quisqueyana Inc. (1)
1550 N Brown Rd Ste 145, Lawrenceville, GA 30043
Tel.: (678) 407-7010
Sales Range: $75-99.9 Million
Money Transfer, Courier & Telecommunications Services
N.A.I.C.S.: 522320

Source Logistics Center Corp. (1)
812 Union St, Montebello, CA 90640
Tel.: (323) 887-3884
Web Site: http://www.sourcelogistics.net
General Warehousing & Storage
N.A.I.C.S.: 493110
Ken Newman (Dir-Transportation & Logistics)

Subsidiary (Domestic):

Fulfillment Corporation of America (2)
11065 SW 11th St Bldg C Ste 325, Beaverton, OR 97005
Tel.: (503) 906-4101
Web Site: http://www.sourcefca.com
Web & Print Services
N.A.I.C.S.: 323111
David P. Torres (Pres & CEO)
Rashelle Meeks (Mgr-Corp Pur)

Superior Environmental Solutions, LLC (1)
9996 Joseph James Dr, Cincinnati, OH 45246
Tel.: (513) 874-8355
Web Site: https://sesinc.com
Remediation Services
N.A.I.C.S.: 562910

Subsidiary (Domestic):

Mountain Environmental Services, Inc. (2)
1560 Pisgah Dr, Canton, NC 28716-2307
Tel.: (828) 648-5556
Web Site: http://www.mountainenvironmental.com
Environmental Consulting Services
N.A.I.C.S.: 541620
Mathew Blackburn (Mgr-Environment Project)

TransForce, Inc. (1)
5520 Cherokee Ave Ste 200, Alexandria, VA 22312
Tel.: (703) 838-5580
Web Site: http://www.transforce.com
Commercial Truck Drivers Staffing & Recruiting Services
N.A.I.C.S.: 561311
Rafael Andres Diaz-Granados (Chm & CEO)

COMPANIES

David W. Broome *(Pres & CEO)*
Howard Fowler *(CFO & Sr VP)*
Jeff Meyer *(COO)*
Paul Braswell *(VP-Recruiting & Retention)*
Joe Dolan *(Sr VP)*
Torquka Johnson Haggerty *(Dir-Risk Mgmt & Safety)*
Dan Horvath *(Dir-Compliance & Safety)*
Jason B. Arnold *(CIO)*
Diana Poss *(VP-HR)*

PALLADIUM GROUP, INC.
55 Old Bedford Rd, Lincoln, MA 01773
Tel.: (781) 259-3737
Web Site: http://www.thepalladiumgroup.com
Rev.: $12,800,000
Emp.: 225
Management Consulting Services
N.A.I.C.S.: 541611
David Norton *(Founder)*
Marcus Pitt *(Dir-Strategy Execution)*

PALLET CONSULTANTS CORP.
810 NW 13 Ave, Pompano Beach, FL 33069
Tel.: (954) 946-2212
Web Site: http://www.palletconsultants.com
Rev.: $7,000,000
Emp.: 53
Wood Container & Pallet Mfr
N.A.I.C.S.: 321920
Gus Gutierrez *(CEO)*
Carla Gruener *(CFO)*

PALLET DIRECT, INC.
12 Carwick Glen Dr, Michigan City, IN 46360
Tel.: (219) 764-7464
Rev.: $18,000,000
Emp.: 2
Lumber, Plywood, Millwork & Wood Panel Merchant Whslr
N.A.I.C.S.: 423310
Ann Stillwell *(CEO)*

PALLET SERVICES INC.
12998 Farm to Market Rd, Mount Vernon, WA 98273
Tel.: (360) 424-8171
Web Site: http://www.palletservices.com
Rev.: $23,800,000
Emp.: 100
Lumber Plywood Millwork & Wood Panel Merchant Whslr
N.A.I.C.S.: 423310
Darren Bronco *(Pres)*
Jeanine Bronco *(Treas & Sec)*

PALLETMAXX, INC.
4818 137th St, Crestwood, IL 60418
Tel.: (708) 385-9595
Web Site: http://www.palletmaxx.com
Rev.: $15,000,000
Emp.: 12
Wood Container & Pallet Mfr
N.A.I.C.S.: 321920
Todd Conway *(VP)*

PALLIATIVE CARECENTER & HOSPICE OF CATAWBA VALLEY, INC.
3975 Robinson Rd, Newton, NC 28658
Tel.: (828) 466-0466   NC
Web Site: http://www.pchcv.org
Year Founded: 1979
Sales Range: $10-24.9 Million
Emp.: 293
Health Care Srvices
N.A.I.C.S.: 622110
Virginia Jimenez *(Dir-Medical)*
David Cook *(Pres & CEO)*

PALLIOS BROS. INC.
2531 Whitmore Ave, Ceres, CA 95307-2646
Tel.: (209) 538-3000   CA
Year Founded: 1951
Sales Range: $10-24.9 Million
Emp.: 30
Grocery Stores
N.A.I.C.S.: 445110
Steve Wright *(Gen Mgr)*

PALM AUTOMOTIVE GROUP
1801 Tamiami Trl, Punta Gorda, FL 33950
Tel.: (941) 639-1155
Web Site: http://www.palmautomall.com
Sales Range: $25-49.9 Million
Emp.: 250
New & Used Car Dealers
N.A.I.C.S.: 441110
JoAnn Helphenstine *(Owner & Pres)*
Matt Lee *(Mgr-Svc)*
Bob Pilgrim *(Mgr-Svc)*
Damian Bolt *(Mgr-Sls)*
Paul Cleaver *(Mgr-Comml & Fleet)*

PALM BAY INTERNATIONAL, INC.
301 Yamato Rd Ste 3130, Boca Raton, FL 33431
Tel.: (561) 893-9998   FL
Web Site: http://www.palmbay.com
Year Founded: 1978
Sales Range: $25-49.9 Million
Emp.: 150
Wine & Distilled Beverages
N.A.I.C.S.: 424820
Harish Parekh *(CFO)*
Rosemary Olenick *(Mgr-HR)*

PALM BEACH CAPITAL PARTNERS LLC
525 S Flagler Dr Ste 201, West Palm Beach, FL 33401
Tel.: (561) 659-9022
Web Site: http://www.pbcap.com
Year Founded: 2001
Privater Equity Firm
N.A.I.C.S.: 523999
Christopher Felder *(CFO)*
Shaun L. McGruder *(Mng Partner)*
Nathan S. Ward *(Mng Partner)*
Michael J. Chalhub *(COO & Partner)*

Subsidiaries:

Mears Transportation Group, LLC   (1)
324 W Gore St, Orlando, FL 32806-1037
Tel.: (407) 422-4561
Web Site: http://www.mearstransportation.com
Taxi Owner & Operator, Limousine, Bus & Shuttle Services
N.A.I.C.S.: 485310

Pape-Dawson Engineers, LLC   (1)
2000 NW Loop 410, San Antonio, TX 78213-2251
Tel.: (210) 375-9000
Web Site: http://www.pape-dawson.com
Engineeering Services
N.A.I.C.S.: 541330
K. Stephen Bonnette *(Sr VP)*
Mashhood Shah *(VP-Transportation)*
Mark Holliday *(Sr Project Mgr)*
Jason Elms *(VP)*
John A. Tyler *(Sr Project Mgr)*
Yuki S. Williams *(Sr Project Mgr)*
Angie Bowers *(Sr Project Mgr)*
Joseph Ortega *(Sr Project Mgr)*
Gilmer D. Gaston *(Sr VP-Transportation)*
Richard Horn *(Sr Project Mgr)*
Derek Mueller *(Sr Project Mgr)*
Samuel G. Dawson *(CEO)*
Jason Atkinson *(VP)*
Brandon O'Donald *(VP)*
Chris Rogers *(VP-Comml Land Dev)*
Jim Welch *(VP)*
Taylor Dawson *(VP)*

Todd Blackmon *(VP)*
Rebecca Carroll *(VP)*
Caleb Chance *(VP)*
Dustin Goss *(VP)*
Robert Wempe *(VP-Houston)*
Matt B. Garcia *(VP-Dallas)*
James Lutz *(Sr VP)*
Nathan Billiot *(VP)*
Curtis Lee *(VP)*
Jason Diamond *(VP)*
Brad Davis *(Mng Principal-North Texas)*
Dan Thoma *(VP)*
Trey Dawson *(Sr VP)*
Ramon Salazar *(Assoc VP)*
Jocelyn Perez *(VP)*

Subsidiary (Domestic):

Maxwell-Reddick & Associates, Inc.   (2)
40 Joe Kennedy Blvd, Statesboro, GA 30458
Tel.: (912) 489-7112
Web Site: http://www.maxred.com
Rev.: $1,100,000
Emp.: 13
Engineeering Services
N.A.I.C.S.: 541330
Charles Maxwell *(Pres)*
Charles Maxwell *(Owner)*

Q. Grady Minor & Associates, P.A.   (2)
3800 Via Del Rey, Bonita Springs, FL 34134-7556
Tel.: (239) 947-1144
Web Site: http://www.gradyminor.com
Architectural Services
N.A.I.C.S.: 541310
David K. Carlyle *(VP)*
Mark Minor *(Pres)*

United Envelope LLC   (1)
45-11 33rd St, Long Island City, NY 11101
Tel.: (718) 707-0700
Web Site: http://www.unitedenvelope.com
Envelope Mfr
N.A.I.C.S.: 322230
Kenneth Bernstein *(Pres & CEO)*

PALM BEACH IMPORTS INC.
2901 Okeechobee Blvd, West Palm Beach, FL 33409
Tel.: (561) 684-6666
Web Site: http://www.bramanmc.com
Sales Range: $400-449.9 Million
Emp.: 267
Car Dealership
N.A.I.C.S.: 441110
Norman Braman *(Pres)*
Vince Cerone *(COO & Gen Mgr)*

PALM BEACH IMPORTS, INC.
2060 Biscayne Blvd 2nd Fl, Miami, FL 33137
Tel.: (305) 576-1889
Year Founded: 1995
Sales Range: $500-549.9 Million
Emp.: 806
Travel Arrangement Services
N.A.I.C.S.: 441110
Stanley Krieger *(Mgr-Customer Svcs)*

PALM BEACH TAN, INC.
633 E State Hwy 121 Ste 500, Coppell, TX 75019
Tel.: (972) 406-2400   TX
Web Site: http://www.palmbeachtan.com
Rev.: $12,000,000
Emp.: 30
Tanning Salons Operator & Franchisor
N.A.I.C.S.: 812199
Diane Lucas *(Pres & COO)*
Cheryl Davis *(Mgr-People Svcs)*
Nicoleta Balas *(Asst Controller)*
Shannon Naylor *(Sr Dir-Mktg)*
Lisa Staberg *(VP-People & People Dev)*
Brian Nelson *(Mgr-Facilities)*
Adrianna Christian *(Mgr-Retail Support)*

PALM RESTAURANT GROUP

Jennifer Meyer *(Mgr-Trng)*
Rustin Powell *(Reg Mgr)*
Eric Hall *(CFO)*
Roy Sneed *(VP-Franchising)*

PALM CHEVROLET OF GAINESVILLE
2600 N Main St, Gainesville, FL 32609
Tel.: (352) 376-7581
Web Site: http://www.gainesvillechevy.com
Sales Range: $10-24.9 Million
Emp.: 55
Automobiles, New & Used
N.A.I.C.S.: 441110
Don Smith *(Dir-Fixed Ops)*
Brandon Maynard *(Gen Mgr)*

PALM CHRYSLER JEEP DODGE RAM
1901 Tamiami Trl, Punta Gorda, FL 33950-5917
Tel.: (941) 639-1155
Web Site: http://www.palmchryslerjeepdodge.net
Sales Range: $50-74.9 Million
Emp.: 290
Car Whslr
N.A.I.C.S.: 441110
Paul Cleaver *(Gen Mgr)*
Dennis Tagge *(Dir-Svc)*

PALM ENTERTAINMENT PROPERTIES LLC
1460 Broadway, New York, NY 10036
Tel.: (646) 790-1211
Web Site: http://www.palmpictures.com
Year Founded: 1998
Sales Range: $50-74.9 Million
Emp.: 80
Holding Company
N.A.I.C.S.: 551112
Chris Blackwell *(Founder & Chm)*

Subsidiaries:

Palm Pictures, LLC   (1)
1460 Broadway, New York, NY 10036
Tel.: (646) 790-1211
Web Site: http://www.palmpictures.com
Sales Range: $50-74.9 Million.
Emp.: 175
Tapes, Audio & Video Production & Distribution
N.A.I.C.S.: 423690
Chris Blackwell *(Founder)*

PALM HARBOR DERMATOLOGY, P.A.
4197 Woodlands Pkwy, Palm Harbor, FL 34685
Tel.: (727) 786-3810
Web Site: http://www.palmharbordermatology.com
Sales Range: $1-9.9 Million
Dermatology Services
N.A.I.C.S.: 621111
Amy Ross *(Owner)*

PALM PETERBILT-GMC TRUCKS INC.
2441 S State Rd 7, Fort Lauderdale, FL 33317
Tel.: (954) 584-3200
Web Site: http://www.palmtruck.com
Rev.: $51,600,000
Emp.: 90
Tractors, Industrial
N.A.I.C.S.: 423830
David Weiger *(Pres)*
Debbi Demherst *(CFO & VP)*
Heather Martin *(Mgr-Svc)*

PALM RESTAURANT GROUP

PALM RESTAURANT GROUP

Palm Restaurant Group—(Continued)

1730 Rhode Is Ave NW Ste 900,
Washington, DC 20036
Tel.: (202) 775-7256
Web Site: http://www.thepalm.com
Year Founded: 1926
Sales Range: $50-74.9 Million
Emp.: 1,500
Owner & Operator of Restaurants
N.A.I.C.S.: 561110
James Longo *(CFO & Exec VP)*
Jeff Phillips *(Co-COO)*
Jens Baake *(Co-COO)*
Joy Jones *(Gen Counsel)*
Victor Ganzi *(Member-Mgmt Bd)*
Wally Ganzi *(Co-Owner & Co-Chm)*
Walter Ganzi Jr. *(Co-Owner)*
Bruce Bozzi Sr. *(Owner & Co-Chm)*
Bruce Bozzi Jr. *(Exec VP)*

Subsidiaries:

The Atlanta Palm (1)
3391 Peachtree Rd NE, Atlanta, GA 30326
Tel.: (404) 814-1955
Web Site: http://www.thepalm.com
Sales Range: $10-24.9 Million
Emp.: 60
Restaurant Services
N.A.I.C.S.: 722511
Lance Jaglarski *(Gen Mgr)*

The Atlantic City Palm (1)
2801 Pacific Ave Ste 102, Atlantic City, NJ 08401
Tel.: (609) 344-7256
Web Site: http://www.thepalm.com
Sales Range: $10-24.9 Million
Emp.: 65
Restaurant Services
N.A.I.C.S.: 722511
Paul Sandler *(Gen Mgr)*

The Charlotte Palm (1)
6705-B Phillips Place Ct, Charlotte, NC 28210
Tel.: (704) 552-7256
Web Site: http://www.thepalm.com
Sales Range: $10-24.9 Million
Emp.: 35
Restaurant Services
N.A.I.C.S.: 722511
Joseph Profeta *(Gen Mgr)*

The Chicago Palm (1)
323 E Whacker Dr, Chicago, IL 60601
Tel.: (312) 616-1000
Web Site: http://www.thepalm.com
Sales Range: $10-24.9 Million
Emp.: 70
Restaurant Services
N.A.I.C.S.: 722511
Phillip Jahnke *(Gen Mgr)*

The Denver Palm (1)
1672 Lawrence St, Denver, CO 80202
Tel.: (303) 825-7256
Web Site: http://www.thepalm.com
Sales Range: $10-24.9 Million
Emp.: 120
Restaurant Services
N.A.I.C.S.: 722511
Cathy Cooney *(Gen Mgr)*

The Houston Palm (1)
6100 Westheimer Ave, Houston, TX 77057
Tel.: (713) 977-2544
Web Site: http://www.thepalm.com
Sales Range: $10-24.9 Million
Emp.: 70
Restaurant Services
N.A.I.C.S.: 722511
Jim Martin *(Exec Dir)*
Scott Sieck *(Gen Mgr)*

The Las Vegas Palm (1)
3500 Las Vegas Blvd S Ste A7, Las Vegas, NV 89109
Tel.: (702) 732-7256
Web Site: http://www.thepalm.com
Sales Range: $10-24.9 Million
Emp.: 100
Restaurant Services
N.A.I.C.S.: 722511
Lawrence Close *(Gen Mgr)*

The Mexico City Palm (1)
Presidente Intercontinental Hotel Campos Eliseos 218, Polanco, Mexico, DF 11560, Mexico
Tel.: (52) 5553277762
Web Site: http://www.thepalm.com.mx
Sales Range: $10-24.9 Million
Emp.: 80
Restaurant Services
N.A.I.C.S.: 722511

The New York Palm Too (1)
840 2nd Ave, New York, NY 10017
Tel.: (212) 697-5198
Web Site: http://www.thepalm.com
Restaurant Services
N.A.I.C.S.: 722511

The Northbrook Palm (1)
1730 Rhode Island Ave Nw Ste 900, Washington, DC 20036-3113
Tel.: (847) 239-7256
Restaurant Services
N.A.I.C.S.: 722511

The Orlando Palm (1)
5800 Universal Blvd, Orlando, FL 32819
Tel.: (407) 503-7256
Web Site: http://www.thepalm.com
Sales Range: $10-24.9 Million
Emp.: 40
Restaurant Services
N.A.I.C.S.: 722511
Michael Martin *(Gen Mgr)*

The Palm Restaurant (1)
837 2nd Ave, New York, NY 10017
Tel.: (212) 687-7698
Web Site: http://www.thepalm.com
Sales Range: $10-24.9 Million
Emp.: 100
Restaurant Services
N.A.I.C.S.: 722511
Wally Ganzi *(Co-Owner & Co-Chm)*
Jim Longo *(CFO & Exec VP-Fin)*
Jeff Phillips *(COO)*
Bruce Bozzi Sr. *(Co-Owner & Co-Chm)*

The Palm Restaurant (1)
1225 19th St NW, Washington, DC 20036
Tel.: (202) 293-9091
Web Site: http://www.thepalm.com
Sales Range: $10-24.9 Million
Emp.: 70
Restaurant Services
N.A.I.C.S.: 722511
Michael Melore *(Gen Mgr)*

The Palm at the Huntting Inn (1)
94 Main St, East Hampton, NY 11937
Tel.: (631) 324-0411
Web Site: http://www.thepalm.com
Sales Range: $10-24.9 Million
Emp.: 75
Restaurant Services
N.A.I.C.S.: 722511

The Philadelphia Palm (1)
200 S Broad St, Philadelphia, PA 19102
Tel.: (215) 546-7256
Web Site: http://www.thepalm.com
Restaurant Services
N.A.I.C.S.: 722511
Jim Haney *(Gen Mgr)*

The Tampa Bay Palm (1)
205 Westshore Plaza Dr, Tampa, FL 33609
Tel.: (813) 849-7256
Web Site: http://www.thepalm.com
Sales Range: $10-24.9 Million
Emp.: 70
Restaurant Services
N.A.I.C.S.: 722511

PALM USA INC.
1201 N Milwaukee Ave, Chicago, IL 60642
Tel.: (773) 235-7673
Year Founded: 1982
Sales Range: $10-24.9 Million
Emp.: 50
Retailer of Footwear & Clothing
N.A.I.C.S.: 458210
Wan Lee *(VP)*

PALMDALE OIL COMPANY, INC.
911 N 2nd St, Fort Pierce, FL 34950
Tel.: (772) 461-2300
Web Site:
http://www.palmdaleoil.com
Rev.: $3,616,900
Emp.: 10
Petroleum & Petroleum Products Merchant Wholesalers, except Bulk Stations & Terminals
N.A.I.C.S.: 424720
Robert Reskin *(CFO)*
Lachlan Cheatham *(CEO)*

Subsidiaries:

Como Oil Company of Florida (1)
3586 Sw Martin Hwy, Palm City, FL 34990
Tel.: (772) 562-6666
Web Site: https://comoflorida.com
Rev.: $8,680,700
Emp.: 24
Petroleum & Petroleum Products Merchant Wholesalers, except Bulk Stations & Terminals
N.A.I.C.S.: 424720

Maassen Oil Company Inc. (1)
612 N Brevard Ave, Arcadia, FL 34266
Tel.: (863) 494-2253
Web Site: http://www.maassenoil.com
Rev.: $10,000,000
Emp.: 30
Lubricating Oils & Greases
N.A.I.C.S.: 424720
John S. Maassen III *(Pres)*

PALMEN AUTOMOTIVE GROUP INC.
8320 Washington Ave, Racine, WI 53406
Tel.: (262) 886-6800
Web Site: http://www.palmen.com
Rev.: $30,300,000
Emp.: 85
New Car Dealers
N.A.I.C.S.: 441110
Andy Palmen *(VP)*
John Becker *(Mgr-Fin)*

Subsidiaries:

Palmen Dodge Chrysler Jeep of Racine (1)
8320 Washington Ave, Racine, WI 53406 (100%)
Tel.: (262) 886-6800
Web Site: http://www.palmen.com
New & Used Cars Dealer
N.A.I.C.S.: 441120
Steve Kaufman *(Mgr-Fin)*

PALMEN KIA
5301 75th St, Kenosha, WI 53142
Tel.: (262) 697-3100
Web Site: http://www.palmenkia.com
Year Founded: 1938
Sales Range: $10-24.9 Million
Emp.: 100
Car Dealer
N.A.I.C.S.: 441110
Andy Palmen *(Pres)*
Pete Christy *(Mgr-Used Car)*
Brian Ambrogio *(Mgr-Fin)*
Ryan Bodi *(Mgr-Parts)*
Chris LeCount *(Mgr-Fin)*
Maria Ruffolo *(Dir-Mktg)*
Lyman Faber *(Mgr-Customer Care)*
Don Smith *(Mgr-Sls)*
Jose Ayala *(Mgr-Sls-Used Vehicle)*
Niko Giannakakis *(Mgr-Sls-Used Vehicle)*
Giaco Ruffolo *(VP & Dir-Ops)*

PALMER AND SICARD INC.
140 Epping Rd, Exeter, NH 03833
Tel.: (603) 778-1841
Web Site:
http://www.palmerandsicard.com
Rev.: $19,531,255
Emp.: 77
Plumbing Contractor
N.A.I.C.S.: 238220
William Mee *(Controller)*
Marc Dion *(Mgr-HVAC & Svc)*
Rick Desfosses *(Mgr-Warehouse)*
Shawn Earabino *(Project Mgr)*
Philip Lynch *(Gen Mgr)*
Mike Powers *(Project Mgr)*
Ken Radford *(Project Mgr)*
Paul W. Welcome *(Supvr-Plumbing)*
Gerry Potvin *(Supvr-Sheet Metal)*

PALMER AUTO GROUP
4545 E 96th St, Indianapolis, IN 46240
Tel.: (317) 846-5555
Web Site: http://www.palmerauto.com
Year Founded: 1956
Sales Range: $50-74.9 Million
Emp.: 450
Sales of New & Used Automobiles
N.A.I.C.S.: 441110
Eldon Palmer *(Chm)*
Gary Huffman *(Pres)*
Jon Thomas *(Gen Mgr)*
William Demaree *(Partner & VP)*
Don Palmer *(VP)*
Gary Gray *(Parts Mgr)*
Pat McCune *(Controller)*

PALMER BANCSHARES, INC.
8045 N Interstate Hwy 45 Service Rd, Palmer, TX 75152
Tel.: (972) 449-2283
Web Site: http://www.csbpalmer.com
Sales Range: $1-9.9 Million
Emp.: 21
Bank Holding Company
N.A.I.C.S.: 551111
Phillip G. Newsom *(Chm, Pres & CEO)*
Pamela K. Davis *(Pres/Chief Lending Officer-Bank)*
Dana Q. Tucker *(CFO & Exec VP)*

Subsidiaries:

Commercial State Bank (1)
8045 N Interstate Hwy 45 Service Rd, Palmer, TX 75152
Tel.: (972) 449-2283
Web Site: http://www.csbpalmer.com
Commericial Banking
N.A.I.C.S.: 522110
Phillip G. Newsom *(Chm & CEO)*
Pamela K. Davis *(Pres & Chief Lending Officer)*
Dana Q. Tucker *(CFO & Exec VP)*
Jerry D. Watson *(Exec VP & Lending Officer)*
Rhonda E. Land *(Sr VP)*
Brandi McElhaney *(VP)*
Pamela Toumbs *(Asst VP)*
Stacy Willis *(Asst VP)*
Angel Dixon *(Asst VP)*

PALMER CANDY COMPANY
2600 Hwy 75 N, Sioux City, IA 51105
Tel.: (712) 258-5543
Web Site:
http://www.palmercandy.com
Year Founded: 1878
Sales Range: $1-9.9 Million
Emp.: 200
Chocolate & Holiday Confection Mfr
N.A.I.C.S.: 311352
Martin B. Palmer *(Pres)*

PALMER CONTINUUM OF CARE, INC.
PO Box 580700, Tulsa, OK 74158-0700
Tel.: (918) 832-7764
Web Site: http://www.palmer-tulsa.org
Year Founded: 2002
Sales Range: $10-24.9 Million
Emp.: 81
Substance Abuse Rehabilitation Services
N.A.I.C.S.: 623220
Patty Crisp *(Program Dir-Women & Childrens Center)*

COMPANIES

Greg Sneed *(Exec Dir)*
Barry Hesson *(Dir-Adolescent Programs)*
Marilyn Fooshee *(Chm)*
Steve Milam *(Treas)*

PALMER DISTRIBUTION SERVICES, INC.
1040 Lockwood Dr, Houston, TX 77020
Tel.: (713) 673-9084
Web Site:
http://www.palmerlogistics.com
Rev.: $13,129,982
Emp.: 100
General Warehousing & Storage
N.A.I.C.S.: 493110
William Hermann *(CEO)*

PALMER ELECTRIC CO.
875 Jackson Ave, Winter Park, FL 32789-4610
Tel.: (407) 646-8700   FL
Web Site: http://www.palmer-electric.com
Year Founded: 1951
Sales Range: $125-149.9 Million
Emp.: 100
Provider of Electrical Products & Services
N.A.I.C.S.: 238210
Thomas G. Beard *(Owner & Pres)*

PALMER INTERNATIONAL, INC.
2036 Lucon Rd, Skippack, PA 19474
Tel.: (610) 584-4241   PA
Web Site: http://www.palmerint.com
Year Founded: 1946
Sales Range: $75-99.9 Million
Emp.: 50
Mfr of Synthetic Resins, Epoxy & Urea Adhesives
N.A.I.C.S.: 325520
Kevin Palmer *(CEO)*
Roberta Palmer-Body *(VP-HR)*
Andrew Maseloff *(VP-Sls-Intl)*
Marc Ragamuth *(Mgr)*

Subsidiaries:
DMK Mexico, S.A. DE C.V.   (1)
Paso Dela Herradura 401, Mexico, 52786, Mexico   (100%)
Tel.: (52) 5552916080
Web Site: http://www.dmkmexico.com
Sales Range: $10-24.9 Million
Emp.: 20
N.A.I.C.S.: 325212

Palmer (UK) Limited   (1)
Tofts Farm E Industrial Est Brenda Rd, Hartlepool, TS25 2BS, Cleveland, United Kingdom   (100%)
Tel.: (44) 1429233913
Automobile Parts Mfr
N.A.I.C.S.: 441330
Derrick Crowe *(Gen Mgr)*

PALMER JOHNSON ENTERPRISES, INC.
613 Williamson St Ste 202, Madison, WI 53703
Tel.: (800) 341-4334
Web Site:
https://www.palmerjohnsonenterprises.com
Year Founded: 1956
Equipment & Service Providers Distr
N.A.I.C.S.: 811114

Subsidiaries:
Continental Engines, Inc.   (1)
60 Pelham Davis Cir, Greenville, SC 29615
Tel.: (864) 242-5567
Web Site:
http://www.continentalengines.com
Sales Range: $10-24.9 Million
Emp.: 36
Engine & Generator Distr

N.A.I.C.S.: 423830

Palmer Johnson Power Systems LLC   (1)
1835 Haynes Rd, Sun Prairie, WI 53590
Web Site: http://www.pjpower.com
Sales Range: $1-9.9 Million
Emp.: 128
Industrial Diesel Engine Repair Services
N.A.I.C.S.: 811114
Glenn Johnston *(CFO)*
Craig Parsons *(Pres)*
Alex Kiamco *(Mgr-Svc)*
Susan Schuster *(Mgr-Equipment Svcs-Natl)*

Subsidiary (Domestic):
Hamilton Power Solutions   (2)
5540 NE Columbia Blvd, Portland, OR 97218-1236
Tel.: (503) 288-6714
Web Site: https://www.hamiltonpower.com
Commercial, Industrial Machinery & Equipment Repair & Maintenance
N.A.I.C.S.: 811310
Andrew Telford *(Gen Mgr)*
Ryan Manthei *(VP-Sls)*
Josh Spitza *(VP-Ops)*
Brad Borchers *(Pres)*

Mill-Log Equipment Co., Inc.   (2)
90895 Roberts Rd, Coburg, OR 97408
Tel.: (541) 485-2203
Web Site: http://www.milllog.com
Sales Range: $25-49.9 Million
Emp.: 15
Clutches, Transmission & Marine Gears & Torque Convertors Mfr; Heavy-Duty Off-Highway Power Transmission Equipment
N.A.I.C.S.: 336350
Dennis Hoff *(Pres)*
Ken Cotte *(Mgr-Central Mid Atlantic States)*
Ricky White *(Mgr-Southern Mid Atlantic States)*

Subsidiary (Non-US):
Mill-Log Wilson Equipment Ltd.   (2)
3804-53rd Ave, Edmonton, T6B 3N7, AB, Canada
Tel.: (780) 434-9578
Web Site: http://www.milllog.com
Emp.: 10
Power Transmission Equipment Mfr
N.A.I.C.S.: 336350
Dean Belcourt *(Mgr-Ops)*
Ed Lazarenko *(Mgr-Oil Field Product)*

PALMER MOVING & STORAGE CO.
24660 Dequindre Rd, Warren, MI 48091-3332
Tel.: (586) 834-3400   MI
Web Site:
http://www.palmermoving.com
Year Founded: 1910
Sales Range: $10-24.9 Million
Emp.: 40
Local Moving & Storage; Long Distance Moving
N.A.I.C.S.: 484121
Jeffrey W. Palmer *(Pres)*
Tom Estfan *(VP)*

PALMER OIL CO. INCORPORATED
1638 Clay St, Henderson, KY 42420
Tel.: (270) 827-1312
Sales Range: $1-9.9 Million
Emp.: 48
Sales of Petroleum Products
N.A.I.C.S.: 424710
Tony Gonnela *(Gen Mgr)*
Linda Crowder *(Controller)*

PALMER RANCH HOLDINGS LTD.
5589 Marquesas Cir Ste 201, Sarasota, FL 34233
Tel.: (941) 922-0759
Sales Range: $25-49.9 Million
Emp.: 10
Property Developer
N.A.I.C.S.: 237210

Hugh Culverhouse *(Owner)*
Andrea Frank *(Gen Counsel)*

PALMER SNYDER FURNITURE CO.
1050 Chinoe Rd Ste 106, Lexington, KY 40502
Tel.: (859) 266-3472
Web Site:
http://www.palmersnyder.com
Rev.: $13,700,000
Emp.: 45
Chairs, Portable Folding
N.A.I.C.S.: 337127
Roger Clark *(Owner & Pres)*
Beth Clark *(Mgr-Mktg)*

PALMETTO CAR & TRUCK GROUP
1625 Savannah Hwy, Charleston, SC 29407
Tel.: (843) 571-3673
Web Site:
http://www.palmettoford.com
Rev.: $122,499,221
Emp.: 140
Automobiles, New & Used
N.A.I.C.S.: 441110
Bils Back *(VP-Sls)*
Graham M. Eubank Jr. *(Pres & CEO)*

PALMETTO CHEVROLET CO., INC.
1122 4th Ave, Conway, SC 29526-5110
Tel.: (843) 248-4283
Web Site:
http://www.palmettochevy.com
Sales Range: $10-24.9 Million
Emp.: 60
Car Whslr
N.A.I.C.S.: 441110
William O. Marsh *(Pres)*

PALMETTO ELECTRIC COOPERATIVE
4063 Grays Hwy, Ridgeland, SC 29936
Tel.: (843) 726-5551
Web Site: http://www.palmetto.coop
Rev.: $32,600,000
Emp.: 180
Distribution, Electric Power
N.A.I.C.S.: 221122
A. Berl Davis *(Pres & CEO)*
Jane Frederick *(VP-HR)*
Gary E. Jeger *(Sr VP-Info Sys)*
Jeremiah E. Vaigneur *(Chm)*
C. Alex Ulmer *(Vice Chm)*
Eunice Spilliards *(Treas & Sec)*
Wilson Saleeby *(VP-Engrg & Ops)*
Tanya Trull *(VP-Fin)*
Lewis F. Davis *(VP-Customer Svc)*

PALMETTO HEALTH
1301 Taylor St, Columbia, SC 29201-2915
Tel.: (803) 296-2100   SC
Web Site:
http://www.palmettohealth.org
Year Founded: 1998
Sales Range: $200-249.9 Million
Emp.: 10,000
Non-Profit Health Care Management Services
N.A.I.C.S.: 622110
Paul K. Duane *(CFO)*
Sara B. Fisher *(Treas)*
Jerome D. Odom *(Vice Chm)*
Beverly D. Chrisman *(Chm)*
Michelle Edwards *(CIO)*
Mark Mayson *(VP-Sys)*
Ryan Hall *(VP-Sys)*
Robert Brinkerhoff *(VP-Sys & HR)*
Deborah J. Tapley *(VP-Sys-Clinical & Support Sys)*

PALMETTO STATE BANKSHARES, INC.

Charles D. Beaman Jr. *(CEO)*
John J. Singerling III *(Pres)*
John M. Brabham Jr. *(Sec)*
Paul V. Fant Sr. *(Vice Chm)*
Benjamin M. Cunningham Jr. *(VP-Sys & Fin)*

Subsidiaries:
Palmetto Health Baptist Easley   (1)
200 Fleetwood Dr, Easley, SC 29640
Tel.: (864) 442-7200
Web Site: http://www.palmettohealth.org
Sales Range: $25-49.9 Million
Emp.: 707
Hospital Operations
N.A.I.C.S.: 622110
John Cooper *(Pres)*
Scott Parker *(First VP)*
Karen Ardis *(Second VP)*

PALMETTO HOSPITAL TRUST
201 Executive Ctr Dr Ste 300, Columbia, SC 29210
Tel.: (803) 731-5300
Web Site: http://www.phts.com
Sales Range: $10-24.9 Million
Emp.: 40
Workers Compensation Insurance
N.A.I.C.S.: 524126
Meg Brooks *(Dir-Comm-PHTS)*
JoAnne Smith *(Asst VP-Fin)*

Subsidiaries:
PHT Services Ltd.   (1)
250 Berryhill Rd Ste 402, Columbia, SC 29210
Tel.: (803) 731-5300
Web Site: http://www.phts.com
Rev.: $4,771,911
Fire, Marine & Casualty Insurance
N.A.I.C.S.: 524126
Brian Teusink *(Pres & CEO)*
Jay Bikofsky *(Vice Chm)*
James A. Pfeiffer *(Chm)*
Norman G. Rentz *(Sec)*
Adam B. Allen *(COO & Exec VP)*
R. Blake Carpenter *(CFO & Exec VP)*
Larry W. Gray *(Exec VP-Claims & Risk Mgmt)*

PALMETTO PAVING CORPORATION
3873 Hwy 701 N, Conway, SC 29526
Tel.: (843) 365-2156
Web Site:
http://www.palmettopavingcorp.com
Sales Range: $10-24.9 Million
Emp.: 20
Provider of Asphalt & Asphaltic Paving Services
N.A.I.C.S.: 324121
G. Marshall Godwin *(Pres)*
Shawn Godwin *(Controller)*

PALMETTO RURAL TELEPHONE COOPERATIVE, INC.
292 Robertson Blvd, Walterboro, SC 29488
Tel.: (843) 538-2020   SC
Web Site: http://www.prtc.coop
Sales Range: $10-24.9 Million
Emp.: 62
Telecommunication Servicesb
N.A.I.C.S.: 517810
Jason J. Dandridge *(CEO)*

PALMETTO STATE BANKSHARES, INC.
601 1st St W, Hampton, SC 29924
Tel.: (803) 943-2671   SC
Web Site:
http://www.palmettostatebank.com
Sales Range: $10-24.9 Million
Emp.: 82
Bank Holding Company
N.A.I.C.S.: 551111
Sterling Laffitte *(Pres)*

PALMETTO STATE BANKSHARES, INC.

U.S. PRIVATE

Palmetto State Bankshares, Inc.—(Continued)

Subsidiaries:

Palmetto State Bank (1)
601 1st St W, Hampton, SC 29924
Tel.: (803) 943-2671
Web Site:
  http://www.palmettostatebank.com
Commericial Banking
N.A.I.C.S.: 522110
Beth Chafin (Asst VP)

PALMS & COMPANY INC.
6421 Lake Washington Blvd NE Ste 404, Kirkland, WA 98033-6876
Tel.: (425) 828-6774
Web Site: http://www.peterpalms.com
Year Founded: 1934
Sales Range: $1-9.9 Million
Emp.: 200
Export/Import of Merchant Banking
N.A.I.C.S.: 424590
Peter J. Palms IV (Pres)

PALMYRA BOLOGNA CO.
230 N College St, Palmyra, PA 17078
Tel.: (717) 838-6336
Web Site:
  http://www.seltzerslebanonbologna.com
Sales Range: $10-24.9 Million
Emp.: 50
Bologna Mfr
N.A.I.C.S.: 311612
Craig Seltzer (Pres)

PALO ALTO VETERANS INSTITUTE FOR RESEARCH
3801 Miranda Ave, Palo Alto, CA 94304-0038
Tel.: (650) 858-3970   CA
Web Site: http://www.pavir.org
Year Founded: 1988
Sales Range: $10-24.9 Million
Emp.: 238
Educational Support & Medical Research Services
N.A.I.C.S.: 611710
Lawrence L. Leung (Treas & Sec)
Mark Nicolls (Chm)
Kerstin Lynam (CEO)
Mary Thornton (Dir-IT)
Elaine Staats (Dir-Sponsored Res)
Bonnie Liang (CFO)
David Luther (Dir-HR)

PALO DURO CAPITAL, LLC
Highland Park Pl 4514 Cole Ave Ste 600, Dallas, TX 75205
Tel.: (214) 295-7520   DE
Web Site:
  http://www.palodurocapital.com
Privater Equity Firm
N.A.I.C.S.: 523999
Matthew Golden (Partner)
Dave Sheridan (Operating Partner)

Subsidiaries:

CCR Specialty Chemicals LLC (1)
305 Madison Ave Ste 1035, New York, NY 10165
Tel.: (214) 769-2221
Investment Services
N.A.I.C.S.: 523999
Matthew Golden (Mgr)

Subsidiary (Domestic):

Crowley Chemical Company, Inc. (2)
1 Grand Central Pl 305 Madison Ave Ste 1035, New York, NY 10165
Tel.: (212) 682-1200
Web Site: http://www.crowleychemical.com
Sales Range: $10-24.9 Million
Emp.: 20
Petrochemicals, Coal Tar Chemicals & Pine Derived Chemical Mfr
N.A.I.C.S.: 325199
Chris Mortensen (Gen Mgr)

Division (Domestic):

Crowley Tar Products Co., Inc. (3)
305 Madison Ave Ste 1035, New York, NY 10165-1036
Tel.: (212) 682-1200
Web Site: http://www.crowleychemical.com
Producer of Coal Tar as in Crudes, Intermediates & Distillates
N.A.I.C.S.: 325194
William Cannon (Pres)

Subsidiary (Domestic):

Rusmar Incorporated (3)
216 Garfield Ave, West Chester, PA 19380
Tel.: (610) 436-4314
Web Site: http://www.rusmarinc.com
Sales Range: $1-9.9 Million
Emp.: 12
Chemical Products Mfr
N.A.I.C.S.: 325998
Christopher Campman (Mgr-Bus Dev)
Ricky van Buren (Mgr-Cellular Concrete & Mining Applications)
Phil Johnson (Pres & CEO)
J. T. Bielan III (Mgr-Sls & Mktg)

Subsidiary (Domestic):

NCM Odor Control, Inc. (4)
120 Rainbow Plz Ln, Brodheadsville, PA 18322
Tel.: (310) 457-5418
Web Site: http://www.ncmodorcontrol.com
Specialty Trade Contractors
N.A.I.C.S.: 238990
Jesse Levin (Pres & CEO)

PALO DURO HARDWOODS INC.
12875 E 42nd Ave Ste 1, Denver, CO 80239-4839
Tel.: (303) 375-0280
Web Site:
  http://www.palodurocollection.com
Rev.: $22,429,120
Emp.: 26
Wood Flooring Whslr
N.A.I.C.S.: 423202
Keith Vigil (Mgr-Credit)
Tom Ruekert (Reg Mgr-Sls)

Subsidiaries:

Diversified Millwork Inc. (1)
3556 Quentin St, Aurora, CO 80011
Tel.: (303) 341-6696
Sales Range: $10-24.9 Million
Emp.: 20
Millwork
N.A.I.C.S.: 321918

PALOMA SYSTEMS, INC.
11250 Waples Mill Rd Ste 420, Fairfax, VA 22030
Tel.: (703) 278-8999
Web Site: http://www.palomasys.com
Year Founded: 1998
Sales Range: $10-24.9 Million
Emp.: 30
Installs, Integrates & Maintains Information & Communications Systems for Government Agencies
N.A.I.C.S.: 541715
Isabel Pedrozo (CEO)

PALOMAR DISPLAY PRODUCTS, INC.
5803 Newton Dr Ste C, Carlsbad, CA 92008-6582
Tel.: (760) 931-3200   CA
Web Site:
  http://www.palomardisplays.com
Year Founded: 1955
Electronic Display Developer & Mfr
N.A.I.C.S.: 334419
Zeev Kalansky (VP-Bus Dev)
Chuck Pridham (VP-Ops)

PALOMAR INSURANCE CORP.
4525 Executive Park Dr Ste 202, Montgomery, AL 36116
Tel.: (334) 270-0105
Web Site: http://www.palomarins.com
Year Founded: 1954
Sales Range: $10-24.9 Million
Emp.: 75
Insurance Agents
N.A.I.C.S.: 524210
Tony Craft (CEO)
Len Skipper (COO)
Terry Henley (Sr VP)
Bill Connell (Sr VP-Mktg)
Allison Strouse (Acct Mgr)
Amanda Russell (Mgr-Acct Benefits)
Toni Jones (VP-Transportation Mktg)
Todd Johnson (VP)
Tammie Little (Coord-Claims)
Susanna Bader (Mgr-Accts Benefits)
Rick Short (Mgr-Facilities)
Portia Anderson (Acct Mgr)
Phil Gargis (Acct Exec)
Austin Golson (Acct Exec)

PALOMAR MOUNTAIN PREMIUM SPRING WATER
1270 W Mission Rd, Escondido, CA 92029
Tel.: (760) 743-0140
Web Site:
  http://www.palomarwater.com
Sales Range: $10-24.9 Million
Emp.: 60
Mineral or Spring Water Bottling
N.A.I.C.S.: 424490
Conrad Pawelski (CFO)

PALOMAR TECHNOLOGIES COMPANIES, LLC
2728 Loker Ave W, Carlsbad, CA 92010
Tel.: (760) 931-3600
Web Site:
  http://www.palomartechnology.com
Year Founded: 1995
Sales Range: $50-74.9 Million
Emp.: 55
Holding Company
N.A.I.C.S.: 551112
Bruce Huehers (Pres & CEO)
Evan Hueners (Product Mgr-Mktg)
Carl Hempel (CFO & VP)
Daniel Evans (CTO)
Rich Hueners (VP-Sls & Mktg)
Rebecca Janzon (Dir-Mktg Comm)

Subsidiaries:

Palomar Technologies GmbH (1)
Am Weichselgarten 30b, 91058, Erlangen, Germany
Tel.: (49) 9131480093
Web Site:
  http://www.palomartechnologies.com
Sales Range: $25-49.9 Million
Emp.: 200
Electronic Components Mfr
N.A.I.C.S.: 334419
Thorsten Scheidler (Mng Dir-Europe)

Palomar Technologies Inc. (1)
2728 Loker Ave W, Carlsbad, CA 92010
Tel.: (760) 931-3600
Web Site:
  http://www.palomartechnologies.com
Rev.: $30,000,000
Emp.: 50
Electronic Components Mfr
N.A.I.C.S.: 334419
Bruce W. Hueners (Pres & CEO)
Daniel Evans (CTO)
Allan Hass (VP-Engrg & Ops)
Carl Hempel (CFO & VP)
Rich Hueners (Mng Dir & VP-Sls-Global)
Tim Hughes (Dir-Global Customer Svc)
David Rasmussen (Gen Mgr-Assembly Svcs)
A. J. Wilson (CMO)

Palomar Technologies Pte Ltd. (1)
8 Boon Lay Way 08-09 Tradehub 21, Pantech Industrial Complex, Singapore, 609964, Singapore
Tel.: (65) 97284988

Web Site:
  http://www.palomartechnologies.com
Sales Range: $10-24.9 Million
Emp.: 60
Electronic Components Mfr
N.A.I.C.S.: 334419

PALOS COMMUNITY HOSPITAL
12251 S 80th Ave, Palos Heights, IL 60463
Tel.: (708) 923-4000   IL
Web Site:
  http://www.paloscommunityhospital.org
Year Founded: 1972
Sales Range: $350-399.9 Million
Emp.: 3,177
Health Care Srvices
N.A.I.C.S.: 622110
Hugh A. Rose (CFO & VP-Fin)
Margaret J. Carroll (CIO)
Mark Sinibaldi (VP-Medical Affairs)

PALOS VERDES BUILDING CORP.
1675 Sampson Ave, Corona, CA 92879
Tel.: (951) 371-8090
Web Site: http://www.usbattery.com
Year Founded: 1926
Sales Range: $125-149.9 Million
Emp.: 400
Storage Batteries Mfr
N.A.I.C.S.: 335910
Steve Kay (CFO)
Terry Agrelius (Pres)

PALS, INC.
3735 W 1st Ave, Willmar, MN 56201
Tel.: (320) 235-8860
Web Site: http://www.palsusa.com
Sales Range: $10-24.9 Million
Emp.: 50
Poultry & Livestock Supplies Distr
N.A.I.C.S.: 423820
Jason Reed (Gen Mgr)
Steve Minnehan (Mgr)
Katie Hoeschen (Gen Mgr)
Jeff Anderson (Mgr-Svc Dept)

PALTALK
Church St Sta, New York, NY 10008
Tel.: (212) 564-9997
Web Site: http://www.paltalk.com
Year Founded: 1998
Rev.: $17,700,000
Emp.: 37
Web Conferencing & Media Services
N.A.I.C.S.: 449210

PALTALK, INC.
122 E 42nd St, New York, NY 10168
Tel.: (212) 594-5050
Software Development Services
N.A.I.C.S.: 541511
Jason Katz (CEO)

PALUMBO LUMBER & MANUFACTURING CO.
1020 W Main St, Lexington, KY 40508
Tel.: (859) 252-1402
Web Site:
  http://www.palumbolumber.com
Sales Range: $10-24.9 Million
Emp.: 25
Lumber: Rough, Dressed & Finished
N.A.I.C.S.: 423310
Stewart Mcintosh (CEO)
Jack Tucker (Co-Pres)

PAMAL BROADCASTING LTD.
6 Johnson Rd, Latham, NY 12110
Tel.: (518) 786-6600
Web Site: http://www.pamal.com
Year Founded: 1996

COMPANIES

Sales Range: $100-124.9 Million
Emp.: 175
Radio Broadcasting Stations
N.A.I.C.S.: 516110
James J. Morrell (Chm & CEO)
John VanDenburgh (Treas & Sec)

PAMBY MOTORS INCORPORATED
665 Danbury Rd, Ridgefield, CT 06877
Tel.: (203) 438-6231
Web Site:
http://www.pambyzone.com
Sales Range: $25-49.9 Million
Emp.: 20
Automobile Sales, New & Used
N.A.I.C.S.: 441110
John Pambianchi (Pres)
Barbara Jones (Office Mgr)

PAMC, LTD.
531 W College St, Los Angeles, CA 90012
Tel.: (213) 624-8411
Web Site: http://www.pamc.net
Year Founded: 1989
Rev.: $36,000,000
Emp.: 600
Holding Company; Hospital Owner & Operator
N.A.I.C.S.: 551112
John Edwards (Pres & CEO)
Allan Shubin (CFO)

Subsidiaries:

Pacific Alliance Medical Center, Inc. (1)
531 W College St, Los Angeles, CA 90012-2315
Tel.: (213) 624-8411
Web Site: http://www.pamc.net
Rev.: $30,251,289
Emp.: 575
General Medical & Surgical Hospitals
N.A.I.C.S.: 622110
John Edwards (Pres & CEO)

PAMCO LABEL COMPANY
2200 S Wolf Rd, Des Plaines, IL 60018-1934
Tel.: (847) 803-2200 DE
Web Site:
http://www.pamcolabel.com
Sales Range: $75-99.9 Million
Emp.: 100
Mfr of Pressure Sensitive Labels & Specialty Printed Products
N.A.I.C.S.: 323111

PAMLICO CAPITAL MANAGEMENT, L.P.
150 N College St Ste 2400, Charlotte, NC 28202
Tel.: (704) 414-7150 NC
Web Site:
http://www.pamlicocapital.com
Year Founded: 1988
Rev.: $2,000,000,000
Emp.: 25
Private Equity Fund Management Services
N.A.I.C.S.: 523940
Tracey M. Chaffin (Partner & CFO)
Scott B. Perper (Partner)
Arthur C. Roselle (Partner)
Walker C. Simmons (Partner)
Scott R. Stevens (Partner)
Eric J. Wilkins (Partner)
Michele D. Bailey (Controller)
Kristy W. Burleigh (Controller)
Leslie F. Bullins (Dir-Tax)
Jay R. Henry (VP)
Andrew B. Tindel (VP)
Gillian Kulman Davis (VP-Bus Dev)
Stuart M. Christhilf IV (Partner & COO)
Frederick Wesley Eubank II (Co-Founder & Partner)
L. Watts Hamrick III (Partner)
R. Scott Glass Jr. (VP)

Subsidiaries:

10th Magnitude Inc. (1)
835 Vernon Ave, Glencoe, IL 60022
Tel.: (312) 940-8109
Web Site: http://www.10thmagnitude.com
Computer Related Services
N.A.I.C.S.: 541519
Brian Blanchard (VP-Cloud Solutions)
Jason Rook (VP-Alliances)
Mark Smith (VP-Sls)
Alex Brown (CEO)
Christopher Lewis (COO)
Claudia Del Valle (Mgr-Bus Dev-New York)
Ira Bell (CTO)

Cartegraph Systems, LLC (1)
3600 Digital Dr, Dubuque, IA 52003
Tel.: (563) 556-8120
Web Site: http://www.cartegraph.com
Software Publisher
N.A.I.C.S.: 513210
Jake Schneider (VP-Product Strategy)
Randy Skemp (Chief Revenue Officer & Exec VP)
Jay Wickham (Mgr-Mkt)
Josh Mallamud (CEO)
Bill Barron (Mng Dir-Buildings & Infrastructure)

Subsidiary (Domestic):

PenBay Solutions LLC (2)
101 Main St, Topsham, ME 04086
Tel.: (703) 270-8480
Web Site: http://www.penbaysolutions.com
Computer Facilities Management Services
N.A.I.C.S.: 541513

Clarity Telecom, LLC (1)
5100 S Broadband Ln, Sioux Falls, SD 57108
Tel.: (605) 965-9393
Holding Company; Cable Television, Internet & Telephone Services
N.A.I.C.S.: 551112
Jim Gleason (CEO)
Keith Davidson (CFO)
Larry Eby (COO)

Subsidiary (Domestic):

NTS, Inc. (2)
1220 Broadway, Lubbock, TX 79401
Tel.: (806) 771-5212
Web Site: http://www.ntscom.com
Sales Range: $50-74.9 Million
Emp.: 200
Holding Company; Long Distance Voice & Data Communications Services
N.A.I.C.S.: 551112
Cyrus Driver (Pres & CEO)

Subsidiary (Domestic):

NTS Communications, Inc. (3)
1220 Broadway St, Lubbock, TX 79401-1610
Tel.: (806) 797-0687
Web Site: http://www.ntscom.com
Sales Range: $50-74.9 Million
Telephone, Internet, Data Products, Point to Point & Voice Mail Communications Services
N.A.I.C.S.: 517810
Cyrus Driver (Pres & CEO)
Deborah Crawford (Exec VP & COO)
Don Pittman (Exec VP & CFO)
Michael McDaniel (VP-Svc Delivery & IT Strategy)
Priscilla Rivas (VP-Network Admin)
Roberto Chang (VP-Products & Mktg)
Wendy J. Lee (VP-HR)
Daniel Wheeler (Gen Counsel & VP)

Subsidiary (Domestic):

Communications Brokers, Inc. (4)
2305 129th Pl SE, Everett, WA 98208-7131
Tel.: (425) 483-8882
Communication Equipment Repair & Maintenance Services
N.A.I.C.S.: 811210

Subsidiary (Domestic):

Xfone USA, Inc. (3)
1220 Broadway, Lubbock, TX 79401
Tel.: (806) 797-0687
Web Site: http://www.ntscom.com
Sales Range: $50-74.9 Million
Emp.: 200
Communications Services Including Local, Long Distance & Data/Internet Solutions
N.A.I.C.S.: 517810

Subsidiary (Domestic):

Gulf Coast Utilities, Inc. (4)
2833 A Brakley Dr, Baton Rouge, LA 70816
Tel.: (800) 565-1536
Integrated Telecommunication Services
N.A.I.C.S.: 517111

Metametrics, Inc. (1)
1000 Park Forty Plz Dr Ste 120, Durham, NC 27713
Tel.: (919) 547-3400
Web Site: http://www.metametricsinc.com
Educational Support Services
N.A.I.C.S.: 611710
A. Jackson Stenner (Co-Founder & Chief Science Officer)
Trilby Berger (Sr VP-Strategic Partnerships)
Timothy J. Klasson (COO)
Eleanor E. Sanford-Moore (Sr VP-R&D)
Anne Schiano (Sr VP-Govt Rels)
Todd Sandvik (Sr VP-Strategy & Ops)
Alistair Van Moere (Chief Product Officer)
Malbert Smith III (Co-Founder, Pres & CEO)

Personify Inc. (1)
6500 River Pl Blvd Bldg III Ste 250, Austin, TX 78730
Tel.: (703) 564-5200
Web Site: http://www.personifycorp.com
Computer Software Development & Applications
N.A.I.C.S.: 513210
Paul Gannon (VP-Mktg)
Dave Cooper (CTO)
Anne-Marie Bitman (VP-Customer Svc)
Bob Wood (VP-Sls)
Sarah Schmall (VP-Pro Svcs-Oak Brook)
Scott Adkins (Chief Revenue Officer-Austin)
Andre Pavlovic (VP-Product Mktg & Mgmt)
Ken Aponte (Sr Dir-Community Solutions)
Kim Horn (Dir-HR)
Marc Bernstein (Principal-Indus & VP)
Michael Wilson (Chief Mktg & Strategy Officer)
Jeff Lyons (COO)
Joe Hermes (CFO)
Cindy Johnson (VP-People Ops-Global)
Scott Collison (Pres & CEO)

Subsidiary (Domestic):

MemberClicks LLC (2)
Piedmont Ctr 3495 Piedmont Rd NE Bldg 12 Ste 110, Atlanta, GA 30305
Tel.: (404) 879-2800
Web Site: http://www.memberclicks.com
Sales Range: $1-9.9 Million
Web-Based Membership Management Software
N.A.I.C.S.: 513210
Mark Sedgley (Pres & CEO)
Adam Kearney (VP-Mktg)
Duncan McCreery (VP-Product)
Brandon Wycherley (Exec VP)
Kinsey Mahan (Dir-Customer Experience)
Paul Plaia III (Chief Revenue Officer)

Subsidiary (Domestic):

WebLink International, Inc. (3)
571 Monon Trl Ste 125, Carmel, IN 46032
Tel.: (317) 872-3909
Web Site:
http://www.weblinkinternational.com
Sales Range: $1-9.9 Million
Emp.: 26
Web-Based Association Management Software Developer
N.A.I.C.S.: 513210
D. J. Muller (Founder & CEO)
Marty Muse (VP-Mktg)
Chris Landis (Chief Strategy Officer)
Colleen Bottorff (Mgr-Content & Comm)
Jacque Shaffer (Dir-Customer Success)
Alex Davis (Brand Mgr)
Chris Phillips (Dir-Product Dev & IT)

PAN AMERICAN GRAIN COMPANY

PAMLICO PACKING COMPANY INCORPORATED
PO Box 336, Grantsboro, NC 28529
Tel.: (252) 745-3688 NC
Web Site:
http://www.bestseafood.com
Year Founded: 1941
Sales Range: $10-24.9 Million
Emp.: 9
Mfr & Distr of Fresh & Frozen Packaged Fish
N.A.I.C.S.: 311710
Doug Cross (VP)

PAMPA CONCRETE CO
220 W Tyng Ave 15th St, Pampa, TX 79065
Tel.: (806) 669-3111
Rev.: $10,000,000
Emp.: 15
Ready Mixed Concrete
N.A.I.C.S.: 327320
Bill J. Williamson (Pres)

PAN AMERICAN COFFEE COMPANY INC.
500 16th St, Hoboken, NJ 07030
Tel.: (201) 963-2329
Web Site:
http://www.panamericancoffee.com
Year Founded: 1960
Sales Range: $10-24.9 Million
Emp.: 72
Coffee Mfr
N.A.I.C.S.: 311920
Ruth Santuccio (VP)

PAN AMERICAN DEVELOPMENT FOUNDATION
1889 F St NW 2nd Fl, Washington, DC 20006
Tel.: (202) 458-3969 DC
Web Site: http://www.padf.org
Year Founded: 1962
Sales Range: $75-99.9 Million
Civil & Social Organization
N.A.I.C.S.: 813410
Kristan Beck (COO)
John Sanbrailo (Exec Dir)
Caterina Valero (Sr Dir-Programs)
Lance Leverenz (Dir-Bus Dev)
Hearly Mayr (Dir-Comm & Pub Affairs)
Luisa Villegas (Deputy Program Dir)

PAN AMERICAN EXPRESS INC.
4848 Riverside Dr, Laredo, TX 78041
Tel.: (956) 723-4848
Web Site: http://www.panamex-zero.com
Year Founded: 1988
Sales Range: $10-24.9 Million
Emp.: 30
Provider of Trucking Services
N.A.I.C.S.: 484121
Ricardo Guardado (Pres)

Subsidiaries:

Southwest Trailers Inc. (1)
4848 Riverside Dr, Laredo, TX 78041
Tel.: (956) 723-4848
Web Site: http://www.panamex-zero.com
Sales Range: $10-24.9 Million
Emp.: 28
Trucking Except Local
N.A.I.C.S.: 484121
Ricardo Guardado (Pres)
Joe Flores (Controller)

PAN AMERICAN GRAIN COMPANY
Calle Claudia Ste 9, Guaynabo, PR 00968
Tel.: (787) 273-6100

PAN AMERICAN GRAIN COMPANY — U.S. PRIVATE

Pan American Grain Company—(Continued)
Web Site:
http://www.panamericangrain.com
Rev.: $24,755,008
Emp.: 72
Prepared Rice & Animal Feeds
N.A.I.C.S.: 311119
Jose Gonzalez (Pres)
Alberto Fernandez (VP-Admin)
Milton Gonzalez (VP)
Eduardo Fernandez (VP-Treasury)

PAN AMERICAN LABORATORIES INC.
4099 Hwy 190, Covington, LA 70433
Tel.: (985) 893-4097
Web Site: http://www.pamlab.com
Rev.: $29,900,092
Emp.: 131
Pharmaceutical Products Developer & Marketer
N.A.I.C.S.: 325412
Frank Jimenez (CEO)

PAN AMERICAN PAPERS, INC.
5101 NW 37th Ave, Miami, FL 33142-3232
Tel.: (305) 635-2534
Web Site: http://www.panampap.com
Year Founded: 1972
Sales Range: $10-24.9 Million
Emp.: 25
Printing & Writing Paper Whslr
N.A.I.C.S.: 424110
Francisco T. Valdes (Co-Founder)
Jesus F. Valdes (Co-Founder)

PAN AMERICAN TOOL CORPORATION
5990 NW 31st Ave, Fort Lauderdale, FL 33309
Tel.: (954) 735-8665
Web Site:
http://www.panamericantool.com
Sales Range: $10-24.9 Million
Emp.: 30
Industrial Supplies Merchant Whslr
N.A.I.C.S.: 423840
Noreen Leon (Pres)
Curtis Finn (Gen Mgr)

PAN ASIAN CURRENCY EXCHANGE CORP.
1939 Alum Rock Ave Ste B, San Jose, CA 95116
Tel.: (408) 251-1250
Rev.: $12,000,000
Emp.: 11
Foreign Currency Exchange
N.A.I.C.S.: 523160
Anita L. Papa (Pres)

PAN COMMUNICATIONS
300 Brickstone Sq 7th Fl, Andover, MA 01810
Tel.: (978) 474-1900
Web Site:
http://www.pancommunications.com
Year Founded: 1995
Sales Range: $1-9.9 Million
Emp.: 60
Public Relations Agency
N.A.I.C.S.: 541820
Mark C. Nardone (Exec VP)
Gary Torpey (Sr VP-Fin)
Elizabeth Famiglietti (Sr VP-HR)
Katherine J. Blair (VP & Gen Mgr-Orlando)
Darlene Doyle (VP)
Rob Adler (Mng Dir & Exec VP)
Tim Munroe (VP)
Michele Frost (VP-Digital)
David Bowker (VP-Tech Practice)
Phil Carpenter (Mng Dir & Exec VP)
Jennifer Malleo (VP)
Ryan M. Wallace (VP & Gen Mgr)
Dan Martin (Sr VP-Healthcare)
Fran Bosecker (VP)
Megan Kessler (VP & Dir-Acct)
Nikki Festa O'Brien (Sr VP)
Adam Cormier (VP-Client Rels)
Catherine Doyle (VP)
Matthew Briggs (Sr VP)
Sian Kilgour (Dir-Client Service-UK)
Gareth Thomas (Mng Dir-UK)
Nia Evans (VP & Gen Mgr-UK)
Adam Novak (VP-Tech)
Emily Holt (VP-Tech)
Kari Hulley (Sr VP & Gen Mgr-San Francisco)
Kathryn McMahon Arrigg (VP)
Philip A. Nardone Jr. (Founder, Pres & CEO)

PAN CONTINENTAL RESOURCES, INC.
2600 Red Bluff Rd, Seabrook, TX 77586
Tel.: (281) 291-8100
Year Founded: 1978
Sales Range: $10-24.9 Million
Emp.: 33
Business Consulting Services; Construction Equipment Whslr
N.A.I.C.S.: 423810
Y.S. Pan (Pres & Treas)

PAN OCEANIC EYEWEAR LTD.
15 W 37th St Fl 6, New York, NY 10018
Tel.: (212) 354-7744
Web Site:
http://www.panoceanicgroup.com
Year Founded: 1968
Sales Range: $10-24.9 Million
Emp.: 60
Mfr & Sales of Sunglasses & Accessories
N.A.I.C.S.: 423990
Ronald Terzi (Owner & Pres)
Elliott Mizrahi (Exec VP)
Kerry Mindick (Mgr-Warehouse)
Jessica Shrier-Levine (Dir-Creative)

PAN PACIFIC EXPRESS CORP.
19481 Harborgate Way, Torrance, CA 90501
Tel.: (310) 638-3887
Web Site:
http://www.panpacificusa.com
Sales Range: $10-24.9 Million
Emp.: 40
Foreign Freight Forwarding
N.A.I.C.S.: 488510
Ivy Wang (Pres)

PAN PACIFIC RV CENTERS INC.
252 W Yettner Rd, French Camp, CA 95231
Tel.: (209) 234-2000
Web Site:
http://www.panpacificrv.com
Rev.: $13,438,557
Emp.: 40
Camper & Travel Trailer Dealers
N.A.I.C.S.: 441210
Matt Jones (Gen Mgr-Sls)

PAN PEPIN INC.
203 Ave Laurel, Bayamon, PR 00959
Tel.: (787) 787-1717
Web Site: http://www.panpepin.com
Rev.: $32,836,902
Emp.: 575
Bread, Cake & Related Products
N.A.I.C.S.: 311812
Jose Teixidor (Chm)
Carolina Rodriguez (VP-Fin)
Angel Vazquez (Pres)

PAN TECHNOLOGY INC.
117 Moonachie Ave, Carlstadt, NJ 07072
Tel.: (201) 438-7878
Web Site:
http://www.pantechnology.com
Rev.: $11,038,140
Emp.: 46
Printing Ink
N.A.I.C.S.: 325910
Robert Rossomando (Pres)
David Bornwell (Controller)
Michael Rossomando (VP)

PAN WEST CORP.
639 McDonald Ave, Brooklyn, NY 11218
Tel.: (718) 438-7340
Sales Range: $10-24.9 Million
Emp.: 25
Plumbing Fittings & Supplies
N.A.I.C.S.: 423720
Michael Panzer (Pres)
Goldie Green (Sec)

PAN-AM EQUITIES, INC.
18 E 50 St Fl 10, New York, NY 10022
Tel.: (212) 837-4800
Sales Range: $10-24.9 Million
Emp.: 50
Apartment Building Operator
N.A.I.C.S.: 524113
David Iwanier (VP)
Geraldine Foley (Dir-Residential Leasing)
Nehad Moughrabi (Mgr-Property)
Virginia Langdet (Controller)

PAN-AMERICAN LIFE INSURANCE GROUP, INC.
601 Poydras St, New Orleans, LA 70130-6029
Tel.: (504) 566-1300
Web Site: http://www.palig.com
Year Founded: 1911
Sales Range: $450-499.9 Million
Emp.: 1,950
Life & Health Insurance Hospital & Medical Service Plans Pension Plans & Administration
N.A.I.C.S.: 524113
Carlos F. Mickan (Vice Chm)
Marta C. Reeves (VP-Corp Mktg)
Scott Reitan (Sr VP-Admin & IT)
Milton Haripaul (Mgr-Ops-Grp Bus)
Valery Sinot (Gen Mgr)
Daniel Costello (Sr VP-Intl Country Mgmt)
Robert DiCianni (Pres-Intl Grp Bus)
Jose S. Suquet (Chm, Pres & CEO)
Anurang Revri (VP-Applications Dev & Architecture)
David Demmon (CFO, Sr VP & Controller)
Bryan Scofield (Sr VP-HR)
Mark Northrup (VP-Application Dev & Infrastructure)
Selig Ehrlich (Chief Actuary & Officer-Risk)
Steven A. Friedman (Chief Investment Officer & Exec VP-Corp Dev & Strategy)
Frank Recio (Exec VP-Ops & Tech)

Subsidiaries:

HolaDoctor, Inc. (1)
900 Old Roswell Lakes Pkwy Ste 230, Roswell, GA 30076
Tel.: (770) 649-0298
Web Site: http://www.holadoctor.net
Sales Range: $1-9.9 Million
Online Health Care Services
N.A.I.C.S.: 513210
Robert Estrada (Pres & CEO)
Cesar Zafra (Controller)
Adriana Hernandez (Mgr-Special Projects & Sls Mktg)
Brianna Oates (Mgr-Health Programs)
Bruno Lopez (Exec VP-Ops)
Chris Butler (CFO)
Dirk Schroeder (Exec VP-Consulting & Res)
Fernando Orfila (Product Dir)
Omar Hernandez (Dir-Database Mktg)
Tania Mancilla (Mgr-SEO & SEM)
Adam Hill (CFO)

Pan-American Life Insurance de Costa Rica, S.A. (1)
Oficentro Fuentes Del Obelisco 2do Piso Oficina 18, San Rafael De Escazu, San Jose, Costa Rica
Tel.: (506) 22880960
Insurance Services
N.A.I.C.S.: 524113

PAN-MAR CORPORATION
88 Sunnyside Blvd Ste 204, Plainview, NY 11803
Tel.: (516) 822-5700
Web Site:
http://www.konigwheels.com
Sales Range: $10-24.9 Million
Emp.: 30
Mfr of Automotive Supplies & Parts
N.A.I.C.S.: 423120
Joe Schaefer (Gen Mgr)

PAN-O-GOLD BAKING CO.
444 E Saint Germain St, Saint Cloud, MN 56304
Tel.: (320) 251-9361
Web Site: http://www.panogold.com
Sales Range: $50-74.9 Million
Emp.: 200
Bread, All Types (White, Wheat, Rye, Etc); Fresh or Frozen
N.A.I.C.S.: 311812
Howard R. Alton Jr. (Chm)

PANA COMMUNITY HOSPITAL
101 E 9th St, Pana, IL 62557
Tel.: (217) 562-2131
Web Site:
http://www.panahospital.com
Year Founded: 1966
Sales Range: $10-24.9 Million
Emp.: 237
Health Care Srvices
N.A.I.C.S.: 622110
Trina Casner (Pres & CEO)
Vickie Coen (Chief Clinical Officer)
James Moon (CFO)
Jean Applegate (Mgr-Cardiopulmonary)
Dianne Bailey (CIO)

PANACEA PRODUCTS CORPORATION
2711 International St, Columbus, OH 43228
Tel.: (614) 850-7000
Web Site:
http://www.panaceaproducts.com
Rev.: $10,000,000
Emp.: 28
Bicycle Parts & Accessories
N.A.I.C.S.: 423910
Tom Mahaffey (Mgr-Ops)
Laurence Damato (Mgr-Mktg)
Mary Smith (Mgr-Direct Import Ops)
Ed Baran (Controller)
Matt Kinne (Mgr-IT)

Subsidiaries:

Grayline Housewares, Inc. (1)
2711 International St, Columbus, OH 43228
Tel.: (614) 850-7000
Web Site:
http://www.graylinehousewares.com
Sales Range: $10-24.9 Million
Houseware Mfr & Distr
N.A.I.C.S.: 326199
Fred K. Rosen (Pres)
Greg Paniccia (Owner)

PANAMERICA COMPUTERS INC.
1386 Bigoak Rd, Luray, VA 22835
Tel.: (540) 635-4402
Web Site: http://www.pcitec.com
Year Founded: 1993
Sales Range: $25-49.9 Million
Emp.: 25
Computer & Computer Peripheral Equipment & Software Merchant Whslr
N.A.I.C.S.: 423430
Rosina Kling (Pres)

PANAMEX PACIFIC, INC
620 E Washington St Ste 118, Petaluma, CA 94952
Tel.: (707) 766-9604   CA
Web Site: http://www.panamex.biz
Emp.: 2
Health Foods Distr
N.A.I.C.S.: 424490
David Brown (Pres & CEO)

Subsidiaries:

Panamex New Zealand (1)
PO Box 6541, Wellesley Street, Auckland, 1010, New Zealand
Tel.: (64) 93791440
Web Site: http://www.panamex.biz
Sales Range: $25-49.9 Million
Emp.: 10
Mfr & Exporter of Specialty Consumer Products for Pacific Island Consumers
N.A.I.C.S.: 325611
Eric Olsen (Mgr-Ops)
Stephen Precious (Mgr-Sls & Mktg)

PANATTONI DEVELOPMENT COMPANY
8775 Folsom Blvd Ste 200, Sacramento, CA 95826-3709
Tel.: (916) 381-1561
Web Site: http://www.panattoni.com
Year Founded: 1986
Sales Range: $25-49.9 Million
Emp.: 130
Commercial, Industrial, Office & Manufacturing Facilities, Construction, Development, Leasing & Management Services
N.A.I.C.S.: 531312
Carl D. Panattoni (Chm)
Adon Panattoni (CEO)
Jacklyn Shelby (Dir-Tax & Treasury)
Paul Kinne (Mgr-Dev-Reno)
Doug Roberts (Partner-Nevada & Arizona)
Jennie Reno (Dir-Asset Mgmt)
Katina Woodbury (Dir-HR)
Willy Accame (Dir-Risk Mgmt)
Christopher Wilson (Exec Dir-Fin Grp)
Bill Bullen (CFO & COO)
Justin Burleson (Exec Dir-Portfolio Mgmt)
Len Psyk (Sr Mgr-Dev-Seattle)
Bart Brynestad (Partner-Seattle)
Brice Hafner (Partner-Dallas)
Dayne Pryor (Partner-Atlanta)
Jacob Leblanc (Partner-Orange County & Inland Empire)
Jason Rosenberg (Partner-Chicago)
John Pagliari (Partner-Chicago)
Mark Branstetter (Partner-Saint Louis & Indianapolis)
Mark Payne (Partner-Los Angeles & San Diego)
Tim Schaedler (Partner-Sacramento)
Todd King (Partner-Houston)
Travis Hale (Partner-Seattle)
Whitfield Hamilton (Partner-Southeast US)

Subsidiaries:

Panattoni Construction, Inc. (1)
8775 Folsom Blvd Ste 100, Sacramento, CA 95826   (100%)
Tel.: (916) 340-2400
Web Site: http://www.panconinc.com
Sales Range: $25-49.9 Million
Emp.: 100
Commercial, Industrial, Office & Manufacturing Facilities Design & Construction Services
N.A.I.C.S.: 236220
Paul Little (CEO)
Pat Hastie (Sr VP & Reg Mgr-Northwest)
Jim Wegman (Sr VP & Mgr-Central Reg)
Matt Clafton (Sr VP & Reg Mgr-Mountain West)

Panattoni Development Company (1)
4601 DTC Blvd Ste 650, Denver, CO 80237   (100%)
Tel.: (303) 790-4737
Web Site: http://www.panattoni.com
Real Estate Development Services
N.A.I.C.S.: 531390
Willy Accame (Dir-Risk Mgmt)
Steve Arthur (Dir-Capital Markets Grp)
Adon Panattoni (CEO)
Carl Panattoni (Chm)
Jennie Reno (Dir-Asset Mgmt)
Jackie Shelby (Dir-Tax & Treasury)
Scott Siegel (Exec Dir-Capital Markets Grp)
Christopher Wilson (Exec Dir-Fin Grp)
Katina Woodbury (Dir-HR)
Mark Branstetter (Partner)

Panattoni Luxembourg Services S.a.r.l (1)
37 Rue Glesener, 1471, Luxembourg, Luxembourg
Tel.: (352) 2621291011
Web Site: http://www.panattonieurope.com
Emp.: 8
Real Estate Manangement Services
N.A.I.C.S.: 531390
Mark Connor (Gen Mgr)

PANAVISE PRODUCTS, INC.
7540 Colbert Dr, Reno, NV 89511-1225
Tel.: (775) 850-2900
Web Site: http://www.panavise.com
Year Founded: 1956
Rev.: $6,000,000
Emp.: 42
Precision Vises, Circuit Board Holders & Specialty Mounts Mfr
N.A.I.C.S.: 333517
Gary Richter (Pres & Mgr-Asian Mfg)
Jennifer Mello (Dir-Engrg)
John Palmer (Engr-Indash Product)
Jose Nolasco (Engr-Sheet Metal)

Subsidiaries:

PanaVise Tool (Changzhou), LLC (1)
Changzhou Export Zone 2 Xingzhu Road Building A9, Changzhou, 213031, Jiangsu, China
Tel.: (86) 51985160871
Web Site: http://www.panavise.com
Machine Tools Mfr
N.A.I.C.S.: 333514
Gary Richter (Mgr-Mfg)

PANCARE OF FLORIDA, INC.
431 Oak Ave, Panama City, FL 32401
Tel.: (850) 747-5599   FL
Web Site: http://www.pancarefl.org
Year Founded: 2005
Sales Range: $10-24.9 Million
Emp.: 60
Health Care Srvices
N.A.I.C.S.: 622110
Tom Brewster (CFO)

PANCOM INTERNATIONAL, INC.
3701 Wilshire Blvd Ste 800, Los Angeles, CA 90010-2816
Tel.: (213) 427-1371   CA
Web Site: http://www.pancom.com

Year Founded: 1981
Sales Range: Less than $1 Million
Emp.: 25
Advetising Agency
N.A.I.C.S.: 541810
Young M. Kim (Pres & CEO)
Joseph Choi (CFO)
Paul Y.S. Moon (Pres & CMO)
Esther Chang (Mgr-Acctg)
Eunice Lee (Mng Dir)
Jiyoung Song (Graphic Designer)

PANCREATIC CANCER ACTION NETWORK
2101 Rosecrans Ave Ste 3200, El Segundo, CA 90245
Tel.: (310) 725-0025   CA
Web Site: https://www.pancan.org
Year Founded: 1999
Sales Range: $10-24.9 Million
Health Care Services
N.A.I.C.S.: 621999
Julie M. Fleshman (Pres & CEO)
Pamela Acosta Marquardt (Founder)
Lynn Matrisian (Chief Science Officer)
Lori Stevens (Chief Dev & Community Engagement Officer)
Karen Young (Vice Chm)
Edwina Mossett (Chief People Officer)
Jodi Lipe (CMO)
Anne-Marie Duliege (Chief Medical Officer)
Sudheer Doss (Chief Bus Officer)
Hilarie Koplow-McAdams (Vice Chm)

PANDA ENERGY INTERNATIONAL INC.
4100 Spring Vly Rd Ste 1001, Dallas, TX 75244-3646
Tel.: (972) 361-2000   TX
Web Site: http://www.pandaenergy.com
Year Founded: 1982
Sales Range: $10-24.9 Million
Emp.: 85
Providers of Electrical Services
N.A.I.C.S.: 238210
Janice Carter (CEO)
Robert K. Simmons (CFO-Fin)
Salwa W. Nicolas (Controller)
Don Thorpe (VP-Ops)

Subsidiaries:

Panda Power Corp. (1)
4100 Spring Vly Rd Ste 1001, Dallas, TX 75244-3646
Tel.: (972) 980-7159
Web Site: http://www.pandaenergy.com
Provider of Electric Services
N.A.I.C.S.: 221122

PANDA RESTAURANT GROUP, INC.
1683 Walnut Grove Ave, Rosemead, CA 91770
Tel.: (626) 799-9898
Web Site: https://www.pandaexpress.com
Year Founded: 1973
Sales Range: $1-4.9 Billion
Emp.: 30,000
Offices of Other Holding Companies
N.A.I.C.S.: 551112
Peggy T. Cherng (Co-Founder)
Andrew Cherng (Co-Founder)
David Landsberg (CFO)

Subsidiaries:

Panda Express Inc. (1)
1683 Walnut Grove Ave, Rosemead, CA 91770   (100%)
Tel.: (626) 799-9898
Web Site: http://www.pandaexpress.com
Sales Range: $10-24.9 Million
Emp.: 100
Eating Place

N.A.I.C.S.: 722513

PANDAAMERICA CORP.
19675 Mariner Ave, Torrance, CA 90503-5812
Tel.: (310) 373-9647   CA
Web Site: http://www.pandaamerica.com
Year Founded: 1968
Sales Range: $10-24.9 Million
Emp.: 12
Provider of Jewelry, Precious Stones & Coins Services
N.A.I.C.S.: 423940
Martin Weiss (Founder)
Peter Yeung (Pres)
William Graessle (VP-Wholesale)

PANDUIT CORP.
17301 Ridgeland Ave, Tinley Park, IL 60477-3093
Tel.: (708) 532-1800   IL
Web Site: http://www.panduit.com
Year Founded: 1953
Sales Range: $600-649.9 Million
Emp.: 3,500
Electrical Wiring Components, Network Wiring Systems & Electronic Connectors Mfr
N.A.I.C.S.: 335932
Andrew Caveney (Chm)
Ron Partridge (Grp VP-Global Sls & Mktg)
Michael G. Kenny (CFO)
Ralph Lolies (Mng Dir-EMEA)
Vipin Sharma (Bus Dir-Network Infrastructure-Middle East & Africa)
Shannon McDaniel (Pres & CEO)

Subsidiaries:

Panduit Canada Corp. (1)
85 Enterprise Blvd, Markham, L6G 0B5, ON, Canada   (100%)
Tel.: (905) 475-6922
Web Site: http://www.panduit.com
Sales Range: $25-49.9 Million
Emp.: 20
Mfr of Electrical Wiring Components, Network Wiring Systems & Electronic Connectors
N.A.I.C.S.: 335931

Panduit Int (1)
Al Shatha Tower 2305, PO Box 500537, Dubai, United Arab Emirates
Tel.: (971) 4 3616933
Web Site: http://www.panduit.com
Sales Range: $10-24.9 Million
Emp.: 11
Wiring & Communication Product Mfr
N.A.I.C.S.: 334290

Panduit Limited (1)
W World Westgate, London, W5 1UD, United Kingdom
Tel.: (44) 2086017200
Web Site: http://www.panduit.co.uk
Sales Range: $25-49.9 Million
Emp.: 60
Mfr of Electrical Wiring Components, Network Wiring Systems & Electronic Connectors
N.A.I.C.S.: 335931

Subsidiary (Non-US):

Panduit Europe Ltd. (2)
Baron De Vironlaan 2, B-1700, Dilbeek, Belgium   (100%)
Tel.: (32) 27143142
Sales Range: $10-24.9 Million
Emp.: 6
Mfr of Electrical Wiring Components, Network Wiring Systems & Electronic Connectors
N.A.I.C.S.: 335931
Filip Koch (Gen Mgr-Benelux)

Panduit Europe Ltd. (2)
Via Lepetit 40, 20020, Lainate, Milan, Italy
Tel.: (39) 0269633270
Web Site: http://www.panduiteurope.com

PANDUIT CORP.   U.S. PRIVATE

Panduit Corp.—(Continued)
Sales Range: $25-49.9 Million
Emp.: 70
Mfr of Electrical Wiring Components, Network Wiring Systems & Electronic Connectors
N.A.I.C.S.: 335931
Sabrina Grifini (Mgr-Mktg)

Panduit GmbH (2)
Am Kronberger Hang 8, Schwalbach, 65824, Germany
Tel.: (49) 6995096129
Web Site: http://www.panduit.com
Sales Range: $10-24.9 Million
Emp.: 30
Mfr of Electrical Wiring Components, Network Wiring Systems & Electronic Connectors
N.A.I.C.S.: 335931

Panduit Nederland (2)
Bedrijvenpark Twente 360, 7602, Almelo, Netherlands
Tel.: (31) 546580480
Web Site: http://www.panduit.com
Emp.: 55
Mfr of Electrical Wiring Components, Network Wiring Systems & Electronic Connectors
N.A.I.C.S.: 335931
Rob Bruims (Mgr)

Panduit Mexico S. EN N.C. (1)
Periferico Pte Manuel Gomez Morin Suite 7225 A, Guadalajara, 45010, Jalisco, Mexico **(100%)**
Tel.: (52) 33 3777 6000
Web Site: http://www.panduit.com
Sales Range: $25-49.9 Million
Emp.: 40
Mfr of Electrical Wiring Components, Network Wiring Systems & Electronic Connectors
N.A.I.C.S.: 335931

Panduit Singapore Pte. Ltd. (1)
60 Tuas Ave 11, Singapore, 639106, Singapore **(100%)**
Tel.: (65) 63796700
Sales Range: $25-49.9 Million
Emp.: 240
Mfr of Electrical Wiring Components, Network Wiring Systems & Electronic Connectors
N.A.I.C.S.: 335931

Subsidiary (Non-US):

Panduit Aust. Pty. Ltd. (2)
30-36 Kitchen Road, Dandenong, 3175, VIC, Australia
Tel.: (61) 1800658280
Web Site: http://www.panduit.com
Sales Range: $10-24.9 Million
Emp.: 40
Mfr of Electrical Wiring Components, Network Wiring Systems & Electronic Connectors
N.A.I.C.S.: 335931

Panduit Corp. Japan Branch (2)
2 chome 13-31 Konan Minato-ku Shinagawa NSS Bldg, Tokyo, 108-0075, Japan **(100%)**
Tel.: (81) 3 6863 6000
Web Site: http://www.panduit.co.jp
Sales Range: $25-49.9 Million
Emp.: 100
Mfr of Electrical Wiring Components, Network Wiring Systems & Electronic Connectors
N.A.I.C.S.: 335931
Masayuki Kambara (Mng Dir)

Panduit Hong Kong (2)
A-3 Business Center 2/F 28-34 Wing Lok Street, 88 Commercial Building, Sheung Wan, Hong Kong, China (Hong Kong) **(100%)**
Tel.: (852) 25342217
Mfr of Electrical Wiring Components, Network Wiring Systems & Electronic Connectors
N.A.I.C.S.: 335931

Panduit Korea Ltd. (2)
4F 415 Korea City Air Terminal 159-6 Samsung-dong, Kangnam-ku, Seoul, 135-728, Korea (South)
Tel.: (82) 2 2182 7300
Web Site: http://www.panduit.co.kr
Mfr of Electrical Wiring Components, Network Wiring Systems & Electronic Connectors
N.A.I.C.S.: 335931

PANEF, INC.
5700 W Douglas Ave, Milwaukee, WI 53218
Tel.: (414) 464-7200
Web Site: http://www.lubriko.com
Year Founded: 1945
Sales Range: $10-24.9 Million
Emp.: 8
Lubricant Supplier
N.A.I.C.S.: 424720
Bruce Moncrieff (Pres)

PANEL PROCESSING, INC.
120 N Industrial Hwy, Alpena, MI 49707-0457
Tel.: (989) 356-9007   MI
Web Site: http://www.panel.com
Year Founded: 1971
Sales Range: $100-124.9 Million
Emp.: 200
Wood Panel Mfr
N.A.I.C.S.: 337212
Stevens Chuck (Acct Mgr)
Tim Witucki (Acct Mgr)
Tonya Spens (Mgr-Bus & Product Dev)

Subsidiaries:

Holland Panel Products, Inc. (1)
615 E 40th St, Holland, MI 49423
Tel.: (616) 392-1826
Wood Panel Mfr
N.A.I.C.S.: 321211

Modular Wood Systems Inc. (1)
1805 Red Bank School Rd, Claudville, VA 24076 **(100%)**
Tel.: (276) 251-5300
Wood Panel Mfr
N.A.I.C.S.: 321211

Panel Processing of Coldwater, Inc. (1)
681 Race St, Coldwater, MI 49036-2121
Tel.: (517) 279-8051
Web Site: http://www.panel.com
Emp.: 41
Hardwood Veneer & Plywood Mfr
N.A.I.C.S.: 321211

Panel Processing of Indiana, Inc. (1)
9250 S Mississippi St, Merrillville, IN 46410
Tel.: (219) 736-0330
Wood Panel Mfr
N.A.I.C.S.: 321211

Panel Processing of Oregon, Inc. (1)
6450 Swan Ct, Klamath Falls, OR 97603
Tel.: (800) 300-1979
Web Site: http://www.panel.com
Sales Range: $10-24.9 Million
Reconstituted Wood Product Mfr
N.A.I.C.S.: 321219
Patrick McNeal (Pres)

Panel Processing of Texas, Inc. (1)
1010 S Bolton St, Jacksonville, TX 75766-0871
Tel.: (903) 586-2423
Web Site: http://www.panel.com
Wood Products Mfr
N.A.I.C.S.: 321999

PANELFOLD INC.
10700 NW 36th Ave, Miami, FL 33167
Tel.: (305) 688-3501
Web Site: http://www.panelfold.com
Sales Range: $10-24.9 Million
Emp.: 250
Wood Partitions & Fixtures
N.A.I.C.S.: 337110
Marsha Kallstroms (VP)
Ed Reed (Reg Mgr-Sls)
Billy C. (Mgr-Customer Svc)
Emily Dixon (Pres & CEO)

PANELIZED STRUCTURES, INC.
5731 Stoddard Rd, Modesto, CA 95356-9000
Tel.: (209) 343-8600   CA
Web Site: http://www.panelized.com
Year Founded: 1989
Sales Range: $25-49.9 Million
Emp.: 50
Roofing, Siding & Sheetmetal Work
N.A.I.C.S.: 238160
Peter Post (CEO-Modesto Office)
Keith Coonce (Pres)
Ron Kozloski (Mgr-Ops)
Chris Brahler (Mgr-Northern Nevada)
Shane Carvalho (Mgr-Southern Nevada)
Tom Eccles (Mgr-Northern California)
Tony Galvan (Mgr-Southern California)
Tim Lessard (Reg Mgr-Sls-Modesto)
Sharon Russell (Controller)
Craig Silva (Mgr-Sacramento)

PANELMATIC INC.
9826 Windmill Park Ln, Houston, TX 77064
Tel.: (281) 890-1678
Web Site: http://www.panelmatic.com
Sales Range: $10-24.9 Million
Emp.: 115
Control Panels, Electric
N.A.I.C.S.: 335313
Richard Leach (Pres)

PANGEA GROUP
2604 S Jefferson Ave, Saint Louis, MO 63118
Tel.: (314) 333-0600
Web Site: http://www.pangea-group.com
Year Founded: 1994
Sales Range: $10-24.9 Million
Emp.: 40
Radioactive Waste Clean-Up Services; Federal Housing Construction; Operation & Installation of Security Devices in Federal Buildings
N.A.I.C.S.: 562112

PANGEA REAL ESTATE
PO Box 809009, Chicago, IL 60680
Tel.: (312) 489-8119
Web Site: http://www.pangeare.com
Year Founded: 2008
Sales Range: $25-49.9 Million
Emp.: 350
Real Estate
N.A.I.C.S.: 531210
Al Goldstein (Founder & Chm)

PANGERE CORPORATION
4050 W 4th Ave, Gary, IN 46406
Tel.: (219) 949-1368
Web Site: http://www.pangere.com
Rev.: $11,400,000
Emp.: 125
Structural Steel Erection
N.A.I.C.S.: 238120
Steve Pangere (Pres)

PANHANDLE BUILDERS & EXCAVATING INC.
222 Langston Blvd, Martinsburg, WV 25404
Tel.: (304) 274-1920
Web Site:
    http://www.panhandlebuilders.com
Rev.: $25,300,000
Emp.: 70
New Single-Family Housing Construction
N.A.I.C.S.: 236115

Allen Henry (Co-Founder)
David Henry (Co-Founder & VP)
Lester A. Henry (Pres)
Carole L. Henry (Co-Founder, Treas & Sec)

PANHANDLE COMMUNITY SERVICES
1309 SW 8th Ave, Amarillo, TX 79101
Tel.: (806) 372-2531   TX
Web Site: http://www.pcsvcs.org
Year Founded: 1964
Sales Range: $10-24.9 Million
Emp.: 136
Community Care Services
N.A.I.C.S.: 624190
Keith Rosicker (Dir-Fin)
Kristina Bodin (Dir-Fin)
Phyllis Cook (Exec Dir)

PANHANDLE PLAINS MANAGEMENT AND SERVICING CORPORATION
1303 23rd St, Canyon, TX 79015
Tel.: (806) 324-4100
Web Site: http://www.ppslc.com
Rev.: $56,122,632
Emp.: 15
Student Loan Services
N.A.I.C.S.: 611710
James Parker (Pres)

PANHANDLE TELEPHONE COOP
603 S Main St, Guymon, OK 73942
Tel.: (580) 338-2556
Web Site: http://www.ptsi.net
Sales Range: $10-24.9 Million
Emp.: 172
Local Telephone Communications
N.A.I.C.S.: 517121
Mitzi Dain (Dir-HR)
Joel Stover (Engr-Special Circuits Field)
Shawn Hanson (CEO)

PANHANDLE-PLAINS HIGHER EDUCATION AUTHORITY INC
1303 23rd St, Canyon, TX 79015
Tel.: (806) 324-4100   TX
Web Site: http://www.pphea.org
Year Founded: 1979
Sales Range: $25-49.9 Million
Emp.: 15
Fundraising Services
N.A.I.C.S.: 561499
Tammy Roark (Treas & Sec)
Rita Craddock (Pres)
Ron Miller (VP)

PANKOW SPECIAL PROJECTS
221 Main St Ste 650, San Francisco, CA 94105-3629
Tel.: (415) 543-4010
Web Site: http://www.pankow.com
Sales Range: $10-24.9 Million
Emp.: 75
Civil Engineering Services
N.A.I.C.S.: 237310
Richard Kunnath (CEO)

PANNELL KERR FORSTER OF TEXAS, P.C.
5847 San Felipe Ste 2600, Houston, TX 77057
Tel.: (713) 860-1400
Web Site: http://www.pkftexas.com
Rev.: $17,500,000
Emp.: 110
Business Consulting, Technology, Assurance, Entrepreneurial Advisory & Tax Solutions Services
N.A.I.C.S.: 541211

COMPANIES

Brian C. Baumler *(Dir-Audit)*
Sonia M. Freeman *(Chief Culture Officer)*
Kenneth J. Guidry *(Pres)*
Marty J. Lindle *(Dir-Audit)*
Michael W. Veuleman *(Dir-Audit)*
J. Del Walker *(Chief Growth Officer)*
Annabella Green *(Dir-Human Capital & Firm Admin)*
Nicole Riley *(Dir-Audit)*
Chris Dodd *(Dir-Tax)*
Emily Smikal *(Dir-Tax)*
Gary Voth *(Chm)*

PANNIER CORPORATION
207 Sandusky St, Pittsburgh, PA 15212-5823
Tel.: (412) 323-4900 PA
Web Site: http://www.pannier.com
Year Founded: 1899
Sales Range: $10-24.9 Million
Emp.: 120
Marking & Identification Systems & Fiberglass Imbedded Sign Mfr
N.A.I.C.S.: 339940
John E. Visconti *(Co-Pres)*
Scott Heddaeus *(Co-Pres)*
Lisa Hohman *(Asst Controller)*
Mike Roy *(Dir-Intl Sls & Mktg)*
Kent Shaver *(Engr-Mechanical)*

Subsidiaries:
Pannier Corporation - Pannier Graphics Division (1)
345 Oak Rd, Gibsonia, PA 15044-8428
Tel.: (724) 265-4900
Web Site: http://www.panniergraphics.com
Fiberglass Sign Mfr
N.A.I.C.S.: 339950

PANORAMA
1751 Cir Ln SE, Lacey, WA 98503-2570
Tel.: (360) 456-0111
Web Site: http://www.panoramacity.org
Year Founded: 1963
Sales Range: $10-24.9 Million
Emp.: 2
Property Management Services
N.A.I.C.S.: 531110
Joseph Di Santo *(Pres & CEO)*

PANORAMA CAPITAL, LLC
1999 Vascom Ave Ste 700, Campbell, CA 95008
Tel.: (650) 234-1420
Web Site: http://www.panoramacapital.com
Year Founded: 2005
Sales Range: $10-24.9 Million
Emp.: 5
Venture Capital Investment Firm
N.A.I.C.S.: 523999
Christopher J. Albinson *(Co-Founder & Mng Dir-Tech)*
Rodney A. Ferguson *(Co-Founder & Mng Dir-Life Sciences)*
Damion E. Wicker *(Co-Founder & Mng Dir-Life Sciences)*
Ann Parsons *(Controller)*
Audrey Vallen *(CFO)*
Srinivas Akkaraju *(Co-Founder)*
Shahan D. Soghikian *(Mng Dir-Tech)*

PANORAMA EYE CARE LLC
2809 E Harmony Rd Ste 210, Fort Collins, CO 80525
Tel.: (833) 777-9001
Web Site: https://panoramaeyecare.com
Eye Clinic
N.A.I.C.S.: 621320
Patrick Arnold *(Chief Medical Officer)*

Subsidiaries:
Michael G. Haas, M.D., LLC (1)
6385 Corporate Dr Ste 307, Colorado Springs, CO 80919-5913
Tel.: (719) 272-3834
Web Site: http://www.haasvisioncenter.com
Offices of Physicians (except Mental Health Specialists)
N.A.I.C.S.: 621111
Janna Haas *(Office Mgr)*

PANTERRA NETWORKS INC.
1153 Bordeaux Dr Ste 102, Sunnyvale, CA 94089
Tel.: (408) 702-2200
Web Site: http://www.panterranetworks.com
Year Founded: 2001
Sales Range: $1-9.9 Million
Emp.: 70
Software
N.A.I.C.S.: 513210
Arthur G. Chang *(Pres & CEO)*

PANTHER MOTOR GROUP INC.
10358 W McNab Rd, Tamarac, FL 33321
Tel.: (954) 682-3693 NV
Web Site: http://www.scootcoupe.com
Sales Range: $1-9.9 Million
Emp.: 2
3 Wheel Scooter Mfr
N.A.I.C.S.: 336991
Dominick Livoti *(Pres, CEO, Treas & Sec)*

PANTHER SUMMIT INDUSTRIES INC.
4807 Beryl Rd, Raleigh, NC 27606-1406
Tel.: (919) 890-4696 NC
Year Founded: 1957
Sales Range: $200-249.9 Million
Emp.: 850
Holding Company
N.A.I.C.S.: 551112
J. Gregory Poole III *(Chm, Pres & CEO)*

Subsidiaries:
Gregory Poole Equipment Company Inc. (1)
4807 Beryl Rd, Raleigh, NC 27606-1406
Tel.: (919) 828-0641
Web Site: http://www.gregorypoole.com
Sales Range: $25-49.9 Million
Emp.: 650
Supplier of Construction & Mining Machinery Services
N.A.I.C.S.: 532412
J. Gregory Poole III *(Chm & CEO)*

PANTHERS FOOTBALL, LLC
800 S Mint St, Charlotte, NC 28202
Tel.: (704) 358-7000 NC
Web Site: http://www.panthers.com
Year Founded: 1993
Sales Range: $25-49.9 Million
Emp.: 130
Professional Football Franchise
N.A.I.C.S.: 711211
Phil Youtsey *(Exec Dir-Ticketing & Sponsorship)*
Marty Hurney *(Gen Mgr)*
Scott Paul *(Dir-Ops-Stadium)*
Mark Hobbs *(Dir-Video)*
Henry Thomas *(Dir-Brdcst)*
Riley Fields *(Dir-Community Rels)*
Matthew Getz *(Mgr-Facility)*
Mark Koncz *(Dir-Pro Scouting)*
Jackie Miles *(Mgr-Equipment)*
Rob Rogers *(Dir-Team Admin)*

Kyle Ritchie *(Dir-PantherVision)*
Mike Dudan *(CFO)*
David Tepper *(Owner)*
Tom Glick *(Pres)*

PANTROPIC POWER PRODUCTS INC.
8205 NW 58th St, Miami, FL 33166-3406
Tel.: (305) 477-3329 FL
Web Site: http://www.pantropic.com
Year Founded: 1986
Sales Range: $25-49.9 Million
Emp.: 210
Generators, Marine Engines, Truck Engines, Rental Equipment, Pumping Systems & Agriculture Engines
N.A.I.C.S.: 423830
Luis Botas *(Chm & Pres)*
Melissa Kowal *(Dir-Mktg)*

PANZURA, INC.
695 Campbell Technology Pkwy 225, Campbell, CA 95008
Tel.: (408) 457-8504
Web Site: http://www.panzura.com
Sales Range: $10-24.9 Million
Emp.: 100
Cloud Storage Solutions
N.A.I.C.S.: 513210
Mark Santora *(Chm)*
John Taylor *(Founder & CTO)*
Rich Weber *(Chief Strategy Officer & VP-Engrg)*
Jeff Herr *(VP-Sls-North America)*
Diptish Datta *(VP-Strategy & Enterprise Applications)*
Patrick Harr *(CEO)*
Barry Phillips *(CMO)*
Caeli Collins *(VP-Support)*
Paul Pu Zhang *(VP-Engrg)*
Brian Brogan *(VP-Sls Channels-Global)*
Dan Waldschmidt *(Chief Revenue Officer)*

PAP-R PRODUCTS COMPANY
1 Harry Glynn Dr, Martinsville, IL 62442
Tel.: (217) 382-4141
Web Site: http://www.paprproducts.com
Rev.: $16,200,000
Emp.: 100
Paper Products Mfr
N.A.I.C.S.: 322299
Scott Ware *(Pres)*

PAPA GINOS-DEANGELO HOLDING CORPORATION, INC.
600 Providence Hwy, Dedham, MA 02026-6804
Tel.: (781) 461-1200 DE
Web Site: http://www.papaginos.com
Year Founded: 1963
Rev.: $135,000,000
Emp.: 100
Holding Company; Pizzeria & Sandwich Shop Restaurants Owner, Operator & Franchisee
N.A.I.C.S.: 551112
Celeste Contois *(Sr VP-HR)*
Rick Wolf *(Pres & CEO)*
Michael McManama *(Sr VP-Brand Dev)*
Lori Whelan *(Exec VP-Fin & Strategic Plng)*

PAPA JOHN'S OF IOWA LLC
5335 Merle Hay Rd 3280, Johnston, IA 50131
Tel.: (515) 251-5909
Sales Range: $10-24.9 Million
Emp.: 600
Eating Place

N.A.I.C.S.: 722513
Tom Donaldson *(Pres)*

PAPAS DODGE INC.
585 E Main St Ste 3, New Britain, CT 06051
Tel.: (860) 225-8751
Web Site: http://www.papasjeep.com
Sales Range: $50-74.9 Million
Emp.: 70
Sales of New & Used Automobiles
N.A.I.C.S.: 441110
Dom Papa *(Co-Owner)*
Ken Papa *(Co-Owner)*
A. J. Maida *(Dir-Digital Mktg)*
Bill Vetre *(Dir-Parts & Svc)*
Lisa Papa-Thiesfeldt *(Mgr-Comm Trng & Mktg)*
Jeff Armington *(Mgr-Used Car)*
Jeromy Berman *(Gen Mgr-Sls)*
Ryan Month *(Mgr-Bus & Fin)*
Martin Mattei *(Mgr-Body Shop)*

PAPE CHEVROLET INC.
425 Westbrook St, South Portland, ME 04106
Tel.: (207) 775-6111
Web Site: http://www.papechevrolet.com
Year Founded: 1969
Sales Range: $10-24.9 Million
Emp.: 75
New Car Dealers
N.A.I.C.S.: 441110
Gary Brookings *(Mgr-Sls)*
Steve Tsujiura *(Mgr-Sls)*
Bill Adams *(Gen Mgr-Sls)*
Mary Palmer *(Dir-F&I)*
Jayne Campbell *(Mgr-F&I)*
Mark Lambert *(Dir-Fixed Ops)*
Tom McCormick *(Mgr-Body Shop)*
Geoff Pulsifer *(Mgr-Internet Sls)*
Trent Smith *(Coord-Svc)*

PAPEL MEDIA NETWORK
4342 Riverwood Ave, Sarasota, FL 34231
Tel.: (941) 234-3677
Year Founded: 1999
Sales Range: Less than $1 Million
Emp.: 10
N.A.I.C.S.: 541810
William Trainor *(Pres)*
Janine Trainor *(COO)*
Stuart Langley *(Dir-Sls)*

PAPER & CHEMICAL SUPPLY CO.
1241 Gnat Palm Rd, Leighton, AL 35646
Tel.: (256) 383-3912
Web Site: http://www.paperandchemical.com
Sales Range: $10-24.9 Million
Emp.: 50
Disposable Plates, Cups, Napkins & Eating Utensils
N.A.I.C.S.: 424130
David M. Muhlendorf *(Pres)*

PAPER CHEMICAL SUPPLY COMPANY
101 Owens Industrial Dr, Savannah, GA 31415
Tel.: (912) 236-1373
Web Site: http://www.paperchemicalsupply.com
Sales Range: $100-124.9 Million
Emp.: 50
Disposable Paper, Packaging, Food Service & Janitorial Sanitary Maintenance Supplies Distr
N.A.I.C.S.: 322291
Michael S. Peebles *(Pres)*
Jerry Peebles *(Mgr-Sls)*

Paper Chemical Supply Company—(Continued)
Karen Beecher *(Mgr-Acctg & Credit)*
Herb Hutson *(Mgr-Pur)*
Paul Waldhour *(Mgr-Sys Admin)*

PAPER CUTTERS INC.
6023 Blvd, Commerce, CA 90040
Tel.: (323) 888-1330
Web Site:
    http://www.papercutters.net
Sales Range: $10-24.9 Million
Emp.: 50
Industrial & Personal Service Paper
N.A.I.C.S.: 424130
Susan Feinstein *(Pres)*

PAPER ENTERPRISES, INC.
770 E 132nd St, Bronx, NY 10454-3429
Tel.: (718) 402-1200   NY
Web Site:
    http://www.paperenterprisesusahome.com
Year Founded: 1961
Sales Range: $25-49.9 Million
Emp.: 100
Wholesale Paper Cups, Bags & Dishes; Janitorial & Restuarant Supplies
N.A.I.C.S.: 424130
Jordan B. Sedler *(Pres)*
Howard Cohen *(VP-Customer Rels)*
Murry Pottruch *(Co-CFO)*
Peter Panagakos *(Chief Comml Ops Officer)*
Corey M. Aronin *(Co-CFO)*

Subsidiaries:

Consolidated Paper Co.   (1)
770 E 132nd St, Bronx, NY 10454 **(100%)**
Tel.: (718) 402-1200
Web Site: http://www.paperenterprises.com
Distribution of Paper Products
N.A.I.C.S.: 424130
Herbert L. Sedler *(Chm)*
Jordan B. Sedler *(Pres)*
Howard Cohen *(VP-Customer Rels)*
Mike Giordano *(Co-COO)*
Murray Pottruck *(CFO)*
Don Sabia *(Co-COO)*

PAPER MACHINERY CORPORATION
8900 W Bradley Rd, Milwaukee, WI 53224
Tel.: (414) 354-8050
Web Site: http://www.papermc.com
Sales Range: $100-124.9 Million
Emp.: 250
Paper Idustry Machinery Mfr
N.A.I.C.S.: 333243
Donald W. Baumgartner *(Founder & Chm)*
Scott Eveland *(VP-Sls-Intl)*
Gary Johnson *(VP-Customer Svc)*
Mike Kazmierski *(Sr VP-Sls)*
Scott B. Koehler *(CFO)*
Cary Kalal *(Sls Mgr-Intl)*
Mike Hansen *(VP-Pkg Div)*
John Fortin *(Pres & CEO)*

PAPER PRODUCTS CO. INC.
36 Terminal Way, Pittsburgh, PA 15219
Tel.: (412) 481-6200
Web Site: http://www.paperproducts-pgh.com
Rev.: $19,600,000
Emp.: 60
Industrial & Personal Service Paper
N.A.I.C.S.: 424130
Tom Lackner *(Mgr-Credit)*
Douglas Townshend *(VP)*
Pat Costello *(Dir-Pur)*
Gary Devlin *(VP-Pkg)*
Paul Lackner *(Pres)*
John Tighe *(Gen Mgr)*
John Lohman *(Acct Mgr)*
Laura Lackner *(Controller)*

PAPER STORE INCORPORATED
20 Main St, Acton, MA 01720
Tel.: (978) 263-2198   MA
Web Site:
    http://www.thepaperstore.com
Year Founded: 1963
Sales Range: $10-24.9 Million
Emp.: 425
Sales of Greeting Cards
N.A.I.C.S.: 459420
Robert Anderson *(Pres)*

PAPER SYSTEMS INC.
185 S Pioneer Blvd, Springboro, OH 45066-3045
Tel.: (937) 746-6841   OH
Web Site:
    http://www.papersystems.com
Year Founded: 1977
Sales Range: $25-49.9 Million
Emp.: 100
Converted Paper Products
N.A.I.C.S.: 322299
Lawrence Curk *(Owner, CEO & Treas)*
Karen Houk *(Mgr-Human Rels)*
Cindy Wallace *(Supvr-Customer Svc)*
Lee Wagoner *(Exec VP-Sls & Mktg)*

PAPER TIGERS INC.
2101 Waukegan Rd Ste 270, Bannockburn, IL 60015
Tel.: (847) 919-6500
Web Site: http://www.papertigers.com
Year Founded: 1967
Rev.: $60,000,000
Emp.: 30
Whslr of Printing & Paper Goods
N.A.I.C.S.: 424110
Robert Kilburg Jr. *(Pres)*

PAPERG
530 Bush St 9th Fl, San Francisco, CA 94108
Tel.: (415) 796-0888
Web Site: http://www.paperg.com
Year Founded: 2008
Sales Range: $1-9.9 Million
Emp.: 30
Custom Advertising for Small & Midsize Budget Campaigns
N.A.I.C.S.: 541430
Victor Wong *(Co-Founder & CEO)*
Roger Lee *(Co-Founder)*
Victor Cheng *(Co-Founder & CTO)*
Dan Chou *(VP-Engrg)*
Andrew Gu *(VP-Product)*
Brooke Frederick *(VP-Sls & Bus Dev)*
Joseph Zahtila *(Chief Revenue Officer)*
Ka Mo Lau *(CFO & COO)*

PAPERLESS BUSINESS SYSTEMS, INC.
1417 4th Ave Ste 4, Seattle, WA 98101
Tel.: (206) 256-0771
Web Site:
    http://www.paperlessbusiness.com
Year Founded: 1997
Sales Range: $1-9.9 Million
Emp.: 30
Software Developer
N.A.I.C.S.: 513210
Randy Pape *(Pres & CEO)*
Scott Pape *(VP-Strategic Rels)*
Ann Donovan *(VP-Mktg)*
Debra Morris *(Mgr-Bus Dev)*

PAPERLESS TRANSACTION CORPORATION
400 E Royal Ln Ste 201, Irving, TX 75039
Tel.: (972) 409-9100
Web Site:
    http://www.paperlesstrans.com
Year Founded: 1998
Rev.: $4,400,000
Emp.: 20
Data Processing & Hosting Services
N.A.I.C.S.: 518210
Tobi McDonald *(Principal)*
George E. Reich *(Principal)*

PAPERSAVE
3150 SW 38 Ave 4th Fl, Miami, FL 33146
Tel.: (877) 959-8655
Web Site: http://www.papersave.com
Document Management, Electronic Workflow & Invoice Automation Services
N.A.I.C.S.: 561499
Nikita Prajapati *(Engr-Quality Assurance)*

Subsidiaries:

Paramount Technologies, Inc.   (1)
1374 EW Maple Rd, Walled Lake, MI 48390-3765
Tel.: (248) 960-0909
Web Site:
    http://www.paramounttechnologies.com
Sales Range: $1-9.9 Million
Emp.: 30
Prepackaged Software
N.A.I.C.S.: 513210
Salim Khalife *(Founder, Pres & CEO)*
Foy Mainor *(Dir-Sls)*

PAPERWEIGHT DEVELOPMENT CORP.
825 E Wisconsin Ave, Appleton, WI 54912
Tel.: (920) 734-9841   WI
Year Founded: 2000
Rev.: $690,364,000
Assets: $387,169,000
Liabilities: $699,468,000
Net Worth: ($312,299,000)
Earnings: ($19,046,000)
Emp.: 1,402
Fiscal Year-end: 12/31/16
Holding Company
N.A.I.C.S.: 551112
Mark R. Richards *(Chm)*
Angela M. Tyczkowski *(Sec & VP)*
Ted A. Goodwin *(VP-Bus Dev)*
Jeffrey J. Fletcher *(Asst Treas)*
Kevin M. Gilligan *(CEO)*
Luke Kelly *(VP-Fin)*

PAPILLON AIRWAYS INC.
12515 Willows Rd NE No 200, Kirkland, WA 98034
Tel.: (425) 820-8800
Web Site: http://www.papillon.com
Year Founded: 1963
Sales Range: $10-24.9 Million,
Emp.: 10
Provider of Air Transportation Services
N.A.I.C.S.: 481219
Brenda Halvorson *(Pres & CEO)*
Robert Graff *(VP-Mktg & Sls)*

PAPOULI'S GREEK GRILL RESTAURANTS
255 E Basse Rd Ste 384, San Antonio, TX 78209
Tel.: (210) 804-1118
Web Site: http://www.papoulis.com
Year Founded: 2002
Sales Range: $1-9.9 Million
Emp.: 70
Greek Restaurant & Catering Services
N.A.I.C.S.: 722513

Nick D. Anthony *(Owner & CEO)*
Alex Moseley *(Dir-Leadership & People Dev)*

PAPPAS ENTERPRISES INC.
655 Summer St, Boston, MA 02210
Tel.: (617) 330-9797
Web Site:
    http://www.courtsquarepress.com
Sales Range: $10-24.9 Million
Emp.: 5
Commercial & Industrial Building Operation
N.A.I.C.S.: 531120
Timothy Pappas *(Pres)*

PAPPAS PARTNERS LP
13939 NW Fwy, Houston, TX 77040-2534
Tel.: (713) 869-0151
Web Site: http://www.pappas.com
Year Founded: 1997
Sales Range: $10-24.9 Million
Emp.: 130
Provider of Dining Services
N.A.I.C.S.: 722511
Harris J. Pappas *(Partner)*

Subsidiaries:

Pappas Restaurants Inc.   (1)
13939 NW Fwy, Houston, TX 77040
Tel.: (713) 869-0151
Web Site: http://www.pappas.com
Seafood Restaurants
N.A.I.C.S.: 722511
Christopher J. Pappas *(Owner)*

PAPPAS REALTY CO.
159 S Main St Ste 302, Akron, OH 44308
Tel.: (330) 762-0535
Web Site:
    http://www.pappasrealtyco.com
Sales Range: $1-9.9 Million
Emp.: 10
Real Estate Services
N.A.I.C.S.: 531210
Michael G. Pappas *(Pres)*
Pete Pappas *(CEO)*

PAPPAS TELECASTING COMPANIES
823 W Center Ave, Visalia, CA 93291-6013
Tel.: (559) 733-7800   NV
Emp.: 100
Holding Company; Television Broadcasting Stations Owner & Operator
N.A.I.C.S.: 551112
Bruce M. Yeager *(CFO & Exec VP)*

PAPPAS VENTURES
2520 Meridian Pkwy Ste 400, Durham, NC 27713
Tel.: (919) 998-3300
Web Site:
    http://www.pappasventures.com
Year Founded: 1994
Rev.: $350,000,000
Equity Investment Firm
N.A.I.C.S.: 523999
Ford S. Worthy *(Partner)*
Scott E. Weiner *(Partner)*
Alex Arfaei *(Partner)*
Matthew Boyer *(CFO)*
Tom Mathers *(Partner)*
Franz B. Humer *(Venture Partner)*
Arthur M. Pappas *(Founder & Mng Partner)*
Michael G. Grey *(Venture Partner)*

PAQ, INC.

8014 Lower Sacramento Rd, Stockton, CA 95210-3724
Tel.: (209) 957-4917
Web Site: http://www.food-4-less.com
Year Founded: 1995
Sales Range: $50-74.9 Million
Emp.: 800
Grocery Store Operator
N.A.I.C.S.: 445110
Wendy McFadden *(Controller)*
Joe Prichard *(Dir-Bakeries)*
Butch Mejia *(Dir-Store)*
Richard Franco *(Dir-Food Svcs)*
Roni Kent *(Dir-Sls Point)*

PAR AVION TRAVEL, INC.
6033 W Century Blvd Ste 780, Los Angeles, CA 90045
Tel.: (310) 670-2970   CA
Web Site: http://www.paravion-inc.com
Year Founded: 1984
Sales Range: $10-24.9 Million
Emp.: 18
Full Service Convention Housing & Travel
N.A.I.C.S.: 561510
Toby Brenner *(Pres & CEO)*
Sherrie Chelini *(VP-Incentives)*
Jo Ann Worthington *(Dir-Sls & Mktg)*
Jill Hungerford *(Mgr-Ops)*
Rosa Gutierrez *(Mgr-Call Center)*

PAR CAPITAL MANAGEMENT, INC.
1 International Pl Ste 2401, Boston, MA 02110
Tel.: (617) 526-8990   DE
Web Site: http://www.parcapital.com
Year Founded: 1990
Sales Range: $1-4.9 Billion
Emp.: 12
Private Investment Firm
N.A.I.C.S.: 523999
Edward L. Shapiro *(Partner)*
David Tobin *(VP)*
Will Moeykens *(VP-Fin)*
John Buchanan *(VP)*
Arthur G. Epker III *(Partner)*
Paul Arlington Reeder III *(Pres)*

Subsidiaries:

Anuvu   (1)
6080 Center Dr Ste 1200, Los Angeles, CA 90045   **(51.4%)**
Tel.: (310) 437-6000
Web Site: https://www.anuvu.com
Rev.: $656,877,000
Assets: $668,580,000
Liabilities: $1,043,734,000
Net Worth: ($375,154,000)
Earnings: ($153,443,000)
Emp.: 1,129
Fiscal Year-end: 12/31/2019
Holding Company; Airline Industry Media Content Delivery & Satellite Telecommunications Services
N.A.I.C.S.: 551112
Michael Pigott *(Sr VP-Aviation Connectivity)*
Christian M. Mezger *(CFO & Exec VP)*
Joshua Benegal Marks *(CEO)*
Per Noren *(Pres)*
R. Jason Everett *(Chief Acctg Officer)*
Zant Chapelo *(Chief People Officer & Sr VP)*
Terri Davies *(Sr VP-Content & Media)*
Cynthia Gillis *(Sr VP-Maritime, Enterprise & Govt)*
Peter Lopez *(VP-Fin & IR)*
Kim Nakamaru *(Gen Counsel, Sec & Sr VP)*
Sean Bratches *(Chm)*

Subsidiary (Domestic):

Emerging Markets Communications LLC   (2)
3044 N Commerce Pkwy, Miramar, FL 33025
Tel.: (954) 538-4000
Web Site: http://www.emcconnected.com
Satellite & Terrestrial Communications
N.A.I.C.S.: 811210
Elisa A. Tinsley *(Sr VP)*
Mark D'Anastasio *(Founder & Pres)*

Post Modern Edit, LLC   (2)
2941 Alton Pkwy, Irvine, CA 92606
Tel.: (949) 608-8700
Web Site: http://www.globaleagle.com
Sales Range: $25-49.9 Million
Emp.: 140
Motion Picture & Video Production, Post-Production & Digital Content Delivery Services
N.A.I.C.S.: 512191
Amir Samnani *(VP-Content)*
Rick Warren *(Mng Partner & CFO)*
Kelli Clark *(Dir-Admin)*

Subsidiary (Domestic):

Ambient, LLC   (3)
4553 Glencoe Blvd, Marina Del Rey, CA 90292
Tel.: (310) 396-7375
Motion Picture & Video Production
N.A.I.C.S.: 512110
Stephen Jackson *(Sr VP-Bus Dev)*

Subsidiary (Domestic):

Row 44, Inc.   (2)
4353 Park Terrace Dr, Westlake Village, CA 91361   **(100%)**
Tel.: (818) 706-3111
Web Site: http://www.row44.com
Airline Passenger Satellite Telecommunications Services
N.A.I.C.S.: 517121
John William LaValle *(CEO)*
John Guidon *(CTO)*
Avani Patel *(Mgr-Fin Analysis)*
Chris Browne *(CIO)*
Dave Cummings *(Sr Dir-Flight Ops)*
Doug Murti *(Dir-Airline Solutions)*
Jane Rizzo *(Mgr-Revenue)*
Lawrence Laffer *(Dir-Bus Dev)*
Marc Springer *(Dir-Billing, Care & Fin)*
Mark Rugg *(Dir-Network Ops)*
Pierre Steffen *(Sr VP-Customer Solutions)*

PAR ENTERPRISES, INC.
200 Straub Dr, Triadelphia, WV 26059
Tel.: (304) 233-2222   WV
Web Site: http://www.straubhonda.com
Year Founded: 1976
Sales Range: $50-74.9 Million
Emp.: 20
Sales of New & Used Automobiles
N.A.I.C.S.: 441110
Kenneth Straub *(Pres)*
Martha Fato *(Treas & Sec)*
Kevin Cook *(Gen Mgr)*
Taylor Presto *(Mgr-Fin)*
Walt Thomas *(Mgr-Body Shop)*

PAR PLUMBING CO. INC.
60 Prospect Ave N, Lynbrook, NY 11563
Tel.: (516) 887-4000
Web Site: http://www.pargroup.com
Rev.: $12,100,000
Emp.: 450
Plumbing Contractor
N.A.I.C.S.: 238220
Martin Levine *(Pres)*
Brendan McMonagle *(VP-New Construction Div)*
Nanci Bloore *(VP-Cust Admin)*

PAR-WAY TRYSON COMPANY
107 Bolte Ln, Saint Clair, MO 63077
Tel.: (636) 629-4545
Web Site: http://www.parwaytryson.com
Year Founded: 1948
Sales Range: $10-24.9 Million
Edible Fats & Oils Mfr
N.A.I.C.S.: 311225
Mandleen Hanson-Hayes *(Pres & CEO)*
Mike Abts *(CFO)*
Mario Murillo *(Mgr-Indus Sls)*
Gary Everson *(Chief Sls & Mktg Officer)*

PARA-PLUS TRANSLATIONS, INC.
2 Coleman Ave, Cherry Hill, NJ 08034
Tel.: (856) 547-3695   NJ
Web Site: http://www.para-plus.com
Year Founded: 1980
Sales Range: $1-9.9 Million
Emp.: 10
Translation & Interpretation Services
N.A.I.C.S.: 541930
Carlos Santiago *(VP)*
Jennifer Bovell *(Project Mgr)*
Robert Santiago III *(COO)*

PARABEL INC.
1901 S Harbor City Blvd Ste 600, Melbourne, FL 32901
Tel.: (321) 409-7500   DE
Web Site: http://www.parabel.com
Sales Range: Less than $1 Million
Emp.: 38
Aquatic Micro-Crops
N.A.I.C.S.: 112519
Anthony John Phipps Tiarks *(Chm & CEO)*

PARACO GAS CORPORATION
800 Westchester Ave S604, Rye Brook, NY 10573
Tel.: (914) 250-3700
Web Site: http://www.paracogas.com
Year Founded: 1968
Gases & Liquefied Petroleum (Propane) Whslr
N.A.I.C.S.: 424720
Joseph Armentano *(CEO)*
Christina Armentano *(COO & Exec VP)*
Jeff Rufner *(Exec VP-Ops)*
Charles Buonincontri *(Dir-Sls)*
Kevin Watson *(CFO)*
Donna Howay *(Dir-Supply Chain Mgmt)*

Subsidiaries:

Bay Gas Service, Inc.   (1)
McGraw St, Shirley, NY 11967
Tel.: (631) 399-3620
Web Site: http://www.baygasservice.com
Liquefied Petroleum Gas (Bottled Gas) Dealers
N.A.I.C.S.: 457210

Paraco South LLC   (1)
15720 John J Delaney Dr Ste 300, Charlotte, NC 28277
Tel.: (704) 944-3246
Propane Gas Distr
N.A.I.C.S.: 424720
Michael Gioffre *(Pres)*

PARADIGM ASSOCIATES
450 De La Constitucion Ave Torre De La Reina Bldg Ste A1, San Juan, PR 00901
Tel.: (787) 782-2929
Web Site: http://www.paradigmpr.com
Year Founded: 1998
Sales Range: $10-24.9 Million
Emp.: 13
Marketing, Advertising, Branding & Public Relations
N.A.I.C.S.: 541810
Guillermo J. Ramis *(CEO)*
Tita Ramirez *(Sr VP)*

PARADIGM CAPITAL PARTNERS
2029 Century Park E, Ste 400, Los Angeles, CA 90067
Tel.: (917) 740-4442
Web Site: https://www.paradigmequitypartners.com
Emp.: 100
Private Equity
N.A.I.C.S.: 523999
Roman Zelinsky *(Founder)*

Subsidiaries:

E & R Industrial Sales, Inc.   (1)
40800 Enterprise Dr, Sterling Heights, MI 48314
Tel.: (586) 795-2400
Web Site: https://www.erindustrial.com
Industrial Supplies Distr
N.A.I.C.S.: 423840

PARADIGM INFOTECH, INC.
8830 Stanford Blvd Ste 312, Columbia, MD 21045
Tel.: (410) 872-1008
Web Site: http://www.paradigminfotech.com
Year Founded: 1997
Sales Range: $25-49.9 Million
Emp.: 600
Customized Software Development Services
N.A.I.C.S.: 541511
Sridhar Gadhi *(Owner)*
Erin Lowman *(Mgr-Accts Receivable)*
Alok Agrawal *(Mgr-Bus Dev)*

PARADIGM METALS INC.
15811 Vision Dr, Pflugerville, TX 78660-3187
Tel.: (512) 255-2622
Web Site: http://www.paradigmmetals.com
Sales Range: $10-24.9 Million
Emp.: 75
Machine & Other Job Shop Work
N.A.I.C.S.: 332710
Daniel J. Chew *(Pres & CEO)*
Steve Chew *(Gen Mgr)*
Matt Casper *(Controller)*

PARADIGM PARTNERS
200 W Lake Pk Blvd Ste 501, Houston, TX 77079
Tel.: (281) 558-7100
Web Site: http://www.hireteh.com
Year Founded: 2006
Sales Range: $1-9.9 Million
Emp.: 35
Tax Consulting
N.A.I.C.S.: 541219
Karim Solanji *(Partner)*
Mike Grenier *(Sr Dir)*
Brian Cameron *(VP-Bus Dev)*
Erica Weinstock *(Mgr-Acctg)*

PARADIGM RECOVERY SOLUTIONS, LLC
17150 Butte Creek Dr Ste 215, Houston, TX 77090
Tel.: (952) 884-0333
Sales Range: $10-24.9 Million
Emp.: 15
Holding Company
N.A.I.C.S.: 561440
John W. Gibson *(CEO)*

Subsidiaries:

Computer Cheque   (1)
17150 Butte Creek 215, Houston, TX 77090
Tel.: (402) 827-5555
Sales Range: $10-24.9 Million
Business Services
N.A.I.C.S.: 561440

PARADIGM SERVICES LLC

PARADIGM SERVICES LLC — U.S. PRIVATE

Paradigm Services LLC—(Continued)
2219 Sanford Dr, Grand Junction, CO 81505
Tel.: (970) 257-7917
Web Site:
 http://www.undergroundlocator.com
Rev.: $19,387,808
Emp.: 20
Petroleum Bulk Stations
N.A.I.C.S.: 424710

PARADISE ADVERTISING & MARKETING, INC.
150 2nd Ave N Ste 800, Saint Petersburg, FL 33701
Tel.: (727) 821-5155
Web Site:
 http://www.paradiseadv.com
Year Founded: 2002
Sales Range: $25-49.9 Million
Emp.: 15
Advertising Agencies
N.A.I.C.S.: 541810
Cedar Hames (*CEO & Chief Strategy Officer*)
Nicole Delaney (*Acct Dir*)
Rudy Webb (*VP-Acct*)
Mary Jane Kolassa (*Acct Dir-PR*)
Lorin Konchak Augeri (*Mgr-PR*)
Tara Tufo (*Dir-PR*)
Eric Snider (*Dir-Strategy & Special Projects*)
Lauren Couturier (*Mgr-Social Media Community*)
John Morgan (*Dir-Res & Analytics*)
Casey Goldstein (*Mgr-Social Media Community*)
Tom Merrick (*Chief Creative Officer*)
Dylan Madigan (*Dir-Art*)
Brian Arndt (*Dir-Creative*)
Melissa Cederquist (*Coord-PR*)
Barbara Karasek (*Co-Owner & CEO*)
Tony Karasek (*Co-Owner & Exec VP*)

Subsidiaries:

Paradise Advertising & Marketing-Naples (1)
646 5th Ave S Ste 213, Naples, FL 34102
Tel.: (239) 465-4972
Web Site: http://www.paradiseadv.com
Advertising Services
N.A.I.C.S.: 541810
Cedar Hames (*CEO & Chief Strategy Officer*)
Tara Tufo (*Dir-PR*)
Jessica Anderson (*Dir-Project Mgmt*)
Brian Arndt (*Dir-Creative*)
Caspar Blattmann (*Sr Dir-Art*)
Glenn Bowman (*Dir-Creative & Digital*)
Eric Hunter (*Dir-Films, Branded Content & Entertainment*)
Jessica Mackey (*Dir-Social Media*)
Dylan Madigan (*Dir-Art*)
John Morgan (*Dir-Res & Analytics*)
Eric Snider (*Dir-Strategy & Special Projects*)

PARADISE BEVERAGES, INC.
94-1450 Moaniani St, Waipahu, HI 96797-4632
Tel.: (808) 678-4049   HI
Web Site:
 http://www.paradisebeverages.com
Year Founded: 1989
Sales Range: $25-49.9 Million
Emp.: 200
Whslr & Marketer of Beer, Wine, Juices, Coffee & Bottled Water
N.A.I.C.S.: 424810
R. John Anderson (*Chm*)

Subsidiaries:

Hawaii Coffee Company (1)
1555 Kalani St, Honolulu, HI 96817
Tel.: (808) 843-4202
Web Site: http://www.lioncoffee.com
Rev.: $25,000,000
Emp.: 120
Coffee Processor & Marketer

N.A.I.C.S.: 424490
Dan Dinell (*Pres*)

Lion Coffee Company (1)
1555 Kalani St, Honolulu, HI 96817
Tel.: (808) 847-3600
Web Site: http://www.lioncoffee.com
Coffee Whslr
N.A.I.C.S.: 424490

PARADISE CHEVROLET
6350 Leland St, Ventura, CA 93003
Tel.: (805) 642-0111   CA
Web Site:
 http://www.paradisechevrolet.com
Year Founded: 1968
Sales Range: $10-24.9 Million
Emp.: 135
New & Used Car Dealer
N.A.I.C.S.: 441110
Bob Lewis (*Bus Mgr-Paradise Chevrolet-Ventura*)

PARADISE CRUISES LTD.
1540 S King St, Honolulu, HI 96826
Tel.: (808) 983-7740
Web Site:
 http://www.starofhonolulu.com
Sales Range: $25-49.9 Million
Emp.: 500
Excursion Cruise Operator
N.A.I.C.S.: 487210
Ronald D. Howard (*Pres*)

PARADISE EXTERIORS LLC
1918 Corporate Dr, Boynton Beach, FL 33426
Tel.: (561) 732-0300
Web Site:
 http://www.paradiseexteriors.com
Year Founded: 2007
Sales Range: $25-49.9 Million
Emp.: 100
General Contractor Services
N.A.I.C.S.: 236210
Dan Beckner (*Owner, Pres & CEO*)
Anthony Beckner (*COO*)
Tina Beckner (*Gen Mgr*)
Jacqueline Molestina (*Mgr-Show & Event*)
Mark Hildreth (*VP-Ops & Sls Mgr*)

PARADISE GALLERIES, INC.
23141 Verdugo Dr Ste 100, Laguna Hills, CA 92653
Tel.: (858) 793-4050
Web Site:
 http://www.paradisegalleries.com
Year Founded: 1991
Sales Range: $10-24.9 Million
Emp.: 60
Doll Retailer
N.A.I.C.S.: 423920
Anthony Seutts (*Pres*)

PARADISE ICE PLANT
PO Box 361807, San Juan, PR 00936
Tel.: (787) 780-6001
Web Site: http://paradiseicepr.com
Sales Range: $10-24.9 Million
Emp.: 25
Ice Mfr
N.A.I.C.S.: 312113
Eduardo Lopez (*Pres*)

PARADISE TOMATO KITCHENS, INC.
1500 S Brook St, Louisville, KY 40208
Tel.: (502) 637-1700
Web Site:
 http://www.paradisetomato.com
Year Founded: 1992
Sales Range: $10-24.9 Million
Emp.: 100
Spice Mfr

N.A.I.C.S.: 311941
Ron Peters (*CEO*)
Justin Uhl (*Dir-Technical*)
Jennifer Vincent (*Dir-Quality Assurance*)
Richard Kern (*Pres*)

PARADISE, INC.
1200 Dr Martin Luther King Jr Blvd, Plant City, FL 33563-5155
Tel.: (813) 752-1155   FL
Web Site:
 https://www.paradisefruitco.com
Year Founded: 1961
PARF—(OTCIQ)
Rev.: $20,134,998
Assets: $24,783,742
Liabilities: $2,036,932
Net Worth: $22,746,810
Earnings: ($613,910)
Emp.: 150
Fiscal Year-end: 12/31/18
Candied Fruit Mfr
N.A.I.C.S.: 311999
Courtney Schulis (*Sls Dir-Glace*)

Subsidiaries:

Paradise Plastics, Inc. (1)
1200 Dr Martin Luther King Jr Blvd, Plant City, FL 33563-5155
Tel.: (813) 752-1155
Web Site: http://www.paradiseplastics.com
Sales Range: $800-899.9 Million
Emp.: 30
Plastic Injection Molding & Thermoforming Services
N.A.I.C.S.: 322220
Randy S. Gordon (*Pres*)

PARADYSZ MATERA COMPANY, INC.
5 Hanover Sq, New York, NY 10004
Tel.: (212) 387-0300
Web Site: http://www.paradysz.com
Year Founded: 1990
Sales Range: $10-24.9 Million
Emp.: 340
Direct Mail Marketing Services
N.A.I.C.S.: 541860
Chris Paradysz (*Founder*)
Michael Cousineau (*CEO*)
Michael Flanagan (*CFO*)
Charles Teller (*Co-Pres*)
John Ernst (*Co-Pres*)
Rob Stagno (*Co-Pres*)

PARAGON ACURA
56-02 Northern Blvd, Woodside, NY 11377
Tel.: (718) 392-8882
Web Site:
 http://www.paragonacura.com
Year Founded: 1929
Rev.: $13,000,000
Emp.: 50
Sales of Automobiles
N.A.I.C.S.: 441110
Murat Deljanin (*Gen Mgr-Sls*)

PARAGON ADVERTISING
65 Park Ave Ste 101, Bay Shore, NY 11706-7359
Tel.: (631) 969-0185   NY
Web Site:
 http://www.thinkparagon.com
Year Founded: 1985
Sales Range: $10-24.9 Million
Emp.: 10
Advetising Agency
N.A.I.C.S.: 541810
Steve A. Starlust (*Owner & CEO*)
Jake Russel (*Exec VP*)
Stu Miller (*Sr Coord-Production*)
Zina Terrya (*VP-Sls*)

PARAGON ADVERTISING
43 Court St, Buffalo, NY 14202-3101

Tel.: (716) 854-7161
Year Founded: 1989
Rev.: $21,000,000
Emp.: 15
N.A.I.C.S.: 541810
Brian Downey (*Chm*)
James Gillan (*Pres & Acct Exec*)
Leo Abbott (*Partner & Dir-Art*)
Eric Goldberg (*Mng Partner*)
Charles Abbott (*Dir-Art*)
Craig Maedl (*VP & Acct Dir*)
Mary Kay Williamson (*VP-Client Svcs*)
Rosemary Witschard (*Mgr-Traffic*)
Andrea O'Bryant (*Mgr-Production*)
Chris Dlugosz (*Mgr-Program*)
Brian Meyer (*Copywriter*)
Scott McCandless (*Dir-Sls & Promos*)

PARAGON BUILDING PRODUCTS INC.
2191 5th St Ste 111, Norco, CA 92860
Tel.: (951) 549-1155   CA
Web Site: http://www.paragonbp.com
Year Founded: 1984
Sales Range: $25-49.9 Million
Emp.: 72
Mfr Concrete Products
N.A.I.C.S.: 327999
Jack Goodman (*Founder*)
Jeff Goodman (*Pres*)

Subsidiaries:

Mohave Block Inc. (1)
6485 S Tampico Rd, Golden Valley, AZ 86401
Tel.: (928) 565-5133
Concrete Products Mfr
N.A.I.C.S.: 327331

Paragon Aggregate Products Inc. (1)
5420 W Bethany Home Rd, Glendale, AZ 85301
Tel.: (623) 435-8271
Web Site: http://www.paragonbp.us
Emp.: 50
Concrete Products Mfr
N.A.I.C.S.: 327331
Ben Hazelton (*Gen Mgr*)

Paragon Building Products Inc. - Nevada Pre-Mix Division (1)
1549 Athol Ave, Henderson, NV 89015-4003
Tel.: (702) 567-0314
Cement Block Product Mfr
N.A.I.C.S.: 327331

Paragon Building Products Inc. - Paragon Concrete Products Division (1)
2305 S Roof Tile Rd, Casa Grande, AZ 85222-7545
Tel.: (520) 836-6454
Emp.: 25
Cement Block Product Mfr
N.A.I.C.S.: 327331
Adam Gallegos (*Asst Plant Mgr*)

PARAGON CERTIFIED RESTORATION
616 Spirit Valley E Dr, Chesterfield, MO 63005-1029
Tel.: (636) 728-0580
Web Site: http://www.paragonstl.com
Year Founded: 2003
Sales Range: $10-24.9 Million
Emp.: 54
Housing Construction Services
N.A.I.C.S.: 236117
Christine McClure (*Dir-HR*)
Randy Wild (*Owner*)
LeAnn Hefner (*Acct Mgr-Bus Dev*)
Steve Stodnick (*Owner*)

PARAGON DECORS INC.
195 Paragon, Albertville, AL 35950
Tel.: (256) 593-4700
Web Site: http://www.paragonpg.com

Year Founded: 1970
Sales Range: $10-24.9 Million
Emp.: 125
Whslr & Mfr of Framed Wall Decor
N.A.I.C.S.: 339999
Wendell Glassco *(Pres & CEO)*
Malanta Glassco-Knowles *(VP-Mktg)*

PARAGON DIE & ENGINEERING COMPANY
5225 33rd St SE, Grand Rapids, MI 49512
Tel.: (616) 949-2220
Web Site: http://www.paragondie.com
Year Founded: 1942
Sales Range: $25-49.9 Million
Emp.: 223
Plastic Injection Mold Mfr
N.A.I.C.S.: 333514
Dave Muir *(Pres)*
Bob Starck *(VP-Bus Dev)*
Greg Eidenberger *(VP-Sls)*
Lucas Bates *(CFO)*
Jon Hamming *(Engr-Sls)*
Dennis McGuinness *(Engr-Sls)*
Dave Van Rooyen *(Engr-Technical Sls)*
Ed Van Rooyen *(Engr-Sls)*
Mark Walcott *(Engr-Technical Sls)*
Charlie Frederick *(VP-Mfg)*

PARAGON ELECTRONIC SYSTEMS INC.
6701 Center Dr W Ste 520, Los Angeles, CA 90045-1540
Tel.: (408) 727-8824　　CA
Web Site: http://www.prgn.com
Year Founded: 1996
Rev.: $27,000,000
Emp.: 300
Mfr of Printed Circuit Boards
N.A.I.C.S.: 334412

PARAGON ENERGY SOLUTIONS, LLC
777 Emory Valley Rd, Oak Ridge, TN 37830
Tel.: (865) 966-5330
Web Site: http://www.paragones.com
Nuclear Power Parts & Services
N.A.I.C.S.: 221113
Douglas VanTassell *(Pres & CEO)*

Subsidiaries:

Nuclear Logistics LLC　　(1)
7410 Pebble Dr, Fort Worth, TX 76118-6961
Tel.: (817) 284-0077
Nuclear Equipment Maintenance & Repair Services
N.A.I.C.S.: 811310

Spectrum Technologies USA, Inc.　　(1)
588 Broadway, Schenectady, NY 12305
Tel.: (518) 382-0056
Web Site: http://www.argoturbo.com
Sales Range: $1-9.9 Million
Emp.: 25
Industrial Supplies Merchant Whslr
N.A.I.C.S.: 423840
Clyde Keaton *(Pres)*

PARAGON FOOD SERVICE
173 Thorn Hill Rd, Warrendale, PA 15086
Tel.: (724) 741-9100
Web Site: http://www.paragonfresh.com
Fresh Food Distr
N.A.I.C.S.: 424480
Elaine M. Bellin *(Pres & CEO)*
John McClelland *(COO)*
Rich Mosgrove *(VP-Ops)*

Subsidiaries:

John V. Heineman Company　　(1)
151 39th St, Pittsburgh, PA 15201-3206
Tel.: (412) 681-9850
Web Site: http://www.jheineman.com
Grocery & Related Products Merchant Whslr
N.A.I.C.S.: 424490
Jack Ketler *(Pres)*

PARAGON GLOBAL RESOURCES, INC.
633 E State Hwy 121 S Ste 250, Coppell, TX 75019
Tel.: (972) 819-5100
Web Site: http://www.paragongri.com
Holding Company; Relocation & Mortgage Services
N.A.I.C.S.: 551112
Joseph A. Morabito *(Pres & CEO)*
Craig Selders *(Pres-Paragon Relocation & Exec VP)*
Mary Legate *(Sr VP)*
Scott McCain *(Sr VP-Global Bus Dev)*
Janelle Gerber *(VP-Real Estate Svcs, Affinity Svcs & Paragon Career Resources)*
Jim Davis *(CFO & VP)*

Subsidiaries:

GenEquity Mortgage, Inc.　　(1)
633 E State Hwy 121 S Ste 510, Coppell, TX 75019
Tel.: (888) 436-3789
Web Site: http://www.genequity.com
Emp.: 10
Mortgage Services
N.A.I.C.S.: 522310
Mary Legate *(Pres)*
Steve Crispin *(VP-Secondary Mktg)*
William Clopton *(VP-Mortgage Ops)*

Subsidiary (Domestic):

Houston Capital Mortgage　　(2)
1717 Saint James Pl Ste 400, Houston, TX 77056-3473
Tel.: (713) 787-6333
Web Site: http://www.houstoncapital.com
Emp.: 20
Mortgage Banker
N.A.I.C.S.: 522310
Christopher A. Viviano *(CEO)*
Stacy G. London *(Pres)*

PARAGON INDUSTRIES INC.
4285 N Golden State Blvd, Fresno, CA 93722
Tel.: (559) 275-5000
Web Site: http://www.bedrosians.com
Rev.: $42,600,000
Emp.: 500
Lumber & Other Building Materials
N.A.I.C.S.: 423310
Larry E. Bedrosian *(Pres & CEO)*
Ernie Ramirez *(Mgr-Warehouse)*

PARAGON INDUSTRIES, INC.
5 Miles E Hwy 117, Sapulpa, OK 74066
Tel.: (918) 291-4459　　OK
Web Site: http://www.paragonindinc.com
Year Founded: 1970
Sales Range: $10-24.9 Million
Emp.: 250
Mfr of Steel Pipe & Tubes
N.A.I.C.S.: 331210
Jack Wachob *(Pres)*
Doug Paschel *(Pres-Sls)*
Derek Wachob *(VP)*
Betsie Willies *(Controller)*

PARAGON INSURANCE HOLDINGS, LLC
45 Nod Rd, Avon, CT 06001
Tel.: (800) 285-4081
Web Site: http://www.paragoninsgroup.com
Year Founded: 2014
Commercial Insurance Services
N.A.I.C.S.: 524298

Ron Ganiats *(Mng Partner)*

Subsidiaries:

Trident Insurance Services, LLC　　(1)
175 E Houston St, San Antonio, TX 78205
Tel.: (210) 342-8808
Sales Range: $200-249.9 Million
Emp.: 350
Insurance Agencies
N.A.I.C.S.: 524210
Mark Watson *(CEO)*
Ron Vindivich *(Pres)*

PARAGON INTERNATIONAL, INC.
2885 N Berkeley Lk Rd Ste 17, Duluth, GA 30096
Tel.: (770) 495-7565
Web Site: http://www.paragonint.net
Data Center Contamination Services
N.A.I.C.S.: 518210
Stephanie King *(Project Mgr)*

PARAGON LEGAL GROUP, P.C.
601 California St Ste 615, San Francisco, CA 94108
Tel.: (415) 738-7870
Web Site: http://www.paragonlegal.com
Year Founded: 2006
Sales Range: $1-9.9 Million
Emp.: 30
Corporate Counsel Services
N.A.I.C.S.: 922130
Mae O'Malley *(Founder & Atty)*
Tam T.T. Pham *(Dir-Recruiting)*
Jennifer Chou-Green *(Mgr-HR)*

PARAGON MECHANICAL INC.
2460 De La Cruz Blvd, Santa Clara, CA 95050
Tel.: (408) 727-7303
Web Site: http://www.paragonmechanical.com
Rev.: $11,300,000
Emp.: 75
Provider of Warm Air Heating & Air Conditioning Services
N.A.I.C.S.: 238220
John T. Watson *(Pres)*
Steven Benakovich *(VP)*

PARAGON MICRO, INC.
Business Technology Ctr 2 Corporate Dr Ste 105, Lake Zurich, IL 60047
Tel.: (847) 637-8371　　IL
Web Site: http://www.paragonmicro.com
Year Founded: 2006
Sales Range: $100-124.9 Million
Emp.: 200
Information Technology Sales & Services
N.A.I.C.S.: 541519
Jeff Reimer *(Pres)*
Dave Lyons *(Acct Mgr-Global)*
Jon Faith *(Acct Mgr-Health Care)*
Tad Dahl *(Founder & CEO)*
Jeff Richards *(Dir-Svcs)*
Forrest Knueppel *(Dir-Corp Sls)*
Todd Cowen *(Sr VP & Gen Mgr)*
Larry Hall *(VP-Pur & Partner Dev)*

PARAGON MOTORS OF WOODSIDE, INC.
57 02 Northern Blvd, Woodside, NY 11377
Tel.: (718) 507-5000
Web Site: http://www.paragonhonda.com
Sales Range: $25-49.9 Million
Emp.: 90
New & Used Car Dealer
N.A.I.C.S.: 441110
William Liang *(Asst Dir-Fin)*
Gary Lin *(Dir-Fin)*

Meto Adovic *(Mgr-Bus)*
Alan D. Gensler *(Mgr-Bus)*
Mitchell J. Levy *(Mgr-Bus)*
Syed Shah *(Mgr-Bus)*
Sasha Kekovic *(Mgr-Proposal)*
Quedwin Medina *(Mgr-Sls)*
Ariel Munoz *(Mgr-Sls)*
Angel Perez *(Mgr-Sls)*

PARAGON PLASTICS, INC.
520 Saint Johns St, Cocoa, FL 32922
Tel.: (321) 631-6212　　FL
Web Site: http://www.paragonplastics.net
Year Founded: 1993
Sales Range: $1-9.9 Million
Emp.: 35
Plastics Products
N.A.I.C.S.: 326199
David Trout *(Pres)*

PARAGON PLUS INC.
7405 E Slauson Ave, Commerce, CA 90040
Tel.: (310) 830-5004
Web Site: http://www.paragonsteel.com
Sales Range: $25-49.9 Million
Emp.: 20
Steel
N.A.I.C.S.: 423510
Doug Carpenter *(Pres)*

PARAGON SPACE DEVELOPMENT CORPORATION
3481 E Michigan St, Tucson, AZ 85714
Tel.: (520) 903-1000　　AZ
Web Site: http://www.paragonsdc.com
Year Founded: 1993
Sales Range: $1-9.9 Million
Emp.: 61
Designs Life-Support, Thermal-Control & Environmental-Control Systems for Extreme Environments
N.A.I.C.S.: 541330
Taber MacCallum *(Co-Founder, Partner & Principal)*
Jane Poynter *(Co-Founder)*
Grant Anderson *(Co-Founder, Pres & CEO)*
Joel Johnson *(CFO)*
Christie Iacomini *(Sr Engr-Aerospace)*
Henry Konopka *(COO)*
Ronald K. Sable *(Chm)*
Kristin Behrens *(Dir-People Dept)*

PARAGON SPORTS CONSTRUCTORS LLC.
5001 Saunders Rd, Fort Worth, TX 76119
Tel.: (817) 916-5000
Web Site: http://www.paragon-sports.com
Sales Range: $10-24.9 Million
Emp.: 25
Civil Engineering Services
N.A.I.C.S.: 237310
Brian Roberts *(CFO)*

PARAGON STEEL ENTERPRISES LLC
4211 County Rd 61, Butler, IN 46721
Tel.: (260) 868-1100
Web Site: http://www.pstparagonsteel.com
Year Founded: 1995
Sales Range: $25-49.9 Million
Emp.: 13
Mfr of Prime & Secondary Steel
N.A.I.C.S.: 423510
Bruce Whitman *(Gen Mgr)*
Jerome F. Henry Jr. *(Pres)*

PARAGON TECHNOLOGIES INC.
U.S. PRIVATE

Paragon Technologies Inc.—(Continued)

PARAGON TECHNOLOGIES INC.
5775 E 10 Mile Rd, Warren, MI 48091
Tel.: (586) 756-9100
Web Site:
http://www.paragontech.com
Rev.: $12,000,000
Emp.: 130
Hydraulic Equipment Repair
N.A.I.C.S.: 811210
Kevin D. Schoensee (Founder & Chm)

PARAGUS STRATEGIC IT
84 Russell St, Hadley, MA 01035
Tel.: (413) 587-2666
Web Site: http://www.paragusit.com
Year Founded: 2004
Sales Range: $1-9.9 Million
Emp.: 35
Information Technology Consulting Services
N.A.I.C.S.: 541512
Delcie D. Bean IV (Founder)

PARALLAX CAPITAL PARTNERS, LLC
23332 Mill Creek Dr Ste 155, Laguna Hills, CA 92653
Tel.: (949) 296-4800   CA
Web Site:
http://www.parallaxcap.com
Year Founded: 1999
Privater Equity Firm
N.A.I.C.S.: 523999
James Richard Hale (Mng Partner)
Michael Hale (Principal & Sr VP-Ops)
Richard Campbell (CFO)
Ryan Kolynych (VP-Private Equity)

Subsidiaries:

Quark Software, Inc.   (1)
1225 17th St Ste 2050, Denver, CO 80202
Tel.: (303) 894-8888
Web Site: http://www.quark.com
Electronic Publishing & Communication Software Solutions
N.A.I.C.S.: 513210
Gavin Drake (VP-Sls & Mktg)
Jim Haggarty (CIO)
Pete Jensen (Gen Counsel)
Claire Hancock (VP-HR)
Dave White (CTO)
Chris Cook (CFO)
John Friske (Pres & COO)
Iresh Mehta (VP-Engrg)
Alex Gorbansky (Gen Mgr-Docurated Bus Unit)
Jason Aiken (Sr Product Mgr)
Nick Howard (Sr Dir-Sls Enablement & Inside Sls)
Chris Hickey (CEO)

Subsidiary (Non-US):

QuarkXPress Publishing R&D (India) Pvt. Ltd.   (2)
A 45 Industrial Area Phase VIII-B Mohali, 160055, Mohali, India
Tel.: (91) 1723049000
Web Site: http://www.quark.com
Electronic Publishing & Communication Software Solutions
N.A.I.C.S.: 334416

VistaSource Inc.   (1)
1900 W Park Dr Ste 280, Westborough, MA 01581
Tel.: (774) 760-1000
Web Site: http://www.vistasource.com
Software Development Services
N.A.I.C.S.: 541511

PARALLAX HEALTH SCIENCES, INC.
1327 Ocean Ave Ste B, Santa Monica, CA 90401
Tel.: (617) 209-7999   NV

Web Site:
http://www.parallaxhealthsciences.com
Year Founded: 2005
Rev.: $23,686,750
Assets: $1,364,357
Liabilities: $7,345,916
Net Worth: ($5,981,559)
Earnings: $16,289,320
Emp.: 6
Fiscal Year-end: 12/31/18
Biotechnology & Health Care Services
N.A.I.C.S.: 541714
Calli R. Bucci (CFO)
Nathaniel T. Bradley (CTO & Chief Product Officer)

PARALLAX POWER SUPPLIES LLC
600 Broadway, Anderson, IN 46012
Tel.: (765) 274-5920
Web Site:
http://www.parallaxpower.com
Sales Range: $25-49.9 Million
Emp.: 14
Electronic Capacitors
N.A.I.C.S.: 334416

PARALLEL INVESTMENT PARTNERS LLC
2525 McKinnon St Ste 330, Dallas, TX 75201
Tel.: (214) 740-3600
Web Site: http://www.parallelip.com
Year Founded: 1999
Sales Range: $25-49.9 Million
Emp.: 16
Privater Equity Firm
N.A.I.C.S.: 523999
Robert J. Taylor (CFO)
F. Barron Fletcher III (Mng Dir)

Subsidiaries:

Mealeys Furniture   (1)
179 Lincoln Hwy, Fairless Hills, PA 19030
Tel.: (215) 949-1111
Web Site: http://www.mealeysfurniture.com
Sales Range: $25-49.9 Million
Furniture Retailer
N.A.I.C.S.: 449110
Dan Mealy (Pres & CEO)

Moosejaw Mountaineering & Backcountry Travel, Inc.   (1)
32200 N Avis Dr Ste 100, Madison Heights, MI 48071
Tel.: (248) 246-4000
Web Site: http://www.moosejaw.com
Sales Range: $25-49.9 Million
Sporting Goods Retailer
N.A.I.C.S.: 459110
Eoin Comerford (Pres & CEO)

Superior Auto, Inc.   (1)
6642 Saint Joe Rd, Fort Wayne, IN 46835
Tel.: (260) 471-5718
Web Site: http://www.superior-auto.com
Sales Range: $10-24.9 Million
Used Car Dealership Operator
N.A.I.C.S.: 441120
Mike English (Controller)
Chad Melchi (Pres & CEO)
Ann Lesperance (Mgr-Acctg)

USA Discounters, Ltd.   (1)
3320 Holland Rd, Virginia Beach, VA 23452
Tel.: (757) 368-3300
Web Site: http://www.usadiscounters.net
Furniture Stores
N.A.I.C.S.: 449210

PARALLEL PRODUCTS OF KENTUCKY, INC.
401 Industry Rd, Louisville, KY 40208
Tel.: (502) 471-2444   KY
Web Site:
http://www.parallelproducts.com
Sales Range: $25-49.9 Million
Emp.: 15

Food, Beverage, Pharmaceutical & Cosmetics Waste Processing, Recycling & Disposal Services
N.A.I.C.S.: 562998
Gene Kiesel (Pres & CEO)
Ken Reese (VP-Sls & Mktg)
Ed Stewart (Dir-Sls-Natl)
Hal Park (Dir-Corp Comm & Mgr-HR)
Russ Hoehn (VP-Fin & Controller)
Denise Gibson (Mgr-Customer Svc-Natl)
Monica Lurie (VP-Sls & Mktg)

PARAMETRIC SOLUTIONS, INC.
900 E Indiantown Rd Ste 200, Jupiter, FL 33477
Tel.: (561) 747-6107   FL
Web Site: http://www.psnet.com
Year Founded: 1993
Sales Range: $1-9.9 Million
Emp.: 160
Engineeering Services
N.A.I.C.S.: 541330
Catherine Haas Barre (Pres)
Joel Haas (CEO)
Daryl Michaelian (VP-Cold Section Engrg)
David Olsen (VP-Hot Section Engrg)
Gary Prus (COO)
David Cusano (VP-Thermal Sciences & IT)

PARAMETRIX, INC.
1002 15th St SW Ste 220, Auburn, WA 98001
Tel.: (253) 269-1330   WA
Web Site: http://www.parametrix.com
Year Founded: 1969
Rev.: $31,019,172
Emp.: 385
Provider of Engineering & Environmental Consulting Services
N.A.I.C.S.: 541690
Jeff Peacock (Pres)
Steve Walker (VP)
Alex Sylvain (Sr Engr-Spokane)
Jeff Fredine (Mgr-Environmental Plng & Compliance-Albuquerque)
Len York (CEO)
Adam Erlandson (Sr Engr-Community Building Div-Bend)
Darby Watson (VP)
Pete Bozin (Sr Engr-Bend)

Subsidiaries:

Krei Architecture Inc   (1)
1119 Pacific Ave Ste 1600, Tacoma, WA 98402-4324   (100%)
Tel.: (253) 383-8700
Sales Range: $10-24.9 Million
Emp.: 40
Provider of Architectural Services
N.A.I.C.S.: 541310

PARAMOUNT APPAREL INTERNATIONAL INC.
1 Paramount Dr, Bourbon, MO 65441
Tel.: (573) 732-4411   MO
Web Site:
http://www.paramountapparel.com
Year Founded: 1929
Sales Range: $50-74.9 Million
Emp.: 500
Hats, Caps & Millinery
N.A.I.C.S.: 315990
Mark Rubenstein (Chm & Co-CEO)
Bruce Levinson (Pres & Co-CEO)
Ada McVay (Brand Mgr)
David Etheridge (Dir-Process Projects)
Debbie Horsefield (Sr Acct Exec)
Jennifer Helmig (Brand Mgr-License)
Katharine Holland (Sr Acct Exec)
Joe Beckett (Mgr-Distr)
Shelly Tindall (Coord-Shipping)
Sonya Sewald (Sr Acct Exec)

Grant Clark (Dir-ASI)
Lori Alyea (Dir-Design)
Mike Jaques (VP-Sls & Mktg)
Steve Lefler (Pres)
Todd Johnson (VP-Ops)
Connie Bourgeois (Dir-Art)
Tim Saling (Sr Acct Exec)

PARAMOUNT BEAUTY DISTRIBUTING ASSOCIATES INC.
41 Mercedes Way Unit 34, Edgewood, NY 11717-8334
Tel.: (631) 242-3737
Web Site:
http://www.paramountbeauty.com
Year Founded: 1966
Sales Range: $10-24.9 Million
Emp.: 110
Beauty Salon Chain
N.A.I.C.S.: 424210
Dave Muir (Pres)
Alan Hagler (Pres)
Susan Nicoletti (Controller)
Jeffrey Hagler (VP)

PARAMOUNT BUILDERS INC.
501 Central Dr, Virginia Beach, VA 23454
Tel.: (757) 340-9000
Web Site:
http://www.paramountbuilders.com
Sales Range: $25-49.9 Million
Emp.: 200
Siding
N.A.I.C.S.: 444110
Edward Augustine (Pres)

PARAMOUNT BUSINESS JETS
673 Potomac Station Dr Ste 707, Leesburg, VA 20176
Web Site:
http://www.paramountbusinessjets.com
Year Founded: 2005
Sales Range: $1-9.9 Million
Emp.: 10
Charter Jet Brokerage
N.A.I.C.S.: 481211
Richard Zaher (Founder & CEO)
Eric Ammon (Sr VP-Sls)

PARAMOUNT CAN COMPANY INC.
16430 Phoebe Ave, La Mirada, CA 90638
Tel.: (714) 562-8410
Web Site:
http://www.paramountglobalservices.com
Sales Range: $10-24.9 Million
Emp.: 55
Commercial Containers
N.A.I.C.S.: 423840
Jack Gample (Pres)

PARAMOUNT CONTRACTING, INC.
219 Witmer Rd, Lancaster, PA 17602
Tel.: (717) 393-9900
Web Site:
http://www.paramountcontracting.biz
Year Founded: 2005
Rev.: $7,000,000
Emp.: 43
Commercial & Institutional Building Construction
N.A.I.C.S.: 236220
Jeff Mylin (Pres)
Brian Zuschmidt (Project Mgr)
Ron Johns (Project Mgr-Northern Tier)

PARAMOUNT EQUIPMENT LLC
805 Lehigh Ave, Union, NJ 07083
Tel.: (844) 276-8283
Web Site:
http://www.paramountth.com

Forklift Dealer
N.A.I.C.S.: 444230
Gary Weisman (VP-Sls & Ops)
Vincent DeRienzo (Sls Mgr)

PARAMOUNT EQUITY MORTGAGE, LLC
8781 Sierra College Blvd, Roseville, CA 95661
Tel.: (916) 290-9999
Web Site: http://www.paramountequity.com
Year Founded: 2003
Sales Range: $25-49.9 Million
Emp.: 356
Mortgage & Nonmortgage Loan Brokers
N.A.I.C.S.: 522310
Jason Walker (Chief Credit Officer)
Hayes Barnard (Founder & Chm)
Ed Fuchs (VP-Capital Markets)
Kelly Resendez (Exec VP-Sls & Bus Dev)
Mike Berte (Pres)
Chiena Choe (Exec VP-Ops)
Cameron Findlay (Exec VP-Capital Markets)
Josh Harmatz (Exec VP-Sls)
Jesse Spina (Exec VP-Sls)
Michael Fahey (CIO)
Matt Murray (Chief Mktg Officer)
Raymond Snytsheuvel (Chief Compliance Officer & Gen Counsel)

PARAMOUNT FOODS INC.
332 NE Blvd, Clinton, NC 28328
Tel.: (910) 592-7611
Rev.: $34,679,297
Emp.: 100
Supermarkets, Chain
N.A.I.C.S.: 445110
Kathy Gautier (Dir-HR)
Michael Lindsay (Pres)

PARAMOUNT HOMES LLC
1 Kathleen Dr Ste 1, Jackson, NJ 08527
Tel.: (732) 886-2900
Web Site: http://www.paramountnewhomes.com
Sales Range: $10-24.9 Million
Emp.: 23
Constructors of Single Family Homes
N.A.I.C.S.: 236115
Jeffrey Fernbach (Pres)
Eli Bleeman (VP)

PARAMOUNT HOTEL GROUP, LLC
710 Route 46 E Ste 206, Fairfield, NJ 07004-1540
Tel.: (973) 882-0505   DE
Web Site: http://www.paramounthotelgroup.com
Year Founded: 1966
Sales Range: $25-49.9 Million
Emp.: 500
Home Management Services
N.A.I.C.S.: 721110
David A. Simon (CEO)
Ethan Kramer (Pres)
Peter Marino (Sr VP-Ops)

PARAMOUNT HOTELS LLC
2003 Western Ave Ste 500, Seattle, WA 98121
Tel.: (206) 826-2710   WA
Web Site: http://www.paramounthotels.com
Sales Range: $10-24.9 Million
Hotel Operator
N.A.I.C.S.: 721110
Tristen Lemieux (Dir-Bus Ops)
Matt Murphy (Exec VP)
Kyle Asher (Gen Mgr-Seattle)

David Frazier (Gen Mgr)
Norm Hwa (Gen Mgr-Portland)
Devon Edwards (VP-Ops)

PARAMOUNT INSURANCE REPAIR SERVICE
2418 Blackgold Ct, Houston, TX 77073
Tel.: (281) 209-0356
Year Founded: 1953
Sales Range: $10-24.9 Million
Emp.: 120
Commercial & Office Buildings, Renovation & Repair
N.A.I.C.S.: 236220
Donald M. Karm (Pres)

PARAMOUNT MANUFACTURING LLC
18259 Westinghouse Rd, Abingdon, VA 24210
Tel.: (276) 623-4300
Web Site: http://www.paramontmfg.com
Rev.: $10,000,000
Emp.: 127
Molding Primary Plastics
N.A.I.C.S.: 326199
James A. Brown (CEO)
Joe Steven (CFO)

PARAMOUNT PRECISION PRODUCTS, INC.
15255 W 11 Mile Rd, Oak Park, MI 48237
Tel.: (248) 543-2100
Web Site: http://www.paramountprecisionproducts.com
Emp.: 100
Fabricated Metal Products Mfr
N.A.I.C.S.: 332710
Norah Lawton (Dir-Fin)
Sheila K. Rossmann (CEO)

Subsidiaries:

Numerical Productions, Inc.   (1)
3901 S Arlington Ave, Indianapolis, IN 46203
Tel.: (317) 783-1362
Web Site: http://www.npcnc.com
Sales Range: $1-9.9 Million
Emp.: 50
Fabricated Metal Products Mfr
N.A.I.C.S.: 332999
Jack Sweeney (Pres)
Andy Gaines (Mgr-Ops)

PARAMOUNT RESIDENTIAL MORTGAGE GROUP, INC.
1265 Corona Point Ct Ste 301, Corona, CA 92879
Tel.: (951) 278-0000
Web Site: http://www.prmg.net
Rev.: $20,300,000
Emp.: 1,000
Real Estate Credit
N.A.I.C.S.: 522292
Paul Rozo (CEO)
Robert Holliday (COO)
Lara Rausch (VP-Products & Trng)
Deborah Goguen (Mgr-Wholesale-Mid Atlantic)
Ryan Goldsmith (Mgr-Sls-Northeast & Mid-Atlantic)
Kevin Peranio (Chief Lending Officer)
Ricky Wilson (Mgr-Georgia)
Steve Levine (Reg Mgr-Sls)
Chris Sorensen (Sr VP & Dir-Natl Retail Production)
Bill Johnson (CFO)
Aimee Johnson (Natl Mgr-Ops)
Jay Boand (Dir-Correspondent Div)
Emily Vondrak (Dir-Strategic Ops & Collateral Mgmt)
Valerie Chopra (Dir-Capital Markets)

Gary Malis (Chief Strategy & Capital Markets Officer & Sr Partner)
Roland Shar (Mgr-Honolulu)

PARAMOUNT RESTAURANT SUPPLY CORPORATION
101 Main St, Warren, RI 02885
Tel.: (401) 247-6500
Web Site: http://www.pararest.com
Sales Range: $50-74.9 Million
Emp.: 51
Commercial Equipment,
N.A.I.C.S.: 423440
Stephen McGarry (Pres & CEO)
Sue McNulty (Sr Acct Exec)
Brian Barer (CEO)

PARAMOUNT SUPPLY CO. INC.
816 SE Ash St, Portland, OR 97214
Tel.: (503) 232-4137   OR
Web Site: http://www.paramountsupply.com
Year Founded: 1954
Sales Range: $10-24.9 Million
Emp.: 25
Industrial Specialties Sales
N.A.I.C.S.: 423720
Kenneth W. Grothe (Pres)

PARAMUS AUTO MALL CHEVROLET-HUMMER
194 Rte 17th N, Paramus, NJ 07652
Tel.: (201) 261-7100
Web Site: http://www.paramuschevrolet.com
Year Founded: 1995
Sales Range: $10-24.9 Million
Emp.: 65
Car Whslr
N.A.I.C.S.: 441110
Bill Brunner (Gen Mgr)

PARANET SOLUTIONS, LLC.
5001 Spring Vly Rd Ste 1050 W, Dallas, TX 75244
Tel.: (214) 623-5150
Web Site: http://www.paranet.com
Year Founded: 1991
Sales Range: $10-24.9 Million
Emp.: 110
Other Management Consulting Services
N.A.I.C.S.: 541618
David W. Truetzel (Chm)
Kris Lamberti (CEO)
Len Blackwell (Vice Chm)

PARASCRIPT LLC
6273 Monarch Park Pl, Niwot, CO 80503-7119
Tel.: (303) 381-3100
Web Site: http://www.parascript.com
Sales Range: $10-24.9 Million
Emp.: 40
Digital Image Analysis & Pattern Recognition Software
N.A.I.C.S.: 513210
Alexander A. Filatov (Pres & CEO)
Ilia Lossev (VP-Advanced R&D)
Greg Council (VP-Mktg & Product Mgmt)
Gloria Canales (Mgr-Channel Mktg)
Igor Kil (Sr VP-R&D)
Kaz Jaszczak (VP-Postal Automation)
Sergey Rudenko (VP-Product Dev)
Dmitry Gershuny (VP-R&D)
Mark Gallagher (VP-Sls)
Ted Niemann (VP-Fin & Admin)

PARASOL TAHOE COMMUNITY FOUNDATION
948 Incline Way, Incline Village, NV 89451
Tel.: (775) 298-0100   NV

Web Site: http://www.parasol.org
Year Founded: 1996
Sales Range: $1-9.9 Million
Emp.: 42
Grantmaking Services
N.A.I.C.S.: 813211
Jean Eick (Mgr-Comm)
Megan Weiss (Dir-Program & Svcs)
Claudia Andersen (CEO)
George Ashley (Treas)
Elbridge Stuart (Vice Chm)
Ron Alling (Sec)
Barbara Collier (Mgr-Ops)
Cari Gutheil (CFO)
Miguel Santiago (Mgr-DWR Center Building)
David C. Hardie (Chm)

PARASOLE RESTAURANT HOLDINGS, INC.
5032 France Ave S, Edina, MN 55410
Tel.: (612) 822-0016   MN
Web Site: http://www.parasole.com
Year Founded: 1986
Sales Range: $10-24.9 Million
Emp.: 22
Holding Company; Restaurants Developer & Operator
N.A.I.C.S.: 551112
Alan Ackerberg (Chief Dev Officer)
Kip Clayton (VP-Bus Dev & Mktg)
Sarah Nerison (Mgr-Social Media Mktg)

Subsidiaries:

Good Earth Restaurants of Minnesota   (1)
1901 Hwy 36 W, Roseville, MN 55113
Tel.: (651) 636-0956
Web Site: http://www.goodearthmn.com
Eating Place
N.A.I.C.S.: 722511
Karen Welder (Gen Mgr)

Good Earth Restaurants of Minnesota   (1)
3460 Galleria, Minneapolis, MN 55435
Tel.: (612) 822-0016
Sales Range: $1-9.9 Million
Emp.: 250
Health Food Restaurant
N.A.I.C.S.: 722513
Barb Marshall (CFO)

PARATECH, INC.
1025 Lambrecht Dr, Frankfort, IL 60423
Tel.: (815) 469-3911
Web Site: http://www.paratech.com
Sales Range: $10-24.9 Million
Emp.: 60
Emergency Rescue Tools Mfr
N.A.I.C.S.: 333991
Robert Trebe (Dir-Mfg)
Brie Brubaker (Mgr-Govt Sls & Indus)

Subsidiaries:

Eagle Compressors Inc.   (1)
3003 Thurston Ave, Greensboro, NC 27406
Tel.: (336) 398-8000
Web Site: http://www.eaglecompressors.com
Sales Range: $10-24.9 Million
Emp.: 30
Breathing Air Systems & Components for Safety Products
N.A.I.C.S.: 333912
Anthony M. Gonzales (Gen Mgr)
Becky Dreier (VP-Fin)

PARATRANSIT SERVICES
4810 Auto Ctr Way, Bremerton, WA 98312
Tel.: (360) 377-7007
Web Site: http://www.paratransit.net
Rev.: $20,040,074
Emp.: 300

PARATRANSIT SERVICES — U.S. PRIVATE

Paratransit Services—(Continued)
Transportation Services
N.A.I.C.S.: 485999
Darlene Riley *(CFO & Exec VP)*
David Baker *(Pres & CEO)*
Christie Scheffer *(COO & Exec VP)*

PARC, INC.
3190 Tyrone Blvd N, Saint Petersburg, FL 33710-2919
Tel.: (727) 345-9111 FL
Web Site: http://www.parc-fl.org
Year Founded: 1953
Sales Range: $10-24.9 Million
Emp.: 518
Disability Assistance Services
N.A.I.C.S.: 624120
April D. Hill *(Chm)*
Michelle Detweiler *(Pres & CEO)*
Lisa Emory *(Asst VP-Dev & Mktg)*

PARCELL STEEL CO., INC.
9550 Warner Ave Ste 336, Fountain Valley, CA 92708
Tel.: (714) 964-5400
Web Site: http://www.parcellsteel.com
Rev.: $32,000,000
Emp.: 100
Structural Steel & Precast Concrete Contractors
N.A.I.C.S.: 238120
Terry Parcell *(Pres)*

PARENT PETROLEUM INC.
37 W 370 Rte 38, Saint Charles, IL 60175
Tel.: (630) 584-2505
Web Site: http://www.parentpetroleum.com
Sales Range: $10-24.9 Million
Emp.: 50
Petroleum Products
N.A.I.C.S.: 424720
Peter Mancini *(Pres)*
Jeff Anderson *(Coord-Safety)*
Joe Notar *(Mgr-Ops)*
Shirin Marvi *(Office Mgr)*

PARENTERAL DRUG ASSOCIATION, INC.
4350 E West Hwy, Bethesda, MD 20814
Tel.: (301) 656-5900 DC
Web Site: http://www.pda.org
Year Founded: 1994
Sales Range: $10-24.9 Million
Emp.: 44
Drug Treatment Services
N.A.I.C.S.: 621420
David Hall *(VP-Sls)*
Craig Elliott *(CFO & Sr VP)*
Wanda O. Neal *(Sr VP-Programs,Meetings & Registration Svcs)*
Walter L. Morris III *(Sr Dir-Publ)*

PARENTHESIS, INC.
405 South Euclid Ave, Oak Park, IL 60302
Tel.: (708) 848-2227
Web Site: http://www.parenthesis-info.org
Emp.: 40
Parenting Education & Support
N.A.I.C.S.: 611710
Laura Zumdahl *(Pres)*
Subsidiaries:
New Moms, Inc. (1)
5317 W Chicago Ave, Chicago, IL 60651
Tel.: (773) 252-3253
Web Site: http://www.newmomsinc.org
Emp.: 106
Community Care Services
N.A.I.C.S.: 624190

Melanie Garrett *(Chief Program Officer)*
Janet Keller *(Dir-Fin)*
Emily White Hodge *(Dir-HR & Ops)*
Anne Schulz *(Dir-Performance Mgmt)*
Ellen Kogstad Thompson *(Founder & Dir-Spiritual Formation)*
Jenna Hania *(Dir-Dev & Comm)*
Luecendia Reed *(Asst Dir-Family Supports)*
Pamela Bozeman *(COO)*
Terry Williams *(CFO)*

PARENTS IN COMMUNITY ACTION, INC.
700 Humboldt Ave N, Minneapolis, MN 55411
Tel.: (612) 377-7422 MN
Web Site: http://www.picaheadstart.org
Year Founded: 1969
Sales Range: $25-49.9 Million
Emp.: 457
Child Day Care Services
N.A.I.C.S.: 624410
Su Melton *(Dir-Fin)*
Candee Melin *(Dir-Child Svcs)*
Brody Burton *(Dir-Facilities)*
Judith D. Baker *(Dir-Parent & Community Rels)*

PARETTI IMPORTS INC.
3000 Richland Ave, Metairie, LA 70002
Tel.: (504) 455-2101
Web Site: http://www.paretti.com
Rev.: $25,000,000
Emp.: 25
Automobiles, New & Used
N.A.I.C.S.: 441110
Karl Schroeder *(Gen Mgr)*
Craig Paretti Jr. *(Owner)*

PARETTI MAZDA
4000 Veterans Blvd, Metairie, LA 70002
Tel.: (504) 888-5420
Web Site: http://www.parettimazda.com
Year Founded: 1950
Sales Range: $10-24.9 Million
Emp.: 50
Car Whslr
N.A.I.C.S.: 441110
Craig Paretti *(VP)*

PARGREEN SALES ENGINEERING CORP.
1224 Capitol Dr, Addison, IL 60101
Tel.: (630) 628-1330
Web Site: http://www.pargreen.com
Rev.: $25,000,000
Emp.: 15
Industrial Machinery & Equipment
N.A.I.C.S.: 423830
Matt Green *(Pres)*
Brandon Cooper *(Mgr-Warehouse)*

PARHAM CONSTRUCTION CO.
1766 Scottsville Rd, Charlottesville, VA 22902
Tel.: (434) 295-9556
Web Site: http://www.parhamconstruction.com
Sales Range: $10-24.9 Million
Emp.: 110
Excavation Services
N.A.I.C.S.: 238910
Ronnie Parham *(Owner)*

PARIC CORP.
689 Craig Rd, Saint Louis, MO 63141
Tel.: (636) 561-9500
Web Site: http://www.paric.com
Year Founded: 1979
Sales Range: $125-149.9 Million
Emp.: 220
Nonresidential Construction Services
N.A.I.C.S.: 236220

Joe McKee *(Pres)*
Earl Strauther *(Dir-Diversity & Inclusion)*
Will Douglas *(CFO)*
Michael Rallo Jr. *(VP-Ops)*

PARIC HOLDINGS, INC.
77 Westport Plz Dr Ste 250, Saint Louis, MO 63146
Tel.: (636) 561-9500 MO
Web Site: https://www.paricholdings.com
Year Founded: 2013
Privater Equity Firm
N.A.I.C.S.: 523940
Kyle Lopez *(CEO)*
Subsidiaries:
Corporate Concepts, Inc. (1)
500 Waters Edge Ste 200, Lombard, IL 60148
Tel.: (630) 691-8800
Web Site: https://www.corpconc.com
Sales Range: $25-49.9 Million
Emp.: 50
Dealer of Furniture & Related Products
N.A.I.C.S.: 423210
Jennifer Cusack *(VP)*
Larry Zerante *(VP)*
Victoria Hansel *(Pres)*

PARIGI GROUP LTD
112 W 34th St 5th Fl, New York, NY 10120
Tel.: (212) 736-0688
Web Site: http://www.parigigroup.com
Year Founded: 1981
Sales Range: $10-24.9 Million
Emp.: 400
Children's Apparel Retail
N.A.I.C.S.: 424350
Marco Srour *(Pres)*
O'Connor Chryse *(VP-Sls & Mdsg)*
Ed Coll *(CEO)*
Jodi Somma *(VP-Sourcing)*
Dora Agajan *(Product Mgr)*
Eddie Miller *(Exec VP-Production & Sourcing)*
Nicole Gabel *(VP-Sourcing & Production)*
Sion Betesh *(Exec VP-Licensing & Mktg)*
Bill Finkelstein *(COO)*
Lena Vladsky *(Dir-HR)*
Morris Srour *(VP & Sec)*
Subsidiaries:
Hartstrings LLC (1)
270 E Conestoga Rd, Strafford, PA 19087
Tel.: (610) 687-6900
Children's Clothing
N.A.I.C.S.: 424350

PARIGI INTERNATIONAL INC.
242 W 38th St, New York, NY 10018-5804
Tel.: (212) 869-1688
Year Founded: 1987
Sales Range: $10-24.9 Million
Emp.: 14
Dresses
N.A.I.C.S.: 424350
Subsidiaries:
Le ARC Corporation (1)
525 7th Ave, New York, NY 10018
Tel.: (212) 869-1688
Sales Range: $10-24.9 Million
Emp.: 1
Real Estate Agents & Managers
N.A.I.C.S.: 531210

PARINGA RESOURCES LIMITED
28 W 44th St Ste 810, New York, NY 10036
Tel.: (812) 406-4400 NY

Web Site: http://www.paringaresources.com
Year Founded: 2012
Assets: $133,949,000
Liabilities: $66,644,000
Net Worth: $67,305,000
Earnings: ($13,097,000)
Emp.: 174
Fiscal Year-end: 06/30/19
Gold, Copper & Other Metal Mining
N.A.I.C.S.: 212220
Ian Middlemas *(Chm)*
David Gay *(Pres)*
Todd Hannigan *(Deputy Chm)*
Dominic Allen *(VP-Fin)*
Egan J. Antill *(CEO & Mng Dir)*
Bruce Czachor *(Gen Counsel & VP)*
Brent Hawley *(Gen Mgr)*
Gregory Swan *(Sec)*
Subsidiaries:
Hartshorne Mining Group, LLC (1)
373 Whobry Rd, Rumsey, KY 42371
Tel.: (812) 406-4400
Coal & Metal Mining Services
N.A.I.C.S.: 212220

PARIS ACCESSORIES, INC.
1385 Broadway 21st Fl, New York, NY 10018
Tel.: (212) 868-0500 NY
Year Founded: 1910
Sales Range: $200-249.9 Million
Emp.: 560
Women's & Men's Scarves, Belts, Hats & Gloves Mfr
N.A.I.C.S.: 315120
Peter Markson *(Chm)*
Marty Kelly *(Treas)*

PARIS BLUES, INC.
2397 Miguel Miranda Ave, Irwindale, CA 91010
Tel.: (310) 605-2000 CA
Web Site: http://www.parisblues.com
Year Founded: 1981
Sales Range: $25-49.9 Million
Emp.: 150
Mfr of Womens & Misses Outerwear
N.A.I.C.S.: 315250

PARIS BROTHERS INC.
8800 NE Underground Dr, Kansas City, MO 64161
Tel.: (816) 455-4188
Web Site: http://www.parisbrothers.com
Sales Range: $10-24.9 Million
Emp.: 33
Whslr of Groceries & General Line
N.A.I.C.S.: 424410
Salvatore J. Paris *(Co-Pres)*
Michael Adams *(Mgr-HR)*
Joseph Parise *(VP)*
Angela Sorisso *(Mgr-Warehouse Coffee Admin)*
Mickey Speir *(Dir-Perishable Sls & Mgr)*
Joe Paris Jr. *(Co-Pres)*

PARIS BUSINESS PRODUCTS, INC.
800 Highland Dr, Westampton, NJ 08060
Tel.: (609) 265-9200 PA
Web Site: http://www.pariscorp.com
Year Founded: 1964
Sales Range: $10-24.9 Million
Emp.: 89
Paper & Custom Business Forms Mfr
N.A.I.C.S.: 323111
Sharon Hennelly *(Dir-Sls & Mktg)*
Christine Bocox *(Mgr-Customer Svc)*
John Murray *(Controller)*

COMPANIES

PARIS CHEVROLET BUICK GMC
1915 N Main St, Paris, TX 75460
Tel.: (903) 784-7446
Web Site:
http://www.parischevrolet.com
Sales Range: $10-24.9 Million
Emp.: 100
Car Whslr
N.A.I.C.S.: 441110
J. B. Lowry (Co-Owner)
Jeff Jones (Co-Owner)

PARIS CLEANERS INC.
67 Hoover Ave, Du Bois, PA 15801
Tel.: (814) 375-9700
Web Site: http://www.parisco.com
Rev.: $21,000,000
Emp.: 600
Supplier of Uniforms
N.A.I.C.S.: 812331
David Stern (Pres & CEO)

PARIS FARMERS UNION
1435 Main St, Oxford, ME 04270
Tel.: (207) 743-8977
Web Site:
http://www.parisfarmersunion.net
Rev.: $15,357,684
Emp.: 120
Distr of Farm Supplies
N.A.I.C.S.: 424910
Alan Gates (Mgr-IT)
Dan Cox (Mgr)
Tammie Smith (Asst Mgr)

PARIS FOODS CORPORATION
1632 Carman St, Camden, NJ 08105-1705
Tel.: (856) 964-0915   NJ
Web Site: http://www.parisfoods.com
Year Founded: 1950
Sales Range: $50-74.9 Million
Emp.: 100
Distr & Packager of Frozen Foods
N.A.I.C.S.: 115114

Subsidiaries:

Paris Securities Corp   (1)
66 Hudson St Ste 201, Hoboken, NJ 07030   (100%)
Tel.: (201) 459-9997
Sales Range: $10-24.9 Million
Emp.: 6
Security & Commodity Trading
N.A.I.C.S.: 541511

PARIS GOURMET OF NEW YORK INC.
145 Grand St, Carlstadt, NJ 07072
Tel.: (201) 939-5656
Web Site:
http://www.parisgourmet.com
Sales Range: $10-24.9 Million
Emp.: 45
Gourmet Food Specialties
N.A.I.C.S.: 424410
Xavier Noel (Pres)
Dominique Noel (VP)

PARIS MAINTENANCE CO. INC.
350 5th Ave Ste 3304, New York, NY 10118-3304
Tel.: (212) 688-4622   NY
Web Site:
http://www.parismaintenance.com
Year Founded: 1958
Sales Range: $100-124.9 Million
Emp.: 1,400
Provider of Building Maintenance Services
N.A.I.C.S.: 561720
Ellen Weglarz (Mgr-Sls)

Subsidiaries:

Metro Computer Facilities Cleaning Corp.   (1)
350 5th Ave Ste 3304, New York, NY 10118
Tel.: (516) 352-3480
Emp.: 100
Janitorial Services
N.A.I.C.S.: 561720

Metro Fire Safety, Inc.   (1)
55 Post Ave Ste 201, Westbury, NY 11590
Tel.: (516) 352-4465
Web Site: http://www.metrofiresafetyny.com
Emp.: 4
Fire & Life Safety Consulting Services
N.A.I.C.S.: 541690
Justin Estosito (Mgr)

Metro Maintenance Service Systems, Inc.   (1)
545 Meacham Ave, New York, NY 11003
Tel.: (516) 352-4430
Emp.: 30
Janitorial Services
N.A.I.C.S.: 561720
Paul Kaplan (Gen Mgr)

Paris Maintenance Co. Inc.   (1)
588 Meacham Ave, Elmont, NY 11003-3866
Tel.: (516) 352-1118
Web Site: http://www.parismaintenance.com
Rev.: $1,300,000
Emp.: 20
Provider of Contracting Services
N.A.I.C.S.: 561720
Charles Loiodice (VP)
Thomas Parissidi (Owner)

PARISH OIL CO. INC.
1910 N Townsend Ave, Montrose, CO 81401
Tel.: (970) 249-4984
Web Site: http://www.parishoil.com
Sales Range: $10-24.9 Million
Emp.: 15
Petroleum Bulk Stations
N.A.I.C.S.: 424710
Greg A. Parish (Pres)
Steve Parish (VP)

PARIVEDA SOLUTIONS, INC.
2811 McKinney Ave Ste 220, Dallas, TX 75204
Tel.: (214) 777-4600
Web Site:
http://www.parivedasolutions.com
Year Founded: 2003
Sales Range: $10-24.9 Million
Emp.: 142
IT Consulting Services
N.A.I.C.S.: 541618
Bruce Ballengee (CEO)
James Kupferschmid (CFO)
Steve Cardwell (Mng VP-Atlanta)
Sean McCall (VP-Houston)
Dbrav Dunkley (VP-Central Reg)
Margaret Rogers (VP-Washington)
Mike Strange (VP-Los Angeles)
Hector Martinez (Chief Strategy & Process Officer)
Kerry Stover (COO & Exec VP)
Brian Orrell (CTO)
Steve Cantonis (VP-Atlanta)
Ed Fikse (Chm)

PARK & SHOP FOOD MART
326 S 5th St, Saint Pauls, NC 28384
Tel.: (910) 865-3344
Web Site:
http://www.piggywiggly.com
Sales Range: $1-9.9 Million
Emp.: 350
Supermarket
N.A.I.C.S.: 445110
Arlene Buie (Office Mgr)
David Drose (VP)
John Drose Jr. (Pres & CEO)

PARK AMERICA INC.
1 Bala Ave Ste 500, Bala Cynwyd, PA 19004
Tel.: (610) 617-2100   PA
Web Site: http://www.parkamerica.net
Year Founded: 1964
Sales Range: $25-49.9 Million
Emp.: 700
Automobile Parking
N.A.I.C.S.: 812930
Jay Weitzman (Pres)
Les Weitzman (VP)
Betsy Touhill (Controller)

PARK AVENUE ARMORY
643 Park Ave, New York, NY 10065
Tel.: (212) 616-3930   NY
Web Site:
http://www.armoryonpark.org
Year Founded: 1999
Sales Range: $10-24.9 Million
Emp.: 221
Art Program Administration Services
N.A.I.C.S.: 926110
Lissa Frenkel (Dir-Project)
Jay T. Dority (Dir-Facilities)
Cassidy Jones (Dir-Education)
Peter Gee (CFO & Chief Admin Officer)
Pierre Audi (Dir-Artistic)
Rebecca Robertson (Pres)

PARK AVENUE BBQ & GRILLE INC.
4425 Military Trl Ste 208, Jupiter, FL 33458
Tel.: (561) 694-2091
Web Site: http://www.pabbqgrille.com
Rev.: $10,699,000
Emp.: 20
Eating Place
N.A.I.C.S.: 722511
Dean Lavallee (Pres)
Chris Walter (Dir-Ops)

PARK AVENUE EQUITY PARTNERS, L.P.
1 E 52nd St 3rd Fl, New York, NY 10022
Tel.: (212) 758-4446
Web Site: http://www.pkave.com
Rev.: $110,000,000
Emp.: 13
Privater Equity Firm
N.A.I.C.S.: 523999
Russell F. Peppet (Partner)
William E. Mayer (Founder & Partner)

PARK AVENUE MOTORS CORP
250 W Passaic St, Maywood, NJ 07607
Tel.: (201) 843-7900
Web Site:
http://www.parkavebmw.com
Sales Range: $10-24.9 Million
Emp.: 52
New & Used Automobiles
N.A.I.C.S.: 441110
Roy Sommerhalter Sr. (Owner)

PARK B SMITH, LTD.
230 5th Ave, New York, NY 10001
Tel.: (212) 889-1818
Web Site: http://www.pbsltd.com
Rev.: $21,200,000
Emp.: 50
Bedspreads
N.A.I.C.S.: 423220
Park B. Smith (CEO)
James J. Davala (VP)
Prerita Manandhar (Coord-Web)
Denise Cox (Dir-Mdse)
Elaine Adams (Coord-Traffic)
Peter Reeves (Asst Mgr-Warehouse)

PARK CHEESE COMPANY INC.
168 E Larsen Dr, Fond Du Lac, WI 54937
Tel.: (920) 923-8484
Web Site:
http://www.parkcheese.com
Sales Range: $75-99.9 Million
Emp.: 25
Cheese; Natural & Processed
N.A.I.C.S.: 311513
Linda Cizek (Office Mgr)
Eric Liebetrau (CEO)

PARK CHRYSLER JEEP
1408 Hwy 13 W, Burnsville, MN 55337-2293
Tel.: (952) 890-5337
Web Site:
http://www.parkchryslerjeep.com
Sales Range: $10-24.9 Million
Emp.: 100
New Car Whslr
N.A.I.C.S.: 441110
David Dworsky (Owner)

PARK CITIES ASSET MANAGEMENT LLC
8214 Westchester Dr Ste 910, Dallas, TX 75225
Tel.: (469) 249-1000
Web Site:
https://www.parkcitiesmgmt.com
Year Founded: 2017
Financial Services
N.A.I.C.S.: 522320
Alex Dunev (Founder & Mng Partner)

Subsidiaries:

Elevate Credit, Inc.   (1)
4150 International Plz Ste 300, Fort Worth, TX 76109
Tel.: (817) 928-1500
Web Site: https://www.elevate.com
Rev.: $416,637,000
Assets: $710,682,000
Liabilities: $601,711,000
Net Worth: $108,971,000
Earnings: ($33,598,000)
Emp.: 436
Fiscal Year-end: 12/31/2021
Online Financial Credit Solution Provider
N.A.I.C.S.: 522390
Jason Harvison (CEO)
Christopher T. Lutes (Chief Strategy Officer)
Kathleen Vanderkolk (Chief Risk Officer)
Steven A. Trussell (CFO)
Eddie Combs (CMO)
Larry Browder (CIO)
Eileen Considine (VP-Digital Mktg)
Kerry Miles (Chief Product Officer)
April Sealy (Exec VP-Operations & Administration)
David Curry Peterson (Chief Credit Officer)

Subsidiary (Domestic):

CC Financial, LLC   (2)
2955 University Dr, Auburn Hills, MI 48326
Tel.: (248) 340-9310
Web Site: http://www.ccfinancial.com
Online Investment Services
N.A.I.C.S.: 523999
Leo Moses (Chm)
Timothy McGlinchey (Vice Chm)
Tim Green (Sec)
Christopher Baker (Treas)

Subsidiary (Non-US):

Elevate Credit International Limited   (2)
Lion Court 25 Procter Street Holborn, London, WC1V 6NY, United Kingdom
Tel.: (44) 2038298403
Web Site: http://www.elevatecredit.co.uk
Financial Investment Services
N.A.I.C.S.: 522291
Christopher T. Lutes (CFO)

Subsidiary (Domestic):

RISE Credit Service of Texas, LLC   (2)

PARK CITIES ASSET MANAGEMENT LLC

U.S. PRIVATE

Park Cities Asset Management LLC—(Continued)
PO Box 101808, Fort Worth, TX 76185
Tel.: (866) 580-1226
Web Site: http://www.risecredit.com
Financial Investment Services
N.A.I.C.S.: 522291

PARK CITIES QUAIL
25 Highland Park Village Ste 100-417, Dallas, TX 75205-2789
Tel.: (214) 632-7460 TX
Web Site:
  http://www.parkcitiesquail.org
Year Founded: 2010
Sales Range: $1-9.9 Million
Environment & Wildlife Preservation Services
N.A.I.C.S.: 813312
Matt Perry-Miller *(Sec)*
Raymond P. Morrow *(Chm-Dinner & Auction)*

PARK CITY FORD
60 North Ave, Bridgeport, CT 06606
Tel.: (203) 366-3425
Web Site:
  http://www.parkcityfordinc.com
Year Founded: 1988
Sales Range: $10-24.9 Million
Emp.: 40
New Car Dealers
N.A.I.C.S.: 441110
David Flint *(Pres)*
Jason W. Flint *(VP)*
Bob Loh *(Mgr-Sls)*
Tyler Heft *(Mgr-Sls)*
Paula Floberg *(Controller)*

PARK CONSTRUCTION COMPANY
1481 81st Ave NE, Minneapolis, MN 55432
Tel.: (763) 786-9800 MN
Web Site:
  http://www.parkconstructionco.com
Year Founded: 1916
Sales Range: $25-49.9 Million
Emp.: 350
Provider of Highway, Bridge & Tunnel Construction Services
N.A.I.C.S.: 237310
John Hedquist *(CFO)*
Bruce Carlson *(VP)*
Jeff Carlson *(Pres)*

PARK CONSTRUCTION CORP.
138 NH Rte 119 E, Fitzwilliam, NH 03447
Tel.: (603) 585-6577
Web Site:
  http://www.parkconstructionco.com
Rev.: $21,000,000
Emp.: 20
Earthmoving & General Contractor
N.A.I.C.S.: 238910
Robert Seppala *(VP)*

PARK CORP.
Intl Exposition Ctr 6200 Riverside Dr, Cleveland, OH 44135
Tel.: (216) 267-4870 NV
Web Site: http://www.parkcorp.com
Sales Range: $10-24.9 Million
Emp.: 20
Industrial Machinery & Equipment
N.A.I.C.S.: 333519
Raymond Park *(Chm & Pres)*
Joseph Adams *(CFO)*
Carin Traffis *(Mgr-Risk)*
Subsidiaries:

WHEMCO, Inc.   (1)
5 Hot Metal St Ste 300, Pittsburgh, PA 15203-2351   **(100%)**
Tel.: (412) 390-2700
Web Site: http://www.whemco.com
Sales Range: $10-24.9 Million
Mfr of Machine Tools & Metal Cutting Tools
N.A.I.C.S.: 333517
Tim Spang *(Dir-HR)*
Al Beeken *(VP-Sls & Mktg)*
Dave Harned *(Gen Mgr)*
Mark Stahl *(Mgr)*

Division (Domestic):

Duraloy Technology   (2)
120 Bridge St, Scottdale, PA 15683   **(100%)**
Tel.: (724) 887-5100
Web Site: http://www.duraloy.com
Specialty Foundry; Heat Resistant & Corrosion Resistant Castings & Fabrications
N.A.I.C.S.: 331513
Paul Rokosz *(Mgr-Major Acct Dev)*

Lehigh Heavy Forge Corp   (2)
275 Emery St, Bethlehem, PA 18015   **(100%)**
Tel.: (610) 317-3113
Web Site: http://www.lhforge.com
Sales Range: $10-24.9 Million
Steel Forging Operations
N.A.I.C.S.: 331110
Allan Robertson *(VP-Sls & Mktg)*
James Romeo *(Pres)*

United Rolls Inc.   (2)
1400 Grace Ave NE, Canton, OH 44705-2099
Tel.: (330) 456-2761
Web Site: http://www.whemco.com
Rolling Mill Machinery Mfr
N.A.I.C.S.: 333519
John Hartwig *(Controller)*

PARK DISTRIBUTORS, INC.
347 RailRd Ave, Bridgeport, CT 06604-5424
Tel.: (203) 366-7200 CT
Web Site:
  http://www.parkdistributors.com
Year Founded: 1966
Sales Range: $1-9.9 Million
Emp.: 12
Electronics Distr
N.A.I.C.S.: 423690
Alan Goodman *(Founder & Pres)*
Subsidiaries:

Universal Relay   (1)
347 Railroad Ave, Bridgeport, CT 06604-5424
Tel.: (203) 579-2140
Web Site: http://www.parkdistributors.com
Rev.: $1,000,000
Emp.: 10
Whslr of Electronic Relays
N.A.I.C.S.: 423690
Alan Goodman *(Owner)*

PARK FINANCIAL GROUP, INC.
1108 Nicollet Mall, Minneapolis, MN 55403
Tel.: (218) 722-3500
Web Site:
  http://www.parkstatebank.com
Year Founded: 2015
Bank Holding Company
N.A.I.C.S.: 551111
David Saber *(CEO)*
Subsidiaries:

Park State Bank, Inc.   (1)
1106 88th Ave W, Duluth, MN 55808
Tel.: (218) 626-2755
Web Site: http://www.parkstatebank.com
State Commercial Bank
Accounting/Auditing/Bookkeeping
N.A.I.C.S.: 522110

PARK HAVEN APARTMENTS
3559 4th Ave, San Diego, CA 92103-4912
Tel.: (619) 238-1957
Rev.: $12,000,000
Emp.: 16
Apartment Building Operator

N.A.I.C.S.: 531110
Leticia Vega *(Asst Mgr)*

PARK HONDA
951 Interstate Pkwy, Akron, OH 44312
Tel.: (330) 644-3322
Web Site: http://www.parkhonda.com
Sales Range: $10-24.9 Million
Emp.: 75
Car Whslr
N.A.I.C.S.: 441110
Tom Flory *(VP & Mgr)*
Sherry Unger *(Office Mgr)*

PARK LANE CONSTRUCTION INC.
100 Village St, Birmingham, AL 35242
Tel.: (205) 995-5658
Web Site: http://www.parklane-construction.com
Rev.: $30,400,000
Emp.: 5
Commercial & Institutional Building Construction
N.A.I.C.S.: 236220
Preston S. Parker *(VP)*
Jay Davis *(Sr Project Mgr)*
Doug Stell *(Project Mgr)*
Chester L. Parker Jr. *(Pres)*

PARK LANE FOODS LLC
2910 Broadway, Astoria, NY 11106-2955
Tel.: (718) 932-7277
Year Founded: 1967
Sales Range: $10-24.9 Million
Emp.: 50
Provider of Grocery Services
N.A.I.C.S.: 445110
Philip Drugin *(CFO)*
Carol Barbara *(Office Mgr)*

PARK OF HOLDING INC.
725 S 72nd St, Omaha, NE 68114
Tel.: (402) 393-8888
Web Site: http://www.sbi-omaha.com
Sales Range: $10-24.9 Million
Emp.: 2
Office Furniture
N.A.I.C.S.: 722513

PARK ONE INCORPORATED
365 Canal St, New Orleans, LA 70130
Tel.: (504) 525-7275
Web Site: http://www.park1.com
Rev.: $10,500,000
Emp.: 25
Parking Lots
N.A.I.C.S.: 812930
Wayne C. Ducote *(Chm)*
Benton Launerts *(Dir-Mktg)*
Richard Moldonado *(Mgr-Opers)*

PARK PLACE CORPORATION
6801 Augusta Rd, Greenville, SC 29605
Tel.: (864) 422-8118
Web Site:
  http://www.parkplacecorp.com
Sales Range: $25-49.9 Million
Emp.: 120
Mattress & Upholstery Mfr & Services
N.A.I.C.S.: 337910
Chuck Stillwell *(Mgr-Network)*

PARK PLACE HOTEL
300 E State St, Traverse City, MI 49684
Tel.: (231) 946-1000
Web Site: http://www.park-place-hotel.com
Year Founded: 1930
Sales Range: $10-24.9 Million

Emp.: 150
Hotel Owner & Operator
N.A.I.C.S.: 721110
Amy Parker *(Gen Mgr)*
Jesse Rollo *(Mgr-Catering & Convention Svcs)*
Lisa Monache *(Mgr-Sls)*
Thomas Maloney *(Mgr-Ops & Front Desk)*

PARK PLACE MOTORCARS, LTD.
6113 Lemmon Ave, Dallas, TX 75209-3135
Tel.: (214) 526-8701 TX
Web Site: http://www.parkplace.com
Year Founded: 1987
Sales Range: $125-149.9 Million
Emp.: 300
New & Used Automobiles Dealer
N.A.I.C.S.: 441110
Cam Mayfield *(Dir-Svc)*
Robert Morris *(Gen Mgr)*
Mike Wasserman *(Dir-Sls)*
Gene Ellison *(Dir-Parts)*
Ken Schnitzer Jr. *(Pres & CEO)*

PARK PLACE VOLVO
3515 Inwood Rd, Dallas, TX 75209-5825
Tel.: (214) 956-5500
Web Site:
  http://dallasvolvo.parkplace.com
Year Founded: 1985
Sales Range: $10-24.9 Million
Emp.: 55
New Car Whslr
N.A.I.C.S.: 441110
Rob Schweizer *(Gen Mgr)*
Donny Lambrecht *(Dir-New Vehicle)*
Stephen Rand *(Dir-Svc Ops)*
Heath Strayhan *(Gen Mgr)*
Paul Lam *(Mgr-E-Commerce & Sls)*
Liz Shafton *(Dir-Mktg)*

PARK RIDGE HEALTH
100 Hospital Dr, Hendersonville, NC 28792
Tel.: (828) 684-8501 NC
Web Site:
  http://www.parkridgehealth.org
Year Founded: 1920
Sales Range: $125-149.9 Million
Emp.: 1,477
Health Care Srvices
N.A.I.C.S.: 622110
Carlo Mainardi *(Chief Medical Officer)*
Craig Richard Lindsey *(Chief Nursing Officer)*
Wendi Barber *(CFO)*
Scott N. Miller *(COO)*
Jimm Bunch *(Pres & CEO)*

PARK RUG COMPANY INC.
9590 Lynn Buff Ct Ste 1, Laurel, MD 20723
Tel.: (301) 776-4000
Web Site:
  http://www.parkrugcompany.com
Sales Range: $1-9.9 Million
Emp.: 15
Carpet & Flooring Mfr & Installer
N.A.I.C.S.: 449121
Nazha Ganim *(Pres)*
Matt Denim *(VP-Ops)*

PARK SOUND ACQUISITION CORPORATION
9454 Wilshire Blvd Ste 612, Los Angeles, CA 90212
Tel.: (310) 888-1870 DE
Year Founded: 2016
Investment Services
N.A.I.C.S.: 523999
James Cassidy *(Pres & Sec)*
James McKillop *(VP)*

PARK SQUARE ENTERPRISES INC.
5200 Vineland Rd Ste 200, Orlando, FL 32811-7617
Tel.: (407) 529-3000 FL
Web Site: http://www.parksquarehomes.com
Year Founded: 1984
Sales Range: $10-24.9 Million
Emp.: 40
Single-Family Housing Construction
N.A.I.C.S.: 236115
Braham Rattan Aggarwal *(Chm)*
Suresh Gupta *(CEO)*
Vishaal Gupta *(Pres)*

PARK WEST HEALTH SYSTEM
3319 W Belvedere Ave, Baltimore, MD 21215
Tel.: (410) 542-7800 MD
Web Site: http://www.parkwestmed.org
Year Founded: 1972
Sales Range: $10-24.9 Million
Emp.: 149
Health Care Srvices
N.A.I.C.S.: 622110
Stanley Arnold *(Treas)*
Louis Parker *(CIO)*
Elizabeth Lee *(CFO)*
Allen Bennett *(Pres & CEO)*
Deborah Woolford *(Sec)*

PARKDALE MILLS INC.
531 Cottonblossom Cir, Gastonia, NC 28054-5245
Tel.: (704) 874-5000 NC
Web Site: http://www.parkdalemills.com
Year Founded: 1916
Sales Range: $300-349.9 Million
Emp.: 3,650
Cotton & Cotton Blend Yarns Mfr
N.A.I.C.S.: 313110
Anderson D. Warlick *(Chm & CEO)*
Charles Heilig *(Pres)*

PARKDALE, INC.
531 Cotton Blossom Cir, Gastonia, NC 28054-5245
Tel.: (704) 874-5000
Cotton Mfr
N.A.I.C.S.: 111920
Anderson D. Warlick *(Chm & CEO)*

Subsidiaries:

Parkdale America, LLC (1)
531 Cotton Blossom Cir, Gastonia, NC 28054
Tel.: (704) 864-8761
Web Site: http://www.parkdalemills.com
Yarn Spinning Mills
N.A.I.C.S.: 313110
Charles Heilig *(Pres)*
Dan Morrison *(VP-Sls)*

PARKE-BELL LTD., INC.
709 W 12th St, Huntingburg, IN 47542-9589
Tel.: (812) 683-3707
Web Site: http://www.touchofclass.com
Year Founded: 1978
Sales Range: $25-49.9 Million
Emp.: 250
Catalog & Mail-Order Houses
N.A.I.C.S.: 449110
Fred Bell *(Pres)*

PARKER & COMPANY INC.
4694 Coffeeport Rd, Brownsville, TX 78522
Tel.: (956) 831-2000
Web Site: http://www.parkerandcompany.com
Sales Range: $10-24.9 Million
Emp.: 55

Customs Broker Services
N.A.I.C.S.: 488510
Abel Medina *(Mgr-Customs)*
David O'Leary *(CFO & VP)*
Frank Parker Jr. *(Owner & Pres)*

PARKER & PARTNERS MARKETING RESOURCES, LLC
134 New Jersey Ave, Absecon, NJ 08201
Tel.: (609) 407-4850
Web Site: http://www.parkerandpartners.com
Year Founded: 1987
Sales Range: Less than $1 Million
Emp.: 10
Full Service
N.A.I.C.S.: 541810
Christine Parker *(Pres)*
Bill Parker *(Founder & Dir-Creative)*
Tina Rotondo *(Mgr-Fin)*
Jenn Shaffor *(Acct Exec)*
Richard Rinck *(VP-Mktg)*
Vincent Sheehy *(Dir-Govt Rels)*

PARKER AUTO GROUP
5105 Warden Rd, North Little Rock, AR 72116
Tel.: (501) 771-1700
Sales Range: $10-24.9 Million
Emp.: 30
Car Whslr
N.A.I.C.S.: 441110
Robert Parker *(Gen Mgr)*
Rick Parker *(Pres)*
Randy Parsley *(Owner)*

PARKER CASSIDY SUPPLY CO.
1940 Lincolnway St, Clinton, IA 52732
Tel.: (563) 242-0683
Year Founded: 1964
Sales Range: $10-24.9 Million
Emp.: 48
Operators of Country General Stores
N.A.I.C.S.: 455219
Robert P. Cassidy *(Pres)*

PARKER CHEVROLET OLDS PONTIAC GEO INC.
PO Box 308, Champlain, NY 12919
Tel.: (518) 292-8272
Sales Range: $25-49.9 Million
Emp.: 28
Car Whslr
N.A.I.C.S.: 441110
Rolla A. Parker *(Pres & Treas)*

PARKER FURNITURE INCORPORATED
10375 S W Beaverton Hillsdale Hwy, Beaverton, OR 97005
Tel.: (503) 644-0155
Web Site: http://www.parker-furniture.com
Rev.: $13,170,113
Emp.: 30
Furniture Retailer
N.A.I.C.S.: 449110
Jeff Parker *(Pres)*

PARKER GAS COMPANY INC.
214 McLamb Rd, Newton Grove, NC 28366
Tel.: (910) 594-0932
Web Site: http://www.parkergas.com
Sales Range: $10-24.9 Million
Emp.: 10
Propane Gas, Bottled
N.A.I.C.S.: 457210
David Parker *(VP)*

PARKER HOLDING COMPANY, INC.
1428 W Danville St, South Hill, VA 23970-3904
Tel.: (434) 447-3146 VA
Year Founded: 1979
Sales Range: $50-74.9 Million
Emp.: 150
Holding Company; Fuel Dealer & Petroleum Terminals Operator
N.A.I.C.S.: 551112
Charles F. Parker *(Pres & CEO)*

Subsidiaries:

Parker Oil Company, Inc. (1)
1428 W Danville St, South Hill, VA 23970-3904
Tel.: (434) 447-3146
Web Site: http://www.parkeroilcompany.com
Fuel Dealers
N.A.I.C.S.: 457210
Charles F. Parker *(Pres & CEO)*

Subsidiary (Domestic):

Bobby Taylor Oil Company, Inc. (2)
4501 Ramsey St, Fayetteville, NC 28311
Tel.: (910) 488-3760
Web Site: https://www.bobbytayloroilnc.com
Sales Range: $10-24.9 Million
Emp.: 40
Petroleum Bulk Stations
N.A.I.C.S.: 424710
Johnny Taylor Jr. *(Pres)*

First Energy Corporation (2)
200 Maury St, Richmond, VA 23224 (100%)
Tel.: (804) 233-8370
Sales Range: $10-24.9 Million
Emp.: 3
Petroleum Terminal Operator
N.A.I.C.S.: 424710
Charles F. Parker *(CEO)*

Division (Domestic):

Parker Oil Company, Inc. - Environmental Management Services Division (2)
1440 W Danville St, South Hill, VA 23970
Tel.: (434) 447-3146
Storage Tank Closure Contracting Services
N.A.I.C.S.: 561990

PARKER HOUSE SAUSAGE COMPANY
4605 S State St, Chicago, IL 60609
Tel.: (773) 538-1112
Web Site: http://www.parkerhousesausage.com
Rev.: $17,100,000
Emp.: 35
Sausages, From Purchased Meat
N.A.I.C.S.: 311612
Regina Parker *(Pres)*
Michael Parker *(CEO)*

PARKER INTERIOR PLANTSCAPE, INC.
1325 Terrill Rd, Scotch Plains, NJ 07076
Tel.: (908) 322-5552
Web Site: http://www.parkerplants.com
Year Founded: 1948
Rev.: $9,800,000
Emp.: 180
Landscape Architectural Services
N.A.I.C.S.: 541320
Richard Parker *(Pres)*

PARKER JEWISH INSTITUTE FOR HEALTH CARE & REHABILITATION
271-11 76th Ave, New Hyde Park, NY 11040-1433
Tel.: (718) 289-2100 NY
Web Site: http://www.parkerinstitute.net
Year Founded: 1968
Sales Range: $100-124.9 Million
Emp.: 1,281

Health Care Srvices
N.A.I.C.S.: 622110
Michael N. Rosenblut *(Pres & CEO)*
Robert M. Werner *(CFO & VP-Fin)*

PARKER LUMBER
2192 Eastex Freeway, Beaumont, TX 77703
Tel.: (409) 898-7000
Web Site: http://www.parkerlumber.net
Year Founded: 1930
Sales Range: $25-49.9 Million
Emp.: 275
Lumber & Other Building Materials Whslr
N.A.I.C.S.: 423310
Scott Parker *(Pres & CEO)*
Brady Laqua *(Mgr)*
Chris Rivers *(Pres)*

PARKER TOWING COMPANY, INC.
1001 3rd St, Northport, AL 35476
Tel.: (205) 391-1131 AL
Web Site: http://www.parkertowing.com
Year Founded: 1941
Sales Range: $25-49.9 Million
Emp.: 230
Provider of Towing & Tugboat Services
N.A.I.C.S.: 488999
Tim Parker *(Chm)*
Charles A. Haun *(Vice Chm & CEO)*
Charles F. Rabbit *(VP-Fin)*
George H. Anderson *(VP-Sls)*
Chris Bushhorn *(VP-Admin Svcs)*
Randy Baygents *(Engr-Port)*
Jared Phillips *(Mgr-Ops)*
Allison Phillips *(Dir-Comm)*

Subsidiaries:

Mobile Shipbuilding & Repair Inc. (1)
1920 Cut Off Rd, Mobile, AL 36610
Tel.: (251) 456-1880
Rev.: $1,800,000
Emp.: 17
Provider of Ship Building & Repairing Services
N.A.I.C.S.: 336611

Pickens County Ports Inc. (1)
2665 Hwy 86 W, Carrollton, AL 35447
Tel.: (205) 373-8852
Rev.: $840,000
Emp.: 7
Provider of Farm Product Warehousing & Storage
N.A.I.C.S.: 493130

PARKER UNIFORMS INC.
2315 Karbach St, Houston, TX 77092
Tel.: (713) 957-1511
Web Site: http://www.parkersu.com
Sales Range: $10-24.9 Million
Emp.: 40
Mfr of Uniforms
N.A.I.C.S.: 315210
Troy Pike *(CEO)*
Allison Balthrope *(Dir-Sls & Mktg)*
Chyrene Mason *(Mgr-Inventory Control)*

PARKER'S CORPORATION
222 Drayton St, Savannah, GA 31401
Tel.: (912) 231-1001
Web Site: http://www.parkersav.com
Year Founded: 1976
Sales Range: $250-299.9 Million
Emp.: 500
Gasoline Stations & Convenience Stores & Gourmet Food Markets
N.A.I.C.S.: 457110
Greg Parker *(Chm & CEO)*
Stephen Hines *(CTO)*
Jeff Bush *(Pres)*

PARKER'S CORPORATION

U.S. PRIVATE

Parker's Corporation—(Continued)
Michelle Weckstein (Dir-HR)
Brandon Hofmann (VP-Mktg)
Teresa Hannigan (CIO)
Bill Bishop (VP-Real Estate & Dev)
Brian J. Prevatt (CFO)
Michael O'Donnell (Project Mgr-Construction)
David Askew (Project Mgr-Construction)
Daniel Ben-Yisrael (Mgr-Real Estate Dev)

PARKER-MCCRORY MANUFACTURING CO.
2000 Forest Ave, Kansas City, MO 64108
Tel.: (816) 221-2000
Web Site: http://www.parmak.com
Sales Range: $10-24.9 Million
Emp.: 90
Electric Fence Chargers
N.A.I.C.S.: 335999
Kenneth D. Turner (Pres)

PARKERGALE, LLC
159 N Sangamon 4th Fl, Chicago, IL 60606
Tel.: (312) 698-6300   DE
Web Site: http://www.parkergale.com
Privater Equity Firm
N.A.I.C.S.: 523940
Devin Mathews (Partner)
Jim Milbery (Partner)
Ryan Milligan (Partner)
Kristina Heinze (Partner)
Corey Dossett (CFO)
Kevin Fitzgerald (Principal)
Jimmy Holloran (Principal)
Kara Master (Principal)

Subsidiaries:

Aircraft Technical Publishers   (1)
101 S Hill Dr, Brisbane, CA 94005
Tel.: (415) 330-9500
Web Site: http://www.atp.com
Aircraft Technical Software Publisher
N.A.I.C.S.: 513210
Ken Aubrey (Chief Revenue Officer)
Rick Noble (CEO)

EditShare, LLC   (1)
3 Brook St, Watertown, MA 02472
Tel.: (617) 782-0479
Web Site: http://www.editshare.com
Software Publisher
N.A.I.C.S.: 513210
Andy Liebman (Co-Founder & Chief Strategy Officer)
Conrad Clemson (CEO)
Tara Montford (Co-Founder & Exec VP-Bus Dev)
Stuart McGeechan (VP-Customer Success)
Alan Dishington (VP-Sls-Asia Pacific)
Tze Ming Ng (Sls Mgr-Asia Pacific)
William Tay (Engr-Pre-Sls-Asia Pacific)
Rob Adams (VP-Sls-Worldwide)
Said Bacho (VP-Sls-Europe, Middle East & Africa)

One Plus Corp.   (1)
3182 MacArthur Blvd, Northbrook, IL 60062
Tel.: (847) 498-0955
Web Site: http://www.onepluscorp.com
Waste Compactor Monitoring & Control Systems Developer, Mfr & Whslr
N.A.I.C.S.: 334513
Jay Simon (Pres)
Klaus Voss (CEO)
Jay Alter (CFO)

PARKHILL, SMITH & COOPER, INC.
4222 85th St, Lubbock, TX 79423-1930
Tel.: (806) 473-2200
Web Site: http://www.team-psc.com
Year Founded: 1945
Emp.: 400
Architectural Services

N.A.I.C.S.: 541310
Kristin Thomas (Coord-Mktg)
Jay Edwards (Pres & CEO)

Subsidiaries:

Lemke Land Surveying, LLC   (1)
3226 Bart Conner Dr, Norman, OK 73072
Tel.: (803) 730-3044
Web Site: http://www.lemke-ls.com
Surveying & Mapping Services
N.A.I.C.S.: 541370
Steve Lemke (Principal)

PARKHOUSE TIRE SERVICE INC.
5960 Shull St, Bell Gardens, CA 90201-6235
Tel.: (562) 928-0421   CA
Web Site: http://www.parkhousetire.com
Year Founded: 1971
Rev.: $85,000,000
Emp.: 350
Distr of Tires & Tubes
N.A.I.C.S.: 441340
James Parkhouse (Pres)
Brian Parkhouse (VP-Mktg)
Frank Ciccone (Controller)

PARKING CONCEPTS INC.
12 Mauchly Bldg I, Irvine, CA 92618
Tel.: (949) 753-7525
Web Site: http://www.parkingconcepts.com
Sales Range: $75-99.9 Million
Emp.: 1,500
Real Estate Managers
N.A.I.C.S.: 531210
Gill Barnett (Pres)
Robert Hindle (VP)

PARKING MANAGEMENT, INC.
1725 Desales St NW Ste 300, Washington, DC 20036-4406
Tel.: (202) 785-9191   DE
Web Site: http://www.pmi-parking.com
Year Founded: 1992
Sales Range: $75-99.9 Million
Emp.: 500
Automobile Parking Services
N.A.I.C.S.: 812930
Shahid Bashir (Mgr-Daytime-Washington DC)
Leul Bogale (Mgr-Suburban Maryland District)

PARKINSON TECHNOLOGIES, INC.
100 Goldstein Dr, Woonsocket, RI 02895
Tel.: (401) 762-2100
Web Site: http://www.parkinsontechnologies.com
Year Founded: 1871
Emp.: 100
Plastics, Nonwovens, Paper & Specialty MaterialsWinding & Web Processing Equipment Mfr & Development
N.A.I.C.S.: 333310
Peter Termyn (Pres & CEO)
Joe Grant (Project Mgr)
Michael Reilly (Mgr-Field Svc)
Cindy Holmes (Coord-Sls)

PARKINSON'S FOUNDATION, INC.
1359 Broadway Ste 1509, New York, NY 10018
Tel.: (212) 923-4700   NY
Web Site: http://www.parkinson.org
Year Founded: 1957
Sales Range: $1-9.9 Million
Emp.: 20

Disease Research Grantmaking Foundation
N.A.I.C.S.: 813211
Andrew B. Albert (Vice Chm)
James Beck (Chief Scientific Officer & Sr VP)
Stephen Ackerman (Treas)
Constance Woodruff Atwell (Sec)
Michael S. Okun (Dir-Medical-Natl)
John L. Lehr (Pres & CEO)
Curt De Greff (CFO & Sr VP)
Christiana Evers (Chief Community Engagement Officer & VP)
Sean Kramer (Chief Dev Officer & VP)
Leilani Pearl (Chief Comm Officer & VP)
Veronica Todaro (COO & Exec VP)
J. Gordon Beckham Jr. (Chm)

PARKLEY HOLDING INC.
700 S Brand Blvd, Glendale, CA 91204
Tel.: (818) 246-1800
Web Site: http://www.calstarmercedes.com
Year Founded: 1987
Rev.: $28,200,000
Emp.: 100
Dealer of New & Used Automobile
N.A.I.C.S.: 441110
Susan Wong (Pres)

Subsidiaries:

Calstar Motors Inc   (1)
700 S Brand Blvd, Glendale, CA 91204
Tel.: (818) 246-1800
Web Site: http://www.calstarmercedes.com
Automobiles, New & Used
N.A.I.C.S.: 441110
Susan Wong (Owner)

PARKS AUTO PARTS INC.
5429 Rivers Ave, North Charleston, SC 29406
Tel.: (843) 747-6656
Web Site: http://www.parksautoparts.com
Sales Range: $10-24.9 Million
Emp.: 175
Automotive Parts
N.A.I.C.S.: 441330
Kevin Gissell (Mgr-Sls & Mktg)

PARKS AUTOMOTIVE INC.
2411 N Main St, High Point, NC 27262
Tel.: (336) 886-7889
Web Site: http://www.parkshighpoint.com
Sales Range: $100-124.9 Million
Emp.: 30
New & Used Car Dealers
N.A.I.C.S.: 441110
Jim Hodges (Mgr)

PARKSIDE MANAGEMENT SERVICES, LLC
5215 Old Orchard Rd Ste 860, Skokie, IL 60077
Tel.: (847) 779-8500
Web Site: http://www.parksidesenior.com
Sales Range: $1-9.9 Million
Emp.: 75
Residential & Assisted Living Community Subdivider & Developer
N.A.I.C.S.: 237210
Michael S. McCarthy (Chm & CEO)

PARKVIEW CAPITAL CREDIT, INC.
2 Post Oak Ctr 1980 Post Oak Blvd 15th Fl, Houston, TX 77056
Tel.: (713) 622-5000   MD

Web Site: http://www.parkviewcapitalcredit.com
Year Founded: 2014
Rev.: $4,299,000
Assets: $67,680,000
Liabilities: $28,190,000
Net Worth: $39,490,000
Earnings: $1,849,000
Fiscal Year-end: 12/31/18
Investment Services
N.A.I.C.S.: 523999

Subsidiaries:

Med-fare Drug & Pharmaceutical Compounding, LLC   (1)
300 W Pine St, Blacksburg, SC 29702
Tel.: (864) 839-6500
Web Site: http://www.medifaredrug.com
Pharmaceuticals Product Mfr
N.A.I.C.S.: 325412

PARKVIEW COMMUNTY HOSPITAL MEDICAL CENTER
3865 Jackson St, Riverside, CA 92503
Tel.: (951) 688-2211   CA
Web Site: http://www.pchmc.org
Year Founded: 1956
Sales Range: $100-124.9 Million
Emp.: 1,454
Health Care Srvices
N.A.I.C.S.: 622110
Patricia Lepe (CFO)
Marlene Burnett (VP-Bus Dev)
Thomas Santos (Chief Nursing Officer)
Douglas Krahn (Dir-Medical)

PARKWAY BANCORP, INC.
4800 N Harlem Ave, Harwood Heights, IL 60706
Tel.: (708) 867-6600   IL
Web Site: http://www.parkwaybank.com
Year Founded: 1984
Sales Range: $50-74.9 Million
Emp.: 242
Bank Holding Company
N.A.I.C.S.: 551111
Rocco Suspenzi (Chm)
Robert Lussier (Pres)

Subsidiaries:

Parkway Bank & Trust Company   (1)
4800 N Harlem Ave, Harwood Heights, IL 60706-3506
Tel.: (708) 867-6600
Web Site: http://www.parkwaybank.com
Sales Range: $50-74.9 Million
Commericial Banking
N.A.I.C.S.: 522110
Rocco Saspenzi (Chm)

Division (Domestic):

Parkway Bank & Trust Company - Arizona Division   (2)
11011 N Tatum Blvd, Phoenix, AZ 85028
Tel.: (602) 765-8500
Web Site: http://www.parkwaybank.com
Regional Corporate Headquarters; Commercial Banking
N.A.I.C.S.: 551114
Frank McGava (Reg Mgr)

PARKWAY BUICK GMC
3314 Texoma Pkwy, Sherman, TX 75090
Tel.: (903) 892-1561
Web Site: http://www.parkwaybuickgmc.com
Sales Range: $50-74.9 Million
Emp.: 30
New & Used Car Dealer
N.A.I.C.S.: 441110
Cathy Lopez (Controller)

PARKWAY CONSTRUCTION & ASSOCIATES LP

1000 Civic Cir, Lewisville, TX 75067-3493
Tel.: (469) 322-3735
Web Site:
http://www.parkwayconstruction.com
Year Founded: 1981
Sales Range: $10-24.9 Million
Emp.: 125
Nonresidential Construction
N.A.I.C.S.: 236220
Anne Cox *(Mgr-HR)*
Bob Murphy *(Dir-Construction)*
Doug Ensign *(Dir-Construction)*
Erik Egan *(Mgr-Bus Dev)*
Greg Klimko *(Dir-Architecture)*
Mel Chadwick *(CFO)*
Rick Wojciechowski *(Pres, CEO & Partner)*
Ted Young *(Dir-Construction)*
Vaughan Hancock *(COO & Partner)*

PARKWAY CORPORATION
150 N Broad St Fl 10, Philadelphia, PA 19102
Tel.: (215) 575-4000
Web Site:
http://www.parkwaycorp.com
Year Founded: 1936
Sales Range: $200-249.9 Million
Emp.: 500
Parking Garage
N.A.I.C.S.: 812930
Joseph Zuritsky *(Chm)*
Robert A. Zuritsky *(Pres & CEO)*
Anna Z. Boni *(Chief Admin Officer & Exec VP)*
Donald Hurford *(VP-HR)*
Howard Trachtman *(Gen Counsel & Sr VP-Fin)*
Paul Ierubino *(COO & Sr VP-Ops)*
Christopher J. Barone *(Chief Acctg Officer & VP)*
Brian Berson *(Sr VP-Real Estate & Dev)*

PARKWAY MOTORCARS
24055 Creekside Rd, Valencia, CA 91355
Tel.: (661) 253-4441
Web Site:
http://www.parkwaymotorcars.com
Year Founded: 1991
Sales Range: $25-49.9 Million
Emp.: 120
New Car Whslr
N.A.I.C.S.: 441110
Bob Javadi *(Gen Mgr-Sls)*

PARKWAY MOTORS OF LEONIA INC.
50 Sylvan Ave, Englewood Cliffs, NJ 07632
Tel.: (201) 944-3300
Web Site:
http://www.parkwaytoyota.com
Sales Range: $10-24.9 Million
Emp.: 30
New & Used Car Dealers
N.A.I.C.S.: 441110
Michael Delacruz *(Gen Mgr)*
Robert Winograd *(Mgr)*
Peter Fleming *(Gen Mgr-Sls)*
H. Dennis Lauzon Jr. *(Owner)*

PARKWEST MEDICAL CENTER
9352 Park West Blvd, Knoxville, TN 37923
Tel.: (865) 373-1000
Web Site: http://www.treatedwell.com
Year Founded: 1990
Sales Range: $300-349.9 Million
Emp.: 2,487
Health Care Srvices
N.A.I.C.S.: 622110

Scott Hamilton *(CFO & VP)*
Em Cobble *(Chief Support Officer & VP)*
Liz Clary *(VP-Behavioral Health)*
Randall Carr *(Dir-HR)*
Mitzi Thomas *(Dir-Care Mgmt & Quality)*
Lynn Cagle *(Chief Nursing Officer & VP)*
Neil Heatherly *(Pres & Chief Admin Ofiicer)*

PARMAN HOLDING CORPORATION
7101 Cockrill Bend Blvd, Nashville, TN 37209
Tel.: (800) 727-7920
Web Site: https://parmancorp.com
Holding Company
N.A.I.C.S.: 551112
Rachel Hockenberger *(CEO)*

Subsidiaries:

Parman Energy Corporation (1)
7101 Cockrill Bend Blvd, Nashville, TN 37209-1005
Tel.: (615) 350-7920
Web Site: http://www.parmanenergy.com
Lubricant & Fuel Products, Services & Solutions
N.A.I.C.S.: 457210
Rachel Hockenberger *(CFO)*
Charley Crichton *(Sr VP)*
David Krause *(Gen Counsel & VP-Supply Chain)*
Keith Pemberton *(Sls Dir-Equipment)*
Kelly Jo Stephens *(Dir-Customer Experience)*
Steve Moore *(Chm & CEO)*
Robert Giffin *(COO)*
Julie Pomeroy *(Chief HR Officer)*

PARMENTER REALTY & INVESTMENT COMPANY
701 Brickell Ave Ste 2020, Miami, FL 33131
Tel.: (305) 379-7500
Web Site: http://www.parmco.com
Year Founded: 1989
Sales Range: $25-49.9 Million
Emp.: 125
Real Estate Investment, Development & Management Services
N.A.I.C.S.: 531390
Darryl Parmenter *(Chm & CEO)*
Andrew R. Weiss *(COO & Mng Principal)*
Stephen K. Bronner *(Vice Chm)*
Christopher McGrew *(Chief Investment Officer & Mng Principal)*
Robert M. Motes *(Gen Counsel & SVP)*
Jeffrey B. Granoff *(CFO)*
Michael G. Loftis *(Mng Principal)*
Areya Keshvari *(VP-Investments & Capital Markets)*
Jasmine Alvarez *(Controller)*
Lyndelle Nieuwkerk *(Dir-Mktg & Comm)*
Ellen Wisniewski *(Mgr-HR)*
Timothy Steve Harrison *(Mng Dir-Facilities & Sustainability)*
Thom Ridnour *(Sr VP-Leasing-Southwest Reg)*
Sarah Buckles *(VP-Property Mgmt)*
Maureen Nez *(VP-Fin & Portfolio Strategy)*

PARMENTER, INC.
103 RailRd St, Odessa, NY 14869
Tel.: (607) 594-7106
Web Site:
http://www.parmenterinc.com
Sales Range: $10-24.9 Million
Emp.: 95
Tires & Tubes, Retails Sales
N.A.I.C.S.: 423130

Sandra Robbins *(Controller)*
Joyce Cole *(Mgr)*

PARNASSUS BOOKS LLC
3900 Hillsboro Pike Ste 14, Nashville, TN 37215
Tel.: (615) 953-2243
Web Site:
https://www.parnassusbooks.net
Year Founded: 2011
Book Stores
N.A.I.C.S.: 459210
Ann Patchett *(Owner)*

Subsidiaries:

Hooks-Yenson LLC (1)
4802 Crescent St, Bethesda, MD 20816-1706
Tel.: (615) 915-4991
Web Site: https://hooksbookevents.com
Professional & Management Development Training
N.A.I.C.S.: 611430
Perry Pidgeon Hooks *(Co-Founder & Pres)*

PARO SERVICES CORP.
1755 Enterprise Pkwy Ste 600, Twinsburg, OH 44087-2277
Tel.: (330) 467-1300
Web Site:
http://www.royalchemical.com
Year Founded: 1938
Sales Range: $100-124.9 Million
Emp.: 200
Chemical Cleaning Compounds Mfr & Distr
N.A.I.C.S.: 325998
Matthew Dailey *(Pres)*

Subsidiaries:

Paro Services Corp. - Royal Chemical Chattanooga Plant
110 Parmenas Ln, Chattanooga, TN 37405
Tel.: (423) 756-3766
Chemical Products Mfr
N.A.I.C.S.: 325998

Paro Services Corp. - Royal Chemical Dallas Plant (1)
2851 Reward Ln, Dallas, TX 75220
Tel.: (214) 358-1861
Emp.: 20
Chemical Products Mfr
N.A.I.C.S.: 325998
Shane Webster *(Plant Mgr)*

Paro Services Corp. - Royal Chemical East Stroudsburg Plant (1)
1336 Crowe Rd, East Stroudsburg, PA 18301
Tel.: (570) 421-7850
Web Site: http://www.royalchemical.com
Chemical Products Mfr
N.A.I.C.S.: 325998

Paro Services Corp. - Royal Chemical Macedonia Plant (1)
8679 S Freeway Dr, Macedonia, OH 44056
Tel.: (330) 467-1300
Chemical Products Mfr
N.A.I.C.S.: 325998

Royal Chemical Company (1)
1755 Enterprise Pkwy Ste 600, Twinsburg, OH 44087-2277
Tel.: (330) 467-1300
Web Site: http://www.royalchemical.com
Sales Range: $25-49.9 Million
Emp.: 40
Cleaning Compounds & Detergents Mfr & Distr
N.A.I.C.S.: 325612
Ed Kubek *(Controller)*
David DeBord *(VP-Dev & Strategy)*
Brian McCue *(COO)*
Barbara Berglund *(Mgr-Quality Assurance)*
Barry Martin *(Dir-Ops-East Stroudsburg)*

Plant (Domestic):

Royal Chemical Company (2)
2498 American Ave, Hayward, CA 94545-1810
Tel.: (510) 782-8727

Web Site: http://www.royalchemical.com
Sales Range: $1-9.9 Million
Emp.: 20
Cleaning Compounds & Detergents Mfr & Distr
N.A.I.C.S.: 325611
Bob Lindsey *(Dir-Ops)*

PARR INSTRUMENT COMPANY
211 53rd St, Moline, IL 61265
Tel.: (309) 762-7716
Web Site: http://www.parrinst.com
Sales Range: $10-24.9 Million
Emp.: 100
Mfr of Calorimeters
N.A.I.C.S.: 334516
Jim Nelson *(Pres)*

PARR LUMBER COMPANY INC.
5630 NW Five Oaks Dr, Hillsboro, OR 97124-9341
Tel.: (503) 614-2500
Web Site: http://www.parr.com
Year Founded: 1930
Sales Range: $25-49.9 Million
Emp.: 550
Lumber, Plywood & Millwork
N.A.I.C.S.: 423310
David Hamill *(CEO)*

Subsidiaries:

Cascade Wholesale Hardware Inc. (1)
5650 NE Wagon Dr, Hillsboro, OR 97124-8510
Tel.: (503) 614-2600
Web Site: http://www.cascade.com
Sales Range: $10-24.9 Million
Emp.: 52
Wholesale Hardware
N.A.I.C.S.: 423710
Michael Parr *(Gen Mgr)*

PARR MEDIA GROUP
13120 Westlinks Terrace Blvd Ste 4, Fort Myers, FL 33913
Tel.: (239) 561-8090
Web Site: http://www.parrmedia.com
Sales Range: $10-24.9 Million
Emp.: 18
Media Buying Services
N.A.I.C.S.: 541830
Dana Parr *(VP-Ops)*
Bill Taylor *(Mng Partner & VP)*
Carrie Nasuta *(Acct Exec)*

PARRATT-WOLFF, INC.
5879 Fisher Rd, East Syracuse, NY 13057
Tel.: (315) 437-1429
Web Site: http://www.pwinc.com
Year Founded: 1969
Sales Range: $10-24.9 Million
Emp.: 55
Contract Drilling Services
N.A.I.C.S.: 213111
Mike Ellingworth *(Pres)*

PARRETT WINDOWS & DOORS, INC.
690 E 2nd Ave, Dorchester, WI 54425
Tel.: (715) 654-6444
Web Site:
http://www.parrettwindows.com
Rev.: $11,600,000
Emp.: 126
Wood Window & Door Mfr
N.A.I.C.S.: 321911
Tyler Kollmansberger *(Engr-Comml Sls)*
Ron Safford *(Mng Dir)*

PARRISH & COMPANY INC.
26995 US Hwy 281 N, San Antonio, TX 78260

PARRISH & COMPANY INC.

Parrish & Company Inc.—(Continued)
Tel.: (830) 980-9595
Web Site:
  http://www.parrishandcompany.com
Year Founded: 1972
Sales Range: $10-24.9 Million
Emp.: 95
Retailer of Home Appliances, Kitchen Cabinets, Lighting Fixtures & Garage Doors
N.A.I.C.S.: 423310
Daniel Parrish *(Pres & Partner)*

PARRISH & PARTNERS, LLC
140 Stoneridge Dr Ste 500, Columbia, SC 29210
Tel.: (803) 978-1600
Web Site:
  http://www.parrishandpartners.com
Year Founded: 2013
Sales Range: $10-24.9 Million
Emp.: 63
Engineeering Services
N.A.I.C.S.: 541330
Ed Parrish *(Pres)*
Adam Parrish *(Principal & Sr Project Mgr)*
Don Freeman *(Principal)*
Chad Rogers *(Principal & Ops Mgr)*
Mark Friendly *(CFO)*

PARRISH ENTERPRISES, LTD.
1414 E Willow Rd, Enid, OK 73701-8714
Tel.: (580) 237-4033   OK
Web Site: http://www.ptcoupling.com
Year Founded: 1981
Sales Range: $75-99.9 Million
Emp.: 350
Industrial Machinery Components & Supplies Mfr & Whslr
N.A.I.C.S.: 423840
James R. Parrish *(Pres)*

Subsidiaries:

Central Machine & Tool Company   (1)
1414 E Willow Rd, Enid, OK 73701-8714
Tel.: (580) 237-4033
Sales Range: $25-49.9 Million
Emp.: 300
Mfr of Industrial Machinery
N.A.I.C.S.: 332710

Mississippi Precision Cast Parts   (1)
356 Langston Cir Golden Triangle Industrial Park, Columbus, MS 39701
Tel.: (662) 245-1155
Sales Range: $1-9.9 Million
Emp.: 32
Steel Investment Castings Foundry
N.A.I.C.S.: 331512
Eddie Houston *(Gen Mgr)*

Oklahoma Investments Casting Company   (1)
708 N 29th St, Blackwell, OK 74631-0580
Tel.: (580) 363-1412
Web Site: http://www.oicc-co.com
Sales Range: $10-24.9 Million
Emp.: 50
Operator of Steel Foundries
N.A.I.C.S.: 331512

P-T Coupling Company   (1)
1414 E Willow Rd, Enid, OK 73702
Tel.: (580) 237-4033
Web Site: http://www.ptcoupling.com
Sales Range: $25-49.9 Million
Emp.: 200
Industrial Supply Distr
N.A.I.C.S.: 423840

Punch-Lok Company   (1)
3001 N 4th, Enid, OK 73701-1372
Tel.: (580) 233-4757
Web Site: http://www.punch-lok.com
Sales Range: $10-24.9 Million
Emp.: 20
Mfr of Clamps, Buckles & Brackets
N.A.I.C.S.: 332510

Seeker Rod Company   (1)
1340 W Cowles St, Long Beach, CA 90813
Tel.: (562) 491-0076
Web Site: http://www.seekerrods.com
Fishing Rod Mfr
N.A.I.C.S.: 339920

Specialty Plastics Company   (1)
2302 N 11th St, Enid, OK 73701-8720
Tel.: (580) 237-1018
Sales Range: $10-24.9 Million
Emp.: 10
Specialty Injection Molded Plastic Products Mfr
N.A.I.C.S.: 326199
Steve Meyer *(Gen Mgr)*

PARRISH EQUIPMENT SUPPLY INC.
171 Hwy 27 S, Nashville, AR 71852
Tel.: (870) 845-2223
Sales Range: $10-24.9 Million
Emp.: 22
Supplier of Poultry Equipment
N.A.I.C.S.: 423820
Don E. Parrish *(Pres)*
Virginia Hartness *(Sec)*

PARRISH TIRE COMPANY, INC.
5130 Indiana Ave, Winston Salem, NC 27106-2822
Tel.: (336) 767-0202   NC
Web Site: http://www.parrishtire.com
Year Founded: 1946
Sales Range: $125-149.9 Million
Emp.: 300
Mfr & Retailer of Tires
N.A.I.C.S.: 423130
W. Logan Jackson *(Chm & Pres)*

Subsidiaries:

Parrish Tire Company, Inc. - Commercial Division   (1)
5130 Indiana Ave, Winston Salem, NC 27106
Tel.: (336) 767-0202
Emp.: 45
Automotive Tire Installation & Maintenance Services
N.A.I.C.S.: 811198
Steve Williard *(Mgr-Comml Sls)*

Parrish Tire Company, Inc. - Wholesale Division   (1)
5130 Indiana Ave, Winston Salem, NC 27106
Automotive Tires Distr
N.A.I.C.S.: 423130

PARRISH-HARE ELECTRICAL SUPPLY CORPORATION
1211 Regal Row, Dallas, TX 75247-3613
Tel.: (214) 905-1001
Web Site: http://www.parrish-hare.com
Year Founded: 1983
Rev.: $38,000,000
Emp.: 60
Electrical Apparatus & Equipment
N.A.I.C.S.: 423610
Pat Hare *(Owner)*
Wes Butler *(COO)*
Diane Beatty *(Mgr-Credit)*
James Butler *(Mgr-Dallas)*
Randy Finklea *(Project Mgr)*
Cheri Kemper *(Mgr-IT)*
Kevin Talbert *(Dir-Inventory Control)*
David Schamber *(Mgr-Warehouse)*
Linda Watson *(Mgr-HR)*
Bryan Land *(Project Mgr)*
Craig Ledbetter *(Mgr-Dallas)*
Greg Johnson *(Mgr-Sls)*
Karen Kypfer *(Project Mgr)*
Kristina Harding *(Project Mgr)*
Kristi Searcy *(Project Mgr)*
Lee Rice *(Mgr-Dallas)*
Sandy Shaw *(Engr-Quality Control)*

PARRISH-MCCALL CONSTRUCTORS, INC.
3455 SW 42nd Ave, Gainesville, FL 32608
Tel.: (352) 378-1571
Web Site: http://www.parrish-mccall.com
Sales Range: $25-49.9 Million
Emp.: 34
Commercial & Office Building Construction
N.A.I.C.S.: 236220
Michael Walsh *(Pres)*
Ed Myers *(Office Mgr)*

PARS INTERNATIONAL CORP.
253 W 35th St 7th Fl, New York, NY 10001
Tel.: (212) 221-9595   NY
Web Site:
  http://www.magreprints.com
Year Founded: 1994
Sales Range: $1-9.9 Million
Emp.: 40
Quick Printing
N.A.I.C.S.: 323111
Cynthia Osborne-McKean *(Co-Founder & Principal)*
Steve Mussman *(Co-Founder & Principal)*
Andy Speter *(VP-Bus Dev)*
Jackie Kurtz *(Dir-Production)*
Robyn L. Roberts *(Dir-Sls)*
Joseph Nunziata III *(VP-Sls Ops)*

PARSEC COMPUTER CORP.
Eight S First Ave, Yakima, WA 98902
Tel.: (509) 248-8309
Web Site:
  http://www.parseccomputer.com
Sales Range: $10-24.9 Million
Emp.: 20
Computer Stores
N.A.I.C.S.: 449210
Kristen Whitener *(Pres & CEO)*
Rick Dibbert *(VP-Ops)*
Robert Guchee *(Owner)*

PARSONS & WHITTEMORE, INC.
4 Intl Dr Ste 300, Rye Brook, NY 10573
Tel.: (914) 937-9009   DE
Year Founded: 1909
Sales Range: $1-4.9 Billion
Emp.: 30
Holding Company; Producer of Market Pulp
N.A.I.C.S.: 322110
George Landegger *(Chm, Pres & CEO)*
Stephen J. Sweeney *(CFO & VP)*
Peggy Jaye *(Dir-PR)*

PARSONS CHEVROLET-BUICK INC.
515 Amron Ave, Antigo, WI 54409
Tel.: (715) 627-4888
Web Site:
  http://www.parsonsofantigo.com
Sales Range: $25-49.9 Million
Emp.: 45
Car Dealership Owner & Operator
N.A.I.C.S.: 441110
Dan Sharon *(Gen Mgr)*
Curt Parson *(Owner)*

PARSONS ELECTRIC LLC
5960 Main St NE, Minneapolis, MN 55432
Tel.: (763) 571-8000
Web Site:
  http://www.parsonscorp.com
Rev.: $36,100,000
Emp.: 750
General Electrical Contractor

N.A.I.C.S.: 238210
Joel Moryn *(Pres)*
Bill Olson *(VP-Field Ops)*
Bonnie Lunzer *(Dir-Safety)*
Dave Karsky *(VP)*
Dave Nielsen *(VP-Electrical Construction)*
Mike Northquest *(CFO)*
Rick Anderson *(VP-Electrical Svc)*
Wendy Boosalis *(VP-Tech)*
M. N. Power *(Owner)*

PARSONS FORD LINCOLN MERCURY
1400 Shepherdstown Rd, Martinsburg, WV 25404
Tel.: (304) 263-3344
Web Site: http://www.parsonsford.com
Sales Range: $200-249.9 Million
Emp.: 50
Used Car Whslr
N.A.I.C.S.: 441120
Meredith Poffenberger *(Mgr-Customer Rels)*

PARSONS ROOFING COMPANY, INC.
605 E Central, Lorena, TX 76655
Tel.: (254) 881-1733   TX
Web Site:
  http://www.parsonsroofing.com
Year Founded: 1978
Sales Range: $25-49.9 Million
Emp.: 140
Roofing Contractors
N.A.I.C.S.: 238160
Ken Wells *(Dir-Ops)*
Tim Jarvis *(Project Mgr)*
Dustin Kelly *(Mgr-Sheetmetal Project)*
Lisa Pechacek *(Project Coord)*
Stuart Parsons Jr. *(Pres)*

PARSONS XTREME GOLF, LLC
15690 N 83rd Way, Scottsdale, AZ 85258
Web Site: http://www.pxg.com
Year Founded: 2014
Sales Range: $75-99.9 Million
Emp.: 196
Golf Equipment Mfr & Distr
N.A.I.C.S.: 339920
Bob Parsons *(Founder)*

PARTICIPANT PRODUCTIONS, LLC
335 N Maple Dr Ste 354, Beverly Hills, CA 90210
Tel.: (310) 550-5100
Web Site:
  http://www.participantmedia.com
Year Founded: 2004
Sales Range: $1-9.9 Million
Emp.: 25
Motion Picture & Video Production
N.A.I.C.S.: 512110
Jim Berk *(Principal)*
Bob Murphy *(Exec VP & CFO)*
Amy Glickman *(Sr VP-Publicity & Corp Comm)*

Subsidiaries:

SoulPancake   (1)
PO Box 39377, Los Angeles, CA 90039
Tel.: (323) 825-1844
Web Site: http://www.soulpancake.com
Sales Range: $1-9.9 Million
Emp.: 12
Motion Picture, Television & Video Production
N.A.I.C.S.: 512110
Alexandra Findlay *(Office Mgr)*
Bayan Joonam *(Head-Production)*
Blaise Leone *(Mgr-Social Media)*
Correy Stoner O'Neal *(Head-Sls & Mktg)*
Devon Gundry *(Co-Founder)*
Rainn Wilson *(Co-Founder)*

COMPANIES — PARTNERS HEALTHCARE SYSTEM, INC.

Shabnam Mogharabi *(CEO)*
Meredith Katz *(Dir-Sls & Bus Dev)*
Mick DiMaria *(VP & Creative Dir)*
Golriz Lucina *(Sr VP & Head-Creative)*
Jordan Allen *(Sr VP-Revenue, Strategy & Ops)*

PARTICLE DRILLING TECHNOLOGIES, LLC
1 City Center 1021 Main St Ste 2650, Houston, TX 77002
Tel.: (713) 223-3031 — NV
Web Site: http://particledrilling.com
Sales Range: $25-49.9 Million
Emp.: 19
Oil & Gas Drilling Services
N.A.I.C.S.: 213111

PARTIDA TEQUILA, LLC
150 California St Ste 500, San Francisco, CA 94111
Tel.: (415) 434-3100
Web Site: http://www.partidatequila.com
Sales Range: $10-24.9 Million
Emp.: 20
Tequila Importer & Distr
N.A.I.C.S.: 424820
J. Gary Shansby *(Founder, Chm & CEO)*

Subsidiaries:

Tequila Partida de Mexico, S.A. de C.V. (1)
Justosierra 2847 Ballartanorte, 1 2 Y 3 Seccion, 44630, Guadalajara, Jalisco, Mexico
Tel.: (52) 3336423303
Web Site: http://www.tequilapartida.com
Sales Range: $10-24.9 Million
Mfr of Tequila Products
N.A.I.C.S.: 312140

PARTIES THAT COOK LLC
601 Minnesota St Ste 115, San Francisco, CA 94107
Tel.: (415) 441-3595
Web Site: http://www.partiesthatcook.com
Year Founded: 2006
Sales Range: $1-9.9 Million
Emp.: 10
Household Cooking Parties Operator
N.A.I.C.S.: 814110
Bibby Gignilliat *(Founder & CEO)*

PARTMINER, INC.
10 Dubont Court, Farmingdale, NY 11735
Tel.: (631) 501-2800 — NY
Year Founded: 1993
Sales Range: $125-149.9 Million
Emp.: 250
Full Service Online Automated Spot & Excess Market-Maker for Electronic Components
N.A.I.C.S.: 423690
L. Christopher Meyer *(CEO)*
Greg Nash *(CFO)*
Morton L. Topfer *(Chm)*

Subsidiaries:

PartMiner Direct (1)
10 Dubon Ct, Farmingdale, NY 11735
Tel.: (631) 501-2800
Electronic Components Distributor
N.A.I.C.S.: 423690

PARTNER ENGINEERING & SCIENCE, INC
2154 Torrance Blvd Ste 200, Torrance, CA 90501
Tel.: (310) 615-4500
Web Site: http://www.partneresi.com
Sales Range: $10-24.9 Million
Emp.: 80
Land Assessment Services
N.A.I.C.S.: 541620

Joseph P. Derhake *(CEO)*
Douglas Lawson *(Dir-Technical-Indus Hygiene)*
Bryan Cortnik *(Dir-Tech)*
Timothy DeBord *(Mgr-Natl Client)*
Alice Ramos *(Principal & Dir-Funds Control)*
William Easley *(Dir-Technical)*
Paul Zavalney *(Dir-Technical-Investment Advisory Grp)*
Douglas Murray *(Dir-Technical-Property Condition Assessments)*
David Regelbrugge *(Partner & Dir-Technical-Indus Hygiene, Health & Safety Svcs)*
Russell Stauffer *(Dir-Technical-Indus Hygiene Svcs)*

Subsidiaries:

Nevada Construction Services (1)
7674 W Lake Mead Blvd Ste 110, Las Vegas, NV 89128
Tel.: (702) 251-1150
Web Site: http://www.ncsnv.com
Engineering, Environmental & Energy Consulting & Design Firm
N.A.I.C.S.: 541330
Terrence L. Wright *(Owner & Chm)*
Debra Vogel *(VP)*
Sonja Eckert *(Mgr-Reno Office)*

PARTNER'S CONSULTING, INC.
1617 Darby Rd Ste 201, Havertown, PA 19083
Tel.: (610) 449-9155
Web Site: http://www.partners-consulting.com
Year Founded: 2006
Sales Range: $1-9.9 Million
Emp.: 42
Information Technology & Human Resource Consulting Services
N.A.I.C.S.: 541512
Peggy Gionta *(Founder & Pres)*

PARTNERPATH, LLC
465 Fairchild Dr Ste 127, Mountain View, CA 94043
Tel.: (650) 810-2220
Web Site: http://www.partner-path.com
Year Founded: 1998
Sales Range: $1-9.9 Million
Emp.: 16
Business Consulting Services
N.A.I.C.S.: 541611
Chris Smith *(VP-Tech)*
David O'Brien *(VP-Client Svcs)*

PARTNERS BOOK DISTRIBUTING
2325 Jarco Dr, Holt, MI 48842
Tel.: (517) 694-3205
Web Site: http://www.partnersbook.com
Rev.: $34,247,769
Emp.: 50
Whslr of Books
N.A.I.C.S.: 424920
Vicky Lynn Eaves *(Pres)*

Subsidiaries:

Partners Book Distributing-West (1)
1901 Raymond Ave SW Ste C, Renton, WA 98057
Tel.: (425) 227-8486
Web Site: http://www.partnersbook.com
Rev.: $3,000,000
Emp.: 25
Books
N.A.I.C.S.: 424920
Sam Speigel *(Pres)*

PARTNERS FOR INCENTIVES INC.
6545 Carnegie Ave, Cleveland, OH 44103

Tel.: (216) 881-3000
Web Site: http://www.pfi-awards.com
Year Founded: 1963
Sales Range: $25-49.9 Million
Emp.: 75
Business-To-Business, Merchandising & Sales Promotion
N.A.I.C.S.: 541810
Joy Smith *(VP-Sls & Mktg)*
Gregory Losh *(Mgr-CIS)*
Jim Kapcar *(Reg Sls Mgr)*

PARTNERS HEALTHCARE SYSTEM, INC.
Prudential Center 800 Boylston St 11th Fl, Boston, MA 02199
Tel.: (617) 278-1000 — MA
Web Site: http://www.partners.org
Year Founded: 1994
Healthcare & Hospital Community Relations Services
N.A.I.C.S.: 621999
Scott M. Sperling *(Chm)*
Gregg Meyer *(Chief Clinical Officer)*
David Torchiana *(Pres & CEO)*

Subsidiaries:

Harbor Medical Associates P.C. (1)
The Stetson Bldg 541 Main St, South Weymouth, MA 02190
Tel.: (781) 952-1240
Web Site: http://www.harbormedical.com
Health Care Srvices
N.A.I.C.S.: 621999
Richard W. Whitney *(Pres)*
Peter Grape *(CEO)*

Newton-Wellesley HealthCare System (1)
2014 Washington St, Newton, MA 02462
Tel.: (617) 243-6000
Web Site: http://www.nwh.in
Emp.: 3,000
Holding Company
N.A.I.C.S.: 551112
Ellen Maloney *(Pres)*

Subsidiary (Domestic):

Newton-Wellesley Children's Corner Inc. (2)
2014 Washington St, Newton, MA 02462
Tel.: (617) 243-6515
Web Site: http://www.nwh.org
Emp.: 15
Child Day Care Services
N.A.I.C.S.: 624410
Kyla McSweeney *(Mng Dir)*

Newton-Wellesley Hospital (2)
2014 Washington St, Newton, MA 02462
Tel.: (617) 243-6000
Web Site: http://www.nwh.org
Hospital Operator
N.A.I.C.S.: 622110
Ellen Maloney *(COO)*
Louis G. Jenis *(Chief Medical Officer & Chief Innovation Officer)*
Vincent McDermott *(CFO)*
Janet C. H. Larson *(Chief Quality Officer & Chief Experience Officer)*
Kevin Whitney *(Chief Nursing Officer & Sr VP-Patient Care Svcs)*

Newton-Wellesley Hospital Charitable Foundation Inc. (2)
2014 Washington St, Newton, MA 02462
Tel.: (617) 724-9841
Charitable Giving & Services
N.A.I.C.S.: 813211
Joan Archer *(Pres)*

Partners Community Healthcare, Inc. (1)
115 4th Ave, Needham, MA 02494
Tel.: (781) 433-3600
Web Site: http://www.partners.org
Healthcare Network Management Services
N.A.I.C.S.: 621111
Caty DiBiase O'Brien *(Acct Dir-Mgmt)*
Amy Seeney *(Acct Mgr)*
Mark Mandell *(Chief Medical Officer)*
Sharon Smith *(Chm)*
Maureen Foley *(Dir-Care Mgmt)*
Carol Peterson *(Exec Dir-RSO)*

Joseph Mcallister *(Mgr-Acctg)*
Lisa Balentine *(Mgr-Clinical Applications)*
Melanie Sylvia *(Mgr-Fin Reporting & Analysis)*
Michelle Bean *(Mgr-Practice Fin)*
Kathleen Moran Garland *(Mgr-Sys Contracting)*
Ruth Neuhaus *(Project Mgr)*
David Connolly *(VP-Fin)*
Kathleen Connolly *(Mgr-Clinical Program Dev)*
Meg Costello *(VP-Network Ops)*
Jill Fiore *(Mgr-Clinical Analytics)*
Kelly Hall *(Exec Dir-Strategic Plng)*
Neeharika Mehta *(Project Mgr-Integrated Care Mgmt Program)*

Partners Continuing Care, Inc. (1)
800 Boylston St Ste 1150, Boston, MA 02199
Tel.: (617) 278-1000
Web Site: http://www.partners.org
Non-Acute Healthcare Services
N.A.I.C.S.: 621498
Gary Gottlieb *(Pres)*

Subsidiary (Domestic):

Partners Home Care Inc. (2)
281 Winter St, Waltham, MA 02451
Tel.: (781) 290-4200
Web Site: http://www.partnersathome.org
Sales Range: $125-149.9 Million
Emp.: 170
Women Healthcare Services
N.A.I.C.S.: 621610
Keren Diamond *(COO & Sr VP)*
Shaune Barry *(Sr Dir-Bus Dev)*
Mary Bures *(Sr Dir-Comm)*
Mary Campbell *(Dir-Customer Svc)*
Maureen N. Chesley *(VP-Strategy & Integration)*
Gary W. Garberg *(VP-Bus Ops)*
Annemarie Martin *(Dir-Client South Reg)*
Octavia Moniz *(Dir-Client North Reg)*
Dana Sheer *(Dir-Advanced Clinical Programs)*
Deborah J. Sullivan *(Dir-Info Sys)*
Judith B. Flynn *(Officer-Compliance & VP-Patient Care Quality)*

Rehabilitation Hospital of the Cape and Islands (2)
311 Service Rd, Sandwich, MA 02537
Tel.: (508) 833-4000
Rehabilitation Hospital Operator
N.A.I.C.S.: 623110
Maureen Banks *(Pres)*

Shaughnessy Kaplan Rehabilitation Hospital (2)
1 Dove Ave, Salem, MA 01970
Tel.: (978) 745-9003
Rehabilitation Hospital Operator
N.A.I.C.S.: 623110

Spaulding Hospital - Cambridge Inc. (2)
1575 Cambridge St, Cambridge, MA 02138
Tel.: (617) 573-2700
Rehabilitation Hospital Operator
N.A.I.C.S.: 623110

Spaulding Rehabilitation Hospital Corporation (2)
300 1st Ave, Charlestown, MA 02129
Tel.: (617) 952-5000
Web Site: http://www.spauldingrehab.org
Rehabilitative Healthcare Services
N.A.I.C.S.: 621498

Partners Harvard Medical International (1)
100 Cambridge St, Boston, MA 02114
Tel.: (617) 535-6400
Web Site: http://www.partners.org
Emp.: 30
Medical Advisory Services
N.A.I.C.S.: 541618
Christopher Coburn *(Chief Innovation Officer)*

Spaulding Rehabilitation Network (1)
300 1st Ave 2nd Fl, Charlestown, MA 02129
Tel.: (617) 952-6200
Web Site: http://www.spauldingrehab.org
Outpatient Health Care Services Organization
N.A.I.C.S.: 813920

PARTNERS HEALTHCARE SYSTEM, INC.

U.S. PRIVATE

Partners HealthCare System, Inc.—(Continued)
David E. Storto *(Pres)*
Maureen Banks *(COO)*
Ross D. Zafonte *(Sr VP-Medical Affairs, Res & Education)*
Cara Babachicos *(CIO)*
Oswald Mondejar *(Sr VP-Mission, Advocacy & Partners Continuing Care)*
Karen S. Nelson *(VP-Quality, Compliance & Regulatory Affairs)*
Steven Patrick *(VP-Dev)*
Nancy Schmidt *(Sr VP-Referral Rels & Network Dev)*
Mary Shaughnessy *(Sr VP-Fin & Plng)*
Joseph Castellana *(VP-Medical Admin)*
Bob McCall *(VP-Inpatient Rehabilitation Svcs)*
Sandra Sedacca *(Chief Dev Officer & Sr VP-Philanthropy)*

The Brigham & Women's Faulkner Hospital (1)
1153 Centre St, Boston, MA 02130
Tel.: (617) 983-7000
Web Site:
http://www.brighamandwomensfaulkner.org
Hospital Operator
N.A.I.C.S.: 622110
David O. McCready *(Pres)*
Margaret Duggan *(Chief Medical Officer & VP-Medical Affairs)*

Subsidiary (Domestic):

Brigham & Women's Physicians Organization (2)
111 Cypress St, Brookline, MA 02445
Tel.: (617) 525-8621
Multi-Specialty Medical Services
N.A.I.C.S.: 621111
Allen B. Smith *(Pres)*

Faulkner Hospital Inc. (2)
1153 Centre St, Boston, MA 02130
Tel.: (617) 983-7000
Web Site:
http://www.brighamwomensfaulkner.com
Emp.: 1,600
Hospital Operator
N.A.I.C.S.: 622110
Michael Gustaffon *(Pres)*

Subsidiary (Domestic):

West Roxbury Medical Group Inc. (3)
1832 Centre St, West Roxbury, MA 02132
Tel.: (617) 469-4000
Web Site:
http://www.brighamandwomens.work
Emp.: 40
Medical Devices
N.A.I.C.S.: 621111
John Lewis *(Dir-Medical)*

Subsidiary (Domestic):

South Shore Hospital (2)
55 Fogg Rd, South Weymouth, MA 02190
Tel.: (781) 624-8000
Web Site: http://www.southshorehospital.org
Rev: $270,606,000
Emp.: 3,900
Hospital Operator
N.A.I.C.S.: 622110
Tim Quigley *(Chief Nursing Officer & VP-Nursing Svcs)*
Brian P. Concannon *(Vice Chm)*
Gene E. Green *(Pres & CEO)*
Stephen Coco *(CFO & Sr VP)*
Timothy R. Lynch *(Sr VP)*
Michael Ayers *(Vice Chm)*
Cara Babachicos *(CIO & Sr VP)*
Justin Campbell *(Vice Chm)*
Joseph R. Driscoll *(Gen Counsel-Legal, Compliance & Audit)*
Jennie Henriques *(Chief Compliance & Audit Officer)*
Nareesa Mohammed-Rajput *(Chief Medical Information Officer)*
Christopher O'Connor *(Chief Dev Officer & Sr VP-External Affairs)*
Wayne Stockbridge *(Chief HR Officer & Sr VP)*

The Brigham & Women's Hospital (2)
75 Francis St, Boston, MA 02115
Tel.: (617) 732-5500
Web Site:
http://www.brighamandwomens.org
Hospital Operator
N.A.I.C.S.: 622110
Christine E. Seidman *(Dir-Cardiovascular Genetics Program)*

The Friends of The Brigham & Women's Hospital (2)
75 Francis Street, Boston, MA 02115
Tel.: (617) 732-8125
Fundraising & Charitable Services
N.A.I.C.S.: 813219

The Massachusetts General Hospital (1)
55 Fruit St, Boston, MA 02114
Tel.: (617) 726-2000
Web Site: http://www.massgeneral.org
Hospital Operator
N.A.I.C.S.: 622110
Rakesh K. Jain *(Dir-Edwin L. Steele Laboratory of Tumor Biology)*
Diane B. Patrick *(Co-Vice Chm)*

Subsidiary (Domestic):

MGH Institute of Health Professions (2)
36 First Ave, Charlestown, MA 02129
Tel.: (617) 726-2947
Web Site: http://www.mghihp.edu
Emp.: 200
Graduate School Operator
N.A.I.C.S.: 611310
Janis P. Bellack *(Pres)*
Lauren Putnam *(Asst Dir-Admission)*
Betsy Rigby *(Chief Dev Officer)*

Martha's Vineyard Hospital Inc. (2)
1 Hospital Rd, Oak Bluffs, MA 02557
Tel.: (508) 693-0410
Web Site: http://www.mvhospital.com
Hospital Operator
N.A.I.C.S.: 622110
Alamjit Virk *(Dir-Medical-Emergency Medicine & Hospitalist Svcs)*
Denise Schepici *(Pres & CEO)*
Rachel Vanderhoop *(Dir-Dev)*
Katrina Delgadillo *(Dir-Comm)*
Earle Ray *(Chm)*
Debra A. Burke *(Vice Chm)*
Susan C. Crampton *(Treas)*

Subsidiary (Domestic):

WNR Inc. (3)
1 Linton Ln, Oak Bluffs, MA 02568
Tel.: (508) 696-6465
Web Site: http://www.windemeremv.org
Nursing Care Facility Operator
N.A.I.C.S.: 623110

Subsidiary (Domestic):

Massachusetts General Physicians Organization, Inc. (2)
55 Fruit St Bullfinch 208, Boston, MA 02114
Tel.: (617) 726-2040
Multi-Specialty Medical Services
N.A.I.C.S.: 621111
Timothy G. Ferris *(Chm & CEO)*

Nantucket Cottage Hospital (2)
57 Prospect St, Nantucket, MA 02554
Tel.: (508) 825-8100
Web Site: http://www.nantuckethospital.org
Hospital Operator
N.A.I.C.S.: 622110
Jason Graziadei *(Officer-Pub Info)*
Catherine S. Ward *(Vice Chm)*
William R. Camp *(Treas)*
Gary Shaw *(Pres & CEO)*

Subsidiary (Domestic):

Nantucket Cottage Hospital Foundation (3)
57 Prospect St, Nantucket, MA 02554
Tel.: (508) 825-8250
Charitable Giving & Services
N.A.I.C.S.: 813211

Subsidiary (Domestic):

North Shore Medical Center Inc. (2)
81 Highland Ave, Salem, MA 01970
Tel.: (978) 741-1200
Web Site: http://www.nsmc.partners.org
Emp.: 600
Hospital Operator
N.A.I.C.S.: 622110
Sarah Andrews *(Sr VP-Dev)*
Janet Barnes *(VP-Quality & Patient Safety)*
Mark Blass *(Exec Dir-North Shore Health System)*
Mary Jo Gagnon *(Sr VP-Ops)*
Francis X. Hinkley *(CIO)*
Steven E. Kapfhammer *(Pres & COO-North Shore Physicians Group)*
Cheryl Merrill *(Sr VP-Patient Care Svcs & CNO)*
Mitchell S. Rein *(Chief Medical Officer & Sr VP-Medical Affairs)*
Roxanne Ruppel *(Sr VP-Ops)*
Christine Blaski *(Pres-Medical Staff)*
Richard E. Holbrook *(Chm)*
Johanna O'Connor *(Chm-Anesthesia)*
Wilfred R. Lewis *(Vice Chm-Anesthesia)*
Everett Lyn *(Chm-Emergency)*
Keith C. Nobil *(Chm-Family Medicine)*
Allyson L. Preston *(Chm-Obstetrics & Gynecology)*
Bruce A. Beckwith *(Chm-Pathology)*
Mark H. Mandell *(Chm-Pediatrics)*
Mark Schechter *(Chm-Psychiatry)*
James Francis McIntyre *(Chm-Radiation Oncology)*
M. Christian Semine *(Chm-Radiology)*
Howard Waldman *(Dir-Medical-Catheterization Lab & PCI)*
Romaine Layne *(Controller)*
Mark Racicot *(CEO)*
Charles Adams *(CFO & Sr VP-Fin)*
Robin Olson *(Sr VP-HR)*
Vinod Narra *(Treas-Medical Staff & Sec)*
Armando Aguilera *(Dir-Emergency Dept)*

Subsidiary (Domestic):

North Shore Physicians Group Inc. (3)
2 Corporation Way Ste 180, Peabody, MA 01960
Tel.: (978) 573-4300
Web Site:
http://www.northshorephysicians.org
Emp.: 25
Multi-Specialty Healthcare Services
N.A.I.C.S.: 621111
Steve Kapfhammer *(Pres)*

The McLean Hospital Corporation (1)
115 Mill St, Belmont, MA 02478
Tel.: (617) 855-3128
Web Site: http://www.mcleanhospital.org
Emp.: 1,900
Psychiatric Hospital Operator
N.A.I.C.S.: 622210
Scott L. Rauch *(Pres)*
Lori Etringer *(Chief Dev Officer & VP)*
Linda M. Flaherty *(Sr VP-Patient Svcs)*
Catharyn Gildesgame *(VP-Strategic Plng & Implementation)*
Joseph Gold *(Chief Medical Officer)*
Michele L. Gougeon *(COO & Exec VP)*
Shelly F. Greenfield *(Chief Academic Officer)*
David A. Lagasse *(Sr VP-Fiscal Affairs)*
Philip G. Levendusky *(Sr VP-Bus Dev & Comm)*
Kerry J. Ressler *(Chief Scientific Officer)*
David S. Barlow *(Chm)*
Adriana Bobinchock *(Dir-Public Affairs & Comm)*
Kirsten W. Bolton *(Dir-Program)*
Paula Bolton *(Mgr-Infection Control)*
Thrassos S. Calligas *(Assoc Dir-Medical)*
Claire Carswell *(Dir-Medical)*
Cristina Berciu *(Mgr-Microscopy Core Facility)*
Eugene V. Beresin *(Exec Dir-)*
Blaise A. Aguirre *(Dir-Medical)*

PARTNERS IN ASSOCIATION MANAGEMENT, INC.
325 John Knox Rd Ste L-103, Tallahassee, FL 32303
Tel.: (850) 224-0711   FL
Web Site:
http://www.yoursearchisdone.com
Year Founded: 1998
Sales Range: $1-9.9 Million
Emp.: 20
Management Consulting Services
N.A.I.C.S.: 541611
Bennett Napier *(Pres & CEO)*
Eric Thorn *(Gen Counsel)*

PARTNERS IN CARE
2075 NE Wyatt Ct, Bend, OR 97701
Tel.: (541) 382-5882   OR
Web Site:
http://www.partnersbend.org
Year Founded: 1981
Sales Range: $10-24.9 Million
Emp.: 140
Women Healthcare Services
N.A.I.C.S.: 621610
Ken Koenig *(Dir-HR)*
Randi Schuyler *(CFO)*
Robyn Tatom *(Dir-Quality & Compliance)*
Lisa Lewis *(Dir-Medical)*

PARTNERS IN HEALTH
888 Commonwealth Ave 3rd Fl, Boston, MA 02215
Tel.: (617) 998-8922   MA
Web Site: http://www.pih.org
Year Founded: 2001
Sales Range: $75-99.9 Million
Emp.: 254
Community Health Care Services
N.A.I.C.S.: 621498
Kenneth A. Himmel *(Chief Program Officer)*
David Whalen *(Chief Dev Officer)*
Ann Quandt *(VP-Fin)*
Joia Mukherjee *(Chief Medical Officer)*
Cynthia Maltbie *(Chief HR Officer)*
Ophelia Dahl *(Founder & Chm)*
Paul E. Farmer *(Founder)*

PARTNERS IN HEALTHCARE, INC.
267 N Canyon Dr, Gooding, ID 83330
Tel.: (208) 934-4433   ID
Web Site: http://www.ncm-c.org
Year Founded: 2008
Sales Range: $25-49.9 Million
Emp.: 192
Health Care Srvices
N.A.I.C.S.: 621610
Tyson Frodin *(Dir-Pharmacy)*
Lucy Osborne *(Chm)*
Elaine Bryant *(Treas & Sec)*
Minon Yates *(Dir-Surgical Svcs)*
Tim Powers *(CEO)*
Jim McCaughey *(Vice Chm)*
Patty McClary *(Dir-Nursing)*
Patrick J. Curtis *(Treas & Sec)*
J' Dee Adams *(COO)*
Sara Demoe *(CFO)*
Sara Otto *(Chief Risk & Compliance Officer)*

PARTNERS MUTUAL INSURANCE CO.
20935 Swenson Dr Ste 200, Waukesha, WI 53186
Tel.: (262) 798-5050
Web Site:
http://www.partnersmutual.com
Sales Range: $10-24.9 Million
Emp.: 40
Fire, Marine, Auto & Casualty Insurance Carriers
N.A.I.C.S.: 524126
Mark H. Ewert *(Mgr-HR)*
Greg Paul *(Mgr-Acct)*
Christine Sears *(Chm)*

PARTNERS PHARMACY, LLC
70 Jackson Dr, Cranford, NJ 07016
Tel.: (908) 931-9111

Web Site:
http://www.partnerspharmacy.com
Year Founded: 1998
Emp.: 900
Pharmacy Services
N.A.I.C.S.: 456110
Marc Altholz *(Exec VP-Sls & Mktg)*
Pooja Desai *(Dir-Billing)*
Patrick Downing *(Pres)*
Anthony Spero *(COO)*

Subsidiaries:

Tech Pharmacy Services, Inc. (1)
8910 Rte 108 Ste C, Columbia, MD 21045
Tel.: (410) 910-9260
Web Site:
http://www.advancedpharmacy.com
Sales Range: $1-9.9 Million
Emp.: 70
Pharmacies & Drug Stores
N.A.I.C.S.: 456110
Mary Ann Miller *(Sr VP-Sls & Mktg)*
Tom Trently *(CFO)*

PARTNERS TWO INC.
12015 San Pedro, San Antonio, TX 78216
Tel.: (210) 545-5850
Web Site: http://www.ptifamily.com
Year Founded: 1970
Emp.: 10
Temporary Staffing Services
N.A.I.C.S.: 561311
Don Decotis *(Co-Owner, Chm & Pres)*
Denise McCauley *(Co-Owner)*

PARTNERSHIP CAPITAL GROWTH LLC
1 Embarcadero Ctr Ste 3810, San Francisco, CA 94111
Tel.: (415) 705-8008
Web Site: http://www.pcg-advisors.com
Year Founded: 2005
Sales Range: $1-9.9 Million
Emp.: 19
Investment Banking
N.A.I.C.S.: 523940
Brent Knudsen *(Founder & Mng Partner)*

PARTNERSHIP EMPLOYMENT
20 Broadway Ste 5, Valhalla, NY 10595
Tel.: (914) 946-3939
Web Site:
http://www.partnershipemployment.com
Year Founded: 1993
Sales Range: $10-24.9 Million
Emp.: 39
Employment Agency
N.A.I.C.S.: 561311
Joseph A. Kelly *(CEO)*
Bill Lewis *(Founder)*

PARTNERSHIP FOR CHILDREN OF CUMBERLAND COUNTY, INC.
351 Wagoner Dr Ste 200, Fayetteville, NC 28303
Tel.: (910) 867-9700   NC
Web Site: http://www.ccpfc.org
Year Founded: 1993
Sales Range: $10-24.9 Million
Emp.: 69
Community Care Services
N.A.I.C.S.: 624190
Carole Mangum *(Mgr-Grants)*
Marie Lilly *(Controller)*
Marie Clark *(COO)*
Van Gunter *(Chm)*
Wendy Lowery *(Sec)*
Mike Yeager *(Mgr-Facility Ops)*
Eileen Cedzo *(Mgr-FRC Counseling)*

Linda Blanton *(Dir-Plng, Dev, & Comm)*
Rebecca Beck *(Mgr-IT)*
Mary Sonnenberg *(Pres)*
Marcus Hedgepeth *(Treas)*

PARTNERSHIP FOR STRONG FAMILIES, INC.
5950 NW 1st Pl Ste A, Gainesville, FL 32607
Tel.: (352) 244-1500   FL
Web Site: http://www.pfsf.org
Year Founded: 2002
Sales Range: $25-49.9 Million
Emp.: 113
Family Support Services
N.A.I.C.S.: 624190
David Glennon *(VP-IT)*
Michael Reneke *(Sr VP-Fin & Admin)*
Robert Holowiak *(VP-HR & Staff Dev)*
Pebbles Edelman *(Sr VP-Clinical & Community Svcs)*

PARTNERSHIP OF PACKER, OESTERLING & SMITH (PPO&S)
122 State St, Harrisburg, PA 17101
Tel.: (717) 232-1898
Web Site: http://www.pposinc.com
Year Founded: 1980
Sales Range: $10-24.9 Million
Emp.: 11
Advertising Agencies
N.A.I.C.S.: 541810
Virginia A. Roth *(Pres)*
Karen M. Gray *(Assoc Dir-Creative)*
Jeffrey S. Miller *(Dir-Creative)*

PARTS AUTHORITY INC.
3 Dakota Dr Ste 110, New Hyde Park, NY 11042
Tel.: (718) 740-4455   PA
Web Site:
http://www.partsauthority.com
Year Founded: 1972
Automotive Supplies & Parts
N.A.I.C.S.: 423120
Yaron Rosenthal *(Co-Founder)*
Randy Buller *(Co-Founder, Pres & CEO)*
David Wotman *(Co-Founder)*
Steve Yanofsky *(Co-Founder)*
David Serrano *(CFO)*
Robert Pesiri *(CIO)*
Robyn Mills *(Chief Talent Officer)*
Rich McMullen *(Sr VP-East Coast Ops)*
Eric Schwartz *(Sr VP-West Coast Ops)*
Howard Cohen *(VP-IT Sys & Data Analysis)*
Rob Blitzstein *(VP-Vendor Mgmt)*
Jason Pugh *(VP-Supply Chain)*
Ben Spitz *(VP-Corp Strategy)*
Jeff Beiser *(VP-Sls)*
Marc Tsutsui *(VP-Warehouse Ops)*

Subsidiaries:

Interamerican Motor Corporation (1)
8901 Canoga Ave, Canoga Park, CA 91304
Tel.: (818) 678-1200
Web Site: http://www.imcparts.com
Automotive Supplies & Parts
N.A.I.C.S.: 423120

PARTS EXPRESS INTERNATIONAL
725 Pleasant Valley Dr, Springboro, OH 45066
Tel.: (937) 743-3000
Web Site: http://www.parts-express.com
Sales Range: $10-24.9 Million
Emp.: 120
Mfr of Electronic Parts
N.A.I.C.S.: 423690

Jeffrey Stahl *(Pres)*
Suzy Fehling *(Coord-HR)*
Dave Hendricks *(Mgr-Network)*
Brian Mitchell *(Mgr-Wholesale)*
Karl Keyes *(Dir-Mktg)*
Rich Taylor *(Product Mgr-Dayton Audio)*
Amy Phillips *(Dir-HR)*

PARTS PLUS OF NEW MEXICO INCORPORATED
5900 Ofc Blvd NE, Albuquerque, NM 87109
Tel.: (505) 341-7000
Web Site:
http://www.partsplusnm.com
Rev.: $10,800,000
Emp.: 76
Automotive Supplies & Parts
N.A.I.C.S.: 423120
Adam Honegger *(VP)*
Andy Dietz *(Mgr-Sls)*

PARTS WHOLESALERS INC.
120 S Cedar St, Spokane, WA 99201
Tel.: (509) 624-2291
Rev.: $14,100,000
Emp.: 105
Motor Vehicle Supplies & New Parts Merchant Whslr
N.A.I.C.S.: 423120
Tim Trudnowski *(Pres & Treas)*
Paul Agather *(Treas & Exec VP)*

PARTSEARCH TECHNOLOGIES
360 Park Ave S 15th Fl, New York, NY 10010
Tel.: (212) 201-0300
Web Site: http://www.partsearch.com
Year Founded: 2001
Sales Range: $25-49.9 Million
Emp.: 255
Computer & Electronics Replacement Parts Whslr & Solutions Services
N.A.I.C.S.: 423690
Glenn C. Laumeister *(Chm)*
Robert E. Calabrese *(Sr VP-Sls & Bus Dev)*
Bob McMullan *(CFO)*

PARTY CITY OF BIRMINGHAM INC.
2750 Carl T Jones Dr, Huntsville, AL 35801
Tel.: (256) 650-0707
Web Site: http://www.partycity.com
Rev.: $25,441,462
Emp.: 16
Party Favors
N.A.I.C.S.: 459420
Stanley Rubenstein *(Chm)*
Esther Rubenstein *(Pres)*

PARTY CITY OF PUERTO RICO INC.
C-22 Gonzalez Giusti St Caparra Office Ctr Ste 226, Guaynabo, PR 00968
Tel.: (787) 781-3605
Web Site: http://www.partycitypr.com
Rev.: $12,097,577
Emp.: 25
Party Favors
N.A.I.C.S.: 459420
Joel Fernandez *(Asst Mgr)*

PARTY RENTAL LTD.
275 N St, Teterboro, NJ 07608
Tel.: (201) 727-4700
Web Site:
http://www.partyrentalltd.com
Rev.: $28,500,000
Emp.: 1,000
Party Supplies Rental Services
N.A.I.C.S.: 532289

Chris Lavarco *(Mgr-Customer Svc)*
Alan Gottlieb *(CFO)*
Gary Halperin *(Pres & COO)*
Rose Rabin *(Mgr-Washington)*
Joseph Nicastro *(Asst Controller)*
Laura Thorne *(Mgr-Bridgehampton)*
Michael Halperin *(CEO)*
Linda Ingram *(Mgr-Customer Rels)*
Diane Morales *(Supvr-Customer Svc)*
Barney Drew *(VP-HR)*
Neal Moran *(VP-Ops)*

PASADENA EYE CENTER
6950 Central Ave, Saint Petersburg, FL 33707
Tel.: (727) 343-3004
Web Site:
http://www.pasadenaeyecenter.com
Sales Range: $1-9.9 Million
Emp.: 20
Ophthalmology Services
N.A.I.C.S.: 621111
David E. Hall *(Pres)*

PASADENA LIQUORS AND FINE WINES
1100 Pasadena Ave S, South Pasadena, FL 33707
Tel.: (727) 347-9607
Web Site:
http://www.pasadenaliquors.com
Sales Range: $1-9.9 Million
Liquor Stores
N.A.I.C.S.: 445320
Jim Valenty *(Owner)*

PASADENA PLAYHOUSE
39 S El Molino Ave, Pasadena, CA 91101
Tel.: (626) 792-8672
Web Site:
http://www.pasadenaplayhouse.org
Sales Range: $10-24.9 Million
Emp.: 50
Theatrical Production
N.A.I.C.S.: 711110
Linda Boyd Griffey *(Sec)*
David DiCristofaro *(Chm)*

PASCH CONSULTING GROUP, LLC
446 Rt 35 S Building C, Eatontown, NJ 07724
Tel.: (732) 734-6993
Web Site:
http://www.pcgdigitalmarketing.com
Year Founded: 2006
Sales Range: $1-9.9 Million
Emp.: 48
Full Service Internet Marketing
N.A.I.C.S.: 541613
Brian Pasch *(Founder)*
Glenn Pasch *(CEO)*
Christine Rochelle *(VP-Ops)*
Renee McGowan *(Mgr-Fin)*
Shawn Hoagland *(Mgr-Web Team)*
Stephen Pasch *(Sr VP-Sls & Bus Dev)*

Subsidiaries:

First Class Educators (FCE) (1)
446 Rte 35 S Bldg C, Eatontown, NJ 07724   (100%)
Tel.: (732) 734-6993
Web Site:
http://www.firstclasseducators.com
Educational Programs, Event Consulting & Dealer Events
N.A.I.C.S.: 711320
Carrie Hemphill *(Mng Dir)*

PASCHAL HOME SERVICES, LLC
280 N Maestri Rd, Springdale, AR 72762
Tel.: (479) 900-0784
Web Site: https://gopaschal.com
Year Founded: 1968
Emp.: 375

PASCHAL HOME SERVICES, LLC

Paschal Home Services, LLC—(Continued)
Professional heating, Air Conditioning, Plumbing & Electrical Services
N.A.I.C.S.: 238220
Charley Boyce (CEO)

Subsidiaries:

Larson, Incorporated (1)
1091 W Kathryn St Ste 4, Nixa, MO 65714
Tel.: (417) 725-8020
Rev.: $1,314,000
Emp.: 9
Site Preparation Contractor
N.A.I.C.S.: 238910

PASCHEN MANAGEMENT CORPORATION
484 Mobil Ave Ste 23, Camarillo, CA 93010
Tel.: (805) 484-0459
Rev.: $10,900,000
Emp.: 850
Fast-Food Restaurant, Chain
N.A.I.C.S.: 722513
Clayton Paschen (Pres)
Matt McInally (Dir-Ops)

PASCO BROKERAGE, INC.
6465 Chase Oaks Blvd, Plano, TX 75023
Tel.: (972) 596-3350
Web Site: http://www.pascoinc.net
Year Founded: 1961
Rev.: $10,000,000
Emp.: 10
Provider of Restaurant Equipment & Supplies
N.A.I.C.S.: 423440
Kasey Hollon (Owner & Pres)
Bill Hollon (VP)

PASCO ECONOMIC DEVELOPMENT COUNCIL, INC.
16506 Pointe Village Dr Ste 101, Lutz, FL 33558
Tel.: (813) 926-0827
Web Site: http://www.pascoedc.com
Sales Range: $1-9.9 Million
Emp.: 8
Economic Development
N.A.I.C.S.: 925120
John Walsh (VP)
Jennifer Lachtara (Coord-Mktg Comm)
Bill Cronin (Pres & CEO)
Juawana Williams (VP)

PASCO SPECIALTY & MANUFACTURING INC.
11156 Wright Rd, Lynwood, CA 90262
Tel.: (310) 537-7782
Web Site: http://www.pascospecialty.com
Year Founded: 1936
Emp.: 100
Mfr & Distrbutor of Specialty Plumbing Fittings & Supplies
N.A.I.C.S.: 423720
Michael J. Hite (Pres)
Trevor King (VP)
Scott Wolosz (Reg Dir-Sls)
Philip McCririe (Mgr)
Michael Head (Reg Dir-Sls)

PASCOAG UTILITY DISTRICT
253 Pascoag Main St, Pascoag, RI 02859
Tel.: (401) 568-6222 RI
Web Site: http://www.pud-ri.org
Year Founded: 2001
Sales Range: $1-9.9 Million
Emp.: 100
Water Supply & Electricity Distr
N.A.I.C.S.: 221310

Mike Kirkwood (Gen Mgr)
Bill Guertin (Asst Gen Mgr-Ops)
Anne Polacek (Vice Chm)
John Demelim (Treas)

PASEK CORPORATION
9 W 3rd St, Boston, MA 02127
Tel.: (617) 269-7110 MA
Web Site: http://www.pasek.com
Year Founded: 1876
Sales Range: $10-24.9 Million
Emp.: 60
Provider of Security Systems Services
N.A.I.C.S.: 561621
Dave Alessandrini (Mgr-Sls)

PASKERT DISTRIBUTING COMPANY
9318 Florida Palm Dr, Tampa, FL 33619
Tel.: (813) 247-4477
Sales Range: $25-49.9 Million
Emp.: 150
Groceries & Related Products
N.A.I.C.S.: 424490

PASKEWITZ ASSET MANAGEMENT LLC
644 Fernandez Juncos Ave, San Juan, PR 00902
Tel.: (732) 393-1600
Web Site: http://www.pamhf.com
Investment Banking & Securities Dealing
N.A.I.C.S.: 523150
Bradford Paskewitz (CEO)

PASQUINELLI CONSTRUCTION CO., INC.
535 Plainfield Rd Ste B, Willowbrook, IL 60527-7608
Tel.: (630) 455-5400 IL
Year Founded: 1956
Rev.: $112,000,000
Emp.: 250
Residential Construction
N.A.I.C.S.: 522292
Bruno A. Pasquinelli (Co-Owner & Pres)
Tony Pasquinelli (Co-Owner & VP)

PASS CREEK RESOURCES LLC
4040 Broadway Ste 508, San Antonio, TX 78209
Tel.: (210) 451-5545 DE
Holding Company; Oil & Natural Gas Exploration Services
N.A.I.C.S.: 551112
Robert G. Watson Jr. (Pres & CEO)

Subsidiaries:

Black Sable Energy, LLC (1)
4040 Broadway Ste 305, San Antonio, TX 78209
Tel.: (210) 451-5545
Oil & Natural Gas Exploration Services
N.A.I.C.S.: 213112

PASSAGEWAYS, LLC
1551 Win Hentschel Blvd, West Lafayette, IN 47906
Tel.: (765) 497-8829
Web Site: http://www.passageways.com
Year Founded: 2003
Rev.: $2,700,000
Emp.: 27
Computer System Design Services
N.A.I.C.S.: 541512
Paroon Chadha (Co-Founder & CEO)
Anne Wertz (Mgr-Customer Support)
Stephanie Scott (Mgr-Implementation)

Bill Arnold (Chief Info Security Officer)
Colin Cunningham (CFO)

PASSAIC VALLEY WATER COMMISSION
1525 Main Ave, Clifton, NJ 07011
Tel.: (973) 340-4300
Web Site: http://www.pvwc.com
Year Founded: 1927
Sales Range: $50-74.9 Million
Emp.: 170
Water Supply
N.A.I.C.S.: 221310
Joseph A. Bella (CEO & Exec Dir)
James Gallagher (Dir-Personnel)
Rigo Sanchez (VP)
Thomas Devita (Pres)

PASSAVANT MEMORIAL HOMES
100 Passavant Way, Pittsburgh, PA 15238
Tel.: (412) 820-1010 PA
Web Site: http://www.passavant.org
Year Founded: 1895
Sales Range: $25-49.9 Million
Emp.: 1,070
Disability Assistance Services
N.A.I.C.S.: 624120
Carol Grant (VP-Corp Compliance)
Larry Kushik (VP-Admin)
Rick D. Senft (Pres & CEO)

PASSAVANT MEMORIAL HOSPITAL ASSOCIATION
1600 W Walnut St, Jacksonville, IL 62650
Tel.: (217) 245-9541 IL
Web Site: http://www.passavanthospital.com
Year Founded: 1906
Sales Range: $75-99.9 Million
Emp.: 909
Health Care Srvices
N.A.I.C.S.: 622110
Reginald Benton (Vice Chm)

PASSERO ASSOCIATES
242 W Main St Ste 100, Rochester, NY 14614
Tel.: (585) 325-1000 NY
Web Site: http://www.passero.com
Year Founded: 1972
Sales Range: $25-49.9 Million
Emp.: 88
Engineeering Services
N.A.I.C.S.: 541330
Wayne F. Wegman (CEO)
David Passero (CFO)
John Caruso (Pres)

PASSPORT GLOBAL INC.
1182 Market St Ste 318, San Francisco, CA 94102
Tel.: (415) 734-0465 DE
Web Site: http://www.passportshipping.com
Year Founded: 2017
Parcel Shipping Services
N.A.I.C.S.: 541618
Alex Yancher (Founder & CEO)
Adam Langston (Chief Comml Officer)

Subsidiaries:

Access Worldwide, Inc. (1)
5192 Southridge Pkwy Ste 112, Atlanta, GA 30349
Tel.: (404) 675-0633
Web Site: http://www.accessworldwide.net
Sales Range: $10-24.9 Million
Emp.: 17
Logistics & Transportation
N.A.I.C.S.: 541860
Daniel Barber (Mgr-IT)
Chassidy Willey (Coord-Customer Svc)

U.S. PRIVATE

PASSPORT HEALTH
921 E Fort Ave Ste 100, Baltimore, MD 21230
Tel.: (410) 727-0556
Web Site: http://www.PassportHealthUSA.com
Year Founded: 1994
Sales Range: $25-49.9 Million
Emp.: 18
Medical Devices
N.A.I.C.S.: 621511
Fran Lessans (Founder, Pres & CEO)
Martin B. Lessans (CFO & General Counsel)
Carol L. Derosa (Sr VP-Clinical Svc & Corp Dev)
Caitlin Bradford (Mgr-Competitive Intelligence & Tech)
Paul Fishburn (COO)

PASSUMPSIC BANCORP INC.
497 RailRd St, Saint Johnsbury, VT 05819
Tel.: (802) 748-3196
Web Site: http://www.passumpsicbank.com
Sales Range: $10-24.9 Million
Emp.: 140
Bank Holding Company
N.A.I.C.S.: 551111
Peter F. Crosby (Pres & CEO)

Subsidiaries:

Passumpsic Savings Bank (1)
497 Railroad St, Saint Johnsbury, VT 05819
Tel.: (802) 748-3196
Web Site: http://www.passumpsicbank.com
Federal Savings Bank
N.A.I.C.S.: 522180
Daniel J. Kimbell (Sr VP & Sr Investment Officer)
Ryan J. Stewart (VP)
Roena Whitehill (Sr VP & Head-Lending)
Bradley J. Gebbie (Chm)
Laurie C. Olszowy (Asst VP)
James Kisch (Pres & CEO)
Richard Lyon (CFO & Sr VP)

PASTA SHOP
5655 College Ave Ste 201, Oakland, CA 94618
Tel.: (510) 547-4005
Web Site: http://www.rockridgemarkethall.com
Year Founded: 1987
Rev.: $12,000,000
Emp.: 250
Owner & Operator of Delicatessen Stores; Wholesaler of Pasta
N.A.I.C.S.: 445110
Sara Wilson (Partner & Owner)

PASTORELLI FOOD PRODUCTS, INC.
162 N Sangamon St, Chicago, IL 60607-2210
Tel.: (312) 666-2041
Web Site: http://www.pastorelli.com
Year Founded: 1931
Sales Range: $75-99.9 Million
Emp.: 17
Italian Foods, Edible Oils & Vinegars
N.A.I.C.S.: 311422
Richard Pastorelli (Pres)
Angela Pastorelli (Treas)

PAT CLEMONS INC.
1720 S Marshall St, Boone, IA 50036
Tel.: (515) 432-5150 IA
Web Site: http://www.patclemons.com
Sales Range: $25-49.9 Million
Emp.: 70
Sales of New & Used Automobiles.
N.A.I.C.S.: 441110

COMPANIES

Pat Clemons *(Pres)*
Chad McDowell *(Controller)*
Joseph Clemons *(Gen Mgr)*

PAT COOK CONSTRUCTION, INC.
1904 Manatee Ave W Ste 300, Bradenton, FL 34205
Tel.: (941) 749-1959   FL
Web Site: http://www.patcook.com
Year Founded: 1992
Sales Range: $10-24.9 Million
Emp.: 15
Commercial & Institutional Building Construction
N.A.I.C.S.: 236220
Darla Cook *(Treas & Sec)*
Pat Cook *(Pres)*
Don Sicking *(VP & Project Mgr)*
Norman Neidert *(Project Mgr)*

PAT MCGRATH DODGE COUNTRY
4610 Ctr Point Rd NE, Cedar Rapids, IA 52402
Tel.: (319) 393-9256
Web Site: http://www.patmcgrathdodgecountry.com
Year Founded: 1975
Sales Range: $25-49.9 Million
Emp.: 100
New Car Whslr
N.A.I.C.S.: 441110
Pat McGrath *(Owner)*

PAT MILLIKEN FORD
9600 Telegraph Rd, Redford, MI 48239
Tel.: (313) 255-3100
Web Site: http://www.patmillikenford.com
Year Founded: 1959
Sales Range: $25-49.9 Million
Emp.: 125
New Car Retailer
N.A.I.C.S.: 441110
Julie Godfrey *(Gen Mgr-Sls)*
Ray Nabozny *(Mgr-New Vehicle Sls)*
Terry Kruse *(Mgr-Lease)*

PAT PECK NISSAN
1015 E Interstate 65 Service Rd S, Mobile, AL 36606
Tel.: (251) 476-7800
Web Site: http://patpecknissanmobile.com
Sales Range: $10-24.9 Million
Emp.: 85
Car Whslr
N.A.I.C.S.: 441110
Mike Neves *(Gen Mgr)*

PAT PECK NISSAN GULFPORT
9480 Highway 49, Gulfport, MS 39503
Tel.: (228) 864-6411
Web Site: http://www.patpecknissangulfport.com
Year Founded: 1987
Sales Range: $10-24.9 Million
Emp.: 74
New Car Dealers
N.A.I.C.S.: 441110
Les Fillingame *(Gen Mgr)*

PAT SALMON & SONS, INC.
3809 Roundtop Dr, North Little Rock, AR 72117-2628
Tel.: (501) 945-0778   AR
Web Site: http://www.patsalmon.com
Year Founded: 1946
Sales Range: $25-49.9 Million
Emp.: 600

Long Distance Trucking Services
N.A.I.C.S.: 484121
Don Salmon *(Pres & CEO)*
Tom Salmon *(COO, Treas & Sec)*
Jeff Boone *(VP & Gen Mgr)*
Patsy Fulfer *(Controller)*
Subsidiaries:
Mail Contractors of America, Inc. (1)
PO Box 15054, Little Rock, AR 72231
Tel.: (501) 280-0500
Web Site: http://www.salmoncompanies.com
Sales Range: $50-74.9 Million
Emp.: 50
Mail Carrier
N.A.I.C.S.: 484220
Don Salmon *(Pres)*

PAT'S PLACE CHILD ADVOCACY CENTER INC.
901 East Blvd, Charlotte, NC 28203
Tel.: (704) 335-2760   NC
Web Site: http://www.patsplacecac.org
Year Founded: 2004
Sales Range: $1-9.9 Million
Emp.: 50
Child Care Services
N.A.I.C.S.: 624110
Janet Harmon *(Dir-Prevention & Education)*
Ann Glaser *(Dir-Clinical Svcs)*
Andrew Oliver *(Exec Dir)*

PATAGONIA WORKS, INC.
259 W Santa Clara St, Ventura, CA 93001
Tel.: (805) 643-8616   CA
Web Site: http://www.patagoniaworks.com
Year Founded: 1973
Holding Company; Investment & Venture Capital Firm
N.A.I.C.S.: 551112
Rose Marcario *(Pres & CEO)*
Subsidiaries:
Patagonia, Inc. (1)
259 W Santa Clara St, Ventura, CA 93001
Tel.: (805) 643-8616
Web Site: http://www.patagonia.com
Outdoor Clothing Designer & Distr
N.A.I.C.S.: 315250
Yvon Chouinard *(Founder)*
Ryan Gellert *(CEO)*
Doug Freeman *(COO)*
Beth Thoren *(Dir-Environmental Action & Initiatives)*

PATCHETT'S MOTORS INCORPORATED
5200 N Golden State Blvd, Turlock, CA 95382
Tel.: (209) 669-5200
Web Site: http://www.patchettsford.com
Rev.: $20,900,000
Emp.: 21
Car Dealership Owner & Operator
N.A.I.C.S.: 441110
Shawn Daly *(Gen Mgr-Sls)*
Richard Rocha *(Dir-Fin)*

PATCO INDUSTRIES, INC.
4830 52nd Ave, Kenosha, WI 53144
Tel.: (262) 658-3590   WI
Web Site: http://www.patcoindustries.com
Year Founded: 1984
Sales Range: $1-9.9 Million
Emp.: 13
Rail Transportation & Communications Equipment Mfr
N.A.I.C.S.: 336999
Armando Covelli *(Dir-Ops)*

PATDAN LLC
249 Market St, Kingston, PA 18704

Tel.: (570) 288-4501
Web Site: http://www.patanddan.com
Sales Range: $10-24.9 Million
Emp.: 23
Sales of New & Used Automobiles
N.A.I.C.S.: 441110
Pat Del Balso *(Owner)*
Dan Del Balso *(Chm)*

PATE-DAWSON COMPANY
402 Commerce Ct, Goldsboro, NC 27534-7048
Tel.: (919) 778-3000   NC
Web Site: http://www.pdco.com
Year Founded: 1885
Sales Range: $50-74.9 Million
Emp.: 325
Wholesale Food Distr
N.A.I.C.S.: 424420
Karen Baker *(Mgr-Sls Support)*
Bob Stewart *(Dir-Multi Unit Sls)*
Tim Wilson *(Gen Mgr-Sls)*
John Pare *(Mgr-Sls-Triangle Area)*
David Stansfield *(Pres)*
Rick Stapleton *(VP-Sls & Mdsg)*
Monae Dean *(Mgr-Transportation & Warehouse)*
Clifton G. Howell *(Dir-Info Sys)*
Jeff Smith *(Dir-Mdsg)*
Clay Enloe *(Dir-Pur & HR)*
Chuck Slappey *(VP-Ops)*

PATEL CONSULTANTS CORPORATION
1525 Morris Ave, Union, NJ 07083
Tel.: (908) 964-7575
Web Site: http://www.patelcorp.com
Year Founded: 1973
Sales Range: $25-49.9 Million
Emp.: 110
IT Staffing Services
N.A.I.C.S.: 561320
Mahendra Patel *(Owner & Pres)*
Nini Olson *(VP-Ops)*

PATEL CONVENIENCE STORES INC.
1300 5th St SE, Cairo, GA 39828
Tel.: (229) 377-9780
Sales Range: $10-24.9 Million
Emp.: 100
Owner & Operator of Convenience Stores
N.A.I.C.S.: 445131
Sanjay Patel *(Pres)*
Cindy Baggett *(Office Mgr)*

PATERSON CARD & PAPER CO.
730 Madison Ave, Paterson, NJ 07501
Tel.: (973) 278-2410   NJ
Web Site: http://www.patersonpapers.com
Year Founded: 1914
Sales Range: $10-24.9 Million
Emp.: 30
Printing Paper Distr
N.A.I.C.S.: 424110
Michael Prell *(Pres)*
Lou Salle *(Mgr-Pur)*
Chuck Furlong *(Mgr-Credit)*
Genie Weisz *(Pres-The Paper Store & More)*

PATH, INC.
8220 Castor Ave, Philadelphia, PA 19152
Tel.: (215) 728-4600   PA
Web Site: http://www.pathcenter.org
Year Founded: 1973
Sales Range: $25-49.9 Million
Emp.: 735
Behavioral Healthcare Services
N.A.I.C.S.: 623220

Alan Brunwasser *(Dir-HR Dept)*
Michael Forchetti *(Chief Comm Officer)*
Nora Kramer *(Dir-Medical)*
Jeffrey Brown *(COO)*
Brad Newman *(Treas)*
Donna Bourgeois *(CIO)*
Jeffrey Wolfenson *(CFO)*
Nancy Greenstein *(Chm)*

PATH-TEC
5700 Old Brim Rd, Midland, GA 31820
Tel.: (706) 569-6368
Web Site: http://www.path-tec.com
Year Founded: 2005
Sales Range: $1-9.9 Million
Emp.: 40
Specimen Collection Kit Design, Manufacturing & Distribution Services
N.A.I.C.S.: 339112
Kevin Boykin *(Founder & CEO)*

PATHFINDER CONSULTANTS LLC
1725 St NW Ste 300, Washington, DC 20006
Tel.: (202) 737-7284
Web Site: http://www.pathfinderconsultants.com
Year Founded: 2010
Sales Range: $1-9.9 Million
Emp.: 42
Management Consulting Services
N.A.I.C.S.: 541690
George Hidy *(CEO & Mgr-Project & Program)*
Kareisa Hidy *(Dir-Ops)*

PATHFINDER, INC.
2520 W Main St, Jacksonville, AR 72078
Tel.: (501) 982-0528   AR
Web Site: http://www.pathfinderinc.org
Year Founded: 1972
Sales Range: $25-49.9 Million
Emp.: 1,595
Developmental Disability Assistance Services
N.A.I.C.S.: 623210
Michael McCreight *(Exec Dir)*
Wendell Dorman *(Sec)*
Joan R. Zumwalt *(Chm)*
Robert D. Ferguson Jr. *(Vice Chm)*

PATHFINDERS
308 W Lancaster Ave Ste 201, Wayne, PA 19087-3944
Tel.: (610) 854-1060
Web Site: http://www.pathfindersinc.net
Year Founded: 1992
Rev.: $3,800,000
Emp.: 16
Employment Placement Agency
N.A.I.C.S.: 561311
Keenan Goggin *(Owner & Pres)*
Mike McErn *(Mgr-Sls)*

PATHFINDERS ADVERTISING & MARKETING GROUP
1250 Pkwy, Mishawaka, IN 46545-3400
Tel.: (574) 259-5908
Web Site: http://www.pathfind.com
Year Founded: 1979
Sales Range: $10-24.9 Million
Emp.: 45
Advertising Agencies
N.A.I.C.S.: 541810
Stephen R. Ball *(CEO)*
Vicky Holland *(Pres)*
Kelly Ball *(VP)*
Nancy Ball *(Office Mgr)*
Kathy Mutka *(Acct Supvr)*
Jeff Staley *(Dir-Art)*
Mike Johnson *(Copywriter)*

PATHGROUP

PathGroup—(Continued)

PATHGROUP
5301 Virginia Way, Brentwood, TN 37027
Tel.: (615) 562-9300
Web Site: https://www.pathgroup.com
Year Founded: 1965
Anatomic, Clinical & Molecular Pathology Services
N.A.I.C.S.: 621511
Ben W. Davis *(Pres & CEO)*

Subsidiaries:

Pathology Consultants, Inc. (1)
8 Memorial Medical Ct, Greenville, SC 29605
Tel.: (864) 295-3492
Web Site:
    http://www.pathologyconsultants.org
Sales Range: $1-9.9 Million
Emp.: 35
Medical Laboratories
N.A.I.C.S.: 621511
Lawrence Minnette *(Pres)*

Southeastern Pathology
Associates (1)
203 Indigo Dr, Brunswick, GA 31525
Web Site: http://www.sepalabs.com
Pathology Services
N.A.I.C.S.: 621511
Vanessa West *(Mgr)*
Mark G. Hanly *(Chief Medical Officer)*

PATHLOCK, INC.
270 S Main St Ste 100, Flemington, NJ 08822-1787
Tel.: (908) 782-5700
Web Site: https://pathlock.com
Emp.: 100
Software Publisher
N.A.I.C.S.: 513210
Anand Adya *(Founder & CEO)*

PATHMARK TRANSPORTATION MARKETING CO.
2875 S Mendenhall Rd Ste 3, Memphis, TN 38115
Tel.: (901) 362-1555
Web Site:
    http://www.pathmarktrans.com
Year Founded: 1989
Sales Range: $25-49.9 Million
Emp.: 20
Provider of Shipping Broker Services
N.A.I.C.S.: 488510
Wesley Kraker *(Pres & CEO)*
Kathy Lineberry *(Mgr-Ops)*
Judie Conner *(Mgr-Admin)*

PATHOS AI, INC.
600 W Chicago Ave Ste 150, Chicago, IL 60654
Tel.: (312) 765-7820
Web Site: https://pathos.com
Emp.: 100
Biotechnology Research
N.A.I.C.S.: 541714
Ryan Fukushima *(CEO)*

Subsidiaries:

Rain Oncology Inc. (1)
8000 Jarvis Ave Ste 204, Newark, CA 94560
Tel.: (510) 953-5559
Web Site: https://www.rainoncology.com
Rev.: $1,415,000
Assets: $135,180,000
Liabilities: $22,144,000
Net Worth: $113,036,000
Earnings: ($75,724,000)
Emp.: 63
Fiscal Year-end: 12/31/2022
Biotechnology Research & Development Services
N.A.I.C.S.: 541714
Lucio Tozzi *(Sr VP-Clinical Ops)*
Vijaya Tirunagaru *(Sr VP & Head-Research)*
Allan Wagman *(VP-Chemistry)*

Nelson Cabatuan *(Sr VP-Fin & Admin)*
Kolbot By *(Sr VP-Technical Ops)*
Jamie S. Blose *(VP & Head-Legal Affairs)*

PATHSTONE CORPORATION
400 E Ave, Rochester, NY 14607-1910
Tel.: (585) 546-7180
Web Site: http://www.pathstone.org
Year Founded: 1969
Provider of Individual & Family Social Services
N.A.I.C.S.: 624190
Stuart J. Mitchell *(Pres & CEO)*
Jeffrey Lewis *(Sr VP-Direct Svcs)*
Kathryn Bryan *(Sr VP-Property Mgmt)*
Alex Castro *(COO)*
Anne R. Babcock-Stiner *(Sr VP-HR)*
Susan Boss *(Sr VP-Housing Svcs)*
Amelia Casciani *(Sr VP-Real Estate Dev)*
Nita R. DAgostino *(Sr VP-Direct Svcs)*
Ruperto Montero *(CFO)*
Leslie W. Kernan Jr. *(Corp Counsel)*

PATHWAY COMMUNITIES INC.
100 World Dr Ste 240, Peachtree City, GA 30269
Tel.: (770) 487-8585
Rev.: $11,022,111
Emp.: 100
Subdividers & Developers
N.A.I.C.S.: 237210
Pat Heaberg *(VP-CID)*
Peggy Sullivan *(Pres)*

PATHWAYS
585 N Mary Ave, Sunnyvale, CA 94085
Tel.: (408) 730-5900
Web Site:
    http://www.pathwayshealth.org
Year Founded: 1986
Sales Range: $50-74.9 Million
Hospice Care Services
N.A.I.C.S.: 621610
Matt Harris *(Treas)*
Tom Harshman *(Sec)*

PATHWAYS COMMUNITY HEALTH
1800 Community Dr, Clinton, MO 64735
Tel.: (660) 885-8131
Web Site:
    http://www.pathwaysonline.org
Year Founded: 1974
Sales Range: $50-74.9 Million
Emp.: 1,223
Behavioral Healthcare Services
N.A.I.C.S.: 623220
Mel Fetter *(CEO)*
Gloria Miller *(Chief Clinical Officer)*

PATHWAYS FINANCIAL CREDIT UNION, INC.
5665 N Hamilton Rd, Columbus, OH 43230
Tel.: (614) 416-7588
Web Site:
    http://www.pathwayscu.com
Year Founded: 1973
Sales Range: $1-9.9 Million
Emp.: 80
Credit Union
N.A.I.C.S.: 522130
Michael Shafer *(CEO)*
Greg Kidwell *(Pres)*
Casey Eckles *(VP-Ops)*
J. Andrew Tarbox *(Chief Intelligence Officer)*
Linda Battaglia *(Dir-Compliance & Trng)*

PATHWAYS HOSPICE
305 Carpenter Rd, Fort Collins, CO 80525
Tel.: (970) 663-3500
Web Site: http://www.pathways-care.org
Year Founded: 1979
Sales Range: $1-9.9 Million
Emp.: 151
Community Care Services
N.A.I.C.S.: 621498
James Danforth *(Dir-Medical)*
Joseph Lopez *(Dir-Medical)*
JoAnn Lovins *(Chm)*
Mary Voggesser *(Vice Chm)*
Michael Towbin *(Dir-Medical)*
David Allen *(Dir-Medical)*

PATIENT ACCESS NETWORK FOUNDATION
805 15th St NW Ste 500, Washington, DC 20005
Tel.: (202) 347-9272
Web Site:
    http://www.panfoundation.org
Year Founded: 2004
Rev.: $535,383,438
Assets: $557,200,700
Liabilities: $133,224,367
Net Worth: $423,976,333
Earnings: $170,746,462
Emp.: 6
Fiscal Year-end: 12/31/18
Health Care Srvices
N.A.I.C.S.: 622110
Daniel J. Klein *(Pres & CEO)*
Ayesha Azam *(VP-Medical Affairs)*
Barbara Barb *(Mgr-HR & Admin)*
Stu Cherande-Friedman *(Sr Dir-Program Ops)*
Liz Eckert *(Dir-Mktg & Comm)*
Nechumah Getz *(COO)*
Thomas Herrmann *(Chief Compliance Officer)*
Karla Kalis *(Mgr-Individual Giving)*
Melissa Kuhta *(Mgr-Compliance)*
Brandon Luzier *(Project Mgr)*
Miriam Million *(Mgr-Mktg & Comm)*
Amy Niles *(Exec VP)*
Gary Owens *(Dir-Medical)*
Leena Patel *(VP-Dev)*
Megan Pawlowski *(Mgr-Digital Mktg & Comm)*
Audrey Quartey *(Sr Mgr-Provider Rels)*
Scott Schlenoff *(CFO)*
Deepak Shrestha *(Sr Project Mgr)*
Victoria Singer *(Mgr-Product Dev)*
Divya Sriram *(Sr Mgr-Dev)*
Joel Straus *(Controller)*
Joan Zhang *(Mgr-Medical Affairs)*

PATIENT CONVERSATION MEDIA, INC.
4315 Guadalupe St Ste 200, Austin, TX 78751
Tel.: (512) 522-0966
Web Site:
    http://www.patientconversation.com
Year Founded: 2008
Sales Range: $1-9.9 Million
Emp.: 29
Healthcare Advertising & Media Buying Services
N.A.I.C.S.: 541810
Donald W. Hackett *(Chm & CEO)*
Lou Scalpati *(CTO)*
Russell J. Ricci *(Chief Medical Officer)*

PATIENT SQUARE CAPITAL, L.P.
2884 Sand Hill Rd Ste 100, Menlo Park, CA 94025
Tel.: (650) 384-6558
Web Site:
    http://www.patientsquarecapital.com

U.S. PRIVATE

Year Founded: 2020
Health Care Investment Firm
N.A.I.C.S.: 523999
Karr Narula *(Founding Partner)*
Trit Garg *(VP)*
Justin Sabet-Peyman *(Mng Dir)*
Adam Fliss *(Founding Partner & Gen Counsel)*
Maria Walker *(Founding Partner & CFO)*
Kaveh Samie *(Partner, Chm & CEO-Middle East & North Africa & Head-Intl Fund Partnerships)*
Jake Cabala *(Partner & Head-Fund Partnerships)*
Jim Momtazee *(Mng Partner)*

Subsidiaries:

Eargo, Inc. (1)
2665 N 1st St Ste 300, San Jose, CA 95134 (100%)
Tel.: (650) 351-7700
Web Site: https://www.eargo.com
Rev.: $37,248,000
Assets: $132,078,000
Liabilities: $31,224,000
Net Worth: $100,854,000
Earnings: ($157,487,000)
Emp.: 243
Fiscal Year-end: 12/31/2022
Hearing Aid Mfr
N.A.I.C.S.: 334510
Mark Thorpe *(CFO & Chief Acctg Officer)*
Donald J. Spence *(Chm)*
Tim Trine *(CTO)*
Christy La Pierre *(Chief Legal Officer & Sec)*

Hanger, Inc. (1)
10910 Domain Dr Ste 300, Austin, PA 17402
Tel.: (512) 777-3800
Web Site: https://corporate.hanger.com
Rev.: $1,120,488,000
Assets: $998,139,000
Liabilities: $887,968,000
Net Worth: $110,171,000
Earnings: $41,982,000
Emp.: 5,200
Fiscal Year-end: 12/31/2021
Orthotic & Prosthetic Patient-Care Centers Developer & Operator
N.A.I.C.S.: 621399
Thomas E. Hartman *(Gen Counsel, Sec & Sr VP)*
Thomas E. Kiraly *(CFO & Exec VP)*
C. Scott Ranson *(CIO & Exec VP-Corp Svcs)*
James H. Campbell *(Chief Clinical Officer & Sr VP)*
Mitchell D. Dobson *(Chief Compliance Officer & Sr VP)*
Peter A. Stoy *(Pres, CEO & COO)*
Dixon LeGrande *(Pres-Products & Svcs)*
Kate Means *(Sr VP-Supply Chain & Customer Ops)*
Kelsey Troy *(Chief HR Officer & Sr VP)*

Subsidiary (Domestic):

Accelerated Care Plus Corp. (2)
4999 Aircenter Cir Ste 103, Reno, NV 89502
Tel.: (775) 685-4000
Web Site: http://info.acplus.com
Electromedical Equipment Mfr
N.A.I.C.S.: 334510
Debbie Koepsel *(Pres)*

Advanced O & P Solutions, L.L.C. (2)
8641 W 95th St, Hickory Hills, IL 60457
Tel.: (708) 237-4084
Web Site: http://www.aopsolutions.com
Orthotic & Prosthetic Product Mfr
N.A.I.C.S.: 339113
Jim Kingsley *(COO)*
Mike Angelico *(Sls Dir)*
Chris Mowrer *(Dir-Clinical & Mfg Tech)*
Jennifer Carlson *(Mgr-Client Svcs)*
Ron Bystrom *(Exec Gen Mgr)*

Advanced Prosthetics & Orthotics, L.L.C. (2)
4537 Emerson St, Jacksonville, FL 32207
Tel.: (904) 858-1515

COMPANIES

Web Site: http://apojax.com
Surgical Appliance Mfr & Distr
N.A.I.C.S.: 339112
Michael D. Richard (Owner & Pres)
Shannon Richard (Office Mgr)

Advanced Prosthetics Center, LLC (2)
9109 Blondo St Ste 1&2, Omaha, NE 68134
Tel.: (402) 399-9993
Web Site: http://www.betterlimbs.com
Surgical Appliance Mfr & Distr
N.A.I.C.S.: 339112
Teresa Eckmann (Office Mgr)

Faith Prosthetic-Orthotic Services, Inc. (2)
1025 Concord Pkwy N, Concord, NC 28027
Tel.: (704) 782-0908
Surgical Appliance Mfr & Distr
N.A.I.C.S.: 339112

Fillauer Companies, Inc. (2)
2710 Amnicola Hwy, Chattanooga, TN 37406
Tel.: (423) 624-0946
Web Site: http://www.fillauercompanies.com
Sales Range: $10-24.9 Million
Holding Company; Orthotic & Prosthetic Devices & Products Designer & Mfr
N.A.I.C.S.: 551112
Michael Fillauer (CEO)
Sheri Hassler (Pres)
Kevin Moore (Pres-Europe)
Rick Anderson (Pres-North Carolina)

Subsidiary (Non-US):

Fillauer Europe AB (3)
Kung Hans Vag 2, 192 68, Sollentuna, Sweden
Tel.: (46) 850533200
Web Site: http://www.fillauer.eu
Orthotic & Prosthetic Device Design & Mfr
N.A.I.C.S.: 339113
Kevin Moore (Pres)
Ulf Gustafsson (Mgr-Key Acct)

Subsidiary (Domestic):

Fillauer LLC (3)
2710 Amnicola Hwy, Chattanooga, TN 37406
Tel.: (423) 624-0946
Web Site: http://www.fillauer.com
Sales Range: $10-24.9 Million
Emp.: 90
Custom Orthopedic Device Designer & Mfr
N.A.I.C.S.: 339113
Sheri Hassler (Pres)

Hosmer-Dorrance Corporation (3)
561 Division St, Campbell, CA 95008
Tel.: (408) 379-5151
Web Site: http://www.hosmer.com
Sales Range: $10-24.9 Million
Emp.: 50
Lower & Upper Extremity Prosthetic Devices Designer & Mfr
N.A.I.C.S.: 339113
Karl Hovland (Pres)
Rich Platt (VP-Ops)

Motion Control, Inc. (3)
115 N Wright Brothers Dr, Salt Lake City, UT 84116
Tel.: (801) 326-3434
Web Site: http://www.utaharm.com
Sales Range: $10-24.9 Million
Emp.: 35
Myoelectric & Externally Powered Prosthetic Arm Systems Designer & Mfr
N.A.I.C.S.: 334510
Arthur Dyck (Pres)
Edwin K. Iversen (VP-R&D)

OTS Corporation (3)
220 Merrimon Ave, Weaverville, NC 28787
Tel.: (828) 658-8330
Web Site: http://www.ots-corp.com
Orthotic Device & PDQ Oven Designer & Mfr
N.A.I.C.S.: 339113
Timothy T. Pansiera (Founder, Pres & Dir-Product Dev)

Stealth Composites, LLC (3)
3938 S 300 W, Salt Lake City, UT 84107
Tel.: (801) 281-9964

Web Site: http://www.e-motis.com
Orthotic Product Mfr
N.A.I.C.S.: 339113
Eric Rubie (Pres)

Subsidiary (Domestic):

Hanger Fabrication Network LLC (2)
4155 E La Palma Ave Ste B400, Anaheim, CA 92807
Tel.: (714) 961-2155
Web Site: http://www.hangerfabrication.com
Orthotic & Prosthetic Surgical Product Mfr
N.A.I.C.S.: 339113

Hanger Prosthetic & Orthotics, Inc. (2)
2 Bethesda Metro Ctr Ste 1200, Bethesda, MD 20814-6320 (100%)
Tel.: (301) 986-0701
Sales Range: $50-74.9 Million
Emp.: 150
Prosthetic & Orthotic Patient Care
N.A.I.C.S.: 621498

Subsidiary (Domestic):

ABI Orthotic/Prosthetic Laboratories, Ltd. (3)
930 Trailwood Dr, Boardman, OH 44512 (100%)
Tel.: (330) 758-1143
Web Site: http://www.hanger.com
Sales Range: $100-124.9 Million
Orthotic & Prosthetic Devices Mfr & Fitting
N.A.I.C.S.: 339112

Advanced Prosthetics of America, Inc. (3)
2763 W Old Us Hwy 441, Mount Dora, FL 32757-3500
Tel.: (352) 383-0396
Surgical Appliance Whslr
N.A.I.C.S.: 423450

Elite Care Incorporated (3)
4114 E Wood St Ste 106, Phoenix, AZ 85040
Tel.: (602) 426-8899
Web Site: http://www.hanger.com
Emp.: 20
Medical Equipment Whslr
N.A.I.C.S.: 423450

Hanger Advanced Bio-Mechanics Inc. (3)
1755 Grass Valley Hwy, Auburn, CA 95603 (100%)
Tel.: (530) 823-3143
Web Site: http://www.hanger.com
Emp.: 40
Prosthetic & Orthotic Services
N.A.I.C.S.: 423450

Hanger Prosthetics & Orthotics East, Inc. (3)
1620 Gateway Blvd Ste 104, Murfreesboro, TN 37129
Tel.: (615) 896-1485
Web Site: https://hangerclinic.com
Orthotic & Prosthetic Patient Care Services
N.A.I.C.S.: 621399

MK Prosthetic & Orthotic Services Inc. (3)
4319 Medical Dr Ste 106, San Antonio, TX 78229
Tel.: (210) 614-9222
Web Site: http://www.hangerclinic.com
Healtcare Services
N.A.I.C.S.: 621999

Orthopedic Rehabilitation Products, Ltd. (3)
5895 E Evans Ste 102, Denver, CO 80222
Tel.: (720) 524-0950
Orthopedic Products Retailer
N.A.I.C.S.: 456199

Shasta Orthotic Prosthetic Service, Inc. (3)
1477 Lincoln St, Redding, CA 96001
Tel.: (530) 246-3333
Web Site: http://www.hanger.com
Sales Range: $100-124.9 Million
Surgical Appliance Mfr
N.A.I.C.S.: 339113

US Orthotics and Prosthetics, Inc. (3)

30 Town Country Dr Ste 103, Fredericksburg, VA 22405
Tel.: (540) 899-2655
Orthotic & Prosthetic Product Mfr
N.A.I.C.S.: 339113

Wasatch Orthotics & Pedorthics, LLC (3)
887 E Vine St 5870 S, Salt Lake City, UT 84107
Tel.: (801) 293-8777
Web Site: http://www.hangerclinic.com
Orthotic Equipment Whslr
N.A.I.C.S.: 423450

Subsidiary (Domestic):

Innovative Neurotronics, Inc. (2)
3600 N Capital of Texas Hwy Ste B150, Austin, TX 78746 (100%)
Tel.: (512) 721-1900
Web Site: http://www.ininc.com
Sales Range: $25-49.9 Million
Emp.: 25
Adaptive & Assistive Technology for People with Disabilities
N.A.I.C.S.: 541713

Linkia, LLC (2)
1375 Piccard Dr Ste 300, Rockville, MD 20850
Tel.: (301) 354-3600
Web Site: http://www.linkia.com
Sales Range: $100-124.9 Million
Insurance Interface Services for Orthotic & Prosthetic Professionals
N.A.I.C.S.: 561499

MMAR Medical Group, Inc. (2)
6025 Shiloh Rd Ste A, Alpharetta, GA 30005
Tel.: (800) 662-7633
Web Site: http://www.mmarmedical.com
Surgical Appliance Mfr & Distr
N.A.I.C.S.: 423450

Nebraska Orthotic & Prosthetic Services, Inc. (2)
722 N Diers Ave, Grand Island, NE 68803
Tel.: (308) 398-2242
Web Site: http://www.hanger.com
Sales Range: $1-9.9 Million
Emp.: 10
Orthotic & Prosthetic Services
N.A.I.C.S.: 621340

Next Step Orthopaedics, Inc. (2)
331 Main St, West Orange, NJ 07052
Tel.: (973) 736-2244
Web Site: http://www.nextsteportho.com
Orthopedic Clinic Services
N.A.I.C.S.: 621111

Orthotic & Prosthetic Technologies, Inc. (2)
2801 Oakmont Dr Ste 1200, Round Rock, TX 78665
Tel.: (512) 255-4400
Health Care Srvices
N.A.I.C.S.: 621111

Prosthetic Laboratories of Rochester, Inc. (2)
121 23rd Ave SW, Rochester, MN 55902
Tel.: (507) 281-5250
Health Care Srvices
N.A.I.C.S.: 621111

SCOPe Orthotics & Prosthetics, Inc. (2)
7863 La Mesa Blvd Ste 100, La Mesa, CA 91942
Tel.: (619) 589-9980
Health Care Srvices
N.A.I.C.S.: 621111

Sawtooth Orthotics and Prosthetics, Inc. (2)
780 S 14th St, Boise, ID 83702
Tel.: (208) 344-9981
Web Site: http://www.sawtoothop.com
Sales Range: $1-9.9 Million
Emp.: 13
Orthotic Medical Product Distr
N.A.I.C.S.: 423450
Desh Anderson (Owner)

Scheck & Siress Prosthetics, Inc. (2)
1S376 Summit Ave Ct E, Oakbrook Terrace, IL 60181

PATIENT SQUARE CAPITAL, L.P.

Tel.: (630) 445-1811
Web Site: http://www.scheckandsiress.com
Health Care Srvices
N.A.I.C.S.: 621999
Samuel Failla (Fin Dir)
Jim Kingsley (COO)
Sheila Boydston (Mgr-Admin Quality Control)
Rob Cressler (CFO)
Tomi Lancaster (Dir-Bus Ops)

Shields Orthotic Prosthetic Services, Inc. (2)
2785 E 3300 S, Salt Lake City, UT 84109
Tel.: (801) 467-5483
Web Site: http://www.shieldsop.com
Health Care Srvices
N.A.I.C.S.: 621111

Southern Prosthetic Supply, Inc. (2)
6530 Corporate Ct, Alpharetta, GA 30005-1706 (100%)
Tel.: (678) 455-8888
Web Site: https://www.spsco.com
Sales Range: $50-74.9 Million
Emp.: 100
Prosthetic Device Distr
N.A.I.C.S.: 423450

Suncoast Orthotics & Prosthetics, Inc. (2)
1838 Hillview St, Sarasota, FL 34239
Tel.: (941) 365-7588
Web Site: http://www.suncoastandp.com
Prosthetic Appliance Distr
N.A.I.C.S.: 423450
Alan Ross (Owner & Pres)
R. John (Mgr-Park)

Superior Orthotics & Prosthetics, LLC (2)
1823 Charlotte Ave, Nashville, TN 37230
Tel.: (615) 340-0068
Web Site: http://www.superioroandp.com
Prosthetic Appliance Distr
N.A.I.C.S.: 423450
Rob Pittman (Founder & Pres)
Eric Kimsey (Dir-Clinical Ops & Prosthetics)
Philip Graves (Dir-Ops)
Donna Boggs (Dir-Admin)
Keith Wilson (Dir-Orthotics)
Erik Larsen (Mktg Dir)
Joey Dixon (Dir-Compliance)

Radius Health, Inc. (1)
22 Boston Wharf Rd 7th Fl, Boston, MA 02210
Tel.: (617) 551-4000
Web Site: https://www.radiuspharm.com
Rev.: $229,973,000
Assets: $181,542,000
Liabilities: $433,846,000
Net Worth: ($252,304,000)
Earnings: ($70,176,000)
Emp.: 293
Fiscal Year-end: 12/31/2021
Pharmaceuticals Mfr
N.A.I.C.S.: 325412
Mark Conley (CFO, Treas & VP)
Chhaya Shah (Chief Bus Officer)
Salvador Grausso III (Chief Comml Officer, Sr VP & Head-Patient Access-US)
Averi Price (Chief Compliance Officer & Gen Counsel)
Maureen Conlan (Head-Oncology)
Bruce Mitlak (Chief Medical Officer & Head-Discovery Science)

SOC Telemed, Inc. (1)
2411 Dulles Corner Park Ste 475, Herndon, VA 20171-5605
Tel.: (866) 483-9690
Web Site: http://www.soctelemed.com
Emp.: 2
Acute Telemedicine Technology & Services
N.A.I.C.S.: 622110
David R. Fletcher (Interim CFO)
David Mikula (COO)
Christopher M. Gallagher (CEO)

Subsidiary (Domestic):

Specialists on Call, Inc. (2)
1768 Business Ctr Dr Ste 100, Reston, VA 20190-5359
Web Site: http://www.soctelemed.com
Acute Telemedicine Technology & Solutions
N.A.I.C.S.: 622110
Chris Gallagher (CEO)
David Mikula (COO)

PATIENT SQUARE CAPITAL, L.P.

U.S. PRIVATE

Patient Square Capital, L.P.—(Continued)
R. Jason Hallock *(Chief Medical Officer)*
Eunice Kim *(Gen Counsel)*
Ron Egan *(Chief Customer Officer)*
Stephanie Harris *(Chief HR Officer)*

Syneos Health, Inc. (1)
1030 Sync St, Morrisville, NC 27560-5468
Tel.: (919) 876-9300
Web Site: https://www.syneoshealth.com
Rev.: $5,393,082,000
Assets: $8,199,218,000
Liabilities: $4,704,217,000
Net Worth: $3,495,001,000
Earnings: $266,497,000
Emp.: 28,768
Fiscal Year-end: 12/31/2022
Holding Company; Biopharmaceutical & Medical Device Mfr
N.A.I.C.S.: 551112
Jim Momtazee *(Mng Partner)*
Colin Shannon *(CEO)*
Michelle Keefe *(CEO)*
Kristen Spensieri *(Head-Corp Comm & Mktg-Global)*
Baba Shetty *(Pres-Tech & Data Solutions)*
Jeanine O'Kane *(Pres-Syneos Health Comm)*
Hillary Bochniak *(Chief HR Officer)*
Larry A. Pickett Jr. *(CIO)*
Ben Rudnick *(Chief Strategy Officer)*
Michael J. Bonello *(CFO)*
Michael Brooks *(COO)*
Costa Panagos *(Co-CEO)*
Max Ghez *(Head-Clinical Bus Dev)*
Larry A. Pickett Jr. *(Chief Info & Digital Officer)*
Margaret Alexander *(Founder)*

Subsidiary (Domestic):

INC Research, LLC (2)
3201 Beechleaf Ct Ste 600, Raleigh, NC 27604-1547
Tel.: (919) 876-9300
Web Site: http://www.incresearch.com
Pharmaceutical Research & Development Services
N.A.I.C.S.: 541715

Division (Domestic):

INC Research (3)
441 Vine St Ste 1200, Cincinnati, OH 45202
Tel.: (513) 381-5550
Web Site: http://www.incresearch.com
Sales Range: $400-449.9 Million
Data Processing of Biopharmaceutical Research
N.A.I.C.S.: 518210
Dana Magly *(Mgr-Facilities)*
Dan Schwartz *(Mgr-IT)*
David Schneider *(Sr Dir-Medical)*

Division (Non-US):

INC Research (3)
River View The Meadows Business Park, Station Approach Blackwater, Camberley, GU17 9AB, Surrey, United Kingdom
Tel.: (44) 1276481000
Web Site: http://www.incresearch.com
Sales Range: $25-49.9 Million
Contract Biopharmaceutical Research & Development Services
N.A.I.C.S.: 541715
Rosie McKellar *(Sr Dir-Central Monitoring)*
Jane Winter *(Sr VP-Global Consulting Unit)*

INC Research (3)
Level 1 20 Atherton Road, Oakleigh, 3166, VIC, Australia
Tel.: (61) 395677600
Sales Range: $10-24.9 Million
Contract Biopharmaceutical Research & Development Services
N.A.I.C.S.: 541715

INC Research (3)
720 King St W, Toronto, M5V 2T3, ON, Canada
Tel.: (416) 963-9338
Web Site: http://www.incresearch.com
Sales Range: $10-24.9 Million
Early Phase Clinical Development Services
N.A.I.C.S.: 541715
Kerry Schoedel *(Dir-Scientific)*

INC Research - Global Clinical Development (3)
Einsteindreef 117-119, 2562 GB, Utrecht, Netherlands
Tel.: (31) 302584600
Sales Range: $25-49.9 Million
Contract Clinical Development Services
N.A.I.C.S.: 541715

INC Research - Munich (3)
Stefan-George-Ring 6, 81929, Munich, Germany
Tel.: (49) 899939130
Web Site: http://www.incresearch.com
Sales Range: $50-74.9 Million
Contract Biopharmaceutical Research & Development Services
N.A.I.C.S.: 541715

INC Research - Saronno (3)
Vicolo del Caldo 36, 21047, Saronno, VA, Italy
Tel.: (39) 029619921
Sales Range: $25-49.9 Million
Contract Biopharmaceutical Research & Development Services
N.A.I.C.S.: 541715

Subsidiary (Domestic):

Syneos Health, LLC (2)
1 Van de Graaff Dr, Burlington, MA 01803
Tel.: (781) 229-8877
Web Site: http://www.syneoshealth.com
Holding Company; Outsourced Clinical Biopharmaceutical Development & Commercialization Services
N.A.I.C.S.: 551112
John M. Dineen *(Chm)*

Subsidiary (Domestic):

Syneos Health US, Inc. (3)
1 Van de Graaff Dr, Burlington, MA 01803
Tel.: (781) 229-8877
Web Site: http://www.syneoshealth.com
Outsourced Clinical Biopharmaceutical Development & Commercialization Services
N.A.I.C.S.: 541618

Subsidiary (Domestic):

Syneos Health Clinical, LLC (4)
301 College Rd E, Princeton, NJ 08540
Tel.: (609) 951-0005
Web Site: http://www.syneoshealth.com
Holding Company; Clinical Research & Drug Development Services
N.A.I.C.S.: 551112

Branch (Domestic):

Syneos Health Clinical, LLC (5)
500 Atrium Dr, Somerset, NJ 08873
Tel.: (800) 416-0555
Web Site: http://www.syneoshealth.com
Clinical Trials Research
N.A.I.C.S.: 541715

Subsidiary (Domestic):

Syneos Health Consulting, Inc. (5)
1030 Sync St, Morrisville, NC 27560
Tel.: (919) 876-9300
Web Site: http://www.syneoshealth.com
Pharmaceutical & Biotechnology Management Consulting Services
N.A.I.C.S.: 541618

Subsidiary (Domestic):

Pharmaceutical Institute, LLC (6)
1030 Sync St, Morrisville, NC 27560
Tel.: (919) 876-9300
Web Site: http://www.syneoshealthlearning.com
Training Solutions for Pharmaceutical & Biotech Industry
N.A.I.C.S.: 611430
Celeste Mosby *(VP-Solution Design & Business Dev)*
Yvonne Ash *(VP-Solution Design)*
Freddy Gozum *(Dir-Solutions Design)*
Marissa Liu-Glaister *(Dir-Learning Strategy)*

Subsidiary (Non-US):

Syneos Health IVH UK Limited (5)
Farnborough Business Park 1 Pinehurst Road, Farnborough, GU14 7BF, Hampshire, United Kingdom
Tel.: (44) 1276 713 000
Web Site: http://www.syneoshealth.com
Phase I-IV Clinical Trials; Data Management & Biostatistics; Regulatory Consulting & Marketing Services
N.A.I.C.S.: 541611

Subsidiary (Non-US):

Syneos Health Germany GmbH (6)
Triforum Haus C1, Frankfurter Strasse 233, 63263, Neu-Isenburg, Germany
Tel.: (49) 6102 8130
Web Site: http://www.syneoshealth.com
Phase I-IV Clinical Trials; Data Management & Biostatistics; Regulatory Consulting & Marketing Services
N.A.I.C.S.: 541611

Syneos Health Italy S.R.L. (6)
Via Gonzaga 7, 201123, Milan, Italy
Tel.: (39) 02 8905 3715
Web Site: http://www.syneoshealth.com
Phase I-IV Clinical Trials; Data Management & Biostatistics; Regulatory Consulting & Marketing Services
N.A.I.C.S.: 541611

Syneos Health Netherlands B.V. (6)
Oval Tower De Entree 99 197 14th floor, 1101 HE, Amsterdam, Netherlands
Tel.: (31) 20 3018 500
Web Site: http://www.syneoshealth.com
Phase I-IV Clinical Trials; Data Management & Biostatistics; Regulatory Consulting & Marketing Services
N.A.I.C.S.: 541611

Subsidiary (Domestic):

i3 Pharmaceutical Services, Inc. (5)
5430 Data Ct Ste 200, Ann Arbor, MI 48108
Tel.: (734) 887-0000
Web Site: http://www.syneoshealth.com
Regulatory Consulting, Clinical Research & Clinical Trial Management Services to Biological & Pharmaceutical Firms
N.A.I.C.S.: 541714

Subsidiary (Domestic):

Syneos Health Communications, Inc. (4)
500 Olde Worthington Rd, Westerville, OH 43082
Tel.: (614) 543-6650
Web Site: http://www.syneoshealth.com
Holding Company; Advertising Agencies
N.A.I.C.S.: 551112

Unit (Domestic):

Chamberlain Healthcare Public Relations (5)
200 Vesey St, New York, NY 10281
Tel.: (212) 884-0650
Web Site: http://www.chamberlainpr.com
Health Care, Public Relations
N.A.I.C.S.: 541820

Subsidiary (Domestic):

Gerbig, Snell/Weisheimer Advertising, LLC (5)
500 Olde Worthington Rd, Columbus, OH 43082
Tel.: (614) 848-4848
Web Site: http://www.gsw-w.com
Advertising Agency
N.A.I.C.S.: 541810
Dan Smith *(Gen Mgr)*
Amanda Joly *(Exec VP- Brand & Experience Strategy)*
Marc Lineveldt *(Exec VP)*
Jen Oleski *(Mng Dir & Exec VP)*
Wendy Rankin *(Sr VP & Dir-Agency Ops)*

Branch (Domestic):

Gerbig, Snell/Weisheimer Advertising, LLC - New York (6)
200 Vesey St 39th Fl, New York, NY 10281
Tel.: (646) 437-4800
Web Site: http://www.gsw-w.com
Advertising Services
N.A.I.C.S.: 541810
Nick Capanear *(Exec VP)*
Bryan Roman *(Sr VP-Creative Tech)*
Michael Austin *(Mng Dir-Creative & Tech)*

Subsidiary (Domestic):

Palio + Ignite, LLC (5)
450 W 15TH St Ste 600, New York, NY 10011-7082
Tel.: (518) 584-8924
Advetising Agency
N.A.I.C.S.: 541810

inVentiv Medical Communications, LLC (5)
1707 Market Pl Blvd Ste 350, Irving, TX 75063
Tel.: (972) 929-1900
Advetising Agency
N.A.I.C.S.: 541810

Subsidiary (Domestic):

Synteract Corp. (2)
5759 Fleet St Ste 100, Carlsbad, CA 92008
Tel.: (760) 268-8200
Web Site: http://www.synteracthcr.com
Sales Range: $25-49.9 Million
Emp.: 800
Human Clinical Drug Trials Services
N.A.I.C.S.: 621511
Matthew Smith *(Sr VP-Comml Ops-Global)*
Martine Dehlinger-Kremer *(VP-Pediatric Dev-Europe)*
Marlo Vasquez *(VP-Biometrics-Global)*
Heather Davis *(Exec Dir-Project Mgmt)*
Zia Haque *(Exec Dir-Clinical Data Mgmt)*
John Whitaker *(Exec Dir-Biostatistics)*
Steve Powell *(CEO)*
Frank Santoro *(Chief Medical Officer)*
Karl Deonanan *(CFO)*
Jack Shannon *(Chief Comml Officer)*
Lisa Dilworth *(VP-Rare & Orphan Diseases)*
Elisabeth Schrader *(Exec Dir-Program Strategy, Pediatrics & Rare Diseases)*
Mary Mattes *(Sr VP-Biometrics)*
Cheryl Murphy *(Sr VP-Clinical Dev)*
Charlotte Oehman *(Gen Counsel)*
Derek Ansel *(Dir-Rare & Orphan Disease Drug Dev)*
Hassan Aly *(Sr Dir-Medical)*

Subsidiary (Non-US):

SynteractHCR Benelux NV (3)
Newsroom Alfons Gossetlaan 30, Sint-Agatha-Berchem, 1702, Groot-Bijgaarden, Belgium
Tel.: (32) 2 4643 900
Web Site: http://www.synteract.com
Clinical Drug Development & Trials
N.A.I.C.S.: 541715
Griet Peeters *(Sr Mgr-Clinical Ops)*
Steve Powell *(CEO)*
Frank Santoro *(Chief Medical Officer)*
Jack Shannon *(Chief Comml Officer)*
Karl Deonanan *(CFO)*
Martina Kroner *(Sr VP-Corp Dev)*
Mary Mattes *(Sr VP-Biometrics)*
Cheryl Murphy *(Sr VP-Clinical Dev)*
Charlotte Oehman *(Gen Counsel)*

SynteractHCR Deutschland GmbH (3)
Albrechtstrasse 14, 80636, Munich, Germany
Tel.: (49) 89 12 66 80 0
Web Site: http://www.synteracthcr.com
Clinical Drug Development & Trials
N.A.I.C.S.: 541715
Martina Kroener *(Mng Dir & VP-Europe)*

SynteractHCR Eastern Europe Forschungsgesellschaft m.b.H. (3)
Spiegelgasse 2/2/41, 1010, Vienna, Austria
Tel.: (43) 1 504 6591.0
Web Site: http://www.synteracthcr.com
Clinical Drug Development & Trials
N.A.I.C.S.: 541715

SynteractHCR France SAS (3)
16 rue Trezel, 92300, Levallois-Perret, France
Tel.: (33) 1 55 90 57 10
Web Site: http://www.synteracthcr.com
Clinical Drug Development & Trials
N.A.I.C.S.: 541715
Sebastien Duval *(VP-Bus Dev-Europe)*

SynteractHCR Iberica, SL (3)

COMPANIES

Carrer del Princep jordi 21-23 Esc B Entresol 1 B, 08014, Barcelona, Spain
Tel.: (34) 93 226 69 64
Web Site: http://www.synteracthcr.com
Clinical Drug Development & Trials
N.A.I.C.S.: 541715
Steve Powell *(CEO)*
Charlotte Oehman *(Gen Counsel)*
Karl Deonanan *(CFO)*
Frank Santoro *(Chief Medical Officer)*
Jack Shannon *(Chief Comml Officer)*

SynteractHCR Limited (3)
Gemini House Bartholomew's Walk, Cambridgeshire Business Park Angel Drove, Ely, CB7 4EA, Cambs, United Kingdom
Tel.: (44) 1353 66 83 39
Web Site: http://www.synteracthcr.com
Emp.: 41
Clinical Drug Trials
N.A.I.C.S.: 541715
Jamie Pearson *(Reg Dir-EMEA)*
Linda Rawlings *(Exec Dir-Strategic Dev)*
Pascale Goujard-Paquette *(Sr Dir-Clinical Ops-Europe)*
Etienne Drouet *(VP-Strategic Dev)*

SynteractHCR S.r.l. (3)
Via Antonio Vivaldi 13, 00043, Ciampino, Rome, Italy
Tel.: (39) 06 79312131
Web Site: http://www.synteracthcr.com
Clinical Drug Development & Trials
N.A.I.C.S.: 541715
Massimo Ildebrando *(Dir-Project Mgmt & Office Mgr)*

SynteractHCR Sweden AB (3)
Ringvagen 100 9E, 11860, Stockholm, Sweden
Tel.: (46) 8 751 10 80
Web Site: http://www.synteracthcr.com
Clinical Drug Development & Trials
N.A.I.C.S.: 541715
Ilari Jauro *(Dir-Clinical Ops)*

PATIENTCO HOLDINGS, INC.
715 Peachtree St NE Ste 900, Atlanta, GA 30308
Tel.: (844) 422-4779
Web Site: http://www.patientco.com
Year Founded: 2009
Sales Range: $1-9.9 Million
Emp.: 33
Application Software Development Services
N.A.I.C.S.: 541511
Bird Blitch *(Co-Founder & CEO)*
Kurt Lovell *(COO)*
Joshua Silver *(Co-Founder & VP-Product Dev)*

PATIENTS & PROVIDERS TO PROTECT ACCESS & CONTAIN HEALTH COSTS
2350 Kerner Blvd Ste 250, San Rafael, CA 94901
Tel.: (415) 389-6800   CA
Year Founded: 2013
Sales Range: $50-74.9 Million
Emp.: 1
Civil & Human Rights Protection Services
N.A.I.C.S.: 813311
Cathy Frey *(VP)*
Dustin Corcoran *(Pres)*
Kathy Kneer *(VP)*
Peter DuBois *(Sec)*
C. Duane Dauner *(Treas)*

PATIENTSAFE SOLUTIONS, INC.
9330 Scranton Rd Ste 325, San Diego, CA 92121
Tel.: (858) 746-3100
Web Site: http://www.patientsafesolutions.com
Year Founded: 2000
Sales Range: $10-24.9 Million
Emp.: 120

Medical, Dental & Hospital Equipment Whslr
N.A.I.C.S.: 423450
Si Luo *(CEO)*
Tim Needham *(Chief Comml Officer)*
Chris Stokes *(CTO)*
Loren Tarmo *(CFO)*

PATIO POOLS OF TUCSON INC.
7960 E 22nd St, Tucson, AZ 85710
Tel.: (520) 886-1211
Web Site: http://www.patiopoolsaz.com
Sales Range: $10-24.9 Million
Emp.: 375
Swimming Pool Construction
N.A.I.C.S.: 238990
Dorothy Ragel *(Owner & Chm)*
Mark Ragel *(Pres)*
Roy Romero *(Asst Mgr)*
Nicole Ragel *(Mgr)*

PATIOSHOPPERS INC.
41188 Sandalwood Cir, Murrieta, CA 92562
Tel.: (951) 696-1700
Web Site: http://www.patioshoppers.com
Year Founded: 2005
Sales Range: $1-9.9 Million
Emp.: 10
Outdoor Furnishings
N.A.I.C.S.: 449129
Todd Chism *(Founder & Pres)*

PATRIARCH PARTNERS, LLC
1 Liberty St 35th Fl, New York, NY 10006
Tel.: (212) 825-0550   DE
Web Site: http://www.patriarchpartners.com
Year Founded: 2000
Sales Range: $25-49.9 Million
Emp.: 50
Privater Equity Firm
N.A.I.C.S.: 523999
Lynn Tilton *(Founder & CEO)*

Subsidiaries:

American LaFrance LLC (1)
1090 Newton Way, Summerville, SC 29483
Tel.: (843) 486-7400
Web Site: http://www.americanlafrance.com
Sales Range: $300-349.9 Million
Emergency Response Vehicle Mfr
N.A.I.C.S.: 336120

Best Textiles Acquisition, LLC (1)
145 N Church St, Spartanburg, SC 29306
Tel.: (864) 641-1966
Web Site: http://www.besttextiles.com
Apparels Mfr
N.A.I.C.S.: 314999
Charles Nichols *(Acting CEO & CFO)*

Croscill, Inc. (1)
1600 George St, Goldsboro, NC 27530
Tel.: (212) 689-7222
Web Site: http://www.croscill.com
Sales Range: $300-349.9 Million
Textile Home Furnishings; Window Treatments & Bed Coverings Mfr
N.A.I.C.S.: 314120
Pat Clemente *(Product Mgr-Hard Bath Accessories)*
Joann DiMaggio *(Mgr-Table Linen Product)*
Joe Granger *(Pres & CEO)*

Subsidiary (Domestic):

Croscill Home (2)
261 5th Ave, New York, NY 10016
Tel.: (212) 689-7222
Sales Range: $25-49.9 Million
Textiles
N.A.I.C.S.: 314120
Joann DiMaggio *(Mgr-Table Linen Product)*
Pat Clemente *(Product Mgr-Hard Bath Accessories)*
Anna Israel *(Coord-Mdse)*
Alex Pellegrino *(Dir-Design-Window & Table Top)*

Global Automotive Systems LLC (1)
2791 Research Dr, Rochester Hills, MI 48309-3575
Tel.: (248) 414-5000
Web Site: http://www.globalautosys.com
Sales Range: $75-99.9 Million
Metal Forming, Welding & Assembly of Vehicle Components
N.A.I.C.S.: 336110

Subsidiary (Domestic):

Saline Metal Systems (2)
905 Woodland Dr, Saline, MI 48176-1625
Tel.: (734) 429-9451
Web Site: http://www.metforming.com
Mfr Dies Stampings & Assemblies For The Automotive Industry
N.A.I.C.S.: 336370

Tubular Metal Systems (2)
401 E 5th St, Pinconning, MI 48650-9321
Tel.: (989) 879-2611
Web Site: http://www.duraauto.com
Sales Range: $25-49.9 Million
Automobile Parts & Accessories
N.A.I.C.S.: 336390
Earl Sibbett *(Gen Mgr)*
Paul Kaczmarek *(Coord-CAD & Mfg)*

Heritage Aviation Ltd. (1)
419 Duncan Perry Rd Ste 109, Arlington, TX 76011
Tel.: (972) 988-8000
Sales Range: $25-49.9 Million
Emp.: 8
Helicopter Completion Services
N.A.I.C.S.: 541990

Intrepid USA Healthcare Services (1)
4055 Valley View Ln Ste 500, Dallas, TX 75244-5048
Tel.: (214) 445-3750
Web Site: http://www.intrepidusa.com
Sales Range: $150-199.9 Million
In-Home Nursing & Therapy Services
N.A.I.C.S.: 621610
Rachel Barrientez *(Mgr-IT-Applications)*
Brian L. Ofenlock *(Coord-IT Facilities)*
Ward Thulin *(Dir-Clinical Svcs)*
Paul Foster *(CEO)*
John Nix *(CFO)*

Libertas Copper, LLC (1)
100 Washington St, Leetsdale, PA 15056-1000
Tel.: (724) 251-4200
Web Site: http://www.husseycopper.com
Sales Range: $50-74.9 Million
Rolled & Drawn Copper Products Mfr
N.A.I.C.S.: 331420
Brian Sprochi *(Dir-Natl Accts)*
Paul Trunzo *(VP-Sls)*

Netversant Solutions LLC (1)
2180 North Loop W Ste 550, Houston, TX 77018-8011
Tel.: (713) 403-3800
Fiber Optic Cable Installation Services
N.A.I.C.S.: 238210

Oasis International (1)
222 E Campus View Blvd, Columbus, OH 43235
Tel.: (614) 861-1350
Web Site: http://www.oasiscoolers.com
Sales Range: $25-49.9 Million
Pressure & Bottled Water Cooler Mfr
N.A.I.C.S.: 312112

Petry Media Corporation (1)
1 Penn Plz 55th Fl, New York, NY 10119
Tel.: (212) 230-5800
Web Site: http://www.petrymedia.com
Sales Range: $75-99.9 Million
Television Advertisement Placement, Sales & Support Services
N.A.I.C.S.: 541840

Subsidiary (Domestic):

Petry Television Inc. (2)
1 Penn Plz 55th Fl, New York, NY 10119-0002
Tel.: (212) 230-5600
Web Site: http://www.petrymedia.com
Sales Range: $25-49.9 Million
Television Advertising Sales & Support Services

PATRIARCH PARTNERS, LLC

N.A.I.C.S.: 541840

Rand McNally & Company (1)
9855 Woods Dr, Skokie, IL 60077
Tel.: (847) 329-8100
Web Site: http://www.randmcnally.com
Sales Range: $75-99.9 Million
Map & Travel Guide Publisher
N.A.I.C.S.: 513199
Jim Rodi *(Sr VP-Mobile Comm)*

Scan-Optics, LLC (1)
169 Progress Dr, Manchester, CT 06042
Tel.: (860) 645-7878
Web Site: http://www.scanoptics.com
Sales Range: $25-49.9 Million
Document Processing; Imaging Solutions & Technologies & Services
N.A.I.C.S.: 334118
Jeff Mitchell *(CEO)*
Seth Murdoch *(CFO)*

Subsidiary (Non-US):

Scan-Optics, Ltd. (2)
Unit 5 Brookside, Colne Way, Watford, WD24 7QJ, Herts, United Kingdom (100%)
Tel.: (44) 1923819581
Web Site: http://www.scanoptics.co.uk
Sales Range: Less than $1 Million
Emp.: 10
Information Processing
N.A.I.C.S.: 518210

Signature Styles, LLC (1)
711 3rd Ave, New York, NY 10017-4014
Tel.: (201) 986-2585
Holding Company; Internet & Mail Order Clothing Sales
N.A.I.C.S.: 551112
Emil Giliotti *(Mng Dir-Consumer Products Platform)*

Holding (Domestic):

Spiegel Brands, Inc. (2)
711 3rd Ave, New York, NY 10017
Tel.: (212) 986-2585
Web Site: http://www.spiegel.com
Sales Range: $100-124.9 Million
Catalog Retail Services
N.A.I.C.S.: 456199

Snelling Staffing Services (1)
4055 Valley View Ln Ste 700, Dallas, TX 75244
Tel.: (972) 239-7575
Web Site: http://www.snelling.com
Sales Range: $350-399.9 Million
Staffing Services
N.A.I.C.S.: 561320
Keith Clark *(Gen Counsel)*
Jim Berry *(CFO)*
Ralph Peterson *(CEO)*

Division (Domestic):

Snelling Personnel Services (2)
103 Carnegie Ctr Ste 111, Princeton, NJ 08540
Tel.: (609) 683-4040
Web Site: http://www.snelling.com
Rev.: $17,000,000
Emp.: 10
Employment Services
N.A.I.C.S.: 561311

Stila Corp. (1)
2801 Hyperion Ave Ste 102, Los Angeles, CA 90027
Tel.: (866) 784-5201
Web Site: http://www.stilacosmetics.com
Sales Range: $25-49.9 Million
Emp.: 24
Cosmetics
N.A.I.C.S.: 325620
Lynn Tilton *(CEO)*

Swift Galey (1)
5 Concourse Pkwy Ste 2300, Atlanta, GA 30328-5350 (100%)
Tel.: (770) 901-6300
Web Site: http://www.swiftgaley.com
Sales Range: $150-199.9 Million
Denim, Twill, Corduroy & Poplins Mfr
N.A.I.C.S.: 313210

eMag Solutions LLC (1)
3495 Piedmont Rd, Atlanta, GA 30305
Tel.: (404) 995-6060

PATRIARCH PARTNERS, LLC

Patriarch Partners, LLC—(Continued)
Web Site: http://www.emaglink.com
Data Management Solutions
N.A.I.C.S.: 518210

PATRICIA ACQUISITION CORP.
2255 Glades Rd Ste 324A, Boca Raton, FL 33431
Tel.: (561) 989-2208   DE
Year Founded: 2020
Assets: $457
Liabilities: $124,000
Net Worth: ($123,543)
Earnings: ($51,354)
Fiscal Year-end: 12/31/22
Investment Services
N.A.I.C.S.: 523999
Ian Jacobs *(Pres, CEO, CFO & Sec)*

PATRICIA FIELD BOUTIQUE
298 Elizabeth St, New York, NY 10012
Tel.: (212) 966-4066
Web Site:
http://www.patriciafield.com
Sales Range: $1-9.9 Million
Emp.: 10
Apparel & Accessories Designer & Retailer
N.A.I.C.S.: 315990
Patricia Field *(Owner)*

PATRICK GALLAGHER TRUCKING INC.
1 PGT Way, Monaca, PA 15061-2255
Tel.: (724) 728-3500   PA
Web Site: http://www.pgttrucking.com
Year Founded: 1975
Sales Range: $25-49.9 Million
Emp.: 210
Provider of Trucking Services
N.A.I.C.S.: 484121
Patrick A. Gallagher *(Founder & Pres)*
Dean Bowman *(Dir-IT Sys)*
Fred Fittante *(Dir-Transportation Pricing Sls)*
Tim Evans *(Exec Dir-Bus Dev)*
Joey Hakim *(VP-Natl Accts)*

PATRICK JAMES INC.
7060 N Marks Ave Ste 117, Fresno, CA 93711-0287
Tel.: (559) 448-0600
Web Site:
http://www.patrickjames.com
Sales Range: $10-24.9 Million
Emp.: 100
Men's & Boys' Clothing Stores
N.A.I.C.S.: 458110
Bill Summers *(CFO & VP)*
Justin Collins *(Mgr-Warehouse)*
Patrick J. Mon Pere Sr. *(Chm & Pres)*

PATRICK LUMBER COMPANY, INC.
812 SW 10th Ave Ste 200, Portland, OR 97205
Tel.: (503) 222-9671   OR
Web Site: http://www.patlbr.com
Year Founded: 1975
Sales Range: $25-49.9 Million
Emp.: 24
Lumber, Plywood & Millwork
N.A.I.C.S.: 423310
Patrick Burns *(Pres)*
Dave Halsey *(Chief Strategic Officer)*
Subsidiaries:

Wood Source, Inc.   (1)
8321 N Steele St, Thornton, CO 80229
Tel.: (303) 297-8310
Web Site: http://www.woodsource.com
Wood Product Mfr & Distr
N.A.I.C.S.: 423310
Martin Schwab *(VP)*

PATRICK MALLOY COMMUNITIES, INC.
851 Cedar St, Carrollton, GA 30117
Tel.: (770) 832-6376
Web Site:
http://www.pmcommunities.com
Sales Range: $10-24.9 Million
Emp.: 40
Broker Of Manufactured Homes, On Site
N.A.I.C.S.: 531210
Patrick Malloy *(Pres)*
Cathy Van Meter *(Dir-HR)*
Scott Sawyer *(VP-Ops)*

PATRICK MOTORS INC.
519 Wasington St, Auburn, MA 01501
Tel.: (508) 756-8364
Web Site:
http://www.patrickmotors.com
Sales Range: $10-24.9 Million
Emp.: 30
Automobiles, New & Used
N.A.I.C.S.: 441110
Matt Patrick *(Gen Mgr)*
Matt Newhouse *(Gen Mgr-Sls)*
Dan Garney *(Mgr-Fin)*
Aaron Tringuk *(Mgr-Used Car)*

PATRICK PONTIAC INC.
4700 W Henrietta, Rochester, NY 14467
Tel.: (585) 359-2200
Web Site:
http://www.patrickbuickgmc.com
Sales Range: $50-74.9 Million
Emp.: 130
Dealer of New & Used Automobiles
N.A.I.C.S.: 441110
David Brick *(Dir-Fin)*
John Tarplee *(Mgr-Svcs)*
Tony Coleman *(Mgr-Sls-Buick & GMC)*
Tracy Monacelli *(Asst Controller-HR)*
Richard Rowlands *(Controller)*
Mark Pennella *(VP)*

PATRICKORTMAN, INC.
11271 Ventura Blvd Ste 492, Studio City, CA 91604
Tel.: (818) 505-1988
Web Site:
http://www.patrickortman.com
Year Founded: 2007
Rev.: $10,000,000
Emp.: 7
Advertising Agencies
N.A.I.C.S.: 541810
Patrick Ortman *(CEO & Creative Dir)*

PATRIOT ADVERTISING INC.
535 E Fernhurst Dr Ste 263, Katy, TX 77450
Tel.: (832) 239-5775   TX
Web Site:
http://www.patriotadvertising.com
Year Founded: 2005
Sales Range: $10-24.9 Million
Emp.: 15
Advertising Services
N.A.I.C.S.: 541810
Tin Runge *(Owner, Pres & CEO)*

PATRIOT CHEVROLET GEO INC.
4401 Fort Campbell Blvd, Hopkinsville, KY 42240
Tel.: (270) 886-1207
Web Site:
http://www.patriotchevy.com
Sales Range: $10-24.9 Million
Emp.: 50
Car Dealership
N.A.I.C.S.: 441110
Charlie Ramsey *(CFO & VP)*
Gene Curtis *(Gen Mgr)*

PATRIOT CONTRACTORS, INC
1600 E Main St Ste 200, Waxahachie, TX 75165
Tel.: (972) 775-4440
Web Site: http://www.patriot1.com
Year Founded: 2007
Sales Range: $1-9.9 Million
Emp.: 20
Architectural Material Installation Services & Distr
N.A.I.C.S.: 541310
John Raftery *(Pres & CEO)*
Mike Wade *(VP & Dir-Quality Control)*

PATRIOT FIRE PROTECTION INC.
2707 70th Ave E, Tacoma, WA 98424
Tel.: (253) 926-2290
Web Site: http://www.patriotfire.com
Sales Range: $10-24.9 Million
Emp.: 70
Fire Sprinkler System Installation
N.A.I.C.S.: 238220
James Boulanger *(Pres)*
Margaret O'Brien *(VP)*
Kevin Marr *(Mgr-Design)*
Mona Keifer *(Office Mgr)*

PATRIOT LOGISTICS
7045 S Fulton St Ste 250, Centennial, CO 80112
Tel.: (209) 942-3111
Web Site:
http://www.patriotadvantage.com
Year Founded: 2005
Sales Range: $1-9.9 Million
Emp.: 25
Retail Reverse Logistics
N.A.I.C.S.: 541614
Steve Weakley *(CEO)*

PATRIOT MEDIA CONSULTING LLC
650 Colleg Rd E Ste 3100, Princeton, NJ 08540
Tel.: (609) 452-8197
Web Site:
http://patriotmediaconsulting.com
Year Founded: 2007
Privater Equity Firm
N.A.I.C.S.: 523940
Stephen J. Simmons *(Chm)*

PATRIOT MORTGAGE CORPORATION
733 Roosevelt Trl Ste 1, Windham, ME 04062
Tel.: (207) 892-9980
Year Founded: 2007
Sales Range: $10-24.9 Million
Emp.: 4
Mortgage Srevices
N.A.I.C.S.: 523910
Raymond Roux *(Co-Owner)*
Nancy Bonafire *(VP)*
G. William Diamond *(Co-Owner)*

PATRIOT NATIONAL, INC.
401 E Las Olas Blvd Ste 1650, Fort Lauderdale, FL 33301
Tel.: (954) 670-2900   DE
Web Site: http://www.patnat.com
Sales Range: $200-249.9 Million
Workers' Compensation Insurance Services
N.A.I.C.S.: 524128
John J. Rearer *(CEO)*
Maria Allen *(Chief Claims Officer)*
John Dennis *(Natl Dir-Premium Audit)*
Anat Veader *(VP-Enterprise Data Architecture)*
Judith L. Haddad *(CTO, CIO & Exec VP)*
Bernard Liburd *(Mgr-Sls)*
Edward Sharples *(VP-Northeast Reg)*
Colin B. Williams *(VP-Texas)*

U.S. PRIVATE

Michael W. Grandstaff *(Exec VP-Strategic Plng & Acq)*
Todd Wilson *(Sr VP-Mergers & Acq)*
Nabeel Tanveer *(Sr VP-Strategic Bus Dev)*
Armand Fernandez *(Exec VP-Loss Control)*
David Andrade *(CMO-Patriot Technology Solutions Inc.)*
Cindy Campbell *(Dir-IR)*
Glenn Hibler *(Chm)*
Kathryn Switzer *(VP-Case Mgmt & Utilization Mgmt-Patriot Care Mgmt)*
Nicole Dutes *(Dir-HR)*
Debi Gorson *(Dir-Facilities & Admin)*
Subsidiaries:

CWI Benefits, Inc.   (1)
715 Congaree Rd, Greenville, SC 29607
Tel.: (864) 234-8200
Web Site: http://www.cwibenefits.com
Sales Range: $1-9.9 Million
Emp.: 20
Management Consulting Services
N.A.I.C.S.: 541618
Ron Ross *(Pres)*
Retha Cox *(Acct Mgr)*
Chuck McKeown *(VP-Mktg & Bus Dev)*
Gina Murphy *(VP)*

Contego Services Group, LLC   (1)
401 E Las Olas Blvd Ste 1540, Fort Lauderdale, FL 33301
Tel.: (215) 665-7273
General Insurance Services
N.A.I.C.S.: 524210

Corporate Claims Management, Inc.   (1)
782 Spirit 40 Park Dr, Chesterfield, MO 63005
Tel.: (636) 519-0330
Web Site: http://www.corporateclaims.com
Fiscal Year-end: 12/31/2006
Risk Managemeng Srvices
N.A.I.C.S.: 524292
Mike Greco *(Pres)*
Mario Lombardi *(VP & Mgr-Natl Sls)*

Forza Lien, Inc.   (1)
PO Box 746, Woodland Hills, CA 91365
Tel.: (818) 449-5021
Business Support Services
N.A.I.C.S.: 541611

Patriot Care, Inc.   (1)
10 Deer Wood Dr, Warren, NJ 07825
Tel.: (973) 572-2116
Ambulance Service
N.A.I.C.S.: 621910

Patriot Services, Inc.   (1)
8949 Brucewood Dr, Richmond, VA 23235
Tel.: (508) 697-9565
Web Site: http://www.patriotservicesma.com
Business Support Services
N.A.I.C.S.: 541611

Patriot Underwriters, Inc.   (1)
401 E Las Olas Blvd Ste 1650, Fort Lauderdale, FL 33301
Tel.: (954) 670-2900
Web Site: http://www.pnigroup.com
Insurance Underwriting
N.A.I.C.S.: 524298
Steven Michael Mariano *(Chm & Pres)*
Scott Palladino *(Mgr-Southeast)*
Shadi Lang *(VP-Mktg & Underwriting-California)*
Maureen McCormick *(VP-Mktg & Underwriting-California)*
Leslie Lewis *(Sr VP)*
John Rearer *(CEO)*
David Hayth *(VP-Southeast)*
Barbie Orr *(Mgr-Underwriting-Gulf)*

Restaurant Coverage Associates, Inc.   (1)
1333 Broad St, Clifton, NJ 07013
Tel.: (973) 472-8600
Web Site: http://www.rca-insurance.com
Insurance Brokerage Services
N.A.I.C.S.: 524210
Maxine Lessard *(Mgr)*
Michael Maher *(VP-Mktg)*

PATRIOT PONTIAC GMC

COMPANIES

BUICK LTD PARTNERSHIP
4600 E Central Texas Expy, Killeen, TX 76543
Tel.: (254) 690-7000
Web Site: http://www.patriotcars.com
Sales Range: $25-49.9 Million
Emp.: 89
Automobiles, New & Used
N.A.I.C.S.: 441110
Mary Kliewer *(Pres)*
William Kliewer *(VP)*

PATSON INC.
4000 Mannheim Rd, Franklin Park, IL 60131
Tel.: (847) 671-7100
Web Site: http://www.nwford.com
Sales Range: $50-74.9 Million
Emp.: 92
Trucks, Commercial
N.A.I.C.S.: 423110
Patrick H. Cayce *(CEO)*
Doug Cayce *(Pres)*
Dave McCarthy *(Treas & Sec)*

PATSON'S MEDIA GROUP
970 Stewart Dr, Sunnyvale, CA 94085
Tel.: (408) 732-0911   CA
Web Site: http://www.patsons.com
Year Founded: 1958
Sales Range: $50-74.9 Million
Emp.: 50
Provider of Commercial Printing Services
N.A.I.C.S.: 323111
Pat Dellamano *(Founder & CEO)*
Joe Dellamano *(VP-Ops)*
Mark Dellamano *(Sr VP)*
John Hessler *(VP-Quality)*
John Dellamano *(VP-Plng)*

PATSY LOU BUICK GMC INC.
G5111 Corunna Rd, Flint, MI 48532
Tel.: (810) 732-7500
Web Site: http://www.patsylou.com
Rev.: $86,000,000
Emp.: 120
New & Used Automobiles
N.A.I.C.S.: 441110
Patsy Lou Williamson *(Pres)*
Teresa Gieierthirt *(Controller)*

PATSY STROCCHIA & SONS IRON WORKS, INC.
84 Withers St, Brooklyn, NY 11211
Tel.: (718) 389-0691
Web Site: http://www.strocchia.com
Year Founded: 1922
Sales Range: $10-24.9 Million
Emp.: 18
Provider of Steel Fabrication, Erection & Supply Services
N.A.I.C.S.: 331110
Leonard D. Strocchia *(VP)*
Ralph J. Strocchia Sr. *(Pres)*
Ralph Strocchia Jr. *(VP)*

PATSY'S, INC.
31 Hall St, Concord, NH 03301
Tel.: (603) 226-2222   NH
Web Site: http://www.patsyco.com
Year Founded: 1929
Provider of Car & Truck Sales, Service & Parts
N.A.I.C.S.: 532120
Anthony M. Waterman *(VP)*
Donal Loughrey *(Controller)*
Joseph R. Alosa Sr. *(Pres & CEO)*
Subsidiaries:

Patsy's Bus Sales & Service   (1)
31 Hall St, Concord, NH 03301
Tel.: (603) 226-2222
Web Site: http://www.patsysbussales.com
Heavy Duty Truck Mfr
N.A.I.C.S.: 336120

Joseph Alosa *(Pres)*

PATTEN AND PATTEN, INC.
555 Walnut St Ste 280, Chattanooga, TN 37402-1308
Tel.: (423) 756-3480   TN
Web Site: https://patteninc.com
Year Founded: 1976
Sales Range: $10-24.9 Million
Emp.: 20
Investment Advisory & Management Services
N.A.I.C.S.: 523940
Janet A. Lawrence *(Mgr-IT Sys & Investment Performance)*
Raymond V. Ryan *(Pres & Portfolio Mgr)*
J. Clay Crumbliss *(Chief Compliance Officer, Principal & VP-Ops & Fin)*
Mark C. Fleck *(Principal & Portfolio Mgr)*
Stephanie P. Graham *(CFO)*
W. A. Bryan Patten *(Founder, Chm, CEO & Portfolio Mgr)*
Frank M. Robbins *(Sec, Sr VP & Portfolio Mgr)*

PATTEN INDUSTRIES, INC.
635 W Lake St, Elmhurst, IL 60126-1409
Tel.: (877) 688-2228   IL
Web Site: http://www.pattenindustries.com
Year Founded: 1938
Sales Range: $50-74.9 Million
Emp.: 450
Repairs & Sells Industrial Machinery & Equipment
N.A.I.C.S.: 423810
Lana Mizina *(Asst Controller)*
Luke Mueller *(Mgr-Used Equipment Sls)*
Tim Hurley *(Mgr-IT)*
Subsidiaries:

Patten Power Systems Inc.   (1)
615 W Lake St, Elmhurst, IL 60126-1409
Tel.: (630) 530-2200
Web Site: http://www.pattenrental.com
Sales Range: $25-49.9 Million
Emp.: 95
Repairs & Sells Industrial Machinery & Equipment
N.A.I.C.S.: 423830

PATTEN SALES & MARKETING, LLC
821 5th Ave S Se 101, Naples, FL 34102
Tel.: (239) 963-9783
Web Site: http://pattenco.com
Sales Range: $125-149.9 Million
Real Estate Development, Acquisition, Construction & Property Management
N.A.I.C.S.: 237210
Michael S. Patten *(CEO)*
John Patten *(VP)*
Thomas A. Gajda *(CFO)*
Steven J. Guy *(Exec VP-Sls & Ops)*
Bill Must *(Mng Dir-Acq & Bus Dev)*
Pete Scerbo *(VP-Acq)*
Gary Sumner *(Mng Partner)*
Joe O'Brien *(Mng Partner-West)*
Katherine Dobbins *(VP-Acq)*

PATTEN SEED COMPANY INC.
235 Valdosta Rd, Lakeland, GA 31635-1550
Tel.: (229) 482-3131   GA
Web Site: http://www.pattenseed.com
Year Founded: 1954
Sales Range: $25-49.9 Million
Emp.: 330
Ornamental Nursery Products, Sod & Seed
N.A.I.C.S.: 111422

Ben Copeland *(Pres)*
Subsidiaries:

Patten Seed Company Inc. - Soil3 Division   (1)
287 Sod Farm Rd, Fort Valley, GA 31030
Tel.: (888) 360-1125
Web Site: http://www.soil3.com
Soil Preparation & Planting Services
N.A.I.C.S.: 115112

Patten Seed Company Inc. - SuperSod Division   (1)
158 Sod Farm Rd, Fort Valley, GA 31030
Tel.: (478) 825-7422
Web Site: http://www.supersod.com
Sod Farming Services
N.A.I.C.S.: 111421

Patten Seed Company Inc. - SuperSod Trees Division   (1)
3086 Five Chop Rd, Orangeburg, SC 29115
Tel.: (803) 531-4443
Web Site: http://www.supersod.com
Sod Farming Services
N.A.I.C.S.: 111421
Mark Burlsof *(Office Mgr)*

PATTERSON BELKNAP WEBB & TYLER LLP
1133 Avenue of the Americas, New York, NY 10036
Tel.: (212) 336-2000
Web Site: http://www.pbwt.com
Year Founded: 1919
Sales Range: $150-199.9 Million
Emp.: 189
Law firm
N.A.I.C.S.: 541110
Michael F. Buchanan *(Partner)*
Laura E. Butzel *(Partner)*
Lisa E. Cleary *(Co-Chm & Mng Partner)*
Michelle W. Cohen *(Partner)*
Gregory L. Diskant *(Partner)*
Peter W. Tomlinson *(Co-Chm)*
Sarah E. Zgliniec *(Partner)*
Saul B. Shapiro *(Partner)*
Stephen P. Younger *(Partner)*
Michelle M. Bufano *(Partner)*
John D. Winter *(Partner)*
Megan E. Bell *(Partner)*
Rachel B. Sherman *(Partner)*
Edward H. Smoot *(Partner)*
H. Gregory Baker *(Partner-Litigation Dept)*
Peter C. Harvey *(Partner)*
William F. Cavanaugh Jr. *(Partner)*
Frederick B. Warder III *(Partner)*

PATTERSON FUEL OIL INC.
477 W John St, Hicksville, NY 11801
Tel.: (516) 354-2160
Web Site: http://www.pattersonenergy.com
Rev.: $12,700,000
Emp.: 40
Fuel Oil Dealers
N.A.I.C.S.: 457210
Gary Ballenweig *(Gen Mgr)*

PATTERSON OIL COMPANY
100 Lincoln Ave, Torrington, CT 06790-0898
Tel.: (860) 489-9271
Web Site: http://www.pattersonoilco.com
Sales Range: $50-74.9 Million
Emp.: 100
Gasoline
N.A.I.C.S.: 424720
Barry S. Patterson *(Pres)*
Michael Beloved *(Treas)*

PATTERSON-ERIE CORPORATION
1250 Tower Ln, Erie, PA 16505-2533
Tel.: (814) 455-8031   DE

PATTON MUSIC CO., INC.

Year Founded: 1967
Sales Range: $75-99.9 Million
Emp.: 1,000
Restaurant
N.A.I.C.S.: 488190
William L. Patterson *(Pres & CEO)*
Cameron McCormick *(CFO)*
Kerry Dougan *(Supvr-Payroll)*

PATTERSON-SCHWARTZ & ASSOCIATES INC.
7234 Lancaster Pike, Hockessin, DE 19707-9273
Tel.: (302) 234-5250   DE
Web Site: http://www.pattersonschwartz.com
Year Founded: 1961
Sales Range: $25-49.9 Million
Emp.: 150
Real Estate Agents & Managers
N.A.I.C.S.: 531210
Joseph Pluscht *(Pres)*

PATTLEN ENTERPRISES INC.
4700 Holly St, Denver, CO 80216
Tel.: (303) 320-1270   CO
Web Site: http://www.lljohnson.com
Year Founded: 1976
Sales Range: $25-49.9 Million
Emp.: 100
Distr of Farm & Garden Machinery
N.A.I.C.S.: 423820
Leonard L. Johnson *(CEO)*
Greg Lamont *(VP)*
Jim Johnson *(Pres & COO)*

PATTON ELECTRONICS CO.
7622 Rickenbacker Dr, Gaithersburg, MD 20882
Tel.: (301) 975-1000   MD
Web Site: http://www.patton.com
Year Founded: 1984
Communications Equipment (Routers, Voip, Gateways, Internet Modems) Mfr
N.A.I.C.S.: 334210
Bruce E. Patton *(VP-Fin & Admin)*
Bryan DuBois *(VP-Special Projects)*
Chris Christner *(Dir-Mktg Comm)*
Robert R. Patton *(Pres & CEO)*
Stephen M. Schrader *(Sr VP-Ops)*
Burton A. Patton *(Exec VP)*
Joachim Wlotzka *(VP-Engrg)*
Buddy Oliver *(VP-Bus Dev)*
Martin Svozil *(VP-Intl Dev)*
Subsidiaries:

FiberPlex Technologies, LLC   (1)
10840 Guilford Rd, Annapolis Junction, MD 20701
Tel.: (301) 604-0100
Web Site: http://www.fiberplex.com
Fiber Optic Mfr
N.A.I.C.S.: 334220
William Linkow *(Pres)*

PATTON INDUSTRIAL PRODUCTS
8410 Pillsbury Ave S, Minneapolis, MN 55420
Tel.: (952) 881-8800
Web Site: http://www.pattonfasteners.com
Sales Range: $10-24.9 Million
Emp.: 55
Fasteners, Industrial: Nuts, Bolts, Screws, Etc.
N.A.I.C.S.: 423840
Scott Buckman *(CFO)*
Terry Houge *(Mgr-Inside Sls)*

PATTON MUSIC CO., INC.
811 Kearny Ave, Modesto, CA 95350-5728
Tel.: (209) 574-1101   CA

PATTON MUSIC CO., INC.

Patton Music Co., Inc.—(Continued)
Web Site:
http://www.pattonamusement.com
Year Founded: 1948
Sales Range: $25-49.9 Million
Emp.: 50
Vending Machine Operators
N.A.I.C.S.: 445132
Jim Ericksen (Owner & Gen Mgr)
James B. Reed Jr. (Pres)

PATTON SALES CORPORATION
1095 E California St, Ontario, CA 91761
Tel.: (909) 988-0661
Web Site:
http://www.pattonscorp.com
Sales Range: $25-49.9 Million
Emp.: 90
Office Furniture
N.A.I.C.S.: 449110
Jon Novack (Pres)

PATTY PECK HONDA
555 Sunnybrook Rd, Ridgeland, MS 39157
Tel.: (601) 957-3400
Web Site:
http://www.pattypeckhonda.com
Year Founded: 1984
Sales Range: $10-24.9 Million
Emp.: 53
Car Whslr
N.A.I.C.S.: 441110
Bob Aubrey (Gen Mgr)
Steve Churchman (Mgr-Used Car Recondition)

PATXI'S PIZZA
822 Irving St, San Francisco, CA 94122
Tel.: (415) 759-9000
Web Site: http://www.patxispizza.com
Year Founded: 2004
Sales Range: $10-24.9 Million
Emp.: 170
Restaurants Serving Quality, Chicago Style Deep Dish Pizzas
N.A.I.C.S.: 722511
Francisco Azpiroz (Co-Founder & Gen Mgr)
William Freeman (Co-Founder & CEO)

PAUL & MARLENE INC.
5115 Alpine Ave NW, Comstock Park, MI 49321
Tel.: (616) 784-0797
Web Site: http://www.grandvalue.com
Rev.: $18,565,584
Emp.: 6
Mobile Home Dealers
N.A.I.C.S.: 459930
Greg Asquith (VP)
Darcy Wright (Head-Sls)

PAUL A. DE JESSE, INC. ADVERTISING
40 Broad St Ste 1, Freehold, NJ 07728
Tel.: (908) 670-8155
Year Founded: 1980
Rev.: $25,000,000
Emp.: 24
Advetising Agency
N.A.I.C.S.: 541810
Paul A. De Jesse (Pres & CEO)
Phyllis S. De Jesse (Exec VP & Creative Svcs Dir)
Ron Leavesley (VP & Mktg Dir Strategic Plng Dir)
Allan Cohen (VP & Medical Dir & Legal Dir)
A. Scott De Jesse (VP & Design Dir)
Rudy Borgersen (VP & Medical Dir)
Dr. William Cohen (VP & Medical Affairs Dir)
Leila Coyle (Controller)
Fred Amster (Grp Art Dir)
John Van Pelt (Grp Art Dir)
Elfi Kraemer (Media Dir)
Tony Fotia (Admin Mgr)
Vincent J. Barone (Acct Dir)
Paul A. De Jesse Jr. (Mngmt Supvr-Client Svcs)

PAUL A. SCHMITT MUSIC COMPANY
2400 Freeway Blvd, Minneapolis, MN 55430
Tel.: (612) 339-4811
Web Site:
http://www.schmittmusic.com
Year Founded: 1896
Sales Range: $150-199.9 Million
Emp.: 380
Retailer of Music Merchandise
N.A.I.C.S.: 459140
Thomas M. Schmitt (Chm, Pres & CEO)
Robert Baker (CFO)

PAUL ARGOE SCREENS, INC.
3224 Savannah Hwy, North, SC 29112
Tel.: (803) 568-2111
Web Site:
http://www.paulargoescreens.com
Year Founded: 1934
Sales Range: $1-9.9 Million
Emp.: 35
Wood Window & Door Mfr
N.A.I.C.S.: 321911
G. Argoe (VP)

Subsidiaries:

The Combination Door Co. (1)
1000 Morris St, Fond Du Lac, WI 54935-5620
Tel.: (920) 922-2050
Web Site: http://www.combinationdoor.com
Millwork & Flooring
N.A.I.C.S.: 321918
David J. Schmidt (Pres)

PAUL ARPIN VAN LINES, INC.
99 James P Murphy Hwy, West Warwick, RI 02893
Tel.: (401) 828-8111
Web Site: http://www.arpin.com
Year Founded: 1900
Sales Range: $100-124.9 Million
Emp.: 325
Local & Long Distance Trucking & Relocation Services
N.A.I.C.S.: 484121
David Arpin (Pres & CEO)
Michael Killoran (Controller)
Conrad Swanson (Sr VP-Agency Dev)
Ed Braks (CFO)

PAUL B. ZIMMERMAN INC.
295 Woodcorner Rd, Lititz, PA 17543
Tel.: (717) 738-7365
Web Site: http://www.pbzinc.com
Sales Range: $10-24.9 Million
Emp.: 130
Provider of Building Supplies
N.A.I.C.S.: 444140
Marvin Horst (Mgr-IT)
Jim Wall (Mgr-Mktg)
Keith Zimmerman (Owner)
Roger L. Zimmerman (Owner, CFO & Exec VP)

PAUL BELLACK INC.
149 Black Horse Ln, North Brunswick, NJ 08902
Tel.: (215) 923-7570
Web Site: http://www.paulbellack.com
Year Founded: 1974
Rev.: $11,000,000
Emp.: 30
Freight Transportation Arrangement Services
N.A.I.C.S.: 488510
Maria Giliati (Mgr-Product Dev)
Kevin Hussey (Pres)

PAUL BROWN MOTORS, INC.
1145 E State St, Olean, NY 14760
Tel.: (716) 372-0080
Web Site:
http://www.paulbrownmotors.com
Sales Range: $10-24.9 Million
Emp.: 58
New & Used Car Dealer
N.A.I.C.S.: 441110
Garth George (Mgr-Fin)
Terence Brairton (Pres)

PAUL BUNYAN COMMUNICATIONS
1831 Anne St NW, Bemidji, MN 56601
Tel.: (218) 444-1234
Web Site: http://www.paulbunyan.net
Year Founded: 1952
Sales Range: $50-74.9 Million
Emp.: 131
Telecommunication Services Provider
N.A.I.C.S.: 517810
Tim Hins (Treas)
Gary Eklund (Sec)
Jim Tarbell (VP)
Kathy Peterson (Pres)

PAUL C. RIZZO ASSOCIATES, INC.
500 Penn Center Blvd Ste 100 Bldg 5, Pittsburgh, PA 15235
Tel.: (412) 856-9700
Web Site: http://www.rizzoassoc.com
Rev.: $15,272,509
Emp.: 148
Energy Consulting Services
N.A.I.C.S.: 541690
Rachelle Rizzo-Eikey (VP-Admin)
Paul C. Rizzo (Chm)

PAUL CERAME FORD
11400 New Halls Ferry Rd, Florissant, MO 63033
Tel.: (314) 838-2400
Web Site: http://www.cerameford.net
Sales Range: $10-24.9 Million
Emp.: 100
New Car Retailer
N.A.I.C.S.: 441110
Emile Williams (Mgr-New Vehicle Sls)
Mike Kufskie (Mgr-Pre-Owned Sls)
Melissa Roberson (Coord-Bus Dev)
Bruce Wicklein (Mgr-Parts)
Stan Blythe (Dir-Comml Accts)

PAUL CONTE CADILLAC, INC.
169 W Sunrise Hwy, Freeport, NY 11520
Tel.: (516) 960-5628
Web Site:
http://www.contecadillac.com
Year Founded: 1979
Sales Range: $10-24.9 Million
New & Used Automobiles Distr
N.A.I.C.S.: 441110
Paul Conte (Pres)
Shai Nadav (Mgr-Svc)

PAUL DE LIMA CO. INC.
7546 Morgan Rd, Liverpool, NY 13090
Tel.: (315) 457-3725
Web Site:
http://www.delimacoffee.com
Rev.: $23,069,321
Emp.: 50

Roasted Coffee
N.A.I.C.S.: 311920
Mike Garlick (Pres)

PAUL DINTO ELECTRICAL CONTRS
121 Turnpike Dr, Middlebury, CT 06762
Tel.: (203) 575-9473
Web Site:
http://www.pauldintoelec.com
Sales Range: $10-24.9 Million
Emp.: 160
Electrical Wiring Services
N.A.I.C.S.: 238210
Debbie Demarco (Dir-Reimbursement)

PAUL ECKE RANCH
441 Saxony Rd, Encinitas, CA 92024-2725
Tel.: (760) 753-1134
Web Site: http://www.ecke.com
Year Founded: 1930
Sales Range: $75-99.9 Million
Emp.: 200
Supplier of Poinsettias, New Guinea Impatiens & Sunscape Daisies Grown in Greenhouses
N.A.I.C.S.: 111422
Daniel Windus (Mgr-IS)
Edgar Engert (Mgr-Sls)

PAUL EVERTS RV COUNTRY
3633 S Maple Ave, Fresno, CA 93725
Tel.: (559) 486-1000
Web Site: http://www.rvcountry.com
Rev.: $25,400,000
Emp.: 200
Recreational Vehicle Dealers
N.A.I.C.S.: 441210
Krik Curtis (Owner)
Alex Mahan (Mgr-Fin)
Stacy Alvarado (Mgr-Parts)

PAUL FISHER OIL COMPANY INC.
365 Mulberry Ave, Selmer, TN 38375
Tel.: (731) 645-3616
Sales Range: $25-49.9 Million
Emp.: 150
Whslr of Petroleum Products
N.A.I.C.S.: 424710

PAUL G. WHITE TILE CO., INC.
50 Allen Ave, Portland, ME 04103
Tel.: (207) 797-4657
Web Site:
http://www.paulwhitetile.com
Year Founded: 1970
Sales Range: $10-24.9 Million
Emp.: 65
Tile & Terrazzo Contracting Services
N.A.I.C.S.: 238340
Paul G. White (Pres)

PAUL HASTINGS LLP
515 S Flower St 25th Fl, Los Angeles, CA 90071
Tel.: (213) 683-6000
Web Site:
https://www.paulhastings.com
Year Founded: 1951
Emp.: 767
Law firm
N.A.I.C.S.: 541110
George W. Abele (Partner)
Nancy L. Abell (Partner)
Leslie L. Abbott (Partner)
Mark W. Atkinson (Partner)
Maria A. Audero (Partner)
Scott Faga (Partner-Washington)
Paul Severs (Partner-Corp Practice-London)
Camilo Cardozo (Partner)

COMPANIES — PAUL, WEISS, RIFKIND, WHARTON & GARRISON LLP

Isaac Ashkenazi *(Partner-Litigation Practice)*
Seth Zachary *(Chm)*
Arun Srivastava *(Partner-Fin Svcs & Regulatory-London)*
Charles Cardon *(Partner)*
Sherrese M. Smith *(Vice Chm-Data Privacy,Cybersecurity Practice & Partner)*

PAUL HEMMER CONSTRUCTION COMPANY
250 Grandview Dr, Fort Mitchell, KY 41017-5667
Tel.: (859) 341-8300   KY
Web Site: http://www.paulhemmer.com
Year Founded: 1982
Sales Range: $75-99.9 Million
Emp.: 50
Provider of Real Estate, Construction & Contracting Services
N.A.I.C.S.: 531210
Barry G. Kienzle *(CFO & Sr VP)*
Jack Levermann *(VP-Bus Dev)*
David Dringenburg *(Dir-Building Svc Grp)*
Paul W. Hemmer Jr. *(Pres & CEO)*
John F. Curtin III *(VP)*

PAUL HEURING MOTORS INC.
720 N Hobart Rd, Hobart, IN 46342
Tel.: (219) 942-3673
Web Site: http://www.heuringford.com
Year Founded: 1942
Sales Range: $25-49.9 Million
Emp.: 45
Car Whslr
N.A.I.C.S.: 441110
David Heuring *(Pres)*
J. R. Heuring *(VP)*

PAUL J. KREZ COMPANY
7831 Nagle Ave, Morton Grove, IL 60053-2712
Tel.: (847) 581-0017   IL
Web Site: http://www.krezgroup.com
Year Founded: 1909
Sales Range: $75-99.9 Million
Emp.: 100
Insulation Contractor
N.A.I.C.S.: 238310
Paul J. Helmer *(Chm)*
Paul K. Helmer *(Pres)*

Subsidiaries:

Barrier Corp.   (1)
7831 Nagle Ave, Morton Grove, IL 60053
Tel.: (847) 581-0017
Web Site: http://www.krezgroup.com
Sales Range: $10-24.9 Million
Emp.: 20
Roof Deck Systems, Floor Leveling, Underlayments, Toppings, Coatings, Geotechnical Engineered Design
N.A.I.C.S.: 238310
Paul K. Helmer *(Pres)*

John Caretti & Co.   (1)
7831 N Nagle Ave, Morton Grove, IL 60106
Tel.: (630) 354-6000
Emp.: 10
Terrazzo Contracting Services
N.A.I.C.S.: 238340
Tom McHugh *(Sr Mgr-Project)*
Chad Rakow *(Project Mgr)*

Spray Insulations, Inc.   (1)
7831 Nagle Ave, Morton Grove, IL 60053-2712
Tel.: (847) 965-7831
Web Site: http://www.krezgroup.com
Sales Range: $10-24.9 Million
Emp.: 20
Fireproofing; Thermal Insulation; Acoustical Insulation
N.A.I.C.S.: 238990

PAUL JARDIN OF USA INC.
60 W Corcoran, Simi Valley, CA 93065
Tel.: (805) 823-8383
Web Site: http://www.3daysuitbroker.com
Sales Range: $10-24.9 Million
Emp.: 20
Retailer of Men's & Boys' Clothing Stores
N.A.I.C.S.: 458110

PAUL JOHNSON DRYWALL, INC.
1720 W Parkside Ln, Phoenix, AZ 85027
Tel.: (602) 254-1320   AZ
Web Site: https://www.pauljohnsondrywall.com
Emp.: 100
Drywall Contractor & Related Construction Services
N.A.I.C.S.: 238310
Robert Cole Johnson *(Pres)*

Subsidiaries:

C & S Drywall Inc.   (1)
1831 E 73rd Ave, Denver, CO 80229
Tel.: (303) 286-9130
Web Site: http://www.cs-drywall.com
Rev.: $3,330,000
Emp.: 30
Drywall & Insulation Contractors
N.A.I.C.S.: 238310
Steve Deeds *(Pres)*

PAUL MILLER AUTO GROUP
179 Rt 46, Parsippany, NJ 07054
Tel.: (973) 575-7750
Web Site: http://www.paulmiller.com
Year Founded: 1976
Sales Range: $200-249.9 Million
Emp.: 250
Owner & Operator of Car Dealerships
N.A.I.C.S.: 441110
Paul Miller *(Pres)*
Mark Sawyer *(Mgr-Mazda & Heavy Trucks Svc)*
Dana Nguyen *(CFO & Sec)*

PAUL OIL COMPANY INC.
524 N Sierra Ave, Oakdale, CA 95361-2762
Tel.: (209) 847-2281   CA
Year Founded: 1974
Sales Range: $10-24.9 Million
Emp.: 60
Provider of Petroleum Products
N.A.I.C.S.: 424720

PAUL PETERS AGENCY INC.
6 Falmouth Hts Rd, Falmouth, MA 02540
Tel.: (508) 548-2500
Web Site: http://www.paulpetersagency.com
Sales Range: $10-24.9 Million
Emp.: 20
Insurance Agents
N.A.I.C.S.: 524210
John Lynch Sr. *(Pres)*

PAUL PIAZZA & SON INC.
1552 Saint Louis St, New Orleans, LA 70112
Tel.: (504) 524-6011
Web Site: http://www.paulpiazza.com
Sales Range: $10-24.9 Million
Emp.: 35
Fish, Fresh
N.A.I.C.S.: 424460
Shepherd Baumer *(VP)*
Kristen Baumer *(Pres)*
Sam Lima *(Dir-Sls & Mktg)*

PAUL REED SMITH GUITARS
380 Log Canoe Cir, Stevensville, MD 21666-2166
Tel.: (410) 643-9970
Web Site: http://www.prsguitars.com
Sales Range: $25-49.9 Million
Emp.: 140
Guitar Mfr
N.A.I.C.S.: 339992
Paul Smith *(Owner)*
Jack Higginbotham *(Pres)*
Geoff Jacobsen *(Mgr-IS)*
Judy Schaefer *(Dir-Mktg)*
David Settimi *(Product Mgr-Accessories)*
Phil Gates *(Mgr-Customer Svc)*
Jim Cullen *(Sls Dir)*

PAUL RISK ASSOCIATES, INC.
11 W State St, Quarryville, PA 17566-1112
Tel.: (717) 786-7308   PA
Web Site: http://www.paulrisk.com
Year Founded: 1932
Sales Range: $10-24.9 Million
Emp.: 75
Provider of Nonresidential Construction Services
N.A.I.C.S.: 236220
Steve Risk *(Pres)*
Linda Read *(Treas & Sec)*
D. J. Risk *(VP)*
Kary Urban *(Mgr-Acctg)*

PAUL SHERRY CHRYSLER-DODGE-JEEP INC.
8645 N County Rd 25 A, Piqua, OH 45356
Tel.: (937) 778-0830
Web Site: http://www.paulsherry.com
Sales Range: $25-49.9 Million
Emp.: 125
New & Used Automobile Dealer
N.A.I.C.S.: 441110
Paul H. Sherry *(Owner)*
Len Clarke *(Gen Mgr)*

PAUL SUSTEK COMPANY INC.
800 Turner Industrial Way, Aston, PA 19014-3006
Tel.: (610) 485-9600   PA
Year Founded: 1978
Sales Range: $10-24.9 Million
Emp.: 25
General Warehousing Storage & Export Packaging
N.A.I.C.S.: 493110
Thomas Wilson *(Pres)*
Travis Traveleeene *(Controller)*
Rich Whitzel *(Mgr)*

PAUL THIGPEN CHEVROLET BUICK GMC
202 W 1st St, Vidalia, GA 30474
Tel.: (866) 435-3167
Web Site: http://www.paulthigpenchevy.com
New & Used Car Dealers
N.A.I.C.S.: 441110
Dave Anderson *(Gen Mgr)*
Stephen Gordon *(Dir-Fixed Operations)*
Gary Gasper *(CFO)*
Shannon Martin *(Sls Mgr)*
Mark Walker *(Sls Mgr)*
Don Sweeney *(Sls Mgr-Internet)*
Mark Stutzman *(Dir-Svc & Parts)*
Jason Hadden *(Asst Mgr-Svc)*
Jamie Whitaker *(Mgr-Customization)*
Bill Hanes *(Mgr-Property)*
Kristen Morris *(Mgr-Parts)*
Gavin Schnelle *(Fin Mgr)*
Rodney Rogers *(Mgr)*

PAUL WALSH NISSAN, INC.
4500 Riverside Dr, Macon, GA 31210
Tel.: (478) 781-8440
Web Site: http://www.butlernissanofmacon.com
Sales Range: $10-24.9 Million
Emp.: 40
Car Whslr
N.A.I.C.S.: 441110
Jay Davis *(Gen Mgr)*

PAUL WINSTON FINE JEWELRY GROUP
151 W 46th St Fl 12, New York, NY 10036
Tel.: (212) 381-2160
Sales Range: $25-49.9 Million
Emp.: 25
Jewelry, Precious Metal
N.A.I.C.S.: 339910
Isaac Gad *(Pres)*

PAUL'S ACE HARDWARE STORES
1800 N Scottsdale Rd, Scottsdale, AZ 85257
Tel.: (480) 947-7281
Web Site: http://www.paulsacehardware.com
Sales Range: $10-24.9 Million
Emp.: 100
Hardware Stores
N.A.I.C.S.: 444140
Carol Michaels *(VP-Admin)*
Mike Rineer *(Sr Acct Mgr)*
Catherine D. Rice *(Mgr-HR)*

PAUL, WEISS, RIFKIND, WHARTON & GARRISON LLP
1285 Avenue of the Americas, New York, NY 10019-6064
Tel.: (212) 373-3000
Web Site: http://www.paulweiss.com
Year Founded: 1946
Sales Range: $750-799.9 Million
Emp.: 737
Legal Advisory Services
N.A.I.C.S.: 541110
Allan J. Arffa *(Partner)*
Robert A. Atkins *(Partner)*
Lynn B. Bayard *(Partner)*
Bruce Birenboim *(Partner)*
Jessica S. Carey *(Partner)*
Lewis R. Clayton *(Partner)*
Jay Cohen *(Partner)*
Alice Belisle Eaton *(Partner)*
Andrew J. Ehrlich *(Partner)*
Gregory A. Ezring *(Partner)*
Andrew C. Finch *(Chm-Antitrust Practice Grp)*
Brad J. Finkelstein *(Partner)*
Roberto Finzi *(Partner)*
Harris B. Freidus *(Partner)*
Manuel S. Frey *(Partner)*
Scott M. Sontag *(Partner)*
Jeffrey Samuels *(Partner)*
Elizabeth Sacksteder *(Partner)*
Scott A. Barshay *(Chm-Corp Dept)*
Brad S. Karp *(Chm)*
Valerie Radwaner *(Deputy Chm)*
J. Steven Baughman *(Partner-Litigation Dept-Washington)*
Kenneth A. Gallo *(Mng Partner-Washington)*
Nicholas Groombridge *(Chm-Intellectual Property Litigation)*
Alvaro Gomez de Membrillera Galiana *(Partner-Mergers & Acq Grp-London)*
David K. Lakhdhir *(Partner-London)*
Mark S. Bergman *(Partner-London)*
Paul M. Basta *(Co-Chm-Bankruptcy & Corp Reorganization Dept)*
Alan W. Kornberg *(Co-Chm-Bankruptcy & Corp Reorganization Dept)*
Jeh Charles Johnson *(Partner & Co-Head-Cybersecurity & Data Protection Practice)*
Sean McNamara *(CFO)*
Hank Miller *(Chief Admin Officer)*

PAUL, WEISS, RIFKIND, WHARTON & GARRISON LLP — U.S. PRIVATE

Paul, Weiss, Rifkind, Wharton & Garrison LLP—(Continued)

Richard D. Drankoski (Chief HR Officer)
Pamela N. Davidson (Chief Legal Personnel & Recruitment Officer)
Nicole Weber (Chief Legal Project Mgmt Officer)
Marjorie S. Kaplan (Chief Professional Dev Officer-Continuing Legal Education)
John C. Hearn (Chief Professional Responsibility Officer)
Mozhgan Mizban (Chief Strategy Officer)
Andreas M. Antoniou (CIO)
Julie Triedman (Dir-Content)
Charles Pesant (Partner)

PAULAUR CORPORATION
105 Melrich Rd, Cranbury, NJ 08512
Tel.: (609) 395-8844
Web Site: http://www.paulaur.com
Year Founded: 1980
Sales Range: $25-49.9 Million
Emp.: 150
Commercial Bakery Services
N.A.I.C.S.: 311812
Andrew Toscano (VP-Mfg)
Michael Toscano (Vp-Engrg)
Mitchell Stefaniak (CFO)
Amanda Lewey (Mgr-Pur)

PAULBECKS INC.
171 Red Oak Dr, Aitkin, MN 56431
Tel.: (218) 927-6919
Web Site: http://www.paulbecks.com
Sales Range: $10-24.9 Million
Emp.: 125
Owner & Operator of Grocery Stores
N.A.I.C.S.: 445110
Greg Paulbeck (Pres)
Mike Paulbeck (Owner)

PAULETTE CARTER DESIGN INC.
1400 NW Irving St Ste 104, Portland, OR 97209
Tel.: (503) 525-2989
Web Site: http://www.pcdgroup.com
Year Founded: 1996
Rev.: $2,100,000
Emp.: 9
Custom Computer Programming Services
N.A.I.C.S.: 541511
Natalya Faden (Dir-Accts)
Danielle Hunt (Dir-Ops)
Paulette Carter (Principal)

PAULMAY CO., INC.
1970 Pitkin Ave, Brooklyn, NY 11207
Tel.: (845) 517-2200   NY
Year Founded: 1987
Plastics Fabrication Company
N.A.I.C.S.: 326199

PAULO PRODUCTS COMPANY INC.
5711 W Park Ave, Saint Louis, MO 63110-1834
Tel.: (314) 647-7500
Web Site: http://www.paulo.com
Year Founded: 1959
Sales Range: $25-49.9 Million
Emp.: 328
Provider of Metal Heat Treating Services
N.A.I.C.S.: 332811
Benjamin F. Rassieur III (Pres)

PAULSCORP, LLC
100 St Paul St, Denver, CO 80206
Tel.: (303) 371-9000   DE

Web Site:
http://thepaulscorporation.com
Capital Management & Real Estate Development Services
N.A.I.C.S.: 531210
William Pauls (Chm)
Brian D. Pauls (Pres)

PAULSEN MARKETING COMMUNICATIONS, INC.
3510 S 1st Ave Cir, Sioux Falls, SD 57105-5807
Tel.: (605) 336-1745
Web Site:
http://www.paulsenmarketing.com
Year Founded: 1951
Rev.: $10,000,000
Emp.: 33
Advetising Agency
N.A.I.C.S.: 541810
Thane E. Paulsen (CEO)
Greg Guse (Pres)
Mark Smither (VP & Dir-Strategic)
Mike Dowling (VP-Creative Svcs)
Kristi Moss (Media Dir)
Alicia DeGeest (Acct Supvr)
Sara Steever (VP-Digital Svcs)
Emily Knutson (Dir-First Impressions)
Jordin Mueller (Acct Coord)
Heather Covrig (Acct Exec)
Kelli Betsinger (Acct Exec)
Marcus Squier (Acct Supvr)
Mindy Dale (Acct Exec)
Jon Marohl (Art Dir)
Katie Levitt (Assoc Dir-Creative)
Danita Tegethoff (Client Svcs Mgr)
Janet Anderson (Mgr-Customer Svc)
Joan Meyers (Mgr-Client Svcs)
Lisa Luening (Mgr-Digital Project)
Tara Young (Coord-Digital Svc)
Michael Napolitano (Lead Web Developer)
Tom Kamnikar (Lead Web Developer)
Susan Janos (Mktg Strategist)
Lee Larson (Media Planner & Buyer)
Marnie Graham (Dir-Art)
Sarah Wolfswinkel (Coord-Production)
Bryan Bjerke (Dir-PR)
Kristie Weiberg (Sr Dir-Art)
Jane Harms (VP-Fin & HR)

PAULSEN, INC.
1116 E Hwy 30, Cozad, NE 69130
Tel.: (308) 784-3333   NE
Web Site: http://www.pauleninc.com
Year Founded: 1946
Sales Range: $25-49.9 Million
Emp.: 300
Highway & Street Construction
N.A.I.C.S.: 237310
Larry Paulsen (Pres)
Dennis Sandrock (Mgr-Dept)
Jim Jewell (Mgr-Dept)

PAULSON & CO. INC.
1251 Ave of the Americas, New York, NY 10020
Tel.: (212) 956-2221   DE
Web Site: http://www.paulsonco.com
Year Founded: 1994
Rev.: $18,000,000,000
Emp.: 120
Alternative Investment Management Services
N.A.I.C.S.: 523940
Stuart L. Merzer (Chief Compliance Officer & Gen Counsel)
Christopher Papagianis (Partner)
Marcelo Kim (Partner)
John Alfred Paulson (Pres & Portfolio Mgr)

Subsidiaries:

Steinway Musical Instruments, Inc.   (1)
800 South St Ste 305, Waltham, MA 02453-1480
Tel.: (781) 894-9770
Web Site: http://www.steinwaymusical.com
Sales Range: $350-399.9 Million
Emp.: 1,698
Musical Instruments Mfr & Distr
N.A.I.C.S.: 339992

Subsidiary (Domestic):

Conn-Selmer, Inc.   (2)
600 Industrial Pkwy, Elkhart, IN 46516-5414
Tel.: (574) 522-1675
Web Site: http://www.conn-selmer.com
Sales Range: $350-399.9 Million
Emp.: 78
Musical Instrument Mfr
N.A.I.C.S.: 339992
John M. Stoner Jr. (Pres & CEO)
Mike Kamphuis (Mng Dir-Education Div)
Tim Lautzenheiser (Chief Education Dev Officer & VP-Education)

Subsidiary (Non-US):

Boston Piano GmbH   (3)
Rondenbarg 10, 22525, Hamburg, Germany
Tel.: (49) 40853910
Musical Instrument Mfr
N.A.I.C.S.: 339992
Werner Husmann (Gen Mgr)

Subsidiary (Domestic):

Kluge Klaviaturen GmbH   (4)
Old Powder Mill 20, 42855, Remscheid, Germany
Tel.: (49) 2191690280
Web Site: http://www.kluge-klaviaturen.de
Wing & Piano Keyboards Mfr
N.A.I.C.S.: 339992

Steinway Haus Dusseldorf GmbH   (4)
Immermannstrasse 14-16, Dusseldorf, 40210, Germany
Tel.: (49) 2114939370
Web Site: http://www.steinway-duesseldorf.de
Musical Instrument Mfr
N.A.I.C.S.: 339992
Walther Steindlegger (Gen Mgr)

Steinway Retail Deutschland GmbH   (4)
Landsberger Strasse 336, Laim, 80687, Munich, Germany
Tel.: (49) 895467970
Web Site: http://www.steinway-muenchen.de
Musical Instrument Retailer
N.A.I.C.S.: 459140
Philipp Avramov (Mgr)

Unit (Domestic):

Ludwig/Musser Percussion Instruments   (3)
600 Industrial Pkwy, Elkhart, IN 46516
Tel.: (574) 522-1675
Web Site: http://www.ludwig-drums.com
Sales Range: $50-74.9 Million
Mfr of Drums, Timpani, Mallet Instruments & Accessories
N.A.I.C.S.: 339992
James A. Catalano (Dir-Sls & Mktg)

Musser   (3)
PO Box 310, Elkhart, IN 46515-0310
Tel.: (574) 522-1675
Web Site: http://www.conn-selmer.com
Sales Range: $10-24.9 Million
Emp.: 750
Mallet Instruments & Accessories Mfr
N.A.I.C.S.: 339992
Perry Richards (Plant Mgr)

Subsidiary (Domestic):

Steinway & Sons   (3)
1 Steinway Pl, Astoria, NY 11105
Tel.: (718) 721-2600
Web Site: http://www.steinway.com
Sales Range: $150-199.9 Million
Mfr & Retailer of Pianos
N.A.I.C.S.: 339992
Dan Miceli (Sr Dir-Retail)
Andrew Horbachevsky (VP-Mfg)

The O.S. Kelly Company   (3)
318 E North St, Springfield, OH 45503-1267
Tel.: (937) 322-4921
Sales Range: $25-49.9 Million
Emp.: 35
Piano Plates Mfr
N.A.I.C.S.: 339992
Ralph Stacy (Plant Mgr)

Unit (Domestic):

Vincent Bach Co.   (3)
500 Industrial Pkwy, Elkhart, IN 46516-5414
Tel.: (574) 522-1675
Web Site: http://www.conn-selmer.com
Sales Range: $350-399.9 Million
Emp.: 150
Mfr of Brass Wind Musical Instruments
N.A.I.C.S.: 339992
Judy Ninik (CFO)

Subsidiary (Non-US):

Vincent Bach International, Ltd.   (3)
Unit 71 Capitol Industrial Park, Capitol Way, London, NW9 0EW, United Kingdom
Tel.: (44) 2083588800
Web Site: http://www.vincentbachonline.com
Sales Range: $10-24.9 Million
Emp.: 8
Musical Instruments Designer & Mfr
N.A.I.C.S.: 339992
Bharath Karia (Gen Mgr)

PAULSON INVESTMENT COMPANY, LLC
5335 Meadows Rd Ste 465, Lake Oswego, OR 97035
Tel.: (503) 243-6000
Web Site:
http://www.paulsoninvestment.com
Year Founded: 1970
Investment Banking Services
N.A.I.C.S.: 523150
Lorraine Maxfield (Sr VP-Corp Fin)
Chris Clark (Chm)
Tanya Durkee Urbach (Exec VP & Head-Legal)
Thomas Parigian (Mng Partner & Dir-Corp Fin)
Trent Donald Davis (CEO)
Robert Setteducati (Mng Partner & Dir-Bus Dev)
Alex Winks (Pres & CFO)
Basil Christakos (Chief Compliance Officer)
Nickolay V. Kukekov (Executives)

PAULUS, SOKOLOWSKI & SARTOR LLC
67 A Mtn Blvd Ext, Warren, NJ 07059-5626
Tel.: (732) 560-9700   NJ
Web Site: http://www.psands.com
Year Founded: 1962
Sales Range: $25-49.9 Million
Emp.: 300
Engineering & Architectural Services
N.A.I.C.S.: 541310
Anthony J. Sastor (Chm)
Emad Youssef (Sr VP)
Luis Miguel Salinas (VP-Environmental Dept)
John Sartor (CEO)

PAULY JAIL BUILDING COMPANY, INC.
17515 Bataan Ct, Louisville, IN 46062
Tel.: (317) 580-0833
Web Site: http://www.paulyjail.com
Sales Range: $10-24.9 Million
Emp.: 22
Contractor of Correctional Equipment
N.A.I.C.S.: 238130
Robert James Pohrer (CEO)
Regina Maltese (VP-Fin)
Jared Bailey (Sr Project Mgr)
Nick Henry (Coord-Hardware)

COMPANIES

Ricky Harrison *(Mgr-Pre-Construction)*
Joseph Pauly Pohrer III *(Pres)*

PAVCO, INC.
1935 John Crosland Jr Dr, Charlotte, NC 28208
Tel.: (704) 496-6800
Web Site: http://www.pavco.com
Year Founded: 1948
Sales Range: $10-24.9 Million
Emp.: 50
Metal Plating Services
N.A.I.C.S.: 332813
Scott Pavlish *(Pres)*

PAVECON INC.
3022 Roy Orr Blvd, Grand Prairie, TX 75050
Tel.: (972) 263-3223
Web Site: http://www.pavecon.com
Year Founded: 1992
Rev.: $18,651,690
Emp.: 115
Parking Lot Construction
N.A.I.C.S.: 238990
Marty Murphy *(VP & Bus Mgr)*
Rick Tuzinski *(Project Mgr-Sls)*

Subsidiaries:

Pavecon Utilities Inc. (1)
3022 Roy Orr Blvd, Grand Prairie, TX 75050
Tel.: (972) 263-3223
Web Site: http://www.pavecon.com
Sales Range: $10-24.9 Million
Emp.: 18
Underground Utilities Contractor
N.A.I.C.S.: 238990

PAVEX INC.
4400 Gettysburg Rd, Camp Hill, PA 17011
Tel.: (717) 761-1502
Web Site: http://www.pavexinc.com
Sales Range: $10-24.9 Million
Emp.: 25
Excavation & Grading, Building Construction
N.A.I.C.S.: 238910
Jodi Goshorn *(Project Coord)*
Robert Kalbach Sr. *(Pres)*

PAVONE
1006 Market St, Harrisburg, PA 17101-2811
Tel.: (717) 234-8886   PA
Web Site: http://www.pavone.net
Year Founded: 1991
Sales Range: $10-24.9 Million
Emp.: 58
Advertising Agencies
N.A.I.C.S.: 541810
Michael R. Pavone *(Pres & CEO)*
Amy S. Beamer *(COO & Partner)*
Robinson Smith *(Dir-Design)*
John Bassounas *(Partner & Dir-Client Svcs)*
Brent Suereth *(Mgr-Resource)*
Carolina Patrick *(Mgr-Brand)*
Cory Blasdell *(Assoc Mgr-Brdcst)*
Darby Hughes *(Dir-Brand Strategy)*
Dave Spink *(Assoc Dir-Creative)*
Isabelle Rousseau *(Sr Mgr-Resource)*
Jeff Odiorne *(Chief Creative & Content Officer)*
Lindsay Abayasekara *(Mgr-Digital Mktg)*
Nate Hileman *(Controller)*

Subsidiaries:

Varsity (1)
532 N Front St, Wormleysburg, PA 17043
Tel.: (717) 652-1277
Web Site: http://www.varsitybranding.com
Sales Range: $10-24.9 Million
Emp.: 50
Advertising Agencies

N.A.I.C.S.: 541810
John Bassounas *(Dir-Client Svcs)*
Amy Beamer *(CFO & Partner)*
Michael Pavone *(Pres & CEO)*
Greg Carney *(Mgr-Integrated Media)*
Derek Dunham *(VP-Client Svcs)*
Jenn Kehler *(Dir-Media)*
Jodi Christman *(Dir-Interactive)*
Robinson Smith *(Dir-Design)*

PAW PAW WINE DISTRIBUTORS COMPANY
2400 Ravine Rd, Kalamazoo, MI 49004
Tel.: (269) 492-9414
Web Site: http://www.pawpawwine.com
Year Founded: 1943
Sales Range: $10-24.9 Million
Emp.: 55
Beer Whslr
N.A.I.C.S.: 424810
David Bogen *(Pres)*

PAW-PAW'S CAMPER CITY INC.
808 Memorial Blvd, Picayune, MS 39466-5635
Tel.: (601) 799-0690   MS
Web Site: http://www.pawpawscampers.com
Year Founded: 1994
Sales Range: $25-49.9 Million
Emp.: 100
Seller & Servicer of Recreational Vehicles
N.A.I.C.S.: 441210
W. B. Herring *(Pres & CEO)*

PAWLING CORPORATION
157 Charles Colman Blvd, Pawling, NY 12564-1121
Tel.: (845) 855-1000   DE
Web Site: http://www.pawlingep.com
Year Founded: 1945
Sales Range: $150-199.9 Million
Emp.: 322
Mfr of Rubber & Molded Rubber Products
N.A.I.C.S.: 326299
Danielle Polverari *(Coord-Mktg)*
Diane Danese *(Mgr-Export Sls)*
Eric Eschbach *(Mgr-Inside Sls)*
Jennifer Killmer *(Coord-Sls)*
Katherine Laboy *(Coord-Inside Sls)*
Kelly Hafford *(Mgr-Quality Assurance, Shipping & Receiving)*
Trish Burd *(Coord-Sls)*
Warren Rozelle *(Mgr-Pur)*

Subsidiaries:

Alpar Architectural Products, LLC (1)
32 Nelson Hill Rd, Wassaic, NY 12592
Tel.: (612) 721-0156
Web Site: http://www.alpararch.com
Wall Protection Sheet & Corner Guard Mfr
N.A.I.C.S.: 326199

Pawling Corporation-Architectural Products Division (1)
32 Nelson Hill Rd, Wassaic, NY 12592-2121
Tel.: (845) 373-9300
Web Site: http://www.pawling.com
Sales Range: $25-49.9 Million
Emp.: 310
Rubber & Plastic Extrusions Mfr
N.A.I.C.S.: 326291
Jason Smith *(Pres)*

Presray Corp. (1)
32 Nelson Hill Rd, Wassaic, NY 12592   (100%)
Tel.: (845) 855-1220
Web Site: http://www.presray.com
Sales Range: $25-49.9 Million
Emp.: 200
Rubber & Plastic Extrusion Mfr
N.A.I.C.S.: 326299
Ted Hollander *(Chm)*
Kevin Harris *(Gen Mgr)*

PAWNEE COUNTY COOPERATIVE ASSOCIATION
103 E 3rd St, Larned, KS 67550
Tel.: (620) 285-2161
Web Site: http://www.pawneecoop.com
Rev.: $100,427,596
Emp.: 40
Petroleum Bulk Stations & Elevators
N.A.I.C.S.: 424910
Hugh Mounday *(Gen Mgr)*

PAWNEE VALLEY COMMUNITY HOSPITAL INC.
923 Carroll Ave, Larned, KS 67550
Tel.: (620) 285-3161   KS
Web Site: http://www.pawneevalleyhospital.com
Year Founded: 2001
Sales Range: $10-24.9 Million
Emp.: 114
Health Care Srvices
N.A.I.C.S.: 622110
John Jeter *(Pres)*
Bryce Young *(VP)*
Kendra Barker *(Interim CEO)*

PAWS/LA
2121 S Flower St, Los Angeles, CA 90007
Tel.: (213) 741-1950   CA
Web Site: http://www.pawsla.org
Year Founded: 1989
Sales Range: $1-9.9 Million
Veterinary Services
N.A.I.C.S.: 541940
Pamela Magette *(Exec Dir)*
Jill Schuberth *(Chm)*
Tomm Wells *(VP)*
Steve Wayland *(Dir-Programs)*
John Meeks *(Coord-Volunteer & Outreach)*
Omar Olivares *(Coord-Client Svc)*
Scott Dunlevie *(Coord-Admin Svcs)*
Michael Jon Smith *(Vice Chm)*

PAWTUCKET CREDIT UNION
1200 Central Ave, Pawtucket, RI 02860
Tel.: (401) 722-2212   RI
Web Site: http://www.pcu.org
Year Founded: 1928
Sales Range: $10-24.9 Million
Emp.: 334
Credit Union
N.A.I.C.S.: 522130
Lynn A. M. Weinstein *(Vice Chm)*
Ronald W. LeClair *(Chm)*
Paul F. Lefebvre *(Sec)*
Tamarah Bacon *(Asst VP)*
Linda Fish *(VP-Info Security)*
Kerri McLaughlin *(Coord-Fin Education)*
Paola Fernandez *(Asst VP-Community Outreach)*
Lenny Silva *(Sr VP-Comml Lending)*
Mark Peloquin *(Asst VP-Collections)*
George J. Charette *(Pres & CEO)*
Carrie Abatiello *(Sr VP)*
Heather Thurber *(Asst VP-HR)*
John B. Richer Jr. *(Treas)*

PAX MACHINE WORKS INC.
5139 Monroe Rd, Celina, OH 45822
Tel.: (419) 586-2337
Web Site: http://www.paxmachine.com
Rev.: $17,000,000
Emp.: 200
Metal Stampings, Nec
N.A.I.C.S.: 332119
Mike Pax *(Pres)*
Deborah Guingrich *(Treas & Sec)*
Stan Reineke *(Mgr-Sls)*

PAXTON MEDIA GROUP LLC

PAX WORLD FUNDS
30 Penhallow St 400, Portsmouth, NH 03801-3828
Tel.: (603) 431-8022   DE
Web Site: http://www.paxworld.com
Year Founded: 1971
Sales Range: $100-124.9 Million
Emp.: 50
Investment Company
N.A.I.C.S.: 523940
Laurence A. Shadek *(Chm)*
Joseph Keefe *(Pres & CEO)*

PAXEN LEARNING CORPORATION
1380 Sarnob Rd, Melbourne, FL 32935
Tel.: (321) 724-1033
Web Site: http://www.paxen.com
Sales Range: $25-49.9 Million
Emp.: 300
Educational Publisher; Tutoring Services
N.A.I.C.S.: 513130
Richard Semancik *(COO)*
Jonathan Zeigler *(VP-Ops)*

PAXIO INC.
2045 Martin Ave Ste 204, Santa Clara, CA 95050-2708
Tel.: (408) 343-8200
Web Site: http://www.paxio.com
Year Founded: 2003
Data Processing, Hosting & Related Services
N.A.I.C.S.: 518210
Viky Vajay *(Office Mgr)*

Subsidiaries:

Fastmetrics LLC (1)
1 Hallidie Plz Ste 838, San Francisco, CA 94102-2817
Tel.: (415) 778-5108
Web Site: http://www.fastmetrics.com
Data Processing, Hosting & Related Services
N.A.I.C.S.: 518210
Andreas Glocker *(CEO)*

PAXION CAPITAL, LP
2494 Sand Hill Rd, Menlo Park, CA 94025
Tel.: (650) 446-7850
Web Site: http://paxion.com
Year Founded: 2015
Privater Equity Firm
N.A.I.C.S.: 523999
Duncan Robertson *(Partner & CFO)*

PAXTON & BALL INC.
541 S Main St, Hartford, KY 42347
Tel.: (270) 298-7401   KY
Year Founded: 1961
Sales Range: $25-49.9 Million
Emp.: 300
Provider of Gasoline Services
N.A.I.C.S.: 457120
David Ball *(Sec)*
Jerry Poole *(Pres)*

PAXTON COMPANY
1111 Ingleside Rd, Norfolk, VA 23502
Tel.: (757) 853-6781
Web Site: http://www.paxtonco.com
Rev.: $21,000,000
Emp.: 85
Marine Supplies
N.A.I.C.S.: 423860
James G. Beale *(Pres)*
Peggy Beale *(CEO & CFO)*
Sue Butler *(VP-Sls & Mktg)*
Elaine Smythe *(VP-Corp Mktg & Sls)*
Dale Clement *(Mgr-Sls-West)*
Paul deLaski *(Mgr-Sls-Northeast)*
Devon Felise *(Mgr-Natl Sls)*

PAXTON MEDIA GROUP LLC

PAXTON MEDIA GROUP LLC

Paxton Media Group LLC—(Continued)
201 S 4th St, Paducah, KY 42003-1524
Tel.: (270) 575-8600
Year Founded: 1938
Sales Range: $75-99.9 Million
Emp.: 2,000
Newspaper Publishers
N.A.I.C.S.: 513110
Jim Paxton (Editor-in-Chief & Publr)
David Paxton (Pres)
Terry Herrin (Mgr-IT & Sys)

Subsidiaries:

Chronicle-Tribune (1)
610 S Adams St, Marion, IN 46953 (100%)
Tel.: (765) 664-5111
Web Site: http://www.chronicle-tribune.com
Sales Range: $50-74.9 Million
Emp.: 196
Newspaper Publishers
N.A.I.C.S.: 513110
Brent Folkner (Mgr-Info & Tech)
Trish Nelson (Mgr-Bus)
David Penticuff (Editor)
Bill Thatcher (Mgr-Distr)
Ben Quiggle (Mng Editor)
Heather Korporal (Mgr-Circulation)
Linda Kelsay (Pres)
Neal Bartrum (Mgr-Distr)
Stan Howard (Dir-Adv)

Connersville News Examiner (1)
406 N Central Ave, Connersville, IN 47331-1926
Tel.: (765) 825-0581
Web Site: http://www.newsexaminer.com
Sales Range: $10-24.9 Million
Emp.: 62
Newspapers
N.A.I.C.S.: 513110

Courier Times Newspaper (1)
201 S 14th St, New Castle, IN 47362-3328
Tel.: (765) 529-1111
Web Site: http://www.thecouriertimes.com
Rev.: $2,500,000
Emp.: 15
Newspapers
N.A.I.C.S.: 513110
Bob Hansen (Pres)
Andrew Byrd (Mgr-Single Copy)
Donna Cronk (Editor-Neighbors)
David Risley (Editor-Sports)
Jack Hutcheson (Dir-Circulation)
Shaun Adkins (Mgr-Home Delivery)
Stacie Wrightsman (Dir-Adv)

Dispatch Publishing Company, Inc. (1)
121 W Michigan Blvd, Michigan City, IN 46360-3274
Tel.: (219) 874-7211
Web Site: http://www.the-dispatch.com
Sales Range: $10-24.9 Million
Emp.: 75
Publisher of Newspapers
N.A.I.C.S.: 513110

Hammond Daily Star Publishing Co. Inc. (1)
725 S Morrison Blvd, Hammond, LA 70403-5401
Tel.: (985) 254-7827
Web Site: http://www.hammondstar.com
Sales Range: $10-24.9 Million
Emp.: 34
Newspapers
N.A.I.C.S.: 513110
Michelle Gallo (Publr)

LaPorte Herald Argus (1)
701 State St, La Porte, IN 46350-3328 (100%)
Tel.: (219) 362-2161
Web Site: http://www.heraldargus.com
Sales Range: $10-24.9 Million
Emp.: 22
Newspaper Services
N.A.I.C.S.: 513110
Bill Hackney (Publr)
Amanda Haverstick (Editor-News)

Log Cabin Democrat, LLC (1)
1121 Front St, Conway, AR 72032 (100%)
Tel.: (501) 327-6621

Web Site: http://www.thecabin.net
Sales Range: $25-49.9 Million
Emp.: 25
Newspaper Publishers
N.A.I.C.S.: 513110
Cindy Malin (Bus Mgr)

Paragould Daily Press (1)
1401 W Hunt St, Paragould, AR 72450-3575 (100%)
Tel.: (870) 239-8562
Web Site: http://www.paragoulddailypress.com
Sales Range: $10-24.9 Million
Emp.: 30
Newspaper Publishers
N.A.I.C.S.: 513110
Brenda Keller (Gen Mgr)
Steve Gillespie (Editor)
Melissa Mitchell (Mgr-Circulation)
Barbara Reichardt (Bus Mgr)

Peru Daily Tribune Publishing Co. Inc. (1)
26 W 3rd St, Peru, IN 46970-2155
Tel.: (765) 473-6641
Web Site: http://www.perutribune.com
Rev.: $1,000,000
Emp.: 10
Publishing Newspapers
N.A.I.C.S.: 513110
Linda Kelsay (Publr)

Russellville Newspapers Inc. (1)
201 E 2nd St, Russellville, AR 72801-5102 (100%)
Tel.: (479) 968-5252
Web Site: http://www.couriernews.com
Sales Range: $10-24.9 Million
Emp.: 40
Commercial Printing
N.A.I.C.S.: 323111
Michelle Harris (Dir-Adv)

Searcy Newspapers Inc. (1)
723 W Beebe-Capps Expy, Searcy, AR 72143-4808
Tel.: (501) 268-8621
Web Site: http://www.thedailycitizen.com
Sales Range: $10-24.9 Million
Emp.: 40
Commercial Printing
N.A.I.C.S.: 323111
Mike Murphy (Publr)
Bud Paxson (Pres)

The Daily Dispatch (1)
304 S Chestnut St, Henderson, NC 27536-4225 (100%)
Tel.: (252) 436-2700
Web Site: http://www.hendersondispatch.com
Rev.: $1,600,000
Emp.: 40
Newspapers
N.A.I.C.S.: 513110
Brent Agurs (Mgr-Circulation)
Carol Venable (District Mgr)
Tim Fulcher (District Mgr)
Matthew Murray (District Mgr)
A. J. Woodell (Mgr-Circulation)

The Durham Herald Co. (1)
2828 Pickett Rd, Durham, NC 27705
Tel.: (919) 419-6500
Web Site: http://www.heraldsun.com
Sales Range: $10-24.9 Million
Emp.: 200
Newspapers
N.A.I.C.S.: 513110
Rick Bean (Publr)
Brent Agurs (Dir-Circulation)
David Jones (Dir-Adv)
Meghan Blackwell (Acct Exec)
Craig Chappell (Acct Exec)
Danielle Christensen (Acct Exec)
Joy Miller (Acct Exec)
Marty Cassady (Acct Exec)
Jennifer Flye (Acct Exec)

The Paducah Sun Newspaper (1)
408 Kentucky Ave, Paducah, KY 42003-1524
Tel.: (270) 575-8600
Web Site: http://www.paducahsun.com
Rev.: $70,100,000
Emp.: 100
Newspapers
N.A.I.C.S.: 323111
Ron Clark (Editor-News)
Gary Adkisson (Gen Mgr)
Carolyn Raney (Dir-Adv)

The Sanford Herald Inc. (1)
208 Saint Clair Ct, Sanford, NC 27330-3916
Tel.: (919) 708-9000
Web Site: http://www.sanfordherald.com
Rev.: $4,000,000
Emp.: 65
Newspapers
N.A.I.C.S.: 513110
Bill Horner (Publr)

The Southern Illinoisan (1)
710 N Illinois Ave, Carbondale, IL 62901-1283
Tel.: (618) 529-5454
Web Site: https://www.thesouthern.com
Sales Range: $50-74.9 Million
Emp.: 180
Newspaper Publishers
N.A.I.C.S.: 513110
Tom English (Exec Editor)
Alee Quick (Editor-Local News)
Shawn Anglin (Editor-Copy)
Sara Treat (Editor-Copy)
Jackson Brandhorst (Editor-Sports & Obits)
Brooke Beckmann (Editor-Copy)
Shad Hicks (Dir-Circulation)
Blake Turpin (Mgr-Circulation)
Kevin Morgan (Mgr-Pkg Center)
Donna Denson (Pres & Dir-Local Sls & Mktg)

The Times Inc. (1)
211 N Jackson St, Frankfort, IN 46041-1906
Tel.: (765) 659-4622
Web Site: http://www.ftimes.com
Sales Range: $10-24.9 Million
Emp.: 14
Newspaper Publishing Services
N.A.I.C.S.: 513110
Thaya Sterrett (Dir-Adv)
Sharon Pardonner (Publr)

Vincennes Newspapers, Inc. (1)
702 Main St, Vincennes, IN 47591
Tel.: (812) 886-9955
Web Site: http://www.suncommercial.com
Sales Range: $10-24.9 Million
Emp.: 17
Publishers of Newspapers
N.A.I.C.S.: 513110
Gayle R. Robbins (Publr & Editor)

Wabash Plain Dealer Company Inc. (1)
123 W Canal St, Wabash, IN 46992-3042 (100%)
Tel.: (260) 563-2131
Web Site: http://www.wabashplaindealer.com
Sales Range: $10-24.9 Million
Emp.: 25
Newspaper Publishing
N.A.I.C.S.: 513110
Eric Seaman (Mng Dir)

PAXTON VAN LINES INCORPORATED

5300 Port Royal Rd, Springfield, VA 22151
Tel.: (703) 321-7600
Web Site: http://www.paxton.com
Sales Range: $25-49.9 Million
Emp.: 200
Local Trucking with Storage
N.A.I.C.S.: 484110
Kevin Callahan (Dir-Safety & Risk Mitigation)

PAXTON-MITCHELL COMPANY

108 S 12th St, Blair, NE 68008
Tel.: (402) 426-3131
Web Site: http://www.paxton-mitchell.com
Sales Range: $10-24.9 Million
Emp.: 9
Gray Iron Ingot Molds, Cast
N.A.I.C.S.: 331511
Al Campbell (Pres)
Mark Pfeffer (Gen Mgr)

PAY TEL COMMUNICATIONS, INC.

PO Box 8179, Greensboro, NC 27419

Web Site: https://www.paytel.com
Year Founded: 1986
Computer Related Services
N.A.I.C.S.: 541519
John Tayloe (VP-Sls)

PAYABILITY, LLC

524 Broadway, New York, NY 10012
Tel.: (646) 494-8675
Web Site: http://www.payability.com
Year Founded: 2014
Sales Range: $10-24.9 Million
Emp.: 54
Online Shopping Services
N.A.I.C.S.: 522390
Keith Smith (Founder & CEO)
Jim Shook (CMO)
Gregor Siwinski (CTO)
Michael Fortugno (VP-Fin)
Jacob Schwartz (Head-Dev & Partnerships)
Anas Sohail (VP & Head-Sls)

PAYCOR, INC.

4811 Montgomery Rd, Cincinnati, OH 45212-2212
Tel.: (513) 381-0505
Web Site: http://www.paycor.com
Year Founded: 1990
Sales Range: $10-24.9 Million
Emp.: 300
Payroll Services
N.A.I.C.S.: 541214
Stacey Browning (Pres)
Ed Woodson (Gen Counsel & Sr VP)
Glenn Cross (CMO)
Adam Ante (CFO)
Chuck Mueller (Chief Revenue Officer)
Alice Geene (Chief Legal Officer & Gen Counsel)
Raul Villar Jr. (CEO)

Subsidiaries:

Paycor, Inc. (1)
10550 Deerwood Park Blvd Ste 306, Jacksonville, FL 32256-2805 (100%)
Tel.: (904) 398-3374
Web Site: http://www.paycor.com
Sales Range: $10-24.9 Million
Emp.: 75
Payroll Services
N.A.I.C.S.: 541214
Bob Coughlin (Founder & CEO)

PAYDAY PAYROLL SERVICES

6465 College Park Sq Ste 200, Virginia Beach, VA 23464
Tel.: (757) 523-0605
Web Site: http://www.paydaypayroll.com
Year Founded: 1985
Rev.: $2,800,000
Emp.: 20
Payroll Services
N.A.I.C.S.: 541214
Andy Kline (Founder & CEO)
Marty Mandelberg (CFO)
Christine Kingery (Mgr-Payroll-Virginia)
Jeff Marbach (Reg Mgr)
Kasam Hamza (Dir-IT Ops)
Rhea Marbach (Mgr-Payroll-Florida)
Danny Kline (Pres)
Aaron Hylton (Dir-Sls & Implementation)

PAYDEN & RYGEL

333 S Grand Ave 32nd Fl, Los Angeles, CA 90071
Tel.: (213) 625-1900
Web Site: http://www.payden.com
Year Founded: 1983
Sales Range: $50-74.9 Million
Emp.: 200
Investment Consultants
N.A.I.C.S.: 523940

Joan A. Payden *(Pres & CEO)*
Mark H. Stanley *(Sr Dir-Portfolio)*
Robin B. B. Creswell *(Mng Principal)*
Justin Bullion *(Mng Principal)*
James Sarni *(Mng Principal)*
Michael E. Salvay *(Mng Principal)*
David P. Ballantine *(Principal)*
Yot Chattrabhutti *(Principal)*
Erinn R. King *(Principal)*
Jeffrey C. Cleveland *(Principal)*
Arthur Hovsepian *(Principal)*
Wade Oosterman *(Pres & CEO)*

Subsidiaries:

Payden & Rygel Global Limited (1)
1 Bartholomew Lane, London, EC2N 2AX, United Kingdom
Tel.: (44) 20 7621 3000
Web Site: http://www.payden.com
Emp.: 19
Financial Advisory Services
N.A.I.C.S.: 523940
Joanne Collins *(Portfolio Mgr)*

PAYETTE ASSOCIATES INC.
285 Summer St, Boston, MA 02210-1518
Tel.: (617) 895-1000   MA
Web Site: http://www.payette.com
Year Founded: 1965
Sales Range: $10-24.9 Million
Emp.: 125
Architectural Services
N.A.I.C.S.: 541310
Roberta F. Haney *(COO)*
Christopher V. Lind *(Mgr-HR)*
Robert J. Schaeffner *(Principal)*
Charles S. Klee *(Principal)*
George E. Marsh *(Principal)*
J. Ian Adamson *(Principal)*
Andrea Love *(Principal & Dir-Building Science)*
Ching-Hua Ho *(Principal)*
Jeffrey H. DeGregorio *(Principal)*
Leon W. Drachman *(Principal)*
Peter Vieira *(Principal)*

Subsidiaries:

Payette Ships Inc. (1)
121 Richmond St, Toronto, ON, Canada (100%)
Tel.: (416) 955-0685
Sales Range: $10-24.9 Million
Emp.: 45
Water Transportation Services
N.A.I.C.S.: 488390

PAYLESS BUILDING CENTER INC.
4600 2nd Ave, Kearney, NE 68847
Tel.: (308) 234-5533
Web Site:
 http://www.builderscrop.com
Sales Range: $10-24.9 Million
Emp.: 105
Lumber & Other Building Materials
N.A.I.C.S.: 237210
Chris Morrgue *(Pres)*

PAYLESS DRUG STORES INC.
16100 SW 72 St, Tigard, OR 97224
Tel.: (503) 626-9436
Web Site:
 http://www.paylessdrug.com
Sales Range: $10-24.9 Million
Emp.: 250
Sales of Pharmaceuticals
N.A.I.C.S.: 424210
Jeffrey Rutz *(CIO & VP-IT)*
Judy Perry *(VP-Sls & Mktg)*
Darwin Pond *(VP-Ops)*
Jackson Leong *(VP-Tech)*
Tom Berkomtas *(CFO)*

PAYLESS HOLDINGS LLC
3231 SE 6th Ave, Topeka, KS 66607
Tel.: (785) 233-5171

Web Site: http://www.payless.com
Year Founded: 2012
Sales Range: $1-4.9 Billion
Holding Company; Footwear Retailer
N.A.I.C.S.: 551112
Betty J. Click *(Sr VP-HR)*
Sally Burk *(VP-Total Rewards)*

Subsidiaries:

Payless ShoeSource Worldwide, LLC (1)
3231 SE 6th Ave, Topeka, KS 66607-2260
Tel.: (785) 233-5171
Web Site: http://www.payless.com
Holding Company
N.A.I.C.S.: 551112

Subsidiary (Non-US):

Payless ShoeSource de Guatemala Ltda. (2)
22-43 Calzada Roosevelt Zone 11 Bldg Tikal Futura,, Niv Moon Tower 12, Guatemala, Guatemala
Tel.: (502) 24401960
Web Site: http://www.paylessguatemala.com
Footwear & Accessories Retailer
N.A.I.C.S.: 458210
Javier Castillo *(Gen Mgr)*

Payless ShoeSource, Inc. (1)
3231 SE Sixth Ave, Topeka, KS 66607-2207
Tel.: (785) 233-5171
Web Site: http://www.payless.com
Sales Range: $1-4.9 Billion
Emp.: 900
Shoe Stores
N.A.I.C.S.: 458210
Michael A. Vitelli *(COO)*
Ellen Junger *(Chief Customer & Mktg Officer)*

Subsidiary (Domestic):

Collective Licensing International, LLC (2)
850 Englewood Pkwy Ste 200, Englewood, CO 80110
Tel.: (303) 761-1345
Web Site: http://www.collectiveintl.com
Brand Development, Licensing & Marketing Services for Youth-Focused Footwear
N.A.I.C.S.: 533110
Dan Brown *(VP-Product)*
Matt Ballard *(VP-Fin & Ops)*

PAYMENTMAX PROCESSING INC.
870 Hampshire Rd, Thousand Oaks, CA 91361
Tel.: (805) 373-8974
Web Site:
 http://www.paymentmax.com
Year Founded: 2004
Sales Range: $10-24.9 Million
Emp.: 20
Business Payment Processing Solutions
N.A.I.C.S.: 522320
Tony Shap *(Owner & Pres)*
Emily Smiley *(CMO)*

PAYMENTONE CORPORATION
5883 Rue Ferrari, San Jose, CA 95138
Tel.: (408) 362-4258
Web Site: http://www.payone.com
Year Founded: 1988
Sales Range: $25-49.9 Million
Emp.: 85
Billing & Collections Services
N.A.I.C.S.: 561440
Joe Lynam *(Founder, Pres & CEO)*
Brad Singer *(Exec VP)*
Mark Snycerski *(VP-Engrg)*

PAYMENTUS CORPORATION
13024 Ballantyne Corporate Pl Ste 400, Charlotte, NC 28277
Tel.: (800) 420-1663
Web Site: http://www.paymentus.

Year Founded: 2004
Electronic Bill Payment Solutions
N.A.I.C.S.: 522320
Dushyant Sharma *(Pres & CEO)*
Elissa Boyet *(Sr Project Mgr-Implementation)*
Jerry Portocalis *(Sr VP)*

PAYNE & DOLAN, INC.
N3 W 23650 Badinger Rd, Waukesha, WI 53188
Tel.: (262) 524-1700
Web Site:
 http://www.payneanddolan.com
Rev.: $11,600,000
Emp.: 70
Highway & Street Construction
N.A.I.C.S.: 237310
Kurt Bechthold *(Pres & CEO)*
Mark Genrich *(Project Mgr)*
Todd Hughes *(Area Mgr)*
Michael Lemke *(Project Mgr)*
Chuck Maxwell *(Mgr-Drill & Blast)*
Raymond Postotnik *(Area Mgr)*

PAYNE-PIKE DEVELOPMENT CO.
2401 E Expy 83, Weslaco, TX 78596
Tel.: (956) 969-2525
Sales Range: $75-99.9 Million
Emp.: 89
Car Whslr
N.A.I.C.S.: 441110
Bob Grooms *(CFO)*
Edwin Bud Payne *(CEO)*

PAYPLUS, LLC
10830 Old Mill Rd Ste 102, Omaha, NE 68154-2609
Tel.: (402) 293-6668   OK
Web Site: http://www.payplusllc.com
Sales Range: $10-24.9 Million
Emp.: 33
Payroll, Tax & Bookkeeping Services
N.A.I.C.S.: 541214
John Hogan *(Pres)*
Ryan Carnahan *(Dir-Payroll)*
Bev Hogan *(Dir-Bookkeeping)*
Jennifer Russell *(Dir-Tax)*
Shawn Fischer *(Specialist-Bus Dev)*

PAYROLL MANAGEMENT, INC.
348 Miracle Strip Pkwy SW Ste 39, Fort Walton Beach, FL 32548-6640
Tel.: (850) 243-5604
Web Site: http://www.pmipeo.com
Year Founded: 1986
Sales Range: $200-249.9 Million
Emp.: 75
Employee Leasing Services
N.A.I.C.S.: 561320
Mike Bonneau *(VP)*
Kelly Thonston *(Mgr-Claims)*

PAYROLL SERVICES PLUS, INC.
606 Halstead Ave, Mamaroneck, NY 10543
Tel.: (914) 472-4796
Web Site:
 http://www.thepspgroup.com
Year Founded: 1999
Rev.: $52,700,000
Emp.: 11
Payroll Services
N.A.I.C.S.: 541214
Dominick Crea *(Founder & Pres)*

PAYSCAPE ADVISORS
729 Lambert Ave, Atlanta, GA 30324
Tel.: (404) 350-6565
Web Site: http://www.payscape.com
Year Founded: 2004
Sales Range: $1-9.9 Million
Emp.: 100

Processor of Credit & Debit Cards, ATM Transactions & Point-of-Sale Equipment & Services to Merchants
N.A.I.C.S.: 522390
Jeremy Wing *(Founder & Pres)*
Adam Bloomston *(CEO & CFO)*
Russ Gambrell *(VP-Fin)*

Subsidiaries:

BillingOrchard (1)
729 Lambert Dr, Atlanta, GA 30324 (100%)
Tel.: (888) 369-1331
Web Site: http://www.billingorchard.com
Online Automated Recurring Billing for Small to Medium Businesses
N.A.I.C.S.: 522320
Jason Robert Swenk *(Chief Innovation Officer)*

PAYSON CASTERS, INC.
2323 N Delany Rd, Gurnee, IL 60031
Tel.: (847) 336-6200   IL
Web Site:
 http://www.paysoncasters.com
Year Founded: 1873
Sales Range: $75-99.9 Million
Emp.: 80
Caster & Wheel Mfr
N.A.I.C.S.: 332991
Harold E. Sullivan III *(Pres)*

Subsidiaries:

American Overhead Conveyor (1)
2335 N Delany Rd, Gurnee, IL 60031-1212 (100%)
Tel.: (847) 336-5033
Web Site: http://www.roll-away.com
Rev.: $1,700,000
Emp.: 23
Mfr of Conveyors
N.A.I.C.S.: 333922
Dan Hopkins *(Mgr-Mktg)*

Nagel Chase Inc. (1)
2323 N Delany Rd, Gurnee, IL 60031-1212
Tel.: (847) 336-4494
Web Site: http://www.paysoncasters.com
Pulley Mfr
N.A.I.C.S.: 332991

Payson Bronco, Inc. (1)
6900 Cherry Ave, Long Beach, CA 90805-1721 (100%)
Tel.: (562) 602-2400
Web Site: http://www.paysoncasters.com
Sales Range: $10-24.9 Million
Emp.: 2
Casters & Wheels
N.A.I.C.S.: 423840
Martin Yaeger *(Gen Mgr)*

Payson Norcross (1)
5034 Singleton Rd, Norcross, GA 30093-2503
Tel.: (770) 923-7753
Web Site: http://www.paysoncasters.com
Sales Range: $10-24.9 Million
Emp.: 1
Caster & Wheel Mfr
N.A.I.C.S.: 332991
Harold E. Sullivan III *(Pres)*

Payson Texas, Inc. (1)
2688 Freewood Dr, Dallas, TX 75220-2511
Tel.: (214) 352-1765
Web Site: http://paysoncasters.com
Sales Range: $10-24.9 Million
Emp.: 3
Mfr of Casters & Wheels
N.A.I.C.S.: 332991

PAYSON PARK THOROUGHBRED TRAINING CENTER INC.
9700 SW Kanner Hwy, Indiantown, FL 34956
Tel.: (772) 597-3555
Web Site:
 http://www.happyhorseswin.com
Sales Range: $1-9.9 Million
Emp.: 24
Horse Racing Training Center
N.A.I.C.S.: 713990
Virginia Payson *(Owner & Pres)*

PAYTON CONSTRUCTION CORP.

Payton Construction Corp.—(Continued)

PAYTON CONSTRUCTION CORP.
124 Washington St, Foxboro, MA 02035
Tel.: (617) 423-9035
Year Founded: 1986
Sales Range: $25-49.9 Million
Emp.: 300
Provider of Nonresidential Construction Services
N.A.I.C.S.: 236220
William B. Payton (Pres & Treas)

PAYZONE DIRECTIONAL SERVICES
4205 Atlas Ct, Bakersfield, CA 93308
Tel.: (661) 616-3111
Web Site: http://www.payzonedirectional.com
Sales Range: $1-9.9 Million
Emp.: 24
Drilling Equipment Services
N.A.I.C.S.: 213111
Shelley Siemens (Office Mgr)
Chad Hathaway (Founder, Pres & CEO)
Mike Kitchen (VP)

PB EXPRESS INC.
20800 Center Ridge Rd Ste 301, Rocky River, OH 44116
Tel.: (440) 356-8988
Web Site: http://www.pbexpress.com
Sales Range: $10-24.9 Million
Emp.: 32
Local Trucking without Storage
N.A.I.C.S.: 484110
Dae Kee Yun (Founder, Pres & CEO)

PB HOIDALE CO. INC.
3801 W Harry St, Wichita, KS 67213
Tel.: (316) 942-1361
Web Site: http://www.hoidale.com
Rev.: $11,515,384
Emp.: 28
Industrial Machinery & Equipment
N.A.I.C.S.: 423830
Richard D. Dixon (Chm)
Steve Wilkening (Branch Mgr)
Mike Keul (Branch Mgr-Kansas)
Brenda Phillips (Coord-Mktg)
Steve Dixon (Pres)

PB INDUSTRIES INC.
361 Bonnie Ln, Elk Grove Village, IL 60007-1915
Tel.: (847) 437-6464
Web Site: http://www.pbindustries.com
Year Founded: 1985
Sales Range: $10-24.9 Million
Emp.: 20
Provider of Local Trucking Services
N.A.I.C.S.: 484110
David Park (CEO)
Tim Park (CFO)
Lisa Giannini (Mgr-Mktg)
Wulf von Schimmelmann (Chm)

PB&J RESTAURANTS INC.
10220 W 87th St, Overland Park, KS 66212
Tel.: (913) 648-6033
Web Site: http://www.eatpbj.com
Year Founded: 1987
Sales Range: $25-49.9 Million
Emp.: 1,000
Provider of Restaurant Services
N.A.I.C.S.: 722511

PBBS EQUIPMENT CORPORATION
W 16500 Greenway Cir, Menomonee Falls, WI 53051
Tel.: (262) 252-7575
Web Site: http://www.pbbs.com
Sales Range: $10-24.9 Million
Emp.: 75
Boiler Repair Shops
N.A.I.C.S.: 811310
Ken Verheyen (Engr-Sls)

PBD, INC.
1650 Bluegrass Lakes Pkwy, Alpharetta, GA 30004-7714
Tel.: (770) 442-8633
Web Site: http://www.pbd.com
Year Founded: 1976
Sales Range: $25-49.9 Million
Emp.: 150
Provider of Fulfillment Services to Certification Programs, Publishers, Associations & Corporations
N.A.I.C.S.: 424920
James E. Dockter (Founder)
Scott A. Dockter (Pres & CEO)
David S. Ferguson (CFO & Sr VP)
Lisa Williams (Sr VP-Ops)
Gregory R. Dockter (Sr VP)
Brion Zaeh (Sr VP-Client Rels)
Jeff Wells (VP & Controller)
Jan Jones (VP-Sls & Gen Mgr-Freight Scouts)

PBE JOBBERS WAREHOUSE INC.
2921 Syene Rd, Madison, WI 53713
Tel.: (608) 274-8797
Web Site: http://www.pbejobbers.com
Year Founded: 1956
Sales Range: $25-49.9 Million
Emp.: 100
Mfr & Distr of Automotive Supplies
N.A.I.C.S.: 423120
Paul Monroe (Pres)
Steve Peterson (VP-Sls)
Coleen Grace (Office Mgr)

PBE WAREHOUSE INC.
12171 Pangborn Ave, Downey, CA 90241
Tel.: (562) 803-4691
Web Site: http://www.pbewarehouse.com
Rev.: $15,800,000
Emp.: 30
Automotive Supplies
N.A.I.C.S.: 423120
Stephen Potter (Pres)

PBE WAREHOUSE SALES INC.
808 N Grove Rd, Richardson, TX 75081
Tel.: (972) 235-3127
Web Site: http://www.pbewarehousesales.com
Year Founded: 1976
Sales Range: $10-24.9 Million
Emp.: 100
Automotive Supplies & Parts Distr
N.A.I.C.S.: 423120
Phil Burnett (Pres)
Melissa Stratton (Coord-Consignment)

PBEX, LLC
223 W Wall St #900, Midland, TX 79701
Tel.: (888) 691-4988
Web Site: http://pbex.com
Oil & Gas Drilling Services
N.A.I.C.S.: 213111
Wes Perry (Chm)
Chas Perry (CEO)

Subsidiaries:

PBEX Resources, LLC (1)
223 W Wall St #900, Midland, TX 79701
Tel.: (888) 691-4988
Oil & Gas Drilling Services
N.A.I.C.S.: 213111
Tom Taccia (Pres)

Subsidiary (Domestic):

E.G.L. Resources, Inc. (2)
508 W Wall St Ste 1250, Midland, TX 79701
Tel.: (432) 687-6560
Web Site: http://www.egloilshale.com
Sales Range: $10-24.9 Million
Emp.: 12
Oil & Gas Well Drilling Services
N.A.I.C.S.: 213111
John Starck (Pres)
William Wesley Perry (CEO)

PBG BUILDERS, INC.
1000 Northchase Dr Ste 307, Goodlettsville, TN 37072
Tel.: (615) 256-2200
Web Site: http://www.pbgbuilders.com
Year Founded: 1991
Nonresidential Construction Services
N.A.I.C.S.: 236220
John Finch (CEO)
Timothy A. Prow (Pres)

PBG CONSULTING, LLC
7925 Jones Branch Dr Ste 2125, McLean, VA 22102
Tel.: (571) 455-1724
Web Site: http://www.pbgconsult.com
Year Founded: 2010
Sales Range: $1-9.9 Million
Emp.: 28
Information Technology Consulting Services
N.A.I.C.S.: 541690
Pawla Ghaleb (Founder, Pres & CEO)
Vanessa Soon (CTO & Exec Mgr)

PBI MARKET EQUIPMENT INC.
2667 Gundry Ave, Signal Hill, CA 90755
Tel.: (562) 595-4785
Web Site: http://www.pbimarketing.com
Rev.: $14,000,000
Emp.: 75
Whslr of Food Service Equipment
N.A.I.C.S.: 423440
Kim Everson (Exec VP)
Jim Ines (Controller)

PBI/GORDON CORPORATION
22701 W 68th Ter, Shawnee, KS 66226
Tel.: (816) 421-4070
Web Site: http://www.pbigordon.com
Year Founded: 1947
Sales Range: $125-149.9 Million
Emp.: 300
Agricultural Chemicals & Lawn & Garden Chemicals Mfr
N.A.I.C.S.: 325320
Donald A. Chew (CEO)
William E. Mealman (Chm)
Glenn E. Mealman (Vice Chm)
Steve Clifford (COO)
Carrie Bergman (Sr Dir-Mktg)
Ashlee Parker-Osborne (Sr Mgr-Corp Comm)

Subsidiaries:

Bunker Properties Inc. (1)
1217 W 12th St, Kansas City, MO 64101-1407
Tel.: (816) 421-4070
Sales Range: Less than $1 Million
Emp.: 3
Nonresidential Building Operators
N.A.I.C.S.: 531120
Tom Holstrom (VP-Ops)

Gordon Corporation (1)
1217 W 12th St, Kansas City, MO 64101-1407
Tel.: (816) 421-4070
Web Site: http://www.pbigordon.com
Sales Range: $10-24.9 Million
Emp.: 80
General Warehousing & Storage
N.A.I.C.S.: 493110
Donald Chew (Pres)

PRN Pharmacal Inc. (1)
8809 Ely Rd, Pensacola, FL 32514
Tel.: (850) 476-9462
Web Site: http://www.prnpharmacal.com
Emp.: 80
Pharmaceuticals Product Mfr
N.A.I.C.S.: 325412

Pegasus Laboratories Inc. (1)
8809 Ely St, Pensacola, FL 32514-7064
Tel.: (850) 478-2770
Web Site: http://www.pegasuslabs.com
Sales Range: $10-24.9 Million
Emp.: 75
Distributes Animal & Human Health Products
N.A.I.C.S.: 325412

PetAg, Inc. (1)
255 Keyes Ave, Hampshire, IL 60140-9449
Tel.: (847) 683-2288
Web Site: http://www.petag.com
Sales Range: $125-149.9 Million
Emp.: 50
Animal Nutritional Products Mfr
N.A.I.C.S.: 311119
Darlene Frudakis (Pres & COO)
George Gill (Chm & CEO)
Will Geary (Controller)

PBM CAPITAL GROUP, LLC
200 Garrett St Ste S, Charlottesville, VA 22902
Tel.: (434) 980-8100
Web Site: http://www.pbmcap.com
Year Founded: 2010
Privater Equity Firm
N.A.I.C.S.: 523999
Gene Scavola (Mng Partner)
Rusty Schundler (Corp Counsel)
Jayson Rieger (Mng Partner)
Chris Martell (Partner)
Sung You (Partner)
Paul B. Manning (Founder, Chm & CEO)
Sean Stalfort (Partner)

PBMARES, LLP
3957 Westerre Pkwy Ste 220, Richmond, VA 23233
Tel.: (804) 323-0022
Web Site: http://www.pbmares.com
Sales Range: $10-24.9 Million
Emp.: 200
Accounting, Auditing & Bookkeeping Services
N.A.I.C.S.: 541219
Mary C. Aldrich (Partner & COO)
Lawrence W. Schwartz (Partner)
Keith L. Wampler (Partner)
David J. Damiani (Partner)
Harvey L. Johnson (CEO)
Nicholas Perrine (Partner)
David E. Bush (Partner-Williamsburg)
Richard G. Smith (Partner & Head-Williamsburg Office)
Brian Windley (Partner)
Jennifer French (Partner-Williamsburg)
Todd Swisher (Sr Mgr-Assurance)
Daniel L. Chenoweth (Partner-Newport News)
Betsy L. Hedrick (Partner)
Craig Ascari (Partner)
Daniel Bender (Partner)

COMPANIES

Daniel Haynes *(Partner)*
Kevin D. Humphries *(Partner)*
Timothy A. Heller *(Partner)*
Neena Shukla *(Partner)*
Dwight Buracker *(Partner)*
Anthony Orsborne *(Partner)*
Bradford Jones *(Partner)*
Carolyn Irwin *(Partner)*
Charles B. Postal *(Partner)*
Daniel B. Martin *(Partner)*
Donald Knotts *(Partner)*
Helaine S. Weissman *(Partner)*
Jackie H. White *(Partner)*
John M. Murray *(Partner)*
Kevin F. Reilly *(Partner)*
Manura Lange *(Partner)*
Matthew B. Dubnansky *(Partner-Healthcare Assurance)*
Merle L. Postal *(Partner)*
Michael A. Garber *(Partner)*
Michael T. Kennison *(Partner)*
Michael P. Straus *(Partner)*
Micheal B. Mendelsohn *(Partner)*
Ricka E. Neuman *(Partner)*
Sean R. O'Connell *(Partner)*
Thomas B. Healy *(Partner)*
Todd E. Levey *(Partner)*
Victoria W. Young *(Partner)*
Joseph S. Mastaler Jr. *(Partner)*

Subsidiaries:

TMDG, LLC (1)
500 E Pratt St Ste 525, Baltimore, MD 21202
Tel.: (443) 743-1277
Web Site: http://www.tmdgllc.com
Accounting, Tax Compliance & Healthcare Consulting Services
N.A.I.C.S.: 541219
Larraine Tompkins *(Sr Mgr-Audit)*
Matthew B. Dubnansky *(Mng Dir)*

PBS CONSTRUCTION INC.
4395 Corporate Sq, Naples, FL 34104-4754
Tel.: (239) 643-6527
Web Site: http://www.pbscontractors.com
Sales Range: $1-9.9 Million
Emp.: 10
Construction Services
N.A.I.C.S.: 236115
Bart Zino *(Pres)*
Russell Budd *(Founder & CEO)*

PBS ENGINEERING & ENVRNMNTL
4412 SW Corbett Ave, Portland, OR 97239
Tel.: (503) 248-1939
Web Site: http://www.pbsenv.com
Rev.: $5,280,000
Emp.: 30
Research & Development in Biotechnology
N.A.I.C.S.: 541714
Bart Phillips *(Mgr-Corp Sls)*
Brian Stanford *(Principal)*
Stephen Smiley *(Owner)*
Scott Grimes *(Project Mgr)*

Subsidiaries:

HDJ Design Group (1)
314 W 15th St, Vancouver, WA 98660
Tel.: (360) 695-3488
Web Site: http://www.hdjdesigngroup.com
Sales Range: $1-9.9 Million
Emp.: 60
Engineeering Services
N.A.I.C.S.: 541330

PBT BANCSHARES, INC.
101 S Main St, McPherson, KS 67460
Tel.: (620) 241-2100
Web Site: http://www.peoples.bank
Banking Services
N.A.I.C.S.: 522110

Tom Pruitt *(Pres & CEO)*

PC AGE, INC.
120 Wood Ave S Ste 511, Iselin, NJ 08830
Tel.: (732) 287-3622
Web Site: http://www.pcage.edu
Sales Range: $1-9.9 Million
Emp.: 20
Computer Training Services
N.A.I.C.S.: 611420
Zafar M. Khizer *(Co-Owner)*
Arifa Z. Khizer *(Co-Owner)*

PC CONSTRUCTION COMPANY
193 Tillui Dr, South Burlington, VT 05403-6118
Tel.: (802) 658-4100   VT
Web Site: http://www.pcconstruction.com
Year Founded: 1958
Sales Range: $450-499.9 Million
Emp.: 1,000
Provider of Contracting & Construction Services
N.A.I.C.S.: 236220
Remo Pizzagalli *(Founder)*
Jay Fayette *(Pres & CEO)*
Kevin Morrissey *(VP)*
John Evans *(Chm)*

PC GROUP, INC.
2840 Hwy 95 Alt S #7, Silver Springs, NV 89429
Tel.: (775) 577-5386   DE
Year Founded: 1971
Orthopedic & Skincare Products Mfr
N.A.I.C.S.: 339113
Christopher P. Vallos *(Pres, CEO, CFO, Treas & Sec)*

Subsidiaries:

The Langer Group (1)
Emerald Way Stone Business Park, Staffordshire, Stone, ST15 0SR, United Kingdom   (100%)
Tel.: (44) 8456780182
Sales Range: $10-24.9 Million
Emp.: 30
Mfr of Custom-Made Foot Products
N.A.I.C.S.: 316210
Andy Barnes *(Mng Dir)*

Twincraft, Inc. (1)
2 Tigan St, Winooski, VT 05404-1326
Tel.: (802) 655-2200
Web Site: http://www.twincraft.com
Sales Range: $100-124.9 Million
Emp.: 200
Soap Developer & Mfr
N.A.I.C.S.: 325611
Peter A. Asch *(Co-Owner)*
Richard Asch *(Co-Owner)*

PC WAREHOUSE INVESTMENT INC.
174 State Rte 17 N Ste C, Rochelle Park, NJ 07662
Tel.: (201) 587-9600
Rev.: $27,700,000
Emp.: 10
Personal Computers
N.A.I.C.S.: 449210
Robin Lu *(Chm)*

Subsidiaries:

Dunwell Computers of California (1)
20655 S Western Ave Ste 116, Torrance, CA 90501-1800
Tel.: (310) 618-9990
Web Site: http://www.dunwell.com
Computers, Peripherals & Software
N.A.I.C.S.: 423430
Richard Tsay *(Gen Mgr)*

PC WHOLESALE LTD.
752 Isom Rd, San Antonio, TX 78216-4026

Tel.: (210) 357-9400
Web Site: http://www.directron.com
Year Founded: 1998
Sales Range: $10-24.9 Million
Emp.: 200
Provider of Computers, Peripherals & Software
N.A.I.C.S.: 423430
Michael Chang *(Pres)*

PCA MANAGEMENT
3165 Garfield Ave, Los Angeles, CA 90040
Tel.: (562) 862-2118
Web Site: http://www.parkpca.com
Year Founded: 1964
Sales Range: $75-99.9 Million
Emp.: 1,250
Parking Services
N.A.I.C.S.: 812930
Eric Chaves *(Pres)*

Subsidiaries:

Parking Company of America, Hotel Division (1)
523 W 6 St Ste 528, Los Angeles, CA 90041
Tel.: (562) 862-2118
Web Site: http://www.parkpca.com
Sales Range: $10-24.9 Million
Emp.: 30
Provider of Parking & Transportation Services for Hotels, Restaurants, Private Parties, Entertainment Events & Self-parking Lots
N.A.I.C.S.: 812930
Lupe Alvarado *(Mgr-HR)*

Parking Company of America, Parking Management Division (1)
523 W 6th St Ste 528, Los Angeles, CA 90014
Tel.: (562) 862-2118
Web Site: http://www.parkpca.com
Sales Range: $25-49.9 Million
Emp.: 500
Manager of Parking Locations
N.A.I.C.S.: 812930
Suzie Cooley *(Dir-Ops)*

PCB APPS, LLC
3 Executive Dr Ste 329, Somerset, NJ 08873
Tel.: (732) 302-0100   NJ
Web Site: http://www.pcbapps.com
Year Founded: 2003
Sales Range: $10-24.9 Million
Emp.: 200
Information Technology Consulting & Managed Services
N.A.I.C.S.: 541519
Nag Karaka *(CEO)*
Mitch Long *(VP-Ops & JDE Program Mgmt)*
Mike Morgan *(Mng Partner & Head-Sls)*
Sunil Paruchuri *(Mng Partner)*
Ravi Chelle *(Mng Partner)*

PCB FINANCLAL, INC
3191 Red Hill Ave Ste 200, Costa Mesa, CA 92626
Tel.: (800) 653-3517
Year Founded: 2002
Commericial Banking
N.A.I.C.S.: 522110
Bill Wilson *(CEO)*
Brian K. Constable *(Chief Credit Officer)*
John Shindler *(CFO)*

Subsidiaries:

Northern California Bancorp, Inc. (1)
601 Munras Ave, Monterey, CA 93940
Tel.: (831) 649-4600
Web Site: http://www.montereycountybank.com
Bank Holding Company; Commercial Banking Services
N.A.I.C.S.: 551111

PCC LOGISTICS

Subsidiary (Domestic):

Monterey County Bank (2)
601 Munras Ave, Monterey, CA 93940
Tel.: (831) 649-4600
Web Site: http://www.montereycountbank.com
Emp.: 20
Commercial Banking
N.A.I.C.S.: 522110
Bruce N. Warner *(CFO, COO & Exec VP)*
Stephanie G. Chrietzberg *(Sr VP)*
Patricia Weber *(Sr VP)*
Dorina A. Chan *(Sec)*
Letitia Garcia *(VP)*
Linda Fernandez *(VP)*
Lillian Mulvey *(VP-Lending)*
Kathy Torres *(VP)*
Charles T. ChrietzbergJr. *(Chm, Pres & CEO)*

PCC LOGISTICS
432 Estudillo Ave, San Leandro, CA 94577
Tel.: (510) 346-6100
Web Site: http://www.pcclogistics.com
Year Founded: 1988
Sales Range: $25-49.9 Million
Emp.: 280
Cargo Warehousing & Trucking Services
N.A.I.C.S.: 488210
Abdel Zaharan *(CFO)*
Chrisy Eberley *(Mgr-Collection)*
Crystal Gallegos *(Office Mgr)*
Walter Jardine *(Mgr-Bus Unit)*

Subsidiaries:

PCC Direct Delivery (1)
2498 W 21st St Bldg 803, Oakland, CA 94607
Tel.: (510) 433-1875
Web Site: http://www.pcclogistics.com
Sales Range: $25-49.9 Million
Emp.: 100
Cargo Loading & Unloading
N.A.I.C.S.: 488210
Mike McDonald *(Pres)*

PCC Logistics (1)
2099 7th St, Oakland, CA 94607
Tel.: (510) 763-8991
Web Site: http://www.pcclogistics.com
Sales Range: $25-49.9 Million
Cargo Loading & Unloading Services
N.A.I.C.S.: 488210
Ellie McWilliams *(Reg Mgr-Support Team)*
Mike McDonald *(CEO)*

PCC Logistics (1)
3200 Occidental Ave, Seattle, WA 98134
Tel.: (206) 622-4030
Web Site: http://www.pcc-cfs.com
Cargo Loading & Unloading
N.A.I.C.S.: 488210

PCC Logistics (1)
2602 Port of Tacoma Rd, Tacoma, WA 98421-4222
Tel.: (253) 922-2423
Web Site: http://www.pcclogistics.com
Sales Range: $10-24.9 Million
Emp.: 30
Cargo Loading & Unloading Distr
N.A.I.C.S.: 488210

PCC Logistics (1)
1830 13th Ave SW, Seattle, WA 98134
Tel.: (206) 223-0551
Web Site: http://www.pcclogistics.com
Sales Range: $25-49.9 Million
Emp.: 65
Cargo Loading & Unloading
N.A.I.C.S.: 488210

PCC Logistics - Watson Center Rd. Facility (1)
1245 E Watson Center Rd, Carson, CA 90745
Tel.: (310) 900-1800
Web Site: http://www.pcclogistics.com
Cargo Loading & Unloading Distr
N.A.I.C.S.: 488210
Peggy Plakos *(Mgr)*

PCC LOGISTICS

PCC Logistics—(Continued)

PCC Transload System (1)
737 Bay St, Oakland, CA 94607
Tel.: (510) 893-5420
Web Site: http://www.pcclogistics.com
Cargo Loading & Unloading Services
N.A.I.C.S.: 484110

PCE CONSTRUCTORS, INC.
13544 Eads Rd, Prairieville, LA 70769
Tel.: (225) 677-9100
Web Site: http://www.constructors-inc.com
Sales Range: $25-49.9 Million
Emp.: 500
Civil Engineering Services
N.A.I.C.S.: 237310
Mark Robards *(Project Mgr)*

PCE, INC.
5120 NW 38th St., Lincoln, NE 68524
Tel.: (402) 474-4690
Year Founded: 1993
Rev.: $13,000,000
Emp.: 12
Holding Company
N.A.I.C.S.: 326199
Sam Featherstone *(CEO)*
Shelly Carpenter *(CFO)*

Subsidiaries:

Geist Manufacturing Inc. (1)
1821 Yolande Ave, Lincoln, NE 68521
Tel.: (402) 474-3400
Web Site: http://www.geistmfg.com
Sales Range: $10-24.9 Million
Power Outlets, Sockets & Cables Mfr
N.A.I.C.S.: 335931

Heinke Technology Inc. (1)
5120 NW 38th St., Lincoln, NE 68524
Tel.: (402) 470-2600
Web Site: http://www.htiplastic.com
Sales Range: $10-24.9 Million
Plastics Processing Services
N.A.I.C.S.: 326199
Richelle Jacobs *(Mgr-Sls)*
Chris Reed *(Dir-Engrg)*
Lisa Sandage *(Project Mgr)*
Troy Just *(Pres)*
Ryan Lund *(Coord-Mktg)*
John Eby *(Dir-Sls & Mktg)*

PCF INSURANCE SERVICES OF THE WEST, LLC
2500 W Executive Pkwy Ste 200, Lehi, UT 84043
Tel.: (385) 273-2270 DE
Web Site: http://www.pcfins.com
Insurance Services
N.A.I.C.S.: 524210
Peter C. Foy *(Founder & Chm)*
Robert Smith *(Pres-Agency Ops)*
Mike Green *(VP-Tech)*
Jeff Hutchins *(VP-HR)*
Felix Morgan *(CEO)*
Kirk Benson *(VP-Ops-Benefits)*
Jenni Lee Crocker *(Sr VP-Growth & Ops)*
Dan Goodwin *(VP-Carrier Rels)*

Subsidiaries:

1 Source Business Solutions, LLC (1)
6966 South Commerce Park Dr, Midvale, UT 84047
Tel.: (801) 352-2333
Web Site: http://www.1sourcebusiness.com
Sales Range: $50-74.9 Million
Human Resource Consulting Services
N.A.I.C.S.: 541612
Justin Harward *(Partner & VP-Sls)*

Andreini & Company (1)
220 W 20th Ave, San Mateo, CA 94403
Tel.: (650) 573-1111
Web Site: http://www.andreini.com
Insurance Brokers
N.A.I.C.S.: 524210

Henry Chen *(CFO)*
Michael Colzani *(Exec VP)*

Hale & Associates, Inc. (1)
100 Cushman St Ste 200, Fairbanks, AK 99701
Tel.: (907) 224-7161
Web Site: http://www.hale-insurance.com
Insurance Agencies & Brokerages
N.A.I.C.S.: 524210
Grace Becker *(Acct Exec)*
David Hale *(Pres & Principal-Agency)*

John E. Peakes Insurance Agency, Inc. (1)
1363 Donlon St, Ventura, CA 93003
Tel.: (805) 650-0199
Web Site: http://www.peakesinsurance.com
Insurance Agencies & Brokerages
N.A.I.C.S.: 524210
John Peakes Jr. *(Pres)*

Professional Warranty Service Corporation (1)
4795 Meadow Wood Ln Ste 300 W, Chantilly, VA 20151
Tel.: (800) 850-2799
Web Site: http://www.pwsc.com
New Home Warranty Products & Administration Services
N.A.I.C.S.: 524298
Charlie Kesmodel *(Reg Dir-Sls-Midwest)*
Gary Dilger *(Reg Dir-Sls-Southwest)*
Mike Scrimo *(Reg Dir-Sls-Northeast)*
Roger Langford *(VP-Sls & Mktg)*
Tyler Gordy *(CEO)*
Russ Weaver *(Sr VP-Ops)*
Paul Weckerly *(Gen Counsel, Sec & Sr VP)*
Carl Sohns *(Mgr-Bus Ops)*
Joseph Alcock *(VP-Fin)*
Lindsay Tingler *(Dir-Enterprise Sales)*
Clinton Fullen II *(Exec VP)*

Wilber-Price Insurance Group Ltd. (1)
420 W Loveland Ave Ste 104, Loveland, OH 45140-2368
Tel.: (513) 239-8610
Web Site: http://www.wilberinsuranceagency.com
Insurance Agencies & Brokerages
N.A.I.C.S.: 524210
John Wilber *(Mgr)*
Dan Chadwell *(COO)*

PCGCAMPBELL
3200 Greenfield Ste 280, Dearborn, MI 48120
Tel.: (313) 336-9000
Web Site: http://www.pcgcampbell.com
Emp.: 100
Automotive, Corporate Communications, Digital/Interactive, Event Planning & Marketing, Financial, Identity Marketing, Market Research, Media Relations, Nonprofit/Social Marketing, Sponsorship
N.A.I.C.S.: 541810
David Scheinberg *(Mng Partner)*
John Scodellaro *(Mng Partner)*
Shane Smith *(Mng Partner)*
David Losek *(CFO)*
Greg Shea *(COO)*

PCI GAMING AUTHORITY
303 Poarch Rd, Atmore, AL 36502
Tel.: (866) 946-3360
Web Site: http://www.windcreekhospitality.com
Casino & Hotel Operator; Gaming & Hospitality Services
N.A.I.C.S.: 721120
James Dorris *(Pres & CEO)*

Subsidiaries:

FlowPlay, Inc. (1)
114 Alaskan Way S Ste 100, Seattle, WA 98104
Tel.: (206) 903-0457
Web Site: http://www.flowplay.com
Online Gambling Services
N.A.I.C.S.: 513210

Derrick Morton *(Co-Founder, Pres & CEO)*
Doug Pearson *(Co-Founder & CTO)*
Craig Robinson *(Chief Revenue Officer)*

Sands Bethworks Gaming LLC (1)
77 Sands Blvd, Bethlehem, PA 18015
Tel.: (877) 727-3777
Web Site: http://www.pasands.com
Casino Resorts & Hotel Operator
N.A.I.C.S.: 721120

PCI INDUSTRIES INC.
700 S Vail Ave, Montebello, CA 90640
Tel.: (323) 728-0004
Web Site: http://www.pci-industries.com
Sales Range: $10-24.9 Million
Emp.: 50
Metal Ventilating Fans
N.A.I.C.S.: 333413
Jack Scilley *(CEO)*
Mike Almaguer *(VP-Sls-Mktg)*
Ali Nikzad *(Plant Mgr & Engr-Mechanical)*

PCI LLC
4899 W Waters Ave Ste A, Tampa, FL 33634
Tel.: (813) 885-7974
Web Site: http://www.pciusa.com
Year Founded: 1983
Sales Range: $1-9.9 Million
Tax Software
N.A.I.C.S.: 513210
Alastair Main *(Pres & COO)*

PCI MEDIA, INC.
523 Victoria Ave, Venice, CA 90291
Tel.: (310) 577-9100 DE
Year Founded: 2018
Emp.: 109
Holding Company
N.A.I.C.S.: 551112
D. Hunt Ramsbottom *(Pres & CEO)*
Thomas Boyle *(CFO)*

PCI MILLWORK
4642 Granite Dr, Tucker, GA 30084
Tel.: (770) 496-4492
Web Site: http://www.pcimillwork.com
Year Founded: 1986
Rev.: $5,500,000
Emp.: 20
Nonresidential Construction
N.A.I.C.S.: 236220
Terry Whitley *(Treas, VP-Facilities & Mgr-Logistics)*

PCI ROADS
14123 42nd St NE, Saint Michael, MN 55376-9564
Tel.: (763) 497-6100 MN
Web Site: http://www.pciroads.com
Year Founded: 1971
Sales Range: $75-99.9 Million
Emp.: 500
Highway & Street Construction
N.A.I.C.S.: 237310
Ted Durkee *(Co-Owner & CEO)*
Tom Sloan *(Co-Owner)*
Steve Gerster *(Co-Owner)*
Alan Sakry *(Mgr)*

PCI STRATEGIC MANAGEMENT, LLC
6811 Benjamin Franklin Dr Ste 200, Columbia, MD 21046
Tel.: (410) 312-0885
Web Site: http://www.pci-sm.com
Year Founded: 2008
Sales Range: $10-24.9 Million
Emp.: 150
Business Management Consulting Services
N.A.I.C.S.: 541611
Sean Battle *(Partner)*
Josh Kinley *(Partner)*

Vance Mitzner *(CTO & Partner)*
Don Whitfield *(Partner)*
Jim Wilson *(Dir-Strategic Programs)*

PCL CIVIL CONSTRUCTORS, INC.
3810 Northdale Blvd Ste 200, Tampa, FL 33624-1873
Tel.: (813) 264-9500
Web Site: http://www.pcl.com
Year Founded: 1906
Sales Range: $10-24.9 Million
Emp.: 200
Civil Engineering Services
N.A.I.C.S.: 237310
M. R. Eveld *(Principal)*
David Morgan *(VP-Fin & Admin)*
Loius S. Ventoza *(COO)*
Jim Schneiderman *(Mgr-Transportation Infrastructure Grp-Raleigh)*
Jim Holtje *(Mgr-Special Projects)*
Eric Chavez *(Mgr-Construction)*

PCL FIXTURES, INC.
275 Ferris Ave, Rumford, RI 02916
Tel.: (401) 334-4646
Web Site: http://www.pclfixtures.com
Year Founded: 1977
Emp.: 100
Store Fixtures Designer & Mfr
N.A.I.C.S.: 423210
Donald Budnick *(CEO)*

PCM SERVICES INC.
10511 Tuckers St, Beltsville, MD 20705
Tel.: (301) 595-3700
Web Site: http://www.pcmservices.com
Sales Range: $200-249.9 Million
Emp.: 250
Construction & Building Maintenance Services
N.A.I.C.S.: 561720
Rollin Bell *(Founder & Chm)*
Todd Cox *(CFO)*
Mark McCaffrey *(Acct Exec)*
John Kile *(Acct Mgr)*
Jan Dinota *(Dir-Admin)*
Richard Nelson *(Principal)*
Michael Coletta *(Sr VP)*
Rick Baxter *(VP-Construction Svcs)*
Aaron Kuzemka *(VP-Sls)*
Agnes Ikotun *(Mgr-Mktg)*
Jason Gebbia *(VP-Process Dev)*

PCN NETWORK
200 Fleet St Ste 1100, Pittsburgh, PA 15220
Tel.: (412) 928-2450
Web Site: http://www.pcnclosings.com
Year Founded: 2004
Sales Range: $10-24.9 Million
Emp.: 18
Mortgage Closing Service
N.A.I.C.S.: 522292
Pritam Advani *(Pres & CEO)*
Ken Smolar *(Sr VP)*
Andrea Goeringer *(Mgr-Customer Rels)*

PCNET INC.
100 Technology Dr, Trumbull, CT 06611
Tel.: (203) 452-8500
Web Site: http://www.pcnet-inc.com
Rev.: $15,000,000
Emp.: 30
Computer & Computer Peripheral Equipment & Software Merchant Whslr
N.A.I.C.S.: 423430
Camilo Soto *(Pres & CEO)*
Nicholas Lentino *(Sr VP-Sls & Mktg)*

COMPANIES

PCO INCORPORATED
23221 E Knox Ave, Liberty Lake, WA 99019
Tel.: (509) 777-6736
Web Site: http://www.pco-inc.com
Year Founded: 1999
Sales Range: $10-24.9 Million
Emp.: 60
Computer Network, Industrial & Residential Security Technologies Mfr
N.A.I.C.S.: 561621
Richard Sheppard *(CEO)*

PCP ENTERPRISE, L.P.
1 Federal St 21st Fl, Boston, MA 02110
Tel.: (617) 960-4000
Web Site: http://www.parthenoncapitalpartners.com
Year Founded: 1998
Privater Equity Firm
N.A.I.C.S.: 523999
Brian P. Golson *(Co-CEO & Mng Partner-San Francisco)*

Subsidiaries:

DaySmart Software, Inc. (1)
3520 Green Ct Ste 250, Brighton, MI 48105
Tel.: (800) 604-2040
Web Site: http://www.daysmart.com
Software Services
N.A.I.C.S.: 513210
Patrick Shanahan *(CEO)*
Cristi Tobelmann *(VP-HR)*

Subsidiary (Domestic):

StormSource LLC (2)
15300 N 90th St Suite 100, Scottsdale, AZ 85260
Tel.: (800) 988-0061
Web Site: http://www.appointment-plus.com
Sales Range: $1-9.9 Million
Emp.: 100
Online Appointment Scheduling Software Mfr
N.A.I.C.S.: 513210
Bob La Loggia *(Founder & CEO)*
Steve Booze *(COO)*
Kendall Matthews *(VP-Global Mktg & Comm)*
Brad Senff *(Dir-IT Ops)*
Derrick Disharoom *(Dir-Quality Assurance)*

Institutional Cash Distributors LLC (1)
580 California St Ste 1335, San Francisco, CA 94104-1034
Tel.: (415) 820-5300
Web Site: http://www.icdportal.com
Investment Advice
N.A.I.C.S.: 523940
Jessica Fischer *(Mgr)*

MRO Corporation (1)
1000 Madison Ave Ste 100, Norristown, PA 19406
Tel.: (610) 994-7500
Web Site: http://www.mrocorp.com
Professional Scientific & Technical Services
N.A.I.C.S.: 541990
Peter Schmitt *(Pres & CFO)*
Stephen Hynes *(CEO)*
Matt O'Connor *(Chief Sls Officer)*

Subsidiary (Domestic):

Cobius Healthcare Solutions, LLC (2)
3149 Dundee Rd Ste 302, Northbrook, IL 60062-2901
Tel.: (847) 656-8700
Web Site: http://www.cobius.com
Rev.: $1,100,000
Emp.: 9
Business Software
N.A.I.C.S.: 334118
Doug Weinberg *(Principal)*

Medi-Copy Services Inc. (2)
210 12th Ave S Ste 201, Nashville, TN 37203
Tel.: (615) 780-2741
Web Site: http://www.medicopy.net

Sales Range: $1-9.9 Million
Emp.: 54
Health Information Management
N.A.I.C.S.: 519290

Parthenon Capital Partners - West Coast Office (1)
4 Embarcadero Ctr Ste 3610, San Francisco, CA 94111
Tel.: (415) 913-3900
Web Site: http://www.parthenoncapitalpartners.com
Sales Range: $50-74.9 Million
Emp.: 13
Privater Equity Firm
N.A.I.C.S.: 523999
Brian P. Golson *(Co-CEO & Mng Partner)*
Andrew C. Dodson *(Mng Partner)*
Scott D. Levine *(Dir-Human Capital)*
Eli Berlin *(VP)*
David J. Ament *(Co-CEO & Mng Partner)*
Lesly J. Schlender *(Dir-Res, Outreach & Dev-Boston)*
Max A. Pinto *(Dir-Strategy & Implementation-Boston)*
Will C. Kessinger *(Chief Investment Officer-San Francisco)*

Payroc LLC (1)
1350 E Touhy Ave Ste 210W, Des Plaines, IL 60018
Tel.: (844) 729-7624
Web Site: http://www.payroc.com
Electronic Payment Services
N.A.I.C.S.: 541214
James Oberman *(Pres & CEO)*
Ryan Hallett *(Chief Revenue Officer)*
Matthew Austin *(COO)*
David Hall *(Exec VP-iTransact Sls)*
Brandon Hallett *(Sr Exec VP-Sls)*
Aaron Johnson *(Exec VP-Payment Solutions)*
Colby Poulson *(Sr VP-Bus Dev)*
Kevin Conroy *(Dir-Ops)*
Rachel Snapp *(Mgr-Relationship)*
Ashley Shereyk *(Mgr-Fin)*
Paul Vienneau *(CTO)*
Kevin Hodges *(CFO)*
Linda Rossetti *(Exec VP-Strategic Initiatives)*
Terri Harwood *(Chief Experience Officer)*
Angela Antrim *(Sr VP-HR)*

Subsidiary (Domestic):

Bluestone Payments, LLC (2)
1029 N Peachtree Pkwy Ste 314, Peachtree City, GA 30269-4210
Tel.: (770) 631-2988
Web Site: http://www.bluestonepayments.com
Office Equipment Merchant Whslr
N.A.I.C.S.: 423420
Linda Rossetti *(Pres)*

White River Capital, Inc. (1)
6051 El Tordo PO Box 9876, Rancho Santa Fe, CA 92067
Tel.: (858) 997-6740
Sales Range: $150-199.9 Million
Emp.: 135
Financial Services Holding Company
N.A.I.C.S.: 551112

Subsidiary (Domestic):

Coastal Credit, LLC (2)
3852 Virginia Beach Blvd, Virginia Beach, VA 23452
Tel.: (757) 340-6000
Web Site: http://www.coastalcreditllc.com
Sales Range: $125-149.9 Million
New & Used Automobile Financing
N.A.I.C.S.: 522299
William E. McKnight *(Founder)*
Martin McFarland *(Pres & CEO)*
Joe O'Brien *(VP-Sls & Mktg)*
Ryan Clements *(VP-Tech)*
Brian Switalski *(VP-Ops)*

Union Acceptance Company LLC (2)
1445 Brookville Way Ste 1, Indianapolis, IN 46206
Tel.: (317) 806-2166
Sales Range: $125-149.9 Million
New & Used Automobile Financing
N.A.I.C.S.: 522299

Zelis Healthcare Corporation (1)
2 Crossroads Dr, Bedminster, NJ 07921

Tel.: (973) 218-9275
Web Site: http://www.zelis.com
Holding Company; Healthcare Industry Claims & Payment Support Services
N.A.I.C.S.: 551112
Brian T. Gladden *(Chief Admin Officer)*
Heather M. Carroll Cox *(Pres-Insights & Empowerment)*
Tom Kloster *(CFO)*
Mark Halloran *(CIO)*
Leo Garneau *(CTO)*
Priscilla Alfaro *(Chief Medical Officer)*
Dunston Almeida *(Exec VP-Strategy, Corp Dev & Product)*
Tom Watson *(Exec VP-Bus Ops)*
Thiyagesan Gnanasekaran *(Sr VP-Enterprise Application Dev)*
Thuy-An Wilkins *(Sr Dir-Media Rels)*
Amanda Eisel *(CEO)*
Dave Ament *(Chm)*
Sue Schick *(Pres & Chief Revenue Officer)*

Subsidiary (Domestic):

EthiCare Advisors, Inc. (2)
22 Route 10 W Ste 201, Succasunna, NJ 07876
Medical Claims Settlements
N.A.I.C.S.: 524298

Payer Compass, LLC (2)
5800 Granite Pkwy Ste 450, Plano, TX 75024
Tel.: (972) 964-6655
Web Site: http://www.payercompass.com
Sales Range: $10-24.9 Million
Emp.: 69
Software Development Services
N.A.I.C.S.: 541511
Gregory S. Everett *(Pres & CEO)*
Roman Gekhter *(CIO)*
Rick Ellsworth *(COO)*
Slayton Gorman *(Chief Revenue Officer)*
Matthew Thompson *(CFO)*

Zelis Claims Integrity, Inc. (2)
2 Crossroads Dr, Bedminster, NJ 07921
Tel.: (973) 218-9275
Web Site: http://www.phx-online.com
Cost Management Solutions
N.A.I.C.S.: 524291
Lori Sempervive *(Co-Pres-Zelis Cost Mgmt)*

Subsidiary (Domestic):

Zelis Payments, Inc. (3)
18167 US Hwy 19 N Ste 300, Clearwater, FL 33764
Web Site: http://www.zelispayments.com
Healthcare Industry Payment Management Services
N.A.I.C.S.: 541219
Ian Drysdale *(Pres)*

Subsidiary (Domestic):

Zelis Network Solutions, LLC (2)
2 Concourse Pkwy Ste 300, Atlanta, GA 30328
Tel.: (404) 459-7201
Web Site: http://www.zellis.com
Healthcare Cost Management Services
N.A.I.C.S.: 561499
Tina Ellex *(Co-Pres-Zelis Cost Mgmt)*

eSecLending LLC (1)
1 Boston Pl 24th Fl, Boston, MA 02108
Tel.: (617) 204-4500
Web Site: http://www.eseclending.com
Sales Range: $75-99.9 Million
Emp.: 100
Securities Lending Services
N.A.I.C.S.: 523150
Richard L. Piccolo *(CFO)*
James Moroney *(Head-Global Equities & Corp Bond Trading)*

Subsidiary (Non-US):

eSecLending (Europe) Limited (2)
1st Floor 10 King William Street, London, EC4N 7TW, United Kingdom
Tel.: (44) 20 7469 6000
Securities Brokerage Services
N.A.I.C.S.: 523150

PCPC DIRECT, LTD.
10690 Shadow Wood Ste 132, Houston, TX 77043

Tel.: (713) 984-8808
Web Site: http://www.pcpcdirect.com
Sales Range: $25-49.9 Million
Emp.: 50
IT Solutions
N.A.I.C.S.: 541519
Cornelia Vaught *(Pres & CEO)*
Joe Vaught *(COO)*
Sam Mouton *(Controller)*

PCRC CORP.
211 College Rd East, Princeton, NJ 08540
Tel.: (609) 720-1468
Web Site: http://www.pcrcorp.com
Rev.: $32,900,000
Emp.: 250
Provides Information Technology & Audio/Visual Solutions
N.A.I.C.S.: 532420

PCS RETIREMENT, LLC
1801 Market St Ste1000, Philadelphia, PA 19103
Tel.: (267) 675-6727
Web Site: http://www.pcs401k.com
Year Founded: 2000
Rev.: $3,700,000
Emp.: 70
Financial Services
N.A.I.C.S.: 541990
Mark Klein *(CEO)*
Jordan Migneault *(Exec VP-Client Experience)*
Christopher Egoville *(VP-Compliance)*
Gerrit A. Fedele *(VP)*
Jim Denon *(VP-Client Svc)*
Lauren Roberts *(Dir-Product Mgmt)*
Peter Adeniran *(Dir-IT)*
Reno Regalbuto *(VP-Institutional Sls)*
Karen Benewith *(VP-Sls-West)*
Jon Clark *(VP-Midwest Reg)*
Patrick Gano *(VP-North Reg)*
Thomas Zlogar Jr. *(Dir-Ops)*

Subsidiaries:

ASPire Financial Services, LLC (1)
4010 Boy Scout Blvd Ste 500, Tampa, FL 33607
Tel.: (813) 874-0671
Web Site: http://www.aspireonline.com
Sales Range: $50-74.9 Million
Emp.: 125
Retirement Plan Solutions
N.A.I.C.S.: 524298
Dipankar Mandal *(CIO & Exec VP)*
Mark Agustin *(COO)*
Steven Shackelford *(Sr VP-Strategic Sls)*
Stephen Tague *(CTO)*
Bille Lee *(VP-Ops)*
Shelia Reed *(VP-Ops)*

PDC FACILITIES INC.
700 Walnut Rdg Dr, Hartland, WI 53029
Tel.: (262) 367-7700
Web Site: http://www.pdcbiz.com
Rev.: $13,623,696
Emp.: 40
Nonresidential Construction
N.A.I.C.S.: 236220
William M. Maslowski *(Pres)*
Paul Bidwell *(CFO)*
Mike Slemin *(Engr-Controls & Design)*
David Knuth *(Project Mgr)*
Greg Glidden *(Project Mgr & Engr-Product)*
Matt Furphy *(Engr-Controls & Design)*

PDI COMMUNICATION SYSTEMS INC.
40 Greenwood Ln, Springboro, OH 45066
Tel.: (937) 743-6010
Web Site: http://www.pdiarm.com
Sales Range: $10-24.9 Million
Emp.: 100

PDI COMMUNICATION SYSTEMS INC.

U.S. PRIVATE

PDI Communication Systems Inc.—(Continued)
Television Broadcasting & Communications Equipment
N.A.I.C.S.: 334220
Lou Vilardo (Owner)

PDI GROUP INC.
5400 Mesa Dr, Houston, TX 77028-3237
Tel.: (713) 635-4200
Rev.: $18,900,000
Emp.: 3
Steel Pipe & Tubing
N.A.I.C.S.: 551112
Stanley T. Rawley (Pres)
Paul Birchfield (VP & Controller)

Subsidiaries:

Pipe Distributors Inc. (1)
5400 Mesa Dr, Houston, TX 77028
Tel.: (713) 635-4200
Web Site: http://www.pipedistributorsinc.com
Pipe & Tubing, Steel
N.A.I.C.S.: 423510

PDK REGENCY HOME FASHIONS INC.
261 5th Ave Rm 1710, New York, NY 10016-7701
Tel.: (212) 889-6144   NY
Year Founded: 1954
Sales Range: $25-49.9 Million
Emp.: 375
Household Furnishings
N.A.I.C.S.: 314120
Paul Zheng (Owner)

PDL BIOPHARMA INC.
932 Southwood Blvd, Incline Village, NV 89451
Tel.: (775) 832-8500   DE
Web Site: http://www.pdl.com
Year Founded: 1986
Rev.: $85,835,000
Assets: $716,119,000
Liabilities: $122,841,000
Net Worth: $593,278,000
Earnings: ($70,411,000)
Emp.: 75
Fiscal Year-end: 12/31/19
Researcher & Developer of Humanized Antibodies to Prevent or Treat Diseases
N.A.I.C.S.: 325414
Christopher L. Stone (Co-CEO, Gen Counsel & Sec)
Dominique Monnet (Pres & Co-CEO)
Christy Horgan (CFO)

PDM COMPANY INC.
185 Ferguson Ave, Shavertown, PA 18708
Tel.: (570) 675-3636
Rev.: $20,000,000
Emp.: 900
Franchise Owner of Fast-Food Restaurants
N.A.I.C.S.: 722513
Steve Morris (Pres)

PDM PRECAST, INC.
220 SE 6th St Ste 310, Des Moines, IA 50309
Tel.: (515) 243-5118
Web Site:
   http://www.pdmprecast.com
Year Founded: 2012
Emp.: 100
Prestressed & Precast Concrete Products Mfr
N.A.I.C.S.: 327390
Adam Petersen (Co-Owner & Pres)
Luke Petersen (Co-Owner & VP-Production)
John Doering (Co-Owner & VP-Engrg)

Mike Meyer (Co-Owner & VP-Ops)
Eric Nixt (Controller)
Carrie Fein (Mgr-Estimating)

PDQ FOOD STORES, INC.
PO Box 620997, Middleton, WI 53562-0997
Tel.: (608) 836-3335   WI
Web Site: http://www.pdqstores.com
Year Founded: 1949
Sales Range: $200-249.9 Million
Emp.: 500
Owner & Operator of Convenient Stores & Gasoline Filling Stations
N.A.I.C.S.: 457120
Michael Arnold (CFO)
Leaha Gerned (Controller)
Dennis Thousand (Dir-IT)
Brandon Dodge (Mgr-Store)
Nicole Harrison (Mgr)
Holly Abel (Mgr)

PDQ PRINT CENTER, INC.
27 Stauffer Industrial Park, Taylor, PA 18517
Tel.: (570) 343-0414
Web Site: http://www.pdqprint.com
Year Founded: 1975
Rev.: $1,800,000
Emp.: 25
Commercial Lithographic Printing
N.A.I.C.S.: 323111
Ann E. Nealon (Mgr-Major Accounts & Customer Care)
David J. Price (COO)
Scott Lynett (CEO)

Subsidiaries:

Times Printing Company, Inc. (1)
100 Industrial Dr, Random Lake, WI 53075-1636
Tel.: (920) 994-4396
Web Site: http://www.timesprintingco.com
Emp.: 300
Commercial Offset Printing Services
N.A.I.C.S.: 323111
Rick Bortolotti (Gen Mgr)

PDQ TEMPORARIES INCORPORATED
704 Hunters Row Ct, Mansfield, TX 76063
Tel.: (817) 477-3515   TX
Web Site:
   http://www.pdqtemporary.com
Year Founded: 1991
Rev.: $21,000,000
Emp.: 65
Temporary Agency
N.A.I.C.S.: 561320
Richard Mumme (CEO)
Erma Ochoa (VP-Corp Svcs)
Mike Moon (Branch Mgr)
Frank Delap (Mgr)
Gena Manning (Asst Mgr)
Ann Thompson (Mgr-Sls)
Lisa Hefner (Reg Dir)

PDR CERTIFIED PUBLIC ACCOUNTANTS
29750 US Hwy 19 N Ste 101, Clearwater, FL 33761
Tel.: (727) 785-4447   FL
Web Site: http://www.pdr-cpa.com
Year Founded: 1974
Sales Range: $1-9.9 Million
Emp.: 35
Certified Public Accountants
N.A.I.C.S.: 541211
William E. Price (Mng Partner)
Mary Pocengal (Mgr-Audit)
Jay Wadsworth (Mgr-Tax)

PDS SERVICES, LLC
37633 Pembroke Ave, Livonia, MI 48152
Tel.: (734) 953-9700

Web Site: http://www.pdsstaffing.com
Year Founded: 2005
Sales Range: $1-9.9 Million
Emp.: 8
Employment Placement Services
N.A.I.C.S.: 561311
Mary Pompea (Pres)
Derek Dyer (Gen Mgr)

PEABODY OFFICE FURNITURE CORPORATION
234 Congress St, Boston, MA 02110-2429
Tel.: (617) 542-1902   MA
Web Site:
   http://www.peabodyoffice.com
Year Founded: 1899
Sales Range: $10-24.9 Million
Emp.: 50
Whslr of Office Furniture
N.A.I.C.S.: 423210
Lester C. Peabody (Owner & Co-Chm)
Jonathan C. Peabody (Co-Chm)
Donald Brooks (Controller)
Richard Baughn (Pres & CEO)

PEABODY PROPERTIES, INC.
536 Granite St, Braintree, MA 02184
Tel.: (781) 794-1000
Web Site:
   http://www.peabodyproperties.com
Year Founded: 1976
Sales Range: $10-24.9 Million
Emp.: 300
Property Management Services
N.A.I.C.S.: 531311
Doreen Bushashia (Pres-Resident Svcs)
Susan Gustin (Dir-PR & Creative)
Kristin Pine (Dir-Trng & Education)
Melissa Fish-Crane (COO)
Doreen Donovan (VP-Compliance & Admin)
Guy Corricelli (CFO)
Adam Kenney (VP-Ops)
John McKee (Reg Dir-Ops)
Maria Oymaian (Dir-Admin & Regulatory Compliance)
Lynne Sales (Dir-Resident Svcs)
Whitney Pulsifer (Sr Dir-Strategic Initiatives)
Scott F. Ployer (VP-Facilities & Capital Plng)
Frank Faticanti (Pres)
Karen Fish-Will (CEO)
Ralph Jordan (VP)
Heather McCann (VP-HR)

Subsidiaries:

Peabody Properties South, LLC (1)
3715 Northside Pkwy Bldg 200 Ste 725, Atlanta, GA 30327
Tel.: (404) 760-8575
Property Management
N.A.I.C.S.: 531311

Division (Domestic):

Tanglewood Park (2)
5355 Sugarloaf Pkwy, Lawrenceville, GA 30043
Tel.: (770) 339-6800
Web Site:
   http://www.peabodypropertiessouth.com
Sales Range: Less than $1 Million
Emp.: 4
Apartment Building Operator
N.A.I.C.S.: 531110

PEABODY SUPPLY COMPANY INC.
58 Pulaski St, Peabody, MA 01960
Tel.: (978) 532-2200
Web Site:
   http://www.peabodysupply.com
Rev.: $22,084,534
Emp.: 42

Plumbing Fittings & Supplies
N.A.I.C.S.: 423720
Dominque Messina (Reg Mgr)

PEACE IN MEDICINE
6771 Sebastopol Ave Ste 100, Sebastopol, CA 95472-3855
Tel.: (510) 251-1856
Web Site:
   http://www.peaceinmedicine.org
Pharmacies & Drug Stores
N.A.I.C.S.: 456110
Jo Leeann (Mgr)

PEACE INDUSTRIES LTD.
1100 Hicks Rd, Rolling Meadows, IL 60008
Tel.: (847) 259-1620   DE
Web Site: http://www.spotnails.com
Pneumatic Tools & Fasteners of Office Supplies Mfr
N.A.I.C.S.: 332618
Mark Wilson (Pres)
Rex A. Jandernoa (CFO)
Win Waterman (VP-Sls & Mktg)

Subsidiaries:

Peace Industries Inc. - Spotnails Division (1)
1100 Hicks Rd, Rolling Meadows, IL 60008
Tel.: (847) 259-1620
Web Site: http://www.spotmnails.com
Power-Driven Handtool Mfr
N.A.I.C.S.: 333991
Mark Wilson (Pres)

PEACE RIVER CITRUS PRODUCTS INC.
4104 NW Hwy 72, Arcadia, FL 34266
Tel.: (863) 494-0440   FL
Web Site:
   http://www.peacerivercitrus.com
Year Founded: 1991
Sales Range: $300-349.9 Million
Emp.: 325
Mfr of Citrus Fruit Juices & Other Related Products
N.A.I.C.S.: 111320
Bart Plymale (VP)
Gregg Vitale (Controller)
Keith Henderson (Mgr-Quality Sys)
Dave Yarina (Mgr-IT)

PEACE RIVER ELECTRIC COOPERATIVE, INC.
210 Metheny Rd, Wauchula, FL 33873-5007
Tel.: (863) 773-4116   FL
Web Site: http://www.preco.coop
Year Founded: 1940
Sales Range: $150-199.9 Million
Emp.: 110
Rural Electric Distribution Cooperative
N.A.I.C.S.: 221122
Andrew Jackson (Gen Counsel & Atty)
Carol Braxton (VP-Fin & Acctg)
Van Crawford (VP)
Randy Shaw (Mgr)

PEACE TEXTILE AMERICA INC.
1605 S Guignard Pkwy, Sumter, SC 29150
Tel.: (803) 773-2177
Web Site: http://epacificsports.com
Year Founded: 1992
Sales Range: $10-24.9 Million
Emp.: 120
Textile Finishing Services
N.A.I.C.S.: 313310
Chang Hwan Bae (Pres)

Subsidiaries:

Pacific Sports Inc. (1)

12407 Slauson Ave Ste E, Whittier, CA 90606
Tel.: (562) 789-1334
Rev.: $4,000,000
Emp.: 5
T-Shirts, Custom Printed
N.A.I.C.S.: 458110

PEACEHEALTH
1115 SE 164th Ave, Vancouver, WA 98683
Tel.: (360) 729-1000
Web Site: http://www.peacehealth.org
Freestanding Ambulatory Surgical & Emergency Centers
N.A.I.C.S.: 621493
Richard DeCarlo (COO & Exec VP)
Liz Dunne (Pres & CEO)

Subsidiaries:

Zoom Care P.C. (1)
11958 SW Garden Place, Tigard, OR 97223
Tel.: (503) 684-8252
Web Site: http://www.zoomcare.com
Health Practitioners
N.A.I.C.S.: 621399
Dave Sanders (Founder)
Bill Frerichs (CEO)

PEACH STATE FEDERAL CREDIT UNION.
1505 Lakes Pkwy, Ste 100, Lawrenceville, GA 30043
Tel.: (678) 889-4328
Web Site: https://www.peachstatefcu.org
Year Founded: 1961
Emp.: 224
Credit Union
N.A.I.C.S.: 522130

PEACH STATE FORD TRUCK SALES, INC.
6535 Crescent Dr, Norcross, GA 30071
Tel.: (770) 449-5300
Web Site: http://www.peachstatetrucks.net
Rev.: $37,700,000
Emp.: 130
Truck Tractors
N.A.I.C.S.: 423110
Ricky Brown (COO)

PEACH STATE ROOFING INC.
1655 Spectrum Dr A, Lawrenceville, GA 30043
Tel.: (770) 962-7885
Web Site: http://www.peachstateinc.com
Sales Range: $10-24.9 Million
Emp.: 75
Roofing Contractors
N.A.I.C.S.: 238160
Marty Kelly (Pres)
Sandy Young (Supvr-Accts Payable)

PEACH STATE TRUCK CENTERS LLC
6535 Crescent Dr, Norcross, GA 30071
Tel.: (770) 449-5300
Web Site: http://www.peachstatetrucks.net
Year Founded: 1974
Rev.: $47,400,000
Emp.: 150
Truck Repair Services
N.A.I.C.S.: 423120
Jim Thompson (Mgr-New Truck)
Bobby Treadwell (Mgr-Fin)
Rick Reynolds (Owner)
Jeff Cook (Dir-New Truck Sls)
Rick Brown (CEO)

PEACH TREE HEALTH
5730 Packard Ave, Marysville, CA 95901
Tel.: (530) 749-3242   CA
Web Site: http://www.pickpeach.org
Year Founded: 1995
Sales Range: $10-24.9 Million
Emp.: 143
Health Care Srvces
N.A.I.C.S.: 622110
Greg Stone (COO)
Carol Furtado (Mgr-Billing Office)
Veronica Avila (Mgr-Acctg)
Kay Sidhu (CFO)
Marcia Myers (Vice Chm)
Ruth Mikkelson (Sec)
Michelle Cowdery (Mgr-HR)
John Nicoletti (Chm)
David Quackenbush (Chief Strategy Officer)
Rosalie Pena (Chief Dev Officer)

PEACHMAC
1850 Epps Bridge Pkwy Ste 207, Athens, GA 30606
Tel.: (706) 208-9990
Web Site: http://www.peachmac.com
Year Founded: 2007
Sales Range: $10-24.9 Million
Emp.: 65
Sales & Repairs of Apple Computers, iPods & iPads, Accessories & Software for Apple Products
N.A.I.C.S.: 449210
Darryl Peck (Co-Founder & Pres)
Anne Lydon Peck (Co-Founder)
Nick Fiedler (Dir-Sls)
Megan Conley (Mgr-Mktg)
Cathy Lilley (Mgr-Store)
Kelly Azabache (Asst Mgr)
Zach Powell (Asst Mgr)

PEACHTREE FABRICS INC.
765 Trabert Ave NW Ste A, Atlanta, GA 30318-4262
Tel.: (404) 351-5400
Web Site: http://www.peachtreefabrics.com
Sales Range: $10-24.9 Million
Emp.: 20
Upholstery Fabrics, Woven
N.A.I.C.S.: 424310
Steve Dutson (Chm & CEO)

PEACOCK ALLEY, INC.
2050 Postal Way, Dallas, TX 75212-6318
Tel.: (214) 744-0399   TX
Web Site: http://www.peacockalley.com
Year Founded: 1973
Sales Range: $10-24.9 Million
Emp.: 40
Bed & Bath Linens Mfr, Importer & Retailer
N.A.I.C.S.: 423220
Mary Ella Gabler (Founder)
Laura Busby (Mgr-E-Commerce)
Melissa Ennis (Mgr)
Jason Needleman (CEO)

PEACOCK OIL CO. OF BAXLEY INC.
429 SE Park Ave, Baxley, GA 31513
Tel.: (912) 367-6601
Sales Range: $10-24.9 Million
Emp.: 9
Petroleum Bulk Stations & Terminals
N.A.I.C.S.: 424710

PEAK ENERGY
PO Box 1110, Waynesville, NC 28786
Tel.: (828) 456-9035   NC
Web Site: http://www.haywoodoil.com
Year Founded: 1973
Rev.: $25,947,517
Emp.: 40
Suppliers of Petroleum Products
N.A.I.C.S.: 457120
David Blevins (CEO)
Rhonda Bucanan (Controller)
Todd Blevins (Pres)

PEAK GLOBAL HOLDINGS, LLC
1141 Jay Ln, Graham, NC 27253
Tel.: (252) 808-3500   DE
Year Founded: 2017
Holding Company
N.A.I.C.S.: 551112
R. Adrian Holler (Mgr)
Edward Small (Mgr)
Jack Baron (Mgr)

Subsidiaries:

Big Rock Sports, LLC (1)
1141 Jay Ln, Graham, NC 27253
Tel.: (252) 808-3500
Web Site: http://www.bigrocksports.com
Sales Range: $25-49.9 Million
Emp.: 400
Retailer of Sporting & Recreation Goods
N.A.I.C.S.: 423910
Gary Zurn (Sr VP-Industry Rels)
Edward Small (CEO)
Andy Melville (Pres)
Bob Hunter (VP-Mdsg)
Brad McNutt (Dir-Sls)
Brian Phillips (Pres-Shooting Sports Div)
Chris Means (Dir-Sls & Mdsg)
Dave Martin (Pres-Fishing)
Eric Hickey (VP-Sls & Mdsg)
Jay Samuels (Chief People Officer)
Patrick Harvey (CFO & Sr VP-Fin)
Mark Harrison (Mng Dir-Canada)
Greg VandeVisser (Creative Dir)
Shannon Farlow (Sr Mgr-Comm)

Subsidiary (Domestic):

AWR Sports LLC (2)
Ste 211 1651 E Main St, El Cajon, CA 92021-5206
Tel.: (619) 593-0872
Web Site: http://www.awrsports.com
Sporting & Recreation Goods Retailer
N.A.I.C.S.: 423910

All-Sports LLC (2)
11245 SE Hwy 212, Clackamas, OR 97015-9160
Tel.: (503) 650-7500
Web Site: http://www.all-sports.com
Sales Range: $25-49.9 Million
Emp.: 80
Sporting And Recreation Goods
N.A.I.C.S.: 423910
Chris McBride (Mgr-Sls)

CSI Sports LLC (2)
360 Industrial Blvd, Sauk Rapids, MN 56379-9785
Tel.: (320) 252-4193
Web Site: http://www.bigrocksports.com
Sales Range: $10-24.9 Million
Emp.: 75
Distribution of Sporting & Recreation Goods
N.A.I.C.S.: 423910
Ed Small (CEO)

Henry's Tackle LLC (2)
173 Hankison Dr, Newport, NC 28570-9170
Tel.: (252) 726-6186
Sales Range: $25-49.9 Million
Emp.: 180
Sporting & Recreation Goods
N.A.I.C.S.: 423910
Linda Morris (Controller & Acct Mgr)
Randy Hendrix (Dir-Distr)

MT Sports LLC (2)
650 Carbon St, Billings, MT 59102
Tel.: (406) 252-1610
Web Site: http://www.mtsports.com
Sales Range: $10-24.9 Million
Emp.: 50
Wholesale of Sporting & Recreation Goods
N.A.I.C.S.: 423910
Steve Edwards (Mgr-Sls)
Adam Comey (Pres & Founding Partner)
Dave S. Swany (Co-Founder & VP)
Eric Heckey (Gen Mgr)
Eric Hickey (Mng Dir)

Maurice Sporting Goods, Inc. (1)
1910 Techny Rd, Northbrook, IL 60065
Tel.: (847) 715-1500
Web Site: http://www.maurice.net
Outdoor Sporting Goods Distr
N.A.I.C.S.: 423910
Jory Katlin (Pres & CEO)
Greg Holmes (Dir-Retail Mktg)
Frank Bruno (VP-Mktg)

PEAK INVESTMENT SOLUTIONS, LLC
1508 Eureka Rd Ste 180, Roseville, CA 95661-2820
Tel.: (916) 772-5022   CA
Web Site: https://www.peakis.net
Year Founded: 1999
Offices of Certified Public Accountants
N.A.I.C.S.: 541211

PEAK METHODS, INC.
1516 S Boston Ave Ste 211, Tulsa, OK 74119
Tel.: (918) 585-8488   OK
Web Site: http://peakuptime.com
Year Founded: 1983
Cloud Managed Service Provider
N.A.I.C.S.: 518210
Gordon Martin (Pres)
Matt Auld (VP-Cloud Svcs)
Jennifer McCuistian (Dir-Pur & Admin)
Brian Toone (VP-Sls)
Kelly Sutton (VP-Svc Delivery)

PEAK RESOURCE GROUP, INC.
410 Peachtree Pkwy Ste 4245, Cumming, GA 30041
Tel.: (770) 888-1659
Web Site: http://www.peak-resource.com
Sales Range: $1-9.9 Million
Emp.: 47
Professional Staffing Services
N.A.I.C.S.: 561311
Jacki Neal (Pres & CEO)

PEAK RESOURCES, INC.
2750 W 5th Ave, Denver, CO 80204
Tel.: (303) 934-1200
Web Site: http://www.peakresources.com
Year Founded: 1991
Sales Range: $25-49.9 Million
Emp.: 37
Information Technology Consulting Services
N.A.I.C.S.: 541512
Thomas D. Brinegar (CFO)
Garrett Covington (Engr-Enterprise Sys)
Kirstin Larson (Mgr)

PEAK ROCK CAPITAL LLC
13413 Galleria Circle Ste Q 300, Austin, TX 78738
Tel.: (512) 765-6520
Web Site: http://www.peakrockcapital.com
Year Founded: 2013
Privater Equity Firm
N.A.I.C.S.: 523999
Anthony DiSimone (CEO)
Steve Martinez (Pres)
Peter Leibman (Mng Dir)
Robert Strauss (Sr Mng Dir)
Thomas Moran (Mng Dir)
Jordan Campbell (Mng Dir)
Nicholas Basso (Mng Dir)

Subsidiaries:

Diamond Crystal Brands, Inc. (1)
3000 Tremont Rd, Savannah, GA 31405
Tel.: (800) 654-5115
Web Site: http://www.dcbrands.com
Food Products, Primarily Refined Cane & Beet Sugar Mfr

PEAK ROCK CAPITAL LLC — U.S. PRIVATE

Peak Rock Capital LLC—(Continued)
N.A.I.C.S.: 311999
Tony Muscato (Pres & CEO)

Subsidiary (Domestic):

Diamond Crystal Bremen, LLC (2)
1090 Pacific Ave, Bremen, GA 30110-2291
Tel.: (770) 537-5813
Meat Product Whslr
N.A.I.C.S.: 424470

Halo Foods Ltd. (1)
Unit 26 Estuary Road Queensway Meadows Industrial Estate, Newport, Gwent, NP19 4XA, Wales, United Kingdom
Tel.: (44) 44 1633 277600
Web Site: http://www.halofoods.co.uk
Health Snack Bars Mfr
N.A.I.C.S.: 722515
Raadhika Sudhir (Fin Dir)
Louis Omare (Mng Dir)
Sean Zhang (Fin Mgr)

Hu-Friedy Mfg. Co., LLC (1)
3232 N Rockwell St, Chicago, IL 60618-5935
Web Site: http://www.hu-friedy.com
Sales Range: $25-49.9 Million
Emp.: 600
Dental Instruments Mfr
N.A.I.C.S.: 339114
Ken Serota (Pres)

Hunters Specialties, Inc. (1)
6000 Huntington Ct NE, Cedar Rapids, IA 52402
Tel.: (319) 395-0321
Web Site: http://www.hunterspec.com
Sales Range: $25-49.9 Million
Emp.: 112
Hunting Equipment Mfr
N.A.I.C.S.: 339920
Craig Cushman (VP-Mktg)
Mike Vrooman (VP-Product Mgmt)
Michael Spencer (VP-Ops)
Tyler Winthers (Dir-Product Mgmt)
Jason McKee (Sr Dir-Art)
MacDonald Plummer III (Sr VP-Sls-Alpharetta)

Louisiana Fish Fry Products Ltd. (1)
5267 Plank Rd, Baton Rouge, LA 70805
Tel.: (225) 356-2905
Web Site: http://www.louisianafishfry.com
Seafood Product Preparation & Packaging
N.A.I.C.S.: 311710
Michael Morse (Pres & CEO)

Natural American Foods, Inc. (1)
10464 Bryan Hwy, Onsted, MI 49265
Tel.: (517) 467-2065
Web Site: http://www.naturalamericanfoods.com
Honey Processor, Packager & Distr
N.A.I.C.S.: 311999
Frank Pyszkowski (Sr VP-Sls & Mktg)
Ed Minson (Dir-Comml Bus Dev)
Peter Paulsen (CFO)
Chris Nubern (Chief Procurement Officer)
Chol Kim (VP-Ops)
John Rzeszut (VP-Mktg)
Lance Chambers (CEO)

Subsidiary (Domestic):

Sweet Harvest Foods Co. (2)
515 Cannon Industrial Blvd, Cannon Falls, MN 55009-1177
Tel.: (507) 263-8599
Web Site: https://www.sweetharvestfoods.com
Sales Range: $1-9.9 Million
Emp.: 20
Honey & Peanut Butter Mfr
N.A.I.C.S.: 311999
Curt Riess (Interim Pres)

Precision Valve Corporation (1)
5711 Old Buncombe Rd, Greenville, SC 29609
Tel.: (864) 246-2200
Web Site: http://www.precisionglobal.com
Aerosol Valves Mfr
N.A.I.C.S.: 332999
Hans Van Der Looij (Mgr-Europe)
Mario Barbero (CEO)

Pretzels, Inc. (1)
123 Harvest Rd, Bluffton, IN 46714-0503
Tel.: (260) 824-4838
Web Site: http://www.pretzels-inc.com
Pretzel & Corn Products
N.A.I.C.S.: 311919
Chip Mann (Exec VP-Sls)
Pamela Koons (Mgr-Quality Assurance)
William Meldahl (VP-Pur)
Bruce Antrim (Coord-Pkg)
Scott Green (VP-Sls & Mktg)
Josh Boone (CFO)
Greg Pearson (CEO)
Mike Kaczynski (VP-Sls)
Tim Jax (VP-Mktg & Innovation)
Carey Hoffman (Dir-R&D)

Seagull Scientific, Inc. (1)
1616 148th Ave SE, Bellevue, WA 98007
Tel.: (425) 641-1408
Web Site: http://www.seagullscientific.com
Custom Computer Programming Services
N.A.I.C.S.: 541511
Jeremy Seigel (Founder & Chm)
Gene Henson (VP-Technical Svcs)
Harold Boe (CEO)
Ian Einman (VP-Tech)
Steve Wilcox (VP-Mktg)
Steve Short (VP-Information Sys & Tech)
Wayne Burns (VP-Fin & Admin)
Nigel LeGresley (Pres & CFO)

Shipley Do-nut Flour & Supply Co. (1)
3410 Ella Blvd, Houston, TX 77018
Tel.: (713) 682-4343
Sales Range: $1-9.9 Million
Emp.: 40
Retail Bakeries
N.A.I.C.S.: 311811
Michael Clark (Owner)

Spatial Business Systems, Inc. (1)
44 Union Blvd, Lakewood, CO 80228
Tel.: (303) 847-4200
Web Site: http://www.spatialbiz.com
Sales Range: $1-9.9 Million
Emp.: 19
Custom Computer Programing
N.A.I.C.S.: 541511
Andrew Street (VP-Tech)
Al Eliasen (Pres)
Dennis Beck (Founder & CEO)

Surveying & Mapping, LLC (1)
4801 SW Pkwy Bldg 2 Ste 100, Austin, TX 78735
Tel.: (512) 447-0575
Web Site: http://www.saminc.biz
Sales Range: $50-74.9 Million
Emp.: 381
Geospatial Surveying & Mapping Services
N.A.I.C.S.: 541370
Samir G. Hanna (Founder & Chm)
Robert E. Butler (Principal & Sr VP)
Michael R. Hatcher (Principal & Sr VP)
Coleman Cunningham (Principal & Sr VP)
Christopher M. Solomon (Pres & CEO)
S. Keith McNease (Principal & Sr VP)
Gregory K. McKnight (Principal & Sr VP)
Robert J. Roy (Principal)
Michael Crain (Mgr-Subsurface Utility Engrg)
M. Brett Smith (VP)
H. Stroud Evans (Principal & VP)
Cookie F. Munson (Gen Counsel)
Dana Smola (Dir-HR)
Kevin Richardson (VP)
Patrick A. Smith (VP)
Travis Engelke (CFO)

Subsidiary (Domestic):

Axis Geospatial LLC (2)
8600 Brooks Dr, Easton, MD 21601
Tel.: (410) 822-1441
Web Site: http://www.axisgeospatial.com
Rev.: $1,896,000
Emp.: 12
Engineeering Services
N.A.I.C.S.: 541330
Justin Lahman (Pres & CEO)
Gary Rockwell (Dir-Data Production)

Carolina Surveying Services Inc. (2)
415 N Lk Dr, Lexington, SC 29072-2803
Tel.: (803) 951-9191
Web Site: http://www.carolinasurveying.com
Surveying & Mapping Services
N.A.I.C.S.: 541370
Dennis Johns (Pres)

Echezabal & Associates, Inc. (2)
108 W Country Club Dr, Tampa, FL 33612
Tel.: (813) 933-2505
Web Site: http://www.echezabal.com
Sales Range: $1-9.9 Million
Emp.: 50
Engineering Services
N.A.I.C.S.: 541330
Edward Wackerman (VP)

Geosolutions, LLC (2)
1440 Lake Front Cir, Spring, TX 77380
Tel.: (281) 681-9766
Web Site: http://www.geosol.biz
Sales Range: $1-9.9 Million
Emp.: 16
Surveying Services
N.A.I.C.S.: 541330
Mary Chruszczak (Principal)

HALIS LLC (2)
1160 Oakpark Dr, McDonough, GA 30253-2212
Tel.: (404) 314-2013
Web Site: http://www.metro-geospatial.com
Geophysical Surveying & Mapping Services
N.A.I.C.S.: 541360
Geoffrey Sease (VP)

John F. Watson & Company (2)
200 N Loraine St Ste 220, Midland, TX 79701-4715
Tel.: (432) 520-2400
Web Site: http://www.windearthwater.com
Architectural Services
N.A.I.C.S.: 541310
John Watson (Pres)

Midland GIS Solutions, LLC (2)
501 N Market St, Maryville, MO 64468-1616
Tel.: (660) 562-0050
Web Site: http://www.midlandgis.com
Stationery & Office Supplies Merchant Whslr
N.A.I.C.S.: 424120
John Teale (Pres)

Wellston Associates Land Surveyors, LLC (2)
506 Osigian Blvd Ste 2, Warner Robins, GA 31088-8985
Tel.: (478) 971-3382
Web Site: https://wellstonassociates.com
Surveying & Mapping Services
N.A.I.C.S.: 541370

Turkey Hill, L.P. (1)
2601 River Rd, Conestoga, PA 17516-9630
Tel.: (717) 872-5461
Web Site: http://www.turkeyhill.com
Holding Company; Dairy Products Mfr & Distr
N.A.I.C.S.: 551112
John Cox (Chm)
Tim Hopkins (CEO)

Subsidiary (Domestic):

Turkey Hill Dairy, Inc. (2)
2601 River Rd, Conestoga, PA 17516
Tel.: (717) 872-5461
Web Site: http://www.turkeyhill.com
Sales Range: $100-124.9 Million
Emp.: 800
Frozen Desserts, Milk & Drinks Processor & Mfr
N.A.I.C.S.: 311511

Zb Importing, Inc. (1)
5400 W 35th St, Cicero, IL 60804
Tel.: (708) 222-8330
Web Site: http://www.ziyad.com
Sales Range: $10-24.9 Million
Other Grocery & Related Products Merchant Whslr
N.A.I.C.S.: 424490
Ibrahim Ziyad (Co-Founder & Pres)
Nemer Ziyad (CEO & VP-Ops & Mktg)
Nassem Ziyad (COO)
Ahmad Ziyad (Co-Founder)

Subsidiary (Domestic):

Vintage Food Corp. (2)
849 Newark Turnpike, Kearny, NJ 07032
Tel.: (201) 955-1505
Web Site: http://www.vintagefood.com
Sales Range: $1-9.9 Million
Emp.: 10
Ret Candy/Confectionery
N.A.I.C.S.: 445292
Suat Demirgil (Pres)

PEAK TECHNICAL SERVICES, INC.
583 Epsilon Dr, Pittsburgh, PA 15238
Tel.: (412) 696-1080 NY
Web Site: http://www.peaktechnical.com
Year Founded: 1968
Sales Range: $10-24.9 Million
Emp.: 75
Help Supply Services
N.A.I.C.S.: 561320
Joseph V. Salvucci (CEO)
Chris Sorisio (Mgr-Info Sys)
Eric Harvey (Acct Mgr)

Subsidiaries:

Peak Technical Services, Irvine (1)
7 Corporate Park Ste 125, Irvine, CA 92606-5154
Tel.: (949) 476-7800
Web Site: http://www.peaktechnical.com
Help Supply Services
N.A.I.C.S.: 561320

Peak Technical Services, National Divison (1)
583 Epsilon Dr, Pittsburgh, PA 15238
Tel.: (412) 825-3160
Web Site: http://www.peaktechnical.com
Contract Staffing Services
N.A.I.C.S.: 561320
Joseph V. Salvucci (Sr VP-Bus Dev)

Peak Technical Services, Troy (1)
850 Stephenson Hwy Ste 214, Troy, MI 48083 (100%)
Tel.: (248) 597-3718
Web Site: http://www.peaktechnical.com
Sales Range: $10-24.9 Million
Emp.: 6
Help Supply Services
N.A.I.C.S.: 561320

PEAK VISTA COMMUNITY HEALTH CENTERS
3205 N Academy Blvd Ste 130, Colorado Springs, CO 80917
Tel.: (719) 632-5700 CO
Web Site: http://www.peakvista.org
Year Founded: 1971
Sales Range: $50-74.9 Million
Emp.: 798
Community Health Care Services
N.A.I.C.S.: 621498
Pam McManus (Pres & CEO)
Kandi Buckland (COO)
Nancy Whitford (Chief Dev Officer & Exec Dir)
Michael Welch (Chief Medical & Dental Officer)
Donna Johnson (Chm)
Rebecca McCay (Chief Nursing & Clinical Officer)

PEAKBIETY INC.
501 E Jackson St Ste 200, Tampa, FL 33602
Tel.: (813) 227-8006 FL
Web Site: http://www.peakbiety.com
Year Founded: 1990
Sales Range: $1-9.9 Million
Emp.: 8
Advetising Agency
N.A.I.C.S.: 541810
Glen C. Peak (Pres)
Donette Arcos (Dir-Media)
Amy Phillips (Dir-Creative)

PEAKE BMW
2630 Veterans Blvd, Kenner, LA 70062
Tel.: (504) 469-6165
Web Site: http://www.peakebmw.com
Year Founded: 1996
Sales Range: $10-24.9 Million
Emp.: 50

Car Whslr
N.A.I.C.S.: 441110
Martin Peake (Pres)

PEAKE PRINTERS, INC.
2500 Schuster Dr, Hyattsville, MD 20781-1123
Tel.: (301) 341-4600   DC
Web Site:
http://www.peakedelancey.com
Year Founded: 1933
Sales Range: $100-124.9 Million
Emp.: 200
Commercial Printing Services
N.A.I.C.S.: 323111
Jay Rupard (Pres)
Mike Reeven (CFO)

PEAKEQUITY PARTNERS
555 E Lancaster Ave Ste 500, Radnor, PA 19087
Tel.: (484) 253-0001
Web Site: http://peakequity.com
Privater Equity Firm
N.A.I.C.S.: 523999
Ric Andersen (Partner)

Subsidiaries:

G5 Search Marketing, Inc.   (1)
550 NW Franklin Ave Ste 200, Bend, OR 97703
Tel.: (541) 306-3374
Web Site: http://www.getg5.com
Sales Range: $10-24.9 Million
Emp.: 100
Online Advertising
N.A.I.C.S.: 541810
Dan Hobin (Founder & CEO)
Patrick Davidson (COO)
Ben Steward (VP-Multifamily)
Karen Blue (VP-Natl Accts)
Kathie Cook (Acct Exec)

PEAKSWARE, LLC.
2770 Dagny Way Ste 212, Lafayette, CO 80026
Tel.: (720) 406-1839
Web Site: http://www.peaksware.com
Year Founded: 1999
Rev.: $2,100,000
Emp.: 20
Computer System Design Services
N.A.I.C.S.: 541512
Gear Fisher (CEO)
Dirk Friel (CMO)
Brad Culberson (CTO)
Jeffrey A. Koch (Chm)

PEANUT BUTTER & CO.
PO Box 200, New York, NY 10101
Tel.: (212) 677-3995   NY
Web Site:
http://www.ilovepeanutbutter.com
Year Founded: 1998
Sales Range: $1-9.9 Million
Emp.: 25
Mfr of Natural Peanut Butter Products
N.A.I.C.S.: 311911
Lee Zalben (Founder & Pres)

PEANUT PROCESSORS INC.
PO Box 160, Dublin, NC 28332
Tel.: (910) 862-2136
Web Site:
http://www.peanutprocessors.com
Sales Range: $75-99.9 Million
Emp.: 30
Nuts, Salted Or Roasted
N.A.I.C.S.: 424450
Houston Nile Brisson (Chm)
Brian Tart (Mgr)

PEAR COMMERCIAL INTERIORS INC.
1515 Arapahoe St, Denver, CO 80202-3150
Tel.: (303) 824-2000   CO
Web Site: http://www.pearwork.com

Year Founded: 1984
Office & Public Building Furniture Retailer & Distr
N.A.I.C.S.: 423210
Kevin McCarthy (VP-Mktg)

PEARCE INDUSTRIES INC.
12320 Main St, Houston, TX 77035-6206
Tel.: (713) 723-1050   TX
Web Site: http://www.wpi.com
Year Founded: 1924
Sales Range: $75-99.9 Million
Emp.: 600
Wholesale Distribution of Gas & Diesel Engines & Construction Machinery; Manufacture & Sales of Oil Field Equipment
N.A.I.C.S.: 423830
Gary M. Pearce (Vice Chm & Pres)
Richard E. Bean (Exec VP)
Stephen R. Pearce (Treas & VP)
Al Bentley (CFO & VP)
Louis M. Pearce Jr. (Chm)
Louis M. Pearce III (Pres-WPI)

Subsidiaries:

Waukesha-Pearce Industries   (1)
12320 S Main St, Houston, TX 77035
Tel.: (713) 723-1050
Web Site: http://www.wpi.com
Sales Range: $50-74.9 Million
Emp.: 400
Distr of Heavy Machinery Tools
N.A.I.C.S.: 423830
Gary Pearce (Pres)

PEARL ARTIST & CRAFT SUPPLY
1033 E Oakland Park Blvd, Fort Lauderdale, FL 33334
Tel.: (954) 564-5700
Web Site: http://www.pearlpaint.com
Rev.: $38,700,000
Emp.: 130
Art & Architectural Supplies
N.A.I.C.S.: 459999
Frank Bassi (Controller)

PEARL CITY ELEVATOR INC.
119 N Main St, Pearl City, IL 61062
Tel.: (815) 443-2512
Web Site: http://www.pce-coop.com
Sales Range: $25-49.9 Million
Emp.: 55
Petroleum Bulk Stations
N.A.I.C.S.: 424710
Todd Block (Gen Mgr)
Ron Bremmer (Pres)

PEARL COMPANIES
1200 E Glen Ave, Peoria Heights, IL 61616
Tel.: (309) 688-9000
Web Site:
http://www.pearlcompanies.com
Sales Range: $10-24.9 Million
Emp.: 180
Holding Company; Insurance; Automotive; Employee Benefits
N.A.I.C.S.: 551112
Gary Pearl (CEO)
Dennis Dietrich (Pres & COO)

PEARL LAW GROUP
567 Sutter S 3rd Fl, San Francisco, CA 94102
Tel.: (415) 771-7500
Web Site:
http://www.immigrationlaw.com
Year Founded: 1995
Sales Range: $1-9.9 Million
Emp.: 30
Legal Advisory & Immigration Services
N.A.I.C.S.: 541199

Christy Nguyen (Partner)
Sameer Khedekar (Mng Partner)
Yvonne Toy (Partner)
Addie Hogan (Partner)
Julie Pearl (CEO)
Michael Ray (VP-Global Bus Svcs)
Elizabeth Jamae (VP-Strategy-Global)
Daniel Park (Mgr-Global Program)

PEARL MEDIA LLC
363 Rt 46 W Ste 260, Fairfield, NJ 07004
Tel.: (973) 492-2300
Web Site:
http://www.pearlmediaus.com
Year Founded: 2008
Sales Range: $1-9.9 Million
Emp.: 12
Outdoor Advertising Services
N.A.I.C.S.: 541850
Joshua Cohen (Pres & CEO)
Anthony Petrillo (Chief Revenue Officer)
Brian Cohen (VP-Real Estate & Acq)
Jesse Sugarman (Sr VP-Bus Dev)
Jen Lee Almeida (COO & Exec VP-Ops)

PEARL MEYER & PARTNERS, LLC
570 Lexington Ave 7th Fl, New York, NY 10022
Tel.: (212) 644-2300
Web Site: http://www.pearlmeyer.com
Year Founded: 1989
Sales Range: $10-24.9 Million
Emp.: 100
Compensation Consulting Services & Survey Data
N.A.I.C.S.: 541612
David N. Swinford (Pres & CEO)
Peter A. Lupo (Mng Dir)
Yvonne Chen (Mng Dir)
Deborah Lifshey (Mng Dir)
Sharon Podstupka (VP)
Theo Sharp (Mng Dir)
Martin J. Somelofske (Mng Dir)
David E. Seitz (Mng Dir-Dallas)
Margaret H. Black (Mng Dir)
Terry Brown (Mng Dir)
Chris Earnest (Mng Dir)
Michael D. Enos (Mng Dir)
Michael T. Esser (Mng Dir)
Beth C. Florin (Mng Dir)
Sandy Godwin (Mng Dir)
Wes Hart (Mng Dir)
Laura A. Hay (Mng Dir)
Jim Heim (Mng Dir)

PEARL PAINT CO. INC.
1033 E Oakland Park Blvd, Fort Lauderdale, FL 33334
Tel.: (954) 564-5700
Web Site: http://www.pearlpaint.com
Year Founded: 1933
Sales Range: $25-49.9 Million
Emp.: 280
Art Supplies
N.A.I.C.S.: 459999
Rosalind Perlmutter (Pres & CEO)

PEARL RIVER VALLEY ELECTRIC POWER ASSOCIATION
1422 Hwy 13 N, Columbia, MS 39429
Tel.: (601) 736-2666
Web Site: http://www.prvepa.com
Rev.: $44,000,000
Emp.: 135
Distribution, Electric Power
N.A.I.C.S.: 221122
Freda Dyess (Mgr-Admin Svcs)
Randy Wallace (Gen Mgr)
Kurt Brautigam (Mgr-Svcs)

PEARL RIVER VALLEY OPPORTUNITY, INC.
756 Highway 98 By-Pass, Columbia, MS 39429
Tel.: (601) 736-9564   MS
Web Site: http://www.prvoinc.org
Year Founded: 1965
Sales Range: $10-24.9 Million
Emp.: 419
Low Income People Assistance Services
N.A.I.C.S.: 624190
Jimmy Richardson (Chm)
Helmon Johnson (Exec Dir)
Arthur Siggers (Vice Chm)
Laura McLain (Sec)

PEARL-PRESSMAN-LIBERTY COMMUNICATIONS GROUP
7625 Suffolk Ave, Philadelphia, PA 19153-1402
Tel.: (215) 925-4900   PA
Web Site: http://www.pplcg.com
Year Founded: 1906
Sales Range: $75-99.9 Million
Emp.: 132
Provider of Printing Services
N.A.I.C.S.: 323111
David Van Dusen (Pres)
Manny Pearl (CFO)
Elliot Schindler (Exec VP-Sls)

PEARLFISHER
455 Broadway Fl 5, New York, NY 10013
Tel.: (212) 604-0601
Web Site: http://www.pearlfisher.com
Year Founded: 2004
Rev.: $2,200,000
Emp.: 8
Business Services
N.A.I.C.S.: 541990
Mike Branson (Mng Partner)
Darren Foley (Dir-Realisation)
Karen Welma (Partner-Creative)
Jonathan Ford (Partner-Creative)
Hamish Campbell (Dir-Creative)
David Ramskov (Mng Dir-Copenhagen)

PEARLMARK REAL ESTATE PARTNERS LLC
200 W Madison St Ste 2800, Chicago, IL 60606
Tel.: (312) 499-1900
Web Site:
http://www.pearlmarkrealestate.com
Year Founded: 1996
Sales Range: $10-24.9 Million
Emp.: 40
Real Estate Investment Services
N.A.I.C.S.: 523999
Douglas W. Lyons (Mng Principal)
Timothy E. McChesney (Mng Dir)
William J. Swackhamer (Mng Dir)
Mark K. Witt (Mng Dir)
Jodi A. Stuart (Mng Dir)
Aaron Robison (Sr VP & Controller-Portfolio)
Blake Williams (COO-Health Care & Life Sciences Bus-Houston)
Christopher Mendez (Sr VP)
Michael O'Malley (Sr VP)
Keith Page (Sr VP)
Stephen R. Quazzo (Co-Founder, CEO & Mng Dir)

Subsidiaries:

Transwestern Commercial Services   (1)
5001 Spring Vly Rd Ste 400W, Dallas, TX 75244-3988
Tel.: (972) 774-2500
Web Site: http://www.transwestern.net

PEARLMARK REAL ESTATE PARTNERS LLC

Pearlmark Real Estate Partners LLC—(Continued)
Sales Range: $25-49.9 Million
Real Estate Services
N.A.I.C.S.: 531120
Jack Eimer (Pres-Central Reg)
Howard Watkins (Principal)
Justin Miller (VP)
Garry Natale (Dir-Mapping)
Alex Hancock (Sr VP-Tenant Advisory Svcs)
Tyler Garrett (VP-Houston)
Grant Walker (Sr VP)
Chris Reyes (VP)
Crystal Allen (Sr VP)
Chace Henke (VP)
Andy Gilpin (VP-Tenant Advisory & Agency Leasing-Washington)
Robert Garcia (VP-Capital Markets)
Josh Delk (Assoc VP)
Steve Harding (CFO)
Tom McNearney (Chief Investment Officer)
Ty Puckett (Exec VP)
Matt Hurd (Sr VP)
Larry Bell (Sr VP)
Lisa Addeo (Dir-Ops-New Jersey)
James Postell (Partner)
Craig Maturi (VP)
Tom Lawyer (Pres)
Bruce Ford (Pres-East)
Robert F. Vicci (Sr VP)

PEARSE-PEARSON COMPANY INC.
22 Tobey Rd, Bloomfield, CT 06002
Tel.: (860) 242-7777
Web Site: http://www.pearse-pearson.com
Year Founded: 1929
Sales Range: $10-24.9 Million
Emp.: 30
Pneumatic Tools & Equipment
N.A.I.C.S.: 423830
Jonathan Pearse (Pres)

PEARSON BUICK GMC
1176 W El Camino Real, Sunnyvale, CA 94087
Tel.: (408) 736-3411
Web Site: http://www.pearsonauto.com
Sales Range: $25-49.9 Million
Emp.: 65
Car Whslr
N.A.I.C.S.: 441110
Greg Meyer (Dir-Svcs)

PEARSON CONSTRUCTION COMPANY, INC.
240 West Britain Ave, Benton Harbor, MI 49022
Tel.: (269) 926-7281   MI
Web Site: https://pearsonconstruction.com
Year Founded: 1918
Rev.: $7,000,000
Emp.: 15
Industrial Building Construction
N.A.I.C.S.: 236220

PEARSON DENTAL SUPPLIES INC.
13161 Telfair Ave, Sylmar, CA 91342-3574
Tel.: (818) 362-2600   CA
Web Site: http://www.pearsondental.com
Year Founded: 1945
Rev.: $66,000,000
Emp.: 150
Medical & Hospital Equipment
N.A.I.C.S.: 423450
Keyhan Kashfian (Owner)
Perry Kashfian (Co-Pres)

PEARSON FORD
10650 N Michigan Rd, Zionsville, IN 46077
Tel.: (317) 873-3333
Web Site: http://www.myindyford.com
Year Founded: 1981
Sales Range: $10-24.9 Million
Emp.: 77
New Car Dealers
N.A.I.C.S.: 441110
Ben Weir (Gen Mgr-Vehicle Ops)
Dave Taylor (Mgr-Used Car)
Don Thompson (Mgr-Used Vehicle Sls)
Randy Bennett (Mgr-Svc)
Chris DeFord (Mgr-Internet Sls)
Robert Denman (Asst Mgr-Fleet)
John Pearson (Mgr-Fin)

PEARSON HOLDING COMPANY INC.
22008 Woodway Dr, Waco, TX 76712
Tel.: (254) 772-2737
Web Site: http://www.pci-gc.com
Sales Range: $10-24.9 Million
Emp.: 25
Industrial Building New Construction
N.A.I.C.S.: 236210
Scott Pearson (Pres)

PEARSON PACKAGING SYSTEMS
8120 West Sunset Hwy, Spokane, WA 99224
Tel.: (800) 732-7766
Web Site: http://www.pearsonpkg.com
Year Founded: 1955
Packaging Systems Mfr
N.A.I.C.S.: 561910
Michael A. Senske (Pres & CEO)
Colby McLean (VP-Systems Solutions Grp)
Ryan Womble (Sls Mgr)
Elaine Morgan (Sr Project Mgr)
Cody Campbell (Engr-Controls)
Susann Roeder (Dir-Mktg)
Jason McCall (Dir-Bus Partner)
Chris Gallagher (VP-Sls)

PEARSON-HUGGINS COMPANIES INC.
14001 Hull St Rd, Midlothian, VA 23112
Tel.: (804) 745-0300
Web Site: http://www.pearsonhonda.net
Year Founded: 1972
Rev.: $35,100,000
Emp.: 50
Dealer of New & Used Automobiles
N.A.I.C.S.: 441110
Frank Pearson (VP)
Bill Biddle (COO)

Subsidiaries:

Gene Huggins Imports Inc.   (1)
7551 Northeast Loop 820, North Richland Hills, TX 76180
Tel.: (817) 485-0300
Web Site: http://www.hugginscars.com
Emp.: 200
Automobiles, New & Used
N.A.I.C.S.: 441110
Ronnie Vaughn (Gen Mgr)

PEASE & CURREN INCORPORATED
75 Pennsylvania Ave, Warwick, RI 02888-3048
Tel.: (401) 739-6350   RI
Web Site: http://www.peaseandcurren.com
Year Founded: 1916
Sales Range: $25-49.9 Million
Emp.: 40
Refinerires for Secondary Nonferrous Metals
N.A.I.C.S.: 331492
Heather Blanchard (Controller)
Francis H. Curren III (Owner & Pres)

PEASE & SONS INC.
10601 Waller Rd E, Tacoma, WA 98448-0100
Tel.: (253) 531-7700
Web Site: http://www.peaseandsons.com
Sales Range: $10-24.9 Million
Emp.: 50
Heavy & Civil Engineering Construction Services
N.A.I.C.S.: 237990
Gordon Pease (VP)

PEAVEY ELECTRONICS CORPORATION
5022 Hartley Peavey Dr, Meridian, MS 39305-5422
Tel.: (601) 483-5365   DE
Web Site: http://www.peavey.com
Year Founded: 1965
Sales Range: $350-399.9 Million
Emp.: 2,000
Audio & Video Equipment Mfr
N.A.I.C.S.: 334310
Hartley D. Peavey (Founder & CEO)
Mary Peavey (Pres)
Courtland Gray (COO)

Subsidiaries:

Crest Audio   (1)
412 Hwy 80 E, Meridian, MS 39301
Tel.: (866) 812-7378
Web Site: http://www.peaveycommercialaudio.com
Designer & Mfr of Power Amplifiers & Mixing Consoles
N.A.I.C.S.: 334310
Hartley Peavey (Founder & CEO)

Peavey Commercial Audio   (1)
5022 Hartley Peavey Dr, Meridian, MS 39305
Tel.: (601) 483-5365
Web Site: http://www.peaveycommercialaudio.com
Audio Visual System Designers & Manufacturers
N.A.I.C.S.: 334310
Kevin Boudloche (Mgr-Web Design)

Peavey Electronics Ltd.   (1)
Great Folds Road, Oakley Hay, Corby, NN18 9ET, United Kingdom
Tel.: (44) 1536461234
Web Site: http://www.peavey-eu.com
Sales Range: $10-24.9 Million
Emp.: 45
Audio & Video Equipment Mfr
N.A.I.C.S.: 334310
Clive Roberts (Mng Dir)

PEAXY, INC.
2380 Bering Dr, San Jose, CA 95131
Tel.: (408) 441-6500
Web Site: http://www.peaxy.net
Year Founded: 2012
Sales Range: $1-9.9 Million
Emp.: 20
Software Development Services
N.A.I.C.S.: 541511
Federico Faggin (Co-Founder)
Manuel Terranova (Co-Founder, Pres & CEO)
Todd Beine (VP-Programs)
Stefan Geens (Dir-Product Design)
Joshua Gallagher (Sr Dir-Software Dev)

PEBBLE BEACH COMPANY
2700 17 Mile Dr, Pebble Beach, CA 93953
Tel.: (831) 647-7500
Web Site: http://www.pebblebeach.com
Year Founded: 1992
Sales Range: $50-74.9 Million
Emp.: 1,800
Hotels & Motels
N.A.I.C.S.: 721110

U.S. PRIVATE

David Stivers (Exec VP)
William L. Perocchi (CEO)
R. J. Harper (Exec VP-Golf & Retail)
Tim Ryan (VP-Bus Dev-Global)
David Heuck (Chief Admin Officer & Exec VP)
Susan Merfeld (Sr VP-Community Affairs)
Mark Stilwell (Exec VP-Real Estate)
Steve Aitchison (Sr VP-Capital Svcs)
Dominic Van Nes (VP-Guest Tech)
Kevin Kakalow (Dir-Retail)
Aaron Flink (Chief Strategy Officer & Exec VP)
Judah Matthews (CFO & VP)
Marcus Jackson (COO & Exec VP)
Mercedes De Luca (CIO & VP)

PEBBLES IN MY POCKET, INC.
1132 S State St, Orem, UT 84097
Tel.: (801) 226-2632
Web Site: http://www.pebblesinmypocket.com
Rev.: $13,400,000
Emp.: 40
Hobbies
N.A.I.C.S.: 459120
Brenda Birrell (Founder, Owner & CEO)

PECCOLE NEVADA CORP
851 S Rampart Blvd Ste 105, Las Vegas, NV 89145
Tel.: (702) 933-1111
Web Site: http://www.peccole.com
Year Founded: 1949
Sales Range: $10-24.9 Million
Emp.: 25
Provider of Land Contracts
N.A.I.C.S.: 237210
Kerry Walters (CFO)

PECHANGA RESORTS & CASINOS
45000 Pechanga Pkwy, Temecula, CA 92592
Tel.: (951) 693-1819
Web Site: http://www.pechanga.com
Year Founded: 1994
Sales Range: $25-49.9 Million
Emp.: 4,500
Gambling Establishment
N.A.I.C.S.: 713290
John Palinkas (Treas)
Willie Ramos (Chm)
Michelle Markstrom (Pres)
Shannon Weidauer (VP-HR & Talent Mgmt)

PECHTER INC.
1128 9th Ave, Altoona, PA 16602-2535
Tel.: (814) 944-1631
Web Site: http://www.pechter.com
Year Founded: 1890
Sales Range: $10-24.9 Million
Emp.: 125
Metals Service Centers & Offices
N.A.I.C.S.: 423510
Ardie Karp (CFO & Controller)
Joel Hollander (Pres, CEO & Dir-Mktg)

PECHTERS BAKING GROUP LLC
840 Jersey St, Harrison, NJ 07029
Tel.: (973) 483-3374
Web Site: http://www.pechters.com
Sales Range: $250-299.9 Million
Emp.: 200
Bread, Cake & Related Products
N.A.I.C.S.: 311812
George Thomas (CEO)

PECKHAM INDUSTRIES, INC.

COMPANIES

20 Haarlem Ave, White Plains, NY 10603-2223
Tel.: (914) 949-2000   NY
Web Site: http://www.peckham.com
Year Founded: 1924
Sales Range: $25-49.9 Million
Emp.: 800
Road Contracting & Construction Services
N.A.I.C.S.: 324121
John R. Peckham *(Pres)*

Subsidiaries:

Byram Concrete & Supply LLC (1)
20 Haarlem Ave 3rd Fl, White Plains, NY 10603
Tel.: (914) 289-0357
Web Site: http://www.byramconcrete.com
Emp.: 25
Readymix Concrete Mfr & Distr
N.A.I.C.S.: 327320
John Peckham *(Pres)*

Dutchess Quarry & Supply Co., Inc. (1)
410 N Rd, Pleasant Valley, NY 12569-7055
Tel.: (845) 635-2174
Sales Range: $25-49.9 Million
Emp.: 130
Concrete Building Products, Sand & Other Construction Materials Distr
N.A.I.C.S.: 423320

Palmer Paving Corp. (1)
25 Blanchard St, Palmer, MA 01069
Tel.: (413) 283-8354
Web Site: http://www.palmerpaving.com
Sales Range: $25-49.9 Million
Emp.: 45
Highway & Street Paving Contractor
N.A.I.C.S.: 237310
Michael Shea *(VP-Ops)*
Janet M. Callahan *(Pres)*
Manuel B. Perry *(VP-Construction Svcs)*
John Fuhrman *(Controller)*
Charles Callahan Jr. *(Founder)*

Patterson Garnet Corp. (1)
Pleasant Ridge Rd, Wingdale, NY 12594
Tel.: (845) 832-0410
Provider of Industrial Garnet
N.A.I.C.S.: 423920

Peckham Asphalt Resale Corp. (1)
20 Haarlem Ave, White Plains, NY 10603
Tel.: (914) 949-2000
Asphalt Mixture Distr
N.A.I.C.S.: 423320

Peckham Materials Corporation (1)
438 Vaughn Rd, Hudson Falls, NY 12839-9644
Tel.: (518) 747-3353
Asphalt Mfr
N.A.I.C.S.: 324121

Peckham Road Corporation (1)
1557 State Route 9, Lake George, NY 12845-3438
Tel.: (845) 621-1415
Road Paving & Construction Services
N.A.I.C.S.: 237310

Putnam Materials Corp. (1)
438 Vaughn Rd, Hudson Falls, NY 12389
Tel.: (518) 747-3353
Web Site: http://www.peckham.com
Asphalt Shingle Mfr
N.A.I.C.S.: 324121
Tim Needham *(Mgr)*

Reclamation, LLC (1)
292 Van Rd, Kingston, NY 12491
Tel.: (845) 331-6500
Web Site: http://www.reclamationllc.net
Sales Range: $10-24.9 Million
Emp.: 40
Cold Recycling Services
N.A.I.C.S.: 238330
Darryl Crespino *(Office Mgr)*
Tony Smith *(Mgr-Shop)*
Emilie Simoneau *(Gen Mgr)*

William E. Dailey Inc. (1)
295 Airport Rd, Shaftsbury, VT 05262
Tel.: (802) 442-9923
Web Site: http://www.peckhamindustries.com
Sales Range: $25-49.9 Million
Emp.: 160
Readymix Concrete Mfr
N.A.I.C.S.: 327320

Wingdale Materials LLC (1)
3206 Pleasant Ridge Rd, Wingdale, NY 12594
Tel.: (845) 832-6000
Asphalt Mfr
N.A.I.C.S.: 324121

PECO CONSTRUCTION COMPANY
5400 W US Hwy 90, San Antonio, TX 78227
Tel.: (210) 432-0971
Web Site: http://www.pecoconstruction.com
Sales Range: $10-24.9 Million
Emp.: 10
Commercial & Office Building, New Construction
N.A.I.C.S.: 236220
James Noland *(Sec)*
Tom Wright *(Pres)*
George Wright *(VP)*

PECO FOODS INC.
1101 Greensboro Ave, Tuscaloosa, AL 35401
Tel.: (205) 345-4711   AL
Web Site: http://www.pecofoods.com
Year Founded: 1969
Sales Range: $250-299.9 Million
Emp.: 3,200
Poultry Hatchery Services
N.A.I.C.S.: 112340
Mark Hickman *(Pres & CEO)*
Steve Conley *(Dir-HR)*
Kevin Phillips *(Dir-Mktg & Sls-Commodity)*
Benny Bishop *(COO)*
William Andersen *(Chief Comml Officer)*
Patrick Noland *(CFO)*
Peter Van Derlyke *(Dir-Health & Safety)*
John Herman Hickman *(Founder)*
Steve Evans *(Chief Commercialization Officer)*
Scott Alexander *(Dir-Sls & Mktg)*

Subsidiaries:

Peco Farms Inc. (1)
145 2nd Ave NW, Gordo, AL 35466-2245 (100%)
Tel.: (601) 764-4964
Web Site: http://www.pecofoods.com
Sales Range: $25-49.9 Million
Emp.: 225
Producer of Broiler, Fryer & Roaster Chickens
N.A.I.C.S.: 112320
Alex Cobb *(Mgr-Feedmill)*
Joe Krebs *(Mgr-Fleet)*
Barry Bennett *(Mgr-Flight Ops)*
Joey Nance *(Mgr-Hatchery)*

Peco Farms of Mississippi, LLC. (1)
Highway 21 S, Sebastopol, MS 39359
Tel.: (601) 625-7819
Poultry Processing Services
N.A.I.C.S.: 311615
Steve McLurin *(Gen Mgr)*

Peco Foods Inc. (1)
95 Commerce Dr, Bay Springs, MS 39422-1905
Tel.: (601) 764-4392
Web Site: http://www.peco.com
Sales Range: $25-49.9 Million
Emp.: 600
Provider of Poultry Hatchery Services
N.A.I.C.S.: 112340

Peco Foods Inc. - Batesville Processing Plant (1)
625 S Allen St, Batesville, AR 72501
Tel.: (870) 793-7511
Emp.: 1,000
Poultry Processing Services
N.A.I.C.S.: 311615

Peco Foods Inc. - Brooksville Processing Plant (1)
559 W Main St, Brooksville, MS 39739
Tel.: (662) 738-5771
Poultry Processing Services
N.A.I.C.S.: 311615

Peco Foods Inc. - Canton Feather Lane Processing Plant (1)
180 Commercial Pkwy, Canton, MS 39046
Tel.: (601) 855-0925
Poultry Processing Services
N.A.I.C.S.: 311615

Peco Foods Inc. - Canton West Fulton Street Processing Plant (1)
1039 W Fulton St, Canton, MS 39046
Tel.: (601) 859-6161
Poultry Processing Services
N.A.I.C.S.: 311615

Peco Foods Inc. - Tuscaloosa Processing Plant (1)
3701 Kauloosa Ave, Tuscaloosa, AL 35401
Tel.: (205) 345-3955
Poultry Processing Services
N.A.I.C.S.: 311615
Tim Daniel *(Plant Mgr)*
Mark Hickman *(Pres & CEO)*

PECO INSPX
1835 Rollins Rd, Burlingame, CA 94010
Tel.: (800) 732-6285   CA
Web Site: http://www.peco-inspx.com
Year Founded: 1955
X-Ray & Inspection Solutions
N.A.I.C.S.: 335314
Jay Parekh *(VP-Engrg & Product)*

PECONIC LAND TRUST, INCORPORATED
296 Hampton Rd, Southampton, NY 11969
Tel.: (631) 283-3195   NY
Web Site: http://www.peconiclandtrust.org
Year Founded: 1983
Sales Range: $10-24.9 Million
Emp.: 40
Land Conservation Services
N.A.I.C.S.: 813312
Julie Zaykowski *(VP)*
Rebecca A. Chapman *(VP)*
Pam Greene *(VP)*
Timothy J. Caufield *(VP)*

PEDATA RESALES, INC.
5151 S Julian Dr, Tucson, AZ 85706-1831
Tel.: (520) 623-6387
Web Site: http://www.pedatarvcenter.com
Year Founded: 1993
Sales Range: $10-24.9 Million
Emp.: 19
Recreational Vehicle Whslr
N.A.I.C.S.: 441210
Don Cottrell *(Mgr-Sls)*
Gerard Pedata *(Pres)*
Grace Pedata *(Sec)*
Amy Warden *(Coord-Customer Care)*

PEDCO E&A SERVICES, INC.
11499 Chester Rd Ste 501, Cincinnati, OH 45246
Tel.: (513) 782-4920
Web Site: http://www.pedcoea.com
Year Founded: 1981
Sales Range: $10-24.9 Million
Emp.: 75
Provider of Architectural Services to Corporate Clients
N.A.I.C.S.: 541330
Kathy Taylor *(Office Mgr)*
Floyd Baker *(Project Mgr)*
Jerome Doerger *(Exec VP)*
Michael Walsh *(Chm & CEO)*

PEDERSEN WORLDWIDE

Steve Weidner *(VP)*
Joseph Hoffman *(Pres & COO)*
Dan Flynn *(Controller)*
Anthony Busch *(Engr-Electrical)*
Douglas Stafford *(Engr-Electrical)*
Megan O'Brien *(Engr-MEP)*
Jeff Zwick *(VP & Sr Project Mgr)*
Ghassan Sudani *(Mgr-Structural Dept)*
Raven Jones *(Sr Engr-Mechanical)*

PEDDINGHAUS CORPORATION
300 N Washington Ave, Bradley, IL 60915-1646
Tel.: (815) 937-3800   DE
Web Site: http://www.peddinghaus.com
Year Founded: 1977
Sales Range: $10-24.9 Million
Emp.: 200
Machine Tools, Metal Cutting Types for Structural & Plate Steel
N.A.I.C.S.: 333517
Lyle Menke *(Mgr-Mktg)*
Greg Kubicka *(CFO)*
Anton Peddinghaus *(CEO)*

PEDDLER'S VILLAGE, INC.
Rt 202 & 263, Lahaska, PA 18931
Tel.: (215) 794-4000
Web Site: http://www.peddlersvillage.com
Sales Range: $10-24.9 Million
Emp.: 300
Lodging & Restaurants
N.A.I.C.S.: 721199
Eve Gelman *(Mgr-PR & Digital Comm)*
Annette Rosenberg *(Coord-Event & Destination Sls)*
Christine Niessen *(Mgr-Sls)*
Darlene Cappa *(Mgr-Hospitality)*
Kevin Hamilton *(Dir-Facilities)*
Terry Ward *(COO)*
Ann Lipcsey *(Mgr-Catering Sls)*

PEDERNALES ELECTRIC CO-OPERATIVE INC.
201 S Ave F, Johnson City, TX 78636
Tel.: (830) 868-7155   TX
Web Site: http://www.pec.coop
Year Founded: 1938
Rev.: $182,206,037
Emp.: 800
Electronic Services
N.A.I.C.S.: 221118
Tracy Golden *(CFO)*
Julie Parsley *(CEO)*
Eddie Dauterive *(COO)*
Emily Pataki *(Chm)*
Lawanda Parnell *(CIO)*

PEDERSEN TOYOTA-VOLVO INC.
4455 S College Ave, Fort Collins, CO 80525
Tel.: (970) 223-3100
Web Site: http://www.pedersentoyota.com
Rev.: $60,000,000
Emp.: 130
Automobiles, New & Used
N.A.I.C.S.: 441110
Gerald Pedersen *(Pres)*

PEDERSEN WORLDWIDE
280 W 10200 S, Sandy, UT 84070
Tel.: (801) 562-3001
Web Site: http://www.pwcompanies.com
Year Founded: 2007
Sales Range: $25-49.9 Million
Emp.: 1,200
Clothing & Bamboo Products

PEDERSEN WORLDWIDE

Pedersen Worldwide—(Continued)
N.A.I.C.S.: 458110
Jeff Pedersen (Chm & CEO)
Brent Rowser (CFO & COO)
Shawn Corbridge (VP-Mktg)
Dustin Tate (Exec VP-Sls)

Subsidiaries:

Cariloha (1)
280 W 10200 S, Sandy, UT 84070
Tel.: (801) 562-3001
Web Site: http://www.cariloha.com
Emp.: 120
Clothing Accessories Retailer
N.A.I.C.S.: 458110
Jefferson G. Pedersen (Pres & CEO)
Aaron Hobson (Exec VP-Mktg)

Del Sol LLC (1)
280 W 10200 S, Sandy, UT 84070
Tel.: (801) 562-3001
Web Site: http://www.delsol.com
Sales Range: $25-49.9 Million
Emp.: 95
Mfr of Color-Change Technology Apparel & Accessories
N.A.I.C.S.: 315250
Jeff Pedersen (Pres & CEO)
Aaron Hobson (Exec VP-Mktg)
Brent Rowser (CFO)
Dustin Tate (Exec VP-Sls)

PEDIATRIC ACADEMIC ASSOCIATION INC.
555 S 18th St 7th Fl, Columbus, OH 43205
Tel.: (614) 722-5958 OH
Year Founded: 1981
Sales Range: $75-99.9 Million
Emp.: 407
Health Care Srvcs
N.A.I.C.S.: 622110
Timothy Feltes (VP)
Michael Brady (Co-Chm)
Timothy Robinson (Treas)
Jeremy Larson (Pres)
J. Philip Saul (Co-Chm)

PEDIGREE TECHNOLOGIES L.L.C.
4776 28th Ave, Fargo, ND 58104
Tel.: (701) 293-9949
Web Site:
http://www.pedigreetechnologies.com
Year Founded: 2004
Sales Range: $1-9.9 Million
Emp.: 65
Fleet Management Software Development Services
N.A.I.C.S.: 541511
Alex Warner (Chm & CEO)
Thomas Konat (VP-Sls)
Richard Gramer (CFO)

PEDONE
49 W 27th St Fl 6, New York, NY 10001
Tel.: (212) 627-3300 NY
Web Site: http://www.pedone.com
Year Founded: 1987
Rev.: $136,000,000
Emp.: 20
Advetising Agency
N.A.I.C.S.: 541810
Michael F. Pedone (Pres & CEO)
Diane Montpelier (Dir-Office Svcs)
Victor Mazzeo (Dir-Creative)

PEDRO FALCON ELECTRICAL CONTRACTORS INC.
31160 Avenue C, Big Pine Key, FL 33043
Tel.: (305) 872-2200
Web Site:
http://www.pedrofalcon.com
Sales Range: $10-24.9 Million
Emp.: 5

Electrical Contractor
N.A.I.C.S.: 238210
Bob Allsbrook (Project Mgr)

PEE DEE ELECTRIC COOPERATIVE INC.
1355 E McIver Rd, Darlington, SC 29532-8112
Tel.: (843) 665-4070 SC
Web Site:
http://www.peedeeelectric.com
Year Founded: 1939
Sales Range: $75-99.9 Million
Emp.: 87
Distr of Electric Power
N.A.I.C.S.: 221122
Robbie Howle (Mgr-Info Tech)
James A. Goodson (Chm)
Mike Fuller (CEO)

PEEK PACKAGING SOLUTIONS
5909 Sea Lion Pl Ste G, Carlsbad, CA 92010
Tel.: (760) 438-1616
Web Site:
http://www.peekpackaging.com
Year Founded: 1994
Sales Range: $1-9.9 Million
Emp.: 7
Packaging Designs & Supplies
N.A.I.C.S.: 561910
Robert Peek (CEO)
Ernie Enriquez (Mgr-Ops)

PEEK'N PEAK RECREATION INC.
1405 Old Rd, Findley Lake, NY 14724
Tel.: (716) 355-4141
Web Site: http://www.pknpk.com
Year Founded: 1985
Sales Range: $10-24.9 Million
Emp.: 500
Owner & Operator of Ski & Golf Resort, Hotel & Restaurant
N.A.I.C.S.: 721199
Jeff TeCulver (Treas & Controller)

PEEL'S BEAUTY SUPPLY INC.
11720 Peel Cir, La Vista, NE 68128
Tel.: (402) 333-0202 NE
Web Site:
http://www.peelssalonservices.com
Year Founded: 1981
Sales Range: $25-49.9 Million
Emp.: 450
Service Establishment Equipment
N.A.I.C.S.: 423850
William Peel (Pres)
Rod Bennink (VP-Fin)

PEELED INC
65 15th St 1st Fl, Brooklyn, NY 11215
Tel.: (212) 706-2001
Web Site:
http://www.peeledsnacks.com
Year Founded: 2005
Sales Range: $1-9.9 Million
Emp.: 10
Organic Fruit Snacks
N.A.I.C.S.: 311919
Noha Waibsnaider (Founder)
Jim Clark (Mgr-Sls-Natl)
Melissa Teegardner (Mgr-Sls-Eastern Reg)

PEEPLES INDUSTRIES INC.
21 E Rd, Savannah, GA 31401
Tel.: (912) 236-1865
Web Site:
http://www.peeplesinternational.com
Sales Range: $10-24.9 Million
Emp.: 11
Stevedoring

N.A.I.C.S.: 488320
Frank Peeples (Chm)

PEER CHAIN COMPANY
2300 Norman Dr, Waukegan, IL 60085
Tel.: (847) 775-4600 IL
Web Site: http://www.peerchain.com
Year Founded: 1969
Industrial & Motor Vehicle Chain Products Mfr
N.A.I.C.S.: 336390
Glenn Spungen (Pres)

Subsidiaries:

Peer Inc. (1)
2300 Norman Dr S, Waukegan, IL 60085
Tel.: (847) 785-2900
Self-Lubricated Ball Bearing Products Mfr
N.A.I.C.S.: 332991

PEER FOODS GROUP, INC.
1200 W 35th St, Chicago, IL 60609-3214
Tel.: (773) 927-1440
Web Site: http://www.peerfoods.com
Year Founded: 1943
Sales Range: $100-124.9 Million
Sausage & Other Prepared Meat Service
N.A.I.C.S.: 311612
Al Salgado (Mgr-Sls)

Subsidiaries:

Emge Foods, LLC (1)
5593 W US Highway 40, Greenfield, IN 46140-8793
Tel.: (317) 894-7777
Web Site: http://www.emgefoods.com
Sales Range: $1-9.9 Million
Emp.: 25
Veal Product Mfr
N.A.I.C.S.: 311612

PEER TO PEER NETWORK
2360 Corporate Cir Ste 400, Henderson, NV 89074-7722
Tel.: (702) 608-7360 NV
Web Site:
http://www.psychicfriendsnetwork.com
Year Founded: 2007
Sales Range: Less than $1 Million
Social Network Operator
N.A.I.C.S.: 516210
Christopher Esposito (Head-Bus Dev)
Dana Lainge (CTO)
James A. Bento (CEO)

PEERLESS DISTRIBUTING CO.
21700 Northwestern Hwy Ste 1160, Southfield, MI 48075-4916
Tel.: (248) 559-1800 MI
Sales Range: $75-99.9 Million
Emp.: 8
Petroleum Products Distr
N.A.I.C.S.: 424710
Marvin H. Fleischman (Pres)
Steve Robinson (Sec)
Naweed Rana (Controller)

PEERLESS ELECTRONICS INC.
700 Hicksville Rd, Bethpage, NY 11714
Tel.: (516) 594-3500 NY
Web Site:
http://www.peerlesselectronics.com
Year Founded: 1945
Sales Range: $10-24.9 Million
Emp.: 110
Electronic Parts & Equipment Distr
N.A.I.C.S.: 423690
Bill Gallucci (VP-Sls)

U.S. PRIVATE

PEERLESS ENTERPRISES INC.
33 W 401 Roosevelt Rd, West Chicago, IL 60185
Tel.: (630) 584-7710
Web Site:
http://www.peerlessfence.com
Rev.: $10,975,542
Emp.: 50
Fence Construction
N.A.I.C.S.: 238990
Lee Lochman (CEO)
Dean White (Vice Chm)

PEERLESS INDUSTRIES INC.
2300 White Oak Cir, Aurora, IL 60502
Tel.: (630) 375-5100 DE
Web Site: http://www.peerless-av.com
Year Founded: 1941
Audio & Visual Mounting Solutions
N.A.I.C.S.: 332510
Brian McClimans (VP-Sls-North America & APAC)
Earl Naegele (Mng Dir-Comml Sls)
Rich Florino (Sr Dir-Natl Accts)
Kevin McDonald (Sr Dir-Natl Accts)
Jeff Blankensop (Dir-Natl Accts)
Therese Cleary (Dir-Channel)
John Johnsen (Reg Sls Mgr)
Lynnette Marshal (Sr Mgr-Strategic Accts)
Maggie Austin (Mgr-Channel)
Maggie Hayes (Mgr-Channel)
Christine Lauber (Mgr-Channel)
Kathy Petrin (Mgr-Strategic Acct)
Megan Zeller (Mgr-Bus Dev)
Robert Branlund (Reg Sls Mgr)
Brian Schumacker (Reg Sls Mgr)
Dave Dahm (Mgr-Natl Accts)
Hut Hutto (Reg Sls Mgr)
Howard Lerner (Reg Sls Mgr)
Dave Zurek (Reg Sls Mgr)
Peter Hopkins (Reg Sls Mgr)
Dwight Jenkins (Reg Sls Mgr)

PEERLESS MIDWEST INC.
55860 Russell Industrial Pkwy, Mishawaka, IN 46545
Tel.: (574) 254-9050
Web Site: http://www.pmidwest.com
Sales Range: $75-99.9 Million
Emp.: 70
Water Well Drilling
N.A.I.C.S.: 237110
James R. Williams (Pres)
Michael J. Williams (VP)
Joel Annable (Project Mgr)
Rod Helmuth (Mgr-Tech Svcs)
Linda Hine (Bus Mgr)
Curt Kent (Project Mgr)

PEERLESS SAW CO.
4353 Directors Blvd, Groveport, OH 43125
Tel.: (614) 836-5790
Web Site:
http://www.peerlesssaw.com
Year Founded: 1931
Sales Range: $10-24.9 Million
Emp.: 110
Saw Blade & Handsaw Mfr
N.A.I.C.S.: 332216
Ken Lloyd (Co-Owner)
Tim Gase (Co-Owner)
Steve Hartshorn (Mgr-Sls)

PEERLESS STEEL COMPANY INC.
2450 Austin Dr, Troy, MI 48083-2030
Tel.: (248) 528-3200 MI
Web Site:
http://www.peerlesssteel.com
Year Founded: 1995
Sales Range: $200-249.9 Million
Emp.: 160
Steel Distr
N.A.I.C.S.: 423510

Douglas Wood (CEO)
Chris Allen (Mgr-Matl)
Jeff Zydeck (CFO)
David Wolff (VP)

PEERLESS SUPPLY INC.
1701 Guthrie Ave, Des Moines, IA 50316
Tel.: (515) 265-9905   IA
Web Site: http://www.peerless-supply.com
Year Founded: 1963
Sales Range: $10-24.9 Million
Emp.: 30
Provider of Machine Tools & Accessories
N.A.I.C.S.: 423830
Bruce Iler (Pres)
Don Scrignoli (VP-Sls)
Connie Terry (Mgr-Acctg)
Gary Schuldt (Mgr-Pur)
John Myers (VP & Gen Mgr)

PEERLESS TECHNOLOGIES CORPORATION
2300 National Rd, Fairborn, OH 45324-2009
Tel.: (937) 490-5000   OH
Web Site: http://www.epeerless.com
Year Founded: 2000
Sales Range: $25-49.9 Million
Emp.: 269
Computer System Design Services
N.A.I.C.S.: 541512
Andrea Kunk (CFO)
Jerry Tritle (VP-Bus Dev)
Michael Bridges (Pres)
Bob Goodman (VP-Strategic Sourcing, Programs & Emerging Programs Div)
Julie Jones (Sr VP-Bus Analytics Grp)
Kurt Harendza (Sr VP-Innovation & Res Grp)
Jack Moore (VP-Charleston Div)
Lee Fuell (Sr Partner)
Chrissy Hardin (VP-Contracts & Mktg)
Steve Lewis (VP-Cyber Mission Solutions Grp)
Mick Feldmeyer (VP-Info Svcs Grp)
Jim Free (VP-Aerospace Sys)
Darren Gero (VP-Ops-Huntsville)
Irv Ramirez (Sr VP-Information Svcs & Solutions)

PEERLESS TYRE CO.
5000 Kingston St, Denver, CO 80239
Tel.: (303) 371-4300   CO
Web Site: http://www.peerlesstyreco.com
Year Founded: 1949
Sales Range: $125-149.9 Million
Emp.: 260
Tire & Gasoline Company
N.A.I.C.S.: 457120
Samuel E. Forbes (Chm & Pres)

PEERLESS UMBRELLA CO., INC.
427 Ferry St, Newark, NJ 07105-3903
Tel.: (973) 578-4900   NJ
Web Site: http://www.peerlessumbrella.com
Year Founded: 1929
Sales Range: $150-199.9 Million
Emp.: 500
Mfr & Distr of Umbrellas & Candles
N.A.I.C.S.: 339999
Gene Moscowitz (Pres)
Rosalynn Leonessa (VP-Mktg)
Dan Edge (Mgr-Sls-Natl)

PEERLESS VALUE OPPORTUNITY FUND
1055 Washington Blvd, Stamford, CT 06901
Tel.: (203) 350-0040   DE
Web Site: http://www.peerless.com
Year Founded: 2011
Investment Services
N.A.I.C.S.: 523999
Timothy E. Brog (Chm & CEO)
Robert Kalkstein (CFO, Sec & Treas)
Yi Tsai (CFO)

PEERLOGIX, INC.
480 6th Ave Ste 351, New York, NY 10011
Tel.: (914) 550-9993   NV
Web Site: http://www.peerlogix.com
Year Founded: 2014
Rev.: $1,096
Assets: $33,156
Liabilities: $3,525,534
Net Worth: ($3,492,378)
Earnings: ($4,996,097)
Emp.: 2
Fiscal Year-end: 12/31/17
Digital Advertisement Software Publisher
N.A.I.C.S.: 513210
William Gorfein (Founder & CEO)

PEG BROADCASTING, LLC
961 Miller Ave, Crossville, TN 38555
Tel.: (931) 707-1102   TN
Web Site: http://www.pegbroadcasting.com
Sales Range: $10-24.9 Million
Emp.: 25
Radio Broadcasting Stations
N.A.I.C.S.: 516110
Jeff Shaw (Gen Mgr)
Kendra Williams (Office Mgr)
Gordon Stack (Mgr-Ops)
Steve Sweeney (Dir-Sls)

Subsidiaries:

PEG Broadcasting - McMinnville/Manchester   (1)
230 W Colville St, McMinnville, TN 37111
Tel.: (931) 473-9253
Web Site: http://www.wowcountry.com
Sales Range: $10-24.9 Million
Emp.: 10
Radio Broadcasting Stations
N.A.I.C.S.: 516110
Kathy Klasek (Office Mgr)
Jay Walker (Dir-News)
Duke Rice (Gen Mgr)

PEG Broadcasting - Sparta   (1)
520 N Spring St, Sparta, TN 38583-1305
Tel.: (931) 836-1055
Web Site: http://www.1050wsmt.com
Sales Range: $10-24.9 Million
Emp.: 2
Radio Broadcasting Stations
N.A.I.C.S.: 516110
Duke Rice (Gen Mgr)

PEGASI ENERGY RESOURCES CORPORATION
218 N Broadway Ste 204, Tyler, TX 75702
Tel.: (903) 595-4139   NV
Web Site: http://www.pegasienergy.com
Sales Range: $1-9.9 Million
Emp.: 3
Oil & Gas Exploration
N.A.I.C.S.: 211120
Oliver C. Waldron (Chm)
Michael H. Neufeld (Pres & CEO)
William L. Sudderth (Exec VP)
Billy Denman (Mgr-Land)
Valerie Holcomb (Controller-Fin)

PEGASUS AUTO RACING SUPPLIES, INC.
2475 S 179th St, New Berlin, WI 53146
Tel.: (262) 317-1234   WI
Web Site: http://www.pegasusautoracing.com
Year Founded: 1980
Sales Range: $1-9.9 Million
Emp.: 15
Auto Parts & Racing Accessories Retailer
N.A.I.C.S.: 441330
Carla J. Heitman (Owner & Pres)
Carrie Schwab (Mgr-Sys)

PEGASUS CAPITAL ADVISORS, L.P.
750 E Main St Ste 600, Stamford, CT 06902
Tel.: (203) 869-4400   CT
Web Site: http://www.pcalp.com
Year Founded: 1996
Sales Range: $25-49.9 Million
Emp.: 40
Provider of Capital Investment & Restructuring Services
N.A.I.C.S.: 525910
Craig M. Kogut (Founder)
Thomas Emmons (Partner-Investment)

PEGASUS COMMERCIAL & RESIDENTIAL CLEANING LLC
7966 Arjons Dr Ste A/B, San Diego, CA 92126
Tel.: (858) 444-2290
Web Site: http://www.pegasusclean.com
Year Founded: 1969
Sales Range: $1-9.9 Million
Emp.: 1,000
Residential Cleaning Services
N.A.I.C.S.: 561720
Jeffrey Becker (Pres)

PEGASUS IMAGING CORPORATION
4001 N Riverside Dr, Tampa, FL 33603
Tel.: (813) 875-7575
Web Site: http://www.accusoft.com
Sales Range: $10-24.9 Million
Emp.: 100
Digital Imaging Software Technology
N.A.I.C.S.: 513210
Jack Berlin (Pres & CEO)

Subsidiaries:

Accusoft Corporation   (1)
4001 N Riverside Dr, Tampa, FL 33603
Tel.: (813) 875-7575
Web Site: http://www.accusoft.com
Sales Range: $10-24.9 Million
Emp.: 95
Software Publisher
N.A.I.C.S.: 513210
Jack Berlin (Founder & CEO)
Russ Puskaric (VP-Sls)
Jim Bean (VP-Architecture)
Anthony Sanchez (CFO)
Steve Wilson (VP-Product)
Susan Gorman (VP-Engrg)
Christine Hairelson (Dir-HR)

Division (Domestic):

Accusoft Corporation   (2)
4 Mount Royal Ave Ste 100, Marlborough, MA 01752
Tel.: (508) 948-0936
Rev.: $3,800,000
Emp.: 30
Software Publisher
N.A.I.C.S.: 513210
Jack Berlin (CEO)

Subsidiary (Domestic):

Snowbound Software Corp.   (3)
309 Waverley Oaks Rd Ste 401, Waltham, MA 02452
Tel.: (617) 607-2010
Web Site: https://snowbound.com
Custom Computer Programming Services

N.A.I.C.S.: 541511
George Farnham (VP-Sls)
Jody Spencer (Dir-Mktg)
Simon Wieczner (Pres & CEO)
Geoff Webb (Mgr-Customer Support)

PEGASUS LOGISTICS GROUP
306 Airline Dr Ste 100, Coppell, TX 75019
Tel.: (469) 671-0300
Web Site: http://www.plg.cc
Year Founded: 1994
Air Courier Services
N.A.I.C.S.: 492110
Kenneth C. Beam (Owner)
Jeremy McClain (Supvr-Ops)
David Cannon (Dir-Ops)
Dennis Degodt (Mgr-Warehouse)
Dan Eminger (Gen Mgr-PDG Trucking & Mgr-Truckload)
Rick Clegg (Acct Mgr)
Chris Moreno (Coord-Logistics)
Jennifer McClelland (Sr Acct Mgr)
Amy McGowen (Mgr-Customer Svc)
Elizabeth Eldredge (Coord-Flowserve Acct)
Jake Flory (Architect-Solutions)
Keith Fretz (Coord-HPES)
Krista Meek (Coord-Ops)
Lisa Martinez (Acct Mgr)
Jason Wylde (Supvr-Warehouse)

PEGASUS ORGANIZATION INTERNATIONAL INC.
138 Deer Run Rd, Kutztown, PA 19530
Tel.: (610) 683-3160
Web Site: http://www.thepegasusorg.com
Year Founded: 2001
Sales Range: $1-9.9 Million
Emp.: 15
Project Management Consulting
N.A.I.C.S.: 541618
Gwenn Carr (Principal)
Gary Englehardt (Principal)
Charles R. Davis (Sr Project Mgr)
Dale R. Donovan (Sr Project Mgr)
Fred Williams (Sr Project Mgr)
Jason W. Melton (Sr Project Mgr)
Tom Howard (Sr Project Mgr)

PEGASUS TECHNOLOGY SOLUTIONS, LLC
Hall Park 2611 Internet Blvd Ste 115, Frisco, TX 75034
Tel.: (972) 332-4144   TX
Web Site: http://www.pegasustechsolutions.com
Year Founded: 2015
Sales Range: $25-49.9 Million
Emp.: 28
Software Development Services
N.A.I.C.S.: 541512
Buck Jones (Founder & CEO)
Dwane Ballard (CTO & Partner)
Terry McGill (Partner & Chief Security Officer)
Sarah Haller (Dir-Ops)
Steve Barnett (Sr VP-Sls)

PEGASUS TRANSPORTATION GROUP, INC.
1675 American Way, Cedar Hill, TX 75104
Tel.: (972) 293-8561
Web Site: http://www.pegasustransport.com
Rev.: $18,328,502
Emp.: 22
Local Trucking with Storage
N.A.I.C.S.: 484110
John M. Mc Fadden (Pres)

PEGASUS TRANSTECH, LLC

PEGASUS TRANSTECH, LLC

Pegasus TransTech, LLC—(Continued)
4301 Boy Scout Blvd Ste 550,
Tampa, FL 33607
Tel.: (813) 386-6000   DE
Web Site:
http://www.pegasustranstech.com
Year Founded: 1998
Sales Range: $10-24.9 Million
Custom Computer Programming Services
N.A.I.C.S.: 541511
Frank Adelman *(Pres & CEO)*
Don Burke *(COO)*
Jeanne Walters *(CFO)*
Salem Elnahwy *(CTO)*
Rick Bradberry *(CMO)*
Mark Spicer *(VP-Integrated Solutions)*
George Abernathy *(Head-Supply Chain Solutions)*

Subsidiaries:

Assured Telematics Inc.   (1)
64 Windsor Rd, Milton, MA 02186-2128
Tel.: (617) 470-3530
Web Site: http://www.assuredtelematics.com
Search, Detection, Navigation, Guidance, Aeronautical & Nautical System & Instrument Mfr
N.A.I.C.S.: 334511
Frank Pellitta *(Pres, Treas & Sec)*

PEGASUSTSI, INC.
5310 Cypress Ctr Dr Ste 200, Tampa, FL 33609
Tel.: (813) 876-2424
Web Site: http://www.pegasustsi.com
Year Founded: 1998
Sales Range: $10-24.9 Million
Emp.: 75
Engineering, Procurement & Construction Management Services
N.A.I.C.S.: 541330
Mary Arnold *(Mgr-HR)*
Lou Giokas *(VP-Bus Dev)*
Karl Ibadulla *(Pres)*
Lucien Richard *(Mgr-Engrg)*

PEGGY ADAMS ANIMAL RESCUE LEAGUE OF THE PALM BEACHES, INCORPORATED
3100/3200 N Military Trl, West Palm Beach, FL 33409
Tel.: (561) 686-3663   FL
Web Site:
http://www.peggyadams.org
Year Founded: 1963
Sales Range: $25-49.9 Million
Emp.: 97
Animal Welfare Services
N.A.I.C.S.: 812910
Rich Anderson *(CEO & Exec Dir)*
Kristi Jackson *(Dir-Fin & Admin Ops)*
Joy Humphries *(Dir-Dev & Mktg)*
Jim Lilli *(Dir-Ops)*
Daniel Hanley *(Treas)*
Laurie Raber Gottlieb *(Sec)*
Nellie Benoit *(VP)*
Joanie Van der Grift *(Pres)*
Lesly Smith *(Chm)*
Sam Hunt *(Vice Chm)*

PEGUES-HURST MOTOR COMPANY
200 Spur 63, Longview, TX 75601
Tel.: (903) 758-6211
Web Site: http://www.pegues-hurstford.com
Sales Range: $25-49.9 Million
Emp.: 85
Automobiles, New & Used
N.A.I.C.S.: 441110

PEI WEI ASIAN DINER, LLC
6191 N Hwy 161 Ste 300, Irving, TX 75038
Tel.: (480) 888-3000   DE
Web Site: http://www.peiwei.com
Year Founded: 2000
Casual Dining Restaurants
N.A.I.C.S.: 722511
John Hedrick *(CEO)*
Chris Andrews *(CIO)*

Subsidiaries:

Pei Wei Asian Diner Two (Dallas) LLP   (1)
3001 Knox St, Dallas, TX 75205-5584
Tel.: (214) 219-0000
Web Site: http://www.peiwei.com
Restaurant Operating Services
N.A.I.C.S.: 722511

Pei Wei Houston, Inc.   (1)
12020 FM 1960 W, Houston, TX 77065
Tel.: (281) 571-4990
Web Site: http://www.peiwei.com
Sales Range: $10-24.9 Million
Emp.: 20
Restaurant Operating Services
N.A.I.C.S.: 722511
Kara Henley *(Gen Mgr)*

PEI, INC.
598 Red Oak Rd, Stockbridge, GA 30281
Tel.: (404) 362-9255   GA
Web Site: http://www.shippei.com
Sales Range: $1-9.9 Million
Emp.: 25
Holding Company; Air Freight Forwarding & Trucking Services
N.A.I.C.S.: 551112
Michele Juneau Wilson *(Co-Founder & Co-CEO)*
Victoria P. Carver *(Co-Founder & Co-CEO)*

Subsidiaries:

PEI Logistics, Inc.   (1)
598 Red Oak Rd, Stockbridge, GA 30281   (100%)
Tel.: (404) 362-9255
Web Site: http://www.shippei.com
Sales Range: $10-24.9 Million
Air Freight Forwarding & Trucking Services
N.A.I.C.S.: 484121
Michele Juneau Wilson *(Co-Founder)*
Victoria P. Carver *(Co-Founder)*
Chris Carver *(Dir-Ops-Atlanta)*
R. Kenny Carver *(Gen Mgr-Atlanta)*

PEI-GENESIS INC.
2180 Hornig Rd, Philadelphia, PA 19116-4289
Tel.: (215) 673-0400   PA
Web Site: http://www.peigenesis.com
Year Founded: 1945
Sales Range: $25-49.9 Million
Emp.: 250
Mfr of Electronic Parts & Equipment
N.A.I.C.S.: 423690
Steven Fisher *(Pres & CEO)*
Jonathan Parry *(Mng Dir-Europe & Sr VP-Global Ops)*
Peter Austin *(COO, Exec VP & Gen Mgr-North America)*
Andy Stump *(Mgr-Ops-South Bend)*
Humberto Morachis *(Mgr-Ops-Nogales)*
Tony Houghton *(Dir-Ops-Europe)*
Euan Sheldon *(Dir-Ops-China)*
Alex Tsui *(Mng Dir-Asia)*
John Hufnagle *(VP-Sls & Engineered Solutions-North America)*
John Rozanski *(Sr Dir-Global Strategic Accts)*

Subsidiaries:

Filconn, Inc.   (1)
3324 N San Marcos Pl, Chandler, AZ 85225
Tel.: (480) 222-3565
Web Site: http://www.filconn.com
Sales Range: $1-9.9 Million
Emp.: 15
Electronic Connectors
N.A.I.C.S.: 334417

Jason Pedruzzi *(Mgr-Sls-Natl)*
Mark Pendergrass *(Pres)*

PEIRCE-PHELPS, INC.
516 E Township Line Rd, Blue Bell, PA 19422
Tel.: (215) 879-7000   DE
Web Site: http://www.peirce.com
Year Founded: 1926
Sales Range: $125-149.9 Million
Emp.: 250
Consumer Electronics & Home Appliance Products; Heating & Air Conditioning Products Distr
N.A.I.C.S.: 423730
Steve Cohen *(Mgr-Sls-New Construction)*
Frank Drybala *(Mgr-Acctg)*
Karen Haynie *(Mgr-Inventory Asset)*
Jack Magrann *(Mgr-Sls)*
Joe Scherer *(Dir-Distr)*
Mike Sullivan *(Mgr-Bryant Sls)*
Gerry DiNenna *(Sec)*
Sam Baum *(Reg Mgr)*
Tom Morgan *(Branch Mgr)*

PEKING HANDICRAFT INC.
1388 San Mateo Ave, South San Francisco, CA 94080
Tel.: (650) 871-3788
Web Site: http://www.pkhc.com
Sales Range: $50-74.9 Million
Emp.: 150
Home Furnishing Mfr
N.A.I.C.S.: 423220
Derrick Lo *(Pres)*
Clinton Chien *(CFO & VP)*

PEKO PRECISION PRODUCTS INC.
1400 Emerson St, Rochester, NY 14606-3009
Tel.: (585) 647-3010
Web Site:
http://www.pekoprecision.com
Year Founded: 1965
Sales Range: $25-49.9 Million
Emp.: 400
Provider of Metal Stampings
N.A.I.C.S.: 332119
Gary Baxter *(Pres & CEO)*
Jim Fisk *(Dir-IT)*
Timothy Christo *(Engr-Mechanical Design)*
Bruce Stafford *(Supvr-Turret Laser)*
Carl Cady *(Engr-Mfg)*
Dan Hartman *(Supvr-Mfg)*
Daniel Fannin *(Engr-Mfg)*
Scott Hiscock *(Engr-Quality)*
Jeff Lake *(VP-Sys Div)*
Jake Leakey *(Engr-Controls)*
Mark Frosino *(Engr-Mechanical)*

PELCO PRODUCTS, INC.
320 W 18th St, Edmond, OK 73013
Tel.: (405) 340-3434   OK
Web Site: http://www.pelcoinc.com
Year Founded: 1985
Sales Range: $25-49.9 Million
Emp.: 260
Traffic Signal Hardware, Utility Products & Decorative Outdoor Lighting Designer & Mfr
N.A.I.C.S.: 335139
Jeff Parduhn *(Controller)*
Shelley Bailey *(Mgr-Customer Svc)*
Paul Koenig *(Dir-Sls & Mktg)*
Steve Parduhn *(Founder, Pres & CEO)*
Mike Gilliland *(Mgr-Mktg)*
John Miller *(Mgr-Quality Assurance)*
Kathy Opp *(Office Mgr)*

PELCO STRUCTURAL, LLC.
1501 N Industrial B, Claremore, OK 74017

Tel.: (918) 283-4004
Web Site:
http://www.pelcostructural.com
Year Founded: 2005
Sales Range: $10-24.9 Million
Emp.: 72
Iron & Steel Mfr
N.A.I.C.S.: 331110
Phil B. Albert *(Pres)*
Kasey Scott *(VP-Sls)*
James Sutphen *(VP-Engrng)*
Kelly Scott *(VP-Ops)*

PELICAN DELIVERS, INC.
3100 Bucklin Hill Rd Ste 220, Silverdale, WA 98383
Tel.: (360) 328-2297   NV
Web Site:
http://www.pelicandelivers.com
Year Founded: 2018
Emp.: 7
Cannabis Delivery Services
N.A.I.C.S.: 492110
David Comeau *(Co-Founder, Chm, Pres & CEO)*
Tina Comeau *(Co-Founder, CFO, Treas & Sec)*
Vadim Tarasov *(CTO)*

PELICAN ENERGY PARTNERS LP
945 Bunker Hill Ste 250, Houston, TX 77024
Tel.: (713) 559-7110
Web Site:
http://www.pelicanenergypartners.com
Emp.: 100
Portfolio Management
N.A.I.C.S.: 523940
John O'Brien *(Mng Dir)*
Mike Scott *(Founder & Mng Partner)*

Subsidiaries:

Stewart Tubular Products, Inc.   (1)
5951 N Houston Rosslyn Rd, Houston, TX 77091
Tel.: (713) 682-1486
Web Site: http://www.stewarttubular.com
Emp.: 100
Mfr of Tubular Accessories
N.A.I.C.S.: 332710
Steven N. Samuel *(Pres, Treas & Sec)*

PELICAN ENGINEERING CONSULTANTS LLC
3073 Horseshoe Dr S Ste 114, Naples, FL 34104
Tel.: (239) 597-7544
Web Site:
http://www.pelicanengineering.com
Year Founded: 1986
Sales Range: $1-9.9 Million
Engineering Consulting Services
N.A.I.C.S.: 541330
Thomas J. Lepore *(Owner)*

PELICAN OIL INC.
1819 Montana Ave, Billings, MT 59101
Tel.: (406) 245-4531
Web Site:
http://www.gmpetroleum.com
Rev.: $14,690,443
Emp.: 9
Petroleum Bulk Stations
N.A.I.C.S.: 424710

PELICAN STATE CREDIT UNION
3232 S Sherwood Forest Blvd, Baton Rouge, LA 70816
Tel.: (225) 408-6100   LA
Web Site:
http://www.pelicanstatecu.com
Year Founded: 1956
Sales Range: $10-24.9 Million
Emp.: 202

COMPANIES

Credit Union
N.A.I.C.S.: 522130
Ronald Stephens *(Sr VP)*
Jeffrey K. Conrad *(CEO)*
Annette Thames *(Sr VP)*
Michelle Ford *(VP-HR)*

PELICAN WASTE & DEBRIS, LLC
172 N Lacarpe Cir, Houma, LA 70360
Tel.: (985) 873-9553
Web Site:
http://www.pelicanwaste.net
Year Founded: 2013
Sales Range: $10-24.9 Million
Emp.: 180
Waste Management Services
N.A.I.C.S.: 562998
Roddie Matherne *(Co-Owner & Gen Mgr)*
Christian Lapeyre *(Co-Owner)*
Corey Callais *(Co-Owner)*

PELICAN WIRE COMPANY, INC.
3650 Shaw Blvd, Naples, FL 34117
Tel.: (239) 597-8555   DE
Web Site: http://www.pelicanwire.com
Year Founded: 1969
Sales Range: $10-24.9 Million
Emp.: 65
Wire & Cable Products Mfr
N.A.I.C.S.: 332618
Ted Bill *(Pres)*

PELICAN WORLDWIDE
14710 Heathrow 4S Pkwy, Houston, TX 77032
Tel.: (713) 862-5557
Web Site: http://www.pelicanww.us
Year Founded: 2002
Rev.: $7,300,000
Emp.: 25
Industrial Manufacturing
N.A.I.C.S.: 339991
Thomas D. Chapman *(Pres)*
Alma Hernandez *(Mgr-Acctg)*

PELLA CORPORATION
102 Main St, Pella, IA 50219
Tel.: (641) 621-1000   IA
Web Site: http://www.pella.com
Year Founded: 1925
Windows, Sliding Glass Doors, Skylights & Entrance Doors Mfr & Marketer
N.A.I.C.S.: 321911
Tim Yaggi *(Pres & CEO)*
Joher Akolawala *(CFO & Exec VP)*
Polly Tousey *(VP)*

Subsidiaries:

Bonelli Enterprises   (1)
330 Corey Way, South San Francisco, CA 94080
Tel.: (650) 873-3222
Web Site: http://www.bonelli.com
Metal Window & Door Mfr
N.A.I.C.S.: 332321
David Bonelli *(Pres)*
Mara Bonelli *(Sec)*

Grabill, Inc.   (1)
7463 Research Dr, Almont, MI 48003
Tel.: (810) 798-2817
Web Site: http://www.grabillwindow.com
Sales Range: $10-24.9 Million
Emp.: 40
Window Mfr
N.A.I.C.S.: 321911
Gregory Grabill *(Pres & CTO)*
Tony Benthem *(Mgr-Pur)*
Todd Collins *(Mgr-Svc & Installation)*
Teresa Grabill *(CFO)*
Tammy Pepper *(Mgr-Fin & Accts)*
Dan Conley *(Mgr-Plant)*
Stacey Muether *(Mgr-Sls)*
Sol Cunningham *(Mgr-Product Dev & Design)*

Lawson Industries Inc.   (1)
8501 NW 90th St, Medley, FL 33166
Tel.: (305) 696-8660
Web Site: http://www.lawson-industries.com
Rev.: $24,996,478
Emp.: 150
Mfr of Windows & Doors
N.A.I.C.S.: 327215
Gaby Cienguegos *(Mgr-IT)*
Larry Olson *(Mgr-Sls)*
Harold Bailey *(Pres)*
Ron Bailey *(VP)*

Pella Windows & Doors, Inc.   (1)
44695 5 Mile Rd, Plymouth, MN 48170
Tel.: (734) 414-6050
Web Site: http://www.pella.com
Distr of Doors & Windows
N.A.I.C.S.: 423310

Pella Windows & Doors, Inc. - Colorado   (1)
4200 Carson St, Denver, CO 80239
Tel.: (303) 371-3750
Web Site: http://www.colorado.pella.com
Distr of Doors & Windows
N.A.I.C.S.: 423310
Tim Bryant *(Pres)*

Pella Windows & Doors, Inc. - Detroit   (1)
1920 Opdyke Ct Ste 100, Auburn Hills, MI 48326
Tel.: (248) 292-5000
Web Site: http://www.detroit.pella.com
Doors & Windows Mfr & Distr
N.A.I.C.S.: 321911

PELLA FINANCIAL GROUP, INC.
800 Main St, Pella, IA 50219
Tel.: (641) 628-2191
Web Site:
http://www.marioncountybank.com
Holding Company
N.A.I.C.S.: 551111

PELLA PRODUCTS OF KANSAS CITY
1602 Jasper St, Kansas City, MO 64116
Tel.: (816) 471-0414   MO
Web Site: http://www.pella.com
Year Founded: 2000
Sales Range: $10-24.9 Million
Emp.: 40
Lumber, Plywood, Millwork & Wood Panel Merchant Whslr
N.A.I.C.S.: 423310
Chan Lundy *(Owner & Pres)*
Chan Lundy *(Pres)*
John Vance *(Gen Mgr)*

PELLA REGIONAL HEALTH CENTER
404 Jefferson St, Pella, IA 50219
Tel.: (641) 628-3150   IA
Web Site: http://www.pellahealth.org
Year Founded: 1958
Sales Range: $50-74.9 Million
Emp.: 903
Health Care Srvices
N.A.I.C.S.: 622110
Robert Kroese *(CEO)*
Erica Marvelli *(Dir-Home Health & Hospice)*

PELLA TRAVEL INC.
1318 E Ave, Pella, IA 50219-1918
Tel.: (641) 628-4224   IA
Web Site: http://www.pellatravel.com
Year Founded: 1982
Sales Range: $1-9.9 Million
Emp.: 3
Travel Agency
N.A.I.C.S.: 561510
Susan Johnson *(Pres)*

PELLA WINDOW & DOOR LLC
120 Dutchman Blvd, Irmo, SC 29063
Tel.: (803) 407-1112

Web Site: http://www.sc.pella.com
Sales Range: $10-24.9 Million
Emp.: 39
Windows & Doors
N.A.I.C.S.: 423310
Denney Znwyk *(CFO)*
Mitch Gaskill *(Mgr-Ops)*

PELLA WINDOWS & DOORS, INC.
12382 Gateway Park Pl Ste B300, Draper, UT 84020-8173
Tel.: (801) 566-4131
Sales Range: $25-49.9 Million
Emp.: 72
Glass Construction Materials
N.A.I.C.S.: 423310
Russ Pettey *(Gen Mgr)*
Eric Lanham *(Gen Mgr-Ops)*
Aaron Wight *(Mgr-Installation)*

PELLA WINDOWS & DOORS, INC. - BOSTON
45 Fondi Rd, Haverhill, MA 01832
Tel.: (978) 373-2500
Web Site:
http://www.boston.pella.com
Sales Range: $10-24.9 Million
Emp.: 100
Distr of Windows & Doors
N.A.I.C.S.: 423310
David Hadley *(Pres)*
Ross Carver *(Mgr-Remodeling Sls)*
Dawn Karactjas *(Mgr-Ops)*

PELLERIN MILNOR CORPORATION
700 Jackson St, Kenner, LA 70062-7774
Tel.: (504) 467-9591   LA
Web Site: http://www.milnor.com
Year Founded: 1947
Sales Range: $50-74.9 Million
Emp.: 650
Commercial Laundry Washer-Extractors; Large Automatic Dryers, Laundry Materials Handling Systems & Continuous Batch Washing Systems Mfr
N.A.I.C.S.: 333310
Charles Ehrensing *(VP-Ops)*
Russ Poy *(VP)*
Peter Youngblood *(VP-Fin)*
Katie Furtado *(Mgr-Adv)*

PELOTON EQUITY LLC
66 Field Point Rd 2nd Fl, Greenwich, CT 06830
Tel.: (203) 532-8011
Web Site:
http://www.pelotonequity.com
Year Founded: 2014
Privater Equity Firm
N.A.I.C.S.: 523999
Carlos Ferrer *(Partner)*
Ted Lundberg *(Partner)*
Theodore Lundberg *(Founder & Partner)*

Subsidiaries:

HealthPlanOne, LLC   (1)
1000 Bridgeport Ave 4th Fl, Shelton, CT 06484
Tel.: (203) 402-2500
Web Site: http://www.healthplanone.com
Sales Range: $1-9.9 Million
Emp.: 45
Health Insurance Services
N.A.I.C.S.: 524210
Bill Stapleton *(CEO)*
Trevor Prout *(VP-Mktg)*
Mike Stapleton *(CTO)*
Winston Haydon *(CFO)*
Scott Kabel *(VP-Call Center Ops)*
David Moser *(VP-HR)*
Paul Stanco *(VP-Mktg)*
Cynthia Ray *(VP-Sls)*
Nancy Williams *(VP-Stars Solutions)*

PEMBROOK REALTY CAPITAL LLC

Journey Health & Lifestyle   (1)
1998 Ruffin Mill Rd, Richmond, VA 23834
Tel.: (800) 958-8324
Web Site:
http://www.journeyhealthandlifestyle.com
Miscellaneous Consumer Goods Distr
N.A.I.C.S.: 423990
Mitchell Yoel *(CEO)*

Subsidiary (Domestic):

firstSTREET for Boomers and Beyond, Inc.   (2)
1998 Ruffin Mill Rd, Colonial Heights, VA 23834-5913
Tel.: (804) 524-9888
Web Site: http://www.firststreetonline.com
Electronics, Computers, Home & Garden Products, Fitness Products, Personal Care Products, Lighting, Automotive Products, Office Products Retailer & Marketer
N.A.I.C.S.: 423990
Dave Modena *(Sr VP-Aging in Home Div)*
Kevin Miller *(CFO, Treas & VP-Fin)*
John Fleming *(VP-Print Media Div)*
Stacy Hackney *(Gen Counsel & Sec)*
Roger Falardeau *(VP-IT)*
Steve Parker *(Sr VP-Mktg)*
Hunter Donaldson *(VP-Sls & Customer Svc)*
Tim Hague *(VP-Mdsg & Catalog)*

PELOTON THERAPEUTICS, INC.
2330 Inwood Rd Ste 226, Dallas, TX 75235
Tel.: (972) 629-4100   DE
Web Site:
http://www.pelotontherapeutics.com
Year Founded: 2010
Rev.: $628,000
Assets: $32,368,000
Liabilities: $8,588,000
Net Worth: $23,780,000
Earnings: ($36,071,000)
Emp.: 64
Fiscal Year-end: 12/31/18
Biotechnology Research & Development Services
N.A.I.C.S.: 541714
John A. Josey *(Pres & CEO)*
Alan A. Musso *(CFO)*
Eli M. Wallace *(Chief Scientific Officer)*
Mohammad Hirmand *(Chief Medical Officer)*
Naseem Zojwalla *(VP-Clinical Dev)*
James P. Rizzi *(VP-Computational Technologies)*
Michael J. Bakes *(VP-Ops)*
Cheryl A. Madsen *(VP-Regulatory Affairs)*
Dean J. Welsch *(VP-Biology)*
Scott N. Cullison *(VP-Bus Dev & Comml Plng)*

PEMBINA COUNTY MEMORIAL HOSPITAL
301 Mountain St E, Cavalier, ND 58220
Tel.: (701) 265-8461   ND
Web Site:
http://www.cavalierhospital.com
Year Founded: 1976
Sales Range: $10-24.9 Million
Emp.: 212
Health Care Srvices
N.A.I.C.S.: 622110
Jeni Schwenzfeier *(CFO)*
Lisa LeTexier *(Dir-Patient Care)*
Tom Ford *(Pres)*
Tom O'Toole *(Sec)*
Tom Vaughn *(VP)*

PEMBROOK REALTY CAPITAL LLC
767 Third Ave 18th Fl, New York, NY 10017
Tel.: (646) 388-5906   DE

PEMBROOK REALTY CAPITAL LLC U.S. PRIVATE

Pembrook Realty Capital LLC—(Continued)
Web Site:
http://www.pembrookgroup.com
Year Founded: 2011
Real Estate Investment Services
N.A.I.C.S.: 525990
Stuart J. Boesky *(CEO)*
Robert Hellman *(Dir-Asset Mgmt)*
John K. Malysa *(Mng Dir)*

PEMCO MUTUAL INSURANCE CO. INC.
1300 Dexter Ave N, Seattle, WA 98109
Tel.: (206) 628-4000 WA
Web Site: http://www.pemco.com
Year Founded: 1948
Sales Range: $100-124.9 Million
Emp.: 700
Provider of Fire, Marine & Casualty Insurance Services
N.A.I.C.S.: 524126
Stan McNaughton *(Chm & CEO)*
Sally Bauer *(Sr Mgr-Sys-Digital Svcs Team)*
Venkata Karumuri *(Mgr-Sys-Digital Bus Center)*
Abeer Abu-Emarah *(Mgr-Underwriting)*
Linda Magee *(Controller)*
Chad Barber *(Dir-Sls Dept)*
Doris Balderrama *(Dir-HR)*
B. Maurice Ward *(Mgr-Diversity & Inclusion)*
Dawn Lee *(VP-Product & Underwriting)*
Emil Dammel *(Dir-Enterprise Quality & Risk)*
Harris Clarke *(VP-Claims, Customer, Scv & Sls)*
Chris Purcell *(CIO & VP)*
Brian Benzel *(Vice Chm)*
Arif Arain *(Dir-Data Governance)*

Subsidiaries:

PEMCO Insurance Company Inc. (1)
1300 Dexter Ave N, Seattle, WA 98109
Tel.: (206) 628-4000
Web Site: http://www.pemco.com
Sales Range: $100-124.9 Million
Emp.: 620
Provider of Fire, Marine & Casualty Insurance Services
N.A.I.C.S.: 524126
Stan Mcnaughton *(CEO)*
Samantha Lewsley *(Mgr-Svc)*
Eric Kwok *(Mgr-Sls & Analysis)*
Paul Barry *(VP-Claims)*
Becky Sorenson *(Sr Mgr-Engrg)*
Mark Olsen *(Mgr-IT Engrg)*
Sally Bauer *(Sr Mgr-Sys-Digital Svcs Team)*
Curt Simonson *(Mgr-Learning & Dev-People & Brand Team)*
Rebecca Jameson *(Product Mgr-Auto Line of Bus)*
Noel Farmer *(Mgr-Technical Support-Infrastructure & Ops)*
Diane Geurts *(Comm Mgr-Mktg Dept)*
Maurice Ward *(Mgr-Diversity & Inclusion)*
M. J. Vigil *(Chief People & Brand Officer)*

PEMCO, INC.
401 W Wea St, Paola, KS 66071
Tel.: (913) 294-9290
Sales Range: $10-24.9 Million
Emp.: 4
Provider of Waste Water & Sewage Treatment Plant Construction
N.A.I.C.S.: 237110
Deb Stifter *(Controller)*
Curt Arndt *(Dir-Customer Svc)*
Keith Theimer *(VP-Tech & Dev)*

PEMISCOT MEMORIAL HEALTH SYSTEMS
PO Box 489, Hayti, MO 63851
Tel.: (573) 359-3415 MO
Web Site: http://www.pemiscot.org
Year Founded: 1949
Sales Range: $25-49.9 Million
Emp.: 753
Health Care Srvices
N.A.I.C.S.: 622110
Russell Gilmore *(Chm)*
Delila Swinger *(Sec)*
Eddie Brooks *(Vice Chm)*
Tim Gardner *(Treas)*
Jim Marshall *(CEO)*

PEMKO MANUFACTURING COMPANY
4226 Transport St, Ventura, CA 93003-5627
Tel.: (805) 642-2600 CA
Web Site: http://www.pemko.com
Year Founded: 1952
Sales Range: $75-99.9 Million
Emp.: 300
Mfr of Weatherstrip, Thresholds, Sills, Continuous Hinges & Glazing
N.A.I.C.S.: 332321
Phil Goossens *(Pres)*

Subsidiaries:

Pemko Manufacturing Company (1)
5535 Distribution Dr, Memphis, TN 38141-8225 (100%)
Tel.: (901) 365-2160
Web Site: http://www.pemko.com
Sales Range: $25-49.9 Million
Emp.: 150
Mfr of Weatherstrip, Thresholds & Continuous Hinges
N.A.I.C.S.: 332321
Phil Goossens *(Pres)*

PEN BOUTIQUE LIMITED
5560 Sterrett Pl Ste 101, Columbia, MD 21044
Tel.: (410) 992-3272
Web Site:
http://www.penboutique.com
Year Founded: 2004
Sales Range: $1-9.9 Million
Emp.: 20
Retailer of Quality Writing Instruments & Accessories
N.A.I.C.S.: 424110
Leena Shrestha *(Founder & Pres)*

PEN-LINK, LTD.
5936 Vandervoort Dr, Lincoln, NE 68516
Tel.: (402) 421-8857 NE
Web Site: http://www.penlink.com
Year Founded: 1987
Sales Range: $10-24.9 Million
Emp.: 68
Software Development Services
N.A.I.C.S.: 541511
Chris Havel *(Engr-Client Svcs)*
Mark Chapin *(VP-R&D)*
Brian Olson *(VP-Ops)*
Kevin Pope *(Pres)*

PENACOOK PLACE
150 Water St, Haverhill, MA 01830
Tel.: (978) 374-0707 MA
Web Site:
http://www.penacookplace.org
Year Founded: 1969
Sales Range: $10-24.9 Million
Emp.: 314
Nursing Care & Rehabilitation Services
N.A.I.C.S.: 623110
Karen Tarzia *(Dir-Admin Svcs & HR)*
David Becker *(Pres & CEO)*
Charlie Carrozza *(CFO)*
Lisa Salterio *(Dir-Nursing)*
Liz Coulter *(Dir-Rehab)*
James Tollman *(Dir-Medical)*
Tracy Howe *(Dir-Dementia Unit)*
Alysia Gomez *(Dir-Dining Svcs)*
Brenda G. Nowers *(Dir-Social Svc)*
Sean Lyden *(Dir-Facilities)*
Richard Sundell *(Treas)*

PENCE BRIGGS INC.
11841 Midlothian Tpke, Midlothian, VA 23113
Tel.: (804) 378-3000
Web Site: http://www.penceauto.com
Sales Range: $10-24.9 Million
Emp.: 5
Automobiles, New & Used
N.A.I.C.S.: 441110

PENCO CORPORATION
1503 W Stein Hwy, Seaford, DE 19973
Tel.: (302) 629-7911 DE
Web Site: http://www.pencocorp.com
Year Founded: 1949
Sales Range: $10-24.9 Million
Emp.: 70
Provider of Plumbing Equipment & Supplies
N.A.I.C.S.: 423720
Fred Glime *(Mgr-Pur)*

PENCOA
5620 1st Ave, Brooklyn, NY 11220
Tel.: (516) 997-2330
Web Site: http://www.pencoa.com
Year Founded: 1978
Sales Range: $10-24.9 Million
Emp.: 106
Pens & Mechanical Pencils
N.A.I.C.S.: 339940
Rick Perlmutter *(CEO)*

PENCOM SYSTEMS INCORPORATED
152 Remsen St, Brooklyn, NY 11201
Tel.: (718) 923-1111 NY
Web Site: http://www.pencom.com
Year Founded: 1973
Technical Recruiting, Staffing, Executive Search & IT Consulting
N.A.I.C.S.: 561311
Wade Saadi *(Founder & Pres)*

PENCOR SERVICES INC.
613 3rd St, Palmerton, PA 18071
Tel.: (610) 826-2552
Web Site: http://www.pencor.com
Sales Range: $10-24.9 Million
Emp.: 150
Provider of Media & Communications Technology
N.A.I.C.S.: 513110
Claude E. Reinhard *(Founder)*

PENDANT AUTOMATION, INC.
514 Young St, Havre De Grace, MD 21078
Tel.: (410) 939-7707 MD
Web Site:
http://www.pendantautomation.com
Year Founded: 2006
Sales Range: $1-9.9 Million
Emp.: 12
Engineeering Services
N.A.I.C.S.: 541330
Rob Ward *(Founder)*

PENDLETON ASSOCIATES INC
85 Sanrico Dr, Manchester, CT 06040
Tel.: (860) 646-4411
Web Site:
http://www.pendletonassoc.com
Sales Range: $10-24.9 Million
Emp.: 12
Plumbing & Hydronic Heating Supplies
N.A.I.C.S.: 423720
Arthur Pendleton *(Pres)*
Rich McCarthy *(Mgr-Inside Sls & Ops)*

PENDLETON FLOUR MILLS, LLC.
PO Box 400, Pendleton, OR 97801
Tel.: (541) 276-6511
Web Site: http://www.pfmills.com
Sales Range: $10-24.9 Million
Emp.: 120
Flour Mfr
N.A.I.C.S.: 311212
Alan Kessler *(Controller)*
Scott Feigner *(Mgr-Production)*

PENDLETON GRAIN GROWERS INC.
PO Box 1248, Pendleton, OR 97801-0830
Tel.: (541) 276-7611 OR
Web Site: http://www.pggcountry.com
Year Founded: 1930
Sales Range: $25-49.9 Million
Emp.: 190
Producer of Grain & Field Beans
N.A.I.C.S.: 424510
Robb Rea *(Dir-AG Supply)*
Terry Potratz *(Mgr-Store)*

PENDLETON WOOLEN MILLS, INC.
220 NW Broadway, Portland, OR 97209-3509
Tel.: (503) 226-4801 OR
Web Site: http://www.pendleton-usa.com
Year Founded: 1863
Sales Range: $450-499.9 Million
Emp.: 1,500
Men's & Women's Sportswear Mfr & Distr
N.A.I.C.S.: 315250
Charles Bishop *(Exec VP-Mfg)*
Peter Bishop *(Exec VP-Design & Mdsg)*
John Bishop *(Chm, Pres & CEO)*
Dennis Simmonds *(CFO)*
Robert Christnacht *(Exec VP-Sls)*
Annetta Young *(Exec VP-Ops & Plng)*

PENDO.IO, INC.
150 Fayetteville St, Raleigh, NC 27601
Web Site: http://www.pendo.io
Year Founded: 2013
Sales Range: $10-24.9 Million
Emp.: 258
Software Development Services
N.A.I.C.S.: 541511
Todd Olson *(Co-Founder & CEO)*
Erik Troan *(Co-Founder & CTO)*
Eric Boduch *(Co-Founder)*
Rahul Jain *(Co-Founder & VP-Bus Dev)*
Leslie Neitzel *(VP-People)*

PENDU MANUFACTURING INC.
718 N Shirk Rd, New Holland, PA 17557
Tel.: (717) 354-4348
Web Site: http://www.pendu.com
Sawmill & Woodworking Machinery Mfr
N.A.I.C.S.: 333243
Marlin J. Hurst *(Owner)*

PENGATE HANDLING SYSTEMS INC.
3 Interchange Pl, York, PA 17406
Tel.: (717) 764-3050
Web Site: http://www.pengate.com
Sales Range: $25-49.9 Million
Emp.: 60

Provider of Materials Handling & Machinery Services
N.A.I.C.S.: 811310
Brian T. Gibbs (Mgr-HR)

Subsidiaries:

Pengate Handling Systems of NY (1)
18 Petra Ln, Albany, NY 12205
Tel.: (518) 452-7793
Web Site: http://www.pengate.com
Rev.: $530,000
Emp.: 55
Materials Handling Machinery
N.A.I.C.S.: 423830
C Joseph Dean (Pres)

PENGUIN POINT FRANCHISE SYSTEMS INC
PO Box 975, Warsaw, IN 46580
Tel.: (574) 267-3107 IN
Web Site: http://www.penguinpoint.com
Year Founded: 1950
Sales Range: $10-24.9 Million
Emp.: 30
Provider of Fast Food Restaurants & Stands
N.A.I.C.S.: 722513
Wallace E. Stouder Jr. (Founder, Chm & Pres)

PENINSULA CAPITAL PARTNERS LLC
1 Detroit Ctr 500 Woodward Ave Ste 2800, Detroit, MI 48226
Tel.: (313) 237-5100 MI
Web Site: http://www.peninsulafunds.com
Year Founded: 1995
Emp.: 10
Mezzanine Capital Investment Firm
N.A.I.C.S.: 523999
Scott A. Reilly (Pres & Chief Investment Officer)
William Y. Campbell (Chm)
Steven S. Beckett (Partner)
Hector A. Bultynck (Partner)
Karl E. Lapeer (Partner)
William F. McKinley (Exec VP)
Dennis A. Murphy (Dir-Reporting & Compliance)
Jon P. Krempel (Dir-Fund Admin)
Dan J. Scanlan (Dir-Portfolio Mgmt)
Ty T. Clutterbuck (Partner)
James Illikman (Partner)

Subsidiaries:

Burlington Medical LLC (1)
3 Elmhurst St, Newport News, VA 23601
Tel.: (757) 888-8994
Web Site: http://www.burmed.com
Sales Range: $1-9.9 Million
Emp.: 125
Protective Medical Supplies Mfr & Distr
N.A.I.C.S.: 339113
John Williams (CEO)

PENINSULA CLEANING SERVICE INC.
12610 Patrick Hendry Dr Ste A, Newport News, VA 23602
Tel.: (757) 833-1603
Web Site: http://www.peninsulacleaning.com
Year Founded: 1990
Sales Range: $1-9.9 Million
Emp.: 200
Industrial & Commercial Building Cleaning Services
N.A.I.C.S.: 561720
Kelvin Copeland (Pres)

PENINSULA COMMUNITY HEALTH SERVICES
400 Warren Ave Ste 300, Bremerton, WA 98337
Tel.: (360) 478-2366 WA
Web Site: http://www.pchsweb.org
Year Founded: 1989
Sales Range: $25-49.9 Million
Emp.: 197
Community Health Care Services
N.A.I.C.S.: 621498
Susan Chesbrough (Dir-HR)
Jennifer Kreidler-Moss (CEO)
Regina Bonnevie Rogers (Dir-Medical)
Aaron Forster (CIO)
Al Pinkham (Pres)
Christopher Cook (CFO)
Paul Hathaway (Treas)
Sharon Tucker (VP)
Yolanda Fong (Sec)

PENINSULA COMMUNITY HEALTH SERVICES OF ALASKA, INC.
230 E Marydale Ave Ste 3, Soldotna, AK 99669
Tel.: (907) 260-7300 AK
Web Site: http://www.pchsak.org
Year Founded: 2001
Sales Range: $10-24.9 Million
Emp.: 180
Community Health Care Services
N.A.I.C.S.: 621498
Jeff Magee (Chief Medical Officer)

PENINSULA COMPONENTS INC.
1300 Industrial Rd Ste 21, San Carlos, CA 94070
Tel.: (650) 593-3288
Web Site: http://www.pencomsf.com
Rev.: $45,000,000
Emp.: 50
Mfr & Distr Industrial Supplies
N.A.I.C.S.: 423840
William A. Gardiner (Founder & Pres)

PENINSULA COPPER INDUSTRIES
220 Calumet St, Lake Linden, MI 49945
Tel.: (906) 296-9918
Web Site: http://www.pencopper.com
Sales Range: $10-24.9 Million
Emp.: 3
Copper Chemicals Mfr
N.A.I.C.S.: 325180
William W. Shropshire Jr. (Chm)

PENINSULA FIBER NETWORK, LLC
1901 W Ridge St Ste 2, Marquette, MI 49855
Tel.: (906) 226-2010
Web Site: https://www.pfnllc.net
Year Founded: 2006
Telecommunications & Transmission Systems
N.A.I.C.S.: 517410
Jim F. Bednarek (Controller)

PENINSULA FLOORS, INC.
6465 Natl Dr, Livermore, CA 94551
Tel.: (925) 449-6000
Web Site: http://www.thepeninsulagroup.com
Year Founded: 1959
Sales Range: $10-24.9 Million
Emp.: 50
Floor Laying & Other Floor Services
N.A.I.C.S.: 238330
Robert Conner (Chm & Pres)

PENINSULA GENERATION CO-OPERATIVE
10125 W Watergate Rd, Cadillac, MI 49601
Tel.: (231) 775-5500 MI
Year Founded: 2010
Electric Energy Distribution Services
N.A.I.C.S.: 221122
Daniel Decoeur (Pres)
Rick Deneweth (Chm)
Janet Kass (Treas)
Brian Valice (Sec)

PENINSULA LIGHT COMPANY
13315 Goodnough Dr NW, Gig Harbor, WA 98332
Tel.: (253) 857-5950
Year Founded: 1925
Sales Range: $25-49.9 Million
Emp.: 92
Distribution, Electric Power
N.A.I.C.S.: 221122
Jafar Taghavi (CEO)

PENINSULA OIL & PROPANE COMPANY
S Market St, Seaford, DE 19973
Tel.: (302) 629-3001
Web Site: http://www.penoil.com
Rev.: $18,500,000
Emp.: 30
Petroleum Bulk Stations
N.A.I.C.S.: 424710
Don Wille (Pres)

PENINSULA PACIFIC STRATEGIC PARTNERS, LLC
10250 Constellation Blvd Ste 2230, Los Angeles, CA 90067
Tel.: (424) 281-0700 DE
Web Site: http://www.peninsulapacific.com
Year Founded: 1999
Investment Services
N.A.I.C.S.: 523999
Mary Ellen Kanoff (Gen Counsel)
Christian Morris (Dir-Corp Dev)
M. Brent Stevens (Founder & Mgr)
Stephen Alarcon (VP)

Subsidiaries:

Brundage-Bone Concrete Pumping, Inc. (1)
500 E 84th Ave Ste A-5, Denver, CO 80229
Tel.: (303) 289-7497
Web Site: http://www.brundagebone.com
Concrete Pumping & Material Placement Services
N.A.I.C.S.: 238110
Timothy Schieck (Controller & Asst Sec)
Randy Waterman (Mgr-Environmental Health Safety & Risk)
Laurel Burnett (Dir-HR)
Greg Mollendor (Asst Controller)
Bruce F. Young (Pres & CEO)

Subsidiary (Domestic):

O'Brien Concrete Pumping Colorado, Inc. (2)
4390 S Windermere St, Englewood, CO 80110 (100%)
Tel.: (303) 778-7474
Web Site: http://www.obrienpumping.com
Concrete Pumping
N.A.I.C.S.: 238110

PENINSULA TRUCK LINES INC.
1010 S 336th St, Federal Way, WA 98003
Tel.: (253) 929-2000
Web Site: http://www.peninsulatruck.com
Sales Range: $25-49.9 Million
Emp.: 300
Local Trucking Services
N.A.I.C.S.: 484110
Stan Vanderpol (Pres & CEO)
Debbie Caporaso (Mgr-HR)
Ron Kieswether (VP-Ops)
Tim Vander Pol (VP-Pricing & Admin)
Brenett Waltos (VP-Sls & Mktg)

PENN CENTER MANAGEMENT CORP.
424 S 27th Ste 300, Pittsburgh, PA 15235
Tel.: (412) 481-8800
Web Site: http://www.sofferorganization.com
Rev.: $20,000,000
Emp.: 25
Real Estate Managers
N.A.I.C.S.: 531210
Brittany Mesing (Mgr-Mktg)

PENN COLOR INC.
400 Old Dublin Pike, Doylestown, PA 18901-2356
Tel.: (215) 345-6550 PA
Web Site: http://www.penncolor.com
Year Founded: 1971
Emp.: 600
Pigment Dispersions Mfr
N.A.I.C.S.: 325130
Dan Bogart (Mgr-Warehouse)
Chris Driscoll (Dir-Info Sys)
David Hill (CFO & VP)
James Meese (Dir-Tech-Building Products & Flexible Vinyl)
Dave Owings (Dir-Procurement)
Bob Rudick (Mgr-Lab)
Al Sylvester (Mgr-Maintenance & Engr-Electrical Control)
Carolyn Torrance (Mgr-Export & Import)
Anthony Zarriello (Plant Mgr)
Asha Abraham (Coord-EHS)
Erik Schneider (Mgr-Quality Control)
Gary Stinson (Plant Mgr)
Margaret Doherty (Sec)
Steve McEntee (Gen Mgr)
Ed Willard (Mgr-Traffic)
Hitesh Patel (Mgr-Global Tech)
Kevin Putman Jr. (Bus Mgr-Pkg)

Subsidiaries:

Penn Color Inc. - Elmwood Park Facility (1)
30 Paul Kohner Pl, Elmwood Park, NJ 07407
Tel.: (201) 791-5100
Pigment Mfr
N.A.I.C.S.: 325130

Penn Color Inc. - Milton Facility (1)
1474 Putman Pkwy, Milton, WI 53563
Tel.: (608) 868-2905
Pigment Mfr
N.A.I.C.S.: 325130

Penn Color Inc. - Ringgold Facility (1)
540 Hackett Mill Rd, Ringgold, GA 30736
Tel.: (706) 937-9200
Web Site: http://www.penncolor.com
Emp.: 40
Pigment Mfr
N.A.I.C.S.: 325130

Penn Color International BV (1)
Smakterweg 31, 5804 AE, Venray, Netherlands
Tel.: (31) 478 554000
Web Site: http://www.penncolor.com
Emp.: 25
Pigment Distr
N.A.I.C.S.: 424950
Bart van Tienen (Mgr-Ops)

Penn Environmental & Remediation, Inc. (1)
2755 Bergey Rd, Hatfield, PA 19440-1758
Tel.: (215) 997-9000
Web Site: http://www.penn-er.com
Sales Range: $10-24.9 Million
Emp.: 30
Provider of Business Consulting Services
N.A.I.C.S.: 541690
Bill Ponticello (Pres)

Sampson Coatings Inc. (1)
1900 Ellen Rd, Richmond, VA 23230-4213 (100%)
Tel.: (804) 359-5011

PENN COLOR INC. — U.S. PRIVATE

Penn Color Inc.—(Continued)
Web Site: http://www.sampsoncoatings.com
Sales Range: $10-24.9 Million
Emp.: 20
Mfr Of Paints And Allied Products
N.A.I.C.S.: 325510
Mike Clarke (Gen Mgr)

PENN COMMUNITY FINANCIAL CORPORATION
3969 Durham Rd, Doylestown, PA 18901
Tel.: (267) 864-1020   PA
Web Site: http://www.penncommunitybank.com
Year Founded: 2004
Sales Range: $75-99.9 Million
Emp.: 324
Bank Holding Company
N.A.I.C.S.: 551111
Jeane M. Vidoni (Pres & CEO)
Charles T. Field (CFO & Exec VP)
Stephanie Schwartzberg (Gen Counsel & Exec VP)

Subsidiaries:

Penn Community Bank (1)
3969 Durham Rd, Doylestown, PA 18901
Tel.: (267) 864-1020
Web Site: http://www.penncommunitybank.com
Commericial Banking
N.A.I.C.S.: 522110
Jeane M. Vidoni (Pres & CEO)
Diane Brown (Chief Admin Officer & Exec VP)
Robert Coffin (Chief Credit Officer & Exec VP)
Todd Hurley (Chief Relationship Officer & Exec VP)
Derek P. B. Warden (Chief Lending Officer & Exec VP)
Charles T. Field (CFO & Exec VP)
Georgann Berger McKenna (Chief HR Officer & Exec VP)

PENN ENERGY RESOURCES, LLC
1000 Commerce Dr Park Place 1 Ste. 400, Pittsburgh, PA 15275
Tel.: (412) 275-3200   DE
Web Site: http://www.pennenergyresources.com
Natural Gas Distribution
N.A.I.C.S.: 221210
Richard D. Weber (Chm & CEO)
Gregory D. Muse (Pres & COO)
John M. Johnston (Chief Dev Officer & Exec VP)
Mark C. Lang (CFO)
S. Casey Bowers (Gen Counsel & Sr VP)
Tommy L. Thompson (Sr VP-Drilling & Completions)

PENN FLORIDA CAPITAL CORP.
1515 N Federal Hwy Ste 306, Boca Raton, FL 33432
Tel.: (561) 750-1030   FL
Web Site: http://www.pennflorida.com
Year Founded: 1987
Sales Range: $50-74.9 Million
Emp.: 50
Real Estate Owner, Developer, Property Manager & Brokerage Services
N.A.I.C.S.: 531311
James R. Applegate (Exec VP & Dir-Club Properties)
M. Scott Collier (Sr VP-Dev)
Mark A. Gensheimer (Pres & CEO)
Bruce G. Sirof (Sr Exec VP)
David K. Warne (Chief Investment Officer)
Dyana Kenney (Exec VP & Dir-Leasing)

Ben Ortega (Sr VP-Dev)
Les Matthews (VP-Dev)
Elena Christodoulou (VP-Sls)

PENN GARRITANO DIRECT RESPONSE MARKETING
701 N 3rd St Ste 201, Minneapolis, MN 55401
Tel.: (612) 333-3775
Year Founded: 1999
Sales Range: $10-24.9 Million
Emp.: 42
N.A.I.C.S.: 541810
Joe Garritano (Pres)
Steve Penn (CEO)
Ryan Campbell (Acct Svcs Dir)
Jerry Mlekoday (Art Dir)
Marty Dietz (Mgr-Graphic Design)

PENN HIGHLANDS HEALTHCARE
100 Hospital Ave, Du Bois, PA 15801
Tel.: (814) 371-2200
Web Site: http://www.phhealthcare.org
Sales Range: $300-349.9 Million
Emp.: 3,800
Hospital Operator
N.A.I.C.S.: 622110
Raymond A. Graeca (Pres)
Mark A. Norman (COO)
Steven M. Fontaine (CEO)
Tarun K. Ghosh (CFO)

Subsidiaries:

Penn Highlands Brookville (1)
100 Hospital Rd, Brookville, PA 15825
Tel.: (814) 849-2312
Web Site: http://www.brookvillehospital.org
Sales Range: $25-49.9 Million
Emp.: 294
Health Care Srvices
N.A.I.C.S.: 622110
Debra Thomas (VP-Patient Care Svcs)
Jessica Park (Dir-Acctg)

PENN JERSEY PAPER CO.
9355 Blue Grass Rd, Philadelphia, PA 19114
Tel.: (215) 671-9800
Web Site: http://www.pjponline.com
Emp.: 500
Paper Products Mfr
N.A.I.C.S.: 322299
William Servis (Dir-Fin)
Glenn Harbison (Dir-Digital Mktg & Ecommerce)
Owen Clarke (Dir-Ops)
Lisa Furia-Cruz (Controller)
Mary Joan Furia-Cocca (Mgr-Customer Svc)
Mark Basher (Dir-Retail Ops)
Thomas R. Furia Sr. (Founder & Owner)
Thomas R. Furia Jr. (Pres & COO)
Thomas R. Furia III (Dir-Supply Chain Mgmt)

PENN LINE CORP.
300 Scottdale Ave, Scottdale, PA 15683-1240
Tel.: (724) 887-9110   PA
Web Site: http://www.pennline.com
Year Founded: 1987
Sales Range: $75-99.9 Million
Emp.: 1,800
Water, Sewer & Utility Line Services
N.A.I.C.S.: 237130
David Linn (CEO)

Subsidiaries:

Penn Line Service, Inc. (1)
300 Scottdale Ave, Scottdale, PA 15683-1299
Tel.: (724) 887-9110
Web Site: http://www.pennline.com

Sales Range: $25-49.9 Million
Emp.: 85
Provider of Water, Sewer & Utility Line Services
N.A.I.C.S.: 237130
Michael Mongell (VP-Tree & Right-of-Way Ops)
David W. Lynn (Pres)

Subsidiary (Domestic):

Forest Construction Company Inc. (2)
300 Scottdale Ave, Scottdale, PA 15683-1240
Tel.: (724) 887-9110
Web Site: http://www.pennline.com
Sales Range: $25-49.9 Million
Emp.: 80
Provider of Water, Sewer & Utility Line Services
N.A.I.C.S.: 237130
Dave Linn (Pres)

Tri-County Electric Company, Inc. (2)
103 Corporate Dr Ste 101, Morgantown, WV 26501
Tel.: (304) 296-3090
Sales Range: $25-49.9 Million
Emp.: 15
Electrical Work & Data Communications Services
N.A.I.C.S.: 238210
Greg Collin (Mgr)

PENN LYON HOMES INC.
195 Airport Rd, Selinsgrove, PA 17870
Tel.: (570) 374-4004
Sales Range: $25-49.9 Million
Emp.: 200
Modular Homes, Prefabricated, Wood
N.A.I.C.S.: 321992
Roger A. Lyons (CEO)
Thomas Ward (Mgr-Svc)

PENN POWER GROUP, LLC
8330 State Rd, Philadelphia, PA 19136
Tel.: (215) 335-0500
Web Site: http://www.pennpowergroupllc.com
Sales Range: $10-24.9 Million
Emp.: 250
Diesel Engine Parts & Repair Services
N.A.I.C.S.: 336310
Philip Fifield (Controller)
Al Clark (Owner & Pres)

Subsidiaries:

Carrier Transicold (1)
8330 State Rd, Philadelphia, PA 19136
Tel.: (215) 335-0500
Sales Range: $10-24.9 Million
Emp.: 75
Trailer Refrigeration Systems Repair
N.A.I.C.S.: 333415
Chris Cannon (Pres)
John Monti (Dir-Eastern Region)

Penn Power Systems (1)
355 Sipe Rd, York Haven, PA 17370
Tel.: (717) 273-4544
Web Site: http://www.pennda.com
N.A.I.C.S.: 332618

PENN SCHOEN BERLAND ASSOCIATES INC.
230 Park Ave S 2nd Fl, New York, NY 10003
Tel.: (212) 534-4000
Web Site: http://www.psbresearch.com
Rev.: $18,000,000
Emp.: 45
Market Analysis Or Research
N.A.I.C.S.: 541910
Michael Pettingill (COO)
Mike Chuter (CEO)
Char Popp (Sr VP-Seattle & Head-Qualitative Res-Global)

Subsidiaries:

Penn Schoen & Berland (1)
1110 Vermont Ave NW Ste 1200, Washington, DC 20005
Tel.: (202) 842-0500
Web Site: http://www.psbresearch.com
Sales Range: $25-49.9 Million
Advertising Agencies
N.A.I.C.S.: 541810
Don Baer (Chm)
Jason Boxt (Exec VP)
Jack Mackenzie (Exec VP & Head-Media & Entertainment Practice-Los Angeles)
John McTernan (Sr VP & Head-Intl Political-London)
Amy Crosby (Mng Dir-Washington DC)
Amy Leveton (Exec VP)
Andy Farkas (Sr VP-Tech)
David James (Sr VP-Washington DC & Seattle)
Jonathan Shingleton (Chm)
Judd Serlen (Pres, Mng Dir & Sr VP-Denver)
Mark Burles (Mng Dir-Seattle)
Megan Rouhier (Sr VP-HR)
Mike Pettingill (CFO & COO)
Nick Crofoot (Sr VP-Denver)
Robert Green (Principal)
Tammy Kaneshige (Sr VP)

PENN SHORE WINERY & VINEYARDS
10225 E Lake Rd Route 5, North East, PA 16428
Tel.: (814) 725-8688
Web Site: http://www.pennshore.com
Year Founded: 1970
Sales Range: $10-24.9 Million
Emp.: 40
Wine Mfr
N.A.I.C.S.: 312130
Jeffrey Ore (Owner)

PENN STATE HEALTH
500 University Dr, Hershey, PA 17033
Tel.: (717) 531-8606   PA
Web Site: http://www.pennstatehealth.org
Health Care Services Organization
N.A.I.C.S.: 813910
A. Craig Hillemeier (CEO)
Rod Dykehouse (Chief IT Officer & Sr VP)
Mark Faulkner (Gen Counsel)
Kimberly Lansford (Chief Compliance Officer & Sr VP)
David Swift (Chief HR Officer & Sr VP)
Sean Young (CMO & Sr VP)
Ross Darrow (Treas & VP)
Steve Massini (CFO, Chief Admin Officer & Exec VP)
Tom Stoessel (Chief Strategy Officer & Sr VP)
Tracy Williams (VP-Fin Reporting, Acctg & Budgets)
Alan L. Brechbill (Pres-Milton S Hershey Medical Center & Exec VP)
John P. Gaspich Jr. (Sr VP & Chief Auditor)

Subsidiaries:

St. Joseph Regional Health Network (1)
2500 Bernville Rd, Reading, PA 19605
Tel.: (610) 378-2000
Web Site: http://www.thefutureofhealthcare.org
Hospital Operator
N.A.I.C.S.: 622110
John R. Morahan (Pres & CEO)
Courtney Coffman (CFO)
Chris Newman (Chief Medical Officer & VP-Medical Affairs)
Sharon Strohecker (Chief Nursing Officer & VP-Clinical Svcs)
Scott Mengle (VP-HR)
Susan Sullivan (VP-Mission & Ministry)

Mary Hahn (VP-Ambulatory Svcs & Bus Dev)
Michael Jupina (VP-Mktg & Comm)

The Milton S. Hershey Medical Center (1)
500 University Dr, Hershey, PA 17033
Web Site: http://hmc.pennstatehealth.org
Rev.: $1,700,000,000
Emp.: 10,000
Medical Center
N.A.I.C.S.: 622110
A. Craig Hillemeier (CEO)
Alan L. Brechbill (Pres)
Paul Swinko (CFO & VP)
Margaret Mikula (Chief Quality Officer & VP)

PENN STATE SEED CO. INC.
RR 1 Hwy 309, Dallas, PA 18612-9781
Tel.: (570) 675-8585   PA
Web Site: http://www.pennstateseed.com
Year Founded: 1938
Sales Range: $10-24.9 Million
Emp.: 5
Provider of Farm Supplies
N.A.I.C.S.: 424910
Jim Harkins (Pres)

PENN STATE TOOL & DIE CORPORATION
260 Westec Dr, Mount Pleasant, PA 15666
Tel.: (724) 613-5500
Web Site: http://www.pennstatetool.com
Year Founded: 1954
Sales Range: $10-24.9 Million
Emp.: 80
Tool & Die Products Mfr
N.A.I.C.S.: 333514
Edna D. Truxal (CEO)
Ralph Ciacco (Pres)
John Elder (Engr-Mfg)
Mike Mangan (Mgr-QC)

PENN TANK LINES INC.
300 Lionville Sta Rd, Chester Springs, PA 19425
Tel.: (484) 713-1500   PA
Web Site: http://www.penntanklines.com
Year Founded: 1995
Sales Range: $100-124.9 Million
Emp.: 300
Provider of Long Distance Trucking Services
N.A.I.C.S.: 484230
Jack McSherry (Chm & CEO)
Ron Grim (Dir-Sls)
Cary Payne (Reg Mgr)
Steve McSherry (Pres)
Jack Williams (COO)

PENN TREATY AMERICAN CORPORATION
2500 Legacy Dr Ste 130, Frisco, TX 75034
Tel.: (469) 287-7044   PA
Web Site: http://www.penntreatyamerican.com
Year Founded: 1972
Sales Range: $75-99.9 Million
Emp.: 322
Holding Company; Accident, Health, Life & Disability Insurance; Long-Term Care & Home Health Care Products Distr
N.A.I.C.S.: 551112
Eugene J. Woznicki (Chm)

Subsidiaries:

American Independent Network Insurance Company of New York (1)
100 N Main St, Elmira, NY 14901
Tel.: (607) 732-3008
Sales Range: $75-99.9 Million
Insurance Services
N.A.I.C.S.: 524298

American Network Insurance Company (1)
3440 Lehigh St, Allentown, PA 18103
Tel.: (610) 965-2222
Web Site: http://www.penntreaty.com
Sales Range: $75-99.9 Million
Insurance Services
N.A.I.C.S.: 524298
Jane Menin Bagley (Sec)

Penn Treaty Network America Insurance Company (1)
3440 Lehigh St, Allentown, PA 18103
Tel.: (610) 965-2222
Web Site: http://www.penntreaty.com
Sales Range: $75-99.9 Million
Emp.: 150
Insurance Services
N.A.I.C.S.: 524298

PENN UNITED TECHNOLOGIES, INC.
799 N Pike Rd, Cabot, PA 16023-2223
Tel.: (724) 352-1507   PA
Web Site: http://www.pennunited.com
Year Founded: 1971
Sales Range: $100-124.9 Million
Emp.: 550
Provider of Special Dies, Tools, Jigs & Fixtures
N.A.I.C.S.: 333514
Bill Jones (Pres)

Subsidiaries:

Penn United Costa Rica SA (1)
Flexipark free zone 300 Mts East from Holcin San Rafael de, 20108, Alajuela, Costa Rica
Tel.: (506) 1 22939310
Industrial Equipment Mfr & Distr
N.A.I.C.S.: 333998
Randall Gonzalez (Gen Mgr)

Penn United Technologies, Inc. - Carbide Division (1)
196 Alwine Rd, Saxonburg, PA 16056
Tel.: (724) 352-5151
Web Site: http://www.pennunited.com
Chemical Products Mfr
N.A.I.C.S.: 325180
Bill Jones (Pres)

Quala-Die, Inc. (1)
1250 Brusselles St, Saint Marys, PA 15857   (100%)
Tel.: (814) 781-6280
Web Site: http://www.quala-die.com
Rev.: $8,700,000
Emp.: 24
Mfr of Tooling for Powdered Compaction & Precision Machining
N.A.I.C.S.: 333514
Dennis P. Schatz (Pres & CEO)
Tom Dorsey (VP & Gen Mgr)
Art Morelli (Mgr-Quality Control)
Todd Taylor (Supvr-Maintenance)

PENN WARRANTY CORPORATION
1081 Hanover St, Wilkes Barre, PA 18706-2028
Tel.: (570) 270-3804
Web Site: http://www.pennwarranty.com
Year Founded: 1988
Warranty Insurance, Automobile
N.A.I.C.S.: 524128
Gale T. Mayorowski (Chief Legal Officer)

PENN WOOD PRODUCTS INC.
102 Locust St, East Berlin, PA 17316
Tel.: (717) 259-9551
Web Site: http://www.pennwoodproducts.com
Rev.: $10,200,000
Emp.: 40
Lumber: Rough, Dressed & Finished
N.A.I.C.S.: 423310
Beth Story Reindollar (Mgr-Sls)
Scott McLaughlin (Mgr-Finishing)
Kraig Coxon (VP-Sls & Mktg)
Ira Lauer (Mgr-Wood Pur)

PENN'S BEST INC.
Route 6 E, Meshoppen, PA 18630
Tel.: (570) 833-5703
Web Site: http://www.pennsbest.net
Year Founded: 1969
Sales Range: $10-24.9 Million
Emp.: 280
Provider of Trucking Services
N.A.I.C.S.: 484121
Patrick Healey (Pres)

PENN-AIR & HYDRAULICS CORP.
580 Davies Dr, York, PA 17402
Tel.: (717) 840-8100
Web Site: http://www.pennair.com
Year Founded: 1968
Sales Range: $10-24.9 Million
Emp.: 60
Pneumatic Tools & Equipment
N.A.I.C.S.: 423830
Jim Conrad (Co-Founder)
Jeff Reinhart (Dir-Bus Ops)
Seth Bray (COO)
Mary Conrad (Co-Founder)
Matt Dearborn (Dir-Logistics)

Subsidiaries:

Konstance Pneumatics (1)
1750 Industrial Hwy, West Chester, PA 17402
Tel.: (610) 430-1225
Web Site: http://www.pennair.com
Emp.: 70
Pneumatic Tools & Equipment
N.A.I.C.S.: 423830
Bob Rhein (Pres)

Pneu-Force (1)
1750 Industrial Hwy, York, PA 17402
Tel.: (717) 840-8100
Web Site: http://www.pennair.com
Pneumatic Tools & Equipment
N.A.I.C.S.: 423830
Jim Conrad (Co-Founder)
Seth Bray (COO)
Mary Conrad (Co-Founder)
Matt Dearborn (Dir-Logistics)

PENN-AIRE AVIATION INC.
316 Allegheny Blvd, Franklin, PA 16323
Tel.: (814) 437-3074
Web Site: http://www.pennaire.com
Sales Range: $10-24.9 Million
Emp.: 8
Sales of Aircrafts
N.A.I.C.S.: 441227
Bruce A. Taylor (Pres)
Ellen Gierlach (CEO)

PENN-MAR ORGANIZATION, INC.
310 Old Freeland Rd, Freeland, MD 21053
Tel.: (410) 343-1069   MD
Web Site: http://www.penn-mar.org
Year Founded: 1981
Emp.: 100
Disability Assistance Services
N.A.I.C.S.: 624120
Gregory T. Miller (Pres & CEO)
Robert Kuhn (CFO)
Roger J. Marquis (Chief Dev Officer)
Laura Tieman (COO)
Kristine A. Crosswhite (Sec)
Anthony Gallo (Chm)
Jonathan Kinsley (Vice Chm & Treas)
Morton F. Zifferer Jr. (Chm)

Subsidiaries:

Change, Inc. (1)
3158 West St, Weirton, WV 26062
Tel.: (304) 797-7733
Web Site: http://www.changeinc.org
Job Training/Related Services Child Day Care Services Individual/Family Services
N.A.I.C.S.: 624310
Judy Raveaux (CEO)
Jordan Savage (CFO)
Rita Coyne (COO-Family Medical Care Div)
James Boniey (COO-Community Svcs Div)

Penn-Mar Organization, Inc. (1)
10709 Susquehanna Trl, Glen Rock, PA 17327
Tel.: (717) 235-8068
Web Site: http://www.penn-mar.org
Disability Assistance Services
N.A.I.C.S.: 624120
Jackie Stevens (Co-COO)
Robert Kuhn (CFO)
Laura Tieman (COO)
Gregory T. Miller (Pres & CEO)

PENN-PLAX, INC.
35 Marcus Blvd, Hauppauge, NY 11788-3733
Tel.: (631) 273-3787
Web Site: http://www.pennplax.com
Rev.: $13,200,000
Emp.: 225
Pet Supplies
N.A.I.C.S.: 459910
Linda Closs (CFO)
Paul Demas (Project Mgr)
Karen Krummel (Mgr-Acctg)

PENNA POWERS BRIAN HAYNES
1706 S Major St, Salt Lake City, UT 84115
Tel.: (801) 487-4800   UT
Web Site: http://www.ppbh.com
Year Founded: 1984
Sales Range: $10-24.9 Million
Emp.: 40
N.A.I.C.S.: 541810
John Haynes (Mng Partner)
David L. Smith (Partner & Dir-Client Svcs)
Chris Menges (Dir-Adv)
Traci Houghton (Dir-Fin)
Stephanie Miller-Barnhart (Dir-PR)
Erico Bisquera (Dir-Creative)
Mike Brian (Partner-Interactive Svcs)
Marc Stryker (Dir-Media)
Chuck Penna (CEO & Partner)

PENNANT SPORTS INC.
5037 Hwy 280 Ste 107, Birmingham, AL 35242
Tel.: (205) 536-7000
Web Site: http://www.pennantsports.com
Year Founded: 1988
Sales Range: $1-9.9 Million
Emp.: 12
Sporting Goods
N.A.I.C.S.: 339920
Robb Dern (CEO)
Rubin Hanan (COO)

PENNCOMP LLC
2050 N Loop W Ste 200, Houston, TX 77018
Tel.: (713) 669-0965
Web Site: http://www.penncomp.com
Year Founded: 1988
Sales Range: $1-9.9 Million
Emp.: 13
Computer & Network Integration
N.A.I.C.S.: 518210
Scott Young (Pres)

PENNDEL MENTAL HEALTH CENTER, INC.
2005 Cabot Blvd Ste 100, Langhorne, PA 19047
Tel.: (267) 587-2300   PA
Web Site: http://www.penndelmhc.org

PENNDEL MENTAL HEALTH CENTER, INC.   U.S. PRIVATE

Penndel Mental Health Center, Inc.—(Continued)
Year Founded: 1973
Sales Range: $10-24.9 Million
Emp.: 188
Mental Health Care Services
N.A.I.C.S.: 623220
Janice Noe *(Dir-Intellectual Disabilities Svcs)*
David Marsden *(Dir-Bus Dev & Tech)*
Karen Buher *(Dir-Child & Family Svcs)*
Karen Graff *(Exec Dir)*
Frank M. Smith *(VP)*
David A. Gruber *(Treas)*
Walter M. Gordon *(Pres)*
Kristen Peak *(Dir-Case Mgmt & Community Treatment Svcs)*
Bernard Solomon *(Dir-Fin)*
Elodie Witkowski *(Dir-Mental Health Outpatient Svcs)*
David Washington *(Dir-BCM, ACM & PATH Svcs)*

PENNFIELD CORPORATION
PO Box 4366, Lancaster, PA 17604-4366
Tel.: (717) 299-2561
Year Founded: 1919
Sales Range: $10-24.9 Million
Emp.: 300
Dairy Feeds & Meat Processing
N.A.I.C.S.: 112210
Jeff Schaum *(COO)*
Steve Isaacson *(Mgr-Dairy Profit)*

PENNFIELD PRECISION INCORPORATED
306 Keystone Dr PO Box 380, Sellersville, PA 18960
Tel.: (215) 257-5191
Rev: $20,000,000
Emp.: 100
Machine Shop, Jobbing & Repair
N.A.I.C.S.: 332216

PENNICHUCK CORPORATION
25 Manchester St, Merrimack, NH 03054
Tel.: (603) 882-5191   NH
Web Site: http://www.pennichuck.com
Year Founded: 1852
Sales Range: $25-49.9 Million
Emp.: 101
Water Utility Company
N.A.I.C.S.: 221310
Donald L. Ware *(COO)*
Larry D. Goodhue *(CEO, CFO & Treas)*
Carol Ann Howe *(Asst Treas)*
Suzanne Ansara *(Sec)*

Subsidiaries:

Pennichuck East Utility, Inc. (1)
25 Manchester St, Merrimack, NH 03054   (100%)
Tel.: (603) 882-5191
Web Site: http://www.pennichuck.com
Supplier of Water
N.A.I.C.S.: 221310

Pennichuck Water Service Corp. (1)
25 Manchester St, Merrimack, NH 03054   (100%)
Tel.: (603) 882-5191
Web Site: http://www.pennichuck.com
Provider of Laboratory Testing, Monitoring & Consulting Services for Water Utilities
N.A.I.C.S.: 221310

Pennichuck Water Works, Inc. (1)
25 Manchester St, Merrimack, NH 03060-3313   (100%)
Web Site: http://www.pennichuck.com
Emp.: 100
Owner & Operator of Community Water Systems
N.A.I.C.S.: 221310
Bonalyn J. Hartley *(VP-Admin)*

Pittsfield Aqueduct Company Inc. (1)
25 Manchester St, Merrimack, NH 03054   (100%)
Tel.: (603) 882-5191
Web Site: http://www.pennichuck.com
Sales Range: $10-24.9 Million
Emp.: 5
Supplier of Water
N.A.I.C.S.: 221310
Stephen J. Densberger *(Pres)*

Southwood Corporation (1)
25 Manchester St, Merrimack, NH 03054   (100%)
Tel.: (603) 882-5191
Web Site: http://www.pennichuck.com
Developer of Commercial & Residential Real Estate
N.A.I.C.S.: 237210
Scarlet Powell *(Sr VP-Bus Dev)*
Jefferson Ellington *(CFO)*
Charles Smith *(Dir-Design)*

PENNINGTONS INC.
911 River Dr S, Great Falls, MT 59405
Tel.: (406) 452-8200
Sales Range: $10-24.9 Million
Emp.: 30
Tobacco & Tobacco Products
N.A.I.C.S.: 424940
Michael Parker *(Pres)*

PENNOCK COMPANY
7135 Colonial Ln, Pennsauken, NJ 08109
Tel.: (215) 492-7900   PA
Web Site: https://www.pennock.com
Year Founded: 1882
Sales Range: $200-249.9 Million
Emp.: 600
Flowers & Related Supplies Whslr
N.A.I.C.S.: 424930
Robert P. Billings *(Pres & CEO)*
Tomas Logue *(VP)*

PENNONI ASSOCIATES INC.
1900 Market St Ste 300, Philadelphia, PA 19103
Tel.: (215) 222-3000
Web Site: http://www.pennoni.com
Year Founded: 1966
Sales Range: $75-99.9 Million
Emp.: 22,000
Engineering & Consulting Services
N.A.I.C.S.: 541330
Andrew Irwin *(Office Dir)*
Peter J. Coote *(Gen Counsel, Sec & VP)*
David A. DeLizza *(Pres & CEO)*
Khaled R. Hassan *(Assoc VP & Dir-King of Prussia Office)*
Joeseph Viscuso *(Sr VP & Dir-Strategic Growth-West Chester)*
David Steigler *(Assoc VP-Dulles)*
John P. Skorupan *(Assoc VP & Dir-Pittsburgh)*
Brian S. Hart *(Office Dir & Mgr-Construction Svcs Div)*
Nathan M. Cline *(Assoc VP & Dir-West Chester)*
Stacey M. McPeak *(CFO, Treas & VP)*
Thomas Davis Rust *(Vice Chm)*
Nelson J. Shaffer *(Exec VP)*
Markus Weidner *(Chief Innovation Officer & Assoc VP)*
Daniel S. DiMucci *(Sr VP)*
Michael McCarthy *(VP)*

Subsidiaries:

Irwin Engineers Inc. (1)
33 W Central St, Natick, MA 01760
Tel.: (508) 653-8007
Web Site: http://www.irwinengineers.com
Rev: $1,264,000
Emp.: 8
Engineering Services
N.A.I.C.S.: 541330

Andrew Irwin *(Pres)*
Lana Carlsson Irwin *(VP-Ops & Bus Dev)*

Jones-Stuckey Ltd., Inc. (1)
5202 Bethel Reed Park Ste 200, Columbus, OH 43220
Tel.: (614) 486-0401
Web Site: http://www.pennoni.com
Sales Range: $1-9.9 Million
Emp.: 17
Civil Engineering Services
N.A.I.C.S.: 541330
David W. Jones *(Pres)*

Mills & Associates, Inc. (1)
3242 Henderson Blvd, Tampa, FL 33609
Tel.: (813) 876-5869
Web Site: http://www.millsandassoc.com
Sales Range: $1-9.9 Million
Emp.: 12
Engineeering Services
N.A.I.C.S.: 541330
Jean Mills *(Sec)*

Pennoni Associates Inc. - New York (1)
460 West 34th St, New York, NY 10001
Tel.: (212) 239-7600
Web Site: http://www.pennoni.com
Sales Range: $1-9.9 Million
Emp.: 25
Engineeering Services
N.A.I.C.S.: 541330
Andrew J. Pennoni *(Reg VP)*
Anthony S. Bartolomeo *(Pres & CEO)*
Daniel S. DiMucci *(Sr VP)*
David Pennoni *(Reg VP)*
Edward P. Guetens *(VP & Dir-Haddon Heights Office)*
Edward P. Pluciennik *(Sr VP)*
Glenn O. McAllister *(VP-Philadelphia)*
Nelson J. Shaffer *(Chief Admin Officer & Exec VP)*
Peter J. Coote *(Gen Counsel, Sec & VP-Philadelphia)*
Stacey M. McPeak *(CFO, Treas & VP-Philadelphia)*
Ronald C. Moore *(Reg VP & Dir-Office-Baltimore & Columbia)*
Susan S. Wolford *(Reg VP-Dulles)*
Todd Hay *(Reg VP)*
Jerry Prevete *(Assoc VP)*
William H. Allen *(VP-Bus Dev)*
Frank H. Donaldson *(Assoc VP)*
Philip Horsey *(Assoc VP & Mgr-Transportation)*
James A. Ruff *(Assoc VP)*
Edward J. Sander *(VP)*
Cecil Whitlock *(Assoc VP)*

PENNSPRING CAPITAL, LLC
1390 Columbia Ave, St 245, Lancaster, PA 17603
Tel.: (973) 985-1539   PA
Web Site: http://www.pennspring.com
Venture Capital & Private Equity Firrm
N.A.I.C.S.: 523999
Lou Castelli *(Mng Partner)*

Subsidiaries:

Burch Materials Co., Inc. (1)
380 Lapp Road, Malvern , PA 19355
Tel.: (610) 640-4877
Web Site: https://burchmaterials.com
Rev: $10,000,000
Emp.: 14
Construction & Mining, except Oil Well, Machinery & Equipment Merchant Whslr
N.A.I.C.S.: 423810

Swing Kingdom LLC (1)
36 Glenbrook Rd, Leola, PA 17540-1301
Tel.: (717) 656-4449
Web Site: http://www.swingkingdom.com
Vinyl Playground Equipment Mfr
N.A.I.C.S.: 339920

PENNSYLVANIA BALLET
1819 JFK Blvd Ste 210, Philadelphia, PA 19103
Tel.: (215) 551-7000   PA
Web Site: http://www.paballet.org
Year Founded: 1964
Sales Range: $10-24.9 Million
Emp.: 247

Ballet Dance Promotion Services
N.A.I.C.S.: 711120
Georgiana Noll *(VP)*
Anthony B. Haller *(VP)*
David A. Pierson *(VP)*
David Hoffman *(Chm)*
Angel Corella *(Dir-Artistic)*
Danthu Phan *(Sec)*
Deborah Gill Hilzinger *(Vice Chm)*
Janet Averill *(VP)*
Jay L. Goldberg *(VP)*
Penny Fox *(VP)*
Robert M. Dever *(Treas)*
Shelly Power *(Exec Dir)*

PENNSYLVANIA BAR INSTITUTE
5080 Ritter Rd, Mechanicsburg, PA 17055-6903
Tel.: (717) 796-0804   PA
Web Site: http://www.pbi.org
Year Founded: 1965
Sales Range: $10-24.9 Million
Emp.: 142
Law firm
N.A.I.C.S.: 541199
Richard L. McCoy *(Exec Dir)*
Emily Barnes *(Program Mgr)*
John B. Hanawalt *(Dir-Fin & Admin)*
Dennis A. Whitaker *(Treas)*
Gail P. Granoff *(Sec)*
Seth A. Mendelsohn *(VP)*
Anita Jones *(Program Mgr)*
Barbara Thornton *(Program Mgr)*
Scott Young *(Program Mgr)*
Beverly Hendry *(Program Mgr)*
Sabina McCarthy *(Program Mgr)*
Stacey Thomas *(Program Mgr)*
Bonnie B. Leadbetter *(VP)*

PENNSYLVANIA COMPENSATION RATING BUREAU
30 S 17th St United Plaza Bldg Ste 1500, Philadelphia, PA 19103-4007
Tel.: (215) 568-2371   PA
Web Site: http://www.dcrb.com
Year Founded: 1915
Sales Range: $1-9.9 Million
Emp.: 120
Worker Compensation Insurance Assistance Services
N.A.I.C.S.: 525190
Andrey Lapchenko *(Mgr-LAN)*
Dave Rawson *(Dir-Technical-Class & Field Ops)*
Prakash Krishnappa *(Mgr-Web Projects)*

PENNSYLVANIA GENERAL ENERGY
120 Market St, Warren, PA 16365
Tel.: (814) 723-3230
Web Site: http://www.penngeneralenergy.com
Sales Range: $25-49.9 Million
Emp.: 125
Crude Petroleum Production
N.A.I.C.S.: 211120
Karen Thomas *(VP-HR)*
Nick Polito *(Engr)*

PENNSYLVANIA LIBRARY ASSOCIATION.
220 Cumberland Pkwy, Mechanicsburg, PA 17055
Tel.: (717) 766-7663   PA
Web Site: http://www.palibraries.org
Year Founded: 1901
Sales Range: $1-9.9 Million
Emp.: 3
Library Association
N.A.I.C.S.: 519210
Paula Gilbert *(Pres)*
Janis Stubbs *(VP)*
Barb Zaborowski *(VP)*

Charity Leonette (VP)
David Schappert (Treas)
Chris Buker (Exec Dir)

PENNSYLVANIA MACARONI COMPANY
2010-12 Penn Ave, Pittsburgh, PA 15222
Tel.: (412) 471-8330   PA
Web Site: http://www.pennmac.com
Year Founded: 1902
Sales Range: $10-24.9 Million
Emp.: 90
Provider of Imported Foods
N.A.I.C.S.: 424410
David Sunseri (Pres)

PENNSYLVANIA NATIONAL MUTUAL CASUALTY INSURANCE COMPANY
2 N 2nd St, Harrisburg, PA 17101-1619
Tel.: (717) 234-4941   PA
Web Site:
  http://www.pennnationalinsurance.com
Year Founded: 1919
Sales Range: $500-549.9 Million
Emp.: 2,388
Property & Casualty Insurance Services
N.A.I.C.S.: 524126
Stephen L. Swanson (Chm)
Christopher D. Markley (VP-Corp Comm)
Karen C. Yarrish (Gen Counsel, Sec & Sr VP)
Robert B. Brandon (Pres & CEO)
Jacquelyn Anderson (CFO, Treas & Sr VP)

Subsidiaries:

Inservco Insurance Services, Inc.   (1)
2 N 2nd St, Harrisburg, PA 17101-1619   (100%)
Tel.: (717) 230-8300
Web Site: http://www.inservco.net
Sales Range: $100-124.9 Million
Emp.: 500
Self Insurance Services
N.A.I.C.S.: 524210

Penn National Holding Corp.   (1)
2 N 2nd St, Harrisburg, PA 17101-1619
Tel.: (717) 234-4941
Web Site:
  http://www.pennnationalinsurance.com
Sales Range: $75-99.9 Million
Emp.: 700
Holding Company
N.A.I.C.S.: 551112
Bob Brandon (VP-Underwriting Ops)

Subsidiary (Domestic):

Penn National Security Insurance Company   (2)
2 N 2nd St, Harrisburg, PA 17101-1619
Tel.: (717) 234-4941
Web Site:
  http://www.pennnationalinsurance.com
Fire, Marine & Casualty Insurance Services
N.A.I.C.S.: 524126

PENNSYLVANIA PROFESSIONAL LIABILITY JOINT UNDERWRITING ASSOCIATION
1777 Sentry Pkwy W VEVA 14 Ste 300, Blue Bell, PA 19422
Tel.: (610) 828-8890   PA
Web Site: http://www.pajua.com
Year Founded: 1976
Sales Range: $1-9.9 Million
Emp.: 5
Insurance Association
N.A.I.C.S.: 813910
Larry S. Roberts (Sec)
Martin Ciccocioppo (Treas)
Susan M. Sersha (Pres)

PENNSYLVANIA PROPERTY AND CASUALTY INSURANCE GUARANTY ASSOCIATION
1617 John F Kennedy Blvd Ste 1850, Philadelphia, PA 19103
Tel.: (215) 568-1007   PA
Web Site: http://www.ppciga.org
Year Founded: 1970
Sales Range: $1-9.9 Million
Emp.: 12
Insurance Association
N.A.I.C.S.: 813910
Stephen F. Perrone (Exec Dir)
Patricia L. Ettore (Mgr-Acctg)
Raymond M. Bauso (Mgr-Claim)

PENNSYLVANIA PSYCHIATRIC INSTITUTE
2501 N 3rd St, Harrisburg, PA 17110
Tel.: (717) 782-6420   PA
Web Site: http://www.ppimhs.org
Year Founded: 2008
Sales Range: $25-49.9 Million
Emp.: 344
Behavioral Healthcare Services
N.A.I.C.S.: 623220
Ruth S. Moore (Dir-Bus Dev)
David Zug (Dir-Informatics)
Theresa Terry-Williams (Chief Nursing Officer)
Wanda Geesey (Dir-HR)
Elisabeth J. Kunkel (Chief Medical Officer)
William Daly (CEO)

PENNSYLVANIA RESOURCES CORP.
400 Keystone Industrial Park Ste 155, Dunmore, PA 18512
Web Site: http://www.pa-resources.com
Rev.: $15,000,000
Emp.: 155
Single-Family Housing Construction
N.A.I.C.S.: 236115

PENNSYLVANIA STATE EMPLOYEES CREDIT UNION
1 Credit Union Pl, Harrisburg, PA 17110
Tel.: (717) 234-8484
Web Site: http://www.psecu.com
Year Founded: 1933
Rev.: $150,589,000
Emp.: 400
State Credit Union Services
N.A.I.C.S.: 522130
Joseph Sassano (Chm)
Joseph A. Lawruk (CEO)
Frank J. Breiner (Sec)
George J. West (Treas)
Jodi Lynne Blanch (Vice Chm)
George Rudolph (Pres)

PENNSYLVANIA STEEL COMPANY, INC
1717 Woodhaven Dr, Bensalem, PA 19020
Tel.: (215) 633-9600
Web Site: http://www.pasteel.com
Year Founded: 1972
Sales Range: $10-24.9 Million
Emp.: 50
Aluminum Bars, Rods, Ingots, Sheets, Pipes, Plates
N.A.I.C.S.: 423510
Joseph M. Dombrowski (Chm & CEO)
Barry Walsh (Pres & COO)
Dan McMullan (VP & Gen Mgr)
Joann Adelsberger (CFO)
Lee M. Kushman (VP & Gen Mgr)
Tony Luongo (Gen Mgr)
John Wolf (Gen Mgr)
Michael Loveland (Gen Mgr)
Stan Millard (Gen Mgr)

Subsidiaries:

Pennsylvania Steel Company - Allentown Division   (1)
1139 Lehigh Ave, Whitehall, PA 18052
Tel.: (610) 432-4541
Web Site: http://www.pasteel.com
Fabricated Structural Metal Mfr
N.A.I.C.S.: 332312

Pennsylvania Steel Company - Connecticut Division   (1)
322 Great Hill Rd, Naugatuck, CT 06770
Tel.: (203) 729-2900
Fabricated Structural Metal Mfr
N.A.I.C.S.: 332312

Pennsylvania Steel Company - Long Island Division   (1)
999 S Oyster Bay Rd Bldg Ste 308, Bethpage, NY 11714
Tel.: (516) 597-5028
Web Site: http://www.pasteel.com
Emp.: 20
Fabricated Structural Metal Mfr
N.A.I.C.S.: 332312

Pennsylvania Steel Company - Richmond Division   (1)
11111 Leadbetter Rd, Ashland, VA 23005
Tel.: (877) 897-2458
Fabricated Structural Metal Mfr
N.A.I.C.S.: 332312

Pennsylvania Steel Company, Lucas Steel Division   (1)
3317 Board Rd, York, PA 17405
Tel.: (717) 767-1066
Web Site: http://www.pasteel.com
Aluminum Bars, Rods, Ingots, Sheets, Pipes, Plates
N.A.I.C.S.: 423510
Lee Kushman (Gen Mgr)

Stark Metal Sales, Inc.   (1)
432 Keystone St, Alliance, OH 44601-1722
Tel.: (330) 823-7383
Web Site: http://www.starkmetal.com
Sales Range: $1-9.9 Million
Emp.: 35
Metal Whslr
N.A.I.C.S.: 423510
Arthur J. Reiber (Pres)
Carole Pennington (Office Mgr)
David B. Rownd (VP)

PENNSYLVANIA TOOL SALES & SERVICE
625 Bev Rd, Youngstown, OH 44512
Tel.: (330) 758-9285
Web Site:
  http://www.penntoolsalesandservice.com
Sales Range: $25-49.9 Million
Emp.: 135
Industrial Tools Distributors
N.A.I.C.S.: 423840
Dennis McMahon (Pres)
Andrew Gentsy (Controller)

PENNSYLVANIA TRUCK CENTERS, INC.
66 Keller Ave, Lancaster, PA 17601
Tel.: (717) 393-3633   PA
Web Site: http://www.patruckctrs.com
Year Founded: 1940
Rev.: $26,600,000
Emp.: 135
Used Trucks & Tractors Sales
N.A.I.C.S.: 441110
Rick Riddle (Mgr-Machine Shop)

PENNSYLVANIA TURNPIKE COMMISSION
700 S Eisenhower Blvd, Middletown, PA 17057
Tel.: (717) 939-9551
Web Site: http://www.paturnpike.com
Sales Range: $350-399.9 Million
Emp.: 2,500
Toll Road Operation
N.A.I.C.S.: 926120

William J. Capone (Dir-Commission Comm)
Nick Gribfhaber (CFO)
Mark P. Compton (CEO)
Leslie S. Richards (Chm)
William K. Lieberman (Vice Chm)
Barry Drew (Treas & Sec)

PENNY AUCTION SOLUTIONS, INC.
330 A St Ste 156, San Diego, CA 92101
Tel.: (866) 275-5260   NV
Web Site:
  http://www.pennyauctionsolutions.com
Year Founded: 2010
Online Auction Services
N.A.I.C.S.: 449210
Micheal Holt (CEO)
Bob van Leyen (CFO)

PENNY NEWMAN GRAIN COMPANY
2691 S Cedar Ave, Fresno, CA 93725-2032
Tel.: (559) 448-8800
Web Site: http://www.penny-newman.com
Year Founded: 1878
Sales Range: $50-74.9 Million
Emp.: 50
Nursery & Garden Centers
N.A.I.C.S.: 424510
Jeff Barnes (VP-HR & IT)
Lisa Young-Brady (Coord-Logistics)
Ly Sy (Coord-Wheat)
James Netto (VP-Production)
Marsha Waller (Mgr-HR)
Scott Malony (Mgr-Rail Logistics)
Thelma Alexander (Mgr-Transportation & Logistics)

PENNY PLATE, INC.
14000 Horizon Way, Mount Laurel, NJ 08054
Tel.: (856) 429-7583   NJ
Web Site: http://www.pennyplate.com
Sales Range: $75-99.9 Million
Emp.: 100
Aluminum Containers Mfr
N.A.I.C.S.: 332431
Paul Cobb (Pres & Gen Mgr)
George Buff III (CEO)

PENNY PUBLICATIONS, LLC
6 Prowitt St, Norwalk, CT 06855
Tel.: (203) 866-6688
Web Site:
  http://www.pennypublications.com
Year Founded: 1996
Sales Range: $10-24.9 Million
Emp.: 150
Periodical Publishers
N.A.I.C.S.: 513120
Sue Haven (Mgr-HR)
Donna Louis (Asst Controller)
Gordon Detlor (Engr-Software)

Subsidiaries:

Asimov's Science Fiction Magazine   (1)
44 Wall St Ste 904, New York, NY 10005
Tel.: (212) 686-7188
Web Site: http://www.asimovs.com
Science Fiction Magazine
N.A.I.C.S.: 513120
Peter Kanter (Publr)
Bruce W. Sherbow (Sr VP-Sls & Mktg)
Sheila Williams (Editor)
Victoria Green (Dir-Art)
Abigail Browning (Mgr-Subsidiary Rights & Mktg)
Christine Begley (VP-Editorial & Product Dev)
Susan Mangan (VP-Design & Production)
Terrie Poly (Mgr-Digital Publ)
Laura Tulley (Sr Mgr-Production)

PENNY'S CONCRETE INC.

PENNY'S CONCRETE INC.

Penny's Concrete Inc.—(Continued)
23400 W 82nd St, Shawnee Mission, KS 66227
Tel.: (913) 441-8781
Web Site: http://www.pennysconcrete.com
Rev.: $27,500,000
Emp.: 5
Ready Mixed Concrete
N.A.I.C.S.: 327320
William J. Penny (Chm)
Chet Kueffer (Coord-Estimating)
Melanie Lorenzo (Dir-Aggregate Ops)
Cory Claxton (Dir-Ready Mix Ops & Safety)

PENNY/OHLMANN/NEIMAN, INC.

1605 N Main St, Dayton, OH 45405-4141
Tel.: (937) 278-0681   OH
Web Site: http://www.ponweb.com
Year Founded: 1949
Rev.: $27,000,000
Emp.: 20
Advetising Agency
N.A.I.C.S.: 541810
Walter Ohlmann (Pres & CEO)
Linda Kahn (Sr Acct Mgr)
Lori Ohlmann (Sr VP-Acct Svcs)
Cindy Zwayer (Production Dir)
Gary Haschart (Dir-Art)
Andy Kittles (Mgr-Graphics)
David Bowman (Chief Mktg Strategist)
Kim Gros (Controller)
Jason Hart (Dir-Art)

PENNYRILE FORD

5505 Ft Campbell Blvd, Hopkinsville, KY 42240
Tel.: (270) 886-8131
Web Site: http://www.pennyrileford.com
Sales Range: $10-24.9 Million
Emp.: 20
Car Dealership
N.A.I.C.S.: 441110
Clay Smith (Pres)
Dan Gardner (Mgr-Sls)

PENNYRILE RURAL ELECTRIC COOPERATIVE CORPORATION

2000 Harrison St, Hopkinsville, KY 42240-3678
Tel.: (270) 886-2555   KY
Web Site: http://www.precc.com
Year Founded: 1937
Sales Range: $25-49.9 Million
Emp.: 150
Electrical Distribution
N.A.I.C.S.: 221122
Sandy Grogan (VP-Fin & Acctg)
John Wheeler (VP-Engrg)
Brent Gilkey (VP-Member Svcs & Comm)
Michelle Small (VP-HR & Benefits)
George D. Brown (Treas & Sec)
Bryson Price (Chm)
James Futrell (Vice Chm)

PENNYROYAL REGIONAL MENTAL HEALTH, MENTAL RETARDATION BOARD, INC.

735 N Dr, Hopkinsville, KY 42240
Tel.: (270) 886-5163   KY
Web Site: http://www.pennyroyalcenter.org
Year Founded: 1967
Mental Health Services
N.A.I.C.S.: 621420
Billy Duvall (Treas)
Bonnie Lynch (Chm)
John Rufli (Vice Chm)

Linda Linda Browder (Sec)
Eric Embry (CEO & Exec Dir)
Beau Roberts (CFO)

Subsidiaries:

LifeSkills, Inc.   (1)
380 Suwannee Trail St, Bowling Green, KY 42103
Tel.: (270) 901-5000
Web Site: http://www.lifeskills.com
Intellectual & Developmental Disability Assistance Services
N.A.I.C.S.: 623210
Alice Simpson (Co-Pres & Co-CEO)
Brian Barczak (Co-Pres & Co-CEO)
Joe Dan Beavers (VP-Fin)

PENNYWORTH HOMES INCORPORATED

679 Blackshear Dr, Thomasville, GA 31792
Tel.: (229) 225-1730
Web Site: http://www.pennyworthhomes.com
Rev.: $11,400,000
Emp.: 15
New Construction, Single-Family Houses
N.A.I.C.S.: 236115
Ebe Walter (Pres)

PENOBSCOT MCCRUM LLC

28 Pierce St, Belfast, ME 04915-6648
Tel.: (207) 338-4360   ME
Web Site: http://www.penobscotmccrum.com
Year Founded: 1948
Sales Range: $100-124.9 Million
Emp.: 210
Frozen Potato Skins, Baked Stuffed Potatoes & other Frozen Potato Products
N.A.I.C.S.: 311412

PENOBSCOT RIVER RESTORATION TRUST

PO Box 5695, Augusta, ME 04332
Tel.: (207) 430-0175   ME
Web Site: http://www.penobscotriver.org
Year Founded: 2004
Sales Range: $10-24.9 Million
Emp.: 7
River Restoration Services
N.A.I.C.S.: 813312
Cheryl Gerrior (Dir-Fin)
Laura Rose Day (Exec Dir)

PENS N MORE

7734 W 99th St, Hickory Hills, IL 60457
Tel.: (888) 453-3058
Web Site: http://www.pensnmore.com
Year Founded: 2006
Sales Range: $1-9.9 Million
Emp.: 30
Discount Office Products Supplier Specializing in Hard-to-Find Writing Instruments & Discontinued Products
N.A.I.C.S.: 459410
Ryan Thornton (Pres)
Nicholas Thornton (Principal & VP)

PENSACOLA READY MIX, LLC

3008 S Hwy 95A, Cantonment, FL 32533-5800
Tel.: (850) 477-2899
Web Site: http://www.readymixusa.com
Year Founded: 1982
Sales Range: $10-24.9 Million
Emp.: 95
Readymix Concrete Mfr
N.A.I.C.S.: 327320
Bobby Linsey (Gen Mgr)

PENSAM CAPITAL, LLC

777 Brickell Ave Ste 1200, Miami, FL 33131
Tel.: (786) 539-4999
Web Site: http://www.pensamcapital.com
Year Founded: 2009
Rev.: $300,000,000
Emp.: 16
Multifamily Housing Investment & Management Services
N.A.I.C.S.: 531390
Michael Stein (Founder & Partner)
Joe Ackerman (Founder & Partner)
Gavin Beekman (Founder & Partner)
Nisha Bhatia (Gen Counsel)
Joseph Brennan (Dir-Capital Markets)
Alex Chediak (Dir-Ops)
Dominic Rechichi (Dir-Asset Mgmt)
Eddie Reiner (Assoc Dir-Asset Mgmt)
Meggan Shaw-Butler (Sr Mgr-Assets)
Hen Shoval (Dir-Acq)
Agustin DeGoytisolo (Accountant)
Alejandro Muelle (Controller-Fin & Mgr-HR)
Javier Herrera (Dir-Bus Dev)
Victoria Griggs (Coord-Design & Project Mgr)

PENSAR DEVELOPMENT INC

900 E Pine St Ste 201, Seattle, WA 98109
Tel.: (206) 284-3134
Web Site: http://www.pensardevelopment.com
Sales Range: $1-9.9 Million
Emp.: 23
Engineeering Services
N.A.I.C.S.: 541330
Clint Schneider (Founder)

PENSERRA SECURITIES LLC

4 Orinda Way, Orinda, CA 94563
Tel.: (800) 456-8850
Web Site: http://www.penserra.com
Year Founded: 2007
Securities Brokerage
N.A.I.C.S.: 523150
George Madrigal (Founder & CEO)
Anthony Castelli (Chief Compliance Officer & COO)
Connie Kreutzer (Mng Dir & Head-Institutional Sls)
Jason M. Valdez (Head-Equity Trading)
Zlatko Martinic (Mng Dir & Head-Transition Mgmt)
Dustin Lewellyn (CIO-Penserra Capital Mgmt)
John Pascente (Mng Dir & Head-Investment Banking Div)
George A. Schmilinsky (Mng Dir & Head-Res Svcs)
Ryan Peterson (Mng Dir & Gen Counsel-Wholesale Trading)

PENSKE BUICK-GMC TRUCKS, INC.

100 S Museum Rd, Shillington, PA 19607
Tel.: (610) 370-6699   PA
Web Site: http://www.penskebuickgmc.com
Sales Range: $10-24.9 Million
Emp.: 60
New & Used Car Dealer
N.A.I.C.S.: 441110
Geoffrey C. Penske (Owner & Pres)
Victor Popescu (Gen Mgr-Sls)
Brad Swavely (Mgr-Parts)
Charlie Weaver (Mgr-Svc)

PENSKE CORPORATION

2555 Telegraph Rd, Bloomfield Hills, MI 48302
Tel.: (248) 648-2000   DE

U.S. PRIVATE

Web Site: http://www.penske.com
Sales Range: $75-99.9 Million
Emp.: 120
Holding Company; Truck Leasing & Auto Dealerships
N.A.I.C.S.: 532120
Roger S. Penske (Founder, Chm & CEO)
Walter P. Czarnecki (Exec VP)
Robert H. Kurnick Jr. (Vice Chm)
Gregory W. Penske (Vice Chm-Entertainment)

Subsidiaries:

DAVCO Technology, LLC   (1)
1600 Woodland Dr, Saline, MI 48176
Tel.: (734) 429-5665
Web Site: http://www.davco.com
Emp.: 100
Fuel Processor & Fluid Level Management Product Mfr
N.A.I.C.S.: 334519
Mark Bara (Pres)

Indianapolis Motor Speedway Corporation   (1)
4790 W 16th St, Indianapolis, IN 46222
Tel.: (317) 492-8500
Web Site: http://www.indianapolismotorspeedway.com
Holding Company; Motor Racetrack & Racing League Owner & Operator
N.A.I.C.S.: 551112

Division (Domestic):

Indianapolis Motor Speedway, LLC   (2)
4790 W 16th St, Indianapolis, IN 46222   (100%)
Tel.: (317) 492-6784
Web Site: http://www.indianapolismotorspeedway.com
Motor Racetrack Operator
N.A.I.C.S.: 711212
Dawn Dyer DeBellis (Dir-Creative Svcs)
Paul Riley (Mgr-Facilities)

Penske Logistics, LLC   (1)
Route 10 Green Hills, Reading, PA 19603   (100%)
Tel.: (610) 775-6000
Web Site: http://www.penskelogistics.com
Logistics, Transportation & Distribution Services
N.A.I.C.S.: 532120
Paul Ott (Sr VP-Fin)
Tom McKenna (Sr VP-Logistics Engrg & Tech)
Jeffrey Stoicheff (Sr VP-HR)
Angela Yang (Mng Dir-Asia Pacific Reg)
Dennis Abruzzi (Sr VP-Enterprise Solutions & Safety)
Joe Carlier (Sr VP-Sls-Global)
Jeffery A. Bullard (Sr VP-Ops-Central Reg)
Andy Moses (Sr VP-Products-Global)
Jeff Jackson (Pres)
Bill Scroggie (Sr VP-Ops-Intl)
Steve Beverly (Sr VP-Ops-Midwest Reg)
Paulo Sarti (Mng Dir-South America)
Brian Hard (Pres-Penske Transportation Solutions)

Subsidiary (Domestic):

Automotive Component Carrier LLC   (2)
675 Okland Ave, Pontiac, MI 48340-2459
Tel.: (248) 758-2150
Sales Range: $10-24.9 Million
Long Distance Trucking Services
N.A.I.C.S.: 484121

Transfreight, LLC   (2)
3940 Olympic Blvd, Erlanger, KY 41018
Tel.: (888) 890-0400
Web Site: http://www.transfreight.com
Third-Party Logistics Services
N.A.I.C.S.: 488510

Penske Racing, Inc.   (1)
200 Penske Way, Mooresville, NC 28115
Tel.: (704) 664-2300
Web Site: http://www.penskeracing.com
Emp.: 500
Race Car Operator
N.A.I.C.S.: 711219

COMPANIES

Travis Geisler *(Dir-Competition)*
Brian Campe *(Engr-Race & Vehicle Dynamics)*
Steve Reis *(Engr-Sprint Cup Car Vehicle Dynamics)*
Roy McCauley *(Mgr-Assembly Ops)*
Clive Howell *(Gen Mgr)*
Brian Wilson *(Engr-Race)*
Chris Yoder *(Coord-Logistics)*

Penske Truck Leasing Company, L.P. (1)
2675 Morgantown Rd, Reading, PA 19607
Tel.: (610) 775-6000
Web Site: http://www.pensketruckleasing.com
Commercial & Consumer Truck Leasing, Contract Maintenance & Rental Services
N.A.I.C.S.: 532120
Don Metcalf *(Dir-Product Mktg)*
Art Vallely *(Pres)*
Sherry Sanger *(Sr VP-Mktg)*
Michael Duff *(Chief Compliance Officer & Sr VP-Govt Rels)*

Subsidiary (Domestic):

Decarolis Truck Rental Inc. (2)
333 Colfax St, Rochester, NY 14606-3107
Tel.: (585) 254-1169
Web Site: http://www.decarolis.com
Sales Range: $400-449.9 Million
Emp.: 500
Truck Rental & Leasing
N.A.I.C.S.: 532120
Paul DeCarolis *(Chm)*
Mark Williams *(VP-Fin)*
Michael Margarone *(Pres)*

Subsidiary (Domestic):

Monroe School Transportation Inc. (3)
970 Emerson St, Rochester, NY 14606-2708 (100%)
Tel.: (585) 458-3230
Web Site: http://www.nellc.com
Sales Range: $25-49.9 Million
Emp.: 300
School Buses & Transportation
N.A.I.C.S.: 485410

Subsidiary (Domestic):

Kris-Way Truck Leasing Inc. (2)
43 Hemco Rd Ste 1, South Portland, ME 04106
Tel.: (207) 799-8593
Web Site: http://www.kris-way.com
Sales Range: $25-49.9 Million
Emp.: 150
Truck Leasing Services
N.A.I.C.S.: 532120
Thomas Keefer *(Pres)*
Evelyn Tonks *(CFO)*
Jim Ryan *(VP-Ops)*
Robert Coale *(VP-Sls)*

Division (Domestic):

Penske Truck Rental (2)
2675 Morgantown Rd, Reading, PA 19607
Tel.: (610) 775-6000
Web Site: http://www.pensketruckrental.com
Sales Range: $125-149.9 Million
Truck Rental Services
N.A.I.C.S.: 532120
Brian Hard *(Pres & CEO)*
Don Mikes *(Sr VP-Rental)*

Subsidiary (Domestic):

Star Truck Rentals Inc. (2)
3940 Eastern Ave SE, Grand Rapids, MI 49508
Tel.: (616) 243-7033
Web Site: http://www.starlease.com
Sales Range: $25-49.9 Million
Emp.: 130
Provider of Tranportation Services
N.A.I.C.S.: 532120
David Bylenga *(Exec VP)*
Brent Larson *(Mgr-Sls)*
Kyle Hillman *(Controller)*
Lonnie Vis *(Dir-Maintenance)*
Theresa Morris *(Mgr-Parts)*
Dave Donbrock *(Branch Mgr)*
Tom Bylenga *(Pres)*

PENSKE MEDIA CORPORATION
11175 Santa Monica Blvd Ste 900, Los Angeles, CA 90025
Tel.: (310) 321-5000 DE
Web Site: http://www.pmc.com
Year Founded: 2004
Online News & Lifestyle Periodical Publisher
N.A.I.C.S.: 513120
Jay Penske *(Chm & CEO)*
Gerry Byrne *(Vice Chm)*
George Grobar *(COO)*
Lauren Utecht *(VP-HR & Corp Comm)*
Ken DelAlcazar *(Sr VP-Fin)*
Gabriel Koen *(VP-Tech)*
Craig Perreault *(Chief Digital Officer)*
Christina Yeoh *(VP-Tech Ops)*
Todd Greene *(Gen Counsel & Exec VP-Bus Affairs)*
Brian Levine *(VP-Revenue Ops)*
Mark Howard *(Chief Adv & Partnerships Officer)*
Mike Monroe *(CMO)*
Rebecca Bienstock *(VP-Talent Rels)*
Brooke Jaffe *(Head-Pub Affairs & Comm)*
Rachel Terrace *(Sr VP-Licensing & Brand Dev)*

Subsidiaries:

Artforum International Magazine, Inc. (1)
350 Seventh Ave 19th Fl, New York, NY 10001
Tel.: (212) 475-4000
Web Site: http://www.artforum.com
Periodical Publishers
N.A.I.C.S.: 513120
John Johnson *(Founder)*
Tony Korner *(Publr)*

BGR Media, LLC (1)
11175 Santa Monica Blvd, Los Angeles, CA 90025
Tel.: (310) 321-5000
Web Site: http://www.bgr.com
Online Consumer Technology Periodical Publisher
N.A.I.C.S.: 513120
Jonathan S. Geller *(Pres)*
Zach Epstein *(Exec Editor)*

Deadline Business Media, LLC (1)
1175 Santa Monica Blvd Ste 900, Los Angeles, CA 90025
Tel.: (310) 321-5000
Web Site: http://www.deadline.com
Online Entertainment Business News Periodical Publisher
N.A.I.C.S.: 513120
Nellie Andreeva *(Editor-Television)*
David Lieberman *(Exec Editor)*
Peter Hammond *(Editor-Awards)*
Patrick Hipes *(Mng Editor)*
Nancy Tartaglione *(Editor-Intl)*
Anita Busch *(Editor-Film)*
Stacey Farishto *(Chief Revenue Officer & Gen Mgr)*

Unit (Domestic):

Footwear News (2)
750 3rd Ave, New York, NY 10017-8100
Tel.: (212) 630-4880
Web Site: http://www.footwearnews.com
Sales Range: $10-24.9 Million
Emp.: 120
Footwear Industry Trade Magazine Publisher
N.A.I.C.S.: 513120
Neil Weilheimer *(Exec Editor)*
Katie Abel *(Dir-Global News)*

Women's Wear Daily (2)
475 5th Ave 3rd Fl, New York, NY 10017-2703
Tel.: (212) 213-1900
Web Site: http://www.wwd.com
Sales Range: $10-24.9 Million
Emp.: 120
Fashion Magazine Publisher
N.A.I.C.S.: 513120

Paul Jowdy *(Chief Bus Officer & Publr-WWD & Fairchild Live)*
Jessica Iredale *(Sr Editor-Fashion Features)*
Miles Socha *(Editor-in-Chief)*

FashInvest, Ltd. (1)
1601 Concord Pike Ste 82-84, Wilmington, DE 19707
Tel.: (302) 777-1616
Web Site: http://www.fashinvest.com
Fashion Tech Related Services
N.A.I.C.S.: 518210

Hollywood Life Media, LLC (1)
11175 Santa Monica Blvd Ste 900, Los Angeles, CA 90025
Tel.: (310) 321-5000
Web Site: http://www.hollywoodlife.com
Emp.: 100
Online Entertainment Periodical Publisher
N.A.I.C.S.: 513120
Bonnie Fuller *(Pres & Editor-in-Chief)*
Michael Fanning *(Pres & Editor-in-Chief)*
Carolyn Davis *(Mng Editor)*

TVLine Media, LLC (1)
11175 St Monica Blvd, Los Angeles, CA 90025
Tel.: (310) 321-5000
Web Site: http://www.tvline.com
Online Entertainment Periodical Publisher
N.A.I.C.S.: 513120
Michael Ausiello *(Founder, Pres & Dir-Editorial)*
Matt Webb Mitovich *(Editor-in-Chief)*
Stacey Farish *(Chief Revenue Officer & Gen Mgr)*

Variety Media, LLC (1)
11175 Santa Monica Blvd, Los Angeles, CA 90025
Tel.: (323) 617-9100
Web Site: http://www.variety.com
Sales Range: $10-24.9 Million
Emp.: 120
Trade Journals Publisher & Information Services
N.A.I.C.S.: 513120
Michelle G. Sobrino-Stearns *(Chief Revenue Officer & Publr)*
Judi Pulver *(Dir-Music Adv)*
Henry Deas *(Dir-Markets & Festivals)*
Steven Gaydos *(VP)*
Dea Lawrence *(CMO)*
Carolyn Horwitz *(Mng Editor)*
Eric Legendre *(Co-Mng Dir-Intl Adv & Strategic Partnerships)*
Celine Rotterman *(Co-Mng Dir-Intl Adv & Strategic Partnerships)*
Alberto Lopez *(Dir-Intl)*
David S. Cohen *(Dir-Digital Features)*
Michelle Fine-Smith *(VP-Global Consumer Partnerships-New York)*
Jordan Moreau *(Editor-Online News)*
Ellise Shafer *(Assoc Editor-Web)*

Wenner Media LLC (1)
1290 Ave of the Americas, New York, NY 10104-0298 (51%)
Tel.: (212) 484-1616
Periodicals & Books Publisher
N.A.I.C.S.: 513120
Jann S. Wenner *(Dir-Editorial)*
Gus Wenner *(Pres & COO)*

Subsidiary (Domestic):

Men's Journal (2)
1290 Avenue of the Americas 2nd Fl, New York, NY 10104
Tel.: (212) 484-1616
Web Site: http://www.mensjournal.com
Publisher of Men's Magazine
N.A.I.C.S.: 513199

Rolling Stone Magazine (2)
1290 Ave Of The Americas 2nd Fl, New York, NY 10104
Tel.: (212) 484-1616
Web Site: http://www.rollingstone.com
Magazine Publisher
N.A.I.C.S.: 513120
Jason Fine *(Editor)*

PENSLER CAPITAL CORPORATION
132 Elm Rd, Princeton, NJ 08540
Tel.: (212) 481-6263 DE

Web Site: http://www.penslercapital.com
Year Founded: 1993
Sales Range: $10-24.9 Million
Emp.: 2
Investment Company
N.A.I.C.S.: 326211
Sanford Pensler *(Pres)*

Subsidiaries:

Korex Corporation (1)
50000 W Pontiac Trl, Wixom, MI 48393-2017
Tel.: (248) 624-0000
Web Site: http://www.korex-us.com
Sales Range: $10-24.9 Million
Mfr of Soap & Other Detergents
N.A.I.C.S.: 325611

ScholarsFirst LLC (1)
100 Park Ave 30th Fl, New York, NY 10017
Tel.: (212) 481-6273
Web Site: http://www.scholarsfirst.com
Educational Support Services611710
N.A.I.C.S.: 611710

PENTA INTERNATIONAL CORP.
50 Okner Pkwy, Livingston, NJ 07039-1604
Tel.: (973) 740-2300
Web Site: http://www.pentamfg.com
Year Founded: 1977
Mfr of Organic Chemicals, Medical Chemicals, Flavor Enhancers, Food Additives & Fragrance Chemicals
N.A.I.C.S.: 325199
Grace Calamito *(Pres & CEO)*

PENTAFOUR SOLUTIONS, LLC
265 Davidson Ave Ste 215, Somerset, NJ 08873
Tel.: (908) 782-8339 DE
Web Site: https://pentafours.com
Emp.: 100
Software Development Services
N.A.I.C.S.: 513210
Nag Karaka *(CEO)*

Subsidiaries:

Winterhawk Consulting LLC (1)
1643 Williamsburg Sq, Lakeland, FL 33803-4279
Tel.: (813) 731-9665
Web Site: http://www.winterhawkconsulting.com
Computer Related Services
N.A.I.C.S.: 541519
Kim Barnett *(Partner)*

PENTAGON FEDERAL CREDIT UNION
2930 Eisenhower Ave, Alexandria, VA 22314
Tel.: (703) 739-3600
Web Site: http://www.penfed.org
Year Founded: 1935
Rev.: $1,097,883,000
Assets: $24,484,751,000
Liabilities: $22,028,122,000
Net Worth: $2,456,629,000
Earnings: $156,028,000
Emp.: 2,164
Fiscal Year-end: 12/31/18
Credit Union
N.A.I.C.S.: 522130
James Raymond Schenck *(Pres & CEO)*
Lisa Jennings *(Sr Exec VP)*
Edward B. Cody *(Chm)*
Winston Wilkinson *(Pres-Mortgage & Exec VP)*
John Kelly *(Chief Admin Officer & Exec VP)*
Jamie Gayton *(Exec VP)*
Ricardo Chamorro *(Exec VP-Consumer Banking & Strategy)*
Shashi Vohra *(Pres-Affiliated Businesses & Sr Exec VP)*

PENTAGON FEDERAL CREDIT UNION

Pentagon Federal Credit Union—(Continued)
Jill Streit *(CFO & Exec VP)*
Scott Lind *(Gen Counsel & Exec VP)*
Joseph Thomas *(CIO & Exec VP)*
Tony Taveekanjana *(VP-Mortgage)*

Subsidiaries:

Pentagon Federal Credit Union
Foundation (1)
2930 Eisenhower Ave, Alexandria, VA 22314
Tel.: (703) 838-1200
Web Site:
http://www.pentagonfoundation.org
Military Grantmaking Foundation
N.A.I.C.S.: 813219
Mark Smith *(Dir-Programs)*
Christine Mahler *(Mgr-Dev)*
Elizabeth Chisolm *(Dir-Donor Engagement)*
Becky Gillespie *(Accountant)*
Douglas W. Webster *(Treas & Sec)*
Fred B. Caprio *(Vice Chm)*
Deborah Lee James *(Chm)*
John W. Nicholson Jr. *(Pres)*

PENTAGON FREIGHT SERVICES, INC.

1211 E Richey Rd, Houston, TX 77073
Tel.: (281) 209-8800
Web Site:
http://www.pentagonfreight.com
Rev.: $23,000,000
Emp.: 60
Provider of Freight Forwarding Services
N.A.I.C.S.: 488510
Les Watson *(Controller)*
Bertha Vincent *(Mgr-Quality Assurance)*
George Booth *(Sr VP)*
William Purvis *(VP)*

PENTAGRAM DESIGN, INC.

204 5th Ave, New York, NY 10010
Tel.: (212) 683-7000 NY
Web Site: http://www.pentagram.com
Year Founded: 1986
Sales Range: $1-9.9 Million
Emp.: 50
Graphic Design Services
N.A.I.C.S.: 541430
Jim Anderson *(Mgr)*
Sarah C. Dobson *(Coord-Partners)*

PENTASTAR AVIATION LLC

7310 Highland Rd, Waterford, MI 48327
Tel.: (248) 666-3630
Web Site:
http://www.pentastaraviation.com
Sales Range: $10-24.9 Million
Emp.: 180
Flying Charter Service
N.A.I.C.S.: 481219
Michael L. Baker *(VP-Safety & Compliance)*
Gary Roberts *(Dir-Quality Control & Assurance)*
Robert L. Sarazin *(VP-FBO Svcs)*
Patricia A. Zikakis *(VP-HR)*
Mark Schenkel *(Controller)*
Douglas Levangie *(VP-Maintenance Ops & Advisory Svcs)*
Brad Bruce *(Exec VP-Maintenance & Sls)*
Edsel B. Ford II *(Owner & Chm)*
Gregory J Schmidt Sr. *(Pres & CEO)*

PENTECH FINANCIAL SERVICES

240 E Hacienda Ave Ste 100, Campbell, CA 95008
Tel.: (408) 879-2200
Web Site:
http://www.pentechfinancial.com
Year Founded: 1978
Sales Range: $25-49.9 Million
Emp.: 12
Lease Financing Services
N.A.I.C.S.: 522220
Benjamin E. Millerbis *(Pres & CEO)*
Bruce Blanco *(CFO & Sr VP)*
Helga Stuart *(Coord-Funding)*

PENTEGRA RETIREMENT SERVICES

701 Westchester Ave Ste 320E, White Plains, NY 10604
Tel.: (914) 694-1300
Web Site: http://www.pentegra.com
Year Founded: 1943
Emp.: 260
Retirement Products & Services
N.A.I.C.S.: 523940
John Schafer *(VP)*
Pete Swisher *(Dir-West Coast)*
Sarah Coxe Lange *(Mng Dir)*
Scott Stone *(Chief Investment Officer & Sr VP)*
Kris Krikorian *(Dir-Qualified Plan Sls-Mission Viejo)*
Laura Grassi *(Reg Dir-Qualified Plan Sls)*
David Barrer *(Dir-Natl)*
Mark Hogan *(Dir-Midwest)*
Michael Wyant *(Dir-Midwest)*
Mary Read *(Dir-Qualified Plan Mktg-Natl)*
Wade Connor *(Dir-Southeast)*
Ken Jackson *(Dir-West)*
Colleen Zanicchi *(Sr VP-HR)*

Subsidiaries:

Pentegra Retirement Services (1)
3 Enterprise Dr Ste 105, Shelton, CT 06484-4694
Tel.: (203) 926-3000
Sales Range: $10-24.9 Million
Emp.: 80
Retirement Benefits & Financial Consulting Services
N.A.I.C.S.: 525110
Gwen Burroughs *(CMO & Sr VP)*

PENTRON CORPORATION

1717 W Collins Ave, Orange, CA 92867
Tel.: (714) 516-7557 DE
Web Site: http://www.pentron.com
Year Founded: 1967
Mfr of Dental Devices & Laboratory Products
N.A.I.C.S.: 339114

PENTUCKET BANK

1 Merrimack St, Haverhill, MA 01830
Tel.: (978) 372-7731 MA
Web Site:
http://www.pentucketbank.com
Year Founded: 1891
Sales Range: $25-49.9 Million
Emp.: 160
Banking Services
N.A.I.C.S.: 522180
David A. Bennett *(CFO, Treas & Sr VP)*
Kevin McKinnon *(Sr VP)*
Michael Milano *(VP)*

PENTWATER CABINETRY, INC.

920 N Lombard Rd, Lombard, IL 60101
Tel.: (630) 487-5811
Web Site:
http://www.pwcabinetry.com
Year Founded: 2014
Sales Range: $1-9.9 Million
Emp.: 18
Home Furnishing Distr
N.A.I.C.S.: 423220
Woon Lee *(Pres)*

PEONY GROVE ACQUISITION CORP

9454 Wilshire Blvd Ste 612, Los Angeles, CA 90212
Tel.: (310) 888-1870 DE
Year Founded: 2017
Investment Services
N.A.I.C.S.: 523999
James Cassidy *(Pres & Sec)*
James McKillop *(VP)*

PEOPLE CREATING SUCCESS, INC.

2225 Sprerry Dr Ste 1500, Ventura, CA 93003
Tel.: (805) 644-9480 CA
Web Site: http://www.pcs-services.org
Year Founded: 2002
Sales Range: $1-9.9 Million
Emp.: 361
Nursing & Personal Care Services
N.A.I.C.S.: 623311
Jason E. Romero *(Pres & CEO)*
Felicia Esperanza Rueff *(Coord-Fade)*
Jeremy Huffman *(Mgr-Acctg)*

PEOPLE FIRST BANCSHARES, INC.

200 S Locust St, Pana, IL 62557 DE
Web Site: http://www.bankpbt.com
Year Founded: 1983
Sales Range: $10-24.9 Million
Emp.: 93
Bank Holding Company
N.A.I.C.S.: 551111

Subsidiaries:

Peoples Bank & Trust (1)
200 S Locust St, Pana, IL 62557
Web Site: http://www.bankpbt.com
Sales Range: $10-24.9 Million
Commericial Banking
N.A.I.C.S.: 522110
John Gardner *(Pres & CEO)*
Craig Deere *(CFO)*
Jim Adcock *(Officer-Loan & Sr VP)*
Carol Furnish *(VP & Mgr-Credit Admin)*
Cindy Whittemore *(Officer-Credit Admin & VP)*
Yvonne Endris *(Asst VP-Ops)*
Karen Kerr *(VP-Fin)*
Carol Schneider *(Asst VP-Credit Ops Acctg)*
Maggie Zahradka *(VP-Ops)*
Jennifer Nagle *(VP-Consumer Banking)*
Joani Jones *(Officer-Consumer Banking)*
Jennifer Mathis *(Officer-Consumer Banking)*
Susan Palliser *(Officer-Consumer Banking)*
Kacie Rankin *(Officer-Consumer Banking)*
Michael M. Trexler *(Chm)*

PEOPLE INC.

1219 N Forest Rd, Williamsville, NY 14221
Tel.: (716) 634-8132
Web Site: http://www.people-inc.org
Year Founded: 1970
Sales Range: $100-124.9 Million
Emp.: 2,400
Services for Developmentally Disabled, Seniors & Their Families; Non-Profit Agency
N.A.I.C.S.: 623311
Rhonda Frederick *(Pres & CEO)*
Bonnie Sloma *(Sr VP)*
Dennis Schrader *(Dir-Mktg & Comm)*
Anne Stone *(CFO)*
Anna Korus *(Sr VP)*
Concetta Ferguson *(Sr VP)*
Mary Beth Iwanski *(Sr VP)*
Denise M. Bienko *(VP)*

PEOPLE INC.

3011 Sutton Gate Dr Ste 140, Suwanee, GA 30024
Tel.: (770) 623-9143
Web Site: http://www.peoplehro.com

U.S. PRIVATE

Sales Range: $150-199.9 Million
Emp.: 15,960
Human Resources & Professional Employer Organization
N.A.I.C.S.: 561330
John W. Hardin *(Owner & CEO)*
Jacob Hardin *(Pres)*

Subsidiaries:

SCI Companies (1)
1420 Kensington Rd 203 Ste 114, Oak Brook, IL 60523-2195
Tel.: (630) 928-4700
Web Site: http://www.peocentral.com
Sales Range: $25-49.9 Million
Emp.: 70
Employee Leasing Services
N.A.I.C.S.: 561330
Daniel Opferman *(Exec VP-Ops)*

PEOPLE OF COLOR NETWORK, INC.

4520 N Central Ave Ste 565, Phoenix, AZ 85012
Tel.: (602) 253-3084 AZ
Web Site: http://www.pcnhealth.com
Year Founded: 2000
Sales Range: $25-49.9 Million
Emp.: 245
Community Health Care Services
N.A.I.C.S.: 621498
Penny Visser *(CFO & Dir-IT)*
Annette White *(Mgr-Bus Dev, Contracts & Mktg)*
Bea Salazar *(Dir-Children's Svcs, Diversity & Learning Center of Excellence)*
Tomas Leon *(Pres & CEO)*
Ramiro Guillen *(Chief Medical Officer)*
Diana Yazzie Devine *(Sec)*
Dora Jackson *(Chm)*
Laura Larson-Huffaker *(Treas)*
Laurie Pierce *(Mgr-Grants & Dev)*
Mark Mazon *(Vice Chm)*

PEOPLE PREMIER, INC.

13600 Alcot Blvd, Clearwater, FL 33760
Tel.: (727) 561-9700
Web Site:
http://www.peoplepremier.com
Sales Range: $1-9.9 Million
Emp.: 7
Professional Employer Organizations
N.A.I.C.S.: 561330
Dale F. Schmidt *(CEO)*

PEOPLE'S COMMUNITY BANK

Hwy 67 & Sycamore St, Greenville, MO 63944
Tel.: (573) 224-3267
Web Site:
http://www.peoplescommunity
bank.com
Year Founded: 1976
Sales Range: $1-9.9 Million
Emp.: 40
Commericial Banking
N.A.I.C.S.: 522110
Keith Wilcett *(Pres)*

PEOPLE'S CREDIT UNION

858 W Main Rd, Middletown, RI 02842
Tel.: (401) 846-8930 RI
Web Site: http://www.peoplescu.com
Year Founded: 1922
Sales Range: $10-24.9 Million
Emp.: 147
Family Support Services
N.A.I.C.S.: 523910
Amy Costello Martel *(COO & Exec VP)*
Melissa Burton *(VP-HR)*
Lyn Dawley *(VP-Lending)*
Ellen Ford *(Pres & CEO)*
Cheryl A. Cady *(Mgr)*

Christopher Eden *(VP-IT & Ops)*
Fatima Estrela *(Mgr)*
Deborah Maxwell *(Mgr-North Kingstown)*
Steven Carneiro *(Mgr-Bus & Residential Lending)*
Sean Daly *(CFO & Exec VP)*
Andrew Plante *(Asst Controller)*
Barry Dunn *(Bus Mgr-Loan)*
Nicole Forte *(Mgr-Member Svc Center)*

PEOPLE'S EQUAL ACTION AND COMMUNITY EFFORT, INC.
217 S Salina St 2nd Fl, Syracuse, NY 13202
Tel.: (315) 470-3300   NY
Web Site: http://www.peace-caa.org
Year Founded: 1968
Sales Range: $10-24.9 Million
Emp.: 503
Community Care Services
N.A.I.C.S.: 624190
David A. Scharoun *(Chm)*
Shirley Copes *(Second VP)*
Joseph E. O'Hara *(Exec Dir)*
Robert T. Tackman *(Treas)*
Erich W. Shafer *(Sec)*

PEOPLE'S JEWELRY COMPANY, INC.
245 23rd St, Toledo, OH 43604
Tel.: (419) 241-4181   OH
Year Founded: 1914
Sales Range: $50-74.9 Million
Emp.: 35
Holding Company; Retail Jewelry & Watch Repair Stores Owner & Operator
N.A.I.C.S.: 551112
David M. Perlmutter *(Pres)*
Jim Kersten *(Controller)*

Subsidiaries:

PTRC, Inc.   (1)
245 23rd St, Toledo, OH 43604   **(100%)**
Tel.: (419) 241-4412
Web Site: http://www.ptrcinc.com
Watch Repair Services
N.A.I.C.S.: 811490

PEOPLE'S TELEPHONE CO-OPERATIVE, INC.
102 N Stephens St, Quitman, TX 75783
Tel.: (903) 763-2214
Web Site: http://www.peoplescom.net
Year Founded: 1954
Sales Range: $10-24.9 Million
Emp.: 80
Local Telephone Communications Services
N.A.I.C.S.: 517121
Scott Thompson *(Controller)*
Steven Steel *(Gen Mgr)*

PEOPLEFINDERS.COM
1821 Q St, Sacramento, CA 95811
Web Site: http://www.peoplefinders.com
Year Founded: 1988
Rev.: $31,200,000
Emp.: 44
Consumer Products & Services
N.A.I.C.S.: 541511
Bryce Lane *(Pres & COO)*
Angela Arriaga-Simpson *(Dir-HR & Ops)*

PEOPLEFORBIKES COALITION LTD
1966 13th St Ste 250, Boulder, CO 80302
Tel.: (303) 449-4893   CO
Web Site: http://www.peopleforbikes.org
Year Founded: 2006
Rev.: $6,909,143
Assets: $4,785,399
Liabilities: $1,919,995
Net Worth: $2,865,404
Fiscal Year-end: 12/31/22
Bicycle Supplier & Retailer Association
N.A.I.C.S.: 813910
Zoe Kircos *(Mgr-Grants)*
Kristy Kibler *(Mgr-Bus Network Events)*
Katy Hartnett *(Dir-Govt Rels)*
Charlie Cooper *(VP-Membership & Dev)*
Tim Blumenthal *(Pres)*
Sarah Braker *(Mgr-Comm)*
Erik Esborg *(VP-Fin)*
Michael Mercuri *(Chm)*
Pat Cunnane *(Vice Chm)*
Elysa Walk *(Treas)*

Subsidiaries:

PeopleForBikes Foundation   (1)
1966 13th St Ste 250, Boulder, CO 80302
Tel.: (303) 449-4893
Web Site: http://www.peopleforbikes.org
Sales Range: $1-9.9 Million
Emp.: 42
Sport Promotion Services
N.A.I.C.S.: 711310
Katy Hartnett *(Dir-Govt Rels)*
Erik Esborg *(VP-Fin)*
Jenn Dice *(VP-Bus Network)*
Sarah Braker *(Sr Mgr-Comm)*
Wendy Mayo *(Dir-Mktg & Comm)*
Jennifer Boldry *(Dir-Res)*
Blair Clark *(Chm)*
Patrick Seidler *(Vice Chm)*
Fred Clements *(Treas)*
Tim Blumenthal *(Pres)*
Charlie Cooper *(VP-Membership & Dev)*

PEOPLEG2
135 S State College Blvd Ste 200, Brea, CA 92821
Tel.: (714) 696-5410
Web Site: http://www.peopleg2.com
Year Founded: 2001
Sales Range: $1-9.9 Million
Emp.: 25
Human Capital Due Diligence Services
N.A.I.C.S.: 541612
Chris Dyer *(CEO)*
James Hall *(VP-Sls)*

PEOPLELINX, LLC
1835 Market St Ste 1105, Philadelphia, PA 19103
Tel.: (267) 773-7320
Year Founded: 2002
Information Technology & Services
N.A.I.C.S.: 541511
Don Nawrocki *(CTO)*
Kevin O'Nell *(CEO)*

PEOPLES BANCORP
3100 Woburn St, Bellingham, WA 98226
Tel.: (360) 715-4200   WA
Web Site: http://www.peoplesbank-wa.com
Year Founded: 1982
Sales Range: $75-99.9 Million
Emp.: 400
Bank Holding Company
N.A.I.C.S.: 551111
Lisa Leslie Holleman *(Chief Risk Officer & Exec VP)*
Charles LeCocq *(Chm & CEO)*
Terry Daughters *(Chief Credit Officer & Exec VP)*
Charlie Guildner *(Chief Lending Officer & Exec VP)*
Michelle Barrett *(Exec VP & Dir-HR & Branch Admin)*

Subsidiaries:

Peoples Bank   (1)
3100 Woburn St, Bellingham, WA 98226
Tel.: (360) 715-4200
Web Site: http://www.peoplesbank-wa.com
Sales Range: $75-99.9 Million
Emp.: 386
Commericial Banking
N.A.I.C.S.: 522110
Charles LeCocq *(Chm & CEO)*
Laura Lee *(Sr VP & Dir-Security)*
Charlie Guildner *(Chief Lending Officer & Exec VP)*
Jan Armstrong *(Mgr-Barkley)*
Mary Compton *(Branch Mgr)*
Pam Langstraat *(Mgr-Lynden)*
Mark Mouw *(Mgr-Coupeville)*
Mark Swanson *(Mgr-Retail Banking-Chelan & Douglas Counties)*
Terry Daughters *(Chief Credit Officer & Exec VP)*
Debbie Hogue *(Branch Mgr)*
Ali Alsos *(Branch Mgr)*
Tom Braaten *(Sr VP)*
Michelle Barrett *(Exec VP & Dir-HR & Branch Admin)*
Christine Lewis *(VP & Dir-HR)*
Casandra Sargent *(Asst VP & Mgr-Retail-Everett Financial Center)*
Tiffany Blair *(Mgr-Retail-Downtown Bellingham)*
Jonathan Ensch *(Sr VP)*
Scott Louia *(VP)*
Lisa Hefter *(Chief Admin & Risk Officer & Exec VP)*
Derek Thornton *(CFO & Sr VP)*

PEOPLES BANK & TRUST COMPANY
524 Main St, Hazard, KY 41701
Tel.: (606) 436-2161
Web Site: http://www.peopleshazard.com
Rev.: $14,489,000
Emp.: 90
State Savings Banks, Not Federally Chartered
N.A.I.C.S.: 522180
Jeff Smith *(CFO)*
Leon Hollon Sr. *(Chm, Pres & CEO)*

PEOPLES BANK AND TRUST
101 S Main St, McPherson, KS 67460
Tel.: (620) 241-2100
Web Site: http://www.peoples.bank
Year Founded: 1898
Commericial Banking
N.A.I.C.S.: 522110
Tom Pruitt *(Pres & CEO)*

Subsidiaries:

Community Bank of the Midwest   (1)
2220 Broadway Ave, Great Bend, KS 67530
Tel.: (620) 792-5111
Web Site: http://www.communitybankmidwest.com
Commericial Banking
N.A.I.C.S.: 522110
Richard Schenk *(CEO)*
Steven Sell *(Pres)*

PEOPLES BANK OF COMMERCE
1528 Biddle Rd, Medford, OR 97504
Tel.: (866) 454-4735
Web Site: http://www.peoplesbank.bank
Year Founded: 1998
Retail & Commercial Banking
N.A.I.C.S.: 522110
Russell E. Milburn *(CFO)*

Subsidiaries:

Steelhead Finance, LLC   (1)
3518 Heathrow Way, Medford, OR 97504
Tel.: (541) 773-3377
Web Site: http://www.steelheadfactoring.com
Finance Services
N.A.I.C.S.: 522299

Bill Stewart *(Pres)*

Willamette Community Bank   (1)
333 Lyon St SE, Albany, OR 97321
Tel.: (541) 926-9000
Web Site: http://www.willamettecommunitybank.com
Commercial Banking Services
N.A.I.C.S.: 522110
David Frances *(Chief Credit Officer & Sr VP)*
Joan Reukauf *(Pres & CEO)*
Robert R. Moore *(Sr VP & Chief Credit Officer)*
Jeff Morris *(Officer-Compliance)*

PEOPLES BANK OF NORTH ALABAMA
1912 Cherokee Ave SW, Cullman, AL 35055
Tel.: (256) 737-7000
Web Site: http://www.peoplebankal.com
Sales Range: $10-24.9 Million
Emp.: 200
State Commercial Banks
N.A.I.C.S.: 522110
James Robin Cummings *(CEO)*
Sheila Sizemore *(VP & Controller)*

PEOPLES BANKSHARES, INC.
45 N Union, Mora, MN 55051
Tel.: (320) 679-3100
Bank Holding Company
N.A.I.C.S.: 551111
Doyle Jelsing *(Pres & CEO)*

Subsidiaries:

Neighborhood National Bank   (1)
45 N Union, Mora, MN 55051
Tel.: (320) 763-2200
Web Site: http://www.neighborhood.bank
Sales Range: $1-9.9 Million
Emp.: 16
Commercial Banking Services
N.A.I.C.S.: 522110
Del Runck *(Exec VP & CFO)*
Heidi Becker *(Mgr-Sls)*
Doyle Jelsing *(Pres & CEO)*

PEOPLES CARE, INC.
13920 City Ctr Dr Ste 290, Chino Hills, CA 91709
Tel.: (626) 869-0558   CA
Web Site: http://www.peoplescare.com
Year Founded: 1997
Sales Range: $10-24.9 Million
Emp.: 400
Residential Care For the Developmentally Disabled
N.A.I.C.S.: 623220
Mike Kaiser *(Founder)*
Catherine Bennage *(Dir-Day Program Svcs)*
Tony Kueter *(COO)*
Brittany Wasson *(Dir-HR)*

PEOPLES ELECTRIC CONTRACTOR, INC.
277 Fillmore Ave E, Saint Paul, MN 55107
Tel.: (651) 227-7711   MN
Web Site: http://www.peoplesco.com
Year Founded: 1922
Sales Range: $100-124.9 Million
Emp.: 200
Electrical, Communications Systems; Building Automation; Temperature Control & Process Automation Construction; Installation, Service & Maintenance
N.A.I.C.S.: 238210
William P. Lindberg *(Pres)*
Matt Lindberg *(VP)*

Subsidiaries:

Peoples Communications System   (1)

PEOPLES ELECTRIC CONTRACTOR, INC. U.S. PRIVATE

Peoples Electric Contractor, Inc.—(Continued)
277 Fillmore Ave E, Saint Paul, MN 55107-1403 (100%)
Tel.: (651) 227-7711
Web Site: http://www.peoplesco.com
Sales Range: $25-49.9 Million
Emp.: 150
Voice & Data Communications Contractor
N.A.I.C.S.: 238210
William Lindberg (Pres)

System One Control (1)
277 Fillmore E Ave, Saint Paul, MN 55107-1403 (100%)
Tel.: (651) 227-7711
Web Site: http://www.peoplesco.com
Sales Range: $1-9.9 Million
Emp.: 30
Building Automation & Temperature Control
N.A.I.C.S.: 238210
William Gausman (Project Mgr)
William P. Lindberg (Pres)

PEOPLES ELECTRIC COOPERATIVE
1600 N Country Club, Ada, OK 74820
Tel.: (580) 272-1500
Web Site: http://www.peoplesec.com
Sales Range: $10-24.9 Million
Emp.: 105
Electric Power Marketers
N.A.I.C.S.: 221122
Randy Ethridge (CEO & Exec VP)
Jennifer Boeck (VP-Comm)
John Hudson (Sr VP-Ops & Engrg)

PEOPLES EXCHANGE BANCSHARES, INC.
2013 Hwy 21 Bypass, Monroeville, AL 36460
Tel.: (251) 575-4555
Web Site: http://www.peoplesexchangebk.com
Year Founded: 1995
Sales Range: $10-24.9 Million
Emp.: 80
Bank Holding Company
N.A.I.C.S.: 551111
Becky B. Snyder (Chm)

Subsidiaries:

Peoples Exchange Bank of Monroe County (1)
2013 Hwy 21 Bypass, Monroeville, AL 36420
Tel.: (251) 575-4555
Web Site: http://www.pebmc.com
Sales Range: $25-49.9 Million
Emp.: 35
Commericial Banking
N.A.I.C.S.: 522110
Harvey Gaston (CEO)
Rebecca Snyder (Chm)

PEOPLES FIRST PROPERTIES INC.
1002 W 23rd St Ste 400, Panama City, FL 32405
Tel.: (850) 769-8981
Web Site: http://www.royalamerican.com
Sales Range: $100-124.9 Million
Emp.: 400
Federal Savings & Loan Associations
N.A.I.C.S.: 522180
Kathy Bossler (VP & Controller)

Subsidiaries:

Royal American Construction (1)
1002 W 23rd St Ste 400, Panama City, FL 32405
Tel.: (850) 769-8981
Web Site: http://www.royalamericancompanies.com
Rev: $990,000
Emp.: 100
Multi-Family & Site Utilities Construction Services
N.A.I.C.S.: 236115

Sandy Bartlett (VP-HR)
Missy Dugas (Reg VP-Ops)
Simon Grindrod (VP-IT)

PEOPLES INDEPENDENT BANCSHARES, INC.
121 Billy B Dyar Blvd, Boaz, AL 35957
Tel.: (256) 593-8844
Bank Holding Company
N.A.I.C.S.: 551111

Subsidiaries:

First Bank (1)
312 Main St, Wadley, AL 36276
Tel.: (256) 395-2255
Web Site: http://www.fbonline.biz
Sales Range: $1-9.9 Million
Emp.: 19
Commericial Banking
N.A.I.C.S.: 522110
Jared Kirby (Pres & CEO)

Peoples Independent Bank (1)
820 S Broad St, Scottsboro, AL 35768
Tel.: (256) 259-8844
Rev.: $1,400,000
Emp.: 8
Commericial Banking
N.A.I.C.S.: 522110
Tim Haston (Pres)
Charleen Lemons (Office Mgr)

PEOPLES MORTGAGE COMPANY
2055 E Centennial Cir, Tempe, AZ 85284
Tel.: (480) 752-3530
Web Site: http://www.peoplesmortgage.com
Sales Range: $125-149.9 Million
Emp.: 500
Mortgage Services
N.A.I.C.S.: 522310
Stan Morris (Pres)
Jay Ray (Mgr-Sls)
Geoff Rooker (Branch Mgr-CMPS)

PEOPLES RURAL TELEPHONE COOPERATIVE
1080 Main St S, McKee, KY 40447 KY
Tel.: (606) 287-7101
Web Site: http://www.prtcnet.org
Year Founded: 1950
Sales Range: $10-24.9 Million
Emp.: 47
Telephone Services
N.A.I.C.S.: 541870
Keith Gabbard (Gen Mgr)
Kendell Norris (VP)
Wendell Gabbard (Sec)
Donald Hughes (Pres)

PEOPLES SERVICES INC.
2207 Kimball Rd SE, Canton, OH 44707
Tel.: (330) 453-3709
Web Site: http://www.peoplesservices.com
Year Founded: 1914
Rev.: $25,495,309
Emp.: 120
General Warehousing
N.A.I.C.S.: 493110
Ronald R. Sibila (Chm)
Douglas J. Sibila (Pres & CEO)
Michelle A. Sibila (Sec)
Dan Stemple (VP-Ops)
Larry P. Kelley (CFO & VP-Fin)
John Matheos (VP-Sls & Mktg)
Joni Locke (VP-Sls & Mktg)
Bill Hanlon (COO & Exec VP)

Subsidiaries:

Central Warehouse Operations, Inc. (1)
2520 Schuette Rd, Midland, MI 48642
Tel.: (989) 496-0880
Logistics & Warehouse Services

N.A.I.C.S.: 541614
Crown Warehousing & Logistics Inc (1)
2160 W 106th St 4, Cleveland, OH 44102-3504
Tel.: (216) 631-1069
Web Site: http://www.peoplesservices.com
Logistics & Warehouse Services
N.A.I.C.S.: 541614
Shelley Habermann (Corp Sec)

Peoples Cartage Inc (1)
2207 Kimball Rd SE, Canton, OH 44707
Tel.: (330) 453-3709
Web Site: http://www.peoplesservices.com
Rev: $8,900,000
Emp.: 8
General Warehousing
N.A.I.C.S.: 493110

Pitzer Transfer & Storage (1)
2050 Cook Dr, Salem, VA 24153
Tel.: (540) 769-2090
Web Site: http://www.peoplesservices.com
Rev: $1,493,676
Emp.: 5
Trucking Except Local
N.A.I.C.S.: 484210

Quick Delivery Service, Inc. (1)
350 W 19th St, Nitro, WV 25143
Tel.: (304) 759-2300
Web Site: http://www.quickdeliveryservice.com
Freight Forwarding Services
N.A.I.C.S.: 484110
George Rash (Mgr-Ops)

Terminal Warehouse, Inc. (1)
1779 Marvo Dr, Akron, OH 44306
Tel.: (330) 773-8207
General Warehousing Services
N.A.I.C.S.: 493110
Candy Kline (Mgr-Ops Info Sys)
Mark Wise (Coord-Day Shift)
Bill Hanlon (Pres)

Total Distribution (1)
164 Spring Grove Dr, Moncks Corner, SC 29461
Tel.: (843) 761-8111
Web Site: http://www.peoplesservices.com
Rev: $410,000
Emp.: 8
Local Trucking without Storage
N.A.I.C.S.: 484110
Doug Sibila (Pres)

Total Distribution Inc. (1)
2207 Kimball Rd SE, Canton, OH 44707
Tel.: (330) 453-3709
Web Site: http://www.peoplesservices.com
Rev: $2,000,000
Emp.: 20
General Warehousing & Storage
N.A.I.C.S.: 493110
Ronald R. Sibila (Chm)
Jim Ehret (Dir-Ops)

Subsidiary (Domestic):

Swafford Warehousing, Inc. (2)
1630 Old Highway 14 S, Greer, SC 29651
Tel.: (864) 848-3854
Web Site: http://www.swaffordtransport.com
Rev: $1,125,000
Emp.: 9
General Warehousing & Storage
N.A.I.C.S.: 493110
Van Swafford (Pres)

PEOPLES WATER SERVICE COMPANY
409 Washington Ave Ste 310, Baltimore, MD 21204
Tel.: (410) 825-3722
Rev: $11,000,000
Emp.: 53
Supplier of Water
N.A.I.C.S.: 221310
Sherlock S. Gillet (Pres)
Iva Gillet (VP)
Charles Gillet Jr. (VP)

PEOPLESBANK
330 Whitney Ave Ste 250, Holyoke, MA 01040-2810

Tel.: (413) 538-9500
Web Site: http://www.bankatpeoples.com
Year Founded: 1885
Sales Range: $100-124.9 Million
Emp.: 311
State Savings Banks, Not Federally Chartered
N.A.I.C.S.: 522180
Thomas Senecal (Pres & CEO)
Michael Oleksak (Chief Credit Officer & Exec VP)
Jacqueline B. Charron (Chief Risk Officer & Sr VP)
Matthew Bannister (First VP-Mktg & Innovation)
Tammy A. Bordeaux (VP & Reg Mgr)
Joseph A. Dias (Asst VP & Asst Controller)
Meghan E. Parnell-Gregoire (VP & Mgr-Bus Lending Center)
Jay C. Seyler (VP-Lending)
Catherine H. Snow (VP-Lending)
Paul Hillsburg (Asst VP-PeoplesWealth Advisory Grp)
Xiaolei Hua (Asst VP)
Matthew Krokov (Asst VP)
Timothy Wegiel (Asst VP)
James A. Sherbo (Sr VP-Lending)
Margaret M. Lenihan (Sr VP-Lending)
Joseph R. Zazzaro (Sr VP-Risk Oversight & IT)
Stacy A. Sutton (Sr VP-Retail)
Karen E. Sinopoli (VP & Controller-Fin)
Donna J. Wiley (VP & Reg Mgr)
Donna M. Charette (First VP-Fin)
Christine A. Phillips (First VP-HR)
Trisha L. Leary (VP-Internal Audit)
Beverly J. Orloski (VP-Lending)
Denise A. Lamory (VP-Lending)
Joseph P. Fimognari (VP-Lending)
Katherine A. St. Mary (VP-Lending)
Kristen P. Hua (VP-Lending)
Wesley D. Tanner (VP-Lending)
Cecile Richard (VP-Ops)
Jeffry A. Kerr (VP-Mktg)
Joan Leahy (VP-Mktg)
Craig W. Kaylor (VP-Risk Oversight)
Lynne A. Gino (VP-Risk Oversight)
Suzanne Rosenberg (Asst VP & Mgr-Springfield Banking Center-West)
Michael Gay (Mgr-Amherst Banking Center)
Brian Canina (CFO, Treas & Exec VP)
Aleda Amistadi (Sr VP-Retail & Ops)
Amy Roberts (Chief HR Officer & Sr VP)
Cheri Mills (Asst VP)

PEOPLESSOUTH BANCSHARES, INC.
203 W Crawford St, Colquitt, GA 39837
Tel.: (229) 758-5511 GA
Web Site: http://www.peoplessouth.com
Year Founded: 1991
Sales Range: $10-24.9 Million
Bank Holding Company
N.A.I.C.S.: 551111
Rickey E. Stuckey (Pres)

Subsidiaries:

PeoplesSouth Bank (1)
203 Crawford St, Colquitt, GA 39837
Tel.: (229) 758-5511
Web Site: http://www.peoplessouth.com
Sales Range: $50-74.9 Million
Emp.: 100
Retail & Commercial Banking
N.A.I.C.S.: 522110
Rickey E. Stuckey (CEO)
Caleb Stuckey (Pres)

PEOPLETEC, INC.

COMPANIES

4901 I Corporate Dr NW, Huntsville, AL 35802
Tel.: (256) 319-3800   AL
Web Site: http://www.peopletec.com
Year Founded: 2005
Sales Range: $10-24.9 Million
Emp.: 150
Engineeering Services
N.A.I.C.S.: 541330
Doug Scalf *(Co-Founder & Pres)*
Terry Jennings *(Co-Founder, Chm & CEO)*
Mark Braun *(VP)*
Brad Blume *(VP)*
Bill Elliott *(VP)*
Tina Nicholson *(VP)*
Dana Tanner *(VP)*
Anna Catherine Cowley *(CFO)*
Dennis Dunaway *(VP)*
Julie Richardson *(Dir-HR)*
Doug Barclay II *(Sr VP)*

PEOPLETOMYSITE.COM, LLC
580 N 4th St Ste 500, Columbus, OH 43215   OH
Web Site:
   http://www.theshipyard.com
Year Founded: 2013
Sales Range: $1-9.9 Million
Advertising & Marketing Consulting Services
N.A.I.C.S.: 541810
Neil Mortine *(Vice Chm)*
Rick Milenthal *(Chm & CEO)*

Subsidiaries:

Fahlgren, Inc.   (1)
4030 Easton Station Ste 300, Columbus, OH 43219
Tel.: (614) 383-1500
Web Site: http://www.fahlgrenmortine.com
Advertising, Public Relations & Marketing Consulting Agency
N.A.I.C.S.: 541810
Neil Mortine *(CEO)*
Brent Holbert *(CFO)*
Amy Dawson *(Exec VP)*
Katie McGrath *(Exec VP & Dir-HR)*
Sean Cowan *(Exec VP-Creative)*
Andy Crawford *(Exec VP-Bus Ops)*
Mark Miller *(Exec VP-Strategy & Insights)*
Aaron Brown *(Exec VP)*
Marty McDonald *(Pres)*

Division (Domestic):

Fahlgren Advertising   (2)
4030 Easton Sta Ste 300, Columbus, OH 43219
Tel.: (614) 383-1500
Web Site: https://www.fahlgrenmortine.com
Advertising Agencies, Brand Development, Direct Marketing
N.A.I.C.S.: 541810
Neil Mortine *(Pres & CEO)*

Fahlgren Grip Digital   (2)
4030 Easton Sta Ste 300, Columbus, OH 43219
Tel.: (614) 383-1500
N.A.I.C.S.: 541810

Fahlgren Mortine Public Relations   (2)
4030 Easton Sta Ste 300, Columbus, OH 43219
Tel.: (800) 731-8927
Web Site: https://www.fahlgren.com
Public Relations Agency
N.A.I.C.S.: 541820
Marty McDonald *(Sr VP)*
Aaron Brown *(Sr VP-Public Rels)*
Julie Exner *(Sr VP)*

Branch (Domestic):

Fahlgren, Inc. - Cincinnati   (2)
414 Walnut St Ste 1006, Cincinnati, OH 45202
Tel.: (513) 665-2344
Web Site: https://www.falgrenmortine.com
Sales Range: $10-24.9 Million
Emp.: 3
N.A.I.C.S.: 541810

Fahlgren, Inc. - Dayton   (2)
9049 Springboro Pike, Miamisburg, OH 45342-4418
Tel.: (937) 560-2840
Web Site: https://www.fahlgren.com
Sales Range: $10-24.9 Million
Emp.: 12
Full Service
N.A.I.C.S.: 541810

Fahlgren, Inc. - Fort Lauderdale   (2)
200 SW 1st St Ste 950, Fort Lauderdale, FL 33301
Tel.: (954) 776-6886
Web Site: https://www.fahlgren.com
Sales Range: $10-24.9 Million
Emp.: 10
N.A.I.C.S.: 541810
John Fahlgren *(Chm)*

Fahlgren, Inc. - Toledo   (2)
One Seagate Ste 901, Toledo, OH 43604
Tel.: (419) 247-5200
Web Site: https://www.fahlgren.com
Sales Range: $10-24.9 Million
Emp.: 1
N.A.I.C.S.: 541810

Fahlgren, inc. - Parkersburg   (2)
418 Grand Park Dr Ste 321, Parkersburg, WV 26105
Tel.: (304) 424-3591
Web Site: https://www.fahlgren.com
Sales Range: Less than $1 Million
Emp.: 20
N.A.I.C.S.: 541810

Subsidiary (Domestic):

Precision Public Relations, Inc.   (2)
3721 Douglas Blvd Ste 350, Roseville, CA 95661-4254
Tel.: (916) 960-5340
Web Site:
   https://www.precisionpublicrelations.com
Marketing Consulting Services
N.A.I.C.S.: 541613
John Sagesegale *(Owner)*

Turner Public Relations, Inc.   (2)
1614 15th St 4th Fl, Denver, CO 80202
Tel.: (303) 333-1402
Web Site: https://www.turnerpr.com
Emp.: 40
Public Relations Agency
N.A.I.C.S.: 541820
Christine Turner *(Founder & Pres)*
Angela Berardino *(Chief Strategy Officer)*
Campbell Levy *(VP-Media Rels)*

Branch (Domestic):

Turner Public Relations, Inc. - New York   (3)
250 W 39th St Ste 1602, New York, NY 10018
Tel.: (212) 889-1700
Web Site: https://www.turnerpr.com
Public Relations Agency
N.A.I.C.S.: 541820
Angela Berardino *(VP)*
Adel Grobler *(VP)*
Malcolm Griffiths *(Sr VP)*

PEORIA DISPOSAL COMPANY/AREA DISPOSAL SERVICE, INC.
4700 N Sterling Ave, Peoria, IL 61615-9071   IL
Tel.: (309) 688-0760
Web Site: http://www.pdcarea.com
Year Founded: 1985
Sales Range: $50-74.9 Million
Emp.: 525
Waste Management Services
N.A.I.C.S.: 562211

Subsidiaries:

C&S Waste Services Inc.   (1)
1540 Titan Dr, Rantoul, IL 61866   (100%)
Tel.: (217) 893-3675
Rev.: $3,000,000
Emp.: 2
Waste Haulers
N.A.I.C.S.: 423620

Clinton Landfill Inc.   (1)
Rte 2 PO Box 216 L, Clinton, IL 61727
Tel.: (217) 935-8028
Web Site: http://www.pdcarea.com
Sales Range: $10-24.9 Million
Emp.: 8
Landfill services
N.A.I.C.S.: 562212

Grimm Bros. Trucking Inc.   (1)
1090 W Jeffrson St, Morton, IL 61550
Tel.: (309) 263-2390
Rev.: $1,400,000
Emp.: 45
Refuse System
N.A.I.C.S.: 484110

Midland Davis Corporation   (1)
3301 4th Ave, Moline, IL 61265
Tel.: (309) 764-6723
Web Site: http://www.midlanddavis.com
Paper & Plastic Products Recycling Services
N.A.I.C.S.: 562219
Mitchell L. Davis *(VP)*
Eric Davis *(Mgr-Bus Dev)*
Martin H. Davis *(Pres)*
Laura Davis *(Controller)*
Michael Davis *(Mgr-Logistics)*

P.D.C. Laboratories Inc.   (1)
2231 W Altorfer Dr, Peoria, IL 61615-1807   (100%)
Tel.: (309) 692-9688
Web Site: http://www.pdclab.com
Sales Range: $10-24.9 Million
Emp.: 45
Testing Laboratories
N.A.I.C.S.: 541715
John Lanpayne *(VP-Laboratory Ops-Illinois)*

P.D.C. Technical Services Inc.   (1)
4349 Southport Rd, Peoria, IL 61615
Tel.: (309) 676-4893
Web Site: http://www.pdcarea.com
Waste Haulers And Landfill Services
N.A.I.C.S.: 541330
George Armstrong *(VP)*

Wigand Disposal Company   (1)
19908 N State Rte 29, Chillicothe, IL 61523-9718
Tel.: (309) 274-4589
Web Site: http://www.pdcarea.com
Rev.: $1,300,000
Emp.: 20
Refuse System
N.A.I.C.S.: 562211

PEORIA PACKING LTD.
1307 W Lake St, Chicago, IL 60607
Tel.: (312) 226-2600
Web Site:
   http://www.peoriapacking.com
Rev.: $27,095,457
Emp.: 10
Meat Packing Plants
N.A.I.C.S.: 311611
Harry Katsiavelos *(Pres)*

PEORIA TOYOTA SCION
7401 N Allen Rd, Peoria, IL 61614
Tel.: (309) 693-7000
Web Site:
   http://www.peoriatoyota.com
Year Founded: 1977
Sales Range: $25-49.9 Million
Emp.: 70
New Car Retailer
N.A.I.C.S.: 441110
Andrew Vanheuklon *(Mgr-Sls)*
Jill McGee *(Mgr-Svc)*
Greg Whitten *(Gen Mgr)*

PEP DIRECT, LLC
19 Stoney Brook Dr, Wilton, NH 03086-0900
Tel.: (603) 654-6141
Web Site: http://www.pep-direct.com
Year Founded: 1973
Direct Marketing Services
N.A.I.C.S.: 541613
Hilary Jandl *(CFO)*
Mark Bender *(VP-Ops)*
Corrine Biggs *(Sr VP-Strategic Dev)*

Charlie Cadigan *(Sr VP-Strategic Bus Ops)*
Michael Elithorpe *(VP-Sls & Mktg)*
Liz Gerardi *(Mgr-Donation Processing Svcs)*
Matt Kennedy *(Dir-Creative)*

PEP PRINTING, INC.
5000 N Basin Ave, Portland, OR 97217
Tel.: (503) 223-4984   OR
Web Site:
   https://www.premierpress.com
Year Founded: 1974
Creative Production & Printing Services
N.A.I.C.S.: 541890
Kyle Gibson *(Dir-Promotional Merchandise)*
Manuel Saez *(VP)*

Subsidiaries:

KG Specialties LLC   (1)
17084 NE Sandy Blvd, Portland, OR 97230
Tel.: (503) 669-8233
Web Site: http://www.kgspecialties.com
Sales Range: $1-9.9 Million
Emp.: 13
Commercial Screen Printing Services
N.A.I.C.S.: 323113
Norma Ball *(Office Mgr-Production)*

PEP-UP, INC.
24987 Dupont Blvd, Georgetown, DE 19947-0556
Tel.: (302) 856-2555   DE
Web Site: http://www.pepupinc.com
Year Founded: 1978
Sales Range: $10-24.9 Million
Emp.: 100
Provider of Liquefied Petroleum Gas, Diesel & Gasoline Services
N.A.I.C.S.: 457210
Larry Martin *(Controller)*

PEPCO MANUFACTURING COMPANY
210 E Evergreen Ave, Somerdale, NJ 08083
Tel.: (856) 783-3700
Web Site:
   http://www.pepcosheetmetal.com
Year Founded: 1960
Sales Range: $10-24.9 Million
Emp.: 75
Metal Products Mfr
N.A.I.C.S.: 332999
John Kennedy *(CEO)*
Beverly Winter *(CFO)*
Edward Miller *(VP-Mktg & Sls)*

Subsidiaries:

Premier Metal Products Co.   (1)
217 Route 303, Valley Cottage, NY 10989-2533
Tel.: (201) 750-4900
Web Site: http://www.premiermetal.com
Rev.: $7,000,000
Emp.: 2
Cabinets, Cases & Accessories Mfr for Electronic Products
N.A.I.C.S.: 337126

PEPE MOTORS CORP.
50 Bank St, White Plains, NY 10606
Tel.: (914) 949-4001
Web Site:
   http://www.mbwhiteplains.com
Sales Range: $25-49.9 Million
Emp.: 200
New & Used Car Dealers
N.A.I.C.S.: 441110
Julie Gafparino *(Controller)*
Gary Turco *(Gen Mgr-Sls)*
Eugene N. Pepe Sr. *(Pres & CEO)*

PEPE'S INC.

PEPE'S INC.

Pepe's Inc.—(Continued)
1325 W 15th St, Chicago, IL 60608-2107
Tel.: (312) 733-2500
Web Site: http://www.pepes.com
Year Founded: 1967
Sales Range: $1-9.9 Million
Emp.: 40
Franchisor of Mexican Restaurants
N.A.I.C.S.: 424490
Mario Dovalina *(Co-Founder & Chm)*
Robert Ptak *(Pres)*
Edwin A. Ptak *(Co-Founder & Gen Counsel)*

PEPIN DISTRIBUTING COMPANY
4121 N 50th St, Tampa, FL 33610
Tel.: (813) 626-6176
Web Site: http://www.pepindistributing.com
Year Founded: 1960
Sales Range: $125-149.9 Million
Emp.: 280
Beer Distr
N.A.I.C.S.: 424810
Thomas A. Pepin *(Pres & CEO)*
Sam Rivera *(Mgr-Market-On-Premise)*

PEPINE REALTY, LLC
4041 NW 37th Pl Ste B, Gainesville, FL 32606
Tel.: (352) 226-8474
Web Site: http://www.pepinerealty.com
Year Founded: 2010
Sales Range: $1-9.9 Million
Real Estate Services
N.A.I.C.S.: 531390
Betsy Pepine *(Owner)*

PEPITONE PROPERTIES CORP.
8890 Salrose Ln Ste 200, Fort Myers, FL 33912
Tel.: (239) 481-5959
Web Site: http://www.pepitonerealty.com
Sales Range: Less than $1 Million
Emp.: 4
Real Estate Broker
N.A.I.C.S.: 531210
Tom Pepitone *(Owner)*

PEPPER CONSTRUCTION GROUP, LLC
643 N Orleans St, Chicago, IL 60654-3608
Tel.: (312) 266-4700   IL
Web Site: http://www.pepperconstruction.com
Year Founded: 1927
Sales Range: $900-999.9 Million
Emp.: 1,250
Holding Company; General Contractor & Construction Management Services
N.A.I.C.S.: 551112
Paul Francois *(Pres)*
Chris Averill *(CFO, COO & Exec VP)*
Keith Dafcik *(VP)*
Scott Nemshick *(Dir-Bus Dev)*
James Nissen *(Pres-Environmental Technologies)*
Tim Cooper *(Exec VP-Ops)*
Russ Pande *(VP-Ops-Milwaukee)*
Jacqueline Lavigne *(CMO, Chief Strategy Officer & Sr VP)*
Jay Ripsky *(Sr VP)*
Jeff Johnson *(Sr VP)*
Tim Sullivan *(Gen Counsel & Sr VP)*
Cam Mallett *(Dir-Mission Critical practice)*

Subsidiaries:

Pepper Construction Co.   (1)
643 N Orleans St, Chicago, IL 60654-3608   (100%)
Tel.: (312) 266-4700
Web Site: http://www.pepperconstruction.com
General Contracting & Construction Management
N.A.I.C.S.: 236220
J. David Pepper *(Chm)*
Chris Averill *(COO)*
Howie Piersma *(VP-IT)*
Tim Sullivan *(Gen Counsel & Sr VP)*
Jake Pepper *(VP)*
Eric Bullion *(VP)*
Mike Grant *(VP)*
Shawn Dziedzic *(VP)*
Susan Heinking *(VP)*
Stephanie Vitner *(VP)*
Stan Pepper *(Pres)*

Pepper Construction Co. of Indiana, LLC   (1)
1850 W 15th St, Indianapolis, IN 46202-2027   (100%)
Tel.: (317) 681-1000
Web Site: http://www.pepperconstruction.com
General Contractor & Commercial Construction Services
N.A.I.C.S.: 236220
Mike McCann *(Pres)*
Dave Pepper *(Chm)*
Steve Allemeier *(COO)*
Bob Eckl *(Sr VP)*

Pepper Construction Company of Ohio   (1)
495 Metro Place S Ste 350, Dublin, OH 43017
Tel.: (614) 793-4477
Web Site: http://www.pepperconstruction.com
Emp.: 30
General Contractor & Commercial Construction Services
N.A.I.C.S.: 236220
Paul Francois *(Pres)*
Jay Jacobsmeyer *(COO)*
Terry Gardner *(Superintendent-Self Perform)*
Brian Lensink *(Project Dir)*
Todd Robertson *(Dir-Bus Dev)*
Jonathan Wilch *(Project Dir-Dev)*
Jerry Noble *(VP & Dir-Cincinnati)*
Evan Caprile *(Project Mgr-High Performance-Local Office)*

Pepper Environmental Technologies, Inc.   (1)
411 Lake Zurich Rd, Barrington, IL 60010
Tel.: (312) 266-4700
Web Site: http://www.pepperconstruction.com
General Contractor & Construction Manager
N.A.I.C.S.: 541219

PEPPER HAMILTON LLP
3000 2 Logan Sq 18 Arch St, Philadelphia, PA 19103
Tel.: (215) 981-4000   PA
Web Site: http://www.pepperlaw.com
Year Founded: 1890
Sales Range: $150-199.9 Million
Emp.: 1,082
Law firm
N.A.I.C.S.: 541110
Josette L. Marsh *(CIO)*
Robert E. Heideck *(Partner)*
Robyn L. Beyer *(Dir-Library & Res Svcs)*
Celeste M. Duke *(Dir-Learning & User Support)*
Craig J. Dunston *(Dir-Office Svcs)*
Patricia Woodson *(Dir-Admin & HR)*
Andrea Toy Ohta *(Partner)*
Michael J. Crumbock *(Partner)*
Daniel P. Pulka *(CMO)*
Ted R. Gropman *(Partner-Construction Practice Grp-Los Angeles)*
Pamela S. Palmer *(Partner-Comml Litigation Dept)*
Thomas M. Gallagher *(Partner)*
Michael G. Connelly *(Partner-Comml Litigation Practice Grp-Pittsburgh)*
Nicholas A. Stawasz *(Partner)*
Gregory D. Len *(Partner)*
William M. Taylor *(Partner)*
John P. Falco *(Partner)*
Andrew Hulsh *(Partner)*
Bradley T. Lennie *(Partner)*
G. Matthew Koehl *(Partner)*
Alva C. Mather *(Partner)*
Maia H. Harris *(Partner)*
Albert Bates *(Partner)*
Kelley P. Doran *(Partner)*
Hilary S. Cairnie *(Partner-Govt Contracts Practice Grp)*
Brian P. Downey *(Partner)*
Christopher W. Wasson *(Partner)*
Goutam Patnaik *(Co-Chm & Partner-Intellectual Property Litigation)*
Joan C. Arnold *(Partner)*
Michael J. Mann *(Partner)*
Michael P. Subak *(Partner)*
Raymond A. Miller *(Partner)*
Sean P. Fahey *(Partner)*
Sven Riethmueller *(Partner)*
Paul E. Pelletier *(Partner-White Collar Litigation & Investigations Practice Grp)*
Sean P. McNally *(Partner-Comml Litigation Practice Grp-Detroit)*
H. Peter Haveles *(Partner)*
Matthew H. Adler *(Chm-Comml Litigation Practice Grp & Partner)*
William D. Belanger *(Chm-Intellectual Property Dept & Partner)*
Mark S. Blaskey *(Chm-Trusts & Estates Practice Grp & Partner)*
John W. Carroll *(Chm-Environmental & Energy Practice Grp & Partner)*
Matthew V. DelDuca *(Chm-Labor & Employment Practice Grp & Partner)*
Todd A. Feinsmith *(Chm-Corp Restructuring & Bankruptcy Practice Grp & Partner)*
Thomas F. Fitzpatrick *(Chm-Intellectual Property Litigation Practice Grp & Partner)*
John M. Ford *(Chm-Fin Svcs Practice Grp & Partner)*
David M. Fournier *(Chm-Corp Restructuring & Bankruptcy Practice Grp & Partner)*
Nina M. Gussack *(Chm-Health Sciences Dept & Partner)*
Jeremy Heep *(Chm-Litigation & Dispute Resolution Dept & Partner)*
David M. Kaplan *(Chm-Employee Benefits Practice Grp & Partner)*
Brian M. Katz *(Chm-Corp & Securities Practice Grp & Partner)*
John D. S. Kelly *(COO)*
Paul J. Kennedy *(Chm-Intellectual Property Litigation Practice Grp & Partner)*
Henry Liu *(Chm-Fin Svcs Practice Grp & Partner)*
Matthew J. Swett *(Chm-Real Estate Practice Grp & Partner)*
Thomas P. Wilczak *(Chm-Environmental & Energy Practice Grp & Partner)*
Deborah L. Spranger *(Partner-Health Sciences Dept-Berwyn)*
Julia D. Corelli *(Partner)*
Callan Stein *(Partner-Health Sciences Dept & White Collar Litigation)*
Justin Brown *(Partner-Tax & Estates Practice Grp)*
John P. Isacson *(Partner-Intellectual Property Dept)*
Howard M. Privette *(Partner-Trial & Dispute Resolution Practice Grp-Orange County)*
Deborah Enea *(Partner-Fin Svcs Practice Grp-Berwyn)*
Lindsay Breedlove *(Partner-Health Sciences Dept)*
Mateusz Saykiewicz *(Partner-Health Sciences Dept-Pittsburgh)*
Tuhin Ganguly *(Partner-Intellectual Property Dept-Washington)*
Frank B. Tripodi *(Partner-Employee Benefits & Exec Compensation Practice Grp)*
Jason C. Spang *(Partner-Construction Practice Grp)*
Jeremy I. Levy *(Partner-Corp & Securities Practice Grp)*
John E. Pooler Jr. *(Chief Admin Officer)*
John L. Schweder II *(Partner-Trial & Dispute Resolution Practice Grp)*
John J. McGrath III *(Partner-Health Sciences Dept)*

PEPPER MILL INC.
380 Brinkby Ave B, Reno, NV 89509
Tel.: (775) 826-8770
Sales Range: $10-24.9 Million
Emp.: 20
Restaurant, Family: Chain
N.A.I.C.S.: 722511
William A. Paganetti *(Pres)*
Terry Cox *(Dir-Race & Sports Book)*

PEPPER SOURCE, LTD.
2720 Athania, Metairie, LA 70002
Tel.: (504) 885-3223
Web Site: http://www.peppersource.com
Year Founded: 1987
Sales Range: $25-49.9 Million
Emp.: 175
Sauce, Marinade & Glaze Mfr
N.A.I.C.S.: 311941
Mark Fisher *(VP)*
Steve Campbell *(Mgr-Pur)*
Brad Palmer *(Plant Mgr)*

PEPPER TREE INC.
595 W 7th St Ste 202, San Pedro, CA 90731
Tel.: (310) 831-1043
Rev.: $11,000,000
Emp.: 6
Lubrication Service, Automotive
N.A.I.C.S.: 811191
Larry A. Kennepohl *(Pres)*
Steve Shields *(Chief Ops Officer)*

PEPPERCOM, INC.
470 Park Ave S 5th Fl, New York, NY 10016
Tel.: (212) 931-6100
Web Site: http://www.peppercomm.com
Year Founded: 1995
Sales Range: $10-24.9 Million
Emp.: 80
Public Relations Services
N.A.I.C.S.: 541820
Steven Cody *(Founder & CEO)*
Deborah Brown *(Partner & Mng Dir-Strategic Dev)*
Jackie Kolek *(Chief Innovation Officer & Exec VP)*
Maggie O'Neill *(Partner & Chief Client Officer)*
Sara Whitman *(Sr Dir-Talent & Strategy)*
Soenke Kisker *(CFO)*
Tara Lilien *(Chief Talent Officer)*
Marissa Dunn *(Sr Strategist-Media)*

Subsidiaries:

Peppercom   (1)
180 Sutter St Fl 2, San Francisco, CA 94104-4010
Tel.: (415) 438-3600

Web Site: http://www.peppercom.com
Sales Range: Less than $1 Million
Emp.: 9
N.A.I.C.S.: 541820
Ann Barlow (Pres & Partner)

Peppercom UK Ltd. (1)
The Timber Yard 107 Drysdale St, London, N1 6ND, United Kingdom
Tel.: (44) 207 033 2660
Web Site: http://www.peppercom.com
Sales Range: $10-24.9 Million
Emp.: 20
N.A.I.C.S.: 541820
Jacki Vause (Mng Dir)

Walek & Associates (1)
317 Madison Ave Ste 2300, New York, NY 10017
Tel.: (212) 889-4113
Web Site: http://www.walek.com
Emp.: 25
Public Relations Services
N.A.I.C.S.: 541820
Thomas Walek (Founder & Pres)
Armel Leslie (Principal)
Mary Beth Kissane (Principal-IR & Leader-Corp Transactions Practice)
Stefan Prelog (Sr Acct Exec)
Morrison Shafroth (VP-Boulder)

PEPPERDASH TECHNOLOGY CORP.
27 Congress St Ste 104, Salem, MA 01970
Tel.: (617) 208-0123
Web Site:
http://www.pepperdash.com
Year Founded: 2000
Rev.: $2,600,000
Emp.: 26
Computer Software Development Services
N.A.I.C.S.: 541511
Philip Walker (CFO)
Howard Nunes (CEO)
David Huselid (COO)
Sumanth Rayancha (CTO)

PEPPERL+FUCHS INC
1600 Enterprise Pkwy, Twinsburg, OH 44087
Tel.: (330) 425-3555
Web Site: http://www.pepperl-fuchs.us
Electrical Component Mfr
N.A.I.C.S.: 333998
Gunther Kegel (CEO)
Werner Guthier (Member-Mgmt Bd)
Mehmet Hatiboglu (Member-Mgmt Bd)

Subsidiaries:

Mactek Corp. (1)
2112 Case Pkwy S Ste 1, Twinsburg, OH 44087
Tel.: (330) 487-5477
Web Site: http://www.mactekccrp.com
Sales Range: $1-9.9 Million
Emp.: 12
Industrial Machinery Mfr
N.A.I.C.S.: 333248
Thomas Holmes (Pres)

PEPPERMILL CASINOS, INC.
2707 S Virginia St, Reno, NV 89502
Tel.: (775) 689-8900 NV
Web Site:
http://www.peppermillreno.com
Year Founded: 1993
Sales Range: $200-249.9 Million
Emp.: 3,000
Owner & Operator of Casinos & Hotels
N.A.I.C.S.: 721120
Nat Carasali (Owner)
Scott Loder (CFO)
Dean Hill (Dir-Security)

Subsidiaries:

Peppermill Hotel Casino (1)
680 Wendover Blvd, Wendover, NV 89883 (100%)
Tel.: (775) 664-2255
Sales Range: $25-49.9 Million
Emp.: 620
Casino
N.A.I.C.S.: 721120
Sonny Longson (Gen Mgr)
Gary Lewis (VP)
Sheyla Mercado (Mgr-Hotel)

PEPPERS AUTOMOTIVE GROUP, INC.
2420 E Wood St, Paris, TN 38242-9598
Tel.: (731) 642-3900
Year Founded: 1993
Sales Range: $10-24.9 Million
Emp.: 40
New Car Whslr
N.A.I.C.S.: 441120
Bobbie Sue Kildebeck (Comptroller)
Doug Peppers (Principal)
Rodney Mckinney (Mgr-Svc)

PEPPERS UNLIMITED OF LOUISIANA, INC.
602 W Bridge St, Saint Martinville, LA 70582-0211
Tel.: (337) 394-8035
Web Site:
http://www.peppersunlimitedofla.com
Year Founded: 1910
Sales Range: $25-49.9 Million
Emp.: 85
Spice Mfr
N.A.I.C.S.: 311941
John B. Bulliard (VP)
Leslie B. Willis (Treas & Sec)
George Bulliard Sr. (Pres)

PEPPERTREE CAPITAL MANAGEMENT, INC.
86 West St, Chagrin Falls, OH 44022
Tel.: (440) 528-0333 OH
Web Site:
http://www.peppertreecapital.com
Year Founded: 2004
Sales Range: $25-49.9 Million
Emp.: 20
Privater Equity Firm
N.A.I.C.S.: 523999
Jeffrey A. Howard (Founder & Mng Dir)
Ryan D. Lepene (Sr Mng Dir)
F. Howard Mandel (Pres)
Cynthia L. Debevec (CFO)
Diane S. Leung (Gen Counsel)
John Ranieri (Mng Dir)
Daniel Weiser (Principal)
John B. Gillette III (VP)

PEPSI COLA BOTTLING CO. OF CENTRAL VIRGINIA INC.
1150 Pepsi Pl, Charlottesville, VA 22901-2865
Tel.: (434) 978-2140 VA
Web Site: http://www.pepsico.com
Year Founded: 1983
Sales Range: $25-49.9 Million
Emp.: 360
Soft Drink Mfr & Bottler
N.A.I.C.S.: 312111
Ralph Campbell (VP-Ops)

PEPSI COLA OGDENSBURG BOTTLERS
1001 Mansion Ave, Ogdensburg, NY 13669
Tel.: (315) 393-1720
Rev.: $18,300,000
Emp.: 40
Soft Drinks
N.A.I.C.S.: 424490
Bonita Wright (Pres)
Richard Wright (VP)
Mike Looney (Controller)

PEPSI MIDAMERICA CO.
2605 W Main St, Marion, IL 62959
Tel.: (618) 997-1377
Web Site:
http://www.pepsimidamerica.com
Sales Range: $100-124.9 Million
Emp.: 695
Soft Drink Distr
N.A.I.C.S.: 312111
Harry L. Crisp II (CEO)
Harry L. Crisp III (Pres & COO)

PEPSI-COLA & NATIONAL BRAND BEVERAGES, LTD.
8275 N Route 130, Pennsauken, NJ 08110-1435
Tel.: (856) 665-6200 PA
Web Site:
http://www.honickmangroup.com
Year Founded: 1957
Sales Range: $500-549.9 Million
Emp.: 5,000
Holding Company; Beverages, Soft Drinks & Juices Bottler & Distr
N.A.I.C.S.: 551112
Jeffrey A. Honickman (CEO)
Harold A. Honickman (Founder & Chm)
Robert Brockway (Pres)
Walt Wilkinson (CFO)

Subsidiaries:

Beverage Capital Corporation (1)
3051 Washington Blvd Ste C, Baltimore, MD 21230-1086
Tel.: (410) 242-7404
Web Site: http://www.beveragecapital.com
Sales Range: $25-49.9 Million
Emp.: 65
Provider of Bottled & Canned Soft Drinks
N.A.I.C.S.: 312111
Rick Smith (VP)

Beverage Distribution Center, Inc. (1)
8275 N Route 130, Pennsauken, NJ 08110-1435
Tel.: (856) 665-4848
Sales Range: $50-74.9 Million
Emp.: 700
Soft Drink Bottler & Distr
N.A.I.C.S.: 312111
Jeffrey A. Honickman (CEO)

Canada Dry Bottling Company of New York, L.P. (1)
11202 15th Ave, College Point, NY 11356
Tel.: (718) 358-2000
Web Site: www.careerbuilders.com
Rev.: $44,700,000
Emp.: 300
Soft Drink Bottler & Distr
N.A.I.C.S.: 312111
Harold A. Honickman (Chm)

Canada Dry Delaware Valley Bottling Company (1)
650 Ships Landing Way, New Castle, DE 19720-4577
Tel.: (302) 322-1856
Rev.: $11,300,000
Emp.: 30
Soft Drink Bottler & Distr
N.A.I.C.S.: 312111

Pepsi-Cola Bottling Co. of New York, Inc. (1)
11202 15th Ave, College Point, NY 11356-1428
Tel.: (718) 392-1000
Sales Range: $150-199.9 Million
Emp.: 950
Soft Drink Bottler & Distr
N.A.I.C.S.: 312111
Mike Buonassissi (VP-Sls & Mktg)
William Wilson (Pres)
Mark Johnson (VP-Fin)

PEPSI-COLA BOTTLING CO. OF LA CROSSE
1900 W Ave S, La Crosse, WI 54601
Tel.: (608) 785-0450

Web Site:
http://www.gillettepepsicola.com
Rev.: $17,500,000
Emp.: 150
Soft Drink Mfr & Bottler
N.A.I.C.S.: 312111
Mike Wolf (Mgr-Ops)
Fritz Truax (CEO)

PEPSI-COLA BOTTLING CO. OF NORTON, VIRGINIA
12th St & Park Ave, Norton, VA 24273
Tel.: (276) 679-1122
Rev.: $18,000,000
Emp.: 376
Soft Drink Mfr & Bottler
N.A.I.C.S.: 312111
George Edward Hunnicutt Jr. (Pres)

PEPSI-COLA BOTTLING OF CORBIN, KENTUCKY INC.
1000 Cumberland Falls Hwy, Corbin, KY 40701-2713
Tel.: (606) 528-1630
Year Founded: 1938
Sales Range: $25-49.9 Million
Emp.: 225
Soft Drink Mfr & Bottler
N.A.I.C.S.: 312111
William Hoover (Pres)
Virgil Webb (Controller)

PEPSI-COLA BOTTLING OF HICKORY, NORTH CAROLINA INC.
2401 14th Ave Cir NW, Hickory, NC 28601
Tel.: (828) 322-8090
Sales Range: $50-74.9 Million
Emp.: 120
Soft Drink Mfr & Bottler
N.A.I.C.S.: 312111
J. Lee Teeter (Pres)

PEPSI-COLA BOTTLING OF WORCESTER
90 Indus Dr, Holden, MA 01520
Tel.: (508) 829-6551
Web Site:
http://www.pepsiworcester.com
Sales Range: $10-24.9 Million
Emp.: 100
Soft Drink Mfr & Bottler
N.A.I.C.S.: 312111
Judy Holeman (Mgr-HR)
Jim Carceo (Head-Sls)
Robert H. Rauh Sr. (Pres)

PEPSI-COLA COMPANY NEW HAVEN
101 Hickory St, New Haven, MO 63068
Tel.: (573) 237-2411
Web Site: http://www.gopepsi.com
Sales Range: $10-24.9 Million
Emp.: 90
Soft Drinks
N.A.I.C.S.: 424490
Ellen Zobrist (CEO)

PEPSI-COLA MEMPHIS BOTTLING CO., INC.
520 E Grand Ave, Memphis, MO 63555
Tel.: (660) 465-8553 MO
Web Site:
http://www.pepsimemphismo.com
Year Founded: 1929
Sales Range: $10-24.9 Million
Emp.: 30
Soft Drinks Mfr & Distr
N.A.I.C.S.: 312111
John Harold Johnson Jr. (CEO)

PEPSI-COLA OF FLORENCE, LLC

Pepsi-Cola Memphis Bottling Co., Inc.—(Continued)

PEPSI-COLA OF FLORENCE, LLC
2499 Florence Harllee Blvd, Florence, SC 29506-8252
Tel.: (843) 662-4532 SC
Sales Range: $25-49.9 Million
Emp.: 250
Soft Drink Mfr & Bottler
N.A.I.C.S.: 312111
Tammy Hicks *(Coord-Pricing)*
Marilyn Tanner *(Dir-HR)*
Brock Graham *(Area Mgr)*
Tim Geddings *(CIO)*

PEQUOT CAPITAL MANAGEMENT INC.
500 Nyala Farms Rd Ste 2, Westport, CT 06880-6270
Tel.: (203) 429-2200 CT
Year Founded: 1999
Sales Range: $50-74.9 Million
Emp.: 170
Investment Advisor
N.A.I.C.S.: 523940
Mike Fox *(Sr VP)*
Kathleen O'Reilly *(Sr VP)*

PER MAR SECURITY SERVICES
1910 E Kimberly Rd, Davenport, IA 52807-2033
Tel.: (563) 359-3200 IA
Web Site:
  http://www.permarsecurity.com
Year Founded: 1953
Sales Range: $75-99.9 Million
Emp.: 1,500
Security Alarms & Guards
N.A.I.C.S.: 561621
Dan Turner *(CIO)*

Subsidiaries:

Midwest Alarm Services Inc. (1)
720 E 2nd St, Des Moines, IA 50309-1832
Tel.: (515) 288-4000
Web Site:
  http://www.midwestalarmservices.com
Sales Range: $1-9.9 Million
Emp.: 40
Alarm Systems Installation Services
N.A.I.C.S.: 423610
Doug Richard *(Pres)*
Tracy Warwick *(Reg Mgr-Svc)*
Michael Wells *(Mgr-Bus Dev)*
Kevin Hess *(Reg Mgr-Ops)*

Subsidiary (Domestic):

Electric Specialties Company (2)
PO Box 24042, Omaha, NE 68124-0042
Tel.: (402) 331-6111
Web Site:
  http://www.electronicspecialty.com
Life Safety Systems Mfr & Distr
N.A.I.C.S.: 423610
Willard Campbell *(Pres)*

PERATON GOVERNMENT COMMUNICATIONS, INC.
12975 Worldgate Dr, Herndon, VA 20170-6008
Tel.: (703) 668-6000
Web Site: http://www.peraton.com
Year Founded: 2017
Satellite Telecommunication Services
N.A.I.C.S.: 517410
Stu Shea *(Chm, Pres & CEO)*
Reggie Brothers *(CTO & Exec VP)*

Subsidiaries:

Strategic Resources International, Inc. (1)
777 Washington Rd Ste 2, Parlin, NJ 08859
Tel.: (732) 253-4001
Web Site: http://www.sriusa.com
Software Development & Consulting Services

N.A.I.C.S.: 541511

PERCEPTICS, LLC
11130 Kingston Pike Ste 6, Farragut, TN 37934
Tel.: (865) 966-9200 TN
Web Site: http://www.perceptics.com
Year Founded: 1979
Security, Traffic Management & Machine Vision Systems Equipment Mfr
N.A.I.C.S.: 335999
Kevin Giles *(VP-Product Engrg)*
Tom Hayes *(VP-Sls & Mktg)*
Claude Bernard *(Engr-Mfg)*
Richard Wheeler *(Mgr-Field Ops)*
Dewayne Lawson *(Sr Engr-Program)*
John Mike *(Pres)*

PERCEPTIONS, INC.
1400 Broadway Lbby 5, New York, NY 10018-5303
Tel.: (212) 944-7717
Year Founded: 1984
Sales Range: $10-24.9 Million
Emp.: 45
Womens, Juniors & Misses Dresses
N.A.I.C.S.: 315250
Sy Blechman *(VP)*

PERCEPTIVE ADVISORS, LLC
Tel.: (646) 205-5300
Web Site:
  https://www.perceptivelife.com
Emp.: 100
Miscellaneous Financial Investment Activities
N.A.I.C.S.: 523999
Michael Altman *(Mng Dir)*

Subsidiaries:

Vapotherm, Inc. (1)
100 Domain Dr, Exeter, NH 03833
Tel.: (603) 658-0011
Web Site: https://www.vapotherm.com
Rev.: $66,801,000
Assets: $96,195,000
Liabilities: $124,385,000
Net Worth: ($28,190,000)
Earnings: $113,259,000
Emp.: 261
Fiscal Year-end: 12/31/2022
Medical Device Mfr & Distr
N.A.I.C.S.: 334510
John Landry *(CFO, Treas, Sec & Sr VP)*
Lindsay Becker *(VP-HR)*
Adrain Lambert Bryant *(Dir-Corp Legal Affairs)*
Brian Lawrence *(CTO & Sr VP)*
Jessica Whittle *(Chief Medical Officer & VP-Clinical Res)*
James Lightman *(Gen Counsel & Sr VP)*

PERCEPTIVE RECRUITING, LLC
5 Creekside Park Ct Ste G, Greenville, SC 29615
Tel.: (864) 256-0203
Web Site:
  http://www.perceptiverecruiting.com
Year Founded: 2014
Sales Range: $1-9.9 Million
Emp.: 5
Software Development Services
N.A.I.C.S.: 541511
Jill Rose *(Pres)*

PERCEPTRONICS SOLUTIONS, INC.
3527 Beverly Glen Boulevard, Encino, CA 91436
Tel.: (818) 788-1025
Web Site:
  http://www.percsolutions.com
Year Founded: 2003
Sales Range: $1-9.9 Million
Emp.: 25
Applied Research & Development of Software Products & Systems

N.A.I.C.S.: 513210
Amos Freedy *(Pres & CEO)*
Gershon Weltman *(Sr VP)*
Elan Freedy *(COO & VP-Engrg)*
Marvin Cohen *(VP-Cognitive Res)*
Ewart De Visser *(Dir-Human Factors & UX Res)*
Paul Scerri *(Dir-Robotics Lab)*

Subsidiaries:

Perceptronics Solutions, Inc. (1)
3141 Fairview Park Dr Ste 415, Falls Church, VA 22042
Tel.: (703) 342-4660
Web Site: http://www.percsolutions.com
Developer of Software Products & Systems
N.A.I.C.S.: 513210
Elan Freedy *(COO & VP-Engrg)*

Perceptronics Solutions, Inc. (1)
16501 Ventura Boulevard, Encino, CA 91436
Tel.: (818) 788-4830
Web Site: http://www.percsolutions.com
Software Research & Development
N.A.I.C.S.: 513210
Marvin Cohen *(VP & Sr Res Scientist)*

PERCEPTYX, INC.
27720 Jefferson Ave Ste 300, Temecula, CA 92590
Tel.: (951) 676-4414
Web Site: http://www.perceptyx.com
Year Founded: 1997
Employee Engagement Services
N.A.I.C.S.: 541612
Jack Morehouse *(COO & Exec VP)*
Andrew Morehouse *(VP-Bus Dev)*
John Borland *(Founder & CEO)*
Cheryl Kim *(CFO)*
Sham Telang *(CTO)*

Subsidiaries:

Waggl, Inc. (1)
1750 Bridgeway Ste B103, Sausalito, CA 94965
Tel.: (415) 399-9949
Web Site: http://www.waggl.com
Software Development Services
N.A.I.C.S.: 541512
Michael Papay *(CEO)*
Jeff Snipes *(Chm)*

PERCHERON INVESTMENT MANAGEMENT LP
One Letterman Dr Ste CP-500, San Francisco, CA 94129
Tel.: (415) 738-4340 DE
Web Site:
  https://percheroncapital.com
Year Founded: 2020
Privater Equity Firm
N.A.I.C.S.: 523940
Ann Rutherford *(Principal)*

Subsidiaries:

Animal Dermatology Group, Inc. (1)
19782 MacArthur Blvd Ste 285, Irvine, CA 92612
Tel.: (949) 390-2990
Web Site:
  https://www.animaldermatology.com
Veterinary Services
N.A.I.C.S.: 541940
Steven Mrha *(CEO)*
Adrian Ford *(VP-Ops)*

Subsidiary (Domestic):

Animal Dermatology & Allergy (2)
5175 Pacific St Ste B, Rocklin, CA 95677-2753
Tel.: (916) 632-2400
Web Site: http://www.adavet.com
Veterinary Services
N.A.I.C.S.: 541940

Animal Dermatology Clinic (2)
2965 Edinger Ave, Tustin, CA 92780
Tel.: (949) 936-0066
Web Site:
  http://www.animaldermatology.com

Sales Range: $1-9.9 Million
Emp.: 50
Veterinary Services
N.A.I.C.S.: 541940
Sharon Peterson *(Exec Dir)*

Animal Dermatology Referral Clinic (2)
4444 Trinity Mills Rd Ste 101, Dallas, TX 75287-7047
Tel.: (972) 267-3800
Web Site: http://www.dermvets.com
Marketing Research & Public Opinion Polling
N.A.I.C.S.: 541910
Reid A. Garfield *(Owner)*

SkinVet Clinic, LLC (2)
15800 Uppr Boones Ferry Rd, Lake Oswego, OR 97035-4085
Tel.: (503) 352-3376
Web Site: http://www.skinvetclinic.com
Ambulatory Surgical & Emergency Centers
N.A.I.C.S.: 621493

PERCHERON, LLC
1904 Grand Pkwy, Katy, TX 77449
Tel.: (832) 300-6400
Web Site:
  http://www.percheronllc.com
Sales Range: $10-24.9 Million
Emp.: 1,000
Land Services, Including Surveying & Environmental Services
N.A.I.C.S.: 541370
Ana Rausch *(Sr VP-Field Svcs)*
Terry L. Rowe *(Dir-GIS & HUB Dev)*
Trent Oglesby *(CEO-Percheron)*
Patrick Brady *(VP-Bus Dev)*
Aaron R. Yost *(Pres & Chief Mktg Officer)*
Cameron Riddels *(Project Mgr)*
Jim Bell *(VP-Bus Dev)*
Steve Grandon *(VP-Bus Dev & Field Svcs)*
Jeff Hieber *(VP-Bus Dev & Survey)*
Justin Lyon *(Sr VP-Field Svcs)*
Arch Stout *(VP-Survey)*
Jeff Trlicek *(Sr VP-Energy)*
Rebecca Harrington *(CFO)*

Subsidiaries:

OGM Land, LLC (1)
7920 FM 1489, Simonton, TX 77476
Tel.: (281) 346-2300
Web Site: http://www.ogmland.com
Sales Range: $10-24.9 Million
Emp.: 6
Land Services, Including Acquisition Management & Geographic Information System (GIS) Mapping Services
N.A.I.C.S.: 541370
Mike Fleniken *(CEO)*
Jeff Trlicek *(VP)*
Walter Hamlin *(Project Mgr)*

Percheron, LLC (1)
320 South View Dr Ste 400, Bridgeport, WV 26330
Tel.: (304) 842-9550
Web Site: http://www.percheronllc.com
Sales Range: $50-74.9 Million
Emp.: 10
Contract Land Services to Oil & Gas Exploration & Production Companies
N.A.I.C.S.: 213112

PERCONA LLC.
4125 Mohr Ave Ste H, Pleasanton, CA 94566
Tel.: (208) 473-2904
Web Site: http://www.percona.com
Year Founded: 2001
Sales Range: $10-24.9 Million
Emp.: 75
Software Product Development Services
N.A.I.C.S.: 541511
Peter Zaitsev *(CEO)*
Vadim Tkachenko *(CTO)*
Matt Yonkovit *(VP-Svcs)*
Jana Carmack *(Coord-Ops)*

Tim Sharp *(Acct Mgr-Technical)*
Kenny Gryp *(Principal & Architect)*
Liz van Dijk *(Sr Dir-Sls Ops)*
Dorothee Wuest *(VP-Sls-EMEA)*
Rob Young *(Exec VP-Product & Svcs)*
Jim Doherty *(Exec VP-Sls & Mktg)*
Andrew Moore *(Mgr-Technical Svcs)*
Ann Schlemmer *(Sr Dir-Customer Success)*
Eliana Yaffe *(Coord-Ops)*
Jamie Rosemary *(Coord-Ops)*
Jarrett Hardester *(Dir-Managed Svcs)*
Joseph Laflamme *(Mgr-Technical Svcs)*
Mark Sexton *(Dir-Contracts & Billing)*
Todd Spain *(COO)*
John Breitenfeld *(Exec VP-Sls)*

Subsidiaries:

Tokutek, Inc. (1)
57 Bedford St Ste 101, Lexington, MA 02420
Tel.: (212) 244-7600
Web Site: http://www.tokutek.com
Software Publisher
N.A.I.C.S.: 513210
John Partridge *(Pres & CEO)*
Dave Rosenlund *(VP-Mktg)*
Michael A. Bender *(Co-Founder & Chief Scientist)*
Martin Farach-Colton *(Co-Founder & CTO)*
Bradley C. Kuszmaul *(Co-Founder & Chief Architect)*

PERCUSSION SOFTWARE INC.

600 Unicorn Park Dr Ste 3, Woburn, MA 01801-3343
Tel.: (781) 438-9900
Web Site: http://www.percussion.com
Sales Range: $10-24.9 Million
Emp.: 100
Content Management Software
N.A.I.C.S.: 513210
Barry Reynolds *(Founder)*
Nancy Devine *(VP-HR)*
Mark Somol *(Pres & COO)*
Alan Matthews *(Founder)*
John Devin *(Founder)*
Jeff Gore *(Chief Revenue Officer)*

PERDUE FARMS INCORPORATED

31149 Old Ocean City Rd, Salisbury, MD 21804
Tel.: (410) 543-3949   MD
Web Site: https://www.perduefarms.com
Year Founded: 1920
Sales Range: $1-4.9 Billion
Emp.: 21,000
Poultry Processing
N.A.I.C.S.: 311615
James A. Perdue *(Chm)*
Steve Evans *(Pres-Perdue Prepared Foods)*
Steve Levitsky *(VP-Sustainability)*
Andrea Staub *(Sr VP-Corp Comm)*
Kelly Fladger *(VP-HR Svcs)*
Mark McKay *(Pres-Premium Meat)*
Eric Christianson *(CMO)*
Herb Frerichs *(Gen Counsel)*
Brenda Galgano *(CFO & Sr VP)*
Jeff Tripician *(Pres-Perdue Premium Meat Company L.L.C)*
Scott Fredericksen *(Pres-Perdue AgriBus)*
Lynn Clark *(Chief HR Officer & Sr VP)*

Subsidiaries:

Coleman Natural Foods, Inc. (1)
1667 Cole Blvd Ste 300, Golden, CO 80401
Tel.: (303) 468-2500
Web Site: http://www.colemannatural.com
Sales Range: $650-699.9 Million
Emp.: 2,300
Poultry, Pork & Processed Meat Mfr & Distr
N.A.I.C.S.: 311611

Unit (Domestic):

Draper Valley Farms Inc. (2)
1000 Jason Ln, Mount Vernon, WA 98273-2490
Tel.: (360) 424-7947
Web Site: http://www.drapervalleyfarms.com
Sales Range: $75-99.9 Million
Emp.: 500
Poultry Hatchery, Feed Mill & Processing Plant
N.A.I.C.S.: 311615

Petaluma Poultry (2)
PO Box 7368, Petaluma, CA 94955
Tel.: (410) 341-2533
Web Site: http://www.petalumapoultry.com
Sales Range: $25-49.9 Million
Emp.: 300
Poultry Feed Mill & Processing
N.A.I.C.S.: 311615
Matt Junkel *(Pres)*

Natural Food Holdings, Inc. (1)
2800 Murray St, Sioux City, IA 51111
Holding Company; Animal Ranch Operator, Meat Processor & Food Whslr
N.A.I.C.S.: 551112
Marlys Werkmeister *(Mgr-Procurement)*

Subsidiary (Domestic):

Niman Ranch, Inc. (2)
1765 W 121st Ave Ste 400, Westminster, CO 80234
Web Site: http://www.nimanranch.com
Emp.: 35
Animal Ranch Operator & Egg Production
N.A.I.C.S.: 112111
Alicja Spaulding *(VP-Mktg)*
Chris Oliviero *(Gen Mgr)*
Alicia LaPorte *(Dir-Comm)*
John Flynn *(VP-Sls)*

Sioux-Preme Packing Co. (2)
4241 US 75 Ave, Sioux Center, IA 51250
Tel.: (712) 722-2555
Web Site: http://www.siouxpremepork.com
Meat Processor, Packer & Whslr
N.A.I.C.S.: 311611
Gary Malenke *(Pres)*
Dick White *(CFO)*

Pennsylvania Agricultural Commodities Marketing Association (1)
475 E High St, Palmyra, PA 17078
Tel.: (717) 838-7050
Web Site: http://www.pacmainc.com
Sales Range: $10-24.9 Million
Emp.: 33
Commodities Pricing Contracts Broker
N.A.I.C.S.: 424510

Perdue Farms Hatchery, Inc. (1)
758 Enterprise Rd, Dillon, SC 29536
Tel.: (843) 841-9451
Web Site: http://www.perdue.com
Poultry Hatcheries
N.A.I.C.S.: 112340
Mike Guzman *(Gen Mgr)*
Carlos Ayala *(VP)*
Jay Simpson *(Dir-Global)*
Mitch Boswell *(Dir-Sls)*

PERDUE INC.

5 W Forsyth St Ste 100, Jacksonville, FL 32202-3603
Tel.: (904) 737-5858
Web Site: http://www.perdueoffice.com
Sales Range: $25-49.9 Million
Emp.: 30
Office Furniture
N.A.I.C.S.: 423210
Vince McCormick *(Pres)*
Gaye Hanley *(Gen Mgr)*

PEREGRIN TECHNOLOGIES INC

1225 NW Murray Rd Ste 112, Portland, OR 97229-5416
Tel.: (503) 690-1111
Web Site: http://www.peregrin.net
Sales Range: $1-9.9 Million
Emp.: 2
Banking Services
N.A.I.C.S.: 522110
Sam Bosch *(Owner)*

PEREGRINE AVIATION SERVICES

505 Main St Ste 208, Hackensack, NJ 07601
Tel.: (201) 342-3700
Web Site: http://www.peregrineaviation.com
Year Founded: 1984
Rev.: $17,555,315
Emp.: 10
Provider of Aircraft Marketing, Consulting Services & Supplies
N.A.I.C.S.: 423860
Scott Dandeneau *(Pres)*
Steven Dandeneau *(VP)*
Patricia Dandeneau *(Dir-Mktg)*

PEREGRINE ENERGY CORP.

220 N Main St Ste 603, Greenville, SC 29601-2129
Tel.: (864) 242-4624
Web Site: http://www.peregrinecorp.net
Year Founded: 1993
Sales Range: $10-24.9 Million
Emp.: 5
Gas Producers, Generators & Other Gas Related Equipment
N.A.I.C.S.: 333998
Ralph H. Walker Jr. *(Pres)*

Subsidiaries:

Kannapolis Energy Partners Llc (1)
1 Lk Cir Dr, Kannapolis, NC 28081
Tel.: (704) 933-1202
Sales Range: $10-24.9 Million
Combination Utilities
N.A.I.C.S.: 541330

PEREGRINE FINANCIAL GROUP, INC.

1 Peregrine Way, Cedar Falls, IA 50613
Tel.: (319) 553-2100   IA
Web Site: http://www.pfgbest.com
Year Founded: 1990
Sales Range: $250-299.9 Million
Emp.: 300
Electronic Futures & Foreign Exchange Brokerage & Dealing Services
N.A.I.C.S.: 523160
Brenda Cuypers *(CFO)*
Rebecca J. Wing *(Gen Counsel)*
Liam J. Boyle *(CIO)*
Susan O'Meara *(Chief Compliance Officer)*
Brian Gelinas *(Mgr-IT)*
Brian Osborne *(Pres)*
Eric Schwarz *(Exec VP)*
Paul Deutch *(Exec Mng Dir)*
Russell R. Wasendorf Sr. *(Chm & CEO)*

Subsidiaries:

Peregrine Financial Group, Inc. - Chicago (1)
311 W Monroe Ste1300, Chicago, IL 60603
Tel.: (312) 775-3000
Web Site: http://www.pfgbest.com
Electronic Futures & Foreign Exchange Brokerage & Dealing Services
N.A.I.C.S.: 523160

Subsidiary (Domestic):

American National Trading Corp. (2)
12300 Wilshire Blvd 2nd Fl, Los Angeles, CA 90025
Tel.: (310) 442-3900
Rev.: $12,000,000
Emp.: 42
Electronic Futures & Foreign Exchange Brokerage & Dealing Services
N.A.I.C.S.: 523160

PEREIRA & O'DELL

215 2nd St, San Francisco, CA 94105
Tel.: (415) 284-9916
Web Site: http://www.pereiraodell.com
Emp.: 100
Digital/Interactive, Integrated Marketing
N.A.I.C.S.: 541810
Andrew O'Dell *(CEO)*
P. J. Pereira *(Founder & Chm-Creative)*
Gary Theut *(Dir-Acct Svc)*
Robert Lambrecht *(Assoc Dir-Creative)*
Jason Apaliski *(Exec Dir-Creative)*
Lauren Harwell *(Assoc Creative Dir)*
Joshua Brandau *(Dir-Media Strategy)*
Nick Chapman *(Dir-Brand Strategy)*
Nancy Daum *(COO & CFO)*
P. J. Pereira *(Founder & Dir-Creative)*
Jonathan Woytek *(Dir-Creative)*
Paulo Coelho *(Assoc Dir-Creative)*
Cory Berger *(Mng Dir-New York)*
Tennille Teague *(Head-Production-New York)*
Matt Herrmann *(Chief Strategy Officer)*
Chris Wilcox *(VP-Partnerships)*
Rob Lambrechts *(Chief Creative Officer)*
Ryan Toland *(Dir-Client Svcs)*
Henry Arlander *(Mng Dir)*

PERELLI ENTERPRISES, INC.

60 Clark Rd, Battle Creek, MI 49037
Tel.: (269) 964-1212
Web Site: http://play.advantagesintered.com
Year Founded: 1990
Sales Range: $10-24.9 Million
Emp.: 140
Rolled Steel Shape Mfr
N.A.I.C.S.: 331221
Jet Perelli *(Pres)*
Bob Dayton *(Exec VP)*
Mihai Atudori *(Sr VP-Global Sls)*
Monica Chen *(Sr VP-Global Sls)*
Tom Haberberger *(Sr VP-Global En-grg)*

PEREZ & MORRIS LLC

8000 Ravines Edge Ct Ste 300, Columbus, OH 43235-5422
Web Site: http://www.perez-morris.com
Emp.: 100
Law firm
N.A.I.C.S.: 541110
Juan Jose Perez *(Owner)*

Subsidiaries:

Giffen & Kaminski, LLC (1)
Penton Media Bldg 1300 E 9th St Ste 1600, Cleveland, OH 44114-1573
Tel.: (216) 621-5161
Web Site: http://www.thinkgk.com
Emp.: 14
Law Firm
N.A.I.C.S.: 541110
Peggy Foley Jones *(Atty)*
Kerin Lyn Kaminski *(Atty)*
Kathleen Nitschke *(Partner)*
William Joseph Baker *(Partner)*
Karen L. Giffen *(Atty)*

PEREZ TRADING CO. INC.

3490 NW 125th St, Miami, FL 33167-2412
Tel.: (305) 769-0761   NY
Web Site: http://www.pereztrading.com
Year Founded: 1947

Perez Trading Co. Inc. — (Continued)
Sales Range: $550-599.9 Million
Emp.: 135
Whslr & Exporter of Paper & Paperboard Equipment & Supplies
N.A.I.C.S.: 424110
John D. Perez (Pres & CEO)
Carl A. Perez (Sr VP)

PERF-FORM PRODUCTS, INC.
1236 Edmonson Ave, Monticello, MN 55362
Tel.: (763) 314-0870
Web Site: http://www.perf-form.com
Year Founded: 1981
Motorcycle Oil Filters Mfr
N.A.I.C.S.: 336991

PERFECT AIR & HOME IMPROVEMENT INC.
4341 Fox Valley Ctr Dr, Aurora, IL 60504
Tel.: (630) 866-3330
Web Site: http://www.perfecthomeservices.com
Year Founded: 1992
Air Conditioning, Furnace & Heating Services
N.A.I.C.S.: 333415

PERFECT CARE INC.
8927 126th St, Richmond Hill, NY 11418
Tel.: (718) 805-7800
Sales Range: $10-24.9 Million
Emp.: 25
Sales of Medical Equipment & Supplies
N.A.I.C.S.: 423450
Kevin Mernone (CEO)

PERFECT COMMERCE HOLDINGS, LLC.
1 Compass Way Suite 120, Newport News, VA 23606
Tel.: (757) 766-8211
Web Site: http://www.perfect.com
Sales Range: $10-24.9 Million
Emp.: 100
Procurement Software Solution Operating Services
N.A.I.C.S.: 423490
Tripp Shannon (CFO)
Nikki Lowe (VP)
Vernon Warner (VP)

Subsidiaries:

Hubwoo S.A. (1)
28 Quai Gallieni, 92153, Suresnes, Cedex, France (88.51%)
Tel.: (33) 153255500
Web Site: http://www.hubwoo.com
On-Demand Supplier Relationship Management Solutions
N.A.I.C.S.: 541519
Sergio Lovera (CFO)
George Hampton Wall (Chm & CEO)
Tripp Shannon (COO & Head-M&A)
Martial Gerardin (Mng Dir)
David Bates (CTO)
Michael Bermudez (Gen Counsel)

PERFECT MARKETING CORPORATION
1650 Broadway Ste 1103, New York, NY 10019
Tel.: (212) 541-4620
Web Site: http://www.pmcglobal.com
Rev.: $10,483,519
Emp.: 5
Theatrical Production Services
N.A.I.C.S.: 711110
George Braun (Pres)

PERFECT SHUTTERS INC.
12213 Hwy 173, Hebron, IL 60034-9610
Tel.: (815) 648-2401
Web Site: http://www.perfectshutters.com
Year Founded: 1976
Component Plastic Shutters Mfr
N.A.I.C.S.: 326199
Dave Thomas (Mgr-Natl Sls)

PERFECTION FOODS COMPANY, INC.
3901 Old York Rd, Philadelphia, PA 19140
Tel.: (215) 455-5400
Web Site: http://www.perfectionfoods.com
Year Founded: 1990
Sales Range: $10-24.9 Million
Emp.: 100
Processed Meat Mfr
N.A.I.C.S.: 311612
Hanh D. Tran (Pres)

PERFECTION GROUP, INC.
2649 Commerce Blvd, Cincinnati, OH 45241-1553
Tel.: (513) 772-7545 OH
Web Site: http://www.perfectiongroup.com
Year Founded: 1952
Sales Range: $100-124.9 Million
Emp.: 250
Plumbing, Heating & Air-Conditioning
N.A.I.C.S.: 238220
Marianne Straley (CFO)
Tony Apro (Pres)
Todd Albrecht (VP)
John Albrecht (VP)

PERFECTION LEARNING CORPORATION
1000 N 2nd Ave, Logan, IA 51546
Tel.: (712) 644-2831
Web Site: http://www.perfectionlearning.com
Year Founded: 1926
Sales Range: $25-49.9 Million
Emp.: 145
Publisher of Books
N.A.I.C.S.: 513130
Steven J. Keay (Pres & CEO)
Mark Hagenberg (Dir-Mktg Ops)
Kristin Hipwell (Dir-Mktg)

PERFECTION MACHINERY SALES, INC.
2550 Arthur Ave, Elk Grove Village, IL 60007-6018
Tel.: (847) 427-3333 IL
Web Site: http://www.perfectionmachinery.com
Year Founded: 1984
Sales Range: $10-24.9 Million
Emp.: 25
Industrial Machinery & Equipment
N.A.I.C.S.: 423830
Jennifer Reiner (Engr-Sls)
Richard Otap (Mgr-Traffic)

PERFECTO INDUSTRIES INC.
1567 Calkins Dr, Gaylord, MI 49735
Tel.: (989) 732-2941
Web Site: http://www.perfectoindustries.com
Year Founded: 1948
Rev.: $12,335,000
Emp.: 65
Rolling Mill Machinery
N.A.I.C.S.: 333519
Heaven Roberts (Owner)

PERFORM GROUP, LLC
333 E 7th Ave, York, PA 17404-2144
Tel.: (717) 852-6900 PA
Web Site: http://www.tighe.com
Year Founded: 1946
Sales Range: $200-249.9 Million
Emp.: 325
Costumes & Leotards for Misses, Men, Juniors & Children Designer & Mfr
N.A.I.C.S.: 315250
Jane A. Deamer (VP-Fin)
John Wayne Misner (Pres & COO)
Leroy A. King Jr. (Chm & CEO)

Subsidiaries:

Perform Group, LLC - Alpha Factor Division (1)
333 E 7th Ave, York, PA 17402
Tel.: (800) 825-7428
Web Site: http://www.alphafactor.com
Gymnastic Apparel Mfr
N.A.I.C.S.: 339920

PERFORMANCE ARCHITECTS INC.
470 Atlantic Ave 4th Fl, Boston, MA 02210
Tel.: (617) 273-8175
Web Site: http://www.performancearchitects.com
Year Founded: 2006
Sales Range: $1-9.9 Million
Emp.: 20
Business & Technology Consulting
N.A.I.C.S.: 541618
Mark Solimini (Co-Founder & CEO)
Ken Chen (Co-Founder & COO)
Andy Tauro (Mgr)
Michael Bender (Dir-Consulting Practice)
Ron Woodlock (Mgr)
Chuck Persky (VP-Consulting Practice)
Doug Ross (Mgr-Consulting Practice)
John McGale (Mgr-Consulting Practice)
Rich Pallotta (Dir-Consulting Practice)
Sreekanth Kumar (Mgr-Consulting Practice)

PERFORMANCE AUTOMOTIVE NETWORK
5726 Dixie Hwy, Fairfield, OH 45014-4204
Tel.: (513) 870-5000 OH
Web Site: http://www.performanceautoplex.com
Year Founded: 1970
Sales Range: $250-299.9 Million
Emp.: 650
Sales of Automobiles
N.A.I.C.S.: 423110
Michael L. Dever (Pres)
Ken Kocher (Dir-Field Ops)
Shane Deber (Dir-Ops)

PERFORMANCE BROKERAGE SERVICES, INC.
7545 Irvine Center Dr Ste 200, Irvine, CA 92618
Tel.: (949) 461-1372
Web Site: http://www.performancebrokerageservices.com
Sales Range: $1-9.9 Million
Automobile & Motorcycle Dealership Brokerage Services
N.A.I.C.S.: 561499
Moshe Stopnitzky (Pres)

PERFORMANCE CHEVROLET LLC
4811 Madison Ave, Sacramento, CA 95841
Tel.: (916) 331-6777
Web Site: http://www.performancechevy.com
Sales Range: $100-124.9 Million
Emp.: 120
Sales of New & Used Cars
N.A.I.C.S.: 441110
John McMichael (Pres)
Kevin Bowers (Gen Mgr)
Valerie McMichael (VP)

PERFORMANCE COATINGS INTERNATIONAL LABORATORIES, LLC
600 S Murray St, Bangor, PA 18013
Tel.: (610) 588-7900 PA
Web Site: http://www.pcoatingsintl.com
High Abrasion Resistance Coatings Mfr
N.A.I.C.S.: 325510
George E. Drazinakis (Pres & CEO)
Colleen Heiser (Gen Mgr)
Rick Longo (Mgr-Tech)
Igor Khudyakov (Dir-Technical-R&D)

PERFORMANCE COMPANIES, INC.
2929 N Stemmons Fwy, Dallas, TX 75247-6102
Tel.: (214) 665-1000 TX
Web Site: http://www.performancecompanies.com
Year Founded: 1981
Sales Range: $125-149.9 Million
Emp.: 250
Specialty Printer & Display Manufacturer; Producer of Transaction Cards
N.A.I.C.S.: 457120
John T. White (Pres & CEO)

PERFORMANCE CONTRACTING GROUP
11145 Thompson Ave, Lenexa, KS 66219
Tel.: (913) 888-8600 DE
Web Site: http://www.performancecontracting.com
Year Founded: 1987
Sales Range: $600-649.9 Million
Emp.: 6,000
Building Insulation Acoustical & Ceiling Work Thermal Insulation Services
N.A.I.C.S.: 238990
William P. Massey (Pres & CEO)
Jason Hendricks (COO)
Tom Gallagher (Sr VP-Ops & ISS Div)
Pat Roth (Sr VP-Ops & Interior Div)

Subsidiaries:

Masthead International, Inc. (1)
3602 S 16th St, Phoenix, AZ 85040
Tel.: (602) 276-5373
Web Site: http://www.mastheadriggingcrating.com
Rigging, Packaging & Crating Services
N.A.I.C.S.: 488991
Anthony Rooney (Gen Mgr)

PCI Ardmac (1)
30 Westbrook Road Trafford Park, Manchester, M17 1AY, United Kingdom
Tel.: (44) 161 848 9002
Web Site: http://www.ardmac.com
Sales Range: $25-49.9 Million
Emp.: 150
Interior Design Services
N.A.I.C.S.: 541410

PCI Insul-Energy Inc. (1)
110 Chain Lake Dr Unit 3-J, Halifax, B3S 1A9, NS, Canada
Tel.: (902) 407-4060
Web Site: http://www.pciinsul-energy.com
Mechanical Insulation Installation Services
N.A.I.C.S.: 541330

PCI Promatec (1)
8846 S Sam Houston Pkwy W Ste 120, Houston, TX 77064
Tel.: (281) 933-7222
Web Site: http://www.promatec.com
Sealant Whslr
N.A.I.C.S.: 424690

COMPANIES

Performance Abatement Services, Inc. (1)
999 Canal St Ste B, Richmond, CA 94804
Tel.: (510) 236-0300
Web Site: http://www.pasmoldsolutions.com
Remediation Services
N.A.I.C.S.: 562910

Performance Contracting Group, Inc. (1)
208 E Woodlawn Rd Ste 200, Charlotte, NC 28217-2230 (100%)
Tel.: (704) 529-8000
Sales Range: $10-24.9 Million
Emp.: 4
Building Insulation; Acoustical & Ceiling Work; Thermal Insulation
N.A.I.C.S.: 238310

Performance Contracting, Inc. - ISS Division (1)
221 Beltway Green Blvd, Pasadena, TX 77503-5837
Tel.: (713) 675-8586
Web Site: http://www.pcg.com
Sales Range: $25-49.9 Million
Emp.: 130
Specialty Contractors
N.A.I.C.S.: 238310
Tim Lampard (Mgr)

PERFORMANCE CONTRACTORS INC.
9901 Pecue Ln, Baton Rouge, LA 70810-2210
Tel.: (225) 751-4156   LA
Web Site: http://www.performance-br.com
Year Founded: 1979
Sales Range: $150-199.9 Million
Emp.: 2,500
Contracting & Construction Services
N.A.I.C.S.: 236210
Ken Carr (Dir-Bus Dev)
Jerome Mabile (Dir-Quality Control)

PERFORMANCE DOOR & HARDWARE, INC.
3710 W Royal Ln Ste 185, Irving, TX 75063
Tel.: (972) 721-1944
Web Site: http://www.performancedoor.com
Year Founded: 1994
Sales Range: $10-24.9 Million
Emp.: 25
Door Frames, All Materials
N.A.I.C.S.: 423310
Jay Kautzman (Chm & Pres)
James Hawxhurst (VP)
Joe Byington (VP-Field Ops)
Rhonda Horton (Mgr-Estimating)
Mark Johnson (Sr Project Mgr)
Jeff Harlan (VP)
Jeff Kerr (Controller)
Gregg Jeter (Sr Project Mgr)
John Stallcup (Project Mgr)

PERFORMANCE ENGINEERED PRODUCTS INC.
3270 Pomona Blvd, Pomona, CA 91768
Tel.: (909) 594-7487
Web Site: https://pepincplastics.com
Emp.: 100
Plastics Product Mfr
N.A.I.C.S.: 326199
Dennis Savalia (Owner & CEO)

Subsidiaries:

Molding Corporation of America (1)
10349 Norris Ave, Pacoima, CA 91331
Tel.: (818) 890-7877
Web Site: http://www.moldingcorp.com
Sales Range: $1-9.9 Million
Emp.: 50
Plastics Product Mfr
N.A.I.C.S.: 326199
David Daws (VP)
John Knight (Mgr-Sls)

PERFORMANCE EQUITY MANAGEMENT, LLC
5 Greenwich Office Park 3rd Floor, Greenwich, CT 06831
Tel.: (203) 742-2400
Web Site: http://www.peqm.com
Year Founded: 2005
Investment Advice Services
N.A.I.C.S.: 523940
John Clark (Pres)
Jeffrey Barman (Mng Dir & Chief Investment Officer)
Marcia Haydel (Mng Dir)
Frank Brenninkmeyer (Mng Dir)
Jeffrey Reals (Mng Dir)
Lawrence Rusoff (Mng Dir)
James Tybur (Mng Dir)
Keith Brocker (VP)
Brian Ward (Head-Bus Dev & Consultant Rels)
Smita Dak (Head-IR)
Taylor Horty (Assoc Dir-Bus Dev)
Jon DeKlerk (COO & Chief Compliance Officer)
Christopher B. Millin (CFO)
Paul Schmitt (Chief Data Officer)
Anita Windels (Dir-HR & Office Admin)
Christopher A. Bach (Mgr-Ops)
Cynthia Vozzo (Mgr-Corp Acctg)
Julianna Murray (Assoc Dir-Bus Dev)

PERFORMANCE FRICTION CORP.
83 Carbon Metallic Hwy, Clover, SC 29710
Tel.: (803) 222-2141   SC
Web Site: http://www.performancefriction.com
Year Founded: 1953
Sales Range: $10-24.9 Million
Emp.: 300
Provider of Motor Vehicle Brake Systems & Parts
N.A.I.C.S.: 336340
Thomas Davis (Treas)

PERFORMANCE GROUP, INC.
22 W Main St, Ephrata, PA 17522
Tel.: (717) 733-6367   PA
Web Site: http://www.tpgworks.com
Year Founded: 1993
Rev.: $13,500,000
Emp.: 50
Temporary Help Service
N.A.I.C.S.: 561320
Justin Doyle (VP & Dir-IS)
Anne McCaulley (VP & Mgr-Risk)
Kimberly Mohr (Dir-Ops)
Paul Mohr (Pres & Owner)
Gregg Monteleone (VP & Dir-Sls)
Todd Hollinger (Asst VP)
Kim Ellis (VP & Dir-Ops)
Barry Harsch (Mgr-Facilities)

PERFORMANCE INDICATOR, LLC
116 John St S Mill 1st Fl, Lowell, MA 01852
Tel.: (978) 459-4500
Web Site: http://www.performanceindicator.com
Year Founded: 2001
Sales Range: $1-9.9 Million
Emp.: 30
Indicator Technology Development Services
N.A.I.C.S.: 561439
Daniel L. Smith (Pres)
Robb J. Osinski (CEO)
Satish Agrawal (CTO)
Paul S. Hovsepian (Sr VP-Corp Continuity)
Lee A. Silvestre (Sr VP-Corp Resource & Responsibility)
Weiyi Jia (VP)

PERFORMANCE INDUSTRIES INC.
7740 E Gelding Dr Ste 2, Scottsdale, AZ 85260
Tel.: (480) 951-1705
Sales Range: $10-24.9 Million
Emp.: 200
Eating Place
N.A.I.C.S.: 722511
Joe Hrudka (Pres)
Donna Monaco (Office Mgr)

PERFORMANCE MARKETING OF IOWA, INC.
1501 42nd St Ste 550, West Des Moines, IA 50266
Tel.: (515) 440-3550
Web Site: http://www.performancemarketing.com
Sales Range: $10-24.9 Million
Emp.: 57
Advertising Services
N.A.I.C.S.: 541810
Kevin Lentz (Owner)
Sarah Miller (Dir-Acct Svcs)

PERFORMANCE MEDICAL GROUP
803 Cajundome Blvd, Lafayette, LA 70506-2307
Tel.: (337) 237-1924   LA
Web Site: http://www.performancemedicalgroup.com
Year Founded: 1972
Sales Range: $125-149.9 Million
Emp.: 22
Retailer of X-Ray Film Chemicals & Equipment
N.A.I.C.S.: 423450
Michelle Hardeman (Pres)

PERFORMANCE PACKAGING
6430 Medical Center St Ste 102, Las Vegas, NV 89148
Tel.: (702) 240-3457
Web Site: http://www.pplv.co
Year Founded: 1994
Sales Range: $1-9.9 Million
Emp.: 9
Packaging Services
N.A.I.C.S.: 561910
Robert Reinders (Pres)
Blair M. Vance (VP-Sls & Mktg)

PERFORMANCE PAPER LLC
6285 E Slauson Ave, Commerce, CA 90040
Tel.: (323) 767-2800
Sales Range: $10-24.9 Million
Emp.: 47
Converted Paper Products
N.A.I.C.S.: 322299
Paul M. Maier (Pres)
Ed Lee (Mgr-Ops)

PERFORMANCE PERSONNEL PARTNERS, LLC
7815 N Dale Mabry Ste 211, Tampa, FL 33614
Tel.: (813) 800-5627
Web Site: http://www.performancepersonnel.com
Year Founded: 2019
Staffing & Recruiting Services
N.A.I.C.S.: 561311
Mike Baker (Mng Dir-Bus Dev)

Subsidiaries:

Oasis Staffing, Inc. (1)
252 N Mosley, Wichita, KS 67202
Tel.: (316) 682-2121
Web Site: http://www.oasisstaffing.com

PERFORMANCE SOFTWARE CORPORATION

Human Resources & Executive Search Consulting Services
N.A.I.C.S.: 541612
Ruth Cyrus (Sr VP-Mktg)
Mike Viola (Exec VP-Sls)
Mark C. Perlberg (Pres & CEO)
Myron Blackmon (Exec VP-Ops)

PERFORMANCE PETROPLEX INC.
2010 Rosa L Park Bld, Nashville, TN 37208
Tel.: (615) 221-5000
Web Site: http://www.nashvillelexus.com
Sales Range: $10-24.9 Million
Emp.: 62
New & Used Car Dealer
N.A.I.C.S.: 441110
J. R. Roper (Gen Mgr)

PERFORMANCE PRESS, INC.
2000 Platinum Rd, Apopka, FL 32703
Tel.: (407) 788-1234   FL
Web Site: http://www.ppiprints.com
Year Founded: 1994
Sales Range: $1-9.9 Million
Emp.: 20
Print & Marketing Logistics Services
N.A.I.C.S.: 323120
Gregory V. Gill (Pres & CEO)
Tod Ellington (COO)
Brian Gill (VP-Sls)
Darren Crampton (Dir-Natl Accts)
Keal Blache (Chief Mktg Officer)
Tiffany Aagaard (CFO)

PERFORMANCE PROCESS, INC.
1515 Reidel Dr, Mundelein, IL 60060
Tel.: (847) 949-4080
Web Site: http://www.ppiinc.com
Sales Range: $10-24.9 Million
Emp.: 40
Mfr of Industrial Defoamers
N.A.I.C.S.: 424690
Robert W. Scobell (Pres)
Mark Smith (VP)
Jack Schuiteman (VP)

Subsidiaries:

Nottingham Company Inc. (1)
1303 Boyd Ave NW, Atlanta, GA 30325-0049
Tel.: (404) 351-3501
Web Site: http://www.chemcompany.com
Rev.: $25,000,000
Emp.: 20
Chemicals & Allied Products
N.A.I.C.S.: 424690

PERFORMANCE REVIEW INSTITUTE, INC.
161 Thorn Hill Rd, Warrendale, PA 15086-7527
Tel.: (724) 772-1616   PA
Web Site: http://www.p-r-i.org
Year Founded: 1990
Sales Range: $1-9.9 Million
Emp.: 75
Business Support Services
N.A.I.C.S.: 561499
Scott Klavon (Dir-Nadoap Program & Aerospace Ops)
Jim Phillis (Controller)
Jon Steffey (Program Mgr-Informatics Solutions)
Dana M. Pless (Sec)
David L. Schutt (Pres)
Etienne Galan (Chm)
Karen Conroy (Mgr-HR & Admin)
Michael J. Hayward (COO & Exec VP)
Randy Daugharthy (Dir-Registrar Program)
Seema Martin (Dir-European Ops)

PERFORMANCE SOFTWARE CORPORATION

PERFORMANCE SOFTWARE CORPORATION

U.S. PRIVATE

Performance Software Corporation—(Continued)
2095 W Pinnacle Peak Rd Ste 120,
Phoenix, AZ 85027
Tel.: (623) 337-8003 AZ
Web Site: http://www.psware.com
Year Founded: 1998
Sales Range: $10-24.9 Million
Emp.: 109
Software Developer & Custom Computer Programming Services
N.A.I.C.S.: 513210
Timothy A. Bigelow *(Chief Dev Officer)*
Mark Latham *(Dir-Fin)*
Raj Ghate *(Dir-Sls & Mktg)*

PERFORMANCE STRENGTH DESIGNS, INC.
PO Box 4664, West Columbia, SC 29171
Tel.: (803) 750-0122
Web Site: http://www.totalstrengthandspeed.com
Year Founded: 1998
Sales Range: $1-9.9 Million
Emp.: 32
Athletic Training & Weight Equipment Mfr
N.A.I.C.S.: 339920
Eric Smith *(VP)*
Scott Williams *(Pres)*

Subsidiaries:
Total Strength and Speed (1)
720 Chris Dr, West Columbia, SC 29169 (100%)
Tel.: (888) 532-8227
Web Site: http://www.totalstrengthandspeed.com
Strength Training Product, Equipment & Accessories Mfr
N.A.I.C.S.: 339920
Eric Smith *(Mgr-Sls)*

PERFORMANCE SUPERSTORE
Loop 59 S, Atlanta, TX 75551
Tel.: (903) 796-2848
Sales Range: $25-49.9 Million
Emp.: 40
New Car Whslr
N.A.I.C.S.: 441110
Jeff Elwood *(Principal)*

PERFORMANCE SYSTEMS INTEGRATION, LLC
7324 SW Durham Rd, Portland, OR 97224
Tel.: (503) 641-2222
Web Site: https://www.psintegrated.com
Fire & Life Safety Protection Services
N.A.I.C.S.: 922160
Travis Everton *(CEO)*

Subsidiaries:
Integrated Fire Systems, Inc. (1)
21235 Canyon Way, Colfax, CA 95713-9296
Web Site: http://www.integratedfiresystems.com
Security System Services
N.A.I.C.S.: 561621
Julie Rios *(Partner)*

PERFORMANCE TOYOTA
5676 Dixie Hwy, Fairfield, OH 45014
Tel.: (513) 874-8797
Web Site: http://www.performancetoyotastore.com
Year Founded: 1976
Sales Range: $10-24.9 Million
Emp.: 76
Car Whslr
N.A.I.C.S.: 441110
Michael L. Dever *(Pres)*

PERFORMANCE TRUCK PRODUCTS
9421 FM 2920 Bldg #3, Tomball, TX 77375
Tel.: (888) 516-4644
Web Site: http://www.performancetruckproducts.com
Year Founded: 2003
Sales Range: $1-9.9 Million
Emp.: 6
Retails Performance Parts & Accessories for Gas & Diesel Equipped Pickup Trucks
N.A.I.C.S.: 441330
Nate Dwyer *(Owner)*
Tedra Ortega *(Mgr-Mktg)*

PERFORMANCE VALIDATION, INC.
Two Park Fletcher 5420 W Southern Ave Ste 100, Indianapolis, IN 46241
Tel.: (855) 737-3825
Web Site: http://perfval.com
Medical Validation Services
N.A.I.C.S.: 621511
Richard Van Doel *(CEO)*

Subsidiaries:
Welsh Commissioning Group, Inc. (1)
4508 Auburn Way N Ste B, Auburn, WA 98002-1381
Tel.: (253) 856-3322
Web Site: http://www.wcxg.com
Engineeering Services
N.A.I.C.S.: 541330
Bryan Welsh *(Pres & Principal)*

PERFORMANT MANAGEMENT COMPANY, LLC
150 N Wacker Dr Ste 1000, Chicago, IL 60606
Tel.: (866) 500-6161 DE
Web Site: http://www.performantcapital.com
Privater Equity Firm
N.A.I.C.S.: 523999
Michael Ciaglia *(Partner)*
Jeff Dillon *(Partner)*

Subsidiaries:
Bolt On Technology, LLC (1)
1105 Industrial Blvd, Southampton, PA 18966-4160
Tel.: (610) 400-1019
Web Site: http://www.boltontechnology.com
Sales Range: $1-9.9 Million
Software Development Services
N.A.I.C.S.: 541511
Michael Risich *(Founder & CEO)*
Tim Cifelli *(Dir-Mktg)*
John Borkowski *(Dir-Sls & Customer Support-Natl)*
Frank Dragoni *(Dir-Sls & Corp Partnerships)*

PERFORMLINE INC.
58 S St, Morristown, NJ 07960
Tel.: (973) 590-2305
Web Site: http://www.performline.com
Software Publisher
N.A.I.C.S.: 513210
Mario Vaccari *(VP-Product Mgmt)*
Alex Baydin *(Founder & CEO)*
Paul Wilmore *(COO)*

Subsidiaries:
LashBack, LLC (1)
4240 Duncan Ave Ste 200, Saint Louis, MO 63110
Tel.: (314) 754-0999
Web Site: http://www.lashback.com
Information Services
N.A.I.C.S.: 519290
Andy McKay *(VP)*
Francis Chmelir *(Pres)*
Sydni Wilson *(Coord-Mktg)*

PERFUMANIA HOLDINGS, INC.
35 Sawgrass Dr Ste 2, Bellport, NY 11713
Tel.: (631) 866-4100 FL
Web Site: http://perfumaniaholdings.com
Year Founded: 1980
Sales Range: $450-499.9 Million
Holding Company; Discount Retail Fragrances
N.A.I.C.S.: 456120
Stephen L. Nussdorf *(Chm)*
Michael W. Katz *(Pres & CEO)*
Neal Montany *(COO)*
Michael Nofi *(CFO)*
Sarah Meehan *(Sec)*
Pat Beh Werblin *(VP-Adv & PR)*
Paolo Rosellini *(VP-Intl)*

Subsidiaries:
Five Star Fragrance Company, Inc. (1)
35 Sawgrass Dri, Bellport, NY 11703 (100%)
Tel.: (631) 866-4073
Sales Range: $10-24.9 Million
Emp.: 30
Perfume Distr
N.A.I.C.S.: 424210

Parlux Fragrances, LLC (1)
5900 N Andrews Ave Ste 500, Fort Lauderdale, FL 33309
Tel.: (954) 316-9008
Web Site: http://www.parlux.com
Sales Range: $100-124.9 Million
Emp.: 135
Fragrances & Related Products Designer, Mfr, Distr & Marketer
N.A.I.C.S.: 325620
Lori Singer *(Pres)*

Perfumania Puerto Rico, Inc. (1)
415 Prime Outlets Blvd, Barceloneta, PR 00617
Tel.: (787) 846-6802
Web Site: http://www.perfumania.com
Cosmetic Product Retailer
N.A.I.C.S.: 456120
Samary Marrero *(Gen Mgr)*

Perfumania, Inc. (1)
251 International Pkwy, Sunrise, FL 33325
Tel.: (954) 335-9100
Web Site: http://www.perfumania.com
Sales Range: $100-124.9 Million
Emp.: 150
Fragrances & Related Products Retailer
N.A.I.C.S.: 456120
Michael W. Katz *(Pres & CEO)*
Donald J. Loftus *(Exec VP)*

Quality King Fragrance, Inc. (1)
35 Sawgrass Dr Ste 2, Bellport, NY 11713-1576
Tel.: (631) 866-4100
Sales Range: $25-49.9 Million
Emp.: 100
Fragrances, Drug Proprietaries & Sundries Whslr
N.A.I.C.S.: 424210
Steven Nussdorf *(Pres)*

PERICH ADVERTISING + DESIGN
117 N 1st St Ste 100, Ann Arbor, MI 48104-1354
Tel.: (734) 769-2215
Web Site: http://www.perich.com
Year Founded: 1987
Rev: $30,000,000
Emp.: 30
Advetising Agency
N.A.I.C.S.: 541810
Ernie Perich *(Pres & Dir-Creative)*
Shirley Perich *(VP-Fin)*
Brad Jurgensen *(VP-Media & Strategic Plng)*
Dan Sygar *(VP & Assoc Dir-Creative)*
Craig Dunaway *(VP-Acct Svcs)*

PERIGON PARTNERS LLC
201 Mission St Ste 1825, San Francisco, CA 94105-8121
Tel.: (415) 430-4140
Web Site: http://www.perigonpartners.com
Investment Advice
N.A.I.C.S.: 523940
Kanoe Cazimero *(Office Mgr-HI)*
Rafia Hasan *(Chief Investment Officer)*
Arthur Ambarik *(CEO)*

PERIGON WEALTH MANAGEMENT LLC
201 Mission St, Ste. 1825, San Francisco, CA 94105-8121
Tel.: (415) 430-4140 DE
Web Site: https://www.perigonwealth.com
Year Founded: 2004
Emp.: 100
Investment Management
N.A.I.C.S.: 523999

Subsidiaries:
Prudeo Partners L.L.C. (1)
602 Meeting St Ste C, West Columbia, SC 29169-7590
Web Site: http://www.assetmgtplanning.com
Investment Advice
N.A.I.C.S.: 523940
Larry Miller *(Owner)*

PERIMETER SECURITY PARTNERS, LLC
5038 Thoroughbred Ln, Brentwood, TN 37027
Tel.: (615) 953-8872
Web Site: http://www.perimetersecuritypartners.com
Year Founded: 2014
Sales Range: $10-24.9 Million
Emp.: 22
Property Protection & Security Services
N.A.I.C.S.: 561612
Wesley M. Foss *(CEO)*
Kenneth J. Grant *(COO)*

PERIMETER TERMINAL, LLC
2970 Parrott Ave NW, Atlanta, GA 30318-1054
Tel.: (404) 799-9199 GA
Web Site: http://www.perimeterterminal.com
Year Founded: 1985
Sales Range: $10-24.9 Million
Emp.: 15
Petroleum Bulk Storage
N.A.I.C.S.: 424710
Vince Kenny *(VP)*
Ben Kenny *(Pres)*

PERIODICAL MANAGEMENT GROUP INTERNATIONAL LTD.
1011 N Frio St 2nd Fl, San Antonio, TX 78207-1811
Tel.: (210) 226-6820
Web Site: http://www.shadowdanceranch.com
Year Founded: 1997
Sales Range: $10-24.9 Million
Emp.: 30
Distr of Books, Periodicals & Newspapers
N.A.I.C.S.: 424920
Brian Weiner *(Chm & Owner)*

Subsidiaries:
Island Periodicals Inc. (1)
52B Sugar Estate Park, Saint Thomas, VI 00801
Tel.: (340) 776-0043
Rev: $40,286,462
Emp.: 5
Books, Periodicals & Newspapers
N.A.I.C.S.: 459210

Lone Star Special Tees Inc. (1)

1011 N Frio St, San Antonio, TX
78207 (100%)
Tel.: (210) 402-0091
Web Site: http://www.lonestartees.com
Sales Range: $10-24.9 Million
Emp.: 26
Custom Screen Prints on T-Shirts
N.A.I.C.S.: 314999
Elaine Blain (Gen Mgr)

PERIPHERAL DEVICES & PRODUCTS SYSTEMS INC.
47027 Benicia St, Fremont, CA
94538-7331
Tel.: (510) 979-1021   CA
Web Site:
    http://www.patriotmemory.com
Year Founded: 1985
Sales Range: $10-24.9 Million
Computer Memory Modules, Peripherals & Software Mfr & Distr
N.A.I.C.S.: 423430
Paul Jones (CEO)

Subsidiaries:

Patriot Memory (1)
11F No 700 Jhong Jheng Road, Jhong He District, New Taipei City, 23552, Taiwan
Tel.: (886) 2 8228 0333
Web Site:
    http://www.info.patriotmemory.com
Computer Memory Module Peripheral & Software Mfr & Distr
N.A.I.C.S.: 334118
Taron Chang (Gen Mgr)

PERIS COMPANIES INC.
282 N Washington St, Falls Church, VA 22046
Tel.: (703) 533-4700
Web Site: http://www.peris.com
Sales Range: $10-24.9 Million
Emp.: 35
Full Service Regional Construction & Office Renovations
N.A.I.C.S.: 236220
Jeffrey R. Pellegrino (Pres, CEO & Principal)
Gary T. Starr (VP-Construction)

PERISCOPE EQUITY LLC
1 N Wacker Dr Ste 4050, Chicago, IL 60606
Tel.: (312) 281-6205   DE
Web Site:
    http://www.periscopeequity.com
Privater Equity Firm
N.A.I.C.S.: 523999
Steven Jarmel (Partner)
Brian Mukherjee (Partner)
John Findlay (Partner)
Eric Hinkle (VP)
Alex Friedman (VP-Bus Dev)
Ralph Carter (Operating Partner)
Will Daly (Operating Partner)
Don Mathis (Operating Partner)
Mark McCall (Operating Partner)
Ujjal Kohli (Operating Partner)

Subsidiaries:

CyberMaxx, LLC (1)
2115 Yeaman Pl Ste 310, Nashville, TN 37206
Tel.: (615) 309-2522
Web Site: https://www.cybermaxx.com
Cyber Security Services
N.A.I.C.S.: 561621
Brian Ahern (CEO)

Subsidiary (Domestic):

Ciphertechs, Inc. (2)
55 Broadway, New York, NY 10006
Tel.: (212) 897-6900
Web Site: http://www.ciphertechs.com
Sales Range: $1-9.9 Million
Emp.: 13
Computer Related Services
N.A.I.C.S.: 541512

Michael Quattrochi (CEO)
Bill Dorney (Dir-Security Solutions)
Marek Surdykowski (Dir-Engrg)

PERISCOPEIQ, INC.
6666 Passer Rd, Coopersburg, PA 18036
Tel.: (484) 863-9119
Web Site:
    http://www.periscopeiq.com
Sales Range: $1-9.9 Million
Emp.: 100
Employee Engagement Software Mfr
N.A.I.C.S.: 513210
K. Paul Singh (Chm)
Pawan Singh (Co-Founder & CEO)
Mohamed Latib (Co-Founder & Chief Customer Officer)
Matthew J. Waite (Dir-Projects)
James P. Murphy (Dir-Mktg Res)
Joel Tolbert (Dir-Tech)

Subsidiaries:

Opinionmeter Inc. (1)
14727 Catalina St, San Leandro, CA 94577
Tel.: (510) 352-4943
Web Site: http://www.opinionmeter.com
Customer Satisfaction Survey Software Mfr
N.A.I.C.S.: 513210
Andrew Pugsley (Partner & Dir-Creative)

PERITUS INC.
222 W Las Colinas Blvd Ste 1650, Irving, TX 75039
Tel.: (817) 380-4200   TX
Web Site: http://www.peritusinc.com
Year Founded: 2000
Sales Range: $1-9.9 Million
Emp.: 72
IT Placement Services
N.A.I.C.S.: 561311
Ramprasad Mavuleti (Pres)
Aditya Varma (Mgr)
Ravi Chandra (Engr-Software)

PERKASIE INDUSTRIES CORPORATION
50 E Spruce St, Perkasie, PA 18944-1285
Tel.: (215) 257-6581   PA
Web Site:
    http://www.perkasieindustries.com
Sales Range: $50-74.9 Million
Emp.: 40
Mfr of Lighting Fixtures, Interior Storm Windows & Wiring Devices
N.A.I.C.S.: 335132
John Hendler (Co-Pres)
Adam Krisco (Co-Pres)

PERKINS & COMPANY, P.C.
1211 SW 5th Ave Ste 1000, Portland, OR 97204-3710
Tel.: (503) 221-0336   OR
Web Site:
    http://www.perkinsaccounting.com
Sales Range: $1-9.9 Million
Accounting, Tax & Corporate Consulting Services
N.A.I.C.S.: 541211
Gary W. Reynolds (Chm)
Jared A. Holum (Pres)
Christopher J. Loughran (Partner & Dir-Tax)
Dave Sullivan (Partner & Dir-Bus Dev)
Chuck Landers (Principal)
Kim Spaulding (Co-Sr Mgr-Tax)
Celeste Ames (Co-Sr Mgr-Tax)
Stephanie Lillengreen (Mgr-HR)

PERKINS COIE LLP
1201 3rd Ave Ste 4800, Seattle, WA 98101-3266
Tel.: (206) 359-8000   WA
Web Site:
    http://www.perkinscoie.com

Year Founded: 1912
Sales Range: $75-99.9 Million
Emp.: 1,300
Law firm
N.A.I.C.S.: 541110
Jordan A. Kroop (Partner)
Nathaniel Ford (Chm-Private Equity Practice)
Theodore W. Wern (Partner)
Ann Schofield Baker (Partner-New York)
Ryan J. Preston (Partner-Dallas)
Janis Claire Kestenbaum (Partner-Comml Litigation)
Clinten N. Garrett (Partner)
Garland W. Allison (Partner-Denver)
Stephanie A. Hirano (Partner)
Michael L. Dunning (Partner)
Angela R. Jones (Partner)
Karl L. Klassen (Partner)
Christina Jordan McCullough (Partner)
Jonathan L. McFarland (Partner)
Bruce Spiva (Mng Partner)
Fabricio Vayra (Partner)
Marc S. Martin (Partner & Atty-Comm & Tech)
Eliot L. Kaplan (Partner)
Nora L. Gibson (Partner)
Justin L. Bastian (Partner)
Stephen J. Schrader (Partner-Corp Practice-San Francisco)
Dana W. Hayter (Partner-Tech Transactions & Privacy Practice-San Francisco)
Patrick S. Thompson (Partner-Comml Litigation Practice-San Francisco)
Graham M. Wilson (Partner)
Gwendolyn A. Williamson (Partner)
Kate Sawyer Keane (Partner)
Barak Cohen (Partner)
Alexandra Magill Bromer (Partner)
Kourtney Mueller Merrill (Partner)
Keith Miller (Partner)
Jon D. Feldhammer (Partner-Trust & Estate Plng Practice-San Francisco)
Paula Leibovitz Goodwin (Partner-Trust & Estate Plng Practice-San Francisco)
Melanie K. Curtice (Partner)
Kelly A. Cameron (Partner)
Christopher D. Thomas (Partner)
Meredith Halama (Partner-Comml Litigation Practice)
Elisabeth Frost (Partner-Political Law Practice)
Brendon Fowler (Partner-Tech Transactions & Privacy Law Practice)
Jonathan Berkon (Partner-Political Law Practice)
Miriam D. Farhi (Partner)
Ryan T. Mrazik (Partner)
Abha Khana (Partner)
Seth J. King (Partner)
William E. Swart (Partner)
Johnny Chiu (Partner-Intellectual Property Practice-Beijing)
James F. Williams (Mng Partner)
Jason M. Quintana (Partner)
Christopher J. Hagan (Partner-Corp Practice-Washington)
Bill Malley (Mng Partner-Washington)
Michael Didiuk (Partner-San Francisco)
Matt Kirmayer (Partner-Emerging Companies & Venture Capital Practice)
Barbara Schussman (Mng Partner-San Francisco)
Geoffrey M. Ossias (Partner/Head-Emerging Companies & Venture Capital Practice)
Buddy Arnheim (Chm-Emerging Companies & Venture Capital Practice)
Jessica Everett-Garcia (Mng Partner-Phoenix)

Jim M. Zimmerman (Partner-Beijing)
Scott J. Palmer (Partner-Beijing)
Geoffrey Vance (Mng Partner-Shanghai)
Lowell Ness (Mng Partner-Palo Alto)
Adrian Rich (Partner-Emerging Companies & Venture Capital Practice-Palo Alto)
Ann Marie Painter (Chm-Labor & Employment Grp)
Andrew Moriarty (Partner-Labor & Employment Grp)
Stephanie Roy (Partner-Washington)
Valerie Dahiya (Partner-Blockchain Tech & Digital Currency Indus Grp)
J. Dax Hansen (Chm-Blockchain Tech & Digital Currency Indus Grp)
Molly Moynihan (Chm-Investment Mgmt Subgroup)
Genhi Givings Bailey (Chief Diversity & Inclusion Officer-Chicago)
John Devaney (Mng Partner)
David Fletcher (Partner-Comml Litigation Practice)
Emily A. Bushaw (Partner)
Elvira Castillo (Partner)
Ulrike Connelly (Partner)
David A. Perez (Partner)
Holly M. Simpkins (Partner)
John Tyler (Partner)
KoKo Huang (Partner)
G. Thomas Stromberg (Partner-Merger & Acq Practice-Los Angeles)
Misha Isaak (Partner-Portland)
Charles G. Curtis Jr. (Partner-Comml Litigation Practice)

PERKINS EASTMAN ARCHITECTS P.C.
115 5th Ave Fl 3, New York, NY 10003-1004
Tel.: (212) 353-7200   NY
Web Site:
    http://www.perkinseastman.com
Year Founded: 1981
Sales Range: $25-49.9 Million
Emp.: 1,000
Architectural Services
N.A.I.C.S.: 541310
Matthew Becker (Assoc Principal)
Hilary Kinder Bertsch (Principal)
Laurie E. Butler (Principal)
Jason Harper (Principal)
Candace Carroll (CFO)
C. Carson Shearon (Principal-Chicago & Dir-Healthcare-Intl)

PERKINS HOME CENTER, INC.
99 A Rte 9, West Chesterfield, NH 03466
Tel.: (603) 256-6844
Web Site:
    http://www.perkinshomecenter.com
Sales Range: $10-24.9 Million
Emp.: 55
Provider of Lumber, Plywood & Millwork
N.A.I.C.S.: 423310
Peter Brady (Owner & Pres)
Karen Haas (Office Mgr)

PERKINS LUMBER CO. INC.
100 10th St NW, Willmar, MN 56201
Tel.: (320) 235-3242
Web Site:
    http://www.perkins.doitbest.com
Rev.: $11,026,505
Emp.: 24
Lumber & Other Building Materials
N.A.I.C.S.: 423310
John Teigland (Pres)

PERKINS MOTOR COMPANY
1205 Motor City Dr, Colorado Springs, CO 80905
Tel.: (719) 475-2330

PERKINS MOTOR COMPANY — U.S. PRIVATE

Perkins Motor Company—(Continued)
Web Site:
http://www.perkinsdodge.com
Year Founded: 1927
Rev.: $40,100,000
Emp.: 130
Automobile Dealers
N.A.I.C.S.: 441120
Jonathan Walter *(Mgr-Sls)*

PERKINS OIL & GAS, INC.
17330 Preston Rd Ste 200D, Dallas, TX 75252
Tel.: (201) 730-6454 NV
Web Site:
http://www.perkinsoilgas.com
Year Founded: 2012
Assets: $304
Liabilities: $86,517
Net Worth: ($86,213)
Earnings: ($23,030,843)
Fiscal Year-end: 06/30/18
Oil & Gas Exploration
N.A.I.C.S.: 211120
Sonny Arandia *(CEO, CFO, Treas & Sec)*

PERKO WORLDWIDE CORP.
2650 SW 18th St, Fort Lauderdale, FL 33312
Tel.: (954) 636-7555 DE
Web Site:
http://www.perkoworldwide.com
Year Founded: 2003
Container Cargo Transportation Vessel Mfr
N.A.I.C.S.: 336612
David E. Perko *(Founder & CEO)*
David Perco *(Founder & CEO)*

PERLEGEN SCIENCES, INC.
35473 Dumbarton Ct, Newark, CA 94560-1100
Tel.: (650) 625-4500 DE
Year Founded: 2000
Sales Range: $25-49.9 Million
Emp.: 105
Developer of Biopharmaceuticals
N.A.I.C.S.: 541714
David R. Cox *(Co-Founder & Chief Scientific Officer)*
Robert G. Middlebrook *(Chief Dev Officer)*
Phyllis E. Whiteley *(Sr VP-Bus Devel & Licensing)*
Stephen P.A. Fodor *(Chm)*

PERLICK CORPORATION
8300 W Good Hope Rd, Milwaukee, WI 53223-4524
Tel.: (414) 353-7060 DE
Web Site: http://www.perlick.com
Year Founded: 1917
Sales Range: $10-24.9 Million
Emp.: 300
Mfr of Refrigeration & Heating Equipment
N.A.I.C.S.: 333415
Richard Palmersheim *(Pres & CEO)*

PERLMART INC.
954 Rte 166, Toms River, NJ 08753-6562
Tel.: (732) 341-0700 NJ
Web Site: http://www.shoprite.com
Year Founded: 1976
Sales Range: $125-149.9 Million
Emp.: 1,500
Grocery Services
N.A.I.C.S.: 445110
Joel Perlmutter *(Pres & CEO)*
John Cardone *(Dir-Produce)*
Glen Holck *(Sr Dir)*
Subsidiaries:
Perlmart Drugs of Lacey Inc. (1)
344 Rte 9 & 1st St, Lanoka Harbor, NJ 08734
Tel.: (609) 693-1152
Sales Range: $50-74.9 Million
Emp.: 300
Drug Store
N.A.I.C.S.: 445110
Glenn Cunningham *(Mgr-Store)*

Perlmart Drugs of Toms River Inc. (1)
954 Route 166, Toms River, NJ 08753-6562
Tel.: (732) 341-0700
Sales Range: $10-24.9 Million
Emp.: 15
Drug Store
N.A.I.C.S.: 456110
Martin Polack *(Controller)*

Perlmart Management Co. Inc. (1)
954 Route 166, Toms River, NJ 08753-6562 (100%)
Tel.: (732) 341-0700
Web Site: http://www.ecoscience.com
Rev.: $290,000
Emp.: 12
Management Services
N.A.I.C.S.: 541611
Michael Perlmutter *(VP)*

Perlmart of Lacey Township Inc. (1)
Rte 9 344 US Hwy, Lanoka Harbor, NJ 08734
Tel.: (609) 693-1152
Web Site: http://www.shoprite.com
Supermarket
N.A.I.C.S.: 445110

PERLOWIN DEVELOPMENT CORP.
7800 NW 61st Ter, Parkland, FL 33067
Tel.: (954) 683-3111 NV
Year Founded: 2014
Emp.: 1
Investment Services
N.A.I.C.S.: 523999
Jed Perlowin *(Pres, CEO, CFO, Chief Acctg Officer, Treas & Sec)*

PERMA-FLEX ROLLER TECHNOLOGY LLC
635 Graves St, Kernersville, NC 27284
Tel.: (704) 633-1201
Sales Range: $75-99.9 Million
Emp.: 60
Mfr of Industrial Roll Coverings
N.A.I.C.S.: 326299
Gail Young *(Mgr-Sls)*
Subsidiaries:
Perma-Flex/ESI (1)
56 55 Timberlea Blvd, Mississauga, L4W 2S4, ON, Canada (100%)
Tel.: (905) 276-3809
Sales Range: $10-24.9 Million
Emp.: 20
Industrial Roll Coverings Sales & Warehousing
N.A.I.C.S.: 326299
Anna Nowak *(Mgr-Fin)*

PERMAL CAPITAL MANAGEMENT, LLC
The Prudential Tower 800 Boylston St Ste 1325, Boston, MA 02199
Tel.: (617) 587-5300
Web Site:
http://www.permalcapital.com
Emp.: 18
Privater Equity Firm
N.A.I.C.S.: 523999
Red Barrett *(Pres & CEO)*

PERMANENT EQUITY MANAGEMENT, LLC
315 N 10th St, Columbia, MO 65201
Tel.: (573) 445-0678
Web Site:
https://www.permanentequity.com
Emp.: 100
Investment Services
N.A.I.C.S.: 523999
Brent Beshore *(Founder & CEO)*
Subsidiaries:
Chance Rides Manufacturing, Inc. (1)
4219 Irving St, Wichita, KS 67209-2613
Tel.: (316) 942-7411
Web Site: http://www.chancerides.com
Sales Range: $75-99.9 Million
Emp.: 150
Carnival & Amusement Park Ride Machine & Equipment Mfr
N.A.I.C.S.: 713990
Aaron Landrum *(Pres & CEO)*

PERMATECH, INC.
911 E Elm St, Graham, NC 27253-1907
Tel.: (336) 578-0701 DE
Web Site: http://www.permatech.net
Year Founded: 1972
Sales Range: $1-9.9 Million
Emp.: 45
Precast Refractory Materials & Systems Mfr
N.A.I.C.S.: 327120

PERMAWICK COMPANY, INC.
255 E Brown St Ste 100, Birmingham, MI 48009
Tel.: (248) 433-3500 DE
Web Site: http://www.permawick.com
Year Founded: 1974
Sales Range: $10-24.9 Million
Emp.: 12
Lubricating Oils/Greases, Bearings & General Industrial Machinery Mfr
N.A.I.C.S.: 324191
Joseph M. Lane *(Chm & Treas)*
John B. Lane *(Pres)*
Subsidiaries:
Permawick Company Inc-Indiana Plant (1)
3110 Permawick Dr, Columbus, IN 47201
Tel.: (812) 372-0703
Web Site: http://www.permawick.com
Sales Range: Less than $1 Million
Ball & Roller Bearings, Lubricant & Industrial Machinery Mfr
N.A.I.C.S.: 332991

PERMIAN BASIN AREA FOUNDATION
3312 Andrews Hwy, Midland, TX 79701
Tel.: (432) 617-3213 TX
Web Site: http://www.pbaf.org
Year Founded: 1989
Sales Range: $10-24.9 Million
Emp.: 8
Charitable Services
N.A.I.C.S.: 813219
Guy McCrary *(Pres & CEO)*
Aaron Bedell *(COO)*
Cyndi Vara *(CFO)*
Cal Hendrick *(Chm)*
Sande Melton *(Sec)*

PERMIAN TANK & MANUFACTURING, INC.
2701 W Interstate 20, Odessa, TX 79766
Tel.: (432) 333-4591 TX
Web Site:
http://www.permiantank.com
Year Founded: 1975
Sales Range: $1-9.9 Million
Emp.: 114
Metal Tank (Heavy Gauge) Mfr
N.A.I.C.S.: 332420
Michael Haynes *(Pres)*

PERNIX THERAPEUTICS HOLDINGS, INC.
10 N Park Place Ste 201, Morristown, NJ 07960
Tel.: (832) 934-1825 MD
Web Site: http://www.pernixtx.com
Year Founded: 1996
Rev.: $146,068,000
Assets: $205,492,000
Liabilities: $379,749,000
Net Worth: ($174,257,000)
Earnings: ($77,141,000)
Emp.: 171
Fiscal Year-end: 12/31/17
Holding Company; Sales, Marketing & Branded Pharmaceutical Products
N.A.I.C.S.: 551112
George P. Jones *(VP-Sls & Mktg)*
Subsidiaries:
Pernix Therapeutics, LLC (1)
10003 Woodloch Forest Dr, The Woodlands, TX 77380
Tel.: (832) 934-1825
Web Site: http://www.pernixtx.com
Pharmaceutical Research & Development Services
N.A.I.C.S.: 541715

Subsidiary (Domestic):
G&S Enterprises, Incorporated (2)
10863 Rockley Rd, Houston, TX 77099
Tel.: (281) 530-3077
Web Site: http://www.greatsouthernlabs.com
Pharmaceutical Preparation Mfr
N.A.I.C.S.: 325412

Joint Venture (Domestic):
Nalpropion Pharmaceuticals, Inc. (2)
3344 N Torrey Pines Ct Ste 200, La Jolla, CA 92037
Tel.: (858) 875-8600
Web Site: http://www.nalpropion.com
Pharmaceuticals Mfr
N.A.I.C.S.: 325412
John Sedor *(Chm & CEO)*
Kenneth R. Pina *(Exec VP)*
Angus Smith
Salma Jutt *(Chief Comml Officer & Sr VP)*
Amy Fox *(VP-HR)*
Amy Halseth *(VP-Clinical Dev)*
Kris Hanson *(VP-Legal & Compliance)*

PERO ENGINEERING & SALES COMPANY, INC.
1144 Tampa Rd, Palm Harbor, FL 34683
Tel.: (813) 962-8001
Web Site:
http://www.peroengineering.com
Sales Range: $1-9.9 Million
Emp.: 5
Chemical & Allied Products Merchant Whslr
N.A.I.C.S.: 424690
Steve Pero *(VP)*

PERPETUAL CAPITAL, LLC
1000 Wilson Blvd Ste 2700, Arlington, VA 22209
Tel.: (703) 647-8700
Web Site:
http://www.perpetualcapitalpartners.com
Private Investment Firm
N.A.I.C.S.: 523999
Robert L. Allbritton *(Exec Chm)*
Duncan L. Evans *(Pres, CEO & Chief Investment Officer)*
Subsidiaries:
California Family Health LLC (1)
8680 Greenback Ln Ste 108, Orangevale, CA 95662
Tel.: (916) 987-2030
Web Site:
http://www.californiafamilyfitness.com
Fitness Centers & Health Clubs
N.A.I.C.S.: 713940

COMPANIES

Randy Karr *(Pres)*
Nick Gury *(VP-Ops)*
Tom Deimler *(Sr VP-Sls, Mktg & Fitness)*
Dave Sedin *(CFO)*

Novatech, Inc. (1)
4106 Charlotte Ave, Nashville, TN 37209
Tel.: (615) 577-7677
Web Site: http://www.novatech.net
Printing Services
N.A.I.C.S.: 323111
Jeff Hoctor *(CFO)*
Carl Pottkotter *(VP-Bus Intelligence)*
John Sutton *(VP-Marketplace-Central)*
Dave Moorman *(Pres-CISO)*
Chas Arnold *(VP-Managed Office Sols)*
Dan Cooper *(CEO)*
Scott Stahl *(COO)*
Kim Barratt *(Chief HR Officer)*
Jim Haney *(VP-Mktg)*

Subsidiary (Domestic):

Atlantic Business Systems (2)
5131 Industry Dr Ste 101, Melbourne, FL 32940
Tel.: (321) 259-7575
Web Site:
 https://atlanticbusinesssystems.com
Rev: $5,328,000
Emp.: 16
Office Supplies & Stationery Stores
N.A.I.C.S.: 459410
Barry Wallingford *(Pres)*

Carolina Business Equipment, Inc. (2)
5123 Bush River Rd, Columbia, SC 29212
Tel.: (803) 798-7522
Web Site: http://www.cbesc.com
Sales Range: $1-9.9 Million
Emp.: 31
Computer & Office Machine Repair & Maintenance Services
N.A.I.C.S.: 811210
John P. Eckstrom *(Pres)*
Stan Sessler *(CFO)*
Kurt Beasley *(CIO)*

DynaSis Integrated Systems Corp. (2)
950 N Point Pkwy Ste 300, Alpharetta, GA 30005
Tel.: (770) 569-4600
Web Site: http://www.dynasis.com
Data Processing, Hosting & Related Services
N.A.I.C.S.: 518210
Brad Bromelow *(VP-Ops)*
Andrew Dunlop *(VP-Network & Data Center Ops)*
Chip Councill *(Mgr-Support)*
Larry Strott *(Architect-Solutions)*
Marcus Berquist *(Mgr-Installation Svcs Project)*
Mike Judd *(Mgr-Network Ops Center)*
Nate Harris *(VP-Support Delivery)*

Kopier Net (2)
1148 Jvl Ct, Marietta, GA 30066
Tel.: (770) 425-5679
Web Site: http://www.kopiernet.com
Sales Range: $1-9.9 Million
Emp.: 12
Refurbished Copiers & Printers Sales & Service
N.A.I.C.S.: 423420
Ted Kolwicz *(Pres)*

Novatech Inc. - Hattiesburg (2)
6401 U S Hwy 49, Hattiesburg, MS 39401
Tel.: (601) 264-3476
Web Site: http://www.novatech.net
Office Equipment & Business Solutions Provider
N.A.I.C.S.: 424120

SmartWater Memphis, Inc. (2)
7251 Appling Farms Pkwy, Memphis, TN 38133
Tel.: (901) 367-9500
Web Site:
 https://www.smartwatermemphis.com
Purified Drinking Water Sales & Dealership
N.A.I.C.S.: 221310
Tom Pease *(Founder & Owner)*

PERPETUAL INSIGHTS LLC
22 Thorndal Cir 3rd Fl, Darien, CT 06820
Tel.: (203) 202-7634
Web Site:
 http://www.beperpetual.com
Year Founded: 2013
Sales Range: $1-9.9 Million
Emp.: 19
Human Resource Requirement Services
N.A.I.C.S.: 541612
Steve Morrissey *(Founder & CEO)*
Pierre Trippitelli *(Mng Partner)*
William Corcoran *(CFO & COO)*
Massimo De Paola *(Mktg Dir)*
Sima Kasyanenko *(Mgr)*

PERRAM ELECTRIC, INC.
6882 Ridge Rd, Wadsworth, OH 44281
Tel.: (330) 239-2661
Web Site:
 http://www.perramelectric.com
Sales Range: $10-24.9 Million
Emp.: 40
Electrical Wiring Services
N.A.I.C.S.: 238210
Zoltan Kovacs *(Pres)*

PERRECA ELECTRIC CO. INC.
520 Broadway, Newburgh, NY 12550
Tel.: (845) 562-4080
Web Site: http://www.perreca.com
Rev.: $32,371,974
Emp.: 250
Electrical Work
N.A.I.C.S.: 238210
Charles C. Tallardy *(Pres)*
Patrick Galietta *(Dir-Safety)*
Mark Talady *(Mgr-Warehouse)*
Julie Forman *(CFO)*
Robert Kaehler *(Pres & COO)*

PERRY & DERRICK CO.
2511 Highland Ave, Cincinnati, OH 45212-2319
Tel.: (513) 351-5800 KY
Year Founded: 1913
Rev.: $17,000,000
Emp.: 140
Paints Mfr
N.A.I.C.S.: 325510
Mark E. Derrick *(Dir-Sls)*
Sally H. Derrick *(Owner & Pres)*

PERRY AUTO MALL
1005 W Ehringhaus St, Elizabeth City, NC 27909
Tel.: (252) 338-3925
Web Site:
 http://www.perryautogroup.com
Sales Range: $25-49.9 Million
Emp.: 70
Automobiles, New & Used
N.A.I.C.S.: 441110
Chris Perry *(VP)*

PERRY BALLARD INCORPORATED
526 Upton Dr E, Saint Joseph, MI 49085
Tel.: (269) 983-0611
Web Site:
 http://www.perryballard.com
Year Founded: 1977
Sales Range: $1-9.9 Million
Emp.: 17
Advetising Agency
N.A.I.C.S.: 541810
Charlotte Burch *(VP & CFO)*
Gary Tipton *(Pres & Dir-Creative)*
Patrice Emmerson *(Creative Strategist & Writer)*
Elisa Broihier *(Creative Strategist & Designer)*
Matt Harlow *(Dir-Acct Svcs)*

PERRY BROTHERS TIRE SERVICE, INC.
610 Wicker St, Sanford, NC 27330
Tel.: (919) 776-9832
Web Site: http://www.perrybros.com
Sales Range: $10-24.9 Million
Emp.: 70
Automotive Tires
N.A.I.C.S.: 441340
Ross Perry *(Co-Owner)*
Paul Perry *(Co-Owner & Pres)*

PERRY BROTHERS, INC.
PO Box 28, Lufkin, TX 75902
Tel.: (936) 634-6686 TX
Year Founded: 1914
Sales Range: $10-24.9 Million
Emp.: 5
Property Management
N.A.I.C.S.: 531210
Charles Acklen *(Pres)*
Sam Baldwin *(Chm)*

PERRY BUICK CO.
6633 E Virginia Beach Blvd, Norfolk, VA 23502
Tel.: (757) 333-0906
Web Site: http://www.perrybuick.com
Year Founded: 1931
Sales Range: $25-49.9 Million
Emp.: 80
New Car Retailer
N.A.I.C.S.: 441110
James Perry *(Pres)*

PERRY CHEMICAL & MANUFACTURING CO. INC.
2335 S 30th St, Lafayette, IN 47909
Tel.: (765) 474-3404
Web Site: http://www.perryfoam.com
Sales Range: $10-24.9 Million
Emp.: 40
Plastics Foam Products
N.A.I.C.S.: 326150
Rick Landrum *(Pres)*

PERRY CHRYSLER DODGE JEEP RAM
2340 National City Blvd, National City, CA 91950
Tel.: (619) 434-0491
Web Site:
 http://www.perrychryslerdodge
 jeepram.com
Year Founded: 1922
Car Whslr
N.A.I.C.S.: 441110
Diamond Valdez *(Mgr-Fin)*
Ramon Gitesatani *(Gen Mgr)*

PERRY COMMUNICATIONS GROUP, INC.
925 L St Ste 260, Sacramento, CA 95814
Tel.: (916) 658-0144 CA
Web Site: http://www.perrycom.com
Rev.: $2,100,000
Emp.: 17
Fiscal Year-end: 12/31/06
Communications, Event Planning & Marketing,
Government/Political/Public Affairs,
Media Relations, Nonprofit/Social Marketing
N.A.I.C.S.: 541810
Anika Butler *(Sec)*
Kassy Perry *(Pres & CEO)*
Julia Spiess *(VP)*
Kristina Davis *(Mgr-Ops)*
Yadira Beas *(Acct Exec)*
Katelyn Downey *(Sr Acct Exec)*
Julia Spiess Lewis *(Sr VP)*
Leia Ostermann *(Sr Acct Exec)*
Alexis Kagarakis *(Acct Coord)*
Anita Gore *(Sr Acct Mgr)*
Marna Davis *(Acct Mgr)*

PERRY ELLIS INTERNATIONAL, INC.

Kaitlin Perry *(Sr Acct Mgr)*
Stephanie McGann Jantzen *(VP)*
Jessica Hice *(Acct Exec)*

PERRY CONSTRUCTION GROUP INC.
1440 W 21st St, Erie, PA 16502
Tel.: (814) 459-8551 PA
Web Site: http://www.perryconst.com
Year Founded: 1990
Sales Range: $10-24.9 Million
Emp.: 64
Contractor of Industrial Buildings & Warehouses
N.A.I.C.S.: 236210
Robert Doyle *(Pres & Treas)*
Michael Doyle *(Sec & VP)*
John J. Doyle *(Chm)*
Rebecca Pollack *(Office Mgr-Fin)*

PERRY CORPORATION
545 W Market St, Lima, OH 45801-4717
Tel.: (419) 228-1360 OH
Web Site:
 http://www.perryproject.com
Year Founded: 1965
Sales Range: $10-24.9 Million
Emp.: 140
Provider of Office Automation Technology
N.A.I.C.S.: 459999
Barry Clark *(CEO)*
Becky Taylor *(Controller)*
Dave Zimerle *(VP-Sls)*
Jeff Bote *(Pres)*

PERRY COUNTY HEALTH SYSTEM
434 N West St, Perryville, MO 63775
Tel.: (573) 547-2536 MO
Web Site: http://www.pchmo.org
Year Founded: 1996
Sales Range: $25-49.9 Million
Emp.: 440
Health Care Srvices
N.A.I.C.S.: 622110
Randy Wolf *(VP-Fin Svcs)*
Barbara Ernst *(VP-Patient Care Svcs)*

PERRY ELLIS INTERNATIONAL, INC.
3000 NW 107th Ave, Miami, FL 33172
Tel.: (305) 592-2830 FL
Web Site: http://www.pery.com
Year Founded: 1978
Rev.: $874,853,000
Assets: $634,162,000
Liabilities: $256,612,000
Net Worth: $377,550,000
Earnings: $56,650,000
Emp.: 2,500
Fiscal Year-end: 02/03/18
Clothing Designer & Marketer
N.A.I.C.S.: 315250
Oscar Feldenkreis *(Pres & CEO)*
Stanley P. Silverstein *(Pres-Intl Dev & Global Licensing)*
Luis Paez *(CIO)*
Jack Voith *(Exec VP-Sportswear Div)*
David Enright *(COO)*

Subsidiaries:

Jantzen Apparel, LLC (1)
411 NE 19th Ave, Portland, OR 97232 (100%)
Tel.: (503) 238-5000
Web Site: http://www.jantzen.com
Sales Range: $75-99.9 Million
Emp.: 75
Women's Casual Clothing & Swimwear Mfr
N.A.I.C.S.: 315250

Division (Domestic):

Jantzen Inc. (2)

PERRY ELLIS INTERNATIONAL, INC.

Perry Ellis International, Inc.—(Continued)
101 Mountain View Dr, Seneca, SC 29672-2124
Tel.: (864) 882-3393
Web Site: http://www.jantzen.com
Sales Range: $125-149.9 Million
Emp.: 100
Women's Sportswear Distr
N.A.I.C.S.: 458110

Jantzen Inc. (2)
1411 Broadway Fl 24, New York, NY 10018-3402
Tel.: (212) 730-1622
Web Site: http://www.jantzen.com
Sales Range: $50-74.9 Million
Emp.: 5
Swimsuits for Women & Children
N.A.I.C.S.: 424350

PEI Licensing, Inc. (1)
3000 NW 107th Ave, Doral, FL 33172
Tel.: (305) 592-2830
Web Site: http://www.pery.com
Emp.: 150
Fashion Apparels Retailer
N.A.I.C.S.: 458110

Perry Ellis Europe Limited (1)
Crittall Road, Witham, CM8 3DJ, Essex, United Kingdom
Tel.: (44) 1376502345
Web Site: http://www.perryellis.co.uk
Sales Range: $75-99.9 Million
Emp.: 100
Clothing & Footwear Whslr
N.A.I.C.S.: 424350
Darren Brown (Accts Mgr)

Perry Ellis International Europe Limited (1)
Pleasants St, Dublin, Ireland
Tel.: (353) 14053840
Web Site: http://www.perry.com
Fashion Apparel Mfr & Retailer
N.A.I.C.S.: 315250
Geroge Seldenkries (Chm)

Perry Ellis International HK Limited (1)
Rm 811-819 8/F Chevalier Commercial Ctr Kowloon Bay, Kowloon, China (Hong Kong)
Tel.: (852) 23374111
Emp.: 76
Clothing Designer & Marketer
N.A.I.C.S.: 315250
Bility Yim (Gen Mgr)

Perry Ellis Menswear, LLC (1)
1120 Ave of the Americas, New York, NY 10036
Tel.: (212) 221-7500
Sales Range: $50-74.9 Million
Emp.: 500
Men's Sportswear, Shirts & Accessories Mfr & Marketer
N.A.I.C.S.: 315250
George Feldenkreis (Chm & CEO)

Rafaella Apparel Group, Inc. (1)
530 7th Ave 2nd fl, New York, NY 10018-3402
Tel.: (212) 403-0300
Web Site: http://www.rafaellasportswear.com
Sales Range: $50-74.9 Million
Emp.: 100
Womens Clothing
N.A.I.C.S.: 424350

PERRY ENGINEERING COMPANY, INC.
1945 Millwood Pike, Winchester, VA 22602-4561
Tel.: (540) 667-4310   VA
Web Site: http://www.perryeng.com
Year Founded: 1951
Sales Range: $50-74.9 Million
Emp.: 300
Heavy Construction
N.A.I.C.S.: 238910
Kevin R. Firebaugh (Project Mgr)
Susan Clem (Project Mgr)
Ken Pracht (Dir-Safety)
Diane Moreland (VP-HR)

PERRY FOAM PRODUCTS INC.
2335 S 30th St, Lafayette, IN 47909
Tel.: (765) 474-3404
Web Site: http://www.perryfoam.com
Rev.: $12,800,000
Emp.: 50
Urethane & Other Foam Product Mfg
N.A.I.C.S.: 326150
David P. Holder (Treas)

PERRY FORD
12740 Poway Rd, Poway, CA 92064
Tel.: (858) 748-1400
Web Site: http://www.perryfordofpoway.com
Year Founded: 1995
Sales Range: $25-49.9 Million
Emp.: 100
Car Whslr
N.A.I.C.S.: 441110
Perry Falk (Pres)

PERRY HILL ACQUISITION CORPORATION
9454 Wilshire Blvd Ste 612, Beverly Hills, CA 90212
Tel.: (310) 888-1870   DE
Year Founded: 2015
Investment Services
N.A.I.C.S.: 523999
James M. Cassidy (Pres & Sec)
James McKillop (VP)

PERRY HOMES INC.
9000 Gulf Fwy Fl 3, Houston, TX 77017
Tel.: (713) 947-1750
Web Site: http://www.perryhomes.com
Rev.: $65,700,000
Emp.: 95
Speculative Builder, Single-Family Houses
N.A.I.C.S.: 236115
Celeste Watlington (Coord-Closing)
Ron Rohrbacher (Dir-Construction Trng & Dev)
Eric Bakk (VP & Controller)
Megan Sigler (VP)
Michael Koons (Mgr-Sls)
Michael Roosth (Dir-Sls Trng)
Todd Chachere (Exec VP)
Kevin Startz (Mgr-Sls)

PERRY LINCOLN MERCURY MAZDA
440 Hitchcock Way, Santa Barbara, CA 93105
Tel.: (805) 682-2411
Sales Range: $10-24.9 Million
Emp.: 45
Car Whslr
N.A.I.C.S.: 441110
Walter Alfaro (Gen Mgr)

PERRY MCCALL CONSTRUCTION INC.
6262 Greenland Rd, Jacksonville, FL 32258
Tel.: (904) 292-2645
Web Site: http://perry-mccall.com
Sales Range: $50-74.9 Million
Emp.: 30
Nonresidential Construction Services
N.A.I.C.S.: 236220
Myron McCall (Pres)

PERRY PRODUCTIONS
602 Dusty Ln, Concord, NC 28027
Tel.: (704) 788-2949
Web Site: http://www.perryproductions.com
Year Founded: 1994
Sales Range: Less than $1 Million
Emp.: 5

Internet/Web Design
Brian Perry (Owner)
Lisa Perry (Owner)

PERRY SUPPLY COMPANY INCORPORATED
2625 Vassar Dr NE PO Box 6486, Albuquerque, NM 87197
Tel.: (505) 884-6972
Web Site: http://www.perrysupply.net
Sales Range: $10-24.9 Million
Emp.: 40
Plumbing & Hydronic Heating Supplies
N.A.I.C.S.: 423720
David Perry Jr. (Pres)

PERRY VIDEX LLC
25 Hainesport - Mt Laurel Rd, Hainesport, NJ 08036
Tel.: (609) 267-1600   NJ
Web Site: http://www.perryvidex.com
Year Founded: 1932
Sales Range: $75-99.9 Million
Emp.: 45
Mfr of Heat Exchangers & Process Vessels; Dealers of Used Process Equipment
N.A.I.C.S.: 423830
Jerome P. Epstein (Chm)
Gregg Epstein (CEO & Pres-Chemicals, Foods & Pharmaceuticals)
Kenneth Miller (Gen Counsel & Exec VP)

Subsidiaries:

Perry Machinery Czech Republic S.R.O. (1)
Prazska 322, 501 01, Hradec Kralove, Czech Republic (100%)
Tel.: (420) 49 582 2270
Web Site: http://www.perryczech.cz
Sales Range: $25-49.9 Million
Emp.: 1
Mfr of Heat Exchangers & Process Vessels; Dealers of Used Process Equipment
N.A.I.C.S.: 425120

Perry Machinery Poland Ltd. (1)
Wolnosci 1A, Ozarow Mazowiecki, 05-850, Poland (100%)
Tel.: (48) 227223270
Web Site: http://www.perry.com.pl
Sales Range: $10-24.9 Million
Emp.: 10
Mfr of Heat Exchangers & Process Vessels; Dealers of Used Process Equipment
N.A.I.C.S.: 425120
Gregg P. Epstein (Pres)
Anna Sawka (Mgr)

Perry Process Equipment Ltd. (1)
Station Road Newton Aycliffe, Durham, DL5 6EQ, United Kingdom
Tel.: (44) 1325315111
Web Site: http://www.perryprocess.co.uk
Sales Range: $10-24.9 Million
Emp.: 18
Mfr of Heat Exchangers & Process Vessels; Dealers of Used Process Equipment
N.A.I.C.S.: 423830
Darren Bentham (Mng Dir)

Perry Products Corporation (1)
25 Mount Laurel Rd, Hainesport, NJ 08036
Tel.: (609) 267-1600
Web Site: http://www.perryproducts.com
Sales Range: $25-49.9 Million
Emp.: 30
Heat Exchanger Mfr
N.A.I.C.S.: 332410
Gregg P. Epstein (Pres)
Robert Parrish (VP-Ops)
David Goodman (Exec VP-Paper & Plastics)
Philip Wallace (Gen Mgr)

PERRY'S AUTO PARTS & SERVICE
113 S F St, Lompoc, CA 93436

U.S. PRIVATE

Tel.: (805) 736-6142
Sales Range: $10-24.9 Million
Emp.: 11
General Automotive Repair Shops
N.A.I.C.S.: 811111
Michael B. Perry (Pres)
Steve Smith (Mgr)

PERRY'S ICE CREAM CO., INC.
1 Ice Cream Plz, Akron, NY 14001-1036
Tel.: (716) 542-5492   DE
Web Site: http://www.perrysicecream.com
Year Founded: 1918
Sales Range: $25-49.9 Million
Emp.: 300
Mfr of Ice Cream
N.A.I.C.S.: 311520
David Hodgson (CIO)
Robert Denning (Pres & CEO)
Michelle Bulan (Exec Dir-Mktg & Corp Comm)
Marissa Wilson (Mgr-Comm)
Joel Bearfield (Dir-Mfg)

PERRYTON EQUITY
4219 S Main St, Perryton, TX 79070-2528
Tel.: (806) 435-4016   TX
Web Site: http://www.myequity.com
Year Founded: 1919
Sales Range: $10-24.9 Million
Emp.: 99
Agricultural Services
N.A.I.C.S.: 424510
Shawn Hughes (Gen Mgr)
Wes Beal (Mgr-Grain Dept & Coord-Safety)
Sandy Earp (Area Mgr)
Sherry Plank (Coord-Fuel Sls)

PERRYTON FEEDERS INC.
Hwy 70, Perryton, TX 79070
Tel.: (806) 435-5466   TX
Year Founded: 1969
Rev.: $25,977,985
Emp.: 75
Beef Cattle Feedlots
N.A.I.C.S.: 112112

PERSAUD COMPANIES INC.
6701 Democracy Blvd Ste 300, Bethesda, MD 20817
Tel.: (301) 896-9798
Year Founded: 1992
Sales Range: $10-24.9 Million
Emp.: 40
Nonresidential Construction Services
N.A.I.C.S.: 236220
Andy Persaud (Owner)

PERSEPHONE CAPITAL PARTNERS LLC
PO Box 198, East Setauket, NY 11733
Tel.: (202) 642-9501
Web Site: http://www.persephonecapital.com
Privater Equity Firm
N.A.I.C.S.: 523999
Jay Lifton (CEO & Mng Partner)
Frank S. Plimpton (Partner)
Alex Sorokin (Partner)

Subsidiaries:

Cella Acquisition Ltd. (1)
Building 148 Sixth Street Thomson Avenue, Harwell Campus, Didcot, OX11 0TR, United Kingdom
Tel.: (44) 1235437740
Web Site: http://cellaenergy.com
Emp.: 8
Advanced Hydrogen Storage Material Mfr
N.A.I.C.S.: 325120

COMPANIES

Alex Sorokin *(CEO)*
Stephen Bennington *(Founder & Mng Dir)*
Nicholas Brunero *(Chief Admin Officer)*
Jay Lifton *(Chm)*
Paul Prince *(Mgr-Ops)*
Chris Hobbs *(Mng Dir)*

Global Relief Technologies, LLC (1)
15 Rye St Ste 305, Portsmouth, NH 03801
Tel.: (603) 422-7333
Web Site: http://www.globalrelieftech.com
Sales Range: $10-24.9 Million
Emp.: 75
Information Services
N.A.I.C.S.: 519290
Suzanne Bresette *(Exec VP)*
Mark Mullin *(CTO)*

PERSEUS BOOKS, LLC
250 W 57th St 15th Fl, New York, NY 10107
Tel.: (212) 340-8100   DE
Web Site:
    http://www.perseusbooksgroup.com
Emp.: 1,100
Holding Company; Book Publisher & Distr
N.A.I.C.S.: 551112
Matthew Goldberg *(VP-Sls & Mktg)*
David Steinberger *(Pres & CEO)*
Heidi Sachner *(VP-Client Svcs)*
Regina Muscatelli *(Mgr-Sls Admin)*
Kristin Kiser *(VP)*

Subsidiaries:

Perseus Books, Inc. (1)
250 W 57th St 15th Fl, New York, NY 10107
Tel.: (212) 340-8100
Web Site:
    http://www.perseusbooksgroup.com
Book Publisher & Distr
N.A.I.C.S.: 513130
Matthew Goldberg *(VP-Sls & Mktg)*
David Steinberger *(Pres & CEO)*
Sabrina McCarthy *(Pres-Client Svcs-Distr)*
Heidi Sachner *(VP-Client Svcs)*

Subsidiary (Domestic):

Consortium Book Sales & Distribution, LLC (2)
The Keg House 34 13th Ave NE, Minneapolis, MN 55413-1007
Tel.: (612) 746-2600
Web Site: http://www.cbsd.com
Book Distr
N.A.I.C.S.: 424920
Jim Nichols *(VP-Sls)*

Legato Publishers Group (2)
814 William St, River Forest, IL 60305
Tel.: (312) 316-9618
Web Site:
    http://www.legatopublishersgroup.com
Book Distr
N.A.I.C.S.: 424920
Mark Suchomel *(Founder)*
Jeff Tegge *(Pres)*

Perseus Distribution, Inc. (2)
210 American Dr, Jackson, TN 38301
Tel.: (731) 423-1973
Web Site:
    http://www.perseusdistribution.com
Book Distr
N.A.I.C.S.: 424920
Celeste Winters *(Dir-Customer Svc)*

Publishers Group West (2)
1700 4th St, Berkeley, CA 94710
Tel.: (510) 809-3700
Web Site: http://www.pgw.com
Emp.: 300
Book Distr
N.A.I.C.S.: 424920
Eric Kettunen *(VP-Mktg & Client Mgmt)*
Suk Lee *(Dir-Intl Sls)*

PERSEUS LLC
2099 Pennsylvania Ave NW 9th Fl, Washington, DC 20006
Tel.: (202) 452-0101   DE
Web Site: http://www.perseusllc.com
Year Founded: 1995
Sales Range: $50-74.9 Million
Emp.: 30
Bank & Private Equity Fund Management Services
N.A.I.C.S.: 523999

Subsidiaries:

Haggar Corporation (1)
1507 Lyndon B Johnson Fwy Ste 100, Farmers Branch, TX 75234-6022
Tel.: (214) 352-8481
Web Site: http://www.haggar.com
Sales Range: $450-499.9 Million
Men's & Women's Apparel Products Marketer, Importer & Mfr
N.A.I.C.S.: 315250
Tim Lyons *(Pres-Sls)*

Subsidiary (Non-US):

Haggar Canada Co. (2)
141 New Huntington Road, Woodbridge, L4H 3R6, ON, Canada
Tel.: (416) 652-3777
Web Site: https://haggarca.wordpress.com
Sales Range: $50-74.9 Million
Women's Apparel Products Marketer & Mfr
N.A.I.C.S.: 424350

PERSHING SQUARE CAPITAL MANAGEMENT, L.P.
888 7th Ave Fl 42, New York, NY 10019
Tel.: (212) 286-0300
Web Site:
    http://www.persiansquareholdings.com
Year Founded: 2003
Sales Range: $5-14.9 Billion
Emp.: 60
Investment & Asset Management Services
N.A.I.C.S.: 523940
William Albert Ackman *(CEO & Portfolio Mgr)*
Stephen Fraidin *(Vice Chm)*
Ben Hakim *(Partner)*

PERSHING SQUARE SPARC HOLDINGS, LTD.
787 11th Ave 9th Fl, New York, NY 10019
Tel.: (212) 813-3700   DE
Web Site:
    https://www.pershingsquaresparcholdings.com
Year Founded: 2021
Rev.: $2
Assets: $30,006,976
Liabilities: $45,297,394
Net Worth: ($15,290,418)
Earnings: ($10,579,787)
Fiscal Year-end: 12/31/23
Holding Company
N.A.I.C.S.: 551112

PERSIS CORPORATION
900 Fort St Mall Ste 1720, Honolulu, HI 96813-3717
Tel.: (808) 599-8000   HI
Web Site: http://www.persis.com
Year Founded: 1967
Sales Range: $75-99.9 Million
Emp.: 3
Provider of Real Estate Services
N.A.I.C.S.: 531120
Easton Manson *(Mng Partner-Persis Asset Mngmt, LLC)*
June Nakahara *(Acctg Mgr & Asst Treas)*

PERSIVIA, INC.
900 Chelmsford St Twr 3 7th Fl, Lowell, MA 01851
Tel.: (978) 856-4600
Web Site: http://www.persivia.com
Year Founded: 2005
Emp.: 50
Computer Software & Services
N.A.I.C.S.: 513210
Mansoor Khan *(CEO)*

Subsidiaries:

IHM Services Company (1)
1 New England Executive Park Ste 225, Burlington, MA 01803-5005
Tel.: (781) 328-3000
Web Site: http://www.ihm-services.com
Computer Related Services
N.A.I.C.S.: 541519
Keith Hagen *(Pres)*
Brent Cosgrove *(COO)*

PERSONAL CARE PRODUCTS COUNCIL FOUNDATION, INC.
1620 L St Nw Ste 1200, Washington, DC 20036
Tel.: (202) 331-1770   DC
Web Site:
    http://www.personalcarecouncil.org
Year Founded: 1985
Sales Range: $10-24.9 Million
Health Care Srvices
N.A.I.C.S.: 813212
David Holl *(Treas)*
Louanne Roark *(Exec Dir)*
Keech Combe Shetty *(Chm)*

PERSONAL COMMUNICATION CENTER
39-40 30th St, Long Island City, NY 11101
Tel.: (718) 764-8300
Web Site:
    http://www.pccwireless.com
Rev.: $13,945,218
Emp.: 43
Telephone Equipment
N.A.I.C.S.: 423690
Patricia Sinha *(Pres)*
Hetal Trivedi *(Mgr-Acct Payable & Receivable)*
Gary Gopalani *(CFO)*

PERSONAL COMPUTER SYSTEMS, INC.
1720 Topside Rd, Louisville, TN 37777
Tel.: (865) 273-1960
Web Site: http://www.pcsknox.com
Year Founded: 1996
Rev.: $20,100,000
Emp.: 58
Computer Peripheral Equipment & Software Merchant Whslr
N.A.I.C.S.: 423430
Edward Waldroop *(CEO)*
Jeremy Waldroop *(Pres)*
Carol Waldroop *(COO)*

PERSONAL ENRICHMENT THROUGH MENTAL HEALTH SERVICES
11254 58th St N Bldg A, Pinellas Park, FL 33782
Tel.: (727) 545-6477   FL
Web Site: http://www.pemhs.org
Year Founded: 1981
Sales Range: $10-24.9 Million
Emp.: 315
Behavioral Healthcare Services
N.A.I.C.S.: 623220
Ken Remming *(Chm)*

PERSONAL MARKETING RESEARCH
322 Brady St, Davenport, IA 52801
Tel.: (563) 322-1960
Web Site:
    http://www.personalmarketingresearch.com
Sales Range: $50-74.9 Million
Emp.: 150
Market Analysis Or Research
N.A.I.C.S.: 541910
Patricia Duffy *(Pres)*

PERSONAL SELLING POWER INC.
150 Riverside Pkwy, Fredericksburg, VA 22406-1126
Tel.: (540) 752-7000
Web Site:
    http://www.sellingpower.com
Sales Range: $1-9.9 Million
Emp.: 38
Customer Relationship Management Information Magazine Publisher
N.A.I.C.S.: 513120
Gerhard Gschwandtner *(Founder & CEO)*

PERSONAL TECHNOLOGY SOLUTIONS LLC
6W 18th St, New York, NY 10011
Tel.: (212) 206-9619   NY
Web Site: http://www.cartwheelit.com
Year Founded: 2003
Sales Range: $1-9.9 Million
Emp.: 20
N.A.I.C.S.:
Josh Feder *(Co-Founder & Mng Partner)*
Allison Pheteplace *(Office Mgr)*
Rafi Kronzon *(Co-Founder & Mng Partner)*

PERSONAL-TOUCH HOME CARE, INC.
222-15 Northern Blvd, Bayside, NY 11361
Tel.: (718) 468-4747
Web Site:
    http://www.pthomecare.com
Year Founded: 1974
Sales Range: $200-249.9 Million
Emp.: 11,500
Women Healthcare Services
N.A.I.C.S.: 621610
Felix Glaubach *(Pres & CEO)*
Robert Marx *(Co-Founder, Chm, Gen Counsel & Exec VP)*
Robert Caione *(CEO)*

Subsidiaries:

Personal Touch Home Care of Baltimore Inc. (1)
200 E Joppa Rd Ste 103, Baltimore, MD 21286-3106   (100%)
Tel.: (410) 321-8448
Web Site:
    http://www.personalhomecare.com
Sales Range: $10-24.9 Million
Emp.: 25
Women Healthcare Services
N.A.I.C.S.: 621610

Personal Touch Home Care of VA. Inc. (1)
5505 Robin Hood Rd Ste C1, Norfolk, VA 23513-2416
Tel.: (757) 855-1355
Web Site: http://www.pthomecare.com
Sales Range: $25-49.9 Million
Emp.: 200
Women Healthcare Services
N.A.I.C.S.: 621610

PERSONALITY HOTELS INC.
440 Geary St, San Francisco, CA 94102
Tel.: (415) 202-8700
Web Site:
    http://www.personalityhotels.com
Sales Range: $10-24.9 Million
Emp.: 30
Hotels & Motels
N.A.I.C.S.: 721110
Yvonne Lembi Detert *(Pres & CEO)*
Dimitar Stanev *(Mgr-Hotel)*
Nathalie Toribio *(Mgr-Local Sls)*

PERSONALITY SOFTWARE SYSTEMS, INC.

PERSONALITY SOFTWARE SYSTEMS, INC.

U.S. PRIVATE

Personality Software Systems, Inc.—(Continued)
11730 W Sunset Blvd Ste 119, Los Angeles, CA 90049
Tel.: (714) 274-9379 NV
Year Founded: 2012
Mobile & Web-Based Software
N.A.I.C.S.: 513210
Uriel Lizama *(Pres, CEO, CFO, Prrincipal Acctg Officer, Treas & Sec)*

PERSONALIZED BEAUTY DISCOVERY, INC.
201 Baldwin Ave, San Mateo, CA 94401
Web Site: http://www.ipsy.com
Cosmetics, Beauty Supplies & Perfume Stores
N.A.I.C.S.: 456120
Marcelo Camberos *(Founder & CEO)*

PERSONALLY YOURS STAFFING
2 S University Dr Ste 304, Plantation, FL 33324
Tel.: (954) 851-0600
Rev.: $11,516,862
Emp.: 18
Help Supply Services
N.A.I.C.S.: 561320
John Messina *(Pres)*

PERSONNEL PARTNERS INC.
2311 Cassopolis St, Elkhart, IN 46514
Tel.: (574) 262-1960
Web Site: http://www.personnelpartners.com
Sales Range: $100-124.9 Million
Emp.: 8
Labor Resource Services
N.A.I.C.S.: 561320
Joan Rhoade *(Pres)*
Randy Rhoade *(CFO)*

PERSONNEL PLACEMENTS LLC
621 Old Hickory Blvd Ste B, Jackson, TN 38305-2911
Tel.: (731) 668-6777
Web Site: http://www.personnelplacement.com
Sales Range: $10-24.9 Million
Emp.: 400
Staffing Company
N.A.I.C.S.: 561320
Susan Gourley *(Mgr-Acctg)*

PERSONNEL PLUS, INC.
111 Filer Ave, Twin Falls, ID 83301
Tel.: (208) 733-7300 ID
Web Site: http://www.personnelinc.com
Rev.: $10,445,400
Emp.: 10
Employment Agencies
N.A.I.C.S.: 561311
Tony Mayer *(Pres)*

PERSONNEL SERVICES
3415 McNiel Ave Ste 101, Wichita Falls, TX 76308-1514
Tel.: (940) 696-3772
Web Site: http://www.psstaffing.com
Year Founded: 1992
Sales Range: $10-24.9 Million
Emp.: 27
Human Resource Management Services
N.A.I.C.S.: 541612
Jesse De Leon *(Mgr-HR)*

PERSONNEL SOURCE INC.
555 Lincoln St, Eugene, OR 97401
Tel.: (541) 342-5310
Web Site: http://www.personnelsource.com
Sales Range: $10-24.9 Million
Emp.: 24
Employment Agencies
N.A.I.C.S.: 561311
Roscoe Divine *(Pres & Owner)*
Derrick Stiltner *(VP)*
Todd Naddau *(Mgr-Accts)*
Jerry Stiltner *(Branch Mgr-Eugene)*

PERSPECTA LLC
1170 Wheeler Way Ste 200, Langhorne, PA 19047
Tel.: (866) 498-4423
Web Site: https://www.goperspecta.net
Emp.: 100
Physician Directories & Data Management Services
N.A.I.C.S.: 518210
Monique Barkett *(Pres-Workers Compensation & Property & Casualty)*
Howard D. Koenig *(Pres & CEO)*
April Stiles *(Founder & Pres-Group Health & Government Div)*

Subsidiaries:
Talisman Systems Group, Inc. (1)
2525 16th St Ste 316, San Francisco, CA 94103
Tel.: (415) 357-1751
Web Site: http://www.talisys.com
Sales Range: $1-9.9 Million
Emp.: 12
Prepackaged Software
N.A.I.C.S.: 513210
Monique Barkett *(Founder)*

PERUVIAN CONNECTION, LTD.
PO Box 990, Tonganoxie, KS 66086-0990
Tel.: (913) 845-2450 KS
Web Site: http://www.peruvianconnection.com
Year Founded: 1976
Sales Range: $50-74.9 Million
Emp.: 150
Women's & Men's Designer Apparel Mail Order & Online Retailer
N.A.I.C.S.: 458110
Annie Hurlbut *(Co-Founder & CEO)*
Biddy Hurlbut *(Co-Founder)*

PERUZZI BUICK GMC
165 Lincoln Hwy, Fairless Hills, PA 19030
Tel.: (215) 943-6000
Web Site: http://www.peruzzigm.com
Rev.: $67,500,000
Emp.: 170
Automotive Retailer
N.A.I.C.S.: 423860
Geno Peruzzi *(Gen Mgr-Sls)*

PERUZZI PONTIAC GMC TRUCK, INC.
156 Lincoln Hwy, Fairless Hills, PA 19030
Tel.: (215) 943-6000
Web Site: http://www.peruzzi.com
Sales Range: $50-74.9 Million
Emp.: 170
Car Whslr
N.A.I.C.S.: 441110
Frederick Peruzzi *(Principal)*

PERVASIP CORP.
430 N St, White Plains, NY 10605
Tel.: (914) 750-9339
Year Founded: 1964
Telecommunication Servicesb
N.A.I.C.S.: 517111
Paul H. Riss *(Chm, Pres & CEO)*

PERYAM & KROLL RE-SEARCH CORP.
6323 N Avondale Ave Ste 211, Chicago, IL 60631
Tel.: (773) 774-3100
Web Site: http://www.pktesting.com
Sales Range: $10-24.9 Million
Emp.: 125
Market Analysis Or Research
N.A.I.C.S.: 541910
Jeffrey J. Kroll *(CEO)*
George Herron *(Supvr-Lab)*
Timothy Croak *(Mgr-Res)*

PESADO CONSTRUCTION COMPANY
7054 Pipestone, Schertz, TX 78154
Tel.: (210) 651-4452
Web Site: http://www.pesadoconstructioncompany.com
Year Founded: 1991
Sales Range: $10-24.9 Million
Emp.: 28
Power & Communication Line & Related Structures Construction Services
N.A.I.C.S.: 237130
Shane Hutson *(Pres)*
Roger Flores *(VP)*
William Hunter *(Principal)*

PESNELL-COTTON
325 5th Ave NW, Attalla, AL 35954
Tel.: (256) 538-7811
Web Site: http://pesnell-cotton.hub.biz
Year Founded: 1986
Sales Range: $10-24.9 Million
Emp.: 3
Provider of Cotton
N.A.I.C.S.: 424590
Edward Pesnell Sr. *(Chm)*

PET ASSISTANT HOLDINGS, LLC
1065 SW 8th St Ste 1865, Miami, FL 33130
Tel.: (800) 935-7280
Web Site: https://www.p3t.vet
Pet Health Services
N.A.I.C.S.: 812910
Rob Levin *(CEO)*

Subsidiaries:
Heartland Veterinary Pharmacy LLC (1)
5052 W 12th St, Hastings, NE 68901
Tel.: (402) 463-2090
Web Site: http://www.heartlandvetsupply.com
Rev.: $3,460,000
Emp.: 10
Veterinary Pharmacy Services
N.A.I.C.S.: 541940

PET DOCTORS OF AMERICA
14333-42 Beach Blvd, Jacksonville, FL 32250
Tel.: (904) 223-5700
Web Site: http://www.petdoctorsofamerica.com
Year Founded: 2001
Sales Range: $10-24.9 Million
Emp.: 40
Pet Care Solution
N.A.I.C.S.: 812910
Stephanie Bennett *(Mgr-Hospital)*

PET FOOD EXPERTS INC.
175 Main St, Pawtucket, RI 02860
Tel.: (401) 334-8535
Web Site: http://www.pfxne.com
Year Founded: 1989
Road Transportation Support
N.A.I.C.S.: 488490
James W. Alden *(CFO)*
Michael Baker *(Prs & CEO)*

Subsidiaries:
United Pacific Pet, LLC (1)
12060 Cabernet Dr, Fontana, CA 92337
Tel.: (951) 360-8550
Web Site: http://www.uppet.com
Nursery & Garden Centers
N.A.I.C.S.: 444240
Kevin Sciullo *(Mgr-Sls)*

PET FOOD WHOLESALE INC.
3160 Enterprise St Ste B, Brea, CA 92821
Tel.: (714) 572-8250
Web Site: http://www.petfoodwholesale.com
Rev.: $37,800,000
Emp.: 60
Nondurable Goods Merchant Whslr
N.A.I.C.S.: 424990
Kent Watts *(Pres)*
Bob Johnson *(Gen Mgr)*

PET HOUSE
5781 Calle Real, Goleta, CA 93117
Tel.: (805) 967-7716
Web Site: http://www.pethouse.org
Sales Range: $10-24.9 Million
Emp.: 12
Retailer Pets
N.A.I.C.S.: 459910
Wendy Guyer *(Owner)*

PET SPECIALTIES LLC
400 S Elliott Rd Ste A1, Chapel Hill, NC 27514
Tel.: (919) 960-3606
Web Site: http://www.phydeauxpets.com
Year Founded: 2002
Sales Range: $1-9.9 Million
Emp.: 22
Pet Supplies
N.A.I.C.S.: 459910

PET STUFF ILLINOIS, LLC
90 S Evergreen Ave, Arlington Heights, IL 60005
Tel.: (773) 372-3073 IL
Web Site: http://www.petstuffchicago.com
Year Founded: 2008
Pet Product Stores
N.A.I.C.S.: 459910
Lisa Senafe *(Founder & Pres)*

Subsidiaries:
Go Dog Go Inc. (1)
8021 S 198th St Bldg 1, Kent, WA 98032
Tel.: (253) 228-4751
Web Site: http://www.godogggoinc.com
Pet Care Services
N.A.I.C.S.: 812910
Kristina Thompson *(Owner)*

Moochie & Co. (1)
652 Radio Dr, Lewis Center, OH 43035
Tel.: (614) 526-3100
Web Site: http://www.moochieandco.com
Retail Stores for Dogs & Cats
N.A.I.C.S.: 459910
Michael Dagne *(Founder & Pres)*

PET WORLD INC.
2148 W Beltline Hwy, Madison, WI 53713
Tel.: (608) 278-7999
Web Site: http://www.petworldstore.net
Rev.: $10,300,000
Emp.: 20
Pets
N.A.I.C.S.: 459910

PETCO PETROLEUM CORPORATION
108 E Ogden Ave Ste 100, Hinsdale, IL 60521
Tel.: (630) 654-2282

Web Site:
http://www.petcopetroleum.com
Sales Range: $10-24.9 Million
Emp.: 100
Oil Field Services
N.A.I.C.S.: 213112
Jay D. Bergman (Pres)

PETE & PETE CONTAINER SERVICE, INC.
4830 Warner Rd, Garfield Heights, OH 44125
Tel.: (216) 441-4422
Web Site:
http://www.peteandpeteinc.com
Year Founded: 1997
Specialized Freight Trucking; Long-Distance
N.A.I.C.S.: 484230

Subsidiaries:

P&P Valley View Holdings, Inc. (1)
11311 Rockside Rd, Cleveland, OH 44125
Tel.: (216) 524-3620
Web Site: http://www.boyasexcavating.com
Wrecking & Demolition Work
N.A.I.C.S.: 237990

PETE BAUR BUICK GMC INC.
14000 Pearl Rd, Strongsville, OH 44136
Tel.: (440) 238-5600
Web Site: http://www.petebaur.com
Year Founded: 1975
Sales Range: $10-24.9 Million
Emp.: 30
Automobile Dealership
N.A.I.C.S.: 441110
Daniel E. Baur (Pres)
Bruce Sykes (Gen Mgr)

PETE HARKNESS AUTO GROUP, INC.
2811 Locust St, Sterling, IL 61081
Tel.: (815) 625-6300   IL
Web Site:
http://www.peteharkness.com
Holding Company; New & Used Car Dealerships Owner & Operator
N.A.I.C.S.: 551112
Peter J. Harkness (Owner & Pres)
Karen Goff (Comptroller)

Subsidiaries:

Harkness Auto Group, Inc. (1)
2502 Locust St, Sterling, IL 61081
Tel.: (815) 499-4888
Web Site:
http://www.peteharknesschryslerdodgejeep.com
Emp.: 139
New & Used Car Dealer
N.A.I.C.S.: 441110
Peter J. Harkness (Pres)
Barry Goodwin (Gen Mgr)

Pete Harkness Chevrolet (1)
627 Lincolnway E, Morrison, IL 61270
Tel.: (815) 772-2171
Web Site:
http://www.peteharknesschevrolet.com
Sales Range: $1-9.9 Million
Emp.: 30
New & Used Car Dealer
N.A.I.C.S.: 441110
Bill Bart (Gen Mgr)

Pete Harkness Chevrolet Buick, Inc. (1)
1003 N 18th St, Centerville, IA 52544
Tel.: (641) 437-4040
Web Site:
http://www.peteharknessautogroup.com
Sales Range: $10-24.9 Million
Emp.: 12
New & Used Car Dealer
N.A.I.C.S.: 441110
Steve Bunch (Gen Mgr)
Delane Kinzler (Mgr-Bus)
Larry Long (Mgr-Parts)
Michael Matusick (Mgr-Svc)

PETE HONNEN EQUIPMENT CO. INC.
5055 E 72nd Ave, Commerce City, CO 80022
Tel.: (303) 287-7506
Web Site: http://www.honnen.com
Sales Range: $25-49.9 Million
Emp.: 90
Construction & Mining Machinery
N.A.I.C.S.: 423810
Pete Honnen (Chm & CEO)
Mark Honnen (Pres)
Bob Lewis (Asst Mgr-Parts)
Dave Cross (Mgr-Parts)
Dean Hirt (VP)
Jim Oller (Mgr-Parts)
Rusty Anderson (VP-Wyoming & Reg Mgr-Idaho)
Jon Asbury (VP-Allied Equipment & Mgr-Territory)
Jeff Jurgena (Mgr-Svc)

PETE LIEN & SONS INC.
3401 Universal Dr, Rapid City, SD 57702
Tel.: (605) 342-7224
Web Site: http://www.petelien.com
Rev.: $46,100,000
Emp.: 415
Ready Mixed Concrete
N.A.I.C.S.: 327320
Peter C. Lien (Pres)
Mike Greear (Mgr-Ops)
Michael Golliher (Mgr-Product Dev)
Bob Richmond (VP-Ops-Lime Plant)
Kevin Hanks (Supvr-Maintenance)
Mary Drumm (Mgr-HR)
Sharon Martin (Dir-Benefits)
Jacki Clucas (Coord-Employment)
Jared Nicolaus (Engr-Sls)

PETE MANKINS AUTO
3707 Summerhill Rd, Texarkana, TX 75503
Tel.: (903) 793-5661
Web Site:
http://www.petemankins.com
Sales Range: $25-49.9 Million
Emp.: 50
Owner & Operator of Car Dealerships
N.A.I.C.S.: 441110
Michael Mankins (VP)

PETE MOORE CHEVROLET INC.
103 New Warrington Rd, Pensacola, FL 32506
Tel.: (850) 456-7000
Web Site: http://www.petemoore.com
Sales Range: $25-49.9 Million
Emp.: 170
Automobiles, New & Used
N.A.I.C.S.: 441110
Pete Moore (Pres)

PETE'S CAR SMART KIA
4701 S Soncy Rd, Amarillo, TX 79119-6286
Tel.: (806) 351-1122
Web Site:
http://www.petescarsmartkia.com
Year Founded: 1983
Sales Range: $10-24.9 Million
Emp.: 38
Car Whslr
N.A.I.C.S.: 441110
Linda Bain (Coord-Customer Care)
Pete Vaughan (Pres)
Lee Gage (Gen Mgr)

PETE'S FRESH MARKET
5724 S Kedzie Ave, Chicago, IL 60629-2408
Tel.: (773) 925-6200
Web Site: http://www.petesfresh.com

Year Founded: 1980
Rev.: $22,000,000
Emp.: 130
Grocery Retailer
N.A.I.C.S.: 445110
James Dremonas (Pres & Sec)
Jan Chesny Heidelmeier (Dir-Floral)
Petro Drimonas (Project Mgr-Dev)
Vlasi Poggas (Mgr)

PETE'S ROAD SERVICE, INC.
2230 E Orangethorpe Ave, Fullerton, CA 92831
Tel.: (714) 446-1207
Web Site: http://www.petesrs.com
Year Founded: 1969
Sales Range: $25-49.9 Million
Emp.: 150
Whslr of Tires
N.A.I.C.S.: 423130
Glenn Fletcher (VP)
Ardy Fletcher (CFO)
Kyle Fletcher (Pres)
Keith Holland (VP)

PETE'S TIRE BARNS, INC.
275 E Main St, Orange, MA 01364
Tel.: (978) 544-8811   MA
Web Site: http://www.petestire.com
Year Founded: 1968
Sales Range: $25-49.9 Million
Emp.: 165
Tire Dealerships & Retreading Facilities Operator
N.A.I.C.S.: 441340
Peter A. Gerry (Pres & CEO)
Arthur Leblanc (VP & Gen Mgr)

PETEDGE
100 Cumming Center Ste 307 B, Beverly, MA 01915
Tel.: (978) 998-8100   MA
Web Site: http://www.petedge.com
Year Founded: 1956
Sales Range: $10-24.9 Million
Emp.: 110
Pet Supplies Mfr & Distr
N.A.I.C.S.: 459910
Ann Kane (Acct Mgr)
David Gordon (Mgr-Pkg Design)
Lori Haraske (Dir-Product Dev)
Sara Roseman (Acct Mgr)
Barry Irmer (Acct Mgr)
Chris MacMillan (Acct Mgr)
Jenna Melvin (Acct Mgr)
Nicholas Alexander (Acct Mgr)
Adrienne Marchese (Asst Acct Exec)
Carolyn Connolly (Mgr-SAP Master Data)
Colleen Ness (Mgr-Sls-Natl & Sr Acct Exec)
Larry Tsoutsis (Supvr-Sls)
Sonya Picariello (Acct Mgr)

PETER A. BASILE SONS, INC.
13000 Newburgh Rd, Livonia, MI 48150-1093
Tel.: (734) 591-4200   MI
Year Founded: 1958
Sales Range: $75-99.9 Million
Emp.: 100
Concrete Paving, Site Utilities Contractor
N.A.I.C.S.: 238110
Michael Bileti (CEO)
Peter Messina (VP-Ops)

Subsidiaries:

Metropolitan Asphalt, Inc. (1)
13000 Newburgh Rd, Livonia, MI 48150-1093
Tel.: (734) 591-4242
Sales Range: $10-24.9 Million
Emp.: 25
Asphalt Paving
N.A.I.C.S.: 238990

PETER A. MAYER ADVERTISING, INC.
324 Camp St, New Orleans, LA 70130-2804
Tel.: (504) 581-7191   LA
Web Site:
http://www.peteramayer.com
Year Founded: 1967
Rev.: $83,000,000
Emp.: 140
Advetising Agency
N.A.I.C.S.: 541810
Mark A. Mayer (Pres)
Ellen F. Kempner (VP & Grp Acct Dir)
David Crane (VP & Grp Acct Dir)
Josh Mayer (Chief Creative Officer)
Christian Howell (Dir-Art & Creative)
Nick Steger (Acct Exec)
George Morse (Designer-Interactive)
Michelle Edelman (Chief Strategy Officer & Exec VP)
Matthew Westfall (Mgr-Mktg)
Rebecca Hollis (Sr Dir-Art)
Desmond LaVelle (VP & Exec Dir-Creative)
Larry Lovell (Dir-PR)

PETER BAKER & SON CO. INC.
1349 Rockland Rd, Lake Bluff, IL 60044-1435
Tel.: (847) 362-3663   IL
Web Site: http://www.peterbaker.com
Year Founded: 1915
Sales Range: $25-49.9 Million
Emp.: 135
Provider of Highway & Street Construction Services
N.A.I.C.S.: 237310
Arthur Baker (Pres)
Rob Baker (Treas, Sec & VP)
Tim Gleason (Mgr-Quality Control)

PETER C. FOY & ASSOCIATES INSURANCE SERVICES, INC.
6200 Canoga Ave Ste 325, Woodland Hills, CA 91367
Tel.: (818) 703-8057   CA
Web Site:
https://foyandassociates.com
Year Founded: 1987
Insurance Brokerage & Employee Benefits Consulting Services
N.A.I.C.S.: 524210
Stephen Foy (Mng Partner & Exec VP)
Cheryl Baldwin (Exec VP)
Ashley Clark (VP-Benefits)
Ashley Kilfoyle (Mktg Mgr-Employee Benefits)

Subsidiaries:

Clark & Associates of Nevada, Inc. (1)
5470 Reno Corporate Dr, Reno, NV 89511
Tel.: (775) 828-7420
Web Site: http://www.clarkandassoc.com
Insurance Agencies & Brokerages
N.A.I.C.S.: 524210
Valerie Clark (Pres)
Brandy Allazetta (Exec VP)
Terrie Mann (Acct Exec)
Kelly McGuire-Shay (Acct Mgr)
Leisa Gandolfo (Acct Mgr)
Nancy Story (Office Mgr)

Colorado Insurance Sales & Service (1)
7901 Southpark Plz Ste 208, Littleton, CO 80120-4505
Tel.: (720) 283-1722
Web Site:
http://www.buycoloradoinsurance.com
Insurance Agencies & Brokerages
N.A.I.C.S.: 524210
Michael Mathisen (Pres)

Grosslight Insurance, Inc. (1)

PETER C. FOY & ASSOCIATES INSURANCE SERVICES, INC. U.S. PRIVATE

Peter C. Foy & Associates Insurance Services, Inc.—(Continued)
21300 Victory Blvd #700, 91367, Woodland Hills, CA
Tel.: (310) 473-9611
Web Site: http://www.grosslight.com
Insurance Agencies & Brokerages
N.A.I.C.S.: 524210
Gilbert F. Grosslight *(CEO)*
Veronica Espinoza *(Acct Mgr)*
Eduardo Vargas *(Acct Mgr-Comml)*
Linda Flanagan *(Gen Mgr)*
Oscar Borge *(Mgr-Comml Lines Div)*
Colleen Malfitano *(Mgr-HR)*
Steven Schiewe *(Pres)*
Chris Chang Dumortier *(Pres-Hospitality Div)*
Hsien-Chen Peng *(Sr Acct Mgr)*
Ed David *(VP)*
Hannah Schiewe *(Dir-Mktg)*
Anthony Ng *(Acct Mgr)*
Eileen Pendleton *(Acct Mgr-Comml)*
Joan Schiewe *(CEO)*
Arpie Simon *(Acct Mgr-Employee Benefits)*

Moulton Insurance Agency, Inc. (1)
143 West St, Ware, MA 01082
Tel.: (413) 967-3327
Web Site: http://www.moultoninsurance.com
Insurance Brokerage Services
N.A.I.C.S.: 524210
Melinda Pelletier *(Mgr-Acctg & Ops)*
Mary Robidoux *(Mgr-Agency & Comml Lines)*
Roy M. St. George *(VP)*
Cynthia Moulton St. George *(Pres)*
Ann Bechard *(Branch Mgr)*
Adam Moulton *(Mgr-Acct & Comml Lines)*

R.L. Milsner, Inc. Insurance Brokerage (1)
1233 Alpine Rd, Walnut Creek, CA 94596
Tel.: (925) 932-0424
Web Site: http://www.rlmilsner.com
Insurance Brokerage Services
N.A.I.C.S.: 524210
Susan Calvert *(Acct Mgr)*
J. J. DiMaso *(Office Mgr)*
Karen Fellezs *(Mgr-Acctg)*
Cynthia Beard *(Mgr-Personal Lines)*
Debbie Bauer *(Acct Mgr)*
Cherrie Lazaro *(Acct Mgr)*
Greg Kelson *(Acct Mgr)*
Eduardo Vega *(Acct Mgr)*
Yvette Primm *(Mgr-Comml Acct)*

Senex Insurance Services, Inc. (1)
21021 Ventura Blvd Ste 310, Woodland Hills, CA 91364
Tel.: (818) 593-3535
Web Site: http://www.senexgroup.com
Insurance Agencies & Brokerages
N.A.I.C.S.: 524210
Bruce Gendein *(Pres)*
Alex Knezevich *(Founder, CFO & Partner)*
Elyse Weise *(COO)*

PETER CONDAKES COMPANY INC.
70 New England Produce Ctr, Chelsea, MA 02150
Tel.: (617) 884-5080 MA
Web Site: http://www.petercondakes.com
Year Founded: 1952
Sales Range: $10-24.9 Million
Emp.: 80
Producers of Fresh Fruits & Vegetables
N.A.I.C.S.: 424480
Peter John Condakes *(Founder & Pres)*

PETER E HAAS JR FAMILY FUND
5 Hamilton Landing Ste 200, Novato, CA 94949
Tel.: (415) 464-2500 CA
Web Site: http://www.marincf.org
Year Founded: 2006
Sales Range: $75-99.9 Million
Emp.: 100
Grantmaking Services
N.A.I.C.S.: 813211

Thomas Peters *(Pres)*
S. A. Hartman *(CFO)*
Alexandra Derby *(VP)*
Cleveland Justis *(Chm)*

PETER KIEWIT SONS', INC.
1000 Kiewit Plz 3555 Farnam St, Omaha, NE 68131-3302
Tel.: (402) 342-2052 DE
Web Site: http://www.kiewit.com
Year Founded: 1884
Sales Range: $5-14.9 Billion
Emp.: 20,989
Holding Company; Heavy Construction Services
N.A.I.C.S.: 551112
Bruce E. Grewcock *(Chm, Pres & CEO)*
Michael J. Piechoski *(CFO & Sr VP)*
Richard A. Lanoha *(Pres & CEO)*

Subsidiaries:

Construction Kiewit Cie (1)
4333 Grande Allee, Boisbriand, J7H 1M7, QC, Canada   **(100%)**
Tel.: (450) 435-5756
Web Site: http://www.kiewit.com
Sales Range: $25-49.9 Million
Emp.: 150
Tunnel & Highway Construction Services
N.A.I.C.S.: 237990

Kiewit Construction Group, Inc. (1)
3555 Farnam St Ste 1000, Omaha, NE 68131-3302   **(100%)**
Tel.: (402) 342-2052
Web Site: http://www.kiewit.com
Sales Range: $50-74.9 Million
Emp.: 550
Construction Contracting
N.A.I.C.S.: 423810

Subsidiary (Domestic):

Buckskin Mining Company (1)
9545 N US Hwy 14 16, Gillette, WY 82717
Tel.: (307) 682-9144
Web Site: http://www.peterkiewit.com
Sales Range: $100-124.9 Million
Emp.: 350
Mining of Bituminous Coal & Lignite-Surface
N.A.I.C.S.: 212114

Kiewit Infrastructure West Co. (2)
Vancouver
2200 Columbia House Blvd, Vancouver, WA 98661
Tel.: (360) 693-1478
Web Site: http://www.kiewit.com
Heavy Construction & Engineering Services
N.A.I.C.S.: 237310

Kiewit Mining Group, Inc. (2)
1550 Mike Fahey St, Omaha, NE 68102   **(100%)**
Tel.: (402) 342-2052
Web Site: http://www.kiewit.com
Sales Range: $25-49.9 Million
Emp.: 25,700
Support Activities for Coal Mining
N.A.I.C.S.: 213113

Kiewit Management Ltd. (1)
11211 215th St, Edmonton, T5S 2B2, AB, Canada   **(100%)**
Tel.: (780) 447-3509
Web Site: http://www.kiewit.ca
Sales Range: $25-49.9 Million
Emp.: 80
Heavy Construction
N.A.I.C.S.: 237990

Kiewit Royalty Trust (1)
1700 Farnam St, Omaha, NE 68102
Tel.: (402) 536-5100
Rev: $1,047,590
Assets: $288,282
Liabilities: $288,281
Net Worth: $1
Earnings: $857,268
Fiscal Year-end: 12/31/2020
Trust Management Services
N.A.I.C.S.: 523940
G. Rosanna Moore *(VP)*

Mass. Electric Construction Co., Inc. (1)
180 Guest St, Boston, MA 02135-2028
Tel.: (617) 254-1015
Web Site: http://www.masselec.com
Sales Range: $10-24.9 Million
Emp.: 110
General Electrical Contractor
N.A.I.C.S.: 238210

Midwest Agencies, Inc. (1)
3555 Farnam St, Omaha, NE 68131-3302
Tel.: (402) 271-2840
Sales Range: $25-49.9 Million
Emp.: 11
Insurance Agents
N.A.I.C.S.: 524210
Philip G. Dehn *(Pres)*

TIC Holdings Inc. (1)
2211 Elk River Rd, Steamboat Springs, CO 80487
Tel.: (970) 879-2561
Web Site: http://www.tic-inc.com
Sales Range: $1-4.9 Billion
Emp.: 9,000
Holding Company
N.A.I.C.S.: 236210
Barbara Judd *(Dir-Personnel)*

Subsidiary (Domestic):

Ibberson, Inc. (2)
828 5th St S, Hopkins, MN 55343
Tel.: (952) 938-7007
Web Site: http://www.ibberson.com
Sales Range: $25-49.9 Million
Emp.: 309
Engineering & Construction Services
N.A.I.C.S.: 237990
Steve Kimes *(Pres)*

Subsidiary (Domestic):

Ibberson Engineering, Inc. (3)
828 5th St S, Hopkins, MN 55343-7750
Tel.: (952) 938-7007
Web Site: http://www.ibberson.com
Sales Range: $25-49.9 Million
Emp.: 80
Design, Engineering & Consulting Services
N.A.I.C.S.: 541330

Ibberson International, Inc. (3)
828 5th St S, Hopkins, MN 55343-7750
Tel.: (952) 938-7007
Web Site: http://www.ibberson.com
Sales Range: $25-49.9 Million
Emp.: 85
International Construction & Engineering Services
N.A.I.C.S.: 237990

T.E. Ibberson Company (3)
828 5th St S, Hopkins, MN 55343-7750
Tel.: (952) 938-7007
Web Site: http://www.ibberson.com
Sales Range: $25-49.9 Million
Emp.: 100
Engineering & Construction Services
N.A.I.C.S.: 237990

Subsidiary (Domestic):

TIC-The Industrial Company (2)
9780 Pyramid Ct, Englewood, CO 80112
Tel.: (970) 879-2561
Web Site: http://www.ticus.com
Rev.: $468,000,000
Emp.: 4,000
Heavy Construction Services
N.A.I.C.S.: 237990
Gary B. McKenzie *(Pres & CEO)*
James F. Kissane *(Treas & VP)*

Subsidiary (Domestic):

TIC Energy & Chemical (3)
6711 E Hwy 332, Freeport, TX 77542-0856
Tel.: (979) 233-5555
Web Site: http://www.ticus.com
Sales Range: $150-199.9 Million
Emp.: 120
Industrial Construction & Maintenance Services
N.A.I.C.S.: 236210
Jim Heath *(VP)*

Unit (Domestic):

TIC Western (3)
1550 James Rd, Bakersfield, CA 93308-9749
Tel.: (661) 391-5700
Web Site: http://www.tic-inc.com
Sales Range: $10-24.9 Million
Emp.: 100
Engineeering Services
N.A.I.C.S.: 237310
Dan Reddick *(Branch Mgr)*

Subsidiary (Domestic):

TIC-The Industrial Company Wyoming, Inc. (3)
1474 Willer Dr, Casper, WY 82604
Tel.: (307) 235-9958
Web Site: http://www.ticus.com
Sales Range: $50-74.9 Million
Emp.: 750
Heavy Construction Services
N.A.I.C.S.: 237990

Western Summit Constructors, Inc. (3)
160 Inverness Dr W Ste 110, Englewood, CO 80112
Tel.: (303) 298-9500
Web Site: http://www.westernsummit.com
Sales Range: $50-74.9 Million
Emp.: 300
Municipal & Industrial Water Treatment Facilities Construction
N.A.I.C.S.: 237110
Chamberlain Jack *(Mgr-Contract)*
Adam Johnsen *(Mgr-Safety)*
Dan Eckdahl *(Area Mgr)*
Eric Ness *(Project Mgr)*

PETER LI EDUCATION GROUP
2621 Dryden Rd Ste 300, Dayton, OH 45439
Tel.: (937) 293-1415
Web Site: http://www.peterli.com
Year Founded: 1971
Sales Range: $25-49.9 Million
Emp.: 80
Publisher of Educational Magazines & Periodicals
N.A.I.C.S.: 513120
Peter J. Li *(Pres & Publr)*
Terry Perkins *(VP-Mktg)*
Patty James *(Dir-Publ)*
Kevin Jensen *(Mgr-Production)*
Chris Osborne *(VP-Ops)*

Subsidiaries:

Peter Li, Inc. (1)
2621 Dryden Rd Ste 300, Dayton, OH 45439   **(100%)**
Tel.: (212) 818-0700
Web Site: http://www.peterli.com
Sales Range: $10-24.9 Million
Emp.: 2
Advertising Sales Office
N.A.I.C.S.: 541211

PETER LUMBER COMPANY
300 E Washington Ave, Pleasantville, NJ 08232
Tel.: (609) 641-9000 NJ
Web Site: http://www.peterlumber.com
Year Founded: 1932
Sales Range: $25-49.9 Million
Emp.: 115
Lumber & Mill Work
N.A.I.C.S.: 423310
Keith Givens *(Mgr-Pur)*
Hugh M. Peter Jr. *(Pres)*

PETER MUELLER, INC.
551 N Washington St, Falls Church, VA 22046
Tel.: (703) 534-0770
Web Site: http://www.internationalsaab.com
Sales Range: $25-49.9 Million
Emp.: 40
Owner & Operator of Car Dealerships
N.A.I.C.S.: 441110
Kurt Schirm *(Owner-Sls & Svc)*
Kevin Panameno *(Mgr-Parts)*
Qui Nguyen *(Mng Partner)*

PETER OGNIBENE ASSOCIATES
3 Iroquois St, Emmaus, PA 18049
Tel.: (610) 928-4062
Year Founded: 1977
Sales Range: Less than $1 Million
Emp.: 3
N.A.I.C.S.: 541810
Peter E. Ognibene (*Pres*)
Dorothy Gasdaska (*Media Dir*)
Ruth Ecker (*Mgr-Traffic*)

PETER P. BOLLINGER INVESTMENT CO.
540 Fulton Ave, Sacramento, CA 95825
Tel.: (916) 489-4600
Web Site: http://www.icalre.com
Rev.: $15,000,000
Emp.: 12
Real Estate Investors, Except Property Operators
N.A.I.C.S.: 523999
Paul Bollinger (*Exec VP*)

PETER PAN BUS LINES, INC.
Union Station Ste 300 1 Peter Pan Way, Springfield, MA 01103
Tel.: (413) 781-2900   MA
Web Site:
   http://www.peterpanbus.com
Year Founded: 1933
Sales Range: $100-124.9 Million
Emp.: 1,500
Interstate Bus Line & Charter Bus Services
N.A.I.C.S.: 485210
Peter A. Picknelly (*Chm*)
Maurice Brodeur (*Controller*)
Chris Crean (*VP-Safety & Security*)
Carl Lajeunesse (*Dir-Charter Sls*)
Bob Montana (*Gen Mgr-Maintenance*)
Thomas Picknally (*Sr VP-Maintenance*)
Frank Dougherty (*VP-Ops*)
Tom Lynch (*Gen Mgr-Boston Div*)
Don Soja (*Gen Mgr-CT Div*)
Kathy Giard (*Sr Dir-Revenue*)

Subsidiaries:

Architectural Windows & Doors   (1)
40 River Rd, Pleasant Valley, CT 06063
Tel.: (800) 448-7809
Web Site: http://www.werawd.com
Window & Door Mfr
N.A.I.C.S.: 321911
Malcolm Getz (*Pres & CEO*)
Kelly Williams (*Mgr-Ops*)
Rusty Boscarino (*Mgr-Svc*)

Belt Technologies, Inc.   (1)
11 Bowles Rd, Agawam, MA 01001
Tel.: (413) 786-9922
Web Site: http://www.belttechnologies.com
Metal Belt & Conveyor System Mfr
N.A.I.C.S.: 326220
Alan Wosky (*Pres*)
Tom Russel (*Mgr-Engrg*)

Bolt Bus   (1)
Newark Penn Sta 1 W Raymond Pl, Newark, NJ 07102
Tel.: (877) 265-8287
Web Site: http://www.boltbus.com
Bus Transportation Services
N.A.I.C.S.: 485210
Giselle Morales (*Supvr-Dispatch*)

Camfour, Inc.   (1)
65 Westfield Industrial Park Rd, Westfield, MA 01085
Tel.: (413) 564-2300
Web Site: http://www.camfour.com
Firearm Distr
N.A.I.C.S.: 423990
Jeff Cinelli (*VP-IT*)

Coach Builders   (1)
2273 Main St, Springfield, MA 01107
Tel.: (413) 737-4494
Web Site: http://www.coachbuilders.com
Sales Range: $10-24.9 Million
Emp.: 25
Bus Repair Services
N.A.I.C.S.: 811111
John Cieplik (*Gen Mgr*)

Duval Precision Grinding Inc.   (1)
940 Sheridan St, Chicopee, MA 01022-1031
Tel.: (413) 593-3060
Web Site: http://www.duvalgrinding.com
Precision Grinding Machinery Mfr
N.A.I.C.S.: 333515
Ron Parlengas (*Pres*)
Brian Gamache (*Mgr-Engrg*)
Darlene Beaulieu (*Office Mgr*)
Jeff Hockenberry (*Mgr-Production*)
Raymond Provencher (*Gen Mgr*)
Paul Iglesias (*Engr-Process*)

Hill Country Wholesale Inc.   (1)
13514 Immanuel Rd, Pflugerville, TX 78660
Tel.: (512) 244-1975
Web Site:
   http://www.hillcountrywholesale.com
Firearms Whslr
N.A.I.C.S.: 423910

Opal Real Estate Group   (1)
PO Box 1776, Springfield, MA 01102
Tel.: (413) 726-9836
Web Site: http://www.opal-re.com
Property Development & Property Management Services
N.A.I.C.S.: 531390
Demetrios N. Panteleakis (*Co-Founder & COO*)
Daniel T. Dodge (*Dir-Dev*)

PETER PARTS ELECTRONICS INC.
6285 Dean Pkwy, Ontario, NY 14519-8939
Tel.: (585) 265-2000   NY
Web Site: http://www.peterparts.com
Year Founded: 1986
Sales Range: $10-24.9 Million
Emp.: 100
Mfr of Electronic Parts & Equipment
N.A.I.C.S.: 423690
Peter Parts (*Pres & VP*)
Tim Radcliffe (*VP-Sls & Mktg*)
Steve Crane (*Gen Mgr*)

PETER PEPPER PRODUCTS, INC.
17929 S Susana Rd, Compton, CA 90224
Tel.: (310) 639-0390
Web Site:
   http://www.peterpepper.com
Year Founded: 1952
Sales Range: $10-24.9 Million
Emp.: 95
Furniture & Commercial Interior Accessories Supplier
N.A.I.C.S.: 423210
Sigi Pepper (*Pres*)
Michael Pepper (*CFO & COO*)
Bob Caseres (*VP-Production*)
Kip Pepper (*VP-Sls & Mktg*)

PETER THOMAS ROTH LABS LLC
460 Park Ave 16th Fl, New York, NY 10022-1829
Tel.: (212) 581-5800
Web Site:
   http://www.peterthomasroth.com
Rev.: $15,000,000
Emp.: 25
Cosmetic Preparation Mfr
N.A.I.C.S.: 325620
Peter Thomas Roth (*Founder*)

Subsidiaries:

June Jacobs Spa Collection   (1)
460 Park Ave 16th Fl, New York, NY 10022-1829
Tel.: (212) 471-4830
Web Site: http://www.junejacobs.com
Sales Range: $10-24.9 Million
Beauty Products
N.A.I.C.S.: 325620
June Jacob (*Pres*)

PETER-DE FRIES INCORPORATED
8525 Jefferson St NE, Albuquerque, NM 87113
Tel.: (505) 858-1010   NM
Web Site: http://www.dionspizza.com
Year Founded: 1978
Sales Range: $10-24.9 Million
Emp.: 1,200
Pizzeria Operator
N.A.I.C.S.: 722513
Jon Patton (*Owner*)

PETERBILT CAROLINA INC.
3502 Jeff Adams Dr, Charlotte, NC 28206
Tel.: (704) 597-8600
Sales Range: $10-24.9 Million
Emp.: 34
Truck Sales
N.A.I.C.S.: 441227

PETERBILT OF LOUISIANA LLC
16310 Commercial Ave, Baton Rouge, LA 70816
Tel.: (225) 273-8300
Web Site:
   http://www.peterbiltoflouisiana.com
Year Founded: 1976
Sales Range: $25-49.9 Million
Emp.: 60
New & Used Truck Dealers; Truck Parts & Servicing
N.A.I.C.S.: 441227
Jack Brabham (*Pres*)

PETERS AUTO SALES INC.
300 Amherst St, Nashua, NH 03063
Tel.: (603) 889-1166
Web Site: http://www.petersauto.com
Sales Range: $100-124.9 Million
Emp.: 150
Sales of New & Used Automobiles
N.A.I.C.S.: 441110
Peter B. Proko Jr. (*Pres*)

PETERS CONCRETE
1516 Atkinson Dr, Green Bay, WI 54303
Tel.: (920) 494-3700
Web Site:
   http://www.petersconcrete.com
Rev.: $10,000,000
Emp.: 80
Ready-Mixed Concrete Products
N.A.I.C.S.: 327320
Jack Peters (*Pres*)

PETERS CONSTRUCTION CORPORATION
901 Black Hawk Rd, Waterloo, IA 50701-2414
Tel.: (319) 236-2003   IA
Web Site:
   http://www.petersconstruction.com
Year Founded: 1951
Sales Range: $75-99.9 Million
Emp.: 60
Engineeering Services
N.A.I.C.S.: 236220
David Peters (*Pres*)
Brad Best (*Pres*)

PETERS CORPORATION
1011 Paseo De Peralta F, Santa Fe, NM 87501
Tel.: (505) 954-5700
Web Site: http://www.gpgallery.com
Rev.: $16,600,000
Emp.: 30
Art Dealers
N.A.I.C.S.: 459920
Gerald P. Peters (*Pres*)
Abigail Schlegell (*Dir-Sls*)
Maria Hajic (*Dir-Naturalism*)
John Macker (*Dir-Publications & Bookstore*)
Robin Roche (*Dir-Registrar*)
Elizabeth Hubbard (*Mgr-Facilities & Contact*)
Elizabeth Hook (*Dir-Gallery*)

PETERS HEATING & AC
4520 Broadway St, Quincy, IL 62305
Tel.: (217) 222-1368
Web Site:
   http://www.petersheatingandair.com
Sales Range: $10-24.9 Million
Emp.: 50
Ventilation & Duct Work Contractor
N.A.I.C.S.: 238220

PETERS MANUFACTURED HOMES
3695 W Riverbend Ave, Post Falls, ID 83854
Tel.: (208) 773-7112
Web Site: http://www.petershms.com
Sales Range: $10-24.9 Million
Emp.: 17
Mobile Home Dealers
N.A.I.C.S.: 459930
Eric Tibesar (*Mgr-Sls*)

PETERSBURG MOTOR COMPANY INC.
100 Myers Dr, Charlottesville, VA 22901
Tel.: (434) 951-1000
Web Site:
   http://www.colonialautocenter.com
Rev.: $97,713,330
Emp.: 200
Automobiles, New & Used
N.A.I.C.S.: 441110
Diane Lawson (*Controller*)
H. Carter Myers III (*CEO*)

PETERSEN HEALTH CARE, INC.
830 W Trailcreek Dr, Peoria, IL 61614
Tel.: (309) 691-8113
Web Site:
   http://www.petersenhealthcare.net
Year Founded: 1974
Sales Range: $25-49.9 Million
Emp.: 55
Nursing Care Services
N.A.I.C.S.: 623110
Mark B. Petersen (*Owner*)
David Oligschlaeger (*Dir-Medical*)

Subsidiaries:

Petersen Health Care - Palm Terrace of Mattoon   (1)
1000 Palm Ave, Mattoon, IL 61938
Tel.: (217) 234-7403
Web Site: http://www.petersenhealthcare.net
Sales Range: $10-24.9 Million
Emp.: 140
Nursing Care Services
N.A.I.C.S.: 623110
Glenna K. Birch (*Reg Dir-Ops*)

PETERSEN MARINE SUPPLY INC.
4455 S 900 W, Ogden, UT 84405
Tel.: (801) 621-7532
Web Site:
   http://www.petersenmarine.com
Rev.: $10,000,000
Emp.: 20
Motor Boat Dealers
N.A.I.C.S.: 441222
Dennis J. Petersen (*Pres*)

PETERSEN-DEAN INC.

PETERSEN-DEAN INC.

U.S. PRIVATE

Petersen-Dean Inc.—(Continued)
39300 Civic Center Dr Ste 300, Fremont, CA 94538
Tel.: (510) 494-9982   CA
Web Site:
http://www.petersendean.com
Year Founded: 1984
Roofing Contractor Services
N.A.I.C.S.: 238160
Joe Dean (Co-Founder)
George K. Milionis (Gen Counsel & Sec)
Mark Volpe (VP-HR)

Subsidiaries:

Maui Roofing   (1)
36 East Waipuilani, Kihei, HI 96753-5225
Tel.: (808) 875-0106
Web Site: http://www.mauiroofing.com
Roofing Contractors
N.A.I.C.S.: 238160

PETERSON BECKNER INDUSTRIES
10700 N Freeway Ste 950, Houston, TX 77037
Tel.: (281) 872-7722
Web Site:
http://www.petersonbeckner.com
Rev.: $18,000,000
Emp.: 60
Structural Steel Erection
N.A.I.C.S.: 238120
Larry Peterson (Pres)
Lance Beckner (VP)

PETERSON COMPANY INC.
10700 W 50th Ave, Wheat Ridge, CO 80033-2287
Tel.: (303) 388-6322   CO
Web Site: http://www.peterson-co.com
Year Founded: 1931
Sales Range: $25-49.9 Million
Emp.: 25
Mfr of Electrical Apparatus & Equipment
N.A.I.C.S.: 423610
Terry Wadworth (Pres)
Bill Kubilus (Treas)
Brian Hurd (Sec)

PETERSON CONTRACTORS, INC.
104 Blackhawk St, Reinbeck, IA 50669
Tel.: (319) 345-2713
Web Site:
http://www.petersoncontractors.com
Year Founded: 1966
Sales Range: $75-99.9 Million
Emp.: 350
Highway & Heavy Construction Services
N.A.I.C.S.: 237310
Cordell Q. Peterson (Founder & Pres)
Mark Peterson (Dir-Personnel)
Jim Peterson (Controller)
Gale M. Peterson Jr. (VP)

PETERSON FARMS, INC.
3104 W Baseline Rd, Shelby, MI 49455-9633
Tel.: (231) 861-7101   MI
Web Site:
http://www.petersonfarms.com
Year Founded: 1984
Sales Range: $25-49.9 Million
Emp.: 200
Fruit Farming, Processing & Whslr
N.A.I.C.S.: 111334
Earl L. Peterson (Chm)
Aaron Peterson (Pres & CEO)
Sarah Schlukebir (VP-Sls & Mktg)
Brad Moul (Dir-HR)
Larry Hicks (Dir-Sls)

Subsidiaries:

Cherry Technologies, Inc.   (1)
3162 W Baseline Rd, Shelby, MI 49455
Tel.: (231) 861-2105
Electric Equipment Mfr
N.A.I.C.S.: 335999

Oceana County Freezer Storage, Inc.   (1)
4730 W Shelby Rd, Shelby, MI 49455
Tel.: (231) 861-6575
Refrigerated Warehousing & Storage
N.A.I.C.S.: 493120

Peterson Farms Fresh, Inc.   (1)
3104 W Baseline Rd, Shelby, MI 49455
Tel.: (231) 861-7101
Web Site: http://www.petersonfarmsinc.com
Fruit Processing
N.A.I.C.S.: 115114
Earl L. Peterson (Chm)
Aaron Peterson (Pres & CEO)

PETERSON GMC-KENWORTH INC.
4330 Poplar Level Rd, Louisville, KY 40213
Tel.: (502) 459-1200
Web Site:
http://www.petersontruckcenter.com
Sales Range: $10-24.9 Million
Emp.: 48
Trucks, Tractors & Trailers: New & Used
N.A.I.C.S.: 441110
Wallace T. Peterson (Pres)
Dave Effinger (Gen Mgr)
Mary Dunlap (Controller)

PETERSON INDUSTRIES LLC
41 N 3rd Ave, Sturgeon Bay, WI 54235-2413
Tel.: (920) 743-5577   WI
Year Founded: 1933
Sales Range: $50-74.9 Million
Emp.: 6
Provider of Ship Repair & Marina Operation Services
N.A.I.C.S.: 336212
Ellsworth L. Peterson (Chm)

PETERSON MANUFACTURING COMPANY INC.
4200 E 135th St, Grandview, MO 64030-2875
Tel.: (816) 765-2000   MO
Web Site: http://www.pmlights.com
Year Founded: 1945
Sales Range: $200-249.9 Million
Emp.: 500
Vehicular Lighting Equipment Mfr
N.A.I.C.S.: 336320
Mark Assenmacher (Dir-Mktg)
Steve Hickerson (VP-Fin)
Steve Meagher (VP-Sls)
Kristen Goodson (VP-Product Mgmt)

Subsidiaries:

Mission Plastics of Arkansas, Inc.   (1)
102 Mission Dr, Nashville, AR 71852-3400
Tel.: (870) 845-4085
Web Site: http://www.pmlight.com
Sales Range: $25-49.9 Million
Emp.: 220
Mfr of Plastic Products
N.A.I.C.S.: 326199

Motorsport Marketing, Inc.   (1)
13312 Fifth St, Grandview, MO 64030-2958
Tel.: (816) 765-8500
Web Site: http://www.gomotorsports.com
Sales Range: $10-24.9 Million
Emp.: 25
Provider of Toys, Hobby Goods & Supplies
N.A.I.C.S.: 423920

Transworld Products, Inc.   (1)
13312 5th St, Grandview, MO 64030-2958
Tel.: (816) 765-6388

Web Site:
http://www.transworldproducts.com
Sales Range: $10-24.9 Million
Emp.: 9
Provider of Business Services
N.A.I.C.S.: 561499
Steve Meagher (CEO)
William Chan (Gen Mgr)
Mike Peteete (Product Mgr)
Steve Schmidt (Pres)

PETERSON MILLA HOOKS
1315 Harmon Pl, Minneapolis, MN 55403-1926
Tel.: (612) 349-9116   MN
Web Site: http://www.pmhadv.com
Year Founded: 1990
Rev.: $60,000,000
Emp.: 48
Brand Development, Fashion/Apparel, Leisure, Retail
N.A.I.C.S.: 541810
David Peterson (Founder)

PETERSON MOTOR COMPANY
9101 W Fairview Ave, Boise, ID 83704-8221
Tel.: (208) 378-9000   ID
Web Site:
http://www.petersontoyota.net
Year Founded: 1958
Sales Range: $125-149.9 Million
Emp.: 200
Retail Sales of New & Used Automobiles
N.A.I.C.S.: 441110
Jason Hamilton (Dir-Mktg)

PETERSON PACIFIC INC.
29408 Airport Rd, Eugene, OR 97402
Tel.: (541) 689-6520   OR
Web Site:
http://www.petersonpacific.com
Year Founded: 1982
Sales Range: $10-24.9 Million
Emp.: 137
Distr of Forestry Related Equipment
N.A.I.C.S.: 333120
Neil Peterson (Chm)

PETERSON PARTNERS, INC.
2825 E Cottonwood Pkwy Ste 400, Salt Lake City, UT 84121
Tel.: (801) 365-0180
Web Site:
http://www.petersonpartnerslp.com
Sales Range: $10-24.9 Million
Emp.: 10
Privater Equity Firm
N.A.I.C.S.: 523999
Joel Clinton Peterson (Founder, Chm & Partner)
Brandon Cope (Partner)
Ben Capell (Partner)
Eric Noble (CFO & Chief Compliance Officer)
Jacob Zornes (Mgr-Fund Acctg)
Kenny Shum (VP)
Marc Fuller (Partner)
Matthew Dadson (Controller)
Matthew Day (Partner)
Robert Hansen (Partner)
Spencer Clawson (VP)
Clint Peterson (Mng Partner)
Aaron Gabbart (VP)
Dan Hanks (VP)
Brian Kelly (VP-Bus Dev)

PETERSON PROBST
701 N Third St Ste 207, Minneapolis, MN 55401
Tel.: (612) 767-3939
Web Site:
http://www.petersonprobst.com
Rev.: $600,000
Emp.: 100

Full Service Advertising
N.A.I.C.S.: 541810
Joe Peterson (Co-Founder & Lead Strategist)
Tom Probst (Co-Founder & Dir-Creative)
Amy Geiger (VP-Bus Dev, Sls & Mktg)

PETERSON STAMPEDE DODGE CHRYSLER JEEP
5801 E Gate Blvd, Nampa, ID 83687
Tel.: (208) 475-3000
Web Site:
http://www.stampededodge.com
Year Founded: 1928
Sales Range: $10-24.9 Million
Emp.: 150
Car Whslr
N.A.I.C.S.: 441110
Mike Moore (Mgr)

PETERSON TOYOTA
4381 Fayetteville Rd, Lumberton, NC 28358-2619
Tel.: (910) 738-5241
Web Site:
http://www.petersontoyota.com
Year Founded: 1981
Sales Range: $10-24.9 Million
Emp.: 50
Car Whslr
N.A.I.C.S.: 441110
A. W. Peterson (Owner)

PETERSON TRACTOR COMPANY
955 Marina Blvd, San Leandro, CA 94577-3440
Tel.: (510) 357-6200   CA
Web Site:
http://www.petersontractor.com
Year Founded: 1936
Sales Range: $75-99.9 Million
Emp.: 100
Agricultural Implements Distr
N.A.I.C.S.: 423810
Duane Doyle (CEO)
John Krummen (VP)

PETES CONNECTION INC.
280 N Benson Ave #7-8, Santee, CA 92071
Tel.: (909) 373-6414
Web Site:
http://www.petesconnection.com
Year Founded: 1987
Sales Range: $10-24.9 Million
Emp.: 50
Cable Television Services
N.A.I.C.S.: 516210

PETES SAKE CANCER RESPITE FOUNDATION
620 W Germantown Pike Ste 250, Plymouth Meeting, PA 19462
Tel.: (267) 708-0510   PA
Web Site:
http://www.takeabreakfromcancer.org
Year Founded: 1999
Rev.: $1,420,479
Assets: $796,713
Liabilities: $13,750
Net Worth: $782,963
Earnings: $307,877
Emp.: 10
Fiscal Year-end: 06/30/14
Cancer Patient Wellness Services
N.A.I.C.S.: 813212
Kate Shields (Chm)
Marcella B. Schankweiler (Founder & CEO)

PETFIRST HEALTHCARE
One Quartermaster Court, Jeffersonville, IN 47130

Web Site:
http://www.petfirsthealthcare.com
Year Founded: 2004
Sales Range: $1-9.9 Million
Emp.: 35
Administers & Sells Pet Insurance for Dogs & Cats
N.A.I.C.S.: 524114
Lansdon B. Robbins *(Co-Founder & Chm)*
A. Brent Hinton *(Co-Founder & Vice Chm)*
Katie Grant Blakeley *(CEO)*
Clint Lawrence *(VP-Sls & Mktg)*
Franklin T. Dog *(Chief Wagging Officer)*
Michael Walling *(CFO)*
Taryn Pearson *(Dir-HR)*

PETFOODDIRECT.COM
2100 Chemical Rd Plymouth Meeting, Plymouth Meeting, PA 19462
Tel.: (215) 513-1999
Web Site:
http://www.petfooddirect.com
Year Founded: 1997
Rev.: $5,000,000
Emp.: 150
Online Pet Supply Store
N.A.I.C.S.: 459910
Mathew Murray *(VP-Fin)*
Jon Roska Jr. *(Founder & VP-Mdsg & Consumables)*

PETIT JEAN ELECTRIC COOPERATIVE
270 Quality Dr, Clinton, AR 72031-0037
Tel.: (501) 745-2493   AR
Web Site: http://www.pjecc.com
Year Founded: 1940
Sales Range: $25-49.9 Million
Electric Power Distr
N.A.I.C.S.: 221122
Sherry Bettis *(Mgr-Fin & Acctg)*
Mike Garbow *(Mgr-Engrg)*
Tom Nowlin *(Mgr-Office Svcs)*
Donnie Collins *(Chm)*
Michael Kirkland *(CEO & Gen Mgr)*

PETLAND DISCOUNTS INC.
355 Crooked Hill Rd, Brentwood, NY 11717-1031
Tel.: (631) 273-6363   NY
Web Site:
http://www.petlanddiscounts.com
Year Founded: 1965
Sales Range: $25-49.9 Million
Emp.: 750
Pet Product Retailer
N.A.I.C.S.: 459910
Amy Eisenberg *(Dir-PR & Special Events)*
Scott Caulfield *(CIO & VP)*
Antonio Martinez *(Mgr)*
Rose Consiglio *(Exec VP)*

PETOSKEY PLASTICS INC.
1 Petoskey St, Petoskey, MI 49770-9723
Tel.: (231) 347-2602   MI
Web Site:
http://www.petoskeyplastics.com
Year Founded: 1969
Sales Range: $75-99.9 Million
Emp.: 400
Unsupported Plastics Film & Sheet
N.A.I.C.S.: 326113
Paul C. Keiswetter *(Pres)*
Susanne K. Maskaluk *(CFO, Treas & Controller)*
Marilyn K. Cummings *(Sec)*

PETPARTNERS, INC.
8051 Arco Corporate Dr Ste 350, Raleigh, NC 27617
Tel.: (919) 215-8222
Web Site: http://www.petpartners.net
Year Founded: 2002
Pet Insurance Product & Services
N.A.I.C.S.: 524128
John Wycoff *(Pres)*

PETR-ALL CORPORATION
7401 Round Pond Rd, Syracuse, NY 13212
Tel.: (315) 446-0125   NY
Web Site:
http://www.expressmart.com
Year Founded: 1975
Sales Range: $75-99.9 Million
Emp.: 510
Petroleum Convenient Store Distributor
N.A.I.C.S.: 424720
Daniel Towmbly *(CFO)*
Mike Askwith *(Pres)*

PETRA ACQUISITION, INC.
5 W 21st St, New York, NY 10010
Tel.: (917) 622-5800   DE
Year Founded: 2020
Investment Services
N.A.I.C.S.: 523999
Andreas Typaldos *(Chm, CEO & Sec)*
Sean Fitzpatrick *(CFO)*

PETRA CAPITAL MANAGEMENT LLC
1370 Ave of the Americas 23rd Fl, New York, NY 10019
Tel.: (212) 812-6170
Web Site: http://www.petracap.com
Investment Services
N.A.I.C.S.: 523999
Andrew Stone *(Chm, Pres & CEO)*

PETRA CAPITAL PARTNERS, LLC
3825 Bedford Ave Ste 101, Nashville, TN 37215
Tel.: (615) 313-5999
Web Site:
http://www.petracapital.com
Year Founded: 1996
Privater Equity Firm
N.A.I.C.S.: 523999
Michael W. Blackburn *(Mng Partner)*
David Fitzgerald *(Partner)*
Douglas B. Owen *(Principal)*
Carol J. Collins *(Chief Admin Officer)*
Melanie L. Beavon *(CFO)*
Charles R. Webb *(VP)*
Matt Sotelo *(VP)*

Subsidiaries:

Acute Behavioral Health, LLC   (1)
424 Church St Ste 2000, Nashville, TN 37219
Tel.: (615) 973-5503
Web Site: https://acutebehavioral.com
Behavioral Healthcare Services
N.A.I.C.S.: 621498

Subsidiary (Domestic):

Hallmark Youthcare-Richmond, LLC   (2)
12800 W Creek Pkwy, Richmond, VA 23238-1116
Tel.: (804) 784-2200
Web Site: http://www.hallmarksystems.com
Sales Range: $10-24.9 Million
Emp.: 150
Psychiatric Hospitals
N.A.I.C.S.: 621420
Wanda Saddler *(VP)*

PETRA GEOTECHNICAL, INC.
3186 Airway Ave Ste K, Costa Mesa, CA 92626
Tel.: (714) 549-8921   CA
Web Site: http://www.petra-inc.com
Year Founded: 1988
Sales Range: $10-24.9 Million
Emp.: 75
Scientific & Technical Consulting Services
N.A.I.C.S.: 541690
Siamak Jafoudi *(Pres)*
Jeanne Krinsky *(VP)*
Robert Ruff *(Sr VP)*

PETRA INCORPORATED
1097 Rosario St, Meridian, ID 83642
Tel.: (208) 323-4500
Web Site: http://www.petrainc.net
Year Founded: 1994
Rev.: $56,500,000
Emp.: 50
Construction Management Services
N.A.I.C.S.: 236210
Jerry Frank *(Pres & CEO)*
Shiloh Holmes *(Mgr-Bus Dev)*
James MacIsaac *(Dir-Bus Dev)*
John Quapp *(CFO & Controller)*

PETRA ROOFING COMPANY, LLC
17338 N May Ave, Edmond, OK 73012
Tel.: (405) 720-2400
Web Site:
http://www.petraroofingco.com
Year Founded: 2004
Sales Range: $1-9.9 Million
Emp.: 6
Construction Services
N.A.I.C.S.: 236220
Nicole Tait *(Owner)*

PETRACCA & SONS INC.
1802 Petracca Pl, Whitestone, NY 11357-6002
Tel.: (718) 746-8000   NY
Web Site: http://psina.weebly.com
Year Founded: 1975
Sales Range: $10-24.9 Million
Emp.: 55
Provider of Industrial Construction Services
N.A.I.C.S.: 237310
Bill Lane *(Mgr)*
James Delaney *(VP)*
Rich Valenza *(VP)*
Bill Robinson *(CFO)*
Eugene Petracca Jr. *(Pres)*

PETRAYS
200 Valley Wood Rd Ste B200, The Woodlands, TX 77380
Tel.: (888) 473-8729
Web Site: http://www.petrays.com
Year Founded: 2006
Sales Range: $1-9.9 Million
Emp.: 8
Veterinary Telemedicine Services
N.A.I.C.S.: 541940
Frank Powell *(Pres)*

PETRELOCATION INC.
1121 E 7th St, Austin, TX 78702
Tel.: (512) 362-6100
Web Site:
http://www.petrelocation.com
Year Founded: 2004
Sales Range: $1-9.9 Million
Emp.: 25
Pet Relocation Services
N.A.I.C.S.: 485999
Kevin O'Brien *(Co-Founder & CEO)*
Angie O'Brien *(Co-Founder)*

PETRICCA INDUSTRIES, INC.
550 Cheshire Rd, Pittsfield, MA 01201-1823
Tel.: (413) 499-1441   MA
Web Site:
http://www.unistresscorp.com
Year Founded: 1936
Sales Range: $25-49.9 Million
Emp.: 300
Prestressed Concrete Product Mfr
N.A.I.C.S.: 327331

Subsidiaries:

Unistress Corporation   (1)
550 Cheshire Rd, Pittsfield, MA 01201
Tel.: (413) 499-1441
Web Site: http://www.unistresscorp.com
Construction Engineering Services
N.A.I.C.S.: 541330
Ralph Schwarzer *(Plant Mgr)*
James Cutler *(Coord-Design)*

PETRO AMIGOS SUPPLY, INC.
757 N Eldridge Pkwy Ste 500, Houston, TX 77079
Tel.: (281) 497-0858
Web Site: http://www.petro-amigos.com
Year Founded: 1988
Sales Range: $250-299.9 Million
Emp.: 20
Energy Related Tubular Products Distr
N.A.I.C.S.: 423130
Cesar Vasquez *(Pres & CEO)*
Stafford Hillman *(VP-Sls)*
Ross Wortham *(VP-Sls)*

PETRO AUTOMOTIVE GROUP, INC.
6248 US Hwy 98, Hattiesburg, MS 39402
Tel.: (601) 264-4411
Year Founded: 1990
Sales Range: $10-24.9 Million
Emp.: 62
Car Whslr
N.A.I.C.S.: 441110
Melissa Lott *(Office Mgr)*

PETRO ENVIRONMENTAL TECHNOLOGIES INC.
7870 E Kemper Rd Ste 240, Cincinnati, OH 45249
Tel.: (513) 489-6789
Web Site: http://www.petroenviro.com
Sales Range: $25-49.9 Million
Emp.: 25
Land Preparation Construction
N.A.I.C.S.: 236210
Pete Mather *(VP)*
Jeff Heltman *(CFO)*
Mark Mather *(Pres)*

PETRO MARINE SERVICES
PO Box 389, Seward, AK 99664
Tel.: (907) 224-3190
Web Site:
http://www.petromarineservices.com
Sales Range: $10-24.9 Million
Emp.: 200
Provider of Fuel Oil Dealer Services
N.A.I.C.S.: 424720
Tony Leichty *(Plant Mgr)*

PETRO SERVICE INC.
17 Avenue East, Bayonne, NJ 07002
Tel.: (732) 721-8000
Web Site:
http://www.petroserviceinc.com
Rev.: $89,172,785
Emp.: 5
Fuel Oil
N.A.I.C.S.: 424720

PETRO-HUNT, L.L.C.
2101 Cedar Springs Rd Ste 600, Dallas, TX 75201-7201
Tel.: (214) 880-8400
Web Site: http://www.petrohunt.com
Year Founded: 1977
Sales Range: $25-49.9 Million
Emp.: 60
Exploration & Production of Oil & Gas

PETRO-HUNT, L.L.C.

Petro-Hunt, L.L.C.—(Continued)
N.A.I.C.S.: 213112
Bruce W. Hunt *(Pres)*
Thomas E. Nelson *(VP-Fin)*
R. Fred Hosey *(Gen Counsel & Sec)*
James M. Mason *(Treas)*
Robert M. Donohue Jr. *(VP)*

Subsidiaries:

Pursue Energy (1)
2173 Shell Oil Rd, Brandon, MS 39043
Tel.: (601) 845-2253
Sales Range: $25-49.9 Million
Emp.: 45
N.A.I.C.S.: 211120

PETRO-LINK, INC.
2901 Arkansas Blvd, Texarkana, AR 71854
Tel.: (870) 772-3300   AR
Sales Range: $10-24.9 Million
Emp.: 7
Gasoline Distributors
N.A.I.C.S.: 424720
Mark Townsend *(Pres)*

PETRO-LOCK INC.
45514 Trevor Ave, Lancaster, CA 93534
Tel.: (661) 948-6044
Web Site: http://www.petrolock.com
Year Founded: 1959
Sales Range: $10-24.9 Million
Emp.: 38
Petroleum Products
N.A.I.C.S.: 424720
Wayne R. Ulberg *(CEO)*

PETROCHEMICAL SERVICES INC.
5600 Jefferson Hwy, New Orleans, LA 70123-5124
Tel.: (504) 947-7825   LA
Year Founded: 1981
Sales Range: $10-24.9 Million
Emp.: 1,000
Providers of Tank Cleaning & Repair Services
N.A.I.C.S.: 811310
James Fallon *(VP-Bus Dev)*
Donna Rachal *(VP-Fin & Admin)*

PETROCHOICE LLC
1300 Virginia Dr Ste 405, Fort Washington, PA 19034
Tel.: (814) 928-4266   DE
Web Site:
http://www.petrochoice.com
Petroleum Lubricant Products Distr
N.A.I.C.S.: 424720
Shane O'Kelly *(CEO)*
Alex Rapp *(Sr VP-Ops)*

Subsidiaries:

Miller Industrial Fluids, LLC (1)
1751 W Raymond St, Indianapolis, IN 46221
Tel.: (317) 634-7300
Web Site: http://www.millerif.com
Oils & Greases, Blending & Compounding
N.A.I.C.S.: 324191
Ross Smith *(Pres & CEO)*

Rex Oil Company (1)
1000 Lexington Ave, Thomasville, NC 27360
Tel.: (336) 472-3000
Web Site: http://www.rexoil.com
Petroleum Product Distr
N.A.I.C.S.: 424720
F. Stuart Kennedy *(VP)*
Harold S. Kennedy *(Pres)*

PETROFLEX NORTH AMERICA, LTD.
1305 N Interstate 35, Gainesville, TX 76240
Tel.: (940) 668-7283
Web Site: http://www.petroflexna.com
Sales Range: $10-24.9 Million
Emp.: 150
Plastics Pipe
N.A.I.C.S.: 326122
Charlesa Woolfolk *(Mgr-Natl Sls)*
Gina Craigie *(CFO)*

Subsidiaries:

Advanced Pedestals, Inc. (1)
2228 N Weaver St, Gainesville, TX 76240
Tel.: (940) 668-4380
Web Site: http://www.petroflexna.com
Rev.: $3,068,594
Emp.: 30
Pedestals, Marble
N.A.I.C.S.: 326122

PETROFLOW ENERGY CORPORATION
15 W 6th St Ste 1100, Tulsa, OK 74119
Tel.: (918) 592-1010   DE
Web Site:
http://www.petroflowenergy.com
Year Founded: 2011
Petroleum & Gas Exploration & Extraction Services
N.A.I.C.S.: 211120
Louis G. Schott *(Gen Counsel)*

PETROGULF CORPORATION
518 17th St Ste 1525, Denver, CO 80202
Tel.: (303) 893-5400
Web Site: http://www.petrogulf.com
Sales Range: $10-24.9 Million
Emp.: 10
Crude Petroleum & Natural Gas
N.A.I.C.S.: 423830
Jerry Goedert *(Engr-Ops)*

PETROLEUM EQUIPMENT & SERVICE, INC.
4125 Sinclair St, Denver, NC 28037
Tel.: (704) 335-8801
Web Site:
http://www.petroleumequipment.net
Year Founded: 1981
Sales Range: Less than $1 Million
Emp.: 14
Sales, Installation & Service of Petroleum Equipment & Convenience Store Fueling Systems
N.A.I.C.S.: 423830
Arthur Wilson *(CEO)*
Chris Wilson *(VP)*

PETROLEUM EQUIPMENT INSTITUTE
6514 E 69th St, Tulsa, OK 74133
Tel.: (918) 494-9696   TN
Web Site: http://www.pei.org
Year Founded: 1951
Rev.: $1,700,000
Emp.: 11
Fiscal Year-end: 12/31/06
Business Associations, Nsk
N.A.I.C.S.: 813910

PETROLEUM INC.
300 W Douglas Ave Ste 1050, Wichita, KS 67202-2911
Tel.: (316) 291-8200   KS
Year Founded: 1948
Sales Range: $125-149.9 Million
Emp.: 3
Oil & Gas Exploration Services
N.A.I.C.S.: 211120
John K. Garvey *(Chm & Pres)*
Aaron Wiechman *(VP-Fin)*

PETROLEUM MARKETING GROUP INC.
2359 Research Ct, Woodbridge, VA 22192
Tel.: (703) 494-5800

Web Site: http://www.petromg.com
Refined Petroleum Products Distr
N.A.I.C.S.: 424720
Amit Sharma *(Mgr-District Dev)*

Subsidiaries:

Leonard E. Belcher, Inc. (1)
615 St James Ave, Springfield, MA 01109
Tel.: (413) 736-5605
Petrochemical Product Distr
N.A.I.C.S.: 424720

Lil Thrift Food Marts Inc. (1)
1007 Arsenal Ave, Fayetteville, NC 28305
Tel.: (910) 433-4490
Web Site:
http://www.shortstopfoodmarts.com
Sales Range: $10-24.9 Million
Emp.: 300
Convenience Store
N.A.I.C.S.: 445131
Chris Neal *(Pres)*

PETROLEUM PRODUCTS CORP.
900 S Eisenhower Blvd, Middletown, PA 17057-5503
Tel.: (717) 939-0466   PA
Web Site:
http://www.ppcterminals.com
Year Founded: 1960
Sales Range: $250-299.9 Million
Emp.: 35
Whslr of Oil, Gasoline & Kerosene
N.A.I.C.S.: 424710
John M. Arnold *(Chm)*
Robert G. Bost *(Pres)*
Michael De Stefano *(CFO)*

PETROLEUM PRODUCTS INC.
500 River E Dr, Belle, WV 25015
Tel.: (304) 926-3000
Web Site:
http://www.petroleumproducts.com
Sales Range: $125-149.9 Million
Emp.: 60
Petroleum Bulk Stations
N.A.I.C.S.: 424710
Peggy White *(Mgr-HR)*

PETROLEUM SALES INC.
1475 2nd St, San Rafael, CA 94901-2754
Tel.: (415) 256-1600
Rev.: $20,100,000
Emp.: 150
Dealer of Liquefied Petroleum Gas
N.A.I.C.S.: 457210
Ben Shimek *(Pres)*

PETROLEUM SALES INC.
2030 Market St NE, Decatur, AL 35602-2624
Tel.: (256) 353-2561   AL
Year Founded: 1970
Sales Range: $10-24.9 Million
Emp.: 105
Petroleum Bulk Plant & Convenience Stores
N.A.I.C.S.: 424710
Rufus W. Orr Jr. *(Chm)*

PETROLEUM TRADERS CORPORATION
7120 Pte Inverness Way, Fort Wayne, IN 46804
Tel.: (260) 432-6622   IN
Web Site:
http://www.petroleumtraders.com
Year Founded: 1979
Sales Range: $75-99.9 Million
Emp.: 130
Whslr of Petroleum Products
N.A.I.C.S.: 424720
Michael Himes *(Pres & CEO)*
Vicki Himes *(VP & Office Mgr)*
Linda Stephens *(Controller)*

PETROLEUM TRANSPORT COMPANY
129 Carson St, Pilot Mountain, NC 27041
Tel.: (336) 368-8974
Web Site:
http://www.petroleumtransport.com
Rev.: $19,109,041
Emp.: 250
Liquid Transfer Services
N.A.I.C.S.: 484220
Jim York *(Pres)*

PETROLEUM WHOLESALE, LP
PO Box 4456, Houston, TX 77210
Tel.: (281) 681-1000   TX
Web Site:
http://www.petroleumwholesale.com
Year Founded: 1971
Sales Range: $10-24.9 Million
Emp.: 60
Independent Petroleum Dealers
N.A.I.C.S.: 424720
Ryan Edone *(CFO)*

PETROLIANCE LLC
1009 Schieffelin Rd, Apex, NC 27502
Tel.: (919) 387-9810
Web Site: http://www.petroliance.com
Sales Range: $250-299.9 Million
Industrial Petroleum Product Automotive & Commercial Lubricant Marine Lubricant Commercial Fuel Distillate & Other Related Product Distr
N.A.I.C.S.: 424710
Robert Crouch *(COO)*
Kevin McCarter *(CEO)*
Linda Strobino *(Chief Mktg Officer)*
Jeff Krizic *(CFO)*

Subsidiaries:

PetroLiance LLC - Chicago (1)
739 N State St, Elgin, IL 60123
Tel.: (847) 741-2577
Web Site: http://www.petroliance.com
Rev.: $40,000,000
Emp.: 70
Distr of Industrial Petroleum Products, Automotive & Commercial Lubricants, Fuels, Distillates & Other Related Products
N.A.I.C.S.: 424710
Kevin McCarter *(CEO)*
Bob Crouch *(COO)*
Jeff Krizic *(CFO)*
Linda Strobino *(CMO)*

PetroLiance LLC - Cleveland (1)
2846 E 37th St, Cleveland, OH 44115
Tel.: (216) 441-7200
Web Site: http://www.petroliance.com
Industrial Lubricants & Metalworking Coolants, Cleaners, Drawing Compounds & Rust Inhibitors Whslr
N.A.I.C.S.: 424720

PETROLOG AUTOMATION, INC.
5565 Mansions Blfs Ste 4602, San Antonio, TX 78245
Tel.: (432) 307-6577
Web Site:
http://www.petrologautomation.com
Year Founded: 2007
Oil & Gas Field Engineering Services
N.A.I.C.S.: 541330
Cesar Chavez *(Founder & CEO)*

PETROMARK INC.
308 Industrial Park Rd, Harrison, AR 72601
Tel.: (870) 741-3226   AR
Web Site:
http://www.whiteoakstation.com
Year Founded: 1978
Sales Range: $25-49.9 Million
Emp.: 300
Petroleum Products Mfr
N.A.I.C.S.: 424720

Steven Turner *(Sec)*
Steve Lair *(Pres)*
Vicki Sterling *(Mgr)*

PETROMAX OPERATING CO., INC.
603 Main St Ste 201, Garland, TX 75040
Tel.: (972) 271-0999
Year Founded: 1988
Sales Range: $10-24.9 Million
Emp.: 20
Oil & Gas Exploration Services
N.A.I.C.S.: 213112
Will Shaw *(VP-Fin)*

PETROMINERALS CORPORATION
25672 Taladro Cir Ste C, Mission Viejo, CA 92691
Crude Petroleum Extraction Services
N.A.I.C.S.: 211120
Ronald Steward *(Chm & Pres)*

PETRON ENERGY II, INC.
17950 Preston Rd Ste 960, Dallas, TX 75252
Tel.: (972) 272-8190   NV
Web Site:
  http://www.petronenergyii.com
Year Founded: 2008
Sales Range: $1-9.9 Million
Emp.: 3
Investment Services
N.A.I.C.S.: 523999
Floyd L. Smith *(Chm, Pres, CEO, Treas & Sec)*

PETROQUEST ENERGY, INC.
400 E Kaliste Saloom Rd Ste 600, Lafayette, LA 70508
Tel.: (337) 232-7028   DE
Web Site: http://www.petroquest.com
Sales Range: $75-99.9 Million
Oil & Gas Exploration & Production
N.A.I.C.S.: 211120
Charles T. Goodson *(Pres & CEO)*
J. Bond Clement *(CFO, Treas & Exec VP)*
Kern Meaux *(Mgr-Property Admin)*

Subsidiaries:

PetroQuest Energy, L.L.C.   (1)
400 E Kaliste Saloom Rd Ste 6000, Lafayette, LA 70508-8508
Tel.: (337) 232-7028
Web Site: http://www.petroquest.com
Sales Range: $150-199.9 Million
Emp.: 86
Gas & Oil Exploration & Production
N.A.I.C.S.: 211120
Charles T. Goodson *(Chm, Pres & CEO)*

PETROSANTANDER INC.
6363 Woodway Dr Ste 350, Houston, TX 77057-1798
Tel.: (713) 784-8700   DE
Year Founded: 1995
Sales Range: $75-99.9 Million
Emp.: 15
Exploration of Crude Petroleum & Natural Gas
N.A.I.C.S.: 211120
Christopher J. Whyte *(Pres & CEO)*
Victor Low *(Controller)*
Ian Gollop *(Exec VP)*

Subsidiaries:

Petrosantander - Columbia Inc.   (1)
6363 Woodway Dr Ste 350, Houston, TX 77057-1798   (100%)
Tel.: (713) 784-8700
Crude Petroleum & Natural Gas
N.A.I.C.S.: 211120
Christopher J. Whyte *(Pres & CEO)*

Petrosantander USA Inc.   (1)
11130 E 7 Mile Rd, Garden City, KS 67846   (100%)
Tel.: (620) 275-2388
Sales Range: $25-49.9 Million
Emp.: 6
Crude Petroleum & Natural Gas
N.A.I.C.S.: 211120
Christopher J. Whyte *(Pres & CEO)*
Pete Kneil *(Mgr-Production)*

PETROSHARE CORP.
9635 Maroon Cir Ste 400, Englewood, CO 80112
Tel.: (303) 500-1160   CO
Web Site:
  http://www.petrosharecorp.com
Year Founded: 2012
Rev.: $20,403,967
Assets: $62,564,475
Liabilities: $66,831,965
Net Worth: ($4,267,490)
Earnings: ($17,307,747)
Emp.: 11
Fiscal Year-end: 12/31/18
Oil & Gas Operations Support Services
N.A.I.C.S.: 213112
Stephen J. Foley *(CEO)*

PETROSKILLS, LLC
2930 S Yale Ave, Tulsa, OK 74114-6252
Tel.: (918) 828-2500   OK
Web Site: http://www.petroskills.com
Year Founded: 2001
Emp.: 75
Petroleum Industry Training & Consulting Services
N.A.I.C.S.: 611519
J. Ford Brett *(CEO)*
W. Dennis Wing *(COO)*
Ron Hinn *(Exec VP)*

PETROSOUTH INC.
234 N Hill St, Griffin, GA 30223
Tel.: (770) 227-8804   GA
Web Site: http://www.petrosouth.com
Year Founded: 1989
Sales Range: $75-99.9 Million
Emp.: 37
Petroleum Product Distr
N.A.I.C.S.: 424720
Mack Arrington *(Gen Mgr)*

PETROTECH SOUTHEAST, INC.
23800 County Rd 561, Astatula, FL 34705
Tel.: (407) 656-8114
Web Site:
  http://www.petrotechse.com
Sales Range: $1-9.9 Million
Emp.: 20
Environmental Services; Oil Recycling
N.A.I.C.S.: 541620
Jeffrey Yates *(Pres)*
Jason Yates *(VP)*
Mike Patterson *(Project Mgr-Sls)*

PETROTEX
1600 S Market St, Brenham, TX 77833
Tel.: (979) 836-4242
Sales Range: $10-24.9 Million
Emp.: 25
Drive-In Restaurant
N.A.I.C.S.: 722513
Robert Mann *(Pres)*

PETROVIC FINANCIAL SOLUTIONS LLC
800 W 47th St Ste 610, Kansas City, MO 64112
Tel.: (816) 531-6700   KS
Web Site:
  http://www.petrovicweaverfinancial.com
Sales Range: $1-9.9 Million
Financial Planning & Investment Management Services
N.A.I.C.S.: 523940
LaDonna Parker *(Dir-Strategic Plng)*
Martha Fitzsimmons *(Mgr-Client Svcs)*
Alex M. Petrovic III *(Pres)*

PETRUS BRANDS, INC.
1425 Ellsworth Industrial Blvd NW, Atlanta, GA 30318
Tel.: (404) 856-4320
Holding Company
N.A.I.C.S.: 551112
Gloria Garrett *(Exec VP-Mktg)*

Subsidiaries:

Shane's Rib Shack   (1)
2136 Hwy 155 N, McDonough, GA 30252
Tel.: (770) 898-7878
Web Site: http://www.shanesribshack.com
Sales Range: $10-24.9 Million
Emp.: 20
Fast-Food Franchiser
N.A.I.C.S.: 722511
Shane Thompson *(Founder & Pres)*

PETRUS RESOURCES CORPORATION
15321 NW 60th Ave Ste 109, Miami Lakes, FL 33014
Tel.: (954) 362-7598   DE
Year Founded: 2011
Investment Services
N.A.I.C.S.: 523999
Miguel Dotres *(Pres, CEO, CFO, Chief Acctg Officer, Treas & Sec)*

PETTICOAT-SCHMITT CIVIL CONTRACTORS, INC.
6380 Philips Hwy, Jacksonville, FL 32216
Tel.: (904) 751-0888
Web Site:
  http://www.petticoatschmitt.com
Year Founded: 2007
Sales Range: $10-24.9 Million
Emp.: 28
Civil Engineering Construction Services
N.A.I.C.S.: 237990
Ryan M. Schmitt *(Founder & Pres)*
Clyde Cross *(VP-Contract Mgmt-Road Div)*
Kimberly Bryan *(Dir-Pre-Construction)*
Lauren Atwell *(VP-Plant Div)*
David Dougherty *(CFO)*

PETTIJOHN AUTO CENTER INC.
1301 S 25th Hwy, Bethany, MO 64424
Tel.: (660) 425-2244
Web Site:
  http://www.pettijohnauto.com
Rev.: $12,000,000
Emp.: 50
New Car Dealers
N.A.I.C.S.: 441110
Tom Pettijohn *(Pres)*

PETTISVILLE GRAIN CO.
18251 County Rd, Pettisville, OH 43553
Tel.: (419) 446-2547   OH
Web Site:
  http://www.pettisvillegrain.com
Sales Range: $10-24.9 Million
Emp.: 17
Grain & Feed Elevators
N.A.I.C.S.: 424510
Neil Rupp *(Pres)*

PETTIT MACHINERY INC.
Hwy 70 W, Ardmore, OK 73401
Tel.: (580) 223-7722
Web Site:
  http://www.pettitmachinery.com
Sales Range: $10-24.9 Million
Emp.: 35
Agricultural Machinery & Equipment
N.A.I.C.S.: 423820
Fred Dunegan *(Gen Mgr)*
Michael Brody Pettit Jr. *(Pres)*

PETTUS OFFICE PRODUCTS, INC.
2 Fwy Dr, Little Rock, AR 72204
Tel.: (501) 666-7226
Web Site: http://www.pettusop.com
Office Equipment Merchant Whslr
N.A.I.C.S.: 423420
Cole Wilson *(VP-Janitorial Div)*

Subsidiaries:

B J S, Inc.   (1)
3509 Asher Ave, Little Rock, AR 72204
Tel.: (501) 661-9200
Web Site:
  http://www.brownjanitorsupply.com
Sales Range: $1-9.9 Million
Emp.: 21
Household Appliance Stores
N.A.I.C.S.: 449210
Gary Acord *(Pres)*

PETTUS PLUMBING & PIPING INC.
12647 Hwy 72, Rogersville, AL 35652
Tel.: (256) 389-8181
Web Site: http://www.pettushvac.com
Sales Range: $10-24.9 Million
Emp.: 60
Plumbing Contractor
N.A.I.C.S.: 238220
Tony Robertson *(Co-Owner)*
Grover Johnson *(Co-Owner)*
Licia House *(Office Mgr)*

PETUNIA PICKLE BOTTOM CORPORATION
305 S Kalorama St Ste F, Ventura, CA 93001
Web Site: http://www.petunia.com
Industrial Design Services
N.A.I.C.S.: 541420
Michael Fowler *(Pres & COO)*

PETWELL PARTNERS LLC
4203 Yoakum Blvd Ste 250, Houston, TX 77006
Tel.: (832) 962-7177
Web Site:
  http://www.petwellpartners.com
Year Founded: 2013
Sales Range: $25-49.9 Million
Emp.: 442
Veterinary Practice Services
N.A.I.C.S.: 541940
David Murvin *(Co-Founder)*
David Strauss *(Co-Founder)*

PEVETO COMPANIES LTD.
320 E Nakoma St, San Antonio, TX 78216
Tel.: (210) 495-4977
Web Site:
  http://www.brakecheck.com
Sales Range: $10-24.9 Million
Emp.: 25
Automotive Repair Shops
N.A.I.C.S.: 811114
David Johnnie *(CEO)*

PEVONIA INTERNATIONAL, LLC
300 Fentress Blvd, Daytona Beach, FL 32114
Tel.: (386) 254-1967
Web Site: http://www.pevonia.com
Year Founded: 1991
Sales Range: $10-24.9 Million
Emp.: 50

PEVONIA INTERNATIONAL, LLC   **U.S. PRIVATE**

Pevonia International, LLC—(Continued)
Skin Care Products Mfr & Retailer
N.A.I.C.S.: 325620
Rob Livingston (CFO)

Subsidiaries:

Pevonia International West (1)
15773 Gateway Cir, Tustin, CA 92780-6470
Tel.: (714) 258-8301
Web Site: http://www.cosmoproshop.com
Skin, Beauty & Health Care Products Distr & Online Retailer
N.A.I.C.S.: 424210

PEX HOLDING INC.
575 Lexington Ave 4th Fl, New York, NY 10022
Tel.: (212) 588-9000
Web Site: http://www.pexglobal.com
Year Founded: 2010
Sales Range: $1-9.9 Million
Emp.: 15
Private Equity Investors
N.A.I.C.S.: 523940
Katherine Hill Ritchie (CEO)
Ken Merlo (Chief Compliance Officer)
Dina Said (Founder)

PEYOTE BIRD DESIGNS
675 Harkle Rd, Santa Fe, NM 87505
Tel.: (505) 983-2480
Web Site: http://www.peyotebird.com
Sales Range: $10-24.9 Million
Emp.: 30
Jewelry, Precious Metal
N.A.I.C.S.: 339910
Colleen Phillips (Controller)
Joy Czmyrid (Acct Coord)
Bonnie Bennett (VP-Creative & Product Dev)

PEZ CANDY, INC.
35 Prindle Hill Rd, Orange, CT 06477-3616
Tel.: (203) 795-0531
Web Site: http://www.pez.com
Year Founded: 1952
Sales Range: $100-124.9 Million
Emp.: 150
Mfr of Candy, Dispensers & Wafers
N.A.I.C.S.: 424450
Lois Anthony (Dir-Field Sls)
Christian Jegen (Pres & CEO)
Jordan Greenstein (Mktg Dir)

PEZOLD MANAGEMENT ASSOCIATES
600 Brookstone Center Pkwy, Columbus, GA 31904-3097
Tel.: (706) 324-1650
Rev.: $25,977,461
Emp.: 7
Fast-Food Restaurant, Chain
N.A.I.C.S.: 722513
John D. Pezold (Pres)

PF MOON AND COMPANY INC.
2207 Hwy 103, West Point, GA 31833
Tel.: (706) 643-1524
Web Site: http://www.pfmoon.com
Sales Range: $10-24.9 Million
Emp.: 90
Waste Water & Sewage Treatment Plant Construction
N.A.I.C.S.: 237110
Keith Steen (VP)
Josh Moon (Pres)

PFBS HOLDINGS, INC.
2805 Ridge Rd, Rockwall, TX 75032
Tel.: (972) 771-8311   TX
Web Site: http://www.lbtexas.com
Year Founded: 2019
Sales Range: $1-9.9 Million
Bank Holding Company
N.A.I.C.S.: 551111
Paul R. Haney (Pres/CEO-Lakeside Bank)

Subsidiaries:

Lakeside Bank (1)
2805 Ridge Rd, Rockwall, TX 75032
Tel.: (972) 722-8311
Web Site: http://www.lbtexas.com
Sales Range: $1-9.9 Million
Emp.: 11
Commercial Banking
N.A.I.C.S.: 522110
Paul R. Haney (Pres & CEO)
Kevin Fowler (Reg Pres-Rockwall)
Kevin Pate (Exec VP)

PFC FURNITURE INDUSTRIES
400 Industrial Dr Ste 400, Richardson, TX 75081
Tel.: (972) 231-7732
Web Site: http://www.pfcind.com
Year Founded: 2008
Sales Range: $1-9.9 Million
Emp.: 12
Household Furniture
N.A.I.C.S.: 337121
Luis Ordonez (Co-Founder & Pres)
Diego Ordonez (Co-Founder)

PFEIFFER & SON LTD.
116 N 16th St, La Porte, TX 77571
Tel.: (281) 471-4222
Web Site: http://www.pfeifferandson.com
Sales Range: $10-24.9 Million
Emp.: 134
General Electrical Contractor
N.A.I.C.S.: 238210
Cindy Gillen (Office Mgr)
Stephen Watson (Mgr-IT)

PFEIFFER LINCOLN-MERCURY INC.
2424 28th St SE, Grand Rapids, MI 49512
Tel.: (616) 949-7800
Web Site: http://www.pfeifferlm.com
Sales Range: $50-74.9 Million
Emp.: 50
Sales of New & Used Automobiles
N.A.I.C.S.: 441110
Daniel Pfeiffer (Pres)
Kim Winkler (Mgr-Sls)

PFG VENTURES L.P.
8800 E Pleasant Vly Rd, Independence, OH 44131
Tel.: (216) 520-8400
Web Site: http://www.proforma.com
Emp.: 100
Commercial Printing Services
N.A.I.C.S.: 323111
Greg Muzzillo (Founder)
Brian Smith (Pres & COO)
Vera Muzzillo (CEO)
Deanna Castello (CMO)
Bob Kimble (Chief Credit & Admin Officer)
Doug Kordel (Chief Strategic Dev Officer & Gen Counsel)
Michele Cardello (Dir-Strategic Partner Dev)
Alan Chippindale (Sr VP-Bus Dev)

PFINGSTEN PARTNERS, LLC
151 N. Franklin St, Ste 2150, Chicago, IL 60606
Tel.: (312) 222-8707
Web Site: http://www.pfingsten.com
Year Founded: 1989
Privater Equity Firm
N.A.I.C.S.: 523999
Thomas S. Bagley (Founder & Sr Mng Dir)
John H. Underwood (Sr Mng Dir)
Scott A. Finegan (Sr Mng Dir)
James J. Norton (Sr Mng Dir)
Denio R. Bolzan (Mng Dir)
John J. Starcevich (Mng Dir)
David H. Johnston (Principal)
Andrew W. Petri (CFO & Chief Compliance Officer)
Phillip D. Bronsteatter (Mng Dir)

Subsidiaries:

Advanced Lighting Concepts, LLC (1)
11235 W Bernardo Ct Ste 102, San Diego, CA 92127
Tel.: (866) 973-1731
Web Site: https://www.environmentallights.com
LED Lighting Products Mfr & Distr
N.A.I.C.S.: 335132
Brad Tedder (CEO)

Subsidiary (Domestic):

City Theatrical, Inc. (2)
475 Barell Ave, Carlstadt, NJ 07072
Tel.: (201) 549-1456
Web Site: http://www.citytheatrical.com
Sales Range: $1-9.9 Million
Emp.: 35
Lighting Equipment Mfr
N.A.I.C.S.: 335139
Gary Fails (Pres & Founder)
Alex Cowan (Mgr-Sls)

Aviation, Power & Marine, Inc. (1)
1811 Corporate Dr, Boynton Beach, FL 33426
Tel.: (561) 732-6000
Web Site: http://www.apm4parts.com
Industrial Gas Turbine Engine Parts Mfr
N.A.I.C.S.: 336412
Greg Young (Pres & CEO)

Bailey International, LLC (1)
2527 Westcott Blvd, Knoxville, TN 37931-3112
Tel.: (865) 588-6000
Web Site: http://www.baileynet.com
Emp.: 130
Hydraulic Cylinder Mfr & Distr
N.A.I.C.S.: 423830
Matt Grussing (Acct Exec)
Angela Cottrell (Dir-HR)
Steve Warnock (Dir-Sls & Svc)
Linda Austin (Office Mgr)

Fire King Security Products, LLC (1)
101 Security Pkwy, New Albany, IN 47150
Tel.: (812) 948-8400
Web Site: http://www.fireking.com
Emp.: 480
Fire Proof Safe & File Mfr
N.A.I.C.S.: 333310
Terry Turner (Mgr-Natl Sls-Western USA)
Scott Canakes (Mgr-Natl Sls-Northwest)
Trista Walk (VP-Office Products)
Philip W. Bradney (COO)
Jim Poteet (Sr VP-Sls & Mktg)
Peter Berens (CTO)
Mark Essig (CEO)
David Goffinet (CIO)
Brenda Lee Lally (VP-HR & Continuous Improvement)
Mike McGunn (VP-Comml Svc)
Mike Smith (VP-Res & Dev)
Gary Weisman (Pres)
Will Wolf (CFO)
Debra Ayres (Sr VP-Cash Mgmt Solutions)
James Currey (Sr VP- Intl Bus Dev)

Kith Kitchens, LLC (1)
280 N Industrial Loop, Haleyville, AL 35565
Tel.: (205) 485-2261
Web Site: http://www.kithkitchens.us
Custom Kitchen & Bath Cabinetry Mfr
N.A.I.C.S.: 337110
Allen Knight (Pres)
Mark Smith (CEO)

Subsidiary (Domestic):

Mouser Custom Cabinetry LLC (2)
2112 N Dixie Ave, Elizabethtown, KY 42701
Tel.: (270) 737-7477
Web Site: http://www.mousercc.com
Rev.: $26,839,966
Emp.: 248
Wood Kitchen Cabinets
N.A.I.C.S.: 337110
Steve Mouser (Pres)

Oliver Printing & Packaging Co., LLC (1)
1760 Enterprise Pkwy, Twinsburg, OH 44087
Tel.: (330) 425-7890
Web Site: http://www.oliverprinting.com
Sales Range: $1-9.9 Million
Commercial Lithographic Printing Services
N.A.I.C.S.: 323111
Dan Oliver (Dir-Ops)
George Oliver (Pres)
Rob van Gilse (Dir-Sls & Mktg)

Subsidiary (Domestic):

Disc Graphics Inc. (2)
10 Gilpin Ave, Hauppauge, NY 11788-4724
Tel.: (631) 234-1400
Web Site: http://www.discgraphics.com
Sales Range: $50-74.9 Million
Emp.: 354
Corrugated & Solid Fiber Box Mfr
N.A.I.C.S.: 322211
Donald Sinkin (CEO)
Margaret M. Krumholz (Pres)
Brian Hartigan (VP-Fin)
Jane Goitia (Mgr-Credit)
Fran Kahn (Acct Mgr)
Richard Roth (Chief Strategy Officer)
John Rebecchi (Sr VP-Mktg & Bus Dev)
Nik Blake (VP-Ops)
Sam John (Mgr-Label Div)

Subsidiary (Domestic):

Disc Graphics Label Group Inc. (3)
10 Gilpin Ave, Hauppauge, NY 11788
Tel.: (631) 234-1400
Web Site: http://www.discgraphics.com
Sales Range: $10-24.9 Million
Paperboard Boxes Supplier
N.A.I.C.S.: 561910
Samuel John (Mgr-Label Dept)

Graph-Corr (3)
4 Corn Rd, Dayton, NJ 08810
Tel.: (732) 355-0088
Paperboard Boxes Supplier
N.A.I.C.S.: 322211
Hugh Murphy (Gen Mgr)

Omega Systems, LLC (1)
1121 Snyder Rd, Reading, PA 19609-1100
Tel.: (610) 678-7002
Web Site: http://www.omegasystemscorp.com
Process, Physical Distribution & Logistics Consulting Services
N.A.I.C.S.: 541614
Bill Kiritsis (Pres)
Jennifer Kiritsis (COO)

Sign Zone LLC (1)
6850 Shingle Creek Pkwy, Brooklyn Center, MN 55430
Tel.: (763) 746-1350
Web Site: http://www.signzoneinc.com
Signs & Displays; Advertising Specialty & Other Promotional Products Mfr
N.A.I.C.S.: 339950
Edward Flaherty (Pres & CEO)

Superior International Industries Inc. (1)
1050 Columbia Dr, Carrollton, GA 30117-8782
Tel.: (770) 832-6660
Web Site: http://www.superiorinternational.com
Sales Range: $25-49.9 Million
Emp.: 300
Mfr & Supplier of Plastics Products for Recreational Use
N.A.I.C.S.: 326199
Randy Beckum (VP-Sls & Mktg)

Subsidiary (Domestic):

Grounds For Play Inc. (2)
1401 E Dallas St, Mansfield, TX 76063-2403
Tel.: (817) 477-5482
Web Site: http://www.groundsforplay.com
Sales Range: $50-74.9 Million
Outdoor Play Environments & Services, Including Designing, Site Planning, Manufacturing & Installing Playground Equipment, Outdoor Classrooms, Safety Surfacing, Shelters & Site Amenities

N.A.I.C.S.: 541490
Eric Strickland (Founder & Chm)
David Reeves (Dir-Sls & Mktg)

Playland Inc. (2)
150 Adamson Industrial Blvd, Carrollton, GA 30117-5408
Tel.: (770) 834-6120
Web Site: http://www.playland-inc.com
Sales Range: $50-74.9 Million
Emp.: 300
Playground Equipment Mfr
N.A.I.C.S.: 326199
Eric Warren (Pres)

PFISTER ENERGY INC.
57 Goffle Rd, Hawthorne, NJ 07506
Tel.: (973) 653-9880
Web Site:
http://www.pfisterenergy.com
Year Founded: 2005
Sales Range: $10-24.9 Million
Emp.: 50
Site Preparation Contractor
N.A.I.C.S.: 238910
Dieter Pfisterer (CEO)
Wayne Pfisterer (Pres)

PFP/SCHMITT-SUSSMAN ENTERPRISES
34 Prindle Hill Rd, Orange, CT 06477
Tel.: (203) 877-9804
Web Site:
http://www.pfpservices.com
Rev.: $15,003,349
Emp.: 165
Life Insurance
N.A.I.C.S.: 524113
Stanley H. Sussman (CEO)
John C. Schmitt II (Chm)
John C. Schmitt III (Sr VP-New Bus Dev)

PGA RESORTS LTD
400 Avenue of the Champions, Palm Beach Gardens, FL 33418
Tel.: (561) 627-2000
Web Site: http://www.pgaresort.com
Sales Range: $10-24.9 Million
Emp.: 1,000
Motel, Franchised
N.A.I.C.S.: 721110
Joe Paige (Gen Mgr)

PGA TOUR, INC.
100 PGA Tour Blvd, Ponte Vedra Beach, FL 32082
Tel.: (904) 285-3700
Web Site: http://www.pgatour.com
Sales Range: $650-699.9 Million
Emp.: 700
Golf Tournament Organizer
N.A.I.C.S.: 713990
Edward L. Moorhouse (Co-COO)
Charles L. Zink (Co-COO)
Ronald E. Price (CFO & Chief Admin Officer)
Gregory T. McLaughlin (CEO-First Tee Foundation)

PGAV INC.
1900 W 47th Pl Ste 300, Westwood, KS 66205
Tel.: (913) 362-6500
Web Site: http://www.pgav.com
Emp.: 120
Architectural Services
N.A.I.C.S.: 541310
Mike Schaadt (Principal)
Steve Troester (Principal)

PGM INCORPORATED
1215 S 1680 W, Orem, UT 84058
Tel.: (801) 434-9546
Web Site: http://www.pgminc.com
Rev.: $16,300,000
Emp.: 450
Market Research Services
N.A.I.C.S.: 541910
Stephen M. Zimmerman (Pres)

PGM PRODUCTS, LLC
1600 Market St Lbby A, Philadelphia, PA 19103-7211
Tel.: (856) 546-0704 NJ
Web Site:
http://www.pgmproducts.com
Sales Range: $50-74.9 Million
Emp.: 65
Distr of Paneling & Hardwood Floors & Italian Ceramic Tiles
N.A.I.C.S.: 423310
Howard Steinberg (Pres)
Mike Dunkes (Mgr-Mktg)
Nick Stango (Mgr Mktg Natl)
Huntington Tile (VP)

Subsidiaries:

Huntington Tile, Inc. (1)
1600 Market St Lbby A, Philadelphia, PA 19103-7211
Tel.: (817) 838-2323
Sales Range: $10-24.9 Million
Emp.: 5
Mfr & Retailer of Ceramic Tile
N.A.I.C.S.: 423320

PHARMA TECH INDUSTRIES INC.
1310 Stylemaster Dr, Union, MO 63084
Tel.: (636) 583-8664
Web Site: http://www.pharma-tech.com
Rev.: $18,700,000
Emp.: 75
Pharmaceutical Preparation Mfr
N.A.I.C.S.: 325412
Richard Loughlin (VP-Bus Dev)
Bryan Cox (VP-Engrg)
Matthew Milner (Dir-Supply Chain)
Jacobo Capuano (COO-Athens)
Eric Kaneps (VP-Bus Dev)
Troy W. Bryce (CFO)
Brisco Harward (Dir-Technical & Quality Svcs)
Kathryn Weingart (VP-Quality)
David VanVliet (Interim CEO)
Edward T. Noland Jr. (Chm)

PHARMACA INTEGRATIVE PHARMACY INC.
4940 Pearl E Cir, Boulder, CO 80301
Tel.: (303) 442-2304
Web Site: http://www.pharmaca.com
Year Founded: 2000
Sales Range: $10-24.9 Million
Emp.: 120
Prescription Services, Complementary & Natural Remedies
N.A.I.C.S.: 456110
Laura Coblentz (VP-Mktg & ECommerce)
Don Summerfield (VP-Integrative Medicine)
Kathryn Bruno (Owner)
Richard S. Willis (Pres & CEO)

PHARMACARE LLC
1251 W Pratt St, Baltimore, MD 21223
Tel.: (410) 209-1100
Web Site: http://www.pharmacare.us
Year Founded: 2006
Sales Range: $25-49.9 Million
Emp.: 105
Pharmacy Chain
N.A.I.C.S.: 456110
Vijay Reddy Annappareddy (Founder)
Marc Inouye (Mgr-Mktg-Hawaii)
Christopher Ayson (Mgr-Quality Improvement-Hawaii)
Brandy Shima (Dir-Community & Long Term Care Pharmacy Svcs-Hawaii)

PHARMACEUTICAL CARE MANAGEMENT ASSOCIATION
325 7th St NW Ste 900, Washington, DC 20004
Tel.: (202) 207-3610 DE
Web Site: http://www.pcmanet.org
Year Founded: 2003
Sales Range: $10-24.9 Million
Emp.: 26
Pharmacy Services
N.A.I.C.S.: 456110
Brenda Palmer (CFO)
Wendy Krasner (VP-Regulatory Affairs)
Jonathan Heafitz (Asst VP-Federal Affairs)
Lauren Barnes (Sr VP-Avalere Health)
J. C. Scott (Pres & CEO)
Alan M. Lotvin (Chm)

PHARMACISTS MUTUAL COMPANIES
808 Hwy 18 W, Algona, IA 50511
Tel.: (515) 295-2461
Web Site: http://www.phmic.com
Year Founded: 1992
Sales Range: $75-99.9 Million
Emp.: 325
Pharmacy Products, Education & Insurance Services
N.A.I.C.S.: 524298
Edward T. Berg (Pres, CEO & Treas)
Thomas E. Claude (VP-Underwriting & Risk Mgmt)
Jonathan Grether (COO)
Shelly Brown (Asst VP-Mktg)

Subsidiaries:

Pharmacists Mutual Insurance Co., Inc. (1)
808 Hwy 18 W, Algona, IA 50511
Tel.: (515) 295-2461
Web Site: http://www.phmic.com
Sales Range: $100-124.9 Million
Emp.: 260
Fire, Marine & Casualty Insurance
N.A.I.C.S.: 524126
Kevin Banwarth (VP-Admin)
Tom Goodrich (VP-Mktg)

Pro Advantage Services, Inc. (1)
219 E State St, Algona, IA 50511-2737
Tel.: (515) 295-9433
Web Site: http://www.phmic.com
Sales Range: $25-49.9 Million
Emp.: 15
Insurance Agents, Brokers & Service
N.A.I.C.S.: 524210
Steve Hoskins (Pres-Pro Advantage Svcs)

The Pharmacists Life Insurance Company Inc. (1)
808 Hwy 18 W, Algona, IA 50511-7234
Tel.: (515) 295-2461
Web Site: http://www.phmic.com
Sales Range: $25-49.9 Million
Emp.: 20
Life Insurance
N.A.I.C.S.: 524113
Steve Haskins (VP)

PHARMACY BUSINESS ASSOCIATION
6300 Enterprise Rd, Kansas City, MO 64120
Tel.: (816) 245-5700
Web Site: http://www.truecarerx.com
Rev.: $21,672,734
Emp.: 45
Drugs, Proprietaries & Sundries
N.A.I.C.S.: 424210
Nickolas Smock (Pres & CEO)
Don Raby (CFO)
Clark Balcom (COO & VP)
Richard Mingori (Dir-Customer Svcs)
Mike Burns (Chm)
David Dubose (Sec)
Gene Forrester (Treas)

PHARMACY TECHNICIAN CERTIFICATION BOARD
2215 Constitution Ave NW Ste 101, Washington, DC 20037
Tel.: (202) 888-1727 DC
Web Site: http://www.ptcb.org
Year Founded: 1995
Sales Range: $25-49.9 Million
Emp.: 28
Pharmacy Technician Certification Provider
N.A.I.C.S.: 561990
Everett B. McAllister (CEO & Exec Dir)
Larry Wagenknecht (Vice Chm)
Paul Abramowitz (Chm)
Thomas Menighan (Treas)

PHARMAHEALTH
132 Alden Rd, Fairhaven, MA 02719
Tel.: (508) 998-8000
Web Site:
http://www.pharmahealthspecialty.com
Year Founded: 1977
Sales Range: $50-74.9 Million
Emp.: 85
Retail & Specialty Pharmacy
N.A.I.C.S.: 456110
Philip Falzarano (COO)
Jennifer Torrey (VP)

PHARMAMED INC.
9435 Bormet Dr Unit 1A, Mokena, IL 60448
Tel.: (708) 267-9998 DE
Year Founded: 2014
Cannabis Industry Services
N.A.I.C.S.: 561499
Daniel Gallagher (CEO, CFO & Principal Acctg Officer)

PHARMASMART INTERNATIONAL INC
3495 Winton Pl Bldg A Ste 1, Rochester, NY 14623
Tel.: (585) 427-0730
Web Site: http://www.pharma-smart.com
Year Founded: 1987
Rev.: $5,700,000
Emp.: 26
Surgical & Medical Instruments
N.A.I.C.S.: 339112
Vanessa L. Thomas (VP-Procurement & Materials Mgmt)
Lisa M. Goodwin (VP-IT)
Joseph P. Sarkis (Chief Strategy Officer, Principal & Gen Mgr)
Ashton S. Maaraba (COO, Partner & Gen Mgr)
Matthew P. Bryant (Controller)
Fred W. Sarkis II (Pres)

PHARMASOL CORPORATION
1 Norfolk Ave, South Easton, MA 02375-1900
Tel.: (508) 238-8501 DE
Web Site: http://www.pharmasol.com
Year Founded: 1973
Sales Range: $100-124.9 Million
Emp.: 300
Pharmaceutical & Personal Care Product Mfr
N.A.I.C.S.: 325620
Howard Katzen (VP-Bus Dev)
Marc Badia (Pres)

PHARMAWORKS INC.
2346 Success Dr, Odessa, FL 33556-3430
Tel.: (727) 232-8200
Web Site:
http://www.pharmaworks.com
Year Founded: 2002
Sales Range: $10-24.9 Million
Emp.: 75

PHARMAWORKS INC.　　　　　　　　　　　　　　　　　　　　　　　　　　　　　　U.S. PRIVATE

Pharmaworks Inc—(Continued)
Pharmaceutical Packaging Machinery Mfr
N.A.I.C.S.: 333993
Peter Buczynsky (Pres)
Ben Brower (VP & Dir-Sls)
Ingo Federle (VP & Dir-Technical)

PHARMORE INGREDIENTS INC.
12569 S 2700 W Ste 201, Riverton, UT 84065
Tel.: (801) 446-8188
Web Site: http://www.pharmore.com
Sales Range: $25-49.9 Million
Emp.: 3
Diet Foods
N.A.I.C.S.: 424490
Gary Jepson (Pres)
Warren Majares (VP)
Elizabeth Haile (Office Mgr)
Allen Gritton (Mgr-Sls)

PHAROS CAPITAL GROUP, LLC
3889 Maple Ave Ste 400, Dallas, TX 75219
Tel.: (214) 855-0194　　　　DE
Web Site:
　　http://www.pharosfunds.com
Sales Range: $25-49.9 Million
Emp.: 30
Privater Equity Firm
N.A.I.C.S.: 523999
Bob Crants (Co-Founder & Chief Investment Officer)
Jim Phillips (Partner)
Joel Goldberg (Partner)
Anna Kovalkova (Partner)
Melinda Cullen (Co-CFO)
Jonathan Youse (Dir-Acctg & Client Svcs)
Adam Persiani (Dir-Bus Dev)
Kimberly Futrell (Co-CFO & Chief Compliance Officer)
Dale LeFebvre (Mng Partner)
Kneeland Conner Youngblood (Co-Founder & Mng Partner)

Subsidiaries:

Charter Health Care Group LLC　(1)
9660 Haven Ave, Rancho Cucamonga, CA 91730
Tel.: (909) 644-4965
Web Site: http://www.charterhcg.com
Health Care Srvices
N.A.I.C.S.: 621999
Steve J. Larkin (CEO)
Jake Panowicz (VP-Home Health)

Subsidiary (Domestic):

Physmed Inc.　(2)
4905 S 107th Ave, Omaha, NE 68127-1965
Tel.: (402) 926-4088
Web Site: http://www.physmedinc.com
Women Healthcare Services
N.A.I.C.S.: 621610
Rowena Sodusta (Mgr)

Lighthouse Holdings, Inc.　(1)
300 Crescent Ct Ste 1380, Dallas, TX 75201
Tel.: (214) 855-0194
Web Site: http://www.pharosfunds.com
Sales Range: $50-74.9 Million
Holding Company
N.A.I.C.S.: 551112
Robert Crants (Co-Founder)

Subsidiary (Domestic):

American Beacon Advisors　(2)
4151 Ammon Carter Blvd, Fort Worth, TX 76155-2450
Tel.: (817) 967-3509
Sales Range: $10-24.9 Million
Emp.: 75
Financial Management
N.A.I.C.S.: 523940

Terri L. McKinney (VP-Enterprise Svcs)
Rosemary K. Behan (VP-Legal & Compliance)
Samuel J. Silver (Chief Fixed Income Officer & VP)
Jeffrey K. Ringdahl (Pres & COO)
Paul Cavazos (Chief Investment Officer)
Gene L. Needles Jr. (Chm & CEO)

Sona MedSpa International, Inc.　(1)
5955 Carnegie Blvd Ste 300, Charlotte, NC 28209
Tel.: (980) 233-3200
Web Site: http://www.sonamedspa.com
Sales Range: $25-49.9 Million
Medical Spa Services Franchisor
N.A.I.C.S.: 621498
Byron Ashbridge (Pres & Co-CEO)
Joseph W. Pitt Jr. (Chm & Co-CEO)

TotalTrax, Inc.　(1)
920 W Basin Rd Ste 402, New Castle, DE 19720
Tel.: (302) 514-0600
Web Site: http://www.totaltraxinc.com
Miscellaneous Electrical Equipment & Component Mfr
N.A.I.C.S.: 335999
Kneeland Youngblood (Exec Chm)
Anthony Andriano (Pres)
Neil O'Connell (Chief Product Officer & CTO)

PHARR R.V 'S, INC.
320 N Loop 289, Lubbock, TX 79403-2717
Tel.: (806) 765-6088
Web Site: http://www.pharrrvs.com
Year Founded: 1969
Sales Range: $10-24.9 Million
Emp.: 33
Recreational Vehicle Retailer
N.A.I.C.S.: 441210
Karl Lathrop (Mgr-Fin)

PHASE 1 TECHNOLOGY CORP.
44 W Jefryn Blvd, Deer Park, NY 11729
Tel.: (631) 254-2600
Web Site:
　　http://www.phase1tech.com
Rev.: $12,000,000
Emp.: 14
Distr of CCD Cameras, Image Acquisition Boards, Lenses & Software Products
N.A.I.C.S.: 423690
Rusty Ponce de Leon (Founder & Pres)
Xavier Molina (Acct Mgr-Sls-Western Reg)
Carole Schara (Controller)

PHASE 2 COMPANY
PO Box 1459, Fort Collins, CO 80522
Tel.: (970) 482-7000
Web Site: http://www.phase2co.com
Year Founded: 1973
Sales Range: $25-49.9 Million
Emp.: 200
Drywall & Insulation Contracting Services
N.A.I.C.S.: 238310
Brian Chastain (Project Mgr)
Karra Damiana (Project Mgr)
Nate Reimer (Project Mgr)
Stu Shoger (Project Mgr)

PHASE 3 MEDIA, LLC
280 Interstate N Cir SE, Atlanta, GA 30339
Tel.: (404) 367-9898
Web Site: http://www.phase3mc.com
Year Founded: 2001
Emp.: 100
Marketing & Graphic Design Services
N.A.I.C.S.: 541430

Ken Holsclaw (Co-Founder & Pres)
Jenny Harris (Sr VP & Gen Mgr-Atlanta)
Jim Cannata (Sr VP & Gen Mgr-Charlotte & Nashville)
Troy McGinnis (Sr VP & Gen Mgr-Dallas)
Gail Turner (Sr VP-Ops & Pur)
Greg Faulkner (VP-Web & Interactive)
Susan Frost (VP-Mktg & Creative Svcs)
Elyse Hammett (VP-PR-Corp & Lifestyle)
Mary Reynolds (VP-PR-Hospitality & Lifestyle)
Robin Konieczny (VP-Strategy)
Emma Major (Coord-Mktg)
Julia Couch (Asst Mgr-PR)
Cherise Stevens (Sr Mgr-PR)
Max Nair (Co-Founder & Chief Investment Officer)

Subsidiaries:

Presentation Services, Inc.　(1)
1575 Northside Dr Bldg 400 Ste 490, Atlanta, GA 30318-5411
Tel.: (404) 351-5800
Printing Services
N.A.I.C.S.: 323111

iDesign Inc.　(1)
2621 Gallatin Pike, Nashville, TN 37216-3743
Tel.: (615) 377-1481
Web Site: http://www.meetidesign.com
Emp.: 11
Graphic Design Services
N.A.I.C.S.: 541430
Anthony Davis (Mgr)

PHASE II PRODUCTS INC.
501 W Broadway Ste 2090, San Diego, CA 92101-8563
Tel.: (619) 236-9648
Sales Range: $10-24.9 Million
Emp.: 15
Mfr of Drapery Hardware & Window Blinds & Shades
N.A.I.C.S.: 337920
Charles Hunt (CEO)

PHASE2 TECHNOLOGY, LLC
1330 Braddock Pl 7th Fl, Alexandria, VA 22314
Tel.: (703) 548-6050
Web Site:
　　http://www.phase2technology.com
Sales Range: $1-9.9 Million
Emp.: 60
Content Management Software
N.A.I.C.S.: 513210
Frank Febbraro (CTO)
Michael Morris (Exec VP-Bus Dev)
Rich Tolocka (VP-Technical Ops)
Jeff Walpole (CEO)
Andrew Hood (Exec VP-Bus Dev)
Nicole Lind (Sr VP-Client Svcs)
Chris Johnson (VP-Engrg)
Doug Marcey (VP-Products)
Steven Merrill (Dir-Dev Ops)
Thomas Tague (COO)
Gretchen Howell (CFO)
Lisa Gilley (Gen Counsel)
Pat Arnold (VP-Creative)

PHASECOM, INC.
1123 Wade Hampton St, Fort Worth, TX 76126
Tel.: (817) 249-0442　　　　TX
Web Site: http://www.phasecom.com
Electronic Parts & Equipment
N.A.I.C.S.: 423690
Scott Trickey (Pres)

PHASERX, INC.
410 W Harrison St Ste 300, Seattle, WA 98119

Tel.: (206) 805-6300　　　　DE
Web Site: http://www.phaserx.com
Year Founded: 2006
Sales Range: Less than $1 Million
Emp.: 19
Biotechnologicall Product Research & Development Services
N.A.I.C.S.: 541714
Robert W. Overell (Pres, CEO, Chief Acctg Officer & Sec)
Gordon C. Brandt (Chief Medical Officer)
Mary G. Prieve (VP-Biology)
Sean Monahan (VP-Chemistry)
James Watson (Head-Corp Dev)
Erin Cox (Head-IR)

PHAT PANDA LLC
2611 N Woodruff Rd, Spokane Valley, WA 99206-4138
Tel.: (504) 612-2673
Web Site: http://www.phatpanda.com
Year Founded: 2014
Sales Range: $25-49.9 Million
Emp.: 420
Cannabis Product Retailer
N.A.I.C.S.: 424210
Robert McKinley (Co-Founder)
Katrina McKinley (Co-Founder)

PHAZAR CORP.
101 SE 25th Ave, Mineral Wells, TX 76067
Tel.: (940) 325-3301　　　　DE
Web Site: http://www.phazarcorp.com
Year Founded: 1991
Sales Range: $1-9.9 Million
Emp.: 66
Holding Company; Antennas & Other Communications Structures Designer, Mfr & Whslr
N.A.I.C.S.: 551112
Robert E. Fitzgerald (Owner, Pres & CEO)

Subsidiaries:

Antenna Products Corporation　(1)
101 SE 25th Ave, Mineral Wells, TX 76067
Tel.: (940) 325-3301
Web Site: http://www.antennaproducts.com
Antennas & Other Communications Structures Designer, Mfr & Whslr
N.A.I.C.S.: 334220
Rob Fitzgerald (CEO)

Subsidiary (Domestic):

Phazar Antenna Corp.　(2)
6300 Columbia Rd, Mineral Wells, TX 76067
Tel.: (940) 325-3301
Web Site: http://www.phazar.com
Wireless Antenna Systems Mfr
N.A.I.C.S.: 334220

PHB INC.
7900 W Ridge Rd, Fairview, PA 16415-1807
Tel.: (814) 474-5511　　　　PA
Web Site: http://www.phbcorp.com
Year Founded: 1985
Sales Range: $150-199.9 Million
Emp.: 900
Precision Aluminum & Zinc Die Castings Mfr
N.A.I.C.S.: 331523
Harold Haibach (Mgr-Mfg)
Dan Langer (VP)
David Rocco (Acct Mgr)
Jack Tipton (Mgr-Molding Div)
William M. Hilbert Sr. (Pres & CEO)

Subsidiaries:

PHB Machining Division　(1)
8150 W Rdg Rd, Fairview, PA 16415
Tel.: (814) 474-1552
Web Site: http://www.phbcorp.com
Sales Range: $25-49.9 Million
Emp.: 200

COMPANIES   PHI

Industrial & Commercial Machinery & Equipment
N.A.I.C.S.: 332710
William M. Hilbert (CEO)
Daniel Langer (VP & Mgr-Pur)
Jack Figurski (VP-Fin)
John Hilbert (Pres)

PHB Molding Division (1)
8152 W Rdg Rd, Fairview, PA 16415-1805 (100%)
Tel.: (814) 474-2683
Web Site: http://www.phbcorp.com
Sales Range: $10-24.9 Million
Emp.: 50
Plastics Materials & Basic Forms & Shapes
N.A.I.C.S.: 331523
Jack Tipton (Mgr-Mfg)
John Hilbert (Pres & CEO)
William M. Hilbert Sr. (Pres & CEO)

PHB Tool & Die (1)
7900 W Ridge Rd, Fairview, PA 16415-0905
Tel.: (814) 474-5511
Sales Range: $10-24.9 Million
Emp.: 30
Die Casting
N.A.I.C.S.: 333514

PHD INC.
9009 Clubridge Dr, Fort Wayne, IN 46809-3000
Tel.: (260) 747-6151   DE
Web Site: http://www.phdinc.com
Year Founded: 1954
Sales Range: $25-49.9 Million
Emp.: 300
Mfr of Fluid Power Cylinders & Actuators
N.A.I.C.S.: 333995
Anna Specht (Project Coord-Creative Svcs)
Donald Walters (Dir-Quality & Engrg Svcs)
Roy Simangunsong (Mng Dir-Indonesia)

PHD MANUFACTURING INC.
44018 Columbiana-Waterford Rd, Columbiana, OH 44408
Tel.: (330) 482-9256
Web Site: http://www.phd-mfg.com
Year Founded: 1972
Sales Range: $10-24.9 Million
Emp.: 98
Pipe Fittings
N.A.I.C.S.: 332919
Joseph Corvino (Pres)
Rick Persing (Mgr-Sls-Sprinkler Div)
Susan Dotson (Mgr-Acctg)
Anthony Kopatich Sr. (CEO)

PHELPS DUNBAR LLP
365 Canal St Ste 2000, New Orleans, LA 70130-6534
Tel.: (504) 566-1311   LA
Web Site: http://www.phelpsdunbar.com
Year Founded: 1853
Sales Range: $100-124.9 Million
Emp.: 501
Legal Advisory Services
N.A.I.C.S.: 541110
Jane E. Armstrong (Partner)
Barbara L. Arras (Partner)
Robert J. Barbier (Sr Partner)
Lee R. Adler (Partner)
M. Nan Alessandra (Partner)
David B. Lawton (Sr Partner)
Alan C. Wolf (Sr Partner)
Kim M. Boyle (Partner)
Michael M. Butterworth (Co-Partner)
Pablo Gonzalez (Co-Partner)
Cecile L. Gordon (Co-Partner)
Rachel A. de Cordova (Partner-Houston)
John Elsley (Sr Partner-Houston)
Jennifer Bonura (Dir-Fin)
Lynne Donaghy (Dir-Mktg & Bus Dev)
Craig Oakman (Dir-Office Svcs & Facilities)
Angie Flaharty (Dir-Practice Grp Support & Reporting)
Bill White (Exec Dir)
Blake A. Bailey (Partner)
James W. Shelson (Partner)
Allen E. Graham (Mng Partner)
Brian D. Wallace (Mng Partner)
William J. Podolsky III (Partner)
Patrick A. Talley Jr. (Partner)

Subsidiaries:

Farris Bobango PLC (1)
618 Church St Ste 300, Nashville, TN 37219-2436
Tel.: (615) 726-1200
Web Site: http://www.farrismathews.com
Law firm
N.A.I.C.S.: 541110
Miller Hogan (Mgr)

PHELPS IMPLEMENT CORPORATION
1502 G Ave, Grundy Center, IA 50638
Tel.: (319) 824-5247
Web Site: http://www.phelpsimp.com
Year Founded: 1944
Sales Range: $25-49.9 Million
Emp.: 95
Mfr of Agricultural Machinery & Equipment
N.A.I.C.S.: 423820
Randy Runge (Mgr-Sls)

PHELPS MEMORIAL HEALTH CENTER
1215 Tibbals St, Holdrege, NE 68949
Tel.: (308) 995-2211   NE
Web Site: http://www.phelpsmemorial.com
Year Founded: 1963
Sales Range: $25-49.9 Million
Emp.: 264
Health Care Srvices
N.A.I.C.S.: 622110
Roger Peterson (VP)
Kathy Canada (Pres)
Phil Hinrichs (Sec)
Steve Kness (Treas)

PHELPS MEMORIAL HOSPITAL CENTER
701 N Broadway, Tarrytown, NY 10591
Tel.: (914) 366-3000   NY
Web Site: http://www.phelpshospital.org
Year Founded: 1952
Sales Range: $200-249.9 Million
Emp.: 1,957
Health Care Srvices
N.A.I.C.S.: 622110
Stere Carniciu (VP)
Frank Foto (Sec)
Jay Weinberger (Treas)
Emil Nigro (Dir-Emergency Medicine Dept)
Glen Taylor (VP-Support Svcs)
Mary Sernatinger (Dir-Mktg & Comm)
Tobe Banc (VP & Dir-Medical)

PHELPS TOINTON INC.
801 8th St Ste 200, Greeley, CO 80631-3943
Tel.: (970) 353-7000   DE
Year Founded: 1989
Sales Range: $100-124.9 Million
Emp.: 10
Mfr & Exporter of Detention Equipment, Jail Locks, Detention Windows, Safes, Custom Woodwork & Precast Concrete
N.A.I.C.S.: 327390
Robert G. Tointon (Pres)
Joe Phelps (VP)
Phelps Tointon (Owner)

Subsidiaries:

Armor Safe Technologies (1)
5916 Stone Creek, The Colony, TX 75056 (100%)
Tel.: (972) 624-5734
Web Site: http://www.armorsafe.com
Sales Range: $25-49.9 Million
Emp.: 18
Aircraft Mfr
N.A.I.C.S.: 332510
Larry A. Robinson (Pres)

Rocky Mountain Prestress, LLC (1)
5801 Pecos St, Denver, CO 80221-6644
Tel.: (303) 480-1111
Web Site: http://www.rmpprestress.com
Sales Range: $50-74.9 Million
Precast & Prestressed Concrete Products Mfr
N.A.I.C.S.: 327390
Dave Holsteen (Pres)

Southern Folger Detention Equipment Company (1)
4634 S Presa St PO Box 2021, San Antonio, TX 78223
Tel.: (210) 240-3086
Web Site: http://www.southernfolger.com
Sales Range: $25-49.9 Million
Prison Locks & Hardware Installers
N.A.I.C.S.: 332510
Don Halloran (Pres)

PHEND & BROWN INC.
367 E 1250 N, Milford, IN 46542
Tel.: (574) 658-4166
Web Site: http://www.phend-brown.com
Year Founded: 1922
Sales Range: $10-24.9 Million
Emp.: 40
Highway & Street Construction
N.A.I.C.S.: 237310
Daniel F. Brown (Pres)
Douglas V. Brown (VP)

PHENIX GOURMET, LLC.
14700 Marquardt Ave, Santa Fe Springs, CA 90670-5125
Tel.: (562) 404-5028
Sales Range: $10-24.9 Million
Emp.: 135
Cookies & Cracker Mfr
N.A.I.C.S.: 311821
Philip Moreau (Mgr-Sls)
Philip Durbin (Mgr-IT)
Stephanie Cigana (VP-Product Dev)

PHENIX SALON LLC
1084 N El Camino Real Ste B Ste 427, Encinitas, CA 92024
Tel.: (719) 785-4858
Web Site: http://www.phenixsalonsuites.com
Year Founded: 2003
Beauty Salons
N.A.I.C.S.: 812112
Jason Rivera (Co-Founder, Pres & CEO)
Gina Rivera (Co-Founder & Pres)
Jerry Griffith (COO)
Ken Aselton (VP-Franchise Dev)
Robert Aertker (Dir-Natl Real Estate)
Sherrie Wilson (VP-Mktg)
Dennis Johanningmeier (CFO)

Subsidiaries:

Phenix Salon Suites Franchising LLC (1)
3578 Hartsel Dr Unit E Ste 352, Colorado Springs, CO 80920
Tel.: (719) 785-4858
Beauty Salon Franchisor
N.A.I.C.S.: 812112

PHENIX SUPPLY COMPANY INC.
5330 Dividend Dr, Decatur, GA 30035
Tel.: (770) 981-2800   GA
Web Site: http://www.phenixsupply.com
Year Founded: 1990
Sales Range: $10-24.9 Million
Emp.: 115
Provider of Service Equipment & Supplies
N.A.I.C.S.: 423850
Robbie Freeman (Pres)

PHENOMENON
6363 Wilshire Blvd Ste 206, Los Angeles, CA 90048
Tel.: (323) 648-4000
Web Site: http://www.phenomenon.com
Year Founded: 2006
Sales Range: $10-24.9 Million
Emp.: 50
Advetising Agency
N.A.I.C.S.: 541810
Krishnan Menon (Chm & CEO)
Chris Adams (Chief Creative Officer)
Jason De Turris (Chief Strategy Officer)
Jay Gelardi (Exec Creative Dir)

PHH INVESTMENTS, LTD.
15725 Dallas Pkwy Ste 220, Addison, TX 75001
Tel.: (972) 233-3367   TX
Web Site: http://www.raa.com
Emp.: 50
Retirement Planning, Personal Risk & Wealth Management Services
N.A.I.C.S.: 523940
Ronald E. Simmons (Chm)
John Bentley (Pres & CEO)
John B. Roberson (Partner)
William F. Hubble (Chm-Investment Policy Committee)
Jeremy Merchant (Chief Investment Officer)
Mark Rubey (VP-Client Svcs)
Brad Bridgewater (VP-Bus Dev)
Tex B. Grubbs (VP & Controller)
Clay Caldwell (VP-Estate Plng)
Carl Youngdale (Dir-Client Svcs-Atlanta)
Michelle Yates (Mgr-Relationship)
Rutledge Gordon (Sr Mgr-Relationship)
Paul Ochel (Mgr-Relationship)
Rick Oldham (Sr Mgr-Relationship)
Josh Pinchek (Mgr-Relationship)
David Robertson (Mgr-Relationship)
Kat Schraeder (Sr Mgr-Relationship)
Earl Williams (Mgr-Relationship)
Richard Winters (Mgr-Relationship)
Jill Pivato (Mgr-Client Experience)
Jeffrey A. Baumert (COO & Sr VP)
Gary Krasnov (Chief Compliance Officer)
Kelly Hammett (VP-Mktg)
Michael Kane (VP)
Josh Spiegel (CFO)
Kenneth H. Mills Jr. (Partner)

PHI
1 Trinity Dr E Ste 201, Dillsburg, PA 17019
Tel.: (717) 502-8840   PA
Web Site: http://www.presbyterianseniorliving.org
Year Founded: 1997
Sales Range: $10-24.9 Million
Emp.: 158
Elder Care Services
N.A.I.C.S.: 624120
Jeffrey J. Davis (CFO & Sr VP)
James Bernardo (COO & Exec VP)

PHI

PHI—(Continued)
Diane Burfeindt (VP-Population Health)
MaryAnne Adamczyk (Sr VP-Corp Rels)
Stephen Proctor (CEO)
Laurel Spagnolo (VP-Resource Dev)

PHI MU FRATERNITY
400 Westpark Dr, Peachtree City, GA 30269
Tel.: (770) 632-2090   GA
Web Site: http://www.phimu.org
Year Founded: 1852
Sales Range: $10-24.9 Million
Emp.: 60
Woman Welfare Services
N.A.I.C.S.: 813410
Tim O'Rourke (Controller)
Darlene Reyes (Exec Dir)
Robin Davis (Dir-Housing)
Jackie Isaacson (Dir-Comm)
Caitlin Dillon (Mgr-Sls)
Hara Henshell (Sr Dir-Member Svcs)
Jessica Sopko (Dir-Collegiate Ops)

PHI, INC.
2001 SE Evangeline Thruway, Lafayette, LA 70508
Tel.: (337) 235-2452   LA
Web Site: http://www.phihelico.com
Year Founded: 1949
Sales Range: $650-699.9 Million
Emp.: 2,207
Helicopter Transportation Services
N.A.I.C.S.: 481219
Robert Bouillion (Dir-HSEQ)
Pat Attaway (Dir-Ops)
James D. Hinch (COO, Chief Admin Officer & VP-PHI Aviation)
Kenneth Highlander (Dir-Supply Chain)
Jeff Juergens (Gen Mgr-Latin America)
Jason Whitley (CFO)
David Treadway (CIO)
Justin Griffin (Treas)
Richard Rome (Sec)
Jeff Skinner (Dir-Risk Mgmt)
Derek Sample (Controller)

Subsidiaries:

Canadian Helicopters Limited   (1)
1215 Montee Pilon, Les Cedres, J7T 1G1, QC, Canada
Tel.: (450) 452-3000
Web Site: http://www.canadianhelicopters.com
Helicopter Transportation Services
N.A.I.C.S.: 481211

HELEX, LLC   (1)
7016 Challenger Ave Blge 40, Titusville, FL 32780
Tel.: (321) 268-4969
Aircraft & Heavy Equipment Repair Services
N.A.I.C.S.: 488190

HNZ Australia Pty Ltd.   (1)
45 Ventor Avenue, West Perth, 6005, WA, Australia
Tel.: (61) 894298890
Helicopter Repair Services
N.A.I.C.S.: 213112

HNZ New Zealand Ltd.   (1)
Hnz Building Trent Drive Nelson Airport, Nelson, 7011, New Zealand
Tel.: (64) 35475255
Helicopter Repair Services
N.A.I.C.S.: 213112

Nampa Valley Helicopters Inc.   (1)
1870 W Franklin Rd, Meridian, ID 83642
Tel.: (208) 362-0551
Web Site: http://www.nvhelicopters.com
Emp.: 22
Helicopter Overhaul & Maintenance Services
N.A.I.C.S.: 488190

Dean Tromburg (Gen Mgr)

PHI Air Medical, L.L.C.   (1)
2800 N 44th St Ste 800, Phoenix, AZ 85008
Web Site: http://www.phiairmedical.com
Air Ambulance Services
N.A.I.C.S.: 621910
Dave Motzkin (Pres)
Paul Julander (VP-Ambulance Ops)
Jeff Stanek (VP-Fin)
Maria Costella (VP-HR)
Linda Whaley (Dir-Admin Svcs)
Graham Pierce (Dir-Air Ambulance)
Sherri Dean (Dir-Air Ambulance)
Kurt Baden (Dir-Ops)
Ed Sangurima (Dir-Maintenance)
Bob Mayberry (Dir-Natl Clinical Standards)
Joe Gallagher (Dir-HSEQ)
Kevin Ruder (Dir-PHI Patient Navigation)
John Blumenstock (Officer-Compliance)

Petroleum Helicopters International, Inc.   (1)
2001 SE Evangeline Thruway, Lafayette, LA 70508
Tel.: (337) 235-2452
Helicopter Transportation Services
N.A.I.C.S.: 481212

PHIBRO LLC
9 W Broad St, Stamford, CT 06902
Tel.: (203) 674-9454   DE
Web Site: http://www.phibro.com
Year Founded: 1901
Commodities Trading Services
N.A.I.C.S.: 523160
Simon Greenshields (CEO & CIO)
Thomas Frank (Head-Trading & Mktg)
Joseph Delaney (CFO)
Martin Mitchell (COO)

PHIDEB PARTNERSHIP
1951 Bernice Rd, Lansing, IL 60438
Tel.: (708) 474-1081
Rev.: $12,000,000
Fast Food Restaurants & Stands
N.A.I.C.S.: 722513

PHIDS, INC.
877 Executive Ctr Dr W Ste 300, Saint Petersburg, FL 33702-2474
Tel.: (727) 576-6630
Web Site: http://www.acquirgy.com
Year Founded: 2001
Sales Range: $50-74.9 Million
Emp.: 50
Advertising Agencies
N.A.I.C.S.: 541810
Irv Brechner (Exec VP-Corp Comm)
Harry Greene (Exec VP-Production)
Steven Morvay (Pres)
Linda Chaney (Sr VP-Bus Dev)
Louis Conte (CFO)
Carrie Burns (VP)
Marc Lalosh (Dir-Creative)
Dorothy Weaver (VP-Digital Mktg Svcs)
Cynthia Tully (VP & Acct Dir)
Paul Soltoff (Chm & CEO)

PHIFER WIRE PRODUCTS INC.
4400 Kauloosa Ave, Tuscaloosa, AL 35401-7042
Tel.: (205) 345-2120   AL
Web Site: http://www.phifer.com
Year Founded: 1952
Sales Range: $25-49.9 Million
Emp.: 950
Supplier of Miscellaneous Fabricated Wire Products & Woven Fabrics For Screening & Related Purposes
N.A.I.C.S.: 332618
Beverly Phifer (Pres & CEO)

PHIL HUGHES AUTO SALES INC.
3200 Atlanta Hwy, Athens, GA 30606
Tel.: (706) 549-3530

Web Site: http://www.philhugheshonda.com
Rev.: $26,050,231
Emp.: 50
Automobiles, New & Used
N.A.I.C.S.: 441110
D. Wilcher (Gen Mgr)

PHIL LONG DENVER VALU-CAR, LLC,
7800 W Stanford Ave, Denver, CO 80123
Tel.: (303) 973-5337
Web Site: http://www.phillongford.com
Sales Range: $10-24.9 Million
Emp.: 60
Car Whslr
N.A.I.C.S.: 441110
Jim Fynes (Gen Mgr)
Lisa Lewis (Mgr-Acctg)
Scott VanSickle (Mgr-Svc)

PHIL LONG LLC
1212 Motor City Dr, Colorado Springs, CO 80905-1313
Tel.: (719) 575-7100   CO
Web Site: http://www.phillongford.com
Year Founded: 1964
Sales Range: $700-749.9 Million
Emp.: 1,000
Auto Retailer
N.A.I.C.S.: 441110
Jay Cimino (Pres & CEO)
Michelle Hill (Mgr-Corp Comm)
Gary Fentiman (COO)

PHIL MEADOR TOYOTA, INC.
1437 Yellowstone Ave, Pocatello, ID 83201
Tel.: (208) 237-2700
Web Site: http://philmeadortoyotas.com
Sales Range: $10-24.9 Million
Emp.: 35
Car Whslr
N.A.I.C.S.: 441110
Phil Meador (Pres)

PHIL SMITH AUTOMOTIVE GROUP
4250 N Federal Hwy, Lighthouse Point, FL 33064
Tel.: (954) 867-1234
Web Site: http://www.philsmithauto.com
Sales Range: $450-499.9 Million
Emp.: 780
Car Dealership Owner & Operator
N.A.I.C.S.: 441110
Phil Smith (Pres)

PHIL WRIGHT AUTOPLEX CO.
3300 E Main St, Russellville, AR 72802
Tel.: (479) 968-1555
Web Site: http://www.philwrightautoplex.com
Rev.: $14,000,000
Emp.: 50
New Car Dealers
N.A.I.C.S.: 441110
Phil Wright (Pres)

PHILADELPHIA 76ERS, L.P.
3601 S Broad St, Philadelphia, PA 19148
Tel.: (215) 339-7676   DE
Web Site: http://www.nba.com
Professional Basketball Team
N.A.I.C.S.: 711211
Michael G. Rubin (Partner)
Joshua J. Harris (Mng Partner)
Allen Lumpkin (Dir-Basketball Admin)
Lara Price (Exec VP-Bus Ops)

Andy Speiser (Sr VP-Fin)
Larry Meli (VP-Fan Experience & Ticket Ops)
Michael Preston (Dir-PR)
Tina Szwak (Controller)
Tom McGinnis (Dir-Radio Brdcst)
Martin Geller (Co-Owner)
David B. Heller (Co-Owner)
Travis Hennings (Partner)
James Lassiter (Partner)
Will Smith (Co-Owner)
Jada Pinkett Smith (Partner)
Art Wrubel (Partner)
Scott Rego (Mgr-Equipment)
Dan Rosci (Asst Mgr-Equipment)
Todd Landrey (Dir-Sixers Camps)
Derrick Hayes (Dir-Game Presentations)
Michael Goings (Mgr-Community Rels)
Scott M. O'Neil (CEO)
Christopher Heck (Chief Revenue Officer)
Jake Reynolds (VP-Ticket Sls & Svc)
Ned Cohen (Assoc VP)
Lara Toscani (Dir-Corp Comm)
Leo Cardenas (Mgr-Grp Sls)
Susan Williamson (VP-Mktg)
Zack Robinson (Dir-Grp Sls)
Elton Brand (Gen Mgr)
Daryl Morey (Pres-Basketball Ops)

PHILADELPHIA BEER WORKS INC.
4120 Main St, Philadelphia, PA 19127-1618
Tel.: (215) 482-8220
Web Site: http://www.manayunkbrewery.com
Sales Range: $10-24.9 Million
Emp.: 110
Malt Mfr
N.A.I.C.S.: 311213
Mike Rose (Owner)

PHILADELPHIA COUNTRY CLUB
1601 Spring Mill Rd, Gladwyne, PA 19035
Tel.: (610) 525-6000   PA
Web Site: http://www.philadelphiacc.net
Year Founded: 1890
Sales Range: $10-24.9 Million
Emp.: 281
Country Club Operator
N.A.I.C.S.: 713910
Toni Keyser (Dir-HR)
Erin Falls (Mgr-Catering & Member Events)
Missi Johnson (Dir-Comm)
Brian Gardner (Dir-Membership)

PHILADELPHIA CRICKET CLUB
415 W Willow Grove Ave, Philadelphia, PA 19118
Tel.: (215) 247-6001   PA
Web Site: http://www.philacricket.com
Year Founded: 1854
Sales Range: $10-24.9 Million
Emp.: 397
Recreation Club Operator
N.A.I.C.S.: 713910
Tim Muessle (COO)
Jacob Smith (Dir-Membership & Bus Dev)
Linda Cook (CFO)
Jim Smith Jr. (Dir-Golf)

PHILADELPHIA EAGLES FOOTBALL CLUB, INC.
1 Novacare Way, Philadelphia, PA 19145-5900
Tel.: (215) 463-2500   PA

COMPANIES

Web Site:
http://www.philadelphiaeagles.com
Year Founded: 1933
Sales Range: $75-99.9 Million
Emp.: 100
Professional Football Franchise
N.A.I.C.S.: 711211
Jeffrey Lurie (*Chm & CEO*)
Don Smolenski (*Pres*)
Frank Gumienny (*CFO & Sr VP*)
Laini DeLawter (*VP-Ticket & Fan Svcs*)
Jason Miller (*Sr VP-Ops*)
Greg McDonald (*Dir-Fin Ops*)
Tony Orazi (*Dir-Fin Reporting*)
Howie Roseman (*Exec VP-Football Ops*)
John Pawling (*VP-IT*)
Julie Hirshey (*Dir-Community Rels*)
Kristie Pappal (*VP-HR*)
Tracy Foster (*Dir-Client Svcs*)
Joe Malatesta (*Mgr-Premium Sls*)
Ari Roitman (*Sr VP-Bus*)
Greg Delimitros (*VP-Equipment Ops*)
Jake Rosenberg (*Dir-Football Admin*)
Dom DiSandro (*VP-Team Security*)
Poorya Nayerahmadi (*Mgr-Mktg Programs*)
Mat Warner (*Dir-Premium Sls*)
Ryan Hummel (*Dir-Facilities*)
Aileen Dagrosa (*Sr VP*)
Erik Rausch (*Mgr-HR*)
Brian Papson (*VP-Mktg*)
J. P. Hayslip (*Dir-Facilities Security*)
Chris Sharkoski (*Dir-Event Ops*)
Brett Strohsacker (*Mgr-PR*)
Dwayne Joseph (*VP-Pro Scouting*)
Eric Long (*Dir-Production*)
Ernie Burrell (*Dir-Corp Partnerships*)
Patrick Dolan (*VP-Football Tech*)
Alec Halaby (*VP-Football Ops & Strategy*)
Andrew Berry (*VP-Football Ops*)
Jon Ferrari (*VP-Football Ops & Compliance*)
Jeremiah Washburn (*Coord-Advanced Projects*)
Joe Pannunzio (*Dir-Team Dev*)
Christina Weiss Lurie (*Pres-Eagle Youth Partnership & Eagles Social Responsibility*)

PHILADELPHIA FEDERATION OF TEACHERS HEALTH AND WELFARE FUND
1816 Chestnut St, Philadelphia, PA 19103
Tel.: (215) 561-2722   PA
Web Site: http://www.pfthw.org
Year Founded: 1971
Sales Range: $25-49.9 Million
Emp.: 38
Health & Welfare Benefit Services
N.A.I.C.S.: 525120
Michael D'Arcy (*Controller*)
Mario Declerico (*Controller*)

PHILADELPHIA FIGHT
1233 Locust St 5th Fl, Philadelphia, PA 19107
Tel.: (215) 985-4448   PA
Web Site: http://www.fight.org
Year Founded: 1990
Sales Range: $10-24.9 Million
Emp.: 107
Health Care Consulting Services
N.A.I.C.S.: 621491
Calenthia Dowdy (*Dir-Faith Initiatives*)
Jane Shull (*Exec Dir*)
Chip Alfred (*PR & Events*)
Barbara L. Bungy (*COO-Community Health Centers*)

PHILADELPHIA FOODS INC.
201 Harvard Ave, Westville, NJ 08093-1444
Tel.: (609) 456-8700   NJ
Year Founded: 1981
Sales Range: $25-49.9 Million
Emp.: 100
Meat Packing Plants
N.A.I.C.S.: 311611

PHILADELPHIA MACARONI CO. INC.
760 S 11th St, Philadelphia, PA 19147-2614
Tel.: (215) 923-3141   PA
Web Site:
http://www.philamacaroni.com
Year Founded: 1961
Sales Range: $100-124.9 Million
Emp.: 1,000
Provider of Macaroni & Spaghetti
N.A.I.C.S.: 311824
Luke Marano Sr. (*Chm & CEO*)

PHILADELPHIA MEDIA HOLDINGS, LLC
801 Market Street Ste 300, Philadelphia, PA 19107
Tel.: (215) 854-2000   DE
Web Site: http://www.pnionline.com
Year Founded: 2006
Sales Range: $1-4.9 Billion
Emp.: 3,800
Holding Company; Newspaper, Magazine & Internet Publisher
N.A.I.C.S.: 551112
H. F. Lenfest (*Owner*)
Fred Groser (*Sr VP-Sls*)
Terrance C. Z. Egger (*CEO & Publr*)
Subsidiaries:

Philadelphia Newspapers, LLC   (1)
400 N Broad St, Philadelphia, PA 19130-4015
Tel.: (215) 854-2000
Web Site: http://www.pnionline.com
Newspaper Publisher & Website Operator
N.A.I.C.S.: 513110
Edward Mahlman (*CMO*)
Robert J. Hall (*CEO & Publr*)

Unit (Domestic):

Philadelphia Daily News   (2)
400 N Broad St, Philadelphia, PA 19130-4099
Tel.: (215) 854-2000
Web Site: http://www.philly.com
Sales Range: $50-74.9 Million
Emp.: 850
Newspaper Publishers
N.A.I.C.S.: 513110
Laurie Conrad (*Editor*)
Anthony Cuffie (*VP-Adv*)
Ben Turk Tolub (*Dir-Product*)
George Kurtas (*CIO*)
Laurence Weilheimer (*Gen Counsel & VP*)
Keith Black (*VP-HR*)
Amy Buckman (*Mgr-PR & Special Events*)
Ed Delfin (*VP-Circulation*)
Fred Groser (*Sr VP-Sls & Mktg*)
Andy Harrison (*CFO*)
H. F. Gerry Lenfest (*Chm*)
Barbara Sadler (*VP-Fin & Controller*)

The Philadelphia Inquirer   (2)
400 N Broad St, Philadelphia, PA 19130
Tel.: (215) 854-2000
Web Site: http://www.philly.com
Sales Range: $300-349.9 Million
Emp.: 2,500
Newspaper Publishers
N.A.I.C.S.: 513110
Brian Toolan (*Editor-Bus*)
Harold Jackson (*Editor-Editorial*)
Sandra Clark (*Mng Editor-Features, Ops & Digital*)
Gabriel Escobar (*Editor*)
Lisa Hughes (*CEO & Publr*)
Patrick Kerkstra (*Mng Editor*)
Ezequiel Minaya (*Deputy Editor-Bus*)

PHILADELPHIA MUSEUM OF ART
26th Benjamin Franklin Pkwy, Philadelphia, PA 19130
Tel.: (215) 763-8100
Web Site:
http://www.philamuseum.org
Year Founded: 1876
Sales Range: $50-74.9 Million
Emp.: 500
Art Gallery, Commercial
N.A.I.C.S.: 712110
Conna Clark (*Mgr-Rights & Reproduction*)
Robert T. Rambo (*CFO*)
Gail Harrity (*Pres & COO*)
Timothy Rub (*CEO*)
Kathleen T. O'Reilly (*Member-Exec Bd*)
Jonathan Peterson (*Dir-Dev*)
Nicole K. Allen White (*Dir-Govt & External Affairs*)

PHILADELPHIA PARENT CHILD CENTER
2515 Germantown Ave, Philadelphia, PA 19133
Tel.: (215) 229-1804   PA
Year Founded: 1971
Sales Range: $50-74.9 Million
Emp.: 104
Child & Family Care Services
N.A.I.C.S.: 624190
Shirley Williams (*CFO*)
Jacqueline Green (*CEO*)
Joseph Aiken (*Chm*)
Sarah Pye-Upshaw (*Vice Chm*)

PHILADELPHIA PRISON SYSTEM
990 Spring Garden St 7th Fl, Philadelphia, PA 19107
Tel.: (215) 686-1234
Web Site: http://www.phila.gov
Emp.: 2,150
Prisons
N.A.I.C.S.: 922140
Louis Giorla (*Commissioner*)
Clyde Gainey (*Deputy Commissioner-Ops & Emergency Svcs*)
Robert Tomaszewski (*Deputy Commissioner-Admin*)
Eugene P. Davey (*Vice Chm*)
Eugene Maier (*Co-Chm*)
James J. O'Connell (*Co-Chm*)
Robert N. C. Nix III (*Sec*)

PHILADELPHIA RESERVE SUPPLY COMPANY
200 Mack Dr, Croydon, PA 19021-6934
Tel.: (215) 785-3141   PA
Web Site: http://www.prsco.org
Year Founded: 1930
Sales Range: $75-99.9 Million
Emp.: 25
Whslr of Lumber & Building Materials
N.A.I.C.S.: 423310
Shawn Lasalle (*Mgr-Warehouse*)

PHILADELPHIA SIGN COMPANY
707 W Spring Garden St, Palmyra, NJ 08065-1732
Tel.: (856) 829-1460   DE
Web Site:
http://www.philadelphiasign.com
Year Founded: 1911
Sales Range: $50-74.9 Million
Emp.: 110
Mfr of Signs & Displays
N.A.I.C.S.: 339950
Robert Mehmet (*Pres & CEO*)
Jennifer Stoughton (*VP-Program Mgmt*)
Joseph Hoban (*VP-Creative Svcs*)
Shelly Robinson (*Dir-HR*)
Jim Ward (*VP-Fin & Ops*)
John Foley (*Exec VP*)
Subsidiaries:

Philadelphia Sign Company - LITTLETON PLANT   (1)
50 Porter Rd, Littleton, MA 01460
Tel.: (978) 486-0137
Sign Mfr
N.A.I.C.S.: 339950

PHILADELPHIA SKATING CLUB & HUMANE SOCIETY
220 Holland Ave, Ardmore, PA 19003-1292
Tel.: (610) 642-8700   PA
Web Site: http://www.pschs.org
Year Founded: 1861
Sales Range: $1-9.9 Million
Emp.: 123
Skating Club
N.A.I.C.S.: 711211
Francis T. Mycek (*Gen Mgr*)
Mary G. Mycek (*Office Mgr*)
Regina Barr (*Dir-Skating*)
Mary Ruth Thompson (*Sec*)
Mike Farrell (*Treas*)
Laura Jaworski (*VP*)
Charlotte Martin (*Pres*)
Cathy Rahab (*VP*)

PHILANTHROPIC VENTURES FOUNDATION
1222 Preservation Pkwy, Oakland, CA 94612-1201
Tel.: (510) 645-1890   CA
Web Site:
http://www.venturesfoundation.org
Year Founded: 1991
Sales Range: $10-24.9 Million
Emp.: 5
Philanthropic Services
N.A.I.C.S.: 813211
Bill Somerville (*Founder & Pres*)
James Higa (*Exec Dir*)
Duncan Beardsley (*Chm*)

PHILHARMONIC SYMPHONY SOCIETY OF NEW YORK INC.
David Geffen Hall 10 Lincoln Ctr Plz, New York, NY 10023-6970
Tel.: (212) 875-5900
Web Site: https://www.nyphil.org
Year Founded: 1842
Emp.: 200
Symphony Orchestra
N.A.I.C.S.: 711320
Zarin Mehta (*Pres & Exec Dir*)
Barbara Shear (*Mgr-Res*)
Marion Cotrone (*Dir-Special Events & Volunteer Svcs*)
Pamela Katz (*Dir-Fin*)
Catherine Williams (*Dir-HR*)
David Snead (*VP-Mktg*)
Ann Hilton (*Dir-Sls*)
John May (*Mgr-Subscriptions*)
Lawrence Rock (*Dir-Audio*)
Carl R. Schiebler (*Mgr-Orchestra Personnel*)
Lucy Kraus (*Editor-Publ*)
Monica Parks (*Dir-Publ*)
Julii Oh (*Dir-Mktg*)
Melanie Forman (*VP-Dev*)
Amy Mugavero (*Dir-Major & Planned Gifts*)

PHILIP PELUSI SALONS
1700 E Carson St Ste 1, Pittsburgh, PA 15203
Tel.: (412) 488-6618
Web Site: http://www.philippelusi.com
Sales Range: $10-24.9 Million
Emp.: 300
Beauty Shops
N.A.I.C.S.: 812112

PHILIP PELUSI SALONS

Philip Pelusi Salons—(Continued)
Philip Pelusi *(Pres)*
Wes Smeltzer *(Supvr-Tech)*
Kate Valentine *(Dir-Salon)*
Kevin Chamberland *(Mgr-Salon)*
Leslie Russell *(Controller)*
Lindsey Welday *(Supvr-Tech)*
Marylou Marino *(Mgr)*

PHILIP/ANDREWS DESIGN
27 Sequoia Rd, Fairfax, CA 94930
Tel.: (415) 454-9509
Year Founded: 1996
Sales Range: $10-24.9 Million
Emp.: 1
Consulting, Electronic Media, Internet/Web Design, Publicity/Promotions
N.A.I.C.S.: 541810

PHILIPP LITHOGRAPHING COMPANY
1960 Wisconsin Ave, Grafton, WI 53024
Tel.: (262) 377-1100
Web Site: http://www.philipplitho.com
Rev.: $18,800,000
Emp.: 47
Commercial Lithographic Printing
N.A.I.C.S.: 323111
Peter Buening *(Pres, Treas & Sec)*
David Kaehny *(Treas)*

PHILIPPEBECKER
55 Union St Fl 3, San Francisco, CA 94111
Tel.: (415) 348-0054
Web Site: http://www.beckersf.com
Year Founded: 2001
Rev.: $4,200,000
Emp.: 24
Designing Products, Advertising & Marketing
N.A.I.C.S.: 541810
Danielle Lalanne *(Coord-Client)*
Philippe Becker *(Principal & Chief Creative Officer)*

PHILIPS INTERNATIONAL REALTY CORP.
295 Madison Ave Ste 2, New York, NY 10017-6304
Tel.: (212) 545-1100
Web Site: http://www.pihc.com
Sales Range: $1-9.9 Million
Emp.: 40
Real Estate Investment Trust
N.A.I.C.S.: 525990
Philip Pilevsky *(Chm, Pres, CEO & Sec)*

PHILLIPPI EQUIPMENT CO.
2875 Hwy 55, Eagan, MN 55121
Tel.: (651) 406-4900
Web Site: http://www.pecoequip.com
Sales Range: $25-49.9 Million
Emp.: 50
General Construction Machinery & Equipment
N.A.I.C.S.: 423810
Wendell A. Phillippi *(Owner)*

PHILLIPS & COHEN ASSOCIATES LTD.
695 Rancocas Rd, Westampton, NJ 08060
Tel.: (609) 518-9000
Web Site: http://www.phillips-cohen.com
Sales Range: $100-124.9 Million
Emp.: 200
Adjustment & Collection Services
N.A.I.C.S.: 561440
Matthew Phillips *(Co-Chm & Co-CEO)*
Adam S. Cohen *(Co-Chm & Co-CEO)*
Tim Webb *(Dir-Sls-Global)*
Gelsomina Paolini *(CFO-Global)*
Nick Cherry *(Mng Dir)*

PHILLIPS & JORDAN INCORPORATED
6621 Wilbanks Rd, Knoxville, TN 37912-1314
Tel.: (865) 688-8342
Web Site: http://www.pandj.com
Year Founded: 1986
Sales Range: $50-74.9 Million
Emp.: 750
Provider of Construction Services
N.A.I.C.S.: 236210
Dudley Orr *(VP-Indus & Comml Grp)*
John West *(VP-Pipeline Svcs Grp)*
Jerry Hill *(VP-Fleet Mgmt)*
Patrick J. McMullen *(Pres)*
Steve Thompson *(VP-Safety & Risk Mgmt)*
William T. Phillips Sr. *(Chm)*

PHILLIPS BUICK PONTIAC GMC
2160 Hwy 27441, Fruitland Park, FL 34731
Tel.: (352) 728-1212
Web Site: http://www.phillips-buick.com
Rev.: $18,200,000
Emp.: 55
Automobiles, New & Used
N.A.I.C.S.: 441110
Larry Phillips *(Pres)*

PHILLIPS BUILDING SUPPLY OF GULFPORT
9185 Hwy 49, Gulfport, MS 39503
Tel.: (228) 868-1101
Web Site: http://www.phillipsbuildingsupply.com
Sales Range: $10-24.9 Million
Emp.: 150
Lumber & Other Building Materials
N.A.I.C.S.: 423310
Patty Spires *(Office Mgr)*
William J. Hough Sr. *(CEO)*
Bill Hough Jr. *(Gen Mgr)*

PHILLIPS CHRYSLER JEEP DODGE RAM
3440 S Pine Ave, Ocala, FL 34471-6615
Tel.: (352) 732-7577
Web Site: http://www.phillipschryslerjeep.net
Sales Range: $25-49.9 Million
Emp.: 37
Car Whslr
N.A.I.C.S.: 441110
Steve Ryerkerk *(Principal)*
John Cherry *(Gen Mgr)*

PHILLIPS COMMUNICATION & EQUIPMENT CO.
31 Commerce Dr, Ruckersville, VA 22968
Tel.: (434) 985-3600
Web Site: http://www.phillipscomm.com
Rev.: $37,944,398
Emp.: 25
Communications Equipment
N.A.I.C.S.: 423690
Chad Morris *(Gen Mgr)*

PHILLIPS CORPORATION
7390 Coca Cola Dr, Hanover, MD 21076
Tel.: (301) 490-6800
Web Site: http://www.phillipscorp.com
Sales Range: $50-74.9 Million
Emp.: 300
Metalworking Machinery
N.A.I.C.S.: 423830
Allen Phillips *(Pres)*
Matthew Phillips *(CFO)*
Tim McClanahan *(Product Mgr)*

PHILLIPS DE PURY & COMPANY
450 Park Ave, New York, NY 10022
Tel.: (212) 940-1200
Web Site: http://www.phillips.com
Year Founded: 1796
Sales Range: $100-124.9 Million
Emp.: 200
Fine Art Auctioneers & Appraisers
N.A.I.C.S.: 561990
Sean Cleary *(Mng Dir)*

PHILLIPS DEVELOPMENT & REALTY, LLC
142 W Platt St, Tampa, FL 33606
Tel.: (813) 686-3100
Web Site: http://www.pdrllc.com
Sales Range: $1-9.9 Million
Emp.: 10
Real Estate Developer & Realtor
N.A.I.C.S.: 531210
Donald E. Phillips *(Mng Dir)*
Phil Baker *(VP-Construction Svcs)*
Kevin Johnston *(COO)*

PHILLIPS DEVELOPMENT CORP.
1501 N University Ave # 740, Little Rock, AR 72207
Tel.: (501) 666-9629
Web Site: http://www.pdccompanies.com
Rev.: $21,089,913
Emp.: 26
Multi-Family Dwellings, New Construction
N.A.I.C.S.: 236116
Chester D. Phillips *(Chm)*
Elizabeth S. Small *(Pres)*

PHILLIPS DISTRIBUTING CORP
3010 Nob Hill Rd, Madison, WI 53713
Tel.: (608) 222-9177
Web Site: http://www.phillipsdistributing.com
Rev.: $20,000,000
Emp.: 35
Distribution Of Liquor
N.A.I.C.S.: 424820
Marv Levy *(Pres)*
Paul Steinke *(Mgr-Sls & Ops)*

PHILLIPS EDISON & COMPANY LLC
11501 Northlake Dr, Cincinnati, OH 45249
Tel.: (513) 554-1110
Web Site: http://www.phillipsedison.com
Rev.: $311,543,000
Assets: $3,526,082,000
Liabilities: $2,047,400,000
Net Worth: $1,478,682,000
Earnings: $(38,391,000)
Emp.: 304
Fiscal Year-end: 12/31/17
Real Estate Development
N.A.I.C.S.: 531210
Jeffrey S. Edison *(Chm & CEO)*
R. Mark Addy *(Exec VP)*
Ron Meyers *(Sr VP-Leasing)*
Cherilyn Megill *(Chief Mktg Officer & Sr VP)*
John Caulfield *(CFO)*
Shaun Smith *(CIO & Sr VP)*
Jennifer L. Robison *(Chief Acctg Officer)*
Dawn Stamper *(Sr VP-Customer Experience)*
Eric Richter *(Sr VP-Property Mgmt)*
Greg H. Clough *(VP-Redevelopment)*
Jim Farmer *(Reg VP-Leasing)*
Joel Strause *(VP-Leasing-Mid-Atlantic Reg)*
Keith A. Rummer *(Chief Compliance Officer, Chief HR Officer & Sr VP)*
Mike Conway *(VP-Accts & Retailer Partnerships-Natl)*
Stuart Shapiro *(VP-Leasing-Southeast Reg)*
Tracey Hall *(Dir-Property Mgmt)*
Tony Haslinger *(Sr VP-Construction)*
Vasili Lyhnakis *(VP-Leasing-West Reg)*
Tanya Brady *(Gen Counsel & Sr VP)*
David Wik *(Sr VP-Acquisition)*
Paul Mittmann *(Reg VP-Acquisition)*
Corrine Cecil *(VP-Leasing)*
Will Ponder *(Reg VP-Acquisitions)*
K. C. Bills *(VP-Portfolio Mgmt & Dev)*
Gregory Hausfeld *(Reg VP-Portfolio Mgmt)*
Ryan Moore *(Sr VP-Investment Mgmt)*
Erin Majors *(Reg VP-Portfolio Mgmt)*
Theresa C. Burian *(VP & Asst Gen Counsel)*
Aaron Morris *(VP-Acctg)*
Scott Adair *(VP-Economic Dev)*
Stephen Bien *(VP-Transactions)*
Charles Douglas Johnson *(Sr VP)*
Brian Gibson *(Sr VP-Fin)*
Kevin J. McCann *(CIO)*
Thomas L. Meyers III *(Reg VP-Portfolio Mgmt)*

Subsidiaries:

Bear Creek Station LLC (1)
19380 Tuolumne Rd, Tuolumne, CA 95379
Tel.: (209) 928-9550
Real Estate Development Services
N.A.I.C.S.: 531210

Phillips Edison & Company Inc. (1)
11501 Northlake Dr, Cincinnati, OH 45249
Tel.: (513) 554-1110
Web Site: https://www.phillipsedison.com
Rev.: $610,124,000
Assets: $4,865,666,000
Liabilities: $2,212,315,000
Net Worth: $2,653,351,000
Earnings: $56,848,000
Emp.: 290
Fiscal Year-end: 12/31/2023
Real Estate Investment Trust
N.A.I.C.S.: 525990
Jeffrey S. Edison *(Co-Founder, Chm & CEO)*
Joseph G. Schlosser *(COO & Exec VP)*
Jennifer L. Robison *(Chief Acctg Officer & Sr VP)*
John P. Caulfield *(CFO, Treas & Sr VP)*
Cherilyn Megill *(CMO)*
Greg Clough *(Sr VP)*
Tony Haslinger *(Sr VP)*
Joe Hoffmann *(Sr VP)*
Ron Meyers *(Sr VP)*
Aaron L. Morris *(Sr VP-Finance)*
David Wik *(Sr VP)*
Robert F. Myers *(Pres)*
Keith A. Rummer *(Chief People Officer & Sr VP)*
Tanya F. Brady *(Chief Ethics Officer, Gen Counsel, Sec & Exec VP)*
Gary G. Bailey *(CIO & Sr VP)*
Kc T. Bills *(Sr VP Portfolio Mgmt-Development)*
Vasili Lyhnakis *(Sr VP-Leasing)*

Phillips Edison Grocery Center REIT II, Inc. (1)
11501 Northlake Dr, Cincinnati, OH 45249
Tel.: (833) 347-5717
Web Site: http://www.grocerycenterREIT2.com
Rev.: $162,577,000
Assets: $1,652,317,000
Liabilities: $869,038,000
Net Worth: $783,279,000
Earnings: $(9,531,000)
Fiscal Year-end: 12/31/2017
Real Estate Investment Services
N.A.I.C.S.: 523999

COMPANIES
PHIPPS & BIRD, INC.

Devin I. Murphy *(Pres)*
R. Mark Addy *(Pres & COO)*

White Oaks Station LLC (1)
308 W Industrial Park Rd, Harrison, AR 72601
Tel.: (870) 741-3226
Real Estate Development Services
N.A.I.C.S.: 531210

PHILLIPS FOODS INC.
3761 Commerce Dr Ste 413, Baltimore, MD 21227
Tel.: (443) 263-1200
Web Site: http://www.phillipsfoods.com
Sales Range: $200-249.9 Million
Emp.: 500
Seafood Restaurant Operator & Seafood Product Sales
N.A.I.C.S.: 722511
Steve Phillips *(Pres & CEO)*
Dean E. Flowers *(Pres/COO-Global)*
John Knorr *(Sr VP)*
Sarah Palmer *(VP-Foodservice Sls)*

Subsidiaries:

Phillips Foods Asia Co., Ltd. (1)
Unit 4 11th Floor 1011 Supalai Grand Tower Rama III Road, Chongnonsee Yannawa, Bangkok, 10120, Thailand
Tel.: (66) 2 683 0470
Restaurant Operators
N.A.I.C.S.: 722511
Michael Hallager *(VP-Sls)*

Phillips Seafood Restaurant (1)
301 Light St, Baltimore, MD 21202
Tel.: (410) 685-6600
Web Site: http://www.phillipsseafood.com
Full-Service Restaurants
N.A.I.C.S.: 722511

PHILLIPS INDUSTRIES
12012 Burke St, Santa Fe Springs, CA 90670-2676
Tel.: (562) 781-2121   CA
Web Site: http://www.phillipsind.com
Year Founded: 1928
Rev.: $50,000,000
Emp.: 500
Truck Parts Mfr & Distr
N.A.I.C.S.: 336390
Bob A. Phillips *(Founder, Chm & CEO)*
Randy Walker *(Dir-Aftermarket Sls-North America)*
Ron Alvarez *(Dir-Sls-OEM & OES-Global & North America)*
Rob Myers *(Pres-Phillips Aftermarket Bus Unit)*
Filiberto Coello *(Pres-Phillips OEM Bus Unit)*
Tom Peterson *(Sr Engr-Mechanical Design)*

Subsidiaries:

Commercial Vehicle Products Division (1)
12070 Burke St, Santa Fe Springs, CA 90670-2676   **(100%)**
Tel.: (562) 781-2100
Sales Range: $25-49.9 Million
Emp.: 200
N.A.I.C.S.: 336212
Robert Phillips *(Pres)*

Shanghai Phillips Industries Vehicle Components Manufacturing Ltd. (1)
No 935 Bai'an Road International, Automobile City Anting, Shanghai, 201805, China
Tel.: (86) 21 6957 4800
Electrical Equipment Distr
N.A.I.C.S.: 423610

PHILLIPS INSURANCE ASSOCIATES, INC.
1600 W Main St, Wilmington, OH 45177-2236
Tel.: (937) 382-5545
Web Site: http://www.phillipsia.com
Year Founded: 1977
Fire, Marine & Casualty Insurance Services
N.A.I.C.S.: 524210
Michael D. Phillips *(Pres)*
Chip Phillips *(VP)*

PHILLIPS MACHINE SERVICE INC.
367 George St, Beckley, WV 25801
Tel.: (304) 255-0537
Web Site: http://www.phillipsmachine.com
Sales Range: $25-49.9 Million
Emp.: 140
Industrial Machinery & Equipment Repair
N.A.I.C.S.: 811210
Bruce Dickerson *(CEO)*

PHILLIPS MANUFACTURING INC.
4949 S 30th St, Omaha, NE 68107
Tel.: (402) 339-3800
Web Site: http://www.phillipsmfg.com
Year Founded: 1955
Rev.: $12,800,000
Emp.: 130
Metal Moldings & Trim Mfr
N.A.I.C.S.: 332321
George J. Kubat *(Owner, Pres & CEO)*

PHILLIPS MUSHROOM FARMS
1011 Kaolin Rd, Kennett Square, PA 19348
Tel.: (610) 925-0520   PA
Web Site: http://www.phillipsmushroomfarms.com
Year Founded: 1962
Sales Range: $10-24.9 Million
Emp.: 200
Specialty Mushroom Farming
N.A.I.C.S.: 111411
Jim Angioletti *(Gen Mgr)*
Peter Gray *(Mgr-Grower)*
Tina Ellor *(Dir-Tech)*
William Steller *(Controller)*

Subsidiaries:

Phillips Gourmet, Inc. (1)
1011 Kaolin Rd, Kennett Square, PA 19348   **(100%)**
Tel.: (610) 925-0520
Web Site: http://www.phillipsmushroomfarms.com
Prepared Gourmet Foods
N.A.I.C.S.: 311412
Kevin Donovan *(Mgr-Sls)*

PHILLIPS PAINTING
6905 K Ave Ste 206, Plano, TX 75074
Tel.: (972) 867-9792
Web Site: http://www.phillipspainting.com
Year Founded: 1997
Sales Range: $1-9.9 Million
Emp.: 90
Painting Services
N.A.I.C.S.: 238320
Jason Phillips *(Owner & Pres)*
Ian Jones *(Dir-Mktg)*
Steve Lewis *(Mgr-Roofing)*

PHILLIPS PET FOOD & SUPPLIES
3747 Hecktown Rd, Easton, PA 18045
Web Site: http://www.phillipspet.com
Year Founded: 1938
Emp.: 200
Pet Food & Supplies Sales
N.A.I.C.S.: 311119

Dan Vaughn *(Gen Mgr-Pricing)*
Todd Shelton *(CEO)*
Kent Weldon *(Chm)*
Greg Cyr *(Chief Comml Officer)*

PHILLIPS SERVICE INDUSTRIES, INC. (PSI)
14492 Sheldon Rd Ste 300, Plymouth, MI 48170
Tel.: (734) 853-5000   MI
Web Site: http://www.psi-online.com
Year Founded: 1967
Sales Range: $150-199.9 Million
Emp.: 500
Global Manufacturing & Services Holding Company
N.A.I.C.S.: 551112
Jay Hollingsworth *(Dir-PB & Mktg)*

Subsidiaries:

Evana Automation Specialists (1)
5825 Old Boonville Hwy, Evansville, IN 47715-2136
Tel.: (812) 479-8246
Web Site: http://www.evanaautomation.com
Sales Range: $10-24.9 Million
Emp.: 55
Systems Integrator & Mfr of Custom, Automated Assembly & Test Systems
N.A.I.C.S.: 541511
Randy Wire *(Gen Mgr)*
Pete Hayes *(Project Mgr)*
Janice Wilson *(Mgr-Pur)*

Mountain Secure Systems (MSS) (1)
1350 Kansas Ave, Longmont, CO 80501-6546
Tel.: (303) 678-9898
Web Site: http://www.mountainsecuresystems.com
Sales Range: $10-24.9 Million
Emp.: 31
Ruggedized Electronic Data Storage Solutions for Harsh Climactic Conditions
N.A.I.C.S.: 334112
Ken Dickson *(Pres)*
Rod Copeland *(Mgr-Sls)*

POWERTHRU (1)
11825 Mayfield, Livonia, MI 48150
Web Site: http://www.power-thru.com
Emp.: 50
Flywheel Energy Storage Systems Mfr for Commercial Applications
N.A.I.C.S.: 334112
Jim Diroff *(Dir-Ops, Sr Leader & Production Strategist)*

PSI Repair Services, Inc. (1)
11900 Mayfield, Livonia, MI 48150-1710
Tel.: (734) 853-5000
Web Site: http://www.psi-repair.com
Sales Range: $25-49.9 Million
Emp.: 200
Industrial Component Repair Services
N.A.I.C.S.: 334419
Scott Phillips *(Pres & CEO)*
Michael Fitzpatrick *(Gen Counsel-Phillips Svc Industries & Gen Mgr-PSI Repair)*

PSI Semicon Services (1)
11900 Mayfield, Livonia, MI 48150
Tel.: (734) 853-5000
Web Site: http://www.psisemiconservices.com
Emp.: 50
Repair & Spare Parts Semiconductor Supplier
N.A.I.C.S.: 541614
John Festa *(Exec Dir)*

Sciaky, Inc. (1)
4915 W 67th St, Chicago, IL 60638-6408
Tel.: (708) 594-3800
Web Site: http://www.sciaky.com
Sales Range: $10-24.9 Million
Emp.: 100
Mfr of Electron Beam, Advanced Arc, Resistance & Laser Welding Systems
N.A.I.C.S.: 335999
John O'Hara *(Mgr-Sls)*

Subsidiary (Non-US):

Sciaky Welding Machines Ltd. (2)
212 Bedford Ave, Slough, SL1 4RH, Berks, United Kingdom   **(46%)**
Tel.: (44) 1753525551
Web Site: http://www.sciaky.co.uk
Rev.: $15,000,000
Emp.: 18
Mfr & Refurbishing Welding Machines
N.A.I.C.S.: 333992

Skytronics, Inc. (1)
14100 Alondra Blvd, Santa Fe Springs, CA 90670
Tel.: (562) 741-5475
Web Site: http://www.skytronicsinc.com
Emp.: 50
Mfr, Repair & Overhaul Services for Commercial & Military Aircraft Ball Screw Assemblies & Actuation Systems
N.A.I.C.S.: 336413
Earlvin Cruz *(Controller)*
Don Sliger *(Mgr-Quality Assurance)*
Jeff Vanosse *(Mgr-Ops)*
Sueli Kwak *(Mgr-Sls)*

PHILLIPS SERVICES, LLC
515 Lycaste St, Detroit, MI 48214
Tel.: (313) 824-5840
Web Site: http://www.pscnow.com
Sales Range: $75-99.9 Million
Emp.: 200
Recycling, Waste Materials
N.A.I.C.S.: 562920
Allen Jones *(Gen Mgr)*

PHILLIPS SUPPLY CO. INC.
1230 Findlay St, Cincinnati, OH 45214
Tel.: (513) 579-1762
Web Site: http://www.phillipssupply.com
Sales Range: $10-24.9 Million
Emp.: 80
Janitors' Supplies
N.A.I.C.S.: 423850
Pamela Rossmann *(Pres)*
Steve Garvey *(Branch Mgr-Sls)*

PHILLIPS' FLOORS, INC.
2714 N Jefferson Way, Indianola, IA 50125-9448
Tel.: (515) 961-7300
Web Site: http://www.phillipsfloors.com
Sales Range: $10-24.9 Million
Emp.: 93
Floor Laying Services
N.A.I.C.S.: 238330
Tim Phillips *(Owner)*
Laura Phillips *(Sec)*

PHILWAY PRODUCTS, INC.
521 E 7th St, Ashland, OH 44805-2553
Tel.: (419) 281-7777   OH
Web Site: http://www.philway.com
Year Founded: 1950
Sales Range: $50-74.9 Million
Emp.: 70
Mfr of Printed Circuit Boards & Plated Circuitry
N.A.I.C.S.: 334412
Terri Danals *(Mgr-Quality)*

PHIPPS & BIRD, INC.
1519 Summit Ave, Richmond, VA 23230-4511
Tel.: (804) 254-2737   VA
Web Site: http://www.phippsbird.com
Year Founded: 1925
Sales Range: $1-9.9 Million
Emp.: 14
Laboratory Equipment, Medical Aspirators, Compressors, Educational Physiology Equipment & Water Treatment Apparatus Mfr
N.A.I.C.S.: 339113
Wes Skaperdas *(Pres & Gen Mgr)*
Pat Skaperdas *(Exec VP)*
George Catlin *(Mgr-Production)*

PHIPPS & BIRD, INC.

Phipps & Bird, Inc.—(Continued)

Subsidiaries:

Intelitool, Inc. (1)
1519 Summit Ave, Richmond, VA 23230 (100%)
Tel.: (804) 254-2737
Web Site: http://www.intelitool.com
Emp.: 12
Mfr of University-Level Physiology Experimentation Apparatus
N.A.I.C.S.: 334516
Wes Skaperdas (Pres)

PHIPPS HOUSES

902 Broadway 13th Fl, New York, NY 10010
Tel.: (212) 243-9090 NY
Web Site: http://www.phippsny.org
Year Founded: 1905
Emp.: 500
Low Income Housing Services
N.A.I.C.S.: 624229
Adam Weinstein (Pres & CEO)
Ronay Menschel (Chm)

PHIPPS VENTURES INC.

3110 Capital Cir NE, Tallahassee, FL 32308
Tel.: (850) 386-2332
Sales Range: $10-24.9 Million
Emp.: 4
Investment Holding Companies, Except Banks
N.A.I.C.S.: 551112
John E Phipps (Chm)
Dennis Boyle (Pres)

PHMC, INC.

106 E Lincolnway Blvd Ste 307, Cheyenne, WY 82001
Tel.: (408) 402-1573 WY
Year Founded: 2012
Holding Company; Artificial Intelligence-Driven Software Applications Developer & Marketer
N.A.I.C.S.: 551112
Stephen Kim (Pres, CEO, CFO, Treas & Sec)

Subsidiaries:

U-Mind Club, Inc. (1)
99 S Almaden Blvd Ste 600, San Jose, CA 95113
Tel.: (408) 402-1573
Web Site: http://www.u-mind.club
Online Artificial Intelligence-Driven Retail Marketing Platform Developer & Operator
N.A.I.C.S.: 518210
Sehee Lee (Chm)
Jae Yoon Chung (Pres, CEO & CFO)

PHOBIO, LLC

3100 Cumberland Blvd SE Ste 200, Atlanta, GA 30339
Web Site: http://www.phobio.com
Year Founded: 2010
Sales Range: $75-99.9 Million
Emp.: 59
Software Development Services
N.A.I.C.S.: 541511
Stephen Wakeling (Co-Founder & CEO)
Drew Yeaton (Co-Founder)
Denny Juge (Co-Founder & Officer-Solutions)
Korey Klugman (Chief Product Officer)
Mike Gergye (COO)

PHOENICIAN PROPERTIES REALTY

5111 N Scottsdale Rd Ste 155, Scottsdale, AZ 85250
Tel.: (480) 663-1400
Web Site:
http://www.phoenicianproperty.com
Year Founded: 2001

Sales Range: $1-9.9 Million
Emp.: 5
Residential & Commercial Properties
N.A.I.C.S.: 531210

PHOENIX AIR GROUP INC.

100 Phoenix Air Dr SW, Cartersville, GA 30120
Tel.: (770) 387-2000
Web Site: http://www.phoenixair.com
Sales Range: $10-24.9 Million
Emp.: 100
Air Transportation, Nonscheduled
N.A.I.C.S.: 481219
Mark H. Thompson (Pres)
Dent Thompson (VP)

Subsidiaries:

Phoenix Air Racing Inc (1)
100 Phoenix Air Dr SW, Cartersville, GA 30120
Tel.: (770) 387-2000
Web Site: http://www.phoenixair.com
Sales Range: Less than $1 Million
Stock Car Racing
N.A.I.C.S.: 711219
Mark Thompson (Pres & CEO)

PHOENIX AMERICAN INCORPORATED

2401 Kerner Blvd, San Rafael, CA 94901
Tel.: (415) 485-4500
Web Site: http://www.phxa.com
Year Founded: 1972
Sales Range: $25-49.9 Million
Emp.: 110
Computer Rental & Leasing
N.A.I.C.S.: 516210
Andrew N. Gregson (CFO & VP)
Joseph Horgan (Sr VP-Phoenix American Fin Svcs)

Subsidiaries:

Phoenix American Financial Services, Inc. (1)
2401 Kerner Blvd, San Rafael, CA 94901-5529
Tel.: (415) 485-4500
Web Site: http://www.pafsi.com
Sales Range: $10-24.9 Million
Emp.: 100
Outsourcing Services
N.A.I.C.S.: 561499
Gus Constantin (Founder, Chm, Pres & CEO)
Andrew N. Gregson (CFO & VP)
Jeff Iverson (Asst VP)
Tony Olivo (Dir-Bus Dev)
Zane Doyle (Chief Strategy Officer-Bus Dev & VP)
Michael Hawn (Sr Dir-Sls)
Justin Deitrick (Sr VP-Fund Acctg)
Samuel Petrecky (VP-Fund Acctg)
Andrew Constantin (Sr VP-Ops)
Robyn Holloway (VP-Strategic Sls)
John McInerney (Mng Dir-PAFS Ireland Limited)

Phoenix American SalesFocus Solutions, Inc. (1)
2401 Kerner Blvd, San Rafael, CA 94901-5529 (100%)
Tel.: (415) 485-4500
Web Site: http://www.sfsmars.com
Sales Range: $10-24.9 Million
Emp.: 25
Sales Force Automation, CRM Solutions & Computer Programming Related Services
N.A.I.C.S.: 541511
Tom Oprendek (COO)
Anil Peggerla (CTO & VP)

Phoenix Leasing Portfolio Services, Inc. (1)
2401 Kerner Blvd, San Rafael, CA 94901-5529
Tel.: (415) 485-4500
Web Site: http://www.phxa.com
Sales Range: $50-74.9 Million
Emp.: 100
Outsourcing Lease & Loan Portfolio Products

N.A.I.C.S.: 522310
Gus Constantin (Pres & CEO)
Andrew N. Gregson (CFO & VP)

Division (Domestic):

Phoenix Leasing Bank Services (2)
2401 Kerner Blvd, San Rafael, CA 94901-5529
Tel.: (415) 485-4500
Web Site: http://www.phxa.com
Sales Range: $75-99.9 Million
Emp.: 100
Leasing Solutions For Community Banks
N.A.I.C.S.: 522110
Andrew Gregson (CFO)

PHOENIX ASSET MANAGEMENT LLC

1205 Franklin Ave Ste 110, Garden City, NY 11530
Tel.: (516) 248-3094
Web Site: http://www.phx-am.com
Privater Equity Firm
N.A.I.C.S.: 523999
Christopher Wall (Partner)

PHOENIX ASSET MANAGEMENT, LLC

1999 Bdwy Ste 4350, Denver, CO 80202
Tel.: (303) 892-7070
Web Site:
http://www.phoenixtma.com
Asset Management & Disposition Services
N.A.I.C.S.: 523940
Jim Steffen (Pres)
David Francis (VP)

PHOENIX ASSOCIATES OF SOUTH FLORIDA, INC.

13180 Livingston Rd Ste 204, Naples, FL 34109
Tel.: (239) 596-9111 FL
Web Site: http://www.phoenix-associates.com
Year Founded: 1992
Sales Range: $1-9.9 Million
Emp.: 28
Nonresidential Construction & Single-Family House Construction
N.A.I.C.S.: 236220
Brian Howell (VP)

PHOENIX BEVERAGES, INC.

2 Atlantic Ave, Brooklyn, NY 11201
Tel.: (718) 609-7221 NY
Web Site:
http://www.phoenixbeverages.com
Year Founded: 1983
Sales Range: $25-49.9 Million
Emp.: 300
Beer & Ale
N.A.I.C.S.: 424810
Dominick Valenza (Mgr-Sls)

Subsidiaries:

Demon Trucking Inc. (1)
3788 Review Ave, Long Island City, NY 11101-2018
Tel.: (718) 472-2550
Sales Range: $10-24.9 Million
Emp.: 90
Local Trucking without Storage
N.A.I.C.S.: 484110

PHOENIX CHILDREN'S FOUNDATION

2929 E Camelback Rd Ste 122, Phoenix, AZ 85016
Tel.: (602) 933-4483
Web Site:
https://www.phoenixchildrensfoundation.org
Year Founded: 1986
Health Care Srvices
N.A.I.C.S.: 621610

U.S. PRIVATE

PHOENIX COAL COMPANY, INC.

551 S Wilson St, Vinita, OK 74301
Tel.: (918) 256-7873 OK
Web Site:
http://www.phoenixcoal.com
Year Founded: 1991
Sales Range: $10-24.9 Million
Emp.: 5
Coal & Mineral & Ore Whslr
N.A.I.C.S.: 423520
Robert I. Hartley (Pres)

PHOENIX CREATIVE CO.

611 N 10th St Ste 700, Saint Louis, MO 63101
Tel.: (314) 421-5646
Web Site:
http://www.phoenixcreative.com
Year Founded: 1989
Sales Range: $1-9.9 Million
Emp.: 30
Advetising Agency
N.A.I.C.S.: 541810
Deborah Finkelstein (Dir-Creative)
Matt O'Neill (Partner)
David Dolak (Chief Creative Officer & Partner)
Keith Schwahn (Partner & Dir-Production Svcs)

PHOENIX ENERGY TECHNOLOGIES

165 Technology Dr Ste 150, Irvine, CA 92618
Web Site: http://www.phoenixet.com
Year Founded: 2004
Sales Range: $1-9.9 Million
Emp.: 54
Energy Efficiency Software
N.A.I.C.S.: 513210
Lisa Varga (Founder & CEO)

PHOENIX FABRICATORS & ERECTORS INC.

182 S County Rd 900 E, Avon, IN 46123
Tel.: (317) 271-7002 IN
Web Site:
http://www.phoenixtank.com
Year Founded: 1986
Sales Range: $50-74.9 Million
Emp.: 200
Producer of Fabricated Plate Work
N.A.I.C.S.: 332420
Tim Yohler (Pres)

PHOENIX FINANCIAL SERVICES, LLC

PO Box 361450, Indianapolis, IN 46236
Tel.: (855) 342-6567
Web Site:
http://www.phoenixfinancial.com
Year Founded: 2014
Sales Range: $10-24.9 Million
Emp.: 105
Debt Collection Services
N.A.I.C.S.: 561440
David A. Hoeft (Founder & CEO)

PHOENIX FORGING COMPANY, INC.

800 Front St, Catasauqua, PA 18032
Tel.: (610) 264-2861
Web Site:
http://www.phoenixforge.com
Year Founded: 1985
Sales Range: $10-24.9 Million
Emp.: 75
Mfr of Iron & Steel Forgings
N.A.I.C.S.: 332111
Nick Thee (CEO)

COMPANIES

Subsidiaries:

Capitol Manufacturing Co. (1)
1125 Capitol Rd, Crowley, LA 70526
Tel.: (337) 783-8626
Web Site: http://www.capitolcamco.com
Industrial Pipe Fittings
N.A.I.C.S.: 332996

PHOENIX GROUP HOLDINGS LLC
121 Chanlon Rd 3rd Fl, New Providence, NJ 07974
Tel.: (908) 222-4800 NJ
Web Site: http://www.phoenixgrp.net
Year Founded: 2004
Sales Range: $10-24.9 Million
Emp.: 60
Holding Company; Medical Communications & Integration Marketing Products & Services
N.A.I.C.S.: 551112
Tracy Doyle *(Pres & CEO)*

Subsidiaries:

Phoenix Marketing Solutions LLC (1)
121 Chanlon Rd 3rd Fl, New Providence, NJ 07974
Tel.: (908) 222-4800
Web Site: http://www.phoenixgrp.net
Sales Range: $10-24.9 Million
Medical Communications & Integration Marketing Products & Services
N.A.I.C.S.: 561499
Tracy Doyle *(Pres & CEO)*
Angela Fiordilino *(COO & Exec VP)*
Spiro Yulis *(Sr VP-Acct Svcs)*

PHOENIX HOUSE FOUNDATION, INC.
164 W 74th St, New York, NY 10023
Tel.: (646) 505-2021 NY
Web Site: http://www.phoenixhouse.org
Year Founded: 1968
Sales Range: $10-24.9 Million
Emp.: 181
Behavioral Healthcare Services
N.A.I.C.S.: 623220
Michael D. Berkowitz *(Sr VP & Dir-HR & Workforce Dev)*
Ann Bray *(Pres & CEO)*
Maria Alvarez *(VP-Florida)*
Mitch Rosenthal *(Founder)*

PHOENIX HOUSES OF LOS ANGELES, INC.
11600 Eldridge Ave, Lake View Terrace, CA 91342
Tel.: (877) 769-9698 CA
Web Site: http://www.phoenixhouse.org
Year Founded: 1970
Sales Range: $10-24.9 Million
Emp.: 262
Assisted Living Services
N.A.I.C.S.: 623312
Shawn R. Morris *(Sr VP)*
Timothy Noonan *(Chm)*

PHOENIX INDUSTRIES, LLC
621 Snively Ave, Winter Haven, FL 33880
Tel.: (863) 293-1151
Web Site: http://www.phoenixfl.com
Year Founded: 1978
Freight Transportation & Storage Services
N.A.I.C.S.: 488510
John Fleming *(Pres)*
Mike Porter *(Mgr-Ops)*
Erica Simpkins *(Controller)*
Jeremy Perez *(Mgr-Warehouse Transportation)*

PHOENIX LOGISTICS, INC.
1840 W 1st Ave, Mesa, AZ 85202

Tel.: (602) 231-8616 AZ
Web Site: http://www.phxlogistics.com
Year Founded: 1991
Sales Range: $1-9.9 Million
Emp.: 150
Electronic Components Mfr
N.A.I.C.S.: 334419
Al Funderburk *(Pres & CEO)*
Greg William *(Sr VP-Program Dev-Orlando & Florida)*
Reed Dent *(CFO)*

Subsidiaries:

Silverado Cable Company (1)
1840 W 1st Ave, Mesa, AZ 85202-1144 (100%)
Tel.: (480) 655-8751
Web Site: http://www.silveradocable.com
Rev.: $6,000,000
Emp.: 65
Custom Wire Harnesses & Cable Assemblies Mfr to Aviation & Aerospace Companies
N.A.I.C.S.: 332618
Robert Simpson *(Co-Owner)*
Mitch Simpson *(Co-Owner)*

PHOENIX MANAGEMENT INC.
10313 Lake Creek Pkwy, Austin, TX 78750
Tel.: (512) 335-5663
Web Site: http://www.pmiaus.com
Rev.: $18,042,995
Emp.: 400
Airports, Flying Fields & Services
N.A.I.C.S.: 488119
Marjorie Strickland *(Pres)*
Gary Giarratano *(VP-Mktg & Bus Dev)*
Susan Sutton *(Coord-Proposal)*

PHOENIX MARKETING GROUP, INC.
6750 Maple Terr, Milwaukee, WI 53213
Tel.: (414) 771-1044
Web Site: http://www.phoenixmgi.com
Year Founded: 1979
Sales Range: $1-9.9 Million
Emp.: 4
Advetising Agency
N.A.I.C.S.: 541810
Jean Radtke *(Pres & CEO)*
Charles J. Radtke *(Creative Dir & VP)*

PHOENIX MARKETING INTERNATIONAL, INC.
6423 Montgomery St Ste 12, Rhinebeck, NY 12572
Tel.: (845) 876-8228 FL
Web Site: http://www.phoenixmi.com
Year Founded: 1999
Emp.: 200
Advertising & Marketing Services
N.A.I.C.S.: 541810
Lane H. Mann *(Pres-Mobile)*
John Antonello *(Mng Dir-Travel & Leisure)*
Allen R. DeCotiis *(Chm & CEO)*
John Schiela *(Pres-Technology)*
Scott A. Spry *(COO)*
Edye Twer *(Pres-Media)*
David M. Thompson *(Mng Dir-Affluent & Wealth)*
Martha Rea *(Pres & Chief Res Officer)*
R. Neal Chambliss *(Pres-Fin Svcs, Innovation & Analytics)*
Andrew Scott *(Mng Dir-Healthcare Intl)*
Brian Maraone *(Pres-Automotive)*
Elizabeth L. Trachte *(Exec VP-Fin Ops)*

Heather Still *(Chief Privacy Officer & Exec VP-HR)*
Jaime Hodges *(Exec VP-Comm & Brand)*
Steve Wakefield *(Pres-Healthcare)*
Steve Wolf *(CMO & Chief Client Officer)*
Mark Willard *(Exec VP-Customer Experience)*
Richard Frazita *(Exec VP)*
Andrew Grant *(Head-Europe)*
Leslie Martin *(Mng Dir-Customer Experience)*
Anne-Marie Duffy *(Pres-Comm & Brand Analytics Practice)*
Pritica Hogg *(Reg Mng Dir-Asia Pacific)*
Bill McCracken *(Pres-Phoenix Synergistics)*
Genie Driskill *(Dir-Res)*
Tamilselvan Gurusamy *(CTO-Oldsmar)*
Caryn Brouwer *(Sr VP-Client Svcs)*
Monte Salsman *(Pres-Winsupply Acq Grp)*

Subsidiaries:

Phoenix Synergistics (1)
3091 Governors Lk Dr Ste 520, Norcross, GA 30071
Tel.: (800) 423-4229
Web Site: http://synergisticsresearch.com
Emp.: 50
Administrative Management & General Management Consulting Services
N.A.I.C.S.: 541611
William H. McCracken *(Pres & CEO)*
Genie M. Driskill *(COO & Sr VP-Res)*
Kenneth R. Owenby *(VP & Sr Dir-Res)*
Stacy W. Casebier *(VP, Editor & Dir-Res)*
Mark Sutin *(VP-Client Rels)*

PHOENIX MEDICAL SOFTWARE, INC.
604 Creekview, Ovilla, TX 75154 NV
Web Site: http://www.phoenixortho.net
Year Founded: 2006
Sales Range: Less than $1 Million
Emp.: 1
Healthcare Related Software
N.A.I.C.S.: 513210
Paul Morgan McCune *(Pres, CEO, CFO, Chief Acctg Officer, Treas & Sec)*

PHOENIX ONE SALES, MARKETING, MANAGEMENT + COMMUNICATIONS LLC
115 Franklin Turnpike Ste # 361, Mahwah, NJ 07430
Tel.: (201) 934-5600
Web Site: http://www.phoenixonesales.com
Sales Range: $1-9.9 Million
Internet Marketing Consulting
N.A.I.C.S.: 541613
Bill Simmel *(CEO)*

PHOENIX PACKAGING INC.
1160 E Main St, Mount Joy, PA 17552
Tel.: (717) 653-2345
Web Site: http://www.phoenixpackaging.com
Year Founded: 1983
Sales Range: $1-9.9 Million
Emp.: 40
Corrugated Cartons & Custom Packaging Products
N.A.I.C.S.: 322211
William Davidson *(Pres)*

PHOENIX PARTNERS INC.
12400 Coit Rd, Dallas, TX 75251-4227
Tel.: (214) 630-6655 TX

Investment Company
N.A.I.C.S.: 541611
Brooks Reed *(Mng Partner)*
Richard C. Waghorne *(Mng Partner)*
Beth Durett *(Controller)*

PHOENIX PERSONNEL
1350 Scribner Ave NW, Grand Rapids, MI 49504
Tel.: (616) 249-0044
Web Site: http://www.phoenixpersonnel.net
Sales Range: $10-24.9 Million
Emp.: 26
Temporary Industrial Staffing Services
N.A.I.C.S.: 561320
Brian Paavola *(CEO)*

PHOENIX PICTURES INC.
Santa Monica Blvd Ste 400, Los Angeles, CA 90067
Tel.: (424) 298-2788
Web Site: http://www.phoenixpictures.com
Sales Range: $50-74.9 Million
Emp.: 8
Motion Picture & Video Production
N.A.I.C.S.: 512110
Arnold W. Messer *(Pres & COO)*
Christopher Trunkey *(CFO & Exec VP)*
David Thwaites *(Co-Pres-Production)*

PHOENIX PROCESS EQUIPMENT
2402 Watterson Trl, Louisville, KY 40299
Tel.: (502) 333-9623
Web Site: http://www.dewater.com
Year Founded: 1984
Sales Range: $25-49.9 Million
Emp.: 47
Dewatering Systems
N.A.I.C.S.: 221310
Michael Fetter *(VP-Mktg)*

PHOENIX RETAIL GROUP
38 Southern Ct, Hiram, GA 30141
Tel.: (678) 567-0775
Web Site: http://www.phxfixinc.com
Rev.: $10,443,205
Emp.: 5
Store & Office Display Cases & Fixtures
N.A.I.C.S.: 337212
Michael Snipes *(Pres)*

PHOENIX ROOFING, INC.
230 Coraopolis Rd, Coraopolis, PA 15108
Tel.: (412) 778-8845
Web Site: http://www.phoenixrfg.com
Year Founded: 1992
Sales Range: $10-24.9 Million
Emp.: 20
Roofing Services
N.A.I.C.S.: 238160
Nancy Bartholomew *(Pres)*
W. Bruce Bartholomew *(VP)*

PHOENIX SOLUTIONS CO.
5480 Nathan Ln N Ste 110, Plymouth, MN 55442
Tel.: (763) 544-2721
Web Site: http://www.phoenixsolutionsco.com
Sales Range: $10-24.9 Million
Emp.: 35
Developer of High Intensity Heaters
N.A.I.C.S.: 335999
J. Leonard Frame *(CFO)*
Gary J. Hanus *(CTO & Sr VP)*
Douglas Frame *(Pres & CEO)*

PHOENIX TECHNOLOGY LTD
2 Progress Dr, Burgaw, NC 28425

PHOENIX TECHNOLOGY LTD — (Continued)
Tel.: (910) 259-6804
Web Site: http://www.kicklitestocks.com
Rev.: $5,000,000
Emp.: 10
All Other Plastics Product Mfr
N.A.I.C.S.: 326199
Zeljko Vesligaj (Pres)

PHOENIX TELECOM SOLUTIONS, INC.
3200 El Camino Real Ste 200, Irvine, CA 92602
Tel.: (714) 564-9044
Web Site: http://www.phoenix-ts.com
Year Founded: 2007
Sales Range: $10-24.9 Million
Emp.: 50
Telecommunication Equipment Sales & Maintenance Services
N.A.I.C.S.: 423690
Douglas Geier (VP-Professional Svcs)
Doug Theobald (CEO)
Kelly Styskal (CFO)
Michael Johnson (COO)

PHOENIX TEXTILE CORPORATION
21 Commerce Dr, O'Fallon, MO 63366
Tel.: (314) 291-2151
Web Site: http://www.phoenixtextile.com
Year Founded: 1983
Sales Range: $10-24.9 Million
Emp.: 130
Homefurnishings
N.A.I.C.S.: 423220
Palmer A. Reynolds (CEO)
Gene Rogers (VP-Ops)
Lisa Meyers (CFO)

PHOENIX TRADING INC.
640 Lofstrand Ln, Rockville, MD 20850
Tel.: (240) 396-1988
Web Site: http://www.ptimd.com
Year Founded: 2006
Sales Range: $10-24.9 Million
Emp.: 18
Replacement Parts & Equipment for the Military & Government Agencies
N.A.I.C.S.: 423490
Mukesh Sethi (Pres)

PHOENIX TRANSPORTATION SERVICES LLC
335 E Yusen Dr, Georgetown, KY 40324
Tel.: (502) 863-0108
Web Site: http://www.phoenix-transportation.net
Rev.: $13,674,192
Emp.: 250
Trucking Service
N.A.I.C.S.: 484121
Kevin Warren (Pres & CEO)
Thomas Brieske (VP-Sls & Mktg)

PHOENIX VINTNERS, LLC
4 S Main St Ste 2, Ipswich, MA 01938
Tel.: (707) 234-4747
Web Site: http://www.travelingvineyard.com
Year Founded: 2001
Wines & Wine-Related Merchandise Direct Marketer & Retailer
N.A.I.C.S.: 445320
Rick Libby (Pres & Founder)
Tim Wrightington (Dir-Ops)

Katie Gentile (Compliance Mgr)
Sheryl Kenney (Fulfillment Mgr)
Christine Bondola (Mgr-Comm & Mktg)

PHOENIX WELDING SUPPLY, CO.
701 S 7th St, Phoenix, AZ 85034-3216
Tel.: (602) 253-1108
Web Site: http://www.phxwelding.com
Sales Range: $10-24.9 Million
Emp.: 60
Welding Equipment & Supply Distr
N.A.I.C.S.: 423830
Douglas L. Seaman (Gen Mgr)
Scott G. Cogswell (Mgr-Pur)
Michael L. Dye (Pres)
Rick Hackerott (Dir-Fin)

PHOENIX ZOO
455 N Galvin Pkwy, Phoenix, AZ 85008
Tel.: (602) 286-3800
Web Site: https://www.phoenixzoo.org
Year Founded: 1961
Animal Zoos Operator
N.A.I.C.S.: 712130

PHOENIXVILLE FEDERAL BANK & TRUST
564 Nutt Rd, Phoenixville, PA 19460
Tel.: (610) 933-1171
Web Site: http://www.phoenixfed.com
Rev.: $12,365,000
Emp.: 60
Federal Savings & Loan Associations
N.A.I.C.S.: 522180
Carol Buckwalter (VP-Customer Rels)
Cathleen Kabacki (Head-Teller)
Richard A. Kunsch Sr. (Pres & CEO)

PHONE POWER, LLC
20847 Sherman Way, Winnetka, CA 91306
Web Site: http://www.phonepower.com
Year Founded: 2005
Sales Range: $1-9.9 Million
Emp.: 55
Telecommuication & Internet Service Providers
N.A.I.C.S.:
Jim Murphy (Pres)

PHONE.COM INC.
184 S Livingston Ave Ste 9 222, Livingston, NJ 07039
Tel.: (973) 577-6380
Web Site: http://www.phone.com
Year Founded: 2007
Sales Range: $1-9.9 Million
Emp.: 25
VoIP, Cloud & API Based Phone Service
N.A.I.C.S.: 517112
Ari Rabban (Co-Founder & CEO)
Alon Cohen (CTO & Exec VP)
Richard Hardman (Sr Dir-Digital Mktg)

PHONETEC LP
3300 N A St Bldg 1 Ste 108, Midland, TX 79705
Tel.: (432) 684-1140
Web Site: http://www.phonetec.com
Rev.: $24,000,000
Emp.: 13
Prepaid Phone Card & Prepaid Digital Cell Phone Services
N.A.I.C.S.: 423690

PHONETICS, INC.
901 Tryens Rd, Aston, PA 19014-1522

Tel.: (610) 558-2700
Web Site: http://www.sensaphone.com
Year Founded: 1985
Sales Range: $25-49.9 Million
Emp.: 43
Mfr of Environmental Monitors
N.A.I.C.S.: 334512
Robert J. Douglass (VP-Sls & Mktg)
Laura Drout (Treas & Sec)

PHOTIZO GROUP
107 West Main St, Midway, KY 40347
Tel.: (859) 846-9830
Web Site: http://www.photizogroup.com
Year Founded: 2006
Sales Range: $1-9.9 Million
Emp.: 22
Research & Consulting for the Imaging Industry
N.A.I.C.S.: 541618
Edward Crowley (Founder, Pres & CEO)
J. Wash (Mgr-HR)
Mario Diaz (VP-Consulting)

PHOTO SYSTEMS INC.
7200 Huron River Dr, Dexter, MI 48130
Tel.: (734) 424-9625
Sales Range: $10-24.9 Million
Emp.: 15
Photographic Equipment & Supplies Mfr & Distr
N.A.I.C.S.: 423410
Christa Fisher (Pres)

PHOTO-SONICS INC.
820 S Mariposa St, Burbank, CA 91506
Tel.: (818) 842-2141
Web Site: http://www.photosonics.com
Sales Range: $10-24.9 Million
Emp.: 60
Photographic Equipment & Supplies
N.A.I.C.S.: 333310
John Kiel (Pres)
Kate Treesuwan (CFO)
Conrad Kiel (VP-Ops)
Graham Jones (Mgr-IMC Sls)
Ken Rhodes (Mgr-Engrg)
Greg Holder (Mgr-Quality Control)
Russ Bunting (Mgr-Sls)

PHOTOBUCKET CORPORATION
2399 Blake St Ste 160, Denver, CO 80205
Tel.: (303) 226-6800
Web Site: http://www.photobucket.com
Year Founded: 2003
Sales Range: $100-124.9 Million
Online Photo & Video Sharing Services
N.A.I.C.S.: 516210
Michael Clark (CTO)
John Corpus (CEO)
Kate Hare (CMO & Chief Product Officer)

Subsidiaries:
Milyoni, Inc. (1)
7901 Stoneridge Dr Ste 210, Pleasanton, CA 94588
Tel.: (925) 251-1701
Web Site: http://www.milyoni.com
Emp.: 11
Online Video Publishing Services
N.A.I.C.S.: 516210
John Corpus (Co-Founder & CEO)
David Raycroft (VP-Performance)
Dean Alms (VP-Experience)

PHOTON MACHINES INC
15030 NE 95th St, Redmond, WA 98052
Tel.: (440) 296-6400
Web Site: http://www.photon-machines.com
Year Founded: 2006
Sales Range: $1-9.9 Million
Emp.: 15
Laboratory Instrument Mfr
N.A.I.C.S.: 334516

PHOTOREFLECT, LLC
303 Camp Craft Rd Ste 360, Austin, TX 78746
Tel.: (512) 891-9322
Web Site: http://www.photoreflect.com
Photography Software Solutions
N.A.I.C.S.: 513210
Brian Woodchek (CEO)
Charlie Meyer (VP-Sls & Mktg)
Alicia Otto (Mgr-Ops)
Kevin McFarland (Gen Mgr)

Subsidiaries:
Express Digital Graphics, Inc. (1)
9200 E Panorama Cir # 150, Englewood, CO 80112
Tel.: (303) 681-5909
Sales Range: $1-9.9 Million
Emp.: 33
Prepackaged Software
N.A.I.C.S.: 513210

Imaging Spectrum Inc. (1)
1101 Summit Ave, Plano, TX 75074
Tel.: (214) 342-9290
Web Site: http://www.imagingspectrum.com
Sales Range: $10-24.9 Million
Emp.: 20
Photographic Equipment & Supplies
N.A.I.C.S.: 423410
Eric Woodchek (Controller)
Steve Behen (Mgr-Sls)

PHX AP ACQUISITIONS LLC
13970 SW 72nd Ave, Portland, OR 97223-8036
Tel.: (503) 286-9300
Web Site: http://www.phoenixgold.com
Year Founded: 2006
Rev.: $20,000,000
Emp.: 50
Holding Company
N.A.I.C.S.: 523999
Jonathan Cooley (Founder)

Subsidiaries:
Phoenix Gold (1)
13190 56th Ct Ste 401, Clearwater, FL 33760
Tel.: (727) 803-0297
Web Site: http://www.phoenixgold.com
Earnings: ($3,000,000)
Emp.: 20
Designer, Marketer & Distr of Mobile & Home Audio Speakers, Amplifiers, Subwoofers & Cables
N.A.I.C.S.: 334310

PHYSICAL DISTRIBUTION SERVICES
55 W 78th St, Bloomington, MN 55420
Tel.: (952) 884-0765
Web Site: http://www.physicaldistributionservices.com
Rev.: $23,000,000
Emp.: 300
Truck Driver Supply Services
N.A.I.C.S.: 561320
Randy Kos (Controller)
Dale B. Robinson (Pres)

PHYSICAL SCIENCES INC.
20 New England Business Ctr, Andover, MA 01810-1077

Tel.: (978) 689-0003
Web Site: http://www.psicorp.com
Year Founded: 1973
Sales Range: $1-9.9 Million
Emp.: 100
Commercial Physical Research
N.A.I.C.S.: 541715
Steven Genestreti (CFO)
B. David Green (Pres & CEO)
Mark Allen (Exec VP-Applied Science)

Subsidiaries:

Faraday Technology, Inc. (1)
315 Huls Dr, Englewood, OH 45315
Tel.: (937) 836-7749
Web Site:
http://www.faradaytechnology.com
Emp.: 200
Electrochemical Engineering Services
N.A.I.C.S.: 541330
Maria Inman (Dir-Res)

NightSea LLC (1)
34 Dunelm Rd, Bedford, MA 01730
Tel.: (781) 791-9508
Web Site: http://www.nightsea.com
Emp.: 3
Development of Undersea Fluorescence Photography Equipment
N.A.I.C.S.: 541715
Charles Mazel (Founder)

Q-Peak (1)
135 South Rd, Bedford, MA 01730 (100%)
Tel.: (781) 275-9535
Web Site: http://www.qpeak.com
Emp.: 14
Development of Solid State Laser Systems
N.A.I.C.S.: 541715
Eric Park (VP)

Research Support Instruments, Lanham Operations (1)
4325 B Forbes Blvd, Lanham, MD 20706
Tel.: (301) 306-0010
Web Site: http://www.researchsupport.com
Developer of Space Instrumentation & Researcher In Space Sciences, Theoretical & Experimental Plasma Physics, Optics & Radiometry
N.A.I.C.S.: 541715
Chris Rollins (VP)

Research Support Instruments, Princeton Operations (1)
57 Hamilton Ave Ste 208, Hopewell, NJ 08525-1840
Tel.: (732) 329-3700
Research & Development Firm Specializing In Diagnostic Equipment & Materials Science, Plasma Physics & Electric Propulsion
N.A.I.C.S.: 541715

PHYSICIAN PARTNERS OF AMERICA, LLC
501 N Reo St, Tampa, FL 33609
Tel.: (813) 549-2134 DE
Web Site:
https://www.physicianpartners ofamerica.com
Year Founded: 2013
Healthcare Professional Organization
N.A.I.C.S.: 813920
Josh Helms (CEO)

PHYSICIAN'S PRACTICE ORGANIZATION INC.
2400 E 17th St, Columbus, IN 47201
Tel.: (812) 373-3060 IN
Year Founded: 1993
Sales Range: $25-49.9 Million
Emp.: 402
Health Care Srvices
N.A.I.C.S.: 621111
John Alessi (Pres)
Kurt G. Ellis (Sec)

PHYSICIANS DEVELOPMENT GROUP LLC
10300 W Maple St, Wichita, KS 67209
Tel.: (316) 448-0850
Web Site:
http://www.physdevgroup.com
Healthcare Services
N.A.I.C.S.: 621610
Greg Lakin (Co-Founder & Partner)
Frederick Hermes (Co-Founder & Partner)
Matthew Lillie (Co-Founder & Partner)
Stephanie Wiens (VP-IR)

PHYSICIANS GROUP MANAGEMENT, INC.
1050 Wall St W, Lyndhurst, NJ 07109
Tel.: (973) 751-7515 NJ
Web Site: http://www.pgmbilling.com
Year Founded: 1981
Sales Range: $1-9.9 Million
Emp.: 51
Accounting Services
N.A.I.C.S.: 541219
Albert Saviano (Chm, Pres, CEO & Controller)
Martha Culver (COO)
Roey Hine (Sr VP-Practice Mgmt)
Giulia Ennis (VP-Ops)
David Seebode (VP-IT)
Chris Saviano (VP-Bus Dev)
Carola Cornejo (Asst VP-Client Svcs & Ops)
Greg Perini (Dir-Sls)

PHYSICIANS INSURANCE, A MUTUAL COMPANY
1301 2nd Ave Ste 2700, Seattle, WA 98101
Tel.: (206) 343-7300
Web Site: http://www.phyins.com
Year Founded: 1982
Sales Range: $75-99.9 Million
Emp.: 100
Insurance Agents, Brokers & Services
N.A.I.C.S.: 524210
Kristin L. Kenny (Co-CFO, Co-Treas & Sr VP)
Mary-Lou Misrahy (Pres & CEO)
Alison Talbot (Sr VP-HR & Admin)
Rod Pierson (CFO, Treas & Sr VP)
Leslie Mallonee (CIO & Sr VP)
Josephine Young (Vice Chm)
Ralph A. Rossi (Chm)

PHYSICIANS MUTUAL INSURANCE CO.
2600 Dodge St, Omaha, NE 68131-2671
Tel.: (402) 633-1000 NE
Web Site:
http://www.physiciansmutual.com
Year Founded: 1902
Sales Range: $700-749.9 Million
Emp.: 1,300
Life, Accident & Health Insurance Services
N.A.I.C.S.: 525190
Robert Reed (Pres & CEO)

Subsidiaries:

Physicians Life Insurance Company (1)
2600 Dodge St, Omaha, NE
68131-2671 (100%)
Tel.: (402) 633-1000
Web Site: http://www.physiciansmutual.com
Sales Range: $250-299.9 Million
Life & Annuity Sales
N.A.I.C.S.: 524130

PHYSICIANS SURGERY CENTER, LLC
6355 Topanga Canyon Blvd Ste 430, Woodland Hills, CA 91367
Tel.: (818) 654-9301
Web Site: http://www.psc-asc.com
Emp.: 100
Surgical & Emergency Center Operator
N.A.I.C.S.: 621493
Glenn Cozen (Principal)
Bob Trevathan (Principal)
Tony Knapp (Principal)
Tim O'Brien (Principal)

PHYSICIANS' PHARMACEUTICAL CORPORATION
8930 Cross Park Dr Ste 3, Knoxville, TN 37923
Tel.: (865) 692-5066
Web Site: http://www.ppcdrx.com
Year Founded: 2005
Sales Range: $1-9.9 Million
Emp.: 10
Wholesale Distr of Pharmaceutical Medications to Physicians
N.A.I.C.S.: 325412
Jim Stiles (Treas)
Christopher Jaffurs (Co-Owner & VP-Bus Dev)

PHYSIQUE 57
24 W 57th St Ste 805, New York, NY 10019
Tel.: (212) 399-0570
Web Site:
http://www.physique57.com
Year Founded: 2005
Sales Range: $1-9.9 Million
Emp.: 58
Cardiovascular Workout Program & Facilities
N.A.I.C.S.: 713940
Jennifer Maanavi (Co-Founder)
Tanya Becker (Co-Founder)

PI COMPANY
1 Riverfront Pl Ste 700, North Little Rock, AR 72115
Tel.: (501) 374-0036
Web Site:
http://www.thepicompany.com
Year Founded: 2000
Sales Range: $1-9.9 Million
Emp.: 6
Tenant Screening, Credit Reports & Criminal Background Checks
N.A.I.C.S.: 541611
John Lindsey (Owner)

PI INC.
213 Dennis St, Athens, TN 37303
Tel.: (423) 745-6213
Web Site: http://www.pi-cm.com
Rev.: $37,395,045
Emp.: 250
Furniture Mfr
N.A.I.C.S.: 337126
Jeff Beene (Pres)
Roger Fairman (Plant Mgr & Mgr-Maintenance & Tooling)
Todd Harris (Mgr-Sls)

PI, INC.
704 Berkeley Av NW Ste A-1, Atlanta, GA 30318
Tel.: (404) 579-0800
Year Founded: 1967
Sales Range: $25-49.9 Million
Emp.: 6
Cable T.V., Co-op Advertising, Financial, Legal Services, Magazines, Newspaper, Newspapers & Magazines, Point of Sale, Real Estate, Seniors' Market, T.V., Yellow Pages Advertising
N.A.I.C.S.: 541810
Heather I. Stobi (Art Dir)

PIANTEDOSI BAKING CO. INC.
240 Commercial St, Malden, MA 02148
Tel.: (781) 321-3400 MA
Web Site: http://www.piantedosi.com
Year Founded: 1916
Sales Range: $10-24.9 Million
Emp.: 216
Bakery Products Mfr
N.A.I.C.S.: 311812
Thomas Piantedosi (Pres)
Nada Somasundram (Dir-Engrg)

PIASA MOTOR FUELS LLC
1 Piasa Ln, Hartford, IL 62048-1504
Tel.: (618) 254-7341 MO
Web Site:
http://www.piasamotorfuels.com
Year Founded: 1932
Sales Range: $75-99.9 Million
Emp.: 350
Petroleum Product Distr
N.A.I.C.S.: 424720
R. William Schrimpf (CEO)
Dave Fritz (Mgr-Fin)

Subsidiaries:

HWRT Oil Company, LLC. (1)
1 Piasa Ln, Hartford, IL 62048
Tel.: (618) 254-2855
Web Site: http://www.hwrtoil.com
Refined Petroleum Distr
N.A.I.C.S.: 424720
Bill Schrimpf (CEO)
Matt Schrimpf (Pres)
Bryan Hatfield (VP)
Dave Fritz (Office Mgr)
Jeff Donahue (Project Mgr & Mgr-Terminal)

Hartford-Wood River Terminal LLC (1)
1 Piasa Ln, Hartford, IL 62048-1504
Tel.: (618) 254-7341
Sales Range: $75-99.9 Million
Emp.: 10
Wholesale Bulk Petroleum Products
N.A.I.C.S.: 424720

Piasa Oil Transport LLC (1)
1 Piasa Ln, Hartford, IL 62048-1504
Tel.: (618) 254-7341
Sales Range: $10-24.9 Million
Emp.: 15
Wholesale & Retail Petroleum Products
N.A.I.C.S.: 488510
Bill Schrimpf (CEO)

Piasa Real Estate, Inc. (1)
1 Piasa Ln, Hartford, IL 62048-1504
Tel.: (618) 254-7341
Real Estate Manangement Services
N.A.I.C.S.: 531390

PIATT COUNTY SERVICE CO.
427 W Marion St, Monticello, IL 61856
Tel.: (217) 762-2133
Web Site: http://www.piattfs.com
Sales Range: $10-24.9 Million
Emp.: 30
Feed & Farm Supply
N.A.I.C.S.: 459999
John W. Hendrix (Pres)
Bill Olson (Treas)
Danny Carroll (Sec)

PIAZZA ACURA OF ARDMORE
150 W Lancaster Ave, Ardmore, PA 19003
Tel.: (610) 896-8600
Web Site:
http://www.piazzaacuraofard more.com
Year Founded: 1987
Sales Range: $10-24.9 Million
Emp.: 40
Car Dealer
N.A.I.C.S.: 441110
Randy Bridegam (Gen Mgr)
Michael Kain (Mgr-Pre Owned Car)
Pete Maxwell (Mgr-Sls)
Mike Spangler (Mgr-Svc)
Samantha Wilbert (Mgr-Internet Sls)

PIAZZA HONDA OF PHILADELPHIA

PIAZZA HONDA OF PHILADELPHIA

Piazza Honda of Philadelphia—(Continued)
6935 Essington Ave, Philadelphia, PA 19153
Tel.: (215) 492-1115
Web Site: http://www.piazzahondaphiladelphia.com
Sales Range: $10-24.9 Million
Emp.: 82
Car Whslr
N.A.I.C.S.: 441110
Ross Polinow (Gen Mgr)

PIC QUIK STORES INC.
2240 Missouri Ave Ste A, Las Cruces, NM 88001
Tel.: (575) 523-5611
Sales Range: $10-24.9 Million
Emp.: 100
Convenience Store
N.A.I.C.S.: 445131
Oscar Andrade (Pres)

PICERNE INVESTMENT CORPORATION
75 Lambert Lind Hwy, Warwick, RI 02886
Tel.: (401) 732-3700
Web Site: http://www.picerne.com
Year Founded: 1925
Sales Range: $25-49.9 Million
Land Subdividing Services
N.A.I.C.S.: 237210
Jason Cornicelli (Controller)

PICERNE REAL ESTATE GROUP
75 Lambert Lind Hwy, Warwick, RI 02886-1131
Tel.: (401) 732-3700
Web Site: http://www.picerne.com
Year Founded: 1929
Sales Range: $50-74.9 Million
Emp.: 800
Subdividers & Developers
N.A.I.C.S.: 237210
Ronald R. S. Picerne (Chm)

Subsidiaries:

Kelly & Picerne Inc. (1)
75 Lambert Lind Hwy, Warwick, RI 02886-1131 (100%)
Tel.: (401) 732-3700
Web Site: http://www.picernehomes.com
Sales Range: $10-24.9 Million
Emp.: 50
Real Estate Agents & Managers
N.A.I.C.S.: 531210

Picerne Construction Corp. (1)
1420 E Missouri Ave Ste 100, Phoenix, AZ 85014-2470
Tel.: (602) 279-8484
Web Site: http://www.picerne.com
Nonresidential Construction
N.A.I.C.S.: 236220
David R. Picerne (Pres & CEO)
Ernesto Alvarez (CFO)

Picerne Development Corp. (1)
1420 E Missouri Ave, Phoenix, AZ 85014-2470
Tel.: (602) 279-8484
Web Site: http://www.picerne.com
Sales Range: $10-24.9 Million
Emp.: 50
Subdividers & Developers
N.A.I.C.S.: 237210
David R. Picerne (Pres & CEO)
Ernesto Alvarez (Controller)

PICEU GROUP LIMITED, INC.
24671 Telegraph Rd, Southfield, MI 48034-3035
Tel.: (248) 353-3035
Year Founded: 1997
Rev.: $27,000,000
Emp.: 100

Mfr & Distributor of Paints & Allied Products
N.A.I.C.S.: 325510
Robert LaCasse (Pres)

Subsidiaries:

United Paint & Chemical Corporation (1)
24671 Telegraph Rd, Southfield, MI 48033-3035
Tel.: (248) 353-3035
Web Site: http://www.unitedpaint.com
Sales Range: $10-24.9 Million
Emp.: 60
Mft & Distributor of Paints & Allied Products
N.A.I.C.S.: 325510
Robert LaCasse (Pres)
Geoff Piceu (Pres)
Damien Smith (Mgr-Seating & Soft Trim Bus Dev)
Linda Keller (Mgr-HR)

PICK QUICK FOODS
445 Westbury Blvd, Hempstead, NY 11550
Tel.: (718) 296-9100
Year Founded: 1976
Sales Range: $125-149.9 Million
Emp.: 145
Owner & Operator of Supermarkets
N.A.I.C.S.: 445110
Howard Lipman (VP)
Jim McCullough (Mgr-Store)
Stuart Myers (Dir-Maintenance)
Katherine Rodriguez (Coord-Scanning)
Bejamin Levine (Pres)

PICKARD CHRYSLER DODGE JEEP
530 E Cumberland Gap Pkwy, Corbin, KY 40701
Tel.: (606) 528-6681
Web Site: http://www.pickardchryslerdodgejeep.com
Sales Range: $10-24.9 Million
Emp.: 35
Car Whslr
N.A.I.C.S.: 441110
Donald Ray Pickard (Pres)
June Pickard (Treas)
Charles Dion Pickard (VP)
Dowanna Pickard Ramsey (Sec)

PICKELNER FUEL CO. INC.
210 Locust St, Williamsport, PA 17701
Tel.: (570) 323-9488
Year Founded: 1932
Sales Range: $10-24.9 Million
Emp.: 26
Provider of Heating Services
N.A.I.C.S.: 457210
Eric Wertz (Mgr-HR)

PICKERING CREATIVE GROUP
8001 S 13th St, Lincoln, NE 68512
Tel.: (402) 423-5447
Web Site: http://www.pickeringcreative.com
Year Founded: 1979
Sales Range: $10-24.9 Million
Emp.: 20
Advertising Services
N.A.I.C.S.: 541810
Gary Pickering (Chm)
Trenton Wilcox (Pres)
Scott Claypool (Dir-Art)
Deb Pickering (Mgr-Admin Svcs)
Sam Tetherow (Dir-Web Tech)

PICKERSGILL RETIREMENT COMMUNITY
615 Chestnut Ave, Towson, MD 21204
Tel.: (410) 825-7423

Web Site: http://www.pickersgillretirement.org
Year Founded: 1802
Sales Range: $10-24.9 Million
Emp.: 168
Assisted Living Services
N.A.I.C.S.: 623312
Janice Harris (Dir-Admissions)
Jim Strom (Sr Dir-Dev & Mktg)
John Goodwin (Dir-Support Svcs)
Brian W. Brooke (Chm)
Barry Eisenberg (Exec Dir)
Ken Gerberg (Dir-Acctg Svcs)
Vici Heineman (Dir-Nursing)

PICKFORD REALTY INC.
12544 High Bluff Dr Ste 420, San Diego, CA 92130
Tel.: (858) 792-6085
Web Site: http://www.prudentialcal.com
Year Founded: 1985
Sales Range: $50-74.9 Million
Emp.: 200
Real Estate Agents & Managers
N.A.I.C.S.: 531210
David Cabot (CEO)

PICKWICK COMPANY INC.
4200 Thomas Dr SW, Cedar Rapids, IA 52404
Tel.: (319) 393-7443
Web Site: http://www.pickwick.com
Year Founded: 1939
Emp.: 150
Sheet Metal & Structural Contract Manufacturing Services
N.A.I.C.S.: 332322
Walter F. Corey (Pres)

PICKWICK ELECTRIC COOPERATIVE
530 Mulberry St, Selmer, TN 38375
Tel.: (731) 645-3411
Web Site: http://www.pickwick-electric.com
Year Founded: 1935
Sales Range: $25-49.9 Million
Emp.: 72
Electric Power Distr
N.A.I.C.S.: 221122
Harold Finley (Vice Chm)
Ray W. Allison (Treas)
Ronnie Fullwood (Chm)
Shawn Smith (Sec)

PICTOMETRY INTERNATIONAL CORP.
100 Town Centre Dr Ste A, Rochester, NY 14623
Tel.: (585) 486-0093
Web Site: http://www.pictometry.com
Year Founded: 2000
Sales Range: $25-49.9 Million
Emp.: 178
Aerial Photography Equipment Mfr
N.A.I.C.S.: 541370
Frank D. Giuffrida (Exec VP-Engrg)

PICTORIAL OFFSET CORPORATION
111 Amor Ave, Carlstadt, NJ 07072
Tel.: (201) 935-7100
Web Site: http://www.pictorialoffset.com
Rev.: $50,000,000
Emp.: 275
Commercial Printing, Lithographic
N.A.I.C.S.: 323111
Garry Venegas (Sr VP-Mfg & Prepress)
Arnie Savin (VP-Strategic Plng)
Bill Camarco (Mgr-Press Room)
Lisa Gerolimos (Mgr-Pur & Inventory)
Robert Lopez (VP-Sls)

Savonije Adrian (Coord-Logistics)
Stacy White (Coord-Production)
Wayne Angley (Coord-Production)

PICTURE MARKETING, INC.
1202 Grant Ave Ste D, Novato, CA 94945
Tel.: (949) 623-9889
Web Site: http://www.picturemarketing.com
Year Founded: 2002
Sales Range: $75-99.9 Million
Emp.: 30
Event & Promotional Marketing
N.A.I.C.S.: 541820

PICUT MANUFACTURING COMPANY
140 Mount Bethel Rd, Warren, NJ 07059
Tel.: (908) 754-1333
Web Site: http://www.picut.com
Year Founded: 1966
Rev.: $20,900,000
Emp.: 100
Industrial Valves
N.A.I.C.S.: 332911

Subsidiaries:

Picut Acquisition Corp (1)
610 Rahway Ave, Union, NJ 07083
Tel.: (908) 687-4100
Web Site: http://www.amerprod.com
Rev.: $10,500,000
Emp.: 180
Industrial Valves
N.A.I.C.S.: 332911

PIED PIPER PET & WILDLIFE, INC.
423 E Lake Dr, Austin, TX 79520
Tel.: (325) 576-2277
Year Founded: 1978
Sales Range: $10-24.9 Million
Emp.: 99
Dog & Cat Food Mfr
N.A.I.C.S.: 311111
Robert B. Moore (Principal)
Derek Moore (Owner)

PIEDMONT AIR CONDITIONING CO.
1031 Nowell Rd, Raleigh, NC 27607
Tel.: (919) 851-5800
Web Site: http://www.piedmontac.com
Year Founded: 1971
Sales Range: $10-24.9 Million
Emp.: 170
Warm Air Heating & Air Conditioning Contractor
N.A.I.C.S.: 238220
Marvin C. Perkins (Dir-Safety)
Leslie Horton (Mgr-HR)

PIEDMONT AUTOMOTIVE OF ANDERSON
4011 Clemson Blvd, Anderson, SC 29621
Tel.: (864) 224-6632
Web Site: http://www.piedmontcars.com
Sales Range: $50-74.9 Million
Emp.: 88
New & Used Car Dealers
N.A.I.C.S.: 441111
Greg Smith (Owner)

PIEDMONT BANCORP, INC.
5100 Peachtree Pkwy, Norcross, GA 30092
Tel.: (770) 246-0011
Web Site: http://www.piedmont.bank
Sales Range: $25-49.9 Million
Emp.: 114
Bank Holding Company
N.A.I.C.S.: 551111
Monty W. Watson (Chm, Pres & CEO)
Kelly J. Johnson (CFO & Sr VP)

COMPANIES

Subsidiaries:

The Piedmont Bank (1)
5100 Peachtree Pkwy, Norcross, GA 30092
Tel.: (770) 246-0011
Web Site: http://www.piedmont.bank
Sales Range: $10-24.9 Million
Commericial Banking
N.A.I.C.S.: 522110
Monty W. Watson (Chm, Pres & CEO)
Chris Elsevier (Sr VP & Sr Credit Officer)
Philip F. Resch (CFO)

Division (Domestic):

Mountain Valley Community
Bank (2)
136 N Main St, Cleveland, GA 30528
Tel.: (706) 348-6822
Web Site: http://www.mvcbank.com
Sales Range: $1-9.9 Million
Commericial Banking
N.A.I.C.S.: 522110
Donald E. Allison (Reg Pres-North Georgia)

Westside Bank (1)
56 Hiram Dr, Hiram, GA 30141-1834
Tel.: (404) 218-1665
Web Site: http://www.westsidebank.net
Commericial Banking
N.A.I.C.S.: 522110
Ford Thigpen (Pres)

PIEDMONT BOBCAT LLC
1015 NC Hwy 66 S, Kernersville, NC 27284
Tel.: (336) 993-5529
Web Site:
  http://www.piedmontbobcat.com
Sales Range: $10-24.9 Million
Emp.: 25
Stores & Yards Equipment Rental
N.A.I.C.S.: 532289
Luelle Crumpler (Controller)

PIEDMONT BOTTLING & VENDING, INC.
1826 Brian Dr NE, Conover, NC 28613
Tel.: (828) 322-8301
Web Site:
  http://www.piedmontvending.com
Year Founded: 1940
Sales Range: $10-24.9 Million
Emp.: 2
Vending Machine & Corporate Dining Services
N.A.I.C.S.: 445132
Aaron Speagle (Owner)

PIEDMONT CHEMICAL INDUSTRIES, INC.
331 Burton Ave, High Point, NC 27262-8071
Tel.: (336) 885-5131   NC
Web Site:
  http://www.piedmontchemical.com
Year Founded: 1938
Sales Range: $25-49.9 Million
Emp.: 200
Manufactures Soap & Other Detergents
N.A.I.C.S.: 325611
Fred E. Wilson Jr. (Chm & Pres)
Mike Chestnut (Dir-Compliance & Regulations)
Ray Soyars (CFO)

Subsidiaries:

Custom Synthesis, LLC (1)
1704 Denver Rd, Anderson, SC 29623-5254 (100%)
Tel.: (864) 261-3067
Web Site: http://www.altcorp.com
Sales Range: $10-24.9 Million
Emp.: 20
Mfr of Specialty Chemicals
N.A.I.C.S.: 325613
Chris Carnell (Mgr-Special Projects)

Dooley Chemicals LLC (1)
2400 E 24 St, Chattanooga, TN 37407-0951
Tel.: (423) 624-0086
Web Site: http://www.piedmontchemical.com
Sales Range: $10-24.9 Million
Emp.: 10
MfrOf Textile Specialty Chemicals
N.A.I.C.S.: 325613
Rick Jensen (VP)
Denise Theobalt (Office Mgr)
David Halstead (Dir-Tech Svc)

Ethox Chemicals LLC (1)
1801 Perimeter Rd, Greenville, SC 29605-5260
Tel.: (864) 277-1620
Web Site: http://www.ethox.com
Sales Range: $10-24.9 Million
Emp.: 125
Mfr Surface Active Agents
N.A.I.C.S.: 325613
Michael Fisher (Engr-Maintenance)

Piedmont Chemical Industries I, LLC (1)
331 Burton Ave, High Point, NC 27262
Tel.: (336) 885-5131
Emp.: 83
Chemical Products Mfr
N.A.I.C.S.: 325998
Mike Bralkowski (Acct Mgr-Sls)
Pam Bartlett (Coord-Regulations)

RWM Technologies LLC (1)
3801 N Hawthorne St, Chattanooga, TN 37406-1310
Tel.: (423) 648-4556
Chemical Product Whslr
N.A.I.C.S.: 424690
Tony Snider (Plant Mgr)

PIEDMONT CONSTRUCTION GROUP LLC
107 Gateway Dr Ste B, Macon, GA 31210
Tel.: (478) 405-8907
Web Site:
  http://www.piedmontconstructiongroup.com
Sales Range: $75-99.9 Million
Emp.: 100
General Contractors
N.A.I.C.S.: 236220
Scott Thompson (Co-Founder & CFO)
David G. Thompson (Co-Founder & CEO)
Erica Royals (Mgr-Contracts)

PIEDMONT ELECTRIC MEMBERSHIP CORP.
2500 NC 86 S, Hillsborough, NC 27278
Tel.: (919) 732-2123   NC
Web Site: http://www.pemc.org
Year Founded: 1938
Sales Range: $25-49.9 Million
Emp.: 115
Provider of Electric Services
N.A.I.C.S.: 221122
Larry Hopkins (VP-Engrg)
Bill Barber (Chm)
Paul Bailey (Vice Chm)
Richal Vanhook (Treas)
Sam Woods (Sec)
Lisa Kennedy (VP-Fin Svcs)
Robert Riley (VP-Ops)
Susan Cashion (Chief Compliance Officer, Chief Admin Officer & VP)

PIEDMONT FINANCIAL HOLDING COMPANY
201 S Stratford Rd, Winston Salem, NC 27103
Tel.: (336) 830-0065
Bank Holding Companies
N.A.I.C.S.: 551111

Subsidiaries:

Piedmont Federal Savings Bank (1)
16 W 3rd St, Winston Salem, NC 27101
Tel.: (336) 770-1000
Web Site: http://www.piedmontfederal.com
Sales Range: $25-49.9 Million
Emp.: 120
Federal Savings Bank
N.A.I.C.S.: 522180
Bruce B. Humphries (Chief Risk & Compliance Officer)
Michael L. Hauser (Pres)
David R. Smelcer (Chief Product Officer)
Richard F. Wagner Jr. (Pres & CEO)

PIEDMONT HEALTH, INC.
299 Lloyd St, Carrboro, NC 27510
Tel.: (919) 933-8494   NC
Web Site:
  http://www.piedmonthealth.org
Year Founded: 1970
Sales Range: $25-49.9 Million
Emp.: 401
Health Care Srvices
N.A.I.C.S.: 622110
Brian Toomey (CEO)
Katrina Mattison (Dir-Dental)
Abigail DeVries (Dir-Medical)
Carl D. Taylor (Dir-Pharmacy Svcs)
Ashley Brewer (Dir-Health Support Svcs)
Demond Thorne (Dir-Fin)
Emily Volk (Dir-Nursing)
Lydia Mason (CFO)
Marianne Ratcliffe (Sr Dir-Care)
Marni Holder (Dir-Program Dev)
Roz Freeman (Dir-HR)
Sudha Rathie (Dir-Lab Svcs)

PIEDMONT HEALTHCARE, INC.
2727 Paces Ferry Rd NW, Atlanta, GA 30309
Tel.: (404) 605-5000   GA
Web Site: http://www.piedmont.org
Year Founded: 1983
Sales Range: $50-74.9 Million
Emp.: 859
Health Care Srvices
N.A.I.C.S.: 622110
Sidney Kirschner (Chief Philanthropy Officer & Exec VP)
Ed Lovern (Chief Admin Officer & Exec VP)
Leigh Hamby (Chief Medical Officer)
Michael McAnder (CFO)
Kevin Brown (Pres & CEO)
Janine Brown (Chm)
Kelly Hulsey (Chief Nursing Officer)
Charles A. Peck (CEO-Athens Reg)
Deborah Armstrong (CEO-Piedmont Henry)
Denise Ray (CEO-Mountainside)
Geoff Brown (CIO)
Greg Hurst (COO)
Jim Weadick (CEO-Piedmont Newton)
Matt Gove (Chief Consumer Officer)
Michael J. Burnett (CEO-Piedmont Fayette)
Michelle Fisher (Chief Strategy & Performance Improvement Officer)
Mike Robertson (CEO-Piedmont Newnan)
Patrick Battey (CEO-Piedmont Atlanta)
Harry M. McFarling III (Vice Chm)

PIEDMONT INVESTMENT ADVISORS, LLC
2605 Meridian Pkwy Ste 105, Durham, NC 27713
Tel.: (919) 688-8600
Web Site:
  http://www.piedmontinvestment.com
Investment Advisory & Portfolio Management Services
N.A.I.C.S.: 523940
Sumali Sanyal (COO, Exec VP & Portfolio Mgr)
Isaac H. Green (Pres, CEO, Co-Chief Investment Officer & Portfolio Mgr)
Charles L. Curry (Co-Chief Investment Officer-Fixed Income, Exec VP & Portfolio Mgr)
Marion White (CFO, Chief Compliance Officer & Sr VP)
Lorenzo Newsome Jr. (Exec VP, Chief Investment Strategist & Portfolio Mgr)

PIEDMONT LIMOUSINE
2410 S Church St, Burlington, NC 27215
Tel.: (336) 228-0141
Year Founded: 1981
Sales Range: $10-24.9 Million
Emp.: 75
Car Whslr
N.A.I.C.S.: 441110
Robyn Grinstead (Office Mgr)
David W. (Pres)

PIEDMONT MECHANICAL, INC.
116 John Dodd Rd, Spartanburg, SC 29303-4642
Tel.: (864) 578-9114   SC
Web Site:
  http://www.piedmontmechanical.com
Year Founded: 1977
Sales Range: $10-24.9 Million
Emp.: 100
Mechanical Contractor; Machinery Installation & Fabrication; Process Piping, HVAC Fabrication & Installation
N.A.I.C.S.: 238220
Paul K. Norris (VP-Georgia Engrg)
Thomas Holt (Project Mgr)
Gene Smith (Pres)
Robert B. Dannelly Sr. (VP-Fin & Controller)

Subsidiaries:

Piedmont Mechanical, Inc. - Lagrange (1)
103 Cooley Industrial Dr, LaGrange, GA 30241-0006
Tel.: (706) 882-4277
Web Site:
  http://www.piedmontmechanical.com
Mechanical Contractor
N.A.I.C.S.: 238220

PIEDMONT NATIONAL CORPORATION
1561 Southland Cir, Atlanta, GA 30318
Tel.: (404) 351-6130   GA
Web Site: http://www.pncorp.com
Year Founded: 1950
Sales Range: $10-24.9 Million
Emp.: 120
Supplier of Nondurable Goods
N.A.I.C.S.: 424990
Albert Marx (Chm & CEO)
Jack DeLeon (VP-Pur)
Lin Carter (VP-Pkg)
Gary Marx (Pres & COO)
Philip Shaw (CFO)
Inge Robbins (Sec)
Brianna Hodges (Dir-Sls-Carolinas)

PIEDMONT NEWNAN HOSPITAL
745 Poplar Rd, Newnan, GA 30265
Tel.: (770) 253-1912   GA
Web Site:
  http://www.piedmontnewnan.org
Sales Range: $25-49.9 Million
Emp.: 1,000
General Medical & Surgical Hospital Services
N.A.I.C.S.: 622110

Piedmont Newnan Hospital—(Continued)
Kelly Loftin (Dir-Major Gifts)
John Miles (Co-CFO)
Michael Robertson (Chm & CEO)
Michael McAnder (Co-CFO)
Jeffrey Folk (Chief Medical Officer)
Jennifer Key (Chief Nursing Officer)

PIEDMONT PETROLEUM CORP.
5 Michael Dr, Greenville, SC 29611
Tel.: (864) 269-5956
Rev.: $18,600,000
Emp.: 100
Convenience Store
N.A.I.C.S.: 445131
Kenneth Cosgrove (Pres)
Sarilla Cosgrove (VP)

PIEDMONT PLASTICS, INC.
5010 W WT Harris Blvd, Charlotte, NC 28269-1861
Tel.: (704) 597-8200   NC
Web Site: http://www.piedmontplastics.com
Year Founded: 1968
Sales Range: $200-249.9 Million
Emp.: 200
Plastic Sheet, Rod Tube & Film Products Distr, Fabricator & Film Converter
N.A.I.C.S.: 424610
Craig Young (CFO)
Henry G. Booth Jr. (Co-Owner & Pres)
Owen H. Whitfield Jr. (Co-Owner & VP)

Subsidiaries:

Regal-Piedmont Plastics, LLC (1)
5261 S Rio Grande St, Littleton, CO 80120
Tel.: (303) 794-9823
Web Site:
   http://www.regalpiedmontplastics.com
Sales Range: $25-49.9 Million
Emp.: 30
Plastic Sheet, Rod Tube & Film Products Distr
N.A.I.C.S.: 424610

PIEDMONT REGIONAL HEALTH
1005 Boulder Dr, Gray, GA 31032
Tel.: (478) 621-2100   GA
Web Site: http://www.ethicahealth.org
Year Founded: 2003
Sales Range: $10-24.9 Million
Emp.: 478
Health Care Srvices
N.A.I.C.S.: 622110
Kay F. Gray (Co-Pres)
Lorraine T. Taylor (Sec & VP)
Lucy M. Rogers (Co-Pres)
Mark A. Waldrop (COO)
Teresa W. Moody (Sec)

PIEDMONT RURAL TELEPHONE COOPERATIVE INC.
201 Anderson Dr, Laurens, SC 29360
Tel.: (864) 682-3131
Web Site: http://www.prtcnet.com
Rev.: $11,691,766
Emp.: 55
Local Telephone Communications
N.A.I.C.S.: 517121
Sharon O' Bryant (Dir-PR & HR)

PIEGE CO, INC.
20120 Plummer St, Chatsworth, CA 91311-5448
Tel.: (818) 727-9100   CA
Web Site: http://www.felinausa.com
Year Founded: 1981
Sales Range: $10-24.9 Million
Emp.: 108
Supplier of Lingerie

N.A.I.C.S.: 315250
Robert K. Zarabi (Pres & CEO)

PIEHLER PONTIAC CORP.
755 Rdg Rd, Rochester, NY 14580
Tel.: (585) 458-4540
Web Site: http://www.piehler.com
Rev.: $37,100,000
Emp.: 85
Automobiles, New & Used
N.A.I.C.S.: 441110
Michael J. Piehler (Pres)
Kevin Leonard (VP)

PIELET BROS TRADING INC.
2720 S River Rd St 216, Des Plaines, IL 60018
Tel.: (847) 803-0460
Sales Range: $10-24.9 Million
Emp.: 10
Ferrous Metal Scrap & Waste
N.A.I.C.S.: 423930
Irving Pielet (Pres)

PIEPER ELECTRIC INC.
5477 S Westridge Drive Ct, New Berlin, WI 53151-5302
Tel.: (414) 462-7700   WI
Web Site:
   http://www.pieperpower.com
Year Founded: 1960
Sales Range: $50-74.9 Million
Emp.: 700
Electrical Contractor
N.A.I.C.S.: 238210
Al Czajka (Project Mgr)
Matthew Stefanski (Project Mgr)
Nathen Welch (Project Mgr)
Scott Riemer (Mgr-Estimating)
Christine Komp (Mgr-Ops)
Thomas Scherer (Project Mgr)
Mark Schroeder (Project Mgr)

PIER 39 L.P.
Beach St & The Embarcadero, San Francisco, CA 94133
Tel.: (415) 705-5500
Web Site: http://www.pier39.com
Year Founded: 1981
Sales Range: $100-124.9 Million
Emp.: 800
Nonresidential Building Operators; Specialty Shops, Restaurants, Attractions
N.A.I.C.S.: 531120
Jodi Cumming (Mgr-Sls)
Sina von Reitzenstein (VP-Leasing)
Elinor Heller (VP & Controller)
Sue Muzzin (Dir-PR & Adv)
Taylor Safford (Pres & CEO)

Subsidiaries:

Blue & Gold Fleet Inc. (1)
Pier 41 Marine Terminal, San Francisco, CA 94133
Tel.: (415) 705-8200
Web Site: http://www.blueandgoldfleet.com
Sales Range: $10-24.9 Million
Emp.: 70
Water Passenger Transportation
N.A.I.C.S.: 487210

Pier Restaurants L.P. (1)
Beach St The Embarcadero, San Francisco, CA 94133-1016
Tel.: (415) 434-2288
Web Site: http://www.pier39restaurants.com
Sales Range: $25-49.9 Million
Emp.: 150
Eating Place
N.A.I.C.S.: 493110

PIER PARK, LLC.
225 W Washington St, Indianapolis, IN 46204
Tel.: (317) 363-1600
Year Founded: 2011
Sales Range: $1-4.9 Billion
Real Estate Development Services

N.A.I.C.S.: 531190
Richard S. Sokolov (Exec Dir)

PIERATTS INC.
110 Mt Tabor Rd, Lexington, KY 40517
Tel.: (859) 268-6000
Web Site: http://www.pieratts.net
Sales Range: $10-24.9 Million
Emp.: 90
Electrical Household Appliance Repair & Sales
N.A.I.C.S.: 811412
Bruce Pieratt (Pres)
Kenny Mills (Mgr-Sls)

PIERCE ALUMINUM COMPANY INC.
34 Forge Pkwy, Franklin, MA 02038-0816
Tel.: (508) 541-7007   MA
Web Site:
   http://www.piercealuminum.com
Year Founded: 1967
Sales Range: $10-24.9 Million
Emp.: 100
Provider of Metal Products & Services
N.A.I.C.S.: 423510
Jim Pringle (VP)
Dave Devine (VP-Ops)
Robert W. Pierce Jr. (Owner, Chm & CEO)

PIERCE ASSOCIATES INC.
4216 Wheeler Ave, Alexandria, VA 22304-6413
Tel.: (703) 751-2400   VA
Web Site: http://www.pai.us
Year Founded: 1961
Sales Range: $25-49.9 Million
Emp.: 280
Provider of Plumbing, Heating & Air Conditioning Services
N.A.I.C.S.: 238220
Stephen C. Pierce (Pres)
John Dunleazy (VP)

PIERCE COMMUNICATIONS, INC.
208 E State St, Columbus, OH 43215-4311
Tel.: (614) 365-9494
Web Site:
   http://www.piercecomm.com
Year Founded: 1985
Sales Range: $1-9.9 Million
Emp.: 5
Advertising Agencies
N.A.I.C.S.: 541810
Gene H. Pierce (Pres)

PIERCE COUNTY PUBLIC TRANSPORTATION BENEFIT AREA CORPORATION
3701 96th St SW, Lakewood, WA 98499
Tel.: (253) 581-8080
Web Site: http://www.piercetransit.org
Year Founded: 1979
Sales Range: $10-24.9 Million
Emp.: 1,100
Provider of Bus Transportation
N.A.I.C.S.: 485113
Bill Spies (Dir-Maintenance)
Sue Dreie (CEO)

PIERCE ENTERPRISES INC.
Ste 105 6100 Seagull St NE, Albuquerque, NM 87109-2500
Tel.: (505) 344-1443
Rev.: $16,300,000
Emp.: 4
Air Passenger Carriers, Nonscheduled
N.A.I.C.S.: 481211

Subsidiaries:

Ross Aviation Inc (1)
Ste 105 6100 Seagull St NE, Albuquerque, NM 87109-2500
Tel.: (505) 344-1443
Aircraft Servicing & Repairing
N.A.I.C.S.: 488190
Tim Goulet (Gen Mgr-Thermal FBO)
Jeff Ross (CEO)

PIERCE FLOORING & DESIGN
2950 King Ave W, Billings, MT 59102
Tel.: (406) 652-4666
Web Site:
   http://www.pierceflooring.com
Sales Range: $25-49.9 Million
Emp.: 150
Floor Covering Stores
N.A.I.C.S.: 449121
G. Ron Pierce (Pres)
Meg Erlenbush (Controller)

PIERCE MANAGEMENT GROUP
8829 Goodwill Church Rd, Belews Creek, NC 27009
Tel.: (336) 595-1075
Rev.: $16,800,000
Emp.: 12
Investment Holding Companies, Except Banks
N.A.I.C.S.: 551112
Scott Pierce (Pres)
Larry Needham (Mgr-Fleet)

PIERCE MATTIE COMMUNICATIONS
62 W 45th St 3 Fl, New York, NY 10036
Tel.: (212) 243-1431
Web Site:
   http://www.piercemattie.com
Year Founded: 2001
Public Relations & Communications
N.A.I.C.S.: 541820
Joshua Blaylock (Dir-Bus Dev)

PIERCE MEMORIAL BAPTIST HOME, INC.
44 Canterbury Rd, Brooklyn, CT 06234
Tel.: (860) 774-9050   CT
Web Site: http://www.piercecare.org
Year Founded: 1951
Sales Range: $10-24.9 Million
Emp.: 253
Residential Care Services
N.A.I.C.S.: 623990
Patty Morse (Pres & CEO)
Linda Silvia (Exec Dir)
Trisha Hall (Dir-Nursing)
Dave Bamber (Dir-Mktg)
Carol Tucker (Dir-Admissions)

PIERCE PACKAGING CO.
2028 E Riverside Blvd, Loves Park, IL 61111
Tel.: (815) 636-5650
Web Site:
   http://www.piercedistribution.com
Sales Range: $10-24.9 Million
Emp.: 450
Packing Goods For Shipping
N.A.I.C.S.: 488991
Kevin Hogan (Pres & CEO)
Tony Chiobini (CFO)

PIERCE'S FLOORING
800 Dewey Blvd, Butte, MT 59701
Tel.: (406) 494-3313
Sales Range: $25-49.9 Million
Emp.: 50
Curtain Whslr
N.A.I.C.S.: 449122
Jon Pierce (Gen Mgr)

PIERCE-PACIFIC MANUFACTURING INC.
4424 NE 158th St, Portland, OR 97230
Tel.: (503) 808-9110
Web Site: http://www.piercepacific.com
Year Founded: 1931
Sales Range: $10-24.9 Million
Emp.: 125
Mfr of Logging Equipment
N.A.I.C.S.: 333120
Michael Hildebrandt *(Pres)*
Shari Schneider *(Treas, Sec & Controller)*

PIERIANDX, INC.
77 Maryland Plz, Saint Louis, MO 63108
Tel.: (314) 812-8003
Web Site: http://www.pieriandx.com
Year Founded: 2011
Emp.: 60
N.A.I.C.S.:
Rakesh Nagarajan *(Chief Biomedical Informatics Officer)*
Jim Howard *(Sr VP-Sls)*
Brad Herrick *(CMO)*
Andy Bredemeyer *(Dir-Customer Ops)*
Joshua Phillips *(VP-Product Dev & Ops)*
Mayuresh Phadke *(Dir-Engrg & Ops)*
Andy Olson *(Sr VP)*
Josh Forsythe *(VP-Sls)*
Bryce Daines *(VP-Product Dev)*
Lisa Weingartner *(VP-Sls)*
Joe Boorady *(Chm)*
Mark McDonough *(CEO)*

PIERPOINT CAPITAL LLC
477 Madison Ave Ste 730, New York, NY 10022
Tel.: (212) 895-8029
Web Site: http://pierpointcap.com
Year Founded: 2014
Private Investment Firm
N.A.I.C.S.: 551112
Jarret Fass *(Mng Partner)*

PIERPONT COMMUNICATIONS, INC.
1233 W Loop S Ste 1300, Houston, TX 77027-3210
Tel.: (713) 627-2223
Web Site: http://www.piercom.com
Year Founded: 1987
Sales Range: $1-9.9 Million
Emp.: 20
Public Relations Agency
N.A.I.C.S.: 541820
Philip A. Morabito *(CEO)*
Clint Woods *(COO)*
Chris Wailes *(VP-Media Rels-Natl)*
Sally Ramsay *(Sr VP)*
Stacy Armijo *(Exec VP)*
Dave Stump *(VP-Bus Dev)*
James Savage *(Sr VP & Gen Mgr-Dallas)*
Tyler Sumrall *(Asst Acct Exec)*
Brian Banks *(CFO)*
Chris Jones *(Sr VP)*
Kenneth Kracmer *(VP-Client Dev)*

Subsidiaries:

Pierpont Communications, Inc. (1)
10900-B Stone Lke Blvd Ste 110, Austin, TX 78759
Tel.: (512) 448-4950
Web Site: http://www.piercom.com
Sales Range: Less than $1 Million
Emp.: 10
Public Relations Agency
N.A.I.C.S.: 541820
Stacy Armijo *(VP)*
Phil Morabito *(CEO)*
Lara Zuehlke *(Dir-Content)*

Danielle Urban *(Sr Acct Exec)*
Hunter Dodson *(Acct Exec)*
Mike Gehrig *(Gen Mgr)*
Dori Ludwig *(Dir-Mktg)*
Linda Madden *(Asst Acct Exec)*

PIERRE DEUX FRENCH COUNTRY
625 Madison Ave, New York, NY 10022
Tel.: (212) 521-8012
Web Site: http://www.pierredeux.com
Rev.: $17,000,000
Emp.: 22
Piece Goods & Notions
N.A.I.C.S.: 449110
Andre J. Cointreau *(Pres & CEO)*

PIERRE'S FRENCH ICE CREAM COMPANY
6200 Euclid Ave, Cleveland, OH 44103
Tel.: (216) 432-1144
Web Site: http://www.pierres.com
Year Founded: 1932
Sales Range: $25-49.9 Million
Emp.: 150
Ice Cream Mfr & Sales
N.A.I.C.S.: 311520

PIERSON AUTOMOTIVE INC.
3456 S Dixie Hwy, Franklin, OH 45005
Tel.: (513) 437-0241
Web Site: http://www.piersonautomotive.com
Sales Range: $10-24.9 Million
Emp.: 20
Automobile Sales & Service
N.A.I.C.S.: 441110
Brenda Pierson *(Owner & Gen Mgr)*

PIERSON FORD LINCOLN MERCURY INC.
701 Auto Plz Dr, Aberdeen, SD 57401
Tel.: (605) 225-3720
Web Site: http://www.piersonford.com
Sales Range: $10-24.9 Million
Emp.: 42
Car Whslr
N.A.I.C.S.: 441110
Barbara Pierson *(VP)*

PIERSON INDUSTRIES INC.
7 Astro Pl, Rockaway, NJ 07866
Tel.: (973) 627-7945
Web Site: http://www.piersonindustriesinc.com
Rev.: $10,400,000
Emp.: 70
Injection Molds & Plastic Products Mfr
N.A.I.C.S.: 333511
Richard Carle *(Plant Mgr)*
Maria Pierson *(VP)*
Ted Pierson *(Pres)*

PIERSON-GIBBS HOMES INC.
706 Gratiot Ave, Columbus, MI 48063
Tel.: (586) 727-2050
Web Site: http://www.p-ghomes.com
Rev.: $12,036,061
Provider of New Construction Services
N.A.I.C.S.: 236115
Carl Leonard *(VP-Sls & Mktg)*
Eric Pierson *(CFO)*
Tim Pierson *(Pres-Quality Lumber)*

PIEZO MOTION CORP.
6700 Professional Pkwy W, Sarasota, Fl 34240
Tel.: (941) 907-4444 DE
Emp.: 100
Appliances, Electrical & Electronics Mfr

N.A.I.C.S.: 335999

Subsidiaries:

Brain Scientific, Inc. (1)
6700 Professional Pkwy, Lakewood Ranch, FL 34240
Tel.: (917) 388-1578
Rev.: $544,275
Assets: $440,218
Liabilities: $5,237,042
Net Worth: ($4,796,824)
Earnings: ($4,284,785)
Emp.: 7
Fiscal Year-end: 12/31/2020
Supplementary Product Distr
N.A.I.C.S.: 456191
Mark Corrao *(CFO)*
Hassan Kotob *(Chm & CEO)*

PIGEON FALLS STATE BANK
40214 S Ekern Ave, Pigeon Falls, WI 54760
Tel.: (715) 983-2295 WI
Web Site: http://www.pigeonfallsstatebank.com
Year Founded: 1920
Sales Range: $25-49.9 Million
Emp.: 17
Commericial Banking
N.A.I.C.S.: 522110
Norma Sletteland *(Owner)*
Debra Fremstad *(VP)*
William Debruyckere *(Pres)*

Subsidiaries:

Bank of Augusta (1)
1214 W Lincoln St, Augusta, WI 54722
Tel.: (715) 286-4444
Web Site: http://www.pigeonfallsstatebank.com
Sales Range: $25-49.9 Million
Emp.: 9
Banking Services
N.A.I.C.S.: 522110
Donna Rongstad *(VP)*

PIGGLY WIGGLY ALABAMA DISTRIBUTING CO.
2400 J Terrell Wooten Dr, Bessemer, AL 35020
Tel.: (205) 481-2300
Web Site: http://www.pwadc.com
Sales Range: $800-899.9 Million
Emp.: 600
Groceries, General Line
N.A.I.C.S.: 424410
Eddie Frye *(Mgr-Sls)*

PIGGLY WIGGLY CAROLINA COMPANY
176 Croghan Spur Rd Ste 301, Charleston, SC 29407
Tel.: (843) 554-9880
Web Site: http://www.thepig.net
Year Founded: 1947
Sales Range: $450-499.9 Million
Emp.: 4,500
Supermarket
N.A.I.C.S.: 445110
Robert Masche *(COO & Sr VP)*
David R. Schools *(Pres & CEO)*
Lynn Willard *(VP-Supermarket Ops)*
Jeff Harrell *(Coord-Event)*
Joseph T. Newton *(Founder)*

PIGGLY WIGGLY CENTRAL INC.
114 E Calhoun St, Sumter, SC 29150
Tel.: (803) 775-4712
Web Site: http://www.pigglywiggly.com
Sales Range: $75-99.9 Million
Emp.: 165
Supermarkets, Chain
N.A.I.C.S.: 445110
William R. McLeod *(Co-Pres)*
Ricky R. McLeod *(Co-Pres)*

PIGGLY WIGGLY FOOD STORES OF JEFFERSON COUNTY, INC.
3000 Montgomery Hwy, Birmingham, AL 35209
Tel.: (205) 879-0884
Web Site: http://www.pigglywiggly.com
Sales Range: $10-24.9 Million
Emp.: 100
Supermarket Operator
N.A.I.C.S.: 445110
Stanley Vircigilio *(Pres)*

PIGGLY WIGGLY HALEYVILLE INC.
811 20th St, Haleyville, AL 35565
Tel.: (205) 486-9598
Sales Range: $10-24.9 Million
Emp.: 200
Supermarket Operator
N.A.I.C.S.: 445110
Ricky Hicks *(Gen Mgr)*

PIGGLY WIGGLY OF CRYSTAL SPRING INC
509 W Marion Ave, Crystal Springs, MS 39059
Tel.: (601) 892-3009
Web Site: http://www.rameysmarketplace.com
Sales Range: $10-24.9 Million
Emp.: 60
Grocery Store Operator
N.A.I.C.S.: 445110
Brad Ramey *(Owner)*

PIGOTT INC.
3815 Ingersoll Ave, Des Moines, IA 50312
Tel.: (515) 279-8879 IA
Web Site: http://www.pigottnet.com
Year Founded: 1942
Sales Range: $10-24.9 Million
Emp.: 30
Whslr of Office Furniture
N.A.I.C.S.: 423210
John Stenberg *(Owner & Pres)*
Jeannette Smith *(Mgr-Sls-Eastern Iowa)*
Mo Schreiber *(VP-Ops)*
Tina Mutchler *(Controller)*
Scot Nation *(Project Mgr)*
Tami Anderson *(VP-Sls & Mktg)*
Cari Trilk *(VP-Design Svcs)*
Dave Edaburn *(Mgr-Corp Installation)*
Tana Nichol *(CFO)*

PIGOTT OIL COMPANY INC.
5806 Plz Dr, Tylertown, MS 39667
Tel.: (601) 876-2172
Sales Range: $10-24.9 Million
Emp.: 12
Gasoline Distr
N.A.I.C.S.: 424720
Blaze Holmes *(Sec)*
Cindy Pigott *(VP)*

PIKE STREET CAPITAL, LP
300 E Pike St Ste 2000, Seattle, WA 98122
Tel.: (206) 686-3340
Web Site: https://www.pikestreetcapital.com
Privater Equity Firm
N.A.I.C.S.: 523940
Paul Caragher *(Mng Partner)*
Colin Fekkes *(CFO)*

Subsidiaries:

PTNW Equity, Inc. (1)
12020 SE 32nd St Ste 2, Bellevue, WA 98005
Tel.: (425) 614-1698
Web Site: http://www.pumptechnw.com

PIKE STREET CAPITAL, LP

Pike Street Capital, LP—(Continued)
Sales Range: $1-9.9 Million
Emp.: 15
Industrial Machinery & Equipment Merchant Whslr
N.A.I.C.S.: 423830
Doug Davidson (Pres)
Chris Suskie (Gen Mgr)
Tom Long (VP-Field Ops)

Subsidiary (Domestic):

PumpTech, LLC (2)
12020 SE 32nd St Ste 2, Bellevue, WA 98005
Tel.: (425) 644-8501
Web Site: https://pumptechnw.com
Pumping Products & Systems Mfr & Distr
N.A.I.C.S.: 333996

Subsidiary (Domestic):

Alpha Southwest, Inc. (3)
205 Rossmoor Ave SW, Albuquerque, NM 87105
Tel.: (505) 877-0287
Web Site: http://www.alphasw.com
Sales Range: $1-9.9 Million
Emp.: 31
Industrial Machinery & Equipment Merchant Whslr
N.A.I.C.S.: 423830
Thomas Yates (CEO & COO)

Pipestone Equipment LLC (3)
676 Moss St Ste A, Golden, CO 80401-4077
Tel.: (303) 579-9658
Web Site: http://www.pipestoneeq.com
Industrial Supplies Merchant Whslr
N.A.I.C.S.: 423840

PIKES PEAK COMMUNITY FOUNDATION
730 N Nevada Ave, Colorado Springs, CO 80903
Tel.: (719) 389-1251 CO
Web Site: http://www.ppcf.org
Year Founded: 1994
Sales Range: $10-24.9 Million
Emp.: 9
Philanthropic Services
N.A.I.C.S.: 813211
Trudy Strewler Hodges (CEO)
Whitney Calhoun (Program Mgr & Mgr-Special Events)
Eric Cefus (Dir-Philanthropic Svcs)
Kate Singh (Mgr-Event & Comm)

PIKES PEAK DISTRIBUTORS LLC
3166 Tampa Rd Ste 1, Oldsmar, FL 34677
Tel.: (727) 474-1720
Web Site: http://www.floridaidoctor.com
Sales Range: $1-9.9 Million
Mobile Phone Repair Services
N.A.I.C.S.: 811210
Richard Haug (Mng Dir)

PIKES PEAK HARLEY DAVIDSON
5867 N Nevada Ave, Colorado Springs, CO 80918
Tel.: (719) 278-2301
Web Site: http://www.pikespeakharleydavidson.com
Sales Range: $10-24.9 Million
Emp.: 150
Motorcycle Dealers
N.A.I.C.S.: 441227
Rob Brooks (VP)
Joe Denning (Gen Mgr)
Vic Vickers (Mgr-Inventory & IT)

PIKES PEAK IMPORTS LTD.
655 Automotive Dr, Colorado Springs, CO 80906
Tel.: (719) 633-1500
Web Site: http://www.pikespeakacura.com
Year Founded: 1986
Sales Range: $10-24.9 Million
Emp.: 100
New & Used Car Dealers
N.A.I.C.S.: 441110
Carrie Burkhardt (Controller)

PIKES PEAK LIBRARY DISTRICT
2418 W Pikes Peak Ave, Colorado Springs, CO 80904
Tel.: (719) 634-1698
Web Site: http://www.ppld.org
Year Founded: 1903
Rev.: $17,963,334
Emp.: 326
Library Services
N.A.I.C.S.: 519210
Greg Roes (Mgr-Circulation)
Jocelyne Sansing (Branch Mgr-Old Colorado City & Ute Pass)
Janice McPherson (Mgr-Adult Svcs)
Paula J. Miller (Exec Dir)

PIKES PEAK OF TEXAS INC.
4340 Directors Row, Houston, TX 77092
Tel.: (713) 686-4500
Web Site: http://www.pikespeakfloral.com
Sales Range: $10-24.9 Million
Emp.: 35
Flowers, Fresh
N.A.I.C.S.: 424930
Jim Haley (Pres)
Wil Guzman (Branch Mgr)

PIKSEL, INC.
1250 Broadway Ste 1902, New York, NY 10001
Tel.: (646) 553-4845 DE
Web Site: http://www.piksel.com
Year Founded: 2003
Sales Range: $200-249.9 Million
Emp.: 1,000
Digital Media Services
N.A.I.C.S.: 541519
Ralf Tillmann (CEO-Interim)
Mark Christie (CTO)
K. Peter Heiland (CEO)
Kris Brown (Co-Mng Dir)
Kristan Bullett (Co-Mng Dir)
Ruth Patterson (Gen Counsel)

Subsidiaries:

KIT digital Limited (1)
17c Curzon Street, Mayfair, London, W1J 5HU, United Kingdom
Tel.: (44) 1904 438000
Web Site: http://www.piksel.com
Digital Media Services
N.A.I.C.S.: 541519

KIT digital Prague a.s. (1)
Kavci Hory Office Park Na Hrebenech II 1718/8, 140 00, Prague, Czech Republic
Tel.: (420) 270 008 100
Digital Media Services
N.A.I.C.S.: 513199

Kewego Deutschland GmbH (1)
Stiglmaierplatz Dachauer Strasse 37, Maxvorstadt, 80335, Munich, Germany
Tel.: (49) 8954558320
Video Management Software Publisher
N.A.I.C.S.: 513210

Polymedia S.p.A. (1)
Via Ernesto Breda 176, Milan, 20126, Italy
Tel.: (39) 02842781
Web Site: http://www.piksel.com
Emp.: 30
Video Management Software Publisher
N.A.I.C.S.: 513210
Patrizia Celi (Gen Mgr)

Sezmi Corporation (1)
1301 Shoreway Rd, Belmont, CA 94002
Tel.: (650) 631-7100
Web Site: http://www.sezmi.com
Sales Range: $10-24.9 Million
Emp.: 80
Cloud-Based Software Publisher
N.A.I.C.S.: 513210

PILES CHEVROLET-OLDS-PONTIAC-BUICK, INC.
30 Ferguson Blvd, Dry Ridge, KY 41035
Tel.: (859) 824-3337
Year Founded: 1956
Sales Range: $10-24.9 Million
Emp.: 35
Car Whslr
N.A.I.C.S.: 441110
Steve Davis (Mgr-Svc)
Randy Mann (Gen Mgr-Sls)
William Piles (Pres)
Buck Walter (Owner)

PILGRIM CAPITAL PARTNERS, LLC
The Harbor House 163 Oldfield Rd, Fairfield, CT 06824
Tel.: (203) 292-6616
Web Site: http://www.pilgrimcap.com
Year Founded: 2006
Privater Equity Firm
N.A.I.C.S.: 523999
Christopher M. Daley (Founder & Partner)
Christopher D. Wright (Partner)

PILGRIM CLEANERS INC.
4001 N Bellaire Blvd, Houston, TX 77005
Tel.: (713) 520-1960 TX
Web Site: http://www.pilgrimcleaners.com
Sales Range: $25-49.9 Million
Emp.: 600
Owner & Operator of Dry Cleaning Facilities
N.A.I.C.S.: 812320

PILGRIM FURNITURE CITY
55 Graham Pl, Southington, CT 06489
Tel.: (860) 276-0030
Web Site: http://www.pilgrimfurniturecity.com
Sales Range: $25-49.9 Million
Emp.: 112
Furniture Whslr
N.A.I.C.S.: 449110

PILGRIM PETROLEUM CORP.
5057 Keller Springs Rd Ste 300, Addison, TX 75001
Tel.: (972) 655-9870
Web Site: http://www.pilgrimpetroleum.com
Year Founded: 1997
Oil & Gas Exploration Services
N.A.I.C.S.: 213112
Samuel Carl Smith (Chm & CEO)

PILGRIM PLASTIC PRODUCTS COMPANY
1200 W Chestnut St, Brockton, MA 02301-5574
Tel.: (508) 436-6300 MA
Web Site: http://www.pilgrimplastics.com
Year Founded: 1913
Sales Range: $400-449.9 Million
Emp.: 32
Plastics Product Mfr
N.A.I.C.S.: 326130
Mark Abrams (Pres)

PILLAR CONSTRUCTION INC.
5649 S General Washington, Alexandria, VA 22312
Tel.: (703) 941-5891

U.S. PRIVATE

Web Site: http://www.pillarconstruction.com
Rev.: $10,400,000
Emp.: 150
Plastering, Drywall & Insulation
N.A.I.C.S.: 238310
Raja Khoury (Pres)
Mike Shelby (VP)
Shawn Gooden (Project Mgr)

PILLARSTONE CAPITAL REIT
Tel.: (281) 747-9997 MD
Web Site: https://pillarstone-capital.org
Year Founded: 1994
PRLE—(OTCBB)
Rev.: $9,273,000
Assets: $57,583,000
Liabilities: $18,667,000
Net Worth: $38,916,000
Earnings: $474,000
Fiscal Year-end: 12/31/21
Real Estate Investment Trust
N.A.I.C.S.: 525990
John J. Dee (CFO & Sr VP)
James C. Mastandrea IV (Chm, Pres & CEO)
Paul T. Lambert (Trustee)
Bradford Johnson (Trustee, Pres & CEO)
Dan Kovacevic (CFO)
William Carter (COO)
Priscilla Gonzalez (Chief Admin Officer)

PILLSBURY WINTHROP SHAW PITTMAN LLP
1540 Broadway, New York, NY 10036-4039
Tel.: (212) 858-1000
Web Site: http://www.pillsburylaw.com
Year Founded: 1868
Sales Range: $550-599.9 Million
Emp.: 1,001
Legal Advisory Services
N.A.I.C.S.: 541110
Takeo Akiyama (Partner-Corp & Securities-New York)
David S. Baxter (Partner-Corp & Securities-New York)
Shinya Akiyama (Partner-Corp & Securities-New York)
Mark N. Lessard (Partner-Fin-New York)
Peter A. Baumgaertner (Partner-Corp & Securities-New York)
Mark D. Litvack (Partner-Intellectual Property-New York)
Jennifer Jordan McCall (Partner-Estates, Trusts & Tax Plng)
Anthony P. Raven (Partner-Energy & Project Fin-Tokyo)
Simon P. Barrett (Partner-Fin-Tokyo)
Mercedes Tunstall (Partner)
Michael Wu (Partner)
Andrew D. Lanphere (Partner-Litigation-San Francisco)
Andrew Smith (Partner)
Andrew L. Strong (Partner-Environment, Land Use & Natural Resources Practice)
Cecily A. Dumas (Partner-Insolvency & Restructuring Practice-San Francisco)
Josh Tucker (Partner-Intellectual Property-Austin & Silicon Valley)
Casey Low (Partner-Austin)
James Lloyd (Partner-Houston)
Jenny Liu (Partner)
Michael Torosian (Partner)
George Willman (Partner)
Brooke Daniels (Partner)
Nora Burke (Partner)
Deborah Ruff (Head-Intl Abitration-Global)

Deborah Baum *(Head-Litigation)*
Amanda Halter *(Partner)*
Osama Abu-Dehays *(Mng Partner)*
Ahmad A. Anani *(Mng Partner)*
Carrie L. Bonnington *(Mng Partner)*
Kimberly Buffington *(Mng Partner)*
Thomas A. Campbell *(Mng Partner)*
Edward A. Cavazos *(Mng Partner)*
Thomas F. Chaffin *(Mng Partner)*
R. J. Davis *(Mng Partner)*
Debra Erni *(Mng Partner)*
Edward Flanders *(Mng Partner)*
Jeffrey B. Grill *(Mng Partner)*
Paul P. Jebely *(Mng Partner)*
Jack Ko *(Mng Partner)*
Eric A. Kremer *(Mng Partner)*
Martin K. Metz *(CIO)*
Edward A. Perron *(Mng Partner)*
Roxane A. Polidora *(Mng Partner)*
Geoffrey Sant *(Partner-Litigation)*
Dillon J. Ferguson *(Partner)*

PILOT CATASTROPHE SERVICES INC.
1055 Hillcrest Rd, Mobile, AL 36695
Tel.: (251) 607-7700 AL
Web Site: http://www.pilotcat.com
Year Founded: 1989
Sales Range: $100-124.9 Million
Emp.: 833
Provider of Insurance Services
N.A.I.C.S.: 524291

Subsidiaries:

Pilot and Associates Inc. (1)
1055 Hillcrest Rd Ste B1, Mobile, AL 36695
Tel.: (251) 607-7700
Web Site: http://www.pilotcat.com
Rev.: $10,000,000
Emp.: 155
Insurance Claim Adjustment Services
N.A.I.C.S.: 524291

PILOT CHEMICAL COMPANY
2744 E Kemper Rd, Cincinnati, OH 45241
Tel.: (513) 326-0600
Web Site: http://www.pilotchemical.com
Year Founded: 1952
Surface Active Agent Mfr
N.A.I.C.S.: 325613
Paul Morrisroe *(Chm)*
Glynn E. Goertzen *(VP-Corp Dev)*
Susan K. Leslie *(VP-Environmental, Health, Safety & Quality)*
David Waizmann *(Bus Dir)*
Catherine Ochterski *(Dir-HR)*
Derek Houck *(CFO)*
Chris Leedy *(VP-Mfg & Engrg)*
Bert Gutierrez *(Gen Mgr-Latin America)*
Sarah Mester *(Dir-Corp Dev)*
Jeff Crume *(Reg Sls Mgr-Northeast)*
Jason Denlinger *(Mgr-Corp Environmental, Health & Safety)*
William Woods *(Mktg Mgr)*
Paul Washlock *(Mgr-Distr Sls)*
Jeff Baxter *(Dir-Supply Chain)*
Mike Clark *(CEO)*
Bartley Morrisroe *(Gen Counsel & Mgr-Corp Comm)*
Rick Shook *(VP-Res & Dev)*
Chris Urban *(Acct Mgr-Distr Key)*
Patrick Conover *(Acct Mgr-Distr)*
Cathi Mowery *(Sr Acct Mgr)*
Hannah Davis *(Acct Mgr-Inside)*
Drew McCandlish *(Sr Acct Mgr)*
Frank D. Nataro *(Sls Mgr-North America)*

Subsidiaries:

Liquid Minerals Group LTD. (1)
PO Box 1700, New Waverly, TX 77358
Tel.: (936) 291-2424
Web Site: http://www.liquidminerals.com
Sales Range: $1-9.9 Million
Emp.: 18
Oil Soluble Organic Metallic Additives Mfr
N.A.I.C.S.: 324110
Mark D. Hughes *(CEO)*
Daniel Smith *(Pres)*

Mason Chemical Company (1)
723 W Algonquin Rd, Arlington Heights, IL 60005
Tel.: (847) 290-1621
Web Site: http://www.masonsurfactants.com
Chemical Product Whslr.
N.A.I.C.S.: 424690

Pilot Chemical Co. of California, Inc. (1)
2744 E Kemper Rd, Cincinnati, OH 45241-1818
Tel.: (562) 945-1867
Web Site: http://www.pilotchemical.com
Sales Range: $10-24.9 Million
Emp.: 15
Soap & Other Detergents
N.A.I.C.S.: 325613

Pilot Chemical Co. of Ohio Inc. (1)
3439 Yankee Rd, Middletown, OH 45044
Tel.: (513) 424-9700
Web Site: http://www.pilotchemical.com
Sales Range: $10-24.9 Million
Emp.: 45
Soap & Other Detergents
N.A.I.C.S.: 325611

Pilot Industries of Texas Inc. (1)
11623 N Houston Rosslyn Rd, Houston, TX 77086 (100%)
Tel.: (281) 448-3222
Web Site: http://www.pilotchemical.com
Sales Range: $10-24.9 Million
Emp.: 30
Petroleum Refining
N.A.I.C.S.: 325199

Pilot Laboratories Inc. (1)
267 Homestead Ave, Avalon, NJ 07001
Tel.: (732) 634-6613
Web Site: http://www.pilotchemical.com
Sales Range: $10-24.9 Million
Emp.: 22
Soap & Other Detergents
N.A.I.C.S.: 325611
Dwight Wilmot *(Office Mgr)*

Pilot Polymer Technologies, Inc. (1)
855 William Pitt Way, Pittsburgh, PA 15238-1334
Tel.: (412) 735-4799
Web Site: http://www.pilotpolymertech.com
Specialty Polymers Design & Mfr
N.A.I.C.S.: 325998
Patrick McCarthy *(Pres & CEO)*

PILOT CORPORATION
5508 Lonas Dr, Knoxville, TN 37909-3221
Tel.: (865) 588-7487 VA
Web Site: https://pilotcompany.com
Year Founded: 1958
Truck Stops & Convenience Stores Operator
N.A.I.C.S.: 457120
Dan Fleming *(VP-Ops)*
Angie Cody *(Dir-Inclusion, Diversity & Equity)*
Paul Shore *(Chief People Officer)*

PILOT GROUP, LLC
75 Rockefeller Plz 23rd Fl, New York, NY 10019
Tel.: (212) 486-4446
Web Site: http://www.thepilotgroup.us
Year Founded: 2003
Sales Range: $25-49.9 Million
Emp.: 20
Privater Equity Firm
N.A.I.C.S.: 523999

Subsidiaries:

North American Membership Group, Inc.
12301 Whitewater Dr, Minnetonka, MN 55343-4104
Tel.: (952) 936-9333
Sales Range: $125-149.9 Million
Lifestyle Membership Organization Operator & Marketer
N.A.I.C.S.: 713910

PILOT GROVE SAVINGS BANK
410 S Grand Ave, Mount Pleasant, IA 52641-1866
Tel.: (319) 469-3951
Web Site: http://www.pilotgrovesavingsbank.com
Commericial Banking
N.A.I.C.S.: 522110
Matthew Morrison *(VP)*

PILOT TRADING COMPANY INC.
308 Dorla Ct Ste 205, Zephyr Cove, NV 89448
Tel.: (775) 588-8850
Web Site: http://www.pilotbrands.com
Sales Range: $25-49.9 Million
Emp.: 24
Importer of Meats & Meat Products
N.A.I.C.S.: 424470

PILOTMALL.COM, INC.
4040 Laird Blvd, Lakeland, FL 33811
Tel.: (863) 226-1106
Web Site: http://www.pilotmall.com
Year Founded: 1998
Sales Range: $1-9.9 Million
Aviation Supplies & Gifts Retailer
N.A.I.C.S.: 459999
Neil Glazer *(Pres)*

PIMCO CAPITAL SOLUTIONS BDC CORP.
650 Newport Ctr Dr, Newport Beach, CA 92660
Tel.: (949) 720-6000 DE
Year Founded: 2021
Rev.: $10,886,000
Assets: $235,816,000
Liabilities: $2,021,000
Net Worth: $233,795,000
Earnings: $9,951,000
Fiscal Year-end: 12/31/22
Investment Management Service
N.A.I.C.S.: 523999
Crystal Porter *(Treas)*
John W. Lane *(Pres)*
Wu-Kwan Kit *(VP)*

PIMCO DYNAMIC CREDIT INCOME FUND
1633 Broadway, New York, NY 10019
Tel.: (212) 739-3222
Web Site: http://www.allianzinvestors.com
Investment Services
N.A.I.C.S.: 523999
Lawrence G. Altadonna *(CFO, Chief Acctg Officer & Treas)*
Hans W. Kertess *(Chm)*

PIMCO REIT, INC.
650 Newport Centre Dr Ste 100, Newport Beach, CA 92660
Tel.: (949) 720-6000 MD
Web Site: http://www.PIMCO.com
Year Founded: 2011
Real Estate Investment Trust
N.A.I.C.S.: 525990
Daniel Ivascyn *(Mng Dir & Grp Chief Investment Officer)*
Scott Simon *(Co-Chief Investment Officer)*
Danielle Luk *(Exec VP & Portfolio Mgr)*
Tiffany Wilding *(Sr VP)*
Josh Thimons *(Mng Dir & Portfolio Mgr)*
Joachim Fels *(Mng Dir)*
David Lown *(Chief Admin Officer)*
Drew Vaden *(CTO)*
Emmanuel Roman *(CEO)*
Jinhy Yoon *(Exec VP & Analyst-Credit)*

PIN BUSINESS NETWORK
8055 E Tufts Ave #950, Denver, CO 80237
Tel.: (720) 613-2249
Web Site: http://pinbusinessnetwork.com
Digital Marketing Services
N.A.I.C.S.: 518210
Keith Sawarynski *(Pres & COO)*

Subsidiaries:

Precis E-Buisness Systems (1)
6295 Greenwood Pl Blvd, Greenwood Village, CO 80111
Tel.: (877) 366-0200
Web Site: http://www.precis.us
Process, Physical Distribution & Logistics Consulting Services
N.A.I.C.S.: 541614
Brian Miesbauer *(Dir-Ops)*

PINCH A PENNY, INC.
6385 150th Ave N, Clearwater, FL 33760
Tel.: (727) 531-8913
Web Site: http://www.pinchapenny.com
Year Founded: 1974
Sales Range: $10-24.9 Million
Emp.: 300
Franchiser of Pool Supply Stores
N.A.I.C.S.: 533110
Jim Eisch *(VP)*
Fred Thomas *(Founder & Chm)*

PINCHERS CRAB SHACK, INC.
28580 Bonita Crossing Blvd, Bonita Springs, FL 34135
Tel.: (239) 948-1313 FL
Web Site: http://www.pinchersusa.com
Year Founded: 1997
Sales Range: $10-24.9 Million
Emp.: 500
Restaurant
N.A.I.C.S.: 722511
Anthony Phelan *(Owner & Pres)*
Grant Phelan *(Dir-Ops)*

PINCHME.COM, INC.
874 Walker Rd Ste C, Dover, DE 19904
Tel.: (917) 512-6936 DE
Web Site: http://www.pinchme.com
Year Founded: 2012
Rev.: $9,363,777
Assets: $3,472,659
Liabilities: $2,058,714
Net Worth: $1,413,945
Earnings: ($4,514,321)
Fiscal Year-end: 12/31/18
Marketing & Advertising Services
N.A.I.C.S.: 541870
Jeremy Reid *(Founder & CEO)*

PINCKNEY HUGO GROUP
760 W Genesee St, Syracuse, NY 13204-2306
Tel.: (315) 478-6700 NY
Web Site: http://www.pinckneyhugo.com
Year Founded: 1940
Sales Range: $10-24.9 Million
Emp.: 20
Advetising Agency
N.A.I.C.S.: 541810
Kathleen Brogan *(VP-Media Svcs)*
Douglas Pinckney *(Pres)*
Chris Pinckney *(Exec Dir-Creative)*
Aaron Hugo *(Exec VP)*
Scott McNany *(Sr Dir-Art)*

PINCKNEY HUGO GROUP

Pinckney Hugo Group—(Continued)
Jennifer Foust *(Sr Dir-Art)*
Robyn Jonick *(Sr Dir-Art)*
Robin Moore *(VP)*
Rachel Vaughn *(Acct Mgr-Pub Rel)*
Rick Humphrey *(VP)*
Bryan Weinsztok *(Acct Mgr)*
Meriel McCaffery *(Office Mgr)*
Colleen O'Mara *(Sr Mgr-PR)*
Cathy Van Order *(Dir-Production Svcs)*
Pamela Woodford *(Acct Mgr-Pub Rel)*
Tracy Nhek *(Acct Mgr)*
Maggie Gotch *(Acct Mgr)*
Katie Duerr *(Sr Mgr-Digital Media)*
Susan Muench *(Assoc Dir-Media)*

PINDLER & PINDLER INC.
11910 Poindexter Ave, Moorpark, CA 93021-1748
Tel.: (805) 531-9090   CA
Web Site: http://www.pindler.com
Year Founded: 1939
Rev.: $27,000,000
Emp.: 70
Fabric Distr
N.A.I.C.S.: 424310
Curt Pindler *(Pres)*
Bill Crawford *(Exec VP)*
Jeanne Wade *(Gen Mgr-Warehouse)*

PINE BELT ENTERPRISES
1088 Rte 88, Lakewood, NJ 08701
Tel.: (732) 363-2900
Web Site:
 http://www.pinebeltcars.com
Year Founded: 1942
Sales Range: $25-49.9 Million
Emp.: 100
Sales of New & Used Automobiles
N.A.I.C.S.: 441110
Igor Sidorov *(Mgr-Inventory)*
Joseph Pagano *(Dir-ECommerce)*
Dan Ariel *(Gen Mgr)*
Alana Hackshaw *(Mgr-Internet Sls)*
Brian Brown *(Mgr-Fin)*
Jared Neumann *(Mgr-Fin)*
Ryan Concord *(Mgr-Sls)*
Kenny Martin *(VP)*

PINE BELT NISSAN OF TOMS RIVER
229 Route 37 E, Toms River, NJ 08753
Tel.: (732) 349-3030
Web Site: http://www.nissan37.com
Year Founded: 1986
Sales Range: $50-74.9 Million
Emp.: 210
Car Whslr
N.A.I.C.S.: 441110
Stephen Malara *(CFO & Controller)*
Ernie Marino *(Gen Mgr)*
Arnold Manresa *(Mgr-Comml Sls)*

PINE BLUFF SAND AND GRAVEL CO
1501 Heartwood St, White Hall, AR 71602
Tel.: (870) 534-7120
Rev.: $14,200,000
Emp.: 60
Dams, Waterways, Docks & Other Marine Construction
N.A.I.C.S.: 236210
W. Scott McGeorge *(Chm & Pres)*

PINE BRANCH COAL SALES INC.
4497 Kentucky Hwy 28, Hazard, KY 41701
Tel.: (606) 436-3712   KY
Web Site:
 http://www.pinebranchcoal.com
Year Founded: 1963
Sales Range: $25-49.9 Million
Emp.: 120
Provider of Coal
N.A.I.C.S.: 212114
David Duff *(Pres)*

PINE BROOK PARTNERS, LLC
60 E 42nd St 50th Fl, New York, NY 10165
Tel.: (212) 847-4333   DE
Web Site:
 http://www.pinebrookpartners.com
Year Founded: 2006
Privater Equity Firm
N.A.I.C.S.: 523999
Andre Burba *(Partner-Energy Investment)*
Oliver Goldstein *(Partner-Fin Svcs Investment)*
Nicholaos C. Krenteras *(Partner-Fin Svcs Investment Team)*
Richard Aube *(Mng Partner)*
Scott Schaen *(Partner)*
William L. Spiegel *(Mng Dir-Fin Svcs)*
Ted Maa *(Partner-Energy Investment)*
James P. Rutherfurd *(Partner-IR)*
Emily Sharko *(COO & Partner)*
Joseph Kopilak *(CFO, Chief Compliance Officer & Partner)*
Bharath Srikrishnan *(Partner-Fin Svcs Investment Team)*
Howard H. Newman *(Chm & CEO)*

Subsidiaries:

Comet Ridge Resources, LLC   (1)
600 17th St Ste 800-S, Denver, CO 80202
Tel.: (303) 226-1300
Web Site:
 http://www.cometridgeresources.com
Oil & Gas Exploration
N.A.I.C.S.: 213111

United PanAm Financial Corp.   (1)
18191 Von Karman Ave Ste 300, Irvine, CA 92612-7105
Tel.: (949) 224-1917
Web Site: http://www.upfc.com
Sales Range: $200-249.9 Million
Emp.: 685
Holding Company; Automobile Financing
N.A.I.C.S.: 551112
James Vagim *(Pres & CEO)*

Subsidiary (Domestic):

United Auto Credit Corporation   (2)
18191 Von Karman Ave Ste 300, Irvine, CA 92612   **(100%)**
Tel.: (949) 224-1917
Web Site: http://www.upfc.com
Sales Range: $25-49.9 Million
Emp.: 50
Automobile Loans
N.A.I.C.S.: 522291
Jeff Whiteman *(Dir-Infrastructure)*
Peter Krogh *(Gen Counsel)*
Steve Singh *(COO)*

PINE BROOK ROAD PARTNERS, LLC
60 E 42nd St 50th Fl, New York, NY 10165
Tel.: (212) 847-4333
Web Site:
 http://www.pinebrookpartners.com
Year Founded: 2006
Investment Services
N.A.I.C.S.: 523940
Howard H. Newman *(Mng Partner)*
Richard Aube *(Mng Partner)*
Joseph Kopilak *(Partner, CFO & Chief Compliance Officer)*
Emily Sharko *(Partner & COO)*
Michael J. Martinez *(Dir-Compliance & Assoc Gen Counsel)*
Elan Stukov *(Controller)*
Jen Zheng *(Dir-Tax)*
Rachel Amendolagine *(VP-IR)*

PINE BUSH EQUIPMENT CO. INC.
97 RTE 302, Pine Bush, NY 12566
Tel.: (845) 744-2006   NY
Web Site: http://www.pbeinc.com
Year Founded: 1956
Sales Range: $150-199.9 Million
Emp.: 60
Supplier of Construction & Mining Machinery
N.A.I.C.S.: 813410
Steven Boniface *(CEO)*
Joe Antonuccio *(Mgr-Construction)*
Simra Alfonsa *(Controller)*

PINE CREEK PARTNERS, LLC
1025 Thomas Jefferson St NW Ste 308 E, Washington, DC 20007
Tel.: (202) 333-7780   DE
Web Site:
 http://www.pinecreekpartners.com
Sales Range: Less than $1 Million
Emp.: 4
Privater Equity Firm
N.A.I.C.S.: 523999
Carl J. Rickertsen *(Founder & Mng Partner)*

PINE GATE RENEWABLES LLC
130 Roberts St, Asheville, NC 28801
Tel.: (855) 969-3380
Web Site:
 http://www.pinegaterenewables.com
Solar Engergy & Electricity Distr
N.A.I.C.S.: 221118
Ben Catt *(CEO)*

Subsidiaries:

Horne Brothers Construction Inc   (1)
1662 Middle River Loop, Fayetteville, NC 28312
Tel.: (910) 323-0320
Web Site: http://www.hbc-inc.com
Sales Range: $25-49.9 Million
Emp.: 35
Commercial & Office Building, New Construction
N.A.I.C.S.: 236220
Charles J. Horne *(Pres)*
Tavia Buie *(Sec)*
Tanya Wright *(Coord-Construction)*

PINE GROVE HOLDINGS, LLC
559 West Diversey Pkwy Ste 344, Chicago, IL 60614
Tel.: (773) 260-0209
Web Site:
 https://www.pinegroveholdings.com
Year Founded: 2011
Holding Company
N.A.I.C.S.: 551112
Nelda J. Connors *(Founder, Chm & CEO)*

Subsidiaries:

KKSP Precision Machining, LLC   (1)
1688 Glen Ellyn Rd, Glendale Heights, IL 60139
Tel.: (630) 260-1735
Web Site: http://www.kksp.com
Screw Machine Product Mfr
N.A.I.C.S.: 332721
Chuck Spears *(Exec Chm)*
Dave Dolan *(Pres & CEO)*

Subsidiary (Domestic):

Grove Industries, Inc.   (2)
10790 Green Bay Rd, Pleasant Prairie, WI 53158
Tel.: (800) 726-5187
Web Site: http://www.grovefittings.com
Machine Shops
N.A.I.C.S.: 332710

PRO-Manufactured Products, Inc.   (2)
29 Ctr Pkwy, Plainfield, CT 06374
Tel.: (860) 564-7884
Web Site: http://www.promanufactured.com
Precision Turned Product Mfr
N.A.I.C.S.: 332721

U.S. PRIVATE

PINE HALL BRICK CO. INC.
2701 Shorefair Dr, Winston Salem, NC 27116
Tel.: (336) 721-7500
Web Site:
 http://www.pinehallbrick.com
Year Founded: 1922
Rev.: $25,000,000
Emp.: 370
Brick & Structural Clay Tiles Mfr & Distr
N.A.I.C.S.: 327120
W. Fletcher Steele *(Founder & Pres)*
Jack Lauer *(CFO)*

PINE INSTRUMENT COMPANY
101 Industrial Dr, Grove City, PA 16127
Tel.: (724) 458-6391
Web Site: http://www.pineinst.com
Sales Range: $10-24.9 Million
Emp.: 80
Industrial Controls & Push Button Selector Switches
N.A.I.C.S.: 335314
Joseph Hines *(Pres & VP)*
Doug Buchanan *(Mgr-Electronics Mfg)*
Ed Kaltenbaugh *(Engr-Software)*
Robin Vaughn *(Mgr-HR)*

PINE ISLAND CAPITAL PARTNERS LLC
Fort Lauderdale 2455 E Sunrise Blvd 1205, Fort Lauderdale, FL 33304
Tel.: (239) 292-5635
Web Site: https://pineislandcp.com
Privater Equity Firm
N.A.I.C.S.: 523999

Subsidiaries:

Precinmac, LP   (1)
79 Prospect Ave, South Paris, ME 04281
Tel.: (207) 743-6344
Web Site: https://www.precinmac.com
High Tolerance Precision Machined Components & Assemblies Mfr
N.A.I.C.S.: 332721
Eric C. Wisnefsky *(CEO)*

Subsidiary (Domestic):

Petersen Inc.   (2)
1527 N 2000 W, Ogden, UT 84404
Tel.: (801) 732-2000
Web Site: http://www.PetersenInc.com
Sales Range: $50-74.9 Million
Emp.: 445
Machinery Equipment Distr
N.A.I.C.S.: 423810
Jon Ballantyne *(CEO)*
Mark Jenkins *(CEO)*
Rob Despain *(VP-Bus Dev)*
Stephen Grange *(VP-Ops)*
Kirk Douglass *(Dir-Quality)*
Tom Burkland *(Mgr-Engrg)*
Dave Dixon *(Mgr-HR)*
Frank Shaw *(Dir-Program Office)*

PINE MANOR INC.
2704 S Main St, Goshen, IN 46526-5417
Tel.: (574) 533-4186   IN
Web Site:
 http://www.millerpoultry.com
Year Founded: 1942
Sales Range: $25-49.9 Million
Emp.: 300
Poultry Products & Services
N.A.I.C.S.: 311119
Galen D. Miller *(Owner & Pres)*
Karen Brenneman *(Mgr-Fin)*

PINE RIVER CAPITAL MANAGEMENT, LP

601 Carlson Pkwy 7th Fl, Minnetonka, MN 55305
Tel.: (612) 238-3300
Web Site:
http://www.pinerivercapital.com
Year Founded: 2002
Sales Range: $800-899.9 Million
Emp.: 54
Asset Management Services
N.A.I.C.S.: 523999
Brian Curtis Taylor *(CEO, Partner & Co-Chief Investment Officer)*
Thomas Edwin Siering *(Partner)*
Paul Richardson *(Chief Risk Officer & Partner)*
Bill Roth *(CIO & Partner-Two Harbors)*
James Clark *(Co-Chief Investment Officer & Partner)*
David Kelly *(CTO & Partner)*
Nikhil Mankodi *(Partner & Co-Head-Asian Trading)*
Aaron Yeary *(Pres & Partner)*
Stephen Alpart *(Mng Dir)*
Tim O'Brien *(Partner, Co-Chief Investment Officer & Gen Counsel)*
Nick Nusbaum *(Partner & CFO)*
Phil Prince *(Partner & Head-Treasury)*

PINE STATE TRADING CO.
100 Enterprise Ave, Gardiner, ME 04345-7199
Tel.: (207) 622-3741   ME
Web Site:
http://www.pinestatetrading.com
Year Founded: 1941
Sales Range: $200-249.9 Million
Emp.: 800
Wholesale Alcoholic Beverages & Groceries Distr
N.A.I.C.S.: 424490
P. Nicholas Alberding *(Co-Owner)*
Keith Canning *(Co-Owner)*
Gena Canning *(Co-Owner)*

Subsidiaries:

Maine Spirits   (1)
100 Enterprise Ave, Gardiner, ME 04345
Web Site: http://www.mainespirits.com
Distilled Alcoholic Beverage Distr
N.A.I.C.S.: 424820
P. Nicholas Alberding *(CEO)*

Pine State Beverage Co.   (1)
100 Enterprise Ave, Gardiner, ME 04345
Tel.: (207) 622-3741
Web Site:
http://www.pinestatebeverage.com
Sales Range: $10-24.9 Million
Emp.: 3
Wholesale Beer, Wine & Non-Alcoholic Beverage Distr
N.A.I.C.S.: 424810
P. Nicholas Alberding *(CEO)*

Town & Country Foods, Inc.   (1)
72 Daggett Hill Rd, Greene, ME 04236
Tel.: (207) 946-5489
Web Site: http://www.tandcfoods.com
Grocery Whslr & Delivery Services
N.A.I.C.S.: 424410
P. Nicholas Alberding *(CEO)*

PINE STREET ALTERNATIVE ASSET MANAGEMENT LP
590 Madison Ave 34th Fl, New York, NY 10022
Web Site:
http://www.pinestreetalt.com
Year Founded: 2011
Investment Services
N.A.I.C.S.: 523999
Caroline Lovelace *(Partner)*

Subsidiaries:

A.R. Schmeidler & Co., Inc.   (1)
500 5th Ave 14th Fl, New York, NY 10110
Tel.: (212) 687-9800
Web Site: http://www.arschmeidler.com

Money Management Services
N.A.I.C.S.: 523940
Arnold R. Schmeidler *(Founder & Chm)*
Andrew J. Schmeidler *(Portfolio Mgr)*
Stephen Burke *(CEO)*
Jared M. Levin *(Portfolio Mgr)*
Sam Weinstock *(Portfolio Mgr)*
Gregory S. Markel *(Portfolio Mgr)*
Brian P. Barry *(Portfolio Mgr)*
Brian C. Molinaro *(Controller)*
Richard L. Motta *(VP-Trading)*
Peter G. Kandel Jr. *(CFO)*

PINE STREET INN INC.
444 Harrison Ave, Boston, MA 02118-2404
Tel.: (617) 482-4944   MA
Web Site:
http://www.pinestreetinn.org
Year Founded: 1968
Sales Range: $300-349.9 Million
Emp.: 600
Shelter & Resources for Homeless People
N.A.I.C.S.: 623990
Terri Gagney *(CFO)*
John A. Sullivan *(Treas)*
Tim Barrett *(Controller)*

PINE TREE EQUITY MANAGEMENT, LP.
1515 Sunset Dr Ste 32, Miami, FL 33143
Tel.: (305) 808-9820   DE
Web Site:
http://www.pinetreeequity.com
Holding Company
N.A.I.C.S.: 551112
Jeff C. Settembrino *(Mng Partner)*

PINE TREE LUMBER CO. INC.
707 N Andreasen Dr, Escondido, CA 92029-1415
Tel.: (760) 745-0411   CA
Web Site:
http://www.pinetreelumber.com
Year Founded: 1945
Sales Range: $25-49.9 Million
Emp.: 200
Provider of Lumber
N.A.I.C.S.: 423310
Jerry Stubblefield *(Gen Mgr)*

PINE TREE SOCIETY FOR HANDICAPPED CHILDREN AND ADULTS, INC.
149 Front St, Bath, ME 04530
Tel.: (207) 443-3341   ME
Web Site:
http://www.pinetreesociety.org
Year Founded: 1936
Disability Afflicted Assistance Services
N.A.I.C.S.: 624120
Erin Rice *(Dir-Mktg & Dev)*
Noel Sullivan *(Pres & CEO)*
Timothy J. Kittredge *(Chm)*
Stefa Normantas *(Sec)*
Dean Paterson *(Vice Chm)*
Denise White *(Dir-HR)*
R. J. Gagnon *(CFO)*
Terry Berkowitz *(COO)*
Matthew Prunier *(Treas)*

PINE VALLEY FOODS, INC.
131 Forest Commercial Dr, West Monroe, LA 71292
Tel.: (318) 397-1124
Web Site:
http://www.pinevalleyfoods.com
Year Founded: 1998
Sales Range: $10-24.9 Million
Emp.: 122
N.A.I.C.S.: 311821
Joseph Giildenzopf *(CEO)*
Dixie Hall *(Dir-HR)*

PINECREST CAPITAL PARTNERS, LLC
8222 Douglas Ave Ste 200, Dallas, TX 75225
Tel.: (214) 295-4901
Web Site:
http://www.pinecrestcap.com
Year Founded: 2014
Privater Equity Firm
N.A.I.C.S.: 523999
Barrett D. Kingsriter *(Co-Founder & Sr Mng Dir)*
Bobby D. Renkes *(Co-Founder & Mng Dir)*

PINEHURST, LLC
80 Carolina Vista, Pinehurst, NC 28374
Tel.: (910) 235-6811
Web Site: http://www.pinehurst.com
Year Founded: 1895
Sales Range: $10-24.9 Million
Golf Course, Country Club & Resort Owner & Operator
N.A.I.C.S.: 713910
Jay Biggs *(Sr VP-Golf & Club Ops)*
Thomas M. Pashley *(Pres)*
Eric Kuester *(Dir-Grp Sls)*
Kimberly Bryan *(Sr Dir-Accounts-Natl)*
Don Bostic *(Dir-Natl Accts)*
Tiffani Sheppard *(Sls Mgr-State Associations)*
Nimisha Birath *(Mgr-Sls)*

Subsidiaries:

National Golf Club, Inc.   (1)
1 Royal Troon Dr, Pinehurst, NC 28374
Tel.: (910) 295-4300
Web Site: http://www.nationalgolfclub.com
Sales Range: $1-9.9 Million
Emp.: 70
Golf Course & Country Club Operator
N.A.I.C.S.: 713910
Ken Crow *(Gen Mgr)*
Tess Brubaker-Burke *(Dir-Fin)*
Tom Parsons *(Dir-Golf)*

PINELAND TELEPHONE CO-OPERATIVE, INC.
30 S Roundtree St, Metter, GA 30439
Tel.: (912) 685-2121
Web Site: http://www.pineland.net
Year Founded: 1951
Sales Range: $10-24.9 Million
Emp.: 70
Local Telephone Communications
N.A.I.C.S.: 517121
Dustin Durden *(Gen Mgr)*
Eddy Jones *(Dir-Plant Ops)*
Jinks Durden *(Dir-Ops)*
Mike Purvis *(Mgr-Engrg & Construction)*
Wayne Foskey *(Plant Mgr)*
Steven McComas *(CFO)*

Subsidiaries:

Pineland Cogentes, Inc.   (1)
30 S Rountree St, Metter, GA 30439
Tel.: (912) 685-2121
Web Site: http://pineland.net
Telephone, Cable TV, Internet, Security, Alarm, Fire Testing, Commercial Computer Services & Managed Services
N.A.I.C.S.: 517810
Tom Glover *(CEO)*

Subsidiary (Domestic):

First Service Carolina, Inc.   (2)
3933 Arrow Dr, Raleigh, NC 27612
Tel.: (919) 832-5553
Web Site: http://www.fscarolina.com
Computer & Software Stores
N.A.I.C.S.: 449210
Jackie Abbott *(Pres)*
Kerry Ray *(Engr-Sys)*

PINELLAS COUNTY HOUSING AUTHORITY
11479 Ulmerton Rd, Largo, FL 33778
Tel.: (727) 443-7684
Web Site: http://www.pin-cha.org
Sales Range: $25-49.9 Million
Housing Administrative Services
N.A.I.C.S.: 925110
Debra Johnson *(CEO & Exec Dir)*
Omar Arce *(Dir-Plng & Modernization)*
Regina Booker *(Dir-Resident Svcs & Programs)*
Ray DiRusso *(Dir-Compliance & Fraud Recoveries)*
Elisa Galvan *(Dir-Housing Choice Voucher Program)*
Leslie Plassman *(Mgr-HR)*

PINELLAS COUNTY UTILITIES
14 S Ft Harrison Ave, Clearwater, FL 33756-5146
Tel.: (727) 464-4000
Web Site:
http://www.pinellascounyt.org
Year Founded: 1937
Sales Range: $25-49.9 Million
Emp.: 800
Utilities
N.A.I.C.S.: 925120
Bob Peocock *(Dir-Customer Svcs)*

PINELLAS OPPORTUNITY COUNCIL INC
501 First Ave N Ste 517, Saint Petersburg, FL 33713
Tel.: (727) 823-4101   FL
Web Site: http://www.poc-inc.org
Year Founded: 1968
Emp.: 115
Develop Programs Helping Families & Individuals Alleviate Conditions of Poverty Through Empowerment & Self-Sufficiency
N.A.I.C.S.: 624190
Carolyn W. King *(Exec Dir)*
Kathy Russell *(Program Dir-Chore Services)*
Gregg Rose *(Program Dir-Retired & Senior Volunteer Program)*
Eleanor Brooks *(Program Dir-Emergency Svcs, Family Dev & EHEAP)*

PINELLAS SUNCOAST TRANSIT AUTHORITY
3201 Scherer Dr N, Saint Petersburg, FL 33716-1004
Tel.: (727) 540-1800
Web Site: http://www.psta.net
Sales Range: $75-99.9 Million
Emp.: 600
Transportation Services
N.A.I.C.S.: 485999
Debbie Leous *(CFO)*

PINES HEALTH SERVICES
74 Access Hwy, Caribou, ME 04736
Tel.: (207) 498-2356   ME
Web Site: http://www.pineshealth.org
Year Founded: 1981
Sales Range: $10-24.9 Million
Emp.: 185
Healtcare Services
N.A.I.C.S.: 622110
Lisa Caron *(COO)*
Jim Davis *(CEO)*
Norm Collins *(Chm)*

PINES INTERNATIONAL, INC.
1992 E 1400 Rd, Lawrence, KS 66044
Tel.: (785) 841-6016
Web Site:
http://www.wheatgrass.com
Sales Range: $1-9.9 Million
Emp.: 20
Whole Foods Mfr

PINES INTERNATIONAL, INC.

Pines International, Inc.—(Continued)
N.A.I.C.S.: 624210
Ron Siebold *(Pres)*
Steve Malone *(Co-Founder & CEO)*

PINES OF SARASOTA, INC.
1501 N Orange Ave, Sarasota, FL 34236
Tel.: (941) 365-0250 FL
Web Site:
  http://www.pinesofsarasota.org
Year Founded: 1948
Sales Range: $10-24.9 Million
Emp.: 300
Intermediate Care Facilities
N.A.I.C.S.: 623110
Dawn Crable *(Dir-HR)*
Paul Hartman *(Dir-Plant Ops)*
Kyle Booth *(Asst Sec)*
Jane Hunder *(Vice Chm)*
Joyce A. Johnson *(Sec)*
Carl G. Smith *(Treas)*
Peter Abbott *(Chm)*
Loris Dixon *(CFO)*
Mike Ward *(Pres & CEO)*

PINEWELL CAPITAL LLC
9481 N 114th Way, Scottsdale, AZ 85259
Tel.: (602) 315-2391
Web Site: http://pinewellcapital.com
Year Founded: 2014
Investment Services
N.A.I.C.S.: 523940
Yuta Matsui *(Mng Partner)*
Ziv Bendor *(Mng Partner)*
Richard Heath *(Ops Partner)*
Adi Knishinsky *(Ops Partner)*

Subsidiaries:

Fogco Systems Inc. (1)
600 S 56th St Ste 9, Chandler, AZ 85226
Tel.: (480) 507-6478
Web Site: http://www.fogco.com
Air-Conditioning & Warm Air Heating Equipment & Commercial & Industrial Refrigeration Equipment Mfr
N.A.I.C.S.: 333415
Gary Wintering *(Pres & CEO)*

PINKARD CONSTRUCTION COMPANY
9195 W 6th Ave, Lakewood, CO 80215
Tel.: (303) 986-4555
Web Site: http://www.pinkardcc.com
Sales Range: $10-24.9 Million
Emp.: 60
Commercial & Office Building, New Construction
N.A.I.C.S.: 236220
Jeff Barnes *(COO)*
Tony Burke *(Pres)*

PINKERTON & LAWS INC.
1165 Northchase Pkwy SE Ste 100, Marietta, GA 30067-6427
Tel.: (770) 956-9000 GA
Web Site: http://www.pinkerton-laws.com
Year Founded: 1955
Sales Range: $75-99.9 Million
Emp.: 100
Commercial & Industrial Construction Services
N.A.I.C.S.: 236220
Lawrence Coil *(Pres & CEO)*
Jeff Jernigan *(Exec VP)*

PINKERTON CHEVROLET-GEO, INC.
925 N Electric Rd, Salem, VA 24153
Tel.: (540) 562-1337
Web Site:
  http://www.pinkertonchevy.com
Sales Range: $10-24.9 Million

Emp.: 42
Car Whslr
N.A.I.C.S.: 441110
William J. Pinkerton *(Pres)*
Jeff Wilson *(Coord-Customer Care)*

PINKIE'S INC.
1426 E 8th St, Odessa, TX 79761-4803
Tel.: (432) 580-0504 TX
Web Site:
  http://www.pinkiesonline.com
Year Founded: 1934
Sales Range: $25-49.9 Million
Emp.: 180
Liquor Stores
N.A.I.C.S.: 445320
David Hernandez *(Mgr-Abilene)*
Stefanie Anderson *(Mgr-Abilene)*
Larry Hostick *(Mgr-Lubbock)*
Michelle Brown *(Mgr-Odessa)*
Paula Henderson *(Mgr-Lubbock)*
Bryan Kramer *(Mgr-Odessa)*
Heather Maxey *(Mgr-Midland)*
Kathy Hale *(Mgr-Midland)*
Chuck Gesting *(Mgr-Midland)*
Theresa Allen *(Mgr-Lubbock)*

PINKS ORIGINAL BAKERY, INC.
22330 68th Ave S, Kent, WA 98032-1948
Tel.: (253) 872-8390
Web Site:
  http://www.pinksoriginalbakery.com
Year Founded: 1987
Sales Range: $10-24.9 Million
Emp.: 2
Bakery Products Mfr
N.A.I.C.S.: 311812
Ruth Perdue *(Controller)*

PINN BROTHERS CONSTRUCTION
1475 Saratoga Ave Ste 250, San Jose, CA 95129
Tel.: (408) 252-9131 CA
Web Site: http://www.pinnbros.com
Year Founded: 1973
Rev.: $10,894,387
Emp.: 15
New Construction, Single-Family Houses
N.A.I.C.S.: 236115
Alan Pinn *(Pres)*
Alyson Willliams *(Mgr-HR & Payroll)*

PINNACLE ADVISORY GROUP
6345 Woodside Ct Ste 100, Columbia, MD 21046
Tel.: (410) 995-6630
Web Site:
  http://www.pinnacleadvisory.com
Year Founded: 1993
Sales Range: $1-9.9 Million
Emp.: 28
Wealth Management & Financial Advisory Services
N.A.I.C.S.: 523940
Richard Donald Vollaro *(Co-Partner)*
Michael E. Kitches *(Co-Partner & Dir-Res)*
John Robert Hill *(Principal)*
Dwight Andrew Mikulis *(Principal)*
Anne Purcell *(VP-Washington)*

PINNACLE ASSET MANAGEMENT, L.P.
712 5th Ave 29th Fl, New York, NY 10019
Tel.: (212) 750-1778 DE
Web Site: http://www.pinnacle-lp.com
Investment Advisory & Asset Management Services
N.A.I.C.S.: 523940

Jason M. Kellman *(Mng Partner & Chief Investment Officer)*
John Lee *(CFO)*

Subsidiaries:

Five Rivers Cattle Feeding, LLC (1)
4848 Thompson Pkwy Ste 410, Johnstown, CO 80534
Tel.: (970) 408-0178
Web Site: http://www.fiveriverscattle.com
Cattle Feedlots Owner & Operator
N.A.I.C.S.: 112112
Mike Thoren *(Pres & CEO)*
Russ Danner *(VP-IT)*
Luke Lind *(Chief Risk Officer & Sr VP)*
Tom McDonald *(VP-Environ Affairs)*
Jerri Lynn Magana *(CFO)*
Donna Hendren *(VP-HR)*
John Foley *(COO & VP-Ops)*

Subsidiary (Domestic):

Interstate Feeders, LLC (2)
1710 S 2450 E, Malta, ID 83342-8608
Tel.: (833) 450-1889
Cattle Feedlots
N.A.I.C.S.: 112112
Guthrie Newell *(Gen Mgr)*
Arvid Carlson *(Gen Mgr)*

PINNACLE ASSOCIATES, LTD.
335 Madison Ave Fl 11, New York, NY 10017
Tel.: (212) 652-3210 NY
Web Site: http://www.pinnacle-ny.com
Year Founded: 1984
Sales Range: $1-9.9 Million
Emp.: 48
Investment Advice
N.A.I.C.S.: 523940
Thomas Passios *(Pres)*
Alice Gabriele *(VP & Portfolio Mgr)*

Subsidiaries:

Investment Management of Virginia, LLC (1)
919 E Main St Fl 16, Richmond, VA 23219
Tel.: (804) 643-1100
Web Site: http://www.imva.net
Rev.: $1,100,000
Emp.: 15
Other Management Consulting Services
N.A.I.C.S.: 541618
Bradley H. Gunter *(Pres & Portfolio Mgr)*
William E. Sizemore *(Mng Dir-Res)*
Henry H. George *(Mng Dir & Portfolio Mgr)*
John H. Bocock *(Chm, Principal & Portfolio Mgr)*

PINNACLE BANCORP, INC.
18081 Burt St, Omaha, NE 68022
Tel.: (402) 697-5990 NE
Year Founded: 1977
Sales Range: $125-149.9 Million
Emp.: 532
Bank Holding Company
N.A.I.C.S.: 551111
Roy G. Dinsdale *(Chm)*
Arlene Porzelt *(VP-HR)*
Justin Horst *(CFO)*
Mark Hesser *(Pres)*

Subsidiaries:

Bank of Colorado (1)
1609 E Harmony Rd, Fort Collins, CO 80525
Tel.: (303) 857-6651
Web Site: http://www.bankofcolorado.com
Sales Range: $10-24.9 Million
Emp.: 30
Retail & Commercial Banking
N.A.I.C.S.: 522110
Collyn Florendo *(Pres-Colorado Springs)*
Cameron Armagost *(Pres-Fort Morgan)*
Shawn Osthoff *(Pres)*
Chris Cox *(Pres-Delta)*
David Finkelstein *(Dir-Mktg)*
Kaycee Lytle *(Pres-Market)*
Tamara Byrd *(Pres-Longmont)*

U.S. PRIVATE

Jonathan Rogers *(Pres-Denver)*
Peter Armstrong *(Sr VP)*
Mitch Kendrick *(Pres-Akron)*

Pinnacle Bank (1)
1401 N St, Lincoln, NE 68508
Tel.: (402) 434-3127
Web Site: http://www.pinnbank.com
Sales Range: $25-49.9 Million
Emp.: 16
Retail & Commercial Banking
N.A.I.C.S.: 522110
Mark Hesser *(Pres)*
Nancy Duckett *(Asst VP)*
Amy Guenther *(Dir-Mktg & VP)*
Curt Denker *(Pres-Market)*
Amy Siffring *(Asst VP)*

Pinnacle Bank (1)
309 S Old Betsy Rd, Keene, TX 76059
Tel.: (817) 645-8861
Web Site: http://www.pinnbanktx.com
Emp.: 25
Retail & Commercial Banking
N.A.I.C.S.: 522110
Peter G. Bennis *(Pres)*

Pinnacle Bank - Wyoming (1)
2000 Main St, Torrington, WY 82240
Tel.: (307) 532-2181
Web Site: http://www.wypinnbank.com
Retail & Commercial Banking
N.A.I.C.S.: 522110
Todd Peterson *(Pres)*

Pinnacle Bank Sioux City (1)
1901 Morningside Ave, Sioux City, IA 51106-2403
Tel.: (712) 276-5331
Web Site: http://www.pinnbanksc.com
Sales Range: $1-9.9 Million
Emp.: 14
Retail & Commercial Banking
N.A.I.C.S.: 522110

PINNACLE BUSINESS SYSTEMS, INC.
3824 S Boulevard St Ste 200, Edmond, OK 73013
Tel.: (918) 587-1500
Web Site: http://www.pbsnow.com
Sales Range: $10-24.9 Million
Emp.: 7
Computer Peripheral Equipment & Software Merchant Whslr
N.A.I.C.S.: 423430
Mark Morris *(Dir-Info Sys)*
Charles Moore *(VP)*
George Hill *(Mgr)*
Jim Young *(CFO)*
Buddy Emig *(Mgr-Acctg)*
Addie Scott *(Mgr-Solution Sls)*

Subsidiaries:

St. Croix Solutions, Inc. (1)
6031 Culligan Way, Minnetonka, MN 55345
Tel.: (952) 653-2900
Web Site: http://www.stcroixsolutions.com
Sales Range: $10-24.9 Million
Data Processing, Hosting & Related Services
N.A.I.C.S.: 518210

PINNACLE COATING & CONVERTING, INC.
212 Natl Ave, Spartanburg, SC 29303-6316
Tel.: (864) 574-8400 SC
Web Site: http://www.pccpaper.com
Year Founded: 1955
Sales Range: $50-74.9 Million
Emp.: 35
Specialty Paper Mfr
N.A.I.C.S.: 322299
Mike Greer *(Pres & CEO)*
Eric Carpin *(Mgr-Inventory)*

PINNACLE COMMUNICATION SERVICES
730 Fairmont Ave, Glendale, CA 91203
Tel.: (818) 241-6009

Web Site: http://www.pinnacleinc.com
Year Founded: 1990
Sales Range: $10-24.9 Million
Emp.: 110
System Integration Services
N.A.I.C.S.: 541690
Avo Amirian *(CEO)*
Joe Licursi *(Pres)*
Arica Simpson *(Project Dir-Admin)*
Karine Ghazarian *(Dir-HR)*

PINNACLE CONSTRUCTION GROUP
1000 Frnt St NW, Grand Rapids, MI 49504
Tel.: (616) 451-0500
Web Site:
http://www.askourclients.com
Sales Range: $10-24.9 Million
Emp.: 20
Commercial & Office Building Contractors
N.A.I.C.S.: 236220
Michael A. Garrett *(Pres)*
Lance Ebenstein *(Mgr-Facility)*

PINNACLE DERMATOLOGY LLC
5141 Virginia Way, Brentwood, TN 37027
Tel.: (833) 257-7546
Web Site:
http://www.pinnacleskin.com
Year Founded: 2004
Skin Health Services
N.A.I.C.S.: 621111
Chad A. Eckes *(CEO)*

Subsidiaries:

Spectrum Dermatology, PLLC (1)
9500 E Ironwood Sq Dr Ste 110, Monterey, CA 85258
Tel.: (480) 923-7528
Web Site:
http://www.spectrumdermatology.com
Offices of Physicians (except Mental Health Specialists)
N.A.I.C.S.: 621111
Esther Ferroni *(Office Mgr)*
Nancy Kim *(Founder)*

PINNACLE ENVIRONMENTAL CORPORATION
200 Broad St, Carlstadt, NJ 07072
Tel.: (201) 939-6565
Web Site: http://www.pinenv.com
Year Founded: 1997
Sales Range: $25-49.9 Million
Emp.: 956
Environmental Remediation Services
N.A.I.C.S.: 562910
Paul O'Brien *(Pres & Principal)*
Robert Ryan *(Principal & VP)*
Joseph A. Whelan *(CFO & Principal)*
Richie Doran *(Mgr-Operating)*
Ray Kinsella *(Project Mgr)*
Joseph Patrick *(Project Mgr)*
John Tancredi *(Div Mgr)*

PINNACLE EXHIBITS, INC.
22400 NW Westmark Dr, Hillsboro, OR 97124
Tel.: (503) 844-4848
Web Site: http://www.pinnacle-exhibits.com
Year Founded: 1998
Sales Range: $25-49.9 Million
Emp.: 114
Interactive Marketing Services
N.A.I.C.S.: 541810
Chris Jensen *(CFO)*
Brad Hogan *(CEO)*
Eric Gavin *(Gen Mgr-Chicago)*
David Lund *(Acct Exec)*

Subsidiaries:

New 24, Inc (1)
345 McCausland Court,, Cheshire, CT 06410
Tel.: (203) 250-6500
Web Site: https://gowithcd.com
Rev.: $6,666,666
Emp.: 40
Institutional Furniture Mfr
N.A.I.C.S.: 337127

PINNACLE FINANCIAL CORPORATION
884 Elbert St, Elberton, GA 30635
Tel.: (706) 283-2854
Web Site:
http://www.pinnaclebank.com
Sales Range: $10-24.9 Million
Emp.: 140
Bank Holding Company
N.A.I.C.S.: 551111
Jackson McConnell Jr. *(Pres & CEO)*
D. Scott Wilson *(CFO)*
John Fortson *(VP)*
Doug Long *(Founder)*

Subsidiaries:

Pinnacle Bank (1)
884 Elbert St, Elberton, GA 30635
Tel.: (706) 283-2854
Web Site: http://www.pinnaclebank.com
Sales Range: $50-74.9 Million
Emp.: 35
Retail, Commercial & Investment Banking
N.A.I.C.S.: 522110
Jackson McConnell Jr. *(Pres & CEO)*
Mike Starrett *(Sr VP)*

Pinnacle Investment Services, Inc. (1)
67 E Franklin St, Hartwell, GA 30643
Tel.: (706) 213-3325
Financial Management Services
N.A.I.C.S.: 523999

PINNACLE HEALTH CARE
7 Halsted Cir, Rogers, AR 72756
Tel.: (479) 636-5716
Rev.: $27,400,000
Emp.: 100
Nursing Care Facilities
N.A.I.C.S.: 623110
Meredith Hutchins *(Office Mgr)*

PINNACLE INSURANCE & FINANCIAL SERVICES, LLC
7791 Belfort Pkwy, Jacksonville, FL 32256
Tel.: (904) 296-4100
Web Site: http://www.pinnacleifs.com
Year Founded: 2007
Sales Range: $1-9.9 Million
Emp.: 48
General Insurance & Financial Management Services
N.A.I.C.S.: 524210
Jim Ludwick *(Pres & CEO)*
Mike Miller *(COO)*
Edgar Morales *(CMO & Sr VP-Multicultural Markets)*
Dave Fastenberg *(CFO)*
Tom Klose *(Mng Partner)*
Austin Knowles *(Mng Partner-Atlanta)*
Michael Becher *(Mng Partner-Atlanta)*
Sean Shea *(Exec VP)*

PINNACLE MACHINE TOOLS, INC.
745 S Church St Ste 307, Murfreesboro, TN 37130
Tel.: (615) 904-7786
Sales Range: $10-24.9 Million
Emp.: 6
Distr of Machine Tools & Accessories
N.A.I.C.S.: 423830
Don Roberts *(Pres)*
Kim Smith *(Office Mgr)*
Dennis McCurry *(VP)*
Jerry Edwards *(VP)*

Subsidiaries:

Pinnacle Machine Tools, Inc. (1)
PO Box 580, Meridianville, AL 35759
Tel.: (256) 828-2600
Sales Range: $10-24.9 Million
Emp.: 2
Distr of Machine Tools & Accessories
N.A.I.C.S.: 423830

PINNACLE MATERIALS, INC.
1200 Tices Ln Ste 202, East Brunswick, NJ 08816-1335
Tel.: (732) 254-7676   NJ
Web Site:
http://www.pinnaclematerials.com
Year Founded: 1996
Sales Range: $10-24.9 Million
Construction Sand & Gravel Mining & Distr
N.A.I.C.S.: 212321
Christine Yackman *(Co-Owner)*
Edward Herbert *(Co-Owner)*

PINNACLE MOUNTAIN HOMES, INC.
335 N Main St, Breckenridge, CO 80424
Tel.: (970) 453-0727
Web Site:
http://www.pinnaclemtnhomes.com
Year Founded: 2005
Sales Range: $10-24.9 Million
Emp.: 14
Home Construction Engineering Services
N.A.I.C.S.: 236115
Paul Steinweg *(Head-Ops)*

PINNACLE NISSAN
7601 E Frank Lloyd Wright Blvd, Scottsdale, AZ 85260
Tel.: (480) 998-9800
Web Site:
http://www.pinnaclenissan.com
Year Founded: 1996
Sales Range: $100-124.9 Million
Emp.: 150
New & Pre-Owned Automobile Dealership
N.A.I.C.S.: 441110
Larry Van Tuyl *(Pres)*
Anna Algiene *(Office Mgr)*
Chris Matchett *(Mgr-Sls)*
Daniel Sanchez *(Mgr-Svc)*
Bobby Krotonsky *(Dir-Svc)*

PINNACLE PRECISION SHEET METAL
5410 E La Palma Ave, Anaheim, CA 92807
Tel.: (714) 632-7910
Web Site:
http://www.pinnacleprecisionsheetmetal.com
Sales Range: $10-24.9 Million
Emp.: 50
Rigidizing Metal
N.A.I.C.S.: 332119
Brian McLaughlin *(VP)*
Tom Flores *(Mgr-Quality Assurance)*

PINNACLE RESTAURANT GROUP LLC
6340 International Pkwy, Plano, TX 75093
Tel.: (972) 220-0200
Rev.: $20,000,000
Emp.: 35
Steak Restaurant
N.A.I.C.S.: 722511
Mark Bromberg *(Pres)*

PINNACLE RISK MANAGEMENT SERVICES, INC.
4000 Kruse Way Pl Ste 1-300, Portland, OR 97035
Tel.: (503) 245-9756
Web Site:
http://www.pinnaclerisk.com
Sales Range: $10-24.9 Million
Emp.: 85
Provider of Third-Party Claims Services
N.A.I.C.S.: 524291
Steven Self *(COO)*
Robert H. Shorit *(Pres & CEO)*
Cortlane Firth *(CFO)*

PINNACLE SERVICES, INC.
724 Central Ave NE, Minneapolis, MN 55414
Tel.: (612) 977-3100
Web Site:
http://www.pinnacleservices.org
Year Founded: 1999
Sales Range: $1-9.9 Million
Emp.: 448
Housing, Employment, Financial & In-Home Services for Elderly & Disabled
N.A.I.C.S.: 624190
Nicolas Thomley *(Founder)*
Jill Cihlar *(Pres & CEO)*
Jessica Reno *(Program Dir)*
Laura Boss *(Program Dir)*
Rose Hoye *(Dir-HR Recruiting)*

PINNACLE STAFFING INC.
127 Tanner Rd, Greenville, SC 29607
Tel.: (864) 297-4212
Web Site:
http://www.pinnaclestaffing.com
Rev.: $20,000,000
Emp.: 16
Help Supply Services
N.A.I.C.S.: 561320
Ryan D. Hendley *(CEO)*
David R. Ballinger *(Pres)*

PINNACLE TECHNICAL RESOURCES, INC.
5501 LBJ Freeway Ste 600, Dallas, TX 75240
Tel.: (214) 740-2424
Web Site: http://www.pinnacle1.com
Sales Range: $25-49.9 Million
Emp.: 275
Custom Information Technology Solutions
N.A.I.C.S.: 541512
Nina G. Vaca *(Chm & CEO)*
Jim Humrichouse *(Pres)*
Jessica Narvaez *(VP-HR)*

Subsidiaries:

Provade, Inc. (1)
999 Baker Way Ste 120, San Mateo, CA 94404
Tel.: (650) 931-1000
Web Site: http://www.provade.com
Sales Range: $1-9.9 Million
Emp.: 31
Procurement Services
N.A.I.C.S.: 541512
Nina G. Vaca *(Chm)*
Hans Bukow *(Pres)*
Tom Rumberg *(CTO)*
Peter Parks *(COO)*

PINNACLE TELECOMMUNICATIONS, INC.
6205 S Walnut St, Loomis, CA 95650
Tel.: (916) 625-8400
Web Site: http://www.pinnacle-telecom.com
Year Founded: 1984
Sales Range: $10-24.9 Million
Emp.: 86
Telephone & Telephone Equipment Installation
N.A.I.C.S.: 238210
Barbara Winters *(Pres)*
Cecilia Lakatos Sullivan *(CEO)*

PINNACLE TEXTILE INDUSTRIES, LLC

Pinnacle Textile Industries, LLC—(Continued)

PINNACLE TEXTILE INDUSTRIES, LLC
440 Drew Ct, King of Prussia, PA 19406-2608
Web Site:
http://www.pinnacletextile.com
Textile & Fabric Finishing Mills
N.A.I.C.S.: 313310
Patrick Methven (Founder, Pres & Mng Partner)

Subsidiaries:

Topps Safety Apparel, Inc. (1)
2516 E State Rd 14, Rochester, IN 46975
Tel.: (574) 223-4311
Web Site:
http://www.toppssafetyapparel.com
Leather Goods Mfr
N.A.I.C.S.: 315990
Alan Dorrell (Pres)

PINNACLEART INTERNATIONAL, LLC
1 Pinnacle Way, Pasadena, TX 77504
Tel.: (281) 598-1330
Web Site: http://www.pinnacleart.com
Year Founded: 2006
Sales Range: $10-24.9 Million
Emp.: 104
Asset Management Services
N.A.I.C.S.: 523940
John Campo (Sr Dir-Ops)

Subsidiaries:

Advanced Reliability Technologies, LLC (1)
One Pinnacle Way, Pasadena, TX 77504
Tel.: (281) 333-3236
Web Site: http://www.artrcm.com
Emp.: 10
Administrative Management & General Management Consulting Service
N.A.I.C.S.: 541611
Walter T. Sanford (Co-Founder & Pres)
James F. Haas (Mgr-IT)
Alan L. Rasmussen (Mgr-Technical Svcs)

PINNACOL ASSURANCE
7501 E Lowry Blvd, Denver, CO 80230
Tel.: (303) 361-4000
Web Site: http://www.pinnacol.com
Year Founded: 1915
Sales Range: $550-599.9 Million
Emp.: 600
Workers Compensation Insurance
N.A.I.C.S.: 524126
Robert Norris (CIO)
Philip B. Kalin (Pres & CEO)
Edie Sonn (VP-Comm & Pub Affairs)
Kathy Kranz (CFO)
Barbara Brannen (VP-HR)
Dana Held (Assoc VP-Medical Ops)
Howard L. Carver (Chm)
Jeffrey L. Cummings (Vice Chm)
David Bomberger (Chief Investment Officer)
Mark Isakson (Chief Customer Officer)
Terrence Leve (Chief Legal & Corp Resources Officer)
Thomas Denberg (Sr Dir-Medical)
Quincy Douglass (VP-Ops)

PINO TILE HOLDINGS LLC
1711 Powerline Rd, Pompano Beach, FL 33069
Tel.: (954) 978-9704
Web Site: http://www.pinotile.com
Rev.: $12,000,000
Emp.: 10
Mfr & Distributor of Tile
N.A.I.C.S.: 449121
Ted Bohne (Pres)

PINOLE VALLEY TRUCKING, INC.
202 S Rochester, Ontario, CA 91761
Tel.: (909) 390-6161
Web Site: http://www.pvtusa.com
Year Founded: 1965
Sales Range: $10-24.9 Million
Emp.: 30
Provider of Trucking Services
N.A.I.C.S.: 484121
Lewis Geleng (VP)
Gloriza Villalba (Project Mgr-Intl)

PINPROS
785 Fairfield Rd-127, Layton, UT 84041
Tel.: (866) 345-7467
Web Site: http://www.pinpros.com
Year Founded: 2003
Sales Range: $1-9.9 Million
Emp.: 14
Designs, Manufactures & Sells Handcrafted Custom Lapel Pins
N.A.I.C.S.: 339993
Craig Fry (Owner & Pres)

PINSLY RAILROAD CO. INC.
53 Southampton Rd, Westfield, MA 01085-1375
Tel.: (413) 568-6426
Web Site: http://www.pinsly.com
Year Founded: 1938
Sales Range: $10-24.9 Million
Emp.: 10
Railroads, Line-Haul Operating
N.A.I.C.S.: 482111
John P. Levine (Pres)
Angela Depalo (Dir-HR)

Subsidiaries:

Florida Central Railroad (1)
3001 W Orange Ave, Apopka, FL 32703
Tel.: (407) 880-8500
Web Site: http://www.fcrr.com
Sales Range: $10-24.9 Million
Railroad
N.A.I.C.S.: 488210
Andre Roberts (Branch Mgr)
Andrew Ikensaa (Mgr-Admin)

Florida Midland Railroad (1)
3001 Orange Ave, Plymouth, FL 32768-0967
Tel.: (407) 880-8500
Web Site: http://www.fcrr.com
Sales Range: $10-24.9 Million
Emp.: 60
Railroad
N.A.I.C.S.: 488210
Bennett J. Biscan (VP)

Florida Northern Railroad (1)
3001 Orange Ave, Plymouth, FL 32703-0967
Tel.: (407) 880-8500
Sales Range: $10-24.9 Million
Railroad
N.A.I.C.S.: 488210
Pete Petree (VP)

Pioneer Valley Railroad (1)
100 Springdale Rd, Westfield, MA 01085
Tel.: (413) 568-3331
Web Site: http://www.pvrr.com
Sales Range: $10-24.9 Million
Railroad
N.A.I.C.S.: 488510
Mike Rennicke (VP & Gen Mgr)
Justin Shelton (Mgr-Ops)
Dave Swirk (Project Mgr)

Railroad Distribution Services, Inc. (1)
2951 US Hwy 17, Eagle Lake, FL 33839
Tel.: (863) 533-6911
Railroad Distribution Services
N.A.I.C.S.: 423310

Railroad Distribution Services, inc. (1)
100 Springdale Rd, Westfield, MA 01085
Tel.: (413) 562-9721
Web Site: http://www.rrdistribution.com

Railroad Distribution Services
N.A.I.C.S.: 488510

PINSTRIPE MARKETING, INC.
695 Central Ave Ste 200, Saint Petersburg, FL 33701
Tel.: (727) 214-1555
Web Site:
http://www.pinstripemarketing.com
Sales Range: $1-9.9 Million
Emp.: 5
Advetising Agency
N.A.I.C.S.: 541810
Ginger Reichl (Pres)
Jeff Zampino (Dir-Creative)

PINT SIZE CORPORATION
99-1287 Waiua Pl, Aiea, HI 96701
Tel.: (808) 487-0030
Web Site:
http://www.pintsizehawaii.com
Year Founded: 1979
Sales Range: $25-49.9 Million
Emp.: 90
Mfr of Ice Cream & Ices
N.A.I.C.S.: 424430
Bordon Christenson (Pres)

PINT, INC.
2105 Garnet Ave Ste E, San Diego, CA 92109
Tel.: (858) 270-2086
Web Site: http://www.pint.com
Year Founded: 1994
Sales Range: $1-9.9 Million
Emp.: 40
Internet Marketing & Related Services
N.A.I.C.S.: 541613
Eric Samuelson (VP & Gen Mgr)
Jimmy Tam (Dir-Technical)

PIONEER AG-CHEM INC.
4100 Glades Rd, Fort Pierce, FL 34981
Tel.: (772) 464-7237
Web Site: http://www.diamond-r.com
Sales Range: $25-49.9 Million
Emp.: 40
Fertilizers & Agricultural Chemicals
N.A.I.C.S.: 325311
Mike Michaels (Pres & CEO)

PIONEER BANK
3000 N Main St, Roswell, NM 88201-6676
Tel.: (575) 624-5200
Web Site: http://www.pioneerbnk.com
Year Founded: 1901
Rev.: $27,709,939
Emp.: 106
Federal Savings & Loan Associations
N.A.I.C.S.: 522180
Karen Koster (Mgr-Sls & Team-Cohoes)
Davis Bennett (VP & Dir-Internal Audit)
Eric Heathwaite (VP-Comml Lending)
Chad Cole (CFO & Sr VP)
Mohamad Mustafa (Branch Mgr)
Michelle Kearnan (VP-HR Admin)
Stephen P. Puntch (CEO)
Christopher Palmer (Pres & COO)
Nicole Austin (Chief Lending Officer & Exec VP)
Anil Mulchandani (Mgr-Sls & Team-Queensbury)
Zachary Ogden (Mgr-Sls & Team)
J. David Webster (Pres-Houston)
Ted DeConno Jr. (Mgr-Comml Relationship)

PIONEER BUILDERS SUPPLY CO.
5401 S Burlington Way, Tacoma, WA 98409

U.S. PRIVATE

Tel.: (253) 474-6000
Web Site: http://www.pioneer-roostop.com
Rev.: $11,900,000
Emp.: 75
Roofing & Siding Materials
N.A.I.C.S.: 423330

PIONEER CENTER FOR HUMAN SERVICES
4001 W Dayton St, McHenry, IL 60050
Tel.: (815) 344-1230
Web Site:
http://www.pioneercenter.org
Year Founded: 1959
Sales Range: $10-24.9 Million
Emp.: 694
Individual & Family Support Services
N.A.I.C.S.: 624190
Laurie Bivona (Dir-Mktg)
Jeff Kurth (CFO)
Christin Kruse (Chief Dev Officer)
Tom Janik (Mgr-Facilities)
Rebecca Heisler (Vice Chm)
Mark LeFevre (Treas)
Sandra Hess Moll (Sec)
Michael Snider (Dir-Fin)
Ronica Patel (Dir-Behavioral Health)
Dan McCaleb (Chm)
Sam Tenuto (CEO)

PIONEER CENTRES INC.
2950 S Havana St, Aurora, CO 80014
Tel.: (303) 751-1500
Web Site:
http://www.pioneercentres.com
Sales Range: $10-24.9 Million
Emp.: 43
Automobiles, New & Used
N.A.I.C.S.: 441110
Robert Jensen (Pres)

PIONEER CONCRETE PUMPING SERVICE
6400 Highlands Pkwy Ste C SE, Smyrna, GA 30082
Tel.: (770) 434-0600
Web Site:
http://www.pioneerconcrete.com
Year Founded: 1973
Sales Range: $10-24.9 Million
Emp.: 75
Concrete Pumping Services
N.A.I.C.S.: 238110
Patrick Inglese (Pres)
June Robinson (Mgr-Accts)
Phylica Wilkerson (Controller)

PIONEER CREDIT COMPANY INC.
1870 Executive Park NW, Cleveland, TN 37312
Tel.: (423) 476-6511
Web Site:
http://www.pioneercredit.net
Year Founded: 1974
Sales Range: $25-49.9 Million
Emp.: 35
Consumer Finance Companies
N.A.I.C.S.: 522291
John W. Holden Jr. (Founder, Pres & CEO)

PIONEER ELECTRIC COOPERATIVE
300 Herbert St, Greenville, AL 36037
Tel.: (334) 382-6636
Web Site:
http://www.pioneerelectric.com
Sales Range: $10-24.9 Million
Emp.: 50
Distribution, Electric Power
N.A.I.C.S.: 221122

COMPANIES

Cleveland Poole *(VP-Economic Dev & Legal Affairs)*
Terry Moseley *(Exec VP & Gen Mgr)*
Linda Horn *(VP-Member Svcs, Mktg & Comm)*
Patti Presley *(Coord-HR)*
Lauren Smith *(CFO & Mgr-Acctg)*

PIONEER EXPLORATION COMPANY
15603 Kuykendahl Rd, Houston, TX 77090
Tel.: (281) 893-9400
Web Site: http://www.pecogas.com
Rev.: $12,000,000
Emp.: 30
Crude Petroleum Production
N.A.I.C.S.: 211120
Younas Chaudhary *(VP)*

PIONEER FARM EQUIPMENT CO.
2589 N Air Fresno Dr Ste 109, Fresno, CA 93727-1554
Tel.: (559) 253-0526   CA
Web Site: http://www.pioneerequipment.com
Year Founded: 1994
Sales Range: $25-49.9 Million
Emp.: 280
Suppliers of Farm & Garden Machinery
N.A.I.C.S.: 423820
Dave Hatfield *(Dir-Mktg)*

PIONEER GARAGE, INC.
525 Commercial Ave NE, Highmore, SD 57345
Tel.: (605) 852-2217   SD
Web Site: http://www.pioneergarage.com
Year Founded: 1972
Sales Range: $25-49.9 Million
Emp.: 10
New & Used Car Dealer
N.A.I.C.S.: 441110
Jan Busse *(Pres)*

PIONEER HOMES, INC.
46 W Lemon St, Tarpon Springs, FL 34689
Tel.: (727) 938-1561
Web Site: http://www.pioneerhomesfla.com
Sales Range: $50-74.9 Million
Emp.: 10
New Single-Family Housing Construction
N.A.I.C.S.: 236115
George Stamas *(Treas, Sec & VP)*
George C. Zutes *(Pres)*

PIONEER HUMAN SERVICES, INC.
7440 W Marginal Way S, Seattle, WA 98108
Tel.: (206) 768-1990   WA
Web Site: http://www.pioneerhumanservices.org
Year Founded: 1963
Sales Range: $50-74.9 Million
Social Service Organization
N.A.I.C.S.: 813410
Karen Lee *(CEO)*
Anthony Wright *(COO)*
Hilary Young *(VP-Policy & Comm)*
Joe Wilczek *(Treas)*
Dick Zais *(Sec)*
Michael Langhout *(Chm)*
Stephanie Welty *(CFO)*
Mark Behrends *(VP-Enterprises)*
Julie Lord *(VP-Client & Community Svcs)*
Steve Woolworth *(VP-Treatment & Reentry Svcs)*
Randy Wilcox *(Vice Chm)*
Jack Dalton *(Founder)*

PIONEER INDUSTRIAL CORPORATION
400 Russell Blvd, Saint Louis, MO 63104
Tel.: (314) 771-0700
Web Site: http://www.pioneerindustrial.com
Sales Range: $10-24.9 Million
Emp.: 45
Seals, Industrial
N.A.I.C.S.: 423840
Jeff Joyce *(Controller)*
Jack Deeken *(Mgr-Safety & Quality Control)*
Joe Niemoeller *(Mgr-Valve Ops)*
Steve Darner *(Supvr-Field Svc)*
Rusty Jaycox *(Mgr-Ops)*
Christy Otto *(Product Mgr-Sls-Natl)*
Mark Sauter *(Mgr-Bus Dev)*

PIONEER INDUSTRIES, INC.
155 Irving Ave N, Minneapolis, MN 55405-1731
Tel.: (612) 374-2280   MN
Web Site: http://www.pioneerintl.com
Year Founded: 1974
Sales Range: $50-74.9 Million
Emp.: 250
Recycle Scrap & Waste Materials
N.A.I.C.S.: 423930
David Yormack *(CEO)*

Subsidiaries:

Batliner Paper Stock Company, Inc. (1)
2501 Frnt St, Kansas City, MO 64120-1647
Tel.: (816) 483-3343
Web Site: http://www.batlinerpaperstock.com
Emp.: 50
Recycle Scrap & Waste Materials
N.A.I.C.S.: 423930
Nick Sterbach *(Pres)*

Batliner Recycling (1)
2501 Front St, Kansas City, MO 64120
Tel.: (816) 483-3343
Emp.: 50
Paper Recycling Services
N.A.I.C.S.: 562920
Nick Sterbach *(Gen Mgr)*

Fibers, Inc. (1)
880 Mark St, Elk Grove Village, IL 60007
Tel.: (630) 543-7676
Industrial Supplies Whslr
N.A.I.C.S.: 423840
Ed Lehner *(Mgr)*

Pioneer Industries, Inc. - Batliner Converting Division (1)
305 Sunshine Rd, Kansas City, KS 66115
Tel.: (816) 483-3343
Packing Paper Mfr
N.A.I.C.S.: 322220

Pioneer Paper Stock Co. of Texas, Inc. (1)
5000 Singleton Blvd, Dallas, TX 75212
Tel.: (214) 630-9881
Web Site: http://www.pioneerintl.com
Emp.: 30
Paper Recycling Services
N.A.I.C.S.: 562920
Febino Rodriguez *(Gen Mgr)*

Pioneer Paper Stock Company (1)
155 Irving Ave N, Minneapolis, MN 55405
Tel.: (612) 374-2280
Web Site: http://www.pioneerpaperstock.com
Paper Recycling Services
N.A.I.C.S.: 562920

PIONEER LANDSCAPING MATERIALS
310 N Pasadena St, Gilbert, AZ 85233-4504
Tel.: (480) 926-8200
Web Site: http://www.pioneersand.com
Rev.: $20,000,000
Emp.: 18
Construction Sand & Gravel
N.A.I.C.S.: 212321
Rob Hall *(Mgr-Store)*

PIONEER MANUFACTURING COMPANY
4529 Industrial Pkwy, Cleveland, OH 44135-4541
Tel.: (216) 671-5500
Web Site: http://www.pioneerathletics.com
Sales Range: $10-24.9 Million
Emp.: 130
Mfr of Building & Ground Maintenance Products
N.A.I.C.S.: 423850
Doug Schattinger *(Pres)*

Subsidiaries:

Revere Products (1)
4529 Industrial Pkwy, Cleveland, OH 44135-4541
Tel.: (216) 671-5500
Web Site: http://www.revereproducts.com
Construction Materials Distr
N.A.I.C.S.: 423320
Jack Nesser *(VP-Ops)*
Doug Schattinger *(Pres)*

PIONEER NEWSPAPERS INC.
221 1st Ave W Ste 405, Seattle, WA 98119-4224
Tel.: (206) 284-4424   WA
Web Site: http://www.pioneernewsgroup.com
Year Founded: 1976
Sales Range: $25-49.9 Million
Emp.: 700
Newspapers
N.A.I.C.S.: 513110
Mike Gugliotto *(CEO)*
Jeffrey Hood *(CFO)*
Eric Johnston *(COO)*

Subsidiaries:

Big Sky Publishing Co. Inc. (1)
221 1st Ave W Ste 405, Seattle, WA 98119-4238
Tel.: (206) 284-4424
Web Site: http://www.pioneernewspapers.com
Rev.: $4,300,000
Emp.: 2
Newspapers
N.A.I.C.S.: 513110

Cache Valley Publishing Company (1)
75 W 300th N, Logan, UT 84321-3971
Tel.: (435) 752-2121
Web Site: http://www.hjnews.com
Rev.: $4,000,000
Emp.: 90
Publishing Newspapers
N.A.I.C.S.: 513110
Charlie McCollum *(Mng Editor)*

Daily Record Newspaper (1)
401 N Main St, Ellensburg, WA 98926-3107 (100%)
Tel.: (509) 925-1414
Web Site: http://www.dailyrecordnews.com
Rev.: $1,400,000
Emp.: 30
Newspaper Publishing
N.A.I.C.S.: 513110
Josh Crawford *(Dir-Circulation)*
Robyn Smith *(Mgr-Outside Sls)*

Havre Daily News Inc. (1)
119 Second Ave N, Seattle, WA 98109-4906
Tel.: (406) 265-6795
Web Site: http://www.havredailynews.com
Rev.: $1,200,000
Emp.: 3
Newspapers
N.A.I.C.S.: 513110

Idaho Press-Tribune Inc. (1)
1618 N Midland Blvd, Nampa, ID 83651
Tel.: (208) 467-9251
Web Site: http://www.idahopress.com
Rev.: $7,400,000
Emp.: 175
Newspaper Publishing
N.A.I.C.S.: 513110
Joe Hansen *(Dir-Digital Tech)*
Rhonda McMurtrie *(Dir-Fin)*
Michelle Robinson *(Dir-Adv)*
Roger Stowell *(Dir-Ops)*

Klamath Publishing Co. Inc. (1)
221 1st Ave W Ste 405, Seattle, WA 98119-4238
Tel.: (206) 284-4424
Web Site: http://www.heraldandnews.com
Sales Range: $10-24.9 Million
Emp.: 6
Newspapers
N.A.I.C.S.: 513110

Klamath Publishing Co. LLC (1)
2701 Foot Hills Blvd, Klamath Falls, OR 97603
Tel.: (541) 885-4410
Web Site: http://www.heraldandnews.com
Sales Range: $10-24.9 Million
Emp.: 80
Newspaper Publishers
N.A.I.C.S.: 513130
Mark Dobie *(Publr)*
Debbie Gribble *(Mgr-Credit)*
Christine Vontersch *(District Mgr-Circulation)*

PIONEER OIL LLC
1728 Lampman Dr Ste A, Billings, MT 59102
Tel.: (406) 254-7071
Web Site: http://www.pioneeroil-co.com
Sales Range: $25-49.9 Million
Emp.: 5
Asphalt Mixture
N.A.I.C.S.: 423320
Tad Butt *(Pres)*
Jason Chen *(CFO)*

PIONEER PACKING INC.
2430 S Grand Ave, Santa Ana, CA 92705-5211
Tel.: (714) 540-9751   CA
Web Site: http://www.pioneerpackinginc.com
Year Founded: 1976
Sales Range: $75-99.9 Million
Emp.: 228
Moving, Storage & Corrugated Boxes
N.A.I.C.S.: 424130

Subsidiaries:

Baycorr Packaging Incorporated (1)
6850 Brisa St, Livermore, CA 94550-7334
Tel.: (925) 449-1148
Web Site: http://www.heritagepaper.com
Rev.: $10,272,246
Emp.: 99
Paperboard Mills
N.A.I.C.S.: 322130
Mike Mora *(Mgr-Sls)*

Heritage Paper Co. (1)
2400 S Grand Ave, Santa Ana, CA 92705-5211
Tel.: (714) 540-9737
Web Site: http://www.heritage-paper.net
Sales Range: $10-24.9 Million
Emp.: 70
Industrial Packaging
N.A.I.C.S.: 424130
Ryan Petersen *(Engr-Pkg)*

Northwest Pioneer Inc. (1)
6006 S 228th St, Kent, WA 98032
Tel.: (253) 872-9693
Web Site: http://www.pioneerseattle.com
Sales Range: $10-24.9 Million
Emp.: 35
Industrial & Personal Service Paper
N.A.I.C.S.: 561720
Robert M. Steele *(Pres)*

PIONEER PACKING INC.

U.S. PRIVATE

Pioneer Packing Inc.—Continued

Pioneer Northern Inc. (1)
6850 Brisa St, Livermore, CA 94550-2356
Tel.: (925) 273-0230
Web Site: http://www.heritagepaper.com
Rev.: $21,140,079
Emp.: 150
Industrial & Personal Service Paper
N.A.I.C.S.: 424130

Pioneer Packaging Inc. (1)
730 E University Dr, Phoenix, AZ 85034-6509
Tel.: (602) 528-4140
Web Site: http://www.pioneerpackaging.com
Rev.: $9,747,090
Emp.: 25
Packaging
N.A.I.C.S.: 322220
Dan Rotner (Gen Mgr)

PIONEER PHOTO ALBUMS INC.
9801 Deering Ave, Chatsworth, CA 91311-4304
Tel.: (818) 882-2161   CA
Web Site: http://www.pioneerphotoalbum.com
Year Founded: 1952
Sales Range: $50-74.9 Million
Emp.: 300
Retail of Photo Albums
N.A.I.C.S.: 323111
Shell Plutsky (Pres)
Tiffany Boxer (Sr VP)

PIONEER PIPE, INC.
2021 Hanna Rd, Marietta, OH 45750
Tel.: (740) 376-2400   OH
Web Site: http://www.pioneergroup.us
Year Founded: 1981
Sales Range: $100-124.9 Million
Emp.: 600
Large Metal Pipe Fabrication, Construction & Maintenance Services
N.A.I.C.S.: 332996
Mike Archer (Pres & CEO)

PIONEER PRODUCTS, INC.
1917 S Memorial Dr, Racine, WI 53403
Tel.: (262) 633-6304
Web Site: http://www.pioneerproducts.com
Rev.: $37,100,000
Emp.: 95
Machine Shops
N.A.I.C.S.: 332710
Rich Gorske (Dir-Mfg Staff)
Todd Westervelt (Dir-Quality Control)
Kevin Parco (Engr)
Michael Mainland (VP)
Donald Mainland (Treas)
F. Jerome Beere (Pres)

PIONEER RAILCORP
1318 S Johanson Rd, Peoria, IL 61607
Tel.: (309) 697-1400   IA
Web Site: http://www.pioneer-railcorp.com
Year Founded: 1986
Sales Range: $10-24.9 Million
Emp.: 130
Shortline Railroad Services
N.A.I.C.S.: 482111
Scott Isonhart (Sec & Controller)
Catherine Busch (Dir-Mktg)
Nathan Johns (VP-Mktg & Govt Affairs)
Tom S. Black (VP-Safety & Transportation)
Dennis Johnson (Mgr-AAR Billing)
Kenneth Pilgrim (Mgr-Revenue Acctg)
Robert Athen (Dir-Ops Center)
Shane D. Cullen (VP-Mechanical & Ops)
Erica Kelsey (Asst Controller)
Dale Montgomery (VP-Bus Dev-Pioneer Railroad Services, Inc.)
Alex Yeros (CEO)
Ross Grantham (COO)
Carrie Genualdi (CFO)

Subsidiaries:

Garden City Western Railway, Inc. (1)
1318 S Johanson Rd, Peoria, IL 61607   (100%)
Tel.: (309) 697-1400
Sales Range: $1-9.9 Million
Emp.: 2
Line-Haul Operating Railroads
N.A.I.C.S.: 482111

PIONEER RIM AND WHEEL COMPANY
2500 Kennedy St NE, Minneapolis, MN 55413
Tel.: (612) 331-1311
Web Site: http://www.pioneerwheel.com
Sales Range: $25-49.9 Million
Emp.: 35
Wheels, Motor Vehicle & Automotive Parts
N.A.I.C.S.: 423120
John H. Cousins (Pres)
Todd Anderson (Mgr-Sls)
Bill Cousins (VP)
Steve Fix (Mgr-Industrial Products)
Shawn McDonald (Mgr-Madison)
Kyle Wanner (Mgr-Automotive & Tow Product)
Mark Padellford (VP)

PIONEER RURAL ELECTRIC COOPERATIVE INC.
344 W US Route 36, Piqua, OH 45356-9255
Tel.: (937) 773-2523
Web Site: http://www.pioneerec.com
Year Founded: 1936
Sales Range: $50-74.9 Million
Emp.: 60
Providers of Electrical Services
N.A.I.C.S.: 221122
Ron Salyer (Pres & CEO)

PIONEER SALES GROUP, INC.
6066 Shingle Creek Pkwy, Minneapolis, MN 55430
Tel.: (763) 546-6880
Web Site: http://www.pioneersalesgroup.com
Year Founded: 1994
Commercial & Industrial Lighting & Electrical Products Whslr
N.A.I.C.S.: 423610
Tim Horsch (Founder)

PIONEER SAVINGS BANK
652 Albany Shaker Rd, Albany, NY 12211
Tel.: (518) 274-4800
Web Site: http://www.pioneerbanking.com
Year Founded: 1889
Sales Range: $50-74.9 Million
Emp.: 300
Savings Institutions
N.A.I.C.S.: 522180
Karl Johnson (Chief Retail Officer & Sr VP)
Elbert Watson (Portfolio Mgr-Comml)
Thomas L. Amell (Pres & CEO)
Trudy Hudson (Area Mgr)
Rob Nichols (Sr VP-Comml Dev)

Subsidiaries:

Anchor Agency, Inc. (1)
61 Colvin Ave Ste 1, Albany, NY 12206
Tel.: (518) 458-8908
Web Site: http://www.anchoragency.com
Sales Range: $1-9.9 Million
Emp.: 21
Insurance Agencies & Brokerages
N.A.I.C.S.: 524210
Marvin A. Freedman (CEO)
Fred Stemp (Pres)
Steve Lobel (VP-Sls & Mktg)
Patricia Ross (VP-Fin Svcs)
Cindy Collins (Mgr-Acct-Bus Insurance)
Nancy Marr (Mgr-Acct-Employee Benefits & Fin Strategies)
Marylyn Raleigh (Mgr-Acct)

Pioneer Commercial Bank (1)
652 Albany Shaker Rd, Albany, NY 12211
Tel.: (518) 730-3999
Banking Services
N.A.I.C.S.: 522110

PIONEER STATE MUTUAL INSURANCE CO.
1510 N Elms Rd, Flint, MI 48532
Tel.: (810) 733-2300
Web Site: http://www.psmic.com
Sales Range: $50-74.9 Million
Emp.: 140
Auto & Home Insurance
N.A.I.C.S.: 524126
Lisa Lott (Treas & VP)

PIONEER STEEL CORPORATION
7447 Intervale St, Detroit, MI 48238
Tel.: (313) 933-9400
Web Site: http://www.pioneersteel-usa.com
Rev.: $17,400,000
Emp.: 55
Plates, Metal
N.A.I.C.S.: 423510
Gloria La Grant (Mgr-Inventory)
Jill Ryan (Dir-Admin)
Ronald Bebes (VP)

PIONEER SUPPLY COMPANY INC.
1710 N Franklin St, Pittsburgh, PA 15233
Tel.: (412) 471-5600
Web Site: http://www.pioneersupply.com
Year Founded: 1948
Sales Range: $10-24.9 Million
Emp.: 45
Supplier of Sign Making & Screen Printing Supplies
N.A.I.C.S.: 423840
James Davis (Pres)

PIONEER TELEPHONE
39 Darling Ave, South Portland, ME 04106
Web Site: http://www.pioneertelephone.com
Year Founded: 1995
Sales Range: $10-24.9 Million
Emp.: 32
Telephone Communication Services
N.A.I.C.S.: 517112
Susan Bouchard (Pres)

PIONEER TELEPHONE ASSOCIATION INC.
120 West Kansas Ave, Ulysses, KS 67880
Tel.: (620) 356-3211
Web Site: http://www.pioncomm.net
Year Founded: 1951
Rev.: $27,931,940
Emp.: 150
Local Telephone Communications
N.A.I.C.S.: 517121
Catherine Moyer (CEO & Gen Mgr)

PIONEER TELEPHONE COOPERATIVE
1304 Main St, Philomath, OR 97370
Tel.: (541) 929-3135
Web Site: http://www.pioneer.net
Rev.: $13,516,771
Emp.: 60
Local Telephone Communications
N.A.I.C.S.: 517121
Mike Whalen (Gen Mgr)
Ruth Witter (Mgr-Acctg)
Traci Landauer (Supvr-IT & Admin)

PIONEER TELEPHONE COOPERATIVE INC.
108 E Robberts Ave, Kingfisher, OK 73750-2742
Tel.: (405) 375-4111   OK
Web Site: http://www.ptci.com
Year Founded: 1953
Sales Range: $50-74.9 Million
Emp.: 600
Telephone Communications
N.A.I.C.S.: 517121
Richard Ruhl (Gen Mgr)
Tina Armentrount (Sec)

PIONEER TITLE COMPANY
8151 W Rifleman St, Boise, ID 83704
Tel.: (208) 377-2700
Web Site: http://www.pioneertitleco.com
Year Founded: 1949
Emp.: 250
Title Insurance
N.A.I.C.S.: 524127
Tim Bundgard (Pres & CEO)
Mike Ranieri (Sr VP & Mgr-Ada)
Jake Tunison (Mgr-Title Production-Boise)
John Doria (Dir-Corp Comm)
Cindy Truchot (CFO)
Jayna Wiesemann (Dir-HR)
Shellie Allen (VP & Mgr-Escrow)
Mark Anderson (Officer-Comml Title)
Heather Jensen (Officer-Long Term Escrow)
Sue Rich-Merritt (Officer-Escrow-Residential & Comml)

PIONEER TITLE COMPANY OF ADA COUNTY
8151 W Rifleman St, Boise, ID 83704
Tel.: (208) 377-2700
Web Site: http://www.pioneertitleco.com
Year Founded: 1949
Sales Range: $10-24.9 Million
Emp.: 98
Direct Title Insurance Services
N.A.I.C.S.: 524127
Tim Bundgard (Pres)

PIONEER TRANSPORTATION CORP.
2890 Arthur Kill Rd, Staten Island, NY 10309-1103
Tel.: (718) 984-8077   NY
Web Site: http://www.pioneerbus.com
Year Founded: 1972
Sales Range: $10-24.9 Million
Emp.: 50
School Bus Transportation Services
N.A.I.C.S.: 485410
Neil Strahl (Pres)

PIONEER VALLEY BOOKS
155A Industrial Dr, Northampton, MA 01060
Tel.: (413) 548-3906
Web Site: http://www.pioneervalleybooks.com
Year Founded: 1998
Sales Range: $1-9.9 Million
Emp.: 20
Retailer of Fiction, Nonfiction Books, Resources & Teaching Materials for Elementary Schools & Early Literacy Programs
N.A.I.C.S.: 611710

Michele Dufresne *(Principal)*
Lauri Yanis *(Dir-Sls & Mktg)*
Glen Bertrand *(Engr-Logistics)*

PIONEER WINDOW HOLDINGS INC.
3 Expressway Plz, Roslyn Heights, NY 11577
Tel.: (516) 822-7000
Web Site: http://www.pioneerwindows.com
Rev.: $31,573,000
Emp.: 200
Storm Doors Or Windows, Metal
N.A.I.C.S.: 332321
Joe Scolaro *(CFO)*
Vincent J. Amato Jr. *(Chm & CEO)*

Subsidiaries:

Pioneer Window & Door Mfg. Ltd. (1)
8 Fast Lane Headingley, Winnipeg, R4H 0C5, MB, Canada
Tel.: (204) 832-5586
Web Site: http://www.pioneerwindowanddoor.com
Window & Door Mfr
N.A.I.C.S.: 332321
Mike Marykuca *(Pres)*

Pioneer Windows Inc. (1)
15 Frederick Pl, Hicksville, NY 11801
Tel.: (516) 746-6337
Web Site: http://www.pioneerwindows.com
Window & Door (Prefabricated) Installation
N.A.I.C.S.: 238130
Vincent J. Amato *(Chm & CEO)*
Eric Miller *(Exec VP-Mfg)*

PIPE FABRICATING & SUPPLY COMPANY
1235 N Kraemer Ave, Anaheim, CA 92806
Tel.: (714) 630-5200
Web Site: http://www.pipefab.com
Year Founded: 1946
Sales Range: $10-24.9 Million
Emp.: 110
Mfr of Piping Equipment
N.A.I.C.S.: 332996
John Eagle *(VP)*
Ernest Simmons *(Pres)*
Jeff Huggard *(Mgr-Production)*

Subsidiaries:

Pipe Fabricating & Supply Company - Utah Plant (1)
2389 S 1100 West St, Woods Cross, UT 84087
Tel.: (801) 292-4471
Web Site: http://www.pipefabricatingandsupply.com
Emp.: 80
Fabricated Pipe Mfr
N.A.I.C.S.: 332996
Jeff Huggard *(VP & Plant Mgr)*

PIPE SYSTEMS INC.
199 Kay Industrial Dr, Lake Orion, MI 48359
Tel.: (248) 614-1700
Web Site: http://www.pipesystems.net
Year Founded: 1972
Sales Range: $10-24.9 Million
Emp.: 5
Mechanical Contractor
N.A.I.C.S.: 238220
Brent C. Gatecliff *(Pres, Treas & Sec)*

PIPE WELDERS INC.
2965 W State Rd 84, Fort Lauderdale, FL 33312
Tel.: (954) 587-8400
Web Site: http://www.pipewelders.com
Year Founded: 1956
Sales Range: $10-24.9 Million
Emp.: 80
Fabricated Structural Metal For Ships
N.A.I.C.S.: 332312
George M. Irvine Jr. *(Chm)*

Subsidiaries:

High Seas Technology, Inc. (1)
2965 W State Rd 84, Fort Lauderdale, FL 33312-4823
Tel.: (954) 584-6000
Web Site: http://www.highseastechnology.com
Sales Range: $1-9.9 Million
Emp.: 30
Marine Electronic Products Distr
N.A.I.C.S.: 423690
Steve Houle *(Mgr-Matls & Quality Control)*

P & R Canvas, Llc. (1)
2945 W State Rd 84, Fort Lauderdale, FL 33312
Tel.: (954) 689-8920
Web Site: http://www.prcanvas.com
Sales Range: $1-9.9 Million
Emp.: 16
Sporting & Recreational Goods & Supplies Merchant Whslr
N.A.I.C.S.: 423910

PIPECO SERVICES
20465 State Highway 249 Ste 200, Houston, TX 77070-2609
Tel.: (281) 955-3500 TX
Web Site: http://www.pipeco.com
Year Founded: 1981
Sales Range: $75-99.9 Million
Emp.: 25
Market Pipes; Pipe Fittings; Drilling Pipes
N.A.I.C.S.: 423810
Steve Tait *(VP-Ops)*

PIPEDRIVE INC.
460 Park Ave S, New York, NY 10016
Web Site: http://www.pipedrive.com
Year Founded: 2010
Pipeline Software Services
N.A.I.C.S.: 513210
Phillip T. Mellet *(Gen Counsel)*
Urmas Purde *(Founder)*
Jens Oberbeck *(VP-Sls)*
Laurence Capone *(CFO)*
Dan Dizon *(VP-Fin Plng & Analysis)*
Heidrun Luyt *(CMO)*
Dominic Allon *(CEO)*
Lisa Davis *(VP-Customer Success)*
Pete Harris *(COO)*
Andrea C. Johnson *(CIO)*

Subsidiaries:

Mailigen Limited (1)
Mailigen International Ltd 13A/F Podium Plaza, 5 Hanoi Road, Central, China (Hong Kong)
Tel.: (852) 58083721
Web Site: http://www.mailigen.com
Email Marketing Software
N.A.I.C.S.: 513210
Janis Rose *(Founder & CEO)*
Svetlana Rozenblate *(Head-Bus Dev and Partnerships)*
Monta Grinberga *(Mgr-Customer Service)*
Natalja Mihejeva *(Project Mgr)*
Janis Geranins *(Acct Mgr)*
Jason Adams Drake *(Head-Customer Success)*

Subsidiary (Non-US):

Mailigen China (2)
Landscape 1215 Chaoyang, Jingtai Xi Lu, Beijing, China
Tel.: (86) 1314 1353 182
Email Marketing Software
N.A.I.C.S.: 513210

Mailigen Europe (2)
Baznicas str 31 5th floor, LV-1010, Riga, Latvia
Tel.: (371) 67491059
Web Site: http://www.mailigen.com
Email Marketing Software
N.A.I.C.S.: 513210

Mailigen Russia (2)
Northern Tower 19th floor Testovskaya ulitsa 10, 123317, Moscow, Russia
Tel.: (7) 4995005614
Email Marketing Software
N.A.I.C.S.: 513210

PIPELINE BRICKELL
1101 Brickell Ave S Tower 8th Fl, Miami, FL 33131
Tel.: (305) 728-8830
Web Site: http://www.pipelinebrickell.com
Sales Range: $1-9.9 Million
High-Design Shared Workspace
N.A.I.C.S.: 561499
Todd Oretsky *(Co-Founder)*
Philippe Houdard *(Co-Founder)*
John Ramsey *(Dir-Ops & Fin)*
Josh Dubin *(Dir-Programs & Strategy)*
Seidy Sleiman *(Gen Mgr-Doral)*

PIPELINE OIL SALES INC.
744 E S St, Jackson, MI 49203-4462
Tel.: (517) 784-3400 MI
Year Founded: 1987
Sales Range: $10-24.9 Million
Emp.: 93
Sales of Petroleum Products
N.A.I.C.S.: 424720
James F. Ahearn *(Chm & Pres)*
Jeffery L. Hansen *(VP-Fin)*

Subsidiaries:

Buddy's Mini Marts, Inc. (1)
744 E South St, Jackson, MI 49203-4462
Tel.: (517) 784-3400
Sales Range: $10-24.9 Million
Emp.: 5
Convenience Store Services
N.A.I.C.S.: 445131

PIPELINE PETROLEUM, INC.
Shippers Rd, Macungie, PA 18062
Tel.: (610) 967-2227 PA
Web Site: http://www.pipelineonline.com
Year Founded: 1968
Sales Range: $25-49.9 Million
Emp.: 170
Supplier of Petroleum Products
N.A.I.C.S.: 424720
Stanley Ebert *(Founder)*

PIPELINE PUBLIC RELATIONS & MARKETING
6823 SE 18th Ave Ste D, Portland, OR 97202
Tel.: (503) 546-7811
Web Site: http://www.pipelineprm.com
Year Founded: 2008
Sales Range: Less than $1 Million
Emp.: 1
Public Relations & Marketing
N.A.I.C.S.: 541820
Timm Locke *(Principal)*

PIPELINE RESEARCH COUNCIL INTERNATIONAL
3141 Fairview Park Dr Ste 525, Falls Church, VA 22042
Tel.: (703) 205-1600 DE
Web Site: http://www.prci.org
Year Founded: 1999
Sales Range: $10-24.9 Million
Emp.: 15
Research & Development Services
N.A.I.C.S.: 541715
Jason Riley *(Mgr-Facility)*
Natalie M. Tessel *(Mgr-Membership & Comm)*
Max Toch *(Sr Mgr-Res)*
Steven Trevino *(Program Mgr-Ops & Integrity)*
Hans Deeb *(Project Mgr)*

PIPELINE SUPPLY INCORPORATED
620 16th Ave S, Hopkins, MN 55343-7833
Tel.: (952) 935-0445 MN
Web Site: http://www.pipeline-supply.com
Year Founded: 1977
Sales Range: $10-24.9 Million
Emp.: 80
Provider of Plumbing & Pipe Supplies
N.A.I.C.S.: 423720
Dan Normandin *(Mgr-Warehouse)*
Mike Bickman *(Mgr)*
Kurt Christopherson *(Mgr)*

PIPELINERX
600 California St Ste 520, San Francisco, CA 94108
Tel.: (847) 696-9101
Web Site: http://www.pipelinerx.com
Year Founded: 2009
Sales Range: $10-24.9 Million
Emp.: 120
Medication Management Services
N.A.I.C.S.: 456110
Brian Roberts *(CEO)*
Chuck Dunlap *(Exec VP-Customer Dev & Experience)*
Chris Ciolko *(Sr VP-Bus Dev)*
Eric Carter *(CTO)*
Ben Buxton *(VP-Engrg)*
Steve Lien *(CFO)*

Subsidiaries:

Evolute Consolidated Holdings, Inc. (1)
6455 S Yosemite St Ste 715, Greenwood Village, CO 80111-5139
Tel.: (425) 463-4400
Web Site: http://www.evolutechi.com
Information Technology Consulting Services
N.A.I.C.S.: 541690

Subsidiary (Domestic):

Midtech Partners, Inc. (2)
7000 S Yosemite St Ste 200, Centennial, CO 80112
Tel.: (303) 694-6029
Web Site: http://www.midtechpartners.com
Computer Related Services
N.A.I.C.S.: 541512

PIPER AIRCRAFT, INC.
2926 Piper Dr, Vero Beach, FL 32960
Tel.: (772) 567-4361 DE
Web Site: http://www.piper.com
Year Founded: 1995
Sales Range: $125-149.9 Million
Emp.: 750
Personal, Training, Utility & Business Aircraft Mfr
N.A.I.C.S.: 336411
Chuck Glass *(Dir-Fleet Sls)*
John Calcagno *(CFO)*
Drew McEwen *(VP-Intl & Direct Sls)*
Jim Funk *(COO)*
Enrico Evers *(Dir-Sls-EMEA)*
Hans Stancil *(Gen Mgr-Sls-America)*
Ron Gunnarson *(VP-Sls, Mktg & Customer Support)*
R. D. Wooten *(Dir-Sls-Arizona, Nevada & New Mexico Territory)*
Kevin M. Keegan *(Gen Counsel)*

PIPER PLASTICS INC
1840 Enterprise CT, Libertyville, IL 60048
Tel.: (847) 367-0110 IL
Web Site: http://www.piperplastics.com
Year Founded: 1982
Sales Range: $10-24.9 Million
Emp.: 135
Machine Shop, Jobbing & Repair Services
N.A.I.C.S.: 332710

Piper Plastics Inc—(Continued)

Pamela Teixeira *(Mgr-Production Control)*
Janet Bennett-Hanchon *(Coord-Production)*

PIPERGY, INC.
2096 Skull Creek Rd, Sundance, WY 82715
Tel.: (307) 746-8673 WY
Year Founded: 2020
Oil & Gas Pipeline Maintenance Services
N.A.I.C.S.: 237120
Thomas J. Mohnen *(CEO & Interim CFO)*
Alan Josselyn *(Pres)*
J. Paul Geeding Jr. *(Chm & COO)*

PIPING & EQUIPMENT CO., INC.
1111 E 37th St N, Wichita, KS 67219-3516
Tel.: (316) 838-7511
Web Site: http://www.pipingequ.com
Year Founded: 1946
Sales Range: $25-49.9 Million
Emp.: 120
Sewer Construction Services
N.A.I.C.S.: 237110
John Wadsworth *(Pres)*

PIPING ALLOYS INC.
13899 W 101st St, Lenexa, KS 66215-1211
Tel.: (913) 677-3833
Web Site: http://www.pipingalloys.com
Sales Range: $10-24.9 Million
Emp.: 15
Plumbing Fittings & Supplies
N.A.I.C.S.: 423720
William G. Wilt *(Pres)*

PIPING ROCK CLUB
150 Piping Rock Rd, Locust Valley, NY 11560
Tel.: (516) 676-2332 NY
Web Site: http://www.pipingrockclub.org
Year Founded: 1911
Sales Range: $10-24.9 Million
Emp.: 216
Golf Club
N.A.I.C.S.: 713910
Andy Hauser *(Gen Mgr)*
Jose A. Alvarez *(Mgr-Maintenance)*
Michael Curti *(Controller)*
Daniel Rekus *(Asst Mgr)*

PIPING TECHNOLOGY & PRODUCTS INC.
3701 Holmes Rd, Houston, TX 77051
Tel.: (713) 731-0030
Web Site: http://www.pipingtech.com
Year Founded: 1975
Sales Range: $25-49.9 Million
Emp.: 6,700
Spring Hangers & Miscellaneous Steel Fabricated Items Mfr
N.A.I.C.S.: 332919
Randy Bailey *(VP)*
Durga D. Agrawal *(Pres)*
John Demusz *(Mgr-US Bellows)*
Aundrela Durham *(Mgr-Small & Fast Quotations)*
Ram K. Garg *(Mgr-Engrg)*
Courtney Chadwell *(Mgr-Mfg)*
David Baker *(Gen Mgr)*
David Smith *(Mgr-Admin & Material Control)*
Jerry Godina *(Mgr-Quality Control)*
R. K. Agrawal *(VP)*
Vijay Jaswal *(Mgr-Quotations)*
Woodie Osteen *(Mgr-Safety)*

Subsidiaries:

Fronek Anchor Darling Enterprises, Inc   (1)
86 Doris Ray Ct, Laconia, NH 03246
Tel.: (603) 528-1931
Web Site: http://www.pipingtech.com
Sales Range: $25-49.9 Million
Emp.: 10
Mechanical & Hydraulic Snubbers Mfr
N.A.I.C.S.: 332912
Walter Paszul *(Gen Mgr)*

Pipe Shields, Inc.   (1)
5199 Fulton Dr, Fairfield, CA 94534
Tel.: (800) 538-7007
Pipe Clamp Mfr
N.A.I.C.S.: 332722

Sweco Fab, Inc.   (1)
3701 Holmes Rd, Houston, TX 77051-1545
Tel.: (713) 731-0030
Web Site: http://www.swecofab.com
Rev.: $1,100,000
Emp.: 700
Pressure Vessels & Tank Mfr
N.A.I.C.S.: 332919
Randy Bailey *(VP)*
Durga D. Agrawal *(Pres & CEO)*

U.S. Bellows, Inc.   (1)
3701 Holmes Rd, Houston, TX 77051
Tel.: (281) 241-9418
Web Site: http://www.usbellows.com
Fabricated Structural Metal Mfr
N.A.I.C.S.: 332312
John T. Demusz *(Mgr)*

PIPITONE GROUP
3933 Perrysville Ave, Pittsburgh, PA 15214
Tel.: (412) 321-0879
Web Site: http://www.pipitonegroup.com
Graphic Design Services
N.A.I.C.S.: 541430
Augie Aggazio *(VP-Interactive)*
Vince Maffessanti *(Mgr-Creative Svcs)*
Scott Witalis *(VP-Client Mktg)*
Gary Adams *(Principal)*
Kim Tarquinio *(Dir-Acct Svcs)*
Marc Newman *(CFO)*
Ron Moehler *(Principal)*
Scott Pipitone *(Pres & CEO)*
Grace Calland *(Acct Suprv)*
Leah Moore *(Dir-Digital Mktg)*
Ian Syphard *(Sr Project Mgr-Interactive)*

Subsidiaries:

Push Seven, Inc.   (1)
100 1st Ave Ste 700, Pittsburgh, PA 15222
Tel.: (412) 745-7777
Web Site: http://www.push7agency.com
Sales Range: $1-9.9 Million
Advertising & Public Relations Agency
N.A.I.C.S.: 541810
John Millea *(Pres)*

PIRAEUS DATA LLC.
1408 4th Ave Ste 400, Seattle, WA 98101
Tel.: (206) 577-0025
Web Site: http://www.piraeusdata.com
Year Founded: 2006
Sales Range: $1-9.9 Million
Emp.: 33
Information Technology Consulting Services
N.A.I.C.S.: 541512
Abel Gonzalez *(Dir-Fin & Ops)*

PIRS CAPITAL, LLC
40 Exchange Pl, New York, NY 10005
Web Site: http://www.pirscapital.com
Year Founded: 2012
Sales Range: $10-24.9 Million
Emp.: 12
Financial Consulting Services

N.A.I.C.S.: 541611
Andrew Mallinger *(COO)*
Igor Shliosberg *(Chief Compliance Officer)*
Jacob Shimon *(CMO)*
Mitchell Rubin *(CFO)*
Matt Washington *(Chief Revenue Officer)*

PISCATAQUA LANDSCAPIING & TREE SERVICE
26 Maclellan Ln, Eliot, ME 03903
Tel.: (207) 439-2241
Web Site: http://piscataqualandscaping.com
Landscaping Services
N.A.I.C.S.: 561730
Justin Gamester *(Pres)*

PISCHKE MOTORS, INC.
1460 W City Hwy 16, West Salem, WI 54669
Tel.: (608) 786-1150
Web Site: http://www.pischke.com
Sales Range: $10-24.9 Million
Emp.: 40
Car Whslr
N.A.I.C.S.: 441110
Callie Stanhope *(Office Mgr)*

PISMO COAST VILLAGE, INC.
165 S Dolliver St, Pismo Beach, CA 93449
Tel.: (805) 773-5649 CA
Web Site: https://www.pismocoastvillage.com
Year Founded: 1975
Rev.: $9,750,627
Assets: $27,253,168
Liabilities: $3,228,687
Net Worth: $24,024,481
Earnings: $988,463
Emp.: 48
Fiscal Year-end: 09/30/23
Resort Management Services
N.A.I.C.S.: 721211
Rodney Enns *(VP-Ops)*
Terris Hughes *(Chm)*
Jack Williams *(CFO & VP-Fin)*
Karen King *(VP)*
Brian J. Skaggs *(Sec)*
George Pappi Jr. *(Exec VP)*

PISTON GROUP, LLC
12723 Telegraph Rd, Redford, MI 48239-1489
Tel.: (313) 541-8674 MI
Web Site: https://www.pistongroup.com
Year Founded: 1995
Sales Range: $200-249.9 Million
Emp.: 10,340
Offices of Other Holding Companies
N.A.I.C.S.: 551112
Vinnie Johnson *(Bd of Dirs, Founder, Founder, Chm, Chm, CEO, CEO & Grp Chm)*
Bob Holloway *(Grp COO)*
Hughey Newsome *(CFO)*
Rosana Moura Garbacik *(Gen Counsel)*
Mamadou Diallo *(CEO)*

Subsidiaries:

Piston Automotive   (1)
12723 Telegraph Rd, Redford, MI 48239-1489   (100%)
Tel.: (313) 541-8674
Web Site: http://www.pistongroup.com
Sales Range: $75-99.9 Million
Emp.: 98
Automotive Parts Assemblies of Cooling Modules & Brake Corner Modules
N.A.I.C.S.: 336110

Subsidiary (Domestic):

Irvin Automotive Products Inc.   (2)
2600 Centerpoint Pkwy, Pontiac, MI 48341
Tel.: (248) 451-4100
Web Site: http://www.irvinautomotive.com
Automotive Interior Trim Mfr & Distr
N.A.I.C.S.: 336360
Justin Szerlong *(VP)*

PIT STOP GAS INC.
PO Box 4412, Topeka, KS 66604-0412
Tel.: (785) 478-9787
Sales Range: $10-24.9 Million
Emp.: 8
Petroleum Brokers
N.A.I.C.S.: 424720
John Akin *(Pres)*

PITA PIT USA, INC.
105 N 4th St Ste 208, Coeur D'Alene, ID 83814
Tel.: (208) 765-3326 ID
Web Site: http://www.pitapitusa.com
Year Founded: 2004
Sales Range: $10-24.9 Million
Emp.: 110
Restaurant Franchise
N.A.I.C.S.: 722513
Jack T. Riggs *(Chm)*
Nelson Lang *(Founder)*
Brenda Zosel Bookholtz *(VP-Acctg & Fin)*
Paul Erwin *(VP-Admin)*
Corey Bowman *(VP)*
Peter Riggs *(CEO)*
Benjamin Drake *(VP-Product Dev)*
Bill Wilfong *(VP-Restaurant Ops)*
Stephanie Powers *(VP-Field Ops)*
C. Lee Strait *(VP-Legal Affairs)*
Robert J. Fasnacht *(Gen Counsel & Sec)*
Doug Reifschneider *(VP-Mktg)*

PITCAIRN FINANCIAL GROUP
1 Pitcairn Pl 165 Township Line Rd Ste 3000, Jenkintown, PA 19046
Tel.: (215) 887-6700
Web Site: http://www.pitcairn.com
Year Founded: 1923
Sales Range: $10-24.9 Million
Emp.: 60
Investment Counseling Services
N.A.I.C.S.: 523940
Leslie C. Voth *(Chm, Pres & CEO)*
Brett Scola *(Dir-Family Wealth Strategy-Washington)*
Eric W. Gaul *(CFO)*
Harold F. Pitcairn *(Chief Investment Officer)*
Laurie Ressin Martin *(Mng Dir & Head-Washington)*
Richard E. Borowy *(Dir-Alternative Investments)*
Susan Devlin *(Dir-IT)*
Ronna J. Gyllenhaal *(Dir-Mktg)*
Dain Kistner *(Dir-Strategy)*
Matthew R. Hilbert *(Dir-Tax)*
Alanson B. Houghton *(Mng Dir)*
Andrew L. Busser *(Mng Dir)*

PITLIK & WICK, INC.
8075 County Road D, Eagle River, WI 54521
Tel.: (715) 479-7488
Web Site: http://www.pitlikandwick.com
Construction Company
N.A.I.C.S.: 236220
Austin Pitlik *(Civil Engr)*

Subsidiaries:

Northern Lakes Concrete, Inc.   (1)
8075 County Road D, Eagle River, WI 54521
Tel.: (715) 479-5014
Web Site: http://www.northernlakesconcrete.com

COMPANIES

Ready Mixed Concrete & Concrete Pumping
N.A.I.C.S.: 238110
Brian Stefonik (Mng Dir)

PITMON OIL & GAS CO.
101 N C St, Davis, OK 73030
Tel.: (580) 369-3135
Rev.: $15,493,774
Emp.: 60
Gasoline Services
N.A.I.C.S.: 424720
Jack Pitmon (CEO)

PITSCO INC.
915 E Jefferson St, Pittsburg, KS 66762
Tel.: (620) 231-0000
Web Site: http://www.pitsco.com
Sales Range: $10-24.9 Million
Emp.: 200
Commercial Equipment
N.A.I.C.S.: 423440
Harvey Dean (CEO)
Lisa Paterni (Pres)
Nancy Peterson (Dir-Educator Insights & Bus Intelligence)
Kelly Reddin (Mgr-Educational Svcs)
Kyle Bailey (Mgr-Mfg)
Robin White-Mussa (VP-Sls)
Matt Frankenbery (VP-Education)
Sharon Dean (Treas & Sec)
Jason Hill (Engr-Education & R&D)

PITSS AMERICA LLC
3150 Livernois Rd Ste 285, Troy, MI 48083
Tel.: (248) 740-0935
Web Site: http://www.pitss.eu
Year Founded: 2007
Sales Range: $1-9.9 Million
Emp.: 10
Application Software Distr
N.A.I.C.S.: 423430
Andreas Gaede (Co-Founder & Co-Pres-Global)
Michael Kilimann (Co-Founder & Co-Pres-Global)

PITT AUTO ELECTRIC COMPANY
4085 Alpha Dr, Allison Park, PA 15101-2961
Tel.: (412) 487-5075   PA
Web Site: http://www.pittauto.com
Year Founded: 1938
Distributes Industrial Machinery & Equipment
N.A.I.C.S.: 423830
Thomas M. Tiernan (Pres)
Dick Eiseman (VP)

PITT-OHIO EXPRESS INC.
15 27th St, Pittsburgh, PA 15222-4729
Tel.: (412) 232-3015   PA
Web Site: http://www.pittohio.com
Year Founded: 1990
Sales Range: $75-99.9 Million
Emp.: 1,750
Provider of Local Trucking Services
N.A.I.C.S.: 484122
Charles L. Hammel (Pres)
Ron Uriah (VP-Safety)
Candi Cybator (Mgr-Mktg & PR)

PITTCON INDUSTRIES
6409 Rhode Island Ave, Riverdale, MD 20737
Tel.: (301) 927-1000
Web Site: http://www.pittconindustries.com
Year Founded: 1956
Sales Range: $1-9.9 Million
Emp.: 25
Metalwork Producer
N.A.I.C.S.: 332119
Jerry Weberman (Gen Mgr)
Sheila Kovalchick (Mgr-Acctg)
Nathan Goldstein (Mgr-Credit)
Bob Welgand (Project Mgr)
Bob Wiest (Project Mgr)

Subsidiaries:

Architectural Art Mfg. Inc.   (1)
6409 Rhode Island Ave, Riverdale, MD 20737
Tel.: (316) 838-4291
Web Site: http://www.archart.com
Bronze, Aluminum, Stainless Steel & Component Expansion Joint Covers Railing System Mfr
N.A.I.C.S.: 332312
Jerry Weberman (Gen Mgr)

PITTMAN CONSTRUCTION COMPANY
1487 Farmer Rd NW, Conyers, GA 30012
Tel.: (770) 922-8660
Web Site: http://www.pittman-construction.com
Sales Range: $10-24.9 Million
Emp.: 20
General Contractor, Highway & Street Construction
N.A.I.C.S.: 237310
Louie A. Pittman (CEO)
Jim Mann (CFO)

PITTS TOYOTA INC.
210 N Jefferson St, Dublin, GA 31021
Tel.: (478) 272-3244
Web Site: http://www.pittstoyota.com
Rev.: $20,000,000
Emp.: 50
Automobiles, New & Used
N.A.I.C.S.: 441110
James Dixon (Mgr-Sls)
Joey Wilson (Asst Mgr-Estimator Pitts Collision Center)
Nick Camarota (Gen Mgr)
Steve Winter (Mgr-Sls)

PITTSBURG TANK & TOWER CO., INC.
1 Watertank Pl, Henderson, KY 42420
Tel.: (270) 826-9000   KS
Web Site: http://www.watertank.com
Year Founded: 1983
Rev.: $30,160,966
Emp.: 400
Fabricated Plate Work
N.A.I.C.S.: 332420
Ben Johnston (Exec VP-Specialty Svcs-Elevated Div)
Rick Dizinno (VP)
Don Johnston (CEO)

PITTSBURGH CULTURAL TRUST
803 Liberty Ave, Pittsburgh, PA 15222
Tel.: (412) 471-6070   PA
Web Site: http://www.trustarts.org
Year Founded: 1984
Sales Range: $50-74.9 Million
Emp.: 492
Arts Promotion Services
N.A.I.C.S.: 711310
Carroll de Vera Roberts (Mgr-Bd Engagement & Exec Special Projects)
Vanessa Braun (Mgr-Employee Engagement & Inclusion & Asst Dir-Accessibility)
Tracy Edmunds (VP-Arts Education)
Rona L. Nesbit (Exec VP)
Lisa Leibering (Mgr-School & Community Programs)

PITTSBURGH FOUNDATION
5 PPG Pl Ste 250, Pittsburgh, PA 15222
Tel.: (412) 391-5122   PA
Web Site: http://www.pittsburghfoundation.org
Year Founded: 1945
Sales Range: $100-124.9 Million
Emp.: 45
Grantmaking Services
N.A.I.C.S.: 813211
Jonathan Brelsford (VP-Fin & Investments)
Katie , Robson (Dir-IT)
Maxwell King (Pres & CEO)
Yvonne Maher (Sr VP-Dev & Donor Svcs)
Edith L. Shapira (Chm)
John C. Harmon (Vice Chm)
Walter H. Smith (Sec)
Kim Fleming (Treas)
Doug Root (VP-Comm)
Jeanne Pearlman (Sr VP-Program & Policy)

PITTSBURGH HISTORY & LANDMARKS FOUNDATION
100 W Station Square Dr Ste 450, Pittsburgh, PA 15219
Tel.: (412) 471-5808   PA
Web Site: http://www.phlf.org
Year Founded: 1964
Sales Range: $1-9.9 Million
Emp.: 29
Historical Resource Preservation Services
N.A.I.C.S.: 712110
Louise Sturgess (Exec Dir)
Thomas Keffer (Mgr-Property & Construction)
Umer Humayun (Project Mgr)
Jack Norris (Chm)
Kevin P. Allen (Co-Vice Chm)
David M. Brashear (Co-Vice Chm)
Selene L. Davis (Sec)
Mary Lu Denny (Dir-Membership Services)
Arthur P. Ziegler Jr. (Pres)
Ronald C. Yochum Jr. (CIO)

PITTSBURGH MERCY HEALTH SYSTEM, INC.
1200 Reedsdale St, Pittsburgh, PA 15233
Tel.: (412) 323-4542
Web Site: http://www.pmhs.org
Healthcare Services & Programs
N.A.I.C.S.: 813410
Susan Welsh (Pres & CEO)
Todd Wahrenberger (Chief Medical Officer)
Richard L. Finley (Chm)

Subsidiaries:

Bethlehem Haven   (1)
Fifth Ave Commons 905 Watson St, Pittsburgh, PA 15219
Tel.: (412) 391-1348
Web Site: http://www.bethlehemhaven.org
Sales Range: $1-9.9 Million
Emp.: 50
Emergency Shelter, Health & Employment Services
N.A.I.C.S.: 624221
Caroline Woodward (Chief Officer-Philanthropic Engagement & Strategic Initiatives)
Sharon R. H. Higginbotham (COO)
Deborah W. Linhart (CEO)
Sarah Dittoe (Mgr-Residential)

PITTSBURGH OPERA
2425 Liberty Ave, Pittsburgh, PA 15222
Tel.: (412) 281-0912   PA
Web Site: http://www.pittsburghopera.org
Year Founded: 1955
Sales Range: $1-9.9 Million
Emp.: 246

PITTSBURGH WATER & SEWER AUTHORITY

Opera Concert Organizer
N.A.I.C.S.: 711130
Michele Fabrizi (Chm)
Antony Walker (Dir-Music)
Susan Solito (Office Mgr)
William J. Powers (Dir-Admin & Artistic Ops)
Emily Grand (Mgr-Ops & Resident Artist Program)
Marilyn Michalka Egan (Dir-Education)
Gene Welsh (Treas)
Christopher Hahn (Gen Dir)
Michele Atkins (Sec)

PITTSBURGH PIPE & SUPPLY CORP
170 Humboldt Ave, Saint Louis, MO 63147
Tel.: (314) 383-5300
Web Site: http://www.pittsburghpipe.com
Sales Range: $25-49.9 Million
Emp.: 95
Steel Pipe & Tubes
N.A.I.C.S.: 331210
Joseph A. Bergfeld (CEO)
Jerry Brookshire (Mgr-Pur)
Jenny Cavinder (CFO)
Steve Crane (Mgr-Ops)
Kevin Davidson (Mgr-Sls-Steel Products)
Robert Naumann (Mgr-Sls-Telecom Products)

PITTSBURGH POND CO.
331 Coxcomb Hill Rd, New Kensington, PA 15038
Tel.: (724) 335-6688
Year Founded: 2000
Sales Range: $25-49.9 Million
Emp.: 8
Nursery, Garden Center & Farm Supply Retailer
N.A.I.C.S.: 444240
Bill Kubrick (Owner)

PITTSBURGH STEELERS SPORTS INC.
3400 S Water St, Pittsburgh, PA 15203-2349
Tel.: (412) 432-7800   PA
Web Site: http://www.steelers.com
Year Founded: 1933
Sales Range: $50-74.9 Million
Emp.: 130
Professional Football Franchise & Sports Arena
N.A.I.C.S.: 711211
Kevin Colbert (Vice Pres & Gen Mgr)
John Wodarek (Mgr-Entertainment & Mktg)
Omar Khan (VP-Football & Bus Admin)
John L. Stallworth (Owner)
Blayre Holmes Davis (Dir-Community Rels)
Arthur J. Rooney II (Co-Owner & Pres)

Subsidiaries:

PSSI Stadium Corporation   (1)
900 Art Rooney Ave, Pittsburgh, PA 15212-5721
Tel.: (412) 697-7150
Web Site: http://www.steelers.com
Sports & Entertainment Facility Operator
N.A.I.C.S.: 711310
Jim Sacco (VP-Stadium Ops & Mgmt)

PITTSBURGH WATER & SEWER AUTHORITY
1200 Penn Ave Penn Liberty Plz, Pittsburgh, PA 15222-2219
Tel.: (412) 255-8935
Web Site: http://www.pgh2o.com

PITTSBURGH WATER & SEWER AUTHORITY

Pittsburgh Water & Sewer Authority—(Continued)
Year Founded: 1984
Sales Range: $25-49.9 Million
Emp.: 241
Provider of Water Services
N.A.I.C.S.: 221310
Margaret L. Lanier (Vice Chm)
Rick Obermeier (Dir-Field Svcs)
Barbara Curry (Mgr-HR)
Tracy Smith (Officer-Open Records)
Kelley Benson (Dir-HR)
Kent Lindsay (Dir-Fin)
Deb Gross (Asst Sec)
Paul Leger (Treas)

PITTSFIELD CO-OPERATIVE BANK
70 S St, Pittsfield, MA 01201
Tel.: (413) 447-7304   MA
Web Site:
   http://www.pittsfieldcoop.com
Year Founded: 1889
Sales Range: $10-24.9 Million
Emp.: 50
Provider of Banking Services
N.A.I.C.S.: 522110
Evan Robitaille (VP)
Jay Anderson (Pres & CEO)
Eric Padelford (CTO & Sr VP)

PITTSFIELD PRODUCTS INC.
5741 Jackson Rd, Ann Arbor, MI 48103
Tel.: (734) 665-3771
Web Site:
   http://www.pittsfieldproducts.com
Rev.: $23,400,000
Emp.: 45
Filters, General Line: Industrial
N.A.I.C.S.: 333998
Theodore Fosdick (Pres)
Diane Bach (Mgr-Traffic)

PIVOT INTERIORS INC.
2740 Zanker Rd Ste 100, San Jose, CA 95134
Tel.: (408) 432-5600
Web Site:
   http://www.pivotinteriors.com
Year Founded: 1973
Sales Range: $150-199.9 Million
Emp.: 130
Office & Public Building Furniture
N.A.I.C.S.: 423210
Ken Baugh (Pres & Acting CFO)
Donna Clervi (VP & Dir-Healthcare)
Heidi Ferguson (Office Mgr)
Caryn Fairlie (Dir-A&D)

PIVOT INTERNATIONAL, INC.
10932 Strang Line Rd, Shawnee Mission, KS 66215
Tel.: (913) 312-6900   KS
Web Site: http://www.pivotint.com
Year Founded: 1972
Sales Range: $50-74.9 Million
Emp.: 50
Timing Devices, Electronic
N.A.I.C.S.: 335314
Mark Dohnalek (Pres & CEO)
Dave Coughlin (Dir-Global Ops)
Tom Tougas (Dir-Global Engrg)
Daryl Seck (Dir-Acct Mgmt & Bus Dev)
Adam Kiburz (Sr Dir-Field Application Solutions & Bus Dev)
Chris Kielian (Owner)
Steve Brown (VP-Global Quality)
Robert Spaedy (CFO)
Subsidiaries:
Digittron Technologies, Inc.   (1)
23875 W 83rd Ter, Shawnee, KS 66227
Tel.: (913) 441-0221
Web Site: http://www.digittron.com
Rev.: $2,900,000

Emp.: 24
Bare Printed Circuit Board Mfr
N.A.I.C.S.: 334412
Joann Turnbaugh (CFO)

PIVOT3, INC.
816 Congress Ave Ste 970, Austin, TX 78701
Tel.: (512) 807-2666
Web Site: http://www.pivot3.com
Year Founded: 2003
Sales Range: $25-49.9 Million
Emp.: 95
Software Publishing Services
N.A.I.C.S.: 513210
Curt Wittich (VP-Worldwide Sls)
Bill Galloway (Founder & CTO)
Ron Nash (Chm & CEO)
Mike Dansby (CFO & VP)
Daniel Keelan (Exec VP)
Brad Ross (VP)
Bruce Milne (CMO & VP)
Ahmad Chamseddine (COO & VP)
Mark Maisano (VP-Channel Sls)
Rance Poehler (Chief Revenue Officer & VP-Global Sls)
Dan Flood (VP-Sls)
Jeff Jordan (VP-Federal Sls)

PIVOTAL ACQUISITION CORP.
The Chrysler Bldg 405 Lexington Ave 11th Fl, New York, NY 10174
Tel.: (212) 818-8800   DE
Web Site: http://www.pivotalac.com
Year Founded: 2018
Assets: $152,342
Liabilities: $128,469
Net Worth: $23,873
Earnings: ($1,127)
Fiscal Year-end: 12/31/18
Investment Services
N.A.I.C.S.: 523999
Subsidiaries:
KLDiscovery, Inc.   (1)
9023 Columbine Rd, Eden Prairie, MN 55347
Tel.: (703) 288-3380
Web Site: https://www.kldiscovery.com
Rev.: $317,432,000
Assets: $619,442,000
Liabilities: $585,751,000
Net Worth: $33,691,000
Earnings: ($43,174,000)
Emp.: 1,163
Fiscal Year-end: 12/31/2022
Electronic Discovery Software Development Services
N.A.I.C.S.: 541511
Ferdinand Cami (VP-Hosting Svcs-Global)
Dawn M. Wilson (CFO)
Robert Hunter (Exec VP-IT & eDiscovery Ops-Global)
Andy Southam (Gen Counsel)
Daniel Balthaser (Exec VP-Engrg)
Meghan Del Monaco (VP-LT Project Mgmt-Global)
Gabriela P. Baron (Exec VP-Strategy)
Lindsey Hammond (Sr VP)
Jill Wickenden (VP-LT Sls)
Christopher J. Weiler (CEO)
Danny Zambito (COO)
Krystina Jones (Chief Revenue Officer)
Mike Burmeister (VP-Ops-Global, Data, Storage Technologies)
Julian Sheppard (VP-Forensic Svcs & Smp-EMEA Ops, Global)
Lawrence B. Prior III (Chm)
Lawrence B. Prior III (Chm)
Subsidiary (Domestic):
Kroll Ontrack, LLC   (2)
9023 Columbine Rd, Eden Prairie, MN 55347-4182
Tel.: (952) 937-5161
Web Site: http://www.krollontrack.com
Emp.: 1,100
Lost Data Protection & Recovering Services
N.A.I.C.S.: 518210
Todd R. Johnson (VP-Data & Storage Tech-Americas & Asia Pacific)

Gregory A. Olson (Sr VP-Worldwide Data Recovery & Software)
Cathleen Peterson (Sr VP-Consulting, Client Svcs & Ops)
Steve Schley (VP-Mktg)
Shawn Abbas (VP-Fin)
Christopher Weiler (CEO)
Subsidiary (Non-US):
KLDiscovery Ontrack Canada Co.   (3)
155 Gordon Baker Road Suite 100, Toronto, M2H 3N7, ON, Canada
Tel.: (416) 491-1650
Web Site: https://www.ontrack.com
Data Recovery Software Publisher Services
N.A.I.C.S.: 513210
Kroll Ontrack (HK) Ltd.   (3)
148 Electric Road 12/F Unit1203A North Point, Wanchai, China (Hong Kong)
Tel.: (852) 2586 5805
Web Site:
   http://www.ontrackdatarecovery.com.hk
Data Recovery Software Publisher
N.A.I.C.S.: 513210
Christopher Weiler (CEO)
Peter Bohret (COO)
Phil Bridge (Pres)
Kroll Ontrack (Switzerland) GmbH   (3)
Hertistrasse 25, 8304, Wallisellen, Switzerland
Tel.: (41) 448773090
Web Site: http://www.datenrettung.ch
Software Development Services
N.A.I.C.S.: 513210
Kroll Ontrack Belgium   (3)
Bargiestraat 15b, 8400, Ypres, Belgium
Tel.: (32) 2 512 30 22
Web Site:
   http://www.ontrackdatarecovery.be
Software Development Services
N.A.I.C.S.: 541511
Kroll Ontrack GmbH   (3)
Hanns-Klemm-Strasse 5, Boblingen, 71034, Germany
Tel.: (49) 7031 644 0
Web Site: http://www.krollontrack.de
Emp.: 60
Software Development Services
N.A.I.C.S.: 513210
Peter Boehret (VP)
Kroll Ontrack Limited   (3)
Global House 1 Ashley Avenue, Epsom, KT18 5AD, Surrey, United Kingdom
Tel.: (44) 1372741999
Web Site: http://www.ontrack.com
Emp.: 30
Computer Services
N.A.I.C.S.: 541519
Philip Bridge (Mng Dir)
Kroll Ontrack Pty Ltd.   (3)
9/28 Donkin St, West End, 4101, QLD, Australia
Tel.: (61) 299591035
Web Site: http://www.ontrack.com
Software Development Services
N.A.I.C.S.: 513210
Adrian Briscoe (Gen Mgr)
Kroll Ontrack SARL   (3)
2 impasse de la Noisette, 91371, Verrieres-le-Buisson, Cedex 413, France
Tel.: (33) 169536699
Web Site: http://www.ontrack.fr
Lost Data Protection & Recovering Services
N.A.I.C.S.: 518210
Kroll Ontrack Sp. z o.o.   (3)
ul Jana III Sobieskiego 11, 40-082, Katowice, Poland
Tel.: (48) 327799999
Web Site: http://www.krollontrack.pl
Software Development Services
N.A.I.C.S.: 541511
Branch (Domestic):
LDiscovery, LLC - Fort Lauderdale   (2)
3215 NW 10th Ter Ste 210, Fort Lauderdale, FL 33309
Tel.: (954) 462-0855

U.S. PRIVATE

Web Site: http://ldiscovery.com
Electronic Discovery Management Solutions
N.A.I.C.S.: 513210
LDiscovery, LLC - Philadelphia   (2)
321 Norristown Rd Ste 110, Ambler, PA 19002
Tel.: (215) 646-1299
Web Site: http://ldiscovery.com
Other Business Service Centers, including Copy Shops
N.A.I.C.S.: 561439
Subsidiary (Domestic):
Superior Document Service Inc.   (2)
700 E Main St, Richmond, VA 23219
Tel.: (804) 648-2800
Web Site: http://www.sdsdiscovery.com
Other Computer Related Services
N.A.I.C.S.: 541519
Kriss Wilson (Pres)
Renee Covington (Founder)
Robert Frampton (Mgr-Production)
Carla Monroe (Mgr-Imaging)
Justin Barbour (Mgr-eDiscovery)
Justin Blessing (VP-Ops)
Sara Skeens (Mgr-Projects)

PIVOTAL GROUP, INC.
3200 E Camelback Rd Ste 295, Phoenix, AZ 85018-2343
Tel.: (602) 956-7200
Web Site:
   http://www.pivotalgroup.com
Sales Range: $400-449.9 Million
Emp.: 1,200
Investment & Real Estate Development Services
N.A.I.C.S.: 523999
F. Francis Najafi (Founder)
Gita Moftacghimi (Controller)

PIVOTAL GROUP, INC.
53 Cahaba Lily Way, Helena, AL 35080
Tel.: (205) 977-7755   DE
Year Founded: 2011
Investment Services; Commercial Construction
N.A.I.C.S.: 523999
Malcolm Duane Lewis (Pres & CEO)

PIVOTAL RESOURCES, INC.
1646 N California Blvd Ste 520, Walnut Creek, CA 94596
Tel.: (925) 975-0500
Web Site:
   http://www.pivotalresources.com
Year Founded: 1993
Sales Range: $10-24.9 Million
Emp.: 10
Organizational Improvement Consulting Services
N.A.I.C.S.: 561499
Peter Pande (Pres)

PIVOTAL SYSTEMS CORPORATION
48389 Fremont Blvd Ste 100, Fremont, CA 94538
Tel.: (925) 924-1480
Web Site: https://www.pivotalsys.com
Year Founded: 2003
PVS—(ASX)
Sales Range: $1-9.9 Million
Emp.: 21
Relays & Industrial Controls Mfr
N.A.I.C.S.: 335314
Joseph Monkowski (Pres & CTO)

PIXELED BUSINESS SYSTEMS
350 W 9th Ave Ste 106, Escondido, CA 92025-5053
Tel.: (858) 566-6060
Web Site: http://www.pixeled.net
Year Founded: 1997
Rev.: $2,200,000
Emp.: 12
Computer Software Services

N.A.I.C.S.: 518210
David M. Morris (Pres & CEO)

PIXLEE, INC.
625 Market St 9th Fl, San Francisco, CA 94105
Tel.: (855) 474-9533
Web Site: http://www.pixlee.com
Marketing Content Services
N.A.I.C.S.: 541910
Kyle Wong (CEO)

Subsidiaries:

TurnTo Networks, Inc. (1)
330 7th Ave Ste 1203, New York, NY 10001
Tel.: (800) 491-7876
Web Site: http://www.turntonetworks.com
Sales Range: $1-9.9 Million
Online Ecommerce Socialization Applications
N.A.I.C.S.: 513210
George Eberstadt (Founder & CEO)
Jan Vejsada (VP-Engrg)
John Swords (Chief Product Officer)
Lance Goler (VP-Sls)
Cathie O'Callaghan (Dir-Mktg)
Cindy Smith (CFO)
Monica Maltby (VP-Customer Success)

PIZZA HUT OF ARIZONA INC.
5902 E Pima St, Tucson, AZ 85712
Tel.: (520) 886-5271
Web Site: http://www.pizzahut.com
Sales Range: $25-49.9 Million
Emp.: 1,000
Pizzeria Operator
N.A.I.C.S.: 722513
Brent Kyte (Chm)
Pat McConaughey (Pres)

PIZZA HUT OF IDAHO INC.
504 N Phillippi St, Boise, ID 83706
Tel.: (208) 323-7767
Web Site: http://www.pizzahut.com
Sales Range: $10-24.9 Million
Emp.: 21
Pizza Restaurant
N.A.I.C.S.: 722513

PIZZA HUT OF MARYLAND INC.
7070 Oakland Mills Rd, Columbia, MD 21046
Tel.: (410) 720-6336
Web Site:
  http://www.pizzahutpizza.com
Sales Range: $25-49.9 Million
Emp.: 1,500
Pizzeria Operator
N.A.I.C.S.: 722513
Robert Schulze Jr. (Pres)

PIZZA KING INC.
221 Farabee Dr, Lafayette, IN 47905
Tel.: (765) 447-2172
Web Site:
  http://www.theoriginalpizzaking.com
Sales Range: $10-24.9 Million
Emp.: 25
Pizza Supplies
N.A.I.C.S.: 424490
Steve Schutz (CEO)
Betty Benjamin (Exec VP)
Chad McQueary (Owner)

PIZZA VENTURE SAN ANTONIO LLC
1248 Austin Hwy Ste221, San Antonio, TX 78209
Tel.: (210) 494-0073
Web Site: http://www.papajohns.com
Rev.: $10,100,000
Emp.: 300
Pizzeria Services
N.A.I.C.S.: 722513
Clark Mandigo (Pres)

Subsidiaries:

Pizza Ventures West Texas Llc (1)
15050 Jones Maltsberger Rd, San Antonio, TX 78247
Tel.: (210) 495-7272
Web Site: http://www.papajohns.com
Sales Range: $10-24.9 Million
Emp.: 30
Pizzeria Services
N.A.I.C.S.: 722513

PIZZA WHOLESALE LEXINGTON INC.
PO Box 757, Paris, KY 40361
Tel.: (859) 987-5482
Web Site:
  http://www.huntbrotherspizza.com
Rev.: $19,645,378
Emp.: 200
Pizza Supplies
N.A.I.C.S.: 424490
James S. Hunt (Pres)

PIZZACO INC.
121 W Marlin St Ste 300, McPherson, KS 67460
Tel.: (620) 241-0303
Web Site: http://www.pizzaco.net
Year Founded: 1972
Sales Range: $10-24.9 Million
Emp.: 650
Pizzeria Operator
N.A.I.C.S.: 722513
Carol Schroeder (Pres)
Kerry Gillis (Mgr-Info Sys)

PJ TRAILERS INC.
1807 FM 2352, Sumner, TX 75486
Tel.: (903) 785-6879
Web Site: http://www.pjtrailers.com
Year Founded: 1991
Sales Range: $10-24.9 Million
Emp.: 300
Trailer Mfr
N.A.I.C.S.: 336214
Aaron Varnes (Gen Mgr)

PJ&J, INC.
226 2nd Ave S, Great Falls, MT 59405
Tel.: (406) 453-4632 MT
Sales Range: $75-99.9 Million
Emp.: 15
Commercial & Residential Fence Erection
N.A.I.C.S.: 423390
Jesse B. Wilson Sr. (Pres)

PJA ADVERTISING & MARKETING, INC.
12 Arrow St, Cambridge, MA 02138-5105
Tel.: (617) 492-5899 MA
Web Site: http://www.agencypja.com
Year Founded: 1988
Sales Range: $10-24.9 Million
Emp.: 60
Advetising Agency
N.A.I.C.S.: 541810
Philip Johnson (CEO)
Mike O'Toole (Pres & Partner)
Hugh Kennedy (Partner & Exec VP-Plng)
Christopher Frame (VP & Dir-Creative-San Francisco)
Nicole Ciacciarelli (Sr VP-Fin)
Greg Straface (Sr VP-Bus Dev)
Janet Carlisle (Exec VP-Client Svcs)
Aaron DaSilva (Exec VP & Exec Dir-Creative)

Subsidiaries:

PJA Advertising & Marketing, Inc. - San Francisco (1)
600 California St Ste 14-035, San Francisco, CA 94109
Tel.: (415) 851-2906
Web Site: http://www.agencypja.com
Sales Range: $10-24.9 Million
Emp.: 8
Advetising Agency
N.A.I.C.S.: 541810
Phil Johnson (CEO)
Robert Davis (Exec VP & Dir-Strategy)
Janet Carlisle (Exec VP-Client Svcs)
Nicole Ciacciarelli (Sr VP-Fin)
Hugh Kennedy (Partner & Exec VP-Plng)
Greg Straface (Sr VP-Bus Dev)

PK INTERNATIONAL INC.
5445 N Elston Ave, Chicago, IL 60630
Tel.: (773) 282-8080
Web Site:
  http://www.pktotalbeauty.com
Rev.: $17,000,000
Emp.: 30
Drugs & Druggists' Sundries Merchant Whslr
N.A.I.C.S.: 424210
Kyu M. Kim (Pres)

PK STUDIOS INC.
2550 Goodlette Frank Rd, Naples, FL 34103
Tel.: (239) 434-5800
Web Site: http://www.pkstudios.com
Sales Range: $1-9.9 Million
Emp.: 6
Architectural, Landscape Architectural & Interior Design Services
N.A.I.C.S.: 541310
Rey Pezeshkan (CEO)

PKC CONSTRUCTION
520 W 103rd St Ste 299, Kansas City, MO 64114-4503
Tel.: (913) 782-4646
Web Site: http://www.pkcc.com
Rev.: $25,489,854
Emp.: 10
Commercial & Office Buildings, Renovation & Repair
N.A.I.C.S.: 236220
Perry Kessler (Pres)

PKDM HOLDINGS, INC.
1407 N Dixie Hwy, Elizabethtown, KY 42701
Tel.: (270) 765-5216
Year Founded: 2008
Holding Company
N.A.I.C.S.: 551112
Richard Urbach (Owner & Pres)
Jim Barnes (CFO & Treas)

Subsidiaries:

Keith Monument Company, Inc. (1)
1407 N Dixie Hwy, Elizabethtown, KY 42701
Tel.: (270) 769-5925
Web Site: http://www.keithmonument.com
Memorial Monuments & Marker Distr
N.A.I.C.S.: 459999

North American Heritage Services, Inc. (1)
310 Peterson Dr, Elizabethtown, KY 42702-0370 (100%)
Tel.: (270) 769-3565
Sales Range: $25-49.9 Million
Emp.: 15
Retail Sales of Memorial Products
N.A.I.C.S.: 459999

PKDW EQUITY PARTNERS, LLC
1 PPG Place, Ste 3030,, Pittsburgh, PA 15222
Tel.: (412) 586-7651
Web Site: https://www.continuim.com
Privater Equity Firm
N.A.I.C.S.: 523940
Henry Watson (Pres & Partner)

PKF O'CONNOR DAVIES, LLP
500 Mamaroneck Ave, Harrison, NY 10528
Tel.: (914) 381-8900 NY
Web Site: http://www.pkfod.com
Year Founded: 1947
Sales Range: $100-124.9 Million
Emp.: 700
Accounting, Auditing, Tax & Advisory Services
N.A.I.C.S.: 541211
Brian M. Flynn (Partner)
Kevin J. Keane (Mng Partner)
Sanders Davies (Sr Partner)
Edward O'Connor (Partner)
Thomas F. Blaney (Partner & Dir-Foundation Svcs)
Clare E. Cella (Partner)
Jerry O'Neil (Partner)
Leo Parmegiani (Partner-Tax)
Mark J. Piszko (Partner)
Daniel L. Effron (Partner-Tax-Paramus)
Kevin J. Keane (Mng Partner)
Joseph Centofanti (Partner-Govt Svcs)
Thomas P. Kennedy (Head-Bus Dev-Hudson Valley)
Felix A. Addeo (Partner)
Joseph L. Ali (Partner)
Michael J. Andriola (Partner)
John Apisa (Partner)
Leonard J. Asch (Partner)
Keith S. Balla (Partner)
Michael I. Banker (Partner)
Susan M. Barossi (Partner)
Peter D. Baum (Partner)
Lawrence A. Baye (Principal)
Mark Bednarz (Partner)
Barbara Bel (Partner)
Bruce Blasnik (Partner)
Joseph Bodan (Partner)
Shelley Brown (Principal)
Alexander K. Buchholz (Partner)
Ann Buscaglia (Partner)
Christopher Casini (Partner)
Emmanuel T. Chirico (Partner)
Patricia Ciardullo (Partner)
Robert Cordero (Partner)
Matthew Corona (Partner)
John Cosgrove (Partner)
Ciro V. Cuono (Partner)
Robert Daniele (Partner)
Yossi Messafi (Partner)
Keith Solomon (Partner-Health Care Practice)
Joshua Burgher (Principal-Mgmt Advisory Practice)
Truphena Martin (Mgr-Diversity, Equity & Inclusion)
Dawn Perri (Chief HR Officer)
Anan Samara (Principal)
Victor Pena (Partner)
Thomas DeMayo (Principal-Cybersecurity & Privacy Practice)
Michael J. Corcione (Principal-Cybersecurity & Privacy Advisory Practice)
Michelle Skrobacz (Partner)
Laurie J. Austin (Mng Partner-New England)
Ilyana Ezhaghi (Partner)
Alan Kufeld (Partner)

Subsidiaries:

PKF O'Connor Davies Capital, LLC (1)
3801 PGA Blvd Ste 600, Palm Beach Gardens, FL 33410
Tel.: (561) 337-5324
Web Site: https://pkfib.com
Investment Banking Services
N.A.I.C.S.: 523150
Robert F. Murphy (Sr Mng Dir)

Subsidiary (Domestic):

Technical Traffic Consultants Corp. (2)

PKF O'CONNOR DAVIES, LLP

PKF O'Connor Davies, LLP—(Continued)
30 Hemlock Dr, Congers, NY 10920
Tel.: (845) 623-6144
Web Site: http://www.technicaltraffic.com
Management Consulting Services Data Processing/Preparation
N.A.I.C.S.: 541614
John Mecchella (Co-Founder)
Robert Mecchella (Founder & Pres)

PKF-MARK III, INC.
17 Blacksmith Rd Ste 101, Newtown, PA 18940
Tel.: (215) 968-5031 PA
Web Site: http://www.pkfmarkiii.com
Year Founded: 1969
Provider of General Construction Services
N.A.I.C.S.: 237110
Craig L. Kolbman (Exec VP)
Glenn A. Ely (VP)
Mark J. Reisinger (VP)

PL CUSTOM BODY & EQUIPMENT CO.
2201 Atlantic Ave, Manasquan, NJ 08736
Tel.: (732) 223-1411
Web Site: http://www.plcustom.com
Sales Range: $10-24.9 Million
Emp.: 200
Ambulance Assembly
N.A.I.C.S.: 336110
Deborah Smock Thomson (Pres)

PL DEVELOPMENT, INC.
609-2 Cantiague Rock Rd, Westbury, NY 11590
Tel.: (516) 986-1700 NY
Web Site:
  http://www.pldevelopments.com
Year Founded: 1988
Emp.: 1,100
Pharmaceutical Mfr & Distr
N.A.I.C.S.: 325412
Mitch Singer (Founder & CEO)
John Francis (Chief Comml Officer)
Dana S. Toops (Chief Scientific Officer)
Thomas Crowe (Chief Supply Chain Officer)
Adam Singer (VP-Infrastructure & Projects)
Evan Singer (Pres)
Linda Singer (VP-Creative Svcs)
Donald Mordas (Sr VP-Pharmaceutical Ops)
Edward Grimm (VP-Ops)
Brad Larson (VP-Sls)
Sophia Sutphen (VP-HR)
Charles Cain (Chief Admin Officer & Gen Counsel)
Peter Napoli (Chief Acctg Officer)
Subsidiaries:
Health-Chem Diagnostics LLC (1)
3341 SW 15th Street, Pompano Beach, FL 33069-4808 (100%)
Tel.: (954) 979-3845
Web Site:
  http://www.healthchemdiagnostics.com
Emp.: 25
Manufactures Medical Home Diagnostic Products
N.A.I.C.S.: 456199
Jack Aronowitz (Pres)

PL Development, Inc. - Lynwood Plant (1)
11865 S Alameda St, Lynwood, CA 90262
Tel.: (323) 567-2482
Web Site: http://www.pldevelopments.com
Pharmaceutical Mfr & Distr
N.A.I.C.S.: 325412

PL INDUSTRIES, LLC
3730 Glen Lk Dr Ste 100, Charlotte, NC 28208
Tel.: (704) 357-1966 DE
Year Founded: 1987
Sales Range: $10-24.9 Million
Emp.: 10
Mfr & Distributor of Men's & Boys' Trousers & Slacks
N.A.I.C.S.: 315250
Eric Plotts (CFO)

PL&P ADVERTISING
200 NE 44th St, Fort Lauderdale, FL 33334-1442
Tel.: (954) 567-1455
Web Site: http://www.plpadv.com
Year Founded: 1974
Sales Range: $10-24.9 Million
Emp.: 6
Advetising Agency
N.A.I.C.S.: 541810
Alfred A. Padron (Owner)
Mercy Padron (Mgr-Traffic)
Justyna Stancel (Graphic Artist)
Euripidez Velazquez (Webmaster)

PLACE MOTOR INC.
19 Thompson Rd, Webster, MA 01570
Tel.: (508) 943-8011
Web Site: http://www.placemotor.com
Sales Range: $10-24.9 Million
Emp.: 40
Car Whslr
N.A.I.C.S.: 441110
Steven Place (Pres)
Mathew Place (Principal)
Stephane Despres (Mgr-Svc)

PLACER COUNTY WATER AGENCY
144 Ferguson Rd, Auburn, CA 95603
Tel.: (530) 823-4850
Web Site: http://www.pcwa.net
Rev.: $50,921,985
Emp.: 150
Water Supply
N.A.I.C.S.: 221118
Brent Smith (Dir-Technical Svcs)
Tom Reeves (Dir-Field Svcs)
Ross Branch (Mgr-Pub Affairs)
Einar Maish (Gen Mgr)
Subsidiaries:
Weimar Water Co. (1)
PO Box 598, Weimar, CA 95736
Tel.: (530) 637-4441
Web Site: https://www.weimarwater.com
Water Supply & Irrigation Systems
N.A.I.C.S.: 221310
Paul Fejes (Mgr)

PLACER ELECTRIC INCORPORATED
5439 Stationers Way, Sacramento, CA 95621
Tel.: (916) 338-4400
Web Site:
  http://www.placerelectric.com
Sales Range: $10-24.9 Million
Emp.: 150
General Electrical Contractor
N.A.I.C.S.: 423830
Richard Nogleberg (Pres, Branch Mgr-Truckee & Co-Owner)

PLACESTER, INC.
100 High St 7th Fl, Boston, MA 02110
Tel.: (617) 430-0050
Web Site: http://www.placester.com
Emp.: 150
Computer Softwares Mfr
N.A.I.C.S.: 513210
Matthew Barba (Co-Founder & CEO)
Frederick Townes (Co-Founder)
Sham Sao (Chief Revenue Officer)
Adam von Reyn (VP-Mktg)

Subsidiaries:
HomeFinder.com, LLC (1)
6789 Quail Hill Pkwy Suite 415, Irvine, CA 92603
Tel.: (888) 912-2719
Web Site: http://www.homefinder.com
Online Residential Real Estate Advertising Services
N.A.I.C.S.: 531390

PLACID HOLDING COMPANY
1601 Elm St Ste 3400, Dallas, TX 75201-7201
Tel.: (214) 880-8479
Year Founded: 1983
Sales Range: $10-24.9 Million
Emp.: 3
Petroleum Refining
N.A.I.C.S.: 551112
Petro Hunt (Owner)
Subsidiaries:
Placid Refining Company LLC (1)
1940 Louisiana Hwy 1 N, Port Allen, LA 70767
Tel.: (225) 387-0278
Web Site: http://www.placidrefining.com
Fuel Refinery
N.A.I.C.S.: 213112
Keith Passman (Gen Mgr-Refinery)
Mike Sims (Mgr-Pur)

PLACON CORPORATION
6096 McKee Rd, Madison, WI 53719
Tel.: (608) 271-5634
Web Site: http://www.placon.com
Year Founded: 1966
Rev.: $45,000,000
Emp.: 340
Mfr of Plastic Products
N.A.I.C.S.: 326113
Dan Mohs (Chm)
Bonnie Groff (Mgr-Commodity)
Michael Knight (Mgr-Sls-Custom)
Tanya King (Mgr-Commodity)
Dannie Stark Jr. (Mgr-Production Shift)
Subsidiaries:
Brookdale Plastics, Inc. (1)
9900 13th Ave N, Plymouth, MN 55441 (100%)
Tel.: (763) 797-1000
Web Site: http://www.brookdaleplastics.com
Sales Range: $1-9.9 Million
Emp.: 78
Manufactures, Designs & Markets Plastic Thermoforms
N.A.I.C.S.: 326150
Joseph Meixell (Pres & CEO)
Brian Cerar (Mgr-Ops)
Cameron Koeppe (Mgr)

PLAGEMAN ASSOCIATES INC.
4333 Mayhew Ave, Cincinnati, OH 45238
Tel.: (513) 921-5400
Web Site:
  http://www.plagemanassociates.net
Rev.: $10,000,000
Emp.: 4
Industrial Machinery & Equipment
N.A.I.C.S.: 423830
Pat Plageman (Pres)

PLAID INC.
85 2nd St Ste 400, San Francisco, CA 94105-3462
Tel.: (510) 610-9000 DE
Web Site: http://www.plaid.com
Year Founded: 2013
Financial Infrastructure API Developer
N.A.I.C.S.: 541511
Zach Perret (Co-Founder & CEO)
William Hockey (Co-Founder)

PLAID PANTRIES, INC.
10025 SW Allen Blvd, Beaverton, OR 97005-4124
Tel.: (503) 646-4246 GA
Web Site: http://www.plaidpantry.com
Year Founded: 1960
Sales Range: $150-199.9 Million
Emp.: 800
Convenience Store Chain
N.A.I.C.S.: 445131
Chris Girard (Chm & CEO)
Brent Chadwick (VP & Corp Controller)
Jonathan Polonsky (Pres & COO)
Tim Cote (VP-Mktg)
Bahman Rostamirad (VP-Ops)

PLAIN 'N FANCY KITCHENS INC.
Oak St & Rte 501, Schaefferstown, PA 17088
Tel.: (717) 949-6571
Web Site:
  http://www.plainfancycabinetry.com
Sales Range: $10-24.9 Million
Emp.: 120
Wood Kitchen Cabinet Mfr
N.A.I.C.S.: 337110
George Achey (Pres & CEO)
Todd Lawrence (Controller)

PLAINFIELD LUMBER COMPANY
3669 Plainfield Ave NE, Grand Rapids, MI 49525
Tel.: (616) 363-9021
Web Site:
  http://www.plc.doitbest.com
Sales Range: $10-24.9 Million
Emp.: 20
Building Materials & Equipment Supplier
N.A.I.C.S.: 423310
Pieter Van Vliet (Pres)

PLAINFIELD PRECISION COMPANIES
24035 Riverwalk Ct, Plainfield, IL 60544-8145
Tel.: (508) 746-6082
Year Founded: 1959
Rev.: $36,000,000
Emp.: 300
Metal Stampings & Custom Injection Molding
N.A.I.C.S.: 332119
Greg Conrad (CEO)
Carolyn Mills (Mgr-Quality)
Kerry Deufel (Mgr-Tooling & Facilities Maintenance)
Subsidiaries:
Plainfield Molding, Inc. (1)
24035 Riverwalk Ct, Plainfield, IL 60544-8145
Tel.: (815) 436-7806
Sales Range: $25-49.9 Million
Emp.: 150
Mfr of Plastic Products
N.A.I.C.S.: 326199
Jim Van Dahm (Gen Mgr)

Plainfield Stamping Texas, Inc. (1)
11530 Pellicano Dr, El Paso, TX 79936-6019
Tel.: (915) 598-1214
Rev.: $5,000,000
Emp.: 20
Metal Stampings & Custom Injection Molding
N.A.I.C.S.: 332119

PLAINFIELD TOBACCO & CANDY INC.
25 Van Dyke Ave, New Brunswick, NJ 08901
Tel.: (732) 296-8900
Web Site:
  http://www.resnickdistributors.com
Rev.: $43,000,000
Emp.: 80

Distr of Smoking Tobacco & Confectionery Products
N.A.I.C.S.: 424940
Lawrence Resnick *(Pres)*
Steven Resnick *(VP)*
Eileen Resnick *(VP)*

PLAINS COMMERCE BANK
220 Main St, Hoven, SD 57450
Tel.: (605) 948-2216
Web Site:
http://www.plainscommerce.com
Year Founded: 1931
Sales Range: $25-49.9 Million
Emp.: 200
Provider of Banking Services
N.A.I.C.S.: 522320
Jerome Hageman *(Chm)*
Steve Hageman *(CEO)*
Brent Heinert *(Pres)*

PLAINS COTTON COOPERATIVE ASSOCIATION
3301 E 50th St, Lubbock, TX 79404
Tel.: (806) 763-8011 TX
Web Site: http://www.pcca.com
Year Founded: 1953
Sales Range: $450-499.9 Million
Cotton Farming, Warehousing & Marketing Association
N.A.I.C.S.: 813910
Joe Tubb *(VP-Info Sys)*
John Johnson *(Sec & Dir-PR & Legislative Affairs)*
Sam Hill *(Treas & Exec VP-Fin)*
Carlos Garcia *(Mgr-Export Sls)*
Grady Martin *(Dir-Sls)*
Lonnie Winters *(VP-Mktg)*
Eddie Smith *(Chm)*
Lexie Fennell *(Vice Chm)*
Greg Bell *(VP-Admin & HR)*
Jay Cowart *(VP-Warehouse Ops)*
Kevin Brinkley *(Pres & CEO)*

Subsidiaries:

Plains Cotton Cooperative Association - Altus Warehouse (1)
End Of West Ridgecrest St, Altus, OK 73521
Tel.: (580) 482-3227
Farm Product Warehousing Services
N.A.I.C.S.: 493130

Plains Cotton Cooperative Association - Sweetwater Warehouse (1)
303 County Rd 142 W Alabama St, Sweetwater, TX 79556
Tel.: (325) 236-6614
Farm Product Warehousing Services
N.A.I.C.S.: 493130

PLAINS EQUITY EXCHANGE & COOPERATIVE UNION
206 E Indiana St, Plains, KS 67869
Tel.: (620) 563-7269
Web Site:
http://www.plainsequity.com
Sales Range: $10-24.9 Million
Emp.: 36
Grain Elevators
N.A.I.C.S.: 424510
Stacy McVey *(Gen Mgr)*

PLAINS TRANSPORTATION INC.
6699 S Washington St, Amarillo, TX 79120
Tel.: (806) 372-9290
Web Site:
http://www.plainstransportation.com
Sales Range: $25-49.9 Million
Emp.: 100
Trucking Service
N.A.I.C.S.: 484121
Dorothy Jane Gripp *(Owner & Pres)*
Sharla Trimble *(VP)*
Martha Fields *(Mgr-Settlement)*

PLAINSMAN TIRE CO. INC.
4955 Top Line Dr, Dallas, TX 75247
Tel.: (214) 630-9381
Web Site:
http://www.plainsmantire.com
Rev.: $15,177,096
Emp.: 30
Automobile Tires & Tubes
N.A.I.C.S.: 423130
Albis Shavers *(VP)*

PLAINVIEW MILK PRODUCTS ASSOCIATION
130 2nd St SW, Plainview, MN 55964
Tel.: (507) 534-3872
Web Site:
http://www.plainviewmilk.com
Sales Range: $75-99.9 Million
Emp.: 50
Powdered Milk
N.A.I.C.S.: 311514
Donny Schreiber *(Mgr-Plant)*
Becky Pearson *(Controller)*

PLAINVILLE STOCK COMPANY, INC.
104 S St, Plainville, MA 02762-2042
Tel.: (508) 699-4434 MA
Year Founded: 1872
Sales Range: $50-74.9 Million
Emp.: 100
Mfr of Precious Jewelry
N.A.I.C.S.: 339910
William Weisman *(Pres)*
Robert Weisman *(Treas)*

PLAMONDON ENTERPRISES INC.
4991 New Design Rd Ste 109, Frederick, MD 21703-7072
Tel.: (301) 695-5051
Web Site:
http://www.royrogersrestaurant.com
Sales Range: $10-24.9 Million
Emp.: 600
Owner & Operator of Restaurants & Hotels
N.A.I.C.S.: 722513
Jim Plamondon *(Co-Pres)*
Lou Schaab *(CFO)*
Peter Plamondon Sr. *(Chm)*
Peter Plamondon Jr. *(Co-Pres)*

PLAN ASIA, INC.
3486 Bahia Blanca W 2-G, Laguna Woods, CA 92637
Tel.: (310) 563-6970
Web Site:
http://www.asialuxeholidays.com
Year Founded: 1992
Tour Operator
N.A.I.C.S.: 561520
Helen Clausen *(Owner)*

PLAN B (THE AGENCY ALTERNATIVE)
116 W Illinois St 2W, Chicago, IL 60654
Tel.: (312) 222-0303
Web Site: http://www.thisisplanb.com
Year Founded: 1998
Rev.: $14,000,000
Emp.: 20
Advetising Agency
N.A.I.C.S.: 541810
Ric Van Sickle *(COO & Partner)*
Clay Cooper *(Partner & Dir-Client Svcs)*
Kim Hildreth *(Dir-Strategic Plng)*
Don Weaver *(Partner)*
Frank Angeletti *(Dir-Creative)*
Joe Popa *(Grp Dir-Creative)*

PLAN INTERNATIONAL USA
155 Plan Way, Warwick, RI 02886
Tel.: (401) 738-5600 NY

Web Site: http://www.planusa.org
Year Founded: 1937
Sales Range: $50-74.9 Million
Emp.: 164
Child Care & Development Services
N.A.I.C.S.: 624110
Tessie San Martin *(Pres & CEO)*
Carol Donnelly *(VP-HR)*
David Cannata *(CFO)*
Chip Carter *(CIO)*
John Glover *(Sr VP-Programs & Policy)*
Ann Chiarucci O'Brien *(Vice Chm)*

PLAN USA, INC.
155 Plan Way, Warwick, RI 02886
Tel.: (401) 738-5600 NY
Web Site: http://www.planusa.org
Year Founded: 1937
Sales Range: $10-24.9 Million
Emp.: 77
Grassroots Assistance In Health, Education, Family Livelihood & Community Development to Help Sponsored Children & their Families In Developing Countries towards Long-term Goal of Self-sufficiency
N.A.I.C.S.: 624110
Carol Donnelly *(VP-HR)*

PLANALYTICS, INC.
920 Cassatt Rd Ste 300, Berwyn, PA 19312-1178
Tel.: (610) 640-9485 PA
Web Site: http://www.planalytics.com
Rev.: $14,000,000
Emp.: 60
Prepackaged Software
N.A.I.C.S.: 513210
Frederic D. Fox *(Founder & CEO)*
Scott Bernhardt *(Pres)*
Paul Corby *(Sr VP-Energy)*
Derron Simon *(COO)*
Kelly Carroll *(VP-Client Support)*
David Frieberg *(VP-Mktg)*
Evan Gold *(Exec VP-Svcs-Global)*
Jed Lafferty *(Mng Dir-Life Sciences)*
Eli Miller *(Sr VP-Tech)*
Adam Moyer *(Sr VP-Customer Success)*
Bernie Wojcik *(VP-Fin)*

PLANES MOVING & STORAGE, INC.
9823 Cincinnati Dayton Rd, West Chester, OH 45069-3825
Tel.: (513) 759-6000 OH
Web Site:
http://www.planescompanies.com
Year Founded: 1921
Sales Range: $100-124.9 Million
Emp.: 197
Interstate & Local Trucking
N.A.I.C.S.: 484121
John Planes *(CEO)*

Subsidiaries:

Planes Moving & Storage Company of Columbus (1)
2000 Dividend Dr, Columbus, OH 43228-3847
Tel.: (614) 777-9090
Web Site: http://www.planes-movingstorage.com
Sales Range: $25-49.9 Million
Emp.: 40
Local, National & International Moving & Storage Services
N.A.I.C.S.: 484121
John J. Planes *(CEO)*
Raymond M. Gundrum *(VP-Fin)*

Planes Moving & Storage of Chicago, LLC (1)
1100 Bilter Rd, Aurora, IL 60502 (100%)
Tel.: (630) 851-3700
Web Site: http://www.planescompanies.com

Sales Range: $25-49.9 Million
Emp.: 25
Provider of Moving & Storage Services
N.A.I.C.S.: 484210
John Planes *(Pres)*
John Sabatalo *(Exec VP)*
Raymond M. Gundrum *(CFO)*
Robert W. Martin *(Gen Mgr)*

Planes Moving & Storage of Dayton, Inc. (1)
9370 Byers Rd, Miamisburg, OH 45342-4352 (100%)
Tel.: (937) 866-0485
Web Site: http://www.planesmoving.com
Sales Range: $25-49.9 Million
Emp.: 13
Local, National & International Moving & Storage Services
N.A.I.C.S.: 493190
John J. Planes *(Chm & CEO)*
Raymond M. Gundrum *(VP-Fin)*
John Sabatalo *(Exec VP)*

Planes Moving & Storage of Indianapolis, Inc. (1)
2635 Planes Dr, Indianapolis, IN 46219-1433
Tel.: (317) 895-1444
Web Site: http://www.planesunited.com
Sales Range: $10-24.9 Million
Emp.: 50
Local, National & International Moving & Storage Services
N.A.I.C.S.: 484121
John J. Planes *(CEO)*
John Sabatalo *(Pres)*
Raymond M. Gundrum *(VP-HR & Treas)*
Don Mueller *(Asst Gen Mgr)*

PLANET ACP, INC.
96 Danbury Road, Ridgefield, CT 06877
Tel.: (203) 438-9580 DE
Year Founded: 1983
Sales Range: $1-9.9 Million
Emp.: 40
Allergy Control Products Online Retailer
N.A.I.C.S.: 455219
Ed Steube *(Pres)*
Jeffrey Tauber *(Owner)*

PLANET AID, INC.
6730 Santa Barbara Ct, Elkridge, MD 21075
Tel.: (410) 796-1510 MA
Web Site: http://www.planetaid.org
Year Founded: 1997
Sales Range: $25-49.9 Million
Emp.: 540
Waste Material Recycling Services
N.A.I.C.S.: 562920
Fred Olsson *(COO)*
Thomas Meehan *(CFO)*

PLANET BEACH FRANCHISING CORPORATION
5145 & 5161 Taravella Rd, Marrero, LA 70072
Tel.: (504) 361-5550 DE
Web Site:
http://www.planetbeach.com
Year Founded: 1996
Sales Range: $10-24.9 Million
Emp.: 42
Tanning & Day Spa Franchisor
N.A.I.C.S.: 812112
Stephen P. Smith *(Chm & CEO)*
Nancy M. Price *(Sr VP-Sls)*
Craig M. Berner *(CFO)*
David Mesa *(Pres-Franchise Ops)*

PLANET CHRYSLER JEEP
400 E Central St, Franklin, MA 02038
Tel.: (508) 520-1550
Web Site: http://www.planetcjd.com
Year Founded: 2004
Sales Range: $25-49.9 Million
Emp.: 30
Car Whslr

PLANET CHRYSLER JEEP

Planet Chrysler Jeep—(Continued)
N.A.I.C.S.: 441110
John Morrill (Mgr-Customer Rels)

PLANET DEPOS, LLC
451 Hungerford Dr Ste 400, Rockville, MD 20850-5327
Web Site:
http://www.planetdepos.com
Court Reporting & Stenotype Services
N.A.I.C.S.: 561492
Jennifer Parratt (VP-Sls)
Bill DiMonte (Founder)
Cindy Miklos (Acct Exec)
Gus Shuwayhat (Acct Exec)
Alison Barberi (Acct Exec)
Kyle Hill (Acct Exec)
Nate Pascal (Acct Exec-Baltimore)
Joseph DiMonte (Founder & Mng Partner)
Karen Bergmann (CFO)
Lisa DiMonte (CEO)
Nico DiMonte (Founder & COO)
Blake Olson (Acct Exec-Southern California)
Josh Kearns (Sls Mgr)

Subsidiaries:

M.A.R. Reporting Group, LLC. (1)
8500 Leesburg Pike Ste 211, Tysons Corner, VA 22182
Tel.: (703) 534-1225
Web Site: http://www.mar-reporting.com
Court Reporting Service
N.A.I.C.S.: 561492
Mario A. Rodriguez (Pres)

PLANET FINANCIAL GROUP, LLC
321 Research Pkwy Ste 303, Meriden, CT 06450
Tel.: (888) 966-9044
Web Site:
https://planetfinancialgroup.com
Emp.: 100
Financial Services
N.A.I.C.S.: 523999
Lee M. Gross (Sr VP)
Michael R. Dubeck (Pres & CEO)

Subsidiaries:

Planet Home Lending, LLC (1)
321 Research Pkwy, Meriden, CT 06450
Tel.: (866) 828-8187
Web Site: https://planethomelending.com
Emp.: 100
Financial Services
N.A.I.C.S.: 523999

Subsidiary (Domestic):

Platinum Home Mortgage Corporation (2)
2200 Hicks Rd, Rolling Meadows, IL 60008
Tel.: (847) 797-9500
Web Site: http://www.phmc.com
Real Estate Credit
N.A.I.C.S.: 522292
Lee M. Gross (Pres & CEO)
Lori Pelinski (Dir-Corp Compliance)
Mike McEvoy (Mgr-Tustin)
Francisco Ramirez (Mgr-Covina)

PLANET HOLLYWOOD INTERNATIONAL, INC.
4700 Millenia Blvd Ste 400, Orlando, FL 32839
Tel.: (407) 903-5500
Web Site:
http://www.planethollywoodintl.com
Year Founded: 1991
Theme Restaurant & Retail Store Operator
N.A.I.C.S.: 722511
Robert Ian Earl (Founder)

Subsidiaries:

Buca, Inc. (1)
1204 Harmon Pl, Minneapolis, MN 55403-2606
Tel.: (612) 288-0138
Web Site: http://www.bucainc.com
Sales Range: $200-249.9 Million
Family-Style Italian Restaurants Operator
N.A.I.C.S.: 722511

Subsidiary (Domestic):

Buca di Beppo Minneapolis (2)
1204 Harmon Pl, Minneapolis, MN 55403
Tel.: (612) 288-0138
Web Site: http://www.bucadibeppo.com
Sales Range: $10-24.9 Million
Emp.: 75
Italian Restaurant
N.A.I.C.S.: 722511
Brier Veit (Mgr-Sls)

PLANET HYUNDAI SAHARA
7150 W Sahara Ave, Las Vegas, NV 89117-2835
Tel.: (702) 483-2487
Web Site:
http://www.planethyundaisahara.com
Sales Range: $10-24.9 Million
Emp.: 100
Car Whslr
N.A.I.C.S.: 441110

PLANET PRODUCTS CORPORATION
4200 Malsbary Rd, Cincinnati, OH 45242-5510
Tel.: (513) 984-5544
Web Site: http://www.planet-products.com
Year Founded: 1947
Sales Range: $75-99.9 Million
Emp.: 75
Machinery & Equipment Mfr for the Food & Meat Packing Industries
N.A.I.C.S.: 333241
Phil Young (Supvr-Pur)

PLANET SHOES
135 2nd Ave, Waltham, MA 02451
Tel.: (781) 547-7177
Web Site:
http://www.planetshoes.com
Year Founded: 1999
Sales Range: $1-9.9 Million
Emp.: 18
Online Shoe Retailer
N.A.I.C.S.: 458210
Brandy Josefson (Supvr-Multi Media Lab)

PLANET SOLAR INC.
719 E Haley St, Santa Barbara, CA 93103
Tel.: (805) 692-2700
Web Site: http://www.planetsolar.com
Year Founded: 2008
Sales Range: $1-9.9 Million
Emp.: 35
Solar Energy Installation
N.A.I.C.S.: 221114
Ben Siebert (CEO)

PLANET SUBARU CAR DEALER
596 Washington St, Hanover, MA 02339
Tel.: (781) 826-4444
Web Site:
http://www.planetsubaru.com
Year Founded: 1998
Sales Range: $25-49.9 Million
Emp.: 30
Car Whslr
N.A.I.C.S.: 441110
Jeff Morrill (VP)

PLANET TOYOTA-SCION
5540 Auto Ct, Matteson, IL 60443
Tel.: (708) 720-8600
Web Site:
http://www.planettoyotaonline.com
Sales Range: $10-24.9 Million
Emp.: 70
New & Used Car Dealer
N.A.I.C.S.: 441110
Ronald Postma (Owner)
Angie Remes (Controller)
Shadi Nassar (Gen Mgr-Sls)

PLANET TRUST BANK CORPORATION
109 Comml St NE, Salem, OR 97301
Tel.: (503) 363-3136
Sales Range: $10-24.9 Million
Emp.: 70
National Commercial Banks
N.A.I.C.S.: 522110
Randy Compton (Pres)
John Willburn (CFO & VP)

Subsidiaries:

Pioneer Trust Bank NA Inc (1)
109 Commercial St NE, Salem, OR 97301
Tel.: (503) 363-3136
Web Site: http://www.pioneertrustbank.com
Sales Range: $50-74.9 Million
Emp.: 80
National Commercial Banks
N.A.I.C.S.: 522110
Randy Compton (Pres)

PLANETRISK, INC.
8280 Greensboro Dr Ste 800, McLean, VA 22102
Tel.: (703) 760-9729
Web Site: http://www.planetrisk.com
Year Founded: 2014
Data Acquisition, Mapping & Geo-Analysis Services
N.A.I.C.S.: 518210
Paul McQuillan (Pres & CEO)
Mark Dumas (Chief Strategy Officer)
Abdul Omar (CFO)

PLANETTRAN
3 Charlton St No 6, Everett, MA 02149
Tel.: (617) 944-9224
Web Site: http://www.planettran.com
Year Founded: 2003
Rev.: $4,000,000
Emp.: 150
Transportation Services
N.A.I.C.S.: 485999
Lori van Dam (Pres)
Steve McCaffrey (Mgr-Dispatch)
Jay Althoff (CEO)

PLANK ENTERPRISES INC.
4404 Anderson Dr, Eau Claire, WI 54703
Tel.: (715) 839-1225
Web Site:
http://www.plankenterprises.com
Rev.: $11,500,000
Emp.: 6
Trucks, Tractors, Loaders, Carriers & Similar Equipment
N.A.I.C.S.: 333924
Leon Plank (Pres)
Lisa Elliott (Mgr-Acctg)
Gary Fenner (VP)
Sue Caterer (Mgr-Info Tech)

PLANNED COMMUNITY DEVELOPERS LTD
15958 City Walk Ste 250, Sugar Land, TX 77479
Tel.: (281) 242-2000
Web Site: http://www.pcdltd.com
Rev.: $20,000,000
Emp.: 30
Subdividers & Developers

U.S. PRIVATE

N.A.I.C.S.: 236115
Les A. Newton (Pres)

PLANNED FURNITURE PROMOTIONS, LLC
9 Moody Rd Bldg D Ste 18, Enfield, CT 06082
Tel.: (860) 749-1472
Web Site:
http://www.pfpromotions.com
Year Founded: 1962
Sales Range: $25-49.9 Million
Emp.: 4
Furniture Sales Promotion Services
N.A.I.C.S.: 423210
Gene Rosenberg (Co-Founder & Chm)
Paul Cohen (Co-Founder & CFO)
Rob Rosenberg (Pres)
Rick Duffey (Mgr-Sls-West Coast)
Tom Liddell (Mng Dir & Sr VP)
Ed Hendon (Dir-Ops-Natl)
Roy Hester (Sr VP)
Bobbie Savickas (Co-Treas)
Evelyn Keene (Co-Treas)

PLANNED PARENTHOOD GREAT PLAINS
4401 W 109th St Ste 100, Overland Park, KS 66211
Tel.: (913) 345-1400
Web Site:
http://www.plannedparenthood.org
Year Founded: 1916
Reproductive Health Care, Family Planning & Educational Services
N.A.I.C.S.: 621410
Brandon Hill (Pres & CEO)

PLANNED SYSTEMS INTERNATIONAL, INC.
10632 Little Patuxent Pkwy Ste 200, Columbia, MD 21044
Tel.: (410) 964-8000
Web Site: http://www.plan-sys.com
Year Founded: 1988
Emp.: 500
Computer Systems Analysts & Design
N.A.I.C.S.: 541512
Eric Skiff (CTO)
Sandra Kelly (Chief HR Officer)
Terry Lin (CEO)
Mike Snyder (COO)
David Truong (COO)
Dean Smith (Chief Medical Officer)

Subsidiaries:

Kinex Inc. (1)
14420 Eagle Is Ct, Gainesville, VA 20155-3888
Tel.: (703) 995-4885
Computer System Design Services
N.A.I.C.S.: 541512

Pro-Sphere Tek, Inc. (1)
1101 King St Ste 200, Alexandria, VA 22314
Tel.: (703) 810-3030
Web Site: http://www.prosphere.com
Information Technology Consulting Services
N.A.I.C.S.: 541690
Rodger Blevins (CEO)
Kevin Rice (Pres)
Mark Walker (Controller)
Carola Ammer (Dir-HR)
Shon Anderson (VP-Corp Strategic Growth)
Shannon Hattersley (VP-DoD Programs)
Eric Hughes (VP-Bus Ops)
Roger Sam (VP-Bus Dev & Mktg)
Don Shea (VP-Health Svcs)

QuarterLine Consulting Services, LLC (1)
13873 Park Center Road, Ste 330, Herndon, VA 20171
Tel.: (866) 972-7111
Web Site: http://www.quarterline.com
General Medical & Surgical Hospitals
N.A.I.C.S.: 622110

COMPANIES

PLANO MARINE SERVICE
1105 Ave K, Plano, TX 75074
Tel.: (972) 423-3134
Web Site: http://www.planomarine.com
Rev.: $15,000,000
Emp.: 25
Motor Boat Dealers
N.A.I.C.S.: 441222
James Benny Ray (*Owner*)
Steve DeWoody (*Mgr-Parts*)
Tom Lewis (*Mgr-Sls*)
Judith Burns (*Mgr-Fin*)

PLANT FANTASIES INCORPORATED
224 W 29th St, New York, NY 10001
Tel.: (212) 268-2886
Web Site: http://www.plantfantasies.com
Year Founded: 1987
Sales Range: $1-9.9 Million
Emp.: 35
Landscape Design Services
N.A.I.C.S.: 541320
Teresa Carleo (*Founder & Pres*)
E. MacKenzie Sharp (*Mgr-Landscape Production*)
Michael Tull (*VP-Design*)
Steve Martucci (*VP-Ops*)
John Goodman (*Mgr-Floral & Event Design*)

PLANT IMPROVEMENT CO. INC.
1800 Briarcliff Rd NE, Atlanta, GA 30329
Tel.: (404) 325-9350
Sales Range: $10-24.9 Million
Emp.: 14
Heavy Construction Equipment Rental
N.A.I.C.S.: 532412
W. Clyde Shepherd III (*Pres*)

PLANT MAINTENANCE SERVICE CORPORATION
3000 Fite Rd, Memphis, TN 38127
Tel.: (901) 353-9880   TN
Web Site: http://www.pmscmphs.com
Year Founded: 1967
Sales Range: $75-99.9 Million
Emp.: 150
Mfr of Design, Fabrication & Field Services for Industries
N.A.I.C.S.: 332313
Jeff Turner (*VP-Fabrication Sls*)
Rick Edwards (*Mgr-Pur*)

Subsidiaries:

Plant Maintenance Service Corporation - Field Construction Division (1)
5679 Old Millington Rd, Millington, TN 38053
Tel.: (901) 353-8471
Industrial Plant Maintenance Services
N.A.I.C.S.: 811310

PLANT MAINTENANCE, INC.
3773 Pacheco Blvd PO Box 48, Martinez, CA 94553-0115
Tel.: (925) 228-3285   CA
Sales Range: $100-124.9 Million
Emp.: 300
Refinery & Oil Service Contractors
N.A.I.C.S.: 561320
Tim Holz (*Pres*)

PLANT MARKETING LLC
819 W Shorewood Dr, Eau Claire, WI 54703
Tel.: (715) 836-8224
Web Site: http://www.plantorders.com
Rev.: $13,600,000
Emp.: 25
Flower Sales
N.A.I.C.S.: 424930
Chris Matter (*Controller*)

PLANT PERFORMANCE SERVICES INC.
4800 Sugar Grove Ste 450, Stafford, TX 77477
Tel.: (918) 245-6606
Web Site: http://www.p2sworld.com
Rev.: $17,100,000
Emp.: 100
Welding On Site
N.A.I.C.S.: 333992
Robert Frawley (*Gen Mgr*)

PLANT PROCESS EQUIPMENT INC.
280 Reynolds Ave, League City, TX 77573
Tel.: (281) 332-2589
Web Site: http://www.plant-process.com
Sales Range: $10-24.9 Million
Emp.: 75
Engineering & Construction Services
N.A.I.C.S.: 236220
Clark V. Kennedy (*Pres & CEO*)
Steven Kennedy (*VP*)

PLANT RECLAMATION
912 Harbour Way S, Richmond, CA 94804
Tel.: (510) 233-6552
Web Site: http://www.plantreclamation.com
Sales Range: $10-24.9 Million
Emp.: 25
Wrecking & Demolition Work
N.A.I.C.S.: 238910
Fred Glueck (*Pres*)
Anthony Gillispie (*Superintendent*)

PLANT SCIENCES INC.
342 Green Vly Rd, Watsonville, CA 95076
Tel.: (831) 728-7771
Web Site: http://www.plantsciences.com
Rev.: $10,999,210
Emp.: 45
Agricultural Research
N.A.I.C.S.: 541720
Steve Cahilig (*Mgr-Ops*)
Kim Cronin (*Mgr-Intellectual Property*)

PLANT TELEPHONE COMPANY
1703 Hwy 82 W, Tifton, GA 31793
Tel.: (229) 528-4777
Web Site: http://www.plantel.net
Sales Range: $10-24.9 Million
Emp.: 61
Residential Telephone Service
N.A.I.C.S.: 517121
Danny E. Sterling (*Pres*)
Beverly Sterling (*VP*)

PLANTAIN PRODUCTS COMPANY
5821 E Causeway Blvd, Tampa, FL 33619
Tel.: (813) 626-9486   FL
Web Site: http://www.chifleschips.com
Year Founded: 1963
Sales Range: $1-9.9 Million
Emp.: 30
Food Preparations Mfr
N.A.I.C.S.: 311423
Margaret Argudo (*Pres & CEO*)

PLANTATION CORP.
514 Grand Ave Ste 161, Laramie, WY 82070
Tel.: (307) 370-1717   WY
Year Founded: 2017
Assets: $220
Liabilities: $55,968
Net Worth: ($55,748)
Earnings: ($65,959)
Emp.: 2
Fiscal Year-end: 12/31/18
Telephone Communication Services
N.A.I.C.S.: 517111
Adrian Bray (*CFO & Sec*)

PLANTATION PETROLEUM HOLDINGS IV, LLC (PPH)
10355 Centrepark Dr Ste 100, Houston, TX 77043
Tel.: (281) 296-7222
Web Site: http://www.plantationpetroleum.com
Sales Range: $10-24.9 Million
Emp.: 20
Holding Company; Petroleum Products
N.A.I.C.S.: 551112
Thomas C. Meneley (*Pres & CEO*)
Donald P. Dotson (*Exec VP & COO*)
Donald L. Adams (*VP-Land*)

Subsidiaries:

Maynard Oil Co. (1)
8080 N Central Expy, Dallas, TX 75206-1838
Tel.: (214) 891-8880
Producer of Crude Oil & Natural Gas
N.A.I.C.S.: 211120

PLANTATION PRODUCTS INC
202 S Washington St, Norton, MA 02766
Tel.: (508) 285-5800   DE
Web Site: http://www.plantationproducts.com
Year Founded: 1990
Sales Range: $25-49.9 Million
Emp.: 400
Home Gardening Products
N.A.I.C.S.: 424910
Michael Pietrasiewicz (*CEO*)
David Sbordon (*VP-Sls*)
Jennifer Masiello (*Reg Mgr-Sls*)

PLANTERS COOPERATIVE ASSOCIATION
500 S Rock Is St, Lone Wolf, OK 73655
Tel.: (580) 846-9008
Web Site: http://www.planterscoop.org
Sales Range: $10-24.9 Million
Emp.: 17
Grain Elevators
N.A.I.C.S.: 424910
Lurman Helwer (*Branch Mgr*)

PLANTERS COTTON OIL MILL INC.
2901 Planters Dr, Pine Bluff, AR 71601
Tel.: (870) 534-3631
Web Site: http://www.plantersoil.com
Sales Range: $10-24.9 Million
Emp.: 90
Cottonseed Oil Mills
N.A.I.C.S.: 311224
Teresa McMillan (*CFO*)
John Jefferson (*Sr VP*)
John Fricke (*CEO & Gen Mgr*)
Debbie Ashcraft (*Mgr-Oil Traffic*)

PLANTERS ELECTRIC MEMBERSHIP CORP
1740 Hwy 25 N, Millen, GA 30442
Tel.: (478) 982-4722
Web Site: http://www.eastga.net
Sales Range: $10-24.9 Million
Emp.: 50
Electronic Services
N.A.I.C.S.: 221118

Matt Brinson (*Gen Mgr*)

PLANTERS FINANCIAL GROUP, INC.
1312 S Main St, Hopkinsville, KY 42240
Tel.: (270) 886-9030   TN
Web Site: http://www.plantersbankonline.com
Year Founded: 2002
Sales Range: $25-49.9 Million
Emp.: 120
Bank Holding Company
N.A.I.C.S.: 551111
Elizabeth McCoy (*Pres & CEO*)

Subsidiaries:

Planters Bank, Inc. (1)
1312 S Main St, Hopkinsville, KY 42240
Tel.: (270) 886-9030
Web Site: http://www.plantersbankonline.com
Sales Range: $25-49.9 Million
Commericial Banking
N.A.I.C.S.: 522110
Janet Calhoun (*Sr VP-Comml Banking*)
Mickey Dunbar (*Asst VP & Branch Mgr*)
Jan Greene (*Branch Mgr*)
Barry Meade (*Sr VP-Credit Admin*)
Eyvette Sellers (*Asst VP-Treasury Mgmt*)
Angie Smith (*Asst VP-Mortgage Lending*)
Eric Miller (*Pres-Greenwood*)
Kelley Workman (*Pres*)
Leigh Durden (*Chief Credit Officer*)
Rick Davis (*CFO & Exec VP*)
Doug Lawson (*Sr VP-Ag & Comml Lending*)
Catherine Lacy (*Mng Dir*)
Alan Hargett (*CEO*)
Jimmy Clayton (*Chm*)

PLANTERS GRAIN COOP ODEM TEXAS
200 N Voss Ave, Odem, TX 78370
Tel.: (361) 368-4111
Web Site: http://www.cfafs.com
Sales Range: $10-24.9 Million
Emp.: 15
Farm Supplies Grain Elevator
N.A.I.C.S.: 424910

PLANTERS HOLDING COMPANY INC.
212 Catchings Ave, Indianola, MS 38751
Tel.: (662) 887-3363
Web Site: http://www.planters-bank.com
Sales Range: $1-9.9 Million
Emp.: 200
Bank Holding Company
N.A.I.C.S.: 551111
James B. Randall (*Pres*)
James H. Clayton (*CEO*)
Henry Paris (*Chm*)

Subsidiaries:

Planters Bank & Trust Company (1)
212 Catchings Ave, Indianola, MS 38751
Tel.: (662) 887-3363
Web Site: http://www.planters-bank.com
Rev.: $27,623,205
Emp.: 30
State Commercial Banks
N.A.I.C.S.: 522110
Chris Makamson (*VP*)
LeAnn Cummins (*Asst VP-Compliance*)
Jim Quinn (*Chief Credit Officer & Exec VP*)

PLANTERS RICE MILL LLC.
403 S Washington St, Abbeville, LA 70510
Tel.: (337) 898-3056
Web Site: http://www.plantersllc.com
Sales Range: $50-74.9 Million
Emp.: 48
Rice Milling Services
N.A.I.C.S.: 311212
Anissa Mouton (*Asst Mgr*)

PLANTERS WAREHOUSE & LOAN CO. U.S. PRIVATE

Planters Warehouse & Loan Co.—(Continued)

PLANTERS WAREHOUSE & LOAN CO.
217 S Main St, Fitzgerald, GA 31750
Tel.: (229) 423-2231
Rev.: $15,735,230
Emp.: 12
Petroleum Products
N.A.I.C.S.: 424720
William Dorminy (Pres)

PLANTRON, INC.
1700 Morrissey Dr, Bloomington, IL 61704
Tel.: (309) 663-1800 — DE
Web Site: http://www.owennursery.com
Year Founded: 1969
Sales Range: $1-9.9 Million
Emp.: 11
Mail Order Flowers & Gardening Supplies
N.A.I.C.S.: 444240
Deanne College (Pres)

Subsidiaries:

Inter-State Nurseries, Inc. (1)
1800 Hamilton Rd, Bloomington, IL 61704
Tel.: (309) 663-6797
Web Site: http://www.interstatenurseries.com
Roses, Perennials, Flower Bulbs & Other General Nursery Stock
N.A.I.C.S.: 111421

PLANTSCAPES, INC.
1127 Poplar Pl S, Seattle, WA 98144
Tel.: (206) 623-7100 — WA
Web Site: http://www.plantscapes.com
Year Founded: 1989
Sales Range: $10-24.9 Million
Emp.: 70
Business Services, Nec, Nsk
N.A.I.C.S.: 561990
Terry Posner (Pres & CEO)
Debbie Bowers (Mgr-Bus)
Dustin Madden (Mgr-Landscape Div)
Kathie Madsen (Mgr-Quality Control)
Louise Fair (Gen Mgr-Ops & Interior)

Subsidiaries:

Highridge (1)
1085 12th Ave NW Ste D1, Issaquah, WA 98027
Tel.: (425) 392-0905
Web Site: http://www.highridge.com
Landscape Contractors
N.A.I.C.S.: 561730
Terry Posner (Pres)

PLANVISTA CORPORATION
4515 George Rd, Tampa, FL 33634
Tel.: (813) 353-2300 — DE
Year Founded: 1994
Sales Range: $10-24.9 Million
Emp.: 155
Provider of Health Management Services
N.A.I.C.S.: 541611

Subsidiaries:

RE Harrington Unemployment Tax Service (1)
353 Sweetmans Ln, Perrineville, NJ 08535-1217
Tel.: (732) 446-7112
Sales Range: $10-24.9 Million
Emp.: 1
Provider of Health Management Services
N.A.I.C.S.: 541611

PLASCAL CORPORATION
361 Eastern Pkwy, Farmingdale, NY 11735
Tel.: (516) 249-2200 — NY
Web Site: http://www.plascal.com
Sales Range: $50-74.9 Million
Emp.: 25
Vinyl Film Mfr
N.A.I.C.S.: 326113
Fred Hurd (Pres)
Sheldon Eskowitz (Treas & Sec)
Ray Brown (VP)

PLASCO INC.
3075 Plainfield Rd, Kettering, OH 45432
Tel.: (937) 254-8444
Web Site: http://www.plascoincorporated.com
Year Founded: 1957
Sales Range: $10-24.9 Million
Emp.: 9
Plastics Processing
N.A.I.C.S.: 326199
Ronald L. Schweller (CEO)
Kevin Stewart (Exec VP, Dir-Quality Control & Mgr-Sls)
Bonnie Zornes (Mgr-Admin)

PLASCON GROUP
2375 Traversefield Dr, Traverse City, MI 49686
Tel.: (231) 935-1580
Web Site: http://www.plascongroup.com
Year Founded: 1999
Sales Range: $10-24.9 Million
Emp.: 80
Plastic Packaging
N.A.I.C.S.: 322220
David Peterson (CEO)

PLASMA AUTOMATION, INC.
1801 Artic Ave, Bohemia, NY 11716
Tel.: (631) 563-7234 — NY
Year Founded: 1992
Sales Range: $1-9.9 Million
Emp.: 45
Machine Tool (Metal Cutting Types) Mfr
N.A.I.C.S.: 333517
Chris Hamilton (Mgr)

Subsidiaries:

Vicon Machinery, LLC (1)
300 Biltmore Dr Ste 220, Fenton, MO 63026
Tel.: (636) 349-8999
Web Site: http://www.viconmachinery.com
Sales Range: $1-9.9 Million
Emp.: 15
Sheet Metal Work Mfg
N.A.I.C.S.: 332322
Mike Fischer (COO)

PLASMA COMPUTING GROUP, INC.
3010 LBJ Freeway Ste 1515, Dallas, TX 75234
Tel.: (972) 763-1500
Web Site: http://www.plasmacomp.com
Year Founded: 2003
Sales Range: $10-24.9 Million
Emp.: 75
Internet Marketing & Other Related Services
N.A.I.C.S.: 541519
Yasser Khan (CTO)

PLASMA TECHNOLOGY, INCORPORATED
1754 Crenshaw Blvd, Torrance, CA 90501-3311
Tel.: (310) 320-3373 — CA
Web Site: http://www.ptise.com
Year Founded: 1969
Sales Range: $75-99.9 Million
Emp.: 120
Mfr of Plasma Coatings
N.A.I.C.S.: 332812
Robert D. Dowell (Pres & CEO)

Subsidiaries:

Plasma Technology, Incorporated - East Coast Facility (1)
70 Rye St, South Windsor, CT 06074
Tel.: (860) 282-0659
Surface Engineering Services
N.A.I.C.S.: 541330

PLASMA-THERM, LLC
10050 16th St N, Saint Petersburg, FL 33716
Tel.: (727) 577-4999
Web Site: http://www.plasmatherm.com
Year Founded: 1974
Sales Range: $25-49.9 Million
Emp.: 140
Semiconductor Devices Mfr
N.A.I.C.S.: 334413
Abdul Lateef (CEO)
Ed Ostan (Exec VP-Mktg)
Jim Pollock (COO)
Russ Westerman (Exec VP-Tech)
Grace Smoker (Dir-HR)
David Masterson (Dir-Ops)
Phil Quince (Dir-Customer Focus Team)
Mike Burns (Dir-Global Sls)
Cody Heinze (Mgr-Customer Svc-Global)

Subsidiaries:

Thin Film Equipment S.R.L. (1)
Viale delle Scienze 23, 20082, Binasco, MI, Italy
Tel.: (39) 0290092460
Web Site: https://www.thinfilmequipment.net
Semiconductor Distr
N.A.I.C.S.: 423690

PLASMET CORP.
2345 Stevens Dr, Richland, WA 99352
Tel.: (509) 375-4231 — DE
Web Site: http://www.plasmetcorp.com
Sales Range: $10-24.9 Million
Emp.: 5
Metallurgical Research Services
N.A.I.C.S.: 541715
Les Peterson (Mgr-Test & Ops)

PLASS APPLIANCES AND FURNITURE INC.
22 W 001 Army Trl Rd, Addison, IL 60101
Tel.: (630) 351-4020
Web Site: http://www.plassappliance.com
Sales Range: $50-74.9 Million
Emp.: 35
Household Appliance Stores
N.A.I.C.S.: 449210
Harold Plass (CEO)
Dale Plass (Pres)

PLASTAKET MANUFACTURING COMPANY INC.
6220 E Hwy 12, Lodi, CA 95240
Tel.: (209) 369-2154 — CA
Web Site: http://www.championjuicer.com
Year Founded: 1950
Juicers Mfr & Distr
N.A.I.C.S.: 335210

PLASTATECH ENGINEERING LTD.
725 Morley Dr, Saginaw, MI 48601-9401
Tel.: (989) 754-6500 — MI
Web Site: http://www.plastatech.com
Year Founded: 1990
Sales Range: $50-74.9 Million
Emp.: 150
Coated Fabrics Mfr

N.A.I.C.S.: 313320
Kathy Allen (Pres)
Jim Chrysler (Controller)
Mark Knipp (Mgr-Tech Sls)

PLASTER CASTER, INC.
1000 Country Club Rd, Ann Arbor, MI 48105
Tel.: (734) 719-0867 — MI
Year Founded: 2007
Travel Services
N.A.I.C.S.: 561599
J.D. Klamka (Chm, Pres, CEO & CFO)

PLASTERER EQUIPMENT CO. INC.
2550 E Cumberland St, Lebanon, PA 17042-9214
Tel.: (717) 273-2616 — PA
Web Site: http://www.plasterer.com
Year Founded: 1912
Sales Range: $25-49.9 Million
Emp.: 90
Servicing of Construction & Mining Machinery
N.A.I.C.S.: 423810

PLASTI-FAB, INC.
5985 S 6th Way, Ridgefield, WA 98642
Tel.: (503) 692-5460
Web Site: http://www.plasti-fab.com
Sales Range: $10-24.9 Million
Emp.: 45
Fiberglass Composite Products Mfr
N.A.I.C.S.: 339999
Ron Schneberger (Dir-Intl Markets)
Kurt W. Ostermiller (Pres)
Jim Coskey (Mgr-Sls-Pacific Northwest Reg)
Nolan Allen (Mgr-Sls-Western Reg)
Corbin Hutchinson (Mgr-Mktg)

PLASTIC COMPONENTS, INC.
9051 Nw 97th Ter, Miami, FL 33178
Tel.: (305) 885-0561
Web Site: http://www.plasticomponents.com
Rev.: $14,300,000
Emp.: 38
Plastics Product Mfr
N.A.I.C.S.: 326199
Raymond A. Barnes (Controller)
Thomas Stark (Pres)
Herman Guevara (Mgr-Sls)
Eugene Stark Jr. (Sec)

PLASTIC INGENUITY INC.
1017 Park St, Cross Plains, WI 53528-9630
Tel.: (608) 798-3071 — WI
Web Site: http://www.plasticingenuity.com
Year Founded: 1972
Sales Range: $25-49.9 Million
Emp.: 450
Plastics Products
N.A.I.C.S.: 326199
Chris Hogg (Acct Exec-Sls)
AnnaMarie Shanahan (Dir-HR)
Steve Buss (Dir-IT)

PLASTIC MOLD TECHNOLOGY, INC.
4201 Broadmoor Ave SE, Grand Rapids, MI 49512
Tel.: (616) 698-9810 — MI
Web Site: http://www.plasticmold.com
Year Founded: 1974
Sales Range: $10-24.9 Million
Emp.: 45
Industrial Molds
N.A.I.C.S.: 333511

COMPANIES

Gary Scott Proos *(Gen Mgr)*
Mike Mayhew *(Plant Mgr)*
Bob Gillett *(Project Mgr)*

PLASTIC PRODUCTS COMPANY, INC.
30355 Akerson St, Lindstrom, MN 55045-9456
Tel.: (651) 257-7778 MN
Web Site: http://www.plasticproductsco.com
Year Founded: 1962
Sales Range: $100-124.9 Million
Emp.: 700
Sales of Plastics Products
N.A.I.C.S.: 326199
Marlene A. Messin *(Owner & Pres)*
Bill Gardner *(CFO)*
Lorna Lumke *(Sec)*

Subsidiaries:

Plastic Products Company, Inc. - Greenfield Facility (1)
239 Parker Dr, Greenfield, TN 38230
Tel.: (731) 235-9189
Plastics Product Mfr
N.A.I.C.S.: 326199
Rick Carlson *(CEO)*

Plastic Products Company, Inc. - Greenville Facility (1)
105 Industrial Dr, Greenville, KY 42345
Tel.: (270) 338-7461
Web Site: http://www.plasticproductscl.com
Emp.: 100
Plastics Product Mfr
N.A.I.C.S.: 326199
Bob Griessel *(Gen Mgr)*

Plastic Products Company, Inc. - Lebanon Facility (1)
630 Metts Dr, Lebanon, KY 40033
Tel.: (270) 692-2025
Web Site: http://www.plasticproductsco.com
Emp.: 100
Plastics Product Mfr
N.A.I.C.S.: 326199
Donald Brockman *(Plant Mgr)*

Plastic Products Company, Inc. - Moline Facility (1)
4600 44th St, Moline, IL 61265
Tel.: (309) 762-6532
Plastics Product Mfr
N.A.I.C.S.: 326199

Plastic Products Company, Inc. - Princeton Facility (1)
610 County Rd 18 S, Princeton, MN 55371
Tel.: (763) 389-3683
Plastics Product Mfr
N.A.I.C.S.: 326199

Plastic Products Company, Inc. - West Branch Facility (1)
228 Tidewater Dr, West Branch, IA 52358
Tel.: (319) 643-3690
Web Site: http://www.plasticproductsco.com
Plastics Product Mfr
N.A.I.C.S.: 326199

Smith Metal Products Inc (1)
15045 Per Rd, Center City, MN 55012
Tel.: (651) 257-3143
Web Site: http://www.smithmetals.com
Emp.: 50
Fabricated Structural Metal Mfr
N.A.I.C.S.: 332312
Todd Jensen *(Gen Mgr)*

PLASTIC RECYCLING, INC.
2015 S Pennsylvania St, Indianapolis, IN 46225-1907
Tel.: (317) 780-6100 IN
Web Site: http://plastic-recycling.net
Year Founded: 1988
Sales Range: $1-9.9 Million
Emp.: 50
Materials Recovery Facilities
N.A.I.C.S.: 562920
Alan Shaw *(Pres)*
Gary Redick *(Mgr-Safety, Trng & Matls)*
Jim Banther *(Plant Mgr)*

PLASTIC REVOLUTIONS, INC.
1704 Barnes St, Reidsville, NC 27323
Tel.: (336) 349-2800
Web Site: http://www.plasticrevolutions.com
Year Founded: 1991
Sales Range: $10-24.9 Million
Emp.: 80
Plastic Recycler Services
N.A.I.C.S.: 423930
Angel Cain *(Office Mgr)*
Emily Kelly *(Mgr-Sls & Pur-Natl)*
John Hagan *(Pres)*
Mitzie Purdy *(Mgr-Shipping & Receiving)*
Ed Handy *(VP & Gen Mgr)*
Dee Pyrtle *(Plant Mgr)*

PLASTIC SUPPLIERS, INC.
2887 Johnstown Rd, Columbus, OH 43219-1719
Tel.: (614) 471-9100 OH
Web Site: http://www.plasticsuppliers.com
Year Founded: 1949
Sales Range: $125-149.9 Million
Emp.: 370
Plastic Films Mfr & Distr
N.A.I.C.S.: 326113
Felicia Benton *(Mgr-Acctg)*
Derek Shannon *(Mgr-Converted Products)*
Brad McDaniel *(Mgr-Mfg)*
Gary Hutto *(Mgr-Quality)*

Subsidiaries:

Sidaplax v.o.f. (1)
Edda Straat 40, 9050, Gentbrugge, Belgium (100%)
Tel.: (32) 92108010
Web Site: http://www.sidaplax.com
Sales Range: $25-49.9 Million
Emp.: 70
Plastic Films Mfr & Distr
N.A.I.C.S.: 326113
B. De Keyser *(Gen Mgr)*
M. Debaets *(Mgr-Sls & Mktg)*

PLASTIC SYSTEMS, LLC.
15055 32 Mile Rd, Romeo, MI 48065
Tel.: (586) 336-9696
Web Site: http://www.plastic-systems.net
Year Founded: 2001
Sales Range: $10-24.9 Million
Emp.: 350
Plastics Product Mfr
N.A.I.C.S.: 326199
Steve Belleville *(CEO)*

PLASTICRAFT MANUFACTURING COMPANY, INC.
115 Plasticraft Dr, Albertville, AL 35951
Tel.: (256) 878-4105
Web Site: http://www.plasticraftmfg.com
Year Founded: 1972
Sales Range: $25-49.9 Million
Emp.: 140
Injection Molded Plastics Products
N.A.I.C.S.: 326199
Martha R. Ingram *(Controller)*

PLASTICS ENGINEERING COMPANY INC.
3518 Lakeshore Rd, Sheboygan, WI 53083-2903
Tel.: (920) 458-2121 WI
Web Site: http://www.plenco.com
Year Founded: 1937
Sales Range: $25-49.9 Million
Emp.: 400
Plastic Mfr
N.A.I.C.S.: 325211
Michael R. Brotz *(Pres)*

PLASTICS GROUP INC.
7409 S Quincy St, Willowbrook, IL 60527
Tel.: (630) 325-1210 MD
Web Site: http://www.theplasticsgroup.net
Year Founded: 2000
Sales Range: $75-99.9 Million
Emp.: 200
Plastic & Plastic Products Mfr
N.A.I.C.S.: 326199
Brian Beth *(Pres)*

PLASTICS RESEARCH CORPORATION
1400 S Campus Ave, Ontario, CA 91761
Tel.: (909) 391-2006 CA
Web Site: http://www.prccal.com
Year Founded: 1972
Sales Range: $10-24.9 Million
Emp.: 100
Fiberglass Reinforced Plastic Containers Designer & Mfr
N.A.I.C.S.: 326199
Gene Gregory *(CEO)*
Sarah Posey *(Mgr-Contracts)*

PLASTILITE CORPORATION
4930 Battlefield Dr, Omaha, NE 68152
Tel.: (402) 453-7500
Web Site: http://www.plastilite.com
Sales Range: $10-24.9 Million
Emp.: 80
Plastics Product Mfr
N.A.I.C.S.: 326199
Jon Ehly *(CEO)*
Rick Drew *(VP-Sls & Mktg)*
Tom Colligan *(Dir-Sls-Natl-Cold Chain & Protective Pkg)*

PLASTIMAYD CORPORATION
14151 Fir St, Oregon City, OR 97045
Tel.: (503) 654-8502
Web Site: http://www.plastimayd.com
Sales Range: $25-49.9 Million
Emp.: 170
Swimming Pool Liners, Space-Arena Air Enclosure & Liners For Industrial Use
N.A.I.C.S.: 326113
Eric Porteous *(VP-Ops)*

PLASTIPAK HOLDINGS, INC.
41605 Ann Arbor Rd, Plymouth, MI 48170
Tel.: (734) 455-3600
Web Site: https://www.plastipak.com
Year Founded: 1967
Sales Range: $1-4.9 Billion
Emp.: 6,000
Offices of Other Holding Companies
N.A.I.C.S.: 551112
William C. Young *(Chm, Pres & CEO)*
David Daugherty *(CIO & VP-Talent Mgmt)*
Frank Pollock *(Chief Comml Officer, Pres-Ops & Bus Dev-Intl)*
Pradeep Modi *(Chief Acctg Officer & VP-Admin & Strategic Plng)*
Thomas Busard *(Chief Procurement & Product Supply Officer-Global)*
Tom Jabero *(Gen Counsel)*

Subsidiaries:

LuxPET A.G./S.A. (1)
Pet Packaging Zone Industrielle Bommelscheuer, L 4940, Bascharage, Luxembourg (100%)
Tel.: (352) 3587191
Web Site: http://www.luxpet.com
Sales Range: $10-24.9 Million
Emp.: 100
Injection Molding PET Preforms for the Beverage Industry
N.A.I.C.S.: 326160

Plastipak Packaging, Inc. (1)
41605 Ann Arbor Rd, Plymouth, MI 48170-4621
Tel.: (734) 455-3600
Web Site: http://www.plastipak.com
Sales Range: $25-49.9 Million
Emp.: 300
Plastic Containers & Manufacturing Technologies, Equipment & Services
N.A.I.C.S.: 326199
William C. Young *(Pres & CEO)*

Subsidiary (Non-US):

Plastipak Argentina SA (2)
Carlos Pellegrini 713/715 Piso 12, C1009ABO, Buenos Aires, Argentina
Tel.: (54) 1152528500
Sales Range: $10-24.9 Million
Emp.: 1
Plastic Mfr
N.A.I.C.S.: 325211

Group (Non-US):

Plastipak Europe (2)
Ellice Way Wrexham Technology Park, Wrexham, LL13 7YL, United Kingdom
Tel.: (44) 1978856111
Web Site: http://www.plastipakeurope.com
Holding Company; Rigid Plastic Packaging Products Mfr & Distr
N.A.I.C.S.: 551112
Simon Lawrence *(Dir-Plant)*
Stenson Martin *(Sls Mgr-UK & Ireland)*

Subsidiary (Non-US):

Plastipak Belgium (3)
Ringlaan 7, B-2960, Brecht, Belgium
Tel.: (32) 33300811
Web Site: http://www.plastipakeurope.com
Emp.: 120
Rigid Plastic Packaging Products Mfr & Distr
N.A.I.C.S.: 326160
Wim Verreet *(Plant Mgr)*

Plastipak Czech Republic s.r.o. (3)
K Vypichu 1242, 252 19, Rudna, Czech Republic
Tel.: (420) 311549171
Web Site: http://www.plastipak.com
Sales Range: $10-24.9 Million
Emp.: 60
Plastic Mfr & Distr
N.A.I.C.S.: 325211

Plastipak Deutschland GmbH (3)
Ernst-Abbe-Strasse 20, 56743, Mendig, Germany
Tel.: (49) 26525850
Web Site: http://www.plastipak.com
Rigid Plastic Packaging Products Mfr & Distr
N.A.I.C.S.: 326160
Christoph Michels *(Coord-Quality)*

Plastipak Iberia (3)
Avenida de la ConstituciAn s/n Parcelas 290-293, 45950, Casarrubios del Monte, Spain
Tel.: (34) 918609200
Web Site: http://www.plastipakeurope.com
Rigid Plastic Packaging Products Mfr & Distr
N.A.I.C.S.: 326160

Subsidiary (Non-US):

Plastipak Maroc (4)
83 Zone Industrielle, El Jadida, 24040, Sarlau, Morocco
Tel.: (212) 523 354 544
Web Site: http://www.plastipakeurope.com
Rigid Plastic Packaging Products Distr
N.A.I.C.S.: 424610
Jose Antonio Torres P. *(Dir Gen)*

Subsidiary (Non-US):

Plastipak Packaging France (3)
Zone d'Enterprises de Bergues, BP 103, 59380, Bierne, France
Tel.: (33) 328227300
Web Site: http://www.plastipakeurope.com
Rigid Plastic Packaging Products Mfr & Distr; Plastic Recycling Services
N.A.I.C.S.: 326160

PLASTIPAK HOLDINGS, INC.

Plastipak Holdings, Inc.—(Continued)

Subsidiary (Domestic):

Plastipak UK Ltd. (3)
Gresford Industrial Park, Gresford, Wrexham, LL12 8LX, United Kingdom
Tel.: (44) 1978856111
Web Site: http://www.plastipakeurope.com
Rigid Plastic Packaging Products Mfr & Distr
N.A.I.C.S.: 326160
Simon Lawrence (Dir-Plant)
Martin Stenson (Sls Mgr-UK & Ireland)

Subsidiary (Non-US):

Plastipak Packaging Do Brasil Ltda. (2)
Avenida Madrid No 325, Vairro Cascapa Paulina, Paulinia, 13140-000, SP, Brazil
Tel.: (55) 1938442100
Web Site: http://www.plastipak.com.br
Sales Range: $10-24.9 Million
Emp.: 50
Plastic Packaging Materials Mfr
N.A.I.C.S.: 561910

Plant (Domestic):

Plastipak Packaging Inc. - Jackson Center (2)
300 Washington St, Jackson Center, OH 45334
Tel.: (937) 596-5166
Web Site: http://www.plastipak.com
Sales Range: $25-49.9 Million
Emp.: 25
Plastics Bottles
N.A.I.C.S.: 326160
William Young (Pres)

Subsidiary (Non-US):

Plastipak Packaging da Amazonia (2)
Av Grande Circular 1000 Distrito Industrial, Cidade Nova, Manaus, EP 69 085 000, Amazonas, Brazil
Tel.: (55) 9236183111
Web Site: http://www.plastipak.com
Plastic Mfr
N.A.I.C.S.: 325211

Whiteline Express Ltd. (2)
9000 General Dr, Plymouth, MI 48170-4621
Tel.: (734) 455-4700
Web Site: http://www.whiteline-express.com
Rev.: $33,000,000
Emp.: 200
Freight Transportation & Logistics Distr
N.A.I.C.S.: 484121

PLASTIPRINT INC.
575 Union Blvd Ste 103, Lakewood, CO 80228
Tel.: (303) 987-0450
Web Site: http://www.plastiprint.com
Sales Range: $10-24.9 Million
Emp.: 2
Plastics Film
N.A.I.C.S.: 424610
Douglas H. Meyer (Pres)
Matt Meyer (Coord-Mktg & Sls)

PLASTOMER CORP.
37819 Schoolcraft Rd, Livonia, MI 48150-5031
Tel.: (734) 464-0700   MI
Web Site: http://www.plastomer.com
Year Founded: 1954
Sales Range: $25-49.9 Million
Emp.: 150
Mfr of Gaskets, Packing & Sealing Devices, Polyurethane Foam & Laminates
N.A.I.C.S.: 326150
George Baughman (Founder)
David Baughman (Exec VP)
Donald Show (Controller)
Walter Baughman III (Pres)

PLASTPRO, INC.
5200 W Century Blvd, Los Angeles, CA 90045

Tel.: (310) 693-8600
Web Site: http://www.plastproinc.com
Year Founded: 1994
Sales Range: $10-24.9 Million
Emp.: 132
Glass Products Mfr
N.A.I.C.S.: 327215
Michelle Pang (Coord-Production)
Franco An (Pres)
Shirley Wang (Founder & CEO)
Johnny Mai (CFO)
Peini Spinazzola (Dir-Mktg)

PLASTYC INC.
55 Broad St Ste 7-B, New York, NY 10004
Tel.: (646) 485-5267
Web Site: http://www.plastyc.com
Year Founded: 2005
Sales Range: $1-9.9 Million
Emp.: 7
Electronic Financial Payment Processing Services
N.A.I.C.S.: 522320
Patrice Peyret (CEO)
Justin Surman (CTO)
Daniel Clark (Dir-Fin)
Jon C. Hennen (Dir-Ops)
Carles Guillot (CMO)
Kari Zylla (Dir-Consumer Svcs)
Mindy DaBros (Sr Project Mgr)

PLATEAU ELECTRIC COOPERATIVE
16200 Scott Hwy, Oneida, TN 37841
Tel.: (423) 569-8591
Web Site: http://www.plateauelectric.com
Rev.: $22,496,260
Emp.: 44
Distribution, Electric Power
N.A.I.C.S.: 221122
Maxwell Huff (Pres)
Vic Davis (VP)
Jim Litton (Treas & Sec)
Dave Cross (CEO)

PLATEAU GROUP INC.
2701 N Main St, Crossville, TN 38555
Tel.: (931) 484-8411
Web Site: http://www.plateaugroup.com
Rev.: $11,400,000
Emp.: 60
Insurance Holding Company
N.A.I.C.S.: 551112
Dick Williams (Pres)

PLATFORM CAPITAL, LLC
1550 Larimer St Ste 118, Denver, CO 80202
Tel.: (877) 733-7483
Web Site: https://www.platformcap.com
Emp.: 100
Privater Equity Firm
N.A.I.C.S.: 523999
Brian Burns (Mng Partner)

Subsidiaries:

Platform Waste Solutions, LLC (1)
1550 Larimer St Ste 118, Denver, CO 80202
Tel.: (877) 733-7483
Solid Waste Collection, Recycling & Disposal Services
N.A.I.C.S.: 562998

PLATFORM PARTNERS LLC
1717 W Loop S Ste 1900, Houston, TX 77027
Tel.: (713) 335-2300   DE
Web Site: http://www.platformllc.com
Year Founded: 2006
Privater Equity Firm
N.A.I.C.S.: 523999

Frederick W. Brazelton (CEO)
Fred Lummis (Chm)
Brad Morgan (Pres)
Kathy Mattina (Chief Compliance Officer)
Vik Kalra (VP)

Subsidiaries:

Dynamic Glass, LLC (1)
9419 Windfern Rd, Houston, TX 77064
Tel.: (713) 895-0080
Web Site: http://dynamicglass.com
Glass & Glazing Contractor
N.A.I.C.S.: 238150
Scott Coulter (CFO)
Kevin Carey (Exec VP)

Subsidiary (Domestic):

Colorado Window Systems, Inc. (2)
10665 E 51st Ave, Denver, CO 80239
Tel.: (303) 227-0559
Web Site: http://coloradowindowsystems.com
Sales Range: $1-9.9 Million
Emp.: 12
Glass & Glazing Contractors
N.A.I.C.S.: 238150
Heidie Skinner (Pres, CEO & CFO)
Dave McManis (Project Mgr)

GHR Acquisition, LLC (1)
24 Greenway Plz Ste 965, Houston, TX 77046
Tel.: (713) 585-3579
Web Site: http://www.ghresources.com
Holding Company
N.A.I.C.S.: 551112
Laura Magner (COO & Partner)
Cheryl Wilhelm (Chief Dev Officer & Partner)

Subsidiary (Domestic):

General Healthcare Resources, LLC (2)
2250 Hickory Rd Ste 240, Plymouth Meeting, PA 19462-2225
Tel.: (610) 834-1122
Web Site: http://www.ghresources.com
Healtcare Services
N.A.I.C.S.: 622110
Laura Magner (COO)

Subsidiary (Domestic):

Meleeo, LLC (3)
17633 Gunn Hwy Ste 110, Odessa, FL 33556
Tel.: (813) 333-0688
Web Site: http://www.meleeo.com
Sales Range: $1-9.9 Million
Emp.: 200
Health Care Srvices
N.A.I.C.S.: 621610
Jason Chiappetta (Founder, Pres & Mng Partner)

PLATFORMQ, LLC
100 Crescent Rd, Needham, MA 02494
Tel.: (617) 938-6000
Web Site: http://www.platformq.com
Sales Range: $1-9.9 Million
Emp.: 65
Online Conferences & Events
N.A.I.C.S.: 611710
Robert Rosenbloom (CEO-PlatformQ Health)
Hal Garnick (Chm)
Chris Charron (COO)
Kathryn Pucci (Sr VP-Education)
Jeff Arnold (Gen Mgr-Cardiology & Urology-PlatformQ Health)
Mallory Willsea (VP-Strategy & Ops)
Gil Rogers (Exec VP)
Jim Phelan (VP-Video Engrg)
Marie Elliott (Mktg Mgr-Interactive)
Anthony Pinto (Dir-Engagement Mktg Strategy)

PLATING TECHNOLOGY INC.
800 Frebis Ave, Columbus, OH 43206

Tel.: (614) 228-2326
Web Site: http://www.platingtech.com
Rev.: $20,000,000
Emp.: 110
Electroplating Services
N.A.I.C.S.: 332813
Keith Goudy (Dir-Safety)
Kirk Urmey (CEO)
Daniel Ott (Plant Mgr)
Richard Hamilton (Gen Mgr)
Tim Caudill (Mgr-Quality)

PLATINUM BANK
802 W Lumsden Rd, Brandon, FL 33511
Tel.: (813) 655-1234
Web Site: http://www.platinumbank.com
Year Founded: 1997
Sales Range: $10-24.9 Million
Emp.: 77
Banking Services
N.A.I.C.S.: 522110
Jerry Kyle (Pres & CEO)
Kenneth D. Ely (Pres-Polk County Reg)
William G. Little (Chief Credit Officer & Sr Exec VP)
William C. Williams (Chief Real Estate Officer & Sr Exec VP)
Julie K. Longabach (CFO & Exec VP)
David M. Sullivan (Sr Exec VP)
David Jones (Sr Exec VP)
Robert F. Cobb (Exec VP)
Gina Hamilton (Sr VP & Dir-Ops & IT)
Tanner Johnson (VP & Mgr-Comml Banking & Relationship)
Pete Odell (Sr VP-Comml Lending)
Heather Velez (VP)

PLATINUM ENERGY RESOURCES, INC.
Galleria Tower 1 2700 Post Oak Blvd Site 1000, Houston, TX 77056
Tel.: (713) 364-7822   DE
Web Site: http://www.platenergy.com
Year Founded: 2005
Sales Range: $10-24.9 Million
Emp.: 163
Oil & Gas Operations
N.A.I.C.S.: 211120
Ralph Schofield (COO)
John Ghermezian (Pres & CEO)

PLATINUM EQUITY, LLC
360 N Crescent Dr, Beverly Hills, CA 90210
Tel.: (310) 712-1850   DE
Web Site: http://www.platinumequity.com
Year Founded: 1995
Privater Equity Firm
N.A.I.C.S.: 523999
Tom Gores (Founder, Chm & CEO)
Johnny O. Lopez (Partner)
Mark Barnhill (Partner)
Robert J. Wentworth (Partner)
Robert Wymbs (Partner)
Roger House (Principal)
Todd Golditch (Principal)
Eva Monica Kalawski (Exec VP)
Mary Ann Sigler (CFO & Chief Compliance Officer)
Dave Aroesty (Principal)
Robert Klap (Principal)
Philip E. Norment (Partner)
David Boutry (Principal)
Adam Cooper (Mng Dir)
Christian Cook (Principal)
Brandon Crawley (Mng Dir)
Soo Jin Goh (Principal)
Craig Ashmore (Principal)
Stephanie Barter (Partner)
Bibi Di Serio (Principal)
Dan Frich (Principal)
Fernando Goni (Principal)

COMPANIES

PLATINUM EQUITY, LLC

Dan Krasner *(Mng Dir)*
Renee Koontz *(Principal)*
Bryan Kelln *(Partner)*
Igor Chacartegui *(Mng Dir)*
Alex Done *(Mng Dir)*
Jacob T. Kotzubei *(Co-Pres)*
Louis Samson *(Co-Pres)*
David Glatt *(Mng Dir & Principal)*

Subsidiaries:

American & Efird, LLC (1)
22 American St, Mount Holly, NC
28120-2150 **(100%)**
Tel.: (704) 951-2996
Web Site: http://www.amefird.com
Industrial Sewing Thread Mfr & Marketer
N.A.I.C.S.: 313110
Craig G. Stover *(Sr VP-Fin)*
Mark Hatton *(VP-Sls)*
Les Miller *(Exec VP-Sls & Ops)*
A. Knox Winget III *(Sr VP-Global Supply Chain Ops)*
James F. Love III *(Asst Sec)*

Subsidiary (Non-US):

A&E Bangladesh Ltd. (2)
4th Floor Plot 38 Gulshan Avenue, Dhaka, 1212, Bangladesh
Tel.: (880) 2 791 4850
Web Site: http://www.amefird.com
Sewing Thread & Industrial Yarn Supplier
N.A.I.C.S.: 424310
Angelo Leanage *(Mng Dir)*
Syed Arefin *(Dir-Sls & Mktg)*
Anwarul Alam *(Dir-Mfg)*

Hilos A&E Dominicana LTD (2)
Zona Franca, Santiago, Dominican Republic
Tel.: (809) 576 9404
Web Site: http://www.amefird.com
Sewing Thread Distr
N.A.I.C.S.: 424310
Kevin Cabral *(Country Mgr)*

Hilos A&E de Honduras, S.A. (2)
Complejo Elca, Choloma, Cortes, Honduras
Tel.: (504) 669 5151
Web Site: http://www.amefird.com
Industrial Sewing Thread Whslr
N.A.I.C.S.: 423840
Javier Vega *(Country Mgr)*

Hilos A&E de Mexico SA de CV (2)
Calle 21 No 93-E x 14 Col Itzimna, 97100, Merida, Yucatan, Mexico
Tel.: (52) 999 942 9800
Web Site: http://www.amefird.com
Sewing Thread Distr
N.A.I.C.S.: 424310
Felipe Fernandez *(Gen Mgr)*

American Commercial Lines Inc. (1)
1701 E Market St, Jeffersonville, IN 47130-4747
Tel.: (812) 288-0100
Web Site: http://www.aclines.com
Sales Range: $800-899.9 Million
Emp.: 2,572
Inland Waterway Marine Transportation Services
N.A.I.C.S.: 483211
Tim Allen *(Dir-Liquid Sls)*
Mike Ellis *(CEO)*
John Giles *(Chm)*
Rich Bruns *(VP-HR)*

American Traffic Solutions, Inc. (1)
1150 N Alma School Rd, Mesa, AZ 85201
Tel.: (480) 443-7000
Web Site: http://www.atsol.com
Sales Range: $1-9.9 Million
Emp.: 81
Transportation Solutions Provider
N.A.I.C.S.: 488999
Patricia Chiodo *(CFO)*
David Roberts *(Pres & CEO)*
Rebecca Kozloff Collins *(Gen Counsel)*
Vincent Brigidi *(Exec VP-Emerging Markets)*
Jason Rivera *(CTO)*
Anat Gan Eden *(Chief People Officer)*

Artesyn Embedded Technologies, Inc. (1)
2900 S Diablo Way Ste 190, Tempe, AZ 85282
Tel.: (602) 438-5720
Web Site: http://www.artesyn.com

Emp.: 16,000
Designer, Mfr & Distr of Embedded Power & Computing Products, Systems & Solutions
N.A.I.C.S.: 334419
Brian Korn *(Sr Dir-Data Center Solutions)*
Barry Dolan *(VP-Sls & Mktg)*
Peter Rowley *(CFO)*

Broadway Systems & Technology Co., Ltd. (1)
No 8 Guxu Road, Pudong New District, Shanghai, 201209, China
Tel.: (86) 21 5863 2133
Web Site: http://www.broadway-grp.com
Holding Company; Foam Plastic & Packaging Products Mfr
N.A.I.C.S.: 551112
Daniel Chen *(CEO)*
Vivian Tan *(Fin Dir)*
Lin Lin *(Gen Counsel)*
Chris Liu *(VP-Transformation)*
Thomas Xu *(VP-Sls & Bus Dev)*
Weifeng Dai *(Dir-Bus Dev)*

Subsidiary (Domestic):

Shanghai Broadway Packaging & Insulation Materials Co., Ltd. (2)
No 8 Guxu Road, Pudong New District, Shanghai, 201209, China
Tel.: (86) 2158632133
Foam Plastics & Packaging Products Mfr
N.A.I.C.S.: 326140

Subsidiary (Domestic):

Chongqing Broadway Foam Applications & Total Packaging Co., Ltd. (3)
12 Yinshan Road, Bishan District, Chongqing, 402760, China
Tel.: (86) 23 6430 2133
Foam Plastics & Packaging Products Mfr
N.A.I.C.S.: 326140
Dragon Chen *(Gen Mgr)*

Subsidiary (Domestic):

Shenzhen Broadway Total Packaging Solution Co., Ltd. (2)
2500034 Dasan Village Dasan Community Guanlan Street, Longhua New District, Shenzhen, 518110, China
Tel.: (86) 75529561539
Foam Plastics & Packaging Products Mfr
N.A.I.C.S.: 326140
Frank Liu *(Gen Mgr)*

Centerfield Media Holdings, LLC (1)
12130 Millenium Dr Ste 600, Los Angeles, CA 90094
Tel.: (310) 341-4420
Web Site: http://www.centerfield.com
Sales Range: $50-74.9 Million
Emp.: 73
Digital Advertising Services
N.A.I.C.S.: 541850
Jason Cohen *(Co-Founder & Co-CEO)*
Brett Cravatt *(Co-Founder & Co-CEO)*
Brad Green *(VP-Fin)*
Sarah Greene *(VP-HR)*
Kevin Miao *(Gen Counsel)*
Scott Norwalk *(VP)*
Gary Pak *(COO & CTO)*
Cali Tran *(Chief Bus Officer)*
Jaimie Clark *(VP-SEO)*
Kuntal Shah *(Exec VP-Tech)*

Subsidiary (Domestic):

Datalot Inc. (2)
65 Jay St, Brooklyn, NY 11201
Tel.: (888) 235-1697
Web Site: http://www.datalot.com
Sales Range: $10-24.9 Million
Emp.: 40
Advertising Software Developer
N.A.I.C.S.: 513210
Josh Reznick *(CEO)*

Savings.com (2)
2225 S Carmelina Ave, Los Angeles, CA 90064
Tel.: (310) 820-5221
Web Site: http://www.savings.com
Online Shopping Offering Discounts, Coupons & Deals on Various Consumer Products
N.A.I.C.S.: 459999
Braian Lee *(Head-Consumer Experience)*

Subsidiary (Non-US):

Savoo Ltd. (3)
22 Long Acre Covent Garden, WC2E 9LY, London, United Kingdom - England **(100%)**
Tel.: (44) 20 3005 7501
Web Site: http://www.savoo.co.uk
Online Discounter of Consumer Products & Services
N.A.I.C.S.: 517810
Simon Bird *(Dir-Retail Partnerships)*

Chassix, Inc. (1)
300 Galleria Officentre Ste 501, Southfield, MI 48034
Tel.: (248) 728-8700
Web Site: http://www.chassix.com
Sales Range: $75-99.9 Million
Emp.: 500
Industrial Machinery Mfr
N.A.I.C.S.: 333998
Safi Hamid *(VP-Sls)*
Eric Rouchy *(VP-Engrg)*
Iwona Niec Villaire *(Gen Counsel & VP)*
Michael Beyer *(CFO)*
Tom Bane *(VP-Ops)*
Joel Tokarz *(VP-HR)*
Alexandre Debrye *(VP/Gen Mgr-Asia)*
Cemal Aydogan *(VP-Ops-Americas)*
Andreas Weller *(Pres & CEO)*

Cision Ltd. (1)
130 E Randolph St 7th Fl, Chicago, IL 60601
Tel.: (312) 922-2400
Web Site: http://www.cision.com
Rev.: $730,373,000
Assets: $1,866,376,000
Liabilities: $1,578,059,000
Net Worth: $288,317,000
Earnings: ($24,394,000)
Emp.: 4,500
Fiscal Year-end: 12/31/2018
Medical Software Publisher
N.A.I.C.S.: 513210
Jack Pearlstein *(CFO & Exec VP)*
Pritham Shetty *(CTO)*
Steve Solomon *(Chief Acctg Officer)*
Yujie Chen *(Pres-Asia Pacific)*
David Barker *(Pres-Data Solutions & Innovation)*
Gregg Spratto *(COO)*
Laura Roman *(Dir-Corp Comm)*
Peter Low *(Mng Dir-EMEA)*
Keir Fawcus *(Sr VP-Sls-EMEA)*
Kate Walker *(VP-Earned Media Mgmt)*
Nicole Guillot *(Chief Content Officer & Pres-Canada & Latam)*
Tim Moylan *(Chief Revenue Officer)*
Rebecca Dersh *(Mgr-PR)*

Subsidiary (Non-US):

Atodia AB (2)
Linnegatan 87A, Stockholm, 115 23, Sweden
Tel.: (46) 850741400
Computer Software Development Services
N.A.I.C.S.: 541511

Cision Finland Oy (2)
Salomonkatu 17 B, 100, Helsinki, Finland **(100%)**
Tel.: (358) 20 786 2590
Sales Range: $25-49.9 Million
Emp.: 14
Business Communication Media Planning, Connection, Monitoring & Analysis Products & Services
N.A.I.C.S.: 561499
Juho Itkonen *(Mgr-Bus Dev)*
Jenni Salomaa *(Mgr-Mktg)*
Magnus Theill *(Mgr-Nordic)*

Cision Germany GmbH (2)
Hanauer Landstr 287, Frankfurt am Main, 60314, Germany
Tel.: (49) 69 244 3288 300
Web Site: http://www.cision.de
Emp.: 25
Business Communication Media Planning, Connection, Monitoring & Analysis Products & Services
N.A.I.C.S.: 561499
Clemens Hammacher *(Mgr-Sls & Mktg)*

Cision Global Solutions AB (2)
Linnegatan 87, Stockholm, 115 23, Sweden
Tel.: (46) 850741000

Web Site: http://www.cision.com
Computer Software Development Services
N.A.I.C.S.: 541511
Magnus Phell *(CEO)*

Cision Portugal S.A. (2)
Avenida Fontes Pereira de Melo No 21 5o, 1050-116, Lisbon, Portugal **(100%)**
Tel.: (351) 213 190 570
Web Site: http://www.cision.com
Business Communication Media Planning, Connection, Monitoring & Analysis Products & Services
N.A.I.C.S.: 561499
Jose Santos *(Mng Dir)*

Cision Scandinavia AS (2)
Akersgatan 16, 0158, Oslo, Norway
Tel.: (47) 8442 7020
Business Communication Media Planning & Connection Products & Services
N.A.I.C.S.: 561499

Cision Sverige AB (2)
Linnegatan 87 A, Box 24194, 104 51, Stockholm, Sweden
Tel.: (46) 8 507 410 00
Web Site: http://www.cision.com
Public Relations & Communication Services
N.A.I.C.S.: 541820
Anders Kall *(CFO)*
Mats Backlund *(Dir-IT)*
Helen Lundstrom *(Mgr-Customer Ops)*
Alexander Mason *(Dir-Sls & Mktg)*
Karin Persson *(Mgr-HR)*
Krister Wennberg *(Dir-Bus Dev)*

Cision UK Ltd. (2)
16-22 Baltic Street West, London, EC1Y 0UL, United Kingdom **(100%)**
Tel.: (44) 207 689 1160
Web Site: http://www.cision.com
Sales Range: $25-49.9 Million
Business Communication Media Planning, Connection, Monitoring & Analysis Products & Services
N.A.I.C.S.: 561499
Kester Ford *(Head-Product & Mktg)*
Jody Clark *(Head-New Bus)*
Marc Munier *(Mng Dir)*

Subsidiary (Domestic):

Gorkana (3)
140 Old Street, London, EC1V 9BJ, United Kingdom
Tel.: (44) 2074206808
Web Site: http://www.gorkana.com
Public Relations Services
N.A.I.C.S.: 541840
Jeni Lee Chapman *(Mng Dir-US)*
Dermot Corrigan *(Chief Comml Officer)*
Myles Johnson *(CFO)*
Jeremy Thompson *(Mng Dir)*
Andrew Brown *(CIO)*
Paul Hender *(Head-Insight)*
Stephen Wicks *(CTO)*
Ciara Jordan *(Dir-Ops)*
Tom Ritchie *(Dir-Product)*
Lorna Mattis *(Dir-HR)*

Subsidiary (Domestic):

Cision US Inc. (2)
130 E Randolph St 7th Fl, Chicago, IL 60601 **(100%)**
Tel.: (312) 922-2400
Web Site: http://www.cision.com
Sales Range: $100-124.9 Million
Business Communication Media Planning, Connection, Monitoring & Analysis Products & Services
N.A.I.C.S.: 561499
Peter Granat *(Chm)*
Kevin Akeroyd *(CEO)*
Maureen Calabrese *(Chief People Officer)*
Mark Jones *(Chief Product Officer)*
Jack Pearlstein *(CFO & Exec VP)*
Paul Salay *(Chief Comml Officer)*
Chris Lynch *(CMO)*
David Barker *(Chief Data & Res Officer)*
Emir Lindo *(Sr VP-Global Partnerships)*
Dustin Johnson *(Sr VP-Svcs Strategy & Ops)*
Michael Piispanen *(COO)*
Pat Galvin *(Chief Revenue Officer-North America)*
Stacey Miller *(Sr Dir-Corp Comm)*

Subsidiary (Non-US):

Data Presse SAS (3)

PLATINUM EQUITY, LLC

U.S. PRIVATE

Platinum Equity, LLC—(Continued)
137 rue du 8 mai 1945 Park Bp 29, Ri-orges, 42153, France
Tel.: (33) 1 76 21 12 00
Web Site: http://www.datapresse.com
Applications Software Programming Services
N.A.I.C.S.: 513210

Subsidiary (Domestic):

PR Newswire Association LLC (3)
350 Hudson Ste 300, New York, NY 10014
Tel.: (800) 776-8090
Web Site: http://www.prnewswire.com
Emp.: 5,000
News, Content Distribution & Public Relations Services
N.A.I.C.S.: 516210
Alex Perez (Sr Engr-Windows Sys)
Nicoletta Nicoli (Grp Dir-Sls-EMEA & India)
Kevin Akeroyd (CEO)
Jack Pearlstein (CFO & Exec VP)
Robert Coppola (CIO)
Whitney Benner (Chief HR Officer)
Dave Haapaoja (Sr VP-Global Ops)
Yujie Chen (Sr VP-Asia-Pacific)
Jeremy Thompson (CEO-EMEA & India)
Sean O'Driscoll (Chief Strategy & Insights Officer)
Chris Lynch (CMO)
Jason Edelboim (Pres-Americas)

Affiliate (Non-US):

PR Newswire Asia Ltd (4)
Unit 1806-1808 Tian An Center 338 West Nanjing Road, Shanghai, 200003, China
Tel.: (86) 21 8017 9500
Web Site: http://en.prnasia.com
Public Relations & News Distribution Network Services
N.A.I.C.S.: 541820
John Williams (Exec VP & Mng Dir-China)
Yujie Chen (Sr VP-Asia-Pacific)

Subsidiary (Domestic):

Visible Technologies (3)
3535 Factoria Blvd SE Ste 400, Bellevue, WA 98006
Tel.: (425) 957-6100
Sales Range: $1-9.9 Million
Emp.: 95
Software Applications to Protect Online Personnel & Corporate Brands
N.A.I.C.S.: 513210
Blake D. Cahill (Sr VP-Mktg)
Elizabeth Morgan (Sr VP-Bus Dev)
Jack Denault (Sr VP-Worldwide Sls & Svcs)
Joseph J. Grano Jr. (Chm)

Subsidiary (Non-US):

Vocus Europe Limited (3)
Longbow House 20 Chiswell Street, London, EC1Y 4TW, United Kingdom
Tel.: (44) 20 3426 4001
Web Site: http://www.vocus.co.uk
Sales Range: $75-99.9 Million
Software Solutions for Public Relations Management
N.A.I.C.S.: 513210
Andrew Muir (Mng Dir)

Vocus UK Limited (3)
Longbow House 20 Chiswell Street, London, EC1Y 4TW, United Kingdom
Tel.: (44) 2034264001
Sales Range: $25-49.9 Million
Emp.: 100
Applications Software Programming Services
N.A.I.C.S.: 513210
Charlie O'rourjke (Mng Dir)

Subsidiary (Non-US):

Public and Investor Relations PIR Sverige AB (2)
Saltmatargatan 9, Stockholm, 113 59, Sweden
Tel.: (46) 8 20 17 00
Web Site: http://www.pirab.se
Public Relations & Communication Consulting Services
N.A.I.C.S.: 541820

Runtime Collective Limited (2)
Sovereign House Church Street 2nd Floor, Brighton, BN1 1UJ, United Kingdom
Tel.: (44) 1273 234 290
Web Site: http://www.brandwatch.com
Emp.: 300
Social Media Monitoring Software Developer
N.A.I.C.S.: 513210
Ben Goodband (CFO)
Ulrik Bo Larsen (Pres)
Anders Hay Kloster (COO)
Chris Bingham (CTO)
Katja Garrood (Chief Brand Officer)
Michael Amsinck (Chief Product Officer)
Edward Crook (Chief Strategy Officer)

Clipper Windpower, LLC (1)
6305 Carpinteria Ave Ste 300, Carpinteria, CA 93013
Tel.: (805) 690-3275
Web Site: http://www.clipperwind.com
Sales Range: $50-74.9 Million
Emp.: 750
Wind Turbine Mfr
N.A.I.C.S.: 333611
Jason DeGroot (Dir-Sls & Supply Chain)
Marty Stimson (Mgr-Engrg)
Jodi Zahner (Office Mgr)

Club Car, LLC (1)
4125 Washington Rd, Evans, GA 30809-3067
Tel.: (706) 955-0081
Web Site: http://www.clubcar.com
Electric & Gasoline Golf Cars & Light Utility Carryalls Mfr
N.A.I.C.S.: 336999
Marc Dufour (Pres & CEO)

Subsidiary (Domestic):

Garia Inc. (2)
14820 N Fwy, Ste 200, Houston, TX 77090
Tel.: (281) 923-0291
Web Site: https://www.garia.com
Emp.: 100
Motorcycle, Bicycle & Parts Mfr
N.A.I.C.S.: 336991

Contego Packaging Holdings Limited (1)
Windlebrook House, Guildford Rd, Bagshot, GU195NG, Surrey, United Kingdom
Tel.: (44) 1276452266
Web Site: http://www.contegopackaging.com
Sales Range: $150-199.9 Million
Emp.: 1,800
Coated & Laminated Packaging Paper & Plastics Film Mfr
N.A.I.C.S.: 322220

Subsidiary (Domestic):

Contego Packaging (2)
Cockburn Fields, Middleton Grove, Leeds, LS115LX, United Kingdom (100%)
Tel.: (44) 1133832296
Web Site: http://www.graphicpackaging.com
Sales Range: $50-74.9 Million
Emp.: 450
Paperboard Box Mfr
N.A.I.C.S.: 322219
David Scheible (CEO)

Subsidiary (Non-US):

Contego Packaging B.V. (2)
Koolweg 12, 4631SZ, Hoogerheide, Netherlands (100%)
Tel.: (31) 164611500
Web Site: http://www.contegopackaging.com
Sales Range: $50-74.9 Million
Emp.: 350
Coated & Laminated Packaging Paper & Plastics Film Mfr
N.A.I.C.S.: 322220
A. J. Luten (Gen Mgr)
Juan Arjona (Gen Mgr)

Contego Packaging Ireland Ltd. (2)
Unit 629 IDA Industrial Park Northern Ext, Old Kilmeaden Road, Waterford, Ireland (100%)
Tel.: (353) 51376484
Web Site: http://www.contegopackaging.com
Sales Range: $25-49.9 Million
Emp.: 36

Coated & Laminated Packaging Paper & Plastics Film Mfr
N.A.I.C.S.: 322220

DCA Services Inc. (1)
300 N Meridian Ave Ste 115, Oklahoma City, OK 73107-6560
Tel.: (405) 951-9300
Web Site: http://www.dcaservices.com
Sales Range: $25-49.9 Million
Emp.: 55
Long Distance Billing Software Applications
N.A.I.C.S.: 517112

DMT Solutions Global Corporation (1)
37 Executive Dr, Danbury, CT 06810-4147 (100%)
Web Site: http://www.bluecrestinc.com
Provider of Hardware & Software Tools for Mail Processing & Transaction Management
N.A.I.C.S.: 333310
Dennis P. Lestrange (CEO)
John P. Capasso (CFO)
Brian K. Davis (COO)

Subsidiary (Domestic):

BCC Software, LLC (2)
75 Josons Dr, Rochester, NY 14623-3494
Tel.: (800) 453-3130
Web Site: http://bccsoftware.com
Software Publisher
N.A.I.C.S.: 513210
Chris Lien (Pres)
Eric Narowski (CFO)
Shawn Ryan (VP-Product Strategy)
Jim Mann (VP-Ops)
Michael Machonkin (VP-Sls)

Subsidiary (Domestic):

Satori Software Inc. (3)
1301 5th Ave Ste 2200, Seattle, WA 98101
Tel.: (206) 357-2900
Sales Range: $10-24.9 Million
Emp.: 20
Data Quality & Mailing Preparation Solutions
N.A.I.C.S.: 541511
Corey Smith (VP-Production Mailing Solutions)
Bob Schimek (Sr Dir-Postal Affairs)

Subsidiary (Domestic):

Monticello Software, Inc. (4)
6411 Carter Ln, Mineral, VA 23117
Tel.: (540) 854-4200
Web Site: http://www.montsoft.com
Sales Range: $10-24.9 Million
Emp.: 7
Software Publisher
N.A.I.C.S.: 513210
Joe Bailey (Pres & CEO)

Subsidiary (Domestic):

Window Book, Inc. (2)
300 Franklin St, Cambridge, MA 02139
Tel.: (617) 441-3500
Web Site: http://www.windowbook.com
Software Publisher
N.A.I.C.S.: 513210
Monica Lundquist (Mgr-Affairs)
Michael Spier (CTO)
Steve Lopez (COO)

Data2Logistics, LLC (1)
12631 Westlinks Dr Ste 3, Fort Myers, FL 33913-8627
Tel.: (239) 936-2800
Web Site: http://www.data2logistics.com
Sales Range: $25-49.9 Million
Emp.: 350
Freight Transportation Arrangement
N.A.I.C.S.: 488510
Harold B. Friedman (Sr VP-Global Corp Dev)
Leif Holm-Andersen (Exec Dir-Pro Svcs)
Kevin Brown (CFO)
Brian Keon (Sr Dir-Ops)
David C. Schembri (Pres & CEO)
Dustin P. Baker (CTO)

Subsidiary (Non-US):

Data2Logistics Europe BV (2)
Rivium 1e straat 101, Capelle aan den IJssel, 2909 LE, Netherlands
Tel.: (31) 10 2661040

Web Site: http://www.data2logistics.com
Emp.: 25
Freight Transportation Arrangement
N.A.I.C.S.: 488510

Doskocil Manufacturing Company Inc. (1)
2300 E Randol Mill Rd, Arlington, TX 76004-1246
Tel.: (877) 738-6283
Web Site: http://www.petmate.com
Plastics Product Mfr
N.A.I.C.S.: 326199
Alice Tillett (CEO)

Subsidiary (Domestic):

Pet Qwerks, Inc (2)
9 Studebaker Dr, Irvine, CA 92618
Tel.: (949) 347-8492
Web Site: http://www.petqwerks.com
Toy & Hobby Goods & Supplies Merchant Whslr
N.A.I.C.S.: 423920
Andrew Gick (VP)
Jim Gick (Founder)

Electro Rent Corporation (1)
6060 Sepulveda Blvd, Van Nuys, CA 91411-2512 (100%)
Tel.: (818) 786-2525
Web Site: http://www.electrorent.com
Rev.: $175,300,033
Assets: $284,577,000
Liabilities: $63,078,000
Net Worth: $221,499,000
Earnings: $4,784,000
Emp.: 386
Fiscal Year-end: 05/31/2016
Electronic Test & Measurement Equipment, Workstations & Personal Computers Sales, Rental & Leasing
N.A.I.C.S.: 532420
Steven Markheim (Pres & CEO)
Herb Ostenberg (Sr VP-Sls-North America)
Michael Clark (CEO-Global)
Dirk de Waart (COO-Global)
Jonathan Watson (CFO)

Subsidiary (Non-US):

Electro Rent (Beijing) Test & Measurement Equipment Rental Co., Ltd. (2)
Laiguangying West Road Chao Lai Hi-Tech Industrial Park Building No10, Chaoyang District, Beijing, 100102, China
Tel.: (86) 1058302699
Web Site: http://www.electrorent.cn
Electronic Test & Measurement Equipment Rental & Leasing
N.A.I.C.S.: 532420

Branch (Domestic):

Electro Rent Corporation (Eastern Regional Office) (2)
1770 Corporate Dr Ste 550, Norcross, GA 30093-2945 (100%)
Tel.: (770) 813-7000
Web Site: http://www.electrorent.com
Emp.: 20
Test Measurement Equipment Computers & Workstations Whslr & Leasing
N.A.I.C.S.: 532210

Subsidiary (Non-US):

Electro Rent Europe NV (2)
Intercity Business Park Generaal de Wittelaan 9/18, Mechelen, 2800, Belgium
Tel.: (32) 15740800
Web Site: http://www.electrorent-europe.com
Electronic Test & Measurement Equipment Rental & Leasing
N.A.I.C.S.: 532420
David Saeys (Mng Dir)
Mike Sullivan (Bus Mgr-UK)

Microlease Limited (2)
Unit 1 Waverley Industrial Park Hailsham Drive, Harrow, HA1 4TR, Mddx, United Kingdom
Tel.: (44) 2084200200
Web Site: http://www.microlease.com
Emp.: 500
Electronic Test Equipment Distr & Leasing
N.A.I.C.S.: 423840

COMPANIES — PLATINUM EQUITY, LLC

David Knights *(Dir-Asset Mgmt Svcs-EMEA)*
Michael Clark *(CEO-Americas)*
Nigel Brown *(CEO)*
Peter Spillman *(Dir-Inventory Plng)*
David Whitfield *(Mng Dir-Asia)*
Gordon Curwen *(VP-Ops-Americas)*
David Sherve *(VP-Product Mgmt & Mktg-Americas)*
Paul Smith *(Dir-Global Fin)*
Paul McCloskey *(Dir-Sls Ops-EMEA)*
Wayne Harris *(Dir-Ops-EMEA)*

Subsidiary (Non-US):

Microlease France (3)
Parc Tertiaire Icade 43 Avenue Robert Schuman, PO Box 10181, 94563, Rungis, Cedex, France
Tel.: (33) 145126565
Web Site: http://www.microlease.com
Electronic Test Equipment Distr
N.A.I.C.S.: 423830
Peter Collingwood *(CEO-EMEA)*
Paul McCloskey *(Dir-Sls Ops-EMEA)*
Nigel Brown *(Co-CEO)*
Michael Clark *(Co-CEO)*
David Whitfield *(Mng Dir-Asia)*

Microlease S.r.l. (3)
Via Piero Gobetti 2/C Cernusco Sul Naviglio, 20063, Milan, Italy
Tel.: (39) 02 9239 2801
Web Site: http://www.microlease.com
Electronic Test Equipment Distr & Leasing
N.A.I.C.S.: 423610
Paul McCloskey *(Dir-Sls Ops)*
Peter Collingwood *(CEO-EMEA)*

Subsidiary (Domestic):

Rush Computer Rentals Inc. (2)
6060 Sepulveda Blvd, Van Nuys, CA 91411
Tel.: (818) 781-2221
Web Site: http://www.rushcomputer.com
Computer Hardware Rental & Leasing Services
N.A.I.C.S.: 532420
Susan Weisberg *(Mgr-Sls)*
Michael Van Den Broek *(Acct Mgr)*

Elevate Textiles Inc. (1)
804 Green Valley Rd Ste 300, Greensboro, NC 27408
Tel.: (336) 379-6220
Web Site: http://www.elevatetextiles.com
Sales Range: $600-649.9 Million
Automotive, Apparel & Interior Furnishings Fabric & Textile Mfr & Distr
N.A.I.C.S.: 313210
Kenneth T. Kunberger *(Pres & CEO)*
Delores Sides *(Dir-Corp Comm & HR)*
Robert E. Garren *(Sr VP & Chief HR Officer)*

Subsidiary (Domestic):

Burlington WorldWide Inc. (2)
804 Green Valley Rd, Greensboro, NC 27408
Tel.: (336) 379-6220
Web Site: http://www.burlingtonfabrics.com
Fabrics Mfr
N.A.I.C.S.: 314999

Carlisle Finishing, LLC (2)
3863 Carlisle Chester Hwy, Carlisle, SC 29031-9307
Tel.: (864) 466-4100
Apparel & Home Furnishing Fabric Finishing Services
N.A.I.C.S.: 313310

Cone Denim LLC (2)
804 Green Valley Rd Ste 300, Greensboro, NC 27408
Tel.: (336) 379-6220
Denim Fabric Mfr
N.A.I.C.S.: 314999

Safety Components Fabric Technologies, Inc. (2)
40 Emery St, Greenville, SC 29605-4572
Tel.: (864) 240-2600
Web Site: http://www.safetycomponents.com
Fabrics Mfr
N.A.I.C.S.: 336390

Enbi Indiana, Inc. (1)
1703 McCall Dr, Shelbyville, IN 46176
Tel.: (317) 398-3267
Web Site: http://www.enbigroup.com
Paper Making Machinery Mfr

Subsidiary (Non-US):

Enbi (Zhuhai) Industrial Co., Ltd (2)
Level 1-2 B1 Level 1-4 B2 Block 1-11 1-13 Technology Park, Xiang Zhou District, Zhuhai, 519060, Guangdong, China
Tel.: (86) 756 8817 188
Web Site: http://www.enbigroup.com
Paper Making Machinery Mfr
N.A.I.C.S.: 333243

Enbi Germany GmbH (2)
Stauffenbergstrasse 3, 51379, Leverkusen, Germany
Tel.: (49) 2171 580 0
Web Site: http://www.enbigroup.com
Paper Transport & Image Transfer Rollers Mfr
N.A.I.C.S.: 333243

Subsidiary (Domestic):

Enbi Rochester, Inc. (2)
1661 Lyell Ave, Rochester, NY 14606
Tel.: (585) 647-1651
Web Site: http://www.enbigroup.com
Paper Making Machinery Mfr
N.A.I.C.S.: 333243
Tuan Doan *(Mgr-Ops & Production)*
Katherine Eisenhauer *(Mgr-HR & Safety)*
Mylene Santos *(Controller)*

Subsidiary (Non-US):

Hungary Enbi Kft. (2)
Ipari Park 6, 2651, Retsag, Hungary
Tel.: (36) 35 551 600
Web Site: http://www.enbigroup.com
Paper Making Machinery Mfr
N.A.I.C.S.: 333243
Rob Pagen *(Mng Dir)*

Exterion Media (1)
84 Theobald's Road, London, WC1X 8NL, United Kingdom
Tel.: (44) 20 7482 3000
Web Site: http://www.exterionmedia.com
Emp.: 250
Holding Company; Outdoor Advertising Services
N.A.I.C.S.: 551112
Pablo Gonzalez *(Chief Sls Officer & Mng Dir-France)*
Karen Rumble *(Dir-People & Culture)*
Jason Cotterrell *(Mng Dir & Grp Chief Strategy Officer)*
Dave King *(Mng Dir)*
Josko Grljevic *(Grp CTO)*
Simon Worthington *(Grp Dir-Comml Initiatives, Mergers & Acq)*
Richard Simkins *(Dir-Creative Solutions)*
Leon Taviansky *(CEO)*

Subsidiary (Non-US):

Exterion Media (Ireland) Limited (2)
6th Floor 25-28 Adelaide Road, Dublin, D02 RY98, Ireland
Tel.: (353) 16694500
Web Site: http://www.exterionmedia.com
Emp.: 27
Transit Billboard & Special Display Advertising Services
N.A.I.C.S.: 541850
Colin Leahy *(Mng Dir)*

Exterion Media (Netherlands) B.V. (2)
The Yard - Etage 4 & 5 Karspeldreef 8, 1101 CJ, Amsterdam, Netherlands
Tel.: (31) 205620562
Web Site: http://www.exterionmedia.com
Emp.: 80
Transit Billboard & Special Display Advertising Services
N.A.I.C.S.: 541850
Eric Keep *(Mng Dir)*

Exterion Media Spain, S.A. (2)
Rue Montoyer 3 1st Fl, Madrid, 28034, Spain
Tel.: (34) 915775757
Web Site: http://www.exterionmedia.es
Sales Range: $10-24.9 Million
Emp.: 40
Transit, Billboard & Special Display Advertising Services
N.A.I.C.S.: 541850
Borja Balanzat *(Mng Dir)*

HarbisonWalker International, Inc. (1)
1305 Cherrington Pkwy Ste 100, Moon Township, PA 15108
Tel.: (412) 375-6600
Web Site: http://www.thinkhwi.com
Sales Range: $10-24.9 Million
Emp.: 2,000
Holding Company; Refractory Products Mfr & Distr
N.A.I.C.S.: 551112
Don Abrino *(Sr Dir-External Tech & Open Innovation)*
Ross Wilkin *(CFO & Treas)*
Michael Werner *(Sr VP-Comml)*
Brad Cramer *(Chief Compliance Officer, Gen Counsel, Sec & VP)*
Judy Weisseg *(VP-HR)*
Martha J. Collins *(CTO)*
Douglas Hall *(Sr VP-Integrated Supply Chain)*
Melissa Bihary *(VP-People & Organizational Effectiveness)*

Subsidiary (Domestic):

A.P. Green Refractories, Inc. (2)
Cherrington Corporate Ctr 400 Fairway Dr, Moon Township, PA 15108
Tel.: (412) 375-6600
Refractory Products Mfr & Distr
N.A.I.C.S.: 327120
Jon A. Allegretti *(Pres)*
Steve Delo *(Pres)*

Subsidiary (Non-US):

AP Green de Mexico, S.A. de C.V. (3)
Carr Monterey-Colombia KM 23 2, 65500, Salinas Victoria, Nuevo Leon, Mexico
Tel.: (52) 81 8237 0570
Refractory Products Mfr & Distr
N.A.I.C.S.: 327120

Subsidiary (Non-US):

ANH Refractories Europe Limited (2)
Dock Road South, Bromborough, Wirral, CH62 4SP, United Kingdom
Tel.: (44) 1516415900
Web Site: http://www.anheurope.co.uk
Sales Range: $10-24.9 Million
Emp.: 31
Refractory Products Mfr & Distr
N.A.I.C.S.: 327120

Empresa de Refractarios Colombianos S.A. (2) (49%)
Calle 24 No 44 01, Medellin, Colombia
Tel.: (57) 42322600
Web Site: http://www.erecos.com
Mfr of Refractory Products
N.A.I.C.S.: 327120

Subsidiary (Domestic):

Harbison-Walker Refractories Company (2)
Cherrington Corporate Ctr 400 Fairway Dr, Moon Township, PA 15108
Tel.: (412) 375-6600
Web Site: http://www.hwr.com
Refractory Products Mfr & Distr
N.A.I.C.S.: 327120

Subsidiary (Non-US):

P.T. Harbison-Walker Refractories (3)
Jl Austalia II Kav N1, Kawasan Industri KIEC, Cilegon, 42443, West Java, Indonesia
Tel.: (62) 254 398 750
Web Site: http://www.anhrefractories.com
Refractory Products Mfr & Distr
N.A.I.C.S.: 327120
Donald Schlanker *(Pres)*

Highway Toll Administration, LLC (1)
11 Grace Ave Ste 108, Great Neck, NY 11021
Tel.: (866) 285-6050
Web Site: http://www.htallc.com
Measuring & Controlling Device Mfr
N.A.I.C.S.: 334519

Hop Lun (Hong Kong) Limited (1)
33/F 9 Wing Hong Street, Cheung Sha Wan, Kowloon, China (Hong Kong)
Tel.: (852) 23599568
Web Site: https://www.hoplun.com
Textile Mfr
N.A.I.C.S.: 315250
Erik Ryd *(Founder & CEO)*

Subsidiary (US):

Rainbow West Apparel, Inc. (2)
12923 S Spring St, Los Angeles, CA 90061
Tel.: (310) 538-2471
Sales Range: $1-9.9 Million
Emp.: 12
Women's, Children's & Infants' Clothing & Accessories Merchant Whslr
N.A.I.C.S.: 424350
Marvin Aranda *(Gen Mgr)*

Husky Injection Molding Systems Ltd. (1)
500 Queen St S, Bolton, L7E 5S5, ON, Canada
Tel.: (905) 951-5000
Web Site: http://www.husky.co
Injection Molding Equipment Mfr
N.A.I.C.S.: 333248
John Galt *(Pres & CEO)*
John Hafferty *(CFO)*
Wesley Grove *(COO)*
Stacie Kordts *(VP-HR)*
Michael Nicholas *(VP-Strategy Deployment)*
Joachim Niewels *(VP-Innovation & Sustainability)*

Subsidiary (Non-US):

Husky CIS LLC (2)
Kuskovskaya ul 20A Block A 5th Floor of 511, 111141, Moscow, Russia
Tel.: (7) 4952329450
Web Site: http://www.husky.co
Injection Molding Equipment Mfr
N.A.I.C.S.: 333248

Husky Injection Molding Systems (India) Private Limited (2)
P-47 8th Avenue Domestic Tariff Area Mahindra World City, Anjur Post Chengalpattu Kancheepuram District, Chennai, 603004, Tamil Nadu, India
Tel.: (91) 44 2747 6400
Web Site: http://www.husky.co
Injection Molding Equipment Mfr
N.A.I.C.S.: 333248

Husky Injection Molding Systems (Israel) Ltd. (2)
Haeshel St 7 Zone 2 Caesarea Industrial Park, PO Box 3593, 38900, Caesarea, Israel
Tel.: (972) 46218080
Web Site: http://www.husky.co
Injection Molding Equipment Mfr
N.A.I.C.S.: 333248

Husky Injection Molding Systems (Nordic) A/S (2)
Orestes Blvd 73, 2770, Copenhagen, Denmark
Tel.: (45) 32486200
Web Site: http://www.husky.co
Injection Molding Equipment Mfr
N.A.I.C.S.: 333248

Husky Injection Molding Systems (Shanghai) Ltd. (2)
Beijing Branch Office Unit 506 Tower E1 The Towers Oriental Plaza, No 1 East Chang An Avenue Dong Cheng District, Beijing, 100738, China
Tel.: (86) 10 85185177
Web Site: http://www.husky.co
Injection Molding Equipment Mfr
N.A.I.C.S.: 333248

Husky Injection Molding Systems (South Africa) Pty. Ltd. (2)
Parade on Kloof office Park No 1 the Parade Street, 3A-5 Eton Road, Bedfordview, 2007, South Africa
Tel.: (27) 11417 0680
Web Site: http://www.husky.co
Injection Molding Equipment Mfr

PLATINUM EQUITY, LLC

U.S. PRIVATE

Platinum Equity, LLC—(Continued)
N.A.I.C.S.: 333248

Husky Injection Molding Systems (Thailand) Ltd. (2)
252/100 Unit B Muang Thai-Phatra Complex Building 20th Floor Tower B, Rachadapisek Road Huaykwang, Bangkok, 10310, Thailand
Tel.: (66) 269317003
Web Site: http://www.husky.co
Injection Molding Equipment Mfr
N.A.I.C.S.: 333248

Husky Injection Molding Systems Argentina S.A. (2)
Zapiola 2375 6 A, 1428, Buenos Aires, Argentina
Tel.: (54) 1168414400
Web Site: http://www.husky.co
Injection Molding Equipment Mfr
N.A.I.C.S.: 333248

Husky Injection Molding Systems Colombia Ltd. (2)
Carerra 69 No 25B - 45 Oficina 611, Edificio World Business Port, Bogota, Colombia
Tel.: (57) 14165626
Web Site: http://www.husky.co
Injection Molding Equipment Mfr
N.A.I.C.S.: 333248

Husky Injection Molding Systems Iberia S.L.U. (2)
Ronda Can Fatijo 5 edificio D-local Db, Parc Tecnologic del Valles, 08290, Cerdanyola del Valles, Spain
Tel.: (34) 935948550
Web Site: http://www.husky.co
Injection Molding Equipment Mfr
N.A.I.C.S.: 333248

Husky Injection Molding Systems Korea Inc (2)
Rm 1110 Ace Twin Tower 1 285 Digital-ro, Guro-gu, Seoul, 08381, Korea (South)
Tel.: (82) 221096400
Web Site: http://www.husky.co
Injection Molding Equipment Mfr
N.A.I.C.S.: 333248

Husky Injection Molding Systems S.A. (2)
Zone Industrielle Riedgen Technical Center, BP 93, 3451, Dudelange, Luxembourg
Tel.: (352) 521151
Web Site: http://www.husky.co
Injection Molding Equipment Mfr
N.A.I.C.S.: 333248

Husky Injection Molding Systems Singapore Pte. Ltd. (2)
80 Changi Road #A-15 and #05-15 Centro-Pod, Singapore, 419715, Singapore
Tel.: (65) 69096003
Web Site: http://www.husky.co
Injection Molding Equipment Mfr
N.A.I.C.S.: 333248

Subsidiary (US):

Husky Injection Molding Systems, Inc. (2)
55 Amherst Villa Rd, Buffalo, NY 14225-1432
Tel.: (716) 630-7300
Web Site: http://www.huskey.co
Injection Molding Equipment Mfr
N.A.I.C.S.: 333248

Subsidiary (Non-US):

Husky do Brasil Sistemas de Injecao Ltda. (2)
Rodovia Dom Gabriel Paulino Bueno Couto Km 66-5, PO Box 2503, 13216-990, Jundiai, Brazil
Tel.: (55) 1145897200
Web Site: http://www.husky.co
Injection Molding Equipment Mfr
N.A.I.C.S.: 333248

Innovative Water Care, LLC (1)
1400 Bluegrass Lakes Pkwy, Alpharetta, GA 30004
Tel.: (800) 222-2348
Water Treatment Solutions
N.A.I.C.S.: 221310

Subsidiary (Domestic):

Solenis International, L.P. (2)
3 Beaver Vly Rd Ste 500, Wilmington, DE 19803
Tel.: (302) 594-5000
Web Site: http://www.solenis.com
Sales Range: $1-4.9 Billion
Emp.: 3,000
Specialty Chemicals Mfr
N.A.I.C.S.: 325998
John Panichella (Pres)

Subsidiary (Domestic):

Solenis LLC (3)
2475 Pinnacle Dr, Wilmington, DE 19803
Tel.: (866) 337-1533
Web Site: https://www.solenis.com
Specialty Chemicals Mfr
N.A.I.C.S.: 325998
John Panichella (CEO)

Subsidiary (Domestic):

Cedarchem, LLC (4)
105 Plantation Ave, Cedartown, GA 30125
Tel.: (770) 748-3863
Web Site: http://www.cedarchem.com
Chemical & Allied Products Merchant Whslr
N.A.I.C.S.: 424690
Candi Wright (Office Mgr)

Clearon Corp. (4)
95 MacCorkle Ave SW, Charleston, WV 25303
Tel.: (304) 746-3000
Web Site: https://www.clearon.com
Emp.: 200
Chlorine Whslr
N.A.I.C.S.: 325180
Melissa Wandling (Mgr-HR)
Matthew C. White (CFO)
David Helmstetter (Gen Mgr)
Bryan Kitchen (Pres & CEO)

Diversey Holdings, Ltd. (4)
1300 Altura Rd Ste 125, Fort Mill, SC 29708
Tel.: (803) 746-2200
Web Site: http://www.diversey.com
Rev: $2,765,900,000
Assets: $4,254,700,000
Liabilities: $3,581,700,000
Net Worth: $673,000,000
Earnings: ($169,300,000)
Emp.: 9,000
Fiscal Year-end: 12/31/2022
Holding Company
N.A.I.C.S.: 551112
Edwin van der Heijden (VP-North America-Food & Beverage)

Subsidiary (Domestic):

Birko Corporation (5)
9152 Yosemite St, Henderson, CO 80640
Tel.: (303) 289-1090
Web Site: http://www.birkocorp.com
Sales Range: $10-24.9 Million
Emp.: 60
Food Safety Chemical Solutions Mfr
N.A.I.C.S.: 325180
Kelly Green (Chm & Pres)
Terry MacAninch (VP-R&D)
Brett Burrough (Dir-Pur)
Fred Gonzales (Mgr-IT)
Jerry Oates (Engr-Svc)
Bob Ogren (VP-Equipment)
John Flynn (VP-Sls)
Mark Swanson (CEO)

Diversey, Inc. (5)
1300 Altura Rd Ste 125, Fort Mill, SC 29708
Web Site: http://diversey.com
Commercial Sanitation Products & Detergents Mfr, Marketer & Distr
N.A.I.C.S.: 325612
Gaetano Redaelli (Chief Strategy Dev Officer)
Phil Wieland (CEO)
Todd Herndon (CFO)
Paul Budsworth (Pres-North America)
Sinead Kwant (Pres-Western Europe)
Himanshu Jain (Pres-APAC)
Jorge Hileman (Pres-LATAM)
Somer Gundogdu (Pres- Emerging Markets)
Ruud Verheul (Pres-Food & Beverage Division)
Michael Del Priore (CIO)

Co-Headquarters (Non-US):

Diversey Europe B.V. (6)
Maarssenbroeksedijk 2, 3542 DN, Utrecht, Netherlands
Tel.: (31) 302476885
Holding Company; Corporate Office
N.A.I.C.S.: 551112

Subsidiary (Non-US):

Diversey (France) S.A.S. (7)
201 rue Carnot, 94120, Fontenay-sous-Bois, France
Tel.: (33) 145147676
Web Site: http://diversey.fr
Commercial Sanitation Products & Detergents Mfr, Marketer & Distr
N.A.I.C.S.: 325612

Diversey Austria Trading GmbH (7)
Wagenseilgasse 3, 1120, Vienna, Austria
Tel.: (43) 1605570
Web Site: http://diversey.at
Commercial Sanitation Products & Detergents Wholesale Trade Distr
N.A.I.C.S.: 425120

Subsidiary (Domestic):

Diversey B.V. (7)
Maarssenbroeksedijk 2, 3542 DN, Utrecht, Netherlands
Tel.: (31) 302476911
Web Site: http://diversey.nl
Commercial Sanitation Products & Detergents Mfr, Marketer & Distr
N.A.I.C.S.: 325612

Subsidiary (Non-US):

Diversey Belgium BVBA (7)
Zoning Kampenhout Sas Zone 2, 672, Kampenhout, Belgium
Tel.: (32) 16617777
Web Site: http://diversey.be
Commercial Sanitation Products & Detergents Mfr, Marketer & Distr
N.A.I.C.S.: 325612

Diversey Canada, Inc. (7)
6150 Kennedy Road Unit 3, Mississauga, L5T 2J4, ON, Canada
Web Site: http://diversey.ca
Commercial Sanitation Products & Detergents Mfr, Marketer & Distr
N.A.I.C.S.: 325612
Lane Crosser (VP)

Diversey Care (7)
29 Chifley Street, Smithfield, 2164, NSW, Australia
Tel.: (61) 297570300
Web Site: http://diversey.com.au
Commercial Sanitation Products & Detergents Mfr, Marketer & Distr
N.A.I.C.S.: 325612

Diversey Ceska republika s.r.o. (7)
K Hajum 1233 Stodulky, 155 00, Prague, Czech Republic
Tel.: (420) 296357111
Web Site: http://diverseysolutions.com
Commercial Sanitation Products & Detergents Mfr, Marketer & Distr
N.A.I.C.S.: 325612
Libor Karel (Dir-Sls & Mktg)

Diversey Deutschland GmbH & Co. OHG (7)
Mallaustrasse 50-56, D 68219, Mannheim, Germany
Tel.: (49) 62187570
Web Site: http://diversey.de
Commercial Sanitation Products & Detergents Mfr, Marketer & Distr
N.A.I.C.S.: 325612

Diversey Eastern & Central Africa Limited (7)
Outer Ring Rd, PO Box 41939, Nairobi, 00100, Kenya
Tel.: (254) 722754074
Web Site: http://www.diversey.com
Commercial Sanitation Products & Detergents Distr
N.A.I.C.S.: 424690

Diversey Espana, S.L. (7)
C Antonio Machado 78-80 3rd floor Vilade-cans Business Park, 8840, Barcelona, Spain
Tel.: (34) 902011106
Web Site: http://diversey.com.es
Commercial Sanitation Products & Detergents Mfr, Marketer & Distr
N.A.I.C.S.: 325612

Diversey Hong Kong Limited (7)
Rm 2001-12 20/F Metroplaza Twr 1 223 Hing Fong Rd Kwai Fong, New Territories, Hong Kong, China (Hong Kong)
Tel.: (852) 23080188
Web Site: http://diversey.hk
Commercial Sanitation Products & Detergents Mfr, Marketer & Distr
N.A.I.C.S.: 325612

Diversey Hygiene (Taiwan) Ltd. (7)
6F No 51 Ln 188 Ruei Guang Rd Neihu District, Taipei, 114, Taiwan
Tel.: (886) 287514888
Web Site: http://diversey.com.tw
Commercial Sanitation Products & Detergents Distr
N.A.I.C.S.: 424690
Terry Liu (Dir-Bus)

Diversey Korea Co., Ltd. (7)
337 Eonju-ro Gangnam-gu Seoul, 7th Floor, Dong-English Center, Seoul, 06226, Korea (South)
Tel.: (82) 234163160
Web Site: http://diversey.co.kr
Commercial Sanitation Products & Detergents Distr
N.A.I.C.S.: 424690

Dyersey Limited (7)
Pyramid Cl, Northampton, NN3 8DP, United Kingdom
Tel.: (44) 800525525
Web Site: http://diversey.co.uk
Commercial Sanitation Products & Detergents Mfr, Marketer & Distr
N.A.I.C.S.: 325612

Diversey Polska Sp. z o.o. (7)
Al. Jerozolimskie 134, 02-305, Warsaw, Poland
Tel.: (48) 221611700
Web Site: http://diversey.com.pl
Commercial Sanitation Products & Detergents Mfr, Marketer & Distr
N.A.I.C.S.: 325612
Robert Karas (Dir-Fin)
Beata Mularska (Dir-Mktg)
Robert Kucinski (Dir-European Sls)
Anna Rybak (Coord-Comm)

Diversey Trading (Shanghai) Co., Ltd. (7)
China Headquarters 3rd Floor Quanhua Information Building No 455, Fushan Road Pudong New Area, Shanghai, 200122, China
Tel.: (86) 2150509900
Web Site: http://www.diversey-china.com
Commercial Sanitation Products & Detergents Wholesale Trade Distr
N.A.I.C.S.: 425120

Diversey de Argentina S.A. (7)
Avenue Marquez 970 1682, Villa Bosch, B1682BAQ, Argentina
Tel.: (54) 1170794363
Web Site: http://diversey.com.ar
Commercial Sanitation Products & Detergents Distr
N.A.I.C.S.: 424690
Jorge Hileman (Pres-Latin America)

Diversey s.r.l. (7)
via Philips 12, Cologno Monzese, 20900, MI, Italy
Tel.: (39) 0399591150
Web Site: http://diversey.it
Commercial Sanitation Products & Detergents Mfr, Marketer & Distr
N.A.I.C.S.: 325612

Subsidiary (Non-US):

Lilleborg AS (4)
Drammensveien 149, 0277, Oslo, Norway
Tel.: (47) 81536000
Web Site: http://www.lilleborg.no
Sales Range: $300-349.9 Million
Household Products; Detergents, Toiletries & Cosmetics; Edible Oils

COMPANIES — PLATINUM EQUITY, LLC

N.A.I.C.S.: 325620

Subsidiary (Non-US):

Peri-dent Ltd. (5)
Tweedbank Industrial Estate, Galashiels, TD1 3RS, Selkirkshire, United Kingdom (100%)
Tel.: (44) 1896754400
Web Site: http://www.dentalfloss.co.uk
Sales Range: $25-49.9 Million
Emp.: 15
Dental Equipment & Supplies Mfr
N.A.I.C.S.: 339114

Subsidiary (Non-US):

Solenis Technologies Germany GmbH (3)
Futingsweg 20, 47805, Krefeld, Germany
Tel.: (49) 21513803
Web Site: http://www.solenis.com
Chemical Products Mfr
N.A.I.C.S.: 325998

Interior Logic Group Holdings, LLC (1)
10 Bunsen, Irvine, CA 92008
Tel.: (760) 929-6700
Web Site: http://www.interiorlogicgroup.com
Holding Company; Interior Design Services
N.A.I.C.S.: 551112
Alan K. Davenport *(Pres & CEO)*
Mark Fikse *(Exec VP-Bus Dev & Ops)*

Subsidiary (Domestic):

Coleman Floor, LLC (2)
8020 Arco Corporate Dr Ste 200, Raleigh, NC 27617
Tel.: (919) 431-1000
Web Site: http://www.colemanfloors.com
Floor Installation Services
N.A.I.C.S.: 238330
Mike Hagen *(Mgr-Market-NE)*

Branch (Domestic):

Coleman Floor Co. (3)
400 Innovation Ave Ste 150, Morrisville, NC 27560
Tel.: (919) 936-9301
Web Site: http://www.colemanfloor.com
Drywall & Insulation Contractors
N.A.I.C.S.: 238310
Brad Ellis *(Gen Mgr)*

Coleman Floor Company (3)
6162 Lawyers Hill Rd, Elkridge, MD 21075-5208
Tel.: (410) 037-0441
Web Site: http://www.colemanfloors.com
Floor Covering Stores
N.A.I.C.S.: 449121
Tim Coleman *(Owner)*

Subsidiary (Domestic):

Interior Logic Group, Inc. (2)
2270 NW Pkwy SE, Marietta, GA 30067
Tel.: (770) 693-9668
Web Site: http://www.interiorlogicgroup.com
Interior Design Services
N.A.I.C.S.: 541410
Alan Davenport *(Chm & CEO)*

Subsidiary (Domestic):

L.A.R.K. Industries, Inc. (3)
4900 E Hunter Ave, Anaheim, CA 92807
Tel.: (714) 701-4200
Design Services
N.A.I.C.S.: 541490

Subsidiary (Domestic):

Intown Design, Inc. (4)
250 Villanova Dr, Atlanta, GA 30336
Tel.: (404) 812-3820
Web Site: http://www.intowndesigninc.com
Other Building Material Dealers
N.A.I.C.S.: 444180

Division (Domestic):

T.A.C. Ceramic Tile Co. (4)
11951 Tac Ct, Manassas, VA 20109
Tel.: (703) 690-2556
Flooring Contractors
N.A.I.C.S.: 238330

Subsidiary (Domestic):

Interior Specialists, Inc. (2)
1630 Faraday Ave, Carlsbad, CA 92008
Tel.: (760) 929-6700
Interior Design & Installation Services
N.A.I.C.S.: 541410
Alan K. Davenport *(Pres & CEO)*
Jeffrey M. Fenton *(COO & Sr VP)*
Robert Hess *(CFO)*
James J. DeGeorge *(Chief Sls Officer & Sr VP)*
Anne Liu *(Chief Acctg Officer)*
Steffani Stevens *(Gen Counsel & Sr VP)*
Randy Bafus *(Sr VP-Comml Sls & Sr Living)*
Jodi Bossak *(Sr VP-Strategic Plng & Bus Dev)*
Katie Prekel *(VP-HR)*

JELD-WEN Australia Pty Ltd (1)
78 Waterloo Road Level 3, Macquarie Park, 2113, NSW, Australia
Tel.: (61) 296843400
Web Site: http://www.jeld-wen.com.au
Sales Range: $25-49.9 Million
Emp.: 5,000
Wood Window & Door Mfr
N.A.I.C.S.: 321911

JM Swank, LLC (1)
395 Herky St, North Liberty, IA 52317
Tel.: (800) 593-6375
Web Site: http://www.jmswank.com
Food Ingredient Distr
N.A.I.C.S.: 722310
Randy Cimorelli *(CEO)*

Subsidiary (Domestic):

Lentz Milling Company (2)
2045 N 11th St, Reading, PA 19612-3159
Tel.: (610) 463-3600
Web Site: http://www.lentzmilling.com
Grocery & Related Products Merchant Whslr
N.A.I.C.S.: 424490

Jostens, Inc. (1)
3601 Minnesota Dr Ste 400, Minneapolis, MN 55435
Tel.: (952) 830-3300
Web Site: http://www.jostens.com
School-Related Affinity Products & Marketing & Photography Services
N.A.I.C.S.: 541922
Charles W. Mooty *(Pres & CEO)*

L&R Distributors, Inc. (1)
88 35th St Bldg 4 5th Fl Ste D, Brooklyn, NY 11232
Tel.: (718) 272-2100
Web Site: http://www.lrdist.com
Durable Goods Merchant Whslr
N.A.I.C.S.: 423990
Olivia Lucas *(Designer-Graphic)*
Marc Bodner *(Chm)*
E.Reilly Murray *(Pres)*
Craig Zumbo *(CFO)*
Jim Athey *(CEO)*
Jonathan J. Banegas *(VP-HR)*

Subsidiary (Domestic):

SJ Creations, Inc. (2)
731 N Vulcan Ave, Encinitas, CA 92024
Web Site: http://www.sjcreationsinc.com
Trade Agents & Brokers Whslr
N.A.I.C.S.: 425120
Sundi Yousko *(Owner)*

LifeScan, Inc. (1)
965 Chesterbrook Blvd, Wayne, PA 19087
Tel.: (408) 263-9789
Web Site: http://www.lifescan.com
Sales Range: $1-4.9 Billion
Emp.: 60
Personal Blood Glucose Monitoring Kits & Blood Derivative Diagnostic Agents Mfr
N.A.I.C.S.: 325412
Valerie L. Asbury *(Pres & CEO)*

Subsidiary (Non-US):

LifeScan Canada Ltd. (2)
Suite 300-4170 Still Creek Drive, Burnaby, V5C 6C6, BC, Canada
Tel.: (604) 293-2266
Web Site: http://www.onetouch.ca
Sales Range: $10-24.9 Million
Emp.: 80
Medicinal Product Mfr
N.A.I.C.S.: 339112

Subsidiary (Domestic):

LifeScan, LLC (2)
6500 Paseo Padre Pkwy, Fremont, CA 94555
Tel.: (408) 263-9789
Web Site: http://www.lifescan.com
Sales Range: $100-124.9 Million
Personal Blood Glucose Monitoring Kits & Blood Derivative Diagnostic Agents Mfr
N.A.I.C.S.: 339112

Livingston International Inc. (1)
405 The West Mall Ste 400, Toronto, M9C 5K7, ON, Canada (100%)
Tel.: (416) 626-2800
Web Site: http://www.livingstonintl.com
Customs Brokerage, Logistics & Transportation Services
N.A.I.C.S.: 488510
Roy G. Coburn *(Pres-Brokerage Svcs-North American)*
Craig E. Conway *(CTO)*
Cora Di Pietro *(VP-Consulting)*
Brian Henderson *(Chief Legal Officer)*
Robert Smith *(Chief Mktg Officer & Chief Sls Officer)*
Candace Sider *(VP-Govt & Regulatory Affairs)*
Tom Cronin *(CFO)*
David Rish *(Pres-Global Trade Mgmt)*
Stacy Brown *(Chief HR Officer)*
Michael Meierkort *(Pres-Freight & Transportation Solutions-Intl)*
John P. Clancey *(Chm)*

Subsidiary (US):

Livingston International, Inc. (2)
141 W Jackson Ste 1510A, Chicago, IL 60604
Tel.: (312) 516-4100
Web Site: http://www.livingstonintl.com
Customs Brokerage & Compliance, International Trade Consulting & Freight Forwarding Services
N.A.I.C.S.: 488510
Tom Cronin *(CFO)*
Roy G. Coburn *(Pres-North American Brokerage Svcs)*
Michael Meierkort *(Pres-Freight & Transportation Solutions-Intl)*
David Rish *(Pres-Trade Mgmt-Global)*
Craig Conway *(CTO)*
Stacy Brown *(Chief HR Officer)*
Robert Smith *(Chief Mktg Officer & Chief Sls Officer)*
Brian Henderson *(Chief Legal Officer)*

Mad Engine, LLC (1)
6740 Cobra Way, San Diego, CA 92121
Tel.: (858) 558-5270
Web Site: http://www.madengine.com
Licensed Apparel Whslr
N.A.I.C.S.: 424350
Curry McKinney *(Project Mgr)*

Subsidiary (Domestic):

Neff, LLC (2)
850 Calle Plano M, Camarillo, CA 93012-8053
Tel.: (424) 383-6333
Web Site: http://www.neffheadwear.com
Core Snow & Skate Headwear Mfr
N.A.I.C.S.: 315990
Shaun Neff *(Founder)*

McGraw-Hill Education, Inc. (1)
2 Penn Plz 20th Fl, New York, NY 10121
Tel.: (646) 766-3199
Web Site: http://www.mheducation.com
Rev.: $1,855,779,000
Assets: $2,747,296,000
Liabilities: $3,124,905,000
Net Worth: ($377,609,000)
Earnings: ($330,963,000)
Emp.: 5,000
Fiscal Year-end: 12/31/2014
Educational Materials Publishing
N.A.I.C.S.: 513199
David B. Stafford *(Gen Counsel & Sec)*
Catherine J. Mathis *(Chief Comm Officer)*
Patrick Milano *(Chief Admin Officer & Exec VP)*

Larry Berg *(Chm)*
Angelo T. DeGenaro *(COO & CIO)*
Simon Allen *(CEO)*
Garet Guthrie *(CFO)*
Anthony Lorin *(Pres-Intl Grp)*
Scott Grillo *(Pres-Professional-Grp)*
Nathan Olson *(Sr VP-Digital Platform Ops-Grp)*
Sheila M. O'Neil *(Chief Culture & Talent Officer)*
Micheal Ryan *(Pres-Higher Education Grp)*
Sean Ryan *(Pres-School Grp)*
Justin Singh *(Sr VP-Growth & Transformation)*

Subsidiary (Domestic):

ALEKS Corporation (2)
15460 Laguna Canyon Rd, Irvine, CA 92618
Tel.: (714) 245-7191
Web Site: http://www.aleks.com
Sales Range: $10-24.9 Million
Emp.: 150
Education Software Developer
N.A.I.C.S.: 513210
Jean-Claude Falmagne *(Co-Founder & Chm)*
Nicolas Thiery *(CTO)*
Eric Cosyn *(Co-Founder & Dir-Applied Res)*
R. G. Wilmot Lampros *(Chief Product Officer)*
Lori Anderson *(VP-Technical Product Mgmt)*
Damien Lauly *(Sr Dir-Quality Control & Intl Product Dev)*
Adrien Blanchi *(Sr Dir-Software Engrg & Applications)*
Gildas Cadin *(Sr Dir-Software Engrg, Architecture & Quality Assurance)*
Sean Cuddihy *(Dir-Math Content)*
Christopher Grayce *(Sr Dir-Product Dev Chemistry Content)*
Shidan Habibi *(Dir-User Experience)*
Michael Kanaly *(Dir-Program Mgmt)*
Manisha Patel *(Dir-Quality Engrg)*
Harold Baker *(Dir-Advanced Customer Solutions)*

Glencoe/McGraw-Hill (2)
8787 Orion Pl, Columbus, OH 43240
Tel.: (614) 430-4000
Web Site: http://www.glencoe.com
Sales Range: $75-99.9 Million
Emp.: 500
Teaching & Learning Aid Materials Publisher
N.A.I.C.S.: 513130

Division (Domestic):

McGraw-Hill (3)
1333 Burr Ridge Pkwy, Burr Ridge, IL 60527
Tel.: (630) 789-4000
Web Site: http://www.mhhe.com
Sales Range: $10-24.9 Million
Emp.: 500
Text Books in Home Economics, Industrial Education, Career Education
N.A.I.C.S.: 513130

Subsidiary (Domestic):

Key Curriculum Press, Inc. (2)
1150 65th St, Emeryville, CA 94608
Tel.: (510) 595-7000
Web Site: http://www.keycurriculum.com
Sales Range: $25-49.9 Million
Emp.: 100
Educational Materials Publisher
N.A.I.C.S.: 513130

Affiliate (Non-US):

McGraw-Hill Education India Private Limited (2)
B-4 Sector - 63 Dist Gautam Budh Nagar, Noida, 201301, Uttar Pradesh, India
Tel.: (91) 1204383400
Web Site: http://www.tatamcgrawhill.com
Sales Range: $25-49.9 Million
Emp.: 30
Book Publishers
N.A.I.C.S.: 513130
Poonam Suyal *(Sec)*

Subsidiary (Domestic):

McGraw-Hill Higher Education (2)
1333 Burr Ridge Pkwy, Burr Ridge, IL 60521 (100%)

PLATINUM EQUITY, LLC

Platinum Equity, LLC—(Continued)
Tel.: (630) 789-4000
Web Site: http://www.mhhe.com
Sales Range: $100-124.9 Million
Emp.: 300
Books & Instructional Materials Publishing
N.A.I.C.S.: 513130
Edward Stanford *(Pres)*

Subsidiary (Non-US):

McGraw-Hill Ryerson Limited (2)
300 Water Street, Whitby, L1N 9B6, ON, Canada
Tel.: (800) 565-5758
Web Site: http://www.mheducation.ca
Sales Range: $50-74.9 Million
Emp.: 200
Books & Information Services, Professional Information, Training Systems
N.A.I.C.S.: 513130

Subsidiary (Domestic):

SRA/McGraw Hill (2)
8787 Orion Pl, Columbus, OH 43240
Tel.: (614) 430-4000
Sales Range: $900-999.9 Million
Emp.: 550
Educational Materials, Tests & Training Programs Mfr
N.A.I.C.S.: 513130

Tegrity, Inc. (2)
1333 Burr Ridge Pkwy, Burr Ridge, IL 60527
Tel.: (408) 369-5150
Web Site: http://www.tegrity.com
Sales Range: $10-24.9 Million
Emp.: 30
Designs, Develops & Distributes Educational Software Products Mfr
N.A.I.C.S.: 513210

Triad Interactive, Inc. (2)
1101 Conn Ave Nw, Washington, DC 20036
Tel.: (202) 347-0900
Web Site: http://www.tri.ad
Custom Computer Programming Services
N.A.I.C.S.: 541511
Cheryl Manning *(Pres)*

Multi-Color Corporation (1)
4053 Clough Woods Dr, Batavia, OH 45103
Tel.: (513) 381-1480
Web Site: http://www.mcclabel.com
Rev.: $1,725,554,000
Assets: $2,652,472,000
Liabilities: $2,023,769,000
Net Worth: $628,703,000
Earnings: ($29,041,000)
Emp.: 8,300
Fiscal Year-end: 03/31/2019
Printed Labels & Engravings for Brand Name Consumer Products
N.A.I.C.S.: 323111
David G. Buse *(COO-Wine & Spirit Markets)*
Sharon E. Birkett *(CFO, Sec & VP)*
Timothy P. Lutz *(Chief Acctg Officer & VP)*
Oliver Apel *(COO-Food & Beverage)*
Michael D. Cook *(COO-Consumer Product Goods)*

Subsidiary (Non-US):

Collotype Labels Chile SA (2)
Panamericana Norte 5201, Conchali, Santiago, 522-0633, Chile
Tel.: (56) 25807100
Web Site: http://www.collotype.cl
Emp.: 160
Packaging & Labeling Services
N.A.I.C.S.: 561910
Marcelo Muller *(Gen Mgr)*

Collotype Labels International Pty. Ltd. (2)
381 South Road, Adelaide, 5031, SA, Australia
Tel.: (61) 884050500
Commercial Gravure Printing Services
N.A.I.C.S.: 323111

Collotype Labels Ireland Limited (2)
Drogheda Industrial Estate, Donore Road, Drogheda, Ireland
Tel.: (353) 419875600
Commercial Gravure Printing Services
N.A.I.C.S.: 323111

Subsidiary (Domestic):

Collotype Labels USA Inc. (2)
21 Executive Way, Napa, CA 94558-6271
Tel.: (707) 603-2500
Web Site: http://www.collotype.com
Sales Range: $50-74.9 Million
Emp.: 150
Commercial Printing Services
N.A.I.C.S.: 323111

Subsidiary (Non-US):

La Cromografica SrL (2)
via del Campostino da, Mezzana, 59100, Prato, Italy
Tel.: (39) 0574562810
Web Site: http://www.cromografica.biz
Packaging & Labeling Services
N.A.I.C.S.: 561910

MCC Polska SA (2)
ul Poznanska 129/133, Mazowiecki, Ozarow, 05-850, Poland
Tel.: (48) 225125900
Commercial Gravure Printing Services
N.A.I.C.S.: 323111
Artur Lesinski *(Dir-Sls)*

Subsidiary (Domestic):

MCC-Norway, LLC (2)
512 E 9th Ave, Norway, MI 49870-1300
Tel.: (906) 563-9261
Web Site: http://www.mcclabel.com
Emp.: 50
Packaging & Labeling Services
N.A.I.C.S.: 561910

Subsidiary (Non-US):

Multi-Color (Barossa) Pty. Ltd. (2)
3 Para Road, Tanunda, 5352, SA, Australia
Tel.: (61) 885636300
Packaging & Labeling Services
N.A.I.C.S.: 561910

Multi-Color (Griffith) Pty. Ltd. (2)
106 Wakaden St, Griffith, 2680, NSW, Australia
Tel.: (61) 269603333
Commercial Gravure Printing Services
N.A.I.C.S.: 323111

Multi-Color (QLD) Pty Ltd (2)
4 Currumbin Ct, Capalaba, Brisbane, 4157, Australia
Tel.: (61) 732454333
Web Site: http://www.mcclabel.com
Emp.: 60
Packaging & Labeling Services
N.A.I.C.S.: 561910
Chad McNamara *(Mgr-Sls)*

Multi-Color Clydebank Scotland Limited (2)
Mulvenny House 2 Murdoch Drive, Clydebank Business Park, Glasgow, G81 2QQ, Scotland, United Kingdom
Tel.: (44) 1419529600
Commercial Gravure Printing Services
N.A.I.C.S.: 323111

Plant (Domestic):

Multi-Color Corporation - Watertown Plant (2)
1222 Perry Way, Watertown, WI 53094-6052
Tel.: (920) 262-1195
Web Site: http://www.multicolorcorp.com
Sales Range: $100-124.9 Million
Emp.: 85
Printing Company
N.A.I.C.S.: 323111
Nigel Vinecombe *(Chm)*

Subsidiary (Non-US):

Multi-Color Daventry England Ltd. (2)
Sopwith Way, Drayton Fields Industrial Estate, Daventry, NN11 8PB, Northants, United Kingdom
Tel.: (44) 1327301181
Commercial Gravure Printing Services
N.A.I.C.S.: 323111

Multi-Color Haro Spain, S.L. (2)
Calle de los Alamos 65, 26200, Haro, La Rioja, Spain
Tel.: (34) 941311629
Commercial Gravure Printing Services
N.A.I.C.S.: 323111

Multi-Color Italia S.p.A. (2)
via del Campostino da Mezzana, 59100, Prato, Italy
Tel.: (39) 0574562810
Commercial Gravure Printing Services
N.A.I.C.S.: 323111

Multi-Color Label Canada Corporation (2)
2850 Rue Botham, Montreal, H4S 1J1, QC, Canada
Tel.: (514) 341-4850
Packaging & Labeling Services
N.A.I.C.S.: 561910

Multi-Color Suisse S.A. (2)
Chemin de Buchaux 36, 2022, Bevaix, Switzerland
Tel.: (41) 328479510
Commercial Gravure Printing Services
N.A.I.C.S.: 323111

Subsidiary (Domestic):

Southern Atlantic Label Co., Inc. (2)
1300 Cavalier Blvd, Chesapeake, VA 23323
Tel.: (757) 487-2525
Commercial Gravure Printing Services
N.A.I.C.S.: 323111

WS Packaging Group Inc. (2)
2571 S Hemlock Rd, Green Bay, WI 54229
Tel.: (800) 818-5481
Web Site: http://www.wspackaging.com
Packaging Products Mfr & Printing Services
N.A.I.C.S.: 322299

Subsidiary (Domestic):

Label Art (3)
1 Riverside Way, Wilton, NH 03086-2000
Tel.: (603) 654-6131
Web Site: http://www.labelart.com
Pressure Sensitive Labels Mfr
N.A.I.C.S.: 561910

Unit (Domestic):

WS Packaging Group Inc. - Franklin (3)
1642 DeBence Dr, Franklin, PA 16323-5211
Tel.: (800) 372-1313
Sheetfed Offset Printing Services
N.A.I.C.S.: 323111

WS Packaging Group Inc. - Mason (3)
7500 Industrial Row Dr, Mason, OH 45040-1307
Sheetfed Offset Printing Services
N.A.I.C.S.: 323111

PCI Limited (1)
35 Pioneer Road North, Singapore, 628475, Singapore
Tel.: (65) 62658181
Web Site: http://www.pciltd.com
Rev.: $288,673,000
Assets: $166,518,000
Liabilities: $65,998,000
Net Worth: $100,520,000
Earnings: $18,181,000
Fiscal Year-end: 06/30/2018
Electronic Products & Components Designer & Mfr
N.A.I.C.S.: 334419
Eng Lin Teo *(CEO)*
Kwee Chim Peh *(Chm)*
Thomas Muljadi Handojo *(Sr VP-Bus Dev)*
Dominic Jin Hou Chan *(Sr VP-Ops)*
Quee Lim Tan *(VP-Mfg)*
Valerie May Wei Tan *(Sec)*
Terence Siong Woon Peh *(Vice Chm)*
Eldon Wan *(Exec Dir)*
Mei Liew Hong *(CFO)*

Subsidiary (Non-US):

PCI-Shanghai Electronic Company Ltd. (2)
No. 1199 Blk 87 Shanghai Caohejing Hi-tech Park, Qin Zhou Bei Lu, Shanghai, 200233, China
Tel.: (86) 2164852487
Web Site: http://www.pciltd.com.sg

Sales Range: $150-199.9 Million
Emp.: 700
Electronic Components Mfr
N.A.I.C.S.: 334419

Subsidiary (US):

Printed Circuits International Incorporated (2)
407 Lee Ave, Highland Springs, VA 23075-1514
Tel.: (804) 737-7979
Web Site: http://www.pciltd.com
Electric Component Whslr
N.A.I.C.S.: 334416

Subsidiary (Domestic):

Quijul Pte. Ltd. (2)
322 Jalan Ahmad Ibrahim, Jurong Indus Estate, Singapore, Singapore
Tel.: (65) 66638244
Sales Range: $50-74.9 Million
Emp.: 10
Property Rental Services
N.A.I.C.S.: 531190

Palace Sports & Entertainment, Inc. (1)
6 Championship Dr, Auburn Hills, MI 48326
Tel.: (248) 377-0100
Web Site: http://www.palacenet.com
Sales Range: $600-649.9 Million
Emp.: 2,300
Holding Company; Sports Teams & Entertainment Centers Owner & Operator
N.A.I.C.S.: 551112
Brad Lott *(VP-Corp Sls)*
Arn Tellem *(Vice Chm)*
Tom Gores *(Owner)*
Greg Campbell *(CFO & Exec VP)*
Mario Etemad *(Exec VP-Ops)*
Charlie Metzger *(Chief Mktg & Comm Officer & Exec VP)*
Mike Zavodsky *(Chief Bus Officer)*

Holding (Domestic):

Detroit Pistons Basketball Company (2)
6 Championship Dr, Auburn Hills, MI 48326-1753
Tel.: (248) 377-0100
Sales Range: $50-74.9 Million
Emp.: 300
Professional Basketball Franchise
N.A.I.C.S.: 711211
Troy Weaver *(Gen Mgr)*
Mike Zavodsky *(Chief Bus Officer)*
Tom Gores *(Owner)*
Michael-Leonard Anderson *(Creative Dir-Innovation)*

Paramount Global Surfaces (1)
18000 NE 5th Ave, Miami, FL 33162
Tel.: (310) 712-1850
Porcelain Tile & Other Hard Surface Floor Coverings Distr & Importer
N.A.I.C.S.: 314999

Subsidiary (Domestic):

Stone Source LLC (2)
215 Park Ave S Ste 700, New York, NY 10003
Tel.: (212) 979-6400
Web Site: http://www.stonesource.com
Sales Range: $25-49.9 Million
Emp.: 25
Marble Building Stone
N.A.I.C.S.: 423320
Joe Macisaac *(Pres & CEO)*
Ron Pierce *(COO & Exec VP)*
Wesley Pearse *(Dir-Projects)*
Patricia Jimenez *(Mgr-Sample Dept)*
Edan Algazy *(Project Mgr)*
Riham LaRussa *(Project Mgr-Special)*

Pattonair Limited (1)
1 Pride Park View, Derby, DE24 8AN, Derbs, United Kingdom
Tel.: (44) 1332886200
Web Site: http://www.pattonair.com
Inventory Management Systems & Aerospace & Defense Industries Components Mfr
N.A.I.C.S.: 561949
Wayne Hollinshead *(CEO)*
Dave Fawcett *(Chief Comml Officer)*
Louise Tommasi *(Chief People Officer)*
John Griffiths *(COO)*

COMPANIES

Subsidiary (US):

Pattonair (2)
1900 Robotics Pl, Fort Worth, TX 76118
Tel.: (817) 284-4449
Web Site: http://www.pattonair.com
Component Kitting Services for Overhaul of Military Equipment & Aircraft Systems
N.A.I.C.S.: 336992
Wayne Hollinshead *(CEO)*
John Griffiths *(COO)*
Dave Fawcett *(Chief Comml Officer)*
Louise Tommasi *(Chief People Officer)*
Andrew Jones *(Chief Procurement Officer)*

Subsidiary (Domestic):

Pattonair Derby Limited (2)
Ascot Business Park 50 Longbridge Lane, Derby, DE24 8UJ, United Kingdom
Tel.: (44) 1332 886 200
Web Site: http://www.pattonair.com
Inventory Management Systems (for Aerospace Industry)
N.A.I.C.S.: 561499

Subsidiary (Non-US):

Pattonair SAS (2)
ZAC du Chene Bocquet, Boulevard Henri Navier, 95150, Taverny, Cedex, France
Tel.: (33) 134186100
Web Site: http://www.pattonair.com
Inventory Management Systems
N.A.I.C.S.: 561499

Pearl Engineered Solutions Pte. Ltd. (1)
No 3 Ang Mo Kio Street 62 #02-08, Singapore, 569139, Singapore
Tel.: (65) 65422338
Web Site: http://www.pearlengineeredsolutions.com
Plastic Component Mfr
N.A.I.C.S.: 325199

Subsidiary (Domestic):

Fischer Medtech Pte Ltd. (2)
No 3 Ang Mo Kio Street 62 #02-08, Singapore, 569139, Singapore
Tel.: (65) 6542 2338
Plastics Product Mfr
N.A.I.C.S.: 326199

Subsidiary (Non-US):

Fischer Solution (Suzhou) Co., Ltd. (2)
Block C Unit 16 Suzhou New & Hi-tech District Export Processing Zone, No 20 Datong Road Suzhou New & Hi-Tech District, Suzhou, 215151, Jiangsu, China
Tel.: (86) 51288606555
Injection Molded Plastic Products Mfr
N.A.I.C.S.: 326121

Fischer Tech (Suzhou) Co., Ltd. (2)
No 288 Tang Zhuang Road Loufeng North District, Hi-Tech Development Zone, Suzhou, 215021, Jiangsu, China
Tel.: (86) 51262746288
Injection Molded Plastic Products Mfr
N.A.I.C.S.: 326121

Subsidiary (Domestic):

Fischer Technology Pte Ltd. (2)
No 3 Ang Mo Kio Street #02-08, Singapore, 569139, Singapore
Tel.: (65) 6542 2338
Injection Molded Plastic Products Mfr
N.A.I.C.S.: 326121

Subsidiary (Non-US):

Fischer-tech Malaysia (2)
No 31 Jalan Petaling Kawasan, Perindustrian Larkin, Johor Bahru, 80350, Johor, Malaysia
Tel.: (60) 72381648
Injection Molded Plastic Products Mfr
N.A.I.C.S.: 326121

Fischer-tech Thailand (2)
109/519 Moo 7 Tumbol Klongsong, Amphua Klongluang, Pathumthani, 12120, Thailand
Tel.: (66) 2 9016011
Plastics Product Mfr
N.A.I.C.S.: 326199

Pelican Products, Inc. (1)
23215 Early Ave, Torrance, CA 90505
Tel.: (310) 326-4700
Web Site: http://www.pelican.com
Sales Range: $75-99.9 Million
Sports & Marine Accessories Mfr & Distr
N.A.I.C.S.: 335139
James Curleigh *(CEO)*
Scott Ermeti *(Pres-Bus-Intl)*
Lyndon J. Faulkner *(Chm)*
Kevin Deighton *(VP-Res & Product Dev)*
Dave Williams *(Pres-BioThermal)*
Sharon Ward *(Dir-Corp Mktg & Comm)*
David Becker *(VP-Sls-Consumer Electronics)*
Bob Shortt *(Pres-Consumer Div)*
Sunil Malhotra *(Sr VP-Worldwide Ops)*
Stephan Corti *(Pres-Comml & Govt Div)*
Jeff Cushing *(VP-IT)*
Ellenmary Michel *(VP-Worldwide HR)*
Scott Nicholson *(VP-Worldwide Quality)*
Phil Gyori *(Pres)*
Frank Gennaco *(Dir-Worldwide Procurement)*
George Platisa *(CFO)*
Bruce Gonzalez *(Controller & VP)*
Lance Ralls *(CIO)*
Brad Antoine *(VP-Fin Plng & Analysis)*

Subsidiary (Domestic):

Minnesota Thermal Science, LLC (2)
3020 Niagara Lane N, Plymouth, MN 56425
Tel.: (218) 824-8533
Web Site: http://www.mnthermalscience.com
Sales Range: $1-9.9 Million
Emp.: 11
Thermal Packaging
N.A.I.C.S.: 423330

Subsidiary (Non-US):

Peli Products, S.L.U, (2)
C/ Provenca 388 Planta 7, 08025, Barcelona, Spain
Tel.: (34) 934674999
Web Site: http://www.peli.com
Protective Case Distr
N.A.I.C.S.: 423990

Pelican Products Australia Pty Ltd (2)
West Wing Platinum Building Suite 2 33 4 Ilya Av, Erina, Gosford, 2250, NSW, Australia
Tel.: (61) 2 4367 7022
Web Site: http://www.pelican.com
Emp.: 10
Protective Case Distr
N.A.I.C.S.: 423990
Christian Nvman *(Dir)*

Pelican Products K.K. (2)
Nisso 22 Bldg 9F 1-11-10 Azabu Dai, Minato, Tokyo, 106-0041, Japan
Tel.: (81) 33 585 9100
Protective Case Distr
N.A.I.C.S.: 423990

Pelican Products Korea Ltd (2)
2616 Hyundai 41 Tower 917-9 Mok-dong, Yangchon-gu, Seoul, 158-050, Korea (South)
Tel.: (82) 2 6092 4700
Protective Case Distr
N.A.I.C.S.: 423990

Pelican Products Singapore Pte Ltd (2)
30 Merchant Road 02-08 Riverside Point, Singapore, 058282, Singapore
Tel.: (65) 64385418
Protective Case Distr
N.A.I.C.S.: 423990

Pelican Products ULC (2)
10221-184th Street, Edmonton, T5S 2J4, AB, Canada
Tel.: (780) 481-6076
Web Site: http://www.pelican.com
Emp.: 14
Protective Case Distr
N.A.I.C.S.: 423990
George Platisa *(CFO)*

Subsidiary (Domestic):

Pelican Products, Inc. (2)
147 N Main St, South Deerfield, MA 01373-1026
Tel.: (413) 665-2163
Web Site: http://www.pelican.com
Rotational & Injection Molded Plastic Storage Cases & Containers Designer, Mfr & Distr
N.A.I.C.S.: 326199
Lyndon Faulkner *(Pres & CEO)*

Subsidiary (Non-US):

Hardigg UK Limited (3)
Unit 4 Brookfield Industrial Estate, Leacon Road, Ashford, TN23 4TU, Kent, United Kingdom
Tel.: (44) 1233895895
Web Site: http://www.peli.com
Sales Range: $10-24.9 Million
Emp.: 30
Rotational & Injection Molded Plastic Storage Cases & Containers Designer, Mfr & Distr
N.A.I.C.S.: 326199
Maurice Morsia *(Dir-Sls-UK)*

Subsidiary (Non-US):

Hardigg France SAS (4)
Urbaparc Bat A2 6/8 boulevard de la Liberation, F-93200, Saint Denis, France
Tel.: (33) 148131550
Web Site: http://www.hardiggeurope.com
Rotational & Injection Molded Plastic Storage Cases & Containers Designer, Mfr & Distr
N.A.I.C.S.: 326199

Plasticard - Locktech International (1)
605 Sweeten Creek Industrial Park, Asheville, NC 28803
Tel.: (828) 210-4754
Web Site: http://www.plicards.com
Plastic Card Mfr
N.A.I.C.S.: 326199
Jeff Imes *(VP-Ops)*
David Ide *(Dir-Sls)*
Shannon Brinkley *(Mgr-Sls-Hospitality, Casino & Cruise Lines)*
Jennifer Carter *(Mgr-Sls-Gift)*
Robert A. Keshura *(Dir-Mfg)*

Platinum Equity Advisors, LLC (1)
360 N Crescent Dr, Beverly Hills, CA 90210
Tel.: (310) 712-1850
Web Site: https://www.platinumequity.com
Investment Advice
N.A.I.C.S.: 523940
Matthew Louie *(Mng Dir)*

Subsidiary (Domestic):

Augusta Sportswear, Inc. (2)
425 Park West Dr, Grovetown, GA 30813
Tel.: (706) 860-4633
Web Site: http://www.augustasportswear.com
Sales Range: $10-24.9 Million
Sports Apparel Designer, Mfr & Whslr
N.A.I.C.S.: 315250
Maria Brockhaus *(Dir-Mktg)*
Wade Vann *(CIO & VP-IT)*
Dave Elliott *(CEO)*

Subsidiary (Domestic):

Holloway Sportswear, Inc. (3)
2633 Campbell Rd, Sidney, OH 45365
Tel.: (937) 497-7575
Web Site: http://www.hollowayusa.com
Sales Range: $10-24.9 Million
Sportswear Designer, Mfr & Whslr
N.A.I.C.S.: 315250
Mark S. Vondenhuevel *(Pres)*
Doug McBurney *(Sr VP-Ops)*
Ray Ziolkowski *(Mktg & Customer Svc)*
Brad Sullivan *(Dir-Mktg)*

Subsidiary (Domestic):

Founder Sport Group (2)
1930 Camden Rd, Charlotte, NC 28203
Tel.: (704) 871-0990
Sports Goods Mfr
N.A.I.C.S.: 339920

Subsidiary (Domestic):

Alleson of Rochester, Inc. (3)

PLATINUM EQUITY, LLC

2921 Brighton Henrietta Town Line Rd, Rochester, NY 14623
Tel.: (585) 272-0606
Athletic Sportswear Mfr
N.A.I.C.S.: 315250

Badger Sportswear, LLC (3)
111 Badger Ln, Statesville, NC 28625
Tel.: (704) 871-0990
Sports Apparel & Accessories Mfr
N.A.I.C.S.: 315250

Subsidiary (Domestic):

The HC Companies, Inc. (2)
2450 Edison Blvd Ste 3, Twinsburg, OH 44087
Web Site: http://www.hc-companies.com
Horticultural Container Mfr
N.A.I.C.S.: 325211
Jeffry Walker *(Mgr-Production-Dillen Products)*
Joshua Whitmore *(Mgr-Production-Dillen Products Retail Div)*
Bob Mayer *(Pres & CEO)*

Platinum Equity, LLC - New York (1)
52 Vanderbilt Ave Ph 1, New York, NY 10017-3824
Tel.: (212) 856-7500
Web Site: http://www.platinumequity.com
Sales Range: $100-124.9 Million
Emp.: 7
Private Equity Firm & Business Management Services
N.A.I.C.S.: 523999
Michael Fabiano *(Mng Dir/Head-Credit-Credit Investing Div)*

Pro-Mark, LLC (1)
845 N Overland Rd, North Salt Lake, UT 84054
Tel.: (801) 299-5555
Web Site: http://www.orbitonline.com
Irrigation Products Mfr
N.A.I.C.S.: 238220
Paul Archibald *(Pres)*
Stuart Eyring *(CEO-Orbit)*

Subsidiary (Domestic):

Arizona Mist Inc. (2)
845 N Overland Rd, North Salt Lake, UT 84054 (80%)
Tel.: (801) 299-5555
Web Site: http://www.orbitonline.com
Sales Range: $10-24.9 Million
Emp.: 9
Outdoor Misting & Cooling Systems
N.A.I.C.S.: 333111

Orbit Irrigation Products Inc. (2)
845 N Overland Rd, North Salt Lake, UT 84054-0328 (100%)
Tel.: (801) 299-5555
Web Site: http://www.orbitonline.com
Sales Range: $25-49.9 Million
Emp.: 207
Mfr of & Wholesale Distribution of Irrigation Products
N.A.I.C.S.: 332919
Mitch Lord *(Dir-Mktg)*
Stuart Eyring *(CEO)*

SVP Worldwide, LLC (1)
1224 Heil Quaker Blvd, La Vergne, TN 37086
Tel.: (615) 213-0880
Web Site: http://www.svpworldwide.com
Holding Company; Sewing Machine Designer, Mfr & Distr
N.A.I.C.S.: 551112
Hilmi Kelleci *(Sr VP-Intl Sls & Bus Dev)*
Paul R. Block *(CEO)*

Subsidiary (Non-US):

SVP Canada Inc. (2)
3781 Victoria Park Ave Unit 8, Toronto, M1W 3K5, ON, Canada
Tel.: (416) 759-4486
Emp.: 15
Sewing Machine Whslr
N.A.I.C.S.: 423830

SVP Europe SpA (2)
Via IV Novembre 92/M, 20021, Bollate, Italy
Tel.: (39) 02333391
Sewing Machine Whslr
N.A.I.C.S.: 423830

PLATINUM EQUITY, LLC

Platinum Equity, LLC—(Continued)

Subsidiary (Domestic):

Singer Sewing Company (2)
1224 Heil Quaker Blvd, La Vergne, TN 37086-3515
Tel.: (615) 213-0880
Web Site: http://www.singerco.com
Sales Range: $75-99.9 Million
Sewing Machine Designer, Mfr & Distr
N.A.I.C.S.: 333248
Gary Jones (Pres-Mass Market)

Subsidiary (Non-US):

Happy Japan Inc. (3)
3515-chome Tachiyagawa, Yamagata, 990-2251, Yamagata, Japan
Tel.: (81) 236862272
Web Site: http://www.happyjpn.com
Sewing Machine Mfr & Whslr
N.A.I.C.S.: 333248
Keitaro Harada (Pres)

SSMC Limited (3)
19/F Boldwin Industrial Building, 16-18 Wah Sing Street, Kwai Chung, NT, China (Hong Kong)
Tel.: (852) 28581551
Web Site: http://www.singer.com.hk
Sewing Machine Whslr
N.A.I.C.S.: 423830
Joe Leung (Mgr)

Singer Africa Middle East Limited (3)
PO Box 249, Amman, 1111, Jordan
Tel.: (962) 6 5927768
Web Site: http://www.singer-sam.com
Sewing Machine Mfr & Distr
N.A.I.C.S.: 333248

Subsidiary (Non-US):

VSM Group AB (2)
Drottinggatan 2, 561 84, Huskvarna, Sweden
Tel.: (46) 36146000
Web Site: http://www.husqvarnaviking.com
Sales Range: $250-299.9 Million
Holding Company; Sewing Machine Designer, Mfr & Distr
N.A.I.C.S.: 551112
Lasse Olsson (Country Mgr)

Subsidiary (Non-US):

VSM (UK) Ltd (3)
Ravensbank House Ravensbank Drive, Redditch, B98 9NA, Worcestershire, United Kingdom
Tel.: (44) 1527 519480
Web Site: http://www.husqvarnaviking.com
Emp.: 10
Sewing Machine Mfr & Whslr
N.A.I.C.S.: 333248
Mike Harris (Mng Dir)

VSM Austria GmbH (3)
Moosstrasse 60, 5020, Salzburg, Austria
Tel.: (43) 66283068117
Web Site: http://www.vsmaustria.com
Sewing Machine Whslr
N.A.I.C.S.: 423830

VSM Belgie BVBA (3)
Culliganlaan 1b, 1831, Diegem, Belgium
Tel.: (32) 33 450 2050
Sewing Machine Whslr
N.A.I.C.S.: 423830

VSM Germany GmbH (3)
An der RaumFabrik 34, 76227, Karlsruhe, Germany
Tel.: (49) 721 4001 0
Web Site: http://www.vsm-deutschland.de
Sewing Machine Whslr
N.A.I.C.S.: 423830

VSM Netherlands BV (3)
Spacelab 35, 3824 MR, Amersfoort, Netherlands
Tel.: (31) 33 450 2050
Sewing Machine Whslr
N.A.I.C.S.: 423830

Subsidiary (US):

VSM Sewing Inc. (3)
PO Box 7017, La Vergne, TN 37086-7017
Tel.: (800) 446-2333

Web Site: http://www.husqvarnaviking.com
Sales Range: $50-74.9 Million
Sewing Machines Distr
N.A.I.C.S.: 423620

Subsidiary (Domestic):

VSM Sverige AB (3)
Drottinggatan 2, 561 84, Huskvarna, Sweden
Tel.: (46) 36146000
Emp.: 100
Sewing Machine Designer, Mfr & Distr
N.A.I.C.S.: 333248
Ulrika Stromberg (CEO)

Subsidiary (Non-US):

VSM Switzerland GmbH (3)
Hauptstr 91, 5070, Frick, Switzerland
Tel.: (41) 62 871 56 65
Web Site: http://www.vsmswitzerland.ch
Sewing Machine Whslr
N.A.I.C.S.: 423830
Wolfgang Endres (Mng Dir)

Schutt Sports (1)
710 S Industrial Dr, Litchfield, IL 62056
Tel.: (217) 324-3978
Web Site: http://www.schuttsports.com
Sales Range: $50-74.9 Million
Sports Helmet & Safety Equipment Mfr
N.A.I.C.S.: 339920
Robert Erb (Pres & CEO)
Glenn Beckmann (Dir-Mktg Comm)
Vincent Long (Mgr-Engrg)

Startec Global Communications Corporation (1)
7361 Calhoun Pl Ste 520, Derwood, MD 20855-2775
Tel.: (301) 610-4300
Web Site: http://www.startec.com
Rev: $100,000,000
Emp.: 12
International & Long Distance Telecommunications Services
N.A.I.C.S.: 517121

Tarter Gate Company, LLC (1)
10739 US 127 Bypass, Dunnville, KY 42528
Tel.: (606) 787-7455
Web Site: http://www.tarterusa.com
Ornamental & Architectural Metal Work Mfr
N.A.I.C.S.: 332323
Keith Tarter (Mgr)
Stephen Frazier (CEO)

Tecumseh Power Company (1)
900 N St, Grafton, WI 53024-1412
Tel.: (262) 377-2700
Web Site: http://www.tecumsehpower.com
Snow Thrower & Industrial Engines & Transmissions
N.A.I.C.S.: 333613

Plant (Domestic):

Tecumseh Power Company (2)
1604 Michigan Ave, New Holstein, WI 53061-1153
Tel.: (920) 898-5711
Sales Range: $100-124.9 Million
Emp.: 900
Combustion Engines Mfr
N.A.I.C.S.: 333611

The Cook & Boardman Group, LLC (1)
3064 Salem Industrial Drive, Winston Salem, NC 27127
Tel.: (336) 768-8872
Web Site: http://www.cookandboardman.com
Holding Company; Architectural Products Distr & Engineering Services
N.A.I.C.S.: 551112
Mark K. Duato (Sr VP-Strategic Integration Solutions)
David Eisner (CEO)

Subsidiary (Domestic):

A3 Communications Inc. (2)
1038 Kinley Rd Bldg B, Irmo, SC 29063
Tel.: (803) 744-5000
Web Site: http://www.a3communications.com
Computer Software Development Services
N.A.I.C.S.: 541511

F. Joseph Thomas (Founder & Chm)
Brian Thomas (Pres & CEO)
Dave Lewis (CFO)
Chad Hendrix (VP-Infrastructure)
Scott Grainger (VP-Physical Security)

American Building Services LLC (2)
7343 W Friendly Ave, Greensboro, NC 27410
Tel.: (336) 854-1612
Web Site: http://www.americanbuildingservice.com
Rev: $5,400,000
Emp.: 75
Other Services to Buildings & Dwellings
N.A.I.C.S.: 561790

Architectural Building Supply Co. (2)
2965 S Main St, Salt Lake City, UT 84115
Tel.: (801) 486-3481
Web Site: http://www.absdoors.com
Rev: $36,000,000
Emp.: 100
Fiscal Year-end: 12/31/2006
Residential & Commercial Door & Door Hardware Whslr
N.A.I.C.S.: 423710

Bass Security Services Inc. (2)
26701 Richmond Rd, Bedford, OH 44146
Tel.: (216) 755-1200
Web Site: http://www.bass-security.com
Sales Range: $25-49.9 Million
Emp.: 140
Security System Services
N.A.I.C.S.: 561621
Dale Bass (Pres)

Builders' Hardware & Specialty Co. (2)
2002 W 16th St, Erie, PA 16505
Tel.: (814) 453-4736
Web Site: http://www.builders-hardware.net
Sales Range: $10-24.9 Million
Emp.: 60
Fiscal Year-end: 12/31/2015
Doors, Sliding
N.A.I.C.S.: 423390
James P. McBrier (CEO)
Susan Baker (Controller & Dir-HR)

Building Specialties Company, Inc. (2)
2171 Ruffner Rd, Birmingham, AL 35210
Tel.: (205) 956-1600
Web Site: http://www.bscoinc.com
Distr of Metal Doors, Frames & Finish Hardware
N.A.I.C.S.: 423310
William P. Caddell III (CEO)

Bunting Door & Hardware Co., Inc. (2)
9351G Philadelphia Rd, Baltimore, MD 21237
Tel.: (410) 574-8123
Web Site: http://www.buntingdoor.com
Sales Range: $10-24.9 Million
Emp.: 40
Builders Hardware
N.A.I.C.S.: 423710
Doug McGinnis (CEO)
Alicia McDavid (Office Mgr)

Cook & Boardman, LLC (2)
3916 Westpoint Blvd, Winston Salem, NC 27103
Tel.: (336) 837-0673
Web Site: http://www.cookandboardmanllc.com
Doors, Door Frames & Related Hardware Whslr
N.A.I.C.S.: 423310
Darrin Anderson (CEO)
Joe Harrell (Branch Mgr)

Branch (Domestic):

Cook & Boardman, LLC - Simpsonville (3)
1028 Old Stage Rd, Simpsonville, SC 29681
Tel.: (864) 963-3414
Web Site: http://www.cookandboardmanllc.com
Doors, Door Frames & Related Hardware Whslr
N.A.I.C.S.: 423310
J. E. Buchanan (Branch Mgr)

U.S. PRIVATE

Subsidiary (Domestic):

Delta Door & Hardware, LLC (2)
1710 N Shelby Oaks Dr Ste 7, Memphis, TN 38134-7403
Tel.: (901) 372-6908
Web Site: http://www.delta-door.com
Commercial Doors, Frames & Hardware Distr
N.A.I.C.S.: 423990
Scott Woodward (Mgr-Ops)
Kris Whitson (Pres)

Discovery Door, Inc. (2)
4440 Yankee Hill Rd, Rocklin, CA 95677-1629
Tel.: (916) 315-1834
Web Site: http://www.discoverydoor.com
Commercial & Institutional Building Construction
N.A.I.C.S.: 236220
Jack Yoder (Project Mgr)

Door Components, L.P. (2)
6711 Bingle Rd, Houston, TX 77092
Tel.: (713) 462-0860
Web Site: http://www.cookandboardman.com
Door & Related Hardware Mfr & Distr
N.A.I.C.S.: 332321
Kenneth A. Hajduk (Branch Mgr)

Exactitude, Inc. (2)
12 Sky View Dr, Cumberland Foreside, ME 04110
Tel.: (207) 829-8631
Web Site: http://www.exactitudeinc.com
Sales Range: $1-9.9 Million
Door, Door Frames & Related Hardware Whslr
N.A.I.C.S.: 423710
Bryan McMakin (Branch Mgr)

Division (Domestic):

Hardware Consultants (3)
59 Banair Rd Unit A, Bangor, ME 04401
Tel.: (207) 942-3411
Web Site: http://www.exactitudeinc.com
Door Hardware Distr
N.A.I.C.S.: 423710

Unit (Domestic):

Girtman & Associates (2)
345 Mason Rd, La Vergne, TN 37086-3606
Tel.: (615) 350-6000
Web Site: http://www.girtmanblog.com
Rev: $7,500,000
Emp.: 31
Lumber, Plywood, Millwork & Wood Panel Merchant Whslr
N.A.I.C.S.: 423310
Charles Girtman (Pres)

Subsidiary (Domestic):

H&H Door Co., Inc. (2)
17610 NW Zac Lentz Pkwy, Victoria, TX 77905
Tel.: (361) 572-3667
Web Site: http://www.hhdoor.com
Doors, Frames, Fire Systems & Bathroom Accessories Distr
N.A.I.C.S.: 444180
Rick Huegele (Founder & Pres)

HC HoodCo, Inc. (2)
Penn Eagle Industrial Park 649 E Rolling Ridge Dr, Bellefonte, PA 16823-8135
Tel.: (814) 355-5000
Metal Window & Door Mfr
N.A.I.C.S.: 332321

Hollow Metal Specialists, Inc. (2)
3135 Lakewood Ranch Blvd Ste 101, Bradenton, FL 34211
Tel.: (941) 379-1970
Web Site: http://www.hmsdoors.com
Sales Range: $1-9.9 Million
Emp.: 33
Door & Door Hardware Distr
N.A.I.C.S.: 423310
David Beckham (Mgr-Sls)
Kelly Cromer (Sr Project Mgr)

James Doorcheck, Inc. (2)
9027 Torresdale Ave, Philadelphia, PA 19136
Tel.: (215) 624-2500
Web Site: http://www.jamesdoorcheck.com

COMPANIES

PLATINUM EQUITY, LLC

Hardware
N.A.I.C.S.: 423710
Raymond Battaglia Jr. *(Pres)*

Mcbride Door & Hardware, Inc. (2)
2067 Wineridge Pl Ste C, Escondido, CA 92029
Tel.: (760) 546-1400
Sales Range: $1-9.9 Million
Emp.: 18
Home Center Operator
N.A.I.C.S.: 444110
Dale Hart *(Exec VP-Admin)*

Mullins Building Products, Inc. (2)
5631C Clifford Cir, Birmingham, AL 35210-4453
Tel.: (205) 836-0011
Web Site:
http://www.mullinsbuildingproducts.com
Clay Building Material & Refractories Mfr
N.A.I.C.S.: 327120
Jeff Mullins *(VP)*

Pinnacle Door & Hardware, Inc. (2)
2165 Sunnydale Blvd Ste K, Clearwater, FL 33765-1273
Tel.: (727) 447-7300
Web Site:
http://www.cookandboardman.com
Sales Range: $1-9.9 Million
Emp.: 11
Architectual Door & Hardware Distr
N.A.I.C.S.: 423710
Mark Ventsam *(VP)*
Steve Kenneman *(VP)*
Rob Humphrey *(Gen Mgr)*

Precision Doors & Hardware (2)
6295 Edsall Rd Ste 80, Alexandria, VA 22312
Tel.: (703) 461-8282
Web Site: http://www.pdoor.com
Rev.: $25,000,000
Emp.: 70
Distr of Hollow Metal, Wooden Doors & Frames, Washroom Accessories & other Metal Specialties
N.A.I.C.S.: 423310
Steve Murdoch *(Gen Mgr-Sls)*
Jeff Hull *(Gen Mgr-Sls)*
Raul Mulero *(Project Mgr)*
Jonathan McCoid *(Project Mgr)*

Branch (Domestic):

Precision Doors & Hardware - Fredericksburg (3)
10941 Pierson Dr, Fredericksburg, VA 22408
Tel.: (540) 373-7300
Web Site: http://www.pdoor.com
Rev.: $7,994,000
Emp.: 14
Inland Water Passenger Transportation
N.A.I.C.S.: 483212
Cliff Salvia *(Mgr)*

Subsidiary (Domestic):

RDL LI, Ltd. (2)
11240 Gemini Ln, Dallas, TX 75229
Tel.: (214) 630-3965
Web Site: http://www.rdlsupply.com
Sales Range: $10-24.9 Million
Emp.: 53
Metal Window & Door Mfr
N.A.I.C.S.: 332321
Eric Martin *(Pres)*

Transworld Systems, Inc. (1)
150 N Field Dr Two Conway Park Ste 200, Lake Forest, IL 60045
Tel.: (888) 446-4733
Web Site: http://www.tsico.com
Collection Products & Services
N.A.I.C.S.: 561440
Neal Stern *(COO)*
Paul Brennan *(VP-Strategic Engagements)*
Joseph Laughlin *(CEO)*
Joel Petersen *(Pres)*
Jeff Mersmann *(Exec VP)*
Jonathan Thompson *(Chief Legal & Compliance Officer)*

Subsidiary (Domestic):

Account Control Technology Holdings, Inc. (2)
PO Box 8012, Canoga Park, CA 91309

Tel.: (800) 394-4228
Web Site:
http://www.accountcontrolholdings.com
Emp.: 3,900
Holding Company
N.A.I.C.S.: 551112
Sameer Maini *(CIO)*
Mark Boeder *(Dir-Mktg)*
Tara Furiani *(Exec VP-Talent)*
Ryan Stearns *(CFO)*
Tracey Carpentier *(CEO)*
Dale Van Dellen *(Chm)*

Subsidiary (Domestic):

Account Control Technology, Inc. (3)
PO Box 8012, Canoga Park, CA 91309
Tel.: (661) 395-5985
Web Site: http://www.accountcontrol.com
Sales Range: $25-49.9 Million
Emp.: 398
Debt Collection & Management Agency
N.A.I.C.S.: 561440
Sameer Maini *(CIO)*
Chad Benson *(COO)*
Fabian Grijalva *(Chief HR Officer)*
Jeff Hunter *(Chief Admin Officer)*
Maureen Burke *(CFO)*
Mike Meyer *(CEO)*

Subsidiary (Domestic):

Convergent Resources, Inc. (4)
6 Concourse Pkwy NE Ste 2920, Atlanta, GA 30328
Tel.: (770) 730-0015
Web Site: http://www.convergentusa.com
Commercial Collection, Revenue Cycle Management & Customer Care Services
N.A.I.C.S.: 561440
Derek Whitaker *(CTO)*
Kevin Shiotelis *(Controller)*
Kathy Myhand *(Dir-HR)*

Subsidiary (Domestic):

Convergent Commercial, Inc. (5)
925 Westchester Ave 1st Fl, White Plains, NY 10604
Tel.: (914) 421-7900
Web Site: http://www.convergentusa.com
Commercial Collection Services
N.A.I.C.S.: 561440
Dennis Casey *(VP)*
Robert Rothenberg *(Mgr-Collection)*

Convergent Healthcare Recoveries, Inc. (5)
121 NE Jefferson St Ste 100, Peoria, IL 61602
Tel.: (309) 671-0525
Web Site: http://www.convergentusa.com
Healthcare Revenue Cycle Management Services
N.A.I.C.S.: 561440
Derek A. Pickell *(CEO)*

Convergent Outsourcing, Inc. (5)
800 SW 39th St, Renton, WA 98057
Tel.: (206) 322-4500
Web Site: http://www.convergentusa.com
Sales Range: $50-74.9 Million
Emp.: 600
Inbound & Outbound Customer Care & Accounts Receivable Management Services
N.A.I.C.S.: 561440
Michael G. Meyer *(CEO)*
Chad Benson *(COO)*
Adam Bury *(Sr VP-Ops)*
Joseph Partain *(Gen Counsel & Sr VP)*

Subsidiary (Domestic):

NCC Business Services Inc. (2)
9428 Baymeadows Rd Ste 200, Jacksonville, FL 32256-7912
Tel.: (605) 228-2388
Web Site: http://www.nccbusiness.com
Emp.: 80
Collection Agencies
N.A.I.C.S.: 561440
Irv Pollan *(Pres)*

TruckPro, LLC (1)
1900 Charles Bryan Ste 100, Cordova, TN 38016
Tel.: (901) 252-4200
Web Site: http://www.truckpro.com
Heavy Duty Truck Parts & Accessories Distr
N.A.I.C.S.: 423140

Chuck Broadus *(Pres & CEO)*
Chris Hoshell *(CFO)*

Subsidiary (Domestic):

Arizona Brake & Clutch Supply (2)
2211 N Black Canyon Hwy, Phoenix, AZ 85009
Tel.: (602) 256-7966
Web Site: http://www.truckpro.com
Automotive Parts & Accessories Stores
N.A.I.C.S.: 441330

BH Partners, LLC (2)
311 Marion St, Saint Louis, MO 63104
Tel.: (314) 231-5047
Web Site: http://www.bhpartnersllc.com
Rev.: $9,400,000
Emp.: 70
Fiscal Year-end: 12/31/2009
Motor Vehicle Supplies & New Parts Merchant Whslr
N.A.I.C.S.: 423120
Louis Boggeman Sr. *(Founder)*
Benken Greg *(CFO & Mgr-IT)*
Paul Boggeman *(Gen Mgr)*
Louis J. Boggeman Jr. *(Pres)*

CCC Heavy Duty Truck Parts Company (2)
2470 Route 73, Cinnaminson, NJ 08077
Tel.: (856) 662-7373
Web Site: http://www.cccparts.com
Sales Range: $10-24.9 Million
Emp.: 20
Rebuilt Truck Parts Mfr
N.A.I.C.S.: 333998

Crane Carrier Company (2)
1925 N Sheridan Rd, Tulsa, OK 74115-3602
Tel.: (918) 836-0151
Web Site: http://www.cranecarrier.com
Sales Range: $25-49.9 Million
Emp.: 250
Heavy Duty On & Off Highway Carrier Concrete Mixer Drilling Rig & Bulk Material Handling Mfr
N.A.I.C.S.: 336211
Jeremy Cooper *(Reg Mgr-Parts & Svc)*

Drivelines NW, Inc. (2)
1943 4th Ave S, Seattle, WA 98134
Tel.: (206) 622-8760
Web Site: http://www.drivelinesnw.com
Rev.: $4,032,000
Emp.: 9
Heavy & Light Duty Truck Parts, Fabrication & Driveline Repair Services
N.A.I.C.S.: 811198
Roger Shannon *(Mgr-Ops)*

Hearron Sales, Inc. (2)
3001 Gateway Ave, Bakersfield, CA 93307
Tel.: (661) 324-1011
Sales Range: $1-9.9 Million
Emp.: 14
Industrial Supplies Merchant Whslr
N.A.I.C.S.: 423840

Pascale Service Corporation (2)
51 Delta Dr, Pawtucket, RI 02860
Tel.: (401) 722-2030
Web Site: http://www.pscpartsstore.com
Truck Parts Distr & Services
N.A.I.C.S.: 811198
Michael Toye *(Asst Mgr-Store)*

Power Train Services Inc. (2)
2334 Production Dr, Indianapolis, IN 46241
Tel.: (317) 241-9393
Web Site: http://www.pwrtrain.com
Distr of Truck Equipment & Parts
N.A.I.C.S.: 441330
Lyle Bass *(Pres)*

San Loma, Inc. (2)
3440 Girard Blvd NE, Albuquerque, NM 87107
Tel.: (505) 880-1999
Web Site: http://www.westfleet.com
Sales Range: $1-9.9 Million
Emp.: 11
Motor Vehicle Supplies & New Parts Merchant Whslr
N.A.I.C.S.: 423120
Ana Pedroncelli *(Acct Mgr)*

Turf Care Supply Corp (1)
50 Pearl Rd Ste 200, Brunswick, OH 44212
Tel.: (330) 558-0910

Web Site: http://www.turfcaresupply.com
Emp.: 30
Granular & Liquid Fertilizer Mfr & Whslr
N.A.I.C.S.: 424910
William Milowitz *(Pres & CEO)*
Gary Platek *(VP-Regulatory Affairs)*
Brian Mengeu *(Plant Mgr)*
Todd McCoy *(VP-Mfg & Ops)*
Mark Mangan *(COO)*

United Site Services, Inc. (1)
118 Flanders Rd, Westborough, MA 01581
Tel.: (800) 864-5387
Web Site: http://www.unitedsiteservices.com
Portable Toilet Rental Services
N.A.I.C.S.: 562991
Kenneth S. Ansin *(Co-Founder)*
Mike Marrapese *(VP-IT)*
Rich Vegter *(Sr VP-Sls)*
Ed Simoneau *(Sr VP)*
Mark Bartholomew *(Sr VP-Field Ops)*
Jim Cashman *(COO & Sr VP)*
Nancy Pawlowski *(CIO & Sr VP)*
Kathy Gillis *(Sr VP-HR)*
Adam Jacobs *(Sr VP & Gen Counsel)*
Asit Goel *(Sr VP-Mktg & Comm)*
Ed Mevic *(VP-Bus Dev)*
Steve Ferry *(VP-Customer Care)*
Amy Wilson *(VP-Acquisition & Integration)*
Jerry Zaabel *(VP-Safety & Compliance)*
Kevin Podmore *(VP-Fleet & Strategic Sourcing)*
Asterios Satrazemis *(CEO)*
Scott Jamroz *(CFO)*

Urbaser, S.A. (1)
Camino de Hormigueras n 171, 28031, Madrid, Spain
Tel.: (34) 91 412 20 00
Web Site: http://www.urbaser.com
Solid Waster Treatment & Management Services
N.A.I.C.S.: 562111
Jose Maria Lopez Pinol *(CEO)*
Eduardo Fernandez *(Dir-Innovation)*

Subsidiary (Non-US):

Urbaser Environnement, S.A.S. (2)
1140 Avenue Albert Einstein, PO Box 51, 34935, Montpellier, Cedex, France
Tel.: (33) 4 67 99 41 00
Web Site:
http://www.urbaserenvironnement.fr
Waste Treatment Services
N.A.I.C.S.: 562998
Claude Saint-Joly *(Chm & CEO)*
Bertrand Hyllaire *(Dir-Publication)*

Urbaser Venezolana S.A. (2)
Av Bolivar Norte Urbanizacion Camoruco Centro Comercial, Profesional Camoruco Piso 16 Oficinas 1 y 2, Valencia, 2001, Venezuela
Tel.: (58) 241 826 42 42
Web Site: http://www.urbaser.com
Solid Waste Collection & Street Cleaning Services
N.A.I.C.S.: 562111

Urbaser, Ltd. (2)
First Floor Westmoreland House 80-86 Bath Road, Cheltenham, GL53 7JT, United Kingdom
Tel.: (44) 1242 248880
Web Site: http://www.urbaser.co.uk
Solid Waste Management Services
N.A.I.C.S.: 924110
Javier Peiro *(Mng Dir)*

V P Holdings, Inc. (1)
805 Executive Center Dr W Ste 100, Saint Petersburg, FL 33702
Tel.: (727) 399-3000
Web Site: http://www.skulocal.com
Marketing Consulting Services
N.A.I.C.S.: 541613
Chris Cate *(COO)*
Craig O'Neill *(Head-Sls)*
Jay Loeffler *(Sr Dir-Natl Accts-CPG, OTC & Retail Grocery)*
Mike Hayes *(Dir-Natl Sls)*

Wesco Aircraft Holdings, Inc. (1)
27727 Ave Scott, Valencia, CA 91355
Tel.: (817) 284-4449
Web Site: https://www.incora.com
Rev.: $1,696,450,000
Assets: $1,794,798,000
Liabilities: $1,081,458,000

PLATINUM EQUITY, LLC

Platinum Equity, LLC—(Continued)
Net Worth: $713,340,000
Earnings: $21,369,000
Emp.: 3,302
Fiscal Year-end: 09/30/2019
Holding Company; Aircraft Parts
N.A.I.C.S.: 551112

Subsidiary (Non-US):

Fasteq Limited (2)
Unit 9 Mill Road Industrial Estate, Linlithgow, EH49 7SF, West Lothian, United Kingdom
Tel.: (44) 1506841230
Web Site: http://www.fasteq.co.uk
Hardware Merchant Whslr
N.A.I.C.S.: 423710
John Ward (CEO & Dir-Fin)
Mike Connelly (Mng Dir)
Mike Wilson (Dir-Sls)
Alan Clark (Mgr-Sls-UK)
Rona Haig (Dir-Ops)

Flintbrook Limited (2)
Park Mill Way Clayton West, Huddersfield, HD8 9XJ, West Yorkshire, United Kingdom
Tel.: (44) 1484867740
Investment Management Service
N.A.I.C.S.: 523940

Haas FineChem (Shanghai) Co. Ltd. (2)
355 Kang Qiao East Road, Kang Qiao Industrial Zone Pudong, Shanghai, China
Tel.: (86) 2158131133
Web Site: http://www.haasfinechem.com
Chemical Product Whslr
N.A.I.C.S.: 424690
Michael Chen (Gen Mgr)

Haas Group Australia Pty Limited (2)
Hawker De Havillan Bg 6 224 Lorimer Street, Melbourne, 3207, VIC, Australia
Tel.: (61) 396818054
Aircraft Parts & Auxiliary Equipment Mfr
N.A.I.C.S.: 336413
Steven Watts (Mng Dir)

Subsidiary (Domestic):

Haas Group International Inc. (2)
1475 Phoenixville Pike, West Chester, PA 19380
Tel.: (484) 564-4500
Web Site: http://www.haasgroupintl.com
Sales Range: $550-599.9 Million
Emp.: 1,300
Chemical Management Services
N.A.I.C.S.: 424690

Subsidiary (Domestic):

Avchem, Inc. (3)
6827 Hazelwood Ave, Saint Louis, MO 63134-1019
Tel.: (314) 524-1611
Industrial Chemicals Mfr
N.A.I.C.S.: 325998
Paula Norris (Mgr-HR)

Subsidiary (Non-US):

Haas Group International GmbH (3)
Gutenbergring 53 H, 22848, Norderstedt, Germany
Tel.: (49) 40 54 80 20
Web Site: http://www.haasgroupintl.com
Sales Range: $25-49.9 Million
Emp.: 13
Aviation Lubricants, Chemicals, Composite Materials, Adhesives, Sealants & Coatings Distr
N.A.I.C.S.: 424690

Haas Group International SCM Ireland Limited (3)
Unit 4A Western Business Park, Ballymurtagh, Shannon, Clare, Ireland
Tel.: (353) 6171 9099
Web Site: http://www.haasgroup.com
Aviation Chemical Distr
N.A.I.C.S.: 424690

Haas Group International SCM Limited (3)
Newton Road, Crawley, RH10 9TY, West Sussex, United Kingdom
Tel.: (44) 1293 459500

Web Site: http://www.haasgroupintl.com
Sales Range: $25-49.9 Million
Emp.: 80
Aviation Chemical Supply Services
N.A.I.C.S.: 424690

Division (Domestic):

MAXCOM Services Division (3)
1846 E Innovation Park Dr, Oro Valley, AZ 85755
Web Site: http://www.maxcomonline.com
Software Development Services
N.A.I.C.S.: 541511

Subsidiary (Domestic):

NetMRO Inc. (3)
8490 NW 24th Ter, Miami, FL 33172
Tel.: (305) 717-6577
Web Site: http://www.netmro.com
Aviation Lubricants, Chemicals, Composite Materials, Adhesives, Sealants & Coatings Distr
N.A.I.C.S.: 424690

Subsidiary (Non-US):

R.D. Taylor & Company Limited (3)
240 Edmiston Drive, Glasgow, G51 2YT, United Kingdom
Tel.: (44) 1414275103
Web Site: http://www.rdtaylor.co.uk
Sales Range: $25-49.9 Million
Emp.: 20
Adhesives, Sealants & Lubricants Distr
N.A.I.C.S.: 424690

Subsidiary (Domestic):

Haas Group, LLC (2)
2215 Plank Rd Ste 300, Fredericksburg, VA 22401
Tel.: (540) 402-1306
Web Site: http://www.haasgroup.info
Roofing Contractors
N.A.I.C.S.: 238160

Haas Holdings, LLC (2)
10747 Webster Ter, Dallas, TX 75229-5362
Tel.: (214) 350-8296
Emp.: 3
Holding Company
N.A.I.C.S.: 551112

Subsidiary (Non-US):

Haas TCM Group of the UK Limited (2)
Aeropia House Newton Road, Crawley, RH10 9TY, West Sussex, United Kingdom
Tel.: (44) 1293459500
Chemical Product Merchant Whslr
N.A.I.C.S.: 424690

Haas TCM Italia Srl (2)
Via Puccini 3, 20121, Milan, Italy
Tel.: (39) 0116932461
Chemical Product Merchant Whslr
N.A.I.C.S.: 424690

Haas TCM Singapore Pte. Ltd. (2)
10 Anson Road13-01, International Plaza, Singapore, 079903, Singapore
Tel.: (65) 65422108
Chemical Product Merchant Whslr
N.A.I.C.S.: 424690
Hong Woon Koay (Mgr-Ops)

Haas TCM of Israel Inc. (2)
PO Box 666, Yokneam, 20692, Israel
Tel.: (972) 49937510
Chemical Product Merchant Whslr
N.A.I.C.S.: 424690
Sabeza Yehuda (Gen Mgr)

Wesco Aircraft Canada Inc. (2)
22 Worcester Rd, Toronto, M9W 5X2, ON, Canada
Tel.: (416) 674-0770
Fastener Distr
N.A.I.C.S.: 423710

Wesco Aircraft Europe, Ltd (2)
Lawrence House Riverside Drive, Cleckheaton, BD19 4DH, West Yorkshire, United Kingdom
Tel.: (44) 1274024600
Web Site: http://www.wescoair.com
Aerospace Hardware & Electronic Component Distr

N.A.I.C.S.: 423860
Andrew Straughan (Mgr-Facilities-Wesco Europe)

Wesco Aircraft France SAS (2)
25 Avenue Georges Brassens, Zone De Fontgrasse, 31700, Blagnac, France
Tel.: (33) 534571665
Web Site: http://www.az-france.com
Aircraft Management Services
N.A.I.C.S.: 488190
Mhairi-Claire Welsh (Mgr-Outside Sls)

Wesco Aircraft Germany GmbH (2)
Buschbohe 10, 28357, Bremen, Germany
Tel.: (49) 421163280
Web Site: http://www.wescoair.com
Emp.: 16
Aerospace Hardware & Electronic Component Distr
N.A.I.C.S.: 423860
Bjoern Henkel (Mgr)

Subsidiary (Domestic):

Wesco Aircraft Hardware Corp. (2)
24911 Ave Stanford, Valencia, CA 91355
Tel.: (661) 775-7200
Web Site: http://www.wescoair.com
Sales Range: $25-49.9 Billion
Emp.: 950
Air Transportation Components & Supplies
N.A.I.C.S.: 423710
Randy J. Snyder (Chm)

Subsidiary (Domestic):

Wesco Aircraft Hardware Corp. - Electrical Products Group (3)
3851 N Webb Rd, Wichita, KS 67226-8137
Tel.: (316) 315-1206
Web Site: http://www.wescoair.com
Sales Range: $50-74.9 Million
Emp.: 150
Aircraft Electronic Parts & Equipment Mfr
N.A.I.C.S.: 334419
Michael Kennedy (Pres)

Subsidiary (Non-US):

Wesco Aircraft Italy Srl (2)
Via Porta Est 17, 30020, Marcon, Italy
Tel.: (39) 0415951875
Web Site: http://www.wescoair.com
Emp.: 12
Aerospace Hardware & Electronic Component Distr
N.A.I.C.S.: 423860

Winc Australia Pty. Limited (1)
Level 5 163 O'Riordan Street, Mascot, 2020, NSW, Australia
Tel.: (61) 800 782 753
Web Site: http://www.winc.com.au
Office Supply & Stationery Store Operator
N.A.I.C.S.: 459410
Petter Kelly (CEO)

Subsidiary (Domestic):

CEI Pty. Ltd. (2)
75 Rushdale Street, Knoxfield, 3180, VIC, Australia
Tel.: (61) 1300727231
Web Site: http://www.raeco.com.au
Office Supply & Stationery Store Operator
N.A.I.C.S.: 459410
Atesh Singh (Mgr-Comml)
Chhaya Patel (Gen Mgr)
Trevor McCann (Dir-Sls)
Dean Parker (Mgr-Mktg)

Subsidiary (Non-US):

NXP Limited (2)
49 Waiouru Rd East Tamaki Manukau, 2013, Auckland, New Zealand
Tel.: (64) 800800547
Web Site: http://www.nxp.nz
Office Supply & Stationery Store Operator
N.A.I.C.S.: 424120
Joe Taylor (CEO)

Subsidiary (Domestic):

OfficeMax New Zealand Limited (3)
30 Sir Woolf Fisher Drive East Tamaki, Manukau, Auckland, 2013, New Zealand
Tel.: (64) 800426473
Web Site: http://www.officemax.co.nz

U.S. PRIVATE

Office Supplies & Furniture Stores & Printing Services
N.A.I.C.S.: 459410

Subsidiary (Domestic):

OfficeMax Australia Limited (2)
Level 1 Building 3 658 Church Street, Richmond, Melbourne, 3121, VIC, Australia
Tel.: (61) 132644
Web Site: http://www.welcome.winc.com.au
Office Supplies & Furniture Stores & Printing Services
N.A.I.C.S.: 459410

PLATINUM GUILD INTERNATIONAL (USA) JEWELRY, INC.
125 Park Ave 25th Fl, New York, NY 20017
Tel.: (800) 208-7528   NY
Web Site: http://platinumjewelry.com
Year Founded: 1975
Platinum & Platinum Jewelry Products Promotion
N.A.I.C.S.: 423940
Kevin Reilly (VP)

PLATINUM PROPERTIES, LLC.
9757 Westpoint Dr Ste 600, Indianapolis, IN 46256
Tel.: (317) 818-2900
Year Founded: 1997
Sales Range: $10-24.9 Million
Emp.: 7
Real Estate Development Services
N.A.I.C.S.: 237210
Paul Rioux (Pres)
Kathy Tekulve (Controller)

PLATINUM WARRANTY CORPORATION
2923 Chautauqua Dr, Stow, OH 44224-3840
Tel.: (216) 587-9990
Year Founded: 1985
Sales Range: $50-74.9 Million
Emp.: 217
Automobile Warranty Insurance
N.A.I.C.S.: 524128

PLATINUM WEALTH PARTNERS, INC.
100 N Tampa St Ste 1600, Tampa, FL 33602
Tel.: (813) 579-1660
Web Site:
http://platinumwealthpartners.com
Sales Range: $1-9.9 Million
Emp.: 20
Portfolio Management & Investment Advisory Services
N.A.I.C.S.: 523940
David Potter (Mng Partner)
Julie Koch (Mgr-Relationship)
Rob Dobbs (Mng Partner)
Alex Cross (Partner)
David Henderson (Partner)
Melissa Robertson (Mgr-Client Svcs)
Thomas Alessi (Mng Partner)
James Abraham (Partner)
John Padilla (Mng Partner)
Dale Boettcher (Mng Partner)
Philip F. Morrissey (Mng Partner)
Alan Rosenfield (Chief Investment Officer)

PLATT CONSTRUCTION, INC.
7407 S 27th St, Franklin, WI 53132
Tel.: (414) 761-3868
Web Site: http://www.plattcon.net
Rev: $18,800,000
Emp.: 100
Commercial & Institutional Building Construction
N.A.I.C.S.: 236220
Michael Peratt (Sec)
Richard A. Platt (Pres & Treas)

COMPANIES

Vicky Piche *(Dir-HR & Office Mgr)*
Gary Sadler *(Project Mgr)*
Todd Czarnecki *(Project Mgr)*

PLATTE RIVER NETWORKS INC.
2955 Inca St Ste 2K, Denver, CO 80202
Tel.: (303) 255-1941
Web Site: http://www.platteriver.com
Year Founded: 2002
Sales Range: $1-9.9 Million
Emp.: 21
Technology Consulting Services
N.A.I.C.S.: 541512
Brent Allshouse *(Co-Founder, CFO & Co-Partner)*
Treve Suazo *(Co-Founder, CEO & Co-Partner)*

Subsidiaries:

Applied Tech Solutions Inc (1)
203 S Paterson St, Madison, WI 53703
Tel.: (608) 257-6051
Web Site: http://www.appliedtech.us
Rev.: $1,300,000
Emp.: 13
Data Processing, Hosting & Related Services
N.A.I.C.S.: 518210
Kurt Sippel *(Pres)*
Anne Vitale *(Dir-Support Svcs)*
Cliff McDonald *(COO)*
Daniel Petersen *(Dir-Bus Intelligence)*
Gary Steuck *(VP)*
Tracy Buttel *(Mgr-Acctg)*

PLATTE RIVER POWER AUTHORITY
2000 E Horsetooth Rd, Fort Collins, CO 80525
Tel.: (970) 226-4000
Web Site: http://www.prpa.org
Year Founded: 1973
Sales Range: $25-49.9 Million
Emp.: 200
Distribution, Electric Power
N.A.I.C.S.: 221122
John R. Bleem *(Mgr-Customer Svc)*
David Smalley *(CFO)*
Jason Frisbie *(CEO & Gen Mgr)*
Todd Alyn Jirsa *(Chm)*

PLATTE RIVER VENTURES, LLC
200 Fillmore St Ste 200, Denver, CO 80206
Tel.: (303) 292-7300 CO
Web Site: http://www.platteriverequity.com
Year Founded: 2006
Privater Equity Firm
N.A.I.C.S.: 523999
J. Landis Martin *(Founder, Chm & Mng Dir)*
Gregory A. Sissel *(Mng Dir)*
Peter W. Calamari *(Mng Dir)*
Mark A. Brown *(Mng Dir)*
Kristian M. Whalen *(Mng Dir)*
Derria D. Banta *(CFO)*
Kelly R. Bischoff *(Controller)*
Eric Crawford *(Principal)*
Brian P. Klaban *(Dir-Bus Dev & Debt Capital Markets)*
Edward C. Hutcheson Jr. *(Mng Dir)*

Subsidiaries:

Belt Power LLC (1)
2197 Canton Road Suite 208, Marietta, GA 30066
Tel.: (404) 419-3700
Web Site: http://www.beltpower.com
Conveyor System Component Mfr & Distr
N.A.I.C.S.: 333922
Travis Wilson *(Exec VP)*
Doug Winnette *(Controller)*
Jason Jones *(Mgr-Customer Experience)*
John Shelton *(Exec VP)*
Robert Lockridge *(Mgr-Ops)*
Don Heitmeier *(Pres & CEO)*

Subsidiary (Domestic):

Dunham Rubber & Belting Corp. (2)
682 Commerce Pkwy W Dr, Greenwood, IN 46143
Tel.: (317) 888-3002
Web Site: http://www.dunhamrubber.com
Rev.: $3,420,000
Emp.: 6
Industrial Supplies Merchant Whslr
N.A.I.C.S.: 423840
Brian Swalve *(Mgr)*
Mark Voigt *(Reg Mgr-Sls)*
Gary Buchanan *(Pres)*

Regional Supply, LLC (2)
2197 Canton Rd Ste 208, Marietta, GA 30066
Tel.: (404) 419-3700
Web Site: http://www.beltpower.com
Conveyor & Conveying Equipment Mfr
N.A.I.C.S.: 333922
Paul Barrett *(Owner)*

Sun Belt Inc. (2)
3603 Ventura Dr W, Lakeland, FL 33811
Tel.: (863) 701-9898
Web Site: http://www.beltpower.com
Conveyor System Component Mfr & Distr
N.A.I.C.S.: 333922
Gunnar Henning *(Pres)*

Jameson, LLC (1)
1451 Old N Main St, Clover, SC 29710
Tel.: (803) 222-6400
Web Site: http://www.jamesonllc.com
Emp.: 45
Tools & Lighting Solutions Mfr
N.A.I.C.S.: 332216
Brad Kokoski *(Product Mgr)*
Shannon Forrest *(Plant Mgr)*
Cathey Hayes *(Mgr-Mktg)*

MFG Chemical, LLC (1)
1804 Kimberly Park Dr, Dalton, GA 30720
Tel.: (706) 226-4114
Web Site: http://www.mfgchemical.com
Chemical & Allied Products Merchant Whslr
N.A.I.C.S.: 424690
Dave Driggers *(VP-Engrg & Special Projects)*
Guido De Stefano *(Chief Science & Technology Officer)*
Joe Welch *(Dir-Environmental, Health, Safety & Security)*
Darin Gyomory *(CFO)*
Paul Turgeon *(Pres & CEO)*
Jonathan O'Dwyer *(VP-Comml Ops)*
Tim Haggerty *(VP-Oil & Gas)*
Joe Dymecki *(Dir-Sls)*
George Graham *(VP-Ops)*
Chad Ayers *(Mgr-Site-Pasadena-Texas)*

Subsidiary (Domestic):

Gulf Bayport Chemicals L.P. (2)
9700 Bayport Blvd, Pasadena, TX 77507
Tel.: (713) 783-7081
Web Site: http://www.gulfbayport.com
Specialty Chemicals Mfr
N.A.I.C.S.: 325998
David Chelette *(Ops Mgr)*

Subsidiary (Domestic):

Clear Lake Chemicals LLC (3)
9700 Bayport Blvd, Pasadena, TX 77507
Tel.: (281) 291-2300
Chemicals Mfr
N.A.I.C.S.: 325998
John Nowlan *(CEO)*

Municipal Emergency Services, Inc. (1)
12 Turnberry Ln Fl 2, Sandy Hook, CT 06482
Tel.: (203) 364-0620
Web Site: http://www.mesfire.com
Fire Protection Equipment & Gears Distr
N.A.I.C.S.: 423990
Tom Hubregsen *(CEO)*
John Skaryak *(VP)*

Subsidiary (Domestic):

Blue Ridge Rescue Suppliers, Inc. (2)
1273 Colonial Fort Dr, Montvale, VA 24122-2953
Web Site: http://www.brrs.net
Service Establishment Equipment & Supplies Merchant Whslr
N.A.I.C.S.: 423850

Profile Products LLC (1)
750 W Lake Cook Rd Ste 440, Buffalo Grove, IL 60089
Tel.: (847) 215-1144
Web Site: http://www.profileevs.com
Environment-Friendly Erosion Prevention & Vegetation Support Products Developer, Mfr & Whslr
N.A.I.C.S.: 339999
James Tanner *(Pres & CEO)*
Adam Dibble *(Dir-Mktg)*
Cal Stuart *(CFO & VP)*
Michelle Lee *(Dir-HR)*
Andrew Yablonski *(Mgr-Sls-Northeast)*
Michael Schupp *(Mgr-Sls-Natl)*

Sierra Alloys Company (1)
5467 Ayon Ave, Irwindale, CA 91706
Tel.: (626) 969-6711
Web Site: http://www.sierraalloys.com
Sales Range: $1-9.9 Million
Forged Titanium & Steel Products
N.A.I.C.S.: 332112
Carla Kennelly *(Engr-Sls)*
Diane Farley *(Engr-Sls)*
Edward J. Brennan *(VP-Sls & Mktg)*

Tiger-Sul Products LLC (1)
4 Armstrong Rd Ste 220, Shelton, CT 06484
Tel.: (203) 635-0190
Web Site: http://www.tigersul.com
Agricultural Chemical Product Mfr
N.A.I.C.S.: 325320
Don T. Cherry *(Pres & CEO)*
Mark Hochgesang *(Dir-Bus Dev & Agency Trading)*
Mike Dennerlein *(Dir-Product Mgmt)*
Manuel Zavala *(Sls Mgr-Intl)*
Usman Khalid *(Mktg Mgr-Crop Performance Div)*
Crystal Moye *(Coord-Inside Sls)*
Angel Cedeno *(CFO)*
Brad Miller *(Dir-Ops)*
Carlos Dragonetti *(Fin Controller)*
Steve Mansfield *(VP)*

Subsidiary (Non-US):

Tiger-Sul Products (Canada) Co. (2)
275137 Range Road 263, PO Box 126, Irricana, T0M 1B0, AB, Canada
Tel.: (403) 935-4197
Web Site: http://www.tigersul.com
Fertilizer Mfr
N.A.I.C.S.: 325314
Don T. Cherry *(Pres & CEO)*

Subsidiary (Domestic):

Tiger-Sul Products LLC (2)
Hwy 31 - W Industrial Park, Atmore, AL 36504
Tel.: (251) 202-3850
Web Site: http://www.tigersul.com
Fertilizer Mfr
N.A.I.C.S.: 325314

Plant (Domestic):

Tiger-Sul Products LLC - Stockton Plant (3)
65 Stork Rd, Stockton, CA 95203
Tel.: (877) 299-3399
Web Site: http://www.tigersul.com
Fertilizer Mfr
N.A.I.C.S.: 325314

Womack Machine Supply Co. (1)
13835 Senlac Dr, Farmers Branch, TX 75234
Tel.: (214) 357-3871
Web Site: http://www.womack-machine.com
Sales Range: $200-249.9 Million
Emp.: 300
Hydraulic Systems Equipment & Supplies
N.A.I.C.S.: 423830
Mike J. Rowlett *(Chm & CEO)*

PLATTE VALLEY FINANCIAL SERVICE COMPANIES INC.
1212 Cir Dr, Scottsbluff, NE 69361
Tel.: (308) 632-7004 WY
Web Site: http://www.pvbankne.com
Year Founded: 1934
Sales Range: $550-599.9 Million
Emp.: 200
Bank Holding Company
N.A.I.C.S.: 551111
H. Hod Kosman *(Chm, Pres & CEO)*
Ann K. Burkholder *(VP)*
Sandy Massey *(Sr VP & Dir-HR)*
Mark Payne *(Sr VP & Dir-IT)*

Subsidiaries:

C. H. Brown Co., LLC (1)
20 W Frontage Rd, Wheatland, WY 82201
Tel.: (307) 322-2545
Web Site: http://www.chbrownco.com
Emp.: 17
Automobile Financing Services
N.A.I.C.S.: 522220

J.G. Elliott Insurance Center (1)
1110 Circle Dr, Scottsbluff, NE 69361
Tel.: (308) 635-2023
Web Site: http://www.jgelliott.com
Emp.: 25
General Insurance Services
N.A.I.C.S.: 524210
Larry Neuwirth *(Mgr-Life & Health Dept)*
Eliasar Kanno *(Mgr-Processing Unit)*
Kerry Meyer *(Acct Exec)*
Kim Hurst V *(VP-Ops)*

McBrayer Insurance Center (1)
302 W 21st Ave, Torrington, WY 82240
Tel.: (307) 532-2147
Web Site: http://www.mcbrayerinsurance.com
Emp.: 4
General Insurance Services
N.A.I.C.S.: 524210
Brennan Malm *(Pres)*
Vickie Snyder *(Mgr-Ops)*

PV Mortgage Company (1)
1212 Cir Dr, Scottsbluff, NE 69363
Tel.: (308) 635-3006
Real Estate, Commercial Financing & Refinancing
N.A.I.C.S.: 522310
Earl Warren *(Pres)*
Jim Zitterkopf *(COO & Sr VP)*
Marci Meyer *(VP)*
Tammy Viessman *(VP)*
Debbie Patrick *(Asst VP)*

Platte Valley Ag Credit Co. (1)
1212 Circle Dr, Scottsbluff, NE 69363
Tel.: (308) 635-7733
Web Site: http://www.pvbankne.com
Sales Range: $25-49.9 Million
Emp.: 7
Credit Lending Services for Agri-Producers & Agri-Businesses
N.A.I.C.S.: 522291

Platte Valley Bank (1)
421 Vandehei Ave, Cheyenne, WY 82003-3260
Tel.: (307) 778-0021
Web Site: http://www.pvbank.com
Emp.: 6
Commercial Banking
N.A.I.C.S.: 522110
Zac Karpf *(Co-COO & Exec VP)*
Joe Guth *(Co-COO & Exec VP)*
Jody Miles *(CFO & Sr VP)*
Nena Kueck *(Sr VP)*
Nathan Hendee *(Sr VP-NMLS# 1026232)*

Platte Valley Bank Nebraska (1)
1212 Cir Dr, Scottsbluff, NE 69363
Tel.: (308) 632-7004
Web Site: http://www.pvbankne.com
Commericial Banking
N.A.I.C.S.: 522110
H. Hod Kosman *(Chm, Pres & CEO)*
Clark Wisniewski *(COO-PVB Trust Div)*

Platte Valley Bank Wyoming (1)
2201 Main St, Torrington, WY 82240-1057
Tel.: (307) 532-2111
Web Site: http://www.pvbankwy.com
Sales Range: $25-49.9 Million
Emp.: 17
Commericial Banking
N.A.I.C.S.: 522110
Joe Guth *(Pres & CEO)*

PLATTE VALLEY FINANCIAL SERVICE COMPANIES INC.   U.S. PRIVATE

Platte Valley Financial Service Companies Inc.—(Continued)

Platte Valley Investment Center Inc. (1)
1212 Circle Dr, Scottsbluff, NE 69361
Tel.: (308) 635-7766
Financial Investment Services
N.A.I.C.S.: 523940

PLATTE-CLAY ELECTRIC COOP
1000 Hwy 92, Kearney, MO 64060
Tel.: (816) 628-3121
Web Site: http://www.pcec.coop
Rev.: $25,011,502
Emp.: 62
Distribution, Electric Power
N.A.I.C.S.: 221122
Mike Torres (CEO)
Cheryl Chandler (Mgr-HR)
Tim Hill (Mgr-Ops)
Sally McGinnis (Mgr-IT)
Julie Morrison (Coord-GIS)
Jerry Maxwell (Supvr-Ops)
Rhonda Nash (Supvr-Acctg)
Gary Shanks (Pres)
Dennis Fulk (Sec)
Theresa Wren (Treas)
Debi Stewart (VP)

PLATTNER AUTOMOTIVE GROUP, INC.
1891 Porter Lake Dr, Sarasota, FL 34240
Tel.: (941) 341-9794
Web Site: http://www.plattnerautomotivegroup.com
Rev.: $23,689,083
Emp.: 3
Automobiles, New & Used
N.A.I.C.S.: 441110
Doug Plattner (Pres)
Janice Bondeson (Mgr-Trade Dealer & Auction)

Subsidiaries:

Plattner's Winter Park Superstore (1)
1050 N Orlando Ave, Winter Park, FL 32789
Tel.: (407) 644-1919
Sales Range: $10-24.9 Million
Automobile Dealership
N.A.I.C.S.: 441120

PLATYPUS ADVERTISING + DESIGN
N29 W23810 Woodgate Ct W Ste 100, Pewaukee, WI 53072
Tel.: (262) 522-8181
Web Site: http://www.platypus-ad.com
Year Founded: 1987
Sales Range: $10-24.9 Million
Emp.: 17
Advertising Agencies
N.A.I.C.S.: 541810
Dan Trzinski (Pres)
Tracey Wieder (Bus Mgr)
Rich Ratay (Assoc Partner & Dir-Creative)
Kathy Sorcan (Dir-Media)
Gary Haas (Assoc Partner & Dir-Creative)
Mary Adamczak (Sr Dir-Art)
Walter Grace (Sr Dir-Art)
Nancy Wilkes (Dir-PR)

PLAY IT AGAIN SPORTS
2211 South Florida Ave, Lakeland, FL 33803
Tel.: (863) 687-7500
Web Site: http://www.playitagainsports.com
Sales Range: $10-24.9 Million
Emp.: 15

Buys, Sells & Trades Quality Used & New Sporting Goods & Equipment
N.A.I.C.S.: 459110

PLAY VISIONS, INC.
19180 144th Ave NE, Woodinville, WA 98072-4371
Tel.: (425) 482-2836
Web Site: http://www.playvisions.com
Year Founded: 1990
Sales Range: $10-24.9 Million
Emp.: 30
Toy Distr
N.A.I.C.S.: 423920
Mark Chernick (CEO)
Jay Keron (CFO)
Webb Nelson (Pres)

PLAYBILL INCORPORATED
525 7th Ave Ste 1801, New York, NY 10018-4918
Tel.: (212) 557-5757
Web Site: http://www.playbill.com
Year Founded: 1884
Sales Range: $10-24.9 Million
Emp.: 30
Publisher of Theater Guides, Programs & Information
N.A.I.C.S.: 513120
Philip S. Birsh (Pres & CEO)
Bruce Hallett (Publr)
Glenn Asciutto (Sr Acct Mgr)
Robert Cusanelli (Dir-Mfg)
Alex Near (Mgr-Production)

PLAYERS HEALTH COVER USA INC.
718 Washington Ave N Ste 402, Minneapolis, MN 55401
Tel.: (612) 345-9683
Web Site: https://playershealth.com
Sports Management
N.A.I.C.S.: 711219
Tyrre Burks (Founder & CEO)

Subsidiaries:

Monarch Management Corporation (1)
3201 Cherry Ridge Dr Ste D405, San Antonio, TX 78230
Tel.: (210) 524-7135
Web Site: https://www.mmc-ins.com
Insurance Agencies & Brokerage Services
N.A.I.C.S.: 524210
Mark Nordstrom (Pres)

PLAYFIELD INTERNATIONAL, INC.
1220 Green Rd, Chatsworth, GA 30705-7319
Tel.: (706) 695-4581   DE
Web Site: http://www.playfieldinternational.com
Year Founded: 1971
Sales Range: $10-24.9 Million
Emp.: 40
Indoor & Outdoor Synthetic Turf Golfmats, Target Greens & Playgrounds Mfr & Distr
N.A.I.C.S.: 314110
Steve Linville (Owner & CEO)

PLAYFLY SPORTS PROPERTIES, LLC
22 Cassatt Ave, Berwyn, PA 19312
Tel.: (203) 461-5461   DE
Web Site: https://playfly.com
Year Founded: 2020
Sports Marketing Services
N.A.I.C.S.: 711219
Michael Schreiber (CEO & Founder)

Subsidiaries:

The Aspire Group, Inc. (1)
1320 Elsworth Blvd NW, Atlanta, GA 30318-7213

Tel.: (404) 389-9100
Web Site: http://www.theaspiregroupinc.com
Marketing Consulting Services
N.A.I.C.S.: 541613
Bernard Mullin (Founder)
John Zeleznock (Mgr-West Michigan University Fan Relationship Mgmt Center)
Trevor Allison (Mgr-USA Natl Sls Center)
A. J. Smith (Dir-Client & Partner Dev)
Christian Wayne (Coord-Performance Analytics)
Bill Fagan (Pres & CEO)

PLAYGIRL INDUSTRIES, INC.
10 W 33rd St, New York, NY 10001
Tel.: (212) 714-1800   NY
Web Site: http://www.stagelightcosmetics.com
Rev.: $13,700,000
Emp.: 35
Cosmetics
N.A.I.C.S.: 424210
Victor Braha (Pres)

Subsidiaries:

Bentley Manufacturing Inc. (1)
10 W 33rd St, New York, NY 10001
Tel.: (212) 714-1800
Disposable Diaper Mfr
N.A.I.C.S.: 322291

PLAYGROUND GROUP INC
18 Bridge St Ste 2D, Brooklyn, NY 11201
Tel.: (718) 797-9529
Web Site: http://www.playgroundgroup.com
Sales Range: $10-24.9 Million
Emp.: 2
N.A.I.C.S.: 541810
Noah Gaynin (CEO & Dir-Creative)
Dana Alia (Dir-Bus Dev)

PLAYHOUSE SQUARE FOUNDATION
1501 Euclid Ave Ste 200, Cleveland, OH 44115
Tel.: (216) 771-4444
Web Site: http://www.playhousesquare.org
Rev.: $40,000,000
Emp.: 300
Theatrical Production
N.A.I.C.S.: 711110
Leanne Dewyer (Asst Dir-Dev)
Jason Swank (Asst Dir-Mktg)
Tim McDonald (Controller)
Tonia Brown (Coord-Ticket & Guest Svcs)
Michelle Ryan Stewart (VP-Dev)
Edward Broderick (Mgr-Front of House)
Carl Dettlebach (Mgr-Facilities)
Joe Benz (Mgr-Food & Beverage Ops)
Stephanie Keefer (Mgr-Mktg & PR)
Chris Meyers (Mgr-Sls)
Nathan Scott (Mgr-Venue Booking)
James Ratner (Chm)

PLAYNEXT, INC.
150 S Almaden Blvd Ste 1500, San Jose, CA 95113
Tel.: (408) 216-1107   DE
Web Site: http://www.playnext.com
Year Founded: 2006
Emp.: 200
Mobile Video Game Developer
N.A.I.C.S.: 513210
Lan Hoang (Founder & CEO)

PLAYSCRIPTS INC.
450 7th Ave Ste 809, New York, NY 10123
Web Site: http://www.playscripts.com
Year Founded: 2000
Sales Range: $1-9.9 Million
Emp.: 11

Online Play Publishing Library
N.A.I.C.S.: 513199
Doug Rand (Co-Founder)
Jonathan Rand (Co-Founder)

PLAYWIRE MEDIA, LLC
1000 E Hillsboro Blvd Ste 103, Deerfield Beach, FL 33441
Tel.: (954) 418-0779
Web Site: http://www.playwiremedia.com
Year Founded: 2007
Emp.: 60
Advertising Agency Specializing in Game Integration
N.A.I.C.S.: 541810
Jayson Dubin (CEO)
Steven Berger (Pres)
Jonthan Trevisani (Mgr-Ops)
James Haley (VP-Sls-Europe)
Chris Giomblanco (COO)
Nick Branstator (CTO)
Tanya Brown (VP-Global Revenue)
Justin Stefanoviv (VP-Sls-US)
Rolf Dinsdale (Dir-Sls-Canada)
Nathan Thomas (VP-Network Ops)

PLAZA ADVISORS, INC.
3412 Bay to Bay Blvd, Tampa, FL 33629
Tel.: (813) 837-1300   FL
Web Site: http://www.plazadvisors.com
Sales Range: $1-9.9 Million
Real Estate Investment Advisory & Brokerage Firm
N.A.I.C.S.: 531390
Jim P. Michalak (Founder & Pres)

PLAZA APPLIANCE MART INC.
5431 Monroe Rd, Charlotte, NC 28212
Tel.: (704) 568-7600
Web Site: http://www.plazaappliancemart.com
Sales Range: $10-24.9 Million
Emp.: 40
Household Appliance Stores
N.A.I.C.S.: 449210
Donald Meekins (Mgr)
Rob Erwin (Mgr-Mdse)
William J. Pleasants Sr. (Owner)
William J. Pleasants Jr. (VP)

PLAZA BELMONT MANAGEMENT GROUP II LLC
8016 State Line Rd Ste 215, Shawnee Mission, KS 66208-3710
Tel.: (913) 381-7177   DE
Web Site: http://www.plazabelmont.com
Year Founded: 1998
Privater Equity Firm
N.A.I.C.S.: 523999
Robert J. Parnow (Pres & COO)
John S. Dalton (Exec VP)
John T. Stout Jr. (Founder, Chm & CEO)

PLAZA LINCOLN MERCURY INC.
8925 US Hwy 441, Leesburg, FL 34788
Tel.: (352) 787-1255
Web Site: http://www.plazalm.com
Rev.: $42,300,000
Emp.: 60
New & Used Automobiles Whslr
N.A.I.C.S.: 441110
Joseph H. Nolette (Pres)
Louis Nolette (Gen Mgr)

PLAZA MAKOTI EQUITY ELEVATOR
101 Railroad Ave, Plaza, ND 58771
Tel.: (701) 497-3707

Web Site:
http://www.plazamakotielevator.com
Sales Range: $10-24.9 Million
Emp.: 12
Grain Elevators
N.A.I.C.S.: 424510
Carl Nannenga (Gen Mgr)

PLAZA MOTORS COMPANY
11830 Olive Blvd, Saint Louis, MO 63141
Tel.: (314) 301-1700
Web Site:
http://www.plazamotors.com
Rev.: $82,300,000
Emp.: 430
New & Used Automobiles
N.A.I.C.S.: 441110
Gary Schulz (CFO)
John R. Capps (Pres & CEO)

PLAZA MOTORS OF BROOKLYN
2740 Nostrand Ave, Brooklyn, NY 11210
Tel.: (718) 253-8400
Web Site:
http://www.plazaautomall.com
Rev.: $18,565,214
Emp.: 350
Sales of Automobiles
N.A.I.C.S.: 441110
John Rosatti (Owner)

PLAZA PROPERTIES INC.
3016 Maryland Ave, Columbus, OH 43209-1590
Tel.: (614) 237-3726   OH
Web Site:
http://www.plazaproperties.com
Year Founded: 1958
Sales Range: $10-24.9 Million
Emp.: 100
Operator of Apartment Buildings & Corporate Buildings
N.A.I.C.S.: 531110
Stephen Campbell (VP)
Larry Ruben (Pres)
Ann Taylor (Mgr-Building & Construction)

PLAZA PROVISION COMPANY
Carretera 165 Esquina Carr 28 Av El Cano, Guaynabo, PR 00965
Tel.: (787) 781-2070   PR
Web Site:
http://www.plazaprovision.com
Year Founded: 1907
Sales Range: $25-49.9 Million
Emp.: 300
Foods & Household Products Distr
N.A.I.C.S.: 424410
Robert A. Cimino (CEO)
Angel Torres (Pres & COO)

Subsidiaries:

Plaza Food Systems   (1)
Carretera 1 Km 27 9 Barrio Rio Canas Cruce Trujillo Alto, Caguas, PR 00725
Tel.: (787) 653-4950
Web Site: http://www.plazafoodsystems.com
Emp.: 200
Grocery Delivery Services
N.A.I.C.S.: 492210
Ivan Alvarez (Gen Mgr)

Plaza Warehousing & Realty Corporation   (1)
Hc 05, Caguas, PR 00725
Tel.: (787) 781-2070
Web Site: http://www.plazaprovision.com
Sales Range: $25-49.9 Million
Emp.: 200
Provider of Packaged Frozen Goods
N.A.I.C.S.: 424420

PLAZA SWEETS, INC.
521 Waverly Ave, Mamaroneck, NY 10543
Tel.: (914) 698-0233
Web Site:
http://www.plazasweetsbakery.com
Year Founded: 1983
Sales Range: $10-24.9 Million
Emp.: 90
Commercial Bakery Services
N.A.I.C.S.: 311812
Rodney Holder (CEO)

PLAZA TIRE SERVICE INC.
3075 Corporate Cr, Cape Girardeau, MO 63703-5817
Tel.: (573) 334-5037   MO
Web Site:
http://www.plazatireservice.com
Year Founded: 1963
Sales Range: $25-49.9 Million
Emp.: 180
Provider of Tire Products & Services
N.A.I.C.S.: 423130
Marc Rhodes (Pres)
Francis Don (Project Mgr)

PLC ENTERPRISES INC.
300 Plaza Dr, Vestal, NY 13850
Tel.: (607) 729-9331
Sales Range: $25-49.9 Million
Emp.: 6
Short-Term Business Credit Institution
N.A.I.C.S.: 522299
Burton I. Koffman (Pres)

PLC MEDICAL SYSTEMS, INC.
10 Forge Pk, Franklin, MA 02038
Tel.: (508) 541-8800
Web Site: http://www.plcmed.com
Sales Range: $1-9.9 Million
Medicinal Product Mfr
N.A.I.C.S.: 339112
Andrew Halpert (Dir-Mktg & Engrg)
Mark Tauscher (Pres & CEO)

PLC TRENCHING CO., LLC.
24 Robinson Rd, Clinton, NY 13323
Tel.: (315) 853-6183
Web Site:
http://www.plctrenching.com
Rev.: $11,300,000
Emp.: 50
Electrical Contractor
N.A.I.C.S.: 238210
Steven P. Bonsted (Controller)
David L. Critell (Owner)
Delores Y. Critelli (Treas)
Steven M. Critelli (Gen Counsel & VP)

PLCS PLUS INTERNATIONAL, INC.
12418-B Rosedale Hwy, Bakersfield, CA 93312
Tel.: (661) 322-4470   NV
Web Site: http://www.bkppi.com
Year Founded: 1996
Sales Range: $1-9.9 Million
Emp.: 38
Designs, Installs, Programs & Integrates Industrial Control & Automation Technology for Manufacturers
N.A.I.C.S.: 541511
Robert Riley (Owner & CEO)

PLEASANT HILL GRAIN LLC
210 S 1st St, Hampton, NE 68843
Tel.: (402) 725-3835
Web Site:
http://www.pleasanthillgrain.com
Year Founded: 1976
Sales Range: $10-24.9 Million
Emp.: 30
Kitchen Equipment & Appliances
N.A.I.C.S.: 332215
Gary Hansen (Principal)

PLEASANT HOLIDAYS LLC
2404 Townsgate Rd, Westlake Village, CA 91361-2505
Tel.: (818) 991-3390
Web Site:
http://www.pleasantholidays.com
Year Founded: 1959
Sales Range: $150-199.9 Million
Emp.: 650
Wholesale Tour Operator
N.A.I.C.S.: 561520
Jerry Healy (VP-Sls)
Kevin Burnett (Dir-Creative)
Margaret Forton (Mgr-Sls-Midwest & East)
Steven M. Hattem (Sr Dir-Sls)
Lisa Pisaturo (VP-Sls-Strategy)
Jack Richards (Pres & CEO)
Davion Jones (Mgr-Bus Dev-Northeast)
Janet Yacoub (Mgr-Bus Dev-Combined Sls Team-Fremont)
Chris Ames (Mktg Mgr-Destination-Mexico, Central & South America)
Chanda Vudmaska (VP-Sls)
Steven Perry (Mgr-Natl Accounts & Trng)
Natalia Pirumyan (Mgr-Bus Dev-Southern California Region)
Lydia Torres (Mgr-Bus Dev-Southern California Region)

PLEASANT MATTRESS CO., INC.
375 S West Ave, Fresno, CA 93706
Tel.: (559) 268-6446
Web Site:
http://www.pleasantmattress.com
Year Founded: 1959
Mattress Mfr
N.A.I.C.S.: 337910
Ernst Morgenstern (Founder)
Rion Morgenstern (CEO)
Carter Gronbach (Pres)

Subsidiaries:

Mcroskey Mattress Company   (1)
1687 Market St, San Francisco, CA 94103
Tel.: (415) 874-7531
Web Site: http://www.mcroskey.com
Sales Range: $1-9.9 Million
Mattress Mfr
N.A.I.C.S.: 337910
Vanessa Contreras (CEO)

PLEASANT RIDGE MANOR
8300 W Ridge Rd, Girard, PA 16417
Tel.: (814) 474-5521   PA
Web Site:
http://www.pleasantridgemanor.com
Year Founded: 1976
Sales Range: $25-49.9 Million
Emp.: 518
Elder Care Services
N.A.I.C.S.: 623212
Robert V. Smith (Exec Dir)
Eardley Wickramsinghe (Dir-Medical)
Tracy Johns (Dir-Rehabilitation Svcs)
Karen Simpson (Dir-Food Svc)
Mary Venezia (Dir-Nursing)

PLEASANT STREET HOMES LLC
51700 Lovejoy Dr, Middlebury, IN 46540
Tel.: (574) 825-3700
Sales Range: $25-49.9 Million
Emp.: 200
Mobile Homes, Personal Or Private Use
N.A.I.C.S.: 321991
Lisa McGlashen (CFO)
Jim Jones (Pres & COO)

Subsidiaries:

Indiana Building Systems Llc   (1)
51700 Lovejoy Dr, Middlebury, IN 46540
Tel.: (574) 825-3700
Mobile Homes, Personal Or Private Use
N.A.I.C.S.: 321991

PLEASANT VIEW RETIREMENT COMMUNITY
544 N Penryn Rd, Manheim, PA 17545
Tel.: (717) 665-2445   PA
Web Site:
http://www.pleasantviewrc.org
Year Founded: 1954
Sales Range: $10-24.9 Million
Emp.: 360
Lifecare Retirement Community Operator
N.A.I.C.S.: 623311
Melissa Mervine (VP-Ops)
Paul W. Brubaker (Sec)
J. Glen Hostetler (VP)
James F. Devine (Chm)
Patrick J. Gendrue II (Treas)

PLEASANTVILLE FORD INC.
47 Pleasantville Rd, Pleasantville, NY 10570
Tel.: (914) 769-1800
Web Site: http://www.pvilleford.com
Rev.: $31,601,547
Emp.: 67
Automobiles, New & Used
N.A.I.C.S.: 441110
Cheryl Borrelly (Gen Mgr)
Wayne Fallica (Mgr-Svcs)

PLEASURELAND INCORPORATED
25064 Augusta Dr, Saint Cloud, MN 56301
Tel.: (320) 251-7588   MN
Web Site:
http://www.pleasurelandrv.com
Year Founded: 1971
Sales Range: $25-49.9 Million
Emp.: 300
Supplier of Recreational Vehicles
N.A.I.C.S.: 441210
Daniel R. Pearson (Pres & CEO)
Brad Bacon (Controller)

PLEDGE PETROLEUM CORP.
576 S Foothills Plz Dr Ste 163, Maryville, TN 37801
Tel.: (865) 227-4818   DE
Year Founded: 2008
Assets: $171,378
Liabilities: $103,508
Net Worth: $67,870
Earnings: ($33,746)
Emp.: 1
Fiscal Year-end: 12/31/18
Investment Services
N.A.I.C.S.: 523999
John Zotos (Interim CFO & Sec)
Christopher L. Headrick (CEO)
John W. Huemoeller II (Chm)

PLENUS GROUP INC.
101 Phoenix Ave, Lowell, MA 01852
Tel.: (978) 970-3832
Web Site: http://www.plenus-group.com
Year Founded: 2002
Sales Range: $10-24.9 Million
Emp.: 40
Frozen Specialty Food Mfr
N.A.I.C.S.: 311412
Joseph Jolly (Pres)

PLESSER HOLLAND ASSOCIATES
20 W 22nd St Ste 903, New York, NY 10010
Tel.: (212) 420-8383
Year Founded: 1992

PLESSER HOLLAND ASSOCIATES U.S. PRIVATE

Plesser Holland Associates—(Continued)
Sales Range: Less than $1 Million
Emp.: 8
Public Relations
N.A.I.C.S.: 541820
Andrew P. Plesser *(Founder)*
Kent Holland *(Partner)*

PLEUNE SERVICE COMPANY
750 Himes St SE, Grand Rapids, MI 49548
Tel.: (616) 243-6374
Web Site:
http://www.pleuneservice.com
Year Founded: 1974
Rev.: $21,796,130
Emp.: 150
Mechanical Contractor
N.A.I.C.S.: 238220
John H. Pleune *(Chm & Pres)*
Jill M. Malone *(VP-HR & Admin)*
Larry Plank *(VP-Sls)*

PLEWS, INC.
1550 Franklin Grove Rd, Dixon, IL 61021
Tel.: (815) 288-3344 DE
Web Site: http://www.plews-edelmann.com
Automotive Parts & Tools Designer, Mfr & Distr
N.A.I.C.S.: 336390
Wes Sherman *(VP-Category Mgmt)*
Joanie Mulligan *(Mgr-Pricing)*
Tami Borum *(CFO & VP-Fin)*
Brett Mueller *(Pres)*
Ron Colby *(Dir-Supply Chain-Global)*
Andrew Moe *(Dir-Mktg Svcs-Aftermarket Retail Markets-Worldwide)*
Dan Billie *(Chief Comml Officer)*
David Rashid *(Chm)*
Brandi Johnson *(Dir-Category Mgmt-Retail-Aftermarket & Retail Markets Worldwide)*
Micah Cram *(Reg Sls Mgr-Western U.S & Canada)*
Tony Edwards *(VP-Bus Dev)*

PLEXENT
16479 Dallas Pkwy Ste 140, Addison, TX 75001
Tel.: (972) 381-0077 TX
Year Founded: 2001
Sales Range: $50-74.9 Million
Emp.: 38
Information Technology Service Management
N.A.I.C.S.: 519290
Gordon Brown *(Founder & Pres)*

PLEXUS CAPITAL, LLC
200 Providence Rd Ste 210, Charlotte, NC 28207
Tel.: (704) 927-6245 NC
Web Site: http://www.plexuscap.com
Year Founded: 1995
Rev.: $255,000,000
Privater Equity Firm
N.A.I.C.S.: 523999
Michael S. Becker *(Co-Founder & Partner)*
Michael K. Painter *(Co-Founder & Mng Partner)*
Will Anders *(Partner)*
Lisa Dunning *(Dir-Acctg)*
Paula Newsome *(Office Mgr)*
Alex Bean *(Partner)*
Subsidiaries:
Practis Inc. (1)
8720 Red Oak Blvd #220, Charlotte, NC 28217
Tel.: (704) 887-5300
Web Site: http://www.practisinc.com
Landscape Architectural Services

N.A.I.C.S.: 541320
Elizabeth Pettrone *(Founder & Mng Partner)*

PLEXUS SCIENTIFIC CORPORATION
7130 Minstrel Way Ste 215, Columbia, MD 21045
Tel.: (410) 715-3865
Web Site: http://www.plexsci.com
Sales Range: $1-9.9 Million
Emp.: 100
Engineeering Services
N.A.I.C.S.: 541330
Ali Sadrieh *(VP-Environmental Svcs & Facilities Mgmt)*
Michael McCrory *(VP)*
David Bell *(VP)*

PLEZ U STORES INC.
2315 N Main St Ste 207, Anderson, SC 29621
Tel.: (864) 224-9695
Year Founded: 1977
Sales Range: $25-49.9 Million
Emp.: 290
Convenience Store
N.A.I.C.S.: 445131
Irvin L. Cauthen *(Pres)*

PLH PRODUCTS, INC.
6655 Knott Ave, Buena Park, CA 90620
Tel.: (714) 739-6600 CA
Web Site:
http://www.plhproducts.com
Year Founded: 1992
Wood Saunas & Infrared Wellness Products Mfr
N.A.I.C.S.: 321992
Kyung Min Park *(Pres, Sec & Dir)*
Seung Woo Lee *(Chm & CEO)*
Sang Lee *(VP-Sls)*

PLIBRICO CO. LLC
1935 Techny Rd, Northbrook, IL 60062
Tel.: (312) 337-9000 DE
Web Site: http://www.plibrico.com
Year Founded: 1914
Sales Range: $75-99.9 Million
Emp.: 73
Monolithic Refractories Mfr & Other Monolithic Refractory Technology Services
N.A.I.C.S.: 238220
Pamela Gaul *(Dir-Mktg)*
Brad Taylor *(Pres & CEO)*

PLIMPTON & HILLS CORPORATION
2 Brainard Rd, Hartford, CT 06114
Tel.: (860) 522-4233
Web Site:
http://www.plimptonhills.com
Sales Range: $10-24.9 Million
Emp.: 125
Plumbing Fittings & Supplies
N.A.I.C.S.: 423720
Anthony Pellegrino *(Dir-Sls-Hartford)*
Nicole Cacciatore *(Product Mgr-Tile)*
Jason Smith *(Branch Mgr)*

PLITEK, LLC.
69 Rawls Rd, Des Plaines, IL 60018
Tel.: (847) 827-6680
Web Site: http://www.plitek.com
Year Founded: 1968
Sales Range: $10-24.9 Million
Emp.: 62
Laminated Plastic Plate Mfr
N.A.I.C.S.: 326130
Karl Hoffman *(Pres)*

PLJ INFORMATION SYSTEMS, INC.

20327 E Calle De Flores, Queen Creek, AZ 85282
Tel.: (480) 222-6020 AZ
Web Site:
http://www.nothingbutnetaz.com
Year Founded: 2001
Sales Range: $10-24.9 Million
Emp.: 7
Managed Service Solutions
N.A.I.C.S.: 513199
Steven Brown *(VP)*
Robert Cox *(Pres)*
Subsidiaries:
Nothing But NET, LLC (1)
615 N 48th St Ste 1027, Phoenix, AZ 85008
Tel.: (480) 222-6020
Web Site: http://www.nothingbutnet.com
Sales Range: $1-9.9 Million
Managed Service Solutions
N.A.I.C.S.: 541511
Robert Cox *(Co-Founder & Pres)*
Steve Brown *(Co-Founder & VP)*

PLN CONTRACTING INC.
230 E 124 St, New York, NY 10035
Tel.: (212) 376-5576
Rev.: $12,000,000
Emp.: 7
General Contracting
N.A.I.C.S.: 236118

PLOCHMAN, INC.
1333 N Boudreau Rd, Manteno, IL 60950-9384
Tel.: (815) 468-3434
Web Site: http://www.plochman.com
Year Founded: 1852
Sales Range: $75-99.9 Million
Emp.: 90
Prepared Mustard Mfr
N.A.I.C.S.: 311941
Carl M. Plochman *(Chm)*
Diane Kintz *(CFO)*

PLOTE CONSTRUCTION, INC.
1100 Brandt Dr, Hoffman Estates, IL 60192
Tel.: (847) 695-9300 IL
Web Site: http://www.plote.com
Year Founded: 1964
Heavy Highway Construction, Asphalt Paving, Snow Removal, Project Management, Concrete Paving & Excavation
N.A.I.C.S.: 238910
Mike Waller *(VP-Ops)*
Michael Mejia *(Dir-HR)*

PLS LOGISTICS SERVICES
3120 Unionville Rd Bldg 110, Cranberry Township, PA 16066
Tel.: (724) 709-9000
Web Site: http://www.plslogistics.com
Year Founded: 1986
Sales Range: $200-249.9 Million
Emp.: 223
Freight Transportation Arrangement
N.A.I.C.S.: 488510
Greg Burns *(Pres & CEO)*
Jon Herberger *(CIO)*
Mark Kummer *(Sr VP-Corp Dev)*

PLUM HEALTHCARE GROUP, LLC
1620 W Fern Ave, Redlands, CA 92373
Tel.: (909) 793-2609 CA
Year Founded: 1999
Sales Range: $1-9.9 Million
Emp.: 80
Nursing Care Facility Operator
N.A.I.C.S.: 623110
Mark Baliff *(Principal & CEO)*
Christi Chapin *(Dir-Rehab Svcs)*
Christy Ingram *(Dir-Mktg)*

Dani Lorenz *(Coord-HR & Payroll)*
Deborah Marks *(Dir-Facility Rehab)*
Ellen Subia *(Dir-Reimbursement)*
Jim Mathews *(Dir-Facility Rehab)*
Kimberly Uecker *(Dir-Bus Dev)*
Leticia Guerrero *(Mgr-Bus Office)*
Myrna Deguzman *(Controller)*
Nanci Wilson *(Dir-Rehab Svcs)*
Paul Hubbard *(Owner)*
Thomas Knoebel *(Mgr-Info Sys)*
Tiaseuoalii Faiai *(Dir-Engrg)*
Vivian Cuenca *(Mgr-Acctg)*
Maria Jackson *(Mgr-HR & WC)*
Gregory LaDuca *(Dir-Facility Rehabilitation)*
Paulina Salazar *(Dir-Fin)*
Liza Munoz *(Dir-Staff Dev)*

PLUM LOGIC, LLC
100 Crossways Park Dr W, Woodbury, NY 11797
Web Site:
http://www.bookkeeper360.com
Year Founded: 2012
Sales Range: $1-9.9 Million
Emp.: 30
Financial Consulting Services
N.A.I.C.S.: 541611
Nick Pasquarosa *(Founder)*

PLUMB HOUSE INC.
10 Industrial Rd, Milford, MA 01757-3587
Tel.: (508) 482-1971
Web Site:
http://www.plumbhouse.com
Sales Range: $100-124.9 Million
Emp.: 30
Commercial & Office Building, New Construction
N.A.I.C.S.: 236220
Helga Coffey *(Dir-Safety)*
Jeff Bergeron *(Project Mgr)*
Dave Erickson *(Head-Preconstruction Div)*

PLUMB INC.
1663 W Sherman Blvd, Muskegon, MI 49441-3564
Tel.: (231) 759-0918 MI
Web Site:
http://www.plumbsmarket.com
Year Founded: 1985
Sales Range: $10-24.9 Million
Emp.: 25
Grocery Store Services
N.A.I.C.S.: 445110
James Nader *(Owner, Pres & CEO)*

PLUMB LINE MECHANICAL, INC.
449 W Commercial St, Elko, NV 89801
Tel.: (775) 753-7586 NV
Web Site:
http://www.plumblineinc.com
Year Founded: 2004
Sales Range: $1-9.9 Million
Emp.: 70
Plumbing, Heating & Air Conditioning Services
N.A.I.C.S.: 238220
Michael Ayala *(Pres)*

PLUMBERS SUPPLY CO. INC.
1000 E Main St, Louisville, KY 40206-1841
Tel.: (502) 582-2261 KY
Web Site: http://www.plumbers-supply-co.com
Year Founded: 1947
Sales Range: $25-49.9 Million
Emp.: 306
Plumbing Fixtures & Related Products Mfr
N.A.I.C.S.: 423720

Jay Johnson (VP)
Jay Wilson (CFO)

PLUMBERS SUPPLY COMPANY
429 Church St, New Bedford, MA 02745
Tel.: (508) 675-7478   MA
Web Site: http://www.plumberssupplyco.com
Year Founded: 1953
Sales Range: $25-49.9 Million
Emp.: 25
Plumbing & Hydronic Heating Supplies Whslr
N.A.I.C.S.: 423720
J. Thomas Jones (Pres)

PLUMBING & INDUSTRIAL SUPPLY CO.
12224 Philadelphia St, Whittier, CA 90039
Tel.: (562) 698-7749
Web Site: http://www.pandico.com
Year Founded: 1968
Sales Range: $10-24.9 Million
Emp.: 30
Whslr of Plumbing & Hydronic Heating Supplies
N.A.I.C.S.: 423720
John Herrera (Controller)

PLUMBING DISTRIBUTORS INC.
1025 Old Norcross Rd, Lawrenceville, GA 30046-5492
Tel.: (770) 963-9231   GA
Web Site: http://www.relyonpdi.com
Year Founded: 1973
Sales Range: $10-24.9 Million
Emp.: 105
Provider of Plumbing Equipment & Supplies
N.A.I.C.S.: 423720
Kenny Rogers (Mgr-Sls)
Lyn Wright (Chm)
Nick Kolb (Coord-Vendor Returns)
Sean Moran (Branch Mgr)
Thomas Tom Perrotta (Branch Mgr)
Adam Brown (Mgr-Outside Sls)
Coley Herrin (Pres & COO)
Fielding Alderman (Mgr-Show Room)
Heather Weinstein (Mgr-Alpharetta Show Room)
Jay Wilson (Mgr-Supply Chain)
Mildred Puckett (Mgr-HR)
Aimee A. Gillen (Controller)

Subsidiaries:

W A Bragg & Co Inc.   (1)
2513 Mike Padgett Hwy, Augusta, GA 30906
Tel.: (706) 798-8257
Web Site: http://www.wabragg.com
Rev.: $7,455,000
Emp.: 15
Plumbing & Heating Equipment & Supplies, Hydronics, Merchant Whslr
N.A.I.C.S.: 423720
Brian Bragg (Pres)

PLUMBING-HEATING-COOLING CONTRACTORS ASSOCIATION
180 S Washington St Suite 100, Falls Church, VA 22046
Tel.: (703) 237-8100
Web Site: http://www.phccweb.org
Year Founded: 1883
Emp.: 130
Trade Association in the Construction Industry
N.A.I.C.S.: 238990
Charlotte R. Perham (VP-Comm)
Cynthia A. Sheridan (COO-Foundation)

Julie A. Turner (Dir-Creative Production & MIS)
Robin J. Maher (COO)
Michael Copp (Exec VP)
John Lieske (Dir-Fin)

PLUMGOOD FOOD, LLC
4015 Hillsboro Pike Ste 214, Nashville, TN 37215-2788
Tel.: (615) 248-4448
Web Site: http://www.plumgoodfood.com
Grocery Delivery Services
N.A.I.C.S.: 424410
Eric Satz (Co-Founder & Pres)
Kate Satz (Co-Founder)
Sarah Voter (Dir-Customer Svc)

PLUMMERS INC.
2250 S McDowell Ext, Petaluma, CA 94954
Tel.: (707) 778-1600
Web Site: http://www.plummers.com
Sales Range: $10-24.9 Million
Emp.: 5
Household Furniture Retailer
N.A.I.C.S.: 449110
Erling Eide (CEO)

PLUNKETT & LYNCH ASSOCIATES
307 7th Ave Rm 2007, New York, NY 10001-6035
Tel.: (212) 631-7526
Web Site: http://www.plunkettandlynch.com
Rev.: $15,000,000
Emp.: 5
Wrap Lighting Manufacturers
N.A.I.C.S.: 541990
Kathy Romano (Mgr-Acctg)
Rob Lynch (VP)
Jim Lynch Sr. (Pres)

PLUNKETT'S PEST CONTROL, INC.
40 NE 52nd Way, Minneapolis, MN 55421-1014
Tel.: (763) 571-7100
Web Site: http://www.plunketts.net
Exterminating & Pest Control Services
N.A.I.C.S.: 561710
Wayne Hardison (Dir-Environmental Svcs, Engrg, Presbyterian Homes & Svcs)

Subsidiaries:

Varment Guard Environmental Services, Inc.   (1)
1001 Chekrein Ave Ste B, Columbus, OH 43229
Web Site: http://varmentguard.com
Wildlife Removal & Bir Management Services
N.A.I.C.S.: 813312
Jared Miller (Dir)

Subsidiary (Domestic):

American Animal Control, LLC   (2)
72298 State Rd 13 N, Syracuse, IN 46567
Web Site: http://www.americananimalcontrol.com
Environment, Conservation & Wildlife Organizations
N.A.I.C.S.: 813312

PLURIBUS CAPITAL MANAGEMENT LLC
770 Broadway, New York, NY 10003
Tel.: (646) 654-5106   DE
Privater Equity Firm
N.A.I.C.S.: 523999
James A. Finkelstein (Co-Founder)
George Green (Co-Founder)
Matthew Doull (Co-Founder)

PLUS DELTA CONSULTING, LLC
10940 Wilshire Blvd Ste 1600, Los Angeles, CA 90024
Tel.: (310) 456-1159
Web Site: http://www.plusdelta.net
Year Founded: 2002
Rev.: $2,200,000
Emp.: 11
Business Consulting Services
N.A.I.C.S.: 541618
Jeremy S. Lurey (CEO)

PLUS GROUP INC.
7425 Janes Ave Ste 201, Woodridge, IL 60517
Tel.: (630) 515-0500   IL
Web Site: http://www.theplusgroup.com
Year Founded: 1975
Sales Range: $10-24.9 Million
Emp.: 90
Staffing Services
N.A.I.C.S.: 561320
John Seelander (VP)

PLUS ONE HEALTH MANAGEMENT, INC.
77 Water St, New York, NY 10038
Web Site: http://www.plusone.com
Year Founded: 1986
Sales Range: $25-49.9 Million
Emp.: 1,500
Health Services
N.A.I.C.S.: 621111
Heather Hannig (Dir-Spa Ops)
Dan Naylon (Dir-Bus Dev)
Veronica Shaw-Hyatt (VP-Acctg)
Dave Shelby (Reg VP-New England)
Mindy Roess (Reg VP-Soth)
Lemont Platt (Reg VP-Mid-Atlantic)
Richard Little (Reg VP-Midwest)
John Holding (Reg VP-West)
Elysa Silbersmith (Dir-Nutrition)
Kristin Shaw (Dir-Spa Svcs)
Gregory Hullstrung (Dir-Physical Therapy)
Mike Motta (Co-Founder, Pres & CEO)
Tom Maraday (Sr VP)
Doug Naumann (Dir-Mktg)
Grace De Simone (Dir-Grp Fitness)
David Todhunter (CFO)
Matt Sylvestre (CIO)
Jamie Macdonald (VP)
Dave Milani (VP-HR)
Nancy Ngai (VP-Health Promo & Clinical Integration)

PLUS RELOCATION SERVICES, INC.
600 Hwy 169 S Ste 500, Minneapolis, MN 55426
Tel.: (952) 512-5500   MN
Web Site: http://www.plusrelocation.com
Year Founded: 1970
Corporate Moving Services
N.A.I.C.S.: 484210
Mick Lee (Chm & CEO)
Susan Schneider (Pres)
Sandra Lee (Exec VP)
Joseph V. Benevides (Sr VP-Global Rels)
Lauren Schroeder (VP-Org Effectiveness)
Stacey Myhro (VP-Supplier Rels)
Chris Pardo (VP-Consulting & Mktg)
Jennifer Lutgen (VP-Client Svcs)
Brian Fudenberg (VP-Bus Dev)
Phillip J. Kronlage (CFO-Acctg)
Pascal Cheung (Mgr-Client Svcs)
Tracey Gatlin (VP-Supply Chain-Global)

PLUSPHARMA, INC.
2460 Coral St, Vista, CA 92081
Tel.: (760) 597-0200   CA
Web Site: http://www.pluspharm.com
Year Founded: 1991
Sales Range: $1-9.9 Million
Emp.: 10
Groceries & Related Products Mfr & Distr
N.A.I.C.S.: 424490
Alice Chen (CFO)

Subsidiaries:

The Coromega Company, Inc.   (1)
2525 Commerce Way, Vista, CA 92081
Tel.: (619) 254-7741
Web Site: http://www.coromega.com
Omega 3 Fish Oil & Gummie Vitamins Mfr
N.A.I.C.S.: 456191

PLUTON BIOSCIENCES LLC
11754 Westline Industrial Dr, Saint Louis, MO 63146
Web Site: http://plutonbio.com
Scientific Laboratories
N.A.I.C.S.: 621511
Charlie Walch (CEO)

Subsidiaries:

Microbe Inotech Laboratories   (1)
11754 Westline Industrial Dr, Saint Louis, MO 63146
Tel.: (314) 344-3030
Web Site: http://www.microbeinotech.com
Research & Development in Biotechnology
N.A.I.C.S.: 541714
Bruce Hemming (Chm)
Douglas Bodily (Mgr-IT)

PLUZYNSKI/ASSOCIATES, INC.
26 W 17th St 10th Fl, New York, NY 10011
Tel.: (212) 645-1414   NY
Web Site: http://www.pluzynski.com
Year Founded: 1977
Rev.: $18,000,000
Emp.: 50
N.A.I.C.S.: 541810
Edward Pluzynski (Founder)
Lawrence B. Ocamb (VP-Print Production)
Scott Pluzynski (Pres)

PLY-TRIM INC.
550 N Meridian Rd, Youngstown, OH 44509
Tel.: (330) 799-7876
Web Site: http://www.plytrim.com
Rev.: $12,500,000
Emp.: 22
Lumber, Plywood & Millwork
N.A.I.C.S.: 423310
Harry Hoffman (Chm)

PLYCO CORPORATION
500 Indus Dr, Elkhart Lake, WI 53020
Tel.: (920) 876-3611
Web Site: http://www.plyco.com
Sales Range: $10-24.9 Million
Emp.: 50
Window Frames & Sash, Plastics
N.A.I.C.S.: 332321
Garry Matz (Pres)
Todd Matz (Pres)

PLYMOUTH FOAM INCORPORATED
1800 Sunset Dr, Plymouth, WI 53073
Tel.: (920) 893-0535
Web Site: http://www.plymouthfoam.com
Year Founded: 1978
Sales Range: $10-24.9 Million
Emp.: 100
Insulation Or Cushioning Material; Packaging Material
N.A.I.C.S.: 326150
David Bolland (Pres & CEO)

PLYMOUTH FOAM INCORPORATED U.S. PRIVATE

Subsidiaries:

Plymouth Foam, Inc. - Minnesota (1)
13900 Industry Ave, Becker, MN 55308
Tel.: (763) 261-4900
Web Site: http://www.plymouthfoam.com
Emp.: 25
Polystyrene Foam Product Mfr
N.A.I.C.S.: 326140

PLYMOUTH HARBOR INC.
700 John Ringling Blvd, Sarasota, FL 34236
Tel.: (941) 365-2600
Web Site:
    http://www.plymouthharbor.org
Year Founded: 1966
Sales Range: $10-24.9 Million
Emp.: 273
Continuing Care Retirement Facility
N.A.I.C.S.: 623311
Harry Hobson (Pres & CEO)
Gary Jackson (CFO & Sr VP)
Joe Devore (VP-Health Svcs)
Gordon Okawa (VP-Mktg & Community Affairs)
Becky Pazkowski (VP-Philanthropy)
Dinah Stamp (VP-Residential Svcs)
Tena Wilson (VP-Support Svcs)
Alyson Harris (Dir-Acctg Svcs)
Lyall Smith (Dir-Concierge & Security Svcs)
Rene Weder (Dir-Dining Svcs)
Jim Myers (Dir-Environmental Svcs)
Karen Novak (Dir-Health Svcs)
Maryanne Shorin (Dir-Resident Svcs & Programs)
Chris Valuck (Dir-Wellness)

PLYMOUTH PLACE INC.
315 N La Grange Rd, La Grange Park, IL 60526
Tel.: (708) 354-0340   IL
Web Site:
    http://www.plymouthplace.org
Year Founded: 1938
Sales Range: $25-49.9 Million
Emp.: 405
Lifecare Retirement Community Services
N.A.I.C.S.: 623311
Dale Lilburn (CEO)
Raymond P. Felson (Exec Dir)
Christopher Campise (Dir-Dining Svcs)
Pat Dance (Dir-HR)
Barbara Erlenbush (Dir-Nursing)
Ellen Masuret (Dir-Resident Svcs)
Robin Tanis (Dir-Fin)
Allyson Zak (Dir-Dev & PR)
Dan Weiler (Dir-Facilities & Ops)
Rita Lopienski (Dir-Life Enrichment)
Sharon Sleezer (Dir-Sls)
R. Conlin (Chm)

PLYMOUTH PRINTING CO. INC.
450 N Ave, Cranford, NJ 07016
Tel.: (908) 276-8100
Web Site:
    http://www.plymouthprinting.com
Sales Range: $10-24.9 Million
Emp.: 100
Pharmaceutical Printing
N.A.I.C.S.: 323111
H. D. Auerbach (Chm & CEO)
Keith Dovel (Pres & COO)

PLYMOUTH ROCK ASSURANCE
695 Atlantic Ave, Boston, MA 02111
Tel.: (617) 720-1620   NJ
Web Site:
    http://www.plymouthrock.com
Year Founded: 1982

Automobile Insurance Services
N.A.I.C.S.: 524128
James M. Stone (Founder & Chm)
Hal R. Belodoff (COO)
Mary Boyd (Pres & CEO)
Gerry Wilson (Pres/CEO-Plymouth Rock Assurance Direct Grp)
Bill Martin (Pres-Plymouth Rock Home Assurance Corp & CEO-Plymouth Rock Home Assurance Corp)
Marc Buro (CEO-InsuraMatch)
Ethan Tarby (CMO)
Paul Measley (Chief Claims Officer)
Rachel Switchenko (VP-Customer Solutions-Plymouth Rock Home Assurance Corp)

PLYMOUTH TUBE COMPANY
29W150 Warrenville Rd, Warrenville, IL 60555-3528
Tel.: (630) 393-3556   MI
Web Site: http://www.plymouth.com
Year Founded: 1924
Steel Pipes & Tubes Mfr & Distr
N.A.I.C.S.: 331210
Drew Van Pelt (Pres & CEO)
Fede Barreto (CFO)
David Crouch (Grp VP)
Chuck Banker (Grp VP)
Ajay Ramaswami (VP-Strategic Iniatives)

Subsidiaries:

Plymouth Tube Company - Chicago Processing Mill (1)
4555 W Armitage Ave, Chicago, IL 60639
Tel.: (773) 489-0226
Steel Coil Processing Mfr
N.A.I.C.S.: 331221

Plymouth Tube Company - East Troy Mill (1)
2056 Young St, East Troy, WI 53120
Tel.: (262) 642-8201
Stainless Steel Tubing Mfr
N.A.I.C.S.: 331210

Plymouth Tube Company - Eupora Mill (1)
212 Industrial Park Rd, Eupora, MS 39744
Tel.: (662) 258-2420
Steel Tubing Mfr
N.A.I.C.S.: 331210

Plymouth Tube Company - Hopkinsville Mill (1)
201 Commerce Ct, Hopkinsville, KY 42240
Tel.: (270) 886-6631
Steel Products Mfr
N.A.I.C.S.: 333111

Plymouth Tube Company - Salisbury Mill (1)
2000 Industrial Pkwy, Salisbury, MD 21801
Tel.: (410) 749-1666
Web Site: http://www.plymouth.com
Steel Tube Mfr
N.A.I.C.S.: 331210
Tony Campell (Gen Mgr)

Plymouth Tube Company - Streator Mill (1)
1209 E 12th St, Streator, IL 61364
Tel.: (815) 673-1515
Sales Range: $25-49.9 Million
Emp.: 45
Steel Tubing Mfr
N.A.I.C.S.: 331210

Plymouth Tube Company - The Winamac Cold Draw Mill (1)
572 W State Rd 14, Winamac, IN 46996
Tel.: (574) 946-3125
Web Site: http://www.plymouth.com
Steel Tube Mfr
N.A.I.C.S.: 331210

Plymouth Tube Company - Trent Mill (1)
2056 Young St, East Troy, WI 53120
Tel.: (262) 642-7321
Web Site: http://www.plymouth.com
Steel Welding & Tubing Mfr

N.A.I.C.S.: 332111

Plymouth Tube Company - West Monroe Mill (1)
601 Grantham Ave, West Monroe, LA 71292
Tel.: (318) 388-3360
Web Site: http://www.plymouth.com
Fabricated Stainless Steel Mfr
N.A.I.C.S.: 332111
Tony Campbell (Gen Mgr)

White Metals Group (1)
201 Commerce Ct, Hopkinsville, KY 42240
Tel.: (270) 886-6631
Metals Mfr
N.A.I.C.S.: 332999
Mark Baker (Pres)

PLYWOOD & DOOR MANUFACTURERS
1435 Morris Ave, Union, NJ 07083
Tel.: (908) 687-7890
Web Site: http://www.finnform.com
Rev.: $10,000,000
Emp.: 12
Plywood
N.A.I.C.S.: 423310
Juhani Haikala (Pres)

PLYWOOD & LUMBER SALES INCORPORATED
2401 Poplar St, Oakland, CA 94607
Tel.: (510) 547-7257
Sales Range: $10-24.9 Million
Emp.: 5
Hardwood Lumber: Rough, Dressed & Finished
N.A.I.C.S.: 423310

PM & M ELECTRIC, INC.
525 W Baseline Rd, Mesa, AZ 85210
Web Site:
    http://www.titansolarpower.com
Year Founded: 2013
Sales Range: $1-9.9 Million
Emp.: 1,000
Electronic Services
N.A.I.C.S.: 238210
David Williamson (CEO)

PM ADVERTISING
1375 Broadway Ste 2700, New York, NY 10024-5140
Tel.: (212) 777-0000
Year Founded: 1990
Sales Range: $1-9.9 Million
Emp.: 12
N.A.I.C.S.: 541810
Himanshu Goodluck (Acct Exec)
Tanay Hurst (Pres-Ops)
Christian Barrant (Mgr)
Caroline Walsh (Mgr-Bus-Lexington)
Jon Siegel (Mng Partner)

Subsidiaries:

PM Advertising (1)
123 Main St, Chicago, IL 60606
Tel.: (312) 123-4567
Rev.: $200,000
Emp.: 3
Advetising Agency
N.A.I.C.S.: 541810
Tania Hurston (Gen Mgr)
Brenda Hurst (Mgr-Ops)

PM COMPANY LLC
9220 Glades Dr, Fairfield, OH 45011
Tel.: (513) 825-7626   DE
Web Site:
    http://www.pmcompany.com
Year Founded: 1905
Sales Range: $10-24.9 Million
Emp.: 100
Mfr of Converted Paper Products
N.A.I.C.S.: 322299
Mike Webster (Pres & CEO)

PM CONSTRUCTION CO. INC.
19 Industrial Park Rd, Saco, ME 04072
Tel.: (207) 282-7697
Web Site:
    http://www.pmconstruction.com
Sales Range: $10-24.9 Million
Emp.: 25
Construction of Commercial & Office Buildings
N.A.I.C.S.: 236220
Phillip Morin (CEO)
George G. Deely (CFO)
William S. Nason (COO)

PM MACKAY GROUP
5 Pine St Ext 6 Mill Annex, Nashua, NH 03060
Tel.: (603) 882-2991
Web Site:
    http://www.pmmackaygroup.com
Sales Range: $10-24.9 Million
Emp.: 135
Residential Construction
N.A.I.C.S.: 236220
Julie Boilard (VP)

PM PARTIES INC.
704 C Matthews-Mint Hill Rd, Matthews, NC 28105
Tel.: (704) 841-1370
Web Site: http://www.partycity.com
Sales Range: $10-24.9 Million
Emp.: 500
Party Favors Supplies
N.A.I.C.S.: 459420
Jeffrey A. Peters (Pres)

PM PEDIATRICS
596 Jericho Tpke, Syosset, NY 11791
Tel.: (516) 677-5437
Web Site:
    http://www.pmpediatrics.com
Sales Range: $10-24.9 Million
Emp.: 134
Health Care Srvices
N.A.I.C.S.: 621999
Steven Katz (Co-CEO)
David J. Biehl (Gen Counsel & Exec VP)
Jill Cysner (VP & Controller)
Rachel Friedman (Chief Culture Officer)
Pascaline Romain (Mgr-Ops)
Sharyn Traub (Dir-Comm)
David Mathison (Dir-Medical-Mid Atlantic)
Mordechai Raskas (Dir-Telemedicine & Clinical Informatics)
Jeffrey Schor (Co-Founder)
Karin Sadow (VP-Quality)
Michael Bachman (VP-Clinical Ops)
Sheryl Cohen (Dir-Medical-Southern New York)
Andre Persaud (Dir-Medical-Northern New York)
Yvette Young (Dir-Medical-New Jersey)
Toni Clare Hogencamp (Dir-Medical-New England)

PM PUBLICIDAD
1776 Peachtree St Ste N600, Atlanta, GA 30309
Tel.: (404) 870-0099
Web Site:
    http://www.pmpublicidad.com
Year Founded: 2003
Rev.: $15,000,000
Emp.: 21
Advetising Agency
N.A.I.C.S.: 541810
Patricio Montalbetti (Co-Founder & Chief Creative Officer)
Eduardo Perez (Pres & CEO)

Ricky Echegaray *(VP & Exec Dir-Creative)*
Patricia Ramon *(Controller)*
Sebastian Otero *(Dir-New Bus)*

PM REALTY GROUP LP
1000 Main St, Houston, TX 77002-5386
Tel.: (713) 209-5800
Web Site: http://www.pmrealtygroup.com
Rev.: $22,600,000
Emp.: 1,000
Real Estate Agent, Commercial
N.A.I.C.S.: 531210
Rick Kirk *(Chm & CEO)*
James C. Gunn *(Pres-Property Svcs)*
John S. Dailey *(Mng Dir & Exec VP)*
William Roger Gregory *(Pres-PMRG Investments)*
Wade Bowlin *(Pres-Central Div)*
Pat Rains *(Exec VP-Risk Mgmt & HR)*
Kim Grizzle *(Sr VP-Leasing-Houston)*
Ariel Guerrero *(Sr VP-Res)*
Zach Wooten *(VP-Leasing-Atlanta)*
Brett Williams *(Sr VP-Property Mgmt-Central Div-Houston)*

PM RECOVERY INCORPORATED
106 Calvert St, Harrison, NY 10528
Tel.: (914) 835-1900
Web Site: http://www.pmrecovery.com
Sales Range: $10-24.9 Million
Emp.: 100
Metals Service Centers & Offices
N.A.I.C.S.: 423510
Mark Spano *(Pres & CEO)*
Gary Boigon *(COO & Sr VP)*
B. Trentman *(Mgr-Customer Svc)*

PM SERVICES COMPANY
2220 Central Ave, Saint Petersburg, FL 33712
Tel.: (727) 323-1060
Web Site: http://www.pmservicescompany.net
Year Founded: 1986
Sales Range: $25-49.9 Million
Emp.: 220
Facility Support Services
N.A.I.C.S.: 561210
Carole Metour *(Pres & CEO)*
James Butland *(Assoc VP-Facility Svcs)*
Michael Korosi *(Dir-IT)*

PM TECHNOLOGIES
5775 Glenridge Dr Bldg B Ste 500, Sandy Springs, GA 30328
Tel.: (678) 323-1600
Web Site: http://www.pmtechno.com
Sales Range: $1-9.9 Million
Emp.: 65
Business Management Consulting Services
N.A.I.C.S.: 541618
Tom Meyers *(Founder & CEO)*
George Ferguson *(VP)*
David Barron *(VP)*
Tracy Wilson *(Dir-Tech Svc & Support)*
Angelo Panousis *(Sr Dir-Pro Svcs)*
Fibia Costea *(Dir-Bus Dev & Recruiting)*

PMA FINANCIAL NETWORK, LLC
2135 CityGate Ln 7F, Naperville, IL 60563
Tel.: (630) 657-6400
Web Site: http://www.pmanetwork.com
Year Founded: 1984
Public Funds Products And Solutions Provider
N.A.I.C.S.: 525990
James Davis *(CEO)*
D. James Lutter *(Sr VP-Trading & Ops)*
John Huber *(Sr VP & Chief Investment Officer)*
Greg Kubitz *(Sr VP)*

Subsidiaries:

Miles Capital, Inc. (1)
1415 28th St Ste 200, West Des Moines, IA 50266
Tel.: (515) 453-8400
Web Site: http://www.miles-capital.com
Rev.: $4,000,000,000
Emp.: 27
Investment Management Service
N.A.I.C.S.: 523940
Amy Mitchell *(Dir-Pub Fund Svcs & Admin)*
Gregory Boal *(CEO)*
Steve S. Stotts *(Dir-Alternative Markets Solutions)*
Doug Earney *(Dir-Fixed Income)*
Courtney Clarke *(Dir-Mktg & Comm)*
David W. Miles *(Chm)*
Ann Blume *(Dir-Asset Mgmt-Portland)*

PMALLIANCE, INC.
2075 Spencers Way Ste 201, Stone Mountain, GA 30087
Tel.: (770) 938-4947
Web Site: http://www.pm-alliance.com
Year Founded: 2003
Rev.: $11,500,000
Emp.: 35
Management Consulting Services
N.A.I.C.S.: 541611
Thomas P. Stevens *(Founder, Pres & Partner)*

PMC CAPITAL PARTNERS, LLC
12243 Branford St, Sun Valley, CA 91352
Tel.: (818) 896-1101   DE
Web Site: http://www.pmcglobalinc.com
Year Founded: 1971
Sales Range: $25-49.9 Million
Emp.: 3,600
Investment Holding Company
N.A.I.C.S.: 551112
Philip E. Kamins *(CEO)*
David Keller *(Controller)*
Mark Hubis *(Mgr-Bus Dev)*
Tirsha Ryder *(Office Mgr)*
Michel Tamer *(Mng Partner)*

Subsidiaries:

PMC, Inc. (1)
12243 Branford St, Sun Valley, CA 91352-1010 (100%)
Tel.: (818) 896-1101
Web Site: http://www.pmcglobalinc.com
Sales Range: $50-74.9 Million
Emp.: 250
Holding Company
N.A.I.C.S.: 551112
Gary Kamins *(Pres)*

Subsidiary (Domestic):

All State Packaging, Inc. (2)
600 Williamson Ave, Opelika, AL 36804
Tel.: (334) 745-6239
Web Site: http://www.allstatepackaging.net
Emp.: 50
Folding Cartons Mfr
N.A.I.C.S.: 322299
David Adams *(Plant Mgr)*
Christie Weed *(Office Mgr)*

Custom Cutlery, Inc. (2)
12243 Branford St, Sun Valley, CA 91352
Tel.: (818) 686-2546
Web Site: http://www.customcutleryinc.com
Sales Range: $25-49.9 Million
Emp.: 15
Disposable Dinnerware & Cutlery Mfr
N.A.I.C.S.: 326140
Trevor Thompson *(Pres)*

Direct Pack, Inc. (2)
1025 W 8th St, Azusa, CA 91702
Tel.: (626) 380-2360
Web Site: http://www.directpackinc.com
Thermoformed Packaging Product Mfr
N.A.I.C.S.: 326140
Craig Snedden *(Pres)*
Gandhi Sifuentes *(VP-Design & Engrg)*
Laura Murphy *(VP-Sls & Mktg)*
Mike Drozek *(VP-Mfg)*

Gedney Foods Company (2)
2100 Stoughton Ave, Chaska, MN 55318
Tel.: (952) 448-2612
Web Site: http://www.gedneypickle.com
Pickle Mfr & Distr
N.A.I.C.S.: 311421

General Plastics Group, Inc. (2)
55 La France Ave, Bloomfield, NJ 07003
Tel.: (973) 748-5500
Web Site: http://www.generalplasticscorp.com
Teflon Coating Services
N.A.I.C.S.: 238150

North Penn Technology, Inc. (2)
2294 N Penn Rd, Hatfield, PA 19440
Tel.: (215) 997-3200
Web Site: http://www.northpenntech.com
Sales Range: $10-24.9 Million
Emp.: 25
Lead Attaching to Service Mounts
N.A.I.C.S.: 334413

PMC Financial Service Group LLC (2)
3816 E La Palma Ave, Anaheim, CA 92807-1713
Tel.: (714) 967-7226
Web Site: http://www.pmcfsg.com
Investment Advice
N.A.I.C.S.: 523940
Walter E. Buttkus III *(Pres)*

Subsidiary (Domestic):

High Road Craft Ice Cream, Inc. (3)
2241 Perimeter Park Dr Ste 7, Atlanta, GA 30341-1309
Tel.: (678) 701-7623
Web Site: http://www.highroadcraft.com
Ice Cream & Frozen Dessert Mfr
N.A.I.C.S.: 311520
Randy Weaver *(CEO)*

Subsidiary (Non-US):

PMC Science-Tech Industries (Nanjing) Co LTD (2)
No 299 Kaiyuan Road, Nanjing, 211100, China
Tel.: (86) 25 57928777
Web Site: http://www.pmc-china.com
Sales Range: $10-24.9 Million
Emp.: 100
Electrical Component Mfr
N.A.I.C.S.: 335999
Robert Chen *(Pres)*

Subsidiary (Domestic):

PMC Specialties Group, Inc. (2)
501 Murray Rd, Cincinnati, OH 45217
Tel.: (513) 482-7373
Web Site: http://www.pmcsg.com
Sales Range: $10-24.9 Million
Emp.: 175
Industrial Inorganic Chemicals
N.A.I.C.S.: 325180

Subsidiary (Non-US):

PMC Specialties Group, Co., Inc. (3)
Ste 512 LG Twintel II 157-3 Samsung-Dong, Kangnam-gu, Seoul, 135-090, Korea (South)
Tel.: (82) 70 8740 6815
Chemical Intermediates Mfr
N.A.I.C.S.: 325998

Subsidiary (Domestic):

PMC Specialty Leaders In Chemicals, Inc. (2)
12243 Branford St, Sun Valley, CA 91352
Tel.: (818) 896-1101
Subsidiary Management Services
N.A.I.C.S.: 551114

Subsidiary (Non-US):

Moehs Iberica, S.L. (3)
Pol Ind Cova Solera C/ Roma 8-12, 08191, Rubi, Spain
Tel.: (34) 93 586 05 20
Web Site: http://www.moehs.com
Sales Range: $25-49.9 Million
Emp.: 115
Chemical Products Mfr
N.A.I.C.S.: 325998
Francisco Escribano *(Gen Mgr)*

Subsidiary (Non-US):

Benechim S.P.R.L. (4)
rue Rene Magritte 163, 7860, Lessines, Belgium
Tel.: (32) 68 33 49 13
Web Site: http://www.benechim.com
Sales Range: $10-24.9 Million
Emp.: 42
Organic Intermediate Mfr
N.A.I.C.S.: 325199
Jougleux Romain *(Gen Mgr)*

Chemische Fabrik Berg GmbH (4)
Mainthalstrasse 3, 6749, Bitterfeld-Wolfen, Germany
Tel.: (49) 3493 78180
Web Site: http://www.cfb.de
Sales Range: $10-24.9 Million
Emp.: 16
Pharmaceutical Ingredient Mfr
N.A.I.C.S.: 325412
M. Grosse *(CEO & Mng Dir)*

Norchim S.A.S. (4)
33 Quai d'Amont, 60340, Saint Leu d'Esserent, France
Tel.: (33) 3 44 56 09 20
Web Site: http://www.norchim.com
Active Pharmaceutical Ingredients Mfr
N.A.I.C.S.: 325412
Khalid Diker *(Officer-Safety)*

Subsidiary (Domestic):

Proteos Biotech, S.L. (4)
62 Gran Via Street 4th left, 28013, Madrid, Spain
Tel.: (34) 967 192 741
Web Site: http://www.proteosbiotech.com
Reagent Mfr
N.A.I.C.S.: 325998

Subsidiary (Non-US):

Raschig GmbH (3)
Mundenheimer Str 100, PO Box 211128, Ludwigshafen, 67061, Germany
Tel.: (49) 62156180
Web Site: http://www.raschig.de
Sales Range: $125-149.9 Million
Emp.: 600
Asphalt Emulsion & Bromine Compounds & Plastics Materials Mfr
N.A.I.C.S.: 325211
Heinz Neis *(Chm)*
Thomas Kraemer *(Mng Dir-Plastics)*

Plant (Domestic):

Raschig GmbH - Espenhain (4)
Werk Espenhain Leipziger Strasse 40
Rotha, Espenhain, 04571, Germany
Tel.: (49) 6215618650
Web Site: http://www.raschig.de
Emp.: 50
Industrial Chemicals Mfr
N.A.I.C.S.: 325199

Subsidiary (Non-US):

Raschig UK Ltd. (4)
Trafford Road Salford Quays, Salfords, M5 2XB, Surrey, United Kingdom
Tel.: (44) 1618773933
Chemicals Mfr
N.A.I.C.S.: 325998

Synres-Almoco B.V. (4)
kulkweg 102, 3150 AA, Hoek van Holland, Netherlands
Tel.: (31) 174389999
Web Site: http://www.almoco.nl
Sales Range: $25-49.9 Million
Emp.: 24

PMC CAPITAL PARTNERS, LLC

PMC Capital Partners, LLC—(Continued)
Moulding Compound for the Electrical Industry Mfr
N.A.I.C.S.: 326199
Rols Zers (Mgr)

Subsidiary (Non-US):

Yarra Valley Chocolaterie & Ice Creamery (3)
35 Old Healesville Rd, Yarra Glen, 3775, VIC, Australia
Tel.: (61) 3 9730 2777
Web Site: http://www.yvci.com.au
Chocolate & Ice Cream Distr
N.A.I.C.S.: 445298

Subsidiary (Domestic):

PSC Industries, Inc. (2)
1100 W Market St, Louisville, KY 40201-0429
Tel.: (502) 625-7700
Nonmetallic Product Fabrication Services
N.A.I.C.S.: 332813

Subsidiary (Domestic):

ERCON ASSOCIATES (3)
667 S 31st St, Louisville, KY 40211
Tel.: (502) 772-3652
Web Site: http://www.ercon.com
Tip Forming & Hole Punching Equipment Mfr
N.A.I.C.S.: 333248

Falls City Machine Technology (3)
667 S 31st St, Louisville, KY 40211
Tel.: (502) 772-3621
Web Site: http://www.fallscitymachinetechnology.com
Industrial Engineering Services
N.A.I.C.S.: 541330
Doug McWhorter (Plant Mgr)
Bill Niekamp (Mgr-Sls)
Garry Thomas (Chief Engr)

PSC Fabricating, Inc (3)
3001 W Kentucky St, Louisville, KY 40211
Tel.: (502) 772-4238
Web Site: http://www.pscfabricating.com
Fiberglass & Foam Product Fabrication Services
N.A.I.C.S.: 238150
Christopher Hart (CFO)
Daven Osborne (Pres)

Division (Domestic):

PSC Industries, Inc. - Glasrite Division (3)
1612 W Broadway, Louisville, KY 40203
Tel.: (502) 589-5602
Web Site: http://www.glasrite.com
Emp.: 32
Fiberglass & Foam Product Fabrication Services
N.A.I.C.S.: 238150
John Kemme (Bus Mgr)

PSC Industries, Inc. - Graham Hydraulics Division (3)
667 S 31st St, Louisville, KY 40211
Tel.: (502) 772-3641
Web Site: http://www.grahamhydraulics.com
Hydraulic Equipment Mfr
N.A.I.C.S.: 333995

Subsidiary (Domestic):

Plastic Color Corporation, Inc. (2)
14201 Paxton Ave, Calumet City, IL 60409
Tel.: (708) 868-3800
Masterbatch Mfr
N.A.I.C.S.: 325130

Polyurethane Machinery Corporation (2)
1 Komo Dr, Lakewood, NJ 08701
Tel.: (732) 415-4400
Web Site: http://www.polymac-usa.com
Polyurethane Sprayer Mfr
N.A.I.C.S.: 333248
Bill Hrynkiewicz (VP)
Mike Kolibas (Pres)
Murphy Mahaffey (Dir-Intl Sls)
Craig Griffin (Mgr-Accts-Natl)
Tom Rivera (Mgr-Technical Svc)

VCF Films, Inc. (2)

1100 Sutton Ave, Howell, MI 48843-1716
Tel.: (517) 546-2300
Web Site: http://www.vcffilms.com
Sales Range: $25-49.9 Million
Emp.: 26
Plastic Flexible Packaging Materials Mfr
N.A.I.C.S.: 326113
Jean-Christophe Brouet (Engr-Tech Sls)

Zenith Global, Inc. (2)
1100 Sutton Ave, Howell, MI 48843
Tel.: (517) 546-7402
Web Site: http://www.zenithglobal.net
Plastic Container Mfr
N.A.I.C.S.: 326199
Matt James (Pres-Brand)

Ransom & Randolph Company (1)
3535 Briarfield Blvd, Maumee, OH 43537
Tel.: (419) 865-9497
Web Site: http://www.ransom-randolph.com
Investment Casting Supplier
N.A.I.C.S.: 327910
Mike Hendricks (VP-Tech)
Daniel Nixon (Pres)
Scott Todd (Sls Mgr-Global)
Ralph Carter (Mgr-Product Dev)
Eric Hodges (Mgr-Quality Assurance)
Marti Hunyor (Mktg Mgr)
Alisa Rawski (Coord-Digital Mktg & Events)

UniversalPegasus International, Inc. (1)
4848 Loop Central Dr Ste 137, Houston, TX 77081
Tel.: (713) 425-6000
Web Site: http://www.universalpegasus.com
Sales Range: $300-349.9 Million
Emp.: 430
Oil & Gas Operations Engineering, Inspection, Survey & Project Management Services
N.A.I.C.S.: 541330
Tom Davison (Pres)
Fermeen Fazal (VP)
Elaine Shine (VP-Fin)
Jack Yarbrough (VP-Engrg & Construction)
Roy Meredith (VP-Bus Dev)
David Parker (Sr VP-Canadian Ops)

Subsidiary (Domestic):

Universal Ensco, Inc. (2)
4848 Loop Central Dr Loop Central 2, Houston, TX 77081
Tel.: (713) 977-7770
Ship Building & Repair Services
N.A.I.C.S.: 336611

PMC GROUP, INC.

PMC Group Bldg 1288 Rte 73 S Ste 401, Mount Laurel, NJ 08054-3237
Tel.: (856) 533-1866   DE
Web Site: http://www.pmc-group.com
Year Founded: 1994
Sales Range: $125-149.9 Million
Holding Company; Specialty Chemicals & Plastic Products Mfr & Distr
N.A.I.C.S.: 551112
Paritosh M. Chakrabarti (Founder & CEO)
Debtosh Chakrabarti (Pres & COO)

Subsidiaries:

Crystal, Inc. - PMC (1)
601 W 8th St, Lansdale, PA 19446-1809   (100%)
Tel.: (215) 368-1661
Web Site: http://www.crystalinc-pmc.com
Sales Range: $10-24.9 Million
Emp.: 60
Mfr of Polymers, Waxes & Soaps
N.A.I.C.S.: 325998
Paritosh Chakrabarti (Pres)

Lenco, Inc. - PMC (1)
10240 Deer Park Rd, Waverly, NE 68462-1416   (100%)
Tel.: (402) 786-2000
Web Site: http://www.lencopmc.com
Sales Range: $25-49.9 Million
Emp.: 300
Injection Molded Plastic Product Assembly & Mfr
N.A.I.C.S.: 326199
Gary Knaub (Mgr-Customer Svc)
Nat Svela (Bus Mgr)

Ouvrie PMC, SAS (1)
64 Rue Faidherbe, PO Box 127, 59811, Lesquin, France   (100%)
Tel.: (33) 320870510
Web Site: http://www.ouvrie.com
Sales Range: $25-49.9 Million
Emp.: 45
Mfr of Polymers
N.A.I.C.S.: 325211
Christian Reuland (Gen Mgr)

PMC Biogenix Korea Ltd. (1)
101-908 Island Park 38 Uisadang-Daero Yeondeunpo-Gu, 150-874, Seoul, Korea (South)
Tel.: (82) 2 2090 7360
Web Site: http://pmcbiogenix.com
Emp.: 137
Specialty Chemicals Mfr
N.A.I.C.S.: 325998
Konghyun Hwang (Gen Mgr)

PMC Biogenix, Inc. (1)
1231 Pope St, Memphis, TN 38108
Tel.: (901) 325-4930
Web Site: http://www.pmc-group.com
Sales Range: $25-49.9 Million
Emp.: 200
Chemical Products Mfr
N.A.I.C.S.: 325199
Kyle Walker (Plant Mgr)
Mike Chapman (Sr Engr-Process)
James Thaxter Hodum (Controller-Plant)

PMC Group - Cincinnati (1)
2000 W St, Cincinnati, OH 45215-3431
Tel.: (513) 733-2100
Sales Range: $25-49.9 Million
Emp.: 75
Methyl Tin Stabilizers & Lubricants Mfr
N.A.I.C.S.: 325998
Mike Rouse (Plant Mgr)

PMC Organometallix, Inc. (1)
The PMC Group Bldg 1288 Route 73 Ste 401, Mount Laurel, NJ 08054
Tel.: (855) 638-2549
Web Site: http://www.pmcorganometallix.com
Emp.: 40
Heat Stabilizer & Catalyst Mfr
N.A.I.C.S.: 325998

PMC Rubber Chemicals India Private Limited (1)
103 G T Road West, Hooghly, Rishra, 712248, West Bengal, India
Tel.: (91) 33 26724734
Web Site: http://www.pmc-rc.com
Rubber Chemical Mfr
N.A.I.C.S.: 325998

Polymer Products Company, Inc. (1)
100 Sta Ave, Stockertown, PA 18083
Tel.: (610) 759-3690
Web Site: http://www.polymerproductscompany.com
Sales Range: $10-24.9 Million
Emp.: 30
Mfr of Polymers
N.A.I.C.S.: 325180
Don Demko (Mgr-Product Dev)

PMC HOMES CORPORATION

14716 S Grant St, Bixby, OK 74008
Tel.: (918) 366-4144
Web Site: http://pmchomes.com
Year Founded: 1983
Sales Range: $25-49.9 Million
Emp.: 22
Housing Construction Services
N.A.I.C.S.: 236117
Steve Harris (Owner & Pres)

PMC SMART SOLUTIONS, LLC

9825 Kenwood Rd Ste 302, Blue Ash, OH 45242
Tel.: (513) 921-5040   OH
Web Site: http://www.pmcsmartsolutions.com
Year Founded: 1929
Custom Plastic Molding Services
N.A.I.C.S.: 326199
Lisa Jennings (Pres & CEO)

PMDSOFT INC.

1 Letterman Dr Bldg D, San Francisco, CA 94129
Tel.: (415) 814-9781
Web Site: http://www.pmd.com
Year Founded: 1999
Sales Range: $1-9.9 Million
Emp.: 9
Wireless Applications for Physicians' Office Automation
N.A.I.C.S.: 541519

PMG WORLDWIDE INC.

7454 Brokerage Dr, Orlando, FL 32809
Tel.: (407) 850-9400
Rev.: $14,310,544
Emp.: 20
Freight Forwarding
N.A.I.C.S.: 488510

PMG WORLDWIDE LLC

2821 W 7th St Ste 270, Fort Worth, TX 76107
Tel.: (817) 420-9970   TX
Web Site: http://www.pmg.co
Sales Range: $1-9.9 Million
Emp.: 44
Information Technology Consulting Services
N.A.I.C.S.: 541511
Geroge Popstefanov (Founder & CEO)

Subsidiaries:

Camelot Communications Ltd. (1)
8140 Walnut Hill Ln Ste 700, Dallas, TX 75231
Tel.: (214) 373-6999
Web Site: http://www.camelotsmm.com
Rev.: $421,700,000
Emp.: 70
Media & Advertising
N.A.I.C.S.: 541810

PMHCC INC

123 S Broad St 23rd Fl, Philadelphia, PA 19109
Tel.: (215) 546-0300   PA
Web Site: http://www.pmhcc.org
Year Founded: 1987
Sales Range: $50-74.9 Million
Emp.: 323
Behavioral Healthcare Services
N.A.I.C.S.: 623220
Bernard Borislow (Exec Dir)
Valerie Byrd (Chm)
Pearl B. Schaeffer (Treas)
Ayana Bradshaw (Sec)
James P. Baker Jr. (Vice Chm)

PMI LUBRICANTS, INC.

3643 Aerial Way Dr, Roanoke, VA 24018
Tel.: (540) 982-0600
Web Site: http://www.pmilubricants.com
Lubricant Distr
N.A.I.C.S.: 424720
Sherrill Vaught (Mgr-Inside Sls)

PMOLINK LLC

2001 Lakeshore Dr, Mandeville, LA 70448
Tel.: (985) 674-5968
Web Site: http://www.pmolink.com
Sales Range: $1-9.9 Million
Emp.: 41
Management Consulting Services
N.A.I.C.S.: 541618
Geoffrey C. Hingle (Pres & CEO)
Charles Rosen (VP-Fin & Consulting Svcs)
Lee Pearson (VP-Ops)
Demetris Demetriou (VP-IT)

PMSQUARE LLC

2100 Clearwater Dr Ste 330, Oak Brook, IL 60523
Tel.: (708) 575-4000
Web Site: http://www.pmsquare.com
Year Founded: 2014
Sales Range: $10-24.9 Million
Emp.: 50
Computer Programming Services
N.A.I.C.S.: 541519
Ryan Dolley (Dir-Tech)

PMT GROUP INC
800 Union Ave, Bridgeport, CT 06607
Tel.: (203) 366-3224 CT
Web Site: http://www.pmt-group.com
Year Founded: 1928
Jig Grinders, Tooling Components, Measuring Systems & Other Precision Tools Mfr
N.A.I.C.S.: 333517
Newman Marsilius (Pres)

Subsidiaries:

Moore Nanotechnology Systems LLC (1)
230 Old Homestead Hwy, Swanzey, NH 03446
Tel.: (603) 352-3030
Web Site: http://www.nanotechsys.com
Sales Range: $10-24.9 Million
Emp.: 40
Ultra Precision Machine Tools Mfr
N.A.I.C.S.: 332216
Ralph Murray (Mgr-Supply Chain)
Mitch Schadler (Mgr-Svc)

Moore Tool Company, Inc. (1)
800 Union Ave, Bridgeport, CT 06607-0088
Tel.: (203) 366-3224
Web Site: http://www.mooretool.com
Sales Range: $50-74.9 Million
Emp.: 184
Jig Boring, Jig Grinding & Measuring Machines, Diamond Turning Machines & Accessories, Flexible Machining Systems
N.A.I.C.S.: 333517

Holding (Non-US):

Moore Special Tool AG (2)
In der Leberzen 25, 8902, Urdorf, Switzerland
Tel.: (41) 788819516
Web Site: http://www.mooretool.com
Sales Range: $50-74.9 Million
Emp.: 6
Precision Machine Tools & Metrology Equipment
N.A.I.C.S.: 423830

The Producto Machine Co. (1)
800 Union Ave, Bridgeport, CT 06607-1137
Tel.: (203) 367-8675
Web Site: http://www.producto.com
Sales Range: $25-49.9 Million
Mfr of Tooling Components
N.A.I.C.S.: 333517

Holding (Non-US):

Producto Diemakers Supplies Ltd. (2)
22 Worcester Rd, Etobicoke, M9W 5X2, ON, Canada
Tel.: (905) 856-9990
Web Site: https://www.dieco.ca
Sales Range: $50-74.9 Million
Emp.: 4
Other Chemical & Allied Products Merchant Wholesalers
N.A.I.C.S.: 424690
Nalin Jayasinghe (Reg Mgr-Sls)

Subsidiary (Domestic):

Producto/Dieco (2)
5835 Harper Rd, Solon, OH 44139
Tel.: (440) 542-0000
Web Site: http://www.dieco.us
Sales Range: $25-49.9 Million
Emp.: 5
Mfr of Tooling Components
N.A.I.C.S.: 423840
Sandi Rysell (Gen Mgr)

Division (Domestic):

Ring Precison Components (2)
2980 Turner Rd, Jamestown, NY 14701
Tel.: (716) 484-7131
Web Site: http://www.ringprecision.com
Sales Range: $25-49.9 Million
Emp.: 115
Tooling Components for Metal Forming, Rubber & Plastics Molding, Injection & Mold Components Tooling & Metal Stamping Mfr
N.A.I.C.S.: 333514

PMX COMMUNITIES, INC.
2700 North Military Trail Ste 130, Boca Raton, FL 33431
Tel.: (561) 210-5349 NV
Web Site: http://www.pmxgold.com
Year Founded: 2004
PMXO—(OTCBB)
Gold Exploration, Production & Marketing Services
N.A.I.C.S.: 212220
Sumeet Malik (Dir-Bus Dev)
Lindsey R. Perry Jr. (CEO, CFO, Controller & Dir-Ops)

PN HOFFMAN INC.
680 Water St, Washington, DC 20016
Tel.: (202) 686-0010
Web Site: http://www.pnhoffman.com
Rev.: $16,779,197
Emp.: 50
Single-Family Housing Construction
N.A.I.C.S.: 236115
Lamont H. Hoffman (CEO)
John Bradley (Sr VP-Ops)
Bao Vuong (VP-Dev)
Paul Nassetta (COO)
Frank Underwood (Sr VP-Ops)
Mark Dorigan (Pres & Gen Counsel)
Shawn Seaman (Principal & Exec VP)

PNEC CORPORATION
2406 Port of Tacoma Rd, Tacoma, WA 98421-3605
Tel.: (253) 475-7600
Web Site: http://www.heatingoil.com
Sales Range: $25-49.9 Million
Emp.: 40
Provider of Heating Oil
N.A.I.C.S.: 238220

PNEO LLC
204 Cardinal Dr, Denton, TX 76209
Year Founded: 2008
Sales Range: $1-9.9 Million
Emp.: 15
Business Consulting Services
N.A.I.C.S.: 541611
Peter Wenham (Exec Dir)
Chris Carignan (CEO)

PNEU-MECH SYSTEMS MFG. LLC
201 Pneu Mech Rd, Statesville, NC 28625
Tel.: (704) 873-2475
Web Site: http://www.pneu-mech.com
Sales Range: $10-24.9 Million
Emp.: 91
Paint Finishing Systems & Equipment for Metal, Plastics, Wood & Composite Affairs
N.A.I.C.S.: 333248
Jerry Trostle (Mgr-Sls-North America)

PNY TECHNOLOGIES, INC.
100 Jefferson Rd, Parsippany, NJ 07054-0218
Tel.: (973) 515-9700 DE
Web Site: http://www.pny.com
Sales Range: $300-349.9 Million
Emp.: 300
Computer Memory Upgrades Mfr & Distributor
N.A.I.C.S.: 334413

POAG SHOPPING CENTERS, LLC
2650 Thousand Oaks Blvd Ste 2200, Memphis, TN 38118
Tel.: (901) 761-7604 DE
Web Site: http://www.poagllc.com
Year Founded: 2012
Shopping Centers Development, Property Management & Leasing Services
N.A.I.C.S.: 531120
Dean Shauger (Sr VP-Mgmt & Mktg)
Joshua D. Poag (Pres & CEO)
G. Dan Poag (Chm)
Bob Rogers (Chief Admin Officer & Gen Counsel)
David Selberg (CFO)
Scott Kern (COO & Sr VP-Dev)
Alesia Kempe (Sr VP-Asset Mgmt)
Brian Smith (Chief Strategy Officer & Exec VP)
Tim Thompson (VP & Controller)

POBLOCKI SIGN COMPANY, LLC
922 S 70th St, West Allis, WI 53214
Tel.: (414) 453-4010
Web Site: http://www.poblocki.com
Sales Range: $50-74.9 Million
Emp.: 200
Sign Design & Installation Services
N.A.I.C.S.: 339950
Bryan Johnson (Pres)

POCH PERSONNEL, INC.
5555 Gull Rd, Kalamazoo, MI 49048
Tel.: (269) 345-0150 MI
Web Site: http://www.trilliumstaffing.com
Sales Range: $25-49.9 Million
Emp.: 150
Temporary Help Service
N.A.I.C.S.: 561320
Oskar Rene Poch (Founder & CEO)

Subsidiaries:

Atlantic Associates, Inc. (1)
1208 VFW Parkway Suite 203, West Roxbury, MA 02132 (100%)
Tel.: (617) 327-1328
Web Site: http://www.atlanticai.com
Strategic IT & Engineering Staffing & Workforce Solutions
N.A.I.C.S.: 611420
Patrick McNamara (Reg Mgr)
John F. Harrington (Principal)
John F. Fitzgerald (Principal)

POCKET GAMES, INC.
1732 1st Ave 25955, New York, NY 10128
Tel.: (347) 464-7532 FL
Web Site: http://www.pocketgamesinc.com
Year Founded: 2013
PKGM—(OTCBB)
Mobile Sports Games
N.A.I.C.S.: 513210
David Lovatt (CEO)

Subsidiaries:

Viximo, Inc. (1)
1 Camp St, Cambridge, MA 02140
Tel.: (617) 583-5671
Web Site: http://www.viximo.com
Computer Related Services
N.A.I.C.S.: 541519
Shamoon Siddiqui (CTO)
Sutton Trout (VP-Bus Dev)
Ravi Mehta (VP-Product)

POCKET GEMS, INC.
220 Montgomery St Ste 750, San Francisco, CA 94104
Tel.: (415) 371-1333
Web Site: http://www.pocketgems.com
Year Founded: 2009

Mobile Video Game Developer
N.A.I.C.S.: 513210
Daniel Terry (Co-Founder, Exec Chm & Chief Compliance Officer)
Harlan Crystal (Co-Founder & CTO)

POCKET HERCULES
510 1st Ave N Ste 210, Minneapolis, MN 55403
Tel.: (612) 709-1376
Web Site: http://www.pockethercules.com
Sales Range: $10-24.9 Million
Emp.: 7
Brand Development & Integration
N.A.I.C.S.: 541810
Tom Camp (Partner & Dir-Creative)
Jason Smith (Partner & Dir-Creative)
Jack Supple (Chief Creative Officer)

POCKET OUTDOOR MEDIA, INC.
4745 Walnut St Unit A, Boulder, CO 80301
Tel.: (303) 440-0601 CO
Web Site: http://www.pocketoutdoormedia.com
Publishing Services
N.A.I.C.S.: 513199
Robin Thurston (CEO)

Subsidiaries:

Big Stone Publishing, Inc. (1)
417 Main St Unit N, Carbondale, CO 81623
Tel.: (970) 704-1442
Web Site: http://www.rockandice.com
Sales Range: $1-9.9 Million
Emp.: 17
Periodical Publishers
N.A.I.C.S.: 513120
Duane Raleigh (Pres)
Randall Levensaler (Dir-Art)

POCONO MANOR GOLF RESORT & SPA
1 Manor Dr, Pocono Manor, PA 18349
Tel.: (570) 839-7111
Web Site: http://www.poconomanor.com
Year Founded: 1902
Sales Range: $1-9.9 Million
Emp.: 150
Resort Hotel Facility; Other Related Convention Facilities
N.A.I.C.S.: 721110

POCONO PRODUCE CO. INC.
Chipperfield Dr RR 191, Stroudsburg, PA 18360
Tel.: (570) 421-4990 PA
Web Site: http://www.poconoproduce.com
Year Founded: 1944
Sales Range: $75-99.9 Million
Emp.: 191
Packaged Frozen Goods
N.A.I.C.S.: 423740
Diane Mack (Asst Controller)
Rosemary Driebe Olofsson (Exec VP)
Neil Cooper (CFO)

POCONO RV SALES & SERVICE INC.
489 Bushkill Plz Ln, Wind Gap, PA 18091
Tel.: (610) 863-5239
Web Site: http://www.poconorv.com
Year Founded: 1998
Sales Range: $400-449.9 Million
Emp.: 15
Recreational Vehicle Whslr
N.A.I.C.S.: 441210
Charles Roberts (Owner)

POD PACK INTERNATIONAL, LTD.

Pocono RV Sales & Service Inc.—(Continued)

POD PACK INTERNATIONAL, LTD.
26 Tower Hill Ln, Kinnelon, NJ 07405
Tel.: (973) 492-3244
Web Site: http://www.podpack.com
Year Founded: 1996
Sales Range: $1-9.9 Million
Emp.: 22
Coffee Mfr
N.A.I.C.S.: 311920
William Powell (Pres & CEO)

POE ASPHALT PAVING INC.
302 15th St, Clarkston, WA 99403-2300
Tel.: (509) 758-5561
Web Site: http://www.poeasphalt.com
Year Founded: 1967
Sales Range: $50-74.9 Million
Emp.: 80
Road & Highway & Driveway Construction Services
N.A.I.C.S.: 237310
Mark Poe (Pres)

POET, LLC
4615 North Lewis Ave, Sioux Falls, SD 57104
Tel.: (605) 965-2200
Web Site: http://www.poet.com
Biofuel Company
N.A.I.C.S.: 221112
Jeff Broin (Founder & CEO)
Subsidiaries:
Poet Research, Inc.   (1)
4615 N Lewis Ave, Sioux Falls, SD 57104
Tel.: (605) 965-2200
Web Site: http://www.poet.com
Commercial Scale Ethanol Plant
N.A.I.C.S.: 541715

POGOTEC, INC.
4502 Starkey Rd Ste 109, Roanoke, VA 24018
Web Site: http://www.pogotec.com
Year Founded: 2014
Emp.: 20
Smartphone Application Development Services
N.A.I.C.S.: 541511
Brendan Sheil (Pres & CEO)
Ronald Blum (Founder & Chief Visionary Officer)
Diane Munn (CFO)
Timothy Haley (COO)
Joshua Schoenbart (Chief Comml Officer)
William Kokonaski (CTO)
Svetlana Samoilova (VP-Augmented Reality)

POGUE LABEL & SCREEN, INC.
205 E Davis St, Saint Louis, MO 63111
Tel.: (314) 571-7577
Web Site: http://www.poguelabel.com
Year Founded: 1946
Sales Range: $1-9.9 Million
Emp.: 31
Decoration Services
N.A.I.C.S.: 459420
Michael Meuser (Pres)

POHANKA AUTO NORTH INC.
1772 Ritchie Station Ct, Capitol Heights, MD 20743
Tel.: (301) 423-1100
Web Site:
http://www.pohankahyundai.com
Rev.: $60,000,000
Emp.: 50
Automobiles, New & Used
N.A.I.C.S.: 441110

Geoffrey Pohanka (Pres)
Subsidiaries:
Pohanka Auto Imports Inc.   (1)
1770 Ritchie Station Ct, Capitol Heights, MD 20743
Tel.: (301) 423-1100
Web Site: http://www.pohanka.com
Sales Range: $25-49.9 Million
New & Used Car Dealers
N.A.I.C.S.: 441110
Richard Harris (CFO)

Pohanka Properties Inc.   (1)
4601 Saint Barnabas Rd, Temple Hills, MD 20748
Tel.: (301) 423-1100
Web Site: http://www.pohanka.com
New & Used Car Dealers
N.A.I.C.S.: 441110
Jeffrey Pohanka (Chm)

Pohanka of Salisbury   (1)
2013 N Salisbury Blvd 2, Salisbury, MD 21801
Tel.: (410) 749-2301
Web Site:
http://www.pohankaofsalisbury.com
Sales Range: $25-49.9 Million
New & Used Car Dealers
N.A.I.C.S.: 441110
Chris Hagel (Mgr-Mktg)
Linda Donahoe (Controller)
Dale WinazaK (Mgr-Shop)
Shane Williams (Mgr-Sls)

POHANKA HONDA
1772 Ritchie Sta Ct, Capitol Heights, MD 20743
Tel.: (301) 899-7800
Web Site:
http://www.pohankahonda.com
Sales Range: $10-24.9 Million
Emp.: 50
Car Whslr
N.A.I.C.S.: 441110
Richard L. Harri (Principal)

POHANKA TOYOTA SERVICE DEPARTMENT
2010 N Salisbury Blvd Ste A, Salisbury, MD 21801-3337
Tel.: (410) 543-2000
Year Founded: 2006
Sales Range: $10-24.9 Million
Emp.: 50
Car Whslr
N.A.I.C.S.: 441110
Wayne Bowen (Dir-Svc)
Jeremy Gilmore (Principal)

POHLAD COMPANIES
60 S 6th St Ste 3900, Minneapolis, MN 55402-4437
Tel.: (612) 661-3880
Web Site:
http://www.pohladcompanies.com
Year Founded: 1969
Investment Holding Company
N.A.I.C.S.: 551112
Dennis J. Goetz (CFO)
Robert C. Pohlad (Pres)
Albert J. Colianni (CEO)
Matt Carter (Chief Admin Officer)
Chase Hawkins (Sr VP-Teatail Ops)
Pamela Lampert (Chief HR Officer)
Denise Mallery (Chief Mktg & Comms Officer)
Erryn Williams (Chief Talent & Diversity Officer)
Subsidiaries:
Carousel Motor Group   (1)
15802 Wayzata Blvd 3900, Minnetonka, MN 55391
Tel.: (952) 303-7500
Web Site:
http://www.carouselmotorgroup.com
Car Dealership
N.A.I.C.S.: 441110

Jack Shimota (VP)
Timothy Kraemer (Sr VP)
Facets Fine Jewelry, LLC   (1)
901 Nicollet Mall, Minneapolis, MN 55402
Tel.: (612) 338-5950
Web Site: http://www.jbhudson.com
Sales Range: $1-9.9 Million
Emp.: 32
Jewelry Stores
N.A.I.C.S.: 458310
Jeannie Joas (Pres)

J. B. Hudson Jewelers Co   (1)
901 Nicollet Mall, Minneapolis, MN 55402
Tel.: (612) 338-5950
Web Site: http://www.jbhudson.com
Jewelry Retailer
N.A.I.C.S.: 458310

Marquette Capital Partners, LLC   (1)
60 S 6th St Ste 3510, Minneapolis, MN 55402
Tel.: (612) 661-3990
Web Site:
http://www.marquettecapitalpartners.com
Rev.: $255,000,000
Privater Equity Firm
N.A.I.C.S.: 523999
Thomas H. Jenkins (Pres & CEO)
Greg Dames (Sr Mng Dir)
Maggie Yanez (Sr VP & Portfolio Mgr)
David Shapiro (Mng Dir)
Andrea Grosz (Mng Dir)
Looe Baker (VP)
Aaron Price (Asst VP)

NorthMarq Companies LLC   (1)
3500 American Blvd W Ste 200, Bloomington, MN 55431
Tel.: (952) 831-1000
Web Site:
http://www.northmarqcompanies.com
Holding Company; Real Estate Investment & Management Services
N.A.I.C.S.: 551112
Jessie Timmerman (Mgr-Comm)
Bert Roberds (VP-Atlanta)

Subsidiary (Domestic):
Kinghorn Driver Hough & Co.   (2)
14100 San Pedro Ave, San Antonio, TX 78232-4362
Tel.: (210) 828-2112
Web Site:
http://www.kinghorn.q10capital.com
Real Estate Credit
N.A.I.C.S.: 522292
Alan Warren (Mgr)

NorthMarq Capital, LLC   (2)
3500 W American Blvd Ste 500, Bloomington, MN 55431
Tel.: (952) 356-0100
Web Site: http://www.northmarq.com
Sales Range: $50-74.9 Million
Emp.: 125
Commercial Real Estate Financing, Mortgage, Property Management & Advisory Services
N.A.I.C.S.: 531390
Eduardo Padilla (CEO)
Paul Cairns (Sr VP & Mgr-Capital Markets)
Michael Myers (COO & Sr Exec VP)
Mark Jeffries (VP-Denver)
Timothy Greisman (VP)
Noah D. Juran (VP-Production)
Lisa Divalentino (Mng Dir-Servicing & Exec VP)
Greg Duvall (VP-Kansas)
Robert Delitsky (Sr VP-New York)
William Ross (Pres)
Bob Toland (VP-Chicago)
Alex Quenzler (VP)
Gary Cohen (Mng Dir-New Jersey)
Michael Chase (Mng Dir-Boston)
Ed Riekstins (Mng Dir)
Christina Grimme (VP)

Branch (Domestic):
NorthMarq Capital, LLC   (3)
1600 Market St Ste 1300, Philadelphia, PA 19103
Tel.: (215) 496-3000
Web Site: http://www.northmarq.com
Sales Range: $75-99.9 Million
Emp.: 40

U.S. PRIVATE

Commercial Real Estate Financing, Mortgage, Property Management & Advisory Services
N.A.I.C.S.: 531390
Eugene Veneziale (COO)
Randy Waddell (Sr VP)

NorthMarq Capital, LLC   (3)
1 Tampa City Ctr Ste 2570, Tampa, FL 33602
Tel.: (813) 223-3088
Web Site: http://www.northmarq.com
Sales Range: $1-9.9 Million
Emp.: 6
Real Estate Credit
N.A.I.C.S.: 522292
Robert P. Hernandez (Mng Dir & Sr VP)
Scott Davis (Sr VP & Sr Dir)
Paul Whalen (VP)

Subsidiary (Domestic):
Quest Commercial Capital Corp.   (3)
4625 Red Bank Rd Ste 101, Cincinnati, OH 45227
Tel.: (513) 985-4000
Web Site: http://www.questccc.com
Real Estate Credit
N.A.I.C.S.: 522292
Susan G. Branscome (Pres)

PaR Systems, LLC   (1)
707 County Rd E W, Shoreview, MN 55126-1912
Tel.: (651) 484-7261
Web Site: http://www.par.com
Automation Systems & Material Handling Equipment Mfr
N.A.I.C.S.: 333248
Tom Pohlad (CEO)

Subsidiary (Domestic):
CAMotion, Inc.   (2)
554 North Ave NW, Atlanta, GA 30318
Tel.: (404) 874-0090
Web Site: http://www.camotion.com
Case Packing, Palletizing & Depalletizing Machines Mfr
N.A.I.C.S.: 333922

Jered, LLC   (2)
3000 Sidney Lanier Dr, Brunswick, GA 31525-6813
Tel.: (912) 262-2000
Web Site: http://www.par.com
Automation Systems & Material Handling Equipment Mfr
N.A.I.C.S.: 333923

Pepsi-Cola Bottling Co. of Aberdeen, LLC   (1)
5305 Hwy 12 E, Aberdeen, SD 57401-9519
Tel.: (605) 225-0700
Sales Range: $10-24.9 Million
Emp.: 35
Soft Drink Mfr, Bottler & Distr
N.A.I.C.S.: 312111
Robert C. Pohlad (CEO)

Pepsi-Cola Bottling Company of Estervile Inc.   (1)
108 S 18th St, Estherville, IA 51334
Tel.: (712) 362-7282
Sales Range: $10-24.9 Million
Emp.: 35
Soft Drink Mfr & Bottler
N.A.I.C.S.: 424490

Pepsi-Cola Bottling Company of Fargo Inc.   (1)
3802 15th Ave N, Fargo, ND 58102
Tel.: (701) 282-5544
Web Site: http://www.pepsi.com
Sales Range: $25-49.9 Million
Emp.: 145
Soft Drink Mfr & Bottler
N.A.I.C.S.: 312111
Robert C. Pohlad (CEO)

Twins Sports, Inc.   (1)
1 Twins Way, Minneapolis, MN 55403
Tel.: (612) 375-1366
Web Site: http://www.twinsbaseball.com
Sales Range: $150-199.9 Million
Emp.: 1,000
Holding Company; Professional Baseball Club
N.A.I.C.S.: 551112
Robert C. Pohlad (Member-Exec Bd)

COMPANIES

Subsidiary (Domestic):

Minnesota Twins, LLC (2)
1 Twins Way, Minneapolis, MN 55403
Tel.: (612) 659-3400
Web Site: http://minnesota.twins.mlb.com
Sales Range: $75-99.9 Million
Emp.: 600
Professional Baseball Club
N.A.I.C.S.: 711211
James O. Pohlad *(Chm-Exec Bd)*
Dave St. Peter *(Pres, CEO & Member-Exec Bd)*
Matt Hoy *(Sr VP-Ops)*
Raenell Dorn *(VP-HR & Diversity)*
Kip Elliott *(CFO, Chief Admin Officer & Exec VP)*
Mike Radcliff *(VP-Player Personnel)*
Rob Antony *(VP & Asst Gen Mgr)*
Nancy O'Brien *(VP-Community Engagement)*
Paul Froehle *(VP-Ticket Ops)*
John Avenson *(VP-Tech)*
Mike Herman *(Dir-Team Travel)*
Laura Day *(Chief Bus Officer & Exec VP)*
Eric Hudson *(Sr Dir-Ticket Svc & Retention)*
Jerry McLaughlin *(Sr Mgr-Ticket Acctg)*
Mike Clough *(Sr VP-Ticket Sls & Svc)*
Derek Falvey *(Chief Baseball Officer & Exec VP)*
Sean Johnson *(Dir-Scouting)*
Joe Pohlad *(Exec VP-Brand Strategy & Growth)*
Bill Pohlad *(Member-Exec Bd)*
Thad Levine *(Sr VP & Gen Mgr)*
Mary Giesler *(Gen Counsel & Sr VP)*

Affiliate (Domestic):

Elizabethton Twins Baseball Club (3)
208 Holly Ln, Elizabethton, TN 37643
Tel.: (423) 547-6441
Web Site: http://www.elizabethtontwins.com
Sales Range: $25-49.9 Million
Emp.: 4
Professional Baseball Club
N.A.I.C.S.: 711211
Mike Mains *(Gen Mgr)*

Fort Myers Miracle Professional Baseball (3)
Lee County Stadium 14400 6 Mile Cypress Pkwy, Fort Myers, FL 33912
Tel.: (239) 768-4210
Web Site: http://www.miraclebaseball.com
Sales Range: $25-49.9 Million
Emp.: 13
Professional Baseball Club
N.A.I.C.S.: 711211
Terry Simon *(Sr Dir-Sls & Mktg)*
Suzanne Reaves *(Bus Mgr)*

New Britain Baseball Club, Inc. (3)
New Britain Stadium 230 John Kirbonic Way Willowbrook Park Complex, New Britain, CT 06051
Tel.: (860) 224-8383
Web Site: http://www.rockcats.com
Sales Range: $25-49.9 Million
Emp.: 15
Professional Baseball Club
N.A.I.C.S.: 711211
Andres Levy *(Mgr-Corp Sls & Hospitality)*
Jeff Dooley *(Dir-Brdcst Production)*

United Properties LLC (1)
3600 American Blvd W Ste 750, Bloomington, MN 55431
Tel.: (952) 835-5300
Web Site: http://www.uproperties.com
Sales Range: $1-9.9 Million
Real Estate Manangement Services
N.A.I.C.S.: 531390
Bill Katter *(Co-Pres/Co-Chief Investment Officer-Dev)*
Eva Stevens *(Pres & COO)*
Frank Dutke *(CEO)*
Rick McKelvey *(VP-Dev)*
Brenda Arnold *(Asst VP)*
Jamie Pollock *(Asst VP & Mgr-Asset)*
John Saunders *(Sr VP-Acq & Dispositions)*
Keith Ulstad *(Sr VP-Retail)*
Richard Student *(Sr VP-Fin & Asset Mgmt)*
Brandon Champeau *(VP)*
Eric Skalland *(CFO & Exec VP-Capital Markets)*
Gordy Stofer *(VP-Office Dev)*
Alicia Rhymer *(VP-Retail Dev)*
Mark Nelson *(Exec VP-Residential Dev)*
Kevin Kelley *(Exec VP-Comml Dev-Denver)*
Mike Dailey *(Sr VP-Dev)*
Bruce McGrath *(Chief Risk Officer)*
Peter Ulstad *(Controller)*
Matt Van Slooten *(Co-Pres/Co-Chief Investment Officer-Dev)*
Judy Jandro *(VP-Capital Markets)*

POHLMAN, LLC
2316 Schuetz Rd, Saint Louis, MO 63146
Tel.: (636) 537-1909
Web Site: http://www.pohlman.com
Year Founded: 1946
Screw Machine Product Mfr
N.A.I.C.S.: 332721
Mike Keithly *(Gen Mgr)*

POINDEXTER EXCAVATING, INC.
10443 E 56th St, Indianapolis, IN 46236
Tel.: (317) 823-6837
Web Site: http://www.poindexterexcav.com
Year Founded: 1974
Sales Range: $10-24.9 Million
Emp.: 250
Land Subdivision Services
N.A.I.C.S.: 237210
Billy Poindexter *(Founder)*
James Fohl *(CFO)*
Frances R. Wertenberger *(Sec)*
Tom Flannery *(Mgr-Shop)*
Jim Myers *(Dir-Safety)*

POINSETT FERTILIZER INC.
10415 Stuckey Ln, Trumann, AR 72472
Tel.: (870) 483-7625
Web Site: http://www.taylorstuckey.com
Rev.: $13,466,507
Emp.: 8
Fertilizer & Fertilizer Materials
N.A.I.C.S.: 424910
Tom Rose *(Pres)*

POINSETT RICE & GRAIN, INC.
6211 SW Dr, Jonesboro, AR 72404
Tel.: (870) 336-2268   AR
Web Site: http://www.poinsettrice.com
Year Founded: 1988
Sales Range: $25-49.9 Million
Emp.: 50
Grain Storage & Logistics Services
N.A.I.C.S.: 493130
Randy McNeil *(Pres)*
Ryan Carwell *(VP)*

Subsidiaries:

Poinsett Rice & Grain, Inc. - Cherry Valley (1)
227 Martin Dr, Cherry Valley, AR 72324
Tel.: (870) 588-3381
Web Site: http://www.poinsettrice.com
Sales Range: $25-49.9 Million
Emp.: 3
Grain Storage & Logistics Services
N.A.I.C.S.: 493130
Ryan Carwell *(VP)*

Poinsett Rice & Grain, Inc. - Marked Tree (1)
300 Adamson Rd, Marked Tree, AR 72365-1631
Tel.: (870) 358-2130
Web Site: http://www.poinsettrice.com
Grain Storage & Logistics Services
N.A.I.C.S.: 493130
John Skelley *(Gen Mgr)*
Caitlin Earls *(Mgr-Logistics)*
John Hawkins *(Ops Mgr)*

POINSETTIA GROVES INC.
1481 US Hwy 1, Vero Beach, FL 32960-5733
Tel.: (772) 562-3356   FL
Web Site: http://www.poinsettiagroves.com
Year Founded: 1947
Sales Range: $10-24.9 Million
Emp.: 50
Citrus Fruits & Gift Packages Retailer
N.A.I.C.S.: 111339
Jeb B. Hudson *(Pres)*

POINT & PAY LLC
110 State St E Ste D, Oldsmar, FL 34677
Tel.: (888) 891-6064
Web Site: http://www.pointandpay.com
Sales Range: $10-24.9 Million
Emp.: 25
Credit, Debit & Electronic Payment Processing Services
N.A.I.C.S.: 522320
Keven C. Connell *(Pres)*
Frank Pollock *(VP-Products & Svcs)*
Martha Greer *(VP-Ops)*
Ryan Pieszak *(Dir-Tech Svcs)*

POINT B
1001 Euclid Ave, Atlanta, GA 30307
Tel.: (404) 888-1700
Year Founded: 1988
Sales Range: Less than $1 Million
Emp.: 12
Advetising Agency
N.A.I.C.S.: 541810
Patricia Babuka *(CEO)*
Colleen Golden *(Pres)*
Betty Orsey *(VP-Comm)*
Kathleen Goodman *(Sr Dir)*
Shelley Holm *(Sr Dir)*
Ben Burke *(Sr Dir)*
Sicely Donaldson *(Sr Dir-Portland Market)*
Stephanie Hart *(Dir-Bus Dev)*

POINT B COMMUNICATIONS
750 N Orleans St Ste 505, Chicago, IL 60654-5040
Tel.: (312) 867-7750
Web Site: http://www.pointbcommunications.com
Year Founded: 1974
Rev.: $18,000,000
Emp.: 30
N.A.I.C.S.: 541810
Robert Grusin *(Pres)*
Tim Grob *(Controller)*
Cary Lahucik *(Dir-Production)*
Jessica Stone-Grusin *(VP-Bus Dev)*
Carol Holderfield *(Sr Dir-Art)*
Cindy Davis *(Dir-Acct Svcs)*
Tarra Rossi *(Sr Art Dir)*
John Sieruta *(Assoc Dir-Creative)*

POINT BANCORP INC.
200 S Hwy 377, Pilot Point, TX 76258
Tel.: (940) 686-5526
Web Site: http://www.pointbank.com
Rev.: $10,166,466
Emp.: 80
National Commercial Banks
N.A.I.C.S.: 522110
Kathy Chambers *(Exec VP)*

POINT BREEZE CREDIT UNION
11104 Mccormick Rd, Hunt Valley, MD 21031
Tel.: (410) 584-7228   MD
Web Site: http://www.pbcu.com
Year Founded: 1935
Sales Range: $10-24.9 Million
Emp.: 103
Credit Union Operator
N.A.I.C.S.: 522130
Cynthia M. Harrell *(VP-Ops Support)*
Genie Briggs *(Sr VP & Dir-Mktg)*
Bernard McLaughlin *(CEO)*
Tricia Harrison *(Chief Lending Officer & Sr VP)*
Michael J. Gallagher *(Chm)*
C. Joseph Marschall *(Sec)*
Ralph S. Pagano *(Treas)*
Kim Mangrum *(Chief Member Svcs Officer & Sr VP)*
Tonia Niedzialkowski *(COO & Exec VP)*
Kristin M. Reynolds *(Sr VP-HR)*
Stewart Holbrook *(VP-IT & Security)*
Beth Bavis *(VP-Member Bus Lending)*
William B. Davis Jr. *(Vice Chm)*

POINT BROADCASTING COMPANY
2284 Victoria Ave Ste 2G, Ventura, CA 93003
Tel.: (805) 654-0414   CA
Web Site: http://pointbroadcastingllc.com
Year Founded: 1994
Holding Company; Radio Broadcasting Stations
N.A.I.C.S.: 551112
John Hearne *(Pres & CEO)*
Miles Sexton *(COO)*
Marissa Garcia *(Grp Dir-HR)*

Subsidiaries:

Gold Coast Broadcasting LLC (1)
2284 S Victoria Ave Ste 2G, Ventura, CA 93003
Tel.: (805) 289-1400
Web Site: http://www.goldcoastbroadcasting.com
Sales Range: $1-9.9 Million
Emp.: 60
Radio Broadcasting Stations
N.A.I.C.S.: 516110
Steve Hess *(Mgr-Local Sls)*
Jack L. Clarke *(Mgr-Natl Sls)*

High Desert Broadcasting LLC (1)
570 E Ave Ste Q-9, Palmdale, CA 93550
Tel.: (661) 947-3107
Web Site: http://www.highdesertbroadcasting.com
Sales Range: $10-24.9 Million
Emp.: 30
Radio Broadcasting Stations
N.A.I.C.S.: 516110
Miles Sexton *(Pres)*
Renee Flores *(Mgr-Local Sls)*

Rincon Broadcasting LLC (1)
414 E Cota St, Santa Barbara, CA 93101-1624
Tel.: (805) 879-8300
Web Site: http://www.rinconbroadcasting.com
Sales Range: $10-24.9 Million
Emp.: 25
Radio Broadcasting Stations
N.A.I.C.S.: 516110
Miles Sexton *(Pres)*
Lin Aubuchon *(Dir-Mktg & Promotions)*
Keith Royer *(Exec VP & Gen Mgr)*
Jose Fierros *(Program Dir-Spanish-Language Radio Stations)*
Sandy Vera *(Coord-Promos)*

POINT BUILDERS, LLC
PO Box 5513, Cedar Rapids, IA 52406
Tel.: (319) 364-5053   IA
Web Site: http://www.pointbuilders.com
Year Founded: 1988
Sales Range: $25-49.9 Million
Emp.: 25
General Construction Contractor
N.A.I.C.S.: 236220
Pam Dafara *(Office Mgr)*
Monica Funk *(CFO & VP-HR)*
Tim Hoftender *(Dir-Bus Dev)*

POINT GUARD PARTNERS LLC   U.S. PRIVATE

Point Builders, LLC—(Continued)

POINT GUARD PARTNERS LLC
400 N Ashley Dr Ste 2150, Tampa, FL 33602
Tel.: (813) 579-2550
Web Site: http://www.pointguardllc.com
Year Founded: 2010
Sales Range: $1-9.9 Million
Emp.: 40
Business Consulting Services
N.A.I.C.S.: 541611
Barry Butler (Mng Partner)
Jeremy Brace (Partner)
Drey Coleman (Partner)
Haley Butler (Partner)
William F. Stringer (Partner)
Yvonne Gallimore (Partner)
Colin Butler (Partner)
Philippe Boulangeat (Partner)

POINT HEALTH TECH, INC.
9501 B Manchaca Rd Ste 100, Austin, TX 78748
Tel.: (512) 292-9560   DE
Web Site: http://www.pointhealth.com
Year Founded: 2020
Health Care Management Services
N.A.I.C.S.: 541618
Matt Dale (CEO)
Doug Bain (Chief Growth Officer)

POINT JUDITH CAPITAL PARTNERS, LLC
4 Liberty Sq 4 Fl, Boston, MA 02109
Tel.: (617) 600-6260
Web Site: https://www.pjc.vc
Emp.: 100
Investment Services
N.A.I.C.S.: 523999
David Martirano (Mng Partner)

POINT LIGHTING CORPORATION
61 W Dudley Town Rd, Bloomfield, CT 06002
Tel.: (860) 243-0600
Web Site: http://www.pointlighting.com
Sales Range: $1-9.9 Million
Emp.: 20
Other Lighting Equipment Mfr
N.A.I.C.S.: 335139
Michael J. Callahan (Pres)
Megan Pugliese (Mgr-Sls)

POINT LOMA CREDIT UNION
9420 Farnham St, San Diego, CA 92123
Tel.: (858) 495-3400   CA
Web Site: http://www.plcu.com
Year Founded: 1948
Sales Range: $10-24.9 Million
Emp.: 155
Consumer Lending Services
N.A.I.C.S.: 522130
Steven R. Auguston (Chm)
Salvatore J. Lupo (Vice Chm)
Linda O. Stay (Treas)
Mark R. Moeller (Sec)
David R. Brooke (Pres & CEO)

POINT OF CARE NANOTECHNOLOGY, INC.
100 Europa Dr, Chapel Hill, NC 27517
Tel.: (732) 723-7395
Web Site: https://pointofcarenano.com
Year Founded: 2010
Assets: $124,643
Liabilities: $141,414
Net Worth: ($16,771)
Earnings: ($78,017)
Fiscal Year-end: 07/31/23
Medical Diagnostic Product Mfr
N.A.I.C.S.: 325414
Nicholas DeVito (CEO)

POINT RECOGNITION
1015 Industrial Pkwy, Brunswick, OH 44212
Tel.: (330) 220-6777
Web Site: http://www.pointrecognition.com
Year Founded: 1985
Sales Range: $1-9.9 Million
Emp.: 8
Employee Award & Recognition Programs
N.A.I.C.S.: 541612
Jeff Geary (Pres)

POINT SPRING & DRIVESHAFT COMPANY
7307 Grand Ave, Pittsburgh, PA 15225
Tel.: (412) 264-3152
Web Site: http://www.pointspring.com
Rev.: $28,000,000
Emp.: 180
Automotive Parts
N.A.I.C.S.: 441330
William F. Ryan (Chm & CEO)
John Reder (VP)
Kenneth Briggs (Controller)

POINT TO POINT INC.
23240 Chagrin Blvd Ste 200, Beachwood, OH 44122
Tel.: (216) 831-4421   OH
Year Founded: 1981
Rev.: $12,000,000
Emp.: 18
Advetising Agency
N.A.I.C.S.: 541810
Mark Goren (CEO)
Bradley Cohen (VP-Media & Interactive)
Ken Holmes (Sr Dir-Interactions)

POINT TO POINT TRANSPORTATION SERVICES INC.
2505 2nd Ave Ste 505, Seattle, WA 98121
Tel.: (206) 805-3050   WA
Web Site: http://www.p2ptransportation.com
Year Founded: 2002
Sales Range: $1-9.9 Million
Emp.: 25
Freight Transportation Arrangement
N.A.I.C.S.: 488510
Daniel E. Rogers (Pres)

POINT4 DATA CORPORATION
PO Box 991090, Redding, CA 96099
Tel.: (714) 755-6550   CA
Web Site: http://www.point4data.com
Year Founded: 1978
Emp.: 100
Computer Support Organization Including On-going Training, Software Support, Software Customization, Hardware Sales & Maintenance
N.A.I.C.S.: 513210

POINT72 ASSET MANAGEMENT, L.P.
72 Cummings Point Rd, Stamford, CT 06902
Tel.: (203) 890-2000   DE
Web Site: http://www.point72.com
Year Founded: 2014
Investment Services
N.A.I.C.S.: 523940
Steven A. Cohen (Chm, Pres & CEO)
Douglas D. Haynes (Pres)
Andrew B. Cohen (Mng Dir)
Rachel D'Antonio (Chief Admin Officer, Treas & Head-Broker Rels)
Marc Desmidt (CEO-Asia Pacific)
Ross Garon (Mng Dir & Head-Cubist Systematic Strategies LLC)
Seetharam Gorre (CIO & Mng Dir)
Matthew Granade (Chief Market Intelligence Officer)
Mark Herr (Mng Dir & Head-Corp Comm)
Mike Jemiolo (Mng Dir & Chief Risk Officer)
Jonathan Jones (Head-Investment Talent Dev)
Dean Maki (Mng Dir)
Howard Man (Head-Asia-Japan)
Jeanne Melino (Dir-Community Matters)
Seiji Onoe (Mng Dir & Head-Japan)
Timothy S. Shaughnessy (COO & Mng Dir)
Michael C. Sullivan (Mng Dir & Head-External Affairs)
Vincent Tortorella (Mng Dir, Chief Compliance Officer & Chief Surveillance Officer)
Phil Villhauer (Mng Dir & Head-Global Trading)

POINTCLEAR, LLC
3550 Engineering Dr Ste 300, Norcross, GA 30092
Tel.: (678) 533-2700
Web Site: http://www.pointclear.com
Year Founded: 1997
Sales Range: $1-9.9 Million
Emp.: 40
Lead Generation Services
N.A.I.C.S.: 541890
Dan McDade (Founder, Pres & CEO)
Karla Blalock (COO)
Brian Bagwell (Controller)

POINTE GROUP LTD.
7500 N Dremydrawdey Ste 215, Phoenix, AZ 85020
Tel.: (602) 956-4300   AZ
Web Site: http://pointeinternational.com
Sales Range: $10-24.9 Million
Emp.: 20
Owner & Operator of Hotel & Resort Properties
N.A.I.C.S.: 236115
Robert A. Gosnell (CEO)
Lee Midtun (CFO)

Subsidiaries:

Gosnell Builders   (1)
7500 N Dreamy Draw Dr Ste 215, Phoenix, AZ 85020   **(100%)**
Tel.: (602) 956-4300
Web Site: http://www.pointeinternational.com
Sales Range: $10-24.9 Million
General Contractor of Single Family Homes; Nonresidential & Industrial Buildings Hotel & Warehouse Operators Subdivider & Developer
N.A.I.C.S.: 236116
Lee Midtun (CFO)

Pointe Builders   (1)
3130 Bonita Rd Ste 200, Chula Vista, CA 91910
Tel.: (619) 691-1800
Web Site: http://www.pointeinternational.com
Sales Range: $10-24.9 Million
Emp.: 10
General Builders
N.A.I.C.S.: 237210
Rick Williams (Pres)

POINTE VISTA DEVELOPMENT LLC
PO Box 1009, Kingston, OK 73439-1009
Tel.: (580) 564-2581
Web Site: http://www.pointe-vista.com
Year Founded: 2006
Sales Range: $1-9.9 Million
Emp.: 60
Real Estate Developers
N.A.I.C.S.: 531390
Scott Fischer (COO)

POINTENORTH INSURANCE GROUP LLC
1100 Cir 75 Pkwy Ste 140, Atlanta, GA 30339
Tel.: (770) 858-7540   GA
Web Site: http://www.pointenorthins.com
Year Founded: 2009
Commercial, Benefit & Life & Personal Insurance Services
N.A.I.C.S.: 524113
William H. Skeeles (Pres, CEO & Principal)
Pamela M. Gibson (CFO)
Mary E. Skeeles (COO & Principal)
Matthew G. Wells (Principal & VP-Bus Dev)
Lee O'Neal (Sr VP)

Subsidiaries:

Caribou Insurance Agency, Inc.   (1)
3500 Blue Lake Dr Ste 195, Birmingham, AL 35243
Tel.: (205) 822-7577
Web Site: http://www.caribouins.com
Sales Range: $1-9.9 Million
Emp.: 6
Insurance Agencies & Brokerages
N.A.I.C.S.: 524210

Holmes Shaw, Inc.   (1)
2860 Johnson Ferry Rd Ste 200, Marietta, GA 30062
Tel.: (770) 642-2150
Web Site: http://www.holmesshaw.com
Insurance Services
N.A.I.C.S.: 524210

McCrary Daniels Insurance Agency   (1)
120 Madison Ave N, Douglas, GA 31533-4604
Tel.: (912) 384-2130
Web Site: https://www.mccrarydaniels.com
Insurance Related Activities
N.A.I.C.S.: 524298

POINTER PR LLC
1026 1st Ave W, Seattle, WA 98119
Tel.: (206) 390-0204
Web Site: http://www.pointerpr.com
Sales Range: Less than $1 Million
Emp.: 1
Communications, Media Relations, Media Training, Planning & Consultation, Public Relations
N.A.I.C.S.: 541820
Mark S. Peterson (Principal)

POIRIER SERVICE CORPORATION
1015 Washington St, Norwood, MA 02062
Tel.: (781) 769-2446
Web Site: http://www.poiriersales.com
Rev.: $11,940,681
Emp.: 28
Household Appliance Stores
N.A.I.C.S.: 449210
Kris Grady (VP-Fin)
Michael Poirier (Pres)

POKAGON BAND OF POTAWATOMI INDIANS
PO Box 180, Dowagiac, MI 49047
Tel.: (269) 462-4267
Web Site: http://www.pokagon.com
Executive Office
N.A.I.C.S.: 921110

COMPANIES

Matt Clay *(Dir-Infoal Tech)*
Frank Freedman *(COO-Four Winds Casinos)*

Subsidiaries:

Mno-Bmadsen (1)
415 E Prairie Ronde St, Dowagiac, MI 49047
Tel.: (269) 783-4111
Web Site: http://www.pokagonband-nsn.gov
Sales Range: $25-49.9 Million
Emp.: 19
Holding Company
N.A.I.C.S.: 551112
Linda Cook *(Chm)*
Sean Winters *(Vice Chm)*
Ronald Sorce *(Treas)*
Bruce Molnar *(Sec)*
Julio Martinez *(CEO)*

Subsidiary (Domestic):

Accu-Mold, LLC (2)
7622 S Sprinkle Rd, Portage, MI 49002
Tel.: (269) 323-0388
Web Site: http://www.accu-moldinc.com
Sales Range: $10-24.9 Million
Emp.: 20
All Other Plastics Product Mfr
N.A.I.C.S.: 326199
Dave Felicijan *(Pres)*

Cressy & Everett Commercial Corporation (2)
3930 Edison Lakes Pkwy, Mishawaka, IN 46545-3443
Tel.: (574) 271-4060
Web Site: http://www.cressyandeverett.com
Offices of Real Estate Agents & Brokers
N.A.I.C.S.: 531210
Leah Cooper *(Dir-Mktg)*
Chris Fielding *(CEO)*

D.A. Dodd, LLC (2)
14 E Michigan Rd, Rolling Prairie, IN 46371
Tel.: (219) 778-4302
Web Site: http://www.dadodd.com
Sales Range: $10-24.9 Million
Mechanical Contractor
N.A.I.C.S.: 238220
Mark McKnight *(Pres)*
Jason DeMeyer *(Exec VP)*
Troland Clay *(CEO)*
Mark Druzbicki *(Mgr-Mishawaka)*
Scott Perez *(Mgr-Indus-Northwest)*

POLAMER INC.
3094 N Milwaukee Ave, Chicago, IL 60618-6637
Tel.: (773) 685-8222   IL
Web Site:
 http://www.polamerusa.com
Year Founded: 1973
Sales Range: $150-199.9 Million
Emp.: 60
Freight Transportation Arrangement
N.A.I.C.S.: 488510
Walter K. Kotaba *(Pres)*
Michalski Ryszard *(Mgr)*
Joanna Bochenek *(VP)*

POLAR BEVERAGE INC.
202 Front St Ste 3, Schenectady, NY 12305-1349
Tel.: (518) 346-7424
Sales Range: $10-24.9 Million
Emp.: 70
Cookies & Cracker Mfr
N.A.I.C.S.: 311821
Floyd A. Simone *(Pres)*

POLAR BEVERAGES
1001 Southbridge St, Worcester, MA 01610-2218
Tel.: (508) 753-4300   MA
Web Site:
 http://www.polarbeverages.com
Year Founded: 1882
Sales Range: $350-399.9 Million
Emp.: 1,000
Carbonated Beverages & Bottled Water
N.A.I.C.S.: 312111

Christopher Crowley *(Exec VP)*
Denis M. Crowley *(Chm)*

Subsidiaries:

Adirondack Beverages (1)
701 Corporations Park, Scotia, NY 12302-1060
Tel.: (518) 370-3621
Web Site:
 http://www.adirondackbeverages.com
Sales Range: $25-49.9 Million
Emp.: 175
Mfr of Beverages
N.A.I.C.S.: 551112
Doug Martin *(VP)*
V. Mattas *(Dir-Demand Plng,Ops)*

POLAR COVE, INC.
40 South St Ste 203, Marblehead, MA 01945-3274
Tel.: (401) 454-3949   RI
Year Founded: 1999
Sales Range: $10-24.9 Million
Emp.: 100
Information Security Services
N.A.I.C.S.: 561499
Bruce Eissner *(CEO)*

POLAR CRUISES
20310 Empire Ave Ste A 102, Bend, OR 97703
Tel.: (541) 330-2454
Web Site:
 http://www.polarcruises.com
Year Founded: 1996
Sales Range: $1-9.9 Million
Emp.: 5
Travel Services
N.A.I.C.S.: 561599
Jim Taylor *(Partner)*

POLAR WARE COMPANY
502 Hwy 67, Kiel, WI 53042
Tel.: (920) 458-3561   WI
Web Site: http://www.polarware.com
Year Founded: 1907
Sales Range: $75-99.9 Million
Emp.: 150
Mfr of Stainless Steel Utensils & Deep Drawn Stainless Steel Components
N.A.I.C.S.: 332119
Mike Scharinger *(VP-Ops)*
Mark Liebzeit *(Mgr-Engrg)*

POLARIS GROWTH MANAGEMENT, LLC
1 Marina Park Dr 10th Fl, Boston, MA 02210
Tel.: (781) 290-2770   DE
Web Site:
 http://www.polarisgrowthfund.com
Year Founded: 2018
Venture Capital & Private Equity Firm
N.A.I.C.S.: 523940
Bryce Youngren *(Mng Partner)*

Subsidiaries:

Knowledge Factor, Inc. (1)
1553 Platte St, Denver, CO 80202
Tel.: (720) 214-4874
Web Site: https://www.amplifire.com
Rev: $2,900,000
Emp.: 31
Custom Computer Programming Services
N.A.I.C.S.: 541511
Charles Smith *(Chief Res Officer)*

POLARIS LABORATORIES
7451 Winton Dr, Indianapolis, IN 46268
Tel.: (317) 808-3750
Web Site: http://www.polarislabs.com
Year Founded: 2009
Sales Range: $10-24.9 Million
Emp.: 135
Testing Laboratories
N.A.I.C.S.: 541380

Bryan Debshaw *(CEO)*
Jeff White *(Chief Science Officer)*
Don Woods *(CIO)*
Brett Minges *(VP-Sls)*
Scott Cherniwchan *(Mgr-Sls-Canada Territory)*
Randy Clark *(Mgr-Mining Program)*
Gwyn Simmonds *(Mgr-Sls-European Territory)*

POLARIS LOGISTICS GROUP, INC.
104 N Summit St Ste 100, Toledo, OH 43604
Tel.: (419) 851-0032
Web Site:
 http://www.polarislogisticsgroup.com
Year Founded: 2013
Sales Range: $10-24.9 Million
Emp.: 20
Logistic & Transportation Services
N.A.I.C.S.: 541614
Dan Nester *(Founder, Pres & CEO)*

POLARIS PACIFIC
850 7th St, San Francisco, CA 94107
Tel.: (415) 361-4800
Web Site:
 http://www.polarispacific.com
Sales Range: $10-24.9 Million
Property Sales & Marketing Firm
N.A.I.C.S.: 531390
Paul Zeger *(Partner)*
Chris Foley *(Partner)*
Garrett Frakes *(Mng Partner)*
Johanna Gunther *(Project Dir)*
Miles Garber *(VP-Res)*
Matt Felt *(VP & Project Dir)*
Irina Chernikova *(Mgr-Res)*
Kathryn Baker *(VP-Design Svcs)*
Gina Reidinger *(VP-Bus Dev)*
Ashley Camps *(Mgr-Mktg)*
Dana Van Galder *(Mgr-Mktg)*
Jennifer Smith *(Project Dir)*
Lindsay Lessman *(Dir-Mktg)*
Lorin Horosz *(VP-Mktg)*
Johanna Williams *(Mgr-Mktg)*
Wendy Novia *(VP-Sls)*
Rachel Weaver *(Mgr-Bus Dev)*
Mike Akerly *(VP & Reg Mgr)*

POLARIS RECRUITMENT COMMUNICATIONS
12 W Ave, Miamisburg, OH 45342
Tel.: (937) 847-1100
Web Site: http://www.polarisrc.com
Year Founded: 2001
Emp.: 7
Advertising Agencies
N.A.I.C.S.: 541810
Daniel L. Price *(Partner)*
Michael Langham *(Dir-Creative)*

POLARIS TECHNOLOGIES
45 Karago Ave, Youngstown, OH 44512-5950
Tel.: (330) 726-7000   OH
Web Site:
 http://www.polaristechnologies.com
Year Founded: 1995
Sales Range: $50-74.9 Million
Emp.: 750
Builders Materials-Vinyl Windows & Patio Doors
N.A.I.C.S.: 423320
Larry Leggett *(Pres)*
Taylor Evans *(Controller)*
Jack Marstellar *(Dir-Engrg)*

POLARIS VENTURE MANAGEMENT CO., LLC
1000 Winter St Ste 3350, Waltham, MA 02451
Tel.: (781) 290-0770   DE

POLEN CAPITAL MANAGEMENT, INC.

Web Site:
 http://www.polarispartners.com
Year Founded: 1996
Rev.: $4,000,000,000
Emp.: 30
Privater Equity Firm
N.A.I.C.S.: 523999
Alan L. Crane *(Partner)*
Mary Blair *(CFO)*
Peter Flint *(Venture Partner)*
Brian Chee *(Mng Partner-San Francisco)*
Paulina Hill *(Principal)*
Pat Kinsel *(Venture Partner)*
Dan Lombard *(Principal)*
Noel Ruane *(Venture Partner)*
Gary Swart *(Partner)*
Bryce D. Youngren *(Mng Partner)*
Dave Barrett *(Mng Partner)*
Brendan Hannigan *(Venture Partner)*
Kevin Bitterman *(Partner)*
Terrance McGuire *(Founder)*
Terrance G. McGuire *(Founder)*

Subsidiaries:

Polaris Venture Partners (1)
1000 2nd Ave Ste 3100, Seattle, WA 98104.
Tel.: (206) 652-4555
Sales Range: $50-74.9 Million
Emp.: 4
Privater Equity Firm
N.A.I.C.S.: 523999
Amir H. Nashat *(Mng Partner)*

POLARIS WIRELESS
301 N Whisman Rd, Mountain View, CA 94043
Tel.: (408) 492-8900
Web Site:
 http://www.polariswireless.com
Year Founded: 1999
Sales Range: $10-24.9 Million
Emp.: 105
Surveillance Software Development Services
N.A.I.C.S.: 541511
Manoio Allegra *(Founder, Pres & CEO)*
Bhavin Shah *(VP-Mktg & Bus Dev)*

POLARIZED MEAT CO., INC.
107 Keystone Indus Park, Dunmore, PA 18512-1518
Tel.: (570) 347-3396
Sales Range: $25-49.9 Million
Emp.: 315
Processed Meat Mfr
N.A.I.C.S.: 311612
Ken Kozel *(Head-Fin)*

POLEN CAPITAL MANAGEMENT, INC.
1825 NW Corporate Blvd Ste 300, Boca Raton, FL 33431
Tel.: (561) 241-2425   NY
Web Site:
 http://www.polencapital.com
Year Founded: 1979
Sales Range: $1-9.9 Million
Emp.: 11
Securities Brokerage
N.A.I.C.S.: 523150
Dan Davidowitz *(CIO & Portfolio Mgr)*
Stan C. Moss *(CEO)*
Damon Ficklin *(Mgr-Portfolio)*
Andrew Powers *(Dir-IT)*
Anthony Xuereb *(Mgr-Relationship)*
Brian Goldberg *(Chief Compliance Officer)*
Jim Haymes *(Dir-Institutional Rels)*
John Gross *(Mgr-Relationship)*
Todd Morris *(Dir-Res)*
George Devino *(Officer-Compliance & Controller)*
John Gunther *(Sr Mgr-Relationship)*

POLEN CAPITAL MANAGEMENT, INC.

Polen Capital Management, Inc.—(Continued)
Chip Jones (Dir-Advisor Rels)
Ian Podbelski (Sr Mgr-Relationship)
Brian Yacko (Mgr-Ops & Trading)

Subsidiaries:

DDJ Capital Management, LLC (1)
Stony Brook Office Park 130 Turner St Bldg 3 Ste 600, Waltham, MA 02453
Tel.: (781) 283-8500
Web Site: http://www.ddjcap.com
Sales Range: $350-399.9 Million
Emp.: 30
Investment Advisory & Special Situation Securities Investing Services
N.A.I.C.S.: 523940
David John Breazzano (Pres, Chief Investment Officer & Portfolio Mgr)
John J. Russell (CFO)
James R. Kime (Mng Dir)
Joshua L. McCarthy (Chief Compliance Officer & Gen Counsel)
Elizabeth B. Duggan (Assoc Gen Counsel)
John F. O'Connor (Sr VP & Head-Bus Dev & Client Svc)
Michael Weissenburger (Mng Dir & Head-Origination)
Roman Rjanikov (Asst Portfolio Mgr & Dir-Res)
Benjamin J. Santonelli (Portfolio Mgr)
John W. Sherman (Portfolio Mgr)

Holding (Domestic):

Miami Valley Steel Service Inc. (2)
201 Fox Dr, Piqua, OH 45356
Tel.: (937) 773-7127
Web Site: http://www.miamivalleysteel.com
Sales Range: $150-199.9 Million
Steel Product Mfr & Distr
N.A.I.C.S.: 331221
Jill A. Kindell (CFO)
Louis J. Moran (CEO)
Len Stahl (VP-Sls)

POLESTAR LABS, INC.
1223 Pacific Oaks Pl Ste 102, Escondido, CA 92029-1934
Tel.: (760) 480-2600   DE
Web Site:
   http://www.polestarlabs.com
Year Founded: 1988
Sales Range: $100-124.9 Million
Emp.: 100
Provides Point-of Care Testing Services to Physicians; Furnish Clinical Labs, Including Equipment, Supplies & Professional Staff
N.A.I.C.S.: 456199
Michael Dunaway (Owner & CEO)
Karen McKim (VP-Sls)

POLICY ADM SOLUTIONS INC.
1902 Whitestone Expy Ste 301, Whitestone, NY 11357
Tel.: (718) 357-0771
Web Site:
   http://www.pasolutions.com
Sales Range: $10-24.9 Million
Emp.: 25
Computer Software Development
N.A.I.C.S.: 541511

POLIFORM USA, INC.
150 E 58th St, New York, NY 10155
Tel.: (212) 421-1800
Web Site:
   http://www.poliformusa.com
Year Founded: 1995
Importer, Retailer & Wholesaler of Furniture
N.A.I.C.S.: 423210
Jessica Chepovsky (Mgr-Show Room & Design)

POLIN POULTRY COMPANY INC.
59 W Church St, Selbyville, DE 19975-2001
Tel.: (302) 436-5191   DE
Year Founded: 1984
Sales Range: $75-99.9 Million
Emp.: 12
Poultry & Poultry Products
N.A.I.C.S.: 424440
Bernard Polin (Pres)
Joan Davis (Mgr-Acctg)

POLINGER SHANNON & LUCHS COMPANY
5530 Wisconsin Ave Ste 1000, Chevy Chase, MD 20815
Tel.: (301) 657-3600
Web Site: http://www.polingerco.com
Sales Range: $10-24.9 Million
Emp.: 95
Property Mangement
N.A.I.C.S.: 531210
Arnold Polinger (Pres)
Jean Cleary (Sr Mgr-Property)
Elliot Schnitzer (Sr Exec VP)
David Newcome (Sr VP-Property Mgmt)
Christopher J. Modica (Sr VP-Construction Svcs)
Brian P. Danhauser (VP-Corp Fin)

POLISH NATIONAL ALLIANCE OF US
6100 N Cicero Ave, Chicago, IL 60646
Tel.: (773) 286-0500
Web Site: http://www.pna-znp.org
Sales Range: $25-49.9 Million
Emp.: 100
Insurance Services
N.A.I.C.S.: 524113
Charles A. Komosa (Sec)
David G. Milcinovic (VP)
Marian Grabowski (Treas)

POLISH NATIONAL CREDIT UNION
46 Main St, Chicopee, MA 01020
Tel.: (413) 592-9495   MA
Web Site: http://www.pncu.com
Year Founded: 1921
Sales Range: $10-24.9 Million
Emp.: 107
Credit Union Operator
N.A.I.C.S.: 522130
Rick Kane (VP-Member Svcs)
Melinda Tulloch (Mgr-Southampton)
David Barszcz (VP-Comml Lending)
James Kelly (Pres & CEO)
Pamela Sanborn (Asst Mgr-Westfield)
Kathi Donahue (Sr VP-Comml Lending)
Tracey Egloff (VP-Residential Lending)
Martha Rickson (Asst VP)

POLISH NATIONAL UNION OF AMERICA
1002 Pittston Ave, Scranton, PA 18505
Tel.: (570) 344-1513
Web Site: http://www.pnu.org
Year Founded: 1908
Sales Range: $25-49.9 Million
Emp.: 20
Insurance Services
N.A.I.C.S.: 524113
John Andrzejewski (CFO)

POLISH ROMAN CATHOLIC UNION OF AMERICA
984 N Milwaukee Ave, Chicago, IL 60642
Tel.: (773) 782-2600   IL
Year Founded: 2000
Sales Range: $25-49.9 Million
Fraternal Organization
N.A.I.C.S.: 813410
Joseph A. Drobot Jr. (Pres)

POLK COUNTY FARMERS CO-OP INC.
9055 Rickreall Rd, Rickreall, OR 97371-9701
Tel.: (503) 363-2332   OR
Web Site:
   http://www.agwestsupply.com
Year Founded: 1932
Sales Range: $10-24.9 Million
Emp.: 105
Farm & Garden Machinery
N.A.I.C.S.: 423820
Max Smith (Gen Mgr)

POLK MECHANICAL COMPANY, LLC.
2425 Dillard St, Grand Prairie, TX 75051-1004
Tel.: (972) 339-1200
Web Site:
   http://www.polkmechanical.com
Sales Range: $75-99.9 Million
Emp.: 250
Electrical Wiring Services
N.A.I.C.S.: 238210
Fran Mccann (Pres)

POLK OIL COMPANY INC.
1422 S 1st St, Lufkin, TX 75904
Tel.: (936) 634-8787
Web Site: http://www.polkoil.com
Sales Range: $25-49.9 Million
Emp.: 6,000
Petroleum Bulk Stations
N.A.I.C.S.: 424710
Marla Kern (Mgr)

POLK'S MEAT PRODUCTS
1801 Simpson Hwy 49, Magee, MS 39111
Tel.: (601) 849-9997
Web Site: http://www.polksmeat.com
Year Founded: 1969
Sales Range: $10-24.9 Million
Emp.: 105
Smoked Meat Product Mfr & Distr
N.A.I.C.S.: 311611
John Polk (Chm)
Randy Lamana (Reg Mgr-Sls)
Laura Tillman (Acct Mgr-Natl)

POLK-BURNETT ELECTRIC COOPERATIVE
1001 State Rd 35, Centuria, WI 54824
Tel.: (715) 646-2191
Web Site: http://www.polkburnett.com
Year Founded: 1938
Rev.: $37,520,000
Assets: $95,398,000
Liabilities: $44,067,000
Net Worth: $51,331,000
Earnings: $2,877,000
Fiscal Year-end: 12/31/18
Electric Power Distr
N.A.I.C.S.: 221122
Edward O. Gullickson (Pres)
Michael X. Morris (VP)
Charles A. Brookshaw (Treas & Sec)

POLKA DOT DAIRY
110 E 17th St, Hastings, MN 55033
Tel.: (651) 438-2793   MN
Web Site:
   http://www.polkadotdairy.com
Year Founded: 1956
Sales Range: $50-74.9 Million
Emp.: 23
Dairy Mfr & Distr
N.A.I.C.S.: 112120
Brenda Fahey (Sec)

POLKTON MANUFACTURING COMPANY
220 E Main St, Marshville, NC 28103
Tel.: (704) 624-3200

Web Site: http://www.seafarer.com
Sales Range: $10-24.9 Million
Emp.: 2
Men's & Boys' Uniforms Mfr
N.A.I.C.S.: 315250
Aaron Efird (VP)

POLLACK
150 Varick St Fl 10, New York, NY 10013
Tel.: (212) 627-7766
Web Site:
   http://www.pollackassociates.com
Year Founded: 1988
Rev.: $12,456,117
Emp.: 35
Textile Mfr
N.A.I.C.S.: 424310
Rick Sullivan (Pres & CEO)
Susan Sullivan (Partner)
Melissa Villa (Mgr-Reg Sls)
Brad Bloom (VP-Sls)

POLLACK CORPORATION
600 Roundwood Dr, Scarborough, ME 04074-8247
Tel.: (207) 883-8455   ME
Web Site: http://www.gmpollack.com
Year Founded: 1954
Sales Range: $50-74.9 Million
Emp.: 130
Jewelry, Watches & Giftware Retailer
N.A.I.C.S.: 458310

POLLACK SHORES REAL ESTATE GROUP, LLC
One Premier Plz 5605 Glenridge Dr Ste 775, Atlanta, GA 30342
Tel.: (404) 835-1475
Web Site:
   http://www.pollackshores.com
Rev.: $56,000,000
Emp.: 160
Real Estate Investment & Management Services
N.A.I.C.S.: 523999
Marc Pollack (Co-Founder)
Steven Shores (Co-Founder, Chm & CEO)
Michael Blair (Mng Dir-Dev)
Tracy H. Bowers (Pres & Mng Dir-Matrix Residential)
Bruce Sanders (Mng Dir & CFO)
Andrew Wittgen (Dir-Asset Mgmt)
Graham Carpenter (Mng Dir-Acq)
Brian Metzler (Dir-Dev)
Anthony M. Everett (Dir-Central Florida)
Anna Loomis (Mgr-Construction)
Bill Moyer (Mgr-Construction)
James R. Winston (Mgr-Construction)
Mike Harty (Mgr-Construction)
Palmer McArthur (Mgr-Dev)
Tyler Gaines (Mgr-Dev)
Jeremy Reynolds (Mgr-Fin Plng & Analysis)
Brendan Whalen (VP-Acq)
Alex Geeslin (VP-Asset Mgmt)
Matt Tracy (Mng Dir-Innovation & Tech)

POLLARD ENTERPRISES INC.
4749 Hwy 80 W, Jackson, MS 39209
Tel.: (601) 922-9425
Rev.: $15,199,172
Emp.: 6
Travel Trailers: Automobile, New & Used
N.A.I.C.S.: 441210
Billy Eugene Pollard (Pres)

Subsidiaries:

RV Repair & Sales Inc. (1)
4749 Hwy 80 W, Jackson, MS 39209
Tel.: (601) 922-9425
Web Site: http://www.rvsalesandrentals.com
Rev.: $1,200,000

Emp.: 5
Recreational Vehicle Repair Services
N.A.I.C.S.: 811111

POLLARD FRIENDLY FORD
3301 S Loop 289, Lubbock, TX 79423
Tel.: (806) 797-3441
Web Site: http://www.pollardford.com
Sales Range: $100-124.9 Million
Emp.: 180
Automobiles, New & Used
N.A.I.C.S.: 441110
Glen R. Pollard *(Owner)*
Michael P. Edwards *(Gen Mgr)*
Mike Lewis *(Dir-Adv)*

POLLER & JORDAN ADVERTISING AGENCY, INC.
373 NW Shore View Dr, Port Saint Lucie, FL 34986
Tel.: (305) 470-8005
Web Site:
http://www.advertisingmiami.com
Year Founded: 1972
Sales Range: $10-24.9 Million
Emp.: 6
N.A.I.C.S.: 541810
Robert Poller *(Pres)*
Kelly Williams *(Art Dir)*
Shari Goldstein *(Dir-Pub Rels)*

POLLOCK COMMUNICATIONS
205 E 42nd St, New York, NY 10017
Tel.: (212) 941-1414
Web Site: http://www.lpollockpr.com
Year Founded: 1991
Sales Range: $1-9.9 Million
Emp.: 16
Fiscal Year-end: 03/31/14
Public Relations, Communications, Brand Identity Services
N.A.I.C.S.: 541820
Lis Pollock *(Pres)*
Moses M. Sanzo *(Controller)*

POLLOCK CORPORATION
Industrial Hwy Keim St, Pottstown, PA 19464
Tel.: (610) 323-5500
Web Site:
http://www.mayerpollock.com
Sales Range: $10-24.9 Million
Emp.: 20
Scrap & Waste Materials
N.A.I.C.S.: 423930
Mayer Pollock *(Chm & Pres)*
Scott Orr *(VP)*

POLLOCK INVESTMENTS INC.
1 Pollock Pl, Grand Prairie, TX 75050-7939
Tel.: (972) 263-2126
Web Site:
http://www.pollockpaper.com
Year Founded: 1918
Sales Range: $50-74.9 Million
Emp.: 700
Provider of Industrial & Personal Paper
N.A.I.C.S.: 424130
Paul A. Garcia *(CFO)*

POLLY'S FOOD SERVICE INC.
1821 Spring Arbor Rd, Jackson, MI 49203-2703
Tel.: (517) 787-6081
Web Site:
http://www.countrystatefarm.com
Year Founded: 1963
Sales Range: $50-74.9 Million
Emp.: 400
Owner & Operator of Grocery Stores
N.A.I.C.S.: 445110
Tim Corby *(Pres)*

POLSINELLI PC
900 W 48th Pl Ste 900, Kansas City, MO 64112
Tel.: (816) 753-1000
Web Site: http://www.polsinelli.com
Emp.: 750
Law Firm
N.A.I.C.S.: 541199
W. Russell Welsh *(Chm & CEO)*
Aaron Chickos *(Atty)*
Paul A. Gomez *(Principal)*
Patrick C. Woolley *(Chm-Intellectual Property)*
Jonathon E. Cohn *(Principal)*
Gary E. Hood *(Vice Chm)*
Adam S. Weiss *(Vice Chm)*
Suni Sukduang *(Vice Chm-Patent Post Grant Practice Grp)*
Gregory V. Novak *(Vice Chm-IP Dept)*
Jittaun A. Dill *(Coord-Diversity & Inclusion-Natl)*
Anna Suda *(Atty)*
Erin L. Muellenberg *(Principal-Los Angeles)*
Richard K. Rifenbark *(Principal-Los Angeles)*
Brian McEvoy *(Chm/Mng Partner-Govt Investigations & Compliance Practice)*

POLSINELLO FUELS INC.
241 Riverside Ave, Rensselaer, NY 12144-2900
Tel.: (518) 463-0084
Web Site:
http://www.polsinellofuels.com
Year Founded: 1953
Sales Range: $25-49.9 Million
Emp.: 100
Petroleum Products
N.A.I.C.S.: 424720
Greg Bobersky *(Comptroller)*
Louis Polsinello Jr. *(Pres)*

POLU KAI SERVICES LLC
137 N Washington St Ste 301, Falls Church, VA 22046
Tel.: (703) 533-0039
Web Site:
http://www.polukaiservices.com
Year Founded: 2003
Sales Range: $10-24.9 Million
Emp.: 71
Environmental & Construction Services
N.A.I.C.S.: 541620
Sean P. Jensen *(Pres)*

POLY PAK AMERICA, INC.
2939 E Washington Blvd, Los Angeles, CA 90023-4277
Tel.: (323) 264-2400
Web Site: http://www.polypak.com
Year Founded: 1972
Sales Range: $50-74.9 Million
Emp.: 125
Mfr of Plastic Mailers, Bags & Packaging
N.A.I.C.S.: 326113
Richard Gurewitz *(Pres)*
Jezabel Weeks *(Office Mgr)*
Mark Freedman *(Controller)*

POLY PORTABLES INC.
99 Crafton Dr, Dahlonega, GA 30533
Tel.: (706) 864-3776
Web Site:
http://www.polyportables.com
Sales Range: $10-24.9 Million
Emp.: 100
Portable Chemical Toilets Mfr
N.A.I.C.S.: 332999

POLY VINYL CO.
320 Range Line Rd, Sheboygan Falls, WI 53085
Tel.: (920) 467-4685
Web Site: http://www.polyvinyl.com
Sales Range: $1-9.9 Million
Emp.: 120
Plastics Product Mfr
N.A.I.C.S.: 326199
James Schnettler *(VP)*
Thomas R. Schnettler *(Pres)*
Mark Schnettler *(Engr-Production & Process)*

POLY VINYL CREATIONS, INC.
11313 State Rd 52, Hudson, FL 34669
Tel.: (727) 857-9618
Web Site: http://www.polyvinylc.com
Year Founded: 1996
Rev.: $11,237,000
Emp.: 32
Vinyl Fence Mfr
N.A.I.C.S.: 444180
Matthew Von Kaenel *(VP-Ops-Georgia)*
Jessica L. Burton *(VP-Sls & Mktg)*
Robert L. Burton *(Owner & CEO)*

POLY-AMERICA LP
2000 W Marshall Dr, Grand Prairie, TX 75051-2709
Tel.: (972) 647-4374
Web Site: http://www.poly-america.com
Year Founded: 1976
Sales Range: $100-124.9 Million
Emp.: 1,800
Provider of Plastic Services
N.A.I.C.S.: 326113
Doug Dawson *(Plant Mgr)*
Tim Hagood *(Mgr-Product Info)*
Devin Pflueger *(Coord-Section)*
Jonathan Bradshaw *(Supvr-Production)*
Kirk Duckworth *(Engr-Electrical)*
Sean Conroy *(Asst Mgr-Laboratory)*
Ronnie Beam *(Controller)*
David Burkel *(Engr-Electrical)*

POLY-FLEX CORP
250 Executive Dr, Edgewood, NY 11717
Tel.: (631) 586-9500
Web Site: http://www.poly-flexcorp.com
Sales Range: $10-24.9 Million
Emp.: 10
Printing Envelopes
N.A.I.C.S.: 323111
Barry Neustein *(Pres)*

POLY-PAK INDUSTRIES, INC.
125 Spagnoli Rd, Melville, NY 11747
Tel.: (631) 293-6767
Web Site: http://www.poly-pak.com
Sales Range: $25-49.9 Million
Emp.: 290
Mfr of Plastic Bags
N.A.I.C.S.: 326111
Leonard Levy *(Chm)*
Michael Losak *(Controller)*
Bruce Steifman *(VP-Svc Div)*

POLY-TAINER INC.
450 W Los Angeles Ave, Simi Valley, CA 93065
Tel.: (805) 526-3424
Web Site: http://www.polytainer.com
Sales Range: $10-24.9 Million
Emp.: 98
Injection Molding Of Plastics
N.A.I.C.S.: 326160
Paul G. Strong *(Pres)*
Johannes Sutedja *(Mgr-Maintenance)*

Julie Williams *(VP)*
Gabriela Llamas *(Dir-HR)*
Karrie Brooks *(Controller)*

POLYCEL HOLDINGS INC.
68 County Line Rd, Somerville, NJ 08876
Tel.: (908) 725-5254
Web Site: http://www.polycel.com
Rev.: $28,000,000
Emp.: 3
Holding Company
N.A.I.C.S.: 551112
Otto J. del Prado *(Pres)*

Subsidiaries:

Polycel Structural Foam, Inc. (1)
68 County Line Rd, Somerville, NJ 08876-3467
Tel.: (908) 722-5254
Web Site: http://www.polycel.com
Sales Range: $25-49.9 Million
Emp.: 175
Injection Molder of Structural Foam
N.A.I.C.S.: 326199

POLYCLEAN INNOVATIONS, LLC
2510 S Brentwood Blvd Ste 301, Saint Louis, MO 63144
Tel.: (314) 961-2700
Web Site: http://www.polycleaninnovations.com
Year Founded: 1992
Sales Range: $10-24.9 Million
Emp.: 6
Broom, Brush & Mop Mfr
N.A.I.C.S.: 339994
Lisa Ladage *(Mgr-Acctg & Admin Svcs)*

POLYFAB CORPORATION
1705 Martin Ave, Sheboygan, WI 53083
Tel.: (920) 459-2525
Web Site:
http://www.polyfabcorp.com
Sales Range: $10-24.9 Million
Emp.: 80
Plastics Product Mfr
N.A.I.C.S.: 326199
Richard A. Gill *(Chm & Pres)*
Carol A. Janssen *(CFO, Treas & Sec)*
Craig Weidman *(Dir-Engrg)*
Steve Olsen *(Mgr-Quality)*
Kent Kuecherer *(Plant Mgr)*

POLYGON COMPANY
103 Industrial Park Dr, Walkerton, IN 46574
Tel.: (574) 586-3145
Web Site:
http://www.polygoncompany.com
Sales Range: $10-24.9 Million
Emp.: 250
Unsupported Plastics Profile Shapes
N.A.I.C.S.: 326121
Bob Fadorsen *(VP-Sls)*
Tim Schobert *(Pres)*

POLYGON SOLUTIONS, INC.
16770 Link Ct Ste 106, Fort Myers, FL 33912
Tel.: (239) 628-4800
Web Site:
http://www.polygonsolutions.com
Year Founded: 2010
Sales Range: Less than $1 Million
Emp.: 7
Special Purpose Tool Mfr
N.A.I.C.S.: 333514
Steve Derbin *(Pres)*

POLYMEDCO, INC.
510 Furnace Dock Rd, Cortlandt Manor, NY 10567-6220
Tel.: (914) 739-5400

POLYMEDCO, INC.

Polymedco, Inc.—(Continued)
Web Site: http://www.polymedco.com
Year Founded: 1980
Sales Range: $10-24.9 Million
Emp.: 80
Clinical Diagnostic Test Kit & Device Mfr
N.A.I.C.S.: 334516
Drew Cervasio (Pres)
Diane Robinson (Supvr-Product Support)
Marie Longo (Coord-Mktg)
Rick De Alto (VP-Ops)
Chrystal Smith (Mgr-IT)
Pablo Rodriguez (Coord-Instrument)
John Milazzo (Supvr-Product Support)

POLYMER ENGINEERED PRODUCTS
595 Summer St Ste 2, Stamford, CT 06901
Tel.: (203) 324-3737
Web Site: http://www.prlresins.com
Sales Range: $10-24.9 Million
Emp.: 75
Injection Molding Of Plastics
N.A.I.C.S.: 326199
Leslie Klein (Chm)
Stephanie Vollano (Mgr-Accts)
Rollie Washburn (Plant Mgr)

POLYMER ENTERPRISES INC.
1600 Washington St, Indiana, PA 15701
Tel.: (724) 838-2340
Web Site: http://www.stausaonline.com
Year Founded: 1915
Sales Range: $25-49.9 Million
Emp.: 600
Mfr of Tires & Inner Tubes
N.A.I.C.S.: 326211
Jack W. Armstrong (CIO & VP)

Subsidiaries:

Race Tires America Inc. (1)
1600 Washington St, Indiana, PA 15701-2894 (100%)
Tel.: (724) 349-9010
Web Site: http://www.americanraceronline.com
Sales Range: $10-24.9 Million
Emp.: 5
Tire & Tube Distr
N.A.I.C.S.: 423130
Scott Junod (Dir-Racing)

Rubber Technology Inc. (1)
Berkshire Ctr Ste 401, Greensburg, PA 15601
Tel.: (724) 838-2340
Sales Range: $10-24.9 Million
Emp.: 20
Mfr of Fabricated Rubber Products
N.A.I.C.S.: 326299

Specialty Tires of America Inc. (1)
1600 Washington St, Indiana, PA 15701-2893
Tel.: (724) 349-9010
Web Site: http://www.stausaonline.com
Sales Range: $25-49.9 Million
Tires & Inner Tube Mfr
N.A.I.C.S.: 326211
Don Mateer (Chm, Pres & CEO)
Mark Grant (Exec VP)

POLYMER INDUSTRIES
Hwy 40, Henagar, AL 35978
Tel.: (256) 657-5197
Web Site: http://www.polymerindustries.com
Rev.: $11,012,566
Emp.: 150
Plastics Processing
N.A.I.C.S.: 326199
Chris Tanner (Mgr-HR & Pur)

POLYMER SOLUTIONS (PSI)
135 Technology Dr, Christiansburg, VA 24073
Tel.: (540) 961-4300
Web Site: http://www.polymersolutions.com
Year Founded: 1987
Emp.: 37
Chemical Testing Laboratories
N.A.I.C.S.: 541380
James Rancourt (Founder)

Subsidiaries:

SASCO Chemical Group, LLC (1)
827 Pine Ave, Albany, GA 31701
Web Site: http://www.sascochemical.com
Proprietary Specialty Chemical Mfr
N.A.I.C.S.: 325180
Marc Skalla (Pres)

POLYMER SOLUTIONS INTERNATIONAL, INC.
11 St Albans Ave, Newtown Square, PA 19073
Tel.: (610) 325-7500
Web Site: http://www.prostack.com
Year Founded: 1997
Sales Range: $25-49.9 Million
Emp.: 21
Plastic Pallet Mfr & Distr
N.A.I.C.S.: 322211
Daniel E. Kelly (CEO)

POLYMERICS, INC.
2828 2nd St, Cuyahoga Falls, OH 44221
Tel.: (330) 928-2210
Web Site: http://www.polymericsinc.com
Year Founded: 1974
Rev.: $20,000,000
Emp.: 75
Custom Compounding Of Rubber Materials
N.A.I.C.S.: 326299
Tim Samples (Pres)
Nanette Phillips (Mgr-Customer Svc)

POLYMET CORPORATION
10073 Commerce Pk Dr, Cincinnati, OH 45246-1333
Tel.: (513) 874-3586
Web Site: http://www.polymet.us
Year Founded: 1967
Sales Range: $50-74.9 Million
Emp.: 60
Mfr of Specialty Alloy Wire
N.A.I.C.S.: 332618
Bill Mosier (Pres)
Randy Norris (Mgr-Customer Svc)
Bob Unger (Mgr-Sls)
Wes Price (Mgr-Welding & Hardfacing Sls)

POLYNESIAN CULTURAL CENTER
55-220 Kam Hwy, Laie, HI 96762
Tel.: (808) 293-3000
Web Site: http://www.polynesia.com
Rev.: $36,000,000
Emp.: 1,100
Tourist Attraction
N.A.I.C.S.: 712190
Von D. Orgill (Pres)
Shelly A. Easton (Mgr-Retail)
Raymond Magalei (Dir-Mktg)

POLYSCIENCES INC.
400 Valley Rd, Warrington, PA 18976
Tel.: (215) 343-6484
Web Site: http://www.polysciences.com
Year Founded: 1961
Sales Range: $10-24.9 Million
Emp.: 82
Research Products
N.A.I.C.S.: 325998

Michael H. Ott (Owner, Pres & CEO)
Joe Dudenbostel (Mgr-Pur)
Chad Owen (VP-Microspheres & Particles)
Jennifer Tenfelde (Dir-Strategic HR)
Joel Coret (CTO)
Tom Foster (Dir-Ops)
Scott Knorr (Exec Dir-Specialty Products & Contract Mfg)
David Harwood (Gen Mgr)
Andrew Ott (COO & Exec VP)
Ryan Ott (Exec VP)

POLYSONICS CORPORATION
405 Belle Air Ln, Warrenton, VA 20186
Tel.: (540) 341-4988
Web Site: http://www.polysonicscorp.com
Year Founded: 1958
Rev.: $3,300,000
Emp.: 38
Engineeering Services
N.A.I.C.S.: 541330
Gordon E. Jacobs (Pres)
Denise A. Jacobs (VP)

POLYSOURCE, LLC
1003 Industrial Dr, Pleasant Hill, MO 64080
Tel.: (816) 540-5300
Web Site: http://www.polysource.net
Year Founded: 2000
Sales Range: $10-24.9 Million
Emp.: 15
Resins Supplier
N.A.I.C.S.: 325991
Patty Sudhoff (Mgr-Customer Svc)
Damien Couch (VP)
Grant Johnson (Pres & CEO)
Greg Jacobson (Founder)
Ryan Koenig (CFO)

POLYSYSTEMS INC.
30 N La Salle St Ste 3600, Chicago, IL 60602
Tel.: (312) 332-5670
Web Site: http://www.polysystems.com
Year Founded: 1970
Sales Range: $10-24.9 Million
Emp.: 75
Computer Time-Sharing
N.A.I.C.S.: 518210
Roger W. Smith (Pres)
Bob Keating (VP)
Michael Leung (VP)
Chris Zuiker (VP)
Al Dickey (Mgr-Actuarial Svcs)
Victor Kwong (VP)
John Adducci (VP)
Jason Kehrberg (VP)
Scott Bright (Mgr-Client Data Svcs)
Cathy Gainer (VP)
David McManus (VP)
Matt Covalle (VP)
Brett Morris (VP)
Gary Stanton (VP)

POLYVENTIVE LLC
140 Executive Dr., Calhoun, GA 30701
Tel.: (706) 659-0300
Web Site: https://www.polyventive.com
Chemicals & Wholesale Distr
N.A.I.C.S.: 424690
Zay Risinger (Pres)

Subsidiaries:

Fibro Chem LLC. (1)
1804 Kimberly Park Dr, Dalton, GA 30720
Tel.: (706) 278-3514
Web Site: http://www.fibrochem.com
Rev.: $9,450,000
Emp.: 30
Power Boiler & Heat Exchanger Mfr

N.A.I.C.S.: 332410

POLYVINYL FILMS, INC.
19 Depot St, Sutton, MA 01590
Tel.: (508) 865-3558
Web Site: http://www.stretchtite.com
Year Founded: 1965
Sales Range: $75-99.9 Million
Emp.: 100
Mfr of Polyvinylchloride Film
N.A.I.C.S.: 326113
John W. Baldwin (Pres)
John J. Connor II (VP)
John Connor Jr. (Treas)

POLYWELL COMPUTERS, INC.
1461 San Mateo Ave, South San Francisco, CA 94080-6505
Tel.: (650) 583-7222
Web Site: http://www.polywell.com
Year Founded: 1987
Rev.: $8,000,000
Emp.: 60
Mfr & Marketer of Computers & Components
N.A.I.C.S.: 334111
Chin Lo (Pres)
Ava Lo (Controller)
Jerry Tighe (Mgr-Tech & Sls)

POMA AUTOMATED FUELING INC.
571 W Slover Ave, Bloomington, CA 92316-0479
Tel.: (909) 421-2280
Web Site: http://www.pomafuel.com
Year Founded: 1991
Sales Range: $25-49.9 Million
Emp.: 100
Provider of Petroleum Products
N.A.I.C.S.: 424720
Jim Tebeau (Dir-Sls)

POMARE LTD.
670 Auahi St Ste I-03, Honolulu, HI 96813
Tel.: (800) 233-8912
Web Site: http://www.hilohattie.com
Year Founded: 1963
Fashion Apparel, Accessories, Gifts & Souvenirs Mfr & Whslr
N.A.I.C.S.: 459420
Donald B.S. Kang (Pres & CEO)
Mark Storfer (COO & Exec VP)
John DesJardins (Mgr-Visual)
Joao Oppenheim (Dir-Sls & Mktg)

Subsidiaries:

Pomare International Corp. (1)
700 N Nimitz Hwy, Honolulu, HI 96817-5034
Tel.: (808) 524-3966
Web Site: http://www.hilohattie.com
Sales Range: $1-9.9 Million
Emp.: 250
Family Clothing Stores
N.A.I.C.S.: 458110

POMOCO NISSAN
1134 W Mercury Blvd, Hampton, VA 23666
Tel.: (757) 838-6111
Web Site: http://www.pomoconissan.com
Year Founded: 1970
Sales Range: $10-24.9 Million
Emp.: 55
New Car Whslr
N.A.I.C.S.: 441110
Stanle Baker (Mgr-Sls)

POMONA CAPITAL
780 3rd Ave FL 46, New York, NY 10017
Tel.: (212) 593-3639

Web Site:
http://www.pomonacapital.com
Rev.: $13,850,898
Emp.: 40
Private Equity Investing
N.A.I.C.S.: 523940
Michael Granoff (CEO)
Fran Janis (Sr Partner)
James Rorer (Partner)
Steve Futrell (Partner)
Lorraine Hliboki (Partner)
Oliver Gardey (Partner)
John Stephens (Partner & CFO)
Jay Mai (Asst Controller)
Jeremy Dardick (Chief Compliance Officer & Gen Counsel)
Elaine Hsu (Controller)
Lawrence Fang (Mgr-Acctg)
Wei Fang (Mgr-Acctg)
Vivian Flynn (Mng Dir-IR)
Sebastien Bowen (Principal)
Lisa Markowitz (Principal)
Patrick Madaus (Partner)

POMONA VALLEY HOSPITAL MEDICAL CENTER
1798 N Garey Ave, Pomona, CA 91767
Tel.: (909) 865-9500   CA
Web Site: http://www.pvhmc.org
Year Founded: 1903
Sales Range: $450-499.9 Million
Emp.: 3,214
Health Care Srvices
N.A.I.C.S.: 622110
Michael Nelson (CFO, Treas & Sec)

POMP'S TIRE SERVICE INC.
1123 Cedar St, Green Bay, WI 54301-4703
Tel.: (920) 435-8301   WI
Web Site: http://www.pompstire.com
Year Founded: 1965
Rev.: $118,463,082
Emp.: 1,000
Tires & Tubes Mfr
N.A.I.C.S.: 423130
James Wochinske (Pres)
Tom Snider (Treas)
Mark Revall (Dir-Safety)

POMPANETTE COMPANY LLC
73 S W St, Charlestown, NH 03603
Tel.: (603) 826-5791
Web Site:
http://www.pompanette.com
Year Founded: 1978
Sales Range: $10-24.9 Million
Emp.: 70
Marine Hardware
N.A.I.C.S.: 332510
Richard Truell (Pres)
James Bailey (Controller)

POMPANO NISSAN
1345 S Federal Hwy, Pompano Beach, FL 33062
Tel.: (954) 781-7700
Web Site:
http://www.pompanonissan.com
Rev.: $44,435,125
Emp.: 50
New & Used Automobiles
N.A.I.C.S.: 441110
Bobby Serpentini (Gen Mgr)

POMPANOOSUC MILLS CORPORATION
Rte 5, East Thetford, VT 05043
Tel.: (802) 785-4851
Web Site: http://www.pompy.com
Year Founded: 1973
Rev.: $14,401,069
Emp.: 150
Furniture Retailer
N.A.I.C.S.: 449110

Dwight O. Sargent (Founder & Owner)
Ed O'Keefe (VP-Sls)
Robert Chapin (VP-Mktg)
Donald Blake (CFO)

POMPEIAN, INC.
4201 Pulaski Hwy, Baltimore, MD 21224-1603
Tel.: (410) 276-6900   MD
Web Site: http://www.pompeian.com
Sales Range: $75-99.9 Million
Emp.: 50
Olive Oil, Vinegar, Cooking Wines, Olives & Artichokes Importer
N.A.I.C.S.: 311225
Bob Eckoff (Mgr-Mktg & Sls)
Bill Monroe (CEO)

POMS & ASSOCIATES INSURANCE BROKERS, INC.
5700 Canoga Ave Ste 400, Woodland Hills, CA 91367
Tel.: (818) 449-9300
Web Site:
http://www.pomsassoc.com
Year Founded: 1991
Sales Range: $1-9.9 Million
Emp.: 150
Insurance Agencies & Brokerages
N.A.I.C.S.: 524210
David Poms (Founder & Pres)
Seth Ford Gilman (Exec VP)
Naureen McMillan (Dir-HR)
Lori Ann Cain (Sr VP & Dir-Employee Benefits)
Chris Poveromo (Exec VP)
Julie C. Garcia (Dir-New Mexico)
Cara Rhyner (Sr VP)
Matthew Getty (CFO)
Jennifer M. Schirtz (VP-Insurance Placement)

PONCE CASH & CARRY INC.
Reparada Industrial Park, Ponce, PR 00732
Tel.: (787) 840-5000   PR
Web Site:
http://www.poncecashandcarry.com
Year Founded: 1971
Sales Range: $50-74.9 Million
Emp.: 510
Grocery Stores
N.A.I.C.S.: 445110
Juan Luna Rodriguez (Pres)
Johanna Leuna (Office Mgr)
Minerva Luna (Operations Mgr)
Jessica Luna (Mgr-HR)
Angel Rodriguez (Mgr)
Angelo Rodriguez (Mgr)
Mirta Melendez (Mgr)
Jose Rivas (Mgr)

PONCE DE LEON FEDERAL BANK
2244 Westchester Ave, Bronx, NY 10462
Tel.: (718) 931-9000
Web Site:
http://www.poncedeleonbank.com
Year Founded: 1960
Rev.: $24,446,000
Emp.: 30
Federal Savings & Loan Associations
N.A.I.C.S.: 621399
Ioannis Kouzilos (VP-Credit Admin)
Mario Pastorino (CFO)
Laura Perez (VP)
Sandra Viera (Branch Mgr)
Howard Jimerson (Asst VP)
Steven A. Tsavaris (Chm & CEO)

PONDELWILKINSON INC.
1880 Century Park E Ste 350, Los Angeles, CA 90067
Tel.: (310) 279-5980

Web Site: http://www.pondel.com
Year Founded: 1981
Sales Range: $10-24.9 Million
Emp.: 11
Financial, Health Care, High Technology, Industrial, Information Technology, Investor Relations, Public Relations
N.A.I.C.S.: 541810
Roger S. Pondel (Pres & CEO)
Robert M. Whetstone (Mng Dir & Principal)
Laurie Berman (Sr VP)
Robert Jaffe (Sr VP & Principal)
Evan Pondel (VP)
Judy Lin Sfetcu (VP)
George Medici (Sr VP)
Ron Neal (VP)

PONDER IDEAWORKS
20291 Ravenwood Ln, Huntington Beach, CA 92646
Tel.: (949) 801-4113   CA
Web Site:
http://www.ponderideaworks.com
Year Founded: 1991
Rev.: $3,200,000
Emp.: 3
Fiscal Year-end: 12/31/01
Advetising Agency
N.A.I.C.S.: 541810
Claudia Ponder (CEO)
Maria Nepite (Dir-Creative)

PONDEROSA TELEPHONE CO
47034 Rd 201, O Neals, CA 93645
Tel.: (559) 868-3312
Web Site:
http://www.goponderosa.com
Rev.: $32,762,253
Emp.: 60
Local Telephone Communications
N.A.I.C.S.: 517121
Elizabeth L. Silkwood (Pres)
Matthew Bose (Gen Mgr)

PONDS & SONS CONSTRUCTION COMPANY, INC.
24 Gabriel Dr, Ehrhardt, SC 29082
Tel.: (843) 846-2500
Web Site:
http://www.pondsconstruction.com
Year Founded: 2003
Sales Range: Less than $1 Million
Emp.: 8
Single-Family House Construction
N.A.I.C.S.: 236115
William Ponds (Owner & Pres)

PONGO RESUME
168 E Main St, Northborough, MA 01532
Tel.: (508) 393-4528
Web Site: http://www.pongo.com
Year Founded: 2004
Rev.: $4,700,000
Emp.: 18
Software Publisher
N.A.I.C.S.: 513210
Rodney Capron Jr. (Pres & CEO)

PONTCHARTRAIN FOODS INC.
71711 Riverside Dr, Covington, LA 70433
Tel.: (985) 892-6173
Sales Range: $350-399.9 Million
Emp.: 500
Fast-Food Restaurant Owner & Operator
N.A.I.C.S.: 722513
Glen Jacobs (VP)
Barbara Gennusa (Controller)

PONTIAC IGA FOOD CENTER

1925 N Perry St, Pontiac, MI 48340-0953
Tel.: (248) 373-1111   MI
Year Founded: 1981
Sales Range: $25-49.9 Million
Emp.: 50
Grocery Stores
N.A.I.C.S.: 445110
Sam Denha (Pres)

PONTIAC RV INC.
15481 E 2000 N Rd, Pontiac, IL 61764
Tel.: (815) 844-5000
Web Site: http://www.pontiacrv.com
Sales Range: $10-24.9 Million
Emp.: 50
Recreational Vehicle Dealers
N.A.I.C.S.: 441210
Gail Kafer (Sec)

PONTIFLEX INC.
45 Main St Ste 636, Brooklyn, NY 11201
Tel.: (800) 420-6086
Web Site: http://www.pontiflex.com
Year Founded: 2006
Sales Range: $10-24.9 Million
Emp.: 41
Online Advertising Software & Services
N.A.I.C.S.: 513210
Sujay Jhaveri (CEO)
Steve Kempisty (VP-Bus Dev)
Patrick J. Molloy (VP-Sls)

PONTOON BOAT, LLC
2805 Decio Dr, Elkhart, IN 46514
Tel.: (574) 264-6336   DE
Web Site:
http://www.benningtonmarine.com
Small Recreational Boat Mfr & Whslr
N.A.I.C.S.: 336612
Steve Vogel (Founder & Chm)
Jacob Vogel (CEO)

PONTOTOC ELECTRIC POWER ASSOCIATION
12 S Main St, Pontotoc, MS 38863
Tel.: (662) 489-3211
Web Site: http://www.pepa.com
Sales Range: $1-9.9 Million
Emp.: 62
Distribution, Electric Power
N.A.I.C.S.: 221122
Chuck Howell (Gen Mgr)
Mark Patterson (Dir-Acctg & Fin)
Jennifer Johnson (Mgr-HR)
Kathy Williamson (Mgr-Collections)

PONY EXPRESS BANCORP, INC.
209 Roseport Rd, Elwood, KS 66024
Tel.: (913) 365-5156
Bank Holding Company
N.A.I.C.S.: 551111
Robert Means (Pres & CEO)

Subsidiaries:

Pony Express Community Bank (1)
624 Felix St, Saint Joseph, MO 64501
Tel.: (816) 671-2265
Web Site: http://www.ponyexpr.com
Rev.: $1,743,000
Emp.: 19
Commericial Banking
N.A.I.C.S.: 522110
Robert A. Means (Pres)
Luke Moore (Asst VP)

POOL & ELECTRICAL PRODUCTS INC.
1250 E Francis St, Ontario, CA 91761
Tel.: (909) 673-1160
Web Site:
http://www.poolelectrical.com

POOL & ELECTRICAL PRODUCTS INC.

Pool & Electrical Products Inc.—(Continued)
Sales Range: $10-24.9 Million
Emp.: 60
Swimming Pool & Hot Tub Service & Maintenance
N.A.I.C.S.: 561790
Andres Becerra *(Pres)*
Sandra Becerra *(CFO)*
Marta Testa *(Controller)*

POOL CITY INC.
5555 Mountain View Dr, West Mifflin, PA 15122
Tel.: (412) 892-2620
Web Site: http://www.poolcity.net
Sales Range: $10-24.9 Million
Emp.: 25
Sales of Above Ground Swimming Pools
N.A.I.C.S.: 459999
Mark Blohm *(Dir-Svc & Installation)*
Marty Horvitz *(Mgr)*
Chris Alberta *(Mgr-Warehouse)*

POOL COVERS, INC.
4925 Fulton Dr, Fairfield, CA 94534
Tel.: (707) 864-6674   CA
Web Site:
http://www.poolcoversinc.com
Year Founded: 1984
Sales Range: $1-9.9 Million
Emp.: 40
Safety Swimming Pool Covers
N.A.I.C.S.: 459999
Bonnie Pickens *(Owner)*
Claire King *(Pres)*

POOL WATER PRODUCTS INC.
17872 Mitchell N, Irvine, CA 92614-6034
Tel.: (949) 756-1666   CA
Web Site: http://www.poolwater.com
Year Founded: 1964
Sales Range: $25-49.9 Million
Emp.: 200
Pooling Chemical Supply Services
N.A.I.C.S.: 423910
Dean C. Allred *(Pres)*
James Bledsoe *(VP)*

POOLDAWG.COM, INC.
PO Box 552, Lafayette, CO 80026
Tel.: (720) 214-3668
Web Site: http://www.pooldawg.com
Year Founded: 2003
Sales Range: $10-24.9 Million
Emp.: 10
Online Pool & Billiards Products Retailer
N.A.I.C.S.: 423910
Kevin Engelke *(Pres)*

POOLE & POOLE ARCHITECTURE, LLC
3736 Winterfield Rd Ste 102, Midlothian, VA 23113
Tel.: (804) 225-0215
Web Site: http://www.2pa.net
Sales Range: $1-9.9 Million
Emp.: 10
Architectural Services
N.A.I.C.S.: 541310
Michael R. Poole *(CEO & Mng Partner)*
Nea May Poole *(COO & Mng Partner)*

POOLE & SHAFFERY, LLP
400 S Hope St Ste 1100, Los Angeles, CA 90071
Tel.: (213) 439-5390
Web Site:
http://www.pooleshaffery.com
Year Founded: 1998

Law Firm
N.A.I.C.S.: 541110
Chris S. Jacobsen *(Partner)*
David S. Poole *(Partner)*
Brian E. Koegle *(Partner)*
Jaion Chung *(Partner)*
Michael S. Little *(Partner)*
Samuel R. W. Price *(Partner)*

POOLE CHEMICAL CO. INC.
111 N 1st St, Texline, TX 79087
Tel.: (806) 362-4261   TX
Web Site:
http://www.poolechemical.com
Year Founded: 1962
Sales Range: $10-24.9 Million
Emp.: 100
Mfr of Agricultural Chemicals
N.A.I.C.S.: 424910
James D. Poole *(Pres)*

POP CAPITAL LLC
200 Varick St Ste 606, New York, NY 10014
Tel.: (212) 488-1701
Web Site: http://www.pop-capital.com
Privater Equity Firm
N.A.I.C.S.: 523940
Alexander Duckworth *(Partner)*
Elijah Duckworth-Schachter *(Partner)*
Ray Simpson *(Partner)*

Subsidiaries:

Douglas Gill International Limited   (1)
Manor House Road, Long Eaton, Nottingham, NG10 1LR, United Kingdom
Tel.: (44) 115 946 0844
Web Site: http://www.gillmarine.com
Sailing Specialty Apparel Designer, Mfr, Whslr & Online Retailer
N.A.I.C.S.: 315250
Jamie Thomas Tunnicliffe *(CEO)*
Ian Graydon Poore *(CFO)*

Subsidiary (US):

Gill North America, Ltd.   (2)
1025 Pkwy Industrial Park Dr, Buford, GA 30518
Tel.: (770) 271-2669
Web Site: http://www.gillna.com
Sales Range: $1-9.9 Million
Emp.: 15
Specialty Sailing Apparel Distr & Online Retailer
N.A.I.C.S.: 458110
David Pritchard *(Sr VP)*

POP LABS, INC
7850 Parkwood Cir Ste B3, Houston, TX 77036
Tel.: (713) 243-4500
Web Site: http://www.poplabs.com
Year Founded: 2001
Rev.: $10,000,000
Emp.: 60
Internet/Web Design, Search Engine Optimization, Web (Banner Ads, Pop-ups, etc.)
N.A.I.C.S.: 541810
Gene McCubin *(Founder)*
Victoria Rabin *(Dir-Bus Dev & Intl)*
Audra Jackson *(Dir-Client Svcs)*
Stephanie Elsy *(CFO)*

POP WARNER LITTLE SCHOLARS INC.
586 Middletown Blvd Ste C100, Langhorne, PA 19047
Tel.: (215) 752-2691   PA
Web Site: http://www.popwarner.com
Year Founded: 1929
Rev.: $4,002,784
Assets: $3,195,759
Liabilities: $677,721
Net Worth: $2,518,038
Earnings: ($127,886)
Emp.: 10
Fiscal Year-end: 03/31/14

Sport Promotion Services
N.A.I.C.S.: 711310
Mary Fitzgerald *(COO)*
Jon C. Butler *(Exec Dir)*
Wynn Jessup *(Chm)*
Larry Hayes *(VP)*
Dennis Donovan *(Sec)*
Anthony Visco Jr. *(Treas)*

POP2LIFE LLC
7 W 18th St 6th Fl, New York, NY 10011
Tel.: (212) 965-8230
Web Site: http://www.pop2life.com
Year Founded: 2003
Sales Range: $1-9.9 Million
Emp.: 10
Management Consulting Services
N.A.I.C.S.: 541613
Eric Murphy *(Founder & CEO)*
Dan Severs *(Dir-Music Initiatives)*
Michele Wiltshire *(Pres & Mng Dir)*
Jeff Bardin *(Exec Dir-Bus Dev)*
Lauren Collins *(Acct Dir)*
Ryan Brown *(Exec Dir-Creative Strategy)*
Kimberly Tittle *(Sr Project Mgr)*
Laura Ostendorf *(Sr Project Mgr)*
Sara Stile *(Sr Project Mgr)*
Tanya Gelman *(Mgr-Project)*
Anthony Dobrini *(Mgr-Project)*

POPCORN PALACE
16W030 83rd St, Burr Ridge, IL 60527
Tel.: (847) 801-1900
Web Site:
http://www.popcornpalace.com
Year Founded: 1998
Sales Range: $1-9.9 Million
Emp.: 26
Gourmet Popcorn
N.A.I.C.S.: 445298
Tim Heitmann *(Founder & CEO)*

POPCORN, INDIANA LLC
1 Cedar Ln, Englewood, NJ 07631
Web Site:
http://www.popcornindiana.com
Year Founded: 2002
Sales Range: $50-74.9 Million
Emp.: 154
Gourmet Popcorn
N.A.I.C.S.: 311999
Hitesh Hajarnavis *(Pres & CEO)*

POPE GOLF, LLC
438 Interstate Ct, Sarasota, FL 34240
Tel.: (941) 444-6600
Web Site: http://www.popegolf.net
Sales Range: $10-24.9 Million
Emp.: 500
Golf Courses & Clubs Management Services
N.A.I.C.S.: 713910
Keith Pope *(CEO)*
Ingrid Pope *(CFO)*
Brad Compton *(VP-Ops)*
Ryan Henderson *(Dir-Mktg)*
Denny Albert *(Dir-Agronomy)*
Nicole Mattei *(Dir-HR)*

POPEJOY CONSTRUCTION COMPANY INC.
123 Oklahoma Ave, Ulysses, KS 67880-2543
Tel.: (620) 356-3404   KS
Year Founded: 1945
Sales Range: $25-49.9 Million
Emp.: 4
Provider of Construction Products & Services
N.A.I.C.S.: 212321
Donald G. Popejoy *(Pres)*
David Kinkall *(Office Mgr)*

U.S. PRIVATE

POPEYES LIMITED PARTNERSHIP I
12150 Tech Rd, Silver Spring, MD 20904
Tel.: (301) 625-5920
Web Site:
http://www.popeyeschicken.com
Rev.: $11,000,000
Emp.: 800
Fast Food Restaurant Operator
N.A.I.C.S.: 722513
Hank Jorgenson *(CEO)*

POPLAR CAPITAL PARTNERS LLC
22343 La Palma Ave Ste 110, Yorba Linda, CA 92887
Tel.: (646) 586-3060
Web Site:
http://www.poplarpartners.com
Investments in Market Research Software & Data Services
N.A.I.C.S.: 523999
Alex Gelman *(Founder & Mng Partner)*

Subsidiaries:

mTAB LLC   (1)
1100 E Orangethorpe Ave Ste 251, Anaheim, CA 92801
Tel.: (714) 693-3110
Web Site: http://www.mtab.com
Sales Range: $1-9.9 Million
Emp.: 15
Computer System Design Services
N.A.I.C.S.: 541512
Mark Lummas *(Dir-Client Svcs)*

POPLAR HEALTHCARE, PLLC
3495 Hacks Cross Rd, Memphis, TN 38125-8803
Tel.: (901) 526-1912   TN
Web Site:
http://www.poplarhealthcare.com
Year Founded: 1995
Laboratory Services Company
N.A.I.C.S.: 541380
James P. Sweeney *(CEO)*
Patrick J. Dean *(Chm)*
Grant D. Carlson *(Chief Dev Officer)*
Tracy K. Emery *(CFO)*
Jackie M. Makapugay *(Dir-Gastrointestinal Pathology)*
Brett Kirkman *(Sr VP)*
Anami Patel *(VP-Genomics Ops & Dev)*
Susan T. Williams *(Sr VP)*

Subsidiaries:

Bostwick Laboratories, Inc.   (1)
3495 Hacks Cross Rd, Memphis, TN 38125
Tel.: (407) 992-0984
Web Site: http://www.uropathdiagnostics.com
Anatomic Pathology Laboratories
N.A.I.C.S.: 621511
David G. Bostwick *(Chief Medical Officer)*
C. Michael Choi *(Dir-Non-GYN Cytology)*
Hillel Kahane *(Dir-Medical-New York)*
Karla M. Perrizo *(Dir-Genitourinary Pathology)*
Anita S. Kulharya *(Dir-Cytogenetics)*

POPMAIL.COM, INC.
1331 Corporate Dr Ste 350, Irving, TX 75038
Tel.: (972) 550-5500
Food Service
N.A.I.C.S.: 722310
Jesse Berst *(COO)*

POPPER AND COMPANY LLC
413 South Blvd of the Presidents, Sarasota, FL 34326
Tel.: (941) 586-9188
Web Site:
http://www.popperandco.com
Year Founded: 2003
Sales Range: $1-9.9 Million

M&A Advisory & Specialty Consulting Services
N.A.I.C.S.: 541611
Caroline Popper (Co-Founder & Pres)
Ken Walz (Co-Founder)

POPPLE CONSTRUCTION, INC.
215 E Saylor Ave, Wilkes Barre, PA 18702
Tel.: (570) 823-0531
Web Site: http://www.poppleconstruction.com
Year Founded: 1989
Sales Range: $10-24.9 Million
Emp.: 175
Water Works Construction & Contractor
N.A.I.C.S.: 238910
Mark Popple (Owner & Pres)
Carolyn Gruver (Controller)
Joe Phillips (Mgr-Pur)

POPS MART FUELS, LLC
418 Piney Grove Rd, Columbia, SC 29210-3835
Web Site: https://popsmartfuels.com
Emp.: 100
Gasoline Stations with Convenience Stores
N.A.I.C.S.: 457110

Subsidiaries:

Fuel Service - DJ's Mart LLC (1)
337 E Park Ave, Chippewa Falls, WI 54729-3163
Tel.: (715) 723-1701
Web Site: https://www.fuelservicellc.com
Sales Range: $25-49.9 Million
Emp.: 140
Provider of Retail Services
N.A.I.C.S.: 445131
John Salden (Pres)

Scully Oil Co , Inc. (1)
150 Flint St, Lyndon Station, WI 53944
Tel.: (608) 666-2662
Web Site: http://www.scullyoil.com
Sales Range: $1-9.9 Million
Emp.: 30
Gasoline Service Stations
N.A.I.C.S.: 457120
Jeff Scully (Pres)

POPULAR FORD SALES INC.
2505 Coney Is Ave, Brooklyn, NY 11223
Tel.: (718) 376-5600
Web Site: http://www.popularford.com
Rev.: $41,500,000
Emp.: 65
Automobiles, New & Used
N.A.I.C.S.: 441110

POPULATION SERVICES INTERNATIONAL
1120 19th St NW Ste 600, Washington, DC 20036
Tel.: (202) 785-0072 NC
Web Site: http://www.psi.org
Year Founded: 1970
Sales Range: $550-599.9 Million
Emp.: 392
Community Health Care Services
N.A.I.C.S.: 621498
Karl Hofmann (Pres & CEO)
Kimberly Schwartz (CFO & Sr VP)
Peter Clancy (COO & Exec VP)
Desmond Chavasse (Sr VP-Malaria Control & Child Survival)
Colleen Gregerson (VP-New Bus Dev)
J. Brian Atwood (Chm)
Gail Harmon (Vice Chm)
Brandon Guzzone (Chief HR Officer)

PORCARO COMMUNICATIONS
433 W 9th Ave, Anchorage, AK 99501-3519
Tel.: (907) 276-4262
Web Site: http://www.porcarocommunications.com
Year Founded: 1982
Rev.: $10,000,000
Emp.: 15
Advertising Agencies, Communications
N.A.I.C.S.: 541810
Michael F. Porcaro (CEO)
Mark Hopkin (Pres)
John Hume (Sr Dir-Art)
Janis Plume (Mgr-Production & Traffic)
Matt Twohy (Sr Copywriter)
Joy Diane Mark Anthony (Mgr-Pur)
Scott Banks (Sr Acct Mgr)
Daryl Hoflich (Dir-Creative)
Vince Penman (Dir-Art, Producer & Interactive Cowboy)
Tyler Johnson (Mgr-Production-Traffic)
Brendan Dowd (Dir-Art)

Subsidiaries:

Porcaro Vancouver (1)
504-221 West Esplanade, Vancouver, V7M 3J3, BC, Canada
Tel.: (604) 985-2400
Emp.: 7
N.A.I.C.S.: 541810
Barbara Moreira (Mng Partner)
Wendy Kearns (VP)

PORCELANOSA NEW YORK INC.
200 Lexington Ave Ste 609, New York, NY 10016
Tel.: (212) 252-7370
Web Site: http://www.porcelanosa-usa.com
Rev.: $10,000,000
Emp.: 8
Tile, Ceramic
N.A.I.C.S.: 444180
Jose Alareu (Mgr)
William Pistone (Mgr-Warehouse)
Eunice Woods (Mgr-Freight)
Donna Levy (Mgr-Sls-NJ)
Susan Gilberg (Mgr)
Joe Rinaldi (Acct Mgr)
Diane Saylor (Mgr-HR)
Andrea Ramsden (Mgr-Kitchen Sls)
John Penta (Mgr-Sls)
Robinson Brian (Acct Exec)
Rocio Raventos Domenech (Asst Mgr-Pur)

PORK KING GOOD
Tel.: (414) 483-6562
Web Site: https://porkkinggood.com
Year Founded: 2018
Emp.: 100
Pork snack Mfr
N.A.I.C.S.: 311919
Lauren Koston (Founder)

Subsidiaries:

Porkie Company of Wisconsin (1)
3113 E Layton Ave, Cudahy, WI 53110
Tel.: (414) 483-6562
Web Site: http://www.porkiesofwisconsin.com
Sales Range: $1-9.9 Million
Emp.: 24
Snack Food Mfr
N.A.I.C.S.: 311919

PORK KING PACKING, INC.
8808 S State Route 23, Marengo, IL 60152
Tel.: (815) 568-8024
Web Site: http://www.porkkingpacking.com
Year Founded: 1988

Sales Range: $25-49.9 Million
Emp.: 250
Processed Pork Mfr
N.A.I.C.S.: 311611
Maria Faso (Office Mgr)
Kazimierz Koziol (Mgr-Facility)
Arturo Cabrera (Mgr-Quality Control)
Tom Miles (Co-Owner & Dir-Sls & Livestock)
Stanley Pajerski (Co-Owner & Dir-Production)

PORKY PRODUCTS INC.
400 Port Carteret Dr, Carteret, NJ 07008-0609
Tel.: (732) 359-9100 NY
Web Site: http://www.porkyproducts.com
Year Founded: 1961
Sales Range: $300-349.9 Million
Emp.: 175
Meats & Meat Products
N.A.I.C.S.: 424470
Anthony Giaconelli (VP-Fin)

POROCEL INDUSTRIES, LLC
10300 Arch St Pike, Little Rock, AR 72206
Tel.: (832) 688-9696
Web Site: http://www.porocel.com
Catalyst Innovation Services
N.A.I.C.S.: 213112
Terence J McHugh (Pres & COO)

Subsidiaries:

Porocel Corp. (1)
12777 Jones Rd Ste 280, Houston, TX 77070-4689
Tel.: (281) 469-8555
Web Site: http://www.porocel.com
Chemicals Mfr
N.A.I.C.S.: 325180
Peter Douvry (Mgr)

PORRECO NISSAN
8890 Peach St, Erie, PA 16509
Tel.: (814) 860-8377
Web Site: http://www.porreconissan.com
Sales Range: $10-24.9 Million
Emp.: 55
Automobile Sales
N.A.I.C.S.: 441110
Michael Clement (Mgr-Pre-Owned Vehicles)
Jeff Carden (Mgr-Bus)
Elise Loya (Office Mgr)
Chris Krepps (Asst Mgr-Svc)
Mike Taylor (Dir-Svc & Parts)
Paul DeDionisio (Mgr-Bus)
Joe Londo (Mgr-Fixed Ops)
Sean Stone (Mgr-Gen Sls)
Ashley Angerer (Mgr-Internet)
Bryon Kehl (Mgr-New Car Sls)
Steve Fleishell (Mgr-Vehicle Restoration)

PORT AMHERST, LTD.
2 Port Amherst Dr, Charleston, WV 25306-6637
Tel.: (304) 926-1140 WV
Web Site: http://www.amherstmadison.com
Year Founded: 1983
Sales Range: $25-49.9 Million
Emp.: 250
Holding Company
N.A.I.C.S.: 551112
Charles T. Jones (Chm)
Jeromy Hodges (Treas)

Subsidiaries:

Amherst Madison, Inc. (1)
2 Port Amherst Dr, Charleston, WV
25306-6637 (100%)
Tel.: (304) 926-1100

Web Site: http://www.amherstmadison.com
Rev.: $2,032,184
Emp.: 35
Coal Loading Services; Barge & Boat Repair Services
N.A.I.C.S.: 213113
Charles T. Jones (Pres)
Drema Woods (Sec)

PORT AUTHORITY OF ALLEGHENY COUNTY INC.
345 6th Ave 3rd Fl, Pittsburgh, PA 15222
Tel.: (412) 566-5500
Web Site: http://www.portauthority.org
Year Founded: 1956
Sales Range: $75-99.9 Million
Emp.: 1,400
Intercity & Rural Bus Transportation Services
N.A.I.C.S.: 485210
Dante Bongiorni (Asst Mgr-Road Ops)
Dottie Buchanan (Supvr-Customer Svc)
Bruce Grover (Dir-Svc Delivery)
Constance McCarthy (Mgr-EAP)
Scott Vetere (Dir-Svc Plng & Schedules)
Paul Zatek (Coord-Fleet Maintenance)
Don Rivetti (Dir-Main Shop)
Ed Greene (Coord-DBE)
Inez Colon (Dir-Employment & Dev)
Loretta Wolfe (Sec)
Tim Frank (Dir-Creative)
Jeff Letwin (Chm)
Katharine Eagan Kelleman (CEO)

PORT AUTHORITY OF NEW YORK & NEW JERSEY
4 World Trade Ctr 150 Greenwich St 24th Fl, New York, NY 10007
Tel.: (212) 435-7777
Web Site: http://www.panynj.gov
Year Founded: 1921
Rev.: $5,344,008,000
Assets: $47,868,583,000
Liabilities: $31,990,189,000
Net Worth: $15,878,394,000
Earnings: ($30,282,000)
Emp.: 195
Fiscal Year-end: 12/31/18
Transportation, Port & Commerce Facilities & Services
N.A.I.C.S.: 485999
Rick Cotton (Exec Dir)

Subsidiaries:

Newark Legal & Communications Center Urban Renewal Corporation (1)
1037 Raymond Blvd, Newark, NJ 07102-5418
Tel.: (973) 624-8500
Web Site: http://www.panynj.gov
Sales Range: $50-74.9 Million
Emp.: 150
Community & Governmental Operations for the NY/NJ Port Authority
N.A.I.C.S.: 921190
Patrick J. Foye (Pres)

Port Authority Trans-Hudson Corp. (1)
1 Path Plz, Jersey City, NJ 07306-2905
Tel.: (201) 216-6015
Web Site: http://www.panynj.gov
Sales Range: $100-124.9 Million
Emp.: 1,000
Rail Transit
N.A.I.C.S.: 485112

PORT BROKERS INC.
152-60 Rockaway Blvd, Jamaica, NY 11434-2800
Tel.: (718) 723-8210 NY
Web Site: http://www.portgroupusa.com
Year Founded: 1967
Sales Range: $25-49.9 Million

PORT BROKERS INC.

U.S. PRIVATE

Port Brokers Inc.—(Continued)
Emp.: 40
Freight Transportation Arrangement
N.A.I.C.S.: 541618
Joseph Shen *(Mgr-Compliance)*
Ted Gapinski *(Mgr-Import)*

PORT CITY BAKERY INC.
PO Box 12706, Green Bay, WI 54307-2706
Tel.: (920) 499-3111
Web Site: http://www.akcrust.com
Rev.: $10,000,000
Emp.: 120
Doughs, Frozen Or Refrigerated: From Purchased Flour
N.A.I.C.S.: 311824
Gail Bush *(Mgr-Pur)*

Subsidiaries:

Alive & Kickin (1)
1326 Cornell Rd, Green Bay, WI 54313
Tel.: (920) 662-0304
Web Site: http://www.akcrust.com
Sales Range: $10-24.9 Million
Emp.: 100
Pizza Restaurant
N.A.I.C.S.: 722513
Randy Charles *(CEO)*
Nick Charles *(Pres)*

PORT CONSOLIDATED INC.
3141 SE 14th Ave, Fort Lauderdale, FL 33316
Tel.: (954) 522-1182
Web Site:
http://www.portconsolidated.com
Sales Range: $10-24.9 Million
Emp.: 85
Provider of Lubricating Oils & Greases & Fuel
N.A.I.C.S.: 424720
Michael Simmons *(Owner & COO)*
Joe Siska *(CFO)*

PORT ERIE PLASTICS, INC.
909 Troupe Rd, Harborcreek, PA 16421
Tel.: (814) 899-7602
Web Site: http://www.porterie.com
Year Founded: 1953
Sales Range: $25-49.9 Million
Emp.: 350
Plastics Product Mfr
N.A.I.C.S.: 326199
John Johnson *(Pres)*
Jon Connole *(Mgr-Sls & Mktg)*
Jeff Horneman *(Mgr-Support Ops)*
Jim Malloy *(Mgr-HR)*
Joe Deutsch *(Mgr-Mfg)*
Tom Brzozowski *(Mgr-Engrg)*
Joe Winkler *(Sr Project Engr)*
Mike Malinowski *(Mgr-Quality Assurance)*
Marsha Miller *(Controller)*

PORT HARBOR MARINE INC.
1 Spring Point Dr, South Portland, ME 04106
Tel.: (207) 767-3254
Web Site:
http://www.portharbormarine.com
Sales Range: $10-24.9 Million
Emp.: 70
Retailer of Motor Boats & Marine Supplies
N.A.I.C.S.: 441222
Robert C. Soucy Jr. *(Pres)*

PORT JEFF CHRYSLER PLYMOUTH JEEP EAGLE INC.
5130 Nesconset Hwy, Port Jefferson Station, NY 11776
Tel.: (631) 474-3939
Web Site:
http://portjesschryslerjeep.com
Sales Range: $10-24.9 Million

Emp.: 47
Car Whslr
N.A.I.C.S.: 441110
Peter Rhein *(Pres)*

PORT JERSEY LOGISTICS
200 Liberty Way, Cranbury, NJ 08512
Tel.: (609) 860-1010
Web Site: http://www.portjersey.com
Sales Range: $10-24.9 Million
Emp.: 120
Special Warehousing & Storage
N.A.I.C.S.: 493190
Erik Holck *(Dir-Bus Dev)*
Leila Davis *(Controller)*

Subsidiaries:

Tyler Distribution Centers (1)
7 Corn Rd, Dayton, NJ 08810
Tel.: (732) 274-9371
Web Site: http://www.portjersey.com
Provider of Total Supply Chain Management Services: General Warehousing
N.A.I.C.S.: 493110

PORT LOGISTICS GROUP, INC.
288 Mayo Ave, City of Industry, CA 91789
Tel.: (877) 901-6472
Web Site: http://www.whiplash.com
Year Founded: 2008
Gateway Logistics Services
N.A.I.C.S.: 541614
Brian Weinstein *(Sr VP-Bus Dev)*
Jeffrey Wolpov *(CEO)*
Greg Morello *(Pres & Chief Comml Officer)*
James Stephens *(CIO)*
Sarah Drazetic *(Chief Process Officer & Chief Engr)*

Subsidiaries:

Enlinx, LLC (1)
2620 S Decker Lake Blvd Ste 500, Salt Lake City, UT 84119
Tel.: (801) 903-1035
Web Site: http://www.enlinx.com
Fulfillment & Warehousing Services
N.A.I.C.S.: 493110
Dave Burns *(CEO)*
Lee Payne *(VP-Mktg)*
Brent Ainsworth *(CFO)*
David Bretey *(COO)*
Mike Higgins *(CIO)*

Whiplash Merchandising Inc. (1)
2075 W Stadium Blvd #1878, Ann Arbor, MI 48108
Tel.: (415) 349-0141
Web Site: https://whiplash.com
E-Commerce, Fulfillment & Logistics
N.A.I.C.S.: 541614

PORT MORRIS TILE & MARBLE
1285 Oakpoint Ave, Bronx, NY 10474
Tel.: (718) 378-6100
Web Site:
http://www.portmorristile.com
Rev.: $50,000,000
Emp.: 400
Terrazzo, Tile, Marble & Mosaic Work
N.A.I.C.S.: 238340
Patrick Barrett *(Pres)*
Don Durnell *(Project Mgr)*
Aurelio Elias *(VP-Production)*
Frank Juranich *(CFO)*
Vincent P. DeLazzero II *(CEO)*

PORT OF EVERETT
1205 Craftsman Way, Everett, WA 98201
Tel.: (425) 259-3164
Web Site:
http://www.portofeverett.com
Rev.: $12,469,378
Emp.: 90
Marine Terminals

N.A.I.C.S.: 488320
Carl Wollebek *(COO)*
Ed Madura *(Dir-Security)*
John Carter *(CFO)*
Lisa Lefeber *(Acting CEO)*

PORT OF GALVESTON
123 Rosenberg Ave, Galveston, TX 77553
Tel.: (409) 765-9321
Web Site:
http://www.portofgalveston.com
Year Founded: 1825
Rev.: $43,514,516
Assets: $188,085,292
Liabilities: $53,324,527
Net Worth: $134,760,765
Earnings: $7,048,669
Emp.: 86
Fiscal Year-end: 12/31/18
Marine Cargo Handling Services
N.A.I.C.S.: 488310
Victor M. Hernandez *(Sr Controller)*
H. L. Smith *(Dir-Cruise Ops)*
Cristina Bujaucius *(Mgr-PR)*
Mark R. Murchison *(Treas & Dir-Fin)*
Roger Quiroga *(Dir-Economic Dev & External Affairs)*
Robert Pierce *(Dir-Safety & Security)*
Peter Simons *(Dir-Facilities & Ops & Deputy Dir-Port)*
Bill Dell *(Asst Mgr-Cruise Terminal)*
Brett B. Milutin *(Officer-Facility Security)*
J. Ross Soileau *(Supvr-EOC)*
Ted O'Rourke *(Chm)*
Rodger E. Rees *(Dir-Port)*
John G. Peterlin III *(Sr Dir-Mktg & Admin)*

PORT OF HOUSTON AUTHORITY
111 E Loop N, Houston, TX 77029-4326
Tel.: (713) 670-2400
Web Site:
http://www.portofhouston.com
Year Founded: 1914
Sales Range: $250-299.9 Million
Emp.: 528
Port Operator
N.A.I.C.S.: 488310
Erik A. Eriksson *(Chief Legal Officer)*
Janiece M. Longoria *(Chm-Port Commission)*
Maxine N. Buckles *(Chief Audit Officer)*
Ricky W. Kunz *(Chief Comml Officer)*
Roger D. Guenther *(Exec Dir)*
Jeff Davis *(Chief Port Ops Officer)*
Tim Finley *(CFO)*
Phyllis Saathoff *(Chief People Officer)*
Marcus Woodring *(Chief Health, Safety, Security & Emergency Ops Officer)*
Orlando Sanchez *(Treas-County)*
Thomas J. Heidt *(COO)*
Charles Thompson *(CIO)*
Curtis E. Duncan *(Controller)*
Wendolynn Montoya Cloonan *(Commissioner)*

PORT OF MIAMI TERMINAL OPERATING COMPANY, LC
1007 N America Way Ste 400, Miami, FL 33132
Tel.: (305) 416-7600
Web Site: http://www.pomtoc.com
Sales Range: $10-24.9 Million
Emp.: 20
Marine Cargo Handling
N.A.I.C.S.: 488320
Charles O'Malley *(CFO)*
Howard Weintraub *(Mgr-Safety & Security)*
Ana Toledo *(Controller)*

Hilda Torres *(Mgr-EDI & Customer Svc)*
Carlos Garcia *(Mgr-Billing)*
Robert Stark *(Mgr-Terminal Operating Sys)*
Bert Cedeno *(Mgr-Terminal)*

PORT OF OAKLAND
530 Water St, Oakland, CA 94607-3746
Tel.: (510) 627-1100
Web Site:
http://www.portofoakland.com
Year Founded: 1927
Sales Range: $250-299.9 Million
Emp.: 600
Operator of Airport, Marine Terminals, Restaurants, Shopping Complexs, Office & Marina Complex & Business Park
N.A.I.C.S.: 926120
Kristi McKenney *(COO)*
Richard Sinkoff *(Dir-Environmental Programs & Plng)*
Robert Bernardo *(Acting Dir-Comm)*
Beth Frisher *(Mgr-Bus Dev & Intl Mktg)*
Arnel Atienza *(Chief Audit Officer)*
Amy Tharpe *(Dir-Social Responsibility)*
Bryant L. Francis *(Dir-Aviation)*
Danny Wan *(Exec Dir)*
Pamela Kershaw *(Dir-Comml Real Estate)*
Sara Lee *(CFO)*
Christopher Boucher *(Dir-HR)*
Matt Davis *(Dir-Govt Affairs)*
Bryan Brandes *(Dir-Maritime)*

PORT OF PORTLAND
7200 NE Airport Way, Portland, OR 97218-4049
Tel.: (503) 944-7000
Web Site:
http://www.portofportland.com
Year Founded: 1891
Sales Range: $200-249.9 Million
Emp.: 787
Marine Cargo; Industrial Parks; Aviation & Distr; Industrial & Commercial Property Development
N.A.I.C.S.: 926120
David Zielke *(Dir-Air Svcs Dev)*
Christine White *(Dir-Community Affairs)*
Craig Johnsen *(Mgr-Contracts & Procurement)*
Donna Eaves *(Partner-HR Bus)*
Keith Leavitt *(Chief Comml Officer)*
Martha Richmond *(Dir-Corp Comm)*
Vince Granato *(COO)*
Cindy Nichol *(CFO)*
Curtis Robinhold *(Deputy Exec Dir)*
Steve Nakana *(Mgr-Social Equity)*
Bob Burket *(Controller)*
Daniel Blaufus *(Gen Counsel)*
Mark Greinke *(CIO)*
Bobbi Stedman *(Chief Admin Officer)*
Rob Fix *(Exec Dir)*

PORT OF SUBS INC.
5365 Mae Anne Ave Ste A29, Reno, NV 89523
Tel.: (775) 747-0555
Web Site: http://www.portofsubs.com
Year Founded: 1975
Sales Range: $100-124.9 Million
Emp.: 300
Sandwiches & Submarines Shop
N.A.I.C.S.: 722513
John Larsen *(CEO)*
David Burns *(Mgr-IT)*
Jennifer Wallace *(Coord-Admin Support)*
Jaci Hall *(Mgr-Mktg)*
Josh Ashworth *(Asst Mgr)*
Mike Powell *(Pres)*

PORT OF TACOMA
1 Sitcum Way, Tacoma, WA 98421
Tel.: (253) 383-5841
Web Site:
http://www.portoftacoma.com
Sales Range: $50-74.9 Million
Emp.: 235
Commercial & Industrial Building Operation
N.A.I.C.S.: 531120
Clare Petrich *(Chm)*
Erin Galeno *(CFO)*
John Wolfe *(CEO)*
Jane Vandenberg *(Dir-Engrg)*
Eric Johnson *(Exec Dir)*

PORT TO PORT INTERNATIONAL CORP.
32 Pyles Ln, New Castle, DE 19720
Tel.: (302) 654-2444
Web Site:
http://www.ptpshipping.com
Year Founded: 1998
Sales Range: $10-24.9 Million
Emp.: 36
Freight Transportation & Logistics Services
N.A.I.C.S.: 488510
Anabel Panayotti *(Pres & CEO)*
Gwen North *(VP)*

PORTABLE CHURCH INDUSTRIES, INC.
1923 Ring Dr, Troy, MI 48083
Tel.: (248) 585-9540
Web Site:
http://www.portablechurch.com
Year Founded: 1994
Sales Range: $1-9.9 Million
Emp.: 30
Consulting Services & Equipment for Churches Meeting in Rented Venues
N.A.I.C.S.: 541618
Daniel Hodgson *(Mgr-Shipping)*
Kevin Jones *(Dir-Sls, Mktg & Client Rels)*
Matthew Brumm *(Mgr-Mfg)*
David Laughlin *(Coord-Material Integration)*
Brandon Sweeten *(Coord-Production Team)*
Justin Sweeten *(Coord-Tech Wiring, Testing & Integration)*
Curt Banter *(Dir-Consulting)*
Andy Wissman *(Dir-Fulfillment)*
Jim Smiley *(Dir-Ops)*
Brett Hollifield *(Mgr-Fin)*
Steve Hollis *(Mgr-Pur)*
Julianne Naum *(Project Mgr)*

PORTABLE PRACTICAL EDUCATIONAL PREPARATION, INC
802 E 46th St, Tucson, AZ 85713
Tel.: (520) 622-3553
Web Site: http://www.ppep.org
Year Founded: 1970
Sales Range: $50-74.9 Million
Emp.: 753
Educational Support Services
N.A.I.C.S.: 611710
Kari Hogan *(Co-Chief Admin Officer)*
Gina K. Judy *(Co-Chief Admin Officer)*
Barbara Coronado *(COO & Dir-Fin)*
Robert Riggs *(Dir-IT)*
Johnson Bia *(Co-Chief Admin Officer)*
John David Arnold *(Founder & CEO)*

PORTABLES UNLIMITED INC.
136 1st St, Nanuet, NY 10954
Tel.: (845) 507-8200
Web Site:
http://www.portablesunlimited.com
Year Founded: 1999
Sales Range: $1-9.9 Million
Emp.: 30

Cellular Products Distr
N.A.I.C.S.: 423690
Irene Coughlin *(CFO)*
Raja Amar *(Pres & CEO)*
Larry Melchionda *(COO)*
Monika Amar *(VP-HR)*
Mo Jagota *(VP-Pur)*
Sonny Massand *(VP-Sls)*

PORTAGE PATH BEHAVIORAL HEALTH
340 S Broadway St, Akron, OH 44308
Tel.: (330) 253-3100
Web Site: http://www.portagepath.org
Year Founded: 1968
Sales Range: $10-24.9 Million
Emp.: 178
Mental Health Care Services
N.A.I.C.S.: 623220
Phillip Heisman *(Sr VP)*
Tracy Yaeger *(Pres)*
Sarah Beth Emberger *(Sec)*
James Gable *(Chm)*
John Zoifo *(Treas)*
Duane Angel *(Vice Chm)*
James A. Crouse *(Sr VP)*
Sean Blake *(VP & Dir-Medical)*

PORTAGE PHARMA LTD.
7966 Lovers Ln, Portage, MI 49002
Tel.: (269) 327-0033
Web Site:
http://www.portagepharmacy.com
Year Founded: 1972
Sales Range: $25-49.9 Million
Emp.: 300
Holding Company Drug Store & Pharmacy Services
N.A.I.C.S.: 551112
Larry Curtis *(Owner)*
Subsidiaries:

PMC Pharmacy Inc. (1)
1241 W Broadway St, Three Rivers, MI 49093-8319 **(100%)**
Tel.: (269) 279-5722
Sales Range: $10-24.9 Million
Emp.: 10
Drug Stores & Proprietary Stores
N.A.I.C.S.: 456110

Portage Pharmacy Inc. (1)
7966 Lovers Ln, Portage, MI 49002-5510 **(100%)**
Tel.: (269) 327-0033
Web Site: http://www.portagepharmacy.com
Sales Range: $10-24.9 Million
Emp.: 11
Drug Stores & Proprietary Stores
N.A.I.C.S.: 456110
Larry Curtis *(Co-Owner)*

Richland Village Drug Inc. (1)
8900 Gull Rd, Richland, MI 49083 **(100%)**
Tel.: (269) 629-9550
Web Site:
http://www.richlandvillagedrug.com
Sales Range: $10-24.9 Million
Emp.: 9
Drug Stores & Proprietary Stores
N.A.I.C.S.: 456110
Tom Bradley *(Branch Mgr)*

PORTAL SERVICE CO.
50101 Hwy 52 N, Kenmare, ND 58746
Tel.: (701) 933-2314
Web Site:
http://www.portalservicecompany.com
Year Founded: 1963
Sales Range: $10-24.9 Million
Emp.: 65
Oil Pipeline Seller & Installer
N.A.I.C.S.: 237120
Douglas Johnson *(CEO)*

PORTAL SOLUTIONS, LLC

2301 Research Blvd Ste 105, Rockville, MD 20850
Tel.: (240) 406-9960
Web Site:
http://www.portalsolutions.net
Year Founded: 2002
Sales Range: $10-24.9 Million
Emp.: 30
Computer System Design Services
N.A.I.C.S.: 541512
Daniel Cohen-Dumani *(Founder & CEO)*
Jill Hannemann *(Dir-Advisory Svcs)*
Rick Hinton *(VP-Products & Solutions)*
Val Orekhov *(CTO)*
Mark Bramhall *(Dir-Tech)*
Adam Krueger *(Dir-UI & UX Design Capability)*
Jenny Lynch *(Dir-Mktg)*
Dale Tuttle *(COO)*
Josh Steiner *(Dir-Practice)*

PORTCO CORPORATION
PO Box 2130, Woodland, WA 98674
Tel.: (360) 696-1641
Web Site: http://www.portco.com
Sales Range: $10-24.9 Million
Emp.: 100
Packing Paper
N.A.I.C.S.: 322220
Bryan Williamson *(VP-Production & Mktg)*
Kent Wall *(Founder, Chm & Pres)*

PORTE ADVERTISING, INC.
462 7th Ave 6th Fl, New York, NY 10018
Tel.: (212) 354-6906
Year Founded: 1993
Sales Range: $10-24.9 Million
Emp.: 2
Brand Development, Collateral, Public Relations
N.A.I.C.S.: 541810
Jay H. Heyman *(Principal & Dir-Creative)*
Paul C. Mesches *(Principal & Dir-Mktg)*

PORTE BROWN LLC
845 Oakton Steet, Elk Grove Village, IL 60007
Tel.: (847) 956-1040
Web Site:
https://www.portebrown.com
Emp.: 100
Accounting & Consulting Firm
N.A.I.C.S.: 541211
Joseph A. Gleba *(CEO & Mng Partner)*
Subsidiaries:

RVG Partners, LLC (1)
1110 Jorie Blvd Ste 350, Oak Brook, IL 60523
Tel.: (630) 472-0800
Offices of Certified Public Accountants
N.A.I.C.S.: 541211
Tom Pruim *(Partner)*

PORTEOUS FASTENER COMPANY INC.
12801 Leffingwell Ave., Santa Fe Springs, CA 90670
Tel.: (310) 847-6776
Web Site:
http://www.porteousfastener.com
Year Founded: 1966
Sales Range: $25-49.9 Million
Emp.: 400
Hardware Services
N.A.I.C.S.: 423710
Chris Saenz *(CFO)*

PORTER BURGESS COMPANY

2805 N Dallas Pkwy Ste 240, Plano, TX 75093
Tel.: (214) 373-6699
Web Site: http://www.flairdata.com
Sales Range: $25-49.9 Million
Emp.: 40
Communications Equipment
N.A.I.C.S.: 423690
Robert P. Burgess *(Pres)*
David Austin *(Controller)*

PORTER CAPITAL CORPORATION
2112 1st Ave N, Birmingham, AL 35203-4202
Tel.: (205) 322-5442
Web Site: http://www.portercap.net
Year Founded: 1992
Sales Range: $25-49.9 Million
Emp.: 35
Short-Term Business Credit
N.A.I.C.S.: 522299
Marc L. Porter *(Pres & CEO)*
Ron Williamson *(Founder & VP)*
Bob Reagan *(Bus Dev Officer)*
John Cox Miller *(Sr VP & Natl Sls Mgr)*
Tanya Fontenot *(Officer-Bus Dev)*
Robert Reagan *(Officer-Bus Dev & Sr VP)*
Karen Small *(Officer-Bus Dev & Sr VP)*

PORTER CHEVROLET HYUNDAI
414 E Cleveland Ave, Newark, DE 19711
Tel.: (302) 453-6800
Year Founded: 1952
Sales Range: $10-24.9 Million
Emp.: 70
Car Whslr
N.A.I.C.S.: 441110
Richard C. Porter II *(Owner)*

PORTER COMPANY/MECHANICAL CONTRACTORS
2105 FM 1626, Manchaca, TX 78652
Tel.: (512) 282-9691
Web Site:
http://www.theporterco.com
Rev.: $26,000,000
Emp.: 40
Mechanical Contractor
N.A.I.C.S.: 238220
David M. Richards *(Pres & CEO)*

PORTER COUNTY SCHOOL EMPLOYEES' INSURANCE TRUST
750 Ransom Rd, Valparaiso, IN 46385
Tel.: (219) 762-2278
Year Founded: 1997
Sales Range: $10-24.9 Million
Employee Welfare Services
N.A.I.C.S.: 525120
Mark Krom *(Sec)*
Rod Gardin *(Treas)*
Wanda Vawter *(VP)*
John Hunter *(Pres)*

PORTER GROUP, INC.
10320 Little Patuxent Pky Ste 1100, Columbia, MD 21044
Tel.: (410) 992-7776
Web Site:
http://www.portergroup.com
Year Founded: 1977
Rev.: $3,400,000
Emp.: 22
Personnel Agency
N.A.I.C.S.: 561311
James C. Porter *(Pres)*

PORTER NISSAN INFINITI
303 E Cleveland Ave, Newark, DE 19711

PORTER NISSAN INFINITI

Porter Nissan Infiniti—(Continued)
Tel.: (302) 368-6300
Web Site:
http://www.porternissan.com
Year Founded: 2000
Sales Range: $50-74.9 Million
Emp.: 75
Car Whslr
N.A.I.C.S.: 441110
Kevin Carroll *(Gen Mgr)*

PORTER PIPE & SUPPLY COMPANY
401 S Rohlwing Rd, Addison, IL 60101
Tel.: (630) 543-8145
Web Site: http://www.porterpipe.com
Sales Range: $50-74.9 Million
Emp.: 130
Distr of Pipe Valves Fittings
N.A.I.C.S.: 423720
James G. Porter *(Pres)*
Ralph G. Porter *(VP)*
Kevin Roche *(Mgr-Sls)*

PORTER PRECISION PRODUCTS COMPANY
2729 Banning Rd, Cincinnati, OH 45239
Tel.: (513) 923-3777
Web Site:
http://www.porterpunch.com
Sales Range: $10-24.9 Million
Emp.: 80
Punches, Forming & Stamping
N.A.I.C.S.: 333514
Doug Cox *(Mgr-Customer Svc)*
Mike Sizemore *(Plant Mgr)*
John Cipriani Jr. *(Pres)*

PORTER ROOFING CONTRACTORS
2454 Nashville Hwy, McMinnville, TN 37110
Tel.: (931) 668-2298
Web Site: http://www.porter-roofing.com
Sales Range: $10-24.9 Million
Emp.: 100
Roofing Contractors
N.A.I.C.S.: 238160
Melssa Cason *(Gen Mgr)*

PORTER TRUCK SALES INC.
135 McCarty St, Houston, TX 77029
Tel.: (713) 672-2400
Web Site: http://www.portertrk.com
Sales Range: $10-24.9 Million
Emp.: 16
Trucks, Commercial
N.A.I.C.S.: 423110
Bob Porter Sr. *(Pres)*
Robert Porter Jr. *(VP)*

PORTER WARNER INDUSTRIES LLC
2 E 38th St, Chattanooga, TN 37410-1423
Tel.: (423) 266-4735
Web Site:
http://www.porterwarner.com
Year Founded: 1922
Sales Range: $10-24.9 Million
Emp.: 85
Distr of Foundry Supplies
N.A.I.C.S.: 423510
Doug Warner *(Pres)*
Randy Smith *(VP-Mktg)*
David Garvey *(VP-Fin & Admin)*
Gerald Hilton *(Mgr-Mfg)*
Steve Soares *(Mgr-Ops)*
Randy Richardson *(Mgr-Ops)*
Sue Burgess *(Office Mgr)*

PORTER WRIGHT MORRIS & ARTHUR LLP
41 S High St Ste 2900, Columbus, OH 43215-6194
Tel.: (614) 227-2000
Web Site:
http://www.porterwright.com
Year Founded: 1846
Sales Range: $100-124.9 Million
Emp.: 201
Legal Advisory Services
N.A.I.C.S.: 541110
Karim A. Ali *(Co-Partner)*
Andrew W. Bojko *(Co-Partner)*
John C. Beeler *(Co-Partner)*
Brian L. Buzby *(Co-Partner)*
Robert H. Cohen *(Co-Partner)*
Molly S. Crabtree *(Co-Partner)*
James D. Curphey *(Co-Partner)*
Greg M. Daugherty *(Co-Partner)*
Joyce D. Edelman *(Co-Partner)*
Andrew C. Emerson *(Co-Partner)*
Jill Okun *(Partner-Litigation-Cleveland)*
Megan Bailey *(Partner)*
Matthew Moberg *(Partner)*
Christopher Cathey *(Partner)*
Lev Martyniuk *(Partner-Cincinnati)*
Susan K. Cliffel *(Partner-Cincinnati)*
Brian Augustine *(Partner-Litigation)*
William C. Sjoberg *(Partner-Bus & Trade Practice-Intl)*
Jeremy Mercer *(Partner)*
Robert J. Tannous *(Mng Partner)*
David Goldberg *(Partner)*
David S. Bloomfield Jr. *(Co-Partner)*

PORTER, LEVAY & ROSE, INC.
7 Penn Plz Ste 810, New York, NY 10001
Tel.: (212) 564-4700
Web Site: http://www.plrinvest.com
Year Founded: 1970
Sales Range: $1-9.9 Million
Emp.: 9
Public Relations, Investor Relations
N.A.I.C.S.: 541820
Lucille Belo *(COO)*
Marlon Nurse *(Sr VP-IR)*
Michael J. Porter *(Pres)*

PORTER-LEATH
868 N Manassas St, Memphis, TN 38107
Tel.: (901) 577-2500
Web Site: http://www.porterleath.org
Year Founded: 1860
Sales Range: $10-24.9 Million
Emp.: 355
Child & Family Support Services
N.A.I.C.S.: 624190
Derick Hayes *(Dir-IT)*
Mike Haase *(VP-Facilities)*
Rob Hughes *(VP-Dev)*
Rafel Hart *(VP)*

PORTERS BUILDING CENTER
18806 M 92 Hwy, Kearney, MO 64060
Tel.: (816) 628-6111
Web Site:
http://www.portersbuilding.com
Sales Range: $25-49.9 Million
Emp.: 150
Building Materials
N.A.I.C.S.: 423310
Craig Porter *(Treas & Sec)*
Kent Porter *(VP)*
Barbara Wilson *(Controller)*

PORTFOLIO CREATIVE
777 Goodale Blvd Ste 300, Columbus, OH 43212
Tel.: (614) 839-4897
Web Site:
http://www.portfoliocreative.com
Year Founded: 2005
Sales Range: $1-9.9 Million
Emp.: 12
Employment Services for Illustrators, Marketing Specialists, Designers, Illustrators & Web Developers
N.A.I.C.S.: 561311
Catherine Lang-Cline *(Co-Owner)*
Kristen Harris *(Co-Owner)*
Jennifer Brown *(Mgr-Mktg)*
Chris Cochran *(Sr Dir-Client Svcs)*
Eileen Jenkins *(Mgr-HR)*
Nikki White *(Mgr-Fin)*

PORTFOLIO MARKETING GROUP
200 S Broad St, Philadelphia, PA 19102
Tel.: (215) 875-0489
Sales Range: $10-24.9 Million
Emp.: 12
N.A.I.C.S.: 541810
John Costo *(Dir)*

PORTFOLIO SOLUTIONS, LLC.
900 Wilshire Dr Ste 200, Troy, MI 48084
Tel.: (248) 689-1550
Web Site:
http://www.portfoliosolutions.com
Year Founded: 1999
Sales Range: $1-9.9 Million
Emp.: 21
Investment Management Service
N.A.I.C.S.: 523999
Florence A. Affatato *(Chief Compliance Officer & Gen Counsel)*
Anthony R. Watson *(CIO)*
Brad Cox *(Mgr-Trading Ops)*
Tony R. Brumley *(CTO)*
John R. Bergmann *(CFO & COO)*

PORTFOLIOS FINANCIAL SERVICES, INC.
4250 Veterans Memorial Hwy Ste 420E, Holbrook, NY 11741
Tel.: (631) 439-4600
Web Site:
http://www.americanportfolios.com
Year Founded: 2001
Rev.: $70,600,000
Emp.: 100
Financial Services
N.A.I.C.S.: 541219
Thomas J. LoManto *(Sr VP-Advisory Svcs)*
Lisa G. DiBella *(VP-HR)*
Frank Giacchetto *(Sr VP-Compliance)*
Dean Bruno *(COO)*
Melissa Grappone *(Dir-Corp Comm)*
Tom M. Wirtshafter *(Pres)*
Frank A. Tauches Jr. *(Sr VP)*

PORTICO BED & BATH INCORPORATED
431 W 14th St, New York, NY 10014
Tel.: (212) 366-1163
Web Site:
http://www.porticohome.com
Sales Range: $10-24.9 Million
Emp.: 18
Beds & Accessories
N.A.I.C.S.: 449110
Marci Zaroff *(Chief Mktg & Sustainability Officer)*

PORTILLOS HOT DOGS INCORPORATED
2001 Spring Rd Ste 500, Oak Brook, IL 60523
Tel.: (630) 954-3773
Web Site: http://www.portillos.com
Rev.: $12,600,000
Emp.: 4,000
Fast-Food Restaurant, Chain
N.A.I.C.S.: 722513

U.S. PRIVATE

Richard J. Portillo *(Pres)*
Michael Osanloo *(CEO)*
Mike Miles *(Chm)*

PORTIONPAC CHEMICAL CORP.
400 N Ashland Ave, Chicago, IL 60622
Tel.: (312) 226-0400
Web Site:
http://www.portionpaccorp.com
Rev.: $20,000,000
Emp.: 55
Cleaning Product Mfr
N.A.I.C.S.: 325199
Burt Klein *(Pres)*
Caryn Stets *(Chief Strategy Officer)*
Natasha Stiles *(Mgr-Brand Natl Sls)*

PORTLAND AIR FREIGHT, INC.
75 Postal Service Way, Scarborough, ME 04074
Tel.: (207) 510-6900
Web Site: http://www.paftrans.com
Year Founded: 1950
Sales Range: $10-24.9 Million
Emp.: 128
General Freight Truck Transportation & Logistics Services
N.A.I.C.S.: 484121
Allen Reed *(Pres)*

PORTLAND ART MUSEUM
1219 SW Park Ave, Portland, OR 97205
Tel.: (503) 226-2811
Web Site:
http://www.portlandartmuseum.org
Year Founded: 1892
Sales Range: $10-24.9 Million
Emp.: 297
Museum Operator
N.A.I.C.S.: 712110
J. S. May *(Chief Advancement Officer)*
Gareth A. Nevitt *(CFO)*
Rob Bearden *(Dir-Ops)*

PORTLAND BOLT & MANUFACTURING CO., LLC
3441 NW Guam St, Portland, OR 97210
Tel.: (503) 718-7125
Web Site:
https://www.portlandbolt.com
Bolt, Nut, Screw, Rivet & Washer Mfr
N.A.I.C.S.: 332722
Greg Lindsay *(Gen Mgr)*

Subsidiaries:

Southern Anchor Bolt Co. (1)
1 Henry Miller St, Harlem, GA 30814
Tel.: (706) 556-6564
Rev.: $1,571,884
Emp.: 10
Iron & Steel Pipe & Tube Manufacturing from Purchased Steel
N.A.I.C.S.: 331210
Steven M. Yanizeski *(Pres)*

PORTLAND CEMENT ASSOCIATION
5420 Old Orchard Rd, Skokie, IL 60077-1083
Tel.: (847) 966-6200
Web Site: http://www.cement.org
Year Founded: 1971
Sales Range: $25-49.9 Million
Emp.: 84
Cement Manufacturer Association
N.A.I.C.S.: 813910
Lawrence C. Novak *(Dir-Structural Engrg)*
Alpa Swinger *(Mgr-Market Dev)*
Jennifer Johnson *(Mgr-Acctg)*
Patricia A. Flesher *(Sr Dir-Comm)*

COMPANIES

Stephen S. Szoke (Sr Dir-Codes & Standards)
John Stull (Chm)
A. Todd Johnston (Exec VP-Govt Affairs)
Michelle L. Wilson (Dir-Concrete Tech)
Paul D. Tennis (Dir-Product Standards & Tech)
Richard P. Bohan (Dir-Mfg Tech)
Michael Schon (VP-Govt Affairs)
Douglas W. Burns (Exec Dir-North Central Reg)
Rachel Derby (VP-Govt Affairs)
Jan E. Farnsworth (VP-Membership Svcs & Ops & Sec)
Kenneth M. Justice (Dir-Promotion)
Mark A. Justman (VP-Market Dev)
Laura M. Nedli (CFO & VP-Fin & Admin)
Randall Palm (Dir-IT)
Erik J. Rancatore (Dir-Comm)
Donn Thompson (Dir-Market Dev)
David Zwicke (Dir-Economic Res)
Michael Ireland (Pres & CEO)
Sean O'Neill (Sr VP-Govt Affairs)
Nick Ferrari (Sr VP-Comm & Media Rels)
Debra Adlis (CFO & Treas)
Libby Pritchard (Dir-Construction Matls Safety & Policy-Govt Affairs Team)

PORTLAND GROUP INC.
74 Salem Rd, North Billerica, MA 01862
Tel.: (978) 262-1444
Web Site: http://www.theportlandgroup.com
Year Founded: 1930
Sales Range: $10-24.9 Million
Emp.: 310
Wholesale Plumbing & Hydronic Heating Supplies
N.A.I.C.S.: 423720
Claire Prue (Controller)

Subsidiaries:

Portland Group Inc. - Newton (1)
10 Westwood St, Newton, MA 02165-1825
Tel.: (617) 527-7040
Rev.: $3,600,000
Emp.: 25
Supplier of Plumbing Products
N.A.I.C.S.: 423720

PORTLAND VALVE & FITTING COMPANY
5216 NE 158th Ave, Portland, OR 97230
Tel.: (503) 288-6901
Web Site: http://www.swagelok.com
Sales Range: $10-24.9 Million
Emp.: 40
Plumbing Fittings & Supplies
N.A.I.C.S.: 423720
Dan McGrath (Mgr-Customer Svc)
Jason Yamamoto (Mgr-Ops)

PORTLAND WATER DISTRICT
225 Douglass St, Portland, ME 04104-2526
Tel.: (207) 774-5961
Web Site: http://www.pwd.org
Year Founded: 1907
Sales Range: $10-24.9 Million
Emp.: 200
Provider of Water Utility Services
N.A.I.C.S.: 221320
Ronald Miller (Gen Mgr)
Christopher Crovo (Exec Dir-Plng)
James Wallace (Exec Dir-Water Ops)

PORTLAND YACHT SERVICES, INC.
58 Fore St, Portland, ME 04101
Tel.: (207) 774-1067
Web Site: http://www.portlandyacht.com
Rev.: $4,380,000
Emp.: 30
Marinas
N.A.I.C.S.: 713930
Phineas Sprague (Co-Founder)
Joanna Sprague (Co-Founder)
Phineas Sprague Jr. (Co-Founder)

Subsidiaries:

White Rock Outboard, Inc. (1)
351 Sebago Lake Rd, Gorham, ME 04038
Tel.: (207) 892-9606
Web Site: https://www.whiterockoutboard.com
Boat Whslr
N.A.I.C.S.: 441222
George Gherardi Jr. (Pres)

PORTO ENERGY CORP.
Suite 350 24 Waterway Ave, The Woodlands, TX 77380
Tel.: (713) 975-1725 BC
Web Site: http://www.portoenergy.com
Sales Range: Less than $1 Million
Emp.: 10
Oil & Gas Exploration & Production Services
N.A.I.C.S.: 211120
Ian B. McMurtrie (Chm)
Joseph Patrick Ash (Pres & CEO)
Patric H. Monteleone (Exec VP)
Richard Pawluk (Sec)

PORTRAIT INNOVATIONS HOLDING COMPANY
2016 Ayrsley Town Blvd Ste 200, Charlotte, NC 28273
Tel.: (704) 499-9300 DE
Web Site: http://www.portraitinnovations.com
Sales Range: $100-124.9 Million
Emp.: 1,432
Commercial Photography
N.A.I.C.S.: 541921
John Grosso (Pres & CEO)
John M. Davis (Chief Dev Officer, Sec & Exec VP)
William K. Bailey II (CFO & VP-Fin & IR)
John J. Grosso III (VP-Ops)

PORTSIDE BUILDERS, INC.
810 S Lansing Ave, Sturgeon Bay, WI 54235
Tel.: (920) 746-1092
Web Site: http://www.portsidebuilders.com
Sales Range: $10-24.9 Million
Emp.: 60
Single-Family Housing Construction
N.A.I.C.S.: 236115
Fran Shefchik (Owner)

PORTUGESE BAKING COMPANY LP
113-129 Kossuth St, Newark, NJ 07105
Tel.: (973) 589-8875
Rev.: $18,686,087
Emp.: 225
Bread, Cake & Related Products
N.A.I.C.S.: 311811
Manuel Teixeira (Pres)

PORTUS HOLDINGS INC.
110 E Broward Blvd Ste 1700, Fort Lauderdale, FL 33301
Tel.: (954) 778-8211 NV
Web Site: http://www.portus-inc.com
Year Founded: 2011
Emp.: 2
Food & Beverage Service Software
N.A.I.C.S.: 513210

L. Clay Edmonds (Exec VP)
George Dale Murray II (Pres, CEO & CFO)

POS WORLD, INC.
2000 Riveredge Pkwy Ste 200, Atlanta, GA 30328
Tel.: (770) 984-0241
Web Site: http://www.posworld.com
Year Founded: 1999
Rev.: $14,900,000
Emp.: 14
Mail-Order Houses
N.A.I.C.S.: 513210
Daniel Dwyer (VP)

POSADOS CAFE INC.
1307 Dominion Plz, Tyler, TX 75703
Tel.: (903) 534-1076
Web Site: http://www.posados.com
Sales Range: $25-49.9 Million
Emp.: 500
Mexican Restaurant
N.A.I.C.S.: 722511
Andrew Gugar (Pres)
Paul Roseberry (Controller)
David Kiefer (Mgr)
Jeremiah Cagle (Mgr-Front House)

POSEY COUNTY FARM BUREAU COOP ASSOCIATION
817 W 4th St, Mount Vernon, IN 47620
Tel.: (812) 838-4468
Web Site: http://www.poseynet.com
Sales Range: $25-49.9 Million
Emp.: 28
Farm Supplies
N.A.I.C.S.: 424910
Chris Cash (Gen Mgr)

POSH BOUTIQUE
4027 Hillsboro Pike, Nashville, TN 37215
Tel.: (615) 269-6250
Web Site: http://www.poshonline.com
Year Founded: 1999
Rev.: $3,600,000
Emp.: 5
Women's Clothing Store
N.A.I.C.S.: 458110
Kathy Hadley (Owner)
Jan Martens (Mgr)

POSIGEN LLC
2424 Edenborn Ave Ste 550, Metairie, LA 70001
Tel.: (504) 835-2510
Web Site: http://www.posigen.com
Year Founded: 2011
Sales Range: $50-74.9 Million
Emp.: 146
Solar Device Installation Services
N.A.I.C.S.: 238220
Peter T. Shaper (CEO)
Thomas Neyhart (Founder & Exec Chm)
Adja Ba (Exec VP-HR)
John Ross (VP-Mktg)
Steven Burt (Chief Compliance & Policy Officer)
Dan Black (Chief Legal Officer)
Naren Yenduri (COO & CTO)
Elizabeth Teel Galante (Sr VP-Energy Efficiency Sols)

Subsidiaries:

New England Conservation Services LLC (1)
15 Lunar Dr, Woodbridge, CT 06525
Tel.: (203) 389-3342
Web Site: http://www.neconserves.com
Human Resource Consulting Services
N.A.I.C.S.: 541612

POSILLICO, INC.
1750 New Hwy, Farmingdale, NY 11735
Tel.: (631) 249-1872 NY
Web Site: https://posillicoinc.com
Year Founded: 2007
Holding Company; Civil Engineering Services
N.A.I.C.S.: 551112
Joseph K. Posillico (Pres & CEO)

Subsidiaries:

Posillico Civil, Inc. (1)
1750 New Hwy, Farmingdale, NY 11735
Tel.: (631) 390-5738
Web Site: https://posillicoinc.com
Rev.: $7,500,000
Emp.: 54
Highway, Street, Bridge & Other Civil Engineering Construction
N.A.I.C.S.: 237310
Joseph K. Posillico (Pres & CEO)

Subsidiary (Domestic):

Martins Construction Corp. (2)
210 Little Falls St, Falls Church, VA 22046
Tel.: (703) 533-8700
Web Site: http://www.martinscorp.com
Sales Range: $10-24.9 Million
Emp.: 100
Highway, Street & Bridge Construction
N.A.I.C.S.: 237310
Maria Martins (CFO)
Pooya Azar (COO & Project Mgr)

Posillico Materials, LLC (1)
1610 New Hwy, Farmingdale, NY 11735
Tel.: (631) 249-1872
Web Site: https://www.posillicomaterials.com
Sales Range: $1-9.9 Million
Emp.: 11
Asphalt Paving Mixture & Block Mfr
N.A.I.C.S.: 324121
Paul F. Posillico (Mng Dir)
Andy Burns (Mgr-Ops)
Fred Locher (VP-Pur)
Lisa M. Dippel (Dir-HR)
Peter Brindley (VP-Ops)

POSITIVEID CORPORATION
1690 S Congress Ave Ste 201, Delray Beach, FL 33445
Tel.: (561) 805-8000 DE
Web Site: http://www.positiveidcorp.com
Rev.: $5,359,000
Assets: $1,725,000
Liabilities: $11,426,000
Net Worth: ($9,701,000)
Earnings: ($8,733,000)
Emp.: 9
Fiscal Year-end: 12/31/17
Human Implantable Radio Frequency Identification Microchip Mfr for Patient Identification
N.A.I.C.S.: 334290
Allison Tomek (Sr VP-Corp Dev)
Gary O'Hara (CTO-Thermomedics)

Subsidiaries:

E-N-G Mobile Systems, Inc. (1)
1690 S Congress Ave Ste 201, Delray Beach, FL 33445
Tel.: (561) 805-8008
Web Site: http://www.e-n-g.com
Automobile Mfr
N.A.I.C.S.: 336110

ExcitePCR, Corporation (1)
1252 Quarry Ln Ste A, Pleasanton, CA 94566
Tel.: (925) 474-2180
Web Site: http://www.excitepcr.com
Pharmaceutical Product Mfr & Distr
N.A.I.C.S.: 325412

MicroFluidic Systems (1)
1252 Quarry Lane Ste A, Pleasanton, CA 94566
Tel.: (925) 474-2180
Biological Research & Development Services
N.A.I.C.S.: 541714

POSITRON CORP.

U.S. PRIVATE

PositiveID Corporation—(Continued)

POSITRON CORP.
530 Oakmont Ln, Westmont, IL 60559
Tel.: (317) 576-0183
Web Site: http://www.positron.com
Sales Range: $1-9.9 Million
Emp.: 19
Molecular Imaging Devices & Radio-pharmaceutical Products Mfr
N.A.I.C.S.: 334510
Corey N. Conn (CFO)
Lawrence Pitt (Mgr-Quality Assurance)
Adel Abdullah (Pres)
Aaron Hargrave (VP)

POSITRONIC INDUSTRIES, INC.
423 N Campbell Ave, Springfield, MO 65806
Tel.: (417) 866-2322   MO
Web Site:
  http://www.connectpositronic.com
Year Founded: 1966
Sales Range: $150-199.9 Million
Emp.: 773
Mfr of Electronic Connectors
N.A.I.C.S.: 334417
John Gentry (CEO)
Mark Martin (VP-Engrg)
Gregory Rocque (Pres)
Subsidiaries:
Positronic Asia Pte Ltd.   (1)
Block 3014 A Ubi Rd 0701, Singapore, 408703, Singapore   (100%)
Tel.: (65) 68421419
Web Site: http://www.connectpositronic.com
Sales Range: $25-49.9 Million
Emp.: 160
Provider of Connectors
N.A.I.C.S.: 334417
Christopher D. Payne (Founder)

Positronic Industries Caribe, Inc.   (1)
101 El Tuque Industrial Park Rd 591, Ponce, PR 00728
Tel.: (787) 841-0920
Sales Range: $25-49.9 Million
Emp.: 206
Electronic Connector Mfr
N.A.I.C.S.: 334417
Willam Gary Sorrells (Gen Mgr)

Positronic Industries S.A.S.   (1)
46 Rte Dengachies, F 32020, Auch, France   (100%)
Tel.: (33) 562634491
Web Site: http://www.connectpositronic.com
Sales Range: $10-24.9 Million
Emp.: 120
Provider of Connectors
N.A.I.C.S.: 334417
William D. Gentry (VP)

Positronic Interconnects Pvt. Ltd.   (1)
Sr No 51/2A/3 & 8 Off Mumbai Bangalore Highway, Pune, 411041, India
Tel.: (91) 20 2469 9910
Electronic Connector Mfr
N.A.I.C.S.: 334417
Ajit Kshirsagar (Mgr-Production)
Roshan Ballamwar (Mgr-Mktg)

Positronic Japan Co Ltd   (1)
Sugamo 3-12-18-201, Toshima-Ku, Tokyo, 170-0002, Japan
Tel.: (81) 3 6310 5830
Electronic Connector Mfr
N.A.I.C.S.: 334417

POSMAN COLLEGIATE STORES INC.
Times Square Sta, New York, NY 10108
Tel.: (718) 894-9696
Web Site:
  http://www.posmancollegiate.com
Sales Range: $25-49.9 Million
Emp.: 50
College Book Store

N.A.I.C.S.: 459210
Eugene Posman (CEO & CFO)
Maxene Posman (Pres)

POSNAVITAS RETAIL SERVICES, INC.
5735 Old Shakopee Rd W Ste 100, Bloomington, MN 55437
Tel.: (952) 936-9280   MN
Web Site: http://www.posnavitas.com
Year Founded: 1981
Sales Range: $10-24.9 Million
Emp.: 55
Holding Company; Back Office, Point-of-Sale, Data Collection & Networking Equipment Maintenance, Repair Services & Whslr; Retailer Loss Prevention Software, Products & Services
N.A.I.C.S.: 551112
Kelly Bennewitz (CEO)
Subsidiaries:
Xerxes Computer Company, LLC   (1)
5735 Old Shakopee Rd W Ste 100, Bloomington, MN 55437   (100%)
Tel.: (952) 936-9280
Web Site: http://www.tdxtech.com
Back Office, Point-of-Sale, Data Collection & Networking Equipment Maintenance, Repair Services & Whslr
N.A.I.C.S.: 811210

POSNER ADVERTISING
30 Broad St 33rd Fl, New York, NY 10004
Tel.: (212) 867-3900   NY
Web Site: http://www.posneradv.com
Year Founded: 1959
Rev.: $35,000,000
Emp.: 25
Advetising Agency
N.A.I.C.S.: 541810
Peter S. Posner (Pres)
Robert K. Posner (Principal)
Christine Shum (CFO)
Bob Posner (Principal)
Subsidiaries:
Posner Advertising   (1)
731 S Highway 101 Ste 1E, Solana Beach, CA 92075-2628
Tel.: (858) 350-7800
Web Site: http://www.posneradv.com
Emp.: 7
Recruitment
N.A.I.C.S.: 541810

POSNER INDUSTRIES INC.
8641 Edgeworth Dr, Capitol Heights, MD 20743
Tel.: (301) 350-1000
Web Site: http://www.posners.com
Sales Range: $10-24.9 Million
Emp.: 70
Steel Distr
N.A.I.C.S.: 423710

POST ACUTE MEDICAL, LLC
1828 Good Hope Rd Ste 102, Enola, PA 17025
Tel.: (717) 731-9660
Web Site:
  http://www.postacutemedical.com
Year Founded: 2006
Acute Care & Rehabilitation Hospitals
N.A.I.C.S.: 622310
Anthony F. Misitano (Principal, Pres & CEO)
John Bauer (Exec VP)
Karick Stober (CFO & Exec VP)
Adam Burick (Chief Medical Officer & Exec VP)
Lisa MacLean (Chief Strategy Officer & Sr Exec VP)
Robert J. Tribeck (Chief Legal Officer & Exec VP)
Bryan Munchen (Sr VP-IT)

Kathleen Brown (Chief Clinical Officer & Exec VP)
Waynea Finley (Sr VP-HR)
Jason Carter (COO)
Kristen Smith (Exec VP-Dev & Hospital Analytics)
Anne Rotoloni Leon (Chief Dev Officer & Exec VP)
Subsidiaries:
LifeCare Hospital   (1)
2550 Kings Hwy, Shreveport, LA 71103
Tel.: (318) 212-6860
Web Site: http://www.lifecare-hospitals.com
Sales Range: $25-49.9 Million
Emp.: 175
General Medical & Surgical Hospitals
N.A.I.C.S.: 622110

PAM Rehabilitation Hospital of Beaumont   (1)
3340 Plaza 10 Blvd, Beaumont, TX 77701
Tel.: (409) 835-0835
Web Site: http://www.warmsprings.org
Emp.: 128
Medical Rehabilitation Services
N.A.I.C.S.: 622310

POST ACUTE PARTNERS, LLC
641 Lexington Ave 31st Fl, New York, NY 10022
Tel.: (212) 802-7600   DE
Web Site: http://www.postacute.com
Year Founded: 2010
Health Care-Focused Equity Investment Firm
N.A.I.C.S.: 523999
Jeffrey Rubin (Co-CEO)
Nancy Dichiora (Dir-Interior Design)
Subsidiaries:
Elderwood Administrative Services, LLC   (1)
500 Seneca St Ste 100, Buffalo, NY 14204
Tel.: (716) 633-3900
Web Site: http://www.elderwood.com
Senior Living & Other Residential Health Care Facilities Operator
N.A.I.C.S.: 561110
Philip Quillard (COO)
Danelle Wotka (Chief Nursing Officer)
Clay Bozard (CIO)
Susan M. Robinson (VP-Risk Mgmt)
Richard Kamats Jr. (Dir-Fin Reporting)

Unit (Domestic):
Elderwood at Tonawanda   (2)
111 Ensminger Rd, Tonawanda, NY 14150-6719
Tel.: (716) 871-1814
Web Site: http://www.tonawandamanor.com
Emp.: 51
Assisted Living Facility Operator
N.A.I.C.S.: 623312
Jim Connelly (Partner)

POST CAPITAL PARTNERS, LLC
747 3rd Ave Fl 19, New York, NY 10017
Tel.: (212) 888-5700   DE
Web Site: http://www.postcp.com
Privater Equity Firm
N.A.I.C.S.: 523999
Michael S. Pfeffer (Co-Founder & Co-Mng Dir)
Mitchell A. Davidson (Co-Founder & Co-Mng Dir)
Christopher P. H. Cheang (Head-Bus Dev)
Subsidiaries:
E.C. Waste, Inc.   (1)
Km 1/7 Rr 923 17, Humacao, PR 00791
Tel.: (787) 852-4444
Solid Waste Disposal Services
N.A.I.C.S.: 562212
Randy Jensen (CEO)

POST GLOVER LIFELINK INC.

167 Gap Way, Erlanger, KY 41018
Tel.: (859) 212-9942
Web Site: http://www.pglifelink.com
Year Founded: 1957
Power Panels & Accessories Mfr
N.A.I.C.S.: 334417
Judith Kathman (Pres)

POST PRINTING CO. INC.
205 W 4th St, Minster, OH 45865
Tel.: (419) 628-2321
Web Site:
  http://www.postprinting.com
Sales Range: $10-24.9 Million
Emp.: 120
Offset Printing; Commercial Printer
N.A.I.C.S.: 323111
Tim Thompson (VP)
Jane J. Thompson (Pres)
Jeff Ahlers (Mgr-Sls)

POST WORKS
100 Avenue of the Americas, New York, NY 10013
Tel.: (212) 894-4050
Web Site: http://www.pwny.com
Sales Range: $10-24.9 Million
Emp.: 100
Motion Picture & Video Production
N.A.I.C.S.: 512199
Rob Demartin (CEO)
Corey Stewart (Chief Engr)
David Rosen (Chm)
Patrick Fallon (Controller)
Dan Porcelli (Sr Dir-Non-Linear Svcs)
Anthony Caputo (VP-Production Svcs)

POST+BEAM
95 Morton St Ground Fl, New York, NY 10014
Tel.: (403) 453-1977   NY
Web Site: http://postandbeam.is
Year Founded: 1999
Sales Range: $25-49.9 Million
Emp.: 35
Design, Development, Marketing & Public Relation Services
N.A.I.C.S.: 541820
Duke Sherman (Mng Partner & Founder)
Jason Warnock (CEO)
Darren Scott (Dir-Digital)
Kelly Howard (Dir-Media)
Candace Warnock (Fin Dir)

POSTAL CENTER INTERNATIONAL
10561 Satellite Blvd, Orlando, FL 32837-8427
Tel.: (407) 852-0978
Web Site: http://www.surfpci.com
All Other Personal Services
N.A.I.C.S.: 812990
Bill Sleeper (Mgr)
Larissa Schenck (VP-Sls & Mktg)
William Sweeney (CIO)
Ismael Diaz (Pres)
Subsidiaries:
Original Impressions, LLC   (1)
12900 SW 89th Ct, Miami, FL 33176-5803
Web Site:
  http://www.originalimpressions.com
Printing
N.A.I.C.S.: 323111
Peter Amaro (Pres & COO)

POSTAL CONNECTIONS OF AMERICA, INC.
6136 Frisco Sq Blvd Ste 400, Frisco, TX 75034
Tel.: (619) 294-7550
Web Site:
  http://www.postalconnections.com
Year Founded: 1995

Franchise Chain of Retail Stores with Office Services, Including Packing, Mailing & Shipping, Copying, Faxing, Mail Boxes & Office Supplies
N.A.I.C.S.: 459410
Fred Morache *(Co-Owner)*

POSTCARD INN ON THE BEACH
6300 Gulf Blvd, Saint Pete Beach, FL 33706
Tel.: (727) 367-2711
Web Site: http://www.postcardinn.com
Year Founded: 2009
Emp.: 100
Hotel Operations
N.A.I.C.S.: 721110
Barry Sternlicht *(Owner)*
Bob Sauerwine *(Gen Mgr)*

POSTCARDMANIA
2145 Sunnydale Blvd Bldg 102, Clearwater, FL 33765
Tel.: (727) 441-4704
Web Site: http://www.postcardmania.com
Year Founded: 1998
Sales Range: $25-49.9 Million
Emp.: 192
Direct Marketing Postcard Design & Printing Services
N.A.I.C.S.: 541860
Joy Gendusa *(Founder & CEO)*
Melissa Bradshaw *(Pres)*
Jill Carey *(Officer-Ops)*
Chris Miller *(VP-Mfg)*
Anthony Heald *(VP-Mail Delivery & Logistics)*
Rob Bradshaw *(Sr VP-Client Acq)*
Saskia Murphy *(VP-Corp Relationships)*
Mike Custer *(VP-Pre-Press & Digital Printing)*
Mark Glasstetter *(VP-Quality Control)*
Sarah Kicinski *(CMO)*
Ashlie Acosta *(VP-Client Mktg Specialists & Mgr-Sls)*
Aubrey Magnie *(Mgr-Sls)*
Ali Freeman *(Mgr-Sls Admin)*
Adam Sene *(Dir-Search Engine Mktg)*
Jessica Lalau *(Dir-Mktg Comm, PR & Social Media)*
Preston Litton *(CTO)*

POSTGRADUATE CENTER FOR MENTAL HEALTH
158 E 35th St, New York, NY 10016
Tel.: (212) 889-5500 NY
Web Site: http://www.pgcmh.org
Year Founded: 1948
Sales Range: $25-49.9 Million
Emp.: 463
Mental Health Care Services
N.A.I.C.S.: 623220
Marcia B. Holman *(VP-Amulatory Ops)*
Jacob Barak *(Pres & CEO)*
Harold E. Moss *(VP-Residential Ops)*

POSTLER & JAECKLE CORP.
615 S Ave, Rochester, NY 14620-1315
Tel.: (585) 546-7450 NY
Web Site: http://www.postlerandjaeckle.com
Year Founded: 1964
Sales Range: $25-49.9 Million
Emp.: 200
Plumbing, Heating & Air Conditioning Services
N.A.I.C.S.: 238220
Erich K. Postler *(CEO)*
Mary Anne Schum *(Controller)*
Dominick Mancini *(COO)*
Paul Tesch *(Mgr-Svc-Refrigeration)*
Kenneth Peck *(Dir-Safety)*
Joseph Valentine *(VP-Construction)*
Fred Costanza *(Mgr-Svc)*
Carmen Perry *(Mgr-Controls & Automation)*
Steve Jaeger *(Mgr-Estimating)*
Amy Smith *(Sec-Construction)*
John Dineen Jr. *(VP-Sls & Mktg)*

POSTON OF DALTON INC.
1001 N Glenwood Ave, Dalton, GA 30721
Tel.: (706) 278-1222
Rev.: $10,500,000
Emp.: 85
Carpets & Rugs
N.A.I.C.S.: 314110

POTAMKIN MANHATTAN CORP
2495 2nd Ave, New York, NY 10035
Tel.: (212) 433-1700
Web Site: http://www.potamkinmitsubishi.com
Sales Range: $10-24.9 Million
Emp.: 60
Automobiles, New & Used
N.A.I.C.S.: 441110
George Spallina *(VP)*

POTAMKIN NEW YORK L.P.
2495 2nd Ave, New York, NY 10035
Tel.: (212) 433-1700
Year Founded: 1989
Sales Range: $10-24.9 Million
Emp.: 100
Car Whslr
N.A.I.C.S.: 441110
Saul Jericho *(Pres)*
George Spallina *(VP)*

POTASH BROS INC.
875 N State St, Chicago, IL 60610
Tel.: (312) 266-4200
Web Site: http://www.potashmarkets.com
Sales Range: $10-24.9 Million
Emp.: 85
Grocery Stores, Independent
N.A.I.C.S.: 445110
Art Potash *(Pres)*

POTENTIAL INDUSTRIES INC.
922 E E St, Wilmington, CA 90744-6145
Tel.: (310) 549-5901 CA
Year Founded: 1975
Sales Range: $10-24.9 Million
Emp.: 150
Provider of Refuse Systems Services
N.A.I.C.S.: 562920
Tony Fan *(Pres)*
Jessica Chen *(Controller)*

POTHOS, INC.
2260 El Cajon Blvd Ste 474, San Diego, CA 92104
Tel.: (619) 546-0621
Web Site: http://www.pothos.us
Year Founded: 2002
Sales Range: $1-9.9 Million
Emp.: 8
Travel Agency Services
N.A.I.C.S.: 561510
Michael Patton *(Pres, CEO & Commanding Officer)*

POTNETWORK HOLDINGS, INC.
3531 Griffin Rd, Fort Lauderdale, FL 33312 CO
Web Site: http://www.potnetworkholding.com
Year Founded: 1996
Rev.: $9,680,543
Assets: $709,931
Liabilities: $5,007,338
Net Worth: ($4,297,407)
Earnings: ($5,584,669)
Emp.: 13
Fiscal Year-end: 12/31/20
Holding Company
N.A.I.C.S.: 551112
Gary Blum *(Chm)*
Kevin Hagen *(Pres)*
Sohail Quraeshi *(CEO)*

POTOMAC CORPORATION
2063 Foster Ave, Wheeling, IL 60090-6520
Tel.: (847) 259-0546 IL
Web Site: http://www.crescentcardboard.com
Year Founded: 1902
Sales Range: $50-74.9 Million
Emp.: 300
Provider of Converted Paper Products
N.A.I.C.S.: 322299
Margie Sundstrom *(Mgr-Acctg & Payroll)*

Subsidiaries:

Crescent Cardboard Company, L.L.C. (1)
100 W Willow Rd, Wheeling, IL 60090-6522
Tel.: (847) 537-3400
Web Site: http://www.cresentcardboard.com
Rev.: $21,400,000
Emp.: 200
Cardboard, Drafting & Drawing Boards, Mat Boards, Posterboard, Photograph & Showcard Mounts Mfr
N.A.I.C.S.: 322299
Scott Ozmun *(Pres)*

Subsidiary (Non-US):

Crescent Europe GmbH (2)
Robert-Bosch-Strasse 10, 89564, Nattheim, Germany
Tel.: (49) 7321 27225 0
Web Site: http://www.crescent-europe.com
Emp.: 15
Office Supplies Mfr
N.A.I.C.S.: 339940
Wolfgang Gugerel *(Mgr-Sls)*

POTOMAC EQUITY PARTNERS, LLC
5111 Yuma Pl NW Ste 200, Washington, DC 20016
Tel.: (202) 827-6050 WA
Web Site: http://www.potomacequitypartners.com
Privater Equity Firm
N.A.I.C.S.: 523999
John Bates *(Founder & Partner)*
Chris Blythe *(Principal)*
Robert Christie *(Partner-Advisory)*
Tony Coelho *(Partner-Advisory)*
Pascal Denis *(Principal)*
Peter Masanotti *(Partner-Advisory)*
Michael Platt *(Partner-Advisory)*
Ray Smith *(Partner-Advisory)*

POTOMAC RIVER GROUP, LLC
19775 Belmont Executive Plz Ste 525, Ashburn, VA 20147-7608
Tel.: (703) 771-3003
Web Site: http://www.potomacrivergroup.com
Year Founded: 2003
Specialized Training, Security & Protection Equipment Products & Support Services
N.A.I.C.S.: 611430
Frank J. Frysiek *(Pres & CEO)*
Charlie Rash *(VP-Ops)*
Richard C. Krueger *(VP-Training)*
Danielle Baird *(Mgr-Bus Dev)*

POTOMAC VALLEY PROPERTIES INC.
Mountain Lk Rd, Hedgesville, WV 25427
Tel.: (304) 754-3358
Web Site: http://www.thewoods.com
Rev.: $11,297,078
Emp.: 17
Membership Sports & Recreation Clubs
N.A.I.C.S.: 713940
Sally Johnston *(Pres)*
Robert Uccellini *(Project Mgr)*
Madeline V. Johnston *(VP-Conference Sls)*
Joy D. Johnson *(VP)*

POTTER & SIMS FOODS, INC.
333B Hwy 12 E, Kosciusko, MS 39090-3420
Tel.: (662) 289-9964 MS
Year Founded: 1991
Sales Range: $25-49.9 Million
Emp.: 300
Grocery Stores
N.A.I.C.S.: 445110
Roy Sims *(Pres)*
Harrel Potter *(VP)*

POTTER CONCRETE LTD
2400 E Pioneer Dr, Irving, TX 75061
Tel.: (214) 630-2191
Sales Range: $100-124.9 Million
Emp.: 540
Concrete Work
N.A.I.C.S.: 238110
Gregory D. Potter *(Owner & Pres)*
Lyn Wesley *(VP)*
Debbie Monroe *(Coord-Benefits)*
Alan Dugger *(Project Mgr)*
Noel Nalls *(VP)*

POTTER DISTRIBUTING INCORPORATED
4037 Roger B Chaffee Blvd SE, Grand Rapids, MI 49548
Tel.: (616) 531-6860
Web Site: http://www.potterdistributing.com
Sales Range: $25-49.9 Million
Emp.: 23
Warm Air Heating & Air Conditioning
N.A.I.C.S.: 423730
Douglas Potter *(Pres)*
Martin Denbraber *(Controller)*

POTTS & CALLAHAN INC.
500 W 29th St, Baltimore, MD 21211
Tel.: (410) 235-9400
Web Site: http://www.pottscallahan.com
Rev.: $24,000,000
Emp.: 16
Excavation Work
N.A.I.C.S.: 238910
Ron Bender *(Pres)*
Paul Collison *(Project Mgr)*
Collison Tim *(Exec VP)*

POTTS COMPANY INC.
981 E Freeway Dr SE Ste A, Conyers, GA 30094
Tel.: (770) 483-9299
Year Founded: 1986
Emp.: 40
Contractors of Commercial, Industrial, Institutional Facilities
N.A.I.C.S.: 236220
Michael R. Potts *(CEO)*
David C. Buser *(Controller)*
Stephen W. Heyward *(VP)*

POTTSTOWN AUTO SALES INC.
629 N Lewis Rd, Limerick, PA 19468
Tel.: (610) 495-7076
Year Founded: 1975
Sales Range: $10-24.9 Million

POTTSTOWN AUTO SALES INC.

Pottstown Auto Sales Inc.—(Continued)
Emp.: 30
Car Whslr
N.A.I.C.S.: 441110
Vincent Piazza (Pres)

POUDRE VALLEY TRUSS, INC.
201 NW Frontage Rd, Fort Collins, CO 80524-9265
Tel.: (970) 484-7313
Web Site:
http://www.fortcollinstruss.com
Sales Range: $10-24.9 Million
Emp.: 12
Truss Mfr
N.A.I.C.S.: 321215
Mike Beebe (Pres)
Mark Weishaup (Sec)
Art Beebe (VP)

POUGHKEEPSIE-HIGHLAND RAILROAD BRIDGE CO. INC.
82 Washington St, Poughkeepsie, NY 12601
Tel.: (845) 454-9649   NY
Web Site: http://www.walkway.org
Year Founded: 1994
Sales Range: $10-24.9 Million
Emp.: 5
Walkway Recreational Services
N.A.I.C.S.: 721211
Elizabeth Waldstein-Hart (Exec Dir)
Jill Romeo (Mgr-Fin)
Ellen Henneberry (Mgr-Dev)
Susanne O'Neil (Program Mgr)

POULIN GRAIN INC.
24 Railroad Sq, Newport, VT 05855
Tel.: (802) 334-6731
Web Site: http://www.poulingrain.com
Year Founded: 1932
Emp.: 100
Prepared Feeds & Agricultural Products Mfr
N.A.I.C.S.: 311119
Josh Poulin (Co-Owner, Pres & CEO)
Jenna Poulin (Co-Owner & Mgr-HR)

POULIN LUMBER INC.
3639 US Rte 5, Derby, VT 05829
Tel.: (802) 766-4971
Web Site:
http://www.poulinlumber.com
Rev: $14,651,689
Emp.: 46
Lumber & Other Building Materials
N.A.I.C.S.: 423310
Bill Hartman (Dir-Fin)

POULIN VENTURES LLC
10010 Indian School Rd NE, Albuquerque, NM 87112
Web Site: http://www.ladyboss.com
Year Founded: 2014
Sales Range: $25-49.9 Million
Emp.: 57
Personal Fitness Training Services
N.A.I.C.S.: 812990
Kaelin Tuell Poulin (Co-Founder)
Brandon Poulin (Co-Founder & CEO)

POULTRY PRODUCTS COMPANY INC.
11 Bemis Rd, Hooksett, NH 03106-2622
Tel.: (603) 668-7414   NH
Web Site: http://www.ppcnew.com
Year Founded: 1978
Sales Range: $100-124.9 Million
Emp.: 250
Distr of Poultry & Poultry Products
N.A.I.C.S.: 424440
Julian Stogniew (Pres)
Gary Wischan (Asst Treas)

POUNDS PHOTOGRAPHIC LABS, INC.
901 Regal Row, Dallas, TX 75247
Tel.: (214) 688-1425
Web Site:
http://www.poundslabs.com
Sales Range: $10-24.9 Million
Emp.: 100
Film Processing & Finishing Laboratory
N.A.I.C.S.: 812921
Danny Pounds (Owner)
Steve Oatman (Controller)
Chris Oelker (Product Mgr-Solutions & Integration)

POUSCHINE COOK CAPITAL MANAGEMENT LLC
599 Lexington Ave Ste 38-B, New York, NY 10022
Tel.: (212) 784-0620
Web Site:
http://www.pouschinecook.com
Sales Range: $1-9.9 Million
Emp.: 8
Privater Equity Firm
N.A.I.C.S.: 523999
John L. Pouschine (Owner & Mng Dir)
Everett R. Cook (Founder)
Robert L. Jenkins (Mng Dir)
Bonnie L. Harland (Dir-Mktg & Ops)

Subsidiaries:

Strategic Distribution, Inc.   (1)
Tel.: (215) 633-1900
Web Site: https://www.sdi.com
Sales Range: $400-449.9 Million
Holding Company; Supply Chain Services
N.A.I.C.S.: 551112
Veronica Abarca (VP-Pur)
Scott Doyle (VP-Application Dev)
Ron Fijalkowski (CIO & Exec VP-Tech)
Chris Moore (Pres & CEO)
Jeremy Jordan (COO)
Neil Clover (CTO)
Adrian Mantini (CFO & Sr VP)
Lorraine Serva (Chief People Officer)
Jerome Blanc (Sr VP-Transformation)
Vee Browne (Dir-Operational Compliance)
Haitham Khudayri (VP-Operations)
Blaze Kurz (VP-Finance)
Chuck Doherty (VP-Operations)
Brian Harmon (VP-Procurement)

Subsidiary (Domestic):

SDI, Inc.   (2)
1414 Radcliffe StSte300, Bristol, PA 19007
Tel.: (215) 633-1900
Web Site: https://www.sdi.com
Sales Range: $25-49.9 Million
Digital Supply Chain Management Services
N.A.I.C.S.: 541614
Sharon Malcolm (Office Mgr)
Scott Morehouse (VP-Bus Dev)
Kelley Ferguson (VP-MRO Supply Chain Solutions)
Jim Owens (Sr VP-Bus Dev)
Glenn Pierce (VP-Ops)
Chris Moore (Pres & CEO)

Subsidiary (Non-US):

Strategic Distribution Marketing de Mexico, S.A. de C.V.   (2)
Ave Hermanos Escobar 7046-4, Col Partido Diaz, C.P. 32310, Ciudad Juarez, Chihuahua, Mexico
Tel.: (52) 6566270457
Sales Range: Less than $1 Million
Supply Chain Solutions
N.A.I.C.S.: 561499

Strategic Distribution Services de Mexico, S.A. de C.V.   (2)
Ave Hermanos Escobar 7046-4, Col Partido Diaz, 32310, Ciudad Juarez, Chihuahua, Mexico
Tel.: (52) 6566270415
Sales Range: Less than $1 Million
Industrial Supplies Whslr
N.A.I.C.S.: 423840

William Robert Berkley (Chm)

POVERTY SOLUTIONS, INC.
3699 Wilshire Blvd Ste 530, Los Angeles, CA 90010-2729
Tel.: (213) 325-3037   CA
Web Site: http://www.povsol.com
Year Founded: 2008
Sales Range: $1-9.9 Million
Emp.: 9
Antipoverty Social Advocacy Services
N.A.I.C.S.: 813319
Frank I. Igwealor (Pres & CEO)
Rita P. Gatewood (Chief Program Officer)
Ausanta Nebbitt (Mgr-Ops)
Roy Watson (Dir-Fin)
Patricia E. Bigay (Mgr-Community Outreach)
Ambrose Egbuonu (Chm)
Martin Nwaege (Treas)
Andrew Jeong (Mgr-Program)

POWDER COTE II INC.
80 N Rose St, Mount Clemens, MI 48043
Tel.: (586) 463-7040
Web Site:
http://www.powdercoteii.com
Rev: $13,000,000
Emp.: 185
Coating Of Metals & Formed Products
N.A.I.C.S.: 332812
Greg Morrow (Supvr-Maintenance)
Stacy Sechan (Supvr-Line)

POWDER RIVER ENERGY CORPORATION
221 Main St, Sundance, WY 82729
Tel.: (307) 283-3531   WY
Web Site: http://www.precorp.coop
Year Founded: 1947
Sales Range: $25-49.9 Million
Emp.: 150
Providers of Electrical Services
N.A.I.C.S.: 221122
Curtis Mock (CFO & Chief Admin Officer)
Reuben Ritthaler (Pres)
Philip Habeck (Treas & Sec)
Les Penning (COO & Deputy Gen Mgr)
Brian Mills (CEO)
Doug Wilson (CIO)
Mike Pommarane (Sr VP-Sys Ops)
Jeff Bumgarner (VP-Member Svcs)
Quentin Rogers (VP-Engrg & Technical Svcs)

POWDER RIVER INC.
PO Box 50758, Provo, UT 84605
Tel.: (208) 345-9325
Web Site:
http://www.powderriver.com
Rev: $20,100,000
Emp.: 3
Barn, Silo, Poultry, Dairy & Livestock Machinery
N.A.I.C.S.: 333111
Matt Johnson (Mgr-Mktg)

POWDR CORP.
1794 Olympic Pkwy Ste 210, Park City, UT 84098
Tel.: (435) 658-5820   DE
Web Site: http://www.powdr.com
Year Founded: 1994
Holding Company; Ski Resort Owner & Operator
N.A.I.C.S.: 551112
David Cumming (Sec & VP)
John D. Cumming (Chm, Pres & CEO)

Subsidiaries:

Boreal Ridge Corp   (1)
19659 Boreal Ridge Rd, Truckee, CA 95724
Tel.: (530) 426-3666
Web Site: http://www.rideboreal.com
Sales Range: $25-49.9 Million
Emp.: 500
Ski Resort Services
N.A.I.C.S.: 721199

Copper Mountain, Inc.   (1)
209 Ten Mile Cir, Frisco, CO 80443
Tel.: (970) 968-2882
Web Site: http://www.coppercolorado.com
Sales Range: $350-399.9 Million
Emp.: 2,700
Ski Resort
N.A.I.C.S.: 713990

Eldora Mountain Resort   (1)
2861 Eldora Ski Rd Ste 140, Nederland, CO 80466
Tel.: (303) 440-8700
Web Site: http://www.eldora.com
Traveler Accommodation
N.A.I.C.S.: 721199
Bill Killebrew (Partner)

Greater Park City Company Inc.   (1)
2600 Alpine Meadows Rd, Tahoe City, CA 96146-9854
Tel.: (530) 583-4232
Web Site: http://www.skialpine.com
Sales Range: $10-24.9 Million
Emp.: 20
Provider of Ski Resort Services
N.A.I.C.S.: 721191

Killington Limited   (1)
4763 Killington Rd, Killington, VT 05751
Tel.: (802) 422-3333
Web Site: http://www.killington.com
Sales Range: $100-124.9 Million
Emp.: 1,000
Resort & Ski Area Operator
N.A.I.C.S.: 487990
Tracy Taylor (Mgr-Pico)

Subsidiary (Domestic):

Killington Resort   (2)
4763 Killington Rd, Killington, VT 05751
Tel.: (802) 422-6200
Web Site: http://www.killington.com
Ski Resort
N.A.I.C.S.: 713920

POWELL CLINCH GAS UTILITY DISTRIBUTION
203 1st St, Lake City, TN 37769
Tel.: (865) 426-2822
Web Site:
http://www.powellclinch.com
Year Founded: 1959
Sales Range: $25-49.9 Million
Emp.: 60
Natural Gas Distribution
N.A.I.C.S.: 221210
Richard McIntosh (VP)

POWELL COMPANIES INC.
3622 Bristol Hwy, Johnson City, TN 37601-1324
Tel.: (423) 282-0111   TN
Web Site:
http://www.powellcompanies.net
Year Founded: 1969
Sales Range: $50-74.9 Million
Emp.: 550
Nonresidential Construction Services
N.A.I.C.S.: 236220
James J. Powell (Founder & Pres)
Bill Polis (Dir-Bus Dev-Bellevue)

POWELL ELECTRONICS INC.
200 Commodore Dr, Logan Township, NJ 08085-1270
Tel.: (856) 241-8000   PA
Web Site: http://www.powell.com
Year Founded: 1946
Sales Range: $100-124.9 Million
Emp.: 200

Wholesale Distribution of Electronic Components
N.A.I.C.S.: 423690
Sjaak Bontje *(Gen Mgr)*
Brill Chan *(Mgr-Sls-China)*
Gary Evans *(Mng Dir-Europe)*
Nicola Della Malva *(Country Mgr-Italy & South East Europe)*

Subsidiaries:

Powell Electronics Europe BV (1)
Kuifmees 58, 3435 RG, Nieuwegein, Netherlands
Tel.: (31) 30 6014666
Web Site: http://www.powell.com
Emp.: 8
Electrical Component Distr
N.A.I.C.S.: 423690
Sjaak Bontje *(Gen Mgr-Agricultural Div)*
Gary Evans *(Mng Dir)*

POWELL GROUP INC.
PO Box 788, Baton Rouge, LA 70809
Tel.: (225) 922-4540
Web Site:
    http://www.powellgroup.com
Sales Range: $10-24.9 Million
Emp.: 20
Radio Broadcasting Stations
N.A.I.C.S.: 516110
Nanette Noland *(Pres)*

POWELL SALES INC.
3622 Bristol Hwy, Johnson City, TN 37601
Tel.: (423) 282-0111
Web Site:
    http://www.powellcompanies.net
Rev.: $27,269,000
Emp.: 1
Mining Machinery & Equipment, Except Petroleum
N.A.I.C.S.: 423810
James J. Powell *(Pres)*

POWELL VALLEY ELECTRIC COOPERATIVE
325 Straight Creek Rd, New Tazewell, TN 37825
Tel.: (423) 626-5204
Web Site: http://www.pve.coop
Year Founded: 1938
Sales Range: $25-49.9 Million
Emp.: 65
Electric Power Distr
N.A.I.C.S.: 221122
Randell W. Meyers *(CEO & Gen Mgr)*
Roger A. Ball *(Pres)*
Bo Goodin *(Dir-Engrg)*

POWELL VALLEY HEALTHCARE
777 Avenue H, Powell, WY 82435
Tel.: (307) 754-2267 WY
Web Site: http://www.pvhc.org
Year Founded: 1992
Sales Range: $25-49.9 Million
Emp.: 598
Healtcare Services
N.A.I.C.S.: 622110
Arleen Campeau *(VP-Patient Care Svcs)*
Nicole Ostermiller *(VP-Resident Care Svcs)*
Cassie Tinsley *(Dir-HR)*
Mike Gilmore *(VP-Outpatient Svcs)*
Terry Odom *(CEO-Interim)*
Lisa Horton *(Dir-Clinic Nursing)*

POWELL'S BOOKS INC.
7 NW 9th Ave, Portland, OR 97209
Tel.: (503) 228-0540 OR
Web Site: http://www.powells.com
Year Founded: 1971
Sales Range: $25-49.9 Million
Emp.: 500
Book Stores
N.A.I.C.S.: 459210
Emily Powell *(Owner & Pres)*
John Kingsbury *(COO)*

POWELL, CARNEY, MALLER, P.A.
1 Progress Plz 200 Central Ave Ste 1210, Saint Petersburg, FL 33701
Tel.: (727) 898-9011
Web Site:
    http://www.powellcarneylaw.com
Sales Range: $1-9.9 Million
Emp.: 15
Law Office
N.A.I.C.S.: 541110
James N. Powell *(Partner)*
Mary Jo Carney *(Partner)*
Karen E. Maller *(Partner)*
Don Douglas Ramsay *(Atty)*

POWELL-WATSON MOTORS INC.
1 S Auto Rd, Laredo, TX 78041
Tel.: (956) 722-5182
Web Site:
    http://www.toyotaoflaredo.com
Sales Range: $25-49.9 Million
Emp.: 88
Automobiles, New & Used
N.A.I.C.S.: 441110
Michael Powell *(VP)*
Mary Cortez *(Controller)*
Mike Adams *(Mgr-Parts)*

POWER & ENERGY, INC.
106 Railroad Dr, Ivyland, PA 18974-1449
Tel.: (215) 942-4600 PA
Web Site:
    http://www.powerandenergy.com
Year Founded: 1993
Sales Range: $1-9.9 Million
Emp.: 15
Hydrogen Purification & Membrane Separation Technologies Mfr
N.A.I.C.S.: 333248
Peter Bossard *(Chm & CEO)*

POWER & PUMPS INC.
803 N Myrtle Ave, Jacksonville, FL 32204
Tel.: (904) 356-5881 FL
Web Site:
    http://www.powerandpumps.com
Year Founded: 1979
Sales Range: Less than $1 Million
Emp.: 25
Industrial Supplies
N.A.I.C.S.: 423840
David Williams *(Pres)*

POWER & TELEPHONE SUPPLY COMPANY
2673 Yale Ave, Memphis, TN 38112-3335
Tel.: (901) 324-6116 TN
Web Site: http://www.ptsupply.com
Year Founded: 1963
Sales Range: $100-124.9 Million
Emp.: 1,500
Wholesale Telephones & Data Communications Equipment
N.A.I.C.S.: 423610
Dale Stevenson *(Pres)*
Jennifer Pentecost Sims *(CEO)*
Thomas Tighe *(Exec VP-Sls)*
Matt Spinolo *(COO)*
Mike Kruszewski *(Exec VP-Sls)*

Subsidiaries:

Power & Telephone Supply Company do Brasil (1)
Rua Dos Tres Irmaos 62 Conj 804 Ed West Tower, Sao Paulo, 05615-190, Brazil
Tel.: (55) 11 3804 9724

Networking & Communication Equipment Distr
N.A.I.C.S.: 423690
Paulo Vasilvd *(Gen Mgr)*

Power & Telephone Supply S.A. DE C.V. (1)
Poniente 146 759-B Col Industrial Vallejo, Del Azcapotzalco, 2300, Mexico, Mexico
Tel.: (52) 55 5719 0502
Web Site: http://www.ptsupply.com
Telecommunication Equipment & Supplies Distr
N.A.I.C.S.: 423690
Paulo Eduardo de Silva *(Intl Mng Dir)*
Nidia Tenorio *(Mgr-Sls-Telecom)*

Power & Telephone Supply of Canada (1)
1141 King Road Unit 1, Burlington, L7R 3X5, ON, Canada (100%)
Tel.: (289) 288-3260
Web Site: http://www.ptsupply.ca
Sales Range: $10-24.9 Million
Emp.: 7
Distr of Telecommunication Materials
N.A.I.C.S.: 517810
Kevin Sweeting *(Dir-Sls)*

POWER ADS CORP.
Mercantil Plz Ste 802, San Juan, PR 00918
Tel.: (787) 528-1303
Web Site:
    http://www.poweradspr.com
Year Founded: 2005
Sales Range: $1-9.9 Million
Emp.: 3
Media Buying Services
N.A.I.C.S.: 541810
Ivan Velez Correa *(Owner)*

POWER AUTO GROUP
500 SW Sublimity Blvd, Sublimity, OR 97385-9629
Tel.: (503) 769-7691
Web Site:
    http://www.powerautogroup.com
Sales Range: $10-24.9 Million
Emp.: 60
New Car Whslr
N.A.I.C.S.: 441110
Roddy Sloper *(Dir-Internet)*

POWER CONSTRUCTION COMPANY
8750 W Bryn Mawr Ave Ste 500, Schaumburg, IL 60631
Tel.: (847) 925-1300 DE
Web Site:
    http://www.powerconstruction.net
Year Founded: 1926
Sales Range: $100-124.9 Million
Emp.: 350
Provider of General Contracting Services
N.A.I.C.S.: 236220
Alvin L. Gorman *(Chm)*
Bob Gallo *(Exec VP)*
Terry Graber *(Pres & CEO)*
Gary Schreiber *(VP)*
Jeff Geier *(Exec VP)*
Dave Anderskow *(CFO & Sr VP)*
Dwight Blake *(Sr VP)*
Bob Van Deven *(VP)*
Jamie Hendricks *(VP)*
Pat Donley *(VP)*

POWER CREATIVE
11701 Commonwealth Dr, Louisville, KY 40299-2358
Tel.: (502) 267-0772 KY
Web Site:
    http://www.powercreative.com
Year Founded: 1976
Sales Range: $75-99.9 Million
Emp.: 150
Advertising Agencies
N.A.I.C.S.: 541810

M. David Power *(CEO)*
Mark Bird *(VP-Architectural Mktg)*
Tim Lucas *(Pres)*
Holly Turney *(Dir-Acct Svcs)*

POWER CURBERS INC.
727 Bendix Dr, Salisbury, NC 28146
Tel.: (704) 636-5871
Web Site:
    http://www.powercurbers.com
Sales Range: $10-24.9 Million
Emp.: 110
Road Construction & Maintenance Machinery
N.A.I.C.S.: 333120
Dwight Messinger *(Pres & CEO)*
Stephen Bullock *(COO)*
David Midgley *(Mgr-Intl Sls)*
Steve Milam *(Mgr-East)*
Steve Peacock *(Mgr-Product Support)*

POWER DESIGN INC.
3753 Eagle Loop, Hood River, OR 97031
Tel.: (541) 354-3222 OR
Web Site:
    http://www.powerdesigninc.com
Year Founded: 1991
Sales Range: $10-24.9 Million
Fiberglass Sectionalizing Electrical Cabinet, Pad Mounted Switchgear & Metering Enclosure Mfr
N.A.I.C.S.: 326199
Eric R. Cederstam *(Pres)*

POWER DESIGN, INC.
11600 9th St N, Saint Petersburg, FL 33716
Tel.: (727) 210-0492 FL
Web Site:
    http://www.powerdesigninc.us
Year Founded: 1989
Sales Range: $125-149.9 Million
Emp.: 370
Electrical Contractor
N.A.I.C.S.: 238210
Mitch Permuy *(Chm)*
Dana Permuy *(Chief Risk Officer)*
Meredith Zdon *(CEO)*
Frank Musolino *(COO)*
David Redden *(Gen Counsel & Mgr-Risk)*
Joseph Micallef *(Exec VP-Construction)*
Marlene Velez *(Chief People & Culture Officer)*
Raghu Kutty *(CIO)*
Lauren Permuy *(VP-Bus Dev)*
Rob McMillian *(Reg VP-West)*
Heather Ford *(CFO)*
Misha Zeltser *(VP-Engrg)*
Carter Hastings *(Reg VP)*
Michael Wells *(VP-Sys)*
Chris Hughes *(VP-Power Design Resources)*
Jaime Castaneda *(Coord-Preconstruction)*

POWER DIRECT
23456 Madero Ste 105, Mission Viejo, CA 92691
Tel.: (949) 253-3441
Web Site: http://www.powerdirect.net
Year Founded: 2001
Sales Range: $25-49.9 Million
Emp.: 46
Advertising & Marketing
N.A.I.C.S.: 541890
Ann Marie Dryden *(COO)*

POWER DISTRIBUTORS, LLC
3700 Paragon Dr, Columbus, OH 43228
Tel.: (800) 554-3336

POWER DISTRIBUTORS, LLC

U.S. PRIVATE

Power Distributors, LLC—(Continued)
Web Site:
  http://www.powerdistributors.com
Year Founded: 2014
Emp.: 230
Outdoor Power Equipment Whslr
N.A.I.C.S.: 423830
Matthew Finn *(Pres)*
Patrick Eberly *(Dir-HR)*
John DeNiro *(VP-Sls)*
Stephanie DeMarco *(Controller)*

Subsidiaries:

Magneto Power, LLC (1)
3500 Thurston Ave Ste 200, Anoka, MN 55303
Tel.: (855) 879-5094
Web Site: http://www.magnetopower.com
Sales Range: $10-24.9 Million
Emp.: 40
Outdoor Power Equipment & Parts Wholesale Distr
N.A.I.C.S.: 423830

POWER DRIVES INC.
133 Hopkins St, Buffalo, NY 14220
Tel.: (716) 822-3600
Web Site:
  http://www.powerdrives.com
Rev.: $19,731,078
Emp.: 175
Hydraulic Systems Equipment & Supplies
N.A.I.C.S.: 423830
Suzanne Elliott *(VP-HR)*
Jim LaMancuso *(Mgr-Inside Sls)*
Jennifer Sheehan *(Controller)*
Rick Luce *(Coord-Maintenance)*
William Frey *(Mgr-Sls)*
Joster Macedo *(CFO)*
Jerome Di Virgilio *(Mgr-Corp Engrg)*
Michael Moffett *(VP/Mgr-Ops)*

POWER EFFICIENCY CORPORATION
5744 Pacific Center Blvd Ste 311, San Diego, CA 92121
Tel.: (858) 750-3875 DE
Web Site:
  http://www.powerefficiency.com
Year Founded: 1994
Sales Range: Less than $1 Million
Emp.: 13
Electric Motor Energy Management Solutions
N.A.I.C.S.: 336320
Steven Z. Strasser *(Vice Chm & CEO)*
Philip L. Meisel *(Chm)*

POWER ENGINEERING, INC.
16632 Millikan Ave, Irvine, CA 92606
Tel.: (949) 260-9716 CA
Web Site:
  http://www.powerengineering.com
Year Founded: 1989
Emp.: 25
Engineeering Services
N.A.I.C.S.: 541330
Cynthia Rhodes *(Pres)*

POWER EQUIPMENT CO. MEMPHIS
3050 Broad Ave, Memphis, TN 38112
Tel.: (901) 327-8261
Web Site: http://www.powereq.com
Sales Range: $10-24.9 Million
Emp.: 45
Pumps & Pumping Equipment Compressor & Boilers
N.A.I.C.S.: 423830
Joe Brackett *(Pres & CEO)*
Carla Roe *(Controller)*

POWER EQUIPMENT COMPANY

2329 River Rd, Grand Junction, CO 81505-1326
Tel.: (970) 024-0722
Web Site: http://www.power-
  equip.com
Construction Machinery Mfr
N.A.I.C.S.: 333120
Clancy Walsh *(Mgr)*
Will Ricketts *(Pres)*

Subsidiaries:

Golden Equipment Company (1)
721 Candelaria Rd NE, Albuquerque, NM 87107
Tel.: (505) 345-7811
Web Site: http://www.goldenequipment.com
Sales Range: $10-24.9 Million
Emp.: 60
Provider of General Construction Machinery & Equipment
N.A.I.C.S.: 423810
Michael Bahrmann *(VP-Ops)*

POWER EQUIPMENT COMPANY INC
3300 Alcoa Hwy, Knoxville, TN 37920-5558
Tel.: (865) 577-5563 DE
Web Site:
  http://www.powerequipco.com
Year Founded: 1946
Sales Range: $75-99.9 Million
Emp.: 125
Construction & Mining Machinery
N.A.I.C.S.: 423810
Jim McNeillie *(VP-Fin & Mgr-Fin)*
Shawn Robins *(Sr VP-Products Support)*
Andy Moon *(Pres)*
Michael Brennan *(CEO)*
Mike Paradis *(Chm)*

POWER FORD
1101 Montano Rd NE, Albuquerque, NM 87107
Tel.: (505) 766-6600
Web Site:
  http://www.powerfordnm.com
Sales Range: $50-74.9 Million
Emp.: 140
Car Dealership Owner & Operator
N.A.I.C.S.: 441110
Gary Timmons *(Mgr-Sls-Fleet)*
Jennifer Germain *(Dir-Customer Rels)*
Jim Lopez *(Mgr-Fin)*
Jawad Moussa *(Mgr-Fin)*
John Chavez *(Gen Mgr-Sls)*

POWER HOLDING CORPORATION
3050 Horseshoe Dr N Ste 105, Naples, FL 34104-7909
Tel.: (239) 775-2230
Web Site: http://www.powercorp.net
Rev.: $17,338,936
Emp.: 10
Subdividers & Developers For Residental & Commercial
N.A.I.C.S.: 237210

POWER HOME REMODELING GROUP, INC.
2501 Seaport Dr First Fl, Chester, PA 19013
Tel.: (610) 874-5000
Web Site: http://www.powerhrg.com
Year Founded: 1992
Sales Range: $100-124.9 Million
Emp.: 900
Building Construction Services
N.A.I.C.S.: 213112
Adam Kaliner *(CFO)*
Jeffrey Kaliner *(Partner)*
Bennet Andelman *(Dir-Mktg Comm)*
Kerry McGovern *(Sr VP-Brand)*

Asher Raphael *(CEO)*
Andrea Recine *(Mgr-PR)*
Sean Flanagan *(VP-Creative Svcs)*

POWER HOME TECHNOLOGIES INC.
4905 Green Rd Ste 107A, Raleigh, NC 27616
Web Site: http://www.pht.com
Year Founded: 2004
Sales Range: $10-24.9 Million
Emp.: 116
Security Systems
N.A.I.C.S.: 561621
Ben Brookhart *(CEO)*

POWER LLC
6402 Deere Rd, Syracuse, NY 13206
Tel.: (315) 374-8439
Web Site: http://www.pwrllc.com
Electrical Apparatus & Equipment
N.A.I.C.S.: 423610
Rod Law *(Pres)*
Ron Rio *(Exec VP-Ops & Engrg)*
Joe Miller *(Project Mgr)*
Andy Huntington *(Mgr-Warehouse)*
Greg Lessard *(Acct Mgr)*
Mark Bandy *(Acct Mgr)*
Richard Wray *(Mgr-Maintenance)*
Mike Shaefer *(Mgr-Pur)*
Vincent Giampietro *(Project Mgr)*

POWER MAINTENANCE & CONSTRUCTORS LLC
201 Tower Plz, Belleville, IL 62220
Tel.: (618) 277-1245
Web Site: http://www.pmcllc.com
Rev.: $10,300,000
Emp.: 100
Boiler Maintenance Contractor
N.A.I.C.S.: 238220
Alan R. Howkins *(Pres)*
Larry Grieff *(CEO)*

POWER MOTIVE CORPORATION
5000 Vasquez Blvd, Denver, CO 80216-3029
Tel.: (303) 355-5900 CO
Web Site:
  http://www.powermotivecorp.com
Year Founded: 1979
Rev.: $35,000,000
Emp.: 150
Construction & Mining Machinery
N.A.I.C.S.: 423810
Bob Davis *(Pres)*
Ric Lechman *(CFO)*
Gary Klipp *(Area Mgr)*
Sheryl Perko *(Mgr-HR)*

POWER PLUMBING, INC.
12507 Telge Rd, Cypress, TX 77429
Tel.: (281) 304-9392
Web Site: http://www.powerlp.com
Year Founded: 1988
Sales Range: $50-74.9 Million
Emp.: 250
Multi-Family Residential Construction Plumbing Contractor
N.A.I.C.S.: 238220
James Power *(Founder & Exec VP-Sls & Estimating)*
Guy Mathieu *(Dir-Vendor Rels)*
Dick Pearsall *(Pres & CEO)*
Nick Freeman *(Mgr-Drafting & Design-Houston)*
John Perry *(Mgr-Drafting & Design-Dallas & Fort Worth)*
Mason Pearsall Jr. *(CFO)*

POWER PROCESS EQUIPMENT INC.
1660 Lake Dr W, Chanhassen, MN 55317
Tel.: (952) 937-1000

Web Site:
  http://www.powerprocess.net
Year Founded: 1958
Emp.: 44
Distr of Industrial Equipment & Supplies
N.A.I.C.S.: 423840
Tony Gilbertson *(VP)*
John Gilbertson Sr. *(Pres)*
John Gilbertson Jr. *(CEO)*

POWER PROCESS PIPING, INC.
45780 Port St, Plymouth, MI 48170-6049
Tel.: (734) 451-0130 MI
Web Site: http://www.ppphq.com
Year Founded: 1974
Sales Range: $500-549.9 Million
Emp.: 150
Fabricator & Installer of Piping Systems
N.A.I.C.S.: 238220
Graham Williams *(Pres & CEO)*
Jerry L. Palmer *(VP & Project Mgr)*
Norman Sunamoto *(VP)*
Mark Johnson *(VP-Shop & Field Ops)*

POWER QUALITY INTERNATIONAL, INC.
2404 Merchant Ave, Odessa, FL 33556
Tel.: (727) 478-7284
Web Site:
  http://www.powerqualityinternatio
  nal.com
Sales Range: $1-9.9 Million
Emp.: 9
Ultra-Efficient & Harmonic-Mitigating Transformers & Filters Mfr
N.A.I.C.S.: 335311
Greg Ferguson *(Founder & Pres)*

POWER SERVICE PRODUCTS, INC.
513 Peaster Hwy, Weatherford, TX 76086
Tel.: (817) 599-9486 TX
Web Site:
  http://www.powerservice.com
Year Founded: 1956
Sales Range: $10-24.9 Million
Emp.: 45
Fuel Additives Mfr
N.A.I.C.S.: 324110
Ed M. Kramer *(Owner & Pres)*
Ruth B. Swain *(COO)*
Bob Sellers *(Sr VP-Sls)*
Mandy Kramer *(VP)*
Al Kramer *(Founder)*

POWER SOLUTIONS
PO Box 100, Barrington, RI 02806
Tel.: (401) 434-5785
Web Site: http://www.power-
  solutions.com
Rev.: $11,000,000
Emp.: 8
Electronic Parts & Equipment
N.A.I.C.S.: 423690
Guy Lacerte *(Pres)*

POWER SOLUTIONS LLC
17201 Melford Blvd Ste A-K, Bowie, MD 20715
Tel.: (301) 794-0330
Web Site: http://www.powersolutions-
  llc.com
Sales Range: $25-49.9 Million
Emp.: 342
Electrical Work
N.A.I.C.S.: 238210
Mary Ways *(Controller)*
Eric Boehm *(Project Mgr)*
John King *(Project Mgr)*
Kevin Howell *(Mgr-Ops)*

COMPANIES

POWER STOP LLC
6112 W 73rd St, Chicago, IL 60638-6115
Tel.: (708) 575-9745
Web Site: http://www.powerstop.com
Year Founded: 2005
Sales Range: $50-74.9 Million
Emp.: 50
Automotive Components Mfr
N.A.I.C.S.: 336390
Mark Pritt *(VP-Special Markets)*
Arvin Scott *(CEO)*
Joe Stephan *(COO)*
Griff Jordan *(Exec VP)*
Bob Van Gorkom *(VP-Bus Dev)*

POWER SUPPLY COMPONENTS INC.
2307 Calle Del Mundo, Santa Clara, CA 95054
Tel.: (408) 737-1333
Web Site: http://www.pscelex.com
Year Founded: 1985
Rev.: $13,699,692
Emp.: 19
Whslr & Distributor of Magnetic, Interconnect, Electro-Mechanical & Passive Components
N.A.I.C.S.: 423690
Ed Morris *(CEO)*
Rick Maciaszek *(Mgr-Cable Assembly)*
David Bonine *(Mgr-Field Sls)*
Ed Donahue *(Product Mgr)*
Charlie Colson *(Mgr-Bridgeport)*

POWER TECHNOLOGY, INC.
16302 Alexander Rd, Alexander, AR 72002
Tel.: (501) 407-0712
Web Site:
http://www.powertechnology.com
Year Founded: 1969
Sales Range: $25-49.9 Million
Emp.: 45
Laser Power Supplies & Laser Diode Modules Mfr
N.A.I.C.S.: 334419
Thomas H. Burgess *(Pres)*
Kara Guire *(CEO)*

POWER TEST, INC.
N60 W22700 Silver Spring Dr, Sussex, WI 53089
Tel.: (262) 252-4301 WI
Web Site:
http://www.powertestdyno.com
Year Founded: 1976
Measuring & Controlling Device Mfr
N.A.I.C.S.: 334519
Alan D. Petelinsek *(Pres)*
Rick Ballo *(Mgr-Sls-Intl)*
Pat Koppa *(Pres)*

Subsidiaries:
Land & Sea, Inc. (1)
25 Henniker St, Concord, NH 03301
Tel.: (603) 226-3966
Web Site: http://www.land-and-sea.com
Boat Building
N.A.I.C.S.: 336612
Robert Bergeron *(Pres)*

POWER TOOLS & SUPPLY INC.
8551 Boulder Ct Unit 1, Walled Lake, MI 48390
Tel.: (248) 363-5650
Web Site: http://www.pts-mi.com
Sales Range: $10-24.9 Million
Emp.: 26
Industrial Supplies
N.A.I.C.S.: 423840
Jeffrey T. McClure *(Pres)*

POWER-FLO TECHNOLOGIES INC.
270 Park Ave, Garden City Park, NY 11040-5318
Tel.: (516) 812-6800
Web Site:
http://www.unitedelectricpower.com
Rev.: $20,300,000
Emp.: 150
Electrical Supplies Distr & Mfr; Motor & Pump Repair Services
N.A.I.C.S.: 423610
Gerald DiCunzolo *(Pres)*

POWER-SONIC CORPORATION
7550 Panasonic Way, San Diego, CA 92154
Tel.: (619) 661-2020
Web Site: http://www.power-sonic.com
Year Founded: 1970
Sales Range: $10-24.9 Million
Emp.: 50
Electrical Apparatus & Equipment
N.A.I.C.S.: 423610
Guy C. Clum *(Pres)*
Bob Lindemann *(Mgr-IT)*
Amy Simcox *(Mgr-Customer Svc)*

Subsidiaries:
PLASTICOS AMC, DE MEXICO, S.A. DE C.V. (1)
Calle 9 Sur 1510, Ciudad Industrial Nueva, Tijuana, 22500, Mexico
Tel.: (52) 6646235911
Web Site: http://www.plasticosamc.com
Emp.: 700
Plastic Component Mfr
N.A.I.C.S.: 326199

Power-Sonic Europe Ltd. (1)
3 Buckingham Square Hurricane Way, Wickford, Basildon, SS11 8YQ, United Kingdom (100%)
Tel.: (44) 1268560686
Web Site: http://www.power-sonic.com
Sales Range: $10-24.9 Million
Emp.: 20
Electrical Apparatus & Equipment
N.A.I.C.S.: 423610
Guy Clum *(Mng Dir)*

POWER/MATION
1310 Energy Ln, Saint Paul, MN 55108
Tel.: (651) 605-3300
Web Site:
http://www.powermation.com
Sales Range: $25-49.9 Million
Emp.: 71
Industrial Supplies
N.A.I.C.S.: 423840
Bob Mergens *(Sr Acct Mgr)*
Mike Ryan *(Mgr-Matl Handling)*
Todd Carlson *(Mgr-Engrg)*

POWERCHORD, INC.
100 2nd Ave S Ste 200 S Tower, Saint Petersburg, FL 33701
Tel.: (727) 823-1530
Web Site:
http://www.powerchordsystem.com
Sales Range: $1-9.9 Million
Emp.: 40
Online Channel Management Software
N.A.I.C.S.: 513210
Patrick Schunk *(Chm)*
Brigitte Hoffstetter *(Dir-Acct Svc)*
Teague Perry *(Dir-Product Implementation)*
Nikki Vegenski *(VP-Mktg & Strategy)*
William Volmuth *(Pres)*

POWERCOMM HOLDINGS INC.
9701 Fallard Ct, Upper Marlboro, MD 20772
Tel.: (703) 746-8980 DE
Web Site:
http://www.PowerCommConstruction.com
Year Founded: 2015
Rev.: $13,621,599
Assets: $5,177,123
Liabilities: $4,207,198
Net Worth: $969,925
Earnings: $775,608
Emp.: 1
Fiscal Year-end: 12/31/18
Investment Services
N.A.I.C.S.: 523999
Laura Kwasnik *(VP-Acctg-PowerComm Construction Inc)*
John Bonilla *(VP-Bus Dev, Intl & Domestic-PowerComm Construction Inc)*
Harry Ahlfeldt *(Superintendent-Underground Ops-PowerComm Construction Inc)*
Louis Burgher *(Mgr-Underground Utilities-PowerComm Construction Inc)*
Sherry Farless *(VP-HR-PowerComm Construction Inc)*
David Kwasnik Sr. *(Pres, CEO, Treas & Sec)*
David Kwasnik Jr. *(VP-HR-PowerComm Construction Inc)*

POWERDMS, INC.
200 E Robinson St Suite 425, Orlando, FL 32801
Tel.: (800) 749-5104
Web Site: http://www.powerdms.com
Year Founded: 2000
Sales Range: $1-9.9 Million
Emp.: 79
Cloud-Based Solution Software Services
N.A.I.C.S.: 513210
Joshua Brown *(Founder)*
Heath Hensley *(CTO)*
Craig Petersen *(VP-Tech)*
David DiGiacomo *(CEO)*

POWERFILM, INC.
2337 230th St, Ames, IA 50014
Tel.: (515) 292-7606
Web Site:
http://www.powerfilmsolar.com
Year Founded: 1988
Sales Range: Less than $1 Million
Solar Panel Mfr
N.A.I.C.S.: 221118
Julia Stone *(Dir-Distr Rels)*
Wesley White *(Dir-Military Bus Ops)*

POWERLAB INC.
1145 Hwy 34 S, Terrell, TX 75160-4556
Tel.: (972) 563-1477 TX
Web Site:
http://www.powerlabinc.com
Year Founded: 1973
Sales Range: $10-24.9 Million
Emp.: 60
Industrial Inorganic Chemicals
N.A.I.C.S.: 325180
Russ Tipton *(Controller)*
Chris Brady *(Engr-Ops)*
Don Rabon *(Mgr-Engrg)*

POWERLINK LLC.
3011 W Grand Blvd, Detroit, MI 48202
Tel.: (313) 309-2020
Web Site:
http://www.powerlinkonline.com
Year Founded: 2002
Sales Range: $10-24.9 Million
Emp.: 400

POWERS AGENCY

Environmental Consulting Services
N.A.I.C.S.: 541620
Scott Rice *(COO)*
Link Howard III *(Founder, Pres & CEO)*

POWERNET GLOBAL COMMUNICATIONS
100 Commercial Dr, Cincinnati, OH 45014
Year Founded: 1992
Sales Range: $25-49.9 Million
Emp.: 308
Telecommunication Servicesb
N.A.I.C.S.: 517810
John Putnam *(VP-Sls)*
Christian Gartner *(CFO)*

POWERON SERVICES, INC.
8801 Washington Blvd Ste 101, Roseville, CA 95678
Tel.: (916) 677-6227
Web Site: http://www.poweron.com
Year Founded: 1994
Sales Range: $10-24.9 Million
Emp.: 43
Computer & Software Dealers
N.A.I.C.S.: 449210
Kevin Hardy *(COO)*

POWERPAY
320 Cumberland Ave, Portland, ME 04101
Tel.: (207) 775-6900
Web Site: http://www.powerpay.biz
Year Founded: 2003
Rev.: $100,000,000
Emp.: 125
Financial Transactions Processing Reserve & Clearinghouse Activities
N.A.I.C.S.: 522320
Jim Raftice *(Pres)*
Lisa Fisher *(Partner-Rels & VP)*
Eran Vail *(Sr VP-Fin)*
Jay Meyers *(Sr VP-IT)*

POWERPLANT MAINTENANCE SPECIALISTS INC.
2900 Bristol St Ste H202, Costa Mesa, CA 92626
Tel.: (714) 427-6900
Web Site: http://www.pmsipower.com
Sales Range: $50-74.9 Million
Emp.: 10
Boiler & Heating Repair Services
N.A.I.C.S.: 236210
James McEachern *(Pres & CEO)*

POWERS & SONS CONSTRUCTION CO., INC.
2636 W 15th Ave, Gary, IN 46404
Tel.: (219) 949-3100
Web Site:
http://www.powersandsons.com
Year Founded: 1967
Sales Range: $25-49.9 Million
Emp.: 100
Provider of Commercial & Office Building Construction Services
N.A.I.C.S.: 236220
Claude Powers *(Exec VP)*
Mamon Powers Jr. *(Pres & CEO)*

POWERS AGENCY
1 W 4th St 5th Fl, Cincinnati, OH 45202-3623
Tel.: (513) 721-5353 OH
Web Site:
http://www.powersagency.com
Year Founded: 1986
Sales Range: $75-99.9 Million
Emp.: 15
Advertising Agencies
N.A.I.C.S.: 541810
Charles W. Powers *(Chm)*
Krista Taylor *(CMO)*
Jim Lindsay *(Mgr-Client Ops)*

POWERS AGENCY

Powers Agency—(Continued)

Katie Copeland (Acct Supvr)
Mary Bailey (Asst Dir-Art)
Rhonda Johnson (Supvr-Acctg)
Samantha Sowder (Asst Dir-Art)
Steve Bleh (Sr Acct Mgr)
Terry Dillon (VP & Dir-Creative)

Subsidiaries:

Pinger PR at Powers (1)
1 W 4th St 5th Fl, Cincinnati, OH 45202-3623
Tel.: (513) 721-5353
Web Site: http://www.powersagency.com
Sales Range: $10-24.9 Million
Advertising Agencies
N.A.I.C.S.: 541810
Charles W. Powers (Chm)

POWERS CONSTRUCTION CO., INC.
3091 S Cashua Dr, Florence, SC 29501-6328
Tel.: (843) 669-5213 SC
Year Founded: 1969
Sales Range: $10-24.9 Million
Emp.: 10
Provider of Construction & Contracting Services
N.A.I.C.S.: 236116
W.O. Powers (Chm)
Ann Powers (Sec)
John T. Rabun Jr. (Pres)

POWERS HOLDINGS, INC.
2400 S 43rd St, Milwaukee, WI 53219
Tel.: (414) 649-4200
Sales Range: $10-24.9 Million
Emp.: 90
Holding Company
N.A.I.C.S.: 551112
Richard Powers (COO)
Steven Powers (Pres)

Subsidiaries:

Curtis Industries Inc. (1)
2400 S 43rd St, Milwaukee, WI 53219
Tel.: (414) 649-4200
Web Site: http://www.curtisind.com
Electrical Components Terminal Blocks & RFI Filters Distr
N.A.I.C.S.: 423610
Stephen Powers (Pres)

POWERS PRODUCTS CO.
1003 E Lincolnway, Cheyenne, WY 82001
Tel.: (307) 632-5521
Web Site: http://www.powersproducts.com
Year Founded: 1941
Sales Range: $10-24.9 Million
Architectural Materials Whslr & Distr
N.A.I.C.S.: 423390
Larry Enomoto (Mgr-Ops)
M. Brent Powers (CEO)
Ken Senour (Product Mgr-Daylighting)
Dave Steele (Product Mgr-Space Flexibility)
Charlie Thompson (Dir-Fin & Admin)
Keith Lunsford (Product Mgr-Fire & Smoke Separation)

POWERS-SWAIN CHEVROLET INC.
4709 Bragg Blvd, Fayetteville, NC 28303
Tel.: (910) 864-9500
Year Founded: 1961
Sales Range: $25-49.9 Million
Emp.: 70
New Car Whslr
N.A.I.C.S.: 441110
W. C. Powers (Mgr-Mktg)

POWERSOUTH ENERGY CO-OPERATIVE
2027 E 3 Notch St, Andalusia, AL 36421
Tel.: (334) 222-2571 AL
Web Site: http://www.powersouth.com
Year Founded: 1941
Sales Range: $300-349.9 Million
Emp.: 600
Electric Power Distr
N.A.I.C.S.: 221122
Gary L. Smith (Pres & CEO)
Horace Horn (VP-External Affairs)
Seth Hammett (VP-Bus Dev)
Damon Morgan (COO)
Beth Woodard (VP-Legal & Corp Affairs Div)
Leigh V. Grantham (VP-Member Svcs & Comm)
Brian Matheson (Dir-Engrg)
David Powell (Dir-Power Production)

POWERSPHYR INC.
4115 Blackhawk Plaza Cir Ste 100, Danville, CA 94506
Tel.: (925) 736-8299 DE
Web Site: http://www.powersphyr.com
Year Founded: 2016
Wireless Power Technology
N.A.I.C.S.: 334220
Bernard M. Notàs (CFO & COO)

Subsidiaries:

Gill Industries, Inc. (1)
5271 Plainfield Ave NE, Grand Rapids, MI 49525
Tel.: (616) 559-2700
Web Site: http://www.gill-industries.com
Precision Engineered Assemblies Supplier
N.A.I.C.S.: 335999

POWERSPORTS EAST
620 Pulaski Hwy, Bear, DE 19701
Tel.: (302) 322-4120
Web Site: http://www.powersportseast.com
Year Founded: 1985
Motorcycle Dealers
N.A.I.C.S.: 441227
Lynn Nathan (Principal)
Gina Moussa (Controller)
Pete Clarkin (Mgr-Fin)
Rebecca Fasten (Gen Mgr)
Steven Shields (Mgr-Parts)

POWERSTORM HOLDINGS, INC.
31244 Palos Verdes Dr W Ste 245, Rancho Palos Verdes, CA 90275-5370
Tel.: (424) 327-2991 DE
Web Site: http://www.powerstormcapital.com
Year Founded: 2011
Sales Range: Less than $1 Million
Telecommunications Infrastructure Equipment
N.A.I.C.S.: 334220
Anamaria Pruteanu (Pres)
Michael J. Freni (Chm & CEO)
Sherry Li (VP-Global Mktg & New Product Dev)
Shailesh Upreti (CTO & Dir-Engrg)
Kirstin L. Gooldy (CFO)

POWERSTRIDE BATTERY CO. INC.
122 Enterprise Ct, Corona, CA 92882
Tel.: (951) 273-2200
Web Site: http://www.powerstridebattery.com
Year Founded: 1926
Sales Range: $10-24.9 Million
Emp.: 45

Battery & Battery-Related Products Distr
N.A.I.C.S.: 423690
Richard Alvord (Owner)
Deanna Willis (Mgr-Acctg)

POWERTEK CORPORATION
9420 Key W Ave Ste 210, Rockville, MD 20850
Tel.: (301) 795-0400
Web Site: http://www.powertekcorporation.com
Year Founded: 2001
Rev.: $16,900,000
Emp.: 150
Business Consulting Services & Computer Related Services
N.A.I.C.S.: 518210
Nancy E. Scott (Pres & CEO)
Samar Ghadry (Exec VP)
Steve Miller (VP-Fin)
Chuck Ellis (VP-Enterprise Tech Engrg)

POWRTEC INTERNATIONAL CORP.
1669 Hollenbeck Ave Ste 142, Sunnyvale, CA 94087-5402
Tel.: (408) 374-1900 DE
Web Site: http://www.powrtec.com
Year Founded: 2006
Metering System Mfr
N.A.I.C.S.: 334514
Grant Jasmin (Founder & CEO)
Rolf Wendt (Sr Dir-Engrg)
Simon Westbrook (Chief Fin & Acctg Officer)

PP+K
1102 N Florida Ave, Tampa, FL 33602
Tel.: (813) 496-7000
Web Site: http://www.uniteppk.com
Year Founded: 2004
Sales Range: $75-99.9 Million
Emp.: 50
Advertising Agencies
N.A.I.C.S.: 541810
Rebecca Cardin (Bus Mgr & Controller)
Tom Kenney (Partner & Exec Dir-Creative)

PPC EVENT SERVICES, LLC
36 Cabot Rd, Woburn, MA 01801
Tel.: (781) 503-2144
Web Site: http://www.peakeventservices.com
Event & Tent Rental Resource Services
N.A.I.C.S.: 711310
Nichole Wardle (VP-Sls-Core Div)
Zachary Zasloff (VP-Ops-Core Div)

PPI TECHNOLOGIES GLOBAL, LLC
1610 Northgate Blvd, Sarasota, FL 34234
Tel.: (941) 359-6678
Web Site: http://www.ppitechnologies.com
Year Founded: 1996
Sales Range: $25-49.9 Million
Emp.: 47
Packaging Machinery & Equipment Mfr
N.A.I.C.S.: 333993
R. Charles Murray (CEO)
Stuart C. Murray (Owner)
Robert C. Libera (Dir-Sls)
Karena Thomas (CFO)

Subsidiaries:

Profile Packaging Inc (1)
1710 Northgate Blvd, Sarasota, FL 34234
Tel.: (941) 359-6678

Web Site: http://www.profilepac.com
Packaging Machinery & Equipment
N.A.I.C.S.: 423830
R. Charles Murray (CEO)
Stewart Murray (Pres)
Sandy Christians (VP)

PPM CONSULTANTS, INC.
1600 Lamy Ln, Monroe, LA 71202
Tel.: (318) 323-7270
Web Site: http://www.ppmco.com
Sales Range: $10-24.9 Million
Emp.: 111
Provider of Environmental & Engineering Consulting Services
N.A.I.C.S.: 541690
L. Todd Perry (Owner)
Shawn Ivey (Principal & Reg Mgr)
Keith Pyron (Co-Owner)
Jere Hess (Dir-Brownfields & Economic Dev)
Annie Mcilwain (Project Mgr-Jackson)

PPS, INC.
14824 W 117th St, Olathe, KS 66062
Tel.: (913) 791-9595
Web Site: http://www.ppsinc.com
Rev.: $6,000,000
Emp.: 64
Commercial Lithographic Printing
N.A.I.C.S.: 323111
Janice Green (Chm)
Matt Wilson (Mgr-Fin)
Mike Farmer (Pres)

Subsidiaries:

Pine Decals (1)
14824 West 117th St, Olathe, KS 66062
Tel.: (913) 791-0164
Web Site: http://www.pinedecals.com
Commercial Screen Printing
N.A.I.C.S.: 323113

PPS, INC.
620 Guilbeau Rd Ste D, Lafayette, LA 70506
Tel.: (337) 262-9777
Web Site: http://www.ppspharm.com
Sales Range: $75-99.9 Million
Emp.: 1,500
Holding Company; Pharmacy Management Solutions
N.A.I.C.S.: 551112
Don Nickleson (CEO)

Subsidiaries:

Comprehensive Pharmacy Services, Inc. (1)
6409 Quail Hollow Rd, Memphis, TN 38120-1414
Tel.: (901) 748-0470
Web Site: http://www.cpspharm.com
Sales Range: $100-124.9 Million
Emp.: 25
Pharmacy Services for Hospitals, Medical Centers & Healthcare Facilities
N.A.I.C.S.: 541618
H. Walker Upshaw (Chief Dev Officer)
Ira Poltorak (Pres-Western Ops & Exec VP)
Marney Wilkerson (Pres-Eastern Ops)
Edward Choy (Pres-Health Sys Ops)
Rod Recor (Chief Strategy Officer)
Gentry Hughes (Pres)
Marvin Finnefrock (Pres-Clinical & Pur Svcs Div)
Sherry Piotraschke (Pres-Compliance & Regulatory Svcs Div)
Leanne Ebert Murphy (Gen Counsel & Exec VP)
Frank Segrave (Chm & CEO)
Jeff Foreman (Grp Pres)
Benjamin R. Hansen (CFO)
Chuck Ball (Pres-Sls)

PPSC, INC.
88 Rowland Way Ste 300, Novato, CA 94945
Tel.: (415) 893-1518 CA
Web Site: http://www.ppsc.com
Sales Range: $25-49.9 Million

COMPANIES

Emp.: 1,500
Medical Apparatus & Supplies
N.A.I.C.S.: 456199
Carolyn McElroy *(Gen Counsel & VP)*
Chris Kane *(COO)*
Jim Doty *(VP-Mktg)*
John Alsterlind *(VP-Fin)*
Jason Anderson *(Sr VP-Sls & Ops)*
Alan Winters *(Sr VP-Customer Svc)*
Timothy Smith *(VP-IT)*
Wendy Thomas *(VP-HR)*

Subsidiaries:

Pacific Pulmonary Service (1)
2705 Broad Bent Pkwy, Albuquerque, NM 87107
Tel.: (505) 341-4141
Web Site: http://www.ppsc.com
Rev.: $650,000
Emp.: 7
Medical Equipment Rental
N.A.I.C.S.: 532283

PPX HOSPITALITY BRANDS INC.
101 Station Landing, Medford, MA 02155
Tel.: (617) 600-3500
Web Site:
  http://www.ppxhospitalitybrand.com
Restaurant Management & Services
N.A.I.C.S.: 722511
Oliver Munday *(CEO)*

Subsidiaries:

Legal Sea Foods Inc. (1)
1 Sea Food Way, Boston, MA 02210
Tel.: (617) 530-9000
Web Site: http://www.legalseafoods.com
Sales Range: $125-149.9 Million
Emp.: 150
Seafood Restaurants
N.A.I.C.S.: 722511
Roger S. Berkowitz *(Pres & CEO)*
Mary Corroin *(Controller)*

PRAB, INC.
5801 E N Ave, Kalamazoo, MI 49048
Tel.: (269) 665-1085 MI
Web Site: http://www.prab.com
Year Founded: 1950
Sales Range: $10-24.9 Million
Emp.: 81
Conveyors, Metal Scrap Reclamation Systems & Related Equipment Mfr
N.A.I.C.S.: 333922
Kimberly Wood *(CEO & Mgr-Portfolio)*

Subsidiaries:

Envirodyne Technologies, Inc. (1)
7574 E Michigan Ave, Kalamazoo, MI 49048
Tel.: (269) 342-1918
Web Site: http://www.kalfab.com
Sales Range: $1-9.9 Million
Emp.: 45
Sheet Metal Mfr
N.A.I.C.S.: 332322
Tim Hanna *(Pres)*
Stan Runyon *(Dir-Acctg & Auditing)*

Division (Domestic):

Kalamazoo Fabricating (2)
7574 E Michigan Ave, Comstock, MI 49048
Tel.: (269) 342-1918
Web Site: http://www.kalfab.com
Sheet Metal Work Mfg
N.A.I.C.S.: 332322
Rob Hokenmaier *(Mgr-Engrg)*

MonlanGroup (2)
7574 E Michigan Ave, Kalamazoo, MI 49048
Tel.: (269) 382-6348
Web Site: http://www.monlangroup.com
Sales Range: $1-9.9 Million
Structural Metal Fabrication Refuse System Mfg
N.A.I.C.S.: 332312

STC Dip Spin (2)
5801 E N Ave, Kalamazoo, MI 49048
Tel.: (269) 382-6349
Web Site: http://www.stc-tech.com
Emp.: 150
Paint Spinners, Custom Machinery, Tool & Die & Stampings Mfr
N.A.I.C.S.: 333248
Dave Steffens *(Gen Mgr)*

PRACTICAL COMPUTER APPLICATIONS, INC.
175 Highland Ave, Needham, MA 02494
Tel.: (617) 527-4722
Web Site: http://www.pcapps.com
Year Founded: 1992
Sales Range: $10-24.9 Million
Emp.: 24
Custom Computer Programming Services
N.A.I.C.S.: 541511
Kent Summers *(Mng Partner)*
Indra Sugianto *(Partner)*

PRACTICE MANAGEMENT INFORMATION CORPORATION
4727 Wilshire Blvd Ste 300, Los Angeles, CA 90010
Tel.: (323) 954-0224 CA
Web Site: http://www.pmiconline.com
Year Founded: 1986
Sales Range: $10-24.9 Million
Emp.: 15
Book Publishing
N.A.I.C.S.: 513130
James B. Davis *(Founder & Pres)*
Greg Trupiano *(VP)*

PRACTICE PROMOTIONS, LLC
7305 Hancock Village Dr Ste 117, Chesterfield, VA 23832
Web Site:
  http://www.practicepromotions.net
Year Founded: 2012
Sales Range: $1-9.9 Million
Emp.: 30
Advertising Agency Services
N.A.I.C.S.: 541810
Neil Trickett *(CEO)*
Amy Trickett *(Mng Partner)*
Deena Fournier *(VP-Ops)*
Gwen Tinsley *(Sls Dir)*
Jacob Siner *(Mktg Dir)*

PRACTICEFORCES
2410 Northside Dr, Clearwater, FL 33761-2236
Tel.: (727) 771-1300
Web Site:
  http://www.practiceforces.com
Year Founded: 2003
Sales Range: $1-9.9 Million
Emp.: 15
Medical Billing Services
N.A.I.C.S.: 541219
Kunal Jain *(CEO)*
Parul Garg *(VP-Revenue Cycle Mgmt)*
Carmel Boswell *(Dir-Client Rels)*

PRACTICELINK, LTD
415 2nd Ave, Hinton, WV 25951
Web Site: http://www.practicelink.com
Sales Range: $1-9.9 Million
Emp.: 36
Staffing Services
N.A.I.C.S.: 561311
Tammy Hager *(Dir-Client Rels & Sls)*
Brian Brown *(Mgr-Physician Rels)*

PRADON CONSTRUCTION & TRUCKING CO.
PO Box 14969, Odessa, TX 79768
Tel.: (432) 362-4186
Web Site: http://www.pradon.net
Sales Range: $10-24.9 Million

Emp.: 150
Haulage, Oil Field
N.A.I.C.S.: 213112
Donald Pradon *(Pres)*
Rodney Roberts *(Controller)*

PRAECIPIO CONSULTING LLC
501 Congress Ave Ste 150, Austin, TX 78701
Tel.: (512) 266-8271
Web Site: https://www.praecipio.com
Year Founded: 2006
Information Technology Consulting Services
N.A.I.C.S.: 541690
Michael Rapp *(CEO)*

Subsidiaries:

The Gurnet Group LLC (1)
800 Boylston St Ste 1600, Boston, MA 02199
Web Site: http://www.gurnet.com
Sales Range: $1-9.9 Million
Emp.: 20
Technology Strategy & Project Management Services
N.A.I.C.S.: 541618
Martin J. King *(CEO)*

PRAEMITTIAS GROUP INC.
8871 Ridgeline Blvd, Highlands Ranch, CO 80129
Tel.: (720) 344-0611
Web Site: http://www.praemittias.com
Year Founded: 2006
Sales Range: $25-49.9 Million
Emp.: 178
Consulting & Engineering Services for the Government
N.A.I.C.S.: 541618
James Stover *(CEO)*
Emily Hamlyn *(Dir-HR)*
Linda Ruch *(Mgr-Acctg)*
Phil Wentzel *(CFO)*

PRAESES, LLC
330 Marshall St Ste 800, Shreveport, LA 71101
Tel.: (318) 424-8125
Web Site: http://www.praeses.com
Sales Range: $25-49.9 Million
Emp.: 77
Telecommunications Resellers
N.A.I.C.S.: 517121
Peggy Blount *(Office Mgr)*
Frank M. Auer *(CEO)*
Kempten L. Schwab *(Pres)*

PRAESIDIAN CAPITAL CORP.
2 Madison Ave, Larchmont, NY 10538
Tel.: (212) 520-2600
Web Site: http://www.praesidian.com
Year Founded: 2002
Private Investment Firm
N.A.I.C.S.: 551112
Jason D. Drattell *(Founder)*
Tom Duffy *(Mng Dir)*
Glenn C. Harrison *(Partner)*

Subsidiaries:

Brand & Oppenheimer Co., Inc. (1)
208 Clock Twr Sq, Portsmouth, RI 02871
Tel.: (401) 293-5500
Web Site:
  http://www.brandandoppenheimer.com
Textiles Converter & Mfr
N.A.I.C.S.: 313310
Lauren Sousa *(Mgr-Bus Rels)*

Subsidiary (Domestic):

Cutting Edge TexStyles, LLC (2)
PO Box 249, Bedford, MA 01730
Tel.: (781) 271-0000
Web Site: http://www.cetexstyles.com
Fabric, Binding & Trim Products
N.A.I.C.S.: 313310

Performance Textiles, Inc. (2)

42 Tremont St Ste 3, Duxbury, MA 02332-5315
Tel.: (781) 934-7055
Web Site: http://www.perftex.com
Sales Range: $1-9.9 Million
Emp.: 15
Broadwoven Fabric Mill Services
N.A.I.C.S.: 313210
Peter Sullivan *(VP & Mgr-Ops)*
Bill Gerrow *(Founder & Pres)*

Round 2 Corp., LLC (1)
4073 Meghan Beeler Ct, South Bend, IN 46628-6628
Tel.: (574) 243-3003
Web Site: http://www.round2corp.com
Metal Service Centers & Other Metal Merchant Whslr
N.A.I.C.S.: 423510
Craig Lundquist *(COO)*
Tom Lowe *(CEO)*

PRAETORIAN DIGITAL, INC.
200 Green St Ste 200, San Francisco, CA 94111
Tel.: (415) 962-8300 DE
Web Site:
  http://www.praetoriandigital.com
Year Founded: 1999
Sales Range: $1-9.9 Million
Emp.: 70
Digital Media Services
N.A.I.C.S.: 519290
Alexander S. Ford *(CEO)*
Michael Herning *(Chm)*
Pam Hinz *(VP-Client Rels)*
Robert Dippell *(VP-Corp Dev)*
Jon Hughes *(VP-Content)*
Aaron Barnes *(COO)*
Ker Thao *(VP-Ops & Fin)*
Bob Bradley *(Sr VP)*
Nick Bruckner *(VP-Media Div)*
Sarah Wilson *(VP-Grants Div)*

PRAGER & CO., LLC
1 Maritime Plz Ste 1000, San Francisco, CA 94111
Tel.: (415) 403-1900
Web Site: http://www.prager.com
Rev.: $20,000,000
Emp.: 50
Investment Banking
N.A.I.C.S.: 523150
Fred Prager *(Chm & Mng Dir)*
Remy Hathaway *(Mng Dir)*
Saul Rosenbaum *(Mng Dir)*
Lynn Hutton *(Mng Dir & COO)*

PRAGER METIS CPAS, LLC
14 Penn Plz Ste 1800, New York, NY 10122
Tel.: (212) 643-0099 NY
Web Site:
  http://www.pragermetis.com
Year Founded: 1987
Emp.: 100
Accounting Services
N.A.I.C.S.: 541211
Glenn L. Friedman *(Co-Mng Partner)*
Alfred Pruskowski *(Partner)*
David R. Neste *(Co-Mng Partner)*
Brian Goldblatt *(Partner)*

Subsidiaries:

Nagano Morita LLP (1)
970 W 190th St, Torrance, CA 90502
Tel.: (310) 324-6868
Web Site: http://www.nagano-morita.com
Sales Range: $1-9.9 Million
Emp.: 50
Accounting, Auditing, And Bookkeeping
N.A.I.C.S.: 541219
Yoshinaga Nagano *(Founder)*
Chikara Nagano *(Partner)*

PRAGER METIS INTERNATIONAL LLC
14 Penn Plz Ste 1800, New York, NY 10122
Tel.: (212) 643-0099

PRAGER METIS INTERNATIONAL LLC

Prager Metis International LLC—(Continued)

Web Site:
http://www.pragermetis.com
Year Founded: 2013
Sales Range: $25-49.9 Million
Accounting Services Organization
N.A.I.C.S.: 813920
David R. Neste (Chm)
Glenn L. Friedman (CEO)
Martin Greenberg (Mng Partner)
Walter J. Brasch (Chief Success Officer)
Steven Bernknopf (Principal)
Benjamin W. Block (Principal)
Joseph Cain (Partner)
Joseph Callaghan (Partner)
Theresa Card (Principal)
Robbin E. Caruso (Partner)
Jenny Y. Chen (Principal)
Stephen Cobell (Partner)
Robert Crowley (Partner)
Francis Decker (Partner)
George Dinar (Partner)
Donna M. DiSclafani (Partner)
Stuart A. Ditsky (Partner)
David F. Fromowitz (Partner)
Thomas P. Gallo (Partner)
Charles B. Goebel (CFO)
Jay Goldberg (Partner)
Brian Goldblatt (Partner)
Mark J. Ackerman (Partner)
Ileana Alvarez (Partner)
Curtis Arluck (Principal)
Jackie Bai (Principal)
John C. Barka (Partner)
Edward Benedetto (Partner)
Dawn M. Bergen (Partner)

PRAGER UNIVERSITY FOUNDATION

15021 Ventura Blvd Ste 552, Sherman Oaks, CA 91403
Web Site: https://www.prageru.com
Year Founded: 2011
Educational Support Services
N.A.I.C.S.: 611710

PRAGER WINERY & PORT WORKS, INC.

1281 Lewelling Ln, Saint Helena, CA 94574-2235
Tel.: (707) 963-3720
Web Site: http://www.pragerport.com
Sales Range: $10-24.9 Million
Emp.: 9
Wine Mfr
N.A.I.C.S.: 312130
James Prager (COO)

PRAGMATICS INC.

1761 Business Center Dr, Reston, VA 20190
Tel.: (703) 761-4033
Web Site: http://www.pragmatics.com
Year Founded: 1985
Rev.: $14,873,890
Emp.: 500
Computer Related Consulting Services
N.A.I.C.S.: 541512
Andy Vogt (Dir-Quality Assurance)
Long Nguyen (Founder & CEO)
Joe Brock (COO)
Ronald Gornto (VP)
Sean Cohan (VP-Tech Solutions Grp)
Richard Silver (Chief Bus Dev Officer)
Michael Froelich (VP & Deputy Gen Mgr-Federal Civilian)
Dennis Lauer (Deputy COO & VP)
Yihong Sun (VP-Fin)

PRAIRIE AG COOPERATIVE

409 W Railroad St, Mount Union, IA 52644
Tel.: (319) 865-1450   IA
Web Site:
http://www.prairieagcoop.com
Year Founded: 1910
Sales Range: $10-24.9 Million
Emp.: 6
Marketer of Grain & Field Beans
N.A.I.C.S.: 424510
Tom McAllister (Pres)

PRAIRIE BANCSHARES CORPORATION

320 Main St, Shelby, MT 59474
Tel.: (406) 434-5567   MT
Web Site: http://www.fsbshelby.com
Year Founded: 1981
Sales Range: $1-9.9 Million
Emp.: 26
Bank Holding Company
N.A.I.C.S.: 551111
Byron H. Kluth (Pres)

Subsidiaries:

The First State Bank of Shelby   (1)
320 Main St, Shelby, MT 59474
Tel.: (406) 434-5567
Web Site: http://www.fsbshelby.com
Emp.: 20
Banking Services
N.A.I.C.S.: 522110
Byron H. Kluth (Pres)

PRAIRIE BAND POTAWATOMI NATION

16281 Q Rd, Mayetta, KS 66509
Tel.: (877) 715-6789
Web Site:
https://www.pbpindiantribe.com
Tribal Organization
N.A.I.C.S.: 921150

Subsidiaries:

Prairie Band, LLC   (1)
19035 US Hwy 75, Holton, KS 66436
Tel.: (785) 364-2328
Web Site: https://prairiebandllc.com
Holding Company
N.A.I.C.S.: 551112
Mario Burgos (Chief Strategy Officer)
Jacob Wamego (CEO)

Subsidiary (Domestic):

Burgos Group LLC   (2)
4700 Lincoln Rd NE, Albuquerque, NM 87109-2303
Web Site: http://www.burgosgroup.com
Facilities Support Services
N.A.I.C.S.: 561210

PRAIRIE CABLE LLC.

2700 Evans Ave, Valparaiso, IN 46383
Tel.: (219) 548-2822
Rev.: $32,600,000
Emp.: 86
Other Fabricated Wire Product Mfr
N.A.I.C.S.: 332618
Mary Oziemkowski (CFO)

PRAIRIE CONTRACTORS, INC.

9318 Gulfstream Rd Unit C, Frankfort, IL 60423
Tel.: (815) 469-1904
Web Site:
http://www.prairiecontractors.com
Sales Range: $10-24.9 Million
Emp.: 40
Commercial & Institutional Building Construction
N.A.I.C.S.: 236220
Jerry V. Files (Owner, Project Mgr & Exec VP)
Peter C. Hegarty (Pres & Project Mgr)
Bethany Howe (Sec)
James M. Winford Jr. (Pres)

PRAIRIE FARMERS ASSOCIATION, INC.

927 Hwy 70 West PO Box 724, Hazen, AR 72064
Tel.: (870) 255-4527
Year Founded: 1953
Sales Range: $10-24.9 Million
Emp.: 15
Petroleum Products, Feed & Seed Distr
N.A.I.C.S.: 424720
Barbara Huffer (Office Mgr)
Troy Young (Gen Mgr)

PRAIRIE FARMS DAIRY, INC.

3744 Staunton Rd, Edwardsville, IL 62025
Tel.: (618) 659-5700   IL
Web Site:
http://www.prairiefarms.com
Year Founded: 1938
Dairy Food Products Mfr
N.A.I.C.S.: 311511
Edward Mullins (Co-CEO)
Tom Weber (CFO)
Gary Aggus (Co-CEO)
Ryan Murphy (Ops Mgr)

Subsidiaries:

Hiland Dairy Foods Company, LLC   (1)
1133 E Kearney, Springfield, MO 65803
Tel.: (417) 862-9311
Web Site: http://www.hilanddairy.com
Dairy Foods & Beverages Mfr & Distr
N.A.I.C.S.: 311511

Ice Cream Specialties, Inc.   (1)
8419 Hanley Indus Ct, Saint Louis, MO 63144-1917
Tel.: (314) 962-2550
Web Site:
http://www.northstarfrozentreats.com
Sales Range: $10-24.9 Million
Emp.: 90
Produce Ice Cream Novelties
N.A.I.C.S.: 311520
Mary Looper (Office Mgr)

Ice Cream Specialties, Inc.   (1)
2600 Concord Rd, Lafayette, IN 47909-2773
Tel.: (765) 474-2989
Sales Range: $10-24.9 Million
Emp.: 120
Produce Ice Cream Novelties
N.A.I.C.S.: 311520

Muller-Pinehurst Dairy Inc.   (1)
2110 Ogilby Rd, Rockford, IL 61102-3482
Tel.: (815) 968-0441
Web Site: http://www.prairiefarms.com
Rev.: $67,910,614
Emp.: 184
Fluid Milk
N.A.I.C.S.: 311511
Bruce Mussigman (Supvr)
Scott Runyard (Asst Plant Mgr)

Prairie Farms Dairy Supply Corp.   (1)
1800 Adams St, Granite City, IL 62040-3300   (100%)
Tel.: (618) 451-5600
Sales Range: $10-24.9 Million
Emp.: 100
Service to Fast Food Outlets
N.A.I.C.S.: 311520

Swiss Valley Farms Co.   (1)
247 Research Pkwy, Davenport, IA 52808
Tel.: (563) 468-6600
Web Site: http://www.swissvalley.com
Dairy Products
N.A.I.C.S.: 424430
Jim Kutchma (Plant Mgr)

PRAIRIE GARDENS INC.

3000 W Springfield Ave, Champaign, IL 61822
Tel.: (217) 356-5558
Web Site:
http://www.prairiegardens.com
Rev.: $18,000,000
Emp.: 125

U.S. PRIVATE

Gift Shop
N.A.I.C.S.: 459420
Jeffrey A. Wandell (Owner)
Craig Dickson (Controller)

PRAIRIE GRAIN PARTNERS LLC

1120 County Rd 24, Clarkfield, MN 56223
Tel.: (320) 669-7501   MN
Web Site:
http://www.prairiegrainpartners.com
Year Founded: 1997
Sales Range: $10-24.9 Million
Emp.: 50
Provider of Grain Products & Services
N.A.I.C.S.: 424510
Scott Mauch (Gen Mgr)
Greg Manning (Mgr-Ops)

PRAIRIE INTERNATIONAL TRUCKS

401 S Dirksen Pkwy, Springfield, IL 62703
Tel.: (217) 523-5631
Web Site:
http://www.prairieinternational.com
Sales Range: $75-99.9 Million
Emp.: 72
Truck Tractors
N.A.I.C.S.: 423110
Mike Joyce (Pres)
Diane Krauss (Treas)
Mike Beasley (Gen Mgr)
Tim Fanter (Gen Mgr-Retail Sls)
Roger Lindgren (Gen Mgr)

PRAIRIE ISLAND INDIAN COMMUNITY

5636 Sturgeon Lake Rd, Welch, MN 55089
Tel.: (651) 385-4124
Web Site: http://www.prairieisland.org
Casino
N.A.I.C.S.: 713210
Nicci Lehto (Sec)
Shelley Buck (Pres)
Melanie Urich (Treas)
Johnny Johnson (Treas)

PRAIRIE LAKES COOP

524 Pope St, Starbuck, MN 56381
Tel.: (320) 239-2226
Web Site:
http://www.prairielakescoop.com
Sales Range: $25-49.9 Million
Emp.: 55
Grains
N.A.I.C.S.: 424510
Brad Manderschied (Gen Mgr)
Gene Muller (Controller)

PRAIRIE LAND COOPERATIVE

115 E Oak St, Hubbard, IA 50122
Tel.: (641) 864-2266   IA
Web Site:
http://www.prairielandcoop.com
Year Founded: 1994
Sales Range: $10-24.9 Million
Emp.: 107
Provider of Grain Products & Servives
N.A.I.C.S.: 424510
Rick Vaughn (Gen Mgr)
Shane Coughenour (Controller)
Becky Nederhoff (Mgr-Tech)

PRAIRIE MANAGEMENT & DEVELOPMENT

333 N Michigan Ave Ste 1700, Chicago, IL 60601
Tel.: (312) 644-1055
Rev.: $12,500,000
Emp.: 25
Real Estate Development Services

N.A.I.C.S.: 237210
Anthony Augustine (Pres)
Paul Levy (VP)
Peter Condich (Gen Mgr)

PRAIRIE MATERIAL
12005 W Hampton Ave, Milwaukee, WI 53208
Tel.: (414) 258-7000
Web Site: http://www.centralreadymixed.com
Year Founded: 1948
Sales Range: $10-24.9 Million
Emp.: 90
Readymix Concrete Mfr
N.A.I.C.S.: 327320
Judy Neubauer (Dir-Sls)

PRAIRIE MECHANICAL CORPORATION
2842 Tucker St, Omaha, NE 68112
Tel.: (402) 331-4050 NE
Web Site: http://www.prairiemech.com
Year Founded: 2002
Sales Range: $10-24.9 Million
Emp.: 38
Plumbing, Heating & Air-Conditioning Services
N.A.I.C.S.: 238220
Brett Lundin (Pres)
Joe Barnhart (Project Mgr)

PRAIRIE PELLA INC.
2163 NW 111th Ct, Des Moines, IA 50325
Tel.: (515) 278-8781
Web Site: http://www.pella.com
Rev.: $21,000,000
Emp.: 54
Doors & Windows
N.A.I.C.S.: 423310
Christopher C. Boley (Pres)
Keith Rudd (Dir-Customer Svcs)
Gordon Staley (Mgr-Sls-Eastern)
Bruce Grenier (VP-Fin)

PRAIRIE POWER, INC.
3130 Pleasant Run, Springfield, IL 62711
Tel.: (217) 245-6161 IL
Web Site: http://www.ppi.coop
Year Founded: 1963
Sales Range: $100-124.9 Million
Emp.: 62
Electric Power Distr
N.A.I.C.S.: 221122
Cyndie Stiles (Dir-HR)
Dan Breden (CEO)
Lyndon Gabbert (VP-Fin & Acctg)
Robert Reynolds (VP-Member Cooperative Svcs)
Dick Chapman I (VP-Engrg & Ops)

PRAIRIE PRIDE COOPERATIVE
1100 E Main St, Marshall, MN 56258-2505
Tel.: (507) 532-9686 MN
Web Site: http://www.prairiepride.com
Year Founded: 1924
Sales Range: $25-49.9 Million
Emp.: 85
Retailer of Petroleum & Refined Fuels
N.A.I.C.S.: 457120
Allen Steffes (Pres)
Curt Fried (Mgr-Petroleum Dispatch)

PRAIRIE QUEST, INC.
4211 Hobson Ct Ste A, Fort Wayne, IN 46815
Tel.: (260) 420-7374
Web Site: http://www.pqcworks.com
Year Founded: 2006
Sales Range: $10-24.9 Million
Emp.: 160
Consulting Services
N.A.I.C.S.: 541611
Stacey Smith (Pres & CEO)

PRAIRIE STATE BANK AND TRUST
340 Main St, Mount Zion, IL 62549
Tel.: (217) 864-2353
Web Site: http://www.psbank.net
Rev.: $10,758,000
Emp.: 150
State Commercial Banks
N.A.I.C.S.: 522110
Kyle Pflum (Pres)

PRAISE INTERNATIONAL NORTH AMERICA, INC.
14071 Stage Rd, Santa Fe Springs, CA 90670
Tel.: (949) 752-5282
Sales Range: $10-24.9 Million
Emp.: 40
Holding Company
N.A.I.C.S.: 551112
Tony Falls (Mgr-HR)

Subsidiaries:

Gloria Jean's, Inc. (1)
33 Coffee Ln, Waterbury, VT 05676-8900
Tel.: (949) 260-1600
Web Site: http://www.gloriajeans.com
Coffee Retailer
N.A.I.C.S.: 445298

PRAJIN 1 STOP DISTRIBUTORS
6802 Pacific Blvd, Huntington Park, CA 90255
Tel.: (323) 588-9323
Web Site: http://www.prajin1stop.com
Sales Range: $10-24.9 Million
Emp.: 50
Compact Discs
N.A.I.C.S.: 423990
Antonio Prajin (Pres)

PRATE ROOFING & INSTALLATIONS, LLC
368 W Liberty St Ste F, Wauconda, IL 60084
Tel.: (847) 865-5626
Web Site: http://www.pratei.com
Year Founded: 1974
Sales Range: $10-24.9 Million
Emp.: 100
Roofing Installation Services
N.A.I.C.S.: 238390
F. Randy Worozaken (VP)

PRATESI LINENS INC.
381 Pk Ave S Rm 1223, New York, NY 10016
Tel.: (212) 689-3150
Web Site: http://www.pratesi.com
Sales Range: $10-24.9 Million
Emp.: 8
Linens
N.A.I.C.S.: 449129
Antonio Dibari (Pres)

PRATT CONSTRUCTION INCORPORATED
3500 Willow Lake Blvd, Saint Paul, MN 55110
Tel.: (651) 429-8032
Web Site: http://www.pratthomes.com
Year Founded: 1973
Sales Range: $10-24.9 Million
Emp.: 35
New Construction, Single-Family Houses
N.A.I.C.S.: 236115
Lowell H. Pratt (Pres)

PRATT MANAGEMENT COMPANY LLC
PO Box 1937, Longmont, CO 80502
Tel.: (303) 776-4496
Web Site: http://www.prattprop.com
Rev.: $24,100,000
Emp.: 15
Land Subdividers & Developers, Commercial
N.A.I.C.S.: 237210
Al Linton (CFO)
James Unger (Gen Mgr)
Maggi Sharp (Project Mgr)

PRAXIS ENGINEERING
135 National Business Pkwy Ste 310, Annapolis Junction, MD 20701
Tel.: (301) 490-4299
Web Site: http://www.praxiseng.com
Year Founded: 2002
Rev.: $25,500,000
Emp.: 148
Custom Computer Programming Services
N.A.I.C.S.: 541511
Paul Larsen (Dir-DoD & Special Programs)
Charlie Duren (Dir-Strategic Markets)
Mark Klein (Co-Founder & Principal)
Jeremy Kaufman (CTO & VP)
Shawn Berry (Mgr-Fin)
Mike Schepers (Mgr-IT)
William S. Dunahoo (Pres)
Tarisa Holbrook (Dir-Mission Capabilities)
Quentin P. Smith Jr. (Dir-Collect & Protect Programs)
Margaret Jarrett (Dir-Emerging Markets)

PRAXSYN CORPORATION
1803 Sky Park Cir Ste A, Irvine, CA 92614
Tel.: (949) 777-6112 IL
Web Site: http://www.praxsyn.com
Year Founded: 2005
Sales Range: $50-74.9 Million
Emp.: 66
Pharmaceutical Mfr & Retailer
N.A.I.C.S.: 325412
Edward F. Kurtz (VP-Sls & Mktg)
Greg Sundem (Chm & CEO)
Stephanie Kaitz (Controller-Fin)
Scot Silber (Pres)

PRE CON INC.
109 Perry St, Petersburg, VA 23803
Tel.: (804) 733-4633
Year Founded: 1975
Sales Range: $10-24.9 Million
Emp.: 100
Polytetrafluoroethylene Resins, Teflon
N.A.I.C.S.: 325211
Charles Reilly (Mgr-Facilities)
Easter Jimmy (Mgr-Warehouse)
Lynda Easter (Supvr-Quality Sys)

PRE-CON PRODUCTS
240 W Los Angeles Ave, Simi Valley, CA 93065
Tel.: (805) 527-0841
Web Site: http://www.pre-conproducts.com
Rev.: $10,576,991
Emp.: 65
Pipe, Concrete Or Lined With Concrete
N.A.I.C.S.: 327332
Kimberly Pinto (Mgr-Project, Pur & Trucking)
Shannon Mulhearn (Mgr-Sls)

PRE-MIX MARBLE TITE MANUFACTURING COMPANY
1259 NW 21st St, Pompano Beach, FL 33069
Tel.: (954) 917-7665
Web Site: http://www.premixmarbletite.com
Sales Range: $75-99.9 Million
Emp.: 20
Lumber & Other Building Materials
N.A.I.C.S.: 423310
Howard L. Ehler Jr. (Pres & CFO)

PRECASH INC.
5120 Woodway Dr Ste 6001, Houston, TX 77056
Tel.: (713) 600-2200 TX
Web Site: http://www.precash.com
Year Founded: 1998
Sales Range: $25-49.9 Million
Emp.: 140
Real-Time Payment Systems that Convert Cash into Electronic Payments
N.A.I.C.S.: 522320
Steven Taylor (CEO)
Matt Callanan (CTO)
Blair Jeffrey (COO)
Richard Wong (VP-Natl Sls)
Michael Pinto (VP & Grp Head-Sls & Bus Dev)
Lee Schoenberger (CFO & Sr VP)
Ross Kennedy (Chief Compliance Officer & Gen Counsel)
Kimberly Frye (Co-Chief Compliance Officer & Gen Counsel)
Doren Helterline (VP & Head-Product Grp)

PRECAST SERVICES INC.
8200 Boyle Pkwy, Twinsburg, OH 44087
Tel.: (330) 425-2880
Web Site: http://www.precastservices.com
Sales Range: $10-24.9 Million
Emp.: 11
Provider of Concrete Services
N.A.I.C.S.: 238110
Ron Cooper (VP)
Bo Kusznir (Pres)
Lorri Sroka (Controller)

PRECEPT MINISTRIES OF REACH OUT, INC.
7324 Noah Reid Rd, Chattanooga, TN 37422
Tel.: (423) 892-6814 TN
Web Site: http://www.precept.org
Year Founded: 1970
Sales Range: $10-24.9 Million
Emp.: 171
Religious Organizations
N.A.I.C.S.: 813110
David Arthur (CEO)

PRECHECK HEALTH SERVICES, INC.
100 Biscayne Blvd Ste 1611, Miami, FL 33132
Tel.: (305) 203-4711
Web Site: https://www.precheckhealth.com
Year Founded: 1983
Helathcare Devices Mfr
N.A.I.C.S.: 334510
Douglas W. Samuelson (CFO)

PRECHECK HEALTH SERVICES, INC.
305 W Woodard Ste 221, Denison, TX 75020
Tel.: (903) 337-1872 FL
Web Site: http://www.precheckhealth.com
Year Founded: 2014
Rev.: $70,000
Assets: $254,909
Liabilities: $1,172,813

PRECHECK HEALTH SERVICES, INC.

PreCheck Health Services, Inc.—(Continued)
Net Worth: ($917,904)
Earnings: ($7,926,516)
Emp.: 3
Fiscal Year-end: 12/31/18
Medical Screening Device Distr
N.A.I.C.S.: 334510
Douglas W. Samuelson (Pres, CEO, CFO & Sec)

PRECIOUS METAL REFINING SERVICES INC.
1531 S Grove Ave Ste 104, Barrington, IL 60010
Tel.: (847) 756-2700
Web Site: http://www.pmrs-refining.com
Year Founded: 1980
Sales Range: $100-124.9 Million
Emp.: 30
Precious Metals Refining Services
N.A.I.C.S.: 331410
Sheldon Goldner (Pres)
Dan Boro (Acct Mgr-Natl)

PRECISE CONSTRUCTION INC.
5026 Trenton St, Tampa, FL 33619
Tel.: (813) 241-2403
Web Site: http://www.preciseconstruction.com
Year Founded: 1988
Sales Range: $25-49.9 Million
Emp.: 27
General Contractors
N.A.I.C.S.: 236220
Gregory P. Johnson (Pres)
Scott G. Johnson (VP-Mktg)
Leslie Adams (Coord-Bid)
Cheryl Clark (CFO & Office Mgr)

PRECISE MEDIA AND FULL SERVICE
888 N Vintage Ave, Ontario, CA 91764
Tel.: (909) 481-3305
Web Site: http://www.precisemedia.com
Sales Range: $10-24.9 Million
Emp.: 75
Video Tape Production
N.A.I.C.S.: 334610
Robert Miller (Pres)

PRECISE METAL PRODUCTS COMPANY
3839 N 39th Ave, Phoenix, AZ 85019
Tel.: (602) 272-2625
Web Site: http://www.precise-metals.com
Rev.: $12,725,417
Emp.: 96
Machine & Other Job Shop Work
N.A.I.C.S.: 332710
Alex Allwine (Pres)

PRECISION AEROSPACE CORP.
11155 Jersey Blvd Ste A, Rancho Cucamonga, CA 91730
Tel.: (909) 980-8855
Web Site: http://www.pac.cc
Year Founded: 1989
Sales Range: $1-9.9 Million
Emp.: 70
Aircraft Parts & Auxiliary Equipment Mfr
N.A.I.C.S.: 336413
Jim Hudson (Pres)

PRECISION ASSOCIATES INC.
740 Washington Ave N, Minneapolis, MN 55401
Tel.: (612) 333-7464
Web Site: http://www.precisionassoc.com
Rev.: $11,821,918
Emp.: 172
Synthetic Rubber
N.A.I.C.S.: 325212
Alanna Hjortland (Engr-Mfg)
Gary Vollmer (Mgr-HR)
Bridget Hanson (Mgr-Mktg)
Bradley Arnold Kadue (Pres)

PRECISION AUTOMATION CO., INC.
1841 Old Cuthbert Rd, Cherry Hill, NJ 08034-1415
Tel.: (856) 428-7400
Web Site: http://www.precisionautomationinc.com
Sales Range: $10-24.9 Million
Emp.: 75
Mfr & Designs Automated Machinery
N.A.I.C.S.: 333998
G. Fred Rexon (Founder)
Marie D. Gallo (Controller)

Subsidiaries:

The New Jersey Wire Stitching Machine Co.   (1)
1841 Old Cuthbert Rd, Cherry Hill, NJ 08034-1478
Tel.: (856) 365-0196
Web Site: http://www.newjerseywire.com
Sales Range: $10-24.9 Million
Emp.: 26
Wire Stitching Machine Mfr
N.A.I.C.S.: 333515

PRECISION CAMERA LP
2438 West Anderson Ln, Austin, TX 78757
Tel.: (512) 467-7676
Web Site: http://www.precision-camera.com
Year Founded: 1976
Sales Range: $10-24.9 Million
Emp.: 45
Retailer & Servicer of Cameras & Camera Accessories & Equipment
N.A.I.C.S.: 449210
Jerry Sullivan (Co-Founder, Co-Owner & CEO)
Rosemary Sullivan (Co-Founder, Co-Owner & Pres)
Noel Rankin (Mgr-Svc Dept)

PRECISION CHRYSLER JEEP DODGE RAM
1341 Rte 23 S, Butler, NJ 07405
Tel.: (973) 838-6808
Web Site: http://www.precisionchrysler.com
Sales Range: $25-49.9 Million
Emp.: 24
Car Dealership
N.A.I.C.S.: 441110
Matt Groetsch (Gen Mgr-Sls)
Joe Loonam (Mgr-Sls)
Joe Amato (Mgr-Sls)

PRECISION COATINGS INC.
8120 Goldie St, Walled Lake, MI 48390-4107
Tel.: (248) 363-8361   MI
Web Site: http://www.pcicoatings.com
Year Founded: 1970
Sales Range: $10-24.9 Million
Emp.: 100
Mfr of Plastic Products
N.A.I.C.S.: 326199
Roy A. Ely (Pres)
Bob Wider (CFO)
Cheryl Seymour (Mgr-HR)
Jason Smith (Mgr-Coating & Environmental)

Joe Dikos (Supvr-Production)
Robin van Tilburg (VP-Ops)
Michael P. Newell (Pres)

PRECISION COMPONENTS CORPORATION
500 Lincoln St, York, PA 17405-7101
Tel.: (717) 848-1126
Web Site: http://www.pcc-york.com
Year Founded: 1993
Sales Range: $10-24.9 Million
Emp.: 270
Provider of Fabricated Plate Work Services
N.A.I.C.S.: 332313
Gary Butler (Pres & CEO)

PRECISION COMPONENTS, INC.
1820 S 35th Ave, Phoenix, AZ 85009
Tel.: (602) 272-6566
Web Site: http://www.pcireload.com
Year Founded: 1962
Sales Range: $10-24.9 Million
Emp.: 175
Property Management Services
N.A.I.C.S.: 531120
Rick Malkemus (Treas)

PRECISION COMPUTER SERVICES, INC.
175 Constitution Blvd S, Shelton, CT 06484
Tel.: (203) 929-0000
Web Site: http://www.precisiongroup.com
Year Founded: 1989
Sales Range: $25-49.9 Million
Emp.: 100
Full Service Technology Integrator
N.A.I.C.S.: 541519
Irene Fitzsimons (Pres)
Jeff Clark (CTO)
Arturo Matos Jr. (COO)

PRECISION CONSTRUCTION & ROOFING
7625 Davis Blvd, North Richland Hills, TX 76182
Tel.: (817) 519-8985
Web Site: http://www.precisionconstructionandroofing.com
Year Founded: 2008
Sales Range: $10-24.9 Million
Emp.: 18
Commercial & Residential Roofing Contractor
N.A.I.C.S.: 238160
Eric Hunter (Owner)

PRECISION COUNTERTOPS INC.
8490 SW Warm Springs St, Tualatin, OR 97062
Tel.: (503) 692-6660
Web Site: http://www.precisioncountertop.com
Sales Range: $10-24.9 Million
Emp.: 36
Plywood Sales
N.A.I.C.S.: 337110
Marcus Neff (Pres)

PRECISION DATA PRODUCTS, INC.
5036 Falcon View Ave SE, Kentwood, MI 49512
Tel.: (616) 698-2242
Web Site: http://www.precision.com
Year Founded: 1979
Sales Range: $10-24.9 Million
Emp.: 15
Computer Products Distr
N.A.I.C.S.: 423430

Gail A. Huff (Pres)
Kristen Harden (Acct Mgr-REMC)
John Dinkel (Mgr-Sls)
Andre Phaneuf (Mgr-Sls)
Brian Nikolich (Acct Mgr)
Randy Morris (Mgr-Sls)

PRECISION DEVELOPMENT
1601 Pacific Coast Hwy Ste 175, Hermosa Beach, CA 90254
Tel.: (310) 341-4724
Web Site: http://www.precisiondev.net
Sales Range: $1-9.9 Million
Emp.: 23
Software Development Services
N.A.I.C.S.: 541511
Greg Ferris (Co-Founder & Principal)
Paul Zimny (Co-Founder & Principal)

PRECISION DEVICES INCORPORATED
8840 N Greenview Dr, Middleton, WI 53562
Tel.: (608) 831-4445
Web Site: http://www.pdixtal.com
Sales Range: $10-24.9 Million
Emp.: 104
Quartz Crystals, For Electronic Application
N.A.I.C.S.: 334419
Barry Arneson (VP-Engrg, Frequency Control & Timing Devices)
Sharad Mistry (CFO)
Zachariah J. Mathews (Pres & CEO)
Daniel Phelan (Chm)
Pierre Soulard (Sec)
Zach Mathews (Pres)

PRECISION ELECTRONIC COIL MFG. CO.
18300 Oxnard St, Tarzana, CA 91356
Tel.: (818) 345-7811
Web Site: http://www.pacificresistor.com
Year Founded: 1953
Sales Range: $50-74.9 Million
Emp.: 45
Wire Wound Resistors, Networks & Customs Mfr
N.A.I.C.S.: 334416
Doug Trewhitt (VP)
Steve Trewhitt III (VP-Ops)

PRECISION ENVIRONMENTAL CO.
5500 Old Brecksville Rd, Independence, OH 44131-1508
Tel.: (216) 642-6040
Web Site: http://www.precision-env.com
Year Founded: 1988
Sales Range: $10-24.9 Million
Emp.: 200
Provider of Environment Related Services
N.A.I.C.S.: 562910
Tony Digeronimo (Pres)

Subsidiaries:

Precision Investment Group Llc   (1)
5500 Old Brooksville Rd, Independence, OH 44131
Tel.: (216) 642-6040
Web Site: http://www.precision-env.com
Rev.: $110,000
Emp.: 5
Holding Companies Nec
N.A.I.C.S.: 551112

PRECISION FABRICS GROUP INC.
301 N Elm St Ste 600, Greensboro, NC 27401
Tel.: (336) 510-8000

Web Site:
http://www.precisionfabrics.com
Sales Range: $150-199.9 Million
Emp.: 48
Mfr of Synthetic Broadwoven Fabrics
N.A.I.C.S.: 313210
Walter G. Jones *(Co-CEO)*
Rich Bliton *(Dir-Bus)*
John Smith *(Mgr-Market)*
Terry Montgomery *(VP)*

PRECISION FITTING & GAUGE CO
1214 S Joplin Ave, Tulsa, OK 74112
Tel.: (918) 834-5011
Web Site: http://www.pfandg.com
Year Founded: 1976
Sales Range: $25-49.9 Million
Emp.: 70
Industrial Fittings
N.A.I.C.S.: 423830
Larry Sapp *(Supvr-Instrumentation)*

PRECISION GRINDING & MANUFACTURING
1305 Emerson St, Rochester, NY 14606
Tel.: (585) 458-4300
Web Site: http://www.pgmcorp.com
Year Founded: 1967
Sales Range: $10-24.9 Million
Emp.: 120
Special Dies & Tools
N.A.I.C.S.: 333514
Todd Hackenburger *(VP-Sls)*
Fred Cadwell *(Supvr-Facilities)*
Mike Hockenberger *(Pres & CEO)*

PRECISION GROUP INC.
175 Constitution Blvd S, Shelton, CT 06484
Tel.: (203) 929-0000
Web Site:
http://www.precisiongroup.com
Sales Range: $25-49.9 Million
Computers, Peripherals & Software
N.A.I.C.S.: 423430
Irene Fitzsimons *(Pres)*
Arturo Matos *(COO)*

PRECISION IBC INC
8054 McGowin Dr, Fairhope, AL 36532-1910
Tel.: (251) 990-6789
Web Site:
http://www.precisionibc.com
Year Founded: 1998
Sales Range: $10-24.9 Million
Emp.: 15
Industrial Machinery & Equipment Sales & Service
N.A.I.C.S.: 423830
Anthony P. Beard *(Pres & CEO)*
Chris Kaufman *(VP)*
David Holt *(Mgr-Fairhope Warehouse)*
Joseph Weller *(Acct Exec)*
Tami Chatwood *(Acct Exec)*
Jennie Keyman *(Accountant)*

PRECISION INC.
300 SE 14th St, Pella, IA 50219-2232
Tel.: (641) 628-3115   IA
Web Site: http://www.ppipella.com
Year Founded: 1977
Sales Range: $25-49.9 Million
Emp.: 300
Conveyor Components Mfr
N.A.I.C.S.: 332510
Roger Brown *(Pres & CEO)*

Subsidiaries:

The Chantland Company   (1)
PO Box 69, Humboldt, IA 50548-0069
Tel.: (515) 332-4040
Web Site: http://www.chantlandpulley.com

Conveyors & Conveyor Pulleys & Packaging Equipment Mfr
N.A.I.C.S.: 333922

Van Gorp Corporation   (1)
1410 Washington St, Pella, IA 50219-1502
Tel.: (641) 628-9212
Web Site: http://www.vangorp.biz
Sales Range: $50-74.9 Million
Emp.: 65
Pulleys Mfr
N.A.I.C.S.: 333922
Joseph Canfield *(Owner & Pres)*

PRECISION INDUSTRIES, INC.
222 Riggs Ave, Portland, TN 37148
Tel.: (615) 325-4127
Web Site: http://www.precind.com
Year Founded: 1974
Sales Range: $10-24.9 Million
Emp.: 60
Metal Stamping
N.A.I.C.S.: 332119
Vince Haynes *(VP-Fin)*
Tim Key *(Engr-Info Sys)*
Cheryl Harrison *(Mgr-HR)*
Kenneth J. Best Jr. *(Chm)*

PRECISION INTERCONNECT CONVERSIONS CORP.
161 E 32nd St, New York, NY 10016
Tel.: (212) 784-2000
Web Site:
http://www.precisioninter.com
Rev.: $10,000,000
Emp.: 45
Provider of Electronic Parts & Equipment
N.A.I.C.S.: 423690
James Rigg *(Pres)*

PRECISION LASER SERVICES, INC.
14730 Lima Rd, Fort Wayne, IN 46818
Tel.: (260) 744-4375
Web Site:
http://www.precisionlaser.com
Year Founded: 1941
Sales Range: $1-9.9 Million
Emp.: 30
Miscellaneous Durable Goods Merchant Whslr
N.A.I.C.S.: 423990
Ed Ferrier *(Pres)*

PRECISION LTC PHARMACY
69 Allen Blvd, Farmingdale, NY 11735
Tel.: (516) 466-7700
Web Site: http://www.precisionltc.com
Pharmacies
N.A.I.C.S.: 456110
Frank Longo *(CEO)*

Subsidiaries:

Prime Care Pharmacy Services, Inc.   (1)
5 Odell Plz Ste B&C, Yonkers, NY 10701
Tel.: (914) 375-4300
Web Site:
http://www.primecareltcpharmacy.com
Sales Range: $1-9.9 Million
Emp.: 10
Drugs & Druggists' Sundries Merchant Whslr
N.A.I.C.S.: 424210
Tom Amigdalos *(Pres & CEO)*

PRECISION MACHINE MANUFACTURING CO.
500 Industrial Rd, Grove, OK 74344
Tel.: (918) 786-9094
Web Site:
http://www.precisiongrove.com
Sales Range: $25-49.9 Million
Emp.: 115
Machine Shop, Jobbing & Repair
N.A.I.C.S.: 332710

Tony Caudill *(Pres)*

PRECISION MEDICINE GROUP, INC.
2 Bethesda Metro Ctr Ste 850, Bethesda, MD 20814
Tel.: (240) 654-0726
Web Site:
http://www.precisionmedicine.com
Year Founded: 2012
Holding Company
N.A.I.C.S.: 551112
Ethan D. Leder *(Co-Founder)*
John W. Hubbard *(Chm)*
Mark P. Clein *(Co-Founder & CEO)*
Chad Clark *(Co-Pres & COO)*
Dan Renick *(Co-Pres & Chief Comml Officer)*
Kelly Wilder *(Chief Mktg & Comm Officer)*

Subsidiaries:

Agility Clinical, Inc.   (1)
701 Palomar Airport Rd Ste 270, Carlsbad, CA 92011-1047
Tel.: (760) 658-5900
Web Site: http://www.agility-clinical.com
Biomedical Research & Consulting Services
N.A.I.C.S.: 541715
Ali Sadighian *(VP-Bus Ops)*
Cristina Damatarca *(VP-Medical Affairs & Pharmacovigilance)*
Marilyn Carlson *(Exec VP-Medical, Regulatory & Scientific Affairs)*

PRECISIONscientia, Inc.   (1)
777 Township Line Rd Ste 300, Yardley, PA 19067
Tel.: (215) 867-1900
Web Site: http://www.precisionscientia.com
Administrative Management & General Management Consulting Service
N.A.I.C.S.: 541611
David Sadock *(CEO)*
Eric Toppy *(Chief Comml Officer)*

Precision for Medicine, Inc.   (1)
2 Bethesda Metro Ctr Ste 850, Bethesda, MD 20814
Tel.: (240) 654-0730
Web Site:
http://www.precisionformedicine.com
Emp.: 20
Scientific Services, Infrastructure & Technologies to Support Development of Personalized Medicines & Therapies
N.A.I.C.S.: 423450
Ethan D. Leder *(Chm-Exec Bd)*
Mark P. Clein *(CEO)*
Chad Clark *(Co-Pres & COO)*
Dan Renick *(Co-Pres & Chief Comml Officer)*

Subsidiary (Domestic):

Apocell, Inc.   (2)
2575 W Bellfort St Ste 190, Houston, TX 77054
Tel.: (713) 440-6070
Web Site: http://www.apocell.com
Sales Range: $1-9.9 Million
Emp.: 35
Medical, Dental & Hospital Equipment & Supplies Merchant Whslr
N.A.I.C.S.: 423450
David K. Hasegawa *(VP-Product Dev)*
Natalie Gassen *(CFO)*

Branch (Domestic):

Precision for Medicine   (2)
2686 Middlefield Rd, Redwood City, CA 94063
Tel.: (650) 299-9200
Research & Development in Biotechnology
N.A.I.C.S.: 541714
Rajiv Mahadevan *(Mng Dir)*

Precision for Value - New Jersey   (1)
240 Main St Ste 400, Gladstone, NJ 07934
Tel.: (908) 470-1780
Web Site: http://www.precisionforvalue.com
Sales Range: $10-24.9 Million
Emp.: 140
Advertising & Marketing for the Pharmaceutical Industry
N.A.I.C.S.: 541890
Dan Renick *(Pres)*

Stern Investor Relations, Inc.   (1)
1270 Ave of the Americas 4th Fl, New York, NY 10020
Tel.: (212) 362-1200
Web Site: http://www.sternir.com
Investor Relations Services
N.A.I.C.S.: 541820
Sarah McCabe *(Sr VP)*
Lilian Stern *(Principal)*
Stephanie Ascher *(Mng Dir)*
Michael Schaffzin *(Dir)*
Carl Mauch *(Dir)*
Rachel Frank *(Dir)*
Julie Seidel *(Dir)*
William Gramig *(Assoc Dir)*

PRECISION METAL FABRICATION, INC.
191 Heid Ave, Dayton, OH 45404
Tel.: (937) 233-5806
Web Site: http://www.premetfab.com
Sales Range: $10-24.9 Million
Emp.: 50
Sheet Metalwork
N.A.I.C.S.: 332322
James Hackenberger *(Pres)*
John Lindberg *(Treas)*

Subsidiaries:

Weldments, Inc.   (1)
167 Heid Ave, Dayton, OH 45404
Tel.: (937) 235-9261
Web Site: http://www.premetfab.com
Sales Range: $10-24.9 Million
Emp.: 12
Welding Repair
N.A.I.C.S.: 811490
John Limberg *(Treas)*
Jim Hackenberger *(Pres)*

PRECISION METAL INDUSTRIES, INC.
1408 SW 8th St, Pompano Beach, FL 33069
Tel.: (954) 942-6303   FL
Web Site: http://www.pmiquality.com
Year Founded: 1985
Sales Range: $10-24.9 Million
Emp.: 78
Precision Sheet Metal Mfr
N.A.I.C.S.: 332322
Gregory S. Wilson *(Pres)*
Donna D. Richards *(Mgr-Customer Svc & Plng)*
Robert Hornick *(Plant Mgr)*
Paul Denneau *(Mgr-Quality Assurance)*

PRECISION METAL PRODUCTS INC.
850 W Bradley Ave, El Cajon, CA 92020
Tel.: (619) 448-2711
Web Site: http://www.pmp-elcajon.com
Rev.: $13,700,000
Emp.: 140
Fabricated Structural Metal
N.A.I.C.S.: 332710
Carol Hake *(Coord-HR)*

PRECISION MOTOR CARS INC.
4211 S 144th St, Omaha, NE 68137-1053
Tel.: (402) 408-2000
Web Site:
http://www.acuraofomaha.com
Rev.: $17,500,000
Emp.: 50
Sales of Automobiles
N.A.I.C.S.: 441110
Rod Rhoden *(Pres)*

PRECISION MULTIPLE CONTROLS INC

PRECISION MULTIPLE CONTROLS INC

Precision Multiple Controls Inc—(Continued)
33 Greenwood Ave, Midland Park, NJ 07432
Tel.: (201) 444-0600
Web Site: http://www.precisionmulticontrols.com
Rev.: $11,000,000
Emp.: 135
Electrical Products Supplier
N.A.I.C.S.: 423610
Darren Lilley *(Pres)*

PRECISION PAPER TUBE COMPANY
1033 Noel Ave, Wheeling, IL 60090
Tel.: (847) 537-4250
Web Site: http://www.pptube.com
Rev.: $11,600,000
Emp.: 100
Paper Tube Mfr & Distr
N.A.I.C.S.: 322219
Rick Hatton *(Pres)*

PRECISION PIPELINE SOLUTIONS, LLC.
617 Little Britain Rd Ste 200, Windsor, NY 12553
Tel.: (845) 566-8332
Web Site: http://www.precisionpipelinesolutions.com
Year Founded: 2002
Sales Range: $10-24.9 Million
Emp.: 200
Energy & Pipeline Services
N.A.I.C.S.: 237120
Jon Selander *(Pres)*
Rebecca Tamm *(Mgr-Fin)*

PRECISION PIPING AND MECHANICAL INC.
5201 Middle Mount Vernon Rd, Evansville, IN 47712
Tel.: (812) 425-5052
Web Site: http://www.ppmiconstruction.com
Year Founded: 1986
Sales Range: $50-74.9 Million
Emp.: 150
Provider of Mechanical Contracting Services
N.A.I.C.S.: 238220
Carol Cook *(Sec)*
Brad Smith *(VP)*
Scott Jones *(Chm)*

PRECISION PLASTICS, INC.
900 W Connexion Way, Columbia City, IN 46725-1028
Tel.: (260) 244-6114 IN
Web Site: http://www.pplastic.com
Year Founded: 1953
Sales Range: $100-124.9 Million
Emp.: 150
Plastic Injection Molder
N.A.I.C.S.: 326199
Ronald R. Richey *(Pres & CEO)*
Cindy Berghoff *(Dir-Quality)*
Ryan B. Richey *(Exec VP)*

Subsidiaries:

Columbia Die Mold (1)
900 W Connexion Way, Columbia City, IN 46725-1028
Tel.: (260) 244-6114
Web Site: http://www.pplastic.com
Sales Range: $25-49.9 Million
Mfr of Die Mold
N.A.I.C.S.: 326199

PRECISION PLUS, INC.
840 Koopman Ln, Elkhorn, WI 53121
Tel.: (262) 743-1700 WI
Web Site: http://www.preplus.com
Year Founded: 1988
Sales Range: $1-9.9 Million
Emp.: 40
Mfg Screw Machine Products
N.A.I.C.S.: 332721

Subsidiaries:

Iseli Precision LLC (1)
402 N Main St, Walworth, WI 53184
Tel.: (262) 275-2108
Web Site: http://www.iseli.com
Sales Range: $25-49.9 Million
Emp.: 75
Precision Screw Machine Products
N.A.I.C.S.: 332722
David Atwood *(Mgr-Natl Sls)*

PRECISION PUNCH CORPORATION
304 Christian Ln, Berlin, CT 06037
Tel.: (860) 229-9902
Web Site: http://www.ppunch.com
Rev.: $4,300,000
Emp.: 36
Special Die & Tool, Die Set, Jig & Fixture Mfr
N.A.I.C.S.: 333514
Kevin Gregoire *(Pres)*

Subsidiaries:

Eastern Industries (1)
304 Christian Ln, Berlin, CT 06037-1420
Tel.: (860) 225-4159
Web Site: http://www.easterngage.com
Measuring & Controlling Device Mfr
N.A.I.C.S.: 334519
Dave Peterson *(Pres)*

PRECISION REPORTING, INC.
125 Chardonnay Oaks Dr, McDonough, GA 30252
Tel.: (770) 786-9664
Web Site: http://www.precisionreporting.net
Year Founded: 1997
Emp.: 100
Court Reporting & Stenotype Services
N.A.I.C.S.: 561492
Mary Caldwell *(Owner)*

PRECISION RESOURCE INC.
25 Forest Pkwy, Shelton, CT 06484-6122
Tel.: (203) 925-0012 CT
Web Site: http://www.precisionresource.com
Year Founded: 1967
Sales Range: $75-99.9 Million
Emp.: 200
Precision Metal Stamping Mfr
N.A.I.C.S.: 332119
James Flynn *(Dir-Sls & Mktg)*
Bob Radecki *(Mgr-Sls)*
Scott Fabricant *(CFO)*
Shelby Passacantando *(Coord-Mktg)*

Subsidiaries:

Precision Resource - California (1)
5803 Engineer Dr, Huntington Beach, CA 92649-1127
Tel.: (714) 891-4439
Web Site: http://www.precisionresource.com
Sales Range: $25-49.9 Million
Precision Metal Stampings
N.A.I.C.S.: 332119
Robert Fitzgerald *(Mgr-Div)*

Precision Resource - Illinois (1)
700 Hickory Hill Dr, Vernon Hills, IL 60061-3111 (100%)
Tel.: (847) 821-0700
Web Site: http://www.precisionresource.com
Sales Range: $10-24.9 Million
Emp.: 100
Producer of Precision Metal Stampings
N.A.I.C.S.: 332119

Precision Resource - Kentucky (1)
171 Oak Grove Dr, Mount Sterling, KY 40353-9087
Tel.: (859) 498-5887
Web Site: http://www.precisionresource.com
Sales Range: $10-24.9 Million
Emp.: 100
Precision Metal Stampings
N.A.I.C.S.: 332119
Horst Griesbaum *(Mgr)*
Tina Terrell *(Mgr-Acctg)*

Precision Resource Canada Ltd. (1)
4 Cherry Blossom Road, Cambridge, N3H 4R7, ON, Canada (100%)
Tel.: (519) 653-7777
Web Site: http://www.precisionresource.com
Sales Range: $75-99.9 Million
Emp.: 300
Precision Metal Stampings
N.A.I.C.S.: 332119
Ron Hunt *(Gen Mgr)*

Precision Resource Inc. - Canada - Cambridge Plant (1)
4 Cherry Blossom Road, Cambridge, N3H 4R7, ON, Canada
Tel.: (519) 653-7777
Fabricated Wire Product Mfr
N.A.I.C.S.: 332618

Precision Resource Inc. - Connecticut Division (1)
25 Forest Pkwy, Shelton, CT 06484
Tel.: (203) 925-0012
Web Site: http://www.precisionresource.com
Fabricated Metal Products Mfr
N.A.I.C.S.: 332999

Precision Resource Inc. - Mexico Division (1)
Carr Ant A Arteaga No 2603, Colonia La Aurora, Saltillo, 25298, Coahuila De Zaragoza, Mexico
Tel.: (52) 844 154 1000
Precision Metal Components Mfr
N.A.I.C.S.: 336370

PRECISION RESOURCES INC.
3975 E Railroad Ave, Cocoa, FL 32926-5975
Tel.: (321) 635-2000
Web Site: http://www.precgroup.com
Sales Range: $10-24.9 Million
Emp.: 220
Metal Structure Fabricating & Maintenance Services
N.A.I.C.S.: 332999
Ed Vonhollen *(Controller)*
Jason Shye *(CFO)*
Bob Kelly *(Pres)*

Subsidiaries:

Precision Enterprises Inc (1)
505 Canaveral Groves Blvd, Cocoa, FL 32926
Tel.: (321) 635-2000
Web Site: http://www.precision.com
Rev.: $1,981,627
Emp.: 15
Administrative Management
N.A.I.C.S.: 561110
Jason Shye *(CFO)*

Precision Fabricating & Cleaning Co (1)
3975 E Railroad Ave, Cocoa, FL 32926
Tel.: (321) 635-2000
Web Site: http://www.precweb.com
Sales Range: $10-24.9 Million
Emp.: 60
Process Control Instruments
N.A.I.C.S.: 334513
Robert Kelly *(Pres)*
Todd Gray *(VP)*

Precision Mechanical Inc. (1)
3975 E RR Ave, Cocoa, FL 32926
Tel.: (321) 635-2000
Web Site: http://www.precgroup.com
Rev.: $30,552,589
Emp.: 63
Warm Air Heating & Air Conditioning Contractor
N.A.I.C.S.: 238220
Robert P. Kelly *(Pres)*

PRECISION ROLL GRINDERS, INC.
6356 Chapmans Rd, Allentown, PA 18106-9364
Tel.: (610) 395-6966 DE
Web Site: http://www.precisionrollgrinders.com
Year Founded: 1970
Sales Range: $75-99.9 Million
Emp.: 100
Roll Grinding Mfr & Polisher
N.A.I.C.S.: 561990
James Manley *(Pres)*
Bob Rourke *(Mgr-Natl Sls & Mktg)*

PRECISION SALES & SERVICE, INC.
930 8th Ave S, Nashville, TN 37203
Tel.: (615) 834-8990
Web Site: http://www.americasmotorsport.com
Rev.: $10,000,000
Emp.: 31
Power Motor Sports Sales & Services
N.A.I.C.S.: 441227
Richard Watts *(Pres)*

PRECISION SHOOTING EQUIPMENT INC.
2727 N Fairview Ave, Tucson, AZ 85705-4009
Tel.: (520) 884-9065 DE
Web Site: http://www.pse-archery.com
Year Founded: 1974
Sales Range: $25-49.9 Million
Emp.: 320
Sporting & Athletic Goods Mfr
N.A.I.C.S.: 339920
Pete Shepley *(Founder)*
Blake Shelby *(VP-Sls & Mktg)*

Subsidiaries:

Precision Plating Inc. (1)
2557 W Violet Ave, Tucson, AZ 85705-1936 (100%)
Tel.: (520) 293-9116
Sales Range: $10-24.9 Million
Emp.: 15
Anodizing
N.A.I.C.S.: 332813

PRECISION STAFFING INCORPORATED
2350 Sterlington Rd, Lexington, KY 40517
Tel.: (859) 272-2030
Web Site: http://www.precisionstaffing.net
Rev.: $14,200,000
Emp.: 10
Temporary Help Service
N.A.I.C.S.: 561320
Anne Kelly *(Gen Mgr)*
Kathy O'Daniel *(Owner & Pres)*

PRECISION STEEL SERVICES INC.
31 E Sylvania Ave, Toledo, OH 43612
Tel.: (419) 476-5702
Web Site: http://www.precisionsteel.com
Rev.: $15,000,000
Emp.: 65
Steel
N.A.I.C.S.: 423510
David L. Kelley *(Pres)*

PRECISION STRIP INC.
86 S Ohio St, Minster, OH 45865-1246
Tel.: (419) 628-2343 OH
Web Site: http://www.precisionstrip.com
Year Founded: 1977
Sales Range: $100-124.9 Million
Emp.: 800
Metals Service Centers & Offices
N.A.I.C.S.: 423510

COMPANIES

PRECISION STRUCTURES INCORPORATED (PSI)
1204 1st Ave N, Wellman, IA 52356
Tel.: (319) 646-2430
Web Site:
  http://www.precisionstructures-inc.com
Year Founded: 1983
Sales Range: $10-24.9 Million
Emp.: 10
Design & Construction of Pre-Engineered Buildings for Agricultural, Dairy & Commercial Applications
N.A.I.C.S.: 423390

Subsidiaries:

Precision Structures Inc. (1)
1204 1st Ave N, Wellman, IA 52356
Tel.: (319) 646-2430
Web Site: http://www.precisionstructures-inc.com
Sales Range: $10-24.9 Million
Emp.: 8
Agricultural Construction Services
N.A.I.C.S.: 236117
Claude Greiner (Pres)

PRECISION SWISS PRODUCTS, INC.
1911 Tarob Ct, Milpitas, CA 95035
Tel.: (408) 433-5880
Web Site:
  http://www.precisionswiss.net
Year Founded: 1974
Rev.: $4,800,000
Emp.: 46
Precision Turned Product Mfr
N.A.I.C.S.: 332321
Bob Pomicpic (Dir-Special Ops)
Peter Pichler (Chief Quality Officer)

PRECISION TANK & EQUIP CO.
3503 Conover Rd, Virginia, IL 62691
Tel.: (217) 452-7228
Web Site:
  http://www.precisiontank.com
Emp.: 50
Metal Tank & Agricultural Equipment Mfr
N.A.I.C.S.: 332420
David Hemming (Pres & CEO)

Subsidiaries:

A & B Welding, Inc. (1)
105 Jackson St, Des Moines, IA 50478
Tel.: (641) 584-2900
Web Site: http://www.abweldingmfg.com
Sales Range: $1-9.9 Million
Emp.: 25
Fabricated Structural Metal Mfr
N.A.I.C.S.: 332312
Arlin Kiel (Owner)

PRECISION THERAPEUTICS, INC.
2516 Jane St, Pittsburgh, PA 15203
Tel.: (412) 432-1500
Web Site:
  http://www.precisiontherapeutics.com
Sales Range: $1-9.9 Million
Emp.: 169
Cancer Testing Laboratory Services
N.A.I.C.S.: 541380
Neil J. Campbell (Pres)
Kevin Hungerford (VP-Sls & Mktg-Global)
Carl Schwartz (CEO)
Jean-Paul Rasschaert (VP-Sls-Intl)

PRECISION TRADING CORP.
15800 NW 48th Ave, Miami Gardens, FL 33014
Tel.: (305) 592-4500
Web Site:
  http://www.precisiontrading.com
Year Founded: 1979
Sales Range: $150-199.9 Million
Emp.: 45
Consumer Electronics & Housewares Distr
N.A.I.C.S.: 423620
Israel Lapciuc (Pres)
Marcos Lapciuc (CFO)

PRECISION WALLS, INC.
1230 NE Maynard Rd, Cary, NC 27513-4174
Tel.: (919) 832-0380
Web Site:
  http://www.precisionwalls.com
Year Founded: 1964
Sales Range: $50-74.9 Million
Emp.: 350
Interior Drywall & Exterior Surface Commercial Construction Contractor
N.A.I.C.S.: 238310
Brian C. Allen (Pres)
Elizabeth B. Allen (Co-Founder & CEO)
Christopher Moss (Mgr-Architectural Sls)
Loy C. Allen Sr. (Co-Founder)

Subsidiaries:

Design Specialties, Inc. (1)
3640 Banks Rd, Raleigh, NC 27603
Tel.: (919) 772-6955
Rev.: $3,000,000
Emp.: 26
Interior Design Services & Construction Material Whslr
N.A.I.C.S.: 423320
Loy C. Allen Jr. (Pres)

PRECISION WIRE PRODUCTS INC.
6150 Sheila St, Los Angeles, CA 90040
Tel.: (323) 890-9100
Web Site:
  http://www.precisionwireproducts.com
Sales Range: $10-24.9 Million
Emp.: 200
Miscellaneous Fabricated Wire Products
N.A.I.C.S.: 332618
Edith Ondrasik (Pres)

PRECISIONHAWK INC.
8601 Six Forks Rd Forum 1 Ste 600, Raleigh, NC 27615
Tel.: (844) 328-5326
Web Site:
  http://www.precisionhawk.com
Unmanned Aerial Vehicles & Farm Drones Stores & Mfr
N.A.I.C.S.: 423430
Michael Chasen (CEO)

PRECIX INC.
744 Belleville Ave, New Bedford, MA 02745
Tel.: (508) 998-4000
Web Site: http://www.precixinc.com
Sales Range: $25-49.9 Million
Emp.: 340
Mfr of Gaskets
N.A.I.C.S.: 339991
David Slutz (Pres & CEO)
Lynne Mastera (CFO)
Mario Silva (Mgr-Production Control)

PREDICTIVE SAFETY LLC
6555 S Kenton St Ste 310, Centennial, CO 80111
Tel.: (303) 319-3505

Web Site:
  http://www.predictivesafety.com
Workplace Safety Analysis
N.A.I.C.S.: 561499
Dave D. Lauriski (CEO)

Subsidiaries:

Data Connect Corp. (1)
6555 S Kenton St Ste 310, Centennial, CO 80111
Tel.: (303) 840-7477
Web Site: http://www.dataconnectcorp.com
Sales Range: $1-9.9 Million
Emp.: 33
Computer System Design Services
N.A.I.C.S.: 541512
Timothy Hobbs (CEO)
David Blackburn (CFO)
Lynda Tarufelli (COO)
Todd Lodge (Mgr-Svcs & Support)
Jeff Sease (VP)
Amanda Scrabeck (Dir-Trade Show Sys)
Jacques Van Der Merwe (Head-Channel & Intl Sls)
Micheal Center (Exec VP-Sls & Mktg)

PREECE, INC.
26845 Vista Ter, Lake Forest, CA 92630-8117
Tel.: (949) 770-9411
Web Site: http://www.preeceinc.com
Year Founded: 1962
Sales Range: $10-24.9 Million
Emp.: 90
Mfr of Hoses, Tubes & Meter Valves
N.A.I.C.S.: 332912
Douglas Lincoln (Dir-Engrg)
Ron Kloetzli (Mgr-Sls)

PREFERRED AUTO INC.
9134 Lima Rd, Fort Wayne, IN 46818
Tel.: (260) 489-0489
Web Site:
  http://www.preferredautogroup.com
Sales Range: $50-74.9 Million
Emp.: 100
Used Car Sales
N.A.I.C.S.: 441120
Jay Leonard (Owner & Pres)
Bill Bandor (CFO)

Subsidiaries:

Preferred Auto Credit Inc. (1)
9206 Lima Rd, Fort Wayne, IN 46818
Tel.: (260) 489-0489
Web Site: http://www.preferredautosmotivegroup.com
Rev.: $30,404,420
Emp.: 8
Financing: Automobiles, Furniture & Other Items
N.A.I.C.S.: 522291
Jay Lenord (Pres)

PREFERRED BANCSHARES, INC.
11757 Katy Fwy Ste 100, Houston, TX 77079
Tel.: (281) 556-6443
Web Site:
  http://www.preferredbanktx.com
Bank Holding Company
N.A.I.C.S.: 551111
Donald Najvar (Pres & CEO)

Subsidiaries:

Preferred Bank (1)
11757 Katy Fwy Ste 100, Houston, TX 77079
Tel.: (281) 556-6443
Web Site: http://www.preferredbanktx.com
Rev.: $7,600,000
Emp.: 41
Fiscal Year-end: 12/31/2006
Federal Savings Institutions
N.A.I.C.S.: 522180
Herb Williams (Chm)
Donald J. Najvar (Pres & CEO)

Texas Independent Bancshares, Inc. (1)

PREFERRED ELECTRIC CO. INC.

3232 Palmer Hwy, Texas City, TX 77592
Tel.: (409) 948-3005
Web Site: http://www.texasfirstbank.com
Emp.: 500
Bank Holding Company
N.A.I.C.S.: 551111
Christopher C. Doyle (Pres)
Sam McGee (Chief IT Officer)

Subsidiary (Domestic):

Texas First Bank (2)
3232 Palmer Hwy, Texas City, TX 77590
Tel.: (409) 948-1990
Web Site: http://www.texasfirstbank.com
Emp.: 206
Retail & Commercial Banking
N.A.I.C.S.: 522180
Christopher C. Doyle (Pres & CEO)
Catherine O. Potter (Sec & Mgr-Regulatory & Risk)
Matthew T. Doyle (Chm)
Dickey Campbell (Reg Pres-Loan)
Ruth Osborn (VP-Electronic Payments)
Matt Crable (Sr VP-SBA Lending)
Robin Mizell (VP-Sls & Svc)
Samuel P. McGee (Chief Ops & Info Officer)
Scott Owen (Dir-HR)

PREFERRED BEEF GROUP
910 E Industrial Rd, Booker, TX 79005
Tel.: (806) 658-4561
Web Site:
  http://www.preferredbeef.com
Year Founded: 2006
Sales Range: $10-24.9 Million
Emp.: 210
Processed Beef Mfr & Distr
N.A.I.C.S.: 311611
Roy Goldsmith (Gen Mgr)

PREFERRED CHOICE MANAGEMENT SYSTEMS INC.
825 E Gate Blvd, Garden City, NY 11530-2124
Tel.: (516) 282-8000
Web Site: http://www.magnacare.com
Year Founded: 1990
Sales Range: $50-74.9 Million
Emp.: 200
Hospital & Medical Service Plans
N.A.I.C.S.: 524114
Craig Greenfield (Gen Counsel & VP)
Joseph Berardo (Pres & CEO)
Heather Suris (VP-Sls & Mktg)

PREFERRED CORPORATE HOUSING
9119 Katy Fwy, Houston, TX 77024
Tel.: (713) 722-0344
Web Site: http://www.corporates.com
Year Founded: 1996
Sales Range: $10-24.9 Million
Emp.: 20
Temporary Corporate Housing
N.A.I.C.S.: 624229
Samantha Elliott (Owner)
Jason Polasek (Mgr-Acct)
Michelle Velasquez (Dir-Client Svcs)
Megan FitzGerrell (Dir-Ops)

PREFERRED DATA SYSTEMS LLC
39100 Country Club Dr Ste 200, Farmington Hills, MI 48331
Tel.: (248) 553-6410
Web Site:
  http://www.pdsnetworking.com
Year Founded: 1999
Sales Range: $1-9.9 Million
Emp.: 14
Hardware Integration
N.A.I.C.S.: 541512
Patrick K. Comeaux (Pres)

PREFERRED ELECTRIC CO. INC.
4113 Yancey Rd, Charlotte, NC 28217
Tel.: (704) 347-0446
Web Site: http://www.peci-elect.com

PREFERRED ELECTRIC CO. INC. U.S. PRIVATE

Preferred Electric Co. Inc.—(Continued)
Sales Range: $10-24.9 Million
Emp.: 200
Electrical Work
N.A.I.C.S.: 238210
Terry Lette *(Co-Owner & Pres)*
David Howard *(Co-Owner & VP)*
David Brown *(VP-Estimating)*
Robert Smith *(VP-Ops)*
Angela Schaeffer *(Office Mgr)*

PREFERRED FURNITURE COMPONENTS INC.
2100 Brentwood St, High Point, NC 27263-1808
Tel.: (336) 889-6332 NC
Web Site:
http://www.preferredfurniturecomponents.com
Year Founded: 1983
Sales Range: $25-49.9 Million
Emp.: 80
Hardware
N.A.I.C.S.: 423710
Randy Kennedy *(Mgr-IT)*
Ron Shaw *(VP)*
Jim Hodgin *(Sec)*

PREFERRED GROUP INC.
400 Chapel Rd Ste 1M, South Windsor, CT 06074
Tel.: (860) 528-1220
Web Site:
http://www.preferredgp.com
Year Founded: 1985
Sales Range: $1-9.9 Million
Emp.: 7
Direct Mail & Marketing Services
N.A.I.C.S.: 541860
Wayne Feigenbaum *(Pres)*

PREFERRED HEALTH CARE, INC.
480 New Holland Ave Ste 7203, Lancaster, PA 17602
Tel.: (717) 560-9290
Web Site: http://www.phcunity.com
Direct Health & Medical Insurance Carriers Services
N.A.I.C.S.: 524114
Eric Buck *(Pres & CEO)*
Sherry Wolgemuth *(VP-Ops)*
Gina Dague *(Dir-Bus Plng & Implementation)*
Dan Labezius *(Dir-Claims Admin & Customer Svc)*
Demi Porter *(Dir-Client Svcs)*
Mike McCuen *(Mgr-Client)*
Melanie Horn *(Mgr-Client)*
Wanda Pitt *(Mgr-Csse & Coord-CCM Care)*
Jessica Sorber *(Coord-Care)*
Lynne Ostrowski *(Mgr-Provider Rels)*
David Jani *(VP-Sls & Bus Dev)*
Brynn Kline *(Mgr-Corp Health)*

PREFERRED HOME SERVICES, LLC
4214 Domino Ave, North Charleston, SC 29405
Tel.: (843) 619-3030
Web Site:
http://www.gopreferred.com
Year Founded: 2014
Sales Range: $1-9.9 Million
Emp.: 200
Air Conditioning System Installation Services
N.A.I.C.S.: 238220
John Ellett *(Owner)*

PREFERRED HOTELS GROUP
311 S Wacker Dr Ste 1900, Chicago, IL 60606-6676
Tel.: (312) 913-0400
Web Site:
http://www.preferredhotels.com
Year Founded: 1968
Sales Range: $50-74.9 Million
Emp.: 100
Independent Luxury Hotels & Resorts
N.A.I.C.S.: 813910
Robert Van Ness *(Exec VP-Americas)*
Michelle Woodley *(Exec VP)*
Gail Ueberroth *(Vice Chm & Chief Creative Officer)*
Lindsey Ueberroth *(Pres & CEO)*
Hiren Chandiramani *(CFO)*
Ken Mastrandrea *(COO)*
Philipp Weghmann *(Exec VP-Europe)*
Richard White *(Sr VP-Global Sls)*
Elaine Macy *(Exec VP-Grp Sls)*
Caroline Michaud *(VP-Corp Comm & PR)*
Lori Strasberg *(Sr VP-Mktg)*
Cheryl Williams *(Chief Revenue Officer)*
John A. Ueberroth *(Chm)*

PREFERRED MEDICAL MARKETING CORPORATION
15720 John J Delaney Dr Ste 460, Charlotte, NC 28277-3413
Tel.: (704) 543-8103
Web Site:
http://www.pmmconline.com
Year Founded: 1986
Rev.: $6,000,000
Emp.: 67
Computer Programming Services
N.A.I.C.S.: 541511
Roger Shaul Jr. *(Pres)*
Donna R. Lomax *(CFO)*
Palmer Hamilton *(VP)*
Kelly Coleman *(VP)*
Katherine Dobbs *(Office Mgr)*
Stephen Summers *(VP-Contract Mgmt Ops)*
Justin Wood *(CFO)*
Fred Sheffield *(Chief Sls Officer)*

PREFERRED MEDICAL PLAN, INC.
4950 SW 8th St, Coral Gables, FL 33134
Tel.: (305) 447-8373
Web Site: http://www.pmphmo.com
Year Founded: 1972
Sales Range: $100-124.9 Million
Emp.: 160
Health Insurance Carrier
N.A.I.C.S.: 524114
Tammy Myerson *(Pres & CEO)*

PREFERRED MUTUAL INSURANCE CO. INC.
1 Preferred Way, New Berlin, NY 13411
Tel.: (607) 847-6161
Web Site:
http://www.preferredmutual.com
Year Founded: 1896
Sales Range: $75-99.9 Million
Emp.: 250
Provider of Insurance Services
N.A.I.C.S.: 524126
Christopher P. Taft *(Pres & CEO)*
Andrew Forstenzer *(Gen Counsel, Sec & VP)*
Michelle Raue *(Sr VP-Claims)*
Tim Hyle *(CFO, Treas & Sr VP)*
Yogesh Deshmukh *(VP-Fin)*
Jessie Remillard *(Dir-HR)*
Sheena Moshetti *(Dir-Strategy Execution)*

Subsidiaries:

Preferred Mutual Insurance Co. (1)
1 Preferred Way, New Berlin, NY 13411 (100%)
Tel.: (607) 847-6161
Web Site: http://www.preferredmutual.com
Sales Range: $50-74.9 Million
Emp.: 200
Provider of Insurance Services
N.A.I.C.S.: 524126
Christopher P. Taft *(Pres & CEO)*

PREFERRED PACKAGING & CRATING, INC.
3330 W Cocopah St Ste 1, Phoenix, AZ 85009-6229
Tel.: (602) 272-2040
Sales Range: $10-24.9 Million
Emp.: 44
Corrugated & Solid Fiber Box Mfr
N.A.I.C.S.: 322211
Andrea Eagleton *(VP)*
Sherri Clark *(Mgr-Acctg)*
Mike Eagleton *(Pres)*

PREFERRED POPCORN LLC
1132 9th Rd, Chapman, NE 68827
Tel.: (308) 986-2526
Web Site:
http://www.preferredpopcorn.com
Year Founded: 1997
Popcorn Mfr
N.A.I.C.S.: 311919
Norm Krug *(Co-Founder & Co-Owner)*
Greg Senkbile *(Co-Founder & Co-Owner)*
Daryl Hunnicutt *(Co-Founder & Co-Owner)*
Martin Flaming *(Co-Founder & Co-Owner)*
Chris Vincent *(Co-Founder & Co-Owner)*
Kelly Grossnicklaus *(CFO)*

Subsidiaries:

K & W Popcorn Inc. (1)
PO Box 275, Trenton, MO 64683-0275
Tel.: (660) 359-2030
Web Site: http://www.kwpopcorn.com
Confectionery Merchant Whslr
N.A.I.C.S.: 424450
William Kennebeck *(Pres)*

PREFERRED PROPERTIES OF VENICE INC.
325 W Venice Ave, Venice, FL 34285
Tel.: (941) 485-9602 FL
Web Site:
http://www.veniceflproperties.com
Year Founded: 1990
Sales Range: $25-49.9 Million
Emp.: 22
Real Estate Agents & Managers
N.A.I.C.S.: 531210
Lauren H. Meadows *(Pres & CEO)*

PREFERRED PUMP & EQUIPMENT LP
2201 Scott Ave Ste 100, Fort Worth, TX 76103
Tel.: (817) 536-9800
Web Site:
http://www.preferredpump.com
Sales Range: $75-99.9 Million
Emp.: 30
Provider of Industrial Water Pumps
N.A.I.C.S.: 423830
Bill Pearce *(Branch Mgr)*
Randy Lyne *(Pres)*
Craig Shelton *(Controller)*

PREFERRED REAL ESTATE GROUP INC.
3522 Erie Ave, Cincinnati, OH 45208
Tel.: (513) 533-4111
Web Site:
http://www.preferredgrouprealtors.com
Rev.: $49,609,021
Emp.: 124
Real Estate Agents & Managers
N.A.I.C.S.: 531210
Christine Beresford *(Owner & Pres)*

PREFERRED SANDS, INC.
1 Radnor Corporate Ctr 100 Matsonford Rd Ste 101, Radnor, PA 19087
Tel.: (610) 834-1969 DE
Web Site:
http://www.preferredsands.com
Year Founded: 2007
Emp.: 415
Sand Mining Services
N.A.I.C.S.: 212322
Michael O'Neill *(Founder & CEO)*
Miguel Pena *(Sr VP-Bus Dev)*
Brad Phillips *(VP/Gen Mgr-Eagleford, Midcon, Rockies & Bakken)*
Bryan Schutt *(Reg Mgr-Sls-Bakken/Rockies & Northeast)*
Casey Taylor *(Dir-Sls-Houston)*
Joerg Pokats *(Reg Mgr-Sls-Canada)*
Lauren Boegner *(VP-HR)*
Tony Lee *(Reg Mgr-Sls-Eagleford)*
Sean McGrath *(CFO & Officer-Acctg)*
Robert Stienes *(Gen Counsel)*
Chris Samanns *(VP/Gen Mgr-Sls-Permian)*
Marc McQuesten *(VP/Gen Mgr-Sls-Canada)*
Leighton Tapia *(Reg Mgr-Sls-Permian)*
Thomas J. Doyle Jr. *(Pres & COO)*

PREFERRED SOLUTIONS
21800 Haggerty Rd Ste 315, Northville, MI 48167
Tel.: (248) 679-0130
Web Site: http://www.prefsol.com
Sales Range: $10-24.9 Million
Emp.: 500
Information Technology Training & Staffing Services
N.A.I.C.S.: 611420
Marie Seipenko *(Pres)*
Sue Piotrowski *(VP)*
Jennifer Butkovich *(Dir-Core Svcs Recruiting)*
Stephanie Gibbons *(Dir-Strategic Recruiting)*
Steve Wargo *(Dir-Program Delivery)*

PREFERRED TRAVEL OF NAPLES INC.
801 Laurel Oak Dr Ste 300, Naples, FL 34108
Tel.: (239) 261-1177 FL
Web Site:
http://www.preferrednaples.com
Year Founded: 1980
Sales Range: $25-49.9 Million
Emp.: 25
Travel Agency
N.A.I.C.S.: 561510
Kathleen D'Amico *(Asst Controller)*
John Burgess *(Mgr-Leisure Div)*
Karen Pickrum *(Dir-Mktg)*
Olga Placeres *(Gen Mgr & Controller)*
Wilma Boyd *(Pres & CEO)*

PREGER & WERTENTEIL, INC.
19 W 34th St 3rd Fl, New York, NY 10001
Tel.: (212) 889-7800 NY
Web Site: http://www.goldmedalintl.com
Year Founded: 1954
Women's, Men's & Children's Hosiery & Accessory Items Distr
N.A.I.C.S.: 424350
Paul Rotstein *(Pres & CEO)*

PREISER SCIENTIFIC, INC.
94 Oliver St, Saint Albans, WV 25177
Tel.: (304) 727-2902 WV
Web Site: http://www.preiser.com

Year Founded: 1924
Sales Range: $75-99.9 Million
Emp.: 40
Scientific Instruments, Laboratory Equipment & Related Supplies
N.A.I.C.S.: 423490
Kevin Westfall (VP)

Subsidiaries:

Standard Instrumentation (1)
94 Oliver St, Saint Albans, WV 25177
Tel.: (304) 727-2902
Web Site: http://www.preiser.com
Sales Range: $10-24.9 Million
Emp.: 39
Laboratory Supplies, Equipment, Scientific Instruments, Microscopes, Coal & Water Testing Equipment
N.A.I.C.S.: 423490
A. E. Preiser (Pres)
Gayle Preiser (CEO)

PRELOAD CONCRETE STRUCTURES
49 Wireless Blvd Ste 200, Hauppauge, NY 11788
Tel.: (631) 231-8100
Web Site: http://www.preloadinc.com
Year Founded: 1949
Sales Range: $25-49.9 Million
Emp.: 80
Waste Water & Sewage Treatment Plant Construction
N.A.I.C.S.: 237110
Andrew E. Tripp Jr. (Pres)

PRELUDE FERTILITY, INC.
9160 Carothers Pkwy Ste 201, Franklin, TN 37067
Tel.: (615) 721-6250   DE
Web Site:
http://www.preludefertility.com
Year Founded: 2015
Fertility Clinic
N.A.I.C.S.: 621511
Christopher P. Montville (Partner & Dir-Practice)

Subsidiaries:

Vivere Health LLC (1)
5000 Meridian Blvd Ste 250, Franklin, TN 37067
Tel.: (615) 550-4900
Web Site: http://www.viverehealth.com
Freestanding Ambulatory Surgical & Emergency Centers
N.A.I.C.S.: 621493

PRELUDE SYSTEMS, INC.
1400 Montefino Ave Ste 150, Diamond Bar, CA 91765
Tel.: (909) 457-4157   CA
Web Site: http://www.preludesys.com
Year Founded: 1999
Sales Range: $10-24.9 Million
Emp.: 55
Technology Services
N.A.I.C.S.: 541512
Kiran Babu Chandra (CEO)

PREMARC CORPORATION
7505 E M 71, Durand, MI 48429-9715
Tel.: (989) 288-2661   MI
Year Founded: 1925
Sales Range: $75-99.9 Million
Emp.: 125
Mfr of Concrete Pipes, Manholes, Box Culverts, Prestressed Bridge Beams & Specialty Concrete Products
N.A.I.C.S.: 327390
Thomas Hager (COO)

Subsidiaries:

Grand River Infrastructure (1)
2701 Chicago Dr SW, Grand Rapids, MI 49519
Tel.: (616) 534-9645
Rev.: $11,800,000
Emp.: 100
Provider of Concrete Products
N.A.I.C.S.: 327390

Premarc (1)
4950 White Lk Rd, Clarkston, MI 48346-2639   (100%)
Tel.: (248) 625-8080
Sales Range: $10-24.9 Million
Emp.: 50
Mfr of Concrete Pipes, Manholes, Box Culverts, Prestressed Bridge Beams & Specialty Concrete Products
N.A.I.C.S.: 327332

Premarc/Marsh Products (1)
7505 M 71, Durand, MI 48429-9715   (100%)
Tel.: (989) 288-2661
Web Site: http://www.crafco.com
Rev.: $13,000,000
Emp.: 53
Mfr of Concrete Products
N.A.I.C.S.: 327390

PREMERA BLUE CROSS
7001-220 St SW Bldg 1, Mountlake Terrace, WA 98043
Tel.: (509) 536-4700   WA
Web Site: http://www.premera.com
Year Founded: 1933
Sales Range: $1-4.9 Billion
Emp.: 425
Health Insurance Carrier
N.A.I.C.S.: 524114
Kent Marquardt (CFO & Exec VP)
Richard Maturi (Sr VP-Healthcare Delivery Sys)
John Pierce (Gen Counsel & Sr VP)
Mark Gregory (CIO & Sr VP-IT)
Jeff Roe (Pres & CEO)
David Braza (Sr VP-Health Care Informatics)
Cecily Hall (Sr VP-HR)
Sharon Chastain (Sr VP-Ops)
Dawn Atkin (VP-Medical Mgmt & Population Health)
Gary Strannigan (VP-Congressional & Legislative Affairs)
Lee McGrath (Sr VP-Provider Strategy & Solutions)
Allison Warren-Barbour (VP-HR)

PREMIER & COMPANIES INC
357 W 36th St, New York, NY 10018
Tel.: (212) 947-1365
Web Site:
http://www.premiersupplies.com
Rev.: $12,000,000
Emp.: 26
Printing Paper
N.A.I.C.S.: 424110
Sheldon Lehman (Owner & Pres)

PREMIER ALUMINUM, LLC
3633 S Memorial Dr, Racine, WI 53403
Tel.: (262) 554-2100
Web Site:
http://www.premieraluminum.com
Year Founded: 1988
Rev.: $19,000,000
Emp.: 150
Mold Aluminum Castings Mfr
N.A.I.C.S.: 331523
Kevin Kelly (Mgr-Sls)

PREMIER AMERICA CREDIT UNION
19867 Prairie St, Chatsworth, CA 91313-2177
Tel.: (818) 772-4000   CA
Web Site:
http://www.premieramerica.com
Year Founded: 1957
Sales Range: $50-74.9 Million
Emp.: 283
Credit Union
N.A.I.C.S.: 522130
Marge McNaught (Sr VP-Lending & Collections)
Brad Cunningham (CFO & Sr VP)
Toni Daniels (Sr VP-Admin)
Glen Chrzas (Sr VP-IT)
Rudy Pereira (Pres & CEO)

PREMIER BANK
2866 White Bear Ave N, Maplewood, MN 55109
Tel.: (651) 777-7700
Web Site:
http://www.premierbanks.com
Sales Range: $50-74.9 Million
Emp.: 200
State Commercial Banks
N.A.I.C.S.: 522110
Victoria Campbell (Officer-Admin & VP)
Donald P. Hileman (Exec Chm)
David Howe (CFO)
Tom Kern (Pres-Northwest Area)
Andrew Nath (Exec VP)
Doug Schultze (Officer-Comml Loan & VP)
Brandon Wilcox (Officer-Comml Loan & VP)
Sam Gallo (Pres-Central West Virginia & Exec VP)
Chris Parr (VP-Central West Virginia)
Michael Malfregeot (Mgr-Central West Virginia)
Nancy Kissinger (Sr VP-Comml Banking-Southern West Virginia Div)
Mark Bias (Pres & CEO)
Jeffrey D. Hatton (COO & Officer-Compliance)
Martha Kaufenberg (Officer-Comml Loan & VP)
Robert Mench (Officer-Loan Review & VP)
Donald B. Regan (Founder & Chm)
Gary M. Small (Pres & CEO)

PREMIER BEAUTY SUPPLY INC.
400 Academy Dr, Northbrook, IL 60062
Tel.: (847) 480-0000
Web Site:
http://www.premierbeautysupply.com
Sales Range: $50-74.9 Million
Emp.: 35
Beauty Parlor Equipment & Supplies
N.A.I.C.S.: 423850
Steve Cohn (Pres)
Joshua Wright (Mgr-Pur & Mktg)
Lynn Kattner (Mgr-Credit & Collections)
Michelle Reale (Sr Acct Exec)
Natalia Bernal (Acct Exec)
Sandy Autry (Acct Exec)

PREMIER BEVERAGE GROUP CORP.
501 Madison Ave Ste 501, New York, NY 10022
Tel.: (646) 820-0630   NV
Web Site:
http://www.premierbeveragegroup.com
Year Founded: 1999
Sales Range: Less than $1 Million
Investment Management Service
N.A.I.C.S.: 523940
Fouad Kallamni (Pres & CEO)

PREMIER BRANDS GROUP HOLDINGS LLC
1411 Broadway, New York, NY 10018
Tel.: (212) 642-3860   DE
Web Site: http://www.ninewest.com
Sales Range: $150-199.9 Million

Holding Company; Women's Apparel & Accessories Designer, Whslr & Retailer
N.A.I.C.S.: 551112
Ira M. Dansky (Gen Counsel, Sec & Exec VP)
Kathy Nedorostek (Co-CEO-Nine West Grp)
Jack Gross (Co-CEO-Nine West Jeanswear Grp)
Ralph Schipani (Interim CEO)
Joel Oblonsky (CEO-Nine West & Bandolino Div)

Subsidiaries:

Jones Apparel Group Canada, LP (1)
388 Applewood Crescent, Vaughan, L4K 4B4, ON, Canada
Tel.: (905) 760-6000
Sales Range: $50-74.9 Million
Women Apparel Distr
N.A.I.C.S.: 424350

Jones International Limited (1)
10/Fl Tower I Metroplaza 223 Hing Fong Road, Kwai Fong, New Territories, China (Hong Kong)
Tel.: (852) 31878000
Women's Fashion Apparel & Accessories Whslr
N.A.I.C.S.: 424350

Maquilas Pami, S.A. de C.V. (1)
Blvd Miguel Aleman 2268, Ciudad Lerdo, 35150, Durango, Mexico
Tel.: (52) 87111 55555
Sales Range: $1-9.9 Million
Fabric Mill
N.A.I.C.S.: 313210

Nine West Group, Inc. (1)
Nine West Plz 1129 Westchester Ave, White Plains, NY 10604
Web Site: http://www.ninewest.com
Women's Footwear, Handbags & Accessories Designer, Whslr & Online Retailer
N.A.I.C.S.: 424350
Joel Oblonsky (CEO)

Nine West Jeanswear Group, Inc. (1)
1441 Broadway, New York, NY 10018
Tel.: (212) 575-2571
Women's Jeans & Other Apparel Designer & Whslr
N.A.I.C.S.: 424350
Jack Gross (CEO)

PREMIER COIL SOLUTIONS, INC.
18993 GH Circle Dr, Waller, TX 77484
Tel.: (713) 677-0209
Web Site: http://www.premiercoil.com
Year Founded: 2011
Sales Range: $50-74.9 Million
Emp.: 200
Coiled Tubing Equipment Mfr
N.A.I.C.S.: 334419
Brett Witte (Founder & CEO)

PREMIER COMPUTING, INC.
345 Bearcat Dr, Salt Lake City, UT 84115
Tel.: (801) 487-8400
Web Site:
http://www.premiercomputing.com
Year Founded: 1952
Sales Range: $1-9.9 Million
Emp.: 20
Computer Software & Services
N.A.I.C.S.: 513210
Vi Nguyen (Comptroller)
Julie Potter (VP)
Casey Lawrence (Pres)

PREMIER COOPERATIVE
501 W Main St, Mount Horeb, WI 53572
Tel.: (608) 437-5536   WI

PREMIER COOPERATIVE

Premier Cooperative—(Continued)

Web Site:
http://www.premiercooperative.com
Year Founded: 1893
Lumber & Other Building Materials
N.A.I.C.S.: 423310
Andy Fiene (CEO & Treas)
Deborah Blake (Asst Mgr)

PREMIER COOPERATIVE, INC.
2104 W Park Ct, Champaign, IL 61821
Tel.: (217) 355-1983
Web Site: http://www.premiercooperative.net
Sales Range: $10-24.9 Million
Emp.: 85
Grain Marketing Services
N.A.I.C.S.: 493130
Roger Miller (CEO)
Jim Deters (CFO)
Dean Killion (Mgr-Grain Mktg)
Ron Snyder (Controller)

PREMIER COS.
785 S Marr Rd, Columbus, IN 47201-7490
Tel.: (812) 379-9501
Web Site: http://www.premierag.com
Year Founded: 1927
Sales Range: $75-99.9 Million
Emp.: 95
Whslr of Farm Supplies & Petroleum Products
N.A.I.C.S.: 424510
Mike Lafferty (Controller)
Jim Geis (Chm)
Barbie Bultman (Sec)
Subsidiaries:

White River Cooperative Inc. (1)
610 Church St, Loogootee, IN 47553
Tel.: (812) 295-4835
Web Site: http://www.whiterivercoop.com
Sales Range: $25-49.9 Million
Emp.: 100
Animal Seeds Distr
N.A.I.C.S.: 424910
Rick Madden (Mgr-Propane Div)

PREMIER DESIGN HOMES INC.
11030 N Kendall Dr No 100, Miami, FL 33176
Tel.: (305) 271-6997
Web Site: http://www.premierdesignhomes inc.com
Sales Range: $10-24.9 Million
Emp.: 15
New Construction, Single-Family Houses
N.A.I.C.S.: 236115
Myra Dallias (Adv Dir)

PREMIER ELECTRICAL CORPORATION
4401 85th Ave N, Brooklyn Park, MN 55443-1937
Tel.: (763) 424-6551
Web Site: http://www.premiercorp.net
Year Founded: 1987
Sales Range: $25-49.9 Million
Emp.: 180
Commercial Electrical Contracting Services
N.A.I.C.S.: 238210
Fred Jahnke (CEO)
Lonnie Bellin (Controller)
Doug Olsen (Pres)

PREMIER ENERGY CORP.
1478 Preston Rd Ste 550, Dallas, TX 75254
Tel.: (972) 789-5151
Year Founded: 2006

Sales Range: Less than $1 Million
Emp.: 35
Oil & Gas Exploration & Development Services
N.A.I.C.S.: 211120
Anton Prodanovic (CEO)
Alexey Goleshev (CFO)
Bosko Popovic (COO)
Aslanbi Kodzokov (Sec)

PREMIER GMC LTD.
2000 Eastern Rd, Rittman, OH 44270
Tel.: (330) 925-5010
Web Site: http://www.premiergmc.com
Year Founded: 1945
Sales Range: $10-24.9 Million
Emp.: 45
Car Whslr
N.A.I.C.S.: 441110
Tom Casto (Gen Mgr)
Corrine Swartz (Office Mgr)
Billy Casto (Mgr-Sls)
C. J. Wright (Mgr-Customer Care)
Matt Maxwell (Mgr-Reconditioning)
Sam Becerra (Mgr-Parts)
Tony Semprini (Mgr-Svc)

PREMIER GRAPHICS, LLC
860 Honeyspot Rd, Stratford, CT 06615
Tel.: (203) 378-6200
Web Site: http://www.premieruplink.com
Sales Range: $10-24.9 Million
Emp.: 55
Commercial Flexographic Printing Services
N.A.I.C.S.: 323111
Cesar Garcia (Owner)
Todd Gould (VP-Sls)

PREMIER INK SYSTEMS INC.
10420 N State St, Harrison, OH 45030
Tel.: (513) 367-2300
Web Site: http://www.premierink.com
Year Founded: 1984
Sales Range: $10-24.9 Million
Emp.: 60
Printing Ink Mfr
N.A.I.C.S.: 325910
Thomas Farmer (Pres)
Doug Foster (Mgr-Laboratory)
Judy Fritz (Office Mgr)
Larry Gersbach (CFO)

PREMIER INTEGRITY SOLUTIONS
7 Jamestown St, Russell Springs, KY 42642
Tel.: (270) 866-3144
Web Site: http://www.premierintegrity.com
Year Founded: 1999
Sales Range: $1-9.9 Million
Emp.: 185
Drug & Alcohol Testing, Background Checks & DNA Testing
N.A.I.C.S.: 541380
Brian Walters (Owner)
Heath Reeder (Engr-Network)
Michael West (Exec VP)
Mike Bunch (Exec VP)
Sarah Asman (Coord-Mktg)

PREMIER MACHINERY INC.
990 Sunshine Ln, Altamonte Springs, FL 32714-3803
Tel.: (407) 786-2000
Web Site: http://www.premierequipment.com
Year Founded: 1988
Sales Range: $10-24.9 Million
Emp.: 30

Mfr of Industrial Machinery & Equipment
N.A.I.C.S.: 423830
John Grabenau (Pres)
Subsidiaries:

Premier Equipment Co. Inc. (1)
990 Sunshine Ln, Altamonte Springs, FL 32714-3803 (100%)
Tel.: (407) 786-2000
Web Site: http://www.premierequipment.com
Sales Range: $10-24.9 Million
Emp.: 25
Provider of Business Services
N.A.I.C.S.: 541990
Tom Kohm (Pres & CEO)

PREMIER MAGNESIA, LLC.
300 Barr Harbor Dr Ste 250, Conshohocken, PA 19428
Tel.: (610) 828-6929
Web Site: http://www.premiermagnesia.com
Year Founded: 2001
Sales Range: $75-99.9 Million
Emp.: 205
Ground or Treated Mineral & Earth Mfr
N.A.I.C.S.: 327992
John Gehret (CEO)
Stephen Becker (Gen Counsel, Sec & VP)
Nicole Hill (CFO)
Rick Wrenn Jr. (Pres)

PREMIER MANUFACTURING, INC.
1711 N Madson, Liberty Lake, WA 99019
Tel.: (509) 927-9860
Web Site: http://www.premier-manufacturing.net
Sales Range: $1-9.9 Million
Emp.: 75
Sheet Metal Mfr
N.A.I.C.S.: 332322
Mike Bourcy (Mgr-Quality)

PREMIER MUSHROOMS LP
2880 Niagara Ave, Colusa, CA 95932
Tel.: (530) 458-2700
Web Site: http://www.premiermushrooms.com
Year Founded: 2006
Sales Range: $10-24.9 Million
Emp.: 170
White & Portobello Mushrooms
N.A.I.C.S.: 111411
John Ashbaugh (CEO)
Chris Krebs (CFO)
Robert Murphy (VP-Mktg & Sls)

PREMIER OFFICE CENTERS, LLC
2102 Business Center Dr, Irvine, CA 92612
Tel.: (949) 253-4130
Web Site: http://www.pbcenters.com
Year Founded: 2002
Sales Range: $25-49.9 Million
Emp.: 180
Commercial Office Leasing Services
N.A.I.C.S.: 531120
Jeff Reinstein (CEO)
Theresa Sherman (CFO)
Michael Pollack (VP & Dir-Real Estate)

PREMIER OILFIELD LABORATORIES LLC
11335 Clay Rd Ste 180, Houston, TX 77041
Tel.: (713) 492-2057
Web Site: http://www.premieroilfieldlabs.com
Oilfield Research & Analytics
N.A.I.C.S.: 213112

Matt Bell (CEO)
Subsidiaries:

COREX (UK) LTD (1)
Units B1 2 3 Airport Industrial Park Howe Moss Drive Dyce, Knowsley, Aberdeen, AB21 0GL, United Kingdom
Tel.: (44) 1224 770434
Web Site: http://www.corex.co.uk
Emp.: 200
Oilfield Research & Analytics Services
N.A.I.C.S.: 213112

NSI Technologies, LLC (1)
7146 S Braden Ave, Tulsa, OK 74136
Tel.: (918) 496-2071
Web Site: http://www.nsitech.com
Emp.: 10
Consulting Software Firm
N.A.I.C.S.: 513210
Mike Smith (Pres)

PREMIER ORTHODONTIC SPECIALISTS, PLLC
3230 S Gilbert Rd Chandler Ste 1, Chandler, AZ 85286
Tel.: (480) 907-0142
Web Site: http://yourazbraces.com
Year Founded: 2006
Sales Range: $1-9.9 Million
Dental Services
N.A.I.C.S.: 621210
Dustin Coles (Founder)

PREMIER PACIFIC CONSTRUCTION, INC.
13103 Golden Way, Poway, CA 92064-9805
Tel.: (858) 748-7152
Year Founded: 2000
PPCQ—(OTCBB)
Sales Range: Less than $1 Million
Emp.: 1
Contracting & Construction Services
N.A.I.C.S.: 238910

PREMIER PLACEMENT MEDIA, LTD
12300 Dundee Court Ste 117, Cypress, TX 77429
Tel.: (281) 304-1512
Web Site: http://www.premier-placement.com
Year Founded: 2001
Sales Range: $10-24.9 Million
Emp.: 20
Paid Search Marketing Services
N.A.I.C.S.: 541613
David Gedeon (Pres & Founder)

PREMIER PLASTICS, INC.
2370 S 3600 W, Salt Lake City, UT 84119
Tel.: (801) 975-0133
Web Site: http://www.premierplastics.net
Year Founded: 1989
Sales Range: $1-9.9 Million
Emp.: 26
Plastic Packaging Services
N.A.I.C.S.: 561910
Jim Holbrook (Pres)

PREMIER PRINT & SERVICES GROUP INCORPORATED
10 S Riverside Plz Ste 1810, Chicago, IL 60606
Tel.: (312) 648-2266
Web Site: http://www.premierprint.com
Rev.: $26,000,000
Emp.: 40
Business Forms
N.A.I.C.S.: 424120

PREMIER PRODUCT SALES, INC.
430 Madera St, San Gabriel, CA 91776

Tel.: (626) 293-1250   CA
Web Site:
   http://www.whatshebuys.com
Year Founded: 1993
Sales Range: $1-9.9 Million
Emp.: 28
Store & Online Retailer of Products for Men, Women & Children
N.A.I.C.S.: 423990
Cathy A. Kamimura *(CEO)*

PREMIER PRODUCTS CO.
1710 Romano Dr, Plymouth Meeting, PA 19462-2822
Tel.: (610) 239-6000   PA
Web Site: http://www.premusa.com
Year Founded: 1917
Sales Range: $125-149.9 Million
Emp.: 150
Mfr & Distributor of Dental & Medical Supplies & Instruments
N.A.I.C.S.: 423450
Gary Charlestein *(Chm)*
Kevin J. Brown *(Sr VP-Premier Medical Prods)*
Karen Giannone *(Dir-HR)*
Alan Kegerise *(Mgr-Sls-Premier Dental Products-North America)*
Joe Simon *(VP-Intl)*
Bill McHale *(Sr VP-Product Dev)*
Julie Charlestein *(Pres & CEO)*
John Bonner *(Product Mgr)*
H. Michael Vukosavich *(Mgr-Sls Europe)*
Ann Coyne *(Product Mgr)*
Steven Hayman *(CFO & COO)*
Tadd Zettlemoyer *(Mgr-Customer Svc)*
John Whitner *(VP-Corp Brand & Digital Mktg)*
Metin Yasin *(Dir-Intl Sls)*
Lisa Hughes *(Mgr-Mktg)*
Lillian J. Caperila *(Mgr-Pro Education)*
Genard McCauley *(Mgr-Sls)*
Cara Braslow *(VP-Corp Regulatory Affairs)*

PREMIER PUMP & SUPPLY, INC.
5425 Stationers Way, Sacramento, CA 95842
Tel.: (916) 638-0122   CA
Web Site:
   http://www.premierpumpsupply.com
Year Founded: 1991
Sales Range: $10-24.9 Million
Irrigation Pump & Supplies Distr
N.A.I.C.S.: 423720

PREMIER SALES INC.
8181 W Darryl Dr, Baton Rouge, LA 70815
Tel.: (225) 927-9280
Web Site:
   http://www.premierhvac.com
Sales Range: $10-24.9 Million
Emp.: 15
Warm Air Heating Equipment & Supplies
N.A.I.C.S.: 423730
Paula Oakley *(Controller)*

PREMIER SOTHEBY'S INTERNATIONAL REALTY
4001 Tamiami Trail N Ste350, Naples, FL 34103
Tel.: (239) 262-4242   FL
Web Site:
   http://www.premiersothebysrealty.com
Year Founded: 1983
Sales Range: $75-99.9 Million
Emp.: 90
Real Estate Broker & Real Estate Management & Development

N.A.I.C.S.: 531210
Kristine Stack *(Dir-Mktg-Central Florida)*
Budge S. Huskey *(Pres & CEO)*
Stephanie Lucas *(Mgr-Mktg-North Carolina)*
Corrine Kelly-Brao *(VP-HR)*
Jessica Johnson *(Mktg Mgr-Charlotte)*
Elise Ramer *(VP-Media Rels)*
Kathy Forrester *(CMO)*
Joe Consolino *(VP-IT)*
Abigail Tesniarz *(VP-Fin)*

PREMIER STEEL INC.
25 Rockwood Pl Ste 3, Englewood, NJ 07631
Tel.: (201) 894-5200
Web Site:
   http://www.premiersteelnj.com
Sales Range: $10-24.9 Million
Emp.: 10
Steel Distr
N.A.I.C.S.: 423510
Steven C. Bergman *(Founder, Pres & CEO)*

PREMIER TECHNOLOGY INC.
1858 W Bridge St, Blackfoot, ID 83221
Tel.: (208) 785-2274
Web Site: http://www.ptius.net
Sales Range: $25-49.9 Million
Emp.: 150
Fabricated Structural Metal
N.A.I.C.S.: 423440
Shelly Sayer *(CFO)*
Buck Cooper *(Mgr-Design Dept)*
Travis Roche *(Project Mgr)*
Lyle Freeman *(VP-Bus Dev)*
Brady Bullock *(Project Mgr)*
Mathew Burke *(Mgr-Quality Assurance)*
Thomas Igoe *(Project Mgr)*
Scott Francis *(Project Mgr)*
Joel Christophersen *(Chief Production Officer)*
Doug Wale *(Mgr-Comml Nuclear Bus)*

PREMIER TRANSPORTATION & WAREHOUSES
851 E Watson Ctr Rd, Carson, CA 90745
Tel.: (310) 835-9207
Web Site: http://www.premiertwi.com
Rev.: $15,692,835
Emp.: 29
Trucking
N.A.I.C.S.: 484121
Greg L. Chandler *(Pres)*

PREMIER VENTURES, INC.
519 16th St, Denver, CO 80202
Tel.: (303) 893-1236
Web Site:
   http://www.premierventuresinc.com
Sales Range: $50-74.9 Million
Emp.: 5
Holding Company; Restaurant & Bar Owner & Operator
N.A.I.C.S.: 551112
Mike Plancarte *(Owner)*
Subsidiaries:
Five Eleven Inc. (1)
501 16th St, Denver, CO 80202
Tel.: (303) 595-3700
Web Site: http://www.paramountcafe.com
Sales Range: $10-24.9 Million
Eating Place
N.A.I.C.S.: 722511
John Ott *(Pres)*

PREMIERE CHEVROLET, INC.
4990 Premiere Pkwy, Bessemer, AL 35022-5500
Tel.: (205) 424-4121

Web Site:
   http://www.premierechevy.com
Year Founded: 1987
Sales Range: $10-24.9 Million
Emp.: 72
Car Whslr
N.A.I.C.S.: 441110
Ken Gallo *(Pres)*

PREMIERE EVENTS
1654 Hayes Dr, Manhattan, KS 66502
Tel.: (323) 934-7777
Web Site: http://www.premierela.com
Performing Art Promotion Services
N.A.I.C.S.: 711310
Jenne Andrews *(Owner, Pres & CEO)*
Subsidiaries:
Party Time Rentals, Inc. (1)
1816 Ponderosa Dr, College Station, TX 77845
Tel.: (979) 696-5555
Web Site: http://www.partytimerentals.com
Sales Range: $1-9.9 Million
Emp.: 30
Party Rentals
N.A.I.C.S.: 459420
Patricia Scarmardo *(Pres)*

PREMIERE LOCK COMPANY
10203A E 61st St, Tulsa, OK 74133
Tel.: (918) 294-8179   CA
Web Site: http://www.weslock.com
Year Founded: 1932
Residential Door Locks & Related Hardware Mfr
N.A.I.C.S.: 332510
Mike Driggers *(CFO)*
Clint Brumble *(Pres)*
Lantz Day *(VP-Sls & Mktg)*

PREMIERE PACKAGING, INC.
6220 Lehman Dr, Flint, MI 48507
Tel.: (810) 239-7650   MI
Web Site:
   http://www.premierepkg.com
Year Founded: 1969
Sales Range: $50-74.9 Million
Emp.: 75
Mfr of Sanitation Goods & Related Products
N.A.I.C.S.: 325612
Mark Drolet *(Pres & Treas)*
Kathy Elfworth *(CFO)*

PREMIERE TRUCK CENTERS, INC.
22031 Hwy 72 E, Tuscumbia, AL 35674
Tel.: (256) 383-9546
Web Site:
   http://www.premiertrucks.com
Rev.: $20,564,698
Emp.: 43
Trucks, Tractors & Trailers; New & Used
N.A.I.C.S.: 441110
Thomas Willings *(Gen Mgr)*

PREMIO FOODS, INC.
21-00 State Route 208 Ste 200, Fair Lawn, NJ 07410
Tel.: (973) 427-1106
Web Site:
   http://www.premiofoods.com
Processed Meat Mfr
N.A.I.C.S.: 311612
Joel Goldberg *(Dir-HR)*
Subsidiaries:
Appetito Provision Co., Inc. (1)
609 10th St, Union City, NJ 07087-3003
Tel.: (201) 864-3410
Sausage Mfr
N.A.I.C.S.: 424470

PREMIO INCORPORATED

918 Radecki Ct, City of Industry, CA 91748-1132
Tel.: (626) 839-3100
Web Site: http://www.premioinc.com
Rev.: $151,904,398
Emp.: 145
Computers, Peripherals & Software
N.A.I.C.S.: 423430
Crystal Wu *(Pres & CEO)*
Kevin Wu *(Exec VP-Ops)*
Ken Szeto *(Gen Mgr)*
Harold K. Hutchinson *(Sr VP)*

PREMISE IMMERSIVE MARKETING
1945 B St Ste A, San Diego, CA 92102
Tel.: (619) 233-7979
Sales Range: $10-24.9 Million
Emp.: 15
Advetising Agency
N.A.I.C.S.: 541810
Gregg Witt *(Founding Partner & Dir-Creative)*

PREMIUM 2000+ WARRANTIES
190 Charlois Blvd Ste B, Winston Salem, NC 27103
Tel.: (336) 759-3352
Web Site:
   http://www.premium2000.com
Sales Range: $10-24.9 Million
Emp.: 17
Truck Warranty Services
N.A.I.C.S.: 561990
Alan McDonald *(Dir-Claims)*
Dick Jackson *(Mgr-California)*

PREMIUM BEERS OKLAHOMA LLC
1700 Beachwood Ave, Oklahoma City, OK 73149
Tel.: (405) 619-2600
Rev.: $93,188,426
Emp.: 200
Beer & Other Fermented Malt Liquors
N.A.I.C.S.: 424810
John Cressup *(Pres)*
Carl Milligan *(CFO)*
Bob Natsch *(Mgr-Ops)*

PREMIUM DESTINATIONS, INC.
100 E Granada Blvd, Ormond Beach, FL 32176
Tel.: (386) 756-3422   FL
Web Site: http://www.pditravel.com
Year Founded: 2006
Sales Range: $1-9.9 Million
Emp.: 30
Travel & Trip Planning Services
N.A.I.C.S.: 561599
Steven M. Schlossberg *(Mng Dir & Co-Founder)*
Larry R. Coltelli *(Co-Founder)*

PREMIUM FLOWERS CORP.
1301 NW 84th Ave Ste 115, Doral, FL 33126
Tel.: (305) 592-1222
Web Site:
   http://www.premiumflowers.com
Sales Range: $10-24.9 Million
Emp.: 40
Flower, Nursery Stock & Florists Supplies Whslr
N.A.I.C.S.: 424930
Enrique Paredes *(Pres)*

PREMIUM INC.
2644 Waiwai Loop, Honolulu, HI 96819
Tel.: (808) 839-9802
Web Site: http://www.premiuminc.net
Year Founded: 1985

PREMIUM INC.   U.S. PRIVATE

Premium Inc.—(Continued)
Sales Range: $10-24.9 Million
Emp.: 60
Service Equipment & Supply Whslr
N.A.I.C.S.: 423850
Alohalani Aran *(Mgr-Sls)*
Melanie Wong *(Pres)*

PREMIUM INSPECTION & TESTING, INC.
14950 Heathrow Forest Pkwy, Houston, TX 77032
Tel.: (281) 310-5415
Inspection Services
N.A.I.C.S.: 926150
Todd Nicholson *(CFO)*
Justin Jarski *(COO)*
Rodney Bonvillain *(CEO)*

Subsidiaries:

Quad City Testing Laboratory (1)
21112 Scott Park Rd, Davenport, IA 52807
Tel.: (563) 391-8500
Web Site: http://www.testlab1.com
Emp.: 50
Testing Laboratory Services
N.A.I.C.S.: 541380

PREMIUM MORTGAGE CORPORATION
2541 Monroe Ave, Rochester, NY 14618
Tel.: (585) 241-0000
Web Site:
  http://www.premiummortgage.com
Year Founded: 2000
Sales Range: $50-74.9 Million
Emp.: 35
Mortgage Banker
N.A.I.C.S.: 522310
Michael Donoghue *(Pres)*

PREMIUM MOTOR CARS LLC.
4236 William Flynn Hwy, Allison Park, PA 15101
Tel.: (412) 486-9595
Year Founded: 1975
Sales Range: $10-24.9 Million
Emp.: 15
Used Car Whslr
N.A.I.C.S.: 441120
Vicky Tree *(Office Mgr)*
Ronald W. Wobb *(Pres)*

PREMIUM OILFIELD TECHNOLOGIES LLC
10600 W Sam Houston Pkwy N, Houston, TX 77064
Tel.: (281) 679-6500   DE
Web Site:
  http://www.premiumoilfield.com
Year Founded: 2003
Oil & Gas Equipment & Products Mfr & Distr
N.A.I.C.S.: 213112
Ben Wolfgang *(VP-Ops)*

Subsidiaries:

GDS International, LLC (1)
9841 Windmill Park Ln, Houston, TX 77064
Tel.: (713) 623-1449
Web Site:
  http://www.globaldrillingsupport.com
Oil & Gas Equipment Distr
N.A.I.C.S.: 213112
Keith G. Holliday *(Pres)*
Paul A. Nicholson *(Sr VP)*
PJ Pendlebury *(VP-Sls & Mktg)*
Gavin Thompson *(VP-Ops-Middle East)*

PREMIUM PARKING SERVICE, LLC
601 Poydras St Ste 1500, New Orleans, LA 70130
Tel.: (844) 236-2011
Web Site:
  https://www.premiumparking.com

Emp.: 100
Parking Management Services
N.A.I.C.S.: 812930
Ben Montgomery *(Pres)*

Subsidiaries:

Allpro Parking, LLC (1)
465 Main St Ste 200A, Buffalo, NY 14203
Tel.: (716) 849-7275
Sales Range: $1-9.9 Million
Emp.: 150
Automobile Parking
N.A.I.C.S.: 812930
Brian D. Dusenberry *(CFO)*
Craig E. Barber *(COO & Sr VP)*
Ruben Escobar *(Mgr-Ops)*
Dan Schmidt *(Dir-Ops)*
Daniel Lassiter *(Dir-Bus Dev & Client Svcs)*
Patrick Phillips *(VP)*
Richard A. Serra *(Pres)*

PREMIUM PROTEIN PRODUCTS, LLC.
4611 W Adams St, Lincoln, NE 68524
Tel.: (402) 470-4300
Year Founded: 2003
Sales Range: $10-24.9 Million
Emp.: 170
Processed Meat Mfr
N.A.I.C.S.: 311612
Kevin Miller *(CEO)*
Steve Sands *(Chm & Pres)*
Matt Knobbe *(Mgr-Info Sys Mgmt)*
Kei Kurasawa *(Dir-Mktg)*

PREMIUM RETAIL SERVICES INC.
618 Spirit Dr, Chesterfield, MO 63005
Tel.: (636) 728-0592
Web Site:
  http://www.premiumretail.com
Year Founded: 1985
General Management Consulting Services
N.A.I.C.S.: 541611
Brian Travers *(Owner & Co-CEO)*
Nique Fajors *(VP-Strategic Accts)*
Dick Doyle *(Co-Pres)*
Bill Campbell *(COO)*
Kevin Travers *(Co-CEO)*
Jeff Schremp *(CFO)*
David Yenzer *(Co-Pres)*
Michael Shehadeh *(Exec VP)*
Sandy Clarke *(Exec VP-Canada)*
Pat Balkenbush *(Exec VP-HR)*
Kevin Werner *(VP-Sls & Ops)*
Bill Faulkner *(VP-Fin)*

Subsidiaries:

Premier Concepts LLC (1)
2701 SE J St, Bentonville, AR 72712
Tel.: (479) 845-2843
Web Site: http://www.premiumretail.com
Retail Marketing Services
N.A.I.C.S.: 541613

PREMIUM TRANSPORTATION STAFFING, INC.
190 Highland Dr, Medina, OH 44256
Tel.: (330) 722-7974   OH
Web Site:
  http://www.premiumdrivers.com
Year Founded: 1985
Sales Range: $25-49.9 Million
Emp.: 3,000
Commercial Truck Driver Leasing & Business Support Services
N.A.I.C.S.: 561330
Todd Packard *(Pres & CEO)*
Claire Bolek *(Exec VP)*
Christine Gloeckner *(District Mgr)*
Vera Matusek *(Mgr-Payroll)*

Subsidiaries:

Premium Enterprises Inc. (1)
190 Highland Dr, Medina, OH 44256
Tel.: (330) 723-4131

Web Site:
  http://www.premiumtransportation.com
Sales Range: $10-24.9 Million
Emp.: 24
Help Supply Services
N.A.I.C.S.: 561330

Premium of North Carolina Inc. (1)
190 Highland Dr, Medina, OH 44256-3199
Tel.: (330) 722-7974
Web Site:
  http://www.premiumtransportation.com
Sales Range: $25-49.9 Million
Emp.: 320
Provider of Help Supply Services
N.A.I.C.S.: 561330

Premium of Tennessee Inc. (1)
190 Highland Dr, Medina, OH 44256-3199   (100%)
Tel.: (330) 722-7974
Web Site: http://www.premiumdrivers.com
Sales Range: $25-49.9 Million
Emp.: 7,500
Provider of Help Supply Services
N.A.I.C.S.: 561330
Todd Packard *(CEO)*

PREMIX, INC.
Rte 20 and Harmon Rd, North Kingsville, OH 44068-0281
Tel.: (440) 224-2181   OH
Web Site: http://www.premix.com
Year Founded: 1959
Sales Range: $25-49.9 Million
Emp.: 350
Plastics Product Mfr
N.A.I.C.S.: 326199
Tom Meola *(Pres & COO)*

Subsidiaries:

Quantum Composites Inc. (1)
1310 S Vly Ctr Dr, Bay City, MI 48706
Tel.: (989) 922-3863
Web Site:
  http://www.quantumcomposites.com
Mfr of Plastic Materials & Resins
N.A.I.C.S.: 325211

PRENGER FOODS INC.
275 East Singleton St, Centralia, MO 65240
Tel.: (573) 682-3616
Web Site:
  http://www.prengerfoods.com
Sales Range: $10-24.9 Million
Emp.: 30
Grocery Stores
N.A.I.C.S.: 445110
Kevin Prenger *(Pres)*

PRENGER'S INC.
14 E Main St, Yorkshire, OH 45388
Tel.: (419) 582-2511
Web Site:
  http://www.prengersinc.com
Year Founded: 1949
Rev.: $12,000,000
Emp.: 40
Dairy Equipment Supplier
N.A.I.C.S.: 423820
Roger Houck *(Pres)*
Joshua Vondenhuevel *(Controller)*
Mike Mescher *(Treas)*
David Albers *(Sec)*

PRENGLER PRODUCTS CORPORATION
14865 State Highway 56, Sherman, TX 75092
Tel.: (903) 892-0242
Web Site:
  http://www.prenglerproducts.com
Emp.: 15
Cabinetry Mfr
N.A.I.C.S.: 337110
Craig Prengler *(Pres)*

Subsidiaries:

Garland Woodworks, Inc. (1)

1720 S Elm St, Sherman, TX 75090
Tel.: (903) 892-6668
Sales Range: $1-9.9 Million
Cabinetry Mfr
N.A.I.C.S.: 337110

PRENT CORPORATION
2225 Kennedy Rd, Janesville, WI 53545
Tel.: (608) 754-0276
Web Site: http://www.prent.com
Sales Range: $50-74.9 Million
Emp.: 460
Mfr of Plastic Thermoforming for Custom Packaging of Blisters, Plastic Trays & Clamshell Packaging
N.A.I.C.S.: 326113
Joseph T. Pregont *(Pres & CEO)*
Sara Lemke *(VP-Fin)*
Jim O'Dierno *(VP-Sls)*
Mark Rothlisberger *(VP-Mfg-Americas)*

PRENTICE CAPITAL MANAGEMENT, LP
33 Benidict Pl 2nd Fl, Greenwich, CT 06830
Tel.: (212) 756-8040   DE
Year Founded: 2005
Sales Range: $1-9.9 Million
Emp.: 17
Privater Equity Firm
N.A.I.C.S.: 523999
Michael Zimmerman *(CEO, Chief Investment Officer & Mgr-Investment)*
Mario Ciampi *(Partner)*

PRENTKE ROMICH COMPANY
1022 Heyl Rd, Wooster, OH 44691
Tel.: (330) 262-1984
Web Site: http://www.prentrom.com
Year Founded: 1964
Sales Range: $10-24.9 Million
Emp.: 100
Environmental Controls
N.A.I.C.S.: 334512
David Moffatt *(Pres)*
Lee Miller *(CFO)*

Subsidiaries:

Words+, Inc. (1)
42505 10th St W, Lancaster, CA 93534   (100%)
Tel.: (661) 723-6523
Web Site: http://www.words-plus.com
Communication Systems & Software for People with Disabilities
N.A.I.C.S.: 513210

PREP SPORTSWEAR
2211 Allied Ave Ste 601, Seattle, WA 98121
Tel.: (206) 876-2800
Web Site:
  http://www.prepsportswear.com
Year Founded: 2003
Sales Range: $1-9.9 Million
Emp.: 32
Customized Athletic Apparel Retail & Webstore Producer
N.A.I.C.S.: 458110
Chad Hartvigson *(Founder & CEO)*
Ivan Chachkov *(CTO)*

PREPAYD, INC.
2850 W Horizon Ridge Pkwy Ste 200, Henderson, NV 89052
Tel.: (702) 534-5531   NV
Web Site: http://www.prepaydinc.com
Sales Range: Less than $1 Million
Emp.: 17
Prepaid Card & Merchant Processing Services
N.A.I.C.S.: 522210
Bruce A. Berman *(Chm & CEO)*

PREPMATTERS

5001 Cordell Ave, Bethesda, MD 20814
Tel.: (301) 951-0350
Web Site:
http://www.prepmatters.com
Year Founded: 1997
Sales Range: $1-9.9 Million
Emp.: 48
Academic Tutoring, Standardized Test Preparation & College Essay & Application Counseling
N.A.I.C.S.: 611691
Ned Johnson *(Founder & Pres)*
Sharon Hanson *(Mgr-Placement)*

PREPNET
3755 36th St SE Suite 250, Grand Rapids, MI 49512
Tel.: (616) 726-8900
Web Site:
http://www.prepnetschools.com
Year Founded: 2008
Sales Range: $1-9.9 Million
Emp.: 77
Network of College Preparatory High Schools
N.A.I.C.S.: 611310
J.C. Huizenga *(Founder)*
Jason Pater *(Pres)*

PRESBYTERIAN COMMUNITY HOSPITAL INC
1451 Avenida Ashford, San Juan, PR 00902-0032
Tel.: (787) 721-2160
Web Site: http://www.presbypr.com
Sales Range: $50-74.9 Million
Emp.: 740
Health Care Srvices
N.A.I.C.S.: 622110
Francisco de Torres Font *(Dir-Medical)*
Pedro Gonzalez Cruz *(Exec Dir)*

PRESBYTERIAN HEALTHCARE FOUNDATION
PO Box 26666, Albuquerque, NM 87125-6666
Tel.: (505) 724-6580
Web Site: https://www.phs.org
Year Founded: 1967
Health Care Srvices
N.A.I.C.S.: 621610

PRESBYTERIAN HEALTHCARE SERVICES
9521 San Mateo NE, Albuquerque, NM 87113
Tel.: (505) 841-1234 NM
Web Site: http://www.phs.org
Year Founded: 1908
Sales Range: $400-449.9 Million
Emp.: 6,000
Hospital & Health Care Services
N.A.I.C.S.: 622110
Diane Fisher *(Gen Counsel & Sr VP)*
Renee Ennis *(CFO-Presbyterian Delivery Sys Fin & VP)*
Lisa Fallert *(COO)*
Jordan Erp *(Chief Actuarial & Underwriting Officer & VP)*
Dale Maxwell *(Interim CEO)*
Jason Mitchell *(Chief Medical & Clinical Transformation Officer)*
Neal Spero *(Chief Sls & Mktg Officer-Comml Product Sls & VP)*
Todd Sandman *(Chief Strategy Officer & Sr VP)*
Jana Burdick *(Chief Svc Officer & VP)*
Joanne Suffis *(Sr VP-HR)*
Mary Eden *(VP-Govt Programs)*
Carolyn Green *(Chief Nursing Officer-Delivery Sys)*
Troy Clark *(VP-Reg Delivery Sys Ops)*
Elizabeth Tibbs *(COO-Presbyterian Medical Grp)*

PRESBYTERIAN HOMES
3200 Grant St, Evanston, IL 60201
Tel.: (847) 570-3422 IL
Web Site:
http://www.presbyterianhomes.org
Year Founded: 1904
Sales Range: $100-124.9 Million
Community Housing Services
N.A.I.C.S.: 624229
Andrew Wissel *(Chief Compliance Officer & VP-HR)*
Nadim M. Abi-Antoun *(COO)*
Robert A. Werdan *(VP-Mktg & PR)*
Mark Havrilka *(CFO)*
Leland E. Hutchinson *(Chm)*
J. Marshall Peck *(Treas)*
Todd F. Swortzel *(Pres & CEO)*
Mary Ann Anichini *(VP-Continuous Quality Improvement)*
Paula Noble *(Sec)*
Nancy Tolan *(VP-Facilities, Plng & Construction)*
Danny Weinberger *(VP-IT)*

PRESBYTERIAN HOMES & SERVICES OF KENTUCKY, INC.
1030 Alta Vista Rd, Louisville, KY 40205
Tel.: (502) 259-9101 KY
Web Site: http://www.phsk.org
Year Founded: 1985
Sales Range: $10-24.9 Million
Emp.: 800
Community Housing Services
N.A.I.C.S.: 624229
Hattie Wagner *(Pres & CEO)*
Craig Jennings *(VP-Strategic Dev)*
Douglas Humphrey *(Sec)*
Harold Smith *(Vice Chm)*
James M. Garrett *(Chm)*

PRESBYTERIAN HOMES INC.
2109 Sandy Ridge Rd, Colfax, NC 27235
Tel.: (336) 886-6553
Web Site:
http://www.presbyhomesinc.org
Rev.: $26,258,230
Emp.: 100
Retirement Hotel Operation
N.A.I.C.S.: 531110
Julia Hanover *(CFO)*
Ronda Cummons *(Controller)*
Tim Webster *(Pres)*

PRESBYTERIAN HOMES OF GEORGIA
301 E Screven St, Quitman, GA 31643-2131
Tel.: (229) 263-6191 GA
Web Site: http://www.phgainc.org
Year Founded: 1946
Sales Range: $10-24.9 Million
Emp.: 700
Elder Care Services
N.A.I.C.S.: 623312
Dianne Arrendale *(CFO)*
Susan E. Stone *(Dir-Dev)*

PRESBYTERIAN HOMES OF TENNESSEE, INC.
7424 Middlebrook Pike, Knoxville, TN 37909
Tel.: (865) 690-3411 TN
Web Site:
http://www.shannondaletn.com
Year Founded: 1968
Sales Range: $25-49.9 Million
Emp.: 662
Senior Living Services
N.A.I.C.S.: 623311
William R. Thomas Jr. *(Pres & CEO)*

PRESBYTERIAN INTERCOMMUNITY HOSPITAL, INC.
12401 Washington Blvd, Whittier, CA 90602
Tel.: (562) 698-0811 CA
Web Site: http://www.pihhealth.org
Year Founded: 1959
Healtcare Services
N.A.I.C.S.: 621999
Kenton Woods *(Treas)*
Richard Atwood *(Chm)*
James R. West *(Pres & CEO)*
Anita Chou *(CFO)*
Amy Fitzgerald *(VP)*
Nicole Jackson *(Dir-Major Gifts & Planned Giving)*
GinA Adams *(Officer-Major Gifts)*

Subsidiaries:

Good Samaritan Hospital, Los Angeles (1)
1225 Wilshire Blvd, Los Angeles, CA 90017
Tel.: (213) 977-2121
Web Site: http://www.goodsam.org
Health Care Srvices
N.A.I.C.S.: 621999
Andrew B. Leeka *(Pres & CEO)*
Charles Thomas Munger *(Chm)*

Los Angeles Cardiology & Associates (1)
700 Warner Ave, Los Angeles, CA 90024-2500
Tel.: (213) 977-0419
Web Site: http://www.lacard.com
All Other Miscellaneous Ambulatory Health Care Services
N.A.I.C.S.: 621999
Anil K. Bhandari *(Mgr)*

PIH Health Hospital - Downey (1)
11500 Brookshire Ave, Downey, CA 90241
Tel.: (562) 904-5000
Web Site: http://www.pihhealth.org
Health Care Srvices
N.A.I.C.S.: 622110
J. Richard Atwood *(Chm)*
Ramona Pratt *(COO)*
Paulette Heitmeyer *(Chief Nursing Officer-Whittier)*
Richard Trogman *(Pres & COO)*

Pioneer Medical Group, Inc. (1)
17777 Center Court Dr Ste 400, Cerritos, CA 90703
Tel.: (562) 229-9452
Multi-Specialty Healthcare Services
N.A.I.C.S.: 621111

PRESBYTERIAN MANORS OF MID-AMERICA INC.
6525 E Mainsgate Rd, Wichita, KS 67226-1062
Tel.: (316) 685-1100 KS
Web Site:
http://www.presbyterianmanors.org
Year Founded: 1978
Sales Range: $50-74.9 Million
Emp.: 1,800
Retirement Facility
N.A.I.C.S.: 561110
William M. Ward *(Pres & CEO)*
Bruce H. Shogren *(CFO & Treas)*
Joan M. Miller *(Controller)*

PRESBYTERIAN PUBLISHING CORPORATION
100 Witherspoon St, Louisville, KY 40202-1396
Tel.: (800) 523-1631
Web Site: http://www.ppcbooks.com
Religious Books Publisher
N.A.I.C.S.: 513130
Marc Lewis *(Pres & Publr)*
Monty Anderson *(COO, Treas & VP)*
Michael Hilliard *(Mgr-Trade Sls & Events)*

PRESBYTERIAN RETIREMENT COMMUNITIES NORTHWEST
715 9th Ave Ste 400, Seattle, WA 98104
Tel.: (206) 826-2111
Web Site: http://www.prcn.net
Rev.: $13,037,844
Emp.: 352
Retirement Hotel Operation
N.A.I.C.S.: 531110
Eileen Christenson *(CFO)*
Larry Dart *(Corp Dir-HR)*
Torsten Hirche *(Pres & CEO)*
Greg Robinson *(Chm)*
Eve Jakoboski *(VP-HR)*
DeAnne Clune *(VP-Mktg)*

PRESBYTERIAN SENIORCARE
1215 Hulton Rd, Oakmont, PA 15139
Tel.: (412) 828-5600 PA
Web Site: http://www.srcare.org
Year Founded: 1928
Sales Range: $10-24.9 Million
Emp.: 851
Elder Care Services
N.A.I.C.S.: 623312
Paul M. Winkle *(Pres)*
Laura W. Synnott *(Vice Chm)*
Peter McLlroy II *(Chm)*

PRESCIENT MEDICAL, INC.
2005 S Easton Rd Ste 204, Doylestown, PA 18901
Tel.: (215) 933-1150
Web Site:
http://www.prescientmedical.com
Year Founded: 2004
Medical Device Mfr
N.A.I.C.S.: 339112
Patricia K. Scheller *(Pres & CEO)*

PRESCIENT MEDICINE HOLDINGS LLC
1214 Research Blvd Ste 1000, Hummelstown, PA 17036-9153
Web Site:
http://www.prescientmedicine.com
Year Founded: 2014
Medical Research & Development
N.A.I.C.S.: 541714
Keri J. Donaldson *(CEO & Medical Dir)*
Brian Eichenberger *(CIO)*
Kevin Stineman *(COO)*

Subsidiaries:

AutoGenomics, Inc. (1)
2980 Scott St, Vista, CA 92081
Tel.: (760) 477-2248
Web Site: http://www.autogenomics.com
Sales Range: $10-24.9 Million
Automated Microarray Based Multiplexing Molecular Diagnostic Platform Developer
N.A.I.C.S.: 334516
Fareed Kureshy *(Co-Founder, Chm, Pres & CEO)*
Shailendra Singh *(Co-Founder & VP-Sys Dev)*
Ramanath Vairavan *(Co-Founder & Sr VP-Lab Ops)*
Robert B. Cole *(Chief Medical Officer)*
Evelyn Lopez *(VP-Regulatory Affairs)*
Saeed Kureshy *(VP-Ops)*
Jim Canfield *(VP-Sls & Mktg)*

PRESCIENT, INC.
2600 Douglas Rd, Coral Gables, FL 33134
Tel.: (305) 854-1711 FL
Web Site: http://www.4prescient.net
Year Founded: 1999
Sales Range: $10-24.9 Million
Real Estate Asset Management Services
N.A.I.C.S.: 531390
Arthur Torano *(Principal)*
Sam Igal *(Pres)*
Emiliano De La Fuente *(CFO)*

Prescient, Inc.—(Continued)
Richard Hernandez (Principal)
Eric Torano (Principal)
Amy Sanchez (VP-Strategic Initiatives & Client Svcs)
Rob DeWald (Dir-Ops-Component Servicing)
Sonny Escarment (Dir-IT)
Brandon Schubert (Dir-Ops-Asset Mgmt)
Shelly Smith (Dir-Ops-Govt Contracting)
Magued Eldaief (CEO)
Satyen Patel (Chm)

PRESCOTT AEROSPACE, INC.
6600 E 6th St, Prescott Valley, AZ 86314
Tel.: (928) 772-7605   AZ
Web Site:
http://www.prescottaerospace.com
Year Founded: 1983
Sales Range: $1-9.9 Million
Emp.: 45
Mfr of Precision Parts & Hardware for Military Aircraft & Commercial Helicopters
N.A.I.C.S.: 336413
Michael K. Dailey (Pres & Gen Mgr)
David Holly (Mgr-Production)
Jack Wildvank (Mgr-Quality)

Subsidiaries:

CSC Machining   (1)
3744 W Roanoke Ave Ste 5, Phoenix, AZ 85009
Tel.: (602) 278-7932
Machine Shops
N.A.I.C.S.: 332710
John Brad Morris (Mgr-Production)
Jill Wall (Office Mgr)

PRESCOTT BROTHERS, INC.
PO Box 708, Mendota, IL 61342-0708
Tel.: (815) 539-9388
Web Site:
http://www.prescottbrothers.com
Sales Range: $25-49.9 Million
Emp.: 26
Car Whslr
N.A.I.C.S.: 441110
Nancy Pienta (Principal)
Jason Leifheit (Gen Mgr)

PRESCOTT HOLDINGS, INC.
PO Box 686144, Franklin, TN 37068
Tel.: (615) 778-8767   NV
Web Site:
http://www.octagonsportsnutrition.com
Year Founded: 2010
Supplements & Nutraceuticals Mfr
N.A.I.C.S.: 325412
Jeff Prescott (Pres, CEO, CFO, Chief Acctg Officer, Sec & Treas)
Noelle Federico (VP)

PRESCRYPTIVE HEALTH, INC.
Tel.: (206) 686-9016
Web Site: https://prescryptive.com
Healthcare Technology Solutions & Services
N.A.I.C.S.: 519290
Chris Blackley (Co-Founder & CEO)

Subsidiaries:

Northwest Pharmacy Services   (1)
2479 Griffin Ave Ste 102, Enumclaw, WA 98022
Tel.: (253) 840-5604
Web Site: http://www.nwpsrx.com
Pharmacy Services
N.A.I.C.S.: 456110
Anja Kraemer (CEO)

PRESENCE FROM INNOVATION, LLC
4847 Park 370 Blvd, Hazelwood, MO 63042
Tel.: (314) 635-9031   MO
Web Site:
http://www.pfinnovation.com
Year Founded: 1956
Showcases, Partitions & Other Merchandising Displays Mfr
N.A.I.C.S.: 337215
Chris Hundley (Mgr-Bus Dev)

Subsidiaries:

Butler Merchandising Solutions, Inc.   (1)
2233 Delmar Blvd, Saint Louis, MO 63103
Tel.: (314) 347-0527
Web Site: http://www.butlermsi.com
Converted Paper Product Mfr
N.A.I.C.S.: 322299
Ken Butler (Pres & CEO)

PRESENTATION MINISTRIES
3230 Mchenry Ave, Cincinnati, OH 45211
Tel.: (513) 662-5378   OH
Web Site:
http://www.presentationministries.com
Year Founded: 1985
Sales Range: $1-9.9 Million
Christian Ministry Services
N.A.I.C.S.: 813110

PRESERVATION NON-PROFIT HOUSING CORPORATION
1118 S Washington Ave, Lansing, MI 48910
Tel.: (517) 482-8555   MI
Year Founded: 1988
Sales Range: $10-24.9 Million
Community Housing Services
N.A.I.C.S.: 624229
Fred Hash (Pres)
Deborah Toby (Treas & Sec)

PRESERVATION OF AFFORDABLE HOUSING, INC.
40 Court St Ste 700, Boston, MA 02108
Tel.: (617) 261-9898   IL
Web Site: http://www.poah.org
Year Founded: 1998
Sales Range: $50-74.9 Million
Emp.: 450
Community Housing Services
N.A.I.C.S.: 624229
Julie A. Klump (VP-Design & Technical Svcs)
Catherine M. Dunham (VP-Resident Svcs & Community Improvement)
Allison J. Adduci (VP-Fin & Acctg)
Amos Allen (VP-Fin & Acctg)
Rochelle Beeks (COO & Exec VP)
Brad R. Blake (VP-IT)
Kathleen M. Carpenter (VP-HR)
Cory Fellows (VP-Real Estate Dev)
Bart W. Lloyd (Gen Counsel & Mng Dir-Acquisitions)
Cory S. Mian (Sr VP-Real Estate Dev)
Randy J. Parker (Mng Dir & CFO)
Rodger L. Brown Jr. (Mng Dir-Real Estate Dev)

PRESERVATION TECHNOLOGIES L.P.
111 Thomson Park Dr, Cranberry Township, PA 16066
Tel.: (724) 779-2111
Web Site: http://www.ptlp.com
Year Founded: 1992
Sales Range: $10-24.9 Million
Emp.: 67
Chemical Product & Preparation Mfr
N.A.I.C.S.: 325998
James E. Burd (Pres & COO)

PRESIDENT AND FELLOWS OF HARVARD COLLEGE
Massachusetts Hall, Cambridge, MA 02138
Tel.: (617) 495-1000
Web Site: http://www.harvard.edu
Year Founded: 1636
Colleges & Universities
N.A.I.C.S.: 611310
Alan M. Garber (Professor-Kennedy School of Govt)
David Gergen (Professor-Public Svcs)
Richard J. Benjamin (Asst Professor-Pathology)
Richard B. Peiser (Professor-Real Estate Devel)
Stephen A. Greyser (Faculty)
Lee M. Nadler (Sr VP-Experimental Medicine)
Robert J. Blendon (Professor-Health Policy)
Paul W. Marshall (Professor-Management Practice)
Dennis J. Selkoe (Professor-Neurology & Neuroscience)
Katherine N. Lapp (Exec VP)
Lisa Hogarty (VP-Campus Svcs)
Rick Calixto (Exec Dir-Harvard Trademark Program)
Sarah E. Thomas (VP-Harvard Library)
Tez Chantaruchirakorn (Project Mgr)
Rakesh K. Jain (Professor-Radiation Oncology)
Lawrence S. Bacow (Pres)
Angelika Fretzen (Dir-Tech Translation-Wyss Institute)
Donald Ingber (Founder-Wyss Institute)
Ayis Antoniou (Dir-Admin-Wyss Institute)
Anne Margulies (CIO & VP)
Sherri A. Charleston (Chief Diversity & Inclusion Officer)
Isaac T. Kohlberg (Sr Assoc Provost & Chief Tech Dev Officer)
Augustus A. White III (Professor-Orthopaedic Surgery)
Srikant Madhav Datar (Professor-Graduate School of Bus Admin)
Paul J. Finnegan (Treas)
H. Kent Bowen (Professor-Bus Admin)

PRESIDENT ASSET GROUP LLC
260 Newport Center Dr 3rd Fl, Newport Beach, CA 92660
Tel.: (949) 999-3368
Web Site: http://www.president-llc.com
Provider of Real Estate Investment Services
N.A.I.C.S.: 531120

PRESIDENT CONTAINER GROUP, INC.
200 W Commercial Ave, Moonachie, NJ 07074
Tel.: (201) 933-7500
Web Site:
http://www.presidentcontainergroup.com
Year Founded: 1947
Corrugated Product Mfr
N.A.I.C.S.: 322211
Marvin Gossbard (Co-Founder)
George Grossbard (Co-Founder)

Subsidiaries:

Artisan Display & Packaging   (1)
200 W Commercial Ave, Moonachie, NJ 07074
Tel.: (201) 933-7500
Web Site:
http://www.presidentcontainergroup.com
Point-of-Purchase Display Mfr & Packaging Services
N.A.I.C.S.: 339999

President Container Inc.   (1)
200 W Commercial Ave, Moonachie, NJ 07074-1610
Tel.: (201) 933-7500
Web Site:
http://www.presidentcontainer.com
Sales Range: $25-49.9 Million
Emp.: 400
Corrugated & Solid Fiber Boxes Mfr
N.A.I.C.S.: 322211
Marvin Grossbard (Co-Founder)

President Industrial Products   (1)
200 W Commercial Ave, Moonachie, NJ 07074
Tel.: (201) 863-8844
Web Site: http://www.pippkg.com
Corrugated & Other Packaging Products & Services
N.A.I.C.S.: 322211
Larry Grossbard (Pres)

Tech-Pak   (1)
100 Blum Blvd, Wood Ridge, NJ 07075
Tel.: (201) 935-3800
Web Site:
http://www.presidentcontainergroup.com
Packaging Services
N.A.I.C.S.: 561910

PRESIDENTIAL BANK, FSB
4520 E W Hwy, Bethesda, MD 20814
Tel.: (301) 652-0700
Web Site:
http://www.presidential.com
Year Founded: 1995
Sales Range: $300-349.9 Million
Emp.: 120
Banking Services
N.A.I.C.S.: 522180
A. Bruce Cleveland (Pres & CEO)
Robert R. Giraldi (Exec VP-Comml Lending)
John Schoemer (Exec VP-Mortgage Lending)
Douglas C. Haskett II (CFO & Exec VP)

Subsidiaries:

Presidential Bank FSB - Mortgage Division   (1)
6 Montgomery Village Ave Ste 330, Gaithersburg, MD 20879
Tel.: (301) 590-8911
Web Site:
http://www.presidentialbankmortgage.com
Rev.: $1,800,000
Emp.: 8
Mortgage Banking Services
N.A.I.C.S.: 522292

Presidential Mortgage Corp   (1)
4600 E Way Hwy 415, Bethesda, MD 20814
Tel.: (301) 951-3700
Web Site: http://www.pcbank.com
Rev.: $2,300,000
Emp.: 25
Loan Correspondents
N.A.I.C.S.: 522390
Bruce Cleveland (Pres)
John Schoemer (Exec VP)
Robert R. Giraldi (Exec VP-Comml Lending)
Douglas C. Haskett (CFO & Exec VP)

Realty Home Mortgage Co. Llc   (1)
4600 E W Hwy 415, Bethesda, MD 20814
Tel.: (301) 718-3038
Web Site: http://www.pcbank.com
Sales Range: $25-49.9 Million
Emp.: 6
Mortgage Banker
N.A.I.C.S.: 522292

PRESIDIO INVESTORS LLC
98 San Jacinto Blvd, Suite 2010, Austin, TX 78701

COMPANIES

Tel.: (512) 772-1725
Web Site:
http://www.presidioinvestors.com
Year Founded: 2007
Venture Capital & Private Equity Firm
N.A.I.C.S.: 523999
Karl Schade *(Mng Partner)*
Chris Puscasiu *(Mng Partner)*
Victor Masaya *(Mng Dir)*
Mark Goldman *(Operating Partner)*
Mallory Baker *(Head-Bus Dev)*

Subsidiaries:

Bravas LLC (1)
9009 W 95th St, Overland Park, KS 66212
Tel.: (913) 948-6000
Web Site: http://www.bravas.com
Smart Home Systems Installer
N.A.I.C.S.: 811210
Ryan Anderson *(CEO)*

Subsidiary (Domestic):

BRAVAS Minneapolis (2)
550 Oak Grove Pkwy, Vadnais Heights, MN 55127
Tel.: (651) 641-1376
Web Site: http://www.bravas.com
Home Automation Solutons
N.A.I.C.S.: 811210
Keith Stanze *(Gen Mgr)*

Residential Systems, Inc. (2)
7661 Shaffer Pkwy, Littleton, CO 80127
Tel.: (303) 277-9983
Web Site:
http://www.residentialsystemsinc.com
Radio, Television & Other Electronics Stores
N.A.I.C.S.: 449210
Brad Fowler *(VP-Ops)*
Skip White *(Sr Project Mgr)*

PRESIDIO PARTNERS
1 Letterman Dr Bldg C Ste CM500, San Francisco, CA 94129
Tel.: (415) 352-1520   CA
Web Site:
http://www.presidiopartners.com
Year Founded: 1984
Privater Equity Firm
N.A.I.C.S.: 523999
Jim Watson *(Mng Dir)*
Faysal Sohail *(Mng Dir)*
Peter Gajdos *(Mng Dir & Portfolio Mgr)*
David Collier *(Mng Dir)*
Lee Pantuso *(CFO)*
Adam Wilczek *(Controller)*
Victoria Jenks *(Mgr-Ops)*

PRESILIENT, LLC
12303 Airport Way Ste 250, Broomfield, CO 80021-2729   NV
Web Site: http://www.presilient.com
Sales Range: $125-149.9 Million
Emp.: 265
IT Support Services
N.A.I.C.S.: 334112
Frank DiTirro *(CFO)*
Jeff Gallo *(VP-Ops)*

Subsidiaries:

Incentra Solutions NW (1)
1100 Dexter Ave N Ste 250, Seattle, WA 98109-3598
Tel.: (425) 828-4223
Rev.: $21,000,000
Emp.: 30
Computer System Design Services
N.A.I.C.S.: 541512

PRESLEY GROUP LTD
226 Hilliard Ave, Asheville, NC 28801
Tel.: (828) 252-4785
Web Site:
http://www.hayesandlunsford.com
Sales Range: $10-24.9 Million
Emp.: 250
General Electrical Contractor
N.A.I.C.S.: 238210

Eugene L. Presley *(Pres)*
John Sizemore *(Controller)*
Michael Lindsay *(VP)*
Jeff Eubanks *(Project Mgr)*
David Stanford *(Gen Mgr)*
Dexter Williams *(Dir-Safety)*
Roy Rector *(VP, Project Mgr)*
Michael Presley *(VP)*

PRESONUS AUDIO ELECTRONICS, INC.
18011 Grand Bay Ct, Baton Rouge, LA 70809
Tel.: (225) 216-7887   LA
Web Site: http://www.presonus.com
Year Founded: 1995
Electronic Audio Equipment Designer & Mfr
N.A.I.C.S.: 335999
Brian Smith *(VP-Engrg)*
Rick Naqvi *(Sr VP-Sls)*

Subsidiaries:

Nimbit, Inc. (1)
47 Mellen St, Framingham, MA 01702
Tel.: (508) 820-8738
Web Site: http://www.nimbit.com
Online Music Marketing, Sales, Distribution & CD Reproduction Services
N.A.I.C.S.: 518210
Philip Antoniades *(Founder)*
Patrick Faucher *(Founder)*
Joseph Twarog *(Founder)*

PRESORT SOLUTIONS
1020 Frontenac Rd, Naperville, IL 60563
Tel.: (630) 428-9000
Web Site: http://www.presort-sol.com
Year Founded: 2002
Sales Range: $10-24.9 Million
Emp.: 110
Mail Presorting Services
N.A.I.C.S.: 561431
Mary L. Williams *(Owner & Pres)*
Kimberly Dunham *(VP-Sls & Mktg)*
Brian Yambor *(VP-Ops)*

PRESQUE ISLE ELECTRIC & GAS CO-OP
19831 M 68 Hwy, Onaway, MI 49765
Tel.: (989) 733-8515
Web Site: http://www.pieg.com
Sales Range: $25-49.9 Million
Emp.: 65
Distr of Electric Power
N.A.I.C.S.: 221122
Brian Burns *(Pres & CEO)*
Richard P. Kieliszewski *(Mgr-Information Sys)*
Maire Chagnon-Hazelman *(Dir-Member Svcs, Mktg & Comm)*
Randy Stempky *(Dir-Supply Chain Mgmt)*
Andrew Bischer *(Dir-Engrg & Right-of-Way)*
Allan Berg *(Vice Chm)*
Sandy Borowicz *(Sec)*

PRESRITE CORPORATION
7105 W Marr St, Cleveland, OH 44105-2048
Tel.: (216) 441-0057   OH
Web Site: http://www.presrite.com
Year Founded: 1969
Sales Range: $25-49.9 Million
Emp.: 400
Iron & Steel Forgings Services
N.A.I.C.S.: 332111
Donald J. Diemer *(Chm & CEO)*
George Longauer *(CFO)*
Bill Burland *(VP-Ops)*
Chris Charman *(Pres)*

PRESS COMMUNICATIONS, LLC
1329 Campus Pkwy, Neptune, NJ 07753-6822
Tel.: (732) 751-1119   DE
Web Site:
http://www.presscommradio.com
Year Founded: 1997
Sales Range: $75-99.9 Million
Emp.: 50
Operating Radio Stations
N.A.I.C.S.: 516120
Rich Morena *(CFO)*
Robert E. McAllan *(CEO)*
Don Dalesio *(COO & Pres-Monmouth & Ocean)*

PRESS-ENTERPRISE INC.
3185 Lackawanna Ave, Bloomsburg, PA 17815
Tel.: (570) 784-2121
Web Site:
http://www.pressenterpriseonline.com
Year Founded: 1902
Sales Range: $25-49.9 Million
Emp.: 265
Commercial Printing & Newspaper Publishing Combined
N.A.I.C.S.: 513110
Brandon R. Eyerly *(Publr-Admin)*
James T. Micklow *(Treas & Controller)*
Rick Marcera *(Mgr-Single Copy Sls)*
James L. Sachetti *(Editor)*
Pam Taylor *(Mgr-District)*
Tim Hare *(Editor-Sports)*
Al Jensen *(Bus Mgr)*
Paul R. Eyerly IV *(Pres)*

PRESSCO TECHNOLOGY INC.
29200 Aurora Rd, Cleveland, OH 44139
Tel.: (440) 498-2600
Web Site: http://www.pressco.com
Year Founded: 1966
Sales Range: $10-24.9 Million
Emp.: 120
Physical Property Testing Equipment
N.A.I.C.S.: 334519
Don W. Cochran *(Pres & CEO)*
Fritz Awig *(VP-Engrg)*
Scott Johnston *(Dir-Mfg)*
Tom Murphy *(VP-Sls)*
Michael Coy *(Mgr-Sls)*

PRESSMAN TOY CORPORATION
3701 W Plano Pkwy Ste 100, Plano, TX 75075
Tel.: (855) 258-8214
Web Site:
http://www.pressmantoy.com
Year Founded: 1922
Toys & Games Mfr
N.A.I.C.S.: 423920

PRESSMAN-GUTMAN CO. INC.
237 W 35th St Ste 601, New York, NY 10001-1905
Tel.: (212) 244-5556   NY
Year Founded: 1909
Sales Range: $50-74.9 Million
Emp.: 27
Piece Goods & Notions
N.A.I.C.S.: 424310
Alvin P. Gutman *(Chm)*

PRESSMASTERS INC.
55 Reality Dr Ste 100, Cheshire, CT 06410
Tel.: (860) 793-0644
Web Site:
http://www.pressmasters.com
Sales Range: $10-24.9 Million
Emp.: 10
Plastic Products Machinery Distr
N.A.I.C.S.: 423830

John H. Cluney *(Pres)*
Cindy Forlenzo *(Office Mgr)*

PRESTAGON LLC
1452 Hamilton Ave, Palo Alto, CA 94301
Tel.: (650) 440-2282
Web Site: http://www.platetopper.com
Sales Range: $1-9.9 Million
Plastics Product Mfr
N.A.I.C.S.: 326199
Michael Tseng *(Pres)*

PRESTERA CENTER
3375 US Route 60 E, Huntington, WV 25705
Tel.: (304) 525-7851   WV
Web Site: http://www.prestera.org
Year Founded: 1968
Sales Range: $25-49.9 Million
Emp.: 1,109
Behavioral Healthcare Services
N.A.I.C.S.: 623220
Sallie Lazaro *(CFO)*
Jerri Tyson-Rollins *(Dir-HR)*
Kim Miller *(Dir-Dev)*
Catherine Luikart *(Program Dir)*
Ken Fitzwater *(Program Dir)*
Karen Yost *(CEO)*
Lisa Kaplan *(Dir-Clinical)*

PRESTIGE BOX CORPORATION
115 Cuttermill Rd, Great Neck, NY 11021
Tel.: (516) 773-3115
Web Site:
http://www.prestigebox.com
Rev.: $39,200,000
Emp.: 30
Folding Paperboard Boxes
N.A.I.C.S.: 322212
Irving Warren *(Chm)*
Sherry Warren *(Pres)*

PRESTIGE CAPITAL CORPORATION
2157 S Lincoln St Ste 220, Salt Lake City, UT 84106
Tel.: (801) 323-2395   NV
Year Founded: 1986
Assets: $873
Liabilities: $297,491
Net Worth: ($296,618)
Earnings: ($30,114)
Emp.: 4,600
Fiscal Year-end: 12/31/22
Investment Services
N.A.I.C.S.: 523999
Christopher Foss *(Mgr-Direct Sls)*
Stuart Rosenthal *(Co-Pres)*
Alan Eliasof *(Co-CEO)*
Harvey L. Kaminski *(Founder)*
Rachel Hersh *(Sls Dir-North America)*
Kristin Brough *(Treas & Sec)*
Deven L. Taylor *(Co-Pres & Co-CEO)*

PRESTIGE CHRYSLER DODGE INC.
200 Alpine St, Longmont, CO 80501
Tel.: (303) 651-3000
Web Site:
http://www.prestigedodge.com
Sales Range: $25-49.9 Million
Emp.: 60
Car Dealership
N.A.I.C.S.: 441110
Roger Weibel *(Pres)*
Steve Leahy *(Mgr-Svc)*

PRESTIGE CORP.
1099 Wall Street W Ste 100, Lyndhurst, NJ 07071
Web Site:
http://www.prestigecorp.com
Year Founded: 1996

PRESTIGE CORP.

Prestige Corp.—(Continued)
Sales Range: $25-49.9 Million
Emp.: 430
Commercial Laundry Services for Hotels
N.A.I.C.S.: 812320
Sang Cho (CEO)

PRESTIGE COSMETICS CORP.
5001 NW 13 Ave SWE I Pompano Beach, Deerfield Beach, FL 33064
Tel.: (954) 480-9202
Web Site:
http://www.prestigecosmetics.com
Sales Range: $10-24.9 Million
Emp.: 20
Cosmetics
N.A.I.C.S.: 325620
Ignacio Rodriguez (Gen Mgr)

PRESTIGE DELIVERY SYSTEMS INC.
9535 Midwest Ave, Cleveland, OH 44125-2428
Tel.: (216) 332-8033
Web Site:
http://www.prestigedelivery.com
Year Founded: 1986
Rev.: $37,500,000
Emp.: 130
Courier Service
N.A.I.C.S.: 492110
Joe Bernon (Pres)
Laura Valentine (Dir-HR)
Chuck Fleming (Project Mgr)

PRESTIGE ENTERPRISE INTERNATIONAL, INC.
11343 Grooms Rd, Cincinnati, OH 45242
Tel.: (513) 469-6044
Web Site:
http://www.prestigefloor.com
Year Founded: 1978
Sales Range: $150-199.9 Million
Emp.: 54
Cut Stock, Resawing Lumber & Planing Services
N.A.I.C.S.: 321912
Charles K. Gabbour (Pres)

PRESTIGE FARMS INC.
7120 Orr Rd, Charlotte, NC 28213-6447
Tel.: (704) 596-2824
Web Site:
http://www.prestigefarms.com
Year Founded: 1965
Sales Range: $25-49.9 Million
Emp.: 215
Poultry & Poultry Products
N.A.I.C.S.: 424440
Edward Thompson (Pres)
Steve Thompson (Gen Mgr)
Clayton Watson (Plant Mgr)
Randall Thompson (CEO)

PRESTIGE MOTORS, INC.
405 S State Route 17, Paramus, NJ 07652
Tel.: (201) 265-7800
Web Site:
http://www.mercedesbenzparamus.com
Car Dealership Owner & Operator
N.A.I.C.S.: 423110
Randy Smith (Supvr-Parts)
Subsidiaries:
Prestige Motors, Inc. (1)
401 Rte 17 S, Paramus, NJ 07652
Tel.: (201) 987-8900
Rev.: $41,440,502
Emp.: 25
Used Car Dealers
N.A.I.C.S.: 441120

PRESTIGE MOTORWORKS INC.
985 State Rt 17 S, Ramsey, NJ 07446
Tel.: (201) 327-2525
Web Site:
http://www.prestigebmw.com
Sales Range: $100-124.9 Million
Emp.: 40
Automobiles, New & Used
N.A.I.C.S.: 441110
Joseph Dockery (Pres & CEO)
Michael Morganstein (Mgr-Sls)

PRESTIGE OF BERGEN INC.
1096 State Rt 17, Ramsey, NJ 07446
Tel.: (201) 825-2700
Web Site:
http://www.prestigetoyota.com
Sales Range: $75-99.9 Million
Emp.: 60
New Car Retailer
N.A.I.C.S.: 441110
Nicholas Pak (Mgr-Sls)
William Berardino (VP)
Craig Malise (Mgr-Svc)

PRESTIGE PONTIAC BUICK GMC
444 James L Hart Pkwy, Ypsilanti, MI 48197
Tel.: (734) 483-0322
Web Site:
http://www.prestigepontiacbuickgmc.com
Sales Range: $25-49.9 Million
Emp.: 60
Automobiles, New & Used
N.A.I.C.S.: 441110

PRESTIGE SERVICES INC.
743 Pierce Rd, Clifton Park, NY 12065
Tel.: (518) 877-7426
Web Site:
http://www.prestigeservicesinc.com
Sales Range: $10-24.9 Million
Emp.: 190
Merchandising Machine Operators
N.A.I.C.S.: 445132

PRESTIGE STAFFING
8010 Roswell Rd Ste 330, Atlanta, GA 30350
Tel.: (770) 200-3565
Web Site:
http://www.prestigestaffing.com
Year Founded: 1999
Sales Range: $10-24.9 Million
Emp.: 35
Employment Placement Agencies
N.A.I.C.S.: 561311
Kevin Floyd (COO)

PRESTIGE TOY CORP.
240 W 35th St 15th Fl, New York, NY 10001-2908
Tel.: (212) 736-8977
Web Site: http://www.prestigetoy.com
Year Founded: 1970
Rev.: $25,000,000
Emp.: 18
Toys & Hobby Goods & Supplies
N.A.I.C.S.: 423920
Robert Gershin (Pres)
Brian Fagen (VP)
Randi Fagen (VP)

PRESTIGE TRAVEL SYSTEMS, INC.
2803 W Busch Blvd Ste 100, Tampa, FL 33618
Tel.: (813) 289-7772
Web Site:
http://www.prestigetravelsystems.com

Year Founded: 1988
Sales Range: $10-24.9 Million
Emp.: 38
Travel Agency
N.A.I.C.S.: 561510
Ron LaScala (Pres)
Anita LaScala (Sr Exec VP)

PRESTIGE TRAVEL, INC.
9895 Montgomery Rd, Cincinnati, OH 45242-6424
Tel.: (513) 793-6586
Web Site: http://www.prestige-travel.com
Sales Range: $25-49.9 Million
Emp.: 20
Travel Management Services
N.A.I.C.S.: 561510
Robin Hershberger (Pres)

PRESTIGE TRAVEL, INC.
6175 Spring Mountain Rd, Raleigh, NC 27612
Tel.: (919) 787-8083
Web Site:
http://www.prestigecruises.com
Year Founded: 1980
Sales Range: $50-74.9 Million
Emp.: 50
Travel Agencies
N.A.I.C.S.: 561510
Kathy Falkensammer (Co-Owner & Pres)
Leo Falkensammer (Co-Owner, CEO, Sec & Treas)
Subsidiaries:
TripReservations.com (1)
6145 Spring Mtn Rd, Las Vegas, NV 89146-8812
Tel.: (702) 946-5200
Web Site: http://www.tripreservations.com
Sales Range: $10-24.9 Million
Internet Booking Service for Las Vegas Hotel Room Reservations
N.A.I.C.S.: 561510

PRESTIGE VOLKSWAGEN
1416 S Harbor City Blvd, Melbourne, FL 32901-3211
Tel.: (321) 309-8989
Web Site:
http://www.melbournevw.com
Year Founded: 1992
Sales Range: $10-24.9 Million
Emp.: 60
New Car Retailer
N.A.I.C.S.: 441110
William Dingman (Owner)
Mike Mistretta (Gen Mgr)

PRESTIGE WHOLESALE INC.
5645 Coral Ridge Dr, Coral Springs, FL 33076
Tel.: (954) 444-7928
Web Site: http://scrapphones.com
Year Founded: 2005
Sales Range: $1-9.9 Million
Emp.: 5
Whslr & Distributor of Environmentally Cellular Phones
N.A.I.C.S.: 517810
Andrew Weissman (Pres)

PRESTIGE YACHT SALES INC.
217 Riverside Dr N, Wall Township, NJ 08724
Tel.: (732) 292-1500
Web Site:
http://www.prestigeyachtsales.com
Year Founded: 1998
Sales Range: $10-24.9 Million
Emp.: 9
Boat Whslr
N.A.I.C.S.: 441222
John R. Schachel (VP)

PRESTO FOOD STORES, INC.
2204 Parkview Dr, Plant City, FL 33563-2120
Tel.: (813) 754-3511
Year Founded: 1976
Sales Range: $10-24.9 Million
Emp.: 4
Retailer of Gasoline
N.A.I.C.S.: 424720
Daniel Coton (Gen Counsel)
Greg Robinson (Exec VP)

PRESTON CHEVROLET CADILLAC KIA INC.
13600 W Center St, Burton, OH 44021
Tel.: (440) 834-9700
Web Site:
http://www.prestoncars.com
Year Founded: 1993
Sales Range: $10-24.9 Million
Emp.: 55
Car Whslr
N.A.I.C.S.: 441110
Patrick Preston (Owner)

PRESTON FORD INC.
218 S Main St, Preston, MD 21655
Tel.: (410) 673-7171
Web Site:
http://www.prestonmotor.com
Sales Range: $10-24.9 Million
Emp.: 100
Automobiles, New & Used
N.A.I.C.S.: 441110
David Wilson (Pres)
Stephanie Lee (Controller)

PRESTON KELLY, INC.
222 1st Ave NE, Minneapolis, MN 55413
Tel.: (612) 843-4000
Web Site:
http://www.prestonkelly.com
Year Founded: 1950
Advetising Agency
N.A.I.C.S.: 541810
Chuck Kelly (CEO)
Chris Preston (Exec VP & Creative Dir)
Mark Jenson (VP & Acct Dir)
Peter Tressel (VP & Creative Dir-Digital)
Scott Dahlgren (Dir-Connections & Media)
Beth Elmore (Dir-Production Svcs)
Yuliya Crevier (Assoc Dir-Digital)
Katia Holmes (VP & Acct Dir)
Kim Seaton (Controller)
Jennifer Gove (Pres)

PRESTON MEATS INC
121 W Farley St, Preston, IA 52069
Tel.: (563) 689-5611
Rev.: $12,000,000
Emp.: 14
Meats, Fresh
N.A.I.C.S.: 424470

PRESTON MEMORIAL HOSPITAL
150 Memorial Dr, Kingwood, WV 26537
Tel.: (304) 329-1400
Web Site:
http://www.prestonmemorial.org
Year Founded: 1955
Sales Range: $10-24.9 Million
Health Care Srvices
N.A.I.C.S.: 622110
Melissa Lockwood (Pres & CEO)
Jennifer Nestor (VP-Clinical Ops)
Terrie Roth (Chief Nursing Officer)
Michele Batiste (Dir-HR)
Megan Allender (Sec)
Kevin Gessler Jr. (Treas & VP-Fin Svcs)

COMPANIES

PRESTON REFRIGERATION COMPANY INC.
3200 Fiberglass Rd, Kansas City, KS 66115-1212
Tel.: (913) 621-1813
Web Site: http://www.prestonrefrigeration.com
Year Founded: 1946
Sales Range: $25-49.9 Million
Emp.: 75
Plumbing, Heating & Air-Conditioning
N.A.I.C.S.: 238220
Cliff Preston (Owner & Pres)
Brian Schnepf (Pres)
Dave Smreker (CEO)
Joe Guevel (CFO)

PRESTON VINEYARDS, INC.
9282 W Dry Creek Rd, Healdsburg, CA 95448
Tel.: (707) 433-3372
Web Site: http://www.prestonvineyards.com
Year Founded: 1970
Sales Range: $10-24.9 Million
Emp.: 10
Vineyard & Wine Mfr
N.A.I.C.S.: 111332
Marjorie Preston (Owner)
Robbie Tonkin (Mgr-Mktg)

PRESTRESS SERVICES INDUSTRIES LLC
5501 Briar Hill Rd, Lexington, KY 40516
Tel.: (859) 299-0461
Web Site: http://www.prestressservices.com
Rev.: $48,663,117
Emp.: 110
Prestressed Concrete Products
N.A.I.C.S.: 327390
Martin Cohen (CEO)
Laurie Linkous (Dir-HR)
David Szydlik (VP-Sls & Pur-Lexington)
Barry Barger (VP-Sls)
Greg Harville (CFO & VP-Fin)
Conn Abnee (VP-Comml Div)

PRETIUM PARTNERS, LLC
810 7th Ave 24th Fl, New York, NY 10019
Web Site: http://pretium.com
Year Founded: 2012
Rev.: $15,900,000,000
Privater Equity Firm
N.A.I.C.S.: 523999
Don Mullen (CEO)
Lee Alexander (Sr Mng Dir-Opr)
Jason Lewis (Portfolio Mgr-Real Estate & Mng Dir)
Josh Pristaw (Sr Mng Dir & Head-Real Estate)

Subsidiaries:

Front Yard Residential Corporation (1)
5100 Tamarind Reef, Christiansted, VI 00820
Tel.: (340) 692-0525
Web Site: http://www.frontyardresidential.com
Sales Range: $200-249.9 Million
Real Estate Manangement Services
N.A.I.C.S.: 531390
Brian Chappell (VP-Fin Reporting)

Subsidiary (Domestic):

ARNS, Inc. (2)
640 Main St, Northport, NY 11768
Tel.: (631) 757-7959
Residential Building Leasing Services
N.A.I.C.S.: 531110

PREVACUS, INC.
2035 E Paul Dirac Dr Ste 106, Tallahassee, FL 32310
Tel.: (850) 765-5054
Web Site: http://www.prevacus.com
Sales Range: $10-24.9 Million
Emp.: 15
Pharmaceuticals Mfr
N.A.I.C.S.: 325412
Jacob VanLandingham (Founder & Pres)
Jamie Mark Grooms (Interim CEO)
Michael Lewandowski (Chief Scientific Officer)

PREVENTICE, INC
1717 N Sam Houston Pkwy W Ste 100, Houston, TX 77038
Tel.: (612) 746-6700
Web Site: http://www.preventicesolutions.com
Year Founded: 2004
Computer Softwares Mfr
N.A.I.C.S.: 513210
Jon P. Otterstatter (CEO)
Emily Benner (Exec VP-Res & Product Dev)
Ryan Ranweiler (CFO)
Jason Spees (Chief Comml Officer)
Tim Miller (Exec VP-Ops)

PREVENTIVE DIAGNOSTICS, INC.
12 Spencer St, Brooklyn, NY 11205
Tel.: (800) 749-9729 NY
Web Site: http://www.pdihealth.com
Year Founded: 2010
Mobile X-rays & Ultrasounds Provider
N.A.I.C.S.: 621512
Mark Tauber (CEO)

Subsidiaries:

Radiation Physics, Inc. (1)
10133 Bacon Dr, Beltsville, MD 20705-2143
Tel.: (301) 937-4072
Web Site: http://www.rpixray.com
Diagnostic Imaging Centers
N.A.I.C.S.: 621512
Kenneth Miller (Pres & CEO)
Thomas Doyle (VP)
Richard Berry (Dir-Mktg)

PRG PACKING CORP.
PO Box 5000, Bronx, NY 10460
Tel.: (718) 328-0059
Web Site: http://stahlmeyer.com
Sales Range: $10-24.9 Million
Emp.: 96
Processed Meat Mfr & Distr
N.A.I.C.S.: 311611
Zenaida Hochman (Plant Mgr)

PRGX GLOBAL, INC.
600 Galleria Pkwy Ste 100, Atlanta, GA 30339-5986
Tel.: (770) 779-3042 GA
Web Site: http://www.prgx.com
Year Founded: 1990
Rev.: $169,758,000
Assets: $125,466,000
Liabilities: $72,416,000
Net Worth: $53,050,000
Earnings: ($13,720,000)
Emp.: 1,500
Fiscal Year-end: 12/31/19
Financial Recovery Services
N.A.I.C.S.: 561499
Michael Cochrane (COO-Global Audit Ops & Sr VP)
Victor Allums (Gen Counsel)
Gregory J. Owens (Chm)
Jim Fisher (CIO)
Anis Hadj-Taieb (VP-Sls-Global)
Kurt J. Abkemeier (CFO, Principal Acctg Officer, Treas, Exec VP & Controller)
Alicia Jackson (VP-Global Privacy, Security & Data Governance)
Carol O'Kelley (CMO)
James Sly (Sr VP-Retail Ops)
Lynn Howard (Chief HR Officer)
Mark Kilgore (VP-Client Dev-Global)
Tony Massanelli (Sr VP-Comml Ops)

Subsidiaries:

Lavante Inc. (1)
5285 Hellyer Ave Ste 200, San Jose, CA 95138-1081
Tel.: (408) 754-1410
Web Site: http://www.lavante.com
Software Development Services
N.A.I.C.S.: 541511
Vinay Ambekar (VP-Engrg)
Doug Markle (VP-Sls & Bus Dev)
Tom Flynn (Co-Founder & VP-Mktg)
Joe Flynn (Co-Founder & VP-Strategy & Alliances)
Ed Zunzunegui (VP-Ops)

PRGX Asia, Inc. - Thailand (1)
3354 43 Manorom Building 12th Floor Rama IV Road, Bangkok, 10110, Thailand
Tel.: (66) 8887997976
Web Site: http://www.prgx.com
Sales Range: $10-24.9 Million
Emp.: 21
Auditing & Corporate Financial Consulting Services
N.A.I.C.S.: 541618

PRGX Australia, Inc. (1)
Level 2 Building 2 20 Bridge Street, Pymble, 2073, NSW, Australia
Tel.: (61) 294490700
Financial Auditing & Corporate Financial Consulting
N.A.I.C.S.: 541618
James Sly (VP-Europe & Asia Pacific Retail Ops)

PRGX Belgium, Inc. (1)
Esplanade 1 Brussel Hoofdstad, 1020, Brussels, Belgium
Tel.: (32) 25580558
Web Site: http://www.prgx.com
Analytics & Recovery Audit Services
N.A.I.C.S.: 541211

PRGX Brasil Ltda. (1)
Av Angelica 2491- 19 andar- Cj 191, Consolacao, Sao Paulo, 01227-200, Brazil
Tel.: (55) 1133650265
Business Consultancy Services
N.A.I.C.S.: 813920

PRGX Canada Corp. (1)
115 Turnbull Court, Cambridge, N1T 1C6, ON, Canada
Tel.: (519) 740-9117
Sales Range: $10-24.9 Million
Emp.: 55
Auditing & Corporate Financial Consulting Services
N.A.I.C.S.: 541618

PRGX Colombia Ltda. (1)
Calle 93 Bis 19 40 Of 402, Bogota, 814, Colombia
Tel.: (57) 15302324
Emp.: 14
Process, Physical Distribution & Logistics Consulting Services
N.A.I.C.S.: 541614

PRGX Deutschland GmbH (1)
Grunerstrasse 133, 40239, Dusseldorf, Germany
Tel.: (49) 21153819395
Web Site: http://www.prgx.com
Sales Range: $75-99.9 Million
Emp.: 15
Auditing & Corporate Financial Consulting Services
N.A.I.C.S.: 541618

PRGX France, Inc. (1)
140-144 rue Victor Hugo, 92300, Levallois-Perret, France
Tel.: (33) 155905500
Web Site: http://www.prgx.com
Sales Range: $25-49.9 Million
Emp.: 90
Auditing & Corporate Financial Consulting Services
N.A.I.C.S.: 541618

PRGX India Private Limited (1)

PRGX GLOBAL, INC.

201-202 Amar Paradigm Baner Road, Baner, Pune, 411 045, Maharashtra, India
Tel.: (91) 2067250300
Web Site: http://www.prgx.com
Emp.: 300
Recovery Audit & Transaction Assurance Services
N.A.I.C.S.: 541211

PRGX International Pte. Ltd. (1)
128 Tanjong Pagar Road, Singapore, 088535, Singapore
Tel.: (65) 67353834
Web Site: http://www.prgx.com
Sales Range: $75-99.9 Million
Emp.: 40
Auditing & Corporate Financial Consulting Services
N.A.I.C.S.: 541618

Branch (Non-US):

PRGX International Pte. Ltd. - Hong Kong (2)
Pottinger Street 10, Kowloon Bay, Central, China (Hong Kong)
Tel.: (852) 26901885
Web Site: http://www.prgx.com
Sales Range: $10-24.9 Million
Emp.: 14
Auditing & Corporate Financial Consulting Services
N.A.I.C.S.: 541618

PRGX Mexico S de RL de CV (1)
Torre Zentrum Av Santa Fe 495 Col Cruz Manca, Mexico, 5349, Mexico
Tel.: (52) 5550816030
Web Site: http://www.prg.com
Sales Range: $25-49.9 Million
Emp.: 120
Auditing & Corporate Financial Consulting Services
N.A.I.C.S.: 541618

PRGX Portugal, Inc. (1)
Av da Boavista 1773B 2nd andar esc 2.7, 4100-133, Porto, Portugal
Tel.: (351) 226090186
Web Site: http://www.prgx.com
Sales Range: $25-49.9 Million
Emp.: 7
Recovery Audit & Contract Management Services
N.A.I.C.S.: 541211

PRGX Spain, Inc. (1)
Calle Albasanz 65 2 A, Madrid, 28037, Spain
Tel.: (34) 913430880
Web Site: http://www.prgx.com
Sales Range: $75-99.9 Million
Emp.: 15
Auditing & Corporate Financial Consulting Services
N.A.I.C.S.: 541618
Nina Mauchand (Dir Gen & Mng Dir)

PRGX Suzhou Co., Ltd. (1)
1402 Room 738 Shang Cheng Road Suncome Liauw's Plaza, Pudong New District, Shanghai, China
Tel.: (86) 2158361698
Web Site: http://www.prgx.com
Sales Range: $10-24.9 Million
Emp.: 40
Auditing & Corporate Financial Consulting Services
N.A.I.C.S.: 541618

PRGX Svenska AB (1)
Karlsbergvagen 55, 113 35, Stockholm, Sweden
Tel.: (46) 852227000
Sales Range: $1-9.9 Million
Emp.: 7
Auditing & Corporate Financial Consulting Services
N.A.I.C.S.: 541618
Adam Simon (Mng Dir)

PRGX UK Holdings Ltd (1)
731 Capability Green, Luton, LU1 3LU, Bedfordshire, United Kingdom
Tel.: (44) 1582395800
Investment Management Service
N.A.I.C.S.: 551112

PRGX UK Ltd. (1)
1st Fl 731 Capability Green, Luton, LU1

PRGX GLOBAL, INC.

PRGX Global, Inc.—(Continued)
3LU, United Kingdom
Tel.: (44) 1582395800
Web Site: http://www.prgx.com
Sales Range: $10-24.9 Million
Emp.: 50
Auditing & Corporate Financial Consulting Services
N.A.I.C.S.: 541618

Profit Recovery Brasil Ltda. (1)
Angelica 2491 2 Andar, Sao Paulo, 01227-200, Brazil
Tel.: (55) 1133650265
Web Site: http://www.prgx.com
Sales Range: $10-24.9 Million
Emp.: 30
Auditing & Corporate Financial Consulting Services
N.A.I.C.S.: 541618

PRI MAR PETROLEUM INC.
1207 Broad St, Saint Joseph, MI 49085
Tel.: (269) 983-7314
Web Site:
http://www.primarpetro.com
Sales Range: $75-99.9 Million
Emp.: 150
Independent Convenience Store
N.A.I.C.S.: 445110
Craig Marzke *(COO & Exec VP)*
Richard L. Marzke *(Chm)*
Tom Kuhar *(CFO & Exec VP)*
Kurt Marzke *(Pres & CEO)*
Kevin Marzke *(CTO & VP)*

PRIAM PROPERTIES INC.
102 Woodmont Blvd Ste 100, Nashville, TN 37205
Tel.: (615) 296-0483   MD
Web Site:
http://www.priamproperties.com
Year Founded: 2018
Emp.: 10
Real Estate Investment Services
N.A.I.C.S.: 531210
Abhishek Mathur *(CEO)*
Brian C. Adams *(Pres)*
W. Michael Madden *(CFO & Treas)*
Michael E. Harris *(Chm)*

PRIBUSS ENGINEERING, INC.
523 Mayfair Ave, South San Francisco, CA 94080
Tel.: (650) 588-0447
Web Site: http://www.pribuss.com
Sales Range: $10-24.9 Million
Emp.: 70
Mechanical Construction & Engineering Services
N.A.I.C.S.: 541330
Janette Bachman *(Project Mgr)*
Jaime Soriano *(Mgr-Shop)*
Ronald Sanchez *(Project Mgr)*
Nel Lukovsky *(Mgr-Credit)*

PRICE & ASSOCIATES CPAS, LLC
400 N Ashley Dr Ste 1325, Tampa, FL 33602
Web Site: http://www.a-lign.com
Year Founded: 2009
Sales Range: $1-9.9 Million
Financial Consulting Services
N.A.I.C.S.: 523940
Scott G. Price *(CEO)*
Jason Torgler *(Chief Revenue Officer)*
Michael Branca *(CFO)*
Mike Herdegen *(CTO)*
Steve Simmons *(COO)*

PRICE BROS EQUIPMENT CO
619 S Washington St, Wichita, KS 67211
Tel.: (316) 265-9577
Web Site:
http://www.pricebroseq.com

Sales Range: $10-24.9 Million
Emp.: 30
Agricultural Machinery & Equipment; Light Industrial
N.A.I.C.S.: 423820
Randy Smith *(VP)*
Richard H. Price Jr. *(Pres)*

PRICE CARS LLC
445 Francisco Blvd E, San Rafael, CA 94901
Tel.: (415) 460-6800
Web Site:
http://www.toyotamarin.com
Sales Range: $50-74.9 Million
Emp.: 85
Owner & Operator of Car Dealerships
N.A.I.C.S.: 441110
Tom Price *(Pres)*

PRICE CHOPPER, INC.
6958 Venture Cir, Orlando, FL 32807
Tel.: (407) 679-1600   FL
Web Site: http://www.pchopper.com
Year Founded: 1997
Sales Range: $1-9.9 Million
Emp.: 40
Commercial Lithographic Printing
N.A.I.C.S.: 323111
Jeff Sooknarine *(Chm)*

PRICE CONSTRUCTION INC.
Hwy 350, Big Spring, TX 79720
Tel.: (432) 267-1691   TX
Web Site:
http://www.priceconstruction.com
Year Founded: 1954
Sales Range: $50-74.9 Million
Emp.: 630
Highway & Street Construction
N.A.I.C.S.: 237310
Bobby W. Price *(Pres)*

PRICE ENGINEERING COMPANY INC.
1175 Cottonwood Ave, Hartland, WI 53029
Tel.: (262) 369-3700
Web Site: http://www.priceeng.com
Sales Range: $10-24.9 Million
Emp.: 95
Industrial Machinery & Equipment Merchant Whslr
N.A.I.C.S.: 423830
Joseph E. Konyn *(CFO & Sec)*
Thomas Price Jr. *(Owner & Pres)*
Rod Vannatta *(Mgr-Ops)*

PRICE FOR PROFIT
6140 Parkland Blvd Ste 200, Cleveland, OH 44124
Tel.: (440) 646-9490
Web Site:
http://www.priceforprofit.com
Year Founded: 2006
Sales Range: $1-9.9 Million
Emp.: 14
Price Control Agency Services
N.A.I.C.S.: 926150
Ryan White *(Pres & CEO)*
Agnes McGeever *(Dir-Mktg)*
Keith Hohman *(Partner)*
Andy Fauver *(VP-Bus Dev)*
Jay Yellen *(VP-Software Dev)*
Joe Bogner *(VP-Res & Dev)*
Regina Loiko *(VP-Talent Dev)*
Robert Elmore *(VP-Fin & Admin)*
Sean Arnold *(Principal)*
Terry Oblander *(Mng Dir)*
Chaz Napoli *(Mng Dir)*
Chaz Napoli *(Mng Dir)*

PRICE FORD LINCOLN
3311 E Hwy 101, Port Angeles, WA 98362
Tel.: (360) 457-3333

Web Site: http://www.priceford.com
Sales Range: $10-24.9 Million
Emp.: 35
Car Dealership
N.A.I.C.S.: 441110
David Price *(Owner)*
Craig Smith *(Controller)*

PRICE GREGORY INTERNATIONAL, INC.
920 Memorial City Way Ste 600, Houston, TX 77024
Tel.: (713) 780-7500   TX
Web Site:
http://www.pricegregory.com
Year Founded: 1980
Sales Range: $25-49.9 Million
Emp.: 448
Infrastructure Services, Including Pipeline Construction & Related Services
N.A.I.C.S.: 237120
Ronnie F. Wise *(Pres)*
Tommy N. Jones *(Sr VP)*
Irene E. Schaffer *(CEO & Exec VP)*
Robert E. Bell Jr. *(Exec VP)*

PRICE INDUSTRIES INC.
211 Dallas St, Ennis, TX 75119
Tel.: (972) 878-5050
Rev.: $10,000,000
Emp.: 5
Commercial & Industrial Building Operation
N.A.I.C.S.: 531120
Thomas R. Price *(Owner & Pres)*

PRICE KING WHOLESALE INC.
10 Malcolm Ave Unit 5, Teterboro, NJ 07608
Tel.: (201) 365-6500   NJ
Web Site: http://www.priceking.com
Year Founded: 1975
Office Supplies, Food & Grocery Supplies Distr
N.A.I.C.S.: 424410
Edward Soffer *(Pres)*

PRICE LEBLANC
13200 Airline Hwy, Baton Rouge, LA 70817
Tel.: (225) 751-1100
Web Site:
http://priceleblanctoyota.com
Sales Range: $25-49.9 Million
Emp.: 307
Car Whslr
N.A.I.C.S.: 441110
Nancy Bondy *(Principal)*
Brent LeBlanc *(Principal)*
Emily LeDeaux *(Dir-Mktg)*

PRICE MART INC.
16524 Jamaica Ave, Jamaica, NY 11432
Tel.: (718) 526-7634
Rev.: $14,003,741
Emp.: 35
Department Store Owner & Operator
N.A.I.C.S.: 455110
Robert Terzi *(Pres)*
Jeffery Terzi *(VP)*
Angela Atarnie *(Controller)*

PRICE MASTER CORPORATION
5707 31st Ave, Woodside, NY 11377
Tel.: (718) 626-7779
Web Site:
http://www.pricemaster.com
Sales Range: $10-24.9 Million
Emp.: 15
Convenience Store Merchandise Distr
N.A.I.C.S.: 423690

Abdul Sater Najimi *(Pres)*
Hakim Najimi *(VP)*

PRICE MODERN LLC
2604 Sisson St, Baltimore, MD 21211-3118
Tel.: (410) 366-5500   MD
Web Site:
http://www.pricemodern.com
Year Founded: 1904
Sales Range: $50-74.9 Million
Emp.: 158
Office Furniture Retailer
N.A.I.C.S.: 449110
Milford Marchant *(Chm & CEO)*
Thomas J. Morton *(CFO & Exec VP)*
Robert Carpenter *(Pres & COO)*
Brent Matthews *(Sr VP)*
Christine Loechel *(Sr VP)*
Joe Albrecht *(Sr VP)*

PRICE RUBBER CORP.
2733 Gunter Pk Dr W, Montgomery, AL 36109-1013
Tel.: (334) 277-5470   AL
Web Site: http://www.pricerubber.com
Year Founded: 1960
Sales Range: $10-24.9 Million
Emp.: 100
Mfr of Conveyor Belts
N.A.I.C.S.: 326220
John W. Price *(VP)*
Charles Herndon *(Branch Mgr)*
Clark Ward *(Treas)*

PRICE TRANSFER INC.
2790 E Delamo Blvd, Rancho Dominguez, CA 90221
Tel.: (310) 639-6074
Web Site:
http://www.pricetransfer.com
Rev.: $11,904,877
Emp.: 80
Local Trucking with Storage
N.A.I.C.S.: 484110
Steve Straub *(CFO)*
Frank Aguirre *(Mgr-Main Street Facility)*
Laurie Crandall *(Project Mgr)*
Raul Rodriguez *(Mgr-Price Intermodal SW)*
Marga Martin *(Mgr-Control)*
James Luzanilla *(Asst Dir-Transportation)*

PRICE TRUCK LINES INC.
4931 S Victoria, Wichita, KS 67216
Tel.: (316) 945-6915
Web Site:
http://www.pricetruckline.com
Rev.: $12,000,000
Emp.: 180
Provider of Trucking Services
N.A.I.C.S.: 484121
Ed Toon *(VP)*
John Bergkamp *(Controller)*

PRICE-DAVIS, INC.
3882 E Highway 27 PO Box 190, Iron Station, NC 28080   NC
Web Site:
http://www.pricedavisinc.com
Year Founded: 1987
Sales Range: $10-24.9 Million
Emp.: 57
Commercial Retail Fixtures & Food Services Equipment
N.A.I.C.S.: 423440
Skeeter Davis *(Principal & VP)*

PRICE-LESS DRUG STORES INC.
2210 Sunrise Blvd, Rancho Cordova, CA 95670-4377
Tel.: (916) 638-0214   CA
Year Founded: 1983

Sales Range: $25-49.9 Million
Emp.: 195
Drug Stores & Proprietary Stores
N.A.I.C.S.: 456110
Jim Veeck *(Pres)*
Craig Peterson *(CFO)*

PRICELESS PARENTING, LLC
11107 NE 174th St, Bothell, WA 98011
Tel.: (425) 770-1629
Web Site:
http://www.pricelessparenting.com
Child & Youth Services
N.A.I.C.S.: 624110
Kathy Slattengren *(Pres)*

PRICEWATERHOUSECOOPERS LLP (USA)
300 Madison Ave 24th Fl, New York, NY 10017-6204
Tel.: (646) 471-4000   DE
Web Site: http://www.pwc.com
Year Founded: 1982
Accounting, Tax Preparation, Risk Management, Business Assurance, Human Resource, Regulatory, Operational Management & Advisory Services
N.A.I.C.S.: 541211
Gary Price *(Chief Admin Officer)*
Mark Mendola *(Vice Chm & Mng Partner)*
Carol A. Sawdye *(COO)*
Diana Weiss *(Partner)*
Dwight Blackman *(Principal)*
Dan Chavez *(Partner)*
Arjun Banerjee *(Partner)*
Neil Dhar *(Head-Fin Svcs)*
Reggie Walker *(Chief Comml Officer)*
Mike Dillon *(Chief Diversity & Inclusion Officer)*
Laurie Endsley *(Chief Ethics & Compliance Officer)*
Mike Fenlon *(Chief People Officer)*
Shannon Schuyler *(Chief Purpose Officer, Pres-Charitable & Principal)*
Mary Waldron *(Chief Risk Officer)*
Caroline Cheng *(Gen Counsel)*
Roz Brooks *(Mng Dir-Pub Policy)*
Jim Flanagan *(Vice Chm & Mng Partner)*
Victoria Brennan *(Partner)*
Lucas Carpenter *(Partner)*
Glenn Tallon *(Partner)*
Michael Bellin *(Partner)*
Vitaly Vishnitsky *(Partner)*
Kenyon Willhoit *(Partner)*
Nicholas Kray *(Partner-Assurance)*
Nathan Jerkins *(Partner-Tax-Mergers & Acq)*
Mori Contreras *(Partner-Tax)*
Michael Drubin *(Partner-Advisory-Deals Practice)*
Marcus Simms *(Partner-Deals Advisory-Delivering Deal Value Practice-Atlanta)*
Kevin Simmonds *(Partner-Advisory Cybersecurity-Atlanta)*
Keith Palmer *(Partner-Assurance-Actuarial Svcs Practice-Atlanta)*
David Ames *(Partner-Advisory-Atlanta)*
Andrew Gaudin *(Partner-Tax-Atlanta)*
Amber Cutler *(Partner-Assurance)*
Toni Lockett Cromwell *(Partner-Assurance)*
Holly Trotter *(Partner-Tax)*
Toby Spry *(Partner-Advisory, Cybersecurity & Privacy)*
Renee Maillet *(Partner-Risk Assurance)*
Sarah Yakots Warren *(Partner-Assurance-Private Company Svcs)*
Matthew Naro *(Partner-Deals Practice)*
Russell Fields *(Partner-Advisory)*
Nicole Yesbik *(Partner-Risk Assurance)*
Angela Konkle *(Partner-Assurance)*
Robert Kianos *(Partner-Assurance)*
Deborah Pena *(Partner-Assurance-South Florida Practice)*
Marcela Cortes *(Partner-Transfer Pricing)*
Michael Castro *(Partner-Assurance)*
Paul Gomez *(Partner-Risk Assurance-Ft. Lauderdale)*
Beth Payne *(Partner-Advisory-Fin Svcs)*
John Wilcox *(Partner-Advisory)*
Mike Costanzo *(Partner-Assurance-Private Company Svcs)*
Kerri Hines *(Partner-Tax)*
Dmitry Danilenko *(Partner-Advisory-Consumer Markets Sector-Tampa)*
Courtney Deverall *(Partner-Assurance)*
Tim Ryan *(Chm & Sr Partner)*
John Linn IV *(Partner)*
Sigal Zarmi *(CIO)*
Subsidiaries:
PwC Strategy& (US) Inc.   (1)
101 Park Ave 18th Fl, New York, NY 10178
Tel.: (212) 551-3828
Web Site: http://www.strategyand.pwc.com
Management Consulting Services
N.A.I.C.S.: 541611
Eduardo Alvarez *(Principal)*
Peter Bertone *(Principal)*
Rick Edmunds *(Principal)*
Vinay Couto *(Principal)*

PRICEWEBER MARKETING COMMUNICATIONS, INC.
10701 Shelbyville Rd, Louisville, KY 40243
Tel.: (502) 499-9220   KY
Web Site: http://www.priceweber.com
Year Founded: 1968
Sales Range: $1-9.9 Million
Emp.: 60
Advertising Agencies
N.A.I.C.S.: 541810
Tony Beard *(Pres, Chief Creative Officer & Partner)*
Jeremy Schell *(Chief Digital Officer & VP)*
Fred Davis *(CEO & Partner)*
Elizabeth Bone *(Acct Exec-Hershey Acct)*
Liz Taylor *(Assoc Acct Exec)*
Clint Martin *(Assoc Dir-Creative)*
Mike Nickerson *(VP-Ops)*
Lindsay Carter *(Acct Supvr)*
Joel Villaflor *(Dir-Creative)*
Chris Johnson *(Acct Supvr)*
Brad Mercer *(VP & Dir-Acct)*
Richard Johnson *(Chief Creative Officer, VP & Dir-Creative)*
Robert Trinkle *(Partner, VP & Dir-Acct)*

PRICKETTS DISTRIBUTING INC.
123 M St, Fresno, CA 93721
Tel.: (559) 268-0201
Web Site: http://www.pricketts.com
Year Founded: 1966
Sales Range: $1-9.9 Million
Emp.: 50
Wholesale Distributor of Soft Drinks
N.A.I.C.S.: 424490
Russ Prickett *(Pres)*

PRIDA GUIDA & COMPANY, P.A.
1106 N Franklin St, Tampa, FL 33602
Tel.: (813) 226-6091
Web Site: http://www.pridacpas.com
Year Founded: 1957
Sales Range: $10-24.9 Million
Emp.: 20
Accounting Services
N.A.I.C.S.: 541211
George K. Guida *(Partner)*
Jessica Chase *(Mgr-Intl Tax)*
Luciano L. Prida Jr. *(Pres)*

PRIDE AND JOYS INC.
1400 Broadway Rm 503, New York, NY 10018
Tel.: (212) 594-9820
Sales Range: $10-24.9 Million
Emp.: 26
Women's Sportswear
N.A.I.C.S.: 315250
Eli Russo *(Pres)*
Neal Russo *(VP)*

PRIDE CONVENIENCE INC.
246 Cottage St, Springfield, MA 01104
Tel.: (413) 737-6992
Web Site: http://www.pridestores.com
Sales Range: $10-24.9 Million
Emp.: 20
Convenience Store
N.A.I.C.S.: 445131
Robert Bolduc *(Pres)*

PRIDE HYUNDAI OF SEEKONK
11 Taunton Ave, Seekonk, MA 02771
Tel.: (508) 336-7880
Web Site:
http://www.hyundaiofseekonk.com
Sales Range: $25-49.9 Million
Emp.: 35
Automobiles, New & Used
N.A.I.C.S.: 441110
Alfred Dosanjos *(Pres)*
Nancy Lopes *(Controller)*
Lisa Anjos *(VP)*
David Rosendahl *(Mgr-Bus Dev)*

PRIDE INDUSTRIES INC.
10030 Foothills Blvd, Roseville, CA 95747-7102
Tel.: (916) 788-2100   CA
Web Site:
http://www.prideindustries.com
Year Founded: 1966
Sales Range: $75-99.9 Million
Emp.: 5,594
Lawn & Garden Services
N.A.I.C.S.: 561720
Tina Oliveira *(Sr VP-HR)*
Bob Olsen *(Chm)*
Mike Snegg *(Treas)*
Sandy Smoley *(Sec)*
Judson Riggs *(Vice Chm)*
Peter Berghuis *(COO)*
Jeffery Dern *(Pres & CEO)*
Gene Walker *(Mgr-Customer Svc-Mfg & Logistics Svcs Div)*
Alan McMillan *(CIO)*
Steve Twitchell *(Sr VP-Mktg, Bus Dev & Strategy)*
Vic Wursten *(Sr VP-Rehabilitation)*
Judson T. Riggs *(Vice Chm)*
Luis Torres-Acosta *(Sr VP-Mfg, Logistics, and Engrg & Property Svcs)*

PRIDE MOBILITY PRODUCTS CORP.
182 Susquehanna Ave, Exeter, PA 18643
Tel.: (570) 655-5574   PA
Web Site:
http://www.pridemobility.com
Year Founded: 1986
Sales Range: $75-99.9 Million
Emp.: 1,000
Lift Chairs, Scooters, Power Wheelchairs & Scooter Lifts Mfr & Distr
N.A.I.C.S.: 339113
Subsidiaries:
Pride Mobility Products Australia Pty. Ltd.   (1)
21 Healey Road, Dandenong, 3175, VIC, Australia
Tel.: (61) 397064611
Lift Chairs, Scooters, Power Wheelchairs & Scooter Lifts Mfr & Whslr
N.A.I.C.S.: 339113

Pride Mobility Products Company   (1)
5096 South Service Road, Beamsville, L3J 1V4, ON, Canada
Tel.: (905) 682-2665
Web Site: https://pridemobility.ca
Sales Range: $25-49.9 Million
Emp.: 65
Lift Chairs, Scooters, Power Wheelchairs & Scooter Lifts Mfr & Whslr
N.A.I.C.S.: 423450

Pride Mobility Products Corp. - Quantum Rehab Division   (1)
182 Susquehanna Ave, Exeter, PA 18643
Tel.: (570) 655-5574
Web Site: http://www.quantumrehab.com
Surgical & Medical Instrument Mfr
N.A.I.C.S.: 339112

Pride Mobility Products Europe BV   (1)
De Zwaan 3, 1601 MS, Enkhuizen, Netherlands
Tel.: (31) 850408630
Web Site: http://pridemobility.eu
Sales Range: $10-24.9 Million
Emp.: 12
Lift Chairs, Scooters, Power Wheelchairs & Scooter Lifts Mfr & Whslr
N.A.I.C.S.: 423450
James Ormel *(Gen Mgr)*

Pride Mobility Products Italia S.r.l.   (1)
Via del Progresso ang Via del Lavoro, Prato della Corte, Rome, 00065, Italy
Tel.: (39) 0765451143
Web Site: http://www.pridemobility.com
Lift Chairs, Scooters, Power Wheelchairs & Scooter Lifts Mfr & Whslr
N.A.I.C.S.: 423450
Federica Pozzi *(Gen Mgr)*

Pride Mobility Products Ltd.   (1)
32 Wedgwood Rd, Bicester, OX26 4UL, Oxfordshire, United Kingdom
Tel.: (44) 1869324600
Web Site: http://www.pridemobility.com
Sales Range: $10-24.9 Million
Emp.: 100
Lift Chairs, Scooters, Power Wheelchairs & Scooter Lifts Mfr & Whslr
N.A.I.C.S.: 423450
Nick Allen *(Mng Dir)*
Paul Rising *(VP-Intl Sls)*

Pride Mobility Products New Zealand Ltd.   (1)
38 Lansford Crescent, Avondale, Auckland, 1007, New Zealand
Tel.: (64) 98280337
Web Site: http://www.pridemobility.com
Sales Range: $10-24.9 Million
Emp.: 1
Lift Chairs, Scooters, Power Wheelchairs & Scooter Lifts Mfr & Whslr
N.A.I.C.S.: 423450
Dai Lowry *(Mgr-Sls)*

Pride Mobility Products SARL   (1)
69 rue Ampere, PO Box 1243, 75017, Paris, France
Tel.: (33) 1 570 655 5574
Web Site: http://www.pridemobility.com
Lift Chairs, Scooters, Power Wheelchairs & Scooter Lifts Mfr & Whslr
N.A.I.C.S.: 423450

PRIDE PRODUCTS CORP
4333 Veterans Memorial Hwy, Ronkonkoma, NY 11779
Tel.: (631) 737-4444
Web Site:
http://www.prideproducts.com
Sales Range: $75-99.9 Million
Emp.: 93

PRIDE PRODUCTS CORP

U.S. PRIVATE

Pride Products Corp—(Continued)

Disposable Plates, Cups, Napkins & Eating Utensils
N.A.I.C.S.: 424130
David Emrani *(Pres)*

PRIDE PRODUCTS, INC.
5 Slater Dr, Elizabeth, NJ 07206
Tel.: (908) 353-6800 NJ
Web Site: http://www.prideprod.com
Year Founded: 1982
Sales Range: $75-99.9 Million
Emp.: 75
Household Appliances & Toys Mfr
N.A.I.C.S.: 561910
William Yuan *(Chm)*

PRIDE SOLVENTS & CHEMICAL COMPANY
6 Long Island Ave, Holtsville, NY 11742
Tel.: (631) 758-0200
Web Site: http://www.pridesol.com
Year Founded: 1970
Rev.: $16,000,000
Emp.: 65
Chemicals & Allied Products
N.A.I.C.S.: 424690
Dave Sticht *(Mgr)*
Arthur W. Dhom Sr. *(CEO)*

Subsidiaries:

Pride Solvents & Chemical Co. Of New Jersey, Inc. (1)
211 Randolph Ave, Avenel, NJ 07001-2402 (100%)
Tel.: (732) 499-0125
Web Site: http://www.pridesol.com
Sales Range: $10-24.9 Million
Emp.: 60
Industrial Chemicals
N.A.I.C.S.: 424690
Art Jones Dhom *(CEO)*

PRIDE TREE HOLDINGS, INC.
2711 Centerville Rd Ste 400, Wilmington, DE 19808
Tel.: (302) 636-5401
Holding Company
N.A.I.C.S.: 551112

Subsidiaries:

Direct Brands, Inc. (1)
1 Penn Plz, New York, NY 10119-0002
Tel.: (212) 596-2000
Web Site: http://www.bookspan.com
Rev.: $400,000,000
Emp.: 300
Direct Order Books, Music & Movies Supplier
N.A.I.C.S.: 459210
Jennifer Canzone *(Dir-Art)*
Ariel Alvarado *(Dir-Mailing Ops)*
Amanda Beekharry *(Mgr-Mktg)*
Craig Polizzotto *(Sr Dir-Art)*

Subsidiary (Domestic):

Columbia House (2)
1 Penn Plz 250 W 34th St 5th Fl, New York, NY 10119
Tel.: (212) 596-2000
Web Site: http://www.columbiahouse.com
Sales Range: $450-499.9 Million
Mail Order Retailer of CDs, Tapes & Books
N.A.I.C.S.: 459210
Michael Chauliac *(Dir-Online Mktg)*

Subsidiary (Non-US):

Columbia House Canada (3)
5900 Finch Ave E, Scarborough, M1B 5X7, ON, Canada
Tel.: (416) 299-9400
Web Site: http://www.bmg.com
Sales Range: $25-49.9 Million
Emp.: 100
Music Mail-Order Services
N.A.I.C.S.: 512250

Subsidiary (Non-US):

Doubleday Canada Limited (2)
5900 Finch Ave E, Scarborough, M1B 5X7, ON, Canada
Tel.: (416) 977-7891
Sales Range: $25-49.9 Million
Emp.: 156
Book Club Mail Order & Telemarketing Services
N.A.I.C.S.: 561422

PRIDESTAFF, INC.
7535 N Palm Ave Ste 101, Fresno, CA 93711-5504
Tel.: (559) 432-7780
Web Site: http://www.pridestaff.com
Year Founded: 1978
Sales Range: $100-124.9 Million
Emp.: 50,000
Human Resources & Executive Search Consulting Services
N.A.I.C.S.: 541612
George Rogers *(Founder & Chm)*
Tammi Heaton *(Co-CEO)*
Mike Aprile *(Co-CEO & CFO)*
John-Reed McDonald *(COO)*
Paula Turner Pizarro *(VP-Franchise Dev)*
Ryan Williams *(VP-Fin)*
Rob Hale *(CIO)*
Bill Hamrick *(VP-Trng & Dev)*
Jeremy Thacker *(Owner-Memphis & Partner-Strategic-Memphis)*
Sean Akin *(Partner-Strategic)*

PRIDGEON & CLAY, INC.
50 Cottage Grove St SW, Grand Rapids, MI 49507-1622
Tel.: (616) 241-5675 MI
Web Site: http://www.pridgeonandclay.com
Year Founded: 1948
Sales Range: $150-199.9 Million
Emp.: 700
Mfr of Automotive & Metal Stampings, Special Dyes, Tools & Weldments
N.A.I.C.S.: 336370
Dawn Stanton *(Mgr-Customer Svc)*

Subsidiaries:

Pridgeon & Clay, KFT (1)
Vasut ut 35/A, 6088, Apostag, Hungary
Tel.: (36) 78428352
Metal Stamping Mfr
N.A.I.C.S.: 332119
Shown Vanlare *(Gen Mgr)*

Pridgeon & Clay, S.de R.L. de C.V. (1)
Privada Industrial Ojo de Agua 380 Desarrollo Industrial GP, Apodaca, 66632, Nuevo Leon, Mexico
Tel.: (52) 81 1331 0026
Emp.: 104
Metal Stamping Mfr
N.A.I.C.S.: 332119

PRIESTER PECAN CO., INC.
208 Old Fort Rd E, Fort Deposit, AL 36032
Tel.: (334) 227-4301
Web Site: http://www.priesters.com
Year Founded: 1935
Sales Range: $25-49.9 Million
Emp.: 118
Roasted Nuts & Peanut Butter Mfr
N.A.I.C.S.: 311911
Thomas Ellis *(VP)*
Faye Hood *(Office Mgr)*
Ned T. Ellis Jr. *(Pres)*

PRIMA COMMUNICATIONS, INC.
230 N Grand St, Schoolcraft, MI 49087
Tel.: (269) 679-3800 MI
Web Site: http://primacommunications.com
Year Founded: 1991

Communication Services Secy/Court Reporting Svc Business Services Coml Art/Graphic Design Misc Publishing
N.A.I.C.S.: 517810
Charlotte Hubbard *(CEO)*
Kristen Crandle *(Controller)*
John Kroggel *(VP)*
Jason Young *(Dir-Ops-Indiana)*

PRIMA LIGHTING CORPORATION
13615 Marquardt Ave, Santa Fe Springs, CA 90670
Tel.: (562) 407-3079 CA
Web Site: http://www.primalighting.com
Sales Range: $1-9.9 Million
Emp.: 16
Designs, Manufactures & Installs Lighting Systems
N.A.I.C.S.: 335132
Adam Y. Lee *(Pres)*

PRIMA PUBLIC RELATIONS, LTD.
57 E Washington St Ste LL5, Chagrin Falls, OH 44022
Tel.: (440) 893-9676
Sales Range: Less than $1 Million
Emp.: 3
Advertising Agencies
N.A.I.C.S.: 541810

PRIMACY
1577 New Britain Ave, Farmington, CT 06032
Tel.: (860) 679-9332
Web Site: http://www.theprimacy.com
Sales Range: $1-9.9 Million
Emp.: 75
Website Development & Digital Marketing
N.A.I.C.S.: 541613
Andy Berling *(VP-Bus Dev)*
Deb Peterson *(Sr VP-Org Dev)*
Lino Ribolla *(Exec Dir-Creative)*
Stan Valencis *(Pres)*
Rosie Walker *(Exec VP-Mktg)*
Melissa Tait *(Sr VP-Tech & Project Mgmt)*
Jeff Johnson *(Mng Dir & Sr VP)*
Matt Cyr *(VP-Strategic Practices)*

PRIMAL PET FOODS INC.
109 S Blvd, San Mateo, CA 94402-2446
Tel.: (415) 642-7400
Web Site: http://www.primalpetfoods.com
Year Founded: 2001
Sales Range: $10-24.9 Million
Emp.: 12
Dog & Cat Food Mfr
N.A.I.C.S.: 311111
Matt Koss *(Owner)*
Matthew Pirz *(VP-Sls)*

PRIMARILY CARE, INC.
75 Sockanosset Cross Rd Ste 300, Cranston, RI 02920
Tel.: (401) 946-4441
Web Site: http://www.primarilycare.com
Sales Range: $10-24.9 Million
Emp.: 11
Administrative Management & General Management Consulting Services
N.A.I.C.S.: 541611
Pete Tarmey *(CFO)*
George Trudel *(CIO)*

PRIMARY AIM, LLC
947 Adair Ave, Zanesville, OH 43702
Tel.: (740) 454-2569 OH

Web Site: http://www.primaryaimllc.com
Year Founded: 1999
Sales Range: $25-49.9 Million
Emp.: 1,000
Fast-Food Restaurant Franchise Owner & Operator
N.A.I.C.S.: 722513
Steve Thompson *(CFO)*
Tim Thompson *(COO)*
Robin Denman *(Dir-Payroll)*
Carol Friel *(Dir-Acctg)*

PRIMARY CARE HEALTH SERVICES, INC.
7227 Hamilton Ave, Pittsburgh, PA 15208
Tel.: (412) 244-4700 PA
Web Site: http://www.pchspitt.org
Year Founded: 1977
Sales Range: $10-24.9 Million
Emp.: 50
Health Care Srvices
N.A.I.C.S.: 622110
Elizabeth Quinn *(Dir-Ops)*
Chelsey Simmons III *(Dir-Fin)*

PRIMARY COLOR SYSTEMS CORP
265 Briggs Ave, Costa Mesa, CA 92626
Tel.: (949) 660-7080
Web Site: http://www.primarycolor.com
Rev.: $11,400,000
Emp.: 350
Color Separation, Photographic & Movie Film
N.A.I.C.S.: 541922
Ron Hirt *(VP-Sls & Mktg)*

PRIMARY FLOW SIGNAL INC.
800 Wellington Ave, Cranston, RI 02910
Tel.: (401) 461-6366
Web Site: http://www.pfsflowproducts.com
Rev.: $12,000,000
Emp.: 17
Flow Meters Distr
N.A.I.C.S.: 423830
Roger Evans *(Engr-Sls & Svc)*

PRIMARY FREIGHT SERVICES INC.
6545 Caballero Blvd, Buena Park, CA 90620
Tel.: (310) 635-3000
Web Site: http://www.primaryfreight.com
Rev.: $13,000,000
Emp.: 40
Freight Transportation Arrangement
N.A.I.C.S.: 488510
Art Sell *(Mgr-Air Freight-United States)*

PRIMARY HEALTH CARE INC.
1200 University Ste 200, Des Moines, IA 50314
Tel.: (515) 248-1447 IA
Web Site: http://www.phcinc.net
Year Founded: 1989
Sales Range: $10-24.9 Million
Emp.: 210
Health Care Srvices
N.A.I.C.S.: 622110
Sherry Gomis *(Dir-HR)*
Bery Engebretsen *(Dir-Medical)*
Rachel Adams *(Dir-Ops)*
Kelly Huntsman *(Exec Dir)*

PRIMARY PACKAGING INCORPORATED
10810 Industrial Pkwy NW, Bolivar, OH 44612

COMPANIES

Tel.: (330) 874-3131
Web Site:
http://www.primarypackaging.com
Sales Range: $10-24.9 Million
Emp.: 64
Plastic Bags: Made From Purchased Materials
N.A.I.C.S.: 326111
Jeff Thrams *(Pres)*
Chuck McComb *(Dir-Sls Dev)*
Gail Chew *(Mgr-Quality Assurance)*

PRIMARY RESIDENTIAL MORTGAGE, INC.
1480 No 2200 W, Salt Lake City, UT 84116
Tel.: (800) 255-2792
Web Site:
http://www.primaryresidentialmortgage.com
Year Founded: 1998
Sales Range: $200-249.9 Million
Emp.: 1,640
Residential Mortgage Lender
N.A.I.C.S.: 522310
Dave Zitting *(Co-Founder)*
Steve Chapman *(Co-Founder)*
Tom George *(COO & Exec VP)*
Ruth Green *(Sr VP-Ops)*
Christopher Jones *(Pres-Retail)*
Burton Embry *(Chief Compliance Officer & Exec VP)*
Scott Mattern *(Mgr-Northwest)*
Kyndle Quinones *(Branch Mgr)*
Kenneth Knudson *(Pres & CEO)*
A. J. Swope *(Exec VP-Secondary Mktg)*
Darryl Lee *(Chief Legal Officer & Exec VP)*
Mathew Whitebrook *(VP-Capital Markets)*
Brandi Hume *(Sr VP-Risk Mgmt)*
Hollie Wylie *(VP-Compliance)*

PRIMARY SERVICES LP
520 Post Oak Blvd Ste 550, Houston, TX 77027
Tel.: (713) 850-7010
Web Site:
http://www.primaryservices.com
Sales Range: $10-24.9 Million
Emp.: 25
Provider of Temporary Help Services
N.A.I.C.S.: 561320
Natalie Scheiffele *(Sr Acct Mgr)*
Sabra Phillips *(VP)*

PRIMARY SUPPLY INC.
PO Box 398, Mission, KS 66201-0398
Tel.: (636) 896-0990
Web Site:
http://www.dougmccullough.com
Rev.: $11,500,000
Emp.: 6
Electrical Apparatus Equipment Wiring Supplies & Related Equipment Merchant Whslr
N.A.I.C.S.: 423610
Darcy Mccullough *(VP)*

PRIMARY SYSTEMS, INC.
4000 Green Park Rd, Saint Louis, MO 63125
Tel.: (314) 880-9977
Web Site: http://www.primary-systems.com
Year Founded: 1976
Sales Range: $10-24.9 Million
Emp.: 25
Communications, Security & Fire Alarm Systems Contractor
N.A.I.C.S.: 238210
Steven Potts *(Pres)*
Jim Faber *(CFO)*

Paul Light *(Exec VP)*
Erik Pemberton *(Mgr-Svcs)*
Jeff Jarvis *(VP-Ops)*

PRIMCO MANAGEMENT INC.
2211 Elliott Ave Ste 200, Seattle, WA 98121
Tel.: (206) 455-2940   DE
Year Founded: 2010
Sales Range: Less than $1 Million
Emp.: 1
Real Estate Manangement Services
N.A.I.C.S.: 531390
David Michery *(Pres & CEO)*

Subsidiaries:

ESMG Inc.   (1)
1875 Century Park E 6th Fl Ste 73, Century City, CA 90067
Tel.: (562) 565-9967
Web Site: http://www.esmgusa.com
Multimedia Production Services
N.A.I.C.S.: 516210
David Michery *(Pres)*

PRIME CAPITAL INVESTMENT ADVISORS, LLC
6201 College Blvd 7th Fl, Overland Park, KS 66211
Tel.: (913) 491-6226   KS
Web Site: http://www.pciawealth.com
Rev.: $1,700,000
Emp.: 24
Asset & Wealth Management Services
N.A.I.C.S.: 541618
Glenn Spencer *(CEO)*
Terra McBride *(CMO)*
Scott Colangelo *(Chm & Mng Partner)*

Subsidiaries:

Cornerstone Retirement Group, Inc.   (1)
5525 Kietzke Ln Ste 100, Reno, NV 89511-4001
Tel.: (775) 853-9033
Web Site:
http://www.cornerstoneretirement.com
Investment Advice
N.A.I.C.S.: 523940
Chris Abts *(Pres)*

PRIME CHOICE FOODS, INC.
1400 Newton St, Bristol, VA 24201
Tel.: (276) 466-8785
Web Site:
http://www.primechoicefoods.com
Year Founded: 2000
Sales Range: $10-24.9 Million
Emp.: 40
Organic Snacks Mfr
N.A.I.C.S.: 311919
Jose Gomez *(Owner)*
Truman King *(Supvr-Production)*

PRIME COMMUNICATIONS LP
12550 Reed Rd Ste 100, Sugar Land, TX 77478-2867
Tel.: (281) 240-7800
Web Site:
http://www.primecomms.com
Rev.: $16,000,000
Emp.: 30
Cellular Telephone Services
N.A.I.C.S.: 517112
Farid Virani *(CEO)*
Akbar Mohamed *(Pres)*

Subsidiaries:

Spring Communications Holding, Inc.   (1)
2150 E Walnut Ave, Dalton, GA 30721-4504
Tel.: (706) 226-9660
Web Site: http://www.springmobile.com
Wireless Components Distr
N.A.I.C.S.: 517121

Subsidiary (Domestic):

Spring Communications   (2)
3939 S Wasatch Blvd Ste 1, Salt Lake City, UT 84124
Tel.: (801) 277-7777
Web Site: http://www.springmobile.com
Sales Range: $25-49.9 Million
Emp.: 500
Wireless Telecommunications Products Retailer
N.A.I.C.S.: 517112
Jason Ellis *(Pres & CEO)*
Brett Bradshaw *(Sr VP-Sls & Ops)*

PRIME CONTRACTORS INC.
17355 Village Green Dr, Houston, TX 77040
Tel.: (281) 999-0875
Web Site:
http://www.primecontractorsinc.com
Sales Range: $10-24.9 Million
Emp.: 49
General Contractor Specializing in Commercial Construction & Renovation
N.A.I.C.S.: 236220
Lee Dodson *(Pres)*
Jim Lingenfelter *(Controller)*
Kimberly Vopat *(Project Coord)*

PRIME CONTROLS, LP
1725 Lake Point Dr, Lewisville, TX 75057
Tel.: (972) 221-4849
Web Site: http://www.prime-controls.com
Year Founded: 1991
Rev.: $27,300,000
Emp.: 125
Electronic Parts & Equipment
N.A.I.C.S.: 423690
Jace McNiel *(Pres)*
Gary McNiel *(Sr VP-Acct Sls & Mktg)*
Jim McMillon *(VP-Ops)*
Scott Ogletree *(Project Mgr)*
Bill Bivens *(VP-Sls & Mktg)*

PRIME FOOD PROCESSING CORP.
300 Vandervoort Ave, Brooklyn, NY 11211-1715
Tel.: (718) 963-2323
Sales Range: $10-24.9 Million
Emp.: 80
Meat Product Production & Distribution Services
N.A.I.C.S.: 311612
Laymont Dofon *(Dir-Quality Control)*

PRIME HEALTHCARE SERVICES, INC.
3300 E Guasti Rd, Ontario, CA 91761
Tel.: (909) 235-4400   DE
Web Site:
http://www.primehealthcare.com
Year Founded: 2001
Holding Company; Hospital Operator
N.A.I.C.S.: 551112
Prem Reddy *(Chm, Pres & CEO)*
Harsha Upadhyay *(Exec VP-Clinical Ops & Reg CEO-Div II)*
Luis Leon *(Pres-Ops-Div II)*
Michael Sarian *(Pres-Ops)*
Ravi Reddy Alla *(VP-Pro Svcs)*
Dan Merel *(VP-Health Plan Ops)*
Mike Heather *(CFO)*
Paryus Patel *(Chief Medical Officer-Div II)*
Kavitha Bhatia *(Chief Medical Officer-Strategy)*
Sunny Bhatia *(Chief Medical Officer-Div 1)*
Soni Mehta *(Chief Medical Officer-Corp & Reg CEO-Pennsylvania)*
Marc Goldstone *(Gen Counsel & Sr VP)*

Raghu Chennareddy *(CTO)*
Will Conaway *(CIO)*
Christina Hutchinson *(VP-Nursing Svcs)*

Subsidiaries:

Chino Valley Medical Center   (1)
5451 Walnut Ave, Chino, CA 91710-2609
Tel.: (909) 464-8600
Web Site: http://www.cvmc.com
Sales Range: $25-49.9 Million
Emp.: 520
General Medical & Surgical Hospitals
N.A.I.C.S.: 622110
Edward Matthews *(CFO)*
Timothy Moran *(CEO)*

Harlingen Medical Center, LP   (1)
5501 S Expy 77, Harlingen, TX 78550   (34.83%)
Tel.: (956) 365-1000
Web Site:
http://www.harlingenmedicalcenter.com
Sales Range: $75-99.9 Million
Emp.: 500
General Acute Care Hospital
N.A.I.C.S.: 621112
Brenda Ivory *(COO)*

La Palma Intercommunity Hospital   (1)
7901 Walker St, La Palma, CA 90623-1722
Tel.: (714) 670-7400
Web Site:
http://www.lapalmaintercommunityhospital.com
Sales Range: $50-74.9 Million
Emp.: 450
Hospital Operator
N.A.I.C.S.: 622110
Sami Shoukair *(Chm & Co-Chief Medical Officer)*
Hilda Manzo-Luna *(Chief Nursing Officer)*
Hassan Alkhouli *(Co-Chief Medical Officer)*
Mylinh Bui *(CFO)*
Allen Stefanek *(Vice Chm & CEO)*

Landmark Medical Center   (1)
115 Cass Ave, Woonsocket, RI 02895
Tel.: (401) 769-4100
Web Site: http://www.landmarkmedical.org
Hospital Operator
N.A.I.C.S.: 622110
Michael R. Souza *(Chm & CEO)*

Lehigh HMA, LLC   (1)
1500 Lee Blvd, Lehigh Acres, FL 33936
Tel.: (239) 369-2101
Web Site: https://www.lehighregional.com
Sales Range: $50-74.9 Million
Hospital Services
N.A.I.C.S.: 622110
Cheryl McIntire *(CFO)*

Lone Star HMA, L.P.   (1)
1011 N Galloway Ave, Mesquite, TX 75149
Tel.: (214) 320-7000
Web Site:
https://www.dallasregionalmedicalcenter.com
Hospital Operator
N.A.I.C.S.: 622110
Glenda Matchett *(CEO)*
Cindi Jobe *(Chief Nursing Officer)*
Michael Metts *(CFO)*

Subsidiary (Domestic):

Dallas Regional Medical Center - Wound Care & Hyperbaric Center   (2)
901 N Galloway Ave Ste 101, Mesquite, TX 75149
Tel.: (214) 660-2580
Web Site: http://www.dallasregionalmedicalcenter.com
Outpatient Wound Care Center Operator
N.A.I.C.S.: 621498

Prime Healthcare Foundation-Coshocton, LLC   (1)
1460 Orange St, Coshocton, OH 43812
Tel.: (740) 622-6411
Web Site: http://www.coshoctonhospital.org
Health Care Srvices
N.A.I.C.S.: 622110

Riverview Regional Medical Center, LLC   (1)
600 S 3rd St, Gadsden, AL 35901

PRIME HEALTHCARE SERVICES, INC.

U.S. PRIVATE

Prime Healthcare Services, Inc.—(Continued)
Tel.: (256) 543-5200
Web Site: http://www.riverviewregional.com
Hospital Services
N.A.I.C.S.: 622110
K. J. Shah *(Chief Medical Officer)*
James P. Davis *(CEO)*
John Langlois *(CEO)*
Tom Moore *(CFO)*

San Dimas Community Hospital (1)
1350 W Covina Blvd, San Dimas, CA 91773
Tel.: (909) 599-6811
Web Site: http://www.sandimashospital.com
Sales Range: $50-74.9 Million
Hospital Services
N.A.I.C.S.: 622110
Zuhair Yahya *(Chief Medical Officer)*
Donna A. Dye *(Dir-Medical Staff Svcs)*

Southern Regional Health System (1)
11 Upper Riverdale Rd SW, Riverdale, GA 30274-2600
Tel.: (770) 991-8000
Web Site: http://www.southernregional.org
Sales Range: $75-99.9 Million
Emp.: 2,300
Full-Service Hospital
N.A.I.C.S.: 622110
Kim Ryan *(Pres & CEO)*

St. Joseph Medical Center (1)
1000 Carondelet Dr, Kansas City, MO 64114-4673
Tel.: (816) 942-4400
Web Site: http://www.stjosephkc.com
Hospital Services
N.A.I.C.S.: 622110
Debra L. Cartwright *(CFO)*
Jodi Fincher *(CEO)*
Kirk Sloan *(Chief Medical Officer)*
Trish Feilmeier *(Chief Nursing Officer)*

St. Mary's Medical Center (1)
201 NW R D Mize Rd, Blue Springs, MO 64014-2518
Tel.: (816) 228-5900
Web Site: http://www.stmaryskc.com
Hospital Operator
N.A.I.C.S.: 622110
Deb Ohnoutka *(CEO)*
Lorie Herrman *(Chief Nursing Officer)*
Debra L. Cartwright *(CFO)*
Alex Colley *(Mgr-Mktg)*

PRIME MASONRY MATERIALS
2800 Teal Club Rd, Oxnard, CA 93030
Tel.: (805) 985-1953 CA
Web Site: http://www.primemasonrymaterials.com
Sales Range: $10-24.9 Million
Emp.: 40
Brick, Stone & Related Materials Distr
N.A.I.C.S.: 423320
Shawn Campbell *(CEO)*

PRIME MORTGAGE USA INC.
1811 N Meridian St, Indianapolis, IN 46202
Tel.: (317) 396-5520
Rev.: $36,000,000
Emp.: 12
Mortgage Banker
N.A.I.C.S.: 522310

PRIME PLASTIC PRODUCTS, INC.
1351 Distribution Way Ste 8, Vista, CA 92081
Tel.: (760) 734-3900
Web Site: http://www.primeplastic.com
Year Founded: 1993
Sales Range: $10-24.9 Million
Emp.: 10
Recyclable Material Merchant Whslr
N.A.I.C.S.: 423930
Pradip Gupta *(Dir-Global Sourcing)*
Vince Gupta *(Pres)*
Rhea Gupta *(VP-Raw Matls Pur)*

PRIME PROPERTY INVESTORS, LTD.
333 Skokie Blvd Ste 113, Northbrook, IL 60062
Tel.: (847) 562-1800
Web Site: http://www.primepropertyinvestors.com
Year Founded: 1993
Sales Range: $25-49.9 Million
Emp.: 15
Real Estate Investments & Developments
N.A.I.C.S.: 525990
Michael H. Zaransky *(Co-Founder & Co-CEO)*
Barbara J. Gaffen *(Co-Founder & Co-CEO)*

PRIME REALTY INCOME TRUST, INC.
c/o The Prime Group North Clark St Ste 2500, Chicago, IL 60654
Tel.: (312) 917-1500 MD
Year Founded: 2009
Sales Range: $25-49.9 Million
Emp.: 75
Real Estate Investment Services
N.A.I.C.S.: 525990
Michael W. Reschke *(CEO)*
Mark K. Cynkar *(CFO)*
David M. Trandel *(COO)*

PRIME SERVICES GROUP INC.
5885 La Ribera St Ste C, Livermore, CA 94550
Tel.: (925) 294-5188
Web Site: http://www.psg-usa.com
Sales Range: $150-199.9 Million
Emp.: 19
Communications Specialization
N.A.I.C.S.: 238210

PRIME STAFFING INC.
3806 N Cicero, Chicago, IL 60641
Tel.: (773) 685-9399
Web Site: http://www.primestaffing.com
Sales Range: $10-24.9 Million
Emp.: 14
Temporary Help Service
N.A.I.C.S.: 561320
Robert Lewis *(Pres)*
Barry Bruckman *(Exec VP)*

PRIME SYSTEMS, INC.
416 Mission St, Carol Stream, IL 60188
Tel.: (630) 681-2100
Web Site: http://www.primeuv.com
Sales Range: $10-24.9 Million
Emp.: 33
Mfr.of Ultraviolet Lamp Fixtures & Machines for Dryers
N.A.I.C.S.: 335139
Elinor Midlik *(Pres)*

PRIME TECHNICAL SERVICES INC.
3495 Piedmont Rd NE Bldg 11-404, Atlanta, GA 30305
Tel.: (678) 585-4822
Web Site: http://www.prime-ts.com
Year Founded: 2014
Sales Range: $10-24.9 Million
Emp.: 210
Professional Consultancy Services
N.A.I.C.S.: 541690
Kurt Sobotka *(Co-Founder & Pres)*
Kyle Sobotka *(Co-Founder)*

PRIME TECHNOLOGICAL SERVICES, LLC
2925 Shawnee Industrial Way Ste 200, Suwanee, GA 30024
Tel.: (770) 232-7300
Web Site: http://www.prime-ems.com
Year Founded: 1989
Sales Range: $10-24.9 Million
Emp.: 90
Radio & Television Broadcasting & Wireless Communications Equipment Mfr
N.A.I.C.S.: 334220
Jerry Stern *(VP-Sls & Mktg)*
Greg Chesnutt *(Pres & CEO)*
Nancy Nunn *(VP-Fin & Admin)*
Lisa Nickerson *(Dir-Ops)*
Eddie Fox *(Dir-Supply Chain)*
Jay Jackson *(Mgr-Quality & Trng)*
Jim Liptak *(Mgr-Engrg & Mfg Tech)*
Sonny Sapp *(Mgr-Production Ops)*
Joe Litavis *(Chief Sls Officer & CMO)*

Subsidiaries:

I. Technical Services LLC (1)
6245 Shiloh Rd Ste D, Alpharetta, GA 30005
Tel.: (850) 420-4376
Web Site: http://www.itechserv.com
Rev.: $1,600,000
Emp.: 16
Bare Printed Circuit Board Mfr
N.A.I.C.S.: 334412
Mike Thompson *(Pres & CEO)*

TeligentEMS, LLC (1)
102 Technology Way, Havana, FL 32333-2000
Tel.: (850) 539-2509
Web Site: http://www.teligentems.com
Printed Circuit Assembly Mfr
N.A.I.C.S.: 334418
Mike Wallace *(Mgr-Bus Dev)*

PRIME WHEEL CORPORATION
17705 S Main St, Gardena, CA 90248
Tel.: (310) 516-9126
Web Site: http://www.primewheel.com
Year Founded: 1989
Sales Range: $150-199.9 Million
Emp.: 800
Wheels, Motor Vehicle
N.A.I.C.S.: 336390
Albert Huang *(CFO & VP)*
Darren Mizuno *(Mgr-Bus Dev)*
Philip Chen *(Vice Chm)*
Ernesto Cruz *(Mgr-Safety)*
Fernando Macias *(Coord-SPC)*
Guillermo Weidmann *(Mgr-Quality)*
Peter Liang *(Plant Mgr)*
Mac Charoensub *(Coord-Logistics)*

PRIME, INC.
2740 N Mayfair, Springfield, MO 65803
Tel.: (417) 521-6886
Web Site: http://www.primeinc.com
Year Founded: 1970
Sales Range: $650-699.9 Million
Emp.: 600
Long Distance Trucking Services
N.A.I.C.S.: 484230
Robert E. Low *(Founder & Pres)*
Steve Wutke *(VP-Sls-Refrigerated Div & Mktg)*
Keith McCoy *(Dir-Mktg)*
Pat Leonard *(Dir-Ops)*
Patricia Hicks *(Mgr-Taxes & Permits)*
Zach Whitehead *(Mgr-Credit)*
Don Lacy *(Dir-Safety)*
Jim Wilkins *(Dir-Flatbed & Tanker Ops)*
Steve Crawford *(Gen Counsel)*
David Pfitzner *(Mgr-Pricing-Natl)*
Rodney Rader *(Dir-Tech)*
Brett Vonwiller *(Mgr-Tanker)*

Subsidiaries:

LHP Transportation Services (1)
2032 E Kearney Ste 213, Springfield, MO 65803
Tel.: (417) 865-7577
Web Site: http://www.lhptransport.com
Rev.: $20,649,986
Emp.: 6
Freight Transportation Arrangement
N.A.I.C.S.: 488510
Lee Hampton *(Pres)*
Robert Low *(VP)*

PRIME-LINE PRODUCTS COMPANY
26950 San Bernardino Ave, Redlands, CA 92374
Tel.: (909) 887-8118 CA
Web Site: http://www.primeline.net
Year Founded: 1978
Window, Door & Safety & Security Product Replacement Hardware Sales
N.A.I.C.S.: 423710
Karl Pomeroy *(Dir-Engrg)*

PRIME-LINE, INC.
314 Reynolds Rd Bldg 4, Malvern, AR 72104
Tel.: (501) 844-4429
Web Site: http://www.primelineinc.com
Year Founded: 1996
Sales Range: $10-24.9 Million
Emp.: 65
Steel Products Mfr
N.A.I.C.S.: 331513
Brian Feeney *(Pres & CEO)*
Bristol Reeves *(Mgr-Inside Sls)*
Don Barnett *(COO & Project Mgr)*
Tom Maddox *(CFO)*
Zac Havens *(Plant Mgr)*

PRIMECARE, INC.
562 Watertown Ave Ste 3, Waterbury, CT 06708
Tel.: (203) 597-8525 CT
Web Site: http://www.primecareinc.org
Year Founded: 1991
Sales Range: $10-24.9 Million
Emp.: 187
Developmental Disability Assistance Services
N.A.I.C.S.: 623210
Richard Smyle *(Pres)*
Tammy Campanelli *(VP)*
Karlene Hylton *(Sec)*
Mark P. Holnbeck *(Treas)*

PRIMED MANAGEMENT CONSULTING SERVICES INC.
PO Box 5080, San Ramon, CA 94583
Tel.: (925) 820-8300 CA
Web Site: http://www.hillphysicians.com
Year Founded: 1984
Sales Range: $25-49.9 Million
Emp.: 377
Health Care Management
N.A.I.C.S.: 541611
Steve McDermott *(Co-Founder, Pres & CEO)*
Darryl Cardoza *(Co-Founder & COO)*
Dan Robinson *(Chief Admin Officer)*
Rosaleen Derington *(Chief Medical Officer)*
Tim Richards *(CFO)*

Subsidiaries:

Hill Physicians Medical Group, Inc. (1)
2409 Crow Canyon Rd, San Ramon, CA 94583-0980
Tel.: (925) 820-8300
Web Site: http://www.hillphysicians.com
Sales Range: $25-49.9 Million
Emp.: 350
Health Care Managment
N.A.I.C.S.: 621111

Robert C. Feldman *(Treas)*
Elisabeth H. Renner *(Vice Chm & Dir-Primary Care Medical)*
David Joyner *(CEO)*
Alvin M. Sockolov *(Sec)*
Wendy Chow *(Chief Legal & Contracting Officer)*
Rosaleen Derington *(Chief Medical Svcs Officer)*
Craig Lanway *(CIO)*

PRIMEDIA, INC.
1775 Bald Hill Rd, Warwick, RI 02886-4210
Tel.: (401) 826-3600   RI
Web Site: http://www.primediahq.com
Year Founded: 1990
Sales Range: $25-49.9 Million
Emp.: 16
Media Buying Services
N.A.I.C.S.: 541830
Edward Valenti *(Founder & COO)*
Stephen Romanello *(VP-Acct Svcs)*
Candice McHugh *(Media Buyer)*
James J. Cooney Jr. *(Pres, CEO & Dir-Creative)*

PRIMEGROUP INSURANCE, INC.
5402 W Laurel St Ste 220, Tampa, FL 33607
Tel.: (813) 288-8270
Web Site: http://www.primegroupins.com
Year Founded: 1999
Sales Range: $25-49.9 Million
Emp.: 40
Insurance Services
N.A.I.C.S.: 524210
Kevin Dugan *(VP)*
Ed Ellsasser *(Pres)*

PRIMEMEDICAL SUPPLY COMPANY
3915 Banson Ave, Baltimore, MD 21227
Tel.: (410) 787-2069
Web Site: http://www.primemedicalsupply.com
Year Founded: 2001
Sales Range: $10-24.9 Million
Emp.: 27
Medical & Surgical Supply Distr
N.A.I.C.S.: 339113
Denise Schaefer *(Office Mgr)*

PRIMENET DIRECT MARKETING SOLUTIONS, LLC
7320 Bryan Dairy Rd, Largo, FL 33777
Tel.: (727) 447-6245   FL
Web Site: http://www.primenet.com
Year Founded: 1962
Sales Range: $25-49.9 Million
Emp.: 100
Direct Mail Marketing Services
N.A.I.C.S.: 541860
Mark J. Keefe *(Pres & Owner)*
Georgia Woitas *(Dir-Product Dev)*

PRIMEPAK COMPANY
133 Cedar Ln, Teaneck, NJ 07666-4416
Tel.: (201) 836-5060   NJ
Web Site: http://www.primepakcompany.com
Year Founded: 1974
Sales Range: $75-99.9 Million
Emp.: 40
Mfr of Plastic Bags
N.A.I.C.S.: 424610
John J. Verrier *(CEO)*
William G. Poppe Jr. *(Pres)*

PRIMEPAY, LLC
1487 Dunwoody Dr, West Chester, PA 19380
Tel.: (610) 296-4500   DE
Web Site: http://www.primepay.com
Year Founded: 1986
Payroll Services
N.A.I.C.S.: 541214
John Cuellar *(CTO)*
Michael Myshrall *(CFO)*
Robert R. Ellis *(COO)*
Yancy Oshita *(CMO)*
Tim Beadnell *(Chief Revenue Officer)*
Scott Johnson *(CEO)*
Matthew Schubert *(Chief Strategy Officer)*
Stephen Feldman *(Chief Compliance Officer)*
Frank McNamara *(Chief Legal Officer)*
Adil Shabbir *(Chief Product & Tech Officer)*

PRIMEREVENUE, INC
1349 W Peachtree St Ste 1800, Atlanta, GA 30309
Tel.: (678) 904-7100
Web Site: http://www.primerevenue.com
Year Founded: 2004
Sales Range: $10-24.9 Million
Emp.: 85
Financial Transaction Processing Services
N.A.I.C.S.: 522320
PJ Bain *(CEO)*
Nathan Feather *(CFO & Gen Mgr-Europe)*
Eugene Buckley *(VP & Gen Mgr-Asia-Pacific)*
Matt Doorley *(VP & Gen Mgr-Americas)*
Dan Juliano *(Sr VP-Bus Dev)*
Robert Kramer *(VP-Working Capital Products & Solutions)*
David Quillian *(Gen Counsel & VP)*
Oliver Belin *(VP-Receivables Fin)*
Nicole Bjugger *(Mgr-Global Program)*
Dominic Capolongo *(Exec VP & Head-Funding-Global)*

PRIMESKILL STAFFING SERVICES
400 E Esplanade Dr Ste 105, Oxnard, CA 93036
Tel.: (805) 988-1500
Web Site: http://www.PrimeSkillStaffing.com
Year Founded: 2007
Sales Range: $10-24.9 Million
Emp.: 23
Human Resource Consulting Services
N.A.I.C.S.: 541612
Dalia Estrada *(Mgr-HR & Acctg)*

PRIMESOURCE FOODSERVICE EQUIPMENT
1409 S Lamar St Ste 1007, Dallas, TX 75215
Tel.: (214) 273-4900
Web Site: http://www.primesourcefse.com
Sales Range: $125-149.9 Million
Emp.: 108
Commercial Cooking & Food Service Equipment
N.A.I.C.S.: 423440
Pilar Nordin *(Mgr-Intl Bus Dev)*
Darren Anderson *(Pres & COO)*
Robb Gibbins *(CFO)*

PRIMESOUTH BANCSHARES, INC.
3473 US Hwy 84, Blackshear, GA 31516
Tel.: (912) 449-6685
Web Site: http://www.primesouth.com
Year Founded: 2000
Bank Holding Company
N.A.I.C.S.: 551111
Paul Kirtley *(CFO)*
James Walker *(Pres & CEO)*

Subsidiaries:

PrimeSouth Bank   (1)
3473 US Hwy 84, Blackshear, GA 31516
Tel.: (912) 449-6685
Web Site: http://www.primesouth.com
Commercial Banking
N.A.I.C.S.: 522110
James Walker *(Pres & CEO)*

PRIMETIME AMUSEMENTS OF SOUTH FLORIDA LLC
5300 Powerline Rd Ste 210, Fort Lauderdale, FL 33309
Tel.: (305) 770-4263
Web Site: http://www.primetimeamusements.com
Year Founded: 1992
Sales Range: $1-9.9 Million
Emp.: 12
Video Arcade Machines & Simulators Operator, Sales & Rental
N.A.I.C.S.: 713120
David Goldfarb *(Pres)*

PRIMITIVES BY KATHY INC.
1817 William Penn Way, Lancaster, PA 17601
Tel.: (717) 394-4220
Web Site: http://www.primitivesbykathy.com
Year Founded: 1997
Sales Range: $10-24.9 Million
Emp.: 75
Decorative Giftware
N.A.I.C.S.: 459420
Kathy Phillips *(Owner)*
Julie Phipps *(Acct Mgr-Key)*
Megan Leonard *(Dir-Art)*
Anita Kolibas *(Mgr-HR)*

PRIMMS LP
950 Warrenville Rd, Lisle, IL 60532
Tel.: (630) 572-3322
Rev.: $35,000,000
Emp.: 140
Truck, Utility Trailer & RV Rental & Leasing
N.A.I.C.S.: 532120
Michael Bruno *(VP-HR)*
Marc Cialoni *(Mgr)*
Craig Clemens *(VP-Sls)*
Phil Hirsch *(VP-Mktg)*
John Wixom *(VP)*

PRIMROSE CANDY CO.
4111 W Parker Ave, Chicago, IL 60639-2111
Tel.: (773) 276-9522
Web Site: http://www.primrosecandy.com
Year Founded: 1928
Sales Range: $25-49.9 Million
Emp.: 170
Candy & Popcorn Confection Mfr
N.A.I.C.S.: 311351
Richard Griseto *(VP-Sls & Mktg)*
Nicole Puch *(Coord-Production)*

PRIMUS BUILDERS, INC.
8294 Hwy 92 Ste 210, Woodstock, GA 30189
Tel.: (770) 928-7120
Web Site: http://www.primusbuilders.com
Year Founded: 2000
Sales Range: $75-99.9 Million
Emp.: 30
Specialized Design, General Contracting & Construction of Refrigerated Facilities to Food & Beverage Distribution
N.A.I.C.S.: 493120
Michael D. Jones *(Pres-Design Svcs)*
Richard O'Connell *(CEO & Partner)*
Erik Gunderson *(Partner & Exec VP)*
Paul Grenier *(Sr VP)*
Matthew Hirsch *(Pres)*
Antony Pitrone *(VP)*
Jordan Kuhn *(Dir-Mktg)*
Christopher Mann *(VP-California)*
Ian Smith *(VP-Process Plng)*

Subsidiaries:

Primus Design Services   (1)
8294 Hwy 92 Ste 210, Woodstock, GA 30189   (100%)
Tel.: (770) 928-7120
Web Site: http://www.primusbuilders.com
Fully Integrated Design Services
N.A.I.C.S.: 541420
Michael D. Jones *(Pres)*
Tony Ooten *(Engr)*
Erik Gunderson *(Exec VP)*
John H. Navarro *(COO)*
Paul Voss *(Dir-Ethics & Compliance)*

PRIMUS CAPITAL PARTNERS, INC.
Eton Tower 28601 Chagrin Blvd Ste 525, Woodmere, OH 44122
Tel.: (440) 684-7300
Web Site: http://www.primuscapital.com
Year Founded: 1983
Sales Range: $10-24.9 Million
Emp.: 16
Private Equity Firm
N.A.I.C.S.: 523999
Loyal W. Wilson *(Mng Dir)*
Jonathan E. Dick *(Mng Dir)*
Phillip C. Molner *(Mng Dir)*
Aaron W. Davis *(Principal)*
Chris Welch *(Principal)*
Stefanie Seidner *(Controller)*
Dominic E. Offredo *(CFO)*
William Charles Mulligan *(Mng Partner)*
Ronald C. Hess Jr. *(Mng Dir)*

PRIMUS GLOBAL SERVICES INC.
1431 Greenway Dr Ste 750, Irving, TX 75038-2492
Tel.: (972) 753-6500
Web Site: http://www.primusglobal.com
Year Founded: 2002
Sales Range: $10-24.9 Million
Emp.: 80
Staffing & Technology Services
N.A.I.C.S.: 561311
Anil Kilaru *(CEO)*
Govardhan Mutluru *(Engr-Sys)*

PRIMUS PHARMACEUTICALS, INC.
7373 N Scottsdale Rd Ste B 200, Scottsdale, AZ 85253
Tel.: (480) 483-1410
Web Site: http://www.primusrx.com
Year Founded: 2000
Sales Range: $10-24.9 Million
Emp.: 65
Prescription Metabolic Product Distr
N.A.I.C.S.: 424210
James D. Weir *(Founder)*
Calvin M. Mitchell *(Sr VP-Product Supply)*
Frank J. Strocchio *(Controller)*
Michael J. Martin *(CFO)*
Kathleen E. Arendt *(Dir-HR & Admin)*

PRIMUS THERAPEUTICS, INC.
23 Orchard Rd Ste 105, Skillman, NJ 08558   DE
Year Founded: 2010
Sales Range: $10-24.9 Million
Emp.: 2
Pharmaceuticals Mfr

PRIMUS THERAPEUTICS, INC.

Primus Therapeutics, Inc.—(Continued)
N.A.I.C.S.: 325412
Dennis M. O'Donnell *(Pres & CEO)*
Mark I. Massad *(CFO)*
Joseph A. Falsetti *(Chm)*

PRINCE & IZANT COMPANY
12999 Plz Dr, Cleveland, OH 44130
Tel.: (216) 362-7000 — OH
Web Site: http://www.princeizant.com
Year Founded: 1927
Sales Range: $1-9.9 Million
Emp.: 68
Mfr & Supplier of Metal Joining Services
N.A.I.C.S.: 423510
Kim Brandenburg *(VP)*
Gus Salamalekis *(Mgr-Sls)*

PRINCE AUTOMOTIVE GROUP INC.
1410 Hwy 82 W, Tifton, GA 31793
Tel.: (229) 382-2525
Web Site: http://www.princeauto.com
Rev.: $38,200,000
Emp.: 75
Automotive Distr
N.A.I.C.S.: 441110
Joe Tinsley *(Gen Mgr)*

PRINCE CORPORATION
8351 E Connie Rd H, Marshfield, WI 54449
Tel.: (715) 384-3105 — WI
Web Site: http://www.prince-corp.com
Year Founded: 1909
Sales Range: $25-49.9 Million
Emp.: 110
Wholesale Distributor & Manufacturer of Animal Feeds
N.A.I.C.S.: 423310
Jay Emling *(Pres)*
Brian Stainbrook *(Supvr-IT)*
Jeffrey Gotter *(Mgr-Lawn & Garden Div)*

PRINCE GEORGE'S COUNTY MEMORIAL LIBRARY SYSTEM
9601 Capital Ln, Largo, MD 20774
Tel.: (301) 699-3500 — MD
Web Site: http://www.pgcmls.info
Year Founded: 1946
Sales Range: $25-49.9 Million
Emp.: 327
Library Operator
N.A.I.C.S.: 519210
Michael B. Gannon *(COO-Support Svcs)*
Alease J. Christy Wright *(Partner)*
Robin Jacobsen *(Dir-Community Engagement)*

PRINCE GOLF
1 Advantage Ct Ste G, Bordentown, NJ 08505
Tel.: (609) 291-5981
Year Founded: 1988
Sales Range: $50-74.9 Million
Emp.: 5
Mfr of Golf Clubs
N.A.I.C.S.: 339920
Chuck Stickelmaier *(Pres)*
Mark Zehfuss *(Mktg Dir & Sls Dir)*

PRINCE MANUFACTURING CORPORATION
612 N Derby Ln, North Sioux City, SD 57049-7000
Tel.: (605) 235-1220 — SD
Web Site: http://www.princehyd.com
Year Founded: 1950
Sales Range: $25-49.9 Million
Emp.: 450
Fluid Power Cylinders & Actuators
N.A.I.C.S.: 333995

Pete Mullen *(Sr VP-Fin)*
Dan D. Vaneldik *(Reg Mgr-Sls)*
Gary Flammang *(Mgr-Distr & Natl Sls)*

PRINCE OF PEACE ENTERPRISES
3536 Arden Rd, Hayward, CA 94545
Tel.: (510) 887-1899
Web Site: http://www.popus.com
Rev.: $11,200,000
Emp.: 36
Health Foods
N.A.I.C.S.: 424490
Kenneth Yeung *(Pres)*

PRINCE RUBBER & PLASTICS CO., INC.
137 Arthur St, Buffalo, NY 14207
Tel.: (716) 877-7400
Web Site: http://www.princerp.com
Rev.: $10,000,000
Emp.: 36
Plastics Processing
N.A.I.C.S.: 326199
Larry Terzain *(Controller)*
Jennifer Bronstein *(VP-Mktg)*
S. Warren Prince Jr. *(Chm)*

PRINCE-BUSH INVESTMENTS
227 W New England Ave, Winter Park, FL 32789-4260
Tel.: (407) 629-4776 — FL
Web Site: http://www.princebush.com
Year Founded: 1985
Rev.: $30,000,000
Emp.: 400
Hotels & Motels
N.A.I.C.S.: 721110
Robert C. Bush *(Partner)*
Thomas P. Prince *(Partner)*
Patrick F. Olson *(Pres)*
Mark Dana *(Sr VP & Mng Partner)*
William P. Reilly Jr. *(Sr VP & Mng Partner)*

PRINCETON AREA COMMUNITY FOUNDATION
15 Princess Rd, Lawrenceville, NJ 08648
Tel.: (609) 219-1800 — NJ
Web Site: http://www.pacf.org
Year Founded: 1991
Sales Range: $10-24.9 Million
Emp.: 8
Grantmaking Services
N.A.I.C.S.: 813211
Laura J. Longman *(CFO)*
Michelle Cash *(VP-Grants & Programs)*
Trisha Volk *(Dir-Donor Svcs)*
Elizabeth B. Wagner *(VP-Dev)*
Jeffrey M. Vega *(Pres & CEO)*
Diana Leighton *(VP-Dev Programs)*
Anthony Cimino *(Chm)*
Carolyn Sanderson *(Vice Chm)*
Meredith Moore *(Vice Chm)*
Andrew Lieu *(Sec)*
Marguerite Mount *(Treas)*

PRINCETON BIOMEDITECH CORP.
4242 US Hwy 1, Monmouth Junction, NJ 08852
Tel.: (732) 274-1000
Web Site: http://www.pbmc.com
Rev.: $13,000,000
Emp.: 120
In Vitro Diagnostics
N.A.I.C.S.: 325413
Jemo Kang *(Pres)*
Gun Soo Han *(Mgr)*
Kiyong Jang *(Product Mgr)*

PRINCETON BMW
3630 Quakerbridge Rd, Hamilton, NJ 08619
Tel.: (609) 452-9400
Web Site: http://www.princetonbmw.com
Rev.: $19,300,000
Emp.: 50
New & Used Automobile Dealer
N.A.I.C.S.: 441110
Vincent Lorenti *(Mgr-Parts)*

PRINCETON CLUB OF NEW YORK
15 W 43rd St, New York, NY 10036
Tel.: (212) 596-1200 — NY
Web Site: http://www.princetonclub.com
Year Founded: 1899
Sales Range: $10-24.9 Million
Emp.: 153
Recreation Club Operator
N.A.I.C.S.: 713910
Larry Hines *(Gen Mgr)*
Abraham Ajewole *(Dir-Fin)*
Wanda Mann *(Dir-Comm & Events)*

PRINCETON COMMUNITY HOSPITAL
1222 Twelfth St, Princeton, WV 24740
Tel.: (304) 487-7000
Web Site: http://www.pchonline.org
Year Founded: 1970
Medical Hospital
N.A.I.C.S.: 441110
James Sarver III *(Pres)*

Subsidiaries:

Bluefield Hospital Company, LLC (1)
500 Cherry St, Bluefield, WV 24701
Tel.: (304) 327-1100
Web Site: http://www.bluefieldregional.net
Health Care Srvices
N.A.I.C.S.: 622110
Brian Kelbaugh *(VP-Fin)*

PRINCETON LAND ROVER
1125 Route 206, Princeton, NJ 08540
Tel.: (609) 921-7788
Web Site: http://www.princetonlandrover.com
Year Founded: 1996
Sales Range: $10-24.9 Million
Emp.: 54
Car Whslr
N.A.I.C.S.: 441110
Joshua T. Kalafer *(Owner)*

PRINCETON PACKET INC.
300 Witherspoon St, Princeton, NJ 08540
Tel.: (609) 924-3244
Web Site: http://www.centraljersey.com
Sales Range: $25-49.9 Million
Emp.: 26
Newspapers, Publishing & Printing
N.A.I.C.S.: 513110
James B. Kilgore *(Pres)*
Beth Gandy *(Mgr-Pre Press)*

PRINCETON PARTNERS, INC.
205 Rockingham Row, Princeton, NJ 08540
Tel.: (609) 452-8500
Web Site: http://www.princetonpartners.com
Year Founded: 1965
Sales Range: $1-9.9 Million
Emp.: 25
Advertising Agencies
N.A.I.C.S.: 541810
Thomas Sullivan *(CEO)*
Jeff Chesebro *(Pres)*
Jan Sullivan *(Mgr-HR)*
Paul Federico *(Dir-Creative)*
Chris Sullivan *(VP-Cross Media)*

U.S. PRIVATE

Tim Burr *(Assoc Dir-Creative)*
Aaron Stoker-Ring *(Assoc Dir-Creative)*
Giselle Herrera *(Controller)*
Leigh Cesanek *(Coord-Social Media & Digital Content)*
Robert Groves *(Mgr-Media)*

PRINCETON PROPERTY MANAGEMENT
520 SW Yamhill St Ste 600, Portland, OR 97204-1329
Tel.: (503) 794-9004
Web Site: http://www.princetonproperty.com
Year Founded: 1984
Sales Range: $10-24.9 Million
Emp.: 600
Real Estate Brokerage Services
N.A.I.C.S.: 531210
Freddy Lunt *(CEO)*
Leif Anderson *(Dir-Bus Dev)*
Amy Alcala *(Dir-Ops)*
Colleen Argentine *(Dir-HR)*
Allison Brown *(Sr Portfolio Mgr)*
Joletta Lorio *(Portfolio Mgr)*
Laura Lunsford *(Sr Portfolio Mgr)*
Greg Knakal *(Sr Portfolio Mgr)*
Laura Flores *(Portfolio Mgr)*
Leslie Johnstone *(Portfolio Mgr)*
Michele Lovin *(Portfolio Mgr)*
Jenny McCord *(Assoc Portfolio Mgr)*
Sylvia Walker *(Portfolio Mgr)*

PRINCETON UNIVERSITY PRESS
41 William St, Princeton, NJ 08540-5237
Tel.: (609) 258-4900 — DE
Web Site: http://www.press.princeton.edu
Year Founded: 1905
Sales Range: $75-99.9 Million
Emp.: 100
Publisher of Scholarly Books
N.A.I.C.S.: 513120
Patrick Carroll *(Controller)*
Adam Fortgang *(Dir-Asst Press & Dir-Mktg)*
Neil Litt *(Design & Production)*

PRINCIPAL BUILDING SERVICES, INC.
505 8th Ave Ste 1000, New York, NY 10018
Tel.: (212) 643-0101
Web Site: http://www.principalbuildingservices.com
Year Founded: 1999
Sales Range: $10-24.9 Million
Emp.: 150
Janitorial Services
N.A.I.C.S.: 561720
Howard Fox *(Principal)*
Sal Mincone *(Principal)*
Jan Hirschhorn *(CFO)*
Ramo Cosovic *(VP-Ops)*

PRINCIPAL MANUFACTURING CORP.
2800 S 19th Ave, Broadview, IL 60155
Tel.: (708) 865-7500
Web Site: http://www.principalmfg.com
Year Founded: 1939
Sales Range: $25-49.9 Million
Emp.: 300
Stamping & Plastic Injection Molding Mfr
N.A.I.C.S.: 333511
Paul Barnett *(Owner & Pres)*

PRINCIPAL MARITIME TANKERS CORPORATION

COMPANIES

3530 Post Rd, Southport, CT 06890
Tel.: (203) 292-9580　　MH
Web Site: http://www.princimar.com
Year Founded: 2014
Deep Sea Petroleum Products Transportation
N.A.I.C.S.: 483111
Bart B. Kelleher (COO)
Kevin M. Kilcullen (CFO)
Michael J. Mitchell (Exec VP & Head-Global Ops)
Arthur L. Regan (Pres & CEO)

PRINCIPLE CONSTRUCTION CORP.
9450 West Bryn Mawr Ave Ste 765, Rosemont, IL 60018
Tel.: (847) 615-1515
Web Site: http://www.pccdb.com
Year Founded: 1999
Rev.: $43,700,000
Emp.: 11
Design Build Construction Services
N.A.I.C.S.: 236210
James A. Brucato (Co-Founder & Pres)
Mark Augustyn (Co-Founder & COO)
James Molzahn (Mgr-Acctg)
Michael Long (VP)
Dennis Crawford (Superintendent)
Phil VanDuyne (Dir-Pre Construction Svcs)

PRINCIPLE POWER, INC.
5901 Christie Ave Ste 303, Emeryville, CA 94608
Tel.: (510) 280-5180
Web Site: http://www.principlepowerinc.com
Year Founded: 2007
Marine Engineering Services
N.A.I.C.S.: 541330
Dominique Roddier (CTO)
Joao Metelo (CEO)
Ralph Sahrmann (Gen Counsel)
Guillaume Ardoise (Sr Mgr-Dev)
Kevin Banister (VP & Head-Dev)
Antoine Peiffer (Mgr-Dev & Supply Chain)
Alexia Aubault (VP & Head-Engrng)
Cyril Giraud (Coord-Design)
Lea Itkin (Designer)
Mitch Aldridge (Mgr-Offshore Ops)
Thomas Marty (Project Mgr)
Joao Mendonca Santos (Mgr-Fabrication)
Fernando Hilario (Controller-Fin)
Alda Martins (Mgr-Compliance)
Aaron Smith (VP & Head-Strategy)

PRINCIPLES GROUP LLC
26 Church St PO Box 305, Liberty Corner, NJ 07938
Tel.: (973) 795-2232
Web Site: http://www.principlesgroup.com
Year Founded: 2002
Sales Range: $1-9.9 Million
Emp.: 12
Management Consulting Services
N.A.I.C.S.: 541618
Mike Tierney (Mng Partner)
Doug Shurts (Mng Partner)

PRINSBURG FARMERS CO-OP
404 RailRd Ave, Prinsburg, MN 56281
Tel.: (320) 978-8100　　MN
Web Site: http://www.prccoop.com
Year Founded: 1927
Sales Range: $75-99.9 Million
Emp.: 40
Grain & Field Beans Supplier
N.A.I.C.S.: 424510
Harvey Van Eps (Gen Mgr)
Don Grussing (Pres)

PRINSCO INC.
108 Hwy 7 W, Prinsburg, MN 56281
Tel.: (320) 978-4116
Web Site: http://www.prinsco.com
Sales Range: $10-24.9 Million
Emp.: 125
Plastics Pipe
N.A.I.C.S.: 326122
Jason Ahrenholz (Engr-Application)
Steve Broten (Mgr-Dispatch)
Mandy Heinen (Mgr-Travel & Coord-Mktg Projects)
Brad Nelson (Project Mgr)
Byron Brouwer (Plant Mgr)
Dave Carlson (Product Mgr)

PRINT IT 4 LESS
601 N Congress Ave, Delray Beach, FL 33445
Tel.: (561) 368-6884
Web Site: http://www.printit4less.com
Year Founded: 1999
Sales Range: $1-9.9 Million
Emp.: 12
Office Products & Custom Printed Forms
N.A.I.C.S.: 459410
Shawn Samaei (Pres)

PRINT NW LLC
9914 32nd Ave S, Tacoma, WA 98499
Tel.: (253) 284-2300
Web Site: http://www.printnw.net
Sales Range: $10-24.9 Million
Emp.: 45
Commercial Flexographic Printing Services
N.A.I.C.S.: 323111
Jeffery Beardemphl (Co-Owner)
Jeff Stallings (Co-Owner)
Bruce Dammeier (Co-Owner)

PRINT REACH, INC.
240 14th St S, Jacksonville Beach, FL 32250
Tel.: (888) 581-3100　　FL
Web Site: http://www.printreach.com
Year Founded: 2019
Print & Mail Productivity Software Provider
N.A.I.C.S.: 513210
Chris Huber (CEO)
Greg Witek (COO)

Subsidiaries:

PagePath Technologies, Inc.　(1)
13 East Main St, Plano, IL 60545
Tel.: (630) 689-4111
Web Site: http://www.pagepath.com
Software Publisher
N.A.I.C.S.: 513210
Jim Dummer (Mgr-Sls)

Virtual Information Systems Corp.　(1)
15600 NE 8th St Ste B1-994, Bellevue, WA 98008
Tel.: (425) 828-9495
Web Site: http://www.virtualsystems.com
Custom Computer Programming Services
N.A.I.C.S.: 541511

PRINT RESOURCES, INC.
1500 E Riverside Dr, Indianapolis, IN 46202
Tel.: (317) 833-7000
Web Site: http://www.printindy.com
Year Founded: 2000
Sales Range: $1-9.9 Million
Emp.: 11
Professional, Scientific & Technical Services
N.A.I.C.S.: 541990
Kurt Ellinger (Treas)
Timothy J. Browning (Pres)

PRINT SOUTH CORPORATION
1115 Tyler St, Fredericksburg, VA 22401
Tel.: (404) 349-4514　　GA
Web Site: http://www.printsouth.com
Year Founded: 1993
Rev.: $75,000,000
Emp.: 350
Commercial Printing, Lithographic
N.A.I.C.S.: 323111
Samuel L. Peters (Pres)
Patti Hikendal (Controller)
Mark Clabaugh (VP-Sls & Mktg)
Jerri Griffin (Prepress Mgr)
Mike Smith (Mgr-Plant)

PRINT TIME INC.
8016 State Line Rd Ste 111, Shawnee Mission, KS 66208-3710
Tel.: (913) 642-1700
Web Site: http://www.printtime.com
Sales Range: $10-24.9 Million
Emp.: 125
Commercial Lithographic Printing
N.A.I.C.S.: 323111
Melody Fillman (Office Mgr)
Richard J. Grindinger (Pres)

PRINT-O-TAPE, INC.
755 Tower Rd, Mundelein, IL 60060-3817
Tel.: (847) 362-1476　　IL
Web Site: http://www.printotape.com
Year Founded: 1946
Sales Range: $10-24.9 Million
Emp.: 50
Mfr of Pressure Sensitive Labels & Specialty Pressure Sensitive Coatings
N.A.I.C.S.: 322220
Carl J. Walliser (Pres)
Bob Ryan (Mgr-Traffic)
Jennifer Zemba (Mgr-Airline Transportation Bus)
Robert Ellison (Acct Mgr)
Ron Cuba (VP-Ops)

PRINTEK INC.
1517 Townline Rd, Benton Harbor, MI 49022
Tel.: (269) 925-3200
Web Site: http://www.printek.com
Rev.: $13,000,000
Emp.: 50
Mfr of Computer Printers
N.A.I.C.S.: 334118
Thomas C. Yeager (Owner)
Dean Driscoll (Controller)
Russ Corace (Exec VP)
Rhonda McMichael (Mgr-Sls)
Linda Eding (Mgr-Ops)

PRINTELECTRIC, INC.
2540 Elm St, Dallas, TX 75226
Tel.: (214) 655-6832
Web Site: http://www.printelectric.com
Year Founded: 1997
Sales Range: Less than $1 Million
Emp.: 4
Advetising Agency
N.A.I.C.S.: 541810
Scott Benton (Principal & Dir-Creative)
Mark Roberts (Principal & Mgr-Production)
Bruce McElroy (Principal & Acct Dir)
Terisa Davis (Dir-Creative)

PRINTERS SQUARE, INC.
105 Faltin Ave, Manchester, NH 03103
Tel.: (603) 703-0795　　NH
Web Site: http://www.talientactiongroup.com
Year Founded: 1985
Sales Range: $1-9.9 Million

Emp.: 16
Commercial Printing Services
N.A.I.C.S.: 323111
Sean Owen (Pres & CEO)
Denise Gendron (Comptroller)
Vicki Coleman (Mgr-Prepress)

PRINTERS' SERVICE, INC.
26 Blanchard St, Newark, NJ 07105
Tel.: (973) 589-7800　　NJ
Web Site: http://www.prisco.com
Year Founded: 1902
Sales Range: $75-99.9 Million
Emp.: 300
Printing Trades Machinery, Equipment & Supplies
N.A.I.C.S.: 423830
Bruce Liroff (Founder, Pres & COO)

Subsidiaries:

IGEPA Belux N.V.　(1)
Nijverheidslaan 4, 9880, Aalter, Belgium
Tel.: (32) 93254545
Web Site: http://www.igepa.be
Sales Range: $25-49.9 Million
Emp.: 135
Printing Trades Machinery Mfr
N.A.I.C.S.: 333248
Fernane Gfessa (Mgr-Supplies)

Mid-West Merchandising Corp.　(1)
312 Stewart Ave, Addison, IL 60101
Tel.: (630) 543-4600
Web Site: http://www.prisco.com
Sales Range: $10-24.9 Million
Emp.: 102
Provider of Printing Trades Machinery, Equipment & Supplies
N.A.I.C.S.: 423830
Frosty Botkin (Pres)
Tim Finegan (Mgr-Sls)

Printers Merchandising Corp.　(1)
35 Commerce Rd, Hingham, MA 02043
Tel.: (781) 749-4590
Web Site: http://www.prisco.com
Sales Range: $10-24.9 Million
Emp.: 9
Printing Trades Machinery, Equipment & Supplies
N.A.I.C.S.: 333248
Bruce Federman (Gen Mgr)

Printers Service of Florida, Inc.　(1)
1580 NW 27th Ave, Pompano Beach, FL 33069
Tel.: (954) 971-0436
Web Site: http://www.prisco.com
Sales Range: $10-24.9 Million
Emp.: 9
Printing Trades Machinery, Equipment & Supplies
N.A.I.C.S.: 333248
John Leo (Gen Mgr)

Prisco Digital, LLC　(1)
7055 Amwiler Industrial Dr Ste E, Atlanta, GA 30360
Tel.: (678) 602-4140
Web Site: http://www.prisco.com
Sales Range: $10-24.9 Million
Emp.: 25
Provider of Printing Trade Machinery Equipment Distr
N.A.I.C.S.: 459999
Jay Friedman (VP-Natl Acct)
Steve Zunde (Pres)

Prisco Europe Bvba　(1)
President Kennedypark 21 B, 8500, Kortrijk, Belgium
Tel.: (32) 56404182
Web Site: http://www.prisco.com
Sales Range: $25-49.9 Million
Emp.: 4
Mfr & Distr of Printing Chemicals & Miscellaneous Pressroom Supplies
N.A.I.C.S.: 333248
Jean Decoene (Mgr)

Prisco Europe Ltd.　(1)
Hammerain House, Hookstone, Harrogate, HG2 8ER, United Kingdom
Tel.: (44) 1423810320
Web Site: http://www.prisco.com
Sales Range: $25-49.9 Million
Emp.: 1

PRINTERS' SERVICE, INC.

Printers' Service, Inc.—(Continued)
Printing Trades Machinery, Equipment & Supplies
N.A.I.C.S.: 423830

Prisco Graphics of Canada, Inc. (1)
1210 Kerrisdale Boulevard Unit 3, Newmarket, L3Y 8Z9, ON, Canada
Tel.: (905) 953-9893
Sales Range: $25-49.9 Million
Emp.: 20
Printing Chemical & Product Distr
N.A.I.C.S.: 424690

Prisco/Pacific, Inc. (1)
1880 S Carlos Ave, Ontario, CA 91761
Tel.: (909) 923-1879
Web Site: http://www.prisco.com
Sales Range: $10-24.9 Million
Emp.: 15
Printing Trades Machinery, Equipment & Supplies
N.A.I.C.S.: 423830
Brian Rodriguez (Gen Mgr)

PRINTFLEX GRAPHICS, INC.
2201 January Ave, Saint Louis, MO 63110
Tel.: (314) 781-0030
Web Site: http://www.print-flex.com
Sales Range: $10-24.9 Million
Emp.: 25
Commercial Printing of Labels, Stickers & Coupons
N.A.I.C.S.: 323111
Elizabeth Pecha-Poeker (CEO)
Jeff Feeney (Gen Mgr)
Steve Baum (Pres)

PRINTFLY CORP.
2727 Commerce Way, Philadelphia, PA 19154
Web Site: http://www.printfly.com
Year Founded: 2002
Custom Printing Services
N.A.I.C.S.: 323111
Kane Posner (Exec VP)
Jason Haft (Exec VP-Ops & Growth)
Kimberly Tricome (Coord-HR)
Subsidiaries:

Tonic Design Co. (1)
441 N 5th St Ste 301, Philadelphia, PA 19123
Tel.: (215) 860-1982
Software Design & Development Services
N.A.I.C.S.: 541511

PRINTFUL, INC.
11025 Westlake Dr, Charlotte, NC 28273
Tel.: (818) 351-7181
Web Site: http://www.printful.com
Year Founded: 2013
Sales Range: $75-99.9 Million
Emp.: 500
Printing & Embroidery Services
N.A.I.C.S.: 323111
Davis Siksnans (Co-Founder)
Alex Saltonstall (CEO)
Zane Levsa (COO)
Lauris Liberts (Co-Founder & Chm)

PRINTGLOBE, INC.
4115 Freidrich Ln Ste 200, Austin, TX 78744
Tel.: (512) 454-5985
Web Site: http://www.printglobe.com
Year Founded: 1995
Sales Range: $1-9.9 Million
Emp.: 30
Custom Printing
N.A.I.C.S.: 561499
Priscilla Stevens (Acct Mgr)
John Bohls (Acct Mgr)
Kristin Ungar (CFO)
Shane Auippa (Acct Mgr)
Karen Boman (Acct Mgr)
Virginia Underwood (Acct Mgr)

Stephanie Zieman (Acct Mgr)
Chris Love (Acct Mgr)
Crystal Bobbitt (Dir-Mktg)
Kitty Tinsman (Dir-Mdsg)
Kimberli Larson (Acct Mgr)

PRINTING MANAGEMENT ASSOCIATES
17128 Edwards Rd, Cerritos, CA 90703
Tel.: (562) 407-9977
Web Site: http://www.printmgt.com
Rev.: $12,300,000
Emp.: 20
Printing Paper
N.A.I.C.S.: 424110
Rich Russel (CEO)

PRINTINGFORLESS.COM, INC.
100 PFL Way, Livingston, MT 59047
Tel.: (406) 222-2689   DE
Web Site: http://www.printingforless.com
Year Founded: 1996
Sales Range: $1-9.9 Million
Emp.: 100
Online Commercial Printing Services
N.A.I.C.S.: 323111
Andrew S. Field (Founder & CEO)
Nick Runyon (CMO)
Casey Bartz (CTO)
Daniel Gaugler (Chief Product & Innovation Officer)
Erin Ortega (VP-Fin)
Subsidiaries:

CreativePro, Inc. (1)
14241 NE Woodinville Duvall Rd 285, Woodinville, WA 98072
Tel.: (425) 252-1292
Web Site: http://www.creativepro.com
Product Updates, News, Reviews & Affiliate Services
N.A.I.C.S.: 323111
Mike Rankin (Editor-in-Chief)

PRINTPACK INC.
2800 Overlook Pkwy, Atlanta, GA 30339
Tel.: (404) 460-7000   GA
Web Site: http://www.printpack.com
Year Founded: 1956
Sales Range: $1-4.9 Billion
Emp.: 3,900
Packaging Mfr
N.A.I.C.S.: 322220
Tripp Seitter (VP-Fin & Admin)
Terrence P. Harper (VP-Tech & Support)
Dave Kenny (Treas)
Mike Alto (Controller)
Jimmy Love (CEO)
Subsidiaries:

Printpack Inc. (1)
2800 Overlook Pkwy NE, Atlanta, GA 30339
Tel.: (404) 460-7000
Web Site: http://www.printpack.com
Rev.: $30,000,000
Emp.: 4
Plastic Bags
N.A.I.C.S.: 326111

PRINTPLACE.COM, LLC
1130 Ave H East, Arlington, TX 76011
Tel.: (817) 701-3555
Web Site: http://www.printplace.com
Year Founded: 2006
Sales Range: $25-49.9 Million
Emp.: 110
Full-Color Offset Printing Specialists
N.A.I.C.S.: 323111
Shawn Petersen (Founder & CEO)
Bill Becker (Co-Founder)
Lisa Hoffman (Product Mgr)
Stephanie Giotes (Gen Counsel & VP)

PRINTRON ENGRAVERS INC.
955 Breezewood Ln, Neenah, WI 54956
Tel.: (920) 725-3077
Web Site: http://www.printron.com
Sales Range: $10-24.9 Million
Emp.: 100
Marking Machine Printing Dies Mfr
N.A.I.C.S.: 339940
Steven Barry (Pres)

PRINTRUNNER, INC.
9673 Topanga Canyon Pl, Chatsworth, CA 91311
Tel.: (818) 993-9111   CA
Web Site: http://www.printrunner.com
Year Founded: 1999
Sales Range: $1-9.9 Million
Emp.: 64
Full Service Printing Company
N.A.I.C.S.: 323111
Seth Staszower (Pres)

PRINTSOUTH CORPORATION
7800 Third Flag Pkwy, Austell, GA 30168
Tel.: (404) 349-4514
Web Site: http://www.printsouth.com
Year Founded: 1993
Rev.: $10,700,000
Emp.: 25
Commercial Lithographic Printing Services
N.A.I.C.S.: 323111
Lynn Rogge (VP-Sls & Mktg)

PRINTVISION, INC.
31 W 34th St 8th Fl, New York, NY 10001
Tel.: (212) 398-4670
Web Site: http://www.printvision.com
Year Founded: 2005
Emp.: 25
Print Procurement Software Mfr
N.A.I.C.S.: 513210
Paul Trolio (Sr VP)
Chiaki Fujino (Pres & CEO)
Ivor Durham (CTO-Consulting)

PRINZ GRAIN & FEED INC.
575 S Main St, West Point, NE 68788
Tel.: (402) 372-2495
Web Site: http://www.printsouth.com
Sales Range: $10-24.9 Million
Emp.: 15
Grains
N.A.I.C.S.: 424510
David Prinz (Pres)
Glenn Prinz (Treas & Sec)

PRIORIA ROBOTICS, INC.
606 SE Depot Ave, Gainesville, FL 32601
Tel.: (352) 505-2188
Web Site: http://www.prioria.com
Year Founded: 2003
Sales Range: $1-9.9 Million
Emp.: 26
Search & Navigation Equipment Mfr
N.A.I.C.S.: 334511
Bryan da Frota (Co-Founder & CEO)
Jason Grzywna (Co-Founder & VP-Ops & Engrg)
Derek Lyons (VP-Sls)

PRIORITY AMERICA, INC.
7680 Universal Blvd Ste 650, Orlando, FL 32819-8971
Tel.: (407) 475-0122   FL
Web Site: http://www.priority-trans.com
Year Founded: 1985
Sales Range: $250-299.9 Million
Emp.: 2,150
Owner & Operator of Trucking Services

U.S. PRIVATE

N.A.I.C.S.: 484121
James Falmon (CEO)

PRIORITY AVIATION, INC.
309 N Oak St, Telluride, CO 81435
Investment Holding Company
N.A.I.C.S.: 551112
Yasmine Acebo (CEO)

PRIORITY DISPATCH INC.
4665 Malsbary Rd, Cincinnati, OH 45242
Tel.: (513) 791-3900
Web Site: http://www.prioritydispatch.com
Rev.: $22,077,324
Emp.: 65
Delivery Service Vehicular
N.A.I.C.S.: 484110
Richard Thomas (Founder & Chm)
R. Jeffrey Thomas (Pres & CEO)

PRIORITY LEASING, INC.
174 Green St, Melrose, MA 02176
Tel.: (781) 321-8778
Web Site: http://www.priorityleasing.com
Year Founded: 1997
Sales Range: $10-24.9 Million
Emp.: 50
Equipment Leasing Services
N.A.I.C.S.: 532490
Brian Gallucci (Mgr-Sls)
Christopher Morrissey (VP-Ops)
Gary Bacher (Dir-Bus Dev)
Jennifer Turner (Sr Acct Mgr)
Sean Hilliard (Dir-Vendor Svcs)

PRIORITY MARKETING
8200 College Pkwy Ste 201, Fort Myers, FL 33919
Tel.: (239) 267-2638
Web Site: http://www.prioritymarketing.com
Sales Range: $1-9.9 Million
Emp.: 30
Advetising Agency
N.A.I.C.S.: 541810
Teri Hansen (Pres & Dir-Creative)
Ava Bickel (Mgr-Production)
Linda Hatch (Office Mgr)
Holly Boldrin (Dir-PR)
Phillip Barrera (Mgr-Art)
Kim Barrera (Mgr-Production)
Lora-Lynn Chuffo (Dir-Fin & Admin)
Allie Schotanus (Dir-Digital Mktg)
Tyrone Belford (Dir-Digital Solutions)
Melissa Cofta (Mgr-Mktg & PR Acct)

PRIORITY ONE FINANCIAL SERVICES INC.
742 2nd Ave S, Saint Petersburg, FL 33701
Tel.: (727) 822-7171
Web Site: http://www.p1fs.com
Sales Range: $1-9.9 Million
Emp.: 56
Recreational & Equipment Financial & Insurance Services
N.A.I.C.S.: 522310
Heather Mariscal (Pres)
Mark Siler (VP-Tech)
Jason Edwards (Mgr-Comml Fin)
Rina Aponte (Mgr-Ops)
Dave Homan (VP-Fin)

PRIORITY ONE SERVICES INC.
6600 Fleet Dr, Alexandria, VA 22310
Tel.: (703) 971-5505
Web Site: http://www.priorityoneservices.com
Year Founded: 1986
Sales Range: $25-49.9 Million
Emp.: 480

Life Sciences & Transportation Research Services
N.A.I.C.S.: 541715
Venee Alicea (Controller)
Pamela Fontenot (VP-Admin & Dir-HR)
Jose Figueroa (Pres)
Ervin Walter (VP-Fin)
Vicky Mayoral (VP-Ops & Dir-Life Sciences)

PRIORITY PAYMENT SYSTEMS, LLC
2001 Westside Pkwy Ste 55, Alpharetta, GA 30004
Tel.: (678) 315-6205   GA
Web Site:
   http://www.prioritypaymentsystems.com
Year Founded: 2005
Emp.: 492
Financial Transaction Processing Services
N.A.I.C.S.: 522320
John V. Priore (Pres & CEO)
Bruce Mattox (CFO)
Robert Black (Sr VP-Fin Svcs)
Sean Kiewiet (CIO)
Sheila Hernandez (Sr VP-Merchant Ops)
Thomas Liney (Sr VP-Client Dev)
Anthony Bonventre (Chief Credit Officer)
Tom Della Badia (Sr VP-Indirect Sls)
Adriana Guaderrama (VP-Compensation)
Chris Prince (Gen Counsel)
Michael Breier (Asst VP-Risk Mgmt)
Mike Haskett (Asst VP-Special Svcs)
Scott Derryberry (VP-Client Svcs)
Tom Della Badia (Sr VP-Indirect Sls)
Bill Christensen (Asst VP-Credit & Underwriting)
Cindy O'Neill (Pres-Comml Payments)

Subsidiaries:

American Credit Card Processing Corp.   (1)
25 Newbridge Rd, Hicksville, NY 11803
Tel.: (877) 202-0667
Web Site: http://www.accpconline.com
Financial Transaction Processing Services
N.A.I.C.S.: 522320
Audree Oser (CEO)

Priority Payment Systems California   (1)
10970 Arrow Rte Ste 203, Rancho Cucamonga, CA 91730-4839
Tel.: (678) 486-1963
Web Site:
   http://www.prioritypaymentsystemsca.com
Financial Transaction Processing Services
N.A.I.C.S.: 522320

Priority Payment Systems RSM   (1)
27702 Crown Vly Pkwy D4-179, Ladera Ranch, CA 92694
Tel.: (949) 364-3220
Web Site: http://www.ppsrsm.com
Financial Transaction Processing Services
N.A.I.C.S.: 522320
Jmaes Ing (Mgr)

Priority Payment Systems West   (1)
15635 SE 114th Ave Ste 205, Clackamas, OR 97015-9029
Tel.: (503) 501-2415
Web Site:
   http://www.prioritypaymentsystemswest.com
Financial Transaction Processing Services
N.A.I.C.S.: 522320

PRIORITY PLASTICS, INC.
500 Industrial Park Dr, Portland, IN 47371
Tel.: (260) 726-7000
Web Site:
   http://www.priorityplastics.com
Year Founded: 1968
Sales Range: $50-74.9 Million
Emp.: 250
Plastic Container Mfr
N.A.I.C.S.: 326199
Andrew Srenco (Pres & CEO)
Gary Turner (COO)

Subsidiaries:

CCW Products, Inc.   (1)
5861 Tennyson St, Arvada, CO 80003
Tel.: (303) 427-9663
Web Site: http://www.ccwproducts.com
Sales Range: $10-24.9 Million
Emp.: 103
Plastic Container Mfr
N.A.I.C.S.: 326199
Dakota Cervenka (Mgr-Mfg)

PRIORITY PUBLIC RELATIONS
2118 Wilshire Blvd Ste 835, Santa Monica, CA 90403
Tel.: (310) 954-1375
Web Site: http://www.prioritypr.net
Year Founded: 1990
Emp.: 10
Public Relations Agency
N.A.I.C.S.: 541820
Jeff Pryor (Pres-PR & Brand Strategist)
Kristien Brada-Thompson (Mng Dir & VP)

Subsidiaries:

Priority Public Relations   (1)
12 Avenue Reine Victoria, Nice, 06000, France
Tel.: (33) 6 87 77 4989
Web Site: http://www.prioritypr.net
Emp.: 2
Public Relations
N.A.I.C.S.: 541820

PRIORITY STAFFING SOLUTIONS, INC.
42 W 38th St Rm 503, New York, NY 10018-0070
Tel.: (212) 213-2277   NY
Web Site: http://www.prioritystaff.com
Year Founded: 1999
Sales Range: $1-9.9 Million
Emp.: 14
Employment Agencies
N.A.I.C.S.: 561311
Deborah Wainstein (Founder)

PRIORITY WASTE LLC
42822 Garfield Rd, Clinton Township, MI 48038
Tel.: (586) 228-1200
Web Site:
   http://www.prioritywaste.com
Waste & Recycling Services
N.A.I.C.S.: 562998
Todd Stamper (CEO)

Subsidiaries:

J. Fons Co Inc   (1)
6451 E Mcnichols Rd, Detroit, MI 48212
Tel.: (313) 893-6656
Hazardous Waste Treatment & Disposal
N.A.I.C.S.: 562211

PRIORITY WIRE & CABLE INC.
1800 E Roosevelt Rd, Little Rock, AR 72206
Tel.: (501) 372-5444
Web Site: http://www.prioritywire.com
Rev.: $36,719,034
Emp.: 200
Electrical Apparatus & Equipment
N.A.I.C.S.: 423610
Candy Grey (Controller)
Robert Strahs (VP-Accts & Mktg-Natl)
Dorothy Tully-Petersen (Sls Mgr-Natl)
Todd Thurston (VP-Natl Accts)

Subsidiaries:

Priority-1 Inc   (1)
1800 E Roosevelt Rd, Little Rock, AR 72206
Tel.: (501) 371-9814
Web Site: http://www.priority1inc.com
Rev.: $3,500,000
Emp.: 30
Local Trucking without Storage
N.A.I.C.S.: 484110
Kenneth Hamilton (Pres)

PRIORITYONE CAPITAL CORPORATION
220 N Main Ave, Magee, MS 39111
Tel.: (601) 849-3311
Web Site:
   http://www.priorityonebank.com
Sales Range: $25-49.9 Million
Emp.: 172
Bank Holding Company
N.A.I.C.S.: 551111
Odean Busby (Chm, Pres & CEO)
Christine Shoemaker (Sec)
Jerry Deas (CFO & Exec VP)
Robert Barnes (Chief Lending Officer & Pres-Simpson Div)
Jane Walker (Exec VP)

Subsidiaries:

PriorityOne Bank   (1)
220 N Main Ave, Magee, MS 39111
Tel.: (601) 849-3311
Web Site: http://www.priorityonebank.com
Rev.: $23,584,000
Emp.: 20
Fiscal Year-end: 12/31/2012
State Commercial Banks
N.A.I.C.S.: 522110
Ethan Leake (Vice Chm)
Fountaine McNair (Pres)
Meaghan Ahlberg (Branch Mgr-Brandon)

PRISKE-JONES COMPANY
711 Daily Dr Ste 105, Camarillo, CA 93010
Tel.: (805) 987-7877
Rev.: $20,000,000
Emp.: 10
Land Subdividers & Developers, Commercial
N.A.I.C.S.: 237210

Subsidiaries:

Priske Jones Southeast   (1)
2740 Bert Adams Rd Ste 100, Atlanta, GA 30339
Tel.: (770) 433-1624
Rev.: $837,929
Emp.: 4
Townhouse Developers
N.A.I.C.S.: 236116

PRISM GAS SYSTEMS I, LP
2350 Airport Freeway Ste 505, Bedford, TX 76022
Tel.: (817) 684-0158
Web Site: http://www.prismgas.com
Rev.: $21,000,000
Emp.: 40
Natural Gasoline Production
N.A.I.C.S.: 211130
Robert E. Dunn (Sr VP)
Chris Booth (Gen Counsel, Sec & VP)

PRISM HEALTH CARE SERVICES, INC.
1337 Basswood Rd, Schaumburg, IL 60173-0173
Tel.: (847) 592-5700
Web Site: http://www.prismhc.com
Health Care Srvices
N.A.I.C.S.: 621399
James Leach (Mgr-IT Ops)
David Shade (Co-Founder & Chm)
Bradley Fetters (COO)
Mukesh Gangwal (Pres & CEO)
Ramona G. Lacy (Co-Founder)

Subsidiaries:

Principle Valuation, LLC   (1)
190 S La Salle St Ste 2900, Chicago, IL 60603
Tel.: (312) 422-1010
Web Site: http://www.principlevaluation.com
Emp.: 100
Valuation & Advisory Services
N.A.I.C.S.: 531320
Timothy H. Baker (Mng Partner)

PRISM VENTURE MANAGEMENT, LLC
117 Kendrick St Ste200, Needham, MA 02494
Tel.: (781) 302-4000
Web Site:
   http://www.prismventure.com
Year Founded: 1996
Rev.: $1,250,000,000
Emp.: 15
Privater Equity Firm
N.A.I.C.S.: 523999
Dina Ciarimboli (Gen Counsel)
Gordon E. Nye (Partner)
Jim Counihan (Partner)
Anthony Natale (Partner)

PRISMA GRAPHIC CORPORATION
2937 E Broadway Rd, Phoenix, AZ 85040-2784
Tel.: (602) 243-5777
Web Site:
   http://www.prismagraphic.com
Sales Range: $10-24.9 Million
Emp.: 60
Commercial Printing Services
N.A.I.C.S.: 323111
Robert Anderson (CEO)
Simon Beltran (Pres)
Alan McAbee (VP-Strategic Accounts)
Victor Martinez (CFO)

PRISON REHABILITATIVE INDUSTRIES AND DIVERSIFIED ENTERPRISES, INC.
223 Morrison Rd, Brandon, FL 33511
Tel.: (727) 556-3300
Web Site: http://www.pride-enterprises.org
Year Founded: 1981
Sales Range: $50-74.9 Million
Emp.: 290
Prison Inmate Rehabilitation & Training Services
N.A.I.C.S.: 624310
Jack Edgemon (Pres)
Pete Radanovich (CFO)
Dee Kiminki (Chief Admin Officer)
H. Gregg Nicklaus (Treas)
Carlyle Holder (Sec)
James J. Reeves (Chm)
Wilbur E. Brewton (Gen Counsel)

PRITCHARD AUTO CO
980 Hwy 18, Britt, IA 50423
Tel.: (641) 843-3871   IA
Web Site: http://www.pritchards.com
Year Founded: 1929
Sales Range: $50-74.9 Million
Emp.: 60
Sales of New & Used Automobiles.
N.A.I.C.S.: 441110
Joseph Pritchard (Owner)
Paul Kumsher (Controller)
Cal Thomazin (VP-Fixed Ops)
Brad Sifert (Mgr-Svc)

PRITCHARD BROADCASTING CORP.
610 N 4th St Ste 300, Burlington, IA 52601
Tel.: (319) 752-5402   IA
Web Site:
   http://www.burlingtonradio.com
Year Founded: 1991

PRITCHARD BROADCASTING CORP.

Pritchard Broadcasting Corp.—(Continued)
Sales Range: $10-24.9 Million
Emp.: 25
Radio Broadcasting Stations Owner & Operator
N.A.I.C.S.: 516110
John T. Pritchard *(Owner)*
Chet Young *(Gen Mgr-Sls)*
Mark Morris *(Dir-News)*
Sherry Porterfield *(Dir-Production)*
Steve Hexom *(Program Dir)*
Joe Bates *(Program Dir)*

Subsidiaries:

Galesburg Broadcasting Co. (1)
154 E Simmons St, Galesburg, IL 61401
Tel.: (309) 342-5131
Web Site: http://www.galesburgradio.com
Emp.: 20
Radio Broadcasting Stations
N.A.I.C.S.: 516110
Roger Lundeen *(Gen Mgr)*

Titan Broadcasting, LLC (1)
610 N 4th St Ste 310, Burlington, IA 52601
Tel.: (319) 752-2701
Web Site: http://www.titanburlington.com
Emp.: 10
Radio Broadcasting Stations Owner & Operator
N.A.I.C.S.: 516110
Steve King *(Program Dir-KBKB-FM)*

PRITCHARD BROWN, LLC.
6501 Erdman Ave, Baltimore, MD 21205-3510
Tel.: (410) 483-5600
Web Site: http://www.pritchardbrown.com
Year Founded: 1947
Sales Range: $10-24.9 Million
Emp.: 105
Electric Equipment Mfr
N.A.I.C.S.: 334419
Michael Witkowski *(COO)*

PRITCHARD ELECTRIC COMPANY, INC.
2425 8th Ave, Huntington, WV 25703
Tel.: (304) 529-2566
Web Site: http://www.pritchardelectric.com
Rev.: $22,300,000
Emp.: 200
Electrical Contractor
N.A.I.C.S.: 238210
Jack M. Reynolds *(VP)*
Stephen Stacks *(Controller)*
Carolyn Powers *(Mgr-Pay Roll)*

PRITCHETT TRUCKING INC.
1050 SE 6th St, Lake Butler, FL 32054
Tel.: (386) 496-2630
Web Site: http://www.pritchetttrucking.com
Sales Range: $10-24.9 Million
Emp.: 500
Local Trucking without Storage
N.A.I.C.S.: 484110
Marvin H. Pritchett *(Founder, Owner & Chm)*
Don Montgomery *(VP-Ops)*
John Pritchett *(Pres)*
Phillip Pritchett *(VP)*

PRITIKIN LONGEVITY CENTER & SPA
8755 NW 36th St, Miami, FL 33178
Tel.: (305) 935-7131
Web Site: http://www.pritikin.com
Year Founded: 1975
Provides Nutritional & Medical Services; Lodging on Premises
N.A.I.C.S.: 721110

PRITZLAFF WHOLESALE MEATS INC.
17025 W Glendale Dr, New Berlin, WI 53151
Tel.: (262) 786-1151
Rev.: $12,800,000
Emp.: 50
Meat & Meat Product Merchant Whslr
N.A.I.C.S.: 424470
Michael Pritzlaff *(VP)*
Bruce Pritzlaff Jr. *(Pres)*

PRIVACY & VALUE INC.
2261 Rosanna St, Las Vegas, NV 89117
Tel.: (269) 692-9418   WY
Year Founded: 2021
Software Development Services
N.A.I.C.S.: 541511
Daniel Okelo *(Pres, CEO, CFO & Sec)*

PRIVATE CAPITAL INCORPORATED
207 Heymann Blvd, Lafayette, LA 70503
Tel.: (337) 233-6678
Rev.: $14,000,000
Emp.: 3
Provider of Financial Services
N.A.I.C.S.: 522299
Joe Kite *(Pres)*

PRIVATE CAPITAL MANAGEMENT, LLC
8889 Pelican Bay Blvd Ste 500, Naples, FL 34108-7512
Tel.: (239) 254-2500   DE
Web Site: http://www.private-cap.com
Year Founded: 1986
Investment Advisory & Asset Management Services
N.A.I.C.S.: 523940
David Joyce *(COO & CFO)*
Jeffrey Fortier *(Mng Dir-Client Svcs)*
Gregg Joseph Powers *(CEO, CIO & Portfolio Mgr-Lead)*
Andrew L. Martin *(Partner & Portfolio Mgr)*
Erick A. E. Sonne *(Sr VP)*
David A. Sissman *(Mng Dir-Res & Portfolio Mgr)*
Chad D. Atkins *(Pres & Chief Compliance Officer)*
Jano P. Janoyan *(Mng Dir-Trading & Ops)*
Max H. Deifik *(VP-Client Svcs)*

PRIVATE ENERGY SYSTEMS, INC.
434 Hale Ave Ste 160, Oakdale, MN 55128
Tel.: (651) 236-8118
Web Site: http://www.privateenergysystems.com
Renewable Energy System Design & Construction Services
N.A.I.C.S.: 541330
David Ault *(CEO)*

PRIVATE EQUITY CAPITAL CORPORATION
5168 Linea del Cielo, Rancho Santa Fe, CA 92067
Tel.: (858) 342-1994   DE
Web Site: http://www.pecc.com
Year Founded: 1998
Privater Equity Firm
N.A.I.C.S.: 523999
John M. Ramey *(Founder & Partner)*

PRIVATE EQUITY GROUP, LLC
12800 University Dr Ste 275, Fort Myers, FL 33907
Tel.: (239) 509-9066

Web Site: http://www.privateequitygroup.net
Year Founded: 1985
Rev.: $2,000,000,000
Real Estate Private Equity Firm
N.A.I.C.S.: 523999
O. J. Buigas *(Founder)*
Howard M. Baum *(Chm)*
Gregory M. Morris *(VP)*
Carol A. Douglas *(Pres)*
Michelle A. Preiss *(VP)*
Amanda M. Bokan *(VP)*
Donald R. Schrotenboer *(CEO)*
Andrew A. Bokan *(VP)*

PRIVATE EYES, INC.
2700 Ygnacio Vly Rd Ste 100, Walnut Creek, CA 94598
Tel.: (925) 927-3333
Web Site: http://www.privateeyesinc.com
Year Founded: 1989
Sales Range: $1-9.9 Million
Emp.: 24
Background Verification Services for Employment
N.A.I.C.S.: 561611
Sandra James *(Founder & Pres)*
Nenita Reyes *(VP)*
Frank Santa Elena *(Mgr-IT Sys)*
Kevin Gillen *(Dir-Supply Chain Strategy)*
Michael Borchard *(VP-Bus Dev)*

PRIVATE LABEL BY G INC.
6015 Obispo Ave, Long Beach, CA 90805
Tel.: (562) 531-1116
Web Site: http://www.kennethwinston.com
Rev.: $13,800,000
Emp.: 28
Women & Children Clothing Mfr
N.A.I.C.S.: 424350
Ty Yeh *(Pres)*

PRIVATE LABEL NUTRACEUTICALS, LLC.
1900 Beaver Ridge Cir, Norcross, GA 30071
Tel.: (678) 328-3701
Web Site: http://www.privatelabelnutra.com
Year Founded: 2008
Sales Range: $25-49.9 Million
Emp.: 120
Pharmaceutical Preparation Whslr
N.A.I.C.S.: 424210
Kai Kalfas *(Acct Mgr)*

PRIVATE MINI STORAGE REALTY LP
10575 Westoffice Dr, Houston, TX 77042
Tel.: (713) 464-6944
Web Site: http://www.private-mini.com
Rev.: $25,000,000
Emp.: 200
Real Estate Managers
N.A.I.C.S.: 531210
Douglas L. Mulvaney Sr. *(Pres)*

PRIVATE VISTA LLC
1 N LaSalle St 33rd Fl, Chicago, IL 60602
Tel.: (312) 831-4370
Web Site: http://www.myprivatevista.com
Year Founded: 1992
Financial Investment Planning
N.A.I.C.S.: 523999
Steve Merdinger *(Partner)*
Jeff Toner *(Partner)*

Jim Weil *(Partner)*
Bob Westrick *(Partner)*
Doug Brown *(Partner)*

PRIVATEERIT, LLC
1101 W Hibiscus Blvd Ste 210, Melbourne, FL 32901
Tel.: (321) 499-3993
Web Site: http://www.privateerit.com
Year Founded: 2014
Sales Range: $1-9.9 Million
Emp.: 22
Information Technology Management Services
N.A.I.C.S.: 541512
Jerry Bennett *(CEO)*
Christa Evans *(Dir-Bus Ops)*
Britney Bennett *(Mgr-Personnel & Fin)*
Samantha Worman *(Officer-Facility Security)*

PRIVATPATH DIAGNOSTICS, INC.
330 W 38th St #405, New York, NY 10018
Tel.: (315) 515-5571
Web Site: http://www.letsgetchecked.com
Healthcare Solutions & Services
N.A.I.C.S.: 621999
Peter Foley *(CEO)*
Ronan Ryan *(COO)*
Derek Newell *(Pres)*

PRIVCO MEDIA LLC
19 W 21st St, New York, NY 10010
Tel.: (212) 645-1686
Web Site: http://www.privco.com
Year Founded: 2009
Sales Range: $10-24.9 Million
Emp.: 40
Corporate Information Directory Publisher
N.A.I.C.S.: 513140
Sam Hamadeh *(Founder)*

PRIVE JETS, LLC
1250 E Hallandale Beach Blvd Ste 505, Hallandale, FL 33009-4638
Tel.: (305) 917-1600
Web Site: http://www.privejets.com
Year Founded: 2007
Sales Range: $1-9.9 Million
Emp.: 10
Long Freight Travelling Services
N.A.I.C.S.: 532411
Isaac Grimberg *(CEO)*

PRIVECO INC.
352 Oliver Dr, Troy, MI 48084
Web Site: http://www.priveco.com
Year Founded: 1998
Rev.: $3,600,000
Emp.: 9
Retail Services
N.A.I.C.S.: 311811
Tom Nardone *(Pres)*
Lisa LoGrasso *(Dir-Mktg)*

PRIVET FUND MANAGEMENT, LLC
79 W Paces Ferry Rd 2nd Fl, Atlanta, GA 30305
Tel.: (404) 419-2670
Web Site: http://www.privetfund.com
Investment Services
N.A.I.C.S.: 523999
Benjamin L. Rosenzweig *(Partner)*
Ryan J. Levenson *(Principal & Portfolio Mgr)*
Paul Bottinelli *(COO, CFO & Chief Comml Offcer)*
Christos Asimakopoulos *(VP)*

COMPANIES

Subsidiaries:

Hardinge Inc. (1)
1235 Westlakes Dr Ste 410, Berwyn, PA 19312
Web Site: http://www.hardinge.com
Sales Range: $300-349.9 Million
Machine Tools Mfr & Distr
N.A.I.C.S.: 333517
Charles P. Dougherty (Pres & CEO)
Randy Bahr (Sr VP-Corp Dev)
Kevin Marvel (VP-HR)
Greg Young (VP-IT)
Gregory Knight (Pres & CEO)

Subsidiary (Domestic):

Forkardt Inc. (2)
2155 Traversefield Dr, Traverse City, MI 49686
Tel.: (231) 995-8300
Web Site: http://www.forkardt
Machine Tool Workholding Device Mfr
N.A.I.C.S.: 333515
John Roselli (CFO & Sr VP)
Tom McGrail (VP-Ops)
Chuck Douherty (Pres & CEO)

Subsidiary (Non-US):

Forkardt Deutschland GmbH (3)
Lachenhauweg 12, D-72766, Reutlingen, Germany
Tel.: (49) 71275812 0
Web Site: http://www.forkardt.com
Machine Tool Workholding Device Mfr
N.A.I.C.S.: 333515

Subsidiary (Non-US):

Forkardt France SAS (4)
28 avenue de Bobigny, F-93135, Noisy-le-Sec, Cedex, France
Tel.: (33) 141831240
Web Site: http://www.forkardt.com
Machine Tool Workholding Device Distr
N.A.I.C.S.: 333515
Roland Ackerman (Reg Pres)

Subsidiary (Domestic):

Hardinge Brothers, Inc. (2)
1 Hardinge Dr, Elmira, NY 14902 (100%)
Tel.: (607) 734-2281
Web Site: http://www.hardinge.com
Grinding Machines & Machine Tools Mfr
N.A.I.C.S.: 333517

Subsidiary (Non-US):

Hardinge GmbH (2)
Europark Fichtenhain A 13 C, 47807, Krefeld, Germany (100%)
Tel: (49) 2151496490
Web Site: http://www.hartdrehen.com
Industrial Machinery Mfr
N.A.I.C.S.: 333517
Victor Gaspar (Reg Pres)

Hardinge Machine (Shanghai) Co., Ltd. (2)
No 1388 East Kang Qiao Road, Pudong, Shanghai, 201319, China
Tel.: (86) 2138108686
Web Site: http://www.hardinge.com
Industrial Machinery Mfr
N.A.I.C.S.: 333517
Alison Zhang (Reg Pres)

Hardinge Machine Tools B.V. (2)
Zalmweg 36, 4941 VX, Raamsdonksveer, Netherlands
Tel.: (31) 162519565
Web Site: http://www.bmtmachines.nl
Grinding Machines & Machine Tools Mfr
N.A.I.C.S.: 333515
Victor Gaspar (Reg Pres)

Subsidiary (Non-US):

Forkardt India LLP (3)
Plot No 39 D No 5-5-35 Ayyanna Ind Park, IE Prasanthnagar Kukatpally, Hyderabad, 500 072, India
Tel.: (91) 4040020571
Web Site: http://www.forkardt.com
Machine Tools Mfr
N.A.I.C.S.: 333517

Representative Office (Non-US):

Hardinge Machine Tools B.V. - Taiwan Representative Office (3)

4 Tzu Chiang 3rd Road, Nant'ou, 540, Taiwan
Tel.: (886) 492260536
Web Site: http://www.hardinge.com
Industrial Machinery Mfr

Subsidiary (Non-US):

Jones & Shipman S.A.R.L. (2)
8 allee des Ginkgos B P 112, F-69672, Bron, Cedex, France
Tel.: (33) 472812660
Web Site: http://www.hardinge.com
Grinding Machines & Machine Tools Mfr
N.A.I.C.S.: 333517

L. Kellenberger & Co. AG (2)
Buetigenstrasse 80, 255/, Studen, Switzerland (100%)
Tel.: (41) 323441152
Web Site: http://www.hardinge.com
Grinding Machine Mfr
N.A.I.C.S.: 333517

Subsidiary (Non-US):

Jones & Shipman Hardinge Limited (3)
Europark Unit 4 Watling Street, Rugby, CV23 OAL, United Kingdom
Tel.: (44) 1162013047
Web Site: http://www.hardinge.com
Cylindrical Grinding Machines & Machine Tools Mfr
N.A.I.C.S.: 333517
Michael Duignan (Mng Dir)

PRIVY, INC.
38 Chauncy St, Boston, MA 02111
Web Site: http://www.privy.com
Year Founded: 2012
Sales Range: $1-9.9 Million
Emp.: 30
Online Shopping Services
N.A.I.C.S.: 541511
Ben Jabbawy (Founder & CEO)
Dave Gerhardt (CMO)
Peter Cai (VP-Engrg)
Alison Aldrich (VP-Partnerships)
Ted Johnson (VP-Sls)

PRL INC.
64 Rexmont Rd, Cornwall, PA 17016
Tel.: (717) 273-2470
Web Site: http://www.prlincom
Sales Range: $10-24.9 Million
Emp.: 150
Laminating Steel
N.A.I.C.S.: 332813
Barbara Herschkowitz (Chm)
Pat Herwschkowitz (Mgr-Adv & PR)

Subsidiaries:

LTC, Inc. (1)
330 N 7th Ave, Lebanon, PA 17046
Tel.: (717) 273-3711
Industrial Supplies Whslr
N.A.I.C.S.: 423840

Regal Cast Inc (1)
307 N 9th Ave, Lebanon, PA 17046
Tel.: (717) 270-1888
Web Site: http://www.prlinc.com
Rev.: $5,000,000
Emp.: 17
Steel Foundries, Nec
N.A.I.C.S.: 331513
Greg Raudenbush (Gen Mgr)

PRO ACTION OF STEUBEN & YATES, INC.
117 E Steuben St, Bath, NY 14810
Tel.: (607) 776-2125   NY
Web Site: http://www.proactioninc.org
Year Founded: 1965
Sales Range: $10-24.9 Million
Emp.: 554
Community Action Services
N.A.I.C.S.: 624190
Debbi Deats (Pres)
Dave Pels (VP)

Debra Hafleigh (Treas)
Judy Duquette (Sec)
Laura Rossman (CEO)

PRO ADVANTAGE
77917 209th St, Albert Lea, MN 56007-5629
Tel.: (507) 377-8838
Web Site: http://www.theproadvantagemn.com
Specialized Freight (except Used Goods) Trucking, Long-Distance
N.A.I.C.S.: 484230
Daniel DeBoer (Pres)

PRO CHRYSLER JEEP INC.
1800 W 104th Ave, Denver, CO 80234
Tel.: (303) 469-1931
Web Site: http://www.lhmdenverjeep.com
Sales Range: $25-49.9 Million
Emp.: 67
New & Used Car Dealer
N.A.I.C.S.: 441110
Jeff Schenden (Gen Mgr)

PRO COMPUTER SERVICE, LLC
304 Harper Dr Ste 130, Moorestown, NJ 08057
Tel.: (856) 596-4446
Web Site: http://www.helpmepcs.com
Year Founded: 2002
Sales Range: $1-9.9 Million
Emp.: 80
Onsite & Remote IT Support Services
N.A.I.C.S.: 519290
Anthony W. Mongeluzo (Founder & CEO)
Traci Jordan (COO)

PRO COOPERATIVE INC.
17 3rd Ave NE, Pocahontas, IA 50574
Tel.: (712) 335-3060   IA
Web Site: http://www.procooperative.com
Year Founded: 1933
Sales Range: $75-99.9 Million
Emp.: 200
Grain & Field Beans
N.A.I.C.S.: 424510
Kyle Kuepker (CEO)

PRO EM OPERATIONS, LLC
1450 E Grant Street, Phoenix, AZ 85034
Tel.: (480) 507-0999
Web Site: https://proem.org
Emp.: 100
Events Management & Planning Services
N.A.I.C.S.: 711310
Amir Glogau (Chm & CEO)

Subsidiaries:

Kirby Rentals, LLC (1)
411 Hames Ave, Orlando, FL 32805
Tel.: (407) 422-1001
Web Site: http://www.kirbytent.com
Tents & Other Camping Equipment Rental Services
N.A.I.C.S.: 532289
Jeff Frame (VP)
John Baszewski (Specialist-Tent)
Steve Flegel (Acct Exec)
Raymond Batista (Acct Exec)
Rebecca Boaz (Acct Exec)
Brenda Brown (Office Mgr)

PRO EQUINE PRODUCTS INC.
5116 E State Hwy 97, Pleasanton, TX 78064
Tel.: (830) 569-4666
Web Site: http://www.cactusropes.com

PRO GROUP, INC.

Year Founded: 2007
Emp.: 35
Mfr of Apparel & Accessories for Equine Industry
N.A.I.C.S.: 315250
Dru Stewart (VP-Mktg)

Subsidiaries:

RHE Hatco, Inc. (1)
601 Marion Dr, Garland, TX 75042-7930
Tel.: (972) 494-0511
Sales Range: $250-299.9 Million
Emp.: 600
Hats Mfr
N.A.I.C.S.: 315990
Matthew Range (Dir-Mktg)
Dennis Henson (Dir-IT)

Subsidiary (Domestic):

Stetson Hat Co. (2)
3601 S Lenard St, Saint Joseph, MO 64503
Tel.: (816) 233-8031
Web Site: http://www.stetsonhat.com
Sales Range: $10-24.9 Million
Emp.: 5
Western Hats Mfr
N.A.I.C.S.: 315990

PRO FASTENING SYSTEMS INC.
44 E University Dr, Arlington Heights, IL 60004
Tel.: (847) 577-7185
Web Site: http://www.profastening.net
Rev.: $10,000,000
Emp.: 30
Bolts
N.A.I.C.S.: 423710
Ben Ahrens (Branch Mgr)

PRO FEET INC.
2220 Anthony Rd, Burlington, NC 27215
Tel.: (336) 226-0237
Web Site: http://www.profeet.com
Sales Range: $10-24.9 Million
Emp.: 17
Socks
N.A.I.C.S.: 315120
Russell R. Wilson (Founder & CEO)

PRO FOOD SYSTEMS, INC.
170 Commerce Dr, Holts Summit, MO 65043
Tel.: (573) 896-2500   MO
Web Site: http://www.champchicken.com
Year Founded: 1999
Sales Range: $10-24.9 Million
Emp.: 100
Distr of Wholesale Deli Products & Food Service Equipment
N.A.I.C.S.: 311999
Shawn Burcham (Co-Founder & CEO)
Carla Dowden (VP-HR)
Lise Fuller (Controller)
Darrell Hale (VP-Equipment Div)

PRO FOOTBALL WEEKLY, LLC
7717 S IL Route 31, Crystal Lake, IL 60014
Tel.: (815) 526-4603   IL
Web Site: http://www.profootballweekly.com
Year Founded: 1967
Newspaper & Magazine Publisher
N.A.I.C.S.: 513110
Rich Murowski (Natl Sls Mgr)

PRO GROUP, INC.
8480 E Orchard Rd Ste 3000, Greenwood Village, CO 80111-5017
Tel.: (303) 792-3000   CO
Web Site: http://www.pro-group.com
Year Founded: 1956
Sales Range: $75-99.9 Million

PRO GROUP, INC.

PRO Group, Inc.—(Continued)

Emp.: 25
Hardware Distribution & Merchandising Consultation
N.A.I.C.S.: 423710
Steve Synnott (Pres & CEO)
Shari Kalbach (Mng Dir-PRO Hardware)
Michele Simes (Dir-Events)

Subsidiaries:

GardenMaster (1)
8480 E Orchard Rd Ste 3000, Greenwood Village, CO 80111-5017
Tel.: (303) 792-3000
Web Site: http://www.gardenmaster.com
Sales Range: $25-49.9 Million
Emp.: 20
Indoor & Outdoor Plants, Flowers, Seeds, Gardening Tools, Supplies & Services
N.A.I.C.S.: 444240

PRO Group, Inc. - Farm Mart Division (1)
8480 E Orchard Rd Ste 3000, Greenwood Village, CO 80111-5017
Tel.: (303) 792-3000
Web Site: http://www.farmmart.com
Farm Supplies Retailer
N.A.I.C.S.: 444240

PRO MARKETING SALES INC.
1350 Bluegrass Lakes Pkwy, Alpharetta, GA 30004-0749
Tel.: (770) 442-2534 GA
Web Site:
    http://www.promarketingsales.com
Year Founded: 1980
Sales Range: $50-74.9 Million
Emp.: 15
Marketing & Sales Consulting Services
N.A.I.C.S.: 541613
Carmen Stuart (Mgr-HR)
J. Harvey Hall Jr. (Co-Owner)

PRO METCO INC.
27071 Cabot Rd Ste 110, Laguna Hills, CA 92653
Tel.: (949) 348-8998
Rev.: $11,000,000
Emp.: 3
Iron & Steel (Ferrous) Products
N.A.I.C.S.: 423510

PRO MOTION, INC.
18405 Edison Ave, Saint Louis, MO 63005
Tel.: (314) 997-0101
Web Site: http://www.promotion1.com
Year Founded: 1995
Sales Range: $10-24.9 Million
Emp.: 20
Consumer Marketing, Publicity/Promotions, Sales Promotion
N.A.I.C.S.: 541870
Steve Randazzo (Pres)
Cathi Kennedy (Dir-Acct)
Becky Fitzgibbon (Head-Acctg)
Brian Dooley (Mgr-Mktg)

PRO MUJER INC.
253 W 35th St Fl 11, New York, NY 10001
Tel.: (646) 626-7000 NY
Web Site: http://www.promujer.org
Year Founded: 1990
Sales Range: $50-74.9 Million
Emp.: 31
Woman Welfare Services
N.A.I.C.S.: 813410
Mary McCaffrey (Treas)
Mark Roy McMahon (Co-Treas)
Gillian Shepherd Mestre (Chm)
Maria Cavalcanti (Pres & CEO)
Raul Espejel (CFO)

Diana de Castro (Chief Alliance Officer)
Samantha Akins (Chief Relationship Officer)
Mohit Nagpal (COO)

PRO OIL INC.
1820 Main Rd, Silver Creek, NY 14136-9779
Tel.: (716) 934-7726 NY
Web Site: http://www.tpsfuel.com
Year Founded: 1991
Sales Range: $10-24.9 Million
Emp.: 40
Trucking Service
N.A.I.C.S.: 484220
Michael A. Jimerson (Pres & CEO)
Terri Nickerson (Mgr-Ops)

PRO PLASTICS INC.
9530 Baythorne Dr, Houston, TX 77041
Tel.: (713) 690-9000
Web Site: http://www.proplastics.com
Sales Range: $10-24.9 Million
Emp.: 150
Plastic Bags: Made From Purchased Materials
N.A.I.C.S.: 326111
Ramy Law (Owner)

PRO PRINT, INC.
3920 Airpark Blvd, Duluth, MN 55811
Tel.: (218) 722-9805 MN
Web Site:
    http://www.proprintduluth.com
Year Founded: 1977
Sales Range: $1-9.9 Million
Emp.: 40
Commercial Digital & Offset Printing
N.A.I.C.S.: 323111
Creston Dorothy (Co-Owner & Pres)

PRO PUBLICA INC.
155 Avenue of the Americas 13th Fl, New York, NY 10013
Tel.: (212) 514-5250 DE
Web Site: http://www.propublica.org
Year Founded: 2007
Sales Range: $10-24.9 Million
Emp.: 80
Investigative Journalism
N.A.I.C.S.: 513120
Heather Troup (Dir-Dev Ops)
Nicholas Lanese (Dir-IT)
Cynthia Gordy (Dir-Mktg)
Barbara Zinkant (Fin Dir & Dir-Ops)
Paul Steiger (Chm)
Richard Tofel (Pres)
Alexis Stephens (Dir-PR)
Lynn Dombek (Editor-Res)
Eric Umansky (Deputy Mng Editor)

PRO RESOURCES INC.
1728 Spy Run Ave, Fort Wayne, IN 46805
Tel.: (260) 420-2117
Web Site:
    http://www.proresources.net
Sales Range: $10-24.9 Million
Emp.: 20
Temporary Help Service
N.A.I.C.S.: 561320
Bill Becker (Pres)
Jeremy Guy (Office Mgr)

PRO SERV SANDERS INC.
101 Tech Dr, Sanford, FL 32771
Tel.: (407) 324-5666
Year Founded: 1997
Sales Range: $10-24.9 Million
Emp.: 150
Building Equipment Installation Services
N.A.I.C.S.: 238290

Terry Hill (Pres)
Robert Terrell (Gen Mgr)

PRO SOUND INC.
1375 NE 123rd St, Miami, FL 33161
Tel.: (305) 891-1000
Web Site: http://www.prosound.net
Year Founded: 1975
Sales Range: $10-24.9 Million
Emp.: 40
Sound Equipment Specialization
N.A.I.C.S.: 238210
R. Sintow (CEO)
Jack Figaro (Pres)
Rick Scharmann (VP-Sls)
Lisa Lane (CFO)

PRO SOURCE INC.
333 Wyman St Ste 225, Waltham, MA 02451
Tel.: (781) 890-8000
Web Site:
    http://www.prosourceinc.com
Sales Range: $1-9.9 Million
Emp.: 45
Computer Related Consulting Services
N.A.I.C.S.: 561320
John Mallin (Pres)

PRO SYSTEMS CORP
1271 Hwy 10 W, Detroit Lakes, MN 56501
Tel.: (218) 847-9277
Web Site: http://www.psys.com
Rev.: $21,475,260
Emp.: 20
Computer Peripheral Equipment
N.A.I.C.S.: 449210
Mike Brodsho (CEO)

PRO TECK EARNS INC.
307 Waverley Oaks Rd Ste 305, Waltham, MA 02452
Tel.: (781) 899-4949
Web Site:
    http://www.proteckservices.com
Sales Range: $25-49.9 Million
Emp.: 195
Real Estate Valuation Services
N.A.I.C.S.: 531390
Matt Jenkins (COO)
Tom O'Grady (CEO)
Basil Pallone (CFO)
Donna Daniels (VP-HR)
Jeff Dickstein (Chief Compliance Officer)
Paul Gomez (CTO)
Thomas Hoff (VP-Mktg & Comm)

PRO THERAPY SUPPLIES
1750 Breckinridge Pkwy Ste 200, Duluth, GA 30096
Tel.: (770) 441-9808
Web Site:
    http://www.protherapysupplies.com
Year Founded: 2003
Sales Range: $10-24.9 Million
Emp.: 20
Physical Therapy Supplies
N.A.I.C.S.: 334510
Sean Tang (Owner)
Tony Tony (Office Mgr)

PRO TOUR MEMORABILIA
20362 Plummer St, Chatsworth, CA 91311
Tel.: (818) 909-5900
Web Site: http://www.ptmimages.com
Rev.: $16,000,000
Emp.: 55
Miscellaneous Durable Goods Merchant Whslr
N.A.I.C.S.: 423990
Jeff Toothaker (Mgr-Sls)
Luke Almour (VP-Sls)

U.S. PRIVATE

PRO-AG FARMERS COOPERATIVE
601 E Soo St Ste A, Parkers Prairie, MN 56361
Tel.: (218) 338-3001
Web Site:
    http://www.proagfarmers.com
Sales Range: $10-24.9 Million
Emp.: 100
Distr of Farm Supplies
N.A.I.C.S.: 424910
Mark Jaskowiak (Gen Mgr)

PRO-AIR SERVICES
3444 Valley Ave SW, Decatur, AL 35603
Tel.: (256) 353-4446 AL
Web Site: http://www.pro-air.net
Year Founded: 1986
Sales Range: $1-9.9 Million
Emp.: 40
Installs & Maintains Heating, Air Conditioning & Refrigeration Equipment
N.A.I.C.S.: 811412
Marshall Putman (Founder & Pres)
Marshall Putman (Pres)
Jason Putman (VP-Ops & Bus Dev)
Carolyn Putman (Comptroller)
Steve Gilder (Project Coord)
Jason Putman (VP-Ops & Bus Dev)
Calvin Colbert (Mgr-Svc Dept)

PRO-AM SAFETY, INC.
551 Keystone Dr, Warrendale, PA 15086
Tel.: (724) 776-1818
Web Site:
    http://www.proamsafety.com
Sales Range: $10-24.9 Million
Emp.: 59
Fire Safety Product Distr
N.A.I.C.S.: 922160
Lauren Skinner (Mgr-Customer Svc)
Lora Shar (Office Mgr)
John Gieder (Mgr-Sls)

PRO-CON PROGRESSIVE CONVERTING, INC.
2430 E Glendale Ave, Appleton, WI 54911
Tel.: (920) 832-8844
Web Site: http://www.pro-con.net
Rev.: $27,300,000
Emp.: 250
Converted Paper Product Mfr
N.A.I.C.S.: 322299
Dan Curtin (Pres)

PRO-COPY TECHNOLOGIES, INC.
4720 Glendale Milford Rd, Cincinnati, OH 45242
Tel.: (513) 769-0606
Web Site:
    http://www.totalprosource.com
Sales Range: $25-49.9 Million
Emp.: 200
Business Machines & Equipment
N.A.I.C.S.: 459999
Ben Russert (Chm)
Brad Cates (Pres & CEO)
Pete Findley (CFO)
Sean Sullins (VP-New Market Dev)

Subsidiaries:

Infitech, LLC (1)
7116 Sennet Pl, West Chester, OH 45069
Tel.: (513) 779-5700
Web Site: http://www.infitech.net
Sales Range: $1-9.9 Million
Emp.: 10
Computer Programming & Other Related Services
N.A.I.C.S.: 541511

PRO-FAC COOPERATIVE, INC.

590 Willow Brook Office Park, Fairport, NY 14450
Tel.: (585) 218-4210 NY
Web Site: http://www.profaccoop.com
Year Founded: 1960
Sales Range: $1-9.9 Million
Emp.: 4
Agricultural Marketing Cooperative Services
N.A.I.C.S.: 424410
Steven D. Koinzan *(Second VP)*
Allan W. Overhiser *(Treas & First VP)*
Shari Burgo *(Asst Sec & Asst Treas)*
David M. Mehalick *(Sec)*
Thomas Willett *(Asst Treas)*
Chris Jagel *(Asst Sec)*

PRO-PAK INDUSTRIES
1125 Ford St, Maumee, OH 43537
Tel.: (419) 729-0751
Web Site: http://www.pro-pakindustries.com
Year Founded: 1948
Rev.: $20,000,000
Emp.: 100
Mfr of Corrugated Boxes
N.A.I.C.S.: 322211
Leo G. Deiger *(Pres)*
Dick Bauman *(Controller)*
Bill Peters *(Engr-Pkg)*
Josh Baum *(Plant Mgr)*
Scott Armey *(Mgr-HR)*
Melody Martin *(Mgr-Quality)*

PRO-SAFE, INCORPORATED
5825A Live Oak Pkwy, Norcross, GA 30093
Tel.: (770) 441-3300
Web Site: http://www.crimefreeusa.com
Sales Range: $10-24.9 Million
Emp.: 5
Security Control Equipment & Systems
N.A.I.C.S.: 423690
James Caperton *(Pres & CEO)*

PRO-SPEC INC.
5824 S 129th E Ave, Tulsa, OK 74134-6705
Tel.: (918) 461-0066
Web Site: http://www.prospecinc.com
Year Founded: 1985
Sales Range: $10-24.9 Million
Emp.: 4
Representative for Plumbing Products Manufacturers
N.A.I.C.S.: 423720
Wayne France *(Owner)*
Harold W. France Jr. *(Pres)*

PRO-TECH AIR CONDITIONING & HEATING SERVICE, INC.
2425 Silver Star Rd, Orlando, FL 32804-3311
Tel.: (407) 291-1644
Web Site: http://www.protechac.com
Plumbing, Heating & Air-Conditioning Contractors
N.A.I.C.S.: 238220
Thomas T. Nixon *(Pres)*

PRO-TECH INDUSTRIES INC.
14113 NE 3rd Ct, Vancouver, WA 98685
Tel.: (360) 573-6641
Web Site: http://www.protech.net
Rev.: $19,678,097
Emp.: 96
Motor Vehicle Parts & Accessories
N.A.I.C.S.: 336390

PROACTIVE CAPITAL GROUP, LLC
641 Lexington Ave, New York, NY 10022
Tel.: (646) 863-6341
Web Site: http://www.proactivecapital.com
Sales Range: $1-9.9 Million
Capital Market Advisory Services
N.A.I.C.S.: 523940
Kirin M. Smith *(Pres)*
Jeff Ramson *(Founder & CEO)*
Adam Holdsworth *(Mng Dir-IR)*
Gregory Barton *(Mng Dir-Digital Svcs & Social Media)*
Stephanie Prince *(Mng Dir-IR)*
Vivian Cervantes *(Mng Dir-IR)*
Chuck Harbey *(Mng Dir-IR)*

PROALLIANCE CORPORATION
6140 Parkland Blvd Ste 300, Mayfield Heights, OH 44124
Tel.: (440) 229-3420
Web Site: http://www.evergreen-national.com
Sales Range: $25-49.9 Million
Emp.: 10
Insurance Holding Company
N.A.I.C.S.: 551112
Charles Hamm *(Pres)*

Subsidiaries:

Evergreen National Indemnity Co. (1)
6140 Parkland Blvd Ste 321, Mayfield Heights, OH 44124
Tel.: (440) 229-3420
Web Site: http://www.evergreen-national.com
Sales Range: $25-49.9 Million
Emp.: 8
Provider of Surety Insurance Services
N.A.I.C.S.: 524128

PROAMERICAS
8174 South Holly #405, Centennial, CO 80122
Tel.: (303) 520-4524
Web Site: http://www.proamericas.com
Sales Range: Less than $1 Million
Advertising, Business-To-Business, Computers & Software, Co-op Advertising, Digital/Interactive, Direct Response Marketing, Email, Exhibit/Trade Shows
N.A.I.C.S.: 541820
Mark Rieger *(Mng Dir)*

PROARCH IT SOLUTIONS, INC.
57 Waddell St SE, Marietta, GA 30060
Tel.: (404) 602-9229 GA
Web Site: http://www.proarch.com
Emp.: 215
Cloud Consulting & Engineering Services
N.A.I.C.S.: 541618
Santosh Kaveti *(CEO)*
Michael Spoont *(Pres)*

Subsidiaries:

Enhops Solutions Private Limited (1)
Plots 1 And 2 Ground Floor Sai Krupa Enclave Manikonda Jagir, Near Lanco Hills Golconda Post, Hyderabad, 500008, Telangana, India
Tel.: (91) 4067364700
Web Site: http://www.enhops.com
Software Testing Services
N.A.I.C.S.: 541511

IV4, Inc. (1)
1387 Fairport Rd Ste 730, Fairport, NY 14450
Tel.: (585) 598-3300
Web Site: http://www.iv4.com
Emp.: 60
Information Technology Consulting Services

N.A.I.C.S.: 541519
Peter Bruu *(COO)*
Alvin Rodriguez *(Dir-Engrg)*
Jim Ockenden *(Chief Sls Officer)*
Mike Spoont *(Pres & CEO)*
Jeanne Morelli *(VP)*
Michael Montagliano *(CTO & VP-Consulting)*
Tony Harris *(Dir-Sls)*

PROBITY INTERNATIONAL CORPORATION
421 N Beverly Dr Ste 350, Beverly Hills, CA 90210
Tel.: (310) 888-1882
Web Site: http://www.probityinternational.com
Year Founded: 1989
Sales Range: $1-9.9 Million
Emp.: 18
Real Estate Investment & Development Services
N.A.I.C.S.: 531210
Robert Zarnegin *(Pres & CEO)*
Daniel Parks *(CFO)*
Monica Esquivel *(Head-Fin & Treasury)*
Michael Tenner *(Gen Counsel)*
David Maffit *(Sr VP-Design & Dev)*

Subsidiaries:

Belvedere Hotel Partnership (1)
421 N Beverly Dr Ste 350, Beverly Hills, CA 90210
Tel.: (310) 888-1882
Hotel
N.A.I.C.S.: 721110

PROBST ELECTRIC INC.
441 W Powerline Rd, Heber City, UT 84032-3865
Tel.: (435) 657-1955
Web Site: http://www.probstelectric.com
Sales Range: $25-49.9 Million
Emp.: 85
Construction Engineering Services
N.A.I.C.S.: 237310
Mary Argyle *(Office Mgr)*
Redgie Probst *(Owner)*

PROCACCI HOLDINGS LLC
3333 S Frnt St, Philadelphia, PA 19148
Tel.: (215) 463-8000
Web Site: http://www.procaccibrothers.com
Holding Company
N.A.I.C.S.: 551112
Joseph M. Procacci *(CEO)*

Subsidiaries:

Procacci Brothers Sales Corporation (1)
3333 S Frnt St, Philadelphia, PA 19148-5605
Tel.: (215) 463-8000
Web Site: http://www.procaccibros.com
Sales Range: $125-149.9 Million
Emp.: 500
Whslr of Fresh Fruits & Vegetables
N.A.I.C.S.: 424480
Bob Goodwin *(Dir-Facilities)*
Christopher Czumbil *(Dir-Transportation)*
Joe Tighe *(Mgr-Maintenance)*
Ken White *(Dir-Sls)*
Kevin Higgins *(Mgr-Transportation)*
Todd Huber *(Mgr-Ops)*
George Binck *(Exec VP)*
Frank Paone *(Dir-Mktg)*
Mike Maxwell *(Pres)*

PROCACCIANTI HOTEL REIT, INC.
1140 Reservoir Ave, Cranston, RI 02920-6320
Tel.: (401) 946-4600 MD
Web Site: https://www.prochotelreit.com

Year Founded: 2016
Rev.: $30,608,705
Assets: $113,846,620
Liabilities: $70,886,292
Net Worth: $42,960,328
Earnings: $4,392,534
Fiscal Year-end: 12/31/22
Real Estate Investment Services
N.A.I.C.S.: 531210
James A. Procaccianti *(Chm, Pres & CEO)*
Gregory D. Vickowski *(CFO & Treas)*
Ron M. Hadar *(Gen Counsel & Sec)*
Elizabeth A. Procaccianti *(COO)*
Mark Bacon *(Chief Construction Officer)*
Robert Leven *(Chief Investment Officer)*

PROCARE LTC HOLDING LLC
111 Executive Blvd, Farmingdale, NY 11735
Tel.: (631) 843-0500 NY
Web Site: http://www.procareltc.com
Pharmacy Services; Health & Personal Care Stores
N.A.I.C.S.: 456199
Hammad Shah *(CEO)*

Subsidiaries:

Allen's Pharmaserv, Inc. (1)
PO Box 2208, Youngstown, OH 44504-0208
Tel.: (330) 744-0707
Web Site: http://www.allensrx.com
Pharmacies & Drug Stores
N.A.I.C.S.: 456110
Alan Mirkin *(Pres)*

PROCE INC.
848 W Bartlett Rd Ste 3E, Bartlett, IL 60103-4493
Tel.: (630) 540-2848
Web Site: http://www.proce.com
Year Founded: 1999
All Other Miscellaneous Ambulatory Health Care Services
N.A.I.C.S.: 621999
Gail Townley *(Mgr)*
Richard Lewis *(CEO)*

PROCESS CONTROL SYSTEMS INTERNATIONAL
11993 Ravenna Rd Ste 5A, Chardon, OH 44024
Tel.: (440) 286-4440
Web Site: http://www.proconsysint.com
Microprocessors & Computer-Based Controllers, Counters & Digital & Analog Panel Meters Mfr
N.A.I.C.S.: 423830

PROCESS DISPLAYS CO
7108 31st Ave N, Minneapolis, MN 55427
Tel.: (763) 546-1133
Web Site: http://www.processdisplays.com
Sales Range: $25-49.9 Million
Emp.: 120
Posters, Lithographed
N.A.I.C.S.: 323111
Rick Anderson *(VP-Sls)*

PROCESS EQUIPMENT COMPANY OF TIPP CITY INC.
6555 S State Rte 202, Tipp City, OH 45371
Tel.: (937) 667-4451 OH
Web Site: http://www.peco-us.com
Year Founded: 1946
Sales Range: $25-49.9 Million
Emp.: 190
Industrial Machinery
N.A.I.C.S.: 332710
Bill Rosenberg *(CEO)*

PROCESS MACHINERY INC.

Process Equipment Company of Tipp City Inc.—(Continued)

PROCESS MACHINERY INC.
1636 Isaac Shelby Dr, Shelbyville, KY 40065
Tel.: (502) 633-5665
Web Site: http://www.processmachinery.com
Sales Range: $10-24.9 Million
Emp.: 70
General Construction Machinery & Equipment
N.A.I.C.S.: 423810
David H. Miles (Owner & Pres)
Charlene Barnes (Mgr-Accts)

PROCESS PLUS LLC
135 Merchant Street Swe 300 4524, Cincinnati, OH 45246
Tel.: (513) 742-7590
Web Site: http://www.processplus.com
Year Founded: 1996
Sales Range: $10-24.9 Million
Emp.: 100
Provider of Engineering Services
N.A.I.C.S.: 541330
Grant Mitchell (Pres & Principal)
Wayne Fischer (Treas)
Tom Hirt (Mgr-IT)
Dennis Gaige (Principal)
Dan Clevenger (Principal)
Jack Obszarski (Principal & Sec)
Jeffrey G. Rankin (Principal-Instrumentation & Controls)
Larry Greis (Principal-Process Design)
Andy Tate (Principal-Project Engrg)
Jim McMillan (Principal-Project Mgmt)

PROCLICK VENTURES, INC.
101 Southwestern Blvd Ste 130, Sugar Land, TX 77478
Tel.: (800) 591-8907
Web Site: http://www.proclickventures.com
Year Founded: 2007
Portfolio Management
N.A.I.C.S.: 523940
Al Panjwani (Partner)
Nimroz Momin (Partner)
Shakil Prasla (Partner)
Parvez Panjwani (Partner)
Thomas Finch (CEO-Engr Supply)

Subsidiaries:

Engineer Supply, LLC (1)
21430 Timberlake Rd Ste 349, Lynchburg, VA 24502-7248
Tel.: (800) 591-8907
Web Site: http://www.engineersupply.com
Professional Equipment & Supplies Merchant Whslr
N.A.I.C.S.: 423490

PROCO PRODUCTS INC.
2431 Wigwam Dr, Stockton, CA 95205
Tel.: (209) 943-6088
Web Site: http://www.procoproducts.com
Sales Range: $10-24.9 Million
Emp.: 24
Mfr Hard Rubber & Molded Rubber Products
N.A.I.C.S.: 326299
Robert Coffee (Mgr-Sls & Mktg-Natl)
Ed Marchese (Pres)

PROCOMM, INC.
1105 Industrial Pkwy, Brick, NJ 08724
Tel.: (732) 206-0660
Web Site: http://www.procomm222.com
Year Founded: 1989

Research & Development in the Physical Engineering & Life Sciences
N.A.I.C.S.: 541715
Robert Sepulveda (Founder)

PROCON AND ASSOCIATES, INC
108 Case Ct, Little River, SC 29597
Tel.: (843) 399-8918
Web Site: http://www.proconglobal.com
Rev.: $12,721,735
Emp.: 34
Building Repair & Renovation Services
N.A.I.C.S.: 236118
Randall G. Mitchem (Mgr-Field Ops)
Robert A. Gallagher (Pres)

PROCONCEPT MARKETING GROUP, INC.
18915 Bull Rapids Rd, Spencerville, IN 46788
Tel.: (260) 238-5000
Year Founded: 2006
Management Consulting Services
N.A.I.C.S.: 541618
Reid Stone (VP-Sls)

PROCONEX MANAGEMENT GROUP INC.
103 Enterprise Dr, Royersford, PA 19468-1281
Tel.: (610) 495-1835
Web Site: http://www.proconexdirect.com
Year Founded: 1994
Sales Range: $10-24.9 Million
Emp.: 131
Mfr of Industrial Machinery & Equipment
N.A.I.C.S.: 423830
Genna Armato (Mgr-Mktg)
Cliff Greider (VP)
Henry Alexander (Acct Mgr)
James Hunter (Engr-Sls)
Jarrett Young (Engr-Sys)
Jim Herron (Mgr-Bus Dev)
Mark Stayton (Engr-Sys)
Phil Russo (Mgr-Inside Sls)
Bill Diehl (Mgr-Sls Support)
David Henn (Mgr-Facilities)
Susan Deegan (Mgr-HR)
Donald Bockman (Acct Mgr)
Collin Bozzarello (Acct Mgr)

Subsidiaries:

Herron Valve, Inc. (1)
103 Enterprise Dr, Royersford, PA 19468-1281
Tel.: (610) 569-4100
Web Site: http://www.herronvalve.com
Sales Range: $10-24.9 Million
Emp.: 6
Mfr of Industrial Supplies
N.A.I.C.S.: 423830
Charlie Hannum (Gen Mgr)

Proconex Inc. (1)
103 Enterprise Dr, Royersford, PA 19468-1281
Tel.: (610) 495-1835
Web Site: http://www.proconexdirect.com
Emp.: 200
Disributors Of Industrial Machinery & Equipment
N.A.I.C.S.: 423830

PROCTOR CONSTRUCTION COMPANY INC.
2050 Us Hwy 1, Vero Beach, FL 32960
Tel.: (772) 234-8164
Web Site: http://www.proctorcc.com
Year Founded: 1977
Sales Range: $50-74.9 Million
Emp.: 35
Provider of Nonresidential Construction Services

N.A.I.C.S.: 236220
Donald Proctor (Chm & CEO)
Donald Tolliver (Pres & COO)
Ronald V. Dhaeseleer (CFO)
Michael McCabe (Dir-Project Dev)

PROCTOR SALES INC.
20715 50th Ave W, Lynnwood, WA 98036-7608
Tel.: (425) 774-1441
Web Site: http://www.gopsi.com
Year Founded: 1957
Sales Range: $25-49.9 Million
Emp.: 55
Warm Air Heating Services
N.A.I.C.S.: 423720
Brent Zefkeles (CFO & COO)
Jason Patterson (Pres)

PRODEA SYSTEMS, INC.
2435 N Central Expy Ste 500, Richardson, TX 75024
Tel.: (214) 278-1800
Web Site: http://www.prodea.com
Computer Software Design & Mfr
N.A.I.C.S.: 513210
Kathy Lam (VP-HR)
Hamid Ansari (Co-Founder & Pres)
Michael Cooper (VP-Engrg & Ops)
Amir Ansari (Co-Founder & CTO)
Tyson King (VP-Sls-Worldwide)
Peter Radsliff (VP-Mktg)
Andrew Tauhert (COO)
Anousheh Ansari (Co-Founder)

Subsidiaries:

Arrayent, Inc. (1)
2317 Broadway St Ste 140, Redwood City, CA 94063
Tel.: (650) 260-6502
Web Site: http://www.arrayent.com
Computer & Electronic Equipment Distr
N.A.I.C.S.: 423690
Shane Dyer (Founder)
Bob Dahlberg (VP-Bus Dev)
Cyril Brignone (CEO)
William Oget (VP-Engrg)

PRODIGAL MEDIA COMPANY
8544 Hickory Hill Dr, Poland, OH 44514
Tel.: (330) 707-2088
Web Site: http://www.prodigalmedia.com
Year Founded: 1994
Rev.: $10,000,000
Emp.: 15
Advetising Agency
N.A.I.C.S.: 541810
Jeff Hedrich (Pres & Dir-Creative)
Maggie Courtney-Hedrich (VP-Bus Dev)
Vince Bevacqua (VP-Media-PR)
Kelly Lipka (CFO)
Jill Jenkins (Acct Exec)

PRODIGY RESOURCES LLC
3773 Cherry Creek N Dr Ste 700 W, Denver, CO 80209
Tel.: (303) 297-7700
Web Site: http://www.prodigyr.com
Year Founded: 2007
Sales Range: $1-9.9 Million
Emp.: 17
Staffing
N.A.I.C.S.: 561311
Todd De Marco (Pres)

PRODIRECTIONAL
850 Conroe Park W Dr, Conroe, TX 77303
Tel.: (936) 441-7266
Web Site: http://www.prodirectional.com
Year Founded: 2001
Sales Range: $10-24.9 Million
Emp.: 350

Oil & Gas Operating Services
N.A.I.C.S.: 213112
Karen O'Neal (CEO)

PRODOS CAPITAL MANAGEMENT LLC
757 3rd Ave Ste 1703, New York, NY 10117
Tel.: (212) 972-3619
Web Site: http://www.prodoscapital.com
Privater Equity Firm
N.A.I.C.S.: 523999
Douglas Song (Principal)

PRODPI INC.
3890 S Windermere St, Englewood, CO 80110
Tel.: (303) 416-9212
Web Site: http://www.prodpi.com
Year Founded: 2004
Sales Range: $1-9.9 Million
Emp.: 25
Photographic Printing
N.A.I.C.S.: 333310
Caitlin Revell (Co-Founder & CEO)
Jeffrey Revell (Co-Founder & COO)

PRODUCE EXCHANGE CO INC.
2801 E Hillsborough Ave, Tampa, FL 33610
Tel.: (813) 237-3374
Rev.: $64,500,000
Emp.: 90
Fresh Fruit & Vegetable Merchant Whslr
N.A.I.C.S.: 424480
Chris Garmendia (Mgr)
John T. Grizzaffe (VP)
James T. Guida (VP)
Charles P. Grizzaffe (Pres)
Virginia Flemming (Treas & Sec)

PRODUCERS AG MARKETING ASSOCIATION
228 S Main St, Kensington, KS 66951
Tel.: (785) 476-2211
Web Site: http://www.proagmarketing.com
Rev.: $14,078,684
Emp.: 15
Grain Elevators
N.A.I.C.S.: 424510
Sam Scofield (Gen Mgr)

PRODUCERS CO-OP ASSOCIATION, INC.
300 Buffalo St, Girard, KS 66743
Tel.: (620) 724-8241
Web Site: http://www.girardcoop.com
Year Founded: 1948
Sales Range: $75-99.9 Million
Emp.: 50
Provider Of Agricultural Services
N.A.I.C.S.: 424910
Loren Reith (Chm)
Joe Ludlum (Sec)
Jack Beezley (Vice Chm)

PRODUCERS COOP OIL MILL
6 SE 4th St, Oklahoma City, OK 73129
Tel.: (405) 232-7555
Web Site: http://www.producerscoop.net
Sales Range: $50-74.9 Million
Emp.: 65
Cottonseed Oil Processor
N.A.I.C.S.: 311224
Gary Conkling (Pres & CEO)

PRODUCERS DAIRY FOODS, INC.

250 E Belmont Ave, Fresno, CA 93701-1405
Tel.: (559) 264-6583 CA
Web Site: http://www.producersdairy.com
Year Founded: 1932
Sales Range: $50-74.9 Million
Emp.: 430
Producer of Dairy Products
N.A.I.C.S.: 424430
Joanne Heredia (Mgr-Mktg)
Daryle Tate (Branch Mgr)
Victor Lai (Gen Counsel)

PRODUCERS GRAIN CO. INC.
1200 S Main St, El Dorado Springs, MO 64744
Tel.: (417) 876-2422
Web Site: http://www.producersgrain.com
Sales Range: $10-24.9 Million
Emp.: 45
Grains
N.A.I.C.S.: 424510
Greg Reynolds (Gen Mgr)

PRODUCERS HYBRIDS
54542 840 Rd W McAllister St, Battle Creek, NE 68715
Tel.: (402) 675-2975
Web Site: http://www.producershybrids.com
Rev.: $10,000,000
Emp.: 65
Seeds & Bulbs
N.A.I.C.S.: 424910
Bill McGuire (Reg Mgr-Sls-Eastern Team)

PRODUCERS LIVESTOCK MARKETING ASSOCIATION
230 W Ctr St, North Salt Lake, UT 84054-2804
Tel.: (801) 936-2424 UT
Web Site: http://www.producerslivestock.com
Year Founded: 1935
Sales Range: $10-24.9 Million
Emp.: 150
Provider of Livestock Marketing Services
N.A.I.C.S.: 424520
Rick O'Brien (Gen Mgr)

PRODUCERS RICE MILL, INC.
518 E Harrison St, Stuttgart, AR 72160-3700
Tel.: (870) 673-4444 AR
Web Site: http://www.producersrice.com
Year Founded: 1943
Rice Drying, Milling & Processing
N.A.I.C.S.: 311212
Keith Glover (Pres & CEO)
Kent Lockwood (VP-Fin & Admin)
Subsidiaries:
Sage V Foods, LLC - Stuttgart Plant (1)
603 N Park Ave, Stuttgart, AR 72160
Tel.: (870) 672-7606
Sales Range: $25-49.9 Million
Food Products Mfr
N.A.I.C.S.: 311999

PRODUCT DEVELOPMENT CORPORATION
20 Ragsdale Dr Ste 100, Monterey, CA 93940-5780
Tel.: (831) 333-1100 CA
Web Site: http://www.teampdc.com
Year Founded: 1939
Sales Range: $75-99.9 Million
Emp.: 2,000
Distr of Telephone Directories
N.A.I.C.S.: 561499
Subsidiaries:
PDC Logistics (1)
4091 McConnell Court, Burnaby, V5A 3L8, BC, Canada
Tel.: (604) 421-9171
Web Site: http://www.pdclogistics.ca
Emp.: 500
Logistics Consulting Servies
N.A.I.C.S.: 541614
Product Development Corporation Australia Pty Ltd (1)
Level 1 Suite 15/202-220 Ferntree Gully Road, Notting Hill, 3168, VIC, Australia
Tel.: (61) 3 92633000
Web Site: http://www.deliverphonebooks.com.au
Newspaper Publishing Services
N.A.I.C.S.: 513110

PRODUCT HANDLING DESIGN INC.
2322 Parker Rd Ste 410, Carrollton, TX 75010
Tel.: (972) 231-4628
Web Site: http://www.producthandling.com
Rev.: $11,115,717
Emp.: 50
Materials Handling Machinery
N.A.I.C.S.: 423830
Ron Walker (Gen Mgr)

PRODUCT MOVERS, LLC
6834 Spring Valley Dr Ste 202, Holland, OH 43528
Tel.: (419) 868-8999
Web Site: http://www.productmovers.com
Year Founded: 2007
Sales Range: $1-9.9 Million
Emp.: 44
Reusable Packaging & Material Handling Solutions Design & Mfr
N.A.I.C.S.: 333993
Devan C. Capur (Founder & CEO)
Joseph Bublick (Mgr-Product & Quality)

PRODUCT QUEST MANUFACTURING, LLC.
330 Carswell Ave, Daytona Beach, FL 32117
Tel.: (386) 239-8787
Web Site: http://www.productquestmfg.com
Year Founded: 1996
Sales Range: $10-24.9 Million
Emp.: 105
Pharmaceuticals Product Mfr
N.A.I.C.S.: 325412
Bill Jennings (CFO)
John Regan (CEO)
Rick Webb (Exec VP)

PRODUCT VENTURES, LTD
55 Walls Dr, Fairfield, CT 06824
Tel.: (203) 319-1119
Web Site: https://www.productventures.com
Rev.: $4,725,000
Emp.: 15
Commercial & Institutional Building Construction
N.A.I.C.S.: 236220
Peter Clarke (Founder & CEO)
Eric Hartman (VP-Tech & Commlization)
Sean Bisceglia (CFO)

PRODUCTION CASTINGS INC.
1410 W Lark Industrial Dr, Fenton, MO 63026
Tel.: (636) 677-3364
Web Site: http://www.productioncastings.com
Sales Range: $10-24.9 Million
Emp.: 125
Zinc & Zinc-Based Alloy Die-Castings
N.A.I.C.S.: 331523
Alan Loeffelman (Pres)

PRODUCTION COMPONENTS, INC.
2657 Aero Dr, Grand Prairie, TX 75052
Tel.: (817) 784-1006
Web Site: http://www.productioncomponents.com
Sales Range: $10-24.9 Million
Emp.: 10
Industrial Product Distr
N.A.I.C.S.: 423840
Richard F. Duly (Owner)
Thomas P. Duly (Owner)
Michael Holt (Owner)
Deborah Duly (Office Mgr)

PRODUCTION CONTROL UNITS, INC.
2280 W Dorothy Ln, Moraine, OH 45439-1892
Tel.: (937) 299-5594 DE
Web Site: http://www.pcuinc.com
Year Founded: 1946
Sales Range: $10-24.9 Million
Emp.: 100
Process & Special Industrial Equipment Designer & Mfr
N.A.I.C.S.: 333248
Thomas H. Hoge (CEO)
Mark Leiter (Sr Engr-Controls)
Jason Reese (Engr-Controls)
William Ware (Engr-Controls)
Bill Budde (Pres)
Joseph Osterday (CFO)

PRODUCTION DESIGN SERVICES
401 Fame Rd, Dayton, OH 45449
Tel.: (937) 866-3377
Web Site: http://www.p-d-s-i.com
Year Founded: 1955
Sales Range: $10-24.9 Million
Emp.: 202
Robots, Assembly Line: Industrial & Commercial
N.A.I.C.S.: 561320

PRODUCTION ROBOTICS, INC.
562 Whitney St, San Leandro, CA 94577
Tel.: (510) 777-0375
Web Site: http://www.productionrobotics.com
Year Founded: 1992
Rev.: $3,400,000
Emp.: 28
Engineeering Services
N.A.I.C.S.: 541330
Leonard Ginsburg (Pres & Chief Engr)
Cuizhu Ma Ginsburg (VP-Ops)

PRODUCTION SERVICE COMPANY
827 Silvernail Rd, Pewaukee, WI 53072
Tel.: (262) 547-4900
Web Site: http://www.oberlinfilter.com
Sales Range: $10-24.9 Million
Emp.: 85
Industrial Filter Mfr
N.A.I.C.S.: 333998
Mike Ignatowski (Controller)
Subsidiaries:
Oberlin Filter Company (1)
404 Pilot Ct, Waukesha, WI 53188
Tel.: (262) 547-4900
Web Site: http://www.oberlinfilter.com
Sales Range: $10-24.9 Million
Emp.: 80
Fiscal Year-end: 08/31/2014
Mfr of Industrial Filters
N.A.I.C.S.: 333998
Thomas L. Oberlin (CEO)
Subsidiary (Non-US):
Oberlin Filter GmbH (2)
Gartenstrasse 38, 52249, Eschweiler, Germany
Tel.: (49) 2403 50 43 0
Web Site: http://www.oberlin-filter.de
Automatic Filtration System Mfr
N.A.I.C.S.: 333413
Joerg Koslowki (Mng Dir)
Oberlin Filter Ltd. (2)
2 Hurworth Road Aycliffe Business Park, Newton Aycliffe, DL5 6UD., Durham, United Kingdom
Tel.: (44) 1325 317900
Web Site: http://www.oberlinfilter.com
Emp.: 7
Automatic Filtration System Mfr
N.A.I.C.S.: 333413

PRODUCTION TOOL CORPORATION
1229 E 74th St, Chicago, IL 60619-2009
Tel.: (773) 288-4400 WI
Web Site: http://www.productiontoolcompany.com
Year Founded: 1957
Sales Range: $10-24.9 Million
Emp.: 35
Industrial Machinery Mfr
N.A.I.C.S.: 332710

PRODUCTION TOOL SUPPLY COMPANY, LLC
8655 E 8 Mile Rd, Warren, MI 48089-3019
Tel.: (586) 755-7770 MI
Web Site: http://www.pts-tools.com
Year Founded: 1951
Sales Range: $200-249.9 Million
Emp.: 500
Industrial Tools & Supplies Whslr
N.A.I.C.S.: 423840
Lawrence A. Wolfe (Pres)
John Beaudoin (Dir-Sls & Mktg)
Craig Fishel (Controller)
Subsidiaries:
Rex Supply Company (1)
14751 Kirby Dr, Houston, TX 77047
Tel.: (713) 222-2251
Web Site: http://www.rex-supply.com
Sales Range: $25-49.9 Million
Emp.: 50
Industrial Sales
N.A.I.C.S.: 423830
Tom Wright (Pres)

PRODUCTIONHUB INC.
1806 Hammerlin Ave, Winter Park, FL 32789
Tel.: (407) 629-4122 FL
Web Site: http://www.productionhub.com
Year Founded: 1998
Sales Range: $1-9.9 Million
Emp.: 10
Telephone Communications Motion Picture/Video Production
N.A.I.C.S.: 517810
John Pokorny (Founder)
Steve Rotz (VP)
Mark J. Foley (Editor-Tech)

PRODUCTIVE DATA SOLUTIONS INC.
6870 West 52nd Ave Ste 107, Arvada, CO 80002
Tel.: (303) 220-7165 CO
Web Site: http://www.pdsinc.com
Year Founded: 1987

PRODUCTIVE DATA SOLUTIONS INC.

Productive Data Solutions Inc.—(Continued)
Information Technology Recruiting & Consulting Services; Custom Computer Programming Services
N.A.I.C.S.: 541511
Brian Hinshaw (VP-Sls)
Tom Sweetman (Pres & CEO)
Kevin Mackie (CFO)
Brian Gephart (VP-Staffing Solutions)

PRODUCTIVE DENTIST ACADEMY
404 Commercial Ave, Anacortes, WA 98221
Tel.: (360) 588-4353
Web Site:
http://new.productivedentist.com
Year Founded: 2005
Sales Range: $1-9.9 Million
Emp.: 10
Dental Practice Consulting
N.A.I.C.S.: 541618
Bruce Baird (Founder)
Vicki McManus (CEO)

PRODUCTIVITY ASSOCIATES, INC.
5625 Ruffin Rd Ste 220, San Diego, CA 92123
Tel.: (800) 247-8776
Web Site: http://www.gotopai.com
Year Founded: 1991
Sales Range: $1-9.9 Million
Emp.: 107
Outsourced Call Center Services; Service Desk & Technical Support Services
N.A.I.C.S.: 541690
Kenneth McLoughlin (CEO)

PRODUCTIVITY INC.
15150 25th Ave N, Plymouth, MN 55447
Tel.: (763) 476-8600
Web Site: http://www.productivity.com
Year Founded: 1968
Sales Range: $10-24.9 Million
Emp.: 100
Machine Tools & Accessories
N.A.I.C.S.: 423830
Greg Buck (Pres)
Kevin Kim (Controller)

PRODUCTS ENGINEERING CORP
2645 Maricopa St, Torrance, CA 90503
Tel.: (310) 787-4500
Web Site:
http://www.productsengineering.com
Sales Range: $10-24.9 Million
Emp.: 110
Measuring Tools & Machines Mfr
N.A.I.C.S.: 332216
Martin Lubovinski (Pres)
Rich Luboviski (VP)
Bernard Brooks (Controller)

PRODUCTS SUPPORT INC.
8331 Bristol Ct, Jessup, MD 20794
Tel.: (410) 792-4754
Web Site:
http://www.productssupport.com
Rev.: $21,000,000
Emp.: 50
Machine & Other Job Shop Work
N.A.I.C.S.: 332710
E. Scott Wiley (Pres)
Cathy Herzing (Mgr-Sls)
Jim Turner (Mgr-Govt Product Sls & Support)

PROEQUITIES, INC.
2801 Hwy 280 S, Birmingham, AL 35223-2407
Tel.: (205) 268-3035 AL
Web Site: http://www.proequities.com
Year Founded: 1985
Sales Range: $10-24.9 Million
Emp.: 90
Securities Broker & Dealer
N.A.I.C.S.: 523150
Rory Hartley (Mng Dir-Protective Securities)
Darren Guerrera (CFO)
Christopher W. Flint (CEO)
Blaine Miller (Chief Supervision Officer)
Steve Youhn (Chief Compliance Officer)
Libet Anderson (Pres)
Kim Davis (VP-Bus Dev)

PROEQUITY ASSET MANAGEMENT CORPORATION
4980 Hillsdale Cir, El Dorado, CA 95762
Web Site:
http://www.proequityam.com
Year Founded: 2011
Sales Range: $1-9.9 Million
Emp.: 33
Asset Management Services
N.A.I.C.S.: 531390
Michael Turner (Mng Dir)
Jeffrey Fanzo (Mng Dir)
Tyler Sheldon (Mng Dir)
Brett Birkeland (Mng Dir)
Adam Nelson (Mng Dir)

PROFECTUS, LLC
3000 Sage Rd, Houston, TX 77056
Tel.: (281) 740-0185
Web Site:
http://www.profectusllc.com
Consulting Services
N.A.I.C.S.: 541618
Gilbert Alba III (CEO)
Subsidiaries:
Excel Search Group, LLC (1)
3000 Sage Rd, Houston, TX 77056
Tel.: (281) 740-0185
Web Site: http://www.excelsearchgroup.com
Employment Placement Agencies
N.A.I.C.S.: 561311
Gilbert Alba (Pres)

PROFESSIONAL ASSOCIATION FOR CHILDHOOD EDUCATION
436 14th St Ste 205, Oakland, CA 94612
Tel.: (415) 749-6851 CA
Web Site: http://www.pacenet.org
Year Founded: 1955
Rev.: $203,977
Assets: $166,345
Liabilities: $77,400
Net Worth: $88,945
Earnings: ($234,930)
Emp.: 2
Fiscal Year-end: 06/30/14
Professional Association
N.A.I.C.S.: 813920
Estela Alvarez (Dir-Events & Education)
Gina Ayllon (Exec Dir)
Cathy Vaughn (VP-Community Outreach)
Sue Houweling (VP-Admin)
R. Ann Whitehead (Treas)
Mary Lou Johnson (Pres)
Sherri Springer (Chm)

PROFESSIONAL BUILDERS SUPPLY, LLC
10405 Chapel Hill Rd, Morrisville, NC 27560
Tel.: (919) 380-3400
Web Site: http://www.pb-supply.com
Year Founded: 2003
Rev.: $29,000,000
Emp.: 54
Lumber & Building Materials
N.A.I.C.S.: 444110
Van Isley (Chm & CEO)
Mike Jones (Mgr-Ops-Charlotte)
Katherine Johnson (Mgr-Credit)
Joey Self (Mgr-Installed Window, Door & Interior Trim)
Wesley Jones (Acct Mgr-Multifamily)
Kim Solomita (Coord-Installed Sls)
Trae McElheny (Pres-Charleston)
Gene Tomczak (CFO)
Steve Hansen (Exec VP-Pur)
Subsidiaries:
SouthEnd Exteriors, Inc. (1)
1500 1 Continental Blvd, Charlotte, NC 28273
Tel.: (704) 527-8551
Web Site: http://www.southendexteriors.com
Siding Installation
N.A.I.C.S.: 238170
James M. Oliver (Pres)
Ryan Roberts (VP)

PROFESSIONAL COMMUNITY MANAGEMENT
27051 Towne Centre Dr Ste 200, Foothill Ranch, CA 92610
Tel.: (949) 768-7261
Web Site:
http://www.pcminternet.com
Sales Range: $25-49.9 Million
Emp.: 1,500
Real Estate Managers
N.A.I.C.S.: 531210
James V. Fraker (VP)
Michelle Thomson (Dir-Associa Svcs-West Coast Reg)
Brian Kruppa (Deputy Gen Counsel & Sr VP)
Matthew Williams (Pres)
Jessica Flicker (Dir-Developer Svcs)
Faye Burian (Coord-Delinquency-Acctg Dept)

PROFESSIONAL COMPUTER CENTER INC.
1433 Hamilton Pkwy, Itasca, IL 60143
Tel.: (630) 285-0500
Web Site: http://www.pccval.com
Sales Range: $10-24.9 Million
Emp.: 150
Computers & Accessories Sales
N.A.I.C.S.: 423430
Robert F. Green (CEO)

PROFESSIONAL CONCESSIONS, INC.
9067 Southern Blvd, West Palm Beach, FL 33411
Tel.: (561) 793-1971 FL
Web Site:
http://www.professionalconcessions.com
Year Founded: 1986
Sales Range: $1-9.9 Million
Emp.: 125
Management of Food, Beverage & Merchandise Concessions at Concerts, Sports & Event Venues
N.A.I.C.S.: 713990
Bruce Beck (VP)
P. J. Wear (Gen Mgr)

PROFESSIONAL CONSTRUCTION SERVICES INC.
6 E 3rd St, Kenner, LA 70062
Tel.: (504) 241-8001 LA
Web Site: http://www.pcsbuilds.com
Year Founded: 1974
Sales Range: $10-24.9 Million

Emp.: 20
Heavy Construction Services
N.A.I.C.S.: 237990
Edward Abate (Pres)

PROFESSIONAL CONTROL CORPORATION
N11 4W 18770 Clinton Dr, Germantown, WI 53022-3118
Tel.: (262) 251-3000 WI
Web Site: http://www.pccweb.com
Year Founded: 1980
Sales Range: $75-99.9 Million
Emp.: 20
Software Programs Integrator for Offices & Factories
N.A.I.C.S.: 423430
Robert D. Dumke (Owner)
Jack Dumke (CFO)
David Martin (VP)
Subsidiaries:
PCC Systems LLC (1)
N 114 W 18770 Clinton Dr, Germantown, WI 53022
Tel.: (262) 251-3000
Web Site: http://www.pccweb.com
Sales Range: $10-24.9 Million
Business Software Solutions
N.A.I.C.S.: 541512
Jack Dunke (CFO)

PROFESSIONAL CONVENTION MANAGEMENT ASSOCIATION
35 E Wacker Dr Ste 500, Chicago, IL 60601
Tel.: (312) 423-7262 IL
Web Site: http://www.pcma.org
Year Founded: 1958
Sales Range: $10-24.9 Million
Emp.: 60
Professional Management Services
N.A.I.C.S.: 611430
Mary Pat Heftman (Treas & Sec)
Ray Kopcinski (Chm)
Bruce MacMillan (CMO)
Michelle Crowley (Chief Growth & Innovation Officer)
Sherrif Karamat (Pres & CEO)
Mona Cotton (Chief Bus Officer)
Robert Haas (Chief Admin Officer)
Meredith Rollins (Chief Community Officer-Community Engagement & Member Growth)

PROFESSIONAL COURSE MANAGEMENT, INC.
10500 Taft St, Pembroke Pines, FL 33026
Tel.: (954) 433-8800 FL
Web Site: http://www.pcmgolf.com
Year Founded: 1971
Sales Range: $1-9.9 Million
Emp.: 116
Golf Course Manager, Owner & Operator
N.A.I.C.S.: 713910
Johnny LaPonzina (Founder & Pres)
Subsidiaries:
Miami Beach Golf Club (1)
2301 Alton Rd, Miami Beach, FL 33140
Tel.: (305) 532-3350
Web Site:
http://www.miamibeachgolfclub.com
Golf Course & Golf Club
N.A.I.C.S.: 713910
Steve Farrell (Dir-Golf)
Jim Nourse (Dir-Food & Beverage)
Jeff Hunt (Dir-Mktg)
Johnny LaPonzina (Pres)
Jim McLean (Dir-Ops)

Miami Shores Country Club (1)
10000 Biscayne Blvd, Miami Shores, FL 33138
Tel.: (305) 795-2360
Web Site: http://www.miamishoresgolf.com
Emp.: 80
Golf Course & Country Club
N.A.I.C.S.: 713910

COMPANIES

Alberto Pozzi *(Gen Mgr)*
Pavel Arutyunov *(Mgr-Food & Beverage)*
Resa Strickland *(Mgr-Catering)*
Chris Baetzel *(Dir-Golf)*
Howie Orlin *(Dir-Tennis)*

Normandy Shores Golf Club (1)
2401 Biarritz Dr, Miami Beach, FL 33141
Tel.: (305) 868-6502
Web Site: http://www.normandyshoresgolfclub.com
Emp.: 20
Golf Course & Golf Club
N.A.I.C.S.: 713910
Jeff Hunt *(Dir-Mktg)*
Johnny LaPonzina *(Pres)*
Jim Nourse *(Dir-Food & Beverage)*

PROFESSIONAL DATA DIMENSIONS
200 S Meridian St Ste 301, Indianapolis, IN 26225
Tel.: (317) 636-7355
Web Site: http://www.pdd.com
Rev.: $5,200,000
Emp.: 45
Data Processing Hosting & Related Services
N.A.I.C.S.: 518210
Clarissa Nowlin *(Controller)*

PROFESSIONAL EDUCATION INSTITUTE
7020 High Grove Blvd, Burr Ridge, IL 60527
Tel.: (630) 382-1000
Web Site: http://www.thepei.com
Year Founded: 1983
Sales Range: $150-199.9 Million
Emp.: 500
Personal Finance, Educational & Other Products Retailer
N.A.I.C.S.: 541840
Mark Holecek *(Chm)*
Michael E. Hussey *(Pres)*
Roger Sinnes *(Chief Revenue Officer)*

PROFESSIONAL ELECTRIC PRODUCTS COMPANY, INC.
33210 Lakeland Blvd, Eastlake, OH 44095-5205
Tel.: (440) 946-3790   OH
Web Site: http://www.pepconet.com
Year Founded: 1968
Sales Range: $10-24.9 Million
Emp.: 87
Provider of Telecommunication Supplies & Services
N.A.I.C.S.: 423610
Joseph C. Borkey *(Pres)*
John C. Borkey *(VP-Ops)*

PROFESSIONAL EMERGENCY CARE PC
38935 Ann Arbor Rd, Livonia, MI 48150
Tel.: (734) 632-0175
Web Site: http://www.er-one.org
Year Founded: 1996
Sales Range: $50-74.9 Million
Emp.: 100
Temporary Staffing Services
N.A.I.C.S.: 561320
Jeffrey Sendi *(Dir-Health)*
David Weaver *(Dir-Medical)*

PROFESSIONAL EMPLOYMENT SOLUTIONS, INC.
14350 N 87th St Ste 165, Scottsdale, AZ 85260-2658
Tel.: (480) 315-8600   AZ
Web Site: http://www.pesinc.com
Year Founded: 2003
Sales Range: $1-9.9 Million
Emp.: 29
Employment Agencies
N.A.I.C.S.: 561311

Phil Graham *(CEO)*

PROFESSIONAL ENGINEERING CONSULTANTS, P.A.
303 S Topeka Ave, Wichita, KS 67202
Tel.: (316) 262-2691
Web Site: http://www.pec1.com
Year Founded: 1946
Rev.: $14,400,000
Emp.: 250
Engineering Consultancy Services
N.A.I.C.S.: 541330
Rod Young *(CEO & Mgr-Civil Dept)*
Dan Biby *(Mgr-Facilities)*
Dennis Downes *(Mgr-Electrical)*
Britt Clubb *(Mgr-Matls Testing & Geotechnical)*
Marc Jones *(Principal)*
Steve Hauck *(Mgr-Mktg)*

PROFESSIONAL EXAMINATION SERVICE
475 Riverside Dr Ste 600, New York, NY 10115
Tel.: (212) 367-4200   MO
Web Site: http://www.proexam.org
Year Founded: 1971
Sales Range: $10-24.9 Million
Emp.: 96
Professional Certification Provider
N.A.I.C.S.: 561990
Sandra Logorda *(CFO)*
Martin S. Brutosky *(VP-Tech Solutions)*
Simmy Ziv-El *(VP-Corp Dev)*
Bob Block *(Pres & CEO)*

PROFESSIONAL FITNESS CONCEPTS, INC.
521 Vera Ct, Joliet, IL 60436-1895
Tel.: (815) 741-5328   IL
Web Site: http://www.pfc-fitness.com
Year Founded: 2001
Rev.: $3,700,000
Emp.: 10
Sales of Pre-Owned Fitness Equipment
N.A.I.C.S.: 423910
Michael Lyons *(Pres, Owner & Reg Mgr)*

PROFESSIONAL GROUNDS MANAGEMENT
2241 2nd Ave S, Saint Petersburg, FL 33712
Tel.: (727) 328-9686
Web Site: http://www.pgminfo.com
Sales Range: $1-9.9 Million
Emp.: 25
Landscaping Services
N.A.I.C.S.: 561730
Tom Burke *(Pres)*

PROFESSIONAL HAIR LABS, INC.
4775 Allen Rd, Zephyrhills, FL 33541
Tel.: (813) 788-7468
Web Site: http://www.prohairlabs.com
Year Founded: 1994
Sales Range: $1-9.9 Million
Emp.: 8
Cosmetic Product Mfr & Distr
N.A.I.C.S.: 325620
Howard Margolin *(Founder & CEO)*
Daryl Margolin *(VP)*
Ryan Margolin *(Dir-EU Mktg)*
Dave Margolin *(Ops Mgr)*

PROFESSIONAL HEALTHCARE RESOURCES, INC.
7619 Little River Tnpk Ste 600, Annandale, VA 22003-2625
Tel.: (703) 752-8700
Web Site: http://www.phri.com
Year Founded: 1994

Home Health, Hospice & Personal Care Services
N.A.I.C.S.: 621610
Ronald DeCesare *(CEO)*
Eileen DeCesare *(Founder)*

PROFESSIONAL IMPLEMENTATION CONSULTING SERVICES, INC.
46 High St, Mount Holly, NJ 08060
Tel.: (609) 614-3261
Web Site: http://www.pics-itech.com
Year Founded: 1994
Sales Range: $1-9.9 Million
Emp.: 30
Information Technology Services
N.A.I.C.S.: 541511
Terry Rossi *(Co-Founder & CIO)*
Richard J. Rosenthal *(Co-Founder)*
Brian Atchison *(Chief Revenue Officer)*
Sharon Doele *(Controller)*
Alan Lawson *(Mgr-Svc Delivery)*

PROFESSIONAL INSURANCE ASSOCIATES
1100 Industrial Rd Ste 3, San Carlos, CA 94070
Tel.: (650) 592-7333
Web Site: http://www.piainc.com
Sales Range: $10-24.9 Million
Emp.: 55
Insurance Services
N.A.I.C.S.: 524210
Paula Hammack *(Pres)*
Michelle Lozada *(Acct Mgr-Comml Lines)*
Jordan Zan *(Partner)*

PROFESSIONAL MEDIA MANAGEMENT
528 Bridge St NW Ste 7, Grand Rapids, MI 49504
Tel.: (616) 456-5555   MI
Web Site: http://www.professionalmediamanagement.com
Year Founded: 1977
Media Buying Services
N.A.I.C.S.: 541810
Jack Ponstine *(Pres & CEO)*
Randy Dykstra *(Mgr-Bus)*
Lee Amundson *(Sr Mgr-Database)*
Leigh Engelbrecht *(Mgr-Ops & Customer Svc)*

PROFESSIONAL METAL CORPORATION
390 River Ridge Dr, Elgin, IL 60123
Tel.: (847) 879-0200
Web Site: http://www.prometco.net
Sales Range: $25-49.9 Million
Emp.: 11
Strip Coil & Sheet Metal
N.A.I.C.S.: 423510
Jack Thompson *(Pres)*
Charles Barnes *(VP)*
Robert Kravit *(VP)*

PROFESSIONAL NATIONAL TITLE NETWORK, INC.
70 W Madison St Ste 1600, Chicago, IL 60602
Tel.: (312) 696-2700
Web Site: http://www.pntn.com
Rev.: $15,000,000
Emp.: 200
Mortgage Banking Services
N.A.I.C.S.: 522310
Kevin J. Cooney *(Pres)*
Joan Moss *(VP)*
Joe Burke *(VP)*

PROFESSIONAL OFFICE ENVIRONMENTS

222 Millwell Dr, Maryland Heights, MO 63043
Tel.: (314) 621-0606
Web Site: http://www.poe-inc.com
Year Founded: 1988
Rev.: $13,619,068
Emp.: 30
Office Furniture Distr & Interior Design Services
N.A.I.C.S.: 423210
Mark Prost *(Controller)*
Stacey Hudson *(Dir-Facility Svcs)*
Jennifer Klaverkamp *(VP-Sls)*

PROFESSIONAL OFFICE SERVICES INC.
2757 Burton Ave, Waterloo, IA 50703-9638
Tel.: (319) 235-6777   IA
Web Site: http://www.poscorp.com
Year Founded: 1976
Sales Range: $25-49.9 Million
Emp.: 375
Mfr of Manifold Business Forms
N.A.I.C.S.: 323111
Mike Williams *(Pres)*
Matt Bigler *(Sr VP-Sls)*
H. Williams *(CEO)*

Subsidiaries:

Professional Office Services (1)
355 6th Ave N, Waite Park, MN 56387
Tel.: (320) 255-8937
Web Site: http://www.poscorp.com
Sales Range: $1-9.9 Million
Emp.: 23
Commercial Lithographic Printing
N.A.I.C.S.: 323111

PROFESSIONAL PACKAGE COMPANY
22360 Royalton Rd, Strongsville, OH 44149
Tel.: (440) 572-1771
Web Site: http://www.a-roo.com
Rev.: $15,000,000
Emp.: 55
Mfr & Distributor of Packing Materials
N.A.I.C.S.: 326113
Scott Gilbert *(Founder, Pres & CEO)*
Sharon Gilbert *(Treas & Sec)*
Phil Basak *(Controller)*

PROFESSIONAL PACKAGING SYSTEMS INC.
2010 S Great SW Pkwy, Grand Prairie, TX 75051
Tel.: (972) 988-0777
Web Site: http://www.propac.com
Year Founded: 1971
Sales Range: $10-24.9 Million
Emp.: 100
Whslr of Packaging Materials
N.A.I.C.S.: 424990
John H. Cruce *(Owner)*

PROFESSIONAL PAVEMENT PRODUCTS, INC.
8081 Philips Hwy Ste 22, Jacksonville, FL 32256
Tel.: (904) 448-4074
Web Site: http://www.pppcatalog.com
Year Founded: 1996
Sales Range: $1-9.9 Million
Emp.: 20
Pavement & Construction Products Distr
N.A.I.C.S.: 423810
Greg Driskell *(Pres)*
Glenn Milton *(VP)*
Debbie Driskell *(Exec Mgr-Acctg)*
Jason Adair *(Mgr-Bridgeport)*
Jentson Beasley *(Mgr-Bridgeport)*
Ryan Cannady *(Mgr-Bridgeport)*
Michael Perez *(Mgr-Bridgeport)*
Monika Thompson *(Mgr-Bridgeport)*
Pete Vasquez *(Mgr-Bridgeport)*

Professional Pavement Products, Inc.—(Continued)
Steve Norkus (Mgr-Relationship & RoadVista Product-Natl)
Sergio Sandoval (Mgr-Relationship-Intl)

PROFESSIONAL PHOTOGRAPHERS OF AMERICA
229 Peachtree St NE Ste 2200, Atlanta, GA 30303
Tel.: (404) 522-8600 GA
Web Site: http://www.ppa.com
Year Founded: 1931
Sales Range: $10-24.9 Million
Emp.: 55
Photography Association
N.A.I.C.S.: 813920
Carla Plouin (Dir-Mktg & Comm)
Scott Morgan (Dir-IT & Admin)
Wilda Oken (Dir-HR)
Scott Kurkian (CFO & COO)
Lori Craft (Chm)
Stephen Thetford (VP)
Rob Behm (Pres)
Audrey Wancket (Treas)
Becky Young (Mgr-IT Project)
Cheryl Pearson (Mgr-Adv Svcs)
David Trust (CEO)
Debbie Todd (Dir-Art)
Gregory Aide (Mgr-Production)
Jane Gaboury (Dir-Publ)
Julia Boyd (Dir-Certification)
Kristen Hartman (Dir-Member Value & Experience)
Sharon Palmer (Mgr-Events)
Wayne Jones (Dir-Sls & Strategic Alliances)

PROFESSIONAL PLASTICS, INC.
1810 E Valencia Dr, Fullerton, CA 92831-4847
Tel.: (714) 446-6500 CA
Web Site: http://www.professionalplastics.com
Year Founded: 1984
Sales Range: $25-49.9 Million
Emp.: 200
Supplier of Plastics Materials
N.A.I.C.S.: 424610
David Kietzke (CEO)
Michael Kietzke (Sr VP)
Chris Kietzke (Exec VP)
John Maglione (CFO)

Subsidiaries:

Professional Plastics Co. Ltd. (1)
Section 1 - No 10 Tiedao Rd, Dong District, Hsin-chu, 300, Taiwan
Tel.: (886) 3 5357850
Plastic Product Whslr
N.A.I.C.S.: 424610

Professional Plastics Pte Ltd. (1)
No 7 Yishun Industrial Street 1 #05-32
North Spring Biz Hub, Singapore, 768162, Singapore
Tel.: (65) 6266 6193
Web Site: http://www.professionalplastics.com.sg
Emp.: 12
Plastic Product Whslr
N.A.I.C.S.: 424610
Wilson Tan (Gen Mgr-Asia)

PROFESSIONAL PRODUCE
2570 E 25th St, Vernon, CA 90058
Tel.: (323) 277-1550
Web Site: http://www.profproduce.com
Rev.: $17,900,000
Emp.: 85
Fresh Fruit & Vegetable Merchant Whslr
N.A.I.C.S.: 424480
Wendell Araki (Gen Mgr-Warehouse)
Rafael Barba (Mgr)
Ted Kaplan (Pres & CEO)
Maribel Reyes (CFO)

PROFESSIONAL PRODUCTION PRODUCTS, INC.
1122 E Hwy 2, Oldtown, ID 83822
Tel.: (208) 437-2412
Web Site: http://www.triprocedar.com
Year Founded: 1990
Rev.: $40,000,000
Emp.: 50
Cut Stock, Resawing Lumber & Planing
N.A.I.C.S.: 321912
Ron Cluster (VP-Procurement & Sls)
Steve Liton (Pres)

PROFESSIONAL PRODUCTS, INC.
9116 Gaither Rd, Gaithersburg, MD 20877-1422
Tel.: (240) 864-4000 MD
Web Site: http://www.professionalproducts.com
Year Founded: 1964
Sales Range: $10-24.9 Million
Emp.: 75
Supplier of Video & Audio Parts & Equipment
N.A.I.C.S.: 423690
Bruce Kaufman (Pres)
Jim Hatcher (CTO)

PROFESSIONAL PROJECT SERVICES, INC.
1100 Bethel Valley Rd, Oak Ridge, TN 37830
Tel.: (865) 220-4300
Web Site: http://www.p2s.com
Year Founded: 1996
Engineeering Services
N.A.I.C.S.: 541330
Mike Webster (CFO)
Mark DeGraff (Pres)
Denis Morgan (VP & Sr Mgr-Environ Program)

PROFESSIONAL REBUILD & OPTIMAL SERVICE LLC
601 Texas Ave, Lubbock, TX 79401
Tel.: (806) 749-7761
Web Site: http://www.theprosco.com
Emp.: 20
Screw Compressors & Gearboxes Mfr & Repair
N.A.I.C.S.: 332710
Rhett Newberry (Pres)
Lee Levisay (Sls Mgr)

Subsidiaries:

Washington Iron Works, Inc. (1)
400 E Lamar St, Sherman, TX 75090
Tel.: (903) 892-8145
Sales Range: $1-9.9 Million
Machine Shops
N.A.I.C.S.: 332710
Jack Westmoreland (Supvr)
Mark Sitte (Pres)

PROFESSIONAL RESOURCES IN INFORMATION SYSTEMS MANAGEMENT, INC.
1801 Old Reston Ave Ste 202, Reston, VA 20190
Tel.: (703) 264-1200
Web Site: http://www.prisminc.com
Year Founded: 1994
Temporary IT Help Service
N.A.I.C.S.: 561320
Mark Johnson (Founder, Pres & CEO)
Carol Cornman (Partner & Exec VP)
Kaushik Rathi (VP-Recruiting)
Rhonda Marstreller (Officer-Facility Security & VP-Fin & Ops)
Kirsten Baker (Mng Dir)

PROFESSIONAL RODEO COWBOYS ASSOCIATION
101 Pro Rodeo Dr, Colorado Springs, CO 80919
Tel.: (719) 593-8840
Web Site: http://www.prorodeo.org
Year Founded: 1936
Sales Range: $10-24.9 Million
Emp.: 80
Sports Promotion
N.A.I.C.S.: 813910
Amy Fast (Coord-Mktg & Social Media)
Dan Martinez (VP-Tech)
George Taylor (CEO)

PROFESSIONAL ROOFING & EXTERIORS
5790 Lamar St, Arvada, CO 80002
Tel.: (303) 420-0986
Web Site: http://www.professionalroof.com
Year Founded: 2005
Sales Range: $1-9.9 Million
Emp.: 22
Full Service Roofing Products
N.A.I.C.S.: 238160
Daniel J. Cupit (Owner & Pres)

PROFESSIONAL SECURITY TECHNOLOGIES LLC
43 River Rd, Nutley, NJ 07110-3411
Tel.: (973) 661-9000 NJ
Web Site: http://www.prosecurity.com
Year Founded: 1967
Sales Range: $50-74.9 Million
Emp.: 20
Security Systems Installation & Services
N.A.I.C.S.: 561621
Richard D. Rockwell (Chm)

PROFESSIONAL SOFTWARE ENGINEERING INC.
780 Lynnhaven Pkwy Ste 350, Virginia Beach, VA 23452-7349
Tel.: (757) 431-2400 VA
Web Site: http://www.prosoft-eng.com
Year Founded: 1984
Sales Range: $25-49.9 Million
Emp.: 200
Computer Integrated Systems Design
N.A.I.C.S.: 541519
Paul K. Wong (Pres & CEO)
Michael D. Adolphi (Exec VP)
Dawn L. Chapman (Dir-HR)
Philip M. Eagan (Dir-Fin)

PROFESSIONAL SOLUTIONS
5510 Cherokee Ave Ste 4, Alexandria, VA 22312
Tel.: (703) 823-2696
Web Site: http://www.prosol1.com
Year Founded: 2002
Sales Range: $10-24.9 Million
Emp.: 230
Employment Agency
N.A.I.C.S.: 561311
LuAnn Dean (Pres)
Michael J. Dean (CEO)

PROFESSIONAL STAFFING A BTS INC.
17757 Us Highway 19 N Ste 660, Clearwater, FL 33764-6598
Tel.: (727) 771-1111 FL
Year Founded: 1990
Sales Range: $150-199.9 Million
Emp.: 170
Temporary Employment Services
N.A.I.C.S.: 561320
Mike Traina (Pres)

PROFESSIONAL STAFFING CORPORATION
PO Box 910569, San Diego, CA 92191
Tel.: (858) 587-7900 CA
Web Site: http://www.culvercareers.com
Year Founded: 1979
Sales Range: $10-24.9 Million
Emp.: 25
Temporary Staffing Services
N.A.I.C.S.: 561320

PROFESSIONAL SUPPORT INC.
26 N Cayuga Rd, Williamsville, NY 14221
Tel.: (716) 634-0253
Web Site: http://www.psi4jobs.com
Year Founded: 1980
Sales Range: $10-24.9 Million
Emp.: 40
Computer Systems Analysts & Design
N.A.I.C.S.: 541512

PROFESSIONAL TRADING SOLUTIONS, INC.
1001 Ave of the Americas 16th Fl, New York, NY 10018
Tel.: (646) 393-4800
Web Site: http://www.professionaltradingsolutions.com
Year Founded: 2006
Sales Range: $25-49.9 Million
Emp.: 100
Security Brokers & Dealers
N.A.I.C.S.: 523150
Farid Naib (CEO)
Keith Petzold (Chief Compliance Officer)
Radford Laney (CIO)

Subsidiaries:

Sterling Trader, Inc. (1)
225 W Washington St Ste 400, Chicago, IL 60606
Tel.: (312) 346-9600
Web Site: http://www.sterlingtradingtech.com
Emp.: 26
Trading Platforms Solutions & Services
N.A.I.C.S.: 541511
Mark Stephens (COO)
Vincent Tseng (CTO)
Jim Nevotti (Pres)

PROFICIO, INC.
PO Box 710130, San Diego, CA 92171
Tel.: (949) 679-9188
Web Site: https://www.proficio.com
Year Founded: 2010
Ambulatory Health Care Services
N.A.I.C.S.: 621999
John Humphreys (VP-Mktg & Ops)
Mike McGrath (VP-Global Sls)
Tim McElwee (Chm & Pres)
Brad Taylor (Founder & CEO)
Barron Nydam (CFO)
Huong Vo (Gen Counsel)
Chris Kane (VP-Sales & Channels-Americas,Europe)
Jessica Doyle (VP-Global SOC Ops)
Jordan Knopp (VP-Product Development)
Bryan Borra (VP-Product & Content Mgmt)
Jay Joshi (VP-Global Engrg & Managed Svcs)

PROFILE CABINET & DESIGN
7400 E 12th St, Kansas City, MO 64126
Tel.: (816) 231-4601
Web Site: http://www.profilecabinet.com
Sales Range: $200-249.9 Million
Emp.: 113

Wood Kitchen Cabinet & Countertop Mfr
N.A.I.C.S.: 337110
Ken Wright *(Controller)*
Doug Lytle *(Pres & Owner)*
Steve Nelson *(Mgr-Sls)*

PROFILE DEVELOPMENT, LLC
1305 W 18th St., Sioux Falls, SD 57105
Tel.: (866) 206-2989
Web Site: https://www.profileplan.com
Year Founded: 2012
Wellness & Fitness Services
N.A.I.C.S.: 713940
Ryan Niparts *(CEO)*

Subsidiaries:

Profile Extrusion Company Inc.

HMR Plan LLC (1)
99 Summer St Ste 1200, Boston, MA 02110
Tel.: (617) 357-9876
Web Site: http://www.hmrprogram.com
Weight Loss Management Services
N.A.I.C.S.: 923120

PROFILE EXTRUSION COMPANY INC.
1850 Taylor Ave Ste 8, Louisville, KY 40213-1594
Tel.: (502) 459-8374 OH
Year Founded: 1994
Sales Range: $10-24.9 Million
Emp.: 100
Aluminum Extruded Product Mfr
N.A.I.C.S.: 331318
James E. Phillips *(CEO)*
James C. Stout *(Controller)*
William R. Weber *(CFO)*
Patti Rizer *(Sec)*

Subsidiaries:

Profile Precision Extrusions (1)
7225 W Sherman St, Phoenix, AZ 85043
Tel.: (623) 936-5599
Web Site: http://www.profileprecisionextrusions.com
Sales Range: $10-24.9 Million
Emp.: 20
Aluminum Extruded Product Mfr
N.A.I.C.S.: 331318

PROFILE METAL FORMING INC.
370 Republic Dr, McKenzie, TN 38201
Tel.: (731) 352-5341
Web Site: http://www.profilemetalray.com
Year Founded: 1986
Sales Range: $10-24.9 Million
Emp.: 24
Provider of Forming, Stamping, Punching & Sizing Services
N.A.I.C.S.: 333517
George Donovan *(CEO)*

PROFILE SYSTEMS, INC.
5300 4th Ave S, Seattle, WA 98108
Tel.: (206) 624-7715 WA
Web Site: http://www.magnumlaser.com
Year Founded: 1988
Sales Range: $1-9.9 Million
Emp.: 12
Photographic Film, Paper, Plate & Chemical Mfr
N.A.I.C.S.: 325992
Stephen Seavecki *(Pres & CEO)*

PROFILES IN HISTORY
26901 Agoura Rd Ste 150, Calabasas Hills, CA 91301
Tel.: (310) 859-7701
Web Site: http://www.profilesinhistory.com
Year Founded: 1985
Sales Range: $1-9.9 Million
Emp.: 10
Antique Dealer
N.A.I.C.S.: 459510
Joseph M. Maddalena *(Pres & CEO)*
Lou Bustamante *(Dir-Art)*
Brian Chanes *(Head-Acq)*

PROFIT RANK, INC.
1320 Tower Rd, Schaumburg, IL 60173
Tel.: (847) 496-7810
Web Site: http://www.profitrank.com
Year Founded: 2004
Sales Range: Less than $1 Million
Emp.: 5
Affiliate Marketing Management
N.A.I.C.S.: 541613
Michael A. Gunn *(Pres & CEO)*
Mike Gunn *(VP-Ops)*

PROFIT SENSE INNOVATIONS
26 Journal Sq, Jersey City, NJ 07306
Web Site: http://www.profitsi.com
Year Founded: 2009
Sales Range: $1-9.9 Million
Emp.: 40
Web Development, Market Research, Tax Preparation, Business Planning & Drop-Shipping Services
N.A.I.C.S.: 541213
Jerry Khemraj *(Owner & CEO)*
Ashley Romero *(Mgr)*

PROFLOORS, LLC
5884 Peachtree Rd, Atlanta, GA 30341
Tel.: (770) 797-2765
Web Site: http://www.profloorsllc.com
Year Founded: 2000
Sales Range: $1-9.9 Million
Emp.: 20
Flooring Installation & Other Interior Materials for Multi-Family Residential & Commercial Properties
N.A.I.C.S.: 238330
Robert Walker *(Pres)*

PROFORMA ALBRECHT & COMPANY
1040 Techne Center Dr, Milford, OH 45150
Tel.: (513) 576-9900 OH
Web Site: http://www.albrechtco.com
Year Founded: 1999
Sales Range: $25-49.9 Million
Emp.: 120
Custom Printing & Promotional Products
N.A.I.C.S.: 424990
Fred Albrecht *(VP)*

PROFORMA BRAND PROFORMANCE
11511 Katy Freeway Ste 555, Houston, TX 77079
Tel.: (832) 448-0770
Web Site: http://www.proforma.com
Year Founded: 2005
Rev.: $2,200,000
Emp.: 12
Advertising & Marketing
N.A.I.C.S.: 541810
Mike Tracy *(Co-Owner)*

PROFORMA GPS GLOBAL PROMOTIONAL SOURCING
4425 W Sunset Rd, Las Vegas, NV 89118
Tel.: (702) 938-2250
Web Site: http://www.proforma.com
Year Founded: 2001
Sales Range: $1-9.9 Million
Emp.: 8
Commercial Printing & Promotional Products
N.A.I.C.S.: 323111
Steve Raucher *(Pres)*

PROFORMA GRAPHIC SERVICES
6341 Nicholas Dr, Columbus, OH 43235
Tel.: (614) 760-5800
Web Site: http://www.proforma.com
Year Founded: 1998
Sales Range: $1-9.9 Million
Emp.: 20
Commercial Printing & Promotional Products
N.A.I.C.S.: 323111
Tom Etgen *(CFO)*

PROFORMA POWERHOUSE SOLUTIONS
9730 Evergreen Ave N, Brooklyn Park, MN 55443
Tel.: (763) 488-1522
Web Site: http://www.proforma.com
Year Founded: 2009
Sales Range: $1-9.9 Million
Emp.: 5
Commercial Printing & Promotional Products
N.A.I.C.S.: 323111
Brad Klingman *(Owner)*

PROFORMA PRINT & PROMOTIONS
71 Commercial St Ste 304, Boston, MA 02109
Tel.: (617) 464-1120
Web Site: http://www.proforma-promotions.com
Sales Range: $1-9.9 Million
Emp.: 7
Advertising Material & Commercial Printing Services
N.A.I.C.S.: 323111
Greg Muzzillo *(Founder)*
Vera Muzzillo *(CEO)*
Brian Smith *(Pres & COO)*
Deanna Castello *(CMO)*
Bob Kimble *(Chief Admin Officer & Chief Credit Officer)*

PROFORMA PROGRESSIVE MARKETING
6600 District Blvd, Bakersfield, CA 93313
Tel.: (661) 617-6117
Web Site: http://www.goproforma.com
Year Founded: 2004
Sales Range: $1-9.9 Million
Emp.: 6
Commercial Printing & Promotional Products
N.A.I.C.S.: 323111
Cat Rayhill *(Office Mgr)*

PROFORMA PROMOTION CONSULTANTS
1074 Hope St Ste 202, Stamford, CT 06907
Tel.: (203) 322-1507
Web Site: http://www.proforma.com
Year Founded: 2002
Sales Range: $10-24.9 Million
Emp.: 6
Promotional Merchandise & Marketing
N.A.I.C.S.: 323111
Stephen Garst *(Owner)*

PROFORMA PROMOTIONALLY YOURS
1155 Adams St Ste 100, Kansas City, KS 66103
Tel.: (913) 814-7802
Web Site: http://www.thinkproforma.com
Year Founded: 2004
Rev.: $26,800,000
Emp.: 1
Promotional & Advertising Products
N.A.I.C.S.: 561499
Sarah Borota *(Mgr-Acct)*
Jeff Bowles *(Mng Partner)*

PROFORMA SIGNATURE SOLUTIONS
4597 Van Epps Rd Ste 100, Brooklyn Heights, OH 44131
Web Site: http://www.proforma.com
Year Founded: 2000
Sales Range: $1-9.9 Million
Emp.: 14
Commercial Printing & Promotional Products
N.A.I.C.S.: 323111
Rich Bewley *(Partner)*
Dennis Funk *(Partner)*

PROFORMA STEWART & ASSOCIATES
PO Box 220, Simpsonville, MD 21150
Tel.: (410) 312-5050
Web Site: http://www.proforma.com
Year Founded: 1981
Sales Range: Less than $1 Million
Emp.: 4
Business-To-Business
N.A.I.C.S.: 541810
Bruce S. Copeland *(Owner)*
Sean Phillips *(Art Dir)*

PROFRAC SERVICES LLC
333 Shops Blvd Ste 301, Dallas, TX 76087
Tel.: (254) 776-3722
Web Site: http://profrac.com
Measuring And Dispensing Pumps Services
N.A.I.C.S.: 423830
Ladd Wilks *(CEO)*

PROFROMGO INTERNET MARKETING, LLC
18 Terminal Way, Pittsburgh, PA 15219
Tel.: (412) 530-5027 PA
Web Site: http://www.profromgo.com
Year Founded: 2007
Web Design, Search Engine Optimization & Web Video Services
N.A.I.C.S.: 541890
Chris Vendilli *(CEO)*
Rob Donaldson *(Dir-Ops)*

Subsidiaries:

Media Post Inc. (1)
306 E Grandview Ave, Zelienople, PA 16063
Tel.: (724) 453-1290
Web Site: http://www.mediapostinc.com
Rev.: $2,198,000
Emp.: 7
Motion Picture & Video Production
N.A.I.C.S.: 512110

PROGENY SYSTEMS CORPORATION
9500 Innovation Dr, Manassas, VA 20110
Tel.: (703) 368-6107
Web Site: http://www.progeny.net
Year Founded: 1995
Rev.: $61,877,362
Emp.: 148
Electronic System & Software Developers
N.A.I.C.S.: 541512
David Moessbauer *(Engr-SW)*
Tom Barns *(Dir-Bus Dev)*
Jonathan Railsback *(Engr-Software)*

Progeny Systems Corporation—(Continued)

Pat Sullivan *(Mgr-Functional & Engr-Testing)*
Susan Borgrink *(Engr-Software)*
Gregory Inners *(Engr-Sys)*
Mike Mackay *(VP-Tech)*
Stephen Cook *(Mgr-Engrg)*
Alexander Kot *(CFO)*

PROGRAM PARTNERS, INC.
818 Hampton Dr Ste 1, Venice, CA 90291
Tel.: (310) 399-4499
Web Site: http://www.programpartners.com
Sales Range: $50-74.9 Million
Emp.: 50
Independent TV Distribution Company
N.A.I.C.S.: 516120
David Hutchinson *(VP)*
Ryan Craig *(Dir-West Coast)*

PROGRAM PLANNING PROFESSIONALS
1340 Eisenhower Pl, Ann Arbor, MI 48108-2774
Tel.: (734) 741-7770
Web Site: http://www.pcubed.com
Year Founded: 1994
Sales Range: $25-49.9 Million
Emp.: 400
Provider of Business Consulting Services
N.A.I.C.S.: 541611
Graham Wallace *(CFO)*

PROGRAM PRODUCTIONS, INC.
870 Oak Creek Dr, Lombard, IL 60148
Tel.: (630) 792-9700
Web Site: http://programproductions.com
Year Founded: 1974
Sales Range: $1-9.9 Million
Emp.: 3,000
Commercial Photography
N.A.I.C.S.: 541922
Bob Carzoli *(Pres)*
Steve Spurlock *(VP-Live Events)*

PROGREEN US, INC.
2667 Camino del Rio S Ste 312, San Diego, CA 92108-3763
Tel.: (619) 487-9585
Web Site: http://www.progreenus.com
Rev.: $24,819
Assets: $1,951,128
Liabilities: $3,482,482
Net Worth: ($1,531,354)
Earnings: ($1,011,147)
Emp.: 1
Fiscal Year-end: 04/30/18
Real Estate Investment Services
N.A.I.C.S.: 531390
Jan Telander *(Pres & CEO)*

PROGRESS EQUITY PARTNERS, LLC
6136 Frisco Sq Blvd Ste 400, Frisco, TX 75034
Tel.: (214) 978-3838
Web Site: http://www.progressequity.com
Year Founded: 1993
Privater Equity Firm
N.A.I.C.S.: 523999
Michael L. Bailey *(Partner)*
Stephen N. Sangalis *(Partner)*
Paul A. Yeoham *(Partner)*
Carolina B. Hensley *(Principal)*

Subsidiaries:

Medical Indicators, Inc. (1)
16 Thomas J Rhodes Indus Dr, Hamilton, NJ 08619
Tel.: (609) 737-1600
Web Site: http://www.medicalindicators.com
Sales Range: $1-9.9 Million
Emp.: 14
Medical, Dental & Hospital Equipment & Supplies Merchant Whslr
N.A.I.C.S.: 423450

PROGRESS GLASS CO. INC.
25 Patterson St, San Francisco, CA 94124
Tel.: (415) 824-7040
Web Site: http://www.progressglass.com
Sales Range: $10-24.9 Million
Emp.: 105
Glass & Glazing Work
N.A.I.C.S.: 238150
Chris Vann *(Supvr-Glazier & Shop)*
Thomas C. Burkard Jr. *(CEO)*

PROGRESS INDUSTRIES
1017 E 7th St N, Newton, IA 50208
Tel.: (641) 792-6119
Web Site: http://www.progressindustries.org
Year Founded: 1979
Sales Range: $10-24.9 Million
Emp.: 440
Disability Assistance Services
N.A.I.C.S.: 624120
Kelly Decker *(VP-HR)*
Mark Cahill *(CFO)*

PROGRESS PARTNERS, INC.
10 Winthrop Sq 6th Fl, Boston, MA 02110
Tel.: (617) 401-2700
Web Site: http://www.progresspartners.com
Year Founded: 2002
Corporate Finance Services & M&A Advisory Firm
N.A.I.C.S.: 523999
Nick MacShane *(Founder)*
Richard Gallagher *(Partner)*

Subsidiaries:

Progress Ventures, Inc. (1)
10 Winthrop Square 6th Floor, Boston, MA 02110
Tel.: (617) 401-2700
Web Site: http://www.progressventures.com
Venture Capital Firm
N.A.I.C.S.: 523999
Chris Legg *(Partner)*

Joint Venture (Domestic):

Skyword Inc. (2)
33 Arch St, Boston, MA 02110
Tel.: (617) 720-4000
Web Site: http://www.skyword.com
Business Support Services
N.A.I.C.S.: 561499
Jim P. Manzi *(Chm)*
Tom Gerace *(Founder)*
Andrew Wheeler *(CEO)*

PROGRESS PLASTIC PRODUCTS INC.
1780 S County Road 1, Tiffin, OH 44883-9746
Tel.: (419) 483-3538
Web Site: http://www.progressplastic.com
Year Founded: 1969
Sales Range: $25-49.9 Million
Emp.: 225
Mfr of Plastics, Resins & Polymer Products
N.A.I.C.S.: 326119
Kathleen Dick *(Dir-HR)*

PROGRESS PRINTING COMPANY
2677 Waterlick Rd, Lynchburg, VA 24502-4861
Tel.: (434) 239-9213
Web Site: http://www.progressprinting.net
Year Founded: 1962
Sales Range: $100-124.9 Million
Emp.: 200
Commercial Offset Printing Services
N.A.I.C.S.: 323111
Stan Smith *(VP-Mfg)*
Tom Thornton III *(Dir-Info Svcs)*

PROGRESSIVE ACUTE CARE LLC
2210 7th St Ste B, Mandeville, LA 70471
Tel.: (985) 626-6134
Web Site: http://www.progressiveacute.com
Hospital Operator
N.A.I.C.S.: 622110
Dan Rissing *(CEO)*
Wayne Thompson *(CFO)*
Mike Hurlburt *(COO)*
Donna Varnado *(VP-Bus Svcs)*

Subsidiaries:

Avoyelles Hospital (1)
4231 LA-1192, Marksville, LA 71351
Tel.: (318) 253-8611
Web Site: http://www.avoyelleshospital.com
Sales Range: $10-24.9 Million
Emp.: 200
Hospital Operator
N.A.I.C.S.: 622110
David M. Mitchel *(CEO)*

Oakdale Community Hospital (1)
130 Hospital Dr, Oakdale, LA 71463
Tel.: (318) 335-3700
Web Site: http://www.oakdalecommunityhospital.com
Sales Range: $10-24.9 Million
Emp.: 250
Hospital Operator
N.A.I.C.S.: 622110
Kare Brousard *(Chief Nursing Officer)*

Winn Parish Medical Center (1)
301 W Boundary St, Winnfield, LA 71483
Tel.: (318) 648-3000
Web Site: http://www.winnparishmedical.com
Sales Range: $10-24.9 Million
Emp.: 50
Hospital Operator
N.A.I.C.S.: 622110
Bryan Bogle *(CEO)*

PROGRESSIVE ALLOY STEELS UNLIMITED, LLC
2217 Bobo Newsom Hwy, Hartsville, SC 29550
Tel.: (843) 383-2182
Web Site: http://www.progressivealloy.com
Year Founded: 1999
Sales Range: $10-24.9 Million
Emp.: 22
Specialty Steel Products
N.A.I.C.S.: 423510
Bruce Olson *(Principal)*

PROGRESSIVE ARCHITECTURE ENGINEERING PLANNING, INC.
1811 4 Mile Rd NE, Grand Rapids, MI 49525
Tel.: (616) 361-2664
Web Site: http://www.progressiveae.com
Year Founded: 1962
Architectural & Engineering Services
N.A.I.C.S.: 541310
Kathy Ball *(Sr Mgr-HR)*

PROGRESSIVE AUTO STEREO INC.
15640 E 14th St, San Leandro, CA 94578
Tel.: (510) 481-7811
Rev.: $15,800,000
Emp.: 9
Radio, Television & Electronic Stores
N.A.I.C.S.: 449210

PROGRESSIVE BUSINESS PUBLICATIONS
370 Technology Dr, Malvern, PA 19355
Tel.: (610) 695-8600
Web Site: http://www.pbp.com
Year Founded: 1989
Sales Range: $25-49.9 Million
Emp.: 600
Newsletters & Book Publishing Services
N.A.I.C.S.: 513130
Pieter VanBennekom *(Dir-Editorial)*

PROGRESSIVE COMPONENTS INTERNATIONAL CORPORATION
235 Industrial Dr, Wauconda, IL 60084
Tel.: (847) 487-1000
Web Site: http://www.procomps.com
Sales Range: $10-24.9 Million
Emp.: 55
Industrial Machinery & Equipment Whslr
N.A.I.C.S.: 423830
Tammy Alongi *(Mgr-Mktg)*
Glenn Starkey *(Co-Owner & Pres)*
Don Starkey *(Co-Owner & Chm)*
DeAnn Springer *(Chief Process Officer)*
Michael Bolton *(CFO)*

PROGRESSIVE CONTRACTING CO
10 N Ritters Ln, Owings Mills, MD 21117
Tel.: (410) 356-9096
Web Site: http://www.progressivecci.com
Sales Range: $10-24.9 Million
Emp.: 40
Commercial & Office Building, New Construction
N.A.I.C.S.: 236220
Karen Stromberg *(Controller)*

PROGRESSIVE CONTRACTING INCORPORATED
297 Hilton Dr Ste 3, Saint George, UT 84771
Tel.: (435) 628-6662
Year Founded: 1984
Rev.: $20,488,081
Emp.: 119
Pipeline Construction
N.A.I.C.S.: 237110
Russell Limb *(Pres)*
John Slack *(Controller)*

PROGRESSIVE CONTRACTORS INC.
14123 42nd St NE, Saint Michael, MN 55376-0416
Tel.: (612) 282-1384
Sales Range: $50-74.9 Million
Emp.: 450
Highway & Street Construction Services
N.A.I.C.S.: 237310
Larry Butts *(Principal)*

PROGRESSIVE DISTRIBUTION SERVICES, INC.

COMPANIES

PROGUARD ACQUISITION CORP.

5505 36th St SE, Grand Rapids, MI 49512
Tel.: (616) 957-5900   MI
Web Site: http://www.prodist.com
Year Founded: 1984
Sales Range: $10-24.9 Million
Emp.: 30
Warehousing & Distribution Services
N.A.I.C.S.: 493190
John McGovern *(Pres)*

PROGRESSIVE DRIVER SERVICES, INC.
2000 Corporate Sq Blvd, Jacksonville, FL 32216-0326
Tel.: (904) 724-2864   FL
Year Founded: 1969
Sales Range: $150-199.9 Million
Emp.: 600
Provider of Contract Driver Services
N.A.I.C.S.: 561311

PROGRESSIVE DYNAMICS, INC.
507 Industrial Rd, Marshall, MI 49068-1750
Tel.: (269) 781-4241
Web Site: http://www.progressivedyn.com
Year Founded: 1964
Sales Range: $25-49.9 Million
Emp.: 100
Mfr of Twelve Volt Lighting & Power Convertors; Fibre Optic Light Sources; Patient Warming Devices
N.A.I.C.S.: 334419
Roger Eby *(Mgr-Sls)*
Barry Lemons *(Mgr-Sls)*
Jeff Cornell *(Mgr-Mechanical Engrg)*
William James *(Dir-Info Sys)*
Mary Mestemaker *(Mgr-HR)*
Mike Walters *(VP-Sls & Mktg)*

PROGRESSIVE ELDERCARE SERVICES - DREW INC.
1052 Old Warren Rd, Monticello, AR 71655-9720
Tel.: (870) 367-0044   AR
Year Founded: 2010
Sales Range: $1-9.9 Million
Elderly Health Care Services
N.A.I.C.S.: 624120
Lisa M. Hensley *(Pres)*

PROGRESSIVE ELDERCARE SERVICES MORRILTON INC.
1000 Brookridge Ln, Morrilton, AR 72110-1558
Tel.: (501) 354-4585   AR
Year Founded: 2010
Sales Range: $1-9.9 Million
Elderly Health Care Services
N.A.I.C.S.: 624120
Matt Manning *(Pres)*

PROGRESSIVE ENERGY INC.
3224 W Broadway, Ardmore, OK 73401
Tel.: (580) 223-2365
Web Site: http://www.progressive-energyfuel.com
Rev.: $16,000,000
Emp.: 50
Petroleum Bulk Stations
N.A.I.C.S.: 424710
Charles M. Clowe *(Co-Owner)*

PROGRESSIVE ENGINEERING & CONSTRUCTION, INC.
3912 W Humphrey St, Tampa, FL 33614
Tel.: (813) 930-0669   FL
Web Site: http://www.progressiveec.com
Year Founded: 1999
Sales Range: $1-9.9 Million
Emp.: 10
Engineering & Environmental Consulting Services
N.A.I.C.S.: 541330
Bridget S. Morello *(Pres)*

PROGRESSIVE FOAM TECHNOLOGIES, INC.
6753 Chestnut Ridge Rd, Beach City, OH 44608
Tel.: (330) 756-3200
Web Site: http://www.progressivefoam.com
Year Founded: 1992
Sales Range: $10-24.9 Million
Emp.: 150
Wood Products Mfr
N.A.I.C.S.: 321999
Pat Culpepper *(Founder & Pres)*
Ben Higl *(CFO & VP-Ops)*
Jason Culpepper *(VP-Sls)*
Scott Foreman *(Dir-Mfg)*
Jim MacDonald *(Dir-Field Sls)*

PROGRESSIVE FURNITURE INC.
502 Middle St, Archbold, OH 43502
Tel.: (419) 446-4500   OH
Web Site: http://www.progressivefurniture.com
Year Founded: 1986
Sales Range: $75-99.9 Million
Emp.: 17
Wood Household Furniture
N.A.I.C.S.: 337122
Mike France *(VP-Sls & Mktg)*
Dan Kendrick *(Exec VP & Gen Mgr)*

PROGRESSIVE HEALTH GROUP, LLC
265 N Lamar Blvd, Oxford, MS 38655
Web Site: https://www.phghealth.com
Year Founded: 2019
Hospitals & Health Care
N.A.I.C.S.: 621610
Quentin Whitwell *(Founder & CEO)*

PROGRESSIVE HEALTH SYSTEMS INC.
600 S 13th St, Pekin, IL 61554
Tel.: (309) 347-1151   IL
Web Site: http://www.pekinhospital.org
Year Founded: 1986
Sales Range: $25-49.9 Million
Medical Education & Treatment Services
N.A.I.C.S.: 621999
Delores M. Eagleson *(Vice Chm)*
Crystal Elliot *(VP-HR)*
Subsidiaries:
Pekin Hospital (1)
600 S 13th St, Pekin, IL 61554-4936
Tel.: (309) 347-1151
Web Site: http://www.pekinhospital.org
Provider of Health Services
N.A.I.C.S.: 622110
Ronald H. Miller *(Chm)*
Bob Haley *(CEO)*
Gordon Cross *(Pres-Medical Staff)*
Delores M. Eagleson *(Treas & Sec)*
James R. Smalley *(Vice Chm)*

ProHealth Inc. (1)
2040 Alameda Padre Serra 101, Santa Barbara, CA 93103
Tel.: (805) 564-3064
Web Site: http://www.prohealth.com
Health Care Srvices
N.A.I.C.S.: 621999
Sheila Cruthirds *(Mgr-Print Mktg)*
Subsidiary (Domestic):
Procare Home Health Services, Inc. (2)
1416 N 8th St, Pekin, IL 61554
Tel.: (309) 347-4663
Web Site: http://www.procareillinois.com
Medical Equipment Distr
N.A.I.C.S.: 456199
Scott Haynes *(Gen Mgr)*

ProHealth Medical Group (1)
19 Olt Ave, Pekin, IL 61554
Tel.: (309) 353-6301
Web Site: http://www.pekinprohealth.com
Emp.: 20
General Healthcare Services
N.A.I.C.S.: 622110
Lisa Guzman *(Dir-Bus Dev)*
Bob Haley *(CEO)*

PROGRESSIVE HYDRAULICS, INC.
350 N Midland Ave, Saddle Brook, NJ 07663
Tel.: (201) 791-3400
Web Site: http://www.phionline.com
Year Founded: 1969
Sales Range: $10-24.9 Million
Emp.: 35
Provider of Hydraulic & Pneumatic Pistons & Valves
N.A.I.C.S.: 423830
David Schatteman *(Pres)*
Maria Panza *(CFO)*

PROGRESSIVE LIFE CENTER
1704 17th St NE, Washington, DC 20002
Tel.: (202) 842-4570   DC
Web Site: http://www.plcntu.org
Year Founded: 1983
Sales Range: $10-24.9 Million
Emp.: 108
Behavioral Healthcare Services
N.A.I.C.S.: 623220
Kofi Boateng *(CFO)*
Andrea Sakyi *(Dir-Fin)*
Laurence E. Jackson *(Pres & CEO)*
Mark Boothe *(Dir-Independent Living Program)*
Anthony L. Williams *(Chm)*
Maurice Hawkins *(Mgr-IT)*

PROGRESSIVE LIGHTING INC.
3130 N Berkeley Lk Rd NW, Duluth, GA 30096
Tel.: (770) 476-8537   GA
Web Site: http://www.progressivelighting.com
Year Founded: 1965
Sales Range: $25-49.9 Million
Emp.: 175
Sales of Electrical Apparatus & Equipment
N.A.I.C.S.: 423610
Mark Lloyd *(Mgr-Compliance)*
Raymond Humphrey *(Mgr-Mdsg)*
Rolanda Barnes *(Mgr-Acctg)*

PROGRESSIVE LOGISTICS INC.
980 W Main St B, Jerome, ID 83338
Tel.: (208) 324-4255
Web Site: http://www.giltner.com
Rev.: $30,654,560
Emp.: 200
Refrigerated Products Transport
N.A.I.C.S.: 484230
Doug Blevins *(Pres)*

PROGRESSIVE PLUMBING INC.
1064 W Hwy 50, Clermont, FL 34711
Tel.: (352) 394-7171
Web Site: http://www.progressiveplumbing.com
Sales Range: $10-24.9 Million
Emp.: 60
Plumbing Contractor Services
N.A.I.C.S.: 238220
William E. Lawson *(Pres)*

PROGRESSIVE PLUMBING SUPPLY, CO.
23950 Ryan Rd, Warren, MI 48091
Tel.: (586) 756-8662   MI
Year Founded: 1993
Sales Range: $1-9.9 Million
Emp.: 10
Plumbing & Heating Equipment & Supplies (Hydronics) Merchant Whslr
N.A.I.C.S.: 423720
Aa Agnello *(Treas)*
Subsidiaries:
Delwood Supply Company (1)
4823 Leafdale Blvd, Royal Oak, MI 48073
Tel.: (248) 280-2880
Web Site: http://www.delwood-supply.com
Rev.: $2,231,000
Emp.: 7
Plumbing & Heating Equipment & Supplies, Hydronics, Merchant Whslr
N.A.I.C.S.: 423720
Mark Fisher *(Pres)*

PROGRESSIVE SAVINGS BANK
500 N Main St, Jamestown, TN 38556
Tel.: (931) 752-2265
Web Site: http://www.psbgroup.net
Year Founded: 1980
Sales Range: $25-49.9 Million
Emp.: 110
Banking Services
N.A.I.C.S.: 522180
Steve Raines *(Pres)*
Kathy Perdue *(Asst VP-IT)*
Mike Wood *(Dir-Online Comm & Creative)*

PROGRESSIVE SERVICES INC.
23 N 35th Ave, Phoenix, AZ 85009
Tel.: (602) 278-4900
Web Site: http://www.progressiveroofing.com
Sales Range: $25-49.9 Million
Emp.: 500
Roofing Contractors
N.A.I.C.S.: 238160
John W. Farrell *(Pres)*
Rhett Myers *(Controller)*
Mark Farrell *(VP)*

PROGRESSIVE TRACTOR & IMPLEMENT COMPANY
I 49 S, Opelousas, LA 70570
Tel.: (337) 942-5689
Web Site: http://www.progressive-tractor.com
Sales Range: $25-49.9 Million
Emp.: 250
Farm Supply
N.A.I.C.S.: 459999
Eddie Villemarette *(Pres)*

PROGREXION HOLDINGS INC.
330 N Cutler Dr, North Salt Lake, UT 84054
Tel.: (801) 384-4100
Web Site: http://www.progrexion.com
Year Founded: 2000
Sales Range: $100-124.9 Million
Emp.: 1,500
Consumer Credit Report Repair Services
N.A.I.C.S.: 561450
Michael DeVico *(Pres)*
James Potter *(Chief Legal Officer)*
Celeste Edmunds *(Dir-Corp Comm & Community Affairs)*

PROGUARD ACQUISITION CORP.
3400 SW 26 Terrace Ste A-8, Fort Lauderdale, FL 33312

PROGUARD ACQUISITION CORP.

Proguard Acquisition Corp.—(Continued)
Business Product Retailer
N.A.I.C.S.: 456120
David A. Kriegstein (Pres & CEO)

PROHEALTH CARE, INC.
N17 W24100 Riverwood Dr Ste 130, Waukesha, WI 53188
Tel.: (262) 928-1000
Web Site: http://www.prohealthcare.org
Year Founded: 1986
Sales Range: $250-299.9 Million
Emp.: 4,800
Provider of Data Processing Services
N.A.I.C.S.: 518210
Susan Edwards (CEO)

Subsidiaries:

National Employee Assistance Services Inc. (1)
N17 W24100 Riverwood Dr Ste 300, Waukesha, WI 53188
Tel.: (262) 574-2500
Web Site: http://www.neas.com
Sales Range: $10-24.9 Million
Emp.: 100
Provider of Individual & Family Services
N.A.I.C.S.: 624190
Philip Chard (Pres & CEO)
Carol Wilson (COO & Sr VP)

Waukesha Health Care, Inc. (1)
725 American Ave, Waukesha, WI 53188-5031
Tel.: (262) 928-1000
Web Site: http://www.waukeshamemorial.org
Sales Range: $50-74.9 Million
Emp.: 734
Health Care
N.A.I.C.S.: 518210
Ed Olson (Pres & CEO)

PROHEALTH PHYSICIANS
3 Farm Glen Blvd, Farmington, CT 06032-2573
Tel.: (860) 284-5200
Web Site: http://www.prohealthmd.com
Year Founded: 1997
Sales Range: $25-49.9 Million
Emp.: 1,000
Management Services For Physicians
N.A.I.C.S.: 813410
Jack Reed (Pres & CEO)
Cheryl Lescarbeau (VP-Clinical Performance)
Bethany Kieley (VP-Practice Programs & Svcs)
John Lynch (VP-Res & Govt Affairs)
Maura Geirin (Officer-Compliance)
Richard Lugli (Gen Counsel, Sr VP & Officer-Privacy)

PROJECT DEVELOPERS, INC.
PO Box 440, Sterling, VA 20167-0440
Tel.: (703) 709-0000
Web Site: http://www.projectdevelopers.com
Year Founded: 1989
Rev.: $11,800,000
Emp.: 55
Security Construction Contractors
N.A.I.C.S.: 561621
Dominick Carducc (Pres)

PROJECT DEVELOPMENT INTERNATIONAL, INC.
424 Skinner Blvd Ste C, Dunedin, FL 34698
Tel.: (727) 734-8589
Web Site: http://www.pdiusa.com
Year Founded: 1980
Sales Range: $1-9.9 Million
Emp.: 4
Construction Consulting Services
N.A.I.C.S.: 541618

James E. Lalumiere (Pres)

PROJECT DEVELOPMENT SERVICES, INC.
3715 Northside Pkwy NW Bldg 400 Ste 700, Atlanta, GA 30327
Tel.: (404) 869-9300
Web Site: http://www.pdsi.us
Year Founded: 2001
Sales Range: $10-24.9 Million
Emp.: 34
Building Contractors
N.A.I.C.S.: 236220
Ralph Engelberger (CEO)
Vickie Smith (Dir-Project)
Don Leonard (VP-Ops-Denver)

PROJECT ENHANCEMENT CORPORATION
20300 Century Blvd Ste 175, Germantown, MD 20874
Tel.: (240) 686-3059
Web Site: http://www.projectenhancement.com
Year Founded: 1998
Sales Range: $10-24.9 Million
Emp.: 96
Project Management Consulting Services
N.A.I.C.S.: 541618
Ricardo Martinez (Pres & CEO)
Charles A. Negin (Sr VP)
Leo Carey (VP-Analytical Svcs)
Getachew Worku (VP-Technical Svcs)
Diane Burnes (Dir-Ops)

PROJECT FOR PRIDE IN LIVING, INC.
1035 E Franklin Ave, Minneapolis, MN 55404
Tel.: (612) 455-5100
Web Site: http://www.ppl-inc.org
Year Founded: 1972
Sales Range: $10-24.9 Million
Emp.: 293
Community Development Services
N.A.I.C.S.: 624190
Paul Williams (Pres & CEO)
Julie Brekke (Sr VP-Employment Readiness)
Jack Katzmark (CFO)
Barbara McCormick (Sr VP-Housing With Svcs)

PROJECT FROG, INC.
501 2nd St Ste 120, San Francisco, CA 94107
Tel.: (415) 814-8500
Web Site: http://www.projectfrog.com
Year Founded: 2006
Sales Range: $25-49.9 Million
Emp.: 33
Construction Materials Mfr
N.A.I.C.S.: 327120
Marijke Smit (Sr VP-Education)
John Jackson (Dir-Architecture)
Nikki Lowy (Sr Mgr-Strategic Accts & Partnerships)
Keiron Ryan (Sr Project Mgr)
Diane Shortz (Mgr-HR & Acctg)
Drew A. Buechley (CFO)
Jennifer Graham (Mgr-Supply Chain)
Karen Vegas (VP-Enterprise Dev)
Mike Eggers (VP-Product & Innovation)
Rick Willison (VP-Construction)
Shirin Arnold (VP-Software Sls)

PROJECT HOLLYWOOD LLC
2255 Glades Road Ste 221A, Boca Raton, FL 33431
Tel.: (561) 998-8001
Investment & Management Services
N.A.I.C.S.: 523999

Mitchell Rubenstein (Partner)
Laurie S. Silvers (Partner)

PROJECT HOPE
255 Carter Hall Ln, Millwood, VA 22646
Tel.: (540) 837-2100   DC
Web Site: http://www.projecthope.org
Year Founded: 1958
Sales Range: $250-299.9 Million
Emp.: 164
Voluntary Health Services
N.A.I.C.S.: 813212
Thomas Kenyon (Chief Health Officer)
Reynold W. Mooney (Vice Chm)
Curt M. Selquist (Treas)
Rabih Torbay (Pres & CEO)
Franklin Guerrero (Chief Dev & Comm Officer & VP)
Chris Skopec (Exec VP)
Julia Soyars (Chief Legal & Compliance Officer & VP)
Alan Weil (VP & Editor-in-Chief-Health Affairs)
Viren Mehta (Sec)
Viren Mehta (Sec)

PROJECT HOSPITALITY, INC.
100 Park Ave, Staten Island, NY 10302
Tel.: (718) 448-1544   NY
Web Site: http://www.projecthospitality.org
Year Founded: 1984
Sales Range: $10-24.9 Million
Emp.: 340
Community Care Services
N.A.I.C.S.: 624210
Joanne Hanson (CFO)
Jaclyn Stoll (COO)
Terry Troia (Exec Dir)
Mary Haas (Second VP)
Frank Puleo (First VP)
Gerald Sussman (Pres)

PROJECT LEADERSHIP ASSOCIATES, INC.
120 S Lasalle Ste 1200, Chicago, IL 60603
Tel.: (312) 441-0077
Web Site: http://www.projectleadership.net
Year Founded: 1998
Sales Range: $25-49.9 Million
Emp.: 170
Computer Programming Services
N.A.I.C.S.: 541511
Gordon Dunkley (Dir-Practice)
Neil Parekh (Partner)
Douglas E. Klatt (Dir-Bus Dev)
Steven Getto (CFO)
Lee Hovermale (CEO)
Kevin Callozzo (Exec VP-Small Bus Svcs)
Daniel Porcaro (Pres)
Andy Adsetts (Reg Dir)
Deb Keating (Dir-HR)
Kris Gronert (Dir-Practice)
Mike Kramer (Mgr-Indiana)
Mike Mete (Dir-Practice)
Rudy Campos (VP-Sls & Mktg)

Subsidiaries:

Project Leadership Associates, Inc. (1)
2710 Gateway Oaks Dr Ste 300 S, Sacramento, CA 95833
Tel.: (916) 436-8757
Web Site: http://www.projectleadership.net
Sales Range: $10-24.9 Million
Emp.: 15
IT Outsourcing Services
N.A.I.C.S.: 541519
Andy Adsetts (Reg Dir)

PROJECT LIGHTING CO. INC.

U.S. PRIVATE

3373 Rauch St, Houston, TX 77029-1311
Tel.: (713) 674-3555
Web Site: http://Www.projectlighting.shopced.com
Rev.: $11,724,628
Emp.: 17
Lighting Fixtures, Residential
N.A.I.C.S.: 423610
Cullen Plaag (Pres)

PROJECT NOW, INC.
418 11th St, Rock Island, IL 61201
Tel.: (309) 793-6391   IL
Web Site: http://www.projectnow.org
Year Founded: 1968
Sales Range: $10-24.9 Million
Emp.: 164
Community Action Services
N.A.I.C.S.: 624190
Maureen Hart (Exec Dir)
Cathy Bizarri (Co-Chm)
Tim Wells (Treas)
Jessie Lisle (Co-Chm)
Linda Work (Sec)
Robert Hepner (Vice Chm)

PROJECT RENEWAL
200 Varick St 9th Fl, New York, NY 10014
Tel.: (212) 620-0340   NY
Web Site: http://www.projectrenewal.org
Year Founded: 1967
Sales Range: $50-74.9 Million
Emp.: 845
Community Care Services
N.A.I.C.S.: 621420
Steven Jones (CFO & Chief Admin Officer)
Doug Warn (Dir-Trng & Clinical Dev)
Mitchell Netburn (Pres & CEO)
Allison Grolnick (Dir-Medical & Psychiatric Svcs)
Nicole Scanlin (Dir-Dev)
Patrick Germain (Dir-Strategy & Evaluation)
R. Aaron La Mar (CIO)
Claudia Rosen (Chm)
Morgan Stanley (Exec Dir)

PROJECT: WORLDWIDE, INC.
3600 Giddings Rd, Auburn Hills, MI 48326-1515
Tel.: (248) 475-2500   MI
Web Site: http://www.project.com
Year Founded: 1914
Advertising, Content, Experiential, Public Relations, Shopper Marketing & Brand Strategy
N.A.I.C.S.: 541810
Chris Meyer (CEO)
Brian Martin (Sr VP-Mktg & Comm)
Beth Bock (Dir-HR Ops)

Subsidiaries:

Affinitive LLC (1)
135 W 26th St 8th Fl, New York, NY 10001
Tel.: (415) 278-9100
Web Site: http://www.beaffinitive.com
Rev.: $3,000,000
Emp.: 15
Advertising Agency
N.A.I.C.S.: 541810
Rob Marscher (VP-Engrg)

GPJ (Singapore) Pte. Ltd (1)
300 Beach Road Unit 22-07 The Concourse, 199555, Singapore, Singapore
Tel.: (65) 6 733 1218
Web Site: http://www.gpj.com
Emp.: 30
N.A.I.C.S.: 541810
Sabrina Leong (Mgr-HR)

George P. Johnson (Australia) Pty. Ltd. (1)
Level 4 70 Riley Street, Pyrmont, Sydney, 2010, NSW, Australia

COMPANIES

Tel.: (61) 2 8569 7600
Web Site: http://www.gpj.com.au
Sales Range: $10-24.9 Million
Emp.: 60
N.A.I.C.S.: 541810
Will Halliday *(Head-Strategy)*
Caleb Bush *(Mng Dir)*
Marc Iacono *(Dir-Ops)*
Luke Clifton *(Exec Dir-Creative)*

George P. Johnson (France) SARL (1)
74 Rue Rouget de Lisle, 92150, Suresnes, France
Tel.: (33) 1 4783 7587
Sales Range: $10-24.9 Million
Emp.: 1
N.A.I.C.S.: 541810

George P. Johnson (Japan) Ltd. (1)
Lapiross Roppongi 6F 6-1-24 Roppongi, Minato-ku, Tokyo, 106-0032, Japan
Tel.: (81) 3 5786 3161
Web Site: http://www.gpj.co.jp
Sales Range: $25-49.9 Million
Emp.: 60
Advertising Agency Services
N.A.I.C.S.: 541810

George P. Johnson (Korea) LLC (1)
Korea World Trade Ctr 27th Fl Trade Tower 159 1, Samsung dong Kangnam ku, Seoul, 135 729, Korea (South)
Tel.: (82) 2 6007 2140
N.A.I.C.S.: 541810

George P. Johnson (UK) Ltd (1)
53 Great Suffolk Street, London, SE1 0DB, United Kingdom
Tel.: (44) 208 879 2200
Web Site: http://www.gpj.co.uk
Sales Range: $10-24.9 Million
Emp.: 70
Marketing Management Services
N.A.I.C.S.: 541613
Jason Megson *(Mng Dir-UK & Nordics)*
Neil Mason *(Exec Dir-Creative)*
Jonathan McCallum *(Mng Dir)*
Peter Davies *(Dir-Bus Dev)*

George P. Johnson Brasil Ltda. (1)
Rua Grajau 662, Sumare, 01253-000, Sao Paulo, Brazil
Tel.: (55) 11 3670 5577
Marketing Consulting Services
N.A.I.C.S.: 541613

George P. Johnson Co. - Boston (1)
711 Atlantic Ave Fl 6, Boston, MA 02111
Tel.: (617) 535-9800
Web Site: http://www.gpj.com
Sales Range: $25-49.9 Million
Emp.: 60
N.A.I.C.S.: 541810
David Rich *(VP-Strategic Mktg-Worldwide)*
Chris Meyer *(CEO)*
Sharon Crichton *(VP & Gen Mgr-Boston)*
Tara Higgins *(Exec VP-Ops)*
Scott Kellner *(VP-Mktg)*
Otto Rosenbusch *(Sr VP & Dir-Acct-Global)*
Mike Rossi *(Exec VP-Ops)*
Jennifer Shifman *(VP & Gen Mgr-Austin)*
John Trinanes *(Sr VP-Creative)*
George Bear *(Dir-Creative Svcs)*
Merethe Bergnord-Ashby *(Dir-Event-Oslo)*

George P. Johnson Co. - EMT Division (1)
11301 Burnet Rd 2nd Fl, Austin, TX 78758
Tel.: (512) 286-2066
N.A.I.C.S.: 541810

George P. Johnson Co. - G7 Entertainment Marketing (1)
4000 Centre Pointe Dr, La Vergne, TN 37086
Tel.: (615) 768-3200
Web Site: http://www.g7marketing.com
Sales Range: $10-24.9 Million
Emp.: 25
N.A.I.C.S.: 541810

George P. Johnson Co. - San Carlos (1)
999 Skyway Rd Ste 300, San Carlos, CA 94070
Tel.: (650) 226-0600
Web Site: http://www.gpj.com
Sales Range: $25-49.9 Million
Emp.: 100
N.A.I.C.S.: 541810

Kenny Lauer *(VP-Digital Experience)*

George P. Johnson Company - Belgium (1)
Avenue du Gui 85, 1180, Brussels, Belgium
Tel.: (32) 1040 2665
Web Site: http://www.project.com
N.A.I.C.S.: 541810

George P. Johnson Event Marketing Co. Ltd (1)
Rm 2601 Hong Kong New World Tower, No 300 Huaihai Mid Rd, Shanghai, 200021, China
Tel.: (86) 21 5117 2288
Web Site: http://www.gpj.com
Sales Range: $10-24.9 Million
Emp.: 20
N.A.I.C.S.: 541810

George P. Johnson Event Marketing Co. Ltd. (1)
Unit 1202 Capital Tower 6A Jianguomenwai St, Chaoyang District, Beijing, 100022, China
Tel.: (86) 10 5166 7333
Sales Range: $10-24.9 Million
Emp.: 40
N.A.I.C.S.: 541810

George P. Johnson Event Marketing Pvt, Ltd. (1)
401 3rd Fl Prestige Tudor Court, 40 Lavelle Rd, Bengaluru, 560 001, India
Tel.: (91) 988 603 8898
N.A.I.C.S.: 541810

George P. Johnson Event Marketing Pvt., Ltd. (1)
B-501 5th Fl Crystal Plaza New Link Rd, Andheri (W), 400053, Mumbai, India
Tel.: (91) 22 2674 0321
Web Site: http://www.gpj.com
N.A.I.C.S.: 541810

George P. Johnson GmbH (1)
Max Eyth Strasse 1, Ostfildern Ruit, Stuttgart, 73760, Germany
Tel.: (49) 7 114 401 250
Web Site: http://www.gpj.de
Emp.: 100
N.A.I.C.S.: 541810
Robin Heim *(Acct Dir)*

George P. Johnson Hong Kong Ltd. (1)
45/F The Lee Gardens 33 Hysan Ave, Causeway Bay, Hong Kong, China (Hong Kong)
Tel.: (852) 2295 2686
Sales Range: $25-49.9 Million
Emp.: 10
N.A.I.C.S.: 541810

JUXT (1)
576 Folsom St Fl 3, San Francisco, CA 94105
Tel.: (415) 671-7840
Web Site: http://www.juxt.com
Marketing Consulting Services
N.A.I.C.S.: 541613
Michael Polivka *(Pres)*

Motive (1)
2901 Blakes St Ste 180, Denver, CO 80205
Tel.: (303) 302-2100
Web Site: http://www.thinkmotive.com
Emp.: 75
Marketing Consulting Services
N.A.I.C.S.: 541613
Matt Statman *(CEO & Chief Creative Officer)*
Elizabeth Seltzer *(Sr VP-Brand Experience)*

Partners + Napier Inc. (1)
192 Mill St Ste 600, Rochester, NY 14614-1022
Tel.: (585) 454-1010
Web Site: http://www.partnersandnapier.com
Sales Range: $10-24.9 Million.
Emp.: 100
Advertising Management Services
N.A.I.C.S.: 541810
Sharon Napier *(CEO)*
Jeffery Gabel *(Chief Creative Officer)*
Greg Smith *(Dir-Retail Mktg)*
Courtney Cotrupe *(Mng Dir)*
Pete VonDerLinn *(Exec Dir-Creative)*
Scott Chapman *(Exec Dir-Fin)*
Mike Baron *(Grp Dir-Creative)*

Dan O'Donnell *(Grp Dir-Creative)*
Elaine Naum *(Sr VP)*
Julie DeRoller *(Sr VP/Grp Dir-Vine Creative Studios)*
Katrina Busch *(Sr VP & Dir-Acct)*

Branch (Domestic):

Partners + Napier Inc. - Atlanta Office (2)
5 Concourse Pkwy Corporate Ctr 5 Ste 2550, Atlanta, GA 30328
Tel.: (678) 443-7400
Web Site: http://www.partnersandnapier.com
Rev.: $5,000,000
Emp.: 20
N.A.I.C.S.: 541810

Project: Worldwide, Inc. - Los Angeles (1)
18500 Crenshaw Blvd, Torrance, CA 90504
Tel.: (310) 965-4300
Web Site: http://www.project.com
Sales Range: $10-24.9 Million
Emp.: 130
Advertising Agencies Services
N.A.I.C.S.: 541810

Raumtechnik Messebau & Event Services GmbH (1)
Plieninger Strasse 54, 73760, Ostfildern, Germany
Tel.: (49) 71 58 98 74 0
Emp.: 280
Marketing Management Consulting Services
N.A.I.C.S.: 541613
Achim Reinhuber *(Gen Mgr)*
Bernd Schury *(CEO & Mng Dir)*

School (1)
1711 Pearl 300, Boulder, CO 80302
Tel.: (720) 390-6000
Web Site: http://www.schoolhelps.com
Emp.: 8
Marketing Consulting Services
N.A.I.C.S.: 541613
Courtenay Bedell *(Mgr-Studio)*

Shoptology, Inc. (1)
7800 N Dallas Pkwy Ste 160, Plano, TX 75024
Tel.: (469) 287-0002
Web Site: http://www.goshoptology.com
Marketing Consulting Services
N.A.I.C.S.: 541613
Charlie Anderson *(CEO)*
Julie Quick *(Sr VP & Head-Insights & Strategy)*
Dino De Leon *(Sr VP & Head-Creative)*
Ken Madden *(Sr VP & Head-Engagement)*

Spinifex Group (1)
Level 4 70 Riley St, Sydney, 2010, NSW, Australia
Tel.: (61) 2 8332 1300
Web Site: http://www.spinifexgroup.com
Emp.: 60
Marketing Consulting Services
N.A.I.C.S.: 541613
Glen Joseph *(Chm)*
Cathy Fahy *(Mgr-Ops)*
Rob Stock *(Gen Mgr)*
Richard Lindsay *(Head-Creative)*
Hai Tran *(Head-Tech)*
Ben Casey *(Acting CEO)*
Cyril Debaecqua *(Mng Dir)*

PROJECTION PRESENTATION TECHNOLOGY

5803 Rolling Rd Ste 207, Springfield, VA 22152
Tel.: (703) 912-1334   VA
Web Site: http://www.projection.com
Year Founded: 1971
Audio-Visual Equipment & Supply Rental
N.A.I.C.S.: 532289
David O. Campbell *(Pres & CEO)*
Mark Nasser *(CFO)*
Karen Moore Cuviello *(VP-Natl Div)*
Larry Taylor *(Corp VP- Convention Center Div)*

PROJECTIONS UNLIMITED INC.

PROJET AVIATION

15311 Barranca Pkwy, Irvine, CA 92618
Tel.: (714) 544-2700   CA
Web Site: http://www.gopui.com
Year Founded: 1956
Sales Range: $75-99.9 Million
Emp.: 45
Distr of Electronic Components
N.A.I.C.S.: 423690
David Herring *(Pres)*
Tom Colantuoni *(Mgr-Sls)*

PROJECTIONS, INC.

3264 Medlock Bridge Rd, Norcross, GA 30092
Tel.: (770) 448-9741
Web Site: http://www.projectionsinc.com
Year Founded: 1979
Sales Range: $1-9.9 Million
Emp.: 20
Custom Employee Communications
N.A.I.C.S.: 334290
Walter E. Orechwa *(CEO)*

PROJECTLINE SERVICES, INC.

562 1st Ave S Ste 400, Seattle, WA 98104
Tel.: (206) 382-2025
Web Site: http://www.projectlineinc.com
Year Founded: 2003
Rev.: $16,500,000
Emp.: 93
Marketing Consulting Services
N.A.I.C.S.: 541613
Mike Kichline *(Principal)*
Anika Lehde *(Principal)*
Jeremy Russell *(Office Mgr)*

PROJECTMANAGER.COM, INC.

3721 Executive Center Dr Ste 200, Austin, TX 78731
Tel.: (512) 219-5789
Web Site: http://www.projectmanager.com
Year Founded: 2008
Sales Range: $1-9.9 Million
Emp.: 16
Software Development Services
N.A.I.C.S.: 541511
Jason Westland *(Founder)*
Thomas Aylor *(CFO)*
Campbell Anderson *(CTO)*
Stephanie Ray *(VP-Product)*
Craig Nicholson *(VP-Sys)*
Ryan Buma *(Pres & CEO)*
Kevin Riegelsberger *(Chm)*
Sara McConnell *(Head-People & Culture)*

PROJECTS UNLIMITED, INC.

6300 Sand Lake Rd, Dayton, OH 45414-2649
Tel.: (937) 918-2200   OH
Web Site: http://www.pui.com
Year Founded: 1940
Sales Range: $200-249.9 Million
Emp.: 130
Mfr of Solid State Audio Indicators, Audio Transducers, Power Transistor Pockets & Electronic Assemblies & Sub-Assemblies
N.A.I.C.S.: 334412
Gene Nesbit *(Pres)*
John Mowad *(Mgr-Matls)*
Rose Plummer *(CFO)*

PROJET AVIATION

957 Sycolin Rd, Leesburg, VA 20175
Tel.: (703) 889-8558
Web Site: http://www.projetaviation.com
Year Founded: 2007

ProJet Aviation—(Continued)
Sales Range: $1-9.9 Million
Emp.: 38
Aircraft Management Services
N.A.I.C.S.: 488119
Shye Gilad *(Mng Partner)*
Julie O'Brien *(Dir-Flight Support & Mktg)*
Tina Gray *(Controller)*

PROJILITY
1900 Campus Commons Dr Ste 410, Reston, VA 20191
Tel.: (703) 448-6777
Web Site: http://www.projility.com
Sales Range: $1-9.9 Million
Emp.: 18
Management & Technology Consulting Services
N.A.I.C.S.: 541618
Jose A. Marroig *(CEO)*
Rob Hirschmann *(VP)*
Kristen Stevens *(Mgr-Tech)*

PROLER STEEL INTERNATIONAL, LLC
3730 Kirby Dr Ste 1175, Houston, TX 77098-3983
Tel.: (713) 226-8000
Web Site: http://www.prolersteelintl.com
Sales Range: $10-24.9 Million
Emp.: 50
Metal Recycling Services
N.A.I.C.S.: 213114
Cris Proler *(Pres & CEO)*
Shane Leonard *(COO)*
Jonathan Hansen *(CFO)*
Bryan Wallace *(Sr VP)*

PROLIANT
1100 Abernathy Rd NE Ste 1000, Atlanta, GA 30328
Tel.: (770) 395-6615
Web Site: http://www.proliant.com
Year Founded: 1993
Sales Range: $10-24.9 Million
Emp.: 67
Payroll Processing & HR Consulting
N.A.I.C.S.: 541214
Kevin Clayton *(CEO)*
Tim Clark *(Mgr-Sls)*
Bruce Gilbert *(Dir-Trng)*

PROLIFT INDUSTRIAL EQUIPMENT CO., LLC
12001 Plantside Dr, Louisville, KY 40299
Tel.: (502) 267-2565 KY
Web Site: http://www.proliftequipment.com
Year Founded: 1978
Sales Range: $1-9.9 Million
Emp.: 280
Industrial Machinery & Equipment
N.A.I.C.S.: 423830
Doug Simcox *(CFO)*
David Grassy *(Pres)*
Chris Frazee *(VP-Sls)*

PROLIM PLM
30445 Northwestern Hwy Ste 380, Farmington Hills, MI 48334
Tel.: (248) 522-2575
Web Site: http://www.prolim.com
Sales Range: $50-74.9 Million
Emp.: 180
Software Service Provider
N.A.I.C.S.: 513210
Prabhu Patil *(Pres & CEO)*
Rich Solti *(Dir-Global Sls)*
Sha Jonna *(Head-Talent Acq)*
Ashwini Kumar *(Head-HR & Dir-Sls)*
Arun Ganesan *(Head-Delivery)*

PROLINK STAFFING LLC
10700 Montgomery Rd Ste 226, Cincinnati, OH 45242
Tel.: (513) 489-5300
Web Site: http://www.prolinkstaff.com
Year Founded: 2011
Sales Range: $75-99.9 Million
Emp.: 290
Recruitment Consulting Services
N.A.I.C.S.: 541612
Tony Munafo *(Co-Founder & CEO)*
Mike Munafo *(Co-Founder)*

PROLOG SERVICES
330 E Kilbourn Ave Ste 1085, Milwaukee, WI 53202-3146
Tel.: (414) 304-3096
Sales Range: $10-24.9 Million
Emp.: 150
Transportation Carrier
N.A.I.C.S.: 488490
Subsidiaries:
Tandem Transport Inc. (1)
9809 South Franklin Dr, Franklin, WI 53132-8849
Tel.: (414) 304-3096
Sales Range: $10-24.9 Million
Emp.: 71
Trucking Service
N.A.I.C.S.: 484121

PROLUXE PROPERTIES
6911 Pistol Range Rd Ste 101B, Tampa, FL 33635
Tel.: (727) 532-3020
Web Site: http://www.proluxeproperties.com
Year Founded: 1986
Sales Range: $10-24.9 Million
Emp.: 5
Residential Real Estate Services
N.A.I.C.S.: 531390
Anna M. West *(VP)*
Michael J. Bednarski *(Pres)*

PROM KROG ALTSTIEL INC.
1009 W Glen Oaks Ln Ste 107, Mequon, WI 53092-3382
Tel.: (262) 241-9414
Web Site: http://www.pkamar.com
Year Founded: 1986
Sales Range: $10-24.9 Million
Emp.: 15
Advertising Services
N.A.I.C.S.: 541810
Bruce Prom *(Pres, Partner & Dir-Art/New Bus)*
Tom Altstiel *(Partner, Treas & Dir-Creative)*
Sandy Mercier *(Acct Exec)*
George Wamser *(Mgr-Art Production)*
Sarah Nohr *(Mgr-Acct)*

PROMAC, INC.
1153 Timber Dr, Elgin, IL 60123
Tel.: (847) 695-8181 IL
Web Site: http://www.promac.com
Year Founded: 1981
Sales Range: $10-24.9 Million
Emp.: 25
Promotional Custom Marketing Services
N.A.I.C.S.: 236220
James A. Rouzer *(Pres & CEO)*
Mike Trump *(Owner)*

PROMARK DIRECT INC.
PO Box 258, Ramsey, NJ 07446-0258
Tel.: (201) 398-9000
Web Site: http://www.promarkdirect.com
Year Founded: 1977
Sales Range: $1-9.9 Million
Emp.: 4
Advetising Agency

N.A.I.C.S.: 541810
Donna Johns *(Pres)*

PROMARK INTERNATIONAL INC.
1268 Humbracht Cir, Bartlett, IL 60103
Tel.: (630) 830-2500
Web Site: http://www.promarkbrands.com
Lighting Equipment Mfr
N.A.I.C.S.: 335132
Ken Orlando *(Pres)*
Bob Otis *(Mgr-Natl Sls)*
Subsidiaries:
Photogenic Professional Lighting (1)
1268 Humbracht Cir, Bartlett, IL 60103-1631
Tel.: (630) 830-2500
Web Site: http://www.photogenic.com
Photographic Lighting Equipment & Accessories Mfr
N.A.I.C.S.: 333310
Smith-Victor Corporation (1)
1268 Humbracht Cir, Bartlett, IL 60103
Tel.: (630) 830-9200
Web Site: http://www.smithvictor.com
Sales Range: $1-9.9 Million
Emp.: 30
Photographic Lighting Equipment & Home Video Accessories Mfr
N.A.I.C.S.: 333310
Ken Orlando *(Pres)*
Speedotron Corporation (1)
1268 Humbracht Cir, Bartlett, IL 60103-1631
Tel.: (630) 246-5001
Web Site: http://www.speedotron.com
Sales Range: $1-9.9 Million
Emp.: 25
Photographic Equipment Mfr.
N.A.I.C.S.: 333310

PROMAXBDA
5700 Wilshire Blvd Ste 275, Los Angeles, CA 90404
Tel.: (310) 788-7600 CA
Web Site: http://www.promaxbda.org
Year Founded: 1956
Sales Range: $1-9.9 Million
Marketing Professional Association
N.A.I.C.S.: 813910
Lucian Cojescu *(CIO)*
Stacy La Cotera *(VP-Global Awards & Gen Mgr)*
Steph Sebbag *(Vice Chm)*
Steve Kazanjian *(Pres & CEO)*
Scot Chastain *(Chm)*
Andy Chua *(Dir-India Conference)*
Angie Panelo *(Dir-Latin American Rels)*
Anush Payaslyan *(Mgr-Member Svcs)*
Christina Graziano *(Dir-Events & Global Conferences)*
Janet Alcantara *(Dir-Asia Conference)*
Jonathan Hallett *(Mng Dir-Africa & Asia Pacific)*
Lester Mordue *(Dir-European Conference & Rels)*
Max Follmer *(Mgr-Mktg & Editorial)*
Paige Albiniak *(Dir-Editorial)*
Wolfgang Thiele *(Accountant)*
Laurel Bernard *(Treas)*
Vicky Free *(Sec)*
Katie Nichols *(Coord-Event)*
Rick Swanson *(VP-Mktg & Programming)*
Kristin Craik *(Coord-Social Media)*
Rachel Wyatt *(Project Coord)*
Stephen Early *(VP-Strategic Partnerships)*
Steve Kalal *(Engr-Software)*
Aurelio Farrell II *(Mgr-Strategic Insights & Analysis)*

PROMAXIMA MANUFACTURING LTD

5310 Ashbrook Dr, Houston, TX 77081
Tel.: (713) 667-9606
Web Site: http://www.promaximamfg.com
Sales Range: $10-24.9 Million
Emp.: 250
Exercise Equipment
N.A.I.C.S.: 339920
Bob Leppke *(Pres)*

PROMED MOLDED PRODUCTS, INC.
15600 Medina Rd, Plymouth, MN 55447
Tel.: (763) 331-3800
Web Site: http://www.promedmolding.com
Year Founded: 1987
Sales Range: $25-49.9 Million
Emp.: 176
Mechanical Rubber Goods Mfr
N.A.I.C.S.: 326220
Connie Laumeyer *(Dir-Customer Sls & Mktg)*
Carol Knutson *(Mgr-HR)*
Craig Morris *(Mgr-Bus Unit)*
James Arps *(Dir-Pharma Svcs)*
Tina Roach *(Mgr-Lean Six Sigma)*
Wayne Kelly *(Pres & CEO)*
Jim Kozlowski *(Mgr-Bus Dev)*

PROMED WASTE SOLUTIONS LLC
750 5th Ave S, Saint Petersburg, FL 33701
Tel.: (727) 527-0300
Web Site: http://www.promedicalwaste.com
Medical Waste Disposal & Treatment
N.A.I.C.S.: 562219
Paul E. Reddish *(Pres)*
Travis Deering *(Gen Mgr-Ops)*
Subsidiaries:
Biotran Inc. (1)
55 Oxford Business Pkwy Ste C, Oxford, GA 30054
Tel.: (770) 570-9831
Web Site: http://www.biotraninc.com
Medical Waste Disposal
N.A.I.C.S.: 562219
Terry Barnett *(Pres)*

PROMEDEV, LLC
11335 NE 122nd Way Ste 140, Kirkland, WA 98034 WA
Web Site: http://www.relieffactor.com
Year Founded: 2015
Sales Range: $10-24.9 Million
Emp.: 18
Health Supplements Distr
N.A.I.C.S.: 424210
Seth Talbott *(Co-Owner)*
Pete Talbott *(Co-Owner)*

PROMEGA CORPORATION
2800 Woods Hollow Rd, Madison, WI 53711-5300
Tel.: (608) 274-4330 WI
Web Site: http://www.promega.com
Year Founded: 1978
Sales Range: $10-24.9 Million
Emp.: 60
Mfr of Biological Products
N.A.I.C.S.: 325414
Han Willems *(Gen Mgr-Promega Benelux)*
Thierry Colin *(Mgr-Sls-Promega Switzerland)*
Brigitta Saul *(Specialist-Product-Promega AG)*
William A. Linton *(Chm, Pres & CEO)*

PROMETHEUM, INC.
120 Wall St Fl 25, New York, NY 10005

Tel.: (212) 514-8369
Web Site: http://www.prometheum.com
Privater Equity Firm
N.A.I.C.S.: 523999
Martin H Kaplan (Chm)

Subsidiaries:

InteliClear, LLC (1)
2 King Arthur Ct, Ste A, North Brunswick, NJ 08902
Tel.: (860) 866-4300
Web Site: http://www.inteliclear.com
Electronics Stores
N.A.I.C.S.: 449210
Bob Victor (Mng Dir)

PROMETHEUS PARTNERS, L.P.
1340 Hamlet Ave, Clearwater, FL 33756
Tel.: (727) 443-5656
Web Site:
http://www.prometheuspartners.com
Year Founded: 1996
Private Equity Firm Focusing on Restaurant Industry
N.A.I.C.S.: 523999
Nicholas Peters (Pres & CEO)
Chris Suh (VP)
Michelle Knight (Controller)
Jeffrey Flynn (Controller)

Subsidiaries:

Coastal QSR, LLC (1)
1340 Hamlet Ave, Clearwater, FL 33756
Tel.: (727) 443-5656
Private Equity Firm
N.A.I.C.S.: 523999

PROMETHEUS REAL ESTATE GROUP, INC.
1900 S Norfolk St Ste 150, San Mateo, CA 94403
Tel.: (650) 931-3400
Web Site:
http://www.prometheusapartments.com
Year Founded: 1965
Rev.: $11,600,000
Emp.: 700
Real Estate Managers
N.A.I.C.S.: 531210
Jonathan Moss (Partner-Dev & Exec VP)
John Millham (Pres)
Jackie Safier (Pres)
Rick Jacobsen (CFO)
Kevin Wilkinson (Sr VP-Acctg)
Pat Calihan (VP-Acq)
Justin Halada (Sr VP-Asset Mgmt)
Eron Kosmowski (VP-Fin)
Vik Lu (VP-Tech)
Dan Emerson (Sr VP)

Subsidiaries:

Kimco Realty Inc (1)
3333 New Hyde Park Rd Ste 100, New Hyde Park, NY 11042-0020
Tel.: (516) 869-9000
Web Site: http://www.kimcorealty.com
Sales Range: $125-149.9 Million
Emp.: 250
Owner & Operator of Retail Shopping Centers
N.A.I.C.S.: 525990
Ross Cooper (Chief Investment Officer & Exec VP)
Raymond Edwards (VP-Retailer Svcs)
Robert Nadler (Pres-Central)
Wilbur Simmons (Pres-Mid-Atlantic)
Kelly Smith (Mng Dir-Canadian Ops)
Thomas R. Taddeo (CIO & Sr VP)
Armand Vasquez (Pres-Western)
Joshua Weinkranz (Pres-Northeast)

PROMETHEUS RESEARCH, LLC
55 Church St 7th Fl, New Haven, CT 06510
Tel.: (203) 928-0102
Web Site: http://www.prometheusresearch.com
Year Founded: 1999
Sales Range: $1-9.9 Million
Emp.: 31
Data Management Services
N.A.I.C.S.: 541513
Owen McGettrick (CTO)
Jennifer Pearce (CFO)

PROMGIRL, LLC
1450 Broadway 21st Fl, New York, NY 10018
Tel.: (302) 279-1052
Web Site: http://www.promgirl.com
Year Founded: 1998
Sales Range: $10-24.9 Million
Emp.: 68
Special Occasion Dresses Online Retailer
N.A.I.C.S.: 424350
David Wilkenfeld (Pres & CEO)
Gregory Hall (Mgr-Special Projects)

PROMINENT CONSTRUCTION, LLC
2855 Anthony Ln S Ste 130, Minneapolis, MN 55418
Tel.: (612) 345-4799
Web Site:
http://www.prominentconstructionllc.com
Year Founded: 2011
Sales Range: $1-9.9 Million
Emp.: 10
General Contractor Services
N.A.I.C.S.: 236210
Justin Krein (Pres)
Chad Ormberg (VP)

PROMINENT TITLE LLC
3101 Bee Caves Rd, Austin, TX 78746-5574
Tel.: (512) 498-3500
Web Site: http://www.ptaustin.com
Title Abstract & Settlement Offices
N.A.I.C.S.: 541191
A. J. Waight (Owner)

PROMINIC.NET
PO Box 7301, Champaign, IL 61826
Tel.: (217) 356-2888
Web Site: http://www.prominic.net
Year Founded: 1998
Sales Range: $1-9.9 Million
Emp.: 12
It Consulting
N.A.I.C.S.: 541690
Douglas Robinson (VP-Customer Svc)
Eric McCartney (Mgr-Data Center)
Joel Anderson (Engr-Software)

PROMISE HOLDINGS, LLC
1455 W Fargo Unit 2, Chicago, IL 60626-0000
Tel.: (312) 543-3729
Web Site: https://www.promise-holdings.com
Emp.: 100
Holding Company
N.A.I.C.S.: 551112
Gordon C. C. Liao (Founder)

Subsidiaries:

Catalina Finer Food Corporation (1)
4710 W Cayuga St, Tampa, FL 33614
Tel.: (813) 876-3910
Web Site: http://www.catalinafoods.com
Meat Processed from Carcasses
N.A.I.C.S.: 311612
Alejandro Cepero (Pres)

Edward Marc Brands, LLC (1)
1705 E Carson St, Pittsburgh, PA 15203-1772
Tel.: (412) 488-1809
Web Site: http://www.edwardmarc.com
Confectionery & Nut Stores
N.A.I.C.S.: 445292

PROMMIS SOLUTIONS HOLDING CORP.
400 Northridge Rd, Atlanta, GA 30350 DE
Web Site: http://www.prommis.com
Year Founded: 2006
Sales Range: $250-299.9 Million
Emp.: 1,375
Residential Mortgage Processing Services
N.A.I.C.S.: 531390
Jennifer H. Dorris (Pres)
George W. Dunaway (CFO & Sec)
Brandon J. Barnett (Exec VP-Bus Dev)
Jay M. Duff (CIO)
Daniel D. Phelan (Chm)
John Marecki (VP-Foreclosure Ops Unit-East Coast)
Phil Johnsen (Sr VP-Sls & Mktg)
Ed Hill (Sr VP-Trustee Svcs)
Charlie Piper (COO)

PROMOPEDDLER.COM
20015 SW Pacific Hwy, Sherwood, OR 97140
Tel.: (503) 783-1480
Web Site:
http://www.promopeddler.com
Year Founded: 1999
Sales Range: $1-9.9 Million
Emp.: 50
Incentive & Promotion Product Distr
N.A.I.C.S.: 459999
Brian Kraft (Mgr-IT)

PROMOTION IN MOTION, INC.
25 Commerce Dr, Allendale, NJ 07401-0008
Tel.: (201) 784-5800 DE
Web Site:
http://www.promotioninmotion.com
Year Founded: 1980
Sales Range: $200-249.9 Million
Emp.: 500
Food & Confectionery Products, Fruit Snacks, Juices & Bottled Water Mfr, Marketer, Exporter & Distr
N.A.I.C.S.: 311340
Michael G. Rosenberg (Founder, Pres & CEO)
Jeff Scudillo (VP-Sls)
Josh Shapiro (VP-Mktg)

Subsidiaries:

Farmers Choice Food Brands (1)
43 W Knowlton Rd, Media, PA 19063
Tel.: (610) 499-9477
Fruit Snack Mfr & Distr
N.A.I.C.S.: 311340

PIM Brands, LLC (1)
500 Pierce St, Somerset, NJ 08873-1270
Tel.: (732) 560-8300
Web Site:
http://www.promotioninmotion.com
Candy & Confectionery Mfr
N.A.I.C.S.: 311919
Michael G. Rosenberg (Pres & CEO)
Norman Ross (VP-Govt Affairs)

PROMOTIONAL PRODUCTS ASSOCIATION INTERNATIONAL
3125 Skyway Cir N, Irving, TX 75038-3526
Tel.: (972) 252-0404 TX
Web Site: http://www.ppai.org
Year Founded: 1904
Sales Range: $10-24.9 Million
Emp.: 80
Professional Association
N.A.I.C.S.: 813920
Khris Harris (Mgr-Ops)
Kim R. Todora (Mgr-PR)
Dale Denham (Pres & CEO)
Rick Brenner (COO)
Tom Goos (Chm)

PROMOTIONAL SLIDEGUIDE CORP.
15 Giltin Ave, Hauppauge, NY 11788
Tel.: (631) 648-1200 NY
Web Site:
http://www.positivepromotions.com
Year Founded: 1947
Sales Range: $25-49.9 Million
Emp.: 170
Catalog & Mail Order Services
N.A.I.C.S.: 455219

PROMUS HOLDINGS, LLC
156 N Jefferson St Ste 300, Chicago, IL 60661
Tel.: (312) 784-3990 IL
Web Site:
http://www.promusholdings.com
Year Founded: 2006
Holding Company; Private Equity, Investment Advisory & Asset Management Services
N.A.I.C.S.: 551112
Brian Musso (Mng Partner)
Zach Musso (Mng Partner)
Terence John Toth (Partner)
Steven Brown (Partner)
Andy Code (Founder & Partner)
Bob Newman (Partner)
Sarah Wuellner (Partner)
Patrick Fisher (Partner)
Ryan Crawford (Chief Compliance Officer & Gen Counsel)
Blake Thoele (Investment Admin Officer)
Meredith Mays (Dir-Mktg & Client Svc)

Subsidiaries:

Promus Capital, LLC (1)
30 S Wacker Dr Ste 1600, Chicago, IL 60606
Tel.: (312) 784-3990
Web Site: http://www.promuscapital.com
Investment Advisory & Asset Management Services
N.A.I.C.S.: 523940
Ryan Crawford (Chief Compliance Officer)
Shanna Otto (Accountant)
Terence John Toth (Co-Founder)

Promus Equity Partners, LLC (1)
156 N Jefferson St Ste 300, Chicago, IL 60661
Tel.: (312) 784-3990
Web Site: http://www.promusequity.com
Privater Equity Firm
N.A.I.C.S.: 523999
Andrew W. Code (Partner)
Steven Brown (Partner)
Sarah Wuellner (Partner)
Anders R. Rosenquist (Principal)
David Code (Principal)

Joint Venture (Domestic):

ADI American Distributors LLC (2)
2 Emery Ave, Randolph, NJ 07869
Tel.: (973) 328-1181
Web Site: http://www.americandistr.com
Sales Range: $10-24.9 Million
Electronic Parts & Equipment Mfr
N.A.I.C.S.: 423690
David Beck (Pres & CEO)
David Kasner (VP-Sls & Mktg)
Michele Almeida (VP-Sls & Mktg)
Bart Mallory (VP-Quality)

Holding (Domestic):

Associated Steel Group, LLC (2)
PO Box 1316, Batesville, MS 38606
Tel.: (615) 714-6234
Holding Company; Metal Building Products Mfr
N.A.I.C.S.: 551112

PROMUS HOLDINGS, LLC

Promus Holdings, LLC—(Continued)

Subsidiary (Domestic):

ACI Building Systems, LLC (3)
10125 Hwy 6 W, Batesville, MS 38606
Tel.: (662) 563-4574
Web Site:
  http://www.acibuildingsystems.com
Metal Buildings & Roofing Systems Designer, Mfr & Sales
N.A.I.C.S.: 332311
Tim Davis (Mgr-Sls)
Timothy W. Ritchie (Pres & CEO)

AIM Metals, LLC (3)
1724 Northside Industrial Blvd, Columbus, GA 31904
Tel.: (706) 660-1877
Web Site: http://www.ai-metals.com
Sales Range: $10-24.9 Million
Emp.: 30
Metal Roof & Related Wall Products Mfr
N.A.I.C.S.: 332311
Stuart Webb (Pres)
John Edward Hatfield (Mgr-Sls)
Mike Gilbert (CFO)
Ron Cumbie (Plant Mgr)

Alliance Steel, Inc. (3)
3333 S Council Rd, Oklahoma City, OK 73179
Web Site: http://www.allianceokc.com
Structural Steel Products Mfr & Distr
N.A.I.C.S.: 332312
Bill Cralley (Pres)
Lisa Steward (CFO)
Mike Heidary (VP-Engrg)
Joel Williams (VP-Mfg)

Holding (Domestic):

Auto Meter Products, Inc. (2)
413 W Elm St, Sycamore, IL 60178
Tel.: (815) 895-8141
Web Site: http://www.autometer.com
Sales Range: $25-49.9 Million
Emp.: 300
Aftermarket Automotive Instrumentation & Video Data Recording Systems Designer, Mfr & Marketer
N.A.I.C.S.: 334514
Scott Zettek (VP-Sls & Mktg)

Subsidiary (Domestic):

Cobb Tuning Products, LLC (3)
2311 W Rundberg Ln Ste 500, Austin, TX 78758
Web Site: http://www.cobbtuning.com
Sales Range: $1-9.9 Million
Automotive Aftermarket Performance Products Designer, Mfr, Whslr & Retailer
N.A.I.C.S.: 336390
Roland Trey Cobb III (Founder & Chief Technologist)

Joint Venture (Domestic):

Kith Kitchens, LLC (2)
280 N Industrial Loop, Haleyville, AL 35565
Tel.: (205) 485-2261
Web Site: http://www.kithkitchens.us
Custom Kitchen & Bath Cabinetry Mfr
N.A.I.C.S.: 337110
Allen Knight (Pres)
Mark Smith (CEO)

Subsidiary (Domestic):

Mouser Custom Cabinetry LLC (3)
2112 N Dixie Ave, Elizabethtown, KY 42701
Tel.: (270) 737-7477
Web Site: http://www.mousercc.com
Rev.: $26,839,966
Emp.: 248
Wood Kitchen Cabinets
N.A.I.C.S.: 337110
Steve Mouser (Pres)

Holding (Domestic):

ProSteel Security Products, Inc. (2)
1400 S State St, Provo, UT 84606
Tel.: (801) 373-2385
Web Site: http://www.prosteelsecurity.com
Sales Range: $10-24.9 Million
Safe & Special Vault, Security & Storm-Resistant Metal Door Mfr
N.A.I.C.S.: 332999

QCC, LLC (2)
7315 W Wilson Ave, Harwood Heights, IL 60706-4707
Tel.: (708) 887-5400
Web Site: http://www.qccorp.com
Sales Range: $100-124.9 Million
Emp.: 180
Precision Machined Metal Components & Assemblies Mfr
N.A.I.C.S.: 332710
Victor Prawica (Mgr-Value Stream)
Gore Ham (Pres & CEO)

Subsidiary (Domestic):

A&K C.N.C. Machining, LLC (3)
1852 Janke Dr, Northbrook, IL 60062-6711
Tel.: (847) 559-1760
Machine Shop Operator
N.A.I.C.S.: 332710

Holding (Domestic):

Quest Products, Inc. (2)
8201 104th St Ste 200, Pleasant Prairie, WI 53158
Web Site: http://www.questproductsinc.com
Health Related Consumer Products
N.A.I.C.S.: 325412
Don Ryan (Founder, Co-Owner & Partner)
Michael Brennan (Co-Owner & Partner)
Mark McGreevy (Partner)
Megan Russo (Dir-Sls-E-Commerce)
Tim Koers (Sr VP-Ops)
Jeff Featherstone (Sr. VP-Sls)
Jon Romanow (Dir-Mktg)

Subsidiary (Domestic):

Tec Laboratories, Inc. (3)
7100 Tec Labs Way, Albany, OR 97321
Tel.: (541) 926-4577
Web Site: http://www.teclabsinc.com
Rev.: $8,722,990
Emp.: 35
Pharmaceutical Preparation Mfr
N.A.I.C.S.: 325412
Steven Smith (CEO)
Larry Burris (Dir-Sls)
Bill Coppoolse (Mgr-Acct-Natl)
Kathlene Cowan (Mgr-IT)
Steve Ness (Mgr-Pur)
Teri Siefker (Controller)
Vern Smith (VP)

PROOF ADVERTISING
114 W 7th St Ste 500, Austin, TX 78701
Tel.: (512) 345-6658   TX
Web Site: http://www.proof-advertising.com
Year Founded: 1989
Sales Range: $50-74.9 Million
Emp.: 120
Advertising Services
N.A.I.C.S.: 541810
Bryan Christian (Pres & Principal)
Lynn Dobson (CFO & VP)
Craig Mikes (Dir-Creative & Dir-Art)
Rob Story (Assoc Dir-Creative)
Trish Malatesta (Acct Dir)
Kara McCoy (Acct Dir)
Josh McGonigle (Dir-Art)
Ly Tran (Dir-Digital Strategy & Architecture)
James Hill (Dir-Media)
Jeff Solmundson (Dir-Media)
Tim Hicks (Dir-Studio Svcs)
Jocelyn Friedman (Grp Acct Dir)
Drew Hammond (Sr Dir-Art)
Terry Ilse (Sr Dir-Art)

PROOF AUTHENTICATION CORPORATION
16 Pleasant St, Wayland, MA 01778
Tel.: (585) 325-3610   DE
Web Site:
  http://www.proofauthentication.com
Year Founded: 2019
Anticounterfeiting Authentication Solutions Services
N.A.I.C.S.: 561621
Daniel McKinnon (CEO)

Subsidiaries:

DSS Digital Inc. (1)
28 E Main St Ste 1525, Rochester, NY 14614
Tel.: (585) 325-3610
Web Site: http://www.dssdigitalgroup.com
Software Development Services
N.A.I.C.S.: 513210
Vincent Lum (Pres)

PROOF RESEARCH, INC.
10 Western Village Ln, Columbia Falls, MT 59912
Tel.: (406) 756-9290
Web Site:
  http://www.proofresearch.com
Rifle Mfr
N.A.I.C.S.: 335999
Jeff Badelt (Dir-Sls-Natl)
Christopher Potts (VP-Fin & Admin)
Larry Murphy (CEO)

Subsidiaries:

Performance Polymer Solutions Inc. (1)
2711 Lance Dr, Moraine, OH 45409
Tel.: (937) 298-3713
Web Site: http://www.p2si.com
Emp.: 15
Adhesive Mfr
N.A.I.C.S.: 325520
David B. Curliss (Pres)

PROPANE EDUCATION & RESEARCH COUNCIL, INC.
1140 Connecticut Ave NW Ste 1075, Washington, DC 20036
Tel.: (202) 452-8975   DE
Web Site:
  http://www.propanecouncil.org
Year Founded: 1997
Sales Range: $10-24.9 Million
Emp.: 35
Propane Gas Research Support Services
N.A.I.C.S.: 813910
Stuart Flatow (VP-Safety & Trng)
Patrick Hyland (Dir-Industry Programs)
Tucker Perkins (Pres & CEO)
Paula Wilson (Dir-Industry Engagement)
Jeremy Wishart (Dir-Off-Road Bus Dev)
Erin Hatcher (Sr VP-Comm & Mktg)
Gavin Hale (VP-Bus Dev)

PROPARK, INC.
1 Union Pl, Hartford, CT 06103
Tel.: (860) 527-2378
Web Site: http://www.propark.com
Year Founded: 1984
Premier Parking Management Services
N.A.I.C.S.: 812930
David Schmid (CEO)
Peter Thorson (Exec VP)
John Schmid (Exec Chm)
Richard DiPietro (Pres)
Joe Coppola (Mng Partner)
Patrick Boeshans (Chief Administrative Officer)
Tim Willey (CFO)
Tom Bechard (Chief Development Officer)
Deana Gore (VP-Admin Div)
Marc Schreiber (VP-Natl Transportation)
Lan Zhang (VP-Fin & Corp Controller)
Kristen Sokich (Exec VP)
Luis Garcia (Sr VP-West Reg)
Sean Lampert (VP-Reg)
Tamer Shaban (VP-Ops-Connecticut)
Ida Inoue (Mgr-Parking Ops)
Greg Tyler (Exec VP-Hospitality & Healthcare)

U.S. PRIVATE

John Reimers (COO)
Stephen Duffy (Chief Strategy Officer)
Kyle Hunter (VP-Corp Analytics)
Alexander Piech (Reg VP-New Jersey)
Joshua Crain (VP-Tech)
Joe Caputo (Sr VP-Southwest)
Courtney Keany (Chief Legal Officer)

Subsidiaries:

Atlantic Services Group, Inc. (1)
2131 K St NW, Washington, DC 20037
Tel.: (202) 466-3175
Web Site:
  http://www.atlanticservicesgroup.com
Rev.: $5,100,000
Emp.: 175
Limousine Service
N.A.I.C.S.: 485320

California Parking Company, Inc. (1)
768 Sansome St, San Francisco, CA 94111
Tel.: (415) 468-4860
Web Site: http://www.californiaparking.com
Sales Range: $1-9.9 Million
Emp.: 90
Parking Lot & Lease Real Property
N.A.I.C.S.: 531190

FLY Away Airport Parking Services LLC (1)
1671 Murfreesboro Rd, Nashville, TN 37217-2917
Tel.: (615) 367-2200
Web Site: http://www.flyawayparking.com
Parking Lots & Garages
N.A.I.C.S.: 812930
J. R. Fraley (Pres)

Imperial Parking Industries, Inc. (1)
6420 Wilshire Blvd, Los Angeles, CA 90048
Tel.: (323) 651-5588
Web Site: http://www.iplcorp.net
Automobile Parking, Nsk
N.A.I.C.S.: 812930
Kia Shakoori (Pres)

Pilgrim Parking Inc. (1)
60 Temple Pl Ste 401, Boston, MA 02111
Tel.: (617) 723-1488
Web Site: http://www.pilgrimparking.com
Rev.: $30,000,000
Emp.: 250
Parking Garage
N.A.I.C.S.: 812930

Sovereign Services Inc. (1)
6363 Richmond Ave Ste 300, Houston, TX 77074
Tel.: (713) 777-0571
Web Site: http://www.sovereignservices.com
Automobile Parking, Nsk
N.A.I.C.S.: 812930
Chris Rockwell (Pres)

PROPEL EQUITY PARTNERS, LLC
10 Glenville St 1st Fl, Greenwich, CT 06831-3680
Tel.: (203) 930-7711
Web Site:
  http://www.propelequity.com
Year Founded: 2012
Emp.: 4
Privater Equity Firm
N.A.I.C.S.: 523999
John M. Belniak (Partner)
Robert M. Farinholt (Partner)

Subsidiaries:

Poof-Slinky, LLC (1)
4280 S Haggerty Rd, Canton, MI 48188
Tel.: (734) 454-9552
Web Site: http://www.poof-slinky.com
Sales Range: $10-24.9 Million
Emp.: 50
Children's Toys Mfr & Marketer
N.A.I.C.S.: 339930
Fred Keller (Pres)

Subsidiary (Domestic):

Alex Panline USA, Inc. (2)

COMPANIES

251 Union St, Northvale, NJ 07647
Tel.: (201) 750-8010
Web Site: http://www.alextoys.com
Sales Range: $10-24.9 Million
Children's Toys Mfr & Marketer
N.A.I.C.S.: 339930

Summit Products, Inc. (1)
7291 Gadsden Hwy, Trussville, AL 35173
Tel.: (205) 661-1774
Web Site: http://www.summittoy.com
Sales Range: $1-9.9 Million
Emp.: 20
Game, Toy & Children's Vehicle Mfr
N.A.I.C.S.: 339930
Dan Henderson *(Pres)*

PROPEL FUELS, INC.
1815 19th St, Sacramento, CA 95811
Tel.: (650) 241-7800
Web Site: http://www.propelfuels.com
Year Founded: 2004
Sales Range: $10-24.9 Million
Emp.: 35
Builds, Owns & Operates a Network of Green-Built Fueling Stations
N.A.I.C.S.: 457210
Rob Elam *(CEO)*

PROPEL INC.
690 Broadway St, Redwood City, CA 94063
Tel.: (650) 241-7800
Web Site: http://www.propelfuels.com
Year Founded: 2007
Sales Range: $10-24.9 Million
Emp.: 27
Green Built Fueling Stations
N.A.I.C.S.: 457120
Matt Horton *(CEO)*

PROPELLER MEDIA WORKS, LLC
208 Flynn Ave 2i, Burlington, VT 05401
Tel.: (802) 864-8251
Web Site: http://www.propellermediawork.com
Year Founded: 1997
Sales Range: $1-9.9 Million
Emp.: 6
Computer System Design Services
N.A.I.C.S.: 541512
David Gibson *(Pres & CEO)*

PROPELLER, INC.
6420 S Macadam Ave, Portland, OR 97239
Tel.: (503) 278-7055
Web Site: http://www.propellerconsulting.com
Year Founded: 2012
Sales Range: $1-9.9 Million
Emp.: 200
Venture Capital Funding Services
N.A.I.C.S.: 523910
Ashley Stuparich *(Office Mgr)*
Jenni Jayne *(Sr Mgr-Mktg)*
Brooke Graham *(Mgr-Ops & Sls)*
Kerri Evans *(Mgr-Proposal & People Dev)*
Donna Prentice *(Office Mgr)*
Sunil Kasturi *(CEO)*
AJ Oberland *(VP-Ops)*
Maura Koehler-Hanlon *(Mng Dir)*

PROPER FOODS, INC.
1319 E Pine, Deming, NM 88030
Tel.: (575) 546-4442
Web Site: http://www.properfoods.com
Year Founded: 1990
Sales Range: $10-24.9 Million
Emp.: 150
Frozen Specialty Food Mfr
N.A.I.C.S.: 311412
Cindy Pfluger *(Dir-Customer Care)*
M. E. Bartley *(Mgr-Utility)*

Tammy Zumwalt *(Dir-HR)*
Judy Leatherwood *(Mgr)*
Eileen Holik *(Mgr-HR)*

PROPER GROUP INTERNATIONAL
13870 E Eleven Mile Rd, Warren, MI 48089
Tel.: (586) 779-8787
Web Site: http://www.propergroupintl.com
Year Founded: 1971
Rev.: $16,100,000
Emp.: 275
Forms (Molds), For Foundry & Plastics Working Machinery
N.A.I.C.S.: 333511
Geoff O'Brien *(Pres)*
Greg Dante *(Dir-Sls)*
Kevin Kowalski *(Engr-Design)*
Dennis Pearson *(Sr Acct Mgr)*
Heather Scott *(Acct Mgr)*

Subsidiaries:

Proper Polymers of Anderson (1)
101 Clemson Research Blvd, Anderson, SC 29625
Tel.: (864) 646-1990
Web Site: http://www.pmecompanies.com
Sales Range: $10-24.9 Million
Emp.: 50
Mold & Polymer Manufacturing
N.A.I.C.S.: 333511

Proper Tooling (1)
13870 E 11 Mile Rd, Warren, MI 48089
Tel.: (586) 779-9777
Web Site: http://www.propergroupintl.com
Sales Range: $25-49.9 Million
Emp.: 230
Dimensional & Small Mold Manufacturing, Specializing in Hardened Steel & Multi Cavity Tooling
N.A.I.C.S.: 333511
David Karnes *(VP)*

PROPERTY CARE SPECIALISTS INC.
2004 Florida St, Valrico, FL 33594
Tel.: (813) 654-3143
Web Site: http://www.propertycarespecialists.com
Sales Range: $1-9.9 Million
Emp.: 25
Landscaping Services
N.A.I.C.S.: 561730
Mike Rustenberghe *(CEO)*
Eric Schultz *(Pres)*
Keith Curran *(Owner)*
Nick Deangelo *(Mgr-Sweeping & Porter)*
Joshua Troyer *(Acct Exec)*

PROPERTY LINK INTERNATIONAL
435 Meadow Lark Ln, Palm Harbor, FL 34683-4824
Tel.: (727) 938-5566
Rev.: $54,000,000
Emp.: 40
Real Estate Purchasing Services
N.A.I.C.S.: 533110

PROPERTY MASTERS INC
1051 Hayes Industrial Dr, Marietta, GA 30062
Tel.: (770) 792-5533
Web Site: http://www.propertymasters.com
Year Founded: 1998
Sales Range: $10-24.9 Million
Emp.: 39
Construction & Remodeling Services
N.A.I.C.S.: 236220
Kyle Cooper *(Pres)*
Scott Berezo *(Dir-Renovations)*
Jackie Jaegle *(Project Coord-REO)*

Alice Barnett *(Controller)*
Heather Pool *(Project Coord)*
Jennifer Williams *(Project Coord)*
Daniel Frangione *(Project Mgr)*
Emilio Samuels *(Supvr-Mechanical)*
Kimberly Campuzano *(Mgr-Client Svcs-REO Div)*
Kristin Glass *(Project Coord)*

PROPERTY RESOURCES CORP.
125 Brazilian Ave, Palm Beach, FL 33480
Tel.: (561) 655-9510
Web Site: http://www.propertyresourcescorporation.com
Sales Range: $75-99.9 Million
Emp.: 5
Investment Services
N.A.I.C.S.: 523999
Joseph Bagby *(Founder & Pres)*
Meredith Bagby *(VP)*

PROPERTY RESOURCES CORP.
240 Madison Ave, White Plains, NY 10606
Tel.: (212) 734-9191
Web Site: http://www.prcny.com
Rev.: $13,900,000
Emp.: 36
Property Management
N.A.I.C.S.: 531110
Frank E. Linde *(Pres)*
David Gartenlaub *(Exec VP)*
John Chatzky *(Owner)*

Subsidiaries:

Melcara Corp. (1)
10 Bank St Ste 550, White Plains, NY 10606
Tel.: (212) 861-8025
Web Site: http://www.prcny.com
Street Apartments & Property Mangement
N.A.I.C.S.: 236116

PROPERTY SOLUTIONS INTERNATIONAL, INC.
522 S 100 W, Provo, UT 84601
Tel.: (801) 375-5522
Web Site: http://www.propertysolutions.com
Year Founded: 2003
Sales Range: $1-9.9 Million
Emp.: 52
Rental Property Management Software
N.A.I.C.S.: 513210
David Bateman *(CEO)*
Ben Zimmer *(Pres)*
John Hanna *(Dir-Sls)*
Dharmesh Schroff *(CIO)*
Chase Harrington *(Exec VP)*

PROPERTYROOM.COM INC.
26421 Crown Valley Pkwy Ste 200, Mission Viejo, CA 92691
Tel.: (949) 282-0121
Web Site: http://www.propertyroom.com
Year Founded: 1999
Sales Range: $10-24.9 Million
Emp.: 50
Electronic Auctions of Police Seized, Found, Stolen, Recovered & Surplus Items
N.A.I.C.S.: 455219
Andrew J. Nash *(CEO)*
Aaron Thompson *(CFO)*
Kevin Felichko *(CTO)*
Donald Nemer *(Sr VP-Sls)*

PROPETRO SERVICES, INC.
1706 S Midkiff Bldg B, Midland, TX 79701

PROPHET BRAND STRATEGY, INC.

Tel.: (432) 688-0012
Web Site: http://www.propetroservices.com
Year Founded: 2005
Sales Range: $10-24.9 Million
Emp.: 300
Oil & Gas Well Drilling Services
N.A.I.C.S.: 213111
Dale Redman *(CEO)*
David Sledge *(COO)*
Jeff Smith *(CFO)*

PROPHARMA SALES LLC
2 City Pl Dr, Saint Louis, MO 63141
Tel.: (314) 812-2767
Web Site: http://www.propharmasales.com
Year Founded: 2013
Sales Range: $1-9.9 Million
Emp.: 32
Digital Marketing Services
N.A.I.C.S.: 541810
Matt Johnson *(Pres)*

PROPHET BRAND STRATEGY, INC.
150 Spear St Ste 1500, San Francisco, CA 94105
Tel.: (415) 677-0909 CA
Web Site: http://www.prophet.com
Year Founded: 1992
Sales Range: $10-24.9 Million
Emp.: 100
Brand & Marketing Consulting Services
N.A.I.C.S.: 541613
Andrew Pierce *(Pres-US)*
Simon Marlow *(CFO & COO)*
Cindy Levine *(Chief Strategy Officer)*
Scott M. Davis *(Chief Growth Officer)*
Rune Gustafson *(Pres-EMEA)*
Scott Drummond *(Partner)*
Ted Moser *(Sr Partner)*
Chan Suh *(Chief Digital Officer & Sr Partner)*
Ed Rhoads *(Partner)*
Jan Doring *(Partner)*
Jeani Vance *(CIO)*
John Baglivo *(CMO)*
Joseph Gelman *(Partner)*
Laurie Santos *(Dir-Firm Ops)*
Peter Dixon *(Chief Creative Officer)*
Tom Agan *(Partner)*
Jorge Aguilar *(Partner)*

Subsidiaries:

Altimeter Group, LLC (1)
1 Bush St 7th Fl, San Francisco, CA 94104
Tel.: (415) 363-0004
Web Site: http://www.altimetergroup.com
Business Consulting Services
N.A.I.C.S.: 541611
Charlene Li *(Founder & CEO)*
Omar Akhtar *(Mng Dir)*
Leslie Candy *(Mgr-Bus Dev)*

Figtree Creative Services Ltd. (1)
Northburgh House 10 Northburgh St, London, EC1 V0AT, United Kingdom
Tel.: (44) 20 70997088
Web Site: http://www.figtreenetwork.com
Sales Range: $10-24.9 Million
Emp.: 35
Advetising Agency
N.A.I.C.S.: 541810
Simon Myers *(CEO)*

Branch (Non-US):

Figtree Creative Services-Wanchai (2)
11-4 St John's Bldg 35th Garden Rd, Central, China (Hong Kong)
Tel.: (852) 2528 0983
Web Site: http://www.prophet.com
Emp.: 20
Advertising & Brand Services
N.A.I.C.S.: 541810
David Brabbins *(Mng Dir)*
Oscar Lam *(Office Mgr)*

PROPHET CORP.   U.S. PRIVATE

Prophet Brand Strategy, Inc.—(Continued)

PROPHET CORP.
2525 LeMond St SW, Owatonna, MN 55060
Tel.: (507) 451-7470
Web Site: http://www.gophersport.com
Sales Range: $25-49.9 Million
Emp.: 90
Physical Education; Athletic & Fitness Equipment
N.A.I.C.S.: 423910
Todd Jennings (Pres)
Michael Dunn (Chm & CEO)
Benoit Garbe (Sr Partner-Shanghai)
Leon Zhang (Partner-Shanghai)
Tom Doctoroff (Sr Partner)
David A. Aaker (Vice Chm)

PROPHET EQUITY L.P.
1460 Main St Ste 200, Southlake, TX 76092
Tel.: (817) 898-1500
Web Site: http://www.prophetequity.com
Privater Equity Firm
N.A.I.C.S.: 523999
Ross Gatlin (CEO & Mng Partner)
Charles Collie (Mng Dir-Leveraged Fin)
Brian Hegi (Mng Dir)
Ben Eakes (Mng Dir)
John P. Tatum (Mng Dir)
David Rex (Mng Dir & Gen Counsel)
Greg Balliro (Sr VP)
Michael Hirschfeld (VP)

Subsidiaries:

Altec Lansing LLC (1)
535 Rte 6 & 209, Milford, PA 18337-0277
Tel.: (570) 296-4434
Web Site: http://www.alteclansing.com
Sales Range: $50-74.9 Million
Emp.: 15
Audio Entertainment Equipment Mfr
N.A.I.C.S.: 334310

Cummings Resources LLC (1)
15 Century Blvd Ste 200, Nashville, TN 37214
Tel.: (615) 244-5555
Web Site: http://www.cummingssigns.com
Sales Range: $25-49.9 Million
Sign Mfr
N.A.I.C.S.: 339950

Derby Fabricating Solutions, LLC (1)
4500 Produce Rd, Louisville, KY 40218
Tel.: (502) 964-9135
Web Site: http://www.derbyfab.com
Custom Plastic & Magnesium Molded Products Mfr
N.A.I.C.S.: 326199
Doug Stahl (Pres & CEO)

Subsidiary (Domestic):

FabSol, LLC (2)
277 Industrial Dr, Cadiz, KY 42211
Tel.: (270) 522-1070
Rubber Sheeting & Adhesive Laminating Services
N.A.I.C.S.: 326299

Total Plastics, Inc. (1)
2810 N Burdick St, Kalamazoo, MI 49004
Tel.: (269) 344-0009
Web Site: http://www.totalplastics.com
Plastic Sheet, Rod, Tube, Film & Tape Distr
N.A.I.C.S.: 326130
Chad Wittkopp (Mgr-Corp Quality)
Timothy Russell (Dir-Info Sys)

Division (Domestic):

Total Plastics, Inc. - Grand Rapids (2)
1652 Gezon Pkwy, Grand Rapids, MI 49519
Tel.: (616) 530-0055
Web Site: http://www.totalplastics.com
Plastic Sheet, Rod, Tube, Film & Tape Distr
N.A.I.C.S.: 326130

Paul Hermann (Branch Mgr)

Total Plastics, Inc.- Life Sciences (2)
7508 Honeywell Dr, Fort Wayne, IN 46825
Tel.: (260) 489-3656
Web Site: http://www.totalplastics.com
Medical Grade Plastics Whslr
N.A.I.C.S.: 423990
Michael Kell (Mgr-Bus Dev)
Teresa Parsons (Mgr-Sls & Product)

WM Coffman Resources LLC (1)
2603 Technology Dr, Plano, TX 75074
Web Site: https://www.wm-coffman.com
Emp.: 100
Hardwood & Iron Stair Parts Mfr
N.A.I.C.S.: 321999
Derek Barksdale (Pres)

Subsidiary (Domestic):

Ideal Wood Products, Inc. (2)
225 W Main St, Little Falls, NY 13365
Tel.: (315) 823-1124
Web Site: http://www.idealstairparts.com
Sales Range: $1-9.9 Million
Emp.: 40
Millwork Services
N.A.I.C.S.: 321918

PROPHETSTOWN EQUIPMENT INC.
200 N St, Prophetstown, IL 61277
Tel.: (815) 537-2304
Web Site: http://www.birkeys.com
Sales Range: $125-149.9 Million
Emp.: 47
Farm Equipment; Lawn & Garden
N.A.I.C.S.: 423820
Donald Bartlett (Pres)

PROPHOENIX INC.
502 Pleasant Vly Ave, Moorestown, NJ 08057
Tel.: (609) 953-6850
Web Site: http://www.prophoenix.com
Year Founded: 2004
Sales Range: $1-9.9 Million
Emp.: 85
Public Safety & Security Software
N.A.I.C.S.: 513210
Jeff Reit (VP-Bus Dev)

PROPPER INTERNATIONAL, INC.
17 Research Park Dr, Saint Charles, MO 63304
Tel.: (636) 685-1000
Web Site: http://www.propper.com
Year Founded: 1967
Sales Range: $250-299.9 Million
Emp.: 3,000
Military Uniforms Distr
N.A.I.C.S.: 315250
Earl Weinman (Chm)

PROPPER MANUFACTURING COMPANY, INC.
36-04 Skillman Ave, Long Island City, NY 11101-1730
Tel.: (718) 392-6650   NY
Web Site: http://www.proppermfg.com
Year Founded: 1935
Sales Range: $25-49.9 Million
Emp.: 75
Mfr & Importer of Medical & Laboratory Supplies & Diagnostic Instruments
N.A.I.C.S.: 339112
Kevin Donovan (Mgr-Territory)
Wayne Schultz (Mgr-Territory)
Andrew Sharavara (CTO & Dir-Bus Dev-Intl)
John Vivenzio (Dir-GPO & IDN Bus Dev)
Joe Looney (Pres & CEO-Medical)
Lionel Florus (VP-Ops)
Monica Minore (VP-Sls & Mktg)

PROPRIETARY CAPITAL LLC
1225 17th St Ste 1500, Denver, CO 80202
Tel.: (303) 951-2515
Web Site: http://www.proprietarycapital.com
Investment Advice
N.A.I.C.S.: 523940
Mark Robertson (Dir-Bus Dev)

Subsidiaries:

American Financial Resources, Inc. (1)
9 Sylvan Way, Parsippany, NJ 07054
Tel.: (973) 983-5626
Sales Range: $1-9.9 Million
Emp.: 300
Mortgage & Nonmortgage Loan Brokers
N.A.I.C.S.: 522310
Paul Impagliazzo (Dir-Natl Sls)
Richard Dubnoff (CEO)

PROPRIETORS OF UNION WHARF
36 Union Wharf, Portland, ME 04101
Tel.: (207) 772-8160
Rev.: $10,000,000
Emp.: 1
Salts, Industrial
N.A.I.C.S.: 531120
Charles Poole (Pres)

PROPRIUM CAPITAL PARTNERS, L.P.
1 Landmark Sq 19th Fl, Stamford, CT 06901
Tel.: (203) 883-0355   DE
Web Site: http://www.proprium.com
Year Founded: 2012
Real Estate Investment Firm
N.A.I.C.S.: 531390
J. Timothy Morris (Co-Founder & Partner)
Willem de Geus (Co-Founder & Partner)
Anthony Kingsley (Partner)
Tony Martin (Partner)
Philipp Westermann (Partner)
Thomas Wong (Partner)
Thomas Carey (Mng Dir-Investments)
Rajat Tandon (Mng Dir-Investments)
John Curran (CFO)
Jonathan Harper (COO)
Diane Citron (Chief Compliance Officer & Gen Counsel)
John Clingan (Principal-Investments)
Yash Ravel (Principal-Investments)
Frank Shu (Principal-Investments)
Javier Perez Lecumberri (Principal-Investments)
Raju Patel (Principal-Reporting & Ops)
Siddharth Sangal (VP-Investments)

Subsidiaries:

Admiral Taverns Ltd. (1)
4th Floor HQ Building 58 Nicholas Street, Chester, CH1 2NP, United Kingdom
Tel.: (44) 1244321171
Web Site: https://www.admiraltaverns.co.uk
Pub Operator
N.A.I.C.S.: 722410
David Wigham (Comml Dir)

PROPST BROTHERS DISTRIBUTORS
829 Davidson Dr NW, Concord, NC 28025
Tel.: (704) 788-2102
Web Site: http://www.propstbrothers.com
Sales Range: $10-24.9 Million
Emp.: 54
Petroleum Products
N.A.I.C.S.: 424720
Trent Propst (Pres)

PROPST PROPERTIES, LLC
305 Church St SW Ste 715, Huntsville, AL 35801
Tel.: (256) 319-7800   DE
Web Site: http://www.propst.com
Year Founded: 2008
Real Estate Firm
N.A.I.C.S.: 531210
John Hughey (Pres)
Chris Brown (Principal)
Jenny Anderson (Mgr-Acctg)
Wes Hardin (Sr VP)
Ben Hughey (Mgr-Property & Leasing Agent)
Hugo Isom (Principal)

Subsidiaries:

MYCO Trailers, LLC (1)
2703 29th Ave E, Bradenton, FL 34208
Tel.: (941) 748-2397
Web Site: http://www.mycotrailers.com
Transportation Equipment Mfr
N.A.I.C.S.: 336214

PROPULSION CONTROLS ENGINEERING
1620 Rigel St, San Diego, CA 92113
Tel.: (619) 235-0961   CA
Web Site: http://www.pceshiprepair.com
Year Founded: 1974
Rev.: $16,683,472
Emp.: 275
Boiler Repair Shop
N.A.I.C.S.: 811310
David Clapp (Pres)

PROSCAPE LANDSCAPE MANAGEMENT CORPORATION
PO Box 231, East Greenwich, RI 02818
Tel.: (401) 886-7000
Web Site: http://www.proscaperi.com
Year Founded: 1995
Sales Range: $1-9.9 Million
Emp.: 50
Commercial & Residential Landscaping Services
N.A.I.C.S.: 561730
John Pontarelli (Owner)

PROSEK PARTNERS
1552 Post Rd, Fairfield, CT 06824
Tel.: (203) 254-1300
Web Site: http://www.prosek.com
Emp.: 165
Public Relations Agency
N.A.I.C.S.: 541820
Jennifer Prosek (Founder & Mng Partner)
Mark Kollar (Partner)
Andy Merrill (Partner)
Mike Geller (Mng Dir)
Caroline Gibson (Partner)
Daniel Allocca (Mng Dir)
Jake Daubenspeck (Sr VP)

Subsidiaries:

Prosek Partners (1)
1 Fetter Lane, London, EC4A 1BR, United Kingdom
Tel.: (44) 20 3440 5801
Web Site: http://www.prosekuk.com
Emp.: 18
Communications & Public Relations
N.A.I.C.S.: 541820
Laura Thorburn (Acct Mgr)
Frederick Duff Gordon (Assoc Dir)
Fiona Laffan (Mng Dir)

Prosek Partners (1)
350 5th Ave Ste 3901, New York, NY 10118
Tel.: (212) 279-3115
Web Site: http://www.prosek.com
Emp.: 30
Public Relations & Communications
N.A.I.C.S.: 541820

Mark Kollar *(Partner)*
Thomas Rozycki *(Mng Dir)*
Karen Niovitch Davis *(Partner)*
Josette Robinson *(Sr VP)*
Russell Sherman *(Partner)*
Andrew Waterworth *(Mng Dir)*
Susan Etkind *(Dir-Content Creation-Connecticut)*
Caroline Gibson *(Mng Dir-New York)*
Frederick Duff Gordon *(Assoc Dir-London)*
Josh Passman *(Mng Dir-New York)*
Russell Polin *(CFO)*
Bernardo Torres *(Assoc Dir-Creative-Connecticut)*
Dave Zamba *(Dir-Creative-Connecticut)*
Caroline Harris-Gibson *(Partner)*
Chris Byrne *(VP)*

PROSERVICE HAWAII
6600 Kalanianaole Hwy Ste 200, Honolulu, HI 96825-1298
Tel.: (808) 725-6877   HI
Web Site: http://www.proservice.com
Year Founded: 1994
Sales Range: $550-599.9 Million
Emp.: 108
Human Resource Management Services
N.A.I.C.S.: 541612
Jason Daley *(Mgr-Sls)*
Jill Eckart *(Mgr-Sls)*
Joseph Pigato *(Chief Innovation Officer)*
Jon Yee *(Dir-IT)*
Kayla Kanetake *(Mgr-Talent Dev)*
Michelle Leon-Guerrero *(Dir-Client Benefits)*
Jordan Conley *(CFO)*
Dan Riordan *(COO)*
Mark Synek *(Chief Sls Officer)*
Ben Godsey *(Pres & CEO)*
Rana Kanaan *(Chief Product Officer)*

Subsidiaries:

Hawaii Human Resources, Inc.   (1)
745 Fort St, Honolulu, HI 96813
Tel.: (808) 695-2222
Web Site: http://www.hihrhawaii.com
Payroll & Administrative Services
N.A.I.C.S.: 541611
John Demarco *(VP-Sls)*
Harry Byerly *(Pres)*
Trisha Nomura *(COO)*
Kalani Morse *(VP-HR)*

PROSHARES TRUST II
7272 Wisconsin Ave 21st Fl,
Bethesda, MD 20814
Tel.: (240) 497-6400   DE
Web Site: https://www.proshares.com
Rev.: $44,947,305
Assets: $3,944,857,469
Liabilities: $57,070,723
Net Worth: $3,887,786,746
Earnings: $95,781,413
Fiscal Year-end: 12/31/22
Investment Fund Management Services
N.A.I.C.S.: 523940
Edward J. Karpowicz *(CFO)*
Michael L. Sapir *(CEO)*
Eric Dash *(Chief Content & Comm Officer)*
Steve Vanourny *(Mng Dir & Head-Corp Dev, Strategy, and Plng)*

PROSKAUER ROSE LLP
11 Times Sq, New York, NY 10036
Tel.: (212) 969-3000
Web Site: http://www.proskauer.com
Year Founded: 1875
Sales Range: $600-649.9 Million
Emp.: 675
Law firm
N.A.I.C.S.: 541110
Elisabeth D. Bernard *(Dir-HR)*
Michael T. Mervis *(Partner)*
Robert Cleary *(Partner)*
Ronald Kornreich *(Partner)*
Kenneth Rubenstein *(Partner)*
Colleen M. Hart *(Partner)*
Liz Ricossa *(Mgr-Bus Dev)*
Christopher M. Wells *(Partner)*
Joanne S. Ollman *(Chief Pro Resources Officer)*
Christine A. Angie *(Dir-Lateral Partner Recruitment)*
Caroline K. Menes *(Officer-Legal Recruiting)*
Deborah Esposito *(Dir-Tech Support)*
Raymond Chow *(Engr-Desktop)*
Ann Barkey *(Head-HR)*
Jacob I. Friedman *(Partner)*
Melissa Santiago *(Mgr-Client Dev)*
Joan Falchi *(Mgr-Employee Rels)*
Peter M. Fass *(Partner)*
Allen I. Fagin *(Partner)*
Amanda Nussbaum *(Partner)*
Betsy Plevan *(Partner)*
Bruce E. Fader *(Partner)*
Carlos Martinez *(Partner)*
Charles S. Sims *(Partner)*
David Grunblatt *(Partner)*
Elise M. Bloom *(Partner)*
Frank Lopez *(Partner)*
Gregory Rasin *(Partner)*
Hank Goldsmith *(Partner)*
Ira G. Bogner *(Partner)*
John Gross *(Partner)*
Joseph Baumgarten *(Partner)*
Justin Breen *(Partner)*
Kristen Mathews *(Partner)*
Larry Sandak *(Partner)*
Lauren Boglivi *(Partner)*
Leibowitz Henry *(Partner)*
Lloyd B. Chinn *(Partner)*
Marc Persily *(Partner)*
Margaret Dale *(Partner)*
Ori Solomon *(Partner)*
Perry A. Cacace *(Partner)*
Steven L. Kirshenbaum *(Partner)*
Bradley I. Ruskin *(Partner)*
Dave Chiarello *(Supvr-Network Ops)*
Christopher E. Ondeck *(Partner)*
Joseph M. Leccese *(Chm)*
Brendan J. O'Rourke *(Partner & Co-Chm-Litigation)*
James R. Howe *(Partner-Merger & Acq-London)*
William Silverman *(Partner)*
Scott Bowman *(Partner)*
Guy Brenner *(Partner)*
Michael Ellis *(Partner)*
Ali Fawaz *(Partner)*
Robin Feiner *(Partner)*
Stephen Gruberg *(Partner)*
Russell Hirschhorn *(Partner)*
Vincenzo Lucibello *(Partner)*
Catherine Sear *(Partner)*
David Miller *(Partner-Tax)*
Joshua Newville *(Partner-Market Lending Comml Litigation & Securities Litigation)*
Bart Williams *(Partner-White Collar Defense & Sports Law)*
Manuel Cachan *(Partner-White Collar Defense & Sports Law)*
Claudia Alston *(Dir-Paralegal Recruiting)*
Seth Safra *(Partner-Employee Benefits & Executive Compensation Grp-Washington)*
Joanne Owen *(Partner-Private Equity Real Estate Grp-London)*
Jeffrey A. Horwitz *(Head-Private Equity Real Estate Grp)*
Mary Kuusisto *(Mng Partner-London)*
Vikki McKay *(Partner-Private Equity Real Estate Grp-London)*
Steven Davis *(Partner-Merger & Acq Grp-London)*
Matt Rees *(Partner-Merger & Acq-London)*
Bruno Bertrand-Delfau *(Partner-Merger & Acq-London)*
Alex Griffith *(Partner-Fin-London)*
Robert Gaut *(Partner-Tax-London)*
Joanne Southern *(CMO)*
Ben Davis *(Partner-Fin Practice-London)*
Steven Ellis *(Head-Multi Tranche Fin Grp)*
Eleanor Shanks *(Partner-London)*
Monica Arora *(Partner-Private Investment Funds Grp)*
Howard Beber *(Head-Private Investment Funds Grp)*
Chip Parsons *(Head-Private Equity Real Estate Funds Practice)*
Stephen Pevsner *(Partner-London)*
Jonathan O'Brien *(COO)*
William Tuttle *(Partner-Corp Dept-Washington)*
Pippa Bond *(Head-Capital Markets Grp-Global)*
Monica Shilling *(Head--Global)*
Karen Garnett *(Partner-Washington)*
Samuel Waldon *(Partner-Litigation-Washington)*
Ryan Blaney *(Partner-Health Care Practice)*
Rick Zall *(Partner & Chm-Health Care Dept & Indus Practice)*
Paul Hamburger *(Head-Washington)*
Jennifer Talbott *(Mgr-Media Rels)*
Warren Allan *(Partner-Global Private Funds Practice)*
Lily Cabianca *(Mgr-Comm)*
Leith Moghli *(Partner)*
Nigel van Zyl *(Head-Private Funds Grp)*
Warren Allen *(Partner)*
Kirsten Lapham *(Partner-Global Private Funds Practice-London)*
Nigel Van Zyl *(Head-Private Funds Grp)*

PROSOCO, INC.
3741 Greenway Cir, Lawrence, KS 66046
Tel.: (785) 865-4200
Web Site: http://www.prosoco.com
Year Founded: 1939
Sales Range: $25-49.9 Million
Emp.: 70
Chemical Preparations
N.A.I.C.S.: 325998
David Boyer *(Pres & CEO)*
Martha Lanpher *(CFO)*

Subsidiaries:

Problem Solving Company LLC   (1)
3741 Greenway Cir, Lawrence, KS 66046
Tel.: (785) 832-8000
Web Site: http://www.psc-solutions.com
Sales Range: $10-24.9 Million
Emp.: 60
Specialty Cleaning & Sanitation Preparations
N.A.I.C.S.: 424690
Gerald Boyer *(Founder & CEO)*

PROSOFT TECHNOLOGY GROUP INC.
2001 Butterfield Rd Ste 240, Downers Grove, IL 60515
Tel.: (630) 725-1800
Web Site:
http://www.prosoftcyberworld.com
Sales Range: $25-49.9 Million
Emp.: 300
Computer Related Consulting Services
N.A.I.C.S.: 541512
Rajeev Gupta *(Pres)*
Dan Dorsey *(Controller)*
Ashok Singh *(VP)*

PROSPECT AIRPORT SERVICES INC.
2130 S Wolf Rd, Des Plaines, IL 60018-1932
Tel.: (847) 299-3636   IL
Web Site: http://www.prospectair.com
Year Founded: 1966
Sales Range: $25-49.9 Million
Emp.: 1,800
Airports Flying Fields & Services
N.A.I.C.S.: 488190
Vicki Strobel *(Pres & CEO)*
Mary Strobel *(Sr VP)*

PROSPECT BANK
177 W Wood St PO Box 400, Paris, IL 61944
Tel.: (217) 465-4154   IL
Web Site:
    http://www.bankprospect.com
Year Founded: 1873
Banking Services
N.A.I.C.S.: 522110
W. Eric Volkmann *(Pres & CEO)*
Richard W. Thompson *(Sr VP & Chief Lending Officer)*
Carol A. Hughes *(Sr VP)*
Jenelle Adams *(Exec VP)*
Donna Grag *(Sr VP & COO)*
Brian Adams *(CIO)*
Sean Pruiett *(Info Sys Officer)*

PROSPECT EDUCATION LLC
750 Sandhill Rd Ste 100, Reno, NV 89521
Tel.: (775) 849-9900
Web Site:
    http://www.prospecteducation.com
Year Founded: 2003
Rev.: $22,400,000
Emp.: 283
School & Educational Services
N.A.I.C.S.: 611699
Michael L. Dawson *(Pres & CEO)*
Susan Hamilton *(Mgr-HR)*
Brandi Anderson *(Mgr-Mktg)*

PROSPECT ENTERPRISES INC.
550 Ceres Ave, Los Angeles, CA 90013
Tel.: (213) 612-0350
Web Site:
    http://www.americanfish.com
Rev.: $209,705,000
Emp.: 125
Fish, Fresh
N.A.I.C.S.: 424460
Veronica McDiarmid *(Dir-HR & Risk Mgmt)*

Subsidiaries:

Southwind Foods LLC   (1)
2900 Ayers Ave, Los Angeles, CA 90023
Tel.: (323) 262-8222
Web Site: https://www.southwindfoods.com
Rev.: $36,200,000
Emp.: 36
Fish & Seafoods
N.A.I.C.S.: 424460
Jim Elie *(Controller)*

Subsidiary (Domestic):

Caito Fisheries Inc.   (2)
19400 S Harbor Dr, Fort Bragg, CA 95437
Tel.: (707) 964-6368
Web Site: https://www.caitofisheries.com
Rev.: $15,100,000
Emp.: 100
Prepared Fresh Fish
N.A.I.C.S.: 311710
Joseph A. Caito *(Pres)*

PROSPECT GLOBAL RESOURCES INC.
1401 17th St Ste 1550, Denver, CO 80202
Tel.: (303) 990-8444   NV
Web Site: http://www.prospectgri.com
Year Founded: 2008

PROSPECT GLOBAL RESOURCES INC.

U.S. PRIVATE

PROSPECT GLOBAL RESOURCES INC.—(Continued)
Emp.: 8
Potash Mining
N.A.I.C.S.: 212390
Barry A. Munitz (Chm)
Gregory M. Dangler (Pres, CEO & CFO)

PROSPECT HILL GROWTH PARTNERS, L.P.
230 Third Ave, 6th F, Waltham, MA 02451
Tel.: (617) 753-1100   DE
Web Site: http://www.prospecthillgrowth.com
Year Founded: 1995
Privater Equity Firm
N.A.I.C.S.: 523999
Jeffrey J. Teschke (Partner)
Lewis D. Gold (Operating Partner)
Jeffrey Miller (Partner)
Joseph M. Fortunato (Operating Partner)
Kyle Casella (Partner)
Lewis Gold (Operating Partner)
Philip Damiano (Operating Partner)
Mitchell Eisenberg (Operating Partner)
Adam L. Suttin (Mng Partner)
William E. Watts (Partner)

Subsidiaries:

Acxion Foodservice (1)
1701 Crossroads Dr, Odenton, MD 21113
Tel.: (410) 381-1239
Web Site: https://acxion.com
Foodservice Sales & Marketing Services
N.A.I.C.S.: 541890

Subsidiary (Domestic):

Advantage Waypoint LLC (2)
2900 Collier Canyon Rd, Livermore, CA 94551-9224
Tel.: (813) 358-5851
Web Site: http://www.asmwaypoint.com
Sales & Marketing Services
N.A.I.C.S.: 541613
David Divelbiss (Mgr)

KeyImpact Sales & Systems, Inc. (2)
1701 Crossroads Dr, Odenton, MD 21113
Tel.: (410) 381-1239
Web Site: http://www.kisales.com
Independent Food Serive Sales & Marketing Services
N.A.I.C.S.: 311999
Dan Cassidy (CEO)
Sharon Bass (Mgr-Education Segment)
Erik Cook (Mgr-Warehouse)
Brenda Lotesta (CMO)
Randy Wieland (Pres)
Colin Quinn (CFO)
Carl Benkovich (COO)
Neil Johnson (CIO)
Rob Monroe (Exec VP-Client Mgmt)
Butch Cassidy (Sr VP-Sysco Sls Div)
Joe Hargadon (Sr VP-Field Sls)
Rob Bull (Dir-Market-Las Vegas)

Cycle Gear Inc. (1)
4705 Industrial Way, Benicia, CA 94510
Tel.: (707) 747-5053
Web Site: http://www.cyclegear.com
Motorcycle Parts & Accessories
N.A.I.C.S.: 441227

EbLens LP (1)
299 Industrial Ln, Torrington, CT 06790
Tel.: (860) 489-3073
Web Site: http://www.eblens.com
Casual Clothing & Footwear Mfr
N.A.I.C.S.: 458110
Richard Seaman (CEO)

Motis Brands, Inc. (1)
N102 W19400 Willow Creek Wy, Germantown, WI 53022
Tel.: (888) 651-3431
Web Site: https://motisbrands.com
Online Retailer of Loading, Hauling & Transportation Products

N.A.I.C.S.: 336999

Subsidiary (Domestic):

Cargo Equipment Corp. (2)
640 Church Rd, Elgin, IL 60123
Tel.: (847) 741-7272
Web Site: http://www.cargoequipmentcorp.com
Rev: $6,040,000
Emp.: 8
Transportation Equipment & Supplies, except Motor Vehicle, Merchant Whslr
N.A.I.C.S.: 423860
Jeff Iden (Pres)

Shoe Sensation, Inc. (1)
253 America Pl, Jeffersonville, IN 47130
Tel.: (812) 288-7659
Web Site: http://www.shoesensation.com
Emp.: 700
Shoe Store Operator
N.A.I.C.S.: 458210
Dave Schoengart (Sr VP-Ops)
Mike Zawoysky (CEO)

The Kyjen Company, LLC (1)
7337 S Revere Pkwy, Englewood, CO 80112
Tel.: (303) 792-9600
Web Site: http://www.outwardhound.com
Dog Toys Mfr & Distr
N.A.I.C.S.: 339930
Michael Black (CEO)

Subsidiary (Domestic):

Dublin Dog Company, Inc. (2)
1435 W Morehead St Ste 120, Charlotte, NC 28208
Web Site: http://www.dublin-dog.outwardhound.com
Pet & Pet Supplies Stores
N.A.I.C.S.: 459910

Petstages, Inc. (2)
333 Skokie Blvd, Northbrook, IL 60062-1621
Web Site: http://www.petstages.com
Pet Products Mfr & Distr
N.A.I.C.S.: 459910

Sentiments Inc. (2)
5635 Smithway St, Los Angeles, CA 90040
Tel.: (323) 843-2080
Web Site: http://www.sentimentshome.com
Home & Pet Decorative Pillows, Throw Blankets & Table Linens Products Mfr & Distr
N.A.I.C.S.: 423920

The NutraSweet Company (1)
222 Merchandise Mart Plz Ste 936, Chicago, IL 60654-1001   (100%)
Tel.: (312) 873-5000
Web Site: http://www.nutrasweet.com
Sales Range: $75-99.9 Million
Low Calorie Sweetener Mfr
N.A.I.C.S.: 325199
William L. DeFer (CEO)
True Knowles (Chm)

Walker Edison Furniture Company LLC (1)
1553 West 9000 S, West Jordan, UT 84088
Tel.: (801) 433-3008
Web Site: http://www.walkeredison.com
Furniture Merchant Whslr
N.A.I.C.S.: 423210

PROSPECT PARTNERS, LLC
200 W Madison St Ste 2710, Chicago, IL 60606
Tel.: (312) 782-7400   DE
Web Site: http://www.prospect-partners.com
Privater Equity Firm
N.A.I.C.S.: 523999
Louis W. Kenter (Founder & Principal)
Maneesh K. Chawla (Principal)
Erik E. Maurer (Principal)
Lauren B. Sinai (Dir-Mktg)
Richard C. Tuttle (Principal)
Bill Lump (CFO & COO)
Brett Holcomb (VP)

Subsidiaries:

Linkage Inc. (1)
200 Wheeler Rd, Burlington, MA 01803
Tel.: (781) 402-5400
Web Site: http://www.linkageinc.com
Sales Range: $50-74.9 Million
Emp.: 95
Business Consulting Services
N.A.I.C.S.: 541611
Richard Pumfrey (COO)
Jennifer McCollum (CEO)
Mark Hannum (Chief Res Officer)
Maria Howard (Chief Revenue Officer)
Kristen Howe (Chief Product Officer)
Jillian Ihsanullah (Chief Experience Officer)

PROSPECT PROPERTY GROUP
477 Commerce Way Ste 115, Longwood, FL 32750
Tel.: (407) 712-2001
Web Site: http://www.prospectproperties.com
Year Founded: 1994
Sales Range: $1-9.9 Million
Real Estate Investment & Management
N.A.I.C.S.: 523999
Alexander D. Walker (Founding Partner)
John Fossum (VP-Residential Mgmt)
Shana Gerwen (Mgr-Residential Mgmt)
Tim Moxley (VP-Land Dev)
Larry D. Kiem (CFO)
Frank Tetel (VP-Underwriting & Acq)
Jackie Williams (Dir-Sls)
Mark C. Filburn (Founding Partner)

PROSPECT RESEARCH & DEVELOPMENT STRATEGIES
173 Washington St, Freeport, PA 16229
Tel.: (724) 295-0679
Web Site: https://www.researchprospects.com
Year Founded: 1999
Prospect Research & Development Services
N.A.I.C.S.: 541720

PROSPECT TRANSPORTATION INC.
630 Industrial Rd, Carlstadt, NJ 07072
Tel.: (201) 933-9999
Web Site: http://www.prospect-trans.com
Rev.: $19,000,000
Emp.: 60
Petroleum Haulage, Local
N.A.I.C.S.: 484220
Vin Zupanovich (Supvr-Dispatch)
Ken Hugo (Mgr-Maintenance & Facilities)
Donald Peck (Mgr-Safety)
Melissa Eichholz (Pres)
Jack McNamara (VP-Mktg & Sls)
Patricia Eichholz (Pres)
Bob McCloughy (Controller)

PROSPECTSPLUS!, INC.
10510 Portal Crossing Ste 107, Bradenton, FL 34211
Tel.: (941) 723-2400
Web Site: http://www.prospectsplus.com
Year Founded: 1994
Sales Range: $1-9.9 Million
Emp.: 20
Real Estate Marketing & Advertising Services
N.A.I.C.S.: 541890
Jim Morton (Pres)
Jim Studebaker (Dir-Ops)
Julie Escobar (Dir-Corp Mktg)
Ramona Williams (Mgr-Inside Sls)

John Studebaker (CTO)
Jason Waid (Dir-Creative Print)
Jeff Flood (Mgr-Production)

PROSPECTUS BERCO
840 William Ln, Reading, PA 19604-1551
Tel.: (610) 372-4637   PA
Web Site: http://www.proberco.org
Year Founded: 1977
Sales Range: $10-24.9 Million
Emp.: 550
Disability Assistance Services
N.A.I.C.S.: 624120
Susan Stalnecker (Dir-Dev)
Jody H. Wagner (Exec Dir)

PROSPER BUSINESS DEVELOPMENT CORP.
400 W Wilson Bridge Ste 200, Worthington, OH 43085
Tel.: (614) 846-0146   OH
Web Site: http://www.goprosper.com
Year Founded: 1990
Emp.: 15
Business Intelligence & Software Applications Developer
N.A.I.C.S.: 513210
Philip Rist (Principal)
Gary Drenik (Founder)
Jim Crawford (VP-Ops)

PROSPER MARKETPLACE, INC.
221 Main St 3rd Fl, San Francisco, CA 94105
Tel.: (415) 593-5400   DE
Web Site: https://www.prosper.com
Year Founded: 2005
Rev.: $199,881,000
Assets: $1,128,404,000
Liabilities: $1,476,410,000
Net Worth: ($348,006,000)
Earnings: $23,232,000
Emp.: 468
Fiscal Year-end: 12/31/22
Peer-to-Peer Lending Marketplace
N.A.I.C.S.: 522310
David Kimball (Chm & CEO)
Usama Ashraf (Pres & CFO)
Jared Brown (VP-People & Places)
Haiyan Huang (Head-Credit Risk)
Don Au Yeung (VP-Fin)
Edward R. Buell III (Chief Compliance Officer, Gen Counsel & Sec)

Subsidiaries:

BillGuard, Inc. (1)
221 Main St Ste 300, San Francisco, CA 94105
Tel.: (888) 483-7783
Web Site: http://www.prosper.com
Mortgage Loan Broker Services
N.A.I.C.S.: 522310

Prosper Funding LLC (1)
221 Main St 3rd Fl, San Francisco, CA 94105
Tel.: (415) 593-5400
Web Site: https://www.prosper.com
Rev.: $63,224,000
Assets: $448,583,000
Liabilities: $421,868,000
Net Worth: $26,715,000
Earnings: ($2,066,000)
Emp.: 403
Fiscal Year-end: 12/31/2023
Peer-To-Peer Online Credit Platform
N.A.I.C.S.: 513199
David Kimball (Pres & CEO)
Usama Ashraf (CFO & Treas)

PROSPERA FINANCIAL SERVICES
5429 LBJ Fwy Ste 400, Dallas, TX 75240
Tel.: (972) 581-3000

Web Site:
http://www.prosperafinancial.com
Rev.: $14,430,081
Emp.: 50
Security Brokers & Dealers
N.A.I.C.S.: 523150
David Stringer (Pres)
Abel Garcia (Dir-Compliance)
Barbara Hale (Sr VP-Ops)
Richard Pascuzzi (Principal & VP)
Tim Edwards (Principal & VP-Sls & Mktg)

PROSPERITY GROUP HOLDINGS, LP
1 Penn Plz Ste 3806, New York, NY 10119
Tel.: (332) 282-2099
Web Site:
https://www.prosperitylife.com
Emp.: 100
Insurance Services
N.A.I.C.S.: 524298
Nicholas Von Moltke (Pres & CEO)
Ann-Kelley Winn (Chief Compliance Officer, Gen Counsel & Sec)
Zachary Jones (CFO)
Drew Westall (Treas)

Subsidiaries:

SBLI USA Mutual Life Insurance Company, Inc. (1)
100 W 33, New York, NY 10001-2320
Tel.: (212) 356-0300
Web Site: http://www.sbliusa.com
Sales Range: $250-299.9 Million
Emp.: 250
Insurance Services
N.A.I.C.S.: 524113
Robert Damante (CFO & Exec VP)
Ralph Meola (Chief Acctg Officer & Sr VP)
Evelyn Murphy (Chm)

Subsidiary (Domestic):

S.USA Life Insurance Company, Inc. (2)
PO Box 1050, Newark, NJ 07101
Tel.: (212) 356-0327
Insurance Brokerage Services
N.A.I.C.S.: 524210

Subsidiary (Domestic):

National Western Life Group, Inc. (3)
10801 N Mopac Expy Bldg 3, Austin, TX 78759-5415
Tel.: (512) 836-1010
Web Site:
https://www.nationalwesternlife.com
Rev.: $558,397,000
Assets: $13,100,227,000
Liabilities: $11,093,016,000
Net Worth: $2,007,211,000
Earnings: $101,144,000
Emp.: 267
Fiscal Year-end: 12/31/2022
Offices of Other Holding Companies
N.A.I.C.S.: 551112

Subsidiary (Domestic):

National Western Life Insurance Company (4)
10801 N Mopac Expy Bldg 3, Austin, TX 78759-5415
Tel.: (512) 836-1010
Web Site:
https://www.nationalwesternlife.com
Emp.: 400
Fiscal Year-end: 12/31/2014
Life Insurance & Annuities Products & Services
N.A.I.C.S.: 524113

Subsidiary (Domestic):

N.I.S. Financial Services, Inc. (5)
500 E 9th St, Kansas City, MO 64106-2627
Tel.: (816) 842-8685
Rev.: $10,045,849
Emp.: 10
Mutual Fund Investment Services
N.A.I.C.S.: 523999

NWL Financial, Inc. (5)
850 E Anderson Ln, Austin, TX 78752 (100%)
Tel.: (512) 836-1010
Web Site:
http://www.nationalwesternlife.com
Sales Range: $300-349.9 Million
Emp.: 290
Investment
N.A.I.C.S.: 523999

NWL Services, Inc. (5)
850 E Anderson Ln, Austin, TX 78752 (100%)
Tel.: (512) 836-1010
Sales Range: $50-74.9 Million
Emp.: 300
Life Insurance Carrier Services
N.A.I.C.S.: 524113
Brian M. Pribyl (Treas)
Kitty Nelson (Pres & CEO)

Ozark National Life Insurance Company (5)
500 E 9th St, Kansas City, MO 64106-2627
Tel.: (816) 842-6300
Web Site: https://www.ozark-national.com
Rev.: $102,499,488
Emp.: 80
Fire Insurance Services
N.A.I.C.S.: 524113
Charles N. Sharpe Jr. (Chm & Pres)

PROST BUILDERS INC.
3617 Rte CC, Jefferson City, MO 65109
Tel.: (573) 635-0211
Web Site:
http://www.prostbuilders.com
Sales Range: $10-24.9 Million
Emp.: 25
Commercial & Office Building Construction Services
N.A.I.C.S.: 236220
Vaughn X. Prost (Owner & Pres)
Rich Northeimer (Project Mgr)
Pam Long (Sr VP-Ops)

PROSTAR COMPUTER, INC.
837 S Lawson St, City of Industry, CA 91748
Tel.: (626) 839-6472
Web Site: http://www.pro-star.com
Year Founded: 1992
Sales Range: $10-24.9 Million
Emp.: 25
Retailer of Computers
N.A.I.C.S.: 423430
Terry Wang (Mgr-Sls & Inventory)

PROSTROLLO ALL-AMERICAN AUTO MALL
1001 S Washington Ave, Madison, SD 57042
Tel.: (605) 256-9111 SD
Web Site:
http://www.prostrolloautomall.com
Year Founded: 1957
Sales Range: $25-49.9 Million
Emp.: 75
Retailer of New & Used Automobiles
N.A.I.C.S.: 441110
Pat Prostrollo (Pres)
Roger Eich (Controller)
David Tischke (Mgr-Fin)

PROSTROLLO MOTOR SALES, INC.
500 4th St NE, Huron, SD 57350-1415
Tel.: (605) 352-6411 SD
Web Site: http://www.prostrollo.com
Year Founded: 1982
Sales Range: $100-124.9 Million
Emp.: 56
Retailer of New & Used Automobiles
N.A.I.C.S.: 441110
John Deniger (Pres)
Doug Chilson (Gen Mgr)
Rick Sabers (Mgr-Sls)

PROSUM, INC.
2201 Park Pl Ste 102, El Segundo, CA 90245
Tel.: (310) 426-0600
Web Site: http://www.prosum.com
Year Founded: 1996
Sales Range: $10-24.9 Million
Emp.: 85
IT Consulting Services
N.A.I.C.S.: 541690
Ravi Chatwani (CEO)
Rick Tyner (Pres-Bus Dev)

PROSYNC TECHNOLOGY GROUP LLC
6021 University Blvd Ste 300, Ellicott City, MD 21043
Tel.: (410) 772-7969
Web Site: http://www.prosync.com
Year Founded: 2000
Sales Range: $1-9.9 Million
Custom Computer Programming Services
N.A.I.C.S.: 541512
Michael Lessing (Founder & CEO)
Scott Dudash (COO)

PROTAMEEN CHEMICALS INC.
375 Minnisink Rd, Totowa, NJ 07511
Tel.: (973) 256-4374
Web Site: http://www.protameen.com
Year Founded: 1969
Sales Range: $10-24.9 Million
Emp.: 30
Mfr of Industrial Inorganic Chemicals
N.A.I.C.S.: 325180
Emmanuel Balasmides (Pres)
John Carola (Mgr-Domestic Sls)

PROTEA BIOSCIENCES GROUP, INC.
1311 Pineview Dr Ste 501, Morgantown, WV 26505
Tel.: (304) 292-2226 DE
Web Site: https://www.proteabio.com
Year Founded: 2005
PRGB—(OTCBB)
Sales Range: $1-9.9 Million
Emp.: 25
Pharmaceutical Preparation Mfr
N.A.I.C.S.: 325412
David Halverson (Chief Bus Officer & VP)
Matthew Powell (Chief Science Officer, Chief Scientific Officer & Dir-R&D)
Stanley Hostler (Sec & VP)
Stephen Turner (Chm & CEO)
Haddon Goodman (VP-Corporate Development)

PROTECH SOLUTIONS, INC.
303 W Capitol Ave, Little Rock, AR 72201
Tel.: (501) 687-2400
Web Site:
http://www.protechsolutions.com
Year Founded: 1995
Sales Range: $10-24.9 Million
Emp.: 70
Information Technology Solutions
N.A.I.C.S.: 541511
Satish Garimalla (CEO)
Arellia Williams (Coord-Mktg)
Shiva Duvvuru (CFO)
Debra Jackson (Project Mgr)

PROTEGRITY HOLDINGS, INC
260 Wekiva Springs Rd, Longwood, FL 32779
Tel.: (407) 788-1717
Year Founded: 1997
Sales Range: $25-49.9 Million
Emp.: 325
Insurance Services

N.A.I.C.S.: 524210
Emma Apablaza (Controller)

PROTEIN HOLDINGS INC.
10 Moulton St, Portland, ME 04101-5039
Tel.: (207) 771-0965 DE
Year Founded: 1997
Sales Range: $10-24.9 Million
Emp.: 10
Holding Company
N.A.I.C.S.: 311511

PROTEIN POLYMER TECHNOLOGIES, INC.
11494 Sorrento Valley Rd, San Diego, CA 92121
Tel.: (858) 558-6064 DE
Web Site: http://www.ppti.com
Year Founded: 1988
Sales Range: Less than $1 Million
Emp.: 2
Biomaterials Developer
N.A.I.C.S.: 325412
James B. McCarthy (Interim CEO)
Joseph Cappello (CTO, VP-R&D & Dir-Clinical Res)
Janis A. Neves (Sec)
J. Thomas Parmeter (Chm)

PROTEIN SOLUTIONS, LLC
3800 E 32nd St, Joplin, MO 64804
Tel.: (417) 624-4966 MO
Web Site: http://www.3dcorpsol.com
Year Founded: 2004
Sales Range: $1-9.9 Million
Emp.: 70
Pet Food Mfr
N.A.I.C.S.: 311111
Mike Livingston (Plant Mgr)

PROTEIN SOURCES, LLP.
503 Silver St E, Mapleton, MN 56065
Tel.: (507) 524-4511
Web Site:
http://www.proteinsourcesmanagement.com
Year Founded: 1999
Sales Range: $10-24.9 Million
Emp.: 77
Swine Production & Financial Management Services
N.A.I.C.S.: 311119
John Fitzsimmons (Partner)
John Hollerich (Partner)
Bron Scherer (Partner)
Paul FitzSimmons (Partner)
William FitzSimmons (Partner)
Richard FitzSimmons (Partner)
Pat FitzSimmons (Partner)
Dan Sohre (Partner)

PROTEINONE
6931 Arlington Rd, Bethesda, MD 20814
Tel.: (301) 657-1405
Web Site: http://www.proteinone.com
Rev.: $900,000
Emp.: 16
Research & Development in the Physical Engineering & Life Sciences
N.A.I.C.S.: 541715
Peter Shin (Founder & Chm)
Hui Ge (VP & Chief Scientific Officer)

PROTEINTECH GROUP, INC.
5400 Pearl St Ste 300, Rosemont, IL 60018
Tel.: (312) 455-8498 IL
Web Site: http://www.ptglab.com
Year Founded: 2001
Clinical Reagent Mfr & Whslr
N.A.I.C.S.: 325413
Jason Jianxun Li (CEO)
Frank Schestag (Comml Dir-Europe)
Jeff Lee (COO)

PROTEINTECH GROUP, INC. (Continued)

Subsidiaries:

HumanZyme, Inc. (1)
2201 W Campbell Park Dr Ste 24, Chicago, IL 60612
Tel.: (312) 738-0127
Web Site: http://www.humanzyme.com
Sales Range: $10-24.9 Million
Emp.: 45
Recombinant Human Proteins Mfr
N.A.I.C.S.: 325414
Mark Azam (VP-R&D & Ops)

PROTEL COMMUNICATIONS, INC.
13851 Danielson St, Poway, CA 92064
Tel.: (858) 218-2000 CA
Web Site: http://www.goprotel.com
Year Founded: 1997
Sales Range: $1-9.9 Million
Emp.: 25
Telecommunications Resellers
N.A.I.C.S.: 517121
Jerry Harder (CTO)
David Krietzberg (CFO)
Michael Promotico (CEO)

Subsidiaries:

Xtelesis Corp. (1)
800 Airport Blvd Ste 417, Burlingame, CA 94010
Tel.: (650) 239-1400
Web Site: http://www.xtelesis.com
Sales Range: $1-9.9 Million
Emp.: 30
Telephone Communications
N.A.I.C.S.: 517810
Scott Strochak (CEO)
Allen Hebron (Engr-VOIP)
Dan Helvering (Acct Mgr)
Adam Smith (Dir-Sls)
Aaron Hancock (Dir-Network Ops)
Alan Steele (Mgr-Implementations Sys)
Alicia Steward (Acct Mgr)
Anna Kraus (Mgr-Acct & Renewals)
Avinash Kumar (Engr-Tier 1 Support)
Brandon Gregrich (Engr-Microsoft Sys)
Brea Hronek (Dir-Ops & Carrier Svcs)
Butch Brown (Dir-Customer Support)
Dave Maughan (Acct Mgr)
David Anderson (Sr Acct Exec)
Deb Howe (Coord-Svc)
Dennis May (Dir-Implementation Svcs)
John Durkin (CFO)
Eric Hoy (VP-Data Svcs)
Marty Paris (VP-Customer Experience)
Christoph Pluchar (CQO)

PROTERRA ADVERTISING
5055 Keller Springs Rd Ste 560, Addison, TX 75001
Tel.: (972) 732-9211
Web Site: http://www.proterraadvertising.com
Year Founded: 1993
Rev.: $29,500,000
Emp.: 8
Advetising Agency
N.A.I.C.S.: 541810
Danny Sanchez (Pres & CEO)
Lisa De Leon (Pres & Acc Exec)

PROTERRA INVESTMENT PARTNERS LP
33 S 6th St Ste 4100, Minneapolis, MN 55402
Tel.: (612) 257-7900 DE
Web Site: http://www.proterrapartners.com
Year Founded: 2015
Rev.: $2,147,000,000
Emp.: 49
Privater Equity Firm
N.A.I.C.S.: 523999
Rich Gammill (Mng Partner-Food)
Brent Bechtle (Partner-Agriculture)
Ned Dau (Chief Mktg Officer & Head-IR)

Tom Howell (Mng Dir-Credit)
Rob Hutter (Mng Dir-Agriculture)
Andrzej Kabarowski (Mng Dir & Head-Risk & ESG)
Nannette Kordus (Mng Dir-HR)
Michael Lesage (Mng Dir-Agriculture)
Jonathan Logan (Mng Dir-Credit)
Eugenio Meschini (Mng Dir-Agriculture)
Jim Sayre (Partner-Food)
Matthew Swanson (Mng Dir & Deputy Gen Counsel-Credit)
Matt Waller (COO-Fin & Ops)
James Warren (Chief Compliance Officer & Gen Counsel-Legal)

PROTEUS B2B
3615 29th St SE, Grand Rapids, MI 49512
Tel.: (616) 235-1122
Web Site: http://www.proteusb2b.com
Sales Range: $1-9.9 Million
Emp.: 14
Advertising & Marketing Services
N.A.I.C.S.: 541810
Galen De Young (Mng Dir)
Brian Vander Maas (Dir-Art)

PROTEUS FUND
15 Research Dr Ste B, Amherst, MA 01002
Tel.: (413) 256-0349 MA
Web Site: http://www.proteusfund.org
Year Founded: 1994
Sales Range: $10-24.9 Million
Emp.: 47
Grantmaking Services
N.A.I.C.S.: 813211
Paul A. Di Donato (Pres)
Beery Adams Jimenez (Mgr-Grants)
Muthoni Magua (CFO)
Dini Merz (Dir-Peace & Security Program)
Jill Price Marshall (COO)

PROTEXT MOBILITY, INC.
16885 River Birch Cir, Delray Beach, FL 33445
Tel.: (800) 215-4212 DE
Web Site: http://www.protextmobility.net
Year Founded: 2001
Sales Range: Less than $1 Million
Emp.: 1
Protection & Family Safety Mobile Applications Software
N.A.I.C.S.: 513210
David M. Lewis (Exec Dir)
Steve Berman (Interim CEO)

PROTHRO CHEVROLET BUICK GMC
452 N Brooks St, Manning, SC 29102-3323
Tel.: (803) 433-2535
Web Site: http://www.prothrochevy.com
Sales Range: $10-24.9 Million
Emp.: 32
Car Whslr
N.A.I.C.S.: 441110
Lannes Prothro (Pres)
William Prothro (VP)

PROTOCALL NJ INC.
1 Mall Dr Ste 203, Cherry Hill, NJ 08002
Tel.: (856) 667-7500
Web Site: http://www.protocallstaffing.com
Year Founded: 1965
Sales Range: $75-99.9 Million
Emp.: 1,900
Temporary Help Service
N.A.I.C.S.: 561320

Janis Lebude (Pres)
Darlene Melfi (VP-Health Care Ops)

PROTOCOL INC.
2805 Fruitville Rd, Sarasota, FL 34237
Tel.: (941) 906-9000 MA
Web Site: http://www.apaccustomerservices.com
Year Founded: 1998
Sales Range: $150-199.9 Million
Emp.: 2,200
Direct Marketing Services
N.A.I.C.S.: 561499
Dan Sullivan (Sr VP-Relationship Mgmt)

Subsidiaries:

Protocol Global Solutions (1)
1000 Corporate Blvd Ste B, Aurora, IL 60505-6401
Tel.: (630) 820-4000
Rev.: $4,300,000
Emp.: 131
Business Services
N.A.I.C.S.: 561499

PROTOM INTERNATIONAL, INC.
1100 Parker Square Ste 230, Flower Mound, TX 75028
Tel.: (972) 410-3551
Web Site: http://www.protominternational.com
Year Founded: 2008
Sales Range: $25-49.9 Million
General Healthcare Services
N.A.I.C.S.: 621610
Nancy E. Corbett (Sr VP-Ops)
Stephen L. Spotts (Pres & CEO)
Vahagn Nazaryan (Sr VP-Physics)
James P. Bennett (CFO)

PROTON ENERGY SYSTEMS, INC.
10 Technology Dr, Wallingford, CT 06492
Tel.: (203) 678-2000 DE
Web Site: http://www.protononsite.com
Year Founded: 1996
Sales Range: $25-49.9 Million
Emp.: 70
Proton Exchange Membrane Electrochemical Systems & Hydrogen Generators Designer & Mfr
N.A.I.C.S.: 333611
Sheldon A. Paul (CFO)
David T. Bow (Sr VP-Bus Dev)
Anders Soreng (CTO)
John A. Zagaja III (Sr VP-Engrg)

PROTOTYPE INDUSTRIES, INC.
1545 26th St Ste 200, Santa Monica, CA 90404
Tel.: (310) 255-9987 CA
Web Site: http://www.prototypeindustries.com
Year Founded: 1988
Sales Range: $1-9.9 Million
Emp.: 25
Publisher of Catalogs & Technical Manuals for Commercial Airlines & System/Equipment Manufacturers
N.A.I.C.S.: 513199
Irene Grigoriadis (CEO)

PROTOTYPE MACHINE CO. INC.
2119 FM 1626, Manchaca, TX 78652
Tel.: (512) 282-1590
Web Site: http://www.randolphaustin.com
Rev.: $12,250,543

Emp.: 5
Measuring & Dispensing Pumps
N.A.I.C.S.: 332710

PROTOTYPE PLASTICS, LLC
3637 131st Ave N, Clearwater, FL 33762
Tel.: (727) 572-0803 FL
Web Site: http://www.pplasticsllc.com
Year Founded: 1978
Sales Range: $1-9.9 Million
Emp.: 15
Plastics Product Mfr
N.A.I.C.S.: 326199
Mark Beane (Gen Mgr)
David Balliett (Mgr-Production)

PROTOTYPES
1000 N Alameda St Ste 390, Los Angeles, CA 90012
Tel.: (213) 542-3838 CA
Web Site: http://www.prototypes.org
Year Founded: 1986
Sales Range: $10-24.9 Million
Emp.: 284
Mental Health Services
N.A.I.C.S.: 621420
Cassandra Loch (Pres & CEO)
April Wilson (VP-Residential)
Nial Stimson (VP-Bus Dev)
Ashley Hernandez (Mgr-Comm & Dev)
Ann McClanathan (Chm)
Ron Burkhardt (Sec)
Jim Quinn (Treas)
Michael Kemp (Vice Chm)
Levi Martin (CFO)
Amy Carlton (Dir-Individual Giving)

PROTRANS INTERNATIONAL INC.
PO Box 42069, Indianapolis, IN 46242
Tel.: (317) 240-4100
Web Site: http://www.protransintl.com
Sales Range: $10-24.9 Million
Emp.: 150
Foreign Freight Forwarding
N.A.I.C.S.: 488510
Craig Roeder (Founder)

PROTRANSPORT-1
720 Portal St, Cotati, CA 94931
Web Site: http://www.protransport-1.com
Year Founded: 2000
Sales Range: $25-49.9 Million
Emp.: 379
Health Care Transportation Services
N.A.I.C.S.: 485991
Rick Gillespie (Controller)
Dennis Robinson (Exec VP)
Mike Sechrist (Co-Founder & CEO)
Heidi Runyon (VP-Billing & Collections)
Elena Whorton (Co-Founder & Pres)
Kevin Gorman (CFO)
Sira Mohamed (Dir-Medical Event Plng)
David Ott (Exec Dir-Clinical Ops)
Cynthia Caldwell (Mgr-Quality & Compliance)

Subsidiaries:

PRN Ambulance, LLC (1)
8928 Sepulveda Blvd, North Hills, CA 91343
Tel.: (818) 810-3600
Web Site: http://www.prnambulance.com
Ambulance Service
N.A.I.C.S.: 621910
Avo Avetisyan (Founder & Pres)
Pete Avetisyan (VP)
Victoria Tatloyan (Gen Mgr)
Paul Scarborough (Exec VP)
Shant Shekherdimian (Dir-Med)
Pete Sturn (Dir-IT)
Alfred Jacobs (Mgr-Ops-South Svc Area)
Ryan Ferguson (Mgr-Ops-North Svc Area)

COMPANIES

Ian Wilson (Coord-Critical Care)
Christine Miyahara (Mgr-Comm)
Bruce West (Mgr-HR)
Ted Milano (Mgr-Risk & Safety)
Josh Parker (Mgr-Training)
Michael Gorman (Acting CEO & COO)
Kevin Gorman (CFO)
Kathleen Loya (Chief Compliance Officer)
Heidi Runyon (VP-Billing & Collections)
Dave Lawson (Exec VP-Ops)
Dennis Robinson (Exec VP)
David Odd (Exec Dir-Clinical Ops)
Carly Clements (Dir-Mktg Comm)
Sira Mohamed (Dir-Medical Event Plng)
Stephanie Monroy (Dir-Scheduling)
Cynthia Caldwell (Mgr-Quality & Compliance)

PROTREND LIMITED
6409 Gayhart St, Commerce, CA 90040
Tel.: (323) 832-9323
Rev.: $12,000,000
Emp.: 3
Mfr of Women's & Juniors' Blouses
N.A.I.C.S.: 315250
Peter Kim (Chm)

PROTRIALS RESEARCH, INC.
800 W California Ave Ste 110, Sunnyvale, CA 94086
Tel.: (650) 864-9180 CA
Web Site: http://www.protrials.com
Year Founded: 1996
Sales Range: $10-24.9 Million
Emp.: 75
Business Consultants
N.A.I.C.S.: 541618
Janie Johnson (Dir-Clinical Ops)
Connie Cyras (Dir-Project Mgmt)

PROV INTERNATIONAL, INC.
502 N Rocky Point Dr Ste 896, Tampa, FL 33607
Tel.: (813) 281-2959
Web Site: http://www.provintl.com
Year Founded: 2003
Sales Range: $10-24.9 Million
Emp.: 300
Information Technology Consulting
N.A.I.C.S.: 541690
Ajit Nair (Founder, Chm-Supervisory Bd & Pres-Americas)
Marcus Leeb (CEO)

PROVANA LLC
901 Warrenville Rd Ste 525, Lisle, IL 60532
Tel.: (331) 229-8642
Web Site: http://www.provana.com
Year Founded: 2011
Business Process Outsourcing Services
N.A.I.C.S.: 522320
Sandeep Bhargava (Co-Founder & CEO)
Karen Powell (Co-Founder & Exec VP)
Sean Clark (Sr VP-Platforms)

Subsidiaries:
TriVium Systems, Inc. (1)
1865 NW 169th Pl Ste 210, Beaverton, OR 97006-7310
Tel.: (503) 439-9338
Web Site: http://www.triviumsys.com
Computer & Computer Peripheral Equipment & Software Merchant Whslr
N.A.I.C.S.: 423430
Mathews Manaloor (CEO)

PROVEN INC.
9444 Waples St Ste 440, San Diego, CA 92121
Tel.: (858) 412-1111
Web Site: http://www.proveninc.com
Year Founded: 2007
Sales Range: $1-9.9 Million
Emp.: 117
Human Resource Consulting Services
N.A.I.C.S.: 541612
Ron Bell (Mng Dir-San Diego)
Poya Hooshim (Sr Mng Partner-Los Angeles)

PROVEST LLC
4520 Seedling Cir, Tampa, FL 33614
Tel.: (813) 877-2844
Web Site: http://www.provest.us
Year Founded: 1991
Sales Range: $75-99.9 Million
Emp.: 500
Legal & Business Support Services
N.A.I.C.S.: 541199
Scott Strady (Founder)
Jim Ward (CEO)
Victor Draper (Exec VP)
Bill Monaghan (VP & Controller)
Carl Turro (Sr VP-Ops)
Lori Liburdi (VP-HR)
Lynda Smith (VP-IT)
Neil Heath (Sr VP-Ops)

PROVIA DOOR, INC.
2150 State Rt 39, Sugarcreek, OH 44681
Tel.: (330) 852-4711
Web Site: http://www.proviaproducts.com
Year Founded: 1977
Sales Range: $125-149.9 Million
Emp.: 586
Mfr of Professional-Class Residential Doors, Storm & Patio Doors
N.A.I.C.S.: 321911
Bill Mullet (Owner)
Brian Miller (Pres)
Keith Yutzy (VP-Ops)
Brent Mullet (VP-IT)

PROVIAS CONSTRUCTION, L.L.C.
PO Box 1614, Brandon, MS 39043
Tel.: (601) 932-1674
Sales Range: $10-24.9 Million
Emp.: 2
Civil Engineering Services
N.A.I.C.S.: 237310
Tammy Parker (Office Mgr)

PROVIDENCE CAPITAL FUNDING, INC.
3070 Saturn St Ste 100, Brea, CA 92821
Tel.: (714) 986-1220
Web Site: http://www.providencecapitalfunding.com
Year Founded: 2003
Sales Range: $1-9.9 Million
Emp.: 16
Construction, Mining & Forestry Machinery & Equipment Rental & Leasing
N.A.I.C.S.: 532412
Ofer Horn (CFO)
Bryce Harrill (Sr Acct Mgr)
Davie Lee (CEO)
Jason Zeager (Acct Mgr)

Subsidiaries:
All Media Capital, Inc. (1)
3070 Saturn St Ste 100, Brea, CA 92821
Tel.: (714) 671-4100
Web Site: http://www.allmediacapital.com
Consumer Lending Services
N.A.I.C.S.: 522291
Onya Swanson (Mgr-Credit)
Jeff Thomas (CEO & Mgr-Vendor Rels)

PROVIDENCE EQUITY PARTNERS L.L.C.
50 Kennedy Plz 18th Fl, Providence, RI 02903-2393

PROVIDENCE EQUITY PARTNERS L.L.C.

Tel.: (401) 751-1700 RI
Web Site: http://www.provequity.com
Year Founded: 1989
Private Equity & Debt Investment Management Firm
N.A.I.C.S.: 523999
Jonathan M. Nelson (Founder & Chm)
Karim A. Tabet (Sr Mng Dir)
David Phillips (Sr Mng Dir)
Andrew A. Tisdale (Sr Mng Dir)
Scott M. Marimow (Mng Dir)
Laura B. Desmond (Operating Partner-Media & Tech Practice)
Marc G. Puglia (Mng Dir & CFO)
Paul G. Stocker (CTO)
Davis Noell (Sr Mng Dir)
Michael J. Dominguez (Chief Investment Officer)
Christopher C. Ragona (Mng Dir)

Subsidiaries:
All Media Baltics (1)
Dzelzavas iela 120G, Riga, 1021, Latvia
Tel.: (371) 6707 0200
Media Holding Company
N.A.I.C.S.: 551112
Pierre Danon (Chm)
Arvil Kupris (COO)
Christian Anting (Grp CEO)

Subsidiary (Non-US):
AS All Media Eesti (2)
Peterburi tee 81, 11415, Tallinn, Estonia (100%)
Tel.: (372) 6220200
Web Site: http://www.tv3.ee
Television Broadcasting
N.A.I.C.S.: 516120

AS Star FM (2)
Petersburi Tee 81 V Korrus, EE 11415, Tallinn, Estonia (100%)
Tel.: (372) 6220288
Web Site: http://www.starfm.tv3.ee
Radio Stations
N.A.I.C.S.: 516110

AS TV Play Baltics (2)
Peterburi tee 81, EE 11415, Tallinn, Estonia
Tel.: (372) 6 024 750
Television Programming Subscription & Distribution Services
N.A.I.C.S.: 517121

Subsidiary (Domestic):
SIA All Media Latvia (2)
Dzelzavas iela 120G, Riga, 1021, Latvia (100%)
Tel.: (371) 67479000
Web Site: http://www.tv3group.eu
Television Broadcasting
N.A.I.C.S.: 516120

SIA Star FM (2)
120G Dzelzavas Street, LV-1021, Riga, Latvia (100%)
Tel.: (371) 7621110
Web Site: http://www.starfm.lv
Radio Stations
N.A.I.C.S.: 516110

Subsidiary (Non-US):
UAB All Media Lithuania (2)
Kalvariju g 135, 08221, Vilnius, Lithuania (100%)
Tel.: (370) 5 20 30 101
Web Site: http://www.tv3group.eu
Television Broadcasting
N.A.I.C.S.: 516120

Chime Communications Limited (1)
62 Buckingham Gate, London, SW1E 6AJ, United Kingdom (100%)
Tel.: (44) 207 096 5888
Web Site: http://www.chimegroup.com
Holding Company; Advertising Agencies
N.A.I.C.S.: 551112
Adrian Coleman (Co-CEO)
Jo Parker (COO)
Matthew Vandrau (Co-CEO)
David Crowther (Dir-Fin)
Stephanie Brimacombe (Mng Dir)
Paul Steven Walsh (Chm)

Subsidiary (Domestic):
Brand Marketing Team Ltd. (2)
Wigglesworth House 69 Southwark Bridge Road, London, SE1 9HH, United Kingdom
Tel.: (44) 203 740 5348
Web Site: http://www.bmtlondon.co.uk
Advetising Agency
N.A.I.C.S.: 541810
Simon Melville (Partner)
Henry Powell (Partner & Dir)
Claire Papadopoulou (Project Mgr)

Bullnose Limited (2)
62 Buckingham Gate, London, SW1E 6AJ, United Kingdom
Tel.: (44) 20 7592 5200
Web Site: http://www.chimegroup.com
Graphic Design Services
N.A.I.C.S.: 541430

Subsidiary (US):
CSM Motorsports, Inc. (2)
10960 Bennett Pkwy, Zionsville, IN 46077
Tel.: (317) 344-1900
Web Site: http://www.csm.com
Motor Sports Industry Corporate Marketing Services
N.A.I.C.S.: 711320

Subsidiary (Non-US):
Just Marketing International Ltd. (3)
3rd Floor 62 Buckingham Gate, London, SW1E 6AJ, United Kingdom
Tel.: (44) 207 593 5200
Web Site: http://www.csm.com
Motor Sports Marketing & Promotional Services
N.A.I.C.S.: 711310

Subsidiary (Domestic):
Chime Insight & Engagement Limited (2)
5th Floor Holborn Gate 26 Southampton Buildings, London, WC2A 1AH, United Kingdom
Tel.: (44) 20 7861 2540
Web Site: http://www.cie.uk.com
Methodology Neutral Research Services
N.A.I.C.S.: 561499
Claire Carter (Dir-Fin)
Crispin Beale (CEO)
Mark Hirst (Dir-Engagement)

De Facto Communications Ltd. (2)
1 Quality Court off Chancery Lane, London, WC2A 1HR, United Kingdom
Tel.: (44) 20 3735 8165
Web Site: http://www.defacto.com
Marketing & Advertising Agency
N.A.I.C.S.: 541810
Kevin Payne (Co-Founder & Dir)
Tristan Jervis (Mng Partner & Dir)
Alex Heeley (Partner)
Matthew Gould (Head-Design)

GRP Public Relations Limited (2)
62 Buckingham Gate, London, SW1P 9ZP, United Kingdom
Tel.: (44) 20 7592 5200
Public Relations Services
N.A.I.C.S.: 541820

Good Relations Limited (2)
Greencoat House Francis Street, London, SW1P 1DH, United Kingdom
Tel.: (44) 20 7932 3600
Web Site: http://www.goodrelations.co.uk
Public Relations & Corporate Communications Services
N.A.I.C.S.: 541820
Annie Fossey (Chm)
Phil Brady (Exec Dir-Property)
Robert Anderson (Exec Dir-Digital)
Richard Moss (CEO)
Neil Bayley (Exec Dir-Corp)
Sophie Taylor-Roberts (Exec Dir-Health & Wellbeing)
Oliver Dove (Exec Creative Dir)
Lawrence Collis (Exec Dir-Consumer)
David Wiles (Exec Dir-Consumer)
Phil Caplin (Dir-Broadcast)
Holly Dedman (Head-Bus Dev)
Huw Morgan (Dir-Internal Comm)

InEvidence Limited (2)
Pinewood Court Larkwood Way Tythering-

PROVIDENCE EQUITY PARTNERS L.L.C.

U.S. PRIVATE

Providence Equity Partners L.L.C.—(Continued)
ton Business Park, Macclesfield, SK10 2XR, United Kingdom
Tel.: (44) 1625 500 800
Web Site: http://www.inevidencecrp.com
Marketing & Advertising Agency
N.A.I.C.S.: 541810
Robin Hamilton *(Mng Dir)*
Melissa Talbot *(Dir)*
John Butters *(Dir)*
Kate Hickson *(Assoc Dir)*

Subsidiary (US):

Method Communications, Inc. (2)
47 W 200 S Ste 402, Salt Lake City, UT 84101
Tel.: (801) 461-9790
Web Site: http://www.methodcommunications.com
Public Relations & Communications Services
N.A.I.C.S.: 541613
Clayton Blackham *(Exec VP)*
David Parkinson *(Co-Founder & CEO)*
Jacob Moon *(Co-Founder & Gen Mgr-Salt Lake City)*
Heather England *(COO)*
Maria Camarena *(VP-Fin)*
Jeanine Bran *(VP-Ops)*
Jenni Holladay *(Exec VP-Mktg)*
Martin Harkin *(Sr VP & Head-Bus Dev-Global)*

Subsidiary (Domestic):

Opinion Leader Research Limited (2)
5th Floor Holborn Gate 26 Southampton Buildings, London, WC2A 1AH, United Kingdom
Tel.: (44) 20 7861 3080
Web Site: http://www.opinionleader.co.uk
Emp.: 20
Marketing Research Service
N.A.I.C.S.: 541910
Pam Armstrong *(Mng Dir)*
Neil Samson *(Dir)*
Sinead Jefferies *(Dir)*
Sian Kerr *(Dir-Res)*
Chloe Woolger *(Mgr-Mktg & Comm)*
Heather Norrington *(Sr Mgr-Res)*
Lydia Fellows *(Assoc Dir)*
Chris Sausman *(Assoc Dir)*

Pure Media Limited (2)
Greencoat House Francis Street, Victoria, London, SW1P 1DH, United Kingdom
Tel.: (44) 207 592 9331
Web Site: http://www.puremedia.co.uk
Media Buying Services
N.A.I.C.S.: 541830
Hugh Walker *(Mng Dir & Dir-Media)*
Paul Capleton *(Head-Trading & Dir-Media)*
Tara Marus *(Mng Dir)*

Teamspirit Limited (2)
Holborn Gate 326-330 High Holborn, London, WC1V 7PP, United Kingdom
Tel.: (44) 20 7360 7878
Web Site: http://www.teamspirit.uk.com
Advetising Agency
N.A.I.C.S.: 541810
Joanne Parker *(Chm)*
Kirsty Maxey *(CEO)*
Montserrat Tojeiro *(Dir-Client Svcs-Comm)*
David McCann *(Dir-Plng)*
Mark Baker *(Head-Res)*
Ursula Delaney *(Dir-PR)*
Crispin Heath *(Dir-Digital)*
James Maxwell *(Exec Creative Dir)*
Jo Preston *(Dir-PR)*
Jim Poulter *(Client Svcs Dir-Comm)*
Adam Smith *(Mng Dir)*
James Terry *(Dir-PR)*
Sam Turner *(Dir-Client Svcs & Comm)*
Duncan Walters *(Dir-Digital)*

VCCP Limited (2)
Greencoat House Francis Street, London, SW1P 1DH, United Kingdom
Tel.: (44) 20 7592 9331
Web Site: http://www.vccp.com
Advetising Agency
N.A.I.C.S.: 541810
Charles Vallance *(Co-Founder & Chm)*
Adrian Coleman *(Co-Founder & Grp CEO)*
Michael Sugden *(CEO)*
Darren Bailes *(Exec Creative Dir)*
Michael Lee *(Chief Strategy Officer)*
Maggie Frost *(CFO)*
Andrew Peake *(Mng Dir)*
Julian Douglas *(Vice Chm)*
Sophie Maunder *(CEO-VCCPme)*
David Boscawen *(Grp Mng Dir)*
Peter Polster *(COO-Intl)*
Stephanie Brimacombe *(CMO)*
Pete Grenfell *(Mng Dir-VCCP Kin)*
Paul Mead *(Chm-VCCP Media)*
Sian Richards *(Head-Diversity & Inclusion)*
Lesley John *(Head-Client Svcs-Singapore)*
Craig Mapleston *(Dir-Asia Pacific)*
Andrew Hook *(Exec Creative Dir-Singapore)*
Dan Colley *(Exec Creative Dir-Retail Div)*
Laura Muse *(Creative Dir)*

Subsidiary (Domestic):

VCCP Blue Limited (3)
Greencoat House Francis Street, London, SW1P 1DH, United Kingdom
Tel.: (44) 20 7592 9331
Web Site: http://www.vccp.com
Advertising Agency Services
N.A.I.C.S.: 541810
Cliff Hall *(CEO)*

VCCP Health Limited (3)
Greencoat House Francis Street, London, SW1P 1DH, United Kingdom
Tel.: (44) 20 7592 9331
Web Site: http://www.vccphealth.com
Pharmaceutical Advertising Agency Services
N.A.I.C.S.: 541810
Brett O'Connor *(Creative Dir)*
Beverley Newbury *(Mng Dir)*

Subsidiary (Non-US):

VCCP Pty. Ltd. (3)
1 Blackburn Street, Surry Hills, 2010, NSW, Australia
Tel.: (61) 2 8284 7200
Web Site: http://www.vccp.com.au
Advertising Agency
N.A.I.C.S.: 541810
David Kennedy-Cosgrove *(Mng Partner)*
Kim Feitelberg *(Exec Dir-Plng)*
Beth Duddy *(Dir-Customer Experience-VCCP Cx)*
Suzie Roberts *(Mng Dir)*
Scott Huebscher *(Exec Creative Dir)*
Will Frew *(Dir-Client Svcs)*

Subsidiary (Domestic):

VCCP Search Limited (3)
Greencoat House Francis Street, London, SW1P 1DH, United Kingdom
Tel.: (44) 20 7592 9331
Web Site: http://www.vccp.com
Advertising Agency Services
N.A.I.C.S.: 541810

Subsidiary (Non-US):

VCCP s.r.o. (3)
Portheimka Namesti, 150 00, Prague, Czech Republic
Tel.: (420) 255 711 801
Web Site: http://www.vccpprague.com
Emp.: 30
Advertising Agency Services
N.A.I.C.S.: 541810
Helena de la Barre *(Mng Dir)*
Dejan Stajnberger *(Creative Dir)*
Henri de la Barre *(Dir-Plng)*
Jan Faflik *(Dir-Bus)*
Peter Polster *(COO-Intl)*

ESI International, Inc. (1)
901 N Glebe Rd, Arlington, VA 22203-1808
Tel.: (703) 558-3000
Web Site: http://www.esi-intl.com
Sales Range: $25-49.9 Million
Emp.: 200
Project & Contract Management Training & Consulting Services
N.A.I.C.S.: 541618
John Elsey *(Pres & CEO)*
Read S. Haddad *(Mng Dir)*
Alan Garvey *(Mng Dir)*
Bill Damare *(VP-Govt Markets)*
Tim clarke *(VP-Comml Markets)*
Mark Bashrum *(VP-Corp Mktg & Public Programs)*
Patrice Collins *(VP-Global Learning, Tech & Delivery)*

GlobalTranz Enterprises, Inc. (1)
7350 N Dobson Rd Ste 130, Scottsdale, AZ 85256
Tel.: (866) 275-1407
Web Site: http://www.globaltranz.com
Freight Forwarding Services
N.A.I.C.S.: 488510
Peter Malling *(VP-Software Engineering)*
Jeffrey R. Simmons *(Chief Legal Officer)*
Robert J. Farrell *(Chm & CEO)*

Subsidiary (Domestic):

Cerasis, Inc. (2)
3200 Cthouse Ln, Eagan, MN 55121
Tel.: (651) 686-4725
Web Site: http://www.cerasis.com
Software Publisher
N.A.I.C.S.: 513210
Steve M. Ludvigson *(Pres & CEO)*

Circle 8 Logistics, LLC (2)
555 Water Edge Ln Ste 225, Elmhurst, IL 60148
Tel.: (708) 343-6703
Freight Transportation Arrangement
N.A.I.C.S.: 488510

Global Freight Source (2)
4600 W Loomis Rd Suite 214, Greenfield, WI 53220
Tel.: (888) 414-8700
Web Site: http://www.globaltranz.com
Freight Management Services
N.A.I.C.S.: 488510
Jim Weatherly *(Pres & CEO)*

Hall Enterprises, Inc. (2)
731 Bielenberg Dr Ste 108, Woodbury, MN 55125-1701
Tel.: (651) 789-4931
Web Site: http://shiplps.com
Rev.: $4,000,000
Emp.: 24
Logistic Services
N.A.I.C.S.: 541614
Justin M. Hall *(CEO)*

Home Shopping Europe GmbH (1)
Munchener Strasse 101 h, Ismaning, 85737, Germany
Tel.: (49) 89 960 600
Web Site: http://www.hse24.de
Sales Range: $75-99.9 Million
Emp.: 700
Household Equipment Whslr
N.A.I.C.S.: 423220
Richard Reitzner *(CEO)*
Koen Verbrugge *(Head-Svc & Ops)*

Huthwaite Inc. (1)
901 N Glebe Rd Ste 200, Arlington, VA 22203
Tel.: (703) 467-3800
Web Site: http://www.huthwaite.com
Sales & Marketing Performance Training Services
N.A.I.C.S.: 611430
Julia Thiel *(Asst VP-Faculty Dev)*
Stephanie Woods *(Exec VP-Sls & Mktg)*
Tara Cash *(Mgr-Production)*
Colleen VanDyke *(VP-Design & Product Dev)*

Hyve Group plc (1)
2 Kingdom Street, London, W2 6JG, United Kingdom
Tel.: (44) 2035459400
Web Site: https://www.hyve.group
Rev.: $74,947,502
Assets: $571,476,567
Liabilities: $358,837,250
Net Worth: $212,639,318
Earnings: ($27,181,554)
Emp.: 914
Fiscal Year-end: 09/30/2021
Trade Exhibitions & Conference Organizer
N.A.I.C.S.: 561920
Andrew Beach *(CFO)*
Mark Shashoua *(CEO)*
Helen Kennedy Shamir *(Corp Counsel)*
James Warsop *(Fin Dir)*
Nikki Griffiths *(Dir)*
Marina Calero *(Head)*
Jessica Natinsky *(Dir)*
Grant Altson *(CIO)*
Rachel Brodie *(Mng Dir)*
Robert Chillman *(Mng Dir)*
Sophie Wawro *(Pres)*
Thomas Whelan *(Dir)*

Subsidiary (Non-US):

ABEC Exhibitions & Conferences Pvt. Ltd. (2)
530 Laxmi Plaza New Link Road, Laxmi Industrial Estate Andheri West, Mumbai, 400053, India
Tel.: (91) 224 286 3900
Web Site: https://www.abec.asia
Travel Arrangement Services
N.A.I.C.S.: 561599
Sumit Gandhi *(CEO & Chm)*
Manish Gandhi *(Exec Dir & COO)*

Fin-mark S.r.l. (2)
Via Pindaro 82, 00125, Rome, Italy
Tel.: (39) 065 093 1045
Web Site: https://www.finmark.it
Personal Care Product Mfr & Distr
N.A.I.C.S.: 325620

GiMA International Exhibition Group GmbH & Co. KG (2)
Schleidenstrasse 3, 22083, Hamburg, Germany
Tel.: (49) 4 023 5240
Web Site: https://www.gima.de
Sales Range: $300-349.9 Million
Emp.: 30
Organizing International Commercial Events
N.A.I.C.S.: 711310
Mathias Lauk *(Mng Dir)*

Hyve Beauty Fuarcilik AS (2)
19 Mayis Caddesi No 3 Golden Plaza Kat 7, Sisli, 34360, Istanbul, Turkiye
Tel.: (90) 212 266 7010
Web Site: https://hyvebeautyfuarcilik.com
Cosmetics Product Distr
N.A.I.C.S.: 456199

Hyve India Private Ltd. (2)
Innov8 2nd Floor 44 Regal Building Outer Circle Connaught Place, New Delhi, 110001, India
Tel.: (91) 112 644 7591
Web Site: https://india.hyve.group
Event Management Services
N.A.I.C.S.: 561920
Gordon Payne *(Reg Dir)*
Gaurav Sood *(Gen Mgr)*
Gagan Sahni *(Dir-Business Development)*

Hyve Worldwide B.V. (2)
Arthur van Schendelstraat 650, 3511 MJ, Utrecht, Netherlands
Tel.: (31) 30 700 9713
Web Site: https://www.thehyve.nl
Information Technology Services
N.A.I.C.S.: 541519
Harry Van Haaften *(CEO)*
Nivethika Mahasivam *(Project Mgr)*
Jolanda Strubel *(Mgr)*

ITE China (2)
Room1703 HongkouSOHO No 575 Wusong Road, Hongkou, Shanghai, 200030, China
Tel.: (86) 2161806789
Web Site: http://eng.ite-china.com.cn
Sales Range: $50-74.9 Million
Emp.: 14
Organizer of International Trade Exhibitions, Conferences & Events
N.A.I.C.S.: 711310

ITE Eurasian Exhibitions FZ LLC (2)
Al Shatha Tower 26th Floor Office No 2613 Media City Sheikh Zayed Road, PO Box 502778, Dubai, United Arab Emirates
Tel.: (971) 4 457 2926
Web Site: https://www.ite-eurasian.com
Event Management Services
N.A.I.C.S.: 561920

ITE GULF FZ LLC (2)
Shatha Tower office 2514 Dubai Media City, PO Box 503021, Dubai, 503021, United Arab Emirates
Tel.: (971) 44332970
Web Site: http://www.ite-gulf.com
Sales Range: $50-74.9 Million
Emp.: 6
International Commercial Events Organizing Services
N.A.I.C.S.: 711310
Mehdi Ogtay Taghiyev *(Gen Mgr)*

ITE LLC Moscow (2)
3 bldg 2 Verkhnyaya Krasnoselskaya str., 107140, Moscow, Russia

COMPANIES
PROVIDENCE EQUITY PARTNERS L.L.C.

Tel.: (7) 4957995585
Web Site: http://www.russia.hyve.group
Sales Range: $75-99.9 Million
Emp.: 270
Organizing International Commercial Events
N.A.I.C.S.: 711310

Subsidiary (Domestic):

ITE Moda Ltd. (2)
Lewisham Rd, The Old Town Hall, Huddersfield, HD7 5AL, West Yorkshire, United Kingdom
Tel.: (44) 1484846069
Web Site: http://www.moda-uk.co.uk
Sales Range: $25-49.9 Million
Emp.: 40
Fashion Accessories
N.A.I.C.S.: 541490
Silvia Collins *(Dir-Event)*
Jodie Goss *(Mgr-New Bus Sls)*
Luke Murphy *(Mgr-Mktg)*

Subsidiary (US):

ITE North America Inc. (2)
2500 Plaza 5 Harborside Financial Ctr, Jersey City, NJ 07311
Tel.: (201) 633-4785
Web Site: http://www.ite-northamerica.com
International Commercial Events Organizing Services
N.A.I.C.S.: 711310

Subsidiary (Non-US):

ITE Poland Sp. z o.o. (2)
Ul Niegolewskich 22/1, 60-231, Poznan, Poland
Tel.: (48) 61 662 7241
Web Site: https://iec-poland.com
Sales Range: $50-74.9 Million
Emp.: 7
Organizing International Commercial Events
N.A.I.C.S.: 711310

ITE TURKEY (2)
19 Mayis Caddesi Golden Plaza Kat 7, Golden Plz Kat 9, 34360, Istanbul, Turkiye
Tel.: (90) 2122918310
Web Site: http://www.ite-turkey.com
Sales Range: $25-49.9 Million
Emp.: 45
Organizing International Commercial Events
N.A.I.C.S.: 711310

ITE Uzbekistan (2)
3rd Floor 59A Mustakillik Avenue, Tashkent, 100000, Uzbekistan
Tel.: (998) 712051818
Web Site: http://www.iteca.uz
Sales Range: $50-74.9 Million
Emp.: 25
International Commercial Events Organizing Services
N.A.I.C.S.: 711310

ITECA ALATOO (2)
Ibrahimova Street 115 A Business Center Dordoi Plaza 6th Floor, Bishkek, Kyrgyzstan
Tel.: (996) 312 698994
Web Site: http://www.ite-exhibitions.com
Organizing International Commercial Events
N.A.I.C.S.: 711310

ITECA Kazakhstan (2)
8th floor C block World Trade Center Almaty 42 Timiryazev Str, Almaty, Kazakhstan
Tel.: (7) 727 258 3434
Web Site: https://www.iteca.kz
Organizing International Commercial Events
N.A.I.C.S.: 711310

Premier Expo (2)
4a Verkhniy Val str, Kiev, 04071, Ukraine
Tel.: (380) 444968645
Web Site: http://www.pe.com.ua
Sales Range: $50-74.9 Million
Emp.: 90
International Commercial Events Organizing Services
N.A.I.C.S.: 711310

Primexpo (2)
24 Litera A Yakubovicha St, Saint Petersburg, 190000, Russia
Tel.: (7) 8123806000
Web Site: http://www.primexpo.ru
Sales Range: $25-49.9 Million
Emp.: 50

International Commercial Events Organizing Services
N.A.I.C.S.: 711310
Irina Belova *(Mgr)*

Subsidiary (US):

Retail Meetup, LLC (2)
605 3rd Ave 26th Fl, New York, NY 10158
Tel.: (646) 598-6644
Web Site: https://staging-env.retailmeetup.com
Online Meeting Services
N.A.I.C.S.: 518210

Subsidiary (Non-US):

SIBERIAN FAIR LLC (2)
220/10 Krasny Prospekt, 630049, Novosibirsk, Russia
Tel.: (7) 3832106290
Web Site: https://sibfair.ru
Sales Range: $150-199.9 Million
Emp.: 400
Organizing International Commercial Events
N.A.I.C.S.: 711310
Sergei Tsoi *(Dir Gen)*

Istituto Marangoni S.r.l. (1)
Via Pietro Verri 4, 20121, Milan, Italy
Tel.: (39) 02 7631 6680
Web Site: http://www.istitutomarangoni.com
Fashion & Design School
N.A.I.C.S.: 611519
Roberto Riccio *(Pres)*
Malcolm McInnes *(Grp Dir-Education)*
Barbara Toscano *(Dir-Milan Campus)*

KPA Services, LLC (1)
1380 Forest Park Cir, Lafayette, CO 80026
Tel.: (303) 228-8750
Web Site: http://www.kpaonline.com
Environmental, Health & Safety Compliance & Human Resource ManagementSolutions for Automotive & Service Industries
N.A.I.C.S.: 541620
Vane Clayton *(Chm & CEO)*
Gabe Orvis *(CFO)*
Bill Duclos *(Sr VP-Ops)*
Eric Schmitz *(Sr VP-Product & Bus Dev)*
Kathryn Carlson *(VP-HR Mgmt Products)*
Bill Reidy *(VP-Sls)*
Jessica Gard *(VP-HR)*
Brandi Vandegriff *(Sr Dir-Tech)*
Jeannie Zaemes *(Sr Dir-Mktg)*

Subsidiary (Domestic):

Succeed Management Solutions, LLC (2)
4000 Kruse Way Pl Bldg 1 Ste 310, Lake Oswego, OR 97035
Tel.: (503) 766-6063
Web Site: http://www.succeedms.com
Emp.: 50
Web-Based Enterprise Risk Management Systems Mfr
N.A.I.C.S.: 513210
Curt Shaw *(Founder & CEO)*
Lisa Sauerwein *(Office Mgr)*

Netsurion, LLC (1)
514 NE 13th St, Fort Lauderdale, FL 33304
Tel.: (713) 929-0200
Web Site: http://www.netsurion.com
Computer System Design Services
N.A.I.C.S.: 541512
Kevin Watson *(CEO)*
Jay Conn *(COO)*
Brad Cyprus *(Co-Founder, Chief Compliance Officer & Chief Security Officer)*
Mark Bartig *(Chief Revenue Officer)*
A. N. Ananth *(Chief Strategy Officer & CEO-Eventracker)*
Susan Greenstein *(Gen Counsel)*
Jagat Shah *(CTO)*

Newport Television LLC (1)
460 Nichols Rd Ste 250, Kansas City, MO 64112
Tel.: (816) 751-0200
Web Site: http://www.newporttv.com
Sales Range: $25-49.9 Million
Emp.: 20
Television Broadcasting
N.A.I.C.S.: 516120

Unit (Domestic):

KMTR-TV (2)

3825 International CT, Springfield, OR 97477
Tel.: (541) 746-1600
Web Site: http://www.kmtr.com
Sales Range: $10-24.9 Million
Television Broadcasting
N.A.I.C.S.: 516120
Jr Jackson *(Gen Mgr)*

KMYT-TV (2)
2625 S Memorial, Tulsa, OK 74129
Tel.: (918) 491-0023
Web Site: http://www.fox23.com
Television Broadcasting Station
N.A.I.C.S.: 516120
Holly Allen *(VP & Gen Mgr)*
Amie Price *(Bus Mgr)*
Amber Musselman *(Dir-Mktg)*
Jim Hanning *(Dir-Sls)*
Kari Barrett *(Mgr-Natl Sls)*
Joan King *(Mgr-Traffic)*
Chooi Ning *(Dir-Programming)*
Matt Rolison *(Mgr-New Media Sls)*
David Brace *(Mgr-Sls)*

KOKI-TV (2)
2625 S Memorial Dr, Tulsa, OK 74129
Tel.: (918) 388-5100
Web Site: http://www.fox23.com
Sales Range: $10-24.9 Million
Television Broadcasting Operations
N.A.I.C.S.: 516120
Amie Price *(Bus Mgr)*

WAWS-TV (2)
11700 Central Pkwy 2, Jacksonville, FL 32224-2600
Tel.: (904) 642-3030
Web Site: http://www.actionnewsjax.com
Sales Range: $50-74.9 Million
Television Broadcasting Station
N.A.I.C.S.: 516120
Dennis McDermott *(Mgr-Local Sls)*
Jim Zerwekh *(Gen Mgr)*

Providence Equity Advisors India Private Limited (1)
Birla Tower 25 Barakhamba Road 6th Floor, New Delhi, 110001, India
Tel.: (91) 11 3041 9000
Web Site: http://www.provequity.com
Privater Equity Firm
N.A.I.C.S.: 523999
Biswajit A. Subramanian *(Mng Dir)*
Gopi Vaddi *(Dir-Investment)*

Providence Equity Asia Limited (1)
100 Queen's Rd 9th Fl Ste 902, Central, China (Hong Kong)
Tel.: (852) 3653 3800
Web Site: http://www.provequity.com
Privater Equity Firm
N.A.I.C.S.: 523999
Niklas R. Rowald *(Mng Dir)*
Jessica E. Huang Pouleur *(VP)*

Providence Equity Investment Consulting (Beijing) Co., Ltd. (1)
China World Trade Center 47th Floor No 1 Jianguomenwai Avenue, Chaoyang District, Beijing, 100004, China
Tel.: (86) 10 5706 1300
Web Site: http://www.provequity.com
Privater Equity Firm
N.A.I.C.S.: 523999
Mary Zha *(VP-Bus Dev)*
Ming Jin *(VP)*

Providence Equity LLC (1)
9 W 57th St Ste 4700, New York, NY 10019
Tel.: (212) 588-6700
Web Site: http://www.providenceequity.com
Emp.: 40
Privater Equity Firm
N.A.I.C.S.: 523999
Charles E. Gottdiener *(Mng Dir)*
R. Davis Noell *(Principal)*
Michael Song *(VP-Portfolio Ops)*
Louise N. Tabbiner *(VP)*
A. J. Washington *(Dir-Bus Dev)*

Providence Equity LLP (1)
28 Central George Street, London, W1S2FA, United Kingdom
Tel.: (44) 2075148800
Web Site: http://www.providencequity.com
Privater Equity Firm
N.A.I.C.S.: 523999
John C. Hahn *(Mng Dir)*
Karim A. Tabet *(Mng Dir)*

Andrew A. Tisdale *(Mng Dir)*
Edward FL. Hughes *(VP)*
Dany H. Rammal *(Mng Dir)*
Charles Vernudachi *(Mng Dir)*

SeatAdvisor, Inc. (1)
2655 Camino Del Rio N Ste 470, San Diego, CA 92108
Tel.: (858) 257-4000
Web Site: http://www.seatadvisor.com
Ticketing & Patron Management Services
N.A.I.C.S.: 541511
Steve Souza *(CTO)*
Jolly Desai *(Controller)*
Steve Garcia *(VP-Customer Success)*
Joe Tish *(Gen Mgr)*
Rory O'Donnell *(Dir-Product Support)*

Study Group Pty. Limited (1)
Level 8 97-99 Bathurst Street, Sydney, 2000, NSW, Australia
Tel.: (61) 282631888
Web Site: http://www.studygroup.com
Sales Range: $125-149.9 Million
Emp.: 2,000
University Preparation & Traditional Secondary Education Programs
N.A.I.C.S.: 611710
John Hood *(Chm)*
David Leigh *(CEO)*
Treacy Bell *(Exec Dir-People & Culture)*

Subsidiary (Domestic):

Study Group Australia Pty. Limited (2)
Level 8 97-99 Bathurst Street, Sydney, 2000, NSW, Australia
Tel.: (61) 2 8263 1888
Web Site: http://www.studygroup.com
Emp.: 85
Educational Support Services
N.A.I.C.S.: 611710
Alex Chevrolle *(Mng Dir & COO)*

Subsidiary (US):

Study Group USA, Inc. (2)
330 Seventh Ave, New York, NY 10001
Tel.: (212) 497-0050
Web Site: http://www.studygroup.com
Sales Range: $10-24.9 Million
Emp.: 60
University Preparation & Traditional Secondary Education Programs
N.A.I.C.S.: 611710

Tenstreet LLC (1)
120 West 3rd Street, Tulsa, OK 74103
Tel.: (877) 219-9283
Web Site: https://www.tenstreet.com
Emp.: 100
Software Solutions
N.A.I.C.S.: 513210

The Forum Corporation (1)
265 Franklin St 4th Fl, Boston, MA 02110-3113
Tel.: (617) 523-7300
Web Site: http://www.forum.com
Sales Range: $25-49.9 Million
Emp.: 100
Professional Development & Training Services
N.A.I.C.S.: 611430
Shail Chotai *(VP-Global Delivery & Ops)*
Aaron Coury *(VP-Sls)*
Brian Hawthorne *(Head-Global Mktg)*

Subsidiary (Non-US):

Forum Equity Partners (2)
Brookfield Place 181 Bay Street Suite 2810, Toronto, M5J 2T3, ON, Canada
Tel.: (416) 947-0389
Web Site: http://www.forumequitypartners.com
Sales Range: $10-24.9 Million
Emp.: 23
Infrastructure & Real Estate Investment & Development
N.A.I.C.S.: 531390
Richard Abboud *(Founder & CEO)*
Rupesh Amin *(Sr VP-Infrastructure & Investments)*
Kyle Duignan *(VP)*
Mark Griller *(Dir-Investment)*
Ryan Gow *(Dir-Investment)*

PROVIDENCE EQUITY PARTNERS L.L.C.   U.S. PRIVATE

Providence Equity Partners L.L.C.—(Continued)
Nikolas Novograd *(Principal-Energy & Renewables-San Francisco)*
Colin Yee *(CFO)*
Nicole Sale *(Dir-Mktg & Comm)*

Forum Europe Ltd. (2)
7 Bisshops Gate, London, EC2N 3AR, United Kingdom
Tel.: (44) 0203743295
Web Site: http://www.forumemea.co.uk
Emp.: 13
Management Consulting Services & Corporate Training
N.A.I.C.S.: 611430
Cindy Stuckey *(Mng Dir)*

TwentyEighty, Inc. (1)
10901 W Toller Dr Ste 202, Littleton, CO 80127
Tel.: (866) 506-7725
Web Site: http://www.twentyeighty.com
Training & Workforce Performance Services
N.A.I.C.S.: 611430
Andrew Huddart *(CEO)*

Untangle, Inc. (1)
100 W San Fernando St Ste 565, Sunnyvale, CA 95113
Tel.: (408) 598-4299
Web Site: http://www.untangle.com
Emp.: 20
Network Security, Data Protection & Protocol Control Services
N.A.I.C.S.: 541511
Dirk Morris *(Founder & Chief Product Officer)*
Lori Booroojian *(CFO)*
Amy Abatangle *(CMO)*
Scott R. Devens *(CEO)*
Timur Kovalev *(CTO)*
Mark A. Hatton *(Chm)*
Gopi Vaddi *(Mng Dir-Providence Equity)*
John F. Rizzo *(Pres/COO-Deem)*

VectorLearning, Inc. (1)
4890 W Kennedy Blvd Ste 300, Tampa, FL 33609
Tel.: (866) 526-0637
Web Site: http://www.vectorlearning.com
Online Continuing Education & Professional Development Training Services
N.A.I.C.S.: 611710
R. Kevin Adamek *(CFO)*
Jon Katz *(Exec VP-Corp Dev)*
Victoria Zambito *(Pres-B2B & VP-Mktg & Product Mgmt)*
Jeff Gordon *(CEO)*

Subsidiary (Domestic):

RedVector.com, LLC (2)
4890 W Kennedy Blvd Ste 300, Tampa, FL 33609
Web Site: http://www.redvector.com
Online Education & Training Services
N.A.I.C.S.: 611430
Victoria Zambito *(Sr VP-Content & Comm)*
David English *(CFO)*
Smitha Oliviera *(VP-Program Mgmt)*
Nancy D. Allen *(Sr VP-Sls)*
Jeff Gordon *(CEO)*
Tammy Daigle *(Sr VP-Customer Experience)*
Carla Luke *(CFO)*
Gary Weisenborn *(CIO)*

Vistage Worldwide, Inc. (1)
11452 El Camino Real Ste 400, San Diego, CA 92130
Tel.: (858) 523-6800
Web Site: http://www.vistage.com
Sales Range: $10-24.9 Million
Emp.: 123
Management Training & Development Programs
N.A.I.C.S.: 541618
Dan Barnett *(COO)*
Jim Higham *(Gen Counsel)*
Dale T. Robinette *(CEO-Coach&Master Cha)*
Robert J. Finocchio Jr. *(Chm)*

Unit (Domestic):

Vistage Florida (2)
8286 Bayberry Rd, Jacksonville, FL 32256
Tel.: (904) 636-0770
Web Site: http://www.vistageflorida.com

Management Training & Development Programs
N.A.I.C.S.: 611430
Kelly Scott *(CEO)*
Charlie Davis *(Pres)*
K. W. Wells *(CFO)*

PROVIDENCE FINANCIAL CORPORATION
630 E 162nd St, South Holland, IL 60473
Tel.: (708) 333-0700
Web Site:
http://www.providencebank.com
Year Founded: 2014
Sales Range: $25-49.9 Million
Bank Holding Company
N.A.I.C.S.: 551111
Steven G. Van Drunen *(Pres & CEO)*
Kevin L. Botma *(Sec & Exec VP)*
Terry L. Van Der Aa *(Chm)*

Subsidiaries:

Providence Bank & Trust (1)
630 E 162nd St, South Holland, IL 60473
Tel.: (708) 333-0700
Web Site: http://www.providencebank.com
Commericial Banking
N.A.I.C.S.: 522110
Steven G. Van Drunen *(Pres & CEO)*
Kevin L. Botma *(COO)*
David A. DeGroot *(CFO)*
Doug A. DeGroot *(Officer-Trust & Exec VP)*
Clair J. Johnson *(Exec VP)*
Wayne J. Postma *(Exec VP)*
Tenay Mazumdar *(Exec VP-Credit Admin)*
Doris R. Hoeksema *(VP & Controller)*
Brian Granato *(Officer-Trust & VP)*
Donnie Chestnutt *(VP-Comml Svcs)*
Nathan Diepstra *(VP-Comml Svcs)*
Derrick Mars *(VP-Comml Svcs)*
Christine Obbagy *(VP-Comml Svcs)*
Thomas E. Alexander *(VP-Consumer Lending)*
Rick Schultz *(VP-Consumer Lending)*
Valerie Breuker *(Officer-Deposit Ops)*
Maria Dadirlat *(Asst Branch Mgr)*
Vincent Martinez *(VP-Mktg & Product Dev)*
Eric Holtrop *(VP-Cash Mgmt)*
Michele Madia-Bradley *(VP-Retail Banking & Cash Mgmt-Orland Park)*
Daniel Faragoi *(VP-Cash Mgmt-Orland Park)*
Monica Tures *(VP-Deposit Delivery-Indiana)*
Judy Jefferson *(Branch Mgr)*
Cathy Majerczyk *(Mgr-Orland Park)*
Cheryl Dalton *(Officer-Trust & Asst VP)*
Jillian Gurney *(Officer-Trust & Asst VP)*
Nick Parisi *(Sr VP-Residential Lending)*
George Caraballo *(VP & Branch Mgr)*
Michele R. Nielsen *(VP & Branch Mgr)*
Christine Zima *(VP-Comml Svcs)*
David Schnepper *(VP-Comml Svcs)*
David Stephenson *(VP-Comml Svcs)*
Kim Cunnea *(VP-Comml Svcs)*
Mark Daniels *(VP-Comml Svcs)*

Subsidiary (Domestic):

The Leaders Bank (2)
2001 York Rd Ste 150, Oak Brook, IL 60523
Tel.: (630) 572-5323
Web Site: http://www.leadersbank.com
Rev.: $16,541,000
Assets: $368,040,000
Liabilities: $340,505,000
Net Worth: $27,535,000
Earnings: ($4,032,000)
Fiscal Year-end: 12/31/2012
Commericial Banking
N.A.I.C.S.: 522110
Kathy Hardy *(Chief Credit Officer & Exec VP)*
Bill Navolio *(Gen Counsel & Exec VP)*
Chas Hall *(Exec VP-Comml Banking)*
Mary Ruminski *(Controller)*

PROVIDENCE HOSPITAL
6801 Airport Blvd, Mobile, AL 36608
Tel.: (251) 633-1000   AL
Web Site:
http://www.providencehospital.org
Year Founded: 1858

Sales Range: $200-249.9 Million
Emp.: 1,832
Healthcare Services
N.A.I.C.S.: 622110
Susan Cornejo *(CFO & Sr VP)*
William Lightfoot *(VP-Medical Svcs)*

PROVIDENCE LIFE SERVICES
18601 N Creek Dr, Tinley Park, IL 60477
Tel.: (708) 342-8100   IL
Web Site:
http://www.providencelifeservices.com
Year Founded: 1956
Sales Range: $75-99.9 Million
Emp.: 1,612
Elder Care Services
N.A.I.C.S.: 624120
Richard Schutt *(CEO)*
Justin Kats *(Treas & Sec)*
Tim Breems *(Chm)*

PROVIDENCE MANAGEMENT COMPANY, LLC
1247 Waukegan Rd Ste 200, Glenview, IL 60025
Tel.: (847) 904-2000
Web Site: http://www.provman.com
Year Founded: 1986
Sales Range: $25-49.9 Million
Emp.: 30
Multi-Family Residential Management & Investment
N.A.I.C.S.: 531311
Bruce LaMotte *(Co-Founder & Pres)*
Alan Pollack *(Co-Founder & Chm)*
Lisa Croushorn *(Reg VP)*
Karen Phillips *(Dir-HR)*
Ray Hutchinson *(COO & Principal)*
David Connolly *(VP)*
Vondie Andrews *(Reg VP)*
Jon Schneider *(CFO)*
Adrienne Leslie *(Dir-Sls)*
Kevin Finkel *(Exec VP)*
Jim Collins *(VP)*

PROVIDENCE MEDICAL CENTER
1200 Providence Rd, Wayne, NE 68787
Tel.: (402) 375-3800   NE
Web Site:
http://www.providencemedical.com
Year Founded: 1975
Sales Range: $10-24.9 Million
Emp.: 218
Health Care Srvices
N.A.I.C.S.: 622110
James R. Frank *(CEO)*

PROVIDENCE PERFORMING ARTS CENTER
220 Weybosset St, Providence, RI 02903
Tel.: (401) 421-2997
Web Site: http://www.ppacri.org
Rev.: $14,086,849
Emp.: 50
Performing Arts Center Production
N.A.I.C.S.: 711310
Joseph W. Walsh *(Chm)*
Ellen Barnes *(Sec)*

PROVIDENCE REST
3304 Waterbury Ave, Bronx, NY 10465
Tel.: (718) 931-3000   NY
Web Site:
http://www.providencerest.org
Year Founded: 1921
Sales Range: $25-49.9 Million
Emp.: 360
Elder Care Services
N.A.I.C.S.: 624120

Julio Rosario *(Dir-Mktg)*
Nikolaos Migias *(Dir-Medical)*
Rosemarie Hofstein *(Dir-Social Svc)*
John Decina *(Chm)*

PROVIDENCE ST. JOSEPH HEALTH
1801 Lind Ave SW, Renton, WA 98057
Tel.: (425) 525-3355   WA
Year Founded: 2015
Health Care Services Organization
N.A.I.C.S.: 813910
Rod Hochman *(Pres & CEO)*
Mike Butler *(Pres-Ops)*
Debra Canales *(Chief Admin Officer & Exec VP)*
Amy Compton-Phillips *(Chief Clinical Officer & Exec VP)*
Shannon Dwyer *(Gen Counsel & Exec VP)*
Jo Ann Escasa-Haigh *(Exec VP)*
Kristina Hansen Smith *(VP & Chief of Leadership Svcs)*
Orest Holubec *(Chief Comm Officer, Chief External Affairs Officer & Sr VP)*
Aaron Martin *(Chief Digital Officer)*
Rhonda Medows *(Pres-Population Health Mgmt)*
Marian Schubert *(Chief Mission Officer & Exec VP)*
Cindy Strauss *(Chief Legal Officer & Exec VP)*
B. J. Moore *(CIO)*

Subsidiaries:

Engage IT Services, Inc. (1)
601 W 1st Ave, Spokane, WA 99201
Tel.: (509) 232-8301
Web Site: http://www.thinkengage.com
Medical Information Technology Services
N.A.I.C.S.: 541511
Fred Galusha *(CEO)*

Subsidiary (Domestic):

Navin, Haffty & Associates LLC (2)
1900 W Park Dr Ste 180, Westborough, MA 01581
Tel.: (781) 871-6770
Web Site: http://www.navinhaffty.com
Rev.: $1,885,900
Emp.: 17
Information Technology Consulting Services
N.A.I.C.S.: 541611
Scott Blanchette *(Exec Dir-Svc Delivery)*
Charlie Caruso *(Sr Dir-Svc Delivery)*
Brenda Fallon *(Sr Dir-Svc Delivery)*
Jan Moore *(VP-Svc Delivery)*

Providence Health & Services (1)
1801 Lind Ave SW, Renton, WA 98057
Tel.: (425) 525-3355
Web Site: http://www.providence.org
Emp.: 73,018
Health Care Services Organization
N.A.I.C.S.: 813910
Rod Hochman *(Pres & CEO)*
Michael Butler *(Pres-Ops & Svcs)*
Erik G. Wexler *(COO)*
Hector Boirie *(Sr VP-Supply Chain Mgmt)*
Deborah Burton *(Chief Nursing Officer & Sr VP)*
Debra A. Canales *(Chief Admin Officer & Exec VP)*
Rhonda Medows *(Chief Population Health Officer & Exec VP)*
Janice Newell *(CIO & Sr VP)*
Cindy Strauss *(Chief Legal Officer & Exec VP)*
Michelle L. Edwards *(Chief Experience Officer)*
Amy Compton-Phillips *(Chief Clinical Officer & Exec VP)*

Unit (Domestic):

Institute for Systems Biology (2)
401 Terry Ave N, Seattle, WA 98109-5263

COMPANIES

Tel.: (206) 732-1200
Web Site: http://www.systemsbiology.org
Rev.: $94,735,000
Assets: $83,865,000
Liabilities: $12,992,000
Net Worth: $70,873,000
Earnings: $70,873,000
Emp.: 185
Fiscal Year-end: 12/31/2016
Biomedical Research Services
N.A.I.C.S.: 541715
Kathy Scanlan (COO & Treas)
Nitin Baliga (Professor & Sr VP)
Cynthia Shumate (Chief Legal Officer, Chief Compliance Officer & Sec)
David A. Sabey (Chm)
Nathan Price (Professor & Assoc Dir)
Jamie Creola (VP-Education)
John Aitchison (Professor)
Sui Huang (Professor)
Robert Moritz (Professor)
Jeff Ranish (Professor)
Ilya Shmulevich (Professor)
David Campbell (Sr Software Engr)
Robert Hubley (Sr Software Engr)
Chris Lausted (Sr Engr-Research)
William Longabaugh (Sr Software Engr)
Paul Shannon (Sr Software Engr)
Joe Slagel (Sr Software Engr)

Providence Tarzana Medical Center (2)
18321 Clark St, Tarzana, CA 91356
Tel.: (818) 881-0800
Web Site: http://www.california.providence.org
Sales Range: $650-699.9 Million
Emp.: 1,300
Hospital
N.A.I.C.S.: 622110
Nick Lymberopoulos (CFO)

St. Joseph Health System (1)
3345 Michelson Dr Ste 100, Irvine, CA 92612
Tel.: (949) 381-4000
Web Site: http://www.stjhs.org
Health Care Services Organization
N.A.I.C.S.: 813910
Richard F. Afable (Pres/CEO-St Joseph Hoag Health)
Jo Ann Escasa-Haigh (CFO)
Jack Cox (Chief Medical Officer & Sr VP)
Kevin Manemann (Pres/CEO-St Joseph Heritage Health)
Kevin Klockenga (Exec VP-Northern California Reg)
Richard Parks (Exec VP-West Texas & Eastern New Mexico Reg)
Roberta Luskin-Hawk (CEO-Humboldt County)
David Southerland (COO-Humboldt County)
Dave Olsen (Vice Chm)
Richard Blair (Chm)
Bruce Lamoureux (Sr VP)
Elaine Couture (Exec VP)
Janice Newell (CIO-Information Svcs & Exec VP)
Robert Hellrigel (Sr VP)

Tegria Holdings LLC (1)
1255 Fourier Dr 101, Madison, WI 53717
Tel.: (608) 729-7355
Web Site: https://www.tegria.com
Consulting & Technology Services
N.A.I.C.S.: 541690
Brian Cahill (CEO)

PROVIDENT FINANCIAL MANAGEMENT, INC.
3130 Ocean Park Blvd Ste 600, Santa Monica, CA 90403
Tel.: (310) 282-0477
Web Site: http://www.providentfm
Rev.: $11,700,000
Emp.: 130
Certified Public Accountants
N.A.I.C.S.: 561110
Barry J. Siegel (CEO)
Linda Lapetino (Acct Mgr)
Rosa Grimes (Bus Mgr)
Ivan Axelrod (COO)

PROVIDENT FUNDING
851 Traeger Ave Ste 100, San Bruno, CA 94066
Tel.: (650) 652-1300
Web Site: http://www.providentfunding.com
Sales Range: $25-49.9 Million
Emp.: 620
Mortgage Banker
N.A.I.C.S.: 522292
Jeremy Kelly (CFO)
Glenn Wertheim (Exec VP)

PROVIDENT JEWELRY & LOAN, INC.
331 Clematis St, West Palm Beach, FL 33401
Tel.: (561) 833-7755
Web Site: http://www.providentjewelry.com
Year Founded: 1993
Sales Range: $1-9.9 Million
Jewelry Retailer
N.A.I.C.S.: 458310
Robert Samuels (Pres)
Lara Pansolli (Dir-PR)

PROVIDENT MORTGAGE CAPITAL ASSOCIATES, INC.
851 Traeger Ave Ste 380, San Bruno, CA 94006
Web Site: http://www.pmca-reit.com
Year Founded: 2011
Real Estate Investment Services
N.A.I.C.S.: 525990
Craig Pica (Chm)
Mark E. Lefanowicz (Pres & CEO)
John Kubiak (Chief Investment Officer)
Jeremy Kelly (CFO, Treas, Sec & Exec VP-Strategy & IR)
Michelle Blake (Chief Admin Officer & Sec)

PROVIDEO MANAGEMENT, INC.
1934 Old Gallows Rd Ste 350, Tysons Corner, VA 22182-4050
Tel.: (703) 731-7694
Web Site: http://www.provideomanagement.com
Year Founded: 2004
Sales Range: $1-9.9 Million
Emp.: 4
Supports Federal Agencies & Military Offices with Strategy, IT & Financial Services
N.A.I.C.S.: 921190
Guillermo Calvo (Founder, Pres & CEO)

PROVIDGE CONSULTING, LLC
2207 Concord Pike 537, Wilmington, DE 19803
Tel.: (888) 927-6583
Web Site: http://www.providge.com
Year Founded: 2002
Sales Range: $1-9.9 Million
Emp.: 28
Customizes Financial, Human Resources & Customer Service Software Applications
N.A.I.C.S.: 541511
Joe Miscione (Mng Dir)
Michael Carr (Mng Dir)
Tim Lampe (Mng Dir)
Greg Dill (Mng Dir)

PROVIDUS GROUP
1177 W Loop S Ste 1550, Houston, TX 77027
Tel.: (713) 586-6586
Web Site: http://www.providusgroup.com
Year Founded: 1988
Sales Range: $10-24.9 Million

Emp.: 24
Contract Legal Staffing Services
N.A.I.C.S.: 561311
Lisa Moore Turano (Chm & Gen Counsel)
Jackie Bedczuk (Dir-Placement)
Joseph A. Turano III (Pres)

PROVIMI FOODS INC
W 2103 County Rd VV, Seymour, WI 54165-9168
Tel.: (920) 833-6861
Web Site: http://www.provimifoods.com
Year Founded: 1961
Sales Range: $10-24.9 Million
Emp.: 40
Veal Processing Services
N.A.I.C.S.: 311611
Dan Schober (Gen Mgr)
Sue Greenen (Controller)

PROVING GROUND MEDIA, INC.
8 New Port Dr Ste D, Forest Hill, MD 21050
Tel.: (410) 420-6343
Web Site: http://www.pgmedia.tv
Year Founded: 2003
Sales Range: $10-24.9 Million
Emp.: 6
Media Buying Services
N.A.I.C.S.: 541830
Debra Payne (Founder & Pres)
Michelle Mason (Acct Supvr)

PROVINSURE, INC.
9700 International Dr, Orlando, FL 32819-8114
Tel.: (407) 370-0776
Web Site: http://www.provinsure.com
Year Founded: 1995
Sales Range: $1-9.9 Million
Emp.: 11
Insurance Brokerage Services
N.A.I.C.S.: 524210
Ashley Bacot (Pres)
Jonathan Rivera (Mgr-Safety & Investigations)
Sandra Kornegay (Mgr-Claims)
Brad Levine (VP-Sls)

PROVIS MEDIA GROUP
1985 Eastwood Rd Ste 200, Wilmington, NC 28403
Tel.: (910) 256-6252
Web Site: http://www.provismedia.com
Year Founded: 2002
Sales Range: Less than $1 Million
Emp.: 20
N.A.I.C.S.: 541810
Matthew Summers (Pres & Dir-Ops)
Jeff Angel (Dir-Creative)

PROXIMITY DESIGN
1107 Fair Oaks Ave Ste 802, South Pasadena, CA 91030
Tel.: (626) 524-3549
Web Site: http://www.proximitydesigns.org
Year Founded: 2009
Sales Range: $10-24.9 Million
Emp.: 8
Individual & Family Services
N.A.I.C.S.: 624190
Zaw Min Soe (Coord-Delta Sls)
Debbie Aung Din (Co-Founder)
Myo Myint (Mgr-FAS)
James D. Taylor (Co-Founder)

PROXIMO SPIRITS, INC.
2 Park Ave, Manhasset, NY 11030
Tel.: (516) 504-9773
Web Site: http://www.proximospirits.com

PRUDENTIAL AMERICANA GROUP REALTORS

Year Founded: 2007
Sales Range: $10-24.9 Million
Emp.: 80
Alcoholic Beverages Producer, Importer & Marketer
N.A.I.C.S.: 424820
Daniel Schwarz (Mgr)
Sara Epstein (Mgr-POS)
Michael Keyes (Pres & CEO)
Jennifer Webb (Dir-PR)

PROXY PERSONNEL LLC
1100 H St NW Ste 260, Washington, DC 20005
Tel.: (202) 639-9300
Web Site: http://www.proxypersonnel.com
Year Founded: 2004
Sales Range: $1-9.9 Million
Emp.: 85
Employee Placement
N.A.I.C.S.: 561311
Ronald Jean-Baptist (Owner)

PRP WINE INTERNATIONAL INC.
1701 Howard St Ste A, Elk Grove Village, IL 60007
Tel.: (847) 290-7800
Web Site: http://www.prpwines.com
Rev.: $12,400,000
Emp.: 8
Winery
N.A.I.C.S.: 424820
Roberta Shupert (Mgr-Mktg)
Tim O'Brien (Mgr-Sls-Wisconsin)

PRU-ONE INC.
1220 20th Ave SE, Salem, OR 97302
Tel.: (503) 371-3013
Web Site: http://www.prudentialhomefinder.com
Year Founded: 1978
Sales Range: $10-24.9 Million
Emp.: 280
Real Estate Agent, Commercial
N.A.I.C.S.: 531210
Sue Turths (VP)
Ken Howe (Dir-Tech)
Gwen Petersen (Mgr-Stayton Branch)

PRUDENT PUBLISHING COMPANY, INC.
65 Challenger Rd Fl 5, Ridgefield Park, NJ 07660
Tel.: (201) 641-7900
Web Site: http://www.gallerycollection.com
Year Founded: 1929
Rev.: $16,000,000
Emp.: 85
Business-To-Business Mail Order Publisher of Greeting Cards
N.A.I.C.S.: 513199
Allen Greenwald (Pres)
H. L. Devore (CMO)

PRUDENT TECHNOLOGIES INC.
8080 Ward Pkwy Ste 201, Kansas City, MO 64114
Tel.: (816) 363-3703
Web Site: http://www.prudentweb.com
Year Founded: 1998
Sales Range: $10-24.9 Million
Emp.: 130
Environmental Assessment, Remediation, Restoration & Construction
N.A.I.C.S.: 541620
Samuel P. Mudumala (Pres)
Pavan Ram Ilipilla (Engr-Environmental)

PRUDENTIAL AMERICANA GROUP REALTORS

PRUDENTIAL AMERICANA GROUP REALTORS

Prudential Americana Group Realtors—(Continued)
2140 E Pebble Rd 160, Las Vegas, NV 89123
Tel.: (702) 796-7777
Web Site: http://www.lasvegashomes.americanagroup.com
Year Founded: 1979
Sales Range: $10-24.9 Million
Emp.: 949
Real Estate Manangement Services
N.A.I.C.S.: 531390
Mark Stark *(Owner & CEO)*
Gordon Miles *(COO)*
Forrest Barbee *(Mgr-Pebble)*
Mitch Fulfer *(Mgr-Sahara)*
Heidi Kasama *(Mgr-Summerlin)*
Aldo Martinez *(Mgr-Southwest Branch)*
Tony Prato *(Mgr-Northwest Branch)*

PRUDENTIAL LIGHTING CORP
1774 E 21st St, Los Angeles, CA 90058
Tel.: (213) 746-0360
Web Site: http://www.prulite.com
Rev.: $22,000,000
Emp.: 150
Fluorescent Lighting Fixtures, Commercial
N.A.I.C.S.: 335132
Jon Steele *(Gen Mgr)*
Jay Weiss *(Mgr-Sls-Reg)*
Rob Empfield *(Mgr-Mktg)*
Jeff Ellis *(Pres)*

PRUDENTIAL NEW JERSEY PROPERTIES
220 Davidson Ave, Somerset, NJ 08873
Tel.: (732) 627-8400
Web Site: http://www.prunewjersey.com
Year Founded: 1985
Sales Range: $50-74.9 Million
Emp.: 550
Real Estate Services
N.A.I.C.S.: 531210
Seymour Litwin *(Vice Chm)*
Nancy Litwin *(Co-Pres)*
Liz Mills *(Sr VP & Dir-Re-Location)*
Susan Magenta *(Dir-Relocation)*

PRUDENTIAL OVERALL SUPPLY INC.
1661 Alton Pkwy, Irvine, CA 92606
Tel.: (949) 250-4855 CA
Web Site: http://www.pos-clean.com
Year Founded: 1932
Sales Range: $75-99.9 Million
Emp.: 2,000
Industrial Launderers
N.A.I.C.S.: 812332
Thomas C. Watts *(Pres)*
John Thompson *(VP-Fin)*
Jerry Martin *(VP-Sls & Mktg)*
Stefan Schurter *(Sr VP-Ops)*

PRUDENTIAL REALTY COMPANY
3700 S Water St Ste 100, Pittsburgh, PA 15203
Tel.: (412) 261-6500
Web Site: http://www.prudentialrealty.com
Year Founded: 1918
Rev.: $30,000,000
Emp.: 125
Real Estate Services
N.A.I.C.S.: 531210
Howard Engelberg *(Mng Partner)*
Mark Hannah *(Controller)*

PRUDENTIAL UTAH REAL ESTATE
6975 S Union Pk Ste 620, Midvale, UT 84047
Tel.: (801) 990-0400
Web Site: http://www.pru-utah.com
Sales Range: $50-74.9 Million
Emp.: 450
Sales of Homes & Properties
N.A.I.C.S.: 531210
Steve Rooney *(Pres & Co-Owner)*
Kathy Rothe *(Dir-Relocation)*
Sarah Colbert *(Owner)*
Tom Roney *(Dir-Comm)*

PRUDENTIAL WOODMONT REALTY INC
5107 Maryland Way, Brentwood, TN 37027-2032
Tel.: (615) 292-3552 TN
Web Site: http://www.woodmontrealty.com
Year Founded: 1990
Sales Range: $10-24.9 Million
Emp.: 50
Real Estate Agents & Managers
N.A.I.C.S.: 531210
Henry H. Gildemeister *(Pres)*

PRUESLER & ASSOCIATES INC.
244 NW 9th St, Ocala, FL 34475
Tel.: (352) 732-2322
Web Site: http://www.restorationspecialist.com
Rev.: $10,500,000
Emp.: 47
General Remodeling, Single-Family Houses
N.A.I.C.S.: 236118
Bob Preusler *(Pres, CEO & Gen Mgr)*

PRUETT FOREST PRODUCTS INC.
1647 Mcfarland Blvd N Ste A1, Tuscaloosa, AL 35406
Tel.: (205) 349-4973 AL
Year Founded: 1987
Sales Range: $50-74.9 Million
Emp.: 3
Lumber, Plywood & Millwork Whslr
N.A.I.C.S.: 423310
Henry Pruett *(Pres & CFO)*

PRUGEN, INC.
8714 E Vista Bonita Dr, Scottsdale, AZ 85255
Tel.: (480) 585-0122
Web Site: http://www.prugen.com
Year Founded: 2006
Sales Range: $1-9.9 Million
Emp.: 5
Pharmaceutical Products Mfr & Distr
N.A.I.C.S.: 325412
Sean Lonergan *(Chm & CEO)*
Tommy Smith *(CFO & Exec VP)*
Bhiku Patel *(Sr VP-R&D)*
Matt Raiff *(COO)*
Linda Carter *(Dir-Mktg)*
Mike Pinto *(Dir-Sls)*

PRUITTS FOOD INC.
1002 E Main St, Antlers, OK 74523
Tel.: (580) 298-5577
Web Site: http://www.pruettsfood.com
Rev.: $12,600,000
Emp.: 95
Supermarket
N.A.I.C.S.: 445110
Raymond C. Pruitt *(Pres & CEO)*
Barbara Pruitt *(Sec)*

PRWT SERVICES, INC.
1835 Market St 8th Fl, Philadelphia, PA 19103
Tel.: (215) 569-8810
Web Site: http://www.prwt.com
Year Founded: 1988
Sales Range: $150-199.9 Million
Emp.: 1,350
Back-Office & Clerical Support Services
N.A.I.C.S.: 561499
Willie F. Johnson *(Founder & Chm)*
Althea Caruth *(VP-Admin & Facilities)*
Kathy Martin *(VP & Controller)*
Alton Shaw *(VP-Ops)*
Harold T. Epps *(Vice Chm)*
Don Peloso *(CFO & Sr VP)*
Malik Majeed *(Pres, CEO & Gen Counsel)*
Ne'Quel Armstead *(Dir-HR & Community Rels)*

Subsidiaries:

U.S. Facilities, Inc. (1)
30 N 41st St Ste 400, Philadelphia, PA 19104 (100%)
Tel.: (215) 564-1448
Web Site: http://www.usfacilities.com
Facilities Management & Support Services
N.A.I.C.S.: 561210
Karl G. Letterman *(Sr VP-Ops)*
Edward F. Daisey *(Pres & CEO)*
James D. Dobrowolski *(Pres & CEO)*
Anita Pirrone *(Dir-HR & Risk Mgmt)*
James R. Dorris *(VP)*
David L. Groomes *(Sr VP-Supply Chain Mgmt)*

PRXDIGITAL
991 W Hedding St Ste 201, San Jose, CA 95126
Tel.: (408) 287-1700 CA
Web Site: http://www.prxdigital.com
Year Founded: 1975
Sales Range: $1-9.9 Million
Emp.: 25
Public Relations Agency
N.A.I.C.S.: 541820
Brenna Bolger *(Founder & CEO)*

PRYOR GIGGEY CO., INC.
2501 Alexandria Rd, Anniston, AL 36201
Tel.: (256) 237-3373 DE
Web Site: http://www.pryorgiggey.com
Year Founded: 1988
Plastic Refractories & Distr
N.A.I.C.S.: 327120
Preston Insley *(Sec)*
Mike Chieppor *(Pres)*

PRYSM, INC.
180 Baytech Dr Ste 200, San Jose, CA 95134
Tel.: (408) 586-1100
Web Site: http://www.prysm.com
Year Founded: 2005
Cloud-Based Digital-Canvas Solutions
N.A.I.C.S.: 541519
Amit Jain *(Founder & CEO)*
Roger Hajjar *(CTO & Sr VP)*
Jasbir Singh *(CFO & VP-Fin)*
Asaf Kharal *(VP & Gen Counsel)*
Stuart Monks *(Sr VP-Collaboration Solutions)*
Hannah Grap *(VP-Mktg)*
Kathy Omaye-Sosnow *(Sr VP-HR)*
Sreeni Garlapati *(CIO & VP-Cust Success & Support)*

PRYSTUP PACKAGING PRODUCTS
101 Prystup Dr, Livingston, AL 35470
Tel.: (205) 652-9583
Web Site: http://www.prystup.com
Sales Range: $10-24.9 Million
Emp.: 100
Folded Paperboard Boxes
N.A.I.C.S.: 322212
Erin McGahey *(Mgr-Supplier Diversity)*

Mike Closson *(VP-Mktg & Bus Dev)*
Carl Sudduth *(Mgr-HR)*
B. J. Parten *(Mgr-Pre-Press)*

PS&S INTEGRATED SERVICES
3 Mountainview Rd, Warren, NJ 07059
Tel.: (732) 560-9700
Web Site: http://www.psands.com
Year Founded: 1962
Architectural & Engineering Services
N.A.I.C.S.: 541310
Jennifer Nevins *(Sr Dir)*
John Sartor *(Pres & CEO)*
Andrew Malek *(Chief Growth Officer)*
Harry Osborne *(Exec VP-Architecture & Engrg)*
L. Miguel Salinas *(Exec VP-Environmental & Energy)*
James La Maire *(CIO & CTO)*
Renard Barnes *(Chief Risk Officer, Gen Counsel & Sec)*
Thomas Heim *(CFO)*
Stacy Lombardi *(Chief People Officer)*
Lisa DiGerolamo *(Sr VP-Site Civil Engineering)*
Thomas Murphy *(Sr VP-Survey)*

Subsidiaries:

Barbara Thayer Pe Arch, Landscape Architecture, L S, PC (1)
100 Crossways Park Dr W Ste 104, Woodbury, NY 11797
Tel.: (516) 364-0660
Web Site: http://www.bthayerassociates.com
Architectural Services
N.A.I.C.S.: 541310
Barbara Thayer *(Pres)*

PSA HOLDINGS, INC.
11311 McCormick Rd, Hunt Valley, MD 21031
Tel.: (410) 821-7766 MD
Web Site: http://www.psafinancial.com
Year Founded: 1978
Sales Range: $75-99.9 Million
Emp.: 100
Holding Company; Insurance & Employee Benefits Brokerage, Financial Planning, Investment & Wealth Management Services
N.A.I.C.S.: 551112
Tammi Nash *(Sr VP-Ops)*
Craig A. English *(Sr VP & Dir-Property & Casualty Insurance)*
Kenneth R. Huber *(Sr VP-Employee Benefit Grp)*
Trevor C. Lewis Jr. *(Mng Dir)*
Frank Giachini *(Sr VP-Ops)*
Donna M. Teets *(Chief Compliance Officer)*
Justin Hoffman *(CMO & Sr VP-Bus Dev)*
Ray Sweet *(CFO)*
Joel Ellis Jr. *(Acct Mgr-Comml Lines)*
Victor Traub III *(Sr Mgr-Relationship)*

Subsidiaries:

P.S.A. Financial, Inc. (1)
11311 McCormick Rd Ste 500, Hunt Valley, MD 21031-8622
Tel.: (410) 821-7766
Web Site: http://www.psafinancial.com
Sales Range: $150-199.9 Million
Emp.: 140
Financial Planning, Investment & Wealth Management Services
N.A.I.C.S.: 523940

Subsidiary (Domestic):

P.S.A. Financial Advisors, Inc. (2)
11311 McCormick Rd, Hunt Valley, MD 21031
Tel.: (410) 821-7766
Web Site: http://www.psafinancial.com

Investment & Employee Benefit Advisory & Portfolio Management Services
N.A.I.C.S.: 523940

P.S.A. Financial Center, Inc. (2)
11311 McCormick Rd, Hunt Valley, MD 21031
Tel.: (410) 821-7766
Web Site: http://www.psafinancial.com
Client Financial Resource Services
N.A.I.C.S.: 812990
Tammi Nash (Sr VP-Ops)
Todd Lehman (VP)

P.S.A. Insurance, Inc. (1)
11311 McCormick Rd Ste 500, Hunt Valley, MD 21031
Tel.: (410) 821-7766
Web Site: http://www.psafinancial.com
Sales Range: $50-74.9 Million
Emp.: 160
Insurance Brokerage Services
N.A.I.C.S.: 524210
Craig A. English (Sr VP & Dir-Property & Casualty Insurance Div)
Gernot Hucek (VP)
James P. McManus III (VP-Comml Property & Casualty Insurance)

PSC COMMUNITY SERVICES INC
120 Jewel St 2nd Fl, Brooklyn, NY 11222
Tel.: (718) 389-7060 NY
Year Founded: 1979
Sales Range: $25-49.9 Million
Emp.: 1,291
Senior Living Services
N.A.I.C.S.: 623312
Christopher Olechowski (Dir-Program)
Renata Warchhol (Asst Dir-Field Ops)
Monica Baldeo (Dir-Patient Svcs)
Wieslaw Szczech (Asst Dir-Admin Svcs)

PSCH, INC.
142-02 20th Ave 3rd Fl, Flushing, NY 11357
Tel.: (718) 559-0516 NY
Web Site: http://www.psch.org
Year Founded: 1980
Sales Range: $75-99.9 Million
Emp.: 1,580
Individual & Family Services
N.A.I.C.S.: 624190
Pamela Weinberg (Sr VP-Medical Affairs)
Sherry Tucker (CFO)
Alan Weinstock (CEO)

PSCU FINANCIAL SERVICES, INC.
560 Carillon Pkwy, Saint Petersburg, FL 33716-1294
Tel.: (727) 572-8822 FL
Web Site: http://www.pscu.com
Year Founded: 1981
Sales Range: $650-699.9 Million
Emp.: 1,600
Provider of Business Services
N.A.I.C.S.: 522320
Tom Gandre (COO)
Sam Esfahani (CIO)
Scott Wagner (Exec VP-Membership Dev)
Dan Rosen (Sr VP-Ops Svcs)
Leah Knepper (VP)
Kimberly Barber (VP-New Bus)
Karen Postma (VP-Implementations)
Eric Brown (Mgr-Implementation Quality)

PSF INDUSTRIES INC.
65 S Horton St, Seattle, WA 98134
Tel.: (206) 622-1252
Web Site:
    http://www.psfindustries.com
Sales Range: $25-49.9 Million
Emp.: 100
Heavy Steel Construction; Manufacturer; Fabricated
N.A.I.C.S.: 332313
Brien Harrison (CFO)
David M. Gibson (Mgr-Sls)
Jeff Brown (Pres)

PSFK LLC
466 Broome St, New York, NY 10012
Tel.: (917) 595-2227
Web Site: http://www.psfk.com
Year Founded: 2005
Rev.: $2,500,000
Emp.: 10
Business Products & Services
N.A.I.C.S.: 424350
Dave Pinter (Sr Editor)
Scott Lachut (Sr Editor)
Piers Fawkes (Editor-in-Chief)

PSG EQUITY L.L.C.
401 Park Dr. Ste 204, Boston, MA 02215
Tel.: (617) 544-8800
Web Site: https://www.psgequity.com
Year Founded: 2014
Emp.: 1,126
Financial Services
N.A.I.C.S.: 523999
Lizzy Acock (Sr VP)

Subsidiaries:

Formstack, LLC (1)
8606 Allisonville Rd Ste 260, Indianapolis, IN 46250
Tel.: (317) 542-3125
Web Site: http://www.formstack.com
Sales Range: $10-24.9 Million
Online Form Integration Software
N.A.I.C.S.: 513210
Chris Byers (CEO)
Duane Hunt (Mgr-Support)
Ashley Walsh (Dir-Mktg)
Matt Taylor (VP-Product)
Dustin Sapp (COO)

Subsidiary (Domestic):

Vroman Systems Inc. (2)
5202 Washington St Ste 11, Downers Grove, IL 60515-4758
Tel.: (630) 737-1890
Web Site: http://www.formsite.com
Custom Computer Programming Services
N.A.I.C.S.: 541511

Sign In Solutions Inc. (1)
150 2nd Ave N sTE 1540, Saint Petersburg, FL 33701
Tel.: (727) 440-9080
Web Site: https://signinsolutions.com
Software Publisher
N.A.I.C.S.: 513210
Jeff Gordon (CEO)

PSI HEALTH SOLUTIONS, INC.
1013 Morse Dr, Pacific Grove, CA 93950
Tel.: (831) 373-7712
Web Site: http://www.psibands.com
Sales Range: $1-9.9 Million
Medicinal Product Mfr
N.A.I.C.S.: 339112
Romy Taormina (Owner)

PSI INTERNATIONAL, INC.
4000 Legato Rd Ste 850, Fairfax, VA 22033
Tel.: (703) 621-5825 VA
Web Site: http://www.psiint.com
Year Founded: 1977
Sales Range: $50-74.9 Million
Emp.: 99
Information Technology Support Services
N.A.I.C.S.: 541519
Richard Seol (Chm, Pres & CEO)
Terri Johng (VP)
Jinwook Kim (Dir-Technical)
Paul Kwon (CFO)
Tim Joo (CTO)
Andy Park (Chief Strategy Officer)
Fred Williams (VP-State & Local Domain)
Samina Qureshi (VP-Healthcare & Pharmaceutical Domain)
Jaimi B. Tyler (VP-HR)
Siv Kannon (Chief Knowledge Officer)

PSI PREMIER SPECIALTIES, INC.
8800 Shoal Creek Blvd Ste B, Austin, TX 78757
Tel.: (512) 371-1700
General Healthcare Services
N.A.I.C.S.: 621610
Kyle Elliott (COO)

PSI PROFESSIONAL SERVICE INDUSTRIES INC
1901 S Meyers Rd, Oakbrook Terrace, IL 60181
Tel.: (630) 691-1490
Web Site: http://www.psiusa.com
Sales Range: $10-24.9 Million
Emp.: 2,500
Residential Construction, Nec
N.A.I.C.S.: 236115
Tom Boogher (CMO & Exec VP)

PSILOS GROUP MANAGERS, LLC
140 Broadway 51st Fl, New York, NY 10005
Tel.: (212) 242-8844 DE
Web Site: http://www.psilos.com
Year Founded: 1998
Rev.: $600,000,000
Healthcare Equity Investment Firm
N.A.I.C.S.: 523999
Albert S. Waxman (Founder & Mng Partner)
Patrick Farrell (VP-Fin)
Stephen M. Krupa (CEO & Mng Partner)
Joseph R. Riley (Mng Partner)
David A. Eichler (Mng Partner)

Subsidiaries:

TriFoil Imaging (1)
9457 De Soto Ave, Chatsworth, CA 91311
Tel.: (818) 709-2468
Web Site: http://www.trifoilimaging.com
Sales Range: $10-24.9 Million
Emp.: 70
Medical Imaging Equipment Designer & Mfr
N.A.I.C.S.: 334510
Alan Crunkleton (Pres & CEO)

PSINAPSE TECHNOLOGY LTD.
1063 Serpentine Ln Ste A, Pleasanton, CA 94566
Tel.: (925) 225-0400 CA
Web Site: http://www.psinapse.com
Year Founded: 1998
Sales Range: $1-9.9 Million
Emp.: 123
Technology Staffing, Consulting & Project Management
N.A.I.C.S.: 561311
Sylvia Luneau (Pres & CEO)
Nicole Foster (Dir-Staffing & Govt Svcs)

PSK SUPERMARKETS INC.
444 S Fulton Ave, Mount Vernon, NY 10553-1718
Tel.: (914) 667-6400 NY
Year Founded: 1970
Sales Range: $50-74.9 Million
Emp.: 550
Grocery Stores
N.A.I.C.S.: 445110

Sydney Katz (Pres)
Maureen Duggan (Controller)

PSOMAS
555 S Flower St Ste 4300, Los Angeles, CA 90071
Tel.: (310) 954-3700 CA
Web Site: http://www.psomas.com
Year Founded: 1946
Sales Range: $150-199.9 Million
Emp.: 400
Provider of Surveying, Engineering & Planning Services
N.A.I.C.S.: 541330
Joan P. Kelly (Dir-Environmental Plng & Resource Mgmt Grp)
Caroline Yontez (Head-HR)
Debra Lambeck (Gen Counsel)
Jeff Gillis (Dir-IT)
Julie Shepard (Dir-Mktg)
Lee Whiteley (Dir-Survey & Mapping)
Matt Clark (Dir-Engrg)
Steve Margaroni (CEO)
Brian Bullock (Mgr-North)
Scott Bryant (Principal)
Karen Carr (Mgr-Mktg-North)
David Cern (Mgr-HR-Northern California)
Tanya Gross (Mgr-Proposal-Sacramento)

Subsidiaries:

Micropolitan, LLC (1)
555 S Flower St Ste 4300, Los Angeles, CA 90071
Tel.: (213) 223-1493
Web Site: http://www.micropolitanco.com
Emp.: 5
Real Estate Manangement Services
N.A.I.C.S.: 531390
Jacob Lipa (CEO)

Pfeiler & Associates Engineer Inc. (1)
14181 Fern Ave, Chino, CA 91710
Tel.: (909) 993-5800
Web Site: http://www.pfeilerassociates.com
Rev.: $4,000,000
Emp.: 28
Engineeering Services
N.A.I.C.S.: 541330
Mark Pfeiler (Pres)
Donald Masukawa (VP)
Mark Gasperino (Mgr-Mapping & Surveying)
Glenn Holmes (VP-Design)
Rob Scipio-Blume (Mgr-Field Survey Crew)

PsomasFMG, LLC (1)
7777 Center Ave Ste 200, Huntington Beach, CA 92647
Tel.: (714) 408-2982
Web Site: http://www.psomasfmg.com
Emp.: 23
Solar Power Structure Installation Services
N.A.I.C.S.: 237130
Louis Kwiker (Chm & CEO)
Paul Mikos (Exec VP-Sls & Mktg)
Alex Smith (VP-Bus Dev)
Al Tsai (Dir-Maintenance & Ops)

PSP CAPITAL PARTNERS, LLC
300 N LaSalle Ste 1500, Chicago, IL 60654
Tel.: (312) 873-4800
Web Site: http://www.pspcapital.com
Year Founded: 2012
Private Investment Firm
N.A.I.C.S.: 523999
John Kevin Poorman (CEO)
Ronald D. Wray (COO & CFO)
Troy Noard (Mng Dir-Private Investments)
Michael Oleshansky (Mng Dir-Private Investments)
Seth Martin (Pres-Real Estate)
John McGuire (Chief Investment Officer-Funds & Partnerships)
Penny S. Pritzker (Founder & Chm)

PSPRINT LLC

PSPRINT LLC — U.S. PRIVATE

PsPrint LLC—(Continued)
2861 Mandela Pkwy, Oakland, CA 94608
Tel.: (510) 444-3933
Web Site: http://www.psprint.com
Year Founded: 1990
Sales Range: $25-49.9 Million
Emp.: 150
Commercial Printing, Lithographic
N.A.I.C.S.: 323111

PSR COMPANY INC.
298 SE Winchester Hill Dr, Chehalis, WA 98532-3003
Tel.: (206) 932-0445 WA
Year Founded: 1994
Sales Range: $1-9.9 Million
Emp.: 6
Provider of Wood & Lumber Services
N.A.I.C.S.: 423990
Cami Carris (VP)

PSYCHOLOGICAL ASSESSMENT RESOURCES, INC.
16204 N Florida Ave, Lutz, FL 33549
Tel.: (813) 968-3003 FL
Web Site: http://www4.parinc.com
Year Founded: 1978
Sales Range: $1-9.9 Million
Emp.: 65
Psychological Assessment Materials Publisher
N.A.I.C.S.: 513199
Bob R. Smith (Owner)
Cathy Smith (VP-Community Rels)
Kay Cunningham (Pres & CEO)

PSYCHOLOGICAL SOFTWARE SOLUTIONS, INC.
4119 Montrose Blvd 5th Fl, Houston, TX 77006
Tel.: (713) 965-6941
Web Site: http://www.psiwaresolutions.com
Year Founded: 2000
Sales Range: $1-9.9 Million
Emp.: 27
Web-Based Education Software Applications
N.A.I.C.S.: 513210
Rosemarie Allen (VP-Educational Ops)
Forrest B. Bruch Jr. (CFO)

PSYCHSOFT
PO Box 232, Quincy, MA 02171
Tel.: (617) 471-8733
Web Site: http://www.psych-soft.com
Year Founded: 1987
Sales Range: $25-49.9 Million
Emp.: 25
IT Software & Services
N.A.I.C.S.: 541512
Tim Lynch (Pres & Partner)

PTA CORPORATION
148 Christian St, Oxford, CT 06478
Tel.: (203) 888-0585 CT
Web Site: http://www.ptacorp.com
Year Founded: 1953
Sales Range: $75-99.9 Million
Emp.: 75
Industrial Molds & Plastic Products Mfr
N.A.I.C.S.: 326199
Jim Meyer (Dir-Application Dev)

PTI ENGINEERED PLASTICS INC.
50900 Corporate Dr, Macomb, MI 48044
Tel.: (586) 263-5100
Web Site: http://www.teampti.com
Rev.: $35,000,000
Emp.: 150
Forms (Molds), For Foundry & Plastics Working Machinery
N.A.I.C.S.: 326199
Mark Rathbone (CEO)

PTI ROYSTON, LLC.
West Washington Bldg 125 W Washington St Ste 795, Athens, GA 30601
Tel.: (706) 246-3555 MO
Web Site: http://www.pharma-tech.com
Year Founded: 1972
Sales Range: $25-49.9 Million
Emp.: 200
Toilet Product Mfr
N.A.I.C.S.: 325620
Rich Loughlin (VP-Strategic Sls)

PTM CORPORATION
6560 Bethuy Rd, Fair Haven, MI 48023
Tel.: (586) 725-2211
Web Site: http://ptmcorporation.com
Rev.: $13,811,622
Emp.: 85
Tools & Accessories For Machine Tools
N.A.I.C.S.: 333515
Charles T. Russell (Pres)
Frank Podsiadlik (Acct Mgr)
Steve Kuhr (Dir-Sls)
Donna Russell-Kuhr (VP)
Stacie Fampier (Office Mgr)

PTMW INC.
5040 NW US Hwy 24, Topeka, KS 66618-3815
Tel.: (785) 232-7792
Web Site: http://www.ptmw.com
Sales Range: $10-24.9 Million
Emp.: 130
Railroad Equipment & Supplies
N.A.I.C.S.: 334290
Patti Christensen (Pres)
Janice Bates (Mgr-HR)
Fred Gantz (Sr Dir-Ops)
Pam Beal (Mgr-Customer Svc)
William Goff (VP-Sls)
John Stallbaumer (Dir-Mfg & Engrg Svcs)

PTS ADVANCE
2860 Michelle Dr Ste 150, Irvine, CA 92606
Tel.: (949) 268-4000
Web Site: http://www.ptsadvance.com
Year Founded: 1995
Staffing & Recruiting Services
N.A.I.C.S.: 541612
Dane Groeneveld (CEO)

Subsidiaries:
R.J. Roberts, Inc. (1)
PO Box 6204, Concord, CA 94524
Tel.: (925) 689-8080
Web Site: http://www.ptsadvance.com
Exterminating & Pest Control Services
N.A.I.C.S.: 561710
Ella Marie Kallios (Pres)

PTS STAFFING SOLUTIONS
9960 Research Dr Ste 200, Irvine, CA 92618
Tel.: (888) 787-3711 CA
Web Site: http://www.ptsstaffing.com
Year Founded: 1995
Employment Placement Agencies
N.A.I.C.S.: 561311
June Stein (Pres)
Ronald Stein (Founder)
Randy Nodalo (VP-Sls)
Greg Fodell (Acct Mgr)
Kathy Golding (Acct Mgr)
Jenny McCambridge (Acct Mgr)
Bernadette McKenzie (Acct Mgr)
Jimi Reed (Acct Mgr)

PUBCO CORPORATION
3830 Kelley Ave, Cleveland, OH 44114
Tel.: (216) 881-5300 DE
Year Founded: 1958
Sales Range: $100-124.9 Million
Emp.: 260
Holding Company
N.A.I.C.S.: 551112
Stephen R. Kalette (Gen Counsel, Sec & VP-Admin)
Jay A. Goldblatt (Asst Sec)
Leo L. Matthews (Pres-Construction Prods)
Robert H. Kanner (Chm, Pres & CEO)

Subsidiaries:
Kroy LLC (1)
3830 Kelley Ave, Cleveland, OH 44114 (100%)
Tel.: (216) 426-5600
Web Site: http://www.kroy.com
Sales Range: $10-24.9 Million
Emp.: 35
Designer, Mfr & Distr of Labeling Machines, Interior Architectural Sign Systems, Bar Code Printers & Supplies
N.A.I.C.S.: 333310
Benny Bonanno (VP-Sls & Mktg)

Subsidiary (Domestic):
Kroy Sign Systems, LLC (2)
7575 E Redfield Rd Ste 113, Scottsdale, AZ 85260-2998
Tel.: (480) 948-2222
Web Site: http://www.kroysignsystems.com
Sales Range: $10-24.9 Million
Emp.: 30
Mailing Letter Handling & Addressing Machines
N.A.I.C.S.: 339950

Smith Corona Corporation (1)
3830 Kelley Ave, Cleveland, OH 44114 (94%)
Tel.: (216) 881-5300
Web Site: http://www.smithcorona.com
Sales Range: $10-24.9 Million
Emp.: 95
Printer Products & Accessories Mfr
N.A.I.C.S.: 459410

PUBLIC AUTOS LTD
925 S Buckner Blvd, Dallas, TX 75217
Tel.: (214) 391-4118
Web Site: http://www.publicautosales.com
Sales Range: $10-24.9 Million
Emp.: 50
Automobiles, Used Cars Only
N.A.I.C.S.: 441120
Fidel Rodriguez (Acct Mgr)

PUBLIC BROADCASTING SERVICE
2100 Crystal Dr, Arlington, VA 22202-1649
Tel.: (703) 739-5000
Web Site: http://www.pbs.org
Year Founded: 1969
Sales Range: $500-549.9 Million
Emp.: 500
TV Programming & Related Services
N.A.I.C.S.: 516120
Lesli Rotenberg (Gen Mgr-Children's Media & Education)
Mario Vecchi (CTO)
Ira Rubenstein (CMO & Chief Digital Officer)
Donald A. Baer (Chm)
Brian J. Reddington (Exec Dir-Foundation)
Jonathan Barzilay (COO)
Tom Tardivo (CFO & Treas)
Afsaneh Beschloss (Vice Chm)
Kevin Martin (Vice Chm)
Jeremy Gaines (Sr VP-Corp Comm)
Jim Dunford (Sr VP-Station Svcs)
Maximilian Duke (VP-Station Strategy & Dev)
Katherine Lauderdale (Chief Legal Officer & Sec)

Subsidiaries:
PBS Enterprises, Inc. (1)
1320 Braddock Pl, Alexandria, VA 22314-1649
Tel.: (703) 739-5400
Web Site: http://www.pbsnationaldatacast.com
Sales Range: $25-49.9 Million
Emp.: 7
Holding Company; Data Delivery Services
N.A.I.C.S.: 551112

PUBLIC CLOTHING COMPANY INC.
499 7th Ave 10 Fl N, New York, NY 10018
Tel.: (212) 768-8440
Web Site: http://www.publicclothing.com
Year Founded: 1993
Womens Clothing
N.A.I.C.S.: 424350
Dan Shamasani (CEO)
Naresh Teckwani (CFO)
Derek Lam (Chief Creative Officer)
Wendy Kahn (Pres)

Subsidiaries:
Derek Lam International, LLC (1)
10 Crosby St, New York, NY 10013
Tel.: (212) 929-1338
Web Site: http://www.dereklam.com
Sales Range: $1-9.9 Million
Emp.: 30
Women's Clothing Retailer
N.A.I.C.S.: 458110

PUBLIC COMMUNICATIONS SERVICES, INC.
11859 Wilshire Blvd, Los Angeles, CA 90025-6616
Tel.: (310) 473-6222 CA
Year Founded: 1988
Rev.: $28,420,622
Emp.: 120
Telephone Communication Services for Correctional Facilities
N.A.I.C.S.: 517810
Paul Jennings (Founder & CEO)
Doyle Schaefers (VP-Ops)
Lucien C. Jervis (Dir-HR)
Steve Cadwell (Gen Mgr-Sls)

Subsidiaries:
PCS Development Inc. (1)
11859 Wilshire Blvd Ste 600, Los Angeles, CA 90025-6616
Tel.: (310) 473-6222
Rev.: $550,000
Emp.: 10
Real Estate Services
N.A.I.C.S.: 531210

PUBLIC COMPANY ACCOUNTING OVERSIGHT BOARD
1666 K St NW, Washington, DC 20006-2803
Tel.: (202) 207-9100
Web Site: http://www.pcaobus.org
Year Founded: 2002
Sales Range: $25-49.9 Million
Audit Standard Compliance Monitoring Services
N.A.I.C.S.: 813920
James R. Doty (Chm)
Marc B. Dorfman (Chief Hearing Officer)
Martin F. Baumann (Dir-Pro Standards & Chief Auditor)
Phoebe W. Brown (Sec)
Suzanne Kinzer (Chief Admin Officer)
Keith Wilson (Deputy Chief Auditor)

COMPANIES

Kent Bonham *(Dir-Govt Rels)*
Nirav Kapadia *(Dir-IT)*
Peter Schleck *(Dir-Internal Oversight & Performance Assurance)*
S. Bruce Wilson *(Dir-Intl Affairs)*
Mary M. Sjoquist *(Dir-Outreach & Small Bus Liaison)*
Colleen Brennan *(Dir-Pub Affairs)*
Brent Han *(Deputy Dir-Bus Intelligence)*
Michael Lofing *(Deputy Dir-Res & Analysis)*
Claudius B. Modesti *(Dir-Enforcement & Investigations Div)*
Helen A. Munter *(Dir-Registration & Inspections Div)*
Sarah Williams *(Deputy Dir-Registration & Inspection)*
William Ryan *(Atty)*

PUBLIC CONSULTING GROUP, INC.

148 State St 10th Fl, Boston, MA 02109
Tel.: (617) 426-2026
Web Site: http://www.publicconsultinggroup.com
Year Founded: 1986
Sales Range: $75-99.9 Million
Emp.: 1,100
Healthcare & Human Resource Agencies Management Consulting Services
N.A.I.C.S.: 541618
William S. Mosakowski *(Founder, Pres & CEO)*
Diane Santoro *(Chief HR Officer)*
Rick Dwyer *(Mgr-Health)*
Jay Egan *(Mgr-Pub Partnerships)*
Matt Brazier *(Dir-Practice Area)*
Grant Blair *(Dir-Practice Area)*
Debra V. Clark *(Dir-Facilities-Corp)*
Mitch Dobbins *(Dir-Acting Practice Area)*
Kathy Fallon *(Dir-Practice Area)*
Marc H. Fenton *(Principal-Pub Partnerships)*
Edward Forth *(CIO)*
Dan Heaney *(CFO)*
Rich Maguire *(Dir-Intl Svcs)*
Jim McInnis *(CFO-Pub Partnerships)*
William Weddleton *(Dir-Acting Practice Area)*
John Shaughnessy *(Dir-Practice Area)*
Stephen Skinner *(Principal & Dir-Mktg)*

Subsidiaries:

University Instructors, Inc. (1)
427 Lee Jackson Hwy Ste 101, Staunton, VA 24401 **(100%)**
Tel.: (540) 886-2483
Web Site: http://ui.pcgus.com
Educational Services & Academic Programs
N.A.I.C.S.: 611710

PUBLIC EDUCATION HEALTH TRUST

4003 Iowa Dr, Anchorage, AK 99517
Tel.: (907) 274-7526 **AK**
Web Site: http://www.pehtak.com
Year Founded: 1996
Health Care Information Provider
N.A.I.C.S.: 525120
Rhonda Kitter *(CFO)*

PUBLIC FINANCIAL MANAGEMENT, INC.

1735 Market St 43rd Fl, Philadelphia, PA 19103
Tel.: (215) 567-6100 **PA**
Web Site: http://www.pfm.com
Year Founded: 1975
Investment Advisory & Asset Management Services
N.A.I.C.S.: 523940
F. John White *(Mng Dir)*
Marty Margolis *(Founder & Mng Dir)*
Michael Nadol *(Mng Dir)*
Marc Ammaturo *(Mng Dir)*
John Bonow *(Mng Dir)*
Robert Delany *(Mng Dir)*
Kerry Benson *(Mng Dir)*
Jim Link *(Mng Dir)*
Dean Kaplan *(Mng Dir)*
Biagio Manieri *(Mng Dir)*
Daniel H. Kozloff *(Mng Dir)*
Michael Aileo *(Mng Dir)*
Tyler Braun *(Mgr-Portfolio Analytics)*
Katherine Clupper *(Mng Dir)*
Alex Gurvich *(Dir-Res)*
Cheryl Maddox *(Mng Dir)*
Christi Fletcher *(Sr Portfolio Mgr-Fixed Income)*

Subsidiaries:

A.C. Advisory, Inc. (1)
150 N Wacker Dr Ste 2160, Chicago, IL 60606
Tel.: (312) 346-0154
Web Site: http://www.acadvisoryinc.com
Financial Investment Activities
N.A.I.C.S.: 523999
Robert Rodriguez *(VP)*
Adela Cepeda *(Founder & Pres)*

Fiduciary Capital Management, Inc. (1)
1062 Barnes Rd Ste 202, Wallingford, CT 06492
Tel.: (203) 269-0440
Administrative Management & General Management Consulting Services
N.A.I.C.S.: 541611
Robert J. McEvitt *(Exec VP & Portfolio Mgr)*
Wayne Gates *(Pres & Chief Investment Officer)*

PFM Financial Advisors LLC (1)
1735 Market St 43rd Fl, Philadelphia, PA 19103
Tel.: (215) 567-6100
Financial Services
N.A.I.C.S.: 523999
John White *(Mng Dir)*

Subsidiary (Domestic):

Fishkind & Associates, Inc. (2)
12051 Corporate Blvd, Orlando, FL 32817
Tel.: (407) 382-3256
Web Site: http://www.fishkind.com
Administrative Management & General Management Consulting Services
N.A.I.C.S.: 541611
Darren M. Weimer *(Sr Engr)*
Henry H. Fishkind *(Pres)*
John Gallagher *(Dir-Association Ops)*
Byron Walden *(CFO)*

PUBLIC HEALTH FOUNDATION ENTERPRISES

12801 Crossroads Pkwy S Ste 200, City of Industry, CA 91746-3505
Tel.: (562) 222-7894 **CA**
Web Site: http://www.phfe.org
Year Founded: 1968
Sales Range: $100-124.9 Million
Emp.: 1,339
Fundraising Services
N.A.I.C.S.: 813219
Darrell B. Baricuatro *(Dir-IT)*
Peter Dale *(Dir-Contracts & Grants Mgmt)*
Blayne Cutler *(Pres & CEO)*
Margarita R. Buitrago *(CFO)*
Tamara Joseph *(Vice Chm)*
Bob Jenks *(Treas)*
Delvecchio Finley *(Sec)*
Erik D. Ramanathan *(Chm)*

PUBLIC HEALTH MANAGEMENT CORPORATION

Ctr Sq E 1500 Market St Ste 1500, Philadelphia, PA 19102
Tel.: (215) 985-2500 **PA**
Web Site: http://www.phmc.org
Year Founded: 1972
Nonprofit Health Care Research & Consulting Services
N.A.I.C.S.: 541715
Celeste Collins *(Chief People Officer & Chief Inclusion Officer)*
Bill Weber *(Mng Dir-Fin)*
Richard J. Cohen *(Pres & CEO)*
Stephen P. Fera *(Sec)*
Michael K. Pearson *(Chm)*
Michele Volpe *(Vice Chm)*
Lauren Nestler *(Chief Comm Officer & Chief Strategy Officer)*
Nina Boffa *(Mng Dir-Total Quality Mgmt)*
Jill Schulson *(Chief Legal Officer)*
Natalie Renew *(Sr Mng Dir-Education & Family Svcs)*
Mike McCain *(CIO)*
Michelle Williams *(Sr Mng Dir-Integrated Health Svcs)*
Lisa Bond *(Mng Dir-Res & Evaluation)*
Rhonda Coleman *(Mng Dir-Real Estate & Facilities)*
Sara Molina Robinson *(Mng Dir-Social Svcs)*
Lauren Lambrugo *(COO)*
Angelita Alomar-Gilbert *(Mng Dir-Behavioral Health Svcs)*
Patty Griffin *(Mng Dir-Comm)*
Kathleen Kinslow *(Treas)*
Pamela Mattel *(Chief Program Officer)*
Robert Block *(CFO)*
Malcolm Yates *(Dir-Govt Rels)*

Subsidiaries:

Interim House Inc. (1)
333 W Upsal St, Philadelphia, PA 19119-4010 **(100%)**
Tel.: (215) 849-4606
Web Site: http://www.interimhouse.org
Sales Range: $10-24.9 Million
Emp.: 25
Residential Care for Women
N.A.I.C.S.: 623990

Interim House West Facilities, Inc. (1)
4108 Parkside Ave, Philadelphia, PA 19104
Tel.: (215) 871-0300
Health Care Srvices
N.A.I.C.S.: 621999

The Public Health Management Services Corporation (1)
1500 Market St Ste 1500, Philadelphia, PA 19102-5085
Tel.: (215) 985-2503
Health Care Srvices
N.A.I.C.S.: 621999

Treatment Research Institute (1)
Ctr Sq E 1500 Market St Ste 1500, Philadelphia, PA 19102
Tel.: (215) 399-0980
Web Site: http://www.tresearch.org
Medical Research Services
N.A.I.C.S.: 541715
Kathleen A. Geary *(VP-Ops)*
Adam Brooks *(Dir-Res)*
Brook Burkley *(Project Mgr)*
Carolyn Carpenedo *(Sr Project Mgr)*
Elizabeth Byrne *(Dir-Clinical Implementation)*
Mary Tabit *(Sr Project Dir)*
Meghan Love *(Dir-Products)*
Kristen Glodek-Oestergaard *(Product Mgr)*
A. Thomas McLellan *(Founder & Chm)*

PUBLIC IMAGERY

7703 Anderson Rd, Tampa, FL 33634
Tel.: (813) 985-9000
Web Site: http://www.publicimagery.com
Sales Range: $1-9.9 Million
Emp.: 23
Interior Decor & Sign Mfr
N.A.I.C.S.: 339950

Jim Stefan *(Pres)*

PUBLIC INTEREST COMMUNICATION

7700 Leesburg Pike 301 N, Falls Church, VA 22043
Tel.: (703) 847-8300
Web Site: http://www.pubintcom.com
Sales Range: $10-24.9 Million
Emp.: 25
Fundraising Organization
N.A.I.C.S.: 561990
Dave Andelman *(Dir-Creative)*
Joyce Brundage *(VP)*
Ken Whitaker *(Pres)*

PUBLIC INTEREST REGISTRY

1775 Wiehle Ave Ste 100, Reston, VA 20190
Tel.: (703) 889-5778 **PA**
Web Site: http://www.pir.org
Year Founded: 2002
Sales Range: $75-99.9 Million
Emp.: 29
Community Care Services
N.A.I.C.S.: 624190
Nancy Giusti *(Controller)*
David Maher *(Sr VP-Law & Policy)*
Paul Diaz *(VP-Policy)*
Marc Saitta *(VP-Fin & Admin)*
Eric Burger *(Sec)*
Roberto Gaetano *(Chm)*
Ingrid Srinath *(Vice Chm)*
Elizabeth Finberg *(Gen Counsel & VP)*
Dave Stewart *(VP-Sls & Mktg)*
Jonathon Nevett *(Pres & CEO)*
Anand Vora *(VP-Bus Affairs)*
Laurie Tarpey *(CFO)*
Rick Wilhelm *(CTO)*

PUBLIC INVESTMENT CORPORATION

528 Arizona Ave Ste 206, Santa Monica, CA 90401
Tel.: (310) 451-5227 **CA**
Sales Range: $10-24.9 Million
Emp.: 3
General Warehousing
N.A.I.C.S.: 493110
Druscilla Alphson *(Pres)*

Subsidiaries:

National Distribution (1)
7025 Central Ave, Newark, CA 94560
Tel.: (510) 487-6226
Web Site: http://www.pcwc.com
Sales Range: $10-24.9 Million
General Warehousing
N.A.I.C.S.: 493110

RH Bophelo Ltd. (1)
RH Bophelo Unit 12 1st floor 1 Melrose Boulevard, Melrose Arch, Johannesburg, 2191, South Africa
Tel.: (27) 100072171
Web Site: https://www.rhbophelo.co.za
Rev.: $15,271,456
Assets: $66,242,979
Liabilities: $9,913,179
Net Worth: $56,329,800
Earnings: $9,946,795
Fiscal Year-end: 02/29/2024
Healthcare Services
N.A.I.C.S.: 621999
Quinton Zunga *(CEO)*
Dion Mhlaba *(CFO)*
Colin Clarke *(Exec Dir)*
Ragni Naicker *(Sec)*
Vuyokazi Nomvalo *(Exec Dir)*

PUBLIC OPINION STRATEGIES LLC

214 N Fayette St, Alexandria, VA 22314
Tel.: (703) 836-7655
Web Site: http://www.pos.org
Year Founded: 1991

PUBLIC OPINION STRATEGIES LLC — U.S. PRIVATE

Public Opinion Strategies LLC—(Continued)
Sales Range: $1-9.9 Million
Emp.: 35
Public Opinion & Market Research
N.A.I.C.S.: 541910
Robert Blizzard (Partner)
Alex Bratty (Partner)
Glen Bolger (Co-Founder & Partner)
Elizabeth Harrington (Partner)
Patrick Lanne (Partner)
Nicole McCleskey (Partner)
Bill McInturff (Co-Founder & Partner)
Neil Newhouse (Co-Founder & Partner)
Lori Weigel (Partner)
Jim Hobart (VP)
Micah Roberts (VP)
Gene Ulm (Partner)

PUBLIC PENSION CAPITAL, LLC
500 Park Ave 4th Fl, New York, NY 10022
Tel.: (212) 768-4554 DE
Web Site: http://www.ppcenterprises.com
Privater Equity Firm
N.A.I.C.S.: 523999
Perry Golkin (Co-Founder & CEO)
Michael T. Tokarz (Co-Founder)
Max Alper (Head-Indus Svcs Grp)
James R. Fisher (Head-Fin Institutions Grp)
Jeffrey Krauss (Head-Healthcare Grp)
Shivani Khurana (Co-Head-Specialty Chemicals Grp)
Puneet Sanan (Co-Head-Specialty Chemicals Grp)
Peter Seidenberg (Mng Dir)
Michael Noonan (Principal)
Annette Guarnaccio (Chief Admin Officer)
Scott Schuenke (CFO)

Subsidiaries:

Life Science Outsourcing, Inc. (1)
830 Challenger St, Brea, CA 92821
Tel.: (714) 672-1090
Web Site: http://www.lso-inc.com
Sales Range: $1-9.9 Million
Emp.: 80
Surgical & Medical Instrument Mfr
N.A.I.C.S.: 339112
Barry Kazemi (Pres)
Charlie Ricci (VP-Sls)
Ken Shagagi (Mgr-Bus Dev)
Mireya Lozano (Dir-Medical Device Mfg)
Armando Arriaga (Dir-Sterilization Validation Svcs)
Jim Fletcher (Mgr-Package Testing)
Paul Trujillo (Dir-Incubator Svcs & Quality & Regulatory)
Yiorgos Polizos (VP-Sls & Mktg)
John Nino (CEO)

Subsidiary (Domestic):

J-Pac, LLC (2)
25 Centre Rd, Somersworth, NH 03878
Tel.: (603) 692-9955
Web Site: http://www.j-pacmedical.com
Contract Medical Packaging & Device Assembly Services
N.A.I.C.S.: 561910
Rick Crane (VP-Innovation Svcs Grp)
Michael Dolge (CFO)
Phil Littlefield (VP-Ops)
Jeff Barrett (Pres & CEO)

PUBLIC SERVICE MORTGAGE, INC.
5101 Hwy 28 E, Pineville, LA 71360
Tel.: (318) 442-4252
Web Site: http://www.endurancemtg.com
Real Estate Credit
N.A.I.C.S.: 522292
Misti Morgan (Office Mgr)

PUBLIC SERVICE TELEPHONE CO
8 N Winston St, Reynolds, GA 31076
Tel.: (478) 847-4111
Web Site: http://www.pstel.com
Rev.: $18,277,350
Emp.: 43
Local Telephone Communications
N.A.I.C.S.: 517121
Jeff Wesselman (Controller)

PUBLIC SUPPLY COMPANY
1236 NW 4th St, Oklahoma City, OK 73106
Tel.: (405) 272-9621
Web Site: http://www.publicsupply.net
Sales Range: $75-99.9 Million
Emp.: 200
Window & Door Frames
N.A.I.C.S.: 332321
Bob Bennett (Pres)

PUBLIC UTILITIES REPORTS, INC.
11410 ISAAC Newton Sq N Ste 220, Reston, VA 20190
Tel.: (703) 847-7720
Web Site: http://www.fortnighty.com
Sales Range: Less than $1 Million
Emp.: 14
Public Utilities Reports
N.A.I.C.S.: 513130
Bruce Radford (Pres & CEO)
Joseph Paparello (Dir-Sls)
Louis Turner (Treas)
Jean Cole (Mgr-Mktg)

PUBLIC UTILITY DISTRICT 1 LEWIS COUNTY
321 NW Pacific Ave, Chehalis, WA 98532
Tel.: (360) 748-9261 WA
Web Site: http://www.lcpud.org
Year Founded: 1936
Rev.: $85,323,869
Assets: $262,209,438
Liabilities: $123,300,747
Net Worth: $138,908,691
Earnings: $3,454,696
Fiscal Year-end: 12/31/18
Electric Power Generation
N.A.I.C.S.: 221118
Chris Roden (Gen Mgr)
Joe First (Mgr-Generation)
Jennifer Bush (Mgr-Customer Svc)

PUBLIC UTILITY DISTRICT 1 OF BENTON COUNTY
2721 W 10th Ave, Kennewick, WA 99336
Tel.: (509) 582-2175
Web Site: http://www.bentonpud.org
Sales Range: $75-99.9 Million
Emp.: 160
Distribution, Electric Power
N.A.I.C.S.: 221122
James Sanders (Gen Mgr)
Jeff Hall (VP)
Allison Walsh (Mgr-HR)
Chad Bartram (Dir-Fin & Admin)

PUBLIC UTILITY DISTRICT 1 OF DOUGLAS COUNTY
1151 Vly Mall Pkwy, East Wenatchee, WA 98802
Tel.: (509) 884-7191
Web Site: http://www.douglaspud.org
Year Founded: 1945
Sales Range: $50-74.9 Million
Emp.: 200
Electric Power Distr
N.A.I.C.S.: 221122
Gary Ivory (Gen Mgr)

PUBLIC UTILITY DISTRICT 1 OKANOGAN
1331 2nd Ave N, Okanogan, WA 98840
Tel.: (509) 422-3310
Web Site: http://www.okanoganpud.org
Sales Range: $25-49.9 Million
Emp.: 83
Distribution, Electric Power
N.A.I.C.S.: 221122
Donald E. Johnson (Sec)
Don Coppock (Dir-Fin)
Jorn Grubich (Gen Mgr)

PUBLIC UTILITY DISTRICT 2 PACIFIC COUNTY
405 Duryea St, Raymond, WA 98577
Tel.: (360) 942-2411
Web Site: http://www.pacificpud.org
Sales Range: $10-24.9 Million
Emp.: 50
Distribution, Electric Power
N.A.I.C.S.: 221122
Douglas Miller (Gen Mgr)
Marc Wilson (Mgr-IT)
Jim Dolan (Mgr-Customer & Energy Svcs)
Jeanne Ledford (Treas & Sec)
Craig Murray (Mgr-Engrg & Ops-Willapa)
Humaira Falkenberg (Mgr-Power Resource)
Danny Avalon (Mgr-Engrg & Ops-Peninsula)
Mike Swanson (VP)
Diana Thompson (Pres)

PUBLIC UTILITY DISTRICT KLICKITAT COUNTY
1313 S Columbus Ave, Goldendale, WA 98620
Tel.: (509) 773-5891
Web Site: http://www.klickitatpud.com
Year Founded: 1938
Rev.: $21,948,559
Emp.: 75
Distribution, Electric Power
N.A.I.C.S.: 221122
Jim Smith (Gen Mgr)

PUBLIC UTILITY DISTRICT NO. 1 CHELAN COUNTY
327 N Wenatchee Ave, Wenatchee, WA 98801
Tel.: (509) 663-8121
Web Site: http://www.chelanpud.org
Sales Range: $150-199.9 Million
Emp.: 650
Distr & Generator of Electric Power
N.A.I.C.S.: 221118
John Stoll (Dir-Customer Svc)

PUBLIC UTILITY DISTRICT NO. 1 OF PEND OREILLE COUNTY
130 N Washington Ave, Newport, WA 99156
Tel.: (509) 447-3137
Web Site: http://www.popud.org
Year Founded: 1936
Sales Range: $25-49.9 Million
Emp.: 85
Electric & Water Utility
N.A.I.C.S.: 221118
Karen Willner (Officer-Pub Records)
Kenna Tornow (Mgr-Comm & Pub Contracts)

PUBLIC UTILITY DISTRICT NO. 2 OF GRANT COUNTY
PO Box 878, Ephrata, WA 98823-1876
Tel.: (509) 754-0500 WA
Web Site: http://www.grantpud.org
Year Founded: 1938
Sales Range: $300-349.9 Million
Emp.: 450
Electronic Services
N.A.I.C.S.: 221122
Sheryl Dotson (Supvr-Property Mgmt)

PUBLIC WORKS COMMISSION
955 Old Wilmington Rd, Fayetteville, NC 28301
Tel.: (910) 483-1401
Web Site: http://www.faypwc.com
Year Founded: 1905
Sales Range: $125-149.9 Million
Emp.: 600
Combination Utilities
N.A.I.C.S.: 221118
Wilson A. Lacy (Chm)
Terri Union (Vice Chm)
Luis Olivera (Sec)
David Trego (Gen Mgr)

PUBLICATION FULFILLMENT SERVICES, INC.
10564 Progress Way, Cypress, CA 90630
Tel.: (714) 226-9782
Web Site: http://www.pfsmag.com
Sales Range: $1-9.9 Million
Emp.: 9
Magazine Fulfillment & Marketing Consulting Services
N.A.I.C.S.: 518210
Jan Edwards-Pullin (Owner & Principal)

PUBLICATIONS & COMMUNICATIONS, INC.
13581 Pond Springs Rd 450, Austin, TX 78729-4108
Tel.: (512) 250-9023 TX
Web Site: http://www.pcinews.com
Year Founded: 1980
Sales Range: Less than $1 Million
Emp.: 15
Computer Trade Publications
N.A.I.C.S.: 513120
Gary Pittman (Pres)

PUBLICATIONS INTERNATIONAL, LTD.
7373 N Cicero Ave, Lincolnwood, IL 60712-1613
Tel.: (847) 676-3470 IL
Web Site: http://www.pubint.com
Year Founded: 1967
Sales Range: $25-49.9 Million
Emp.: 225
Book Publishing Company
N.A.I.C.S.: 513130
Lou Weber (Founder)
Richard Maddrell (Pres)
Tim Light (Controller)

PUBLICENGINES INC.
11781 S Lone Peak Pkwy Ste 200, Draper, UT 84020
Tel.: (801) 828-2700
Web Site: http://www.publicengines.com
Year Founded: 2007
Sales Range: $1-9.9 Million
Emp.: 25
Cloud Based Crime Mapping Network
N.A.I.C.S.: 561621
William Kilmer (CEO)

PUBLICIDENTITY INC.
1220 S Boyle Ave, Los Angeles, CA 90023
Tel.: (323) 266-1360
Web Site: http://www.publicidentity.com
Year Founded: 2001
Sales Range: $1-9.9 Million
Emp.: 5
Branded Promotional Merchandise
N.A.I.C.S.: 455219
Leland Felsenthal (Pres)
Sonita Butalia (Project Mgr)

COMPANIES

PUBLISHER'S CREATIVE SYSTEMS
119 E Grand Ave, Escondido, CA 92025
Tel.: (800) 847-9910
Web Site: http://www.pcspublink.com
Year Founded: 1991
Sales Range: $1-9.9 Million
Emp.: 45
Subscription Fulfillment Services
N.A.I.C.S.: 561499
Michael J. Ciuffreda (CEO)
Tony Theiss (VP-Sls & Mktg)
Joseph Kelly Ciuffreeda (Pres & Dir-Info Tech)
Jens Kalisch (Mgr-IT)
Angie De Leon (Gen Mgr & Dir-Ops)

PUBLISHERS ADVERTISING ASSOCIATES
237 Park Ave 15Fl, New York, NY 10017
Tel.: (212) 364-1100
Web Site: http://www.hachettebookgroup.com
Year Founded: 1973
Rev: $10,000,000
Emp.: 30
Entertainment
N.A.I.C.S.: 541810
Chris Barba (Exec VP-Sls & Mktg)
Martha Otis (Sr VP-Adv & Promo)
Oscar Stern (Dir-Art)
Cheryl Rozier (Dir-Adv)
Brad Negbaur (Dir-Copy)
Janice Wilkins (Assoc Dir)

PUBLISHERS CIRCULATION FULFILLMENT INC.
502 Washington Ave Ste 500, Towson, MD 21204-5017
Tel.: (410) 821-8614   MD
Web Site: http://www.pcfcorp.com
Year Founded: 1980
Sales Range: $250-299.9 Million
Emp.: 5,000
Newspaper Circulation Services
N.A.I.C.S.: 561499
Gerard Giordana (CEO)
Thomas D. Foard (CFO & Exec VP)
Kevin Daly (Exec VP-Distr Svcs)
Joe Neuhof (VP-Bus Dev)

PUBLISHERS CLEARING HOUSE, INC.
300 Jericho Quadrangle Dept 300, Jericho, NY 11753-2219
Tel.: (516) 883-5432   NY
Web Site: http://www.pch.com
Year Founded: 1953
Sales Range: $150-199.9 Million
Emp.: 500
Catalog, Mail Order & Television Sales
N.A.I.C.S.: 513140
Andy Goldberg (Chm & CEO)
Rick Busch (Sr VP)
Jason John (CMO-Digital)
James Jones (Gen Mgr-PCH Digital Entertainment Properties)
Noah Jessop (Head-Data)
Tim Braz (Chief Revenue Officer)
Kurt Kendall (Chief Analytics Officer)
Subsidiaries:
Zandica, Inc.   (1)
1001 Elwell Court, Palo Alto, CA 94303
Tel.: (650) 461-8300
Web Site: http://www.topix.net
Sales Range: $75-99.9 Million
Online News & Information Services
N.A.I.C.S.: 516210

PUBLISHERS' GRAPHICS, LLC.
140 Della Ct, Carol Stream, IL 60188
Tel.: (630) 221-1850   IL
Web Site: http://www.pubgraphics.com
Year Founded: 1996
Short Run Book Printing Services
N.A.I.C.S.: 323117
Nick Lewis (Pres)
Catherine Hoffmann (Mgr-Ops)

PUBLISHING GROUP OF AMERICA
341 Cool Springs Blvd Ste 400, Franklin, TN 37067
Tel.: (615) 468-6000
Web Site: http://pgoamedia.com
Year Founded: 2000
Sales Range: $10-24.9 Million
Emp.: 35
Magazine Publisher
N.A.I.C.S.: 513199

PUBLIX SUPER MARKETS, INC.
3300 Publix Corporate Pkwy, Lakeland, FL 33811
Tel.: (863) 688-1188   FL
Web Site: https://www.publix.com
Year Founded: 1930
Rev: $48,393,907,000
Assets: $31,524,347,000
Liabilities: $9,486,482,000
Net Worth: $22,037,865,000
Earnings: $4,412,220,000
Emp.: 232,000
Fiscal Year-end: 12/25/21
Offices of Other Holding Companies
N.A.I.C.S.: 551112
David P. Phillips (CFO, Treas & Exec VP)
Randall Todd Jones Sr. (Exec Chm)
Marc H. Salm (VP)
Kevin S. Murphy (CEO)
Merriann M. Metz (Gen Counsel, Sec & VP)
Robert J. McGarrity (VP)
John F. Provenzano (VP)
Marcy P. Benton (VP)
Dain Rusk (VP)
Robert J. Bechtel (VP)
John L. Goff Jr. (Pres)
Randolph L. Barber (VP)
L. Renee Kelly (VP)
Michael E. Lester (VP)
Steven B. Wellslager (VP)
Kris Jonczyk (VP)
Brad E. Oliver (VP)
Norman J. Badger (VP)
Chris Mesa (VP)
Doug Stalbaum (Controller)
Joey Riddle (VP-Charlotte)
John L. Goff Jr. (Chm & Pres)
Christopher J. Mesa (VP)
Douglas Stalbaum (VP)
Monica A. Allman (VP)
Adrian Bennett (VP)
Matthew I. Crawley (VP)
Kyle C. Davis (VP)
Christopher P. Haake (VP)
Bridgid A. O'Connor (VP)
Charles B. Roskovich Jr. (VP)
Marsha C. Singh (VP)
Laurie Z. Douglas (CIO)
Douglas A. Harris Jr. (VP)
William W. Rayburn IV (VP)
Subsidiaries:
Lone Palm Golf Club, LLC   (1)
800 Lone Palm Dr, Lakeland, FL 33815
Tel.: (863) 499-5481
Web Site: https://www.lonepalmgc.com
Sales Range: $25-49.9 Million
Emp.: 35
Golf Course & Country Club Services
N.A.I.C.S.: 713910

Publix Alabama, LLC   (1)
4851 Whitesburg Dr SE Ste B, Huntsville, AL 35802
Tel.: (256) 650-2396
Mail Order Pharmaceutical Services
N.A.I.C.S.: 445110

Publix Asset Management Company   (1)
3300 Publix Corporate Pkwy, Lakeland, FL 33811-3311
Tel.: (863) 688-1188
Web Site: https://www.publix.com
Sales Range: $75-99.9 Million
Trademark Management Services
N.A.I.C.S.: 533110

Publix Super Markets, Inc. - GA, SC, TN & AL   (1)
2600 Delk Rd SE, Marietta, GA 30067-6202
Tel.: (770) 952-6601
Web Site: http://www.publix.com
Sales Range: $75-99.9 Million
Emp.: 180
Regional Managing Office
N.A.I.C.S.: 551114

Publix Super Markets, Inc. - North Florida/Southeast Georgia   (1)
9786 W Beaver St, Jacksonville, FL 32220
Tel.: (904) 781-8600
Web Site: http://www.publix.com
Sales Range: $25-49.9 Million
Emp.: 600
Regional Managing Office & Grocery Distribution Center
N.A.I.C.S.: 551114

Publix Super Markets, Inc. - South East Florida   (1)
100 NE 183 St, Miami, FL 33179-9030
Tel.: (305) 652-2411
Web Site: http://www.publixsupermarkets.com
Sales Range: $10-24.9 Million
Emp.: 400
Regional Managing Office & Grocery Distribution Center
N.A.I.C.S.: 551114

Real Sub, LLC   (1)
1936 George Jenkins Blvd, Lakeland, FL 33815
Tel.: (863) 688-1188
Land Subdivision Services
N.A.I.C.S.: 237210

PUBSQUARED LLC
111 W 28th St, New York, NY 10001
Tel.: (646) 845-9382
Web Site: http://www.pubsqrd.com
Advertising Services
N.A.I.C.S.: 541810
Matthew Dearborn (CEO)
Subsidiaries:
Local Yokel Media LLC   (1)
1 N Frnt St Ste 203, Stamford, CT 06901
Tel.: (917) 952-4887
Web Site: http://www.localyokelmedia.com
Advertising Agencies
N.A.I.C.S.: 541810
Dick O'Hare (Co-Founder & CEO)

PUCKETT GROCERY CO. INC.
115 E Maple Ave, Sayre, OK 73662
Tel.: (580) 928-3280
Sales Range: $10-24.9 Million
Emp.: 100
Grocery Stores
N.A.I.C.S.: 445110
M. Craig Puckett (Pres)

PUCKETT MACHINERY COMPANY INC.
100 Caterpillar Dr, Flowood, MS 39232
Tel.: (601) 969-6000   MS
Web Site: http://www.puckettmachinery.com
Year Founded: 1970
Sales Range: $50-74.9 Million
Emp.: 350
Industrial Machinery Distr
N.A.I.C.S.: 423810

PUEBLO BONITO HOTELS & RESORTS

Richard H. Puckett (Chm & CEO)
Bill Morgan (Mgr-Used Equipment)
Subsidiaries:
Puckett Rents Inc   (1)
9207 W Oaklawn Rd, Biloxi, MS 39532-8047   (100%)
Tel.: (228) 392-2211
Web Site: http://www.puckett.com
Sales Range: $10-24.9 Million
Emp.: 10
Provider of Rental Services
N.A.I.C.S.: 459999
Harvey Page (Mgr-Parts)

SITECH South MS, LLC   (1)
404 Hwy 49, Richland, MS 39218
Tel.: (601) 397-6155
Web Site: http://www.sitechsouthms.com
Construction Machinery Mfr
N.A.I.C.S.: 333120

PUCKETT'S FLOORING COMPANY
8057 S Priest Dr, Tempe, AZ 85284
Tel.: (480) 990-8191
Web Site: http://www.puckettsflooring.com
Year Founded: 1988
Sales Range: $10-24.9 Million
Emp.: 18
Floor Coverings Whslr
N.A.I.C.S.: 449121
Theodore Fluegel (Pres)

PUEBLO BANCORPORATION
301 W 5th St, Pueblo, CO 81003
Tel.: (719) 545-1834
Web Site: http://www.pbandt.com
Year Founded: 1982
Sales Range: $25-49.9 Million
Emp.: 200
Bank Holding Company
N.A.I.C.S.: 551111
Michael Moore (Pres & CEO)
Subsidiaries:
Pueblo Bank & Trust Co. Inc.   (1)
301 W 5th St, Pueblo, CO 81003   (100%)
Tel.: (719) 545-1834
Web Site: http://www.pbandt.com
Sales Range: $50-74.9 Million
Emp.: 190
Banking Services
N.A.I.C.S.: 522110

PUEBLO BONITO HOTELS & RESORTS
1450 Frazee Rd Ste 602, San Diego, CA 92108
Tel.: (858) 642-2050
Web Site: http://www.pueblobonito.com
Year Founded: 1987
Sales Range: $10-24.9 Million
Emp.: 9
Hotel Owner & Operator
N.A.I.C.S.: 721110
Ernesto Coppel (Owner)
Subsidiaries:
Pueblo Bonito Emerald Bay   (1)
Av Ernesto Coppel Compana S N Camino Al Delfin, Zona Nuevo Mazatlan, 82110, Mazatlan, Sinaloa, Mexico
Tel.: (52) 6699890525
Web Site: http://www.pueblobonitoemeraldbay.com
Hotel Operations
N.A.I.C.S.: 721110

Pueblo Bonito Los Cabos   (1)
Playa El Medano S N, 23410, Cabo San Lucas, Mexico
Tel.: (52) 6241429797
Web Site: http://www.pueblobonito-loscabos.com
Sales Range: $10-24.9 Million
Hotel Operations
N.A.I.C.S.: 721110
Ernesto Coppel (Co-Owner)

PUEBLO BONITO HOTELS & RESORTS
U.S. PRIVATE

Pueblo Bonito Hotels & Resorts—(Continued)

Pueblo Bonito Mazatlan (1)
Avenida Camaron Sabalo 2121 Norte, 82110, Mazatlan, Sinaloa, Mexico
Tel.: (52) 6699898900
Web Site: http://www.pueblobonito.com.mx
Sales Range: $10-24.9 Million
Hotel Operations
N.A.I.C.S.: 721110
Ernesto Coppel *(Co-Owner)*
Marcus Kronemeyer *(Co-Owner)*

Pueblo Bonito Pacifica Holistic Retreat and Spa (1)
Cabo Pacifica S/N, 23450, Cabo San Lucas, Mexico
Tel.: (52) 6241429696
Web Site: http://www.pueblobonitopacifica.com
Sales Range: $10-24.9 Million
Hotel Operations
N.A.I.C.S.: 721110

Pueblo Bonito Rose (1)
Playa El Medano S N, 23410, Cabo San Lucas, Mexico
Tel.: (52) 6241429898
Web Site: http://www.pueblobonito-rose.com
Hotel Operations
N.A.I.C.S.: 721110
Ernesto Coppel *(Owner)*
Liliana Zatarain *(Mgr-Reservations)*

Pueblo Bonito Sunset Beach (1)
Predioparaiso Esconbido, 23450, Cabo San Lucas, Mexico
Tel.: (52) 6241429999
Web Site: http://www.pueblobonitosunsetbeach.mx
Hotel Operations
N.A.I.C.S.: 721110
Ernesto Coppel Kelly *(Owner & Pres)*
Veronica Escamilla *(Mgr-Reservations)*

PUENTES BROTHERS INC.
3060 Industrial Way NE, Salem, OR 97301
Tel.: (503) 370-9710
Web Site: http://www.donpancho.com
Sales Range: $10-24.9 Million
Emp.: 350
Tortilla Mfr
N.A.I.C.S.: 311830
George Puentes *(Pres)*
Phillis Puentes *(VP)*
Ricardo Bayez *(Pres-Ops)*
Tom Hoffert *(Mgr-Sls & Mktg)*

PUERTO RICAN ACTION BOARD
90 Jersey Ave, New Brunswick, NJ 08901
Tel.: (732) 828-4510   NJ
Web Site: http://www.prab.org
Year Founded: 1971
Sales Range: $10-24.9 Million
Emp.: 318
Community Care Services
N.A.I.C.S.: 624190
Stephen Eisdorfer *(Sec)*
Betty Reba *(Vice Chm)*
Blanquita Valenti *(Chm)*
Chris Blount *(Dir-Site)*
Darshna Amarnani *(Dir-Site)*
Jose Carlos Montes *(CEO)*
Ellen Tully III *(Dir-Site)*

PUERTO RICAN FAMILY INSTITUTE, INC.
145 W 15th St 2nd Fl, New York, NY 10011
Tel.: (212) 924-6320   NY
Web Site: http://www.prfi.org
Year Founded: 1960
Sales Range: $25-49.9 Million
Emp.: 745
Family Support Services
N.A.I.C.S.: 624190
Abigail Juarez-Karic *(Program Dir)*
Maria Elena Girone *(Pres & CEO)*
Iran Rodriguez *(Pres & CEO)*

David Ortiz *(Program Dir)*
Angela Cabrera *(Sec)*
John Robert *(Chm)*
Mildred Allen *(Treas)*
Yolanda Alicea-Winn *(VP)*

PUERTO RICO CONSERVATION TRUST FUND
PO Box 9023554, San Juan, PR 00902
Tel.: (787) 722-5834   PR
Year Founded: 1970
Sales Range: $25-49.9 Million
Emp.: 132
Natural Resource Preservation Services
N.A.I.C.S.: 813312
Jorge A. Baez *(Dir-Ops)*
Fernando Lloveras *(Exec Dir)*
Maria M. Marques *(CFO)*
Neida Pumarejo *(Dir-Acq)*

PUERTO RICO ELECTRIC POWER AUTHORITY
PO Box 364267, San Juan, PR 00936-4267
Tel.: (787) 521-3434
Web Site: http://www.prepa.com
Year Founded: 1941
Electricity Provider & Distr
N.A.I.C.S.: 221122
Ernesto Sgroi-Hernandez *(Chm)*
Jose Ortiz *(CEO)*

PUERTO RICO FARM CREDIT A C A
213 Avenue Domenech, San Juan, PR 00918
Tel.: (787) 753-0587
Web Site: http://www.puertoricofarmcredit.com
Sales Range: $25-49.9 Million
Emp.: 34
Agricultural Credit Institutions
N.A.I.C.S.: 522299
Antonio Marichal *(Chm)*
Ricardo Fernandes *(Pres & CEO)*

PUERTO RICO INDUSTRIAL DEVELOPMENT COMPANY
355 Franklin Delano Roosevelt Ave, San Juan, PR 00918
Tel.: (787) 764-1175
Web Site: https://pridco.pr.gov
Sales Range: $25-49.9 Million
Emp.: 350
Business Development Agency
N.A.I.C.S.: 926110
Javier Bayon *(Exec Dir)*
Jerman Monroig *(Gen Mgr)*

Subsidiaries:

Rums of Puerto Rico (1)
135 W 53 St 22nd FL, New York, NY 10020-1599
Tel.: (212) 245-1200
Web Site: https://rumcapital.pr.gov
Rum Promoter & Distr
N.A.I.C.S.: 424820

PUERTO RICO LEGAL SERVICES, INC.
PO Box 9134, San Juan, PR 00908-9134
Tel.: (787) 728-8686
Web Site: http://www.servicioslegales.org
Sales Range: $10-24.9 Million
Emp.: 327
Legal Consulting Services
N.A.I.C.S.: 541110
Anamari Melecio Rivera *(Dir-HR)*
Charles S. Hey Maestre *(Exec Dir)*
Viviam Godineaux Villaronga *(Pres)*
Glorimar Acevedo Cruz *(Sec)*
Eddie Olivera Robles *(Treas)*

Francis D. Nina Estrella *(VP)*
Jesus Garcia Oyola *(VP)*
Brenda Cruz *(Dir-Litigation)*
Juan Ocasio *(Dir-Info Sys)*
Lisandra Rodriguez *(Dir-Admin)*

PUERTO RICO PUBLIC BROADCASTING CORP
570 Hostos Ave, San Juan, PR 00918
Tel.: (787) 766-0505
Web Site: http://www.prnet.pr
Sales Range: $10-24.9 Million
Emp.: 570
Radio & Television Broadcasting Stations
N.A.I.C.S.: 516110
Tetro Rua *(VP)*
Marietty Lasanta *(Pres)*

PUERTO RICO SUPPLY GROUP
Luchetti Industrial Park Marginal Rd PR 5, Bayamon, PR 00961
Tel.: (787) 780-4043
Web Site: http://www.prsupplies.com
Year Founded: 1971
Sales Range: $300-349.9 Million
Emp.: 450
Holding Company; General Grocery; Tobacco & Personal Care Products Distr
N.A.I.C.S.: 551112
Edwin Hernandez Perez *(Pres)*

Subsidiaries:

Puerto Rico Supplies Co. Inc. (1)
C St Cnr B St Luchetti Industrial Park, Bayamon, PR 00961
Tel.: (787) 780-4043
Web Site: http://www.prsupplies.com
Sales Range: $100-124.9 Million
Emp.: 200
Tobacco & Tobacco Products Distr
N.A.I.C.S.: 424940
Edwin Hernandez Perez *(Pres)*
Carmen Laura Marrero *(VP)*

PUERTO RICO TOURISM COMPANY
Princes Bulding Number 2 Princes Work Way, San Juan, PR 00902-3960
Tel.: (787) 721-2400   PR
Year Founded: 1970
Sales Range: $250-299.9 Million
Emp.: 600
Tourist Products & Services
N.A.I.C.S.: 561520
Nydza Irizarry *(Dir-Legal)*

Subsidiaries:

Puerto Rico Tourism Company - New York (1)
135 W 50th St 22 Fl, New York, NY 10020
Tel.: (212) 586-6262
Web Site: http://www.puerto-rico-tourism.com
Sales Range: $10-24.9 Million
Emp.: 20
Tourism Bureau
N.A.I.C.S.: 561920
Gabriel Emanuelli *(Mng Dir)*

PUERTO RICO WIRE PRODUCTS INC.
Urban Industrial Corujo Carr 866 Lot 8, Bayamon, PR 00961
Tel.: (787) 288-8080
Web Site: http://www.puertoricowire.com
Rev.: $31,400,000
Emp.: 150
Building Materials, Interior
N.A.I.C.S.: 423810
Jose Cestero Yordan *(Pres)*
Jose Cestero Ramirez *(VP)*

PUFF N STUFF CATERING, LLC
250 Rio Dr, Orlando, FL 32810
Tel.: (407) 629-7833   FL
Web Site: http://www.puffnstuff.com
Year Founded: 1980
Sales Range: $1-9.9 Million
Emp.: 240
Caterers
N.A.I.C.S.: 722320
Emerald Proulx *(Mgr-Trng & Svcs)*
Mary Dickson *(Dir-Fin)*
Warren Dietel *(Owner & Pres)*

PUFFER SWEIVEN
4230 Greenbriar Dr, Stafford, TX 77477
Tel.: (281) 240-2000
Web Site: http://www.puffer.com
Sales Range: $10-24.9 Million
Emp.: 20
Indicating Instruments & Accessories
N.A.I.C.S.: 423830
Andy Bauml *(Acct Mgr)*
Jerry Siler *(Exec VP)*
Blake Coburn *(Mgr-Ops)*
Dave Buse *(VP-Bus Dev)*
Fred Burban *(Acct Mgr)*
James Hill *(Mgr-Sls)*
Jeff Cassidy *(Acct Mgr)*
Maria Bocaranda *(Engr-Outside Sls)*
Mario Cadena *(Coord-Logistics)*
Mark Lincecum *(Bus Mgr-Fisher Severe Svc)*
Scott Nicely *(Mgr-Staging Centre)*
Tim Vautherine *(Mgr-Asset)*
Bart Thomas *(Mgr-Sls)*
Jennifer Stolting *(Mgr)*
Bryan McGowan *(Acct Mgr)*
Gary Rhodes *(Acct Mgr)*
Jim McLaughlin *(Acct Mgr)*
Mike Taylor *(Acct Mgr)*
Robert Meinecke *(Acct Mgr)*
Shannon Sanders *(Acct Mgr)*
Brian Frame *(Acct Mgr-Asset Reliability & Optimization)*
Albert Grobmyer *(Pres)*
Shelly Marshall *(Project Coord)*
Michael Wagner *(Project Mgr)*
Sherry Camet *(Sr Mgr-Sls)*
Carla Pruneda *(Supvr-Sls)*
Shawn Chambers *(Acct Mgr)*
Wayne Bland *(Mgr-Inside Sls-Field Instrumentation)*

PUGET SOUND INTERNATIONAL, INC.
33400 8th Ave S Ste 205, Federal Way, WA 98003
Tel.: (253) 272-1099
Web Site: http://www.psi-intl.com
Rev.: $10,500,000
Emp.: 150
General Warehousing & Storage
N.A.I.C.S.: 493110
Mike O'Malley *(VP)*

PUGET SOUND PILOTS
101 Stewart St Ste 900, Seattle, WA 98101
Tel.: (206) 728-6400
Web Site: http://www.pspilots.org
Sales Range: $10-24.9 Million
Emp.: 15
Piloting Storage Vessels Mfr
N.A.I.C.S.: 488330
David Grove Smith *(Pres)*

PUGET SOUND PIPE & SUPPLY CO
7816 S 202nd St, Kent, WA 98032
Tel.: (253) 796-9350
Web Site: http://www.pugetpipe.com
Rev.: $40,000,000
Emp.: 100
Pipes & Fittings, Plastic

COMPANIES

N.A.I.C.S.: 423720
Gary Stratiner *(Pres & CEO)*
Steve Lewis *(CFO & Exec VP)*
Kara Harmon *(Mgr-Billing)*

PUGH OIL COMPANY
1001 Michigan Blvd, Racine, WI 53402-4915
Tel.: (262) 632-4492 WI
Sales Range: Less than $1 Million
Emp.: 5
Retailer & Distributor of Gas, Diesel & Home Fuels
N.A.I.C.S.: 457120
Joseph Arvai *(VP)*
William Pugh Jr. *(Pres & Treas)*

Subsidiaries:

Pugh Marina (1)
1001 Michigan Blvd, Racine, WI 53402
Tel.: (262) 632-8515
Web Site: http://www.pughmarina.com
Marina & Restaurant
N.A.I.C.S.: 457120
William Pugh Jr. *(Pres)*

Quick Flash Oil Co. (1)
11815 W Bradley Rd, Milwaukee, WI 53224
Tel.: (414) 359-1100
Web Site: http://www.quickflash.com
Retailer & Distributor of Gas, Diesel & Home Fuels
N.A.I.C.S.: 424710
Charles Jacobus *(Mng Dir)*

PUGH OIL COMPANY INC.
701 McDowell Rd, Asheboro, NC 27205-7370
Tel.: (336) 629-2061 NC
Web Site: http://www.pughoil.com
Year Founded: 1982
Sales Range: $50-74.9 Million
Emp.: 100
Wholesalers of Petroleum Products
N.A.I.C.S.: 424720
Ronald Pugh *(CEO)*
Tom Morris *(Controller)*

PUGLIA ENGINEERING INC.
2216 E 11th St, Tacoma, WA 98421
Tel.: (253) 627-7232
Web Site: http://www.pugliaengineering.com
Sheet Metal Work Mfg
N.A.I.C.S.: 332322
Karen Hedrick *(Controller)*
Neil Turney *(Owner)*

Subsidiaries:

BAE Systems (1)
Foot of 20th St, San Francisco, CA 94107
Tel.: (415) 861-7447
Sales Range: $75-99.9 Million
Emp.: 400
Ship Building & Repairing
N.A.I.C.S.: 336611

PUGLIESE INTERIOR SYSTEMS INC.
30182 Esperanza, Rancho Santa Margarita, CA 92688
Tel.: (949) 837-9194 CA
Web Site: http://www.puglieseaccessfloors.com
Year Founded: 1976
Sales Range: $10-24.9 Million
Emp.: 5
Providers of Demountable Floor Installation
N.A.I.C.S.: 238990
Gene Anawalt *(Pres)*

PUGMIRE AUTOMOTIVE GROUP
1865 Cobb Pkwy S, Marietta, GA 30060
Tel.: (770) 952-2261
Web Site: http://www.pugmire.com
Sales Range: $50-74.9 Million
Emp.: 70
Sales & Service For New & Used Automobiles
N.A.I.C.S.: 441110
Richard H. Pugmire *(Pres)*

PUKLICH CHEVROLET, INC.
3701 State St, Bismarck, ND 58503
Tel.: (701) 223-5800
Web Site: http://www.puklichchevrolet.com
Sales Range: $25-49.9 Million
Emp.: 95
Car Whslr
N.A.I.C.S.: 441110
Chris Davis *(Mgr)*

PULASKI ELECTRIC SYSTEM, INC. (PES)
128 S 1st St, Pulaski, TN 38478-3216
Tel.: (931) 363-2522 TN
Web Site: http://www.pulaskielectric.org
Year Founded: 1891
Sales Range: $25-49.9 Million
Emp.: 60
Municipal Electric System
N.A.I.C.S.: 221122
Anita King *(Mgr-HR)*

PULASKI-WHITE RURAL TELEPHONE COOPERATIVE, INC.
306 S State Rd 39, Buffalo, IN 47925
Tel.: (574) 278-7121
Web Site: https://www.lightstream.coop
Emp.: 100
Internet Service Provider
N.A.I.C.S.: 517111
Brent Gillum *(Pres & CEO)*

PULAU CORPORATION
12633 Challenger Pkwy Ste 200, Orlando, FL 32826
Tel.: (407) 380-9191
Web Site: http://www.pulau.com
Year Founded: 1975
Medical & Government Training, Logistics & Supply Chain Management Services
N.A.I.C.S.: 541519
Michael J. Armstrong *(Pres)*

PULIDO ASSOCIATES INC.
4924 Old Benbrook Rd, Fort Worth, TX 76116
Tel.: (817) 731-4241
Web Site: http://www.pulidosrestaurant.com
Sales Range: $10-24.9 Million
Emp.: 40
Mexican Restaurant
N.A.I.C.S.: 722511
Robert Pulido Sr. *(Pres)*

PULSAR ADVERTISING, INC.
8383 Wilshire Blvd Ste 334, Beverly Hills, CA 90211
Tel.: (323) 302-5110 NY
Web Site: http://www.pulsaradvertising.com
Year Founded: 1992
Rev.: $17,000,000
Emp.: 35
Advetising Agency
N.A.I.C.S.: 541810
Alberto Gonzalez *(Pres, Exec Dir-Creative)*
Morgan Daniels *(Assoc Dir-Creative)*
David Uratsu *(CFO)*
James Wright *(Reg Dir-East Coast)*

Subsidiaries:

Pulsar Advertising, Inc. (1)
1023 15th St NW Ste 800, Washington, DC 20005
Tel.: (202) 775-7456
Web Site: http://www.pulsaradvertising.com
Sales Range: $10-24.9 Million
Emp.: 8
N.A.I.C.S.: 541810
Katherine Carlson *(Mng Dir)*

Pulsar Advertising, Inc. (1)
830 E Main St Ste 2310, Richmond, VA 23219
Tel.: (804) 225-8300
Web Site: http://www.pulsaradvertising.com
Sales Range: Less than $1 Million
Emp.: 8
N.A.I.C.S.: 541810
Jim Wright *(Reg Dir-East Coast)*
Sandy Snead *(Acct Supvr)*
Tamara Neil *(Account Exec-PR)*

PULSEPOINT INC.
20 Broad St 6th Fl, New York, NY 10005
Tel.: (212) 706-4800
Web Site: http://www.pulsepoint.com
Emp.: 150
Advertising Software Developer
N.A.I.C.S.: 513210
Sloan Gaon *(CEO)*
Darline Jean *(COO)*
Mitchell Eisenberg *(Gen Counsel & Sr VP-Corp Dev)*
Jad Nehme *(CTO)*
Andrew Stark *(Sr VP-Content Solutions)*
Chris Neuner *(Sr VP & Gen Mgr-Digital Health Solutions)*
Jack Dempsey Southerland III *(Sr VP-Programmatic Solutions)*

Subsidiaries:

Pulsepoint Ltd. (1)
The Euston Office One Euston Square 40 Melton St, London, NW1 4FD, United Kingdom
Tel.: (44) 203 574 4607
Web Site: http://www.pulsepoint.com
Emp.: 15
Advertising Software Developer
N.A.I.C.S.: 513210
Gareth Shaw *(Mng Dir)*

PULSETECH PRODUCTS CORPORATION
1100 S Kimball Ave, Southlake, TX 76092-9009
Tel.: (817) 329-6099 TX
Web Site: http://www.pulsetech.net
Year Founded: 1994
Battery Maintenance & Testing Products Mfr; Solar Panel Mfr
N.A.I.C.S.: 334413
Zena Johnson *(Mgr-Mktg)*
Pete Smith *(CEO)*

PULTE ACQUISITION CORP.
321 N Clark St Ste 500, Chicago, IL 60654
Tel.: (312) 445-6523 DE
Year Founded: 2015
Emp.: 3
Investment Services
N.A.I.C.S.: 523999
Charles Heinzelman *(Chm)*
William J. Pulte *(CEO)*
Marc Urbach *(CFO & Treas)*

PUMC HOLDING CORPORATION
31-35 S St, Danbury, CT 06810
Tel.: (203) 743-6741
Web Site: http://www.preferred-mfg.com
Sales Range: $10-24.9 Million
Emp.: 73
Manufacture Gas Burners, Industrial

N.A.I.C.S.: 333414
David G. Bohn *(Pres)*
David G. Paddock *(CFO & Sec)*

Subsidiaries:

Preferred Utilities Manufacturing Corporation (1)
31 35 S St, Danbury, CT 06810-8147
Tel.: (203) 743-6741
Web Site: http://www.preferred-mfg.com
Sales Range: $10-24.9 Million
Combustion Equipment; Combustion Controls & Data Acquisition Systems; Fuel Oil Handling Equipment, Pump Sets, Day Tanks Filtration Systems & Oil & Gas Burners Mfr
N.A.I.C.S.: 334519
Chuck White *(VP)*
David Eoff *(Mgr-Sls-Natl)*

Subsidiary (Domestic):

W.N. Best (2)
31-35 S St, Danbury, CT 06810-8147
Tel.: (203) 743-6741
Web Site: http://www.preferred-mfg.com
Mfr of Industrial Heat & Process Burners; Specialty Burners for Waste & Acid Sludge Decomposition; Skimmings Burners
N.A.I.C.S.: 334519
David G. Paddock *(Sec)*

PUMFORD CONSTRUCTION INC.
1674 Champagne Dr N, Saginaw, MI 48604-9202
Tel.: (989) 754-6262
Web Site: http://www.pumford.com
Year Founded: 1972
Rev.: $25,155,329
Emp.: 100
Industrial Buildings & Warehouses
N.A.I.C.S.: 236220
Matt Pumford *(Pres)*
Greg Turner *(COO)*
Pamela Rees *(Controller & Dir-HR)*
Eric Wagner *(Chief Estimator Officer & VP)*
James Jacobs *(VP-Corp Accounts)*

Subsidiaries:

Gregory Construction Inc. (1)
1674 Champagne Dr, Saginaw, MI 48708-5468
Tel.: (989) 892-4551
Web Site: http://www.gregoryconstructionco.com
Sales Range: $10-24.9 Million
Emp.: 50
Industrial Buildings & Warehouses
N.A.I.C.S.: 236220
Gordon Burnside *(Dir-Corp Safety)*

PUMP & METER SERVICE INC.
11303 Excelsior Blvd, Hopkins, MN 55343
Tel.: (952) 933-4800
Web Site: http://www.pump-meter.com
Rev.: $12,000,000
Emp.: 46
Provider of Service Station Equipment
N.A.I.C.S.: 238990
Joe Radermacher *(CEO)*

PUMPING SYSTEMS INC.
1100 Vijay Dr, Atlanta, GA 30341
Tel.: (770) 458-9555
Web Site: http://www.pumping-systems.com
Year Founded: 1978
Sales Range: $10-24.9 Million
Emp.: 16
Pumps & Pumping Equipment
N.A.I.C.S.: 423830
John Kokoska *(Pres & CEO)*
Steve Peters *(VP-Ops)*

PUMPING SYSTEMS INC.   U.S. PRIVATE

Pumping Systems Inc.—(Continued)
Becky Lowry (Engr-Application)
Collier Jackson (VP-Special Accts)
Jay Hunsberger (Engr-Sls Application)

PUMPS PARTS & SERVICE INC.
9325 Forsyth Park Dr, Charlotte, NC 28273
Tel.: (704) 588-6250
Web Site: http://www.pp-s.com
Sales Range: $10-24.9 Million
Emp.: 56
Mfr of Pumps & Pumping Equipment
N.A.I.C.S.: 423830
William Ray Miller (Pres)
Mike Dysart (VP)
Tyra Bean (Mgr-Mktg)

PUNA PLANTATION HAWAII LTD.
50 E Puainako St, Hilo, HI 96720-5243
Tel.: (808) 959-9111
Web Site: http://www.ktasuperstores.com
Year Founded: 1916
Sales Range: $100-124.9 Million
Emp.: 125
Supermarkets, Chain
N.A.I.C.S.: 445110
Barry Taniguchi (Chm & CEO)
Craig Hamamoto (Exec VP)
Hoku Kamakau (Dir-Store-KTA Express)

PUNCH PRESS PRODUCTS, INC.
2035 E 51st St, Vernon, CA 90058-2818
Tel.: (323) 581-7151
Web Site: http://www.punch-press.com
Year Founded: 1953
Sales Range: $75-99.9 Million
Emp.: 87
Provider of Metal Stamping, Welding & Assembly
N.A.I.C.S.: 332119
C. J. Matiszik (Pres)
Ruth Noriega (Mgr-HR)
Helen Wesley (Controller)
Miguel Moncada (Mgr-Production)

Subsidiaries:

Auto Trend Products (1)
2035 E 51st St, Vernon, CA 90058-2818 (100%)
Tel.: (323) 581-9191
Sales Range: $10-24.9 Million
Mfr of Drip & Drain Pans
N.A.I.C.S.: 332119

PUNDMANN MOTOR CO. INC.
2727 W Clay St, Saint Charles, MO 63301
Tel.: (636) 724-1220
Web Site: http://www.pundmannford.com
Sales Range: $25-49.9 Million
Emp.: 300
New & Used Car Dealers
N.A.I.C.S.: 441110
Tom Pundmann (Pres)
Marc Buchholz (Mgr-Fleet & Comml Sls)
John Foley (Mgr-New Car)
Matt Muraski (Gen Mgr-Sls)

PUPPET LABS INC.
926 NW 13th Ave Ste 210, Portland, OR 97209
Tel.: (877) 575-9775
Web Site: http://www.puppetlabs.com
Year Founded: 2005
Sales Range: $10-24.9 Million
Emp.: 235
Software Publisher
N.A.I.C.S.: 513210
Luke Kanies (Founder)
Deepak Giridharagopal (CTO)
Simon Hayes (Sr VP-Bus & Corp Dev)
Jamie Hull (VP-Product)
Justin Dorff (Mgr-PR)
Gary Green (Sr VP-Worldwide Sls)
Marianne Calder (Mng Dir & VP-EMEA)
Nick Smyth (VP-Engrg-Belfast)
Sandra Hamilton (VP-Customer Success)
Omri Gazitt (Chief Product Officer)
Tim Zonca (VP-Worldwide Mktg)
Tanya Webb (Sr Mgr-Diversity & Inclusion)
Mark Iserloth (CFO)
Darryl McKinnon (Mng Dir-Asia Pacific & Japan & VP)
Tom Broderick (VP)
John Schwan (VP & Partner-Sls & Program-Global)
Terry Wrightson (VP-Americas)
Reza Morakabati (VP-Bus & Tech Ops)
Rahul Singh (VP-Engrg)
Gert Drapers (VP-Engrg & Dir-Seattle Site)
Katie Abbott (VP-Legal & People)
Abby Kearns (CTO)

PUPPET WORKSHOP INC.
295 E 10th Ct, Hialeah, FL 33010-5148
Tel.: (305) 666-2655
Web Site: http://www.puppetworkshop.com
Year Founded: 1977
Rev.: $11,800,000
Emp.: 208
Puppets & Marionettes
N.A.I.C.S.: 339999
Ronnie Burns (Pres)
Gerald Burns (Treas & VP)

PUR-O-ZONE, INC.
345 N Iowa St, Lawrence, KS 66044
Tel.: (785) 843-0771
Web Site: http://www.purozone.com
Sales Range: $10-24.9 Million
Emp.: 36
Janitorial Supplies Distr
N.A.I.C.S.: 424690
Joe Bosco (Office Mgr)
Terry Boyle (Mgr-Sls)
Mike Lane (Mgr-Sls)
Rick Link (Dir-Mktg)
Mike Lockhart (Mgr-Warehouse)
Dave Rethman (Coord-Svc Dept)
Mark McFarland (Mgr-Sls-Wichita-Kansas)

PURA NATURALS, INC.
23615 El Toro Rd X300, Lake Forest, Ca 92630
Year Founded: 2005
PNAT—(OTCBB)
Emp.: 100
Cleaning Products Marketer & Sales
N.A.I.C.S.: 325612

PURACAP PHARMACEUTICAL LLC
20 Kingsbridge Rd, Piscataway, NJ 08854
Tel.: (908) 941-5456
Web Site: http://www.puracap.net
Pharmaceuticals & Healthcare Products Mfr & Sales
N.A.I.C.S.: 325412
Mark Bolling (Exec VP-Sls & Mktg-OTC & Generic Rx)
Dahai Guo (Founder & CEO)
Elise Klein Geiger (Exec VP & Gen Mgr-Sls-Branded Rx)
Xiaofeng Meng (VP-Quality & Regulatory Affairs)
Adam Feng (Sr Dir-R&D)
Mahboob Rahman (VP-Mfg-Global)

Subsidiaries:

PuraCap Caribe LLC (1)
Road 698 Km 0.8 Barrio Mameyal, Dorado, PR 00646
Tel.: (787) 796-0258
Pharmaceuticals Mfr
N.A.I.C.S.: 325412
Gilberto Lleras (Assoc Mgr)
Julio Vallejo (Specialist-IT)

PuraCap Laboratories LLC (1)
301 Robey St, Franklin, KY 42134-1032
Tel.: (270) 586-6386
Web Site: http://www.puracap.net
Emp.: 36
Pharmaceuticals Mfr
N.A.I.C.S.: 325412
Sharon Bigay Luster (Mng Dir)

PURAMED BIOSCIENCE INC.
1326 Schofield Ave, Schofield, WI 54476
Tel.: (715) 359-6373
Web Site: http://www.puramedbioscience.com
Year Founded: 2006
Emp.: 3
Pharmaceuticals Mfr
N.A.I.C.S.: 325412
Russell W. Mitchell (Chm, CEO & CFO)
Patricia McMurtrie (Pres & COO)

PURCELL CO., INC.
4401 E Aloha Dr, Diamondhead, MS 39553-3303
Tel.: (228) 255-7773
Year Founded: 1969
Sales Range: $50-74.9 Million
Emp.: 10
Real Estate Development; Resort, Municipal & Commercial Operations
N.A.I.C.S.: 236115
Bill Alexander (CFO & VP-Fin)
Carl H. Joffe (Gen Counsel & Sec)

Subsidiaries:

Lake Arrowhead Div. (1)
2419 Lake Arrowhead Dr, Waleska, GA 30183 (100%)
Tel.: (770) 720-2700
Web Site: http://www.lakearrowheadga.com
Sales Range: $25-49.9 Million
Emp.: 2
Real Estate Development, Resort & Municipal Operations
N.A.I.C.S.: 237210
Kay Williams (Dir-Mktg)

Sandpiper Cove Div. (1)
775 Gulf Shore Dr, Destin, FL 32541-3138 (100%)
Tel.: (850) 837-9121
Web Site: http://www.sandpipercove.com
Sales Range: $10-24.9 Million
Emp.: 100
Real Estate Development
N.A.I.C.S.: 813990

PURCELL CONSTRUCTION CORP
566 Coffeen St, Watertown, NY 13601
Tel.: (315) 782-1050
Web Site: http://www.purcellconstruction.com
Sales Range: $10-24.9 Million
Emp.: 20
Commercial & Office Building, New Construction
N.A.I.C.S.: 236220
Dale Kraybill (VP-Construction Ops)
Christina Schneider (CFO)
Jim Kingsley (Dir-Safety, Environmental & HR)

PURCELL CONSTRUCTION INC.
277 Dennis St, Humble, TX 77338-4978
Tel.: (281) 548-1000
Web Site: http://www.purcellc.com
Year Founded: 1989
Sales Range: $25-49.9 Million
Emp.: 45
Nonresidential Construction
N.A.I.C.S.: 236220
Larry E. Purcell (Founder)
Glenda Marshall (Controller)

PURCELL INTERNATIONAL INC.
2499 N Main St, Walnut Creek, CA 94596-7161
Tel.: (925) 933-6100
Web Site: http://www.purcell-intl.com
Year Founded: 1950
Sales Range: $10-24.9 Million
Emp.: 13
Supplier of Food
N.A.I.C.S.: 424470
William E. Purcell (Pres)

PURCELL MURRAY COMPANY INC.
235 Kansas St, San Francisco, CA 94103
Tel.: (415) 468-6620
Web Site: http://www.purcellmurray.com
Year Founded: 1981
Sales Range: $75-99.9 Million
Emp.: 100
Large Appliance Mfr & Distr
N.A.I.C.S.: 335999
Kevin Murray (Dir-Mktg)
Mike Maramba (Dir-Ops)
Larissa Taboryski (Dir-Culinary & Mgr-Brisbane Showroom)
Laura Clifton (Gen Mgr-Builder Sls Div)
Curtis Roe (Dir-Fin)
Tim McLoughlin (Gen Mgr-Sls)
Virginia Gonzalez (Mgr-Territory-Southern California)
Larry Chatfield (Mgr-Svc)
Denis Zapata (Mgr-Warehouse-Santa Fe Springs)
Matt Murray (Mng Dir)
Anne Murray Puricelli (Dir-La Cornue)
Helen Adams (Mgr-Inside Sls)
Judy Trigonis (Mgr-Showroom)
Maureen Ashe (Mgr-Territory-Northern California)
Mayra Zavala (Asst Mgr-Warehouse)
Tiffany Stanley (Mgr-Territory-Southern California)

PURCELL TIRE & RUBBER COMPANY INC.
301 N Hall St PO Box 100, Potosi, MO 63664-1403
Tel.: (573) 438-2131
Web Site: http://www.purcelltire.com
Year Founded: 1936
Sales Range: $300-349.9 Million
Emp.: 1,000
Tire Retreading & Repair Services
N.A.I.C.S.: 811198
Roger Lucas (Pres & CEO)

Subsidiaries:

Jacks Tire & Oil Management Co. (1)
1795 N Main St, Logan, UT 84341
Tel.: (435) 752-7987
Web Site: http://www.jackstireandoil.com

COMPANIES

Sales Range: $1-9.9 Million
Emp.: 110
Automotive Tires
N.A.I.C.S.: 441340
J. David Bowen (Pres)
Rob Bowen (VP)

Subsidiary (Domestic):

Jacks Tire & Oil Inc. (2)
1795 N Main St, Logan, UT 84341
Tel.: (435) 752-7811
Web Site: http://www.jackstireandoil.com
Rev.: $7,500,000
Emp.: 25
Automotive Tires
N.A.I.C.S.: 441340
J. David Bowen (Owner)

Purcell Tire & Rubber Company (1)
1505 E Newlands Dr, Fernley, NV 89408
Tel.: (775) 575-3321
Sales Range: $10-24.9 Million
Emp.: 80
Tire Retreading & Repair Services
N.A.I.C.S.: 811198
Harry Costopoulos (Asst Mgr)

Purcell Tire Company of Kentucky (1)
1029 N Green St, Henderson, KY 42420-2753 (100%)
Tel.: (270) 826-3931
Web Site: http://www.purcelltire.com
Sales Range: $10-24.9 Million
Emp.: 15
Mfr of Tires & Tubes
N.A.I.C.S.: 423130
Robert G. Purcell (Pres)

PURCH GROUP, INC.
150 5th Ave 9th Fl, New York, NY 10011
Tel.: (212) 703-5800 DE
Web Site: http://www.purch.com
Emp.: 350
Digital Content & Services
N.A.I.C.S.: 541890
Greg Mason (CEO)
Mike Kisseberth (Chief Revenue Officer)
Doug Llewellyn (Pres & COO)
Antoine Boulin (Head-Corp & Bus Dev & Gen Mgr-Europe)
John Potter (CTO)
Becky Snyder (VP-Org Dev)
Molly Baab (Sr VP & Gen Mgr-Bus-to-Consumer Div)
Aaron Bailey (Sr VP & Gen Mgr-Bus-to-Bus Div)
Phil Barrett (Sr VP & Gen Mgr-Mktg & Shopper Svcs)

Subsidiaries:

Bestofmedia, LLC (1)
9696 Culver Blvd Ste 104, Culver City, CA 90232-2737
Tel.: (310) 279-5500
Web Site: http://www.tomshardware.com
Resource for PC Hardware Reviews & News
N.A.I.C.S.: 513199

BuyerZone.com LLC (1)
225 Wyman St, Waltham, MA 02451-1209
Tel.: (781) 734-8000
Web Site: http://www.buyerzone.com
Sales Range: $10-24.9 Million
Emp.: 50
Business-to-Business Online Marketplace
N.A.I.C.S.: 425120
Aaron R. Bailey (Sr VP & Gen Mgr)
Anne Kelly (VP-Sls)
Jeff Gordon (VP-Product Mktg)
Maureen McCarthy (Sr Dir-Ops)

PURCHASE FORD LINCOLN, INC.
1352 US Hwy 45 N, Mayfield, KY 42066
Tel.: (270) 247-9300
Web Site:
  http://www.purchaseford.com
Year Founded: 2000

Sales Range: $10-24.9 Million
Emp.: 40
Car Whslr
N.A.I.C.S.: 441110
Al Page (Gen Mgr)
Clay Smith Jr. (Pres)

PURCHASES SALES INC.
525 Dickerson Rd, Gaylord, MI 49735
Tel.: (989) 732-5101
Sales Range: $25-49.9 Million
Emp.: 25
Storage, Frozen Or Refrigerated Goods
N.A.I.C.S.: 493120

PURDIE ROGERS, INC.
5447 Ballard Ave NW, Seattle, WA 98107
Tel.: (206) 628-7700 WA
Web Site:
  http://www.purdierogers.com
Year Founded: 1990
Rev.: $12,750,000
Emp.: 12
Advertising Agencies, Full Service, Media Buying Services, Planning & Consultation, Public Relations
N.A.I.C.S.: 541810
George Purdie (Principal)
Andy Rogers (Principal)
Jim McKellar (Exec VP)
Barnett Turk (Dir-Creative)
Kris Nystrom (Sr Art Dir)
Adam Ganz (Acct Supvr)
Andrew Rogers (Pres)

Subsidiaries:

Purdie Rogers, Inc. (1)
2000 Oaks Pl, Arcadia, CA 91006
Tel.: (626) 355-5201
Web Site: http://www.purdierogers.com
N.A.I.C.S.: 541810
Jim McKellar (Exec VP)

PURDUE PHARMA LP
1 Stamford Forum 201 Tresser Blvd, Stamford, CT 06901-3431
Tel.: (203) 588-8000
Web Site:
  http://www.purduepharma.com
Year Founded: 1892
Sales Range: $1-4.9 Billion
Emp.: 1,150
Pharmaceuticals Mfr & Distr
N.A.I.C.S.: 325412
Edward B. Mahony (Head-Due Diligence & Integration Mgmt)
Craig Landau (Pres & CEO)
David Lundie (Head-Technical Ops)
Josephine Martin (Sr VP & Head-Corp Affairs & Comm)
Carina Vassilieva (VP-HR-Canada)
Sarah L. Robertson (Dir-Comm-Canada)
Marcelo Bigal (Chief Medical Officer)
Danielle Lewis (Dir-Corp Comm)
Lisa C. Miller (Head-Corp Social Responsibility)
Steve Miller (Chm)
Marc Kesselman (Sr VP & Gen Counsel)
Julie Ducharme (Chief Scientific Officer & VP)

Subsidiaries:

Mundipharma International Ltd. (1)
191 Cambridge Science Park Milton Road Unit 194 196 & 198, Cambridge, CB4 0GW, United Kingdom
Tel.: (44) 1223424211
Web Site: http://www.mundipharma.com
Sales Range: $10-24.9 Million
Emp.: 800
Mfr & Marketer of Biopharmaceuticals
N.A.I.C.S.: 325414

Susie Hackett (Head-Corp Comm)
Alberto Martinez (Pres & CEO)
Philippe Mazas (CIO)

Napp Pharmaceuticals Ltd. (1)
Cambridge Science Park Milton Rd, Cambridge, CB4 0GW, United Kingdom
Tel.: (44) 1223424444
Web Site: http://www.napp.co.uk
Sales Range: $25-49.9 Million
Emp.: 800
Mfr of Prescription Drug Delivery Systems
N.A.I.C.S.: 339114
Hywel Day (Mng Dir)

Purdue Pharmaceuticals L.P. (1)
4701 Purdue Dr, Wilson, NC 27893
Tel.: (203) 588-8000
Web Site: http://www.purduepharma.com
Pharmaceuticals Mfr
N.A.I.C.S.: 325412
Alan Johnson (Asst Dir-Quality Assurance)
Ann Kraft (Exec Dir-Licensing & Bus Dev)
Brianne Weingarten (Exec Dir-Licensing & Bus Dev)
Corey Adams (Dir-Licensing & Bus Dev)
Kathryn Gregory (Exec Dir-Licensing & Bus Dev)

Purdue Products L.P. (1)
1 Stamford Forum 201 Tresser Blvd, Stamford, CT 06901-3431
Tel.: (203) 588-8000
Pharmaceutical Product Whslr
N.A.I.C.S.: 424210

Rhodes Technologies L.P. (1)
498 Washington St, Coventry, RI 02816
Tel.: (401) 262-9200
Web Site: http://www.rhodestec.com
Pharmaceuticals Mfr
N.A.I.C.S.: 325412

The P.F. Laboratories Inc. (1)
700 Union Blvd, Totowa, NJ 07512
Tel.: (973) 256-3100
Sales Range: $10-24.9 Million
Emp.: 100
Pharmaceuticals Mfr
N.A.I.C.S.: 325412

PURE BRAND COMMUNICATIONS, LLC
2401 Larimer St, Denver, CO 80205-2122
Tel.: (303) 297-0170
Web Site: http://www.pure-brand.com
Year Founded: 2003
Rev.: $4,600,000
Emp.: 18
Fiscal Year-end: 12/31/06
Advertising Agencies
N.A.I.C.S.: 541810
Dan Igoe (Owner & Mng Partner)
Gregg Bergan (Owner)
Anna Ziverts (Acct Exec-PR)
Rachel George (Sr Acct Mgr-PR)
Carly Murphy (Acct Exec)

Subsidiaries:

Pure Brand Communications (1)
1815 Evans Ave, Cheyenne, WY 82001
Tel.: (307) 634-5871
Emp.: 3
N.A.I.C.S.: 541810
Mike Lane (Principal)

PURE FINANCIAL ADVISORS, INC.
3131 Camino Del Rio N Ste 1550, San Diego, CA 92108
Tel.: (619) 814-4100
Web Site:
  http://www.purefinancial.com
Year Founded: 2007
Sales Range: $1-9.9 Million
Emp.: 19
Investment Management Service
N.A.I.C.S.: 523940
Michael Fenison (Founder & CEO)
Bobby Gahvari (Dir-Institutional Advisory)
Anthony Amato (CTO)
Kathryn Bowie (Dir-Client Rels)

PURE POWER TECHNOLOGIES, LLC

Babak Gahvari (Dir-Institutional Advisory)
Maiken Jorgensen (Coord-Mktg)
Danielle Martin (Chief Compliance Officer & Dir-Ops)
Danny Michael (Branch Mgr)
Wendy Miller (Dir-Client Rels-Irvine)
Paul M. Miller (Founder & COO)

Subsidiaries:

HK Financial (1)
4330 La Jolla Vlg Dr Ste 330, San Diego, CA 92122-6241
Tel.: (858) 550-0425
Web Site: http://www.hkfinancial.com
Investment Advice
N.A.I.C.S.: 523940

PURE FRUIT TECHNOLOGIES, LLC
1276 S 820 E Ste 150, American Fork, UT 84003
Tel.: (801) 216-8300
Web Site:
  http://www.purefruittechnology.com
Year Founded: 2002
Sales Range: $1-9.9 Million
Emp.: 11
Botanical Products Mfr & Marketer
N.A.I.C.S.: 325411
Michael Drabiuk (Mgr)

PURE H2O BIO-TECHNOLOGIES, INC.
370 W Camino Gardens Blvd Ste 332, Boca Raton, FL 33432
Tel.: (561) 347-2771
Water Purification Equipment Mfr
N.A.I.C.S.: 333310
Joseph P. Doxey (Pres)

PURE INTEGRATION, LLC
13454 Sunrise Valley Dr Ste 500, Herndon, VA 20171
Tel.: (703) 707-9680
Web Site:
  http://www.pureintegration.com
Year Founded: 2004
Rev.: $13,400,000
Emp.: 50
Management Consulting Services
N.A.I.C.S.: 541618
Greg Stayin (COO)

PURE MARKETING GROUP
5155 Shiloh Rd Ste 200, Cumming, GA 30040
Tel.: (678) 297-1188
Web Site:
  http://www.puremarketinggroup.net
Year Founded: 2006
Sales Range: $1-9.9 Million
Emp.: 10
Promotional Products & Services
N.A.I.C.S.: 541613
Dane VanBreene (Founder & Owner)
Marie Bryan (Acct Exec)
Dane Van Breene (Owner)

PURE POWER TECHNOLOGIES, LLC
1410 N Point Blvd, Blythewood, SC 29016
Tel.: (803) 744-7020
Web Site:
  http://www.purepowertech.com
Diesel Truck Fuel Injection Systems & Other Related Precision Machining Products Mfr
N.A.I.C.S.: 336310
Jerry Sweetland (Pres & CEO)
Richard Marsden (CFO)
Chuck Henderson (Dir-Ops)
Steffen Martin (Chief Engr)

PURE ROMANCE PARTIES, INC.   U.S. PRIVATE

Pure Romance Parties, Inc.—(Continued)

PURE ROMANCE PARTIES, INC.
161 Commerce Blvd, Loveland, OH 45140
Tel.: (513) 248-8656   OH
Web Site: http://www.pureromance.com
Year Founded: 1993
Sales Range: $1-9.9 Million
Emp.: 150
Miscellaneous Personal Services
N.A.I.C.S.: 459420
Patricia Brisben (Founder & Chm)
Cheryl Force (Sr VP-Sls & Trng)
Christopher Cicchinelli (Pres & CEO)
Josh Ephron (Exec VP-Ops)
Heather Battles (Sr VP-Creative)
Rieley Scott (Sr VP-Strategic Initiatives)

Subsidiaries:

Petra Fashions Inc.   (1)
1 2nd St, Peabody, MA 01960-4907
Tel.: (978) 777-5853
Web Site: http://www.petrafashions.com
Lingerie & Sleepwear for Women & Men Whslr
N.A.I.C.S.: 458110

PURE TRANSIT TECHNOLOGIES, INC.
9710 Research Dr, Irvine, CA 92618
Tel.: (949) 798-6600
Fuel Bus Mfr & Distr
N.A.I.C.S.: 336320
Suzanne Herring (CFO)

PURECOAT INTERNATIONAL, LLC
3301 Electronics Way, West Palm Beach, FL 33407
Tel.: (561) 844-0100
Web Site: http://www.purecoat.com
Sales Range: $1-9.9 Million
Emp.: 43
Steel Plating
N.A.I.C.S.: 332111
George Bognar (Pres)
Marshall Menachem (VP-Sls)
Ronald Keohan (Mgr-Production)
Anjel Throckmorton (Mgr-Quality Assurance)
Rachel Trabada (Office Mgr & Mgr-Acctg)

PURECOMMERCE
5600 Post Rd #114-274, East Greenwich, RI 02818
Tel.: (401) 274-8991   RI
Web Site: http://www.purecommerce.com
Year Founded: 1994
Sales Range: $25-49.9 Million
Emp.: 65
E-Commerce Software
N.A.I.C.S.: 513210
Nancy Greenwood (VP)

PUREFORMULAS.COM
11801 NW 100th Rd Ste 4, Miami, FL 33178-1047
Web Site: http://www.pureformulas.com
Year Founded: 2005
Sales Range: $1-9.9 Million
Emp.: 20
Vitamins & Food Supplement Retailers
N.A.I.C.S.: 456191
Jose Prendes (CEO)
Lars Furtwaengler (VP-ECommerce & Mdsg)

PUREFUN! INC.
401 Industrial Park Dr, Lawrenceville, GA 30046
Tel.: (770) 682-8880
Web Site: http://www.purefuninc.com
Year Founded: 1999
Sales Range: $1-9.9 Million
Emp.: 50
Wholesale Food Service, Paper, Janitorial & Classroom Supplies & Apparel for the Child Care Industry
N.A.I.C.S.: 424910
Todd Harrison (Pres)
Michael Jones (Mgr-Ops)
Amy Bowman (Supvr-Sls)

PURELY ALASKAN WATER INC.
1800 Glenn Hwy, Palmer, AK 99645
Tel.: (907) 745-2464
Web Site: http://www.purelyalaskan.com
Year Founded: 1999
Sales Range: $10-24.9 Million
Emp.: 4
Bottled Water & Block Ice Mfr
N.A.I.C.S.: 312112
Robert Gottstein (Pres)

PURETEK CORPORATION
1050 Arroyo St, San Fernando, CA 91340
Tel.: (818) 361-3316   CA
Web Site: http://www.d-care.com
Year Founded: 1992
Sales Range: $25-49.9 Million
Emp.: 250
Pharmaceuticals Mfr
N.A.I.C.S.: 325412
Stephen Pressman (VP-Sls & Mktg)
Millard Delos Santos (Dir-Production & Tech Ops)
Hope Keifer (Mgr-Pur)
Gary Tippitt (VP-Sls)
Jeff Soska (Dir-IT)

PURGATOIRE VALLEY CONSTRUCTION
117 Pine St, Trinidad, CO 81082-2428
Tel.: (719) 846-8449
Web Site: http://www.pvc1inc.com
Year Founded: 2011
Sales Range: $10-24.9 Million
Emp.: 20
Site Preparation Services
N.A.I.C.S.: 238910
Glenn Moltrer (Pres)

PURITAN BAKERY, INC.
1624 E Carson St, Carson, CA 90745-2504
Tel.: (310) 830-5451   CA
Web Site: http://www.puritanbakery.com
Year Founded: 1938
Sales Range: $100-124.9 Million
Emp.: 170
Mfr of Bakery Products
N.A.I.C.S.: 311812
Mark Markulis (Mgr-Sls)

PURITAN CHRYSLER-PLYMOUTH INC.
1200 Cranston St, Cranston, RI 02920
Tel.: (401) 942-7800
Web Site: http://www.puritanchrysler.com
Rev.: $12,925,104
Emp.: 40
Sales of New & Used Cars
N.A.I.C.S.: 441110
Susan Brill (Controller)

PURITAN CLEANERS
1807 Staples Mill Rd, Richmond, VA 23230
Tel.: (804) 355-5726
Web Site: http://www.puritancleaners.com
Drycleaning & Laundry Services (except Coin-Operated)
N.A.I.C.S.: 812320
Debbie Oldham (Mgr)
Gary Glover (Pres)

Subsidiaries:

Handcraft Cleaners and Launderers Inc.   (1)
2733 McRae Rd, North Chesterfield, VA 23235
Tel.: (804) 323-1936
Web Site: http://www.handcraftdrycleaners.com
Industrial Launderers
N.A.I.C.S.: 812332
Jay Nichols (Owner)

PURITAN CLOTHING COMPANY OF CAPE COD
408 Main St, Hyannis, MA 02601
Tel.: (508) 775-2400
Web Site: http://www.puritancapecod.com
Sales Range: $10-24.9 Million
Emp.: 80
Family Clothing Stores
N.A.I.C.S.: 458110
Richard A. Penn (Pres)

PURITY CYLINDER GASES INC.
2580 28th St SW, Wyoming, MI 49509
Tel.: (616) 532-2375
Web Site: http://www.puritygas.com
Year Founded: 1938
Rev.: $25,000,000
Emp.: 250
Gases, Compressed & Liquefied
N.A.I.C.S.: 424690
Gary Nyhuis (Chm)
Glenn Garman (Pres)
Paulette Kooistra (Asst Controller)
Scott Berg (Product Mgr)
Kirk DeWeerd (Mgr-Distr)
Nancy Keegstra (Asst Mgr-Credit)
Ray Leonard (Mgr-Ops)
Jim Brower (Office Mgr)

PURITY WHOLESALE GROCERS, INC.
5300 Broken Sound Blvd NW Ste 110, Boca Raton, FL 33487-3517
Tel.: (561) 994-9360   FL
Web Site: http://www.puritywholesale.com
Year Founded: 1982
Sales Range: $700-749.9 Million
Emp.: 170
Grocery Whslr
N.A.I.C.S.: 424410
Alan Rutner (Co-Pres)
Thomas Jankus (VP-Acctg)
Jeffrey Levitetz (Founder & Chm)
David Groomes (Co-Pres)

Subsidiaries:

Cherin Transportation, Inc.   (1)
300 Purity Dr, Lebanon, IN 46052
Tel.: (765) 483-3730
Web Site: http://www.cherin-inc.com
Logistics Consulting Servies
N.A.I.C.S.: 541614

PURMORT & MARTIN INSURANCE AGENCY, LLC
2301 Ringling Blvd, Sarasota, FL 34237
Tel.: (941) 366-7070   FL
Web Site: http://www.purmort.com
Year Founded: 1958

Sales Range: $1-9.9 Million
Emp.: 36
Insurance Brokerage
N.A.I.C.S.: 524210
Jaime Purmort (Co-Owner)
Russ Bobbitt (Co-Owner)

Subsidiaries:

Lovinger Insurance, Inc   (1)
4106 Henderson Blvd Ste E, Tampa, FL 33629-5750
Tel.: (813) 258-8909
Web Site: http://www.lovingerinsurance.com
Insurance Agencies & Brokerages
N.A.I.C.S.: 524210
Lynne Lovinger (Owner)

PUROHIT NAVIGATION, INC.
233 S Wacker Dr Ste 6220, Chicago, IL 60606-4303
Tel.: (312) 341-8100   IL
Web Site: http://www.purohitnavigation.com
Year Founded: 1985
Sales Range: $75-99.9 Million
Advetising Agency
N.A.I.C.S.: 541810
Ahnal Purohit (CEO)
Monica Noce Kanarek (Chief Creative Officer)
Kim Hogen (CFO)
Anshal Purohit (Pres)
Brad Sherrill (VP-Acct Svcs-West Coast Dev)

PUROSYSTEMS, INC.
Franchise Support Ctr 6001 Hiatus Rd Ste 13, Tamarac, FL 33321
Tel.: (954) 722-6618
Web Site: http://www.puroclean.com
Year Founded: 1990
Rev.: $8,700,000
Emp.: 30
Management Consulting Services
N.A.I.C.S.: 541611
Lesley Wechter (Mgr-Client Svcs)
Will Southcombe (Dir-Trng & Tech Svcs)
David Olson (VP-Trng)
Timothy Courtney (VP-Franchise Dev)
Mark Davis (Chm & CEO)
Steve White (Pres & COO)
Duane Marker (Controller)

PURPLE WAVE, INC
825 Levee Dr, Manhattan, KS 66502
Tel.: (785) 537-7653
Web Site: http://www.purplewave.com
Sales Range: $1-9.9 Million
Emp.: 55
Online Auction Services
N.A.I.C.S.: 459420
Aaron McKee (Founder & CEO)
Eric Williams (CFO)
Suzy McKee (Dir-Resource Allocation)
Richard Bates (VP-Sls)
Jeff Wilson (Dir-Auction)
John Rogers (Dir-Auction)
James Beal (Mgr-Territory)
Jackie Black (Mgr-Territory)
Michael Braun (Mgr-Territory)
Amy Shaneyfelt (Mgr-Mktg)
Rod Hoover (Mgr-Creative & Design)
Bob McBride (Mgr-Territory)
Chuck Fischer (Mgr-Client Svcs)
Clarence Collister (Mgr-Territory)
Jason Moore (Dir-HR)
York Hekel (Dir-Customer Svc)
David Brotton (VP-Mktg)

PURPLE WINE COMPANY
9119 Graton Rd, Graton, CA 95444
Tel.: (707) 938-9229
Web Site: http://www.purplewine.com

Year Founded: 2001
Sales Range: $50-74.9 Million
Emp.: 30
Wine Mfr & Distr
N.A.I.C.S.: 312130
Ron Janowczyk (Sr VP)
Jeff Lubin (VP-Mktg)

PURPLEREAL.COM, CORP.
6371 Business Blvd Ste 200, Sarasota, FL 34240
Tel.: (941) 730-1079 FL
Web Site: http://www.purplereal.com
Year Founded: 2014
Silk Products & Costume Jewelry Internet Retailer
N.A.I.C.S.: 424350
Diane J. Harrison (Chm, Pres, CFO & Chief Acctg Officer)
Anna L. Williams (Treas & Sec)

PURSUIT OF EXCELLENCE, INC.
10440 N Central Expy Ste 1250, Dallas, TX 75231
Tel.: (214) 452-7881
Web Site:
  http://www.pursuitofexcellence.com
Year Founded: 1994
Sales Range: $10-24.9 Million
Emp.: 200
Human Resources Outsourcing Specialist
N.A.I.C.S.: 541612
Marie Diaz (Founder & Chief Visionary Officer)
Myla Galvan (Dir-Special Events)
Mark Galvan (Pres & Chief Strategy Officer)
Ryan T. Veale (Dir-Ops)

PURVIS BEARING SERVICE LTD.
10500 N Stemmons Fwy, Dallas, TX 75220
Tel.: (214) 358-5500
Web Site:
  http://www.purvisindustries.com
Year Founded: 1945
Rev.: $50,000,000
Emp.: 300
Power Transmission Products, Bearings & Linear Components Distr
N.A.I.C.S.: 423830
Robert W. Purvis (Pres)
Gail Purvis (Treas & Sec)

Subsidiaries:

Acadiana Bearing Co (1)
400 Jefferson Blvd, Lafayette, LA 70501
Tel.: (337) 261-0101
Rev.: $2,850,000
Emp.: 5
Industrial Supplies Merchant Whslr
N.A.I.C.S.: 423840

Conveyor Aggregate Products Corp. (1)
10500 N Stemmons Fwy, Dallas, TX 75220 (100%)
Tel.: (214) 358-5588
Web Site: http://www.capcorp.com
Sales Range: $10-24.9 Million
Emp.: 75
Provider of Conveyor Belting Services
N.A.I.C.S.: 333922
Cameron Barker (Dir-Ops)

PURVIS BROTHERS INC.
321 Mars Valencia Rd, Mars, PA 16046
Tel.: (724) 625-1566 PA
Web Site: http://www.purvisbros.com
Year Founded: 1928
Sales Range: $25-49.9 Million
Emp.: 70
Provider of Fuel
N.A.I.C.S.: 424710

Denise Kristofic (Office Mgr)

PURVIS FORD, INC.
3660 Jefferson Davis Hwy, Fredericksburg, VA 22408
Tel.: (540) 898-3000
Web Site: http://purvisford.net
Year Founded: 1970
Sales Range: $75-99.9 Million
Emp.: 110
Car Whslr
N.A.I.C.S.: 441110
Dave Eadie (Coord-Customer Care)
R. Eli Patrick (Pres)

PUSH
101 Ernestine St, Orlando, FL 32801-2317
Tel.: (407) 841-2299
Web Site: http://www.pushhere.com
Year Founded: 1996
Sales Range: $25-49.9 Million
Emp.: 35
Full Service
N.A.I.C.S.: 541810
John Ludwig (CEO)
Gary LaPage (Sr VP & Dir-Media)
Chris Robb (Partner & Chief Creative Officer)
Mark Unger (Dir-Creative & New Media)
Erik Schroeder (Dir-Mktg)
Corey Miller (Assoc Dir-Media)
Lynn Whitney-Smith (Dir-Project Mgmt)
Laura Dagner (Project Mgr)
Jason Poinsette (Dir-Acct Mgmt)
Ron Boucher (Dir-Creative)
Andy MacMillin (Assoc Dir-Creative)
Heather McBride (Sr Acct Exec-PR)
Susan Watts (Jr Media Planner & Buyer)
Bree Adamson (Copywriter)
Kevin Harrell (Copywriter)

PUSH CREATIVE
1697 Broadway Suite 500, New York, NY 10019
Tel.: (212) 269-0700
Web Site: http://www.pushcreative.tv
Year Founded: 2000
Emp.: 100
Branding Services Agency
N.A.I.C.S.: 541810
Rudy Gaskins (CEO & Exec Dir-Creative)
Joan Baker (Sr VP-Pub Rel)
Frank Rodrigues (Exec Producer)
Sean Miller (Dir-Comm)

PUSH INC.
1100 Lindy St, Rice Lake, WI 54868
Tel.: (715) 236-7874
Web Site: http://www.push-inc.com
Year Founded: 1974
Sales Range: $10-24.9 Million
Emp.: 135
Cable Laying Construction
N.A.I.C.S.: 237130
Jack Lapcinski (Pres)
Lynn Haugen (Office Mgr)
Pat Mattmiller (Bus Mgr)

PUSH PEDAL PULL, INC.
2306 W 41st St, Sioux Falls, SD 57105
Tel.: (605) 334-7740
Web Site:
  http://www.pushpedalpull.com
Sales Range: $10-24.9 Million
Emp.: 120
Exercise Equipment
N.A.I.C.S.: 459110
Martin Bruder (Pres)

PUSH, INC.
501 Church St Ste 317, Vienna, VA 22180
Tel.: (703) 938-7500 NV
Year Founded: 2009
Wellness Care Products Distr
N.A.I.C.S.: 424210
Ted Wong (Pres & CEO)
Howard Sidman (CFO, Treas & Sec)

PUTNALS PREMIUM PINESTRAW INC.
4987 E US Hwy 27, Mayo, FL 32066
Tel.: (386) 294-1075 GA
Web Site:
  http://www.putnalspinestraw.com
Year Founded: 1971
Sales Range: $10-24.9 Million
Emp.: 15
Producer of Farm Supplies
N.A.I.C.S.: 424910
James Carlsen (Pres)

PUTNAM COMPANY
11499 Rte 6, Wellsboro, PA 16901
Tel.: (570) 723-8000
Web Site:
  http://www.acornmarkets.com
Year Founded: 1938
Sales Range: $25-49.9 Million
Emp.: 250
Owner & Operator of Convenience Stores
N.A.I.C.S.: 445131
Edward H. Owlett III (Pres & CEO)

PUTNAM COUNTY BANK INC.
2761 Main St, Hurricane, WV 25526
Tel.: (304) 562-9931 WV
Web Site: http://www.putcopk.com
Year Founded: 1901
Sales Range: $25-49.9 Million
Emp.: 80
State Commercial Banks
N.A.I.C.S.: 522110
John R. Wilson (Pres & CEO)

PUTNAM COUNTY SAVINGS BANK
2477 Rte 6, Brewster, NY 10509-0417
Tel.: (845) 279-7101
Web Site: http://www.pcsb.com
Year Founded: 1871
Sales Range: $1-4.9 Billion
Emp.: 178
Federal Savings Bank
N.A.I.C.S.: 522180
Michael Goldrick (Exec VP & Chief Lending Officer)
Ruth Leser (Sec, Sr VP & Dir-HR)
Rich Petrone (Chief Credit Officer & Sr VP)
Robert Farrier (Officer-Retail Banking & Sr VP)
Joseph D. Roberto (Chm, Pres & CEO)
Scott Nogles (CFO, Treas & Exec VP)
Carol Bray (CIO & Sr VP)
Dave McNamara (Officer-Compliance & Sr VP)
Dominick Petramale (Officer-Retail Banking, Sr VP & Dir-Cash Mgmt Svcs)
Clifford Weber (Chief Risk Officer, Gen Counsel & Sr VP)

PUTNAM LEXUS
390 Convention Way, Redwood City, CA 94063-1405
Tel.: (650) 363-8500
Web Site:
  http://www.putnamlexus.com
Year Founded: 1989
Sales Range: $10-24.9 Million
Emp.: 75

Car Whslr
N.A.I.C.S.: 441110
Candace Francesconi (Bus Mgr)

PUTNAM PLASTICS, INC.
30 W Stardust Rd, Cloverdale, IN 46120
Tel.: (765) 795-6102
Web Site:
  http://www.putnamplasticsinc.com
Sales Range: $10-24.9 Million
Emp.: 60
Plastics Bag Mfr
N.A.I.C.S.: 326111
Debbie Underwood (Office Mgr)

PUTNAM SOURCING GROUP
2133 E 38th St, Los Angeles, CA 90058
Tel.: (323) 583-2501
Web Site:
  http://www.putnamsource.com
Year Founded: 1983
Sales Range: $10-24.9 Million
Emp.: 18
Provider of Men's & Boy's Clothing
N.A.I.C.S.: 315250
Brad Eisman (Dir-Sls)

PUTNAM-GREENE FINANCIAL CORPORATION
100 S Madison St, Eatonton, GA 31024
Tel.: (706) 485-9941 GA
Year Founded: 1986
Bank Holding Company
N.A.I.C.S.: 551111
Lurner O. Benton III (Pres)

Subsidiaries:

Farmers & Merchants Bank (1)
100 S Madison Ave, Eatonton, GA 31024
Tel.: (706) 485-9941
Web Site: http://www.ibankfmb.com
Rev.: $7,559,000
Assets: $201,666,000
Liabilities: $179,733,000
Net Worth: $21,933,000
Earnings: $90,000
Emp.: 49
Fiscal Year-end: 12/31/2013
Retail & Commercial Banking
N.A.I.C.S.: 522110
Lurner O. Benton III (Pres & CEO)

First Bank of Coastal Georgia (1)
250 W Bacon St, Pembroke, GA 31321
Tel.: (912) 653-4396
Web Site: http://www.firstbankofcg.com
Rev.: $4,622,000
Assets: $130,996,000
Liabilities: $116,509,000
Net Worth: $14,487,000
Earnings: $981,000
Emp.: 30
Fiscal Year-end: 12/31/2012
Retail & Commercial Banking
N.A.I.C.S.: 522110

The Citizens Bank of Cochran (1)
124 E Dykes St PO Box 427, Cochran, GA 31014
Tel.: (478) 934-6277
Web Site:
  http://www.citizensbankcochran.com
Rev.: $2,486,000
Assets: $70,522,000
Liabilities: $62,880,000
Net Worth: $7,642,000
Earnings: $987,000
Emp.: 22
Fiscal Year-end: 12/31/2013
Retail & Commercial Banking
N.A.I.C.S.: 522110
Lurner O. Benton III (Pres & CEO)
Brian Bazemore (Sr VP)

The Farmers Bank (1)
202 S Main St, Greensboro, GA 30642
Tel.: (706) 453-2335
Web Site: http://www.farmbk.com

PUTNAM-GREENE FINANCIAL CORPORATION U.S. PRIVATE

Putnam-Greene Financial
Corporation—(Continued)
Sales Range: $1-9.9 Million
Emp.: 15
Commericial Banking
N.A.I.C.S.: 522110
A. Sidney Lane (Pres)

PUTT-PUTT, LLC
300 S Liberty St Ste 110, Winston Salem, NC 27101
Tel.: (336) 714-3950   NC
Web Site: http://www.putt-putt.com
Year Founded: 2004
Sales Range: Less than $1 Million
Emp.: 3
Miniature Golf Recreational Centers Franchisor
N.A.I.C.S.: 713940
David M. Callahan (Partner)
Robin Kerr (Exec VP-Mktg)
David E. Cassels III (Partner)
Joseph E. Warner III (Partner)

Subsidiaries:

The Professional Putters Association   (1)
8105 Timberlake Rd, Lynchburg, VA 24502
Tel.: (434) 237-7888
Web Site: http://www.proputters.com
Professional Putting Organization
N.A.I.C.S.: 813920
Jim Evans (Partner)

PUTUMAYO WORLD MUSIC INC.
28 W 25th St 5th Fl, New York, NY 10010
Tel.: (212) 625-1400   NY
Web Site: http://www.putumayo.com
Year Founded: 1993
Sales Range: $10-24.9 Million
Emp.: 100
Whslr of Tapes & Cassettes; Prerecorded
N.A.I.C.S.: 423990
Dan Storper (Founder & CEO)
Hy Shiloff (Mgr-Accts)

PUYALLUP TRIBAL HEALTH AUTHORITY
2209 E 32nd St, Tacoma, WA 98404
Tel.: (253) 593-0232   WA
Web Site: http://www.eptha.com
Year Founded: 1981
Sales Range: $25-49.9 Million
Emp.: 222
Health Care Srvices
N.A.I.C.S.: 622110
Christine Henry (Exec Dir)
Alan Shelton (Dir-Medical)
Mike Crocker (CFO)

PUYALLUP TRIBE OF INDIANS
3009 E Portland Ave, Tacoma, WA 98404
Tel.: (253) 573-7800
Web Site: http://puyallup-tribe.com
Business Support Services
N.A.I.C.S.: 561499
Bill Sterud (Chm)

Subsidiaries:

Ames International Inc.   (1)
4401 Industry Dr E, Fife, WA 98424
Tel.: (253) 235-4866
Web Site: https://www.emilyschocolates.com
Sales Range: $10-24.9 Million
Emp.: 45
Packaged Chocolates, Nuts & Snack Mfr
N.A.I.C.S.: 424450
George Paulose (Founder)
Ryan Clark (Coord-Shipping)
Manu Kurian (Mgr-Ops)
Leo Schultz (Controller)
Amy Palouse (Pres)

PVE SHEFFLER, LLC
Waterfront Corp Park III 2000 Georgetowne Dr Ste 101, Sewickley, PA 15143-8992
Tel.: (724) 444-1100
Web Site: http://www.pvesheffler.com
Engineering, Surveying & Environmental Services
N.A.I.C.S.: 541330
Robert Macomber (Chief Growth Officer)

PVPII - FNSS ACQUISITION, INC.
277 Mallory Station Rd Ste 112, Franklin, TN 37067
Tel.: (615) 224-0400   DE
Web Site: http://grabglobal.com
Perimeter Security, Installation & Specialty Construction Management Services
N.A.I.C.S.: 237990
Brian Cooper (CEO)
Paul Bazzano (VP-Sls & Bus Dev)
Natalie Hill (VP-Fin)
Chris Tucker (Dir-Project Mgmt & Engrg)
Robert Saldana (Mgr-Info Sys)

Subsidiaries:

CatsClaw Americas, LLC   (1)
1489 Barker Dr, Randleman, NC 27317-7873
Tel.: (336) 339-0204
Web Site: http://www.catsclawamericas.com
Specialty Trade Contractors
N.A.I.C.S.: 238990

PVS CHEMICALS, INC.
10900 Harper Ave, Detroit, MI 48213-3364
Tel.: (313) 921-1200   MI
Web Site: http://www.pvschemicals.com
Year Founded: 1945
Sales Range: $200-249.9 Million
Emp.: 350
Industrial Chemicals Production
N.A.I.C.S.: 424690

Subsidiaries:

Chantland MHS Co.   (1)
502 7th St N, Dakota City, IA 50529
Tel.: (515) 332-4045
Web Site: http://www.chantland.com
Sales Range: $10-24.9 Million
Emp.: 70
Conveyor & Conveying Equipment Mfr
N.A.I.C.S.: 333922
Jamie Flot (Pres & COO)

Fanchem, Ltd.   (1)
1012 Gore Road, Freelton, L8B 0Z5, ON, Canada   (100%)
Tel.: (313) 626-2414
Sales Range: $10-24.9 Million
Emp.: 3
Distr & Transporters of Chemicals
N.A.I.C.S.: 424690

PVS Chemical Solutions, Inc.   (1)
10900 Harper Ave, Detroit, MI 48213
Tel.: (313) 921-1200
Web Site: http://www.pvschemicals.com
Emp.: 25
Chemicals Mfr
N.A.I.C.S.: 325998

Unit (Domestic):

PVS Chemicals Solutions Inc. - Buffalo   (2)
55 Lee St, Buffalo, NY 14210-2109   (100%)
Tel.: (716) 825-5762
Web Site: http://www.pvschemicals.com
Sales Range: $10-24.9 Million
Emp.: 48
Mfg. of Chemicals
N.A.I.C.S.: 325180
James B. Nicholson (Pres & CEO)

PVS Chemicals Solutions Inc. - Copley   (2)
3149 Copley Rd, Copley, OH 44321-2127   (100%)
Tel.: (330) 666-0888
Web Site: http://www.pvschemicals.com
Rev.: $12,400,000
Emp.: 18
Chemical Distr
N.A.I.C.S.: 424690

PVS Chemicals Solutions, Inc. - Chicago   (2)
12260 S Carondolet Ave, Chicago, IL 60633-1197   (100%)
Tel.: (773) 933-8800
Web Site: http://www.pvschemicals.com
Sales Range: $10-24.9 Million
Mfr & Distribution of Chemicals
N.A.I.C.S.: 331313

PVS Chemicals Belgium N.V.   (1)
Panterschipstraat 80, Gent, 9000, Belgium   (100%)
Tel.: (32) 92577700
Web Site: http://www.pvs.be
Sales Range: $10-24.9 Million
Emp.: 36
Chemicals Mfr
N.A.I.C.S.: 325998
David Engelen (Gen Mgr)

PVS Technologies, Inc.   (1)
10900 Harper Ave, Detroit, MI 48213-3364   (100%)
Tel.: (313) 921-1200
Web Site: http://www.pvschemical.com
Rev.: $18,200,000
Emp.: 59
Mfr of Chemicals
N.A.I.C.S.: 325998

PVS Transportation, Inc.   (1)
11001 Harper Ave, Detroit, MI 48213-3319   (100%)
Tel.: (313) 921-1200
Web Site: http://www.pvschemicals.com
Sales Range: $1-9.9 Million
Emp.: 60
Trucking Company Responsible for Pickup & Delivery of Chemicals
N.A.I.C.S.: 484110
Brian Wodetzki (Gen Mgr)

PVS-Nolwood Chemicals, Inc.   (1)
10900 Harper Ave, Detroit, MI 48213-3364   (100%)
Tel.: (313) 925-0300
Web Site: http://www.pvschemicals.com
Rev.: $53,000,000
Emp.: 90
Chemical Distr
N.A.I.C.S.: 424690
Timothy Nicholson (Pres)

Siam PVS Chemicals Company Limited (SPVS)   (1)
Thai Virawat Building 7th Floor 86/1 Krungthonburi Rd Banglumpoolang, Bangkok, 10600, Klongsan, Thailand
Tel.: (66) 2 860 8920
Web Site: http://www.siampvs.com
Sales Range: $25-49.9 Million
Emp.: 12
Liquid Ferric Chloride Mfr
N.A.I.C.S.: 325998

PW&D INC.
54 Weldon Pkwy, Maryland Heights, MO 63043
Tel.: (314) 432-3555
Web Site: http://www.power.com
Year Founded: 1992
Sales Range: $25-49.9 Million
Emp.: 50
Windows & Doors Whslr
N.A.I.C.S.: 423310
Cynthia Earl (Controller)

PWH CO MFG, INC.
172 E Industrial Blvd Ste 108, Pueblo West, CO 81007
Tel.: (719) 766-9347
Web Site: http://www.stratoscbd.com
Year Founded: 2014
Sales Range: $1-9.9 Million

Emp.: 50
Pharmaceuticals Product Mfr
N.A.I.C.S.: 325412
Jason Neely (Founder & Pres)

PWI CONSTRUCTION INC.
3903 W Martin Ave, Las Vegas, NV 89118
Tel.: (480) 461-0777
Web Site: http://www.pwiconstruction.com
Year Founded: 1986
Sales Range: $25-49.9 Million
Emp.: 100
Residential Construction
N.A.I.C.S.: 236115
Jeffrey D. Price (Pres)
Marc D. Ferguson (CFO & VP)
Mark Izdepski (VP-Ops)
Nicole Flier (Dir-Mktg & Bus Dev-East)

PWR, LLC.
6402 Deere Rd, Syracuse, NY 13206
Tel.: (315) 701-0210
Web Site: http://www.pwrllc.com
Year Founded: 2000
Sales Range: $10-24.9 Million
Emp.: 74
Telecommunications Industry
N.A.I.C.S.: 517810
Andy Huntington (Mgr-Warehouse)
David Snowman (CFO)
Greg Lessard (Acct Mgr)
Joe Miller (Project Mgr)
Rod Law (Pres)
Ron Rio (Exec VP-Ops)

PWS INVESTMENTS, INC.
6500 Flotilla St, Los Angeles, CA 90040-1714
Tel.: (323) 721-8832   CA
Web Site: http://www.pwslaundry.com
Year Founded: 1968
Sales Range: $10-24.9 Million
Emp.: 100
Holding Company
N.A.I.C.S.: 551112
Morton Pollack (Chm)
Brad Pollack (Pres)

PYCO INDUSTRIES, INC.
2901 Ave A, Lubbock, TX 79404-2231
Tel.: (806) 747-3434   TX
Web Site: http://www.pycoindustries.com
Year Founded: 1936
Sales Range: $200-249.9 Million
Emp.: 330
Cooperative Cotton Seed Processor
N.A.I.C.S.: 311224
Robert Lacy (Pres)
Ronnie Gilbert (Sr VP-Mktg)
Tony Morton (VP-Fin)
Jeff Tucker (Dir-IT)
Thomas W. Horsford (Chm)
Lewis Harvill (VP-Ops)

PYE AUTOMOBILE SALES OF CHATTANOOGA
2131 Chapman Rd, Chattanooga, TN 37421
Tel.: (423) 855-5454
Web Site: http://www.pyeacura.com
Rev.: $11,900,000
Emp.: 35
Automobiles, New & Used
N.A.I.C.S.: 441110
L. F. Pye Jr. (Pres)

PYE-BARKER FIRE & SAFETY, LLC
11605 Haynes Bridge Rd Ste 350, Alpharetta, GA 30009
Tel.: (800) 927-8610

Web Site: https://pyebarkerfs.com
Year Founded: 1946
Masonry Contractors
N.A.I.C.S.: 238140
Anthony Reynolds *(Mgr)*
Bart Proctor *(CEO)*
Chuck Reimel *(VP-Bus Dev)*
Joseph Hightower *(COO)*
Eric Garner *(Pres-Alarm Div)*

Subsidiaries:

AAA Fire Safety & Alarm Inc. (1)
334 N Marshall Way Ste G, Layton, UT 84041-4041
Web Site: http://www.aaafireutah.com
Security System Services
N.A.I.C.S.: 561621
Scott Shriber *(Pres)*

Alarm Specialists, Inc. (1)
333 Old Tarrytown Rd, White Plains, NY 10603
Tel.: (914) 946-1998
Sales Range: $1-9.9 Million
Emp.: 16
Security Systems Services (except Locksmiths)
N.A.I.C.S.: 561621
Gary Davis *(Pres)*
David Levey *(Supvr-Ops)*
Nancy Rout *(Mgr-Sls)*

Alarmguard Security Inc. (1)
305 S Westgate Dr A, Greensboro, NC 27407
Tel.: (336) 854-3281
Web Site:
   http://www.alarmguardsecurity.com
Rev.: $5,341,000
Emp.: 7
Security & Fire Detection Services
N.A.I.C.S.: 561621

Amherst Alarm, Inc. (1)
435 Lawrence Bell Dr, Buffalo, NY 14221
Tel.: (716) 632-4600
Web Site: http://www.amherstalarm.com
Security Systems Services Electrical Contractor
N.A.I.C.S.: 561621
Timothy Creenan *(CEO)*
Mike Saxer *(Mgr-Tech Svc)*
Joseph Schmitt *(Mgr-Installation)*

Automatic Fire Sprinklers, Inc. (1)
7272 Mars Dr, Huntington Beach, CA 92647-4428
Tel.: (714) 841-2066
Web Site: https://www.afsfire.com
Sales Range: $10-24.9 Million
Emp.: 50
Fire Sprinkler System Installation
N.A.I.C.S.: 238220
Susan McClymonds *(VP)*
Gary Peterson *(Pres & CEO)*
Bill Warren *(Dir-Information Technology)*

B Safe Inc. (1)
109 Baltimore Aave, Wilmington, DE 19805
Tel.: (302) 633-1833
Web Site: http://bsafealarms.com
Security Systems Services, except Locksmiths
N.A.I.C.S.: 561621
Philip H. Gardner *(Pres)*
Mary Cakir *(Mgr-Customer Svc)*

Subsidiary (Domestic):

Diamond Electronics LLC (2)
299 Ward St Ste A, Hightstown, NJ 08520
Tel.: (609) 371-9500
Web Site:
   http://www.diamondelectronicsnj.com
Electrical Contractor
N.A.I.C.S.: 238210

Bates Security, LLC (1)
3166 Custer Dr, Lexington, KY 40517-4014
Tel.: (312) 867-9177
Web Site: https://www.batessecurity.com
Locksmiths
N.A.I.C.S.: 561622
Regina Hoover *(Mgr)*

Bender & Modlin Fire Sprinkler, Inc. (1)
170 College Dr Ste G, Orange Park, FL 32065
Tel.: (904) 298-2637
Web Site: http://www.bendermodlin.com
Sales Range: $1-9.9 Million
Emp.: 25
Plumbing, Heating & Air-Conditioning Contractors
N.A.I.C.S.: 238220
C. Allen Bender *(Pres)*
Terry W. Modlin *(Treas & Sec)*
J. R. Holestin *(VP)*

Bevan Security Systems Inc. (1)
190 Tenby Chase Dr., Delran, NJ 08075
Tel.: (856) 461-2234
Web Site: http://www.bevansecurity.com
Rev.: $6,104,000
Emp.: 8
Electrical Apparatus & Equipment, Wiring Supplies & Related Equipment Merchant Whslr
N.A.I.C.S.: 423610
Randall J. Bevan *(Founder)*

Boyd Properties, LLC (1)
3601 N Potsdam Ave, Sioux Falls, SD 57104
Tel.: (605) 367-3176
Web Site: http://www.justicefire.com
Specialty Trade Contractors
N.A.I.C.S.: 238990
Jerry Justice *(Gen Mgr)*

Briscoe Protective Systems, Inc. (1)
99 Mark Tree Rd Ste 201, Centereach, NY 11720
Tel.: (631) 471-2562
Web Site: http://www.briscoeprotective.com
Sales Range: $1-9.9 Million
Emp.: 22
Electrical Work, Nsk
N.A.I.C.S.: 561621
David Miranda *(COO-Comml Svcs)*
Denise Rueda *(Dir-PR)*
Robin Caputo *(Supvr-Acctg)*
Michael Petrone *(Dir-Project Ops)*
Frank Iovino *(Chief Revenue Officer)*
Alexander Schuil *(CEO)*

Subsidiary (Domestic):

Bellringer Security, Inc. (2)
830 County Rd 39, Southampton, NY 11968
Tel.: (631) 283-3400
Web Site: http://www.bellringer.com
Sales Range: $1-9.9 Million
Installs & Services Detection & Security Systems
N.A.I.C.S.: 561621
Edwin J. Thompson *(Pres & CEO)*

Communication Electronics Inc. (1)
800 W Collins Dr, Casper, WY 82601
Tel.: (307) 265-8838
Web Site: http://www.comtronix.biz
Security Systems Services, except Locksmiths
N.A.I.C.S.: 561621
Robert Dobler *(Founder, Treas & Sec)*
Bruce Kopperud *(Founder & Pres)*

Comtron Systems, Inc. (1)
41651 Corporate Way 6, Palm Desert, CA 92260
Tel.: (760) 776-8811
Web Site: http://www.comtronalarm.com
Rev.: $9,870,000
Emp.: 15
Electrical Apparatus & Equipment, Wiring Supplies & Related Equipment Merchant Whslr
N.A.I.C.S.: 423610
Monty Sonensen *(Mgr)*

Cox Fire Protection, Inc. (1)
7910 Professional Pl, Tampa, FL 33637
Tel.: (813) 980-3282
Web Site: https://www.coxfire.com
Sales Range: $1-9.9 Million
Emp.: 120
Fire Protection, Sprinklers & Alarms Installation & Service
N.A.I.C.S.: 238210
Linda Cox *(CEO)*
Scott Cox *(Pres)*
Kevin Palmberg *(Mgr-Alarms Div)*
Shane Rushlo *(Dir-Preconstruction Svcs)*

Dacsis LLC (1)
5110 NE Evangeline Trwy, Carencro, LA 70520
Tel.: (337) 756-2521
Web Site: http://www.dacsis.com
All Other Support Services
N.A.I.C.S.: 561990
Laurie Hohensee *(Owner)*

Fire Alarm Services, Inc. (1)
4800 W 60th Ave, Arvada, CO 80003
Tel.: (303) 466-8800
Web Site: http://www.firealarmservices.com
Security System Services
N.A.I.C.S.: 561621
Shannon Smith *(Co-Founder & Reg Mgr)*

Iowa Fire Equipment Company (1)
2800 Delaware Ave, Des Moines, IA 50317-3543
Tel.: (515) 265-8030
Web Site: http://www.iafire.com
Durable Goods Merchant Wholesalers
N.A.I.C.S.: 423990

Pacific Fire And Security, Inc. (1)
828 Poplar Pl S, Seattle, WA 98144
Tel.: (206) 957-0907
Web Site: http://www.pacificfiresecurity.com
Rev.: $2,700,000
Emp.: 27
Electrical Contractor
N.A.I.C.S.: 238210
Adam Pinsky *(CFO)*
Kelsey Lutton *(Coord-Safety)*
Paul Dalton *(Pres)*

Phoenix Fire Systems, Inc. (1)
744 W Nebraska St, Frankfort, IL 60423
Tel.: (815) 464-9300
Web Site: http://www.phoenixfire.com
Rev.: $7,000,000
Emp.: 30
Site Preparation Contractor
N.A.I.C.S.: 238910
Kirk Humbrecht *(Pres)*

Protect Alarms (1)
1932 S 4th St, Allentown, PA 18103
Tel.: (610) 797-7000
Web Site: http://www.protectalarms.com
Rev.: $4,100,000
Emp.: 50
All Other Miscellaneous Store Retailers, except Tobacco Stores
N.A.I.C.S.: 459999
Albert Taylor *(Pres)*

Rapid Fire Protection, Inc. (1)
1530 Samco Rd, Rapid City, SD 57702
Tel.: (605) 348-2342
Web Site: http://rapidfireinc.com
Fire Protection Services
N.A.I.C.S.: 922160
Matt Hammon *(CEO)*
Brent Peterson *(Mgr-Svc)*
Matt Batie *(VP)*
Rod DiBona *(COO)*
Jared Willson *(Mgr-Sls)*
Melody Sime *(Office Mgr)*
Randy Ables *(Mgr-North Dakota)*
Ross Batie *(Mgr-Utah)*

Subsidiary (Domestic):

Aegis Fire Systems, Inc. (2)
500 Boulder CT Ste A, Pleasanton, CA 94566
Tel.: (925) 417-5550
Web Site: http://www.aegisfire.com
Rev.: $9,000,000
Emp.: 90
Site Preparation Contractor
N.A.I.C.S.: 238910
Thomas McKinnon *(Pres)*
Timothy Higgins *(VP)*

Strickland Fire Protection, Inc. (2)
5113 Berwyn Rd, College Park, MD 20740-4107
Tel.: (301) 474-1136
Web Site: http://www.stricklandfire.com
Plumbing, Heating & Air-Conditioning Contractors
N.A.I.C.S.: 238220
Manning J. Strickland *(Pres)*

S & S Sprinkler Co LLC (1)
14054 Jefferson Hwy, Baton Rouge, LA 70817
Tel.: (225) 753-8512
Web Site: https://www.sssprinkler.com
Rev.: $8,650,000
Emp.: 25

Cosmetics, Beauty Supplies & Perfume Stores
N.A.I.C.S.: 456120

Sentry Watch Inc. (1)
8203 Piedmont Triad Pkwy Ste H, Greensboro, NC 27409
Tel.: (336) 292-6468
Web Site: http://www.sentrywatch.com
Electrical Apparatus & Equipment, Wiring Supplies & Related Equipment Merchant Whslr
N.A.I.C.S.: 423610

Shiver Security Systems, Inc. (1)
15 Pinnacle Point Dr, Miamisburg, OH 45342
Tel.: (937) 228-7301
Web Site: http://www.shiversecurity.com
Rev.: $1,000,000
Emp.: 30
Security System Services
N.A.I.C.S.: 561621
Randy Jackson *(Mgr-Technical)*
Alison Shiver *(Head-Mktg)*
Dwayne Tackett *(Mgr-Ops)*
Hank Little *(Mgr-Svo)*
Wayne Lisle *(VP)*
Chip Shiver *(Pres)*

Systems Design Group LLC (1)
146 Main St Ste A, Flemington, NJ 08822-1616
Tel.: (908) 284-0121
Web Site: http://www.sdg-security.com
Electrical Contractor
N.A.I.C.S.: 238210
Robert Shore *(Pres & CEO)*

The Hartline Alarm Co, LLC (1)
401 N Scenic Hwy, Lake Wales, FL 33853
Tel.: (863) 678-0678
Web Site: http://hartlinealarm.com
Sales Range: $1-9.9 Million
Emp.: 30
Security System Services
N.A.I.C.S.: 561621
Alan Hart *(Pres & CEO)*
Mark Jones *(Gen Mgr)*

Treasure Valley Fire Protection, Inc. (1)
2731 Saturn Way, Boise, ID 83709
Tel.: (208) 362-1888
Web Site: http://www.tvfp.us
Fire Protection
N.A.I.C.S.: 922160
Greg Patrick *(VP)*

PYPHA ENERGY, LLC.
10777 Westheimer Rd Ste 1100, Houston, TX 77042
Tel.: (713) 267-9323
Web Site: http://www.pypha.com
Sales Range: $10-24.9 Million
Emp.: 12
Energy Marketing Services
N.A.I.C.S.: 211130
Ola Oladeji *(Pres)*

PYRAMID ADVISORS LLC
1 Post Office Sq Ste 1950, Boston, MA 02109
Tel.: (617) 412-2800
Web Site:
   http://www.pyramidhotelgroup.com
Year Founded: 1999
Sales Range: $5-14.9 Billion
Emp.: 7,200
Investment Services; Hotel Owner & Operator
N.A.I.C.S.: 523999
Warren Q. Fields *(Chief Investment Officer & Principal)*
James R. Dina *(COO & Principal)*
Richard M. Kelleher *(CEO & Principal)*
John S. Hamilton *(Sr VP-Bus Dev & Acq)*
Caroline Warren *(Chief People Officer & Exec VP)*
Chris Pfohl *(Sr VP-Bus Dev & Acquisition)*
Christopher Devine *(CFO)*
Jim Merrill *(Exec VP-Ops)*

PYRAMID ADVISORS LLC

Pyramid Advisors LLC—(Continued)

Subsidiaries:

Pyramid Hotel Group LLC (1)
1 Post Office Sq Ste 1950, Boston, MA 02109
Tel.: (617) 412-2800
Web Site: http://www.pyramidhotelgroup.com
Emp.: 9,000
Hotel Operator
N.A.I.C.S.: 721110
Warren Q. Fields *(CEO & Principal)*
James R. Dina *(COO & Principal)*
John Hamilton *(Sr VP-Acq & Bus Dev)*
Christopher Devine *(CFO)*
Jim Merrill *(Exec VP-Ops)*

Pyramid Project Management (1)
1 Post Office Sq Ste 3100, Boston, MA 02109
Tel.: (617) 412-2800
Web Site: http://www.pyramidadvisors.com
Sales Range: $25-49.9 Million
Emp.: 50
Hotel Renovation Management Services
N.A.I.C.S.: 236210
Edward Riley *(Sr VP-Project Mgmt)*
Michael Kubick *(VP-Project Mgmt)*

Pyramid Resort Group (1)
1 Post Office Sq Ste 3100, Boston, MA 02109
Tel.: (617) 946-2033
Web Site: http://www.pyramidhotelgroup.com.com
Sales Range: $10-24.9 Million
Emp.: 60
Resort Operator & Manager
N.A.I.C.S.: 721110
Doug Cole *(VP-Asset Mgmt-West)*
Jim Merrill *(VP-Asset Mgmt East)*
Greg Gooding *(Gen Mgr-Westin Lake Las Vegas Resort & Spa)*

PYRAMID BROKERAGE COMPANY INC.
5786 Widewaters Pkwy, De Witt, NY 13214
Tel.: (315) 445-1030
Web Site: http://www.pyramidbrokerage.com
Rev.: $13,000,000
Emp.: 120
Provider of Real Estate Services
N.A.I.C.S.: 531210
John L. Clark *(Pres)*
Robert Berkey *(Chm & CEO)*
Julie Seeley *(Dir-Mktg & Res)*
Karen Bowman-Sangster *(Office Mgr)*
Christopher D. Giunta *(Dir-Sls-Rochester)*
Michael Kalet *(Dir-Sls-Syracuse & Watertown)*
David Schiller *(Dir-Sls-Buffalo)*

PYRAMID CONSULTING, INC.
11100 Atlantis Pl, Alpharetta, GA 30022
Tel.: (770) 248-0024
Web Site: http://www.pyramidci.com
Year Founded: 1996
Sales Range: $50-74.9 Million
Emp.: 75
IT Staff Augmentation, Software Development & Outsourcing Services
N.A.I.C.S.: 541519
Sanjeev Tirath *(Co-Founder, Pres & CEO)*
Ramesh Maturu *(Co-Founder, VP & Dir-Solutions Delivery)*
Namita Tirath *(VP-Mktg & Sls)*

PYRAMID FLOOR COVERING, INC.
38 Harbor Park Dr, Port Washington, NY 11050
Tel.: (516) 932-7200 NY
Web Site: http://www.pyramidfloors.com
Year Founded: 1974
Sales Range: $10-24.9 Million
Emp.: 70
Floor Laying & Floor Work
N.A.I.C.S.: 238330
Tammy Dreher *(Controller)*

PYRAMID HEALTH CARE LP
1894 Plank Rd, Duncansville, PA 16635
Tel.: (814) 944-3035
Web Site: http://www.pyramidhealthcarepa.com
Rev.: $16,900,000
Emp.: 348
Alcoholism & Drug Addiction Rehabilitation Center
N.A.I.C.S.: 622210
Jonathan Wolf *(CEO)*

PYRAMID HOTELS & RESORTS, INC.
30 Rowes Wharf Ste 530, Boston, MA 02110
Tel.: (617) 412-2800 MD
Web Site: http://www.pyramidhotelgroup.com
Year Founded: 2009
Emp.: 10,000
Real Estate Investment Services
N.A.I.C.S.: 525990
Warren Q. Fields *(CIO-Business dev & CIO)*
Richard M. Kelleher *(CEO)*
Jack A. Levy *(Sr VP-Fin Analysis)*
Christopher Devine *(CFO)*
James R. Dina *(COO)*
John Green *(Sr VP-Asset Mgmt)*

Subsidiaries:

Hamilton Hotel Partners Ltd (1)
Exchange Tower harbour Exchange Square Ste 602, London, E14 9GE, England, United Kingdom
Tel.: (44) 2036961947
Hotels Asset Management Services
N.A.I.C.S.: 721110
Frank Croston *(Partner)*

PYRAMID INDUSTRIES, INC.
2200 Secaucus Rd, North Bergen, NJ 07047
Tel.: (201) 348-6300
Web Site: http://www.resources-warehouse.com
Sales Range: $25-49.9 Million
Emp.: 75
Local Trucking & Storage Services
N.A.I.C.S.: 484110
Frank Folise *(Pres)*

Subsidiaries:

Land Bridge Terminals, Inc. (1)
2200 Secaucus Rd, North Bergen, NJ 07047
Tel.: (201) 348-6756
Web Site: http://www.resources-warehouse.com
Sales Range: $10-24.9 Million
Emp.: 15
Local Trucking Services
N.A.I.C.S.: 484110

Resources Trucking, Inc. (1)
2200 Secaucus Rd, North Bergen, NJ 07047
Tel.: (201) 348-6300
Web Site: http://www.resources-warehouse.com
Sales Range: $10-24.9 Million
Emp.: 35
Local Trucking Services
N.A.I.C.S.: 484110
Frank Folise *(Pres)*
Craig Folise *(Treas & Sec)*

PYRAMID MANAGEMENT GROUP, INC.
The Clinton Exch 4 Clinton Sq, Syracuse, NY 13202
Tel.: (315) 422-7000 NY
Web Site: http://www.pyramidmg.com
Year Founded: 1970
Sales Range: $200-249.9 Million
Emp.: 500
Provider of Real Estate Development Services
N.A.I.C.S.: 531120
Cindy Wheeler *(Mgr-HR)*
James DeWolf *(Mgr-IT)*
Molly Moore *(Supvr-Revenue Mgmt)*
Peter Berardi *(Dir-Leasing)*
Melissa Pello *(Supvr-Fin)*
Stephen J. Congel *(CEO)*
Jennifer Smith *(Mgr-Pricing)*

Subsidiaries:

Kingston Collection (1)
101 Kingston Collection Way, Kingston, MA 02364
Tel.: (781) 582-2445
Web Site: http://www.kingstoncollection.com
Shopping Mall Operator
N.A.I.C.S.: 531120
David Gilmore *(Gen Mgr)*

PYRAMID MASONRY CONTRACTORS
2330 Mellon Ct, Decatur, GA 30035
Tel.: (770) 987-4750
Web Site: http://www.pyramidmasonry.net
Sales Range: $25-49.9 Million
Emp.: 200
Bricklaying
N.A.I.C.S.: 238140
John C. Doherty *(Pres)*
Tim Tracy *(VP-Atlanta Div)*
Jim Cook *(Dir-Safety)*
Karen Swords *(Project Mgr)*

PYRAMID MOUNTAIN LUMBER
379 Boy Scout Rd, Seeley Lake, MT 59868
Tel.: (406) 677-2201 MT
Web Site: http://www.pyramidlumber.com
Year Founded: 1949
Sales Range: $10-24.9 Million
Emp.: 135
Supplier of Lumber
N.A.I.C.S.: 321113
Loren Rose *(Controller)*
Charlie Parke *(VP)*
Gordy Sanders *(Mgr-Resource)*

PYRAMID SERVICES, INC.
624-A S Fayetteville St, Asheboro, NC 27203
Tel.: (336) 636-5551
Year Founded: 1990
Sales Range: $50-74.9 Million
Emp.: 5
Facilities Support Services
N.A.I.C.S.: 561210
George Crowell *(CFO & VP)*
Laura J. Wilson *(Pres & CEO)*

PYRAMID SOLUTIONS, INC.
30200 Telegraph Rd Ste 440, Bingham Farms, MI 48025
Tel.: (248) 549-1200 MI
Web Site: http://www.pyramidsolutions.com
Year Founded: 1990
Emp.: 200
Computer Software Development Services
N.A.I.C.S.: 541511
Glenn Beal *(Sr Acct Exec-NCIM)*
Anna Goldsworthy Morris *(Acct Exec)*
Daniel Kosmalski *(CEO)*
Tom Walma *(Engr-Sys & Software)*
Robert DuBois *(Pres)*

U.S. PRIVATE

PYRAMID SYSTEMS, INC.
2677 Prosperity Ave Ste 700, Fairfax, VA 22031
Tel.: (703) 553-0800
Web Site: http://www.pyramidsystems.com
Year Founded: 1995
Sales Range: $10-24.9 Million
Emp.: 85
IT Consulting & Software Engineering
N.A.I.C.S.: 423430
Sherry Hwang *(Owner & Pres)*
Chuck Harris *(COO)*
Daekyu Lee *(VP-Client Ops)*
Kim Weaver *(VP-Fin Tech Solutions)*
Jeff Hwang *(Founder & CEO)*
Stacy Cleveland *(Sr VP-Client Delivery)*
Doug Sickler *(Chief Growth Officer & Sr VP)*

PYRAMID TECHNOLOGIES INC.
1927 Harbor Blvd, Costa Mesa, CA 92627-7600
Tel.: (949) 753-0333
Web Site: http://www.pyramidtechnologiesinc.com
Sales Range: $10-24.9 Million
Emp.: 30
Electronic Parts & Equipment
N.A.I.C.S.: 459920
Tony Mavusi *(Pres)*
Nick Freischlag *(Mgr-QA)*

PYROPURE, INC.
5 Commerce Dr, Aston, PA 19014
Tel.: (610) 497-1743 PA
Web Site: http://www.pyromet999.com
Year Founded: 1969
Sales Range: $10-24.9 Million
Emp.: 30
Precious Metal Refiner
N.A.I.C.S.: 331410
Tony D'Angelo *(VP-Sls)*
Duane Breece *(Plant Mgr)*
Toni Russo *(Mgr-Refining Acct)*
Vicki Pitner *(Mgr-Production Acct)*

Subsidiaries:

Sun Valley Film Wash, Inc. (1)
5 Commerce Dr, Aston, PA 19014
Tel.: (610) 497-1743
Web Site: http://www.sunvalleyfilmwash.com
Silver Recycling Services
N.A.I.C.S.: 423930

PYROTEK INCORPORATED
9503 E Montgomery Ave, Spokane Valley, WA 99206-4115
Tel.: (509) 926-6211 WA
Web Site: http://www.pyrotek-inc.com
Year Founded: 1956
Sales Range: $25-49.9 Million
Emp.: 650
Clay Refractory Services
N.A.I.C.S.: 327120
Allan Roy *(Pres & CEO)*
Paul A. Rieckers *(CFO)*
Mark Palmer *(Dir-Product R&D)*
Steve Davis *(Dir-Mktg)*

Subsidiaries:

EMP Technologies, Ltd. (1)
Faraday House Eastern Avenue, Burton-on-Trent, DE13 0BB, Staffordshire, United Kingdom
Tel.: (44) 1283 741147
Web Site: http://www.emptechnologies.com
Electromagnetic Product Mfr & Distr
N.A.I.C.S.: 333310

Metaullics Systems Co. LP - Sanborn (1)
2040 Cory Rd, Sanborn, NY 14132
Tel.: (716) 731-3221
Web Site: http://www.metaullics.com

COMPANIES

Sales Range: $1-9.9 Million
Emp.: 60
Molten Metal Filtration Services
N.A.I.C.S.: 335991

Metaullics Systems Co. LP - Solon (1)
31935 Aurora Rd, Solon, OH 44139-2717
Tel.: (440) 349-8800
Web Site: http://www.metaullics.com
Sales Range: $25-49.9 Million
Emp.: 95
Molten Metal Filtration Services
N.A.I.C.S.: 335991
Heather Stalanker *(Dir-HR)*

PT. Pyrotek Indonesia (1)
Rukan Niaga III Jl Puri Kencana Blok M 8 No 2F, Kembangan, Jakarta, 11610, Indonesia
Tel.: (62) 21 583 50625
Web Site: http://www.pyrotek.com
Emp.: 12
Industrial Equipmnt Mfr & Distr
N.A.I.C.S.: 333248
Imam Pramutianto *(Country Mgr)*

Pyrobras Comercio e Industria Ltda. (1)
Rua Jose Ruscitto 245 Vila Das Oliveiras Taboao da Serra, Taboao da Serra, 06765-490, Sao Paulo, Brazil
Tel.: (55) 11 2699 6720
Industrial Equipmnt Mfr & Distr
N.A.I.C.S.: 333248

Pyrotek (Asia) Ltd. (1)
20A Kee On Building 200 Hollywood Road Sheung Wan, Hong Kong, China (Hong Kong)
Tel.: (852) 75526951362
Industrial Equipment Distr
N.A.I.C.S.: 423830

Pyrotek (Guangxi Nanning) High Temperature Materials Co., Ltd. (1)
18 Jianye No 1 Road Yinhai Boulevard, Liangquing District, Nanning, 530221, Guangxi, China
Tel.: (86) 771 401 9113
Industrial Equipmnt Mfr & Distr
N.A.I.C.S.: 333248

Pyrotek (Xi'an) Metaullurgical Materials Co., Ltd. (1)
The North of Xihu Rd Qindu Town Hu Country, Xi'an, 710309, Shanxi, China
Tel.: (86) 29 8494 5446
Industrial Equipmnt Mfr & Distr
N.A.I.C.S.: 333248

Pyrotek Bahrain SPC (1)
Building 1349 Road 5136, PO Box 26170, Askar, 951, Bahrain
Tel.: (973) 17 831001
Industrial Equipmnt Mfr & Distr
N.A.I.C.S.: 333248

Pyrotek CZ, s.r.o. (1)
Dolni Lhota, Case Postale 203, Blansko, 678 01, Czech Republic
Tel.: (420) 516 527 111
Emp.: 120
Industrial Equipmnt Mfr & Distr
N.A.I.C.S.: 333248

Pyrotek Dongguan Limited (1)
Caotang Industry Park Hadi, Nancheng District, Dongguan, 523000, Guangdong, China
Tel.: (86) 769 2285 5023
Industrial Equipmnt Mfr & Distr
N.A.I.C.S.: 333248
Robin Wu *(Mgr-Ops)*

Pyrotek Engineering Materials (Pty) Ltd. (1)
Unit 18 Eagle Industrial Park, PO Box 1295, Alton, Richards Bay, 3900, South Africa
Tel.: (27) 35 797 4039
Web Site: http://www.pyrotek.info
Emp.: 15
Fiberglass & Refractory Product Distr
N.A.I.C.S.: 424310
Cylvia Broodryk *(Mgr-Fin)*

Pyrotek Engineering Materials Ltd. (1)
Garamonde Drive Wymbush, Milton Keynes, MK8 8LN, Bucks, United Kingdom

Tel.: (44) 1 908 561155
Web Site: http://www.pyrotek.com
Emp.: 25
Industrial Product Distr
N.A.I.C.S.: 423840
John Thurman *(Gen Mgr)*

Pyrotek FZE (1)
Warehouse No RA08SC07, Jebel Ali, Dubai, United Arab Emirates
Tel.: (971) 48 837 700
Industrial Product Distr
N.A.I.C.S.: 423840

Pyrotek High-Temperature Industrial Products Inc. (1)
221 Enterprise Avenue, Kitimat, V8C 2C8, BC, Canada
Tel.: (250) 632-2717
Emp.: 3
Filtration & Gasket Product Mfr
N.A.I.C.S.: 339991
Derick Steinson *(Branch Mgr)*

Pyrotek Inc. (1)
9601 E Montgomery Ave, Spokane Valley, WA 99206-4115
Tel.: (509) 926-6211
Web Site: http://www.pyrotek-inc.com
Sales Range: $25-49.9 Million
Emp.: 81
Mfr of Asphalt Felts & Coatings
N.A.I.C.S.: 327212
Don Ting *(COO)*
Emma Thompson *(Gen Counsel)*
Mark Arnold *(Mgr-Bus Dev-Advanced Matls Div)*
Beth Winter *(Mgr-Fin Reporting)*
Gordon Albers *(Gen Mgr-Continental Europe)*
Harvey Chalker *(Gen Mgr-Engrg Svcs & Oceania)*
Rejean Dault *(Gen Mgr-Canada)*
Steve Davis *(Gen Mgr-Glass)*
Bruce Gallaher *(Gen Mgr & Dir-Mktg)*
Alex Louie *(Gen Mgr-Asia)*
Paul A. Rieckers *(CFO)*

Pyrotek Inc. (1)
Ricardo Rojas 1064, Puerto Madryn, 9120, Chubut, Argentina
Tel.: (54) 280 4475714
Emp.: 5
Industrial Product Distr
N.A.I.C.S.: 423840
Andres Pascual *(Gen Mgr)*

Pyrotek India Pvt. Ltd. (1)
205 SIDCO Industrial Estate, Thirumazhisai, Chennai, 600 124, India
Tel.: (91) 44 26811071
Industrial Equipmnt Mfr & Distr
N.A.I.C.S.: 333248

Pyrotek Japan Co., Ltd. (1)
1-6 8-Chome Gokohdori Chuo-Ku, Chuo-Ku, Kobe, 651-0087, Japan
Tel.: (81) 78 265 5590
Emp.: 20
Industrial Equipmnt Mfr & Distr
N.A.I.C.S.: 333248
Takami Yoshiyuki *(Gen Mgr)*

Pyrotek Korea (1)
135 A-Dong Taebaek B/D 1171-8 Jungri-Dong, Seo-Gu, Daegu, Korea (South)
Tel.: (82) 53 523 5202
Industrial Product Distr
N.A.I.C.S.: 423840

Pyrotek Ltd. (1)
65 Shakhterov Street, 660020, Krasnoyarsk, Russia
Tel.: (7) 3912020800
Refractory Material Mfr
N.A.I.C.S.: 327120

Pyrotek Mexico, S. de R. L. de C. V. (1)
Decada 5008 Parque Industrial Milenium, Apodaca, 66600, Nuevo Leon, Mexico
Tel.: (52) 811 247 8000
Industrial Product Distr
N.A.I.C.S.: 423840

Pyrotek Netherlands B.V. (1)
Boonsweg 83a, Heinenoord, 3274 LH, Netherlands
Tel.: (31) 186 600007
Industrial Product Distr

N.A.I.C.S.: 423840

Pyrotek Products Ltd. (1)
69 Cryers Road East Tamaki Manukau, Auckland, 2013, New Zealand
Tel.: (64) 9 272 2056
Web Site: http://www.protek.info
Emp.: 30
Ceramic Product Mfr & Distr
N.A.I.C.S.: 327910
Robin Stanley *(Gen Mgr)*

Pyrotek Pty. Ltd. (1)
147 149 Magowar Road, Girraween, 2145, NSW, Australia
Tel.: (61) 288682000
Industrial Equipmnt Mfr & Distr
N.A.I.C.S.: 333248

Pyrotek Refrakter Sanayi ve Ticaret Ltd. Sti. (1)
Siracevizler Cad No14-16 D 9 Bomonti Sisli, 34381, Istanbul, Turkiye
Tel.: (90) 212 233 88 98
Industrial Product Distr
N.A.I.C.S.: 423840

Pyrotek SA (1)
Ile Falcon, 3960, Sierre, Switzerland
Tel.: (41) 27 455 8264
Web Site: http://www.pyrotek.info
Industrial Product Distr
N.A.I.C.S.: 423840

Pyrotek Scandinavia AB (1)
Hokedalen Ed, 668 92, Dals-Ed, Sweden
Tel.: (46) 53462000
Web Site: http://www.pyrotek.info
Emp.: 45
Refractory Material Mfr
N.A.I.C.S.: 327120
Lennart Skoogh *(Mng Dir)*

Pyrotek Thailand Co. Ltd. (1)
424 SOI 68 Sukhumvit Road Bangna, Bangkok, 10260, Thailand
Tel.: (66) 2 361 4870
Industrial Product Distr
N.A.I.C.S.: 423840

Pyroven C.A. (1)
Zona Industrial Matanzas Sur Final Calle Arboleda Con Bucare, PO Box 160, Puerto Ordaz, 8015, Estado Bolivar, Venezuela
Tel.: (58) 286 994 1894
Industrial Product Distr
N.A.I.C.S.: 423840

SNIF Systems (1)
100 Clearbrook Rd Ste 325, Elmsford, NY 10523-1116
Tel.: (914) 345-4740
Aluminum Refining Services
N.A.I.C.S.: 331313
Ozgur Cakmak *(Mgr-Field Engrg)*
Stam Bisiotis *(Mgr-Fin)*

Shenzhen Pyrotek Inc. (1)
Suite 301 Block A Huahan Innovation Park Keyuan Rd, Shenzhen, 518057, Guangdong, China
Tel.: (86) 755 2663 2324
Industrial Product Distr
N.A.I.C.S.: 423840

TAB Refractory Construction & Maintenance Co. Ltd. (1)
Parkdale Industrial Estate Wharf Street Unit 7, Warrington, WA1 2HT, Cheshire, United Kingdom
Tel.: (44) 1925 230 222
Web Site: http://www.tabrefractory.com
Refractory Contracting Services
N.A.I.C.S.: 238140

PYURE BRANDS, LLC
2277 Trade Center Way, Naples, FL 34109
Tel.: (305) 509-5096
Web Site: http://www.pyuresweet.com
Year Founded: 2008
Sales Range: $1-9.9 Million
Sweetener Products Mfr
N.A.I.C.S.: 311999
Ben Fleischer *(Founder)*

PYXERA GLOBAL

1030 15th St NW Ste 730 E, Washington, DC 20005
Tel.: (202) 872-0933 DE
Web Site: http://www.pyxeraglobal.org
Year Founded: 1990
Sales Range: $10-24.9 Million
Emp.: 32
Management Consulting Services
N.A.I.C.S.: 541611
Deirdre White *(CEO)*
Laura E. Asiala *(VP-Client Rels & Pub Affairs)*
Moussa Diouf *(CFO & VP-Fin & Admin)*
Kimberli Jeter *(Chief Learning & Partnership Officer)*
Amanda MacArthur *(VP-Global Pro Bono & Engagement)*

PYXIS TECHNOLOGIES, LLC
45911 Port St, Plymouth, MI 48170
Tel.: (734) 414-0261
Web Site: http://www.pyxistechnologies.com
Year Founded: 2000
Sales Range: $10-24.9 Million
Emp.: 22
Gauge, Test & Assembly Equipment
N.A.I.C.S.: 334519
Jeffrey Wickens *(Owner)*

Q & D CONSTRUCTION
1050 S 21st St, Sparks, NV 89431-5596
Tel.: (775) 786-2677
Web Site: http://www.qdconstruction.com
Sales Range: $50-74.9 Million
Emp.: 650
Construction Engineering Services
N.A.I.C.S.: 237310
Norman L. Dianda *(Pres)*
Laura J. Dianda *(Sec)*
Duane Boreham *(VP-Aviation Svcs)*

Q BLACK, LLC
43 Norfolk St, San Francisco, CA 94103
Tel.: (415) 252-7987
Sales Range: $25-49.9 Million
Emp.: 50
New Media Investment Services
N.A.I.C.S.: 523999
Joseph Q. Bretz *(CEO)*
David E. Blackford *(COO)*
Brian Lillquist *(VP-Bus Dev)*
Richard Verdoni *(CIO)*

Q INTERNATIONAL COURIER, LLC
175-28 148th Ave, Jamaica, NY 11434-5516
Tel.: (718) 995-3616 NY
Web Site: http://www.quick.aero
Year Founded: 1981
Time-critical Transportation & Logistics Services
N.A.I.C.S.: 541614
Nick Tarzia *(Mgr-Logistics)*
Dominique Bischoff-Brown *(COO)*
Mohammed Siddiqi *(Fin Mgr)*
Christopher Curti *(CFO)*

Subsidiaries:

Quick International Courier UK Limited (1)
Unit 1 & 2 Prescott Road Colnbrook Berkshire, Heathrow, Colnbrook, SL3 0AE, Berkshire, United Kingdom (100%)
Tel.: (44) 2088977273
Web Site: http://www.quick.co.uk
Sales Range: $10-24.9 Million
Emp.: 100
Courier Service
N.A.I.C.S.: 492110
Justin Cassin *(Gen Mgr)*

Q INTERNATIONAL COURIER, LLC

Q International Courier, LLC—(Continued)

Unitrans Corporation, Inc. (1)
3789 Groveport Rd, Obetz, OH 43207
Tel.: (614) 492-1144
Web Site: http://www.unitransinc.com
Freight Transportation Services
N.A.I.C.S.: 484121

Q MODEL MANAGEMENT INC.
354 Broadway, New York, NY 10013
Tel.: (212) 807-6777
Web Site: http://www.qmodels.com
Year Founded: 1998
Sales Range: $1-9.9 Million
Emp.: 15
Modeling Agency
N.A.I.C.S.: 711410

Q THERAPEUTICS, INC.
417 S Wakara Way Ste 3510, Salt Lake City, UT 84108
Tel.: (801) 582-5400
Web Site: http://www.qthera.com
Year Founded: 2005
Sales Range: Less than $1 Million
Biopharmaceutical Researcher & Mfr
N.A.I.C.S.: 325412
Steven J. Borst (Chm, Pres & CEO)
James T. Campanelli (VP-R&D)
Mahendra Rao (Chief Strategy Officer)

Q-CELLS NORTH AMERICA
400 Spectrum Ctr Dr Ste 1400, Irvine, CA 92618
Tel.: (949) 748-5996
Web Site: http://www.q-cells.us
Solar Cells And Modules Mfr
N.A.I.C.S.: 221114

Q-LAB CORP.
800 Canterbury Rd, Cleveland, OH 44145
Tel.: (440) 835-8700
Web Site: http://www.q-lab.com
Year Founded: 1956
Sales Range: $1-9.9 Million
Emp.: 60
Instruments & Related Products Mfr for Measuring, Displaying & Controlling Industrial Process Variables
N.A.I.C.S.: 334513
Douglas Grossman (Pres)
Gary Cornell (Mgr-Standards, Quality & Calibration)
James Gauntner (Mgr-Sls-North America)
Smrithi Kumar (Mgr-Sls-Intl)
Jeffrey Quill (Dir-Tech Applications)
Kirk Wilhelm (CFO)
George Grossman (Founder)
Subsidiaries:
ADT, LLC (1)
21212 W Patton Rd, Wittmann, AZ 85361
Tel.: (623) 388-9500
Web Site: http://www.aztest.com
Rev: $1,430,000
Emp.: 10
Testing Laboratories
N.A.I.C.S.: 541380

Q-MATION INC.
425 Caredean Dr, Horsham, PA 19044
Tel.: (215) 675-5800
Web Site: http://www.qmation.com
Sales Range: $10-24.9 Million
Emp.: 25
Industrial Machinery & Equipment
N.A.I.C.S.: 423830
Russ Fadel (Pres)

Q-TECH CORPORATION
10150 W Jefferson Blvd, Culver City, CA 90232-3502
Tel.: (310) 836-7900
Web Site: http://www.q-tech.com
Year Founded: 1972
Rev.: $17,000,000
Emp.: 160
Oscillators Mfr
N.A.I.C.S.: 334419
Richard Taylor (Owner)
Charles Peot (Deputy Dir-Quality Assurance)
Kent Del Rosso (Mgr-Info Tech)
Alex Kris (Mgr-IT & ERP Software Dev & Support)
Curtis Hooper (Engr-Design)

Q/W COIN SERVICES LTD.
420 Throckmorton St, Fort Worth, TX 76102-3708
Tel.: (817) 332-1219
Year Founded: 1991
Sales Range: $25-49.9 Million
Emp.: 55
Coin Laundry Services
N.A.I.C.S.: 532289
David Sykes (VP)
Gary Pace (Pres)

Q10 CAPITAL, L.L.C.
700 12th Ave S Ste 302, Nashville, TN 37203
Tel.: (615) 279-1631
Web Site: http://www.q10capital.com
Real Estate Investment Firm
N.A.I.C.S.: 531390
James M. Murphy (Chm)

Q1MEDIA
11401 Century Oaks Terrace Ste 470, Austin, TX 78758-0007
Tel.: (512) 388-2300
Web Site: http://www.q1media.com
Year Founded: 2004
Sales Range: $10-24.9 Million
Emp.: 20
Brand Development
N.A.I.C.S.: 541810
Bill Wiemann (Founder & Pres)
Keith Eddleman (VP-Tech)
Hunter Temperton (Dir-Ad Ops)
Lene Lay (VP-Sls)
Jessica Sanders (Controller)
Alissa Vrabel (Dir-HR)
Jason Appelbaum (Dir-Mktg)
Zac Hornsey (Dir-Publr Dev)
Andrew Price (Dir-Yield Ops)
Fabio Bartolai (Mgr-Sls-Natl)
Gaines Jonakin (Sr VP-Product & Ops)
Matt Bentley (Sr VP-Sls & Mktg)
Jimmy Short (VP-Bus Dev)

Q3 STAMPED METAL
777 Manor Pk Dr, Columbus, OH 43228-9522
Tel.: (614) 870-0195
Year Founded: 1992
Sales Range: $100-124.9 Million
Emp.: 207
Metal Products
N.A.I.C.S.: 336370
Francis Price (Pres & CEO)
Vernon Bell (CFO & Gen Mgr)
Subsidiaries:
Q3 Industries (1)
605 Miami St, Urbana, OH 43078-1907
Tel.: (937) 652-2181
Sales Range: $50-74.9 Million
Emp.: 150
Mfr of Air & Vacuum Reservoirs; Plastic & Fabricated Metal Products; High Pressure Cylinders & Composites
N.A.I.C.S.: 326199
Rymac Enterprises (1)
240 Berkley St, High Point, NC 27260-8102 (100%)
Tel.: (336) 889-8084

Sales Range: $10-24.9 Million
Emp.: 40
Custom Injection Molding
N.A.I.C.S.: 326199

QA SYSTEMS INC.
503 Oakland Ave, Austin, TX 78703
Tel.: (512) 637-1000
Web Site: http://www.qasystems.com
Sales Range: $1-9.9 Million
Emp.: 25
System Integration Services
N.A.I.C.S.: 541512
Marcos Gutierrez (Pres)

QATALYS INCORPORATED
222 W Las Colinas Blvd Ste 550E, Irving, TX 75039
Tel.: (214) 630-1480
Web Site: http://www.qatalys.com
Year Founded: 1995
Sales Range: $25-49.9 Million
Emp.: 25
Custom Computer Programming Services
N.A.I.C.S.: 541511
Rao Telidevara (Chm & Pres)

QBR BRAKE, INC.
5100 W Goldleaf Cir Ste 215, Los Angeles, CA 90056
Tel.: (323) 299-0004
Web Site: http://www.nugeon.com
Sales Range: $10-24.9 Million
Emp.: 5
Motor Vehicle Brake Parts Mfr & Distr
N.A.I.C.S.: 336340
Daniel Collins (Office Mgr)
Sonny Riddle (VP-Sls & Mktg)

QC ALLY, LLC
36 Discovery, Irvine, CA 92618
Tel.: (844) 824-5644
Web Site: https://qcally.com
Audit Services
N.A.I.C.S.: 522320
Jeffrey Flory (CEO)
Subsidiaries:
Inglet Blair LLC (1)
6207 Bee Cave Rd, Austin, TX 78746-5048
Tel.: (512) 732-0498
Web Site: http://www.ingletblair.com
Real Estate Credit
N.A.I.C.S.: 522292
Craig Inglet (Founder & Mng Dir)

QC VENTURES LLC
730 SW 34th St, Renton, WA 98055-4814
Tel.: (206) 768-7000
Web Site: http://www.aquaquip.com
Sales Range: $10-24.9 Million
Emp.: 85
Swimming Pools, Hot Tubs & Sauna Equipment & Supplies
N.A.I.C.S.: 459999

QC VERIFY, LLC
216 Centerview Dr Ste #280, Brentwood, TN
Tel.: (615) 591-2528
Web Site: https://www.qcverify.com
Year Founded: 1992
Emp.: 100
Software Publisher
N.A.I.C.S.: 513210

QCE FINANCE LLC
7595 Technology Way Ste 200, Denver, CO 80237
Tel.: (720) 359-3300
Web Site: http://www.quiznos.com
Holding Company; Sandwich Shops Developer, Operator & Franchisor
N.A.I.C.S.: 551112

Doug Pendergast (Pres & CEO)
George Jeffrey (Global COO)
Subsidiaries:
The Quizno's Operating Company LLC (1)
1001 17th St Ste 200, Denver, CO 80202
Tel.: (720) 359-3300
Web Site: http://www.quiznos.com
Sales Range: $125-149.9 Million
Emp.: 450
Sandwich Shops Developer, Operator & Franchisor
N.A.I.C.S.: 533110
Douglas N. Benham (Chm)

QCI TECHNOLOGY
1500 NW 118th St, Des Moines, IA 50325
Tel.: (515) 440-4960
Web Site: http://www.qci.com
Year Founded: 1995
Sales Range: $10-24.9 Million
Emp.: 140
Other Management Consulting Services
N.A.I.C.S.: 541618
Bruce Logan (Pres)
Chris Kyil (COO)
Mike Davidson (CFO)

QCUE, INC.
210 Barton Springs Rd Ste 160, Austin, TX 78704
Tel.: (512) 853-9462
Web Site: http://www.qcue.com
Year Founded: 2007
Sales Range: $10-24.9 Million
Emp.: 12
Software Publisher
N.A.I.C.S.: 513210
Barry Kahn (Founder & CEO)
Walter Bodwell (VP-Engrg)
Dan Meehan (Dir-Pricing & Ops)
Doug Mitarotonda (VP)

QED NATIONAL
350 7th Ave 10th Fl, New York, NY 10001
Tel.: (212) 481-6868
Web Site: http://www.qednational.com
Sales Range: $1-9.9 Million
Emp.: 47
Information Technology Staffing Services
N.A.I.C.S.: 561330
Colleen Molter (Founder & Pres)

QED SYSTEMS, INC.
4646 N Witchduck Rd, Virginia Beach, VA 23455
Tel.: (757) 490-5000
Web Site: http://www.qedsysinc.com
Year Founded: 1969
Sales Range: $25-49.9 Million
Emp.: 400
Information Technology, Engineering, Logistics & Industrial Services
N.A.I.C.S.: 541990
Willie Hardee (Dir-Engrg Svcs)
James G. Bohannan (Project Mgr-Engrg Svcs)
Lauren Pierce (Mgr-Contracts)
Mike Neibert (Dir-Technical Svcs-East Coast)
Subsidiaries:
QED Systems, Inc. - Honolulu Office (1)
96-1185 Waihona St Ste D-6, Pearl City, HI 96782
Tel.: (808) 484-5616
Web Site: http://www.qedsysinc.com
Information Technology, Engineering, Logistics & Industrial Services
N.A.I.C.S.: 541990

COMPANIES

Ricky Fleming *(Reg Mgr-Technical Svcs-Hawaii)*

QED Systems, Inc. - Port Orchard Office (1)
1455 Lumsden Rd, Port Orchard, WA 98367
Tel.: (360) 876-7100
Web Site: http://www.qedsysinc.com
Information Technology, Engineering, Logistics & Industrial Services
N.A.I.C.S.: 541990
Dave Jack *(Reg Mgr-Technical Svcs-Bremerton)*

QED Systems, Inc. - San Diego Office (1)
1010 W 19th St, National City, CA 91950
Tel.: (619) 802-0020
Web Site: http://www.qedsysinc.com
Information Technology, Engineering, Logistics & Industrial Services
N.A.I.C.S.: 541990
Glen Hofert *(Dir-West Coast & Hawaii)*
Kirk Burgamy *(Reg Mgr-Technical Svcs-San Diego)*

QGENDA, LLC
3280 Peachtree Rd NE Ste 1400, Atlanta, GA 30305
Web Site: http://www.qgenda.com
Year Founded: 2006
Medical Information Technology Services
N.A.I.C.S.: 519290
Greg Benoit *(CEO)*

Subsidiaries:

Shift Administrators, LLC (1)
2818 Canterbury Rd, Columbia, SC 29204-2312
Web Site: http://www.shiftadmin.com
Custom Computer Programming Services
N.A.I.C.S.: 541511
Patrick Hunt *(Founder & CEO)*

QGS DEVELOPMENT INC.
17502 County Rd 672, Lithia, FL 33547
Tel.: (813) 634-3326
Web Site: http://www.qgsdevelopment.com
Year Founded: 1982
Sales Range: $10-24.9 Million
Emp.: 100
Golf Course Contractors
N.A.I.C.S.: 561730
Howard Barnes *(Co-Owner & Pres)*
J. W. Thomas *(Co-Owner)*
Jim Armstrong *(VP-Golf)*
Donald Thomas *(Treas & Sec)*
Thomas H. Barnes *(VP-Site)*
Greg Fowler *(Controller)*
Paul Cope *(Mgr-Irrigation)*
Joe Rodi *(Mgr-Ops)*
Ted Rush *(Mgr-Estimating)*
Glenda Booker *(Office Mgr)*
Larry Woody *(Asst VP & Officer-Ops)*

QHP CAPITAL, L.P.
2626 Glenwood Ave Ste 550, Raleigh, NC 27608
Tel.: (919) 261-5250
Web Site: https://www.qhpcapital.com
Year Founded: 2020
Investment Management
N.A.I.C.S.: 523999

Subsidiaries:

Applied Stemcell, Inc. (1)
1165 Obrien Dr Ste A, Menlo Park, CA 94025-1440
Tel.: (408) 773-8007
Web Site: http://www.appliedstemcell.com
Research & Development in Biotechnology
N.A.I.C.S.: 541714
Michael Cleary *(Co-Founder)*

Spectra Medical Devices, LLC (1)
260 Fordham Rd H, Wilmington, MA 01887

Tel.: (978) 657-0889
Web Site: http://www.spectramedical.com
Rev.: $2,200,000
Emp.: 12
Medical, Dental & Hospital Equipment & Supplies Merchant Whslr
N.A.I.C.S.: 423450
Peter Comeau *(Engr-Intl Sls)*
Phyllis Dias *(Controller)*
Raymond Charbonneau *(Mgr-Intl R&D)*
Agustin Turriza *(Mgr-Ops)*
Casey Campolini *(Coord-Matls Control)*
Ray W. Nute *(CFO)*
W. S. Kang *(Pres-Ops-Korean)*
Chad Nikel *(CEO)*

Subsidiary (Non-US):

XL Precision Technologies, Ltd. (2)
79 Sadler Forster Way, Teesside Industrial Estate, Stockton-on-Tees, TS17 9JY, United Kingdom
Tel.: (44) 1642 766960
Web Site: http://www.xlprecisiontechnologies.com
Emp.: 60
Medical Equipment Mfr
N.A.I.C.S.: 339112
Tom Graham *(Mng Dir)*

QM CORPORATION
515 Nichols Blvd, Sparks, NV 89431
Tel.: (775) 355-4040
Web Site: http://www.qmcorp.com
Rev.: $34,400,000
Emp.: 120
Condominium Developers
N.A.I.C.S.: 236117
Charlene McCoy *(Controller)*
Larry Allison *(CFO)*
Sherilyn Nemedez *(Dir-Owner Svcs)*

Subsidiaries:

Interval Management Inc. (1)
515 Nichols Blvd, Sparks, NV 89431
Tel.: (775) 355-4040
Web Site: http://www.qmcorp.com
Rev.: $3,100,000
Emp.: 20
Management Services
N.A.I.C.S.: 541611
Larry Roberts *(CEO)*

QMC SYSTEMS, INC.
3995 Hagers Grove Rd, Salem, OR 97317
Tel.: (360) 470-8634   WY
Year Founded: 2015
Sales Range: Less than $1 Million
Emp.: 1
Financial Planning, Education & Consulting Services Focusing On Asian Investors
N.A.I.C.S.: 541611
Renae Bell *(Pres, CEO, CFO, COO & Chief Acctg Officer)*

QMI SECURITY SOLUTIONS
1661 Glenlake Ave, Itasca, IL 60143-1004
Tel.: (630) 782-0911   IL
Web Site: http://www.roll-a-way.com
Year Founded: 1986
Rev.: $3,800,000
Emp.: 52
Mfr of Commercial & Residential Metal Storm Doors & Security Products
N.A.I.C.S.: 332321
James Daluga *(VP-Procurement & Quality Assurance)*

QNARY LLC
256 W 36th St 7th Fl, New York, NY 10018
Tel.: (866) 499-2946
Web Site: http://www.qnary.com
Year Founded: 2012
Sales Range: $1-9.9 Million
Emp.: 16
Software Development Services

N.A.I.C.S.: 513210
Timothy E. Breen *(Founder)*
Mark Pilatowski *(Chief Product Officer)*
Marc Reichel *(Dir-Bus Dev & Growth)*
Mary Snauffer *(Pres-US)*
Ray Carbonell *(Pres-Global)*
Savina Kotorov *(Dir-Ops)*
Anna Wilgan *(Mgr-PR)*

QNEXIS INC
11800 Sunrise Valley Dr Ste 400, Reston, VA 20191
Tel.: (703) 464-5100
Web Site: http://www.qnexis.com
Year Founded: 2001
Sales Range: $1-9.9 Million
Emp.: 10
Management & Communications Solutions
N.A.I.C.S.: 541618
Kurt Nguyen *(Pres & CEO)*
Liz Dunn *(VP-Mktg)*

QOMO HITEVISION, LLC.
46950 Magellan Dr, Wixom, MI 48393
Tel.: (248) 960-0985
Web Site: http://www.qomo.com
Year Founded: 1990
Sales Range: $10-24.9 Million
Emp.: 12
Electronic Parts & Equipment Whslr
N.A.I.C.S.: 423690
Gregory Vincent *(Mgr-Intl Sls)*
Kevin Talentino *(VP-Ops & Dir-Bus Dev)*

QOMPLX, INC.
1775 Tysons Blvd Ste 800, Tysons, VA 22102
Tel.: (703) 995-4199
Web Site: http://qomplx.com
Year Founded: 2015
Software Publisher
N.A.I.C.S.: 513210
Jason Crabtree *(Co-Founder & CEO)*
Andrew Sellers *(Co-Founder & CTO)*
John Ferrari *(CFO & Chief Admin Officer)*
Abha DasGupta *(Chief Strategy Officer)*
Carol DiBattiste *(Gen Counsel & Sec)*
Brian Hale *(VP-Global Market Dev & Public Private Partnerships)*
James Faeh *(Dir-Corp Comm)*

QORVAL, L.L.C.
5150 Tamiami Trl N Ste 301, Naples, FL 34103
Tel.: (239) 430-0303
Web Site: http://www.qorval.com
Sales Range: $1-9.9 Million
Emp.: 25
Management Consulting Services
N.A.I.C.S.: 541611
James R. Malone *(Mng Partner)*
Paul Fioravanti *(CFO, COO & Chief Restructuring Officer)*
Eric Glassman *(Mng Dir)*
Keith M. Northern *(Mng Dir)*
John A. Pryor *(Mng Dir)*
Richard N. Reighard *(Mng Dir)*

QOSINA CORP.
150-Q Executive Dr, Edgewood, NY 11717-8329
Tel.: (631) 242-3000
Web Site: http://www.qosina.com
Year Founded: 1980
Sales Range: $25-49.9 Million
Emp.: 94
Medical Device Mfr
N.A.I.C.S.: 339112
Stuart Herskovitz *(Chm)*
Alfred Rivera *(CFO)*

QSACK & ASSOCIATES, INC.

Gerry Quinn *(COO)*
Joseph Walsh *(Mgr-IT)*
Judy Randolph *(Mgr-HR)*
Michael Gillis *(Mgr-Supplier Relationship)*
Peggy Wilson *(Dir-Sls)*
Steve Parisi *(Controller)*
Nancy Klimpel *(Coord-Mktg)*
Thomas Iavarone *(Dir-Ops)*
Edson Oncebay *(Coord-Logistics)*
Scott Herskovitz *(Pres & CEO)*
Lee Pochter *(Exec VP)*

QPHARMA, INC.
22 South St, Morristown, NJ 07960
Tel.: (973) 656-0011
Web Site: http://www.qpharmacorp.com
Year Founded: 1994
Emp.: 140
Compliance & Commercial Services to Life Sciences Industry
N.A.I.C.S.: 541715
Patrick P. Den Boer *(Founder, Pres & CEO)*
Reno Amadori *(CFO)*
John Cunningham *(Exec VP-Sls & Mktg)*
Dawn L. Gabriel *(Chief Compliance Officer)*
Brendan Middleton *(Dir-Mktg & PR)*
Jonathan Wright *(Chief Legal Officer & Gen Counsel)*
Michael Strubbe *(Mng Dir-Samples, Direct to Practitioner & Fulfillment)*
Kerrie Coleman *(Mng Dir-Learning Mgmt Sys)*
Badal Shah *(Mng Dir-KOL & Targeting)*
Lori Peters *(Sr VP-Comml Ops)*

QPM AEROSPACE INC.
17383 Ne Sacramento St, Portland, OR 97230-5943
Tel.: (425) 233-6170
Web Site: http://www.qpmaerospace.com
Sales Range: $10-24.9 Million
Emp.: 100
Machine Tools, Metal Forming Type
N.A.I.C.S.: 333517
Eva Cherry *(Exec VP)*
Bill Zang *(CFO)*
Terry Gaab *(CFO & Gen Mgr)*

QPS COMPANIES INC.
139 Bishops Dr Ste 330, Brookfield, WI 53005
Tel.: (262) 754-9000
Web Site: http://www.qpsemployment.com
Year Founded: 1985
Sales Range: $10-24.9 Million
Emp.: 200
Employment Agency Services
N.A.I.C.S.: 561311
Scott A. Mayer *(Pres & CEO)*
Mary Remington *(Chief Acctg Officer & Exec VP)*
Mark Immekus *(Chief Sls Officer & Exec VP)*
Dan McNulty *(COO & Exec VP)*
Steve Waller *(Reg VP)*
Anne Jabusch *(Coord-Mktg)*
Janet Agnello *(Exec VP-HR)*

QSACK & ASSOCIATES, INC.
2111 Wilson Blvd Ste 700, Arlington, VA 22201
Tel.: (703) 351-5035
Web Site: http://www.qsack1.com
Year Founded: 2001
Rev.: $5,200,000
Emp.: 53
Business Consulting Services
N.A.I.C.S.: 541618

QSACK & ASSOCIATES, INC.

U.S. PRIVATE

QSACK & Associates, Inc.—(Continued)
C. Anthony Cusack (Pres & CEO)

QSC, INC.
22 Salesbarn Rd, Carrollton, GA 30116
Tel.: (770) 838-0830
Sales Range: $1-9.9 Million
Emp.: 15
Construction Management Services
N.A.I.C.S.: 237990
Charles Chestnut (CEO & CFO)
Sadie Simpson (Sec)

QSC, LLC
1675 MacArthur Blvd, Costa Mesa, CA 92626
Tel.: (714) 754-6175
Web Site: https://www.qsc.com
Year Founded: 1968
Sales Range: $25-49.9 Million
Emp.: 300
Audio Systems Mfr
N.A.I.C.S.: 334310
Joe Pham (Chm & CEO)
Barry Ferrell (Chief Strategy Officer & Sr VP)
Jatan Shah (Pres & COO)
Mark Mayfield (Mgr-Cinema Mktg)
Christopher Jaynes (Sr VP-Software Technologies)
Anna Csontos (Chief Market Officer & Exec VP)
Danny Pickett (Dir-Sls-Global Cinema)
Pat Quilter (Founder)
Aravind Yarlagadda (CTO & Exec VP-Product Dev)
William Chan (Sr Dir-North Asia)
Markus Winkler (Sr VP-Asia & EMEA)
Ron Marchant (Sr Dir-Sls & Mktg-EMEA)
Andy Pearce (Sr Dir-Southeast Asia & Pacific)
Kristine Fowler (Sr Mgr-Digital Mktg & Global Comm)
Vanessa Genesius (Mgr-Mktg Comm)
Jason Moss (VP-Alliances & Market Dev)
Frank West (VP-Sys-US, Canada & Latin America)
Sandra Rothe (Mgr-Media & PR)

Subsidiaries:

Attero Tech, LLC (1)
1315 Directors Row Ste 107, Fort Wayne, IN 46808-1284
Tel.: (260) 496-9668
Web Site: https://www.qsys.com
Computer Programming Services
N.A.I.C.S.: 541511

QSI INC.
3375 Koapaka St Ste D108, Honolulu, HI 96819
Tel.: (808) 831-0811
Web Site: http://www.timessupermarkets.com
Rev.: $108,200,000
Emp.: 1,000
Supermarkets & Other Grocery Stores
N.A.I.C.S.: 445110
Gaeton Cavarocchi (Mgr-IT)
Robert Stout (CEO)

QSR STEEL CORPORATION, LLC
300 Locust St, Hartford, CT 06114
Tel.: (860) 548-0248
Web Site: http://www.qsrsteel.com
Year Founded: 2000
Rev.: $7,800,000
Emp.: 31
Fabricated Structural Metal Mfr

N.A.I.C.S.: 332312
Glenn Salamone (Pres)
David Ruscon (Dir-Ops)
Roger N. Carrier (Dir-Sls & Estimating)
Gary Krajewski (Mgr-Production)

QSS INTERNATIONAL INC.
10301 Democracy Ln Ste 401, Fairfax, VA 22030
Tel.: (703) 766-0211
Web Site: http://www.qssinternational.com
Year Founded: 2004
Sales Range: $1-9.9 Million
Emp.: 14
General Contractors
N.A.I.C.S.: 236210
Pramod Banavar (Pres)
Prakash Banavar (Dir-Fin)
Pavithra Banavar (VP)
Vincent Jae Yang (Project Mgr)
Derrick Moore (Project Mgr)
John Taylor (Asst Project Mgr)

QST INDUSTRIES, INC.
550 W Adams St Ste 200, Chicago, IL 60661
Tel.: (312) 930-9400 DE
Web Site: http://www.qst.com
Year Founded: 1880
Sales Range: $200-249.9 Million
Emp.: 30
Textiles & Converter of Pocketing for Men's Wear Mfr; Trim Components for the Apparel Industry Mfr & Distr
N.A.I.C.S.: 314999
Jack Janusek (Controller)

Subsidiaries:

QST Asia Ltd. Hong Kong (1)
9 F Playmates Factory Bldg, 1 Tin Hau Rd, Tuen Mun, NT, China (Hong Kong) (100%)
Tel.: (852) 27978880
Web Site: http://www.qst.com
Sales Range: $1-9.9 Million
Mens Womens & Childrens Apparel Construction Component Mfr
N.A.I.C.S.: 315990
Matthew Wong (Gen Mgr)

QST Dominicana LLC (1)
Calle la Bobina Edificio A-14 Caribbean Industrial Park, Matanzas, Santiago, 31000, Dominican Republic
Tel.: (809) 8095826400
Mfr of Trim Components for Apparel Industry
N.A.I.C.S.: 315210
Albert Madera (Mgr)

QST INDUSTRIES (SHANGHAI) CO., LTD. (1)
No 500 Shen Yu Road Ma Lu Town, Jia Ding District, Shanghai, 201818, China
Tel.: (86) 21 5990 1104
Clothing Apparel Distr
N.A.I.C.S.: 424350
Kendy Wong (Gen Mgr)

QST INDUSTRIES ASIA (S) PTE. LTD. (1)
629 Aljunied Road 07 15 Cititech Industrial Building, Singapore, 389838, Singapore
Tel.: (65) 6 227 9233
Web Site: http://www.qst.com
Sales Range: $10-24.9 Million
Emp.: 9
Garment & Apparel Mfr & Distr
N.A.I.C.S.: 315990
Julina Lee (Gen Mgr)

QST Industrias de Mexico, S.A. de R.L. de C.V. (1)
Parque Industrial Toluca 2000 Calle 4 Norte No 201, Toluca, Mexico, Mexico (100%)
Tel.: (52) 7222769960
Sales Range: $1-9.9 Million
Trim Component Mfr
N.A.I.C.S.: 315210

QST VIETNAM CO., LTD (1)

Unit 3A 3rd floor Standard Factory Bldg Lot No 04b 10 Street No 14, Tan Thuan Dong Ward District 7, Ho Chi Minh City, Vietnam
Tel.: (84) 8 377 08008
Sales Range: $10-24.9 Million
Emp.: 27
Leisure Clothing Mfr
N.A.I.C.S.: 315250

QUICK SERVICE TEXTILE GUATEMALA S.R.L (1)
37 Avenida 3-13 zona 7, Colonia El Rodeo, Guatemala, 01007, Guatemala
Tel.: (502) 2431 5353
Sales Range: $10-24.9 Million
Emp.: 4
Garment & Apparel Accessory Supplier
N.A.I.C.S.: 315990

QUICK SERVICE TEXTILE MAROC (1)
Z I Ain Sebaa Route 110 Boulevard Fuessanta Hangar N 10 km 12500, Casablanca, 20590, Morocco
Tel.: (212) 5 2267 2811
Web Site: http://www.qst.com
Sales Range: $10-24.9 Million
Emp.: 25
Apparel Accessory Mfr & Supplier
N.A.I.C.S.: 315990
El-Hassani Hassan (Gen Dir)

QST TRAVEL GROUP INC.
PO Box 3127, Tustin, CA 92781
Tel.: (949) 660-9200 CA
Year Founded: 1966
Sales Range: $10-24.9 Million
Emp.: 110
Provider of Travel Agency Services
N.A.I.C.S.: 561510

QT INDUSTRIES LLC
7410 Ambassador Row, Dallas, TX 75247
Tel.: (972) 221-0537
Web Site: http://www.qtmfg.com
Year Founded: 1990
Injection Mold Mfr & Plastic Injection Molding Services
N.A.I.C.S.: 333511
Anand Patel (CEO & CFO)
Bill Gilliland (Owner)

QTEC SOLUTIONS, INC.
355 E Rincon St Ste 219, Corona, CA 92879
Tel.: (951) 270-5357 DE
Web Site: http://www.qtec.us
Year Founded: 1996
Electronic Component Obsolescence Management Services
N.A.I.C.S.: 541611

QTEROS, INC.
99 Pulpit Hill Rd, Amherst, MA 01002
Tel.: (413) 531-6884
Web Site: http://www.qteros.com
Year Founded: 2007
Sales Range: $10-24.9 Million
Emp.: 45
Ethanol Fuel Developer & Mfr
N.A.I.C.S.: 325414
Stephan Rogers (CEO)

QTM, INC.
300 Stevens Ave, Oldsmar, FL 34677
Tel.: (813) 891-1300 FL
Web Site: http://www.qtminc.com
Year Founded: 1989
Sales Range: $1-9.9 Million
Emp.: 30
Precision Machining, Welding, Fabricating & Abrasive Waterjet Machining
N.A.I.C.S.: 332710
Richard K. Peck (CEO)

QUABAUG CORPORATION
18 School St, North Brookfield, MA 01535
Tel.: (508) 867-7731

Web Site: http://www.quabaug.com
Rev.: $18,500,000
Emp.: 315
Soles, Boot Or Shoe: Rubber, Composition, Or Fiber
N.A.I.C.S.: 326299
Kevin M. Donahue (Chm & CEO)
John J. McLoughlin (VP-Customer Satisfaction)
Brian Hanrahan (VP)

QUABBIN WIRE & CABLE CO. INC.
10 Maple St, Ware, MA 01082
Tel.: (413) 967-3117
Web Site: http://www.quabbin.com
Year Founded: 1975
Sales Range: $10-24.9 Million
Emp.: 80
Nonferrous Wiredrawing & Insulating
N.A.I.C.S.: 332618
Paul Engel (Pres)
Dan Griswold (VP-Fin)
Debi Engel (Exec VP)
Stacy Gilmour (VP-HR)
Michael LaPlaca (Mgr-Natl Sls)

QUACKENBUSH CO., INC.
495 Kennedy Rd, Buffalo, NY 14227-1031
Tel.: (716) 894-4355 NY
Web Site: http://www.qcoinc.com
Year Founded: 1932
Sales Range: $75-99.9 Million
Emp.: 100
Provider of Mechanical Contracting Services
N.A.I.C.S.: 238220
Richard Wagner (Controller)
Larry Szalay (Project Mgr)
Marc Timblin (Asst Project Mgr)

QUAD AREA COMMUNITY ACTION AGENCY INC.
45300 N Baptist Rd, Hammond, LA 70401
Tel.: (225) 567-2350 LA
Web Site: http://www.quadarea.org
Year Founded: 1976
Sales Range: $10-24.9 Million
Emp.: 122
Low Income Individual & Family Support Services
N.A.I.C.S.: 624190
Wallace Sibley (Exec Dir)

QUAD PARTNERS, LLC
570 Lexington Ave 36th Floor, New York, NY 10022
Tel.: (212) 724-2200
Web Site: https://www.quadpartners.com
Year Founded: 2000
Emp.: 100
Investment Services
N.A.I.C.S.: 523999
Lincoln E. Frank (Co-Founder & Mng Partner)
Daniel P. Neuwirth (Co-Founder & Mng Partner)

Subsidiaries:

The ILSC Education Group, Inc. (1)
443 University Ave, Toronto, M5G 2H6, ON, Canada
Tel.: (416) 323-1770
Web Site: https://www.ilsc.com
Emp.: 500
Administration of Education Programs
N.A.I.C.S.: 923110
Paul Schroeder (CEO)

Subsidiary (US):

Berlitz Corporation (2)
7 Roszel Rd 3rd Fl, Princeton, NJ 08540-6306

COMPANIES

QUADRANGLE DEVELOPMENT CORPORATION

Tel.: (609) 514-9650
Web Site: http://www.berlitz.com
Holding Company; Language Schools Operator & Franchisor; Translation Services; Language Educational Materials Publisher
N.A.I.C.S.: 551112

QUAD PLUS LLC.
1919 Cherry Hill Rd, Joliet, IL 60433
Tel.: (815) 740-0860   IL
Web Site: http://www.quadplus.com
Year Founded: 1990
Sales Range: $10-24.9 Million
Emp.: 50
Industrial Control Systems Services
N.A.I.C.S.: 541420
Chris Tooley *(Pres)*
Joe Kowalkowski *(Mgr-Large Drive Indus)*

QUAD VIDEO HOLDINGS CORPORATION
14999 Wunderlich Dr Unit 109, Houston, TX 77069-2048
Tel.: (713) 553-7884   TX
Web Site:
  https://www.quadvideohalo.com
Year Founded: 2022
Medical Videography Equipment Designer, Mfr & Whslr
N.A.I.C.S.: 334310
Bryan C. Becker *(CEO & Dir-Customer Rels)*

Subsidiaries:

Quad Video Halo, Inc.   (1)
7411 Songwind Ln, Spring, TX 77379-4005
Tel.: (713) 553-7884
Web Site: https://www.quadvideohalo.com
Medical Videography Equipment Designer, Mfr & Whslr
N.A.I.C.S.: 334310

QUAD-C MANAGEMENT, INC.
240 W Main St Ste 600, Charlottesville, VA 22902
Tel.: (434) 979-2070   DE
Web Site:
  http://www.quadcmanagement.com
Year Founded: 1989
Privater Equity Firm
N.A.I.C.S.: 523999
Terrence D. Daniels *(Founder & Chm)*
Anthony R. Ignaczak *(Mng Partner)*
Stephen M. Burns *(Mng Partner)*
Frank Winslow *(Partner)*
Sara Cutts *(Controller)*
Tom Hickey *(Partner)*
Thad Jones *(Partner)*
Tim Billings *(Partner)*
Michael Brooks *(Partner)*
Jack Walker *(Partner)*
Matt Trotta *(Principal)*

Subsidiaries:

Apps Associates LLC   (1)
289 Great Rd Ste 308, Acton, MA 01720-3425
Tel.: (978) 399-0230
Web Site: http://www.appsassociates.com
Business Software Installation & Support Services
N.A.I.C.S.: 541519
Bill Saltys *(Sr VP-Alliances)*
Christian Mueller *(Gen Mgr-Ops-European & VP)*
John Schmottlach *(Sr VP-Delivery)*
Chandru Muthuukkaruppan *(VP-India Ops)*
Adrian King *(CEO)*
Larry Jones *(Chm)*
Lydie Fox *(Chief People Officer)*

Subsidiary (Non-US):

Apps Associates GmbH   (2)
Airport Dortmund Forum 4, Flughafenreng 11, 44319, Dortmund, Germany
Tel.: (49) 2312222790
Emp.: 20

Software Installation & Support Services
N.A.I.C.S.: 541519
Christian Mueller *(Gen Mgr)*

Apps Associates Pvt. Ltd.   (2)
1-3-23 2 Street No 4 Habsiguda, Hyderabad, 500 007, India
Tel.: (91) 4030212601
Web Site: http://www.appsassociates.com
Emp.: 500
Software Installation & Support Services
N.A.I.C.S.: 541519

Subsidiary (Domestic):

Forcivity, Inc.   (2)
1000 Elm St Ste 800, Manchester, NH 03101
Web Site: http://www.forcivity.com
Software Development Services
N.A.I.C.S.: 541511
Jeff Oskin *(CEO)*
Steve Baines *(Pres & Chief Growth Officer)*
Jim Coleman *(CTO)*
Ivan Moore *(Chief Client Officer)*

SmartDog Services, LLC   (2)
7004 Bee Cave Rd Bldg 3 Ste 100, Austin, TX 78746-5004
Tel.: (512) 279-2528
Web Site: http://www.smartdogservices.com
Information Technology & Services
N.A.I.C.S.: 541690
Paul McCarthy *(Founder & Chm)*
Scott Elequin *(Pres)*
Garth Hernandez *(COO)*
Mihir Patel *(CTO)*
Al Veach *(VP-Sls)*

HaystackID LLC   (1)
15 W 39th St 16th Fl, New York, NY 10018
Tel.: (212) 748-9492
Web Site: http://www.haystackid.com
Emp.: 50
Electronic Discovery Services for Legal Industry
N.A.I.C.S.: 541519
Kevin D. Glass *(Pres)*
Alexander Gessen *(Dir-Forensics-Natl)*
Jason M. Glass *(VP-Client Svcs)*
Eric Singer *(Exec VP)*
Laurence D. Lieb *(Mng Dir-Forensics-Chicago)*
Larry Marshall *(CFO)*
Hal Brooks *(CEO)*
John Wilson *(Chief Info Security Officer)*
Rob Robinson *(CMO)*
Andrew Parrish *(Sr VP-Ops)*
Sergio Garcia *(VP-Forensics First Practice)*
Evan Craghead *(CTO)*
John Brewer *(Chief Artificial Intelligence Officer)*

Subsidiary (Domestic):

Business Intelligence Associates, Inc.   (2)
39 Broadway 26th Fl, 10006, New York, NY
Tel.: (212) 240-2282
Web Site: http://www.biaprotect.com
Data Processing, Hosting & Related Services
N.A.I.C.S.: 518210
Brian Schrader *(Pres)*
Jason Park *(VP-Digital Forensic Svcs)*
Adam Feinberg *(Exec VP-Professional Svcs)*
Jamir Munoz *(VP-Litigation Tech)*
Mark MacDonald *(Sr VP-Bus Dev)*
Colleen Freeman *(Sr Dir-Accts-Natl)*
Monica DaSilva *(Assoc VP-Managed Review Svcs)*
Lisa Moini *(VP-Managed Review Svcs)*

eTERA Consulting LLC   (2)
1100 17th St NW Ste 605, Washington, DC 20036
Tel.: (202) 349-0177
Web Site: http://www.eteraconsulting.com
Litigation & Legal Management Consulting
N.A.I.C.S.: 541618
Scott Holec *(Pres)*
Mike Garner *(Sr Exec VP)*
Mary McGinness *(Mgr-All1ance One Partnership Program)*
Greg Bufithis *(Mng Dir-Europe)*
Cassey Elder *(Mgr-PR)*
Margaret Lindsay *(CFO)*
Bruce Malter *(VP-Consulting Solutions)*

Emily Burdeshaw *(Mgr-Campaigns & Content)*
Stacey Webb *(Mgr-HR)*
Chris Hurlebaus *(Dir-Client Engagement)*
Jon Forst *(CIO)*

Learners Edge, Inc.   (1)
2805 Dodd Rd Ste 200, Eagan, MN 55121
Tel.: (952) 469-3454
Web Site: http://www.learnersedge.com
Law firm
N.A.I.C.S.: 541199
Kyle Pederson *(Owner)*

QED Technologies International, Inc.   (1)
1040 University Ave, Rochester, NY 14607
Tel.: (585) 256-6540
Web Site: http://www.qedmrf.com
Emp.: 60
Optical Lens Grinding Machinery Mfr
N.A.I.C.S.: 333310
Andrew Kulawiec *(Pres)*

Retina Associates of New Jersey, P.A.   (1)
628 Cedar Ln, Teaneck, NJ 07666
Tel.: (908) 458-8333
Web Site: http://www.njretina.com
Freestanding Ambulatory Surgical & Emergency Centers
N.A.I.C.S.: 621493

SEI Group, LLC   (1)
5470 Oakbrook Pkwy, Norcross, GA 30093
Tel.: (770) 840-7625
Web Site: https://seigroupusa.com
Rev.: $2,800,000
Emp.: 20
Building Products Distr & Insulation Sevices
N.A.I.C.S.: 238290
Joseph Carrington *(CEO)*
Mark Moore *(Pres)*

Subsidiary (Domestic):

G5 Enterprises, Inc.   (2)
1539 N Commercial Ste 5, Nixa, MO 65714
Tel.: (417) 761-8001
Web Site: https://www.g5ec.com
Construction Supply Mfr & Services
N.A.I.C.S.: 236220
Ian Yates *(Coordinator-Mktg)*
Maribeth Gardner *(Pres)*

Subsidiary (Domestic):

Bolivar Insulation Co   (3)
2050 E Trafficway St, Springfield, MO 65802
Tel.: (417) 862-5575
Web Site: http://www.bolivarinsulation.com
Sales Range: $10-24.9 Million
Emp.: 65
Insulation Material, Building
N.A.I.C.S.: 444110

Judy's Insulation Co., Inc.   (3)
504 E Stephenson Ave, Harrison, AR 72601
Tel.: (870) 741-6712
Web Site: https://www.judysinsulation.com
Insulation & Gutter Installation Services
N.A.I.C.S.: 238310

Subsidiary (Domestic):

Professional Foam Insulators Ltd.   (2)
1006 FM 1819, Pollok, TX 75969-3241
Tel.: (936) 853-3626
Web Site: http://www.profoaminsulators.com
Drywall & Insulation Contractors
N.A.I.C.S.: 238310
Robert Slack *(Mgr)*

Stanton Carpet Corporation   (1)
100 Sunnyside Blvd Ext Ste 100, Woodbury, NY 11797
Tel.: (516) 822-5878
Web Site: http://www.stantoncarpet.com
Carpet Designer, Mfr & Marketer
N.A.I.C.S.: 449121

QUAD-CITY PETERBILT INC.
8100 N Fairmount St, Davenport, IA 52806
Tel.: (563) 391-4300

Web Site:
  http://www.quadcitypeterbilt.com
Rev.: $35,200,000
Emp.: 55
Trucks, Commercial
N.A.I.C.S.: 423110
Doug Emard *(Mgr-Fin)*
Paul Grask *(Dir-Used Equipment & Truck Sls)*

QUAD-COUNTY READY MIX CORP
300 W 12th St, Okawville, IL 62271
Tel.: (618) 243-6430
Web Site: http://www.qcrm4.com
Rev.: $15,000,000
Emp.: 10
Ready Mixed Concrete
N.A.I.C.S.: 327320
Carol Husteddi *(Office Mgr)*

QUADAX INC.
3690 Orange Pl, Cleveland, OH 44122
Tel.: (216) 765-1144
Web Site: http://www.quadax.net
Year Founded: 1973
Sales Range: $25-49.9 Million
Emp.: 320
Billing & Bookkeeping Service
N.A.I.C.S.: 541219
John Leskiw *(Pres)*
Phil Conard *(VP)*
Walt Williams *(Dir-Revenue Cycle Optimization & Strategy)*

QUADCO INCORPORATED
1390 E Murray Dr, Farmington, NM 87401
Tel.: (505) 327-0486
Web Site: http://www.quadcoinc.com
Sales Range: $10-24.9 Million
Emp.: 40
Aircraft & Heavy Equipment Repair Services
N.A.I.C.S.: 444140
Mike Connelly *(Pres)*
David Baggett *(VP-Ops)*

QUADGEN WIRELESS SOLUTIONS INC.
200 N Warner Rd Ste 110, King of Prussia, PA 19406
Tel.: (484) 944-0009
Web Site:
  http://www.quadgenwireless.com
Year Founded: 2007
Sales Range: $10-24.9 Million
Emp.: 175
Telecommunications
N.A.I.C.S.: 517810
Srikalahasti Vagvala *(Pres)*

QUADRANGLE DEVELOPMENT CORPORATION
1001 G St NW Ste 900, Washington, DC 20001-4549
Tel.: (202) 393-1999   DE
Web Site:
  http://www.quadrangledevcorp.com
Year Founded: 1965
Sales Range: $125-149.9 Million
Emp.: 180
Real Estate Development
N.A.I.C.S.: 531120
Christopher Gladstone *(Pres)*
Robert Gladstone *(Chm)*
Douglas Zimmerman *(Chief Acctg Officer)*

Subsidiaries:

Quadrangle Management Company   (1)
1001 G St NW Ste 900, Washington, DC 20001-4549
Tel.: (202) 393-1999

3315

QUADRANGLE DEVELOPMENT CORPORATION U.S. PRIVATE

Quadrangle Development Corporation—(Continued)
Sales Range: $25-49.9 Million
Property Management Services
N.A.I.C.S.: 531312
William A. Holvey (VP-Ops)

QUADRANGLE GROUP LLC
437 Madison Ave 34th Fl, New York, NY 10022
Tel.: (212) 418-1700   DE
Web Site:
  http://www.quadranglegroup.com
Year Founded: 2000
Rev.: $6,000,000,000
Investment & Asset Management Services
N.A.I.C.S.: 523999
Brian Bytof (COO)
Susan Yee (Chief Admin Officer)
Michael Anthony Huber (Pres & Mng Principal)

QUADRANT MANAGEMENT, INC.
320 Park Ave, New York, NY 10022
Tel.: (212) 231-3906
Web Site:
  http://www.quadrantmgt.com
Year Founded: 1978
Privater Equity Firm
N.A.I.C.S.: 523999
Marco Vega (CFO & COO)
Bruce Bunner (Mng Dir)
Ted Deinard (Mng Dir)
Luke McGee (Principal)
Weston Quasha (Principal)
Eli Davidai (Mng Dir)
Alan Grant Quasha (Chm & CEO)

Subsidiaries:

Applied Underwriters, Inc. (1)
950 Tower Ln 14th Fl, Foster City, CA 94404
Tel.: (415) 656-5000
Web Site: http://www.auw.com
Sales Range: $300-349.9 Million
Emp.: 500
Workers Compensation Insurance Services
N.A.I.C.S.: 525190
Steve Menzies (CEO)
Ron Fiamma (Pres-Applied Fine Art & Collectibles)
Christopher Walsh (Sr VP-Underwriting)
Rand Silver (Sr VP-Risk Mgmt)

Subsidiary (Domestic):

Applied Underwriters Captive Risk Assurance Company, Inc. (2)
10805 Old Mill Rd, Omaha, NE 68154
Tel.: (402) 827-3424
Financial Services
N.A.I.C.S.: 518210

Centauri Specialty Insurance Holdings Inc. (1)
5391 Lakewood Ranch Blvd Ste 303, Lakewood Ranch, FL 34240
Tel.: (866) 318-4113
Web Site: http://www.centauriinsurance.com
Sales Range: $50-74.9 Million
Emp.: 20
Property Insurance
N.A.I.C.S.: 524126
Ricardo A. Espino (Pres & CEO)
Victoria Gomez (Chief Risk Officer)
Petra Charbonneau (VP-Product)
Brooke Adler (Asst Sec & Asst Gen Counsel)
Mark Jones (CFO)
Jenna Feverston (Coord-Sls & Mktg)
Caroline Hallett (Mgr-Sls-Florida)
Wyatt Hall (Mgr-Sls-South Carolina)
Joseph McCormick (Mgr-Sls-Texas)
Kelsey Baker (VP-Specialty Lines)
Andria Moore (VP-Territory Sls-Florida)
Tom Brady (VP-Claims)
Rick Moore (VP-Sls & Agency Rels)
Paul Knutson (VP-Capital & Reinsurance Strategy)

General Flange & Forge LLC (1)
2381 Philmont Ave Ste #125, Huntingdon Valley, PA 19006
Tel.: (215) 938-6900
Web Site: http://www.generalflange.com
Flanges Mfr
N.A.I.C.S.: 332111
Jeanne Paskus (Dir-Mktg & Sls)

Landauer-Medstar (1)
1 Bradford Rd, Mount Vernon, NY 10553
Tel.: (914) 665-9050
Healthcare Services
N.A.I.C.S.: 621399
Zeb Pirzada (Pres & CEO)

Subsidiary (Domestic):

Galloping Hill Surgical Corporation (2)
4470 Bordentown, Sayreville, NJ 08872
Tel.: (732) 251-8000
Web Site: http://www.allcaremedical.net
Sales Range: $10-24.9 Million
Health Care Equipment & Supplies Distr
N.A.I.C.S.: 423450
Richard Lerner (Pres)
Win Hayes (CEO)
Brian M. Sullivan (Coord-Inside Sls)

Subsidiary (Domestic):

Allcare Medical SNJ Corp. (3)
8 E Stow Rd Ste 200, Marlton, NJ 08053
Tel.: (732) 727-8292
Web Site: http://www.allcaremedical.net
Health Care Equipment & Supplies Distr
N.A.I.C.S.: 423450

QUADRAS, INC.
3176 Marjan Dr, Atlanta, GA 30340
Tel.: (770) 458-2170
Web Site: http://www.quadrasinc.com
Sales Range: $10-24.9 Million
Emp.: 35
Provider of Commercial Photography
N.A.I.C.S.: 541922
Cynthia Morgan (Co-Pres)
Sara S. Harris (Co-Pres)
Emily Brooks (Dir-Art)
Jere Brookshire (Coord-Preflight)
Stacey Mumford (Dir-Art)

QUADREP INCORPORATED
Ste 110 2901 Moorpark Ave, San Jose, CA 95128-2555
Tel.: (408) 432-3300   CA
Web Site: http://www.quadrep.com.tw
Year Founded: 1968
Sales Range: $25-49.9 Million
Emp.: 135
Mfr of Electronic Parts & Equipment
N.A.I.C.S.: 423690

QUADRIVIUS, INC.
Quad Ctr, Rochester, PA 15074
Tel.: (724) 709-9000
Year Founded: 1991
Sales Range: $10-24.9 Million
Emp.: 250
Freight Transportation Arrangement
N.A.I.C.S.: 488510
James G. Ruiz (VP-Bus Devel)
John Grallardo (Pres & CEO)
Brian Volkos (VP-Fin)

Subsidiaries:

Pittsburgh Logistics Systems, Inc. (1)
3120 Unionville Rd, Cranberry Township, PA 16066
Tel.: (724) 709-9000
Web Site: http://www.plslogistics.com
Sales Range: $10-24.9 Million
Transportation Services
N.A.I.C.S.: 484230
Greg Burns (Chm)

QUAESTUS HOLDINGS, LLC
6 Executive Park Drive, Clifton Park, NY 12065
Tel.: (518) 348-0060
Investment Banking
N.A.I.C.S.: 523999

Subsidiaries:

Etico Partners, LLC (1)
1795 Route 9,, Clifton Park, NY 12065
Tel.: (518) 348-0060
Web Site: https://www.eticofinancial.com
Securities Broker & Dealer; Investment Management & Advisory Services
N.A.I.C.S.: 523150

Subsidiary (Domestic):

Third Avenue Management LLC (2)
675 3rd Ave Ste 2900-05, New York, NY 10017-2023   (60%)
Tel.: (212) 888-5222
Web Site: http://www.thirdave.com
Sales Range: $100-124.9 Million
Emp.: 100
Investment Advisory & Management Services
N.A.I.C.S.: 523940
Ryan Dobratz (Portfolio Mgr-Real Estate)
Matthew Fine (Portfolio Mgr-Value)
Jason Wolf (Portfolio Mgr-Real Estate)
Quentin Velleley (Portfolio Mgr-Intl Real Estate)
Michael Buono (CFO)
Michael Warlan (Head-Global Trading)
Erik C. Kleinbeck (Head-Bus Dev)

Holding (Domestic):

Home Products International, Inc. (3)
4501 W 47th St, Chicago, IL 60632-4451
Tel.: (773) 890-1010
Web Site: http://www.homzproducts.com
Mfr of Home Organizational Products
N.A.I.C.S.: 423220
George Hamilton (CEO)

QUAIL CREEK BANCSHARES INC.
12201 N May Ave, Oklahoma City, OK 73120
Tel.: (405) 755-1000
Web Site:
  http://www.quailcreekbank.com
Year Founded: 1974
Sales Range: $25-49.9 Million
Emp.: 75
National Commercial Banks
N.A.I.C.S.: 522110
Doug Fuller (Pres & CEO)

QUAIL H FARMS, LLC.
5301 Robin Ave, Livingston, CA 95334
Tel.: (209) 394-8001
Web Site:
  http://www.quailhfarms.com
Sales Range: $10-24.9 Million
Emp.: 505
Potato Farming
N.A.I.C.S.: 111211
J. Michael Hennigan (Co-Owner & Chm)
Jack E. Smith (Co-Owner & CEO)

QUAIL MOUNTAIN INC.
4033 Miller Ave, Klamath Falls, OR 97603
Tel.: (541) 884-1313
Rev.: $10,000,000
Emp.: 50
Distributions Soft Drinks
N.A.I.C.S.: 445298
Tony Bocchi (Controller)
John Bocchi (Pres)

QUAINTANCE-WEAVER INC.
324 W Wendover Ave Ste 300, Greensboro, NC 27408
Tel.: (336) 370-0966
Web Site: http://www.qwrh.com
Rev.: $10,000,000
Emp.: 600
Hotel
N.A.I.C.S.: 721110

Dennis Quaintance (Pres)
Christina White (Controller)

QUAKE GLOBAL, INC.
4711 Viewridge Ave Ste 150, San Diego, CA 92123
Tel.: (858) 277-7290   CA
Web Site:
  http://www.quakeglobal.com
Year Founded: 1998
Sales Range: $10-24.9 Million
Emp.: 56
Modem Designer, Mfr & Support Services
N.A.I.C.S.: 541512
Eduardo Hernandez (Mgr-IT)
Juan Ibarra (Sr Mgr-Matls)

Subsidiaries:

ODIN Technologies (1)
21631 Red Rum Dr Ste 165, Ashburn, VA 20147
Tel.: (703) 968-0000
Web Site: http://www.odintechnologies.com
Rev.: $6,300,000
Emp.: 15
Computer System Design Services
N.A.I.C.S.: 541512

QUAKER CITY CHEMICALS INC.
7360 Milnor St, Philadelphia, PA 19136
Tel.: (215) 333-2000
Web Site: http://www.chemical.net
Rev.: $14,400,000
Emp.: 37
Chemicals & Allied Products
N.A.I.C.S.: 424690
Lori Szwanki-Scott (Sec-Customer Svc)

QUAKER CITY MERCANTILE
114-120 S 13th St, Philadelphia, PA 19107
Tel.: (215) 922-5220
Web Site:
  http://quakercitymercantile.com
Year Founded: 1988
Sales Range: $25-49.9 Million
Emp.: 60
Advetising Agency
N.A.I.C.S.: 541810
Steven Grasse (CEO)
Ron Short (Dir-Art)
Ron Pushkar (Dir-Creative)

QUAKER EQUITIES LTD., INC.
245 5th Ave, New York, NY 10016
Tel.: (212) 473-1100   NY
Web Site:
  http://www.chathamimports.com
Year Founded: 1987
Sales Range: $100-124.9 Million
Emp.: 1,178
Wine & Distilled Beverages
N.A.I.C.S.: 424820
Joseph J. Magliocco (Pres)

Subsidiaries:

Brescome Barton Inc. (1)
69 Defco Pk Rd, North Haven, CT 06473-1129   (100%)
Tel.: (203) 239-4901
Web Site: http://www.brescomebarton.com
Sales Range: $25-49.9 Million
Emp.: 200
Wine & Distilled Beverages Distributor
N.A.I.C.S.: 424820
Glenn Ackerman (Dir-Mktg-Sls)

Chatham Imports Inc (1)
245 5th Ave Ste 1402, New York, NY 10016-7304   (100%)
Tel.: (212) 473-1100
Web Site: http://www.chathamimports.com
Rev.: $9,500,000
Emp.: 10
Wine And Distilled Beverages
N.A.I.C.S.: 424820

COMPANIES

Joanne Goldberg (CFO)
Vincent Arlotta (Dir-Fin)
Connie Kam (Dir-Mktg)
Joanne Renne (Dir-Traffic Mgmt)
Joseph J. Magliocco (Pres)
Dennis Eidson (CEO)

QUAKER MAID MEATS INC.
521 Carroll St, Reading, PA 19611-2010
Tel.: (610) 376-1500   PA
Web Site:
http://www.quakermaidmeats.com
Year Founded: 1960
Rev.: $29,410,954
Emp.: 98
Prepared Meats
N.A.I.C.S.: 311612
Robert Parsons (Mgr-Logistics)
Joey Piazza (Dir-Mktg)

QUAKER MFG. CORP.
187 Georgetown Rd, Salem, OH 44460-0449
Tel.: (330) 332-4631
Web Site: http://www.quakermfg.com
Year Founded: 1962
Sales Range: $10-24.9 Million
Emp.: 150
Metal Stamping Services
N.A.I.C.S.: 332119
B. E. Smith (VP-Dev)
William D. Blanton (Pres & COO)
Robert Russell (Bus Mgr-Stamping)
Darrin Ackerman (Bus Mgr-Tooling)
Jim Wykle (Program Mgr)
Greg Harrold (Program Mgr)

QUAKER VALLEY FOODS INC.
2701 Red Lion Rd, Philadelphia, PA 19114-1019
Tel.: (215) 992-0900
Web Site:
http://www.quakervalleyfoods.com
Rev.: $168,563,055
Emp.: 300
Packaged Foods
N.A.I.C.S.: 424420
Kenneth Fleekop (VP)

QUAL-PRO CORPORATION
18510 S Figueroa St, Gardena, CA 90248
Tel.: (310) 329-7535
Web Site: http://www.qual-pro.com
Year Founded: 1971
Sales Range: $10-24.9 Million
Emp.: 128
Electronics Manufacturing Services
N.A.I.C.S.: 334412
Brian Shane (Pres & CEO)
David Soden (VP-Engrg & Sls)
Kirk A. Waldron (CFO & Exec VP)

QUALCARE
7334 Center St, Mentor, OH 44060
Tel.: (440) 729-5888
Web Site:
http://www.homeinstead.com
Year Founded: 2000
Sales Range: $1-9.9 Million
Emp.: 296
Senior Home Care Services
N.A.I.C.S.: 621610
Therese Kovatch (Pres)

QUALI TRADE INC.
287 Marschall Rd Ste 104, Shakopee, MN 55379
Tel.: (952) 403-0606
Sales Range: $10-24.9 Million
Emp.: 5
Fertilizer & Fertilizer Materials
N.A.I.C.S.: 424910
Harland Hohenstein (Pres)
Alan Hohenstein (VP)
Norma Bendzick (Controller)
Josh Heimkes (Mgr-Reg Sls)

QUALI-PRO
4515 Falls of Neuse Rd Ste 300, Raleigh, NC 27609
Tel.: (206) 812-8600
Web Site: http://www.quali-pro.com
Year Founded: 2000
Sales Range: $10-24.9 Million
Emp.: 20
Farming Products Mfr & Online Marketer
N.A.I.C.S.: 424910
Allan Las (Chief Product Dev Officer)
Jerry Corbett (Mgr-Tech Svc)
Nicholas Strain (Dir-Bus-Brand)

QUALIA, INC.
37 W 28th St 5th Fl, New York, NY 10001
Tel.: (646) 723-4657
Web Site: http://www.qualia-media.com
Advertising Services
N.A.I.C.S.: 541810
Kathy Leake (Founder & CEO)
Niels Meersschaert (CTO)
Emily Keith (VP-Sls)
Roger Juntilla (VP-Bus Dev)
Tami Kelly (VP-Customer Success Mgmt & Ops)
Robin Kim (VP-Fin)
John Cattarulla (Dir-Data & Media)

QUALICO STEEL COMPANY INC.
7797 E State Hwy 52, Webb, AL 36376-5755
Tel.: (334) 793-1290   AL
Web Site:
http://www.qualicosteel.com
Year Founded: 1976
Sales Range: $10-24.9 Million
Emp.: 700
Fabricated Structural Metals Mfr
N.A.I.C.S.: 332312
John E. Downs (CEO)
Thomas Defnall (Exec VP-Bus Dev)
Mike Downs (VP-Project Mgmt)

QUALIS, CORPORATION
689 Discovery Dr NW Ste 400, Huntsville, AL 35806
Tel.: (256) 971-1707   AL
Web Site: http://www.qualis-corp.com
Year Founded: 1993
Sales Range: $25-49.9 Million
Emp.: 200
Engineering Analysis & Design Testing
N.A.I.C.S.: 541330
Elizabeth A. Morard (Chm & CEO)
John Baugher (Dir-Contracts)
Roderick Duke (Pres & CFO-Interim-Mng Corp Bus Ops & Infrastructure)
Carlos Kingston (COO)

QUALITEK INTERNATIONAL INC.
315 Fairbank St, Addison, IL 60101-3123
Tel.: (630) 628-8083   IL
Web Site: http://www.qualitek.com
Year Founded: 1980
Sales Range: $10-24.9 Million
Emp.: 200
Chemical Preparation Services
N.A.I.C.S.: 325998
Phodi Han (Pres)
Debbie Ligouri (Mgr-Mktg)

Subsidiaries:

Qualitek (Shanghai) Trading Co., Ltd.   (1)
1028 ShuYu Building FanYu Road XuHui District Room 103, Shanghai, 200030, China
Tel.: (86) 21 51557072
Soldering Product Whslr
N.A.I.C.S.: 424690

Qualitek Delta Philippines   (1)
Phase 1 Qualitek Ave (1st Ave), Bataan Economic Zone, Mariveles, 2106, Batan, Philippines
Tel.: (63) 845 4028
Web Site: http://www.qualitek.com
Soldering Products Mfr
N.A.I.C.S.: 333992

Qualitek Electronic Shenzhen China   (1)
3B/F YiFa Print Building Tong Yi Industrial Zone 351 JiHua Rd Buji, Shenzhen, 518112, China
Tel.: (86) 75528522814
Web Site: http://www.qualitek.com
Soldering Products Mfr
N.A.I.C.S.: 333992

Qualitek Europe Ltd.   (1)
9 Apex Ct Bassendale Rd Wirral Intl Business Park, Wirral, CH62 3RE, Bromborough, United Kingdom
Tel.: (44) 01513340888
Web Site: http://www.qualitek-europe.com
Sales Range: $10-24.9 Million
Emp.: 0
Lead Free Alloy Mfr
N.A.I.C.S.: 331110

Qualitek Singapore Pte. Ltd   (1)
6 Tuas South Street 5, Singapore, 637790, Singapore
Tel.: (65) 67957757
Sales Range: $10-24.9 Million
Emp.: 10
Solder & Lead Free Powder Mfr
N.A.I.C.S.: 333992
Veroinica Hong (Gen Mgr)

QUALITEMPS INC.
702 E Washington Ave, Madison, WI 53703
Tel.: (608) 257-1057
Web Site: http://www.qtigroup.com
Sales Range: $10-24.9 Million
Emp.: 45
Provider of Temporary Help Services
N.A.I.C.S.: 561320
David Silverberg (Chm)

QUALITEST GROUP
1 Post Rd 3rdFl, Fairfield, CT 06824
Web Site:
http://www.qualitestgroup.com
Software Publishing, Developing, Testing & Quality Assurance
N.A.I.C.S.: 513210
David Cotterell (Chief Acquisition Officer)

Subsidiaries:

Experior Group Ltd.   (1)
Charta House 30-38 Church Street, Staines-upon-Thames, TW18 4EP, United Kingdom
Tel.: (44) 1784 618005
Web Site: http://www.experiorgroup.com
SAP Testing & Assurance
N.A.I.C.S.: 513210
Simon Evans (Co-CEO)
Debbie Burton (Co-CEO)
Christian Maloney (Dir-Svcs Delivery)
Michelle Heaselgrave (Head-HR)
Chris Barker (Head-Fin)

QUALITY AGGREGATES INC.
4955 Steubenville Pike Ste 245, Pittsburgh, PA 15205-9604
Tel.: (412) 777-6701
Sales Range: $10-24.9 Million
Emp.: 75
Limestone Quarry Operator

QUALITY BEVERAGE LP

N.A.I.C.S.: 212114
Craig Bryan (Dir-Safety)
Greig McCoy (Mgr-Fleet)
Bob Snyder (Mgr-IT)
Michelle Greene (Treas & VP)
Jeff Ankrom (VP-Ops)
Dave Jessloski (VP-Sls)

QUALITY ASSURED ENTERPRISES, INC.
1600 5th St S, Hopkins, MN 55343-7814
Tel.: (952) 933-7800   MN
Web Site: http://www.qal.com
Year Founded: 1988
Sales Range: $10-24.9 Million
Emp.: 40
Provider of Commercial Printing Services
N.A.I.C.S.: 323111
Robert Westmyer (Chm & CEO)

Subsidiaries:

Quality Assured Label, Inc.   (1)
1600 5th St S, Hopkins, MN 55343-7814
Tel.: (952) 933-7800
Web Site: http://www.qal.com
Sales Range: $10-24.9 Million
Emp.: 35
Commercial Printing Services Supplier
N.A.I.C.S.: 323111
Robert Westmyer (Pres)

QUALITY BAKERS GROUP, INC.
30521 Palos Verdes Dr E, Palos Verdes Peninsula, CA 90275-6351
Tel.: (310) 514-0762
Sales Range: $10-24.9 Million
Emp.: 100
Bakery Products Mfr
N.A.I.C.S.: 311812
Peter Dreyer (Pres)

QUALITY BAKERS OF AMERICA COOPERATIVE, INC.
1055 Parsippany Blvd Ste 201, Parsippany, NJ 07054
Tel.: (973) 263-6970   NY
Web Site: http://www.qba.com
Year Founded: 1922
Sales Range: $50-74.9 Million
Emp.: 4
Bakers Cooperative; Bread
N.A.I.C.S.: 541618
Donald C. Cummings (CFO)

QUALITY BAKERY PRODUCTS, INC.
14330 Interdrive W, Houston, TX 77032
Tel.: (281) 449-4977
Web Site:
http://www.qualitybakeryproducts.net
Year Founded: 1993
Sales Range: $10-24.9 Million
Emp.: 65
Commercial Bakery Services
N.A.I.C.S.: 311812
Henry Wellborn (Sec & Mgr-Pur)
Mike Tills (VP & Gen Mgr)
Joel Wagstaff (Dir-Ops)

QUALITY BEVERAGE LLC
1413 Jake Alexander Blvd PO Box 697, Salisbury, NC 28145
Tel.: (704) 637-5881
Rev.: $18,200,000
Emp.: 90
Soft Drinks
N.A.I.C.S.: 311930
Cliff Ritchie (Pres)
Conrad Wetterau (Chm & CEO)

QUALITY BEVERAGE LP

QUALITY BEVERAGE LP

Quality Beverage LP—(Continued)

525 Myles Standish Blvd, Taunton, MA 02780
Tel.: (508) 822-6200 MA
Web Site: http://www.qblp.com
Year Founded: 1994
Alcoholic Beverage Distr
N.A.I.C.S.: 424810
T. Conrad Wetterau *(Pres & CEO)*
Theodore Audet *(COO & Exec VP)*

Subsidiaries:

Quality Beverage (1)
12 Saint Mark St, Auburn, MA 01501-3237
Tel.: (508) 832-5311
Web Site: http://www.qblp.com
Sales Range: $25-49.9 Million
Emp.: 80
Alcoholic Beverage Distr
N.A.I.C.S.: 424810
Craig Colonero *(Dir-Sls & Mktg)*

QUALITY BOLT & SCREW CORP.

5290 Gateway Dr, Geismar, LA 70734
Tel.: (225) 744-1100
Rev.: $11,200,000
Emp.: 30
Bolts, Nuts & Screws
N.A.I.C.S.: 423710
James L. Power *(Pres)*
Pat McGrail *(Gen Mgr)*

QUALITY BONELESS BEEF INC.

700 Ctr St, West Fargo, ND 58078
Tel.: (701) 282-0202
Web Site:
  http://www.qualitymeats.com
Sales Range: $10-24.9 Million
Emp.: 60
Sausages & Other Prepared Meats
N.A.I.C.S.: 311612
Blair Kemmer *(CFO)*
Lee McCleary *(Pres & Dir-Pur)*
Ron Jansen *(CEO & Mgr-Quality)*

QUALITY CARE FOR CHILDREN, INC.

2751 Buford Hwy Ste 500, Atlanta, GA 30324
Tel.: (404) 479-4200
Web Site:
  http://www.qualitycareforchildren.org
Sales Range: $25-49.9 Million
Emp.: 61
Child Care Services
N.A.I.C.S.: 624410
Jon Tuuri *(Dir-Fin & Ops)*
Pam Runkle *(Exec VP-Early Care & Learning)*
Pam Tatum *(CEO)*
Reynaldo Green *(VP-Nutrition & Health)*
Jeff Ader *(Dir-Mktg & Corp Engagement)*
Leng Leng Chancey *(VP-Dev & Mktg)*

QUALITY CARE SITTER SERVICE, INC.

3442 Eastex Freeway, Beaumont, TX 77703
Tel.: (409) 832-0011 TX
Web Site:
  http://www.qualitycares.com
Year Founded: 1996
Sales Range: $1-9.9 Million
Emp.: 289
Women Healthcare Services
N.A.I.C.S.: 621610
Nancy Carlisle *(Pres)*

QUALITY CARTON INC.

617 Little Britain Rd, New Windsor, NY 12553
Tel.: (201) 529-6900
Web Site:
  http://www.qualitycarton.com
Year Founded: 1978
Sales Range: $10-24.9 Million
Emp.: 68
Corrugated Boxes, Partitions & Point-of-Purchase Displays Mfr & Distr
N.A.I.C.S.: 322212
Liam Quinn *(VP-Sls)*

QUALITY CASTINGS COMPANY

1200 N Main St, Orrville, OH 44667
Tel.: (330) 682-6010
Web Site: http://www.qcfoundry.com
Rev.: $21,500,000
Emp.: 350
Gray Iron Castings
N.A.I.C.S.: 331511
Dave Yonto *(Pres)*
Bob Nicholas *(Controller)*
Dick Nicholas *(Chm-Mgmt Bd)*

QUALITY CHEKD DAIRIES, INC.

901 Warrenville Rd Ste 405, Lisle, IL 60532
Tel.: (630) 717-1110 IL
Web Site: http://www.qchekd.com
Year Founded: 1944
Sales Range: $10-24.9 Million
Emp.: 10
Dairy Processor
N.A.I.C.S.: 112120
Peter Horvath *(Pres)*
Mary DeMarco *(Mgr-Acctg & Admin)*
Steve Drabek *(Dir-HR & Trng)*
Chuck Yarris *(Dir-Quality & Food Safety)*

QUALITY CHRISTMAS TREE CO. INC.

5345 W Loop S, Houston, TX 77081
Tel.: (713) 218-0860
Web Site:
  http://www.houstongardencenters.com
Year Founded: 1978
Sales Range: $25-49.9 Million
Emp.: 15
Retailer of Garden Supplies
N.A.I.C.S.: 444240
Matt Hooper *(Pres)*

QUALITY CIRCUITS INC.

1102 Progress Rd, Fergus Falls, MN 56537
Tel.: (218) 739-9707
Web Site: http://www.qciusa.com
Year Founded: 1988
Sales Range: $10-24.9 Million
Emp.: 70
Printed Circuit Boards
N.A.I.C.S.: 334412
Wayne Dirkman *(Owner)*
Cory Fiedler *(Supvr-Shift)*

QUALITY COILS INCORPORATED

748 Middle St, Bristol, CT 06010
Tel.: (860) 584-0927
Web Site: http://www.qualitycoils.com
Year Founded: 1965
Sales Range: $10-24.9 Million
Emp.: 160
Coil Windings, Electronic
N.A.I.C.S.: 334416
Keith A. Gibson *(VP)*
Mark Gibson *(Pres)*
Erin Mullin *(Asst VP)*

QUALITY COMPANIES USA, LLC.

425 Griffin Rd, Youngsville, LA 70592
Tel.: (337) 857-6000
Web Site:
  http://www.qualitycompanies.com
Year Founded: 2002
Sales Range: $50-74.9 Million
Emp.: 654
Construction Engineering Services
N.A.I.C.S.: 541330
Jody Broussard *(Sr VP)*

QUALITY CONCRETE & RENTAL INC.

230 Bus Pk Way, West Palm Beach, FL 33411
Tel.: (561) 798-4509
Sales Range: $25-49.9 Million
Emp.: 420
Concrete Work
N.A.I.C.S.: 238110

QUALITY CONTRACTORS INCORPORATED

11245 Indian Trl Ste 2, Dallas, TX 75229-3519
Tel.: (972) 238-5567
Sales Range: $10-24.9 Million
Emp.: 65
Industrial Buildings & Warehouses
N.A.I.C.S.: 236220
Theresa Cox *(Pres & CEO)*

QUALITY CONTROLLED MANUFACTURING, INC

9429 Abraham Way, Santee, CA 92071
Tel.: (619) 443-3997 CA
Web Site:
  http://www.qualitycontrolledmanufacturinginc.com
Year Founded: 1978
Sales Range: $10-24.9 Million
Emp.: 95
Precision Machined Component & Assembly Mfr
N.A.I.C.S.: 333248
Jane Currie *(Treas)*
William R. Grande *(CEO)*

QUALITY CUSTOM CABINETRY INC.

125 Peters Rd, New Holland, PA 17557
Tel.: (717) 656-2721
Web Site: http://www.qcc.com
Year Founded: 1968
Sales Range: $10-24.9 Million
Emp.: 300
Mfr of Wood Kitchen Cabinets
N.A.I.C.S.: 337110
Bill Mullineaux *(Dir-Mktg)*

QUALITY CUSTOMS BROKER INC.

4464 S Whitnall Ave, Milwaukee, WI 53235
Tel.: (414) 482-9447
Web Site:
  http://www.qualitybrokers.com
Sales Range: $1-9.9 Million
Emp.: 45
Customhouse Brokers
N.A.I.C.S.: 488510
Karin LaFreniere *(Pres)*
Kathy Zimmer *(Sec)*
Jarad Currier *(VP-Corp Logistics)*
Darrell Toth *(VP-Chicago Branch)*

QUALITY DAIRY COMPANY

111 W Mount Hope Ave, Lansing, MI 48910
Tel.: (517) 319-4100
Web Site: http://www.qdcplastics.com
Sales Range: $10-24.9 Million
Emp.: 750
Milk Production

U.S. PRIVATE

N.A.I.C.S.: 445298
Stan Martin *(Pres)*
Ron Bolinsky *(CFO)*
Lorena Conlin *(Supvr-Retail Acctg)*

QUALITY DINING, INC.

4220 Edison Lks Pkwy, Mishawaka, IN 46545-1420
Tel.: (574) 271-4600 IN
Web Site: http://www.qdi.com
Year Founded: 1981
Sales Range: $200-249.9 Million
Emp.: 7,200
Restaurant Franchise
N.A.I.C.S.: 722511
Christopher L. Collier *(VP-Fin)*
James K. Fitzpatrick *(Chief Dev Officer & Sr VP)*
Daniel B. Fitzpatrick *(Founder, Chm & CEO)*
Jeanne M. Yoder *(VP & Controller)*
Lindley E. Burns *(Sr VP-Full Svc Dining Div)*
Gerald O. Fitzpatrick *(Sr VP-Burger King Div)*
Joseph E. Olin *(VP)*
William J. Lee *(VP-Burger King Div)*
Thomas D. Hanson *(VP-Mktg)*
Steven C. Hunter *(VP-Chilis Grill & Bar Div)*
John C. Firth *(Pres)*

QUALITY DISTRIBUTING COMPANY

199 1st St, Los Altos, CA 94022
Tel.: (650) 941-5630
Rev.: $39,400,000
Emp.: 100
Groceries, General Line
N.A.I.C.S.: 722513
James Olson *(CEO)*
Jim Beglin *(VP)*
Vern Wardle *(VP)*

Subsidiaries:

Quality Distributing Union City (1)
2850 Volpey Way, Union City, CA 94587
Tel.: (510) 429-7920
Sales Range: $10-24.9 Million
Emp.: 55
Poultry & Poultry Products
N.A.I.C.S.: 424440

QUALITY DISTRIBUTORS, LLC

2424 S 21st St, Phoenix, AZ 85034
Tel.: (602) 445-2600
Web Site:
  http://www.mandalayhomes.com
Sales Range: $200-249.9 Million
Emp.: 130
Distr of Wireless Products
N.A.I.C.S.: 423690
Kathy Gauthier *(Dir-People Svcs)*
Donna Juarez *(Mgr-Mktg)*

QUALITY ENGINEERING SOLUTIONS, INC.

405 Water St, Conneaut Lake, PA 16316
Tel.: (814) 382-0373
Web Site:
  http://www.qespavements.com
Year Founded: 1997
Sales Range: $10-24.9 Million
Emp.: 60
Engineeering Services
N.A.I.C.S.: 541330
Sherry Morian *(Pres)*
Lydia H. Kennard *(Pres & CEO)*

QUALITY EQUIPMENT DISTRIBUTORS INC.

75 Bank St, Orchard Park, NY 14127
Tel.: (716) 681-7703
Web Site: http://www.qeddirect.com
Year Founded: 2000
Sales Range: $1-9.9 Million

COMPANIES

Emp.: 7
Nondestructive Testing Equipment
N.A.I.C.S.: 335999
Daniel Sisson (Pres)

QUALITY FABRICATORS INC.
1035 W Fullerton Ave, Addison, IL 60101
Tel.: (630) 543-0540
Web Site: http://www.qfi-usa.com
Year Founded: 1973
Sales Range: $10-24.9 Million
Emp.: 100
Sheet Metalwork
N.A.I.C.S.: 332322
Tom Lovelace (Pres)
Mark Lovelace (VP-Sls & Mktg)
Victor Camacho (VP-Ops)
Mike Piento (Controller)

QUALITY FARM EQUIPMENT CO. INC.
655 Pugh Rd, Clinton, NC 28328
Tel.: (910) 592-5559
Web Site: http://www.qualityequip.com
Rev.: $10,000,000
Emp.: 15
Farm Tractors
N.A.I.C.S.: 459999
Greg Morgan (CEO)

QUALITY FINISHERS, INC.
355 Old Dalton Rd NE, Calhoun, GA 30701
Tel.: (706) 226-4712
Rev.: $27,600,000
Emp.: 30
Dyeing & Finishing of Tufted Rugs & Carpets
N.A.I.C.S.: 314110
Greg Brock (Owner)

QUALITY FLOAT WORKS, INC.
1382 Payne Rd, Schaumburg, IL 60173
Tel.: (847) 781-8960
Web Site: http://www.metalfloat.com
Year Founded: 1915
Sales Range: $10-24.9 Million
Emp.: 26
Metals Mfr
N.A.I.C.S.: 423510
Sandra Westlund-Deenihan (Pres & Design Engr)
Jason W. Speer (VP & Gen Mgr)

QUALITY FLOORING 4 LESS
101 California St, San Francisco, CA 94111
Tel.: (510) 698-5142
Web Site: http://www.qualityflooring4less.com
Year Founded: 2008
Sales Range: $10-24.9 Million
Emp.: 20
Flooring Products
N.A.I.C.S.: 449121
Aaron David (Owner)

QUALITY FOOD COMPANY, INC.
25 Bath St, Providence, RI 02908
Tel.: (401) 421-5668
Web Site: http://www.qualityfoodcompany.com
Year Founded: 1931
Sales Range: $50-74.9 Million
Emp.: 65
Meat Product Whslr
N.A.I.C.S.: 424470
Richard Spinella (Mgr-Credit)
William P. Catauro Jr. (Pres)

QUALITY FOODS CORPORATION
537 Rochester Rd, Pittsburgh, PA 15237-1747
Tel.: (412) 364-3399   PA
Web Site: http://www.kuhonsmarket.com
Year Founded: 1967
Sales Range: $50-74.9 Million
Emp.: 600
Provider of Grocery Services
N.A.I.C.S.: 445110
Jodi Zema (Controller)

QUALITY FOODS INC.
5425 S E St Ste A, Indianapolis, IN 46227
Tel.: (317) 784-4061
Sales Range: $10-24.9 Million
Emp.: 5
Convenience Store
N.A.I.C.S.: 445131

QUALITY FROZEN FOODS INC.
1663 62nd St, Brooklyn, NY 11204
Tel.: (718) 256-9100
Web Site: http://www.qualityfrozenfoods.com
Rev.: $25,283,907
Emp.: 44
Packaged Frozen Goods
N.A.I.C.S.: 424420
Moses Semel (Pres)
Rachel Leibler (Sec)

QUALITY HYDRAULICS & PNEUMATICS INC.
1415 Wilhelm Rd, Mundelein, IL 60060
Tel.: (847) 680-8400
Web Site: http://www.qualityhydraulics.com
Rev.: $13,700,000
Emp.: 22
Industrial Machinery & Equipment Merchant Whslr
N.A.I.C.S.: 423830
John Felsenthal Jr. (Pres)

QUALITY IMPLEMENT COMPANY
10576 US Hwy 277 S, Munday, TX 76371
Tel.: (940) 422-4534
Web Site: http://www.qualityimplement.com
Sales Range: $10-24.9 Million
Emp.: 100
Farm Equipment Parts & Supplies
N.A.I.C.S.: 423820
Floyd Reed (Pres)
Brant Reed (Controller)

QUALITY INGREDIENTS CORPORATION
14300 Rosemount Dr, Burnsville, MN 55306
Tel.: (952) 898-4002   MN
Web Site: http://www.qic.us
Year Founded: 1987
Sales Range: $10-24.9 Million
Emp.: 90
Powdered Food Ingredients Mfr & Contract Spray Drying Services
N.A.I.C.S.: 311999
Mona Hiserodt (Office Mgr)

QUALITY INNOVATIVE SOLUTIONS INC.
1741 Ives Ave Ste B, Oxnard, CA 93033
Tel.: (805) 983-8200   CA
Web Site: http://www.qi-solutions.com
Year Founded: 2004
Sales Range: $1-9.9 Million
Emp.: 31

Engineeering Services
N.A.I.C.S.: 541330
Bobby Mullins (Pres)

QUALITY INSULATION & ROOFING
2323 N. Frazier St Ste E, Conroe, TX 77303
Tel.: (936) 539-9739
Web Site: https://www.qualityinsulationandroofing.com
Year Founded: 2012
Sales Range: Less than $1 Million
Emp.: 10
Drywall & Insulation Contractors
N.A.I.C.S.: 238310
Jason Smith (Founder & Pres)

QUALITY IT PARTNERS INC.
2960 Lonesome Dove Rd Ste 2000, Mount Airy, MD 21771
Tel.: (301) 607-8744
Web Site: http://www.qitp.com
Year Founded: 2000
Sales Range: $1-9.9 Million
Emp.: 25
It Consulting
N.A.I.C.S.: 541690
Karen Donoghue (Dir-Mktg)

QUALITY JEEP-CHRYSLER, INC.
8101 Lomas Blvd NE, Albuquerque, NM 87110
Tel.: (505) 265-3753
Web Site: http://www.qualitydeal.com
Sales Range: $25-49.9 Million
Emp.: 90
Car Whslr
N.A.I.C.S.: 441110
Vince DiLorenzo (Gen Mgr)

QUALITY KING DISTRIBUTORS INC.
35 Sawgrass Dr Ste 1, Bellport, NY 11713
Tel.: (631) 737-5555   NY
Web Site: http://www.qkd.com
Year Founded: 1955
Sales Range: $1-4.9 Billion
Emp.: 1,400
Health & Beauty Aids Distr
N.A.I.C.S.: 424210
Glenn F. Nussdorf (CEO)
Marc Garrett (VP-DP)
Ellen Ryder (Mgr-Accts Payable)

Subsidiaries:

QK Healthcare, Inc.   (1)
35 Sawgrass Dr, Bellport, NY 11713   (100%)
Tel.: (631) 737-5555
Web Site: http://www.qkrx.com
Generic & Branded Pharmaceuticals Distr
N.A.I.C.S.: 424210
Michael W. Katz (CFO, Treas & Exec VP)

QUALITY LIQUID FEEDS INC.
3586 State Hwy 23, Dodgeville, WI 53533
Tel.: (608) 935-2345
Web Site: http://www.qlf.com
Year Founded: 1977
Sales Range: $50-74.9 Million
Emp.: 130
Animal Feed
N.A.I.C.S.: 424910
Cory Berg (Pres & CEO)
Joe Saini (VP-Mfg & Procurement)
Stuart Sliter (VP-Transportation)
Steve Freeman (Mgr-Regulatory & Res)
Larry Berg (Mgr-Ingredient Procurement & Logistics)
Mary Kay Esser (VP-Acctg)
Michelle Fredrich (Mgr-Inventory)

QUALITY MILL SUPPLY CO. INC.

Tony Bunn (Mgr-Transportation Logistics)
Steve Peterson (Mgr-Equipment)
Jim Steil (VP-IT)
Howard Blalock (VP-Technical Svcs)
Lisa Davis (Mgr-Dairy Product)
Randy Davis (Mgr-Bus Dev)
Jim Lere (Reg Mgr-Sls)
Brent Molldrem (Mgr-Credit)
Jeff Dugan (CFO)
Megan Mieden (Mgr-Payroll)
Sara Gabor (Mgr-Mktg)

QUALITY LOGO PRODUCTS, INC.
724 N Highland Ave, Aurora, IL 60506
Tel.: (630) 896-1627
Web Site: http://www.qualitylogoproducts.com
Year Founded: 2003
Rev.: $6,500,000
Emp.: 30
Business Services
N.A.I.C.S.: 561990
Bret Bonnet (Co-Owner & Pres)
Michael Wenger (Co-Owner & VP)
Ben Britz (Acct Mgr-Customer Dev)
Jessica Sund (Asst Mgr-Sls)
Michelle Karpus (Mgr-Acctg)

QUALITY MANAGEMENT SOLUTIONS INC.
146 Lowell St Ste 300 B, Wakefield, MA 01889
Web Site: http://www.qmsinc.com
Year Founded: 2008
Sales Range: $1-9.9 Million
Emp.: 40
It Consulting
N.A.I.C.S.: 541690
Carl Dunlap (Co-Founder)
Michael Krug (Co-Founder)

QUALITY MANUFACTURING CORP.
4300 NW Urbandale Dr, Urbandale, IA 50322
Tel.: (515) 331-4300
Web Site: http://www.qualitymfgcorp.com
Sales Range: $10-24.9 Million
Emp.: 80
Fabricated Structural Metal Mfr
N.A.I.C.S.: 332312
Tom Carder (Pres)

QUALITY MARBLE, INC.
3860 70th Ave N, Pinellas Park, FL 33781
Tel.: (727) 527-1676
Web Site: http://www.qualitymarble.com
Year Founded: 1960
Sales Range: $1-9.9 Million
Emp.: 25
Marble & Granite Importing & Fabrication Services
N.A.I.C.S.: 238340
Mark West (Pres)
Scott Corrigan (Mgr-Warehouse)

QUALITY METAL WORKS, INC.
1207 Wood Ct, Plant City, FL 33563
Tel.: (813) 752-6015
Web Site: http://www.qmwcom.com
Rev.: $23,200,000
Emp.: 30
Sheet Metal Work Mfg
N.A.I.C.S.: 332322
Mark Telese (VP)

QUALITY MILL SUPPLY CO. INC.
2159 Early Ln, Franklin, IN 46131
Tel.: (317) 346-1000

QUALITY MILL SUPPLY CO. INC.

Quality Mill Supply Co, Inc.—(Continued)
Web Site: http://www.qualitymill.com
Rev.: $26,898,359
Emp.: 65
Industrial Supplies
N.A.I.C.S.: 423840
Alan Gilbert (Chm)

QUALITY MOLD INC.
2200 Massillon Rd, Akron, OH 44312-4234
Tel.: (330) 645-6653
Web Site: http://www.qualitymold.com
Year Founded: 1978
Sales Range: $10-24.9 Million
Emp.: 300
Provider of Special Dies, Tools, Jigs & Fixtures
N.A.I.C.S.: 333511
Greg Kaliaks (Pres)
Mert Yazici (Dir-Pur)
Tara DeRita (Coord-Acctg)

QUALITY MORTGAGE SERVICES LLC
1111 Lakeview Dr, Franklin, TN 37067-3072
Tel.: (516) 409-5555
Web Site: http://www.nationalmortgageprofessional.com
Real Estate Credit
N.A.I.C.S.: 522292
Mark MacKey (CEO)

QUALITY MOTOR CARS STOCKTON
2222 E Hammer Ln, Stockton, CA 95210
Tel.: (209) 476-1640
Web Site: http://www.acuraofstockton.com
Sales Range: $10-24.9 Million
Emp.: 20
Sales of Automobiles, New & Used
N.A.I.C.S.: 441110
S. Robert Zamora (Pres)

QUALITY NATURALLY FOODS
18830 E San Jose Ave, City of Industry, CA 91748
Tel.: (626) 854-6363 CA
Web Site: http://www.qnfoods.com
Year Founded: 1971
Sales Range: $125-149.9 Million
Emp.: 50
Mfr of Baking Mixes & Custom Blending
N.A.I.C.S.: 424490
Frank H. Watase (Chm & Pres)
Charles Lee (VP-Ops)

QUALITY OIL CO. INC.
1734 E Parrish Ave, Owensboro, KY 42303-0908
Tel.: (270) 684-0215
Sales Range: $25-49.9 Million
Emp.: 23
Petroleum Bulk Stations
N.A.I.C.S.: 424710
Larry Clark (Pres)
Lynn Northern (Controller)

QUALITY OIL COMPANY LLC
1540 Silas Creek Pkwy, Winston Salem, NC 27127-3758
Tel.: (336) 722-3441 NC
Web Site: http://www.qualityoilnc.com
Year Founded: 1929
Sales Range: $50-74.9 Million
Emp.: 475
Provider of Gasoline Station Services
N.A.I.C.S.: 457120
Tim Lowman (Sr VP-Convenience Store Ops)

Carol Holt (Sr VP-IT)
Andy Sayles (Sr VP-Sls)
Graham Bennett (Pres)
Donn McIver (Sr VP)
Thomas Rieke (VP-IT)
Michael O'Connor (VP-Fin & Controller)
Michael Robb (VP-Mktg)
Rodney Cheek (VP-Construction)
Kyle Armentrout (VP-Real Estate)

Subsidiaries:

Reliable Tank Line, LLC (1)
1540 Silas Creek Pkwy, Winston Salem, NC 27127
Tel.: (336) 721-9520
Web Site: http://www.reliabletankline.com
Sales Range: $1-9.9 Million
Emp.: 16
General Freight Trucking, Long-Distance, Truckload
N.A.I.C.S.: 484121
Robert Bramlett (Mgr)
Buddy Jenkins (Sr VP)
Josh McClure (VP)
Evan Wooten (Mgr-Fleet)
Justin Lambert (Mgr-Terminal-Charlotte)
Boone Cooke (Mgr-Terminal-Greensboro)
Mike Cole (Mgr-Terminal-Chesapeake)
Scott Vestal (Mgr-Terminal-Richmond)
Randy Spencer (Mgr-Terminal-Roanoke)
Chris Barnes (Mgr-Terminal-Selma)
Michael Cole (Mgr-Terminal-Spartanburg)

QUALITY PACKAGING SPECIALISTS, INC.
5 Cooper St, Burlington, NJ 08016
Tel.: (609) 239-0503
Web Site: http://www.qpsima.com
Year Founded: 1994
Sales Range: $150-199.9 Million
Emp.: 250
Contract Packaging, Fulfillment & Third-Party Logistics Services
N.A.I.C.S.: 561910
K. Michael Ricketts (Chm & CEO)
Dan Seniff (Controller)
Steve Alemi (COO)
James Wozniak (Exec VP-Sls)

Subsidiaries:

QPSI / IPC (1)
2030 US 130 N, Burlington, NJ 08016
Tel.: (609) 239-0503
Web Site: http://www.qpsiusa.com
Packaging & Fulfillment Logistics Services
N.A.I.C.S.: 561910
Brian Frost (Sr VP-Corp Quality)
Shawn Smith (CFO)

QUALITY PACKAGING, INC.
851 Sullivan Dr, Fond Du Lac, WI 54935
Tel.: (920) 923-3633
Web Site: http://www.qpack.com
Sales Range: $25-49.9 Million
Emp.: 75
Industrial Machinery & Equipment Merchant Whslr
N.A.I.C.S.: 423830
John Strupp (Mgr-Ops)

QUALITY PARTS SUPPLY, INC.
15844 S Hwy 35, Bruceville, TX 76630
Tel.: (254) 857-4629 TX
Web Site: http://www.qualitypartssupply.com
Year Founded: 1970
Sales Range: $25-49.9 Million
Emp.: 100
Motor Vehicle Parts, Used
N.A.I.C.S.: 423140
Billy G. Hoover (Pres)

QUALITY PERFORATING, INC.
166 Dundaff St, Carbondale, PA 18407-1565
Tel.: (570) 282-4344

Web Site: http://www.qualityperf.com
Perforated Sheets, Coils & Component Parts
N.A.I.C.S.: 332119

QUALITY PETROLEUM CORP.
1625 George Jenkins Blvd, Lakeland, FL 33815-3729
Tel.: (863) 687-2682 FL
Web Site: http://www.qpetro.com
Year Founded: 1971
Sales Range: $75-99.9 Million
Emp.: 50
Petroleum & Oil/Grease Lubricant Whslr
N.A.I.C.S.: 424710
Stephen Weeks (Pres)

Subsidiaries:

Quality Petroleum of Alabama, Inc. (1)
112 Trade Center Dr, Birmingham, AL 35244
Tel.: (205) 988-4600
Web Site: http://www.qualityfuels.net
Fuel Retailer & Whslr
N.A.I.C.S.: 424710
David Melton (VP)
Davis Milton (Office Mgr)
Karen Thomason (Office Mgr)

Smith Brothers Oil Company, Inc. (1)
765 W Main St, Bartow, FL 33830
Tel.: (863) 533-3163
Web Site: http://www.smithbrother.com
Rev.: $10,016,479
Emp.: 20
Engine Fuels & Oils
N.A.I.C.S.: 424720
Ralph Weeks (Chm)

QUALITY PETROLEUM INC.
11610 Maybelline Dr, North Little Rock, AR 72117
Tel.: (501) 955-2166
Web Site: http://www.qualitypetroleuminc.com
Year Founded: 1960
Sales Range: $10-24.9 Million
Emp.: 50
Lubricating Oils & Greases Whslr
N.A.I.C.S.: 424720
Sam Edmondson (Pres)
Tim Colclasure (Gen Mgr)

Subsidiaries:

Quality Petroleum (1)
9000 E Hwy 66, El Reno, OK 73036-9205
Tel.: (405) 272-3200
Petroleum Bulk Stations & Terminals
N.A.I.C.S.: 424710

QUALITY PLUS SERVICES INC.
2929 Quality Dr, Petersburg, VA 23805
Tel.: (804) 863-0191
Web Site: http://www.qpsisbest.com
Sales Range: $25-49.9 Million
Emp.: 200
Electrical Contractor
N.A.I.C.S.: 238210
Dianna Bradbury (CFO)

QUALITY PLYWOOD SPECIALTIES, INC.
13000 Automobile Blvd Ste 400, Clearwater, FL 33762
Tel.: (727) 572-0500
Web Site: http://www.qualityplywoodspec.com
Year Founded: 1994
Sales Range: $1-9.9 Million
Emp.: 40
Plywood, Lumber, Veneers & Other Wood Products Wholesale Distr
N.A.I.C.S.: 423310
Michael A. Jankowsi (Pres)

QUALITY PONTIAC GMC BUICK
7901 Lomas Blvd NE, Albuquerque, NM 87110-7916
Tel.: (505) 765-1300 NM
Web Site: http://www.qualitydeal.com
Year Founded: 1957
Sales Range: $25-49.9 Million
Emp.: 100
Retailer of New & Used Automobiles & Related Parts & Service
N.A.I.C.S.: 441110
Charles V. DiLorenzo (Pres & CEO)

QUALITY POOL SUPPLY CO.
5303 W Vienna Rd, Clio, MI 48420
Tel.: (810) 686-3010
Web Site: http://www.qualitypool.com
Year Founded: 1971
Sales Range: $10-24.9 Million
Emp.: 60
Swimming Pools Equipment & Supplies
N.A.I.C.S.: 423910
Cary Engelhart (Pres)
John Schofield (Controller)
Jack Engelhart (Founder & Chm)

QUALITY PORK PROCESSORS, INC.
711 Hormel Century Pkwy, Austin, MN 55912
Tel.: (507) 434-6300
Web Site: http://www.qppinc.net
Year Founded: 1987
Emp.: 2,000
Meat Packing & Slaughtering Services
N.A.I.C.S.: 311611
Mel Gilbertson (Co-Owner & Sr VP-Ops)
Nate Jansen (VP-HR & Quality Svcs)
Ken Kay (VP-Fin)
Melissa Jochumsen (Production Mgr)
Danny Joseph (Mgr-Packaging)
John Berglund (Mgr-Acctg)
Dale Wicks (Dir-HR)
Claude Pulliam (Mgr-Plant)
Angela Stout (Mgr-QS)
Kelly Boerhave (Plant Engr)
Didacus Guzman (Dir-Safety)

QUALITY PRODUCTS INC.
2222 S 3rd St, Columbus, OH 43207
Tel.: (614) 228-0185 OH
Web Site: http://www.multipress.com
Year Founded: 1998
Sales Range: $10-24.9 Million
Emp.: 80
Holding Company; Aircraft Ground Support Equipment & Hydraulic Machine Tools Mfr & Distr
N.A.I.C.S.: 551112
Tac Kensler (CFO & Sec)
Richard Drexler (Chm)
David Somers (CEO)

Subsidiaries:

Columbus Jack Corporation (1)
2222 S 3rd St, Columbus, OH 43207
Tel.: (614) 443-7492
Web Site: http://www.columbusjack.com
Sales Range: $1-9.9 Million
Emp.: 65
Mfr of Hydraulic Jacks
N.A.I.C.S.: 333998
Maria Conley (Mgr-Govt Sls)
Ron Bivens (Mgr-Customer Svc)
Jason Drexler (Coord-Ops & Sls)
Karen K. Hart (COO & Pres)
Rick Parise (Coord-Repair & Refurbish)

PPT Industrial Machines Inc. (1)
714 Walnut St, Mount Carmel, IL 62863
Tel.: (618) 262-8666
Emp.: 60
Press Brakes, Hydraulic Presses & Shears Mfr & Servicer

N.A.I.C.S.: 333248
Amy Clodfelter *(Mgr-Inside Sls)*
Chris Robinson *(Dir-Sls & Mktg)*

QPI Multipress, Inc. (1)
1250 Refugee Ln, Columbus, OH 43207
Tel.: (614) 228-0185
Web Site: http://www.multipress.com
Sales Range: $1-9.9 Million
Emp.: 52
Mfr of Industrial Hydraulic Bench Presses & Floor Presses
N.A.I.C.S.: 333517
Karen Hart *(Controller)*
Barney Raye *(Pres)*

QUALITY PROJECT MANAGEMENT LLC
1702 E McNair Dr, Tempe, AZ 85283
Web Site: http://www.qpmllc.com
Year Founded: 1995
Sales Range: $10-24.9 Million
Emp.: 96
Industrial Building Construction
N.A.I.C.S.: 236210
Gus Guerrero *(VP-Construction Svcs)*
Paul R. Masica *(VP-Ops)*

QUALITY RESTAURANT CONCEPTS
601 Vestavia Pkwy Ste 1000, Birmingham, AL 35216
Tel.: (205) 824-5060
Sales Range: $50-74.9 Million
Emp.: 23
American Restaurant
N.A.I.C.S.: 722511
Fred Gustin *(Owner)*
Alan Darden *(Coord-IT)*
Kim Hartzog *(Coord-Tax & License)*
Tom Winston *(Dir-Ops Admin)*
Blake Sly *(Dir-Ops)*
Brett Verhaar *(Mgr)*
Heath Barnett *(Mgr)*
Christopher Phillips *(Mgr-Svc)*
Tammy Strickland *(Controller-Cash)*
Jason Williams *(Dir-IT)*
Daniel Martin *(Gen Mgr)*

QUALITY ROOFING CENTER OF SOUTHEAST MISSOURI
9350 Hwy C, Senath, MO 63876
Tel.: (573) 738-2683
Web Site:
http://www.qualityroofingcontractors.com
Sales Range: $10-24.9 Million
Emp.: 50
Roofing, Siding & Sheetmetal Work
N.A.I.C.S.: 238160
Terry Whitlock *(Pres)*

QUALITY SAFETY EDGE
14676 Diamondhead S, Montgomery, TX 77356
Tel.: (936) 588-1130
Web Site:
http://www.qualitysafetyedge.com
Sales Range: $1-9.9 Million
Emp.: 20
Safety Consulting Services
N.A.I.C.S.: 541690
Terry McSween *(Pres & CEO)*
Jerry Pounds *(Pres-Intl Div)*
Michael Johnson *(VP-Domestic Sls)*
Beth Foate *(Sr Project Mgr)*
Angelica C. Grindle *(Sr VP)*
Bob Foxworthy *(VP-Market-Latin America)*
Christian Ingle *(Mng Dir)*
Grainne Matthews *(VP-Europe)*
Daniel J. Moran *(Sr VP)*
Judith E. Stowe *(Founder & Sr Dir-Program & Quality Safety Edge)*
Francisco Ugalde *(Sr Project Mgr)*
Christopher Stubenberg *(VP-Latin America)*

QUALITY SAUSAGE COMPANY
1925 Lone Star Dr, Dallas, TX 75212-6302
Tel.: (214) 634-3400
Web Site:
http://www.qualitysausage.com
Year Founded: 1990
Sales Range: $25-49.9 Million
Emp.: 250
Producer of Sausages & Other Prepared Meats
N.A.I.C.S.: 311612
Gene Eisen *(Pres)*
Steve O'Brien *(CFO)*

QUALITY SERVICES FOR THE AUTISM COMMUNITY
253 W 35th St 16th FL, New York, NY 10001
Tel.: (212) 244-5560 NY
Web Site: http://www.qsac.com
Year Founded: 1978
Sales Range: $25-49.9 Million
Emp.: 1,146
Behavioral Healthcare Services
N.A.I.C.S.: 624120
Cory Polshansky *(COO)*
Gary A. Maffei *(CEO & Exec Dir)*
Andrew Linden *(Sr Dir-Adult Programs)*
Paul Naranjo *(CFO)*
Mijung Choi *(CFO)*

QUALITY STATE OIL CO. INC.
2201 Calumet Dr, Sheboygan, WI 53083-4602
Tel.: (920) 459-5640 WI
Web Site:
http://www.qualitystate.com
Year Founded: 1988
Sales Range: $25-49.9 Million
Emp.: 225
Provider of Petroleum Services
N.A.I.C.S.: 424710
Gregory B. Bultman *(Pres & CFO)*
John Winter *(VP-Plng & Dev)*
Kris Dirks *(Supvr-Acctg)*

QUALITY STEEL FABRICATION
2339 Industrial Dr, Sidney, OH 45365
Tel.: (937) 492-9503
Web Site: http://www.qsfab.com
Year Founded: 2002
Sales Range: $1-9.9 Million
Emp.: 21
Fabricated Structural Metal
N.A.I.C.S.: 332312
Robert P. Brunswick *(Pres)*

QUALITY SYNTHETIC RUBBER INCORPORATED
1700 Highland Rd, Twinsburg, OH 44087
Tel.: (330) 425-8472
Web Site: http://www.qsr-inc.com
Sales Range: $50-74.9 Million
Emp.: 250
Custom Compounding Of Rubber Materials
N.A.I.C.S.: 326299
Paul Norton *(Mgr-Shipping)*
Toni Haneberg *(Mgr-Indus Sls)*

QUALITY TEMPORARY SERVICES
5361 Gateway Ctr Ste D, Flint, MI 48507-3943
Tel.: (810) 230-0368
Web Site: http://www.q-staffing.com
Rev.: $17,396,004
Emp.: 4
Temporary Help Service
N.A.I.C.S.: 561320
David Wujciak *(Pres)*

QUALITY TOOL INC.
1220 Energy Park Dr, Saint Paul, MN 55108
Tel.: (651) 646-7433
Web Site: http://www.qualitytool.com
Sales Range: $10-24.9 Million
Emp.: 160
Mfr of Die Sets For Metal Stamping (Presses)
N.A.I.C.S.: 333514
Chuck Proulx *(Pres)*

QUALITY TRUCK CARE CENTER INC.
5725 Green Valley Rd, Oshkosh, WI 54904
Tel.: (920) 231-2122
Web Site:
http://www.qualitytruckcarecenter.net
Sales Range: $10-24.9 Million
Emp.: 50
Commercial Trucks
N.A.I.C.S.: 423110
Kenneth J. Balda *(Owner & Pres)*
Lori Lane *(Controller)*

QUALITY TRUSS INC.
3635 Park Court Blvd, Pompano Beach, FL 33064
Tel.: (954) 975-3384
Web Site:
http://www.flqualitytruss.com
Year Founded: 1992
Sales Range: $10-24.9 Million
Emp.: 6
Truss Mfr
N.A.I.C.S.: 321215
Tolgs Adeck *(Pres)*

QUALITY TURNING INC.
9155 Alabama Ave Ste D, Chatsworth, CA 91311
Tel.: (818) 349-8734
Rev.: $500,000
Emp.: 4
Aircraft Parts & Auxiliary Equipment Mfr
N.A.I.C.S.: 336413
Jorge Cassan *(Pres)*

QUALITY VISION INTERNATIONAL INC.
850 Hudson Ave, Rochester, NY 14621
Tel.: (585) 544-0450
Web Site: http://www.qvii.com
Sales Range: $15-24.9 Billion
Emp.: 322
Optical Test & Inspection Equipment
N.A.I.C.S.: 561110
Len Mills *(Supvr-Marcom)*
Bill Stickles *(Dir-Production)*
Boris Gelman *(Sr VP-Engrg & Tech & Dir-Quality)*
Aaron Wagner *(Engr-Applications)*
Ian Ober *(Engr-Electrical)*
Richard Crist *(Engr-Electrical)*
Randy Weaver *(CIO & Dir-Electronics Mfg Grp)*
Wade Cook *(VP-Optics Mfg)*
Bob Scheidt *(Pres-Quality Vision Svcs)*
Keith Polidor *(COO & Sr VP)*

Subsidiaries:

Kotem Hungary Ltd. (1)
2 Gyar Str, Budaors, 2040, Hungary
Tel.: (36) 23 444 002
Web Site: http://www.kotem.com
Software Development Services
N.A.I.C.S.: 541511

Subsidiary (Non-US):

Kotem Technologies Inc. (2)
1971 Marquis Ave, Ottawa, K1J 8J5, ON, Canada

Tel.: (613) 749-0200
Software Development Services
N.A.I.C.S.: 541511

OGP Messtechnik GmbH (1)
Nassaustrasse 11, 65719, Hofheim, Germany
Tel.: (49) 6122 99 68 0
Web Site: http://www.ogpgmbh.de
Multi Sensor System Mfr
N.A.I.C.S.: 334513
Karl Lenz *(Mng Dir)*

OGP Shanghai Co. Ltd. (1)
Building 8 No 11 Galileo Road, Pu Dong New District, Shanghai, 201203, China
Tel.: (86) 21 50458383
Web Site: http://www.smartscope.com.cn
Multi Sensor System Mfr
N.A.I.C.S.: 334513
Viki Lv *(Gen Mgr)*

Optical Gaging (S) Pte, Ltd (1)
21 Tannery Road, Singapore, 347733, Singapore
Tel.: (65) 6741 8880
Web Site: http://www.smartscope.com.sg
Measuring Equipment Mfr
N.A.I.C.S.: 334513
Kelly Chee *(Gen Mgr)*

Optical Gaging Products Inc. (1)
850 Hudson Ave, Rochester, NY 14621-4896
Tel.: (585) 544-0400
Web Site: http://www.ogpnet.com
Optical Instruments & Lenses Mfr
N.A.I.C.S.: 333310
Tom Groff *(VP-Sls-North America)*
R. Stephen Flynn *(Pres)*

Quality Vision International Inc. - Certified Comparator Products Division (1)
1174 Grange Hall Rd, Beavercreek, OH 45430
Tel.: (937) 426-9677
Web Site:
http://www.certifiedcomparator.com
Optical Comparator Mfr
N.A.I.C.S.: 333310

RAM Optical Instrumentation Inc. (1)
1175 North St, Rochester, NY 14621
Tel.: (585) 758-1300
Web Site: http://www.ramoptical.com
Measuring Equipment Mfr
N.A.I.C.S.: 334513
Frank Opett *(Dir-Ops)*

VIEW Micro-Metrology, Inc. (1)
1711 W 17th St, Tempe, AZ 85281
Tel.: (480) 295-3150
Web Site: http://www.viewmm.com
Sales Range: $10-24.9 Million
Emp.: 12
Video Measurement Technologies
N.A.I.C.S.: 334519
Justin Rucker *(Dir-Ops)*

QUALITY WHOLESALE BUILDING PRODUCTS INC.
11701 Kinard Rd, North Little Rock, AR 72117-9635
Tel.: (501) 945-3442 AR
Year Founded: 1987
Sales Range: $50-74.9 Million
Emp.: 65
Lumber, Plywood & Millwork Whslr
N.A.I.C.S.: 423310
Randy Wright *(Pres & CEO)*
Cheryl McCullough *(Controller)*
Tim Shuttleworth *(Mgr-Sls)*

QUALITY WOODS INC.
605 50th St SE, Charleston, WV 25304
Tel.: (304) 925-9546
Year Founded: 1981
Sales Range: $10-24.9 Million
Emp.: 60
Hardwood Moldings, Paneling Doors, Millwork & Flooring Whslr
N.A.I.C.S.: 423310

QUALITY WOODS INC.

Quality Woods Inc.—(Continued)
Sal Rossi (Pres)
Anna Rossi (Accountant)
Iris Rossi (Treas & Sec)

QUALLY & COMPANY, INC.
1187 Wilmette Ave, Ste 160, Wilmette, IL 60091-2719
Tel.: (312) 280-1898
Web Site:
  http://www.quallycompany.com
Year Founded: 1979
Rev.: $11,800,000
Emp.: 18
N.A.I.C.S.: 541810
Robert Qually (Chm Emeritus)
Michael Iva (Pres & Dir-Creative)
Betty Knox (CFO & VP)
Curtis Sahakian (Gen Counsel & VP)
Grey Ryerson (VP-Mktg)

QUALMETRIX INC.
3810 Executive Wy, Miami, FL 33025
Tel.: (786) 431-0418
Web Site: http://www.qualmetrix.com
Sales Range: $1-9.9 Million
Post-Acute Healthcare Software Applications
N.A.I.C.S.: 513210
Cristian Ilie (CTO)
Daryl Wansink (Sr VP-Analytics)
Richard Krol (Sr VP-Bus Dev)

QUALSTAR CREDIT UNION
PO Box 96730, Bellevue, WA 98009-7730
Tel.: (425) 643-3400
Web Site: http://www.qualstarcu.com
Year Founded: 1952
Sales Range: $10-24.9 Million
Emp.: 113
Credit Union Operator
N.A.I.C.S.: 522130
Michael G. Elfstrom (CFO)
Robert D. Arbuckle (Chief Admin Officer)
Mark R. Nelson (Pres & CEO)

QUALTEX LABORATORIES
6211 IH-W, San Antonio, TX 78201
Tel.: (210) 757-9505
Web Site: http://www.qualtexlabs.org
Year Founded: 2007
Sales Range: $125-149.9 Million
Emp.: 267
Testing Laboratory
N.A.I.C.S.: 541380
Linda Kay Myers (Pres, CEO & COO)
Thomas Scott Jones (VP-Scientific Affairs)
Irma G. Villarreal (VP-Bus Integration)
Jose R. Garcia (VP-Mktg & Customer Rels)

QUALUS CORPORATION
100 Colonial C Pkwy Ste 400, Lake Mary, FL 32746
Tel.: (321) 244-0170
Web Site: https://qualuscorp.com
Year Founded: 2020
Emp.: 480
Electric Power Engineering Services
N.A.I.C.S.: 541330
Hisham Mahmoud (Chm & CEO)

Subsidiaries:
Tri Sage Consulting (1)
5418 Longley Ln, Reno, NV 89511
Tel.: (775) 336-1300
Web Site: http://www.trisage.com
Rev.: $3,000,000
Emp.: 10
Engineeering Services
N.A.I.C.S.: 541330
Karen P. E. Schlichting (Pres)
Lori Williams (Sr Project Mgr)

Dave Porter (Engr-Utility)
James Demuth (Mgr-Construction)
Jim Bengochea (Mgr-Engrg)
Jim Bessey (Mgr-Construction & Supvr Quality Assurance)
Kayla L. Cass (Engr-Civil)
Mary Shrigley-LeMay (Office Mgr)
Alissa K. Turner (Project Mgr & Sr Engr)

QUAM-NICHOLS COMPANY
234 E Marquette Rd, Chicago, IL 60637-4091
Tel.: (773) 488-5800
Web Site:
  http://www.quamspeakers.com
Year Founded: 1930
Sales Range: $10-24.9 Million
Emp.: 250
Commercial & Industrial Loudspeakers & Mounting Accessories
N.A.I.C.S.: 334310
Bruce Arndt (CFO)
Randy Moore (VP & Gen Mgr)
Craig Tayler (Mgr-Sls-Natl)
William G. Little (Pres & CEO)

QUANT SYSTEMS, INC.
546 Long Point Rd, Mount Pleasant, SC 29464
Tel.: (843) 571-2825
Web Site:
  http://www.hawkeslearning.com
Year Founded: 1979
Sales Range: $1-9.9 Million
Emp.: 25
Software Publisher
N.A.I.C.S.: 513210
Hallie Hurwitz (Mgr-Software Product)

QUANTA ADVERTISING
968 James St, Syracuse, NY 13217
Tel.: (315) 472-2809
Year Founded: 1975
Sales Range: Less than $1 Million
Emp.: 3
N.A.I.C.S.: 541810
Dan Accordino (Pres)
Marie Irwin (Dir Mktg & Dir Adv)
Jim Jackson (Assoc Dir-Creative)
Adam Donnelley (Exec VP & Dir-Client Solutions)
Andreas Brueckner (Mng Dir)
Dave Hohman (Sr VP)
Donald Patrick Lim (Mng Dir)

QUANTASY, LLC
5855 Green Vly Cir, Culver City, CA 90230
Tel.: (310) 945-4100
Web Site: http://www.quantasy.com
Year Founded: 2011
Marketing & Advertising Services
N.A.I.C.S.: 541810
Will Campbell (Founder)

Subsidiaries:
Muse Communications, Inc. (1)
2001 Wilshire Blvd 6th Fl, Santa Monica, CA 90403
Tel.: (310) 945-4100
Advertising & Marketing Services
N.A.I.C.S.: 541810
Shelley Yamane (Pres)

QUANTECH SERVICES, INC.
91 Hartwell Ave, Lexington, MA 02421
Tel.: (781) 271-9757
Web Site:
  http://www.quantechserv.com
Year Founded: 1999
Sales Range: $10-24.9 Million
Emp.: 400
Program Management, Systems Engineering, Cost & Financial Management Consulting Services for Government Agencies & Commercial Clients
N.A.I.C.S.: 541611

Jim Monopoli (Pres)
Bert Rogers (Dir-Strategic Plng & Bus Dev)
Rick Sette (CFO)
Maryanne Cromwell (Dir-HR & Security)
Dave Mirra (VP-IT)
Susan Thibodeau (VP-Southern Reg)

QUANTEGY INC.
2230 Marvyn Pkwy, Opelika, AL 36804
Web Site: http://www.quantegy.com
Sales Range: $75-99.9 Million
Emp.: 700
Magnetic Tape
N.A.I.C.S.: 334610
Peter Hutt (CEO)

QUANTEM AVIATION SERVICES
175 Ammon Dr, Manchester, NH 03103
Tel.: (603) 647-1717
Web Site:
  http://www.quantemaviation.com
Sales Range: $10-24.9 Million
Emp.: 600
Cargo Loading & Unloading Services
N.A.I.C.S.: 488210
James Jolck (Sr VP-Bus Dev)
Karen L. Fortin (VP-Fin)
Rich Moletteire (Gen Mgr)
Pat Bealmear (Reg Dir)

QUANTEM FBO GROUP LLC
27499 Riverview Ctr Blvd Ste 206, Bonita Springs, FL 34134
Tel.: (603) 647-6763
Web Site:
  https://www.odysseyaviation.com
Year Founded: 1997
Emp.: 82
Aviation & Aerospace Component Mfg.
N.A.I.C.S.: 334511
Ken Allison (Pres & CEO)
Larry Wade (Partner)

Subsidiaries:
Golden Isles Aviation (1)
115 Terminal Wy, St Simons Island, GA 31522
Tel.: (912) 263-8617
Web Site:
  http://www.goldenislesaviation.com
Support Activities for Air Transportation
N.A.I.C.S.: 488190
Lawrence Wade (Owner)

QUANTIFI, INC.
17 Union Pl 2nd Fl, Summit, NJ 07901
Tel.: (908) 273-9455
Web Site:
  http://www.quantifisolutions.com
Year Founded: 2002
Rev.: $9,000,000
Emp.: 45
Software Publisher
N.A.I.C.S.: 513210
Rohan Douglas (Founder & CEO)
Dmitry Pugachevsky (Dir-Res)

QUANTIX, INC.
7600 E Eastman Ave Ste 408, Denver, CO 80231
Tel.: (720) 493-8980
Web Site: http://www.quantixinc.com
Year Founded: 2002
Sales Range: $10-24.9 Million
Emp.: 111
Professional Staffing Services
N.A.I.C.S.: 561320
Jill Renolds (Pres)

QUANTRONIX, INC.

U.S. PRIVATE

380 S 200 W, Farmington, UT 84025-2409
Tel.: (801) 451-7000
Web Site: http://www.cubiscan.com
Year Founded: 1999
Sales Range: $10-24.9 Million
Emp.: 50
Optical Scanning Equipment Mfr
N.A.I.C.S.: 333310
Clark P. Skeen (Pres)
Mike Stucki (Mgr-Svc)

QUANTROS, INC.
690 N McCarthy Blvd Ste 200, Milpitas, CA 95035
Tel.: (408) 957-3300
Web Site: http://www.quantros.com
Sales Range: $10-24.9 Million
Emp.: 50
Health Care Information Technology Services
N.A.I.C.S.: 541511
Trey Cook (Pres & CEO)
Ray Olson (Gen Counsel, Sec & VP)

Subsidiaries:
MediQual Systems, Inc. (1)
293 Boston Post Rd W Ste 100, Marlborough, MA 01752
Tel.: (508) 571-5100
Web Site: http://www.mediqual.com
Computer-Based Clinical Information Management Systems Developer
N.A.I.C.S.: 513210

QUANTUM BUSINESS STRATEGIES, INC.
1260 N Slone Lane, Las Vegas, NV 89110
Tel.: (702) 296-2754
Year Founded: 2016
Assets: $2,220,741
Liabilities: $2,263,965
Net Worth: ($43,224)
Earnings: ($76,645)
Fiscal Year-end: 12/31/18
Business Management Consulting Services
N.A.I.C.S.: 541611
Holly Roseberry (CEO & Principal Fin Officer)

QUANTUM CAPITAL GROUP LLC
Bank of America Tower 800 Capitol St Ste 3600, Houston, TX 77002
Tel.: (713) 452-2000
Web Site:
  https://www.quantumcap.com
Year Founded: 1998
Private Equity Firm
N.A.I.C.S.: 523940

QUANTUM COLOR GRAPHICS LLC
6511 Oakton St, Morton Grove, IL 60053-2728
Tel.: (847) 967-3600
Web Site:
  http://www.quantumgroup.com
Year Founded: 1992
Sales Range: $25-49.9 Million
Emp.: 150
Printing Services
N.A.I.C.S.: 323120
William W. White (CEO)

QUANTUM COMMUNICATIONS
101 Sullys Trl Bldg 20, Pittsford, NY 14534-4552
Tel.: (585) 248-8250
Web Site:
  http://www.quantumcommunications.net
Year Founded: 1983
Sales Range: Less than $1 Million
Emp.: 3

Automotive, Graphic Design, Internet/Web Design, Print, Retail, T.V.
N.A.I.C.S.: 541810
Chris Nation *(Dir-Client Svcs)*

QUANTUM DESIGN INC.
10307 Pacific Ctr Ct, San Diego, CA 92121
Tel.: (858) 481-4400
Web Site: http://www.qdusa.com
Rev.: $22,803,115
Emp.: 200
Analytical Instruments
N.A.I.C.S.: 334516
Ronald E. Sager *(Chm)*
Jerry Daviess *(Pres)*
Dave Schultz *(CFO)*
Stefano Spagna *(Dir-Engrg)*

QUANTUM ENERGY PARTNERS, LLC
5 Houston Ctr 1401 McKinney St Ste 2700, Houston, TX 77010
Tel.: (713) 452-2000
Web Site: http://www.quantumep.com
Year Founded: 1998
Rev.: $6,500,000,000
Investment Management Service
N.A.I.C.S.: 523940
Franklin Myers *(Dir-Advisory)*
James V. Baird *(Partner & Gen Counsel)*
Garry A. Tanner *(Partner)*
Jeffrey A. Jones *(Dir-Technical)*
Michael A. Denham *(CFO)*
Michael P. Dalton *(Mng Dir-IR)*
William C. Montgomery *(Mng Dir)*
Eric Nielsen *(Mng Dir-Bus Dev)*
Charles D. Davidson *(Venture Partner)*
Mark Traylor *(VP-IR & Plng)*
Dheeraj Verma *(Pres)*
Jeff Donahue *(Mng Dir)*
Tom Field *(Mng Dir)*
Sean O'Donnell *(Mng Dir)*
Jonathan Regan *(Mng Dir)*
Blake Webster *(Mng Dir)*
Jon Grimmer *(Sr VP-Technical)*
Basak Kurtoglu *(Sr VP-Technical)*
Sebastian T. Gass *(CTO)*
S. Wil VanLoh Jr. *(Founder & CEO)*

Subsidiaries:

Ceritas Energy, LLC (1)
3 Allen Ctr 333 Clay St Ste 750, Houston, TX 77002
Tel.: (713) 439-5000
Web Site: http://www.ceritasgroup.com
Natural Gas Pipeline Transportation
N.A.I.C.S.: 486210
John Herbert *(VP-Legal & Regulatory Affairs)*
David Litchfield *(VP)*
Len Hesseltine *(VP)*

Chalker Energy Partners III, LLC (1)
2 Shell Plz 777 Walker St Ste 2520, Houston, TX 77002
Tel.: (713) 586-6858
Web Site: http://www.chalkerenergy.com
Oil & Gas Exploration & Production
N.A.I.C.S.: 211120
Doug Krenek *(Pres)*
Larry Tolleson *(VP-Ops)*
Bill Dukes *(VP-Land & Bus Dev)*
Janie Isbell *(Mgr)*

Quantum Utility Generation, LLC (1)
5 Houston Ctr 1401 McKinney St Ste 1800, Houston, TX 77010
Tel.: (713) 485-8600
Web Site: http://www.quantumug.com
Emp.: 16
Utility Investment Holding Company
N.A.I.C.S.: 551112
Larry Kellerman *(CEO)*
Sean O'Donnell *(Pres & CFO)*
Lance Schuler *(Gen Counsel)*
Dirk Straussfeld *(COO & Exec VP)*
Christopher Sanders *(VP & Controller)*

Mike Beckner *(VP-Renewables)*
Akhil Unni *(VP & Dir-Fin Plng & Analysis)*
Mark Breen *(Sr VP-Ops)*
Averill Conn *(VP & Assoc Gen Counsel)*
Stacy Guidry *(Dir-Plant Acctg)*
Myphuong Lam *(Mgr-Asset)*
Matthew Nicklos *(VP-Project Acq & Fin)*
Jason Pillai *(Chief Comml Officer)*
Irene Robinson *(Office Mgr)*
Suriyun Sukduang *(VP-Engrg & Project Dev)*

Subsidiary (Domestic):

Pasco Cogen, Ltd. (2)
14850 Old State Rd 23, Dade City, FL 33523-2845
Tel.: (352) 523-0062
Electric Power Distribution Services
N.A.I.C.S.: 221122

Ute Energy LLC (1)
1875 Lawrence St Ste 200, Denver, CO 80202
Tel.: (720) 420-3200
Crude Petroleum & Gas Exploration, Drilling, Extraction & Transportation
N.A.I.C.S.: 213112
Robert E. Ogle *(CFO)*

Vantage Energy Inc. (1)
116 Inverness Dr E Ste 220, Englewood, CO 80112
Tel.: (720) 458-6601
Web Site: http://www.vantageenergy.com
Emp.: 63
Holding Company; Petroleum & Natural Gas Extraction
N.A.I.C.S.: 551112
Roger J. Biemans *(Chm & CEO)*
W. Worth Carlin *(Sr VP-Land)*
Mike L. Hopkins *(VP-Midstream)*
Seth Urruty *(VP-Dev)*
Mark Brown *(VP-Land & Bus Dev)*
Christopher L. Valdez *(VP-Mktg & Midstream Bus Dev)*
Richard Starkey *(VP-Subsurface Tech)*
Ryan T. Gosney *(Chief Acctg Officer & VP-Controller)*
John J. Moran Jr. *(Sr VP-Ops)*
Thomas B. Tyree Jr. *(Pres & CFO)*

QUANTUM ENERGY, LLC.
35010 Chardon Rd Ste 200, Willoughby, OH 44094
Tel.: (440) 954-5022
Year Founded: 1996
Rev.: $3,000,000
Emp.: 25
Fiscal Year-end: 12/31/06
Oil & Gas Exploration
N.A.I.C.S.: 213112
Paul Mysyk *(Principal)*

QUANTUM GROUP, INC.
9835 Lk Worth Rd Ste 16-237, Lake Worth, FL 33467
Tel.: (561) 904-9473 NV
Web Site: http://www.quantummd.com
Sales Range: $10-24.9 Million
Emp.: 57
Medical Technology & Business Consulting Services
N.A.I.C.S.: 541519
Susan Darby Gallagher *(Sec)*
Cheryl Kahanec *(CEO)*
Peter Cahall *(Chm)*
Alan Darling *(VP-Info Sys)*
Michele Brennan *(VP-Accts & Bus Dev-Natl)*
Noel J. Guillama *(Pres)*

QUANTUM INK COMPANY
4651 Melton Ave, Louisville, KY 40213
Tel.: (502) 364-8900
Web Site: http://www.quantumink.com
Sales Range: $1-9.9 Million
Emp.: 26
Aqueous Borne Flexographic Ink Mfr & Distr

N.A.I.C.S.: 325910
Robert Bodner *(Co-Founder)*
Dan Bland *(Co-Founder)*

QUANTUM MARKET RESEARCH, INC.
1015 N 98th St Ste 301, Omaha, NE 68114-2357
Tel.: (402) 250-8302 DE
Web Site: http://www.quantumworkplace.com
Human Resource Consulting Services
N.A.I.C.S.: 541612
Greg Harris *(CEO)*

Subsidiaries:

Talent Keepers, Inc. (1)
280 W Canton Ave Ste 100, Winter Park, FL 32789
Tel.: (407) 660-6041
Web Site: http://www.talentkeepers.com
Sales Range: $1-9.9 Million
Emp.: 100
Direct Property & Casualty Insurance Carriers
N.A.I.C.S.: 524126
Fredric Frank *(CEO)*
Christian Grover *(Dir-Tech)*
Christopher P. Mulligan *(Founder & CEO)*
Craig R. Taylor *(VP-Client Svcs)*
Kerri Weber *(Dir-Strategy)*

QUANTUM MATERIALS CORP.
3055 Hunter Rd, San Marcos, TX 78666
Tel.: (512) 245-6646 NV
Web Site: http://www.qmcdots.com
Rev.: $20,120
Assets: $2,614,281
Liabilities: $6,185,578
Net Worth: ($3,571,297)
Earnings: ($9,401,069)
Emp.: 4
Fiscal Year-end: 06/30/18
Solar Technology & Quantum Dot Mfr
N.A.I.C.S.: 334419
Robert Phillips *(CFO)*
Payal Patel *(Dir-HR)*
Peter Cona *(COO)*
Nicholas P. Vitalari *(Chief Strategy Officer)*

Subsidiaries:

Solterra Renewable Technologies, Inc. (1)
ASU Research Pk 7700 S River Pkwy, Tempe, AZ 85284
Tel.: (214) 701-8779
Web Site: http://www.solterrasolarcells.com
Solar Technology & Quantum Dot Mfr
N.A.I.C.S.: 334419
Stephen B. Squires *(Pres, CEO & Mng Dir)*

QUANTUM PLASTICS, INC.
21 N Main St, Aberdeen, SD 57401
Tel.: (605) 229-7001 SD
Year Founded: 1997
Sales Range: $1-9.9 Million
Emp.: 36
Plastics Product Mfr
N.A.I.C.S.: 326199
Dennis Chasteen *(Pres)*

Subsidiaries:

3D Plastics, Inc. (1)
1095 E Commerce Ave, Gladewater, TX 75647
Tel.: (903) 844-9333
Web Site: http://www.3dplasticsinc.com
Sales Range: $1-9.9 Million
Emp.: 65
Plastics Product Mfr
N.A.I.C.S.: 326199
David Frye *(Pres)*
Dena Wood *(VP)*

QUANTUM RESEARCH INTERNATIONAL, INC.
991 Discovery Dr, Huntsville, AL 35806
Tel.: (256) 971-1800
Web Site: http://www.quantum-intl.com
Year Founded: 1987
Rev.: $64,100,000
Emp.: 400
Computer System Design Services
N.A.I.C.S.: 541512
D. Frank Pitts *(Pres & CEO)*
Dick Wilbanks *(COO & Sr VP)*
Tim Bloechl *(Dir-Cybersecurity Bus Dev)*

QUANTUM RESEARCH SERVICES, INC.
5505 Central Ave, Boulder, CO 80301
Tel.: (303) 786-9500
Web Site: http://www.aspenonnet.com
Year Founded: 1989
Sales Range: $1-9.9 Million
Emp.: 175
Marketing Research & Public Opinion Polling
N.A.I.C.S.: 541910
Eric Hall *(CFO)*
Trey Cowhig *(VP-Mktg)*

QUANTUM VENTURES OF MICHIGAN, LLC
1030 Doris Rd, Auburn Hills, MI 48326
Tel.: (248) 292-5680
Web Site: http://www.qvmllc.com
Private Equity Fund
N.A.I.C.S.: 525910
Robert J. Skandalaris *(Pres & CEO)*
Aaron Witalec *(VP-Acquisitions)*
David Puro *(Gen Counsel & VP-Acquisitions)*
Carey Sienkiewicz *(Assoc Gen Counsel)*
Linda Liphardt *(Corp Controller)*
Kristin Puro *(Dir-Philanthropy)*

QUANTUM, INC.
PO Box 2791, Eugene, OR 97402
Tel.: (541) 345-5556
Web Site: http://www.quantumhealth.com
Sales Range: $25-49.9 Million
Emp.: 25
Vitamins & Herbal Supplement Mfr
N.A.I.C.S.: 325411
Jason Pellegrini *(CEO)*

QUANTUMDIGITAL, INC.
8702 Cross Park Dr Ste 200, Austin, TX 78754
Tel.: (512) 837-2300
Web Site: http://www.quantumdigital.com
Year Founded: 1986
Sales Range: $10-24.9 Million
Emp.: 75
Direct Mail Printing & Mailing Services
N.A.I.C.S.: 541860
Steve Damman *(CEO & CFO)*
Freddie Baird *(Pres & COO)*
Eric Cosway *(Exec VP & CMO)*
J. Chris Anderson *(VP & CTO)*
Angela McMurray *(Dir-HR)*
Jonathan Peterson *(VP-Bus Dev)*
Matthew Kemp *(Sr Mgr-Acct)*

QUARDEV, INC.
2707 NE Blakeley St, Seattle, WA 98105
Tel.: (206) 547-7771 WA
Web Site: http://www.quardev.com
Year Founded: 2000
Sales Range: $1-9.9 Million

Quardev, Inc.—(Continued)
Emp.: 45
Software Testing, Technical Documentation Writing, Project Management & Consulting Services
N.A.I.C.S.: 541690
Joseph Dillon (Pres & CEO)
Tom Armitage (Sr Mgr-Fin, Contracts & Scheduling)

QUARLES & BRADY LLP
411 E Wisconsin Ave Ste 2350, Milwaukee, WI 53202
Tel.: (414) 277-5000
Web Site: http://www.quarles.com
Year Founded: 1892
Sales Range: $200-249.9 Million
Emp.: 1,000
Law firm
N.A.I.C.S.: 541110
Thomas Schoewe (CFO)
John J. Peterburs (Exec Dir)
Robert James Kline (Partner)
Kimberly Leach Johnson (Chm)
Brian Sirower (Chm-Restructuring, Bankruptcy & Creditor's Rights Grp-Natl)
Patrick J. Bitterman (Chm-Estate, Trust & Wealth Preservation Practice Grp)
Larry P. Cote (Mng Partner & Partner-Washington Office)
Paul Langer (Mng Partner-Chicago)
Randall R. Fearnow (Partner)
Edward D. Rickert (Partner)
Mark W. Bina (Partner)
Jeffery M. Monberg (Partner)
David E. Worthen (Partner)
Jonathan Hudis (Partner)
Anthony C. Marino (Partner)
Jeffrey Shear (Partner)
Marian M. Zapata-Rossa (Partner)
Rowan P. Smith (Partner)
Cathleen T. Yu (Partner)
Nicole A. Bashor (Partner)
Brian A. Hartstein (Partner)
Valerie P. Vidal (Partner-Litigation & Alternative Dispute Resolution Grp)
Jonathan W. Hackbarth (Partner)
Daniel J. Ark (Partner)
Mary Ann Murray (Partner-Chicago)
Susan McCaffery Zoeller (Partner)
Theodore M. Sullivan (Partner)
Mark M. Yacura (Partner)
Peter F. Asaad (Partner)
Stephanie J. Quincy (Chm-Labor & Employment Practice Grp & Partner)
Anne M. O'Brien (Partner)
Lucy Dollens (Mng Dir-Indianapolis)
Edward A. Salanga (Chm-Comml Litigation & Dispute Resolution Practice Grp)
Kelli Edson (Mng Partner-Tampa)
Jennifer Sucher (Partner-Bankruptcy, Restructuring, & Creditor's Rights Practice)
Derek Neathery (Vice Chm-Real Estate Practice Grp)
Douglas S. Buck (Partner-Real Estate Law Practice Grp)
Julie H. Cole (Chief Client Rels Officer)
Andrew Hargitt (Chief HR Officer)
Karen R. Mazin (Chief Legal Practice Admin Officer)
Richard A. Raether (CIO)
Charyn Ullrick (Co-CFO)
David Blank (Partner-Washington)
Meghan O'Connor (Partner)
Caroline Hennessy (Sr Mgr-Digital Mktg & PR)
Lori Meddings (Partner-Intellectual Property Practice Grp-Madison)
Jack Cook (Chm-Intellectual Property Grp-Natl)
Michael Aldana (Mng Partner-Natl)
Ryan Haas (Partner-Bus Law Grp)
Mark Kornfield (Partner-Tampa)
David Cellitti (Partner-Bus Law Practice Grp-Tampa)
Rasha Elganzouri Gad (Partner-Real Estate Grp-Chicago)
Kevin Delorey (Chm-Real Estate Practice Grp-Natl & Partner)
Katya Zelenovskiy (Mng Partner-Bus Law Practice Grp)
Kevin Long (Mng Partner)
David Wiese (Partner-Washington)
Rasha Elganzouri (Partner-Real Estate Grp-Chicago)
M. Scott McBride (Partner-Intellectual Property Grp)
Jonodev Osceola Chaudhuri (Chm-Law & Policy Grp-India)
Joel Tragesser (Mng Partner-Indianapolis)
Kevin Halloran (Partner-Bus Law Practice Grp)

QUARLES PETROLEUM INCORPORATED
1701 Fall Hill Ave Ste 200, Fredericksburg, VA 22401
Tel.: (540) 371-2400   VA
Web Site: http://www.quarlesinc.com
Year Founded: 1940
Provider of Petroleum Bulk Stations & Terminals
N.A.I.C.S.: 424710
Paul Giambra (Pres & CEO)

Subsidiaries:
Artag Holdings, Inc. (1)
3302 Patterson Ave, Richmond, VA 23111
Tel.: (804) 746-8283
Petroleum & Petroleum Products Merchant Wholesalers, except Bulk Stations & Terminals
N.A.I.C.S.: 424720

Northern Neck Oil Company (1)
11549 History Land Hwy, Warsaw, VA 22572
Tel.: (804) 333-3835
Sales Range: $1-9.9 Million
Fuel & Petroleum Products Distr
N.A.I.C.S.: 457210

Quarles Truck Stop Inc. (1)
9719 James Madison Hwy, Warrenton, VA 20187-7814   (100%)
Tel.: (540) 439-3000
Sales Range: $10-24.9 Million
Emp.: 15
Gasoline Service Stations
N.A.I.C.S.: 457120

Revere Gas, Inc. (1)
11080 General Puller Hwy, Hartfield, VA 23071
Tel.: (540) 736-8303
Web Site: http://www.reveregas.com
Wholesale Trade Agents & Brokers
N.A.I.C.S.: 425120
Craig Revere (COO)

QUARRIES DIRECT INTERNATIONAL LLC
2633 N 24th Dr, Phoenix, AZ 85009
Tel.: (602) 269-7900
Web Site: http://www.qdistone.com
Year Founded: 2005
Sales Range: $10-24.9 Million
Emp.: 35
Natural Stone Supplier
N.A.I.C.S.: 327991
Arif Surmen (Pres & CEO)

QUARRY CAPITAL MANAGEMENT LLC
37 Walnut St Ste 310, Wellesley Hills, MA 02481
Tel.: (508) 655-3540
Web Site: http://www.quarrycapital.com
Privater Equity Firm
N.A.I.C.S.: 523999
Brent P. Johnstone (Mng Dir)

Subsidiaries:
Royal Pet Supplies Inc. (1)
60 Rodeo Dr, Brentwood, NY 11717
Tel.: (631) 243-2300
Web Site: http://www.royalpetsupplies.com
Sales Range: $75-99.9 Million
Emp.: 400
Pet Supply Distr
N.A.I.C.S.: 423990

QUARRYVILLE PRESBYTERIAN RETIREMENT COMMUNITY
625 Robert Fulton Hwy, Quarryville, PA 17566-1400
Tel.: (717) 786-7321   PA
Web Site: http://www.quarryville.com
Year Founded: 1948
Sales Range: $10-24.9 Million
Emp.: 491
Lifecare Retirement Community Operator
N.A.I.C.S.: 623311
Diane Aston (CFO)

QUARTER HORSE RACING INC.
4961 Katella Ave, Los Alamitos, CA 90720-2721
Tel.: (714) 820-2800
Web Site: http://www.losalamitos.com
Year Founded: 1974
Sales Range: $25-49.9 Million
Emp.: 500
Provider of Racing & Track Operation Services
N.A.I.C.S.: 711212
Ed Allred (Owner)
Orlando Gutierrez (Dir-Mktg)

Subsidiaries:
Horsemen's Quarter Horse Racing Association, Inc. (1)
4961 Katella Ave, Los Alamitos, CA 90720-2721
Tel.: (714) 820-2800
Web Site: http://www.losalamitos.com
Provider of Racing & Track Operation Services
N.A.I.C.S.: 711219

QUARTERWAY GIN, INC.
1380 W US Hwy 70 B, Plainview, TX 79072-0744
Tel.: (806) 889-3391
Web Site: http://www.quarterwaygin.com
Year Founded: 1972
Sales Range: $1-9.9 Million
Emp.: 10
Crop Preparation Services
N.A.I.C.S.: 115114
Bill Mason (VP)
Steve Mason (Owner & Pres)

QUASAR BIO TECH LLC
1465 Tellavast Rd, Sarasota, FL 34243
Tel.: (941) 306-5812
Web Site: http://www.quasarbiotech.com
Year Founded: 2001
Sales Range: $1-9.9 Million
Emp.: 10
Light-Based Skin Therapy Devices
N.A.I.C.S.: 339112
Peter Nesbit (Pres & CEO)

QUASAR INDUSTRIES INC.
1911 Northfield Dr, Rochester Hills, MI 48309
Tel.: (248) 852-0300
Web Site: http://www.quasar.com
Year Founded: 1967
Rev.: $13,000,000
Emp.: 80
Mfr of Precision-Quality Prototype & Short Run Production Parts
N.A.I.C.S.: 332710
Jeanette Burch (Controller)
Stephen Patterson (Project Mgr)

QUASIUS INVESTMENT CORP.
4805 Independence Pkwy Ste 100, Tampa, FL 33634
Tel.: (813) 249-2514   FL
Web Site: http://www.gca.net
Year Founded: 1987
Sales Range: $1-9.9 Million
Emp.: 25
Computer Training & Other Computer Services
N.A.I.C.S.: 611420
Jim Quasius (Pres & CEO)

QUATRINE FURNITURE INC.
2300 Curry St, Long Beach, CA 90805
Tel.: (562) 616-6370
Web Site: http://www.quatrine.com
Sales Range: $10-24.9 Million
Emp.: 78
Furniture Retailer
N.A.I.C.S.: 449110
Gina Quatrine (Owner & Pres)

QUATRIS HEALTH LLC
2350 Airport Freeway Ste 300, Bedford, TX 76022
Tel.: (817) 282-0300
Web Site: http://www.quatris.com
Year Founded: 2000
Sales Range: $10-24.9 Million
Emp.: 70
Medical Practice Management & Electronic Medical Record Software Developer
N.A.I.C.S.: 513210
Mitch Weld (Pres-Bus Dev)
Mark Spates (Pres & CEO)
DeAnna Archer (Project Coord-Implementation)

Subsidiaries:
Alliance Healthcare Solutions, Inc. (1)
2543 Warren Dr, Rocklin, CA 95677
Tel.: (916) 722-1111
Sales Range: $10-24.9 Million
Emp.: 25
Medical Practice Management & Electronic Medical Record Software Developer
N.A.I.C.S.: 513210
Mitch Weld (CEO)
Jamie Jahnke (Mgr-Pur)

QUATRX PHARMACEUTICALS CO.
777 E Eisenhower Pkwy Ste 100, Ann Arbor, MI 48108
Tel.: (734) 913-9900   DE
Web Site: http://www.quatrx.com
Year Founded: 2000
Sales Range: $10-24.9 Million
Emp.: 58
Endocrine, Metabolic & Cardiovascular Therapeutic Pharmaceutical Developer
N.A.I.C.S.: 325412
Stuart Dombey (Co-Founder & Chief Scientific & Regulatory Officer)
Christopher Nicholas (COO, Co-Founder & Chief Bus Officer)
Gary Onn (CFO)
Risto Lammintausta (Mng Dir-Hormos Medical)
Rochelle Hanley (Chief Medical Officer)

QUATTRO DIRECT LLC

COMPANIES

200 Berwyn Park Ste 310, Berwyn, PA 19312
Tel.: (610) 993-0070
Web Site: http://www.quattro.agency
Advetising Agency
N.A.I.C.S.: 541810
Scott Cohen *(Mng Dir)*
Dan Boerger *(Mng Dir)*
Tom McNamara *(Mng Dir & Partner)*
Julie Herbster *(VP-Strategy)*
Lynda Taylor *(VP & Grp Acct Dir)*
Chris Matsinger *(VP-Ops & Tech)*
Stacey Greiner *(VP & Grp Acct Dir)*
Dan Lawler *(VP & Dir-Acct Grp)*
Eric Hellberg *(VP-Production)*
Jason Koscho *(VP-Creative Svcs)*
John Siemienski *(VP-Digital Svcs)*
Michael Marchesani *(VP-Bus Dev)*
Tom Pitcherella *(Mng Dir)*

QUAYSIDE ASSOCIATES LTD.
1 Quay Blvd, Miami, FL 33138
Tel.: (305) 895-7100
Rev.: $21,900,000
Emp.: 67
New Housing Operative Builders
N.A.I.C.S.: 236117
Tom Davis *(Mgr)*

QUEBEDEAUX BUICK GMC
3566 E Speedway Blvd, Tucson, AZ 85716-3940
Tel.: (520) 777-1142   AZ
Web Site: http://www.qbuickgmc.com
Year Founded: 1958
Sales Range: $100-124.9 Million
Emp.: 100
Retailer of New & Used Automobiles
N.A.I.C.S.: 441110
Thomas Quebedeaux *(Pres)*
Leroy Masseth *(Controller)*
Basilio Gonzalez *(Dir-Svcs)*
Stuart Tawney *(Mgr-Sls)*
Paul Quist *(Mgr-Sls)*

QUEBIT CONSULTING, LLC
49 Secor Rd, Scarsdale, NY 10583
Web Site: http://www.quebit.com
Year Founded: 2002
Rev.: $5,000,000
Emp.: 28
Computer System Design Services
N.A.I.C.S.: 541512
Catherine Jirak *(COO & Principal)*
Gary Quirke *(Founder, CEO & Principal)*
Michael Cowie *(Dir-Strategic Solutions)*
Scott Mutchler *(VP-Advanced Analytics & Gen Mgr)*
Ann-Grete Tan *(Sr VP-Ops & Gen Mgr-FOPM Svcs)*
Gary Corrigan *(Sr VP)*

Subsidiaries:

Applied Analytix Inc.   (1)
49 Secor Rd, Scarsdale, NY 10583   (100%)
Tel.: (800) 783-2481
Web Site: http://www.quebit.com
Emp.: 50
Software & Consulting Services
N.A.I.C.S.: 541618
Robin Stevens *(Principal)*

QUEEN CITY MOTORS CO.
1900 North Ave, Spearfish, SD 57783
Tel.: (605) 642-2766
Web Site: http://www.queencitymotors.com
Year Founded: 1984
Sales Range: $10-24.9 Million
Emp.: 50
New Car Whslr
N.A.I.C.S.: 441110
Randy Harms *(Gen Mgr)*

QUEEN CITY TELEVISION SERVICE CO. INC.
2430 Queen City Dr, Charlotte, NC 28208-2715
Tel.: (704) 391-6000   NC
Web Site: http://www.queencitytv.com
Year Founded: 1952
Sales Range: $25-49.9 Million
Emp.: 130
Retail of Household Appliances
N.A.I.C.S.: 722511
Roddey Player *(CFO)*

QUEENS SYMPHONY ORCHESTRA
c/o Queens College 65-30 Kissena Blvd, Flushing, NY 11367
Tel.: (718) 570-0909
Web Site: http://www.queenssymphony.org
Year Founded: 1953
Sales Range: Less than $1 Million
Emp.: 5
Symphony Orchestra
N.A.I.C.S.: 711130
Daniel DeLoma *(Gen Mgr)*
Kenichi Wilson *(Pres)*

QUEENSBORO FARM PRODUCTS INC.
156-02 Liberty Ave, Jamaica, NY 11433
Tel.: (718) 658-5000   NY
Web Site: http://www.queensborofarmproducts.com
Year Founded: 1909
Sales Range: $50-74.9 Million
Emp.: 80
Dairy Products Mfr
N.A.I.C.S.: 424430
Allen Miller *(Pres & CEO)*
Andrew Flitt *(Controller)*

QUEENSTOWN BANK OF MARYLAND
7101 Main St, Queenstown, MD 21658
Tel.: (410) 827-8881   MD
Web Site: http://www.queenstown-bank.com
Year Founded: 1899
Sales Range: $10-24.9 Million
Banking Services
N.A.I.C.S.: 522110
Christina Wilkins *(Sr VP)*
James P. Shaw *(CFO & Sr VP)*
T. Douglas Pierson *(Vice Chm)*
Patrick E. Thompson *(Chm)*
Peggy E. Lewis *(Sr VP)*
Stephanie V. Morris *(Officer-Loan & Sr VP)*
C. Franklin Russum *(Sr VP)*
Tracy Whitby-Fairall *(COO & Sr VP)*
Joellen Calloway *(VP)*
Karen Dean *(Officer-Loan & VP)*
Patrica Tarr *(VP)*
Judy Vera *(VP)*
John Ludwig *(VP)*
Helen Aytch *(Asst VP)*
Jamie Dulin *(Sr VP)*
Heather Jarrell *(Asst VP)*
Diane Xander *(Officer-Loan & Asst VP)*
Karen Clough *(Officer-Loan & Asst VP)*
Brooke Horney *(Sr VP)*
Lauren Pfisterer *(VP)*
Katie Anderson *(VP)*
Tammy Taylor *(Asst VP)*
Heather Dodd *(Officer-Loan & Asst VP)*
Michael Lucas *(Officer-Loan & Asst VP)*

QUELL INDUSTRIAL SERVICES
PO Box 1058, Portland, TX 78374
Tel.: (361) 643-2618
Web Site: http://www.quellservices.com
Sales Range: $10-24.9 Million
Emp.: 250
Labour Services
N.A.I.C.S.: 115115
Tracy Weitzel *(Acct Exec)*

QUES INDUSTRIES, INC.
5420 W 140th St, Cleveland, OH 44142
Tel.: (216) 267-8989   OH
Web Site: http://www.quesinc.com
Year Founded: 1983
Sales Range: $1-9.9 Million
Emp.: 18
Mfr of Chemicals Used for Water Treatment, Cleaners & Industrial Applications
N.A.I.C.S.: 325998
Bill Kelly *(Mgr-Technical)*
Colton Meng *(Mgr-Ops)*
Bob Hallas *(Plant Mgr)*

QUEST CE
10850 W Park Ste 1000, Milwaukee, WI 53224
Tel.: (414) 375-3400
Web Site: http://www.questce.com
Sales Range: $1-9.9 Million
Emp.: 22
Compliance Training & Continuing Education Services
N.A.I.C.S.: 611710
Patrick Torhorst *(CIO)*
Alex Krenke *(Exec VP-Sls, Mktg & Client Svcs)*
Linda Mieth-Krenke *(Pres & CEO)*

QUEST CONTROLS, INC.
208 9th St Dr W, Palmetto, FL 34221
Tel.: (941) 729-4799
Web Site: http://www.questcontrols.com
Year Founded: 1989
Sales Range: $10-24.9 Million
Emp.: 50
Electronic Monitoring, Control & Test Solutions
N.A.I.C.S.: 334519
Edward Goggin *(Pres)*
Randy Aura *(Mgr-Ops)*
Todd Carlin *(Coord-Sls & Support)*
George Kubes *(Sr Engr-Sls)*
Ritchie S. Bufkin *(Dir-Sls-Intl)*

QUEST CORPORATION OF AMERICA, INC.
17220 Camelot Ct, Land O Lakes, FL 34638
Tel.: (813) 926-2942   FL
Web Site: http://www.qcausa.com
Year Founded: 1995
Sales Range: $1-9.9 Million
Emp.: 45
Advertising Agencies
N.A.I.C.S.: 541810
Sharlene Francois Lairscey *(Owner & Pres)*
Diane Hackney *(Sr VP)*
Mary Brooks *(VP)*
Tish Burgher *(VP)*
Jill Cappadoro *(VP)*

QUEST CREDIT UNION
610 SW 10th St, Topeka, KS 66612-1673
Tel.: (785) 233-5556   KS
Web Site: http://www.quest-cu.org
Year Founded: 1974
Sales Range: $10-24.9 Million
Emp.: 76

Credit Union Operator
N.A.I.C.S.: 522130
Don Frick *(Sec)*
Bryan Vargas *(Treas)*
Mike Lackey *(Chm)*
Bobb Collie *(Vice Chm)*

QUEST ENGINEERING, INC.
2300 Edgewood Ave S, Minneapolis, MN 55426
Tel.: (952) 546-4441
Web Site: http://www.questenginc.com
Sales Range: $10-24.9 Million
Emp.: 50
Industrial Machinery & Equipment Whslr
N.A.I.C.S.: 423830
Peter Kinney *(Owner)*

QUEST ENVIRONMENTAL & SAFETY PRODUCTS, INC.
1414 South West St Ste 200, Indianapolis, IN 46225
Tel.: (317) 594-4500
Web Site: http://www.questsafety.com
Year Founded: 1991
Sales Range: $10-24.9 Million
Emp.: 26
Asbestos & Lead Abatement Products Distr
N.A.I.C.S.: 423840
Sam Yadav *(Pres)*
Vanita K. Yadav *(CFO)*
Garry Rady *(Controller)*
Kelli Marti *(Mgr-Ops)*

QUEST EVENTS, LLC
2591 Dallas Pkwy, Frisco, TX 75034
Tel.: (214) 436-4161
Web Site: https://www.questevents.com
OLKR—(OTC)
Events Services
N.A.I.C.S.: 711310
Robert Young *(Reg Mgr)*
Lee Dunlap *(CEO)*

Subsidiaries:

PeachTree Tents and Events, LLC   (1)
1422 Chattahoochee Ave, Atlanta, GA 30318
Tel.: (404) 574-6655
Web Site: http://www.peachtreetents.com
Sales Range: $1-9.9 Million
Emp.: 40
Tents & Camping Stores
N.A.I.C.S.: 459110
Trish Dreyer *(Mgr-Sls)*
Mike Schmidt *(Founder & CEO)*

QUEST INTEGRATED, LLC
19823 58th Pl S Ste 200, Kent, WA 98032-6103
Tel.: (253) 872-9500   WA
Web Site: http://www.qi2.com
Year Founded: 1970
Emp.: 50
Non-contant Measurement & Sensor Solutions; Printed Electronics Research & Development Services
N.A.I.C.S.: 334516
Kelli Kirk *(Mgr-HR)*

Subsidiaries:

Quest Inspar, LLC   (1)
19823 58th Pl S Ste 200, Kent, WA 98032
Tel.: (713) 391-8660
Web Site: http://www.questinspar.com
Oil & Gas Pipeline Construction Services
N.A.I.C.S.: 237120
David Voigt *(VP-Fin & Admin)*
Kelli Kirk *(Mgr-HR)*
Kent Weisenberg *(Founder & CTO)*
Scott A. Wise *(VP-Sls & Mktg)*

QUEST LINER INC.

Quest Liner Inc.—(Continued)

QUEST LINER INC.
2099 Southpark Ct Ste 1, Dubuque, IA 52003
Tel.: (563) 381-1051
Web Site: http://www.foodliner.com
Sales Range: $10-24.9 Million
Emp.: 110
Trucking Service
N.A.I.C.S.: 484121
Greg McCoy (Pres)

QUEST NATIONAL SERVICES LLC
933 Lee Rd Ste 250, Orlando, FL 32810
Web Site: http://www.questns.com
Year Founded: 2008
Sales Range: $1-9.9 Million
Emp.: 16
Software Development Services
N.A.I.C.S.: 541511
Adam Nager (Founder & CEO)

QUEST OIL CORP.
222 Sydney Baker S Ste 350H, Kerrville, TX 78028
Year Founded: 1999
Oil & Gas Exploration Services
N.A.I.C.S.: 213112
Joseph A. Wallen (Pres & CEO)

QUEST RECYCLING SERVICES LLC
6175 Main St Ste 420, Frisco, TX 75034
Tel.: (972) 464-0004
Web Site: http://www.questrecycling.com
Year Founded: 2007
Sales Range: $100-124.9 Million
Emp.: 55
Recycling Programs
N.A.I.C.S.: 541620
Brian Dick (CEO)
Ashley Dailey (Dir-Retail Svcs)

QUEST TECHNOLOGY INTERNATIONAL, INC.
11200 NW 138th St, Miami, FL 33178
Tel.: (305) 513-8583
Web Site: http://www.qtinet.com
Sales Range: $10-24.9 Million
Emp.: 22
Electronic Parts & Equipment Whslr
N.A.I.C.S.: 423690
Nestor Novo (Pres)

QUESTAR CORPORATION
6204 Ingham Rd, New Hope, PA 18938-9663
Tel.: (215) 862-5277 PA
Web Site: http://www.questarcorporation.com
Year Founded: 1950
Sales Range: $50-74.9 Million
Emp.: 5
Telescopes & Telephoto Lenses & other Optical Systems Including Long-Distance Microscopes & Computer Analytic Systems Mfr & Distr
N.A.I.C.S.: 333310
Donald J. Bandurick (Pres)

Subsidiaries:

Q-Machine (1)
Ctr & Lemon St, Stowe, PA 19464 (100%)
Tel.: (610) 323-7264
Sales Range: $10-24.9 Million
Emp.: 4
Machine Shops
N.A.I.C.S.: 332710

QUESTE CAPITAL
170 S Green Vly Pkwy Ste 300, Las Vegas, NV 89012
Tel.: (702) 685-8200 NV
Web Site: http://www.questecapital.com
Year Founded: 2010
Investment Holding Company
N.A.I.C.S.: 551112

QUESTIONS & SOLUTIONS ENGINEERING, INC.
1079 Falls Curve, Chaska, MN 55318
Tel.: (612) 308-4716
Web Site: http://www.qseng.com
Sales Range: $1-9.9 Million
Emp.: 15
Building & Facility Consulting Engineering Services
N.A.I.C.S.: 541330
Rebecca Ellis (Pres)
Cathy Melander (Engr-Electrical)
Stephanie Gallatin (Engr-Mechanical)
Mathieu Lindquist (Engr-Mechanical)
Matthew Malinosky (Engr-Mechanical)

QUESTOR MANAGEMENT COMPANY, LLC
700 E Maple Rd, Birmingham, MI 48009
Tel.: (248) 593-1930 DE
Web Site: http://www.questor.com
Investment Funds Management
N.A.I.C.S.: 541611
Albert A. Koch (Vice Chm & Mng Dir)
Jay Alix (Co-Founder & Co-Mng Principal)
Wallace L. Rueckel (Mng Dir)

Subsidiaries:

Polar Corporation (1)
12810 County Rd 17, Holdingford, MN 56340-9773
Tel.: (320) 746-2255
Web Site: http://www.polartank.com
Sales Range: $150-199.9 Million
Emp.: 1,100
Tank Trailer Mfr
N.A.I.C.S.: 332420
Donald Stover (CFO)
Randy Arlt (VP-Bus Dev)
Michael Evans (Pres-Svc Centers)
Jim Painter (Pres-Tank Trailer)
Chris Dietemann (Pres-Quality Trailer Products)
Robert D. Denious (Pres)
Doug Chapple (CEO)

Subsidiary (Domestic):

Polar Service Centers, Inc. (2)
1015 W Saint Germain St, Saint Cloud, MN 56301
Tel.: (800) 826-6589
Web Site: http://www.polarservicecenters.com
Industrial Supplies Whslr
N.A.I.C.S.: 423840
Mike Besson (Pres)

Rockwell American (2)
604 W Main St, Azle, TX 76020
Web Site: http://www.rockwellamerican.com
Automotive Parts Mfr & Distr
N.A.I.C.S.: 336390
Christy Dietemann (Pres)

QUEUE CREATIVE
410 S Cedar St Ste F, Lansing, MI 48912
Tel.: (517) 374-6600
Web Site: http://www.queueadvertising.com
Year Founded: 2004
Sales Range: Less than $1 Million
Emp.: 5
Advetising Agency
N.A.I.C.S.: 541810
Lori Cunningham (Partner)
Tom Helderman (Partner)
Melissa Devine (Dir-New Bus)

QUEXCO INCORPORATED
2777 N Stemmons Fwy, Dallas, TX 75207-2501
Tel.: (214) 631-6070 DE
Year Founded: 1984
Sales Range: $300-349.9 Million
Emp.: 725
Private Investment Firm; Holding Company
N.A.I.C.S.: 551112
Howard M. Meyers (Chm, Pres & CEO)

Subsidiaries:

RSR Corporation (1)
2777 N Stemmons Fwy Ste 1800, Dallas, TX 75207-2277 (100%)
Tel.: (214) 631-6070
Web Site: http://www.rsrcorp.com
Sales Range: $25-49.9 Million
Emp.: 50
Recycling Lead-Based Batteries for Refined Lead & Lead Alloys
N.A.I.C.S.: 331492
Robert Finn (Pres & CEO)

Subsidiary (Domestic):

Bestolife Corporation (2)
2777 N Stemmons Fwy Ste 1800, Dallas, TX 75207-2277 (100%)
Tel.: (214) 631-6070
Web Site: http://www.bestolife.com
Emp.: 8
Pipe Thread Compound Mfr
N.A.I.C.S.: 325520
Gary Stufflebeme (Pres)

Quemetco Metals Limited, Inc. (2)
602 S Swanson St, Casa Grande, AZ 85122 (100%)
Tel.: (214) 631-6070
Web Site: http://www.rsrcorp.com
Sales Range: $25-49.9 Million
Emp.: 50
Mfr of Fabricated Lead Products
N.A.I.C.S.: 331492

Quemetco Realty, Inc. (2)
2777 N Stemmons Freeway Ste 1800, Dallas, TX 75207-2277 (100%)
Tel.: (214) 631-6070
Sales Range: $25-49.9 Million
Realty Holdings
N.A.I.C.S.: 531120
Robert Finn (Pres)

Quemetco, Inc. (2)
2777 N Stemmons Fwy Ste 1800, Dallas, TX 75207-2277 (100%)
Tel.: (214) 631-6070
Sales Range: $25-49.9 Million
Emp.: 50
Mfr of Antimonal Lead
N.A.I.C.S.: 331492

QUIBIDS, LLC
4 NE 10th St Ste 242, Oklahoma City, OK 73104
Tel.: (405) 253-3883
Web Site: http://www.quibids.com
Sales Range: $50-74.9 Million
Emp.: 120
Online Auctions
N.A.I.C.S.: 449210
Jeff Geurts (CFO)
Shaun Tilford (CTO)
Kevin Elliott (Dir-Mdse)

QUICK BOX, LLC
11551 E 45th Ave Unit C, Denver, CO 80239
Tel.: (720) 990-5642
Web Site: http://www.quickbox.com
Year Founded: 2009
Sales Range: $25-49.9 Million
Emp.: 180
Logistic Services
N.A.I.C.S.: 488510
Stephen Adele (CEO)

QUICK CHEK FOOD STORES INC.
3 Old Hwy 28, Whitehouse Station, NJ 08889
Tel.: (908) 534-2200 NJ
Web Site: http://www.qchek.com
Year Founded: 1966
Sales Range: $900-999.9 Million
Emp.: 1,400
Convenience Store
N.A.I.C.S.: 445131
Dean C. Durling (CEO)
Bob Vallario (Mgr-Real Estate-New Jersey)
Rob Easley (Sr VP-Mktg & Mdsg)
Scott Zoeller (VP-Food Svc)

QUICK POINT INCORPORATED
1717 Fenpark Dr, Fenton, MO 63026
Tel.: (636) 343-9400
Web Site: http://www.quickpoint.com
Rev.: $16,700,000
Emp.: 180
Advertising Novelties
N.A.I.C.S.: 339950
Kim Smith (Mgr-Credit)
John G. Goessling Sr. (Pres)

QUICK QUALITY RESTAURANT INC.
2 Ethel Rd Ste 205a, Edison, NJ 08817
Tel.: (732) 248-8200
Rev.: $11,900,000
Emp.: 20
Fast-Food Restaurant, Chain
N.A.I.C.S.: 722513
Joseph Bijou (Pres)
Bruce Garza (VP-Fin)

QUICK SOLUTIONS INC.
440 Pollaris Pkwy Ste 500, Westerville, OH 43082
Tel.: (614) 825-8000
Web Site: http://www.quicksolutions.com
Sales Range: $10-24.9 Million
Emp.: 200
Computer Integrated Systems Design
N.A.I.C.S.: 541512
Tom Campbell (CEO)
Valerie Hedges (Office Mgr)

QUICK TANKS INC.
545 Krueger St, Kendallville, IN 46755
Tel.: (260) 347-3850
Web Site: http://www.quicktanks.com
Sales Range: $10-24.9 Million
Emp.: 80
Mfr Water Storage Tanks
N.A.I.C.S.: 332812
Tom Quick (Pres)

QUICKSILVER EXPRESS COURIER INC.
203 E Little Canada Rd, Little Canada, MN 55117-1681
Tel.: (651) 484-1111 MN
Web Site: http://www.qec.com
Year Founded: 1982
Sales Range: $50-74.9 Million
Emp.: 750
Local Trucking Services
N.A.I.C.S.: 484110
Mike Crary (Founder & Chm)

Subsidiaries:

Quicksilver Express Courier of Colorado, Inc. (1)
1400 Quail St, Lakewood, CO 80215-4421
Tel.: (303) 232-5800
Web Site: http://www.qec.com
Sales Range: $25-49.9 Million
Emp.: 150
Provider of Courier Services
N.A.I.C.S.: 492210
Chuck Miller (Pres)

COMPANIES

Quicksilver Express Courier of Minnesota Inc. (1)
203 Little Canada Rd E, Little Canada, MN 55117-1681 **(100%)**
Tel.: (651) 484-1111
Web Site: http://www.qec.com
Sales Range: $25-49.9 Million
Emp.: 296
Provider of Local Trucking Services
N.A.I.C.S.: 484110
Kurt Sloan (VP)

Quicksilver Express Courier of Missouri Inc. (1)
1126 Adams St, Kansas City, KS 66103-1306
Tel.: (913) 321-5959
Web Site: http://www.qec.com
Sales Range: $10-24.9 Million
Emp.: 85
Provider of Local Trucking Services
N.A.I.C.S.: 484110

Quicksilver Express Courier of Wisconsin, Inc. (1)
11220 W Lincoln Ave, Milwaukee, WI 53227 **(100%)**
Tel.: (414) 645-4000
Web Site: http://www.qec.com
Sales Range: $10-24.9 Million
Emp.: 75
Provider of Trucking Services
N.A.I.C.S.: 484110
Janice Patterson (Gen Mgr)

QUICKWAY DISTRIBUTION SERVICES LLC
1116 Polk Ave, Nashville, TN 37210
Tel.: (615) 834-9470
Web Site: http://www.quickwaycarriers.com
Year Founded: 1994
Sales Range: $25-49.9 Million
Emp.: 350
Provider of Trucking Services
N.A.I.C.S.: 484230
Roger Blume (Dir-Ops)
William Provost (Pres)

Subsidiaries:

Quickway Carriers Inc. (1)
5209 Linbar Dr Ste 602, Nashville, TN 37211-3135 **(100%)**
Tel.: (615) 834-9470
Web Site: http://www.quickwaycarriers.com
Sales Range: $10-24.9 Million
Emp.: 20
Provider of Trucking Services
N.A.I.C.S.: 484230
Bill Prebost (Pres & CEO)
Chris Tate (CFO)

QUICKWAY EXPRESS INC.
5209 Linbar Dr Ste 602, Nashville, TN 37211
Tel.: (615) 834-9470
Web Site: http://www.quickwaycarriers.com
Rev.: $15,700,000
Emp.: 20
Local Trucking without Storage
N.A.I.C.S.: 484110
William Prevost (Pres & CEO)

QUIET ANGEL FOUNDATION
2325 Dulles Corner Blvd Ste 670, Herndon, VA 20171
Tel.: (703) 437-9720   VA
Year Founded: 2009
Sales Range: $1-9.9 Million
Child Care Services
N.A.I.C.S.: 624110
Jeff Saplis (Pres)
Anna Saplis (Treas)
Craig Cote (Sec)

QUIET LIGHT COMMUNICATIONS INC.
220 E State St, Rockford, IL 61104
Tel.: (815) 398-6860

Web Site: http://www.quietlightcom.com
Sales Range: $1-9.9 Million
Emp.: 15
Advetising Agency
N.A.I.C.S.: 541810
Terry Schroff (CEO)

QUIGLEY MANUFACTURING INC.
38880 Grand River Ave, Farmington Hills, MI 48335
Tel.: (248) 426-8600
Web Site: http://www.qmi.com
Sales Range: $1-9.9 Million
Emp.: 30
Metal Stamping
N.A.I.C.S.: 332119
Carol C. Quigley (Pres)

QUIK PRINT
217 N Pennsylvania Ave, Wichita, KS 67214
Tel.: (316) 942-2208   KS
Web Site: http://www.quikprintwichita.com
Year Founded: 1963
Commercial Lithographic Printing, Quick Printing & Photocopying Services
N.A.I.C.S.: 323111
Johnny Tarrant (VP)
Susie Tarrant (Pres)
Rob Galaway (Gen Mgr)

QUIK STOP QUIK WASH
2774 Sawmill Rd, Santa Fe, NM 87505
Tel.: (505) 473-7328
Web Site: http://www.quikstop.com
Car Wash & Gasoline Service Stations
N.A.I.C.S.: 457120
Jim Polk (Pres)

QUIK THRIFT FOOD STORES, INC.
2200 Powder Springs Rd SW Ste 200, Marietta, GA 30064
Tel.: (770) 422-2948
Web Site: http://www.quikthrift.com
Year Founded: 1967
Sales Range: $10-24.9 Million
Emp.: 125
Owner & Operator of Grocery Stores
N.A.I.C.S.: 445110
Thomas J. Sanders (CEO)
Susan Bethea (Office Mgr)
Esther Walker (Mgr-Accts Payable)
Margie Royal (Mgr-District)
Jerry Ennis (Mgr-Maintenance)
Jim Barlow Jr. (Pres)
James Barlow Sr. (CFO)

QUIK-MART STORES INC.
8351 E Broadway Blvd, Tucson, AZ 85710
Tel.: (520) 298-8929
Web Site: http://www.quikmartstores.com
Sales Range: $10-24.9 Million
Emp.: 157
Convienice Stores, Chain
N.A.I.C.S.: 445110
Troy Little (Pres)
Shelly Gibbons (VP)

QUIK-WAY FOODS OF DALLAS INC.
8350 N Central Exwy Ste M1015, Dallas, TX 75206-6611
Tel.: (214) 750-9313
Web Site: http://www.beveragecity.com
Year Founded: 1966
Sales Range: $25-49.9 Million

Emp.: 200
Operator of Convenience Stores
N.A.I.C.S.: 445320
Donald L. Golman (Pres)
Dennis Wright (Dir-Fuel Dispatch)
Mary Kuhkendahl (Mgr-Payroll)
Klay Beavert (Controller)

QUIKEY MANUFACTURING CO. INC.
1500 Industrial Pkwy, Akron, OH 44310
Tel.: (330) 633-8106
Web Site: http://www.quikey.com
Sales Range: $10-24.9 Million
Emp.: 230
Advertising Novelties
N.A.I.C.S.: 339950
Michael W. Burns (Pres)

QUIKTRIP CORPORATION
4705 S 129th E Ave, Tulsa, OK 74134-7008
Tel.: (918) 615-7700   OK
Web Site: https://www.quiktrip.com
Year Founded: 1958
Sales Range: $5-14.9 Billion
Emp.: 28,679
Other Gasoline Stations
N.A.I.C.S.: 457120
Chester Edward Cadieux III (Chm, Pres & CEO)

Subsidiaries:

Quik Trip Distribution (1)
822 Quicktrip Way, Belton, MO 64012 **(100%)**
Tel.: (816) 331-2810
Web Site: http://www.quiktrip.com
Sales Range: $100-124.9 Million
Emp.: 800
Warehouse Distribution of Packaged Food Products for Convenience Stores
N.A.I.C.S.: 311999
Jason Cooper (Mgr-Personnel)

QuikTrip West, Inc. (1)
I-44 Exit 222A Tulsa W, Tulsa, OK 74107
Tel.: (918) 446-7997
Web Site: http://www.quiktrip.com
Emp.: 8,000
Convenience Store & Gasoline Retailer
N.A.I.C.S.: 457120
Bill Williamson (Mgr-Stores)

QUILL/AWA ENTERPRISES
1111 W Mockingbird Ln Ste 1300, Dallas, TX 75247
Tel.: (214) 630-8316   TX
Web Site: http://www.quilladvertising.com
Year Founded: 1986
Rev.: $15,000,000
Emp.: 9
N.A.I.C.S.: 541810
Stephen M. Utley (Pres & Exec Dir-Creative)
Patty Whitt (VP-Acct Svcs)
Jennifer Sullivan (Mgr-Acct Svcs)

QUILLIN'S INC.
700 N 3rd St, La Crosse, WI 54601
Tel.: (608) 785-1424
Web Site: http://www.quillinsfoods.com
Sales Range: $50-74.9 Million
Emp.: 860
Owner & Operator of Grocery Stores
N.A.I.C.S.: 445110
Mike Quillin (Pres)
Timothy Quillin (VP)

QUINCANNON ASSOCIATES, INC.
10 Rockefeller Ste 1120, New York, NY 10020
Tel.: (212) 246-0060   NY

Web Site: http://www.quincannon.com
Year Founded: 1974
Ship Brokerage Services
N.A.I.C.S.: 488510
Tim Orwin (Mgr-Ops)

Subsidiaries:

Braemar Quincannon Pte Limited (1)
8 Cross Street 09-06 Manulife Tower, Singapore, 048424, Singapore **(50%)**
Tel.: (65) 65330069
Web Site: http://www.braemarseascope.com
Deep Sea Freight Transportation
N.A.I.C.S.: 483111
Mark Sorgo (Mng Dir)

QUINCY BIOSCIENCE
726 Heartland Trl Ste 300, Madison, WI 53717
Tel.: (608) 827-8000
Web Site: http://www.quincybioscience.com
Year Founded: 2004
Sales Range: $10-24.9 Million
Emp.: 58
Biological Product Research & Development Services
N.A.I.C.S.: 541715
Michael Beaman (CEO)
Mark Underwood (Pres)

QUINCY COMMUNITY ACTION PROGRAMS, INC.
1509 Hancock St, Quincy, MA 02169
Tel.: (617) 479-8181   MA
Web Site: http://www.qcap.org
Year Founded: 1965
Sales Range: $10-24.9 Million
Emp.: 156
Anti-Poverty Advocacy Services
N.A.I.C.S.: 813319
Beth Ann Strollo (CEO)
Josephine Shea (Pres)
Timothy McAloon (VP)

QUINCY MUTUAL FIRE INSURANCE COMPANY
57 Washington St, Quincy, MA 02169
Tel.: (617) 770-5100   MA
Web Site: http://www.quincymutual.com
Year Founded: 1851
Sales Range: $250-299.9 Million
Emp.: 220
Home Owners, Automobile, Commercial Multi-Peril & Business Owners Insurance Services
N.A.I.C.S.: 524126
Harold E. Gerbis (VP-Personal Lines Underwriting)
K. Douglas Briggs (Pres & CEO)
Kevin M. Meskell (Exec VP)
Thomas A. Harris (Chief Risk Officer & Sr VP)
Steven H. Briggs (Sr VP-Claims)
Lu-Ann R. Smith (VP-HR)
Lisa M. Schooley (Treas & VP)
Mark A. Giuliani (VP-Info Sys)
James J. Moran Jr. (Gen Counsel, Sec & Sr VP)

Subsidiaries:

Patrons Oxford Insurance Company (1)
Auburn Business Park, Auburn, ME 04211
Tel.: (207) 783-2258
Web Site: http://www.patrons.com
Sales Range: $25-49.9 Million
Emp.: 43
Property & Casualty Insurance Services
N.A.I.C.S.: 524128
Mark Pettingill (CEO)
Rachel Bannister (Asst VP-Mktg)

QUINCY PEPSI-COLA BOTTLING CO.

U.S. PRIVATE

Quincy Pepsi-Cola Bottling Co.—(Continued)

QUINCY PEPSI-COLA BOTTLING CO.
1121 Locust St, Quincy, IL 62301-1919
Tel.: (217) 223-8600 DE
Year Founded: 1927
Sales Range: $10-24.9 Million
Emp.: 80
Soft Drinks
N.A.I.C.S.: 424490
Ronald Vecchie *(Chm & CEO)*
Jack Keiler *(Controller)*
Mike Bartel *(Pres)*
Shawn Vecchie *(VP)*

QUINCY SYMPHONY ORCHESTRA ASSOCIATION
200 N 8th St Ste 102, Quincy, IL 62301-3062
Tel.: (217) 222-2856
Web Site: http://www.qsoa.org
Year Founded: 1947
Sales Range: Less than $1 Million
Emp.: 3
Symphony Orchestra
N.A.I.C.S.: 711320
Jane Polett *(Gen Mgr)*

QUINLAN MARKETING COMMUNICATIONS
550 Congressional Blvd Ste 350, Carmel, IN 46032
Tel.: (317) 573-5080 IN
Web Site: http://www.quinlanmarketing.com
Year Founded: 1937
Sales Range: $50-74.9 Million
Emp.: 15
N.A.I.C.S.: 541810
Jay Koenig *(Dir-Art)*
Linda Fosnight *(Dir-Admin)*
Jackie Donaldson *(Dir-Media)*

QUINN APPAREL INC.
19440 Peachland Blvd, Port Charlotte, FL 33948
Tel.: (941) 235-7222 FL
Web Site: http://www.quinnshop.com
Year Founded: 2012
Men & Women Clothing Distr & Whslr
N.A.I.C.S.: 424350
Jean Kollof *(Pres & CEO)*

QUINN CO.
3500 Shepherd St, City of Industry, CA 90601
Tel.: (562) 463-4000
Web Site: http://www.quinncompany.com
Year Founded: 1924
Sales Range: $25-49.9 Million
Emp.: 500
Rental of General Construction Machinery & Equipment
N.A.I.C.S.: 423810
Don Davis *(Mgr-Mktg)*

QUINN COMPANY INC.
10273 S Golden State Blvd, Selma, CA 93662-9410
Tel.: (559) 896-4040
Web Site: http://www.quinncompany.com
Year Founded: 1919
Sales Range: $50-74.9 Million
Emp.: 580
Construction & Mining Machinery
N.A.I.C.S.: 423810

Subsidiaries:

Quinn Used Parts Inc (1)
5253 S Peach Ave, Fresno, CA 93725-9708 (100%)
Tel.: (559) 445-1616
Web Site: http://www.quinn.com

Sales Range: $10-24.9 Million
Emp.: 9
Provider of Industrial Machinery & Equipment Services
N.A.I.C.S.: 423810

QUINN EMANUEL URQUHART & SULLIVAN, LLP.
865 S Figueroa St 10th Fl, Los Angeles, CA 90017
Tel.: (213) 443-3000
Web Site: http://www.quinnemanuel.com
Year Founded: 1986
Sales Range: $800-899.9 Million
Emp.: 501
Legal Advisory Services
N.A.I.C.S.: 541110
John B. Quinn *(Co-Mng Partner)*
Eric J. Emanuel *(Partner)*
Jeremy Andersen *(Partner)*
Anthony P. Alden *(Partner)*
Yury Kapgan *(Partner)*
Steven M. Anderson *(Partner)*
James R. Asperger *(Partner)*
Harold A. Barza *(Partner)*
Robert J. Becher *(Partner)*
Fred G. Bennett *(Partner)*
Kristen Bird *(Partner)*
Jeffrey N. Boozell *(Partner)*
Jon C. Cederberg *(Partner)*
Kenneth R. Chiate *(Partner)*
John P. D'Amato *(Partner)*
Susan Estrich *(Partner)*
Michael L. Fazio *(Partner)*
Gary E. Gans *(Partner)*
Danielle L. Gilmore *(Partner)*
Ryan S. Goldstein *(Partner)*
John S. Gordon *(Partner)*
David M. Grable *(Partner)*
Justin C. Griffin *(Partner)*
Tigran Guledjian *(Partner)*
J. D. Horton *(Partner)*
Charles Eskridge *(Partner)*
Tara Lee *(Partner)*
Richard C. Smith *(Partner-Washington)*
Steven Cherny *(Partner-New York)*
Edward J. DeFranco *(Chm-National Intellectual Property Litigation Practice & Partner)*
Elizabeth Urquhart *(Dir-Mktg & Bus Dev)*
Andrew Schapiro *(Partner)*
Christopher Landau *(Partner)*
Liu Xiao *(Partner-Litigation-Shanghai)*
Sam Williamson *(Mng Partner-Shanghai)*
Leonid Feller *(Partner)*
William A. Burck *(Co-Mng Partner)*

QUINN EVANS ARCHITECTS INC.
2121 Ward Place, NW, 4th Fl, Washington, DC 20037
Tel.: (202) 298-6700
Web Site: http://www.quinnevans.com
Year Founded: 1984
Rev.: $4,000,000
Emp.: 29
Architectural Services
N.A.I.C.S.: 541310
Larry Barr *(Principal)*
Daniel Curry *(Principal)*
Tom Jester *(Principal)*
Randall Wong *(Project Mgr)*
Brenda Williams *(Principal)*
Robert Fink *(Dir-Design Tech)*
Marcos Molina *(Coord-Mktg & Comm)*
Alyson Steele *(Chief Design Officer & Exec VP)*
Rima Namek *(Principal-Baltimore)*
Joe Cellucci *(Principal-Baltimore)*
Kathryn Slattery *(Principal)*
Julie Siple *(Dir-Sustainability)*

Subsidiaries:

BCWH, Inc. (1)
1840 W Broad St, Richmond, VA 23220
Tel.: (804) 788-4774
Web Site: http://www.bcwh.com
Sales Range: $1-9.9 Million
Architectural Services
N.A.I.C.S.: 541310
Syd Knight *(Principal-ASLA)*
Roger D. Richardson *(Principal-AIA & REFP)*
Robert E. Comet Jr. *(Pres, Partner & Principal)*

QUINN FABLE ADVERTISING
131 W 35th St, New York, NY 10001
Tel.: (212) 974-8700
Web Site: http://www.quinnfable.com
Year Founded: 1988
Rev.: $55,000,000
Emp.: 40
N.A.I.C.S.: 541810
Kathy Fable *(Pres & CEO)*
Julie Curtis *(Exec VP-Tech Svcs)*
Loren Fass *(Acct Coord)*
Susanne Dunlap *(Assoc Dir-Creative)*

QUINN/BREIN PUBLIC RELATIONS
403 Madison Ave N Ste 101, Bainbridge Island, WA 98110
Tel.: (206) 842-8922 WA
Web Site: http://www.quinnbrein.com
Year Founded: 1979
Sales Range: $1-9.9 Million
Emp.: 4
Public Relations Agency
N.A.I.C.S.: 541820
Jeff Brein *(Pres)*
Ginger Vaughan *(Client Svcs Dir)*
Elizabeth Scott *(Dir-Market Res)*

QUINNOX, INC.
2056 Westings Ave Ste 190, Naperville, IL 60563
Tel.: (630) 548-4800
Web Site: http://www.quinnox.com
Sales Range: $25-49.9 Million
Emp.: 70
Computer Related Consulting Services
N.A.I.C.S.: 541512
Ninan George *(Exec VP-Human Capital Mgmt)*
Ashoke Dutt Sr. *(Pres)*

QUINTANA CAPITAL GROUP, L.P.
1415 Louisiana St Ste 2400, Houston, TX 77002
Tel.: (713) 751-7500 DE
Web Site: http://www.qeplp.com
Year Founded: 1932
Sales Range: $25-49.9 Million
Emp.: 27
Privater Equity Firm
N.A.I.C.S.: 523999
Corbin J. Robertson Jr. *(Mng Partner & Principal)*
Donald L. Evans *(Principal & Sr Partner)*
Warren S. Hawkins *(Principal)*
Eva Clark *(Chief Compliance Officer)*
Dwight Dunlap *(Mng Dir & CFO)*
Gbolade Odeneye *(VP-Fin & Acctg)*
John W. Wessels *(Mng Dir-Engrg)*
Paul Cornell *(Mng Dir & CFO)*

Subsidiaries:

Corsa Coal Corp. (1)
199 Bay Street Suite 5300, Commerce Court West, Toronto, M5L 1B9, ON, Canada (56%)
Tel.: (416) 214-9800
Web Site: http://www.corsacoal.com
Rev.: $128,486,000
Assets: $210,152,000
Liabilities: $122,435,000

Net Worth: $87,717,000
Earnings: ($63,723,000)
Emp.: 280
Fiscal Year-end: 12/31/2020
Coal Mining Services
N.A.I.C.S.: 212390

Subsidiary (US):

Kopper Glo Fuel, Inc. (2)
200 Prosperity Rd, Knoxville, TN 37923
Tel.: (865) 824-2749
Web Site: http://www.kopperglo.com
Coal Mining & Distr
N.A.I.C.S.: 212114
Keith Dyke *(Pres & Partner)*
Johnny L. Gaertner *(Controller)*
Wesley S. Gilmer *(Mgr-Engrg)*
James Thacker *(Mgr-Surface & Plant Ops)*

PBS Coals, Inc. (2)
1576 Stoystown Rd, Friedens, PA 15541
Tel.: (814) 443-4668
Web Site: http://pbscoals.severstal.com
Coal Mining & Distr
N.A.I.C.S.: 212114
D. Lynn Shanks *(Pres & CEO)*
Dmitry Goryachev *(CFO)*
Betsy Wright *(Dir-HR)*
Peter J. Vuljanic *(Exec VP-Strategy, Project Dev & Surface Mining)*
Robert Kudlawiec *(VP)*
Mark Amyot *(Dir-Sls-Domestic & Logistics)*
Hank Parke *(Dir-Bus Dev & PR)*
Raymond J. McElhaney *(VP-Domestic Sls & Logistics)*

Subsidiary (Domestic):

RoxCoal, Inc. (3)
1576 Stoystown Rd, Friedens, PA 15541-7402
Tel.: (814) 445-3876
Web Site: http://www.corsacoal.com
Coal Mining
N.A.I.C.S.: 212115
Pete Meritts *(Pres & CEO)*

Subsidiary (US):

Wilson Creek Energy, LLC (2)
140 W Union St, Somerset, PA 15501
Tel.: (814) 443-4600
Mineral Mining Services
N.A.I.C.S.: 212390
Melissa Santiago *(Mgr-Permits & Land)*
Steve Meehan *(VP-Mktg)*

QUINZEL ACQUISITION COMPANY
535 Madison Ave 30th Fl, New York, NY 10022
Tel.: (646) 432-3736 DE
Year Founded: 2021
Investment Services
N.A.I.C.S.: 523999
Joel Greenblatt *(Co-Chm & Co-CEO)*
Robert Goldstein *(Co-Chm & Co-CEO)*
Bernard Seibert *(CFO & Sec)*

QUIRK AUTO PARK
293 Hogan Rd, Bangor, ME 04402-1386
Tel.: (207) 945-9401 ME
Web Site: http://www.quirkauto.com
Sales Range: $10-24.9 Million
Emp.: 100
Retailer of New & Used Automobiles
N.A.I.C.S.: 441110
John E. Quirk *(Pres & CEO)*
Jack Ouirk *(Owner)*
Julie McCluskey *(Mgr-HR)*
Joshua Conley *(Gen Mgr-Sls)*

QUIRK CHEVROLET PORTLAND
1000 Brighton Ave, Portland, ME 04102-1010
Tel.: (207) 774-5971 ME

COMPANIES

Web Site:
http://www.forestcityauto.com
Year Founded: 1983
Sales Range: $50-74.9 Million
Emp.: 115
Sales of New & Used Automobiles
N.A.I.C.S.: 441110
Bryan Wickerham *(Mgr-F&I)*
Jack Quirk Jr. *(Pres)*

QUIRKY INC.
606 W 28th St Fl 7, New York, NY 10001
Tel.: (212) 401-2868
Web Site: http://www.quirky.com
Sales Range: $50-74.9 Million
Emp.: 300
Invention Development Services
N.A.I.C.S.: 339999
Ben Kaufman *(Founder)*
Viresh Chopra *(Chief Design Officer)*
Ed Kremer *(CEO)*
Charlie Kwalwasser *(Gen Counsel)*
Rochelle DiRe *(Chief People Officer)*
Graham Blache *(VP-Platform)*
Steve Heintz *(CTO)*

Subsidiaries:

Undercurrent LLC (1)
270 Lafayette St Ste 1300, New York, NY 10012
Tel.: (212) 431-4808
Web Site: http://www.undercurrent.com
Emp.: 33
Organizational Design, Strategy & Management Services
N.A.I.C.S.: 541611
Mike Arauz *(Partner)*
Aaron Dignan *(CEO)*
Clay Parker Jones *(Mng Dir)*

QUIROGA LAW OFFICE, PLLC
505 N Argonne Rd B-109, Spokane Valley, WA 99212
Tel.: (509) 927-3840
Web Site:
http://www.quirogalawoffice.com
Year Founded: 2009
Sales Range: $1-9.9 Million
Emp.: 42
Law firm
N.A.I.C.S.: 541110
Casey Quiroga *(Co-Founder)*
Hector Quiroga *(Co-Founder)*
Stevan Veselinovic *(CTO)*
Joseph Rouse *(Dir-Ops)*
Kari Milich *(Mng Dir)*

QUISITIVE TECHNOLOGY SOLUTIONS, INC.
1431 Greenway Dr Ste 1000, Irving, TX 75038
Tel.: (972) 573-0995
Web Site: http://www.quisitive.com
Year Founded: 2016
Cloud Solution Services
N.A.I.C.S.: 519290
Mike Reinhart *(Founder & CEO)*
Sue Darrow *(Sr VP-HR & Culture)*

QUIXOTE ENTERPRISE INC.
130 Noxen Rd, Harveys Lake, PA 18618
Tel.: (570) 639-5536
Rev.: $16,600,000
Emp.: 20
Gifts & Novelties
N.A.I.C.S.: 424990
Eric Morrow *(Pres)*
Larry Schemery *(Controller)*

QUIXOTE RESEARCH, MARKETING & PUBLIC RELATIONS
3107 Brassfield Rd, Greensboro, NC 27410
Tel.: (336) 605-0363

Web Site:
http://www.quixotegroup.com
Year Founded: 1999
Sales Range: Less than $1 Million
Emp.: 12
Research, Marketing & Public Relations
N.A.I.C.S.: 541820
Chuck Mattina *(Co-Founder, Pres, CFO & Partner)*
Kim Doran *(CEO)*
Lisa Kornblum *(Office Mgr)*

QUIZZ SPORTSWEAR INC.
1410 Broadway Fl 24, New York, NY 10018-5007
Tel.: (212) 869-8630 NY
Year Founded: 1991
Sales Range: $10-24.9 Million
Emp.: 25
Women's, Children's & Infants' Clothes
N.A.I.C.S.: 424350
Mariette Wilson *(Pres)*

QUOIN INC.
200 Lincoln St Fl 4th, Boston, MA 02111
Tel.: (617) 357-5233
Web Site: http://www.quoininc.com
Sales Range: $25-49.9 Million
Emp.: 25
Painting, Coating & Hot Dipping
N.A.I.C.S.: 541618
Brad Kain *(Pres)*
Jean Pierre LeJacq *(Founder & CTO)*
Antonio Gallardo *(Dir-Tech & Support Practice)*
Sue Willard *(Dir-Project Mgmt Practice)*

Subsidiaries:

Almond Products Inc (1)
17150 148th Ave, Spring Lake, MI 49456
Tel.: (616) 844-1813
Web Site: http://www.almondproducts.com
Painting Of Metal Products
N.A.I.C.S.: 332812

Miller Products Inc. (1)
980 N Michigan Ave Ste 1900, Chicago, IL 60611-7505
Tel.: (616) 454-8341
Painting, Coating & Hot Dipping
N.A.I.C.S.: 332812

QUORUM ARCHITECTS, INC.
3112 W Highland Blvd, Milwaukee, WI 53208
Tel.: (414) 265-9265
Web Site:
http://www.quorumarchitects.com
Architectural Services
N.A.I.C.S.: 541310
Allyson Nemec *(Architect)*
Brian Scotty *(Project Mgr)*
Mark Knapp *(Architect)*
Chris Hau *(Project Mgr)*
Natalie Strohm *(Project Mgr)*

QUORUM HEALTH CORPORATION
1573 Mallory Ln Ste 100, Brentwood, TN 37027
Tel.: (615) 221-1400 DE
Web Site:
http://www.quorumhealth.com
Year Founded: 2016
Rev.: $1,689,626,000
Assets: $1,491,885,000
Liabilities: $1,727,879,000
Net Worth: ($235,994,000)
Earnings: ($163,927,000)
Emp.: 6,900
Fiscal Year-end: 12/31/19
Holding Company; Healthcare Services
N.A.I.C.S.: 551112

Martin D. Smith *(Pres & CEOO)*
Shaheed Koury *(Chief Medical Officer & Pres-Clinical Ops)*
Hal McCard *(Gen Counsel, Sec & Sr VP)*
Glenn A. Hargreaves *(Chief Acctg Officer & Sr VP)*
Dan Slipkovich *(CEO)*

Subsidiaries:

Ambulance Services of Lexington, Inc. (1)
200 W Church St, Lexington, TN 38351
Tel.: (731) 968-1841
Health Care Srvices
N.A.I.C.S.: 622110

Ambulance Services of McKenzie, Inc. (1)
161 Hospital Dr, McKenzie, TN 38201
Tel.: (731) 660-6369
Health Care Srvices
N.A.I.C.S.: 622110

Anna Clinic Corp. (1)
515 N Main St Ste C, Anna, IL 62906-1668
Tel.: (618) 833-2872
Health Care Srvices
N.A.I.C.S.: 622110
Nancy Russell *(Office Mgr)*

Anna Hospital Corporation (1)
517 N Main St, Anna, IL 62906
Tel.: (618) 833-4511
Web Site:
http://www.unioncountyhospital.com
Sales Range: $25-49.9 Million
Health Care Srvices
N.A.I.C.S.: 622110
James Farris *(CEO)*
Mike Harbor *(CFO)*
Charles R. Sanders *(Chief Nursing Officer)*

Augusta Health System, LLC (1)
78 Medical Ctr Dr, Fishersville, VA 22939
Tel.: (540) 332-4000
Web Site: http://www.augustahealth.com
Medical & Surgical Hospitals
N.A.I.C.S.: 622110
Laurel L. Landes *(Vice Chm)*
Victor M. Santos *(Chm)*
Mary N. Mannix *(Pres & CEO)*
Burnie Powers *(Treas & Sec)*
Alex Brown *(Gen Counsel & VP-Legal Affairs)*
Mike Canfield *(CIO & VP)*
Karen C. Clark *(VP-Ops)*
Crystal Farmer *(Chief Nursing Officer & VP)*
D. Scott Jones *(Chief Compliance Officer)*
J. Scott Just *(VP)*
John Katsianis *(CFO & VP)*
Mark LaRosa *(Chief Strategy Officer & VP-Bus Dev)*
Daniel O'Connor *(VP-HR)*
Tami G. Radecke *(VP-Community Partnerships)*

Augusta Physician Services, LLC (1)
2258 Wrightsboro Rd Ste 200, Augusta, GA 30904
Tel.: (706) 736-2273
Emp.: 3
Health Care Srvices
N.A.I.C.S.: 622110

Big Spring Hospital Corporation (1)
1601 W 11th Pl, Big Spring, TX 79720
Tel.: (432) 263-1211
Web Site: http://www.smmccares.com
Health Care Srvices
N.A.I.C.S.: 622110
Vivian Gordon *(Dir-Radiology)*

Blue Island Clinic Company, LLC (1)
12935 Gregory St, Blue Island, IL 60406-2428
Tel.: (708) 597-2000
Web Site:
http://www.metrosouthmedicalcenter.com
Health Care Srvices
N.A.I.C.S.: 622110

CSRA Holdings, LLC (1)
2803 Wrightsboro Rd Ste 38, Augusta, GA 30909
Tel.: (706) 729-6000
Health Care Srvices
N.A.I.C.S.: 622110

QUORUM HEALTH CORPORATION

Centre Clinic Corp. (1)
395 Northwood Dr, Centre, AL 35960-1045
Tel.: (256) 927-4900
Health Care Srvices
N.A.I.C.S.: 622110
Amber Morrie *(Gen Mgr)*

Centre HBP Services, LLC (1)
400 Northwood Dr, Centre, AL 35960-1023
Tel.: (256) 927-5531
Health Care Srvices
N.A.I.C.S.: 621610

Centre Hospital Corporation (1)
400 Northwood Dr, Centre, AL 35960
Tel.: (256) 927-5531
Web Site:
http://www.cherokeemedicalcenter.com
Emp.: 140
Women Healthcare Services
N.A.I.C.S.: 621610
Jay Hinesley *(CEO)*

Clinton Hospital Corporation (1)
24 Cree Dr, Lock Haven, PA 17745
Tel.: (570) 893-5000
Web Site: http://www.lockhavenhospital.com
Emp.: 40
Health Care Srvices
N.A.I.C.S.: 622110
Sheila Daly *(Pres)*
William T. McGrail *(Chm)*

Crossroads Physician Corp. (1)
209 Crossroads Pl Ste 150, Mount Vernon, IL 62864-6546
Tel.: (618) 244-6710
Emp.: 4
Health Care Srvices
N.A.I.C.S.: 622110

Deming Hospital Corporation (1)
900 W Ash St, Deming, NM 88030
Tel.: (575) 546-5800
Web Site: http://www.mimbresmemorial.com
Emp.: 200
Health Care Srvices
N.A.I.C.S.: 622110

Doctors Hospital Physician Services, LLC (1)
6225 Frank Ave NW, North Canton, OH 44720-8439
Tel.: (330) 497-6555
Health Care Srvices
N.A.I.C.S.: 622110
Spring Baulieu *(Gen Mgr)*

Edwardsville Ambulatory Surgery Center, L.L.C. (1)
12 Ginger Creek Pkwy, Glen Carbon, IL 62034
Tel.: (618) 656-8200
Web Site:
http://www.edwardsvillesurgery.com
Health Care Srvices
N.A.I.C.S.: 622110
Sonja Schwebke *(Coord-Clinic)*

Evanston Clinic Corp. (1)
107 N Main St, Lyman, WY 82937
Tel.: (307) 787-3313
Health Care Srvices
N.A.I.C.S.: 622110

Evanston Hospital Corporation (1)
190 Arrowhead Dr, Evanston, WY 82930
Tel.: (307) 789-3636
Web Site:
http://www.evanstonregionalhospital.com
Emp.: 50
Health Care Srvices
N.A.I.C.S.: 622110
Tony Gillies *(Chm)*
Gary Spencer *(Vice Chm)*
Cheri Willard *(CEO-Interim)*
Pete Finelli *(CFO)*

Forrest City Arkansas Hospital Company, LLC (1)
1601 New Castle Rd, Forrest City, AR 72335
Tel.: (870) 261-0000
Web Site:
http://www.forrestcitymedicalcenter.com
Emp.: 19
Health Care Srvices
N.A.I.C.S.: 622110

Forrest City Clinic Company, LLC (1)

3329

QUORUM HEALTH CORPORATION

U.S. PRIVATE

Quorum Health Corporation—(Continued)
904 Holiday Dr 400, Forrest City, AR 72335
Tel.: (870) 630-9354
Web Site:
http://www.forrestcitymedicalcenter.com
Health Care Srvices
N.A.I.C.S.: 622110

Fort Payne Hospital Corporation (1)
200 Medical Ctr Dr, Fort Payne, AL 35968
Tel.: (256) 845-3150
Web Site: http://www.dekalbregional.com
Sales Range: $25-49.9 Million
Emp.: 480
Health Care Srvices
N.A.I.C.S.: 622110

Fort Payne RHC Corp. (1)
415 Medical Ctr Dr SW, Fort Payne, AL 35968-3421
Tel.: (256) 997-2820
Health Care Srvices
N.A.I.C.S.: 622110

Galesburg Hospital Corporation (1)
695 N Kellogg St, Galesburg, IL 61401
Tel.: (309) 343-8131
Web Site: http://www.cottagehospital.com
Health Care Srvices
N.A.I.C.S.: 622110

Granite City Clinic Corp. (1)
2044 Madison Ave Ste 27, Granite City, IL 62040-4641
Tel.: (618) 451-7600
Emp.: 8
Health Care Srvices
N.A.I.C.S.: 622110
Edward Cunningham (CEO)

Granite City Illinois Hospital Company, LLC (1)
2100 Madison Ave, Granite City, IL 62040
Tel.: (618) 798-3000
Web Site: http://www.gatewayregional.net
Health Care Srvices
N.A.I.C.S.: 622110

Granite City Orthopedic Physicians Company, LLC (1)
4802 S State Route 159, Glen Carbon, IL 62034-1904
Tel.: (618) 288-4388
Health Care Srvices
N.A.I.C.S.: 622110

Granite City Physicians Corp. (1)
2044 Madison Ave Ste 22, Granite City, IL 62040
Tel.: (618) 877-6800
Sales Range: $75-99.9 Million
Emp.: 3
Health Care Srvices
N.A.I.C.S.: 622110
Mark Bethell (CEO)

Greenville Clinic Corp. (1)
1502 S Colorado St, Greenville, MS 38703
Tel.: (662) 332-9872
Web Site: http://www.greenvilleclinic.com
Women Healthcare Services
N.A.I.C.S.: 621610

Greenville Hospital Corporation (1)
29 LV Stabler Dr, Greenville, AL 36037
Tel.: (334) 382-2671
Web Site: http://www.lvstabler.com
Sales Range: $25-49.9 Million
Emp.: 224
General Medical & Surgical Hospitals
N.A.I.C.S.: 622110
Connie Nicholas (CEO)

Heartland Rural Healthcare, LLC (1)
3331 W Deyoung St Ste 305, Marion, IL 62959
Tel.: (618) 985-9140
Health Care Srvices
N.A.I.C.S.: 622110

Hospital of Barstow, Inc. (1)
820 E Mtn View St, Barstow, CA 92311
Tel.: (760) 256-1761
Web Site: http://www.barstowhospital.com
Emp.: 360
Health Care Srvices
N.A.I.C.S.: 622110

Hospital of Louisa, Inc. (1)
2485 Hwy 644, Louisa, KY 41230
Tel.: (606) 638-9451
Web Site:
http://www.threeriversmedicalcenter.com
Health Care Srvices
N.A.I.C.S.: 622110

Jackson Hospital Corporation (1)
540 Jett Dr, Jackson, KY 41339
Tel.: (606) 666-6000
Web Site: http://www.kentuckyrivermc.com
Emp.: 30
Health Care Srvices
N.A.I.C.S.: 622110
John J. Ballard (CEO)
Wanda Robinette (Chief Nursing Officer)
Valerie Bryant (CFO)

Jackson Physician Corp. (1)
1151 Main St, Jackson, KY 41339
Tel.: (606) 666-8771
Health Care Srvices
N.A.I.C.S.: 622110

Kentucky River HBP, LLC (1)
540 Jett Dr, Jackson, KY 41339-9622
Tel.: (606) 666-6479
Health Care Srvices
N.A.I.C.S.: 621610

King City Physician Company, LLC (1)
4117 S Water Tower PIC, Mount Vernon, IL 62864
Tel.: (618) 242-0672
Health Care Srvices
N.A.I.C.S.: 622110
Jackie Campbell (Office Mgr)

Knox Clinic Corp. (1)
834 N Seminary St, Galesburg, IL 61401
Tel.: (309) 345-4513
Emp.: 600
Health Care Srvices
N.A.I.C.S.: 622110
James Flinn (CEO)

Lexington Family Physicians, LLC (1)
102 W Medical Park Dr, Lexington, NC 27292
Tel.: (336) 249-3329
Web Site:
http://www.lexingtonfamilyphysicians.com
Health Care Srvices
N.A.I.C.S.: 622110
Martin D. Smith (Pres-Div III Ops)

Lexington Hospital Corporation (1)
200 W Church St, Lexington, TN 38351
Tel.: (731) 968-3646
Web Site:
http://www.hendersoncohospital.com
Health Care Srvices
N.A.I.C.S.: 622110
Regina Maness (Mng Dir)
Denise Mills (Mgr-Clinic)

MMC of Nevada, LLC (1)
1299 Bertha Howe Ave, Mesquite, NV 89027
Tel.: (702) 346-8040
Web Site: http://www.mesaviewhospital.com
Health Care Srvices
N.A.I.C.S.: 622110
Mitchell Fransen (CFO)

Marion Hospital Corporation (1)
3333 W DeYoung, Marion, IL 62959
Tel.: (618) 998-7000
Web Site: http://www.heartlandregional.com
Health Care Srvices
N.A.I.C.S.: 622110
Melisa Adkins (CEO)

McKenzie Physician Services, LLC (1)
960 N 16th St Ste 207, Springfield, OR 97477-4175
Tel.: (541) 744-8400
Health Care Srvices
N.A.I.C.S.: 622110

McKenzie-Willamette Regional Medical Center Associates, LLC (1)
1460 G St, Springfield, OR 97477
Tel.: (541) 726-4400
Web Site: http://www.mckweb.com
Health Care Srvices
N.A.I.C.S.: 622110

Memorial Management, Inc. (1)
3331 W Deyoung, Marion, IL 62959
Tel.: (618) 998-7297
Emp.: 3
Health Care Srvices
N.A.I.C.S.: 622110

Mesa View PT, LLC (1)
1140 W Pioneer Blvd, Mesquite, NV 89027
Tel.: (702) 346-1899
Web Site:
http://www.mesaviewphysicaltherapy.com
Emp.: 20
Health Care Srvices
N.A.I.C.S.: 622110
Parvis Wakefielet (Pres)

Monroe HMA, Inc. (1)
2151 W Spring St, Monroe, GA 30655
Tel.: (770) 267-8461
Web Site:
http://www.clearviewregionalmedicenter.com
Emp.: 450
Hospital Services
N.A.I.C.S.: 622110
Jon-Paul Croom (COO)
Michael Johnson (CEO)

National Healthcare of Mt. Vernon, Inc. (1)
Ste 8 Doctors Park Rd, Mount Vernon, IL 62864
Tel.: (618) 244-5500
Health Care Srvices
N.A.I.C.S.: 622110

National Imaging of Carterville, LLC (1)
10419 Fleming Rd, Carterville, IL 62918
Tel.: (618) 985-8007
Health Care Srvices
N.A.I.C.S.: 622110

National Imaging of Mount Vernon, LLC (1)
4119 S Water Tower Pl Ste A, Mount Vernon, IL 62864-6293
Tel.: (618) 246-9595
Health Care Srvices
N.A.I.C.S.: 622110

Our Healthy Circle (1)
1573 Mallory Ln Ste 100, Brentwood, TN 37027
Tel.: (800) 462-5266
Web Site: http://www.ourhealthycircle.com
Healtcare Services
N.A.I.C.S.: 621999

Paintsville Hospital Company, LLC (1)
625 James S Trimble Blvd, Paintsville, KY 41240
Tel.: (606) 789-3511
Web Site: http://www.pbhrmc.com
Sales Range: $50-74.9 Million
Emp.: 250
Health Care Srvices
N.A.I.C.S.: 622110
Deborah L. Trimble (CEO)
Patricia Major (CFO)
June Blankenship (Officer-Hospital Compliance)

Subsidiary (Domestic):

Paintsville HMA Physician Management, LLC (2)
830 S Mayo Trl, Paintsville, KY 41240-1384
Tel.: (606) 789-8749
Web Site: http://www.pbhrmc.com
Health Care Srvices
N.A.I.C.S.: 622110
Deborah Trimble (CEO)
Patricia Major (CFO)
June Blankenship (Hospital Compliance Officer)

Phillips Clinic Corp. (1)
1801 Marting Luther King Jr Dr, Helena, AR 72342-8998
Tel.: (870) 338-8682
Web Site: http://www.phillipsclinic.com
Health Care Srvices
N.A.I.C.S.: 622110

Phillips Hospital Corporation (1)
1801 Martin Luther King Dr, Helena, AR 72342
Tel.: (870) 338-5800

Web Site: http://www.helenarmc.com
Health Care Srvices
N.A.I.C.S.: 622110

Quorum Solutions, LLC (1)
3133 Caswell Dr, Troy, MI 48084
Tel.: (248) 709-0742
Health Care Srvices
N.A.I.C.S.: 622110

Red Bud Clinic Corp. (1)
415 W S 4th St, Red Bud, IL 62278
Tel.: (618) 939-1551
Health Care Srvices
N.A.I.C.S.: 622110

Red Bud Illinois Hospital Company, LLC (1)
325 Spring St, Red Bud, IL 62278
Tel.: (618) 282-3831
Health Care Srvices
N.A.I.C.S.: 622110
Wayne Smith (Pres)

Red Bud Regional Clinic Company, LLC (1)
325 Spring St, Red Bud, IL 62278
Tel.: (618) 282-3831
Web Site: http://www.redbudregional.com
Healthcare Provider
N.A.I.C.S.: 622110

River to River Heart Group, LLC (1)
3331 W Deyoung St Ste 203, Marion, IL 62959-5896
Tel.: (618) 997-4733
Emp.: 15
Health Care Srvices
N.A.I.C.S.: 622110
Rachelle Mueller (Gen Mgr)

SMMC Medical Group (1)
2301 S Gregg St, Big Spring, TX 79720
Tel.: (432) 268-4801
Web Site: http://www.smmccare.com
Health Care Srvices
N.A.I.C.S.: 622110
Kellie Tubb (Gen Mgr)

San Miguel Clinic Corp. (1)
2301 7th St, Las Vegas, NM 87701
Tel.: (505) 454-4000
Health Care Srvices
N.A.I.C.S.: 622110

Southern Illinois Medical Care Associates, LLC (1)
3411 Professional Park Dr, Marion, IL 62959
Tel.: (618) 997-2161
Web Site: http://www.simcaproviders.com
Health Care Srvices
N.A.I.C.S.: 622110

Sunbury Clinic Company, LLC (1)
337 Arch St, Sunbury, PA 17801-2212
Tel.: (570) 286-0303
Emp.: 11
Health Care Srvices
N.A.I.C.S.: 622110
Elaine Dietrich (Gen Mgr)

Three Rivers Medical Clinics, Inc. (1)
2483 Hwy 644 Ste 102, Louisa, KY 41230
Tel.: (606) 638-7488
Web Site:
http://www.threeriversmedicalcenter.com
Health Care Srvices
N.A.I.C.S.: 622110
Greg Kifer (CEO)

Tooele Clinic Corp. (1)
196 E 2000 N, Tooele, UT 84074
Tel.: (435) 882-9035
Health Care Srvices
N.A.I.C.S.: 622110

Vista Physician Group (1)
200 S Greenleaf St Ste A, Gurnee, IL 60031-3398
Tel.: (847) 360-3000
Web Site:
http://www.vistaphysiciangroup.com
Health Care Srvices
N.A.I.C.S.: 622110

Waukegan Illinois Hospital Company, LLC (1)
1324 N Sheridan Rd, Waukegan, IL 60085
Tel.: (847) 360-4000
Web Site: http://www.vistahealth.com

Emp.: 1,300
Health Care Srvices
N.A.I.C.S.: 622110

Williamston HBP Services, LLC (1)
310 S McCaskey Rd, Williamston, NC 27892-2150
Tel.: (252) 809-6179
Web Site: http://www.martingeneral.com
Emp.: 250
Health Care Srvices
N.A.I.C.S.: 622110
Craig Fichter *(Gen Mgr)*

QUORUM INTEGRATED, INC.
816 Evanson Rd PO Box 1057, Hockessin, DE 19707
Tel.: (302) 239-4822 DE
Year Founded: 1990
Sales Range: Less than $1 Million
Emp.: 4
N.A.I.C.S.: 541810
William Nimtz *(Founder & Pres)*
Cheryl Wolfe Jackson *(Dir-PR & Copywriter)*
Ted Karwowski *(Dir-Art)*

QUPACO INC.
300 N Sherman St, York, PA 17403
Tel.: (717) 843-9061 PA
Web Site:
  http://www.quakercitypaper.com
Year Founded: 1946
Sales Range: $10-24.9 Million
Emp.: 25
Paper Products Whslr & Distr
N.A.I.C.S.: 424130
Paul E. Newcomer *(CEO)*
Kathleen S. Bergdoll *(Pres)*

QVS HOLDING INC.
4814 Technology Dr, Martinez, GA 30907
Tel.: (706) 796-8934
Web Site:
  http://www.cleanwateraugusta.com
Year Founded: 1985
Sales Range: $25-49.9 Million
Emp.: 10
Water Distribution Services
N.A.I.C.S.: 221310
Jimmy Holt *(Pres)*

QVT FINANCIAL, LP
1177 Avenue of the Americas, New York, NY 10036
Tel.: (212) 705-8800
Web Site: http://www.qvt.com
Year Founded: 2003
Sales Range: $1-9.9 Million
Emp.: 20
Portfolio Management
N.A.I.C.S.: 523940
Daniel Gold *(CEO & Mng Partner)*
Michael Coursen *(Controller)*
Keith S. Manchester *(Partner & Head-Life Sciences)*

QWINIX TECHNOLOGIES, INC.
9155 E Nichols Ave Ste 300, Centennial, CO 80112
Tel.: (303) 459-4310
Web Site: http://www.qwinix.io
Year Founded: 2012
Sales Range: $10-24.9 Million
Emp.: 17
Software Development Services
N.A.I.C.S.: 541511
Darshan Puttannaiah *(Founder & CEO)*
Amaresh Veer *(COO)*
Leonardo Murillo *(CTO)*
Chandra Sekhar Chaganti *(VP-Dev & Ops)*

R & L CARRIERS, INC.
600 Gillam Rd, Wilmington, OH 45177-0271
Tel.: (937) 382-1494 OH
Web Site: http://www.rlcarriers.com
Year Founded: 1967
Sales Range: $1-4.9 Billion
Emp.: 10,000
Motor Freight Carriers
N.A.I.C.S.: 484121
Jeff Copsey *(VP-HR)*
Bob Zimmerman *(Pres)*

Subsidiaries:

AFC Worldwide Express Inc. (1)
3658 Atlanta Industrial Dr NW, Atlanta, GA 30349
Tel.: (770) 919-0400
Web Site: http://www.afcexpress.com
Sales Range: $10-24.9 Million
Emp.: 50
Provider of Freight Forwarding Services
N.A.I.C.S.: 488510
Mike Shroyer *(CFO)*

Greenwood Motor Lines Inc. (1)
600 Gilliam Rd, Wilmington, OH 45177-9089
Tel.: (937) 382-1494
Transportation Services
N.A.I.C.S.: 484121

R & L CONSTRUCTION INC.
904 Nepperhan Ave, Yonkers, NY 10703
Tel.: (914) 423-2400
Web Site: http://www.rlcon.com
Sales Range: $10-24.9 Million
Emp.: 96
Engineeering Services
N.A.I.C.S.: 236220
Colin Barton *(Dir-Interior Div)*
Michael Brady *(Dir-Masonry Div)*
Brendan O'Brien *(Dir-Sls & Mktg)*
Jim Troilo *(Mgr-Ops)*
Michael Riegler *(VP-Field Ops)*

R & R AUTO GROUP
PO Box 619, Schuylkill Haven, PA 17972
Tel.: (570) 385-2881
Web Site:
  http://www.rnrautogroup.com
Year Founded: 1985
Sales Range: $10-24.9 Million
Emp.: 50
Car Whslr
N.A.I.C.S.: 441110
John Smith *(VP)*

R & R DIRECT MAIL, INC.
190 Motor Pkwy Ste 103, Hauppauge, NY 11788
Tel.: (631) 249-8710 NY
Web Site: http://www.rickardlist.com
Year Founded: 1978
Sales Range: $1-9.9 Million
Emp.: 18
Direct Mail Advertising Services
N.A.I.C.S.: 541860
Mark L. Rickard *(Pres & CEO)*
Jennifer L. Rickard *(COO & Exec VP)*
Marianne Palumbo *(Dir-List Brokerage Grp)*
Amy Seyler *(Dir-Media Plng)*

R & Y AC COMPRESSOR, INC.
15315 NE 21st Ave, Miami, FL 33162
Web Site:
  http://www.rycompressors.com
Year Founded: 1989
Sales Range: $1-9.9 Million
Emp.: 26
Air Conditioning Parts Mfr
N.A.I.C.S.: 333415
Roy Shaked *(Pres)*
Jacob Shaked *(VP)*
Prosper Asher Mamane *(VP)*
Michael Mizrahi *(Mgr-E-Commerce)*

R CORP FINANCIAL
1900 Round Rock Ave, Round Rock, TX 78681
Tel.: (512) 600-8100 TX
Web Site: http://www.rbanktexas.com
Year Founded: 2012
Bank Holding Company
N.A.I.C.S.: 551111
Steve Stapp *(Pres & CEO)*
Judy Kirkland *(COO & Exec VP)*
Mike Shaw *(Chief Credit Officer & Exec VP)*
Chris Bubela *(Chief Lending Officer & Exec VP)*
J. Hollis Bone *(Exec VP-Comml Lending)*

Subsidiaries:

R Bank (1)
1900 Round Rock Ave, Round Rock, TX 78681
Tel.: (512) 600-8100
Web Site: http://www.rbanktexas.com
Commericial Banking
N.A.I.C.S.: 522110
Steve Stapp *(Pres & CEO)*
Bryon Borchers *(VP)*
Travis Perthuis *(Sr VP)*
Garrett Morgan *(Sr VP-Austin)*
Marc Bone *(CFO)*
Steven Stinson *(COO & Exec VP)*

R E W ENTERPRISES, INC.
200 W Nakoma Dr., San Antonio, TX 78216
Tel.: (210) 349-7866 TX
Web Site:
  http://www.sunncarpets.com
Year Founded: 1977
Sales Range: $10-24.9 Million
Emp.: 10
Home Furnishing Merchant Whslr
N.A.I.C.S.: 423220
Jim Coleman *(Owner)*

R E WEST INC.
14 Blue Grass Dr, Ashland City, TN 37015
Tel.: (615) 792-1526
Web Site: http://www.rewest.com
Rev.: $12,500,000
Emp.: 150
Trucking Except Local
N.A.I.C.S.: 484121
Jenny West *(CFO & Sec)*
Allen Kemp *(VP-IT)*
Donna Tomlinson *(VP-HR, Recruiting & Safety)*
Dustin Stricker *(Mgr-Maintenance)*
Bill West *(VP-Customer Svc)*
Robert E. West Jr. *(Pres & CEO)*

R F STEARNS INC
5200 Meadows Rd Ste 200, Lake Oswego, OR 97035
Tel.: (503) 601-8700
Web Site: http://www.rfstearns.com
Year Founded: 1981
Rev.: $56,500,000
Emp.: 30
Commercial & Institutional Building Construction
N.A.I.C.S.: 236220
Richard Burnham *(Pres)*
Carey Lee *(Mgr-Sls)*

R SQUARE, INC.
5 Independence Way Ste 105, Princeton, NJ 08540
Tel.: (609) 520-8204
Web Site: http://www.r-square.com
Year Founded: 1997
Sales Range: $10-24.9 Million
Emp.: 150
Software Development Services
N.A.I.C.S.: 513210
Heather Mapps *(Mgr-Fin)*

R STREET INSTITUTE
1050 17th St NW Ste 1150, Washington, DC 20036
Tel.: (202) 525-5717 DC
Web Site: http://www.rstreet.org
Year Founded: 2008
Sales Range: $1-9.9 Million
Emp.: 12
Social Advocacy Services
N.A.I.C.S.: 813319
Zach Graves *(Dir-Tech & Innovation Policy)*
Eli Lehrer *(Co-Chm & Pres)*
Andrew Moylan *(Exec Dir)*
Erica Schoder *(Fin Dir & Dir-Ops)*
Marni Soupcoff *(Co-Chm)*
Kevin R. Kosar *(Project Dir)*
Cameron Smith *(VP-Policy)*

R T WESTERN MISSOURI FRANCHISE LLC
402 N Marie St, Nixa, MO 65714
Tel.: (417) 724-0298
Sales Range: $25-49.9 Million
Emp.: 750
Restaurant, Family: Chain
N.A.I.C.S.: 541618

R TO FIFTH, INC.
6688 Cortez Rd W, Bradenton, FL 34210
Tel.: (941) 761-7797 FL
Web Site: http://www.oysterbar.net
Year Founded: 2002
Sales Range: $25-49.9 Million
Emp.: 82
Eating Place
N.A.I.C.S.: 722511
Gary Harkness *(Gen Mgr)*
John Horne *(Pres)*

R&B GRINDING CO. INC.
1900 Clark St, Racine, WI 53403
Tel.: (262) 634-5538
Web Site: http://www.rbgrinding.com
Sales Range: $10-24.9 Million
Emp.: 150
Machine Shop, Jobbing & Repair
N.A.I.C.S.: 332710
Ray Biddle *(Pres)*

R&B RECEIVABLES MANAGEMENT
860 S Northpoint Blvd, Waukegan, IL 60085
Tel.: (847) 887-8502
Web Site:
  http://www.randbreceivables.com
Rev.: $17,300,000
Emp.: 60
Purchasers of Accounts Receivable & Commercial Paper
N.A.I.C.S.: 522299
Dennis A. Brebner *(Pres & CEO)*

R&B WAGNER CO. INC.
10600 West Brown Deer Rd, Milwaukee, WI 53224
Web Site: http://www.rbwagner.com
Rev.: $13,425,567
Emp.: 78
Metal Parts Mfr
N.A.I.C.S.: 332996
Michael MacLeish *(VP-Innovation & Engrg)*
Julius Wagner *(Founder)*

R&B WHOLESALE DISTRIBUTORS
2350 S Milliken Ave, Ontario, CA 91761
Tel.: (909) 230-5401
Web Site: http://www.rbdist.com
Rev.: $18,546,089
Emp.: 47
Appliance Distr

R&B WHOLESALE DISTRIBUTORS

N.A.I.C.S.: 423620
Bob Burggraf *(Pres)*
Connie Espina *(Gen Mgr)*

R&C SERVICES INC.
1407 N Lincoln St, Greensburg, IN 47240
Tel.: (812) 663-1000
Web Site: http://www.acraauto.com
Rev.: $34,136,598
Emp.: 120
Automobiles, New & Used
N.A.I.C.S.: 441110
Richard A. Acra *(Pres)*
Todd Acra *(Mgr-Corp Ops)*

R&D CARY ENTERPRISES
105 W Chatham St, Cary, NC 27511
Tel.: (919) 467-2355
Year Founded: 1969
Sales Range: $10-24.9 Million
Emp.: 15
Greeting Cards
N.A.I.C.S.: 459420
Ralph H. Ashworth *(Pres)*

R&D ENTERPRISES, INC.
20660 US Hwy 31 N, Vinemont, AL 35179-5963
Tel.: (256) 775-6337
Web Site:
 http://www.motorheadproducts.com
Year Founded: 2000
Sales Range: $1-9.9 Million
Emp.: 2
Licensed Products Designer & Mfr
N.A.I.C.S.: 339999
James Loney *(CEO)*

R&D MAINTENANCE SERVICES, INC.
409 N Main St, Hennessey, OK 73742-1017
Tel.: (405) 853-7108
Sales Range: $25-49.9 Million
Emp.: 400
Operation Maintenance Services
N.A.I.C.S.: 236210

R&D THIEL INC.-CARPENTER CONTRACTORS OF AMERICA
2340 Newburg Rd, Belvidere, IL 61008-7842
Tel.: (815) 544-1699
Web Site:
 http://www.carpentercontractor.com
Year Founded: 1955
Sales Range: $50-74.9 Million
Emp.: 400
Carpentry Work
N.A.I.C.S.: 238130

Subsidiaries:

Carpenter Components of Illinois (1)
2340 Newburg Rd, Belvidere, IL 61008-7842 (100%)
Tel.: (815) 544-1699
Web Site: http://www.rdthiel.com
Sales Range: $75-99.9 Million
Carpentry Services
N.A.I.C.S.: 238130
Terry Smith *(CEO)*

Carpenter Contractors of America (1)
3200 NE 14th St Cswy, Pompano Beach, FL 33062
Tel.: (954) 781-2660
Web Site:
 http://www.carpentercontractors.com
Rev.: $250,000,000
Emp.: 35
Home Builder Services
N.A.I.C.S.: 238130
Bill Fritsch *(Pres)*

Carpenter Contractors of America (1)
190 Gillis Hill Rd, Fayetteville, NC 28306-8522
Tel.: (910) 875-7575
Web Site:
 http://www.carpentercontractors.com
Sales Range: $25-49.9 Million
Emp.: 100
Carpentry Work
N.A.I.C.S.: 238130

Carpenter Contractors of America (1)
2160 Andrea Ln, Fort Myers, FL 33912-1901 (100%)
Tel.: (239) 437-1100
Web Site:
 http://www.carpentercontractors.com
Sales Range: $25-49.9 Million
Emp.: 20
Carpentry Work
N.A.I.C.S.: 238130
Ray Coay *(Gen Mgr)*

Carpenter Contractors of America (1)
9950 Princess Palm Ave, Tampa, FL 33619-8302
Tel.: (813) 621-7882
Web Site:
 http://www.carpentercontractors.com
Sales Range: $25-49.9 Million
Emp.: 8
Carpentry Work
N.A.I.C.S.: 238130
Jim Peterlin *(Mgr-Engrg)*

Carpenter Contractors of America (1)
3900 Ave G NW, Winter Haven, FL 33880
Tel.: (863) 294-6449
Web Site:
 http://www.carpentercontractorsofamerica.com
Sales Range: $25-49.9 Million
Emp.: 50
Carpentry Work
N.A.I.C.S.: 238130

R&F INDUSTRIES, INC.
402 W Davis St, Luling, TX 78648-2254
Tel.: (830) 875-6927
Web Site:
 http://www.randfindustries.com
Industrial Machinery & Equipment Merchant Whslr
N.A.I.C.S.: 423830
Raymond McGlothlin *(Owner)*

R&G CONSTRUCTION COMPANY
1700 N Graham St, Charlotte, NC 28206
Tel.: (704) 334-7228
Sales Range: $10-24.9 Million
Emp.: 25
Construction Services
N.A.I.C.S.: 236220
James R. Costin *(Chm)*
Michelle Heape *(Sec)*

R&H CONSTRUCTION CO.
1530 SW Taylor St, Portland, OR 97205
Tel.: (503) 228-7177
Web Site: http://www.rhconst.com
Year Founded: 1979
Rev.: $73,000,000
Emp.: 180
Commercial & Office Building, New Construction
N.A.I.C.S.: 236220
John Ward *(Pres & COO)*
Alisa Castellano *(Controller)*
Jennifer Bianchini *(Dir-People & Culture)*
Alex Coleman *(Mgr-Preconstruction)*
Kenny Herrera *(Dir-Safety, Health & Environmental)*
Trenton Lundquist *(Asst Project Mgr-Buildings Grp)*
Kim Bourgeois *(Project Mgr-Special Projects)*

Subsidiaries:

R&H Construction Co. - Central Oregon (1)
360 SW Bond St Ste 130, Bend, OR 97702
Tel.: (541) 312-2961
Web Site: http://www.rhconst.com
Sales Range: $10-24.9 Million
Emp.: 30
Commercial & Office Building, New Construction
N.A.I.C.S.: 236220
Randy Williams *(CFO & Principal)*
Matt Wycoff *(Sr Mgr-Preconstruction)*

R&H MOTOR CARS LTD
9727 Reisterstown Rd, Owings Mills, MD 21117-4122
Tel.: (410) 363-3900
Web Site:
 http://www.rhmotorcars.com
Year Founded: 1991
Sales Range: $125-149.9 Million
Emp.: 125
Sales of New & Used Automobiles
N.A.I.C.S.: 441110
Tim Sauder *(Mgr-Parts & Svcs)*
Michael Berman *(CFO)*

R&K DISTRIBUTORS INC.
1302 E Whaley St, Longview, TX 75601
Tel.: (903) 758-4494
Web Site: http://www.rkdist.com
Sales Range: $25-49.9 Million
Emp.: 100
Beer & Other Fermented Malt Liquors
N.A.I.C.S.: 424810
Mike Martin *(Pres)*
Carla Hammon *(Office Mgr)*
Todd Morgan *(Gen Mgr)*

R&L DEVELOPMENT COMPANY
153 Swan Lake Ln, New Alexandria, PA 15670
Tel.: (724) 668-2223
Web Site: http://www.rldevco.com
Year Founded: 1969
Sales Range: $25-49.9 Million
Emp.: 150
Provider of Utility Maintenance & Heavy Construction Services
N.A.I.C.S.: 238910
Richard L. Myers *(Pres & COO)*
David A. Zuchegno *(CFO & Sr VP)*
Patricia C. Latimer *(VP-Estimating)*
Steven H. Landers *(Sec & VP-Parts)*
Michael W. Koestler *(Sr VP-Ops)*
Richard T. Miller *(Mgr-Pur Parts)*
Luke A. Latimer *(Chm & CEO)*
Roy D. Cessna *(VP-Ops & Mgr-Equipment)*

R&M INDUSTRIES INC.
2865 Executive Pl, Escondido, CA 92029
Tel.: (760) 233-9770
Web Site:
 http://randmindustries.homestead.com
Sales Range: $10-24.9 Million
Emp.: 179
Pillow Mfr
N.A.I.C.S.: 314120

R&M REALTY INC.
8290 W Sahara Ave Ste 100, Las Vegas, NV 89117
Tel.: (702) 871-9500
Web Site:
 http://www.lasvegashomes.com
Sales Range: $10-24.9 Million
Emp.: 130
Real Estate Agent, Residential
N.A.I.C.S.: 531210
Robert H. Hamrick *(Chm & CEO)*

R&M RICHARDS INC.
1400 Broadway, New York, NY 10018-5300
Tel.: (212) 921-8820   NY
Web Site: http://www.rmrich.com
Year Founded: 1991
Sales Range: $100-124.9 Million
Emp.: 110
Womens, Juniors & Misses Dresses
N.A.I.C.S.: 315250
Mario Dell'Anno *(CEO)*
Richard Dell'Anno *(Pres)*
Robert Dell'Anno *(VP)*
Steve Gardiner *(CFO)*

R&M WHOLESALE CO. INC.
501 S St, Brookston, IN 47923
Tel.: (765) 563-3188
Rev.: $17,000,000
Emp.: 80
Whslr of Tobacco & Tobacco Products; Retailer of General Merchandise
N.A.I.C.S.: 424940
Jeff Schmierer *(Pres)*

R&N KNITTED
544 Park Ave, Brooklyn, NY 11205
Tel.: (718) 522-6990
Sales Range: $10-24.9 Million
Emp.: 30
Hats, Caps & Millinery
N.A.I.C.S.: 424350

R&O CONSTRUCTION COMPANY INC.
933 Wall Ave, Ogden, UT 84404-4800
Tel.: (801) 627-1403   UT
Web Site: http://www.randoco.com
Year Founded: 1979
Sales Range: $10-24.9 Million
Emp.: 130
Provider of Nonresidential Construction Services
N.A.I.C.S.: 236220
Orluff Opheikens *(Founder & CEO)*
Charles Auger *(CFO & VP)*
Frank McDonough *(Sr VP)*
Mike Nicholls *(VP-Special Projects)*
Slade Opheikens *(Pres)*
Chet Opheiken *(VP-Bus Dev-Las Vegas)*

R&R ASSOCIATES LLC
1962 Main St Ste 300, Sarasota, FL 34236
Tel.: (941) 336-7500
Web Site:
 http://www.rrassociates.com
Sales Range: $1-9.9 Million
Emp.: 35
Product Design Engineering & Mfr
N.A.I.C.S.: 541330
Leo Riza *(Co-Owner)*
Erkan Riza *(Co-Owner)*

Subsidiaries:

R&R Associates LLC - Canada (1)
888 3rd Street 10th Floor, Calgary, T2P 5C5, AB, Canada
Tel.: (403) 400-7690
Product Design Engineering & Mfr
N.A.I.C.S.: 541330

R&R Associates LLC - Heavy Production Division (1)
Bahirye Ucok Blvd No 39 Daire 1, Karsiyaka, 35530, Izmir, Turkiye
Tel.: (90) 537 372 2036
Heavy Engineering
N.A.I.C.S.: 237990

R&R Associates LLC - Quality Assurance Division (1)
19S XinBaoHui Building Nanhai Road, Nanshan District, Shenzhen, 518054, China
Tel.: (86) 755 86038533
Quality Assurance Services
N.A.I.C.S.: 561499

COMPANIES

R&R CABLE COMPANY INC.
103 S 2nd St, Roslyn, WA 98941
Tel.: (509) 649-2212
Web Site: http://www.rrcable.com
Rev.: $10,900,000
Emp.: 85
Cable & Other Subscription Programming
N.A.I.C.S.: 516210
Nathan Weis *(Pres)*
Gregory A. Maras *(Sec)*
Marian A. Weis *(Treas)*

R&R INC.
44 Victoria Rd, Youngstown, OH 44515
Tel.: (330) 799-1536   OH
Web Site: http://www.rrtrucks.com
Year Founded: 1952
Sales Range: $25-49.9 Million
Emp.: 150
Sales of Trucks, Tractors & Trailers
N.A.I.C.S.: 441110
Bob Savich *(Mgr-Sls)*

R&R INSURANCE SERVICES, INC.
1581 E Racine Ave, Waukesha, WI 53186
Tel.: (262) 574-7000
Web Site:
   http://www.myknowledgebroker.com
Sales Range: $50-74.9 Million
Emp.: 150
Full Service Insurance Agency
N.A.I.C.S.: 524210
Ken Riesch *(Pres)*
Mike Harrison *(Exec VP-Mktg)*
Jack Riesch *(Owner & Exec VP)*
David Lancaster *(Exec VP-Employee Benefits)*
Jason Navarro *(Acct Exec-Comml)*
Michael Franz *(COO)*
Frank Maurer *(Exec VP-Comml Lines)*
Nora Hauser *(Exec VP-HR)*

Subsidiaries:

Frett Barrington Ltd.   (1)
W239 N3490 Pewaukee Rd Ste 101, Pewaukee, WI 53072
Tel.: (262) 696-5010
Web Site: http://www.frettbarrington.com
Insurance Brokerage
N.A.I.C.S.: 524210
Terrence Frett *(Owner)*
Marie Nienhuis *(Sr VP)*
Patty Frett *(VP)*

Snyder Insurance Agency, Inc.   (1)
100 S Main St, Oconomowoc, WI 53066
Tel.: (262) 567-0288
Web Site: http://www.snyder-ins.com
Sales Range: $1-9.9 Million
Emp.: 16
Insurance Services
N.A.I.C.S.: 524210
Susna Jurgella *(VP-Admin)*
Tom Rutledge *(Acct Exec)*
John Snyder III *(Pres)*

R&R PARTNERS
900 S Pavilion Center Dr, Las Vegas, NV 89144
Tel.: (702) 228-0222   NV
Web Site: http://www.rrpartners.com
Year Founded: 1974
Sales Range: $50-74.9 Million
Emp.: 250
Advetising Agency
N.A.I.C.S.: 541810
Billy Vassiliadis *(CEO)*
Rob Dondero *(Exec VP)*
James King *(CFO & Principal)*
Mary Ann Mele *(Pres & Chief Integration Officer)*
Randy Snow *(Chief Strategic Officer & Principal)*
Don Turley *(VP-Brdcst Production)*
Cindy Dreibelbis *(Chief Admin Officer & Principal)*
Morgan Baumgartner *(Gen Counsel)*
Fran Barr *(HR Dir)*
Ron Lopez *(Dir-Creative)*
Todd Gillins *(Dir-Res)*
Tony Garritano *(Sponsorships Dir)*
Jill Blanchett *(Corp Dir)*
Arnie DiGeorge *(Exec Dir-Creative)*
Pete Ernaut *(Pres-Govt & Pub Affairs Principal)*
Fletcher Whitwell *(VP-Media & Digital Activation)*
Robin Milgrim *(Dir-Art)*
Bob Henrie *(Partner & Pricipal)*
David Weissman *(Dir-PR)*
Steve Andrews *(Assoc Dir-Creative)*
John Lopez *(VP-Govt & Pub Affairs)*
Jessica Hazen *(Sr Dir-Art)*
Peter O'Neill *(Corp Dir-Pub Rel)*
Anna Catlett *(VP-Client Svcs)*
Michelle Mader *(VP-Ops)*
Darrin Munoz *(Deputy Dir-Client Svcs)*
Jeff Zimm *(Dir-Design)*
Lou Flores *(Dir-Creative-Phoenix)*
Monica Bouldin *(VP-Los Angeles)*

Subsidiaries:

R&R Partners   (1)
615 Riverside Dr, Reno, NV 89503-5601
Tel.: (775) 323-1611
Web Site: http://www.rrpartners.com
Emp.: 25
N.A.I.C.S.: 561520
Tim O'Brien *(Dir-Creative)*

R&R Partners   (1)
900 S Pavilion Ctr Dr, Las Vegas, NV 89144
Tel.: (702) 228-0222
Web Site: https://www.rrpartners.com
Emp.: 20
Advertising Agency Services
N.A.I.C.S.: 541810
Pat Buller *(Assoc Dir-Creative)*
Cathie DeNaughen *(Mng Dir)*

R&R Partners   (1)
4150 N DrinkWater Blvd Ste 500, Scottsdale, AZ 85251
Tel.: (480) 317-6040
Web Site: http://www.rrpartners.com
Emp.: 15
N.A.I.C.S.: 541810
Matt Silverman *(Mng Dir-Arizona)*
Billy Vassiliadis *(CEO & Principal)*
Cindy Dreibelbis *(Chief Admin Officer & Principal)*
Jim King *(CFO & Principal)*
Arnie DiGeorge *(Exec Dir-Creative)*
Erik Sandhu *(VP-Fin)*

R&R Partners   (1)
101 Constitution Ave NW Ste L110, Washington, DC 20001
Tel.: (202) 289-5356
Advertising Agencies
N.A.I.C.S.: 541810
Michael Pieper *(Exec VP)*
Doug Richardson *(Dir-PR)*

R&R PLASTICS
2407 US Hwy 20A, Swanton, OH 43558
Tel.: (419) 825-2311
Sales Range: $1-9.9 Million
Emp.: 28
Injection Molding of Thermoplastic Materials
N.A.I.C.S.: 326199

R&R POOL & PATIO INC.
58 Largo Dr, Stamford, CT 06907
Tel.: (203) 353-9663
Web Site: http://www.patio.com
Sales Range: $25-49.9 Million
Emp.: 500
Sales of Patio & Swimming Pool Equipment
N.A.I.C.S.: 423910
David M. Ross *(Founder)*

R&R PROVISION COMPANY
1240 Pine St, Easton, PA 18042
Tel.: (610) 258-5366
Rev.: $19,000,000
Emp.: 40
Meats & Meat Products
N.A.I.C.S.: 424470
Richard W. Rogers Sr. *(Pres)*

R&R TRANSPORTATION INC.
PO Box 216, Audubon, MN 56511
Tel.: (218) 439-6144
Web Site: http://www.rrtransinc.com
Sales Range: $10-24.9 Million
Emp.: 125
Long Haul Trucking
N.A.I.C.S.: 532120
Warren Cadwallader *(Mgr-Maintenance)*

R&S ANTIQUES, INC.
262 N Rodeo Dr, Beverly Hills, CA 90210
Tel.: (310) 273-6660   CA
Web Site: http://www.davidorgell.com
Year Founded: 1933
Sales Range: $10-24.9 Million
Emp.: 70
Luxury Jewelry, Timepieces, Antiques & Gifts Store Owner & Operator
N.A.I.C.S.: 458310
Rahim Soltani *(Pres)*

R&S DAIRY QUEENS, INC.
1555 E Common St, New Braunfels, TX 78130
Tel.: (830) 606-2063
Web Site:
   http://www.randsdairyqueens.com
Sales Range: $10-24.9 Million
Ice Cream Parlor
N.A.I.C.S.: 311520
Melanie Richardson *(Office Mgr)*

R&W CONCRETE CONTRACTOR
1015 Terminal Way, San Carlos, CA 94070
Tel.: (650) 348-1450
Web Site: http://www.rwconcrete.com
Sales Range: $10-24.9 Million
Emp.: 20
Concrete Work
N.A.I.C.S.: 238110

R'CLUB CHILD CARE, INC.
4140 49th St N, Saint Petersburg, FL 33709
Tel.: (727) 578-5437
Web Site: http://www.rclub.net
Year Founded: 1976
Sales Range: $10-24.9 Million
Emp.: 300
Child Day Care Services
N.A.I.C.S.: 624410

R-RANCH MARKET INC.
13985 Live Oak Ave, Irwindale, CA 91706
Tel.: (626) 814-2900
Rev.: $16,500,000
Emp.: 30
Grocery Stores
N.A.I.C.S.: 445110
Farid Shalabi *(Pres)*

R-S-H ENGINEERING, INC.
909 N 18th St Ste 200, Monroe, LA 71201
Tel.: (318) 323-4009   LA
Web Site: http://www.rsh.com
Year Founded: 1984
Sales Range: $10-24.9 Million
Emp.: 100
Industrial Plant & Pipeline Design, Engineering, Inspection & Construction Services
N.A.I.C.S.: 541330
Jeffrey Turner *(VP & Mgr-E&I Section)*
Robert J. Simmons *(VP)*
Charles L. Rand Jr. *(Pres)*

R. BAKER & SON ALL INDUSTRIAL SERVICES
1 Globe Ct, Red Bank, NJ 07701
Tel.: (732) 222-3553
Web Site: http://www.rbaker.com
Year Founded: 1935
Rev.: $16,000,000
Emp.: 100
Construction Services
N.A.I.C.S.: 561210
Walter Baker *(CFO & VP)*
David Baker *(Pres & CEO)*
Joan Schick *(Controller)*
John Malley *(Project Mgr)*
Art Ferlazzo *(Dir-Bus Dev)*

R. C. LACY, INC.
25 Maple Ave Rte 9W, Catskill, NY 12414
Tel.: (518) 943-4300
Web Site: http://www.rclacy.com
Year Founded: 1914
Sales Range: $25-49.9 Million
Emp.: 42
New Car Dealers
N.A.I.C.S.: 441110
James Lacy *(Principal)*
John Luvera *(Gen Mgr-Sls)*
Rock Lacy *(Pres & Treas)*
Cal Lacy *(Sec & VP)*

R. D. WING CO., INC.
517 6th St S, Kirkland, WA 98033
Tel.: (425) 821-7222
Web Site: http://www.rdwing.com
Sales Range: $100-124.9 Million
Emp.: 13
Mineral Products Mfr
N.A.I.C.S.: 327999
Brandon Wing *(Mgr-Ops)*

R. E. GARRISON TRUCKING INC.
1103 County Rd 1194, Vinemont, AL 35179
Tel.: (256) 737-1709
Web Site: http://www.regarrison.com
Sales Range: $10-24.9 Million
Emp.: 25
Trucking
N.A.I.C.S.: 484121
Lanny Samples *(Dir-Safety)*
Carlton Musgrove *(Dir-Maintenance)*
Wyles Griffith *(Pres)*
Donovon Lovell *(VP)*
Donna Lindsey *(CFO)*

R. FRIEDRICH & SONS INC.
619 E Lincoln Way, Ames, IA 50010
Tel.: (515) 663-9999
Web Site: http://www.friedrich-realty.com
Rev.: $10,475,116
Emp.: 10
Real Estate & Rental Construction Services
N.A.I.C.S.: 531110
Kurt Friedrich *(Owner)*

R. HIRT JR. CO.
3000 Chrysler Dr, Detroit, MI 48207
Tel.: (313) 831-2020
Web Site: http://www.rhirt.com
Sales Range: $10-24.9 Million
Emp.: 16
Specialty Food Items Mfr & Distr
N.A.I.C.S.: 424490
David B. DeVries *(Pres)*

R. MCALLISTER SERVICE COMPANY
7116 Park Ave, Pennsauken, NJ 08109
Tel.: (856) 665-4545
Sales Range: $10-24.9 Million
Emp.: 100
Provider of Heating & Air Conditioning Services
N.A.I.C.S.: 457210
George McAllister (CEO)
John Hammond (Controller)

R. MCCLOSKEY INSURANCE AGENCY
4001 MacArthur Blvd No 300, Newport Beach, CA 92660
Tel.: (949) 223-8100
Web Site: http://www.tfgroup.com
Rev.: $12,000,000
Emp.: 100
Insurance Agents
N.A.I.C.S.: 524210
Paul S. Thomas (Mng Partner)

R. ROESE CONTRACTING CO., INC.
2674 S Huron Rd, Kawkawlin, MI 48631
Tel.: (989) 684-5121   MI
Web Site: http://www.rroese.com
Year Founded: 1958
Rev.: $28,000,000
Emp.: 140
Provider of Telephone & Communication Line Construction Services
N.A.I.C.S.: 237130
Richard Roese (Pres)
Robert Woods (Sec)
Don Schmidt (Controller)

R. SISKIND & CO. INC.
1385 Broadway 24th Fl, New York, NY 10018
Tel.: (212) 840-0880
Rev.: $28,295,626
Emp.: 50
Men's & Boy's Clothing Mfr & Distr
N.A.I.C.S.: 424350
Richard Siskind (Chm)

R.A. DINKEL & ASSOCIATES, INC.
4641 Willoughby Rd, Holt, MI 48842
Tel.: (517) 699-7000   MI
Web Site:
http://www.ideasideas.espwebsite.com
Year Founded: 1965
Sales Range: $1-9.9 Million
Emp.: 15
Sales Promotion Services
N.A.I.C.S.: 541810
Liz Dinkel (Co-Pres)
Kim Pipekow (Specialist-Mktg)
Julie Welch (Co-Pres)

R.A. JEFFREYS DISTRIBUTING CO.
2026 US Hwy 70 W, Goldsboro, NC 27530
Tel.: (919) 734-7777
Rev.: $34,600,000
Emp.: 60
Beer Distr
N.A.I.C.S.: 445320
Robert A. Jeffreys (Pres)
Ashlee Rose (Coord-Category Shelf Space)
Kelly O'Gorman (Brand Mgr-Craft)
Kevin Holloman (Mgr-Route)
Rich Whitten (Mgr-Non Alcoholic Brands)

R.A. JOHNSON INC.
4499 Corporate Sq, Naples, FL 34104
Tel.: (239) 643-4415
Web Site: http://www.rjtires.com
Sales Range: $1-9.9 Million
Emp.: 60
Auto Repair & Tire Retailer
N.A.I.C.S.: 811111
Richard A. Johnson (CEO)

R.A. TOWNSEND COMPANY
1100 N Bagley St, Alpena, MI 49707
Tel.: (989) 354-3105   MI
Web Site:
http://www.ratownsend.com
Year Founded: 1932
Sales Range: $10-24.9 Million
Emp.: 56
Heating Oil & Services
N.A.I.C.S.: 423730
Thomas R. Townsend (Pres)

R.A.B. HOLDINGS, INC.
444 Madison Ave, New York, NY 10022
Tel.: (212) 688-4500   DE
Sales Range: $500-549.9 Million
Emp.: 1,810
Holding Company; Kosher & Health Foods
N.A.I.C.S.: 551112
Richard A. Bernstein (Chm, Pres & CEO)
Steven M. Grossman (CFO, Treas & Exec VP)
Ira A. Gomberg (Sr VP-Comm)
Hal B. Weiss (Treas)

Subsidiaries:

Manischewitz Company (1)
80 Ave Ste K, Newark, NJ 07105
Tel.: (201) 333-3700
Web Site: http://www.manischewitz.com
Sales Range: $50-74.9 Million
Emp.: 240
Kosher Foods Mfr
N.A.I.C.S.: 311821
David Rossi (Sr VP-Mktg)
David Sugarman (Pres & CEO)

R.B. EVERETT & COMPANY
8211 Red Bluff Rd, Pasadena, TX 77507
Tel.: (281) 991-8161
Web Site: http://www.rbeverett.com
Rev.: $13,000,000
Emp.: 40
General Construction Machinery & Equipment
N.A.I.C.S.: 423810
J. F. Henderson (Pres)
Dean Henderson (VP)
Retta Webb (Sec)

R.B. INTERNATIONAL INC.
101 S Gary Ave Ste B, Roselle, IL 60172
Tel.: (630) 376-0600   CA
Web Site: http://www.rbibearing.com
Year Founded: 1990
Sales Range: $10-24.9 Million
Emp.: 15
Industrial Machinery & Equipment
N.A.I.C.S.: 423830
Tony Bisante (Pres-RBI Canada)

Subsidiaries:

RBI Bearing Canada - Calgary (1)
4900 64th Ave SE Bay #70, Calgary, T2C 4V3, AB, Canada
Tel.: (403) 236-4280
Web Site: http://www.rbibearing.com
Radial Ball Bearing & Other Custom Machined Parts Distr
N.A.I.C.S.: 423840

RBI Bearing Canada - Toronto (1)
1790 Bonhill Road, Mississauga, L5T 1C8, ON, Canada
Tel.: (905) 670-9733
Web Site: http://www.rbibearing.com
Emp.: 6
Radial Ball Bearing & Other Custom Machined Part Distr
N.A.I.C.S.: 423840
Tony Bisante (Pres)

R.B. MATHESON TRUCKING INC.
9785 Goethe Rd, Sacramento, CA 95827
Tel.: (916) 685-2330   CA
Web Site:
http://www.mathesoninc.com
Year Founded: 1962
Sales Range: $50-74.9 Million
Emp.: 50
Provider of Transportation Services
N.A.I.C.S.: 492110
Michael Wilbourn (Dir-HR)
Mark B. Matheson (Pres & CEO)

R.B. PAMPLIN CORPORATION
6205 SW Lake Rd, Portland, OR 97222
Tel.: (503) 248-1133   DE
Web Site: http://www.pamplin.org
Year Founded: 1957
Sales Range: $550-599.9 Million
Emp.: 4,000
Holding Company
N.A.I.C.S.: 551112
Chuck Nedrow (VP-Fin)
Robert B. Pamplin Jr. (Chm, Pres & CEO)

Subsidiaries:

Mount Vernon Mills, Inc. (1)
503 S Main St, Mauldin, SC 29662
Tel.: (864) 688-7100
Web Site: http://www.mvmills.com
Sales Range: $350-399.9 Million
Emp.: 2,700
Textiles & Home Furnishings Mfr
N.A.I.C.S.: 313210

Division (Domestic):

Mount Vernon Mills, Inc., Riegel Consumer Products Div. (2)
51 Riegel Rd, Johnston, SC 29832
Tel.: (803) 275-2541
Web Site: http://www.riegellinen.com
Sales Range: $75-99.9 Million
Emp.: 30
Mfr of Infants & Domestic Products
N.A.I.C.S.: 314120
Bill Josey (Pres)
Tim Shirley (Plant Mgr)

Mount Vernon Mills, Inc., Riegel Textile Div. (2)
91 4th St, Trion, GA 30753-0007 (100%)
Tel.: (706) 734-2311
Web Site: http://www.mvmills.com
Sales Range: $600-649.9 Million
Emp.: 3,000
Mfr of Textiles
N.A.I.C.S.: 424310

Mount Vernon Mills, Inc., Riegel Textile Div. (Alto) (2)
2850 Gainsville Hwy, Alto, GA 30510-0649
Tel.: (706) 778-2141
Web Site: http://www.mvmills.com
Emp.: 622
Mfr of Textiles
N.A.I.C.S.: 424310

Mount Vernon Mills, Inc. (1)
2850 Gainsville Hwy, Alto, GA 30510 (100%)
Tel.: (706) 778-2141
Web Site: http://www.mvmills.com
Sales Range: $50-74.9 Million
Emp.: 568
Textile Mfr
N.A.I.C.S.: 424310
Robert B. Pamplin Jr. (Chm & CEO)

Pamplin Communications Corporation (1)
6605 SE Lake Rd, Portland, OR 97222-1327
Tel.: (503) 251-1579
Sales Range: $10-24.9 Million
Emp.: 80
Holding Company For Radio Stations, Newspapers, Retail Stores & Entertainment Business
N.A.I.C.S.: 517810

Subsidiary (Domestic):

Christian Supply Centers Inc. (2)
10209 SE Division St, Portland, OR 97266-1327 (100%)
Tel.: (503) 251-1590
Web Site: http://www.christiansupply.net
Providing Christian Book & Gift Store
N.A.I.C.S.: 459210

Ross Island Sand & Gravel Co., Inc. (1)
4315 SE McLoughlin Blvd, Portland, OR 97202 (100%)
Tel.: (503) 239-5504
Web Site: http://www.rossisland.co
Sales Range: $25-49.9 Million
Emp.: 250
Mfr of Concrete, Asphalt & Dry Mix Products; Mining of Sand & Gravel
N.A.I.C.S.: 327320

Subsidiary (Domestic):

K.F. Jacobson & Co. Inc. (2)
4315 SE McLoughlin Blvd, Portland, OR 97282-0245 (100%)
Tel.: (503) 239-5532
Mfr of Concrete, Asphalt & Dry Mix Products; Sand & Gravel Mining
N.A.I.C.S.: 237310

R.C. AULETTA & CO. LLC
59 E 54th St, New York, NY 10022-4271
Tel.: (212) 355-0400
Web Site: http://www.auletta.com
Year Founded: 1965
Sales Range: $1-9.9 Million
Emp.: 8
Public Relations Agency
N.A.I.C.S.: 541821
Richard C. Auletta (Pres)

R.C. BIGELOW, INC.
201 Black Rock Tpke, Fairfield, CT 06825
Tel.: (203) 334-1212
Web Site: http://www.rcbigelow.com
Year Founded: 1945
Sales Range: $150-199.9 Million
Emp.: 425
Mfr of Teas
N.A.I.C.S.: 311920
Eunice Bigelow (Vice Chm)
Marshall Adams (Sr VP-Bus Devel & Strategic Plng)
Donald Janezic (CFO)
Robert Kelly (VP-Mktg & Sls)
Cindy Bigelow (Pres)
Elizabeth Fritz (Product Mgr)
Richard Whalen (VP-HR)

Subsidiaries:

Charleston Tea Plantation (1)
6617 Maybank Hwy, Wadmalaw Island, SC 29487
Tel.: (843) 559-0383
Web Site:
http://www.charlestonteaplantation.com
Sales Range: $1-9.9 Million
Emp.: 10
Tea Farming Services
N.A.I.C.S.: 111998
Jane Knight (Bus Mgr)

R.C. OLSEN CADILLAC
201 Cambridge Rd, Woburn, MA 01801
Tel.: (781) 935-7000

Web Site:
http://www.olsencadillac.com
Year Founded: 1963
Sales Range: $10-24.9 Million
Emp.: 50
Car Whslr
N.A.I.C.S.: 441110
Richard Olsen (Pres)

R.C. OWEN HOLDING COMPANY
310 Blythe Ave, Gallatin, TN 37066
Tel.: (615) 452-5658
Rev.: $19,100,000
Emp.: 7
Chewing Tobacco Mfr & Storage
N.A.I.C.S.: 312230
Richard C. Owen III (Pres)

Subsidiaries:

Gallatin Redrying & Storage Co. (1)
310 N Blythe Ave, Gallatin, TN 37066
Tel.: (615) 452-3355
Tobacco Redrying
N.A.I.C.S.: 312230
R. C. Owen III (Chm)

R.C. Owen Company of
Tennessee (1)
310 N Blythe Ave, Gallatin, TN 37066
Tel.: (615) 452-5658
Chewing Tobacco Mfr & Distr
N.A.I.C.S.: 312230

R.C.A. RUBBER COMPANY
1833 E Market St, Akron, OH 44305-4214
Tel.: (330) 784-1291   OH
Web Site: http://www.rcarubber.com
Year Founded: 1931
Sales Range: $25-49.9 Million
Emp.: 85
Rubber Stair Treads & Flooring Mfr
N.A.I.C.S.: 326299
S. D. Price (VP)
Don Bullock (Mgr-Sls)

Subsidiaries:

Pulaski Rubber Co. (1)
500 S 11th St, Pulaski, TN 38478
Tel.: (931) 363-5583
Sales Range: $10-24.9 Million
Mfr of Molded Rubber Goods; Rubber Stair Treads
N.A.I.C.S.: 326299

R.D. BANKS CHEVROLET, INC.
5729 Mahoning Ave NW, Warren, OH 44483
Tel.: (330) 847-0586
Web Site:
http://www.rdbankschevrolet.com
Year Founded: 1921
Sales Range: $10-24.9 Million
Emp.: 28
Car Whslr
N.A.I.C.S.: 441110
Russell D. Banks (Pres)

R.D. BITZER CO. INC.
776 American Dr, Bensalem, PA 19020-7342
Tel.: (215) 604-6600   PA
Web Site: http://www.rdbitzer.com
Year Founded: 1929
Sales Range: $10-24.9 Million
Emp.: 25
Plumbing & Heating Equipment Distr
N.A.I.C.S.: 423720
John H. Bitzer (Pres)
William Bitzer (CEO)
Mike Deluca (Mgr-Acctg)
Brian Taylor (Mgr-Svc)

R.D. NIVEN & ASSOCIATES LTD.
955 Kimberly Dr, Carol Stream, IL 60188
Tel.: (630) 580-6000
Web Site: http://www.niven.net
Sales Range: $1-9.9 Million
Emp.: 40
Signs & Advertising Specialties; Marketing Consulting Services
N.A.I.C.S.: 339950
Ronald D. Niven (Chm)
Don Hubbard (Pres)

R.D. OFFUTT COMPANY
700 7th St S, Fargo, ND 58103
Tel.: (701) 237-6062   MN
Web Site:
http://www.rdoffuttcompany.com
Year Founded: 1968
Sales Range: $75-99.9 Million
Emp.: 1,900
Holding Company; Agricultural, Industrial, Earth-Moving & Forestry Machinery & Equipment Dealerships Operator
N.A.I.C.S.: 551112
Steven B. Dewald (CFO)
Christi Offutt (Chm)

Subsidiaries:

RDO Equipment Co. (1)
700 S 7th St, Fargo, ND 58103
Tel.: (701) 237-6062
Web Site: http://www.rdoequipment.com
Emp.: 400
Agricultural, Industrial, Earth-Moving & Forestry Machinery & Equipment Dealerships Operator
N.A.I.C.S.: 423820

Subsidiary (Domestic):

RDO Vermeer, LLC (2)
700 S 7th St, Fargo, ND 58103
Tel.: (701) 237-6062
Web Site: http://www.rdoequipment.com
Sales Range: $1-9.9 Million
Branded Agricultural, Industrial, Earth-Moving & Forestry Machinery & Equipment Dealerships Operator
N.A.I.C.S.: 423820
Marshall Anderson (VP & Gen Mgr)

R.D. OLSON CONSTRUCTION
2955 Main St Fl 3, Irvine, CA 92614-2530
Tel.: (949) 474-2001
Web Site: http://www.rdolson.com
Year Founded: 1979
Sales Range: $10-24.9 Million
Emp.: 120
Nonresidential Construction Contracting Services
N.A.I.C.S.: 236220
Joseph G. Cervantes (Sr Exec VP-Ops)
Ian Gardiner (Exec VP)
William J. Wilhelm (Pres)
Robert D. Olson (CEO)
Tim Cromwell (Exec VP & Dir-Bus Dev)

R.E. BULLOCK & COMPANY
1621 N Roberts Rd Ste 130, Kennesaw, GA 30144
Tel.: (770) 426-8200
Web Site: http://www.rebullock.net
Rev.: $10,000,000
Emp.: 10
Insurance Agents, Brokers & Service
N.A.I.C.S.: 524210
Tim Pierce (Pres)

R.E. CARROLL INC.
1570 N Olden Ave, Trenton, NJ 08638
Tel.: (609) 695-6211   NJ
Web Site: http://www.recarroll.com
Year Founded: 1925
Sales Range: $10-24.9 Million
Emp.: 27
Sales of Raw Materials
N.A.I.C.S.: 424690
Richard G. DeLange (CFO)
David Carroll (VP)
Lewis Sawyers (Mgr-Chemical Prods)
Don Harris (Mgr-Petroleum Product)
Simon Bula (Dir-Ops & Pur)
Larry Krock (Dir-Bus Dev)
Denise Bush (Mgr-Customer Svc)
John Boruta (Mgr-Quality Assurance & Compliance)
Stephen Antenucci (Controller)
Lamar Green (Ops Mgr)
Robert E. Carroll III (Pres)

R.E. CHAIX & ASSOCIATES INSURANCE BROKERS, INC.
3200 El Camino Real Ste 290, Irvine, CA 92602
Tel.: (949) 722-4177
Web Site:
http://www.rechaixinsurance.com
Year Founded: 1987
Insurance Agencies & Brokerages
N.A.I.C.S.: 524210
Roger Chaix (Founder & Pres)

Subsidiaries:

National Advantage Insurance Services, Inc. (1)
2000 E 4th St #320, Santa Ana, CA 92705
Tel.: (714) 505-1015
Web Site: http://www.naisins.com
Insurance Agencies & Brokerages
N.A.I.C.S.: 524210

R.E. CRAWFORD CONSTRUCTION LLC
6771 Professional Pkwy W Ste 100, Sarasota, FL 34240
Tel.: (941) 907-0010
Web Site: http://www.recrawford.com
Year Founded: 1979
Sales Range: $10-24.9 Million
Emp.: 35
Retail & Office Construction
N.A.I.C.S.: 236220
Jeffrey T. Smith (Pres & CEO)
Utahna Smith (CFO & Exec VP)
Alan Shapiro (Sr Project Mgr)
Jeff Uselton (Dir-Construction)
Mike Ritzie (Project Mgr)
Susan Courter (Dir-Bus Dev)

R.E. GRIESEMER INC.
51 W Raymond St, Indianapolis, IN 46225
Tel.: (317) 638-4344
Web Site:
http://www.regriesemer.com
Sales Range: $10-24.9 Million
Emp.: 60
Plumbing Contractor
N.A.I.C.S.: 238220
William Powlen (Pres)
Greg Pierle (Mgr-Svcs)

R.E. HANA II ENTERPRISES INC.
600 S 6th Ave, City of Industry, CA 91746-3025
Tel.: (626) 336-3700
Sales Range: $25-49.9 Million
Emp.: 240
Convenience Foods Mfr
N.A.I.C.S.: 311991
Robert E. Hana (Pres)

R.E. HEIDT CONSTRUCTION CO.
3237 Powell Ln, Westlake, LA 70669
Tel.: (337) 433-4466
Rev.: $14,800,000
Emp.: 8
Highway & Street Construction
N.A.I.C.S.: 237310
Troy Gurouen (Dir-Acctg)
Ted Price Jr. (VP)

R.E. MICHEL COMPANY INC.
1 R E Michel Dr, Glen Burnie, MD 21060-6498
Tel.: (410) 760-4000   MD
Web Site: http://www.remichel.com
Year Founded: 1935
Sales Range: $50-74.9 Million
Emp.: 800
Provider of Warm Air Heating & Air Conditioning Services
N.A.I.C.S.: 423730
Frank Schneider (Dir-Tech Svcs)
Stephen Neathery (Dir-Mktg)

R.E. MONKS CONSTRUCTION COMPANY LLC
8355 Vollmer Rd, Colorado Springs, CO 80936
Tel.: (719) 495-3621   CO
Web Site: http://www.remonks.com
Year Founded: 1965
Sales Range: $25-49.9 Million
Emp.: 250
Heavy Construction
N.A.I.C.S.: 236210
Daniel Monks (Gen Mgr)
George Waehner (VP)

R.E. PURCELL CONSTRUCTION COMPANY INCORPORATED
1550 Starkey Rd, Largo, FL 33771
Tel.: (727) 584-3329
Web Site: http://www.repurcell.com
Year Founded: 1973
Sales Range: $25-49.9 Million
Emp.: 110
Highway & Utility Construction; Asphalt Mfr
N.A.I.C.S.: 237310
Scott Williams (VP)

R.E. SWEENEY COMPANY INC.
3700 Noble Ave, Fort Worth, TX 76111-4621
Tel.: (817) 834-7191
Web Site:
http://www.sweeneylumber.com
Year Founded: 1959
Sales Range: $25-49.9 Million
Emp.: 245
Doors, Moulding & Custom Millwork Mfr
N.A.I.C.S.: 423310

Subsidiaries:

Resdoor Company, Inc. (1)
3769 Noble Ave, Fort Worth, TX 76111-4628
Tel.: (817) 654-2151
Web Site: http://www.resdoor.com
Sales Range: $10-24.9 Million
Emp.: 110
Mfr Of Doors Moulding And Custom Millwork
N.A.I.C.S.: 321911
Joe Ward (Gen Mgr)

Sweeney Hardwoods, Inc. (1)
3609 Conway St, Fort Worth, TX 76111
Tel.: (817) 838-3095
Web Site:
http://www.sweeneyhardwoods.com
Hardwood Distr
N.A.I.C.S.: 423990
Steve Staser (Mgr-Mill & Moulding)

R.F. FISHER ELECTRIC CO LLC
1707 W 39th Ave, Kansas City, KS 66103
Tel.: (913) 384-1500
Web Site: http://www.rffisher.com

R.F. Fisher Electric Co LLC—(Continued)
Sales Range: $25-49.9 Million
Emp.: 150
General Electrical Contractor
N.A.I.C.S.: 238210
Stacy Ryan *(CFO)*
Chris Terrell *(COO)*
Jason Kariker *(Gen Mgr-Sign Div)*
Jon Garner *(Mgr-Pur)*
Pam Kruger *(Office Mgr)*
Gavin Seeley *(Owner & Pres)*
Sam Valenti *(VP-Svc)*
Stephanie Boal *(Project Mgr)*
Paul Briggs *(Project Mgr)*
Keegan Monahan *(Project Mgr)*
Troy Thomasson *(VP-Critical Power Solutions)*

R.F. INC.
10400 York Rd, Cockeysville, MD 21030
Tel.: (410) 666-5300
Web Site: http://www.frankelauto.com
Rev.: $13,400,000
Emp.: 87
Automobiles, New & Used
N.A.I.C.S.: 441110
Robert Frankel *(Pres)*

Subsidiaries:

Mid Atlantic Collision Center (1)
105 Beaver Ct, Hunt Valley, MD 21030
Tel.: (410) 667-8555
Web Site: http://www.frankelmidatlantic.com
Rev.: $140,000
Emp.: 2
General Automotive Repair Shops
N.A.I.C.S.: 811111

R.F. KNOX COMPANY, INC.
4865 Martin Ct SE, Smyrna, GA 30082
Tel.: (770) 434-7401
Web Site: http://www.rfknox.com
Year Founded: 1914
Sales Range: $25-49.9 Million
Emp.: 175
Fabricated Metal Components Mfr
N.A.I.C.S.: 332999
Jack Knox *(Pres)*
Tommy Partain *(Exec VP)*

R.F. MACDONALD CO.
25920 Eden Landing Rd, Hayward, CA 94545-3816
Tel.: (510) 784-0110 CA
Web Site:
   http://www.rfmacdonald.com
Year Founded: 1956
Sales Range: $25-49.9 Million
Emp.: 200
Plumbing Fixtures, Equipment, Supplies, Boilers & Pumps
N.A.I.C.S.: 423720
Michael D. MacDonald *(VP)*
James T. MacDonald *(Pres)*
Chris Sentner *(VP-Boiler Div)*
Robert Sygiel *(VP-Pump Div & VP-Mktg)*
Joel Lesser *(VP-Fin & HR)*

R.F. SCURLOCK COMPANY INC.
3220 5th St, Trinway, OH 43842
Tel.: (740) 754-6132
Web Site: http://www.y-city.net
Sales Range: $10-24.9 Million
Emp.: 15
Excavation Work
N.A.I.C.S.: 238910
Ronald Scurlock Jr. *(Pres)*

R.G. RAY CORPORATION
3227 N Wilke Rd, Arlington Heights, IL 60004-1437
Tel.: (847) 459-5900 IL
Web Site:
   http://www.rgrayclamps.com
Year Founded: 1972
Sales Range: $25-49.9 Million
Emp.: 310
Hardware
N.A.I.C.S.: 332510
Robert J. Fabsik *(Pres)*
Glenn Kozak *(CFO)*
Lloyd Pressman *(Mgr-Pur)*

R.G. RILEY & SONS INC.
17700 Duvan Dr, Tinley Park, IL 60477-3669
Tel.: (877) 576-5447 IL
Web Site: http://www.rgriley.com
Year Founded: 1945
Sales Range: $10-24.9 Million
Emp.: 90
Provider of Clothing Services
N.A.I.C.S.: 315220
Millie Kimmons *(Office Mgr-HR)*
Mike Riley *(VP)*

R.G. SMITH CO. INC.
1249 Dueber Ave SW, Canton, OH 44706
Tel.: (330) 456-3415
Web Site:
   http://www.rgscontractors.com
Rev.: $14,859,806
Emp.: 100
Industrial Buildings & Warehouses
N.A.I.C.S.: 236220
Dave Dennison *(Mgr-Safety Div)*

R.H. BARRINGER DISTRIBUTING CO. INC.
1620 Fairfax Rd, Greensboro, NC 27407-4139
Tel.: (336) 854-0555
Year Founded: 1990
Sales Range: $25-49.9 Million
Emp.: 209
Distr of Beer & Ale
N.A.I.C.S.: 424810
Mark Craig *(Pres)*

R.H. FOSTER ENERGY LLC
110 Mecaw Rd, Hampden, ME 04444
Tel.: (207) 947-5336 ME
Web Site: http://www.rhfoster.com
Year Founded: 1965
Sales Range: $50-74.9 Million
Emp.: 348
Distr of Petroleum Products
N.A.I.C.S.: 424720
R. W. Foster *(Pres)*
Robert Tracy *(Exec VP)*
Lynne Coombs *(Controller)*
Brenda Gerow *(Dir-HR)*

R.H. KUHN COMPANY, INC.
2250 Roswell Dr, Pittsburgh, PA 15205
Tel.: (412) 444-2300 PA
Year Founded: 1958
Sales Range: $25-49.9 Million
Emp.: 240
Furniture Retailer
N.A.I.C.S.: 449110
Michael Kuhn *(Chm & Pres)*

R.H. PETERSON CO.
14724 Proctor Ave, City of Industry, CA 91746
Tel.: (626) 369-5085
Web Site: http://www.rhpeterson.com
Rev.: $25,000,000
Emp.: 170
Gas Fireplace Mfr
N.A.I.C.S.: 335220
Leslie Bortz *(CEO)*
Dennis Rodriguez *(Supvr-Tech Svcs)*
Mike Waller *(VP)*

Guillermo Rocha *(Mgr-Quality)*
Jon Bridgwater *(Sr VP)*
Paul Song *(Engr-Mfg)*

R.H. RENY INC.
731 Rte 1, Newcastle, ME 04553
Tel.: (207) 563-3177 ME
Web Site: http://www.renys.com
Year Founded: 1949
Sales Range: $10-24.9 Million
Emp.: 375
Department Stores
N.A.I.C.S.: 455110
Robert H. Reny *(Pres & Treas)*
John E. Reny *(VP)*

R.H. SMITH DISTRIBUTING CO.
315 Wine Country Rd, Grandview, WA 98930
Tel.: (509) 882-3377
Web Site: http://www.rhsmith.com
Rev.: $51,219,560
Emp.: 25
Petroleum Bulk Stations
N.A.I.C.S.: 424710
John Norling *(CFO)*
Eddie Herrera *(Mgr-Transportation)*
Rick Smith *(Pres)*
Doug Smith *(Sec & Treas)*
Rod Smith *(VP)*

R.H. WHITE COMPANIES INC.
41 Central St, Auburn, MA 01501
Tel.: (508) 832-3295
Web Site: http://www.rhwhite.com
Year Founded: 1923
Rev.: $50,297,609
Emp.: 500
Power Plant Construction
N.A.I.C.S.: 237990
David H. White *(Pres & CEO)*
Daniel Horgan *(VP-Utility Construction)*
John Stamatov *(Ops Mgr-Utility Construction)*
Jeff Towle *(VP-Ops)*

Subsidiaries:

R.H. White Construction Co. (1)
41 Central St, Auburn, MA 01501
Tel.: (603) 424-3130
Web Site: http://www.rhwhite.com
Pipeline Construction
N.A.I.C.S.: 237110
David H. White *(Pres & CEO)*
Jim McCarthy *(COO)*

R.H. White Construction Company, Inc. (1)
615 River Rd, Bow, NH 03304
Tel.: (603) 424-3130
Web Site: http://www.rhwhite.com
Sales Range: $10-24.9 Million
Emp.: 600
Heavy Construction Equipment Rental
N.A.I.C.S.: 532412
Aron Govoni *(Div Mgr)*

White Development Corp. (1)
41 Central St, Auburn, MA 01501
Tel.: (508) 832-3295
Web Site: http://www.rhy.com
Rev.: $2,891,921
Emp.: 575
Single-Family Housing Construction
N.A.I.C.S.: 236115
David White *(Pres & CEO)*

Whitewater, Inc. (1)
41 Central St, Auburn, MA 01501
Tel.: (508) 832-3295
Rev.: $5,106,839
Emp.: 5
Business Management Consulting Services
N.A.I.C.S.: 541611
David H. White *(Pres)*

R.H. WYNER ASSOCIATES INC.
208 Manley St, West Bridgewater, MA 02379
Tel.: (508) 588-3300
Web Site:
   http://www.shawmutcorporation.com
Year Founded: 1916
Sales Range: $25-49.9 Million
Emp.: 150
Laminating Of Fabrics
N.A.I.C.S.: 313320
Giang Wyner *(Gen Mgr)*
John Zang *(Gen Mgr)*

R.H.MOORE COMPANY, INC.
PO Box 830, Murrells Inlet, SC 29576-0830
Tel.: (843) 650-2155
Web Site:
   http://www.rhmoorecompany.com
Sales Range: $25-49.9 Million
Emp.: 140
Construction Engineering Services
N.A.I.C.S.: 237310
Henry R. Moore *(Pres)*

R.I.S.N. OPERATIONS INC.
187 Main St, Wakefield, RI 02879
Tel.: (401) 789-9744 DE
Web Site: http://www.ricentral.com
Year Founded: 2007
Holding Company; Newspaper Publisher
N.A.I.C.S.: 551112
Melanie Radler *(Pres)*
Roland McBride *(Treas & Exec VP)*

Subsidiaries:

Southern Rhode Island
Newspapers (1)
187 Main St, Wakefield, RI 02879-3504
Tel.: (401) 789-9744
Web Site: http://www.ricentral.com
Sales Range: $10-24.9 Million
Emp.: 75
Newspaper Publishers
N.A.I.C.S.: 513110
Michael Souza *(Editor-in-Chief)*
Matthew Wunsch *(Editor-Narragansett Times & Chariho Times)*
Holly Moore *(Coord-Adv)*

Subsidiary (Domestic)

Kent County Daily Times (2)
1353 Main St, West Warwick, RI 02893
Tel.: (401) 821-7400
Newspaper Publishers
N.A.I.C.S.: 513110

Narragansett Times (2)
187 Main St, Wakefield, RI 02879-3504
Tel.: (401) 789-9744
Web Site: http://www.ricentral.com
Newspaper Publishers
N.A.I.C.S.: 513110

Pawtucket Times (2)
23 Exchange St, Pawtucket, RI 02860-2026
Tel.: (401) 722-4000
Web Site: http://www.pawtuckettimes.com
Newspaper Publishers
N.A.I.C.S.: 513199
Jody Boucher *(Publr)*

The Chariho Times (2)
187 Main St, Warwick, RI 02879
Tel.: (401) 789-9744
Web Site: http://www.ricentral.com
Newspaper Publishing Services
N.A.I.C.S.: 513110
Matt Wunsch *(Mng Editor)*

The Coventry Courier (2)
1353 Main St, West Warwick, RI 02893
Tel.: (401) 821-7400
Newspaper Publishers
N.A.I.C.S.: 513110

The East Greenwich Pendulum (2)
580 Main St, East Greenwich, RI 02818-3608
Tel.: (401) 884-4662
Web Site: http://www.ricentral.com
Publishers of Weekly Newspapers

COMPANIES

The Evening Call Publishing Company (2)
75 Main St, Woonsocket, RI 02895-0992
Tel.: (401) 762-3000
Web Site: http://www.woonsocketcall.com
Newspaper Publishers
N.A.I.C.S.: 513110
Kathy Needham (Controller)
Jody Boucher (Publr)

The Standard-Times (2)
13 W Main St, North Kingstown, RI 02852-5111
Tel.: (401) 294-4576
Newspaper Publishing Services
N.A.I.C.S.: 513110

R.J. CARROLL COMPANY INC.
1341 Hwy 287 S, Mansfield, TX 76063
Tel.: (817) 477-5664
Web Site: http://www.rjcarrollco.com
Sales Range: $10-24.9 Million
Emp.: 75
System Integration Services
N.A.I.C.S.: 237110
Ron Carroll (COO)
Scott Cook (VP)
Sandi Carroll (CEO)

R.J. CORMAN RAILROAD GROUP LLC
101 R J Corman Dr, Nicholasville, KY 40356
Tel.: (859) 885-9457
Web Site: http://www.rjcorman.com
Sales Range: $100-124.9 Million
Emp.: 1,300
Railroad & Railway Roadbed Construction
N.A.I.C.S.: 236210
Noel Rush (Sr VP)
Jerry Adams (VP-Facility & Shop Svcs)
Fred N. Mudge (Chm)
Duane Barton (VP)
Nathan Henderson (Chief Comml Officer)
Ray Goss (Pres)
Jimmy Spencer (VP)
Justin Broyles (VP-Comml Dev)
Mike Robinson (VP-Comml Dev)
Chase Armstrong (VP-Comml Dev)
Mike Philpot (VP-Ops-South)
John Phillips (VP-Ops-North)
Edward Quinn III (CEO)

Subsidiaries:

R.J. Corman Railpower (1)
2011 Peninsula Dr, Erie, PA 16506
Tel.: (814) 835-2212
Web Site: http://www.railpower.com
Sales Range: $25-49.9 Million
Emp.: 20
Transportation & Power Generation Technology Developer
N.A.I.C.S.: 333613

R.J. DALE ADVERTISING & PUBLIC RELATIONS
211 E Ontario St Ste 200, Chicago, IL 60611
Tel.: (312) 644-2316   IL
Year Founded: 1979
Sales Range: Less than $1 Million
Emp.: 30
Public Relations, Publicity/Promotions
N.A.I.C.S.: 541820
Robert J. Dale (Pres & CEO)
E. Dennis Gardner (Sr VP-Acct Plng)
Mollie West (Dir-Pub Rels)
David Ferris (VP-Creative Svcs)

R.J. DAUM CONSTRUCTION COMPANY
11581 Monarch St, Garden Grove, CA 92841
Tel.: (714) 894-4300
Web Site: http://www.rjdaum.com
Year Founded: 1936
Sales Range: $25-49.9 Million
Emp.: 100
Commercial Construction Services
N.A.I.C.S.: 236220
Harold I. Perong (VP)
Mark Perong (VP)
Frank Ruiz (Project Mgr)
Mike Holliday (Project Mgr)
Tom Lareau (Project Mgr)
Ray Vasquez (Dir-HR & Ops)

R.J. GRONDIN & SONS
11 Bartlett Rd, Gorham, ME 04038
Tel.: (207) 854-1147
Web Site: http://www.grondinconstruction.com
Sales Range: $75-99.9 Million
Emp.: 150
Sewer Line Construction
N.A.I.C.S.: 237110
Philip H. Grondin (Co-Founder)
Robert Grondin (Co-Founder)

R.J. KIELTY PLUMBING INC.
7979 Massachusetts Ave, New Port Richey, FL 34653
Tel.: (727) 863-5486
Web Site: http://www.rjkielty.com
Rev.: $13,302,854
Emp.: 94
Plumbing Contractor
N.A.I.C.S.: 238220
Rod J. Kielty (Pres)

R.J. MILLER & ASSOCIATES INC.
3629 Lovell Ave, Fort Worth, TX 76107
Tel.: (817) 377-0971
Web Site: http://www.rj-miller.com
Rev.: $12,336,993
Emp.: 50
Commercial & Office Building, New Construction
N.A.I.C.S.: 236220
Cynthia Turner (CFO)
R. J. Miller (Pres)
Kenny Buyers (Sr VP)
Trevor Browne (VP)

R.J. NOBLE COMPANY
15505 E Lincoln Ave, Orange, CA 92865-1015
Tel.: (714) 637-1550
Web Site: http://www.rjnoblecompany.com
Sales Range: $25-49.9 Million
Emp.: 145
Highway & Street Construction Services
N.A.I.C.S.: 237310
Jim Ducote (Controller)

R.J. O'BRIEN & ASSOCIATES, LLC
222 S Riverside Plz Ste 1200, Chicago, IL 60606
Tel.: (312) 373-5000   DE
Web Site: http://www.rjobrien.com
Year Founded: 1914
Sales Range: $50-74.9 Million
Emp.: 300
Commodities Brokerage & Trading Services
N.A.I.C.S.: 523160
Gerald F. Corcoran (Chm & CEO)
Matthew Rees (Chief Customer Officer & Exec VP)
James Gabriele (Sr Mng Dir & CFO)
Julie M. DeMatteo (Mng Dir)
Daniel Staniford (Sr Mng Dir-Institutional Sls)
Stephen Brodsky (Chief Strategy Officer)
Patrick J. Melia (Sr VP-Commodity Sls-New York)
Joe Raia (Mng Dir-Global Commodity Futures)
Brad Giemza (Sr Mng Dir & Chief Risk Officer)
Melissa Zierk (Mng Dir & Gen Counsel)
Michael Hoehne (Mng Dir-HR)

Subsidiaries:

R.J. O'Brien & Associates Canada Inc. (1)
195 Commerce Drive, Winnipeg, R3P 1A2, MB, Canada
Tel.: (204) 594-1440
Web Site: https://www.rjobrien.ca
Emp.: 9
Commodities Brokerage & Trading Services
N.A.I.C.S.: 523160
Keith Riddoch (Gen Mgr)

R.J. O'Brien (Europe) Limited (1)
Ground Floor 25 Copthall Avenue, London, EC2R 7BP, United Kingdom
Tel.: (44) 845 686 1756
Web Site: http://www.rjobrien.co.uk
Holding Company; Securities Brokerage & Trading Services
N.A.I.C.S.: 551112
David Mudie (CEO)
Thomas Texier (Dir-Ops)
Peter Jerrom (Sr VP-Listed Foreign Exchange Brokers)
John Burt (Sr VP-Listed Foreign Exchange Brokers)

Subsidiary (Domestic):

R.J. O'Brien (UK) Limited (2)
Ground Floor 25 Copthall Avenue, London, EC2R 7BP, United Kingdom
Tel.: (44) 845 686 1756
Web Site: http://www.rjobrien.co.uk
Securities Brokerage & Trading Services
N.A.I.C.S.: 523150
David Mudie (CEO)
Thomas Texier (Dir-Ops)

R.J. O'Brien Limited (2)
Business Design Centre 52 Upper Street, Islington, London, N1 0QH, United Kingdom
Tel.: (44) 2073907777
Web Site: http://www.rjobrien.co.uk
Sales Range: $50-74.9 Million
Emp.: 150
Derivatives Clearing & Settlement Services
N.A.I.C.S.: 522320
David Mudie (CEO)
Thomas Texier (Mng Dir)
Mark Trafeli (Gen Counsel)
Stefan Giemza (Dir-Compliance)
Adam Solomons (Chief Customer Officer)
Adrian Marrocco (CFO)
John Martin (Dir-Ops)
Devinder Harry (CIO)

Subsidiary (Domestic):

Kyte Broking Limited (3)
Business Design Centre 52 Upper Street, London, N1 0QH, United Kingdom
Tel.: (44) 2073907777
Securities & Commodities Brokerage & Dealing Services
N.A.I.C.S.: 523150

R.J. SCHINNER CO. INC.
N89 W14700 Patrita Dr, Menomonee Falls, WI 53051
Tel.: (262) 797-7180   WI
Web Site: http://www.rjschinner.com
Year Founded: 1951
Sales Range: $10-24.9 Million
Emp.: 60
Industrial & Personal Service Paper
N.A.I.C.S.: 424130
James Schinner (Exec VP)
Linda Schinner (Coord-Rebate)
Derek Dellwo (Dir-Ops)
Kim Boughner (Mgr-Mktg)
Robert J. Schinner Sr. (Exec VP)

R.J. YOUNG CO., INC.

R.J. THROCKMORTON SALES CO.
148 Workman Ct, Eureka, MO 63025
Tel.: (636) 227-7222
Web Site: http://www.rjthrockmorton.com
Year Founded: 1974
Sales Range: $10-24.9 Million
Emp.: 8
Electronic Parts & Equipment
N.A.I.C.S.: 423690
Ronald J. Throckmorton (Pres)
Christine Cameron (Sec)
Doug Kannawarf (VP)

R.J. VAN DRUNEN & SONS INC.
300 W 6th St, Momence, IL 60954-1136
Tel.: (815) 472-3100   IL
Web Site: http://www.vandrunenfarms.com
Year Founded: 1958
Sales Range: $25-49.9 Million
Emp.: 230
Suppliers of Dehydrated Fruits Vegetables & Soups
N.A.I.C.S.: 311423
Kevin Van Drunen (Gen Mgr)

R.J. WALKER CO. INC.
1555 N Keyser Ave, Scranton, PA 18504
Tel.: (570) 344-8221
Web Site: http://www.rjwalker.com
Sales Range: $10-24.9 Million
Emp.: 40
Heating Equipment (Hydronic)
N.A.I.C.S.: 423720
John Walker (VP)
Denise Dcorcoran (Coord-Health Benefits)
Kristie Vaccaro (Mgr-Show Room)

R.J. YOUNG CO., INC.
730A Freeland Station Rd, Nashville, TN 37228
Tel.: (615) 255-8551   TN
Web Site: http://www.rjyoung.com
Year Founded: 1955
Office Equipment Whslr
N.A.I.C.S.: 423420
Jason Bordwine (Sr VP-Ops)
Chip Crunk (Pres & CEO)
Ralph Mello (Gen Counsel)
A. J. Baggott (COO)
Mike Noffsinger (Reg VP-Sls)
Chris Clark (Reg VP-Central Reg)
Chris Bethea (Reg VP-South Reg)
Chad Lagrone (VP-Tech Svcs)
Lauren Kail (Reg VP-Northwest Reg)
Justin Chancellor (Reg VP-West Reg)
Keith Burrell (Reg VP-East Reg)
Harris Delchamps (Reg VP-North Reg)

Subsidiaries:

Automated Imaging Systems, Inc. (1)
105 Pine St, Monroe, LA 71201
Tel.: (318) 322-6118
Copiers, Facsimile, Printer Duplicators & Laser Printers Distr
N.A.I.C.S.: 423420
Earl L. Tarver (Pres)

Bristol Office Supply Inc. (1)
33 Moore St, Bristol, VA 24201
Tel.: (276) 669-7131
Web Site: http://www.rjyoung.com
Office Equipment Whslr
N.A.I.C.S.: 423420
Darrell Ferguson (Mgr-Svc)

Business Electronics Corp. (1)
4001 Farr Rd, Bessemer, AL 35022
Tel.: (205) 847-5465

R.J. Young Co., Inc.—(Continued)
Document Management & IT Solutions, Digital Interactive Whiteboards & Displays, AV, Imaging & Unified Communications Systems
N.A.I.C.S.: 561499
Shawn Brown (Mgr-Acct)

R.J.S. & ASSOCIATES INC.
1675 Savere St, Hayward, CA 94545
Tel.: (510) 670-9111
Rev.: $80,000,000
Emp.: 200
Foundation & Footing Contractor
N.A.I.C.S.: 238110
Robert J. Simmons (Pres)
Patrick Braun (Gen Mgr)

R.K. ALLEN OIL CO., INC.
36002 AL Hwy 21, Talladega, AL 35160
Tel.: (256) 362-4261
Web Site: http://www.rkallenoil.com
Year Founded: 1972
Sales Range: $10-24.9 Million
Emp.: 107
Producer of Petroleum Products
N.A.I.C.S.: 424720
R. K. Allen (Pres)
Jamie Eddins (Mgr-Ops AOC Food-Marts)
Jinny Valentine (Office Mgr)
Subsidiaries:
A.O.C. Foodmarts Inc. (1)
360002 AL Hwy 21, Talladega, AL 35160
Tel.: (256) 362-4261
Provider of Grocery Store Services
N.A.I.C.S.: 445131
Teresa Hays (Office Mgr)

R.K. AUTO GROUP, INC.
502 N Delsea Dr, Vineland, NJ 08360
Tel.: (856) 696-8400
Web Site: http://www.rkautogroup.com
Year Founded: 1982
Sales Range: $10-24.9 Million
Emp.: 55
Car Whslr
N.A.I.C.S.: 441110
Jim Gee (VP)

R.K. BLACK INC.
4111 Perimeter Ctr Pl, Oklahoma City, OK 73112
Tel.: (405) 943-9801
Web Site: http://www.rkblack.com
Sales Range: $10-24.9 Million
Emp.: 75
Office Equipment
N.A.I.C.S.: 423420
Chris Black (Pres)
Andy Taylor (Dir-Svc)

R.K. ELECTRIC INC.
42021 Osgood Rd, Fremont, CA 94539
Tel.: (510) 770-5660
Web Site: http://www.rkelectric.com
Year Founded: 1985
Sales Range: $25-49.9 Million
Emp.: 120
General Electrical Contractor
N.A.I.C.S.: 238210
Lonnie Robinson (Pres & CEO)
Mike Mangaoang (Project Mgr-Electrical Div)
Raul Real (VP)

R.K. MILES
618 Depot St, Manchester Center, VT 05255
Tel.: (802) 362-1952
Web Site: http://www.rkmiles.com
Year Founded: 1940
Sales Range: $10-24.9 Million
Emp.: 185
Other Building Material Retailer
N.A.I.C.S.: 444180
Tammy Heaton (CFO)
Pete Duffany (Mgr)
Zack Dupuis (Mgr)
Brenda Beanland (Mgr-Ops)

R.K. STRATMAN INCORPORATED
680 B Parr Rd, Wentzville, MO 63385
Tel.: (636) 332-5636
Web Site: http://www.rkstratman.com
Sales Range: $25-49.9 Million
Emp.: 250
Screen Printing On Fabric Articles
N.A.I.C.S.: 314999
Carl Stratman (Pres)
Rhonda Thompson (VP)

R.L. ALBERT & SON, INC.
2001 W Main St Ste 155, Stamford, CT 06902
Tel.: (203) 622-8655
Web Site: http://www.albertscandy.com
Year Founded: 1915
Sales Range: $75-99.9 Million
Emp.: 12
Importer & Distr of Confections
N.A.I.C.S.: 424450
Robert Katz (CEO)
Jorge La Sada (Mgr-Sls & Mktg)

R.L. BRINK CORP.
4400 N 24th St, Quincy, IL 62305
Tel.: (217) 222-2760
Rev.: $12,024,026
Emp.: 50
General Contractor, Highway & Street Construction
N.A.I.C.S.: 237310
Ronald L. Brink (Pres)

R.L. CAMPBELL ROOFING CO. INC.
76 S Laura St Ste 2200, Jacksonville, FL 32202
Tel.: (904) 359-8900
Web Site: http://www.rlcampbell.com
Rev.: $10,713,658
Emp.: 30
Roofing, Siding & Sheetmetal Work
N.A.I.C.S.: 238160
Roy L. Campbell (Pres)

R.L. FRENCH CORPORATION
4111 Delaware Ave, Des Moines, IA 50313
Tel.: (515) 265-8111
Web Site: http://www.kenworthmidiowa.com
Sales Range: $100-124.9 Million
Emp.: 50
Trucks, Tractors & Trailers: New & Used
N.A.I.C.S.: 441110
Rod French (Pres)

R.L. FRIDLEY THEATRES INC.
1321 Walnut St, Des Moines, IA 50309
Tel.: (515) 282-9287
Web Site: http://www.fridleytheatres.com
Year Founded: 1973
Sales Range: $25-49.9 Million
Emp.: 500
Owner & Operator of Motion Picture Theaters
N.A.I.C.S.: 512131
Robert L. Fridley (Co-Founder)
Myrna Fridley (Co-Founder)

R.L. HUDSON & COMPANY
2000 W Tacoma St, Broken Arrow, OK 74012
Tel.: (918) 259-6600
Web Site: http://www.rlhudson.com
Sales Range: $10-24.9 Million
Emp.: 90
Supplier of Seals & Custom Molded Products
N.A.I.C.S.: 332710
Richard L. Hudson (Chm & CEO)
Jonathan Steinkirchner (Engr-Quality)
Richard Von Drehle (Pres)

R.L. JAMES INC.
3949 Evans Ave, Fort Myers, FL 33901
Tel.: (239) 936-6002
Web Site: http://www.rljames.com
Year Founded: 1988
Sales Range: $1-9.9 Million
Emp.: 100
General Contractors
N.A.I.C.S.: 238390
Robert L. James (CEO)
Kevin Phillips (Pres)
John Dahin (CFO & VP)
Gary R. Wasser (Mgr-Sls)

R.L. JONES CUSTOMHOUSE BROKERS INC.
1778 Cimetta Rd Ste A, Calexico, CA 92231
Tel.: (760) 357-3177
Web Site: http://www.rljones.com
Year Founded: 1938
Sales Range: $10-24.9 Million
Emp.: 100
Customhouse Brokers
N.A.I.C.S.: 488510
Earl Roberts (Pres & Gen Mgr)
Francisco Brambila (Mgr)

R.L. JORDAN OIL CO
1451 Fernwood Glendale Rd, Spartanburg, SC 29307-3044
Tel.: (864) 585-2784
Web Site: http://www.hotspotstore.com
Year Founded: 1950
Sales Range: $50-74.9 Million
Emp.: 700
Retailer of Groceries
N.A.I.C.S.: 445131
Dan Durbin (Pres)

R.L. KISTLER INC.
300 Mile Crossing Blvd, Rochester, NY 14624
Tel.: (585) 436-1940
Web Site: http://www.rlkistler.com
Year Founded: 1968
Sales Range: $10-24.9 Million
Emp.: 40
Air Conditioning Equipment Whslr
N.A.I.C.S.: 423730
Jeffrey Ingerick (Pres)
Brian Willemsen (VP-Sls)
Terry Switzer (Chm)

R.L. MCCOY, INC.
7898 East Lincolnway, Columbia City, IN 46725
Tel.: (260) 625-3443
Web Site: http://www.rlmccoy.net
Year Founded: 1961
Sales Range: $10-24.9 Million
Emp.: 100
Concrete Pumping & Bridge Construction Services
N.A.I.C.S.: 237310
Mark W. McCoy (Pres)

R.L. MORGAN COMPANY INC.
6429 W Pierson Rd Ste 19, Flushing, MI 48433
Tel.: (810) 659-2291
Web Site: http://www.gillroys.com
Year Founded: 1945
Sales Range: $25-49.9 Million
Emp.: 300
Retailer of Hardware Merchandise
N.A.I.C.S.: 444140
Robert L. Morgan (Pres)

R.L. VALLEE INC.
280 S Main St, Saint Albans, VT 05478
Tel.: (802) 524-8710
Web Site: http://www.rlvallee.com
Rev.: $70,000,000
Emp.: 25
Fuel Oil
N.A.I.C.S.: 424720

R.L. WILLIAMS COMPANY
103 N Mclin Creek Rd, Conover, NC 28613
Tel.: (828) 328-8698
Web Site: http://www.rlwilliamscompany.com
Sales Range: $10-24.9 Million
Emp.: 10
Restroom Product Distr
N.A.I.C.S.: 423850
Robert Williams (Owner)

R.L. ZEIGLER CO. INC.
730 Energy Center Blvd Ste 1403, Tuscaloosa, AL 35473
Tel.: (205) 758-3621
Web Site: http://www.zmeats.com
Year Founded: 1927
Sales Range: $25-49.9 Million
Emp.: 250
Provider of Meat Packing & Processing Services
N.A.I.C.S.: 311612
Matt Norton (Plant Mgr)
Norm Trotter (Project Mgr-Ops)

R.L.E. CORP.
PO Box 4429, Utica, NY 13504
Tel.: (315) 738-4370
Web Site: http://aipi.net
Sales Range: $75-99.9 Million
Emp.: 150
Frozen Specialty Food Mfr
N.A.I.C.S.: 311412
Kathy Wameling (Controller & Dir-IT)
Joel McIntyre (Mgr-Sls)
Philip Casamento (Owner)
Michael Fornino (Mgr-Sls)
Rosalie Fornino (Dir-HR)

R.M. BARROWS, INC. ADVERTISING & PUBLIC RELATIONS
205 Park Rd Ste 208, Burlingame, CA 94010-4220
Tel.: (650) 344-1951
Web Site: http://www.barrows.com
Year Founded: 1980
Sales Range: Less than $1 Million
Emp.: 1
N.A.I.C.S.: 541810
Robert M. Barrows (Pres)

R.M. BURRITT MOTORS, INC.
340 State Rte 104, Oswego, NY 13126
Tel.: (315) 343-8948
Web Site: http://www.burrittmotors.com
Year Founded: 1955
Sales Range: $10-24.9 Million
New & Used Car Dealerhip & Automotive Body Repair Shop Owner & Operator
N.A.I.C.S.: 441110
Chris R. Burritt (Owner)

COMPANIES

Subsidiaries:

R.M. Burritt Motors - Buick Chevrolet
Oswego (1)
340 State Route 104, Oswego, NY 13126
Tel.: (315) 207-4099
Web Site: http://www.burrittchevy.com
Sales Range: $10-24.9 Million
Emp.: 40
New & Used Car Dealer
N.A.I.C.S.: 441110
Chris R. Burritt (Pres & Gen Mgr)

R.M. KERNER CO.
2208 E 33rd St, Erie, PA 16510
Tel.: (814) 898-2000
Web Site: http://www.rmkco.com
Rev.: $34,900,000
Emp.: 50
Machine Shop, Jobbing & Repair
N.A.I.C.S.: 332710
Ronald Mark Kerner (Pres)

R.M. PALMER COMPANY
77 S 2nd Ave, Reading, PA 19611-1223
Tel.: (610) 372-8971   PA
Web Site: http://www.rmpalmer.com
Year Founded: 1948
Sales Range: $200-249.9 Million
Emp.: 800
Chocolate & Confectionery Mfr
N.A.I.C.S.: 311351
Richard M. Palmer (Pres)
Dave Abramson (VP-Sls)
Bruce Tessier (Mgr-Warehouse)
Brielle Monestime (Brand Mgr)
John Kerr (Dir-Mktg)

R.M. PARKS INCORPORATED
1061 N Main St, Porterville, CA 93257
Tel.: (559) 784-2384
Web Site: http://www.rmparksinc.com
Sales Range: $10-24.9 Million
Emp.: 72
Distr of Petroleum Products
N.A.I.C.S.: 424710
R. M. Parks (Pres)
Jason Callison (Gen Mgr-Sls)
David Camarena (Mgr-Fleet)
Sherrill Morris (Mgr-Acctg)

R.M. STARK & CO. INC.
701 SE 6th Ave Ste 203, Delray Beach, FL 33483
Tel.: (561) 243-3815
Web Site: http://www.rmstark.com
Sales Range: $10-24.9 Million
Emp.: 10
Security Brokers & Dealers
N.A.I.C.S.: 523150
Gary L. Stark (Pres)
Ellen Adler (VP)

R.N. EATON & COMPANY INC.
4124 NW Riverside St, Riverside, MO 64150
Tel.: (816) 741-7985
Web Site:
  http://www.eatonchemical.com
Sales Range: $10-24.9 Million
Emp.: 16
Industrial Chemical Distr
N.A.I.C.S.: 424690
Ray N. Eaton (Pres & Gen Mgr)
Jim Eaton (Mgr-Sls)

R.O. WHITESELL & ASSOCIATES, INC.
3334 Founders Rd, Indianapolis, IN 46268-3334
Tel.: (317) 876-9000   IN
Web Site: http://www.whitesell.com
Year Founded: 1946
Sales Range: $75-99.9 Million
Emp.: 62

Sales of Electronics
N.A.I.C.S.: 423690
Steve Underhill (Controller)
Bradley Thinnes (Pres-CPMR)
Carlos Martinez (Mgr-Area)
Gerald Armour (VP)
Rick Oser (VP)

R.O. WILLIAMS & CO., INC
2508 McFaddin St, Beaumont, TX 77702
Tel.: (409) 735-5376
Web Site: http://www.rowilliams.com
Rev.: $10,500,000
Emp.: 15
Insurance Agents
N.A.I.C.S.: 524210
Stewart Chisum (Pres)

R.P. KINCHELOE COMPANY INC.
700 International Pkwy Ste 100, Richardson, TX 75081
Tel.: (214) 828-4545   TX
Year Founded: 1919
Sales Range: $10-24.9 Million
Emp.: 4
Medical & Hospital Equipment Distr
N.A.I.C.S.: 339112
Richard P. Kincheloe (Founder)

R.P. WEDDELL & SONS CO.
4945 E Carey Ave, Las Vegas, NV 89115-5531
Tel.: (702) 248-4829
Sales Range: $10-24.9 Million
Emp.: 50
Underground Utilities Contractor
N.A.I.C.S.: 238990
Chris Weddell (VP)
Dan Weddell (Gen Mgr)

R.P. WILLIAMS & SONS, INC.
400 Summer St, Bristol, NH 03222-3213
Tel.: (603) 744-5446
Web Site: http://www.rpwilliams.com
Year Founded: 1941
Sales Range: Less than $1 Million
Emp.: 21
Lumber & Building Supplies
N.A.I.C.S.: 423310
Craig T. Williams (VP)
Doug Williams (Treas)
Robert M. Williams Jr. (Pres)

R.R. DAWSON BRIDGE COMPANY LLC
1999 Richmond Rd Ste 1, Lexington, KY 40502
Tel.: (859) 269-4644
Sales Range: $25-49.9 Million
Emp.: 8
Bridge Construction
N.A.I.C.S.: 237310
Robert R. Dawson Jr. (Exec Dir)

R.R. SIMMONS CONSTRUCTION CORP.
13112 Telecom Dr, Tampa, FL 33637-0924
Tel.: (813) 632-1200   FL
Web Site: http://www.rrsimmons.com
Year Founded: 1968
Sales Range: $1-9.9 Million
Emp.: 22
Commercial & Institutional Building Construction
N.A.I.C.S.: 236220
Linda O. Simmons (Pres)
Randy Simmons (Chm)
Malinda Webster (VP & Controller)
Cesar Zevallos (Sr VP)

Howard Bruning (VP-Architectural Svcs)
Brent Kitchiner (VP)
Scott Weik (VP)

R.S. ANDREWS ENTERPRISES INC.
3617 Clearview Pkwy, Atlanta, GA 30340
Tel.: (770) 454-1800
Web Site: http://www.rsandrews.com
Year Founded: 1968
Plumbing, Heating, Air-Conditioning
N.A.I.C.S.: 238220

R.S. BRASWELL COMPANY INC.
485 S Cannon Blvd, Kannapolis, NC 28083
Tel.: (704) 933-2269
Web Site: http://www.rsbraswell.com
Year Founded: 1950
Sales Range: $10-24.9 Million
Emp.: 60
Whslr of Materials Handling Machinery
N.A.I.C.S.: 423830
Steve Thigpen (VP)

R.S. DAVIS RECYCLING, INC.
10105 SE Mather Rd, Clackamas, OR 97015
Tel.: (503) 655-5433
Web Site:
  http://www.portlandrecycling.com
Year Founded: 1960
Sales Range: $10-24.9 Million
Emp.: 28
Recyclable Material Whslr
N.A.I.C.S.: 423930
Michael Doane (Pres & Gen Mgr)
Jamie Stateler (Office Mgr)
Hank Doane (VP-Ops)

R.S. HUGHES CO., INC.
1162 Sonora Ct, Sunnyvale, CA 94086-5308
Tel.: (408) 739-3211   CA
Web Site: http://www.rshughes.com
Year Founded: 1954
Sales Range: $200-249.9 Million
Emp.: 390
Industrial Distributor of Adhesives, Tape & Safety Products
N.A.I.C.S.: 423840
Gail Zimmerman (CFO)
Pete Biocini (Pres)
Thomas Shmitt (Controller)

Subsidiaries:

R.S. Hughes Co. (1)
10639 Glenoaks Blvd Ste 1, Pacoima, CA 91331
Tel.: (818) 686-9111
Web Site: http://www.rshughes.com
Sales Range: $25-49.9 Million
Emp.: 15
General Product Warehousing Services
N.A.I.C.S.: 493110
Jon Baeder (Mgr-Sls)

R.S. KNAPP CO. INC.
1000 Wall St W, Lyndhurst, NJ 07071
Tel.: (201) 438-1500
Web Site: http://www.napconet.com
Sales Range: $10-24.9 Million
Emp.: 265
Provider of Drafting Supplies for the Architecture, Engineering & Construction Industries
N.A.I.C.S.: 423490
Gary J. Wilbur (Pres & CEO)
Kevin O'Keefe (Mgr-Internet Svcs)

R.S. LIPMAN BREWING COMPANY, LLC
2815 Brick Church Pike, Nashville, TN 37207
Tel.: (615) 244-2230   TN
Web Site: http://rslipman.com
Beer & Ale Merchant Whslr
N.A.I.C.S.: 424810
Robert S. Lipman (Pres)
Blake Wylie (Dir-IT)
Charles Bader (Dir-Sls Spirits)
Charlie Jackson (Dir-Sls-On-Premise)
Clark Calvert (Dir-Sls-Beer)
Greg Naiser (VP-Sls)
Lowell Goldman (VP-Ops)
Pat Kerrigan (Dir-Sls Wine)
Stefan Banks (Treas, Sec & Gen Mgr)
Michael Kwas (Sls Mgr)
Nic Donahue (VP)

Subsidiaries:

Little Harpeth Brewing LLC (1)
30 Oldham St, Nashville, TN 37213-1107
Tel.: (615) 574-9977
Web Site:
  http://www.littleharpethbrewing.com
Breweries
N.A.I.C.S.: 312120
Matthew Hearn (Dir-Creative)

R.S. OWENS & COMPANY
5535 N Lynch Ave, Chicago, IL 60630-1417
Tel.: (773) 282-6000   IL
Web Site: http://www.rsowens.com
Year Founded: 1938
Sales Range: $10-24.9 Million
Emp.: 150
Provider of Trophies, Plaques, Custom Recognition & Incentive Awards & Gifts
N.A.I.C.S.: 339910
Scott Siegel (Pres)
Joseph Petree (Dir-Design)
Mark Psaros (VP)

R.S. YOUNG EXCAVATING, INC.
G5305 N Dort Hwy, Flint, MI 48505-1832
Tel.: (810) 789-7155   MI
Web Site:
  http://www.youngsenvironmental.com
Year Founded: 1979
Sales Range: $75-99.9 Million
Emp.: 50
Underground Excavating Contractor; Water Mains & Sewer Lines Installation, Repair & Replacement
N.A.I.C.S.: 237110
Robert S. Young (Founder)

Subsidiaries:

Young Environmental Clean Up (1)
G-5305 N Dort Hwy, Flint, MI 48505
Tel.: (810) 789-7155
Sales Range: $25-49.9 Million
Environmental Cleanup Services
N.A.I.C.S.: 562910

R.T. MILORD CO.
9801 Industrial Dr, Bridgeview, IL 60455
Tel.: (708) 598-7900
Web Site: http://www.milord.com
Year Founded: 1887
Sales Range: $300-349.9 Million
Emp.: 30
Operative Builders
N.A.I.C.S.: 237210
Mike Thomas (Treas)
Kevin Milord (Pres)

R.T. VANDERBILT HOLDING COMPANY, INC.
30 Winfield St, Norwalk, CT 06856-5150
Tel.: (203) 295-2141   NY

R.T. VANDERBILT HOLDING COMPANY, INC.

R.T. Vanderbilt Holding Company, Inc.—(Continued)

Web Site:
http://www.rtvanderbiltholding.com
Year Founded: 1916
Holding Company; Rubber, Plastics & Petroleum Markets
N.A.I.C.S.: 551112
Hugh Vanderbilt Jr. *(Chm & CEO)*

Subsidiaries:

Vanderbilt Chemical, LLC (1)
6281 Beach Blvd Ste 204, Buena Park, CA 90621
Tel.: (714) 670-8084
Web Site:
http://www.vanderbiltchemicals.com
Chemical Products Mfr
N.A.I.C.S.: 325998

Vanderbilt International Sarl (1)
29 Route De Pre-Bois, PO Box 870, Geneva, 1215, Switzerland
Tel.: (41) 22 929 5734
Web Site:
http://www.vanderbiltinternational.com
Industrial Chemicals Mfr
N.A.I.C.S.: 325998
Nadia Hess *(Office Mgr)*

Vanderbilt Minerals, LLC (1)
33 Winfield St, Norwalk, CT 06856-5150
Tel.: (203) 295-2140
Web Site:
http://www.vanderbiltminerals.com
Sales Range: $10-24.9 Million
Emp.: 20
Chemical Products Mfr
N.A.I.C.S.: 325998
Randy Johnson *(Pres)*

R.V. CLOUD CO.
3000 Winchester Blvd, Campbell, CA 95008
Tel.: (408) 378-7943
Web Site: http://www.rvcloudco.com
Rev.: $26,098,053
Emp.: 60
Plumbing & Hydronic Heating Supplies
N.A.I.C.S.: 423720

R.V. EVANS COMPANY
2325 E Logan St, Decatur, IL 62526
Tel.: (217) 423-3631
Web Site: http://www.rvevans.com
Sales Range: $10-24.9 Million
Emp.: 47
Distr of Packaging, Fastening & Closure Systems
N.A.I.C.S.: 423840
Kelly Evans *(Pres)*
Tom Evans *(CEO)*
Sheri Kuntz *(Mgr-Acctg)*
Richard V. Evans Jr. *(Chm)*

R.W. BECKETT CORPORATION
38251 Ctr Rdg Rd, North Ridgeville, OH 44039
Tel.: (440) 327-1060   OH
Web Site:
http://www.beckettcorp.com
Year Founded: 1937
Sales Range: $10-24.9 Million
Emp.: 210
Heating Equipment Mfr
N.A.I.C.S.: 333414
Kevin Beckett *(Pres & CEO)*

Subsidiaries:

Delavan Limited (1)
Gorsey Lane, Widnes, WA8 0RJ, Cheshire, United Kingdom
Tel.: (44) 1514246821
Web Site: https://delavan.com
Aircraft Part Mfr
N.A.I.C.S.: 336413

Delavan Spray, LLC (1)
4334 Main Hwy, Bamberg, SC 29003-8456

Tel.: (803) 245-4347
Web Site: https://delavan.com
Industrial Combustion & Spray Nozzles Mfr
N.A.I.C.S.: 332919

R.W. HARRIS INC.
12300 44th St N, Clearwater, FL 33762
Tel.: (727) 572-9200
Web Site: http://www.rwharrisinc.com
Year Founded: 1986
Sales Range: $10-24.9 Million
Emp.: 50
Foundation & Footing Contracting Services
N.A.I.C.S.: 238110
Ronald Harris *(Pres)*

R.W. MERCER COMPANY, INC.
2322 Brooklyn Rd, Jackson, MI 49203-4750
Tel.: (517) 787-2960   MI
Web Site: http://www.rwmercer.com
Year Founded: 1960
Sales Range: $75-99.9 Million
Emp.: 160
Provider of Contracting & Construction Services
N.A.I.C.S.: 238990
Kirk N. Mercer *(CEO)*
Andrew Mercer *(Owner & Pres)*
Bill Hunter *(VP-Petroleum Construction)*
Tracy Saylor *(VP)*
Mike Bullinger *(Project Mgr)*
Mike Decker *(Mgr-Svc-Petroleum)*
Dan Hlywa *(Branch Mgr)*
Tom Snyder *(Mgr-Svc)*
Dan Dubois *(CFO)*
Brian Meyer *(Project Mgr)*
Jerry Daly *(Project Mgr)*
Matt Stoddard *(Project Mgr)*
Tony Hurd *(Dir-Sls-Petroleum)*

R.W. PRESSPRICH & CO., INCORPORATED
452 Madison Ave 12th Fl, New York, NY 10018
Tel.: (212) 832-6200
Web Site: http://www.pressprich.com
Sales Range: $100-124.9 Million
Emp.: 90
Securities Brokerage
N.A.I.C.S.: 523150
Joe Calvo *(Head-Trading)*
Larry Milstein *(Mng Dir-Fixed Income Trading)*
Steve Ruggiero *(Head-Res)*
Edward J. Rappa *(Chm)*

R.W. SAUDER INC.
570 Furnace Hills Pike, Lititz, PA 17543-0427
Tel.: (717) 626-2074   PA
Web Site:
http://www.saudereggs.com
Year Founded: 1946
Sales Range: $125-149.9 Million
Emp.: 425
Poultry & Poultry Products
N.A.I.C.S.: 424440
Paul Sauder *(Owner)*
Greg Rhineer *(Mgr-Quality Control)*

R.W. SIDLEY, INCORPORATED
436 Casement Ave, Painesville, OH 44077-3817
Tel.: (440) 352-9343
Web Site: http://www.rwsidley.com
Year Founded: 1933
Sales Range: $25-49.9 Million
Emp.: 750
Distr of Construction Materials & Supplies
N.A.I.C.S.: 327991
Robert Buescher *(Pres & CEO)*

Subsidiaries:

Carr Concrete Corp. (1)
362 Waverly Rd, Williamstown, WV 26187
Tel.: (304) 464-4441
Web Site: http://www.carrconcrete.com
Concrete Products Mfr
N.A.I.C.S.: 327390
Burr Stanley *(Project Mgr-Bridge & Box Culvert)*
Jason Norman *(Project Mgr-Buildings)*
Keith Kostelac *(Project Mgr)*
Larry E. Miller *(Project Mgr)*

J.P. Jenks, Inc. (1)
7123 Madison Rd, Thompson, OH 44086
Tel.: (440) 428-4500
Sales Range: $10-24.9 Million
Emp.: 35
Provider of Trucking Services
N.A.I.C.S.: 484121

Parking Structures, Inc. (1)
436 Casement Ave, Painesville, OH 44077-3817
Tel.: (440) 352-9343
Web Site: http://www.rwsidley.com
Sales Range: $10-24.9 Million
Emp.: 2
Structural Steel Erection Mfr
N.A.I.C.S.: 238190

Sidley Truck & Equipment (1)
7123 Madison Rd Route 528, Thompson, OH 44086
Tel.: (440) 298-3227
Web Site: http://www.sidleytrucks.com
New & Used Motor Vehicle Equipment Whslr
N.A.I.C.S.: 423120

R.W. ZANT COMPANY
1470 E 4th St, Los Angeles, CA 90033-4236
Tel.: (323) 980-4950   CA
Web Site: http://www.rwzant.com
Year Founded: 1950
Sales Range: $25-49.9 Million
Emp.: 150
Poultry & Poultry Products
N.A.I.C.S.: 424440
Willam Zant *(Pres)*
Mike Jones *(VP-Mktg)*
Peter Mahugh *(Controller)*

R2 INNOVATIVE TECHNOLOGIES INC
11924 Forest Hill Blvd Ste 22-138, Wellington, FL 33414
Web Site: http://www.r2it.com
Year Founded: 1999
Sales Range: $1-9.9 Million
Emp.: 20
Event Management Software
N.A.I.C.S.: 423430
Robert J. Rodgers *(Pres)*

R2 LOGISTICS, INC.
10739 Deerwood Park Blvd Ste 103, Jacksonville, FL 32256
Tel.: (904) 394-4677
Web Site:
http://www.r2logisticsteam.com
Sales Range: $25-49.9 Million
Emp.: 52
Transportation & Logistics Services
N.A.I.C.S.: 488999
Matt Elsass *(VP-Ops)*
Ben Jordan *(VP-Ops)*
Hunter Schwind *(VP-Sls)*
Kees Hiatt *(CFO)*
Dan Knopf *(Mgr-Houston)*
Brad Schneider *(VP-Ops)*
Jordan O'Connor *(Mgr-Seattle)*
Jon Adams *(VP-LTL Solutions)*
Frank Dreischarf *(VP-Supply Chain Solutions)*
Katie Quinn *(CEO & COO)*

R2 QUALITY CASTINGS, LLC

1908 MacArthur Rd, Waukesha, WI 53188-5722
Tel.: (262) 542-0763   WI
Web Site:
http://www.qualitycastingswi.com
Steel Alloy Casting Investment Foundry
N.A.I.C.S.: 331512
Richard Adams *(Pres & Owner)*
Kris Adams *(VP-Admin)*

R2 UNIFIED TECHNOLOGIES
980 N Federal Highway Ste 410, Boca Raton, FL 33432
Tel.: (561) 515-6800
Web Site: http://www.r2ut.com
Year Founded: 2008
Sales Range: $1-9.9 Million
Emp.: 18
Information Technology, Voice & Data Networks, Private & Public Cloud Solutions & Managed Services
N.A.I.C.S.: 519290
Jamie Doherty *(Pres & CEO)*
Ryan Rippo *(Mgr-Svc)*
Jason Doherty *(Dir-Sls)*

R2C GROUP, INC.
207 NW Park Ave, Portland, OR 97209
Tel.: (503) 222-0025
Web Site: http://www.r2cgroup.com
Year Founded: 1998
Rev.: $366,100,000
Emp.: 230
Advertising Agencies
N.A.I.C.S.: 541810
Marilyn Davis *(Mng Partner-Client Rels & Exec VP)*
David Savage *(Chief Compliance Officer & Mng Partner)*
Michelle Cardinal *(Founder & CEO)*
Sue Collins *(VP)*
Steve Diamond *(Exec Dir-Creative)*
Jane Crisan *(Pres & COO)*
Mark Toner *(CMO)*
David Maher *(CFO)*
Baylen Springer *(VP-Mktg Analytics)*
Mark Simon *(VP-New Bus Dev)*
Joy McCammon *(Dir-Talent Mgmt)*
Dan Gallagher *(Sr VP-Brand Strategy & Res)*
Patrick Acosta *(Sr VP & Dir-Media)*
Tony Ferranti *(Mng Partner)*

R3 STRATEGIC SUPPORT GROUP, INC.
875 Orange Ave Suite 210, Coronado, CA 92118
Tel.: (800) 418-2040
Web Site: http://www.r3ssg.com
Year Founded: 2008
Sales Range: $1-9.9 Million
Emp.: 26
Innovative Strategic Solutions & Services to Government & Commercial Domains
N.A.I.C.S.: 921190
David Sadler *(Gen Mgr)*
Linda Runyeon *(VP-Fin)*
Clark Nichols *(Principal)*
Mark Sanders *(Principal)*

RA RODRIGUEZ INC.
20 Seaview Blvd, Port Washington, NY 11050
Tel.: (516) 625-8080
Web Site: http://www.rodriguez-usa.com
Sales Range: $10-24.9 Million
Emp.: 15
Bearings
N.A.I.C.S.: 423840
Rafael A. Rodriguez Jr. *(Pres)*

RAADR, INC.

2432 W Peoria Ave Ste 1346, Phoenix, AZ 85029
Tel.: (480) 755-0591   NV
Web Site: http://www.raadr.com
Year Founded: 2006
Sales Range: Less than $1 Million
Emp.: 1
Digital Marketing Services
N.A.I.C.S.: 513210
Jacob DiMartino *(Founder & CEO)*

RAAMCO INTERNATIONAL INCORPORATED
270 Sylvan Ave, Englewood Cliffs, NJ 07632-2523
Tel.: (201) 567-5991   DE
Web Site: http://www.raamco.com
Year Founded: 1983
Sales Range: $25-49.9 Million
Emp.: 220
Apartment Building Operator
N.A.I.C.S.: 531110
Linda Louis *(VP)*
Abel Sheng *(Pres)*

Subsidiaries:

Sheng-Raamco Management Inc.   (1)
10501 Holy Springs, Houston, TX 77042
Tel.: (713) 785-3410
Sales Range: $25-49.9 Million
Emp.: 3
Real Estate Manangement Services
N.A.I.C.S.: 523150

RAB FOUNDATION REPAIR LLC
13206 Byrd Dr, Odessa, FL 33556
Tel.: (813) 926-2300
Web Site: http://www.rabfoundationrepair.com
Year Founded: 2007
Sales Range: $10-24.9 Million
Emp.: 40
Foundation Repair & Sinkhole Remediation
N.A.I.C.S.: 238190
Michael Manley *(Co-Founder)*
Rodger Bennett Jr. *(Co-Founder)*

RABENHORST FUNERAL HOME INC.
825 Government St, Baton Rouge, LA 70802
Tel.: (225) 383-6831
Web Site: http://www.rabenhorst.com
Rev.: $35,000,000
Emp.: 55
Funeral Home
N.A.I.C.S.: 812210
Karen Rabenhorst-Kerr *(Owner)*
Alvin P. Rabenhorst Jr. *(Pres)*

RABER PACKING CO.
1413 N Raber Rd, Peoria, IL 61604
Tel.: (309) 673-0721
Web Site: http://www.raberpacking.com
Year Founded: 1954
Sales Range: $50-74.9 Million
Emp.: 20
Processed Beef Mfr & Distr
N.A.I.C.S.: 311611
Carroll Wetterauer *(Sec)*

RABIDEAU GRAIN & LUMBER, INC.
745 S Elliott St, Clifton, IL 60927
Tel.: (815) 694-2339   IL
Web Site: http://www.rabideaugrain.com
Sales Range: $10-24.9 Million
Emp.: 15
Grain & Lumber Products Distr
N.A.I.C.S.: 424510
Hanley Tuy *(Mng Dir)*

RABIN WORLDWIDE, INC.
731 Sansome St Fl 2, San Francisco, CA 94111-1723
Tel.: (415) 522-5700
Web Site: http://www.rabin.com
Sales Range: $10-24.9 Million
Emp.: 20
Financial Services for Businesses in Transition
N.A.I.C.S.: 455219
Richard Reese *(Pres & CEO)*
Michael Bank *(Sr VP)*
Irena Okun *(Controller)*

RABINE PAVING AMERICA, LLC
900 National Pkwy Ste 260, Schaumburg, IL 60173
Tel.: (815) 675-0555   IL
Web Site: http://www.rabinegroup.com
Year Founded: 1981
Sales Range: $150-199.9 Million
Emp.: 276
Asphalt, Poured Concrete Foundation & Structure Contractors
N.A.I.C.S.: 238110
Gary T. Rabine *(CEO)*
Dan Gillette *(Sr Dir-Ops)*
Scott Klug *(Chief Sls Officer)*
LeeAnn Atwood *(Dir-Mktg)*

Subsidiaries:

Sealco Asphalt, Inc.   (1)
617 N US Highway 287, Fort Collins, CO 80524
Tel.: (970) 224-1172
Web Site: http://www.sealcoasphalt.com
Sales Range: $1-9.9 Million
Emp.: 10
Asphalt & Paving Services
N.A.I.C.S.: 423390

RABUCK STRANGER
3221 Hutchison Ave Ste H, Los Angeles, CA 90034-3299
Tel.: (310) 815-8225
Web Site: http://www.rabuckstranger.com
Year Founded: 1987
Rev.: $20,000,000
Emp.: 15
N.A.I.C.S.: 541810
Dijana Marsic *(Sr Dir-Art)*
Michelle Di Ciutuis *(Acct Exec)*
Karen Lovett *(Controller)*

RAC ENTERPRISES INC.
104 E Vine St, Hatfield, PA 19440
Tel.: (215) 368-5506
Web Site: http://www.wwstereo.com
Rev.: $10,975,648
Emp.: 70
Video Recorders, Players, Disc Players & Accessories
N.A.I.C.S.: 449210
Robert Cole *(Pres)*
Natalie Sinn *(Dir-Ops)*

RAC TRANSPORT COMPANY INC.
6050 E 56th Ave, Commerce City, CO 80022
Tel.: (303) 289-5500
Web Site: http://www.ractransport.com
Sales Range: $25-49.9 Million
Emp.: 175
Local Trucking without Storage
N.A.I.C.S.: 484110
Jim Perea *(Pres)*
Howard Perea *(VP)*

RACE ROCK GP, L.L.C
1990 Post Oak Blvd Ste 2400, Houston, TX 77056
Tel.: (832) 920-1276   TX

Web Site: http://www.racerockgroup.com
Privater Equity Firm
N.A.I.C.S.: 523940
Michael L. Yates *(Mng Dir)*

Subsidiaries:

Highway Safety LLC   (1)
239 Commerce St, Glastonbury, CT 06033-2492
Tel.: (860) 633-9445
Web Site: https://www.highwaysafety.net
Provider of Galvanizing Services
N.A.I.C.S.: 332322

Structural & Steel Products, Inc.   (1)
1320 S University Dr Ste 701, Fort Worth, TX 76107
Tel.: (817) 332-7417
Web Site: http://www.s-steel.com
Structural & Steel Products Mfr & Distr
N.A.I.C.S.: 332312
Joe Troop *(Pres)*
Bobby Hunnicutt *(VP & Gen Mgr)*
Sheri Schmedt *(Dir-HR)*
Harold V. Price Jr. *(Founder, Chm & CEO)*

RACE STREET FOODS INC.
1130 Olinder Ct, San Jose, CA 95122
Tel.: (408) 294-6161
Web Site: http://www.racestreetfoods.com
Rev.: $40,000,000
Emp.: 100
Seafood, Poultry, Beef & Pork Products Whslr
N.A.I.C.S.: 424440
Gino Barsanti *(Chm)*

RACEBROOK CAPITAL ADVISORS, LLC
635 Madison Ave Ste 1300, New York, NY 10022
Tel.: (212) 672-0020
Web Site: http://www.racebrook.com
Emp.: 10
Private Investment Firm
N.A.I.C.S.: 523999
John J. Cuticelli Jr. *(CEO)*

Subsidiaries:

Sheldon Good & Company International, LLC   (1)
488 Madison Ave Ste 1704, New York, NY 10022
Tel.: (212) 672-0020
Sales Range: $50-74.9 Million
Real Estate Auctioneers
N.A.I.C.S.: 531210
Elizabeth A. Schuette *(Chief Compliance Officer)*
Aaron S. Perl *(Corp Counsel)*
John J. Cuticelli Jr. *(Chm & CEO)*

Subsidiary (Domestic):

Sheldon Good & Company-Mountain Region   (2)
600 Grant St Ste 425, Denver, CO 80203
Tel.: (303) 740-6050
Sales Range: $25-49.9 Million
Emp.: 6
Real Estate Auctions
N.A.I.C.S.: 531390

RACEMARK INTERNATIONAL, LP
1711 Highway 41 South Sw, Calhoun, GA 30701-3624
Tel.: (518) 899-6611   DE
Web Site: http://www.racemark.com
Year Founded: 1963
Rev.: $28,900,000
Emp.: 240
Global Supplier of Automotive Markets
N.A.I.C.S.: 314110
Bob Bailey *(Founder)*

Subsidiaries:

Racemark Industries, SA   (1)

Pre Jorat 18, 2108, Couvet, Switzerland
Tel.: (41) 328645082
Seat Cover Whslr
N.A.I.C.S.: 423120

Racemark International, LLC   (1)
1711 Hwy 41 S, Calhoun, GA 30701
Tel.: (706) 629-4442
Web Site: http://www.racemark.com
Sales Range: $10-24.9 Million
Emp.: 40
Mfr Car Floormats
N.A.I.C.S.: 314110
Daniel Gaines *(Engr-Mfg)*

RACETRAC PETROLEUM, INC.
200 Galleria Pkwy SE Ste 900, Atlanta, GA 30339
Tel.: (770) 431-7600   GA
Web Site: https://www.racetrac.com
Year Founded: 1959
Sales Range: $1-4.9 Billion
Emp.: 10,400
Gasoline Stations with Convenience Stores
N.A.I.C.S.: 457110
Robert J. Dumbacher *(Treas)*
Kristina Appen *(Mgr-Special Projects)*
Jay Peake *(Dir-Fuel Pricing)*
Lori Mullins *(Dir-Field HR)*
Billy Milam *(COO)*
Bolch Jr. McBrayer *(Interim CFO)*
Melanie Isbill *(Chief Mktg Officer)*
Natalie B. Morhous *(CEO)*

RACEWAY PETROLEUM INC.
1411 Stelton Rd, Piscataway, NJ 08854
Tel.: (732) 819-9116
Web Site: http://www.racewaypetroleum.com
Rev.: $74,300,000
Emp.: 20
Gasoline
N.A.I.C.S.: 424720
Nick Kambitsis *(Pres)*

RACHAEL'S FOOD CORPORATION
705 Meadow St, Chicopee, MA 01013
Tel.: (413) 888-1202
Web Site: http://www.rachaelsfoodcorp.com
Prepared Food Distr
N.A.I.C.S.: 311999
Adam Kramer *(Pres)*

Subsidiaries:

Grote & Weigel Inc.   (1)
76 Granby St, Bloomfield, CT 06002
Tel.: (860) 242-8528
Web Site: http://www.groteandweigel.com
Sales Range: $50-74.9 Million
Emp.: 42
Sausages & Other Prepared Meat Products Mfr
N.A.I.C.S.: 311612
Adam Kramer *(Pres)*

RACHAS INC.
1233 Camino Del Rio S, San Diego, CA 92108
Web Site: https://chuzefitness.com
Emp.: 100
Fitness & Recreational Sports Center
N.A.I.C.S.: 713940
Cory Brightwell *(CEO & Founder)*

Subsidiaries:

Baileys Gym, Inc.   (1)
PO Box 8762, Jacksonville, FL 32239
Tel.: (904) 242-4967
Web Site: http://www.baileysgym.com
Golf Courses & Country Clubs
N.A.I.C.S.: 713910
Darryl Bailey *(Sec)*

RACHEL ALLAN, LLC

RACHEL ALLAN, LLC

Rachel Allan, LLC—(Continued)
181 Shore Ct, Burr Ridge, IL 60527-3506
Tel.: (630) 910-8880
Web Site: http://www.rachelallan.com
Fashion & Bridal Dress Mfr
N.A.I.C.S.: 458110
Arun Tandon (Pres)

Subsidiaries:
Mary's Group, Ltd. (1)
12315 Parc Crest Dr, Stafford, TX 77477
Tel.: (281) 933-9678
Web Site: http://www.marysbridal.com
Piece Goods, Notions & Other Dry Goods Merchant Whslr
N.A.I.C.S.: 424310

RACINE INDUSTRIES INC.
1405 16th St, Racine, WI 53403
Tel.: (262) 637-4491
Commercial Cleaning Equipment Mfr & Distr
N.A.I.C.S.: 333310

RACINE SYMPHONY ORCHESTRA ASSOCIATION INC.
PO Box 1874, Racine, WI 53401-1874
Tel.: (262) 636-9285
Web Site: http://www.racinesymphony.org
Sales Range: Less than $1 Million
Emp.: 4
Symphony Orchestra
N.A.I.C.S.: 711130
Nancy DeKraay (Pres)

RACING ASSOCIATION OF CENTRAL IOWA
1 Prairie Meadows Dr, Altoona, IA 50009
Tel.: (515) 967-1000
Web Site: http://www.prairiemeadows.com
Sales Range: $125-149.9 Million
Emp.: 1,100
Casino & Racetrack Operator
N.A.I.C.S.: 711212
Gary Palmer (Pres & CEO-Prairie Meadows)
Clint Pursley (VP-Security-Prairie Meadows)
Derron Heldt (Dir-Racing-Prairie Meadows)
Ann Atkin (COO & Sr VP-Prairie Meadows)
Tony Guzman (Dir-IT-Prairie Meadows)
Pam Nash (Asst Dir-Facilities)
Tony Stork (Asst Dir-IT-Prairie Meadows)
Julie Stewart (Dir-Community Rels-Prairie Meadows)
Elaine Castelline (CFO & VP-Fin-Prairie Meadows)
Clay Willey (VP-Hospitality-Prairie Meadows)
Dustin VandeWeerd (Dir-Facilities-Prairie Meadows)

RACK PROCESSING COMPANY, INC.
2350 Arbor Blvd, Dayton, OH 45439
Tel.: (937) 294-1911
Web Site: http://www.rackprocessing.com
Year Founded: 1948
Sales Range: $10-24.9 Million
Emp.: 70
Electroplating, Plating, Polishing, Anodizing & Coloring Services
N.A.I.C.S.: 332813
Craig Coy (Pres)
Kevyn Coy (Treas & Sec)

RACKMOUNT SOLUTIONS, INC.
2805 200 E Plano Pkwy, Plano, TX 75074
Tel.: (972) 272-6631 TX
Web Site: http://www.rackmountsolutions.net
Year Founded: 2001
Sales Range: $1-9.9 Million
Emp.: 14
Computer Storage Device Mfr
N.A.I.C.S.: 334112
Tom Currier (Pres)

RACKWISE, INC.
2365 Iron Point Rd Ste 190, Folsom, CA 95630
Tel.: (916) 984-6000 NV
Web Site: http://www.rackwise.com
Year Founded: 2009
Sales Range: $1-9.9 Million
Emp.: 15
Software Developer
N.A.I.C.S.: 513210
Doug MacRae (Exec VP-Tech Dev Grp)
Patrick W. M. Imeson (Pres, Treas & Sec)
Edward Higgins (Exec VP)

RACO GENERAL CONTRACTORS INC.
1401 Dalon Rd NE, Atlanta, GA 30306-3156
Tel.: (404) 873-3567 GA
Web Site: http://www.racogc.com
Year Founded: 1952
Sales Range: $10-24.9 Million
Emp.: 50
Contractors of Industrial Buildings & Warehouses
N.A.I.C.S.: 236210
Kevin Cleveland (CEO)

RACO INCORPORATED
2000 Lotus Dr, Gretna, VA 24557
Tel.: (434) 656-6676
Web Site: http://www.raco-construction.com
Sales Range: $10-24.9 Million
Emp.: 100
Provider of Telephone & Communication Line Construction Services
N.A.I.C.S.: 237130
Jean Waller (Pres)
Mike Overstreet (VP-Mktg)
Jack Bellissimo (Brand Mgr)

RACO INDUSTRIES, INC.
5481 Creek Rd, Cincinnati, OH 45242
Tel.: (513) 984-2101 OH
Web Site: http://www.racoindustries.com
Year Founded: 1988
Sales Range: $1-9.9 Million
Emp.: 67
Business Data Services
N.A.I.C.S.: 518210
Roger Klosterman (Sr Acct Mgr-Sls)

Subsidiaries:
Toolworx Information Products, Inc. (1)
7994 Grand River Ave, Brighton, MI 48114
Tel.: (810) 220-5115
Web Site: http://www.toolworx.com
Sales Range: $1-9.9 Million
Emp.: 15
Computer Integrated Systems Design
N.A.I.C.S.: 541512
Brad Oyster (Pres & CEO)
Ed Weber (VP-Sls & Mktg)

RACOM CORPORATION
201 W State St, Marshalltown, IA 50158
Tel.: (641) 752-5820
Web Site: http://www.racom.net
Year Founded: 1972
Rev.: $14,000,000
Emp.: 85
Sales & Services of Mobile Radios
N.A.I.C.S.: 449210
Michael Miller (Pres & CEO)
Nick Loney (CFO & VP-Fin)
Terry Brennan (VP-Sls, Mktg & Bus Dev)
Steve Holmes (COO)

RACON INC.
7300 Commerce Dr, Tuscaloosa, AL 35403
Tel.: (205) 333-8500 AL
Year Founded: 1981
Sales Range: $25-49.9 Million
Emp.: 250
Highway & Street Construction
N.A.I.C.S.: 237310
Ramona M. Andrews (Pres)
Chris Poling (Project Mgr)
Keith Andrews (Owner)

RAD POWER BIKES LLC
1128 NW 52nd St, Seattle, WA 98107
Web Site: http://www.radpowerbikes.com
Year Founded: 2007
Sales Range: $25-49.9 Million
Emp.:
Bicycles Distr
N.A.I.C.S.: 459110
Mike Radenbaugh (Co-Founder)
Ty Collins (Co-Founder)
Joe Flynn (Mgr-Customer Experience)
Tony Thomas (Mgr-Product Support)

RAD-INFO, INC.
16545 Lake Brigadoon Cir, Tampa, FL 33618
Tel.: (813) 963-5884
Web Site: http://www.rad-info.net
Year Founded: 1999
Sales Range: $1-9.9 Million
Telecom Consulting Services
N.A.I.C.S.: 541690
Peter Radizeski (Founder & Pres)

RADAR, INC.
22214 20th Ave SE Ste 101, Bothell, WA 98021-4212
Tel.: (425) 424-2002 WA
Web Site: http://www.radarinc.com
Year Founded: 1958
Sales Range: $25-49.9 Million
Emp.: 65
Electronic Components Distr
N.A.I.C.S.: 423690
Wilbur B. McPherson (Pres)

RADARWORKS, INC.
1929 3rd Ave Ste 200, Seattle, WA 98101
Tel.: (206) 441-6657
Web Site: http://www.radarworks.com
Year Founded: 1995
Sales Range: $10-24.9 Million
Emp.: 30
Advertising Agencies
N.A.I.C.S.: 541810
Kim Latendresse (Dir-Client Svcs)
Lou Maxon (Exec Dir-Creative)

Subsidiaries:
Radarworks, Inc. (1)
5670 Wilshire Blvd Ste 100, Los Angeles, CA 90036
Tel.: (323) 965-5091
Web Site: http://www.radarworks.com
Sales Range: Less than $1 Million
Emp.: 7
Advetising Agency
N.A.I.C.S.: 541810

Mark Taylor (Exec Dir-Creative)
Kazumi Mechling (CEO)

RADCLIFF-ECONOMY MARINE SERVICES
115 Cocran Caldway, Mobile, AL 36602
Tel.: (251) 433-0066
Web Site: http://www.radcliffeconomy.com
Year Founded: 1987
Sales Range: $10-24.9 Million
Emp.: 50
Provider of Petroleum Bulk Station Services
N.A.I.C.S.: 424710
Harold Galemore (Controller)
Brad Jones (Coord-Marine)
Mike Yarbrough (Coord-Creative)
Steve Gordon (Gen Mgr)
Stuart Gordon (Mgr-Terminal)

RADCO INDUSTRIES, INC.
700 Kingsland Dr, Batavia, IL 60510
Tel.: (630) 232-7966
Web Site: http://www.radcoind.com
Year Founded: 1971
Sales Range: $25-49.9 Million
Emp.: 21
Inorganic Chemical Mfr
N.A.I.C.S.: 325180
Michael Damiani (CEO)
Tony Corscadden (VP-Ops)
Lawrence J. Kendzior (VP-Fin)
Brian Finch (VP-Military Products & Lubricants)
Jed Seybold (Sr Mgr-Bus Dev-Heat Transfer Fluids-Global)
John Campbell (Mgr-Sls-Heat Transfer Fluids)
Scott Mondi (Acct Mgr-Military Sls)

RADFORD AUTO AUCTION
2500 Tyler Rd, Radford, VA 24073
Tel.: (540) 639-9011
Web Site: http://www.radfordautoauction.com
Year Founded: 1977
Sales Range: $10-24.9 Million
Emp.: 40
Automotive Retailer
N.A.I.C.S.: 423110
David Sale (Pres)
Karen Sale (Owner)
Penny Linkous (Mgr-Fleet & Lease)

RADIAL DRILLING SERVICES INC.
4921 Spring Cypress Rd, Spring, TX 77379
Tel.: (281) 374-7507
Web Site: http://www.radialdrilling.com
Year Founded: 2004
Sales Range: $10-24.9 Million
Emp.: 120
Oil & Gas Well Drilling Services
N.A.I.C.S.: 213111
Henk H. Jelsma (Pres)
Charlie Guilbeau (Dir-Global Support)
Danny Lindsey (Mgr-Field Support)
Sergey Faerman (Dir-Ops-FSU)
Geza Bethlen (Dir-Ops-Latin America)
James Borne (Mgr-IT)
Ian C. Hatchell (VP-Ops)

RADIAL EQUITY PARTNERS LP
745 5th Ave, New York, NY 10151
Tel.: (212) 551-4575 DE
Web Site: https://www.radialequity.com
Emp.: 100
Financial Services
N.A.I.C.S.: 523940

Swen Kupferschmid-Rojas *(CFO & Chief Compliance Officer)*

Subsidiaries:

Lewisburg Printing, Inc. (1)
135 Legion Ave, Lewisburg, TN 37091
Tel.: (931) 270-3130
Web Site: http://www.lewisburgprinting.com
Rev.: $9,462,400
Emp.: 100
Commercial Lithographic Printing
N.A.I.C.S.: 323111
Dawn Richardson *(Controller)*
Thomas Hale Hawkins IV *(CEO)*

Subsidiary (Domestic):

Huston-Patterson Corporation (2)
123 W N St Fl 4, Decatur, IL 62522-3396
Tel.: (217) 429-5161
Web Site: http://www.hustonpatterson.com
Emp.: 100
Printing
N.A.I.C.S.: 323120
Steve Frantz *(COO)*

RADIANCE TECHNOLOGIES, INC.
350 Wynn Dr, Huntsville, AL 35805
Tel.: (256) 704-3400
Web Site:
http://www.radiancetech.com
Year Founded: 1999
Sales Range: $25-49.9 Million
Emp.: 271
Telecommunications Services & Solutions for Government & Military
N.A.I.C.S.: 517810
Charles Kelly *(Dir-Admin)*
Kacey Clark *(Dir-Mktg, Comm & Brand Engagement)*
Cindy Santy *(Chief Capabilities Officer)*
Jamie N. Jones *(Dir-Radiance University)*
Bill Bailey *(CEO)*
Kristi Looney *(VP/Dir-HR)*
Tim Tinsley *(Pres)*
Darien Hammett *(Exec VP-Defense)*

RADIANS, INC.
5305 Distriplex Farms Dr, Memphis, TN 38141
Tel.: (901) 388-7776
Web Site: http://www.radians.com
Year Founded: 1997
Sales Range: $1-9.9 Million
Protective Apparel & Safety Products Mfr & Distr
N.A.I.C.S.: 339999
Mike Tutor *(CEO)*
Bill England *(Pres)*
Chris Massa *(VP-Retail Sls)*

Subsidiaries:

Radians Carolina (1)
124 Sunrise Center Dr, Thomasville, NC 27360
Tel.: (336) 474-8000
Web Site: http://www.radians.com
Sales Range: $1-9.9 Million
Emp.: 50
Safety Apparel Mfr
N.A.I.C.S.: 315250
Philip W. Young *(VP-Ops)*

VisionAid, Inc. (1)
11 Kendrick Rd, Wareham, MA 02571-3472
Tel.: (508) 295-3300
Web Site: http://www.visionaidinc.com
Safety Eyewear
N.A.I.C.S.: 339115
Daniel McCarthy *(Pres)*
Tim Flaherty *(VP-Mktg)*
Ken Duffie *(VP-Engrg & Mgr-Shipping)*
Donna Groom *(Mgr-Customer Svc)*

Division (Domestic):

Lensclean, Inc. (2)
11 Kendrick Rd, Wareham, MA 02571
Tel.: (508) 295-3300

Web Site: http://www.visionaidinc.com
Mfr of Lens Tissue & Cleaning Liquids
N.A.I.C.S.: 339115
Calum Maclachlan *(Treas & Controller)*
Daniel McCarthy *(Pres & CEO)*

RADIANT COMMUNICATIONS CORP.
5001 Hadley Rd, South Plainfield, NJ 07080
Tel.: (908) 757-7444
Web Site: http://www.rccfiber.com
Sales Range: $10-24.9 Million
Emp.: 60
Mfr of Fiber Optics Strands
N.A.I.C.S.: 327212
David Mandell *(Controller)*
Julie Hou *(Project Mgr)*

RADIANT GROUP LLC
1320 E 9th Ave, Tampa, FL 33605
Tel.: (813) 247-4731
Web Site: http://www.radiant.com
Rev.: $53,800,000
Emp.: 350
Petroleum Bulk Stations
N.A.I.C.S.: 424710
Angelina Capitano *(Pres)*
John Mertney *(CFO)*

RADIANT HOLDINGS INC.
1020 NW 163rd Dr, Miami, FL 33169
Tel.: (305) 914-3434
Web Site:
http://www.radiantholdings.com
Rev.: $250,000,000
Emp.: 200
Telecommunication Equipment Repair (Except Telephones)
N.A.I.C.S.: 517121

Subsidiaries:

Radiant Telecom Inc. (1)
1020 Northwest 163rd Dr, Miami, FL 33169
Tel.: (305) 914-3434
Web Site: http://www.nteraholdings.com
Rev.: $25,600,000
Telephone Communication, Except Radio
N.A.I.C.S.: 517121

RADIANT LOGIC, INC.
75 Rowland Way Ste 300, Novato, CA 94945
Tel.: (415) 209-6800   CA
Web Site:
http://www.radiantlogic.com
Year Founded: 2005
Sales Range: $1-9.9 Million
Emp.: 45
Software Publisher
N.A.I.C.S.: 513210
Cluade Y. Samuelson *(VP-Engrg)*
Dieter Schuller *(VP-Sls & Bus Dev)*
Michael Prompt *(Founder)*
Joe Sander *(CEO)*
Deborah McGinn *(CMO)*
Justin Sollenne *(CFO)*
Jeff Tishgart *(VP-Global Partners & Alliances)*

RADIANT OIL & GAS, INC.
9700 Richmond Ave Ste 124, Houston, TX 77042
Tel.: (832) 242-6000
Web Site:
http://www.radiantoilandgas.com
Year Founded: 1990
Sales Range: Less than $1 Million
Emp.: 6
Oil & Gas Exploration Services
N.A.I.C.S.: 213112
Barry J. Rava *(VP-Exploration)*

RADIANT RFID
12912 Hill Country Blvd Ste F 245, Austin, TX 78738
Tel.: (512) 351-4915   TX

Web Site: http://www.radiantrfid.com
Year Founded: 2004
Sales Range: $1-9.9 Million
Emp.: 14
Radio Frequency Identification Software Development Services
N.A.I.C.S.: 541511
Cynthia Rubio *(Pres & CEO)*
Stephan Schwarze *(CTO)*
Nick Zuniga *(Mgr-Ops)*

RADIATION BILLING SOLUTIONS, INC.
1044 Jackson Felts Rd, Joelton, TN 37080
Tel.: (615) 746-4711   TN
Web Site:
http://radiationbusiness.com
Year Founded: 2004
Emp.: 120
Oncology Management, Billing & Consulting Services
N.A.I.C.S.: 541690
Dan Moore *(CEO)*
Greg Merrill *(Pres)*

Subsidiaries:

MBR Medical Billing Inc. (1)
171 Technology Dr Ste 200, Boalsburg, PA 16827-1530
Tel.: (814) 808-1020
Web Site: http://www.mbri.com
Insurance Agencies & Brokerages
N.A.I.C.S.: 524210
James Matthews *(Pres)*

RADIATION ONCOLOGY SERVICES, INC.
275 Professional Ct, Riverdale, GA 30274
Tel.: (770) 994-1650
Web Site: http://www.radonc.com
Sales Range: $10-24.9 Million
Emp.: 40
Administrative Management & General Management Consulting Service
N.A.I.C.S.: 541611
Pam Morris *(Pres)*
John Warner Ray *(CEO)*

RADIATION TECHNICAL SERVICES CO.
2600 Moss Ln, Harvey, LA 70058
Tel.: (504) 342-4531
Year Founded: 2003
Sales Range: $1-9.9 Million
Emp.: 45
Radiation Waste Identification, Removal & Disposal Services
N.A.I.C.S.: 562211
Andrew Gross *(CEO)*

RADIATION TEST SOLUTIONS, INC.
5030 Centennial Blvd, Colorado Springs, CO 80919
Tel.: (719) 531-0800
Web Site:
http://www.radiationtestsolutions.com
Year Founded: 2015
Radiation Effects Testing
N.A.I.C.S.: 541380
Malcolm Thomson *(Pres)*

Subsidiaries:

Cobham RAD, Inc. (1)
5030 Centennial Blvd, Colorado Springs, CO 80919
Tel.: (719) 531-0800
Web Site: http://ams.aeroflex.com
Radiation Test Services for Domestic Consumers & International Programs
N.A.I.C.S.: 541380

RADIATOR SPECIALTY COMPANY

600 Radiator Rd, Indian Trail, NC 28079-5225
Tel.: (704) 377-6555   NC
Web Site: http://www.rscbrands.com
Year Founded: 1924
Sales Range: $150-199.9 Million
Emp.: 350
Automotive Sealing Chemical & Rubber Product Cleaning Compound Tool & Traffic Safety Device Mfr
N.A.I.C.S.: 325998
Ronald Weiner *(Gen Counsel & VP)*
Don Debouse *(Mgr-Natl Sls)*
Mike Guggenheimer *(VP-Sls & Mktg)*
Aaroen Martin *(Dir-Adv & Mktg)*

Subsidiaries:

Radiator Specialty Company - RSC Chemical Solutions Division (1)
600 Radiator Rd, Indian Trail, NC 28079-5255
Tel.: (704) 821-7643
Web Site: http://www.rscbrands.com
Sales Range: $25-49.9 Million
Emp.: 100
Chemical Products Mfr
N.A.I.C.S.: 325998
Brian Chapman *(Gen Mgr)*

RADICAL COSMETICS, LLC
350 Comstock St, New Brunswick, NJ 08901
Web Site:
http://www.radicalcosmetics.com
Year Founded: 2002
Sales Range: $1-9.9 Million
Emp.: 20
Cosmetics Contract Mfr
N.A.I.C.S.: 325620
Fenton Baijnath *(CEO)*

RADIO DIRECT RESPONSE
1400 N Providence Rd Ste 4000, Media, PA 19063
Tel.: (610) 892-7300   DE
Web Site: http://www.radiodirect.com
Year Founded: 1993
Sales Range: Less than $1 Million
Emp.: 16
Infomercials, Radio, Sales Promotion
N.A.I.C.S.: 541810
Mark Lipsky *(Pres & CEO)*
Vince Raimondo *(VP-Mktg)*
Lisa Sable *(Acct Mgr)*
Barbra Tabnick *(Sr Acct Mgr)*

RADIO DISTRIBUTING CO.
27015 Trolley Dr, Taylor, MI 48180
Tel.: (313) 295-4500
Web Site: http://www.rdc-radio.com
Sales Range: $10-24.9 Million
Emp.: 50
Electrical Appliances, Major
N.A.I.C.S.: 423620
Margie Ratliff *(Dir-HR)*

RADIO ENGINEERING INDUSTRIES
6534 L St, Omaha, NE 68117
Tel.: (402) 339-2200
Web Site: http://www.radioeng.com
Year Founded: 1938
Rev.: $20,000,000
Emp.: 100
Video Camera-Audio Recorders, Household Use
N.A.I.C.S.: 334310
Terri Jukes *(CEO)*
Scott Hays *(Exec VP)*
Michael Lekovich *(VP-Pur)*
Michelle Zappia *(Mgr-HR)*

RADIO FLYER INC.
6515 W Grand Ave, Chicago, IL 60707

RADIO FLYER INC.   U.S. PRIVATE

Radio Flyer Inc.—(Continued)
Tel.: (773) 637-7100
Web Site: http://www.radioflyer.com
Year Founded: 1917
Sales Range: $75-99.9 Million
Emp.: 100
Toys & Sporting Goods Mfr
N.A.I.C.S.: 339930
Robert Pasin (CEO)
Amy Bastuga (Dir-HR)

RADIO FREE ASIA
2025 M St NW Ste 300, Washington, DC 20036
Tel.: (202) 530-4900   DC
Web Site: http://www.rfa.org
Year Founded: 1996
Sales Range: $25-49.9 Million
Emp.: 284
Broadcasting Services
N.A.I.C.S.: 334220
Richard Smith (Treas)
John A. Estrella (VP-Comm & Govt Rels)
Bernadette Burns (Sec)
Rohit Mahajan (Dir-Pub Affairs & Digital Strategy)
Parameswaran Ponnudurai (VP-Programming)
Carolyn Bartholomew (Chm)
Bay Fang (Pres)
Ginny Stein (Mng Editor-Southeast Asia)

RADIO FREQUENCY SYSTEMS, INC.
200 Pond View Dr, Meriden, CT 06450-7195
Tel.: (203) 630-3311   DE
Web Site: http://www.rfsworld.com
Year Founded: 1950
Sales Range: $75-99.9 Million
Emp.: 165
Wireless Telecommunications Infrastructure Products Mfr & Designer
N.A.I.C.S.: 334220
Zhu Du-qing (Dir-Product Mgmt-Asia Pacific North)
Horst Spielkamp (Gen Mgr)
Asad Zoberi (Product Mgr)
Subsidiaries:
Radio Frequency Systems GmbH   (1)
Kabelkamp 20, Hannover, 30179, Germany
Tel.: (49) 511676550
Web Site: http://www.rfsworld.com
Sales Range: $25-49.9 Million
Mfr & Designer of Wireless Telecommunications Infrastructure Product
N.A.I.C.S.: 334220
Monika Maurer (Pres & CEO)
Karl Kirschenhofer (COO)

Radio Frequency Systems Pty. Ltd.   (1)
36 Gdn St, Kilsyth, 3137, VIC, Australia
Tel.: (61) 397518400
Web Site: http://www.rfsworld.com
Sales Range: $10-24.9 Million
Emp.: 100
Providers of Household Audio & Video Equipment
N.A.I.C.S.: 334310

Radio Frequency Systems Singapore Pte Ltd   (1)
750D Chai Chee Road #04-05 Lobby 2, Technopark at Chai Chee, Singapore, 469004, Singapore
Tel.: (65) 6240 8428
Web Site: http://www.rfsworld.com
Household Audio & Video Equipment
N.A.I.C.S.: 334310

RADIO PARTS COMPANY INC.
650 Alpha Dr, Pittsburgh, PA 15238
Tel.: (412) 963-6202
Web Site: http://www.camrpc.com

Sales Range: $10-24.9 Million
Emp.: 22
Electronic Parts
N.A.I.C.S.: 423690
Hersh H. Segall (Pres)
Rosiland Segall (Treas & Sec)

RADIO RESEARCH INSTRUMENT CO.
584 N Main St, Waterbury, CT 06704-3506
Tel.: (203) 753-5840   CT
Year Founded: 1952
Sales Range: $10-24.9 Million
Emp.: 15
Radar Systems & Equipment Mfr
N.A.I.C.S.: 334511
Jane Barber (Pres)

RADIO SYSTEMS CORPORATION
10427 Electric Ave, Knoxville, TN 37932-3369
Tel.: (865) 777-5404   TN
Web Site: http://www.petsafe.net
Year Founded: 1991
Sales Range: $25-49.9 Million
Emp.: 300
Electronic Pet Containment & Training Products
N.A.I.C.S.: 335999
Randy Boyd (Founder & Chm)
Willie Wallace (CEO)
Amy E. Miles (Acct Mgr)
Subsidiaries:
Invisible Fence, Inc.   (1)
10427 Electric Ave, Knoxville, TN 37932
Tel.: (610) 651-0999
Web Site: http://www.invisiblefence.com
Rev.: $12,400,000
Emp.: 200
Electrical Equipment & Supplies
N.A.I.C.S.: 335999

Subsidiary (Domestic):
Canine Fence Cos., Inc.   (2)
493 Danbury Rd, Wilton, CT 06897
Tel.: (203) 762-1294
Web Site: http://www.caninefence.com
Rev.: $2,108,000
Emp.: 17
Commercial & Institutional Building Construction
N.A.I.C.S.: 236220
Carol Hill (Owner)
Jennifer Hill (Pres & CEO)

Premier Pet Products   (1)
14201 Sommerville Ct, Midlothian, VA 23113
Tel.: (804) 379-4702
Web Site: http://www.petsafe.net
Rev.: $19,000,000
Emp.: 95
Pet Product Mfr
N.A.I.C.S.: 459910
Randal D. Boyd (CEO)

Radio Systems PetSafe Europe Ltd.   (1)
2nd Floor Elgee Building Market Square, Dundalk, Louth, Ireland
Tel.: (353) 58 44988
Web Site: http://intl.petsafe.net
Pet Care & Training Product Mfr
N.A.I.C.S.: 812910
Angela Critchley (Mktg Dir-Intl)
Randy Boyd (Chm)

RADIOLOGY REGIONAL CENTER, P.A.
3680 Broadway, Fort Myers, FL 33901
Tel.: (239) 936-2316   FL
Web Site: http://www.radiologyregional.com
Year Founded: 1963
Sales Range: $1-9.9 Million
Emp.: 71
Radiology Services

N.A.I.C.S.: 621111
Brian A. Krivisky (CEO & Mng Dir)
Traci Hotka (Mgr-Mktg)

RADIOMETRICS CORPORATION
4909 Nautilus Ct N Ste 110, Boulder, CO 80301
Tel.: (303) 449-9192
Web Site: http://www.radiometrics.com
Sales Range: $1-9.9 Million
Emp.: 20
Totalizing Fluid Meter & Counting Device Mfr
N.A.I.C.S.: 334514
Eric Plomondon (VP-Mfg)
Victor Markin (Dir-Engrg & R&D)
Dave Patton (Dir-Mfg & Sls)

RADIUMONE, INC.
55 2nd St 18th Fl, San Francisco, CA 94105
Tel.: (415) 418-2840
Web Site: http://www.radiumone.com
Year Founded: 2010
Sales Range: $100-124.9 Million
Emp.: 220
Software Development Services
N.A.I.C.S.: 541511
Bill Lonergan (CEO)
Rupert Staines (Mng Dir-Europe)
Alex Gove (VP-Corp Dev)
Igor Danchenko (VP-Engrg)
Dave Zinman (COO)
Bob Hall (Chief Strategy Officer)
Ann Piper (Sr VP-Sls-North America)
Kerry McCabe (Pres)
Louise Biggs (Dir-Bus Ops)
Emma Hazlehurst (Dir-Bus Dev)
Steve Baunach (VP-Data Svcs)

RADIUS FINANCIAL GROUP, INC.
600 Longwater Dr Ste 107, Norwell, MA 02061
Tel.: (781) 742-6500
Web Site: http://www.radiusgrp.com
Year Founded: 1999
Rev.: $3,800,000
Emp.: 34
Mortgage & Nonmortgage Loan Brokers
N.A.I.C.S.: 522310
Sarah Valentini (Co-Founder & CEO)
Keith Polaski (Co-Founder & COO)
David O'Connor (CTO)
Ryan McKenna (Gen Counsel-Corp Roster)
Subsidiaries:
Freedmont Mortgage Corp.   (1)
50 Scott Adam Rd 200, Cockeysville Hunt Valley, MD 21030
Tel.: (410) 628-0500
Web Site: http://www.freedmont.com
Rev.: $5,970,000
Emp.: 30
Real Estate Credit
N.A.I.C.S.: 522292
Kevin Murphy (Mgr)
Jay Delmont (Pres-Div)
Carl Delmont (Exec VP)

RADIUS GLOBAL MARKET RESEARCH
120 5th Ave Fl 9-10, New York, NY 10011
Tel.: (212) 633-1100
Web Site: http://www.radius-global.com
Rev.: $18,500,000
Emp.: 50
Market Analysis & Research
N.A.I.C.S.: 541910
Chip Lister (Mng Dir)
Glenn Staada (Sr VP)

Bari Weinhausen (Dir-Qualitative Res)
Cindy Han (Mng Dir-Asia)
Joy Liuzzo (VP-Seattle)
Kelly Coyne (VP)
Jill Gress (VP)
Judy Hoffman (Sr VP)
Shari Aaron (Sr VP)
Subsidiaries:
Radius EMEA   (1)
238 Saint John St, London, EC1V 4PH, United Kingdom   (100%)
Tel.: (44) 2031300707
Web Site: http://www.radius-global.com
Full-Service Market Research
N.A.I.C.S.: 541910
Michael Fodor (Mng Dir)
John Storey (Dir-Res)
Jeanette Vivier (Dir-Europe)

Radius Global Market Research   (1)
426 State St, Schenectady, NY 12305   (100%)
Tel.: (518) 631-2585
Web Site: http://www.radius-global.com
Market Research
N.A.I.C.S.: 541910
Jamie Myers (Dir-Client Svcs)

Radius Global Market Research   (1)
400 Galleria Pkwy Ste 1500, Atlanta, GA 30339   (100%)
Tel.: (678) 385-6172
Web Site: http://www.radius-global.com
Sales Range: $10-24.9 Million
Emp.: 1
Market Research
N.A.I.C.S.: 541910

Radius Global Market Research   (1)
5150 E Pacific Coast Highway, Long Beach, CA 90804   (100%)
Tel.: (562) 980-1800
Web Site: http://www.radius-global.com
Market Research
N.A.I.C.S.: 541910

Radius Global Market Research   (1)
533 Versailles Dr, Maitland, FL 32751   (100%)
Tel.: (407) 645-3611
Web Site: http://www.radius-global.com
Market Research
N.A.I.C.S.: 541910

Radius Global Market Research   (1)
500 Office Ctr Dr Ste 400, Fort Washington, PA 19034   (100%)
Tel.: (267) 513-1751
Web Site: http://www.radius-global.com
Market Research
N.A.I.C.S.: 541910
Shira Horn (VP)

Radius Global Market Research   (1)
100 Pine St Ste 1250, San Francisco, CA 94111   (100%)
Tel.: (415) 421-7800
Web Site: http://www.radius-global.com
Market Research
N.A.I.C.S.: 541910
Lesley Brooks (Sr VP)
Mark Vogel (Sr VP)

RADIUS GLOBAL SOLUTIONS LLC
50 W Skippack Pike, Ambler, PA 19002
Tel.: (267) 419-1111
Web Site: http://www.radiusgs.com
Year Founded: 1987
Sales Range: $10-24.9 Million
Emp.: 42
Collection Agencies
N.A.I.C.S.: 561440
Michael J. Barrist (CEO)
Steve Leckerman (COO)
Paul E. Weitzel (Officer-Dev)
William Fischer (CFO)
Steve Elliott (CIO)
Greg Stevens (Chief Compliance Officer)
Jennifer Ditnes (Chief HR Officer & Exec VP)
Scott Ross (Exec VP-Sls & Mktg)

COMPANIES

Subsidiaries:

Northland Group (1)
7831 Glenroy Rd Ste 110, Edina, MN 55439-3115
Tel.: (952) 831-4005
Web Site: http://www.northlandgroup.com
Collection Agencies
N.A.I.C.S.: 561440
Lance Black *(Pres)*

RADIX COMMUNICATIONS, INC.
3399 S Lakeshore Dr, Saint Joseph, MI 49085
Tel.: (269) 982-7400 MI
Web Site: http://www.radixcom.net
Year Founded: 1965
Sales Range: $10-24.9 Million
Emp.: 30
N.A.I.C.S.: 541810
Carl Mosher *(Pres)*
Colleen Stroup *(Mgr-Acctg)*

RADIX WIRE COMPANY
26000 Lakeland Blvd, Cleveland, OH 44132-2638
Tel.: (216) 731-9191 OH
Web Site: http://www.radix-wire.com
Year Founded: 1944
Sales Range: $50-74.9 Million
Emp.: 90
High Temperature Insulated Wire & Cable Mfr
N.A.I.C.S.: 332618
George Doll *(Mgr-IT)*
Pam Kochman *(Mgr-HR)*
Cynthia Lavo *(Controller)*

RADLER ENTERPRISES INC.
5825 N Sam Houston Pkwy W Ste 100, Houston, TX 77086
Tel.: (281) 440-8595
Web Site: http://www.radlertx.com
Rev.: $28,000,000
Emp.: 12
Real Estate Investors, Property Operators
N.A.I.C.S.: 523999
Mishael H. Radom *(Pres)*
Sandy Dyson *(Dir-Fin)*

Subsidiaries:

Radler Financial Inc. (1)
530 Wells Fargo Dr Ste 300, Houston, TX 77090
Tel.: (281) 440-8595
Web Site: http://www.radlertx.com
Sales Range: Less than $1 Million
Emp.: 5
Artists' Agents & Brokers
N.A.I.C.S.: 711410
Mishael H. Radom *(Pres)*

RADLEY ACURA
5823 Columbia Pike, Falls Church, VA 22041
Tel.: (703) 824-5700
Web Site:
 http://www.radleyacura.com
Year Founded: 1986
Sales Range: $25-49.9 Million
Emp.: 120
Car Whslr
N.A.I.C.S.: 441110
Rod Emmons *(Gen Mgr-Sls)*

RADMACHER BROTHERS EXCAVATING CO, INC.
2201 N State Route 7 Ste B, Pleasant Hill, MO 64080
Tel.: (816) 540-3614 MO
Web Site: http://www.radbroex.com
Year Founded: 1981
Highway, Street & Bridge Construction
N.A.I.C.S.: 237310

Robert Radmacher *(Pres & Co-Owner)*
Thomas Radmacher *(VP & Co-Owner)*

RADON MEDICAL IMAGING CORP.
384 Peachoid Rd, Gaffney, SC 29341
Tel.: (864) 487-0450 SC
Web Site:
 http://www.radonmedicalimaging.com
Year Founded: 1976
Sales Range: $1-9.9 Million
Emp.: 14
Repair Services Whol Medical/Hospital Equipment
N.A.I.C.S.: 811210
Anthony R. Bodenheimer *(Pres)*

Subsidiaries:

Alpha Imaging, Inc. (1)
4455 Glenbrook Rd, Willoughby, OH 44094
Tel.: (440) 953-3800
Web Site: https://www.alpha-imaging.com
Sales Range: $25-49.9 Million
Emp.: 50
Medical Imaging Equipment Mfr
N.A.I.C.S.: 339112
Michael Perrico *(CEO)*
Lance Ream *(CFO)*

Subsidiary (Domestic):

Medical Imaging Systems, Inc. (2)
2 Corporate Dr Ste 252, Shelton, CT 06484-6248
Tel.: (203) 944-0303
Web Site:
 http://www.medicalimagingsystems.com
Medical, Dental & Hospital Equipment & Supplies Merchant Whslr
N.A.I.C.S.: 423450
Randy Lester *(Pres)*

Reliant Medical Systems, Inc. (2)
2600 Cabover Dr, Hanover, MD 21076
Tel.: (410) 766-3311
Sales Range: $10-24.9 Million
Emp.: 15
Medical, Dental & Hospital Equipment & Supplies Merchant Whslr
N.A.I.C.S.: 423450
Patrick Veil *(Pres)*

RAF INDUSTRIES, INC.
1 Pitcairn Pl 165 Township Line Rd Ste 2100, Jenkintown, PA 19046-3593
Tel.: (215) 572-0738 PA
Web Site: https://www.rafequity.com
Year Founded: 1979
Sales Range: $10-24.9 Million
Emp.: 11
Equity Investment Firm
N.A.I.C.S.: 523999
Robert A. Fox *(Chm & CEO)*
Richard M. Horowitz *(Pres & COO)*
Amy Fox *(Asst Gen Counsel)*
Cheryl McCullough *(Controller)*
David A. Bennett *(Dir-Logistics)*
Michael F. Daly *(CFO & VP)*
Andrew Souder *(VP-Acq)*
Harry J. Ferguson *(Mgr-Risk)*
Jeffrey Panarey *(Dir-Acq)*
John F. Piree *(VP-Tax)*
Robert J. Pasco *(Dir-Tax)*
Tom Harper *(Pres)*
James Rymer *(CEO)*

Subsidiaries:

Automated Systems Design, Inc. (1)
775 Goddard Ct, Alpharetta, GA 30005
Tel.: (770) 740-2300
Web Site: http://www.asd-usa.com
Sales Range: $10-24.9 Million
Emp.: 36
Communication Equipment Mfr & Distr
N.A.I.C.S.: 517112
Kevin Kiziah *(Pres)*
Evelyn Stephens *(Mgr-Acctg)*

Subsidiary (Domestic):

Strong Systems International, Inc. (2)
6410 Atl Blvd, Norcross, GA 30071
Tel.: (770) 729-1199
Web Site: http://www.strongsystems.com
Rev.: $5,000,000
Emp.: 12
Security Systems Services, except Locksmiths
N.A.I.C.S.: 561621
Chris Verch *(CEO)*
Tim Taskaline *(CFO)*

RAFAEL LUMBER & SUPPLY COMPANY
930 Andersen Dr, San Rafael, CA 94901
Tel.: (415) 453-3043
Web Site: http://www.rafael-lumber.com
Sales Range: $25-49.9 Million
Emp.: 40
Lumber & Other Building Materials Mfr
N.A.I.C.S.: 423310
Donald Kelleher *(Pres)*

RAFFERTY HOLDINGS, LLC
1010 Franklin Ave Ste 300A, Garden City, NY 11530
Tel.: (516) 693-5380 NY
Web Site:
 http://www.raffertyholdings.com
Year Founded: 1987
Emp.: 20
Holding Company; Financial Investment Services
N.A.I.C.S.: 551112
Michael Rafferty *(Pres)*

Subsidiaries:

Hilton Capital Management, LLC (1)
1010 Franklin Ave Ste 300A, Garden City, NY 11530
Tel.: (516) 693-5380
Web Site: http://www.hiltoncm.com
Rev.: $320,000,000
Emp.: 12
Investment Advisory Services
N.A.I.C.S.: 523940
C. Craig O'Neill *(CEO)*
William Garvey *(Founder & Chief Investment Officer)*
Barbara Martens *(Chief Compliance Officer)*
Clark Gillies *(Mgr-Customer Rels)*
Kate DeAngelo *(VP-Ops)*
David W. Jennings *(Mng Dir & Mgr-Relationship)*
Kevin McCarthy *(VP)*
Andrew S. Molloy *(Dir-Mktg)*
Alexander D. Oxenham *(Sr Portfolio Mgr)*
Suzanne Casey *(Mng Dir & Head-Sls & Distr)*
Tim Reilly *(Pres)*

The Direxion Funds (1)
500 5th Ave Ste 415, New York, NY 10110
Tel.: (646) 572-3390
Web Site: http://www.direxionfunds.com
Leveraged Index & Alternative-Class Mutual Fund Investment Solutions
N.A.I.C.S.: 525910
Daniel D. O'Neill *(Pres & Chief Investment Officer)*
Andy O'Rourke *(CMO)*
Edward Egilinsky *(Mng Dir & Head-Alternative Investments)*
Paul Brigandi *(Sr VP-Trading)*

RAFFERTY PONTIAC GMC, SUBARU
4700 W Chester Pike, Newtown Square, PA 19073
Tel.: (610) 353-6900
Sales Range: $10-24.9 Million
Emp.: 50
Car Whslr
N.A.I.C.S.: 441110
Robert Rafferty *(Pres)*

RAFFERTY'S INC.
1750 Scottsville Rd Ste 2, Bowling Green, KY 42104-3375
Tel.: (270) 781-2834 KY
Web Site: http://www.raffertys.com
Year Founded: 1981
Sales Range: $25-49.9 Million
Emp.: 800
Eating Place
N.A.I.C.S.: 722511
Doug Taulbee *(CFO)*
Joe Wathen *(VP & Dir-Ops)*
Jenifer Watkins *(Dir-Mktg)*

RAFT RIVER RURAL ELECTRIC COOPERATIVE, INC.
155 N Main, Malta, ID 83342
Tel.: (208) 645-2211
Web Site: http://www.rrelectric.com
Year Founded: 1939
Sales Range: $10-24.9 Million
Emp.: 32
Electric Power Distribution Services
N.A.I.C.S.: 221122
Heber Carpenter *(Gen Mgr)*
Kim Smith *(Mgr-Ops)*
Andrea Scott *(Supvr-Acctg)*
Kurt Anderson *(Mgr-Fin & Admin)*

RAFTELIS FINANCIAL CONSULTANTS, INC.
227 W Trade St Ste 1400, Charlotte, NC 28202
Web Site: http://www.raftelis.com
Year Founded: 1993
Sales Range: $1-9.9 Million
Emp.: 20
Management Consulting Services
N.A.I.C.S.: 541618
George Raftelis *(Founder)*
Harold Smith *(VP)*
Melissa Levin *(Mgr)*
Sudhir Pardiwala *(Exec VP)*
Bart Kreps *(Sr Mgr)*
Darin Thomas *(Dir-Mgmt Consulting)*
Doug Bean *(Dir-Govt Svcs)*
Elaine Vastis *(Mgr)*
Frank Davis *(Mgr)*
Jon Davis *(Mgr)*
Keith Readling *(Exec VP)*
Mike Rocca *(Dir-Ops-Florida)*
Peiffer Brandt *(Pres & CEO)*
Sanjay Gaur *(Mgr)*
Thomas Beckley *(Sr Mgr)*
Andrew Rheem *(Mgr)*
Habib Isaac *(Mgr)*
Henrietta Locklear *(Sr Mgr)*
Joe Crea *(Mgr)*
Rick Giardina *(Exec VP)*
Rocky Craley *(Mgr)*
Tony Hairston *(Sr Mgr)*

RAGE ADMINISTRATIVE & MARKETING SERVICES, INC.
1313 N Webb Rd Ste 200, Wichita, KS 67206-4077
Tel.: (316) 634-1888
Web Site: http://www.rage-inc.com
Sales Range: $75-99.9 Million
Emp.: 2,500
Restaurant Management Services
N.A.I.C.S.: 541618
Steve Stansbury *(CFO)*
Ronald C. Geist *(Pres & Pres)*
Ron C. Geist *(Pres)*

RAGINGBULL.COM, LLC
62 Calef Hwy Ste 233, Lee, NH 03861
Web Site: http://www.ragingbull.com
Year Founded: 2005
Sales Range: $1-9.9 Million
Emp.: 200
Financial Consulting Services
N.A.I.C.S.: 523940

RAGINGBULL.COM, LLC

RagingBull.com, LLC—(Continued)
William C. Martin *(Co-Founder)*
Jeff Bishop *(Founder)*

RAGLAND BROS. RETAIL COMPANIES INC.
2836 Dug Hill Rd, Huntsville, AL 35811-7933
Tel.: (256) 859-3774   AL
Year Founded: 1984
Sales Range: $50-74.9 Million
Emp.: 450
Provider of Grocery Services
N.A.I.C.S.: 445110
Ward Ragland *(Pres)*

RAGLAND MILLS, INC.
14079 Hammer Rd, Neosho, MO 64850
Tel.: (417) 451-2510
Web Site: http://www.raglandmills.com
Year Founded: 1941
Sales Range: $10-24.9 Million
Emp.: 25
Animal Food Product Mfr
N.A.I.C.S.: 311119
Deborah Ragland *(VP)*
Theresa Miele *(Sec)*
Eloise Ragland *(Owner)*
Judy Ring *(Mgr)*

RAGLE INC.
5266 Vann Rd, Newburgh, IN 47630-8485
Tel.: (812) 853-9558
Web Site: http://www.ragleinc.com
Year Founded: 1993
Sales Range: $10-24.9 Million
Emp.: 50
Construction Engineering Services
N.A.I.C.S.: 237310
Samuel Ragle *(Owner)*

RAGO & SON, INC.
1029 51st Ave, Oakland, CA 94601
Tel.: (510) 536-5700
Web Site: http://www.rago-son.com
Sales Range: $10-24.9 Million
Emp.: 50
Metal Stamping Services
N.A.I.C.S.: 332119
Dominic Rago *(Pres)*
Gerald Accardo *(VP)*

RAGOZZINO FOODS INC.
10 Ames Ave, Meriden, CT 06451
Tel.: (203) 238-2553
Web Site: http://www.ragozzino.com
Rev.: $17,000,000
Emp.: 75
Frozen Specialty Food Mfr
N.A.I.C.S.: 311412
Nancy Ragozzino *(VP-Bus Dev)*
Susan Ragozzino *(VP-Product Dev)*
John Ragozzino *(VP)*
Gloria Ragozzino *(Pres)*

RAGUS MEDIA, LLC
4200 Wanda St, Idaho Falls, ID 83406
Tel.: (208) 201-1977
Web Site: http://www.ragusmedia.com
Year Founded: 2006
Sales Range: Less than $1 Million
Emp.: 3
Advetising Agency
N.A.I.C.S.: 541810
Cameron Andrews *(CEO & Mgr-Bus)*
Michael Cousin *(Sr Acct Mgr)*

RAH INDUSTRIES
24800 Ave Rockefeller, Valencia, CA 91355-3467
Tel.: (661) 295-5190
Web Site: http://www.rah-ind.com
Rev.: $11,194,645
Emp.: 78
Fabricate Sheet Metalwork
N.A.I.C.S.: 332322
Ronald Hansen *(Pres & CEO)*
Sandra Hansen *(CFO & VP)*
Gerry Quintal *(Gen Mgr)*

RAHE INC.
1522 Park Rd, Waynesboro, VA 22980
Tel.: (540) 943-3176
Year Founded: 1971
Sales Range: $10-24.9 Million
Emp.: 450
Fast-Food Restaurant, Chain
N.A.I.C.S.: 722513

RAHN CONTRACTING, LLC
534 N Black Horse Pike, Blackwood, NJ 08012
Tel.: (856) 629-5097
Property Maintenance Service Provider
N.A.I.C.S.: 531312
Matt Rahn *(Owner)*

Subsidiaries:

All-Green Turf Management Corp.   (1)
808 Warsaw Ave, Blackwood, NJ 08012
Tel.: (856) 232-1776
Web Site: http://www.allgreenturf.com
Sales Range: $1-9.9 Million
Emp.: 30
Lawn And Garden Services
N.A.I.C.S.: 561730
Gene Martinez *(Pres)*

RAHR CORPORATION
800 W First Ave, Shakopee, MN 55379
Tel.: (952) 445-1431
Web Site: http://www.rahr.com
Year Founded: 1847
Sales Range: $450-499.9 Million
Emp.: 300
Craft Brewing & Specialty Malts
N.A.I.C.S.: 424810
William Rahr *(Pres & CEO)*

Subsidiaries:

Rahr Malting Co   (1)
800 W First Ave, Shakopee, MN 55379   (100%)
Tel.: (952) 445-1431
Web Site: http://www.rahr.com
Malt Production
N.A.I.C.S.: 311213
Ron Johnson *(Pres)*

Subsidiary (Domestic):

BSG CraftBrewing   (2)
701 W 3rd Ave, Shakopee, MN 55379   (100%)
Tel.: (952) 224-1385
Web Site: http://bsgcraftbrewing.com
Craft Breweries
N.A.I.C.S.: 312120
Chris German *(Mgr-Sls-Midwest)*

RAHR MALTING CO. INC.
800 W 1st Ave, Shakopee, MN 55379-1148
Tel.: (952) 445-1431   MN
Web Site: http://www.rahrcorporation.com
Year Founded: 1847
Sales Range: $25-49.9 Million
Emp.: 135
Produces Malt & Industry Related Brewing Supplies
N.A.I.C.S.: 311213
Tim Dircks *(Mgr)*

Subsidiaries:

Rahr Malting Canada Ltd   (1)
Highway 12 East, PO Box 113, Alix, T0C 0B0, AB, Canada   (100%)
Tel.: (403) 747-2777
Sales Range: $10-24.9 Million
Emp.: 40
Provider of Malting Services
N.A.I.C.S.: 311213

RAIFF PARTNERS, INC.
152 W 57th St 29th Fl, New York, NY 10019
Tel.: (212) 247-4000   DE
Year Founded: 1995
Equity Investment Firm
N.A.I.C.S.: 523999
Robert M. Raiff *(Pres & CEO)*
Sheldon Brody *(CFO)*

RAIL DELIVERY SERVICES, INC.
8600 Banana Ave, Fontana, CA 92335
Tel.: (909) 355-4100   CA
Web Site: http://www.raildelivery.com
Year Founded: 1981
Sales Range: $10-24.9 Million
Emp.: 44
Moving Services
N.A.I.C.S.: 484210
Judi Girard-Stefflre *(Founder, Chm & COO)*
Sharon Brooks *(Pres)*
Erin Stefflre-Garcia *(VP-Fin & Admin)*
Janet Galgani *(Controller)*

RAILMARK HOLDINGS INC.
450 Mamaroneck Ave Fl 4, Harrison, NY 10528-2400
Tel.: (248) 960-9440
Web Site: http://www.railmark.com
Sales Financing
N.A.I.C.S.: 522220
Bradford Holley *(VP)*

RAILROAD CONSTRUCTION COMPANY, INC.
75-77 Grove St, Paterson, NJ 07503
Tel.: (973) 684-0362
Web Site: http://www.railroadconstruction.com
Year Founded: 1926
Sales Range: $75-99.9 Million
Emp.: 100
Bridge Construction
N.A.I.C.S.: 237310
Alfonso Daloisio Jr. *(Pres)*

Subsidiaries:

Beach Electric Company Inc.   (1)
67-69 Grove St, Paterson, NJ 07503-2238   (100%)
Tel.: (973) 413-1900
Web Site: http://www.beachelectricco.com
Sales Range: $10-24.9 Million
Emp.: 35
General Electrical Contractor
N.A.I.C.S.: 238210

RCC Builders & Developers, Inc.   (1)
65 Grove St Ste 67, Paterson, NJ 07503
Tel.: (973) 684-9957
Web Site: http://www.rccbuilders.com
Emp.: 15
Construction Engineering Services
N.A.I.C.S.: 541330

RCC Fabricators, Inc.   (1)
2035 Route 206 S, Southampton, NJ 08088
Tel.: (609) 859-9350
Web Site: http://www.rccfabricators.com
Emp.: 38
Construction Engineering Services
N.A.I.C.S.: 541330
Scott Vesper *(Plant Mgr)*

RAILROAD DEVELOPMENT CORP.
381 Mansfield Ave Ste 500, Pittsburgh, PA 15220-2754
Tel.: (412) 928-0777
Web Site: http://www.rrdc.com
Line-Haul Railroads
N.A.I.C.S.: 482111
Robert Pietrandrea *(Pres)*

Subsidiaries:

Iowa Interstate Railroad, Ltd.   (1)
5900 6th SW, Cedar Rapids, IA 52404   (60%)
Tel.: (319) 298-5400
Web Site: http://www.iaisrr.com
Rail Transport Services
N.A.I.C.S.: 482111
Carrie Evans *(VP-Sls & Mktg)*
Adam C. Sutherland *(Dir-Safety & Security)*
Andy Laurent *(Dir-Bus Dev)*
Cheryl Rangel *(Dir-Sls & Mktg)*
Joe Parsons *(Pres & CEO)*
Mike Stuver *(Chief Transportation Officer)*

RAILS COMPANY
101 Newark Way, Maplewood, NJ 07040
Tel.: (973) 763-4320   CT
Web Site: http://www.railsco.com
Year Founded: 1932
Sales Range: $10-24.9 Million
Emp.: 34
Railroad Equipment
N.A.I.C.S.: 336510
Garwood N. Burwell *(Pres)*
Mik Kinda *(Treas & Sec)*
Kendis Mikloskinda *(Controller)*
Ed T. Oksienik *(Mgr-IT & Admin-Network)*

RAILWAY CLAIM SERVICES INC.
52 S Main St, Lexington, TN 38351
Tel.: (731) 967-1796
Web Site: http://www.railway-claim-services.com
Sales Range: $10-24.9 Million
Emp.: 15
Insurance Claims Adjusting
N.A.I.C.S.: 524291
Phillis Little *(Sec & Owner)*

RAILWAY DISTRIBUTING INC.
675 Emory St, San Jose, CA 95110
Tel.: (408) 866-9266
Web Site: http://www.fbmsales.com
Sales Range: $25-49.9 Million
Emp.: 50
Drywall Materials
N.A.I.C.S.: 423320
Jerry Ferguson *(Mgr-Ops)*
Kai Markee *(Mgr-Campbell)*

RAIN
4 Greenleaf Woods Ste 301, Portsmouth, NH 03801
Tel.: (603) 498-5864
Sales Range: $10-24.9 Million
Emp.: 7
N.A.I.C.S.: 541810
Steve Casey *(Pres)*
Katherine Palm *(Acct Mgr)*

RAIN
610 W 26th St 9th Fl, New York, NY 10001
Tel.: (212) 206-6850
Web Site: http://www.mediarain.com
Year Founded: 2003
Sales Range: $10-24.9 Million
Emp.: 75
Advertising Agency
N.A.I.C.S.: 541810
Brian Edelman *(Founder & Partner)*
Thomas Crowley *(Assoc Dir-Creative)*
Nithya Thadani *(CEO)*
Will Hall *(Exec Dir-Creative)*
Terra Reilly *(Mng Dir-Utah)*
Eric Turkington *(VP-Strategic Partnerships-Seattle)*
Khaya Dlanga *(Chief Mktg Officer-South Africa)*

COMPANIES

RAIN ASSOCIATES
18136 Regents Square Dr, Tampa, FL 33647
Tel.: (813) 349-8626
Web Site: http://www.metro-bay.com
Sales Range: $1-9.9 Million
Real Estate Services
N.A.I.C.S.: 531390
Bill Rain (Pres)

RAIN BIRD CORPORATION
1000 W Sierra Madre Ave, Azusa, CA 91702
Tel.: (626) 812-3400
Web Site: http://www.rainbird.com
Year Founded: 1933
Sales Range: $150-199.9 Million
Emp.: 175
Sprinklers & Valves & Controllers & All Encompassing Automatic Systems Mfr
N.A.I.C.S.: 332919
Dave Johnson (Dir-Corp Mktg)
Shane Russell (Mgr-Ops)
J. R. Bergantino (Dir-Golf & Intl)
Stuart Hackwell (Dir-Golf Strategic Bus Unit)
Michael L. Donoghue (CEO)
Art Ludwick (Chm)

Subsidiaries:

Rain Bird Corporation - Rain Bird Golf Division (1)
6991 E Southpoint Rd Bldg 1, Tucson, AZ 85706
Tel.: (520) 741-6100
Golf Club Operator
N.A.I.C.S.: 713910
Michael McAfee (Dir-Quality)
Ian Williams (Mgr-Golf Specification)

Rain Bird Corporation - Residential Products Division (1)
1000 W Sierra Madre Ave, Azusa, CA 91702
Tel.: (626) 963-9311
Web Site: http://www.rainbird.com
Rev.: $10,200,000
Mfr of Irrigation Products
N.A.I.C.S.: 333112

RAIN GUARD
8280 14th Ave, Sacramento, CA 95826-4719
Tel.: (916) 454-2560
Web Site: http://www.raynguard.com
Sales Range: $10-24.9 Million
Emp.: 6
Road Roller Parts Mfr
N.A.I.C.S.: 325520
Dave Hartman (Plant Mgr)

RAIN HOME ATTENDANT SERVICES INC
811 Morris Park, Bronx, NY 10461
Tel.: (718) 829-2131
Year Founded: 1979
Sales Range: $25-49.9 Million
Emp.: 1,617
Elder Care Services
N.A.I.C.S.: 623312
Sobeida Valdez (Program Dir)

RAINBO OIL COMPANY
2255 Kerper Blvd, Dubuque, IA 52001
Tel.: (563) 582-7291
Web Site: http://www.rainbolubes.com
Rev.: $30,771,807
Emp.: 50
Automotive Supplies & Parts
N.A.I.C.S.: 423120
Paul M. Fahey (Pres)

RAINBO RECORD MANUFACTURING CORP
8960 Eton Ave, Canoga Park, CA 91304-1621
Tel.: (818) 280-1100
Web Site: http://www.rainborecords.com
Year Founded: 1939
Rev.: $16,744,353
Emp.: 115
Prerecorded Records & Tapes
N.A.I.C.S.: 334610
Steve Sheldon (Pres & CEO)
David Dickerson (CFO)

RAINBOW AUTOMOTIVE LLC
1700 Westbank Expy, Harvey, LA 70058
Tel.: (504) 367-1700
Web Site: http://www.rainbowautomotive.com
Rev.: $21,100,000
Emp.: 63
Automobiles, New & Used
N.A.I.C.S.: 441110
Lloyd Guillot (Pres)
Jim Hollis (VP)

RAINBOW CORAL CORP.
871 Coronado Center Dr Ste 200, Henderson, NV 89052
Tel.: (702) 940-2345
Year Founded: 2010
Agricultural Production Services
N.A.I.C.S.: 112990
Kimberly Palmer (CEO & CFO)

RAINBOW DESIGN BUILDERS, INC.
209A Shaun Ln, Hailey, ID 83333
Tel.: (208) 788-5855
Year Founded: 1983
Rev.: $10,000,000
Emp.: 15
New Single-Family Housing Construction
N.A.I.C.S.: 236115
Dan Kurdy (Pres)

RAINBOW GRAPHICS INC.
933 Tower Rd, Mundelein, IL 60060
Tel.: (847) 824-9600
Web Site: http://www.rainbowgraphics.com
Commercial Lithographic Printing
N.A.I.C.S.: 323111
Scott Campbell (VP & Gen Mgr)
Jeff Koszuta (Pres)
Claude Koszuta Jr. (VP-Sls)

RAINBOW INC.
7324 36th Ave N, Minneapolis, MN 55427
Tel.: (763) 535-4041
Web Site: http://www.rainbowincmn.com
Year Founded: 1957
Sales Range: $10-24.9 Million
Emp.: 60
Commercial Painting Services
N.A.I.C.S.: 238320
Paul Haagenson (Pres)
Mike DeBuhr (Mgr-Indus Div)

RAINBOW LIGHT NUTRITIONAL SYSTEMS, INC.
100 Ave Tas Beverage, Santa Cruz, CA 95060
Tel.: (831) 429-9089
Web Site: http://www.rainbowlight.com
Year Founded: 1981
Rev.: $6,000,000
Emp.: 60
Mfr of Medicinal & Botanical Products
N.A.I.C.S.: 325411

Linda Kahler (Founder & Pres)
Sharon Dressen (Sr Mgr-Education & Outreach)
Rona Meakin (Mgr-Mktg Svcs)
Christopher Hobbs (Dir-Integrative Science)

RAINBOW MOVERS INC.
19 National Dr, Franklin, MA 02038
Tel.: (508) 528-4111
Web Site: http://www.rainbowmovers.com
Sales Range: $10-24.9 Million
Emp.: 49
Freight & Furniture Movers
N.A.I.C.S.: 484121
Jim McEnaney (Principal)
Erin McEnaney (Pres)

RAINBOW RASCALS LEARNING CENTER, INC.
1732 Crooks Rd, Troy, MI 48084
Tel.: (248) 569-2500
Web Site: http://www.rainbowchilddevelopment.com
Year Founded: 1986
Sales Range: $1-9.9 Million
Emp.: 500
Child Day Care Services
N.A.I.C.S.: 624410
Patrick Fenton (CEO)
Paul Hafeli (CFO)
Karen Krygier (COO)
Hugh McBride (CMO)
Rodney Blight (Dir-Construction)
Beth Apple (Dir-HR)
Gena Sayej (Dir-Ops-Southeast)
Ted Toloff (Co-CFO)

Subsidiaries:

The Little Red School House, Inc. (1)
3210 200th Pl SW, Lynnwood, WA 98036
Tel.: (425) 775-6070
Web Site: http://www.littlered.org
Sales Range: $1-9.9 Million
Emp.: 42
Child Care Services
N.A.I.C.S.: 624410

RAINBOW RYDERS INC.
5601 Eagle Rock Ave NE, Albuquerque, NM 87113
Tel.: (800) 725-2477
Web Site: http://www.rainbowryders.com
Year Founded: 1984
Hot Air Balloon Flights
N.A.I.C.S.: 487990
Scott Appelman (Founder, Pres & CEO)

Subsidiaries:

Private Balloon Flights LLC (1)
4620 Plume Rd, Albuquerque, NM 87120
Tel.: (505) 550-2677
Hot Air Balloon Flights
N.A.I.C.S.: 487990

RAINBOW STATION INC.
4551 Cox Rd Ste 310, Glen Allen, VA 23060
Tel.: (804) 747-5900
Web Site: http://www.rainbowstation.org
Year Founded: 1989
Sales Range: $1-9.9 Million
Emp.: 150
Child Day Care, Preschool & After Care
N.A.I.C.S.: 624410
Gail W. Johnson (CEO)
Elizabeth Bodenheimer (Dir-Preschool)

RAINBOW TECHNOLOGY

RAINEY ROAD HOLDINGS, INC.

CORPORATION
261 Cahaba Vly Pkwy, Pelham, AL 35124
Tel.: (205) 733-0333
Web Site: http://www.rainbowtech.net
Year Founded: 1971
Sales Range: $10-24.9 Million
Emp.: 30
Chemical Products Mfr & Marketer
N.A.I.C.S.: 325998
Penny Causey (VP-Sls-Telecom Div)
Renee Steeley (Mgr-Quality Assurance)

RAINES IMPORTS, INC.
5102 MacCorkle Ave SW, South Charleston, WV 25309
Tel.: (304) 768-1251
Web Site: http://www.lesterraines.com
Year Founded: 1953
Rev.: $10,000,000
Emp.: 65
Automobiles, New & Used
N.A.I.C.S.: 811121
Greta Smith (Office Mgr)
Snowden Lester Raines III (Pres)

Subsidiaries:

Lester Raines Mazda (1)
5035 MacCorkle Ave SW, Charleston, WV 25309
Tel.: (304) 768-1251
Web Site: http://www.mazdalesterraines.com
Sales Range: $10-24.9 Million
New & Used Car Dealer
N.A.I.C.S.: 441110
Dale Moats (Mgr-Body Shop)
Tim Russell (Mgr-Sls)
Andrew Barr (Mgr-Mazda Svc)
Tim Nichols (Mgr-Parts)

Lester Raines Mitsubishi (1)
5035 MacCorkle Ave SW, Charleston, WV 25309
Tel.: (304) 768-1251
Web Site: http://www.mitsubishilesterraines.com
Sales Range: $10-24.9 Million
New & Used Car Dealer
N.A.I.C.S.: 441110

RAINEY ROAD HOLDINGS, INC.
15600 37th Ave N Cte 100, Plymouth, MN 55446
Tel.: (763) 541-1410
Web Site: http://www.crowntonka.com
Holding Company; Commercial Refrigeration Unit Mfr
N.A.I.C.S.: 551112
Michael Kahler (Chm)

Subsidiaries:

Rainey Road LLC (1)
10700 Highway 55 Ste 300, Plymouth, MN 55441
Tel.: (763) 541-1410
Web Site: http://www.crowntonka.com
Sales Range: $10-24.9 Million
Emp.: 25
Commercial Refrigeration Unit Mfr
N.A.I.C.S.: 333415

Subsidiary (Domestic):

CrownTonka, Inc. (2)
10700 Hwy 55 Ste 300, Plymouth, MN 55441
Tel.: (763) 541-1410
Web Site: http://www.crowntonka.com
Sales Range: $10-24.9 Million
Commercial Refrigeration Equipment Mfr
N.A.I.C.S.: 333415
Greg Sullens (Sr VP-Mktg & Sls)
Dennis Parle (VP-Sls-West)
Terry Brooks (VP-Mfg)
Mike Polis (Controller)
Jim Cook (VP-Sls-West)
Mark Norvold (VP-Sls-Midwest)

RAINEY ROAD HOLDINGS, INC.

Rainey Road Holdings, Inc.—(Continued)
John Stocks (Sr VP-Sls & Mktg)
David Teske (Mgr-Customer Svc)
Scott Wonderly (VP-Sls-Southeast)

Subsidiary (Domestic):

CrownTonka California, Inc. (3)
4215 Airport Dr, Ontario, CA 91761
Tel.: (909) 605-6419
Web Site: http://www.thermalrite.com
Sales Range: $10-24.9 Million
Commercial Refrigeration Equipment Mfr
N.A.I.C.S.: 333415
Jim Cook (VP-Sls-West)
Steve Gill (Sr VP-Sls & Mktg)
Derek Johnson (Mgr-Customer Svc)

RAINFOREST ALLIANCE
298 5th Ave 7th Fl, New York, NY 10001
Tel.: (212) 677-1900 NY
Web Site: https://www.rainforest-alliance.org
Year Founded: 1987
Sales Range: $25-49.9 Million
Emp.: 168
Biodiversity Conservation Services
N.A.I.C.S.: 813312
Leslie Park (Gen Counsel)
Lisa Gauchey (VP-HR)
Ana Paula Tavares (Exec VP)
Richard Z. Donovan (Sr VP & VP-Forestry)
Nigel Sizer (Pres)
Han de Groot (CEO)
Susan Tressler (Chief External Rels Officer)

RAINFOREST DISTRIBUTION CORP
20 Pulaski St, Bayonne, NJ 07002
Tel.: (201) 683-7952
Web Site:
 https://www.rainforestdistribution.com
Emp.: 100
Food & Beverage Distr
N.A.I.C.S.: 424490
Alexander Ridings (CEO)

Subsidiaries:

Associated Buyers, LLC (1)
50 Commerce Way, Barrington, NH 03825
Tel.: (603) 664-5656
Sales Range: $1-9.9 Million
Emp.: 75
Whol Groceries
N.A.I.C.S.: 424490
Karta Owens (Pres)
Nancy McKeton (Controller)

RAINFOREST INC.
420 5th Ave FL 27, New York, NY 10018
Tel.: (212) 575-7620
Web Site: http://www.thermalrite.com
Rev.: $13,000,000
Emp.: 20
Mfr of Wool & Down-Filled Outerwear & Sports Wear
N.A.I.C.S.: 315250
Jack Wu (Founder & Pres)
Alan Bindler (Dir-Men's Fashion)
Weiming Peng (Mgr-Production)

RAINIER INDUSTRIES, LTD.
18375 Olympic Ave S, Seattle, WA 98188
Tel.: (425) 251-1800
Web Site: http://www.rainier.com
Sales Range: $25-49.9 Million
Emp.: 150
Fabric & Display Products Mfr
N.A.I.C.S.: 339950
Scott Campbell (Chm)
Brian Rowinski (VP-Customer Svc)
David Traub (CEO)

RAINIER PARTNERS LP
1111 3rd Ave Ste 3030, Seattle, WA 98101
Web Site:
 http://www.rainierpartners.com
Year Founded: 2020
Holding Company
N.A.I.C.S.: 551112
Lucas Bench (VP)
Jonathan Lo (VP)
Alex Rolfe (Mng Partner)
Jon Altman (Mng Partner)

Subsidiaries:

Calpine Containers Inc. (1)
380 W Spruce Ave Clovis, Fresno, CA 93611
Tel.: (559) 519-7199
Web Site: http://www.calpinecontainers.com
Rev.: $97,000,000
Emp.: 15
Corrugated & Solid Fiber Boxes
N.A.I.C.S.: 424130
Walter D. Tindell (CEO)
Mike Martin (Mgr-Sls)
Marco Mastro (Dir-Art & Creative)
Scott Hickman (VP-Sls & Ops)
Ken Sommers (CFO & VP)

Subsidiary (Domestic):

JS AG Packaging, Inc. (2)
6850 New Kapittel Ct, Shafter, CA 93263
Tel.: (661) 833-9383
Web Site: http://www.jsagpackaging.com
Industrial & Personal Service Paper Merchant Whslr
N.A.I.C.S.: 424130
Bryan Reyes (Mgr-Fleet & Maintenance)
Jeff Smith (Founder)

SCI Floor Covering, Inc. (1)
21440 Melrose Ave, Southfield, MI 48075-5631
Tel.: (248) 359-3500
Web Site: https://commercial-carpet.net
Sales Range: $1-9.9 Million
Emp.: 26
Flooring Contract Services
N.A.I.C.S.: 238330
Tony Hutcheson (Mgr-Project)

Subsidiary (Domestic):

United Carpet Company, Inc. (2)
5434 Eagle Industrial Ct, Hazelwood, MO 63042
Tel.: (314) 731-4280
Web Site: http://www.unitedcarpetinc.com
Sales Range: $1-9.9 Million
Emp.: 30
Floor Laying And Floor Work, Nec
N.A.I.C.S.: 238330
Gary Russo (Pres)

RAINIER SEED INC.
1404 4th St, Davenport, WA 99122
Tel.: (509) 725-1235
Web Site:
 http://www.rainierseeds.com
Sales Range: $10-24.9 Million
Emp.: 24
Oil Nuts, Kernels, Seeds
N.A.I.C.S.: 424590
Ed Johnston (Controller)

RAINIER SYMPHONY
PO Box 58182, Seattle, WA 98138
Tel.: (206) 781-5618
Web Site:
 http://www.rainiersymphony.org
Year Founded: 1981
Sales Range: $10-24.9 Million
Emp.: 100
Symphony Orchestra
N.A.I.C.S.: 711130
Tom Metcalf (Pres)
Susan Reynolds (VP)
Bev Willison (Treas)
David Wayne Waltman (Dir-Music)
Wendy Hilliker (Mgr-Box Office & Coord-Volunteer)
Annette Fanslow (Sec)
Eric Tishkoff (Pres)
Nancy Hall (Treas)

RAINING ROSE, INC.
100 30th Str Dr SE, Cedar Rapids, IA 52403
Tel.: (800) 481-3934
Web Site: http://www.rainingrose.com
Year Founded: 1997
Rev.: $6,900,000
Emp.: 52
Soap & Detergent Mfr
N.A.I.C.S.: 325611
Mike Wehr (Mgr-Contract Sls)
Charles B. Hammond Jr. (Pres)
Nathan Robson (Dir-Promo Sls)
Kyle Hach (VP-Ops)
Katie Beitz (Dir-Mktg)

RAINMAKER CAPITAL, LLC
1315 Bridgeway Sausalito, Sausalito, CA 94965
Tel.: (415) 339-3055
Web Site:
 http://www.rainmakercap.com
Year Founded: 1995
Secondary Market Financing
N.A.I.C.S.: 522299
Edwin Metcalf (Co-Founder)
Scott Lipsitz (Partner)

Subsidiaries:

FacilityONE Technologies, LLC (1)
730 W Main St Ste 2W, Louisville, KY 40202
Tel.: (502) 805-2100
Web Site: http://www.facilityone.com
Computer System Design Services
N.A.I.C.S.: 541512
Renee Farmer (CEO)
Robin Alston (CTO)
Greg Fisher (CFO)
Jennifer Bergman (VP-Bus Dev)
Robert Hamilton (VP-Ops)

RAINS BIRCHARD INC.
1481 NW 13th Ave Ste 545, Portland, OR 97209
Tel.: (503) 297-1791 OR
Web Site:
 http://www.rainsbirchardmarketing.com
Year Founded: 2010
Advetising Agency
N.A.I.C.S.: 541810
Jon Rains (Pres)

RAINTREE SYSTEMS, INC.
27307 Via Industria, Temecula, CA 92590
Tel.: (951) 252-9400 CA
Web Site: http://www.raintreeinc.com
Year Founded: 1982
Sales Range: $1-9.9 Million
Emp.: 90
Medical Administration Software Development Services
N.A.I.C.S.: 541511
Nina Moses (Coord-Implementation)

RAISER SENIOR SERVICES LLC
800 S Claremont St Ste 201, San Mateo, CA 94402
Tel.: (650) 342-9026
Web Site: http://www.raiser.com
Sales Range: $10-24.9 Million
Retirement Community
N.A.I.C.S.: 623311

RAISING CANE'S USA, LLC
3313 Highland Rd, Baton Rouge, LA 70808
Tel.: (225) 387-3533
Web Site:
 http://www.raisingcanes.com
Year Founded: 1996
Sales Range: $100-124.9 Million
Emp.: 2,500
Full Service Restaurants Business

U.S. PRIVATE

N.A.I.C.S.: 722511
Todd Graves (Founder, Chm & CEO)
Shawn Jenkins (VP-Pur)

RAIT FINANCIAL TRUST
2 Logan Sq 100 N 18th St 23rd Fl, Philadelphia, PA 19103
Tel.: (215) 207-2100 MD
Web Site: http://www.rait.com
Sales Range: $25-49.9 Million
Real Estate Investment Trust
N.A.I.C.S.: 525990
David T. Kra (Sr VP)
Siu Yan Lin (Gen Counsel & Sr VP)

Subsidiaries:

Apartments of Mandalay Bay, LLC (1)
6650 S Sandhill Rd, Las Vegas, NV 89120-2933
Tel.: (702) 451-8380
Apartment Building Rental Services
N.A.I.C.S.: 531110

Augusta Apartments Nevada, LLC (1)
10175 Spencer St, Las Vegas, NV 89183
Tel.: (702) 318-3000
Apartment Building Rental Services
N.A.I.C.S.: 531110

Belle Creek Apartments Colorado, LLC (1)
19458 Longspeak Dr Ste 110, Henderson, CO 80640
Tel.: (303) 286-1439
Emp.: 4
Apartment Building Rental Services
N.A.I.C.S.: 531110
Amanda Wright (Gen Mgr)

Colonial Parc Apartments Arkansas, LLC (1)
5813 Baseline Rd, Little Rock, AR 72209
Tel.: (501) 508-4538
Web Site: http://www.colonialparc.com
Emp.: 11
Apartment Building Rental Services
N.A.I.C.S.: 531110

Desert Wind Apartments Arizona, LLC (1)
4140 W McDowell Rd, Phoenix, AZ 85009
Tel.: (602) 272-5994
Web Site:
 http://www.welovedesertwind.com
Sales Range: $25-49.9 Million
Emp.: 3
Apartment Building Rental Services
N.A.I.C.S.: 531110
Virginia Morenl (Office Mgr)

Eagle Ridge Apartments California, LLC (1)
1315 S Meadow Ln, Colton, CA 92324
Tel.: (909) 825-1175
Web Site: http://www.raitresidential.com
Apartment Building Rental Services
N.A.I.C.S.: 531110

Emerald Bay Apartments Nevada, LLC (1)
4701 E Sahara Ave, Las Vegas, NV 89104
Tel.: (702) 444-2168
Web Site:
 http://www.myemeraldbayapartments.com
Apartment Building Rental Services
N.A.I.C.S.: 531110

Grand Terrace Apartments California, LLC (1)
1315 S Meadow Ln, Colton, CA 92324
Tel.: (909) 512-6954
Web Site: http://www.raitresidential.com
Apartment Building Rental Services
N.A.I.C.S.: 531110

Heritage Trace Apartments Virginia, LLC (1)
168-A Heritage Way, Newport News, VA 23602
Tel.: (757) 877-1140
Web Site: http://www.heritagetraceapts.com
Emp.: 5
Apartment Building Rental Services
N.A.I.C.S.: 531110

COMPANIES

Lafayette English Apartments, LP (1)
1919 Burton Dr, Austin, TX 78741-4276
Tel.: (512) 440-1331
Web Site: http://www.raitsresidential.com
Emp.: 9
Apartment Building Rental Services
N.A.I.C.S.: 531110

Mandalay Owner Texas, LLC (1)
12443 Tech Ridge Blvd, Austin, TX 78753
Tel.: (512) 821-3900
Web Site: http://www.mandalayatts.com
Sales Range: $25-49.9 Million
Emp.: 9
Apartment Building Rental Services
N.A.I.C.S.: 531110

McDowell Mountain Arizona, LLC (1)
5711 E Estrid Cir, Scottsdale, AZ 85254
Tel.: (602) 684-2702
Emp.: 1
Apartment Building Rentals
N.A.I.C.S.: 531110
Jeff Nicholson *(Owner)*

Oyster Point Apartments Virginia, LLC (1)
102 Americana Dr Ste 99, Newport News, VA 23606
Tel.: (757) 378-0805
Web Site: http://www.oysterpointplace.com
Sales Range: $25-49.9 Million
Emp.: 6
Apartment Building Rental Services
N.A.I.C.S.: 531110
Cassandra Snyder *(Office Mgr)*

PlazAmericas Mall Texas, LLC (1)
201 Sharpstown Ctr, Houston, TX 77036
Tel.: (713) 777-1111
Web Site: http://www.plazamericas.com
Property Rental & Leasing Services
N.A.I.C.S.: 531120

RAIT Partnership, L.P. (1)
2929 Arch St Ste 17, Philadelphia, PA 19104-2857
Tel.: (215) 861-7900
Investment Management Service
N.A.I.C.S.: 523940

RAIT-Melody 2016 Holdings Trust
Two Logan Sq 100 N 18 Th St 23 Rd Fl, Philadelphia, PA 19103
Tel.: (215) 207-2100
Real Estate Investment Trust Services
N.A.I.C.S.: 525990

River Park West Apartments Owner, LLC (1)
22155 Wildwood Park Rd, Richmond, TX 77469-5200
Tel.: (281) 232-3680
Web Site: http://www.riverparkwestapartments.com
Apartment Construction Services
N.A.I.C.S.: 236116

Stone Creek Apartments Colorado, LLC (1)
1121 W Prospect Rd Ste 110, Fort Collins, CO 80526
Tel.: (970) 221-5328
Web Site: http://www.stonecreekapartmenthomes.com
Sales Range: $25-49.9 Million
Emp.: 3
Apartment Building Rental Services
N.A.I.C.S.: 531110
Liz Logan *(Office Mgr)*

Taberna Capital Management, LLC (1)
450 Park Ave Fl 11, New York, NY 10022-2737
Tel.: (215) 207-2100
Apartment Building Rental Services
N.A.I.C.S.: 531110

Trails at Northpoint Mississippi Member, LLC (1)
600 Northpointe Pkwy, Jackson, MS 39211
Tel.: (601) 956-4353
Emp.: 4
Apartment Building Rental Services
N.A.I.C.S.: 531110
Toni Pope *(Gen Mgr)*

Treasure Island Resort Florida, LLC (1)
11750 Gulf Blvd, Treasure Island, FL 33706
Tel.: (727) 360-7096
Web Site: http://www.tibeachclub.com
Sales Range: $25-49.9 Million
Emp.: 6
Apartment Building Rental Services
N.A.I.C.S.: 531110

Tresa At Arrowhead Arizona, LLC (1)
17722 N 79th Ave, Glendale, AZ 85308
Tel.: (623) 878-2500
Web Site: http://www.tresaapts.com
Emp.: 15
Apartment Building Rental Services
N.A.I.C.S.: 531110
D. Tammy *(Reg Mgr)*

Tuscany Bay Apartments Florida, LLC (1)
12065 Tuscany Bay Dr, Tampa, FL 33626
Tel.: (813) 257-9323
Web Site: http://www.tuscanybaylivingtampa.com
Emp.: 6
Apartment Building Rental Services
N.A.I.C.S.: 531110

Urban Retail Properties Co. of Florida (1)
925 S Federal Hwy Ste 700, Boca Raton, FL 33432
Tel.: (561) 394-6433
Commercial Building Construction Services
N.A.I.C.S.: 236220

Urban Retail Properties Co. of Massachusetts (1)
404 Wyman St Ste 365, Waltham, MA 02451
Tel.: (781) 890-6006
Commercial Building Construction Services
N.A.I.C.S.: 236220

Vista Lago Condos, LLC (1)
10571 SW 156th Pl, Miami, FL 33196
Tel.: (305) 388-6446
Web Site: http://www.raitresidential.com
Emp.: 5
Apartment Building Rental Services
N.A.I.C.S.: 531110
Jennifer Diaz *(Mgr-Property)*

Willow Creek Apartments Investor, LLC (1)
1000 Baltimore Ave, Albertville, AL 35950-2997
Tel.: (256) 878-7877
Web Site: http://www.dalcormgt.com
Emp.: 2
Apartment Building Rental Services
N.A.I.C.S.: 531110
Lary Camp *(Mgr-Property)*

RAJ PATEL, MD LLC
615 1st St N, Alabaster, AL 35007
Tel.: (205) 624-2100
Web Site: https://truedermatology.com
Medical & Surgical Dermatology Services
N.A.I.C.S.: 621111

Subsidiaries:

Aqua Dermatology Management, LLC (1)
163 N Brevard Ave, Arcadia, FL 34266
Tel.: (863) 588-6905
Dermatology Services
N.A.I.C.S.: 621111
Larry Kraska *(CEO)*

Subsidiary (Domestic):

Coast Dermatology & Skin Cancer Center, P.A. (2)
21550 Angela Ln, Venice, FL 34293
Tel.: (941) 493-7400
Web Site: http://www.drneily.com
Sales Range: $10-24.9 Million
Emp.: 13
Dermatology & Skin Cancer Physicians' Office
N.A.I.C.S.: 621111
J. Gregory Neily *(Owner)*

RAK DEVELOPMENT COMPANY
11416 Sw Barber St, Wilsonville, OR 97070-7392
Tel.: (503) 646-8888
Web Site: http://www.costapacific.com
Rev.: $30,000,000
Emp.: 12
New Construction, Single-Family Houses
N.A.I.C.S.: 236115
Rudy Kadlub *(CEO)*

Subsidiaries:

Orenco Station Sales LLC (1)
1509 NE 65th Ave, Hillsboro, OR 97124
Tel.: (503) 640-1230
Web Site: http://www.costapacific.com
Rev.: $890,000
Emp.: 10
Single-Family Housing Construction
N.A.I.C.S.: 236115

RAK INDUSTRIES INC.
625 Jersey Ave, New Brunswick, NJ 08901
Tel.: (732) 846-3399
Web Site: http://www.powerriteproducts.com
Rev.: $11,265,671
Emp.: 20
Power Transmission Equipment & Apparatus
N.A.I.C.S.: 423840
Robert V. Capanelli *(CEO)*

RAKS BUILDING SUPPLY INC
108 Carson Dr, Los Lunas, NM 87031
Tel.: (505) 865-1100
Web Site: http://www.raks.com
Year Founded: 1986
Sales Range: $25-49.9 Million
Emp.: 95
Whslr of Lumber, Rough Dressed & Finished
N.A.I.C.S.: 423310
Richie Tabet *(Partner)*
Kenneth Trujall *(Partner)*

RAL SUPPLY GROUP INC.
24 Dunning Rd, Middletown, NY 10940
Tel.: (845) 343-1456
Web Site: http://www.ralsupply.com
Rev.: $25,000,000
Emp.: 35
Plumbing Fittings & Supplies
N.A.I.C.S.: 423720
Charlie Milich *(Pres)*
Pete Gasiewicz *(VP-Sls)*
John Hildebrandt *(VP-Ops)*

RALAND TECHNOLOGIES LLC
2275 Research Blvd Ste 500, Rockville, MD 20850   NY
Web Site: http://www.raland.com
Year Founded: 1998
Sales Range: $1-9.9 Million
Emp.: 120
Consulting Services
N.A.I.C.S.: 541618
Patricia Rader *(COO, Mng Partner & Exec VP)*
Dorcie McKniff Jasperse *(Exec Dir-Life Sciences)*
Olga Chmilar *(Mng Dir-Translation & Language Svcs)*
Michael Antalek *(Dir-Tech)*
Maria E. Munoz *(Sr Mgr-Language Svcs Project)*

RALCO INDUSTRIES, INC.
2720 Auburn Ct, Auburn Hills, MI 48326
Tel.: (248) 853-3200

RALEIGH MINE & INDUSTRIAL SUPPLY, INC.

Web Site: http://www.ralcoind.com
Year Founded: 1970
Sales Range: $10-24.9 Million
Metal Stamping, Prototyping & Automotive Parts Mfr
N.A.I.C.S.: 336370
Paul Delong *(Fin Mgr)*
Jim Piper *(Pres)*

RALCO NUTRITION, INC.
1600 Hahn Rd, Marshall, MN 56258
Tel.: (507) 532-5748
Web Site: http://www.ralconutrition.com
Year Founded: 1971
Sales Range: $10-24.9 Million
Emp.: 110
Animal Food Product Mfr
N.A.I.C.S.: 311119
Jim Hedges *(VP-Swine Tesh Sls)*
Tom Lattimore *(Mgr-Natl Sls)*
Jon Knochenmus *(Pres)*
Glenn Bader *(VP-Mktg)*
Jerry Lupkes *(Plant Mgr)*

RALEIGH ENTERPRISES
5300 Melrose Ave 4th Fl W Office Bldg, Hollywood, CA 90038
Tel.: (310) 899-8900   CA
Web Site: http://www.raleighenterprises.com
Year Founded: 1955
Sales Range: $25-49.9 Million
Emp.: 400
Hotels, Shopping Centers & Commercial & Industrial Buildings; Studio Property Rentals
N.A.I.C.S.: 721110
George I. Rosenthal *(Founder)*
Mark Rosenthal *(CEO)*

Subsidiaries:

File Keepers, LLC (1)
6277 E Slauson Ave, Los Angeles, CA 90040-3011
Tel.: (323) 728-3133
Web Site: http://www.filekeepers.com
Document Storage & Warehousing Services
N.A.I.C.S.: 493190
Ricardo Lamarque *(VP-Ops)*

Raleigh Studios, Inc. (1)
5300 Melrose Ave, Hollywood, CA 90038
Tel.: (323) 466-3111
Web Site: http://www.raleighstudios.com
Motion Picture & Video Production Services
N.A.I.C.S.: 512110

RALEIGH MINE & INDUSTRIAL SUPPLY, INC.
1500 Mill Creek Rd PO Box 72, Mount Hope, WV 25880-1600
Tel.: (304) 877-5503
Web Site: http://www.raleighmine.com
Year Founded: 1978
Sales Range: $25-49.9 Million
Emp.: 250
Distr of Fabricated Structural Metal & Coal Mining Supplies
N.A.I.C.S.: 237990
Stirl R. Smith *(Pres)*

Subsidiaries:

Blizzard Industrial Supply (1)
PO Box 1259, Bluefield, VA 24605
Tel.: (276) 326-6111
Web Site: http://www.blizzardvirginia.com
Sales Range: $10-24.9 Million
Emp.: 10
Mfr of Construction & Mining Machinery
N.A.I.C.S.: 423810
Richard Smith *(CEO)*

Eastern States Mine Supply Co. (1)
PO Box 538, Madison, WV 25130
Tel.: (304) 369-6010
Web Site: http://www.easternstatesmine.com

3349

RALEIGH MINE & INDUSTRIAL SUPPLY, INC.   U.S. PRIVATE

Raleigh Mine & Industrial Supply, Inc.—(Continued)
Sales Range: $1-9.9 Million
Mining Equipment & Supplies Distr
N.A.I.C.S.: 423840
Cindy Clay (Mgr-Inside Sls)

National Energy Holding Company Inc. (1)
265 Indus Dr, Beckley, WV 25801-9776
Tel.: (304) 255-1416
Sales Range: $10-24.9 Million
Emp.: 20
Distr of Construction & Mining Machinery
N.A.I.C.S.: 423810
Donna Vandko (CFO)

West Virginia Steel Corporation (1)
327 Glass Edition Rd, Poca, WV 25159
Tel.: (304) 755-5638
Web Site: http://www.wvsteelcorp.com
Sales Range: $10-24.9 Million
Emp.: 65
Warehouser of Fabricated Structural Metal
N.A.I.C.S.: 332312
Brian Smith (Mgr-Sls)

RALEIGH TRACTOR & TRUCK COMPANY
1526 S Blount St, Raleigh, NC 27603
Tel.: (919) 832-5871
Web Site:
  http://www.cardinalinternationaltrucks.com
Sales Range: $10-24.9 Million
Emp.: 42
Trucks, Commercial
N.A.I.C.S.: 423110
Karen Haize (Controller)
Paul Howard (Gen Mgr)
John M. Alexander Jr. (Pres)

RALEY'S INC.
500 W Capitol Ave, West Sacramento, CA 95605-2624
Tel.: (916) 373-6370   CA
Web Site: https://www.raleys.com
Year Founded: 1935
Sales Range: $1-4.9 Billion
Emp.: 20,000
Supermarkets & Other Grocery Retailers (except Convenience Retailers)
N.A.I.C.S.: 445110
Kevin Konkel (COO)
Lee Worthy (VP-Pharmacy & Wellness)
Michael Teel (Owner & Chm)
Keith Knopf (Pres & CEO)
Deirdre Zimmermann (Chief Customer Experience Officer)
Paul Gianetto (Sr VP-Sls & Mdsg)
Laura Croff (Chief HR Officer)
Greg Corrigan (Sr Dir-Produce & Floral)
Jennifer Warner (Chief Admin Officer)
Craig Benson (Chief IT Officer)
Helen Singmaster (Gen Counsel & Sr VP)
Matt Hilbrink (VP-Enterprise Risk & Asset Protection)
Tiffanie Burkhalter (CFO)

Subsidiaries:

Bel Air Markets (1)
500 W Capitol Ave, West Sacramento, CA 95605
Tel.: (916) 373-3333
Web Site: http://www.raleys.com
Sales Range: $50-74.9 Million
Emp.: 400
Retail Grocery
N.A.I.C.S.: 445110
Michael Teeo (Pres & CEO)

Nob Hill Foods, Inc. (1)
1st St, Gilroy, CA 95020-4229
Tel.: (800) 725-3977
Web Site: http://www.raleys.com
Rev.: $400,000,000
Emp.: 2,600

Supermarket Chain; Retail Grocer
N.A.I.C.S.: 445110

RALLY AUTO GROUP, INC.
438 Auto Vista Dr, Palmdale, CA 93551
Tel.: (661) 878-9466   CA
Web Site: http://www.4rally.com
Year Founded: 1927
Sales Range: $25-49.9 Million
Emp.: 200
Holding Company; Car Dealerships Owner & Operator
N.A.I.C.S.: 551112

Subsidiaries:

Rally GM Superstore (1)
39012 Carriage Way, Palmdale, CA 93551
Tel.: (661) 349-8017
Web Site: http://www.rallyauto.com
New & Used Car Dealer
N.A.I.C.S.: 441110
Pat Bonas (VP & Gen Mgr)
Kristina Hoerner (Controller)
Brent Carlon (Mgr-Used Car)
Shannon Halverstadt (Office Mgr)
Jerry Gaines (Gen Sls Mgr)
Bill Deem (Sls Mgr)
Lamel Scott (Sls Mgr)
Gregory Radcliffe (Sls Mgr)
Tony Anaya (Sls Mgr)
David Kleinau (Sls Mgr)
Martha Baldridge (Dir-Fin)
Bryan Arana (Mgr-Fin)
John Lee (Mgr-Fin)
Mike Taylor (Mgr-Fin)
Mike Deconza (Dir-Parts & Svc)
Johnny Lopez (Mgr-Svc)
Szabolcs Lengyel (Mgr-Body Shop)

RALLY MANUFACTURING, INC.
7600 Corporate Ctr Dr Ste 400, Miami, FL 33014-6217
Tel.: (305) 628-2886   FL
Web Site: http://www.rallymfg.com
Year Founded: 1980
Rev.: $107,000,000
Emp.: 135
Motor Vehicle Parts & Accessories
N.A.I.C.S.: 336390
Marc Iacovelli (Chm)
Gerald Pointon (Exec VP-Sls)

RALLY POINT MANAGEMENT, LLC
100 Pamela Ann Dr, Fort Walton Beach, FL 32547
Tel.: (850) 226-7589
Web Site:
  http://www.rallypointmanagement.com
Rev.: $3,700,000
Emp.: 28
Computer Management Services
N.A.I.C.S.: 518210
Chris Crutchfield (CEO)
Mike Ward (Pres)
Bob Black (VP-Bus Admin)

RALLYE MOTORS LLC
1600 Northern Blvd, Roslyn, NY 11576
Tel.: (516) 625-1600
Web Site:
  http://www.rallyemotors.com
Year Founded: 1958
Sales Range: $300-349.9 Million
Emp.: 240
Automobile Sales
N.A.I.C.S.: 441110
John Tremaroli (CFO)
Shaun Weissman (Mgr-Bus Dev)
Nick Toomey (VP & Gen Mgr)

RALPH CLAYTON & SONS
10 Havenwood Ct, Lakewood, NJ 08701
Tel.: (732) 751-7600

Web Site: http://www.claytonco.com
Rev.: $75,000,000
Emp.: 740
Concrete Masonry & Sand Mining
N.A.I.C.S.: 423320
William Clayton Jr. (CEO)

RALPH HONDA
3939 W Ridge Rd, Rochester, NY 14626
Tel.: (585) 225-3200
Web Site: http://www.ralphhonda.com
Year Founded: 1933
Sales Range: $10-24.9 Million
Emp.: 60
Car Whslr
N.A.I.C.S.: 441110
Philip Pettinato (Mgr-Parts)
Rhonda Breedlove (Office Mgr)
Bob Tomoser (Mgr-Sls)
Mike Morrill (Mgr-Sls)
Scott Westcott (Mgr-Sls)
Tom Martin (Mgr-Fin)

RALPH L. WADSWORTH CONSTRUCTION COMPANY, INC.
166 E 14000 S Ste 200, Draper, UT 84020
Tel.: (801) 553-1661
Web Site: http://www.wadsco.com
Year Founded: 1975
Rev.: $44,394,198
Emp.: 65
Bridge Construction Services
N.A.I.C.S.: 237310
Tod Wadsworth (Mgr-Bus Dev)
Kip L. Wadsworth (Pres & CEO)

RALPH SELLERS MOTOR CO.
14215 N Airline Hwy, Gonzales, LA 70737
Tel.: (888) 615-9759
Web Site:
  http://www.ralphsellers.com
Automotive Repair & Maintenance
N.A.I.C.S.: 811198
Jimmy Ledbetter (Mgr-Internet Sls)

Subsidiaries:

Sellers 3 Properties, LLC (1)
14215 Airline Hwy, Gonzales, LA 70737
Tel.: (888) 852-6754
Automotive Repair & Maintenance
N.A.I.C.S.: 811198
Paul Ralph Sellers Jr. (Mgr)

Subsidiary (Domestic):

Ralph Sellers Chevrolet (2)
15015 Florida Blvd, Baton Rouge, LA 70819
Tel.: (225) 272-6500
Web Site:
  http://www.ralphsellerschevrolet.com
New & Used Car Dealers
N.A.I.C.S.: 441120

RALPH THAYER CHEVROLET-TOYOTA INC.
1225 N Main St, Bowling Green, OH 43402
Tel.: (419) 353-5751
Year Founded: 1935
Sales Range: $10-24.9 Million
Emp.: 50
Car Whslr
N.A.I.C.S.: 441110
James Benedict (Controller)
Tom Clark (Acct Mgr)
Tony Hernandez (Acct Mgr)
Robert London (Gen Mgr)
Paul Thayer (Pres)

RALPH W. EARL CO., INC.
5930 E Molloy Rd, Syracuse, NY 13211-2109
Tel.: (315) 454-4431
Web Site: http://www.rwearl.com

Year Founded: 1982
Sales Range: $10-24.9 Million
Emp.: 90
Industrial Machinery & Equipment Mfr
N.A.I.C.S.: 423830
Graham Wood (Pres)
Martin Holleran (CFO)
Travis Brown (Engr-Applications)

RALPH'S OF LAFAYETTE INC.
3112 Cameron St, Lafayette, LA 70506
Tel.: (337) 233-0105
Web Site:
  http://www.ralphselectronics.com
Year Founded: 1945
Rev.: $11,000,000
Emp.: 100
Whslr of Electronic Parts
N.A.I.C.S.: 423690
David L. Jordan (Pres)
Kenneth Martin (Treas & Sec)
Alice Jordan (VP)
Dwayne Caillier (Gen Mgr)

RAM CONSOLIDATED INDUSTRIES, INC.
642 W Iris Dr, Nashville, TN 37204
Tel.: (615) 269-7272
Web Site: http://www.pierceusa.com
Sales Range: $1-9.9 Million
Emp.: 5
Holding Company & Manufacturer Industrial Supplies & Machinery
N.A.I.C.S.: 423840
Tom J. Ritter (Pres)

Subsidiaries:

Pierce Equipment (1)
642 W Iris Dr, Nashville, TN 37204
Tel.: (615) 269-7272
Web Site: http://www.pierceusa.com
Printing & Office Equipment Mfr & Distr
N.A.I.C.S.: 333248

RAM CONSTRUCTION SERVICES OF MICHIGAN, INC.
13800 Eckles Rd, Livonia, MI 48150-1041
Tel.: (734) 464-3800   MI
Web Site:
  http://www.ramservices.com
Year Founded: 1918
Sales Range: $25-49.9 Million
Emp.: 100
Special Trade Contracting Services
N.A.I.C.S.: 238990
Robert Magur (Pres)

RAM COUNTRY CHRYSLER DODGE INC.
3611 W Hwy 90, Del Rio, TX 78840
Tel.: (830) 775-7575
Web Site: http://www.ramcountry.com
Year Founded: 1997
Sales Range: $10-24.9 Million
Emp.: 50
Car Whslr
N.A.I.C.S.: 441110
Nick Khoury (Pres)

RAM DEVELOPMENT COMPANY, INC.
3399 PGA Blvd Ste 450, Palm Beach Gardens, FL 33418
Tel.: (561) 630-6110   FL
Web Site:
  http://www.ramrealestate.com
Year Founded: 1996
Sales Range: $1-9.9 Million
Emp.: 17
Land Subdivision
N.A.I.C.S.: 237210
Peter Cummings (Chm)
Ivy Greaner (COO)
Casey Cummings (CEO)
Jim Stine (Chief Investment Officer)

Karen Geller *(Gen Counsel & Exec VP)*
Hugo Pacanins *(Mng Dir-Dev-Residential)*
Jennifer Stull-Wise *(Mng Dir-Asset Mgmt)*

RAM FUNDING SERVICES CORP.
877 N Hwy A1a Apt 307, Indialantic, FL 32903-3020
Tel.: (321) 426-8181
Rev.: $16,000,000
Emp.: 6
High Volume Mortgage Acquisition Company
N.A.I.C.S.: 522310
Guy Ercolini *(Pres)*

RAM GRAPHICS, INC.
2408 S Park Ave, Alexandria, IN 46001
Tel.: (765) 724-7783
Web Site: http://www.ramgraphics.com
Sales Range: $10-24.9 Million
Emp.: 100
Clothing & Accessory Whslr
N.A.I.C.S.: 424350
Rachel Robinson *(Mgr-Sls)*

RAM INC.
PO Box 1850, McAlester, OK 74502
Tel.: (918) 423-3121   OK
Web Site: http://www.weallfordpropane.com
Year Founded: 1987
Sales Range: $10-24.9 Million
Emp.: 88
Sales of Groceries
N.A.I.C.S.: 445131
Twylah Monroe *(Office Mgr)*

RAM INTERNATIONAL INC.
4664 World Pkwy Cir, Saint Louis, MO 63134
Tel.: (314) 427-3000
Web Site: http://www.ram-intl.com
Sales Range: $10-24.9 Million
Emp.: 30
Freight Forwarding
N.A.I.C.S.: 488510
Jan C. Goris *(Pres)*

RAM INTERNATIONAL LTD.
PO Box 99010, Lakewood, WA 98499-0010
Tel.: (253) 588-1788   WA
Web Site: http://www.theram.com
Year Founded: 1971
Sales Range: $75-99.9 Million
Emp.: 1,500
Eateries
N.A.I.C.S.: 722511
Jeffrey Iverson *(Pres)*

RAM TECH SYSTEMS, INC.
200 Biddle Ave Ste 103, Newark, DE 19702-3967
Tel.: (302) 832-6600
Web Site: http://www.rtsiusa.com
Year Founded: 1996
Rev.: $4,700,000
Emp.: 38
Custom Computer Programming Services
N.A.I.C.S.: 541511
Srinivas Lokula *(CEO)*

RAM TECHNOLOGIES, INC.
275 Commerce Dr Ste 100, Fort Washington, PA 19034
Tel.: (215) 654-8810
Web Site: http://www.ramtechnologiesinc.com
Year Founded: 1981
Sales Range: $1-9.9 Million
Emp.: 25
Health Care Technology
N.A.I.C.S.: 621999
Robert A. Tulio *(Pres)*
Christopher P. Minton *(Exec VP-Sls & Mktg)*
Mark A. Wullert *(Dir-Mktg)*
Jose A. Lopez *(VP-Sls)*
Jack Willgruber *(Dir-Implementation Svcs)*
James Kolata *(Chief Strategy Officer)*

RAM TOOL & SUPPLY CO. INC.
4500 5th Ave S Bldg A, Birmingham, AL 35222
Tel.: (205) 714-3300   AL
Web Site: http://www.ramtool.com
Year Founded: 1967
Emp.: 100
Construction Materials Distributor
N.A.I.C.S.: 423840
Pat Murchison *(Branch Mgr)*

Subsidiaries:

Apache Supply, Inc.   (1)
64 Darlington Ave, Wilmington, NC 28403
Tel.: (910) 251-1488
Hardware Whslr
N.A.I.C.S.: 423710

RAMAR FOODS INTERNATIONAL CORPORATION
1101 Railrd Ln, Pittsburg, CA 94565
Tel.: (925) 439-9009
Web Site: http://www.ramarfoods.com
Sales Range: $10-24.9 Million
Emp.: 130
Ice Cream & Cured Meat Mfr
N.A.I.C.S.: 311520
Tom Chisari *(Mgr-Natl Sls)*
Primo Quesada *(CEO)*

RAMCAST ORNAMENTAL SUPPLY CO.
2201 Firestone Blvd, Los Angeles, CA 90002
Tel.: (323) 585-4999
Web Site: http://www.ramcast.net
Rev.: $19,500,808
Emp.: 40
Architectural Metalwork Whslr
N.A.I.C.S.: 423390
Ismael Ramirez *(Pres)*
Rosa Warschaw *(CEO)*

RAMCO - RELIABLE ARCHITECTURAL METALS CO.
9751 Erwin St, Detroit, MI 48213-1103
Tel.: (313) 924-9750
Web Site: http://www.ramcometals.com
Glass Material Distr
N.A.I.C.S.: 423390
Kurt Flonta *(Mgr-Prod)*

RAMCOM INTERNATIONAL CORP.
1729 NW 84th Ave, Miami, FL 33126
Tel.: (305) 446-3410
Web Site: http://www.ramcomcorp.com
Sales Range: $25-49.9 Million
Emp.: 7
Computer & Computer Peripheral Equipment & Software Merchant Whslr
N.A.I.C.S.: 423430
Rafael Fernandez *(Pres)*

RAMEX, INC.
5151 San Felipe Ste 450, Houston, TX 77056
Tel.: (713) 977-5212
Web Site: http://www.ramex.com
Privater Equity Firm
N.A.I.C.S.: 523999
Simon Wachsberg *(VP)*

Subsidiaries:

Countryside Foods, LLC   (1)
5151 San Felipe Ste 450, Houston, TX 77056
Tel.: (713) 977-5212
Investment Activities
N.A.I.C.S.: 523999

RAMEY AUTOMOTIVE INC.
PO Box 790, Richlands, VA 24641
Tel.: (276) 964-2511
Sales Range: $10-24.9 Million
Emp.: 65
Used Car Whslr
N.A.I.C.S.: 441120
Charles Moss *(Gen Mgr)*

RAMEY MOTORS INC.
135 Fairmount Dr, Princeton, WV 24739
Tel.: (304) 425-2134
Web Site: http://www.rameycars.com
Sales Range: $100-124.9 Million
Emp.: 140
New & Used Car Dealership Owner & Operator
N.A.I.C.S.: 441110
Amy Shupe *(Mgr-HR)*
Robert Ramey *(Dir-Dealer Ops)*

RAMI TECHNOLOGY GROUP
10400 NW 33rd St Ste 290, Miami, FL 33172
Tel.: (305) 593-6033
Web Site: http://www.ramitechnology.com
Sales Range: $10-24.9 Million
Emp.: 200
Frequency Component Mfr
N.A.I.C.S.: 334419
Alexander Wolloch *(Pres)*

Subsidiaries:

Raltron Electronics Corp.   (1)
10400 NW 33rd St Ste 270, Miami, FL 33172
Tel.: (305) 593-6033
Web Site: http://www.raltron.com
Sales Range: $100-124.9 Million
Emp.: 20
Crystal Units, Oscillations, Filters & Ceramic Resonators Mfr
N.A.I.C.S.: 334419
Alexandre Wolloch *(Pres)*

Subsidiary (Non-US):

RAMI Technology (S) Pte Ltd   (2)
Block 1003 Bukit Merah Central 04-20 Technopreneur Centre, Singapore, 159836, Singapore
Tel.: (65) 65130280
Web Site: http://www.raltron.com
Sales Range: $10-24.9 Million
Emp.: 12
Mfr of Crystal Units, Oscillations, Filters & Ceramic Resonators
N.A.I.C.S.: 334419

Raltron Israel Ltd.   (2)
West Industrial Zone, PO Box 1028, Beit Shemesh, 99100, Jerusalem, Israel
Tel.: (972) 29993814
Mfr of Crystal Units, Oscillations, Filters & Ceramic Resonators
N.A.I.C.S.: 334419

Raltron Korea Co., Ltd.   (2)
Rm 1102 Hyundai Office Bldg, 9 4 Soo Nae Dong Bundang Ku, Songnam, 463-020, Kyungki Do, Korea (South)
Tel.: (82) 317174884
Web Site: http://www.raltron.com
Sales Range: $10-24.9 Million
Emp.: 4
Crystal Units, Oscillations, Filters & Ceramic Resonators Mfr
N.A.I.C.S.: 334419

RAMMKERR, INC.
221 W 74th Ter, Kansas City, MO 64114-5730
Tel.: (816) 523-5555
Web Site: http://www.topsyspopcorn.com
Year Founded: 1981
Sales Range: $1-9.9 Million
Emp.: 100
Franchised Popcorn & Ice Cream Shop Operator
N.A.I.C.S.: 445292
Robert Ramm *(Pres)*
Julie Winkert *(Office Mgr)*

RAMONA AUTO SERVICES INC.
2350 W Menlo Ave, Hemet, CA 92545
Tel.: (909) 652-4363
Web Site: http://www.ramonatire.com
Sales Range: $10-24.9 Million
Emp.: 5
General Automotive Repair Shops
N.A.I.C.S.: 811111

RAMONA MUNICIPAL WATER DISTRICT
105 Earlham St, Ramona, CA 92065
Tel.: (760) 789-1330
Web Site: http://www.rmwd.org
Year Founded: 1956
Sales Range: $25-49.9 Million
Emp.: 60
Water Supply
N.A.I.C.S.: 221310
David Barnum *(Gen Mgr)*
Jim Hickle *(Treas)*
Richard Hannasch *(CFO)*

RAMONA'S MEXICAN FOOD PRODUCTS
13633 S Western Ave, Gardena, CA 90249
Tel.: (310) 323-1950
Web Site: http://www.ramonas.com
Rev.: $19,900,000
Emp.: 120
Food Preparations
N.A.I.C.S.: 311999
Jackie Betancourt *(Mgr-HR)*

RAMOS OIL CO. INC.
1515 S River Rd, West Sacramento, CA 95691-2810
Tel.: (916) 371-2570   CA
Web Site: http://www.ramosoil.com
Year Founded: 1951
Sales Range: $10-24.9 Million
Emp.: 174
Petroleum Bulk Stations & Terminals
N.A.I.C.S.: 424710
William Ramos *(Founder & Chm)*
Kent Ramos *(Pres)*
Kyle Ramos *(Pres-Ramos Environ Svcs)*
Jan Bard *(Controller)*

RAMP TECHNOLOGY GROUP, LLC
601 108th Ave NE Unit 310, Bellevue, WA 98004
Tel.: (425) 467-1840
Web Site: http://www.rampgroup.com
Year Founded: 2000
Sales Range: $1-9.9 Million
Emp.: 90
Computer Related Services
N.A.I.C.S.: 541512
Vishwa Prasad *(Owner)*

RAMPAGE CLOTHING COMPANY

Rampage Clothing Company—(Continued)
2332 E Pacifica Pl, Rancho Dominguez, CA 90220
Tel.: (323) 325-9851
Web Site: http://www.rampage.com
Sales Range: $100-124.9 Million
Emp.: 180
Dresses, Paper, Cut & Sewn
N.A.I.C.S.: 315250

RAMPART CAPITAL CORPORATION
16401 Country Club Dr, Crosby, TX 77532
Tel.: (713) 223-4610
Web Site: http://www.rampart-capital.biz
Year Founded: 1994
Sales Range: $1-9.9 Million
Emp.: 6
Financial & Business Services
N.A.I.C.S.: 237210
Eileen Fashoro (VP)

Subsidiaries:
Rampart Studios Inc. (1)
PO Box 91983, West Vancouver, V7V4S4, BC, Canada
Tel.: (604) 925-7659
Investment Services
N.A.I.C.S.: 523999
Gerry J. de Klerk (Pres, CFO & Sec)

RAMPART GROUP
1983 Marcus Ave Ste C130, Lake Success, NY 11042
Tel.: (516) 538-7000
Web Site: http://www.rampartinsurance.com
Year Founded: 1965
Sales Range: $25-49.9 Million
Emp.: 150
Insurance Brokers
N.A.I.C.S.: 524210
Stanley Morris (Chm-Rampart Brokerage Corp)
Evan Portnoy (Pres-Rampart Benefit Plng)
Gary Morris (CEO)
Margie Augeri (CFO)
Diane Kelly (Dir-Rampart Brokerage Corp)
Robert Reiss (Mgr-Personal Lines Mktg)
Bo Brown (CIO)
Debra Perillo (Dir-HR)
Gina Gerbino (Mgr-Claims)
Pat Crafton (Mgr-Personal Lines Underwriting)
Kathy D. Leodler (Founder & CEO)

RAMPART PLUMBING & HEATING SUPPLY INC.
1801 N Union, Colorado Springs, CO 80909
Tel.: (719) 471-7200
Web Site: http://www.rampartsupply.com
Year Founded: 1968
Sales Range: $10-24.9 Million
Emp.: 80
Sales of Plumbing-Fixtures, Equipment & Supplies
N.A.I.C.S.: 423720
Colin Perry (Pres)
John McCullom (Dir-Mktg)
Kelli Hines (Gen Mgr)

RAMSAY REALTY
7604 Hwy 238, Jacksonville, OR 97530
Tel.: (541) 899-1184
Web Site: http://www.ramsayrealty.com
Year Founded: 1966
Sales Range: $10-24.9 Million
Emp.: 12
Real Estate Brokers & Agents
N.A.I.C.S.: 531210
Clare Stevens (Owner)

RAMSEY & WALKER, LLC
1791 Frontera St, Navarre, FL 32566
Tel.: (850) 684-3098
Web Site: http://www.ramsey-walker.com
Year Founded: 2012
Sales Range: $10-24.9 Million
Emp.: 5
Building Construction Services
N.A.I.C.S.: 236115
Brett Ramsey (Mng Partner)
Kayleigh Johnson (Office Mgr)
Alex Johnson (Production Mgr)
Bobby Reever (Mgr-Quality Control)

RAMSEY ADVERTISING
3801 W Commercial Blvd, Fort Lauderdale, FL 33309
Tel.: (866) 900-7267
Web Site: http://www.ramseyglobal.com
Year Founded: 1998
Rev.: $10,000,000
Emp.: 75
Automotive, Full Service, Merchandising, Retail
N.A.I.C.S.: 541810
Mark Weaver (Mng Dir)

RAMSEY AUTO GROUP
585 Route 17 N, Ramsey, NJ 07446
Tel.: (201) 327-8170
Web Site: http://www.ramseyvolvonj.com
Year Founded: 1968
Sales Range: $10-24.9 Million
Emp.: 50
Car Whslr
N.A.I.C.S.: 441110
Raymond VanDuren (Pres)

RAMSEY FINANCIAL CORPORATION
300 4th St, Devils Lake, ND 58301
Tel.: (701) 662-4024
Web Site: http://www.ramseybank.com
Year Founded: 1892
Sales Range: $10-24.9 Million
Emp.: 55
Bank Holding Company
N.A.I.C.S.: 551111
Scott A. Thompson (Pres & CEO)

Subsidiaries:
Ramsey National Bank (1)
300 4th St NE, Devils Lake, ND 58301
Tel.: (701) 662-4024
Web Site: http://www.ramseybank.com
Sales Range: $10-24.9 Million
Commericial Banking
N.A.I.C.S.: 522110
Scott A. Thompson (Pres & CEO)

RAMSEY OUTDOOR STORE INC.
240 Rte 17 N, Paramus, NJ 07652
Tel.: (201) 261-5000
Web Site: http://www.ramseyoutdoor.com
Rev.: $15,920,569
Emp.: 50
Sporting Goods & Bicycle Shops
N.A.I.C.S.: 459110
Stuart Levine (Pres)
Marvin Sign (Gen Mgr)

RAMSEY VOLVO
585 Route 17 S, Ramsey, NJ 07446
Tel.: (888) 319-0377
Web Site: http://www.ramseyvolvonj.com

New & Pre-Owned Car Delear
N.A.I.C.S.: 441110
Thomas Gali (Sls Mgr)
Thomas Mandel (Mgr-Svc)
Ron Lombardo (Fin Mgr)

RAN-MAR INC.
149 Partridge Farm Rd, Berlin, VT 05641
Tel.: (802) 223-9571
Web Site: http://www.ran-mar.com
Year Founded: 1977
Sales Range: $10-24.9 Million
Emp.: 5
Manufactured Homes; New & Used
N.A.I.C.S.: 236115
Randy J. Rouleau (Pres)
Greg Rouleau (VP)

RANADIVE GROUP
Sleep Train Arena 1 Sports Pkwy, Sacramento, CA 95834
Tel.: (916) 928-0000
Web Site: http://www.sleeptrainarena.com
Year Founded: 2013
Holding Company; Professional Basketball Team & Sports Arena Owner & Operator
N.A.I.C.S.: 551112
Vivek Ranadive (Owner & Mng Partner)
Ron Burkle (Partner)
Mark Mastrov (Partner)

Subsidiaries:
Sacramento Kings Limited Partnership (1)
Golden 1 Ctr 500 David J Stern Walk, Sacramento, CA 95814 (65%)
Tel.: (916) 928-0000
Professional Basketball Team Services
N.A.I.C.S.: 711211
Matina Kolokotronis (Pres-Bus Ops & COO)
Phil Horn (VP-Ticket Sls & Svc)
Vivek Y. Ranadive (Owner & Chm)
Jeff Risley (VP-Ticket Ops)
Gerri Guzman (Sr Dir-Fin)
Erica Rau (Sr VP-Mktg)
Brian Plumb (VP-A/V & Production)
Kyle Ellington (Dir-HR, Diversity & Inclusion)
Andrew Nicholson (VP-Digital & Content)
Justin Petkus (VP-Ticket Sls & Membership Svcs)
Anthony McClish (Gen Mgr-G-League)
Peja Stojakovic (Asst Gen Mgr)
Brian Hilton (Dir-A/V & Brdcst)
Kevin Curran (Dir-Security)
Mike Herrera (Sr Dir-Bus Dev)
Ryan Brijs (Sr Dir-Creative)
Ryan Spillers (Sr Dir-Mktg)
Luke Bornn (VP-Strategy & Analytics)
Tom Hunt (Exec VP-Bus Ops)
Ryan Montoya (CTO)
Joelle Terry (Sr VP-Comm)
Mike Whitehead (Sr VP-Fin)
Jeff Dorso (Gen Counsel & Sr VP)
Alex Rodrigo (Sr VP & Gen Mgr)
Stacy Wegzyn (Sr VP-HR)

RANCH & HOME SUPPLY LLC
2275 N 7th Ave, Bozeman, MT 59715
Tel.: (406) 587-5846
Web Site: http://www.murdochs.com
Rev.: $68,900,000
Emp.: 600
Farm Supplies
N.A.I.C.S.: 424910
Rick Ungersma (Pres)

RANCH CREEK PARTNERS, LLC
2157 N Northlake Way Ste 230, Seattle, WA 98103
Web Site: http://www.ranchcreekllc.com
Privater Equity Firm
N.A.I.C.S.: 523940
J.D. Kritser (Founder & Chm)

Subsidiaries:
Rainier Welding, Inc. (1)
19020 NE 84th St, Redmond, WA 98053
Tel.: (425) 868-1300
Web Site: http://www.rainierwelding.com
Sales Range: $1-9.9 Million
Emp.: 25
Plate Work Mfr
N.A.I.C.S.: 332313
Rick Forster (Co-Owner)
David Forster (Co-Owner & Project Mgr)
Bob Webster (Project Mgr)
Janice Gaynes (Office Mgr)

RANCHERS SUPPLY COMPANY, INC.
1005 E Olive St, Lamar, CO 81052-0721
Tel.: (719) 336-2236
Web Site: http://www.ranchers-supplyco.com
Year Founded: 1963
Sales Range: $10-24.9 Million
Emp.: 10
Lumber & Building Supplies Distr
N.A.I.C.S.: 423310
John Carder (Pres)

RANCHO FORD, INC.
26895 Ynez Rd, Temecula, CA 92591
Tel.: (951) 699-1302
Web Site: http://www.ranchoford.com
Sales Range: $25-49.9 Million
Emp.: 124
Car Whslr
N.A.I.C.S.: 441110
Jason Noble (Mgr-Ops)

RANCHO MOTOR COMPANY INC.
15425 Dos Palmas, Victorville, CA 92392
Tel.: (760) 955-8200
Web Site: http://www.ranchomotorco.com
Sales Range: $25-49.9 Million
Emp.: 200
New & Used Car Sales
N.A.I.C.S.: 441110
John Wilkins (Principal)
Kathy Wilkins (Principal)

RANCHO SANTA FE FOUNDATION
Rancho Santa Fe Plz 162 S Rancho Santa Fe Rd Ste B-30, Encinitas, CA 92024
Tel.: (858) 756-6557
Web Site: http://www.rsffoundation.org
Year Founded: 1981
Sales Range: $10-24.9 Million
Emp.: 7
Grantmaking Services
N.A.I.C.S.: 813211
Debbie Anderson (Mgr-Programs)
Christy Wilson (Exec Dir)
Dan Beals (Mgr-Fin)
Kevin Crawford (Chm)

RANCHO SANTA FE MINING, INC.
500 N Rainbow Blvd Ste 300, Las Vegas, NV 89107
Tel.: (858) 717-8090
Year Founded: 2015
Metal Mining Services
N.A.I.C.S.: 212290
Michael S. Midlam (Pres & CEO)
Lawrence W. Geeck (CFO, Treas & Sec)
W. David Leavitt (Chm)

RANCHO SIMI RECREATION PARK DISTRICT

1692 Sycamore Dr, Simi Valley, CA 93065
Tel.: (805) 584-4400   CA
Web Site: http://www.rsrpd.org
Year Founded: 1961
Sales Range: $25-49.9 Million
Emp.: 77
Recreational Services
N.A.I.C.S.: 713990
Mark E. Johnson *(Chm)*
Larry Peterson *(District Mgr)*
Brian Pierce *(Coord-Recreation)*
Greg Laranjo *(Coord-Recreation)*

RANCHWOOD HOMES CORPORATION
923a E Pacheco Blvd, Los Banos, CA 93635-4327
Tel.: (209) 826-6200
Rev.: $48,483,095
Emp.: 8
Land Subdividers & Developers, Residential
N.A.I.C.S.: 237210
Greg Hostetler *(Owner)*
Christy Walston *(Mgr-Mktg)*

RANCON REAL ESTATE CORPORATION
27740 Jefferson Ave 100, Temecula, CA 92590
Tel.: (951) 676-8418
Web Site: http://www.rancon.com
Sales Range: $10-24.9 Million
Emp.: 20
Real Estate Brokers & Agents
N.A.I.C.S.: 531210
Michael Diaz *(Pres)*
Sandy Tyler *(VP)*

RAND CONSTRUCTION CORPORATION
1029 N Royal St, Alexandria, VA 22314
Tel.: (703) 553-5511   VA
Web Site: http://www.randcc.com
Year Founded: 1989
Sales Range: $1-9.9 Million
Construction & Renovation Services
N.A.I.C.S.: 236220
Linda D. Rabbitt *(Chm)*
David Fletcher *(Principal & Dir-Preconstruction Svcs)*
Kurt Haglund *(COO)*
Mike Clough *(Principal & Dir-Project Ops)*
Matt Dausch *(Principal & Dir-Austin)*
Cullen McGuire *(Principal & Dir-Denver)*
Tim Welch *(Dir-Field Ops)*
Tim Schmidt II *(Principal & Dir-Preconstruction Svcs)*

RAND ENGINEERING & ARCHITECTURE, PC
159 W 25th St 12th Fl, New York, NY 10001
Tel.: (212) 675-8844   NY
Web Site: http://www.randpc.com
Year Founded: 1987
Sales Range: $1-9.9 Million
Emp.: 80
Construction Management, Engineering & Architectural Services
N.A.I.C.S.: 541310
Stephen Varone *(Founder & Pres)*
Peter Varsalona *(Principal & VP)*

RAND GRAPHICS INC.
500 S Florence St, Wichita, KS 67209
Tel.: (316) 942-1218
Web Site: http://www.randgraphics.com
Sales Range: $10-24.9 Million
Emp.: 193
Commercial Printing Services
N.A.I.C.S.: 323111
Randy Vautravers *(Pres)*
Cheryl Adkisson *(Comptroller)*
Rex Abrahams *(VP-Sls)*
Jason Peebler *(Mgr-Sls)*

RAND INTERNATIONAL LEISURE PRODUCTS
51 Exec Blvd, Farmingdale, NY 11735
Tel.: (631) 249-6000
Web Site: http://www.randinternational.com
Year Founded: 1977
Sales Range: $25-49.9 Million
Emp.: 40
Bicycle Distribution
N.A.I.C.S.: 423910
Mark Worksman *(Pres)*

RAND REALTY LLC
95 S Middletown Rd, Nanuet, NY 10954
Tel.: (845) 825-8060   NY
Web Site: http://www.randrealty.com
Year Founded: 1984
Sales Range: $50-74.9 Million
Emp.: 850
Real Estate Agency
N.A.I.C.S.: 531210
Matt Rand *(CEO)*
Joseph Rand *(VP-Innovation)*
Marsha Rand *(Founder & Pres)*
Deborah Clark *(Branch Mgr)*
Barbara Meyer *(Reg Mgr)*
Daniel Rand *(Pres-Home Svcs)*

RAND TECHNOLOGY INC.
15225 Alton Pkwy Unit 100, Irvine, CA 92618
Tel.: (949) 250-6770
Web Site: http://www.randtech.com
Rev.: $36,700,000
Emp.: 50
Electronic Parts & Equipment Merchant Whslr
N.A.I.C.S.: 423690
Andrea Klein *(Founder & CEO)*
Mustafa Naim *(Acct Mgr-Strategic)*
Karen McAnlis *(Mgr-Acctg)*
Kim Fix *(Exec VP-Strategic Initiatives)*
Frederick Fu *(Mng Dir & Pres-Asia Pacific)*
Nami Mokri *(VP-Sls & Pur-Asia Pacific)*
Kevin Sheehan *(CIO)*
Jennifer Strawn *(Exec VP-Global Solutions & Sourcing)*
Doug Schilletter *(Exec VP-Global Ops)*

RANDA CORP.
417 5th Ave Fl 11, New York, NY 10016
Tel.: (212) 768-8800   NJ
Web Site: http://www.randa.net
Year Founded: 1960
Sales Range: $75-99.9 Million
Emp.: 361
Holding Company; Men's Apparel Accessories Mfr & Distr
N.A.I.C.S.: 551112
Jeffrey Spiegel *(CEO)*
Randy Kennedy *(Sr VP-Ops)*
Judy Person *(Sr VP-Sls & Mdsg)*
David Katz *(CMO & Sr VP)*

Subsidiaries:

Haggar Clothing Co.   (1)
11511 Luna Rd, Dallas, TX 75234
Tel.: (214) 352-8481
Web Site: http://www.haggar.com
Sales Range: $400-449.9 Million
Men's & Women's Apparel Products Marketer, Importer & Mfr
N.A.I.C.S.: 315250
Michael Stitt *(CEO)*

Randa Accessories Leather Goods LLC   (1)
5600 N River Rd 5th Fl, Rosemont, IL 60018-5188
Tel.: (847) 292-8300
Web Site: http://www.randa.net
Sales Range: $25-49.9 Million
Emp.: 200
Leather Accessories Mfr & Distr
N.A.I.C.S.: 316990

Division (Domestic):

Randa Luggage   (2)
200 Broadacres Dr 2nd Fl, Bloomfield, NJ 07003-3154
Tel.: (973) 873-9050
Web Site: http://www.randaluggage.com
Sales Range: $10-24.9 Million
Emp.: 75
Luggage Mfr & Distr
N.A.I.C.S.: 316990

Subsidiary (Domestic):

Swank, Inc.   (2)
417 5th Ave 11th Fl, New York, NY 10016
Tel.: (212) 867-2600
Web Site: http://www.swankinc.com
Sales Range: $75-99.9 Million
Emp.: 245
Jewelry, Leather Goods, Accessories & Toiletries Mfr
N.A.I.C.S.: 316990

The Trafalgar Company   (2)
24 W 40th St 6th Fl, New York, NY 10018
Tel.: (210) 354-6113
Web Site: http://www.trafalgarcompany.com
Sales Range: $25-49.9 Million
Luxury Luggage, Handbags, Belts & Wallets Mfr & Distr
N.A.I.C.S.: 316990

Randa Neckwear Corp.   (1)
120 W 45th St 38th Fl, New York, NY 10036
Tel.: (212) 768-8800
Web Site: http://www.randa.net
Men's Neckwear Distr & Marketer
N.A.I.C.S.: 424350

Subsidiary (Domestic):

Countess Mara, Inc.   (2)
417 5th Ave 11th Fl, New York, NY 10016   (100%)
Tel.: (212) 768-8800
Web Site: http://www.countessmara.com
Sales Range: $25-49.9 Million
Emp.: 30
Men's Ties & Neckwear Designer, Mfr, & Distr
N.A.I.C.S.: 315990
Jeffery Spiegel *(Pres)*

Wemco, Inc.   (1)
200 James Dr E, Saint Rose, LA 70087   (100%)
Tel.: (504) 712-7100
Sales Range: $75-99.9 Million
Men's Clothing Accessories & Luggage Distr, Warehouse & Logistics Services
N.A.I.C.S.: 488510
Randy Kennedy *(Sr VP)*

RANDA SOLUTIONS
722 Rundle Ave, Nashville, TN 37210
Tel.: (615) 467-6387
Web Site: http://www.randasolutions.com
Year Founded: 2003
Sales Range: $1-9.9 Million
Emp.: 23
Design & Implementation of Technology Systems
N.A.I.C.S.: 541519
Martin Reed *(Pres & CEO)*
Adam Engle *(COO)*
Tami Orrange *(Dir-Talent Mgmt)*
Kimberly Wilson Linson *(Dir-Credential Ecosys)*

RANDALL BROTHERS INC.
665 Marietta St NW, Atlanta, GA 30313
Tel.: (404) 892-6666
Web Site: http://www.randallbrothers.com
Sales Range: $10-24.9 Million
Emp.: 110
Lumber, Plywood & Millwork
N.A.I.C.S.: 423310
Jeffery Hullett *(Coord-Sls)*
Michael Reyland *(CFO & Exec VP)*

RANDALL METALS CORPORATION
2483 Greenleaf Ave, Elk Grove Village, IL 60007
Tel.: (847) 952-9690
Web Site: http://www.randallmetals.com
Rev.: $40,000,000
Emp.: 70
Metals Service Centers & Offices
N.A.I.C.S.: 423510
Laurens W. Leffingwell *(Co-CEO)*
Roberto Jimenez *(Mgr-Quality)*

RANDALL MOTORS INC.
801 W Ave N, San Angelo, TX 76903
Tel.: (325) 655-5631
Web Site: http://www.randallmotors.com
Rev.: $10,000,000
Emp.: 44
Automobiles, New & Used
N.A.I.C.S.: 441110
Kerry Goetz *(Parts Mgr)*
George Randall *(Pres)*

RANDALL NOE AUTO GROUP
1608 W Moore Ave, Terrell, TX 75160
Tel.: (972) 524-3775
Web Site: http://www.randallnoe.net
Sales Range: $10-24.9 Million
Emp.: 110
Sales of Automobiles, New & Used
N.A.I.C.S.: 441110
Coby Vickman *(Mgr-Fin)*
Freddie Schei *(Dir-Internet)*
Rick Bayon *(Mgr-Sls)*
Ron Fry *(Mgr-Parts)*
Allan Salinas *(Asst Dir-Fin)*
Kurt Lawrence *(Dir-Fin)*
Andrew McWilliams *(Dir-Ford Sls)*
Silvio Martini *(Mgr-Fin)*
Brandon Nabors *(Mgr-Fin)*
James Chadwick *(Mgr-Pre Owned Sls)*
Vincent Clementi *(Mgr-Pre Owned Sls)*
Manny Carmona *(Mgr-Sls)*

RANDALL PR, LLC
4701 SW Admiral Way Ste 308, Seattle, WA 98116
Tel.: (206) 402-4328
Web Site: http://www.randallpr.com
Year Founded: 2001
Emp.: 6
Public Relations Agency
N.A.I.C.S.: 541820
Lori Randall *(Principal)*

RANDALL REED'S PRESTIGE LINCOLN MERCURY
3601 Shiloh Rd, Garland, TX 75041
Tel.: (972) 468-1171   TX
Web Site: http://www.prestigegarland.com
Year Founded: 1982
Sales Range: $100-124.9 Million
Emp.: 100
Automobile Dealership
N.A.I.C.S.: 441110
Randall Reed *(Owner & Pres)*

RANDOLPH ACQUISITIONS, INC.   U.S. PRIVATE

Randolph Acquisitions, Inc.—(Continued)

RANDOLPH ACQUISITIONS, INC.
4228 1st Ave Ste 15, Tucker, GA 30084
Tel.: (404) 267-7093   DE
Year Founded: 2015
Emp.: 1
Real Estate Investment Services
N.A.I.C.S.: 531390
Laurice Simmonds Wilson (CFO)
Richard James Randolph III (Pres, CEO, & Treas)

RANDOLPH COMPANY
11950 Alief Clodine Rd, Houston, TX 77082
Tel.: (281) 983-4040
Rev.: $14,180,473
Emp.: 50
Measuring & Controlling Devices
N.A.I.C.S.: 334519
Jon A. Tatum (Chm & Pres)
Daniel Thompson (VP)

RANDOLPH ELECTRIC MEMBERSHIP CORPORATION
879 McDowell Rd, Asheboro, NC 27205
Tel.: (336) 625-5177   NC
Web Site:
   http://www.randolphemc.com
Year Founded: 1939
Rev.: $37,295,254
Emp.: 90
Electronic Services
N.A.I.C.S.: 221122
Dale F. Lambert (CEO)
Fred Smith (VP-Member & PR)
Tammy Brady (Mgr-Member Svcs)
Adam Hargett (VP-Fin)
Jeff McDuffie (Coord-Safety & Environmental)
Olivia Simpson (Mgr-HR)
Dennis Mabe (VP-Engrg & Ops)

RANDOLPH GROUP, INC.
1 N Franklin St Ste 310, Chicago, IL 60606
Tel.: (312) 263-4900   DE
Web Site:
   http://www.randolphgrp.com
Year Founded: 1988
Private Family Holding Company
N.A.I.C.S.: 551112
Frederick A. Eck (Pres)
Ken Kunin (Principal)
Rocky Lopez (CFO & Principal)

RANDOLPH PACKING CO.
275 Roma Jean Pkwy, Streamwood, IL 60107
Tel.: (630) 830-3100
Web Site:
   http://www.randolphpacking.com
Year Founded: 1928
Sales Range: $10-24.9 Million
Emp.: 100
Sausage Mfr
N.A.I.C.S.: 424470
Bruce Peterson (Gen Mgr)

RANDOLPH PACKING COMPANY
403 W Balfour Ave, Asheboro, NC 27203-3247
Tel.: (336) 672-1470
Sales Range: $25-49.9 Million
Emp.: 87
Processed Meat Mfr
N.A.I.C.S.: 311611
Rebecca T. Hamlet (Treas & Sec)
A. Rex (VP)

RANDY MARION INCORPORATED
220 W Plz Dr, Mooresville, NC 28115
Tel.: (704) 664-3303   NC
Web Site:
   http://www.randymarion.com
Holding Company New & Used Car Dealerships Owner & Operator
N.A.I.C.S.: 551112
Randall L. Marion (Principal)

Subsidiaries:

Randy Marion Chevrolet-Pontiac-Buick, LLC   (1)
220 W Plz Dr, Mooresville, NC 28117
Tel.: (704) 664-3303
Web Site: http://www.randymarion.com
Sales Range: $75-99.9 Million
Emp.: 110
New & Used Car Dealer
N.A.I.C.S.: 441110
Randall L. Marion (Principal)
Rebecca Frost (Controller)
Ben Goins (Dir-Ops)
Becky Mullery (Dir-Fin)

RANDY MERREN AUTO SALES INC.
5535 S Greenville Rd, Greenville, MI 48838
Tel.: (616) 754-6800
Web Site:
   http://www.randymerrenauto.com
Sales Range: $10-24.9 Million
Emp.: 9
Used Merchandise Stores
N.A.I.C.S.: 459510
David R. Merren Jr. (Pres)

RANDY'S SANITATION, INC.
4351 US Hwy 12 SE, Delano, MN 55328
Tel.: (763) 972-3335   MN
Web Site:
   http://www.randysenvironmentalservices.com
Year Founded: 1979
Sales Range: $10-24.9 Million
Emp.: 135
Garbage Collecting, Destroying & Processing
N.A.I.C.S.: 562111
Randy Roskowiak (Pres)
Fredrick Ron Streitman (Controller)

RANGAIRE MANUFACTURING COMPANY, LP
501 S Wilhite St, Cleburne, TX 76031-6338
Tel.: (817) 556-6511
Web Site:
   http://www.rangairemfg.com
Sales Range: $1-9.9 Million
Emp.: 150
Range Hoods Mfr
N.A.I.C.S.: 332322
Alan M. Crawford (Owner & Pres)

RANGAM CONSULTANTS INC.
270 Davidson Ave Ste 103, Somerset, NJ 08872
Tel.: (908) 704-8843
Web Site: http://www.rangam.com
Year Founded: 1995
Sales Range: $10-24.9 Million
Emp.: 400
Information Technology Consulting Services
N.A.I.C.S.: 541512
Hetal Parikh (Pres)
Nishith Parikh (CEO & CTO)
Geetanjali Moorjani (Mgr-HR)
Sunil Samani (Sr Mgr-Resource)
Chirayu Patel (Sr Mgr-Resource)
Kamal Verma (Controller-Fin)
Ekta Patel (Acct Mgr)
Kirat Raval (Coord-Resource)

RANGE KLEEN MFG., INC.
4240 East Rd, Lima, OH 45807-1533
Tel.: (419) 331-8000   OH
Web Site: http://www.rangekleen.com
Year Founded: 1971
Sales Range: $150-199.9 Million
Emp.: 500
Household Kitchen Products Mfr & Distr
N.A.I.C.S.: 332215
Patrick O'Connor (Pres)
Jill Brown (Mgr-Acctg)

RANGE LIGHT LLC
118 N Clinton St Ste 202, Chicago, IL 60661
Tel.: (312) 466-9911
Web Site:
   http://www.rangelightllc.com
Year Founded: 2012
Privater Equity Firm
N.A.I.C.S.: 523999
Tao Huang (Mng Partner)
Kishore Gangwani (Operating Partner)

RANGE TELEPHONE COOPERATIVE INC.
2325 E Frnt St, Forsyth, MT 59327
Tel.: (406) 347-2226   MT
Web Site: http://www.rangetel.coop
Year Founded: 1955
Sales Range: $10-24.9 Million
Emp.: 45
Provider of Telephone Communication Services
N.A.I.C.S.: 517121
Robert Adams (Pres)
Robin Stephens (Gen Mgr)

Subsidiaries:

Advanced Communications Technology, Inc.   (1)
290 N Brooks St, Sheridan, WY 82801
Tel.: (307) 673-0910
Web Site: http://www.actaccess.net
Telecommunication Servicesb
N.A.I.C.S.: 517810
Aaron Sopko (Gen Mgr)

Dubois Telephone Exchange, Inc.   (1)
12 S 1st St, Dubois, WY 82513-9702
Tel.: (307) 455-2341
Web Site: http://www.duboistelephone.com
Sales Range: $10-24.9 Million
Emp.: 15
Provider of Telephone Communication Services
N.A.I.C.S.: 517121

RT Communications Inc.   (1)
130 S 9th St, Worland, WY 82401-3434
Tel.: (307) 347-8251
Web Site: http://www.rtcom.net
Sales Range: $10-24.9 Million
Provider of Telephone Communication Services
N.A.I.C.S.: 517121
Becky Dooley (Gen Mgr)
David Webb (Mgr-Engrg)

RANGEFORD RESOURCES, INC.
301 Commerce St Ste 3500, Fort Worth, TX 76102
Tel.: (800) 699-9064   NV
Web Site: http://www.rangeford-resources.com
Year Founded: 2007
Assets: $46
Liabilities: $2,338,658
Net Worth: ($2,338,612)
Earnings: ($1,253,662)
Emp.: 2
Fiscal Year-end: 03/31/17
Oil & Gas Exploration
N.A.I.C.S.: 211120

Marc L. Duncan (Pres & COO)
John Lepin (Controller)

RANGELAND COOPERATIVES INC.
250 F St, Phillipsburg, KS 67661
Tel.: (785) 543-2114   KS
Web Site: http://www.rangeland.coop
Year Founded: 1996
Sales Range: $10-24.9 Million
Emp.: 20
Marketer of Grain Elevators
N.A.I.C.S.: 424510
Bruce L. Williams (Pres & Mgr)

RANGER AEROSPACE LLC
Pkwy Plza Ste 250 125 The Pkwy, Greenville, SC 29615
Tel.: (864) 329-9000   DE
Web Site:
   http://www.rangeraerospace.com
Year Founded: 1997
Emp.: 20
Holding Company
N.A.I.C.S.: 551112
Steve Townes (Founder, Pres & CEO)
Brian Nerney (Partner)
Edward Bolden (Pres-Rotorcraft Svcs)

Subsidiaries:

Air Shop B.V.   (1)
Kantoorweg 7, West Knollendam, 1525 RJ, Wormerveer, Netherlands
Tel.: (31) 756226050
Web Site: http://www.aclairshop.com
Air Cargo Container Sales, Repair & Leasing Services
N.A.I.C.S.: 532411
Maurice Van Terheijden (Dir-EMEA)

Subsidiary (Non-US):

ACL Airshop (Shanghai) Limited   (2)
Room 606 Unit C No 1333 Wen Ju Road, Pudong district, Shanghai, 201207, China
Tel.: (86) 21 5096 0855
Web Site: http://www.aclairshop.com
Cargo Container Distr
N.A.I.C.S.: 423840

ACL Airshop Pte Ltd.   (2)
No 29 Changi South Avenue 2 01 01A, Singapore, 486444, Singapore
Tel.: (65) 65420882
Web Site: http://www.aclairshop.com
Cargo Container Distr
N.A.I.C.S.: 423840
Pieter Van Calcar (Gen Mgr & Dir-Asia Pacific)

Subsidiary (US):

Airline Container Leasing, LLC   (2)
436 Saco Lowell Rd, Easley, SC 29640
Tel.: (864) 306-1350
Web Site: http://www.dottiedown.com
Air Cargo Container Sales, Repair & Leasing Services
N.A.I.C.S.: 532411

Unit (Domestic):

Airline Container Leasing, LLC - New York   (3)
3800 Hampton Rd, Oceanside, NY 11572
Tel.: (516) 678-4334
Web Site: http://www.aclairshop.com
Air Cargo Container Sales, Repair & Leasing Services
N.A.I.C.S.: 532411

Subsidiary (Non-US):

DXB ACL Airshop DWC LLC   (2)
Business Park Office E2-O209, Logistics City, Dubai, United Arab Emirates
Tel.: (971) 4 8879169
Web Site: http://www.aclairshop.com
Cargo Container Distr
N.A.I.C.S.: 423840

RANGER GOLD CORP.

20 W Park Ave Ste 207, Long Beach, NY 11561
Tel.: (516) 442-1883
Year Founded: 2007
Liabilities: $3,243
Net Worth: ($3,243)
Earnings: ($21,504)
Fiscal Year-end: 03/31/23
Metal Mining Services
N.A.I.C.S.: 213114
Gurpartap Singh Basrai *(Pres)*

RANGER JOE'S COLUMBUS ARMY SURPLUS CO.
325 Farr Rd, Columbus, GA 31907-6248
Tel.: (706) 689-0082
Web Site: http://www.rangerjoes.com
Year Founded: 1963
Sales Range: $10-24.9 Million
Emp.: 120
Military & Law Enforcement Gear
N.A.I.C.S.: 459999
E. Paul Voorhees *(Owner)*
Rick Weik *(Pres)*

RANGER LIFT TRUCKS
2121 I-10 E, Highlands, TX 77562
Tel.: (281) 843-2430
Web Site:
 http://www.rangerlifttrucks.com
Used Household & Office Goods Moving
N.A.I.C.S.: 484210
Galen Gardner *(Owner)*

Subsidiaries:

Universal Forklift Supply LLC (1)
9159 Wallisville Rd, Houston, TX 77029
Tel.: (281) 992-5438
Web Site: http://www.rangerlifttrucks.com
Sales Range: $1-9.9 Million
Emp.: 20
Forklift Truck Distr
N.A.I.C.S.: 423830

RANGER SPECIALIZED GLASS INC.
19031 Aldine Westfield Rd, Houston, TX 77073
Tel.: (281) 821-3777
Web Site:
 http://www.rangerglass.com
Sales Range: $10-24.9 Million
Emp.: 50
Glass Construction Materials
N.A.I.C.S.: 423390
Robert Malone *(Pres)*
Jan Hildrand *(Mgr-Personnel)*

RANGERS BASEBALL EXPRESS LLC
Globe Life Park 1000 Ballpark Way, Arlington, TX 76011
Tel.: (817) 273-5222   DE
Web Site: http://www.mlb.com
Year Founded: 2010
Emp.: 200
Professional Baseball Club Services
N.A.I.C.S.: 711211
Ray C. Davis *(Co-Chm)*
Bob R. Simpson *(Co-Chm)*

Subsidiaries:

Rangers Baseball LLC (1)
1000 Ballpark Way Ste 400, Arlington, TX 76011-5170
Tel.: (817) 273-5222
Professional Baseball Club
N.A.I.C.S.: 711211
John Blake *(Exec VP-Comm)*
Jon Daniels *(Pres-Baseball Ops & Gen Mgr)*
Mike Call *(Sr Dir-Maintenance & MEP Ops)*
Kellie Fischer *(CFO & Exec VP)*
Chuck Morgan *(Exec VP-Ballpark Entertainment & Productions)*
Rob Matwick *(Exec VP-Bus Ops)*
Richard Price *(Asst VP-Bus Ops)*
Joe Januszewski *(Exec VP, Chief Revenue Officer & CMO)*
Blake Miller *(VP-Security & Parking)*
Sean Decker *(Sr VP-Ops & Events)*
Amy Beam *(Mgr-Ownership Concierge Svcs)*
Ray Davis *(Co-Chm)*
Bob R. Simpson *(Co-Chm)*
Katie Pothier *(Gen Counsel & Exec VP)*
Neil Leibman *(Chm-Ownership Committee)*
Chris DeRuyscher *(Sr Dir-Entertainment & Production)*
David Foster *(Coord-Production)*
Alan Rose *(Coord-Digital Media)*
Jason Abbadie *(Coord-Promotions)*
Jaimie Hibbs *(Coord-Promotions)*
Tanner Leggett *(Coord-Mascot)*
Jack Hill *(Sr VP-Project Dev)*
Mark Neifeld *(VP-Rangers Events)*
Duane Arber *(Sr Dir-Facility Ops)*
Mike Smith *(Sr Dir-Security & Parking)*
Steve Ballard *(Dir-Complex Grounds)*
Dennis Klein *(Dir-Major League Grounds)*
George Dunn *(Dir-Retail)*
Dana Jons *(Asst Dir-Parking & Security)*
Ulisses Campos *(Mgr-Facility Ops)*
Dan Hanrahan *(Mgr-Dan Hanrahan)*
Sherri Morgan *(Coord-Parking)*
Oliver Strickland *(Coord-Security)*
Matt Blood *(Dir-Farm)*

RANI FOODS, INC.
16801 S Central Ave, Carson, CA 90746
Tel.: (310) 324-8877
Web Site: http://www.ranibrand.com
Year Founded: 1979
Sales Range: $75-99.9 Million
Emp.: 100
Spice & Extract Mfr
N.A.I.C.S.: 311942
Ramesh Chander *(Supvr-Production-Pub Rels)*
Suneel Chander *(Pres)*
Sunita Chander *(VP)*
Anupama Chander *(Mgr-HR)*

RANKINGS.IO, LLC
1405 N Green Mt Rd Ste 220, O'Fallon, IL 62269
Web Site: http://www.rankings.io
Year Founded: 2013
Sales Range: $1-9.9 Million
Emp.: 16
Digital Marketing Services
N.A.I.C.S.: 541810
Chris Dreyer *(Founder & Pres)*
Steven Willi *(VP)*
Todd Stager *(Dir-Strategy)*
Sonya Palmer *(Dir-Ops)*
Wil Parker *(Dir-Accounts)*

RANON & PARTNERS INC.
515 W Bay St Ste 200, Tampa, FL 33606
Tel.: (813) 253-3465
Web Site: http://www.ranon.com
Year Founded: 1956
Sales Range: $1-9.9 Million
Emp.: 15
Architectural Services
N.A.I.C.S.: 541310
Sharon Mangione *(Partner & Mgr-Mktg)*
John F. Ranon *(Founder)*
Richard Schmitt *(Partner & Mgr-Technical)*
Rod Tanner *(Mng Partner)*
Kathy Arsenault *(Partner)*

RANTEC MICROWAVE SYSTEMS, INC.
31186 La Baya Dr, Westlake Village, CA 91362
Tel.: (818) 223-5000   NV
Web Site:
 http://www.rantecantennas.com
Year Founded: 1957
Sales Range: $75-99.9 Million
Emp.: 60
Microwave Antennas Mfr
N.A.I.C.S.: 334511
Dennis Lavelle *(Dir-Bus Dev)*

Subsidiaries:

Microwave Specialty Company (1)
520 E Carmel St, San Marcos, CA 92078-4499
Tel.: (760) 744-1544
Web Site:
 http://www.microwavespecialty.com
Antenna Mfr
N.A.I.C.S.: 334220

RANTRONICS INTERNATIONAL LTD.
7660 Shelborne Dr, Granite Bay, CA 95746
Tel.: (916) 788-4305
Web Site: http://www.rantronics.com
Rev: $20,600,000
Emp.: 83
Electrical Apparatus & Equipment Wiring Supplies & Related Equipment Merchant Whslr
N.A.I.C.S.: 423610
Paul Ahdan *(Pres)*

RAO DESIGN INTERNATIONAL, INC.
9451 Ainslie, Schiller Park, IL 60176
Tel.: (847) 671-6182
Web Site: http://www.raodesign.com
Year Founded: 1960
Sales Range: $25-49.9 Million
Emp.: 50
Plastic Packaging Blow Molds Mfr
N.A.I.C.S.: 333511
Rao K. Murukurthy *(Pres)*

Subsidiaries:

American Plastic Technologies, Inc. (1)
9451 Ainslie St, Schiller Park, IL 60176
Tel.: (847) 671-6182
Web Site: http://www.iblowfillseal.com
Plastic Packaging Blow-Fill-Seal Machinery Mfr
N.A.I.C.S.: 333993
Rao K. Murukurthy *(Pres)*

RAPER, TOM, INC.
2250 Williamsburg Pike, Richmond, IN 47374
Tel.: (765) 966-8361
Web Site:
 http://www.campingworld.com
Year Founded: 1961
Sales Range: $50-74.9 Million
Emp.: 215
Recreational Vehicle Whslr
N.A.I.C.S.: 441210
Mark Lemonis *(Owner)*
Mike Halcomb *(Gen Mgr)*

RAPHAEL HOTEL GROUP
200 W 12th St, Kansas City, MO 64105-1638
Tel.: (816) 421-6100
Web Site: http://www.kcmarriott.com
Year Founded: 1989
Sales Range: $25-49.9 Million
Emp.: 500
Management Services
N.A.I.C.S.: 561110
Pis Pilli *(Pres)*
Kevin Pistilli *(Owner)*

Subsidiaries:

Downtown Marriott Hotel (1)
200 W 12th St, Kansas City, MO 64105-1638
Tel.: (816) 421-6800
Hotel Operator
N.A.I.C.S.: 721110
Kevin Pistilli *(Pres)*

RAPHAELS PARTY RENTALS INC.
8606 Miramar Rd, San Diego, CA 92126
Tel.: (858) 689-7368
Web Site: http://www.raphaels.com
Sales Range: $10-24.9 Million
Emp.: 160
Party Supplies Rental Services
N.A.I.C.S.: 532289
Raphael Silverman *(Pres)*
Philip Silverman *(VP)*
Richard Palmer-Jeffery *(Dir-Sls)*
Elizabeth Hannon-Kiss *(Office Mgr)*

RAPID CHEVROLET CO. INC.
2323 E Mall Dr, Rapid City, SD 57701
Tel.: (605) 343-1282
Web Site:
 http://www.rapidchevrolet.com
Sales Range: $75-99.9 Million
Emp.: 115
Automobiles, New & Used
N.A.I.C.S.: 441110
Chad Dingman *(Mgr-Fin)*

RAPID DIE & MOLDING CO.
800 E Amelia St, Cassville, WI 53806
Tel.: (608) 725-5114   IL
Web Site: http://www.rdmco.com
Rev: $25,900,000
Emp.: 12
Speaker Systems
N.A.I.C.S.: 334310
Thomas A. Yocum *(Pres)*

RAPID ENGINEERING INC.
1100 7 Mile Rd NW, Comstock Park, MI 49321-9727
Tel.: (616) 784-0500   MI
Web Site:
 http://www.rapidengineering.com
Year Founded: 1962
Sales Range: $50-74.9 Million
Emp.: 100
Mfr of Industrial Heating Equipment & Painting Systems
N.A.I.C.S.: 333415
Bruce Bellamy *(Pres)*
Larry Weforick *(CFO)*

Subsidiaries:

Bananza Air Management Systems, Inc. (1)
1100 7 Mile Rd NW, Comstock Park, MI 49321-9727   (100%)
Tel.: (616) 726-8800
Web Site: http://www.bananza.com
Sales Range: $10-24.9 Million
Emp.: 12
Commercial Space Heating Equipment Mfr
N.A.I.C.S.: 333994

RAPID FIRE MARKETING, INC.
311 W 3rd St Ste 1234, Carson City, NV 89703
Tel.: (775) 461-5127   DE
Web Site: http://www.rapid-fire-marketing.com
Year Founded: 1989
Sales Range: Less than $1 Million
Emp.: 1
Medical Device Mfr & Whslr
N.A.I.C.S.: 339113

RAPID GLOBAL BUSINESS SOLUTIONS, INC.
31791 Sherman Dr, Madison Heights, MI 48071
Tel.: (248) 589-1135   MI
Web Site: http://www.rgbsi.com
Year Founded: 1997
Sales Range: $50-74.9 Million
Emp.: 1,158
Engineering Design & Staffing Services

RAPID GLOBAL BUSINESS SOLUTIONS, INC.

Rapid Global Business Solutions, Inc.—(Continued)
N.A.I.C.S.: 541330
Nanua Singh *(Founder, Chm & CEO)*
Prakash Sathe *(Sr VP-Engrg & Bus Dev)*
Ravi Kumar *(Pres & CIO)*
Sheenoo Sekhon *(Dir-HR)*
Shweta Kumar *(Program Mgr-Engrg Svcs)*
Scott Aicher *(COO)*

RAPID INDUSTRIES, INC.
4003 Oaklawn Dr, Louisville, KY 40219
Tel.: (502) 968-3645
Web Site: http://www.rapidindustries.com
Year Founded: 1967
Sales Range: $10-24.9 Million
Emp.: 125
Mfr of Industrial Conveyors & Lifts; Provider of Structural Steel Erection, Machine & Equipment Demolition & Machine Moving
N.A.I.C.S.: 333922
Mary J. Sheets *(Pres & CEO)*
Mark Roth *(Engr-Applications)*
Kevin Brown *(Mgr-Logistics)*
Walt Hiner *(Project Mgr)*

RAPID MANUFACTURING, LCR
1044 W Grove Ave, Orange, CA 92865
Tel.: (714) 974-2432
Web Site: http://www.rapidmfg.com
Rev.: $25,000,000
Emp.: 150
Miscellaneous Fabricated Wire Products
N.A.I.C.S.: 532490
Dan Lang *(Pres)*
Louis Palomares *(Sr Acct Mgr & Engr-Quote)*
Luis C. Espinoza *(COO)*
Annie Li *(Dir-Global Sls)*
Joseph Lang *(Office Mgr)*

RAPID PATHOGEN SCREENING, INC.
7227 Delainey Ct, Sarasota, FL 34240
Tel.: (727) 941-1850
Web Site: http://www.rpsdetectors.com
Sales Range: $1-9.9 Million
Emp.: 30
Diagnostic Test Mfr
N.A.I.C.S.: 339112
Robert Sambursky *(Founder, Pres & CEO)*
Ashley Burgan *(Product Mgr-Primary Care & Govt Channels)*
Peter Condon *(VP-Product Dev)*
Amy Schoenthaler *(Dir-HR & Admin)*
Jennifer Frisbie *(Sr Dir-Product Mktg)*
Douglas Bueschel *(VP-Quality Affairs & Bus Sys)*
Uma Mahesh Babu *(VP-Res & Tech)*
Christopher Allen Michaels *(VP-Strategic Dev & Tech Licensing)*

RAPID RACK INDUSTRIES INC.
14421 Bonelli St, City of Industry, CA 91746
Tel.: (626) 333-7225
Web Site: http://www.rapidrack.com
Sales Range: $25-49.9 Million
Emp.: 257
Mfr & Sale of Partitions & Fixtures
N.A.I.C.S.: 337126
Arlene Collins *(Controller)*

RAPID REALTY FRANCHISE LLC
681 4th Ave, Brooklyn, NY 11232
Tel.: (347) 404-5202
Web Site: http://www.rapidnyc.com
Year Founded: 1997
Sales Range: $10-24.9 Million
Emp.: 750
Real Estate Brokerage
N.A.I.C.S.: 531210
Anthony Lolli *(Founder & CEO)*
Carlos Angelucci *(COO)*

RAPID RESPONSE MARKETING LLC
7500 W Lake Mead Blvd Ste 9, Las Vegas, NV 89128-1000
Tel.: (702) 631-9714
Web Site: http://www.rapidresponseonline.com
Year Founded: 2001
Rev.: $24,000,000
Emp.: 18
Fiscal Year-end: 12/31/06
Advetising Agency
N.A.I.C.S.: 541810
Jon Fondy *(Dir-Mktg)*
Rhianna Ross *(Dir-Ops)*

RAPID ROBERTS INC.
1840 S Campbell Ave, Springfield, MO 65807
Tel.: (417) 890-1111
Web Site: http://www.rapidrobertsinc.com
Rev.: $11,900,000
Emp.: 77
Gasoline Stations
N.A.I.C.S.: 457120
Steve Makoski *(Dir-HR)*
Eric Gard *(Mgr-Store)*

RAPID SECURITY SOLUTIONS, LLC
1920 Northgate Blvd Ste A-9, Sarasota, FL 34234
Tel.: (941) 219-4190
Web Site: http://www.rsecurity.net
Sales Range: $1-9.9 Million
Emp.: 23
Security Solutions
N.A.I.C.S.: 561621
Kathy Ritsema *(Coord-Client Svc)*
David Slomak *(Controller)*

RAPIDLD
1775 Woodstock Rd, Roswell, GA 30075
Tel.: (770) 874-1190
Web Site: http://www.rapidld.com
Sales Range: $1-9.9 Million
Emp.: 24
Data Processing, Hosting & Related Services
N.A.I.C.S.: 518210
Steve Owens *(Co-Founder)*
Jim Everidge *(Co-Founder, Pres & CEO)*
Chris Terry *(Co-Founder & VP-Consulting Ops)*
C. Reed Jones *(Co-Founder)*
Will Avery *(Co-Founder)*

RAPIDTRON, INC.
2 Park Plz Ste 1240, Irvine, CA 92614
Tel.: (949) 250-6590
Marketing Research Service
N.A.I.C.S.: 541910
Jack Thomsen *(Pres, CFO & Sec)*

RAPIER SOLUTIONS, INC.
3095 Senna Dr, Matthews, NC 28105
Tel.: (704) 321-2271
Web Site: http://www.rapiersolutions.com
Year Founded: 2002
Sales Range: $1-9.9 Million
Emp.: 32
Information Technology Consulting Services
N.A.I.C.S.: 541512
William Bailey *(Pres)*
Jacques Graves *(Dir-Bus Dev)*
Hazel Bailey *(VP-Ops)*

RAPOCA ENERGY CO. LP
2700 Lee Hwy, Bristol, VA 24202
Tel.: (276) 669-3400
Rev.: $13,900,000
Emp.: 10
Coal Processing & Sales
N.A.I.C.S.: 212115

RAPPAHANNOCK ELECTRIC COOP
247 Indus Ct, Fredericksburg, VA 22408
Tel.: (540) 898-8500
Sales Range: $150-199.9 Million
Emp.: 315
Distribution, Electric Power
N.A.I.C.S.: 221122
Frank B. Boxley *(Sec)*
Nash Johnston *(Vice Chm)*
William C. Frazier *(Chm)*

RAPPAHANNOCK WESTMINSTER-CANTERBURY, INC.
132 Lancaster Dr, Irvington, VA 22480
Tel.: (804) 438-4000
Web Site: http://www.embracelifeatrwc.org
Year Founded: 1980
Sales Range: $10-24.9 Million
Emp.: 307
Lifecare Retirement Community Operator
N.A.I.C.S.: 623311
Alice Coates *(Dir-Social Svcs)*
Penny Smith *(CFO & VP)*

RAPPORT, INC.
13180 W 43rd Dr, Golden, CO 80403
Tel.: (303) 202-9599
Web Site: http://www.rapportinc.com
Year Founded: 1979
Sales Range: $1-9.9 Million
Emp.: 40
Cable Harness, Control Box, Bulk Battery & Charger Mfr
N.A.I.C.S.: 335999
Dale Lehman *(VP)*

RAPTOR TECHNOLOGIES, INC
631 W 22nd St, Houston, TX 77008
Tel.: (713) 880-8902
Web Site: http://www.raptorware.com
Rev.: $4,600,000
Emp.: 15
Computer System Design Services
N.A.I.C.S.: 541512
Lauri Wray *(Controller)*
David Rogers *(CMO)*
Gray Hall *(CEO)*

Subsidiaries:
PAYK12, LLC   (1)
2535 E Southlake Blvd Ste 140, Southlake, TX 76092
Tel.: (765) 683-9374
Web Site: https://www.payk12.com
Software Development Services
N.A.I.C.S.: 541511
Chad Buntin *(Pres & COO)*
TJ Markland *(CEO)*
Matt Bolten *(Engr-Lead Software)*

RARE SYSTEMS INC.
12335 Kingsride Ln No 297, Houston, TX 77024
Tel.: (713) 467-7273
Web Site: http://www.rare.com
Sales Range: $10-24.9 Million
Emp.: 3
Computer Storage Devices
N.A.I.C.S.: 334112
Ron A. Rieke *(Owner, Pres & CFO)*
Montie Tims *(VP)*

RARITAN ADVERTISING AGENCY
10 Patton Dr, West Caldwell, NJ 07006-6405
Tel.: (973) 228-5100
Web Site: http://www.rrmarketing.com
Emp.: 100
Advetising Agency
N.A.I.C.S.: 541810
David C. Lowenstein *(Exec VP, Sec & Member-Board-Managers)*
Dennis M. Portsmore *(CFO & VP)*
Dennis A. Resnick *(VP-Sls & Mktg)*

RASA FLOORS & CARPET CLEANING, LLC
2833 Eisenhower, Carrollton, TX 75007
Tel.: (972) 242-6666
Web Site: http://www.rasafloors.com
Rev.: $29,000,000
Emp.: 135
Carpet Laying
N.A.I.C.S.: 561499
Michael Rasa *(Founder & CEO)*
Barbara Coy *(Dir-Corp Affairs)*
Blaise Spitaleri *(Mgr-Houston)*
Sharon Phillips *(Dir-Bus Ops & Strategy)*
Keith Olinger *(VP-Fin & Controller)*
Debbie Rasa *(Member-Mgmt Bd)*
Paul Rasa *(Member-Mgmt Bd)*
Brad Rasa *(Pres & COO)*
Pierre Rouly *(VP & Dir-Sls)*
Craig Sutton *(CFO & Member-Mgmt Bd)*

RASMUSSEN EQUIPMENT COMPANY
3333 W 2100 S, Salt Lake City, UT 84119
Tel.: (801) 972-5588
Web Site: http://www.rasmussenequipment.com
Rev.: $23,023,211
Emp.: 50
Excavating Machinery & Equipment
N.A.I.C.S.: 423810
Bob Rasmussen *(Owner)*

RASMUSSEN GROUP INC.
5550 NE 22nd St, Des Moines, IA 50313
Tel.: (515) 266-5173
Web Site: http://www.rasmussengroup.com
Year Founded: 1912
Sales Range: $100-124.9 Million
Emp.: 500
Bridge Construction
N.A.I.C.S.: 237310
Kurt Rasmussen *(Pres)*
Justin Wieg *(Controller)*
Tim Mallicoat *(CEO)*
Wayne Nyberg *(CFO)*

Subsidiaries:
Capitol Steel & Iron Company   (1)
1726 S Agnew Ave, Oklahoma City, OK 73108
Tel.: (405) 632-7710
Web Site: http://www.capitol-steel.com
Rev.: $12,400,000
Emp.: 50
Structural Shapes & Pilings, Steel
N.A.I.C.S.: 331110

COMPANIES

John H. Nesom (Pres-Sls)

Ideal Ready-Mix Company Inc. (1)
3902 W Mt Pleasant St, West Burlington, IA 52655
Tel.: (319) 754-4747
Web Site: http://www.idealrm.com
Sales Range: $10-24.9 Million
Ready-Mixed Concrete Supplier
N.A.I.C.S.: 327320
Jay Johnson (Pres)

Jensen Construction Company (1)
5550 NE 22nd St, Des Moines, IA 50313
Tel.: (515) 266-5173
Web Site: http://www.rasmussengroup.com
Rev.: $53,000,000
Emp.: 50
Bridge Construction
N.A.I.C.S.: 237310
Jeff Rasmussen (Pres)

RASPUTIN RECORDS INC.
2401 Telegraph Ave, Berkeley, CA 94704
Tel.: (510) 848-9018
Web Site:
   http://www.rasputinmusic.com
Sales Range: $10-24.9 Million
Emp.: 140
Records
N.A.I.C.S.: 449210
Kenneth Sarachan (Pres)

RASTACLAT, LLC
4007 Paramount Blvd Ste 110, Lakewood, CA 90712
Tel.: (424) 397-7170
Web Site: http://www.rastaclat.com
Year Founded: 2010
Sales Range: $10-24.9 Million
Emp.: 30
Apparel & Fashion Services
N.A.I.C.S.: 458110
Daniel Kasidi (Founder)

RASTELLI BROTHERS INC.
300 Heron Dr, Swedesboro, NJ 08085
Tel.: (856) 803-1100
Web Site: http://www.rastellis.com
Rev.: $15,519,130
Meats, Fresh
N.A.I.C.S.: 424470
Ray Rastelli (Pres)
Tony Rastelli (VP)
Paul Zaun (CFO)

RASTRAC
13809 Research Blvd Ste 735, Austin, TX 78750
Tel.: (512) 918-0700
Web Site: http://www.rastrac.com
Year Founded: 2001
Sales Range: $10-24.9 Million
Emp.: 20
Business Services
N.A.I.C.S.: 561491
Jeff Manning (Pres)
Larry Durbin (COO)

RATEGAIN TECHNOLOGIES INC.
105 Decker Court, Ste 540, Irving, TX 75062
Tel.: (214) 234-4000   DE
Web Site: http://rategain.com
Hospitality & Travel Technology Solutions
N.A.I.C.S.: 561499
Bhanu Chopra (Founder, Chm & Mng Dir)
Tanmaya Das (CFO)

Subsidiaries:

BCV Social LLC (1)
223 W Erie St Ste 2NW, Chicago, IL 60654
Tel.: (224) 333-1255
Web Site: https://www.bcvsocial.com
Digital Marketing Services

N.A.I.C.S.: 541613
Cece Novotny (Dir-HR)
Stephanie Polinski (Sr Dir-Strategy)
Kyle Gilkeson (Dir-Creative)

RATERMANN MANUFACTURING, INC.
601 Pinnacle Pl, Livermore, CA 94550
Tel.: (925) 243-0620   CA
Web Site: http://www.rmimfg.com
Year Founded: 1999
Industrial & Medical Gas Products Mfr & Distr
N.A.I.C.S.: 423840
George Ratermann (Pres)

RATESPECIAL INTERACTIVE
234 E Colorado Blvd Ste 600, Pasadena, CA 91101
Tel.: (626) 376-4702
Web Site: http://www.ratespecial.com
Year Founded: 2007
Sales Range: $10-24.9 Million
Emp.: 28
Marketing Consulting Services
N.A.I.C.S.: 541613
David Tam (Co-Founder & CEO)
Thomas McErlane (Co-Founder & Pres)
Bertrand Seow (Co-Founder, CFO & CTO)
Anna Freeman (Controller)

RATH AUTO RESOURCES
4515 Towson Ave, Fort Smith, AR 72901
Tel.: (479) 646-8251
Web Site:
   http://www.rathautoresources.com
Year Founded: 1970
Sales Range: $10-24.9 Million
Emp.: 40
Car Dealership
N.A.I.C.S.: 441110
Larry Rath (Owner)

RATHBUN REGIONAL WATER ASSOCIATION, INC.
16166 Highway J29, Centerville, IA 52544
Tel.: (641) 647-2416   IA
Web Site: http://www.rrwa.net
Year Founded: 1976
Sales Range: $1-9.9 Million
Emp.: 61
Water Distribution Services
N.A.I.C.S.: 221310
Mindy Payne (Mgr-Admin)
John Humphrey (Chief Admin Officer)
Rod Glosser (CFO)
John Glenn (CEO & COO)

RATHJE ENTERPRISES INC.
1845 N 22nd St, Decatur, IL 62526-5113
Tel.: (217) 423-2593   IL
Web Site:
   http://www.bodineelectricofdecatur.com
Year Founded: 1918
Sales Range: $25-49.9 Million
Emp.: 350
Electrical Work
N.A.I.C.S.: 238210
David W. Rathje (Pres)
Harry Rakers (CFO)

RATIO ARCHITECTS, INC.
101 S Pennsylvania St, Indianapolis, IN 46204-3684
Tel.: (317) 633-4040
Web Site:
   http://www.ratioarchitects.com
Year Founded: 1982
Emp.: 83

Architectural Services
N.A.I.C.S.: 541310
Kevin Huse (Principal-Libraries)
Tracy Imes (Assoc Principal & Dir-Admin)
Tim Barrick (Principal & Exec VP)
Tony Steinhardt (Principal & VP)
Insung Chu (Assoc Principal & Project Designer)
Tom Gallagher (Assoc Principal)
Ed Scopel (Principal)
Craig Smith (Principal)
Bryan Strube (Principal)
Brett Frenier (Mgr-Client Dev-Raleigh & Southeast)
William A. Browne Jr. (Pres & Principal)

RATTLE ADVERTISING
16 Broadway, Beverly, MA 01915-4457
Tel.: (978) 998-7890
Web Site:
   http://www.rattlethemarket.com
Year Founded: 2001
Sales Range: $10-24.9 Million
Emp.: 10
Advertising Agencies
N.A.I.C.S.: 541810
Sally Murphy (Co-Owner)
Rich Swietek (Partner & Dir-Creative)
Joe Higgins (Co-Owner & Partner)

RAUEN INCORPORATED
4099 McDonald Dr Ste 1, Dubuque, IA 52003-5298
Tel.: (563) 584-8000
Web Site:
   http://envisiontees.espwebsite.com
Promotional Products & Services
N.A.I.C.S.: 541890
Tom Rauen (Owner)

Subsidiaries:

Something Unique, Inc. (1)
529 Highway 39, Denison, IA 51442-2727
Tel.: (712) 263-2302
Sales Range: $1-9.9 Million
Emp.: 20
Services Related to Advertising
N.A.I.C.S.: 541890
Kraig Kitt (Pres)

RAUL WALTERS PROPERTIES, LLC
1021 Ashland Rd Apt 601, Columbia, MO 65201
Tel.: (573) 445-8606   MO
Web Site: http://www.raulwalters.com
Year Founded: 1967
Land Subdivision
N.A.I.C.S.: 237210
Art King (Pres)

RAULLI & SONS INC.
213 Teall Ave, Syracuse, NY 13210
Tel.: (315) 479-6693   NY
Web Site:
   http://www.raulliandsons.com
Year Founded: 1967
Sales Range: $50-74.9 Million
Emp.: 105
Provider of Metal Products
N.A.I.C.S.: 332312
Richard Raulli (Pres)
David Nichols (Coord-Safety)

RAV INVESTIGATIVE & SECURITIES SERVICES LTD
44 W 28th St Fl 6, New York, NY 10001
Tel.: (212) 447-7777
Web Site: http://www.ravsecurity.net
Sales Range: $10-24.9 Million
Emp.: 30
Protective Services
N.A.I.C.S.: 561612

RAVING BRANDS, INC.

Ron Allen (Pres & CEO)
Ernest Altamirano (Sr VP)

RAVEN TRANSPORT HOLDING, INC.
6800 Broadway Ave, Jacksonville, FL 32254
Tel.: (904) 880-1515
Web Site: http://www.idriveraven.com
Emp.: 600
Holding Company
N.A.I.C.S.: 484121
Adams Bridge (Pres)

Subsidiaries:

Raven Transport Company Inc. (1)
6800 Broadway Ave, Jacksonville, FL 32254-2762
Tel.: (904) 880-1515
Web Site: http://www.raventrans.com
Sales Range: $25-49.9 Million
Emp.: 300
Contract Haulers
N.A.I.C.S.: 484121
W. Randolph Lee (Owner, Pres & CEO)
Stephen J. Silverman (COO)

RAVENNA DESIGN
4900 Fillmore St, Hollywood, FL 33021-5820
Tel.: (954) 923-6571
Year Founded: 1987
Sales Range: Less than $1 Million
Emp.: 3
Advetising Agency
N.A.I.C.S.: 541810
Tim Ravenna (Founder & Owner)

RAVENNA MOTORS INC.
2700 NE 55th St, Seattle, WA 98105
Tel.: (206) 525-5424
Web Site:
   http://www.bobbyersvolvo.com
Rev.: $16,200,000
Emp.: 43
Automobiles, New & Used
N.A.I.C.S.: 441110
Doug Byers (Pres)

RAVEON TECHNOLOGIES CORPORATION
2320 Cousteau Ct, Vista, CA 92081
Tel.: (760) 444-5995
Web Site: http://www.raveon.com
Year Founded: 2003
Sales Range: $1-9.9 Million
Emp.: 16
Communication Equipment Mfr
N.A.I.C.S.: 334290
John Sonnenberg (CEO)

Subsidiaries:

RF Neulink (1)
2320 Cousteau Ct, Vista, CA 92081
Tel.: (760) 444-5995
Web Site: http://www.rfneulink.com
Wireless Data Radio Modems Design & Mfr
N.A.I.C.S.: 334220
John Sonnenberg (CEO)

RAVING BRANDS, INC.
1718 Peachtree St Nw Ste 1070, Atlanta, GA 30309-2481
Tel.: (404) 355-5400
Year Founded: 2003
Fast-Food Franchiser
N.A.I.C.S.: 722511
Martin Sprock (Co-Founder & CEO)
Daryl Dollinger (Co-Founder & Pres)
Brent Fuller (VP-Ops)

Subsidiaries:

Mama Fu's (1)
1720 Peachtree St Nw Ste 1028, Atlanta, GA 30309-2467
Tel.: (404) 367-5443
Web Site: http://www.mamafus.com
Sales Range: $10-24.9 Million
Emp.: 30
Fast Food Restaurants
N.A.I.C.S.: 722511

RAVING BRANDS, INC.   U.S. PRIVATE

Raving Brands, Inc.—(Continued)
Randy Murphy (CEO)
Jamie Cohen (Chief Mktg Officer)
Hemesh Patel (Dir-Delivery & Guest Logistics)
Erika Lingonblad (Mgr-Digital Mktg)
Steve Burt (Pres & CFO)

RAVISA DISTRIBUTION CENTER LLC.
13485 S Unitec Dr, Laredo, TX 78045
Tel.: (956) 723-6897
Web Site: http://www.ravisa.com
Rev.: $10,300,000
Emp.: 200
Freight Transportation Arrangement
N.A.I.C.S.: 488510
Gerardo Vidales (Pres)

RAW ARTISTS, INC.
155 W Washington Blvd Ste 650, Los Angeles, CA 90015
Tel.: (213) 995-6729
Web Site: http://www.rawartists.com
Year Founded: 2009
Sales Range: $1-9.9 Million
Emp.: 65
Media Advertising Services
N.A.I.C.S.: 541840
Heidi Luerra (Founder & CEO)
Matthew Klahorst (CTO)
Sarah Raeke (Dir-Events)
Kim Powell (Coord-HR)
Jaden Brodie (Mktg Mgr)

RAW MATERIALS CORPORATION
3860 W 11th St, Houston, TX 77055
Tel.: (713) 861-2800 TX
Web Site: http://www.raw-materials.com
Year Founded: 1985
Rev.: $28,000,000
Emp.: 10
Distr of Resins, Additives & Specialty Chemicals
N.A.I.C.S.: 424690
Terry Cogan (Gen Mgr)
J. Colwell (Pres)

RAWLINGS MECHANICAL CORP.
11615 Pendleton St, Sun Valley, CA 91352
Tel.: (818) 764-5346
Web Site: http://www.rawlingsmechanical.com
Sales Range: $10-24.9 Million
Emp.: 45
Plumbing, Heating & Air Conditioning Contractor
N.A.I.C.S.: 238220
Robert S. Bratton (Pres)
Amado DeLeon (Controller)
Patricia Wood (Sec)
Rex Horney Jr. (VP)

RAWSOFT INC.
PO Box 922343, Norcross, GA 30010
Tel.: (770) 456-5455
Web Site: http://www.rawsoft.com
Sales Range: $1-9.9 Million
Software Developer
N.A.I.C.S.: 513210
Rydal Williams (Founder & CEO)

RAWSON-KOENIG, INC.
2301 Central Pkwy, Houston, TX 77092-7720
Tel.: (713) 688-4414 TX
Web Site: http://www.rki-us.com
Year Founded: 1911
Sales Range: $25-49.9 Million
Emp.: 275
Mfr of Truck Equipment, Including Tool Boxes, Utility Service Bodies, Winches & Cranes
N.A.I.C.S.: 336211
Thomas C. Rawson (Chm & CEO)
Richard F. Koenig (VP-Info Sys)
Fredrick Wamhoff (Gen Counsel, Sec & VP)
Les Horvath (Controller)

RAXCO SOFTWARE, INC.
6 Montgomery Vlg Ave Ste 500, Gaithersburg, MD 20879
Tel.: (301) 527-0803
Web Site: http://www.raxco.com
Rev.: $4,000,000
Emp.: 40
Developer & Marketer of High-Performance Systems Administration Software & Resource Management Solutions
N.A.I.C.S.: 541511
Robert E. Nolan (Pres & CEO)
Timothy J. Larkin (CFO)

RAY ALDERMAN & SONS INC.
2209 S Colony Ave, Union Grove, WI 53182
Tel.: (262) 878-3359
Web Site: http://www.rayaldermanandsons.com
Year Founded: 1985
Sales Range: $10-24.9 Million
Emp.: 48
Dairy Product Whslr
N.A.I.C.S.: 424430
Steve Hantschel (Acct Mgr)
Ray Alderman III (Pres)

RAY ANGELINI, INC.
105 Blackwood Barnsboro Rd, Sewell, NJ 08080
Tel.: (856) 228-5566
Web Site: http://www.raiservices.com
Sales Range: $10-24.9 Million
Emp.: 40
Nonresidential Construction Services
N.A.I.C.S.: 236220
Ray Angelini (Pres)
Ken Ezzo (VP)
Lisa Hodge (Mgr-Accts Payable)
Joe Nessler (Dir-Field Ops)
Ellen Salvatore (Asst Controller)
Christopher Tranchina (Project Mgr)
Edward Wells (Mgr-Field Ops)
William Stranahan (Project Mgr)
Doug Eberly (Supvr-Electrical)
Jason Kaplan (COO)
James J. Merkins Jr. (Gen Counsel)

RAY BELL CONSTRUCTION COMPANY INC.
255 Wilson Pike Cir, Brentwood, TN 37027
Tel.: (615) 373-4343 TN
Web Site: http://www.raybellconstruction.com
Year Founded: 1970
Sales Range: $125-149.9 Million
Emp.: 280
Provider of Contracting & Construction Services
N.A.I.C.S.: 236220
Jody Evans (Treas & Sec)
Keith Pyle (Pres)
Elvis Butler (Sr VP)
Bruce Nicely (VP)

RAY BRANDT NISSAN INC.
4000 Lapalco Blvd, Harvey, LA 70058
Tel.: (504) 367-1666 LA
Web Site: http://www.raybrandtauto.com
Year Founded: 1983
Rev.: $39,200,000
Emp.: 125
New & Used Cars Dealer
N.A.I.C.S.: 441110
Ricky Phan (Gen Mgr)
Subsidiaries:
Ray Brandt Chrysler Dodge Jeep (1)
1660 Westbank Expwy, Harvey, LA 70058-4324
Tel.: (504) 363-1999
Web Site: http://www.raybrandtdodge.com
Rev.: $25,000
Emp.: 75
New & Used Car Dealership
N.A.I.C.S.: 441110
Raymond J. Brandt (Owner)

RAY BRANDT TOYOTA OF METAIRIE
2460 Veterans Blvd, Kenner, LA 70062
Tel.: (504) 367-1666
Year Founded: 2003
Sales Range: $25-49.9 Million
Emp.: 129
Car Whslr
N.A.I.C.S.: 441110
David Feicht (Gen Mgr)

RAY CATENA MOTOR CAR
910 US Hwy 1, Edison, NJ 08817
Tel.: (732) 549-6600
Web Site: http://www.raycatena.com
Rev.: $47,500,000
Emp.: 250
Automobiles, New & Used
N.A.I.C.S.: 441110
Raymond Catena (Pres)
John Storm (CFO)
Ken Hessert (Dir-IT)
Glen Gaito (Mgr-Svc)

RAY FOGG BUILDING METHODS INC.
981 Keynote Cir Ste 15, Cleveland, OH 44131-1842
Tel.: (216) 513-3219
Web Site: http://www.rayfogg.com
Year Founded: 1959
Sales Range: $10-24.9 Million
Emp.: 35
Provider of Nonresidential Construction Contracting Services
N.A.I.C.S.: 236220
Michael J. Merle (Pres & CEO)
Richard D. Neiden (VP)
Frank S. Kubicki (CFO)
Mark Ray (VP)
Ray Fogg Sr. (Chm)

RAY HUFFINES CHEVROLET PLANO
1001 Coit Rd, Plano, TX 75075
Tel.: (972) 867-4000
Web Site: http://www.chevyplano.com
Year Founded: 1983
Sales Range: $25-49.9 Million
Emp.: 200
New Car Whslr
N.A.I.C.S.: 441110
Craig Robbins (Gen Mgr)

RAY LAETHEM, INC.
17677 Mack Ave, Grosse Pointe, MI 48224-1470
Tel.: (313) 886-1700 MI
Web Site: http://www.raylaethem.com
Year Founded: 2011
Sales Range: $25-49.9 Million
Holding Company; New & Used Car Dealerships Owner & Operator
N.A.I.C.S.: 551112
Jeffrey Laethem (Pres & Gen Mgr)
Subsidiaries:
Ray Laethem Buick-GMC, Inc. (1)
17677 Mack Ave, Detroit, MI 48224-1470
Tel.: (313) 886-1700
Web Site: http://www.raylaethempontiac.com
Sales Range: $10-24.9 Million
Emp.: 70
New & Used Car Dealer
N.A.I.C.S.: 441110
Jeffrey Laethem (Pres)
Jim Castiglione (Sls Mgr)
Bob Hunwick (Sls Mgr-Fleet)
Matt Frame (Mgr-New Car & Truck Sls)
Walt Bainbridge (Dir-Svc)

Ray Laethem Chrysler Dodge Jeep Ram (1)
18001 Mack Ave, Grosse Pointe, MI 48224
Tel.: (313) 884-7210
Web Site: http://www.raylaethemchryslerdodgejeep.com
Emp.: 125
New & Used Car Dealer
N.A.I.C.S.: 441110
Jeffrey Laethem (Pres & Gen Mgr)
Karen Mirabile (Mgr-Sls)
Greg Scott (Specialist-Parts)

RAY M. WRIGHT INC.
6400 Bradley Park Dr, Columbus, GA 31904
Tel.: (706) 322-2773
Web Site: http://www.raymwrightinc.com
Sales Range: $10-24.9 Million
Emp.: 40
Speculative Builder, Single-Family Houses
N.A.I.C.S.: 236115
Ernie Wright (Treas)
Bill Barnwell (VP-Ops)
Gloria Yearta (Sec)

RAY MURRAY INC.
50 Limestone Rd, Lee, MA 01238
Tel.: (413) 243-2164
Web Site: http://www.raymurray.com
Year Founded: 1973
Sales Range: $10-24.9 Million
Emp.: 55
Industrial Supplies
N.A.I.C.S.: 423840
Cassandra Barry (Reg Mgr-Sls)
John Murray (Co-Owner, Co-Partner & Product Mgr)
Paul Bolduc (Mgr-Sls-Wisconsin)
Mike Hopsicker (Co-Owner, Pres, CEO & Co-Partner)
Bob Rosenbaum (Mgr-Sls-New York)
Jim Wiltshire (Mgr-Sls-Pennsylvania, New Jersey & Long Island)
Larry Doughty (Mgr-Sls-Maine, New Hampshire & Vermont)
Marc Christian (Mgr-Sls-Indiana, Ohio & Kentucky)
Randy Burns (Mgr-Sls-Indiana, Western Kentucky & Chicago Metro)
Woody Markus (Mgr-Sls-Ohio & Eastern Kentucky)

RAY PEARMAN LINCOLN, INC.
2501 Bob Wallace Ave SW, Huntsville, AL 35805
Tel.: (256) 536-7451
Web Site: http://www.raypearman.com
Car Dealer
N.A.I.C.S.: 441110
Serlina Beaty (Mgr-Customer Svc)
Greg Allen (Sls Mgr)
Jack Camariotes (Fin Mgr)
Paige Sandlin (Mgr-New Car)
Mike Mendez (Sls Mgr)
Heath Bell (Sls Mgr-Pre-Owned)
Gina Dilgard (Mgr-Rental)

RAY SERAPHIN FORD, INC.
100 Windsor Ave, Vernon Rockville, CT 06066
Tel.: (860) 875-3369

Web Site:
http://www.rayseraphinfordinc.com
Year Founded: 1941
Sales Range: $10-24.9 Million
Emp.: 50
Car Whslr
N.A.I.C.S.: 441110
Raymond J. Seraphin *(Pres)*

RAY STONE INCORPORATED
550 Howe Ave Ste 200, Sacramento, CA 95825-8339
Tel.: (916) 649-7500
Web Site:
http://www.raystoneinc.com
Sales Range: $10-24.9 Million
Emp.: 150
Land Subdividing Services
N.A.I.C.S.: 237210
Eric Olsen *(Sr VP)*
Todd Stone *(Pres)*
Michael Stone *(Sr VP)*
Lillian Westley *(Mgr-Leasing & Property)*
Aubrey Jones *(Dir-Mktg)*
Elizabeth Lopez *(Sr Mgr-Real Estate-Comml Svcs)*
Natalie Hinkel *(VP-Comml Svcs)*

RAY VARNER FORD, LLC.
2026 N Charles G Seivers Blvd, Clinton, TN 37716
Tel.: (865) 457-0704
Web Site:
http://www.rayvarnerford.com
Sales Range: $10-24.9 Million
Emp.: 75
Car Whslr
N.A.I.C.S.: 441110
Ray Varner *(Gen Mgr)*

RAY'S FLOORING SPECIALIST, INC.
7401 Los Volcanes NW, Albuquerque, NM 87121
Tel.: (505) 883-1967
Web Site:
http://www.raysflooring.com
Year Founded: 1972
Sales Range: $10-24.9 Million
Flooring Retailer & Contractor
N.A.I.C.S.: 449121
Gerald Lucero *(Pres)*
Raymond Lucero Jr. *(Mgr-Retail Sls)*

RAY'S FOOD PLACE
615 5th St, Brookings, OR 97415
Tel.: (541) 469-3113
Web Site: http://www.gorays.com
Year Founded: 1957
Sales Range: $10-24.9 Million
Emp.: 91
Pharmaceutical Product Whslr
N.A.I.C.S.: 424210

RAY-CARROLL COUNTY GRAIN GROWERS, INC.
26274 Hwy 24, Carrollton, MO 64633 MO
Web Site: http://www.ray-carroll.com
Year Founded: 1931
Sales Range: $10-24.9 Million
Emp.: 97
Provider of Agricultural Product Distr
N.A.I.C.S.: 424510
Matt Schuster *(Mgr-Comml Agronomy)*
John Graverson *(Mgr-Grain Dept)*
Paul Harris *(Mgr-Petroleum)*

Subsidiaries:

Ray-Carroll Fuels, L.L.C. (1)
807 W Main, Richmond, MO 64085
Tel.: (816) 776-3114
Emp.: 15
Petroleum & Petroleum Product Whslr
N.A.I.C.S.: 424720

Paul Harris *(Mgr-Fuels)*
Dean McFatrich *(Asst Mgr)*

RAYCLIFF CAPITAL
654 Madison Ave 12th Fl, New York, NY 10065
Tel.: (212) 508-5312
Emp.: 10
Investment Services
N.A.I.C.S.: 523999
Bippy M. Siegal *(Chm & CEO)*
David C. House *(Pres)*

RAYLE ELECTRIC MEMBERSHIP
616 Lexington Ave, Washington, GA 30673
Tel.: (706) 678-2116
Web Site: http://www.rayleemc.com
Rev.: $13,300,000
Emp.: 60
Distribution, Electric Power
N.A.I.C.S.: 221122
Richard Heard *(Dir-Svc)*
Fred McWhorter *(Pres)*

RAYMOND CHEVROLET
118 W IL Route 173, Antioch, IL 60002-1832
Tel.: (847) 395-3600
Web Site:
http://www.raymondchevrolet.com
Sales Range: $25-49.9 Million
Emp.: 85
Car Whslr
N.A.I.C.S.: 441110
Mark Scarpelli *(Pres)*

RAYMOND CONSTRUCTION COMPANY INCORPORATED
4407 N Beltwood Pkwy Ste 106, Dallas, TX 75244
Tel.: (972) 980-4404
Web Site:
http://www.raymondconstruction.com
Sales Range: $25-49.9 Million
Emp.: 30
Commercial & Office Building, New Construction
N.A.I.C.S.: 236220
Charles M. Raymond *(Pres)*
Justin Deming *(Dir-Central Texas)*
Ben Cholick *(Dir-Dev)*
Walker Workman *(Dir-Ops-Austin)*

RAYMOND DE STEIGER INC.
12500 Hall Rd, Sterling Heights, MI 48313-1100
Tel.: (586) 739-9700 MI
Web Site:
http://www.rayelectricsupply.com
Year Founded: 1981
Sales Range: $25-49.9 Million
Emp.: 90
Electrical Apparatus & Equipment
N.A.I.C.S.: 423610
Peter J. De Steiger *(CEO)*
Wes Jones *(COO)*

RAYMOND EXPRESS INTERNATIONAL CORPORATION
320 Harbor Way, South San Francisco, CA 94080
Tel.: (650) 871-8560
Web Site: http://www.reiexpress.com
Year Founded: 1983
Sales Range: $10-24.9 Million
Emp.: 10
Domestic Freight Forwarding
N.A.I.C.S.: 488510
Raymond Wong *(Founder)*

RAYMOND HANDLING CONCEPTS CORPORATION
41400 Boyce Rd, Fremont, CA 94538

Tel.: (510) 745-7500
Web Site:
http://www.raymondhandling.com
Year Founded: 1994
Sales Range: $50-74.9 Million
Emp.: 205
Industrial Machinery & Equipment
N.A.I.C.S.: 423830
Stephen S. Raymond *(Pres)*
Ron Curtis *(VP-Fin)*
Al Silar *(VP-Ops)*
Crystal Brister *(Mgr-Corp Aftermarket Admin)*
Danny Blau *(Mgr-Acct)*
Sue Murray *(Coord-Sls)*
Simon Walker *(VP-Sls & Mktg)*
Lance Emigh *(Dir-Sls)*
Eric Jones *(Mgr-Integrated Sys)*
Shane Fairbanks *(Suprv-Acct)*
Heidi Healy *(VP-HR)*

RAYMOND T. JOHNSON INC.
10313 Kensington Pkwy, Kensington, MD 20895
Tel.: (301) 946-6700
Web Site:
http://www.johnsonsflorists.com
Year Founded: 1933
Sales Range: $10-24.9 Million
Emp.: 100
Retail Florist & Garden Centers
N.A.I.C.S.: 444240
Catherine Harris *(Treas & Sec)*

RAYMOUR & FLANIGAN FURNITURE CO.
7248 Morgan Rd, Liverpool, NY 13090
Tel.: (315) 453-2500 NY
Web Site:
http://www.raymourflanigan.com
Year Founded: 1947
Sales Range: $650-699.9 Million
Emp.: 4,400
Furniture Retailer
N.A.I.C.S.: 449110
Neil Goldberg *(Pres & CEO)*
Steve Goldberg *(Exec VP)*

RAYNER & RINN-SCOTT INC.
6755 S Old Harlem Ave, Bedford Park, IL 60638
Tel.: (708) 458-8800
Web Site: http://www.rrswood.com
Sales Range: $25-49.9 Million
Emp.: 85
Lumber, Plywood & Millwork
N.A.I.C.S.: 423310
Todd Berry *(Controller)*

RAYO WHOLESALE INC.
11495 Woodside Ave, Santee, CA 92071
Tel.: (619) 448-7144
Web Site:
http://www.rayowholesale.com
Rev.: $10,079,813
Emp.: 16
Cleaning & Maintenance Equipment & Supplies
N.A.I.C.S.: 423850
Ed Young *(Pres)*

RAYS CHEVROLET OLDS INC.
716 W Summers Dr, Abbeville, LA 70510
Tel.: (337) 893-1243
Web Site: http://www.raychevy.com
Sales Range: $10-24.9 Million
Emp.: 59
Automobiles, New & Used
N.A.I.C.S.: 441110
Stephen Domingues *(Pres)*

RAYS WHOLESALE MEAT, INC.

2113 S 3rd Ave, Yakima, WA 98903
Tel.: (509) 575-0729
Rev.: $18,000,000
Emp.: 60
Meat & Meat Product Merchant Whslr
N.A.I.C.S.: 424470
Delores Shuel *(Treas & Sec)*

RAYTEX FABRICS INC.
130 Crossways Park Dr, Woodbury, NY 11797
Tel.: (516) 584-1111 NY
Web Site:
http://www.raytexindustries.com
Sales Range: $50-74.9 Million
Emp.: 20
Piece Goods & Notions
N.A.I.C.S.: 424310
Lee Bickell *(CFO)*

RAZ IMPORTS INC.
1020 Eden Rd, Arlington, TX 76001
Tel.: (817) 466-4729
Web Site: http://www.razimports.com
Rev.: $46,000,000
Emp.: 200
General Merchandise, Non-Durable
N.A.I.C.S.: 424990
Stan Wilemon *(Owner)*

RAZER INC.
203 3rd St Ste 900, San Francisco, CA 94103
Tel.: (760) 579-0180
Web Site: http://www.razer.com
Year Founded: 2005
Gaming Hardware Mfr
N.A.I.C.S.: 334118
Min-Liang Tan *(Founder & CEO)*
Edwin Chan *(CFO)*
Khaw Kheng Joo *(COO)*
Mike Dilmagani *(Sr VP-Sls & Mktg)*
Choo Wei-Pin *(Gen Counsel & Sr VP-Corp Dev)*

Subsidiaries:

Razer USA Ltd. (1)
9 Pasteur Ste 100, Irvine, CA 92618
Tel.: (760) 579-0180
Web Site: http://www.razerzone.com
Gaming Computer & Computer Peripheral Equipment Designer, Mfr & Whslr
N.A.I.C.S.: 423430
Min-Liang Tan *(Founder & CEO)*
Edwin Chan *(CFO)*
Khaw Kheng Joo *(COO)*
Mike Dilmagani *(Sr VP-Sls & Mktg)*

Subsidiary (Domestic):

THX Ltd. (2)
1255 Battery St Ste 100, San Francisco, CA 94111
Tel.: (415) 492-3900
Web Site: http://www.thx.com
Entertainment Technical Certification & Content Production Services
N.A.I.C.S.: 541990
Scott Francis *(CTO)*

Uniwiz Trade Sales, Inc. (1)
3F Comworks Corporate Center 1050 Quezon Avenue, Quezon City, Philippines
Tel.: (63) 284412414
Web Site: http://www.loadcentral.com.ph
Electronic Product Distr
N.A.I.C.S.: 423690

RAZMATAZ
2034 W Rose Garden Ln, Phoenix, AZ 85027
Tel.: (623) 215-0500
Year Founded: 1992
Sales Range: $10-24.9 Million
Emp.: 35
Furniture Whslr
N.A.I.C.S.: 449110
Bart Bates *(Principal)*

RAZOR TECHNICAL STAFFING
U.S. PRIVATE

Razor Technical Staffing—(Continued)

RAZOR TECHNICAL STAFFING
350 Clayton St Unit C, Denver, CO 80206
Tel.: (303) 388-6009
Web Site:
http://www.razortechnical.com
Year Founded: 2005
Sales Range: $1-9.9 Million
Emp.: 93
Employee Staffing
N.A.I.C.S.: 561311
Elisabeth Vezzani (VP-Bus Dev)
Clint Dinnel (Mng Partner & VP-Sls)

RAZORBACK CONCRETE CO.
211 N 6th St, West Memphis, AR 72301
Tel.: (870) 735-9580
Web Site:
http://www.razorbackconcrete.com
Rev.: $30,000,000
Emp.: 250
Ready Mixed Concrete
N.A.I.C.S.: 327320
Dan Hogan (Gen Mgr-Matls)
Steve Meggers (CFO)
Keith Wetsell (Gen Mgr)

RAZORBACK FOUNDATION
1295 S Razorback Rd Ste A, Fayetteville, AR 72701
Tel.: (479) 443-9000
Web Site:
http://www.razorbackfoundation.com
Year Founded: 1981
Sales Range: $25-49.9 Million
Emp.: 16
Athlete Funding Services
N.A.I.C.S.: 561499
Billye Veteto (CFO)
Scott Varady (Exec Dir)
Terry Prentice (Asst Dir-RVOICE & Local Advocacy)
Mica Strother (Sr Dir-Dev-Little Rock)
Susannah Shinn (Dir-Dev-Little Rock)
Hunter Yurachek (Dir-Athletics)

RAZORGATOR, INC.
4094 Glencoe Ave Ste A, Marina Del Rey, CA 90292
Tel.: (310) 289-3000
Web Site: http://www.razorgator.com
Sales Range: $25-49.9 Million
Emp.: 20
Entertainment Ticket Sales
N.A.I.C.S.: 561599
Brendan Ross (CEO)
Nima Moayedi (Pres)
Pat Toole (VP)
Jackie Martinoski (Dir-Broker Svcs Grp)

RAZORLEAF CORPORATION
3732 Fishcreek Rd Ste 291, Stow, OH 44224
Tel.: (330) 676-0022
Web Site: http://www.razorleaf.com
Year Founded: 2000
Sales Range: $10-24.9 Million
Emp.: 42
Data Processing & Training Services
N.A.I.C.S.: 611420
Eric Doubell (CEO)
Michael Craffey (Project Mgr)
Joseph A. Stock (CFO)

RAZORSIGHT INC.
12012 Sunset Hills Rd Ste 910, Reston, VA 20190
Tel.: (703) 995-5900
Web Site: http://www.razorsight.com
Year Founded: 2001
Rev.: $8,032,000
Emp.: 150

Accounting & Finance Management Software Developer
N.A.I.C.S.: 513210
Charlie Thomas (CEO)
Marc Bandini (VP-Ops)
Brandon Thorne (VP-Fin & Controller)
Chris Checco (Mng Dir)
Stephen Waldis (Founder, Chm & CEO)
Bob Garcia (Pres & COO)
Lawrence Irving (CFO & Treas)
Ronald Prague (Gen Counsel & Exec VP)
Kevin Hunsaker (Chief HR Officer & Exec VP)
Carlos Montero-Luque (Exec VP-R&D)
Chris Putnam (Exec VP-Sls & Bus Dev-Global)
Joel Silverman (Exec VP & Gen Mgr)
Daniel Rizer (Exec VP-Strategy & Bus Dev)
Leif O'Leary (Exec VP-Strategic Fin)
Pat Doran (CTO & Exec VP)

RAZZARI DODGE CHRYSLER JEEP
1605 Auto Center Dr, Merced, CA 95340-5675
Tel.: (209) 722-7407
Web Site: http://www.razzari.com
Year Founded: 1987
Sales Range: $10-24.9 Million
Emp.: 50
Car Whslr
N.A.I.C.S.: 441110
Tim Razzari (Pres)

RAZZOOS INC.
5080 Spectrum Dr Ste 806 W, Addison, TX 75001
Tel.: (972) 233-6399
Web Site: http://www.razzoos.com
Sales Range: $25-49.9 Million
Emp.: 1,200
Cajun Restaurant
N.A.I.C.S.: 722511
Jeff Powell (Pres)
Chris Degan (VP-Plng & Tech)
Garret Brooks (VP-Ops)
Dianne Slaight (VP-Fin & Acctg)

RB CAR COMPANY
3811 S Michigan St, South Bend, IN 46614
Tel.: (574) 299-4838
Web Site:
http://www.rbcarcompany.com
Sales Range: $25-49.9 Million
Emp.: 60
Car Whslr
N.A.I.C.S.: 441110
Brandon Cretacci (Pres)

RB INTERIOR TRIM
309 S Link Ln Unit C, Fort Collins, CO 80524
Tel.: (970) 484-4401
Year Founded: 2000
Sales Range: $10-24.9 Million
Emp.: 50
Subcontractor & Construction Services
N.A.I.C.S.: 238350
Scott Busteed (Owner & Pres)

RB JERGENS CONTRACTORS INC.
11418 N Dixie Dr, Vandalia, OH 45377
Tel.: (937) 669-9799
Web Site: http://www.rbjergens.net
Sales Range: $25-49.9 Million
Emp.: 70
Highway & Street Construction & Excavating

N.A.I.C.S.: 237310
Dave King (Project Mgr)
David Knoth (Project Mgr)
Greg Siefring (Mgr-Ops)
Victor Roberts (VP)

RB OPPENHEIM ASSOCIATES, INC.
2040 Delta Way, Tallahassee, FL 32303
Tel.: (850) 386-9100
Web Site: http://rboa.com
Year Founded: 1985
Full-service, Marketing-Communications, Advertising & Public Relations Counseling Firm
N.A.I.C.S.: 541613
Rick Oppenheim (Pres & CEO)
Michael Winn (Chief Digital Officer, Exec VP & Mktg Mgr-Digital)

RBA, INC.
294 Grove Ln E Ste 100, Wayzata, MN 55391
Tel.: (952) 404-2676
Web Site:
http://www.rbaconsulting.com
Year Founded: 2006
Sales Range: $1-9.9 Million
Emp.: 300
Technology & Consulting Services
N.A.I.C.S.: 541618
Rick Born (Co-Founder & CEO)
Mike Reinhart (Co-Founder)
Jenna Soule (Dir-Mktg)

Subsidiaries:

Saturn Systems, Inc. (1)
314 W Superior St Ste 1015, Duluth, MN 55802
Tel.: (218) 623-7200
Web Site: http://www.saturnsys.com
Sales Range: $1-9.9 Million
Emp.: 35
Custom Computer Programing
N.A.I.C.S.: 541511
Keith Erickson (Founder)
Mark Chmielewski (Sr VP)
May Joseph (Engr-Quality Assurance Test)
Tyler Carlson (Engr-Quality Assurance Test)
Jon Anderson (Dir-Ops)
Lee Matson (CFO)
Mark Budisalovich (Engr-Software)
Scott Risdal (Pres)

RBB PUBLIC RELATIONS, LLC
355 Alhambra Cir Ste 800, Miami, FL 33134
Tel.: (305) 448-7450
Web Site:
http://www.rbbcommunications.com
Year Founded: 1975
Sales Range: $1-9.9 Million
Emp.: 38
Public Relations Agency
N.A.I.C.S.: 541820
Christine M. Barney (CEO & Mng Partner)
Lisa K. Ross (Pres & Partner)
Tina Elmowitz (Partner & Exec VP)
Maite Velez-Couto (Partner & VP)
Sandra Fine Ericson (Partner, Sr VP & Dir-Results Measurement)
Shawn Warmstein (Partner & VP)
Josh Merkin (Partner & VP)
Laura Guitar (Partner & Exec VP-Health, Crisis Comm & Issue Mgmt)
Abdul Muhammad II (VP-Digital Dev)

RBC, INC.
216 N Walnut Ave, Demopolis, AL 36732
Tel.: (334) 289-3564
Web Site:
http://www.robertsonbanking.com
Year Founded: 1870
Rev.: $16,072,017
Assets: $304,053,685

Liabilities: $269,950,174
Net Worth: $34,103,511
Earnings: $4,662,140
Fiscal Year-end: 12/31/18
Bank Holding Company
N.A.I.C.S.: 551111
William Gary Holemon (Pres & CEO)
Peter Michael Reynolds (CFO & Exec VP)
Lee Pritchett (Sr VP-IT & Ops)
Katie Windham (Officer-HR & Sr VP)
Allen Bishop (Officer-Loan)
Joey Heurion (Sr VP)
Madeline Outlaw (Officer-Loan)
Kristi Parker (Officer-Loan & Asst VP)
Blake Thrasher (VP)
Becky Wharton (VP-Retail & Branch Ops)
Kathleen Wideman (VP)

Subsidiaries:

Robertson Banking Company (1)
216 N Walnut Ave, Demopolis, AL 36732
Tel.: (334) 289-3564
Web Site: http://www.robertsonbanking.com
Sales Range: $50-74.9 Million
Emp.: 79
State Commercial Banks
N.A.I.C.S.: 522110
William Gary Holemon (Pres & CEO)
James L. Stanford (VP & Dir-Mktg)
Joey A. Heurion (Sr VP-Bus Banker)
Peter Michael Reynolds (CFO & Exec VP)
Amy Beshears White (VP)
Whit Bird (Pres-Birmingham)
John Lollar (Pres-Tuscaloosa Market)
Katie Windham (Officer-HR & Sr VP)
Clay Allen Jr. (Sr VP)

RBI CORPORATION
10201 Cedar Rdg Dr, Ashland, VA 23005
Tel.: (804) 550-2210
Web Site: http://www.rbicorp.com
Sales Range: $25-49.9 Million
Emp.: 100
Engines, Gasoline
N.A.I.C.S.: 423830
Lucas Mezzenga (Gen Mgr)

RBO PRINTLOGISTIX, INC.
2463 Schuetz Rd, Maryland Heights, MO 63043-3314
Tel.: (314) 432-1636
Web Site: http://www.rboinc.com
Wholesale Trade Agents & Brokers
N.A.I.C.S.: 425120
Cathy Armstrong (CEO)

Subsidiaries:

Reign Print Solutions, Inc. (1)
550 W Campus Dr, Arlington Heights, IL 60004-1408
Tel.: (847) 590-7091
Web Site: http://www.reignprint.com
Rev.: $800,000
Emp.: 7
Whol Stationery/Offc Sup Computer Related Svcs Ltl
N.A.I.C.S.: 424120
William G. Jourdan (Pres)

RBP CHEMICAL TECHNOLOGY, INC.
150 S 118th St, Milwaukee, WI 53214
Tel.: (414) 240-1399
Web Site:
http://www.rbpchemical.com
Year Founded: 1988
Sales Range: $10-24.9 Million
Emp.: 35
Chemical Preparations
N.A.I.C.S.: 325998
Paul Nowak (CFO, Treas & Sec)
Nancy Antonicci (Sr Mgr-Customer Support)
Mark Kannenberg (Pres)
Ernie Litynski (VP-Ops)

COMPANIES

Michael Carano (VP-Tech & Bus Dev)
Tony Jackson (Mgr-Sls-Electronics-Intl)

RBW LOGISTICS CORPORATION
326 Prep Phillips Dr, Augusta, GA 30903
Tel.: (706) 724-3979
Web Site: http://www.rbwlogistics.com
Rev.: $18,541,559
Emp.: 125
Logistic Services
N.A.I.C.S.: 541614
John Albright (Sr Mgr-Ops)

RC DOLNER LLC
307 5th Ave FL 9, New York, NY 10016
Tel.: (212) 645-2190
Web Site: http://www.rcdolner.com
Sales Range: $25-49.9 Million
Emp.: 35
Provider of Nonresidential Construction Services
N.A.I.C.S.: 236220
Jesse Weinberg (Project Mgr)

RC RASMUSSEN CORPORATION
8727 5th Ave S, Seattle, WA 98108
Tel.: (206) 762-3700
Web Site: http://www.rasmussenco.com
Sales Range: $25-49.9 Million
Emp.: 35
Logging & Forestry Machinery & Equipment
N.A.I.C.S.: 423810
Richard C. Rasmussen (Owner)
Lynn Cobb (Controller)

Subsidiaries:

Rasmussen Equipment Co. (1)
8727 5th Ave S, Seattle, WA 98108
Tel.: (206) 762-3700
Rev.: $7,200,000
Emp.: 18
Logging Equipment & Supplies
N.A.I.C.S.: 423810
Richard C. Rasmussen (Owner & Pres)

Rasmussen Wire Rope Rigging Co (1)
415 S Cloverdale St, Seattle, WA 98108
Tel.: (206) 762-3700
Web Site: http://www.rasmussenco.com
Sales Range: $1-9.9 Million
Rope, Wire (Not Insulated)
N.A.I.C.S.: 423510

RC-1, INC.
301 S. State St Ste S103, Newtown, PA 18940
Tel.: (760) 230-1617 NV
Year Founded: 2007
Rev.: $110,508
Assets: $108,155
Liabilities: $449,622
Net Worth: ($341,467)
Earnings: ($48,985)
Fiscal Year-end: 12/31/19
Motorsport Event Organizer
N.A.I.C.S.: 711219
John E. Parker (Pres, CEO, Chief Financial & Acctg Officer & Sec)
Michael T. Moe (Chm)
Michael J. Newell (Exec VP-Strategy & Bus Dev)
John F. Ford (Exec VP-Sls & Bus Dev)

RCAP HOLDINGS, LLC
405 Park Ave 15th Fl, New York, NY 10022
Tel.: (212) 415-6500 DE

Holding Company; Securities Brokerage & Dealing, Stock Transfer & Investment Advisory Services
N.A.I.C.S.: 551112
Nicholas S. Schorsch (Chm, Co-CEO & Mng Partner)
William M. Kahane (Co-CEO & Mng Partner)
James A. Tanaka (Gen Counsel)

Subsidiaries:

Aretec Group, Inc. (1)
405 Park Ave 14th Fl, New York, NY 10022 (50%)
Tel.: (212) 415-6500
Web Site: http://www.rcscapital.com
Sales Range: $1-4.9 Billion
Emp.: 1,942
Holding Company
N.A.I.C.S.: 551112
Andrew G. Backman (Mng Dir-IR & PR)
Mason L. Allen (Gen Counsel)
Bradley Eric Scher (CEO)
David Orlofsky (Interim CFO & Chief Restructuring Officer)

First Allied Securities, Inc. (2)
655 W Broadway 12th Fl, San Diego, CA 92101-4412
Tel.: (619) 702-9600
Web Site: http://www.firstallied.com
Securities Brokerage, Dealing & Investment Advisory Services
N.A.I.C.S.: 523150
Garrett J. Merrill (Mng Dir-Supervision Dept)
Summer Arnold (Mng Dir-Ops)
Shannon Condra (Sr Mng Dir-Advisor Rels)
Dan Umansky (Mng Dir-Bus Consulting Grp)
Mimi Bock (Pres)

Subsidiary (Domestic):

First Allied Advisory Services, Inc. (3)
15455 Conway Rd, Chesterfield, MO 63017
Tel.: (636) 537-1040
Web Site: http://www.firstallied.com
Investment Advisory Services
N.A.I.C.S.: 523940
Robin Rodermund (COO)

Subsidiary (Domestic):

Girard Securities, Inc. (2)
9560 Waples St Ste B, San Diego, CA 92121
Tel.: (858) 622-2140
Web Site: http://www.joingirard.com
Emp.: 250
Securities Broker & Dealer
N.A.I.C.S.: 523150
John Barragan (Pres & COO)
Jason Rogers (Sr Exec VP)
Susie Woltman Tietjen (Chm & CEO)
Shirley Klicman (CFO & Exec VP)
Brian Jacobsen (Chief Compliance Officer)

Hatteras Funds LLC (2)
6601 Six Forks Rd Ste 340, Raleigh, NC 27615-6520
Tel.: (919) 846-2324
Web Site: http://www.hatterasfunds.com
Sales Range: $1-4.9 Billion
Emp.: 47
Alternative Investment Fund Management Services
N.A.I.C.S.: 551112
David B. Perkins (Founder, Chm & CEO)
Jessica Sherburne (Dir-Mktg)
Matthew Hurd (Sr VP-Natl Accts)
Michael Lee (Exec Dir-Southeast)
Christopher Minton (Dir-Southwest)
Casey Brunner (Mng Dir & Partner)

Investors Capital Holdings, Ltd. (2)
6 Kimball Ln Ste 150, Lynnfield, MA 01940
Tel.: (781) 593-8565
Sales Range: $100-124.9 Million
Emp.: 65
Security Broker & Dealer; Investment Advisory & Asset Management Services
N.A.I.C.S.: 523150
Timothy B. Murphy (Pres & CEO)
Kathleen L. Donnelly (CFO)
James Wallace (COO)
John G. Cataldo (Chief Compliance Officer)

Subsidiary (Domestic):

ICC Insurance Agency, Inc. (3)
6 Kimball Ln Ste 150, Lynnfield, MA 01940 (100%)
Tel.: (781) 593-8565
Insurance Brokerage Services
N.A.I.C.S.: 524210
Peter Acciavatti (Pres)

Investors Capital Corporation (3)
6 Kimball Ln, Lynnfield, MA 01940 (100%)
Tel.: (781) 593-8565
Web Site: http://www.investorscapital.com
Sales Range: $75-99.9 Million
Emp.: 60
Investment Advisory Services
N.A.I.C.S.: 523940
Timothy B. Murphy (Pres & CEO)

Subsidiary (Domestic):

J.P. Turner & Company, LLC (2)
1 Buckhead Plz 3060 Peachtree Rd NW 11th Fl, Atlanta, GA 30305
Tel.: (404) 479-8300
Web Site: http://www.jpturner.com
Sales Range: $25-49.9 Million
Emp.: 90
Security Brokers & Dealers
N.A.I.C.S.: 523150
Timothy W. McAfee (Co-Founder & CEO)
William Mellow (Co-Founder)
Dean Vernoia (COO)
Patrick Power (Mng Dir-Investment Banking)
Jim Attaway (CTO)
Al Pierantozzi (Sr VP-Bus Dev & Branch Support)
Adam Simon (VP-Ops)
Clint Gharib (Dir-Investment Products)
Reed Lengel (Sr VP-Supervision)
Steve Fisher (Principal-Fin & Ops)
Marc Slavny (Dir-Alternative Investments)
Ed Woll (Chief Compliance Officer)

Summit Financial Services Group, Inc. (2)
595 S Federal Hwy Ste 500, Boca Raton, FL 33432
Tel.: (561) 338-2800
Web Site: http://www.summitbrokerage.com
Rev.: $81,837,841
Assets: $17,125,498
Liabilities: $5,034,818
Net Worth: $12,090,680
Earnings: $2,548,565
Emp.: 83
Fiscal Year-end: 12/31/2013
Holding Company; Securities Brokerage & Dealing, Investment Advisory, Insurance Brokerage & Asset Management Services
N.A.I.C.S.: 551112
Marshall T. Leeds (Chm, Pres & CEO)
Steven C. Jacobs (CFO, Sec & Exec VP)

Subsidiary (Domestic):

Summit Brokerage Services, Inc. (3)
595 S Federal Hwy Ste 500, Boca Raton, FL 33432
Tel.: (561) 338-2800
Web Site: http://www.summitbrokerage.com
Securities Broker & Dealer
N.A.I.C.S.: 523150
Marshall T. Leeds (Pres & CEO)
Steven C. Jacobs (CFO & Exec VP)
Rob Crowe (CMO & Exec VP)
Vincent A. Chiera (Chief Admin Officer & Exec VP)
Fred G. Fram (Exec VP-Compliance & Ops)
Bernard Golembe (Exec VP-Brokerage Ops)
Thomas Terpko (Exec VP-Tech)
Dennis Kaminski (Sr VP)
Susan Camacho (Dir-Commissions)

Subsidiary (Domestic):

VSR Group, Inc. (2)
8620 W 110th St, Overland Park, KS 66210
Tel.: (913) 498-2900
Web Site: http://www.vsrfinancial.com
Sales Range: $5-14.9 Billion
Emp.: 275
Holding Company; Securities Brokerage & Dealing Services
N.A.I.C.S.: 551112
J. Michael Stanfield (Co-Founder & CEO)
Jon M. Stanfield (Pres & Corp Counsel)

Chatten W. Scruggs (Sr VP-Tech)
Jim Blosser (VP-Recruiting)
Jeff Eisenhauer (VP & Dir-Trade Desk)
Susan Vargason (VP & Dir-Compliance)
Karen Freeman (Asst VP-Mktg)
Brad Mauderer (Asst VP-Advisory Trading)
Donald J. Beary (Co-Founder & Exec VP)

Subsidiary (Domestic):

VSR Financial Services, Inc. (3)
8620 W 110th St, Overland Park, KS 66210
Tel.: (913) 498-2900
Web Site: http://www.vsrfinancial.com
Securities Broker & Dealer
N.A.I.C.S.: 523150
J. Michael Stanfield (Co-Founder & CEO)
Jim Blosser (VP-Recruiting)
Jon M. Stanfield (Pres & Corp Counsel)
Donald J. Beary (Co-Founder & Exec VP)
Chatten W. Scruggs (Sr VP-Tech)
Jeff Eisenhauer (VP & Dir-Trade Desk)
Susan Vargason (VP & Dir-Compliance)
Karen Freeman (Asst VP-Mktg)
Brad Mauderer (Asst VP-Advisory Trading)

RCB HOLDING COMPANY, INC.
300 W Patti Page Blvd, Claremore, OK 74017
Tel.: (918) 341-6150 OK
Web Site: http://www.rcbbank.com
Year Founded: 1984
Sales Range: $100-124.9 Million
Emp.: 627
Bank Holding Company
N.A.I.C.S.: 551111
Tom Bayless (COO & Sr Exec VP)
Roger Mosier (Pres & CEO)

Subsidiaries:

RCB Bank (1)
300 W Patti Page Blvd, Claremore, OK 74017-8039 (100%)
Tel.: (918) 341-6150
Web Site: http://www.rcbbank.com
Sales Range: $100-124.9 Million
Commericial Banking
N.A.I.C.S.: 522110
Tom G. Bayless (COO & Sr Exec VP)
Roger L. Mosier (Pres & CEO)
Ryan Odom (VP-Comml Lending-Norman)
Amy Hall (VP)
Marc Milleson (VP-Lending)

RCC ASSOCIATES, INC.
255 Jim Moran Blvd, Deerfield Beach, FL 33442
Tel.: (954) 429-3700
Web Site: http://www.rccassociates.com
Sales Range: $75-99.9 Million
Commercial Construction
N.A.I.C.S.: 236220
Beverly Raphael (Pres & CEO)
Richard N. Rhodes (Exec VP)

RCD GENERAL CONTRACTORS
2075 W Park Pl Blvd Ste D, Stone Mountain, GA 30087
Tel.: (770) 465-9032
Web Site: http://www.rcd-atlanta.com
Year Founded: 2002
Sales Range: $1-9.9 Million
Emp.: 13
Nonresidential Construction
N.A.I.C.S.: 236220
Micheal Lyle (Project Mgr)
Mark Farol (VP-Construction)
Dean Smith (Founder)
Richard D. Smith Jr. (Pres)

RCF MANAGEMENT LLC
1400 16th St Ste 200, Denver, CO 80202
Tel.: (720) 946-1444
Web Site: http://www.resourcecapitalfund.com

RCF MANAGEMENT LLC

RCF Management LLC—(Continued)
Year Founded: 1998
Sales Range: $10-24.9 Million
Emp.: 100
Privater Equity Firm
N.A.I.C.S.: 523999
James McClements *(Mng Partner & CIO)*
Ryan T. Bennett *(Partner & Head-Technical)*
Henderson G. Tuten *(Partner)*
Ross Randolph Bhappu *(Partner)*
Russ Cranswick *(Partner)*
Sherri A. Croasdale *(Parent & CFO)*
Mason G. Hills *(Partner)*
Peter B. Nicholson *(Partner)*
David Thomas *(Partner & Mng Dir)*
Martin Valdes *(Partner & Mng Dir)*
Brett Beatty *(Partner)*
Jasper Bertisen *(Partner)*
Jacqueline Murray *(Principal)*
Jeff Mills *(Mng Dir)*
Gregory Honig *(Dir-Origination-Canada)*

Subsidiaries:

Alloycorp Mining Inc. (1)
67 Yonge St, Toronto, M5E 1L8, ON, Canada
Tel.: (416) 847-0376
Web Site: http://www.alloycorp.com
Metal Mining Services
N.A.I.C.S.: 212290
Graham du Preez *(CFO)*
Mario Caron *(Chm)*

Ausenco Limited (1)
144 Montague Road, Brisbane, 4101, QLD, Australia
Tel.: (61) 7 3169 7000
Web Site: http://www.ausenco.com
Sales Range: $100-124.9 Million
Engineering & Project Management Services
N.A.I.C.S.: 541330
George Lloyd *(Chm)*
Zimi Meka *(CEO)*
Neil Trembath *(CTO & Chief People Officer)*
Simon Cmrlec *(Pres-North America)*
Ed Meka *(Exec VP)*
Greg Lane *(Chief Technical Officer)*
Ron Douglas *(Exec VP-Project Delivery)*
Brad Shaw *(Pres-APAC/Africa)*
Chris King-Sidney *(Pres-Consulting)*
Rick Ogden *(CFO)*
Shelley Nixon *(VP-Vancouver)*
Garry Warren *(Pres-Project Delivery-North America)*

Subsidiary (US):

Ausenco PSI LLC (2)
1390 Willow Pass Rd Ste 400, Concord, CA 94520
Tel.: (925) 939-4420
Web Site: http://www.ausenco.com
Emp.: 8
Pipeline System Installation Services
N.A.I.C.S.: 237120

Subsidiary (Domestic):

Ausenco Services Pty. Ltd. (2)
144 Montague Rd, Brisbane, 4101, QLD, Australia
Tel.: (61) 7 3169 7000
Web Site: http://www.ausenco.com
Engineeering Services
N.A.I.C.S.: 541330

First Bauxite Corporation (1)
82 Richmond Street East Suite 200, Toronto, M5C 1P1, ON, Canada
Tel.: (592) 223-4396
Web Site: http://www.firstbauxite.com
Rev.: $6,134
Assets: $2,192,600
Liabilities: $37,868,170
Net Worth: ($35,675,570)
Earnings: ($9,741,823)
Emp.: 43
Fiscal Year-end: 12/31/2017
Mineral Exploration Services
N.A.I.C.S.: 213114

Alan Roughead *(Pres & CEO)*
William White *(CFO)*

NYCO Minerals, Inc. (1)
803 Mtn View Dr, Willsboro, NY 12996
Tel.: (518) 963-4262
Web Site: http://www.nycominerals.com
Sales Range: $75-99.9 Million
Mineral Producers
N.A.I.C.S.: 212390

Subsidiary (Non-US):

Minera Roca Rodando S. de R.L. de C.V. (2)
Carretera Mina Pilares Km 0 00 Carretera A Nogales Km 15 5, Colonia Valle Grande, Hermosillo, 83000, San Mexico, Mexico
Tel.: (52) 6622891000
Web Site: http://www.nycominerals.com
Sales Range: $25-49.9 Million
Emp.: 47
Industrial Mineral Mining
N.A.I.C.S.: 213115
Gerardo Montijo *(Supvr-Gen Ops)*

NorZinc Ltd. (1)
510 Burrard St Suite 907, PO Box 11644, Vancouver, V6C 3A8, BC, Canada (100%)
Tel.: (604) 688-2001
Web Site: https://www.norzinc.com
Rev.: $72,698
Assets: $8,559,209
Liabilities: $3,054,838
Net Worth: $5,504,371
Earnings: ($6,072,945)
Emp.: 9
Fiscal Year-end: 12/31/2019
Zinc & Other Mineral Exploration & Mining
N.A.I.C.S.: 213114
Peter Portka *(CFO)*
Rohan Hazelton *(Pres)*
Claudine Lee *(VP)*

RCG PRODUCTIONS

5645 Coral Ridge Dr Ste 206, Coral Springs, FL 33076
Tel.: (954) 752-5224
Web Site:
http://www.rcgproductions.net
Year Founded: 2002
Sales Range: $10-24.9 Million
Emp.: 2
Audio/Visual, Brand Development, Broadcast, Cable T.V.
N.A.I.C.S.: 541810
Debra Hall-Greene *(VP)*
Robert Greene *(Pres & Mng Dir)*

RCH COMPANY, INC.

208 Louisville Ave, Monroe, LA 71201
Tel.: (318) 387-5335
Web Site:
http://www.rchcompanyinc.com
Year Founded: 2003
Sales Range: $1-9.9 Million
Engineering & Land Surveying
N.A.I.C.S.: 541370
Glenda Morris *(Mgr-Surveying)*
Ron C. Haisty Jr. *(Pres & CEO)*

RCM INDUSTRIES, INC.

3021 Cullerton St, Franklin Park, IL 60131-2204
Tel.: (847) 455-1950 IL
Web Site:
http://www.rcmindustries.com
Year Founded: 1989
Sales Range: $75-99.9 Million
Emp.: 700
Holding Company
N.A.I.C.S.: 331523
Robert Marconi *(CEO)*
Ken Morency *(Pres)*
Phil Burton *(VP-Ops)*

Subsidiaries:

AAllied Die Casting Manufacturing, Inc. (1)
3021 Cullerton Dr, Franklin Park, IL 60131-2204 (100%)
Tel.: (847) 455-1950

Web Site: http://www.rcmindustries.com
Sales Range: $25-49.9 Million
Emp.: 200
Mfr of Aluminum Die Castings
N.A.I.C.S.: 331523

AAllied Die Casting Manufacturing, Inc. (1)
401 Allied Dr, Rutherfordton, NC 28139-1178 (100%)
Tel.: (828) 286-4003
Sales Range: $10-24.9 Million
Emp.: 130
Mfr of Aluminum Die Castings
N.A.I.C.S.: 331523
Don Kilburg *(Pres)*

Imperial Die Casting (1)
2249 Old Liberty Rd, Liberty, SC 29657 (100%)
Tel.: (864) 859-0202
Sales Range: $10-24.9 Million
Emp.: 140
Mfr of Aluminum Die Castings
N.A.I.C.S.: 331523
Dennis Freeman *(CFO)*
Rick Buchhop *(CEO & Gen Mgr)*
Wayne Madden *(Mgr-HR)*

Inland Die Casting (1)
161 Carpenter Ave, Wheeling, IL 60090-6007 (100%)
Tel.: (847) 541-2700
Web Site: http://www.rcmindustries.com
Sales Range: $25-49.9 Million
Emp.: 160
Mfr of Aluminum Die Castings
N.A.I.C.S.: 331523

RCM SOLUTIONS, INC.

16900 Science Dr Ste 112, Bowie, MD 20715
Tel.: (301) 860-0590
Web Site: http://www.rcm-solutions.net
Year Founded: 2004
Sales Range: $1-9.9 Million
Emp.: 40
IT Management Services
N.A.I.C.S.: 541513
Ron Martin *(Founder & CEO)*

RCO ENGINEERING INC.

29200 Calahan Rd, Roseville, MI 48066-1849
Tel.: (586) 774-0100 MI
Web Site: http://www.rcoeng.com
Year Founded: 1973
Sales Range: $50-74.9 Million
Emp.: 700
Design, Development, Tooling & Technical Placements
N.A.I.C.S.: 336390
Stephen Carollo *(CEO)*
Debbie Mack *(CFO)*
Dale Drew *(Gen Mgr)*
Dan Tarvis *(Program Mgr & Supvr-Design)*
Jeff Simek *(Plant Mgr)*
Paul Dowson *(Acct Mgr-Sls)*

RCP BLOCK & BRICK, INC.

8240 Broadway, Lemon Grove, CA 91945-2004
Tel.: (619) 460-9101
Web Site: http://www.rcpblock.com
Year Founded: 1947
Sales Range: $10-24.9 Million
Emp.: 200
Mfr of Concrete Block & Brick Products
N.A.I.C.S.: 327331
Mike Finch *(Pres & CEO)*
Ed Marsh *(Mgr-Store)*
Anthony Rivera *(Dir-Safety)*
Stanley Stephens *(Mgr-IT)*

RCS COMPANY OF TAMPA

422 Hobbs St, Tampa, FL 33619
Tel.: (813) 661-2302
Web Site: http://www.rcs-tampa.com

U.S. PRIVATE

Sales Range: $10-24.9 Million
Emp.: 30
Refrigeration Construction & Repair Services
N.A.I.C.S.: 238220
Alfred Estrada *(Pres)*
Terry Barrett *(Controller)*
Albert Estrada *(Project Mgr)*
Paul Samay *(Mgr-Construction)*
Gene Wahl *(Mgr-Gen Ops)*

RD ENGINEERING & CONSTRUCTION INC.

1660 N Magnolia Ave, El Cajon, CA 92020
Tel.: (619) 562-2255
Web Site:
http://www.rdconstruction.com
Year Founded: 1978
Sales Range: $10-24.9 Million
Emp.: 26
Commercial & Office Building, New Construction
N.A.I.C.S.: 236220
Robert D. Davison *(Pres)*
Joey Atkins *(Superintendent)*

RD MERRILL COMPANY

1938 Fairview Ave E Ste 300, Seattle, WA 98102
Tel.: (206) 676-5600
Web Site:
http://www.merrillgardens.com
Rev.: $13,000,000
Emp.: 45
Retirement Hotel Operation
N.A.I.C.S.: 813110
William D. Pettit *(Pres & COO)*
Charles Wright *(Chm)*
Steve Delmore *(Exec VP)*
Doug Spear *(CFO & Sr VP)*

Subsidiaries:

Merrill Gardens LLC (1)
1938 Fairview Ave E Ste 300, Seattle, WA 98102-3650
Tel.: (206) 676-5300
Web Site: http://www.merrillgardens.com
Sales Range: $200-249.9 Million
Senior Citizen Housing & Independent Living Community Owner & Operator
N.A.I.C.S.: 623312
William D. Pettit *(Pres & COO)*
Charles Wright *(Chm)*
Doug Spear *(CFO & Sr VP)*
David Eskenazy *(Pres)*
Morei Lingle *(Chief Admin Officer & Sr VP)*

Subsidiary (Domestic):

Truewood (2)
3409 26th St W, Bradenton, FL 34205
Tel.: (941) 203-4866
Web Site: http://www.merrillgardens.com
Senior Housing Industry
N.A.I.C.S.: 623312

RD PLASTICS COMPANY, INC.

4825 Trousdale Dr Ste 203, Nashville, TN 37220
Tel.: (615) 781-0007
Web Site: http://www.rdplastics.com
Year Founded: 1975
Sales Range: $10-24.9 Million
Emp.: 25
Supplier of Plastic Materials & Basic Shapes
N.A.I.C.S.: 424610
Lynda Huseman *(Pres)*

RD&G HOLDINGS CORPORATION

1885 W Dartmouth Unit 1, Englewood, CO 80110
Tel.: (720) 883-0600 CO
Sales Range: Less than $1 Million
Emp.: 6
Screen Printing & Embroidery Services

COMPANIES
RDA HOLDING CO.

N.A.I.C.S.: 323113
Larry Parsons *(Pres & CEO)*

RDA CORPORATION
303 International Cir Ste 340, Hunt Valley, MD 21030
Tel.: (410) 308-9300
Web Site: http://www.rdacorp.com
Year Founded: 1988
Sales Range: $10-24.9 Million
Emp.: 200
Computer Software Development & Applications
N.A.I.C.S.: 541511
Tom Cole *(Pres & CEO)*
Patty Weaver *(Dir-Facilities & Admin Svcs)*
Jason Amato *(Controller)*

RDA HOLDING CO.
750 Third Ave, New York, NY 10017
Tel.: (646) 293-6000 DE
Web Site: http://www.rda.com
Sales Range: $1-4.9 Billion
Emp.: 2,100
Holding Company
N.A.I.C.S.: 551112
Paul R. Tomkins *(CFO & Exec VP)*
Joseph Held *(CIO & Sr VP)*
Susan W. Cummiskey *(Sr VP-HR)*
Albert L. Perruzza *(Exec Vp-Bus Dev)*
Susan Fraysse Russ *(VP-Global Comm)*

Subsidiaries:

The Reader's Digest Association, Inc. (1)
Reader's Digest Rd, Pleasantville, NY 10570
Tel.: (914) 238-1000
Web Site: http://www.rd.com
Sales Range: $350-399.9 Million
Emp.: 100
Magazines, Books, Music, Videos, Electronic Publishing & New Media Publisher
N.A.I.C.S.: 513120
Robert E. Guth *(Chm)*
William H. Magill *(Treas & VP)*
Elaine Alimonti *(VP-Mktg & Sls Dev)*
Barbara O'Dair *(Exec Editor)*
Cynthia Hack *(Publr-Selecciones)*
Neil Wertheimer *(VP & Editor-in-Chief-Emerging Bus & Content Dev)*
Harold Clarke *(Publr-Books, Music & Trade Publ)*
Bonnie Kintzer *(Pres & CEO)*
Tom Callahan *(CFO)*
Alec Casey *(CMO)*

Subsidiary (Non-US):

David & Charles plc (2)
Brunel House Forde Close, Newton Abbot, TQ12 4PU, Devon, United Kingdom
Tel.: (44) 1626323200
Web Site: http://www.fwmedia.com
Sales Range: $25-49.9 Million
Emp.: 60
Publisher
N.A.I.C.S.: 513120

Det Beste A/S (2)
Haakon VII's Gate 10 C, 161, Oslo, Norway
Tel.: (47) 22178220
Web Site: http://www.detbeste.no
Sales Range: $25-49.9 Million
Emp.: 15
Magazine Publisher
N.A.I.C.S.: 513120

Distrimedia Services B.V. (2)
Hogehilweg 17, 1101 CB, Amsterdam, Zuidoost, Netherlands
Tel.: (31) 205678911
Magazine Publisher
N.A.I.C.S.: 513120

Subsidiary (Domestic):

R.D. Manufacturing Corporation (2)
Readers Digest Rd, Pleasantville, NY 10570-7000
Tel.: (914) 238-1000
Web Site: http://www.rd.com
Publishing Services
N.A.I.C.S.: 323117

RD Publications, Inc. (2)
750 3rd Ave, New York, NY 10017
Tel.: (914) 238-1000
Web Site: http://www.rd.com
Sales Range: $50-74.9 Million
Emp.: 500
Magazine Publisher
N.A.I.C.S.: 513120
Mary Berner *(Pres & CEO)*

Subsidiary (Domestic):

Home Service Publications, Inc. (3)
1 Readers Digest Rd, Pleasantville, NY 10570-7000
Tel.: (914) 238-1000
Web Site: http://www.familyhandyman.com
Sales Range: $10-24.9 Million
Emp.: 25
Magazine Publisher
N.A.I.C.S.: 513120
Eric W. Schrier *(Pres)*

Reader's Digest Children's Publishing, Inc. (3)
Readers Digest Rd, Pleasantville, NY 10570-7000
Tel.: (914) 238-1000
Web Site: http://www.readersdigest.com
Children Magazine Publisher
N.A.I.C.S.: 513120
Harold Clarke *(Pres)*

Subsidiary (Non-US):

Reader's Digest (Malaysia) Sdn. Bhd (2)
Level 6 Symphony House Blk D13 Pusat Dagangan Dana 1, Jalan PJu 1A/46, 47301, Petaling Jaya, Malaysia
Tel.: (60) 379601111
Web Site: http://www.rdasia.com.my
Magazine Publisher
N.A.I.C.S.: 513120

Reader's Digest (Philippines) Inc. (2)
Unit 1004 Jafford Place Building 19 Eisenhower Saint Greenhill, San Juan, Manila, 1504, Philippines
Tel.: (63) 27259001
Web Site: http://www.rdasia.com
Sales Range: $25-49.9 Million
Emp.: 5
Magazine Publisher
N.A.I.C.S.: 513120
Paul Heath *(CEO)*

Reader's Digest (Thailand) Limited (2)
278 Raintree Office, Garden Rama 9 Road, Kuay Kwang, Bangkok, 10320, Thailand
Tel.: (66) 23199938
Web Site: http://www.readersdigest.co.th
Magazines, Books, Music, Videos, Electronic Publishing & New Media Publisher
N.A.I.C.S.: 513120

Reader's Digest Association Far East Ltd. (2)
PO Box 11852, Hong Kong, China (Hong Kong)
Tel.: (852) 25681117
Web Site: http://www.readersdigest.hk
Sales Range: $25-49.9 Million
Emp.: 100
Magazine Publisher
N.A.I.C.S.: 424920

Reader's Digest Children's Publishing Limited (2)
The Ice House 124 126 Walcot Streey, Bath, BA1 5BG, United Kingdom
Tel.: (44) 1225473200
Web Site: http://www.readersdigest.co.uk
Sales Range: $25-49.9 Million
Emp.: 10
Magazine Publisher
N.A.I.C.S.: 513120

Reader's Digest Colombia, Ltda (2)
Carrera 14 94A 44 Oficina 103, Bogota, Colombia
Tel.: (57) 16 233 039
Web Site: http://www.rd.com
Magazines, Books, Music, Videos, Electronic Publishing & New Media Publisher
N.A.I.C.S.: 513120

Subsidiary (Domestic):

Reader's Digest Consumer Services, Inc. (2)
750 3rd Ave, New York, NY 10017-7000
Tel.: (914) 238-1000
Web Site: http://www.readersdigest.com
Rev: $3,000,000
Emp.: 200
Magazine Publisher
N.A.I.C.S.: 513120

Reader's Digest Entertainment, Inc. (2)
750 3rd Ave, New York, NY 10017
Tel.: (914) 238-1000
Web Site: http://www.rd.com
Magazine Publisher
N.A.I.C.S.: 513120
Bonnie Kintver *(CEO)*

Subsidiary (Non-US):

Reader's Digest Europe Limited (2)
157 Edgware Road, London, W2 2HR, Wiltshire, United Kingdom
Tel.: (44) 2077158000
Web Site: http://www.readersdigest.co.uk
Sales Range: $25-49.9 Million
Emp.: 170
Magazines, Books, Music, Videos, Electronic Publishing & New Media Publisher
N.A.I.C.S.: 513120

Reader's Digest Kiado KFT (2)
Nepfurdo utca 22, BP 1970, 1138, Budapest, Hungary
Tel.: (36) 12963600
Sales Range: $25-49.9 Million
Emp.: 55
Magazines, Books, Music, Videos, Electronic Publishing & New Media Publisher
N.A.I.C.S.: 513120

Reader's Digest Mexico S.A. de C.V. (2)
Av Prol Paseo de la Reforma 1236 10 Piso Sant Fe Cuajimalpa, Mexico, 5348, Mexico
Tel.: (52) 5553512200
Web Site: http://www.selecciones.com
Sales Range: $25-49.9 Million
Emp.: 100
Magazines, Books, Music, Videos, Electronic Publishing & New Media Publisher
N.A.I.C.S.: 513120

Reader's Digest N.V. S.A. (2)
Paapsemlaan 20, 1070, Brussels, Belgium
Tel.: (32) 2 526 8104
Web Site: http://www.rdcompany.be
Sales Range: $25-49.9 Million
Emp.: 30
Magazine Publisher
N.A.I.C.S.: 513120

Reader's Digest Przeglad Sp.z.o.o. (2)
EMPARK Mokotow Business Park Building SATURN Domaniewska 41, Warsaw, 02-672, Poland
Tel.: (48) 223193200
Web Site: http://www.digest.com.pl
Sales Range: $25-49.9 Million
Emp.: 55
Magazines, Books, Music, Videos, Electronic Publishing & New Media Publisher
N.A.I.C.S.: 513120

Reader's Digest S.A. (2)
Raffelstrasse 11, CH 8045, Zurich, Switzerland
Tel.: (41) 14557316
Web Site: http://www.rd.com
Sales Range: $25-49.9 Million
Emp.: 25
Magazine Publisher
N.A.I.C.S.: 513120

Subsidiary (Domestic):

Reader's Digest Sales & Services, Inc. (2)
44 S Broadway, White Plains, NY 10601
Tel.: (914) 238-1000
Web Site: http://www.readersdigest.com
Sales Range: $50-74.9 Million
Emp.: 800
Magazine Advertising Services
N.A.I.C.S.: 541890

Subsidiary (Domestic):

Reader's Digest Sales & Services, Inc. (3)
260 Madison Ave, New York, NY 10016
Tel.: (212) 850-7100
Web Site: http://www.rd.com
Sales Range: $10-24.9 Million
Emp.: 125
Magazine Advertising Services
N.A.I.C.S.: 541890

Subsidiary (Non-US):

Reader's Digest Selecciones S.A. (2)
Azalea 1 Miniparc Edificio B 1 De La Moraleja Alcobendas Planta Ofic, Madrid, 28109, Spain
Tel.: (34) 917688640
Web Site: http://www.rd.com
Sales Range: $25-49.9 Million
Emp.: 3
Magazines, Books, Music, Videos, Electronic Publishing & New Media Publisher
N.A.I.C.S.: 513120

Reader's Digest Vyber s.r.o. (2)
V Celnici 1031 4, 110 00, Prague, Czech Republic
Tel.: (420) 222071111
Web Site: http://www.vybercz.iol.cz
Sales Range: $25-49.9 Million
Emp.: 100
Magazine Publisher
N.A.I.C.S.: 513120

Reader's Digest World Services, S.A. (2)
Boulevard Paepsem, Berchem, 1070, Belgium
Tel.: (32) 25 268 111
Web Site: http://www.rd.com
Magazines, Books, Music, Videos, Electronic Publishing & New Media Publisher
N.A.I.C.S.: 513120

Subsidiary (Domestic):

Reiman Media Group, Inc. (2)
5400 S 60th St, Greendale, WI 53129
Tel.: (414) 423-0100
Web Site: http://www.reimanpub.com
Sales Range: $300-349.9 Million
Emp.: 500
Magazine Publisher
N.A.I.C.S.: 513120
Catherine Cassidy *(Editor-in-Chief-Taste of Home)*

Subsidiary (Non-US):

Seleccoes do Reader's Digest (Portugal) S.A. (2)
Rua Da Industria 4 1Fl Alfragide, 2780-781, Amadora, Portugal
Tel.: (351) 213810000
Web Site: http://www.clients.com
Sales Range: $25-49.9 Million
Emp.: 60
Magazines, Books, Music, Videos, Electronic Publishing & New Media Publisher
N.A.I.C.S.: 513120

The Reader's Digest (New Zealand) Limited (2)
PO Box 90489, Auckland, 1030, New Zealand
Tel.: (64) 95229777
Web Site: http://www.rd.com
Magazines, Books, Music, Videos, Electronic Publishing & New Media Publisher
N.A.I.C.S.: 513120

Subsidiary (Domestic):

The Reader's Digest Association (Russia) Inc. (2)
750 3rd Ave 4Fl, Pleasantville, NY 10070
Tel.: (914) 238-1000
Web Site: http://www.readersdigest.com
Magazine Publisher
N.A.I.C.S.: 513120

RDA HOLDING CO.

RDA Holding Co.—(Continued)

Subsidiary (Non-US):

The Reader's Digest Association Pty Limited (2)
26 Waterloo Street, Surrey Hills, Sydney, 2010, NSW, Australia
Tel.: (61) 29 690 6111
Web Site: http://www.readersdigest.com.au
Sales Range: $25-49.9 Million
Emp.: 110
Magazines, Books, Music, Videos, Electronic Publishing & New Media Publisher
N.A.I.C.S.: 513120

Subsidiary (Domestic):

Reader's Digest (Australia) Pty Ltd. (3)
80 Bay Street, Ultimo, Sydney, 2007, NSW, Australia
Tel.: (61) 290186000
Web Site: http://www.readersdigest.com
Sales Range: $50-74.9 Million
Emp.: 370
Magazine Publisher
N.A.I.C.S.: 513120
Paul Heath (Mng Dir)

Subsidiary (Non-US):

Uitgeversmaatschappij The Reader's Digest N.V.
Hogehilweg 17, 1101 CB, Amsterdam, Zuidoost, Netherlands
Tel.: (31) 205678400
Web Site: http://www.readersdigest.nl
Sales Range: $25-49.9 Million
Emp.: 105
Magazine Publisher
N.A.I.C.S.: 513120
Franz Mueller (Mng Dir)

Verlag Das Beste Ges.m.b.H. (2)
Singerstrasse 2, 1010, Vienna, Austria
Tel.: (43) 15132554
Web Site: http://www.readersdigest.at
Sales Range: $25-49.9 Million
Emp.: 10
Magazine Publisher
N.A.I.C.S.: 513120
Werner Nit (Gen Mgr)

Subsidiary (Domestic):

Weekly Reader Corporation (2)
44 S Broadway, White Plains, NY 10601
Tel.: (914) 242-4000
Web Site: http://www.weeklyreader.com
Sales Range: $25-49.9 Million
Emp.: 162
Supplementary Educational Materials for the School Market
N.A.I.C.S.: 513120

RDA INTERNATIONAL
100 Vandam St 1st Fl, New York, NY 10013
Tel.: (212) 255-7700
Web Site: http://www.rdai.com
Rev.: $80,000,000
Emp.: 64
Advetising Agency
N.A.I.C.S.: 541810
Anthony Bagliani (Dir-Creative)

RDC INC.
1 Sousa St, Rossville, GA 30741
Tel.: (706) 858-1345
Sales Range: Less than $1 Million
Emp.: 3
Nonresidential Building Operators
N.A.I.C.S.: 531120
Hazel Bell (Pres)

RDC MACHINE INC.
384 Laurelwood Rd, Santa Clara, CA 95054
Tel.: (408) 970-0721
Web Site: http://www.rdcmachine.com
Sales Range: $10-24.9 Million
Emp.: 26
Machine Shop, Jobbing & Repair
N.A.I.C.S.: 332710
Randolph D. Cuilla (Pres)
Dana Depew Sr (VP-Ops)

RDI DIAMONDS, INC.
3101 W Ridge Rd 2nd Fl, Rochester, NY 14626
Tel.: (585) 225-3390
Web Site: http://www.rdidiamonds.com
Year Founded: 1992
Sales Range: $10-24.9 Million
Emp.: 22
Diamond Whslr
N.A.I.C.S.: 423940
Andrew Rickard (VP-Ops)
Sara Juett (Acct Mgr)

RDI, INC.
333 N Bedford Rd, Mount Kisco, NY 10549
Tel.: (914) 773-1000
Web Site: http://www.rdiusa.com
Year Founded: 1988
Sales Range: $10-24.9 Million
Electromechanical Component Mfr
N.A.I.C.S.: 334419
Ed Westring (Mgr-Sls Natl)

RDK TRUCK SALES
3214 E Adamo Dr, Tampa, FL 33605
Tel.: (813) 241-0711
Web Site: http://www.rdk.com
Sales Range: $50-74.9 Million
Emp.: 30
Garbage Truck Sales & Services
N.A.I.C.S.: 441227
Richard Kemner (Owner)
Mike Kemner (Mgr-Mktg)

RDR INC
5900 Fort Dr Ste 300, Centreville, VA 20121
Tel.: (703) 266-4000
Web Site: http://www.rdr.com
Year Founded: 1986
Sales Range: $25-49.9 Million
Emp.: 225
Provider of Systems Software Development Services
N.A.I.C.S.: 541512
Michelle Younger (Dir-HR)

RDR PROPERTIES INC.
3000 Dormax St SW, Grandville, MI 49418
Tel.: (616) 538-0120
Rev.: $25,034,222
Emp.: 30
Plastering Services
N.A.I.C.S.: 238310

Subsidiaries:

Herb Ritsema Co. (1)
3000 Dormax St SW, Grandville, MI 49418
Tel.: (616) 538-0120
Web Site: http://www.ritsema.com
Plastering Services
N.A.I.C.S.: 238310
Jim Davis (Gen Mgr-Flooring)
Doug Terpstra (Gen Mgr-Drywall)

RDSK, INC.
17861 Cartwright Rd, Irvine, CA 92614
Tel.: (949) 851-1085 DE
Web Site: http://www.litronic.com
Year Founded: 1997
Identity Management, Assurance & Authentication
N.A.I.C.S.: 541512
Kris Shah (CEO)

RDV CORPORATION
200 Monroe Ave NW, Grand Rapids, MI 49503
Tel.: (616) 454-4114 MI

Year Founded: 1991
Investment Holding Company
N.A.I.C.S.: 551112
Robert H. Schierbeek (COO)

Subsidiaries:

Ottawa Avenue Private Capital, LLC (1)
200 Monroe Ave NW, Grand Rapids, MI 49503
Tel.: (616) 454-4114
Privater Equity Firm
N.A.I.C.S.: 523999
Robert H. Schierbeek (COO)

RDV Sports, Inc. (1)
RDV Sportsplex 8701 Maitland Summit Blvd, Orlando, FL 32810
Tel.: (407) 916-2400
Sales Range: $25-49.9 Million
Emp.: 600
Holding Company; Professional Basketball Franchise & Sports Complex Owner & Operator
N.A.I.C.S.: 551112
Daniel G. DeVos (Chm & Pres)
Alex Martins (Pres/CEO-Orlando Magic)
Jo Wheeler (Coord-Admin)
Joann Thomas (Mgr-Billing)

Subsidiary (Domestic):

Orlando Magic, Ltd. (2)
8701 Maitland Summit Blvd, Orlando, FL 32810
Tel.: (407) 916-2400
Web Site: http://www.nba.com
Professional Basketball Franchise
N.A.I.C.S.: 711211

Unit (Domestic):

RDV Sportsplex (2)
8701 Maitland Summit Blvd, Orlando, FL 32810-5915
Tel.: (352) 674-7000
Web Site: http://www.rdvsportsplex.com
Fitness & Recreational Sports Centers
N.A.I.C.S.: 713940
Rich Devoss (Owner)

RE COMMUNITY HOLDINGS II, INC.
809 W Hill St, Charlotte, NC 28208
Tel.: (704) 697-2000
Web Site: http://www.recommunity.com
Sales Range: $100-124.9 Million
Emp.: 1,150
Recycling Facilities
N.A.I.C.S.: 423930
Andrew D. Lipman (Vice Chm)
Sean Duffy (Pres & COO)
Will Herzog (Dir-Mktg-ReCommunity Recycling LLC)
Jerry White (Mgr-Southeast)
Steve Gray (Mgr-Mid-Atlantic)
Stephen Klemann (Mgr-North Reg)
James E. Devlin (CEO)
David Eisner (CFO)
David Lank (Dir-Operational Improvement)
Kimberli Lasyone (Dir-HR)
Mike Brennan (Gen Counsel)
Dennis McGill (CEO-Interim)

RE KRAMIG & CO. INC.
323 S Wayne Ave, Cincinnati, OH 45215
Tel.: (513) 761-4010
Web Site: http://www.kramiginsulation.com
Rev.: $14,000,000
Emp.: 21
Insulation Of Pipes & Boilers
N.A.I.C.S.: 238990
Andrew J. Kulesza (Pres & CEO)
Bronner Jeff (Superintendent)

RE MONKS CONSTRUCTION COMPANY
PO Box 25579, Colorado Springs, CO 80936-5579
Tel.: (719) 495-3621
Web Site: http://www.remonks.com
Year Founded: 1981
Sales Range: $50-74.9 Million
Emp.: 300
Industrial Building Construction Services
N.A.I.C.S.: 236210
Miguel Lagos (Mgr-IT)

RE STEEL SUPPLY COMPANY INC.
2000 Eddystone Indus Pk, Eddystone, PA 19022
Tel.: (610) 876-8216 PA
Web Site: http://www.resteel.com
Year Founded: 1973
Sales Range: $10-24.9 Million
Emp.: 75
Provider of Fabricated Structural Metal
N.A.I.C.S.: 332312
James Melvin Jr. (Pres)

RE-AD MARKETING INC.
4790 Caughlin Pkwy Ste 387, Reno, NV 89519
Tel.: (775) 232-1950 NV
Year Founded: 2012
Real Estate Advertising Services
N.A.I.C.S.: 541890
Michael F. Smith (Pres, CEO, CFO, Principal Acctg Officer, Treas & Sec)

RE/MAX ACCORD
313 Sycamore Vly Rd W, Danville, CA 94526
Tel.: (925) 838-4100
Web Site: http://www.remaxaccord.com
Year Founded: 1996
Sales Range: $1-9.9 Million
Emp.: 350
Real Estate Agency
N.A.I.C.S.: 531210
Jerry Stadtler (Co-Owner & Realtor)
Stephanie A. Stadtler (Co-Owner & Realtor)
Michael Carter (VP)

RE/MAX ALLEGIANCE
5100 Leesburg Pike Ste 302, Alexandria, VA 22302
Tel.: (703) 824-4800
Web Site: http://www.myallegiancehome.com
Real Estate Agent, Commercial
N.A.I.C.S.: 531210
Judy Austin (Owner & Pres)
Melisa Chavez (Sr VP-Ops)
John Blount (Pres-Affiliated Bus)
Davidson Lunger (Pres-Assoc Dev)
Helen Malakoff (Sr VP-Ops)
Charlie Bengel Jr. (CEO)

Subsidiaries:

RE/MAX Allegiance - Virginia Beach (1)
4000 Virginia Beach Blvd Ste 164, Virginia Beach, VA 23452
Tel.: (757) 490-7300
Web Site: http://www.myallegiancehome.com
Real Estate Brokers & Agents
N.A.I.C.S.: 531210

RE/MAX ALLIANCE GROUP
2000 Webber St, Sarasota, FL 34239
Tel.: (941) 954-5454
Web Site: http://www.alliancegroupfl.com
Sales Range: $25-49.9 Million
Emp.: 20
Real Estate Broker
N.A.I.C.S.: 531210

Peter Crowley (Co-Owner)
Ron Travis (Co-Owner)
Kink Crowley (Gen Mgr)
Karen Cox (Dir-Comm)

RE/MAX CHOICE PROPERTIES
131 Indian Lake Blvd Ste 200, Hendersonville, TN 37075-6207
Tel.: (615) 822-2003 TN
Web Site: http://www.choiceproperties01.remax.tennessee.com
Year Founded: 1995
Sales Range: $25-49.9 Million
Emp.: 25
Real Estate Agents & Managers
N.A.I.C.S.: 531210
Joanne Staler (Co-Owner)

RE/MAX HEARTLAND
1579 NE Rice Rd, Lees Summit, MO 64086
Tel.: (816) 373-8400
Web Site: http://www.kcheartlandrealtors.com
Sales Range: $125-149.9 Million
Emp.: 65
Real Estate Brokers & Agents
N.A.I.C.S.: 531210
T. David Rogers (Pres)

RE/MAX OF NAPERVILLE INC.
1200 Iroquois Ave, Naperville, IL 60563
Tel.: (630) 420-1220
Web Site: http://www.bigbrokers.com
Sales Range: $450-499.9 Million
Emp.: 120
Real Estate Brokers & Agents
N.A.I.C.S.: 531210

RE/MAX PROPERTIES EAST, INC.
10525 Timberwood Cir Ste 100, Louisville, KY 40223
Tel.: (502) 425-6000
Web Site: http://www.homesinlouisville.com
Year Founded: 1986
Sales Range: $10-24.9 Million
Emp.: 12
Real Estate Brokerage Services
N.A.I.C.S.: 531210
Brad Herrick (CEO)

RE/MAX REALTORS INC.
7603 Woodcroft CT, Houston, TX 77095
Tel.: (281) 463-3900
Web Site: http://remax.com
Sales Range: $10-24.9 Million
Emp.: 2
Real Estate Brokers & Agents
N.A.I.C.S.: 531210
Ray Lafuente (Pres)

RE/MAX VILLA REALTORS
7505 Bergenline Ave, North Bergen, NJ 07047
Tel.: (201) 868-3100
Web Site: http://www.remax-villa.com
Year Founded: 1977
Sales Range: $10-24.9 Million
Emp.: 70
Real Estate Brokers & Agents
N.A.I.C.S.: 531210
Orvelio A. Herrera (Pres)

RE:GROUP, INC.
213 W Liberty St, Ann Arbor, MI 48104-1398
Tel.: (734) 213-0200 NY
Web Site: http://www.regroup.us
Year Founded: 1996
Rev.: $23,000,000
Emp.: 18
Advetising Agency
N.A.I.C.S.: 541810
Janet Muhleman (Pres & CEO)
Sharon Costantini (Office Mgr)
Carey Jernigan (VP)
Rhonda Huie (Dir-Creative)
Liz Conlin (VP & Dir-Client Svcs)
Karyn Kozo (VP & Dir-Client Svcs)
Kyle Feliks (Assoc Dir-Creative)
Pat Cuda (Dir-Media)
David Murray (Dir-Social Web Comm)
Matthew Zumstein (Assoc Dir-Digital Media)

RE:INTERACTION
44 Savage St, Charleston, SC 29401
Tel.: (843) 327-8451
Year Founded: 2008
Sales Range: $10-24.9 Million
Emp.: 20
Advetising Agency
N.A.I.C.S.: 541810
Matthew Klein (Pres)

RE:THINK GROUP
700 Canal St 5th Fl, Stamford, CT 06902
Tel.: (203) 357-9004
Web Site: http://www.rethinkgroup.com
Sales Range: $10-24.9 Million
Emp.: 12
Full Service
N.A.I.C.S.: 541810
James Offenhartz (Pres)
Kristy Ashfar (Dir-Acct Plng & Strategy)
Jonathan Sawyer (Partner-Creative)
Janet Evelyn (Dir-Media)

REA & ASSOCIATES, INC.
419 W High Ave, New Philadelphia, OH 44663
Tel.: (330) 339-6651 OH
Web Site: http://www.reacpa.com
Year Founded: 1938
Sales Range: $10-24.9 Million
Emp.: 40
Certified Public Accountants
N.A.I.C.S.: 541211
Don McIntosh (CEO)
Greg Goodie (Principal)
Lee Beall (Exec VP)
Steve Roth (Principal)
Anne Baker (Dir-First Impressions)
Mary Beth Koester (Principal & Dir-Valuation & Transaction Advisory Svcs)
Tim McDaniel (Principal & Dir-Consulting Svcs)
Kerry McElroy (Sr Mgr-Zanesville)
Melissa Dunkle (Mgr-Tax-Dublin)
Joseph Popp (Principal & Dir-State & Local Tax Svcs)
Matt Dasta (Principal & Dir-Tax Svcs)
Greg Speece (Principal)
Lauren Holt (Mgr-Northeast)
Ben Antonelli (Principal-Equity)

REA ENERGY CO-OPERATIVE CORP.
75 Airport Rd, Indiana, PA 15701
Tel.: (724) 349-4800
Web Site: http://www.reaenergy.com
Rev.: $26,702,483
Emp.: 53
Electronic Services
N.A.I.C.S.: 221118
Tom Borusiewicz (Gen Mgr)

REA MAGNET WIRE COMPANY, INC.
3400 E Coliseum Blvd Ste 200, Fort Wayne, IN 46805
Tel.: (260) 421-7321 DE
Web Site: http://www.reawire.com
Year Founded: 1933
Sales Range: $5-14.9 Billion
Emp.: 1,300
Mfr of Copper & Aluminum Magnet Wire
N.A.I.C.S.: 335929
Larry Knepp (VP-Integration & Transition)
Jerry Long (Pres & CEO)
Ryan Kelly (COO & Exec VP)
Michael F. Connolly (Exec VP-Bus Dev)
Pablo Leguina (CMO & Exec VP-Sls)
John Hake (Exec VP-China Joint Ventures)

Subsidiaries:

Algonquin Industries Division (1)
129 Soundview Rd, Guilford, CT 06437-2937
Tel.: (203) 453-4348
Web Site: http://www.algonquin-industries.com
Sales Range: $50-74.9 Million
Emp.: 85
N.A.I.C.S.: 331318

Plant (Domestic):

REA Magnet Wire Company, Inc. - AR Plant (2)
1800 Hwy 61 S, Osceola, AR 72370
Tel.: (870) 563-5207
Emp.: 50
Magnet Wire Mfr
N.A.I.C.S.: 331420
John Rausch (Gen Mgr)

Hanover Manufacturing Plant (1)
10117 Leadbetter Pl, Ashland, VA 23005-3411 (100%)
Tel.: (804) 550-5400
Sales Range: $50-74.9 Million
Emp.: 29
Mfr of Magnet Wire
N.A.I.C.S.: 524126

REA Magnet Wire Company, Inc. - Ashland (1)
10117 Leadbetter Pl, Ashland, VA 23005
Tel.: (804) 550-5401
Sales Range: $25-49.9 Million
Emp.: 20
Silo Mfr
N.A.I.C.S.: 331222

REA Magnet Wire Company, Inc. - Indiana Plant (1)
2800 Concord Rd, Lafayette, IN 47909
Tel.: (260) 421-7321
Magnet Wire Mfr
N.A.I.C.S.: 331420

REA Magnet Wire Company, Inc. - New Haven Avenue Plant (1)
4300 New Haven Ave, Fort Wayne, IN 46803
Tel.: (260) 421-7321
Magnet Wire Mfr
N.A.I.C.S.: 331420

REAC GROUP, INC.
8878 Covenant Ave Ste 209, Pittsburgh, PA 15237
Tel.: (412) 366-8886 FL
Web Site: https://www.realestatecontacts.com
Year Founded: 2005
REAC—(OTCBB)
Sales Range: Less than $1 Million
Emp.: 1
Online Real Estate Advertising & Marketing Services
N.A.I.C.S.: 531390

REACH COMMUNITY DEVELOPMENT, INC.
4150 SW Moody Ave, Portland, OR 97239
Tel.: (503) 231-0682 OR
Web Site: http://www.reachcdc.org
Year Founded: 1982
Sales Range: $10-24.9 Million
Emp.: 104
Community Development Services
N.A.I.C.S.: 624190
Brian Bieler (Dir-Asset Mgmt)
Anthony Petchel (Dir-Philanthropy)
Pamela Benoit (COO)
Rebbecca Maese (VP)
Alma Flores (Dir-Housing Dev)

REACH GENETICS, INC.
4800 Baseline Rd Unit E104 Ste 345, Boulder, CO 80303
Tel.: (855) 369-3687 NV
Web Site: http://www.reachgenetics.com
Genetics Research & Development Services
N.A.I.C.S.: 541714
Cynthia Boerum (Chm, CEO & CFO)
Jeff Hranicka (COO)
Doug Pineda (Dir-Bus Dev)

REACH MARKETING LLC
2 Blue Hill Plz Concourse Level, Pearl River, NY 10965
Tel.: (845) 201-5300
Web Site: http://www.reachmarketing.com
Sales Range: $1-9.9 Million
Emp.: 10
Marketing Services
N.A.I.C.S.: 541890
Wayne Roberts (Pres)
Greg Grdodian (CEO)
Chris Longo (COO)
Sean Sullivan (VP-Sls & Ops)
Aaron Liebson (CFO)
Josephine Messina (VP-Direct Mktg Svcs)
John Lignos (Sr VP-Bus Dev)
Wayne Nagrowski (VP-Mktg Solutions)
Paula Sanchez (VP)
Chris Steele (Dir-Database Tech)
Stevan Roberts (Chm)
David Klein (Sr VP-Product Dev & Database Svcs)
Joel Manning (VP-List Brokerage)
Michelle Roth (VP-Audience Dev Svcs)

REACH MESSAGING HOLDINGS, INC.
44081 Pipeline Plz Ste 310, Ashburn, VA 20147
Tel.: (517) 213-6147 DE
Web Site: http://www.reachmessaging.com
Year Founded: 2007
Sales Range: Less than $1 Million
Emp.: 1
Mobile Applications & Social Gaming Software Products
N.A.I.C.S.: 513210

REACH NOW INTERNATIONAL INC.
3939 S Harvard Ave, Tulsa, OK 74135
Tel.: (918) 361-0452 OK
Web Site: http://www.reachnow.net
Year Founded: 2006
Sales Range: $1-9.9 Million
Emp.: 1
Community Support Services
N.A.I.C.S.: 813219
William C. Meyer (Pres)
Leslie A. Meyer (Sec & VP)
Hal Boehm (Treas)

REACH SPORTS MARKETING GROUP
6440 Flying Cloud Dr Ste 225, Eden Prairie, MN 55344
Tel.: (952) 944-7727

Reach Sports Marketing Group—(Continued)

Web Site:
http://www.reachdigitalsolution.com
Year Founded: 2004
Sales Range: $1-9.9 Million
Emp.: 50
Advetising Agency
N.A.I.C.S.: 541810
Darren Wercinski (Co-Founder & CEO)
Marc Kline (Co-Founder)
Jennifer Lewis (Dir-Sls)

REACT2MEDIA, LLC.
35 W 36th St Ste 4E, New York, NY 10018
Tel.: (212) 239-7070
Web Site:
http://www.react2media.com
Year Founded: 2008
Sales Range: $1-9.9 Million
Emp.: 12
Online Media Marketing Consulting Services
N.A.I.C.S.: 541613
Alexander Schaller (Co-Founder & CEO)
Jordan Galbraith (Co-Founder & COO)

REACTION AUDIO VISUAL LLC
9951 Muirlands Blvd, Irvine, CA 92618
Tel.: (949) 600-8235
Web Site: http://www.reactionav.com
Year Founded: 2005
Sales Range: $1-9.9 Million
Emp.: 15
Event Technology Services
N.A.I.C.S.: 561920
J. Ocana (Pres & COO)

REACTION BIOLOGY CORPORATION
1 Great Vly Pkwy Ste 2, Malvern, PA 19355-1423
Web Site:
http://www.reactionbiology.com
Drug Testing, Screening & Research Services
N.A.I.C.S.: 541380
Matthew Oristano (Chm & CEO)
Richard S. Kollender (CFO & Chief Bus Officer)
John H. Johnson (CEO)

READABOO, INC.
845 3rd Ave 6th Fl, New York, NY 10022
Tel.: (646) 495-0939 DE
Web Site: http://www.readaboo.com
Year Founded: 2013
Sales Range: Less than $1 Million
Emp.: 10
Ebook Subscriptions & Marketing For Independently Published Books
N.A.I.C.S.: 424920
Ajay Tandon (Pres & CEO)

READE COMMUNICATIONS GROUP
850 Waterman Ave, East Providence, RI 02914
Tel.: (401) 433-7000 NJ
Web Site: http://www.reade.com
Year Founded: 1973
Sales Range: $1-9.9 Million
Emp.: 35
Advetising Agency
N.A.I.C.S.: 541810
Charles Reade Jr. (Mgr-Gen Sls & Mktg)

Subsidiaries:

Reade Communications Group (1)
1680 O'Malley Dr, Sparks, NV 89501
Tel.: (775) 352-1000
Web Site: http://www.reade.com
Rev.: $4,000,000
Emp.: 4
High Technology, Industrial
N.A.I.C.S.: 541810
Bethany Satterfield (VP & Reg Mgr)
Charles Reade (Chm & Pres)
E. S. Reade (VP & Gen Mgr)

READER'S WHOLESALE DISTRIBUTORS INC.
8010 Kempwood Dr, Houston, TX 77055
Tel.: (713) 224-8300
Web Site:
http://www.readerswholesale.com
Year Founded: 1978
Sales Range: $50-74.9 Million
Emp.: 99
Flooring Services
N.A.I.C.S.: 423220
Lloyd S. Burke (Chm & Pres)
Ed Mahler (Controller)

READEREST
2201 Long Prairie Rd Ste 107-316, Flower Mound, TX 75022
Tel.: (855) 321-7732
Web Site: http://www.readerest.com
Sales Range: $1-9.9 Million
Plastic Glasses Holder
N.A.I.C.S.: 326199
Rick Hopper (Pres)

READING ANTHRACITE COMPANY
200 Mahantongo St, Pottsville, PA 17901-7200
Tel.: (570) 622-5150 PA
Web Site:
http://www.readinganthracite.com
Year Founded: 1871
Sales Range: $25-49.9 Million
Emp.: 100
Mining, Processing & Sale of Anthracite Coal & Associated Products
N.A.I.C.S.: 212115
John W. Rich (Chm)
Brian R. Rich (Pres)
Frank D. Derrick (Gen Mgr)
Jeffery A. Gliem (Dir-Ops)
Ricardo A. Muntone (Dir-Safety & Special Projects)
Alfred Ty Leinneweber (Project Mgr)
John Rampolla (Treas)

Subsidiaries:

Anthracite Power and Light (1)
10 Gilberton Rd, Gilberton, PA 17934
Tel.: (570) 622-3000
Web Site: http://www.anthracitepower.com
Electric Power Distribution Services
N.A.I.C.S.: 221122

Barakat Associates, LTD (1)
10 Gilberton Rd, Gilberton, PA 17934-1009
Tel.: (570) 874-1602
Anthracite Coal Mining Services
N.A.I.C.S.: 212115

Bear Ridge Machine & Fabrication, Inc. (1)
10 Eleanor Ave, Frackville, PA 17931
Tel.: (570) 874-4083
Web Site: http://www.brmf.net
Fabricating & Welding Equipment Mfr
N.A.I.C.S.: 332999
Jack Wittig (Mgr-Sls & Engrg)

Gilberton Coal Company (1)
10 Gilberton Rd, Gilberton, PA 17934
Tel.: (570) 874-1602
Coal Mining Services
N.A.I.C.S.: 212115

Gilberton Power Company (1)
81 Eleanor Ave, Frackville, PA 17931

Tel.: (570) 874-4119
Emp.: 41
Electric Power Generation Services
N.A.I.C.S.: 221118
Alex Brush (Gen Mgr)

John J Holden Insurance Company (1)
215 S 2nd St, Saint Clair, PA 17970
Tel.: (570) 429-2100
Web Site:
http://www.johnholdeninsurance.com
Insurance Brokerage Services
N.A.I.C.S.: 524210
John Holden (Mgr)

Keller Oil Company (1)
1610 Route 61 S, Schuylkill Haven, PA 17972
Tel.: (570) 385-1030
Web Site: http://www.kelleroil.com
Heating Oil & Kerosene Supplier
N.A.I.C.S.: 457210

Laurel Ridge (1)
10 Gilberton Rd, Gilberton, PA 17934
Tel.: (570) 874-1602
Residential & Commercial Construction Services
N.A.I.C.S.: 236116

Lehigh Engineering LLC (1)
200 Mahantongo St, Pottsville, PA 17901
Tel.: (928) 628-2300
Web Site: http://www.lehighengineer.com
Engineeering Services
N.A.I.C.S.: 541330
William P. Anders (Mgr-Engrg Svcs)
Ted Puschak (Mgr-Mining Engrg)
Michael Hydock (Designer-Project)
Rodd J. White (Mgr-Firm)

Lehigh Fuels (1)
2825 Lehigh St, Whitehall, PA 18052
Tel.: (610) 266-8990
Web Site: http://www.lehighfuels.com
Oil & Kerosene Distr
N.A.I.C.S.: 424720
Peter Smith (Gen Mgr)
Jack Krissinger (Mgr)

R & R Property Managers (1)
10 Gilberton Rd, Gilberton, PA 17934-1009
Tel.: (570) 874-4047
Real Estate Brokerage Services
N.A.I.C.S.: 531390

Reading Stove Company (1)
16 Summer Valley Rd, Orwigsburg, PA 17961
Tel.: (570) 366-7788
Web Site: http://www.readingstove.com
Coal Stove Mfr
N.A.I.C.S.: 335220

WMPI Pty., LLC (1)
10 Gilberton Rd, Gilberton, PA 17934
Tel.: (570) 874-1602
Web Site: http://www.ultracleanfuels.com
Liquid Fuel Product Mfr & DistrFuel Distr
N.A.I.C.S.: 424720

Waste Management & Processors, Inc (1)
10 Gilberton Rd, Gilberton, PA 17934
Tel.: (570) 874-1602
Fuel Distr
N.A.I.C.S.: 424720
Michael Rich (VP)

READING EAGLE COMPANY
345 Penn St, Reading, PA 19601-4029
Tel.: (610) 371-5000 PA
Web Site:
http://www.readingeagle.com
Year Founded: 1904
Sales Range: $150-199.9 Million
Emp.: 500
Provider of Newspaper Publishing, Commercial Lithographic Book Printing & Radio Broadcasting
N.A.I.C.S.: 513110
William S. Flippin (Chm & Publr)
Lori Gerhart (Mgr-Adv & Sls)
Peter D. Barbey (Pres & CEO)
Andy Andrews (Editor-Bus)

Anne T. Chubb (COO)
David R. Gemmell (Sr Dir-Fin)
Christopher J. D'Angelo (Sr Dir-Production)
Evan Jones (Editor-Bus)
Lisa Scheid (Editor-Bus Wwekly)
Harry J. Deitz Jr. (Assoc Publr & Editor)

READING EQUIPMENT & DISTRIBUTION, INC.
1363 Bowmansville Rd, Bowmansville, PA 17507
Tel.: (717) 445-6746 PA
Web Site:
http://www.readingequipment.com
Year Founded: 1972
Sales Range: $25-49.9 Million
Emp.: 200
Provider of Truck Equipment & Related Services
N.A.I.C.S.: 441330
Jim Moorehand (Dir-Standard Sls)
Gordon Treisbach (Exec VP-Fin)
Stephen R. Morton (Dir-Matls)
Kris Ziegler (Dir-Specialty Equipment Sls)
Norman Ziegler Jr. (Pres)
Norman Ziegler Sr. (Founder)

READING FOUNDRY & SUPPLY CO.
650 Chestnut St, Reading, PA 19602
Tel.: (610) 320-6450
Web Site:
http://www.readingfoundry.com
Rev.: $10,000,000
Emp.: 50
Plumbing Fittings & Supplies
N.A.I.C.S.: 423720
Ryck D. Spengler (Pres)
Peter Wright (Treas & Sec)

READING IS FUNDAMENTAL, INC.
750 First ST Ste 920, Washington, DC 20002
Tel.: (202) 536-3400 DC
Web Site: http://www.rif.org
Year Founded: 1973
Sales Range: $1-9.9 Million
Emp.: 37
Child Educational Support Services
N.A.I.C.S.: 611710
John F. Remondi (Chm)
Cammie L. Backus (VP)
Cheryl Clark (VP-Programs)
Christy Moberly (Vice Chm)
J. Johnson (Treas)
Alicia Levi (Pres & CEO)
Ed Deleon (Chief Program & Content Officer)
Beth Meyer (CMO)
Marc Walby (Sec)

READING PARTNERS
180 Grand Ave Ste 800, Oakland, CA 94612
Tel.: (510) 444-9800 CA
Web Site:
http://www.readingpartners.org
Year Founded: 2001
Sales Range: $1-9.9 Million
Emp.: 515
Educational Support Services
N.A.I.C.S.: 611710
Adeola Whitney (CEO)
Dean Elson (Chief Knowledge Officer)
Cathy Cockrum Dean (Chm)
Dan Carroll (Treas)
Hagar Berlin (VP-Dev)
Kathy Taylor (Sec)
Stephanie Cohen (Mng Dir)
Walter Elcock (Vice Chm)

Jessica Vibberts *(Chief People Officer)*
Rosa J. Gutierrez *(Chief Fin & Operating Officer)*

READING ROCK INCORPORATED
4600 Devitt Dr, Cincinnati, OH 45246
Tel.: (513) 874-2345
Web Site:
http://www.readingrock.com
Rev.: $25,000,000
Emp.: 150
Concrete Blocks Mfr
N.A.I.C.S.: 327331
Gordon Rich *(Pres)*
Keven Roberts *(Mgr-Sls, Specification & Market-US)*
Neil Winter *(Mgr-Market)*
Brian Smith *(Mgr-Market-US)*

READY METAL MANUFACTURING COMPANY
4500 W 47th St, Chicago, IL 60632
Tel.: (773) 376-9700   IL
Web Site: http://ready.birkey.com
Year Founded: 1947
Sales Range: $25-49.9 Million
Emp.: 350
Metal Office & Store Fixtures Mfr
N.A.I.C.S.: 337215

READY MIX CONCRETE
331 N Main St, Euless, TX 76039
Tel.: (817) 835-4100
Sales Range: $25-49.9 Million
Emp.: 300
Ready Mixed Concrete
N.A.I.C.S.: 327320

READY MIX CONCRETE SOMERSET INC.
63 Fosterline, Somerset, KY 42503
Tel.: (606) 679-7490
Web Site:
http://www.readymixconcreteky.com
Sales Range: $10-24.9 Million
Emp.: 50
Ready-Mixed Concrete Products Mfr
N.A.I.C.S.: 327320
Joe A. Newell *(Pres)*
Bill Newell *(VP)*

READY MIX USA, INC.
2570 Ruffner Rd, Birmingham, AL 35210
Tel.: (205) 986-4800
Web Site:
http://www.readymixusa.com
Sales Range: $100-124.9 Million
Emp.: 2,500
Holding Company
N.A.I.C.S.: 551112
Herb Gossett *(Dir-Safety)*
Joseph Ryan Mandel *(Plant Mgr)*
Jim Phillips *(CIO)*
Sid Coleman *(Gen Mgr)*
Ben Templin *(Mgr)*
David Rabold *(Mgr-Environmental)*
Hogan Hartzog *(Mgr-Mktg)*
Timothy Baert *(Mgr-Safety)*

Subsidiaries:

Bayou Concrete Company Inc.   (1)
3151 Hamilton Blvd, Theodore, AL 36582-8500
Tel.: (251) 408-0700
Web Site: http://www.bayouconcretellc.com
Sales Range: $25-49.9 Million
Emp.: 250
Mfr of Central-Mixed Concrete
N.A.I.C.S.: 327320

Block USA Alabama Division LLC   (1)
2570 Russner Rd, Birmingham, AL 35210
Tel.: (205) 271-6846

Web Site: http://www.blockusa.com
Rev.: $4,700,000
Emp.: 100
Blocks, Concrete Or Cinder: Standard
N.A.I.C.S.: 327331

Ready Mix USA - Tri-States Div   (1)
419 N Selvidge St, Dalton, GA 30720
Tel.: (706) 278-6044
Web Site: http://www.readymixusa.com
Sales Range: $10-24.9 Million
Emp.: 40
Ready Mixed Concrete
N.A.I.C.S.: 327320
Chris Pack *(Plant Mgr)*

READY WIRELESS LLC
955 Kacena Rd Ste A, Hiawatha, IA 52233
Tel.: (319) 743-4624
Web Site:
http://www.readymobile.com
Year Founded: 2008
Sales Range: $10-24.9 Million
Emp.: 28
Outsourced Devices & Services on a Multi-Carrier Wireless Platform
N.A.I.C.S.: 517112
Fred Haumesser *(Co-Founder & Exec VP-Sls)*
Dennis Henderson *(Co-Founder & CEO)*
Kim Lehrman *(VP-Mktg)*
Joe Peterson *(Pres-Ready Internet of Things)*

READYTALK
1900 16th St Ste 600, Denver, CO 80202
Tel.: (303) 209-1600
Web Site: http://www.readytalk.com
Sales Range: $25-49.9 Million
Emp.: 150
Web Conferencing & Audio Conferencing Solutions
N.A.I.C.S.: 513210
James Kenly *(Mgr-Event)*
Brandon Hess *(Mgr-Inbound Mktg)*
Crystal Ziadeh *(Coord-Event)*
Barb Stevens *(COO)*

REAGAN ASSET MANAGEMENT, LLC
711 S Osprey Ave, Sarasota, FL 34236
Tel.: (941) 954-4044
Web Site:
http://www.reaganasset.com
Sales Range: $25-49.9 Million
Real Estate Asset Management & Maintenance Services
N.A.I.C.S.: 531390
David J. Matthes *(Co-Founder & Pres)*
Rachel C. Anderson *(Dir-Ops)*
Donna A. Triolo *(Dir-Tech & Trng)*

REAGAN-UDALL FOUNDATION
1025 Connecticut Ave NW Ste 1000, Washington, DC 20036
Tel.: (202) 828-1205   MD
Web Site: http://www.reaganudall.org
Year Founded: 2009
Sales Range: $1-9.9 Million
Emp.: 5
Food & Drug Administration Services
N.A.I.C.S.: 813319
Kay Holcombe *(Sec)*
Richard L. Schilsky *(Vice Chm)*

REAL ADVISORS, LLC
60 Ocean Blvd Ste 10, Jacksonville, FL 32233
Web Site:
http://www.realadvisors.com
Year Founded: 2011
Sales Range: $1-9.9 Million

Real Estate Investment Services
N.A.I.C.S.: 531210
Dolmar Cross *(Founder)*

REAL CAPITAL SOLUTIONS INC.
371 Centennial Pkwy Ste 200, Louisville, CO 80027
Tel.: (303) 466-2500
Web Site:
http://www.realcapitalsolutions.com
Sales Range: $25-49.9 Million
Real Estate Investment Services
N.A.I.C.S.: 531390
Marcel Arsenault *(Founder, Chm & CEO)*
Sharon Eshima *(COO)*
Rudy Fettig *(Gen Counsel & VP)*
Jason Esplin *(VP & Dir-Tax)*
Brian Wilson *(Pres-Div)*
Brian Paul *(Pres-Homebuilding & CEO)*
Mariya Chuykova *(Portfolio Mgr)*
Judy Lawson *(VP-Comml Ops)*
Dan Semler *(Chief Acctg Officer)*
Shaun O'Connor *(Pres)*

REAL DATA, INC.
2984-G Austin Springs Blvd, Miamisburg, OH 45342
Tel.: (281) 415-4121
Year Founded: 1984
Software Publisher
N.A.I.C.S.: 513210
William Tunnell *(Sr VP-Mergers & Acq)*
Christine Chiaramonte *(Sr VP-Admin)*
Frank N. Kautzmann III *(Chm, Pres, CEO, Treas & Sec)*

REAL ESTATE GROUP INC.
5355 Schroth Ln, Appleton, WI 54913
Tel.: (920) 993-7001
Web Site:
http://www.coldwellhomes.com
Sales Range: $10-24.9 Million
Emp.: 500
Real Estate Brokers & Agents
N.A.I.C.S.: 531210
Stephen Vertin *(Controller)*

REAL ESTATE III INC.
1160 Pepsi Pl Ste 306, Charlottesville, VA 22901
Tel.: (434) 817-9700
Web Site:
http://www.realestateiii.com
Year Founded: 1972
Sales Range: $10-24.9 Million
Emp.: 50
Real Estate Brokers & Agents
N.A.I.C.S.: 531210
Art Pearson *(Pres)*
Jeff Gaffney *(CEO)*
Donna Patton *(VP-Mng Broker Crossroads)*
Tim Carson *(VP)*

REAL ESTATE INSYNC
Highpoint Ctr Ste 810, 106 E College Ave, Tallahassee, FL 32301
Tel.: (850) 345-9455
Web Site:
http://www.realestateinsync.com
Sales Range: $1-9.9 Million
Real Estate Services
N.A.I.C.S.: 531390
William F. Butler *(Founder & Pres)*

REAL FOUNDATIONS, INC.
13737 Noel Rd Ste 900, Dallas, TX 75240
Tel.: (214) 292-7000
Web Site:
http://www.realfoundations.net
Year Founded: 2000

Sales Range: $25-49.9 Million
Emp.: 180
Management Consultants for the Real Estate Industry
N.A.I.C.S.: 531390
Chris Shaida *(CEO & Exec Mng Dir)*
Mark Callin *(Exec Mng Dir)*
David W. Stanford *(Exec Mng Dir)*
Dan Sterk *(Mng Dir-Dallas)*
Amanda Kennedy *(Chief Acctg Officer)*
Paul Chen *(Dir-Hong Kong)*
Rob Kearnes *(Dir-Melbourne)*
Tony Dodder *(Dir-Talent & Resources)*
Robert Choi *(Mng Dir-Dallas)*
Phillip McCorkle *(Mng Dir-Dallas)*
Andrew Carey *(Mng Dir-London)*
Kevin Harrigan *(Mng Dir-Los Angeles)*
Brent McFerren *(Mng Dir-New York)*

REAL FREEDOM INC.
2637 E Atlantic Blvd Ste 18591, Pompano Beach, FL 33062
Web Site:
http://www.realfreedominc.com
Year Founded: 2005
Sales Range: $1-9.9 Million
Emp.: 4
Online Wealth Building & Real Estate Courses
N.A.I.C.S.: 611710
Andy Proper *(CMO)*
Justin McCormick *(COO)*

REAL GRANDY VALLEY PIZZA HUT, LLC
2101 N 23rd St, McAllen, TX 78501
Tel.: (956) 682-1521
Web Site:
http://www.rgvpizzahut.com
Sales Range: $25-49.9 Million
Emp.: 1,000
Pizzeria Franchises Owner & Operator
N.A.I.C.S.: 722511
Floyd L. Burgen *(Pres)*
Jerry Greenfield *(Controller)*

REAL HOLDING MANAGEMENT CORP.
9688 SW 24th St, Miami, FL 33165-8015
Tel.: (305) 221-8351   FL
Year Founded: 1962
Sales Range: $300-349.9 Million
Emp.: 225
Operator of Grocery & Drug Stores
N.A.I.C.S.: 445110
Manuel A. Herran *(Pres)*
Daniel Valdez *(VP)*

REAL LIVING CYPRESS REALTY, INC.
7270-4 College Pkwy, Fort Myers, FL 33907
Tel.: (239) 275-3321
Web Site:
http://www.cypressrealty.com
Year Founded: 1976
Sales Range: $10-24.9 Million
Emp.: 3
Real Estate Broker
N.A.I.C.S.: 531210
Robert L. Wade *(Pres)*
Tania Archer *(Dir-Relocation & Office Mgr)*
Shane Wilson *(VP)*

REAL LIVING PITTMAN PROPERTIES

REAL LIVING PITTMAN PROPERTIES U.S. PRIVATE

Real Living Pittman Properties—(Continued)
10940 Raven Ridge Rd Ste 100, Raleigh, NC 27614
Tel.: (919) 277-4622
Web Site:
http://www.homesbypittman.com
Sales Range: $150-199.9 Million
Emp.: 100
Real Estate Brokers & Agents
N.A.I.C.S.: 531210
Lou Ann Pittman *(VP-Tech & Mktg)*
Don Batten *(Mgr)*

REAL LIVING, INC.
77 E Nationwide Blvd, Columbus, OH 43215
Tel.: (614) 459-7400
Web Site: http://www.realliving.com
Year Founded: 1953
Sales Range: $1-4.9 Billion
Emp.: 4,000
Real Estate Services
N.A.I.C.S.: 531210
Edward Caldwell *(Sr VP-South East)*
Allan Dalton *(COO)*

REAL PROPERTY SERVICES CORP
9960 W Cheyenne Ave Ste 110, Las Vegas, NV 89129
Tel.: (702) 313-3700
Rev.: $18,600,000
Emp.: 12
Real Estate Managers
N.A.I.C.S.: 531210
Patricia Green *(Pres)*

REAL PROPERTY TAX ADVISORS
575 Pharr Rd, Atlanta, GA 30355
Tel.: (404) 816-2050
Web Site:
http://www.realpropertytaxadvisors.com
Year Founded: 2002
Sales Range: $1-9.9 Million
Emp.: 9
Tax Management Services
N.A.I.C.S.: 541213
Anne Joyner Sheehan *(Founder & CEO)*
Deb Kling *(VP)*

REAL SOCIAL DYNAMICS, INC.
8491 W Sunset Blvd Ste 452, West Hollywood, CA 90069
Tel.: (310) 652-0157
Web Site:
http://www.realsocialdynamics.com
Year Founded: 2002
Sales Range: $25-49.9 Million
Emp.: 100
Dating & Other Personal Coaching Services
N.A.I.C.S.: 812990
Nicholas Kho *(Pres)*

REAL TIME COMPANIES, LLC.
20601 N 19th Ave Ste 110, Phoenix, AZ 85027
Tel.: (623) 792-8946
Web Site: http://www.real-time-companies.com
Year Founded: 1997
Sales Range: $1-9.9 Million
Emp.: 69
Software Product Development Services
N.A.I.C.S.: 541511
Kenneth A. Varga *(Founder & CEO)*
Michelle Hoffman *(CFO)*

REAL VALUE, INC.
1031 Sparkleberry Ln Ext, Columbia, SC 29223
Tel.: (803) 699-1120
Web Site:
http://www.rockofadam.com
Year Founded: 1992
Sales Range: $10-24.9 Million
Emp.: 50
Cut Stone & Stone Product Mfr
N.A.I.C.S.: 327991
Syed Ahamed *(Owner)*
Yong Kim *(Engr-CAD)*

REALCAPITALMARKETS.COM, LLC
5780 Fleet St Ste 130, Carlsbad, CA 92008
Tel.: (760) 602-5080
Web Site: http://www.rcm1.com
Year Founded: 2000
Sales Range: $1-9.9 Million
Emp.: 35
Online Commercial Real Estate Services
N.A.I.C.S.: 531390
Stephen J. Alter *(Founder & CEO)*

REALDEFENSE LLC
150 S Los Robles Ave Ste 400, Pasadena, CA 91101
Tel.: (801) 895-7909
Web Site: https://www.realdefen.se
Software Development & Services
N.A.I.C.S.: 541511
Gary Guseinov *(CEO)*

Subsidiaries:

Support.com, Inc. (1)
Tel.: (650) 556-9440
Web Site: https://www.support.com
Rev.: $43,864,000
Assets: $39,266,000
Liabilities: $4,830,000
Net Worth: $34,436,000
Earnings: $446,000
Emp.: 780
Fiscal Year-end: 12/31/2020
Technical Support Automation Software
N.A.I.C.S.: 513210
Andrew Latimer *(CIO)*
Omeed Jafari *(VP-Global Ops)*

Subsidiary (Non-US):

Support.com India Pvt Ltd (2)
No 110 3rd Floor 4th Cross 5th Block, Coramangla Industrial Layout, Bengaluru, 560095, Karnataka, India
Tel.: (91) 8067616400
Web Site: http://www.support.com
Sales Range: $25-49.9 Million
Emp.: 45
Data Processing & Related Services
N.A.I.C.S.: 518210

REALEFLOW, LLC
6659 Pearl Rd Ste 301, Parma Heights, OH 44130
Tel.: (440) 545-2095
Web Site: http://www.realeflow.com
Year Founded: 2007
Sales Range: $1-9.9 Million
Emp.: 31
Software Products Whslr
N.A.I.C.S.: 541519
Joe Singleton *(COO)*
Aaron Cavano *(Dir-Mktg)*
Austin Hale *(Product Mgr)*
Greg Clement *(Founder & CEO)*
Jimmy Shanahan *(Mgr-Quality Assurance)*
Josh Tobias *(Dir-Customer Happiness)*
Matthew Shumaker *(Product Mgr)*
Tim Radigan *(CFO)*

REALEN PROPERTIES
1550 Vine St, Philadelphia, PA 19102
Tel.: (610) 251-5000

Web Site: http://www.realen.com
Year Founded: 1968
Commercial Property Developers
N.A.I.C.S.: 531210
Dennis Maloomian *(Pres & CEO)*
Steven Cupps *(Mgr-Dev)*

REALGY, LLC
1100 New Britain Ave Ste 15, West Hartford, CT 06110
Tel.: (860) 233-2270
Web Site: http://www.realgy.com
Year Founded: 1998
Sales Range: $10-24.9 Million
Emp.: 9
Energy Conservation Products & Services & Computer Software Publishers & Developers
N.A.I.C.S.: 926130
Michael Vrtis *(Mng Partner)*

REALHOME.COM INC.
3001 Summer St, Stamford, CT 06905
Tel.: (203) 323-7715 DE
Web Site: http://www.ahahome.com
Year Founded: 1994
Sales Range: $10-24.9 Million
Emp.: 37
Online Provider of Information & Services for Homeowners & Homebuyers
N.A.I.C.S.: 812990
Peggy Vincento *(Dir-Mktg)*

REALI, INC.
777 Mariners Is Blvd Ste 210, San Mateo, CA 94404
Tel.: (844) 447-3254 DE
Web Site: http://www.reali.com
Real Estate Technology Company
N.A.I.C.S.: 531390
Amit Haller *(Co-Founder & CEO)*
Ami Avrahami *(Co-Founder)*

Subsidiaries:

Lenda, Inc. (1)
1101 8th St Ste 100, Berkeley, CA 94710
Tel.: (510) 524-0216
Web Site: http://www.bodytime.com
Sales Range: $1-9.9 Million
Emp.: 30
Cosmetics, Beauty Supplies & Perfume Stores
N.A.I.C.S.: 456120
Manda Heron *(Pres & CEO)*

REALIGN CAPITAL STRATEGIES
350 10th Ave Ste 1450, San Diego, CA 92101
Tel.: (619) 333-2500
Web Site:
http://www.realigncapital.com
Privater Equity Firm
N.A.I.C.S.: 523999
Grant Lippincott *(Mng Partner)*

Subsidiaries:

American Summit Insurance Company (1)
510 N Valley Mills Dr-Ste 202, Waco, TX 76710
Tel.: (254) 399-0626
Web Site: http://www.american-summit.com
Property & Casualty Insurance
N.A.I.C.S.: 524126

National Lloyds Insurance Corporation (1)
510 N Valley Mills Dr Ste 202, Waco, TX 76710
Tel.: (254) 399-0626
Web Site: http://www.natlloyds.com
Property & Casualty Insurance
N.A.I.C.S.: 524126

REALLY GOOD COPY CO.
92 Moseley Ter, Glastonbury, CT 06033-3714

Tel.: (860) 659-9487
Year Founded: 1981
Sales Range: Less than $1 Million
Emp.: 5
Advetising Agency
N.A.I.C.S.: 541810
Donna Donovan *(Pres)*

REALLY RAW HONEY
3725 Gough St, Baltimore, MD 21224
Tel.: (410) 675-7233
Web Site:
http://www.reallyrawhoney.com
Sales Range: $50-74.9 Million
Emp.: 60
Honey Production Services
N.A.I.C.S.: 112910
Frantz Walker *(Pres)*
John Cole *(Mgr-Plant Ops)*

REALLY STRATEGIES, INC.
2570 Blvd of the Generals Ste 213, Audubon, PA 19403
Tel.: (610) 631-6770
Web Site: http://www.rsicms.com
Year Founded: 2000
Sales Range: $1-9.9 Million
Emp.: 20
Custom Computer Programming Services
N.A.I.C.S.: 541511
Lisa Bos *(Co-Founder, CTO & Exec VP-Publ Solutions)*
Jeff Wood *(Sr VP-Enterprise Bus Dev)*
Christopher Hill *(VP-Product Mgmt)*
Barry Bealer *(Co-Founder, Pres & CEO)*
Steve Quirke *(VP-Ops)*
Paul Eisenberg *(Dir-Pro Svcs Engagements)*
R. Sivadas *(Head-Content Svcs-Global)*

REALMAD MEDIA, LLC
2401 W Peoria Ave Ste 200, Phoenix, AZ 85029
Web Site: http://www.staylisted.com
Year Founded: 2013
Sales Range: $1-9.9 Million
Emp.: 52
Advertising Agency Services
N.A.I.C.S.: 541810
Mark Mayfield *(Sr Acct Mgr)*

REALMARK DEVELOPMENT, LLC
5789 Cape Harbour Dr Ste 201, Cape Coral, FL 33914
Tel.: (239) 541-1372
Web Site:
http://www.realmarkgroup.com
Sales Range: $1-9.9 Million
Waterfront & Marine Property Developer
N.A.I.C.S.: 237210
Will Stout *(Founder & Pres)*

REALNETWORKS, INC.
568 1st Ave S Ste 600, Seattle, WA 98104
Tel.: (206) 674-2700 WA
Web Site:
https://www.realnetworks.com
Year Founded: 1994
RNWK—(NASDAQ)
Rev.: $58,183,000
Assets: $69,308,000
Liabilities: $23,235,000
Net Worth: $46,073,000
Earnings: ($21,981,000)
Emp.: 281
Fiscal Year-end: 12/31/21
Developer of Digital Media Services & Software
N.A.I.C.S.: 541511
Robert Glaser *(Founder, Chm & CEO)*

COMPANIES

Subsidiaries:

Game House Europe B.V. (1)
Emmasingel 21, Postbus 577, 5611 AZ,
Eindhoven, Netherlands
Tel.: (31) 402391370
Web Site: http://talent.gamehouse.com
Game Developer
N.A.I.C.S.: 513210

GameHouse Europe B.V. (1)
Emmasingel 20-4/Everdiep, PO Box 577,
5611 AZ, Eindhoven, Netherlands
Tel.: (31) 402391370
Web Site: http://talent.gamehouse.com
Internet Game Portal
N.A.I.C.S.: 541511

**RealNetworks Asia Pacific Co.,
Ltd.** (1)
9F Kyewon Building 71 Cheonggyecheon-ro, Jongro-gu, Seoul, 03189, Korea (South)
Tel.: (82) 220145523
Wireless Telecommunication Services
N.A.I.C.S.: 517112

RealNetworks GmbH (1)
Sonystrasse 18, 5081, Anif, Salzburg, Austria
Tel.: (43) 6246770071700
Web Site: http://www.realnetworks.com
Computer Programming Services
N.A.I.C.S.: 541511

RealNetworks, Inc. - Reston (1)
11600 Sunrise Valley Dr Ste 200, Reston,
VA 20191
Tel.: (703) 437-4422
Sales Range: $25-49.9 Million
Emp.: 70
Mobile Internet Applications & Services
N.A.I.C.S.: 517810

RealNetworks, Ltd. (1)
100 New Bridge Street, London, EC4V 6JA,
United Kingdom
Tel.: (44) 2076184000
Computer Programming Services
N.A.I.C.S.: 541511

Slingo, Inc. (1)
411 Hackensack Ave 8th Fl, Hackensack,
NJ 07601
Tel.: (201) 489-6727
Web Site: http://www.slingo.com
Internet Game Portal
N.A.I.C.S.: 541511

REALSELF INC.
1008 Western Ave Ste 206, Seattle,
WA 98104
Tel.: (206) 624-9357
Web Site: http://www.realself.com
Year Founded: 2006
Sales Range: $1-9.9 Million
Emp.: 14
Website for Consumers With Information on Cosmetic Surgery, Dermatology & Dentistry
N.A.I.C.S.: 519290
Tom Seery (Founder & CEO)
Remy Munch (Engr-Software)
Lauren Sato (VP-People)
Lara Devgan (Chief Medical Officer)

REALTECH, INC.
10 Vly Stream Pkwy, Malvern, PA
19355
Tel.: (610) 356-4401
Web Site: http://www.realtech.us
Year Founded: 1994
Computer Integrated Systems Design
Services
N.A.I.C.S.: 541512
David Milano (CEO)

REALTEX DEVELOPMENT CORPORATION
1101 S Capital of Texas Hwy Bldg F
Ste 200, Austin, TX 78746
Tel.: (512) 306-9206
Web Site:
http://www.realtexdevelopment.com
Year Founded: 1998
Sales Range: $1-9.9 Million
Emp.: 30
Real Estate Development & Investment
N.A.I.C.S.: 237210
Ricky J. Deyoe (Founder & Pres)

Subsidiaries:

Realtex Construction, LLC (1)
1101 S Capital of Texas Hwy Bldg F Ste
200, Austin, TX 78746
Tel.: (512) 306-9206
Web Site:
http://www.realtexdevelopment.com
Residential Construction
N.A.I.C.S.: 236116

**Realtex Housing Management,
LLC** (1)
1101 S Capital of Texas Hwy Bldg F Ste
200, Austin, TX 78746
Tel.: (512) 306-9206
Residential Real Estate Management
N.A.I.C.S.: 531311

REALTIME NORTH AMERICA, INC.
1101 Channelside Dr, Tampa, FL
33602
Tel.: (813) 283-0070   FL
Web Site:
http://www.realtimenorthamerica.com
Year Founded: 2002
Sales Range: $1-9.9 Million
Emp.: 112
Security Software
N.A.I.C.S.: 513210
Thomas Neudenberger (COO)

REALTRUCK, INC.
1307 12th Ave NE Ste 4, Jamestown,
ND 58401
Tel.: (701) 253-5906
Web Site: http://www.realtruck.com
Year Founded: 1998
Sales Range: $10-24.9 Million
Emp.: 82
Furniture Merchant Whslr
N.A.I.C.S.: 423210
Shawn Herrick (Dir-Bus Dev)
Jeff Vanlaningham (Pres)
Justin Deltener (CTO)
Katie Feigitsch (Brand Mgr)
Josh Deltener (Dir-IT)
Ryan McDonald (Mgr-Digital Mktg)
Dan Strezo (VP-Mdsg)
Christine Barringer (Chief Acctg Officer)
Baljinder Singh (CFO)
Carl-Martin Lindahl (CEO)

REALTY EXECUTIVES ASSOCIATES INC.
10255 Kingston Pike, Knoxville, TN
37922-3274
Tel.: (865) 693-3232   TN
Web Site:
http://www.realtyexecutivestn.com
Year Founded: 1978
Sales Range: $10-24.9 Million
Emp.: 40
Relocation Experts
N.A.I.C.S.: 531210
Sherry Iles (Office Mgr)

REALTY EXECUTIVES OF TUCSON, INC.
1745 E River Rd Ste 245, Tucson, AZ
85718
Tel.: (520) 615-8400
Web Site: http://www.gotucson.com
Rev.: $470,000,000
Emp.: 200
Real Estate Brokers & Agents
N.A.I.C.S.: 531210
David Jones Jr. (Mgr)

REALTY EXECUTIVES, RIVERSIDE
3610 Central Ave Ste 400, Riverside,
CA 92506-2839
Tel.: (951) 213-3500
Web Site:
http://www.realtyexecutives.com
Year Founded: 1990
Rev.: $133,000,000
Emp.: 110
Real Estate Agents & Managers
N.A.I.C.S.: 531210
Bobbi Feinstein (Co-Owner)
Suzanne McDaniel (Exec Dir-Ops)

REALTY ONE GROUP, INC.
9089 S Pecos Rd Ste 3400, Henderson, NV 89074
Tel.: (702) 898-7575
Web Site: http://www.realtyonelv.com
Year Founded: 2005
Sales Range: $1-4.9 Billion
Emp.: 58
Real Estate Services
N.A.I.C.S.: 531390
Kuba Jewgeniew (Founder & CEO)
Simon Chen (COO)
Lou Gonzalez (Pres-Affiliates)
Katherine Yoshikawa (Mgr-Charity-Cares)
Vinnie Tracey (Pres-Intl)
Robb Spearman (Dir-Heartland)
Mark Pessin (VP-Learning)
Kathy Baker (Dir-Trng)
Cory Vasquez (CMO)

REALTY PARTNERS LLC
1990 Main ST Ste 750, Sarasota, FL
34236
Web Site: http://www.realty-partners.com
Year Founded: 2009
Sales Range: $1-9.9 Million
Emp.: 10
Financial Consulting Services
N.A.I.C.S.: 523940
Thomas Heimann (Founder & CEO)

REALTY RESOURCES CHARTERED
247 Commercial St, Rockport, ME
04856
Tel.: (207) 236-4067
Sales Range: $10-24.9 Million
Emp.: 25
Subdividers & Developers
N.A.I.C.S.: 237210
Joseph M. Cloutier (Pres)

REALTY USA LLC
914 Maple Rd, Williamsville, NY
14221
Tel.: (716) 689-8100   NY
Web Site: http://www.realtyusa.com
Holding Company; Residential &
Commercial Real Estate Brokerage
Services
N.A.I.C.S.: 551112
Merle L. Whitehead (Pres & CEO)

Subsidiaries:

Realty USA CNY, Inc. (1)
5110 W Genesee St, Camillus, NY 13031
Tel.: (315) 487-6551
Web Site: http://www.realtyusa.com
Sales Range: $10-24.9 Million
Emp.: 100
Real Estate Brokerage Services; Regional
Managing Office
N.A.I.C.S.: 531210
Mark W. Re (VP & Gen Mgr-Central New
York Reg)
Bob Kratz (Dir-Mktg-Reg)

Branch (Domestic):

**Realty USA CNY, Inc. - Saratoga
Springs-Broadway Office** (2)

REALWINWIN, INC.

505 Broadway, Saratoga Springs, NY
12866
Tel.: (518) 584-0743
Web Site: http://www.realtyusa.com
Sales Range: $1-9.9 Million
Real Estate Brokerage Services
N.A.I.C.S.: 531210

Realty USA Capital, Inc. (1)
1547 Rte 9, Clifton Park, NY 12065
Tel.: (518) 348-7100
Web Site: http://www.realtyusa.com
Sales Range: $1-9.9 Million
Emp.: 50
Offices of Real Estate Agents & Brokers
N.A.I.C.S.: 531210
Paul Destefano (VP)

Realty USA WNY, Inc. (1)
361 Delaware Ave, Buffalo, NY 14202
Tel.: (716) 689-8100
Web Site:
http://www.realtyusacommercial.com
Rev.: $10,100,000
Emp.: 50
Real Estate Brokerage Services; Regional
Managing Office
N.A.I.C.S.: 531210
Merle L. Whitehead (Pres & CEO)
Daniel Symoniak (VP)
Nan Malysza (Sr Mgr)
Kevin F. Durawa (CIO)

Branch (Domestic):

**Realty USA WNY, Inc. - Pittsford
Office** (2)
57 Monroe Ave Ste A, Pittsford, NY 14534
Tel.: (585) 381-4400
Web Site: http://www.realtyusa.com
Sales Range: $1-9.9 Million
Emp.: 45
Real Estate Brokerage Services
N.A.I.C.S.: 531210
Reinhart Brucker (VP)
Donald Perry (VP)

REALTYWORKS INC.
501 Bagley Dr, Myrtle Beach, SC
29579-8255
Tel.: (843) 650-1652   SC
Year Founded: 1972
Rev.: $10,000,000
Emp.: 6
Real Estate Brokers & Agents
N.A.I.C.S.: 531210
Harold Dixon (Pres)

REALVOICE LLC
4913 Raleigh Common Dr Ste 203,
Memphis, TN 38128-2485   TN
Web Site: http://www.realvoice.com
Online Marketing & Call Center Services
N.A.I.C.S.: 561421
James Mays (CEO)
Heather Dana (Gen Mgr-Ops)

Subsidiaries:

Hawaiian Beach Rentals (1)
151 Hamakua Dr Ste 835, Kailua, HI
96734-3239
Tel.: (808) 826-6968
Web Site:
http://www.hawaiianbeachrentals.com
Online Vacation Rental Services
N.A.I.C.S.: 561599

REALVOLVE, INC.
5445 DTC Pkwy Ste 475, Greenwood
Village, CO 80111
Web Site: http://www.realvolve.com
Year Founded: 2014
Sales Range: $1-9.9 Million
Emp.: 24
Software Development Services
N.A.I.C.S.: 541511
Dave Crumby (Founder & CEO)
Mark Stepp (Chief Innovation Officer)
Dale Warner (COO)

REALWINWIN, INC.

REALWINWIN, INC.

RealWinWin, Inc.—(Continued)
1628 JFK Blvd Ste 2100, Philadelphia, PA 19103
Tel.: (215) 732-4480
Web Site: http://www.realwinwin.com
Sales Range: $1-9.9 Million
Emp.: 23
Energy Management & Software Solutions
N.A.I.C.S.: 513210
Doug Bloom *(Chm & CEO)*
Ross Cowan *(Dir-Bus Dev)*
Dave Burns *(Dir-Ops)*
Lauren Chierici *(Controller)*

REAM'S FOOD STORES
160 E Claybourne Ave, Salt Lake City, UT 84115
Tel.: (801) 485-8451
Web Site: http://www.reamsfoods.com
Sales Range: $125-149.9 Million
Emp.: 750
Owner & Operator of Grocery Stores
N.A.I.C.S.: 445110
Ruby Ream *(Pres)*
Barry Bessey *(Gen Mgr)*
Richard Williams *(Supvr-Produce Supvr)*

REAMES & SON CONSTRUCTION CO.
1208 Cypress St, Valdosta, GA 31601
Tel.: (229) 244-9286
Web Site: http://www.reamesconcrete.com
Sales Range: $10-24.9 Million
Emp.: 80
Grading
N.A.I.C.S.: 237310
Jeff Reames *(Pres)*

REAMS SPRINKLER SUPPLY COMPANY
6001 S 57th St, Lincoln, NE 68516
Tel.: (402) 423-0120
Web Site: http://www.reams.net
Year Founded: 1970
Sales Range: $10-24.9 Million
Emp.: 10
Distr of Irrigation Equipment
N.A.I.C.S.: 423820
Bryce Bousquet *(Pres)*
David Peck *(Dir-Ops)*
Ron Bousquet *(Co-Founder & Sr VP)*

REARDON ASSOCIATES INC.
450 Washington St Ste LL5, Dedham, MA 02026
Tel.: (781) 329-2660
Web Site: http://www.reardonassociates.com
Year Founded: 1964
Sales Range: $10-24.9 Million
Emp.: 10
Placement Agencies
N.A.I.C.S.: 561311
Terry Farmer *(Controller)*

REASORS INC.
200 W Choctaw St, Tahlequah, OK 74464
Tel.: (918) 456-1472
Web Site: http://www.reasors.com
Sales Range: $150-199.9 Million
Emp.: 2,500
Grocery Stores, Independent
N.A.I.C.S.: 445110
Jeff Reasor *(Pres)*
Dave Brumley *(Chief HR Officer & Exec VP)*
Steve Lehto *(COO & Exec VP)*
Steve Martin *(CFO & Exec VP)*
Ward Dunn *(VP-Sls & Mktg)*

REBBEC MOTOR CO.
101 E Front St, El Paso, IL 61738
Tel.: (309) 740-0958 IL
Web Site: http://www.rebbecmotor.com
Sales Range: $10-24.9 Million
Emp.: 45
New & Used Car Dealer
N.A.I.C.S.: 441110
Martin Rebbec *(Owner)*
Jeff Rebbec *(Gen Mgr)*
Karen Castronova *(Bus Mgr)*
John Warren *(Sls Mgr)*
Terry Renfrow *(Mgr-Svc)*
Jeff Kibler *(Mgr-Parts)*
Rick Heiken *(Mgr-Svc)*

REBBL INC.
5900 Hollis St Ste L, Emeryville, CA 94608
Web Site: http://www.rebbl.co
Year Founded: 2011
Sales Range: $10-24.9 Million
Emp.: 40
Food & Beverage Product Mfr
N.A.I.C.S.: 311412
Palo Hawken *(Founder)*
Michele Kessler *(CEO)*
Bonnie Neulight *(CMO)*
Chuck Engle *(Sr VP-Sls)*
Jon Blair *(Sr VP-Fin & Acct)*

REBECCA MINKOFF LLC
16 W 22nd St 2nd Fl, New York, NY 10011
Tel.: (212) 677-7829
Web Site: http://www.rebeccaminkoff.com
Year Founded: 2005
Sales Range: $25-49.9 Million
Emp.: 50
Designs Footwear, Handbags & Ready-to-Wear Apparel
N.A.I.C.S.: 316210
Rebecca Minkoff *(Founder)*
Uri Minkoff *(CEO)*

REBEKAH CHILDREN'S SERVICES.
290 IOOF Ave, Gilroy, CA 95020
Tel.: (408) 846-2100 CA
Web Site: http://www.rcskids.org
Sales Range: $10-24.9 Million
Emp.: 323
Child Care Services
N.A.I.C.S.: 624110
Rebecca Burdett *(COO-Education Svcs)*
Jennifer Grier *(Chief Clinical Officer-Community Svcs)*
Christophe Rebboah *(Exec Dir)*
Mary Lou Lang *(Treas)*
Karolinne Livingston *(Sec)*
Mike Young *(Pres)*

REBEKAH REHAB & EXTENDED CARE CENTER
1070 Havemeyer Ave, Bronx, NY 10462-5310
Tel.: (718) 863-6200 NY
Web Site: http://www.rebekahrehab.org
Year Founded: 1968
Sales Range: $25-49.9 Million
Emp.: 223
Health Care Srvices
N.A.I.C.S.: 622110
Kenneth Gelb *(CEO)*
Michael Felberg *(Fin Dir)*
Sheelagh Martin *(Asst Dir-Nursing)*
Jose Hernandez *(Dir-Facilities Mgmt)*
Anna Leon *(Dir-Nursing)*

REBEL OIL COMPANY, INC.
2200 Highland Dr, Las Vegas, NV 89102-4629
Tel.: (702) 382-5866 NV
Web Site: http://www.rebeloil.com
Year Founded: 1952
Sales Range: $50-74.9 Million
Emp.: 500
Provider of Petroleum Bulk Station Services
N.A.I.C.S.: 424710
Jack Cason *(Pres & CFO)*
Larry Crisp *(CIO)*

REBELMOUSE, INC.
560 Broadway Ste 308, New York, NY 10012
Tel.: (917) 780-2264
Web Site: http://www.rebelmouse.com
Year Founded: 2012
Sales Range: $1-9.9 Million
Emp.: 42
Software Services
N.A.I.C.S.: 513210
Andrea Breanna *(CEO)*

REBO INC.
9481 St Rt 708 N, Russells Point, OH 43348
Tel.: (937) 843-3036 OH
Web Site: http://www.spendaday.com
Year Founded: 1950
Sales Range: $10-24.9 Million
Emp.: 40
Full Line Boating Accessories & Safety Equipment
N.A.I.C.S.: 441222
Bob Culp *(Mgr-Svc)*
Mike Hummel *(Mgr-Parts)*
Greg Koerner *(Mgr-Svc)*

REBOLUCION, LLC
22 W 23rd St 3rd Fl, New York, NY 10010
Tel.: (212) 229-0700 NY
Year Founded: 1999
Sales Range: $10-24.9 Million
Emp.: 7
Advetising Agency
N.A.I.C.S.: 541810
Federico L. Mejer *(Partner & Dir-Integrated Comm)*
Amy Gomez *(Partner & Dir-Acct Svcs)*
Alan Glikin *(Dir-Media)*

REBOOT MARKETING LLC
2006 Acklen Ave, Nashville, TN 37212
Tel.: (800) 304-4202
Web Site: http://www.rebootmarketing.com
Year Founded: 2008
Sales Range: $10-24.9 Million
Emp.: 7
Retailer of Informational How-to Guides for Consumers
N.A.I.C.S.: 512120
Erin Baler *(Partner)*
Brett Phillips *(Dir-Ops)*
Allen Baler *(Partner)*

REBUILD NORTHWEST FLORIDA, INC.
150 W Maxwell St, Pensacola, FL 32501
Tel.: (850) 497-7024 FL
Web Site: http://www.rebuildnwf.org
Year Founded: 2004
Sales Range: $10-24.9 Million
Emp.: 21
Hurricane Mitigation Services
N.A.I.C.S.: 624190
Garrett W. Walton *(CEO)*
Sandra C. Woodbery *(COO)*
William L. Merrill *(VP-Engrg)*

REBUILDERS AUTOMOTIVE SUPPLY CO. INC.
1650 Flat River Rd, Coventry, RI 02816
Tel.: (401) 822-3030
Web Site: http://www.coresupply.com
Sales Range: $10-24.9 Million
Emp.: 60
Automotive Parts & Supplies, Used
N.A.I.C.S.: 423140
Robert Grady *(Pres)*
George Lucas *(Sr VP)*

RECAST SOFTWARE INC.
1660 MN-100 S Suite 528, St Louis Park, MN 55416
Tel.: (612) 430-9691
Web Site: https://www.recastsoftware.com
Emp.: 100
Software Publr
N.A.I.C.S.: 513210
Will Teevan *(CEO)*

Subsidiaries:

Liquit B.V. (1)
Kastanjelaan 6, Ridderkerk, 2982 CM, Netherlands
Tel.: (31) 886383500
Web Site: http://www.liquit.com
Software Development Company
N.A.I.C.S.: 513210
Peter Hermeling *(Co-Founder & COO)*

Subsidiary (US):

Superior Data Solutions Inc. (2)
1 New Hampshire Dr #125, Portsmouth, NH 03801
Tel.: (603) 964-7840
Web Site: http://www.appnostix.com
Workspace Management & Other Related Services
N.A.I.C.S.: 541511
Linda Laporta *(Founder)*

RECELLULAR INCORPORATED
2555 Bishop Cr W, Dexter, MI 48130
Tel.: (734) 205-2200
Web Site: http://www.recell.com
Sales Range: $10-24.9 Million
Emp.: 300
Telephone & Telegraphic Equipment
N.A.I.C.S.: 423690
Charles Newman *(Founder & Chm)*
Steve Manning *(Pres & CEO)*
John Wetherholt *(Mgr-Dexter Plant)*
Woody Anderson *(VP-ECommerce)*

RECHTIEN INTERNATIONAL TRUCKS
7227 NW 74th Ave, Miami, FL 33166
Tel.: (305) 888-0111
Web Site: http://www.rechtieninternationaltrucks.com
Sales Range: $75-99.9 Million
Emp.: 200
Trucks, Tractors & Trailers: New & Used
N.A.I.C.S.: 441110
Carlos Currlin *(Gen Mgr)*

RECIPROCAL RESULTS
193 A Rice Av, Staten Island, NY 10314
Tel.: (718) 370-3977 NY
Web Site: http://www.r2trade.com
Year Founded: 1997
Sales Range: Less than $1 Million
Emp.: 1
Advetising Agency
N.A.I.C.S.: 541810
Roy Moskowitz *(CEO)*

RECKER & BOERGER INC.
10115 Transportation Way, Cincinnati, OH 45246
Tel.: (513) 942-4411 OH

Web Site:
http://www.thecomfortzone.com
Year Founded: 1962
Sales Range: $10-24.9 Million
Emp.: 85
Provider of Heating & Air Conditioning Services
N.A.I.C.S.: 449210
Jackie Johnson (Dir-Adv)
Steve Boerger (Pres)
Roma Mount (Mgr-Sls Store)

RECO CONSTRUCTORS, INC.
710 Hospital St, Richmond, VA 23219
Tel.: (804) 644-2611
Web Site:
http://www.recoconstructors.com
Year Founded: 1914
Sales Range: $10-24.9 Million
Emp.: 100
Plate Work & Metal Coating
N.A.I.C.S.: 332313
John Moss (VP)
Robert C. Courain Jr. (Chm)

RECO EQUIPMENT INC.
41245 Reco Rd, Belmont, OH 43718
Tel.: (740) 782-1314   OH
Web Site: http://www.recoequip.com
Year Founded: 1983
Rev.: $50,000,000
Emp.: 140
Construction & Mining Machinery
N.A.I.C.S.: 423810
Rick Starinchak (Mgr-Svc)
Diane Bakenhester (Office Mgr)
Ed Rowe (Mgr-HR)
Brian Nolan (Reg Mgr-Sls)
Joshua Gasber (VP)
Chad Gilman (Dir-Sls)

RECOGNITION SYSTEMS INC.
30 Harbor Park Dr, Port Washington, NY 11050
Tel.: (516) 625-5000
Web Site: http://www.dotworks.com
Year Founded: 1968
Sales Range: $10-24.9 Million
Emp.: 100
Pre-Press Art Supplies
N.A.I.C.S.: 424990
John McCusker (CEO)
Linda McCusker (Pres)
Jeff McCusker (VP)

RECOMMERCE HOLDINGS, LLC
546 Hillsboro Technology Dr, Deerfield Beach, FL 33441
Tel.: (855) 473-4666
Year Founded: 2013
Brand Agency
N.A.I.C.S.: 541890
Taylor Hamilton (CEO)

Subsidiaries:

Vitamin Discount Center Inc.   (1)
5519 Southern Comfort Blvd, Tampa, FL 33634
Tel.: (813) 542-5756
Web Site:
http://www.vitamindiscountcenter.net
Food & Health Supplement Stores
N.A.I.C.S.: 456191
Jason King (Mgr)

RECON ENGINEERING & CONSTRUCTION, INC.
10741 Los Alamitos Blvd, Los Alamitos, CA 90720
Tel.: (562) 799-7980
Web Site: http://www.recon-inc.com
Sales Range: $10-24.9 Million
Emp.: 100
Specialty Construction, Installation & Repair of High Temperature Refractory & Corrosion Resistant Linings
N.A.I.C.S.: 327120
Mendy Harrington (Mgr-Cost Controls)
Greg Howearth (Supvr-Safety Field)

RECON ENVIRONMENTAL, INC.
1927 5th Ave, San Diego, CA 92101
Tel.: (619) 308-9333
Web Site: http://www.RECON-us.com
Year Founded: 1972
Sales Range: $10-24.9 Million
Emp.: 100
Environmental Consulting Services
N.A.I.C.S.: 541620
Robert MacAller (Pres & CEO)
Lee Sherwood (Dir-California)
Charles Bull (Chm)
Wendy Loeffler (Project Mgr)

RECON LOGISTICS
26901 Cannon Rd Ste 400, Bedford, OH 44146
Tel.: (440) 708-2306
Web Site:
http://www.reconlogistics.com
Year Founded: 2005
Sales Range: $10-24.9 Million
Emp.: 25
Transportation Management, Logistics & Technology Services
N.A.I.C.S.: 488510
Hank Newman (Pres)
Rebecca Kelley (Gen Mgr-Admin)

RECON REFRACTORY & CONSTRUCTION INC.
3914 Cherry Ave Ste B, Long Beach, CA 90807-3727
Tel.: (562) 799-7980
Web Site: http://www.recon-inc.com
Year Founded: 1990
Sales Range: $10-24.9 Million
Emp.: 100
Civil Engineering Services
N.A.I.C.S.: 237310
Janice Allison (Office Mgr)
Virigina Baron (Asst Office Mgr)

RECONCRAFT
320 Nevada St Ste 301, Newton, MA 02460
Tel.: (877) 645-7761
Web Site: http://www.reconcraft.com
Year Founded: 2008
Sales Range: $1-9.9 Million
Emp.: 12
Mfr of Shallow-Draft Workboats for Utility, Maritime Defense, Law Enforcement & Emergency Response Services
N.A.I.C.S.: 336612
Jay B. Hoflich (Co-Founder & CEO)
Joseph F. Silkowski (Co-Founder & COO)
Jonathan R. Hoflich (Co-Founder & Chief Bus Dev Officer)

RECONSERVE, INC.
2811 Wilshire Blvd Ste 410, Santa Monica, CA 90401
Tel.: (310) 458-1574   CA
Web Site: http://reconserve.com
Year Founded: 1938
Sales Range: $75-99.9 Million
Emp.: 400
Bakery Waste Material Processing & Recycling Services & Animal Feed Mfr
N.A.I.C.S.: 311999
Rida Hamed (Sec & Exec VP)
David Luskin (COO)
Bill Barth (Mgr-Bakery Svcs)
Bryan Bergquist (VP-Feed Sls)
Dean Hoy (Mgr-Feed Sls)
Jeff Weber (Mgr-Bakery Svcs-Lower MidWest)
Joe Douglas (VP-Bakery Svcs-South)
John Hawrylko (VP-Bakery Svcs-North)
John Sheldon (Mgr-Bakery Svcs)
Kevin Shore (VP-Bakery Svcs-West)
Rick Cook (Mgr-Bakery Svcs-Upper Midwest)
Rodger Wilson (Mgr-Bakery Svcs-Great Lakes)
Adam Cowan (Mgr-Bakery Svcs-Eastern Midwest)

Subsidiaries:

ReConserve of California-Los Angeles, Inc.   (1)
9112 Graham Ave, Los Angeles, CA 90002
Tel.: (323) 564-5871
Web Site: http://www.reconserve.com
Waste Recycling
N.A.I.C.S.: 311119

Subsidiary (Domestic):

International Processing Corp   (2)
2811 Wilshire Blvd, Santa Monica, CA 90403
Tel.: (310) 458-1574
Web Site: http://www.reconserve.com
Provider of Transportation Services
N.A.I.C.S.: 813990
Meyer Lusken (Pres)

ReConserve of California-Stockton, Inc.   (2)
704 Zephyr St, Stockton, CA 95206   (100%)
Tel.: (209) 982-5085
Web Site: http://reconserve.com
Sales Range: $10-24.9 Million
Emp.: 18
Processor of Recycled Food Products for Animals
N.A.I.C.S.: 311119
Kevin Shore (VP-Bakery Svcs-West)

ReConserve of Maryland   (2)
3220 Sun St, Baltimore, MD 21226   (100%)
Tel.: (410) 354-1417
Recycling of Bakery Products
N.A.I.C.S.: 311119

ReConserve, Inc.   (2)
6160 S River Rd, Hodgkins, IL 60525   (100%)
Tel.: (708) 354-5882
Processor of Recycled Food Products for Animals
N.A.I.C.S.: 311119
Meyer Lusken (CEO)
Peggy Kiser (Office Mgr)

ReConserve, Inc.   (2)
4695 Radford Rd, Flowery Branch, GA 30542-3998
Tel.: (770) 967-0145
Sales Range: $50-74.9 Million
Recycling of Bakery By-Products
N.A.I.C.S.: 449210
Bob McMullin (Pres)

ReConserve, Inc.   (2)
41 N James St, Kansas City, KS 66118   (100%)
Tel.: (913) 621-5619
Sales Range: $10-24.9 Million
Emp.: 15
Processor of Recycled Food Products for Animals
N.A.I.C.S.: 562998

ReConserve, Inc.   (2)
2811 Wilshire Boulevard Suite 410, Santa Monica, CA 90403   (100%)
Tel.: (310) 458-1574
Processor of Recycled Food Products for Animals
N.A.I.C.S.: 311611

Recycle to Conserve, TX, Inc.   (2)
3610 Duncanville Rd, Dallas, TX 75236   (100%)
Tel.: (214) 339-4755
Web Site: http://www.scopeproducts.com
Processor of Recycled Food Products for Animals
N.A.I.C.S.: 311119

Topnotch Foods, Inc.   (2)
1988 E 57th St, Vernon, CA 90058-3464   (100%)
Tel.: (323) 586-2007
Sales Range: $1-9.9 Million
Emp.: 9
Mfr of Bread Crumbs
N.A.I.C.S.: 311999

Scope Energy Resources, Inc.   (1)
2811 Wilshire Blvd ste 410, Santa Monica, CA 90403-1205   (100%)
Tel.: (310) 458-1574
Web Site: http://www.reconserve.com
Sales Range: $50-74.9 Million
Emp.: 100
Oil Production Interests
N.A.I.C.S.: 533110

Scope Properties, Inc.   (1)
2811 Wilshire Blvd Ste 410, Santa Monica, CA 90404   (100%)
Tel.: (310) 458-1574
Sales Range: $1-9.9 Million
Emp.: 30
Real Estate Management
N.A.I.C.S.: 531190

RECORDER PUBLISHING CO.
17 19 Morristown Rd, Bernardsville, NJ 07924
Tel.: (908) 766-3900
Web Site:
http://www.recordernewspapers.com
Sales Range: $10-24.9 Million
Emp.: 30
Newspapers; Publishing & Printing
N.A.I.C.S.: 513110
Diane Howard (Office Mgr)

RECORDTRAK INC.
651 Allendale Rd, King of Prussia, PA 19406
Tel.: (610) 992-5000
Web Site: http://www.recordtrak.com
Sales Range: $10-24.9 Million
Emp.: 130
Personal Investigation Service
N.A.I.C.S.: 541990
Martin H. Marshall (Pres)
Ed Trainor (Project Mgr)
Margaret Castagna (VP)

RECOURSE COMMUNICATIONS, INC.
112 Intracoastal Pointe Dr, Jupiter, FL 33477
Tel.: (561) 686-6800   FL
Web Site:
http://www.rcirecruitmentsolutions.com
Year Founded: 1985
Sales Range: $10-24.9 Million
Emp.: 100
Workforce Recruitment Consulting & Advertising Services
N.A.I.C.S.: 541612
Michael C. Moore (Chm & CEO)
Pat Matarese (Pres & CFO)
Samantha Moore (Exec Vp-Client Svcs)
Amitai Givertz (Mng Dir-RCI Center of Excellence)
Aaron Greider (VP-Sls)
Melody Storms (Dir-Integrated Talent Solutions & Mgr-Social Media)
Tonya Greene (Dir-Natl Recruitment)
Maryanna Choinski (Mgr-Production)

RECOVER GEAR, LLC
822 US Hwy A1A N, Ponte Vedra Beach, FL 32082
Tel.: (904) 280-9660
Web Site:
http://www.110playharder.com
Sales Range: $1-9.9 Million
Emp.: 15

RECOVER GEAR, LLC

Recover Gear, LLC—(Continued)
Sports Socks Mfr
N.A.I.C.S.: 315120
David Green (CEO)
Nathan Fabrick (Dir-Sls)
Brandi Lauderman (Product Dir)
Jenn Vonhagen (Dir-Mktg)
Jason Schoepfer (Dir-Ops)
Peter Bailet (Dir-Fin)
Rachel Stanley (Mgr-Brand Rels)
Austin Chow (Pres)

RECOVER HEALTH, INC.
5900 Green Oak Dr Ste 200, Minnetonka, MN 55343-4797
Tel.: (952) 926-9808   FL
Web Site:
http://www.recoverhealth.org
Year Founded: 2009
Health Care Srvices
N.A.I.C.S.: 621999
Greg Von Arx (CEO)
Kara Von Arx (COO)
Joe Christenson (CFO)
Janet Fehler (VP-Ops)
Jan Daly (Dir-Therapy Svcs)

RECOVERY CENTERS OF AMERICA OPERATIONS, LLC
2701 Renaissance Blvd, King of Prussia, PA 19406
Tel.: (610) 270-3876   PA
Web Site:
http://www.recoverycentersofamerica.com
Residential Rehabilitation Facilities & Outpatient Service Centers Developer, Owner & Operator
N.A.I.C.S.: 623220
J. P. Christen (COO)
Deni Carise (Chief Scientific Officer)
Rich Smith (CMO)
Laura A. Ames (CEO-Danvers)
Bill Koroncai (Dir-Comm)
Adam Brickner (CEO-Southern Maryland & Washington)
Stephanie Anderson (CEO)

Subsidiaries:

Recovery Services of New Jersey, Inc.   (1)
5034 Atlantic Ave, Mays Landing, NJ 08330
Tel.: (609) 625-4900
Web Site:
http://www.recoverycentersofamerica.com
Sales Range: $1-9.9 Million
Emp.: 105
Residential Rehabilitation Facilities & Outpatient Service Centers Operator
N.A.I.C.S.: 623110
Edward Olwell (Supvr-Outpatient Clinical)

RECOVERY HEALTH SERVICES
12101 Lima Rd, Fort Wayne, IN 46818
Tel.: (260) 637-3166   IN
Web Site: http://www.byronhealth.org
Year Founded: 1991
Sales Range: $10-24.9 Million
Emp.: 252
Health Care Srvices
N.A.I.C.S.: 622110
Peter A. Marotti (Exec Dir)

RECREATION CENTERS OF SUN CITY WEST, INC.
19803 N R H Johnson Blvd, Sun City West, AZ 85375
Tel.: (623) 544-6000
Web Site: http://www.rcscw.com
Sales Range: $10-24.9 Million
Emp.: 400
Membership Sports & Recreation Clubs
N.A.I.C.S.: 713940

Russell Boston (Mgr-Facilities Maintenance)
Shari Costa (Mgr-Acctg)

RECREATION WORLD INC.
13906 W Colonial Dr, Winter Garden, FL 34787-4202
Tel.: (407) 656-6444   FL
Web Site:
http://www.giantrecreationworld.com
Year Founded: 1983
Sales Range: $25-49.9 Million
Emp.: 75
Recreational Vehicle Dealers
N.A.I.C.S.: 441210
Donald McNamara (CEO)
Dick Rocha (Pres)
Stewart Mederos (CFO)

RECREATIONAL EQUIPMENT, INC.
6750 S 228th St, Kent, WA 98032
Tel.: (253) 395-3780   WA
Web Site: http://www.rei.com
Year Founded: 1938
Sales Range: $1-4.9 Billion
Emp.: 10,389
Outdoor Gear Retailer & Mfr
N.A.I.C.S.: 459110
Tim Spangler (Sr VP-Retail)
Rick Bingle (VP-Supply Chain)
Kathleen Peterson (VP-Private Brands)
Susan Viscon (Sr VP-Mdsg)
Julie Averill (CIO)
Mark Stoddard (VP-Plng, Inventory Mgmt & Ops)
Ben Steele (Chief Creative Officer)
Steven Hooper (Chm)
Anthony Truesdale (Vice Chm)
Eric F. Artz (Pres & CEO)
Raquel Karls (Sr VP-HR)
Rachel Ligtenberg (VP-Retail)
Jed Paulson (VP-Digital Retail)
Craig Rowley (VP-Mktg)
Chris Speyer (VP-Private Brands)
Chris Arnold (Dir-External Comm & Pub Affairs)
Kelley Hall (CFO & Sr VP)
Analyn Nouri (VP-Platform Engrg)
Todd Wilson (VP-Product Engrg)
Sylvia Wilks (Chief Supply Chain Officer & Sr VP)
Minnie Alexander (Gen Counsel, Sec & VP)

RECREATIONAL SPORTS & IMPORTS INC.
2436 N Woodruff Ave, Idaho Falls, ID 83401
Tel.: (208) 523-5721   ID
Web Site: http://www.rsiinc.com
Year Founded: 1966
Sales Range: $25-49.9 Million
Emp.: 180
Electrical Apparatus & Equipment Mfr & Distr
N.A.I.C.S.: 423610
Randy Anderson (CEO)
Gary Olsen (Pres)

RECRUITICS, LLC
437 5th Ave 5th Fl, New York, NY 10016
Tel.: (646) 612-7181
Web Site: http://www.recruitics.com
Data-Centric Recruitment Marketing Agency
N.A.I.C.S.: 541612
Adam Stafford (CEO)
Dave Tuttle (Chief Revenue Officer)

Subsidiaries:

KRT Marketing, Inc.   (1)
3685 Mt Diablo Blvd Ste 255, Lafayette, CA 94549-3776

Tel.: (925) 284-0444
Web Site: http://www.krtmarketing.com
Rev.: $24,815,000
Emp.: 10
Advertising & Marketing Agnecy
N.A.I.C.S.: 541810

RECRUITING FORCE LLC
1464 E White Stone Blvd Ste 1903, Cedar Park, TX 78613
Tel.: (512) 996-0999
Web Site:
http://www.recruitveterans.com
Year Founded: 2006
Sales Range: $1-9.9 Million
Emp.: 45
Staffing & Recruiting
N.A.I.C.S.: 561311
Rudy J. Uribe (Founder & Pres)

RECRUITWISE
704 S Illinois Ave Ste C-202, Oak Ridge, TN 37830
Tel.: (865) 425-0405
Web Site: http://www.recruitwise.jobs
Year Founded: 1998
Rev.: $4,000,000
Emp.: 53
Human Resource Consulting Services
N.A.I.C.S.: 541612
Terri Reedy (Office Mgr)
Glenn Zahn (Pres)

RECTOR MOTOR CAR CO.
1010 Cadillac Way, Burlingame, CA 94010
Tel.: (650) 348-0111
Web Site:
http://www.rectormotors.com
Rev.: $22,500,000
Emp.: 60
New & Used Car Dealers
N.A.I.C.S.: 441110
James Hannay (Owner & CEO)
Dan Belluomini (VP-Sls)

RECTRIX AVIATION, INC.
777 Virginia Rd, Concord, MA 01742
Tel.: (781) 274-0400
Web Site: http://www.rectrix.aero
Sales Range: $1-9.9 Million
Emp.: 40
Private Jet Services
N.A.I.C.S.: 481211
Richard Cawley (Pres)
Stephanie Sisca (Mgr-Flight Coordination)
Brian Sansiveri (Dir-Ops)
Paul Foley (CEO)

RECURLY, INC.
300 Brannan St Ste 608, San Francisco, CA 94107
Tel.: (415) 800-2042
Web Site: http://www.recurly.com
Sales Range: $1-9.9 Million
Billing Software
N.A.I.C.S.: 513210
Dan Burkhart (Co-Founder & CEO)
Isaac Hall (Co-Founder & Chm)
Renato Mascardo (CTO)
Andy Montgomery (Head-Design)
Ariel Myers (Head-Sls)
Rachel Quick (Sr Dir-Customer Support)
Frederick Felman (VP-Ops)

RECURSION SOFTWARE, INC.
2591 N Dallas Pkwy Ste 200, Frisco, TX 75034
Tel.: (972) 731-8800
Web Site:
http://www.recursionsw.com
Year Founded: 2001
Sales Range: $75-99.9 Million
Emp.: 20

Provider of Java, C++ & Csharp Development Solutions
N.A.I.C.S.: 449210
Paul A. Lipari (Pres & CEO)

RECYCLE TRACK SYSTEMS, INC.
435 Hudson St Ste 404, New York, NY 10014
Tel.: (833) 787-4636
Web Site: http://www.rts.com
Year Founded: 2014
Waste Management Services
N.A.I.C.S.: 562998

Subsidiaries:

Recyclebank LLC   (1)
95 Morton St, New York, NY 10014
Tel.: (212) 659-9900
Web Site: http://www.recyclebank.com
Hazardous Waste Treatment & Disposal
N.A.I.C.S.: 562211

RED 212
5509 Fair Ln, Cincinnati, OH 45227
Tel.: (513) 772-1020
Web Site: http://www.red212.com
Year Founded: 2001
Sales Range: $10-24.9 Million
Emp.: 16
Motion Picture & Video Production Service
N.A.I.C.S.: 512110
Anne Chambers (CEO)
Kara Schwandner (Partner & Dir-Client Svcs)
Donivan Perkins (Partner)
Richard Walker (COO, Partner & Dir-Production)

RED 7 MEDIA, LLC
10 Norden Pl, Norwalk, CT 06855
Tel.: (203) 854-6730
Web Site: http://www.red7media.com
Year Founded: 2002
Sales Range: $10-24.9 Million
Emp.: 50
Periodical Publishers
N.A.I.C.S.: 513120
Dan Hanover (Gen Mgr-Events Grp)
Kerry Smith (Founder, Pres & CEO)
Len Roberts (Bus Mgr)
Mike Westcott (Mng Dir-Corp Mktg & Strategy)
Tony Silber (Gen Mgr-Publ Grp)
Bill Mickey (Dir-Audience Dev)

RED APPLE GROUP, INC.
800 3rd Ave, New York, NY 10022
Tel.: (212) 580-6805
Web Site: https://ragny.com
Sales Range: $1-4.9 Billion
Emp.: 8,000
Offices of Other Holding Companies
N.A.I.C.S.: 551112
John A. Catsimatidis Jr. (Pres & COO)
Matt Wanning (VP)
Louis Palermo (Pres-Real Estate Div)

Subsidiaries:

Gristedes Foods, Inc.   (1)
823 11th Ave, New York, NY 10019-3557   (92%)
Tel.: (212) 956-5803
Web Site: http://www.gristedes.com
Sales Range: $300-349.9 Million
Emp.: 4,000
Supermarket Chain & Holding Company
N.A.I.C.S.: 445110
Francine Rioux (Sr Mgr-Asset Mgmt)
Debbie Clusan (Dir-Payroll)

Subsidiary (Domestic):

Gristedes Supermarkets, Inc.   (2)
907th 8th Ave St, New York, NY 10019-3557
Tel.: (212) 582-5873

Web Site:
http://www.gristedessupermarkets.com
Rev.: $51,792,540
Emp.: 2,000
Supermarket Distr
N.A.I.C.S.: 445110
John A. Catsimatidis Jr. *(Chm, CEO & Treas)*

United Acquisition Corp. (1)
800 3rd Ave 5th Fl, New York, NY 10022
Tel.: (212) 956-5770
Emp.: 40
Holding Company
N.A.I.C.S.: 551112
John A. Catsimatidis Jr. *(Chm & CEO)*

Subsidiary (Domestic):

United Refining Inc. (2)
823 11th Ave, New York, NY 10019
Tel.: (212) 956-5803
Web Site: http://www.redapple.com
Sales Range: $50-74.9 Million
Emp.: 100
Holding Company; Refining Operations
N.A.I.C.S.: 551112
John A. Catsimatidis Jr. *(Chm & CEO)*

Subsidiary (Domestic):

United Refining Company (3)
15 Bradley St, Warren, PA 16365-3299
Tel.: (814) 723-1500
Web Site: http://www.urc.com
Rev.: $2,086,625,000
Assets: $879,717,000
Liabilities: $536,153,000
Net Worth: $343,564,000
Earnings: ($6,362,000)
Emp.: 1,951
Fiscal Year-end: 08/31/2016
Petroleum Products Refiner & Marketer
N.A.I.C.S.: 324110
John A. Catsimatidis Jr. *(Chm & CEO)*
Myron L. Turfitt *(Pres & COO)*
James E. Murphy *(CFO)*
Michael E. Toole *(VP-Refining)*
Roy A. Williams *(Sr VP-Mkt)*

Subsidiary (Domestic):

Country Fair Inc. (4)
15 Bradley St, Warren, PA 16365-3299
Tel.: (814) 898-1500
Web Site: http://www.countryfairstores.com
Sales Range: $125-149.9 Million
Emp.: 55
Convenience Store Operator
N.A.I.C.S.: 445131
John A. Catsimatidis Jr. *(Chm)*
Myron L. Turfit *(Pres & COO)*
James E. Murphy *(VP-Fin & CFO)*
Mike Jara *(Dir-Facilities Dev)*
Damien Zdarko *(Dir-Maintenance & Security)*

RED ARROW LOGISTICS INC.
22605 SE 56th St Ste 270, Issaquah, WA 98029
Tel.: (425) 747-7914
Web Site:
http://www.redarrowlogistics.com
Year Founded: 2003
Sales Range: $1-9.9 Million
Emp.: 12
Freight Transportation Arrangement
N.A.I.C.S.: 488510
Liz Lasater *(CEO)*

RED ARTS CAPITAL, LLC
3 1st National Plz 70 W Madison St Ste 2900, Chicago, IL 60602
Web Site:
http://www.redartscapital.com
Privater Equity Firm
N.A.I.C.S.: 523999
Nicholas Antoine *(Co-Founder & Mng Partner)*
Vanessa D'Cunha *(CFO)*
Chad Strader *(Co-Founder, CEO & Mng Partner)*

Subsidiaries:

Sunset Pacific Transportation, Inc. (1)
13875 Norton Ave, Chino, CA 91710
Tel.: (909) 464-1677
Web Site: http://www.sunsetpacific.com
Local Trucking with Storage
N.A.I.C.S.: 484110
Josh Craig *(CEO)*

RED BALL OXYGEN CO. INC.
609 N Market St, Shreveport, LA 71107
Tel.: (318) 425-3211   LA
Web Site:
http://www.redballoxygen.com
Year Founded: 1930
Sales Range: $10-24.9 Million
Emp.: 140
Supplier of Welding & Industrial Gases
N.A.I.C.S.: 423830
Ralph Thomas *(Treas)*
Robert Ewing *(Pres)*
Paul D. Barron *(Mgr)*
Alex Kennedy *(Chm & CEO)*

RED BALL TIGER
78 Buena Vista Ave, Mill Valley, CA 94941-1243
Tel.: (415) 905-0392   CA
Web Site: http://www.redballtiger.com
Year Founded: 1994
Rev.: $70,000,000
Emp.: 5
N.A.I.C.S.: 541810
Gregory Wilson *(Owner)*

RED BEND SOFTWARE, INC.
400 1 Totten Pond Rd Ste 130, Waltham, MA 02451
Tel.: (781) 890-2090   DE
Web Site: http://www.redbend.com
Mobile Device Software Development Services
N.A.I.C.S.: 513210
Yoram Salinger *(Pres & CEO)*
Sharon Peleg *(Founder & CTO)*
Alon Kleinman *(Exec VP-R&D)*
Lori Sylvia *(Exec VP-Mktg)*
Shykeh Gordon *(Exec VP-Global Sls)*
Sigal Givati *(Exec VP-HR)*
Dean Martin *(VP-EMEA)*
Shlomo Dovrat *(Chm)*
Dvora Nuriel-Valach *(CFO)*

RED BROWN KLE
840 N Old World Third St Ste 401, Milwaukee, WI 53203
Tel.: (414) 272-2600
Year Founded: 2000
Sales Range: Less than $1 Million
Emp.: 5
N.A.I.C.S.: 541810
Carl Brown *(Owner & Pres)*
Kurt Kleman *(VP & Dir-Creative)*
Liz Ruby *(VP & Dir-Copy)*

RED CANOE CREDIT UNION
1418 15th Ave, Longview, WA 98632
Tel.: (360) 425-2130
Web Site:
http://www.redcanoecu.com
Rev.: $28,429,453
Emp.: 150
Credit Union
N.A.I.C.S.: 522130
Charlie Neithardt *(Chm)*
Jeff Haverlack *(VP-IT)*
Caroll Hope *(Sec)*
Debbie Malone *(VP-Ops)*
Deidra Miner *(COO)*

RED CARPET TICKETS INC.
12912 Hill Country Blvd F240, Bee Cave, TX 78738
Tel.: (512) 377-1667
Web Site:
http://www.redcarpettickets.com
Year Founded: 2004
Sales Range: $1-9.9 Million
Emp.: 10
Private Label Event Ticket Sales for Major Corporations
N.A.I.C.S.: 561499
Brian Peters *(Pres & CEO)*
Stephen Saddock *(CFO)*

RED CHAMBER CO.
1912 E Vernon Ave, Vernon, CA 90058-1611
Tel.: (323) 234-9000
Web Site:
https://www.redchamber.com
Year Founded: 1973
Sales Range: Less than $1 Million
Emp.: 1,700
Fish & Seafood Merchant Wholesalers
N.A.I.C.S.: 424460
Ming Bin Kou *(Pres)*
Amy Hui *(Asst Mgr-Credit)*
Andro Chen *(Asst VP)*
Raul Bunelos *(Mgr-Warehouse)*
Sharon Chao *(Controller)*
Wales Yu *(VP-Food Innovation & R&D)*

Subsidiaries:

Neptune Foods (1)
4510 S Alameda St, Vernon, CA 90058
Tel.: (323) 232-8300
Web Site: http://www.neptunefoods.com
Sales Range: $25-49.9 Million
Emp.: 200
Fish & Seafood Processor & Distr
N.A.I.C.S.: 311710
Howard Choi *(Pres)*

OFI Markesa International (1)
1912 E Vernon Ave Ste 110, Vernon, CA 90058
Tel.: (323) 231-1600
Web Site: http://www.ofimarkesa.com
Sales Range: $10-24.9 Million
Emp.: 15
Seafood Marketing
N.A.I.C.S.: 424460

Tampa Bay Fisheries, Inc. (1)
3060 N Gallagher Rd, Dover, FL 33527
Tel.: (813) 752-8883
Web Site: http://www.tbfish.com
Sales Range: $350-399.9 Million
Emp.: 450
Seafood Distr
N.A.I.C.S.: 424460
Robert Patterson *(Pres & CEO)*
Tom Tao *(CFO)*
Wyatt Howard *(VP-Mktg)*
Robert Fields *(VP)*

Division (Domestic):

Singleton Seafood (2)
3060 Gallagher Rd, Dover, FL 33527
Tel.: (813) 750-1850
Sales Range: $10-24.9 Million
Emp.: 350
Seafood Processing & Sales
N.A.I.C.S.: 424460
Nikki Adams *(Mgr-Ops)*

RED CLAY INDUSTRIES INC.
PO Box 241689, Charlotte, NC 28224-1689
Tel.: (704) 523-1018
Web Site:
http://www.redclayindustries.com
Sales Range: $10-24.9 Million
Emp.: 45
Highway & Street Construction Services
N.A.I.C.S.: 237310
James Smith *(Pres)*

RED CLAY INTERACTIVE
22 Buford Village Way Ste 221, Buford, GA 30518
Tel.: (770) 297-2430
Web Site:
http://www.redclayinteractive.com
Year Founded: 2000
Rev.: $2,100,000
Emp.: 18
Data Processing, Hosting & Related Services
N.A.I.C.S.: 518210
Lance Compton *(Pres & CEO)*
Scott Atkinson *(Mgr-Sls)*
Lindsey Marshall *(Dir-Interactive Mktg)*

RED CLOUD PROMOTIONS
1600 Sawtelle Blvd Ste 108, Los Angeles, CA 90025
Tel.: (310) 444-5583
Web Site:
http://www.redcloudpromotions.com
Year Founded: 2002
Rev.: $6,200,000
Emp.: 12
Marketing Consulting Services
N.A.I.C.S.: 541613
Cloud Morrison *(Partner)*
Nathan Maze *(Mgr)*

RED COATS INC.
4520 E W Hwy Ste 200, Bethesda, MD 20814-4500
Tel.: (301) 654-4360   MD
Web Site: http://www.redcoats.com
Year Founded: 1960
Sales Range: $50-74.9 Million
Emp.: 4,000
Building Maintenance Services
N.A.I.C.S.: 561720
Barbara K. Peel *(Chm & Pres)*
Blaine Wilson *(VP-HR)*
Bob Butorac *(Sr VP-Ops)*
Scott Kydd *(Sr VP-Ops)*
William F. Peel *(Founder & Vice Chm)*
W. Mack Wells *(Exec VP)*
Jack Ball *(VP-South Virginia & North Carolina)*
Erick Ireland *(Sr VP-Mktg & Sls)*
Greg Cunningham *(Mgr-Safety)*
Ralph G. Blasey *(VP-Bus Dev)*
Todd Dayton *(VP)*

Subsidiaries:

Admiral Security Services (1)
4520 EW Hwy Ste 101, Bethesda, MD 20814
Tel.: (301) 656-9382
Web Site: http://www.admiralsecurity.com
Security Services
N.A.I.C.S.: 561612
Leon A. Beresford *(VP-Corp Ops)*
George D. Vincent *(Exec VP)*
Cynthia Lunningham *(Mgr-HR)*
Page Wells-Pollock *(Mgr-Bus Dev)*

Branch (Domestic):

Admiral Security Services (2)
240 N Babcock St Ste A, Melbourne, FL 32935
Tel.: (321) 724-4020
Web Site: http://www.admiralsecurity.com
Sales Range: $10-24.9 Million
Emp.: 3
N.A.I.C.S.: 561720
George Vincent *(Exec VP)*
James Boddie *(Dir-Ops DC & MD)*
Leon Beresford *(Mgr-Bus Dev)*
Jay Lombard *(Dir-Ops DC & MD)*
Cynthia Lunningham *(VP-Corp Ops)*

Admiral Security Services (2)
2615 N Magnolia Ave, Ocala, FL 34475-9361
Tel.: (352) 351-5335
Web Site: http://www.admiralsecurity.com
Sales Range: $10-24.9 Million
Emp.: 10
Professional Security Services
N.A.I.C.S.: 561612

Admiral Security Services (2)
1112 Virginia Dr, Orlando, FL 32803-2582
Tel.: (407) 894-4151
Web Site: http://www.admiralsecurity.com

RED COATS INC.

U.S. PRIVATE

Red Coats Inc.—(Continued)
Sales Range: $25-49.9 Million
Emp.: 140
Aircraft services
N.A.I.C.S.: 561720
George D. Vincent (Exec VP)

Red Coats Inc. (1)
1010 Park Ave Ste 100, Baltimore, MD 21201 (100%)
Tel.: (410) 576-0600
Sales Range: $25-49.9 Million
Emp.: 800
N.A.I.C.S.: 561720

Red Coats Inc. - North Carolina Division (1)
2525 Meridian Pkwy Ste 50B, Durham, NC 27713
Tel.: (919) 572-0752
Janitorial Services
N.A.I.C.S.: 561720

Red Coats Inc. - North Florida Division (1)
101 E Kennedy Blvd Ste G 102, Tampa, FL 33602
Tel.: (813) 621-6878
Web Site: http://www.redcoats.com
Sales Range: $10-24.9 Million
Emp.: 700
Janitorial Services
N.A.I.C.S.: 561720
James E. Green (Sr VP-Florida Div)
Jack Ball (VP-Southern Virginia & North Carolina Div)
Ralph G. Blasey (VP-Bus Dev)
Bob Butorac (Sr VP-Ops)
Greg Cunningham (Mgr-Safety)
Todd Dayton (VP-Florida)
Erick Ireland (Sr VP-Mktg & Sls)
Scott Kydd (VP-Ops)
William F. Peel (Chm)
Blaine Wilson (Dir-Admin)
Robert Wolak (VP-Lerner Div)

Red Coats Inc. - South Florida Division (1)
8420 NW 52nd St Ste 101, Doral, FL 33166
Tel.: (800) 785-0020
Web Site: http://www.redcoats.com
Janitorial Services
N.A.I.C.S.: 561720
James Green (Sr VP-Bus Dev-Florida Div)
Todd Dayton (VP-South Florida)
Jack Ball (VP-Southern Virginia & North Carolina Div)
Ralph G. Blasey (VP-Bus Dev)
Bob Butorac (Sr VP-Ops)
Greg Cunningham (Mgr-Safety)
Erick Ireland (Sr VP-Mktg & Sls)
Scott Kydd (VP-Ops)
Barbara K. Peel (Chm & Pres)
William F. Peel (Vice Chm)
W. Mack Wells (Exec VP)
Robert Wolak (VP-Lerner Div)

Red Coats Inc. - Virginia Southern Division (1)
9830 Mayland Dr Ste H, Richmond, VA 23232
Tel.: (804) 253-1800
Web Site: http://www.redcoats.com
Emp.: 700
Janitorial Services
N.A.I.C.S.: 561720
Jack Ball (VP)

RED COLLAR PET FOODS, INC.
1550 W McEwen Dr Ste 250, Franklin, TN 37067
Tel.: (866) 232-0996
Web Site:
  http://www.redcollarpet.com
Animal Feed Mfr
N.A.I.C.S.: 311119
Chris Hamilton (Pres & CEO)
Subsidiaries:

Hampshire Pet Products, LLC (1)
7502 E 26 Ste, Joplin, MO 64804
Tel.: (417) 206-6137
Pet Product Services & Mfr
N.A.I.C.S.: 311119
Julie Larson (VP)

RED COMMA MEDIA, INC.
605 Williamson St, Madison, WI 53703
Tel.: (608) 661-3780
Web Site:
  http://www.redcommamedia.com
Year Founded: 2003
Sales Range: $10-24.9 Million
Emp.: 3
Media Buying Services
N.A.I.C.S.: 541830
Carrie Dellinger (Pres)

RED DELUXE BRAND DEVELOPMENT
120 S Front St, Memphis, TN 38103
Tel.: (901) 522-9242
Web Site: http://www.reddeluxe.com
Year Founded: 2002
Sales Range: $10-24.9 Million
Emp.: 15
N.A.I.C.S.: 541810
Stinson Liles (Founder)
Martin Wilford (Founder)
Kelsey Taylor (Acct Mgr & Acct Supvr)

RED DEVIL, INC.
4175 Webb St, Pryor, OK 74361
Tel.: (918) 585-8111
Web Site: http://www.reddevil.com
Rev.: $12,300,000
Emp.: 95
Hand Tools & Chemical Products Mfr
N.A.I.C.S.: 424690
Larry Brandon (VP-Tech & Gen Mgr)
Jason Ringling (Dir-Mktg Svcs)
Alan Buynak (Mgr-IT)

RED DOG EQUITY LLC
3715 Northside Pkwy NW Bldg 200 Ste 420, Atlanta, GA 30327
Tel.: (404) 458-7777
Web Site:
  http://www.reddogequity.com
Investment Services
N.A.I.C.S.: 523999
Toby Chambers (Co-Founder & Mng Dir)
Tom Connolly (Co-Founder & Mng Dir)
Chance McNamara (VP)
Amy Githens (Mgr-Ops)
Subsidiaries:

Mammoth Holdings, LLC (1)
428 W Pike St, Lawrenceville, GA 30046
Tel.: (404) 609-4233
Web Site:
  http://www.mammothholdings.com
Car Wash Services
N.A.I.C.S.: 811192
David L. Hoffmann (Chm & CEO)
David Hoffmann (CEO)
Corey Joslin (COO)
Mark Hidle (Chief People Officer)
Jennifer Vanderveldt (CFO)
Caleb Jarrett (Dir-IT)
Harsha Musthyala (Sr Dir-Data Analytics)
Chris Donner (VP-Dev)

Holding (Domestic):

Marc1 Carwash (2)
3439 Pelham Pkwy, Pelham, AL 35124
Tel.: (205) 859-2727
Web Site: https://www.marc1carwash.com
Car Wash Services
N.A.I.C.S.: 811192

Today's Car Wash, L.L.C. (2)
514 S Fort Hood St, Killeen, TX 76541-6820
Tel.: (254) 245-8657
Web Site: http://www.todayscarwash.com
Law firm
N.A.I.C.S.: 541110
Tyler Furney (Co-Founder & Mgr)

Wash Me Fast, LLC (2)
2149 Cobb Pkwy NW, Kennesaw, GA 30152
Tel.: (470) 468-5257
Web Site: http://www.washmefast.com
Car Wash Services
N.A.I.C.S.: 811192

Wiggy Wash, LLC (2)
794 S Main St, Spanish Fork, UT 84660
Tel.: (801) 798-6170
Web Site: http://www.wiggywash.com
Car Wash Services
N.A.I.C.S.: 811192
Brent Wignall (CEO)

RED DOOR INTERACTIVE, INC.
350 10th Ave Ste 100, San Diego, CA 92101-8700
Tel.: (619) 398-2670
Web Site: http://www.reddoor.biz
Year Founded: 2002
Sales Range: $1-9.9 Million
Emp.: 60
Advertising Agencies
N.A.I.C.S.: 541810
Reid Carr (Pres & CEO)
Amy Carr (Exec VP-HR)
Dennis Gonzales (VP-Ops)
Erika Werner (VP-Client Svcs)
Grant Brisacher (CFO)
Patrick Cinco (Dir-Creative)
John Faris (VP-Cross Channel Mktg)
Kate De Jong (VP-Employee Experience)

RED DOT CORPORATION
495 Andover Park E, Seattle, WA 98188-7605
Tel.: (206) 575-3840
Web Site: http://www.rdac.com
Year Founded: 1965
Sales Range: $25-49.9 Million
Emp.: 400
Mfr of Motor Vehicle Parts & Accessories
N.A.I.C.S.: 336320
R. Bruce Channer (CFO & VP)
Robert Gardiner (Dir-Aftermarket Sls)
Stephen Machin (VP-Global Mfg)
Bill Jewell (Mgr-Aftermarket Mktg)
Pat Carroll (VP-Sls)
Nick Janus (Pres)
Gary P. Hansen (VP-Engrg)
Scott Latimer (Reg Mgr-Sls)
Ken Montelongo (Reg Mgr-Aftermarket)
John McCormack (Sr Mgr-Supply Chain)
Brian Kennedy (Mgr-Aftermarket)
Steve Lach (COO)
Artak Arakelian (VP-Ops)
Ryan Baker (Dir-Aftermarket Sls)
Rick Freeman (Dir-OEM Sls)

RED FROG EVENTS, LLC
100 W Ohio St Ste 100, Chicago, IL 60654-6567
Tel.: (773) 687-4595
Web Site:
  http://www.redfrogevents.com
Year Founded: 2007
Sales Range: $50-74.9 Million
Emp.: 80
Event Production Services
N.A.I.C.S.: 711320
Joe Reynolds (Co-CEO)
Stephanie Mezzano (VP-Ops)

RED GOLD INC.
1500 Tomato Country Wy, Elwood, IN 46036
Tel.: (765) 754-7527
Web Site: http://www.redgold.com
Rev.: $124,800,000
Emp.: 107
Tomato Products
N.A.I.C.S.: 311421

Larry Brandenburg (Mgr-Special Sls)
Dan Quigley (Mgr-Sls-Midwest Reg)
Subsidiaries:

RGT Logistics, LLC. (1)
PO Box 103, Elwood, IN 46036
Web Site: http://www.rgttransport.com
Logistics Management Services
N.A.I.C.S.: 541614

Red Gold (1)
800 Dougherty St, Bluffton, IN 46714-2915
Tel.: (260) 824-1422
Sales Range: $25-49.9 Million
Emp.: 1
Tomato Canner
N.A.I.C.S.: 311421
Redgold Eric Yeskie (Asst Mgr-Distr Center)
Mike Herrmann (Dir-Engrg)
Greg Metzger (Dir-Mktg)
Maurie Fettig (Exec VP)
Jack Lynch (Mgr-Sls-Natl)
Joe Spencer (Mgr-Sls-Natl)
William Sinclair (Mgr-Trade Mktg)
Conrad Heisner (Plant Mgr)
Joi Johnson (Project Coord-SQF)
Tim Ingle (VP-HR & Strategy)
Lynch Bennett III (Dir-Matls Mgmt)

Red Gold Inc. - Elwood Facility (1)
490 S 22nd St, Elwood, IN 46036
Tel.: (765) 557-5500
Ketchup Mfr
N.A.I.C.S.: 311421

Red Gold Inc. - Geneva Facility (1)
705 S Williams St, Geneva, IN 46740
Tel.: (260) 368-9017
Ketchup Mfr
N.A.I.C.S.: 311421

Red Gold Inc. - Orestes Facility (1)
120 E Oak St, Orestes, IN 46063
Tel.: (765) 754-7527
Ketchup Mfr
N.A.I.C.S.: 311421

RED HERRING, INC.
1900 Alameda de las Pulgas Ste112, San Mateo, CA 94403-1295
Tel.: (650) 215-1520
Web Site: http://www.redherring.com
Year Founded: 1993
Sales Range: $10-24.9 Million
Emp.: 130
Online Magazine Publisher
N.A.I.C.S.: 513120
Alex Vieux (Founder & Chm)
Joel Dreyfus (Editor-in-Chief)
Matt Gallagher (Editor)

RED HOAGLAND HYUNDAI
5325 14th St W Ste 41, Bradenton, FL 34207-3307
Tel.: (941) 756-9544
Sales Range: $10-24.9 Million
Emp.: 60
Car Whslr
N.A.I.C.S.: 441110
Helen Akin (Gen Mgr)
Forrest Fulford (Mgr)
G. M. Hoagland (Pres)

RED HOLDINGS GROUP INC.
2625 W Sunset Dr, Tampa, FL 33629
Tel.: (813) 251-4734
Holding Company
N.A.I.C.S.: 551112
Elliot Kracko (Chm)
Edward W. Easton (Pres)
Kathleen Shanahan (Dir)
Subsidiaries:

Gamma Industries Inc. (1)
6130 Sainte Anne Boulevard, L'Ange-Gardien, Quebec, G0A 2K0, QC, Canada
Tel.: (418) 822-1448
Web Site: http://www.gamma-online.com
Sales Range: $25-49.9 Million
Emp.: 150
Aluminum Products Mfr, Including Windows, Curtain Walls, Doors, Panels & Coverings for Commercial & Institutional Sectors

N.A.I.C.S.: 331318
Pierre Belanger *(Dir-Fin)*

Division (US):

Gamma USA, Inc. (2)
5600 NW 37th Ave, Miami, FL 33142
Tel.: (305) 633-2422
Web Site: http://www.gammana.com
Aluminum Products Mfr, Including Windows, Curtain Walls, Doors, Panels & Coverings for Commercial & Institutional Sectors
N.A.I.C.S.: 331318

RED HORSE OIL COMPANY INCORPORATED
128 Reliance Rd, Rock Springs, WY 82901
Tel.: (307) 362-3649
Web Site: http://www.redhorseoil.com
Sales Range: $25-49.9 Million
Emp.: 60
Petroleum Products
N.A.I.C.S.: 424720
Peter J. Bunning *(Pres & CEO)*

RED HOT & BLUE RESTAURANTS, INC.
154 Charlois Blvd Frnt, Winston Salem, NC 27103-1565
Tel.: (703) 276-8833
Web Site:
http://www.redhotandblue.com
Sales Range: $75-99.9 Million
Emp.: 300
Restaurant Chain
N.A.I.C.S.: 722511
Jeanne Ormsby *(VP-Fin & Admin)*

RED HOUSE NORTH AMERICA, INC.
10 Roswell St Ste 200, Alpharetta, GA 30009
Tel.: (770) 475-2103
Web Site:
http://www.redhouseusa.com
Year Founded: 2001
Sales Range: $1-9.9 Million
Emp.: 25
Advetising Agency
N.A.I.C.S.: 541810
Dan Hansen *(Sr Partner)*
Terry McLane *(Sr Partner)*

RED INC.
1397 Library Cir Ste 201, Grand Forks, ND 58201
Tel.: (701) 775-4006
Sales Range: $10-24.9 Million
Emp.: 400
Fast-Food Restaurant, Chain
N.A.I.C.S.: 722513

RED LAKE GAMING INC.
Hwy 1, Redlake, MN 56671
Tel.: (218) 679-2111
Web Site:
http://www.sevenclanscasino.com
Sales Range: $25-49.9 Million
Emp.: 20
Gambling Establishment
N.A.I.C.S.: 713290
Charles Preneic *(CEO)*

RED LEVEL NETWORKS
24371 Catherine Industrial Dr Ste 223, Novi, MI 48375
Tel.: (248) 412-8200
Web Site:
http://www.redlevelnetworks.com
Sales Range: $1-9.9 Million
Emp.: 21
Infrastructure Software Consulting Services
N.A.I.C.S.: 541512
David King *(Pres & CEO)*
Connie Carr *(Coord-Help Desk)*
Edward Aube *(VP-Managed Svcs)*
Robert Tessanne *(VP-Cloud & Tech Solutions)*
Janet Tyler *(COO)*
Janet Tyler *(COO)*

RED MOON MARKETING LLC
4100 Coca-Cola Plz Ste 215, Charlotte, NC 28211
Tel.: (704) 366-1147
Web Site:
http://www.redmoonmkt.com
Year Founded: 1988
Sales Range: $10-24.9 Million
Emp.: 25
Advertising Agencies
N.A.I.C.S.: 541810
James Bailey *(Pres & CEO)*
Greg Mercer *(Sr VP-Acct Svcs)*
Eddie Burklin *(CFO)*
Shyloe Luehrs *(Sr VP)*
Jim Duncan *(Exec VP-Sls & Mktg)*
Tyler Sigmon *(VP)*
Glenn Wilga *(Dir-Acct)*
Jimmy Harte *(Exec VP)*
Krista Nuzum *(Sr Acct Exec)*
Amanda Maness *(Dir-Acct)*
Jay Martin *(Mng Dir-Strategic Plng)*
Mike Adams *(Sr Acct Dir)*

RED MOUNTAIN CAPITAL PARTNERS LLC
10100 Santa Monica Blvd Ste 925, Los Angeles, CA 90067
Tel.: (310) 432-0200   DE
Web Site: http://www.redmtncap.com
Emp.: 50
Privater Equity Firm
N.A.I.C.S.: 523999
John Christopher Teets *(Partner)*
Jack Watkinson *(Partner, COO & Chief Compliance Officer)*
Jennifer Martin *(CFO & Principal)*
Matthew Hepler *(Partner)*
Willem T. Mesdag *(Mng Partner)*

RED NOLAND CADILLAC
990 Motor City Dr, Colorado Springs, CO 80905-7309
Tel.: (719) 633-4633
Web Site:
http://www.rednolandcadillac.com
Year Founded: 1974
Sales Range: $25-49.9 Million
Emp.: 120
New Car Whslr
N.A.I.C.S.: 441110
Mike Jorgensen *(Pres & Partner)*

RED OAK REALTY
1891 Solano Ave, Berkeley, CA 94707
Tel.: (510) 527-3387   CA
Web Site:
http://www.redoakrealty.com
Year Founded: 1976
Real Estate Services
N.A.I.C.S.: 531390
Vanessa Bergmark *(Owner & CEO)*
Marion Henon *(Sls Mgr)*
Todd Hodson *(Sls Mgr)*
Nicole Aissa *(Pres)*

RED PEACOCK INTERNATIONAL, INC.
19859 Nordhoff St, Northridge, CA 91324
Tel.: (818) 407-8822
Web Site:
http://www.redpeacock.com
Year Founded: 1997
Sales Range: $25-49.9 Million
Emp.: 9
Consumer Electronics Distr
N.A.I.C.S.: 423620
Ruby G. Mansukhani *(Pres & COO)*
John Lalwani *(Exec VP)*

RED PEPPER INC.
110 29th Ave N Ste 100, Nashville, TN 37203
Tel.: (615) 320-9335
Web Site:
http://www.redpepperland.com
Year Founded: 2001
Sales Range: $1-9.9 Million
Emp.: 28
N.A.I.C.S.: 541810
Tim McMullen *(Founder)*

Subsidiaries:

Red Pepper, Inc (1)
113 S Perry St Ste 200, Lawrenceville, GA 30045
Tel.: (678) 749-7483
Web Site: http://www.redpepperinc.com
Emp.: 5
N.A.I.C.S.: 541810
Dave McMullen *(Partner)*

RED RIVER COMPUTER CO., INC.
21 Water St Ste 500, Claremont, NH 03743-2216
Tel.: (603) 448-8880
Web Site: http://www.redriver.com
Emp.: 300
Information Technology Services
N.A.I.C.S.: 541519
Doug Adams *(Mgr-Sls)*
Rick Bolduc *(Chm)*
Alan Dumas *(CEO)*
Dan Kent *(CTO)*

Subsidiaries:

Accunet Solutions (1)
20 Park Plaza 4th Fl, Boston, MA 02116
Tel.: (800) 711-3963
Web Site: http://www.accunetsolutions.com
Information Technology & Consulting Services
N.A.I.C.S.: 541519
Alan Dumas *(Founder & Pres)*
Stephen Stahl *(VP-Sls & Engrg Svcs)*
David Bates *(CFO & COO)*

RED RIVER GRAIN COMPANY
3549 200th Ave, Breckenridge, MN 56520
Tel.: (218) 643-3738
Web Site:
http://www.redrivergrain.com
Sales Range: $10-24.9 Million
Emp.: 15
Producers of Grain & Wheat
N.A.I.C.S.: 424510
David Yaggie *(Pres)*

RED RIVER HUMAN SERVICES FOUNDATION
2506 35th Ave S Ste A, Fargo, ND 58104
Tel.: (701) 235-0971   ND
Web Site: http://www.rrhsf.org
Year Founded: 1979
Sales Range: $10-24.9 Million
Emp.: 345
Developmental Disability Assistance Services
N.A.I.C.S.: 624120
Thomas R Newberger *(CEO)*

RED RIVER INTERMODAL INC.
2285 Ste A 201, Bossier City, LA 71111
Tel.: (318) 686-2020
Web Site: http://www.rrii.com
Sales Range: $25-49.9 Million
Emp.: 7
Transportation Agents & Brokers
N.A.I.C.S.: 488510
Clay Crenshaw *(Treas)*

RED RIVER MACHINERY INC.
2601 N Interstate Hwy, Ennis, TX 75119
Tel.: (972) 438-6592   TX
Web Site:
http://www.redrivermachinery.com
Year Founded: 1983
Sales Range: $10-24.9 Million
Emp.: 10
Distr of Metalworking Machinery
N.A.I.C.S.: 423830
Eddie Richardson *(Pres)*

RED RIVER MOTOR COMPANY
221 Traffic St, Bossier City, LA 71111
Tel.: (318) 742-3411
Web Site:
http://www.redriverchevy.com
Sales Range: $25-49.9 Million
Emp.: 125
New & Used Car Dealers
N.A.I.C.S.: 441110
Loyd Nelson *(Mgr-New Vehicle Sls)*
Billy Woods *(Dir-New Vehicle Sls)*
Patton Fritze *(Gen Mgr-Fixed Ops)*
Alvin Olsan *(Gen Mgr-Variable Ops)*

RED RIVER SOLUTIONS
14800 Quorum Dr Ste 325, Dallas, TX 75254
Tel.: (972) 715-6100   TX
Web Site:
http://www.redriversolutions.com
Year Founded: 2004
Sales Range: $1-9.9 Million
Emp.: 14
Personnel Contractor
N.A.I.C.S.: 561311
Eric Riegelman *(Mgr-Oracle Project)*
Terri Pettit *(Dir-Sls)*

RED RIVER SPECIALTIES INC.
7545 Haygood Rd, Shreveport, LA 71107-3506
Tel.: (318) 425-5944   LA
Web Site: http://www.rrsi.com
Year Founded: 1987
Sales Range: $10-24.9 Million
Emp.: 40
Agriculture & Farm Business
N.A.I.C.S.: 424910
Tad Owens *(Mgr)*
Mike Ream *(Mgr)*
Steven Burd *(Gen Mgr)*

RED RIVER VALLEY RURAL ELECTRIC ASSOCIATION
1003 Memorial Dr, Marietta, OK 73448
Tel.: (580) 276-3364
Web Site: http://www.rrvrea.com
Rev.: $13,871,087
Emp.: 50
Electric Power Distribution
N.A.I.C.S.: 221122
Roger Rhoades *(Mgr-Acctg)*
Brent Hartin *(CEO)*
Winston Warthen *(Dir-Engrg)*

RED ROOF INNS, INC.
2071 N Bechtle Ave, Springfield, OH 45504
Tel.: (614) 744-2600
Web Site: http://www.redroof.com
Year Founded: 1972
Sales Range: $300-349.9 Million
Emp.: 6,500
Economy Lodging Business
N.A.I.C.S.: 721199
Larry Daniel *(Sr VP-Distr)*
Phil Hugh *(Chief Dev Officer)*
Neil Scott *(VP-Sls & Ops)*
Joe Luck *(VP-Franchise Sls & Dev-West Coast)*
Leslie Fisher *(Sr VP-HR & Trng)*
Bill Hall *(Sr VP-Franchise Ops)*

RED SIX MEDIA, LLC

Red Six Media, LLC.—(Continued)

RED SIX MEDIA, LLC
319 3rd St, Baton Rouge, LA 70801
Tel.: (225) 615-8836
Web Site:
http://www.redsixmedia.com
Year Founded: 2009
Sales Range: $1-9.9 Million
Emp.: 16
Advertising Agency Services
N.A.I.C.S.: 541810
Matt Dardenne *(Co-Owner & Creative Dir)*
Joe Martin *(Co-Owner & Creative Dir)*
Kristen Rushing *(Co-Owner & Acct Dir)*
Donny Terrio *(Art Dir)*
Katie Brooks *(Sr Acct Mgr)*

RED SKY BLUE WATER, LLC
999 Northlake Way Ste 200, Seattle, WA 98103
Tel.: (206) 632-1600
Web Site:
http://www.redskybluewater.com
Year Founded: 2007
Sales Range: $1-9.9 Million
Emp.: 17
Business Management Consulting Services
N.A.I.C.S.: 541618
Sharon A. Davison *(CEO)*
Rex Houchins *(CTO)*
Noland Angara *(COO)*

RED SPOT INTERACTIVE
1001 Jupiter Park Dr Ste 124, Jupiter, FL 33458
Tel.: (800) 401-7931
Web Site:
http://www.redspotinteractive.com
Year Founded: 2008
Sales Range: $1-9.9 Million
Emp.: 50
Integrated Marketing & Customer Acquisition Platform Systems
N.A.I.C.S.: 541613
Jason Tuschman *(Co-Founder & Pres)*
Amy Holdener *(Sr Dir-Lead Mgmt & Client Rels)*
Matt Tompkins *(Sr Dir-Client Rels & Ops)*
Niko Ormond *(VP-Ops & Product Dev & Co-Founder)*

RED SPRINGS FUEL OIL COMPANY
614 W 4th Ave, Red Springs, NC 28377
Tel.: (910) 843-4148
Sales Range: $10-24.9 Million
Emp.: 15
Petroleum Bulk Stations & Terminals
N.A.I.C.S.: 424710
Lewis Mcfayden *(Pres)*

RED SQUARE
54 St Emanuel St, Mobile, AL 36602
Tel.: (251) 476-1283
Web Site:
http://redsquaregaming.com
Year Founded: 1977
Sales Range: $25-49.9 Million
Emp.: 60
Advertising Agencies
N.A.I.C.S.: 541810
Rich Sullivan Jr. *(Pres & Exec Dir-Creative)*

RED STAR OIL CO. INC.
802 Purser Dr, Raleigh, NC 27603-4151
Tel.: (919) 772-1944   NC
Web Site: http://www.redstaroil.com

Year Founded: 1972
Sales Range: $10-24.9 Million
Emp.: 30
Fuel Oil Dealers
N.A.I.C.S.: 457210
Amanda Tracy *(Gen Mgr)*

RED STONE TAX EXEMPT PARTNERS LP
2 Grand Central Tower 140 E 45th St, New York, NY 10017
Tel.: (212) 297-1800
Web Site: http://redstoneco.com
Year Founded: 2011
Real Estate Investment Services
N.A.I.C.S.: 525990
John Sokolovic *(Co-Founder)*
David Levine *(Co-Founder)*
Michael Ricci *(CFO & Mng Dir)*

RED THREAD SPACES LLC
101 Seaport Blvd Ste 600, Boston, MA 02210
Tel.: (617) 439-4900   MA
Web Site: http://www.red-thread.com
Year Founded: 1986
Sales Range: $25-49.9 Million
Emp.: 194
Office Furniture Sales & Design Services
N.A.I.C.S.: 423210
John Mitton *(VP-Audiovisual)*
Don Marshall *(Pres-Eastern Massachusetts)*
Larry Levine *(Pres)*
Jeff Keener *(CEO)*
Orlando Corsi Jr. *(CFO & COO)*

RED VENTURES, LLC
1101 Red Ventures Dr, Fort Mill, SC 29707-7146
Tel.: (704) 971-2300   NC
Web Site:
http://www.redventures.com
Year Founded: 2000
Online Marketing Services
N.A.I.C.S.: 541613
Mark Brodsky *(CFO)*
Ricardo Elias *(Co-Founder & CEO)*
Dan Feldstein *(Co-Founder & CMO)*
Courtney Jeffus *(Co-Pres)*
Carlos Angrisano *(Pres-Brazil)*
Hallie Cornetta *(Exec VP-Human Capital)*
Heather Cheney *(Exec VP-Talent Acquisition)*
Jason Carlock *(Pres-Home Svcs)*
Jeff Hallock *(Pres-RV Health)*
John Sutton *(Chief Digital Officer)*
John Thomas *(Exec VP-Data Science)*
Melinda Narciso *(Exec VP-HR)*
Sarah Soule *(Co-Pres)*
Scott Hamer *(Exec VP)*
Steve Sibley *(Co-Pres)*
Tim Kullick *(COO-Home Svcs)*
George Watkins *(Exec VP)*
James LaPlaine *(CTO)*
Carmen Leyton *(Exec VP)*
Marc McCollum *(Exec VP)*
Murphy Clark *(Exec VP)*
Jeff Ross *(Exec VP)*

Subsidiaries:

Bankrate, LLC   (1)
1675 Broadway Fl 22, New York, NY 10019
Tel.: (917) 368-8600
Web Site: http://www.bankrate.com
Internet Consumer Banking Marketplace
N.A.I.C.S.: 525990

Subsidiary (Non-US):

Freedom Marketing Limited   (2)
The Cooperage Copper Row, London, SE1 2LH, United Kingdom
Tel.: (44) 2071951970

Web Site:
http://www.freedommarketing.co.uk
Online Publishing Services
N.A.I.C.S.: 513199

Subsidiary (Domestic):

LinkOffers, LLC   (2)
8920 Business Park Dr Ste 350, Austin, TX 78759
Tel.: (855) 889-5465
Online Publishing Services
N.A.I.C.S.: 513199

NetQuote, Inc.   (2)
7300 RM 2222 Bldg 2 Ste 100, Austin, TX 78730
Tel.: (512) 279-3113
Web Site: http://www.netquote.com
Online Insurance Services
N.A.I.C.S.: 524298

HomeInsurance.com LLC   (1)
4829 Carolina Beach Rd, Wilmington, NC 28412
Tel.: (910) 452-1000
Web Site: http://www.homeinsurance.com
Sales Range: $1-9.9 Million
Emp.: 125
General Insurance Services
N.A.I.C.S.: 524210
Kate Chill *(VP-Policy Sls & Carrier Relationships)*
Adayna Gonzalez *(Dir-Digital Mktg)*
Mike Pesackis *(Dir-Carrier Ops)*
Abhishek Ratani *(Pres)*
David Torrence *(Dir-Bus Dev)*

Imagitas, Inc.   (1)
48 Woerd Ave Ste 101, Waltham, MA 02453
Tel.: (781) 906-4500
Web Site: http://www.imagitas.com
Marketing Services
N.A.I.C.S.: 541910
Rich Hoey *(Sr VP-Fin)*
Bruce Grams *(VP-Production Engrg)*
Don Dittemore *(Sr VP-Tech)*
Judith Frothingham *(Sr VP-Alliances)*
Nina Pralour *(VP-Direct Mail Products)*
Sakina Tawawalla *(Sr VP-Partner Growth)*
Charlie Hadlow *(Exec VP)*
Peter Smul *(Sr VP-Ops)*
Jeff Mumford *(VP-Red Ventures)*
Susan Shanklin *(VP-Human Capital)*

RED WAGON ADVERTISING & DESIGN
4330 25th St, San Francisco, CA 94114-3603
Tel.: (415) 896-5100
Year Founded: 2000
Sales Range: Less than $1 Million
Emp.: 6
N.A.I.C.S.: 541810
Jim Herwitz *(Co-Dir-Creative & Writer)*
Dave Sanchez *(CEO & Dir-Creative)*
Scott Guisti *(Mgr-Production)*

RED WING PROPERTIES, INC.
675 Leetown Rd, Stormville, NY 12582
Tel.: (845) 221-2224
Web Site:
http://www.redwingsandgravel.com
Year Founded: 1969
Sales Range: $10-24.9 Million
Emp.: 75
Brick, Stone & Related Construction Material Whslr
N.A.I.C.S.: 423320
Frank Doherty Jr. *(Pres)*

RED WING SHOE COMPANY, INC.
314 Main St, Red Wing, MN 55066-2300
Tel.: (651) 388-8211   MN
Web Site:
http://www.redwingshoe.com
Year Founded: 1905

Sales Range: $300-349.9 Million
Emp.: 1,850
Footwear Mfr
N.A.I.C.S.: 316210
Dave Baker *(Gen Counsel & Exec VP)*
Peter D. Engel *(Dir-Mktg Comm)*
Wes Thies *(VP-Intl Sls-Ops)*
Don Roberts *(VP-Corp Accts)*
Joe Copinka *(CIO)*
Carrie Heimer *(VP-HR)*

Subsidiaries:

Red Wing Shoe Vasque Div.   (1)
314 Main St Riverfront Ctr, Red Wing, MN 55066
Tel.: (651) 388-8211
Web Site: http://www.vasque.com
Sales Range: $25-49.9 Million
Emp.: 100
Mfr of Outdoor Hiking Footwear For Men & Women
N.A.I.C.S.: 316210
George Curleigh *(VP)*

S.B. Foot Tanning Company   (1)
805 Bench St, Red Wing, MN 55066-9550
Tel.: (651) 388-4731
Web Site: http://www.sbfoot.com
Sales Range: $25-49.9 Million
Emp.: 250
Leather, Tanning & Finishing for Shoes & Upholstery
N.A.I.C.S.: 316110
Carrie Heimer *(VP-HR)*
Silas B. Foot III *(Pres)*

Division (Domestic):

S.B. Foot Tanning Company Cactus Div.   (2)
PO Box 845, Dumas, TX 79029-0845
Tel.: (806) 966-5121
Sales Range: $25-49.9 Million
Emp.: 71
Leather Tanning & Finishing
N.A.I.C.S.: 316110

Saint James Hotel   (1)
406 Main St, Red Wing, MN 55066-2325   (100%)
Tel.: (651) 388-2846
Web Site: http://www.st-james-hotel.com
Rev: $4,900,000
Emp.: 172
Hotel
N.A.I.C.S.: 721110
Michael McKay *(Gen Mgr)*

RED ZONE LLC
1800 Tysons Blvd Ste 550, McLean, VA 22102
Tel.: (703) 726-7133   DE
Year Founded: 2004
Privater Equity Firm
N.A.I.C.S.: 523999
Dwight C. Schar *(Mng Partner)*
Daniel M. Snyder *(Co-Founder & Mng Partner)*

RED'S SHOE BARN INC.
35 Broadway, Dover, NH 03820
Tel.: (603) 742-1893   NH
Web Site:
http://www.redshoebarn.com
Year Founded: 1958
Sales Range: $10-24.9 Million
Emp.: 110
Shoe Stores
N.A.I.C.S.: 458210
Patrick M. Murray *(Owner)*

RED212
637 REDna Terrace, Cincinnati, OH 45215
Tel.: (513) 772-1020
Web Site: http://www.red212.com
Year Founded: 2001
Sales Range: Less than $1 Million
Emp.: 10
N.A.I.C.S.: 541810

COMPANIES

REDDING FREIGHTLINER LLC

Anne Chambers *(CEO)*
Kara Schwandner *(Partner & Dir-Client Svcs)*
Richard Walker *(Partner, COO & Dir-Production)*
Liz Stoner *(Assoc Acct Mgr)*
Bryan Smith *(Mgr-Digital Mktg)*

RED7E
637 W Main St, Louisville, KY 40202-2987
Tel.: (502) 585-3403   KY
Web Site: http://www.red7e.com
Year Founded: 1974
Sales Range: $50-74.9 Million
Emp.: 20
Brand Development, Consumer Marketing, Education, Entertainment, Financial, Health Care, Seniors' Market, Strategic Planning
N.A.I.C.S.: 541810
Dan Barbercheck *(Pres & Exec Dir-Creative)*
Wally Dahman *(Sr Dir-Art)*
Laura Becker *(Mgr-Print Production)*
Jim Hoyland *(COO & VP)*
Mary Zdobylak *(Mgr-Traffic)*
James Williamson *(Assoc Dir-Creative)*
Greg Elliott *(Dir-Media Svcs)*
Matt O'Mara *(Assoc Dir-Media)*
Courtney Lee *(Sr Acct Exec)*

REDAPTIVE, INC.
340 Brannan St Ste 400, San Francisco, CA 94107
Tel.: (415) 413-0445   DE
Web Site: https://www.redaptive.com
Year Founded: 2015
Rev.: $42,307,000
Assets: $139,339,000
Liabilities: $89,156,000
Net Worth: $50,183,000
Earnings: ($19,469,000)
Emp.: 188
Fiscal Year-end: 12/31/20
Energy Efficiency Consulting Services
N.A.I.C.S.: 541690
Arvin Vohra *(CEO)*
John Rhow *(Pres & Chm)*
Matt Gembrin *(CFO)*
Eileen Evans *(Chief Corp Affairs & Legal Officer)*
Steven Farber *(Sr VP-Corporate Development)*

REDARHCS INC.
2312 W Kettleman, Lodi, CA 95242
Tel.: (209) 369-6344
Sales Range: $10-24.9 Million
Emp.: 20
Fast Food Restaurants
N.A.I.C.S.: 722513
Cindy Jones *(Controller)*
Craig Scheder *(Pres)*

REDBIRD CAPITAL PARTNERS L.P.
667 Madison Ave, New York, NY 10065
Tel.: (646) 342-8087   DE
Web Site: http://redbirdcap.com
Rev.: $6,000,000,000
Privater Equity Firm
N.A.I.C.S.: 523999
Gerry Cardinale *(Founder & Mng Partner)*
Robert Covington *(Partner)*
Hunter Carpenter *(Partner)*
Robert Klein *(Partner)*
Tyler Alexander *(Principal)*
Andrew C. Lauck *(Partner)*
Mike Zabik *(Partner)*
Niraj Shah *(Principal)*

Subsidiaries:

Associazione Calcio Milan S.p.A. (1)
Via Aldo Rossi 8, 20149, Milan, Italy
Tel.: (39) 0262281
Web Site: http://www.acmilan.com
Professional Soccer Team & Sports Arena Operator
N.A.I.C.S.: 711211
Adriano Galliani *(Exec VP-Vicarious)*
Barbara Berlusconi *(Exec VP)*
Paolo Berlusconi *(VP)*
Silvio Berlusconi *(Chm)*
Ivan Gazidis *(CEO)*
Vinai Venkatesham *(Mng Dir)*
Raul Sanllehi *(Head-Football)*

Compass Datacenters, LLC (1)
14180 N Dallas Pkwy Ste 610, Dallas, TX 75254
Tel.: (214) 452-2144
Web Site: http://www.compassdatacenters.com
Internet & Data Center Services
N.A.I.C.S.: 518210
Chris Crosby *(Founder & CEO)*
Jay Forester *(Sr VP-Data Center Product Delivery)*
Jared Day *(Pres & CFO)*
Nancy Novak *(Sr VP-Construction)*
Andrew Salcido *(VP-Ops)*
Sudhir Kalra *(Sr VP-Global Ops)*

Conifer Insurance Company (1)
3001 W Big Beaver Rd Ste 200, Troy, MI 48084
Tel.: (248) 559-0840
Web Site: https://www.coniferinsurance.com
Insurance Services
N.A.I.C.S.: 524210
James G. Petcoff *(Pres)*
Nicholas J. Petcoff *(CEO)*

Skydance Media LLC (1)
2900 Olympic Blvd, Santa Monica, CA 90404
Tel.: (424) 291-3400
Web Site: https://skydance.com
Entertainment Media Company
N.A.I.C.S.: 711410

Tally Energy Services (1)
3104 Edloe St, Houston, TX 77027
Tel.: (832) 530-4880
Privater Equity Firm
N.A.I.C.S.: 551112
Chris Dorros *(CEO)*

Holding (Domestic):

Tech-Flo Consulting, LLC (2)
9701 Pozos Ln, Conroe, TX 77303
Tel.: (936) 494-4330
Web Site: http://www.tech-flo.net
Industrial Machinery Equipment Mfr & Whslr
N.A.I.C.S.: 333998
W. J. Jackson *(Pres)*
Erik Reissig *(Exec VP & Gen Mgr)*
Molly Junell *(Office Mgr)*
Chad Musgrove *(VP-Fin & Controller)*
Shubert Willis *(Mgr-Permian Basin Area)*

Vida Capital, Inc. (1)
835 W 6th St Ste 1400, Austin, TX 78703
Tel.: (512) 961-8265
Web Site: http://www.vidacapitalinc.com
Asset Management Firm; Specializes Solely in Insurance-linked Strategies
N.A.I.C.S.: 524127
Jeffrey R. Serra *(Founder & Chm)*
Blair Wallace *(Pres & CEO)*
Zachary Ainsberg *(Mng Dir)*
Michael Kee *(Mng Dir-Analytics)*
Will Ketterer *(CIO & Sr Mng Dir-Portfolio Mgmt)*
Peter Polanskyj *(Head-Structured Credit)*
Matthew Roesler *(Mng Dir-Structured Credit)*

XFL Properties LLC (1)
600 Steamboat Rd Ste 107, Greenwich, CT 06830
Tel.: (203) 989-3399
Web Site: https://www.theufl.com
Holding Company; Professional Football & Sports Entertainment Services
N.A.I.C.S.: 551112

Subsidiary (Domestic):

XFL, LLC (2)
600 Steamboat Rd Ste 107, Greenwich, CT 06830
Tel.: (203) 989-3399
Web Site: http://www.xfl.com
Professional Football League & Sports Entertainment Services
N.A.I.C.S.: 711219

REDBURN TIRE COMPANY
3801 W Clarendon Ave, Phoenix, AZ 85019-3717
Tel.: (602) 272-7601   AZ
Web Site: http://www.rtco.net
Year Founded: 1934
Sales Range: $25-49.9 Million
Emp.: 250
Wholesale Distribution of Automobile & Truck Tires & Tubes, Rebuilding & Retreading Tires, Tire Repair Shop
N.A.I.C.S.: 423130
J. D. Chastain *(Pres)*
Donald Leffler *(CFO, Treas & Sec)*
Randy Lowry *(VP-Sls)*

REDCHIP COMPANIES, INC.
500 Winderely Pl Ste 100, Maitland, FL 32751
Tel.: (407) 644-4256
Web Site: http://www.redchip.com
Year Founded: 1992
Sales Range: $10-24.9 Million
Emp.: 25
Small-Cap Stock Research Services
N.A.I.C.S.: 523940
JP Yoo *(Mng Dir-RedChip South Korea)*
Dave Gentry *(Pres & CEO)*
Jon Cunningham *(VP & Dir-IR)*
Paul Kuntz *(Dir-Comm)*
Thomas Pfister *(Dir-Res)*
Devin Tipton *(Dir-Media)*
Richard T. Schumacher *(CEO)*

Subsidiaries:

RedChip China (1)
712 Block A 7 Dongsanhuan Zhonglu, Beijing, 100020, Chaoyang, China
Tel.: (86) 10 8591 0635
Web Site: http://www.redchip.com
Small-Cap Stock Research Services
N.A.I.C.S.: 523210

RedChip Korea (1)
56-1 SeokChon Dong Suite 301 Songpa-Gu, Seoul, Korea (South) (100%)
Tel.: (82) 10 9474 4811
Web Site: http://www.redchip.com
Small-Cap Stock Research Services
N.A.I.C.S.: 523940
JP Yoo *(Mng Dir)*

REDCLOUD CONSULTING INC.
11000 NE 33rd Pl Ste 100, Bellevue, WA 98004
Tel.: (425) 305-4121
Web Site: http://www.redcloudconsulting.com
Year Founded: 1995
Sales Range: $1-9.9 Million
Business Management Consulting Services
N.A.I.C.S.: 541611
Brett Alston *(Mng Partner)*
Brett Clifton *(Mng Partner)*
Scott Ekman *(Dir-Practice)*
Kam Kiani *(Dir-Practice)*
Ali Spain *(Dir-Practice)*
Corey Artherholt *(Dir-Practice)*
Sophia Stead *(Sr Mgr)*
Teresa Brosche *(Sr Mgr)*

Subsidiaries:

Denny Mountain Media, LLC (1)
1235A NE 88th St, Seattle, WA 98115
Tel.: (425) 831-7130
Web Site: http://www.dennymountain.com
Sales Range: $1-9.9 Million
Emp.: 62
Digital Marketing Services

600 Steamboat Rd Ste 107, Greenwich, CT 06830
Tel.: (203) 989-3399
Web Site: http://www.xfl.com
Professional Football League & Sports Entertainment Services
N.A.I.C.S.: 711219

N.A.I.C.S.: 541613
Brenda Potts *(Project Mgr)*
Brandi Martin *(VP)*
Jill Sherensky *(Co-Founder & Mng Partner)*
Patrick Batson *(Co-Founder & Mng Partner)*
Mia Buse-Stone *(Office Mgr)*
Patrick Shaw *(Acct Mgr)*
Barry Long *(Dir-Mktg & Client Svcs)*

REDD PAPER COMPANY
104 Faulkner St, New Smyrna Beach, FL 32808
Tel.: (407) 299-6656
Web Site: http://www.reddpaper.com
Sales Range: $1-9.9 Million
Emp.: 3
Printing & Writing Paper Merchant Whslr
N.A.I.C.S.: 424110
Sherry Redd *(CEO)*
Johnny Redd *(Pres)*
John Redd Jr. *(VP)*

REDDELL HONDA
1625 S Church St, Murfreesboro, TN 37130
Tel.: (615) 896-3480
Web Site: http://reddellhonda.com
Year Founded: 1995
Sales Range: $10-24.9 Million
Emp.: 44
Car Whslr
N.A.I.C.S.: 441110
Alvin Reddell *(Gen Mgr)*
Eric Reddell *(Mgr-Sls-New Car)*
John Reddell *(Pres)*
Steve Thompson *(Comptroller)*

REDDEN MARINE SUPPLY INC.
1411 Roeder Ave, Bellingham, WA 98225
Tel.: (360) 733-0250
Web Site: http://www.reddenmarine.com
Sales Range: $10-24.9 Million
Emp.: 86
Fishing Equipment
N.A.I.C.S.: 459110
Alan R. Chiabai *(Pres)*
Mike Steiner *(Mgr-Sls)*
Troy Baker *(Mgr-Shipping)*
Randy Chiabai *(Owner)*
Mike Reese *(Exec VP)*

REDDI INDUSTRIES, INC.
6205 E Kellogg Dr, Wichita, KS 67218
Tel.: (316) 858-2083   KS
Web Site: http://www.reddiindustries.com
Year Founded: 1969
Plumbing, Electrical & HVAC Services
N.A.I.C.S.: 238220
Zack Steven *(Owner)*

REDDI SERVICES, INC.
4011 Bonner Industrial Dr, Shawnee Mission, KS 66226
Tel.: (913) 287-5005
Web Site: http://www.reddiservices.com
Year Founded: 1957
Sales Range: $10-24.9 Million
Emp.: 90
Plumbing Contractor
N.A.I.C.S.: 238220
Jason Sheahan *(Gen Mgr)*

REDDING FREIGHTLINER LLC
4991 Caterpillar Rd, Redding, CA 96003
Tel.: (530) 241-4412
Web Site: http://www.reddingfreightliner.com
Sales Range: $10-24.9 Million

REDDING FREIGHTLINER LLC U.S. PRIVATE

Redding Freightliner LLC—(Continued)
Emp.: 40
Trucks, Commercial
N.A.I.C.S.: 423110
Jon Morgan (Mgr-Parts)

REDDING LUMBER TRANSPORT, INC.
4301 Eastside Rd, Redding, CA 96001
Tel.: (530) 241-8193 CA
Web Site: http://www.rlttrucking.com
Year Founded: 1972
Rev.: $19,000,000
Emp.: 130
Trucking Except Local
N.A.I.C.S.: 484121
Albert Shufelberger (Pres)

REDDING OIL CO. INC.
4990 Mtn Lks Blvd, Redding, CA 96003-1455
Tel.: (530) 243-1217
Web Site:
  http://www.reddingoilcompany.com
Year Founded: 1959
Sales Range: $10-24.9 Million
Emp.: 45
Provider of Petroleum Services
N.A.I.C.S.: 424710
John R. Reiser (Pres)
Vince Reiser (CFO)
Chris Reiser (CEO)

REDDING ROOFING SUPPLY INC.
5858 Westside Rd, Redding, CA 96001-4448
Tel.: (530) 241-3510 CA
Year Founded: 1977
Sales Range: $10-24.9 Million
Emp.: 45
Roofing, Siding & Insulation
N.A.I.C.S.: 423330
Alan Shufelberger (Pres)
Roberta Chase (Controller)

REDDY RAW, INC.
1 Ethel Blvd, Wood Ridge, NJ 07075
Tel.: (201) 804-7633 NY
Web Site: http://www.reddyraw.com
Year Founded: 1948
Rev.: $26,600,000
Emp.: 100
Distribute Frozen Goods
N.A.I.C.S.: 424420
Henry Senderowicz (Pres)
Alan Finkelstein (CEO)
Robert Paeprer (VP)
Rich Torre (Mgr-Warehouse)
Jorge Cuevas (Asst Mgr-Warehouse)

REDEMPTION PLUS, LLC.
9829 Commerce Pkwy, Lenexa, KS 66219
Tel.: (913) 563-4300
Web Site:
  http://www.redemptionplus.com
Year Founded: 1996
Sales Range: $10-24.9 Million
Emp.: 50
Miscellaneous Nondurable Goods Merchant Whslr
N.A.I.C.S.: 424990
Steve Jordan (CFO)
Ron L. Hill (CEO)
John Wagner (Supvr-Receiving)

REDEYE COFFEE ROASTING, LLC
1196 Capital Circle NE Dr, Tallahassee, FL 72303
Tel.: (850) 386-7700
Coffee Shop
N.A.I.C.S.: 722511
Mark McNees (CEO)

Subsidiaries:
Catalina Cafe (1)
1208 Capital Cir, Tallahassee, FL 32301-3801
Tel.: (850) 877-5999
Web Site: http://www.catalinacafe.com
Snack & Nonalcoholic Beverage Bars
N.A.I.C.S.: 722515
Maurice Moulton (Co-Owner)
Patricia Allaire (Co-Owner)

REDF
2 Embarcadero Ctr Ste 650, San Francisco, CA 94111
Tel.: (415) 561-6677 CA
Web Site: http://www.redf.org
Year Founded: 2003
Sales Range: $10-24.9 Million
Emp.: 41
Employment Placement Services
N.A.I.C.S.: 561311
Leeann Alameda (Dir-Comm)
Karen Chern (Assoc Dir-Investments & Advisory Svcs)
Christina Garcia (Dir-Strategic Advancement & Pub Affairs)
Christina Gilyutin (Dir-Talent Mgmt)
Kristin Lardas (Dir-Learning & Impact)
Carla Javits (Pres & CEO)
Jeff Bergquist (Mgr-Portfolio)
Mariana Farias (Mgr-HR)
Nicole Simoneaux (Dir-Investments & Advisory Svcs)
Ashley Cordero (Mgr-Initiatives)
Carrie McKellogg (Chief Program Officer)
Laura Murphy (Dir-Fin & Acctg)
Lori Warren (Dir-Mktg & Comm)
Matthew Horgan (Mgr-Facilities & Ops)
Vivienne Lee (Reg Dir)
David Samuels (Chief Fin & Admin Officer)

REDFIELD & COMPANY INC.
1901 Howard St, Omaha, NE 68102
Tel.: (402) 341-0364
Web Site:
  http://www.redfieldandcompany2.com
Sales Range: $10-24.9 Million
Emp.: 40
Business Form & Card Printing, Lithographic
N.A.I.C.S.: 323111
Thomas J. Kearney (Pres)
Thomas Beachler (VP)
Dale Stevens (VP)
Joe Beal (CFO)

REDFIELD ENERGY, LLC.
38650 171st St, Redfield, SD 57469
Tel.: (605) 302-0090
Web Site:
  https://www.redfieldenergy.com
Year Founded: 2005
Sales Range: $1-9.9 Million
Emp.: 40
Crop Postharvest Services
N.A.I.C.S.: 115114
Simon Appel (Dir-Environment & Compliance)
Gary Bentzin (COO)
Leslie Ford (Coord-HR)
Donna Hausvik (CMO)
Tom Hitchcock (CEO)
Robert Ratigan (Supvr-Commodities)
Jill Rude (Office Mgr)
Trent Sherman (Controller)
Kevin Siebrecht (Mgr-Safety & Facility)
Ryan Siebrecht (Mgr-Production)
Dana Siefkes-Lewis (Chief Admin Officer)
Casey Stoner (Mgr-Maintenance)
Angela Turck (Mgr-Lab)

Bruce Blume (Mgr)
Chris Ryan (Mgr)
Craig Johnson (Mgr)
Francis Hass (Mgr)
Jay Esser (Mgr)
Larry Kahnke (Mgr)
Mike Willis (Mgr)
Paul Domke (Mgr)
Jim Klebsch (Chm)
Troy Knecht (Vice Chm)
Doug Deiter (Sec)
Don Pugh (Mgr)
Terry Schmidt (Mgr)

REDFIN NETWORK, INC.
1500 W Cypress Creek Rd Ste 411, Fort Lauderdale, FL 33309-1851
Tel.: (954) 769-1335 NV
Web Site: http://www.redfinnet.com
Year Founded: 1996
E-Commerce Transaction Processing Services
N.A.I.C.S.: 522320
Joseph Jones (CFO)

REDFISH HOLDINGS, INC.
1360 Little Duck Cir, Gulf Breeze, FL 32563
Tel.: (858) 531-4361 WY
Year Founded: 2015
Emp.: 1
Mobile Software Application Development Services
N.A.I.C.S.: 541511
Tom Mahoney (CEO)

REDHAWK GLOBAL, LLC
2642 B Fisher Rd, Columbus, OH 43204
Tel.: (614) 487-8505 OH
Web Site:
  http://www.redhawkglobal.com
Year Founded: 2002
Sales Range: $10-24.9 Million
Emp.: 15
Freight Transportation
N.A.I.C.S.: 488510
Erach Deboo (Principal)

REDHEAD COMPANIES
6011 University Blvd Ste 210, Ellicott City, MD 21043
Tel.: (410) 465-1282
Web Site:
  http://www.redheadcompanies.com
Sales Range: $10-24.9 Million
Emp.: 20
Advertising, Interactive
N.A.I.C.S.: 541810
Missi Brooks (Acct Exec)
Tara Dean (Acct Exec)
Chris Dominiski (Mgr-Production)
Paula Dwyer (Acct Exec)
Jeff Hankin (CFO)
Erin Lake (Co-Creative Dir)
Reggie Bliss (Web Designer)
W. Kirk Lutz (Dir-Creative)
Julie Pelaez (Dir-Creative)
Jane Stelboum (Pres)
Ed Stern (CEO & Writer)
Nana Elsayed (Asst Acct Exec)
Juliet Gilden (Acct Exec)

REDHORSE CORPORATION
363 5th Ave Ste 201, San Diego, CA 92101
Tel.: (619) 241-4609
Web Site:
  http://www.redhorsecorp.com
Year Founded: 2007
Sales Range: $10-24.9 Million
Emp.: 61
Industrial Equipment Installation Services
N.A.I.C.S.: 238990

Matthew Dost (Gen Counsel & VP-Compliance)
Jill McFarlane (CFO)
David Inmon (Co-Founder)
Mark Walsh (Co-Founder & CQO)
William Miner (Dir-Quality Programs)
Ben Hough (VP-Energy Svcs)
Adrienne Barnes (VP-Environmental Svcs)
Kim Reinke (VP-Bus Dev)
Vincent Bridgeman (VP-Intelligence Svcs)
Brian Teeple (VP-Digital Solutions)
Melissa Houghton (VP-Corp Growth)
Melissa Thierry (Dir-Fin, Plng & Analysis)
Mark Shiffer (Dir-Engrg)
Michael Rauseo (Dir-Capture-Security Practice-Natl)
Lance Orr (Dir-Ops-Security Practice-Natl)
Rob Sheen (Chief Growth Officer)
Noah Klemm (Chief Delivery Officer)
John Adamo (VP-Energy & Environment)
Robin Gonzalez (VP-Federal Civilian)
Matt Teschke (CTO)
John A. Zangardi (Pres & CEO)

Subsidiaries:
Allied Associates International, Inc. (1)
6801 Kennedy Rd Ste 302, Warrenton, VA 20187
Tel.: (540) 341-8262
Web Site: http://www.a2ius.com
Sales Range: $10-24.9 Million
Emp.: 57
Engineering Services
N.A.I.C.S.: 541330

REDI-CARPET SALES OF DALLAS
10225 Mula Rd, Stafford, TX 77477
Tel.: (972) 512-8300
Web Site: http://www.redicarpet.com
Year Founded: 1981
Rev.: $20,000,000
Emp.: 30
Carpets, Vinyl & Tile Whslr
N.A.I.C.S.: 423220
Greg Waleke (CEO)
Jerry Hosko (Pres & COO)
Brian Caress (VP)
John Hagan (VP)

REDI-DIRECT MARKETING, INC.
107 Little Falls Rd, Fairfield, NJ 07004-3401
Tel.: (973) 808-4500
Web Site: http://www.redidirect.com
Year Founded: 1990
Sales Range: $25-49.9 Million
Emp.: 450
Technology-Based Sales & Marketing Systems
N.A.I.C.S.: 541613
Thomas R. Buckley (Founder & CEO)
James J. Weaver (Founder & Pres)
Joe Lauda (VP & Gen Mgr-Redi-Data)

REDIFY GROUP INC.
101 N Main St Ste B, Smithfield, UT 84334
Tel.: (435) 563-8080 DE
Year Founded: 1985
Sales Range: Less than $1 Million
Application Software Development Services
N.A.I.C.S.: 513210
Scott Emerson Lybbert (Chm & CFO)
Samuel H. Gaer (CEO)

REDING GRAVEL & EXCAVATING CO., INC.
2001 E Oak St, Algona, IA 50511

Tel.: (515) 295-3661 IA
Web Site: http://www.rgealgona.com
Year Founded: 1948
Rev.: $4,100,000
Emp.: 100
Site Preparation Contractor
N.A.I.C.S.: 238910
Chuck Reding (Pres)
Katie Besch (Controller)
Dan Preuschl (Project Mgr-Farm Drainage)
Lesa Todd (Office Mgr)

Subsidiaries:

Edwards Contracting (1)
1386 B Olive Ave, Hampton, IA 50441
Tel.: (641) 456-5360
Highway & Interstate Subdrain Installations
N.A.I.C.S.: 237310
Larry Edwards (Owner)
Lynn Alcott (Asst Mgr-Projects)

RGE Storm Lake (1)
1420 E Richland St, Storm Lake, IA 50588 (100%)
Tel.: (712) 732-4059
Web Site: http://www.rgealgona.com
Sand & Gravel Excavations, Materials Sales & Hauling
N.A.I.C.S.: 212321
Lesa Todd (Office Mgr)

REDINGTON-FAIRVIEW GENERAL HOSPITAL
46 Fairview Ave, Skowhegan, ME 04976
Tel.: (207) 474-5121 ME
Web Site: http://www.rfgh.net
Year Founded: 1969
Sales Range: $50-74.9 Million
Emp.: 711
Healtcare Services
N.A.I.C.S.: 622110
Richard D. Willett (CEO & Sec)
Dana C. Kempton (CFO)

REDISCOVER
901 NE Independence Ave, Lees Summit, MO 64086
Tel.: (816) 246-8000 MO
Web Site: http://www.rediscovermh.org
Year Founded: 1969
Sales Range: $10-24.9 Million
Emp.: 409
Mental Health & Substance Abuse Rehabilitation Services
N.A.I.C.S.: 623220
Catherine Singleton (Vice Chm)
David Stackelhouse (Treas & Sec)
Shirley Olson (Chm)

REDLINE DESIGN GROUP, P.A.
925 Tuckaseegee Rd Ste 110, Charlotte, NC 28208
Tel.: (704) 377-2990
Web Site: http://www.redlinedg.com
Architectural Services
N.A.I.C.S.: 541310
Thomas Duzan (Principal)
David Eve (Pres)
Jason Byrd (Principal)

Subsidiaries:

Phillips Architecture PA (1)
1110 Navaho Dr, Raleigh, NC 27609
Tel.: (919) 878-1660
Web Site: http://www.phillipsarch.com
Rev.: $3,400,000
Emp.: 26
Architectural Services
N.A.I.C.S.: 541310
Crista Misenheimer (Dir)
Delores Cook (Principal & Mgr-Fin)
Mike Phillips (CEO)
Ryan Suydam (Dir)

REDMILE GROUP LLC
1 Letterman Dr Ste Dm100, San Francisco, CA 94129-2401
Tel.: (415) 677-5340
Web Site: http://www.redmilegroup.com
Offices of Certified Public Accountants
N.A.I.C.S.: 541211
Jeremy Green (Portfolio Mgr)
Robert Faulkner (Mng Dir)

Subsidiaries:

Redx Pharma Plc (1)
Block 33 Mereside Alderley Park Alderley Edge, Macclesfield, SK10 4TG, United Kingdom (91.76%)
Tel.: (44) 1625469900
Web Site: https://www.redxpharma.com
Emp.: 101
Pharmaceuticals Mfr
N.A.I.C.S.: 325412
Andrew Saunders (Chief Medical Officer)
Lisa Mary Whewell Ansonas (CEO)
Richard Armer (Chief Scientific Officer)
Jane Griffiths (Chm)
James Barwell (Head-Business Development)
Inder Bhamra (VP & Head-Chemistry & DMPK)
Peter Collum (CFO)
Nicolas Guisot (VP & Head-Dev Science)
Cliff Jones (Chief Innovation Officer)
Helen McKeever (Head-Nonclinical Dev)
James Mead (COO)
Caitlin Pearson (Head-Communications)
Caroline Phillips (Chief Scientific Officer)
Claire Solk (Chief Legal Officer & Sec)
Craig Tilston (Head-Dev Ops)
Simon Woodcock (VP & Head-Biology)

Subsidiary (Domestic):

Redx Anti-Infectives Ltd (2)
2nd Floor BioHub Mereside Alderley Park, Macclesfield, SK10 4TG, United Kingdom
Tel.: (44) 1625238972
Pharmaceuticals Product Mfr
N.A.I.C.S.: 325412
Derek Lindsay (Mng Dir)
Andrew Ratcliffe (Head-Chemistry)
Neil Stokes (Head-Biology)
Stuart Best (Head-Analytical & DMPK)

REDNER'S MARKETS INC.
3 Quarry Rd, Reading, PA 19605
Tel.: (610) 926-3700 PA
Web Site: http://www.rednersmarkets.com
Year Founded: 1970
Sales Range: $700-749.9 Million
Emp.: 3,000
Grocery Stores
N.A.I.C.S.: 445110
Ryan S. Redner (Pres & CEO)
Gary M. Redner (COO)
Richard Redner (Chm)
Cory Deily (Dir-Security & Loss Prevention)
Tim Twiford (Dir-Food Svc)
Dan Eberhart (VP-Procurement)

REDNISS & MEAD, INC.
22 1st St, Stamford, CT 06905-5101
Tel.: (203) 327-0500
Web Site: http://www.rednissmead.com
Year Founded: 1957
Civil Engineering Services
N.A.I.C.S.: 541330
Richard W. Redniss (Principal-Planner)
Raymond L. Redniss (Principal-Surveyor)
Brian P. McMahon (Principal, VP & Dir-Engrg)
Craig J. Flaherty (Pres, Principal & Sr Engr)
Jorge P. Pereira (Principal)
Lawrence W. Posson (Principal, Sec & Dir-Surveying)
Aubrey E. Mead Jr. (Treas)

Subsidiaries:

Ryan & Faulds LLC (1)
11 Grumman Hill Rd, Wilton, CT 06897
Tel.: (203) 762-9492
Web Site: http://www.ryanandfaulds.com
Surveying & Mapping Services
N.A.I.C.S.: 541370
Douglas R. Faulds (Mgr-Survey)

REDPEG MARKETING, INC.
727 N Washington St, Alexandria, VA 22314
Tel.: (703) 519-9000 VA
Web Site: http://www.redpeg.com
Year Founded: 1995
Sales Range: $10-24.9 Million
Emp.: 48
Advetising Agency
N.A.I.C.S.: 541810
Brad Nierenberg (CEO)
Martin Codd (VP-Production)
Johnny Ward (VP-Brand Partnerships)
Daniel Brienza (Dir-Creative Grp)
John Piester (Pres)
Fredda Hurwitz (CMO)
Eric Hansen (CFO)

REDPOINT BIO CORPORATION
5501 Old York Rd, Philadelphia, PA 19141
Tel.: (215) 456-2312 DE
Web Site: http://www.redpointbio.com
Sales Range: Less than $1 Million
Biotechnology Researcher & Developer
N.A.I.C.S.: 541714
Richard P. Shanley (Chm)

REDPOINT GLOBAL INC.
36 Washington St Ste 120, Wellesley Hills, MA 02481
Tel.: (781) 725-0250 DE
Web Site: http://www.redpoint.net
Year Founded: 2006
Sales Range: $10-24.9 Million
Customer Relationship Management Software Developer & Publisher
N.A.I.C.S.: 513210
Dale H. Renner (Co-Founder & CEO)
George Corugedo (Co-Founder & CTO)
Lewis Clemmens (Co-Founder)
Alex Berton (VP-Sls-Asia Pacific)
Patrick McHugh (Chief Sls Officer)

REDRIDGE FINANCE GROUP, LLC
333 W Wacker Dr 16th Fl, Chicago, IL 60606
Tel.: (312) 443-8500 DE
Web Site: http://www.redridgefg.com
Year Founded: 2009
Corporate Financing, Capital Investment, Due Diligence & Debt Advisory Services
N.A.I.C.S.: 522299
Randolph T. Abrahams (Pres & CEO)
Dave Norris (COO)

Subsidiaries:

ExWorks Capital, LLC (1)
333 W Wacker Dr Ste 1620, Chicago, IL 60606
Tel.: (312) 443-8500
Web Site: http://www.exworkscapital.com
Emp.: 50
International Trade Financing, Capital Investment & Financial Advisory Services
N.A.I.C.S.: 522299
Amanda Roberts (VP-Bus Dev)
Dave Norris (Mng Dir)
Matthew Stanley (Mng Dir-Direct Origination)
Randall Abrahams (Chm)
Alan Beard (Mng Dir)
Ravi Singh V (VP-Logistics)

Branch (Domestic):

ExWorks Capital, LLC - Washington, D.C. Office (2)
1600 Wilson Blvd Ste 1210, Arlington, VA 22209-2594
Tel.: (202) 517-0150
Web Site: http://www.exworkscapital.com
International Trade Financing, Capital Investment & Financial Advisory Services
N.A.I.C.S.: 522299
Brady Edholm (VP)
Jozsef Szamosfalvi (Dir-Emerging Market Project & Structured Fin Underwriting)
Ravi Singh (VP-Logistics)
Alan J. Beard (Mng Dir)
Juan Fronjosa (Dir-Project & Structured Trade Fin)

REDROCK LEADERSHIP
8184 Woodland Center Blvd, Tampa, FL 33614
Tel.: (813) 885-5097
Web Site: http://www.redrockleadership.com
Sales Range: $1-9.9 Million
Emp.: 6
Sales & Management Training Services
N.A.I.C.S.: 611430
Jeff Ruby (Founder & CEO)

REDS BASEBALL PARTNERS, LLC
Great American Ball Park 100 Main St, Cincinnati, OH 45202
Tel.: (513) 765-7000 OH
Web Site: http://cincinnati.reds.mlb.com
Year Founded: 1869
Sales Range: $100-124.9 Million
Emp.: 40
Professional Baseball Club
N.A.I.C.S.: 711211
Robert H. Castellini (CEO)
Bill Reinberger (VP-Corp Sls)
Thomas L. Williams (Vice Chm & Treas)
Phillip J. Castellini (COO)
Chris Buckley (Sr Dir-Amateur Scouting)
Richard H. Stowe (Mgr-Reds Clubhouse & Equipment)
Karen Forgus (Sr VP-Bus Ops)
Ralph Mitchell (VP-Comm & Mktg)
Doug Healy (CFO & Sr VP-Fin)
Bentley J. Viator (Controller)
Nick Krall (VP & Gen Mgr)
Sean Brown (Sr Dir-Ballpark Ops)
Allison Stortz (Dir-HR)
Garry McGuire (Mgr-Employee Rels)
Charles Leddon (Dir-Sports Science Initiatives)
Jeff Graupe (Dir-Player Dev)
Jim Stoeckel (Dir-Global Scouting)
Michael Schatz (Mgr-Baseball Analytics)
Mike Saverino (Mgr-Ops)
Richard Jimenez (Dir-Latin American Scouting)
Rob Coughlin (Mgr-Video Scouting)
Sam Grossman (Asst Gen Mgr)
W. Joseph Williams Jr. (Chm)

REDSALSA TECHNOLOGIES INC.
13800 Montfort Dr Ste 230, Dallas, TX 75240
Tel.: (972) 503-4200
Web Site: http://www.redsalsa.com
Year Founded: 1993
Rev.: $13,600,000
Emp.: 225
Computer System Design Services
N.A.I.C.S.: 541512
Sunita Pradeep (Mgr-HR)

REDSTONE COMMUNICATIONS INC.

U.S. PRIVATE

REDSTONE Communications Inc.—(Continued)

REDSTONE COMMUNICATIONS INC.
10031 Maple St, Omaha, NE 68134
Tel.: (402) 393-5435
Web Site:
 http://www.redstonespark.com
Year Founded: 1983
Sales Range: $10-24.9 Million
Emp.: 24
Advetising Agency
N.A.I.C.S.: 541810
Steve Armbruster (Partner & Dir-Creative)

REDSTONE INVESTMENTS
5050 Belmont Ave, Youngstown, OH 44505
Tel.: (330) 759-4000
Web Site:
 http://www.redstoneinvestment.com
Year Founded: 1991
Sales Range: $50-74.9 Million
Emp.: 25
Real Estate Development, Management & Investment
N.A.I.C.S.: 531390
Jonathan A. Levy (Mng Partner)
Bruce Tamarkin (Sr VP-Property Mgmt)
Jeffrey M. Grinstein (Gen Counsel & Sr VP)
Patrick Kelly (Pres-Comml)
Robert O. Alter (Sr VP-Comml)
Fred J. Hohnadel (Sr VP-Dev)
Baharea Larsen (VP-Comml)
Frank W. Ryon (VP-Comml)
Bradley S. Salzer (Pres-Funding)
William Wamble (VP-Comml)
Lee J. Burdman (Co-Founder & Mng Partner)

REDSTONE PRESBYTERIAN SENIORCARE
6 Garden Center Dr, Greensburg, PA 15601
Tel.: (724) 832-8400 PA
Web Site:
 http://www.redstonehighlands.org
Year Founded: 1980
Sales Range: $25-49.9 Million
Emp.: 536
Senior Living Services
N.A.I.C.S.: 623311
Mark Celigoi (CFO & VP-Fin)
James Hodge (VP-HR)
Francis King (VP-Corp Svcs)
Vicki Loucks (VP-Quality)

REDVISION SYSTEMS INC.
1055 Parsippany Blvd Ste 412, Parsippany, NJ 07054
Tel.: (973) 854-9500
Web Site: http://www.redvision.com
Year Founded: 2001
Sales Range: $25-49.9 Million
Emp.: 494
Web Based Real Estate Search Tool
N.A.I.C.S.: 513140
Brian Twibell (CEO)
Joe Ross (CTO)
Garry Johnson (Chief Product Officer)
Sanford J. Bleich (Chief Title Officer & VP)

REDVISION SYSTEMS, INC
1055 Parsippany Blvd Suite 412, Parsippany, NJ 07054
Tel.: (973) 854-9500
Web Site: http://www.redvision.com
Year Founded: 2001
Emp.: 1,000
Title Searches & Real Property Data Solutions
N.A.I.C.S.: 524121
Brian Twibell (Pres)
Joe Ross (Co-Founder & CTO)
Michael Carus (Pres)
Garry Johnson (Chief Product Officer)
Leanne Zinn (COO)
George Psyllos (CFO & Treas)
Craig J. Muldoon (Exec VP-Product Mktg)
Sanford J. Bleich (Chief Title Officer)
Jacqueline Young (VP & Dir-Title Compliance & Best Practices)
Tim Padgett (VP-Ops)
Ailie Ashton (Dir-Mktg)

REDW STANLEY FINANCIAL ADVISORS LLC
6401 Jefferson St Ne, Albuquerque, NM 87109
Tel.: (505) 998-3216
Web Site: http://www.redw.com
Rev.: $1,000,000
Emp.: 100
Administrative Management & General Management Consulting Service
N.A.I.C.S.: 541611
Chris Tyhurst (Principal)
Gabriel Tevrizian (Dir-Mktg)
Daniel Yu (Chief Investment Officer)
Robert Latimer (Chief Trading Officer)
Lauren Malone (Mgr-Fin Plng)
Dennis Davis (Principal)
Ed Street (Principal)
Ginny Stanley (Principal)
Jimmy Trujillo (Principal)
Marcus Clarke (Principal & Dir-Internal Tech)
Michael T. Allen (Principal)
Mustafa Kamal (Principal)
Tal D. Moore (Principal)

Subsidiaries:

Grove Mueller & Swank PC (1)
475 Cottage St NE Ste 200, Salem, OR 97301-3814
Tel.: (503) 581-7788
Web Site: http://www.gmscpa.com
Other Accounting Services
N.A.I.C.S.: 541219
Thomas E. Glogau (Mgr)

REDWIRE LLC
1136 Thomasville Rd, Tallahassee, FL 32303
Tel.: (850) 219-9473
Web Site: https://redwire.com
Security Guards & Patrol Services
N.A.I.C.S.: 561612
Bryan Andrews (Mgr)

Subsidiaries:

State Alarm, Inc. (1)
5956 Market St, Youngstown, OH 44512
Tel.: (330) 726-8111
Web Site: http://www.state-alarm.com
Sales Range: $1-9.9 Million
Emp.: 35
Miscellaneous Retail Stores, Nec, Nsk
N.A.I.C.S.: 459999
Brenda Dull (Treas & Sec)
Donald P. Shury (Pres & CEO)

REDWOOD CAPITAL GROUP, LLC
1 E Wacker Dr Ste 1100, Chicago, IL 60601
Tel.: (312) 464-0300
Web Site:
 http://www.redwoodcapgroup.com
Year Founded: 2007
Rev.: $600,000,000
Emp.: 10
Multi-Family Real Estate Investment & Management Services
N.A.I.C.S.: 523999
David Carlson (Mng Partner)
Mark Isaacson (Mng Partner)
Bill McDougall (Asst VP-Acq)

REDWOOD CAPITAL INVESTMENTS, LLC
7301 Parkwy Dr, Hanover, MD 21076
Tel.: (410) 402-2000 MD
Web Site: http://www.redcapinv.com
Privater Equity Firm
N.A.I.C.S.: 523999
Ryan Mostrom (Partner)
Patrick Sissman (Partner)
Sarah Walsh (VP-Fin & Acctg)

Subsidiaries:

Camper Country RV (1)
5500 South Kings Highway, Myrtle Beach, SC 29575
Tel.: (843) 238-5678
Web Site:
 https://rvonemyrtlebeach.rvone.com
Recreational Vehicle Dealers
N.A.I.C.S.: 441210

Erickson Living Management, LLC (1)
701 Maiden Choice Ln, Catonsville, MD 21228-3738
Tel.: (410) 242-2880
Web Site:
 http://www.ericksonretirement.com
Sales Range: $25-49.9 Million
Emp.: 300
Developer of Retirement Communities
N.A.I.C.S.: 237210
Debra Doyle (Exec VP-Ops)
Alan Butler (Pres)
Suson Tillman-Taylor (Dir-Human Svcs-Cedar Crest Community-Pompton Plains)
Kathy McCrossin (Dir-Sls-Devonshire at PGA Natl Community-Palm Beach Gardens)

Premier Trailer Leasing, Inc. (1)
3600 William D Tate Ave Ste 300, Grapevine, TX 76051
Tel.: (817) 421-2552
Web Site:
 http://www.premiertrailerleasing.com
Truck, Utility Trailer & Recreational Vehicle Rental & Leasing Services
N.A.I.C.S.: 532120
Jim Aubuchon (Pres)

RV Retailer, LLC (1)
1 Financial Plz 100 SE 3rd Ave Ste 1850, Fort Lauderdale, FL 33394
Tel.: (954) 908-3650
Web Site: http://www.rvretailer.net
Recreational Vehicle Dealers
N.A.I.C.S.: 441210
Famous P. Rhodes (Chief Marketing & Technical Officer & VP)
Jon Ferrando (Pres & CEO)
John Rizzo (CFO, Treas & Exec VP)
Raul Rodriguez (Sr VP-Corp Dev)

Subsidiary (Domestic):

A & S RV Center, Inc. (2)
2375 N Opdyke Rd, Auburn Hills, MI 48326
Tel.: (248) 373-5811
Web Site: http://www.asrvcenter.com
Recreational Motor Vehicle Mfr
N.A.I.C.S.: 532120
Don McKay (Mgr-Internet Sls)

Aloha R.V., Inc. (2)
8212 Pan American Fwy, Albuquerque, NM 87113
Tel.: (505) 298-8444
Web Site: http://www.aloharv.com
Sales Range: $1-9.9 Million
Emp.: 25
Recreational Vehicle Dealers
N.A.I.C.S.: 441210
Ilene Dean (VP)

Family RV Group (2)
9600 Colerain Ave Ste 300, Cincinnati, OH 45251
Tel.: (513) 923-5371
Web Site: http://www.familyrvgroup.com
Recreational Car Dealers-New & Used
N.A.I.C.S.: 441120
Walt Rogers (CEO)

Subsidiary (Domestic):

Candys Campers, Inc. (3)
5905 Veterans Memorial Hwy, Scottsville, KY 42164-8376
Tel.: (270) 622-2010
Web Site: http://www.candyscampers.com
Sales Range: $10-24.9 Million
Emp.: 22
Recreational Vehicle Whslr
N.A.I.C.S.: 441210
Steve Barnett (Owner & VP)

Colerain Trailer Center, LLC (3)
3491 Struble Rd, Cincinnati, OH 45251-4945
Tel.: (513) 813-2523
Web Site: http://www.colerainrv.com
Sales Range: $25-49.9 Million
Recreational Vehicle Dealers
N.A.I.C.S.: 441210
Charles Jung (Founder)

Subsidiary (Domestic):

Colerain Northside, LLC (4)
1630 N Broadway, Lexington, KY 40361
Tel.: (859) 987-7267
Web Site: http://www.northsidervs.com
Sales Range: $10-24.9 Million
Recreational Vehicle Dealers
N.A.I.C.S.: 441210

Colerain RV at Alum Creek, LLC (4)
5742 E State Rte 37, Delaware, OH 43015
Tel.: (740) 548-4068
Web Site: http://www.colerainrv.com
Sales Range: $1-9.9 Million
Emp.: 15
Recreational Vehicle Dealers
N.A.I.C.S.: 441210
Jon M. Cross (Gen Mgr)

Colerain RV of Dayton, LLC (4)
1775 S Dayton Lakeview Rd, New Carlisle, OH 45344
Tel.: (937) 236-0200
Web Site: http://www.colerainrv.com
Recreational Vehicle Dealers
N.A.I.C.S.: 441210

Subsidiary (Domestic):

Golden Gait Trailers, LLC (2)
5051 Davidson Hwy, Concord, NC 28027-8413
Tel.: (704) 743-5280
Web Site: http://www.goldengait.com
Truck Trailer Mfr
N.A.I.C.S.: 336212
Timothy Masud (Mgr)

Marlin Ingram RV Center, LLC (2)
4504 Troy Hwy, Montgomery, AL 36116-5122
Tel.: (334) 288-0331
Web Site: http://www.ingramrvcenter.com
Recreational Vehicle Dealers
N.A.I.C.S.: 441210

Mid-State RV Center, Inc. (2)
131 Peachtree Pkwy, Byron, GA 31008-4016
Tel.: (478) 956-3456
Web Site: http://www.midstaterv.com
Recreational Vehicle Dealers
N.A.I.C.S.: 441210

Ocean Grove R.V. Sales Inc., of St. Augustine (2)
6775 US Hwy 1 S, Saint Augustine, FL 32086-7696
Tel.: (904) 797-5732
Web Site:
 http://www.oceangrovervsales.com
Recreational Vehicle Dealers
N.A.I.C.S.: 441210

Tom's Camperland, Inc. (2)
1301 W Broadway, Mesa, AZ 85202
Tel.: (480) 894-1267
Web Site: http://www.tomscamperland.com
Recreational Vehicle Dealers
N.A.I.C.S.: 441210

REDWOOD COAST DEVELOPMENTAL SERVICES CORPORATION
1116 Airport Park Blvd, Ukiah, CA 95482
Tel.: (707) 462-3832 CA

Web Site:
http://www.redwoodcoastrc.org
Year Founded: 1983
Sales Range: $75-99.9 Million
Emp.: 101
Developmental Disability Assistance Services
N.A.I.C.S.: 624120
Lou Enge *(Mgr-Client Svcs)*
Marilyn De Roe *(Mgr-Office Ops)*

REDWOOD CREDIT UNION
3033 Cleveland Ave Ste 100, Santa Rosa, CA 95403
Tel.: (707) 545-4000   CA
Web Site: http://www.redwoodcu.org
Year Founded: 1950
Sales Range: $100-124.9 Million
Emp.: 469
Credit Union
N.A.I.C.S.: 522130
Tony Hildesheim *(Sr VP-IT)*
Robin McKenzie *(Sr VP-Mktg & Comm)*
Andy Ramos *(Sr VP-Member Experience)*
Robert Steele *(Co-Chm)*
Lisa Wittke Schaffner *(Treas)*
Jim Olmsted *(Sec)*
Robert Eyler *(Co-Chm)*
Diane Berthinier *(Sr VP-Lending)*
Lisa Heath *(Chief Fin & Risk Officer & Exec VP)*
Brett Martinez *(Pres & CEO)*
Matt Martin *(VP-Community & Govt Rels)*
Reid Louie *(Asst VP & Mgr-Marin)*
Sandy Barron *(Mgr-San Rafael)*
Kristina Derkos *(Sr VP-Admin Svcs)*
Ron Felder *(Chief Lending Officer & Exec VP)*
Tom Hubert *(Sr VP-Auto, Insurance & Wealth Mgmt)*
Mishel Kaufman *(Chief Admin & Risk Officer)*
Todd Lindemann *(Sr VP-Payments)*
Ryan Lind *(Mgr-Novato)*
Dave Upham *(Sr VP-Member Experience)*
Wilson Tengnguyen *(Mgr-Mill Valley)*
Eric Maldonado *(Mgr-Bus Dev)*
Penny Cleary *(Mgr-Community Programs)*
Laureen Barnes *(Mgr-Mortgage Lending)*
Jeff Street *(VP-Product & Svc Innovation)*
Bryan Haas *(Sr VP-Product & Member Engagement)*

REDWOOD INDUSTRIES INC.
2345 S CC Hwy, West Valley City, UT 84119
Tel.: (801) 973-9000
Web Site:
http://www.ccimechanical.com
Sales Range: $25-49.9 Million
Emp.: 250
Mechanical Contractor
N.A.I.C.S.: 238220
Davis Mullholand *(Pres)*
Michael R. Kladis *(VP)*
D. Patrick Lynch *(VP)*
Curtis Tate *(Controller)*
David Engel *(Mgr-Quality Control)*
David A. Katsanevas *(Mgr-Svc)*
Nathan M. Brimhall *(Dir-Safety)*

REDWOOD INVESTMENTS LLC
3633 M Street, Washington, DC 20027
Tel.: (202) 333-1395
Web Site:
http://www.redwoodinvestments.net
Year Founded: 2005
Privater Equity Firm
N.A.I.C.S.: 523999
Michael M. Wood *(Founder & Chm)*
Kimberly P. McMillan *(Mgr-Fin)*

REDWOOD MORTGAGE INVESTORS IX, LLC
177 Bovet Rd Ste 520, San Mateo, CA 94402
Tel.: (650) 365-5341   DE
Web Site:
http://www.redwoodmortgage.com
Year Founded: 2008
Rev.: $6,776,000
Assets: $67,810,000
Liabilities: $2,354,000
Net Worth: $65,456,000
Earnings: $3,808,000
Fiscal Year-end: 12/31/23
Mortgage Lender
N.A.I.C.S.: 522310
Michael R. Burwell *(Pres, Treas & Sec)*

REDWOOD OIL COMPANY
50 Professional Ctr Dr Ste 100, Rohnert Park, CA 94928
Tel.: (707) 584-7000
Web Site: http://www.redwoodoil.com
Year Founded: 1972
Rev.: $167,792,200
Emp.: 230
Petroleum Stations & Convenience Stores
N.A.I.C.S.: 424720
Peter Van Alyea *(Founder, Owner & Pres)*
Peter V. Eialia *(Principal)*

REDWOOD SCIENTIFIC TECHNOLOGIES, INC.
250 W First St Ste 310, Claremont, CA 91711
Tel.: (310) 693-5401   NV
Web Site:
http://www.redwoodscientific.co
Year Founded: 2014
Emp.: 15
Pharmaceuticals Product Mfr
N.A.I.C.S.: 325412
Jason Cardiff *(Founder, Pres & CEO)*
Jacques Poujade *(CFO)*

REDWOOD SOFTWARE, INC.
3000 Aerial Center Pkwy 115, Morrisville, NC 27560
Tel.: (919) 460-5400
Web Site: http://www.redwood.com
Rev.: $6,580,000
Emp.: 50
Software Publisher
N.A.I.C.S.: 513210
Mark Farnsworth *(CTO)*

Subsidiaries:

Advanced Systems Concepts, Inc.   (1)
1180 Headquarters Plz West Tower 3rd Fl, Morristown, NJ 07960
Tel.: (973) 539-2660
Web Site: http://www.adcsyscon.com
Sales Range: $10-24.9 Million
Emp.: 25
Custom Computer Programming Services
N.A.I.C.S.: 541511
Benjamin Rosenberg *(Pres)*
Chris Loeschorn *(Engr-Software)*
Eric Chen *(Engr-Software)*
Reed Overfelt *(CEO)*

Subsidiary (Domestic):

JScape LLC   (2)
116 Hwy 99 N Ste 106, Eugene, OR 97402
Tel.: (800) 229-2724
Web Site: http://www.jscape.com
Custom Computer Programming Services
N.A.I.C.S.: 541511

Bonnie Karr *(VP-Sls & Customer Svc)*
Van Glass *(CEO)*

REDYREF INTERACTIVE KIOSKS
100 Riverdale Rd, Riverdale, NJ 07457
Tel.: (800) 628-3603
Web Site: https://redyref.com
Year Founded: 1913
Self Service Kiosk Mfr & Interactive Software Developer
N.A.I.C.S.: 541512
David McCracken *(CTO)*

Subsidiaries:

Livewire Kiosk, Inc.   (1)
1805 Loucks Rd Ste 700, York, PA 17408-7902
Tel.: (717) 718-1241
Web Site: http://www.livewiredigital.com
Computer System Design Services
N.A.I.C.S.: 541512
Ronald Long *(Project Mgr)*

REE INC.
3000 W Cedar St, Beaumont, TX 77702
Tel.: (409) 838-2002
Web Site: http://www.bgfoods.com
Sales Range: $10-24.9 Million
Emp.: 10
Franchise Owner of Fast-Food Restaurants
N.A.I.C.S.: 722513
Rodger Ellis *(Pres)*
Brian Ellis *(VP)*
Donnie Borel *(CFO)*

REEBLE INC.
1020 Merchant St, Emporia, KS 66801
Tel.: (620) 342-0404
Rev.: $13,600,000
Emp.: 55
Supermarkets, Chain
N.A.I.C.S.: 445110

REECE ALBERT INC.
3001 Foster St, San Angelo, TX 76903-9216
Tel.: (325) 653-1241   TX
Web Site:
http://www.reecealbertinc.com
Year Founded: 1942
Sales Range: $25-49.9 Million
Emp.: 300
Highway & Street Construction
N.A.I.C.S.: 237310
Brian Biggerstaff *(Mgr-Environmental)*

Subsidiaries:

CSA Materials, Inc.   (1)
US Hwy 277 N, Del Rio, TX 78840
Tel.: (830) 775-2492
Sales Range: $10-24.9 Million
Emp.: 1
Highway & Street Construction
N.A.I.C.S.: 237310
Wesley Coleman *(Superintendent)*

REECE SUPPLY COMPANY OF DALLAS
3308 Royalty Row, Irving, TX 75062
Tel.: (972) 438-3131   TX
Web Site:
http://www.reecesupply.com
Year Founded: 1936
Sales Range: $10-24.9 Million
Emp.: 100
Sign Material & Equipment Distr
N.A.I.C.S.: 423840
Rick Brown *(Reg Mgr)*

Subsidiaries:

Reece Supply Company of Houston   (1)
2606 Bell St, Houston, TX 77003
Tel.: (713) 228-9496
Web Site: http://www.reecesupply.com
Sales Range: $1-9.9 Million
Industrial Supplies, Nsk
N.A.I.C.S.: 423840

Reece Supply Company of San Antonio   (1)
4955 Stout Dr, San Antonio, TX 78219
Tel.: (210) 662-6898
Web Site: http://www.reecesupply.com
Sales Range: $1-9.9 Million
Whol Industrial Supplies
N.A.I.C.S.: 423840

REECE-CAMPBELL, INC.
320 Southwayne, Cincinnati, OH 45215
Tel.: (513) 542-4600   OH
Web Site:
http://www.reececampbell.com
Year Founded: 1983
Sales Range: $75-99.9 Million
Emp.: 75
Provider of Construction & Contracting Services
N.A.I.C.S.: 236220
Peter W. Chronis *(Pres)*
Joe Shelby *(Project Mgr)*
Dick Dierkes *(Project Mgr)*
Teresa Earls *(Mgr-Acct)*

REECE-HOPPER SALES, LLC
14348 Proton Rd, Farmers Branch, TX 75244
Tel.: (214) 324-9311   TX
Web Site:
http://www.rhsalesreps.com
Year Founded: 2018
Industrial Plumbing Services & Contractors
N.A.I.C.S.: 238220
Don Reece *(Pres)*

Subsidiaries:

RRR Industrial Sales, Inc.   (1)
9010 John W Carpenter Fwy, Dallas, TX 75247
Tel.: (214) 324-9311
Web Site: http://www.rrrind.com
Sales Range: $1-9.9 Million
Emp.: 30
Industrial Machinery And Equipment
N.A.I.C.S.: 423830
Donald G. Reece *(Pres)*

Reece-Hopper Sales, LLC - Houston   (1)
520 E Parker Rd, Houston, TX 77076
Tel.: (713) 691-5103
Web Site: http://www.rhsalesreps.com
Plumbing & Heating Equipment & Supplies (Hydronics) Merchant Whslr
N.A.I.C.S.: 423720

REED & GRAHAM INC.
690 Sunol St, San Jose, CA 95126
Tel.: (408) 287-1400   CA
Web Site: http://www.rginc.com
Year Founded: 1928
Rev.: $44,300,000
Emp.: 127
Petroleum Refining
N.A.I.C.S.: 324110
Gerry Graham Jr. *(Pres & CEO)*

Subsidiaries:

Reed & Graham, Inc. - Geosynthetics Division   (1)
26 Light Sky Ct, Sacramento, CA 95828-1016
Tel.: (916) 381-9900
Web Site: http://www.rginc.com
Sales Range: $10-24.9 Million
Emp.: 18
N.A.I.C.S.: 324110
Carl Springer *(Mgr-Northern California Area)*

Unit (Domestic):

Reed & Graham, Inc. - Geosynthetics Division-San Jose   (2)

REED & GRAHAM INC.

Reed & Graham Inc.—(Continued)
550 Sunol St, San Jose, CA 95126-3763
Tel.: (408) 294-1959
Web Site: http://www.rginc.com
Geosynthetic Products Warehousing & Distribution
N.A.I.C.S.: 493190
Jason Ridgway (Mgr-Warehouse)

REED & PERRINE SALES, INC.
396 Main St, Tennent, NJ 07726
Tel.: (732) 446-6363
Web Site:
http://www.reedandperrine.com
Year Founded: 1916
Sales Range: $10-24.9 Million
Emp.: 24
Nitrogenous Fertilizer Mfr
N.A.I.C.S.: 325311
Ginny Bulkowski (Pres)
Bob Bulkowski (VP)
Jed Erickson (Acct Mgr-Natl)
Tammy Smith (Office Mgr)
Bill Jeannotte (Mgr-Production)
Phil Pudder (Mgr-Warehouse)

REED BEVERAGE, INC.
3701 SE 25th Ave, Amarillo, TX 79103
Tel.: (806) 376-5674
Web Site:
http://www.reedbeverage.com
Beer Mfr & Distr
N.A.I.C.S.: 312120
Vance Reed (Chm)
Chris Reed (Pres & CEO)
Charles Hughes (Pres-Domestic, Imports & N/A)
Rhett Blandford (Pres-Craft, Wine & Spirits)
Dusty Walker (CFO)
Spencer Duncan (Pres-Chain Sls)
Derick Hughes (Pres-Sls)
Steve DeBaets (Pres-Strategy)
Trevor Williams (VP-Ops)

REED CITY POWER LINE SUPPLY CO., INC.
420 S Roth St Ste A, Reed City, MI 49677-9115
Tel.: (231) 832-2297
Web Site: http://www.uscco.com
Year Founded: 1963
Sales Range: $100-124.9 Million
Emp.: 350
Electrical Equipment Distr
N.A.I.C.S.: 423610
Michael Bigford (Pres)
Franklin C. Wheatlake (Chm & CEO)

REED CONTRACTING SERVICES, INC.
2512 Triana Blvd SW, Huntsville, AL 35805
Tel.: (256) 533-0505
Web Site:
http://www.reedalabama.com
Year Founded: 1987
Sales Range: $10-24.9 Million
Emp.: 350
Road Construction; Asphalt Production; Water, Sewer & Storm Drainage Construction; Ready Mix Concrete Mfr
N.A.I.C.S.: 238990
Michael W. Reed (Founder & Pres)
Paul Siskey (Controller)
David Harris (VP)

REED FOOD TECHNOLOGY
3151 Greenfield Rd, Pearl, MS 39208
Tel.: (601) 939-4001
Web Site: http://www.reedfood.com
Year Founded: 1995
Sales Range: $10-24.9 Million
Emp.: 35
Convenience Foods Mfr
N.A.I.C.S.: 311991
Robert J. Reed (Pres)
Merrilee Hall (Mgr-R&D)

REED GRAIN & BEAN COMPANY, INC.
903 Elm St, Buhl, ID 83316
Tel.: (208) 839-4242   ID
Web Site: http://www.reedgrain.com
Year Founded: 1986
Sales Range: $75-99.9 Million
Emp.: 10
Processor of Field Beans & Grains
N.A.I.C.S.: 424510

Subsidiaries:

Reed Brothers Inc.   (1)
903 Elm St, Buhl, ID 83316   (10%)
Tel.: (208) 543-4306
Web Site: http://www.regrain.com
Rev.: $715,000,000
Trucking; Agricultural Commodities
N.A.I.C.S.: 424510
Douglas K. Beames (CFO & Controller)
Earl W. Reed (Pres)
Carol O. Reed (Treas)

REED INC.
802 Ave E, Ely, NV 89301
Tel.: (775) 289-4463
Web Site:
http://www.rplaceonline.com
Sales Range: $10-24.9 Million
Emp.: 8
Convenience Store
N.A.I.C.S.: 445131
Bryan Reed (Pres)

REED LALLIER CHEVROLET, INC.
4500 Raeford Rd, Fayetteville, NC 28304
Tel.: (910) 778-2066
Web Site: http://www.reedlallier.com
Year Founded: 1988
Sales Range: $50-74.9 Million
Emp.: 100
New Car Retailer
N.A.I.C.S.: 441110
John Quinn (Gen Mgr)
Beth Clark (Mgr-Mktg)

REED MACHINERY, INC.
10A New Bond St, Worcester, MA 01606
Tel.: (508) 595-9090   MA
Web Site: http://www.reed-machinery.com
Sales Range: $10-24.9 Million
Emp.: 12
Thread Rolling Machinery
N.A.I.C.S.: 333248
Jim Flanagan (Owner & Pres)
Brian R. Faucher (VP-Ops)

REED MANUFACTURING COMPANY INC.
1321 S Veterans Blvd, Tupelo, MS 38804
Tel.: (662) 842-4472   TN
Web Site:
http://www.reedmanufacturing.com
Year Founded: 1919
Sales Range: $10-24.9 Million
Emp.: 40
Men's & Boy's Work Clothing
N.A.I.C.S.: 315250
Edward R. Nelson (Pres)

REED NISSAN
3776 W Colonial Dr, Orlando, FL 32808
Tel.: (407) 297-7333
Web Site: http://www.reednissan.com
Year Founded: 1950
Automobile & Other Motor Vehicle Merchant Whslr
N.A.I.C.S.: 423110
Vincent Mancuso (Gen Sls Mgr)
Brian Longacre (Sls Mgr)
Brian Wood (Sls Mgr)
Billy Simcox (Mgr-Floor)
John Bedar (Mgr-Floor)
Guy McCumber (Dir-Fixed Ops)
Joe Scuderi (Mgr-Parts)
Robert Keen (Fin Mgr)
Mostafa Elasri (Fin Mgr)
Kris Williams (Fin Mgr)
Carlos Veintimilla (Mgr-Svc Lane)
John Bartolotta (Mgr-Svc Lane)
Raymond Reed (Owner)

REED OIL COMPANY
511 Montgomery Ave, New Castle, PA 16102-1111
Tel.: (724) 658-6691   PA
Web Site: http://www.reedoil.com
Year Founded: 1982
Sales Range: $25-49.9 Million
Emp.: 25
Petroleum Bulk Stations & Terminals
N.A.I.C.S.: 424710

REED SENDECKE KREBSBACH
701 Deming Way, Madison, WI 53717-1937
Tel.: (608) 827-0701   WI
Web Site: http://www.rsandk.com
Year Founded: 1978
Sales Range: $10-24.9 Million
Emp.: 17
Graphic Design Services
N.A.I.C.S.: 541810
Stan Reed (Principal)
Jim Sendecke (Principal)
Kay Krebsbach (Pres & Principal)
Stephanie Brill (Mgr-PR)
Nan Disalvo (Exec VP)
Patti Kessler (Media Coord)
Jim Thackray (VP)
Laurie Wilkinson (CFO)
Kay Krebsbach (Pres & Principal)
Nan DiSalvo (Exec VP)

REED SMITH LLP
Reed Smith Ctr 225 5th Ave, Pittsburgh, PA 15222
Tel.: (412) 288-3131
Web Site: http://www.reedsmith.com
Year Founded: 1877
Sales Range: $800-899.9 Million
Emp.: 1,450
Law Firm Representing Companies in Litigation
N.A.I.C.S.: 541110
Robert A. Nicholas (Partner & Head-Legal Personnel)
Gary A. Sokulski (COO)
Carol C. Honigberg (Partner)
Edward J. Estrada (Partner)
Angela Angelovska-Wilson (Partner)
David A. Surbeck (Partner)
Heather A. Ritch (Partner)
Luke E. Debevec (Partner)
Joel S. Barras (Partner)
James L. Rockney (Partner)
Justin H. Werner (Partner)
Jarrod D. Shaw (Partner)
Michael O'Neil (Partner-Chicago)
Debra H. Dermody (Partner)
Michael A. Yuffee (Partner-Washington)
Katie C. Pawlitz (Partner)
Lilit Asadourian (Partner)
Sean P. Delaney (Partner)
Kenneth M. Siegel (Partner)
Jason E. Hazlewood (Partner)
Kathryn Pourmand Nordick (Partner)
Paul R. Gupta (Partner)
Kevin Cadwell (Partner)
David Adelman (Partner)
Peter J. Chassman (Partner-Houston)
Mark D. Temple (Partner-Houston & Chicago)
Lucy Dillon (Chief Knowledge Officer-London)
Steven W. Agnoli (CIO-Global Customer Centre)
Douglas J. Wood (Partner)
Peter Y. Malyshev (Partner)
Gregory Wang (Partner-Hong Kong)
Calvin Chan (Partner-Singapore)
Kohe Hasan (Partner-Singapore)
Jesse J. Ash (Partner)
Peter J. Stuhldreher (Partner-Houston)
Ericson P. Kimbel (Partner)
Charles Ball (Partner-Singapore)
Derek J. Baker (Partner-Philadelphia & Princeton)
Iain Balkwill (Partner-London)
Jennifer L. Achilles (Partner-New York)
Jason H. Ballum (Partner-Richmond)
Kevin C. Abbott (Partner-Pittsburgh)
Michael A. Banzhaf (Partner)
Rashpaul Bahia (Partner-London)
Siddesh Bale (Partner-Chicago)
Simon T. Adams (Partner-San Francisco)
Daniel K. Winterfeldt (Partner)
Andrew Jenkinson (Mng Partner-London)
Sakil A. Suleman (Partner)
Peter M. Ellis (Partner)
James E. DelBello (Partner)
Douglas E. Cameron (Chm-Litigation Dept-Global & Partner)
Jess Drabkin (Partner)
Leif Cervantes De Reinstein (Partner)
Stephen E. Sessa (Chm-Entertainment & Media Indus Grp & Partner)
John M. Iino (Chm-Diversity & Inclusion-Global & Partner)
Bryan M. Webster (Partner-Complex Litigation Grp-Chicago)
Michael LoVallo (Mng Partner-Chicago)
Jean Kuei (Partner)
Kevin Madagan (Partner)
Paul R. Mohun (Partner-Global Real Estate Grp-San Francisco)
David Thompson (Head-San Francisco)
Dusty Elias (Chm-Real Estate Grp)
Susan Berry (Partner)
William Sheridan (Partner)
Andres Vallejo (Partner)
Daniella Landers (Partner)
Bart Huffman (Partner)
Marlen D. Whitley (Exec Dir-Diversity Recruiting)
Sandy Thomas (Mng Partner-Global)
Andrei Baev (Partner-Energy & Natural Resources)
William Lewis (Partner-Global Real Estate Grp-Chicago)
Joe Sarcinella (Chm-Global Real Estate Grp)
Petar Orlic (Partner-Real Estate Grp-London)
Jay Glunt (Partner-Labor & Employment Practice)
Reginia Speed-Bost (Partner)
Leith Moghli (Partner-Private Equity & Investment Funds Practice-Global)
Michael C. Lynch (Chief HR Officer)
Jay McAveeney (CFO)
Victoria Westcott (Partner-Project, Asset & Export Fin-Fin Industry Grp-Paris)
Jill Vorobiev (Partner-Labor & Employment Practice Grp-Chicago)

COMPANIES

Leonard Bernstein (Mng Partner-Philadelphia)
Matthew Petersen (Co-Chm-Global Corp Grp)
Michael N. Peterson (Partner-Corp Grp-Global)
Lewis D. Zirogiannis (Partner-Regulatory Enforcement Practice-Global)
Edward B. Schwartz (Partner-Washington & Chm-Antitrust & Competition Team-Regulatory)
James Sanders (Chm-Regulatory Enforcement Grp-Global)
Andreas Splittgerber (Partner)
Philip Thomas (Partner-London)
Mark Melodia (Partner & Chm-IP, Tech & Data Grp)
Cynthia O'Donoghue (Partner)
Howard Womersley Smith (Partner-IP, Tech & Data Practice-London)
Barry Spenceley (Dir-Reed Smith Global Solutions-Leeds)
Julia Boyd (Partner-Corporate Grp-Global)
Lorenzo Gasparetti (Mng Partner-Los Angeles)
Julia Zhu-Morelli (Partner-Corp Grp-Global)
Martin Bunning (Partner-Global Corp Grp-Frankfurt)
Delphine Currie (Co-Chm-Global Corp Grp)
Rolf Hunermann (Mng Partner-Frankfurt)
Colette D. Honorable (Partner)
Ronald L. Francis Jr. (Partner)

REEDER CHEVROLET COMPANY
4301 Clinton Hwy, Knoxville, TN 37912
Tel.: (865) 687-7710
Web Site: http://www.reederchevy.com
Sales Range: $50-74.9 Million
Emp.: 85
Automobiles, New & Used
N.A.I.C.S.: 441110
Jim Quinlan (Pres)
Jerry McDaniels (Mgr-Svcs)
Dave Snowden (Mgr-Parts)

REEDER-TRAUSCH MARINE
6950 E US Hwy 36, Rockville, IN 47872
Tel.: (765) 344-1771
Web Site: https://www.reedertrauschmarines.com
Boat Dealers
N.A.I.C.S.: 441222
J Hurless (Mng Partner)
Montey Anderson (Mng Partner)

Subsidiaries:

Denny's Marina Inc. (1)
5550 Kopetsky Dr, Indianapolis, IN 46217
Tel.: (317) 786-9562
Web Site: https://www.dennysmarina.com
Sales Range: $10-24.9 Million
Emp.: 12
Motor Boat Dealers
N.A.I.C.S.: 441222
Daniel A. Decker (Pres)

REEDLEY HIGH SCHOOL
740 W North Ave, Reedley, CA 93654
Tel.: (559) 305-7100
Web Site: http://www.rhs.kcusd.com
Education Services
N.A.I.C.S.: 611710
John Ahlin (Principal)

REEDMAN TOLL AUTO WORLD
1700 E Lincoln Hwy US Rte 1, Langhorne, PA 19047
Tel.: (215) 757-4961
Web Site: http://www.reedmantoll.com
Sales Range: $200-249.9 Million
Emp.: 400
New & Used Cars & Trucks Whslr
N.A.I.C.S.: 441110
Trisha DeMaria (Mgr-Adv)
William O'Flanagan (Pres)
Tracy Bender (Controller)
Bruce Toll (Pres & CEO)

REEDS & SON FURNITURE INC.
28401 Canwood St, Agoura Hills, CA 91301
Tel.: (818) 597-7800
Web Site: http://www.reedsfurniture.com
Rev.: $16,176,446
Emp.: 22
Furniture Retailer
N.A.I.C.S.: 449110
Dru Wickman (Pres)

REEDS JEWELERS, INC.
2525 S 17th St, Wilmington, NC 28401-7705
Tel.: (910) 350-3100 NC
Web Site: http://www.reeds.com
Year Founded: 1946
Sales Range: $100-124.9 Million
Emp.: 685
Retailer of Jewelry
N.A.I.C.S.: 458310
Alan Zimmer (Pres & CEO)

REEF INDUSTRIES INCORPORATED
9209 Almeda Genoa Rd, Houston, TX 77075
Tel.: (713) 507-4200
Web Site: http://www.reefindustries.com
Rev.: $24,000,000
Emp.: 40
Plastics Finished Products, Laminated
N.A.I.C.S.: 326130
Mike McElhany (Mgr-Vapor Protection-Griffolyn Building Products)
Tom Scarborough (Mgr-Product)

REEL LUMBER SERVICE
275 E Santa Ana St, Anaheim, CA 92805
Tel.: (714) 991-7121
Web Site: http://www.reellumber.com
Sales Range: $10-24.9 Million
Emp.: 26
Lumber: Rough, Dressed & Finished
N.A.I.C.S.: 423310
Shirley Reel (Pres)
Jim Nickerson (Controller)

REEL-O-MATIC, INC.
5101 South Council Ste 100, Oklahoma City, OK 73179
Tel.: (405) 672-0000 OK
Web Site: http://www.reelpower.com
Year Founded: 1936
Sales Range: $1-9.9 Million
Emp.: 50
Mfr of Material Handling Equipment for Wire, Cable, Steel Wire Rope, Tubing, Hose & other Flexible or Coilable Products
N.A.I.C.S.: 333998
Don Moreau (VP-Sls)

REELAN INDUSTRIES INC.
623 Stewart Ave Ste 201, Garden City, NY 11530
Tel.: (516) 683-2300
Sales Range: $10-24.9 Million
Emp.: 50
Tank Caulking & Weather, Water & Fireproofing
N.A.I.C.S.: 238990

REELL PRECISION MANUFACTURING CORP.
1259 Willow Lk Blvd, Saint Paul, MN 55110
Tel.: (651) 484-2447
Web Site: http://www.reell.com
Year Founded: 1970
Sales Range: $10-24.9 Million
Emp.: 200
Clutches, Hinges For Computers
N.A.I.C.S.: 333613
John West (CFO)
John Schannach (Sr Mgr-Product Line-Global)
Jack Field (VP-Sls & Customer Svc-Global)
Chet Zaslow (Mgr-Global Sls-Medical Tech)
Metin Kose (Mgr-Sls-Central Europe)
Kyle Smith (Co-CEO)
Ron Nelson (VP-Ops-Global)
Jim Brown (Mgr-Global Product Line-Comml Motion Bus)
Jay Bargas (Mgr-Global Product Line-Automotive Bus)
Tony Wang (Head-Sls-China)
Shari Erdman (Co-CEO)
Michael Naughton (Chm)

REES CONTRACT SERVICE INC.
10111 W 105th St, Overland Park, KS 66212
Tel.: (913) 888-0590
Sales Range: $10-24.9 Million
Emp.: 400
Security Guard Services
N.A.I.C.S.: 561612
B. M. Foster (Pres)
Robert Ayres (VP)
Danny Keith (Gen Mgr)

REES-JONES FAMILY HOLDINGS LP
8111 Westchester Dr 900, Dallas, TX 75225
Tel.: (214) 884-3239 DE
Holding Company
N.A.I.C.S.: 551112
David M. Hundley (Gen Counsel)

REESE ENTERPRISES, INC.
16350 Asher Ave, Rosemount, MN 55068
Tel.: (651) 423-1174 MN
Web Site: http://www.reeseusa.com
Year Founded: 1917
Sales Range: $100-124.9 Million
Emp.: 150
Weather Strips, Plastic Extrusions, Footmats & Gratings Mfr
N.A.I.C.S.: 326199
Robert T. Ellingson (CEO)
Terry Deering (Dir-Mktg & Sls)
Mike Glaus (CFO)
Chester W. Ellingson III (Pres)

Subsidiaries:

Reese Enterprises, Inc. - Astro Plastics Division (1)
16350 Asher Ave E, Rosemount, MN 55068-0459
Tel.: (651) 322-1055
Web Site: http://www.astroplastics.com
Sales Range: $10-24.9 Million
Emp.: 43
Plastic Extrusions Mfr
N.A.I.C.S.: 326199
Robert T. Ellingson (Pres)
James R. Kinville (COO)

Reese Enterprises, Inc. - Weather Strip Division (1)
16350 Asher Ave, Rosemount, MN 55068-6000
Tel.: (651) 423-1126
Web Site: http://www.reeseusa.com
Sales Range: $10-24.9 Million
Emp.: 45
Weather Strips Mfr
N.A.I.C.S.: 326199
Mike Glaus (Controller)

REESE INTEGRATED MARKETING
1875 Morgantown Rd, Reading, PA 19607
Tel.: (610) 378-1835
Web Site: http://www.reeseadv.com
Year Founded: 1981
Sales Range: $1-9.9 Million
Emp.: 10
Integrated Marketing
N.A.I.C.S.: 541613
Eric Rosen (Dir-PR)

REESE, TOMASES & ELLICK, INC. (RT&E)
768 Mount Moro Rd # 100, Villanova, PA 19085-2007
Tel.: (302) 652-3211 DE
Web Site: http://www.rteideas.com
Year Founded: 1957
Rev.: $35,000,000
Emp.: 33
Advetising Agency
N.A.I.C.S.: 541810
Ed Keane (Dir-Creative)
Mark Miller (Sr Dir-Art)
Maureen Poling (Bus Mgr)
Alison Moran (Acct Exec)

Subsidiaries:

GrafikPharm, Inc. (1)
1105 Market St Ste 100, Wilmington, DE 19801
Tel.: (302) 472-5909
Emp.: 6
N.A.I.C.S.: 541810
Tom Planer (Dir)

RT&E Integrated Communications (1)
1105 Market St Ste 100, Wilmington, DE 19801
Tel.: (302) 652-3211
Web Site: http://www.rteideas.com
Rev.: $550,000
Emp.: 15
Public Relations Agency
N.A.I.C.S.: 541820
Kate Densford (Acct Coord)
Brian Cunningham (Mgr-PR)
Chick Housam (CEO)
Maureen Poling (Mgr-Bus)
Edward Keane (Dir-Creative)
Tom Planer (Dir-Grafikpharm)
Mike Stack (Art Dir-Grafikpharm)
Rich Mark (Sr Mgr-Acct-Grafikpharm)

REESMANS EXCAVATING & GRADING, INC.
28815 Bushnell Rd, Burlington, WI 53105
Tel.: (262) 539-2124
Web Site: http://www.reesmans.com
Sales Range: $10-24.9 Million
Emp.: 55
Highway Street & Bridge Construction
N.A.I.C.S.: 237310
Eric Reesman (Project Mgr)
Adam Reesman (Project Mgr)
Michael Church (Project Mgr)
John Mutter (Mgr-Shop)
Jon Snyder (Coord-Safety)
Mark Leclair (Controller)
Chris Reesman (VP)

REEVE STORE EQUIPMENT COMPANY

REEVE STORE EQUIPMENT COMPANY

Reeve Store Equipment Company—(Continued)
9131 Bermudez St, Pico Rivera, CA 90660
Tel.: (562) 949-2535
Web Site: http://www.reeveco.com
Sales Range: $10-24.9 Million
Emp.: 120
Counter & Counter Display Cases Mfr
N.A.I.C.S.: 337126
Mike Leonard *(Mgr-Sls-Wholesale Distr-Natl)*

Subsidiaries:

Clemco-Elite Standard Systems LLC (1)
660 Auburn Folsom Rd, Auburn, CA 95603-5646
Tel.: (909) 483-0141
Web Site: http://www.clemco-elite.com
Fixture Component Mfr
N.A.I.C.S.: 337215
Dan Doke *(Founder & Pres)*

REEVE TRUCKING CO.
5050 Carpenter Rd, Stockton, CA 95215
Tel.: (209) 948-4061
Web Site: http://www.reevetrucking.com
Rev.: $11,519,737
Emp.: 70
Trucking Except Local
N.A.I.C.S.: 484121
Donnie Reeve *(Pres)*

REEVES CONSTRUCTION COMPANY
101 Sheraton Ct, Macon, GA 31210
Tel.: (478) 474-9092
Web Site: http://www.reevescc.com
Year Founded: 1955
Sales Range: $150-199.9 Million
Emp.: 600
Clearing, Grading, Drainage & Asphalt Paving of Roadways & Parking Areas
N.A.I.C.S.: 324121
Randy England *(Dir-HR)*
Terry Looney *(Controller)*
John Cosgrove *(Exec VP-Florida)*
Dean Hayman *(Mgr-West Reg)*
Jarrod Crum *(Dir-Safety)*
Pat Dwyer *(Mgr-Corp Sls)*
Barry Dietrich *(Controller)*
Victoria L. Taffet *(Mgr-Bus Dev-GA & FL)*
Rob Loar *(Mgr-North Reg)*
Tony Felix *(Dir-Quality Control)*
Stoy Marlow *(VP & Reg Mgr)*
Robert Ponton *(Pres)*
Fred Shelton *(CFO)*
Lee Rushbrooke *(Pres)*

Subsidiaries:

Baker Infrastructure Group, Inc. (1)
101 Sheraton Ct, Macon, GA 31210
Tel.: (478) 474-9092
Asphalt Paving of Roadways & Parking Areas
N.A.I.C.S.: 324121

Subsidiary (Domestic):

R.B. Baker Construction Inc. (2)
100 Morgan Industrial Blvd, Garden City, GA 31408-9589
Tel.: (912) 964-6513
Web Site: http://www.rbbaker.com
Highway & Street Construction Services
N.A.I.C.S.: 237310
Stoy F. Marlow *(VP)*
Scott Newman *(Reg Mgr)*
Neal Andrews *(Mgr)*

Sloan Construction Company, Inc. (1)
250 Plemmons Rd, Duncan, SC 29334
Tel.: (864) 968-2250
Web Site: http://www.sloan-construction.com

Construction Services
N.A.I.C.S.: 236220
Rob Loar *(VP-Ops)*

Subsidiary (Domestic):

Granite Contracting, LLC (2)
18606 Northline Dr, Cornelius, NC 28031
Tel.: (704) 892-0341
Web Site: http://www.granitecontracting.com
Rev.: $8,309,700
Emp.: 60
Highway, Street & Bridge Construction
N.A.I.C.S.: 237310
Ryan Haynes *(Controller)*

REEVES FLORAL PRODUCTS, INC.
10288 Hwy 92, Woodstock, GA 30188
Tel.: (770) 924-5230
Web Site: http://www.reevesfloral.com
Year Founded: 1962
Sales Range: $10-24.9 Million
Emp.: 60
Flowers & Florists Supplies
N.A.I.C.S.: 424930
J. Stanley Fitts *(CEO)*

REEVES HARDWARE COMPANY
16 S Main St, Clayton, GA 30525
Tel.: (706) 782-4253
Web Site: http://www.reeveshomefurnishings.com
Rev.: $21,648,758
Emp.: 30
Lumber & Other Building Materials
N.A.I.C.S.: 423310
Chris Hendricks *(Controller)*
Lewis F. Reeves Jr. *(Pres)*

REEVES IMPORT MOTORCARS INC.
11333 N Florida Ave, Tampa, FL 33612
Tel.: (813) 933-2811
Web Site: http://www.drivereeves.com
Year Founded: 1971
Sales Range: $25-49.9 Million
Emp.: 300
Car Dealership Owner & Operator
N.A.I.C.S.: 441110
Vivian C. Reeves *(Pres & CEO)*
Kimberly Rogers *(Mgr-Mktg)*
Terry Jackson *(Mgr-Alignment Center)*

REEVES INTERNATIONAL, INC.
14 Industrial Rd, Pequannock, NJ 07440-1920
Tel.: (973) 694-5006
Web Site: http://www.reevesintl.com
Year Founded: 1946
Toys, Gifts & Collectibles Mfr & Distr
N.A.I.C.S.: 339930
Anthony Fleischmann *(Pres)*
Stephanie Macejko *(VP-Mktg & Product Dev)*

Subsidiaries:

Reeves International, Inc. (1)
34 Owens Dr, Wayne, NJ 07470-2341
Tel.: (973) 956-9555
Web Site: http://www.reeves.com
Emp.: 50
Mfr of Model Horses & Other Animals
N.A.I.C.S.: 339930
Anthony Fleischmann *(Pres)*

REEVES LAVERDURE PUBLIC RELATIONS
7820 Glades Rd Ste 275, Boca Raton, FL 33434-4177

Tel.: (561) 391-8717
Web Site: http://www.reevespr.com
Year Founded: 1994
Sales Range: $10-24.9 Million
Emp.: 3
Public Relations Agency
N.A.I.C.S.: 541820
David Reeves *(Founder & Pres)*

REEVES-WIEDEMAN COMPANY
14861 W 100th St, Lenexa, KS 66215
Tel.: (913) 492-7100
Web Site: http://www.rwco.com
Sales Range: $10-24.9 Million
Emp.: 60
Plumbing Fittings & Supplies
N.A.I.C.S.: 423720
Ted Wiedeman *(Pres)*
Kurt Wiedeman *(Controller)*
Walley Wiedeman *(VP)*

REF-CHEM, L.P.
1128 S Grandview, Odessa, TX 79761
Tel.: (432) 332-8531
Web Site: http://www.ref-chem.com
Year Founded: 1957
Sales Range: $100-124.9 Million
Emp.: 400
Engineering, Construction, EPC & Maintenance Services
N.A.I.C.S.: 237990
S. C. Myers *(CEO)*
Rodney J. Page *(CFO)*
Jeff W. Rashall *(Pres)*
Jeremy S. Huntley *(VP-Construction)*
Jerry L. Pullen *(VP-Bus Dev)*
Dwayne M. Boudreaux *(Sr VP-Mktg & Bus Dev)*
Anthony I. Garza *(VP-Fin & Admin)*
Todd Henderson *(Dir-Transmission & Distr)*

Subsidiaries:

Ref-Chem, L.P. - Brownfield (1)
602 Seagraves Rd, Brownfield, TX 79316
Tel.: (806) 637-0500
Web Site: http://www.ref-chem.com
Sales Range: $10-24.9 Million
Emp.: 50
Engineering, Construction, EPC & Maintenance Services
N.A.I.C.S.: 237990

REFINERY TERMINAL FIRE COMPANY
PO Box 4162, Corpus Christi, TX 78469
Tel.: (361) 882-6253
Web Site: http://www.rtfc.org
Year Founded: 1948
Sales Range: $10-24.9 Million
Emp.: 177
Industrial Fire Protection Services
N.A.I.C.S.: 813319
Lonnie K. Bartlett *(CEO)*

REFLEX SYSTEMS, LLC
53 Perimeter Center E Ste 175, Atlanta, GA 30346
Tel.: (404) 924-2400
Web Site: http://www.reflexsystems.com
Sales Range: $1-9.9 Million
Emp.: 30
Virtualization Management & Security Software Solutions
N.A.I.C.S.: 513210
Brian Cohen *(CEO)*
Eric Farr *(VP-Engrg)*
Heather Foster *(VP-Mktg)*
Steve Cundill *(VP-Sls)*

REFRESHMENT SERVICES INC.

3400 Solar Ave, Springfield, IL 62707
Tel.: (217) 522-6321
Web Site: http://refreshmentservicespepsi.com
Rev.: $97,300,000
Emp.: 10
Soda Syrups, Except For Fountain Use
N.A.I.C.S.: 424490
Ronald J. Vecchie *(Chm)*
Joyce Zaffiri *(Dir-Admin Ops)*

REFRICENTRO INC.
Carr 2 Km 121 8 Interior Bo Caimital Alto, Aguadilla, PR 00603
Tel.: (787) 493-0300
Web Site: http://www.refricentro.com
Sales Range: $10-24.9 Million
Emp.: 80
Warm Air Heating & Air Conditioning Distr
N.A.I.C.S.: 423730
Cirilo C. Hernandez *(Founder)*

Subsidiaries:

Refricenter of Miami Inc. (1)
7101 NW 43rd St, Miami, FL 33166
Tel.: (305) 477-8880
Web Site: http://www.refricenter.net
Sales Range: $100-124.9 Million
Emp.: 120
Air Conditioning Equipment Distr
N.A.I.C.S.: 423730
Jose Hernandez *(Mgr-Intl)*

REFRIGERATED FOOD EXPRESS INC.
57 Littlefield St, Avon, MA 02322-1934
Tel.: (508) 587-4600
Web Site: http://www.rfxinc.com
Year Founded: 1952
Sales Range: $25-49.9 Million
Emp.: 25
Trucking Service
N.A.I.C.S.: 484230

Subsidiaries:

Pioneer Transfer, LLC (1)
2034 S Saint Aubin St, Sioux City, IA 51106
Tel.: (712) 274-2332
Web Site: http://www.pioneertransfer.com
Sales Range: $10-24.9 Million
Emp.: 5
Freight Transportation Brokers
N.A.I.C.S.: 488510
Kari Dobrovolny *(COO)*
Jeff Burke *(Dir-Sls)*
Jim Morse *(Pres)*

REFRIGERATION & ELECTRIC SUPPLY CO.
1222 S Spring St, Little Rock, AR 72202
Tel.: (501) 374-6373
Web Site: http://www.resupplyco.com
Rev.: $10,025,145
Emp.: 9
Refrigeration Equipment & Supplies
N.A.I.C.S.: 423740
Eric Schneblen *(Mgr)*

REFRIGERATION SUPPLIES DISTRIBUTORS
26021 Atlantic Ocean Dr, Lake Forest, CA 92630-8831
Tel.: (949) 380-7878
Web Site: http://www.rsd.net
Rev.: $36,000,000
Emp.: 500
Distr of Refrigeration Equipment
N.A.I.C.S.: 423740
Joe Larson *(Branch Mgr)*
Jose Bravo *(Branch Mgr)*

Subsidiaries:

Refrigeration Supplies Distributors (1)

1201 Monterey Pass Rd, Monterey Park, CA 91754-3616
Tel.: (323) 264-2800
Web Site: http://www.rsd-tc.com
Sales Range: $50-74.9 Million
Wholesale Distribution of Refrigeration Equipment & Supplies
N.A.I.C.S.: 423740
Doug Collins (Controller)

REFRIGERATION SUPPLIES INC.
9700 Manchester Rd, Saint Louis, MO 63119
Tel.: (314) 961-2000
Web Site: http://www.rsikb.com
Sales Range: $10-24.9 Million
Emp.: 52
Kitchen Cabinets
N.A.I.C.S.: 423310
Anthony F. Piazza II (Pres)

REFRIGIWEAR, INC.
54 Breakstone Dr, Dahlonega, GA 30533-6698
Tel.: (706) 864-5757   NY
Web Site: httрs://www.refrigiwear.com
Year Founded: 1954
Sales Range: $10-24.9 Million
Emp.: 110
Industrial Insulated Work Clothing Mfr
N.A.I.C.S.: 315250
Ronald Breakstone (Pres)

REFURBISHED OFFICE FURNITURE, INC.
1212 N 39th St Ste 200, Tampa, FL 33605
Tel.: (813) 241-4515
Web Site: http://www.rofinc.net
Year Founded: 1991
Sales Range: $10-24.9 Million
Emp.: 85
Office Furniture Retailer
N.A.I.C.S.: 449110
Joni Adams (CEO)
Roberto Hursey (Controller)

REG LENNA CENTER FOR THE ARTS
116 E 3rd St, Jamestown, NY 14701
Tel.: (716) 664-2465   NJ
Web Site: http://www.reglenna.com
Year Founded: 1985
Sales Range: $1-9.9 Million
Emp.: 100
Performing Arts & Cultural Center
N.A.I.C.S.: 611519
Kathleen Eads (Exec Dir)
Hillary Meyer (Bus Mgr)
Dennis Drew (Gen Mgr)
Len Barry (Dir-Mktg & Comm)
Matt Hanley (Pres)
Matt Kindberg (Sec)

REGAL ASSETS, LLC
2600 W Olive Ave 5th Fl, Waco, TX 76712
Tel.: (323) 962-1133
Web Site: http://www.regalassets.com
Year Founded: 2003
Sales Range: $10-24.9 Million
Emp.: 33
Precious Metal Investment Services
N.A.I.C.S.: 523940
Tyler Gallagher (Owner)

REGAL AUTOMOTIVE GROUP
2615 Lakeland Hills Blvd, Lakeland, FL 33805-2217
Tel.: (863) 687-8000
Web Site: http://www.regallakeland.com
Year Founded: 1976
Sales Range: $10-24.9 Million
Emp.: 35
New & Used Car Dealerships
N.A.I.C.S.: 441110
Sal Campisi Jr. (Owner)

REGAL BANK
570 W Mt Pleasant Ave, Livingston, NJ 07039
Tel.: (973) 716-0600
Web Site: http://www.regalbanknj.com
Year Founded: 2007
Sales Range: $10-24.9 Million
Emp.: 60
Commericial Banking
N.A.I.C.S.: 522110
Thomas Lupo (Pres & CEO)
David M. Orbach (Chm)
Karen Hall (CFO & Sr VP)
Daniel M. Tower (COO & Exec VP)
Richard Cimo (Chief Credit Officer & Sr VP)
Luke de Araujo (Compliance Officer & VP)
Peter Poquette (VP-IT)
Michael Bono (VP)
Monte Ehrenkranz (VP)
Albena Gargiulo (VP)
Sean Howland (VP)
Annabella Portee (VP)
Peter Schoberl (Sr VP)
Christina E. Slater (VP)

REGAL CORPORATION
1624 Riverside Dr, Knoxville, TN 37915
Tel.: (800) 824-2164
Web Site: http://www.regalcorp.com
Year Founded: 1978
Construction & Mining Machinery Equipment Distr
N.A.I.C.S.: 423810
Mike Conley (Pres)
Linda Beaver (Mgr-Sls, Customer Svc & Accts Receivable)
Mike Beaver (VP)
Thomas Leonard (VP-Fin & Tech)

REGAL ELECTRIC, INC.
19451 S Tamiami Trl Ste 2, Fort Myers, FL 33908
Tel.: (239) 313-4550
Web Site: http://www.regalelectric.net
Year Founded: 1999
Sales Range: $10-24.9 Million
Emp.: 100
Electrical Contractor
N.A.I.C.S.: 238210
Rob Kemp (Mgr-Svc)
Cindy Walters (Controller)
Kevin Broader (Mgr-Warehouse)

REGAL ELECTRONICS, INC.
120 San Lucar Ct, Sunnyvale, CA 94086
Tel.: (408) 988-2288
Web Site: http://www.regalusa.com
Sales Range: $75-99.9 Million
Emp.: 200
Electronic Components Mfr
N.A.I.C.S.: 334419
Madeleine Lee (CEO)
Tony Lee (Pres)

REGAL LAGER, INC.
1100 Cobb Pl Blvd, Kennesaw, GA 30144
Tel.: (770) 955-5060
Web Site: http://www.regallager.com
Sales Range: $10-24.9 Million
Emp.: 20
Sales of Infant & Children's Accessories
N.A.I.C.S.: 423990
Dave Milligan (Mgr-Sls Dev)

REGAL LOGISTICS
6500 26th St E, Fife, WA 98424
Tel.: (253) 922-2250
Web Site: http://www.regallogistics.com
Year Founded: 1970
Logistic Services
N.A.I.C.S.: 541614
Roque Neeves (Pres)
Garry Neeves (VP)

REGAL MARINE INDUSTRIES, INC.
2300 Jetport Dr, Orlando, FL 32809-7800
Tel.: (407) 851-4360   FL
Web Site: http://www.regalboats.com
Year Founded: 1969
Sales Range: $75-99.9 Million
Emp.: 500
Mfr of Pleasure Boats
N.A.I.C.S.: 336612
Paul Kuck (VP-Product Dev & Mfg)
Duane Kuck (Pres & CEO)
Tim Kuck (COO & Exec VP)
Jeff Littlefield (Mgr-Creative)
Jacob Kuck (Sls Mgr-North America)

REGAL MARKETING, INC.
1600 E 2nd St, Scotch Plains, NJ 07076
Tel.: (908) 322-3801
Web Site: http://www.regalmarketing.com
Rev.: $10,998,095
Emp.: 4
Fruits & Vegetables Distr
N.A.I.C.S.: 424480
Hubertus Fladung (Mgr-Sls)
Scott Weinstock (Pres)
David Weinstock (VP)

REGAL METAL PRODUCTS CO.
3615 Union Ave SE PO Box 207, Minerva, OH 44657
Tel.: (330) 868-6343
Web Site: http://www.regalmetalproducts.com
Sales Range: $10-24.9 Million
Emp.: 46
Metal Stamping
N.A.I.C.S.: 332119
John Theodore Tomak (Pres)

REGAL MOTORS INC.
12718 E 55th St, Tulsa, OK 74146
Tel.: (918) 622-0788
Web Site: http://www.regalcars.com
Year Founded: 1983
Rev.: $12,228,983
Emp.: 29
Dealer of Used Automobiles
N.A.I.C.S.: 441120
Robert Mulkey (Pres)

REGAL NISSAN, INC.
1090 Holcomb Bridge Rd, Roswell, GA 30076-1911
Tel.: (770) 998-8686
Web Site: http://www.regalauto.com
Year Founded: 1980
Sales Range: $10-24.9 Million
Emp.: 78
Car Whslr
N.A.I.C.S.: 441110
Bo Scott (Gen Mgr)

REGAL OIL INC.
424 N Main St, San Angelo, TX 76903
Tel.: (325) 658-7521
Web Site: http://www.regaloil.net
Rev.: $26,900,000
Emp.: 100
Distribution & Retail Of Petroleum Products
N.A.I.C.S.: 424720
John D. Phillips (Pres)
Dan Baker (Mgr-Ops)
Doug Phillips (Exec VP)

REGAL PLASTIC SUPPLY CO.
5265 S Rio Grande St, Littleton, CO 80120
Tel.: (303) 794-9823   CO
Web Site: http://www.piedmontplastics.com
Year Founded: 1956
Emp.: 600
Holding Company; Plastic Sheet, Rod Tube & Film Products Distr
N.A.I.C.S.: 551112
Edward F. Statter (Owner)
Bill Barth (Reg Dir)
Hank Booth (CEO)
Rafael Balderrama (Mgr-District)
Tyler Booth (VP)

Subsidiaries:

Regal-Piedmont Plastics, LLC   (1)
5261 S Rio Grande St, Littleton, CO 80120
Tel.: (303) 794-9823
Web Site: http://www.regalpiedmontplastics.com
Sales Range: $25-49.9 Million
Emp.: 30
Plastic Sheet, Rod Tube & Film Products Distr
N.A.I.C.S.: 424610

REGAL PLASTIC SUPPLY COMPANY, INC.
9200 N Royal Line, Irving, TX 75063
Tel.: (972) 484-0741   TX
Web Site: http://www.regal-plastics.com
Year Founded: 1970
Sales Range: $10-24.9 Million
Emp.: 150
Plastic Sheet, Adhesive, Sealant & Sign Supplies Distr
N.A.I.C.S.: 424610
Patricia L. Gono (CFO, Treas, Sec & VP)
Wayne Gono (VP & Gen Mgr)

REGAL PRESS INC.
79 Astor Ave, Norwood, MA 02062
Tel.: (781) 769-3900
Web Site: http://www.regalpress.com
Sales Range: $10-24.9 Million
Emp.: 120
Embossing On Paper
N.A.I.C.S.: 323111
Christine O'Leary (Mng Dir)
Michael Simone (VP-Sls)
William Duffey Jr. (Chm)

REGAL STEEL CO.
2220 Morrissey Ave, Warren, MI 48091
Tel.: (586) 756-8300
Web Site: http://www.regalsteel.com
Sales Range: $10-24.9 Million
Emp.: 30
Steel Supplier
N.A.I.C.S.: 423510
Dianna Weller (Mgr-Quality Assurance)

REGAL SUPPLY COMPANY INC.
111 E 10th Ave, Kansas City, MO 64116-4326
Tel.: (816) 421-6290   MO
Web Site: http://www.regalplastic.com
Year Founded: 1954
Sales Range: $25-49.9 Million
Emp.: 225
Mfr of Plastics Materials

REGAL SUPPLY COMPANY INC.

Regal Supply Company Inc.—(Continued)
N.A.I.C.S.: 424610
Bob McFarlane (VP)
Greg Slavik (VP)

REGAL TEMPORARY SERVICES INC.
2807 Race St, Fort Worth, TX 76111
Tel.: (817) 877-4301
Web Site:
http://www.regalstaffing.com
Sales Range: $10-24.9 Million
Emp.: 20
Help Supply Services
N.A.I.C.S.: 561320
Elsa Maris (Mgr)

REGAL WARE, INC.
1675 Reigle Dr, Kewaskum, WI 53040-8923
Tel.: (262) 626-2121   DE
Web Site: http://www.regalware.com
Year Founded: 1945
Sales Range: $50-74.9 Million
Emp.: 800
Cookware, Kitchen Accessories & Home Water & Air Filters Mfr
N.A.I.C.S.: 335210
Jeffrey A. Reigle (Pres & CEO)
Douglas J. Reigle (VP-Supply Chain Mgmt)
Joseph A. Swanson (Sr VP-Ops)
Tracy Pearson (CFO & Sr VP)
David N. Lenz (COO & Sr VP)
James D. Reigle (Chm)

Subsidiaries:

Regal Ware, Inc. (1)
1675 Regal Dr, Kewaskum, WI 53040   (100%)
Tel.: (262) 334-2311
Web Site: http://www.westbend.com
Sales Range: $50-74.9 Million
Emp.: 500
Mfr of Kitchen Small Appliances & Electronic Timers
N.A.I.C.S.: 335220

Saladmaster (1)
230 W White Pl Ste 101, Arlington, TX 76018
Tel.: (817) 633-3555
Web Site: http://www.saladmaster.com
Sales Range: $10-24.9 Million
Emp.: 20
Mfr of Cookware & Crockery
N.A.I.C.S.: 335220
Veronica Lane (Mgr-Sls-Latin America)
Brenna Patton (Sr Mgr-Sls Promo)

REGAL WINGS, INC.
244 5th Ave Ste 200, New York, NY 10001
Tel.: (212) 444-9942
Web Site: http://www.regalwings.com
Year Founded: 2006
Sales Range: $10-24.9 Million
Emp.: 42
Airline Travel Arrangement Services
N.A.I.C.S.: 561599
Sam Gross (CEO)

REGAN COMMUNICATIONS GROUP, INC.
106 Union Wharf, Boston, MA 02109
Tel.: (617) 488-2800   MA
Web Site:
http://www.regancomm.com
Year Founded: 1984
Sales Range: $10-24.9 Million
Emp.: 30
Public Relations Agency
N.A.I.C.S.: 541820
Mariellen Burns (Chief Strategy Officer)
Julie Kahn (Pres)
Kelly Mayfair Owens (Partner & Dir-Editorial)
Lindsay Rotondi (Sr VP)
Lisa Doucet-Albert (Sr VP)
Scott Mackenzie (Sr VP)
Steve Owens (Partner & Creative Dir)
Thomas Cole (Co-Founder & COO)
George K. Regan Jr. (Co-Founder, Chm & Pres)

Subsidiaries:

Pierce-Cote Advertising, Inc. (1)
683 Main St, Osterville, MA 02655-2015
Tel.: (508) 420-5566
Web Site: http://www.pierce-cote.com
Sales Range: $1-9.9 Million
Emp.: 7
Advetising Agency
N.A.I.C.S.: 541810
Diane McPherson (VP & Dir-Acct)
John Migliaccio (Exec Dir-Creative)
Mary Stengel (Dir-Media & Client Svcs)
Lynn O'Brien (Dir-Art)
Bradford Schiff (Pres)
Jaime Gallagher (Gen Mgr-Admin)
Judith Goetz (Dir-Acct)
Amy Levine (Acct Exec)
Diane Payson (Mgr-Fin)
Pam Shapiro (Acct Exec)

Regan Communications Group, Inc. - Florida (1)
270 S Central Blvd Ste 200B, Jupiter, FL 33458
Tel.: (561) 575-3288
Web Site: http://www.regancomm.com
Public Relations Agency
N.A.I.C.S.: 541820

Regan Communications Group, Inc. - Providence (1)
127 Dorrance St 4th Fl, Providence, RI 02903
Tel.: (401) 351-8855
Web Site: http://www.regancomm.com
Emp.: 4
Public Relations Agency
N.A.I.C.S.: 541820
Lisa Doucet-Albert (Sr VP)
Kate Barba Murphy (Dir-Acct)
George K. Regan Jr. (Chm & Pres)

REGAN HOLDING CORPORATION
2090 Marina Ave, Petaluma, CA 94954-6714
Tel.: (800) 395-1053   CA
Web Site: http://www.legacynet.com
Year Founded: 1993
Holding Company; Insurance Services
N.A.I.C.S.: 551112
Lynda L. Pitts (Founder & CEO)
R. Preston Pitts (Pres)

Subsidiaries:

Legacy Marketing Group (1)
2090 Marina Ave, Petaluma, CA 94954-6714   (100%)
Tel.: (707) 778-8638
Web Site: http://www.legacynet.com
Holding Company for Life Insurance & Financial Service
N.A.I.C.S.: 524210
Lynda Pitts (Founder & CEO)

REGAN TECHNOLOGIES CORPORATION
7 Barnes Industrial Rd S, Wallingford, CT 06492
Tel.: (203) 284-4120
Web Site: http://www.rtcorp.com
Year Founded: 1997
Sales Range: $10-24.9 Million
Emp.: 20
Systems Integrator & Reseller
N.A.I.C.S.: 541512
Donna Regan (Dir-Mktg)

REGBERG & ASSOCIATES, INC.
1036 N Tigertail Rd, Los Angeles, CA 90049-1421
Tel.: (310) 475-5735
Year Founded: 1973
Sales Range: Less than $1 Million
Emp.: 5
N.A.I.C.S.: 541810
Scott Regberg (Pres, Treas & Sec)
Scott Bowman (Art Dir)

REGENCE HEALTH NETWORK, INC.
2801 W 8th St, Plainview, TX 79072
Tel.: (806) 293-8561   TX
Web Site: http://www.rhn.md
Year Founded: 1973
Sales Range: $10-24.9 Million
Emp.: 209
Health Care Srvices
N.A.I.C.S.: 622110
Derek Martin (CFO)
Michael Hemphill (COO)
Cynthia Wetzel (Dir-Clinical Affairs)
Rick Love (CEO)
Robert Martinez (Chm)
Sean Wehrley (Treas)
Bryan Gillespie (Sec)
Steve Martinez (Vice Chm)
Jennifer Pattison (Dir-Employee Rels & Branding)
Sandy Logan (Dir-Revenue Cycle of Mgmt)
Benson Lovett (Reg Dir-Ops)
Morgan Leak (Chief Medical Officer)
Herbert Tabor (Dir-Dental)
Robert Bidwell (Dir-Lab)

REGENCY ENTERPRISES INC.
9261 Jordan Ave, Chatsworth, CA 91311
Tel.: (818) 901-0255
Web Site:
http://www.regencylighting.com
Year Founded: 1981
Sales Range: $25-49.9 Million
Emp.: 260
Provider of Electrical Apparatus & Equipment
N.A.I.C.S.: 423610
Mike Goldstone (Founder, Owner & COO)
Hoon Kim (VP-Fin)
Scott Anderson (Co-Owner & Co-Pres)
Judah Regenstreif (Co-Owner & Co-Pres)
Isaac Regenstreif (Co-Owner & Co-Pres)
Evan Regenstreif (Co-Owner & Co-Pres)
Ron Pilner (VP-Reg Sls)

REGENCY MANAGEMENT SERVICE LLC
2417 Fields S Dr, Champaign, IL 61822
Tel.: (217) 359-7031   IL
Web Site:
http://www.regencyapartments.com
Year Founded: 1982
Sales Range: $100-124.9 Million
Emp.: 113
Investment, Syndication & Development of Apartments & Shopping Centers
N.A.I.C.S.: 531210
Robert A. Pratten (Pres & CEO)

Subsidiaries:

Regency Commercial Associates LLC (1)
330 Cross Pointe Blvd, Evansville, IN 47715-4027   (100%)
Tel.: (812) 424-9200
Web Site: http://www.regency-prop.com
Sales Range: $10-24.9 Million
Emp.: 50
Commercial Property Management/Leasing
N.A.I.C.S.: 531120

U.S. PRIVATE

Jeff Howell (VP-Property Mgmt)
Jim Wittman (VP-Dev & Leasing)
Kevin Hammett (Pres & CEO)
Kevin Rock (CFO & VP-Acctg & Fin)
Tracy Stutz (VP-HR & Admin)
Brian Castellano (Mgr-IT)
Barry Paddock (Controller)
Chris Folz (Dir-Acq)
Diane Ellis (Dir-Admin)
Denny Riffert (Treas)
Emily Neumann (Mgr-Acq)
Mandy Chinn (Mgr-Acctg)
Jamie Edmonson (Sr Dir-Leasing)
Ashley Seyffarth (Coord-Mktg)

REGENCY PLASTICS - UBLY INC.
4147 N Ubly Rd, Ubly, MI 48475
Tel.: (989) 658-8504
Web Site: http://www.geminigroup.net
Rev.: $16,200,000
Emp.: 125
Blow Molded Finished Plastics Products, Nec
N.A.I.C.S.: 326199
Dan Bourcier (Plant Mgr)

REGENCY TECHNOLOGIES, INC.
17000 Preston Rd Ste 230, Dallas, TX 75248-1201
Tel.: (817) 540-6055
Web Site:
http://www.regencytech.com
Sales Range: $10-24.9 Million
Emp.: 80
IT Programming & Consulting Services
N.A.I.C.S.: 541511
Arul Rajah (COO)

REGENCY TRANSPORTATION, INC.
101 Constitution Blvd, Franklin, MA 02038
Tel.: (508) 520-3595
Web Site:
http://www.regencytrans.com
Sales Range: $10-24.9 Million
Emp.: 120
Provider of Trucking Services
N.A.I.C.S.: 484121
Richard Giroux (Pres)
Tom Baldelli (Dir-Fleet & Facility Maintenance)
Paul Giroux (Founder, Pres & CEO)
Daniel Brady (Dir-Bus Support & Analysis)
Charlene McDonald (CFO)
Ed Rodricks (COO & Exec VP)

REGENCY TRAVEL INC.
416 Perkins Extended, Memphis, TN 38117
Tel.: (901) 682-9065   TN
Web Site:
http://www.regencytravel.net
Year Founded: 1978
Sales Range: $25-49.9 Million
Emp.: 30
Travel Agencies
N.A.I.C.S.: 561510
Terry A. Beaty (CEO)
Joe Crews (Mgr)

REGENERATIVE MEDICINE SOLUTIONS LLC
201 E Kennedy Blvd Ste 700, Tampa, FL 33602
Tel.: (877) 867-4551
Web Site:
http://www.myregenmed.com
Emp.: 90
Regenerative Medicine Services
N.A.I.C.S.: 621498
James St. Louis (Chief Medical Officer)
Lynn Flaherty Margnelli (Exec VP)
Jeremy Daniel (CFO)
Jimmy St. Louis (Pres & CEO)

COMPANIES

REGENESIS BIOMEDICAL, INC
5301 N Pima Rd, Scottsdale, AZ 85250
Tel.: (480) 970-4970
Web Site: http://www.regenesisbio.com
Sales Range: $10-24.9 Million
Emp.: 51
Noninvasive Regenerative Medicine Product Mfr & Whslr
N.A.I.C.S.: 325412
Dennis Genge *(CFO & VP)*
Scott Robey *(VP-Mktg)*
Richard D. Shirk *(Chm)*
Mark Davis *(VP-Clinical Res & Regulatory Affairs)*
Adrianne Patti Smith *(VP-Medical Affairs & Clinical Bus Dev)*
Tom Eisiminger Jr. *(Pres & CEO)*

REGENT AEROSPACE CORPORATION
28110 W Harrison Pkwy, Valencia, CA 91355
Tel.: (661) 257-3000
Web Site: http://www.regentaerospace.com
Year Founded: 1993
Aircraft Interior Refurbishment, Aircraft Seating, Parts Support & Window Repair Services
N.A.I.C.S.: 336413
Tim Garvin *(VP-Sls & Mktg)*
Reza Soltanian *(Pres)*
Steve Nale *(Mng Dir)*
Everado Guereca *(VP-Ops)*
Thomas Cecil *(Sr Dir-Sls)*
Ann Allieres *(Sr Program Mgr)*
Peter Blicha *(Dir-Engrg)*
Omid Eslamipour *(Dir-Quality Assurance & Compliance)*
Claudio Escobedo *(Mgr-Quality Assurance)*
Larry Laputka *(Comptroller)*
Hector Hernandez *(Dir-Ops)*
Steven Teeman *(CFO)*

Subsidiaries:

Airbase Services Inc. (1)
4949 Amon Carter Blvd, Fort Worth, TX 76155
Tel.: (214) 677-9623
Web Site: http://www.regentaerospace.com
Sales Range: $25-49.9 Million
Emp.: 40
Aircraft & Heavy Equipment Repair Services
N.A.I.C.S.: 811310
Lena Watters *(Pres)*

REGENT CAPITAL CORPORATION
105 N Maple, Nowata, OK 74048
Tel.: (918) 273-1227
Web Site: https://www.bankregent.com
Year Founded: 2008
Bank Holding Company
N.A.I.C.S.: 551111

Subsidiaries:

Regent Bank Na (1)
212 W Cherokee Ave, Nowata, OK 74048
Tel.: (918) 273-3683
Web Site: http://www.bankregent.com
Rev.: $1,505,000
Emp.: 5
Banking Services
N.A.I.C.S.: 522110
Sean Kouplen *(CEO)*
Darin Kent *(Pres)*

REGENT CONTRACTING CORP.
6105 Transit Rd Ste 140, East Amherst, NY 14051-2611
Tel.: (716) 639-0396
Web Site: http://www.regent-companies.com
Year Founded: 1990
Real Estate Development, Construction, Property Management & Leasing Services
N.A.I.C.S.: 236220
David Huck *(Pres)*

Subsidiaries:

RDI, LLC (1)
6105 Transit Rd Ste 140, East Amherst, NY 14051
Tel.: (716) 639-0396
Web Site: http://www.regent-companies.com
Real Estate Development, Property Management & Leasing Services
N.A.I.C.S.: 531390

REGENT ENTERTAINMENT PARTNERSHIP, L.P.
10990 Wilshire Blvd Ph 1800, Los Angeles, CA 90024
Tel.: (310) 806-4288 TX
Web Site: http://www.regententertainment.com
Sales Range: $25-49.9 Million
Emp.: 12
Holding Company; Motion Picture Production & Distribution
N.A.I.C.S.: 551112
Stephen P. Jarchow *(Co-Founder & Chm)*
Paul A. Colichman *(Co-Founder)*

Subsidiaries:

Regent Entertainment, Inc. (1)
2323 Bryan Street 2200 Americas Towers, Dallas, TX 75201
Tel.: (214) 373-3434
Motion Picture Distribution Services
N.A.I.C.S.: 512120
Mary Garcia *(Dir-Admin)*

REGENT INTERNATIONAL
1411 Broadway 7th Fl, New York, NY 10018
Tel.: (212) 398-1006 NY
Sales Range: $75-99.9 Million
Emp.: 40
Mfr of Women's Apparel
N.A.I.C.S.: 424350
Jack Shweky *(Pres)*
Michael Shweky *(VP)*
Richard Shweky *(VP)*
Grace Cruse *(Mgr-Acctg)*

REGENT SPORTS CORPORATION
45 Ranick Rd, Hauppauge, NY 11788
Tel.: (631) 234-2800
Rev.: $49,800,000
Emp.: 100
Sporting & Recreation Goods
N.A.I.C.S.: 423910
Dan Grill *(Controller)*
Joe Stepnowsky *(Mgr-Premium Sls-Eastern Reg & Intl)*
Denise O'Hara *(Mgr-Pur)*
Ivan Kelley *(Mgr-Inventory Control)*
Jeff Patrissi *(Product Mgr)*
Peter Palazzolo *(Mgr-Warehouse)*

REGENT SQUARE CAPITAL, LLC
Regent Sq, Pittsburgh, PA 15221
Tel.: (412) 387-7660
Web Site: http://www.regentsquarecapital.com
Privater Equity Firm
N.A.I.C.S.: 523999
Jason Lewis *(Mng Partner)*

Subsidiaries:

Generator Source, LLC (1)
625 Baseline Rd, Brighton, CO 80603
Tel.: (720) 996-0865
Web Site: http://www.generatorsource.com
Motor Vehicle Supplies & New Parts
N.A.I.C.S.: 423120

REGENT SYSTEMS, INC.
7590 Paragon Rd, Dayton, OH 45459-4065
Tel.: (937) 640-8010
Web Site: http://www.regentsystems.com
Sales Range: $10-24.9 Million
Emp.: 60
IT Consulting Services
N.A.I.C.S.: 541519
Michael Bernal *(Chm)*
Richard Nagel *(CFO)*
Michaels Account *(CEO)*

REGENT TECHNOLOGIES, INC.
5646 Milton Ste 718, Dallas, TX 75206
Web Site: http://www.regent-tec.com
Year Founded: 1980
Assets: $4,888,519
Liabilities: $135,079
Net Worth: $4,753,440
Earnings: ($112,704)
Fiscal Year-end: 12/31/17
Oil & Natural Gas Exploration Services
N.A.I.C.S.: 211120

REGENT, L.P.
9720 Wilshire Blvd, Beverly Hills, CA 90212
Tel.: (310) 299-4100
Web Site: http://www.regentlp.com
Privater Equity Firm
N.A.I.C.S.: 523999
Michael A. Reinstein *(Founder, Chm & CEO)*

Subsidiaries:

Accell North America, Inc. (1)
6004 S 190th St Ste 101, Kent, WA 98032 (100%)
Tel.: (253) 395-1100
Web Site: http://www.accellconnect.com
Emp.: 70
Bicycles & Parts Dist
N.A.I.C.S.: 423910
Larry Pizzi *(Sr VP-Sls & Mktg)*
Stuart Johnson *(Chief Mktg & Digital Officer)*

Current Media Group, LLC (1)
1025 E Woodmen Rd, Colorado Springs, CO 80920
Tel.: (800) 457-5975
Web Site: http://www.currentcatalog.com
Stationery Product Whslr
N.A.I.C.S.: 424120

Subsidiary (Domestic):

Lillian Vernon Corporation (2)
PO Box 35022, Colorado Springs, CO 80935-3522
Tel.: (800) 545-5426
Web Site: http://www.lillianvernon.com
Assorted Gifts & Products Online Retailer
N.A.I.C.S.: 455219

EDOB Abwicklungs AG (1)
Einsteinring 14-18, 85609, Aschheim, Germany
Tel.: (49) 8999440
Web Site: http://www.escada.com
Women's Clothing & Accessories Designer, Distr & Retailer
N.A.I.C.S.: 424350
Reinhard D. Pollath *(Chm-Supervisory Bd)*
Stephen Croncota *(CMO)*
Megha Mittal *(Chm)*
Marco Raab *(VP-Mktg & Comm)*
Iris Epple-Righi *(CEO)*
Niall Sloan *(Dir-Design)*

Subsidiary (US):

Escada America LLC (2)
26 Main St Ste 101, Chatham, NJ 07928
Tel.: (973) 635-1802
Women's Fashion Apparel & Accessories Distr & Retailer
N.A.I.C.S.: 424350

Subsidiary (Non-US):

Escada Benelux BV (2)
Nieuwstraat 156 D, 5126 CH, Gilze, Netherlands
Tel.: (31) 161745040
Women Apparel Distr
N.A.I.C.S.: 424350

Subsidiary (US):

Escada Canada Inc. (2)
1412 Broadway, New York, NY 10018 (100%)
Tel.: (212) 852-5300
Web Site: http://www.escada.com
Sales Range: $25-49.9 Million
Emp.: 12
Women's Clothing Mfr
N.A.I.C.S.: 315250

Subsidiary (Non-US):

Escada France S.A. (2)
19 32 Paris Ten, 75009, Paris, France (100%)
Tel.: (33) 149701521
Web Site: http://www.escada.com
Sales Range: $25-49.9 Million
Emp.: 80
Provider of Women's Apparel
N.A.I.C.S.: 315210

Escada Hong Kong Ltd. (2)
20/F East Warwick House Taikoo Place 979 Kings Road, Hong Kong, China (Hong Kong) (100%)
Tel.: (852) 28454321
Sales Range: $25-49.9 Million
Emp.: 30
Women's Apparel & Accessories
N.A.I.C.S.: 424350

Escada Italia S.r.l. (2)
Via Solforino 19, Milan, 20121, Italy
Tel.: (39) 0229003141
Web Site: http://www.escada.com
Provider of Women's Apparel
N.A.I.C.S.: 315210

Escada Japan Co. Ltd. (2)
550 Nishihonmachi Mitsui Building, 1-3-15 Awaza, Osaka, Japan
Web Site: http://www.escada.com
Provider of Women's Apparel
N.A.I.C.S.: 315210

Escada Korea Ltd. (2)
4th & 5th Floors Wookyung Building 98-13 Chungdam-dong, Kangnam-ku, Seoul, Korea (South)
Web Site: http://www.escada.com
Provider of Women's Apparel
N.A.I.C.S.: 315210

Escada Monte Carlo S.A.M. (2)
27 Av de la costa, Montemonaco, 98000, Monte Carlo, Monaco
Tel.: (377) 33149701515
Women Apparel Distr
N.A.I.C.S.: 424350

Escada Portugal Unipessoal Limitada (2)
Calcada da Estrela 76, 1200-665, Lisbon, Portugal
Tel.: (351) 213969071
Women Apparel Distr
N.A.I.C.S.: 424350

Escada Switzerland Ltd. (2)
Lussiweg 37, 6301, Zug, Switzerland
Tel.: (41) 498999440
Women Apparel Distr
N.A.I.C.S.: 424350

Escada Textilien-Vertriebsges.m.b.H. (2)
Alter Markt 5, 5020, Salzburg, Austria
Tel.: (43) 662849612
Women Apparel Distr
N.A.I.C.S.: 424350

Escada UK Ltd. (2)
5 Fl W Shropshire House 2-10 Capper St,

REGENT, L.P.

Regent, L.P.—(Continued)
Marylebone, London, W1G9NB, United Kingdom (100%)
Tel.: (44) 2075806066
Web Site: http://www.escada.com
Sales Range: $25-49.9 Million
Emp.: 5
Whslr of Ladies Fashion
N.A.I.C.S.: 541490

Grupo Escada Espana S.A.U. (2)
Fonollar 4, 08241, Manresa, Spain
Tel.: (34) 938751000
Web Site: http://de.escada.com
Women's Apparel Store Operator
N.A.I.C.S.: 458110

Fine Stationery, Inc. (1)
1313 N Market St Ste 303, Wilmington, DE 19801
Tel.: (888) 808-3463
Web Site: http://www.finestationery.com
Emp.: 80
Office Supplies & Stationery Stores
N.A.I.C.S.: 459410
Steve Bach (Sr Dir-IT)

HistoryNet, LLC (1)
1919 Gallows Rd Ste 400, Vienna, VA 22182
Tel.: (703) 771-9400
Web Site: http://www.historynet.com
Historical Magazines Publisher
N.A.I.C.S.: 513120
Dana Shoaf (Editor-Civil War Times Magazine)

La Senza Corporation (1)
1604 St-Regis Boulevard, Dorval, H9P 1H6, QC, Canada
Tel.: (514) 684-3651
Web Site: http://www.lasenzacorporation.com
Sales Range: $300-349.9 Million
Emp.: 100
Lingerie & Apparel Retailer
N.A.I.C.S.: 459999

NexTag, Inc. (1)
555 Twin Dolphin Dr Ste 370, Redwood City, CA 94065
Tel.: (650) 293-0424
Web Site: http://www.nextag.com
Comparison Shopping Search Engine
N.A.I.C.S.: 541519
Amy Jarman (VP-HR)

Private Sale GmbH (1)
Einsteinring 28, 85609, Aschheim, Germany
Tel.: (49) 30890605800
Web Site: http://www.brands4friends.de
Online Shopping Club for Fashion & Lifestyle
N.A.I.C.S.: 458110
Nina Putz (CEO & Mng Dir)
Norbert Domek (Mng Dir & COO)
Torsten Wolf (CMO)
Sebastian Possner (CTO)

Sightline Media Group, LLC (1)
1919 Gallows Rd Ste 400, Vienna, VA 22182
Tel.: (703) 750-7400
Web Site: http://www.sightlinemediagroup.com
Military News Organization
N.A.I.C.S.: 516210
Jill Aitoro (Exec Editor-Bus to Govt Grp)
Christine Aquino (VP-Bus Ops)
Mort Greenberg (Sr VP-Adv Sls)
Jerry Foley (Dir-B2G Global Sls)
Shawn Byers (VP-Audience Dev & Circulation)

Subsidiary (Domestic):

American Police Beat (2)
505 8th Ave Ste 1004, New York, NY 10018
Tel.: (646) 726-4833
Web Site: http://www.apbweb.com
Law Enforcement Monthly Print Publications
N.A.I.C.S.: 513120
Dave Quimby (Dir-Adv Sls)

Army Times Publishing Company (2)
6883 Commercial Dr, Springfield, VA 22159-0001
Tel.: (703) 750-7400
Web Site: http://www.armytimes.com

Sales Range: $25-49.9 Million
Periodical Publisher for Military, Aerospace & Federal Employees
N.A.I.C.S.: 513120
Richard Sandza (Mng Editor)
Kathleen Curthoys (Editor-News)

Sunset Publishing Corporation (1)
80 Willow Rd, Menlo Park, CA 94025-3661 (100%)
Tel.: (650) 321-3600
Web Site: http://www.sunset.com
Magazines & Books Publisher
N.A.I.C.S.: 513120

The Beautiful Group Management, LLC (1)
9720 Wilshire Blvd 6th Fl, Beverly Hills, CA 90212
Tel.: (310) 299-4100
Luxury Salon & Spa Operator
N.A.I.C.S.: 812112

zulily, llc (1)
2601 Elliott Ave Ste 200, Seattle, WA 98121
Tel.: (206) 800-9500
Web Site: https://www.zulily.com
Sales Range: $1-4.9 Billion
Emp.: 2,907
E-Commerce Website
N.A.I.C.S.: 455219
Luke Friang (CIO & Sr VP)
Robert Spieth (COO)
John Lohnas (Sr VP)
Bergitta Trelstad (Gen Counsel & VP)
Ron Kelly (VP-Partner Svcs)
John Starke (VP-Bus Dev)
Rena Wong (CFO & VP-Fin)
Tim Ragland (VP-Analytics)
Terry Boyle (Pres & CEO)

REGIER CARR & MONROE LLP
4801 E Broadway Blvd, Tucson, AZ 85711
Tel.: (520) 624-8229
Web Site: http://www.rcmtulsa.com
Offices of Certified Public Accountants
N.A.I.C.S.: 541211
Jeff Lucas (Mgr-Tax)
Laura Lehmer (Partner)

Subsidiaries:

Kirkpatrick Sprecker & Company, LLP (1)
311 S Hillside St, Wichita, KS 67211-2195
Tel.: (316) 685-1411
Web Site: http://www.kscpa.com
Offices of Certified Public Accountants
N.A.I.C.S.: 541211
Dan Strunk (Partner)
Drew Rooks (Mgr-Tax)
Monty Alen (Partner)

REGINA COMMUNITY NURSING CENTER
550 E Fornance St, Norristown, PA 19401
Tel.: (610) 272-5600 PA
Web Site: http://www.reginanursingcenter.org
Year Founded: 1963
Sales Range: $10-24.9 Million
Emp.: 150
Elder Care Services
N.A.I.C.S.: 623312
Louise McSherry (Dir-Nursing)

REGION 13 EDUCATION SERVICE CENTER
5701 Springdale Rd, Austin, TX 78723
Tel.: (512) 919-5313 TX
Web Site: http://www.esc13.net
Year Founded: 1968
Sales Range: $25-49.9 Million
Emp.: 328
Educational Support Services
N.A.I.C.S.: 611710
Terry Smith (Exec Dir)
Gary L. Barnett (Sec)
Ron McMichael (Chm)
Paul Curtis (Vice Chm)

REGION II COMMISSION ON SERVICES TO THE AGING
102 N Main St, Brooklyn, MI 49230
Tel.: (517) 592-1974 MI
Year Founded: 1974
Sales Range: $10-24.9 Million
Emp.: 59
Senior Living Services
N.A.I.C.S.: 623311
Ginny Wood-Broderick (Sec & Exec Dir)

REGION VII AREA AGENCY ON AGING
1615 S Euclid Ave, Bay City, MI 48706
Tel.: (989) 893-4506 MI
Web Site: http://www.region7aaa.org
Year Founded: 1975
Sales Range: $10-24.9 Million
Emp.: 122
Senior Living Services
N.A.I.C.S.: 623311
Andrew Orvosh (Exec Dir)
Lisa Pijaszek (Mgr-Fiscal)

REGIONAL AIRPORT AUTHORITY
700 Adminstration Dr, Louisville, KY 40209
Tel.: (502) 368-6524
Web Site: http://www.flylouisville.com
Sales Range: $50-74.9 Million
Emp.: 220
Airport
N.A.I.C.S.: 488119
Charles T. Miller (Exec Dir)
Dodie Caulk (Dir-Fin)

REGIONAL CENTER OF THE EAST BAY
500 Davis St Ste 100, San Leandro, CA 94577
Tel.: (510) 618-6100 CA
Web Site: http://www.rceb.org
Year Founded: 1975
Sales Range: $250-299.9 Million
Emp.: 350
Disability Assistance Services
N.A.I.C.S.: 624120
Nancy Kubota (Dir-Fin & Admin)
Pamela Thomas (Dir-Consumer Svcs)
James Burton (Exec Dir)

REGIONAL EMERGENCY MEDICAL SERVICES AUTHORITY
450 Edison Way, Reno, NV 89502
Tel.: (775) 858-5700 NE
Web Site: http://www.remsa-cf.com
Year Founded: 1981
Sales Range: $25-49.9 Million
Emp.: 62
Ambulance Service
N.A.I.C.S.: 621910
Dean Dow (Pres & CEO)
Jim Begbie (Chm)
J. W. Hodge (COO-Healthcare Svcs)
Brenda Staffan (COO-Integrated Svcs)
Barry Duplantis (CFO)

REGIONAL ENERGY HOLDINGS, INC.
535 Connecticut Ave, Norwalk, CT 06854
Tel.: (866) 657-8617
Sales Range: $10-24.9 Million
Holding Company
N.A.I.C.S.: 551112
Michael Fallquist (Pres & CEO)

REGIONAL FOOD BANK OF OKLAHOMA
3355 S Purdue st, Oklahoma City, OK 73179
Tel.: (408) 972-1111 OK
Web Site: https://www.regionalfoodbank.org
Year Founded: 1980
Sales Range: $50-74.9 Million
Emp.: 125
Hunger Relief Services
N.A.I.C.S.: 624210
Rodney W. Bivens (Founder)
James R. Hopper (Treas)
Ray Haefele (Chm)
Karen Jacobs (Sec)
Tressa Madden (Vice Chm)

REGIONAL INDUSTRIAL DEVELOPMENT CORPORATION OF SOUTHWESTERN PENNSYLVANIA INC.
210 6th Ave Ste 3620, Pittsburgh, PA 15222
Tel.: (412) 471-3939 PA
Web Site: http://www.ridc.org
Year Founded: 1955
Sales Range: $25-49.9 Million
Emp.: 24
Industrial Development
N.A.I.C.S.: 541910
Colleen Poremski (Sec)
William C. Kirk (VP-Real Estate Ops)
W. Michael Saul (Controller)
Bobbie J. Snowball (Dir-Leasing)
Donald F. Smith (Pres)
Timothy White (Sr VP-Dev)
Mary Donato (Coord-Property Mgmt)
Ray Maffit (Project Mgr)
Dane Estok (Project Mgr)
Mark McCann (Project Mgr-Construction)
Jim Palochik (Dir-Construction Svcs)
Fred Hayes (Program Mgr)
Beth Hoffman (Asst Controller)
Don Johnson (Sr Mgr-Dev)
Daniel Sharek (Dir-Engrg Svcs)
Dennis Joyce (COO)

REGIONAL INTERNATIONAL CORP.
1007 Lehigh Sta Rd, Henrietta, NY 14467-9311
Tel.: (585) 359-2011 NY
Web Site: http://www.regionalinternational.com
Year Founded: 1989
Sales Range: $25-49.9 Million
Emp.: 80
Trucks, Trailers & Buses Mfr
N.A.I.C.S.: 423110
James D. Carello (Pres)
Mike Jenks (Controller)

REGIONAL MANAGEMENT, INC.
11 E Fayette St, Baltimore, MD 21202-1606
Tel.: (410) 539-2370
Web Site: http://www.regionalmgmt.com
Year Founded: 1959
Sales Range: $10-24.9 Million
Emp.: 300
Real Estate Services
N.A.I.C.S.: 531210
Nadine Hartman (Dir-HR)
Amy Macht (Pres)
Peter Grose (VP)

REGIONAL ONE HEALTH
877 Jefferson Ave, Memphis, TN 38103
Tel.: (901) 545-7100 TN
Web Site: http://www.regionalonehealth.org
Year Founded: 1981

Sales Range: $350-399.9 Million
Emp.: 2,828
Health Care Srvices
N.A.I.C.S.: 622110
Reginald W. Coopwood *(Pres & CEO)*
Sarah Colley *(Sr VP-HR)*
Rick Wagers *(CFO & Sr Exec VP)*
Tammie Ritchey *(VP-Dev)*
Tish Towns *(Sr VP-External Rels)*
Phil Shannon *(Chm)*
Susan Cooper *(Chief Integration Officer & Sr VP)*
Jackie Lucas *(CIO & Sr VP)*
Imad Abdullah *(Chief Legal Officer)*

REGIONAL REPORTING INC.
90 John St Ste 702, New York, NY 10038
Tel.: (212) 964-5973
Web Site: http://www.regionalreporting.com
Year Founded: 1963
Sales Range: $10-24.9 Million
Emp.: 360
Provider of Loss Prevention Consulting Services to Insurance Industry
N.A.I.C.S.: 524298
Martin Myers *(CEO)*
Louis Siegel *(Pres)*
Allan Myers *(Exec VP)*
John Senatore *(Branch Mgr)*
Tammy Seddon *(Branch Mgr)*

REGIONAL TRANSIT AUTHORITY
2817 Canal St, New Orleans, LA 70119
Tel.: (504) 248-3900
Web Site: http://www.norta.com
Year Founded: 1979
Sales Range: $1-9.9 Million
Emp.: 1,700
Local & Suburban Transit Services
N.A.I.C.S.: 485113
John Hertel *(CEO-Southeastern Michigan)*
Greg Cook *(Exec Dir)*
Earline Roth *(Vice Chm)*
Justin T. Augustine III *(Gen Mgr)*
Flozell Daniels Jr. *(Chm)*

REGIONAL TRANSPORTATION AUTHORITY
175 W Jackson Blvd Ste 1650, Chicago, IL 60604
Tel.: (312) 913-3200 IL
Web Site: http://www.rtachicago.org
Year Founded: 1974
Sales Range: $1-4.9 Billion
Emp.: 1,630
Transportation
N.A.I.C.S.: 926120
Bea Reyna-Hickey *(CFO)*
Leanne Redden *(Exec Dir)*
Kirk Dillard *(Chm)*
Nadine Lacombe *(Gen Counsel)*

Subsidiaries:

Chicago Transit Authority (1)
567 W Lake St, Chicago, IL 60661
Tel.: (312) 664-7200
Web Site: http://www.transitchicago.com
Sales Range: $25-49.9 Million
Emp.: 500
Local Passenger Transportation
N.A.I.C.S.: 485999
Eva-Dina Delgado *(Chief Dev Officer)*
Paris Bradley *(Mgr-Rail Customer Svc)*
Karyn Usher *(Mgr)*

Northeast Illinois Regional Commuter Railroad Corporation (1)
547 W Jackson Blvd Ste 1400, Chicago, IL 60661
Tel.: (312) 322-6777
Web Site: http://www.metrarail.com

Sales Range: $10-24.9 Million
Emp.: 300
Rail Passenger Transportation & Commuter Rail Services
N.A.I.C.S.: 485112

Pace (1)
550 W Algonquin Rd, Arlington Heights, IL 60005-4412
Tel.: (847) 364-7223
Web Site: http://www.pacebus.com
Sales Range: $125-149.9 Million
Emp.: 1,500
Suburban Bus Services
N.A.I.C.S.: 485113
Susan Moss *(Dir-Sls)*
David Carter *(Dir-Courier Ops)*

REGIONAL TRANSPORTATION DISTRICT INC.
1600 Blake St, Denver, CO 80202-1324
Tel.: (303) 628-9000
Web Site: http://www.rtd-denver.com
Year Founded: 1969
Sales Range: $100-124.9 Million
Emp.: 2,482
Provider of Local & Suburban Transit Services
N.A.I.C.S.: 485113
Larry Hoy *(Chm)*
Jeff Walker *(Sec)*
Natalie Menten *(Treas)*
Michael Ford *(COO)*
Debra Johnson *(CEO & Gen Mgr)*

REGIONAL UTILITY SERVICES, INC.
2400 Cannons Campground Rd, Spartanburg, SC 29307
Tel.: (864) 327-1993
Web Site: https://rus-inc.com
Year Founded: 2006
Facilities Services
N.A.I.C.S.: 561210
Dan Cothran *(CEO)*

REGIONS FACILITY SERVICES INC.
2314 Circuit Way, Brooksville, FL 34604
Tel.: (352) 848-2591
Web Site: http://www.regionsfacilityservices.com
Year Founded: 2003
Sales Range: $10-24.9 Million
Emp.: 30
Facilities Maintenance, Renovation, & Support Services
N.A.I.C.S.: 561210
Ron Wilhite *(Founder & CEO)*

REGISTRAR & TRANSFER COMPANY
10 Commerce Dr, Cranford, NJ 07016
Tel.: (908) 497-2300
Web Site: http://www.rtco.com
Year Founded: 1899
Sales Range: $50-74.9 Million
Emp.: 170
Security Transfer Agents
N.A.I.C.S.: 523940
William T. Saeger *(VP-Mktg)*
Thomas Montrone *(Pres & CEO)*
Mary Cascaes *(COO & Exec VP)*

REGISTRY NETWORK, INC.
1207 Carlsbad Village Dr Ste X, Carlsbad, CA 92008
Tel.: (760) 966-3700
Web Site: http://www.registrynetwork.net
Sales Range: $1-9.9 Million
Emp.: 160
Medical Help Service
N.A.I.C.S.: 561320

Laura Moeller *(Treas)*
John Fusco *(Pres & CEO)*

REGITAR U.S.A., INC.
2575 Container Dr, Montgomery, AL 36109
Tel.: (334) 244-1885
Web Site: http://www.regitar.com
Rev.: $21,500,000
Emp.: 34
Hardware Merchant Whslr
N.A.I.C.S.: 423710
John Ingle *(Mgr-Warehouse)*
Gary S. Tsai *(Mgr-Ops)*

REGULATORY ASSISTANCE PROJECT
50 State St Ste 3, Montpelier, VT 05602
Tel.: (802) 223-8199 ME
Web Site: http://www.raponline.org
Year Founded: 1992
Sales Range: $10-24.9 Million
Emp.: 20
Management Consulting Services
N.A.I.C.S.: 541611
Christine Salembier *(COO)*
Christopher James *(Principal)*
Yannick Georges *(Mgr-Ops)*
Camille Kadoch *(Mgr-Publ)*
Catherine Mitchell *(Sec)*
Richard Sedano *(Sec)*
Carl Weinberg *(Vice Chm)*
Cheryl Harrington *(Treas)*

REGUS ADVISORS, INC.
13155 Noel Rd, Dallas, TX 75240
Tel.: (972) 764-8000
Web Site: http://www.regusadvisors.com
Strategic & Financial Advisory Services
N.A.I.C.S.: 523999
C.J. Comu *(Chm)*

Subsidiaries:

Southwest Bottling & Co-Packing, LLC (1)
9761 Clifford Dr Ste 100, Dallas, TX 75220
Tel.: (214) 459-3929
Web Site: http://www.southwestbottling.com
Sales Range: $1-9.9 Million
Emp.: 35
Beverages & Juices Mfr & Distr
N.A.I.C.S.: 312111
Jim Webb *(Mgr-Maintenance)*
Sarvesh Sharma *(CEO)*

REH HOLDINGS INC.
150 S Sumner St, York, PA 17404
Tel.: (717) 843-0021
Web Site: http://www.rehholdings.com
Sales Range: $50-74.9 Million
Emp.: 100
Guardrail Construction, Highways
N.A.I.C.S.: 237310
Basil A. Shorb III *(CEO)*

Subsidiaries:

Elderlee, Inc. (1)
729 Cross Rd, Oaks Corners, NY 14518
Tel.: (315) 789-6670
Web Site: http://www.elderlee.com
Highway Safety Product Mfr
N.A.I.C.S.: 332322
Linda Crowther *(Controller)*

L.S. Lee Inc. (1)
152 S Sumner St, York, PA 17404
Tel.: (717) 854-7000
Web Site: http://www.lslee.com
Sales Range: $1-9.9 Million
Emp.: 30
Guardrail Construction, Highways
N.A.I.C.S.: 237310
Basil A. Shorb III *(CEO)*

REH Holdings Inc (1)
150 S Sumner St, York, PA 17404

Tel.: (717) 843-0021
Rev.: $57,000
Emp.: 10
Aircraft Rental
N.A.I.C.S.: 532411
William Shorb *(CEO)*

REHAB ASSOCIATES
159 W Main St, Newark, OH 43055
Tel.: (740) 345-2837
Web Site: http://rehabassociates.net
Year Founded: 1984
Physiotherapy Clinic Operator
N.A.I.C.S.: 621340
Paul Kaple *(Owner & Pres)*
Andrew Godby *(Mktg Dir)*
Kimberly Woolford *(Coord-Clinic Office)*
Kaitlin King *(Coord-Accts)*
Krista Arthur *(Coord-Office)*
Connie Bess *(CEO)*

REHABABILITIES, INC.
8655 Haven Ave Ste 200, Rancho Cucamonga, CA 91730-4891
Tel.: (909) 989-5699 CA
Web Site: http://www.rehababilities.com
Year Founded: 1987
Sales Range: $1-9.9 Million
Emp.: 400
Placement for Rehabilitation Therapy Professionals
N.A.I.C.S.: 561311
Kimberly Jones *(Pres)*

REHABILITATION SUPPORT SERVICES, INC.
5172 Western Tpke, Altamont, NY 12009
Tel.: (518) 464-1511 NY
Web Site: http://www.rehab.org
Year Founded: 1979
Sales Range: $25-49.9 Million
Emp.: 997
Mental Health Care & Substance Abuse Rehabilitation Services
N.A.I.C.S.: 621420
Joy Devita *(Dir-Quality Improvement)*
John Paduano *(Co-Mng Dir)*
Ed Butz *(Co-Mng Dir)*
Gerard Lesczynski *(Co-Mng Dir)*

REHMANN ROBSON PC
5800 Gratiot Rd, Saginaw, MI 48603
Tel.: (989) 799-9580
Web Site: http://www.rehmann.com
Sales Range: $50-74.9 Million
Emp.: 900
Certified Public Accountants
N.A.I.C.S.: 541211
Steven D. Kelly *(Chm & CEO)*
Joan Payne *(CFO)*
Jim Carpp *(Principal & Dir-Consulting)*
Stephen Chang *(Sr Mgr-Audit & Assurance Dept-Troy)*

REHOBOTH MCKINLEY CHRISTIAN HEALTH CARE SERVICES
1901 Red Rock Dr, Gallup, NM 87301
Tel.: (505) 863-7000 NM
Web Site: http://www.rmch.org
Year Founded: 1985
Sales Range: $50-74.9 Million
Emp.: 425
Health Care Srvices
N.A.I.C.S.: 622110
Priscilla Smith *(Chm)*
David Bischoff *(Treas)*
David Dallago *(Vice Chm)*
William Kiefer *(COO)*

REHRIG PACIFIC COMPANY

REHRIG PACIFIC COMPANY

Rehrig Pacific Company—(Continued)
4010 E 26th St, Los Angeles, CA 90058
Tel.: (323) 262-5145   CA
Web Site:
  http://www.rehrigpacific.com
Year Founded: 1913
Sales Range: $150-199.9 Million
Emp.: 450
Provider of Plastic Cases
N.A.I.C.S.: 326199
Will Rehrig *(Pres)*
Brian Yorston *(Dir-Bus Dev-Environmental)*
Scott Lukach *(VP-Environmental)*

Subsidiaries:

Rehrig Pacific Company - Atlanta Plant (1)
1000 Raco Ct, Lawrenceville, GA 30046
Tel.: (770) 339-9888
Plastics Product Mfr
N.A.I.C.S.: 326199

Rehrig Pacific Company - Dallas Plant (1)
625 W Mockingbird Ln, Dallas, TX 75247
Tel.: (214) 631-7943
Plastics Product Mfr
N.A.I.C.S.: 326199

Rehrig Pacific Company - Erie Plant (1)
1738 W 20th St, Erie, PA 16502
Tel.: (814) 455-8023
Web Site: http://www.rehrig.com
Emp.: 160
Plastics Product Mfr
N.A.I.C.S.: 326199
Sam Bernal *(Plant Mgr)*

Rehrig Pacific Company - Kansas Plant (1)
8875 Commerce Dr, De Soto, KS 66018
Tel.: (913) 585-1175
Web Site: http://www.rehrigpacific.com
Emp.: 100
Plastics Product Mfr
N.A.I.C.S.: 326199
Don Hale *(Office Mgr)*

Rehrig Pacific Company - Kenosha Plant (1)
7800 100th St, Pleasant Prairie, WI 53158
Tel.: (262) 947-3312
Plastics Product Mfr
N.A.I.C.S.: 326199

Rehrig Pacific Company - Orlando Plant (1)
7452 Presidents Dr, Orlando, FL 32809
Tel.: (407) 857-3888
Emp.: 20
Plastics Product Mfr
N.A.I.C.S.: 326199
Andres Gutierrez *(Mgr-Plant)*

Rehrig Pacific Company de Mexico S.A. De C.V (1)
La Noria 103 Santa Rosa Jauregui Parque Industrial Queretaro, 76220, Queretaro, Mexico
Tel.: (52) 442 296 2000
Web Site: http://www.rehrigpacific.com.mx
Plastics Product Mfr
N.A.I.C.S.: 326199

REI REAL ESTATE SERVICES LLC
11711 N Pennsylvania St Ste 200, Carmel, IN 46032
Tel.: (317) 573-6050
Web Site: http://www.reires.com
Sales Range: $10-24.9 Million
Emp.: 90
Real Estate Managers
N.A.I.C.S.: 531210
Jeffrey S. Sporleder *(CFO)*
Michael Wells *(Pres)*
Michael D. Napariu *(VP-Sls & Leasing)*
Ryan Wells *(VP-Dev)*

REI SYSTEMS, INC.
45335 Vintage Park Plz, Sterling, VA 20166
Tel.: (703) 256-2245
Web Site: http://www.reisys.com
Year Founded: 1989
Sales Range: $10-24.9 Million
Emp.: 200
Turnkey Web-Enabled Business Management Solutions
N.A.I.C.S.: 541519
Veer Bhartiya *(Co-Founder & Chm)*
Shyam Salona *(Co-Founder & CEO)*
Mamta Pandya *(Engr-QA)*
Sachin Kapoor *(Mgr-Web Design)*
Paul Anninos *(VP)*
Subhash Kari *(VP)*
Jason McGill *(Dir-Bus Dev-Grant Mgmt Sys Line)*
Andrew Zeswitz *(CTO)*
Wagish Bhartiya *(Chief Growth Officer)*
Sid Agarwal *(VP-Health Sys)*

REICH & TANG, INC.
1411 Broadway 28th Fl, New York, NY 10018
Tel.: (212) 830-5240   DE
Web Site:
  http://www.reichandtang.com
Year Founded: 1970
Holding Company; Balance Sheet & Cash Management Services
N.A.I.C.S.: 551112
Michael P. Lydon *(Pres & CEO)*
Joseph Jerkovich *(COO & Exec VP)*
Tom Nelson *(Chief Investment Officer & Exec VP)*
Andrew Mintz *(CIO & Exec VP)*
Steve Genereau *(Chief Deposit Officer & Exec VP)*
Christine Butwill *(Sr VP & Controller)*
Eric Ho *(Sr VP & IT/Security Officer)*
Chris Gill *(Sr VP-Ops)*
Carol Stark *(Sr VP-HR)*
Walter Cotumaccio *(Sr VP-Natl Sls & Relationship Mgmt)*
Jason Blair *(Exec Mng Dir-Strategic Deposit Relationships)*
Teresa Murphy *(VP-Mktg)*

Subsidiaries:

Reich & Tang Deposit Networks, LLC (1)
1411 Broadway 28th Fl, New York, NY 10018
Web Site: http://www.reichandtang.com
Balance Sheet & Cash Management Services
N.A.I.C.S.: 522320
Tom Ormseth *(Exec VP & Head-Banking)*
Joe Jerkovich *(CEO)*
Steve Genereau *(Chief Deposit Officer & Exec VP)*

REICHARD STAFFING, INC.
6622 Southpoint Dr S Ste 190, Jacksonville, FL 32216
Tel.: (904) 296-0414   FL
Web Site:
  http://www.reichardstaffing.com
Year Founded: 2001
Sales Range: $1-9.9 Million
Emp.: 9
Employee Placement
N.A.I.C.S.: 561311
Sean Reichard *(Founder)*
Ashley O'Donnell *(Acct Exec)*

REICHERT CHEVROLET BUICK OF WOODSTOCK
2145 S Eastwood Dr, Woodstock, IL 60098-4604
Tel.: (815) 345-4978
Web Site:
  http://www.reichertwoodstock.com
Sales Range: $25-49.9 Million
Emp.: 26
New & Used Automobile Dealership
N.A.I.C.S.: 441110
John M. Reichert *(Chm)*

REICHHOLD, INC.
1035 Swabia Ct, Durham, NC 27703
Tel.: (919) 990-7500
Web Site: http://www.reichhold.com
Year Founded: 1927
Sales Range: $400-449.9 Million
Emp.: 1,300
Synthetic Resin Coating Resin Latex Polymer & Adhesive Mfr
N.A.I.C.S.: 325211
John Gaither *(Pres & CEO)*

Subsidiaries:

Polynt S.p.A. (1)
Via Enrico Fermi 51, 24020, Scanzorosciate, BG, Italy
Tel.: (39) 035 65 21 11
Web Site: http://www.polynt.com
Intermediate Polymers & Resins Mfr
N.A.I.C.S.: 325180
Rosario Valido *(CEO)*
Mario Novelli *(COO)*
Sergio Moreno *(Sr VP & Gen Mgr-America)*
Paolo Carugati *(CFO)*
Alberto Milesi *(COO-GM Polynt Chemical Changzhou-Asia)*
Massimiliano Schiavi *(Dir-Sites & EMEA HR)*
Maurizio Leonardi *(COO-Polynt Composites EMEA)*

Subsidiary (Non-US):

Polynt Chemical (Changzhou) Co. Ltd. (2)
Chemical Industrial Park Xinbei District N 10 Port Avenue, Chunjiang County, Changzhou, 213033, China
Tel.: (86) 519 5778998
Web Site: http://www.polynt.com
Sales Range: $50-74.9 Million
Emp.: 120
Chemicals Mfr
N.A.I.C.S.: 325998

Polynt Composites Australia Pty Ltd. (2)
Level 1 16 Tullamarine Park Road, Tullamarine, 3043, VIC, Australia
Tel.: (61) 3 9339 7300
Web Site: http://www.ccpcomposites.com.au
Emp.: 30
Resin Mfr
N.A.I.C.S.: 325211
Neil Cesir *(Gen Mgr)*

Polynt Composites France S.A. (2)
Route d Arras CS 50019, Drocourt, 62320, France
Tel.: (33) 3 21 74 84 00
Polyester Product Distr
N.A.I.C.S.: 424610

Polynt Composites Germany GmbH (2)
Kieselstrasse, Miehlen, Germany
Tel.: (49) 67 72 93 21 0
Polyester Product Distr
N.A.I.C.S.: 424610

Polynt Composites Korea Co. Ltd (2)
51 Wanju Sandan 4-ro, Wanju-gun, Bongdong-eup, 55321, Jeollabuk-do, Korea (South)
Tel.: (82) 63 260 2114
Web Site: http://www.polynt.co.kr
Resin Mfr
N.A.I.C.S.: 325211
Rosario Valido *(Pres)*
Seil Kim *(Mng Dir)*

Polynt Composites Malaysia Sdn. Bhd. (2)
Plo n 491 Jalan Keluli, Pasir Gudang Industrial Estate, 81700, Johor, Malaysia
Tel.: (60) 7 256 5610
Web Site: http://www.polynt.com
Emp.: 10
Polyester Product Distr
N.A.I.C.S.: 424610

Polynt Composites Poland Sp. z o.o. (2)
Ul Grabska 11d, Niepolomice, 32005, Poland
Tel.: (48) 12 281 42 00
Polyester Product Distr
N.A.I.C.S.: 424610

Polynt Composites Spain, S.L. (2)
Avenida Republica Argentina s/n, Miranda de Ebro, Burgos, 9200, Spain
Tel.: (34) 947 027 204
Web Site: http://www.polynt.com
Polyester Product Distr
N.A.I.C.S.: 424610

Polynt Composites UK Ltd (2)
Laporte Road Stallingborough Near Grimsby North East, Grimsby, DN 18DR, Lincolnshire, United Kingdom
Tel.: (44) 1 469 552570
Polyester Product Distr
N.A.I.C.S.: 424610

Polynt GmbH (2)
Kieselstrasse 2, Miehlen, 56357, Germany (100%)
Tel.: (49) 677293210
Web Site: http://www.polynt.com
Sales Range: $25-49.9 Million
Production & Sales of Chemicals
N.A.I.C.S.: 325998
Peter Schmidt *(Gen Mgr)*

Subsidiary (US):

Polynt Group Holding Inc. (2)
99 E Cottage Ave, Carpentersville, IL 60110
Tel.: (360) 736-1679
Holding Company; Regional Managing Office
N.A.I.C.S.: 551112

Subsidiary (Non-US):

Polynt Composites Brazil Ltda. (3)
Rua Aurea Tavares 480/580 Parque Industrial das Oliveiras, Taboao da Serra, 06765-440, Sao Paolo, Brazil
Tel.: (55) 11 2147 2700
Web Site: http://www.ccpcomposites.com.br
Resin Mfr
N.A.I.C.S.: 325211

Polynt Composites Canada Inc. (3)
90 Hoka Street, Winnipeg, R2C 3N2, MB, Canada
Tel.: (204) 668-4900
Web Site: http://www.ccpcomposites.ca
Adhesive Product Mfr
N.A.I.C.S.: 325520
Garth Danchuk *(Mgr-Western Canada)*

Branch (Domestic):

Polynt Composites Canada Inc. (4)
2650 Rue Therese-Casgrain, Drummondville, J2A 4J5, QC, Canada
Tel.: (819) 477-4516
Web Site: http://www.ccpcomposites.ca
Emp.: 33
Raw Material for the Composites Industry
N.A.I.C.S.: 424590
Michel Reid *(Branch Mgr)*

Subsidiary (Domestic):

Polynt Composites USA Inc. (3)
99 E Cottage Ave, Carpentersville, IL 60110
Tel.: (847) 428-2657
Web Site: http://www.pccrusa.com
Sales Range: $1-4.9 Billion
Resin & Colorant Mfr
N.A.I.C.S.: 325180
David James *(Coord-Warehouse & Inventory)*
Martin Gudmundson *(Mgr-Site)*
Matthew Hayden *(Product Mgr-Line)*

Subsidiary (Non-US):

Polynt Hong Kong CO., Limited (2)
Flat D 25/F Capital Trade Centre 62 Chun Yip Street, Kwun Tong, Kowloon, China (Hong Kong)
Tel.: (852) 2865 3821
Resin Mfr
N.A.I.C.S.: 325211

Polynt Iberica, S.L. (2)

COMPANIES

Calle Pelayo 11 Principal C, Barcelona, Spain
Tel.: (34) 93 00 47 011
Resin Mfr
N.A.I.C.S.: 325211

Plant (Domestic):

Polynt S.p.A. - Brembate di Sopra Plant (2)
Via Caduti e ispersi dell'Aeronautica 18, Brembate di Sopra, 24030, BG, Italy
Tel.: (39) 035 62 31 00
Web Site: http://www.polynt.com
Sales Range: $25-49.9 Million
Chemicals Mfr
N.A.I.C.S.: 325998

Polynt S.p.A. - Cavaglia Plant (2)
Via Abate Bertone 10, 13881, Cavaglia, BI, Italy
Tel.: (39) 0161 996611
Web Site: http://www.polynt.com
Sales Range: $25-49.9 Million
Chemicals Mfr
N.A.I.C.S.: 325998
Enrico Carrea (Gen Mgr)

Polynt S.p.A. - Ravenna Plant (2)
Via Baiona 192, 48100, Ravenna, Italy
Tel.: (39) 0544 457 011
Web Site: http://www.polynt.com
Sales Range: $25-49.9 Million
Emp.: 65
Chemicals Mfr
N.A.I.C.S.: 325998

Polynt S.p.A. - San Giovanni Valdarno Plant (2)
Via Del Pruneto 40, San Giovanni Valdarno, 52027, AR, Italy
Tel.: (39) 055 91 28 1
Web Site: http://www.polynt.com
Sales Range: $50-74.9 Million
Emp.: 243
Intermediate Polymers & Resins Mfr
N.A.I.C.S.: 325180
Massimo Eapanni (Mgr)

Subsidiary (Non-US):

Polynt Sp. z o.o. (2)
Ul Grabska 11d, 32005, Niepolomice, Poland
Tel.: (48) 12 281 42 00
Web Site: http://www.polynt.com
Sales Range: $25-49.9 Million
Chemicals & Resins Mfr
N.A.I.C.S.: 325998
Thomasz Jirecki (Gen Mgr)

Polynt UK Ltd. (2)
Station Road, Cheddleton Nr Leek, Leek, ST13 7EF, Staffordshire, United Kingdom
Tel.: (44) 1538 369000
Web Site: http://www.polynt.com
Sales Range: $25-49.9 Million
Emp.: 42
Chemicals Mfr
N.A.I.C.S.: 325998
Chris Beff (Gen Mgr)

Reichhold AS (1)
Klinestadmoen 9, Sandefjord, 3241, Norway
Tel.: (47) 33448600
Emp.: 35
Plastic Materials Mfr
N.A.I.C.S.: 325211
Egil Holtmon (Dir-Tech)

Reichhold CZ s.r.o (1)
Veleslavinova 10, Usti nad Labem, 40011, Czech Republic
Tel.: (420) 472707777
Polyester Resin Distr
N.A.I.C.S.: 424610

Reichhold Finance BV (1)
Lichtenauerlaan 102-120, 3062 ME, Rotterdam, Netherlands
Tel.: (31) 102045575
Sales Range: $10-24.9 Million
Emp.: 20
Plastics Product Mfr
N.A.I.C.S.: 326199
Abby Ho (Mgr-Fin)

Reichhold GmbH (1)
Winsbergring 25, 22525, Hamburg, Germany (100%)
Tel.: (49) 408539920

Sales Range: $25-49.9 Million
Emp.: 10
Composites Mfr
N.A.I.C.S.: 424610

Reichhold India Private Limited (1)
F-38 Midc Ranjangaon Industrial Area, Shirur taluka, Pune, 412220, Maharashtra, India
Tel.: (91) 2138675000
Plastics Product Mfr
N.A.I.C.S.: 326199

Reichhold Kimya Sanayi ve Ticaret AS (1)
Kale Agasi Sok No 5/Bm, Rumeli Hisari, Istanbul, Turkiye
Tel.: (90) 2122637821
Plastic Materials Mfr
N.A.I.C.S.: 326199

Reichhold Limited (1)
50 Douglas Street, Port Moody, V3H 3L9, BC, Canada
Tel.: (604) 939-1181
Web Site: http://www.reichhold.com
Sales Range: $25-49.9 Million
Phenolic Resins, Amino Resins, Solvent-Based Polymers, Emulsion Polymers, Thermosetting Polyesters, Molding Compounds & Treated Fiber Products Mfr
N.A.I.C.S.: 325211
John S. Gaither (Pres & CEO)

Reichhold Oy Ab (1)
Hyljeluodontie 3, FIN-02270, Espoo, Finland
Tel.: (358) 974202200
Web Site: http://www.reichhold.com
Composites Mfr
N.A.I.C.S.: 424610

Reichhold Polymers (Tianjin) LTD. (1)
No 28 Bibo St Hangu Modern Industry Park, TEDA, Tianjin, 300480, China
Tel.: (86) 22 2738 9081
Web Site: http://www.reichhold.com
Polyester Resin Distr
N.A.I.C.S.: 424610

Reichhold SAS (1)
Nord Zone Industriale Nord, BP 17-21, 55400, Etain, France
Tel.: (33) 329870308
Sales Range: $10-24.9 Million
Emp.: 51
Polyester Resin Distr
N.A.I.C.S.: 424610
Nembrini Dertrane (Plant Mgr)

Reichhold Srl (1)
Via Romagnoli 23 San Polo di Torrile, 43056, Parma, Italy
Tel.: (39) 0521 812811
Web Site: http://www.reichhold.com
Emp.: 70
Plastics Product Mfr
N.A.I.C.S.: 326199
Elisa Juatteri (Mgr-Sls)

Reichhold Trading (Beijing) LTD. (1)
Room C Floor 5 Bldg 2 No 99 Kechuang 14 Street, Beijing Economy and Technique Development Area, Beijing, 100176, China
Tel.: (86) 10 5975 5318
Polyester Resin Distr
N.A.I.C.S.: 424610

Reichhold UK Limited (1)
54 Willow Lane, Mitcham, CR4 4NA, Surrey, United Kingdom
Tel.: (44) 20 8648 4684
Unsaturated Polyester Resins Mfr
N.A.I.C.S.: 325211

REICO, INC.
6790 Comml Dr, Springfield, VA 22151-4209
Tel.: (703) 256-6400 VA
Web Site: http://www.reico.com
Year Founded: 1952
Sales Range: $100-124.9 Million
Emp.: 400
Provider of Kitchen, Bathroom & Other Household Fixtures
N.A.I.C.S.: 423310
Richard Maresco (Pres)
Tom Beitenbeck (VP)
Thad Whittenburg (VP-Sls)
Paula Hensley (Controller)

REID MIDDLETON INC.
728 134th St SW Ste 200, Everett, WA 98204
Tel.: (425) 741-3800
Web Site: http://www.reidmiddleton.com
Sales Range: $10-24.9 Million
Emp.: 75
Engineeering Services
N.A.I.C.S.: 541330
Hugh Kuyper (Dir-Civil Projects Grp)
Shannon Kinsella (Dir-Waterfront Grp)
Ken Andersen (Principal)
Wendell Johnson (Dir-Dev Svcs)
Bob Galteland (Pres)
Mike Yeoman (Dir-Survey)
Jim Purkey (Dir-Survey)
Brian Moon (Principal-Structural Engrg)
Jason Emoto (Sr Engr-Structural)

REID PETROLEUM CORP.
100 W Genesee St, Lockport, NY 14095
Tel.: (716) 434-2885 NY
Web Site: http://www.reidpetroleum.com
Year Founded: 1991
Sales Range: $25-49.9 Million
Emp.: 43
Disributors of Gasoline
N.A.I.C.S.: 457120
Paul D. Reid (CEO)
Karen Korphals (CFO)
Paul A. Quebral (Pres)

Subsidiaries:

Erie Petroleum (1)
1502 Greengarden Rd, Erie, PA 16501
Tel.: (814) 456-7516
Web Site: http://www.melzersfuel.com
Sales Range: $25-49.9 Million
Petroleum Whslr
N.A.I.C.S.: 424720

REID/O'DONAHUE & ASSOCIATES INC.
419 S Perry St, Montgomery, AL 36104
Tel.: (334) 263-7812 AL
Year Founded: 1979
Rev.: $20,000,000
Emp.: 17
Fiscal Year-end: 07/31/04
N.A.I.C.S.: 541810
Bruce S. Reid (CEO & Mng Partner)
Shannon O'Donahue (Pres, Creative Dir & Acct Exec)
Claudia O'Donahue (Treas, Sec & Mgr-Production)
Janice Alex (Dir-Media)
Susan Bryan (Acct Exec)
Christen Bozeman (Assoc Dir-Media)
Carol Dennis (Dir-Art)

REIDSVILLE GROCERY CO. INC.
PO Box 929, Reidsville, NC 27323-0929
Tel.: (336) 349-4314
Sales Range: $25-49.9 Million
Emp.: 45
Tobacco & Tobacco Products & Groceries
N.A.I.C.S.: 424940
Peyton Balsley (Pres)

REIFF GRAIN & FEED INC.
1935 Hwy 1 N, Fairfield, IA 52556
Tel.: (641) 472-4136 IA
Web Site: http://www.fairfieldag.com
Year Founded: 1937
Sales Range: $10-24.9 Million
Emp.: 20
Mfr of Grains

REINAUER TRANSPORTATION COMPANIES

N.A.I.C.S.: 424910
David S. Reiff (Pres)

REILEY REALTY, INC.
115 E Main St Ste 7, Saint Anthony, ID 83445
Tel.: (208) 624-4088
Year Founded: 1976
Sales Range: $10-24.9 Million
Emp.: 3
Real Estate Brokerage Services
N.A.I.C.S.: 531210
Robert M. Reiley (Mgr)

REILLY CONSTRUCTION CO. INC.
110 Main St, Ossian, IA 52161
Tel.: (563) 532-9211
Web Site: http://www.reilly-construction.com
Sales Range: $25-49.9 Million
Emp.: 285
Provider of Construction Services
N.A.I.C.S.: 237310
Robert M. Reilly (Pres)
Sandy Meyer (Office Coord)
Larry Thompson (VP)

REILLY ELECTRICAL CONTRACTORS
14 Norfolk Ave, South Easton, MA 02375
Tel.: (508) 230-8001
Web Site: http://www.gorelco.com
Sales Range: $10-24.9 Million
Emp.: 130
General Electrical Contractor
N.A.I.C.S.: 238210
James J. Reilly (Pres)
Thomas B. Aborn (VP-Estimating)

Subsidiaries:

Brewer Electric & Utilities (1)
100 Old Town House Rd, South Yarmouth, MA 02664
Tel.: (508) 394-3211
Web Site: http://www.gorelco.com
Rev.: $22,200,000
Emp.: 20
General Electrical Contractor
N.A.I.C.S.: 237110
James J. Reilly (Owner)

REILY FOODS COMPANY
400 Poydras St 10th Fl, New Orleans, LA 70130
Tel.: (504) 524-6131
Web Site: http://www.reilyproducts.com
Year Founded: 1902
Coffee, Tea, Mayonnaise, Salad Dressings, Cake Flour, Peanut Butter & Cooking Oils Mfr
N.A.I.C.S.: 311941
William B. Reily IV (Pres & CEO)

Subsidiaries:

New England Tea & Coffee Company, LLC (1)
100 Charles St, Malden, MA 02148
Web Site: http://www.newenglandcoffee.com
Roaster & Distr of Coffee & Tea
N.A.I.C.S.: 311920
Murray Fish (VP-Fin)

REINAUER TRANSPORTATION COMPANIES
1983 Richmond Ter, Staten Island, NY 10302
Tel.: (718) 816-8167
Web Site: http://www.reinauer.com
Rev.: $13,700,000
Emp.: 500
Canal & Intracoastal Freight Transportation
N.A.I.C.S.: 483211
Joe Lukenda (Gen Mgr)

REINDEER AUTO RELOCATION

REINDEER AUTO RELOCATION
5100 Charles Ct, Zionsville, IN 46077
Tel.: (317) 299-2878
Web Site:
http://www.reindeerauto.com
Year Founded: 1997
Rev.: $20,800,000
Emp.: 47
Management Consulting Services
N.A.I.C.S.: 541614
C. Ritchie Shewmaker (Exec VP & Principal)
Jo E. Donnar (VP)
Timothy Donnar (CEO & Principal)
Jennifer Carolan (Mgr)

REINDERS INCORPORATED
13400 Watertown Plank Rd, Elm Grove, WI 53122
Tel.: (262) 786-3300
Web Site: http://www.reinders.com
Sales Range: $25-49.9 Million
Emp.: 150
Fertilizer & Fertilizer Materials
N.A.I.C.S.: 424910
Bill Sherer (Mgr-Sls)
Tom Rowe (Dir-Mktg)
Dave Berg (Bus Mgr)
Ann Reinders (Branch Mgr)
Phil Zastrow (Mgr-Golf Irrigation)

REINDL PRINTING INC.
1300 Johnson St, Merrill, WI 54452
Tel.: (715) 536-9537
Web Site:
http://www.reindlprinting.com
Sales Range: $10-24.9 Million
Emp.: 80
Commercial Lithographic Printing
N.A.I.C.S.: 323111
Juile Bushor (Controller)
Richard Reindl (Co-Founder & Pres)

REINEKE FAMILY DEALERSHIPS
1303 Perrysburg Rd, Fostoria, OH 44830
Tel.: (419) 435-7741
Web Site:
http://www.reinekefamilydealerships.com
New & Used Car Dealer
N.A.I.C.S.: 441110
Subsidiaries:

Reineke Ford, Inc. (1)
1303 Perrysburg Rd, Fostoria, OH 44830
Tel.: (419) 435-7741
Web Site:
http://www.reinekefamilydealership.com
Sales Range: $25-49.9 Million
Emp.: 50
New & Used Car Dealer
N.A.I.C.S.: 441110
Thomas A. Reineke (Pres)
Joseph Wolph (Mgr-Internet Sls)
Jeff Long (Gen Mgr)
Kathy Hill (Office Mgr)
Robert Nusser (Mgr-Parts)
Bill Squire (Gen Mgr)

Reineke Lincoln Mercury Mazda Inc. (1)
1350 N Cable Rd, Lima, OH 45805
Tel.: (419) 227-7400
Web Site: http://www.reinekelmm.com
Rev.: $20,000,000
Emp.: 45
New & Used Automobiles
N.A.I.C.S.: 441110
Tom Reineke (Pres)

Reineke Motors, Inc. (1)
1045 E Wyandot Ave, Upper Sandusky, OH 43351
Tel.: (419) 294-2386
Web Site: http://www.reinekes.com

Sales Range: $10-24.9 Million
Emp.: 15
New & Used Car Dealer
N.A.I.C.S.: 441110

Tiffin Ford-Lincoln-Mercury Inc. (1)
2020 W State Rte 18, Tiffin, OH 44883
Tel.: (419) 447-9752
Web Site: http://www.tiffinford.com
Sales Range: $25-49.9 Million
Emp.: 50
New & Used Car Dealer
N.A.I.C.S.: 441110

REINGOLD LINK, LLC
14th St NW Bldg 2901, Washington, DC 20009
Tel.: (202) 559-4446
Web Site: http://www.linksp.com
Year Founded: 2012
Sales Range: $1-9.9 Million
Emp.: 50
Marketing Consulting Services
N.A.I.C.S.: 541613
Michael Akin (Pres)
Corey Barenbrugge (COO)
Molly Barker (Mgr-Editorial)
Molly Flores (Project Mgr)
Julian Flores (Project Mgr)

REINHARDT CORP.
3919 State Hwy 23, West Oneonta, NY 13861
Tel.: (607) 432-6635
Web Site:
http://www.reinhardthomeheating.com
Sales Range: $25-49.9 Million
Emp.: 30
Fuel Oil Dealers
N.A.I.C.S.: 457210
David Harder (Pres)

REINHARDT MOTORS INC.
911 Eastern Blvd, Montgomery, AL 36117
Tel.: (334) 272-7147
Web Site:
http://www.reinhardttoyota.com
Sales Range: $50-74.9 Million
Emp.: 127
Automobiles, New & Used
N.A.I.C.S.: 441110
Mike Reinhardt (VP)
T. Ed Reinhardt (Pres)
Linda Wilson (VP)

REINHART INDUSTRIES INC.
12055 Globe St, Livonia, MI 48150-1142
Tel.: (734) 462-9478
Year Founded: 1992
Sales Range: $10-24.9 Million
Emp.: 20
Industrial Machinery
N.A.I.C.S.: 332710
Mark Schloff (Pres)
Matt Sawyer (Controller)

REINHOLD CORP.
1845 Town Center Blvd Ste 105, Orange Park, FL 32003
Tel.: (904) 269-5857
Web Site: http://reinholdcorp.com
Year Founded: 1931
Sales Range: $75-99.9 Million
Emp.: 12
Nursery Product Whslr
N.A.I.C.S.: 424930
Jack Myers (Pres)

REINKE MANUFACTURING COMPANY, INC.
1040 Rd 5300, Deshler, NE 68340
Tel.: (402) 365-7251 NE
Web Site: http://www.reinke.com
Year Founded: 1954
Sales Range: $10-24.9 Million

Emp.: 500
Agricultural Irrigation Equipment Mfr; Steel Tubing & Oil Casing; Truck Trailers
N.A.I.C.S.: 333111
Beth Landau (Mgr-Adv)
John Zhang (Gen Mgr-China)
Chris Roth (Pres)
Marvin Pascual (Mgr-Northwest)

REISCHLING PRESS, INC.
3325 S 116th St Ste 161, Tukwila, WA 98168
Tel.: (206) 905-5999 WA
Web Site: http://www.rpiprint.com
Year Founded: 1979
Sales Range: $10-24.9 Million
Emp.: 120
Lithographic Commercial Printing
N.A.I.C.S.: 323111
Rick Bellamy (CEO)
Ted Reischling (Pres)
Brett Eddy (CTO)
Rix Kramlich (Gen Mgr-eCommerce Div)

Subsidiaries:

Blurb, Inc. (1)
580 California St Ste 300, San Francisco, CA 94104
Tel.: (415) 364-6300
Web Site: http://www.blurb.com
Sales Range: $25-49.9 Million
Book Publishing
N.A.I.C.S.: 513130
Bruce Watermann (Sr VP-Print Ops)
Gene Domecus (CFO)
Rix Kramlich (CEO)
Kelly Leach (COO)

Picaboo Corporation (1)
100 Carlson Rd, Rochester, NY 14610
Tel.: (855) 537-0050
Web Site: http://www.picaboo.com
Custom Computer Programming Services
N.A.I.C.S.: 541511
Kevin B. McCurdy (Co-Founder & Co-CEO)

REISS CORPORATION INC.
75 Mt Vernon Rd, Englishtown, NJ 07726
Tel.: (732) 446-6100
Web Site: http://www.reissbuilt.com
Year Founded: 1896
Rev.: $71,800,000
Emp.: 100
Molding Primary Plastics
N.A.I.C.S.: 326122
Carl Reiss (Pres)

REKCUT PHOTOGRAPHIC INC.
147 San Marco Ave, Saint Augustine, FL 32085
Tel.: (904) 829-6541
Web Site: http://www.leonards.com
Rev.: $12,430,335
Emp.: 100
Photofinishing Laboratory
N.A.I.C.S.: 812921
Donna Santuccio (Controller)
Leonard Tucker Jr. (Pres)

RELATED FLORIDA, INC.
315 S Biscayne, Miami, FL 33131
Tel.: (305) 460-9900 FL
Web Site:
http://www.relatedgroup.com
Year Founded: 1979
Sales Range: $1-4.9 Billion
Emp.: 260
Real Estate Services
N.A.I.C.S.: 237210
Jorge M. Perez (Founder, Chm & CEO)
Steve Patterson (Pres/CEO-Related Dev)
Carlos Rosso (Pres-Condominium Dev)

U.S. PRIVATE

Jeffery Hoyos (Chief Acctg Officer & Sr VP)
Sonia Figueroa (Sr VP-Dev)
Larry Lennon (Pres-TRG Mgmt)
Patrick Campbell (VP)
James M. Werbelow (Sr VP-Construction)
Betsy McCoy (Gen Counsel & VP)
Albert Milo (Principal & Sr VP-Related Urban Dev)

RELATIONAL LLC
3701 Algonquin Rd Ste 600, Rolling Meadows, IL 60008
Tel.: (847) 818-1700
Sales Range: $300-349.9 Million
Emp.: 350
IT Management Consulting Services
N.A.I.C.S.: 541618
Chris Czaja (Treas & VP)
Jeffery Ehlers (CEO)
Frank Swann (VP-Ops)
Dean Frankel (Gen Counsel)

Subsidiaries:

CDI Computer Dealers Inc. (1)
75 Clegg Road, Markham, L6G 1A1, ON, Canada
Tel.: (905) 946-1119
Web Site: http://www.cdicomputers.com
Sales Range: $25-49.9 Million
Emp.: 400
Refurbished Computer Distr
N.A.I.C.S.: 423430
Saar Pikar (CEO)

Relational LLC (1)
Ste 940 19200 Von Karman Ave, Irvine, CA 92612-8521
Tel.: (949) 955-0600
Rev.: $1,100,000
Emp.: 8
Computer Hardware Rental Or Leasing, Except Finance Leasing
N.A.I.C.S.: 522220

Relational Technology Services (1)
12821 Starkey Rd, Largo, FL 33773
Tel.: (727) 524-9668
Web Site: http://www.relationalfunding.com
Sales Range: $10-24.9 Million
Emp.: 52
Appraiser, Real Estate
N.A.I.C.S.: 531320

Relational Technology Solutions (1)
1901 Ulmerton Rd, Clearwater, FL 33762-2300
Tel.: (727) 524-9668
Web Site: http://www.rts.com
Rev.: $92,321,109
Emp.: 50
System Integration Services
N.A.I.C.S.: 541512

RELATIVITY ACQUISITION CORP.
3753 Howard Hughes Pkwy Ste 200, Las Vegas, NV 89169 DE
Web Site:
https://www.relativityacquisition.com
Year Founded: 2021
RACY—(NASDAQ)
Rev.: $8,651
Assets: $1,764,813
Liabilities: $2,157,690
Net Worth: ($392,877)
Earnings: ($2,305,489)
Emp.: 2
Fiscal Year-end: 12/31/23
Investment Holding Company
N.A.I.C.S.: 551112
Tarek K. Tabsh (Chm & CEO)
Steven Berg (CFO)

RELATIVITY MEDIA, LLC
9242 Beverly Blvd Ste 300, Beverly Hills, CA 90210
Tel.: (310) 859-1250 CA
Web Site:
http://www.relativitymedia.com

COMPANIES

Sales Range: $75-99.9 Million
Emp.: 500
Motion Picture, Music & Home Entertainment Production & Distribution Services; Entertainment Websites Developer & Operator
N.A.I.C.S.: 512110
Ryan Kavanaugh (CEO)
Andrew Marcus (Pres & COO)
Rachel Cadden (Exec VP-Mktg)
David Spiegelman (Pres-Distr-Domestic Television & Digital)
Kenneth Halsband (Pres-Physical & Post Production)
Camela Galano (Pres-Intl)
Court Coursey (Chief Investment & Strategy Officer)
Tamoor Shafi (Chief Digital Officer)

Subsidiaries:

ARTISTdirect, Inc. (1)
9046 Lindblade St, Culver City, CA 90232-2513
Tel.: (310) 956-3300
Web Site: http://www.artistdirect.com
Sales Range: $10-24.9 Million
Emp.: 68
Online Music Services
N.A.I.C.S.: 491110

RELATIVITY, INC.
3811 The Oak Rd, Philadelphia, PA 19129
Tel.: (215) 844-3508   PA
Year Founded: 1991
Sales Range: Less than $1 Million
Emp.: 1
Advetising Agency
N.A.I.C.S.: 541810
Mindy Y. Glassman (Founder & Pres)

RELAY EXPRESS
498 Commercial Dr, Fairfield, OH 45014
Tel.: (513) 860-2555
Web Site: http://www.relayexpress.com
Year Founded: 1986
Rev.: $11,700,000
Emp.: 60
Local Trucking Operator
N.A.I.C.S.: 484110
Matt Seiter (Founder)
Robert Smith (Founder)
Mike Bernecker (Founder)

RELAY RESOURCES
5312 NE 148th Ave, Portland, OR 97230-3438
Tel.: (503) 261-1266   OR
Web Site: http://www.relayresources.org
Year Founded: 1951
Disability Assistance Services
N.A.I.C.S.: 624120
Alysa Rose (Pres & CEO)
Tiffini Mueller (Dir-Mktg & Comm)
Deeann Jurgens (CFO)
Tim Moscato (Dir-Ops Bus)
Elizabeth Kurtz (Dir-HR)
Kim Leathley (Chm)
Stephen King (Vice Chm)

RELCO PRODUCTS INC.
1021 Jackson St, Anderson, IN 46016
Tel.: (765) 643-0070
Web Site: http://www.relcoproducts.com
Sales Range: $10-24.9 Million
Emp.: 8
Sales of Lumber, Plywood & Millwork
N.A.I.C.S.: 423310
Randy Loyd (Pres)
John Buckner (Mgr-Sls)
Brody Stock (VP-Sls & Mktg)

RELCO SYSTEMS INC.
7310 Chestnut Rdg Rd, Lockport, NY 14094
Tel.: (716) 434-8100
Web Site: http://www.relcosystems.com
Rev.: $15,700,000
Emp.: 150
Trucking Except Local
N.A.I.C.S.: 484121
Robert E. Lewis (Pres)
Shirley Zimpfer (Controller)

RELECTRIC, INC
2390 Zanker Rd, San Jose, CA 95131
Tel.: (408) 467-2222
Web Site: http://www.relectric.com
Year Founded: 2003
Rev.: $8,500,000
Emp.: 28
Electrical Supplies & Related Equipment Merchant Whslr
N.A.I.C.S.: 423610
Suni Rose (Mgr-Customer Svc)

RELEVANCE INC.
514 S Duke St, Durham, NC 27701-3364
Tel.: (919) 283-2748
Web Site: http://www.ThinkRelevance.com
Year Founded: 2003
Sales Range: $1-9.9 Million
Emp.: 30
Computer Software Services
N.A.I.C.S.: 449210
Justin Gehtland (Pres)

RELEVANT ADS, INC.
10175 Slater Ave Ste 205, Fountain Valley, CA 92708
Tel.: (714) 640-3930   CA
Web Site: http://www.localsplash.com
Year Founded: 2002
Sales Range: $1-9.9 Million
Emp.: 107
Search Engine Marketing Service Providers
N.A.I.C.S.: 541810
Steve Yeich (CEO)
Jeremy Auestad (Dir-Mktg)
David J. Rodecker (Founder & CTO)
Mat Estrada (VP-Fin & Admin)
Nanette Lagos (Office Mgr)
Michael Georgio (Mgr-Quality Assurance)
Kerry Wagoner (Mgr-PPC)
Laure Muller (Dir-Project Mgmt)
Debra Northart (Dir-Product Ops)
Eade Hopkinson II (Mgr-IT)

RELEVANT INDUSTRIAL LLC
2010 McAllister Rd, Houston, TX 77092
Tel.: (800) 779-1414
Web Site: https://relevantsolutions.com
Valve, Purification & Thermal Equipment Solutions
N.A.I.C.S.: 423610
John M. Carte (CEO)

Subsidiaries:

CHEMFLOW Products, LLC (1)
27905 Commercial Park Rd Ste 410, Tomball, TX 77375
Tel.: (281) 354-9594
Web Site: http://www.chemflowproducts.com
Construction & Mining Machinery & Equipment Merchant Whslr
N.A.I.C.S.: 423610
Michael R. Johnson (Pres)

Marshall W Nelson & Associates, Inc. (1)
4300 N Port Washington Rd, Milwaukee, WI 53212
Tel.: (414) 332-6000
Web Site: http://www.marshallwnelson.com
Sales Range: $1-9.9 Million
Emp.: 26
Industrial Machinery & Equipment Merchant Whslr
N.A.I.C.S.: 423830
Marshall W. Nelson (Chm)
Ron Oeltjen (Mgr-Automation)

RELEVANTE, INC.
1400 N Providence Rd Ste 4025 Bldg 2, Media, PA 19063
Tel.: (215) 442-1930
Web Site: http://www.relevante.com
Year Founded: 2002
Sales Range: $10-24.9 Million
Emp.: 120
Accounting & Technology Consulting & Staffing
N.A.I.C.S.: 541690
Eileen Wainwright (COO & Partner)

Subsidiaries:

Relevante Consulting (India) Private Limited (1)
8-2-316/A/6 Rd No 14, Banjara Hills, Hyderabad, 500034, Andhra Pradesh, India
Tel.: (91) 4066467607
Web Site: http://www.relevante.co.in
Accounting & Technology Consulting & Staffing
N.A.I.C.S.: 541690

RELIABLE AUTOMATIC SPRINKLER CO., INC.
103 Fairview Pk Dr, Elmsford, NY 10523
Tel.: (914) 586-4242   NY
Web Site: http://www.reliablesprinkler.com
Year Founded: 1918
Sales Range: $50-74.9 Million
Emp.: 550
Automatic Fire Sprinklers & Sprinkler System Control Equipment Mfr
N.A.I.C.S.: 333998
Kevin T. Fee (Pres)
Michael R. Fee (Exec VP)
Thomas Multer (VP-Product Tech)
Bob Poulton (Mgr-Sls-Orlando)
David Asplund (Dir-Technical Svcs)
J. Todd Bresnahan (Dir-Accounts-US & Canada)
Matt Squirell (Dir-Sls-Canada)
John McNamara (VP-Corp Sls)
Rex K. Schwendiman (VP-Sys Components)
Mark A. Connor (Dir-Sls-Territory 3-Denver)
Guy Devillers (Mgr-Ops-New York)
David J. Rosso (Mgr-Sls-Chicago)
Jerry Holowak (Dir-Distr Center Ops-Dallas)
James A. Mikkila (Mgr-Technical Svcs)
Travis Mitchell (Mgr-Ops-Seattle)
Alan Larson (Mgr-Technical Svcs)
Brandon Telford (Mgr-Technical Svcs)
Cary Webber (Dir-Technical Svcs)
George Nicola (Mgr-Technical Svcs)
Frank J. Fee III (Chm)

Subsidiaries:

Reliable Fire Sprinkler Australia Pty. Ltd. (1)
550 Churchill Road, Kilburn, 5084, SA, Australia
Tel.: (61) 881629555
Fire Sprinkler Mfr
N.A.I.C.S.: 333998
David Kelly (Sls Mgr-Australia)

Reliable Fire Sprinkler Ltd. (1)
Unit 25 Birches Industrial Estate, East Grinstead, RH19 1XZ, West Sussex, United Kingdom
Tel.: (44) 1342 316800
Emp.: 25

RELIABLE CONTRACTING COMPANY INC.

Fire Sprinkler Mfr
N.A.I.C.S.: 333998
Adam Robotham (Dir-Intl Sls)
Michael Billstroem (Dir-Intl Technical Svc)

RELIABLE CARRIERS INC.
41555 Koppernick Rd, Canton, MI 48187-2415
Tel.: (734) 453-9950   MI
Web Site: http://www.reliablecarriers.com
Year Founded: 1983
Sales Range: $10-24.9 Million
Emp.: 100
Provider of Trucking Services
N.A.I.C.S.: 484230
Tom Abrams (Pres)
Bob Sellers (COO & VP)
James Potter (Mgr-Ops-Retail)
Gregory M. Feary (Mng Partner)

RELIABLE CASTINGS CORPORATION
3530 Spring Grove Ave, Cincinnati, OH 45223-2448
Tel.: (513) 541-2627
Web Site: http://www.reliablecastings.com
Year Founded: 1922
Sales Range: $100-124.9 Million
Emp.: 225
Aluminum & Bronze Sand Castings, Aluminum Permanent Mold Castings & Wood & Metal Mfr
N.A.I.C.S.: 331524
R. J. Kuhn (Pres)
Jeff Sams (Mgr-Tooling Sls)

Subsidiaries:

Reliable Castings Corporation - Sidney Plant (1)
1521 W Michigan St, Sidney, OH 45365
Tel.: (937) 492-6171
Sales Range: $25-49.9 Million
Emp.: 150
Aluminum Casting Mfr
N.A.I.C.S.: 331524
Dave Allen (Mgr-Ops)

RELIABLE CHEVROLET
800 N Central Expwy, Richardson, TX 75080
Tel.: (972) 952-1500
Web Site: http://www.reliablechev.com
Year Founded: 1986
Sales Range: $25-49.9 Million
Emp.: 250
Automobile Dealership
N.A.I.C.S.: 441110
Dave Anderson (Gen Mgr)
Brad Kelly (Mgr-Svc)

RELIABLE CONTRACTING COMPANY INC.
1 Church View Rd, Millersville, MD 21108
Tel.: (410) 923-2636
Web Site: http://www.reliablecontracting.com
Rev.: $50,045,017
Emp.: 200
General Contractor, Highway & Street Construction
N.A.I.C.S.: 237310
Jerry Baldwin (Pres)
Joe Zdrojewski (Controller)
Christina Baldwin O'Meara (Owner)

Subsidiaries:

Reliable Group, LLC (1)
2410 Evergreen Rd Ste 200, Gambrills, MD 21054
Tel.: (410) 987-0313
Real Estate Services
N.A.I.C.S.: 531210
Joseph G. Baldwin (Pres)

RELIABLE CONTRACTING COMPANY INC.   U.S. PRIVATE

Reliable Contracting Company Inc.—(Continued)
Subsidiary (Domestic):
Louis Hyatt, Inc. (2)
200 Westgate Cir Ste 502, Annapolis, MD 21401-3374
Tel.: (301) 261-8832
Web Site: http://www.hyattcommercial.com
Offices of Real Estate Agents & Brokers
N.A.I.C.S.: 531210
Louis Hyatt *(Pres)*
Justin Mullen *(Sr VP-Sls, Leasing & Acq)*
Alan Hyatt *(Partner)*

RELIABLE FIRE EQUIPMENT CO.
12845 S Cicero Ave, Alsip, IL 60803
Tel.: (708) 597-4600
Web Site: http://www.reliablefire.com
Sales Range: $10-24.9 Million
Emp.: 88
Alarm Systems
N.A.I.C.S.: 423610
Debra A. Horvath *(Pres)*

RELIABLE GOVERNMENT SOLUTIONS INC.
4061 Powder Mill Rd Ste 700, Beltsville, MD 20705
Tel.: (301) 572-4190
Web Site: http://www.rgsfederal.com
Year Founded: 2001
Sales Range: $1-9.9 Million
Emp.: 30
It Consulting
N.A.I.C.S.: 541690
Chieu Van Le *(Pres & CEO)*
Thuy Le *(Controller)*

RELIABLE INDUSTRIES INC.
5739 G St, New Orleans, LA 70123-3114
Tel.: (504) 738-9644
Web Site: http://www.reliableindustries.com
Industrial Machinery & Equipment
N.A.I.C.S.: 423830
Daina Abadie *(Mgr-Accts Payable)*
Ray Angelette *(Controller)*

RELIABLE JET MAINTENANCE LLC
3900 Airport Rd Hngr 1, Boca Raton, FL 33431
Tel.: (561) 417-3834
Web Site: http://www.reliablejet.com
Year Founded: 2005
Sales Range: $1-9.9 Million
Emp.: 46
Aviation Maintenance
N.A.I.C.S.: 811310
Jonathan Burls *(Founder)*
Donald Chamberlain *(Mgr-Ops)*
Tsunami Gomez *(Mgr-Production)*

RELIABLE KNITTING WORKS, INC.
6737 W Washington Ste 3200, Milwaukee, WI 53214
Tel.: (414) 272-5084   WI
Web Site: http://www.reliableofmilwaukee.com
Year Founded: 1911
Head Wear, Footwear & Accessories Mfr
N.A.I.C.S.: 315120
Mark Blutstein *(Pres & CEO)*

RELIABLE OIL EQUIPMENT INC.
7476 Webster St, Dayton, OH 45414
Tel.: (937) 665-1200   OH
Web Site: http://www.reliableoil.com
Year Founded: 1960
Sales Range: $10-24.9 Million
Emp.: 30

Distr of Service Station Equipment
N.A.I.C.S.: 423850
Tina Dobrzeniecki *(Mgr-Customer Svcs)*

RELIABLE PRODUCTION SERVICE, INC.
1090 Cinclare Dr, Port Allen, LA 70767
Tel.: (225) 637-4835
Web Site: http://www.reliableproduction.com
Rev.: $13,000,000
Emp.: 100
Site Preparation Contractor
N.A.I.C.S.: 238910

RELIABLE SILVER, INC.
302 Platts Mill Rd, Naugatuck, CT 06770
Tel.: (203) 574-7732
Web Site: http://www.reliablesilver.com
Rev.: $3,800,000
Emp.: 14
Primary Smelting & Refining Nonferrous Metal
N.A.I.C.S.: 331410
Roseann D'Alfonso *(Treas)*

RELIABLE SOFTWARE RESOURCES, INC
22260 Haggerty Rd Ste 285, Northville, MI 48167
Tel.: (248) 477-3555
Web Site: http://www.rsrit.com
Year Founded: 2004
Sales Range: $10-24.9 Million
Emp.: 245
Custom Computer Programming Services
N.A.I.C.S.: 541511
Ravi Vallem *(Co-Founder & CEO)*
Venkat Gone *(Co-Founder & Pres)*
Sridhar Kodati *(CFO & Partner)*
Panchaleswar Nayak *(VP-Tech Solutions)*
Steve Scruggs *(VP-Sls)*

RELIABLE TIRE DISTRIBUTORS INC.
805 N Black Horse Pike, Blackwood, NJ 08012-3936
Tel.: (856) 232-0700   NJ
Web Site: http://www.reliabletire.com
Year Founded: 1985
Sales Range: $75-99.9 Million
Emp.: 115
Distr of Tires & Tubes
N.A.I.C.S.: 423130
Richard Betz *(Pres)*
Mike Tofani *(Controller)*

RELIABLE TOOL & MACHINE CO.
300 W Ohio St, Kendallville, IN 46755
Tel.: (260) 347-4000
Web Site: http://www.reliabletool.com
Rev.: $16,500,000
Emp.: 135
Heavy Equipment Component Mfr
N.A.I.C.S.: 336390
Owen Drerup *(VP)*
Charles Drerup *(Pres)*

RELIABLE TRUCKING INC.
5141 Commercial Cir, Concord, CA 94520
Tel.: (925) 685-6799
Web Site: http://www.conconow.com
Rev.: $30,965,813
Emp.: 2,000
Draying, Local; Without Storage
N.A.I.C.S.: 484220
Steven Gonsalves *(Pres)*

RELIABLE VAN & STORAGE CO., INC.
550 Division St, Elizabeth, NJ 07201
Tel.: (908) 352-5300
Web Site: http://www.newjerseymoversnj.com
Year Founded: 1923
Sales Range: $10-24.9 Million
Emp.: 85
General Freight Trucking Services
N.A.I.C.S.: 484121
Peter J. Toscano *(Pres & CEO)*

RELIABLE WHOLESALE LUMBER INC.
7600 Redondo Cir, Huntington Beach, CA 92648-1303
Tel.: (714) 848-8222   CA
Web Site: http://www.rwli.net
Year Founded: 1971
Sales Range: $100-124.9 Million
Emp.: 203
Lumber, Plywood & Millwork
N.A.I.C.S.: 423310
Mitch Mitchell *(VP-BS)*
Bogie Nicols *(Exec VP)*

RELIANCE AEROTECH INC.
1321 Murfreesboro Pike Ste 602, Nashville, TN 37217
Tel.: (615) 627-0740
Web Site: http://www.relianceaerotech.com
Sales Range: $10-24.9 Million
Emp.: 70
Privater Equity Firm
N.A.I.C.S.: 523999
Glynn Wiliams *(Pres & CEO)*
Subsidiaries:
Navhouse Corporation (1)
10 Loring Drive, Bolton, L7E 1J9, ON, Canada (100%)
Tel.: (905) 857-8102
Web Site: http://www.navhouse.com
Sales Range: $10-24.9 Million
Emp.: 15
Navigation Systems & Subassemblies Mfr
N.A.I.C.S.: 811210

RELIANCE BANCORP, INC.
1119 12th St, Altoona, PA 16601
Tel.: (814) 949-6263   PA
Web Site: http://www.reliancebank.com
Year Founded: 2009
Sales Range: $10-24.9 Million
Emp.: 95
Bank Holding Company
N.A.I.C.S.: 551111
Timothy P. Sissler *(Vice Chm)*
Dennis E. Doll *(Pres & CEO)*
Brian H. Lehman *(CFO & Exec VP)*
James F. Kuhn *(Exec VP & Chief Lending Officer)*
Subsidiaries:
Reliance Savings Bank (1)
1119 12th St, Altoona, PA 16601
Tel.: (814) 949-6263
Web Site: http://www.reliancebank.com
Sales Range: $10-24.9 Million
Emp.: 72
Commericial Banking
N.A.I.C.S.: 522110
Timothy P. Sissler *(Chm)*
Dennis E. Doll *(Pres & CEO)*
Brian H. Lehman *(CFO & Exec VP)*
James F. Kuhn *(Chief Lending Officer & Exec VP)*

RELIANCE CAPITAL MARKETS II, LLC
621 S Plymouth Ct 1st Fl, Chicago, IL 60605
Tel.: (312) 870-1500   FL

Web Site: http://www.rcmassetmanagement.com
Futures & Foreign Exchange Asset Management & Brokerage Services
N.A.I.C.S.: 523940
Bobby Schwartz *(Co-Founder & Mng Partner)*
Tammy Sullivan *(Partner & Mng Dir)*
Paul Rieger *(Partner & Mng Dir)*
Jeff Malec *(Partner & Mng Dir)*
Ed Sweeney *(Co-Founder & Partner)*
Jack Malone *(Officer-Compliance)*
Subsidiaries:
Reliance Capital Markets II, LLC - RCM Alternatives Division (1)
318 W Adams St, Chicago, IL 60606
Tel.: (312) 870-1500
Web Site: http://www.rcmalternatives.com
Emp.: 50
Investment Management Service
N.A.I.C.S.: 523940
Lauren Berliner *(Dir-Client Rels)*
John Cummings *(Dir-Investment Res)*
Walter Gallwas *(Mng Dir)*
Jeff Malec *(Mng Dir & Partner)*
Jeff Eizenberg *(Exec Dir)*
Bobby Schwartz *(Mng Partner)*
Tammy Naughton Sullivan *(Mng Dir & Partner)*
Paul Rieger *(Mng Dir & Partner)*
Matthew Bradbard *(Dir-Alternative Investments)*
Ruth Baerman *(Mgr-Relationship)*

RELIANCE HEATING & AIR CONDITIONING COMPANY
1694 Hwy 138 NE, Conyers, GA 30013
Tel.: (770) 483-3850
Web Site: http://www.reliancehvac.com
Rev.: $24,000,000
Emp.: 115
Provider of Warm Air Heating & Air Conditioning Contracting Services
N.A.I.C.S.: 238220
Jim Bilbrey *(Pres)*
Phillip Dooley *(VP)*

RELIANCE HOUSE INC.
40 Broadway, Norwich, CT 06360
Tel.: (860) 887-6536   CT
Web Site: http://www.reliancehouse.org
Year Founded: 1977
Sales Range: $10-24.9 Million
Emp.: 305
Developmental Disability Assistance Services
N.A.I.C.S.: 623210
Sue Caplet *(Mgr-Property)*
Linda Smith *(CFO)*
Jen Brayman *(Dir-Quality Svcs)*
David Burnett *(CEO)*
Kerry Lee *(Dir-Clinical)*

RELIANCE INC.
3940 10th Ave N, Lake Worth, FL 33461
Tel.: (561) 967-5066
Web Site: http://www.relianceinc.com
Year Founded: 2001
Sales Range: $1-9.9 Million
Emp.: 49
Mortgage & Title Agency
N.A.I.C.S.: 522310
Enrique Richard Rodriguez *(Founder & CEO)*
E. I. Cogen *(CTO)*

RELIANCE STAR PAYMENT SERVICES, INC.
475 Northern Blvd Ste 38, Great Neck, NY 11021
Tel.: (516) 321-9888
Web Site: http://www.reliancestar.com
Year Founded: 2004

Sales Range: $1-9.9 Million
Emp.: 15
Financial Transaction Processing
N.A.I.C.S.: 522320
Fenella Yin Fang Kim (Founder & CEO)

RELIANT ASSET MANAGEMENT LLC
2900 S Quincy St Ste 300 A, Arlington, VA 22206-2279
Tel.: (703) 382-2900
Web Site: http://www.rammodular.com
Year Founded: 2010
General Rental Centers
N.A.I.C.S.: 532310
Michael Roman (Co-Founder & VP)
Barry Roman (Co-Founder & Pres)
Peter Eberle (Exec VP)
Saul Rothenberg (CIO)

Subsidiaries:

Aries Building Systems, LLC (1)
1919 Mueller Ln, Troy, TX 76579
Tel.: (888) 598-6689
Web Site: http://ariesbuildings.com
Building Design & Construction Services
N.A.I.C.S.: 236210
Barry A. Roman (Co-Founder & Pres)
Michael I. Roman (Co-Founder & VP)
Peter Eberle (Exec VP)
Christopher Brewer (VP-Bus Dev)
Katie Roman (Mgr-Reg Camp Sls & Ops)
Jim Muller (Controller)
Thomas Browder (VP-Estimating)
Richard J. Brewer (Dir-Ops)
Saul M. Rothenberg (CIO)
Michael A. Bollero Sr. (Pres)
Michael Bollero Jr. (VP-Sls & Mktg)

Division (Domestic):

Aries Building Systems, LLC - PNW
Major Projects (2)
4122 Factoria Blvd SE Ste 402, Bellevue, WA 98006
Tel.: (844) 992-7437
Web Site: http://ariespnw.com
Institutional Building Construction Services
N.A.I.C.S.: 236220
Michael A. Bollero Sr. (Pres)

Subsidiary (Domestic):

Jobsite Trailer Corp. (2)
1393 North Lucas St, Rochester, IN 46975
Tel.: (574) 224-4000
Web Site: http://www.jobsitemobileoffices.com
Mobile Office & Field Office Company
N.A.I.C.S.: 332311
James Guthrie (CEO)

Class Leasing, LLC (1)
1221 Harley Knox Blvd, Perris, CA 92571-7408
Tel.: (951) 943-1908
Web Site: http://www.classleasingllc.com
Institutional Building Construction Services
N.A.I.C.S.: 236220
James Goldenetz (Pres)

RELIANT FINANCIAL SERVICES INC.
1600 Genessee St Ste 961, Kansas City, MO 64102-1137
Tel.: (816) 421-7110
Year Founded: 1995
Sales Range: $75-99.9 Million
Emp.: 30
Financial Consulting Services
N.A.I.C.S.: 523150
Michael Pollakowski (Pres & CEO)
Sandy Warmund (Exec VP)

RELIANT FOODSERVICE
26090 Ynez Rd, Temecula, CA 92591
Tel.: (951) 296-6019
Web Site: http://www.reliantfoods.com
Year Founded: 1996
Sales Range: $1-9.9 Million
Emp.: 19
Quick Service Food Products
N.A.I.C.S.: 311999
David Canada (Owner)

RELIANT INVENTORY SERVICES
2601 S Bayshore Dr Ste 725, Miami, FL 33133
Tel.: (786) 268-4520 FL
Web Site: http://www.reliant-inv.com
Year Founded: 1969
Business Support Services
N.A.I.C.S.: 561499
Steve Miller (Exec VP)

Subsidiaries:

Reliant Inventory Services, Inc. (1)
11050 Fancher Rd Lot 110, Westerville, OH 43082
Tel.: (614) 855-2960
Web Site: http://www.reliant-inv.com
Sales Range: $1-9.9 Million
Business Support Services
N.A.I.C.S.: 561499

RELIANT MISSION, INC.
11002 Lk Hart Dr Ste 100, Orlando, FL 32832
Tel.: (407) 671-9700 OH
Web Site: http://www.reliant.org
Year Founded: 1989
Religious Organizations
N.A.I.C.S.: 813100
Tom Mauriello (Exec Dir)
Cori Crawford Van Oss (Mgr-Mobilization)
Darlene McKay (Dir-Fin Ops)
Dave Meldrum-Green (Treas & Dir-Org Affairs)
Barb Seckler (Ops Mgr-Fin)
Mike Swann (Dir-Missionary Resources)
John Abassian (Engr-Software)
Daniel Cone (Coord-Benefits & Fin)
Diane Wallace (Coord-Accts Payable)

RELIANT REALTY, LLC
4711 Trousdale Dr Ste 121, Nashville, TN 37220
Tel.: (615) 859-7150
Web Site: http://www.reliantrealty.com
Year Founded: 2007
Sales Range: $10-24.9 Million
Emp.: 560
Real Estate Manangement Services
N.A.I.C.S.: 531210
Jennifer Pierce Cook (Comptroller)

RELIANT TRANSPORTATION, INC.
4411 S 86th St Ste 101, Lincoln, NE 68526
Tel.: (402) 464-7771 NE
Web Site: http://www.reliant-transportation.com
Sales Range: $10-24.9 Million
Emp.: 30
Local Trucking Services
N.A.I.C.S.: 484110
Steven J. Miller (Pres)
Matthew Sobotka (VP-Ops)

RELIAQUEST LLC
5100 W Kennedy Blvd Ste 430, Tampa, FL 33602
Tel.: (813) 321-1276
Web Site: http://www.reliaquest.com
Year Founded: 2007
Sales Range: $1-9.9 Million
Emp.: 35
Computer Related Consulting & Other Services
N.A.I.C.S.: 541519

Brian Murphy (Founder & CEO)
Alex Bender (CMO)
Derin McMains (Dir-Mental Conditioning)
Laurie Morylak (Sr VP-Mktg)
Colin O'Connor (COO)

RELIEF INTERNATIONAL
1101 14th St NW Ste 1100, Washington, DC 20005
Tel.: (202) 639-8660 CA
Web Site: http://www.ri.org
Year Founded: 1990
Sales Range: $25-49.9 Million
Emp.: 166
Vulnerable People Support Services
N.A.I.C.S.: 624190
Jamie Jones (VP-Program Dev)
Jamie Hall (Sr VP-Strategy)
Stephen Croll (VP-Ops)
Paul Levengood (Chm)
Nancy Wilson (Pres & CEO)
Ann Koontz (Sr VP)
Elia Makar (VP-HR)
Mary Au (CFO)

RELIGION NEWS LLC
University of Missouri School of Journalism 30 Neff Annex, Columbia, MO 65211
Tel.: (573) 882-9257
Web Site: http://www.religionnewsllc.com
Religious News Publishing
N.A.I.C.S.: 513110
Tiffany McCallen (Mgr-Natl Community)
Don Southworth (Treas)

Subsidiaries:

Religion News Service (1)
National Press Bldg 529 14th St NW Ste 1009, Washington, DC 20045
Tel.: (202) 463-8777
Web Site: http://www.religionnews.com
Sales Range: $10-24.9 Million
Emp.: 15
News Agency
N.A.I.C.S.: 516210
Yonat Shimron (Mng Editor)
Wendy Gustofson (Dir-Mktg)
Sheila Holder (Bus Mgr)
Jerome Socolovsky (Editor-in-Chief)
Tom Gallagher (CEO & Publr)

RELMEC MECHANICAL LLC
4975 Hamilton Ave, Cleveland, OH 44114-3906
Tel.: (216) 391-1030 IL
Year Founded: 2000
Sales Range: $50-74.9 Million
Emp.: 150
Mechanical Contractor
N.A.I.C.S.: 238220
Layne Kendig (Pres)
Jeff Hajek (Project Coord)
Annie Sterle (Project Mgr)
Jerry Filips (VP-Ops- HVAC)

RELOCATION MANAGEMENT RESOURCES, INC.
714 9th St Ste 102, Durham, NC 27705
Tel.: (919) 286-6652 NC
Web Site: http://www.rmronline.com
Year Founded: 1992
Sales Range: $10-24.9 Million
Relocation Services
N.A.I.C.S.: 561990
Robert J. Carbonell Jr. (Pres)

Subsidiaries:

Relocation Management Resources, Inc. - Business Solutions (1)
200 Connecticut Ave 2nd Fl, Norwalk, CT 06854
Web Site: http://www.rmronline.com
Relocation Services

N.A.I.C.S.: 561990

RELOCATION SERVICES INTERNATIONAL
1210 Distribution Way, Vista, CA 92081
Tel.: (760) 597-6100
Web Site: http://www.rsirelo.com
Year Founded: 1992
Freight Transportation Arrangement
N.A.I.C.S.: 488510
Andrew Churchill (Owner & Pres)

RELWARE
32255 Northwestern Hwy, Farmington Hills, MI 48334
Tel.: (248) 406-1800
Web Site: http://www.relware.com
Year Founded: 1999
Rev.: $5,700,000
Emp.: 41
Computer System Design Services
N.A.I.C.S.: 541512
C. Richard Campbell (CFO)
Mark Brown (CIO)
Chris Mansueti (Dir-Client Svcs)
Dann Lemerand (VP-Bus Dev)
Steve Hermans (VP-Interfaces)

RELYANCE BANK, N.A.
912 S Poplar St, Pine Bluff, AR 71601
Tel.: (870) 535-7222 AR
Web Site: http://www.relybank.com
Year Founded: 1965
Commericial Banking
N.A.I.C.S.: 522110
Chuck Morgan (Pres & CEO)
Michael Neathery (Sr VP & Sr Acctg Officer)
LaTasha McNeely Randle (Branch Mgr)
Bryan Castleberry (Asst VP-IT)
Jennifer Milroy (Branch Mgr)
Lynn L Guynn (Asst VP)
Blake Cansler (VP-Comml Lending)
Andy Jenkins (Sr VP & Sr Info Sys Officer)
Steve White (VP-Agricultural Lending)
Carol Cook (Sr VP & Sr Consumer Real Estate Mgr)
Destiny Coleman (Asst Branch Mgr)
Rebekah Biernacki (Asst VP-Loan Ops)
Karen Hall (Asst VP-Ops)
Kristi Barger (VP & Sr Trust Officer)
Steve Williams (VP/Dir-Internal Audit-Little Rock & Pine Bluff)

RELYCO SALES, INC.
121 Broadway, Dover, NH 03820
Tel.: (603) 742-0999 NH
Web Site: http://www.relyco.com
Year Founded: 1989
Printing & Writing Paper Merchant Whslr
N.A.I.C.S.: 424110

REM ELECTRONICS SUPPLY CO. INC.
525 S Park Ave, Warren, OH 44483
Tel.: (330) 373-1300 OH
Web Site: http://www.remelectronics.com
Year Founded: 1955
Sales Range: $10-24.9 Million
Emp.: 21
Distr of Industrial Electronics
N.A.I.C.S.: 423690
Dan Myers (Mgr-Added Value)

REM GLOBAL, INC.
222 W Las Colinas Blvd Ste 2250N, Irving, TX 75039
Tel.: (972) 458-0800
Web Site: http://www.remglobal.com

REM GLOBAL, INC. — *U.S. PRIVATE*

REM Global, Inc.—(Continued)
Restaurant Operators
N.A.I.C.S.: 722511
Kim Forsythe (Owner)

REM MARKET LLC.
130 Tichenal Rd, Cashmere, WA 98815
Tel.: (509) 782-3801
Rev.: $22,200,000
Emp.: 172
Supermarkets & Other Grocery Stores
N.A.I.C.S.: 445110
Kathy Leppert (Mgr-Admin)

REMARK PAPER COMPANY INC.
50 W Dundee Rd, Wheeling, IL 60090-4864
Tel.: (847) 541-8777 IL
Web Site: http://www.remarkpaper.com
Year Founded: 1977
Sales Range: $25-49.9 Million
Emp.: 20
Mfr of Printing, Writing Paper & Newsprint
N.A.I.C.S.: 424110
Dennis Kramer (VP)
Debbie Harmon (Comptroller)

REMBRANDT ENTERPRISES, INC.
1419 480th St, Rembrandt, IA 50576
Tel.: (712) 286-6000
Web Site: http://www.rembrandtinc.com
Year Founded: 1994
Sales Range: $25-49.9 Million
Emp.: 200
Egg Producer
N.A.I.C.S.: 424440
David Rettig (CEO)
Tom Seigfreid (VP-Treasury & Risk Mgmt)
Jim Winterton (Supvr-Production)
Sally Brecher (Mgr-HR)

REMCO SUPPLY INC.
1815 E Wendover Ave, Greensboro, NC 27405
Tel.: (336) 273-3676
Web Site: http://www.remcosupply.com
Sales Range: $10-24.9 Million
Emp.: 18
Industrial Supplies
N.A.I.C.S.: 423840
James B. Remmey (VP)
Richard C. Remmey III (Treas)

REMCON PLASTICS INCORPORATED
208 Chestnut St, Reading, PA 19602
Tel.: (610) 376-2666
Web Site: http://www.remcon.com
Year Founded: 1982
Sales Range: $10-24.9 Million
Emp.: 60
Plastics Finished Products, Laminated
N.A.I.C.S.: 326130
Peter Connors (Owner)
Karen Kramer (Dir-Employee Engagement)
Rich Maguire (COO & VP)
Denise Donaldson (Controller)

REMEDI SENIORCARE HOLDING CORPORATION
9006 Yellow Brick Rd, Baltimore, MD 21237
Tel.: (443) 927-8450 MD
Web Site: http://www.remedirx.com
Year Founded: 2002
Holding Company Long-Term Care Pharmacy Operator
N.A.I.C.S.: 551112
Kathleen Chagnon (Chief Legal Officer)
Alan Bronfein (Sr VP-Strategic Sourcing)
Jim Waller (VP-HR)
John Gould (CFO)
Jeffrey Stamps (Pres & CEO)
Stephen Handelman (Sr VP)
Mark Schroder (COO)
Erin Ascher (Chief HR Officer)
Sean McCarthy (CIO)

Subsidiaries:
Remedi SeniorCare of Ohio - Northeast, LLC (1)
34099 Melinz Pkwy Ste G, Eastlake, OH 44095
Tel.: (440) 953-0604
Web Site: http://www.remedirx.com
Long-Term Care Pharmacy
N.A.I.C.S.: 456110
Alan Bronfein (Sr VP-Strategic Sourcing)
Kathleen Chagnon (Gen Counsel, Sec & Sr VP)
Corey Gauff (Exec VP-Sls & Mktg)
John Gould (CFO)
Jennifer Hardesty (Chief Clinical Officer)
Richard Hood (COO)
Jeffrey Stamps (Pres & CEO)
Scott Walker (CIO)
Jim Waller (VP-HR)

REMEDY INFORMATICS
9350 S 150 E Ste 850, Sandy, UT 84070
Tel.: (801) 733-3300
Web Site: http://www.remedyinformatics.com
Year Founded: 2003
Sales Range: $1-9.9 Million
Emp.: 51
Medical Software Development Services
N.A.I.C.S.: 541511
Gary Kennedy (Founder & CEO)
Jim Hyde (Exec VP-Ops)
Kevin R. Smith (Exec VP-Bus Dev & Sls)
Nate Benson (VP-IT)
Mike Cummens (CMO)
Robert Ludlow (VP-Product Mgmt)
Manish Muzumdar (Sr VP-Products)
Mike Nelson (VP-Dev)
Travis K. Smith (VP-Admin)
Scott C. Howard (Chief Medical Officer)
Dan Baker (Sr VP-Sls)
Cherie D. Zeringue (VP-Mktg)

REMEDY ROOFING, INC.
21925 Franz Rd Ste 402, Katy, TX 77449
Tel.: (281) 391-8555
Web Site: http://www.remedyroofing.com
Year Founded: 2005
Sales Range: $25-49.9 Million
Emp.: 8
Residential & Commercial Roofing Services
N.A.I.C.S.: 238160
Greg Arnim (Co-Founder, Pres & CEO)
Douglas Traylor (Co-Founder & Chief Sls Officer)
Linda Lindsay (Office Mgr)
Jennifer Slivensky (CFO)
Stephan Bergmann (Chief Comm Officer)
Wilson Cifuentes (COO)

REMEGENIX, INC.
4800 Montgomery Ln Ste 800, Bethesda, MD 20814
Tel.: (518) 302-1515
Web Site: http://www.remegenix.com
Year Founded: 2006
Pharmaceuticals Product Mfr
N.A.I.C.S.: 325412

REMER INC. CREATIVE MARKETING
205 Marion St, Seattle, WA 98104
Tel.: (206) 624-1010 WA
Web Site: http://www.remerinc.com
Year Founded: 1993
Sales Range: $10-24.9 Million
Emp.: 12
Communications, Consumer Marketing
N.A.I.C.S.: 541810
David Remer (CEO & Dir-Creative)
Christopher Harwood (Assoc Dir-Creative & Copywriter)
Andrea Jones (VP-Strategy & Client Svcs)
Brett Siemen (Sr Art Dir)

REMINGTON ASSOCIATES LTD.
1834 Walden Ofc Sq Ste 200, Schaumburg, IL 60173
Tel.: (847) 221-0200 IL
Web Site: http://www.halock.com
Year Founded: 1996
Information Security Professional Services Firm
N.A.I.C.S.: 541690
Terry Kurzynski (Sr Partner)
Jim Mirochnik (CEO & Sr Partner)

REMINGTON PRODUCTS COMPANY
961 Seville Rd, Wadsworth, OH 44281
Tel.: (330) 335-1571 OH
Web Site: http://www.remprod.com
Year Founded: 1947
Sales Range: $1-9.9 Million
Emp.: 110
Rubber Products Mfr
N.A.I.C.S.: 326299
John Weisend (Controller)
Rhonda Newman (CEO)
Jennifer Hoane (VP-Mktg & Customer Svc)

Subsidiaries:
Foot Petals, Inc. (1)
13405 Yarmouth Rd NW, Pickerington, OH 43147
Tel.: (866) 847-8632
Web Site: http://www.footpetals.com
Sales Range: $1-9.9 Million
Emp.: 15
Cushions for Women's Shoes Mfr
N.A.I.C.S.: 316210
Jeff Cosgrove (Pres)
Kayla Boyet (Pres-Brand)

REMITDATA, INC.
80 Monroe Ave Ste 300, Memphis, TN 38103
Tel.: (901) 383-5380
Web Site: http://www.remitdata.com
Year Founded: 2000
Sales Range: $1-9.9 Million
Emp.: 56
Information Retrieval Services
N.A.I.C.S.: 517810
Bently C. Goodwin (Founder)
Jim Brady (Chm)
Joel K. Wood (CFO)
David Ellett (CEO)
Jim Harter (CTO)
Mike Issac (Sr VP-Payer Ops)
Jim Freedman (Sr VP-Payer Solutions)
Helen Bardo-Levins (VP-Client Svcs)
Aaron Hood (VP-Mktg & Product Mgmt)

REMO INC.
28101 Industry Dr, Valencia, CA 91355-4102
Tel.: (661) 294-5600 CA
Web Site: http://www.remo.com
Year Founded: 1957
Sales Range: $10-24.9 Million
Emp.: 330
Musical Instruments & Parts
N.A.I.C.S.: 339992
Remo Belli (Founder)
Brock Kaericher (Pres)

REMORA ROYALTIES, INC.
807 Las Cimas Pkwy Ste 275, Austin, TX 78746
Tel.: (512) 579-3590 DE
Web Site: http://www.remoraroyalties.com
Year Founded: 2011
Emp.: 20
Holding Company
N.A.I.C.S.: 551112
Grant W. Livesay (Co-Founder, Pres, CFO & Sec)
Corwin Y. Ames (VP-Reservoir Enrgrg)
Aaron T. Brack (VP-Ops)
Christopher J. Manuel (VP-Land)
George V. Peyton V (Co-Founder, Chm & CEO)

REMOTE BACKUP SYSTEMS INC.
11200 Wexford Dr, Eads, TN 38028-6934
Tel.: (901) 405-1234
Web Site: http://www.remote-backup.com
Year Founded: 1987
Sales Range: $1-9.9 Million
Emp.: 16
Computer & Computer Peripheral Equipment & Software Merchant Whslr
N.A.I.C.S.: 423430
Rob Cosgrove (CEO)

REMOTE MEDICAL INTERNATIONAL, INC.
4259 23rd Ave W Ste 200, Seattle, WA 98199
Tel.: (206) 686-4878
Web Site: http://www.remotemedical.com
Year Founded: 2001
Sales Range: $1-9.9 Million
Emp.: 45
Medical Training, Supply & Rescue Services
N.A.I.C.S.: 423450
Andrew Cull (Founder)
Christopher Price (Project Coord)
Tom Milne (Dir-Sls)
Christine Avakian (Dir-Admin)

REMOTE TIGER
6404 Ivy Lane Ste 320, Greenbelt, MD 20770
Tel.: (301) 703-9669
Web Site: http://www.remotetiger.com
Year Founded: 2007
Sales Range: $1-9.9 Million
Emp.: 26
It Consulting
N.A.I.C.S.: 541690
Gopi Mandela (Pres & CEO)

REN SCOTT CREATIVE MARKETING
9004 Brittany Way, Tampa, FL 33619
Tel.: (813) 872-8350
Web Site: http://www.renscottcreativemarketing.com
Sales Range: $1-9.9 Million
Emp.: 10

Advertising & Marketing Agency
N.A.I.C.S.: 541810
Ren Scott *(Founder & CEO)*
Delanie Wallace *(Acct Coord)*

RENA-WARE DISTRIBUTORS INC.
15885 NE 28th St, Bellevue, WA 98008
Tel.: (425) 881-6171   WA
Web Site: http://www.renaware.com
Sales Range: $75-99.9 Million
Emp.: 50
Direct Sales of Cookware & Other Goods
N.A.I.C.S.: 339910
Russell Zylstra *(Chm)*
Brad Rich *(Pres)*
Benjamin J. Zylstra *(CEO)*

Subsidiaries:

R.W. Distributors   (1)
12 St Johns Close, Bovey Tracey, TQ13 9BU, Devon, United Kingdom
Tel.: (44) 1 626 834 114
Household Appliance Whslr
N.A.I.C.S.: 335220

RW COOKWARE S.L.   (1)
C Montesa 14 16 Nave 2, 28890, Madrid, Spain
Tel.: (34) 91 764 00 90
Household Appliance Whslr
N.A.I.C.S.: 449210

RW Inox de RL de C.V.   (1)
Primo Feliciano Velazquez 3266, Col Vallarta Sur Chapalita, Guadalajara, 44500, Jal, Mexico
Tel.: (52) 33 31 21 68 29
Cooking Utensil Sales & Repair Services
N.A.I.C.S.: 449210
Mariah Samara *(Gen Mgr)*

Rena Ware (Thailand) Limited   (1)
No 78 Country Villa Srinakarin Road Praves, Bangkok, 10250, Thailand
Tel.: (66) 2 721 9634
Household Appliance Whslr
N.A.I.C.S.: 449210

Rena Ware Distributors, C.A.   (1)
Avenida Andres Galarraga Edificio Franca Chacao, Caracas, Venezuela
Tel.: (58) 212 263 7510
Web Site: http://www.renaware.com.ve
Sales Range: $25-49.9 Million
Cooking Utensil Distr
N.A.I.C.S.: 423220

Rena Ware de Chile, S.A.I.C.   (1)
Los Conquistadores 2755, Santiago, Chile
Tel.: (56) 2 2334 4946
Cooking Utensil Repair Services
N.A.I.C.S.: 811412

Rena Ware de Costa Rica, S.A.   (1)
Del cruce Guadalupe-Moravia 500 mts Este, Goicoechea, San Jose, 1000, Costa Rica
Tel.: (506) 2528 4600
Web Site: http://www.renaware.co.cr
Cooking Utensil Distr
N.A.I.C.S.: 423220
Luis Vallecillo *(Mgr-Res)*

Rena Ware del Peru, S.A.   (1)
Av Jorge Basadre 152, San Isidro, Lima, Peru
Tel.: (51) 1 616 6969
Web Site: http://www.renaware.com.pe
Cooking Utensil Sales & Repair Services
N.A.I.C.S.: 449210

Rimbo Ware AG   (1)
Rte De Chesalles 50, PO Box 276, Marly, 1723, Switzerland   **(100%)**
Tel.: (41) 264363640
Sales Range: $25-49.9 Million
Emp.: 3
Direct Sales of Cookware & Other Household Goods
N.A.I.C.S.: 314120
Benito Quingiliani *(Mng Dir)*

RENAISSANCE DOORS & WINDOWS INC.
2425 W Commonwealth, Fullerton, CA 92833
Tel.: (714) 578-0090
Web Site: http://www.renaissance-windows.squarespace.com
Rev.: $11,210,164
Emp.: 80
Millwork
N.A.I.C.S.: 321918
Michael Jenkins *(Pres & CEO)*
Linda Novak *(Controller)*
Tom Jenkins *(VP)*

RENAISSANCE ENTERTAINMENT PRODUCTIONS
5027 Irwindale Ave Ste 200, Irwindale, CA 91706
Tel.: (626) 969-4750
Web Site: http://www.renfair.com
Year Founded: 2005
Sales Range: $10-24.9 Million
Emp.: 32
Holding Company: Specialty Fairs
N.A.I.C.S.: 713990
J. Stanley Gilbert *(Co-Owner)*
Kathryn Cramer *(Mgr-Fin)*

Subsidiaries:

Renaissance Entertainment Corp.   (1)
275 Century Cir Ste 102, Louisville, CO 80027
Tel.: (303) 664-0300
Web Site: http://www.renfair.com
Sales Range: $10-24.9 Million
Renaissance Fair Operator
N.A.I.C.S.: 713990

RENAISSANCE KNITWEAR INC.
1407 Broadway Rm 3607, New York, NY 10018
Tel.: (212) 354-3388
Rev.: $14,394,596
Emp.: 4
Women's & Misses' Outerwear
N.A.I.C.S.: 315250

RENAISSANCE MARINE GROUP, INC.
1061 16th Ave, Clarkston, WA 99403
Tel.: (509) 758-9189
Web Site: http://www.renaissance-marine-group.com
Rev.: $2,333,333
Emp.: 80
Boat Building
N.A.I.C.S.: 336612
Bruce Larson *(Mgr)*
Gerald Wooley *(Pres & COO)*

Subsidiaries:

Northwest Boats Industries, Inc.   (1)
PO Box 580, Clarkston, WA 99403
Tel.: (508) 758-9831
Web Site: http://www.northwest-boats.com
Boatbuilding And Repairing Services
N.A.I.C.S.: 336612

RENAISSANCE MORTGAGE GROUP INC.
585 N Courtenay Pkwy Ste 301, Merritt Island, FL 32953-4853
Tel.: (321) 459-9940   FL
Year Founded: 1997
Sales Range: $25-49.9 Million
Emp.: 13
Mortgage Services
N.A.I.C.S.: 522310
Sergio Crunchaway *(CEO)*

RENAISSANCE SCIENCES CORPORATION
10201 S 51-St Bldg-A Ste-75, Phoenix, AZ 85044
Tel.: (480) 374-1202   AZ
Web Site: http://www.rscusa.com
Year Founded: 2003
Sales Range: $1-9.9 Million
Emp.: 19
Wireless Telecommunications
N.A.I.C.S.: 517112
Brad Colbert *(VP)*

RENAISSANCE SPORTS & ENTERTAINMENT, LLC
9400 W Maryland Ave, Glendale, AZ 85305
Tel.: (623) 772-3200   DE
Year Founded: 2013
Holding Company; Professional Hockey Franchise & Sports Arena Owner & Operator
N.A.I.C.S.: 551112
George Frederick J. Gosbee *(Mng Partner)*
Anthony LeBlanc *(Co-Owner, Pres & CEO)*
Avik Dey *(Co-Owner-Arizona Coyotes)*

Subsidiaries:

Coyotes Hockey, LLC   (1)
6751 N Sunset Blvd Ste 200, Glendale, AZ 85305
Tel.: (623) 772-3200
Web Site: http://coyotes.nhl.com
Sales Range: $10-24.9 Million
Emp.: 150
Professional Hockey Team
N.A.I.C.S.: 711211
George Frederick J. Gosbee *(Chm & Governor)*
Richard Nairn *(VP-Comm)*
Jim O'Neal *(Dir-Security)*
Don Maloney *(Exec VP & Gen Mgr)*
Chris O'Hearn *(VP-Hockey Ops)*
Grant Buckborough *(Sr Dir-Premium & Suite Sls)*
Kimberly Trichel *(Dir-Community Rels)*
Monty Low *(Dir-IT)*
Ari Segal *(COO)*
Andrew Barroway *(Owner & Chm)*
Sam Bays *(Dir-Bus Dev)*
Lamont Buford *(Dir-Game Presentation)*
Olivia Campos *(Dir-Community Rels)*
Matt Carnot *(Coord-Corp Partnerships Svc)*
Amy Dimond *(Sr Dir-Mktg)*
Gregg Olson *(CFO)*
John Pierce *(CMO)*
Rachel Regnier *(Dir-Production)*
John Rozak *(Sr Mgr-Mktg)*

RENAISSANCE SYSTEMS, INC.
1515 S Capital Of Texas H, Austin, TX 78746
Tel.: (512) 367-1155   TX
Web Site: http://www.rsitex.com
Year Founded: 1983
Sales Range: $1-9.9 Million
Emp.: 13
Computer System Design Services
N.A.I.C.S.: 541512
Greg Folkerson *(COO)*
John M. Jackson *(Pres)*
Dianne Howes *(Office Mgr)*
Daniel Bernard *(Mgr-IS)*

Subsidiaries:

Folkerson Communications, Ltd.   (1)
701 Sun Meadows Dr, Harker Heights, TX 76548
Tel.: (254) 698-0016
Web Site: http://www.folkersoncom.com
Telecommunications Resellers
N.A.I.C.S.: 517121

RENAISSANCE TECHNOLOGIES, LLC
800 3rd Ave 34th Fl, New York, NY 10022-7604
Tel.: (212) 486-6780   DE
Web Site: http://www.renfund.com
Year Founded: 1982
Sales Range: $50-74.9 Million
Emp.: 93
Security Brokers & Dealer Services
N.A.I.C.S.: 523150
James H. Simons *(Chm)*
Mark Silber *(CFO)*
James Rowen *(COO)*
Peter Brown *(CEO)*
Paul Broder *(Chief Risk Officer)*

RENAVATIO HEALTHCARE COMMUNICATIONS LLC
27-29 Cambridge Ln, Newtown, PA 18940-3326
Tel.: (215) 968-8890
Web Site: http://www.renavatiogroup.com
Sales Range: $1-9.9 Million
Emp.: 16
Health Care Products Mfr
N.A.I.C.S.: 621610
Sheila Gerus *(Principal)*
Larry Iaquinto *(Principal)*
Joseph Miller *(Supvr-Art Grp)*
Ron Lewis *(Dir-Creative & Art)*
Shari Frost *(Acct Dir)*

RENEGADE
10950 Gilroy Rd Ste J, Hunt Valley, MD 21031
Tel.: (410) 667-1400
Year Founded: 1988
Rev.: $47,000,000
Emp.: 50
Advetising Agency
N.A.I.C.S.: 541810
Tim Watkins *(Pres)*
Jennifer Leo Stine *(COO)*
Chris Beutler *(Chief Vision Officer)*
Paul Field *(Chief Strategy Officer)*
Elizabeth Jackson *(Dir-Acct Svcs)*
Ken Hall *(Dir-Creative-Digital)*
Dave Munley *(Acct Dir-Natl)*
Brian Stetson *(Dir-Post Production)*
Sean Sutherland *(Assoc Acct Exec)*

RENEGADE VENTURES, INC.
8275 S Eastern Ave, Las Vegas, NV 89123
Tel.: (702) 577-2871   DE
Year Founded: 2012
Real Estate Investment
N.A.I.C.S.: 525990
Paul J. Howarth *(Chm & CEO)*
Joseph Wade *(Vice Chm & CFO)*
M.L. Billington *(Pres)*

RENEGY HOLDINGS, INC.
2525 E Camelback Rd Ste 820, Phoenix, AZ 85016-4230
Tel.: (480) 556-5555   DE
Web Site: http://www.renegy.com
Sales Range: $1-9.9 Million
Emp.: 64
Holding Company; Biomass Energy Facility Operator
N.A.I.C.S.: 551112
Robert M. Worsley *(Chm & CEO)*
Scott K. Higginson *(Sr VP-Bus Dev & Pub Affairs)*

Subsidiaries:

Renegy, LLC   (1)
3418 N Val Vista Dr, Mesa, AZ 85213
Tel.: (480) 556-5555
Web Site: http://www.renegy.com
Sales Range: $1-9.9 Million
Emp.: 59
Biomass Energy Facility Operator
N.A.I.C.S.: 221118

RENESAN SOFTWARE
400 Cntnental Blvd Fl 6, Manhattan Beach, CA 90266
Tel.: (310) 598-6223
Web Site: http://www.renesan.com
Electronics Stores
N.A.I.C.S.: 449210

RENESAN SOFTWARE

Renesan Software—(Continued)

Neeraj Sinja *(CEO)*

Subsidiaries:

Visonex, LLC (1)
916 Willard Dr, Green Bay, WI 54304
Tel.: (920) 496-0600
Web Site: http://www.visonex.com
Professional, Scientific & Technical Services
N.A.I.C.S.: 541990
Michael Hess *(VP-Sls)*

RENEW DATA CORP.

9500 Arboretum Blvd Ste L2-120,
Austin, TX 78759-6334
Tel.: (512) 276-5500
Web Site: http://www.renewdata.com
Year Founded: 2001
Sales Range: $25-49.9 Million
Emp.: 130
Data Retrieval & Security Services
N.A.I.C.S.: 518210
Douglas S. Strahan *(CFO)*
Linda Kish *(Chief Acctg Officer & VP-Fin)*
Brian M. Brown *(VP-IT & Security)*
Gina Foster *(VP-Ops & Project Mgmt)*

RENEW INDIANAPOLIS, INC.

202 E Market St, Indianapolis, IN 46204
Tel.: (317) 454-8528
Web Site: http://www.renewindianapolis.org
Real Estate & Consumer Services
N.A.I.C.S.: 531390
Chris Hartley *(Mgr-Data)*
Nicholas Hunot *(Mgr-Proj)*
Osha Brownlee *(Mgr-Program)*
Stephanie Quick *(COO)*

RENEWABLE ENERGY ACQUISITION CORP.

2694 Blackwater Rd NW, Longville, MN 56655
Tel.: (952) 541-1155 NV
Year Founded: 2007
REAI—(NASDAQ)
Assets: $4,573
Liabilities: $188,725
Net Worth: ($184,152)
Earnings: ($12,726)
Fiscal Year-end: 12/31/23
Investment Services
N.A.I.C.S.: 523999
Craig S. Laughlin *(Pres, CEO & CFO)*

RENEWABLE FUEL CORP.

7251 W Lake Mead Blvd 300, Las Vegas, NV 89128
Tel.: (702) 989-8978 NV
Web Site: http://www.rfuelcorp.com
Year Founded: 2007
Sales Range: Less than $1 Million
Emp.: 8
Biodiesel & Glycerin Production
N.A.I.C.S.: 324199
William H. Van Vliet III *(Founder)*
Richard S. Henderson *(Pres)*
Daniel Nam Sang Cho *(VP-Intl Affairs)*

RENEWABLE FUNDING GROUP, INC.

1221 Broadway 4th Fl, Oakland, CA 94612
Tel.: (510) 451-7900 DE
Web Site: http://www.renewfund.com
Year Founded: 2008
Holding Company; Clean Energy Financing Services
N.A.I.C.S.: 551112
Cisco DeVries *(Founder)*
Jack Bernard *(Exec Dir)*
Joanna Karger *(CFO)*
Mimi Frusha *(COO)*
Mary Luevano *(Dir-South California)*
Mark Floyd *(CEO)*
Nicholas Haaf *(Chief Sls Officer)*

Subsidiaries:

Renew Financial II LLC (1)
1221 Broadway 4th Fl, Oakland, CA 94612
Tel.: (510) 451-7900
Web Site: http://www.renewfinancial.com
Clean Energy Financing Services
N.A.I.C.S.: 522299
Francisco DeVries *(Founder)*
Cliff Staton *(Exec VP)*
Mark Floyd *(CEO)*
Roger Goldman *(Chm)*
Joel Eckhause *(Chief Risk Officer)*
Mary Kathryn Lynch *(Exec VP-Fin)*
Sachin Adarkar *(Gen Counsel)*
Stephanie Braun *(VP-Product)*

Subsidiary (Domestic):

Renew Financial Corp. II (2)
1005 Brookside Rd, Allentown, PA 18106
Tel.: (610) 433-7486
Web Site: http://www.afcfirst.com
Emp.: 38
Clean Energy Financing Services
N.A.I.C.S.: 522299
Tessa Shin *(Dir-Programs)*
Susie Tompkins *(Mgr-Customer Svc & Payments)*
Susan Moring *(Project Mgr)*
John M. Hayes *(Pres & COO)*
Teri Stoffey *(Dir-Process & Reporting)*
Joanne Hartman *(Mgr-HR)*
Jeanette Francis *(Dir-Customer Response)*
Jennifer Allen *(Dir-Production)*
Greg Burns *(Mgr-Bus Dev-New England)*
Ken Yeager *(VP-Natl Accts)*
Laura Nelson *(CFO & Exec VP)*
Patricia Stumpp *(Sr Officer-Credit & VP)*
Shawna Hoffman *(Program Mgr)*
Valerie Berdahl *(Coord-Mktg & Bus Dev)*

RENEWABLE RESOURCES GROUP INC.

113 La Brea Ave 3rd Fl, Los Angeles, CA 90036
Tel.: (323) 936-9303
Web Site: http://www.renewablegroup.com
Holding Company
N.A.I.C.S.: 551112
J. Ari Swiller *(Founder)*

Subsidiaries:

Sun World International LLC (1)
16350 Driver Rd, Bakersfield, CA 93308
Tel.: (661) 392-5000
Web Site: http://www.sun-world.com
Sales Range: $800-899.9 Million
Emp.: 905
Fruit & Vegetable Producer & Distr
N.A.I.C.S.: 111332
David Marguleas *(CEO)*
Juliana Escobar *(Dir-Export Sls)*
Jeff Jackson *(Exec VP-Bus Dev)*

RENEWABLE WATER RESOURCES

561 Mauldin Rd, Greenville, SC 29607
Tel.: (864) 299-4000
Web Site: http://www.rewaonline.org
Year Founded: 1925
Sales Range: $25-49.9 Million
Emp.: 185
Wastewater Systems
N.A.I.C.S.: 221320
Patricia Dennis *(Controller)*
Barbara Wilson *(Dir-HR)*
Blake Visin *(Dir-IT)*
Kevin James *(Mgr-Ops)*
Chris Eleazer *(Mgr-Collection Sys)*

RENEWAL DESIGN-BUILD INC.

124 S Columbia Dr, Decatur, GA 30030
Tel.: (404) 378-6962
Web Site: http://www.renewaldesignbuild.com
Year Founded: 2001
Sales Range: $10-24.9 Million
Emp.: 17
Construction Services
N.A.I.C.S.: 236210
Peter Michelson *(CEO)*
David Michelson *(Founder & CEO)*
Shereen Shaw *(Controller)*
Candace Parker *(Dir-First Impressions)*
Clint Tomasino *(Project Mgr)*
Heather Shuster *(Dir-Project Dev)*
Kara Adams *(Dir-Mktg)*
Reed Haley *(Project Mgr)*

RENFROE PECAN CO. INC.

2400 W Fairfield Dr, Pensacola, FL 32505
Tel.: (850) 438-9405
Web Site: http://www.renfroepecan.com
Rev.: $18,415,249
Emp.: 7
Nuts Mfr & Distr
N.A.I.C.S.: 424590
John W. Renfroe Jr. *(Pres)*

RENHILL GROUP INC.

28315 Kensington Ln Ste B, Perrysburg, OH 43551
Tel.: (419) 254-2800
Web Site: http://www.renhill.com
Sales Range: $100-124.9 Million
Emp.: 1,200
Temporary Help Service
N.A.I.C.S.: 561320
Barrie Howell *(Pres)*

RENIX CORP.

265 Radio Rd, Corona, CA 92879
Tel.: (951) 371-8996
Web Site: http://www.newportboats.com
Rev.: $10,200,000
Emp.: 30
Boat Dealers
N.A.I.C.S.: 441222
Marry Shannon *(Branch Mgr)*

RENK SEED COMPANY

6809 Wilburn Rd, Sun Prairie, WI 53590
Tel.: (608) 837-7351
Web Site: http://www.renkseed.com
Sales Range: $10-24.9 Million
Emp.: 30
Farm Supplies Merchant Whslr
N.A.I.C.S.: 424910
Bob Wilms *(Mgr-Northeast Wisconsin)*
Ted Richel *(Mgr-Sls-Northwest Wisconsin)*
Bob Bork *(Mgr-East Central Wisconsin)*
Jeff Taffe *(Mgr-North Dakota & Northern Minnesota)*
Keith Loe *(Mgr-West Central Minnesota)*
Glenn Zarling *(Mgr-Eastern Minnesota)*
John Heying *(Mgr-Northeast Iowa)*
Amy Allen *(Mgr)*
Jeff Renk *(VP)*
Alex Renk *(Pres)*
Jason Fearing *(Mgr-West Central Wisconsin)*

RENKER-EICH-PARKS ARCHITECTS, INC.

1609 Dr Martin Luther King Jr St N, Saint Petersburg, FL 33704-4203
Tel.: (727) 821-2986
Web Site: http://www.reparch.com

U.S. PRIVATE

Sales Range: $1-9.9 Million
Emp.: 7
Architectural Services
N.A.I.C.S.: 541310
Paul Palmer *(Mng Partner)*
Richard Headland *(Mng Partner)*
Sergio DeSanto *(Mng Partner)*
Haley Harmon *(Principal)*
Harmon Haley Jr. *(Mng Partner)*

RENN KIRBY CHEVROLET BUICK, LLC.

791 York Rd, Gettysburg, PA 17325
Tel.: (717) 334-9234
Web Site: http://www.rennkirby.com
Sales Range: $25-49.9 Million
Emp.: 30
Car Whslr
N.A.I.C.S.: 441110
Gary Moser *(Gen Mgr)*

RENN KIRBY MITSUBISHI INC.

5903 Urbana Pike, Frederick, MD 21704-7206
Tel.: (301) 663-4185
Web Site: http://www.rennkirbymitsubishi.com
Sales Range: $10-24.9 Million
Emp.: 48
Car Dealership
N.A.I.C.S.: 441110
Sean Kirby *(Owner)*
Tony Ciorra *(Mgr-Parts)*
Becky Strawsburg *(Office Mgr)*
Russell Hawthorne *(Gen Mgr)*
Chris Mongold *(Mgr-Fin)*
Michael Hadid *(Mgr-Gen Sls)*
Justin Krumpach *(Mgr-Svc-Columbus)*

RENN TRANSPORTATION, INC.

8845 Forest St, Gilroy, CA 95020
Tel.: (408) 842-3545
Web Site: http://www.renntransportation.com
Rev.: $50,000,000
Emp.: 55
Petroleum Bulk Stations
N.A.I.C.S.: 424710
Richard Renn *(Mgr-Maintenance)*

RENNA COMMUNICATIONS

Po Box 651, Shelter Island, NY 11964
Tel.: (917) 757-6123
Sales Range: $10-24.9 Million
Emp.: 5
Communications, Gay & Lesbian Media & Marketing, Media Planning, Media Relations, Media Training, Strategic Planning/Research
N.A.I.C.S.: 541810
Cathy McElrath Renna *(Mng Partner)*

RENNEN INTERNATIONAL

120 19 Rockaway Blvd, Ozone Park, NY 11420
Tel.: (718) 978-6722
Web Site: http://www.renneninternational.com
Year Founded: 2002
Sales Range: $1-9.9 Million
Emp.: 45
Aftermarket Alloy Wheels for Automobiles
N.A.I.C.S.: 326211
Richard Shaw *(Owner)*

RENNER MOTORS, INC.

3055 Central Ave, Columbus, IN 47203
Tel.: (812) 372-1561
Web Site: http://www.rennermotors.com
Year Founded: 1948

Sales Range: $10-24.9 Million
Emp.: 42
Car Dealer
N.A.I.C.S.: 441110
Lisa Hurley (Pres)
Jeroyl Harris (VP)
Belinda Coleman (Gen Mgr-Sls)

RENO CONTRACTING INC.
7584 Metropolitan Dr Ste 100, San Diego, CA 92108
Tel.: (619) 220-0224
Web Site: http://www.renocon.com
Sales Range: $25-49.9 Million
Emp.: 60
Nonresidential Construction
N.A.I.C.S.: 236220
Matthew J. Reno (Founder & CEO)
Walter J. Fegley (Pres & COO)
Joseph L. McCaleb (Dir-Preconstruction)
Joey Miller (Mgr-AR)
Bryan McCarthy (Project Mgr)
Danielle Slagal (Project Mgr)
Andrew Kessler (Gen Counsel)
Greg Carnegie (Mgr-Energy Program)
Toby Foster (Project Mgr)
Wade Richardson (Project Mgr)
Pete Hunter (Sr Project Mgr)
Rick Laferney (Sr Project Mgr)
Victoria Seidler (Sr Project Mgr)
Chris Heim (VP)

RENO LUMBER
680 Spice Islands Dr, Sparks, NV 89431
Tel.: (775) 329-9663
Web Site: http://www.renolumber.com
Sales Range: $10-24.9 Million
Emp.: 30
Lumber & Building Material Whslr
N.A.I.C.S.: 444110
Chris Fleiner (VP-Sls)

RENO TOYOTA INC.
9475 S Virginia St, Reno, NV 89511-8941
Tel.: (775) 828-9666
Web Site: http://www.renotoyota.com
Sales Range: $10-24.9 Million
Emp.: 100
Car Whslr
N.A.I.C.S.: 441110
Ryan M. Dolan (Gen Mgr)
Thomas S. Dolan (Pres)

RENO'S APPLIANCE INC.
11 Kulick Rd, Fairfield, NJ 07004
Tel.: (973) 575-8422
Web Site: http://www.renosappliance.com
Sales Range: $100-124.9 Million
Emp.: 50
Retailer of Kitchen Appliances
N.A.I.C.S.: 449210
John Cioletti (Pres)

RENODIS, INC.
476 Robert St N, Saint Paul, MN 55101-2238
Tel.: (651) 556-1200   MN
Web Site: http://www.renodis.com
Year Founded: 2002
Sales Range: $1-9.9 Million
Emp.: 21
Scientific & Technical Consulting Services
N.A.I.C.S.: 541690
Craig Beason (Founder & CEO)
Myron Braun (VP-Sls)
David Steichen (CFO & Dir-Mergers & Acq)
Matt Spivey (CTO)

Subsidiaries:

12 Points Consulting Corp.   (1)
1613 Main Ave E Ste 2, West Fargo, ND 58078-2135
Tel.: (701) 282-4602
Web Site: http://www.12pointsconsulting.com
Emp.: 100
Management Consulting Services
N.A.I.C.S.: 541618
Curtis Olein (Pres)

Eric Ryan Corporation   (1)
1 Early St Ste A, Ellwood City, PA 16117
Tel.: (724) 752-8900
Web Site: https://www.ericryan.com
Sales Range: $1-9.9 Million
Emp.: 102
Telecommunications Cost Reduction Services
N.A.I.C.S.: 926150
Keith Venezie (Founder & CEO)

RCN Communications LLC   (1)
200 Jennings Ave, Knoxville, TN 37917
Tel.: (865) 293-0350
Web Site: http://www.rcntechnologies.com
Sales Range: $1-9.9 Million
Emp.: 50
Information Technology Management Services
N.A.I.C.S.: 541512
Geoff Yearack (Co-Founder & Pres)
Jennifer Yearack (Co-Founder & CEO)
Gary Menees (VP-Sls)
Ben Moser (VP-Ops)
Nick Conner (Dir-Sls Ops)

RENOSOL CORPORATION
691 S River Rd, Bay City, MI 48708
Tel.: (989) 894-0300
Web Site: http://www.renosol.com
Year Founded: 1981
Polyurethane Systems, Molded Seating & Interior Trim Products Mfr
N.A.I.C.S.: 326199
Larry Adkisson (CEO)

RENOVA LIGHTING SYSTEMS, INC.
36 Bellair Ave, Warwick, RI 02886
Tel.: (404) 737-6700
Web Site: http://www.renova.com
Energy-Efficient Lighting Fixtures & Other Products Mfr & Distr
N.A.I.C.S.: 335132
Rick Edwards (Pres, CEO & Owner)

RENOVO CAPITAL, LLC
14241 Dallas Pkwy Ste 1230, Dallas, TX 75254
Tel.: (214) 699-4960   DE
Web Site: http://www.renovocapital.com
Year Founded: 2009
Rev: $500,000,000
Privater Equity Firm
N.A.I.C.S.: 523999
Don Jungerman (Partner)
David Hull (Partner)
Matthew Farrell (Partner)
Amanda Kennelly (Office Mgr)

Subsidiaries:

Andronico's Community Markets   (1)
1200 Irving St, San Francisco, CA 94122
Tel.: (415) 661-3220
Web Site: http://www.andronicos.com
Sales Range: $25-49.9 Million
Grocery Stores
N.A.I.C.S.: 445110
William Andronico (Pres)
Cheryl Hughes (CFO)

Informatics Holdings, Inc.   (1)
1400 10th St, Plano, TX 75074-8648
Web Site: http://www.systemid.com
Computer & Computer Peripheral Equipment & Software Merchant Whslr
N.A.I.C.S.: 423430
Thomas O. Shea (Pres)

Rochester Sensors, LLC   (1)
1025 S Belt Line Rd Ste 100, Coppell, TX 75019
Tel.: (888) 724-0778
Web Site: https://rochestersensors.com
Measuring & Controlling Device, Industrial Machinery & Equipment Mfr & Whslr
N.A.I.C.S.: 334513

States Industries, LLC   (1)
29545 E Enid Rd, Eugene, OR 97402
Tel.: (541) 688-7871
Web Site: http://www.statesind.com
Sales Range: $75-99.9 Million
Mfr of Plywood, Hardwood Or Hardwood Faced Panels
N.A.I.C.S.: 321211
Mike Taylor (Pres)
Milena Lodestein-Riel (Mgr-Value stream)
David Bell (Mgr-Mktg)
Kristee Neumann (Mgr-HR)
Mario Serra (Dir-OEM Sls)

Subsidiary (Domestic):

Drawer Box Specialties Inc.   (2)
1482 N Batavia St, Orange, CA 92867
Tel.: (714) 744-4247
Web Site: http://www.dbsdrawers.com
Sales Range: $10-24.9 Million
Emp.: 75
Custom Drawer Mfr
N.A.I.C.S.: 423310

RENOVUS CAPITAL PARTNERS
460 E Swedesford Rd Ste 2050, Wayne, PA 19087
Tel.: (610) 848-7705
Web Site: http://renovuscapital.com
Year Founded: 2010
Privater Equity Firm
N.A.I.C.S.: 551112
Daniel Maine (CFO)
Brad Whitman (Founding Partner)
Atif Gilani (Founding Partner)
Jesse Serventi (Founding Partner)
Frederick Hill (Partner)

Subsidiaries:

ARETUM Holdings, LLC   (1)
7315 Wisconsin Ave Ste 500W, Bethesda, MA 20814
Tel.: (240) 800-3001
Web Site: https://www.aretum.com
General Management Consulting Services
N.A.I.C.S.: 541611
Damian DiPippa (CEO)

Subsidiary (Domestic):

Artemis Consulting, Inc.   (2)
2669 Oakton Glen Dr, Vienna, VA 22181-5344
Tel.: (703) 598-0077
Web Site: http://www.artemisconsultinginc.com
Internet Publishing & Broadcasting & Web Search Portals
N.A.I.C.S.: 516210
Rohit Gupta (Pres)

Panum Telecommunications, LLC   (2)
7315 Wisconsin Ave 800 W, Bethesda, MD 20814-3202
Tel.: (301) 470-2683
Web Site: http://www.panum.com
General Management Consulting Services
N.A.I.C.S.: 541611
Sujata Gupta (CEO)
Vijay Mishra (COO)

EducationDynamics, LLC   (1)
111 River St 10th Fl, Hoboken, NJ 07030
Tel.: (201) 377-3000
Web Site: http://www.educationdynamics.com
Higher Education Student Prospecting & Acquisition Services
N.A.I.C.S.: 541612
Bruce Douglas (CEO)
Michael Flores (Chief Mktg Officer)
Pamela Cohen (Chief Revenue Officer)
Greg Clayton (Pres-Solution Svcs)
Aja Baxter (Gen Counsel)
Carol Aslanian (Pres-Aslanian Market Res & Sr VP)
Sandesh Sadalge (VP-Analytics)
Erick Vazquez (VP-IT)
Tom Wright (CFO)

Subsidiary (Domestic):

Dick Jones Communications, LLC   (2)
1370 S Atherton St, State College, PA 16801
Tel.: (724) 260-0198
Web Site: https://www.rwjonesagency.com
Communications & Marketing Services
N.A.I.C.S.: 541613
Laura Snyder (VP)
Maggy Ralbovsky (Pres & Mng Dir)
Scott Willyerd (Mng Partner)

F2 Strategy, Inc.   (1)
1 Blackfield Dri Ste 229, Tiburon, CA 94920
Tel.: (415) 844-0641
Web Site: https://www.f2strategy.com
Financial Services
N.A.I.C.S.: 523999

Subsidiary (Domestic):

Oakbrook Solutions, Inc.   (2)
301 N Main St Ste 2304, Winston Salem, NC 27101
Tel.: (336) 714-0321
Web Site: http://www.oakbrooksolutions.com
Sales Range: $1-9.9 Million
Emp.: 100
Business Consulting Solutions
N.A.I.C.S.: 541618
Craig Cook (Co-Founder & Pres)
Tony Painter (Chm, Co-Founder & CEO)

Rasmussen College, LLC   (1)
8300 Norman Center Dr Ste 300, Bloomington, MN 55437
Tel.: (952) 806-3900
Web Site: http://rasmussen.edu
Graduate & Undergraduate College
N.A.I.C.S.: 611310
Brent Dobsch (CFO)
Tawnie Cortez (VP-Student Affairs)
Thomas M. Slagle (CEO)
Henry S. Bienen (Chm)
Ann Leja (Interim Pres)

Toxstrategies Inc.   (1)
23123 Cinco Ranch Blvd Ste 220, Katy, TX 77494-2297
Tel.: (512) 382-9830
Web Site: http://www.toxstrategies.com
Scientific & Technical Consulting Services
N.A.I.C.S.: 541690
Mark Harris (Co-Founder)

Subsidiary (Domestic):

Modality Solutions, LLC   (2)
2600 S Shore Blvd Ste 364, League City, TX 77573
Web Site: http://www.modality-solutions.com
Sales Range: $1-9.9 Million
Emp.: 8
Biopharmaceutical Research & Development Services
N.A.I.C.S.: 541715
Gary M. Hutchinson (Pres)
Daniel J. Littlefield (Principal)
Hannah Anderson (Mgr-Project & Quality)
Matthew Coker (Engr-Consulting)
Sumika Stansbury (Engr-Consulting)

RENOWN HEALTH
1155 Mill St, Reno, NV 89502
Tel.: (775) 982-4100
Web Site: http://www.renown.org
Year Founded: 1862
Sales Range: $250-299.9 Million
Emp.: 4,565
Medical Health Network
N.A.I.C.S.: 622110
Dawn Ahner (CFO)
Phyllis Freyer (VP-Mktg & Comm)
Chris Bosse (VP-Govt Rels)
Michelle Sanchez-Bickley (VP-HR)
Anthony D. Slonim (Pres & CEO)
Erik Olson (CEO-Renown Reg Medical Center & VP)

RENOWN NETWORK SERVICES
1155 Mill St c/o Tax Treasury Z-5, Reno, NV 89502
Tel.: (775) 982-4404   NV

RENOWN NETWORK SERVICES

Renown Network Services—(Continued)
Year Founded: 1987
Sales Range: $25-49.9 Million
Health Care Srvices
N.A.I.C.S.: 622110
Christine Wells (Dir-Ambulatory Care Svcs)
Lawrence Tnlops III (VP-Ambulatory Svcs)

RENSSELAER HONDA
770 Hoosick Rd, Troy, NY 12180
Tel.: (518) 279-1171
Web Site: http://www.rensselaerhonda.com
Year Founded: 1977
Sales Range: $50-74.9 Million
Emp.: 60
New & Used Car Dealers
N.A.I.C.S.: 441110
Glenn Babineau (Mgr-Fin)

RENT READY, LLC
508 W 5th St Ste 240, Charlotte, NC 28202
Web Site: http://www.rentready.com
Year Founded: 2013
Sales Range: $1-9.9 Million
Emp.: 26
Real Estate Manangement Services
N.A.I.C.S.: 531390
Will Brugh (Co-Founder)
Jonathan Kite (Co-Founder)
Ryan McMillian (Co-Founder)

RENT SOLUTIONS
3502 Henderson Blvd Ste 203, Tampa, FL 33609
Tel.: (813) 579-5597
Web Site: http://www.rentsolutions.com
Sales Range: $25-49.9 Million
Emp.: 40
Property Rental & Management Services
N.A.I.C.S.: 531110
Steve Oehlerking (Pres)
Ralph Corigliano (Dir-Bus Dev)
Tammy Leonard (Dir-Property Mgmt)
Careese Babb (Dir-Acctg)
Cody Richardson (Mgr-Property)

RENTAL MAX LLC
908 East Roosevelt Rd Fl 2, Wheaton, IL 60187
Tel.: (630) 221-1133
Web Site: http://www.rentalmax.com
Rev.: $15,800,000
Emp.: 200
Equipment Rental & Leasing
N.A.I.C.S.: 532490
Harry T. Hagy Jr. (Pres)

RENTAL UNIFORM SERVICE OF FLORENCE
906 S Church St, Florence, SC 29504-2950
Tel.: (843) 669-4444
Web Site: http://www.rentaluniformsvc.com
Sales Range: $10-24.9 Million
Emp.: 182
Industrial Uniform Supply
N.A.I.C.S.: 812332

RENTALS UNLIMITED INC.
24000 Frederick Rd, Clarksburg, MD 20872
Tel.: (301) 972-6200
Web Site: http://www.rentalsunlimited.com
Year Founded: 1956
Sales Range: $10-24.9 Million
Emp.: 90
Rental of Heavy Construction Equipment & Trucks

N.A.I.C.S.: 532412
Jeff Bryant (Pres)

RENTBITS.COM
1062 Delaware St Ste 5, Denver, CO 80204
Tel.: (303) 640-3160
Web Site: http://www.rentbits.com
Year Founded: 2006
Sales Range: $1-9.9 Million
Emp.: 19
Real Estate Rental Search Engine Services
N.A.I.C.S.: 531190
Dan Daugherty (CEO)

RENTECH, INC.
1000 Potomac St NW 5th Fl, Washington, DC 20007
Tel.: (202) 791-9040   CO
Web Site: http://www.rentechinc.com
Year Founded: 1981
Sales Range: $250-299.9 Million
Emp.: 939
Synthetic Fuels & Renewable Power Developer
N.A.I.C.S.: 325998
Julie Dawoodjee Cafarella (VP-IR & Comm)
Joe Herold (Sr VP-HR)
Keith B. Forman (Pres & CEO)
Paul Summers (CFO, Treas & VP)
Nicole M. Powe (Gen Counsel, Sec & Sr VP)
Mark R. Wilson (CEO)

Subsidiaries:

BioFuel Energy Systems, LLC   (1)
415 Squantum Rd, Jaffrey, NH 03452
Tel.: (603) 532-4666
Biofuel Distr
N.A.I.C.S.: 424690

Fulghum Fibrefuels, Ltd.   (1)
PO Box 15395, Augusta, GA 30919
Tel.: (706) 651-1000
Web Site: http://www.fulghumfibrefuels.com
Biofuel Mfr & Distr
N.A.I.C.S.: 325199

Fulghum Fibres Chile S.A.   (1)
Av Costanera S /N Schwager Colonel Reg VIII, Coronel, Chile
Tel.: (56) 412710720
Web Site: http://www.forestalchile.cl
Wood Product Distr
N.A.I.C.S.: 423990
Hiroshi Ogihara (Gen Mgr)
Lorena A. Sanchez (Mgr-Admin & Fin)
Claudio C. Meza (Plant Mgr)
Gerardo Herrera (Plant Mgr)
Ignacio Echevarria (Plant Mgr)

Fulghum Fibres Collins, Inc.   (1)
Highway 121 S, Collins, GA 30421
Tel.: (912) 693-9645
Wood Chip Mfr
N.A.I.C.S.: 321113

New England Wood Pellet, LLC   (1)
141 Old Sharon Rd, Jaffrey, NH 03452
Tel.: (603) 532-9400
Web Site: http://www.pelletheat.com
Emp.: 33
Wood Pellets for Heating Mfr
N.A.I.C.S.: 321912
Rocco A. Bouse (Dir-Sls & Mktg)

Rentech Development Corporation   (1)
10877 Wilshire Blvd 10 fl, Los Angeles, CA 90024
Tel.: (310) 571-9800
Web Site: http://www.rentechinc.com
Sales Range: $125-149.9 Million
Emp.: 30
Owns & Licenses a Proprietary & Patented Process that Converts Synthesis Gas into Liquid Hydrocarbons
N.A.I.C.S.: 333248

Rentech Energy Midwest Corporation   (1)

16675 US Hwy 20 W, East Dubuque, IL 61025-8605
Tel.: (815) 747-3101
Sales Range: $100-124.9 Million
Emp.: 120
Mfr of Nitrogen Fertilizers
N.A.I.C.S.: 325311
Bob Tschiggsrie (Plant Mgr)

Rentech Nitrogen Finance Corporation   (1)
10877 Wilshire Blvd Ste 600, Los Angeles, CA 90024
Tel.: (310) 571-9800
Chemical Products Distr
N.A.I.C.S.: 424690

Rentech Services Corporation   (1)
4150 E 60th Ave, Commerce City, CO 80022-3110   (100%)
Tel.: (303) 286-7233
Web Site: http://www.rentechinc.com
Sales Range: $10-24.9 Million
Emp.: 25
Provider of Business Research Services
N.A.I.C.S.: 541910

Schuyler Wood Pellet, LLC   (1)
172 Diamond Dr, Frankfort, NY 13340
Tel.: (315) 724-7166
Wood Product Distr
N.A.I.C.S.: 423990

RENTWERX, LLC
21222 Gathering Oak 103, San Antonio, TX 78260
Tel.: (210) 497-8686
Web Site: http://www.rentwerx.com
Year Founded: 2011
Sales Range: $1-9.9 Million
Emp.: 26
Residential Leasing & Property Management Services
N.A.I.C.S.: 531110
Melanie Thomas (Dir-Ops)
Ruby Rowan (Mgr-Portfolio)
Valerie Pedraza (Mgr-Portfolio)
Cristina Hinojosa (Mgr-Portfolio)
Brian Hughes (Dir-Sls & Mktg)

RENTZEL PUMP MANUFACTURING, LP
1301 N Globe Ave, Lubbock, TX 79408
Tel.: (405) 360-7865   NE
Web Site: http://www.rentzelpump.com
Year Founded: 1878
Sales Range: $25-49.9 Million
Emp.: 15
Pumps & Fertilizer Spreaders & Sprayers Mfr
N.A.I.C.S.: 423830
Lupe Montalvo (Office Mgr)

RENWOOD REALTYTRAC, LLC
One Venture Plz Ste 300, Irvine, CA 92618
Tel.: (949) 502-8300   NV
Web Site: http://www.realtytrac.com
Year Founded: 1996
Sales Range: $25-49.9 Million
Emp.: 100
Online Real Estate Marketplace
N.A.I.C.S.: 531390
Rick Sharga (Exec VP-Mktg)
Cabell Cobbs (CFO)
Gary Hegenbart (Exec VP-HR)
Ginny Walker (Sr Mgr-PR)
Jennifer von Pohlmann (Mgr-PR)
Michael Sawtell (Exec VP & Gen Mgr-Consumer Solutions)

REO AMERICA, INC.
940 Ctr Cir Ste 2005, Altamonte Springs, FL 32714
Tel.: (407) 339-1108
Web Site: http://www.reo-america.com

U.S. PRIVATE

Year Founded: 2003
Rev.: $3,200,000
Emp.: 7
Real Estate Agents & Brokers
N.A.I.C.S.: 531210
Douglas Gale (Owner)

REOPCO INC.
4930 E State St, Rockford, IL 61108
Tel.: (815) 387-1700
Web Site: http://www.roadrangerusa.com
Sales Range: $10-24.9 Million
Emp.: 25
Convenience Store
N.A.I.C.S.: 445131
Dan Arnold (Founder)

REPACORP INC.
31 Industry Park Ct, Tipp City, OH 45371
Tel.: (937) 667-8496
Web Site: http://www.repacorp.com
Year Founded: 1974
Sales Range: $10-24.9 Million
Emp.: 100
Labels (Unprinted), Gummed: Made From Purchased Materials
N.A.I.C.S.: 322220
Rick M. Heinl (Pres)

REPAIR CENTER, LLC
601 Maryland Ave NE, Grand Rapids, MI 49505
Web Site: http://www.techdefenders.com
Year Founded: 2014
Sales Range: $1-9.9 Million
Electronic Equipment Repair Services
N.A.I.C.S.: 811114
Garry VonMyhr (CEO)
James Doletzky (CFO)
Scott Morey (Dir-Systems)
Victor Del Angel (Dir-Ops)
Mark Hudson (Dir-ITAD Sls)

REPCON, INC.
7501 Uppr River Rd, Corpus Christi, TX 78469
Tel.: (361) 289-6342
Web Site: http://www.repcon.com
Rev.: $23,000,000
Emp.: 200
Heavy & Civil Engineering Construction
N.A.I.C.S.: 237990
R. E. Parker (Pres)
Kirby Morgan (CFO)
Mike Denman (Mgr-Quality)
Malcolm Pace (Supvr-Safety)

REPEQUITY
1211 Connecticut Ave NW Ste 250, Washington, DC 20036
Tel.: (202) 654-0800
Web Site: http://www.repequity.com
Year Founded: 2007
Sales Range: $1-9.9 Million
Emp.: 32
Online Brand Management Services
N.A.I.C.S.: 541810
Tripp Donnelly (Founder & CEO)
Kyong Choe (CFO)
Steve Wanczyk (VP-Search & Social Media)
Eric Gilbertsen (VP-Digital Strategy)
Ashley Barna (VP-Digital Adv & Search Engine Optimization)

REPIPE SPECIALISTS, INC.
146 S San Fernando, Burbank, CA 91503
Tel.: (818) 842-9900
Web Site: http://www.repipespecialists.com
Year Founded: 1991

Sales Range: $1-9.9 Million
Emp.: 20
Plumbing & Heating Contractor
N.A.I.C.S.: 238220
Jeffrey Butler *(Owner)*
Linda Estabrook *(Mgr-Ops)*

REPLACEMENT PARTS INC.
1901 E Roosevelt Rd, Little Rock, AR 72206
Tel.: (501) 375-1215   AR
Web Site:
   http://www.btbautoparts.com
Year Founded: 1988
Rev.: $79,470,312
Emp.: 900
Motor Vehicle Supplies & New Parts
N.A.I.C.S.: 423120
E. Fletcher Lord Jr. *(Chm)*

Subsidiaries:

Crow Burlingame of Conway Inc.   (1)
1740 E Oak St, Conway, AR 72032-4741
Tel.: (501) 329-6823
Sales Range: $10-24.9 Million
Emp.: 7
Motor Vehicle Supplies & New Parts
N.A.I.C.S.: 423120
Michael Dawson *(Mgr-Stores)*

Crow-Burlingame Co.   (1)
610 Hwy 367 N, Newport, AR 72112-4835   (100%)
Tel.: (870) 523-3675
Sales Range: Less than $1 Million
Emp.: 3
Used Motor Vehicle Parts
N.A.I.C.S.: 423140
Bill Mauldin *(Mgr-Store)*

Crow-Burlingame Co. Inc.   (1)
1901 E Roosevelt Rd, Little Rock, AR 72206-2533   (100%)
Tel.: (501) 375-1215
Web Site: http://www.btbautoparts.net
Sales Range: $10-24.9 Million
Emp.: 100
Motor Vehicle Supplies & New Parts
N.A.I.C.S.: 423120

Crow-Burlingame Co. Inc.   (1)
1895 W MLK Blvd, Fayetteville, AR 72701-6204
Tel.: (479) 521-7574
Sales Range: $10-24.9 Million
Emp.: 13
Motor Vehicle Supplies & New Parts
N.A.I.C.S.: 423120
Bryan Jones *(Gen Mgr)*

Parts Warehouse Inc.   (1)
1901 E Roosevelt Rd, Little Rock, AR 72206-2533
Tel.: (501) 375-1215
Web Site: http://www.autoparts.com
Sales Range: $10-24.9 Million
Emp.: 20
Motor Vehicle Supplies & New Parts
N.A.I.C.S.: 423120
Flecther Lord *(Owner)*

Subsidiary (Domestic):

Tri-States Automotive Warehouse, Inc.   (2)
PO Box 5838, Marianna, FL 32447-5838
Tel.: (850) 526-2331
Web Site: http://www.tristatesauto.com
Rev.: $15,170,888
Emp.: 65
Automotive Supplies & Parts
N.A.I.C.S.: 423120
William Stevens *(Gen Mgr)*

REPLACEMENTS, LTD.
1089 Knox Rd, McLeansville, NC 27301-9228
Tel.: (336) 697-3000   NC
Web Site:
   http://www.replacements.com
Year Founded: 1981
Sales Range: $50-74.9 Million
Emp.: 700
Mail Order House Distr of Discontinued China, Crystal & Flatware

N.A.I.C.S.: 449129
Linh Calhoun *(CMO)*

REPLENEX INC.
9815 W 74th St, Eden Prairie, MN 55344
Tel.: (952) 941-9150
Web Site: http://www.replenex.com
Sales Range: $10-24.9 Million
Emp.: 50
Industrial Tools, Cleaners & Abrasives Distr
N.A.I.C.S.: 423840
Ron Veith *(VP-Fin)*
Matthew Cohen *(Pres)*
Rick Kurschner *(Mgr-IT)*
Tom Folska *(VP-Sls)*
Nick Morrissey *(Acct Mgr)*
Ron Johnson *(Mgr-Tech Svcs)*
Allison Caird *(Mgr-On-Site)*
Dan Timmersman *(Reg Mgr-Sls)*
Don Considine *(Reg Mgr-Sls)*
Doug Rovner *(VP-Ops)*
Ken Herbst *(Acct Mgr)*
Max Schultz *(Acct Mgr)*
Ron Frisk *(Acct Mgr)*
Tom Sokol *(Acct Mgr)*
Tony DAquisto *(Reg Mgr-Sls)*

REPLOGLE GLOBES PARTNERS LLC
125 Fencl Lane, Hillside, IL 60162
Tel.: (708) 593-3411
Web Site:
   http://www.reglogeglobes.com
Year Founded: 1930
Sales Range: $600-649.9 Million
Emp.: 100
Mfr of Handcrafted Globes
N.A.I.C.S.: 541370
Melissa Rains *(Mgr-Special Market Distributors)*
Clayton Chang *(Pres)*
Slavica Kutlic *(Dir-Engrg)*
Joe Wright *(CEO)*

REPLY! INC.
12667 Alcosta Blvd Ste 200, San Ramon, CA 94583
Tel.: (925) 983-3400   DE
Web Site: http://www.reply.com
Year Founded: 2001
Sales Range: $25-49.9 Million
Emp.: 200
Online Auction Marketplace & Marketing Services
N.A.I.C.S.: 425120
Adam Carabetta *(VP-Retail Ops)*
Reza Hajebi *(CTO)*
Chris Mancini *(CMO)*
Sonia Hernandez *(VP-Optimization)*
Adam Markowitz *(VP-Engrg)*
Tatiana Rizzante *(CEO)*

Subsidiaries:

HomeGain.com, Inc.   (1)
12667 Alcosta Blvd Ste 200, San Ramon, CA 94583
Tel.: (925) 983-2852
Web Site: http://www.homegain.com
Sales Range: $25-49.9 Million
Emp.: 75
Online Real Estate Marketing & Advertising Services
N.A.I.C.S.: 531390
Louis Cammarosano *(Gen Mgr)*
Vikas Karandikar *(CTO)*
Jim Ridley *(Dir-Website Ops)*

REPROGRAPHICS ONE INC.
15260 Commerce Dr S, Dearborn, MI 48120
Tel.: (734) 542-8800
Web Site:
   http://www.reprographicsone.com
Rev.: $14,500,000
Emp.: 30

Blue Print Cloth Distr
N.A.I.C.S.: 325992
Tim Ginster *(Mgr-Sls)*

REPROTECH LIMITED
33 Fifth Ave NW Ste 900, Saint Paul, MN 55112
Tel.: (651) 489-0827
Web Site: http://www.reprotech.com
Year Founded: 1990
Long-term Cryostorage & Fertility Preservation
N.A.I.C.S.: 493100
Heather Cummins *(Exec Dir)*
Brent Hazelrigg *(Pres)*
Brad Senstra *(CEO)*

REPUBLIC AIRWAYS HOLDINGS INC.
8909 Purdue Rd Ste 300, Indianapolis, IN 46268
Tel.: (317) 484-6000   DE
Web Site: http://www.rjet.com
Year Founded: 1996
Holding Company
N.A.I.C.S.: 551112
Bryan K. Bedford *(Chm, Pres & CEO)*
Jeff Jones *(VP-Market Plng & Dev)*
Paul Kinstedt *(Acting COO & Sr VP-Ops)*
Thomas Duffy *(VP-Tech Svcs)*
Scott Durgin *(VP-Admin & Lean Methods)*
Brad Elstad *(VP-Safety & Regulatory Compliance)*
Joseph P. Allman *(CFO & Sr VP)*
Drew Skaff *(VP-Supply Chain)*
Matt Koscal *(VP-HR)*
Rose Doria *(VP-Labor Rels)*
Pat Gannon *(VP-Sys Ops Control)*
Scott Hornback *(VP-Fin & Acctg)*
Nirav Shah *(VP-IT)*

Subsidiaries:

Chautauqua Airlines Inc.   (1)
8909 Purdue Rd Ste 300, Indianapolis, IN 46268-4962
Tel.: (317) 484-6000
Web Site: http://www.flychautauqua.com
Sales Range: $600-649.9 Million
Emp.: 3,000
Passenger Airline
N.A.I.C.S.: 481111
Bryan K. Bedford *(Pres & CEO)*

Republic Airline Inc.   (1)
8909 Purdue Rd Ste 300, Indianapolis, IN 46268
Tel.: (317) 484-6000
Web Site: http://www.rjet.com
Sales Range: $200-249.9 Million
Emp.: 400
Passenger Airline
N.A.I.C.S.: 481111
Bryan K. Bedford *(Chm, Pres & CEO)*

REPUBLIC BANCORP CO.
2221 Camden Ct, Oak Brook, IL 60523
Tel.: (630) 570-7700   DE
Web Site:
   http://www.republicebank.com
Year Founded: 1969
Sales Range: $75-99.9 Million
Emp.: 284
Bank Holding Company
N.A.I.C.S.: 551111
William H. Sperling *(Pres/CEO-Republic Bank of Chicago)*
Robert Charal *(Pres)*

Subsidiaries:

Republic Bank of Chicago   (1)
2221 Camden Ct, Oak Brook, IL 60523
Tel.: (630) 570-7700
Web Site: http://www.republicebank.com
Sales Range: $75-99.9 Million
Commericial Banking
N.A.I.C.S.: 522110

Aristotle Halikias *(Chm)*
William H. Sperling *(Vice Chm)*
Lillian Miljkovic Vukmirovic *(Chief Risk Officer & Exec VP)*
David Livingston *(Exec VP)*
Thomas Bugielski *(CEO)*
Stephen Clingen *(Sr VP & Grp Head-Comml & Indus Lending & Treasury Mgmt)*
Dave Ryan *(Sr VP & Mgr-MSB)*
John F. Slade *(Exec VP-Credit)*
Lindsay Abrams *(Sr VP-Human Capital)*
Madhu Reddy *(CIO & Sr VP)*
Steven Campanella *(Exec VP-Retail Banking)*
Maria Warden *(Sr VP & Head-Treasury Mgmt)*
Cheryl Meyer *(VP-Comml Banking)*
Brian Griffin *(Sr VP & Head-Leasing)*

REPUBLIC BANCSHARES, INC.
306 W Superior St, Duluth, MN 55802
Web Site:
   http://www.bankrepublic.com
Bank Holding Company
N.A.I.C.S.: 551111
David M. Gaddie *(Chm, Pres & CEO)*

Subsidiaries:

Republic Bank, Inc.   (1)
306 W Superior St Ste 100, Duluth, MN 55802-1806
Tel.: (218) 733-6408
Web Site: http://www.bankrepublic.com
Credit Card Issuing
N.A.I.C.S.: 522210

REPUBLIC BUSINESS CREDIT, LLC
201 St Charles Ave Ste 2210, New Orleans, LA 70170
Tel.: (504) 262-8600
Web Site: http://www.republicbc.com
Year Founded: 2010
Financial Services
N.A.I.C.S.: 522291
Stewart Chesters *(CEO)*
Robert Meyers *(Pres)*
Matt Begley *(COO)*
Vanessa Johnson *(Exec VP-Asset Based Lending)*
Jason Carmona *(Exec VP & Mgr-Western)*
Tae Chung *(Sr VP-Bus Dev-Los Angeles)*
Brian Daray *(Sr VP & Mgr-Underwriting)*
Christy Morgan *(VP & Mgr-Legal)*

Subsidiaries:

Fast A/R Funding   (1)
15303 Ventura Blvd Ste 1000, Sherman Oaks, CA 91403
Web Site: http://www.fastarfunding.com
Financing & Factoring Services
N.A.I.C.S.: 522299
Jonah F. Schnel *(Chm & Pres)*

Subsidiary (Domestic):

Continental Business Credit, Inc.   (2)
21031 Ventura Blvd Ste 900, Woodland Hills, CA 91364
Tel.: (818) 737-3700
Web Site: http://www.cbcredit.com
Emp.: 30
Financing & Factoring Services
N.A.I.C.S.: 522299
Lee N. Hirsch *(Pres)*

REPUBLIC CONTRACTING CORP.
869 Pepper St, Columbia, SC 29209-2138
Tel.: (803) 783-4920   SC
Year Founded: 1956
Sales Range: $75-99.9 Million
Emp.: 130
Provider of Contracting & Construction Services

REPUBLIC CONTRACTING CORP.   U.S. PRIVATE

Republic Contracting Corp.—(Continued)
N.A.I.C.S.: 237310
Walter Deierlein (Pres)
Dave Hutto (Project Mgr)
Joe Simoneau (Controller)
J.N. Deierlein Jr. (Pres)

REPUBLIC CRANE & EQUIPMENT CO.
2023 John Crosland Jr Way, Charlotte, NC 28208-1944
Tel.: (704) 399-7555   NC
Web Site:
  http://www.republiccrane.com
Year Founded: 1976
Sales Range: $25-49.9 Million
Emp.: 25
Provider of Industrial Equipment
N.A.I.C.S.: 423830
Reed B. Mahany (Pres)

REPUBLIC FASTENER PRODUCTS CORP.
1827 Waterview Dr, Great Falls, SC 29055-8929
Tel.: (803) 482-2500   NY
Web Site: http://www.repfast.com
Year Founded: 1949
Sales Range: $50-74.9 Million
Emp.: 15
Mfr of Fasteners, Tools, Cutters, Hooks & Special Wire Forms
N.A.I.C.S.: 339993
Richard A. Barnes (Pres & COO)
Daniel F. Barnes (CEO)

REPUBLIC FINANCE LLC
7031 Commerce Cir, Baton Rouge, LA 70809
Tel.: (225) 927-0005
Web Site:
  http://www.republicfinance.com
Sales Range: $10-24.9 Million
Emp.: 360
Licensed Loan Companies
N.A.I.C.S.: 524113
Rex Ellison (Pres)
Jay Jolly (CFO)
Joy Beale (Controller)

REPUBLIC FINANCIAL CORPORATION
10701 W Kellogg St, Wichita, KS 67209
Tel.: (316) 722-6343
Rev.: $15,000,000
State Commercial Banks
N.A.I.C.S.: 522110
Jerry V. Blue (Pres & CEO)

Subsidiaries:

Southwest National Bank   (1)
2150 Woodrow Ave, Wichita, KS 67203
Tel.: (316) 838-5741
Web Site: http://www.southwestnb.com
Rev.: $10,000,000
Emp.: 55
National Trust Companies With Deposits, Commercial
N.A.I.C.S.: 522110
Janette Brooks (VP & Mgr-Tyler Crossing)
Trish Minard (Pres)
Chris Walker (VP)
Amy Branch (VP-Customer Svc)
Kyle Campbell (Asst Mgr-Tyler Crossing)
Debbie Newman (VP)
Julie Graber (VP-Comml Lending)
Jamie Ranney (Sr VP)
Shannon Poe (Sr VP)
Olivia Becker (VP-Treasury Mgmt)
John Lawrence (Asst VP-Consumer Lending)

REPUBLIC FINANCIAL CORPORATION
5251 Dtc Pkwy Ste 300, Greenwood Village, CO 80111
Tel.: (303) 751-3501

Web Site: http://www.republic-financial.com
Year Founded: 1971
Sales Range: $100-124.9 Million
Emp.: 100
Equipment & Vehicle Finance Leasing Companies
N.A.I.C.S.: 522220
James H. Possehl (Chm)
Robert S. Possehl (Pres)
Chuck Singleton (Pres-Special Assets)
Dennis Bikun (CFO & Treas)
Randy Dietrich (CEO)

Subsidiaries:

Camalloy, Inc.   (1)
1960 N Main St, Washington, PA 15301-0248
Tel.: (724) 222-2022
Web Site: http://www.camalloy.com
Sales Range: $10-24.9 Million
Emp.: 30
Whslr of Metals, Stainless Steel, Coils, Sheets, Bars Plates, Construction Materials & Industrial Supplies
N.A.I.C.S.: 423510
Connie Howard (VP-Fin)
Art Downs (Pres)
Nate Maczuzak (Mgr-Sls & Operating Svcs)
Jason Matuscin (VP-Sls)
John Mawhinney (Mgr-Industrial Products)

Community Bank Funding Company   (1)
5251 DTC Pkwy Ste 300, Greenwood Village, CO 80111
Tel.: (800) 483-6835
Web Site: http://www.cbankfunding.com
Investment Management Service
N.A.I.C.S.: 523940
Christa Gerlach (VP-Bus Dev & Acct Mgr)

GMT Global Republic Aviation Ltd.   (1)
48 Upper Paggot St, Dublin, 4, Ireland
Tel.: (353) 1 210 3504
Aircraft Leasing Services
N.A.I.C.S.: 532411

REPUBLIC INDUSTRIES
3000 W Broadway, Louisville, KY 40211
Tel.: (502) 588-2120
Web Site: http://www.republic-ind.com
Rev.: $25,417,010
Emp.: 95
Mfr of Industrial Machinery & Equipment
N.A.I.C.S.: 423830
Carl Coslow (Pres)
Michael Walling (CFO)

REPUBLIC INDUSTRIES INC.
1400 Warren Dr, Marshall, TX 75672-5893
Tel.: (903) 935-3680   TX
Web Site: http://www.republicind.com
Year Founded: 1987
Sales Range: $25-49.9 Million
Emp.: 500
Kitchen Cabinet Mfr
N.A.I.C.S.: 337110
Joey Little (Mgr-Scheduling & Logistics)

REPUBLIC MORTGAGE HOME LOAN LLC
5241 S State St 2, Murray, UT 84107
Tel.: (801) 288-9400
Web Site: http://www.repmtg.com
Sales Range: $10-24.9 Million
Emp.: 50
Mortgage Banker
N.A.I.C.S.: 522292
Gary Nielson (VP-Retail)
Matt Brumble (CFO)
Ruyth Bagley (Mgr-Sls & Mktg)

REPUBLIC NATIONAL DISTRIBUTING COMPANY
8045 Northcourt Rd, Houston, TX 77040
Tel.: (832) 782-1000   TX
Web Site: http://www.rndc-usa.com
Sales Range: $1-4.9 Billion
Spirits & Wine Wholesale Distr
N.A.I.C.S.: 424820
Joe Gardner (VP-Fine Wine)
Greg Bowdish (VP-Natl Accts & Mktg)
Sam Ray (Mgr-Acct-Natl)

Subsidiaries:

National Distributing Company, Inc.   (1)
1 National Dr SW, Atlanta, GA 30336
Tel.: (404) 696-9440
Web Site: http://www.ndcweb.com
Wines, Spirits & Beer & of Non-Alcoholic Beverages Wholesale Distr
N.A.I.C.S.: 424820
Jay M. Davis (Chm & CEO)
John A. Carlos (Vice Chm & Treas)
Jerry Rosenberg (Vice Chm & Sec)

Republic National Distributing Company   (1)
1010 Isuzu Pkwy, Grand Prairie, TX 75050-7869
Tel.: (972) 595-6100
Web Site: https://www.rndc-usa.com
Sales Range: $75-99.9 Million
Emp.: 14,000
Wine & Distilled Alcoholic Beverage Merchant Wholesalers
N.A.I.C.S.: 424820
Robert Hendrickson (COO & Exec VP)
Nicholas Mehall (CFO)
Dennis Bashuk (Treas & VP)
Scott Lammert (Sr VP-Supplier Bus Dev)
Darrell Riekena (CIO)
H. Alan Rosenberg (Gen Counsel & VP-Legal)
Nick Mehall (Pres)

Republic National Distributing Company   (1)
624 N 44th Ave, Phoenix, AZ 85043-2915
Tel.: (602) 233-1900
Sales Range: $25-49.9 Million
Emp.: 360
Wine & Distilled Beverages
N.A.I.C.S.: 424820

Republic National Distributing Company   (1)
8100 Seaton Pl, Montgomery, AL 36116
Tel.: (334) 420-2902
Web Site: http://www.rndc-usa.com
Spirits & Wine Distr
N.A.I.C.S.: 424820
Tom Cole (CEO)
Nicholas Mehall (CFO)

Republic National Distributing Company   (1)
4901 Savarese Cir N, Tampa, FL 33634
Tel.: (813) 885-3200
Web Site: http://www.ndcweb.com
Sales Range: $50-74.9 Million
Emp.: 325
Wine & Liquor Distr
N.A.I.C.S.: 424820
Bob Kaminski (Gen Mgr)

Republic National Distributing Company   (1)
9423 N Main St, Jacksonville, FL 32218-5749
Tel.: (904) 714-7200
Web Site: http://www.ndcweb.com
Sales Range: $25-49.9 Million
Emp.: 150
Wine & Alcohol Distr
N.A.I.C.S.: 424820
William G. Mansfield (Exec VP-Chain Accounts)
Robert Zinner (Dir-Ops)
Thomas White (Reg Pres)

Republic National Distributing Company - Washington   (1)
4235 Sheriff Rd NE, Washington, DC 20019
Tel.: (202) 388-8400

Web Site: http://www.rndc-usa.com
Liquor & Wine Distr
N.A.I.C.S.: 424820

REPUBLIC PACKAGING CORP.
9160 S Green St, Chicago, IL 60620
Tel.: (773) 233-6530
Web Site: http://www.repcc.com
Sales Range: $10-24.9 Million
Emp.: 25
Packaging & Shipping Materials, Foamed Plastics
N.A.I.C.S.: 326150
Charles R. Wood (Pres & CEO)
Dan Casper (Mgr-Ops)
Edward Olszewski (CFO)

REPUBLIC PLUMBING SUPPLY COMPANY INC.
890 Providence Hwy, Norwood, MA 02062-4741
Tel.: (781) 762-3900   MA
Web Site:
  http://www.republicsupplyco.com
Year Founded: 1977
Sales Range: $25-49.9 Mill on
Emp.: 85
Plumbing Fixtures Equipment & Supply Whslr
N.A.I.C.S.: 423720
James M. Duggan (Treas)
Jane Orseno (Sec)
William E. Duggan Jr. (Pres)

REPUBLIC STATE MORTGAGE CO.
815 Hawthorne St, Houston, TX 77006
Tel.: (713) 520-7791
Web Site:
  http://www.republicstatemortgage.com
Sales Range: $10-24.9 Million
Emp.: 120
Mortgage Bankers & Loan Correspondents
N.A.I.C.S.: 522310
Robert Wagnon (Owner & CEO)
Ellen Brown (Controller)
Paulina McGrath (Pres)
Donna Wright (Mgr-Natl Production)

REPUBLIC STEEL
2633 8th Street, Canton, OH 44704
Tel.: (330) 438-5336
Web Site:
  http://www.republicengineered.com
Sales Range: $300-349.9 Million
Emp.: 5,000
Blast Furnaces & Steel Mills
N.A.I.C.S.: 331110
Jaime Vigel (Pres & CEO)

Subsidiaries:

Republic Technologies International Llc   (1)
3770 Embassy Pkwy, Akron, OH 44333
Tel.: (330) 670-3000
Web Site: http://www.republictech.com
Sales Range: $10-24.9 Million
Emp.: 100
Blast Furnaces & Steel Mills
N.A.I.C.S.: 331110

REPUBLIC TOBACCO LP
2301 Ravine Way, Glenview, IL 60025
Tel.: (847) 832-9700
Rev.: $25,516,000
Emp.: 50
Smoking Tobacco
N.A.I.C.S.: 424940
Donald R. Levin (Founder & Chm)
Gene Pytlewicz (Controller)
Paul Marobella (Pres & CMO)

REPUBLIC WIRE, INC.

5525 Union Centre Dr, West Chester, OH 45069
Tel.: (513) 860-1800 OH
Web Site:
 http://www.republicwire.com
Year Founded: 1982
Sales Range: $150-199.9 Million
Emp.: 85
Mfr of Copper Wire
N.A.I.C.S.: 331420
Mark Huelsebusch (CFO & Treas)

REPUTATION MANAGEMENT CONSULTANTS
92 Corporate Park Ste C700, Irvine, CA 92606
Web Site:
 http://www.reputationmanagementconsultants.com
Year Founded: 2008
Sales Range: $1-9.9 Million
Emp.: 35
Reputation Monitoring Software Platform
N.A.I.C.S.: 513210
Gary P. Hagins (Pres)

REPUTATION PARTNERS, LLC
30 W Monroe St Ste 1410, Chicago, IL 60603
Tel.: (312) 222-9939
Web Site:
 http://www.reputationpartners.com
Year Founded: 2002
Emp.: 20
Advetising Agency
N.A.I.C.S.: 541810
Amy Littleton (Pres)
Nicholas B. Kalm (Founder & CEO)
Jane G. Devron (Founder)
Megan E. Hakes (Founder)
Marilyn Vollrath (Exec VP-Milwaukee)
Jessica Vollrath Huebner (VP-Milwaukee)
Courtney Cherry (Sr VP & Dir-Digital Strategies)
Nick Quirke (Sr VP & Dir-Creative Svcs)
Michael McGrath (Exec VP)
Anna Zeck (Sr VP)
Jeremy Berrington (Sr VP)
Andrew Moyer (Exec VP & Gen Mgr)
Judy Twist (VP-Ops)
Natalie Wanner (Acct Coord)
Stephanie Murray (VP)
Paige Borgman (VP & Head-Digital Strategy)
Ruben Castro (Mgr-Acctg)
Anne Marie Mitchell (Sr VP)
Heidi Zumbahlen (Fin Mgr)

REPUTATION.COM, INC.
1400A Seaport Blvd Ste 401, Redwood City, CA 94063
Tel.: (650) 241-7491
Web Site: http://www.reputation.com
Year Founded: 2006
Software Application Development Services
N.A.I.C.S.: 541511
Joe Fuca (CEO)
Jason Grier (COO & Head-Product)
Manish Balsara (CTO)
Scott Barmmer (Chief Revenue Officer)
Dave Mingle (VP-Customer Experience)
Shannon Hernandez (Gen Counsel & Sec)
Shannon Nash (Chief Acctg Officer)
Andrew Geisse (VP-Sls)
Brent Nixon (Chief Ecosystem Officer)
Liz Carter (CMO)
Pam Dodrill (Chief Customer Officer)

Subsidiaries:

Strategic Internet Marketing Partners, Inc. (1)
141 W Jackson Blvd Ste 1850, Chicago, IL 60604
Web Site: http://www.simpartners.com
Digital Internet Marketing Products & Services
N.A.I.C.S.: 518210
Jon Schepke (CEO)
Niel Mahoney (COO)
Adam Dorfman (Sr VP-Product)
Francois Toubol (Sr VP-Tech)
Jay Hawkinson (VP-Mktg)

REQROUTE INC.
1250 Ames Ave Ste 210, Milpitas, CA 95035
Tel.: (408) 338-0071
Web Site: http://www.reqrouteinc.com
Year Founded: 2008
Sales Range: $10-24.9 Million
Emp.: 25
IT Staffing & Recruiting
N.A.I.C.S.: 541690
Lakshman Larry Visampalli (Client Svcs Mgr)

REQUEST FOODS INC.
3460 John F Donnelly Dr, Holland, MI 49424
Tel.: (616) 786-0900
Web Site:
 http://www.requestfoods.com
Rev.: $29,600,000
Emp.: 400
Frozen Specialty Food Mfr
N.A.I.C.S.: 311412
Jack DeWitt (VP)
Connie Nabb (Controller)
Jeff Gehres (VP-Sls & Mktg)

REQUEST, INC.
100 Saratoga Village Blvd Ste 45, Ballston Spa, NY 12020-3738
Tel.: (518) 899-1254
Web Site: http://www.request.com
Year Founded: 1998
Sales Range: $10-24.9 Million
Emp.: 35
Digital Media Storage, Management, Playback & Integration Equipment Mfr
N.A.I.C.S.: 334310
Peter Cholnoky (Pres & CEO)
Andy Lopez (VP-Sls & Mktg)

REROOF AMERICA CORPORATION
2904 Via Esperanza, Edmond, OK 73013
Tel.: (405) 330-5400
Web Site:
 http://www.reroofamerica.com
Year Founded: 1979
Sales Range: $10-24.9 Million
Emp.: 10
Roofing Contractors
N.A.I.C.S.: 238160
John R. Emrich (Pres)

RES MANUFACTURING COMPANY
7801 N 73rd St, Milwaukee, WI 53223
Tel.: (414) 354-4530
Web Site: http://www.resmfg.com
Sales Range: $25-49.9 Million
Emp.: 125
Stamping Metal
N.A.I.C.S.: 332119
John Wittmann (Exec VP-Sls & Mktg)
Wayne Wilfert (Sr Engr-Design)

RESCAR INC.
1101 31st St Ste 250, Downers Grove, IL 60515-5532
Tel.: (630) 963-1114 TX

Web Site: http://www.rescar.com
Year Founded: 1972
Sales Range: $25-49.9 Million
Emp.: 900
Railroad Rolling Stock Maintenance Services
N.A.I.C.S.: 336510
Susan Schieszler (Sr VP-Customer Svc & Quality Assurance)
Marvin B. Hughes (Sr VP-Sls, Mktg & Customer Svc)
Joseph F. Schieszler Sr. (Chm)

RESCUE MISSION MINISTRIES, INC.
1201 E Main St, Durham, NC 27703
Tel.: (919) 688-9641 NC
Web Site:
 http://www.durhamrescuemission.org
Year Founded: 1973
Sales Range: $10-24.9 Million
Emp.: 39
Community Housing Services
N.A.I.C.S.: 624229
Mike Stephens (Bus Mgr)
Rob Tart (COO)
Jim Cooper (Mgr-IT)
Kristi Zimmerman (Office Mgr)
Brad Williams (VP)
Ernie Mills (Co-Founder & CEO)
Gary Doane (Treas)
Lacy Frye (Pres)
Gail Mills (Co-Founder & CFO)
Joe Stroup (Sec)

RESCUE ONE FINANCIAL
2101 Business Ctr Dr Ste 120, Irvine, CA 92612
Web Site:
 http://www.rescueonefinancial.com
Year Founded: 2007
Sales Range: $10-24.9 Million
Emp.: 31
Debt Reduction & Consolidation
N.A.I.C.S.: 522390
Bradley Smith (Co-Founder & CEO)

RESCUE SOCIAL CHANGE GROUP, LLC.
1000 W Washington St, San Diego, CA 92103
Tel.: (619) 231-7555
Web Site: http://www.rescuescg.com
Rev.: $3,000,000
Emp.: 30
Marketing Consulting Services
N.A.I.C.S.: 541611
Kyle O'Grady (Engr-Young Action)
Meghan McCarthy (Mgr-After School Brand)
Cameron Wiley (Engr-Web Dev)
Valerie Winstrom (Brand Mgr-San Diego)
Ryan Johnson (Dir-Ops)
Tony Callico (Sr Dir-Creative Design)
Aaron Sleeper (Sr Dir-Web Dev)
Benjamin Mervis (Acct Mgr)
Jasmine Ancrum (Mgr-Community)
Jason Lane (Mgr-Production)
Joe Smyser (Dir-Strategy & External Affairs)
Johnathan Thompson (Mgr-Social Media)
K. C. Campbell (Sr Dir-Creative-Ideation)
Kristin Carroll (CEO)
Lucia Napolez (Acct Coord)

RESCUECOM CORPORATION
2560 Burnet Ave, Syracuse, NY 13206
Tel.: (315) 431-4147 NY
Web Site: http://www.rescuecom.com
Year Founded: 1985

Computers, Peripherals & Software Services
N.A.I.C.S.: 423430
David A. Milman (CEO)

RESEARCH AMERICA, INC.
2002 Sproul Rd, Broomall, PA 19008
Tel.: (610) 356-1800
Web Site:
 http://www.researchamericainc.com
Sales Range: $1-9.9 Million
Emp.: 105
Marketing Research & Public Opinion Polling Services
N.A.I.C.S.: 541910
David McGinley (Pres)
DeAnna Lance (Dir-Adv & PR)

Subsidiaries:

The Natural Marketing Institute Inc (1)
272 Ruth Rd, Harleysville, PA 19438
Tel.: (215) 513-7300
Web Site: http://www.nmisolutions.com
Periodical Publishers
N.A.I.C.S.: 513120
Jan Nash (VP-Market Res)
Kathryn Schulte (Project Dir)
Diane Ray (VP-Strategic Innovation)
Kirsten Wingenbach (Dir-Advanced Analytics)

The Sigma Group, LLC (1)
4546 S 86th St, Lincoln, NE 68526
Tel.: (402) 420-7979
Web Site: http://www.sigma-grp.com
Sales Range: $1-9.9 Million
Emp.: 50
Healthcare Marketing Research Services
N.A.I.C.S.: 541910
Dennis Nutter (Pres)
Inta Didrichsons (VP-Analytic Svcs)

Viewpoint Consulting, Inc. (1)
580 Middletown Blvd Ste D215, Langhorne, PA 19047-1876
Tel.: (215) 741-5775
Web Site:
 http://www.viewpointconsulting.net
Pharmaceutical & Healthcare Marketing Research Services
N.A.I.C.S.: 541614
Norman Smith (Founder & Pres)

RESEARCH ANALYSIS & MAINTENANCE, INC.
9440 Viscount Blvd Ste 200, El Paso, TX 79925
Tel.: (915) 592-7047
Web Site: http://www.ramincorp.com
Rev.: $45,335,493
Emp.: 300
Commercial Physical Research
N.A.I.C.S.: 561720
Richard Jones (Program Mgr)
James Sharp (VP & Gen Mgr)

RESEARCH BY DESIGN LLC
2005 Southeastern Rd Ste 300, Doylestown, PA 18901
Tel.: (215) 489-9200
Web Site:
 http://www.adelphigroup.com
Sales Range: $10-24.9 Million
Emp.: 48
Market Analysis or Research
N.A.I.C.S.: 541910

RESEARCH CORPORATION TECHNOLOGIES, INC.
6440 N Swan Rd Ste 200, 85718, Tucson, AZ
Tel.: (520) 748-4400
Web Site: http://www.rctech.com
Year Founded: 1987
Legal Services Office
N.A.I.C.S.: 525990

RESEARCH DATA SERVICES, INC.

RESEARCH DATA SERVICES, INC.   U.S. PRIVATE

Research Data Services, Inc.—(Continued)
777 S Harbour Island Blvd Ste 260, Tampa, FL 33602
Tel.: (813) 254-2975 FL
Web Site: http://www.rdsmarketresearch.com
Year Founded: 1979
Sales Range: $1-9.9 Million
Emp.: 16
Marketing Management & Economic Research & Consulting
N.A.I.C.S.: 541613
Walter J. Klages *(Pres & CEO)*
Ilene Claire Evans-Klages *(VP-Qualitative Res)*

RESEARCH DEVELOPMENT & PROMOTIONS
360 Menores Ave, Coral Gables, FL 33134
Tel.: (305) 445-4997
Web Site: http://www.rdppromotions.com
Sales Range: $10-24.9 Million
Emp.: 6
N.A.I.C.S.: 541810
Robert N. Del Pozo *(Pres)*
Richard G. Amundsen *(Exec VP)*
Victoria Goldstein-Macadar *(VP-PR)*
Peter Ekstein *(Dir-Creative)*

RESEARCH FOUNDATION FOR MENTAL HYGIENE, INC.
150 Broadway Ste 301, Menands, NY 12204
Tel.: (518) 474-5661 NY
Web Site: http://www.corporate.rfmh.org
Year Founded: 1952
Sales Range: $125-149.9 Million
Emp.: 1,779
Behavioral Healthcare Services
N.A.I.C.S.: 621420
Michael Kavanaugh *(Controller & Deputy Treas)*
Robert Burke *(Mng Dir)*
Paul Margolies *(Project Mgr)*

RESEARCH FOUNDATION OF THE CITY UNIVERSITY OF NEW YORK
230 W 41st St, New York, NY 10036-7207
Tel.: (212) 417-8300
Web Site: http://www.rfcuny.org
Grantmaking Foundations
N.A.I.C.S.: 813211
Jarnee M. Bramlette *(Interim Pres, CFO & Treas)*
Jerry Steele *(COO)*
Jeffrey Slonim *(Chief Counsel & Sec)*
Jacek Olszewski *(CIO)*

RESEARCH PRODUCTS CORPORATION
1015 E Washington Ave, Madison, WI 53703-2938
Tel.: (608) 257-8801 WI
Web Site: http://www.aprilaire.com
Year Founded: 1938
Sales Range: $100-124.9 Million
Emp.: 300
Heating, Air-Conditioning & Air Purification Equipment
N.A.I.C.S.: 333415
Larry A. Olsen *(CEO)*
Tom Ruse *(Mgr-Mktg Comm)*
P. M. Graham *(Sr VP)*

Subsidiaries:

Research Products Corporation - Aprilaire Division (1)
1015 E Washington Ave, Madison, WI 53703
Tel.: (608) 310-6163

Humidifier Mfr & Distr
N.A.I.C.S.: 333415
Tim Watson *(Dir-IT)*

RESEARCH PRODUCTS INTERNATIONAL CORPORATION
410 N Business Ctr Dr, Mount Prospect, IL 60056
Tel.: (847) 635-7330
Web Site: http://www.rpicorp.com
All Other Manufacturing
N.A.I.C.S.: 339999
Robert A. Chudy *(Pres)*

Subsidiaries:

Ag Scientific, Inc. (1)
6450 Lusk Blvd Ste E102, San Diego, CA 92121
Tel.: (858) 452-9925
Web Site: http://www.agscientific.com
Sales Range: $1-9.9 Million
Emp.: 11
Chemical & Allied Products Merchant Whslr
N.A.I.C.S.: 424690
Allen Lindgren *(CEO)*

RESEARCH SOLUTIONS GROUP, INC.
100 Tony Holmes Dr Ste 200, Pelham, AL 35124
Tel.: (205) 663-6350
Web Site: http://www.researchsolutionsgroup.com
Year Founded: 1971
Sales Range: $10-24.9 Million
Emp.: 25
Industrial Chemicals, Solvents, Solvent Blends, Specialty Cleaners, Degreasers & Metalworking Lubricants Distr
N.A.I.C.S.: 424690
Douglas Miller *(Controller)*
Jeff Miller *(Pres & CEO)*

RESEARCH SQUARE
601 W Main St Ste 102, Durham, NC 27701
Tel.: (919) 704-4253
Web Site: http://en.researchsquare.com
Year Founded: 2004
Sales Range: $10-24.9 Million
Emp.: 114
Developer of Software & Services for Global Research
N.A.I.C.S.: 513210
Rochelle Cupelli *(VP-Fin)*
Damian Pattinson *(VP-Publ Innovation)*

RESEARCH TRIANGLE INSTITUTE
3040 E Cornwallis Rd, Research Triangle Park, NC 27709-2194
Tel.: (919) 541-6000 NC
Web Site: http://www.rti.org
Year Founded: 1959
Sales Range: $1-4.9 Billion
Emp.: 2,800
Scientific Research on Contract for Industry & Government
N.A.I.C.S.: 541715
James J. Gibson *(COO)*
E. Wayne Holden *(Pres)*
Allen W. Mangel *(Exec VP-RTI Health Solutions)*
G. Edward Story *(Gen Counsel, Sec & Exec VP)*
Lisa May *(Exec VP-HR)*
Paul Weisenfeld *(Exec VP-Intl Dev Grp)*
Rachel Nugent *(VP-Chronic Noncommunicable Diseases Initiative)*
Tim J. Gabel *(Exec VP-Social, Statistical & Environmental Sciences)*

Michael H. Kaelin Jr. *(CFO & Exec VP)*
Peter M. Scott III *(Chm)*

Subsidiaries:

RTI Health Solutions (1)
3005 Boardwalk St Ste 105, Ann Arbor, MI 48108
Tel.: (734) 213-5372
Web Site: http://www.rtihealthsolutions.org
Sales Range: $10-24.9 Million
Emp.: 10
Biotechnology Research & Development Services
N.A.I.C.S.: 541714
Allen W. Mangel *(Exec VP)*
Lawrence N. Bell *(VP-Bus Affairs)*
Josephine A. Mauskopf *(VP-Health Economics)*
Elizabeth B. Andrews *(VP-Pharmacoepidemiology & Risk Mgmt)*
Stephanie R. Earnshaw *(VP-Health Economics)*
Sheri E. Fehnel *(VP-Patient-Reported Outcomes)*
Lynne R. Hamm *(Sr Dir-Clinical & Medical Svcs)*
James Rosenzweig *(Sr Dir-Clinical Consulting)*

RTI Rockville (1)
6110 Executive Blvd, Rockville, MD 20850
Tel.: (301) 816-4621
Web Site: http://www.masimax.com
Sales Range: $25-49.9 Million
Emp.: 115
Biomedical Research
N.A.I.C.S.: 541714

RESER'S FINE FOODS INC.
PO Box 8, Beaverton, OR 97075
Tel.: (503) 643-6431 OR
Web Site: http://www.resers.com
Year Founded: 1951
Sales Range: $300-349.9 Million
Emp.: 3,000
Wholesale Specialty Food Items Mfr
N.A.I.C.S.: 311999
Paul Leavy *(CFO)*
Peter Sirgy *(Exec VP-Sls & Mktg)*
Mike Reser *(VP-Logistics)*

Subsidiaries:

Reser's Fine Foods (1)
1811 W 1700 S, Salt Lake City, UT 84104
Tel.: (801) 972-5633
Web Site: http://www.resers.com
Sales Range: $25-49.9 Million
Emp.: 115
Mfr of Frozen Foods & Specialties
N.A.I.C.S.: 311412

Vaughan Foods, Inc. (1)
216 NE 12th St, Moore, OK 73160
Tel.: (405) 794-2530
Web Site: http://www.vaughanfoods.com
Sales Range: $75-99.9 Million
Emp.: 300
Processed & Packaged Refrigerated Foods Distr
N.A.I.C.S.: 424420
Mark E. Vaughan *(Pres & COO)*
Herbert B. Grimes *(Chm & CEO)*

RESERVE GROUP MANAGEMENT COMPANY
3560 W Market St Ste 300, Akron, OH 44333
Tel.: (330) 665-2900 OH
Web Site: http://www.reservegroup.com
Year Founded: 1995
Sales Range: $1-4.9 Billion
Emp.: 3,000
Privater Equity Firm
N.A.I.C.S.: 523999
R. Mark Hamlin Jr. *(Pres)*

Subsidiaries:

Forged Products, Inc. (1)
6505 N Houston Rosslyn Rd, Houston, TX 77091-1006

Tel.: (713) 462-3416
Web Site: http://www.fpitx.com
Sales Range: $10-24.9 Million
Emp.: 95
Mfr of Large Forgings, Casing Hanger Bodies, Heavy Wall Cylinders & Tube Sheets for Heat Exchangers
N.A.I.C.S.: 336310
Tommy Steward *(Supvr-Forge)*

Gautier Steel, Ltd. (1)
80 Clinton St, Johnstown, PA 15901
Tel.: (814) 535-9200
Web Site: http://www.gautiersteel.com
Emp.: 100
Hot-Rolled Carbon & Alloy Steel Bar Mfr
N.A.I.C.S.: 331110
Darryl DiOrio *(Pres)*
Ken Smith *(VP-Ops)*
Jackie Kulback *(CFO & Controller)*
Jack Mazur *(VP-Sls & Mktg)*
Mark Groebel *(Mgr-Sls)*
Tony Kassander *(Mgr-Matls)*
Rob Gall *(Asst Mgr-Matls)*
Peter Thompson *(VP-Sls & Mktg)*

Subsidiary (Domestic):

Gautier Specialty Metals, LLC (2)
80 Clinton St, Johnstown, PA 15901 (100%)
Tel.: (814) 535-9200
Web Site: http://www.gautierspecialty.com
Specialty Metal Finishing Services
N.A.I.C.S.: 332812
Jack Mazur *(VP-Sls)*
Mark Groebel *(Mgr-Sls)*
Peter Thompson *(VP-Sls)*

Integrated Biometrics, Inc. (1)
121 Broadcast Dr, Spartanburg, SC 29303
Tel.: (864) 990-3711
Web Site: http://www.integratedbiometrics.com
Emp.: 12
Fingerprint Biometric Sensor Mfr
N.A.I.C.S.: 334118
Steve Thies *(CEO)*
Mike Grimes *(VP-Key Accounts)*
David Gerulski *(Sr VP-Global Sls & Mktg)*
Fred Frye *(CTO)*
Thomas McCabe *(CFO)*

Nova Forge Corp. (1)
34 Power Plant Rd, PO Box 150, New Glasgow, Trenton, B0K 1X0, NS, Canada
Tel.: (902) 752-0989
Web Site: http://www.fpitx.com
Emp.: 900
Steel & Iron Die Forging Mfr
N.A.I.C.S.: 332111

Romeo Rim, Inc. (1)
74000 Van Dyke Ave, Romeo, MI 48065-3208
Tel.: (586) 336-5800
Web Site: http://www.romeorim.com
Sales Range: $25-49.9 Million
Emp.: 200
Energy Absorbing Bumper & Custom Reaction Injection Molded Component Mfr
N.A.I.C.S.: 326199
Honey Dennison *(Dir-HR)*
Randy Johnson *(Pres & CEO)*
Tim Howell *(Gen Mgr)*

Scotland Manufacturing Co., Inc. (1)
22261 Skyway Church Rd, Laurinburg, NC 28353
Tel.: (910) 844-3956
Web Site: http://www.scotlandmanufacturing.com
Deep Drawn & Flat Stamping Mfr
N.A.I.C.S.: 332119
Wayne Cain *(Gen Mgr)*

Spartanburg Steel Products, Inc. (1)
1290 New Cut Rd, Spartanburg, SC 29303
Tel.: (864) 585-5211
Web Site: http://www.ssprod.com
Sales Range: $500-549.9 Million
Emp.: 600
Automotive Stampings & Assemblies, Stainless Steel Containers for Beer, Beverages, Food, Chemicals & Pharmaceuticals Mfr
N.A.I.C.S.: 336370
Bill Nunnery *(Engr-Maintenance)*
Chris Griffith *(Mgr-Program)*
Charlene Lane *(VP)*
Chad Raynes *(Pres)*

COMPANIES

Subsidiary (Domestic):

Spartanburg Stainless Products Inc. (2)
121 Broadcast Dr, Spartanburg, SC 29303
Tel.: (864) 699-3200
Stainless Steel Products Mfr
N.A.I.C.S.: 331110

Superior Fabrication Company, LLC (1)
17499 S Dolan St, Kincheloe, MI 49788
Tel.: (906) 495-5634
Web Site: http://www.supfab.com
Fabricated Steel Component & Assembly Mfr
N.A.I.C.S.: 332999

RESERVEAGE, LLC.
5745 SW 75th St Ste 337, Gainesville, FL 32608
Tel.: (352) 374-4760
Web Site: http://www.reserveage.com
Year Founded: 2009
Sales Range: $50-74.9 Million
Emp.: 72
Organic Food Supplement Whslr
N.A.I.C.S.: 456191
Irina Lorenzi (CMO)
Naomi Whittel (Founder)

RESERVOIR CAPITAL GROUP, L.L.C.
767 5th Ave Fl 33, New York, NY 10153
Tel.: (212) 610-9000   DE
Web Site:
http://www.reservoircap.com
Year Founded: 1998
Private Investment Firm
N.A.I.C.S.: 523999
Daniel H. Stern (Co-CEO)
Craig A. Huff (Co-CEO)
Gregg M. Zeitlin (Founder & Sr Mng Dir)
Eric Engler (Sr Mng Dir)

Subsidiaries:

Reservoir Operations, L.P. (1)
650 Madison Ave Ste 26, New York, NY 10022
Tel.: (212) 610-9000
Investment Management Service
N.A.I.C.S.: 523940

RESH MARKETING CONSULTANTS, INC.
22 Surrey Ct, Columbia, SC 29212-3140
Tel.: (803) 798-0009
Web Site: http://www.resh.com
Year Founded: 1979
Sales Range: $10-24.9 Million
Emp.: 5
N.A.I.C.S.: 541810
Hal Von Nessen (Principal)

RESIDENSEA
5200 Blue Lagoon Dr Ste 7, Miami, FL 33126
Tel.: (305) 269-5151
Year Founded: 2001
Rev.: $1,000,000
Emp.: 26
Fiscal Year-end: 12/31/06
Hotel/Motel Operation Drinking Place Eating Place
N.A.I.C.S.: 721110

RESIDENTIAL MORTGAGE, LLC
100 Calais Dr Ste 100, Anchorage, AK 99503-4049
Tel.: (907) 222-8800
Web Site:
http://www.residentialmtg.com
Sales Range: $10-24.9 Million
Emp.: 200
Provider of Mortgage Banking & Loan Services
N.A.I.C.S.: 522310
Roger Aldridge (Owner & Pres)
Rae Guse (Office Mgr)
Linda Hair (VP)
Dave Broline (CFO)
Lynn Houser (VP-Ops)

RESIDENTIAL REALTY GROUP I INC.
510 Bering Dr Ste 230B, Houston, TX 77057
Tel.: (713) 953-9001   DE
Year Founded: 2000
Sales Range: $10-24.9 Million
Emp.: 63
Community Housing Services
N.A.I.C.S.: 624229
David Schwartz (Pres & Sec)

RESILIENCE CAPITAL PARTNERS, LLC
25101 Chagrin Blvd Ste 350, Cleveland, OH 44122
Tel.: (216) 292-0200   OH
Web Site:
http://www.resiliencecapital.com
Privater Equity Firm
N.A.I.C.S.: 523999
Bassem A. Mansour (Co-CEO)
Steven H. Rosen (Co-CEO)
David Glickman (Partner)
Ron Cozean (Operating Partner)

Subsidiaries:

Aero Communications, Inc. (1)
5711 Research Dr, Canton, MI 48188
Tel.: (734) 467-8121
Web Site:
http://www.aerocommunications.com
Sales Range: $200-249.9 Million
Emp.: 1,000
Provider of Electrical Work Services
N.A.I.C.S.: 238210

Aerospace Products International, Inc. (1)
3778 Distriplex Dr N, Memphis, TN 38118-7299
Tel.: (901) 365-3470
Web Site: http://www.apiworldwide.com
Sales Range: $75-99.9 Million
Aircraft Parts & Accessories Distr & Supply Chain Management Services
N.A.I.C.S.: 423860
Andrew R. Trosper (Pres & COO)
Eric Waller (VP-Supply Chain Programs & Product Line Mgmt)
Denis Boucher (VP-Sls & Mktg)
Jim Howell (CFO & VP-Fin)

Branch (Non-US):

Aerospace Products International, Inc. - Asia Pacific (2)
Lisbon-Phil Bldg 5415, Clark Freeport Zone, Pampanga, 2009, Philippines
Tel.: (63) 45 893 5490
Web Site: http://www.apiworldwide.com
Emp.: 16
Aircraft Parts & Accessories Distr
N.A.I.C.S.: 423860
Bernabe Pastrana (Reg Mgr-Sls)

Aerospace Products International, Inc. - Canada (2)
2461 46th Avenue, Lachine, H8T 3C9, QC, Canada
Tel.: (514) 636-5720
Web Site: http://www.apiworldwide.com
Aircraft Parts & Accessories Distr
N.A.I.C.S.: 423860
Moe Godin (Sls Mgr)

Affinity Special Apparel, Inc. (1)
1202 Dayton Yellow Springs Rd, Fairborn, OH 45324
Tel.: (866) 548-8434
Web Site: http://affinityapparel.com
Business Uniforms & Career Apparel Mfr
N.A.I.C.S.: 315250
Jerry Yates (VP-Mfg)

American De Rosa Lamparts, LLC (1)
1945 S Tubeway Ave, City of Commerce, CA 90040-1611
Tel.: (323) 728-6300
Residential Electric Lighting Fixture Mfr
N.A.I.C.S.: 335131

CR Brands, Inc. (1)
8790 Beckett Rd, West Chester, OH 45069-4856
Tel.: (513) 860-5039
Web Site: http://www.crbrandsinc.com
Sales Range: $75-99.9 Million
Emp.: 20
Mfr & Marketer of Household Cleaning & Detergent Products
N.A.I.C.S.: 325611
John Samoya (VP-Fin & Controller)

CableNet Services Unlimited, LLC (1)
7 Chelsea Pkwy Ste 709, Boothwyn, PA 19061
Tel.: (610) 364-9504
Web Site: http://www.cablenetservices.com
Sales Range: $25-49.9 Million
Emp.: 50
Cable Installation Services
N.A.I.C.S.: 238210
Joe Moderski (Partner)
Bernard Kitzinger (Exec VP-Bus Dev)
John Pergolini (Partner)
Ed Birzes (Sr Dir-Ops Reg)

Flight Options LLC (1)
26180 Curtiss Wright Pkwy, Cleveland, OH 44143-1453
Tel.: (216) 261-3500
Web Site: http://www.flightoptions.com
Flight Equipment Rental & Leasing
N.A.I.C.S.: 532411
Kenneth Ricci (Chm)
David H. Davies (CIO)
Joseph Salata (VP-Flight Ops)

Lux Global Label Company, LLC (1)
2025 Joshua Rd, Lafayette Hill, PA 19444-2431
Tel.: (610) 825-3250
Web Site: http://www.luxgloballabel.com
Sales Range: $100-124.9 Million
Emp.: 250
Mfr of Paper Labels, Converted Paper & Paperboard Products
N.A.I.C.S.: 322220
Bruce Winter (Mgr-Svc)
James Shacklett III (CEO)

Subsidiary (Domestic):

Labelworx Inc. (2)
51 Runway Dr, Levittown, PA 19057-4700
Tel.: (215) 945-5645
Web Site: http://www.labelworx.net
Digital Label & Packaging Services
N.A.I.C.S.: 561910
John Lang (VP)
Jack Lang (Co-Founder & Pres)

R & D Enterprises, Inc. (1)
46900 Port St, Plymouth, MI 48170
Tel.: (734) 454-9600
Web Site: http://www.rdent.net
Sales Range: $10-24.9 Million
Emp.: 50
Power Boiler & Heat Exchanger Mfr
N.A.I.C.S.: 332410
Ken Robinson (CEO)

TPS, LLC (1)
2821 Old Rte 15, New Columbia, PA 17856
Tel.: (570) 538-7200
Web Site:
http://www.thermalproductsolutions.com
Industrial Furnace, Oven & Test Chamber Mfr
N.A.I.C.S.: 333994
Ron Cozean (Chm)

Unit (Domestic):

Lindberg/MPH (2)
3827 Riverside Rd, Riverside, MI 49084
Tel.: (269) 849-2700
Web Site: http://www.lindbergmph.com
Mfr of Gas or Electric Large Smelting Furnaces Melting Furnaces & Receiving Furnaces
N.A.I.C.S.: 333914

Joel Shingledecker (Gen Mgr)

Trialon Corporation (1)
1477 Walli Strasse Dr, Burton, MI 48509
Tel.: (810) 742-8500
Web Site: http://www.trialon.com
Sales Range: $10-24.9 Million
Emp.: 400
Testing Engineering & Technical Staffing Services
N.A.I.C.S.: 541380
Patricia L. Crowder (CEO)
Les Hadden (Pres)
Jerry Johnson (CFO)

Division (Domestic):

Indiana Engineering and Test Center (2)
1815 Touby Pike, Kokomo, IN 46901
Tel.: (765) 860-1066
Web Site: http://www.trialon.com
Sales Range: $10-24.9 Million
Emp.: 30
Reliability Testing Services
N.A.I.C.S.: 541380
Les Hadden (VP)

Michigan Engineering and Test Center (2)
1477 Walli Strasse Blvd, Burton, MI 48509
Tel.: (810) 742-8500
Web Site: http://www.trialon.com
Sales Range: $25-49.9 Million
Engineering & Test Services
N.A.I.C.S.: 541380

Technical Staffing Division (2)
5600 New King St Ste 345, Troy, MI 48098
Tel.: (248) 205-2510
Web Site: http://www.trialon.com
Sales Range: $10-24.9 Million
Emp.: 9
Temporary Help Service
N.A.I.C.S.: 561320
Keith Browne (Office Mgr)

Weaber, Inc. (1)
1231 Mount Wilson Rd, Lebanon, PA 17042-4785
Tel.: (717) 867-2212
Web Site: http://www.weaberlumber.com
Sales Range: $50-74.9 Million
Emp.: 300
Mfr & Retailer of Rough, Sawed & Planed Lumber
N.A.I.C.S.: 321918
Matthew Weaber (Pres)
Bill Campoll (CFO)
John Georgelis (VP-Sls)
Marty Daigle (Mgr-Sls)

RESILIENCE TECHNOLOGY CORPORATION
7502 Connelley Dr Ste 101, Hanover, MD 21076-1705
Tel.: (888) 297-8515
Web Site: http://www.resilience.com
Year Founded: 1995
Sales Range: Less than $1 Million
Emp.: 100
Data Security Solutions
N.A.I.C.S.: 423430
Sean Scott (CEO)
Joe Cortes (CFO)
Tom Takesian (VP-Mktg)
Michael Scanlon (Exec VP)
Bob Luders-Gibbs (VP-EMEA)

RESIN PARTNERS INC.
602 S Fairview St, Alexandria, IN 46001
Tel.: (765) 724-7761
Sales Range: $10-24.9 Million
Emp.: 150
Fiberglass & Plastic Furniture Mfr
N.A.I.C.S.: 561499
Sami Sagol (Chm)
Tony Jonas (Pres)
Kathy Eschler (Dir-Info Sys)
Steve Bingman (Plant Mgr)

RESIN TECHNOLOGY LLC

RESIN TECHNOLOGY LLC

Resin Technology LLC—(Continued)
1 Forge Billage Rd Ste A, Groton, MA 01450
Tel.: (978) 448-6926
Web Site: http://www.resintek.com
Sales Range: $25-49.9 Million
Emp.: 9
Plastics Products
N.A.I.C.S.: 424610
James Seidewand (Pres)
Sophie Henry (VP-Ops & Global Logistics)

RESINALL CORP
PO Box 195, Severn, NC 27877
Tel.: (203) 329-7100
Web Site: http://www.resinall.com
Rev.: $80,000,000
Emp.: 150
Thermosetting Materials Mfr
N.A.I.C.S.: 325211
Joe LeVine (Chief Comml Officer & VP)

RESINOID ENGINEERING CORP.
7557 St Louis Ave, Skokie, IL 60076-4033
Tel.: (847) 673-1050
Web Site: http://www.resinoid.com
Year Founded: 1939
Sales Range: $10-24.9 Million
Emp.: 100
Plastics Products
N.A.I.C.S.: 531120
Clarence A. Herberst Jr. (Chm)

RESINTECH INC.
1 Resin Tech Plz 160 Cooper Rd, West Berlin, NJ 08091
Tel.: (856) 768-9600
Web Site: http://www.resintech.com
Year Founded: 1986
Sales Range: $10-24.9 Million
Emp.: 250
Mfr of Ion Exchange Resins
N.A.I.C.S.: 424610
Michael Gottlieb (Pres)
Francis DeSilva (Mgr-Natl Sls)

RESOLUTE ADMINISTRATION, INC.
30 Burton Hills Blvd Ste 350, Nashville, TN 37215
Tel.: (615) 665-3636
Web Site: http://www.resolutecap.com
Year Founded: 2016
Privater Equity Firm
N.A.I.C.S.: 523999
Bill Nutter (Partner)
Casey Hammontree (Partner)
Caroline Ducas (Partner)
Andy Tatman (Partner)
Tyler Augusty (Dir-Investments)
Doyle Rippee (Dir-Dev)

Subsidiaries:

Cole Information Services, Inc. (1)
17041 Lakeside Hills Plz Ste 2, Omaha, NE 68130-4677
Tel.: (402) 323-3505
Web Site: http://www.coleinformation.com
Insurance, Small Business, Real Estate & Home Services Directory Publisher & Information Services
N.A.I.C.S.: 513140
James Eggleston (Pres & CEO)

RESOLUTE PARTNERS LLC.
37 W Ctr St, Southington, CT 06489
Tel.: (860) 628-6800
Web Site: http://www.resolutepartners.com
Rev.: $10,900,000
Emp.: 62

Office Machinery & Equipment Rental & Leasing
N.A.I.C.S.: 532420
Michael S. Blanco (Founder & CEO)
Paul Guertin (VP-Mktg)
Aaron Ezrilov (Dir-Federal Solutions)
Frank Demasi (VP-IT)

RESOLUTE SOLUTIONS CORPORATION
Skyline Tower 10900 NE 4th St Ste 2110, Bellevue, WA 98004
Tel.: (425) 467-9191
Web Site: http://www.resolute.com
Year Founded: 1996
Sales Range: $10-24.9 Million
Emp.: 96
Business & Technology Consulting Services
N.A.I.C.S.: 513210

Subsidiaries:

Kivati Software, LLC (1)
10900 NE 4th St Ste 2110, Bellevue, WA 98004 (100%)
Tel.: (425) 467-9191
Software Developer
N.A.I.C.S.: 513210

RESOLUTE TECHNOLOGIES LLC
6760 Alexander Bell Dr Ste 250, Columbia, MD 21046
Tel.: (410) 910-6686
Web Site: http://www.resolute-tech.com
Year Founded: 2013
Sales Range: $10-24.9 Million
Emp.: 68
Information Technology Consulting Services
N.A.I.C.S.: 541512
Jennifer Walker (CEO)
Robb Jett (CTO)
Chad Walker (CIO)
Beth Kovesdi (Dir-Engagement)
Raynett Colston (Dir-Programs)

RESOLUTION, INC.
327 Holly Ct, Williston, VT 05495
Tel.: (802) 862-8881
Sales Range: $25-49.9 Million
Emp.: 150
Video Tape Production
N.A.I.C.S.: 334610
William H. Schubart (CEO)

RESOLVE MARINE SERVICES, INC.
1510 SE 17th St Ste 400, Fort Lauderdale, FL 33316
Tel.: (954) 764-8700
Web Site: http://www.resolvemarine.com
Year Founded: 1980
Sales Range: $10-24.9 Million
Emp.: 25
Salvage, Emergency Response, Training, Naval Architecture & Marine Engineering Services
N.A.I.C.S.: 811310
Joseph E. Farrell III (Pres & CEO)

RESONANCE EMERGING MARKETS MACRO TRUST
36 E 12th St Ste 200, New York, NY 10003
Investment Services
N.A.I.C.S.: 523999
Benjamin Savage (Co-CEO & CFO)
James Waldinger (Co-CEO)

RESONATE NETWORKS, INC.
11720 Plz America Dr 3rd Fl, Reston, VA 20190
Tel.: (571) 266-3200

Web Site: http://www.resonateinsights.com
Year Founded: 2008
Sales Range: $10-24.9 Million
Emp.: 79
Information Technology Consulting Services
N.A.I.C.S.: 541512
Bryan Gernert (Founder & CEO)
Andy Hunn (COO)
David Wheatley (CFO)
Deborah Correa (VP-Client Svcs)
Marc Johnson (CMO)
Michael Horn (VP-Res)
John Brady (Chm)
Sara T. Fagen (Vice Chm)
David Wyler (VP)
Pat LaPointe (Exec VP)
Jason Schneider (Chief Revenue Officer)
Jonathan Ricard (Sr VP-Bus Dev)
Haidee Hanna (VP-Mktg)
Bryan Eldring (VP-Brand Sls)
Gary Sherwood (VP-Client Solutions)
Joel Pulliam (Chief Product Officer & Sr VP)
Steve Drill (VP-Engrg)
Tom Craig (CTO)

RESONATE, INC.
16360 Monterey Rd Ste 260, Morgan Hill, CA 95037
Tel.: (408) 548-5500
Web Site: http://www.resonate.com
Year Founded: 1995
Sales Range: $10-24.9 Million
Emp.: 188
Develops & Markets Software Products & Services that Monitor, Manage & Control Computer Networks, Server Systems & Internet, Intranet & Extranet Applications
N.A.I.C.S.: 513210
Geoffrey Selzer (Founder)

RESORT ASSOCIATION MANAGEMENT
9550 Shore Dr, Myrtle Beach, SC 29572
Tel.: (843) 449-2204
Web Site: http://www.ramrestors.com
Sales Range: $50-74.9 Million
Emp.: 20
Provider of Property Management & Public Relations Services
N.A.I.C.S.: 531311
Lee Rawcliffe (Owner)
Arron Harrison (VP)

RESORT HOSPITALITY ENTERPRISES LTD.
1002 W 23rd St Ste 400, Panama City, FL 32405-3648
Tel.: (850) 769-8981
Sales Range: $25-49.9 Million
Emp.: 500
Hotel Management & Operations
N.A.I.C.S.: 721110
Jimmy Barr (CEO)

RESORT INNS OF AMERICA INC.
5600 Gulf Blvd, Saint Petersburg, FL 33706
Tel.: (727) 363-2215
Web Site: http://www.tradewindsresort.com
Sales Range: $75-99.9 Million
Emp.: 1,000
Resort Hotel
N.A.I.C.S.: 459420
Tim Bogott (CEO)

Subsidiaries:

TradeWinds Islands Resorts On Saint Pete Beach (1)

5500 Gulf Blvd, Saint Pete Beach, FL 33706
Tel.: (727) 367-6461
Web Site: http://www.tradewindsresort.com
Hotel
N.A.I.C.S.: 721110
Timothy R. Bogott (CEO)
Keith Overton (Pres & COO)
Terry Popelka (VP-Sls)
Travis Johnson (Mgr-Hotel)
Jeffrey Fredrickson (VP-Food & Beverage)
James Metro (VP-Rooms Div)
Shelly Palmquist (VP-Revenue Mgmt)
Elda Vaso (VP-Fin & Acctg)
Bob LaCasse (Mng Dir)
Joe Smith (Owner)

RESOURCE ALLIANCE LLC
1725 Winward Concourse Ste 100, Alpharetta, GA 30005
Tel.: (678) 691-6600
Web Site: http://www.real-hr.com
Human Resource Support Services
N.A.I.C.S.: 541612
Dennis Weyenberg (CEO)

RESOURCE BANK
555 Bethany Rd, Dekalb, IL 60115
Tel.: (815) 756-6321
Web Site: http://www.resourcebank.com
Year Founded: 1910
Sales Range: $10-24.9 Million
Emp.: 35
Bank Holding Company
N.A.I.C.S.: 551111
Richard J. Katz (Pres)

Subsidiaries:

Resource Bank National Association (1)
555 Bethany Rd, Dekalb, IL 60115
Tel.: (815) 756-6321
Web Site: http://www.resourcebank.com
Rev.: $18,662,000
Emp.: 130
National Commercial Banks
N.A.I.C.S.: 522110
Richard J. Katz (Pres)

RESOURCE CENTER FOR INDEPENDENT LIVING, INC.
1137 Laing, Osage City, KS 66523
Tel.: (785) 528-3105
Web Site: http://www.rcilinc.org
Year Founded: 1984
Sales Range: $10-24.9 Million
Emp.: 2,465
Disability Assistance Services
N.A.I.C.S.: 624120
Mike Pitts (Dir-Fin & Tech)
Susan Warner (Dir-Payroll & Benefits)
Tania Harrington (Dir-Disability Svcs)
Becky Brewer (Dir-HCBS Programs & Svcs)
Joyce Lacey (Accountant)

RESOURCE CONSULTING GROUP, INC.
301 E Pine St Ste 600, Orlando, FL 32801
Tel.: (407) 422-0252
Web Site: http://www.resourceconsulting.com
Year Founded: 1988
Sales Range: $1-9.9 Million
Emp.: 22
Financial Planning & Investment Management Consulting Services
N.A.I.C.S.: 541611
Michael H. Davis (Founder & CEO)
Gregg Biro (Dir-Bus Dev)
Steve Mackall (Chief Investment Officer & Dir-Ops)
Mike Masur (CFO)
Kimberly Sterling (VP)
Taylor Mace (Coord-Comm)
Johnnie James (Pres)

COMPANIES

RESOURCE GROUP INTERNATIONAL
2025 1st Ave Ste 830, Seattle, WA 98121
Tel.: (206) 464-0200
Rev.: $11,600,000
Investment Holding Companies, Except Banks
N.A.I.C.S.: 551112
David Herrick (VP)

RESOURCE LENDERS INC.
7330 N Palm 106, Fresno, CA 93711
Tel.: (559) 225-0500
Web Site:
http://www.resourcelenders.com
Sales Range: $75-99.9 Million
Emp.: 90
Mortgage Banker
N.A.I.C.S.: 522292
Richard Barnes (Pres)

RESOURCE MANAGEMENT ENTERPRISES INC.
9999 Anderson Ave, Chicago Ridge, IL 60415
Tel.: (708) 425-8565
Web Site: http://www.rmcrecycle.com
Rev.: $19,500,000
Emp.: 6
Recycling, Waste Materials
N.A.I.C.S.: 562920
Calvin Tigchelaar (Pres & CEO)
William R. Slager (Controller)

Subsidiaries:

Resource Management Rockford LLC (1)
10244 Clow Creek Dr, Plainfield, IL 60544
Tel.: (630) 904-0780
Web Site: http://www.rmcrecycle.com
Rev.: $150,000
Emp.: 3
Recycling, Waste Materials
N.A.I.C.S.: 562920
Dave Kawa (Plant Mgr)

RESOURCE ONE CREDIT UNION
1200 Bellview St, Dallas, TX 75215
Tel.: (214) 319-3131 TX
Web Site: http://www.r1cu.org
Year Founded: 1936
Sales Range: $25-49.9 Million
Emp.: 196
Credit Union
N.A.I.C.S.: 522130
Lee C. Strickhouser (Dir-Lending)
Douglas P. Bedner (COO)
James K. Ladner (CFO)

RESOURCE ONE, INC.
2202 Industrial Blvd, Sarasota, FL 34234
Tel.: (941) 225-7657 FL
Web Site:
http://www.resourceonefl.com
Year Founded: 1975
Sales Range: $1-9.9 Million
Emp.: 30
Chemical & Allied Products Merchant Whslr
N.A.I.C.S.: 424690
Duncan Yull (Pres)

RESOURCE OPTIONS, INC.
200 Highland Ave, Needham, MA 02494
Tel.: (781) 455-0224
Web Site:
http://www.resourceoptions.com
Year Founded: 1998
Sales Range: $10-24.9 Million
Emp.: 25
Staffing Services
N.A.I.C.S.: 541612

Matthew Carlin (Pres & CEO)
Greg Kerr (Mgr-Ops)
Jon Abplanalp (VP-Environmental Svcs)
Ellen Taylor (Coord-Job)
Chris Kuppens (Dir-Staff Dev)

RESOURCE PARTNERS GROUP, INC.
6 Terra Vita Ct, Barrington, IL 60010-7145
Tel.: (847) 713-2900
Web Site: http://www.rpgroup.us
Sales Range: $1-9.9 Million
Emp.: 2
Management Consulting Services
N.A.I.C.S.: 541618
David Jacobs (Exec VP)
Connie M. Jacobs (Pres)

RESOURCE PRO, LLC
1180 Ave of the Americas 16th Fl, New York, NY 10036
Web Site:
http://www.resourcepro.com
Year Founded: 2003
Sales Range: $10-24.9 Million
Emp.: 600
Insurance Industry Focused Remote Back Office Support Solutions
N.A.I.C.S.: 561499
David Watkins (Chm)
Daniel Epstein (CEO)
Laura Downey (VP-Client Integration)

Subsidiaries:

Insurance Licensing Services-America (1)
111 N Railroad St, Groesbeck, TX 89109-3427
Tel.: (254) 729-8002
Web Site: http://www.spearmintrhinolv.com
Insurance Agencies & Brokerages
N.A.I.C.S.: 524210
Arleen Taveras (Pres)

RESOURCE PROVIDERS, INC.
3109 W Martin Luther King Jr Blvd Ste 121, Tampa, FL 33607
Tel.: (813) 282-8889 FL
Web Site: http://www.rpiusa.com
Year Founded: 2001
Sales Range: $1-9.9 Million
Emp.: 20
Fiscal Year-end: 12/31/14
Electronic Medical Transcription & Records Management Services
N.A.I.C.S.: 561499
W. Allen Clifford (Pres & CEO)
Laura A. Kaufman (COO)
Gary P. Posner (VP & Dir-Medical)
Robert G. Isbell (VP-Mktg)
Richard Flick (Dir-IT)

RESOURCE SOLUTIONS INC.
3675 Tampa Rd Ste C, Oldsmar, FL 34677
Tel.: (813) 855-3000
Web Site:
http://www.resourceforsolutions.com
Year Founded: 2009
Sales Range: $1-9.9 Million
Emp.: 20
Direct Mail Marketing
N.A.I.C.S.: 541860
Rick Broom (Owner & Pres)
Gail Hastings Broom (VP-Mktg)
Douglas Gornick (VP-Ops)
Ryan Van Sickle (Mgr-Sls)
Christopher Harrington (Office Mgr)

RESOURCE SYSTEMS GROUP, INC.
55 Railroad Row, White River Junction, VT 05001
Tel.: (802) 295-4999

Web Site: http://www.rsginc.com
Year Founded: 1986
Sales Range: $10-24.9 Million
Emp.: 75
Process, Physical Distribution & Logistics Consulting Services
N.A.I.C.S.: 541614
Thomas Adler (Founder & Pres)
Stacey Falzarano (Sr Dir-HR)
Kevin Hathaway (VP)
Stephen Lawe (CEO)
Maren Outwater (VP)
Colin High (Co-Founder)
Brandon Bohr (Dir-Fin)
Lindsay Coe (Dir-Mktg)
Stephan McCurdy (VP)

RESOURCES FOR HUMAN DEVELOPMENT
4700 Wissahickon Ave Ste 126, Philadelphia, PA 19144-4248
Tel.: (215) 951-0300 PA
Web Site: http://www.rhd.org
Year Founded: 1970
Sales Range: $200-249.9 Million
Emp.: 6,245
Disability Assistance Services
N.A.I.C.S.: 624120
Todd Silverstein (Chief Admin Officer & Treas)
Marco Giordano (CFO)
Stan Shubilla (Assoc Dir-Bus Mgmt)
Dyann Roth (CEO)

RESOURCES GLOBAL PROFESSIONALS
2700 Post Oak Blvd Ste 1600, Houston, TX 77056
Tel.: (713) 403-1960
Web Site:
http://www.resourcesglobal.com
Year Founded: 1996
Sales Range: $10-24.9 Million
Emp.: 45
Provider of Supply Chain Management Services
N.A.I.C.S.: 541613
Tanja Cebula (Chief Innovation Officer & Exec VP)
Elisabeth Dick (Sr VP-Southwest)
Joni Noel (Sr VP-South Central)
Brandon Johnson (CIO)
Shauna Watson (Mng Dir-Fin & Acctg-Global)
Suzanne Stanton (Sr VP-Global Client Dev)
Tracey Figurelli (Sr VP-Integrated Solutions)
Mark Campbell (VP-European)
Kate W. Duchene (Chief Legal Officer & Exec VP)
Michael Carberry (Mng Dir-Carolinas)
John Bower (Chief Acctg Officer)
Thomas Chu (Mng Dir-China, Hong Kong & Singapore Reg)
Steve Barker (Mng Dir-Human Capital-Global)
Hiro Ueda (Reg Mng Dir)

RESOURCES LEGACY FUND
555 Capitol Mall Ste 1095, Sacramento, CA 95814
Tel.: (916) 442-5057 CA
Web Site:
http://www.resourceslegacyfund.org
Year Founded: 1998
Sales Range: $25-49.9 Million
Emp.: 18
Natural Resource Conservation Services
N.A.I.C.S.: 813312
Rosina Bugarin (Dir-Fin)
Mary Scoonover (Exec VP)
Michael Mantell (Pres)
Peggy McNutt (Officer-Program)

RESOURCIS INFORMATION SERVICES, INC.
6055 Southard Trace, Cumming, GA 30040
Tel.: (770) 804-3140 GA
Web Site: http://www.resourcis.com
Year Founded: 1996
Data Processing, Hosting & Related Services
N.A.I.C.S.: 518210

RESPEC INC.
3824 Jet Dr, Rapid City, SD 57703
Tel.: (605) 394-6400
Web Site: http://www.respec.com
Year Founded: 1969
Rev.: $2,000,000
Emp.: 400
Engineeering Services
N.A.I.C.S.: 541330
Philip A. Welling (CFO & Treas)
Dale R. Atkinson (CTO)
Cameron P. Hook (CIO)
Samantha L. Lapin (Sr VP-IT)
Kerry L. Devries (VP)
Leo L. Van Sambeek (VP)
Rick R. Moser (VP)
Karla R. Lipp (Sec)

Subsidiaries:

PDC Engineering, Inc. (1)
1028 Aurora Dr, Fairbanks, AK 99709
Tel.: (907) 452-1414
Web Site: http://www.pdceng.com
Sales Range: $1-9.9 Million
Emp.: 45
Engineeering Services
N.A.I.C.S.: 541330
Dennis Bogren (Principal)
Royce Conlon (CFO & Engr-Civil & Environmental)
Doug Murray (Principal & Engr-Mechanical)
Keith Hanneman (Principal & Engr-Civil & Environmental)
Matt Emerson (Pres)
Mark Pusich (Principal & Engr-Civil)
Mike Story (Principal & Engr-Structural)
Robert Posma (Principal & Head-Electrical Engr Dept)

RESPIRATORY DISTRIBUTORS INC.
110 E Azalea Ave, Foley, AL 36535
Tel.: (251) 943-5844
Web Site: http://www.rdiworld.com
Sales Range: $25-49.9 Million
Emp.: 28
Pharmaceuticals
N.A.I.C.S.: 424210

RESPITEK MEDICAL SERVICES
8257 Causeway Blvd, Tampa, FL 33619
Tel.: (813) 626-3333
Web Site:
http://www.respitekmedical.com
Rev.: $10,000,000
Emp.: 50
Oxygen Therapy Equipment
N.A.I.C.S.: 423450
Gary M. Anzulewicz (Pres)

RESPOND2 CMEDIA
207 NW Park Ave, Portland, OR 97209
Tel.: (503) 222-0025
Web Site: http://www.rtcgroup.com
Year Founded: 1998
Rev.: $225,000,000
Emp.: 135
N.A.I.C.S.: 541810
Tim O'Leary (CEO-Respond2)
David Savage (Exec VP & Mng Partner-Cmedia)
Marilyn Davis (Exec VP & Mng Partner)
Michelle Cardinal (Pres & CEO-Cmedia)

RESPOND2 CMEDIA

Respond2 Cmedia—(Continued)

Subsidiaries:

Marketing & Media Services, LLC (1)
931 Jefferson Blvd Ste 1001, Warwick, RI 02886
Tel.: (401) 737-7730
Emp.: 25
Advertising, Advertising Specialties, Broadcast, Cable T.V., Co-op Advertising, Media Buying Services, Outdoor, Over-50 Market, Seniors' Market, Syndication, T.V., Travel & Tourism
N.A.I.C.S.: 541810
Anthony J. Ferranti (Exec VP)
Sally E. Dickson (Pres)
Tony Ferranti (Exec VP)
Carey White (Supvr-Media)

RESPONSE ENVELOPE INC.
1340 S Baker Ave, Ontario, CA 91761
Tel.: (909) 923-5855
Web Site: http://www.response-envelope.com
Rev.: $27,084,130
Emp.: 150
Envelopes
N.A.I.C.S.: 323111
David Junkin (Gen Mgr)
Lee Larson (Mgr-Ops)
John Gonzales (Mgr-Ops)
Lora Pentheroudakis (Mgr-Sls)

RESPONSE MAIL EXPRESS INC.
4805 Independence Pkwy Ste 250, Tampa, FL 33634
Tel.: (813) 885-8200
Web Site: http://www.rme360.com
Sales Range: $10-24.9 Million
Emp.: 160
Direct Mail Advertising Services
N.A.I.C.S.: 541860
Jorge Villar (Pres)
Jeffrey DiAngelo (VP-Strategic Accts)
Charles Dallacqua (CEO)
Lynn Tyler (CFO)
Ben Porch (CTO)
Sandra Worm (Gen Mgr)

Subsidiaries:

Keeponprospecting.com (1)
4910 Savarese Cir, Tampa, FL 33634
Tel.: (813) 885-8200
Web Site: http://www.keeponprospecting.com
Sales Lead Services
N.A.I.C.S.: 561499
Jorge Villar (Founder & COO)

RESPONSE MARKETING GROUP LLC
8730 Stony Point Pky Ste 250, Richmond, VA 23235-1969
Tel.: (804) 747-3711
Web Site: http://www.rmg-usa.com
Year Founded: 1993
Rev.: $10,400,000
Emp.: 6
Advetising Agency
N.A.I.C.S.: 541810
Stuart Holt (CEO)
Susan King (CMO)
Brian Long (Chief Creative Officer)

RESPONSE MEDIA, INC.
3155 Medlock Bridge Rd, Norcross, GA 30071-1423
Tel.: (770) 451-5478   GA
Web Site: http://www.responsemedia.com
Year Founded: 1979
Rev.: $33,000,000
Emp.: 55
Advetising Agency
N.A.I.C.S.: 541810

Betty Abion (CEO)
Michael McMackin (VP)
Josh Perlstein (Pres)
Connie Minnaugh (Acct Exec)
Patrick Rogge (Chief Innovation Officer)
Douglas Breuer (COO)
Angela Stanhope (Dir-Creative Svcs)
Diane Widerstrom (VP-Integrated Svcs)
Keith Perlstein (CTO)
Ryan Tuttle (COO)
Alvin Glay (VP-Growth & Data-Driven Strategy)

RESPONSE PERSONNEL, INC.
56 W 45th St 2nd Fl, New York, NY 10036
Tel.: (212) 983-8870   NY
Web Site: http://www.responseco.com
Sales Range: $25-49.9 Million
Emp.: 60
Executive Placement
N.A.I.C.S.: 541612
Allen Gutterman (Pres)

Subsidiaries:

RPI Professional Alternatives (1)
56 W 45th St 2nd Fl, New York, NY 10036
Tel.: (212) 983-8870
Web Site: http://www.rpiprofessional.com
Rev.: $20,000,000
Emp.: 50
Temporary Help Service
N.A.I.C.S.: 541611

RESPONSE, LLC
100 Crown St, New Haven, CT 06510
Tel.: (203) 776-2400
Web Site: http://www.thepowertoprovoke.com
Year Founded: 2002
Sales Range: $1-9.9 Million
Emp.: 20
Marketing Consulting Services
N.A.I.C.S.: 541613
Carolyn Walker (CEO & Mng Partner)
David Klineberg (Pres & Partner)
Matt Durand (Sr Dir-Art)
Kim DeMartino (VP-Client Svcs)
Terry Lush (Dir-Creative)
Jenna Coulson (Mgr-Social Media)
Julia Nuara (Sr Acct Mgr)
Marc Broad (VP-Digital)

RESSLER MOTORS
8474 Huffine Ln, Bozeman, MT 59718
Tel.: (406) 587-5501
Web Site: http://www.resslermotors.com
Year Founded: 1999
Automobile Dealers
N.A.I.C.S.: 441120
Jeff Kayser (Gen Mgr)

RESTAURANT BUSINESS INC.
816 E Whittier Blvd, La Habra, CA 90631
Tel.: (562) 690-2011
Web Site: http://www.elcholo.com
Sales Range: $10-24.9 Million
Emp.: 600
Restaurants Owner & Operator
N.A.I.C.S.: 722410
George R. Salisbury (Pres)
Jessie Trejo (Asst Controller)
John Astin (Mgr-Restaurant)
Jonathan Maze (Exec Editor)

RESTAURANT MANAGEMENT CORP.
22 N 6th St, Chambersburg, PA 17201

Tel.: (717) 267-0727
Rev.: $16,300,000
Emp.: 500
Fast-Food Restaurant, Chain
N.A.I.C.S.: 722513
Michael Sipen (Pres)
Bryan Hogge (VP)

RESTAURANT MANAGEMENT INC.
300 Main St, Cincinnati, OH 45202-4159
Tel.: (513) 362-8900   OH
Web Site: http://www.arbys-rmi.com
Year Founded: 1965
Sales Range: $50-74.9 Million
Emp.: 1,850
Eating Place
N.A.I.C.S.: 722513
Grant Troja (Pres & CEO)

RESTAURANT MANAGEMENT OF SOUTH CAROLINA INC.
205 E Liberty St, Sumter, SC 29150-5057
Tel.: (803) 775-9742
Sales Range: $10-24.9 Million
Emp.: 5
Restaurant
N.A.I.C.S.: 722511

RESTAURANT RECRUIT, INC.
611 Market St # 2, Kirkland, WA 98033-5422
Tel.: (512) 342-0110   IL
Web Site: http://www.rradinc.com
Year Founded: 2000
Sales Range: $10-24.9 Million
Emp.: 6
Advetising Agency
N.A.I.C.S.: 541810
Zane Windham (Pres & Mng Partner)
Laura Hackley (Partner & Dir-Creative)
Michelle Hoskins (Acct Exec)
Phil Hedges (Acct Exec)

RESTAURANT SERVICES, INC.
2901 E Randol Mill Rd, Arlington, TX 76011
Tel.: (817) 640-5415
Web Site: http://www.restaurantservices.com
Sales Range: $10-24.9 Million
Emp.: 70
Commercial Equipment Whslr
N.A.I.C.S.: 423440
Gerald L. Durr (Pres)

RESTAURANT SYSTEMS INC.
3880 W Battlefield St, Springfield, MO 65807-8432
Tel.: (417) 883-3600
Sales Range: $10-24.9 Million
Emp.: 600
Fast-Food Restaurant, Independent
N.A.I.C.S.: 722513
Mike Treadwell (Chm)
Brandon Robertson (CFO)

RESTAURANTS NO LIMIT, INC.
4300 Baker Rd Ste 1, Spring Park, MN 55384
Tel.: (952) 938-3000   MN
Web Site: http://www.lordfletchers.com
Year Founded: 1975
Sales Range: $1-9.9 Million
Emp.: 93
Restaurant Services
N.A.I.C.S.: 722511
William Naegele (Principal)

RESTAURANTS OF AMERICA, INC.

U.S. PRIVATE

300 S Jackson St Ste 400, Denver, CO 80209
Tel.: (720) 482-1963   TX
Year Founded: 1989
Holding Company; Franchise Restaurants & Sports Bars Owner & Operator
N.A.I.C.S.: 551112
Brian Weston (Pres & CEO)

Subsidiaries:

Restaurants of America Management, Inc. (1)
300 S Jackson St Ste 400, Denver, CO 80209
Tel.: (720) 482-1963
Franchise Restaurants & Sports Bars Management Services
N.A.I.C.S.: 561110
Suzanne Ringo (Office Mgr)
Brian Weston (Pres & CEO)

Subsidiary (Domestic):

Albuquerque Hooters, Inc. (2)
4601 San Mateo Blvd NE, Albuquerque, NM 87109
Tel.: (505) 884-6600
Web Site: http://www.hootersnewmexico.com
Sales Range: $1-9.9 Million
Restaurant & Sports Bar Operator
N.A.I.C.S.: 722511

Colorado Springs Hooters, Inc. (2)
0750 Citadel Dr, Colorado Springs, CO 80909
Tel.: (719) 596-3111
Web Site: http://www.hooterscolorado.com
Sales Range: $1-9.9 Million
Emp.: 60
Restaurant & Sports Bar Operator
N.A.I.C.S.: 722511

Parker Rd. Hooters, Inc. (2)
2610 S Parker Rd, Aurora, CO 80014
Tel.: (303) 337-7070
Web Site: http://www.hooterscolorado.com
Sales Range: $1-9.9 Million
Emp.: 50
Restaurant & Sports Bar Operator
N.A.I.C.S.: 722511

Phoenix Hooters, Inc. (2)
455 N 3rd St Ste 190, Phoenix, AZ 85004
Tel.: (602) 495-1234
Web Site: http://www.hootersarizona.com
Rev.: $2,500,000
Emp.: 75
Restaurant & Sports Bar Operator
N.A.I.C.S.: 722511

Westminster Hooters, Inc. (2)
1111 W 120th Ave, Westminster, CO 80234
Tel.: (303) 991-4668
Web Site: http://www.hootersroa.com
Sales Range: $1-9.9 Million
Emp.: 51
Restaurant & Sports Bar Operator
N.A.I.C.S.: 722511
Justin McKenney (Gen Mgr)

RESTEK CORPORATION
110 Benner Cir, Bellefonte, PA 16823
Tel.: (814) 353-1300
Web Site: http://www.restek.com
Year Founded: 1985
Sales Range: $10-24.9 Million
Emp.: 300
Mfr & Supplier of Chromatographic Supplies
N.A.I.C.S.: 334513
Bryan Wolcott (Pres)
Sabah Dabby (Chief Innovations Officer)
Sara Hall (Mgr-Environment)
Stan Serafin (Project Mgr)

RESTHAVEN CARE COMMUNITY
9 E 8th St, Holland, MI 49423
Tel.: (616) 796-3500   MI
Web Site: http://www.resthaven.org
Year Founded: 1945

COMPANIES

Sales Range: $10-24.9 Million
Emp.: 472
Elder Care Services
N.A.I.C.S.: 624120
Bev Donahue *(Dir-Fin)*
Glenn Lowe *(Dir-Dev)*
Barb Huls *(Dir-HR)*
Taryn Bradtmueller *(Dir-Home Care)*

RESTOCKIT.COM
4350 Oakes Rd Ste 512, Davie, FL 33314-2223
Tel.: (954) 967-1150
Web Site: http://www.restockit.com
Year Founded: 2003
Rev.: $14,500,000
Emp.: 18
Service Establishment Equipment Whslr
N.A.I.C.S.: 423850
Matt Kuttler *(Co-Founder)*
Lestainia Dyce *(Acct Mgr)*
Brian Goldberg *(Dir-IT)*

RESTON ASSOCIATION
12001 Sunrise Valley Dr, Reston, VA 20191-3404   VA
Tel.: (703) 435-6530
Web Site: http://www.reston.org
Year Founded: 1964
Rev.: $17,591,559
Assets: $34,859,321
Liabilities: $4,970,317
Net Worth: $29,889,004
Emp.: 507
Fiscal Year-end: 12/31/18
Recreational Area Maintenance Services
N.A.I.C.S.: 721214
Melissa Kelley *(Dir-HR & Admin Svcs)*
Mike Leone *(Dir-Comm, Mktg & Community Engagement)*
Laura Kowalski *(Dir-Recreation & Environmental Education)*
Harry P. Lynch *(CEO)*
Julie Bitzer *(Chm)*
Caren Anton *(Vice Chm)*
John Mooney *(Sec)*
Robert T. Petrine *(Treas)*
Cameron Adams *(Dir-Covenants Admin)*
Mike McNamara *(Dir-Maintenance & Natural Resources)*
Clara William *(Dir-IT)*
Anthony Champ *(Gen Counsel)*

RESTON LIMOUSINE & TRAVEL SERVICE, INC.
45685 Elmwood Ct, Dulles, VA 20166
Tel.: (703) 478-0500
Web Site: http://www.restonlimo.com
Year Founded: 1989
Sales Range: $10-24.9 Million
Emp.: 275
Limousine Service
N.A.I.C.S.: 485320
Jim Grey *(Mgr-Contracts-Virginia)*
Melissa Beard *(Controller)*
Rosetta Crutch *(Mgr-Ops)*
Tony Simon *(COO)*
Kristina Bouweiri *(Pres & CEO)*
Margaret Day *(Mgr-Customer Rels)*
Keith Johnson *(Mgr-Safety & Trng)*
Karen Ballard *(Mgr-HR)*
Anna Wilkinson *(Mgr-Mktg)*
Bruce Kudeviz *(CFO)*

RESTONIC MATTRESS CORPORATION
737 Main St 3rd Fl, Buffalo, NY 14203
Tel.: (847) 241-1130   DE
Web Site: http://www.restonic.com
Year Founded: 1938
Sales Range: $50-74.9 Million
Emp.: 3
Mattress Mfr
Ronald Passaglia *(Pres & CEO)*
Julia Rosien *(VP-Brand & Digital Mktg)*

Subsidiaries:

Continental Silverline Products Inc.   (1)
710 N Drennan St, Houston, TX 77003-1321
Tel.: (713) 222-7394
Mattress Mfr
N.A.I.C.S.: 337910
John Robins *(Principal)*

Everton Mattress Factory, Inc.
347 Poleline Rd, Twin Falls, ID 83301
Tel.: (208) 733-8373
Web Site: http://www.evertonmattress.com
Emp.: 15
Mattress Mfr
N.A.I.C.S.: 337910
Derrick Hanson *(Mgr)*
Jessie Boller *(Mgr)*

Johnson City Bedding Company   (1)
250 West Market St, Johnson City, TN 37604-6208
Tel.: (423) 434-1020
Web Site: http://www.restonicjc.com
Sales Range: $10-24.9 Million
Mattress Mfr
N.A.I.C.S.: 337910

McKinney Bedding Company   (1)
718 W Chase St, Springfield, MO 65803-1522
Tel.: (417) 866-2747
Mattress Mfr
N.A.I.C.S.: 337910
Lloyd McKinney *(Pres)*

Oregon Mattress Company   (1)
2751 NE Wynooski Rd, Newberg, OR 97132-7139
Tel.: (503) 538-8875
Web Site: http://www.oregonmattress.com
Mattress Mfr
N.A.I.C.S.: 337910

Restonic Mattress Corporation - Restonic British Columbia Factory   (1)
13137 82a Avenue, Surrey, V3W 9Y6, BC, Canada
Tel.: (604) 501-1010
Web Site: http://www.restonic.ca
Mattress Mfr
N.A.I.C.S.: 337910
Lionel Martin *(Mgr)*

Restonic Mattress Corporation - Restonic Caribbean Factory   (1)
Orange Grove Estate, Orange Grove, WI, Tacarigua, Trinidad & Tobago
Tel.: (868) 6121789
Mattress Mfr
N.A.I.C.S.: 337910

Restonic Mattress Corporation - Restonic Dominican Republic Factory   (1)
Gustavo Mejia Ricart Ste 57, Naco, Santo Domingo, Dominican Republic
Tel.: (809) 5402262
Mattress Mfr
N.A.I.C.S.: 337910

Restonic Mattress Corporation - Restonic Ecuador Factory   (1)
Av Los Shyris Sector San Jose, Via Sangolqui-Amaguana, Quito, Ecuador
Tel.: (593) 2 398 9100
Web Site: http://www.chaideychaide.com
Mattress Mfr
N.A.I.C.S.: 337910

Restonic Mattress Corporation - Restonic Middle East Factory   (1)
Jebel Ali Industrial Area Ste 3 Plot 559-1119, PO Box 700, Dubai, United Arab Emirates
Tel.: (971) 4 880 3444
Web Site: http://www.restonic.ae
Mattress Mfr
N.A.I.C.S.: 337910
Yousif Kooheji *(Gen Mgr)*

Restonic Mattress Corporation - Restonic Quebec Factory   (1)
990 Rue Salaberry, Laval, H7S 2J1, QC, Canada
Tel.: (450) 668-8670
Mattress Mfr
N.A.I.C.S.: 337910
Guy Tousejnant *(Gen Mgr)*

Restonic Mattress Corporation - Restonic of India Factory   (1)
S F No 192 Uthupalayam Road, Arasur Village Palladam Taluk, 641407, Coimbatore, Tamilnadu, India
Tel.: (91) 4222360890
Web Site: http://www.pepsindia.com
Sales Range: $25-49.9 Million
Emp.: 40
Mattress Mfr
N.A.I.C.S.: 337910
Suresh Babu *(Gen Mgr)*

Restonic Mattress Corporation - Restonic of Korea Factory   (1)
92-1 Nokchonri, Hwadoep, Namyangju, Korea (South)
Tel.: (82) 31 594 3377
Mattress Mfr
N.A.I.C.S.: 337910

Sleep Haven, Inc.   (1)
8819 E Industrial Rd, Haven, KS 67543
Tel.: (620) 465-2242
Web Site: http://www.sleephaveninc.com
Mattress Mfr
N.A.I.C.S.: 337910

Sleep Products, Inc.   (1)
901 Park Pl, New Albany, IN 47150-2260
Tel.: (812) 945-4122
Mattress Mfr
N.A.I.C.S.: 337910

Sleep-Rite Industries, Inc.   (1)
1492 Rollins Rd, Burlingame, CA 94010-2307
Tel.: (650) 344-1980
Mattress Mfr
N.A.I.C.S.: 337910

Stevens Mattress Mfg., Inc.   (1)
1251 S 48th St, Grand Forks, ND 58201-3820
Tel.: (701) 775-5461
Sales Range: $10-24.9 Million
Mattress Mfr
N.A.I.C.S.: 337910
Richard Stevens *(Pres)*

Stevens Mattress of Iowa, Inc.   (1)
1000 Prospect Dr, Toledo, IA 52342-2145
Tel.: (641) 484-3344
Mattress Mfr
N.A.I.C.S.: 337910

Stylution Int'l Corp.   (1)
No 10 Hou-Da Rd, Baihuadong Village, Dongguan, Guangdong, China
Tel.: (86) 769 83358888
Web Site: http://www.stylutionintl.com
Mattress Mfr
N.A.I.C.S.: 337910

Stylution Int'l Corp.   (1)
73 Wu Chun Road, New Taipei Industrial Park, Taipei, Taiwan
Tel.: (886) 2 2299 2222
Web Site: http://www.restonic.com.tw
Mattress Mfr
N.A.I.C.S.: 337910

Stylution Japan INC.   (1)
Taki Build 2F, Higawa Nihonbashi, Tokyo, 103-0004, Japan
Tel.: (81) 369141190
Web Site: http://www.stylution.es
Mattress Mfr
N.A.I.C.S.: 337910

RESTOR3D, INC.
Research Triangle Park 4001 E NC 54 Hwy Ste 3160, Durham, NC 27709
Tel.: (984) 888-0593
Web Site: https://www.restor3d.com
Year Founded: 2017
3D Printing & Medical Devices Solutions
N.A.I.C.S.: 339112

Kurt Jacobus *(CEO)*

Subsidiaries:

ConforMIS, Inc.   (1)
600 Technology Park Dr, Billerica, MA 01821
Tel.: (781) 345-9001
Web Site: https://www.conformis.com
Rev.: $62,050,000
Assets: $94,048,000
Liabilities: $39,869,000
Net Worth: $54,179,000
Earnings: ($50,473,000)
Emp.: 295
Fiscal Year-end: 12/31/2022
Surgical Implant & Device Mfr
N.A.I.C.S.: 339112
Denise E. Pedulla *(Chief Legal Officer & Sec)*
Gary Maingot *(Sr VP-Ops)*
Marc Quartulli *(VP-Clinical Affairs & Market Access)*
Bart Lagae *(VP-Intl Mktg)*
Eric Rickenbach *(Sr VP-Sls)*
Jeff Kogl *(VP-Bus Dev)*
Christine Desrochers *(Interim CFO & Controller)*
James Paiva *(VP-Mktg-US)*
Michael Fillion *(COO)*

Subsidiary (Domestic):

ImaTX, Inc.   (2)
12582 W Millennium Dr, Los Angeles, CA 90094
Tel.: (310) 255-5500
Motion Picture Production Services
N.A.I.C.S.: 512110

RESTORATION BUILDERS INC.
3961 E Chandler Blvd, Ste 111-168, Phoenix, AZ 85048
Tel.: (630) 833-6721
Web Site: https://restorbuilders.com
Year Founded: 2017
Commercial & Institutional Building Construction
N.A.I.C.S.: 236220
Jeff Granberry *(Owner)*
John Lorenz *(Chm & CEO)*
Steve Fulgham *(COO)*

Subsidiaries:

Renown Construction of Texas LLC   (1)
1240 Texas St, Lewisville, TX 75057
Tel.: (972) 782-5489
Web Site: http://www.renownconstruction.com
Roof Construction Services
N.A.I.C.S.: 238160
Adam Buttorff *(Founder & Pres)*

RESTORATION BUILDERS INC.
3961 E Chandler Blvd Ste 111-168, Phoenix, AZ 85048
Tel.: (425) 999-6508
Web Site: http://restorbuilders.com
Year Founded: 2017
Residential & Commercial Contractor
N.A.I.C.S.: 236210
John Lorenz *(Chm & CEO)*

Subsidiaries:

AVCO Roofing Inc.   (1)
13437 State Hwy, Tyler, TX 75707-6374
Tel.: (903) 534-8700
Web Site: http://www.avcoroofing.com
Roofing Contractors
N.A.I.C.S.: 238160

Alden Roofing, Inc.   (1)
15635 Vision Dr Ste 100, Pflugerville, TX 78660
Tel.: (512) 251-0880
Web Site: http://www.aldenroofing.com
Roofing Contractors
N.A.I.C.S.: 238160
Josh Knox *(Partner)*

RESTORATION BUILDERS INC.

U.S. PRIVATE

Restoration Builders Inc.—(Continued)

Aspenmark Roofing Solutions LLC (1)
2947 Blystone Ln, Dallas, TX 75220
Tel.: (214) 823-7663
Web Site: http://www.aspenmarkroofing.com
Sales Range: $1-9.9 Million
Emp.: 10
Roofing Installation Services
N.A.I.C.S.: 238160
Chris Zazo (CEO)

RESTORATION CLEANERS, LLC
1500 Brittmoore Ste 501 & 502, Houston, TX 77043
Tel.: (713) 468-8287
Web Site: http://www.restorationcleaners.com
Year Founded: 2002
Sales Range: $1-9.9 Million
Emp.: 90
Restorer & Cleaner of Soft Goods Damaged by Disasters & Water Damage
N.A.I.C.S.: 333310
Brian Adams (Pres & CEO)
Marvin Schauer (Acct Mgr-Hotel Bus Dev)

RESTORATION INDUSTRIES, INC.
211 N 5th Ave, Manhattan, MT 59741
Tel.: (406) 388-3136
Year Founded: 2006
Sales Range: Less than $1 Million
Wall Cavity Drying System Mfr
N.A.I.C.S.: 333415
Thomas Dean Geer (Pres, CEO & Sec)
Lorrie Ann Geer (CFO & VP)

RESTORATION MEDIA
17666 Fitch, Irvine, CA 92614
Tel.: (714) 426-4500
Web Site: http://www.restorationmedia.com
Year Founded: 2001
Sales Range: $10-24.9 Million
Emp.: 35
Advetising Agency
N.A.I.C.S.: 541810
Sammy Sayago (CEO)
Rizaldy Asis (Mgr-Email Ops)

RESTORATIVE CARE OF AMERICA
12221 33rd St N, Saint Petersburg, FL 33716
Tel.: (727) 573-1595
Web Site: http://www.rcai.com
Sales Range: $10-24.9 Million
Emp.: 90
Sales of Orthopedic Appliances
N.A.I.C.S.: 334510
Bud Hess (Pres & CEO)
Heidi Rodriguez (Sec)

Subsidiaries:

Restorative Care of America, Inc. (1)
12221 33rd St N, Saint Petersburg, FL 33716
Tel.: (727) 572-8189
Web Site: http://www.rcai.com
Rev: $980,000
Emp.: 50
Orthopedic Appliances
N.A.I.C.S.: 334510
C. E. Hess (Pres)

RESTORE INCORPORATED
3000 NE 30th Pl Ste 201, Fort Lauderdale, FL 33306
Tel.: (954) 563-7001
Web Site: http://www.restoreusa.com
Year Founded: 1983
Sales Range: $10-24.9 Million

Emp.: 4
Lubricating Oils & Greases
N.A.I.C.S.: 324191
Tim M. Sultan (Pres)
Omar Sultan (Chm & CEO)

RESTORE NEIGHBORHOODS LA, INC.
315 W 9th St Ste 407, Los Angeles, CA 90015
Tel.: (213) 270-1720
Web Site: http://www.rn-la.org
Year Founded: 2009
Sales Range: $25-49.9 Million
Emp.: 30
Community Support Services
N.A.I.C.S.: 624190
John Perfitt (Exec Dir)
Tim Piasky (Deputy Dir)
Jeffrey Schaffer (Pres)
Dan Falcon (Treas)
Tom De Simone (Sec)

RESTORE ONE
PO Box 3278, Greenville, NC 27836
Tel.: (252) 751-0411
Web Site: http://www.restoreonelife.org
Sales Range: $10-24.9 Million
Emp.: 4
Human & Social Services
N.A.I.C.S.: 813410
Andrea Reynolds (Dir-RO Ambassadors)
Anna Smith (Co-Founder)
Brian Maclaszek (Treas)
Chris Smith (Co-Founder)
Justin Cox (Chm)

RESTORE REHAB SERVICES, LLC
16000 Park Ten Pl Ste 204, Houston, TX 77084
Tel.: (832) 321-4728
Web Site: http://www.restorerehab.org
Year Founded: 2009
Sales Range: $1-9.9 Million
Emp.: 34
Women Healthcare Services
N.A.I.C.S.: 621610
Ankush Bhargava (Pres)

RESTORED DIGITAL SOLUTIONS, LLC
1801 NW 135th Ave Ste 900, Miami, FL 33182
Tel.: (305) 468-9965
Web Site: http://www.rdsteam.com
Year Founded: 2010
Digital Printing Solutions
N.A.I.C.S.: 423420
Gustavo Hermida (Founder & CEO)
Mike Martin (Pres)

Subsidiaries:

A1 Printer Repair & Supplies, Inc. (1)
1041 W Commercial Blvd Ste 102, Fort Lauderdale, FL 33309
Tel.: (954) 739-1111
Web Site: http://www.a1printerrepairs.com
Digital Printing Solutions
N.A.I.C.S.: 423420
Giovanni F. Crupi (Pres)
Sheryl Chesler (Dir-Mktg)

RESTRUCTURE INC.
205 S Hoover Blvd, Tampa, FL 33609
Tel.: (813) 287-5571
Sales Range: $10-24.9 Million
Emp.: 34
Petroleum Bulk Stations & Terminals
N.A.I.C.S.: 424710
Jack J. Ceccarelli (Pres)

Subsidiaries:

Restructure Petro Marketing Services (1)
9519 E Dr Martin Luther King Jr Blvd # 100, Tampa, FL 33610-7400
Tel.: (813) 287-5571
Web Site: http://www.rpmsinc.com
Rev.: $16,500,000
Emp.: 1
Petroleum Products, Nec
N.A.I.C.S.: 424720

RESULTS DIRECT MARKETING
555 N Woodlawn Ste 300, Wichita, KS 67208-3683
Tel.: (316) 689-8555
Web Site: http://www.resultsdm.com
Year Founded: 1998
Sales Range: $10-24.9 Million
Emp.: 15
Advertising Agencies
N.A.I.C.S.: 541810
Peter Janssen (VP)
Buddy Kuhn (Pres)
Cinda York (Mgr-Mktg Svcs)
Maia Briggs (Mgr-Mktg)
Danna Voegeli (Coord-Mktg)
Kim Lawrence (Mgr-Production)
Jennifer Joy (Acct Exec)
Ron Kahan (Dir-CRM & Loyalty Strategies)
Carmen Riggle (Mgr-Mktg)
Shyla Boyer (Sr Mgr-Fin)

RESULTS GENERATION
8127 Mesa Dr Ste B 206 319, Austin, TX 78759
Tel.: (512) 799-8108
Web Site: http://www.resultsgeneration.com
Year Founded: 2007
Sales Range: $1-9.9 Million
Emp.: 9
Direct Mail Advertising
N.A.I.C.S.: 541860
Clint Priest (Founder)
Manny Gunawan (VP-Ops)

RESULTS TECHNOLOGY
7939 Flint St, Lenexa, KS 66214
Tel.: (913) 928-8300
Web Site: http://www.ritanow.com
Year Founded: 1995
Sales Range: $10-24.9 Million
Emp.: 70
Information Technology Products & Services
N.A.I.C.S.: 423430
John E. French (Chm & CEO)
Patrick Murphy (Pres)
Nathan Keller (VP-Bus Dev)
Mike Hummel (VP-St. Louis)
Sam Norton (Sr Acct Exec)
Aaron Hite (VP)
Martin Wells (Engr-Infrastructure)
Brandon Quantz (Engr-Sr Network)
Mike Gilmore (CTO)

RESULTSCX
100 NE 3rd Ave. Ste 200, Fort Lauderdale, FL 33001
Tel.: (863) 594-1448
Web Site: https://resultscx.com
Emp.: 11,035
Outsourcing & Resourcing Services
N.A.I.C.S.: 561110
Rajesh Subramaniam (CEO & Mng Dir)

Subsidiaries:

Huntswood CTC Limited (1)
Abbey Gardens Abbey Street, Reading, RG1 3BA, Berkshire, United Kingdom
Tel.: (44) 333 321 7815
Web Site: http://www.huntswood.com

Business Process Outsourcing & Resourcing Services; Technology Delivery & Data Analytics
N.A.I.C.S.: 561110
Matthew Bonfield (CEO)
Paul Scott (Chief Comml Officer)
Dave King (COO)
Donna Knight (CFO)
Steve Mills (CTO & CFO)
Anton Manley (COO)
Helen Maslin (Chief Risk Officer)
Kirk Croal (CTO)

RESURGENCE FINANCIAL, LLC
1161 Lake Cook Rd Ste D, Deerfield, IL 60015-5277
Tel.: (847) 656-2200
Year Founded: 2001
Sales Range: $10-24.9 Million
Emp.: 70
Credit Card Debt & Collection Services
N.A.I.C.S.: 561440
Todd Lansky (COO)

RESURGENS TECHNOLOGY PARTNERS, LLC
3630 Peachtree Rd NE Ste 920, Atlanta, GA 30326
Tel.: (678) 894-1447
Web Site: http://www.resurgenstech.com
Year Founded: 2016
Emp.: 100
Private Investment Firm
N.A.I.C.S.: 523999
John Baumstark (Operating Partner)
Adi Filipovic (Mng Dir)
Lizzy Brown (VP-Talent)
Henry Chancy (Head-Bus Dev)
Danny Carpenter (VP)
Leonora Lesesne (COO)
Bryan West (Head-Talent)

Subsidiaries:

AgencyBloc (1)
2100 Central Ave Ste 104, Boulder, CO 80301
Tel.: (866) 338-7075
Web Site: https://www.agencybloc.com
Software Development Services
N.A.I.C.S.: 513210
Adam Lewis (CEO)

Subsidiary (Domestic):

FormFire, LLC (2)
1360 E 9th St Ste 850, Cleveland, OH 44114
Tel.: (216) 502-2324
Web Site: http://www.formfire.com
Insurance Software Development Services
N.A.I.C.S.: 541511
Colin Ingram (CEO)
Rich Peplin (Project Mgr)
Chris Dinda (Dir-Sls)
Peter Analore (VP-Ops)
Michael Epp (Founder)
Dave Campbell (COO)

Assurance Software, Inc. (1)
800 Adams Ave, Audubon, PA 19403
Web Site: http://www.assurancesoftware.com
Business Continuity Software & Services
N.A.I.C.S.: 513210
Jon Ezrine (CEO)
Jim Corr (CFO)

Subsidiary (Domestic):

Castellan Solutions LLC (2)
323 W Lakeside Ave Ste 410, Cleveland, OH 44113
General Management Consulting Services
N.A.I.C.S.: 541611

Division (Domestic):

BC Management, Inc. (3)
8071 Centerstone Dr, Huntington Beach, CA 92646-8572
Tel.: (714) 969-8006

COMPANIES

Web Site: http://www.bcmanagement.com
Staffing & Research Services
N.A.I.C.S.: 541720
Cheyene Marling *(Mng Dir-Talent Mgmt & Res Analytics)*

EnergyCAP, LLC (1)
360 Discovery Dr, Boalsburg, PA 16827
Tel.: (814) 237-3744
Web Site: http://www.energycap.com
Software Publisher
N.A.I.C.S.: 513210
Chris S. Heinz *(Chief Customer Officer & VP-Customer Svcs)*
Adam C. Hegedus *(CIO & VP-Ops)*
Ryan T. Ohlson *(COO)*
John C. Heinz *(VP-Sls)*
Ryan Booz *(CTO & VP-Software Dev)*
Steven D. Heinz *(Founder & CEO)*
David Ulmer *(VP & Head-Implementation Solutions)*

Investment Metrics LLC (1)
3 Parklands Dr Ste 203, Darien, CT 06820
Tel.: (203) 662-8400
Web Site: http://www.invmetrics.com
Investment Performance Analytics & Reporting Solutions
N.A.I.C.S.: 513210
Scott Bugbee *(Dir-Bus Dev)*
Sanjoy Chatterjee *(CEO)*
Thomas Carlson *(VP-Sls & Mktg)*
Mark Bell *(Chief Mktg Officer)*

Subsidiary (Domestic):

Investor Force Holdings, Inc. (2)
1100 E Hector St Ste 100, Conshohocken, PA 19428
Tel.: (484) 351-7200
Performance Measurement & Reporting Software.
N.A.I.C.S.: 513210

Subsidiary (Domestic):

Insignis, Inc. (3)
1 N Lasalle St Ste 825, Chicago, IL 60602
Tel.: (312) 368-3630
Web Site: http://www.insignis.com
Investment Data Management Services
N.A.I.C.S.: 518210
Harold Sullivan *(CEO)*
Suzanne Streitz *(Sr VP-Client Svcs)*

Investor Force, Inc. (3)
640 Lee Rd Ste 200, Wayne, PA 19087 (80%)
Tel.: (610) 408-3700
Sales Range: $100-124.9 Million
Developer of Online Financial Software Applications
N.A.I.C.S.: 513210

Valant Medical Solutions Inc. (1)
2033 6th Ave Suite 500, Seattle, WA 98121
Tel.: (888) 774-0532
Web Site: http://www.valant.com
Sales Range: $1-9.9 Million
Emp.: 50
SaaS Electronic Health Record-Keeping Products & Services
N.A.I.C.S.: 513210
Ben Lischner *(CTO)*
Brook West *(VP-Sls & Mktg)*
Heather Grube *(Dir-Practice Svcs)*
Micah Adler *(Dir-Practice Consultation)*
Mary Fischer *(Controller)*
Alec Fishburne *(VP-Customer Success)*
Ryan Donahue *(VP-Product & Engrg)*
Kelli Paull *(VP-Customer Experience)*

RETAIL BUSINESS DEVELOPMENT, INC.
111 2nd Ave NE 15th Fl, Saint Petersburg, FL 33701
Tel.: (866) 869-6975
Web Site: http://www.retailbusinessdevelopment.com
Sales Range: $75-99.9 Million
Retail Management, Training & Outsourcing Services
N.A.I.C.S.: 541618
Kevin Killoran *(COO)*
James Ralph *(Pres & CEO)*

RETAIL CLOUD TECHNOLOGIES, LLC
380 Park Pl Blvd Ste 250, Clearwater, FL 33759
Tel.: (727) 210-1700
Web Site: http://www.teamworkcommerce.com
Year Founded: 2007
Sales Range: $10-24.9 Million
Emp.: 175
Software Development Services
N.A.I.C.S.: 541511
Michael Mauerer *(Founder & CEO)*
Chad Willis *(Owner & Partner)*
Amber Hovious *(VP-Mktg & Partnerships)*
Jonathan Mauerer *(VP-Revenue)*
Sergey Kozhevnikov *(VP-Product Dev)*

RETAIL CONCEPTS, INC.
10560 Bissonnet St Ste 100, Houston, TX 77099
Tel.: (281) 340-5000 TX
Web Site: http://www.sunandski.com
Year Founded: 1980
Sales Range: $25-49.9 Million
Emp.: 229
Sporting Goods Retailer
N.A.I.C.S.: 459110
B. Frank Stanley *(CFO & CEO)*
Alison Albrecht *(VP-Mktg)*
Karen Gibson *(Mgr-HR)*
Rick Dodgen *(Mgr-Store Plng)*
Dean Simpson *(Dir-Logistics Distr)*

RETAIL CONSTRUCTION SERVICES
11343 39th St N, Lake Elmo, MN 55042
Tel.: (651) 704-9000
Web Site: http://www.retailconstruction.com
Sales Range: $25-49.9 Million
Emp.: 110
Commercial & Office Building, New Construction
N.A.I.C.S.: 236220
Stephen Bachman *(Pres, CEO & Owner)*
Kelly Odegard *(Mgr-HR)*
Daniel Braun *(Project Mgr)*

RETAIL FIXTURE, LLC.
3000 Wolff St, Racine, WI 53404
Tel.: (262) 619-3040
Web Site: http://www.retailfixture.com
Rev.: $12,000,000
Emp.: 75
Furniture Designer, Engineer & Builder
N.A.I.C.S.: 337211
Bill Lacey *(Mgr-CAD)*
Curt Woodward *(Owner)*
Doug Swenson *(Project Mgr)*
Erik Garcia *(Project Mgr)*
Scot Mitchell *(Project Mgr)*
Tim Mason *(Mgr-Production)*

RETAIL INDUSTRY LEADERS ASSOCIATION
1700 N Moore St Ste 2250, Arlington, VA 22209
Tel.: (703) 841-2300 NY
Web Site: http://www.rila.org
Year Founded: 1969
Sales Range: $10-24.9 Million
Emp.: 61
Retail Industry Professional Association
N.A.I.C.S.: 813920
Deborah White *(Gen Counsel & Exec VP)*
Jennifer Safavian *(Exec VP-Govt Affairs)*
Jenny Keehan *(Exec VP-Member Svcs & Retail Ops)*
Brian Dodge *(COO)*
Evan Armstrong *(VP-Govt Affairs)*
Christin Fernandez *(VP-Comm)*
Talana Lattimer *(Dir-Digital Comm)*
Brian Cornell *(Chm)*
Sandy Kennedy *(Pres)*
Jason Brewer *(Exec VP-Comm & State Affairs)*
Brian Rose *(Dir-State Affairs & Advocacy)*
Lisa LaBruno *(Exec VP-Retail Ops)*
Austen Jensen *(Sr VP-Govt Affairs)*
Melissa Sharp Murdock *(VP-Comm & Media Rels)*
Blake Harden *(VP-Intl Trade)*

RETAIL INFORMATION SYSTEMS, INC.
2555 Westhollow Dr, Houston, TX 77082
Tel.: (281) 558-5910
Web Site: http://www.retailinfosys.com
Year Founded: 1994
Sales Range: $10-24.9 Million
Emp.: 15
Software Publisher
N.A.I.C.S.: 513210
Madhu Bontha *(Founder & CEO)*

RETAIL INVESTORS OF TEXAS, LTD.
2420 Nederland Ave, Nederland, TX 77627-6048
Tel.: (409) 727-3104 TX
Web Site: http://www.marketbasketfoods.com
Year Founded: 1961
Supermarkets & Grocery Services
N.A.I.C.S.: 445110
Skylar Thompson *(Pres)*
Thomas Cormier *(CEO)*
Daniel Geraci *(Controller)*
Paul Woodward *(Coord-Employment & Training)*
Toni Hoffpauir *(Mgr-Benefits)*

RETAIL MAINTENANCE, INC.
45 W Prospect Ave Ste 1650G, Cleveland, OH 44115
Tel.: (216) 574-4844 OH
Web Site: http://www.rmiexpress.com
Year Founded: 1996
Sales Range: $1-9.9 Million
Emp.: 24
Electrical Repair & Maintenance
N.A.I.C.S.: 238210
Brian Caton *(Pres)*
Rose Bir *(Supvr-Customer Svc)*

RETAIL RADIO
7921 Kingswood Dr Ste A3, Citrus Heights, CA 95610
Tel.: (916) 961-8845
Web Site: http://www.retailradio.biz
Year Founded: 2008
Sales Range: $1-9.9 Million
Emp.: 14
Music Software, Sensory Branding & Digital Signage
N.A.I.C.S.: 541890
J. C. Swan *(COO)*
Nick Cocchiola *(Dir-Ops)*

RETAIL SECURITY SERVICES, INC.
3249 Route 112 Bdg 4 Ste 2, Medford, NY 11763
Tel.: (631) 346-3570
Web Site: http://www.retailsecurityservices.net
Year Founded: 2014
Sales Range: $10-24.9 Million
Emp.: 38

RETHINK ROBOTICS, INC.

Security Guard Services
N.A.I.C.S.: 561612
Kathleen Larmour *(Pres)*
Danielle Procida *(Dir-Fin)*
Allison Seguine *(Dir-Ops)*
Bianca McNamara *(Mgr-Natl Sls)*
Casey DeCesare *(Mgr-Client)*

RETAIL THERAPY LLC
24 Wilson Way, Westwood, MA 02090-1806
Tel.: (781) 329-8990 MA
Web Site: http://www.frugalfannies.com
Year Founded: 1983
Sales Range: $50-74.9 Million
Emp.: 710
Women's Clothing Store
N.A.I.C.S.: 458110
John Bonica *(CFO)*
Dina Markowski *(Mgr)*
Katelyn Butler *(Mgr-Store)*

Subsidiaries:

Frugal Fannie's Fashion Warehouse (1)
24 Wilson Way, Westwood, MA 02090 (100%)
Tel.: (781) 329-8990
Web Site: http://www.frugalfannie.com
Sales Range: $25-49.9 Million
Emp.: 120
Retail Warehouse
N.A.I.C.S.: 458110
Orrin Doxer *(Pres)*

RETAILERS & MANUFACTURERS DISTRIBUTION MARKETING SERVICES INC.
401 Clearview Rd, Edison, NJ 08837-3736
Tel.: (732) 225-5572
Year Founded: 1977
Sales Range: $10-24.9 Million
Emp.: 200
Provider of Business Services
N.A.I.C.S.: 493110

RETAILNEXT, INC.
60 S Market St Ste 1000, San Jose, CA 95113-2336
Web Site: http://www.retailnext.net
Information Services
N.A.I.C.S.: 519290
Andrew Golden *(Head-Talent Acq & HR)*
Alexei Agratchev *(CEO)*

Subsidiaries:

Retailnext RP UK Ltd. (1)
Beech House Woodlands Business Park Linford Wood West, Milton Keynes, MK14 6ES, United Kingdom
Tel.: (44) 1908682700
Advertising & Marketing Services
N.A.I.C.S.: 541810

RETELE COMPANY
15 Division St, Greenwich, CT 06830
Tel.: (203) 629-1261
Web Site: http://www.reteleco.com
Year Founded: 1986
Sales Range: Less than $1 Million
Emp.: 3
N.A.I.C.S.: 541810
Ken Tenner *(Dir-Art)*
Steve Katcher *(Dir-Creative)*
Dean C. Gamanos *(Pres)*

RETHINK ROBOTICS, INC.
27 Wormwood St, Boston, MA 02210
Tel.: (617) 500-2487
Web Site: http://www.rethinkrobotics.com
Robotic Machinery Mfr
N.A.I.C.S.: 333248
Rodney Brooks *(Founder, Chrn & CTO)*
Scott Eckert *(Pres & CEO)*

RETHINK ROBOTICS, INC.

Rethink Robotics, Inc.—(Continued)
Jason Barton (Chief Revenue Officer)
Jim Daly (COO)
Jim Lawton (Chief Product & Mktg Officer)
Ann Whittaker (VP-HR & Admin)

RETIF OIL & FUEL, LLC
527 Destrehan Ave, Harvey, LA 70058
Tel.: (504) 349-9000   LA
Web Site: http://www.retif.com
Year Founded: 1965
Sales Range: $25-49.9 Million
Emp.: 77
Petroleum Bulk Stations & Terminals
N.A.I.C.S.: 424710
Kenneth J. Retif (Pres)
David Hacker (Controller)
Tammy Coulon (Office Mgr)
Bob Gaudet (VP-Sls)
Brandon Lorio (CFO)
Chad Harris (Mgr-Ops)

RETINA CONSULTANTS OF SOUTHWEST FLORIDA, INC.
6901 International Ctr, Fort Myers, FL 33912
Tel.: (239) 772-4323
Web Site: http://www.eye.md
Year Founded: 1980
Sales Range: $1-9.9 Million
Emp.: 100
Eye Care Specialists
N.A.I.C.S.: 621111
Joseph P. Walker (Founder & Pres)

RETINA HEALTH CENTER
1567 Hayley Ln Ste 101, Fort Myers, FL 33907
Tel.: (239) 337-3337
Web Site:
http://www.retinahealthcenter.com
Sales Range: $1-9.9 Million
Emp.: 45
Optometrist Offices
N.A.I.C.S.: 621320
Alexander M. Eaton (Founder & Dir)
Christine A. Elkins (Coord-Res)
Cathy Flynn (Officer-Privacy)

RETIREMENT COMMUNITY SPECIALISTS, INC.
11022 S 51st St Ste 204, Phoenix, AZ 85044-4307
Tel.: (480) 947-8600   AZ
Web Site: http://www.rcsmgt.com
Year Founded: 1990
Sales Range: $250-299.9 Million
Emp.: 5
Construction & Operation of Retirement Centers
N.A.I.C.S.: 541611
Eric Johnston (Pres)

RETIREMENT LIVING, INC.
8140 Township Line Rd, Indianapolis, IN 46260
Tel.: (317) 875-9700   IN
Web Site:
http://www.marquetteseniorliving.org
Year Founded: 1979
Sales Range: $25-49.9 Million
Emp.: 351
Lifecare Retirement Community Operator
N.A.I.C.S.: 623312
Stephen Steel (CEO)

RETIREMENT, LLC - SERIES TWO
13838 Quail Pointe Dr Ste B, Oklahoma City, OK 73134
Tel.: (405) 848-8862   IL
Web Site:
http://www.retirementllc.com
Retirement Benefits Administration Services
N.A.I.C.S.: 524292
Bill Robertson (VP-Retirement Plan)

Subsidiaries:
Retirement, LLC - Series Two, Operations Office   (1)
13838 Quail Pointe Dr Ste B, Oklahoma City, OK 73134
Tel.: (405) 848-8862
Web Site: http://www.retirementllc.com
Retirement Benefits Administration Services
N.A.I.C.S.: 524292
Robert J. Krypel (CEO)

Summit Group, Inc.   (1)
1900 NW Expressway Ste 410, Oklahoma City, OK 73118
Tel.: (405) 842-1800
Insurance Related Activities
N.A.I.C.S.: 524298

RETRIEVER MEDICAL/DENTAL PAYMENTS, LLC
115 E Stevens Ave, Valhalla, NY 10595
Web Site:
http://www.rectanglehealth.com
Year Founded: 1993
Sales Range: $50-74.9 Million
Emp.: 150
Payment Processing Services
N.A.I.C.S.: 522320
Dominick Colabella (CEO)
Scott LoPresti (COO)
Mike Peluso (CTO)
Kathy Tuite (CMO)
Martin Veilleux (CFO)

RETRO ELEVATOR CORP.
3241 118th Ave N, Saint Petersburg, FL 33716
Tel.: (727) 895-8144   FL
Web Site:
http://www.retroelevator.com
Year Founded: 1993
Sales Range: $1-9.9 Million
Emp.: 50
Elevator Cab Mfr
N.A.I.C.S.: 333921
Andy Melendez (Pres)
Andrew Safko (Gen Mgr)
Allen Householder (Mgr-Shop)

RETTEW ASSOCIATES INC.
3020 Columbia Ave, Lancaster, PA 17603
Tel.: (717) 394-3721
Web Site: http://www.rettew.com
Year Founded: 1995
Sales Range: $1-9.9 Million
Emp.: 27
Engineeering Services
N.A.I.C.S.: 541330
Mark P. Lauriello (Pres & COO)
Clayton E. Bubeck (Sr VP)
Brian W. Engle (Reg VP)
Robert M. Lauriello (VP-Civil, Municipal & Transportation)
Mary Ellen Eshelman (Dir-HR)

RETZLAFF INCORPORATED
50 Mitchell Blvd, San Rafael, CA 94903-2035
Tel.: (415) 472-1177   CA
Web Site: http://www.celadon.com
Year Founded: 1990
Sales Range: $10-24.9 Million
Emp.: 5
Custom Infrared Remote Control Devices
N.A.I.C.S.: 335314
Robert Z. Retzlaff (CEO)
Kathy Johnson (Pres)

REULAND ELECTRIC COMPANY
17969 Railroad St, City of Industry, CA 91748-1192
Tel.: (626) 854-5192   CA
Web Site: http://www.reuland.com
Year Founded: 1930
Sales Range: $25-49.9 Million
Emp.: 250
Mfr of Motors; Fluid-Shaft & Electric
N.A.I.C.S.: 335312

Subsidiaries:
Reuland Electric Company - Brake Division   (1)
4500 East Grand River Ave, Howell, MI 48843
Tel.: (517) 546-4400
Web Site: http://www.reuland.com
Emp.: 50
Brake Mfr
N.A.I.C.S.: 336340
Debbie Limtao (Mgr-HR)

Reuland Electric Company - Engineering Services Division   (1)
9620 Colerain Ave, Cincinnati, OH 45140
Tel.: (626) 854-7440
Sales Range: $10-24.9 Million
Emp.: 2
Industrial Motor Mfr
N.A.I.C.S.: 335312

Reuland Electric Company - Foundry Division   (1)
17969 Railroad St, City of Industry, CA 91748   (100%)
Tel.: (626) 964-6411
Web Site: http://www.reuland.com
Sales Range: $10-24.9 Million
Emp.: 100
Mfr of Electric Motors, Motor Brakes & Other Related Products
N.A.I.C.S.: 335312
Bill Kramer (CFO)

REUNION HOSPITALITY TRUST, INC.
60 E 42nd St Ste 1901, New York, NY 10165
Tel.: (212) 681-7045   MD
Year Founded: 2010
Real Estate Investment Services
N.A.I.C.S.: 525990
Jason Nathaniel Ader (Chm)
E. Jonathan Falik (CEO)
Andrew P. Nelson (CFO)
Adam C. McMaster (Chief Acctg Officer)
Daniel B. Silvers (Pres)

REUNION TITLE, INC.
2701 W Plano Pkwy Ste 100, Plano, TX 75075-8211
Tel.: (214) 556-0334   TX
Web Site: http://www.reuniontitle.com
Title Insurance
N.A.I.C.S.: 524210
Linda Brown (Pres)

REUTER EQUIPMENT COMPANY
3816 W Lowr Buckeye Rd, Phoenix, AZ 85009
Tel.: (602) 269-1050
Web Site: http://www.rec-reuter.com
Sales Range: $10-24.9 Million
Emp.: 23
General Construction Machinery & Equipment
N.A.I.C.S.: 423810
Carol A. Fellars (Pres)

REUTHER INVESTMENT CO. INC.
11654 Olive Blvd, Saint Louis, MO 63141
Tel.: (314) 432-8408
Web Site: http://www.reuther.com

U.S. PRIVATE

Sales Range: $50-74.9 Million
Emp.: 81
Automobile Sales, New & Used
N.A.I.C.S.: 441110
Janet Reuther Schopp (Pres)

REUTHER JEEP CHRYSLER
11733 Lackland Rd, Saint Louis, MO 63146-4207
Tel.: (314) 432-8408
Web Site: http://www.reuther.com
Year Founded: 1951
Sales Range: $25-49.9 Million
Emp.: 81
Car Whslr
N.A.I.C.S.: 441110
Janet Reuther (Gen Mgr)
Janet Schoop (Pres)

REV IT LOGISTICS LLC
3050 California Ave Ste A B, Salt Lake City, UT 84107
Tel.: (801) 486-6060
Web Site:
http://www.revitlogistics.com
Year Founded: 2005
Sales Range: $1-9.9 Million
Emp.: 18
Logistics & Transportation
N.A.I.C.S.: 488510
Doug Murray (Exec VP-Bus Dev)

REV RENEWABLES, INC.
1700 Broadway 38th Fl, New York, NY 10019
Tel.: (212) 615-3456   DE
Year Founded: 2021
Emp.: 65
Holding Company
N.A.I.C.S.: 551112
Edward Sondey (CEO)
Robert Parker (CFO & Sr VP)
Christopher Shugart (Sr VP-Operations)
Paul Segal (Chm)
Kathryn Wilson (Sec, Sr VP & Gen Counsel)

REV WORLDWIDE, INC.
3571 Far West Blvd Ste 156, Austin, TX 78731
Tel.: (512) 485-2553
Web Site:
https://www.revworldwide.com
Payment Services
N.A.I.C.S.: 522320
Roy Sosa (CEO & Chm)

Subsidiaries:
NetSpend Corporation   (1)
PO Box 2136, Austin, TX 78768-2136
Tel.: (512) 532-8200
Web Site: https://www.netspend.com
Sales Range: $350-399.9 Million
Emp.: 500
Debit Card Issuing
N.A.I.C.S.: 522210
Kelley Knutson (Pres)
Tammy Ting (Sr VP & Gen Mgr)
Derek Tanis (Sr VP-Partner Channel)
Beth Deck (Sr VP-Fin & Acctg)
Calvin M. Holman (Sr VP-Information Technology)
Diana Holgate (Sr VP-Segment)
Austin Smithers (Sr VP-Compliance)
Michael Reiff (VP)
Pat Vogeler (VP-HR)
Walt Granville (Sr VP)
Andrew Garner (Sr VP & Gen Mgr)
Brian Hobbs (Sr VP)
Jason Gonzalez (Sr VP & Asst Gen Counsel)
Rick Cox (Sr VP-Operations)
Shannon Johnston (CTO)
Walt Granville (Sr VP)
Andrew Garner (Sr VP & Gen Mgr)
Brian Hobbs (Sr VP)
Jason Gonzalez (Sr VP & Asst Gen Counsel)
Rick Cox (Sr VP-Operations)

COMPANIES

Shannon Johnston *(CTO)*
Walt Granville *(Sr VP)*
Andrew Garner *(Sr VP & Gen Mgr)*
Brian Hobbs *(Sr VP)*
Jason Gonzalez *(Sr VP & Asst Gen Counsel)*
Rick Cox *(Sr VP-Operations)*
Shannon Johnston *(CTO)*
Roger D. Kidwell Jr. *(COO & Exec VP)*

Subsidiary (Domestic):

Skylight Financial, Inc. (2)
1455 Lincoln Pkwy E Ste 600, Atlanta, GA 30346
Tel.: (404) 720-2000
Web Site: http://www.skylightfinancial.com
Debit Card Issuing
N.A.I.C.S.: 522210

REV.IO, LLC
3340 Peachtree Rd NE Ste 2850, Atlanta, GA 30326
Web Site: http://www.rev.io
Year Founded: 2002
Sales Range: $1-9.9 Million
Emp.: 200
Software Development Services
N.A.I.C.S.: 541511
Ross Overstreet *(Founder & CTO)*
Brent Maropis *(CEO)*
Robert Benoit *(CFO)*
Evan Rice *(Exec VP-Sls & Mktg)*
Matt Robison *(Sr VP-Client Svcs)*

Subsidiaries:

Tigerpaw Software, Inc. (1)
2201 Thurston Cir Ste 7, Bellevue, NE 68005
Tel.: (402) 592-4544
Web Site: http://www.tigerpawsoftware.com
Sales Range: $1-9.9 Million
Emp.: 20
Business Software Developer
N.A.I.C.S.: 513210
James Foxall *(Pres & CEO)*
Corey DeJong *(Dir-Mktg)*
Michelle Jackson-Triplett *(Dir-Support)*
Marudaraj Jivaraj *(Dir-Software Dev)*
Guy Korbitz *(Dir-Fin & Admin)*
Suzy Kratochvil *(Dir-Trng & Implementation)*
Joel Vaslow *(COO)*

REV19, LLC
2535 E Southlake Blvd, Southlake, TX 76092
Tel.: (888) 708-8019 TX
Web Site: https://go-afs.com
Year Founded: 2017
Integrated Payment Solutions
N.A.I.C.S.: 522320
Dustin Siner *(Chief Revenue Officer)*
Corey Young *(CEO)*
John Buchanan *(Sr VP)*
Cortnee Fagundes *(VP-Ops)*
Carol Sawyer *(VP-Risk Mgmt)*

Subsidiaries:

PurePayments LLC (1)
515 Marin St #402, Thousand Oaks, CA 91360
Web Site: http://purepayments.com
Payroll Services
N.A.I.C.S.: 541214

Renaissance Associates Inc. (1)
14241 Dallas Pkwy Ste 520, Dallas, TX 75254
Tel.: (972) 980-9731
Web Site: http://www.rabankcard.com
Credit Card Processing & Services
N.A.I.C.S.: 522320
Daniel Martin *(CEO)*
Michael Rottkamp *(Partner & Exec VP)*
Gina Spina *(Dir-Risk & Acct Boarding)*
Stephen Hogg *(Dir-Ops)*
Keith Patterson *(Mgr-Customer Retention)*

REVA MEDICAL, INC.
5751 Copley Dr, San Diego, CA 92111
Tel.: (858) 966-3000 CA
Web Site: http://www.revamedical.com
Year Founded: 1998
Rev.: $28,508,000
Assets: $22,661,000
Liabilities: $115,474,000
Net Worth: ($92,813,000)
Earnings: $7,134,000
Emp.: 50
Fiscal Year-end: 12/31/17
Medical Device Mfr
N.A.I.C.S.: 339113
Jeffrey A. Anderson *(Pres)*
Erik Wiberg *(CFO)*
Jessica Earley *(VP-Ops & Product Dev)*

REVAL HOLDINGS, INC.
420 Fifth Ave Fifth Fl, New York, NY 10018
Tel.: (212) 901-9845 DE
Web Site: http://www.reval.com
Year Founded: 2007
Sales Range: $25-49.9 Million
Emp.: 350
Holding Company; Software Publisher
N.A.I.C.S.: 551112

REVCO ELECTRICAL SUPPLY, INC.
360 County Rd 39A, Southampton, NY 11968
Tel.: (631) 283-3600
Web Site: http://www.revcoelectric.com
Sales Range: $25-49.9 Million
Emp.: 52
Lighting Fixtures, Commercial & Industrial
N.A.I.C.S.: 423610
Theodora Velys *(Pres)*

REVCOM INC.
Ste 278 5960 W Parker Rd, Plano, TX 75093-7792
Tel.: (972) 488-1847
Web Site: http://www.revcom.com
Rev.: $11,000,000
Emp.: 13
Satellite Earth Stations
N.A.I.C.S.: 517410
Alicia C. Rivera *(VP)*
Erik P. Foster *(VP-Sls)*
Joel D. Valle *(VP-Network Ops)*
Lawrence Foster Jr. *(Pres & CEO)*

REVCON CONSTRUCTION CORP.
500 Industrial Dr, Prairie View, IL 60069
Tel.: (847) 634-3111
Web Site: http://www.revconcorp.com
Rev.: $15,000,000
Emp.: 45
Industrial Building Construction
N.A.I.C.S.: 236210
Guy Revesz *(CEO & Dir-Consulting)*
Rex Revesz *(Pres)*
Marilyn Revesz *(VP)*
Bernie Revesz *(Acct Mgr)*
Jay Luther *(VP-Estimating)*

REVCOR, INC.
251 Edwards Ave, Carpentersville, IL 60110-1941
Tel.: (847) 428-4411 IL
Web Site: http://www.revcor.com
Year Founded: 1946
Sales Range: $150-199.9 Million
Emp.: 450
Blower Wheels, Impeller Fans & Housings (metal & Plastic)
N.A.I.C.S.: 333413

John H. Reichwein Jr. *(Pres & CEO)*
Andrew K. Groharing *(COO)*
Stephen J. Szorc *(CIO)*
Lee Frick *(VP-Materials)*

Subsidiaries:

V2R, LLC (1)
251 Edwards Ave, Carpentersville, IL 60110-1941 (100%)
Tel.: (847) 551-9600
Web Site: http://www.vision2reality.com
Sales Range: $10-24.9 Million
Emp.: 15
Software Designer
N.A.I.C.S.: 333413
John H. Reichwein Jr. *(Pres & CEO)*
Daniel M. Beebe *(Mgr-Technology & Dev)*
Andrew K. Groharing *(CFO)*

REVEL SYSTEMS, INC.
170 Columbus Ave 4th Fl, San Francisco, CA 94133
Tel.: (844) 584-3316
Web Site: http://www.revelsystems.com
Year Founded: 2010
Sales Range: $25-49.9 Million
Emp.: 200
Software & Technology Development Services
N.A.I.C.S.: 513210
Lisa Falzone *(Co-Founder)*
Christopher Ciabarra *(Co-Founder & CTO)*
Vince Cellini *(Controller-Fin)*
Alex Bogachek *(VP-Engrg)*
Greg Dukat *(CEO)*

REVELL COMMUNICATIONS
1 Capital Mall Ste 210, Sacramento, CA 95814-3974
Tel.: (916) 443-3816 CA
Year Founded: 1984
Sales Range: Less than $1 Million
Emp.: 6
Public Relations Agency
N.A.I.C.S.: 541820
Dennis C. Revell *(Pres & CEO)*

REVELS TRACTOR CO. INC.
2217 N Main St, Fuquay Varina, NC 27526
Tel.: (919) 552-5697
Web Site: http://www.revelstractor.com
Sales Range: $25-49.9 Million
Emp.: 82
Lawn & Garden Machinery & Equipment
N.A.I.C.S.: 423820
Charles Turner Revels Jr. *(Pres)*

REVELSTOKE CAPITAL PARTNERS LLC
3033 E 1st Ave ANB Bank Bldg Ste 501, Denver, CO 80206
Tel.: (303) 953-5100
Web Site: http://www.revelstokecp.com
Privater Equity Firm
N.A.I.C.S.: 523999
Mark W. King *(Mng Partner & CEO)*
Simon A. Bachleda *(Co-Founder & Mng Partner)*
Dale J. Meyer *(Co-Founder & Mng Partner)*
Steve Geringer *(Operating Partner)*
Greg Steil *(Operating Partner)*
Eric A. Shuey *(Mng Dir)*
Russell J. Cassella *(Mng Partner)*
Ron Kuerbitz *(Operating Partner)*

Subsidiaries:

Career Step, LLC (1)
2901 Ashton Blvd, Lehi, UT 84043
Tel.: (801) 489-9393
Web Site: http://www.careerstep.com

Emp.: 150
Online Learning Services
N.A.I.C.S.: 611710
Stephen J. Tober *(Pres)*
Christopher F. Charles *(VP-Ops & Client Mgmt)*
Ben Hartman *(VP-Enrollments)*
Laurie A. McBrierty *(VP-Product Mgmt)*
Judson Smith *(VP-Continuing Education)*
Nate Swanson *(COO)*
Jerolyn Robertson *(VP-Academics)*

Encore Rehabilitation Services LLC (1)
30230 Orchard Lk Rd, Farmington, MI 48334
Tel.: (248) 538-9444
Web Site: http://www.encorerehabilitation.net
Rehabilitative Therapy Services
N.A.I.C.S.: 623110
Don Cook *(VP-Bus Dev & Dir-PAC Strategic Dev)*
Linda Shackelford *(Co-Owner & Pres)*
John Rubino *(VP-Recruitment)*
Michael Houlihan *(Co-Owner & Pres-Bus Dev)*
Steve Wilkinson *(VP-HR)*
Sean M. Whelan *(CEO)*

Subsidiary (Domestic):

Metro Therapy, Inc. (2)
1363 Veterans Hwy Ste 8, Hauppauge, NY 11788-9005
Tel.: (631) 366-3876
Web Site: http://www.metrotherapy.com
Home Care & Special Education Itinerant Services
N.A.I.C.S.: 621610
Barbara Kupferman *(VP)*
Conrad Kupferman *(VP)*

Fast Pace Medical Clinic, PLLC (1)
203 S High St, Waynesboro, TN 38485-2605
Tel.: (855) 632-4800
Web Site: http://www.fastpacurgentcare.com
Freestanding Ambulatory Surgical & Emergency Centers
N.A.I.C.S.: 621493
Stan Bevis *(Owner)*
Reams Powers *(Dir-Medical)*

REVELWOOD, INC.
14 Walsh Dr Ste 303, Parsippany, NJ 07054
Tel.: (201) 984-3030 NY
Web Site: http://www.revelwood.com
Year Founded: 1995
Sales Range: $1-9.9 Million
Emp.: 25
Performance Management Software Development
N.A.I.C.S.: 513210
Kenneth Wolf *(Chief Visionary Officer)*

REVENEER, INC.
10 Maguire Rd Bldg 3 Fl 2, Lexington, MA 02421
Tel.: (339) 999-2666
Web Site: http://www.reveneer.io
Year Founded: 2013
Sales Range: $1-9.9 Million
Emp.: 113
Information Services
N.A.I.C.S.: 519290
Greg Casale *(CEO)*
Steve Hill *(CFO)*
Leona Newell *(VP-HR)*
Zac Iovanella *(Mgr-Sls Dev)*
Kara Brown *(Mgr-Mktg)*

REVENUE ENTERPRISES LLC
3131 S Vaughn Way, Aurora, CO 80014
Tel.: (720) 748-3660
Web Site: http://www.revenueenterprises.com
Year Founded: 2004
Sales Range: $1-9.9 Million
Emp.: 60

REVENUE ENTERPRISES LLC — U.S. PRIVATE

Revenue Enterprises LLC—(Continued)
Health Care & Consumer Debt Collection Services
N.A.I.C.S.: 561440
Tim Brainerd *(Owner & CEO)*

REVENUE.COM CORPORATION
137 Bay St #7, Santa Monica, CA 90405
Tel.: (310) 694-0640   NV
Web Site: http://www.revenue.com
Year Founded: 2014
Holding Company; Online Advertising Services
N.A.I.C.S.: 551112
Francisco Diaz-Mitoma *(CEO)*
Geoffrey DeStefano *(Pres)*
Yamir Ortiz-Morales *(Sr Engr-Software)*
James Jago *(CFO)*

Subsidiaries:

Virurl, Inc.   (1)
137 Bay St #7, Santa Monica, CA 90405-1026
Tel.: (310) 694-0640
Web Site: http://www.revenue.com
Emp.: 10
Online Advertising Services
N.A.I.C.S.: 541890
Merrill Brown *(Chm)*
Jeremy Musighi *(Head-Ops)*
James Jago *(CFO)*
Geoffrey DeStefano *(Pres)*
Ashley Wallace *(Acct Exec)*
Francisco Diaz-Mitoma Jr. *(CEO)*

REVERE COPPER PRODUCTS INC.
1 Revere Pk, Rome, NY 13440-5568
Tel.: (315) 338-2022   DE
Web Site: http://www.reverecopper.com
Year Founded: 1801
Sales Range: $200-249.9 Million
Emp.: 300
Copper Rolling & Drawing
N.A.I.C.S.: 331420
Joseph Schoeck *(VP-Sls & Mktg)*

REVERE ELECTRIC SUPPLY COMPANY
8807 187th St, Mokena, IL 60448
Tel.: (708) 995-3251   IL
Web Site: http://www.revereelectric.com
Year Founded: 1919
Sales Range: $100-124.9 Million
Emp.: 200
Whslr of Electrical Products
N.A.I.C.S.: 423610
Robin Weiner Reid *(Dir-Mktg)*
Kathy Becker *(Dir-HR)*
Mike Radanke *(Coord-VMI)*
Paul McCool *(Pres & CEO)*
Christine Bissett *(Dir-Price Mgmt)*
Eric Feige *(Mgr-Custom Assembly)*
Al Gathman *(Mgr-Customer Svc)*
Jim Lisicki *(VP-Ops)*
Greg Kolb *(VP-Automation)*
Sue Nelson *(Mgr-Bus Dev)*
Tom Frary *(Pres)*
Mike Martyn *(Acct Mgr)*
Dave Christoffel *(Dir-Customer Svc)*

Subsidiaries:

Glenbard Electric Supply Inc.   (1)
333 Eisenhower Ln S, Lombard, IL 60148
Tel.: (630) 627-5104
Web Site: http://www.glenbardelectric.com
Rev.: $7,896,000
Emp.: 12
Electrical Apparatus & Equipment, Wiring Supplies & Related Equipment Merchant Whslr
N.A.I.C.S.: 423610

Dominic Vozella *(Pres)*
Maryann Rose *(Office Mgr)*
Bob Lindgren *(Sr Project Mgr)*
Keith Schmidt *(Mgr-Sls)*

REVERE INDUSTRIES, LLC
17005 A Westfield Park Rd, Westfield, IN 46074
Tel.: (419) 547-1868   DE
Web Site: http://www.revereindustries.com
Year Founded: 2005
Sales Range: $300-349.9 Million
Emp.: 2,000
Holding Company; Plastic Injection Molding, Powder Metallurgy, Aluminum Casting & Food Services Packaging Products & Services
N.A.I.C.S.: 551112
Pat Aubry *(Grp Pres & CEO)*
James R. Crews Jr. *(CFO & VP)*

Subsidiaries:

Ross Casting & Innovation, LLC   (1)
402 S Kuther Rd, Sidney, OH 45365
Tel.: (937) 497-4500
Web Site: http://www.rciwheels.com
Sales Range: $25-49.9 Million
Emp.: 300
Aluminum Die-Castings Mfr
N.A.I.C.S.: 331523
Samuel Ramesh *(Pres)*

REVERE MILLS INTERNATIONAL GROUP
2860 S River Rd Ste 250, Des Plaines, IL 60018
Tel.: (847) 759-6800   IL
Web Site: http://www.reveremills.com
Year Founded: 1992
Sales Range: $25-49.9 Million
Emp.: 50
Home Furnishings & Textile Mfr & Whslr
N.A.I.C.S.: 449129
Elaine Aschenbrand *(Dir-Mktg)*
Kathy Bounelis *(Controller)*
Jenifer Buffalo *(VP-Mktg)*
Jeff Gregg *(Pres)*

REVERE PACKAGING
39 Pearce Industrial Rd, Shelbyville, KY 40065
Tel.: (800) 626-2668
Web Site: http://www.reverepackaging.com
Paper Bag & Coated & Treated Paper Mfr
N.A.I.C.S.: 322220
Kate Henninger *(VP-Fin & Controller)*

REVEREIT LLC
402 Amherst St Ste 100, Nashua, NH 03063
Tel.: (603) 889-3000
Web Site: http://www.revereit.com
Year Founded: 2005
Sales Range: $1-9.9 Million
Emp.: 115
IT Consulting for the Pharmaceutical Industry
N.A.I.C.S.: 541690
Gaurav Sharma *(Pres)*

REVERENCE CAPITAL PARTNERS LLC
590 Madison Ave, New York, NY 10022
Tel.: (212) 804-8025
Web Site: https://www.reverencecapital.com
Year Founded: 2013
Privater Equity Firm
N.A.I.C.S.: 523999

Peter C. Aberg *(Co-Founder & Partner)*
Alexander A. Chulack *(Co-Founder & Partner)*

Subsidiaries:

Advisor Group, Inc.   (1)
20 E Thomas Rd Ste 2000, Phoenix, AZ 85012
Tel.: (866) 481-0379
Web Site: http://www.advisorgroup.com
Holding Company; Investment Advisory Services
N.A.I.C.S.: 551112
Andrea Dircks Larsen *(Chief HR Officer)*
Jamie Price *(Pres & CEO)*
Steve Chipman *(Sr VP-Strategic Acq)*
Rob Gulner *(Chief Compliance Officer-Investment Advisory)*
Jon Frojen *(CFO)*
Todd Fulks *(Sr VP-Succession & Acq)*
Kristen Kimmell *(Exec VP-Bus Dev)*
Greg Cornick *(Pres-Advice & Wealth Mgmt)*
Erinn Ford *(Exec VP-Advisor Engagement)*
Susan Theder *(CMO)*

Subsidiary (Domestic):

FSC Securities Corporation   (2)
2300 Windy Rdg Pkwy Ste 1100, Atlanta, GA 30339
Tel.: (800) 547-2382
Web Site: http://www.joinfsc.com
Emp.: 1,200
Securities & Investment Advisory Services
N.A.I.C.S.: 523940
John Dillon *(Chief Compliance Officer)*
Derek Burke *(Pres & CEO)*

Ladenburg Thalmann Financial Services Inc.   (2)
4400 Biscayne Blvd 12th Fl, Miami, FL 33137
Tel.: (305) 572-4100
Web Site: https://www.ladenburg.com
Rev.: $1,469,302,000
Assets: $829,936,000
Liabilities: $588,471,000
Net Worth: $241,465,000
Earnings: $22,767,000
Emp.: 1,510
Fiscal Year-end: 12/31/2019
Holding Company; Asset Management, Securities Brokerage & Investment Banking Services
N.A.I.C.S.: 551112
Diane Chillemi *(CFO & SrVP)*
Peter Blum *(Co-Pres & CEO)*
David Rosenberg *(Co-Pres & CEO)*
Robert Mateicka *(Chief Compliance Officer)*
Joseph Giovaniello Jr. *(Sr VP-Corp & Regulatory Affairs)*

Subsidiary (Domestic):

Highland Capital Brokerage, Inc.   (3)
3535 Grandview Pkwy Ste 600, Birmingham, AL 35243
Tel.: (205) 263-4400
Web Site: http://www.highlandbrokerage.com
Insurance Agencies & Brokerages
N.A.I.C.S.: 524210
Joe Presutti *(Mng Principal-West)*
Marty Dooley *(Principal-Milwaukee)*
Michael Pariano *(Mng Principal-New England)*
Nick Catrini *(Mng Principal-New York Metro)*
Paul M. Harrington *(Principal-Heartland)*
Anthony Lancaster *(CIO)*
Wilma Morales Turner *(VP-Mktg Comm & Events)*
Chase Allen *(VP-Institutional Acct)*
Greg Zahn *(Asst VP-Multiline & Digital Sls)*
Shelley Bondurant *(VP-Ops, Strategy & Bus Consulting)*
Sonya Isbell *(Asst VP-HR)*
Teague Wright *(COO)*
Patrick Mulheran *(Mng Principal-Heartland)*
Lance Barton *(Mng Principal-Southeast)*
Robert Brookie *(Asst VP-Underwriting)*
Nancy Hanson *(VP-Field Ops & New Bus)*
Lauren Sinnott *(Asst VP & Dir-Creative)*
Rhonda Padgett *(VP-Legal & Compliance)*
Chris Godsey *(Dir-IT)*
Angela Blackburn *(Asst VP-Highcap Fin)*
Drew Lawrence *(CFO)*

Trey Wall *(VP-Independent Broker Dealer Strategies)*
Michael C. Sorensen *(Mng Principal-Brokerage Distr)*
James J. Sorebo *(Sr VP-Community Banks & IBDs)*
Greg Mack *(Chief Distr Officer-Life)*
Matt Kroeger *(VP-Sls Support & Carrier Mgmt)*
Jason A. Kestler *(Chief Distr Officer-Annuity)*
Jennifer Tierney Connelly *(VP-Alternative Distr)*
Michael J. Sapyta *(VP-Advanced Plng)*
Austin Jarvis *(VP-Advanced Sls-Taxation)*
Jim Gelder *(CFO)*
Robert W. Finnegan *(Sr VP & Atty-Advanced Plng)*

Highland Capital Holding Corp.   (3)
3535 Grandview Pkwy Ste 600, Birmingham, AL 35243
Tel.: (205) 263-4400
Web Site: http://www.highlandbrokerage.com
Financial Services
N.A.I.C.S.: 523999

Investacorp Advisory Services Inc.   (3)
4400 Biscayne Blvd 11th Fl, Miami, FL 33137
Tel.: (305) 557-3000
Investment Advisory Services
N.A.I.C.S.: 523940

Investacorp, Inc.   (3)
4400 Biscayne Blvd 11th Fl, Miami Lakes, FL 33137
Tel.: (305) 557-3000
Web Site: http://www.investacorp.com
Sales Range: $50-74.9 Million
Emp.: 80
Financial Investment Services
N.A.I.C.S.: 523150
Patrick Farrell *(Pres & CEO)*

Ladenburg Thalmann Annuity Insurance Services, LLC   (3)
3535 Grandview Pkwy Ste 600, Birmingham, AL 35243
Tel.: (844) 422-3375
Web Site: http://www.ladenburgannuity.com
Financial Services
N.A.I.C.S.: 551112
Crystal Duco *(Dir-Annuity Ops)*

Ladenburg, Thalmann & Co. Inc.   (3)
277 Park Ave 26th Fl, New York, NY 10172
Tel.: (212) 409-2000
Web Site: http://www.ladenburg.com
Sales Range: $50-74.9 Million
Emp.: 60
Financial Services
N.A.I.C.S.: 523999
Peter H. Blum *(Co-Pres & Co-CEO)*
Diane Chillemi *(CFO & Sr VP)*
David Rosenberg *(Co-Pres & Co-CEO)*
Joseph Giovaniello *(Gen Counsel & Sr VP)*
Steven Kaplan *(Mng Dir & Head-Capital Markets)*
Mark Green *(Mng Dir & Head-Tech Banking)*
Lionel Leventhal *(Mng Dir-Investment Banking)*
Robert Mateicka *(Chief Compliance Officer)*
Vlad Ivanov *(Mng Dir-Healthcare Investment Banking)*
Nicholas Stergis *(Mng Dir)*
Barry Steiner *(Mng Dir)*
Jonathan Intrater *(Mng Dir)*
Matthew L. Kaplan *(Mng Dir & Head-Healthcare Equity Res)*
Jeffrey S. Cohen *(Mng Dir-Equity Res)*
Wangzhi Li *(Mng Dir-Equity Res-Biotech)*
Michael J. Higgins *(Mng Dir)*
Mickey M. Schleien *(Mng Dir-Equity Res)*
Christopher Nolan *(Exec VP-Equity Res)*
Michael C. Schmitz *(Mng Dir-Equity Res)*
Jon R. Hickman *(Mng Dir-Equity Res)*
Amy Furuno *(VP-Access Institutional Sls & Trading)*
David J. Strupp Jr. *(Mng Dir & Head-Healthcare Investment Banking)*
Glenn G. Mattson Jr. *(VP-Equity Res)*

Premier Trust, Inc.   (3)
4465 S Jones Blvd, Las Vegas, NV 89103

COMPANIES — REVERENCE CAPITAL PARTNERS LLC

Tel.: (702) 507-0750
Web Site: http://www.premiertrust.com
Trust Services
N.A.I.C.S.: 523991
Mark Dreschler (Co-Founder, Pres & CEO)
Stacy Libbey (Sr VP)

Securities America Financial Corporation (3)
12325 Port Grace Blvd, La Vista, NE 68128
Tel.: (800) 747-6111
Web Site: http://www.securitiesamerica.com
Securities Brokerage Services
N.A.I.C.S.: 523999

Subsidiary (Domestic):

Securities America Advisors, Inc. (4)
300 E Willis St Ste D, Prescott, AZ 86301
Tel.: (928) 541-0900
Web Site: http://www.securitiesamerica.com
Financial Services
N.A.I.C.S.: 523999
Janine Wertheim (Pres)
Dennis King (Sr VP-Bus Dev & Fee Based Sls)

Securities America, Inc. (4)
12325 Port Grace Blvd, La Vista, NE 68128
Tel.: (402) 399-9111
Web Site: http://www.securitiesamerica.com
Portfolio Management
N.A.I.C.S.: 523940
David Vaughan (CFO)
Dennis King (Sr VP-Bus Dev & Fee Based Sls-Securities America Advisors)
Doreen Griffith (CIO & Exec VP)
Gregg Johnson (Exec VP-Branch Office Dev & Acquisitions)
Kevin Miller (Gen Counsel & Exec VP)
Jim Nagengast (Pres & CEO)
Janine Wertheim (Chief Mktg Officer, Pres-Securities America Advisors & Sr VP)
Kirk Hulett (Exec VP-Strategy & Practice Mgmt)
Mark Lasswell (Chief Compliance Officer & Sr VP)
Paul Lofties (Sr VP-Wealth Mgmt & Product Strategy)
Jim Norwood (Pres-Fin Institutions Div)
Jim Meyers (COO & Sr VP)
Leon M. Johnson (Chief Information Security Officer & Sr VP-Infrastructure)
Gregory J. Smith (VP-Supervision)
Matt Kinsella (Chief Compliance Officer & VP)

Sunset Financial Services, Inc. (4)
3520 Broadway Blvd, Kansas City, MO 64111
Tel.: (816) 753-7000
Sales Range: $75-99.9 Million
Emp.: 500
Full-Service Brokerage & Investment Services
N.A.I.C.S.: 523940
Kelly Ullom (VP)
Smriti Laxman Popenoe (Founder)

Wall Street Financial Group (4)
255 Woodcliff Dr Ste 6, Fairport, NY 14450 (100%)
Tel.: (585) 267-8000
Web Site: http://www.wsfg.com
Sales Range: $1-9.9 Million
Emp.: 67
Investment Services
N.A.I.C.S.: 523940
Timothy Delaney (Dir-Ops)
Victoria Bach-Fink (Supvr-Branch)
Camille Merrick (Chief Compliance Officer)
D. Robert Anderson (VP)

Subsidiary (Domestic):

Securities Service Network Inc. (3)
9729 Cogvill Rd Ste 301, Knoxville, TN 37932
Tel.: (866) 843-4635
Web Site: http://www.ssnetwork.com
Sales Range: $25-49.9 Million
Emp.: 16
Financial Advisory Services
N.A.I.C.S.: 523999

Triad Advisors, Inc. (3)
5155 Peachtree Pkwy Ste 3220, Norcross, GA 30092
Tel.: (770) 840-0363
Web Site: http://www.triad-advisors.com
Sales Range: $25-49.9 Million
Emp.: 55
Financial Advisory Services
N.A.I.C.S.: 523940
Mark C. Mettelman (Co-Founder & Chm)
Michael C. Bryan (Sr VP-Advisory Svcs)
Marilyn Hosten (Sr VP-Ops)
Jeffrey L. Rosenthal (Pres & CEO)
Nate Stibbs (Chief Strategy Officer & Exec VP)
Kiliaen Ludlow (Sr VP-Relationship Mgmt)
Bernard Breton (Chief Compliance Officer & Exec VP)
Amy Rehn (Sr VP-Advisory Svcs)
Jeff St. John (Sr VP & Dir-Tech)
Hugh M. Tarbutton Jr. (Sr VP-Bus Dev)

Triad Hybrid Solutions, LLC (3)
5155 Peachtree Pkwy Ste 3230, Norcross, GA 30092
Tel.: (866) 580-8219
Web Site: http://www.triad-advisors.com
Emp.: 6
Financial Services
N.A.I.C.S.: 523999
Michael C. Bryan (Sr VP-Advisory Svcs)
Amy Rehn (Sr VP-Advisory Svcs)
Jeffrey L. Rosenthal (Pres & CEO)
Mark C. Mettelman (Founder & Chm)
Nathan M. Stibbs (Chief Strategy Officer & Exec VP)
Hugh Tarbutton (COO & Exec VP)
Kiliaen V. R. Ludlow (Exec VP-Ops & Client Svcs)
Bernard Breton (Chief Compliance Officer & Exec VP)

Subsidiary (Domestic):

Royal Alliance Associates, Inc. (2)
10 Exchange Pl Ste 1410, Jersey City, NJ 07302
Tel.: (212) 551-5100
Web Site: http://www.royalalliance.com
Emp.: 2,000
Securities & Investment Advisory Services
N.A.I.C.S.: 523150
Al Grilli (Sr VP)

Subsidiary (Domestic):

Signator Investors Inc. (3)
397 Little Neck Rd Ste 200, Virginia Beach, VA 23452-5768
Web Site: http://www.signatorinvestors.com
Insurance Agencies & Brokerages
N.A.I.C.S.: 524210
Joseph Terry (Deputy Chief Compliance Officer-St. Petersburg)
Christopher Maryanopolis (Pres)
Thomas Horack (Chief Compliance Officer)

Subsidiary (Domestic):

SagePoint Financial, Inc. (2)
20 E Thomas Rd Ste 2000, Phoenix, AZ 85012
Tel.: (602) 744-3000
Web Site: http://www.sagepointfinancial.com
Emp.: 1,900
Securities & Investment Advisory Services
N.A.I.C.S.: 523150

Woodbury Financial Services, Inc. (2)
7755 3rd St N, Oakdale, MN 55128
Tel.: (800) 800-2638
Web Site: http://www.joinwoodbury.com
Emp.: 1,200
Security & Investment Advisory Services
N.A.I.C.S.: 523150
Rick Fergesen (Pres & CEO)
Amy M. Harbort (Chief Compliance Officer)

Subsidiary (Domestic):

Life Certain Wealth Strategies, LLC (3)
8400 E Prentice Ave Ste 715, Greenwood Village, CO 80111-2919
Tel.: (303) 793-3999
Web Site: http://www.lifecertain.com
Law firm
N.A.I.C.S.: 541110
Herb White (Pres)
Joseph Di Biasi (CEO)
Gregory McElheny (COO)

Diamond Resorts International, Inc. (1)
10600 W Charleston Blvd, Las Vegas, NV 89135
Tel.: (702) 823-7534
Web Site: http://www.diamondresorts.com
Holding Company; Hotel & Resort Owner & Operator
N.A.I.C.S.: 551112
Michael Flaskey (CEO)
Jim Mikolaichik (CFO)
Kenneth S. Siegel (Pres, Chief Admin Officer & Gen Counsel)

Affiliate (Domestic):

Diamond Resorts Corporation (2)
10600 W Charleston Blvd, Las Vegas, NV 89135
Tel.: (702) 684-8000
Hotel Properties Management Services
N.A.I.C.S.: 721110
Lisa Gann (Controller)
Jim Mikolaichik (CFO)

Subsidiary (Domestic):

Diamond Resorts Holdings, LLC (2)
10600 W Charleston Blvd, Las Vegas, NV 89135
Tel.: (702) 823-7534
Web Site: http://www.diamondresorts.com
Holding Company
N.A.I.C.S.: 551112
Jim Mikolaichik (CFO)
Michael Flaskey (CEO)

Unit (Domestic):

Kohl's Ranch Lodge (3)
202 S Kohls Ranch Lodge Rd, Payson, AZ 85541
Tel.: (928) 478-4211
Web Site: http://www.diamondresortsandhotels.com
Hotel & Resort Operator
N.A.I.C.S.: 721110

Los Abrigados Resort & Spa (3)
160 Portal Ln, Sedona, AZ 86336
Tel.: (928) 282-1777
Web Site: http://www.diamondresortsandhotels.com
Hotel, Resort & Spa Operator
N.A.I.C.S.: 721110

Mystic Dunes Resort & Golf Club (3)
7600 Mystic Dunes Ln, Celebration, FL 34747
Tel.: (407) 396-1311
Web Site: http://www.diamondresortsandhotels.com
Hotel & Resort Operator & Time-Share Condominium Exchange Services
N.A.I.C.S.: 721110

Subsidiary (Domestic):

Potter's Mill, Inc. (3)
300 Potter Dr, Bellevue, IA 52001
Tel.: (563) 872-3838
Web Site: https://www.pottersmill.net
Full-Service Restaurants
N.A.I.C.S.: 722511

Unit (Domestic):

The Historic Crags Lodge (3)
300 Riverside Dr, Estes Park, CO 80517
Tel.: (970) 586-6066
Web Site: http://www.diamondresortsandhotels.com
Hotel & Resort Operator
N.A.I.C.S.: 721110

Varsity Clubs of America - South Bend (3)
3800 N Main St, Mishawaka, IN 46545
Tel.: (574) 277-0500
Web Site: http://www.diamondresortsandhotels.com
Hotel & Resort Operator
N.A.I.C.S.: 721110

Varsity Clubs of America - Tucson (3)
3855 E Speedway Blvd, Tucson, AZ 85716
Tel.: (520) 318-3777
Web Site: http://www.diamondresortsandhotels.com
Hotel & Resort Operator
N.A.I.C.S.: 721110
Aldo Dioverti (Mgr-Resort)

Russell Investments Group, LLC. (1)
1301 2nd Ave 18th Fl, Seattle, WA 98101
Tel.: (206) 505-7877
Web Site: http://www.russell.com
Alternative Investment Management Services
N.A.I.C.S.: 523940
Jeff Hussey (Chief Investment Officer-Global)
Brian Meath (Mng Dir & Sr Portfolio Mgr)
Mark Spina (Head-US Private Client Svcs)
Toby Hoden (CMO)
Michelle Seitz (Chm & CEO)
Michael Hall (Mng Dir-Institutional-Americas)
Gene Raffone (Chief HR Officer-Global)
Kate El-Hillow (Co-Pres & Chief Investment Officer-Global)
Kevin Klingert (Co-Pres)

Signature Estate & Investment Advisors, LLC (1)
2121 Ave of the Stars Ste 1600, Los Angeles, CA 90067
Tel.: (800) 723-5115
Web Site: https://www.seia.com
Investment Management & Advisory Services
N.A.I.C.S.: 523940

Sunstar Insurance Group, LLC (1)
530 Oak Ct Dr Ste 250, Memphis, TN 38117
Tel.: (901) 537-7450
Web Site: http://www.sunstarinsurancegroup.com
Holding Company
N.A.I.C.S.: 551112
Christopher R. Parcell (CFO)
Greg Lottes (Pres & COO)
Casey Bowlin (Founder & CEO)
Nicolas Colicchio (VP-Carrier Relations & Strategic Partnerships)

Subsidiary (Domestic):

Campbell & Company, Inc. (2)
2850 Quarry Lake Dr, Baltimore, MD 21209
Tel.: (410) 413-2600
Web Site: http://www.campbell.com
Investment Services
N.A.I.C.S.: 523999
D. Keith Campbell (Chm)
Geoffrey William Andrews (CEO)
Kevin Cole (CIO)
Steve Campbell (Pres)

Holding (Domestic):

Campbell Alternative Asset Trust (3)
2850 Quarry Lake Dr, Baltimore, MD 21209
Tel.: (410) 413-2600
Web Site: http://www.campbell.com
Sales Range: $1-9.9 Million
Emp.: 150
Investment Services
N.A.I.C.S.: 523999
Gregory T. Donovan (CFO)

Subsidiary (Domestic):

Chapman & Hogan Insurance Group (2)
3636 S Geyer Rd Ste 110, Saint Louis, MO 63127
Tel.: (314) 892-8999
Web Site: http://www.chapman-sander.com
Insurance Services
N.A.I.C.S.: 524298
Ron Burlison (Chm)

The Todd Agency, Inc. (2)
10800 Financial Ctr Pkwy Ste 300, Little Rock, AR 72211
Tel.: (501) 225-4485
Web Site: http://www.toddagency.com
Insurance Agencies & Brokerages
N.A.I.C.S.: 524210

Vida Capital, Inc. (1)
835 W 6th St Ste 1400, Austin, TX 78703
Tel.: (512) 961-8265
Web Site: http://www.vidacapitalinc.com
Asset Management Firm; Specializes Solely in Insurance-linked Strategies
N.A.I.C.S.: 524127
Jeffrey R. Serra (Founder & Chm)
Blair Wallace (Pres & CEO)
Zachary Ainsberg (Mng Dir)
Michael Kee (Mng Dir-Analytics)

REVERENCE CAPITAL PARTNERS LLC

Reverence Capital Partners LLC—(Continued)
Will Ketterer *(CIO & Sr Mng Dir-Portfolio Mgmt)*
Peter Polanskyj *(Head-Structured Credit)*
Matthew Roesler *(Mng Dir-Structured Credit)*

REVERSE MORTGAGE INVESTMENT TRUST INC.
1455 Broad St Fl 2, Bloomfield, NJ 07003
Tel.: (973) 542-7170   MD
Web Site:
http://www.reversefunding.com
Year Founded: 2013
Emp.: 165
Real Estate Investment Services
N.A.I.C.S.: 525990
Robert V. Sivori *(COO)*
St. John Bannon *(CFO & Treas)*
Timothy A. Isgro *(Chief Investment Officer)*

REVGEN PARTNERS, INC.
6300 S Syracuse Way Ste 760, Centennial, CO 80111
Tel.: (720) 945-7300   CO
Web Site: http://www.revgen.com
Year Founded: 2008
Sales Range: $1-9.9 Million
Emp.: 80
Business Management Consulting Services
N.A.I.C.S.: 541618
Michael Turner *(Pres & CEO)*
Kirk Mielenz *(Exec Vp-Client Svcs)*
Jason Hansen *(Exec VP-Client Svcs-Delivery)*
Robert Sunker *(VP)*
Emily Sims *(Dir-HR & Ops)*
Cara Athmann *(Dir-Client Svcs)*
Beth Kotarba *(Dir-Client Svcs)*
Neel Pelser *(Dir-Client Svcs)*
Pero Dalkovski *(Dir-Client Svcs)*
Chrissy Winkler *(Dir-Client Svcs)*
Corrina Ruttkar *(VP-Comm)*
Cliff Love *(Dir-Client Svcs)*

REVILLE TIRE CO.
8044 Olde Eight Rd, Northfield, OH 44067
Tel.: (330) 468-1312
Web Site: http://www.revillewhs.com
Sales Range: $10-24.9 Million
Emp.: 130
Automotive Supplies & Parts Whslr
N.A.I.C.S.: 423120
Robert J. Reville *(Pres)*

REVIORA, LLC
19321 US 19 N Ste 412, Clearwater, FL 33764
Tel.: (813) 344-1600
Web Site: http://www.reviora.com
Year Founded: 2007
Sales Range: $1-9.9 Million
Software Developer
N.A.I.C.S.: 513210
Brian Sallee *(CEO)*

REVISION
37 W 28th St 7th Fl, New York, NY 10001
Tel.: (212) 889-0005
Web Site: http://www.revisionnyc.com
Year Founded: 1993
Sales Range: $1-9.9 Million
Emp.: 15
Advetising Agency
N.A.I.C.S.: 541810
Gene Fritz *(Dir-HR)*
Ted Baker *(Mng Dir)*
Chuck Borghese *(Exec Creative Dir)*
Michael Kosowicz *(Dir-Acct)*

REVITALIZE CAPITAL
255 East 5th St Ste 2400, Cincinnati, OH 45202
Tel.: (513) 453-4572
Web Site: http://revitalizecap.com
Holding Company
N.A.I.C.S.: 551112
Eric S. Khan *(Founder & Mng Dir)*
Chris J. Blood *(Mng Dir)*
Matt P. Johnson *(Mng Dir)*

Subsidiaries:

Graphic Village, LLC   (1)
9933 Alliance Rd, Cincinnati, OH 45242
Tel.: (513) 241-1865
Web Site: http://www.graphicvillage.com
Commercial Printer, Printing & Packaging
N.A.I.C.S.: 333248

Subsidiary (Domestic):

DMS ink   (2)
888 Daton St, Yellow Springs, OH 45387
Tel.: (937) 222-5056
Web Site: http://www.dmsink.us
Other Business Service Centers & Copy Services
N.A.I.C.S.: 561439
Christine Soward *(VP-Bus Dev)*

J & P Investments, Inc.   (2)
8100 Reading Rd, Cincinnati, OH 45237
Tel.: (513) 821-2299
Rev: $2,000,000
Emp.: 12
Fiscal Year-end: 12/31/2006
Offset Printing
N.A.I.C.S.: 323111
Doug Chalk *(Mgr)*

REVITUP ENTERPRISES LLC
253 A Pine Ave N, Oldsmar, FL 34677
Tel.: (813) 920-0788
Web Site:
http://www.launchpadonline.com
Year Founded: 1992
Sales Range: $1-9.9 Million
Emp.: 25
Computer Related Services
N.A.I.C.S.: 541512
Ilene Rosoff *(CEO)*

REVIVA INC.
5130 Main St NE, Minneapolis, MN 55421-1528
Tel.: (763) 535-8900   MN
Web Site: http://www.reviva.com
Year Founded: 1944
Sales Range: $50-74.9 Million
Emp.: 250
Rebuilder of Truck Engines & Related Parts
N.A.I.C.S.: 336330
Andy Stewart *(Acct Mgr-Sls)*
Josh Stahl *(Pres)*
Larry Schmidt *(Exec VP-Sls)*

Subsidiaries:

Engine Rebuilders, Inc.   (1)
PO Box 367, Oakes, ND 58474
Web Site: http://www.engreb.com
Automotive Engine Parts Mfr
N.A.I.C.S.: 336310

REVOLENT CAPITAL SOLUTIONS
217 N Howard Ave Ste 200, Tampa, FL 33606
Tel.: (813) 200-8798
Web Site:
https://www.revolentcapitalsolutions.com
Emp.: 100
Private Equity
N.A.I.C.S.: 523940

Subsidiaries:

The Facilities Group National LLC   (1)
217 N Howard Ave Ste 200, Tampa, FL 33606
Tel.: (813) 321-7420
Web Site: https://www.thefacilitiesgroup.com
Facilities Services
N.A.I.C.S.: 561210

Subsidiary (Domestic):

National Healthcare Resources, Inc   (2)
535 Dock St Ste 114, Tacoma, WA 98402-4629
Graphic Design Services
N.A.I.C.S.: 541430
Eric Hokol *(Mgr)*

REVOLUTION
600 W Chicago Ave Ste 220, Chicago, IL 60654
Tel.: (312) 529-5850
Web Site:
http://www.revolutionworld.com
Year Founded: 2001
Sales Range: $25-49.9 Million
Emp.: 70
Sports Marketing & Media Services
N.A.I.C.S.: 541613
John Rowady *(Founder & CEO)*
Darren Marshall *(Exec VP-Consulting & Res)*
Dan Lobring *(Mng Dir-Comm)*
Kent Thomas *(VP-Strategy Grp)*
Brian Quarles *(Dir-Creative)*
Megan Grubbs *(VP-Res)*
Chris Sonntag *(Mng Dir & Head-Sponsorship Consulting-Global)*
Mike Hormuth *(Sr Dir-Mktg Comm)*
Dave Mullins *(Sr VP-Client Dev)*
Emily Szymczak *(CFO)*

REVOLUTION CAPITAL GROUP, LLC
1999 Avenue of The Stars Ste 3430, Los Angeles, CA 90067
Tel.: (310) 229-0800   CA
Web Site:
http://www.revolutionpe.com
Sales Range: $25-49.9 Million
Emp.: 1,000
Privater Equity Firm
N.A.I.C.S.: 523999
Robert Loring *(Founder & Mng Partner)*
Cyrus Nikou *(Founder & Partner)*
Aman Bajaj *(Mng Dir)*
Chongyang Luo *(Dir-Tech)*
Tom Cleary *(Gen Counsel)*
Stanley Huang *(CFO)*
Brian Burns *(Mng Dir)*
Sean Dorney *(Mng Dir)*

Subsidiaries:

Lawrence Schiff Silk Mills, Inc.   (1)
590 California Rd, Quakertown, PA 18951
Tel.: (215) 538-2880
Web Site: http://www.schiffribbons.com
Sales Range: $10-24.9 Million
Emp.: 175
Silk Ribbon Mfr & Distr
N.A.I.C.S.: 313220
Richard J. Schiff *(Owner)*

Subsidiary (Domestic):

LSSM Sales, Inc.   (2)
1385 Broadway Ste 914, New York, NY 10018
Tel.: (212) 679-2185
Web Site: http://www.schiffribbons.com
Silk Ribbon Wholesale Distr
N.A.I.C.S.: 424310

REVOLUTION FOODS, INC.
8383 Capwell Dr, Oakland, CA 94621
Tel.: (510) 596-9024
Web Site: http://www.revfoods.com
Year Founded: 2006
Sales Range: $10-24.9 Million
Emp.: 742

U.S. PRIVATE

Meals & Nutrition Food Suppliers
N.A.I.C.S.: 722310
Kristin Groos-Richmond *(Co-Founder & CEO)*
Kirsten Saenz Tobey *(Co-Founder)*
Diana Fair *(COO)*
Chris Cornyn *(Chief Innovation Officer)*
David de souza *(Exec VP)*
Leslie Lerude *(VP-People)*
Neil Neufeld *(VP-Ops)*
Pat Donovan *(VP-Bus Dev)*
Rhonda Lesinski *(Exec VP-School Meals)*
Denise D. Beckles *(CFO)*
Alvin Crawford *(VP-Sls)*
Mark Welch *(VP-Ops-Central)*

REVOLUTION MANUFACTURING, LLC
2335 Eddy Ln, Eau Claire, WI 54703
Tel.: (844) 835-8016   UT
Web Site:
http://www.101revolution.com
Year Founded: 1996
Snowboard & Ski Mfr
N.A.I.C.S.: 339920
Alex Makar *(Mgr-Floor Sanding Solutions, Machine Mfg, Parts and Drum Recovery)*

REVOLUTION PREP, LLC
710 Wilshire Blvd Ste 501, Santa Monica, CA 90401
Tel.: (310) 458-1000   CA
Web Site:
http://www.revolutionprep.com
Year Founded: 2002
Sales Range: $10-24.9 Million
Emp.: 120
Exam Preparation & Tutoring
N.A.I.C.S.: 611691
Jake Neuberg *(Co-Founder)*
Ramit Varma *(Co-Founder)*

REVOLUTION PUBLIC RELATIONS
4000 E Madison St #202, Seattle, WA 98112
Tel.: (206) 354-8049
Web Site:
http://www.revolutionpr.com
Sales Range: Less than $1 Million
Emp.: 5
Communications, Public Relations, Strategic Planning/Research
N.A.I.C.S.: 541820
Aaron Hilst *(Art Dir & Acct Mgr)*
Cheryl Cink *(Acct Mgr)*

REVOLUTION TECHNOLOGIES, LLC
1000 Revolution Technologies Way, Melbourne, FL 32901
Tel.: (321) 409-4949
Web Site:
http://www.revolutiontechnologies.com
Year Founded: 1993
Sales Range: $10-24.9 Million
Emp.: 100
Business Consulting Services
N.A.I.C.S.: 541618
Ted Parker *(Founder & CEO)*
T. Kent Smith *(Pres & COO)*
Miles Toshie *(Exec VP)*
Colleen Middlebrooks *(Dir-Mktg)*
Jason Decristoforo *(Controller)*
Joslyn Barroso *(Mgr-HR)*
Kevin Burke *(Exec Dir-Svc Delivery)*
Richard Snider *(VP-Sls-MSP Div)*
Stacy Schott *(Acct Dir-ERP-Natl)*
Tom OSullivan *(VP-ERP Grp)*

REVOLUTION, LLC
1717 Rhode Island Ave NW, Washington, DC 20036-3023
Tel.: (202) 776-1400

Web Site: http://www.revolution.com
Emp.: 100
Equity, Venture Capital & Real Estate Investment Firm
N.A.I.C.S.: 523999
Stephen M. Case *(Chm & CEO)*
Philippe Bourguignon *(Vice Chm-Revolution Places)*
Ronald Klain *(Gen Counsel & Exec VP)*
Tige Savage *(Mng Dir & Sr VP)*
John Richardson *(COO & Exec VP)*
David Hall *(VP-Transactions & Strategic Analysis)*
David G. Golden *(Mng Partner)*
Tracy Van Grack *(Sr VP-Comm & Pub Policy)*
Meredith Balenske *(VP-Comm)*
J. D. Vance *(Partner)*

Subsidiaries:

Exclusive Resorts, LLC (1)
1515 Arapahoe Carver St Tower 3 Ste 500, Denver, CO 80202
Tel.: (303) 226-4900
Web Site: http://www.exclusiveresorts.com
Sales Range: $25-49.9 Million
Resort Operator
N.A.I.C.S.: 721110
Stephen M. Case *(Co-Chm)*
Todd Harris *(Sr VP-Hospitality)*
Cathy Ross *(CEO)*
Adam Wegner *(Exec VP-Strategy & Corp Dev)*
Philippe Bourguignon *(Co-Chm)*
Sara Whitford *(Gen Counsel & Sr VP)*
Robert E. Parsons Jr. *(CFO)*

REVOLUTIONARY CONCEPTS, INC.
1914 JN Pease Place, Charlotte, NC 28262
Tel.: (980) 225-5376 NV
Web Site:
http://www.revolutionaryconceptsinc.com
Sales Range: $1-9.9 Million
Development & Design of EyeTalk Communicator, A Smart Camera Technology Product
N.A.I.C.S.: 334310
Ronald Carter *(Chm & Pres)*
Garry Stevenson *(CFO & VP)*
Solomon R.C. Ali *(Sr VP)*

REVOLUTIONS MEDICAL CORPORATION
670 Marina Dr 3rd Fl, Charleston, SC 29492
Tel.: (843) 971-4848 NV
Web Site:
http://www.revolutionsmedical.com
Year Founded: 1997
Sales Range: Less than $1 Million
Emp.: 3
Surgical & Medical Instruments & Apparatus Mfr
N.A.I.C.S.: 339112
Rondald L. Wheet *(Chm, Pres & CEO)*

REVONA PROPERTIES
625 Sheepshead Bay Rd Ste 620, Brooklyn, NY 11224
Tel.: (718) 743-4400
Web Site:
http://www.revonaproperties.com
Residential Homes
N.A.I.C.S.: 531311
Jay Rosenfeld *(CEO)*

Subsidiaries:

Sussex Hall Apartments (1)
16605 Highland Ave, Jamaica, NY 11432
Tel.: (718) 658-9734
Residential Buildings & Dwellings
N.A.I.C.S.: 531110

REVSTREAM INC.
228 Hamilton Ave Third Fl, Palo Alto, CA 94301
Web Site:
http://www.revstreamone.com
Year Founded: 2006
Sales Range: $1-9.9 Million
Emp.: 10
Software Services
N.A.I.C.S.: 513210
Rajiv Chopra *(Founder & CEO)*
Mark Aubin *(Chief Product Officer & VP-Product Strategy)*
Ram Iyer *(VP-Solutions & Support)*
Jon Bloodworth *(VP-Bus & Corp Dev)*

REW INVESTMENTS INCORPORATED
8501 Telephone Rd, Houston, TX 77061
Tel.: (713) 641-9700
Web Site: http://www.iflyaji.com
Rev.: $11,400,000
Emp.: 145
Flying Charter Services
N.A.I.C.S.: 481219
Roger Woolsey *(Pres)*
Laura Williams *(Mgr)*

REWARDSNOW, INC.
383 Central Ave Ste 350, Dover, NH 03820
Tel.: (603) 516-3440 NH
Web Site:
http://www.rewardsnow.com
Year Founded: 1997
Sales Range: $1-9.9 Million
Emp.: 28
Loyalty Marketing Programs for Financial Institutions
N.A.I.C.S.: 561990
Joanne Houle *(CFO & Treas)*

REX DIRECT NET, INC.
100 Springdale Rd A3 Ste 253, Cherry Hill, NJ 08003
Tel.: (856) 489-9581
Web Site:
http://www.rexdirectnet.com
Year Founded: 2001
Sales Range: $10-24.9 Million
Emp.: 20
Advetising Agency
N.A.I.C.S.: 541810
Jennine T. Rexon *(Owner)*
Vito Tonkonog *(VP-Lead Generation & Affiliate Mktg)*
Tami Brewer *(Dir-The Sample Network)*

REX ENGINEERING GROUP, INC.
1000 Corporate Ctr Dr Ste 110, Monterey Park, CA 91754
Tel.: (323) 262-9199
Web Site: http://www.rexeg.com
Engineeering Services
N.A.I.C.S.: 541330
Steven Ueke *(CEO)*
James Pawlikowski *(Principal & Dir-Engrg)*

Subsidiaries:

REX Contruction Services (1)
85 SW 52nd Ave, Ocala, FL 34474
Tel.: (352) 854-6266
Construction & Engineering Services
N.A.I.C.S.: 238120
Patrick Kenny *(Pres)*

Subsidiary (Domestic):

Edwards Construction Services Inc. (2)
85 SW 52nd Ave, Ocala, FL 34474-1892
Tel.: (352) 854-6266
Web Site:
http://www.edwardsconstruction.com

Sales Range: $75-99.9 Million
Emp.: 44
Provider of Industrial Buildings & Warehouses Construction Services
N.A.I.C.S.: 236210
Jeffrey Rudacille *(Mgr-IT)*
Rusty Setzer *(Sr Project Mgr-Southeast)*

REX LUMBER COMPANY
840 Main St, Acton, MA 01720-5806
Tel.: (978) 263-0055 MA
Web Site: http://www.rexlumber.com
Year Founded: 1946
Sales Range: $150-199.9 Million
Emp.: 335
Provider of Lumber & Millwork
N.A.I.C.S.: 321912
Benjamin Forester *(Chm, Pres & CEO)*
Craig Forester *(Mgr-Ops)*
Cheryl Bieren *(Mgr-Mill)*
Mark Bronstein *(Dir-Fin)*

REX MARINE CENTER, INC.
144 Water St 146, Norwalk, CT 06854-3191
Tel.: (203) 866-0383 CT
Web Site: http://www.rexmarine.com
Year Founded: 1936
Sales Range: $10-24.9 Million
Emp.: 25
Sales of Boats
N.A.I.C.S.: 441222
Susan Brown *(Controller)*
William T. Gardella Sr. *(Pres)*
William T. Gardella Jr. *(Gen Mgr)*

Subsidiaries:

Norwalk Cove Marina, Inc. (1)
48 Calf Pasture Beach Rd, Norwalk, CT 06855
Tel.: (203) 838-2326
Web Site: http://www.norwalkcove.com
Yacht Repair & Maintenance Services
N.A.I.C.S.: 336611
Dianne Jewell *(Controller)*
Steve Babbitz *(Gen Mgr)*

REX MOORE ELECTRICAL CONTRACTORS & ENGINEERS
6001 Outfall Cir, Sacramento, CA 95828
Tel.: (916) 372-1300 CA
Web Site: http://www.rexmoore.com
Year Founded: 1922
Sales Range: $50-74.9 Million
Emp.: 500
Provider of Electrical Contracting Services
N.A.I.C.S.: 238210
Rodney R. Weckworth *(Owner)*
William C. Hubbard *(Exec VP)*
David Rex Moore *(Chm)*

REX OIL COMPANY INC.
1970 E 68th Ave, Denver, CO 80229
Tel.: (303) 455-1743 CO
Web Site: http://www.rexoil.com
Year Founded: 1968
Sales Range: $10-24.9 Million
Emp.: 30
Supplier of Petroleum Products
N.A.I.C.S.: 424720
Eric Balenseifen *(Pres)*

REX PIPE & SUPPLY CO.
10311 Berea Rd, Cleveland, OH 44102
Tel.: (216) 651-1900
Web Site: http://www.rexpipe.com
Sales Range: $10-24.9 Million
Emp.: 26
Whslr of Plumbing Fittings & Supplies
N.A.I.C.S.: 423720
Joseph Cleary *(Pres)*
Timothy Cleary *(Mgr-Credit)*

REX-HIDE INC.
705 S Lyons Ave, Tyler, TX 75702
Tel.: (903) 593-7387
Web Site: http://www.rex-hide.com
Rev.: $25,200,000
Emp.: 10
Automotive Rubber Goods (Mechanical)
N.A.I.C.S.: 326291

REXCO EQUIPMENT INC.
1925 Blairs Ferry Rd NE, Cedar Rapids, IA 52402
Tel.: (319) 393-2820 IA
Web Site:
http://www.rexcoequipment.com
Year Founded: 1959
Sales Range: $25-49.9 Million
Emp.: 24
Distr of Heavy Construction Equipment
N.A.I.C.S.: 811210
Sue Fisher *(Mgr-HR)*
Joe Carolan *(Mgr-Parts)*

REXIT, INC.
1550 54th St, Brooklyn, NY 11219
Tel.: (718) 782-9200 MD
Year Founded: 2010
Real Estate Investment Services
N.A.I.C.S.: 523999
Shmuel Eisenberger *(Pres, CEO, CFO, Treas, Sec & VP)*

REXIUS FOREST BY-PRODUCTS
1275 Bailey Hill Rd, Eugene, OR 97402
Tel.: (541) 342-1835
Web Site: http://www.rexius.com
Sales Range: $25-49.9 Million
Emp.: 150
Trucking Except Local
N.A.I.C.S.: 484121
Rusty Rexius *(Co-Pres)*
Jack Hoeck *(VP)*
Dan Sutton *(Sr VP)*
Arlen Rexius *(Co-Pres)*
Jerry Cunningham *(CFO & Sec)*
Jason Giles *(VP)*

REXTON REALTY COMPANY
36 W 25th St Ste 301, New York, NY 10010
Tel.: (646) 336-6519
Web Site: http://rextonnyc.com
Sales Range: $10-24.9 Million
Emp.: 24
Nonresidential Building Operators
N.A.I.C.S.: 531120
Peter Harris *(Pres)*
Marilee Bleetsteenee *(CFO & VP)*
John Engel *(VP)*

REYES HOLDINGS, LLC
6250 N River Rd, Rosemont, IL 60018-4241
Tel.: (847) 916-1193 DE
Web Site:
https://www.reyesholdings.com
Year Founded: 1976
Sales Range: $15-24.9 Billion
Emp.: 36,000
Offices of Other Holding Companies
N.A.I.C.S.: 551112
M. Jude Reyes *(Co-Chm)*
Dean H. Janke *(Exec VP-Bus Dev)*
Nicholas L. Giampietro *(Chief Legal Officer, Sec & Exec VP)*
Alison Chang *(Mgr-Human Capital-Harbor Distributing)*
Brandon Burbridge *(Dir-Security Ops)*
Carver L. Seay *(Mgr-Area Fleet)*

Subsidiaries:

Reyes Beverage Group (1)

REYES HOLDINGS, LLC

Reyes Holdings, LLC—(Continued)
6250 N River Rd Ste 9000, Rosemont, IL 60018
Tel.: (847) 227-6500
Web Site:
http://www.reyesbeveragegroup.com
Sales Range: $1-4.9 Billion
Emp.: 250
Beverage Distr
N.A.I.C.S.: 424810
David K. Reyes (CEO)
Raymond M. Guerin (COO)

Subsidiary (Domestic):

Chesbay Distributing, LLC (2)
3928 Cook Blvd, Chesapeake, VA 23323
Tel.: (757) 558-8170
Food & Beverage Distr
N.A.I.C.S.: 424490
Andrea Weaver (Asst Controller)
Patrick Collins (Pres & Gen Mgr)

Chicago Beverage Systems, LLC (2)
441 N Kilbourne Ave, Chicago, IL 60624
Tel.: (773) 826-4100
Web Site:
http://www.chicagobeveragesystems.org
Sales Range: $25-49.9 Million
Emp.: 192
Distr & Wholesalers of Domestic & Imported Beer
N.A.I.C.S.: 424810
James J. Doney (Pres)
Dwight Gramm (Mgr-Mktg)
Nick Kempen (Supvr-Sls)

Crest Beverage, LLC (2)
8870 Liquid Ct, San Diego, CA 92121-2234
Tel.: (858) 452-2900
Web Site: http://www.crestbeverage.com
Sales Range: $25-49.9 Million
Beer & Wine Distr
N.A.I.C.S.: 424810
Charles Cummins (Mgr-Ops)
Raul Ambriz-Diaz (Acct Mgr)
Kellen Rayner (Acct Mgr-Sls)
Dan Burns (Area Mgr)
Patty Torre (Office Mgr)

Florida Distributing Co. LLC (2)
3964 Shader Rd, Orlando, FL 32808-3132
Tel.: (407) 298-2424
Web Site: http://www.floridadistributing.com
Sales Range: $100-124.9 Million
Emp.: 200
Beer Distr
N.A.I.C.S.: 424810
Melissa Stringer (Supvr-HR)
Bob Johnston (Pres)

Gate City Beverage Distributors (2)
2505 Steele St, San Bernardino, CA 92408
Tel.: (909) 799-1600
Web Site: http://www.gatecitybeverage.com
Sales Range: $25-49.9 Million
Emp.: 225
Beer Distr
N.A.I.C.S.: 424810

Harbor Distributing LLC (2)
1625 S Lewis St, Anaheim, CA 92805
Tel.: (714) 712-2400
Web Site:
http://www.harbordistributingllc.com
Sales Range: $75-99.9 Million
Beer & Ale Distr
N.A.I.C.S.: 424810
Tom Reyes (Pres)
Tim McGuire (VP-Fin)

Subsidiary (Domestic):

T.F. Louderback, Inc. (3)
700 National Ct, Richmond, CA 94804
Tel.: (510) 729-5000
Web Site: http://www.bayareabev.com
Rev.: $30,000,000
Emp.: 200
Beer & Other Fermented Malt Liquors Distr
N.A.I.C.S.: 424810
T.J. Louderback (Pres)
Anthony Avizenis (Gen Mgr-Sls)
Todd Rovelstad (Gen Mgr)
Tom Echaniz (CFO)
William Johnson (Dir-HR)

Subsidiary (Domestic):

Henry J. Lee Distributors Inc. (2)
5802 N Rhett Ave, Hanahan, SC 29410
Tel.: (843) 554-7837
Web Site: http://www.hjleedistributors.com
Sales Range: $50-74.9 Million
Emp.: 100
Beer Distr
N.A.I.C.S.: 424810

Premium Distributors of Maryland, LLC (2)
530 Monocacy Blvd, Frederick, MD 21701
Tel.: (301) 662-0372
Sales Range: $25-49.9 Million
Emp.: 25
Beer Distr
N.A.I.C.S.: 424810
Ryan Broz (Dir-Reg)

Premium Distributors of Virginia, LLC (2)
15001 Northridge Dr, Chantilly, VA 20151 (100%)
Tel.: (703) 227-1200
Web Site: http://www.reyesholdings.com
Sales Range: $25-49.9 Million
Emp.: 220
Distr & Wholesalers of Domestic & Imported Beer
N.A.I.C.S.: 424810
Robby McDonald (Mgr-Mktg)
John Zelter (Pres)

The Martin-Brower Company, LLC (1)
6250 N River Rd, Rosemont, IL 60018 (100%)
Tel.: (847) 227-6500
Web Site: http://www.mbhires.com
Sales Range: $350-399.9 Million
Emp.: 3,000
Distr of Food & Paper Products
N.A.I.C.S.: 424420

Subsidiary (Non-US):

Martin-Brower of Canada Co. (2)
6990 creditview Rd Union 5, Mississauga, L5N 8R9, ON, Canada (100%)
Tel.: (905) 568-8000
Sales Range: $25-49.9 Million
Emp.: 60
Food Distribution
N.A.I.C.S.: 424490

REYNALDOS MEXICAN FOOD COMPANY

3301 E Vernon Ave, Vernon, CA 90058
Tel.: (562) 803-3188
Web Site: http://www.rmfood.com
Rev.: $17,227,000
Emp.: 120
Ethnic Grocery Store
N.A.I.C.S.: 445110
Doug Reed (CFO)
Christiann Arapostathis (Office Mgr)

REYNEN & BARDIS COMMUNITIES, INC.

10630 Mather Blvd, Mather, CA 95655
Tel.: (916) 366-3665   CA
Web Site: http://www.rbhome.us
Year Founded: 1970
Sales Range: $75-99.9 Million
Emp.: 25
Residential Real Estate Development Services
N.A.I.C.S.: 237210
Christo D. Bardis (Pres)
John D. Reynen (Treas & Sec)
Dennis Willard (CFO)

REYNOLDS ASPHALT & CONSTRUCTION COMPANY

701 S Industrial Blvd Ste 100, Euless, TX 76040-7022
Tel.: (817) 267-3131   TX
Web Site:
http://www.reynoldsasphalt.com
Year Founded: 1981
Sales Range: $25-49.9 Million
Emp.: 134
Asphalt Paving Mixtures & Blocks
N.A.I.C.S.: 324121
Gary E. Reynolds (Pres & CEO)
Ned Tankersley (VP)
Alexander Joseph (VP-Construction)

REYNOLDS CONSTRUCTION, LLC

4544 N State Rd 37, Orleans, IN 47452   DE
Web Site:
http://www.reynoldscon.com
Year Founded: 2016
Heavy Civil Construction Services
N.A.I.C.S.: 237990
Les Archer (Pres)
Paul Burton (Exec VP-Midwest Div)
Kevin Shemwell (Exec VP-Southeast Div)
Kevin Strott (Exec VP-Rocky Mountain Div)
Wesley Self (Exec VP-Integrated Svcs)
Liz Smith (Exec VP-Acctg & Admin)

Subsidiaries:

Layne Heavy Civil, Inc. (1)
4520 N State Rd 37, Orleans, IN 47452
Tel.: (812) 865-3232
Water & Sewer Line Construction Services
N.A.I.C.S.: 237110
Les Archer (Pres)

Subsidiary (Domestic):

Layne Southwest, Inc. (2)
7818 Pan American E Freeway Ne, Albuquerque, NM 87109
Tel.: (505) 342-2898
Water & Sewer Line Construction Services
N.A.I.C.S.: 237110

Meadors Construction Co., Inc. (2)
5634 W 5th St, Jacksonville, FL 32254
Tel.: (904) 695-9290
Water & Sewer Line Construction Services
N.A.I.C.S.: 237110

W.L. Hailey & Company, Inc. (2)
2971 Kraft Dr, Nashville, TN 37204-3618
Tel.: (615) 255-3161
Water & Sewer Line Construction Services
N.A.I.C.S.: 237110

REYNOLDS ENTERPRISES OF BROOME, INC.

145 Broad Ave, Binghamton, NY 13904
Tel.: (607) 723-7409   NY
Web Site: http://www.agway.com
Year Founded: 2000
Sales Range: $1-9.9 Million
Emp.: 20
Nursery & Garden Centers
N.A.I.C.S.: 444240
Janet Reynolds (Sec & VP)

REYNOLDS FORD INC.

825 N Interstate Dr, Norman, OK 73069
Tel.: (405) 321-2411
Web Site:
http://www.reynoldsautos.com
Rev.: $33,900,000
Emp.: 115
Automobiles, New & Used
N.A.I.C.S.: 441110
Dale Daniels (Pres)
Mark McClintock (Controller)
Forrest Reining (Mgr-Svc)
Michael Lang (Gen Mgr)
Kenny Hines (Asst Mgr-Svc)

REYNOLDS MOTOR COMPANY

1900 Avenue of the Cities, East Moline, IL 61244-4196
Tel.: (309) 792-9530
Web Site:
http://www.reynoldsmotors.com
Sales Range: $10-24.9 Million
Emp.: 86
Car Whslr
N.A.I.C.S.: 441110
Scott Reynolds (Owner & Mgr)

REYNOLDS OIL COMPANY INC.

741 N Jefferson St, Lewisburg, WV 24901
Tel.: (304) 645-1920
Sales Range: $25-49.9 Million
Emp.: 20
Provider of Heating Oil
N.A.I.C.S.: 424710
W. T. Reynolds (Pres)
Tom Reynolds (VP)

REYNOLDS PACKING CO. INC.

33 E Tokay St, Lodi, CA 95240-4149
Tel.: (209) 369-2725   CA
Year Founded: 1955
Sales Range: $50-74.9 Million
Emp.: 85
Crop Preparation Services for Market
N.A.I.C.S.: 115114
Alan Huynh (Controller)
Don Reynolds (Pres)

REYNOLDS READY MIX LLC

2640 S McKenzie St, Foley, AL 36535
Tel.: (251) 943-2985
Web Site:
http://www.readymixusa.com
Rev.: $24,000,000
Emp.: 25
Ready Mixed Concrete
N.A.I.C.S.: 327320
Walter Pope (Exec VP & Gen Mgr)
Justin Blackwell (Exec VP & Gen Mgr)
Bobby Lindsey (VP)

REYNOLDS, SMITH & HILLS INC.

10748 Deerwood Park Blvd S, Jacksonville, FL 32256-0597
Tel.: (904) 256-2500   FL
Web Site: http://www.rsandh.com
Year Founded: 1941
Sales Range: $150-199.9 Million
Emp.: 250
Architectural & Engineering Services
N.A.I.C.S.: 541310
Kenneth R. Jacobson (CFO, Gen Counsel & Exec VP)
Holt Graves (CFO & Exec VP)
Lisa Robert (VP-Ops, Mktg, Transportation & Infrastructure)
Brian P. Reed (CEO)
John J. Bottaro (Sr VP-Corp, Health & Science)
David T. Sweeney (Pres & CEO)
Donald G. Andrews (Sr VP-Aviation)
Chad H. Critcher (Sr VP-Contractor Delivery)
Douglas D. Geiger (Sr VP-Transportation & Construction Mgmt)
Steven W. Moore (Sr VP-Aerospace & Defense)
Andrew P. Wheeler (Sr VP-Health & Science)
Tom Everett (VP)
Leerie T. Jenkins Jr. (Chm)
James W. Hullett Jr. (Sr VP-Transportation & Infrastructure)

REYTEC CONSTRUCTION RESOURCES, INC.

1901 Hollister Rd, Houston, TX 77080
Tel.: (713) 957-4003
Web Site: http://www.reytec.net

COMPANIES — RFE INVESTMENT PARTNERS

Year Founded: 1996
Sales Range: $25-49.9 Million
Emp.: 150
Construction Contractor
N.A.I.C.S.: 238190
Gregg T. Reyes *(Co-Founder, Pres & CEO)*
Thomas Pena *(VP)*
Reytec-Amy Strother *(Office Mgr)*

REZEK EQUIPMENT
970 Reece St, San Bernardino, CA 92411
Tel.: (909) 885-6221
Web Site: http://www.ronrezek.com
Year Founded: 1957
Emergency Response Equipment Distr & Support Services
N.A.I.C.S.: 624230
Ronald V. Rezek *(Founder & CEO)*

REZN8 PRODUCTIONS, INC.
6430 Sunset Blvd, Hollywood, CA 90028
Tel.: (323) 957-2161
Year Founded: 1987
Rev: $10,000,000
Emp.: 30
N.A.I.C.S.: 541810
Tatiana Derovanessian *(Pres & CEO)*

RF MORSE & SON INC.
22 Cranberry Hwy 28, West Wareham, MA 02576
Tel.: (508) 295-1553
Rev: $20,826,604
Emp.: 12
Retail Nurseries & Garden Stores
N.A.I.C.S.: 444240
Richard Canning *(Pres)*

RFE INVESTMENT PARTNERS
10 Wright Street, Westport, CT 06880
Tel.: (203) 966-2800
Web Site: http://www.rfeip.com
Year Founded: 1979
Privater Equity Firm
N.A.I.C.S.: 523999
James A. Parsons *(Mng Dir)*
Ned Truslow *(Mng Dir)*
Michael J. Foster *(Mng Dir & Chief Compliance Officer)*
Michael Rubel *(Mng Dir)*
Paul Schilpp *(Mng Dir)*
Don Juricic *(CFO & Mng Dir)*
Sean E. Gillick *(Principal)*
Bill Bronander *(Principal)*
R. Peter Reiter Jr. *(Mng Dir-Bus Dev)*

Subsidiaries:

Eagle Operating Corp. (1)
8550 W Bryn Mawr Ave Ste 200, Chicago, IL 60631
Tel.: (773) 992-4450
Web Site: http://www.ensembleiq.com
Periodical Publishers
N.A.I.C.S.: 513120
Peter Hoyt *(Pres)*
Joel Hughes *(COO)*
David Shanker *(CEO)*
Ann Jadown *(Chief HR Officer)*
Dan McCarthy *(CFO)*
Tanner Van Dusen *(Chief Innovation Officer)*
Jennifer Litterick *(Chief Comml Officer)*
Ed Several *(Exec VP-Events & Conferences)*
John Kenlon *(Sr VP-Tech Brands)*

Division (Domestic):

Apparel Magazine (2)
4 Middlebury Blvd, Randolph, NJ 07869
Tel.: (973) 607-1300
Web Site: http://apparel.edgl.com
Magazine Publisher
N.A.I.C.S.: 513120
Susan Nichols *(Publr & Brand Dir)*
Jordan Speer *(Editor-in-Chief)*
Cindy DeBerry *(Sls Mgr)*
Robin Ridgell *(Art Dir)*
Jessica Binns *(Sr Editor)*
Marla Wood *(Acct Exec)*
Patricia Wisser *(Production Mgr)*
John Hall *(Dir-Event Content)*
Pat Benkner *(Dir-Event Plng)*
Jeff Zabe *(Mgr-Audience Dev)*

Consumer Goods Technology (2)
4 Middlebury Blvd, Randolph, NJ 07869
Tel.: (973) 607-1300
Web Site: http://www.consumergoods.com
Magazine Publisher
N.A.I.C.S.: 513120
Peter Breen *(Editor-in-Chief)*
Colette Magliaro *(Creative Dir)*

Hospitality Technology (2)
4 Middlebury Blvd, Randolph, NJ 07869
Tel.: (973) 607-1300
Web Site: http://www.hospitalitytechnology.edgl.com
Magazine Publisher
N.A.I.C.S.: 513120
Abigail Lorden *(Brand Dir)*
Dorothy Creamer *(Editor)*
Michal Christine Escobar *(Mng Editor)*
Leah Segarra *(Sr Acct Exec)*
Megan Lynberg *(Reg Sls Mgr)*
Noell Dimmig *(Acct Exec)*
Patricia Wisser *(Production Mgr)*

RIS News (2)
1 Gateway Center Raymond Plz W 16th Fl, Newark, NJ 07102
Tel.: (201) 855-7600
Web Site: http://www.risnews.com
Magazine Publisher
N.A.I.C.S.: 513120
Joe Skorupa *(Dir-Editorial)*
Tim Denman *(Exec Editor)*
Jamie Grill-Goodman *(Mng Editor)*
Patricia Wisser *(Production Mgr)*
Colette Magliaro *(Creative Dir)*
Lauren Dimeo *(Art Dir)*

Selling Halloween (2)
213 Mooney Rd, Flanders, NJ 07836
Tel.: (973) 270-8078
Web Site: http://www.sellinghalloween.com
Magazine Publisher
N.A.I.C.S.: 513120

Hastings Manufacturing Company (1)
325 N Hanover St, Hastings, MI 49058-1527
Tel.: (269) 945-2491
Web Site: http://www.HastingsPistonRings.com
Sales Range: $25-49.9 Million
Emp.: 400
Motor Vehicle Piston Rings Designer & Mfr
N.A.I.C.S.: 336390
Jeffrey P. Guenther *(Sr VP-Sls & Mktg)*
Robert M. Kollar *(COO)*
Dave Sepesi *(Dir-OEM Sls)*
Tom DeBlasis *(VP-Bus Dev)*
Angela Tindall *(Coord-Mktg)*
Kevin D. Willison *(Dir-IT)*
Randy Lunsford *(Mgr-Product Design & Analysis)*
Ken Holbrook *(Pres & CEO)*
Sarah Kollar *(Mgr-Mktg)*
Dan Qualls *(VP-Bus Dev)*
Natasha Bian *(Mgr-Admin Support)*
Jose Segovia *(Dir-Bus Dev-Latin America)*
Richard L. Zwiernikowski Jr. *(CFO)*

Subsidiary (Non-US):

Hastings East Manufacturing Co., Ltd. (2)
No 2 Plant Jian'an Industrial Park 86 W Rd & Wujin Ave, Wujin Hi-Tech Indus Dev Zone, Changzhou, Jiangsu, China
Tel.: (86) 51986488775
Web Site: http://www.hastingsmfg.com
Sales Range: $10-24.9 Million
Emp.: 50
Motor Vehicle Piston Ring Mfr & Distr
N.A.I.C.S.: 336310

LaunchPad Home Group (1)
8920 Business Park Dr. Ste 200, Austin, TX 78759
Tel.: (203) 966-2800
Web Site: https://launchpadhomegroup.com
Home Inspection Services

N.A.I.C.S.: 541350
Scott Swayze *(CEO)*

Subsidiary (Domestic):

Axium Inspections, LLC (2)
1499 Blake St Ste 9B, Denver, CO 80202-1369
Tel.: (303) 797-6900
Web Site: http://www.axiuminspections.com
Building Inspection Services
N.A.I.C.S.: 541350
Wade Williamson *(Pres)*

Lectrus, Inc. (1)
1919 Polymer Dr, Chattanooga, TN 37421
Tel.: (423) 894-9268
Web Site: http://www.lectrus.com
Sales Range: $25-49.9 Million
Metal Buildings & Electrical Switchgear Enclosure Mfr
N.A.I.C.S.: 332322
Greg Cain *(Mgr-Mfg)*
Tim Vavra *(Mgr-Mfg)*
Lynnette Brady *(Mgr-Quality & Matls-South Dakota)*

Nudo Products Inc. (1)
1500 Taylor Ave, Springfield, IL 62703-5663
Tel.: (217) 528-5636
Web Site: http://www.nudo.com
Sales Range: $25-49.9 Million
Ceiling, Wall, Floor, Exterior & Sign Panels Mfr & Distr
N.A.I.C.S.: 326130
Donna Birnschein *(Mgr-HR)*
Derek Hostetter *(Plant Mgr)*

Subsidiary (Domestic):

High Standard, Inc. (2)
81 Fitzgerald Dr, Jaffrey, NH 03452
Tel.: (603) 532-8000
Web Site: http://www.hsipanels.com
Sales Range: $1-9.9 Million
Architectural Wall Panels Mfr & Distr
N.A.I.C.S.: 423390

Sales Empowerment Group LLC (1)
6 W Hubbard St Ste 400, Chicago, IL 60654
Tel.: (312) 374-3500
Web Site: http://www.salesempowermentgroup.com
Sales Range: $1-9.9 Million
Emp.: 13
Sales Consulting Services
N.A.I.C.S.: 541613
Brian ONeil *(Pres & CEO)*
Charles Andrews *(VP-Sls)*
Doug Boone *(VP-Advisory Svcs)*
Gail Behun *(VP-Sls)*
Gregg Sankovitch *(VP-Recruitment)*

Subsidiary (Domestic):

Square 2 Marketing, Inc. (2)
Valley Sq Ste 210 1501 Main St, Warrington, PA 18976
Tel.: (215) 491-0100
Web Site: http://www.square2marketing.com
Marketing Services
N.A.I.C.S.: 541613
Eric Keiles *(Chief Mktg Officer)*
Mike Lieberman *(CEO)*
Dave Gerhardt *(Chief Revenue Officer)*
Julie Golden *(Pres)*
Justin Phillips *(Dir-Interactive Art)*
Joanne Shorts *(Controller)*
Jessica Hein *(Mgr-Acctg)*
Kristin Stricker *(COO)*
Gabe Wahhab *(Dir-Interactive)*
Cari Baldwin *(Chief Revenue Officer)*
Sean Dazet *(Chief Revenue Officer)*

The Sales Board, Inc. (2)
14505 21st Ave N, Plymouth, MN 55447
Tel.: (763) 473-2540
Web Site: http://www.thesalesboard.com
Sales Range: $1-9.9 Million
Emp.: 15
Sales Training
N.A.I.C.S.: 624310
Duane Sparks *(Chm & Pres)*

Southern Pump & Tank Company (1)
4800 N Graham St, Charlotte, NC 28269-4823
Tel.: (704) 596-4373

Web Site: http://www.spatco.com
Sales Range: $25-49.9 Million
Emp.: 210
Gasoline Equipment Construction & Installation Services; Industrial Pumps, Tanks & Metering Devices Sales; General Contracting Services
N.A.I.C.S.: 423830
John Force *(VP-Mktg)*
Kent Reed *(Branch Mgr-Charlotte)*
Jeff Bailey *(Pres)*

Subsidiary (Domestic):

K&K Electric, Inc. (2)
2517 Country Club Rd, Sanford, FL 32771
Tel.: (407) 323-6300
Web Site: http://www.kkelectric.com
Sales Range: $1-9.9 Million
Emp.: 50
Electrical Contractor
N.A.I.C.S.: 238210
Chris Ferrara *(Pres)*
Pete Hodges *(Mgr-Construction)*
Susan Logan *(Pres-HR)*

Mckinney Petroleum Equipment, Inc. (2)
3926 Halls Mill Rd, Mobile, AL 36693
Tel.: (251) 661-8800
Web Site: http://www.mckinneypetroleum.com
Sales Range: $1-9.9 Million
Emp.: 21
Industrial Machinery & Equipment Whslr
N.A.I.C.S.: 423830
Mike Johnson *(Mgr-Svc)*

Veransa Group, Inc. (1)
36 Grove St, New Canaan, CT 06840
Tel.: (203) 966-2800
Web Site: http://www.veransa.com
Green Waste Collection Centers
N.A.I.C.S.: 562998
Marc Owensby *(CEO)*
Roger Johansson *(Chm)*

Subsidiary (Domestic):

Consolidated Resource Recovery, Inc. (2)
3025 Whitfield Ave, Sarasota, FL 34243
Tel.: (941) 756-0977
Web Site: http://www.teamcrr.com
Materials Recovery Facilities
N.A.I.C.S.: 562920
Douglas Halward *(Pres)*
Alan McCabe *(Mgr-Pur)*
Deborah Brindley *(Mgr-Acctg)*
Glenn Purvis *(Mgr-Ops)*
Robert Gomez *(Dir-Mktg)*

ZRG Partners, LLC (1)
365 W Passaic St Ste 465, Rochelle Park, NJ 07662
Tel.: (201) 560-9900
Web Site: https://www.zrgpartners.com
Human Resources & Executive Search Consulting Services
N.A.I.C.S.: 541612
Larry Hartmann *(CEO)*
Leslie Sharp *(Mng Dir)*
Nate Frank *(Pres & Mng Partner)*
David Hart *(Mng Partner)*
Phoebe Henderson *(Mng Dir)*
Richard Herman *(Mng Partner-Global Private Equity)*
Brian McGowan *(Mng Partner)*
Andy Talkington *(Mng Dir)*
John McLean *(Mng Dir)*
Sharon Stein *(Mng Dir)*
Charles H. King *(Mng Dir)*
Beverly Morgan *(Mng Dir)*
Wendelyne Murphy *(Mng Partner)*
Davonne Helmer *(Mng Dir-Chicago)*
Richard Dowd *(Mng Dir)*
Bruce Robertson *(Mng Dir-Global Financial Officers Practice Leader-New York)*
Brian Meany *(Mng Partner-Global Consumer)*
Shelly Scott *(Mng Dir)*
Brian Kelley *(Mng Dir)*
Chuck Nees *(Mng Dir)*
Abe Doctor *(Mng Partner & Mng Dir)*
Hugo Lara *(Mng Dir)*
Lisa Hooker *(Mng Dir-Technology Practice Leader-Austin)*
Kevin Anderson *(Mng Dir-Dallas)*
Justin Pinchback *(Chief Revenue Officer)*

RFE INVESTMENT PARTNERS

RFE Investment Partners—(Continued)
Melissa Norris *(Co-Head-Asset Management)*
Beth Rustin *(Co-Head-Asset Management)*

Subsidiary (Domestic):

Dowd Associates Inc. (2)
777 Westchester Ave Ste 120, White Plains, NY 10604-3520
Tel.: (914) 251-1515
Professional, Scientific & Technical Services
N.A.I.C.S.: 541990

Jamesbeck Global Partners, LLC (2)
437 Madison Ave Fl 28, New York, NY 10022
Tel.: (212) 616-7400
Web Site: http://www.jamesbeck.com
Sales Range: $1-9.9 Million
Emp.: 20
Employment Agency
N.A.I.C.S.: 541612
Ashton McFadden *(Principal)*

Rose Ryan Inc. (2)
35473 Dumbarton Ct, Newark, CA 94560-1100
Tel.: (510) 456-3056
Web Site: http://www.roseryan.com
Investment Advice
N.A.I.C.S.: 523940
Michael Rose *(Owner)*
Stephen Ambler *(VP-Svc & Delivery)*
Brooks Ensign *(Dir-Strategic Projects)*

Sucherman Consulting Group, Inc. (2)
1212 Ave Of The Americas, New York, NY 10036
Tel.: (212) 827-0101
Web Site: http://www.sucherman.com
Management Consulting Services
N.A.I.C.S.: 541611
Stuart Sucherman *(Founder & Chm)*
Erik Sorenson *(CEO)*

Terra Search Partners, LLC (2)
8 California St Ste 400, San Francisco, CA 94111-4828
Tel.: (415) 433-8888
Web Site: http://www.terrasearchpartners.com
Employment Placement Agencies
N.A.I.C.S.: 561311
Sally Carlson *(Owner)*

RFE/RL INC.
1201 Connecticut Ave NW Ste 1100, Washington, DC 20036
Tel.: (202) 457-6900
Web Site: http://www.rferl.org
Year Founded: 1949
Sales Range: $50-74.9 Million
Emp.: 40
Broadcasting
N.A.I.C.S.: 516110

RFG DISTRIBUTING INC.
7300 49th Ave N, New Hope, MN 55428
Tel.: (763) 540-0335
Web Site: http://www.rfgdistributing.com
Year Founded: 1967
Sales Range: $10-24.9 Million
Emp.: 150
Pet Foods Supplies
N.A.I.C.S.: 459910
Steven Thoeny *(Pres)*

RFID GLOBAL SOLUTION INC.
11921 Freedom Dr Ste 970, Reston, VA 20190
Web Site: http://www.rfidgs.com
Year Founded: 2005
Sales Range: $1-9.9 Million
Emp.: 25
Real Time Asset Management Tools
N.A.I.C.S.: 513210
Diana Hage *(Pres & CEO)*
Thomas Manzagol *(Founder & COO)*

RFIP INC.
100 W Wilshire Blvd Ste C4, Oklahoma City, OK 73116
Tel.: (405) 286-0928
Web Site: http://www.rfip.com
Year Founded: 2005
Sales Range: $10-24.9 Million
Emp.: 40
Wi-Fi Implementation & Cellular Communications
N.A.I.C.S.: 517112
Carson Hulcher *(Mgr-Engrg)*

RFX INCORPORATED
748 Seward St, Hollywood, CA 90038
Tel.: (323) 962-7400
Web Site: http://www.rfx.com
Year Founded: 1978
Sales Range: $10-24.9 Million
Emp.: 10
Reseller of Hardware & Software
N.A.I.C.S.: 512191
Raymond E. Feeney *(Founder & Pres)*

RG ENGINEERING INC.
605 Condado St Ste 322, San Juan, PR 00907
Tel.: (787) 723-4623
Web Site: http://www.rgepr.com
Year Founded: 1982
Rev.: $24,849,776
Emp.: 12
Electrical Apparatus & Equipment
N.A.I.C.S.: 423610
Roberto Camino *(Pres)*

RG INDUSTRIES, INC.
650 N State St, York, PA 17403
Tel.: (717) 846-9300   PA
Web Site: http://www.rg-group.com
Year Founded: 1956
Sales Range: $10-24.9 Million
Emp.: 81
Hydraulic & Pneumatic Fluid Power Products Mfr & Whslr
N.A.I.C.S.: 423830
Randall A. Gross *(Chm)*
Rich Freeh *(Pres & CEO)*
Steve Bennis *(COO)*
Gene Kostelac *(CFO)*
Edward Stum II *(Exec VP-Mfg)*

Subsidiaries:

Weaver Fluid Power, Inc. (1)
2904 Willow St Pike N, Willow Street, PA 17584
Tel.: (717) 464-2776
Web Site: http://www.weaverfluidpower.com
Sales Range: $1-9.9 Million
Hydraulic & Pneumatic Fluid Power Products Whslr & Repair Services
N.A.I.C.S.: 423830
Randy Gross *(Pres)*

RGB MECHANICAL CONTRACTORS INC.
4221 E Johnson Ave, Jonesboro, AR 72401
Tel.: (870) 972-8360
Web Site: http://www.rgbmechanical.com
Sales Range: $10-24.9 Million
Emp.: 80
Warm Air Heating & Air Conditioning Contractor
N.A.I.C.S.: 238220
Ralph Brasher *(Pres)*

RGB SYSTEMS INC.
1025 E Ball Rd, Anaheim, CA 92805
Tel.: (714) 491-1500
Web Site: http://www.extron.com
Rev.: $26,400,000
Emp.: 25,000
Computer Peripheral Equipment
N.A.I.C.S.: 334118

Andrew C. Edwards *(Pres)*
Dave Pincek *(VP-Product Dev)*

RGF ENVIRONMENTAL GROUP
1101 W 13th St, Riviera Beach, FL 33404
Tel.: (561) 848-1826
Web Site: http://www.rgf.com
Sales Range: $10-24.9 Million
Emp.: 70
Water Quality Monitoring & Control Systems
N.A.I.C.S.: 334513
Ronald G. Fink *(Pres)*
Sharon Rinehiner *(Gen Counsel & VP)*
Watler Ellis *(VP)*

Subsidiaries:

AFL Industries, Inc. (1)
1751 W 10th St, Riviera Beach, FL 33404
Tel.: (561) 844-5200
Web Site: http://www.aflindustries.com
Sales Range: $10-24.9 Million
Emp.: 15
Commercial & Service Industry Machinery Mfr
N.A.I.C.S.: 333310

RGF INDUSTRIES INCORPORATED
300 Poplar St, Pittsburgh, PA 15223
Tel.: (412) 449-0044   PA
Web Site: http://www.pittsburghglassblock.com
Year Founded: 1964
Sales Range: $10-24.9 Million
Emp.: 90
Glass Block, Brick, Concrete Block & Masonry Building Materials Sales
N.A.I.C.S.: 444180
Robert V. Friday *(Pres)*

RGL-FORENSIC ACCOUNTANTS & CONSULTANTS
7887 E Belleview Ave Ste 1200, Denver, CO 80111
Tel.: (303) 721-8898
Web Site: http://www.rgl.com
Year Founded: 1997
Sales Range: $10-24.9 Million
Emp.: 125
Accounting & Consulting Services
N.A.I.C.S.: 541219
Paul L. Cadorette *(Partner)*
Matthew Morris *(Partner)*
Angela MacPhee *(CEO)*
Bert Lacativo *(Partner)*

RGP HOLDING, INC.
3411 Silverside Rd, Wilmington, DE 19801-4812
Tel.: (302) 478-6160   DE
Sales Range: $125-149.9 Million
Emp.: 5
Investment Holding Company
N.A.I.C.S.: 551112
Barry L. Katz *(Pres & Gen Counsel)*

Subsidiaries:

Amol Dicalite Ltd. (1)
301 Akshay 53 Shrimali Society Navrangpura, Ahmedabad, 380009, Gujarat, India
Tel.: (91) 7940246246
Web Site: http://www.amoldicalite.com
Emp.: 30
Filteraids & Filler Products Mfr
N.A.I.C.S.: 325510
Shreyas Chinubhai Sheth *(Mng Dir)*

Dicalite Holdings Inc. (1)
1105 North Market Ste 1300, Wilmington, DE 19801
Tel.: (302) 478-6160
Refractory Pumping Mfr
N.A.I.C.S.: 333914

Subsidiary (Domestic):

Dicalite Corporation (2)
36994 Summit Lake Rd, Burney, CA 96013-9636   (100%)
Tel.: (530) 335-5451
Web Site: http://www.greco.com
Sales Range: $50-74.9 Million
Mfr of Diatomite Filter Aids & Fillers
N.A.I.C.S.: 212390

Subsidiary (Non-US):

Dicalite Europe Nord, S.A. (3)
Fcheepzatestrasse100, 9000, Gent, Dusseldorf, Belgium   (100%)
Tel.: (32) 92509550
Web Site: http://www.dicalite-europe.com
Sales Range: $10-24.9 Million
Emp.: 60
Fillers & Filteraids
N.A.I.C.S.: 325510
Geert Remua *(Mng Dir)*

Subsidiary (Domestic):

GREFCO, Inc. (2)
23705 Crenshaw Blvd, Torrance, CA 90505-5236   (100%)
Tel.: (610) 660-8840
Sales Range: $100-124.9 Million
Industrial Filteraids, Fillers, Perlite & Diatomite
N.A.I.C.S.: 212390

GRC Holding, Inc. (1)
1 Bala Ave Ste 310, Bala Cynwyd, PA 19004
Tel.: (610) 660-8803
Sales Range: $25-49.9 Million
Refractory Pumping Mfr
N.A.I.C.S.: 238220
Raymond G. Perelman *(Chm)*

Subsidiary (Domestic):

American Refractories Co. (2)
301 S Keim St, Pottstown, PA 19464   (100%)
Tel.: (610) 718-0450
Sales Range: $25-49.9 Million
Refractory Repair & Installation
N.A.I.C.S.: 238220

Belmont Holdings Corp. (2)
1 Bala Ave Ste 310, Bala Cynwyd, PA 19004-1704
Tel.: (610) 660-8803
Machined Products, Residential Heating Equipment, Lawn & Garden Equipment, Bridge Floors & Grating & Dental Equipment & Supplies Mfr
N.A.I.C.S.: 333111

Subsidiary (Domestic):

Chemrock Corporation (3)
2601 Osage St, Nashville, TN 37208-2348   (100%)
Tel.: (615) 320-1493
Sales Range: $10-24.9 Million
Cryogenic Perlite Mfr
N.A.I.C.S.: 327331
Raymond Perelman *(CEO)*

Induplex, Inc. (1)
Unit 3 A B Mapfre Asian Corp Center 1220 Acasia Avenue, Madrigal Business Park Ayala A, 1770, Muntinlupa, Philippines   (100%)
Tel.: (63) 28076802
Web Site: http://www.induplex.com
Sales Range: $25-49.9 Million
Filteraids & Filler Products
N.A.I.C.S.: 325510

RGT ADVERTISING AGENCY
2468 Sharon Oaks Dr, Menlo Park, CA 94025
Tel.: (650) 854-1490
Year Founded: 1981
Sales Range: Less than $1 Million
Emp.: 1
High Technology, Internet/Web Design, Strategic Planning, Technical Advertising
N.A.I.C.S.: 541810
Richard G. Thau *(Pres)*

COMPANIES

RGW CONSTRUCTION INC.
550 Greenville Rd, Livermore, CA 94550-0221
Tel.: (925) 606-2400 CA
Web Site: http://www.rgwconstruction.com
Year Founded: 1990
Sales Range: $75-99.9 Million
Emp.: 150
Highway & Street Construction
N.A.I.C.S.: 237310
Karrie Souza (CFO)
William S. Stewart (Pres)
Janis Ragone (Controller)
Jake Lewon (Sr Project Mgr)
Mike Betti (Sr Project Mgr)
Robert W. Purdy (Sec & VP)
Steve Genereux (Sr Project Mgr)

RH SCALES CO. INC.
240 University Ave, Westwood, MA 02090
Tel.: (781) 320-0005
Web Site: http://www.rhscales.com
Sales Range: $10-24.9 Million
Emp.: 40
Automotive Supplies & Parts
N.A.I.C.S.: 423120
Richard L. Scales (Pres)
Patrick Hayes (Mgr-Sls)

RHA NORTH CAROLINA MR INC
3060 Peachtree Rd NW Ste 900, Atlanta, GA 30305
Tel.: (404) 364-2900 NC
Web Site: http://www.rhahealthservices.org
Year Founded: 1988
Sales Range: $50-74.9 Million
Emp.: 1,155
Behavioral Healthcare Services
N.A.I.C.S.: 623220
John R. West (CFO-RHA Health Svcs)
Chase Northcutt (VP)
Heather-Dawn Ashley (VP)
Nicklaus N. Sulaiman (CFO-RHA Mgmt Svcs)

RHA SULLIVAN INC
3060 Peachtree Rd NW Ste 900, Atlanta, GA 30305
Tel.: (404) 364-2900 TN
Year Founded: 1989
Sales Range: $10-24.9 Million
Health Care Srvices
N.A.I.C.S.: 623110
John R. West (CFO & Exec VP)
Kathy Green (Sr VP)
Jeanne Duncan (VP)
Chase Northcutt (VP)
John White (VP)

RHC, INC.
965 Veterans Memorial Hwy NE, Rome, GA 30161
Tel.: (706) 291-2674
Year Founded: 1989
Sales Range: $10-24.9 Million
Emp.: 59
New Car Whslr
N.A.I.C.S.: 441110
Michael S. Barron (Mgr-Mktg)
Mike Barron Jr. (Gen Mgr)
Alfred L. Barron Jr. (Pres)

RHEA LANA'S, INC.
1055 Sunflower Dr Suite 104, Conway, AR 72034
Tel.: (501) 499-0009
Web Site: http://www.rhealana.com
Year Founded: 1997
Sales Range: $1-9.9 Million
Emp.: 10
Franchisor & Host of Children's Clothing Consignment Events
N.A.I.C.S.: 813410
Rhea Lana Riner (Pres & Founder)

RHEE BROS. INC.
7461 Coco Cola Dr, Hanover, MD 21076
Tel.: (410) 381-9000 MD
Web Site: http://www.rheebros.com
Year Founded: 1974
Sales Range: $25-49.9 Million
Emp.: 140
Provider of Wholesale Grocery Services
N.A.I.C.S.: 424410
Syngman Steve Rhee (Chm & CEO)

RHG GROUP, INC.
915 5th St NW, Washington, DC 20001
Tel.: (202) 789-0039
Web Site: http://www.rhggroup.com
Year Founded: 1994
Sales Range: $10-24.9 Million
Emp.: 115
Management Consulting Services
N.A.I.C.S.: 541611
Reginald Laurent (Pres)
Charlie Wurz (VP)

RHINE EQUIPMENT COMPANY
1120 112th St E, Tacoma, WA 98445
Tel.: (253) 536-0600
Web Site: http://www.rhineequipment.com
Year Founded: 1982
Sales Range: $10-24.9 Million
Emp.: 15
Provider of Industrial Machinery Services
N.A.I.C.S.: 423830
Stan Hayes (Pres)
Joel Simmonds (CFO)

RHINEBECK BANK
2 Jefferson Plz, Poughkeepsie, NY 12601
Tel.: (845) 454-8555
Web Site: http://www.rhinebeckbank.com
Year Founded: 1860
Sales Range: $25-49.9 Million
Emp.: 135
Commericial Banking
N.A.I.C.S.: 522110
Philip Bronzi (Sr VP & Dir-Comml Lending)
Michael J. Quinn (Pres & CEO)
Louis Tumolo Jr. (Chm)

Subsidiaries:

Brinckerhoff & Neuville, Inc. (1)
1134 Main St, Fishkill, NY 12524
Tel.: (845) 896-4700
Web Site: http://www.brinckerhoffandneuville.com
Sales Range: $1-9.9 Million
Emp.: 10
Insurance Agents
N.A.I.C.S.: 524210
Mary Brinckerhoff (CEO)

New Horizons Asset Management Group, LLC (1)
11 Racquet Rd, Newburgh, NY 12550
Tel.: (845) 567-3930
Web Site: http://www.nhamg.com
Sales Range: $1-9.9 Million
Emp.: 5
Asset Management Services
N.A.I.C.S.: 523940
Thomas E. Hughes (Mng Partner)

RHINEHART EQUIPMENT COMPANY
3556 Martha Berry Hwy NE, Rome, GA 30165
Tel.: (706) 232-8962
Web Site: http://www.rhinehartequipment.com
Year Founded: 1947
Sales Range: $10-24.9 Million
Farm Equipment & Supplies Mfr
N.A.I.C.S.: 459999
Kyle Sherone (Mgr)

RHINO 7 FRANCHISE DEVELOPMENT CORPORATION
431 Keisler Dr, Cary, NC 27518
Tel.: (919) 589-9999
Web Site: http://www.r7fdc.com
Year Founded: 1999
Sales Range: $1-9.9 Million
Emp.: 12
Franchise Sales & Development Services
N.A.I.C.S.: 533110
Doug Schadle (Co-Founder & CEO)
Rita Perkins (Office Mgr & Coord-Franchise)
Pat Cohen (CFO)
Brian Garoutte (VP-Franchise Dev)
John J. Cohen Jr. (Co-Founder & Pres)

RHINO FOODS INC.
79 Industrial Pkwy, Burlington, VT 05401
Tel.: (802) 862-0252
Web Site: http://www.rhinofoods.com
Rev.: $16,600,000
Emp.: 100
Mfr of Doughs
N.A.I.C.S.: 311824
Leighton Patterson (Mgr-Pur & Matls)
Jayne Magnant (Dir-Fin & Admin)
Gillian Bell (Mgr-Mktg)

RHINO LININGS CORPORATION
9747 Businesspark Ave, San Diego, CA 92131
Tel.: (858) 450-0441 CA
Web Site: http://www.rhinolinings.com
Year Founded: 1988
Sales Range: $10-24.9 Million
Emp.: 59
Polymer Coatings Mfr
N.A.I.C.S.: 325510
Pierre Gagnon (Pres & CEO)
Ben Smith (Mng Dir-Rhino Flooring)

Subsidiaries:

Concrete Solutions, Inc. (1)
9747 Businesspark Ave, San Diego, CA 92131
Tel.: (619) 297-3999
Web Site: http://www.concretesolutions.com
Sales Range: $10-24.9 Million
Emp.: 40
Concrete Products Mfr
N.A.I.C.S.: 423320

RHINOCORPS LTD. CO.
1128 Pennsylvania NE Ste 100, Albuquerque, NM 87110
Tel.: (505) 323-9836 NM
Web Site: http://www.rhinocorps.com
Year Founded: 1998
Sales Range: $10-24.9 Million
Emp.: 65
Computer System Design Services
N.A.I.C.S.: 541512
Anthony Contri (Pres)
Fred Jonas (VP)

RHLI INC.
1800 Iowa St, Bellingham, WA 98229
Tel.: (360) 734-8700
Sales Range: $10-24.9 Million
Emp.: 43
Automobiles, New & Used
N.A.I.C.S.: 441110
Allen Meyer (Gen Mgr)

RHM FLUID POWER INC.
375 Manufacturers Dr, Westland, MI 48186-4038
Tel.: (734) 326-5400 MI
Web Site: http://www.rhmfp.com
Year Founded: 1973
Sales Range: $10-24.9 Million
Emp.: 65
Provider of Industrial Machinery & Equipment
N.A.I.C.S.: 423830
Jeffrey Varona (Pres)
Frank Bowles (VP-Mfg)
Neelima Reddy (Project Mgr)
James Warner (Engr-Sls-Test Sys)
Mike Baker (Mgr-Sls)
William W. Tulloch III (Chm)

RHO CAPITAL PARTNERS, INC.
Carnegie Hall Tower 152 W 57th St 23rd Fl, New York, NY 10019
Tel.: (212) 751-6677 NY
Web Site: http://www.rho.com
Privater Equity Firm
N.A.I.C.S.: 523999
Mark Leschly (Mng Partner)
Joshua Ruch (Mng Partner)

Subsidiaries:

Rho Acceleration, L.P. (1)
Carnegie Hall Tower 152 W 57th St 23rd Fl, New York, NY 10019
Tel.: (212) 751-6677
Web Site: http://www.rhoacceleration.com
Investment Holding Company
N.A.I.C.S.: 551112
Habib Kairouz (Mng Partner)
George Bitar (Mng Partner)
Patrick Wack (Operating Partner)
Doug McCormick (Operating Partner)
Mark Roehrenbeck (Principal)

Joint Venture (Domestic):

Skyword Inc. (2)
33 Arch St, Boston, MA 02110
Tel.: (617) 720-4000
Web Site: http://www.skyword.com
Business Support Services
N.A.I.C.S.: 561499
Jim P. Manzi (Chm)
Tom Gerace (Founder)
Andrew Wheeler (CEO)

Rho Ventures LLC (1)
Carnegie Hall Tower 152 W 57th St 23rd Fl, New York, NY 10019
Tel.: (212) 751-6677
Web Site: http://www.rhoventures.com
Venture Capital Firm
N.A.I.C.S.: 523999
Mark Leschly (Mng Partner)

RHOADS METAL FABRICATIONS INC.
1117 Admiral Peary Way Philadelphia Naval Shipyard, Philadelphia, PA 19112
Tel.: (267) 728-6300
Web Site: http://www.rhoadsinc.com
Rev.: $13,806,000
Emp.: 17
Sheet Metalwork
N.A.I.C.S.: 332322
Daniel J. Rhoads (Pres)

RHODA LEE, INC.
525 7th Ave Fl 16, New York, NY 10018
Tel.: (212) 840-5700 NY
Year Founded: 1947
Sales Range: $1-9.9 Million
Emp.: 75
Women's & Girls' Cut & Sew Blouse & Shirt Mfr
N.A.I.C.S.: 315250
Audrey Laufer (VP)

RHODE ISLAND AIRPORT CORP | U.S. PRIVATE

Rhode Island Airport Corp—(Continued)

RHODE ISLAND AIRPORT CORP
2000 Post Rd, Warwick, RI 02886
Tel.: (401) 737-4000
Web Site: http://www.pvdairport.com
Sales Range: $10-24.9 Million
Emp.: 180
Airport
N.A.I.C.S.: 488119
Peter Frazier (Gen Counsel & Sr VP)
Iftikhar Ahmad (Pres & CEO)
Jonathan N. Savage (Chm)
Patti Goldstein (Sr VP-Mktg & Comm)
Eric Seabury (Asst VP-Engrg)

RHODE ISLAND BLOOD CENTER
405 Promenade St, Providence, RI 02908
Tel.: (401) 453-8360 RI
Web Site: http://www.ribc.org
Year Founded: 1979
Sales Range: $25-49.9 Million
Emp.: 411
Blood Distribution Services
N.A.I.C.S.: 621991
Charles R. Reppucci (Vice Chm)
Mark A. Shaw (Chm)
Cynthia Wyman (Sec)
Lawrence F. Smith (Pres & CEO)
Scott J. Asadorian (COO & VP)

RHODE ISLAND COMMUNITY FOOD BANK
200 Niantic Ave, Providence, RI 02907
Tel.: (401) 942-6325 RI
Web Site: http://www.rifoodbank.org
Year Founded: 1981
Rev.: $20,840,736
Assets: $14,683,964
Liabilities: $612,431
Net Worth: $14,071,533
Earnings: $841,840
Emp.: 53,000
Fiscal Year-end: 06/30/19
Community Food Services
N.A.I.C.S.: 624210
Karen Fuller (Dir-Philanthropy)
Lisa Roth Blackman (Chief Philanthropy Officer)
Maribeth Cirelli (Dir-Admin)
Christine Cannata (CFO)
Andrew Schiff (CEO)
Cheryl Powers (Mgr-Food Donations)
Renzo Arteta (Coord-Community Resource)
Jeanne Hebert (Coord-Volunteer)
Kathie Falcone (Fin Dir)
Mary Hunt (Mgr-Accounts Payable)
Lucia Perez (Coord-Fin)
Linda Pickett (Office Mgr)
Jill Gonsalves (Dir-Annual Giving)
Hugh Minor (Dir-Comm)
Kathy Correia (Mgr-Dev Information)
Denise Marques (Coord-Dev)
Doris Moore (Mgr-Grants)
Jen Tomassini (COO)
Amanda Clarke (Dir-Innovation & Plng)
Erica Hanson (Dir-Agency Svcs)
Heather Langlois (Dir-Community Kitchen)
Melissa Martland-Kile (Mgr-Nutrition Education)
Jack Russell (Dir-Ops)
Gary Ivone (Dir-Facility)

RHODE ISLAND CONVENTION CENTER AUTHORITY
Dunkin Donuts Ctr 1 LaSalle Sq, Providence, RI 02903-1058
Tel.: (401) 351-4295
Web Site: http://www.riconvention.com
Year Founded: 1987
Sales Range: Less than $1 Million
Emp.: 3
Provider of Business Services
N.A.I.C.S.: 561990
James P. McCarvill (Exec Dir)
Lawrence J. Lepore (Gen Mgr)
Pamela Bacon (Dir-Fin)
Susan Catanzaro (Dir-Ticketing & Customer Svc)
Cheryl Cohen (Dir-Mktg, PR & Booking)
James Demers (Dir-Complex Security)
Robert Lauro (Dir-Ops)
Kathy Masino (Dir-Food & Beverage)
John J. McGinn (Sr Dir-Sls)
Amanda Marzullo Wilmouth (Sr Dir-Facilities)
Melissa Avedisian (Sr Mgr-Sls & Catering-Corp & Sport Market)
Arleen F. Oliva (Sr Mgr-Natl Sls-Trade Shows & Convention Market)
Breana Quinn (Mgr-Sls & Mktg)
Diane Richards (Mgr-Sls-Religious & Fraternal)
Kerri Dailey (Asst Mgr-Box Office)

RHODE ISLAND CREDIT UNION
160 Francis St, Providence, RI 02903
Tel.: (401) 751-7440 RI
Web Site: http://www.ricreditunion.org
Year Founded: 1946
Sales Range: $10-24.9 Million
Emp.: 78
Credit Union
N.A.I.C.S.: 522130
Milton Bronstein (First VP)
Paul V. Filippone (Treas)
Robert P. Gemma (Sec)
Frank R. Walker III (Asst Treas)

RHODE ISLAND NOVELTY, INC.
350 Commerce Dr, Fall River, MA 02720
Web Site: http://www.rinovelty.com
Year Founded: 1986
Novelty Goods Whslr
N.A.I.C.S.: 423990
Bogdan Nowak (Founder & Pres)
Robert Novack (Pres)

Subsidiaries:

Mistco, Inc. (1)
17160 NW 2nd Ct, Miami, FL 33169
Tel.: (305) 653-2003
Web Site: http://www.mistco.com
Sales Range: $1-9.9 Million
Emp.: 35
Miscellaneous Durable Goods Merchant Whslr
N.A.I.C.S.: 423990

RHODE ISLAND PBS FOUNDATION
50 Park Ln, Providence, RI 02907-3145
Tel.: (401) 222-3636
Web Site: https://www.ripbs.org
Emp.: 100
Grantmaking Foundations
N.A.I.C.S.: 813211

RHODE ISLAND PHILHARMONIC ORCHESTRA INC.
667 Waterman Ave, East Providence, RI 02914
Tel.: (401) 831-3123
Web Site: http://www.riphil.org
Emp.: 145
Symphony Orchestra
N.A.I.C.S.: 711130

RHODE ISLAND TEXTILE COMPANY, INC.
211 Columbus Ave, Pawtucket, RI 02861-3404
Tel.: (401) 722-3700 RI
Web Site: http://www.ritextile.com
Year Founded: 1913
Sales Range: $50-74.9 Million
Emp.: 900
Mfr of Elastic & Non-Elastic Narrow Fabrics, Knits, Braids & Webbing
N.A.I.C.S.: 313220
Paul M. Mahoney (Pres-Indus Sls)
Jim Carria (CFO)
Nella Fonseca (Mgr-Quality)
Deborah OBrien (Mgr-Mgmt Info Sys)

Subsidiaries:

Anahuac South Carolina Elastic S.A. de C.V. (1)
Estano 29 Col Esfuerzo Nacional, CP 55320, Xalostoc, Mexico (100%)
Tel.: (52) 5 5569 6858
Web Site: http://www.anahuacsce.com
Sales Range: $10-24.9 Million
Emp.: 125
Mfr of Elastic Knit & Woven Narrow Fabrics
N.A.I.C.S.: 313210

RHODEN AUTO CENTER INC.
3400 S Expy, Council Bluffs, IA 51501
Tel.: (712) 366-9400
Web Site: http://www.rhodenloancity.com
Rev.: $93,191,000
Emp.: 140
Automobiles, New & Used
N.A.I.C.S.: 441110
Rodney D. Rhoden (Pres)

RHODES ASSOCIATES
555 5th Ave 6th Fl, New York, NY 10017
Tel.: (212) 983-2000
Web Site: http://www.rhodesassociates.com
Sales Range: $10-24.9 Million
Emp.: 15
Executive Placement Services
N.A.I.C.S.: 541612
Steven Littman (Mng Partner)
Ray Hoffman (Principal)
Diane Tarbell (COO)
Penny Dolan (VP-Res)

RHODES GROCERY INC.
310 E Centennial Dr, Pittsburg, KS 66762
Tel.: (620) 231-7920
Web Site: http://rhodesgroceryhiring.blogspot.com
Sales Range: $25-49.9 Million
Emp.: 115
Grocery Stores
N.A.I.C.S.: 445110
Ron Rhodes (Pres)
Barbara Rhodes (Sec & VP)

RHODES INC.
1120 I St, Reedley, CA 93654
Tel.: (559) 638-2275
Web Site: http://www.rhodesinc.com
Sales Range: $10-24.9 Million
Emp.: 7
Petroleum Bulk Stations
N.A.I.C.S.: 424710
David Rhodes (Owner)

RHODES INTERNATIONAL, INC.
PO Box 25487, Salt Lake City, UT 84123-0487
Tel.: (801) 972-0122 NV
Web Site: http://www.rhodesbakenserv.com
Year Founded: 1964
Sales Range: $200-249.9 Million
Emp.: 450
Mfr of Frozen Bread, Roll & Biscuit Dough
N.A.I.C.S.: 311812
Kenny Farnsworth Jr. (Pres)

Subsidiaries:

Rhodes International (1)
W950 Hwy 16, Columbus, WI 53925-0410 (100%)
Tel.: (920) 623-5161
Web Site: http://www.rhodes-bns.com
Sales Range: $25-49.9 Million
Emp.: 100
Mfr of Frozen Bread Dough
N.A.I.C.S.: 311412

RHODES OIL COMPANY INC.
305 Moore St, Walterboro, SC 29488
Tel.: (843) 549-5521
Rev.: $13,000,000
Emp.: 12
Petroleum Products
N.A.I.C.S.: 424720
Robert Smith (Pres)
Leon Langley (VP)

RHODIANA CORP.
6190 Fairmount Ave Ste K, San Diego, CA 92120
Tel.: (619) 280-9992 CA
Web Site: http://www.rhodiana.com
Year Founded: 1985
Sales Range: $1-9.9 Million
Emp.: 45
Mfg & Ret Carrying Cases
N.A.I.C.S.: 316990
Ann Long (VP)

RHODIUM ENTERPRISES, INC.
251 Little Falls Dr, Wilmington, DE 19808
Tel.: (302) 636-5401 DE
Web Site: https://www.rhdm.com
Year Founded: 2021
Emp.: 43
Cryptocurrency Mining Services
N.A.I.C.S.: 523160
Nathan Nichols (Co-Founder & CEO)
Chase Blackmon (Co-Founder & COO)
Cameron Blackmon (Co-Founder & CTO)
Nicholas Cerasuolo (Co-Founder & CFO)

RHOMOBILE, INC.
3031 Tisch Way Ste 1002, San Jose, CA 95128
Tel.: (408) 572-8076
Web Site: http://www.rhomobile.com
Sales Range: $1-9.9 Million
Emp.: 15
Mobile Application Software
N.A.I.C.S.: 513210
Adam Blum (CEO)

RHONE GROUP, LLC
630 5th Ave Ste 2710, New York, NY 10111
Tel.: (212) 218-6700 DE
Web Site: http://www.rhonegroup.com
Year Founded: 1996
Holding Company; Investment Advisory & Private Equity Services
N.A.I.C.S.: 551112
M. Steven Langman (Co-Founder & Mng Dir)
Robert Frank Agostinelli (Co-Founder)

Subsidiaries:

Rhone Capital LLC (1)
630 5th Ave Ste 2710, New York, NY 10111
Tel.: (212) 218-6700

COMPANIES

RHONE GROUP, LLC

Privater Equity Firm
N.A.I.C.S.: 523999

Holding (Non-US):

ASK Chemicals GmbH (2)
Reisholzstrasse 16-18, PO Box 440, Hilden, 40721, Germany
Tel.: (49) 211711030
Web Site: http://www.ask-chemicals.de
Sales Range: $700-749.9 Million
Emp.: 90
Foundry Supply Chemicals Mfr
N.A.I.C.S.: 325998
Frank Coenen (CEO)

Subsidiary (Non-US):

ASK Chemicals Benelux B.V. (3)
Industrieweg 73c, 5145 PD, Waalwijk, Netherlands
Tel.: (31) 416674590
Web Site: http://www.ask-chemicals.com
Sales Range: $50-74.9 Million
Emp.: 10
Oil Based Chemical Intermediates Distr
N.A.I.C.S.: 424690
Jone Whitton (Gen Mgr)

Plant (Domestic):

ASK Chemicals GmbH - Werk Wulfrath (3)
Dieselstrasse 35-41, Wulfrath, 42489, Germany
Tel.: (49) 20587850
Web Site: http://www.ask-chemicals.com
Sales Range: $75-99.9 Million
Emp.: 220
Phenolic Resins Mfr
N.A.I.C.S.: 325211
Frank Coenen (Exec Officer)

Subsidiary (US):

ASK Chemicals LP (3)
5200 Blazer Pkwy, Dublin, OH 43017
Tel.: (614) 790-3333
Web Site: http://www.ask-chemicals.com
Sales Range: $10-24.9 Million
Emp.: 150
Chemical & Resin Mfr
N.A.I.C.S.: 325211
Scott Hoertz (COO)
Thiemo Heinzen (CFO)
Frank Coenen (CEO)
Charles Hoertz (Mgr-Mktg & Comm-Americas)
Verena Sander (Mgr-Corp Mktg & Comm)

Holding (Non-US):

CSM Bakery Solutions Europe Holding B.V. (2)
Piet Heinkade 55, 1112 XE, Amsterdam, Netherlands
Tel.: (31) 205091850
Web Site: http://www.csmbaking.com
Sales Range: $1-4.9 Billion
Emp.: 4,200
Holding Company; Baking Ingredients Mfr & Distr
N.A.I.C.S.: 551112
Roeland De Wolf (Dir-HR)

Subsidiary (Non-US):

BakeMark Ingredients-Canada Ltd. (3)
2480 Viking Way, Richmond, V6V 1N2, BC, Canada
Tel.: (604) 303-1700
Web Site: http://www.bakemarkcanada.com
Bakery Ingredients
N.A.I.C.S.: 311824

CSM (United Kingdom) Ltd. (3)
Stadium Road Bromborough, Wirral, CH62 3NU, United Kingdom
Tel.: (44) 1513431600
Web Site: http://www.csm.co.uk
Sales Range: $25-49.9 Million
Emp.: 500
Bakery Product Distr
N.A.I.C.S.: 311812
David Astles (Product Mgr)
Darren Blake (Dir-Sls)

Subsidiary (Domestic):

Kate's Cakes Ltd (4)
Unit 3 Wiston Business Park London Road A24, Ashington, RH20 3DJ, West Sussex, United Kingdom
Tel.: (44) 1903 891910
Web Site: http://www.katescakes.com
Baked Goods Mfr
N.A.I.C.S.: 311813

Subsidiary (Non-US):

CSM Austria GmbH (3)
Schleppe-Platz 8 Feschnigstrasse 221, 9020, Klagenfurt, Austria
Tel.: (43) 463414030
Emp.: 40
Bakery Product Distr
N.A.I.C.S.: 424420
Christoph Rohschenkel (Mng Dir)

Subsidiary (US):

CSM Bakery Products North America (3)
1912 Montreal Rd, Tucker, GA 30084
Tel.: (770) 938-3823
Web Site: http://www.csmbakerysolutions.com
Bakery Supplies & Ingredients Mfr
N.A.I.C.S.: 311999
Marianne Kirkegaard (Pres & CEO)
James Singh (Chm)
Dennis Murphy (VP-Comm)

Unit (Domestic):

CSM Bakery Products - Colton (4)
2111 W Vly Blvd, Colton, CA 92324
Tel.: (909) 825-7343
Sales Range: $10-24.9 Million
Emp.: 500
Bakery & Frozen Products
N.A.I.C.S.: 311813
John Mayo (Gen Mgr)

CSM Bakery Products - Lancaster (4) (100%)
3765 Walden Ave, Lancaster, NY 14086-1405
Tel.: (716) 685-4000
Sales Range: $50-74.9 Million
Emp.: 120
Produces & Sells Fruit Fillings, Icing Products & Ice Cream Toppings
N.A.I.C.S.: 311421

CSM Bakery Products - Minnetonka (4)
111 Cheshire Ln Ste 100, Minnetonka, MN 55305
Tel.: (952) 404-7500
Sales Range: $75-99.9 Million
Emp.: 285
Food Processing & Distribution Services
N.A.I.C.S.: 311824

Subsidiary (Non-US):

CSM Bakery Supplies Gida San. ve Tic. A.S (3)
Ferhatpasa Mah Anadolu Cad G45 Sok No 48, Atasehir, 34858, Istanbul, Turkiye
Tel.: (90) 216 661 3838
Bakery Food Products Mfr
N.A.I.C.S.: 311813
Burak Ali Aksu (Gen Mgr)

CSM Benelux NV (3)
Ahlers House Noorderlaan 139, 2030, Antwerp, Belgium
Tel.: (32) 3 6417100
Web Site: http://www.csmbakerysolutions.com
Sales Range: $200-249.9 Million
Emp.: 60
Bakery Products Mfr & Distr
N.A.I.C.S.: 311813
Helen Soly (Mgr-HR)

Branch (Non-US):

CSM Benelux - Goes (4) (100%)
Fruitlaan 24, 4462 EP, Goes, Netherlands
Tel.: (31) 113 236400
Web Site: http://www.csmbakerysolutions.com
Sales Range: $50-74.9 Million
Food Ingredients
N.A.I.C.S.: 311999

Subsidiary (Non-US):

CSM Biochem Trading Shanghai Co., Ltd. (3)
Room 601 No 10 Lane 198 Zhang Heng Road, Pudong New District, 201204, Shanghai, China
Tel.: (86) 21 6887 8755
Specialty Chemicals Distr
N.A.I.C.S.: 424690

CSM Deutschland GmbH (3) (100%)
Theodor Heuss Allee 8, 28215, Bremen, 28215, Germany
Tel.: (49) 42135020
Web Site: http://www.csmbaking.com
Sales Range: $25-49.9 Million
Emp.: 220
Basic Ingredients, Combined Ingredients Systems, Semi-Finished Products & Almost-Ready Products for all Bakery Segments
N.A.I.C.S.: 311812
Thomas Tanck (Mng Dir)
Holger Eckmanns (Mng Dir)
Frans Theeuwes (Mng Dir)

Division (Domestic):

CSM Deutschland GmbH (4) (100%)
Mainzer Stasse 152-160, 55411, Bingen, Germany
Tel.: (49) 67217900
Web Site: http://www.csmbakerysolutions.com
Sales Range: $25-49.9 Million
Emp.: 150
Bread Mixes & Bread Improvers
N.A.I.C.S.: 311812
Hans Peter Hertmann (Controller)

Subsidiary (Non-US):

CSM France SAS (3) (100%)
18 Rue De La Robertsau, PO Box 50, 67802, Bischheim, Cedex, France
Tel.: (33) 388838588
Sales Range: $25-49.9 Million
Bakery Ingredient Distr
N.A.I.C.S.: 311812
Florence Machuret (Product Mgr)

CSM Hellas SA (3) (100%)
34A Averof St Northern Ionia, 14232, Athens, Greece
Tel.: (30) 2102589200
Emp.: 35
Bakery Product Distr
N.A.I.C.S.: 311812
Miltiadis Kappatos (Mng Dir)
Aimilia Sotiropoulou (Mgr-Fin)

CSM Iberia SA (3) (100%)
Calle Fructuos Gelabert 6-8 San Joan Despi, 08970, Barcelona, Spain
Tel.: (34) 93 477 51 20
Sales Range: $25-49.9 Million
Emp.: 200
Bakery Product Distr
N.A.I.C.S.: 424490

CSM Italia S.r.l. (3)
Viale S. Maria della Croce 12, 26013, Crema, Cremona, Italy
Tel.: (39) 0373 8961
Bakery Product Distr
N.A.I.C.S.: 311812
Ernesto Dipietro (Country Dir)

CSM Magyarorszag Kft. (3)
Ocsai ut 5, 1239, Budapest, Hungary
Tel.: (36) 1 421 2000
Sales Range: $10-24.9 Million
Emp.: 25
Bakery Product Distr
N.A.I.C.S.: 311812

CSM Nordic A/S (3)
Marsvej 26, 6000, Kolding, Denmark
Tel.: (45) 63418300
Bakery Product Distr
N.A.I.C.S.: 424420

CSM Polska Sp. z o.o. (3) (100%)
Ul Krakowiakow 103, 02-255, Warsaw, Poland
Tel.: (48) 22 575 50 00
Web Site: http://www.csmpolska.pl
Sales Range: $25-49.9 Million
Bakery Product Distr
N.A.I.C.S.: 424490

Stefan Pleban (Mng Dir)

MARGO - CSM Schweiz AG (3) (100%)
Lindenstrasse 16, 6340, Baar, Switzerland
Tel.: (41) 417682222
Web Site: http://www.margo.ch
Sales Range: $10-24.9 Million
Emp.: 34
Bakery Product Distr
N.A.I.C.S.: 311812
Matthias Bollmann (Mgr-Fin)

Holding (Domestic):

Fogo de Chao, Inc. (2)
5908 Headquarters Dr Ste K200, Plano, TX 75024
Tel.: (972) 960-9533
Web Site: http://www.fogodechao.com
Holding Company; Restaurant Operator
N.A.I.C.S.: 551112
George Barry McGowan (CEO)
Anthony D. Laday (CFO)

Joint Venture (Non-US):

Hudson's Bay Company (2)
8925 Torbram Road, Brampton, L6T 4G1, ON, Canada
Tel.: (905) 792-4400
Web Site: http://www3.hbc.com
Rev.: $6,872,326,720
Assets: $7,165,514,720
Liabilities: $5,709,836,300
Net Worth: $1,455,678,420
Earnings: ($397,269,740)
Emp.: 40,000
Fiscal Year-end: 02/02/2019
Specialty Retail & Department Stores Operator
N.A.I.C.S.: 455110
Richard A. Baker (Exec Chm)
Marc J. Metrick (Pres-Saks Fifth Avenue)
Kerry Mader (Chief Customer Officer & Exec VP)
Todd Zator (Chief Acctg Officer)
Ian Putnam (Chief Corp Dev Officer & Pres-Real Estate)
David J. Schwartz (Gen Counsel, Sec & Exec VP)
Andrew Blecher (Chief Comm Officer)
Edward Record (CFO)
Janis Leigh (Chief HR Officer)
Stephen J. Gold (Chief Tech & Digital Ops Officer)
Vanessa LeFebvre (Pres-Lord & Taylor)
Anu Penmetcha (VP-Digital Mdsg & Ops)
Meghan Nameth (Sr VP-Mktg)
Paige Thomas (Pres-Saks OFF 5TH)
Alexander Meyer (Chief Customer Officer)

Division (Domestic):

Home Outfitters (3)
401 Bay Street, Toronto, M5H 2Y4, ON, Canada
Tel.: (416) 861-6404
Web Site: http://www.homeoutfitters.com
Kitchen, Bed & Bath Products Retailer
N.A.I.C.S.: 449129

Subsidiary (US):

Saks Incorporated (3)
611 5th Ave, New York, NY 10022
Tel.: (212) 940-5305
Web Site: http://www.saks.com
Rev.: $3,147,554,000
Assets: $2,090,247,000
Liabilities: $940,398,000
Net Worth: $1,149,849,000
Earnings: $62,882,000
Emp.: 13,900
Fiscal Year-end: 02/02/2013
Holding Company; Department Store Operator & Online Retailer
N.A.I.C.S.: 551112
Richard A. Baker (Chm)
Lucas Evans (Treas & Sr VP)

Subsidiary (Domestic):

Saks Fifth Avenue, Inc. (4)
611 5th Ave, New York, NY 10022
Tel.: (212) 753-4000
Web Site: http://www.saksfifthavenue.com
Sales Range: $1-4.9 Billion
Emp.: 500

RHONE GROUP, LLC

U.S. PRIVATE

Rhone Group, LLC—(Continued)
Department Store Operator & Online Retailer
N.A.I.C.S.: 455110
Eric Jennings (VP & Dir-Mktg-Fashion-Mens & Home Gifts)
Marta Nowakowski (Mgr-Mdsg-Jewelry & Watches)
Romina Nabhen (Dir-New Fashion & Fifth Avenue Club)
Kate Oldham (Sr VP & Gen Mgr-Mdse-Beauty, Fragrance, Lingerie & Swimwear)
Marc J. Metrick (Pres)
Roopal Patel (Dir-Fashion)
Shelley Tadaki Cramer (Gen Mgr-Waikiki)
Jennifer Welch (Mgr-District Asset Protection)
Deb McGinnis (VP & Gen Mgr-Palm Beach Gardens)
Ramona Messore (VP & Gen Mgr-Brickell City Centre)
Alicia Williams (VP-Diversity, Equity & Inclusion)
Cara Chacon (Sr VP-ESG)
Kathleen Shea (VP-Travel & Tourism Strategy)
John Antonini (Sr VP & Dir-Stores)

Division (Domestic):

The Bay (3)
401 Bay Street Suite 700, Toronto, M5H 2Y4, ON, Canada
Tel.: (416) 861-6437
Web Site: http://www.thebay.ca
Sales Range: $100-124.9 Million
Departmental Store Operator
N.A.I.C.S.: 455110
Bonnie R. Brooks (Pres & CEO)

Joint Venture (Domestic):

Neovia Logistics Services, LLC (2)
6363 N State Hwy 161 Ste 700, Irving, TX 75038
Tel.: (469) 513-7000
Web Site: http://www.neovialogistics.com
Third Party Logistics Services
N.A.I.C.S.: 541614
Zach Green (Chief Legal Officer)
Thomas Musgrave (Chief Ops & Tech Officer)
Stephen Boone (Sr Dir-Comm)
Michael Foss (Chief HR Officer)
Christopher Synek (CEO)
Dave Moore (COO)
Carlos Rodriguez (Chm)

Subsidiary (Non-US):

Neovia Logistics Germany GmbH (3)
Tel.: (49) 71176991111
Third Party Logistics Services
N.A.I.C.S.: 541614

Neovia Logistics Services (U.K.) Ltd. (3)
Peckleton Lane, Desford, LE9 9JU, United Kingdom
Tel.: (44) 1162186000
Emp.: 1,000
Logistic Services
N.A.I.C.S.: 488999

Neovia Logistics Services International NV (3)
Steenstraat 20/2, PO Box 2, 1800, Vilvoorde, Belgium
Tel.: (32) 22 63 46 11
Web Site: http://www.neovialogistics.com
Emp.: 65
Logistic Services
N.A.I.C.S.: 488999

Neovia Logistics Services Spain S.A. (3)
Guadalajara Jalisco 5, Guadalajara, 19004, Spain
Tel.: (34) 949325010
Logistic Services
N.A.I.C.S.: 561499

Subsidiary (Domestic):

North Canton Transfer Company (3)
2515 Greensburg Rd, North Canton, OH 44720
Tanker Services
N.A.I.C.S.: 484121

Petro-Chemical Transport (3)
3440 Sojourn Dr 100, Carrollton, TX 75006
Distribution & Logistics Services
N.A.I.C.S.: 541614

Affiliate (Domestic):

Orion S.A. (2)
1700 City Plz Dr Ste 300, Spring, TX 77389
Tel.: (281) 318-2959
Web Site: https://www.orioncarbons.com
Rev.: $2,030,900,000
Assets: $1,888,700,000
Liabilities: $1,429,300,000
Net Worth: $459,400,000
Earnings: $106,200,000
Emp.: 1,600
Fiscal Year-end: 12/31/2022
Holding Company; Carbon Black Mfr
N.A.I.C.S.: 551112
Corning F. Painter (CEO)
Jeffrey F. Glajch (CFO)
Carlos J. Quinones (Sr VP-Ops-Global)
Wendy Wilson (Head-IR & Corp Comm)
Pedro Riveros (Sr VP-Global Rubber Carbon Black & Americas Reg)
Sandra Niewiem (Sr VP-Global Specialty Carbon Black & EMEA Reg)

Subsidiary (Non-US):

Orion Engineered Carbons France SAS (3)
L Aubette BP 21 F, 13131, Berre-l'Etang, France
Tel.: (33) 442102242
Acetylene Mfr & Distr
N.A.I.C.S.: 325120

Orion Engineered Carbons Holdings GmbH (3)
Hahnstrasse 49, 60528, Frankfurt am Main, Germany
Tel.: (49) 69 3650 54 100
Web Site: http://www.orioncarbons.com
Sales Range: $1-4.9 Billion
Holding Company; Carbon Black Mfr & Distr
N.A.I.C.S.: 551112

Subsidiary (Domestic):

Orion Engineered Carbons GmbH (4)
Hahnstrasse 49, 60528, Frankfurt am Main, Germany
Tel.: (49) 69 3650 54 100
Web Site: http://www.orioncarbons.com
Emp.: 500
Carbon Black Mfr & Distr
N.A.I.C.S.: 325180
Charles Herlinger (Mng Dir & CFO)
Christian Eggert (Mng Dir)

Subsidiary (US):

Orion Engineered Carbons LLC (5)
4501 Magnolia Cove Dr Ste 106, Kingwood, TX 77345
Tel.: (832) 445-3300
Web Site: http://www.orioncarbons.com
Emp.: 200
Carbon Black Mfr & Distr
N.A.I.C.S.: 325180
Mark Leigh (Sr VP & Gen Mgr)
Kane Henneke (Mgr-Mktg-Polymers & Inks-Americas)
Mark Peters (Sr VP & Gen Mgr-Americas)
Sanjay Monie (Mgr-Technical Market-Inks, Coatings & Special Applications)
Jennifer S. Granados (Mgr-Mktg-Coatings, Printing Sys & Specialty Applications-Amer)
Rodney Taylor (VP-Innovation-Americas)
Pedro Riveros (Sr VP-Global Rubber Carbon Black & Gen Mgr-Americas)
Sandra Niewiem (Sr VP-Global Specialty Carbon Black & Gen Mgr-EMEA)
Michael Reers (Chief Admin Officer)

Subsidiary (Non-US):

Orion Engineered Carbons Trading (Shanghai) Co., Ltd. (5)
Room 3701-3702 BM InterContinental Business Center 100 Yutong Road, Shanghai, 200070, China
Tel.: (86) 21 6107 0966
Web Site: http://www.orioncarbons.com
Emp.: 30

Carbon Black Distr
N.A.I.C.S.: 424690
Lixing Min (Sr VP & Gen Mgr)

Holding (Domestic):

Rexair, LLC (2)
50 W Big Beaver Ste 350, Troy, MI 48084
Tel.: (248) 643-7222
Web Site: http://www.rainbowsystem.com
Water-based Filtration System Mfr
N.A.I.C.S.: 333310
Paul T. Vidovich (Chm & CEO)

Holding (Non-US):

S.G.M. Distribuzione S.r.l. (2)
Via V Schiaparelli 31, 47122, Forli, Italy
Tel.: (39) 0543 776411
Web Site: http://www.sgmdistribuzione.it
Electronics Retailer
N.A.I.C.S.: 449210

Subsidiary (Domestic):

UniEuro S.p.A. (3)
Strada Statale 231, Zona Industriale 2, 12066, Monticello d'Alba, Cuneo, Italy
Tel.: (39) 01 73 46 64 11
Web Site: http://www.unieuro.it
Sales Range: $800-899.9 Million
Electronics Stores
N.A.I.C.S.: 449210

Subsidiary (Domestic):

Monclick S.r.l. (4)
Via Energy Park 22, 20871, Vimercate, MB, Italy
Tel.: (39) 0269496949
Web Site: http://www.monclick.it
IT Hardware & Software Sales
N.A.I.C.S.: 423430

Rhone Group Advisors LLC (1)
630 5th Ave Ste 2710, New York, NY 10111
Tel.: (212) 218-6765
Investment Advisory & Management Services
N.A.I.C.S.: 523940
M. Steven Langman (Co-Founder & Mng Dir)

RHYMES AND COMPANY ADVERTISING
5909 W Loop S Ste 145, Bellaire, TX 77041
Tel.: (713) 871-8980
Web Site: http://www.rhymes.com
Year Founded: 1981
Sales Range: $25-49.9 Million
Emp.: 4
Advetising Agency
N.A.I.C.S.: 541810
Felix Rhymes (Pres)

RHYTHM AND HUES INC.
5890 W Jefferson Blvd Ste Q, Los Angeles, CA 90016
Tel.: (310) 448-7500
Web Site: http://www.rhythm.com
Sales Range: $50-74.9 Million
Emp.: 750
Cartoon Production & Visual Effects
N.A.I.C.S.: 512110
Pauline Tso (Founder & VP)
Scott Byrt (Dir-Production)
Arish Fyzee (Co-Founder & Creative Dir)

RHYTHM ENGINEERING
12351 W 96th Ter Ste 107, Lenexa, KS 66215
Tel.: (913) 227-0603
Web Site:
  http://www.rhythmtraffic.com
Sales Range: $1-9.9 Million
Emp.: 50
Traffic Signal Optimization Services
N.A.I.C.S.: 238210
Glen Bollinger (Supvr-Signalization)

RHYTHM HOLDING COMPANY, INC.

500 Boylston St 11th Fl, Boston, MA 02116
Tel.: (857) 264-4280   DE
Web Site: http://www.rhythmtx.com
Pharmaceuticals Mfr
N.A.I.C.S.: 325412
Elizabeth Stoner (Chief Dev Officer)
Bart Henderson (Founder)
Leonardus H. T. Van der Ploeg (Chief Scientific Officer)
Nithya Desikan (Chief Comml Officer)
Hunter C. Smith (CFO)
David P. Meeker (Chm)

RIA IN A BOX LLC
125 Maiden Ln Ste 15C, New York, NY 10038
Web Site: http://www.riainabox.com
Year Founded: 2005
Software Publisher
N.A.I.C.S.: 513210
Will Bressman (CEO)

Subsidiaries:

ITEGRIA, LLC (1)
1200 Shermer Rd Ste 475, Northbrook, IL 60062
Tel.: (888) 996-4642
Web Site: http://www.itegria.com
Sales Range: $1-9.9 Million
Information Technology Consulting Services
N.A.I.C.S.: 541512
Richard Mabbun (Co-Founder & CEO)
Julian Makas (Co-Founder)

RIADA TRADING COMPANY INCORPORATED
6730 W Kellogg Dr Ste 2, Wichita, KS 67209
Tel.: (316) 945-2552
Sales Range: $25-49.9 Million
Emp.: 4
Grains
N.A.I.C.S.: 424510
Ron Brock (Pres)

RIATA CAPITAL GROUP LLC
3889 Maple Ave Parkland Hall Ste 220, Dallas, TX 75219
Tel.: (214) 740-3600
Web Site: http://www.riatacapital.com
N.A.I.C.S.:
Jeff S. Fronterhouse (Mng Partner)
James J. Bradford (Partner)
Robert J. Taylor (CFO)
Angie Tade (Controller)
David Parker (VP)
Mitchell Wyly (VP)
F. Barron Fletcher III (Mng Partner)
Glenn W. Askew III (Partner)

Subsidiaries:

Eyetique LLC (1)
2242 Murray Ave, Pittsburgh, PA 15217
Tel.: (412) 422-5300
Web Site: http://www.eyetique.com
Eyecare Centers & Optical Goods Retailer
N.A.I.C.S.: 456130
Brad Childs (Reg VP)

RIB CITY GRILL, INC.
2122 2nd St, Fort Myers, FL 33901
Tel.: (239) 334-8634
Web Site: http://www.ribcity.com
Year Founded: 1989
Sales Range: $25-49.9 Million
Restaurant
N.A.I.C.S.: 722511
Beth Watson (Dir-Mktg)
Paul D. Peden (CEO)
Craig Peden (Pres)

RIB CRIB BBQ INC.
4535 S Harvard Ave, Tulsa, OK 74135-2905
Tel.: (918) 712-7427
Web Site: http://www.ribcrib.com
Rev.: $10,900,000

COMPANIES

Emp.: 23
Eating Place
N.A.I.C.S.: 722320
Bret Chandler *(Owner & CEO)*
Marc Chastain *(Pres)*
Curtis Wyant *(Gen Mgr)*

RIBBONS EXPRESS, INC.
1980 Old Cuthbert Rd, Cherry Hill, NJ 08034
Tel.: (856) 834-5222
Web Site: http://www.ribbons-express.com
Year Founded: 1988
Rev.: $33,700,000
Emp.: 49
Stationery & Office Supplies Merchant Whslr
N.A.I.C.S.: 424120
John Murabito *(Pres)*

RIBECK & CO.
570 Mt Pleasant St, West Rockport, ME 04865
Tel.: (207) 785-4165
Year Founded: 1977
Sales Range: Less than $1 Million
Emp.: 3
N.A.I.C.S.: 541810
Fred Ribeck *(Owner)*
Carol Miller *(Bookkeeper)*

RICARDO BEVERLY HILLS, INC.
6329 S 226th St, Kent, WA 98032
Web Site: http://www.ricardobeverlyhills.com
Year Founded: 1978
Luggage Designer, Mfr, Distr & Online Retailer
N.A.I.C.S.: 316990
Bob Owen *(Chm)*
Greg McNaul *(VP-Fin)*
Karla Pearson *(Coord-Shipment)*
Lynne Johnson *(VP-Design & Product Dev)*
Marcel Tedjasukmana *(Mgr-Office Ops)*
Carmen Negrea *(VP-Mktg)*

Subsidiaries:

Skyway Luggage Company (1)
30 Wall St, Seattle, WA 98121-1320
Tel.: (206) 441-5300
Web Site: http://www.skywayluggage.com
Sales Range: $10-24.9 Million
Emp.: 30
Luggage Wholesale Mfr
N.A.I.C.S.: 316990

RICART FORD INC.
4255 S Hamilton Rd, Groveport, OH 43125-9332
Tel.: (614) 836-6265
Web Site: http://www.ricart.com
Year Founded: 1953
Sales Range: $600-649.9 Million
Emp.: 950
Retailer of New & Used Automobiles
N.A.I.C.S.: 441110
Rhett Ricart *(Owner & Pres)*
Robert Carruthers *(CFO)*
Paul F. Ricart Jr. *(Owner)*

RICCIARDI BROTHERS INC.
1915 Springfield Ave, Maplewood, NJ 07040
Tel.: (973) 762-3830
Web Site: http://www.ricciardibrothers.com
Year Founded: 1929
Sales Range: $10-24.9 Million
Emp.: 15
Paint Sales
N.A.I.C.S.: 424950
Walter Ricciardi *(Pres)*

RICE AUTOMOTIVE GROUP
8330 Kingston Park, Knoxville, TN 37919
Tel.: (865) 693-0610
Web Site: http://www.riceautomotive.com
Year Founded: 1957
Holding Company; New & Used Car Dealerships & Automotive Repair Shop Owner & Operator
N.A.I.C.S.: 551112
Don Campbell *(Co-Owner)*
Scott Campbell *(Co-Owner)*

Subsidiaries:

Rice Buick-GMC, Inc. (1)
8330 Kingston Pike, Knoxville, TN 37919
Tel.: (865) 693-0610
Web Site: http://www.ricegmc.com
Sales Range: $25-49.9 Million
Emp.: 95
New & Used Car Dealer; Automotive Body & Interior Repair Services
N.A.I.C.S.: 441110
Scott Campbell *(Principal)*
Dale Duckett *(Dir-Fin)*
Marshall Myer *(Dir-ECommerce & Mgr-Customer Care)*
Mark Ruckart *(Mgr-Collision Center)*
Mark Beason *(Mgr-Svc)*
Jeff Bolen *(Mgr-Parts)*
Frank Bridges *(Asst Mgr-Fin)*
Gary Dean *(Mgr-Sls)*

Rice Chrysler Dodge, Inc. (1)
3033 Alcoa Hwy, Alcoa, TN 37701
Tel.: (865) 970-7423
Web Site: http://www.ricechryslerdodge.net
Sales Range: $10-24.9 Million
Emp.: 45
New & Used Car Dealer
N.A.I.C.S.: 441110
Curt Wright *(Pres & Gen Mgr-Sls)*
Chris Pass *(Mgr-Sls-New Vehicles)*

RICE CHRIST, INC.
1504 109th St, Grand Prairie, TX 75050
Tel.: (972) 660-6040
Web Site: http://www.rice-christ.com
Year Founded: 1967
Sales Range: $10-24.9 Million
Emp.: 10
Industrial Machinery & Equipment Whslr
N.A.I.C.S.: 423830
Terry Christ *(Pres)*

RICE EPICUREAN MARKET
5333 Gulfton St, Houston, TX 77081-2801
Tel.: (713) 662-7700
Web Site: http://www.riceepicurean.com
Year Founded: 1988
Sales Range: $75-99.9 Million
Emp.: 30
Grocery Stores; Rental Property Management
N.A.I.C.S.: 445110
Gary Friedlander *(Pres & COO)*
Bruce Levy *(CFO & Sr VP)*
Phil Cohen *(VP-Mktg)*

RICE FIELD CORPORATION
14500 Vly Blvd, City of Industry, CA 91746-2918
Tel.: (626) 968-6917
Web Site: http://www.ricefieldcorporation.com
Sales Range: $10-24.9 Million
Emp.: 120
Meat Product Production Services
N.A.I.C.S.: 311612
Derek Lee *(Pres)*

RICE LAKE WEIGHING SYSTEMS, INC.
230 W Coleman St, Rice Lake, WI 54868-2404
Tel.: (715) 234-9171
Web Site: http://www.rlws.com
Year Founded: 1946
Sales Range: $150-199.9 Million
Emp.: 400
Electro-Mechanical Weighing System Component & Instrumentation for the Industrial Scale Marketplace Mfr
N.A.I.C.S.: 333998
Mark O. Johnson *(Pres)*
Kraig Smith *(CFO)*
Scott Herman *(Dir-Matls)*
Pat Ranfranz *(Dir-Mktg)*
Douglas Hagie *(Engr-Tech Sls)*

Subsidiaries:

Heusser Neweigh Metrology Services (1)
1400 Willow Pass Ct, Concord, CA 94520-1008
Tel.: (925) 798-8900
Web Site: http://www.neweigh.com
Emp.: 600
Commercial Equipment Merchant Whslr
N.A.I.C.S.: 423440
R. L. Ruefenacht *(Owner)*

Measurement Systems International, Inc. (1)
14240 Interurban Ave S Ste 200, Seattle, WA 98168-4661
Tel.: (206) 433-0199
Web Site: http://www.msiscales.com
Sales Range: $1-9.9 Million
Scale & Balance Mfr
N.A.I.C.S.: 333998
Ron Wenzel *(Mgr-Intl Sls)*
Tim Carroll *(Mgr-Sls-Natl-North America)*

Rice Lake Weighing Systems Europe B.V. (1)
Weiland 11, 6666 MH, Heteren, Netherlands
Tel.: (31) 88 2349171
Web Site: http://www.ricelake.eu
Scale & Balance Mfr
N.A.I.C.S.: 333998

Rice Lake de Mexico (1)
Rio Madeira PTE 540 Col Del Valle, Garza Garcia, 66220, Mexico
Tel.: (52) 715 234 9171
Web Site: http://www.ricelake.mx
Weighing Machinery Mfr & Distr
N.A.I.C.S.: 333993

RICE PACKAGING, INC.
356 Somers Rd, Ellington, CT 06029
Tel.: (860) 872-8341
Web Site: http://www.ricepackaging.com
Year Founded: 1964
Sales Range: $10-24.9 Million
Emp.: 100
Folding Paperboard Box Mfr
N.A.I.C.S.: 322212
Clifford Rice *(Pres)*
Ed White *(VP-Ops)*

RICE TOYOTA SCION & COLLISION CENTER
2630 Battleground Ave, Greensboro, NC 27408
Tel.: (336) 288-1190
Web Site: http://www.ricetoyota.com
Year Founded: 1956
Sales Range: $25-49.9 Million
Emp.: 159
New Car Whslr
N.A.I.C.S.: 441110
Mary Catherine Curry *(Gen Mgr)*

RICE, HALL, JAMES & ASSOCIATES
600 W Broadway Ste 1000, San Diego, CA 92101-3383
Tel.: (619) 239-9005
Web Site: http://www.ricehalljames.com

RICH & CARTMILL, INC.

Year Founded: 1974
Sales Range: $150-199.9 Million
Emp.: 25
Investment & Asset Management Services
N.A.I.C.S.: 523940
Gary S. Rice *(Portfolio Mgr)*
Cara M. Thome *(Portfolio Mgr)*
Thao N. Buuhoan *(Pres & COO)*
Carl M. Obeck *(CFO)*
Michael Meoli *(Dir-Client Svc Mktg)*
Janine Marquez *(Chief Compliance Officer)*

RICE-KILROY CONSTRUCTION COMPANY INC.
5028 Us Hwy 26, Dubois, WY 82513
Tel.: (307) 455-3405
Rev.: $23,200,000
Emp.: 40
Highway Street & Bridge Construction
N.A.I.C.S.: 237310
James Rice *(Pres)*
Tim Payne *(Treas & Sec)*

RICELAND FOODS, INC.
2120 S Park Ave, Stuttgart, AR 72160
Tel.: (870) 673-5500
Web Site: http://www.riceland.com
Year Founded: 1921
Sales Range: $800-899.9 Million
Emp.: 1,900
Rice & Soybean Milling Services; Farmer-Owned Cooperative
N.A.I.C.S.: 311212
Harry E. Loftis *(CFO & Sr VP)*
Carl W. Brothers *(Sr VP)*
Jerry A. Delatte *(Sr VP-Domestic Food Svc)*
Scott Gower *(VP-Commodity Ops)*
Bill J. Reed *(VP)*
Terry L. Richardson *(VP & Sec)*
Dan Meins *(Dir-Mktg)*
Ben Noble *(COO & Exec VP)*
Danny Kennedy *(CEO)*

RICELAND PETROLEUM COMPANY
321 Travis St, Lafayette, LA 70503
Tel.: (337) 237-5455
Web Site: http://www.ricelandpet.com
Year Founded: 1977
Sales Range: $10-24.9 Million
Emp.: 5
Mfr Crude Petroleum Production
N.A.I.C.S.: 211120
Robert Brown *(VP)*
Clarence Ardoin *(CFO)*
William Gillette Jr. *(Pres & CEO)*

RICETEC, INC.
13100 Space Ctr Blvd Ste 300, Houston, TX 77059
Tel.: (281) 212-5100
Web Site: http://www.ricetec.com
Year Founded: 1988
Sales Range: $25-49.9 Million
Emp.: 140
Rice Seed Production & Whslr
N.A.I.C.S.: 325414
Mark Denman *(COO-Consumer Bus Div)*
Jim Thompson *(Dir-Strategic Mktg)*
Brandon Matherne *(Mgr-Infrastructure)*
Bill Helton *(Mgr-IT Strategic Plng & Dev)*
Rob Grant *(VP-Mktg & Bus Strategy)*
Jim Forgy *(Mgr-Station)*

RICH & CARTMILL, INC.
2738 E 51st St Ste 400, Tulsa, OK 74105
Tel.: (918) 743-8811
Web Site: http://www.rcins.com

RICH & CARTMILL, INC. U.S. PRIVATE

Rich & Cartmill, Inc.—(Continued)
Year Founded: 1922
Insurance Agents
N.A.I.C.S.: 524210

RICH BRANDS, LLC
1819 E Morton Ste 110, Phoenix, AZ 85020
Tel.: (602) 889-4800 GA
Web Site: http://www.richbrands.biz
Year Founded: 1998
Sales Range: $10-24.9 Million
Emp.: 27
Home Fragrances, Bath & Body Soaps & Lotions Mfr
N.A.I.C.S.: 325620
Mark Grodsky *(Pres)*

RICH DAD EDUCATION, INC.
1612 E Cape Coral Pkwy, Cape Coral, FL 33904
Tel.: (239) 542-0643
Web Site: http://www.richdadeducation.com
Emp.: 160
Business Training Schools
N.A.I.C.S.: 611519

RICH DEALERS
2802 Science Dr Unit 201, Orlando, FL 32826
Tel.: (407) 275-8667
Web Site: http://www.richdealers.com
Year Founded: 2004
Sales Range: $1-9.9 Million
Emp.: 48
Car Dealer
N.A.I.C.S.: 441110
Jimmy Vee *(Co-Founder)*
Travis Miller *(Co-Founder)*

RICH DUNCAN CONSTRUCTION INC.
2295 Rural Ave SE, Salem, OR 97302
Tel.: (503) 390-4999
Web Site: http://www.richduncanconstruction.com
Year Founded: 2002
Sales Range: $10-24.9 Million
Emp.: 18
Commercial Building Construction Services
N.A.I.C.S.: 236220
Richard E. Duncan *(Pres)*
Nathan Cooke *(VP-Ops)*
Scott Jackson *(Superintendent-Project)*
Chad Elliott *(Project Mgr)*
Bill McCall *(Project Mgr)*
Michael Richard *(Project Mgr)*

RICH FARMS INC.
2043 Springhill Furnace Rd, Smithfield, PA 15478
Tel.: (724) 564-7644
Web Site: http://www.richfarms.com
Sales Range: $10-24.9 Million
Emp.: 40
Farm Supplies
N.A.I.C.S.: 424910
Thomas A. Rich *(Pres)*
Mark Rich *(VP)*

RICH HOLDINGS, INC.
1 Robert Rich Way, Buffalo, NY 14213-1714
Tel.: (716) 878-8000 DE
Web Site: http://www.richs.com
Year Founded: 1945
Holding Company; Frozen Food Products Mfr & Whslr; Entertainment Media & Sports Team Operator
N.A.I.C.S.: 551112

William G. Gisel Jr. *(Vice Chm)*
Robert E. Rich Jr. *(Co-Chm)*
Melinda R. Rich *(Co-Chm)*
Richard Ferranti *(Pres/CEO-Rich Products Corp)*
James Deuschle *(CFO & Exec VP)*
Ted Rich *(Exec VP-Org Excellence-Rich Products Corp)*

Subsidiaries:

Rich Entertainment Group, LLC (1)
1 Robert Rich Way, Buffalo, NY 14213-1714
Tel.: (716) 878-8000
Web Site: http://www.richentertainmentgroup.com
Holding Company; Sports Teams, Travel Management Services, Restaurants, Theatre Production Services & Entertainment Venues Operator
N.A.I.C.S.: 551112
Melinda R. Rich *(Chm & Pres)*
Michael Buczkowski *(Pres-Baseball Ops)*
Melinda R. Rich *(Vice Chm)*
Joseph W. Segarra *(COO)*
William E. Grieshober Jr. *(Gen Counsel)*

Subsidiary (Domestic):

Bison Baseball, Inc. (2)
1 James D Griffin Plz, Buffalo, NY 14203
Tel.: (716) 846-2000
Web Site: http://www.bisons.com
Sales Range: $10-24.9 Million
Emp.: 50
Professional Baseball Club
N.A.I.C.S.: 711211
Robert E. Rich Jr. *(Chm)*
Michael Buczkowski *(Grp Pres-Baseball Ops & Gen Mgr)*

Naturals Baseball, Inc. (2)
3000 Gene George Blvd, Springdale, AR 72762
Tel.: (479) 927-4900
Web Site: http://www.nwanaturals.com
Professional Baseball Club
N.A.I.C.S.: 711211
Justin Cole *(VP & Gen Mgr)*

The Travel Team, Inc. (2)
2495 Main St Ste 340, Buffalo, NY 14214-2154
Tel.: (716) 862-7600
Web Site: http://www.thetravelteam.com
Travel Agency & Reservation Management Services
N.A.I.C.S.: 561510
Ronald H. Luczak *(VP-Bus Dev)*
Beth O'Donnell *(VP-Fin)*
Denise Wohlfeil *(Mgr-Acctg)*
Janet Herman *(Sr VP)*
Monika McKeel *(Mgr)*
Suzanne Rozak *(Mgr-Exec Svcs)*
Toni McConnaughey *(Mgr-Leisure Travel)*
Luke Thomas *(VP-Bus Alliances-Global)*
Joel Cristall *(VP-Strategic Tech)*
Stefanie Gramkee *(VP-Ops)*
Julie Metzgar *(VP-Leisure & Luxury Travel)*

West Virginia Black Bears Baseball, Inc. (2)
2040 Gyorko Dr, Granville, WV 26534
Tel.: (304) 293-7910
Web Site: http://www.westvirginiablackbears.com
Professional Baseball Club Operator
N.A.I.C.S.: 711211
Matthew Drayer *(Gen Mgr)*

Rich Products Corporation (1)
1 Robert Rich Way, Buffalo, NY 14213-1714
Tel.: (716) 878-8000
Web Site: https://www.richs.com
Emp.: 12,000
Packaged Frozen Food Merchant Wholesalers
N.A.I.C.S.: 424420
Melinda R. Rich *(Chm)*
Melinda R. Rich *(Vice Chm)*
Ted Rich *(Exec VP-Org Excellence)*
Yexi Liu *(CIO)*
Richard Ferranti *(Pres, Pres, CEO & CEO)*
Jeff Kim *(Pres-Global Markets)*
James Deuschle *(CFO & Exec VP-Global Supply Chain & Risk Mgmt)*

Edward Moore *(Chief HR Officer & Exec VP)*
Kara Burke *(VP-Innovation & Growth)*
Ray Burke *(Pres-US & Canada Reg)*
Jim Motos *(Sr VP-Consumer Brands)*
Robert E. Rich Jr. *(Chm)*

Subsidiary (Domestic):

Casa Di Bertacchi (2)
1910 Gallagher Dr, Vineland, NJ 08360-1545
Tel.: (856) 696-5600
Sales Range: $10-24.9 Million
Emp.: 100
Mfr of Italian Food Specialties
N.A.I.C.S.: 311612

Jacquelines Wholesale Bakery, Inc. (2)
96 Swampscott Rd, Salem, MA 01970
Tel.: (978) 744-8600
Web Site: http://www.jacquelinesbakery.com
Commercial Bakeries
N.A.I.C.S.: 311812

Subsidiary (Non-US):

Productos Rich S.A. de C.V. (2)
Carr Federal Mexico-Toluca 5640 Col Lomas de Memetla, Del Cuajimalpa, Mexico, 05330, Mexico
Tel.: (52) 53873600
Web Site: http://www.richs.com.mx
Bakery Products Mfr
N.A.I.C.S.: 311813

Plant (Domestic):

Productos Rich S.A. de C.V. - Ocoyoacac Manufacturing Facility (3)
Km 0 5 Carr Amomoluico, Santiago Tianguistenco, 52740, Ocoyoacac, Mexico
Tel.: (52) 55 5387 3600
Bakery Product Mfr & Distr
N.A.I.C.S.: 311813

Subsidiary (Non-US):

Rich Bakery Products (Tianjin) Co., Ltd. (2)
3 Xinxing Road Wuqing Developing Area, Wuqing District, Tianjin, 301700, China
Tel.: (86) 22 5968 3100
Bakery Products Mfr
N.A.I.C.S.: 311813

Plant (Non-US):

Rich Graviss Products Pvt. Ltd. - Kala Amb Manufacturing Facility (2)
Plot No 254/ 215/8/192/1 Nahan Road Village Ogli, Sirmour, Kala Amb, Himachal Pradesh, India
Tel.: (91) 22 42313500
Web Site: http://www.richgraviss.com
Bakery Product Mfr & Distr
N.A.I.C.S.: 311813

Subsidiary (Non-US):

Rich Products (M) Sdn. Bhd. (2)
3A-9 Level 3A & Mezzanine Floor The Place Jalan PJU 8/5G, Bandar Damansara Perdana, 47820, Petaling Jaya, Selangor, Malaysia
Tel.: (60) 3 7724 2890
Sales Range: $10-24.9 Million
Emp.: 8
Bakery Product Mfr & Distr
N.A.I.C.S.: 311813

Rich Products (Suzhou) Co., Ltd. (2)
15th Fl Greentech Tower 436 Heng Feng Road, Shanghai, 200070, China
Tel.: (86) 21 2419 8000
Web Site: http://www.richs.cn
Sales Range: $10-24.9 Million
Emp.: 50
Bakery Products Mfr
N.A.I.C.S.: 311813
Peter Lei *(Gen Mgr)*

Plant (Domestic):

Rich Products (Suzhou) Co., Ltd. - Suzhou Plant Manufacturing Facility (3)
75 Su Hong West Road Suzhou Industrial

Park, Suzhou, 215021, Jiangsu, China
Tel.: (86) 512 6252 6636
Web Site: http://www.rich.com
Emp.: 400
Bakery Products Mfr
N.A.I.C.S.: 311813
Jeff King *(Gen Mgr)*

Subsidiary (Non-US):

Rich Products Australia Pty Ltd. (2)
1-5 Chalmers Cres, PO Box 567, Mascot, 2020, NSW, Australia
Tel.: (61) 2 9317 4377
Web Site: http://www.richproducts.com.au
Bakery Products Mfr
N.A.I.C.S.: 311813

Representative Office (Non-US):

Rich Products Corp. - South Africa (2)
77 Earp Street Ophirton, Johannesburg, 2016, Gauteng, South Africa
Tel.: (27) 11 429 4000
Sales Range: $75-99.9 Million
Emp.: 500
Bakery Product Mfr & Distr
N.A.I.C.S.: 311813
Anthony Kriel *(Reg Mgr-Sls)*

Plant (Domestic):

Rich Products Corporation - Arlington Manufacturing Facility (2)
5885 Jetway Dr, Arlington, TN 38002
Tel.: (901) 867-2903
Bakery Product Mfr & Distr
N.A.I.C.S.: 311813

Rich Products Corporation - Brownsville Manufacturing Facility (2)
3555 E 14th St, Brownsville, TX 78521
Tel.: (956) 542-0001
Web Site: http://www.richs.com
Sales Range: $50-74.9 Million
Emp.: 270
Bakery Product Mfr & Distr
N.A.I.C.S.: 311813
Eddie Delarosa *(Gen Mgr)*

Rich Products Corporation - Brunswick Manufacturing Facility (2)
200 Glyndale Dr, Brunswick, GA 31520
Tel.: (912) 264-0097
Web Site: http://www.richproducts.com
Emp.: 280
Bakery Product Mfr & Distr
N.A.I.C.S.: 311813
Mike Callaway *(Plant Mgr)*
Mike Carlowa *(Gen Mgr)*

Rich Products Corporation - Burlington Manufacturing Facility (2)
499 Veterans Dr, Burlington, NJ 08016
Tel.: (609) 387-7200
Bakery Product Mfr & Distr
N.A.I.C.S.: 311813
Michael Ball *(Plant Mgr)*

Rich Products Corporation - Eagan Manufacturing Facility (2)
1000 Apollo Rd, Eagan, MN 55121
Tel.: (651) 286-7861
Bakery Product Mfr & Distr
N.A.I.C.S.: 311813

Rich Products Corporation - Fountain Inn Manufacturing Facility (2)
1405 S Main St, Fountain Inn, SC 29644
Tel.: (864) 409-0409
Web Site: http://www.rich.com
Bakery Product Mfr & Distr
N.A.I.C.S.: 311813
Norma Galicia *(Mgr-HR)*

Rich Products Corporation - Fresno Manufacturing Facility (2)
320 0 St, Fresno, CA 93721
Tel.: (559) 486-7380
Web Site: http://www.rich.com
Bakery Products Mfr
N.A.I.C.S.: 311813
Jeremy Haynes *(Mgr)*

Rich Products Corporation - Gallatin Manufacturing Facility (2)
349 W Main St, Gallatin, TN 37066-3240
Tel.: (615) 452-4892
Web Site: http://www.richproducts.com
Sales Range: $10-24.9 Million
Emp.: 120

COMPANIES

Producer of Chicken, Beef & Pork Barbecue Meats
N.A.I.C.S.: 311514
Connie Blackmon (Controller)

Rich Products Corporation - Hilliard Manufacturing Facility (2)
4600 Northwest Pkwy, Hilliard, OH 43026
Tel.: (614) 771-1117
Bakery Product Mfr & Distr
N.A.I.C.S.: 311813
Megan Hoffer (Coord-Quality Assurance)

Rich Products Corporation - Missouri City Manufacturing Facility (2)
13221 S Gessner, Missouri City, TX 77489
Tel.: (281) 410-6600
Food Topping Mfr
N.A.I.C.S.: 311412

Rich Products Corporation - Morristown Manufacturing Facility (2)
5701 Commerce Blvd, Morristown, TN 37814
Tel.: (423) 587-4400
Bakery Product Mfr & Distr
N.A.I.C.S.: 311813

Rich Products Corporation - Murfreesboro Manufacturing Facility (2)
625 Butler Dr, Murfreesboro, TN 37127
Tel.: (615) 890-4211
Bakery Product Mfr & Distr
N.A.I.C.S.: 311813

Rich Products Corporation - New Britain Manufacturing Facility (2)
263 Myrtle St, New Britain, CT 06053
Tel.: (866) 737-8884
Web Site: http://www.rich.com
Bakery Product Mfr & Distr
N.A.I.C.S.: 311813

Rich Products Corporation - Niles Manufacturing Facility (2)
6200 Mulford St, Niles, IL 60714
Tel.: (847) 581-1749
Sales Range: $25-49.9 Million
Emp.: 100
Bakery Product Mfr & Distr
N.A.I.C.S.: 311813

Rich Products Corporation - Rochester Manufacturing Facility (2)
10 White St, Rochester, NY 14608
Tel.: (585) 479-6020
Bakery Product Mfr & Distr
N.A.I.C.S.: 311813

Rich Products Corporation - Santa Ana Manufacturing Facility (2)
3401 W Segerstrom Ave, Santa Ana, CA 92704
Tel.: (714) 338-1145
Web Site: http://www.richs.com
Bakery Products Mfr
N.A.I.C.S.: 311813
Jorge Cancino (Supvr-Warehouse)
Linda Orienza-Gerard (Mgr-HR)

Rich Products Corporation - Santa Fe Springs - Busch Place Manufacturing Facility (2)
12805 Busch Pl, Santa Fe Springs, CA 90670
Tel.: (562) 946-6396
Bakery Product Mfr & Distr
N.A.I.C.S.: 311813

Rich Products Corporation - Santa Fe. Springs - Ann Street Manufacturing Facility (2)
9511 Ann St, Santa Fe Springs, CA 90670
Tel.: (562) 946-6396
Food Topping Mfr
N.A.I.C.S.: 311412

Rich Products Corporation - Union City Manufacturing Facility (2)
1600 Whipple Rd, Union City, CA 94587
Tel.: (510) 491-2950
Web Site: http://www.richs.com
Emp.: 120
Bakery Products Mfr
N.A.I.C.S.: 311813
Craig Eastham (Plant Mgr)

Rich Products Corporation - Vineland Manufacturing Facility (2)
1910 Gallagher Dr, Vineland, NJ 08360
Tel.: (856) 696-5600
Food Topping Mfr
N.A.I.C.S.: 311412

Rich Products Corporation - Waycross Manufacturing Facility (2)
2805 Smith Dr, Waycross, GA 31503
Tel.: (912) 283-2119
Bakery Product Mfr & Distr
N.A.I.C.S.: 311813

Subsidiary (Non-US):

Rich Products Gida Sanayi ve Ticaret Limited Sirketi (2)
Senlikkoy Mah Kirserdar Sok No 53, Florya, Istanbul, 34153, Turkiye
Tel.: (90) 212 573 8855
Bakery Product Mfr & Distr
N.A.I.C.S.: 311813

Rich Products Limited (2)
No 3701A 37/F 148 Electric Road, North Point, China (Hong Kong)
Tel.: (852) 2529 3880
Bakery Product Mfr & Distr
N.A.I.C.S.: 311813

Rich Products Limited (2)
5-7 Solent Gate Speedfields Park, Fareham, PO14 1TL, Hampshire, United Kingdom
Tel.: (44) 1329 228000
Web Site: http://www.richuk.com
Sales Range: $25-49.9 Million
Emp.: 200
Cake & Bakery Product Mfr
N.A.I.C.S.: 311813
David Hunt (Mng Dir)

Plant (Domestic):

Rich Products Limited - Kidderminster Manufacturing Facility (3)
Unit 71 Hartlebury Trading Estate, Hartlebury, Kidderminster, DY10 4JB, United Kingdom
Tel.: (44) 1299 251090
Web Site: http://www.richuk.com
Cake & Bakery Product Mfr
N.A.I.C.S.: 311813

Subsidiary (Non-US):

Rich Products Manufacturing (Thailand) Co., Ltd. (2)
5th Floor Lake Rajada Office Complex 193/25 Ratchadapisek Road, Kwang Klongtoey Khet Klongtoey, Bangkok, 10110, Thailand
Tel.: (66) 2 264 0261
Bakery Products Mfr
N.A.I.C.S.: 311813

Rich Products of Canada, Ltd. (2)
149 Rowntree Dairy Road, Box C8, Woodbridge, L4L6E1, ON, Canada
Web Site: http://www.richscanada.com
Bakery Products Mfr
N.A.I.C.S.: 311813

Plant (Domestic):

Rich Products of Canada, Ltd. - Fort Erie Manufacturing Facility (2)
12 Hagey Avenue, Fort Erie, L2A1W3, ON, Canada
Tel.: (905) 871-2605
Bakery Products Mfr
N.A.I.C.S.: 311813
Scott Verost (Plant Mgr)

Subsidiary (Non-US):

Rich de Argentina S.A. (2)
Arenales 1123 2 Piso, C1061AAI, Buenos Aires, Argentina
Tel.: (54) 11 4816 8553
Bakery Product Mfr & Distr
N.A.I.C.S.: 311813

Rich de Colombia S.A.S. (2)
Carrera 18C 121-40 Oficina 202, Bogota, 0571, Colombia
Tel.: (57) 1 74 26 121
Bakery Product Mfr & Distr
N.A.I.C.S.: 311813

Rich do Brasil Ltda. (2)
Rua Joaquim Floriano no 72 cj 165 Itaim, Sao Paulo, 04534-000, Brazil
Tel.: (55) 11 3708 1800
Web Site: http://www.richs.com.br
Bakery Product Mfr & Distr
N.A.I.C.S.: 311813

Plant (Domestic):

Rich do Brasil Ltda. - Marinique Manufacturing Facility (3)
Av Cargill s/n Horto Florestal, Mairinque, 18120-000, Sao Paulo, Brazil
Tel.: (55) 11 4708 2713
Web Site: http://www.rich.com.br
Emp.: 35
Food Topping Mfr
N.A.I.C.S.: 311412
Claudia Irie (Pres)

Subsidiary (Domestic):

SeaPak Shrimp & Seafood Company (2)
127 Airport Rd, Saint Simons Island, GA 31522
Tel.: (404) 317-0731
Web Site: http://www.seapak.com
Frozen Seafood Products Mfr & Whslr
N.A.I.C.S.: 311412

Subsidiary (Non-US):

Shanghai InstantWhip Foods Co., Ltd. (2)
No 158 Huancheng North Rd, Fengxian District, Shanghai, 201401, China
Tel.: (86) 21 6710 4567
Bakery Products Mfr
N.A.I.C.S.: 311813

Subsidiary (Domestic):

T. R. Rizzuto Pizza Crust, Inc. (2)
3420 E Riverside Ave, Spokane, WA 99202
Tel.: (509) 536-9268
Web Site: http://www.rizzutofoods.com
Sales Range: $1-9.9 Million
Emp.: 40
Flour Mixes & Dough Mfr
N.A.I.C.S.: 311824
Don Curry (VP-Sls)

The Christie Cookie Company (2)
1205 3rd Ave N, Nashville, TN 37208
Tel.: (615) 242-3817
Web Site: http://www.christiecookies.com
Cookie & Cracker Mfr
N.A.I.C.S.: 311821

RICH ICE CREAM CO.
2915 S Dixie Hwy, West Palm Beach, FL 33405
Tel.: (561) 833-7585
Web Site: http://www.richicecream.com
Year Founded: 1910
Sales Range: $10-24.9 Million
Emp.: 134
Ice Cream Mfr
N.A.I.C.S.: 311520
Randy Rich (Pres)
Krista Heath (Mgr-HR)

RICH KRAMER CONSTRUCTION INC.
789 N Miller Ave, Springfield, MO 65802
Tel.: (417) 865-5959
Web Site: http://www.richkramer.com
Rev.: $17,100,000
Emp.: 80
Commercial & Institutional Building Construction
N.A.I.C.S.: 236220
Charles Kramer (Sec)
Richard Kramer (Pres)
Marsha Sulteen (Controller & Office Mgr)
Bob Kramer (VP)

RICH MORTONS GLEN BURNIE LINCOLN MERCURY
51 Mountain Rd, Pasadena, MD 21122
Tel.: (410) 766-4000
Web Site: http://www.richmortons.com
Rev.: $33,300,000
Emp.: 80
New & Used Car Dealers
N.A.I.C.S.: 441110
Richard W. Morton (Pres)

RICH PHARMACEUTICALS, INC.
9595 Wilshire Blvd Ste 900, Beverly Hills, CA 90212
Tel.: (424) 230-7001   NV
Web Site: http://www.richpharmaceuticals.com
Year Founded: 2010
Rev.: $115,000
Assets: $37,429
Liabilities: $6,396,089
Net Worth: ($6,358,660)
Earnings: ($1,692,341)
Emp.: 1
Fiscal Year-end: 03/31/18
Pharmaceuticals Mfr
N.A.I.C.S.: 325412
Harrison Pierce Kordestani (CEO)

RICH SHIPPING (USA) INC.
1055 Corp Ctr Dr 200, Monterey Park, CA 91754
Tel.: (323) 446-8888
Web Site: http://www.richshipping.com
Sales Range: $50-74.9 Million
Emp.: 35
Freight Forwarding
N.A.I.C.S.: 488510

RICHANN LLP
1200 E Laurel Ave, McAllen, TX 78501
Tel.: (956) 630-2838
Year Founded: 1988
Sales Range: $100-124.9 Million
Emp.: 650
Grocery Stores
N.A.I.C.S.: 445110
Steven R. Grill (Partner)

RICHARD BAUER & CO. INC.
310 Cedar Ln, Teaneck, NJ 07666
Tel.: (201) 692-1005
Web Site: http://www.richardbauer.com
Sales Range: $10-24.9 Million
Emp.: 10
Printing Paper
N.A.I.C.S.: 424110
Burke Kimber (Pres)
Robert Cipolaro (Chm & CEO)

RICHARD BRADY & ASSOCIATES, INC.
3710 Ruffin Rd, San Diego, CA 92123
Tel.: (858) 496-0500   CA
Web Site: http://www.richardbrady.com
Year Founded: 1997
Sales Range: $25-49.9 Million
Emp.: 100
Engineering Design, Construction & Environmental & Remediation Services
N.A.I.C.S.: 541330
Richard Brady (Founder, Pres & CEO)
Crystal Kolland (CFO)
Jim Bowen (Chief Performance Officer)
Howard Johnson (Co-COO)
Terry Smith (Co-COO)
Javier Saunders (Exec VP)

RICHARD C. YOUNG & CO., LTD.

U.S. PRIVATE

Richard C. Young & Co., Ltd.—(Continued)

RICHARD C. YOUNG & CO., LTD.
5150 Tamiami Trl North Ste 400,
Naples, FL 34103
Tel.: (239) 213-1789
Web Site:
http://www.younginvestments.com
Year Founded: 1989
Sales Range: $1-9.9 Million
Emp.: 14
Investment Advisory Services
N.A.I.C.S.: 523940
Matthew A. Young (*Pres & CEO*)
Karen Curry (*Mgr-Customer Svc*)

RICHARD CANTRELL
1661 9th St, Santa Monica, CA 90404
Tel.: (310) 399-5511
Web Site:
http://www.hardtailforever.com
Sales Range: $10-24.9 Million
Emp.: 25
Women's & Children's Clothing
N.A.I.C.S.: 424350
Richard R. Cantrell (*Founder*)

RICHARD E. PIERSON CONSTRUCTION COMPANY, INC.
426 Swedesboro Rd, Pilesgrove, NJ 08098-2534
Tel.: (856) 769-8244   NJ
Web Site: http://www.repdemo.com
Year Founded: 1976
Sales Range: $50-74.9 Million
Emp.: 400
Complete Site Development
N.A.I.C.S.: 238910
Richard E. Pierson (*Pres*)

Subsidiaries:

Richard E. Pierson Construction Company, Inc. - Asphalt Plant   (1)
860 Oak Grove Rd, Bridgeport, NJ 08014
Tel.: (856) 467-4199
Asphalt Product Mfr
N.A.I.C.S.: 324122

Richard E. Pierson Construction Company, Inc. - Logan Plant   (1)
220 Floodgate Rd, Swedesboro, NJ 08085
Tel.: (856) 467-1421
Construction Engineering Services
N.A.I.C.S.: 237990

RICHARD G. JENNINGS III ENTERPRISES
2897 Hwy 64 E, Cashiers, NC 28717
Tel.: (828) 743-3684
Web Site:
http://www.jenningsbuilderssupply.com
Year Founded: 1984
Sales Range: $25-49.9 Million
Emp.: 55
Lumber & Other Building Materials
N.A.I.C.S.: 423310
Claire Bumgarner (*Office Mgr & Sec*)
Rob Herstek (*Pres*)
Richard G. Jennings III (*Owner*)

RICHARD GOETTLE INC.
12071 Hamilton Ave, Cincinnati, OH 45231-1032
Tel.: (513) 825-8100   OH
Web Site: http://www.goettle.com
Year Founded: 1956
Sales Range: $10-24.9 Million
Emp.: 130
Construction Services
N.A.I.C.S.: 238990
John Gruber (*Mgr-Equipment*)
Michael Dyer (*VP-Field Resources*)

Dennis Russell (*Dir-Marine Construction*)
Nick Mathews (*Project Mgr*)
Scott Eads (*Mgr-Procurement*)

RICHARD KARR CADILLAC BUICK PONTIAC GMC
900 W Lukes 340, Waco, TX 76711
Tel.: (254) 776-1111
Year Founded: 1960
Sales Range: $10-24.9 Million
Emp.: 60
Car Whslr
N.A.I.C.S.: 441110
Frances Karr Ellis (*Asst Gen Mgr*)
J. Richard Karr (*Pres*)

RICHARD KAY AUTOMOTIVE
1935 Pearman Dairy Rd, Anderson, SC 29625
Tel.: (864) 226-4000
Web Site: http://www.richardkaysuperstore.com
Year Founded: 1984
Sales Range: $10-24.9 Million
Emp.: 90
Car Whslr
N.A.I.C.S.: 441110
Richard Kay (*Pres*)

RICHARD LAYNE
15 Rancho Cir, Lake Forest, CA 92630
Tel.: (714) 325-2003
Web Site:
http://www.richardlayne.com
Rev.: $18,000,000
Emp.: 5
Commercial Art & Graphic Design
N.A.I.C.S.: 541430

RICHARD LEEDS INTERNATIONAL
135 Madison Ave Fl 10, New York, NY 10016
Tel.: (212) 532-4546
Web Site:
http://www.richardleeds.com
Sales Range: $25-49.9 Million
Emp.: 80
Mfr of Women's & Children's Nightwear
N.A.I.C.S.: 315250
Richard M. Leeds (*Chm*)
Beth Shindelman (*CFO*)

RICHARD O'BRIEN COMPANIES, INC.
640 W Tennessee Ave, Denver, CO 80223
Tel.: (303) 778-8771   CO
Sales Range: $10-24.9 Million
Holding Company; Concrete Pumping
N.A.I.C.S.: 551112
Steve O'Brien (*Mgr-Ops*)
Rick O'Dougherty (*Controller*)

RICHARD P. MORTENSON P. C.
413 5th St, Stephen, MN 56757
Tel.: (218) 478-2880
Web Site:
https://www.richmortcpa.com
Offices of Certified Public Accountants
N.A.I.C.S.: 541211
Richard Mortenson (*Owner*)

RICHARD SMYKAL INCORPORATED
1607 Taft Ave Ste 102, Wheaton, IL 60189-6981
Tel.: (630) 665-7440
Web Site:
http://www.smykalhomes.com
Sales Range: $25-49.9 Million

Emp.: 5
Single-Family Housing Construction
N.A.I.C.S.: 236115
John Wozniack (*Pres*)
Frank Johnson (*VP-Design & Dev*)

RICHARD'S BRICK CO.
234 Springer Ave, Edwardsville, IL 62025
Tel.: (618) 656-0230
Web Site:
http://www.richardsbrick.com
Sales Range: $10-24.9 Million
Emp.: 90
Brick Clay Mfr & Distr
N.A.I.C.S.: 327120
John Montley (*Pres & Treas*)

RICHARD'S PAINT MANUFACTURING COMPANY, INC.
200 Paint St, Rockledge, FL 32955
Tel.: (321) 636-6200
Web Site:
http://www.richardspaint.com
Sales Range: $10-24.9 Million
Emp.: 200
Paints & Paint Additives
N.A.I.C.S.: 325510
Edward J. Richard Sr. (*Chm*)

RICHARD'S RESTAURANTS INC.
8341 N 400 E, Bryant, IN 47326
Tel.: (260) 997-6823
Web Site:
http://www.richardsrestaurants.com
Sales Range: $10-24.9 Million
Emp.: 1,000
Owner & Operator of Family Resturants
N.A.I.C.S.: 722511
Donald C. Strong (*Pres*)
Jodie Bales (*Controller*)

RICHARDS BROTHERS OF MOUNTAIN GROVE
N and Union St, Mountain Grove, MO 65711-0866
Tel.: (417) 926-4168   MO
Web Site: http://www.rbfeeds.com
Year Founded: 1937
Sales Range: $75-99.9 Million
Emp.: 45
Operator of Grocery Stores
N.A.I.C.S.: 455219
David Skyles (*VP*)
Robert Skyles (*VP*)
Steven Skyles (*VP*)
Zane Mulberry (*Treas & Controller*)

RICHARDS BUILDING SUPPLY COMPANY
12070 W 159th St, Homer Glen, IL 60491
Tel.: (773) 586-7777
Web Site: http://www.richards-supply.com
Year Founded: 1978
Sales Range: $10-24.9 Million
Emp.: 60
Roofing & Siding Materials; Building Materials Whslr
N.A.I.C.S.: 423330
Richard J. Guzior (*Founder & Chm*)
Ron Guzior (*VP-Ops*)
Christopher Cannonito (*Gen Counsel*)
Ted Dometita (*CFO*)
William D. Swanson (*Pres & CEO*)

Subsidiaries:

Eastern Aluminum Supply of Virginia, A Richards Company   (1)
1351 W Pembroke Ave, Hampton, VA 23661
Roofing, Siding & Insulation Material Merchant Whslr

N.A.I.C.S.: 423330
Gene Pallotta (*Gen Mgr*)

Eastern Aluminum Supply-A Richards Company   (1)
311 N Oak Forest Rd, Goldsboro, NC 27534
Tel.: (919) 751-1440
Web Site: http://www.eastalum.com
Sales Range: $10-24.9 Million
Exterior Building Products Whslr
N.A.I.C.S.: 423330
William S. Hunter (*Mgr*)
Bob Cray (*Reg Mgr-Sls*)
Benito Gutierrez (*Mgr-Ops-North Carolina & South Carolina*)

Jim Waters Corporation   (1)
419 Manchester Rd, Poughkeepsie, NY 12603
Tel.: (845) 452-6310
Web Site: http://www.jimwaters.com
Sales Range: $10-24.9 Million
Emp.: 50
Exterior Building Suppliers Whslr
N.A.I.C.S.: 444180
Clay Dingman (*Mgr-Masonry Product*)
Kevin Washall (*Gen Mgr-Lower Hudson Valley*)
Brian Stewart (*Branch Mgr-Bridgeport*)

Midwest Aluminum Supply Inc.   (1)
1001 Aucutt Rd, Montgomery, IL 60538
Tel.: (630) 897-2333
Web Site: http://www.midwestsiding.com
Rev.: $18,000,000
Emp.: 28
Building Materials, Interior
N.A.I.C.S.: 423310
Gerald L. Enoch (*Pres*)

Subsidiary (Domestic):

Midwest Siding Supply Inc.   (2)
1001 Aucutt Rd, Montgomery, IL 60538
Tel.: (630) 897-2333
Web Site: http://www.midwestsiding.com
Rev.: $7,700,000
Emp.: 23
Building Materials, Interior
N.A.I.C.S.: 423310

RICHARDS CORPORATION
44931 Falcon Pl, Sterling, VA 20166
Tel.: (703) 834-5550
Web Site:
http://www.richardscorp.com
Sales Range: $10-24.9 Million
Emp.: 59
Aerial Cameras
N.A.I.C.S.: 333310
Stephen Snyder (*Controller*)
Dennis Doyle (*Exec VP-Equipment Ops*)
Jeff Levins (*Sr Project Mgr*)
Richard M. Doyle Jr. (*Pres*)

RICHARDS ELECTRIC MOTOR CO.
426 State St, Quincy, IL 62301-4146
Tel.: (217) 222-7154
Web Site:
http://www.richardselectricmotor.com
Year Founded: 1954
Sales Range: $10-24.9 Million
Emp.: 40
Electric Motor Distr
N.A.I.C.S.: 423610
Bill Dietrich (*Pres*)
Steve Smith (*Mgr-Construction*)
Greg Ehrhardt (*Mgr-Engrg*)
Roch Schulte (*Project Mgr*)
Herb Schwartz (*Asst Mgr-Shop*)
Jeremy Rose (*Project Mgr*)
Andy Pepin (*Mgr-Sls & Pur*)
Kirt Brinkley (*Project Mgr*)
Jim Keller (*Comptroller*)
Allen Taylor (*Coord-Water & Wastewater*)
Bryan Gorrell (*Mgr-Shop*)

RICHARDS ELECTRIC SUPPLY CO., INC.
4620 Reading Rd, Cincinnati, OH 45229
Tel.: (513) 242-8800
Web Site:
http://www.richardselectric.com
Year Founded: 1926
Sales Range: $50-74.9 Million
Emp.: 130
Sales of Electrical Supplies, Lighting Fixtures & Supplies, Industrial Automation Equipment, Motors & Drives & Data/Voice & Video Products
N.A.I.C.S.: 423610
Mark Schmidlin *(Gen Mgr)*
Michael Misrach *(Pres)*
Donna Ryan *(Branch Mgr)*
Liz Ransick *(Coord-Lighting)*
Dennis Hetzel *(Mgr)*
Rick Seybold *(Mgr-Lighting Sls)*
Randy Chamberlin *(Mgr-Sls)*

RICHARDS INDUSTRIES VALVE GROUP
3170 Wasson Rd, Cincinnati, OH 45209
Tel.: (513) 533-5600 OH
Web Site: http://www.richardsind.com
Year Founded: 1947
Sales Range: $25-49.9 Million
Emp.: 150
Mfr of Industrial Valves & Related Piping Specialty Products
N.A.I.C.S.: 332911
Jason Cooper *(CFO & VP-Acctg & Mgmt Info Sys)*
Charles Page *(Principal & VP)*
Bruce Broxterman *(Pres)*

RICHARDS PACKAGING INCOME FUND
N.A.I.C.S.:

RICHARDS PLUMBING & HEATING SUPPLIES
400 Mark St, Grand Rapids, MI 49548
Tel.: (616) 247-0965
Web Site:
http://www.richardsplumbing.com
Sales Range: $10-24.9 Million
Emp.: 50
Whslr of Plumbing & Energy Systems
N.A.I.C.S.: 423720

RICHARDS QUALITY BEDDING, INC.
3443 Manderley Dr Ne, Grand Rapids, MI 49525-2033
Tel.: (616) 241-2481 MI
Web Site:
http://www.richardsbedding.com
Year Founded: 1937
Sales Range: $10-24.9 Million
Emp.: 20
Mfr of Mattresses & Bedding Products
N.A.I.C.S.: 337910

RICHARDS SUPPLY COMPANY
2200 Franklin Ave, Waco, TX 76701
Tel.: (254) 754-2351 TX
Web Site:
http://www.richardssupply.com
Year Founded: 1937
Abrasives, Air Tools & Compressors Wholesaler
N.A.I.C.S.: 423830
Steve Wessinger *(CEO)*
Eric Wessinger *(Pres)*
Edwin Sanchez *(Ops Mgr)*
Bill Jones *(Controller)*
Matt Kuehl *(Mgr-E-commerce)*

Subsidiaries:

Manske Material Handling, Inc. (1)
3137 S Main St, Fort Worth, TX 76110-4230
Tel.: (817) 922-9992
Web Site: http://www.manske-inc.com
Industrial Truck, Tractor, Trailer & Stacker Machinery Mfr
N.A.I.C.S.: 333924

RICHARDS TRACTORS & IMPLEMENTS
1995 NE 8th St, Homestead, FL 33033
Tel.: (305) 247-8711
Web Site: http://www.ritrac.com
Rev.: $11,800,000
Emp.: 19
Land Preparation Machinery, Agricultural
N.A.I.C.S.: 423820
Agnes Sevilla *(Mgr-IT)*
Jose Cardenal Sr. *(Pres)*

RICHARDS, INCORPORATED
48 Harris Pl, Brattleboro, VT 05302
Tel.: (802) 254-6016 VT
Web Site:
http://www.therichardsgrp.com
Year Founded: 1867
Sales Range: $10-24.9 Million
Emp.: 80
Insurance Agency, Benefits Administration & Financial Services
N.A.I.C.S.: 524210
Mark Richards *(Pres)*
Peter Richards *(VP-Risk Mgmt)*
Drew Richards *(VP)*
Benjamin Taggard *(VP-Investment Advisory Svcs)*
Christina Flood *(Controller)*
Kathy Ballantine *(Dir-Ops & Comml Lines & Mgr-Claims)*
Barbara Miller *(Asst Mgr-Personal Lines)*
Hayley Hill *(Mgr-Personal Lines)*
Jessica Fleury *(Mgr-Personal Lines Support)*
Shannon Prescott *(Program Dir)*
Cindy Robichaud *(Supvr-Acct)*

RICHARDS-WILCOX, INC.
600 S Lake St, Aurora, IL 60506-5582
Tel.: (630) 897-6951
Web Site:
http://www.richardswilcox.com
Year Founded: 1880
Sales Range: $10-24.9 Million
Emp.: 150
Mfr of Office Storage Products, Conveyor Systems & Specialty Door Hardware
N.A.I.C.S.: 337214
Scott Patrick *(Owner)*

RICHARDS/CARLBERG
1900 W Loop S Ste 1100, Houston, TX 77027
Tel.: (713) 965-0764 NV
Year Founded: 1948
Rev.: $45,000,000
Emp.: 25
Advetising Agency
N.A.I.C.S.: 541810
Chuck Carlberg *(Principal)*
Norma Bolton *(Dir-Admin)*
Gayl Carlberg *(Principal)*
Lynda Boydstun-Nielsen *(Head-Brand Mgmt)*
Kelley Rodriguez *(Dir-Brand Media)*
Karen Holland *(Dir-Brand Creative & Art)*

RICHARDSAPEX INC.
4202 24 Main St, Philadelphia, PA 19127
Tel.: (215) 487-1100
Web Site:
http://www.richardsapex.com
Rev.: $16,000,000
Emp.: 63
Lubricating Oils & Greases
N.A.I.C.S.: 324191

RICHARDSON BOTTLING COMPANY
PO Box 44427, Tacoma, WA 98448
Tel.: (253) 535-6447
Web Site:
http://www.mountainmist.com
Year Founded: 1939
Sales Range: $10-24.9 Million
Emp.: 100
Bottled Water Mfr
N.A.I.C.S.: 312112
Neil Richardson *(Owner)*
Michael Davis *(Mgr-Coffee Svc)*
Paul K. Fischer *(Mgr-Personnel)*

RICHARDSON GROUP INC.
1818 Market St Ste 2800, Philadelphia, PA 19103
Tel.: (215) 940-9255
Web Site: http://www.richardson.com
Sales Range: $25-49.9 Million
Emp.: 110
Global Sales Training & Consulting Services
N.A.I.C.S.: 541618
Joseph Jacobs *(CTO & Sr VP)*
Deborah Antonelli *(Sr VP-Global Sls)*
Christopher Tine *(Chief Product Officer & Sr VP)*
John D. Elsey *(Pres & CEO)*

RICHARDSON HOUSING GROUP INC.
290 Constitution Blvd, Lawrenceville, GA 30046
Tel.: (770) 931-4131
Web Site: http://www.rhghomes.com
Sales Range: $10-24.9 Million
Emp.: 7
Speculative Builder, Single-Family Houses
N.A.I.C.S.: 236115
Allen Richardson *(CEO)*

RICHARDSON INDUSTRIES, INC.
904 Monroe St, Sheboygan Falls, WI 53085-1872
Tel.: (920) 467-2671 WI
Web Site:
http://www.richardsonlumber.doitbest.com
Year Founded: 1848
Sales Range: $150-199.9 Million
Emp.: 750
Mfr of Wooden Dining Room & Bedroom Furniture; Trusses, Wooden Roof & Floor Lumber; Treated Lumber; Lumber & Other Building Materials Dealer; Furniture Dealer
N.A.I.C.S.: 337122

Subsidiaries:

Richardson's Furniture Emporium (1)
202 Pine St, Sheboygan Falls, WI 53085-1560 (100%)
Tel.: (920) 467-6659
Web Site:
http://www.richardsonfurnitureemporium.com
Sales Range: $10-24.9 Million
Emp.: 5
Furniture Mfr & Sales
N.A.I.C.S.: 337215

Richco Structures (1)
W 989 County Hwy FF, Haven, WI 53083
Tel.: (920) 565-3986
Web Site: http://www.richcostr.com
Sales Range: $25-49.9 Million
Emp.: 150
Mfr of Wooden Roof & Floor Trusses
N.A.I.C.S.: 321215

Richco Structures (1)
1409 Red Maple Rd, De Pere, WI 53083
Tel.: (920) 336-9400
Web Site: http://www.richcostr.com
Sales Range: $10-24.9 Million
Emp.: 15
Mfrof Wooden Roof Trusses
N.A.I.C.S.: 321215

RICHARDSON INVESTMENTS, INC.
8601 Lomas Blvd NE, Albuquerque, NM 87112-5048
Tel.: (505) 292-0000 NM
Web Site: http://www.rich-ford.com
Year Founded: 1961
Automobile Dealership
N.A.I.C.S.: 441110
Dennis Snyder *(Pres)*
Della Andersen *(Asst Gen Mgr)*
James Orona *(Mgr-Used Cars)*
Winona Robinson *(Controller)*
John Anderson *(Mgr-Fin)*
Jimmy Griego *(Mgr-Fin)*
Allan Quezada *(Mgr-Fin)*
Ryan Ruff *(Mgr-Fin)*

RICHARDSON METALS, INC.
1080 Ford St, Colorado Springs, CO 80915
Tel.: (719) 597-0801
Web Site: http://www.richmetals.com
Year Founded: 1980
Other Aluminum Rolling & Drawing
N.A.I.C.S.: 331318

RICHARDSON MOLDING, LLC
931 Herman Alford Memorial Hwy, Philadelphia, MS 39350-8701
Tel.: (601) 656-7921 IL
Web Site:
http://www.richardsonmolding.com
Year Founded: 1858
Battery Parts Mfr
N.A.I.C.S.: 326199
David Rodriguez *(Dir-IT)*
Steve Dyer *(Pres & CEO)*
Ben Napier *(VP-HR)*
George Noel *(VP-Engrng & Tooling)*
Keith Toll *(VP-Sls)*
Nathan Lay *(VP-Ops)*

RICHARDSON REALTY AUCTION
Hwy 66, Rogersville, TN 37857
Tel.: (423) 272-7950
Web Site:
http://www.richardsonandrichardson.com
Rev.: $10,000,000
Emp.: 2
Real Estate Brokers & Agents
N.A.I.C.S.: 531210
Max Richardson *(Pres)*

RICHEY CAPACITOR INC.
1219 4th Ave S, Nashville, TN 37210
Tel.: (615) 254-3561
Web Site: http://richeycapacitor.com
Year Founded: 1965
Sales Range: $25-49.9 Million
Emp.: 350
Electronic Capacitors
N.A.I.C.S.: 334416
R. Royce Richey *(Founder & Pres)*

RICHFIELD HOSPITALITY, INC.
7600 E Orchard Rd Suite 230, Greenwood Village, CO 80111
Tel.: (303) 220-2000
Web Site: http://www.richfield.com
Year Founded: 1986
Sales Range: $10-24.9 Million
Emp.: 1,723

RICHFIELD HOSPITALITY, INC.

Richfield Hospitality, Inc.—(Continued)
Home Management Services
N.A.I.C.S.: 721110
Ellen Callas *(VP-Ops)*

RICHFIELD INDUSTRIES, CORP.
3020 Airpark Dr S, Flint, MI 48507
Tel.: (810) 233-0440 — MI
Web Site: http://www.richfieldindustries.com
Year Founded: 1939
Sales Range: $25-49.9 Million
Emp.: 600
Help Supply Services
N.A.I.C.S.: 561330
Al Rennert *(Mgr-Sls)*
Eric Wiltse *(Project Mgr)*
Lisa Dykstra *(Mgr-IT)*

RICHIE PHARMACAL COMPANY INC.
119 State Ave, Glasgow, KY 42141-1449
Tel.: (270) 651-6159
Year Founded: 1972
Rev.: $27,000,000
Emp.: 26
Pharmaceutical Products Distr
N.A.I.C.S.: 325412
Dawn Boyter *(CEO)*

RICHIE'S SUPER PREMIUM ITALIAN ICE
3 Garvey St, Everett, MA 02149
Tel.: (617) 387-3188
Web Site: http://www.richiesitalianice.com
Year Founded: 1956
Sales Range: $10-24.9 Million
Emp.: 15
Ice Cream Mfr
N.A.I.C.S.: 311520
Pamela Cardillo *(VP)*
Tom Fradi *(Gen Mgr)*
Richie Cardillo Jr. *(Pres)*

RICHLAND CHEVROLET COMPANY
511 Central Ave, Shafter, CA 93263-2121
Tel.: (661) 746-4981
Web Site: http://www.richlandchevrolet.com
Year Founded: 1969
Sales Range: $10-24.9 Million
Emp.: 40
New Car Whslr
N.A.I.C.S.: 441110
Jeffrey Millwee *(Partner)*

RICHLAND LIBRARY
1431 Assembly St, Columbia, SC 29201
Tel.: (803) 799-9084 — SC
Web Site: http://www.richlandlibrary.com
Year Founded: 1865
Sales Range: $25-49.9 Million
Emp.: 469
Public Library Operator
N.A.I.C.S.: 519210
Nathaniel A. Barber *(Chm)*
Ida W. Thompson *(Sec)*

RICHLAND PROPERTIES INC.
113-D Emily Ln, Portland, TN 37148
Tel.: (615) 325-3510
Web Site: http://www.portlandtn.com
Year Founded: 1980
Sales Range: $10-24.9 Million
Emp.: 21
Provider of Real Estate Developer Services
N.A.I.C.S.: 531110

Subsidiaries:
Richland Towers Inc. (1)
4890 W Kennedy Blvd, Tampa, FL 33609-2523
Tel.: (813) 286-4140
Web Site: http://www.richlandtowers.com
Sales Range: $10-24.9 Million
Provider of Subdividers & Developer Services
N.A.I.C.S.: 332312
Matt Peterson *(VP-Comm & Employee Dev)*

RICHLAND RESEARCH CORPORATION
3110 N 19th Ave Ste 220, Phoenix, AZ 85015-6055
Tel.: (602) 230-0012
Web Site: http://www.pioneerresearchcorporation.com
Sales Range: $25-49.9 Million
Emp.: 100
Industrial Organic Chemicals
N.A.I.C.S.: 325199
Gabe Young *(Mgr-Sls)*

RICHLAND, LLC
1905 Mines Rd, Pulaski, TN 38478
Tel.: (931) 424-3900
Web Site: http://www.richlandllc.com
Year Founded: 1999
Rev.: $13,500,000
Emp.: 85
Construction Services
N.A.I.C.S.: 333120
Jim Greene *(Pres)*
David Campbell *(VP)*

RICHMOND AMBULANCE AUTHORITY
2400 Hermitage Rd, Richmond, VA 23220-1310
Tel.: (804) 254-1150 — VA
Web Site: http://www.raaems.org
Year Founded: 1991
Sales Range: $10-24.9 Million
Emp.: 295
Ambulance Authority Services
N.A.I.C.S.: 621910
Elizabeth Matish *(Sec)*
J. Stephen Ford *(Treas)*
Terone B. Green *(Chm)*
Joseph Boatwright III *(Vice Chm)*

RICHMOND AREA ASSOCIATION FOR RETARDED CITIZENS
3600 Saunders Ave, Richmond, VA 23227
Tel.: (804) 358-1874 — VA
Web Site: http://www.richmondarc.com
Year Founded: 1954
Sales Range: $10-24.9 Million
Emp.: 488
Behavioral Healthcare Services
N.A.I.C.S.: 621420
Kimberly Watson *(VP-Dev & Comm)*
John B. Walker *(Pres & CEO)*
Julee Fletcher *(CFO & Sr VP)*
Charles Story III *(VP-HR)*

RICHMOND BONDED WAREHOUSE CORP.
326 Prep Phillips Dr, Augusta, GA 30901
Tel.: (706) 724-0106
Web Site: http://www.rbwlogistics.com
Sales Range: $10-24.9 Million
Emp.: 60
Provider of General Warehousing & Storage Services & Trucking Services
N.A.I.C.S.: 493110
Frank Anderson *(VP)*

RICHMOND CORRUGATED BOX INC.
5301 Corrugated Rd, Sandston, VA 23150
Tel.: (804) 222-1300
Web Site: http://www.richmondcorrugatedbox.com
Sales Range: $10-24.9 Million
Emp.: 30
Boxes Corrugated: Made From Purchased Materials
N.A.I.C.S.: 322211
Hobbs Goodwin *(Gen Mgr)*

RICHMOND FORD
4600 W Broad St, Richmond, VA 23230-3206
Tel.: (804) 358-5521
Web Site: http://www.richmondford.com
Automobiles & Trucks
N.A.I.C.S.: 423110

RICHMOND HOME NEED SERVICES INC
3155 Amboy Rd, Staten Island, NY 10306
Tel.: (718) 987-8400 — NY
Year Founded: 1971
Sales Range: $10-24.9 Million
Emp.: 468
Women Healthcare Services
N.A.I.C.S.: 621610
Manuel Lagmay *(Chm)*
Barbara Davis *(Vice Chm)*
Bernard Del Ray *(Treas)*
Cynthia Roberti *(Sec)*

RICHMOND HONAN MEDICAL PROPERTIES INC.
975 Johnson Ferry Rd Ste 450, Atlanta, GA 30342
Tel.: (404) 255-6358 — MD
Web Site: http://richmondhonan.com
Sales Range: $10-24.9 Million
Emp.: 30
Medical Facilities Real Estate Investment Services
N.A.I.C.S.: 525990
Scott C. Honan *(Co-Founder & CEO)*
Lea Richmond III *(Co-Founder)*

RICHMOR AVIATION INC.
Columbia County Airport, Hudson, NY 12534
Tel.: (518) 828-9461
Web Site: http://www.richmor.com
Year Founded: 1967
Sales Range: $25-49.9 Million
Emp.: 300
Provider of Nonscheduled Air Transportation
N.A.I.C.S.: 481219
Mahlon Richards *(Pres)*
David Buono *(Mgr-FBO)*
Valerie Calder *(Office Mgr)*
Peter Shaffer *(Dir-Ops)*

RICHNER COMMUNICATIONS, INC.
2 Endo Blvd, Garden City, NY 11530
Tel.: (516) 569-4000 — NY
Web Site: http://www.liherald.com
Year Founded: 1964
Sales Range: $25-49.9 Million
Emp.: 130
Newspaper Publishers
N.A.I.C.S.: 513110
Michael Bologna *(VP-Ops)*
Rhonda Glickman *(VP-Sls)*
Glenn Oswald *(CFO)*
Lori Berger *(Mgr-Specialty Sls & Digital)*
Ellen Reynolds *(Mgr-Inside Adv Sls & Xpress Coups)*
Diane Ramdass *(Dir-Circulation)*
Anthony Rifilato *(Editor)*
Jeff Bessen *(Editor)*
Scott Brinton *(Exec Editor)*

RICHPORT PROPERTIES INC.
PO Box 427, Tucker, GA 30085
Tel.: (770) 934-0710
Web Site: http://www.richport.com
Sales Range: $10-24.9 Million
Emp.: 8
Operative Builders
N.A.I.C.S.: 236117
Richard Porter *(Owner)*

RICHRELEVANCE, INC.
49 Stevenson St Ste 950, San Francisco, CA 94105
Tel.: (415) 956-1947
Web Site: http://www.richrelevance.com
Software Publisher
N.A.I.C.S.: 513210
David Selinger *(Co-Founder)*
Diane Kegley *(CMO)*
Kevin Duffey *(VP-IT Ops)*
Zach Koekemoer *(CFO)*
Amanda Berger *(Sr VP-Americas)*
Sarath Jarugula *(Chief Product Officer)*
Jim Crumbacher *(Officer-Data Production & Sr VP-Legal & Bus Ops)*
Ricardo Fuchs *(Sr VP-APAC)*
Robb Miller *(Sr VP-Sls-Americas)*
William D. Pearce *(Chm)*

Subsidiaries:
RichRelevance France (1)
9 rue du Quatre Septembre, 75002, Paris, France
Tel.: (33) 1 70 98 31 90
Software Publisher
N.A.I.C.S.: 513210

RichRelevance UK (1)
Soane Point 6-8 Market Place, Reading, RG1 2EG, Berkshire, United Kingdom
Tel.: (44) 118 9255018
Software Publisher
N.A.I.C.S.: 513210

RICHTER & RATNER CONTRACTING CORPORATION
45 W 36th St 12th Fl, New York, NY 10018
Tel.: (212) 936-4500 — NY
Web Site: http://www.richterratner.com
Year Founded: 1912
Sales Range: $50-74.9 Million
Emp.: 100
General Contracting Services
N.A.I.C.S.: 236220
Michael H. Ratner *(Owner & CEO)*
Marc Heiman *(Pres & COO)*
David Brown *(VP-Construction Ops)*

RICHTER7
280 S 400 W Ste 200, Salt Lake City, UT 84101
Tel.: (801) 521-2903 — UT
Web Site: http://www.richter7.com
Year Founded: 1971
Rev.: $42,000,000
Emp.: 37
Advetising Agency
N.A.I.C.S.: 541810
Dave Newbold *(Pres)*
Scott Rockwood *(CEO)*
Tim Brown *(Partner)*
Peggy Lander *(Partner)*
Marcia Winn *(Bus Mgr)*
Tal Harry *(Acct Dir)*
David Martin *(Dir-Media)*
Tony Robinson *(CFO)*

Ryan Anderson *(Dir-Art & Digital Retoucher)*
Gary Sume *(Dir-Creative)*
Peter Brown *(Partner)*

RICHWOOD BANCSHARES, INC.
28 N Franklin St, Richwood, OH 43344
Tel.: (740) 943-2317
Web Site:
    http://www.richwoodbancshare.com
Bank Holding Company
N.A.I.C.S.: 551111
Chad Hoffman *(Pres & CEO)*

Subsidiaries:

The Richwood Banking Company   (1)
28 N Franklin St, Richwood, OH 43344
Tel.: (740) 943-2317
Web Site: http://www.richwoodbank.com
Rev.: $6,000,000
Emp.: 18
Commercial Banking Services
N.A.I.C.S.: 522110
Chad Hoffman *(Pres & CEO)*
Sierra Heaton *(Mgr-Brands)*

RICK BALL GM SUPERSTORE INC
1507 W Ashley Rd, Boonville, MO 65233
Tel.: (660) 882-5688
Web Site: http://www.rickball.com
Sales Range: $10-24.9 Million
Emp.: 50
Automobiles, New & Used
N.A.I.C.S.: 441110
Richard C. Ball *(Pres)*
Debbie Rapp *(Controller)*

RICK CASE ENTERPRISES, INC.
875 N State Rd 7, Fort Lauderdale, FL 33317
Tel.: (954) 581-5885   FL
Web Site: http://www.rickcase.com
Sales Range: $800-899.9 Million
Emp.: 1,000
Holding Company; New & Used Car Dealerships Owner & Operator
N.A.I.C.S.: 551112
Richard J. Case *(Owner, Pres & CEO)*

Subsidiaries:

Rick Case Acura   (1)
875 N State Rd 7, Fort Lauderdale, FL 33317
Tel.: (954) 715-7798
Web Site: http://www.rickcaseacura.com
Sales Range: $25-49.9 Million
Emp.: 200
New & Used Car Distr
N.A.I.C.S.: 441110
Benny Bahal *(Gen Mgr)*
Karim Kassim *(Mgr-Sls-New Cars)*
Sean Segaloff *(Mgr-Sls & Bus Dev Center)*
Mike Lichtenthal *(Mgr-Svc)*
John Evans *(Mgr-Fin)*
Sari Medina *(Mgr-Customer Svc)*
Mike Cortella *(Mgr-Sls)*

Rick Case Hyundai - Ft. Lauderdale   (1)
925 N State Rd 7, Plantation, FL 33317
Tel.: (954) 289-9146
Web Site:
    http://www.ftlauderdalehyundai.com
Rev.: $36,900,000
Emp.: 45
Automobile New & Used Distr
N.A.I.C.S.: 441110
Richard Case *(Owner)*

RICK ENGINEERING COMPANY
5620 Friars Rd, San Diego, CA 92110
Tel.: (619) 291-0707
Web Site:
    http://www.rickengineering.com
Year Founded: 1955
Rev.: $36,100,000
Emp.: 415
Design & Engineering Services
N.A.I.C.S.: 541330
Robert Stockton *(Owner)*
Kai Ramer *(COO)*

RICK JOHNSON & COMPANY, INC.
1120 Pennsylvania St NE, Albuquerque, NM 87110-7408
Tel.: (505) 266-1100   NM
Web Site: http://www.rjc.com
Year Founded: 1977
Rev.: $30,000,000
Emp.: 50
Advetising Agency
N.A.I.C.S.: 541810
Marge White *(Chief Admin Officer & Sr VP)*
James McKenna *(Pres)*
Pam Schneider *(Sr VP & Dir-Client Svcs)*
Judy Cullison *(VP)*
Deborah U. Johnson *(CEO)*
Jess Kowal *(VP & Creative Dir)*
Katie Duberry *(Assoc Dir-Creative)*

RICK KOCH OIL CO.
1501 N Airport Rd, Weatherford, OK 73096
Tel.: (580) 772-6076
Sales Range: $10-24.9 Million
Emp.: 5
Fuel Whslr; Owner & Operator of Convenience Stores
N.A.I.C.S.: 424710
Rick Koch *(Owner)*

RICK WEAVER BUICK-PONTIAC-GMC
714 W 12th St, Erie, PA 16501
Tel.: (814) 455-8071
Web Site:
    http://www.rwbuypower.com
Rev.: $21,300,000
Emp.: 54
New & Used Automobiles
N.A.I.C.S.: 441110
Adam Weaver *(Pres)*

RICK'S CUSTOM FENCING & DECKING
4543 SE Tualatin Valley Hwy, Hillsboro, OR 97123
Tel.: (503) 648-7830   OR
Web Site:
    http://www.ricksfencing.com
Year Founded: 1980
Sales Range: $10-24.9 Million
Emp.: 30
Retailer of Cedar Fencing & Decking
N.A.I.C.S.: 321999
Tom Marshall *(Mgr-Store)*

RICK'S RESTORATIONS
1112 S Commerce St, Las Vegas, NV 89102
Tel.: (702) 655-5544
Web Site:
    http://www.ricksrestorations.com
Sales Range: $25-49.9 Million
Emp.: 28
Restoration Services
N.A.I.C.S.: 562910
Rick Dale *(Owner)*

RICKENBACKER INTERNATIONAL CORPORATION
3895 S Main St, Santa Ana, CA 92707
Tel.: (714) 545-5574
Web Site:
    http://www.rickenbacker.com
Sales Range: $10-24.9 Million
Emp.: 100
Guitars & Musical Instrument Accessories Mfr & Sales
N.A.I.C.S.: 339992
Richard Cannata *(Supvr-Factory)*

RICKETTS FARM SERVICE, INC.
Hwy 24 W 2 Miles, Salisbury, MO 65281
Tel.: (660) 388-6489   MO
Web Site:
    http://www.rickettsfarm.com
Year Founded: 1972
Sales Range: $10-24.9 Million
Emp.: 15
Agricultural Feed For Livestock
N.A.I.C.S.: 424910
Seth Ricketts *(Pres)*

RICKEY'S RESTAURANT & LOUNGE, INC.
4799 Hollywood Blvd, Hollywood, FL 33021
Tel.: (954) 966-1429   FL
Web Site: http://rickeyswings.com
Year Founded: 1955
Fast Food Restaurants
N.A.I.C.S.: 722513

RICKSHAW BAGWORKS
904 22nd St, San Francisco, CA 94107
Tel.: (415) 904-8368
Web Site:
    http://www.rickshawbags.com
Year Founded: 2007
Sales Range: $1-9.9 Million
Emp.: 20
Custom Bag Design & Manufacturing Company
N.A.I.C.S.: 316990
Mark Dwight *(Founder & CEO)*

RICO INDUSTRIES INC.
7000 N Austin Ave, Niles, IL 60714-4602
Tel.: (312) 427-0313
Web Site: http://www.ricoinc.com
Rev.: $12,000,000
Emp.: 80
Wallets
N.A.I.C.S.: 316990
Bev Streitenfeld *(Controller)*
Teryn Frank *(Coord-Mktg & Sls)*

RICO MOTOR COMPANY
220 S 5th St, Gallup, NM 87301-5302
Tel.: (505) 722-2271   NM
Web Site:
    http://www.ricoautocomplex.com
Year Founded: 1919
Sales Range: $50-74.9 Million
Emp.: 100
Retail Sales of New & Used Automobiles
N.A.I.C.S.: 441110
Marty Menapace *(Gen Mgr)*

RICOCHET PARTNERS, INC.
521 SW 11th Ave Ste 400, Portland, OR 97205
Tel.: (503) 220-0212
Web Site:
    http://www.ricochetpartners.com
Sales Range: $10-24.9 Million
Emp.: 10
Brand Development & Integration, Consulting, Integrated Marketing, Local Marketing, Media Relations, New Product Development
N.A.I.C.S.: 541810

Peter Charlton *(CEO & Chief Creative Officer)*
Jeanne McKirchy-Spencer *(Pres & Chief Strategy Officer)*
Ron Spencer *(Pres & Chief Strategy Officer)*
Carrie Wright *(Sr Dir-Art)*

RICS SOFTWARE
7602 E 88th Pl, Indianapolis, IN 46256
Tel.: (317) 275-5992
Web Site:
    http://www.ricssoftware.com
Year Founded: 1983
Sales Range: $1-9.9 Million
Emp.: 36
Retail Software Platform
N.A.I.C.S.: 513210
David B. Becker *(Pres)*
Dan Sanders *(CIO)*
Mark Brown *(CFO)*
Jason Becker *(CEO & COO)*

RIDA DEVELOPMENT CORP.
1777 Walker St Ste 501, Houston, TX 77010
Tel.: (713) 961-3835   TX
Web Site:
    http://www.championsgate.com
Sales Range: $25-49.9 Million
Emp.: 9
Real Estate Investment & Development Services
N.A.I.C.S.: 531390
Dave Mitzner *(Pres)*
Marc Reicher *(Sr VP-Ops)*
Ira Mitzner *(Sr VP-Dev)*
Yvonne Shouey *(Dir-Sls & Leasing & Project Mgr)*

Subsidiaries:

Hyatt Regency Orlando   (1)
9801 International Dr, Orlando, FL 32819
Tel.: (407) 284-1234
Web Site:
    http://www.orlando.regency.hyatt.com
Hotel Operations
N.A.I.C.S.: 721110

RIDDLE VILLAGE
1048 W Baltimore Pike, Media, PA 19063
Tel.: (610) 891-3700   PA
Web Site:
    http://www.riddlevillage.com
Year Founded: 1993
Sales Range: $25-49.9 Million
Emp.: 450
Lifecare Retirement Community Operator
N.A.I.C.S.: 623311
Robert G. Bertolette *(Pres & CEO)*
Kimberly Foster-Roguszewski *(CFO & VP)*
Ronald J. Waterman *(COO & VP)*
Daniel E. Kennedy *(Chm)*
Jon D. Helms *(Sec)*

RIDDLEBERGER BROS., INC.
6127 S Valley Pike, Mount Crawford, VA 22841
Tel.: (540) 434-1731   VA
Web Site: http://www.rbiva.com
Year Founded: 1940
Sales Range: $25-49.9 Million
Emp.: 300
Mechanical Contractor
N.A.I.C.S.: 238220
Kelly Blosser *(CFO)*

RIDDLES GROUP, INC.
2707 Mt Rushmore Rd, Rapid City, SD 57701

RIDDLES GROUP, INC.

Riddles Group, Inc.—(Continued)
Tel.: (800) 741-7609   SD
Web Site:
http://www.riddlesjewelry.com
Year Founded: 1959
Precious or Semi-Precious Metal Jewelry Mfr
N.A.I.C.S.: 339910
J. Brett Riddle (Pres)

RIDE ENTERTAINMENT SYSTEMS, INC.
114 Log Canoe Cir, Stevensville, MD 21666
Tel.: (410) 643-9300   MD
Web Site:
http://www.rideentertainment.com
Sales Range: $50-74.9 Million
Carnival & Amusement Park Equipment
N.A.I.C.S.: 423850
Edward Hiller (Pres)
Adam Sandy (Chief Bus Dev Officer)

RIDE-AWAY HANDICAP EQUIPMENT
54 Wentworth, Londonderry, NH 03053
Tel.: (603) 437-4444
Web Site: http://www.ride-away.com
Year Founded: 1986
Sales Range: $10-24.9 Million
Emp.: 50
Provider of Modification Services for Vehicles
N.A.I.C.S.: 811121
Jim Scruggs (Gen Mgr)
Barry Linder (Mgr-Mktg)
Pete Potvin (Mgr-Production & Svc)
Rick Baldisci (Gen Mgr)
Davis McCabe (VP-Fin & Insurance)
Jesse Lore (Dir-Trng)
Kathy Kittle (CFO & VP)
Ernest Foote (Mgr-Pre-Owned Vehicle)
Ron Hoy (Gen Mgr)

RIDEAU PACKAGING, INC.
1025 Paramount Pkwy, Batavia, IL 60510
Tel.: (630) 761-8544   IL
Web Site:
http://www.greenseedcp.com
Sales Range: $10-24.9 Million
Emp.: 100
Outsourced Consumer Product Packaging Services
N.A.I.C.S.: 561910
Hector Garcia (Dir-Ops)
Donald S. Reed (CEO)
David Gray (Pres & Chief Growth Officer)
Jeff Sawyers (COO)

RIDEGEAR.COM
121 DuBois St, Santa Cruz, CA 95060
Tel.: (831) 425-4044
Web Site: http://www.ridegear.com
Sales Range: $1-9.9 Million
Emp.: 26
Online After-Market Motor Vehicle Accessories Retailer
N.A.I.C.S.: 441330
Tammie McKenzie (Mgr-Mktg)

RIDER DICKERSON, INC.
815 25th Ave, Bellwood, IL 60104
Tel.: (312) 427-2926
Web Site:
http://www.riderdickerson.com
Year Founded: 1903
Printing Services
N.A.I.C.S.: 323111
Florence Breitbarth (Office Mgr)
Frank Cominsky (Mgr-Press Room)

Bill Barta (Pres & CEO)
Dean Petrulakis (Sr VP-Bus Dev)
Derek Phillips (VP-Ops)
Tim Gaber (Mgr-Digital Solutions)

RIDERS BIKE SHOP INC.
4750 Norrel Dr, Trussville, AL 35173
Tel.: (205) 655-1234
Web Site:
http://www.ridersharleydavidson.com
Sales Range: $10-24.9 Million
Emp.: 40
Motorcycle Dealers
N.A.I.C.S.: 441227
Tim Peek (Gen Mgr)
William E. Peek Sr. (Pres)

RIDESAFELY.COM, INC.
78 Cabot Blvd E, Langhorne, PA 19047-1802
Tel.: (215) 289-0300   PA
Web Site: http://www.ridesafely.com
Year Founded: 2002
Sales Range: $10-24.9 Million
Emp.: 18
Online Marketing Service for Salvage Car & Motorcycle Dealers
N.A.I.C.S.: 441227
Max Repik (Co-Founder)

Subsidiaries:

RideSafely Bulgaria   (1)
52 Khan Omurtag St, 1504, Sofia, Bulgaria
Tel.: (359) 887761436
Web Site: http://bg.ridesafely.com
Sales Range: $10-24.9 Million
Emp.: 3
Online Marketing Service for Salvage Car & Motorcycle Dealers
N.A.I.C.S.: 441227

RideSafely Canada, Inc.   (1)
54 Murray Rd, North York, M3K 1T2, ON, Canada
Tel.: (416) 848-3130
Web Site: http://www.RideSafely.ca
Online Marketing Service for Salvage Car & Motorcycle Dealers
N.A.I.C.S.: 441227

RideSafely Europe GmbH   (1)
Sand 9, 21107, Hamburg, Germany
Tel.: (49) 4067303853
Web Site: http://www.RideSafely.eu
Online Marketing Service for Salvage Car & Motorcycle Dealers
N.A.I.C.S.: 441227

RideSafely Middle East   (1)
Dubai Tower Building, PO Box 71719, Baniyas-Dira, Dubai, United Arab Emirates
Tel.: (971) 43958400
Web Site: http://www.ridesafely.com
Online Marketing Service for Salvage Car & Motorcycle Dealers
N.A.I.C.S.: 441227

RIDG-U-RAK, INC.
120 S Lake St, North East, PA 16428-1232
Tel.: (814) 725-8751   PA
Web Site: http://www.ridgurak.com
Year Founded: 1942
Sales Range: $75-99.9 Million
Emp.: 360
Complete Storage Systems & Pallet Storage Racks Designer & Distr
N.A.I.C.S.: 337126
Paul DeRaimo (Dir-Quality)
Ian Hodapp (Supvr-Shipping)
Karen Jendruczak (Sec)
Debbie Mills (Mgr-Acctg)
Julie Monroe (Engr-Safety & Regulatory Compliance)
Steve Smith (Mgr-Traffic)
Donald Spellman (Project Mgr)
Ted Gorniak (Mgr-Inside Sls)
Dave Olson (Mgr-Sls-Natl)

RIDGE DIAGNOSTICS, INC.

4225 Executive Sq Ste 600, La Jolla, CA 92037   DE
Web Site: http://www.ridgdx.com
Neuropsychiatric Disorder Biomarker Developer & Marketer
N.A.I.C.S.: 325413
Lonna J. Williams (CEO)
Lori Henderson (VP-Mktg Strategy & Bus Dev)
Perry Renshaw (Co-Founder & Chief Medical Officer)
Bo Pi (Co-Founder & CTO)
Kelly San George (CFO)
Larry G. Stambaugh (Chm)

RIDGE SERVICES INC.
18 Thatcher Rd, Dayton, NJ 08810
Tel.: (609) 819-8864
Rev.: $17,657,731
Emp.: 400
General Warehousing
N.A.I.C.S.: 493110

RIDGE-FORT WAYNE COMPANY, INC.
630 Ave of Autos, Fort Wayne, IN 46804
Tel.: (260) 459-1650   IN
Web Site:
http://www.ridgecompany.com
Year Founded: 1948
Sales Range: $25-49.9 Million
Emp.: 20
Automotive Parts & Accessories Retailer
N.A.I.C.S.: 441330
Andrew Thomas (VP-Sls)
Matthew Thomas (VP)

RIDGECREST HERBALS, INC.
3683 W 2270 S Ste A, Salt Lake City, UT 84120-2306
Tel.: (801) 978-9633
Web Site: http://www.rcherbals.com
Year Founded: 1986
Sales Range: $10-24.9 Million
Emp.: 25
Perishable Prepared Food Mfr
N.A.I.C.S.: 311991
Matt Warnock (Pres)
Chris Herbert (Mgr-Retail Sls)
Will Christensen (Mgr-Sls-Natl)

RIDGELINE INTERNATIONAL INC.
8281 Greensboro Dr Ste 300, Tysons Corner, VA 22102
Tel.: (703) 544-2424
Web Site:
http://www.ridgelineintl.com
Year Founded: 2015
Sales Range: $25-49.9 Million
Emp.: 125
Software Development Services
N.A.I.C.S.: 541511
Erik Wittreich (CEO)

RIDGELINE MANAGEMENT COMPANY
59 E 11th Ave Ste 200, Eugene, OR 97401
Tel.: (541) 686-1119
Web Site:
http://www.ridgelinemc.com
Sales Range: $25-49.9 Million
Continuing Care Retirement Communities Operator
N.A.I.C.S.: 623311
Louise Bates (Reg Dir)
Myrna Dorfman (Dir-Bus Ops)
Chuck McGlade (CEO)
Crystal Taylor (CFO)

RIDGEMONT PARTNERS MANAGEMENT LLC

101 S Tyron St St 3400, Charlotte, NC 28280
Tel.: (704) 944-0914   DE
Web Site:
http://www.ridgemontep.com
Privater Equity Firm
N.A.I.C.S.: 523999
Travis Hain (Partner)
Rob Edwards (Partner)
Donny Harrison (Partner)
George Morgan (Partner-Dallas)
Scott Poole (Partner-Charlotte)
Walker Poole (Partner-Charlotte)
Trey Sheridan (Partner-Charlotte)
John Shimp (Partner-Charlotte)
Ed Balogh (COO)
Jack Purcell (Partner-Charlotte)
Tim Dillon (Partner)
Charles Anderson (Partner)
Seth Peck (VP-Dallas)
Cay Freihofer (Partner)
John Chirokas (Controller-Charlotte)
Kelly Lineberger (VP-Charlotte)
Laura Fahrney (Principal-Charlotte)
Matt Ibbetson (VP-Ops-Charlotte)
Petri Lindberg (VP-Charlotte)
Daniel Harknett (Partner)
Mary Hunt (Office Mgr)
Jane H. Caldwell (Chief Admin Officer)

Subsidiaries:

Abrasive Products & Equipment, LLC   (1)
3009 Pasadena Fwy Ste 100, Pasadena, TX 77503
Tel.: (281) 930-0808
Web Site: http://www.apeblastandpaint.com
Sales Range: $10-24.9 Million
Portable Air Blast Equipment Sales, Rental & Maintenance Services
N.A.I.C.S.: 423440
Kevin Willis (Gen Mgr)

Subsidiary (Domestic):

BKW Environmental Services, LLC   (2)
2330 Pasadena Blvd, Pasadena, TX 77502
Tel.: (713) 473-4445
Web Site: http://www.bkwenvironmental.com
Portable Air Blast Equipment Sales & Rental Services
N.A.I.C.S.: 423440

Corrosion Specialties, LLC   (2)
2221 Northmont Pkwy Ste 200, Duluth, GA 30096
Tel.: (770) 938-7263
Web Site: http://www.corrosionspec.com
Sales Range: $1-9.9 Million
Emp.: 14
Corrosion Control Products & Equipment Distr
N.A.I.C.S.: 423830
Matt Steinmann (Pres)

Marco Group International, Inc.   (2)
3425 E Locust St, Davenport, IA 52803
Tel.: (563) 324-2519
Abrasive Product Mfr
N.A.I.C.S.: 327910

Subsidiary (Non-US):

Manus Abrasive Systems, Inc   (3)
1040 78 Avenue, Edmonton, T6P 1L7, AB, Canada
Tel.: (780) 468-2588
Web Site: http://www.manusabrasive.com
Abrasive Blast Equipment Mfr & Distr
N.A.I.C.S.: 327910
Cory MacLean (Pres)

Agape Care Group   (1)
110 Dillon Dr, Spartanburg, SC 29307
Tel.: (800) 932-2738
Web Site: http://agapecaregroup.com
Hospital & Outpatient Services
N.A.I.C.S.: 622110
Troy Yarborough (CEO)

Subsidiary (Domestic):

Serenity Hospice Care LLC   (2)

COMPANIES

510 Bellevue Ave, Dublin, GA 31021
Tel.: (478) 275-2023
Web Site:
http://www.serenityhospicecares.com
Sales Range: $1-9.9 Million
Emp.: 97
Specialty Hospitals
N.A.I.C.S.: 622310
Chad Hutcheson (Sec)
John W. Souza (CFO)

Allied 100, LLC (1)
1800 US Hwy 51 N, Woodruff, WI 54568
Tel.: (715) 358-2329
Web Site: http://www.allied100.com
Sales Range: $10-24.9 Million
Medical, Hospital Equipment & Supplies Merchant Whslr
N.A.I.C.S.: 423450
Kenneth Raupach (Co-Founder & Co-Owner)
Jonathan A. Dobbs (Co-Founder & Co-Owner)

Subsidiary (Domestic):

LifeGuard Medical Solutions, LLC (2)
821 Fesslers Pkwy, Nashville, TN 37210
Tel.: (615) 256-1818
Web Site: http://www.lifeguardmed.com
Equipment, Education & Management for Automated External Defibrillator Programs
N.A.I.C.S.: 423450
Chet Frist (Co-Founder & Principal)
John C. Frist (Dir-Medical)

American Outcomes Management, L.P. (1)
5009 S Hulen St, Fort Worth, TX 76132-1937
Tel.: (817) 263-4700
Web Site:
http://www.americanoutcomes.com
Women Healthcare Services
N.A.I.C.S.: 621610
Kevin O'Connor (Pres)
Chris York (Chm)

Anne Arundel Dermatology Management LLC (1)
600 Ridgely Ave Stes 120 & 123, Annapolis, MD 21401
Tel.: (443) 351-3376
Web Site: http://aadermatology.com
Cosmetology & Dermatology Services
N.A.I.C.S.: 622110
Scott Mahosky (CEO)

Subsidiary (Domestic):

Washington Dermatology Center (2)
6163 Executive Blvd, Rockville, MD 20852-3901
Web Site:
http://www.washingtondermatology center.com
Offices of Physicians (except Mental Health Specialists)
N.A.I.C.S.: 621111
Vicki Smith (Office Mgr)

Hemasource, Inc. (1)
4158 Nike Dr, West Jordan, UT 84088
Tel.: (888) 844-4362
Web Site: http://www.hemasource.com
Medical, Dental & Hospital Equipment & Supplies Merchant Whslr
N.A.I.C.S.: 423450
Matt Johnson (CFO)
Tom Jordan (Pres & CEO)
James J. Sielatycki (Exec VP-Sls & Mktg)
Christopher Fletcher (CTO)
Kent F. Janes (Sr VP-Procurement & Ops)
John Utvich (VP & Gen Mgr-New Market Dev)
Joe Malory (VP-Analytics)

Munch's Supply LLC (1)
1901 Ferro Dr, New Lenox, IL 60451
Tel.: (773) 248-0131
Web Site: http://www.munchsupply.com
Heating, Ventilation & Air Conditioning Equipment Distr
N.A.I.C.S.: 423730
Aaron Sanders (Territory Mgr)
Robert Munch (CEO)

Subsidiary (Domestic):

Air Purchases of New Hampshire (2)
190 Zackry Rd, Manchester, NH 03109
Tel.: (603) 668-7810
Sales Range: $10-24.9 Million
Emp.: 40
Distr of Warm Air Heating & Air Conditioning Equipment
N.A.I.C.S.: 423730

Comfort Air Distributing Inc. (2)
5757 E 42nd Ave, Denver, CO 80216
Tel.: (303) 399-1752
Web Site:
http://www.comfortairdistributing.com
Sales Range: $10-24.9 Million
Emp.: 49
Provider of Warm Air Heating Equipment & Supplies Services
N.A.I.C.S.: 423730
Jim O'Mara (Pres)
Dave Schrock (Exec VP)
Jeff Patton (Mgr-Ops)

Wholesale Sheet Metal Inc. (2)
800 Southwest Blvd, Kansas City, KS 66103
Tel.: (913) 432-7100
Web Site: http://www.wsmkc.com
Site Preparation Contractor
N.A.I.C.S.: 238910
Pat Chilen (Pres)

RTS Holdings, LLC (1)
1 Kellaway Dr, Randolph, MA 02368
Tel.: (781) 961-8200
Web Site: http://www.roadone.com
Holding Company; Intermodal Logistics Services
N.A.I.C.S.: 551112
David McLaughlin (Co-Founder & COO)
Paul Miller (VP-Ops-Northeast)
Karen Zima (VP-Ops-West)
Jeremiah Carruthers (VP-Ops-Southeast)
Peter Entwistle (VP-Sls-Northeast)
Kendall P. Kellaway Jr. (Co-Founder, Pres & CEO)

Subsidiary (Domestic):

CTI RP, Inc. (2)
135 Distribution Dr, Savannah, GA 31408-1408
Tel.: (912) 629-0600
Web Site:
http://www.crowntransportation.com
General Warehousing & Storage
N.A.I.C.S.: 493110
Steven Mcallister (COO)

DDI Transportation, Inc. (2)
10235 Timber Rdg Dr, Ashland, VA 23005
Tel.: (804) 550-2334
Web Site: http://www.dditransportation.com
Rev.: $4,500,000
Emp.: 62
General Freight Trucking Services
N.A.I.C.S.: 484121
Fred Huennekens (CEO)
Dan Bugas (Pres)
Rich Mills (VP-Ops)
Jim Gelonese (VP)
Rick Roache (Mgr-Safety)

Division (Domestic):

The Transporter, Inc. (2)
5410 Oates Rd, Houston, TX 77013
Tel.: (713) 675-5578
Web Site:
http://www.houstontransporter.com
Rev.: $1,300,000
Emp.: 25
Fiscal Year-end: 12/31/2006
Local Trucking Operator Trucking Operator-Nonlocal Local Trucking-With Storage
N.A.I.C.S.: 484110
Greg Cook (VP-Sls)
Jeff Ebel (VP-Ops)

Unishippers Global Logistics, LLC (1)
746 E Winchester St Ste 200, Salt Lake City, UT 84107
Tel.: (801) 708-5800
Web Site: http://www.unishippers.com
Logistics & Transportation Services
N.A.I.C.S.: 484121
Dan Lockwood (Chm)
Dennis Heaps (Controller)
Kevin Lathrop (Pres & CEO)
Steve Leavitt (COO-Franchisee & Exec VP)

Robert Rodgers (CFO)
Tim Story (Exec VP-Freight Ops)
Alan Humpherys (VP-Tech)
Alison Smith (Sr Dir-Franchise Ops)
Dolly Wagner-Wilkins (CTO)

Woodridge Behavioral Care (1)
162 Cude Ln, Madison, TN 37115
Tel.: (615) 860-9230
Web Site: http://www.woodridgecare.com
Psychiatric & Substance Abuse Hospitals
N.A.I.C.S.: 622210
Neil Campbell (Pres & CEO)
Mike White (CFO & Exec VP)

Worldwide Express Operations, LLC (1)
2828 Routh St Ste 400, Dallas, TX 75201
Web Site: http://www.wwex.com
Shipping Services
N.A.I.C.S.: 488330
Tom Madine (CEO)
Mike Grayson (Exec VP)
Brendan Newman (Sr VP-Sls)
Joel Clum (COO)
Dolly Wagner-Wilkins (CTO)
Robert Rose Jr. (Pres)

RIDGETOP HOLDING CO., INC.
5910 S 27th St, Omaha, NE 68107-3487
Tel.: (402) 731-7484   NE
Year Founded: 1995
Sales Range: $75-99.9 Million
Emp.: 175
Holding Company; Heavy Construction Equipment Sales & Rental Services
N.A.I.C.S.: 551112
Warren Griffin (CFO)
Jeff Green (CEO)

Subsidiaries:

Davis Erection Co. Inc. (1)
15109 231st St, Gretna, NE 68028
Tel.: (402) 731-7484
Web Site: http://www.daviserection.com
Sales Range: $25-49.9 Million
Emp.: 100
Steel Erection Services
N.A.I.C.S.: 238120
Warren Griffin (CEO)
Mike Dail (VP)
Matt Pilant (Project Mgr)
Don Gausden (Dir-Ops)
Denny Johnston (Project Mgr)
Brendan Joyce (Project Mgr)
Bryan Limley (Dir-Assembly & Disassembly)
Derrick Lindeman (Mgr-Risk)
Eric Newton (Project Mgr)
Russ Siedlik (Project Mgr)

Northwest Steel Erection Co. (1)
5125 Beisser Dr, Des Moines, IA 50111
Tel.: (515) 986-0380
Web Site: http://www.cranerent.com
Sales Range: $10-24.9 Million
Emp.: 50
Structural Steel Erection Services
N.A.I.C.S.: 238120
Warren Griffin (CFO)

RIDGEVIEW INDUSTRIES
3093 Northridge Dr NW, Grand Rapids, MI 49534-9132
Tel.: (616) 453-8636
Web Site:
http://www.ridgeviewindustries.com
Year Founded: 1977
Rev.: $24,200,000
Emp.: 300
Metal Stamping
N.A.I.C.S.: 332119
David Nykamp (Pres)
Leslie Hamann (Mgr-HR)

RIDGEVIEW MEDICAL CENTER
500 S Maple St, Waconia, MN 55387
Tel.: (952) 442-2191   MN
Web Site:
http://www.ridgeviewmedical.org
Year Founded: 1999

RIDGEWOOD INFRASTRUCTURE LLC

Sales Range: $200-249.9 Million
Emp.: 1,804
Health Care Srvices
N.A.I.C.S.: 621610
Monte Johnson (Chm-Credentials)
Andraya Huldeen (Co-Chm-Womens & Childrens Svcs Line)
Jeffrey Mair (Co-Chm-Surgery Svcs Line)
Katherine Hackett (Co-Chm-Womens & Childrens Svcs Line)
Jeff Nelson (Vice Chm)
Wayne Hubin (Treas)
Julie Herman (Sec)
Sandra Z. Beulke (Chm-Medical Staff Quality)
Alvaro Sanchez (Chief Medical Officer)

RIDGEWAY CHEVROLET, INC.
17730 Torrence Ave, Lansing, IL 60438-1857
Tel.: (708) 474-4990
Sales Range: $10-24.9 Million
Emp.: 45
Car Whslr
N.A.I.C.S.: 441110
John Van Ramshorst (Pres)

RIDGEWAY PHARMACY
2824 US Hwy 93 N, Victor, MT 59875
Tel.: (406) 642-6040
Web Site: http://www.ridgewayrx.com
Year Founded: 1998
Sales Range: $10-24.9 Million
Emp.: 32
Drug Stores & Proprietary Stores
N.A.I.C.S.: 456110
James Cloud (CEO)
Klinton Curtis (Pres)

RIDGEWOOD INFRASTRUCTURE LLC
34 E 51st St 9th Fl, New York, NY 10022
Tel.: (212) 867-0050
Web Site:
http://www.ridgewoodinfrastructure.com
Year Founded: 1982
Infrastructure Services
N.A.I.C.S.: 531390
Ross Posner (Mng Partner)
Ryan Stewart (Partner)

Subsidiaries:

Dupuy Storage & Forwarding LLC (1)
4300 Jourdan Rd, New Orleans, LA 70126
Tel.: (504) 245-7600
Web Site: http://www.dupuystorage.com
Rev.: $5,100,000
Emp.: 95
Warehousing & Storage Services
N.A.I.C.S.: 493190
Allan B. Colley (Pres)
Donna Loescher (Dir-Customer Svc)
Garry Luter (Dir-Ops)
Janice Smith (Dir-Fin)
Adam Miller (Controller)
Al Hernandez (VP)
Bob Olmedo (VP)
Brad Lane (Dir-Ops)
Caryn Sawyer (VP)
Curtis Watts (Mgr-Trucking)
Dana Webb (Mgr-Maintenance)
Dwayne Leon (Mgr-Bulk Facility)
Eduardo Montero (Sr Dir-Bus Dev)
Janet Colley Morse (Dir-Bus Dev)
Jay Hurckes (Mgr-Production)
Jeff Hernandez (Dir-Ops)
John Westcott (CIO)
Joseph Breiten (Mgr-Warehouse)
Keith Luter (Mgr-Ces)
Lamar Crumbliss (Mgr-Warehouse)
Michael Wright (Mgr-Silo)

3433

RIDGEWOOD INFRASTRUCTURE LLC
U.S. PRIVATE

Ridgewood Infrastructure LLC—(Continued)
Scotty Fitzgerald *(Dir-Quality Sys & Regulatory Affairs)*
Tom Goodman *(Mgr-Warehouse)*

Sienergy, L.P. (1)
13215 Bee Cave Pkwy Galleria Oaks Bldg B Ste B-250, Bee Cave, TX 78738
Tel.: (281) 778-6250
Web Site: http://www.sienergy.com
Natural Gas Distribution
N.A.I.C.S.: 221210
June M. Dively *(CEO)*
Daniel Pope *(VP-Bus Dev)*
Paul Kennedy *(Sr VP-Ops)*
Julie Myhre *(VP-Engrg & Construction)*

RIDGEWOOD LAKES GOLF & COUNTRY CLUB, INC.
200 Eagle Ridge Dr, Davenport, FL 33837
Tel.: (863) 424-8688
Web Site: http://www.ridgewoodlakesgolf.com
Year Founded: 1993
Sales Range: $10-24.9 Million
Emp.: 40
Golf Course & Country Club Owner & Operator
N.A.I.C.S.: 713910

RIDGEWOOD REAL ESTATE PARTNERS, LLC
25A Hanover Rd Ste 310, Florham Park, NJ 07932
Tel.: (973) 593-0003
Web Site: http://www.ridgewoodrep.com
Year Founded: 2008
Real Estate Developer & Investor
N.A.I.C.S.: 531390
Michael Plotnick *(VP)*
Jonathan S. Grebow *(Pres & CEO)*
Brett H. Owings *(Sr VP-Dev)*

Subsidiaries:
Elmwood Country Club, Inc. (1)
850 Dobbs Ferry Rd, White Plains, NY 10607
Tel.: (914) 592-6600
Web Site: http://www.elmwoodcc.org
Sales Range: $1-9.9 Million
Golf Course & Country Club
N.A.I.C.S.: 713910
Jerry Schurhamner *(Gen Mgr)*
Megan Hopkins *(Asst Mgr)*
Stephen Caspi *(Controller)*

RIDGEWOOD SAVINGS BANK
71-02 Forest Ave, Ridgewood, NY 11385
Tel.: (718) 240-4900
Web Site: http://www.ridgewoodbank.com
Year Founded: 1921
Rev.: $155,488,000
Emp.: 350
Federal Savings Bank
N.A.I.C.S.: 522180
Leonard Stekol *(Chm, Pres & CEO)*
Gelsomina D'Esposito *(Asst VP)*
Connie Manolopoulos *(VP)*
Richard Spiegel *(VP)*
Mirsada Tagani *(VP-Digital Channels)*
Steven Toth *(Asst VP)*

RIDLEY ELECTRIC CO. INC.
5800 Ct St Rd, Syracuse, NY 13206
Tel.: (315) 463-8606
Rev.: $21,385,234
Emp.: 75
General Electrical Contractor
N.A.I.C.S.: 238210
Lee Ridley *(Chm & CFO)*
Benjamin Ridley *(Pres)*
Mike McBride *(VP)*

RIDLEYS FOOD CORP
621 Washington St S, Twin Falls, ID 83301
Tel.: (208) 324-4633
Web Site: http://www.shopridleys.com
Sales Range: $50-74.9 Million
Emp.: 750
Grocery Stores
N.A.I.C.S.: 445110
Jerry L. Ridley *(Pres)*
Kara Leninger *(Controller)*

RIEBE'S AUTO PARTS
200 Palm Ave, Auburn, CA 95603
Tel.: (530) 885-4674
Web Site: http://www.riebes.com
Rev.: $20,000,000
Emp.: 83
Sales of Automotive Parts & Accessories
N.A.I.C.S.: 441330

RIECHESBAIRD, INC.
1 Wrigley, Irvine, CA 92618
Tel.: (949) 586-1200
Web Site: http://www.riechesbaird.com
Year Founded: 1985
Sales Range: $10-24.9 Million
Emp.: 20
Advertising Agencies
N.A.I.C.S.: 541810
Ryan Rieches *(Co-Founder & Partner)*
Pam Walker *(Dir-Fin & HR)*
Alan Brew *(Co-Founder & Partner)*
Michael Dula *(Co-Founder, Chief Creative Officer & Partner)*
Dustin King *(Dir-Brand Mgmt)*
Drew Letendre *(Dir-Brand Strategy)*
Mark Lethbridge *(Co-Founder & Partner-EMEA)*
Tom Golland *(Co-Founder & Partner-EMEA)*
Federico Soto Roland *(Mng Dir-Buenos Aires)*
Stephen Barry *(Mng Dir-Hong Kong)*
Andrea Fabbri *(Mng Dir-New York)*
Raymond W. Baird II *(Co-Founder & Partner)*

RIECHMAN CROSBY HAYS COMPANY, INC.
3250 Millbranch Rd, Memphis, TN 38116-3624
Tel.: (901) 345-2200
Web Site: http://www.rch.distcorp.com
Year Founded: 1963
Rev.: $42,579,471
Emp.: 200
Industrial Supplies
N.A.I.C.S.: 423840
James R. Butler *(Pres & CEO)*

Subsidiaries:
RCH Distributors Inc. (1)
3131 Directors Row, Memphis, TN 38131-0405
Tel.: (901) 345-3100
Sales Range: $1-9.9 Million
Emp.: 22
Lawn & Garden Supplies Distr
N.A.I.C.S.: 423710

RIECHMANN BROS LLC
1000 S Frnt St, Okawville, IL 62271
Tel.: (618) 243-6186
Web Site: http://www.riechmannbros.com
Rev.: $10,000,000
Emp.: 17
Agricultural Machinery & Equipment
N.A.I.C.S.: 423820
Bill Riechmann Sr. *(Pres)*

RIEDEL CRYSTAL
95 Mayfield Ave, Edison, NJ 08818
Tel.: (732) 346-8960
Web Site: http://www.riedel.com
Rev.: $12,000,000
Emp.: 25
Glassware
N.A.I.C.S.: 423220
Maximilian Riedel *(Pres)*
Nikki Marra *(Mgr-Admin)*
Holger Bauer *(Controller)*

RIEDON, INC.
300 Cypress Ave, Alhambra, CA 91801
Tel.: (626) 284-9901
Web Site: http://www.riedon.com
Year Founded: 1960
Electronic Resistor Mfr
N.A.I.C.S.: 334416
Mike Zoeller *(Owner & Pres)*

Subsidiaries:
Deltec Shunts, LLC (1)
300 Cypress Ave, Alhambra, CA 91801
Tel.: (626) 284-9901
Web Site: http://www.deltecco.com
Electronic Components Mfr
N.A.I.C.S.: 334419

RIEGNER & ASSOCIATES, INC.
18481 W 10 Mile Rd, Southfield, MI 48075-2621
Tel.: (248) 569-4242
Emp.: 15
Marketing & Advertising Services
N.A.I.C.S.: 541820
Bryan Riegner *(Pres)*

RIEKES EQUIPMENT COMPANY
6703 L St, Omaha, NE 68117
Tel.: (402) 593-1181
Web Site: http://www.riekesequipment.com
Sales Range: $10-24.9 Million
Emp.: 100
Materials Handling Machinery
N.A.I.C.S.: 423830
Duncan Murphy *(Pres)*
Ron Meyer *(Controller)*

RIEMAN & ARSZMAN CUSTOM DISTRIBUTORS
9190 Seward Rd, Fairfield, OH 45014
Tel.: (513) 874-5444
Web Site: http://www.customdistributors.com
Sales Range: $10-24.9 Million
Emp.: 48
Distr of Major Appliances
N.A.I.C.S.: 423620
Rebeka Peters *(Mgr-Orders)*

RIENZI & SONS, INC.
18-81 Steinway St, Astoria, NY 11105
Tel.: (718) 278-8435
Web Site: http://www.rienzifoods.com
Year Founded: 1967
Sales Range: $10-24.9 Million
Food Products Mfr & Distr
N.A.I.C.S.: 311999
Michael Rienzi *(Pres)*
Joseph Rienzi *(VP)*

RIESBECK FOOD MARKETS INC.
48661 National Rd W, Saint Clairsville, OH 43950
Tel.: (740) 695-7050
Web Site: http://www.riesbeckfoods.com
Rev.: $125,612,369
Emp.: 1,100
Independent Supermarket
N.A.I.C.S.: 445110
Richard L. Riesbeck *(Pres & CEO)*
Greg Bauer *(Dir-LP)*
Jennifer Kiger *(Dir-Acctg)*
Mark Kemp *(Dir-IT)*
Jay Ropietski *(VP-Retail)*

RIESS FORD SALES INC.
768 State Route 13, Marissa, IL 62257
Tel.: (618) 295-3721
Web Site: http://www.riessfordsales.com
Sales Range: $25-49.9 Million
Emp.: 47
Automobiles, New & Used
N.A.I.C.S.: 441110
Jim Dunning *(Controller)*

RIESTER
3344 E Camelback Rd, Phoenix, AZ 85018
Tel.: (602) 462-2200
Web Site: http://www.riester.com
Year Founded: 1989
Sales Range: $10-24.9 Million
Emp.: 120
Advertising Services
N.A.I.C.S.: 541810
Timothy W. Riester *(CEO & Principal)*
Mirja Riester *(Chief Strategic Officer & Principal)*
Tom Ortega *(Chief Creative Officer & Principal)*
Christina Borrego *(Dir-PR)*
Alan Perkel *(Chief Digital Officer & Principal)*
Kurt Krake *(Exec Dir-Media)*
Tricia Kashima *(Dir-Media)*
David Kovacs *(Assoc Dir-Content Strategy)*
Troy Pottgen *(Dir-Creative)*
Mike Ross *(Dir-Creative)*
Stephanie Penteloute *(Dir-Integration)*
Gregg Miskiel *(Dir-Integration Grp)*
Bryan Ojala *(Exec Dir-Consumer Packaged Goods)*

Subsidiaries:
Riester-Robb (1)
132 W Pierpont Ave Ste 300, Salt Lake City, UT 84101-1102
Tel.: (801) 532-7333
Web Site: http://www.riester.com
Emp.: 25
Advertising Services
N.A.I.C.S.: 541810
Skip Branch *(Coord-Client Rels)*
Mike Korologas *(Dir-PR)*

RIESTERER & SCHNELL INC.
N2909 Hwy 32 N, Pulaski, WI 54162
Tel.: (920) 822-3077
Web Site: http://www.rands.com
Sales Range: $50-74.9 Million
Emp.: 140
Farm Implements
N.A.I.C.S.: 423820
Beau Dvorachek *(Reg Mgr-Sls)*

RIETH-RILEY CONSTRUCTION CO., INC.
3626 Elkhart Rd, Goshen, IN 46526-5815
Tel.: (574) 875-5183
Web Site: http://www.rieth-riley.com
Year Founded: 1916
Sales Range: $450-499.9 Million
Emp.: 1,600
Construction Services
N.A.I.C.S.: 237310
Brian Inniger *(Exec VP)*
A. Keith Rose *(CEO)*
Eric Engleking *(VP-Northern Indiana)*
Dan Foreman *(Mgr-Gary)*

COMPANIES

Subsidiaries:

Rieth-Riley Construction Co., Inc. - Big Rapids (1)
20251 19 Mile Rd, Big Rapids, MI 49307
Tel.: (231) 796-7268
Web Site: http://www.riethriley.com
Sales Range: $10-24.9 Million
Emp.: 30
Construction Services
N.A.I.C.S.: 237310

Rieth-Riley Construction Co., Inc. - Grand Valley (1)
220 Chicago Dr, Grand Rapids, MI 49519
Tel.: (616) 245-9263
Sales Range: $1-9.9 Million
Emp.: 65
Construction Services
N.A.I.C.S.: 237310

Rieth-Riley Construction Co., Inc. - Lansing (1)
4150 S Creyts Rd, Lansing, MI 48917
Tel.: (517) 721-0103
Web Site: http://www.riethriley.com
Sales Range: $10-24.9 Million
Emp.: 20
Construction Services
N.A.I.C.S.: 237310
Chad Loney *(Mgr)*

RIFENBURG CONSTRUCTION INC.
159 Brick Church Rd, Troy, NY 12180-8106
Tel.: (518) 279-3265 NY
Web Site: http://www.rifenburg.com
Year Founded: 1958
Sales Range: $25-49.9 Million
Emp.: 400
Provider of Highway & Street Construction
N.A.I.C.S.: 237310
George Rifenburg *(Pres)*
Jack Rifenburg *(VP)*
John Ahearn *(CFO)*

RIFFLE & ASSOCIATES INC.
2671 Crescentville Rd, Cincinnati, OH 45241-1596
Tel.: (513) 771-0002 OH
Web Site: http://www.riffle-assoc.com
Year Founded: 1962
Sales Range: $10-24.9 Million
Emp.: 30
Provider of Electrical Apparatus & Equipment Services
N.A.I.C.S.: 423610
John E. Blust *(Chm)*
Tom J. Cotter *(Pres & Principal)*

RIFT VALLEY EQUITY PARTNERS, LLC
7 World Trade Center 250 Greenwich St 46th Fl, New York, NY 10007
Tel.: (212) 266-0131
Web Site: http://www.riftvalleyequity.com
Privater Equity Firm
N.A.I.C.S.: 523999
David Caputo *(Mng Partner)*
Oliver Ong *(Partner)*
Mark Woolgar *(Partner)*

Subsidiaries:

WHI Global, LLC (1)
90 New Dutch Ln, Fairfield, NJ 07004
Tel.: (973) 276-1377
Web Site: http://www.whiglobal.com
Precision Metal Components & Complex Assemblies Mfr
N.A.I.C.S.: 334413
Albert Altieri *(Pres & CEO)*
Jim Falco *(CFO)*
Duke Peer *(Exec VP-Sls & Mktg)*

Subsidiary (Domestic):

Aero - Bond Corp. (2)
1 Allen St, Springfield, MA 01108
Tel.: (413) 734-2224
Web Site: http://www.aerobondcorp.com
All Other Miscellaneous General Purpose Machinery Mfr
N.A.I.C.S.: 333998

Arlington Machine & Tool Co. (2)
90 New Dutch Ln, Fairfield, NJ 07004
Tel.: (973) 276-1377
Web Site: http://arlingtonmachine.com
Sales Range: $1-9.9 Million
Emp.: 103
Precision-Machined Components Mfr
N.A.I.C.S.: 332721
Susan Blanck *(CEO)*
Attila Mozsolits *(Controller)*
John J. Staudinger Jr. *(Pres & COO)*

M & M Manufacturing, Inc. (2)
13914 E Admiral Pl, Tulsa, OK 74116
Tel.: (918) 933-6500
Web Site: http://www.mm-mfg.com
Sales Range: $1-9.9 Million
Emp.: 50
Components Mfr
N.A.I.C.S.: 332710
Rocky Payton *(Gen Mgr)*

RIGER ADVERTISING AGENCY, INC.
53 Chenango St, Binghamton, NY 13902
Tel.: (607) 723-7441
Web Site: http://www.riger.com
Year Founded: 1950
Sales Range: $10-24.9 Million
Emp.: 12
N.A.I.C.S.: 541810
Peter Cronk *(Mng Partner)*
Laurie Van Kuren *(Acct Exec & Mgr-Media)*
Rob Stiene *(Dir-Creative)*
Barbara Butler *(Mgr-Office & Acctg)*
Paula Johnson *(Acct Coord)*
Patty Farro *(Media Buyer)*
Steve Johnson *(VP-Client Svcs)*
Mark Bandurchin *(VP-Creative Svcs)*
Karen Frobel *(Specialist-Print Production)*

RIGGINS, INC.
3938 S Main Rd, Vineland, NJ 08360-7743
Tel.: (856) 825-7600
Web Site: http://www.rigginsoil.com
Year Founded: 1926
Heating Oil, Gasoline & Diesel Distr
N.A.I.C.S.: 457210
Paul Riggins *(Pres & CEO)*
Steven Riggins *(CFO)*
Richard Cummines *(VP-Ops)*
Matthew Riggins *(Dir-Strategy)*

RIGGS DISTLER & COMPANY INC.
4216 Lousi, Baltimore, MD 21222
Tel.: (410) 633-0300
Web Site: http://www.riggsdistler.com
Year Founded: 1909
Rev.: $28,400,000
Emp.: 500
Mechanical & Electrical Contractors
N.A.I.C.S.: 238210
Joseph Seaman *(VP-Mechanical Grp)*
Paul Bizon *(VP-Electrical Grp)*
Steve Zemaitais Jr. *(VP-Utility Grp)*

RIGGS DISTRIBUTING, INC.
1755 Rollins Rd, Burlingame, CA 94010
Tel.: (650) 240-3000
Web Site: http://www.riggsdistributing.com
Year Founded: 1983
Rev.: $29,900,000
Emp.: 50
Kitchen Appliances Mfr
N.A.I.C.S.: 423620
Robert J. Hostetler *(VP-Retail Sls)*
Katie Post *(Mgr-Mktg)*

RIGGS INDUSTRIES, INC.
PO BOX 86, Boswell, PA 15531
Tel.: (814) 629-5621 PA
Web Site: http://www.riggsindustries.com
Year Founded: 1985
Structural Steel Erection Contractor; Manufacture Truck Bodies & Trailers, Steel Fabrication Equipment; Rental & Mine Construction
N.A.I.C.S.: 236220
Rosanne Novak *(Mgr-Acctg)*
Clyde Long *(Mgr-Quality Assurance & Quality Control)*
Dan Yunetz *(Pres)*

Subsidiaries:

Lincoln Contracting & Equipment Co. Inc (1)
Rte 30 W, Stoystown, PA 15563 (100%)
Tel.: (814) 629-5621
Web Site: http://www.lincolncontracting.com
Sales Range: $10-24.9 Million
Emp.: 130
General Contracting
N.A.I.C.S.: 332312
Harold E. Walker Jr. *(Pres)*
William Friedline *(CFO)*

Lincoln Contracting & Equipment Company, Inc. (1)
2478 Lincoln Hwy, Boswell, PA 15531-0096
Tel.: (814) 629-6641
Web Site: http://www.lceci.com
Sales Range: $50-74.9 Million
Emp.: 60
N.A.I.C.S.: 237110
Harold E. Walker Jr. *(Pres)*
C. Daniel Riggs *(VP)*
Jason Byer *(Chief Engr)*
Gary Leister *(Mgr-Engrg)*

Somerset Steel Erection Company Inc (1)
2478 Lincoln Hwy, Stoystown, PA 15563
Tel.: (814) 629-5621
Web Site: http://www.somersetsteelerection.com
Sales Range: $10-24.9 Million
Emp.: 35
General Contracting
N.A.I.C.S.: 236220
C. Daniel Riggs *(Pres)*
William Friedline *(CFO)*
Clyde B. Long *(Dir-Bus Dev)*
Don Walker *(Sr Project Mgr)*
Harold Walker Jr. *(VP)*

Somerset Welding & Steel, Inc. (1)
10558 Somerset Pike, Somerset, PA 15501
Tel.: (814) 443-2671
Web Site: http://www.jjbodies.com
Sales Range: $25-49.9 Million
Emp.: 200
Mfr of Steel Frames for Industrial Trucks & Trailers
N.A.I.C.S.: 336211
Sidney William Riggs *(Pres)*

Division (Domestic):

Somerset Welding and Steel, Inc. - J&J Truck Bodies & Trailers Division (2)
10558 Somerset Pike, Somerset, PA 15501
Tel.: (814) 444-3400
Web Site: http://www.jjbodies.com
Sales Range: $25-49.9 Million
Emp.: 200
Truck Trailer Mfr
N.A.I.C.S.: 336212
S. William Riggs *(Pres)*
Michael Riggs *(Sr VP)*
Jason Cornell *(Sls Dir)*
Gerald Johnson *(Mgr-Special Projects)*

Somerset Welding and Steel, Inc. - J&J Truck Equipment Division (2)
Facility 422 Riggs Rd, Somerset, PA 15501
Tel.: (814) 444-7000
Web Site: http://www.jjtruckequipment.com
Storage Truck Mfr
N.A.I.C.S.: 336212
David Spear *(Gen Mgr)*

RIGGS OIL COMPANY INC.
1505 E 1st Ave, Big Stone Gap, VA 24219
Tel.: (276) 523-2662
Web Site: http://www.riggsoil.com
Sales Range: $50-74.9 Million
Emp.: 150
Sales of Petroleum Products
N.A.I.C.S.: 212114
Arnold Riggs *(Pres)*

RIGGS PARTNERS
750 Meeting St, West Columbia, SC 29169
Tel.: (803) 799-5972
Web Site: http://www.riggspartners.com
Year Founded: 1987
Sales Range: $1-9.9 Million
Emp.: 10
Public Relations & Brand Management
N.A.I.C.S.: 541820
Cathy Monetti *(Partner)*
Teresa Coles *(Pres & Partner)*
Kevin Smith *(Partner)*
Tom Barr *(Partner)*
Ryon Edwards *(Partner)*

RIGHT AT HOME, INC.
6464 Center St Ste 150, Omaha, NE 68106-2818
Tel.: (402) 697-7537
Web Site: http://www.rightathome.net
Year Founded: 2005
Sales Range: $1-9.9 Million
Emp.: 6,000
Women Healthcare Services
N.A.I.C.S.: 621610
Allen Hager *(Founder & Chm)*
Eric Little *(Chief Dev Officer-Franchise Dev)*
Amy Stanosheck *(Dir-Standards & Quality)*
Dave Creal *(VP-Franchise Dev)*
Jeff Vavricek *(CFO)*
Margaret Haynes *(CEO)*
Mike Flair *(VP-Franchise Bus Solutions)*
Pat Boyd *(VP-Mktg)*
Brady Schwab *(Chief Growth Officer)*

RIGHT COOPERATIVE ASSOCIATION
10881 N Main St, Wright, KS 67882
Tel.: (620) 227-8611
Web Site: http://www.rightcoop.com
Sales Range: $25-49.9 Million
Emp.: 56
Grain & Farm Supply Whslr
N.A.I.C.S.: 424510
Markie Hardy *(Controller)*

RIGHT LANE ACQUISITION I, INC.
5130 S Fort Apache Rd #215-219, Las Vegas, NV 89148
Tel.: (561) 236-5011 NV
Year Founded: 2014
Investment Services
N.A.I.C.S.: 523999
Robin G. Lane *(Pres, CEO, CFO, Chief Acctg Officer, Treas & Sec)*

RIGHT LANE INDUSTRIES, LLC
222 N La Salle St Ste 705, Chicago, IL 60601
Tel.: (312) 766-3368
Web Site: https://www.rightlaneindustries.com
Holding Company
N.A.I.C.S.: 551112
Eric Mara *(CEO)*

RIGHT NETWORKS, LLC
14 Hampshire Dr, Hudson, NH 03051

RIGHT NETWORKS, LLC

Right Networks, LLC—(Continued)
Tel.: (888) 417-4448
Web Site:
http://www.rightnetworks.com
Year Founded: 2002
Cloud Services
N.A.I.C.S.: 541219
M. Darren Root *(Chief Strategist)*
Joel Hughes *(CEO)*
Michael Dionne *(CFO)*
Will Yapp *(VP-Sls & Bus Dev)*
Dave Rosi *(VP-Mktg)*
Jim Walsh *(CIO)*
Eric Brehm *(Chief Product Officer)*
Gary Engel *(VP- Custom Care)*
Joe Dwyer *(VP & Gen Mgr-Right Labs)*
Adam Collicelli *(Gen Counsel)*

RIGHT ON INTERACTIVE, LLC

136 E Market St Ste 400, Indianapolis, IN 46204
Tel.: (317) 225-5868
Web Site:
http://www.rightoninteractive.com
Year Founded: 2006
Sales Range: $1-9.9 Million
Marketing Automation Software
N.A.I.C.S.: 513210
Troy Burk *(Founder & CEO)*
Amol Dalvi *(Co-Founder & CTO)*
Kim Howard *(Mgr-Client Success)*
Anna Harvey *(Controller-Fin)*
Andre Ramsey *(Dir-Client Success)*
Amit Khot *(Dir-Tech)*

RIGHT SIDE CAPITAL MANAGEMENT, LLC

649 Mission St 5th Fl, San Francisco, CA 94105
Tel.: (415) 655-4965   DE
Web Site:
http://www.rightsidecapital.com
Private Equity Firm
N.A.I.C.S.: 551112
Dave Lambert *(Mng Dir)*
Kevin Dick *(Mng Dir)*
Jeff Pomeranz *(Mng Dir)*
Paul Swiencicki *(Partner-Growth)*
John Eng *(Partner-Funding Ecosystem)*

Subsidiaries:

DataRobot, Inc.   (1)
225 Franklin St Fl 13, Boston, MA 02110
Tel.: (617) 765-4500
Web Site: http://www.datarobot.com
Automated Machine Learning & Augmented Analytic Services
N.A.I.C.S.: 518210
Mark Hawkins *(Chm)*
Debanjan Saha *(CEO)*
Michael Schmidt *(CTO)*
Venky Veeraraghavan *(Chief Product Officer)*
Brian Brown *(Gen Counsel)*
Chris Merwin *(CFO)*

Subsidiary (Domestic):

Paxata, Inc.   (2)
1800 Seaport Blvd 3rd Fl, Redwood City, CA 94063
Tel.: (855) 972-9282
Data Preparation & Data Fabric Services
N.A.I.C.S.: 518210

RIGHT SYSTEMS INC.

2600 Williamette Dr NE Ste C, Lacey, WA 98516
Tel.: (360) 956-0414
Web Site: http://www.rightsys.com
Sales Range: $10-24.9 Million
Emp.: 100
Computers, Peripherals & Software, Integration & Consulting
N.A.I.C.S.: 423430

John P. Minor *(CEO)*
Sean Padget *(VP-Mktg & Sls)*

RIGHT WAY AUTO

39 Downeast Hwy, Ellsworth, ME 04605
Tel.: (207) 667-3344   ME
Web Site:
http://www.rightwayauto.com
Rev.: $15,000,000
Emp.: 15
Sell Automobiles, Used Cars Only
N.A.I.C.S.: 441120
Chadd Linnehan *(Owner)*

RIGHTEOUS CLOTHING AGENCY

11495 SE Hwy 212, Clackamas, OR 97015
Tel.: (800) 548-1227
Web Site: http://www.rchq.com
Year Founded: 1989
Sales Range: $1-9.9 Million
Emp.: 40
Uniform Mfr & Supplier of Retail Merchandise Programs for Restaurant Chains
N.A.I.C.S.: 458110
Thomas Johnson *(Chief Creative Officer)*
Alyson Salz *(Owner & Partner)*
Karen Danielson *(Bookkeeper)*
Jay Salz *(COO)*

RIGHTSTAFF, INC.

4919 McKinney Ave, Dallas, TX 75205
Tel.: (214) 953-0900   TX
Web Site:
http://www.rightstaffinc.com
Year Founded: 1998
Sales Range: $1-9.9 Million
Emp.: 13
Staffing & Consulting Services
N.A.I.C.S.: 541612
Shelley Amason *(Pres & CEO)*

RIGHTSURE INSURANCE GROUP

5151 E Broadway Blvd Ste 100, Tucson, AZ 85711
Tel.: (520) 917-5296
Web Site: http://www.rightsure.com
Insurance Services
N.A.I.C.S.: 524210
Felicia Duarte *(VP-Ops)*

Subsidiaries:

American Cornerstone Insurance LLC   (1)
5151 E Broadway Blvd Ste 100, Tucson, AZ 85711
Tel.: (520) 917-5296
Insurance Services
N.A.I.C.S.: 524298

RIGHTWAY GATE, INC.

2720 Loker Ave W Ste Q, Carlsbad, CA 92010
Tel.: (760) 736-3700   CA
Web Site: http://www.rwgusa.com
Year Founded: 1993
Sales Range: $1-9.9 Million
Emp.: 25
Internet Services
N.A.I.C.S.: 517810
Wolfgang Reile *(CEO)*

RIGID GLOBAL BUILDINGS, LLC

18933 Aldine Westfield Rd, Houston, TX 77073
Tel.: (281) 443-9065
Web Site:
http://www.rigidbuilding.com
Sales Range: $25-49.9 Million

Emp.: 250
Structural Steel Erection
N.A.I.C.S.: 238120
Steve Olson *(VP-Sls)*
Arnold Rillera *(Engr-Design)*
Alex Ghodsi *(Mgr)*

RIGIDIZED METALS CORP.

658 Ohio St, Buffalo, NY 14203-3122
Tel.: (716) 849-4760   NY
Web Site: http://www.rigidized.com
Year Founded: 1940
Sales Range: $50-74.9 Million
Emp.: 45
Deep Textured Design-strengthened Metals Mfr
N.A.I.C.S.: 332119
Joshua Smith *(Dir-Ecology)*
Chris Schiller *(Mgr-Bus Dev)*
Ron Konnert *(Mgr-Shipping & Receiving)*
Tom Schunk *(Project Mgr-Fabrication)*
Beth Neel *(Mktg Mgr)*
R. S. Smith III *(Pres)*

RIGMAX, LLC

504 Medical Ctr Dr Ste 300, Conroe, TX 77304
Tel.: (281) 889-3361   TX
Web Site: http://rigmax.com
Energy Projects Consulting Services
N.A.I.C.S.: 541620
Truman Wright *(CEO)*
Joe Page *(Chief Admin Officer & Exec VP)*
Leesa Foster *(pres)*

Subsidiaries:

RigMax H2O, LLC   (1)
504 Medical Ctr Dr Ste 300, Conroe, TX 77304
Tel.: (281) 889-3361
Web Site: http://rigmax.com
Environmental Consulting Services
N.A.I.C.S.: 541620
Truman Wright *(CEO)*

RIHM MOTOR COMPANY

2108 University Ave W, Saint Paul, MN 55114
Tel.: (651) 646-7833   MN
Web Site:
http://www.rihmkenworth.com
Year Founded: 1932
Sales Range: $75-99.9 Million
Emp.: 84
Wholesale Distributor of Trucks & Tractors; General Repair of Trucks
N.A.I.C.S.: 423110
Mark Shide *(Controller)*
Jerome Barney *(Mgr-Parts)*
Terry Wing *(Pres)*

Subsidiaries:

Lawrence Transportation Company   (1)
1515 Indus Dr NW, Rochester, MN 55901
Tel.: (507) 282-6715
Web Site: http://www.lawrencetrans.com
Refrigerated Products Trucking Services
N.A.I.C.S.: 484121
Deri Nordsving *(Gen Mgr)*

RIISER OIL COMPANY INC.

709 S 20th Ave, Wausau, WI 54401-5208
Tel.: (715) 845-7272   WI
Web Site: http://www.riiser.com
Year Founded: 1999
Sales Range: $200-249.9 Million
Emp.: 350
Convenience Stores, Truck Stops & Diesel Fuel Stations
N.A.I.C.S.: 424710
James L. Kemerling *(Pres)*
Todd Kopplin *(VP-Retail Ops)*

U.S. PRIVATE

Subsidiaries:

Riiser Transportation   (1)
709 S 20th Ave, Wausau, WI 54401-5208
Tel.: (715) 845-7272
Web Site: http://www.riiser.com
Sales Range: Less than $1 Million
Emp.: 22
Trucking Service
N.A.I.C.S.: 484121
James L. Kemerling *(Pres)*

RIKE, INC.

3403 Satellite Blvd, Duluth, GA 30096
Tel.: (770) 623-9211
Web Site:
http://www.accuracarland.com
Sales Range: $10-24.9 Million
Emp.: 80
New Car Dealers
N.A.I.C.S.: 441110
Richard Woodruff *(CEO & CFO)*

RIKER PRODUCTS, INC.

4901 Stickney Ave, Toledo, OH 43612-3716
Tel.: (419) 729-1626
Web Site: http://www.rikerprod.com
Sales Range: $25-49.9 Million
Emp.: 160
Heavy Duty Exhaust Systems Mfr & Custom Tube Bending Services
N.A.I.C.S.: 336390
Gary Frye *(Pres)*
Frank Curtis *(Mgr-Quality Assurance)*
Kati Kolinski *(Supvr-AC)*
Shelly Vargo Mills *(Mgr-HR)*

RILEA GROUP INC.

1450 Brickell Ave Ste 1420, Miami, FL 33131
Tel.: (305) 371-5254
Web Site: http://www.rileagroup.com
Year Founded: 1981
Sales Range: $1-9.9 Million
Real Estate Developers
N.A.I.C.S.: 237210
Alan Ojeda *(Pres & CEO)*
Kathy Frias *(Dir-Leasing & Mgmt)*
Amneris Pedroso *(Controller)*

RILEY CONSTRUCTION COMPANY INC.

5301 99th Ave, Kenosha, WI 53144-2237
Tel.: (262) 658-4381
Web Site: http://www.rileycon.com
Year Founded: 1965
Sales Range: $100-124.9 Million
Emp.: 250
Nonresidential Construction Services
N.A.I.C.S.: 236220
Barbara Riley *(Exec VP)*
David R. Riley *(Chm)*
Mark Presterl *(VP)*
Ben Kossow *(VP-Ops)*
Chris Siefert *(VP)*
Matt Prince *(Pres)*
Peter J. Sinsky *(CFO)*

RILEY EXPLORATION GROUP, LLC

2008 N Council Ave, Blanchard, OK 73010
Tel.: (405) 485-8200   DE
Web Site:
http://www.rileyexplorationgroup.com
Year Founded: 2012
Holding Company; Oil & Gas Exploration & Extraction
N.A.I.C.S.: 551112
Corey Riley *(CFO)*
Harold Atkinson *(Sr VP-Land)*
Dennis Duval *(Exec VP-Exploration & Geology)*
Mark Miles *(COO)*
Christie Morrow *(Dir-Comm & PR)*

Bobby D. Riley *(Founder)*
David LaLonde *(CFO)*
Amy Becker *(VP-Land)*
Kevin L. Riley *(Exec VP-Bus Dev)*
Bobby D. Riley *(Founder)*
James J. Doherty Jr. *(Exec VP-Engrg & Ops)*

Subsidiaries:

Cinco Resources, Inc. (1)
2626 Howell St Ste 800, Dallas, TX 75204 (90%)
Tel.: (214) 520-7727
Web Site: http://www.cincoresources.com
Sales Range: $25-49.9 Million
Emp.: 47
Oil & Gas Exploration & Extraction
N.A.I.C.S.: 211120
Jon L. Glass *(Chm, Pres & CEO)*
Wayne B. Stoltenberg *(CFO & Sr VP)*
Edward P. Travis *(COO & Sr VP)*
Leigh T. Prieto *(Chief Acctg Officer & VP)*
Craig D. Pollard *(VP-Exploration)*
Chris M. Kidd *(Sr VP-Bus Dev & Land)*

RILEY GEAR CORPORATION
1 Precision Dr, Saint Augustine, FL 32092
Tel.: (904) 829-5652
Web Site: http://www.rileygear.com
Year Founded: 1946
Sales Range: $10-24.9 Million
Emp.: 50
Gears; Forged Steel
N.A.I.C.S.: 332111
Larry Kent *(Engr-Mfg)*
Kim Hemingway *(Supvr-Maintenance)*
Steve Palmer *(Supvr-Mfg)*
Jack Frost *(Engr-Quality)*

RILEY HAYES ADVERTISING
333 S First St, Minneapolis, MN 55401
Tel.: (612) 338-7161
Web Site: http://www.rileyhayes.com
Year Founded: 1991
Sales Range: $10-24.9 Million
Emp.: 35
N.A.I.C.S.: 541810
Tom Hayes *(Founder & CEO)*
Kerry Krepps *(Creative Dir-Co-Owner)*

RILEY SALES INC.
1719 Romano Dr, Plymouth Meeting, PA 19462
Tel.: (610) 279-4500
Web Site: http://www.rileysales.com
Sales Range: $10-24.9 Million
Emp.: 70
Supplier of Heating & Air Conditioning Products
N.A.I.C.S.: 423730
Michael Riley *(Pres)*
Deb Ott *(Controller)*
Maria Kerridge *(Mgr-IT)*

RILEY TECHNOLOGIES, LLC
170 Overhill Dr, Mooresville, NC 28117
Tel.: (704) 663-6319 NV
Web Site: http://www.rileytech.com
Sales Range: $10-24.9 Million
Emp.: 35
Race Cars & Motor Vehicle Parts Designer & Mfr
N.A.I.C.S.: 336211
William P. Riley *(Pres)*

RIM FOREST LUMBER, CO.
26491 Pine Ave, Rimforest, CA 92378
Tel.: (909) 337-6262
Web Site:
 http://www.rimforestlumber.doitbest.com
Sales Range: $10-24.9 Million
Emp.: 40

Lumberyard & Hardware Services
N.A.I.C.S.: 423310
Edward Baumann *(Pres)*

RIM LOGISTICS LTD
200 N Gary Ave Ste B, Roselle, IL 60172
Tel.: (630) 595-0610
Web Site: http://www.rimlogistics.com
Sales Range: $10-24.9 Million
Emp.: 150
Freight Transportation Arrangement
N.A.I.C.S.: 488510
Robert Mueller *(Founder & Pres)*
Bonita Pizzo *(Mgr-Wisconsin Sls)*
Crystal Lokcinski *(Supvr-Foreign Agent Accts-Front Office)*
Lisa Bieda *(VP-Import Compliance)*
Nancy Kernan *(Mgr-Brokerage)*
Jeremy Arnold *(Supvr-Distr)*
Kris Veneziano *(Dir-IT)*
Linda Frevert *(Coord-Benefits)*
Diana Lozowska *(Coord-Pricing)*
Bill Paul *(Dir-Trng)*
Melissa Kotek *(Mgr-Bus Dev)*
Joe Logsdon *(Mgr-Sls-Chicago)*
Beverly Ericson *(Product Mgr-Inbound-Natl)*
Christin Madro *(Supvr-Import Brokerage)*
Jason Steinke *(Exec VP)*
Mike Powell *(VP-Tech Solutions)*
Rob Krusinski *(Dir-Sls)*
Mike Maiss *(Mgr-Air Export)*
Tim Gerharz *(Mgr-Ops)*
Vicki Perry *(Supvr-Import Customs Brokerage)*
Tom McNulty *(VP-IT)*
Jim McGregor *(CFO)*

RIM OPERATING, INC.
5 Inverness Dr E, Englewood, CO 80112
Tel.: (303) 799-9828
Web Site: http://www.rimop.com
Rev.: $20,000,000
Emp.: 15
Crude Petroleum & Natural Gas
N.A.I.C.S.: 211120
Steven W. Rector *(Co-Owner & Pres)*
Paul Murphy *(Controller)*
Rene Morin *(Owner, Partner & VP)*

RIMA MANUFACTURING COMPANY
3850 Munson Hwy, Hudson, MI 49247
Tel.: (517) 448-8921
Web Site: http://www.rimamfg.com
Rev.: $21,482,778
Emp.: 105
Screw Machine Products
N.A.I.C.S.: 332721

RIMCO INC.
312 John F Kennedy Ave Km 37, Puerto Nuevo, PR 00920
Tel.: (787) 792-4300
Web Site: http://www.rimcocat.com
Sales Range: $25-49.9 Million
Emp.: 110
Industrial Machine Parts
N.A.I.C.S.: 423830
Richard F. McConnie Jr. *(Pres)*

RIMHUB, INC.
11700 Plz America Dr Ste 810, Reston, VA 20190
Tel.: (703) 956-4000
Web Site: http://www.rimhub.com
Business Support Services
N.A.I.C.S.: 561499
Srinath Narayan *(Chm & CEO)*
Su Fan *(CMO)*
Nidhi Sharma *(Mgr-HR)*

Subsidiaries:

Rimhub India Pvt. Ltd. (1)
Second Floor Plot No 880, Udyog Vihar Phase V, 1220016, Gurgaon, India
Tel.: (91) 1244848888
Web Site: http://www.rimhub.com
Business Support Services
N.A.I.C.S.: 561499

Systems Integration, Inc. (1)
7316 Business Pl, Arlington, TX 76001
Tel.: (817) 468-1494
Web Site: http://www.sitexas.com
Sales Range: $1-9.9 Million
Emp.: 30
Management Consulting Services
N.A.I.C.S.: 541611
Rhonda Kirby *(Mgr-Sls)*

RIMKUS CONSULTING GROUP, INC.
12140 Wickchester Ln Ste 300, Houston, TX 77079
Tel.: (713) 621-3550
Web Site: http://rimkus.com
Year Founded: 2003
Sales Range: $1-9.9 Million
Emp.: 15
Management Consulting Services
N.A.I.C.S.: 541618
Robert Ketchum *(Mgr)*
Brian Moore *(Mgr-Mktg)*
Curtis R. Brown *(Chm & Exec Dir)*
Gregory Schuelke *(Sr VP)*
James Jordan *(VP)*
John Dufour *(Mgr)*
Kevin D. Hope *(VP)*
Kyle R. Paulson *(Mgr-Mktg)*
Michael R. Manley *(VP-Reg Mktg)*
Patrick Worsham *(Mgr-Mktg-Reg)*
Walter R. Reifel *(VP)*
Christopher R. Grubbs *(Mgr-Las Vegas)*
Jonathan Higgins *(Mgr-Western Reg)*
Michael N. Bohrer *(Dir-New York)*
Randy Lasure *(Mgr-Eastern Reg)*
Robert Kocher *(CEO)*

Subsidiaries:

Sullivan Engineering, LLC (1)
134 W 29th St 3rd Fl, New York, NY 10001
Tel.: (646) 809-5889
Web Site:
 http://www.sullivanengineeringllc.com
Commercial Construction Services
N.A.I.C.S.: 236220
Brian P. Sullivan *(CEO)*
Mark Sheeran *(Chief Strategy & Operating Officer)*
Michael Frech *(VP-Recruiting)*
Kevin M. Duffy *(VP-Ops)*
Mike Lopez *(Dir-Building Envelope Consultants)*

RIMPULL CORPORATION
15600 S Hwy 169, Olathe, KS 66062
Tel.: (913) 782-4000
Web Site: http://www.rimpull.com
Year Founded: 1971
Sales Range: $10-24.9 Million
Emp.: 192
Mining Machinery
N.A.I.C.S.: 333131
Jeff Scheibel *(CFO & VP)*

RIMROCK AUTO GROUP, INC.
840 S Shiloh Rd, Billings, MT 59106
Tel.: (406) 651-5000 MT
Web Site:
 http://www.rimrockauto.com
Year Founded: 1951
Sales Range: $450-499.9 Million
Emp.: 267
Retail Sale of New & Used Automobile Distr
N.A.I.C.S.: 441110
Ernie Lee *(Chief Admin Officer & Principal)*

Subsidiaries:

Rimrock Suburu, Inc. (1)
2540 Phyllis Ln, Billings, MT 59102-5644
Tel.: (406) 651-5000
Web Site: http://www.rimrocksubaru.com
Sales Range: $10-24.9 Million
Emp.: 25
Retail Sales of New & Used Automobiles
N.A.I.C.S.: 441110
Bj Johnson *(Gen Mgr)*

RIMSTORM, INC.
205 Van Buren St Ste 120, Herndon, VA 20170
Tel.: (703) 345-5833 VA
Web Site: https://www.rimstorm.com
Year Founded: 2018
Emp.: 500
Full-service Managed Security Service Provider
N.A.I.C.S.: 541512
Ben Gerenstein *(Pres & CEO)*

Subsidiaries:

Elevative Networks LLC (1)
1577 Spring Hill Rd Ste 210, Vienna, VA 22182-2284
Tel.: (703) 226-3401
Custom Computer Programming Services
N.A.I.C.S.: 541511
David Cross *(CEO)*

RINCHEM COMPANY INCORPORATED
5131 Masthead St, Albuquerque, NM 87107
Tel.: (505) 345-3655
Web Site: http://www.rinchem.com
Sales Range: $10-24.9 Million
Emp.: 400
Hazardous Waste Collection & Disposal
N.A.I.C.S.: 562211
William W. Moore *(Chm)*
Charles Breinholt *(Pres)*
Michael Campbell *(Mgr-IS Maintenance)*
Gary Michaelson *(Mgr-Facility)*
Gwen Inman *(Dir-HRD & QESH)*

RINCON CONSULTANTS, INC.
180 N Ashwood Ave, Ventura, CA 93003
Tel.: (805) 644-4455 CA
Web Site:
 http://www.rinconconsultants.com
Year Founded: 1994
Sales Range: $10-24.9 Million
Emp.: 55
Environmental Consulting Services
N.A.I.C.S.: 541690
Duane Vander Pluym *(VP)*
Michael P. Gialketsis *(Pres)*
Stephen Svete *(VP)*
Walt Hamann *(VP)*
Joseph Power *(Principal)*
Richard Daulton *(Principal)*
Steve Hongola *(Principal)*
A. Edward Morelan *(Principal-Environmental Site Assessment & Remediation)*
Abe Leider *(Principal-Environmental & Plng Svcs)*
Colby J. Boggs *(Principal)*
Erik Feldman *(Principal-Sustainability Svcs)*
Jennifer Haddow *(Principal)*
Lacrissa Cook Davis *(Principal)*
John Dreher Jr. *(Principal)*

RINEHART OIL, INC.
2401 N State St, Ukiah, CA 95482
Tel.: (707) 462-8811
Web Site: http://www.rinehartoil.com
Rev.: $28,800,000
Emp.: 100

RINEHART OIL, INC.

Rinehart Oil, Inc.—(Continued)
Petroleum & Petroleum Products Merchant Whslr
N.A.I.C.S.: 424720
Joan Bosrock (Mgr-Fuel Pricing)
Mike Babcock (Mgr-Sls)
Reed Rinehart Jr. (Pres)

RING POWER CORPORATION
500 World Commerce Pkwy, Saint Augustine, FL 32092
Tel.: (904) 737-7730
Web Site: http://www.ringpower.com
Year Founded: 1986
Sales Range: $25-49.9 Million
Construction & Mining Services
N.A.I.C.S.: 423810
Lance Ringhaver (Chm & Pres)
Heather Lane Courtney (Mgr-Power Sys Rental Ops)
Frank Streva (Mgr-Used Equipment Sls)
Hubert Norris (Sr VP & Dir-Parts Ops)

Subsidiaries:

Ring Power Corporation (1)
500 World Commerce Pkwy, Saint Augustine, FL 32092
Tel.: (904) 737-7730
Web Site: http://www.ringpower.com
Construction & Mining Machinery Services
N.A.I.C.S.: 423810
Chris Zeras (VP-Sls-HE)
Sue Miller (Sr VP-Mktg & Dir-PR)
Kevin Robbins (Exec VP-Sls)
David Alban (COO & Sec)
Ed Sanford (VP)
Wes MacDonald (Mgr-General Svc & Ops)
Dan Leach (Mgr-Product Support)
Curtis Thompson (Asst Mgr-Sls-Electric Power & Indus Engines)

Subsidiary (Domestic):

Ring Lift (2)
2700 N Caroline Powerline Rd, Pompano Beach, FL 33069
Tel.: (954) 977-5010
Web Site: http://www.ringpowert.com
Rev.: $19,872,020
Emp.: 52
Materials Handling Machinery
N.A.I.C.S.: 423830
Maria Ramos (Mgr-Svc)

RingPower Corp (1)
10421 Ferhill Dr, Riverview, FL 33578 (100%)
Tel.: (813) 671-3700
Web Site: http://www.ringhaver.com
Sales Range: $100-124.9 Million
Emp.: 1,000
Construction Equipment Distr
N.A.I.C.S.: 423810
Randal Ringhaver (Chm, Pres & CEO)

RINGGOLD TELEPHONE CO. INC.
200 Evitt Pkwy, Ringgold, GA 30736
Tel.: (706) 965-2345
Web Site: http://www.catt.com
Sales Range: $10-24.9 Million
Emp.: 75
Telephone Communications
N.A.I.C.S.: 517610
Alice Evitt Bandy (Owner)
Phil Erlie (VP)
Celeste Bandy Weaver (VP-Fin & Regulatory)

RINGLAND CONSTRUCTION INC.
4637 Vincennes Blvd #10, Cape Coral, FL 33904
Tel.: (239) 980-7711
Web Site: http://www.ringlandconstruction.com
Year Founded: 1992
Sales Range: $1-9.9 Million

Construction Services
N.A.I.C.S.: 236115
Russ Ringland (Pres)

RINGLAND-JOHNSON INC.
1725 Huntwood Dr, Cherry Valley, IL 61016-9560
Tel.: (815) 332-8600
Web Site: http://www.ringland.com
Year Founded: 1946
Sales Range: $10-24.9 Million
Emp.: 124
Nonresidential Construction
N.A.I.C.S.: 236220
Brent B. Johnson (Pres & CEO)
Lauren Spencer (CFO, Treas & Sec)

RINGLER ASSOCIATES INC.
27422 Aliso Creek Rd Ste 200, Aliso Viejo, CA 92656
Tel.: (949) 296-9000
Web Site: http://www.ringlerassociates.com
Sales Range: $10-24.9 Million
Emp.: 200
Insurance Agents & Brokers
N.A.I.C.S.: 524210
W. Ross Duncan (Chm)
James M. Early (Exec VP & Dir-Sls-Natl)
Joseph Loseman (CFO & Sr VP)
Duke T. Wolpert (VP & Dir-Mktg)
Geoffrey E. Hunt (Pres & CFO)
Brenda Greenwood (Mgr-Svc Center)
Michael Rickerts (Dir-IT)
Melissa Evola Price (Chief Strategy & Bus Dev Officer)
Andrea L. Haupert (Dir-Mktg & Comm-Denver)
Veni Lanka (Mgr-Ops)
Brian M. Farrell Jr. (Vice Chm)

RINGLING COLLEGE OF ART AND DESIGN, INC.
2700 N Tamiami Trl, Sarasota, FL 34234-5895
Tel.: (941) 351-5100
Web Site: http://www.ringling.edu
Year Founded: 1931
Fine Arts Undergraduate College
N.A.I.C.S.: 611310
Larry R. Thompson (Pres)
Tracy A. Wagner (Exec VP)
Tammy S. Walsh (VP-Student Life & Dean-Students)
Michael Klein (Vice Chm)
George Miles (Chm)
Joel Morganrogh (Co-Treas)
Rosemary Oberndorf (Co-Treas)
Stacey Corley (VP-Advancement)
Christine C. DeGeorge (VP-Human & Org Dev)
Peter A. McAllister (VP-Academic Affairs)

Subsidiaries:

Ringling College Lifelong Learning Academy (1)
Temple Beth Shalom 1050 S Tuttle Ave Bldg 1, Sarasota, FL 34237
Tel.: (941) 309-5111
Web Site: http://www.thelifelonglearningacademy.com
Adult Non-Credit School
N.A.I.C.S.: 611699
Jana Overstreet (Exec Dir)

RINGS END INC.
181 W Ave, Darien, CT 06820-4312
Tel.: (203) 655-2525
Web Site: http://www.ringsend.com
Year Founded: 1902
Sales Range: $25-49.9 Million
Emp.: 350
Lumber, Plywood & Millwork Retailer
N.A.I.C.S.: 423310

Doug Campbell (Chm)
David Campbell (Pres & CEO)
Lou Reda (CFO & Exec VP)
Kel Tyler (Sr VP)
John G. Giardino (Dir-HR)
Claude Hirsch (Controller)
Eddie Abbiati (Gen Mgr-Niantic)
Sue Bell (Mgr-Credit)
Maria DeCarlo (Mgr-Credit-Lewisboro Store)
Henry De La Rosa (Gen Mgr-Architectural Hardware & Kitchen Sls)
Richard Fournier (Mgr-Paint Center)
David Rohr (Gen Mgr)
Judy Koniecko (Mgr-Credit-Niantic Store)
Pete McDonald (Gen Mgr)
Sal Migliorelli (Mgr-Store)
Gordon Milne (Gen Mgr)
Cindy Lewis (Mgr-Credit)
Fernando Queiroz (Mgr-Comml Paint)
Rick Moreau (Gen Mgr-New Milford)
Markens Jeune (Mgr-Paint Center-Lewisboro)
Mike Loya (Gen Mgr)
Matt Rich (Gen Mgr)
Gary Walton (Gen Mgr)
Scott Curcio (Gen Mgr)
Sean Gleason (Mgr-Paint Sls)
Matt Dewing (Mgr-Facilities)
Eileen Loya (Mgr-Credit)
Anthony Capomolla (Mgr-Paint Center-Stamford)
Bill Bolstridge (Mgr-Paint Center-West Haven)
Bill Simek (Mgr-Sls)
Bob Thomas (Mgr-Paint Center-New London)
Brandon Watkins (Mgr-Paint Center-Danbury)
Mike Burkhart Sr. (Dir-Sls & Ops)
John F. Carroll Jr. (Dir-Tech)

Subsidiaries:

Ring's End of Bethel Inc. (1)
9 Taylor Ave, Bethel, CT 06801
Tel.: (203) 797-1212
Web Site: http://www.ringsend.com
Sales Range: $10-24.9 Million
Emp.: 30
Home Center Operator
N.A.I.C.S.: 444110
Mike Loya (Mgr)

RINKER OIL CORPORATION
29 Water St, Cuba, NY 14727
Tel.: (585) 968-3330
Web Site: http://www.rinkeroil.com
Year Founded: 1936
Sales Range: $10-24.9 Million
Emp.: 22
Heating Fuel & Bottled Gas Dealer
N.A.I.C.S.: 457210
Dawn Davis (Office Mgr)

RIO BRAVO OIL, INC.
2425 Fountainview Ste 300, Houston, TX 77057
Tel.: (713) 787-9060
Web Site: http://www.riobravooil.com
Year Founded: 2010
Sales Range: Less than $1 Million
Oil & Gas Exploration Services
N.A.I.C.S.: 211120
Lynden Bernard Rose (Sec)
Seth Alan Nichamoff (Acting Pres & CEO)
Carlos E. Buchanan II (CFO, Chief Acctg Officer & Treas)

RIO FRESH, INC.
FM 2557, San Juan, TX 78589
Tel.: (956) 787-0023
Web Site: http://www.riofresh.com
Sales Range: $10-24.9 Million
Emp.: 250
Fresh Fruit & Vegetable Whslr

N.A.I.C.S.: 424480
Bill Morley (Gen Mgr)
Christine Morley (Pres)
Jeremy Clemmons (Supvr-Field Harvesting)

RIO GRANDE CO.
201 Santa Fe Dr, Denver, CO 80223
Tel.: (303) 825-2211
Web Site: http://www.riograndeco.com
Rev.: $24,800,000
Emp.: 64
Cement
N.A.I.C.S.: 423320
Bruce Peterson (Pres)
Brent Broekemeier (CEO)
Steve Sathoff (Controller)

RIO GRANDE ELECTRIC COOP
Hwy 90 and FM Rd 131, Brackettville, TX 78832
Tel.: (830) 563-2444
Web Site: http://www.rgec.coop
Rev.: $15,510,195
Emp.: 40
Distribution, Electric Power
N.A.I.C.S.: 221122
Daniel G. Laws (Gen Mgr)
Trish Taylor (Dir-HR)

RIO GRANDE STEEL, LTD.
US Hwy 281 E Owassa, Edinburg, TX 78539
Tel.: (956) 702-4434
Web Site: http://www.riograndesteel.com
Rev.: $12,900,000
Emp.: 9
Steel Wire Products Mfr
N.A.I.C.S.: 423510
Hector Maldonado (Pres)

RIO GRANDE TRAVEL CENTERS, INC.
4331 Wyoming Blvd NE, Albuquerque, NM 87111-3143
Tel.: (505) 292-7044
Web Site: http://www.rgtravel.com
Year Founded: 1975
Sales Range: $75-99.9 Million
Emp.: 60
Travel Agency
N.A.I.C.S.: 561510
Joanne Summers (Co-Owner & CFO)
Mike Miller (Exec VP & Co-Owner)
Ed Heron (Mgr-IT)

RIO MOTOR CO.
4343 E US Hwy 83, Rio Grande City, TX 78582
Tel.: (956) 487-2596
Web Site: http://www.riomotors.com
Year Founded: 1994
Sales Range: $10-24.9 Million
Emp.: 30
Car Dealer
N.A.I.C.S.: 441110
Obidio C. Canales (Owner)

RIOJAS ENTERPRISES INC.
9719 Jacob Ln, Lees Summit, MO 64086-8475
Tel.: (913) 281-1600
Web Site: http://www.riojas-able.com
Year Founded: 1988
Sales Range: $10-24.9 Million
Emp.: 80
Temporary Employment Services
N.A.I.C.S.: 561320
Carlos Riojas (Pres)
Brad Johnson (Dir-HR)
James English (Dir-Admin)

COMPANIES

RIORDAN, LEWIS & HADEN, INC.
10900 Wilshire Blvd Ste 850, Los Angeles, CA 90024
Tel.: (310) 405-7200
Web Site: http://www.rlhequity.com
Year Founded: 1982
Investment Management & Financial Services
N.A.I.C.S.: 523999
J. Christopher Lewis *(Founder & Mng Partner)*
Murray E. Rudin *(Mng Dir)*
Ryan A. Smiley *(Mng Dir)*
Adam L. Frankinburger *(CFO & Chief Compliance Officer)*
Michel Glouchevitch *(Mng Dir)*
Rob Rodin *(Pres & CEO)*
Robert A. Zielinski *(Mng Dir)*
Kenneth D. Hubbs *(Mng Dir)*

RIP'S COUNTRY INN
3809 N Crain Hwy, Bowie, MD 20716
Tel.: (301) 805-5900
Web Site: http://www.ripscountryinn.com
Year Founded: 1952
Sales Range: $10-24.9 Million
Restaurant Operators
N.A.I.C.S.: 722511
Matthew Gilstein *(Gen Mgr)*

RIPA & ASSOCIATES, INC.
1409 Tech Blvd Ste 1, Tampa, FL 33619
Tel.: (813) 623-6777   FL
Web Site: http://www.ripatampa.com
Year Founded: 1998
Sales Range: $50-74.9 Million
Emp.: 280
Water, Sewer Line & Related Structures & Roadway Construction
N.A.I.C.S.: 237110
Chris LaFace *(Pres)*

RIPARIUS CORPORATION
25 Schilling Rd, Hunt Valley, MD 21031
Tel.: (410) 785-3002   MD
Web Site: http://www.ripariusconstruction.com
Year Founded: 1985
Sales Range: $100-124.9 Million
Emp.: 40
Nonresidential Construction
N.A.I.C.S.: 531120
Mike McCarthy *(Pres & CEO)*

Subsidiaries:

Riparius Communication Services   (1)
25 Schilling Rd, Hunt Valley, MD 21031
Tel.: (410) 785-3002
Web Site: http://www.ripariuscontruction.com
Sales Range: $10-24.9 Million
Emp.: 10
Communication & Construction Services
N.A.I.C.S.: 517810
Micheal McCarthy *(Pres)*

Riparius Construction Inc.   (1)
25 Schilling Rd, Hunt Valley, MD 21031
Tel.: (410) 785-3002
Web Site: http://www.ripariusconstruction.com
Sales Range: $10-24.9 Million
Emp.: 30
Nonresidential Construction
N.A.I.C.S.: 531120
Debbie Seebach *(Project Coord)*
Ken Kolb *(VP)*
Scott Germer *(Project Mgr)*

RIPKEN BASEBALL, INC.
880 Long Dr, Aberdeen, MD 21001
Tel.: (410) 306-7575
Web Site: https://ripkenbaseball.com
Emp.: 100
Sports Teams & Clubs
N.A.I.C.S.: 711211

Subsidiaries:

Baseball Factory, Inc.   (1)
9212 Berger Rd Ste 200, Columbia, MD 21046
Tel.: (410) 715-5080
Web Site: http://www.baseballfactory.com
Sales Range: $1-9.9 Million
Emp.: 60
Baseball Training, Consulting & Promotional Services
N.A.I.C.S.: 611620
Steve Sclafani *(Founder & CEO)*
Rob Naddelman *(Pres)*
Steve Bernhardt *(Exec VP-Baseball Ops)*
Jason Budden *(Sr VP-Mktg & Brand)*
Dan Forester *(VP-Player Dev)*
Jim Gemler *(Sr VP-Baseball Ops)*
Jeff Brazier *(VP-Youth Baseball)*
Gene Mattingly *(CFO)*
Dave Lax *(Sr Dir-Event Mktg & Partnerships)*
Becky Oldham *(Dir-Social Media)*
Adam Beaver *(Dir-Retail Sls)*
Ryan Liddle *(Dir-Youth Baseball Ops)*
Amanda Beck *(Mgr-Database Mktg)*
Barbara Scott *(Mgr-HR)*
Andy Ferguson *(Sr Dir-Player Dev & Scouting)*
Justin Roswell *(Sr Dir-Tournaments & Showcases)*
Wei Xue *(Sr Dir-Web Dev)*
Joe Lake *(Sr Dir-Youth Baseball Ops)*

RIPON ATHLETIC, INC.
275 June St, Berlin, WI 54923
Tel.: (920) 361-1500
Web Site: http://www.riponathletic.com
Rev.: $10,800,000
Emp.: 151
Cut & Sew Apparel Mfr
N.A.I.C.S.: 315250
Peter Derleth *(VP)*
Henry M. Derleth *(Pres)*
Gretchen Derleth *(Sec)*
Richard L. Madden *(Treas)*

RIPPE & KINGSTON, LLC
1077 Celestial St, Cincinnati, OH 45202-1696
Tel.: (513) 977-4578   OH
Web Site: http://www.rippe.com
Sales Range: $75-99.9 Million
Emp.: 100
Holding Company; Legal Software Development & Network Integration, Law Firm Management & Capital Advisory Services
N.A.I.C.S.: 551112
Jeremy Frye *(Partner)*
Leah Fogle *(Asst Controller)*
Tom Obermaier *(CEO)*
Steve Crossman *(Chief Revenue Officer)*
Ginny Schumacher *(VP-Mktg)*
John Boyd *(Chief Product Officer)*

Subsidiaries:

Rippe & Kingston Systems, Inc.   (1)
1077 Celestial St, Cincinnati, OH 45202-1696
Tel.: (513) 241-1375
Web Site: http://www.rippe.com
Sales Range: $1-9.9 Million
Legal Software Development, Integration & Hosting Services
N.A.I.C.S.: 541511
George Kingston *(Pres)*

RIPPLE INDUSTRIES LLC
1801 Century Park E Ste 1900, Los Angeles, CA 90067
Tel.: (310) 202-5210
Web Site: https://rippleindustries.com
Investment Services
N.A.I.C.S.: 523999

Subsidiaries:

Schumacher Electric Corporation   (1)
801 Business Center Dr, Mount Prospect, IL 60056-2179
Tel.: (847) 385-1600
Web Site: http://www.batterychargers.com
Sales Range: $50-74.9 Million
Emp.: 55
Mfr of Automotive Battery Chargers & Custom Transformers
N.A.I.C.S.: 335999
Donald Schumacher *(CEO)*
John Waldron *(Pres)*
Daniel Frano *(VP-Fin)*

RIPPLEWOOD HOLDINGS LLC
920 Broadway 6th Fl, New York, NY 10010
Tel.: (212) 582-6700   DE
Year Founded: 1995
Emp.: 2,000
Privater Equity Firm
N.A.I.C.S.: 523999
Timothy C. Collins *(Founder)*

Subsidiaries:

AS Citadele Banka   (1)
Republikas laukums 2A, Riga, LV-1010, Latvia   (75%)
Tel.: (371) 6 701 0000
Web Site: http://www.citadele.lv
Rev.: $90,646,558
Assets: $3,583,110,176
Liabilities: $3,311,146,967
Net Worth: $271,963,209
Earnings: $43,525,581
Emp.: 1,603
Fiscal Year-end: 12/31/2016
Banking Services
N.A.I.C.S.: 522110
Guntis Belavskis *(Chm-Mgmt Bd & CEO)*
Valters Abele *(Member-Mgmt Bd & Chief Risk Officer)*
Kaspars Cikmacs *(Member-Mgmt Bd & Chief Ops Officer)*
Santa Purgaile *(Member-Mgmt Bd & Chief Bus Officer)*
Timothy Collins *(Chm-Supervisory Bd)*
Critchley Elizabeth *(Deputy Chm-Supervisory Bd)*
Vladislavs Mironovs *(Member-Mgmt Bd)*
Uldis Upenieks *(Member-Mgmt Bd)*
Slavomir Mizak *(Member-Mgmt Bd)*

Subsidiary (Domestic):

AB "Citadele" Bankas   (2)
Republikas laukums 2A, LV-1010, Riga, Latvia   (100%)
Tel.: (371) 67010 000
Web Site: http://www.citadele.lt
Rev.: $138,784,250
Assets: $4,191,376,172
Liabilities: $3,809,811,874
Net Worth: $381,564,299
Earnings: $40,879,369
Emp.: 1,369
Fiscal Year-end: 12/31/2019
Commericial Banking
N.A.I.C.S.: 522110
Timothy C. Collins *(Chm-Supervisory Bd)*
Elizabeth Critchley *(Deputy Chm-Supervisory Bd)*
Slavomir Mizak *(Chief Tech & Ops Officer & Member-Mgmt Bd)*
Uldis Upenieks *(Chief Compliance Officer & Member-Mgmt Bd)*
Valters Abele *(CFO, Chief Risk Officer & Member-Mgmt Bd)*
Vladislavs Mironovs *(Chief Strategy Officer & Member-Mgmt Bd)*
Johan Akerblom *(Chm-Mgmt Bd & CEO)*
Vaidas Zagunis *(Chief Corp Comml Officer & Member-Mgmt Bd)*
Ruta Ezerskiene *(Chief Retail Comml Officer & Member-Mgmt Bd)*

Subsidiary (Non-US):

AP Anlage & Privatbank AG   (2)
Limmatquai 4, 8001, Zurich, Switzerland
Tel.: (41) 447876200
Web Site: http://www.apbank.ch
Rev.: $8,626,084
Assets: $299,152,444
Liabilities: $270,356,948

RIPPLEWOOD HOLDINGS LLC

Net Worth: $28,795,496
Earnings: $3,466,361
Emp.: 24
Fiscal Year-end: 12/31/2019
Banking Services
N.A.I.C.S.: 522110
Joachim Bodschwinna *(Chief Risk Officer & Member-Mgmt Bd)*
Vladimirs Ivanovs *(Vice Chm)*
Urs E. Hottiger *(Chm)*
Boriss Prudnikovics *(Member-Mgmt Bd & Head-Asset Mgmt)*
Rolf Bauer *(CEO & Member-Mgmt Bd)*
Gian Nay *(Deputy CEO, COO & Member-Mgmt Bd)*

AS Citadele banka Eesti filiaal   (2)
Roosikrantsi 2, Tallinn, 10119, Estonia
Tel.: (372) 7700000
Web Site: http://www.citadele.ee
Banking Services
N.A.I.C.S.: 522110
Sofia Kirsimaa *(CEO)*
Lauri Karner *(Head-Corp & Institutional Banking)*

Shaklee Corporation   (1)
4747 Willow Rd, Pleasanton, CA 94588   (40.5%)
Tel.: (925) 924-2000
Web Site: http://www.shaklee.com
Sales Range: $100-124.9 Million
Emp.: 300
Vitamins & Nutritional Products Distr
N.A.I.C.S.: 424210
Roger Barnett *(Chm & CEO)*
Marjorie Fine *(Gen Counsel, Sec & Exec VP)*
Jamie McManus *(Chm-Medical Affairs, Health Sciences & Education)*
Mike Batesole *(CFO)*
Rich Libby *(CIO)*
Enlie Widjaja *(Gen Mgr)*
Philip Wong *(Gen Mgr)*
Rong Xue *(Chief Supply Officer)*
Laura Evans *(Sr VP-Sls & Field Dev)*
Emanuel Fakoukakis *(Chief Innovation Officer)*
Jon Fieldman *(Chief Supply Officer)*
Brad Harrington *(CMO)*

Subsidiary (Non-US):

Shaklee Canada, Inc.   (2)
529 Michigan Drive Unit 700, Oakville, L6L 0C4, ON, Canada
Tel.: (905) 681-1422
Web Site: http://www.shaklee.com
Sales Range: $25-49.9 Million
Emp.: 32
Industrial Products Mfr
N.A.I.C.S.: 541420
Roger L. Barnett *(CEO)*
Jeff Hill *(Pres)*
Shobhna Asthana *(CFO)*
Franci Kursh *(CIO)*
Melina Baxter *(CMO)*
Matt Town *(Gen Counsel)*
Kelley Moran *(VP)*
James R. Brooks *(Exec VP)*

Shaklee Mexico, S.A. de C.V.   (2)
Juan de la Fontaine 23, Col Chapultepec Polanco, CP 11560, Mexico, Mexico
Tel.: (52) 5591387000
Web Site: http://www.shaklee.com.mx
Sales Range: $25-49.9 Million
Emp.: 23
Nutritional Product Mfr
N.A.I.C.S.: 456191
Julio P. Cepeda *(Gen Mgr)*

Shaklee Products (Malaysia) Sdn. Bhd.   (2)
Level 9 The Pinnacle Persiaran Lagoon Bandar Sunway, 47500, Subang Jaya, Selangor Darul Ehsan, Malaysia
Tel.: (60) 3 5622 3188
Web Site: http://www.shaklee.com.my
Sales Range: $25-49.9 Million
Emp.: 120
Nutritional Products
N.A.I.C.S.: 456191
Helen Lam *(Pres)*
Mike Batesole *(CFO)*
Tony Tucker *(Gen Counsel, Sec & Sr VP)*
Bruce Daggy *(Chief Science Officer & Sr VP-R&D)*

Subsidiary (Domestic):

Shaklee Research Center   (2)

RIPPLEWOOD HOLDINGS LLC

Ripplewood Holdings LLC—(Continued)
1992 Alpine Way, Hayward, CA 94545-1702
Tel.: (510) 781-0713
Web Site: http://www.shaklee.com
Sales Range: $25-49.9 Million
Emp.: 114
Provider of Nutritional Research Services
N.A.I.C.S.: 624190
Roger Barnett *(Pres & CEO)*
Bruce Daggy *(Chief Innovation Officer)*
Rich Libby *(Chief Supply Officer)*
Jennifer Steeves-Kiss *(CFO)*
Todd Tucker *(CIO)*
Enlie Widjaja *(Gen Mgr)*
Philip Wong *(Gen Mgr)*
Laura Evans *(Sr VP-Sls & Field Dev)*
Jon Fieldman *(Chief Supply Officer)*
Brad Harrington *(CMO)*
Cindy Latham *(Sr VP-Global Mktg)*

Shaklee U.S. (2)
4747 Willow Rd, Pleasanton, CA 94588-2763
Tel.: (925) 924-2000
Web Site: http://www.us.shaklee.com
Provider of Nutritional Product Distr
N.A.I.C.S.: 424210

RIPPY CADILLAC, LLC
4951 New Centre Dr, Wilmington, NC 28403
Tel.: (910) 799-2421 NC
Web Site:
  http://www.rippyautomotive.com
Sales Range: $25-49.9 Million
Emp.: 65
Automobiles, New & Used
N.A.I.C.S.: 441110
Allen Rippy *(Pres)*

RIPT APPAREL, LLC
746 N Elizabeth St #1, Chicago, IL 60642
Tel.: (773) 789-7478
Web Site: http://www.riptapparel.com
Online Tee Shirt Retailer
N.A.I.C.S.: 424350
Paul Friemel *(Founder & CMO)*
T. J. Mapes *(Founder & CTO)*
Matt Ingleby *(CEO)*
Whitney Zech *(Mgr-Pre-Production)*
Eric Fisher *(Mgr-Production)*
Renita Kavallieros *(Graphic Designer)*
K. J. Smith *(Dir-Mktg)*
Jason Svatos *(Mgr-Traffic)*

RISDALL MARKETING GROUP, LLC
2685 Long Lake Rd Ste 100, Roseville, MN 55113
Tel.: (651) 286-6700 MN
Web Site: http://www.risdall.com
Year Founded: 1972
Rev.: $200,000,000
Emp.: 46
Advertising & Public Relations Agency
N.A.I.C.S.: 541810
John Risdall *(Founder)*
Ted Risdall *(Chm & CEO)*
Joel Koenigs *(CTO)*
Katie Usem *(Acct Exec)*
Erik Hinds *(VP-Digital Strategy)*
Dave Schad *(Exec VP & Gen Mgr)*

Subsidiaries:

Risdall Public Relations (1)
550 Main St, New Brighton, MN 55112
Tel.: (651) 286-6700
Web Site: http://www.risdallpr.com
Public Relations Agency
N.A.I.C.S.: 541820
Tina Karelson *(Pres-Creative)*
Jennifer Risdall *(CEO-Risdall Online Mktg Grp)*
Glenna Dibrell *(Sr VP & Acct Supvr)*
Andrea Goodall *(VP)*
Maggie Tompkins *(Acct Exec)*
Pete Fabian *(Dir-Creative)*
Joel Koenigs *(Pres-Tech)*
Kelly Mapes *(Mgr-Acctg)*
Michelle Peterson *(Acct Coord)*
John Risdall *(Founder & Chm)*
Ted Risdall *(Pres & CEO)*
Jim Sandstrom *(Pres-Risdall Sandstorm Media Works)*
Melissa Holte *(Assoc Dir & Acct Supvr)*

RISDON INTERNATIONAL, INC.
1100 Buckingham St, Watertown, CT 06795
Tel.: (860) 417-1100 DE
Sales Range: $150-199.9 Million
Emp.: 800
Fragrance & Color Cosmetic Packaging Mfr
N.A.I.C.S.: 561910
Gene Giancarli *(Engr-Design)*
Luba Wagner *(Supvr-Warehouse)*

RISE AGAINST HUNGER
3733 National Dr Ste 200, Raleigh, NC 27612
Tel.: (919) 839-0689 DE
Web Site:
  http://www.riseagainsthunger.org
Year Founded: 1998
Hunger Relief Services
N.A.I.C.S.: 624210
Rod Brooks *(Pres & CEO)*
Bob Dixson *(CFO)*
Anne Bander *(Chm)*
Edna Ogwangi *(Chief Impact Officer)*
Peggy Shriver *(Chief Dev Officer)*
Larry Shepherd *(COO)*
Walter Gaskin *(Vice Chm)*

RISE INTERACTIVE, INC.
1 S Wacker Dr Ste 300, Chicago, IL 60606
Tel.: (312) 281-9933
Web Site:
  http://www.riseinteractive.com
Year Founded: 2004
Sales Range: $10-24.9 Million
Emp.: 230
Advertising Agency & Internet Marketing Company
N.A.I.C.S.: 541810
Jon Morris *(Founder & CEO)*
Scott Conine *(Sr VP-Ops)*
Howard Diamond *(VP-Digital Strategy)*
Larry Fisher *(Chief Client Svc Officer)*
Steven Tazic *(Dir-Digital Media)*
Lou Amodeo *(Assoc Dir-Creative)*
Matthew Zaute *(Sr VP-Client Delivery)*
Josh Zarov *(VP-ECommerce)*
Brent Laufenberg *(VP-Innovation)*
Ben Hurley *(Chief Client Service Officer)*

RISE, INC.
8406 Sunset Rd NE, Spring Lake Park, MN 55432-1387
Tel.: (763) 786-8334 MN
Web Site: http://www.rise.org
Year Founded: 1992
Sales Range: $10-24.9 Million
Disability Assistance Services
N.A.I.C.S.: 624120
Dan Hagberg *(Dir-IT Svcs)*
Tim Dickie *(VP)*
Tom Haglund *(CFO)*
Beth DePoint *(Dir-PR)*
Melinda Dannley *(Coord-DTH)*
Keith Hovland *(Coord-DTH)*
Noel McCormick *(Dir-Advancement)*
Truc Pham *(Dir-MFIP & Welfare-to-Work Programs)*
Jennifer Gajewski *(Dir-Quality Assurance)*
Robert Reedy *(Dir-Vocational Svcs-Twin Cities Metro Area)*
Michele Warren *(Mgr-Production)*
Lynn Noren *(Pres)*

RISING INDIA, INC.
1190 Cleveland Rd, Sandusky, OH 44870
Tel.: (402) 960-6110
Web Site:
  http://www.risingbiosciences.org
Rev.: $15,000
Assets: $193,000
Liabilities: $1,306,000
Net Worth: ($1,113,000)
Earnings: ($139,000)
Fiscal Year-end: 12/31/18
Holding Company
N.A.I.C.S.: 551112

RISING MEDICAL SOLUTIONS, LLC
325 N LaSalle St Ste 475, Chicago, IL 60610
Tel.: (312) 559-8445
Web Site: http://www.risingms.com
Year Founded: 1999
Rev.: $16,800,000
Emp.: 157
Data Processing, Hosting & Related Services
N.A.I.C.S.: 518210
Jason F. Beans *(CEO)*
Tom Galvan *(CFO)*
Kristyn Mullikin *(Office Mgr)*
Timothy Howlin *(Chief Sls Officer)*
Anne Kirby *(Chief Compliance Officer & VP-Care Mgmt)*
Dan Trahan *(CIO)*
Deborah Tschiltsch *(VP-Acct Mgmt)*
Rachel Fikes *(VP-Mktg & Dir-Study Program-Work Comp BenChmarking Study)*
Rick Thompson *(VP-Talent Mgmt)*
Robert Evans *(VP-Repricing Solutions)*
David Huth *(COO)*

Subsidiaries:

Preferred Disability Management, LLC (1)
11711 N Meridian St, Carmel, IN 46032-4534
Tel.: (317) 571-0702
Web Site: http://www.pdmrtw.com
Sales Range: $1-9.9 Million
Emp.: 23
Management Consulting Services
N.A.I.C.S.: 541618
Vernon Poland *(VP)*

RISING PHOENIX HOLDINGS CORPORATION
126 Business Park Dr, Utica, NY 13502
Tel.: (800) 382-2468
Web Site: https://www.rphc.com
Year Founded: 2018
Holding Company
N.A.I.C.S.: 551112
Daniel A. Craig *(CEO)*

RISING SUN FARMS
5126 S Pacific Hwy, Phoenix, OR 97535
Tel.: (541) 535-8331
Web Site:
  http://www.risingsunfarms.com
Year Founded: 1985
Rev.: $4,100,000
Emp.: 27
Frozen Specialty Food Mfr
N.A.I.C.S.: 311412
Sheila McRoy *(Mgr-Sls-Natl)*
Elizabeth Fujas *(Owner & Mgr-Sls-Natl)*

U.S. PRIVATE

RISING SUN SOLAR & ELECTRIC
810 Kokomo Rd Ste 160, Haiku, HI 96708
Tel.: (808) 575-2202
Web Site:
  http://www.risingsunsolar.com
Year Founded: 2004
Sales Range: $1-9.9 Million
Emp.: 100
Solar Electric & Hot Water Systems
N.A.I.C.S.: 221118
Bari Barnes *(Gen Mgr)*
Matias Besasso *(Pres & Owner)*
Brad Albert *(Pres & Owner)*

RISINGER BROS TRANSFER INC.
225 W Courtland St, Morton, IL 61550-1403
Tel.: (309) 266-9555
Web Site:
  http://www.risingerbros.com
Rev.: $20,212,844
Emp.: 70
Trucking Except Local
N.A.I.C.S.: 484121
Michelle Neill *(Controller)*

RISK & INSURANCE MANAGEMENT SOCIETY, INC.
1065 Avenue of the Americas 13th Fl, New York, NY 10018
Tel.: (212) 286-9292
Web Site: http://www.rims.org
Sales Range: $10-24.9 Million
Emp.: 50
Risk & Insurance Management Society
N.A.I.C.S.: 513120
Mary Roth *(CEO)*
Blanca Ferreris *(Sr Mgr-Meetings & Events)*
Nowell R. Seaman *(Pres)*
Gloria Brosius *(Sec)*
Stephen Pottle *(Treas)*
Carol Fox *(VP-Strategic Initiatives)*
Annette Homan *(COO)*
Michael Peters *(VP-IT)*
Paul Pizio *(VP-Fin & Acctg)*
Nikole Tenbrink *(VP-Membership & Mktg)*
Richard J. Roberts Jr. *(Pres)*
Robert Cartwright Jr. *(VP)*

RISK ASSISTANCE NETWORK + EXCHANGE NETWORK, INC.
510 Fifth Ave 3rd Fl, New York, NY 10036
Tel.: (844) 786-7263
Web Site:
  http://www.ranenetwork.com
Risk Management, Safety & Security Services
N.A.I.C.S.: 561621
David Lawrence *(Founder)*

Subsidiaries:

Stratfor Enterprises, LLC (1)
221 W 6th St Ste 400, Austin, TX 78701-3100
Tel.: (512) 744-4300
Web Site: http://www.stratfor.com
Internet Publishing & Broadcasting & Web Search Portals
N.A.I.C.S.: 516210
Dave Sikora *(CEO)*
Joshua Cook *(Dir-PR)*
Ken Maranian *(Chief Product Officer)*
Chip Harmon *(Pres)*
Gemma Postlethwaite *(Chm)*

RISK ENTERPRISE MANAGEMENT LIMITED
2540 Route 130 Ste 109, Cranbury, NJ 08512
Tel.: (609) 495-0001 DE

Web Site: http://www.remltd.com
Sales Range: $100-124.9 Million
Emp.: 400
Property & Casualty Reinsurance Claims & Risk Management Services
N.A.I.C.S.: 524298
Paula Maguire *(Sr VP-Field Claim Ops)*
Matthew Craig *(Sr VP-Sls)*
Linda Naif *(Sr VP-Customer Support & IT)*
John Tobey *(VP-Home Office Claims)*
Tim McIntyre *(Gen Counsel & VP)*
Mike Brambier *(VP-Fin & Analysis)*
Alan Lawrence *(VP-Fin Svcs & Controller)*
Myron Ascher *(VP-HR)*

RISK MITIGATION CONSULTING INC.
2300 Wilson Blvd Ste 752, Arlington, VA 22201
Tel.: (850) 974-2566
Web Site: https://rmcglobal.com
Year Founded: 2011
Scientific & Technical Consulting Services
N.A.I.C.S.: 541690
Brent Hyland *(COO)*

Subsidiaries:

Securicon, LLC (1)
5520 Cherokee Ave, Alexandria, VA 22312
Tel.: (703) 914-2780
Web Site: http://www.securicon.com
Rev.: $2,500,000
Emp.: 15
Other Management Consulting Services
N.A.I.C.S.: 541618

RISKPRONET INTERNATIONAL INC.
PO Box 1149, Menlo Park, CA 94026-1149
Tel.: (650) 323-1929
Web Site: http://www.riskpronet.com
Sales Range: $650-699.9 Million
Insurance Agencies Association
N.A.I.C.S.: 813910
Gary Normington *(Exec Dir)*

Subsidiaries:

The Buckner Company, Inc. (1)
6550 S Millrock Dr Ste 300, Salt Lake City, UT 84121
Tel.: (801) 937-6700
Web Site: http://www.buckner.com
Sales Range: $10-24.9 Million
Commercial Insurance Brokerage & Administration Services
N.A.I.C.S.: 524298
Terry H. Buckner *(Pres & CEO)*
Christian Deputy *(Chief Sls Officer)*
Frank Lancaster *(CFO & Exec VP)*

RISSER OIL CORP.
2865 Exec Dr, Clearwater, FL 33762-3316
Tel.: (727) 573-4000   FL
Web Site: http://www.therissercompanies.com
Year Founded: 1960
Sales Range: $75-99.9 Million
Emp.: 40
Petroleum Retailer & Distr
N.A.I.C.S.: 424710

RISTAL INC.
890 W Elliot Rd Ste 102, Gilbert, AZ 85233-5127
Tel.: (480) 302-5161   AZ
Web Site: http://www.selectblinds.com
Year Founded: 2000
Sales Range: $10-24.9 Million
Emp.: 14
Online Retailer of Window Treatments

N.A.I.C.S.: 449122
Rick Steele *(Founder & CEO)*

RISTKEN SOFTWARE SERVICES, L.P.
15305 N Dallas Pkwy Ste 1300, Addison, TX 75001
Tel.: (972) 991-6300
Web Site: http://www.taillight.com
Year Founded: 1998
Sales Range: $10-24.9 Million
Emp.: 40
Web-Based Software for Automobile Dealerships
N.A.I.C.S.: 513210
Matthew G. Twyman *(Founder & CEO)*
Patrick A. DeMarco *(Pres)*

RITA BLANCA ELECTRIC COOPERATIVE, INC.
12210 Highway 87 N, Dalhart, TX 79022
Tel.: (806) 249-4506   TX
Web Site: http://www.ritablancaelectric.com
Year Founded: 1945
Sales Range: $25-49.9 Million
Emp.: 30
Electric Power Distr
N.A.I.C.S.: 221122
Grace Subealdea *(Office Mgr)*
Brent Wheeler *(CEO & Gen Mgr)*
Tracy Howell *(Mgr-Ops)*

RITA CORPORATION
850 S Rte 31, Crystal Lake, IL 60014
Tel.: (201) 934-0616   IL
Web Site: http://www.ritacorp.com
Year Founded: 1953
Rev.: $45,000,000
Emp.: 118
Provider of Pharmaceuticals
N.A.I.C.S.: 424210
Tom Goode *(VP-Sls)*
Jaime McLeer *(Engr-Logistics)*
Steve Ueck *(Mgr-Matls)*

Subsidiaries:

R.I.T.A International Inc. (1)
850 S Rte 31, Crystal Lake, IL 60014
Tel.: (815) 337-2500
Web Site: http://www.ritacorp.com
Sales Range: $10-24.9 Million
Emp.: 60
Drugs, Proprietaries & Sundries
N.A.I.C.S.: 424210

RITA STAFFING INC.
5150 S Florida Ave, Lakeland, FL 33813
Tel.: (863) 646-5021
Web Site: http://www.ritastaffing.com
Sales Range: $10-24.9 Million
Emp.: 30
Provider of Temporary Staffing Service
N.A.I.C.S.: 561320
Jim Dayvault *(Pres)*

RITA'S FRANCHISE COMPANY
1210 Northbrook Dr Ste 310, Trevose, PA 19053
Tel.: (215) 876-9306
Web Site: http://www.ritasice.com
Year Founded: 1984
Sales Range: $100-124.9 Million
Emp.: 80
Ice Cream & Frozen Desserts
N.A.I.C.S.: 311520
John Dombroski *(CFO & Sr VP)*
Phyllis Savar *(CMO)*

RITCHEY METALS COMPANY INC.
30 Georgetown Rd, Canonsburg, PA 15317

Tel.: (724) 745-7700   PA
Web Site: http://www.ritcheymetals.com
Year Founded: 1965
Sales Range: $25-49.9 Million
Emp.: 50
Supplier of Nonferrous Foundries
N.A.I.C.S.: 331529
Warren T. Richey *(Pres)*

RITCHIE CORPORATION
8100 E 22nd St N Ste 800-103, Wichita, KS 67226-2308
Tel.: (316) 462-0000   KS
Web Site: http://www.ritchiebuilding.com
Year Founded: 1855
Sales Range: $10-24.9 Million
Emp.: 70
Building Materials Supplier; Concrete Construction; Construction Materials Recycling
N.A.I.C.S.: 238110
Lou Bollin *(Sec)*

Subsidiaries:

ICF Solutions, LLC (1)
8401 E Oak Knoll, Wichita, KS 67207 (100%)
Tel.: (316) 944-2131
Web Site: http://www.icfbuild.com
Sales Range: $10-24.9 Million
Emp.: 10
Concrete Construction
N.A.I.C.S.: 238110

RITCHIE ENGINEERING COMPANY
10950 Hampshire Ave S, Bloomington, MN 55438
Tel.: (952) 943-1300
Web Site: http://www.yellowjacket.com
Rev.: $15,100,000
Emp.: 100
Hose, Belting & Packing
N.A.I.C.S.: 423840
Brian Flynn *(Exec VP-Intl Sls)*
Mary Gentry *(Mgr-Mktg Comm)*
Tom Ritchie *(Pres-Product Dev)*
Luke Parry *(Mgr-Sls-UK & Benelux)*

RITCHIE GROCER COMPANY
319 S Washington Ave PO Box 71, El Dorado, AR 71730
Tel.: (870) 863-8191
Sales Range: $10-24.9 Million
Emp.: 15
Groceries, General Line
N.A.I.C.S.: 424410
John S. Benson Sr. *(CEO)*

RITCHIE IMPLEMENT INC.
507 W Main St, Cobb, WI 53526
Tel.: (608) 623-2331
Web Site: http://www.ritchiesinc.com
Year Founded: 1961
Sales Range: $10-24.9 Million
Emp.: 27
Farm Implements
N.A.I.C.S.: 423820
Chelsie Klaas *(Mgr-Fin)*
Connie Ritchie-Hallada *(Owner)*
Ron Ritchie *(Pres)*

RITCHIE INDUSTRIES, INC.
120 S Main St, Conrad, IA 50621
Tel.: (641) 366-2525   IA
Web Site: http://www.ritchiefount.com
Year Founded: 1921
Sales Range: $50-74.9 Million
Emp.: 100
Mfr & Distr of Livestock Watering Equipment
N.A.I.C.S.: 333111
Leon Yantis *(Pres)*
Robert Amundson *(Dir-Engrg)*

RITCHIE TRACTOR COMPANY, LLC.
1746 W Lamar Alexander Pkwy, Maryville, TN 37801
Tel.: (865) 981-3199
Year Founded: 1993
Sales Range: $10-24.9 Million
Emp.: 56
Outdoor Power Equipment Whslr
N.A.I.C.S.: 444230
John Kleinhans *(Mgr)*

RITCHIE-CURBOW CONSTRUCTION CO.
11820 Fountain Way Ste 202, Newport News, VA 23606
Tel.: (757) 873-0123
Web Site: http://www.ritchiecurbow.com
Sales Range: $10-24.9 Million
Emp.: 42
Commercial & Office Building, New Construction
N.A.I.C.S.: 236220
Eugene W. Wilson *(VP)*
Joseph C. Ritchie Jr. *(Pres)*
Carl M. Beale III *(VP-Ops)*

RITE RUG CO.
3949 Business Pk Dr, Columbus, OH 43204
Tel.: (614) 261-6060
Web Site: http://www.riterug.com
Year Founded: 1932
Sales Range: $25-49.9 Million
Emp.: 90
Residential & Commercial Floor Covering Mfr
N.A.I.C.S.: 449121
Michael H. Goldberg *(CEO)*

Subsidiaries:

Rite Rug Co. (1)
3200 Kettering Blvd, Dayton, OH 45439
Tel.: (937) 297-6100
Rev.: $13,000,000
Emp.: 8
Floor Laying & Floor Work, Nec
N.A.I.C.S.: 238330

RITE WAY OIL & GAS CO., INC.
8400 I St, Omaha, NE 68127-1614
Tel.: (402) 331-6400   NE
Year Founded: 1964
Sales Range: $25-49.9 Million
Emp.: 150
Provider of Petroleum Product Services
N.A.I.C.S.: 424720
Greg McNeal *(Supvr-Stores)*
Mike Danielski *(Pres)*

RITE-HITE HOLDING CORPORATION
8900 N Arbon Dr, Milwaukee, WI 53223-2451
Tel.: (414) 355-2600   WI
Web Site: http://www.ritehite.com
Year Founded: 1967
Sales Range: $450-499.9 Million
Emp.: 1,400
Holding Company
N.A.I.C.S.: 423830
Mark Kirkish *(CFO)*
Mary Blaser *(Mgr-Mktg)*

Subsidiaries:

Arbon Equipment Corporation (1)
8900 N Arbon Dr, Milwaukee, WI 53223
Tel.: (704) 559-5722
Web Site: http://www.arbonequipment.com
Loading Dock Equipment Supplier
N.A.I.C.S.: 333922
Doug Arents *(Mgr-Logistics)*
Gerry Timms *(VP & Gen Mgr)*

RITE-HITE HOLDING CORPORATION — U.S. PRIVATE

Rite-Hite Holding Corporation—(Continued)

Arbon Equipment Pty Limited (1)
Unit 2 47 Prime Drive, Seven Hills, 2147, NSW, Australia
Tel.: (61) 3 9349 6800
Web Site: http://www.arbon.com.au
Loading Dock Equipment Distr
N.A.I.C.S.: 423830

DuctSox Corporation (1)
4343 Chavenelle Rd, Dubuque, IA 52002
Tel.: (563) 589-2777
Web Site: http://www.ductsox.com
Fabric Air Dispersion Products Mfr
N.A.I.C.S.: 333415

Frommelt Safety (1)
4343 Chavenelle Rd, Dubuque, IA 52002
Tel.: (563) 556-2020
Sales Range: $25-49.9 Million
Emp.: 40
Mfr Safety Curtains, Barrier Doors & Machine Guards
N.A.I.C.S.: 333322
Gerry Timms (Product Mgr)

Rite-Hite Corporation (1)
8900 N Arbon Dr, Milwaukee, WI 53223-2451
Tel.: (414) 355-2600
Web Site: http://www.ritehite.com
Sales Range: $25-49.9 Million
Emp.: 150
Mfr of Dock Shelters; Traffic & Powered Doors; Safety Curtains
N.A.I.C.S.: 423830
Andy Olson (Mgr-Mktg)

Rite-Hite Door Division (1)
8900 N Arbon Dr, Milwaukee, WI 53224 (100%)
Tel.: (414) 355-2600
Web Site: http://www.ritehite.com
Sales Range: $25-49.9 Million
Emp.: 180
Material Handling Doors
N.A.I.C.S.: 332321
Paul Rowlett (Pres)

Rite-Hite Frommelt Division (1)
8900 N Arbor Dr, Milwaukee WI 53223
Tel.: (414) 355-2600
Web Site: http://www.ritehite.com
Sales Range: $25-49.9 Million
Emp.: 60
Seals & Shelters for Warehouse Door Openings
N.A.I.C.S.: 423830

Rite-Hite Material Handling Equipment (Kunshan) Co., Ltd. (1)
1st Floor 558 Tong Xie Road, Shanghai, 200335, China
Tel.: (86) 21 6237 6333
Web Site: http://www.ritehite.com.cn
Emp.: 110
Conveying Equipment Mfr
N.A.I.C.S.: 333922

RITE-MADE PAPER CONVERTERS
2600 Bi State Dr, Kansas City, KS 66103
Tel.: (913) 621-5000
Web Site: http://www.ritemade.com
Rev.: $28,790,427
Emp.: 85
Telegraph, Teletype & Adding Machine Paper
N.A.I.C.S.: 322230
Stephen Schwartz (Pres & CEO)
Roy Fairchild (CFO)
Fred Brown (Sr VP-Sls)
Curtis Post (Sr VP)

RITE-STYLE OPTICAL CO
12240 Emmet St, Omaha, NE 68164
Tel.: (402) 492-8822
Web Site: http://www.ritestyle.com
Sales Range: $10-24.9 Million
Emp.: 125
Manufacture Eyeglasses
N.A.I.C.S.: 339115
George P. Lee (Founder & CEO)
Larry Lee (Pres)

RITENET CORPORATION
1445 Research Blvd Ste 350, Rockville, MD 20850-6111
Tel.: (301) 251-5636
Web Site: http://www.ritenet.com
Sales Range: $25-49.9 Million
Emp.: 40
Professional, IT & Telecommunications Services
N.A.I.C.S.: 541611
Rao K. Ramineni (Founder & Pres)

RITEWAY BUS SERVICE, INC.
6970 S 6th St, Milwaukee, WI 53154
Tel.: (414) 570-5200
Web Site: http://www.goriteway.com
Year Founded: 1957
Bus Transportation Services Provider
N.A.I.C.S.: 485113
Bob Zanotti (Pres & CEO)
Joshua Smith (CFO)
James O. Christian (VP-Acctg & Fin)
Nate Hamilton (VP-Ops-School Bus Division)
Dave Pape (VP-Ops-School Bus Division)
Mick Howen (VP-Ops-School Bus Division)
Steve Fazlovic (VP-Commercial Services)
Kathi Kaestner (VP-Commercial Services)
Adam Ludovic (VP-Fleet, Tech, and Systems)
Ron Bast (Chm)
RJ Bast (Co-Owner)
Wendy Bast (Co-Owner)
Rochelle Bast (Co-Owner)

Subsidiaries:

Cardinal Buses, Inc. (1)
202 E Winslow St, Middlebury, IN 46540
Tel.: (574) 825-9405
Web Site: http://www.cardinalbuses.com
Bus Charter Service-Nonlocal
N.A.I.C.S.: 485510

RITEWOOD, INC.
3643 S 4000 E, Franklin, ID 83237
Tel.: (208) 646-2213
Rev.: $21,000,000
Emp.: 40
Chicken Egg Production
N.A.I.C.S.: 112310
Ramon Wright (VP)
David K. Woodward (Pres)
Lorraine Wright (Treas & Sec)

RITTENHOUSE MARKETING ASSOCIATES
2 Logan Sq 4th Fl, Philadelphia, PA 19103-2719
Tel.: (215) 448-6014
Web Site: http://www.binswanger.com
Year Founded: 1931
Sales Range: $1-9.9 Million
Emp.: 12
Brand Marketing, E-Brochures, Media Ads & Direct Mailings
N.A.I.C.S.: 541810
Laurie Goldstein (Dir-Mktg)

RITTENHOUSE SENIOR LIVING
880 E Swedesford Rd Ste 210, Wayne, PA 19087
Tel.: (484) 831-5310
Web Site: http://www.rittenhousesl.com
Holding Company; Senior Citizen Assisted Living Facilities
N.A.I.C.S.: 551112
Kathy Galbraith (Dir-Mktg)

Subsidiaries:

Rittenhouse Senior Living of Indianapolis LLC (1)
1251 W 96th St, Indianapolis, IN 46260-1181
Tel.: (317) 575-9200
Web Site: http://www.rittenhousesl.com
Sales Range: $10-24.9 Million
Emp.: 30
Senior Citizen Assisted Living Facility Operator
N.A.I.C.S.: 623312
May Ehresman (Exec Dir)

RITTENHOUSE VENTURES, LLC
The Navy Yard 100 Innovation Ctr 4801 S Broad St Ste 340, Philadelphia, PA 19112
Tel.: (215) 972-1502
Web Site: http://rittenhouseventures.com
Privater Equity Firm
N.A.I.C.S.: 523940
Saul Richter (Mng Partner)

RITTER INSURANCE MARKETING
2600 Commerce Dr, Harrisburg, PA 17110
Tel.: (717) 540-3720
Web Site: http://www.ritterim.com
Year Founded: 2005
Sales Range: $1-9.9 Million
Emp.: 43
Technology Tools & Training for Insurance Agents
N.A.I.C.S.: 524298
Craig J. Ritter (Owner & Pres)
Calvin J. Ritter (Founder & Chm)
David Dietz (VP-Mktg)
April L. Ford (Dir-Mktg)
Chuck Ducharm (VP-Agent Svcs)
Samantha Galeano (Mgr-HR)
Scott Kowalski (VP-Ops)

RITTER LUMBER CO.
1050 Detroit Ave, Nederland, TX 77627
Tel.: (409) 727-0231
Web Site: http://www.ritterathome.com
Rev.: $16,000,000
Emp.: 40
Lumber, Plywood & Millwork
N.A.I.C.S.: 423310
Allan Ritter (Pres)
John Ritter (VP)
Troy Guidry (Mgr-Sls)

RITZ ASSOCIATES
112 Beach St, Boston, MA 02111
Tel.: (617) 439-0800 MA
Web Site: http://www.ritzinc.com
Year Founded: 1990
Sales Range: $10-24.9 Million
Emp.: 10
Contract Furniture Services
N.A.I.C.S.: 449110
Michael MacDonald (Pres)

RITZ SAFETY, LLC
6321 E 30th St, Indianapolis, IN 46219
Web Site: http://www.ritzsafety.com
Construction & Mining Machinery & Equipment Merchant Whslr
N.A.I.C.S.: 423810
Ben Ambler (Mgr-Ops)

Subsidiaries:

Safety Source, Inc. (1)
5865 Rangeline Rd, Theodore, AL 36582
Tel.: (251) 443-7445
Web Site: http://www.safetysourceinc.com
Sales Range: $1-9.9 Million
Emp.: 15

Miscellaneous Durable Goods Merchant Whslr
N.A.I.C.S.: 423990
Thomas Cannon (Reg Mgr-Sls)
Keith Skipworth (Pres)
Frischer Ken (VP)

RITZ-CRAFT CORP. OF PA
15 Industrial Pkwy, Mifflinburg, PA 17844
Tel.: (570) 966-1058
Web Site: http://www.ritz-craft.com
Sales Range: $25-49.9 Million
Emp.: 400
Modular Homes, Prefabricated, Wood
N.A.I.C.S.: 321992
Paul R. John Jr. (Pres & CEO)

RITZVILLE WAREHOUSE CO. INC.
201 E 1st Ave, Ritzville, WA 99169
Tel.: (509) 659-0130
Web Site: http://www.ritzwhse.com
Year Founded: 1893
Sales Range: $25-49.9 Million
Emp.: 55
Grain Elevators
N.A.I.C.S.: 424510
Brian Gordon (CEO)
Avia Thompson (CFO)
Jacob Klein (Pres)
Jarod Wollweber (Sec)

Subsidiaries:

Odessa Trading Company Inc. (1)
112 S Division St, Odessa, WA 99159
Tel.: (509) 982-2661
Web Site: http://www.odessatrading.com
Sales Range: $10-24.9 Million
Emp.: 30
Grain Elevators
N.A.I.C.S.: 424510
H. P. Carstensen (Mgr)
Ted Suchland (Mgr-Parts-Odessa)

RIVA FINANCIAL INC.
6715 E Mission Ave, Spokane, WA 99212
Tel.: (509) 444-3700
Web Site: http://www.kingbeverage.com
Sales Range: $10-24.9 Million
Emp.: 2
Holding Company
N.A.I.C.S.: 551112
Theodore Rusnak (Pres)
Gary Hill (CFO)
Peter Rushnak (VP)

RIVAL DOWNHOLE TOOLS LC
5535 Brystone Dr, Houston, TX 77041
Tel.: (713) 983-8355 TX
Web Site: http://rivaldt.com
Year Founded: 2002
Oil Drilling Services
N.A.I.C.S.: 213111
Doc Gunther (Founder & CTO)
Niel Fletcher (CEO)
Noah Daoust (COO)
Bryan Granier (CFO)

RIVAL HOLDINGS, LLC.
2817 E Dupont Rd, Fort Wayne, IN 46825
Tel.: (260) 452-6951
Web Site: https://www.rival.re
Year Founded: 2023
Construction Services
N.A.I.C.S.: 236220
Brad Crawford (CEO)

Subsidiaries:

Laux Construction, LLC (1)
1535 Jessop Rd, Dansville, MI 48819
Tel.: (517) 623-0117
Web Site: http://www.lauxconstruction.com

Sales Range: $1-9.9 Million
Emp.: 11
Highway, Street & Bridge Construction
N.A.I.C.S.: 237310
David Laux (Owner & Pres)

RIVENDELL MEDIA INC.
1248 Route 22 W, Mountainside, NJ 07092
Tel.: (908) 232-2021   NJ
Web Site:
  http://www.rivendellmedia.com
Year Founded: 1979
Sales Range: $1-9.9 Million
Emp.: 8
Media Buying Services
N.A.I.C.S.: 541830
Todd L. Evans (Pres & CEO)

RIVENROCK CAPITAL LLC
915 Wilshire Blvd Ste 1760, Los Angeles, CA 90017
Tel.: (213) 489-4660
Web Site:
  http://www.rivenrockcapital.com
Privater Equity Firm
N.A.I.C.S.: 523999
John J. Nelson (Principal)
David V. Adams Sr. (Principal)
David V. Adams Jr. (Principal)

Subsidiaries:

Small World Toys   (1)
1451 W Knox St, Torrance, CA 90745
Tel.: (310) 645-9680
Web Site: http://www.smallworldtoys.com
Sales Range: $25-49.9 Million
Emp.: 60
Specialty Toys
N.A.I.C.S.: 423920
Sheri Brownrigg (VP-Product)

RIVER ASSOCIATES INVESTMENTS, LLC
633 Chestnut St Ste 1640, Chattanooga, TN 37450-1600
Tel.: (423) 755-0888
Web Site:
  http://www.riverassociatesllc.com
Year Founded: 1989
Privater Equity Firm
N.A.I.C.S.: 523999
Mark Jones (Partner)
Courtney L. Cudd (Chief Compliance Officer & Treas)
Mike B. Brookshire (Co-Mng Partner)
W. Craig Baker (Partner)
Jonathan Kent (Sr VP)
Blake Lewis (VP)
Stuart Vyule (VP)
Megan Hunt (Dir-Mktg)
Sherry Longley (Controller)
George H. Patten Pettway Jr. (Partner)

Subsidiaries:

Current Solutions, LLC   (1)
3184 Mesa Ave, Grand Junction, CO 81504
Tel.: (970) 256-1175
Electrical Apparatus & Equipment, Wiring Supplies & Related Equipment Merchant Whslr
N.A.I.C.S.: 423610
Greg Tolle (Mgr-Ops)

Double E Company, LLC   (1)
319 Manly St, West Bridgewater, MA 02379
Tel.: (508) 588-8099
Web Site: http://www.ee-co.com
Motor Vehicle Parts Mfr
N.A.I.C.S.: 336390
Tom Pranka (CEO)

Subsidiary (Domestic):

Productive Solutions, Inc.   (2)
1025 Breezewood Ln, Neenah, WI 54956
Tel.: (920) 751-1555
Web Site: http://www.appletonmfg.com

Sales Range: $1-9.9 Million
Emp.: 30
Cutting Tool & Machine Tool Accessory Mfr
N.A.I.C.S.: 333515
Lewis Krueger (CEO)

KK Precision, Inc.   (1)
104 Oakdale Road, Toronto, M3N 1V9, ON, Canada
Tel.: (416) 742-5911
Web Site: http://www.kkprecision.com
Engine Component Mfr & Distr
N.A.I.C.S.: 336412

National Deli, LLC   (1)
7250 NW 35 Ter, Miami, FL 33122
Tel.: (800) 683-9292
Web Site: http://www.nationaldeli.com
Meat Product Whslr
N.A.I.C.S.: 424470
Mark Bergman (CFO)

Omega Environmental Technologies, Inc.   (1)
1401 Valley View Ln Ste 100, Irving, TX 75061
Tel.: (972) 812-7000
Web Site: http://www.omega-usa.com
Emp.: 150
Automobile Parts Distr
N.A.I.C.S.: 441330
Dominick Ferraro (VP-Mktg)
Grace Davis (Pres & CEO)
Rod Means (Mgr-Pur)
Steven Clemens (Controller)

Quikserv Corp.   (1)
11441 Brittmoore Park Dr, Houston, TX 77041
Tel.: (713) 849-5882
Web Site: http://www.quikserv.com
Other Commercial & Service Industry Machinery Mfr
N.A.I.C.S.: 333310
Brian Coble (Mgr-Svc)
Sophia Navarro (Mgr-Office)
Jason T. Epps (Pres & CEO)
Lisa Csikos (VP-Fin)
Hector Vallejo (VP-Sls & Mktg)
Chris Cordle (VP-Ops)
Beth Deragon (Dir-HR)
Brian McCloskey (Dir-Sls)
Wade Arnold (Mgr-Natl Accts)
Gabriela Mendez (Mgr-Inside Sls)
Brian Hanson (Mgr-Sls & Mktg)
Jenny Acosta (Mgr-Project)
Rick Gonzales (Mgr-Project)
Richard Picar (Mgr-Prod)
Joe Facundo (Mgr-R&D)
Jimmy Garcia (Mgr-Purchasing)

Subsidiary (Domestic):

United States Bullet Proofing, Inc.   (2)
16201 Branch Ct, Upper Marlboro, MD 20774
Tel.: (301) 454-0155
Web Site: http://www.usbulletproofing.com
Rev.: $3,600,000
Emp.: 10
Other Construction Material Merchant Whslr
N.A.I.C.S.: 423390
Ken Sampson (Owner)

RIVER BANK HOLDING CO.
145 N Main St, Stoddard, WI 54658
Tel.: (608) 457-2100
Web Site: http://www.riverbank.biz
Year Founded: 1991
Sales Range: $25-49.9 Million
Emp.: 50
Bank Holding Company
N.A.I.C.S.: 522110
Brian Voelker (Pres)
Brian Spreuer (VP & Branch Mgr)
Bryan Simonson (VP & Branch Mgr)
Scott Tourdot (Asst VP)

Subsidiaries:

River Bank   (1)
145 N Main St, Stoddard, WI 54658
Tel.: (608) 457-2100
Web Site: http://www.riverbank.biz
Sales Range: $25-49.9 Million
Emp.: 15
Provider of Banking Services

N.A.I.C.S.: 522110
Brian Voelker (Pres & CEO)

RIVER BEND INDUSTRIES LLC
3730 Wheeler Ave, Fort Smith, AR 72901
Tel.: (479) 646-3473
Web Site:
  http://www.riverbindustries.com
Sales Range: $10-24.9 Million
Emp.: 130
Mfr of Injection-Molded Appliance Parts
N.A.I.C.S.: 326199
Ron Embree (Owner, Pres & CEO)

Subsidiaries:

River Bend Industries-North Liberty Division   (1)
1125-240th St NE, North Liberty, IA 52317-9572
Tel.: (319) 626-7500
Web Site: http://www.riverbindustries.com
Plastics Products
N.A.I.C.S.: 326199

River Bend Industries-Victor Division   (1)
2135 B Ave, Victor, IA 52347-8512
Tel.: (319) 647-3151
Web Site: http://www.riverbindustries.com
Plastics Products
N.A.I.C.S.: 326199
Ryan Embry (Dir-Sls)

RIVER CITIES CAPITAL FUNDS
221 E 4th St Ste 2400, Cincinnati, OH 45202-4151
Tel.: (513) 621-9700
Web Site: http://www.rccf.com
Rev.: $500,000,000
Emp.: 14
Venture Capital
N.A.I.C.S.: 523999
J. Carter McNabb (Mng Dir)
Edward C. McCarthy (Mng Dir)
Daniel T. Fleming (Mng Dir)
R. Glen Mayfield (Co-Founder & Mng Dir)
Edwin T. Robinson (Co-Founder & Mng Dir)
Britney Hamberg (Mgr-Comm)
Laura Mohr (Mgr-Admin)
Adrienne Vannarsdall (Dir-Fin & Ops)
Patrick Dunnigan (Principal)
Parag A. Rathi (VP)
David J. Kereiakes (VP)
Sara Cordell (Controller)
Walker Fuller (VP)

RIVER CITY CONSTRUCTION L.L.C.
101 Hoffer Ln, East Peoria, IL 61611-9334
Tel.: (309) 694-3120
Web Site: http://www.rccllc.com
Year Founded: 1984
Sales Range: $25-49.9 Million
Emp.: 250
Provider of Nonresidential Construction Services
N.A.I.C.S.: 236220
Bernard J. Koch (Pres)
Leanne Skuse (VP)
John C. Hoelscher (VP-Fin & Acctg)
Stephen Dorris (VP)

Subsidiaries:

River City Construction   (1)
1509 N Main St, Benton, IL 62812-1937
Tel.: (618) 435-2612
Web Site: http://www.rccllc.com
Sales Range: $10-24.9 Million
Emp.: 20
Provider of Construction Services
N.A.I.C.S.: 236220

Kent Kampwerth (VP)
John Sutherland (Pres)

RIVER CITY LANDSCAPE SUPPLY
3414 Hog Haven Rd, Sauget, IL 62206
Tel.: (618) 274-1222
Web Site:
  http://www.rivercitylandscape.com
Sales Range: $25-49.9 Million
Emp.: 80
Brick, Stone & Related Material
N.A.I.C.S.: 423320
Tim Thomas (Pres)
Richard Mullen (VP-Sls)

RIVER CITY PETROLEUM, INC.
840 Delta Ln, West Sacramento, CA 95691
Tel.: (916) 371-4960
Web Site: http://www.rcpfuel.com
Year Founded: 1981
Sales Range: $250-299.9 Million
Emp.: 35
Distr & Sales of Petroleum Products
N.A.I.C.S.: 424720
Leonard D. Robinson (Pres)
Kurt Schmidl (CFO)
Greg Michaels (VP)

RIVER COMMUNICATIONS, INC.
333 Westchester Ave, White Plains, NY 10604
Tel.: (914) 686-5599   NY
Web Site: http://www.riverinc.com
Year Founded: 1988
Sales Range: $1-9.9 Million
Advetising Agency
N.A.I.C.S.: 541810
James F. Tobin (Pres)
Justin Meise (Principal)

RIVER COUNTRY CO-OP
1080 W River St, Chippewa Falls, WI 54729
Tel.: (715) 723-2828
Web Site:
  http://www.rivercountrycoop.com
Sales Range: $75-99.9 Million
Emp.: 250
Grain, Agricultural Supplies, Fuel & Other Products & Services Cooperative
N.A.I.C.S.: 424910
Bruce Mlsna (CEO & Gen Mgr)
Mike Prahl (VP-Ag Svcs)
Lee Jensen (Pres)
Randy Mahr (VP)
Tim Hager (Sec)

RIVER COUNTRY COOPERATIVE
9072 Cahill Ave, Inver Grove Heights, MN 55076
Tel.: (651) 451-1151   MN
Web Site:
  http://www.rivercountry.coop
Year Founded: 1935
Fuel, Grain & Agricultural Supplies Cooperative
N.A.I.C.S.: 424910
John Zimmerman (Pres)
Steve Lindstrom (Vice Chm)
Clark Kaisershot (Sec)
John Duchscherer (Gen Mgr & CEO)
Eric Hanson (CFO)
Linda Speetzen (Controller)
Walter Miller (Mgr-Credit)
Jody Serres (Mgr-Accounts Payable)

RIVER FALLS MUTUAL INSURANCE COMPANY
218 N Main St, River Falls, WI 54022
Tel.: (715) 425-5292

RIVER FALLS MUTUAL INSURANCE COMPANY

River Falls Mutual Insurance Company—(Continued)
Web Site:
https://www.riverfallsmutual.com
Emp.: 100
Insurance Services
N.A.I.C.S.: 524210

Subsidiaries:

Trade Lake Mutual Insurance Co, Inc. (1)
11733 State Rd 48, Frederic, WI 54837
Tel.: (715) 327-4800
Web Site: http://www.tradelakemutual.com
Sales Range: $10-24.9 Million
Emp.: 15
Insurance Agencies & Brokerages
N.A.I.C.S.: 524210
Ginger Baker (Mgr)
Wayne Gustafson (VP)
Jackie Coen (Mgr)

RIVER HILL COAL COMPANY INC.
45 Memorial Dr, Kylertown, PA 16847
Tel.: (814) 345-5642
Web Site: http://www.rhcoal.com
Sales Range: $10-24.9 Million
Emp.: 5
Strip Mining, Bituminous
N.A.I.C.S.: 212114
Harry Hanchar (Pres)

RIVER PRODUCTS COMPANY, INC.
3273 Dubuque St NE, Iowa City, IA 52240
Tel.: (319) 338-1184
Web Site:
http://www.riverproducts.com
Sales Range: $10-24.9 Million
Emp.: 108
Crushed Stone, Sand & Gravel Products
N.A.I.C.S.: 212312
Thomas R. Scott (Pres & CEO)
Matthew C. Banning (CFO & VP)
Margaret Tuthill (Asst Mgr-Sls)

RIVER REGION COOPERATIVE
1015 Prescot NW, Sleepy Eye, MN 56085
Tel.: (507) 794-3031
Web Site:
http://www.riverregioncoop.com
Rev.: $20,000,000
Emp.: 6
Feed & Grain Merchant Services
N.A.I.C.S.: 424510
Kevin Subart (Gen Mgr)

RIVER RUN COMPUTERS, INC.
2320 W Camden Rd, Glendale, WI 53209
Tel.: (414) 228-7474
Web Site: http://www.river-run.com
Rev.: $3,094,000
Emp.: 14
Computer System Design Services
N.A.I.C.S.: 541512
Theresa Hietpas (Mgr-Mktg)
Paul T. Riedl Jr. (Owner & CEO)

Subsidiaries:

Alexssa Enterprises Ltd. (1)
801 W Washington St, West Bend, WI 53095
Tel.: (262) 338-3742
Web Site: http://www.alexssa.com
Computer System Design Services
N.A.I.C.S.: 541512
Chris Wenzel (Pres)

RIVER STEEL, INC.
1115 Industrial Dr, West Salem, WI 54669-1739
Tel.: (608) 786-7775
Web Site: http://www.riversteel.com
Year Founded: 1954
Sales Range: $10-24.9 Million
Emp.: 120
All Other Miscellaneous Fabricated Metal Product Mfr
N.A.I.C.S.: 332999
Timothy Brennan (CEO)
James Brennan (Dir-Bus Dev)

RIVER VALLEY AG CREDIT
408 E Broadway, Mayfield, KY 42066
Tel.: (270) 247-5613
Web Site:
http://www.rivervalleyagcredit.com
Year Founded: 1916
Agricultural Credit Institutions
N.A.I.C.S.: 522299
Beth Barkley (CFO)
Kyle Yancey (Pres & CEO)
Kevin Brown (Chief Lending Officer)
Kip Ellington (Reg Mgr-Lending)
Denise Newton (Officer-Capital Markets & SAM)
Jessica Johnson (Mgr-HR)
David Richesin (Chm)
Joe Campbell (Vice Chm)

RIVER VALLEY BANCORPORATION, INC.
327 N 17th Ave Ste 100, Wausau, WI 54401
Tel.: (715) 845-5522
Web Site:
http://www.rivervalleybank.com
Year Founded: 1967
Bank Holding Company
N.A.I.C.S.: 551111
Todd Nicklaus (Co-Owner & Chm)
Todd Nagel (COO)
Greg Nicklaus (Co-Owner)
Mark Wiebe (CFO)

Subsidiaries:

River Valley Bank (1)
327 N 17th Ave Ste 200, Wausau, WI 54401 (100%)
Tel.: (715) 845-5522
Web Site: http://www.rivervalleybank.com
Sales Range: $75-99.9 Million
Emp.: 12
Financial Institution
N.A.I.C.S.: 522180
Paul Schlumberger (VP-Madison)
Todd Nagel (Pres & CEO)
Mark Wiebe (CFO)
Jay Wittman (COO)
Sue Matis (Exec VP-HR & Org Dev)
Paul Rudersdorf (Exec VP-Banking & Wealth Mgmt)

RIVER VALLEY COOPERATIVE
619 Lombard St, Clarence, IA 52216
Tel.: (563) 452-3805
Web Site:
http://www.rivervalleycoop.com
Year Founded: 1932
Sales Range: $50-74.9 Million
Emp.: 150
Grain & Field Beans; Agricultural Services
N.A.I.C.S.: 424510
James Gruenhagen (VP-Ops)
Dale Ford (VP-Feed Bus Unit)
Tim Burress (CEO & Gen Mgr)
Mike Moellenbeck (VP-Grain Bus Unit)
Mike Wagner (Mgr-Feed Ops)
Tom Dale (Mgr-Swine Acct)
Jake Williams (CFO & VP)

RIVER VALLEY FOODS INC.
102 Farrell Rd, Syracuse, NY 13209
Tel.: (315) 451-9521
Web Site:
http://www.rivervalleyfoods.com
Sales Range: $50-74.9 Million
Emp.: 150
Distr of Frozen Food
N.A.I.C.S.: 424420
Gerard Redmond (Pres)

RIVER VALLEY PAPER CO.
120 E Mill St Ste 337, Akron, OH 44309-1911
Tel.: (330) 535-1001
Web Site:
http://www.rivervalleypaper.com
Sales Range: $10-24.9 Million
Emp.: 60
Producer of Industrial & Personal Service Paper
N.A.I.C.S.: 424130
John Sharp (Owner & Pres)
Mary Pamer (Mgr-Admin)
Patrick Conley (VP-Sls)

RIVER VALLEY TRUCK CENTERS
2120 3rd Ave, Mankato, MN 56001
Tel.: (507) 345-1128
Web Site: http://www.rvtc.com
Year Founded: 1994
Sales Range: $50-74.9 Million
Emp.: 150
Trucks, Noncommercial
N.A.I.C.S.: 423110
Gerald Westman (Pres & CFO)

RIVERA FIGUEROA FRANCISCO INC.
41 Calle Comercio, Ponce, PR 00730
Tel.: (787) 844-5730
Web Site: http://www.prtc.net
Sales Range: $25-49.9 Million
Emp.: 200
Supermarket
N.A.I.C.S.: 445110
Francisco Rivera Figueroa (Pres)
Isaac Figueroa (VP)

RIVERENCE HOLDINGS LLC
PO Box AG, Filer, ID 83328
Tel.: (208) 326-3100
Web Site: http://www.riverence.com
Fish Producer & Distr
N.A.I.C.S.: 424460
Rob Young (CEO)
Louis Anello (Sr VP-Sls & Mktg)

Subsidiaries:

Clear Springs Foods, Inc. (1)
1500 E 4424 N Clear Lake Rd, Buhl, ID 83316
Tel.: (208) 543-4316
Web Site: http://www.clearsprings.com
Sales Range: $1-9.9 Million
Emp.: 400
Distr, Researcher & Farm Raiser of Rainbow Trout
N.A.I.C.S.: 112511
Kurt Myers (VP-Mktg)

RIVERFRONT ACTIVITY CENTER, INC.
3000 South Ave, La Crosse, WI 54601
Tel.: (608) 784-9450
Web Site: http://www.riverfrontinc.org
Year Founded: 1977
Sales Range: $1-9.9 Million
Disability Assistance Services
N.A.I.C.S.: 624120
Jennifer Bausch (Dir-HR)
Mary Kessens (Pres & CEO)
Craig Poshepny (Dir-Employment Svcs)
Lisa Duncanson (Dir-Northern Reg Svcs)
Hasmig Tempesta (Dir-Svcs-Southern Reg)
Carissa Pagel-Smith (Dir-Employment Excellence)
Kelly Porter (Coord-Northern Day Svcs)
Jennifer Happ (Coord-Southern Day Svcs)
Ted Roberts (Mgr-Facilities)
Tom Kabat (Dir-Fin)
Darcie Marks (Coord-Community Living)
Joe Stubbs (Mgr-Janesville Production-Employee Svcs)
Ben Smaby (Mgr-IT)
Tami Taylor (Coord-Outcomes)
Nate Hundt (Dir-Mktg & Comm)
Tom Avery (Co-Founder)
Gary Schettle (Co-Founder)

RIVERFRONT PACKING COMPANY, LLC
4889 US Hwy 1, Vero Beach, FL 32967
Tel.: (772) 562-4155
Sales Range: $1-9.9 Million
Fruit Packing & Crating
N.A.I.C.S.: 488991
Dan Richey (Pres & CEO)

RIVERHAWK FAST SEA FRAMES, LLC
5251 W Tyson Ave, Tampa, FL 33611
Tel.: (813) 397-4950
Web Site: http://www.rhfsf.com
Sales Range: $10-24.9 Million
Ship & Boat Building
N.A.I.C.S.: 336611
Mark Hornsby (CEO)

RIVERHEAD BUILDING SUPPLY CORP.
250 David Ct, Calverton, NY 11933
Tel.: (631) 727-1400
Web Site: http://www.rbscorp.com
Year Founded: 1948
Building Materials Mfr
N.A.I.C.S.: 444180
Stacy Yakaboski (Gen Counsel)
Ted Sadowski (Mgr-Hardware)
Jeffrey Bailey (Dir-IT)
John Callahan (Pres)

Subsidiaries:

Riverhead Building Supply Corp. (1)
6000 Post Rd, North Kingstown, RI 02852-0655
Tel.: (401) 541-7400
Web Site: http://www.rbscorp.com
Sales Range: $10-24.9 Million
Emp.: 45
Lumber, Plywood & Mill Work
N.A.I.C.S.: 423310
Ted Sadowski (Gen Mgr)

RIVERLAKE PARTNERS, LLC
1000 SW Broadway Ste 1010, Portland, OR 97205
Tel.: (503) 228-7100
Web Site:
http://www.riverlakepartners.com
Year Founded: 2003
Investment & Holding Company
N.A.I.C.S.: 551112
Eric J. Krieger (Founder & Mng Partner)
Victor G. Petroff (Partner)
Tom Zupan (CFO)

RIVERLAND RESOURCES INC.
7600 Parklawn Ave Ste 410, Minneapolis, MN 55435
Tel.: (952) 835-6600
Sales Range: $10-24.9 Million
Emp.: 5
Canal Barge Operations
N.A.I.C.S.: 483211
Jim Woerner (Pres)

RIVERMARK COMMUNITY CREDIT UNION

COMPANIES

RIVERSIDE PARTNERS, LLC

8505 SW Creekside Pl, Beaverton, OR 97008
Tel.: (503) 626-6600
Web Site: http://www.rivermarkcu.org
Rev.: $16,464,469
Emp.: 99
Finance Insurance & Loan Service
N.A.I.C.S.: 522180
Scott Burgess *(Pres & CEO)*
Jeff Miller *(Mgr-Mortgage Dept)*
Ann Burton *(Mgr-Contact Center)*
Cori Poland *(Branch Mgr-Ops)*
Shelly Arnold *(Branch Mgr)*
Marge Mead *(Mgr-Mortgage Dept)*
Stephanie Strimling *(Project Mgr-Ops)*
Judy Nix *(VP-HR & Employee Dev)*
Teri Jo Zahn *(Mgr-HR)*
Nick Hodson *(CFO)*
Rob Mills *(CTO)*
Seth Schaefer *(Chief Experience Officer)*
David Noble *(VP-Mktg)*

RIVERO, GORDIMER & COMPANY, P.A.
1 Tampa City Ctr Ste 2600 201 N Franklin St, Tampa, FL 33602
Tel.: (813) 875-7774   FL
Web Site: http://www.rgcocpa.com
Year Founded: 1983
Sales Range: $1-9.9 Million
Emp.: 40
Accounting, Auditing & Bookkeeping
N.A.I.C.S.: 541211
Cesar J. Rivero *(Pres)*
Jim O'Connor *(Mgr-Tax)*

RIVERSIDE ACURA
13701 David O Dodd Rd, Little Rock, AR 72210
Tel.: (501) 448-8000
Web Site: http://www.riversideacura.com
Sales Range: $25-49.9 Million
Emp.: 27
New & Used Car Dealers
N.A.I.C.S.: 441110
David Kelly *(Gen Mgr)*
Jeff Corder *(Mgr-Svc)*

RIVERSIDE AUTO SALES INC.
2511 Ludington St, Escanaba, MI 49829
Tel.: (906) 786-6834
Web Site: http://www.riverside-mi.fivestardealers.com
Rev.: $12,977,015
Emp.: 40
Automobiles, New & Used
N.A.I.C.S.: 441110

RIVERSIDE COMMUNITY CARE, INC.
270 Bridge St Ste 301, Dedham, MA 02026
Tel.: (781) 329-0909   MA
Web Site: http://www.riversidecc.org
Year Founded: 1990
Rev.: $81,538,000
Assets: $41,771,000
Liabilities: $16,945,000
Net Worth: $24,827,000
Earnings: $54,000
Fiscal Year-end: 12/31/19
Community Care Services
N.A.I.C.S.: 624190
Michael J. McHugh *(Chm)*
Linda Snyder *(Vice Chm)*
Scott M. Bock *(Founder, Pres & CEO)*
Marsha Medalie *(COO & Exec VP)*
Thomas Hall *(Asst VP-Clinical Svcs)*
Don Hughes *(VP-Community Living Svcs)*
Loren Singer *(VP-Developmental & Cognitive Svcs)*
Joseph Wadlinger *(Treas)*
Susan Flannery *(Sec)*
Patrick Chilcott *(CFO)*
Paulo Fulton *(VP-HR)*

Subsidiaries:

MindWise Innovations   (1)
270 Bridge St, ite 205, Dedham, MA 02026
Tel.: (781) 239-0071
Web Site: http://www.mindwise.org
Mental Health Care Services
N.A.I.C.S.: 621420
Norm Gorin *(VP-Dev)*
Lisa K. Desai *(Dir-Behavioral Health Consulting)*
Nick Hanzel-Snider *(Mgr-Mktg)*
Lea Karnath *(Mgr-Suicide Program)*
Meritt Kelsey *(Mgr-Bus & Product Dev)*
Bryan Kohl *(Sr VP)*
Marjie McDaniel *(VP)*
Kara Neymeyr *(Dir-Suicide Program)*
David Veira *(Mgr-Screening Program)*

RIVERSIDE ELECTRONICS LTD.
1 Riverside Dr, Lewiston, MN 55952-1461
Tel.: (507) 523-3220   MN
Web Site: http://www.rellew.com
Year Founded: 1984
Sales Range: $25-49.9 Million
Emp.: 300
Electronic Assembly of Printed Circuit Boards
N.A.I.C.S.: 334412
Mandy Weilandt *(Controller)*
Stephen H. Craney *(Founder)*
Dan Streich *(Engr-Mfg)*
Katie L. Wohletz *(Mgr-Sls & Mktg)*

RIVERSIDE FOODS, INC.
2520 Wilson St, Two Rivers, WI 54241
Tel.: (920) 793-4511
Web Site: http://www.riversidefoods.com
Sales Range: $10-24.9 Million
Emp.: 100
Frozen Specialty Food Mfr
N.A.I.C.S.: 311412
Mike Coenen *(Mgr-Sls-Natl)*
Mike Yauger *(VP-Quality Assurance)*

RIVERSIDE FORD INC.
2089 Riverside Dr, Macon, GA 31204
Tel.: (478) 464-2900
Web Site: http://www.riversidefordmacon.com
Rev.: $83,000,000
Emp.: 130
Owner & Operator of Car Dealership
N.A.I.C.S.: 441110
William A. Fickling Jr. *(Pres)*

RIVERSIDE FOREST PRODUCTS INC.
2912 Professional Pkwy, Augusta, GA 30907
Tel.: (706) 855-5500
Web Site: http://www.riversideforest.com
Sales Range: $10-24.9 Million
Emp.: 13
Lumber, Plywood & Millwork
N.A.I.C.S.: 423310
Sam Collins *(Pres)*
Ruth Mobley *(Controller)*

RIVERSIDE FURNITURE CORPORATION
1400 S 6th St, Fort Smith, AR 72901-4342
Tel.: (479) 785-8100   AR
Web Site: http://www.riverside-furniture.com
Year Founded: 1946
Sales Range: $10-24.9 Million
Emp.: 140
Wood & Upholstered Furniture
N.A.I.C.S.: 337122
David Dixon *(VP-Admin)*
Beth Brown *(CFO)*
Michelle Miller *(Dir-Creative-Product Dev)*
Michael Charlton *(Sr VP-Product Dev & Mdsg)*

RIVERSIDE GAS & OIL CO. INC.
319 Corinth Rd, Queensbury, NY 12804
Tel.: (518) 615-0515
Sales Range: $10-24.9 Million
Emp.: 25
Fuel Oil Dealers
N.A.I.C.S.: 457210
David L. Moynehan *(Owner & Pres)*

RIVERSIDE METRO AUTO GROUP LLC
8330 Indiana Ave, Riverside, CA 92504
Tel.: (951) 688-9420
Web Site: http://www.riversidemetro.com
Rev.: $120,000,000
Emp.: 160
Automobiles, New & Used
N.A.I.C.S.: 441110
Dan Purinton *(Controller)*
Brian Michaelson *(Mgr-Sls)*
Richard Michaelson *(Principal-Dealer)*
Jim Epsteen *(Mgr-Fleet & Internet Sls)*

RIVERSIDE ORAL SURGERY
130 Kinderkamack Rd, River Edge, NJ 07675
Tel.: (201) 487-6565
Web Site: http://www.riversideoralsurgery.com
Office Of Physician
N.A.I.C.S.: 621111
Jason M. Auerbach *(Founder & Mng Partner)*

Subsidiaries:

Metropolitan Craniofacial Center, P.A.   (1)
101 Old Short Hills Rd, West Orange, NJ 07052
Tel.: (973) 736-7616
Web Site: http://www.metrocraniofacial.com
Office Of Physician
N.A.I.C.S.: 621111
Meredith Mitchell *(Coord-Patient Care)*

RIVERSIDE PAPER COMPANY INC.
3505 NW 112th St, Miami, FL 33167
Tel.: (305) 633-5221
Web Site: http://www.rpconline.com
Year Founded: 1973
Sales Range: $10-24.9 Million
Emp.: 41
Boxes, Paperboard & Disposable Plastic
N.A.I.C.S.: 424130
Marshall L. Stern *(Pres)*

RIVERSIDE PARTNERS, LLC
699 Boylston St 14th Fl, Boston, MA 02116
Tel.: (617) 351-2800   MA
Web Site: http://www.riversidepartners.com
Year Founded: 1989
Privater Equity Firm
N.A.I.C.S.: 523999
Steven F. Kaplan *(Gen Partner)*
Jon Lemelman *(Partner)*
Karen Clark *(Operating Partner)*
Max Osofsky *(Gen Partner)*
Lloyd Rogers *(Operating Partner)*
David L. Belluck *(Gen Partner)*
Mike Magliochetti *(Operating Partner)*
David Del Papa *(Gen Partner)*
Craig Stern *(Principal)*
Daniel H. Berry *(Operating Partner)*
Pat Dooling *(Principal)*
Loren Schlachet *(Mng Partner)*

Subsidiaries:

3Play Media, Inc.   (1)
34 Farnsworth St 4th Fl, Boston, MA 02210
Tel.: (617) 764-5189
Web Site: http://www.3playmedia.com
Teleproduction & Other Postproduction Services
N.A.I.C.S.: 512191
Chris Antunes *(Co-Founder & Co-CEO)*
Jeremy Barron *(Chief Customer Officer)*
Josh Miller *(Co-Founder & Co-CEO)*
Lily Bond *(VP-Mktg)*

Subsidiary (Domestic):

Captionmax, Inc.   (2)
2438 27th Ave S, Minneapolis, MN 55406
Tel.: (612) 341-3566
Web Site: http://www.captionmax.com
Sales Range: $1-9.9 Million
Emp.: 50
Cable & Other Subscription Programming
N.A.I.C.S.: 516210
Max Duckler *(Founder)*
Truck Morrison *(CEO)*

Alcohol Monitoring Systems, Inc.   (1)
9135 Ridgeline Blvd, Littleton, CO 80129
Tel.: (303) 989-8900
Sales Range: $1-9.9 Million
Emp.: 45
Medical, Dental & Hospital Equipment & Supplies Merchant Whslr
N.A.I.C.S.: 423450
Michael Iiams *(CEO)*
Dan Altvater *(Acct Exec)*
Matt Mitchell *(Acct Exec)*
Mike Napolilli *(Acct Exec)*
Murray Brooks *(Acct Mgr-Southeast Reg)*
Patrick Wren *(Acct Exec)*
Terry Fain *(Dir-Sls)*
Tom Krajewski *(Acct Exec)*

American Cadastre, LLC   (1)
13650 Dulles Technology Dr Ste 400, Herndon, VA 20171
Tel.: (540) 896-9952
Web Site: http://www.amcad.com
Sales Range: $1-9.9 Million
Records Management Software & Solutions
N.A.I.C.S.: 513210

Calero Software, LLC   (1)
Eagles Landing Business Park Bldg 100 Ste 120 1565 Jefferson Rd, Rochester, NY 14623
Tel.: (585) 381-6000
Web Site: http://www.calero.com
Telecommunications Design, Production & Servicing; Call Accounting; Web Based Telemanagement Software
N.A.I.C.S.: 513210
Tripp Cox *(Exec VP-Res & Dev)*
Scott Davis *(VP-Mktg)*
Tom DeClerck *(CIO)*
Scott Forbes *(Exec VP & Gen Mgr-Products)*
Albert Spell *(VP-Ops)*
Andrew Taylor *(VP-Global Sls)*
Dave Winters *(CFO & VP-Admin)*
Ron Rijkenberg *(Mng Dir-EMEA)*
Steven F. Kaplan *(Chm)*
Kelly Hunt *(Exec VP-Fin)*
Billy Howes *(VP-Solution Consulting)*
Scott Gilbert *(CEO)*
David Bliss *(Chief Product Officer)*

CarePatrol Franchise Systems, LLC   (1)
1760 E Pecos Rd Ste 338, Gilbert, AZ 85295
Web Site: http://www.carepatrol.com
Assisted Living Senior Placement Services
N.A.I.C.S.: 623312

Contractor Management Services, LLC   (1)

RIVERSIDE PARTNERS, LLC

U.S. PRIVATE

Riverside Partners, LLC—(Continued)
20430 N 19th Ave Ste 230, Phoenix, AZ 85027
Tel.: (623) 561-5681
Web Site: http://www.ictherightway.com
Sales Range: $1-9.9 Million
Emp.: 50
Independent Contractor Services
N.A.I.C.S.: 541611
Dennis Roccaforte (Founder)
Rebecca Collins (Chief Compliance Officer & Gen Counsel)
Drake Pruitt (CEO)
Jeelani Shaik (CTO)
Colleen Shannon (CFO)
Brian Panicko (VP-Sls & Channel Dev)
Christine Chan (VP-Strategic Accts-New York)
Leigh Ann Schneider (Sr Dir-Bus Dev)

Dominion Diagnostics, LLC (1)
211 Circuit Dr, North Kingstown, RI 02852
Tel.: (401) 667-0800
Web Site: http://www.dominiondiagnostics.com
Drug Testing Services
N.A.I.C.S.: 541380
Mark A. McSally (COO & Gen Counsel)
Robert M. Garvey (CEO)
Kenneth F. Indof (VP-Sls & Mktg)
Mary P. Hauser (VP-Addiction Svcs & New Market Dev)
Charlene Johnson (VP-Laboratory Ops & Dir-Laboratory)
Sheri Machado (Dir-HR)
David J. Molusis (VP-IT)

Econoserve Solutions, LLC
21410 N 19th Ave Ste #151, Phoenix, AZ 85027
Tel.: (602) 374-3101
Web Site: https://www.unislink.com
Revenue Cycle & Population Health Management Services
N.A.I.C.S.: 541611

Subsidiary (Domestic):

Doctors Resource Specialists, LLC (2)
2525 W Beryl Ave, Phoenix, AZ 85021-1606
Tel.: (602) 439-6780
Web Site: http://www.doctorsresourcespecialist.com
Sales Range: $1-9.9 Million
Emp.: 50
Administrative Management & General Management Consulting Service
N.A.I.C.S.: 541611
Sue Magalnick (Co-Founder)
Julie Serbin (Co-Founder)

Impact XM (1)
250 Ridge Rd, Dayton, NJ 08810
Tel.: (732) 274-2000
Web Site: http://www.impact-xm.com
Trade Show Marketing Services
N.A.I.C.S.: 541611
David Beach (COO)
Anne Houghton (VP-Creative)
Jared Pollacco (Pres)
Heather Griffin (VP-Mktg)
John Capano (VP-Client Dev)
Erik McKinney (Exec Creative Dir)

John L. Hinkle Holdings Co., Inc. (1)
3680 Stadium Pkwy, Kalamazoo, MI 49009
Tel.: (269) 344-1037
Food & Beverages Devlopment Services
N.A.I.C.S.: 541990
Brian D. Briggs (Pres & CEO)

Subsidiary (Domestic):

Whittle & Mutch, Inc. (2)
712 Fellowship Rd, Mount Laurel, NJ 08054
Tel.: (856) 235-1165
Sales Range: $1-9.9 Million
Emp.: 14
Spice & Extract Mfr
N.A.I.C.S.: 311942
John Mutch (Pres)

Lexipol, LLC (1)
6B Liberty Ste 200, Aliso Viejo, CA 92656
Tel.: (949) 484-4444
Web Site: http://www.lexipol.com
Emp.: 25
Policy Training & Consulting Services

N.A.I.C.S.: 541690
Daniel Merkle (Chm)
Van Holland (CFO)
Ron Wilkerson (CEO)
Murtaza Masood (CTO)

Medical Reimbursements of America, Inc. (1)
7105 Moores Ln, Brentwood, TN 37027-2840
Tel.: (615) 905-2678
Web Site: https://revecore.com
Other Accounting Services
N.A.I.C.S.: 541219
Lyle Beasley (Pres)
Dave Wojczynski (CEO)

Subsidiary (Domestic):

Kemberton Healthcare Services LLC (2)
501 Corporate Ctr Ste 600, Franklin, TN 37067
Tel.: (877) 540-0749
Web Site: http://www.kemberton.net
Insurance Agencies & Brokerages
N.A.I.C.S.: 524210
George Abatjoglou (CEO)
Rainie Kleckner (Chief Customer Officer)
Deanna Gray (Sr VP-Customer Success)
Roze Seale (Reg VP-Sls)

Subsidiary (Domestic):

Advanced Patient Advocacy LLC (3)
175 Admiral Cochrane Dr Ste 403, Annapolis, MD 21401
Tel.: (410) 268-1577
Web Site: http://www.apallc.com
Sales Range: $10-24.9 Million
Emp.: 150
Helps Hospitals Match Uninsured & Underinsured Hospital Patients With Health Care Programs Such As Medicare, Medicaid & Cobra
N.A.I.C.S.: 524210
Kevin A. Groner (Founder & CEO)
Wendy Bennett (Pres)
Michael Wilmoth (COO)

Pilgrim Software Inc. (1)
2807 W Busch Blvd Ste 200, Tampa, FL 33618
Tel.: (813) 915-1663
Web Site: http://www.pilgrimsoftware.com
Sales Range: $10-24.9 Million
Software Publisher
N.A.I.C.S.: 513210
Prashanth Rajendran (COO)
Atulya Risal (Founder)
Elaine Schroeder (VP-Sls)
Thierry Durand (CEO)
Ronald Kozlin (CFO)
Charles Murphy (VP-SaaS Ops)
Erika Deschodt (Dir-HR)
Stanley Curtis (CTO & Sr VP-Software Engrg)

Subsidiary (Non-US):

Pilgrim Quality Solutions EMEA BV (2)
Olympia 1A & B, 1213 NS, Hilversum, Netherlands
Tel.: (31) 8520 80 996
Web Site: http://pilgrimquality.com
Software Publisher
N.A.I.C.S.: 513210
Liz Corey (Sr Dir-HR)
Rick Lowrey (Gen Mgr)

Sir Grout LLC (1)
4840 Plainsman Cir, Cumming, GA 30028
Tel.: (678) 566-3998
Web Site: http://www.sirgrout.com
Drycleaning & Laundry Services (except Coin-Operated)
N.A.I.C.S.: 812320

USA Insulation Franchise, LLC (1)
1351 E 357th St, Eastlake, OH 44095
Tel.: (440) 602-4107
Web Site: http://www.usainsulation.net
Drywall & Insulation Contractors
N.A.I.C.S.: 238310
Jeff Pitrone (Pres)

Uinta Brewing Co. (1)
1722 S Fremont Dr 2375 W, Salt Lake City, UT 84104

Tel.: (801) 467-0909
Web Site: http://www.uintabrewing.com
Emp.: 25
Alcoholic Beverages Mfr
N.A.I.C.S.: 312120
Will Hamill (Founder)
Beckie Britter (Controller & Dir-Procurement)
Lindsay Berk (Dir-Mktg)
Mike Smith (Mgr-System Implementation)
Mark Allen (Dir-Ops)
Rodney Anderson (Accountant)
Chris Kiernan (Mgr-Maintenance)
Shauna Lupcho (CFO)
Joe Mastrorocco (Mgr-Chain Accts-Natl)
Alyssa Nannetti (Coord-Employee Experience)
Darren Penman (Mgr-Chain Accts-Natl)
Tanya Sapula (Office Mgr)
Jeremy Worrell (Mgr-Community Mktg)
Brian Curran (VP-Sls-Boston)
Jeremiah Wallis (Mgr-Accts-Natl)
Jeremy Ragonese (Pres)

RIVERSIDE PAYMENTS, INC.
12500 SE 2nd Cir Ste 240, Vancouver, WA 98684
Web Site: http://www.riversidepayments.com
Year Founded: 2014
Sales Range: $1-9.9 Million
Emp.: 91
Online Payment Services
N.A.I.C.S.: 522320
Brandon Skinner (Co-Owner & CEO)
Jason Reese (Co-Owner & CFO)
Jeremy Shroyer (VP-Sls)
Dan Riddle (Mgr-Natl Sls)
Adam Harden (Mgr-Natl Sls)

RIVERSIDE REALTY GROUP, LLC
2053 W First St, Fort Myers, FL 33901
Tel.: (239) 313-5544
Web Site: http://www.riversiderealtyflorida.com
Sales Range: $1-9.9 Million
Emp.: 12
Real Estate Broker
N.A.I.C.S.: 531210
Tara Molly (Owner)

RIVERSIDE REFRACTORIES, INC.
201 Truss Ferry Rd, Pell City, AL 35128
Tel.: (205) 338-3366
Web Site: http://www.riversiderefractories.com
Year Founded: 1929
Clay Refractory
N.A.I.C.S.: 327120
Lee Morris (VP-Clay & Pre-Cast Sls)
Robert Kuhn (VP-Sls)
Jennifer Brown (VP-Fin)
Bill Morris (VP-Ops)
Ed Morris (VP-Pur & Traffic)
Mike Alexander (VP-Res)
Brent Whitton (Gen Mgr-Canada)
John C. Morris Sr. (Pres)

RIVERSIDE SCRAP IRON & METAL CORPORATION
2993 6th St, Riverside, CA 92507
Tel.: (951) 686-2120
Web Site: http://www.riversidemetalrecycling.com
Year Founded: 1954
Sales Range: $10-24.9 Million
Emp.: 50
Processor of Ferrous & Nonferrous Scrap Metals, Including Copper, Aluminum, Brass & Steel
N.A.I.C.S.: 423930

RIVERSIDE TECHNOLOGY, INC.
3350 Eastbrook Dr, Fort Collins, CO 80525
Tel.: (970) 484-7573
Web Site: http://www.riverside.com
Year Founded: 1985
Sales Range: $10-24.9 Million
Emp.: 149
Engineering & Consulting Services for Water, Energy & Land Resources Management
N.A.I.C.S.: 541690
Douglas Greer (Co-CFO, Treas & Sec)
Larry Brazil (Pres & CEO)
Vernon W. Settle (Co-CFO)
Shawn Sutherland (Dir-HR)

RIVERSIDE TRANSPORT INC.
4001 Kansas Ave, Kansas City, KS 66106
Tel.: (913) 233-5500
Web Site: http://www.riversidetransport.com
Sales Range: $10-24.9 Million
Emp.: 130
Trucking Except Local
N.A.I.C.S.: 484121
Bill Grojean (Pres)
Sean Tulitana (Mgr-Ops)

RIVERSIDE WORLD PUBLISHING, INC.
636 S Oak St, Iowa Falls, IA 50126
Tel.: (641) 648-4271
Rev.: $48,000,000
Emp.: 90
Book Publishers
N.A.I.C.S.: 513130

RIVERSIDE-SAN BERNARDINO COUNTY INDIAN HEALTH, INC.
11555 1/2 Potrero Rd, Banning, CA 92220
Tel.: (951) 849-4761
Web Site: http://www.rsbcihi.org
Year Founded: 1974
Sales Range: $25-49.9 Million
Emp.: 326
Rural Health Care Services
N.A.I.C.S.: 622110
Mark Jensen (CFO)
Jess Montoya (CEO & Exec Dir)
Linwood Killam (Exec Dir)
Angella White (Mgr-Case)
Claudia Magana (Coord-Healthy Heart Data)

RIVERSTONE GROUP, INC.
1701 5th Ave, Moline, IL 61265
Tel.: (309) 757-8250
Web Site: http://www.riverstonegrp.com
Year Founded: 1917
Sales Range: $25-49.9 Million
Emp.: 50
Holding Company; Rock Quarry Owner & Operator
N.A.I.C.S.: 551112
Greg Eckman (CFO)
Amy Castrey (Mgr-HR)
Jim Papenhausen (Mgr-Pur)

Subsidiaries:

Central Stone Co. (1)
1701 5th Ave, Moline, IL 61265-7908
Tel.: (309) 757-8250
Quarry Operator
N.A.I.C.S.: 212312

Knox County Stone Co. Inc. (1)
PO Box 39, Edina, MO 63537
Tel.: (660) 397-3946
Rev.: $3,165,212
Emp.: 12
Crushed & Broken Limestone
N.A.I.C.S.: 212312
Charles C. Ellis (Pres)

COMPANIES

Le Claire Investment Inc. (1)
18965 300 St, Long Grove, IA 52956
Tel.: (309) 757-8250
Rev.: $1,718,367
Emp.: 9
Investor
N.A.I.C.S.: 523999
Charles C. Ellis *(Owner & Pres)*

RIVERSTONE HOLDINGS LLC
712 5th Ave, New York, NY 10019
Tel.: (212) 993-0076   DE
Web Site:
http://www.riverstonellc.com
Year Founded: 2000
Privater Equity Firm
N.A.I.C.S.: 523999
Robert M. Tichio *(Partner)*
David M. Leuschen *(Co-Founder & Sr Mng Dir)*
Christopher A. Abbate *(Partner)*
Pierre F. Lapeyre Jr. *(Co-Founder & Sr Mng Dir)*

Subsidiaries:

Abaco Energy Technologies LLC (1)
713 Northpark Central Dr Ste 400, Houston, TX 77073-6348
Tel.: (281) 869-0700
Emp.: 160
Holding Company; Energy Industry Equipment Mfr & Services
N.A.I.C.S.: 551112
Roger Rivet *(CFO)*
Kenneth Babcock *(Pres & CEO)*

Subsidiary (Domestic):

BasinTek LLC (2)
713 Northpark Central Dr Ste 400, Houston, TX 77073
Tel.: (281) 869-0700
Web Site: http://www.basintek.com
Sales Range: $10-24.9 Million
Emp.: 120
Oil & Gas Field Drilling Equipment Mfr
N.A.I.C.S.: 333132
Royce Trotter *(Dir-Quality Assurance)*
Dan O'Sullivan *(Pres)*
Cecilia Harris *(VP-Sls)*
Jesse Garner *(VP-Sls)*
Peter Cariveau *(VP-Engrg)*
Thomas Bunch *(Mgr-Supply Chain)*
Todd Bablitz *(Mgr-Mfg)*

EP Energy Corporation (1)
601 Travis St Ste 1400, Houston, TX 77002   (12.4%)
Tel.: (713) 997-1000
Web Site: http://www.epenergy.com
Sales Range: $1-4.9 Billion
Emp.: 372
Holding Company; Oil & Natural Gas Exploration, Development & Production Services
N.A.I.C.S.: 551112
Jace D. Locke *(Gen Counsel, Sec & VP)*
Kyle A. McCuen *(CFO, Chief Acctg Officer, Treas & Sr VP)*
Raymond J. Ambrose *(Sr VP-Engrg & Subsurface)*
Chad D. England *(Sr VP-Ops)*
Peter D. Addison *(VP-Land & Land Admin)*
Mark E. Hargis *(VP-Geoscience)*
Dennis M. Price *(VP-Mktg)*
Alan R. Crain Jr. *(Chm)*

Subsidiary (Domestic):

EP Energy LLC (2)
1001 Louisiana St, Houston, TX 77002
Tel.: (713) 997-1200
Web Site: http://www.epenergy.com
Rev.: $1,323,999,999
Assets: $4,180,999,999
Liabilities: $4,779,999,999
Net Worth: ($599,000,000)
Earnings: ($1,002,999,999)
Emp.: 991
Fiscal Year-end: 12/31/2018
Oil & Natural Gas Exploration & Production
N.A.I.C.S.: 211120
Kyle McCuen *(CFO, Treas & Sr VP)*

Hestya Energy BV (1)
Herengracht 480, 1017 CB, Amsterdam, Netherlands
Tel.: (31) 207371456
Web Site: http://www.hestya-energy.com
Dry & Liquid Bulk Terminals
N.A.I.C.S.: 424710
Harry van Rietschoten *(Exec Dir)*
Hans Zuijderwijk *(Fin Dir)*
Barbara Geelen *(CFO & Exec Dir)*

Subsidiary (Non-US):

Wilhelmshavener Raffineriegesellschaft mbH (2)
Raffineriestrasse 1, 26388, Wilhelmshaven, Germany
Tel.: (49) 4421 509 603
Oil Refinery
N.A.I.C.S.: 324110

International-Matex Tank Terminals, Inc. (1)
400 Poydras St Ste 3000, New Orleans, LA 70130   (100%)
Tel.: (504) 586-8300
Web Site: http://www.imtt.com
Emp.: 532
Bulk Liquid Storage Terminals
N.A.I.C.S.: 424710
Matthew Rosenboom *(CFO)*
Carlin G. Conner *(Chm & CEO)*
Carlin Conner *(Chm & CEO)*

Subsidiary (Domestic):

IMTT Holdings LLC (2)
400 Poydras St Ste 3000, New Orleans, LA 70130
Tel.: (504) 586-8300
Web Site: http://www.imtt.com
Holding Company
N.A.I.C.S.: 551112

Subsidiary (Non-US):

IMTT Quebec Inc. (2)
Port of Quebec Pier 50, PO Box 53010, Quebec, G1J 5K3, QC, Canada
Tel.: (418) 667-8641
Web Site: https://www.imtt.com
Petroleum Bulk Storage Services
N.A.I.C.S.: 493190
Marc Dulude *(COO & Exec VP)*
Mike Kelly *(VP & Mgr-Terminal)*

Subsidiary (Domestic):

IMTT-Bayonne (2)
250 E 22nd St, Bayonne, NJ 07002
Tel.: (201) 437-2200
Web Site: http://www.imtt.com
Chemical Products Distr
N.A.I.C.S.: 424690

IMTT-Geismar (2)
8112 Hwy 75, Geismar, LA 70734
Tel.: (225) 474-2514
Chemical Products Distr
N.A.I.C.S.: 424690

IMTT-Illinois (2)
13589 Main St, Lemont, IL 60439
Tel.: (630) 257-6222
Petroleum Product Distr
N.A.I.C.S.: 424720

Subsidiary (Non-US):

IMTT-NTL, LTD (2)
Suite 201 2nd Floor Baine Jonston Centre 10 Fort William Place, Saint John, A1C 1K4, NL, Canada
Tel.: (709) 570-3200
Web Site: https://imtt.com
Petroleum Bulk Storage Services
N.A.I.C.S.: 493190

Subsidiary (Domestic):

IMTT-Richmond-CA (2)
100 Cutting Blvd, Richmond, CA 94804
Tel.: (510) 412-5700
Web Site: http://www.imtt.com
Petroleum Product Distr
N.A.I.C.S.: 424720

IMTT-Virginia (2)
2801 S Military Hwy, Chesapeake, VA 23323
Tel.: (757) 485-3000
Web Site: http://www.imtt.com
Petroleum Product Distr
N.A.I.C.S.: 424720

Proserv Holdings Limited (1)
Proserv House, Prospect Road, Westhill, AB32 6FJ, Aberdeenshire, United Kingdom
Tel.: (44) 1224 737 000
Web Site: http://www.proserv.com
Holding Company
N.A.I.C.S.: 551112
Ally Rule *(CFO)*
Davis Larssen *(COO)*
Stephen Cox *(Pres-UK)*
Andrew Anderson *(Pres-Middle East & Africa)*
Steve Lykins *(Pres-Americas)*
Henrik Johnson *(Pres-Scandinavia)*
Geert Kooi *(Pres-Far East & Australia)*
Iain Smith *(Pres-Subsea Controls)*
Jackie Mann *(Sr VP-HR)*
Andrew Imrie *(Sr VP-Sls & Bus Dev)*
David Currie *(CEO)*
Tore Erntsen *(CTO-Subsea Controls-Trondheim Facility-Norway)*

Subsidiary (Domestic):

Nautronix Ltd (2)
Howe Moss Avenue, Kirkhill, Aberdeen, AB21 0GP, United Kingdom
Tel.: (44) 224 775700
Web Site: http://www.nautronix.com
Acoustic Positioning & Communication Services
N.A.I.C.S.: 541990
Sam Hanton *(VP-Subsea Svcs)*
Alan Buchan *(Ops Mgr)*
Lynne Adu *(VP-Comml Mgmt)*
Lindsay MacDonald *(Sr Mgr-Tech & Engrg)*
Alex Dey *(Mgr-ICS & Product Training)*
Andrew Connelly *(Mgr-NASCoM Product Line)*
Gordon Gourlay *(Mgr-NASDive & NASDrill Product Line)*
Steven Sangster *(Mgr-QHSE)*
Thomas McCudden *(Sls Mgr-Global-NASNet)*

Subsidiary (Non-US):

Nautronix Brasil Ltda. (3)
Av Rio Branco 156 Sala 3222-4, Rio de Janeiro, 20040-003, Brazil
Tel.: (55) 21 252 40071
Web Site: http://www.nautronix.com
Subsea Communication Services
N.A.I.C.S.: 541990
Lynne Adu *(Dir-Comml & HR)*

Riverstone Holdings LLC - Houston Office (1)
1000 Louisiana Ste 1450, Houston, TX 77002
Tel.: (713) 357-1400
Web Site: http://www.riverstonellc.com
Privater Equity Firm
N.A.I.C.S.: 523999
Ralph C. Alexander *(Mng Dir)*
Rajen Mahagaokar *(VP)*
Peter R. Coneway *(Mng Dir)*
Carl L. Williams *(Mng Dir)*
Andrew J. Karian *(Principal)*
Fauzul Lakhani *(VP-New York)*
Mark G. Papa *(Partner)*
Adrian Sackett *(Principal)*

Riverstone Holdings LLC - London Office (1)
3 St James's Square, London, SW1Y 4JU, United Kingdom
Tel.: (44) 20 3206 6300
Emp.: 20
Investment Management Service
N.A.I.C.S.: 523940
Robin J. A. Duggan *(Mng Dir)*
Christopher B. Hunt *(Partner & Mng Dir)*
Alfredo A. Marti *(Mng Dir-New York)*

Talen Energy Corporation (1)
600 Hamilton St Ste 600, Allentown, PA 18101-1179
Web Site: http://www.talenenergy.com
Holding Company; Electric Power Generation & Distribution
N.A.I.C.S.: 551112
Paul A. Farr *(Pres & CEO)*
Todd Martin *(Mgr-Media & Community Rels)*
Julie LaBella *(Sr Dir-External Affairs)*
Stacey L. Peterson *(Treas, Sr VP-Fin & Head-IR)*
Ryan G. Koren *(Sr Mgr-IR & FP&A)*
Mark Allen McFarland *(Pres & CEO)*

RIVERSTONE HOLDINGS LLC

Subsidiary (Domestic):

Burns Mechanical, Inc. (2)
123 Gibraltar Rd, Horsham, PA 19044-2373
Tel.: (215) 674-9000
Web Site: http://www.burnsmechanical.com
Emp.: 200
Warm Air Heating & Air Conditioning Contractors
N.A.I.C.S.: 238220
Tim Snope *(VP-Pre-Construction)*
Mike Browne *(Controller)*
Dan Kerr *(Pres)*
Matt Rafferty *(Gen Mgr-Svc)*

McCarl's, Inc. (2)
1413 9th Ave, Beaver Falls, PA 15010
Tel.: (724) 843-5660
Web Site: http://www.mccarl.com
Plumbing, Heating & Air-Conditioning; Process Piping & Fabrication Services
N.A.I.C.S.: 238220
Jeffrey Hines *(Pres)*

McClure Company (2)
4101 N 6th St, Harrisburg, PA 17110-1643
Tel.: (717) 232-9743
Web Site: http://www.mcclureco.com
Plumbing Contractors & Mechanical Engineering Services
N.A.I.C.S.: 238210
Chip Brown *(Pres)*

Millennium Builders, Inc. (2)
50 Inwood Rd Ste 2, Rocky Hill, CT 06067
Tel.: (860) 571-0555
General Construction Contractor
N.A.I.C.S.: 236220
Peter Carey *(Gen Mgr)*

Talen Energy Marketing, LLC (2)
835 Hamilton St Ste 150, Allentown, PA 18101-1179
Tel.: (888) 211-6011
Web Site: http://www.talenenergy.com
Electric Power Distr
N.A.I.C.S.: 221122

Talen Energy Supply, LLC (2)
835 Hamilton St Ste 150, Allentown, PA 18101-1179
Tel.: (888) 211-6011
Electric Power Generation & Distribution
N.A.I.C.S.: 221122
Alejandro Hernandez *(CFO & Exec VP)*
Ralph Alexander *(CEO)*
Alejandro Hernandez *(CFO & Exec VP)*

Talen Nuclear Development, LLC (2)
835 Hamilton St Ste 150, Allentown, PA 18101-1179
Tel.: (888) 211-6011
Nuclear Power Development Services
N.A.I.C.S.: 221113

USA Compression Partners, LP (1)
111 Congress Ave Ste 2400, Austin, TX 78701
Tel.: (512) 473-2662
Web Site: https://www.usacompression.com
Rev.: $846,178,000
Assets: $2,736,760,000
Liabilities: $3,030,045,000
Net Worth: ($293,285,000)
Earnings: $20,493,000
Emp.: 822
Fiscal Year-end: 12/31/2023
Holding Company; Gas Compression Leasing Services
N.A.I.C.S.: 551112
Eric Dee Long *(Pres & CEO)*
Matthew C. Liuzzi *(CFO, Treas & VP)*
Sean T. Kimble *(VP-HR)*
G. Tracy Owens *(Chief Acctg Officer & VP-Fin)*
Christopher W. Porter *(Gen Counsel, Sec & VP)*
Eric A. Scheller *(COO & VP)*
Thomas E. Long *(Chm)*

Subsidiary (Domestic):

CDM Resource Management LLC (2)
211 E 7th St Ste 620, Austin, TX 78701
Tel.: (281) 516-6500
Natural Gas Contract Compression Services
N.A.I.C.S.: 213112

RIVERSTONE HOLDINGS LLC   U.S. PRIVATE

Riverstone Holdings LLC—(Continued)

USA Compression Partners, LLC (2)
111 Congress Ave Ste 2400, Austin, TX 78701 (100%)
Tel.: (512) 473-2662
Web Site: http://www.usacompression.com
Gas Compression Leasing Services
N.A.I.C.S.: 213112
Eric Dee Long (Pres & CEO)
Sean T. Kimble (VP-HR)
Christopher W. Porter (Gen Counsel, VP & Sec)
Eric A. Scheller (VP)

Utex Industries Inc. (1)
10810 Katy Fwy Ste 100, Houston, TX 77043-5013
Tel.: (713) 467-1000
Web Site: http://www.utexind.com
Sales Range: $50-74.9 Million
Emp.: 425
Seals, Gaskets & Packing Products Mfr
N.A.I.C.S.: 339991
Michael Balas (Pres & CEO)
Mike Blake (VP-Bus Dev)
Pete Sanchez (CFO)
Gary Burton (Mng Dir)
Chuck Rankin (VP-Ops)
Jack Stoner (Gen Mgr)

Subsidiary (Domestic):

CAM Specialty Products, Inc. (2)
11881 Hwy 75 N, Willis, TX 77378
Tel.: (936) 890-0039
Web Site: http://www.utexind.com
Sales Range: $1-9.9 Million
Emp.: 35
Plastics Product Mfr
N.A.I.C.S.: 326199
Bob Adkins (Gen Mgr)

Vantage Energy Inc. (1)
116 Inverness Dr E Ste 220, Englewood, CO 80112
Tel.: (720) 458-6601
Web Site: http://www.vantageenergy.com
Emp.: 63
Holding Company; Petroleum & Natural Gas Extraction
N.A.I.C.S.: 551112
Roger J. Biemans (Chm & CEO)
W. Worth Carlin (Sr VP-Land)
Mike L. Hopkins (VP-Midstream)
Seth Urruty (VP-Dev)
Mark Brown (VP-Land & Bus Dev)
Christopher L. Valdez (VP-Mktg & Midstream Bus Dev)
Richard Starkey (VP-Subsurface Tech)
Ryan T. Gosney (Chief Acctg Officer & VP-Controller)
John J. Moran Jr. (Sr VP-Ops)
Thomas B. Tyree Jr. (Pres & CFO)

RIVERSTONE LOGISTICS, LLC
11225 N Community House Rd, 8th Fl, Charlotte, NC 28277
Tel.: (980) 595-7394
Web Site: https://rlx.us
Year Founded: 2017
Emp.: 179
Transportation, Logistics, Supply Chain & Storage
N.A.I.C.S.: 488510
Charlie Workmon (CEO)

Subsidiaries:

RBAB, Inc. (1)
4531 Oak Fair Blvd, Tampa, FL 33610
Tel.: (813) 612-9372
Sales Range: $1-9.9 Million
Emp.: 42
Used Household & Office Goods Moving
N.A.I.C.S.: 484210

RIVERTON MOTOR COMPANY, INC.
11100 S Jordan Gateway, Sandy, UT 84095
Tel.: (801) 576-4600 UT
Web Site:
  http://www.rivertonmotor.com
Rev.: $75,575,264
Emp.: 75

New & Used Car Dealerships Owner & Operator
N.A.I.C.S.: 441110
Christopher Page (Pres)
Merci Overdiek (Controller)

RIVERVIEW HEALTH & REHAB CENTER INC.
6711 La Roche Ave, Savannah, GA 31406
Tel.: (912) 354-8225 GA
Year Founded: 1961
Sales Range: $10-24.9 Million
Nursing Home Care Services
N.A.I.C.S.: 623110
John Rynell (Controller)
Stan Adams (Exec Dir)
William Wessinger (Pres)
Laura Dow (Treas)
Steve Booker (VP)
Rick Gnann Jr. (Sec)

RIVERVIEW HOTEL
103 Flagler Ave, New Smyrna Beach, FL 32169
Tel.: (386) 428-5858
Web Site:
  http://www.riverviewhotel.com
Sales Range: $1-9.9 Million
Emp.: 16
Hotel Owner & Operator
N.A.I.C.S.: 721110
Wayne Heller (Co-Owner)
Judy Heller (Co-Owner)

RIVERVIEW INTERNATIONAL TRUCKS INC
2445 Evergreen Ave, West Sacramento, CA 95691
Tel.: (916) 371-3110
Web Site: http://www.riverview-trucks.com
Sales Range: $25-49.9 Million
Emp.: 75
New & Used Trucks, Tractors & Trailers Dealership
N.A.I.C.S.: 441110
Lyle Bassett (Pres)

RIVERVIEW MARINA INC.
711 Snake River Ave, Lewiston, ID 83501
Tel.: (208) 746-1412
Web Site: http://www.boatingfun.com
Rev.: $14,400,000
Emp.: 40
Building & Repairing of Motorboats
N.A.I.C.S.: 336612
Barry Barnes (Pres)

RIVERWOOD CAPITAL LP
70 Willow Rd Ste 100, Menlo Park, CA 94025-3652
Tel.: (650) 618-7300
Web Site:
  http://www.riverwoodcapital.com
Year Founded: 2007
Emp.: 25
Privater Equity Firm
N.A.I.C.S.: 523999
Nicholas E. Brathwaite (Co-Founder & Partner)
Jeff Parks (Co-Founder & Mng Partner)
Francisco Alvarez-Demalde (Co-Founder & Mng Partner)
Jeffrey T. Parks (Co-Founder & Mng Partner)
Harish Belur (Partner)
Augustin Hong (Principal)
Sean McArthur (Principal)
Scott Ransenberg (Partner)
Don Standley (VP)
Alexandre Porto (Partner)
Ramesh Venugopal (Partner)
Joaquim Lima (Partner)

Joe De Pinho (Partner)
Thomas J. Smach (Partner)
Chris Varelas (Co-Founder & Mng Partner)
Michael E. Marks (Mng Partner)

RIVERWOODS MILL, INC.
316 E 1400 S, Saint George, UT 84790
Tel.: (435) 673-4145
Web Site:
  http://www.riverwoodsmill.com
Year Founded: 1997
Sales Range: $25-49.9 Million
Emp.: 54
Wood Kitchen Cabinet Mfr
N.A.I.C.S.: 337110
Ryan Brimhall (Plant Mgr)

RIVES & REYNOLDS LUMBER COMPANY, INC.
Hwy 15 N, Louisville, MS 39339
Tel.: (662) 773-5157
Sales Range: $10-24.9 Million
Emp.: 150
Sawmill Operating Services
N.A.I.C.S.: 321113
William B. Reynolds (VP)
Terry E. Reynolds (Pres)
Ann R. Reynolds (Treas & Sec)

RIVES E. WORRELL COMPANY, INC.
708 Christopher Dr, Savannah, GA 31406
Tel.: (912) 354-1386
Sales Range: $10-24.9 Million
Emp.: 13
Commercial & Office Building, New Construction
N.A.I.C.S.: 236220
Walter B. Murphy III (Pres)

RIVIERA DUNES MARINA CONDOMINIUM ASSOCIATION, INC.
102 Riviera Dunes Way, Palmetto, FL 34221
Tel.: (941) 981-5330
Web Site: http://www.rdmarina.com
Sales Range: $1-9.9 Million
Emp.: 4
Homeowners' Association
N.A.I.C.S.: 813410
Bob Crowley (Pres)

Subsidiaries:

Riviera Dunes Marina (1)
102 Riviera Dunes Way, Palmetto, FL 34221
Tel.: (941) 981-5330
Web Site: http://www.rdmarina.com
Sales Range: $1-9.9 Million
Emp.: 8
Marinas
N.A.I.C.S.: 713930
Peggy Trotter (Office Mgr)

RIVIERA FINANCE LLC
220 Ave I, Redondo Beach, CA 90277
Tel.: (310) 540-3993
Web Site:
  http://www.rivierafinance.com
Year Founded: 1969
Sales Range: $25-49.9 Million
Emp.: 15
Factoring of Commercial Paper
N.A.I.C.S.: 522299
Robert B. Waugh (Natl Mgr-Sls)
Tony Liu (Mgr-IT)

RIVIERA PARTNERS
290 King St Ste 9, San Francisco, CA 94107
Tel.: (650) 587-3560

Web Site:
  http://www.rivierapartners.com
Sales Range: $1-9.9 Million
Emp.: 25
Executive & Technical Search Service
N.A.I.C.S.: 921140
Michael A. Morell (Mng Partner)
Kevin Buckby (Partner)
Lain Grant (Partner)
Sandy Ma (Partner)
Michael Ellison (Product Mgr)
Iva Messy (VP-Talent Dev)
Austin Brizendine (Partner)
Crystal Lynn Guerrero (Project Mgr)
Dirk Cleveland (Partner)
Eric K. Johnson (Dir-IT)
Eric Larson (Partner)
George Kaszacs (Partner)
John Simonelli (COO)
Megan Martin (VP-Mktg)
Jeff Crowell (Sr Dir-Partnerships & Bus Dev)
Kara Landon (Sr Dir-Partnerships & Bus Dev)
Jack Gage (VP-Partnerships & Bus Dev)
Will Hunsinger (CEO)

RIVIERA POINT HOLDINGS, LLC
2700 Glades Cir Ste 142, Weston, FL 33327
Tel.: (954) 385-0733
Web Site:
  http://www.rivierapointholdings.com
Sales Range: $1-9.9 Million
Real Estate Developers
N.A.I.C.S.: 237210
Rodrigo Azpurua (CEO)

RIVIERA TRADING INC.
180 Madison Ave Fl 21, New York, NY 10016
Tel.: (212) 949-9000
Rev.: $77,300,000
Emp.: 25
Mfr & Distributing Sunglasses
N.A.I.C.S.: 424310
Orville Ankarlo (Pres)
Kurt Kress (VP-Hat Design)

RIVKIN RADLER LLP
926 RXR Plz, Uniondale, NY 11556-0926
Tel.: (516) 357-3000 NY
Web Site: http://www.rivkinradler.com
Year Founded: 1950
Law firm
N.A.I.C.S.: 541110
Jeffrey P. Rust (Partner-Health Svcs & Corp Practice Grp)
Kenneth Murphy (Partner-Comml Litigation, Compliance, Investigations & White)
Michael J. Twersky (Partner-Banking, Corp, Real Estate, Zoning & Land Use)
William Cornachio (Partner)
Harvey Epstein (Partner)
Stuart Gordon (Partner)
Eric Fader (Partner)
Henry Mascia (Partner)
Carol Hyde (Partner)

RIX INDUSTRIES
4900 Industrial Way, Benicia, CA 94510
Tel.: (707) 747-5900
Web Site:
  http://www.rixindustries.com
Year Founded: 1878
Sales Range: $10-24.9 Million
Emp.: 80

Mfr of Reciprocating Piston Compressors for Industrial Gases & Breathing Air
N.A.I.C.S.: 333912
Bert E. Otterson *(Pres & CEO)*
Dee Hewlett *(CFO)*

RIZVI TRAVERSE MANAGEMENT LLC
260 E Brown St Ste 380, Birmingham, MI 48009
Tel.: (248) 594-4751   DE
Web Site:
   http://www.rizvitraverse.com
Privater Equity Firm
N.A.I.C.S.: 523999
Suhail R. Rizvi *(Founder & Chief Investment Officer)*
John A. Giampetroni *(Co-Founder & COO)*
Ben Kohn *(Mng Partner)*

Subsidiaries:

RealD Inc.   (1)
100 N Crescent Dr Ste 200, Beverly Hills, CA 90210
Tel.: (310) 385-4000
Web Site: http://www.reald.com
Emp.: 200
Stereoscopic 3D Technologies Mfr & Licensor
N.A.I.C.S.: 333310
Michael V. Lewis *(Founder & CEO)*
Travis Reid *(COO)*
Jeff Spain *(CFO)*
John Trafford-Owen *(Mng Dir-Europe, Middle East, Africa & Russia)*

Subsidiary (Non-US):

RealD Europe Limited   (2)
Suite C-1 Breakspear Park Breakspear Way, Hemel Hempstead, HP2 4TZ, United Kingdom
Tel.: (44) 2080905380
Web Site: http://www.reald.com
Stereoscopic 3D Technologies Mfr & Licensor
N.A.I.C.S.: 512131
Roger Harris *(Mng Dir-Europe, Middle East, Africa & Russia)*

RIZZUTI/AUSTIN MARKETING GROUP
1846 Rosemeade Pkwy Ste 150, Carrollton, TX 75007
Tel.: (972) 394-5116   DE
Year Founded: 1992
Rev.: $12,000,000
Emp.: 5
N.A.I.C.S.: 541810
John Rizzuti *(Mng Dir)*
Lisa Austin *(Sr Partner)*

RJ BRANDS LLC
200 Performance Dr, Mahwah, NJ 07495
Web Site: http://www.chefman.com
Year Founded: 2009
Sales Range: $50-74.9 Million
Emp.: 65
Small Kitchen Appliance Mfr
N.A.I.C.S.: 335220
Ralph Newhouse *(CEO)*
Eli Weiss *(Chief Strategy Officer)*
Pinny Kahana *(VP-Sls)*
Josef Gottlieb *(VP-Product & Dev Ops)*
Paul Dupiano *(VP-Product)*

RJ KING & ASSOCIATES
8270 Woodland Ctr Blvd Ste 190, Tampa, FL 33614
Tel.: (813) 874-1515
Web Site:
   http://www.rjkingassociates.com
Year Founded: 1992
Sales Range: $1-9.9 Million
Emp.: 7

Healthcare-Related Real Estate Brokerage, Leasing & Property Management Services
N.A.I.C.S.: 531210
Darren Wagner *(Sr VP-Medical Office Leasing)*
Phillip Faircloth *(Sr VP-Investment Sls)*
Melees McCune *(VP-Property Mgmt)*

RJ LEE GROUP INC.
350 Hochberg Rd, Monroeville, PA 15146
Tel.: (724) 325-1776
Web Site: http://www.rjlg.com
Year Founded: 1980
Rev.: $10,000,000
Emp.: 250
Provider of Consulting, Contract Research & Analytical Laboratory Services
N.A.I.C.S.: 541715
Richard J. Lee *(CEO)*
David K. James *(CFO & Sr VP-Ops)*
Marsha Hess *(Project Coord)*

RJ TORCHING, INC.
5061 Energy Dr, Flint, MI 48505
Tel.: (810) 785-9759   MI
Web Site: http://www.rjtorching.com
Year Founded: 1984
Sales Range: $25-49.9 Million
Emp.: 35
Metal Recycling
N.A.I.C.S.: 423510
Jason Roughton *(Pres)*

RJE BUSINESS INTERIORS INC.
623 Broadway St, Cincinnati, OH 45202-2234
Tel.: (513) 641-3700
Web Site: http://www.rjecincy.com
Year Founded: 1986
Sales Range: $10-24.9 Million
Emp.: 105
Interior Design Services
N.A.I.C.S.: 541410
Kevin McKiernan *(Pres)*
Chris Keller *(VP-Sls)*
Amanda Miller *(VP-Sls & Mktg)*
Annie St. Clair *(Acct Exec)*
Brian MacKenzie *(VP-Sls)*

RJF INTERNATIONAL CORPORATION
3875 Embassy Pkwy Ste 110, Fairlawn, OH 44333-8334
Tel.: (330) 668-7600   OH
Web Site:
   http://www.rjfinternational.com
Year Founded: 1988
Sales Range: $25-49.9 Million
Emp.: 650
Engineered Polymer Products Mfr
N.A.I.C.S.: 326113
John Baechle *(CEO)*
Jim Schubert *(Mgr-Taxation)*

Subsidiaries:

Koroseal Wall Coverings West   (1)
7334 S Alton Way Unit 14j, Centennial, CO 80112
Tel.: (818) 729-7889
Web Site: http://www.koroseal.com
Sales Range: $10-24.9 Million
Emp.: 10
Plastic & Paint Wallcoverings
N.A.I.C.S.: 424950

RJL HOLDING CO. LLC
13520 Evening Creek Dr Ste 300, San Diego, CA 92128
Web Site: http://www.luciacap.com
Investment & Wealth Management Services
N.A.I.C.S.: 523150

Joseph P. Lucia *(Pres)*
Lance Helfert *(Sr VP)*
Richard Plum *(Chief Fin Plng Officer)*
Joseph J. Lucia *(CMO)*
Chris Lloyd *(Sr VP)*
Janean Stripe *(Sr VP)*
Timothy J. Shea *(Sr VP)*
Preston Schumacher *(Sr VP)*
Atticus Lowe *(Sr VP-Res Portfolio Mgmt)*
Raymond J. Lucia Jr. *(Chm & CEO)*

RJM BUILDERS INCORPORATED
15340 Meadow Wood Dr, Wellington, FL 33414-9005
Tel.: (561) 204-3760
Web Site: http://www.rjmhomes.net
Sales Range: $10-24.9 Million
Emp.: 60
New Construction, Single-Family Houses
N.A.I.C.S.: 236115
Ronald Maggio *(Pres)*

RJM CONSTRUCTION LLC
830 Boone Ave N, Golden Valley, MN 55427
Tel.: (952) 837-8600   MN
Web Site:
   http://www.rjmconstruction.com
Year Founded: 1981
Sales Range: $200-249.9 Million
Emp.: 150
Construction Planning & Engineering Services
N.A.I.C.S.: 541330
Joseph Maddy *(COO)*
Robert Jossart *(Co-Owner, Co-Founder & CEO)*
Brian Recker *(Pres)*
Paul Wade *(VP-Fin)*
Ted Beckman *(Sr VP)*
Brad Barickman *(VP-Corp Construction)*
Troy Stutz *(VP-Bus Dev)*
Carter Vargo *(VP-Corp)*
Wayne Peterson *(Superintendent)*
Gary Wikenheiser *(Superintendent)*
Jed Field *(Dir-MEP Design & Coordination)*
Eric Olson *(VP)*

RJMETRICS INC.
1339 Chestnut St Ste 1500, Philadelphia, PA 19107
Tel.: (877) 684-1394
Web Site: http://www.rjmetrics.com
Sales Range: $1-9.9 Million
E-Commerce Software Developer
N.A.I.C.S.: 513210
Irrum Doss *(Co-Founder & Chief Sls Officer)*
Jason Goldberg *(Co-Founder & CEO)*
Antoine Theoret-Poupart *(Mgr-Acq)*

RJMS CORPORATION
6999 South Front Rd, Livermore, CA 94551
Tel.: (510) 675-0500
Web Site: http://www.tmhnc.com
Rev.: $44,591,775
Emp.: 120
Materials Handling Machinery
N.A.I.C.S.: 423830
Richard Andres *(Pres)*
Melissa Coito *(Mgr-Trng)*
Mark Gates *(Mgr-Svc)*
Stephen Andres *(VP-Ops)*
Jerry Lowery *(Mgr-Parts)*

RJR POLYMERS INC.
7875 Edgewater Dr, Oakland, CA 94621
Tel.: (510) 638-5901
Web Site: http://www.rjrpolymers.com

Sales Range: $10-24.9 Million
Emp.: 60
Electrical Equipment & Supplies Mfr
N.A.I.C.S.: 334419
Raymond Bregante *(Founder & Chm)*
Julio Quintana *(Mgr-Automation)*
Bregante Anthony *(CFO)*
Shawn Jehs *(Mgr-Bus-Applied Matls)*
Edward Estelita *(Supvr-Injection Molding)*
Wil Salhuana *(COO & Exec VP)*
John Ni *(Dir-Product Dev & Technical Svc)*

RJS CONSTRUCTION GROUP, LLC
5300 Stinson Ave, Superior, WI 54880
Tel.: (715) 394-7771   WI
Web Site:
   http://www.rjscompanies.com
Rev.: $40,000,000
Emp.: 100
Commercial & Office Building Contractors
N.A.I.C.S.: 236220
Todd L. Johnson *(Chm & CEO)*

RJT COMPUQUEST, INC.
23440 Hawthorne Blvd Ste 210, Torrance, CA 90505
Tel.: (310) 378-6666
Web Site:
   http://www.rjtcompuquest.com
Year Founded: 1998
Sales Range: $50-74.9 Million
Emp.: 289
Information Technology Consulting Services
N.A.I.C.S.: 541512
Amar Shokeen *(CEO)*
Alan Gaddis *(VP-Sls)*
Rita Shokeen *(CFO)*
Mark Shmagin *(VP-Ops, Fin & Legal)*
Wade Sparks *(Sr VP-Sls)*

RJW MEDIA
5830 Ellsworth Ave Ste 200, Pittsburgh, PA 15232-1778
Tel.: (412) 361-6833   PA
Year Founded: 1985
Sales Range: $25-49.9 Million
Emp.: 15
Media Buying Agency
N.A.I.C.S.: 541830
Richard J. Wolk *(CEO)*
Julie O. Smith *(Owner & Pres)*
Ruth Ashcroft *(Mgr-Traffic)*

RJW, INC.
5755 Granger Rd Ste 400, Independence, OH 44131-1456
Tel.: (216) 398-6090   DE
Web Site:
   http://www.bestwaysystems.com
Year Founded: 1986
Sales Range: $10-24.9 Million
Emp.: 14
Holding Company; Freight Trucking Services
N.A.I.C.S.: 551112
Jeffrey Wenham *(CEO)*
Frederick L. Wenham *(Chm)*
Mike Kirschner *(VP-Ops)*

Subsidiaries:

Bestway Systems, Inc.   (1)
5755 Granger Rd Ste 400, Independence, OH 44131-1456   (100%)
Tel.: (216) 398-6090
Web Site: http://www.bestwaysystems.com
Sales Range: $10-24.9 Million
Provider of Trucking Services
N.A.I.C.S.: 484121
Jeffrey Wenham *(CEO)*

RJW, INC.

RJW, Inc.—(Continued)
Division (Domestic):
Bestway Systems, Inc. - Memphis Division (2)
2460 Frisco Ave, Memphis, TN 38114
Tel.: (901) 332-8254
Web Site: http://www.bestwaysystems.com
Freight Trucking Services
N.A.I.C.S.: 484121

Total Transportation Trucking, Inc. (1)
5755 Granger Rd Ste 400, Independence, OH 44131
Tel.: (800) 331-4307
Web Site: http://www.totaltransportationtrucking.com
Emp.: 12
Logistics Consulting Servies
N.A.I.C.S.: 541614
Eric Haldi *(Controller)*

RK CAPITAL PARTNERS, LLC

5555 Glenridge Connector Ste 200, Atlanta, GA 30342
Tel.: (678) 365-0190
Web Site: https://www.rkcapitalpartners.com
Year Founded: 2003
Secondary Market Financing
N.A.I.C.S.: 522299
Randall B. Katz *(Principal)*

RK DISTRIBUTING INC.

1001 W Memorial Rd Ste 15, Oklahoma City, OK 73114
Tel.: (405) 752-9619   OK
Year Founded: 1979
Sales Range: $10-24.9 Million
Emp.: 6
Distribution of Fuel
N.A.I.C.S.: 424720
Thomas Cowden III *(Pres)*

RK ENVIRONMENTAL SERVICES LLC

768 Carver Ave, Westwood, NJ 07675
Tel.: (201) 503-9800
Web Site: http://www.rkenvironmental.com
Year Founded: 2000
Sales Range: $1-9.9 Million
Emp.: 40
Pest Management & Food Safety
N.A.I.C.S.: 561710
Hank Hirsch *(Pres)*
Chris Sweezy *(Reg Mgr-Ops)*
Ricardo John *(Reg Mgr-Ops)*
Talath Witharane *(VP)*

RK MECHANICAL, INC.

3800 Xanthia St, Denver, CO 80238
Tel.: (303) 355-9696   NE
Web Site: http://www.rkmi.com
Year Founded: 1985
Sales Range: $100-124.9 Million
Emp.: 1,100
Mfr of Plumbing, Sheet Metal, HVAC, Process Piping & Design Build Products
N.A.I.C.S.: 238220
Rick L. Kinning *(Pres & CEO)*
Jon L. Kinning *(COO & Exec VP)*
Marc Paolicelli *(Chief Customer Officer)*
Terry Bates *(CFO)*

Subsidiaries:
RK Specialties, Inc. (1)
8221 E 96th Ave Ste B, Henderson, CO 80640
Tel.: (303) 355-9696
Structural Steel Fabrication Services
N.A.I.C.S.: 332312

RKA PETROLEUM COMPANIES, LLC

28340 Wick Rd, Romulus, MI 48174
Tel.: (734) 946-2199
Web Site: http://www.rkapetroleum.com
Sales Range: $200-249.9 Million
Emp.: 120
Petroleum Products Retailer, Terminal Operator & Distr
N.A.I.C.S.: 424720
Keith L. Albertie *(Exec VP & Dir-Wholesale)*
Kari Elliott *(CEO)*
Michael Valerio *(CFO)*

Subsidiaries:
Land & Sea Petroleum, Inc. (1)
6710 NW 15th Way, Fort Lauderdale, FL 33309
Tel.: (954) 978-3835
Web Site: http://www.landandseapetroleum.com
Sales Range: $25-49.9 Million
Emp.: 9
Petroleum Products Retailer & Distr
N.A.I.C.S.: 424720
Anna Alonzo *(Office Mgr)*

RKB HANDYMAN SERVICES, INC.

330 Motor Pkwy Ste 306, Hauppauge, NY 11788
Tel.: (516) 612-7821
Web Site: http://www.rkb247.com
Year Founded: 2014
Sales Range: $1-9.9 Million
Emp.: 12
Facility Management Services
N.A.I.C.S.: 561210
Anthony Franzese *(Pres)*

RKI, INC.

2301 Central Pkwy, Houston, TX 77092
Tel.: (713) 688-4414
Web Site: http://www.rki-us.com
Rev.: $35,500,000
Emp.: 350
Motor Vehicle Body Mfr
N.A.I.C.S.: 336211
Richard F. Koenig *(VP)*
Thomas C. Rawson *(Chm & CEO)*
Fredrick Wamhoff *(Gen Counsel, Sec & VP)*

RKL ESOLUTIONS, LLC

1800 Fruitville Pike, Lancaster, PA 17604
Tel.: (717) 735-9109
Web Site: http://www.rklesolutions.com
Year Founded: 2002
Information Technology Services
N.A.I.C.S.: 513210
Joe Noll *(Pres)*
Bob Gaby *(COO)*
Walter Goodfield *(Exec VP-Sls & Mktg)*

RKON, INC.

328 S Jefferson St Ste 450, Chicago, IL 60661
Tel.: (312) 654-0300
Web Site: http://www.rkon.com
Year Founded: 1998
Sales Range: $25-49.9 Million
Emp.: 75
Computer Peripherals Mfr
N.A.I.C.S.: 334118
Marc Malizia *(CTO)*

RKS ELECTRIC CORP.

94-24 88 St, Ozone Park, NY 11416
Tel.: (718) 843-5555
Year Founded: 1978
Sales Range: $10-24.9 Million

Emp.: 175
Electrical Wiring Services
N.A.I.C.S.: 238210
Steven Weinstein *(Pres)*

RL DEPPMANN COMPANY

46575 Magellan Dr Novi, Novi, MI 48034
Tel.: (248) 354-3710
Web Site: http://www.deppmann.com
Sales Range: $10-24.9 Million
Emp.: 61
Warm Air Heating Equipment & Supplies
N.A.I.C.S.: 423730
Norman E. Hall *(Pres)*
Joe Smolinski *(VP-Bus Dev & Plng)*

RL HAINES CONSTRUCTION, LLC

5500 Vista View Way, Oviedo, FL 32765
Tel.: (407) 384-1908
Web Site: http://www.rlhaines.com
Year Founded: 1991
Sales Range: $10-24.9 Million
Emp.: 55
Construction Services
N.A.I.C.S.: 236220
Richard Hainess *(Founder & Pres)*
Joseph Hurt *(COO)*

RL PUBLIC RELATIONS + MARKETING

11835 W Olympic Blvd Ste 1155E, Los Angeles, CA 90064
Tel.: (310) 473-4422
Web Site: http://www.rlpublicrelations.com
Year Founded: 1995
Emp.: 200
Full-Service Hispanic Public Relations & Marketing Agency
N.A.I.C.S.: 541820
Roxana Lissa *(Founder & Pres)*
Yanka Burgos *(VP)*
Mario Flores *(Partner & Mng Dir)*

Subsidiaries:
RL Public Relations + Marketing (1)
1115 Broadway St Ste 1271, New York, NY 10010
Tel.: (212) 206-8668
Web Site: http://www.rlpublicrelations.com
Sales Range: Less than $1 Million
Emp.: 5
Hispanic Public Relations & Marketing
N.A.I.C.S.: 541810
Roxana Lissa *(Founder & Pres)*
Victoria Capelli *(Head-New York & VP)*
Ana Ceron *(VP)*

RLC HOLDING CO. INC.

1420 W Chestnut Ave, Enid, OK 73703-4307
Tel.: (580) 233-6000   OK
Year Founded: 1992
Sales Range: $25-49.9 Million
Emp.: 150
Highway & Street Construction
N.A.I.C.S.: 237310
Pam Knox *(Treas)*
Ray Feightner *(Pres)*
Robert L. Cummins Jr. *(Chm)*

Subsidiaries:
The Cummins Construction Company Inc. (1)
1420 W Chestnut Ave, Enid, OK 73703-4307
Tel.: (580) 233-6000
Web Site: http://www.cumminsasphalt.com
Highway & Street Construction
N.A.I.C.S.: 237310

RLG INVESTMENTS, INC. -U.S.A

5433 Westheimer Rd, Houston, TX 77056-5399
Tel.: (713) 622-4700
Year Founded: 1978
Sales Range: $25-49.9 Million
Emp.: 426
Mfr of Sanitary Paper Products
N.A.I.C.S.: 322291

RLK & COMPANY

Timberline Ski Area Lodge, Government Camp, OR 97028
Tel.: (503) 272-3311
Web Site: http://www.timberlinelodge.com
Rev.: $18,000,000
Emp.: 200
Resort Hotel
N.A.I.C.S.: 721110
John Tullis *(Dir-Pub Affairs)*
Jeff Kohnstamm *(Pres)*

RLM PUBLIC RELATIONS, INC.

228 E 45 St 11F, New York, NY 10017
Tel.: (212) 741-5106   DE
Web Site: http://www.rlmpr.com
Year Founded: 1991
Public Relations Agency
N.A.I.C.S.: 541820
Richard Laermer *(Founder & CEO)*
Stephen Bradley *(Gen Mgr)*
Jon Lindsay Phillips *(Exec Dir)*

RLR ADVERTISING

150 S Arroyo Pkwy, Pasadena, CA 91105
Tel.: (626) 440-0321
Year Founded: 2005
Sales Range: $10-24.9 Million
Emp.: 19
N.A.I.C.S.: 541810
Mikki Robischon *(Pres)*
Hans Castro Gallo *(Dir-Art & Dir-Creative)*
Roberto Leni *(Copywriter)*
Toby Muller *(Copywriter)*

RLR ADVERTISING INC.

102 Sound Ct, Northport, NY 11768
Tel.: (631) 925-5590
Web Site: http://www.rlradv.com
Year Founded: 1986
Sales Range: Less than $1 Million
Emp.: 3
N.A.I.C.S.: 541810
Wendy Ann Ruehle *(Exec VP)*
Robert L. Ruehle Sr. *(Pres & CEO)*

RLR INDUSTRIES INC.

575 Discovery Pl, Mableton, GA 30126
Tel.: (770) 948-6069
Web Site: http://www.rlrlighting.com
Year Founded: 1956
Sales Range: $10-24.9 Million
Emp.: 75
Plastics Processing
N.A.I.C.S.: 326199
Bartha Covington *(Mgr-HR)*
Andy Lewis *(VP)*
Anthony Gaito *(Mgr-Maintenance)*
Perry Thibaudeau *(Mgr-Engrg)*
Scott Sowers *(Mgr-Shipping & Receiving)*
Stewart Lewis *(Mgr-Mktg)*
Keith Senkyr *(Project Mgr-Design)*
Walter Thompson *(Mgr-Sls-Natl)*

RLR, INC.

14040 Santa Fe Trl Dr, Lenexa, KS 66215-1284
Tel.: (913) 888-5201
Web Site: http://www.smithandloveless.com
Sales Range: $25-49.9 Million

Emp.: 315
Holding Company
N.A.I.C.S.: 551112
Robert L. Rebori *(Chm & Pres)*
Darby Ritter *(Mgr-Mktg Comm)*
Frank Rebori *(Chm & Pres)*

Subsidiaries:

Di-Sep Systems International (1)
15519 Blackburn Ave, Norwalk, CA 90650
Tel.: (562) 407-3432
Web Site: http://www.smithandloveless.com
Sales Range: $10-24.9 Million
Emp.: 5
Water Purification Equipment
N.A.I.C.S.: 423720
Jim Ellis *(Gen Mgr)*

Smith & Loveless, Inc. (1)
14040 Santa Fe Trl Dr, Lenexa, KS 66215-1284
Tel.: (913) 888-5201
Web Site: http://www.smithandloveless.com
Sales Range: $50-74.9 Million
Emp.: 150
Water & Wastewater Pumping Services
N.A.I.C.S.: 221310

Subsidiary (Non-US):

Kalsep UK Ltd. (2)
2F Albany Park Frimley Road, Camberley, GU16 7PL, Surrey, United Kingdom
Tel.: (44) 1276 675675
Web Site: http://www.kalsep.co.uk
Waste Treatment Services
N.A.I.C.S.: 221310

Subsidiary (Domestic):

Smith & Loveless Georgia Inc. (2)
10425 Old Atlanta Hwy, Covington, GA 30014
Tel.: (678) 712-6780
Web Site: http://www.smithandloveless.com
Emp.: 3
Waste Treatment Services
N.A.I.C.S.: 221310
Scott Stephens *(Engr-Sls)*

Subsidiary (Non-US):

Smith & Loveless New Zealand Limited (2)
Unit 3 7 Milford Rd, Milford, Auckland, New Zealand
Tel.: (64) 9 488 6701
Web Site:
http://www.smithandlovelessnz.co.nz
Emp.: 2
Waste Treatment Services
N.A.I.C.S.: 221310
Joe Gill *(Gen Mgr-Sls & Mktg)*

RM CROWE MANAGEMENT COMPANY
5944 Luther Ln 1000, Dallas, TX 75225
Tel.: (214) 369-6192
Web Site: http://www.rmcrowe.com
Year Founded: 1987
Sales Range: $10-24.9 Million
Emp.: 100
Provider of Land Subdivider & Developer Services
N.A.I.C.S.: 551112
Ken Thurmond *(VP)*

RM MECHANICAL INC.
5998 W Gowen Rd, Boise, ID 83709
Tel.: (208) 362-0131
Web Site:
http://www.rmmechanical.net
Sales Range: $25-49.9 Million
Emp.: 200
Plumbing Contractor
N.A.I.C.S.: 238220
Brad Hom *(CFO)*
Tom McGrath *(Project Mgr)*

RM PERSONNEL INC.
4707 Montana Ave, El Paso, TX 79903
Tel.: (915) 565-7674
Web Site:
http://www.rmpersonnel.com
Sales Range: $25-49.9 Million
Emp.: 1,500
Employment Leasing Agencies
N.A.I.C.S.: 561311
Ceci Miles Mulvihill *(Pres)*
Amber Vargas *(Mgr-HR)*
Jose M. Sanchez *(CFO)*

RM WILSON CO. INC.
3434 Market St, Wheeling, WV 26003
Tel.: (304) 232-5860
Web Site: http://www.rmwilson.com
Year Founded: 1966
Sales Range: $50-74.9 Million
Emp.: 30
Whslr of Mining Machinery & Equipment
N.A.I.C.S.: 423810
Pat Popicg *(Pres)*

RMA BROKERAGE LLC
5875 Castle Creek Pkwy N Dr Ste 215, Indianapolis, IN 46250
Tel.: (317) 575-4440
Web Site: http://www.caitlin-morgan.com
Year Founded: 1990
Insurance Agencies & Brokerages
N.A.I.C.S.: 524210

RMA HOME SERVICES INC.
2690 Cumberland Pkwy Se Ste 300, Atlanta, GA 30339-3913
Tel.: (770) 779-1335
Sales Range: $50-74.9 Million
Emp.: 800
Provider of Home Improvement Services
N.A.I.C.S.: 423310

RMA LAND CONSTRUCTION, INC.
2707 Saturn St, Brea, CA 92821
Tel.: (714) 985-2888
Web Site: http://www.rmaland.com
Year Founded: 1981
Rev.: $21,900,000
Emp.: 48
General Contracting Services
N.A.I.C.S.: 236220
Roy Mohammad *(Founder, Pres & CEO)*
Steve Mohammad *(Exec VP)*

RMA TRANSPORTATION SERVICES INC.
22292 Pepper Rd, Lake Barrington, IL 60010
Year Founded: 1997
Rev.: $14,300,000
Emp.: 35
Turnkey Technology Solution
N.A.I.C.S.: 927110
Richard M. Allen *(Pres & CEO)*
Josh Allen *(VP)*

RMAX INC.
13524 Welch Rd, Dallas, TX 75244
Tel.: (972) 387-4500
Web Site: http://www.rmax.com
Insulation Or Cushioning Material, Foamed Plastics
N.A.I.C.S.: 326150
Milledge A. Hart III *(Chm)*

RMB BANCSHARES, INC.
1201 S Missouri, Marceline, MO 64658
Tel.: (660) 376-2077   MO
Web Site:
http://www.regionalmissouri.com
Year Founded: 1990
Sales Range: $1-9.9 Million
Emp.: 32
Bank Holding Company
N.A.I.C.S.: 551111
Don Reynolds *(Chm & CEO)*
Patrick Kussman *(Pres & COO)*

Subsidiaries:

Regional Missouri Bank (1)
1201 S Missouri Ave, Marceline, MO 64658
Tel.: (660) 376-2077
Web Site: http://www.regionalmissouri.com
Retail & Commercial Banking
N.A.I.C.S.: 522110
Kimberly Corbin *(VP-Loan Dept)*
Danielle Head *(Asst VP-Loan Dept)*
Jordan Lichtenberg *(Asst VP-Loan Dept)*

RMC DISTRIBUTING LLC
1525 N Newport Rd, Colorado Springs, CO 80916
Tel.: (719) 598-0772
Web Site:
http://www.rmcdistributing.net
Rev.: $38,000,000
Emp.: 85
Beer & Other Fermented Malt Liquors
N.A.I.C.S.: 424810
Bob Lisko *(Controller)*
Everett Laughlin *(Dir-Tech & Employee Svcs)*
Mark Larson *(Mgr-Allied Brand)*

RMC PROPERTY GROUP LLC
8902 N Dale Hwy Ste 200, Tampa, FL 33614
Tel.: (813) 960-8154
Web Site: http://www.rmcpg.com
Sales Range: $25-49.9 Million
Emp.: 50
Property Leasing, Management, Acquisition & Development Services
N.A.I.C.S.: 531190
Mitchell F. Rice *(CEO)*
Susie Levin Rice *(Pres)*
Bobby Eggleston *(CFO & Chief Real Estate Officer)*
Elysia Ellickson-Tucci *(VP-Asset Mgmt)*
Dea Etlinger *(Dir-Property Mgmt)*
Suzanne Delery *(Controller)*
Cindy Lee *(VP-Ops)*

Subsidiaries:

The Ross Realty Group, Inc. (1)
3001 Executive Dr Ste 250, Clearwater, FL 33762
Tel.: (727) 725-2800
Web Site: http://www.rossrealty.com
Sales Range: $50-74.9 Million
Emp.: 25
Real Estate Brokerage
N.A.I.C.S.: 531210
Elliot Ross *(Pres)*
Norman Leonard *(Sr Mgr-Property)*
Frank Boullosa *(Dir-Lender Svcs)*
Dea Etlinger *(Mgr-Property)*

RMC VANGUARD MORTGAGE CORPORATION
1111 North Loop W Ste 250, Houston, TX 77008
Tel.: (713) 802-6000   TX
Web Site: http://www.rmcv.com
Year Founded: 1996
Sales Range: $10-24.9 Million
Emp.: 115
Originates, Processes, Underwrites & Closes Conventional & Residential Government Loans
N.A.I.C.S.: 522310
Eric R. Kugler *(Sr VP)*
Owen Raun *(Pres)*
Jayne James *(Mgr-Quality)*
Matt Kiker *(CFO)*
Trisha Barnes *(VP-Ops)*

RMCN CREDIT SERVICES, INC.
1611 Wilmeth Rd Ste B, McKinney, TX 75069
Tel.: (972) 529-0900
Web Site:
http://www.repairmycreditnow.com
Year Founded: 1997
Rev.: $7,200,000
Emp.: 93
Credit Reporting Services
N.A.I.C.S.: 561450
Doug Parker *(Founder, Pres & CEO)*

RMD HOLDINGS, LTD.
69951 Lowe Plank Rd, Richmond, MI 48062
Tel.: (586) 749-6900   MI
Web Site:
http://www.nationwideconstructiongroup.com
Sales Range: $10-24.9 Million
Emp.: 90
Specialty Construction Operation Services
N.A.I.C.S.: 238990
Robert E. Demil *(Pres)*
Robert Pietryka *(CFO)*
Scott Keller *(COO)*
Rogue Tyson *(Corp Counsel)*

RMD TECHNOLOGIES, INC.
688 Rancheros Dr, San Marcos, CA 92069
Tel.: (760) 741-2400   CA
Web Site: http://www.rmdt.com
Year Founded: 2001
Sales Range: Less than $1 Million
Emp.: 2
Electronic Waste Recycling Services
N.A.I.C.S.: 562211
Patrick A. Galliher *(CEO)*

RMG MEDIA, LLC
375 Park Ave Ste 2607, New York, NY 10152
Tel.: (646) 600-5222
Web Site: http://www.rmgmedia.com
Year Founded: 2013
Sales Range: $1-9.9 Million
Emp.: 45
Advertising & Marketing Services
N.A.I.C.S.: 541810
Ryan Gellis *(Mng Partner)*
Michael Caruso *(Mng Partner)*

RMG NETWORKS HOLDING CORPORATION
15301 Dallas Pkwy Ste 500, Addison, TX 75001   DE
Web Site:
http://www.rmgnetworks.com
Year Founded: 2011
Rev.: $37,042,000
Assets: $21,948,000
Liabilities: $16,243,000
Net Worth: $5,705,000
Earnings: ($5,193,000)
Emp.: 162
Fiscal Year-end: 12/31/17
Holding Company; Digital Signage Solutions & Media Applications
N.A.I.C.S.: 551112
Jerry Rosen *(Chief Mktg & Creative Officer-Global & Sr VP)*
Gregory H. Sachs *(Chm)*
Jana Ahlfinger Bell *(CFO & Exec VP)*
George Clopp *(CTO & Sr VP)*
Ankur Ahlowalia *(CEO)*

Subsidiaries:

EMN Acquisition Corporation (1)
405 Urban St Ste 150, Lakewood, CO 80228
Tel.: (303) 993-3293
Visual Communication Services
N.A.I.C.S.: 541430

RMG Networks, Inc. (1)

RMG NETWORKS HOLDING CORPORATION

RMG Networks Holding Corporation—(Continued)
15301 Dallas Pkwy Ste 500, Addison, TX 75001
Tel.: (972) 543-9300
Web Site: http://www.rmgnetworks.com
Emp.: 60
Location-Based Targeted Audience Advertising Services
N.A.I.C.S.: 541890

Subsidiary (Non-US):

RMG Networks Limited (2)
Tower 42 Floor 14 25 Old Broad St, London, EC2N 1HQ, United Kingdom
Tel.: (44) 2038686930
Web Site: http://www.rmgnetworks.com
Sales Range: $10-24.9 Million
Emp.: 30
Telecommunications Products Distr
N.A.I.C.S.: 423690

RMH ACQUISITION, LLC.
375 Erie Ave, Morton, IL 61550
Tel.: (309) 266-1500
Year Founded: 2009
Sales Range: $75-99.9 Million
Support Services
N.A.I.C.S.: 561499
Jonathan W. Rocke (Pres)
William D. Morton (Exec Dir)

RMH FRANCHISE CORPORATION
2021 Pine Lake Rd, Lincoln, NE 68542
Tel.: (402) 858-7880
Web Site: http://www.rmhfranchise.com
Year Founded: 2012
Applebee's Franchise Owner & Operator
N.A.I.C.S.: 722511
Howard Hohman (COO)
Mitch Blocher (CFO)
Kevin Bennett (VP-Reg Ops)
Roger Somers (Exec Dir-IT)
Melanie Barichivich (Dir-Mktg)
Jen Hansen (Dir-People Resources)
Matt Cissell (Controller)
Michelle Carlson (Dir-Training)

RMH SYSTEMS, INC.
1130 SE Westbrook Dr, Waukee, IA 50263
Tel.: (515) 987-7999 IA
Web Site: http://www.rmhsystems.com
Materials Handling & Packaging Machinery Mfr & Whslr
N.A.I.C.S.: 333248
Todd Maxwell (COO)
Craig Howard (Gen Mgr-Scale)
Marc Collis (Gen Mgr-Packaging)

Subsidiaries:

Skarnes, Inc. (1)
2100 Niagara Ln N, Minneapolis, MN 55447
Tel.: (763) 231-3600
Materials Handling Machinery & Equipment Mfr & Whslr
N.A.I.C.S.: 333248
Lisa Chelberg (Coord-Svc)

RMI MARKETING & ADVERTISING
436 Old Hook Rd 2nd Fl, Emerson, NJ 07631
Tel.: (201) 261-7000 NJ
Web Site: http://www.rmi-inc.com
Year Founded: 1973
Rev.: $17,000,000
Emp.: 20
Advetising Agency
N.A.I.C.S.: 541810
Jonathan Morgan (VP)

RMI, LLC
3475 Piedmont Rd Ste 250, Atlanta, GA 30305
Tel.: (404) 355-6734
Web Site: http://www.rmiondemand.com
Year Founded: 1979
Sales Range: $25-49.9 Million
Emp.: 162
Software Stores
N.A.I.C.S.: 449210
J. Peter Kleifgen (Chm & CEO)
James A. Day (CFO & Sr VP)

RMK HOLDINGS CORP.
1 E Erie St Ste 410, Chicago, IL 60611
Tel.: (312) 337-2372 DE
Web Site: http://www.rmk123.com
Sales Range: $10-24.9 Million
Emp.: 8
Business Management Services
N.A.I.C.S.: 561499
Ron McLauglin (Pres)

Subsidiaries:

Logisoft Computer Products, LLC (1)
6605 Pittsford-Palmyra Rd Ste E1, Fairport, NY 14450-3405
Web Site: http://www.logisoft.com
Computer Services
N.A.I.C.S.: 541511
Robert Ballard (Pres)

RML HEALTH PROVIDERS LIMITED PARTNERSHIP
5601 S County Line Rd, Hinsdale, IL 60521
Tel.: (630) 286-4000 IL
Web Site: http://www.rmlspecialtyhospital.org
Year Founded: 1996
Sales Range: $75-99.9 Million
Emp.: 826
Health Care Srvices
N.A.I.C.S.: 622110
John Landstrom (VP-HR)
Jim Prister (Pres & CEO)
Tricia Vaisvila (VP-Bus Dev)
Ken Pawola (COO)
Julie Ames (CIO)
Tom Pater (CFO & VP)

RMO INC.
650 W Colfax Ave, Denver, CO 80204
Tel.: (303) 592-8200
Web Site: http://www.rmortho.com
Rev.: $19,000,000
Emp.: 150
Orthodontic Appliances
N.A.I.C.S.: 339114
Adam Wachholtz (Mgr-Sls)
Nancy Molish (Mgr-Sls-West Reg)

RMR & ASSOCIATES, INC.
5870 Hubbard Dr, Rockville, MD 20852-6425
Tel.: (301) 230-0045
Web Site: http://www.rmr.com
Year Founded: 1987
Sales Range: $10-24.9 Million
Emp.: 10
Advetising Agency
N.A.I.C.S.: 541810
Robyn M. Sachs (Pres)
Jim Cavender (Dir-Art)
Seth Menishon (Mgr-PR)
Kate Russell (VP-Acct Svcs)
Sandra Schwartzman (VP-PR)
Laura Asendio (Sr Acct Exec)
Cassey Elder (Acct Exec)
Guy Shields (Sr VP)

RMR PREFERRED INCOME FUND
2 Newton Pl 255 Washington St Ste 300, Newton, MA 02458
Tel.: (617) 332-9530
Investment Services
N.A.I.C.S.: 523999

RMS OMEGA TECHNOLOGIES GROUP, INC.
7410 Coca Cola Dr, Hanover, MD 21076
Tel.: (410) 290-7101
Web Site: http://www.rmsomega.com
Emp.: 100
Electronic & Precision Equipment Repair & Maintenance
N.A.I.C.S.: 811210
Joe Gurreri (Acct Mgr)

Subsidiaries:

New Technology Investments, Inc. (1)
1904 Hilco St, Albemarle, NC 28001
Tel.: (704) 983-1495
Web Site: http://www.scanonline.com
Rev.: $6,300,000
Emp.: 100
Stationery & Office Supplies Merchant Whslr
N.A.I.C.S.: 424120
David Smith (Sec)
Brian Graves (Pres)

RMTS, LLC
Old Mercantile Exchange Bldg 6 Harrison St, New York, NY 10013
Tel.: (212) 925-0017
Web Site: http://www.rmts.net
Rev.: $28,000,000
Emp.: 24
Managing General Underwriters of Medical Stop Loss, Group Life & AD&D Coverage Services
N.A.I.C.S.: 524298
David P. Kalm (Pres & CEO)
Gregory T. Caluri (Sr VP-Underwriting & Sls)
Ronald J. Geck (Sr VP-Claims & Assoc Gen Counsel)
Thomas J. Axon (Founder, Owner & Chm)

RMW ARCHITECTURE & INTERIORS
160 Pine St Ste 509, San Francisco, CA 94111
Tel.: (415) 781-9800
Web Site: http://www.rmw.com
Sales Range: $25-49.9 Million
Emp.: 50
Interior Designer
N.A.I.C.S.: 541410
Thomas B. Gerfen (Principal)
Lisa Smith (CFO)
Steve Worthington (Principal)
Jeff Leonhardt (Principal)
Karen Letteney (Dir-Interiors)
Russ Nichols (Pres)
Stan Lew (Principal)
Stephen Guest (Principal)
Gary Koshaba (Principal)
Terry Kwik (Principal)
Bart McClelland (Principal)
Robbin McDonald (Principal)

RN FIELD CONSTRUCTION INC.
515 Folsom Fl 2, San Francisco, CA 94105
Tel.: (415) 648-8140
Web Site: http://www.rnfield.com
Sales Range: $25-49.9 Million
Emp.: 30
Commercial & Office Buildings, Renovation & Repair
N.A.I.C.S.: 236220
John A. Grcina (Pres & Principal)
Tim Gibbons (CFO & Principal)
Kevin Jacobs (Superintendent)

U.S. PRIVATE

Marla Blanchard (Project Coord)
Randy McCracken (VP)
Seiichi Quartaroli (Principal & Sr Project Mgr)
Tracy Coletta (Principal & Dir-Ops)

RN INDUSTRIES TRUCKING, INC.
PO Box 1168, Roosevelt, UT 84078
Tel.: (435) 722-2800
Web Site: http://www.rnindustries.com
Year Founded: 1990
Sales Range: $10-24.9 Million
Emp.: 300
Oil & Gas Operating Services
N.A.I.C.S.: 213112
Russell Cowan (Mgr-HR)

RNA, INC.
130 W Wenger Rd, Englewood, OH 45322
Tel.: (937) 832-0058 OH
Web Site: http://www.rnahealth.com
Year Founded: 1975
Sales Range: $1-9.9 Million
Emp.: 45
Computer System Design Services
N.A.I.C.S.: 541512
John H. McKee (Chm)
Bonnie Lawhorn (Dir-Sls-Long Term Care)
Frank L. Duke Yetter (Pres)
Philip Lew (CEO)

Subsidiaries:

Castronics, Inc. (1)
4386 E Hwy 30, Kimball, NE 69145
Tel.: (308) 235-4881
Web Site: http://www.castronicspipe.com
Sales Range: $1-9.9 Million
Emp.: 28
Fabricated Pipe & Pipe Fitting Mfr
N.A.I.C.S.: 332996
Bruce Evertson (Pres)
Perry Vannewkirk (CEO & Mng Partner)

RND AUTOMATION & ENGINEERING, LLC
7910 25th Ct E Unit 105, Sarasota, FL 34243
Tel.: (941) 870-5400
Web Site: http://www.rndautomation.com
Sales Range: $1-9.9 Million
Emp.: 12
Custom Automation & Material Handing Machinery Engineer, Designer & Mfr
N.A.I.C.S.: 333248
Sean Dotson (Pres)
Doug Robertson (VP)
Bruce Naylor (VP)
Tim Twitty (Dir-Engrg)

RNK INC.
333 Elm St, Dedham, MA 02026
Tel.: (781) 613-6000
Web Site: http://www.rnktel.com
Sales Range: $10-24.9 Million
Emp.: 150
Telephone Communication, Except Radio
N.A.I.C.S.: 517121
Richard Koch (Pres & CEO)
Joy Tessier (Exec VP)

RNMC INC.
1500 Veterans Memorial Hwy, Rome, GA 30161
Tel.: (706) 291-1981
Web Site: http://www.romenissan.com
Sales Range: $10-24.9 Million
Emp.: 27
Automobile Dealership

N.A.I.C.S.: 441110
Jeff Gamble (Mgr-Parts)
Jorge Ortiz (Dir-Fin)
Kenneth Lackey (Mgr-Sls)
George Barron (Owner)

Subsidiaries:

Heritage of Gainesville Inc. (1)
2400 Browns Bridge Rd, Gainesville, GA 30504
Tel.: (678) 944-8663
Automobiles, New & Used
N.A.I.C.S.: 441110

RNR CONSULTING
1111 Superior Ave E, Cleveland, OH 44114
Tel.: (216) 621-8977 OH
Web Site:
http://www.rnrconsulting.com
Year Founded: 2001
Sales Range: $10-24.9 Million
Emp.: 18
Management Consulting Services
N.A.I.C.S.: 541611
Holly Julius (Pres & CEO)
Rahim N. Rahim (Principal & Owner)
Tiffany Laude (Mgr-Bus Dev)

RNR HOLIDAY RV INC.
23203 E Knox Ave, Liberty Lake, WA 99019
Tel.: (509) 927-9000
Web Site: http://www.rnrrv.com
Sales Range: $25-49.9 Million
Emp.: 120
Recreational Vehicle Dealers
N.A.I.C.S.: 441210
Ray L. Bunney (Owner)
Jason Tiemann (Mgr-Svcs & Parts)
Keith Woodruff (Dir-Fixed Ops)
Mike Duncan (Mgr-Parts)

RO HO HO INC.
1479 Tobias Gadson Blvd, Charleston, SC 29407-4794
Tel.: (843) 402-0710
Web Site: http://www.papajohns.com
Sales Range: $10-24.9 Million
Emp.: 13
Pizzeria, Independent
N.A.I.C.S.: 722513
Don Bauer (VP)
Philip Horn Jr. (Pres)

RO INNOVATION
1624 Market St Ste 202, Denver, CO 80202
Tel.: (888) 731-4002
Web Site:
http://www.roinnovation.com
Customer Reference Management & Sales Enablement Solutions
N.A.I.C.S.: 513210
James Mooney (Founder & CEO)
Tony DeLollis (COO & CTO)
Dan Montoya (VP-Svcs)

RO-MAC LUMBER & SUPPLY INC.
700 E Main St, Leesburg, FL 34748
Tel.: (352) 787-4545
Web Site:
http://www.romaclumber.com
Year Founded: 1945
Sales Range: $25-49.9 Million
Emp.: 300
Lumber Products
N.A.I.C.S.: 444110
Don Magruder (CEO)
Dan Robuck Jr. (Owner & Pres)

RO-MAR TRANSPORTATION SYSTEMS INC.
3500 S Kedzie Ave, Chicago, IL 60632-2726
Tel.: (773) 376-8800 DE
Web Site: http://www.romartrans.com
Year Founded: 1990
Sales Range: $25-49.9 Million
Emp.: 500
Provider of Freight Transportation Services
N.A.I.C.S.: 488510
Michael Marden (Founder & CEO)
Dave Hernandez (Acct Mgr)
Janeen Musillami (Dir-Safety)

ROAD BUILDERS MACHINERY & SUPPLY CO.
1001 S 7th St, Kansas City, KS 66105
Tel.: (913) 371-3822
Web Site:
http://www.roadbuildersmachinery.com
Year Founded: 1985
Sales Range: $50-74.9 Million
Emp.: 172
General Construction Machinery & Equipment
N.A.I.C.S.: 423810
Phil McCoy (Pres)
Bryan McCoy (VP)
Gerry Buser (VP)
Nicole Argard (Mgr-Credit)
Vince McBride (Mgr-Ops)
Ted Christensen (Mgr-Parts-Columbus)
Josh Halte (Mgr-Parts-Columbus)
Mike Hink (Mgr-Parts-Columbus)
Brian Burkert (Mgr-Rental)
Rusty Kilpatrick (Mgr-Svc-Columbus)
Dewayne Thornton (Mgr-Svc-Columbus)

ROAD MACHINERY & SUPPLIES COMPANY
5633 Hwy 13 W, Savage, MN 55378-1215
Tel.: (952) 895-9595 MN
Web Site:
http://www.rmsequipment.com
Year Founded: 1926
Sales Range: $100-124.9 Million
Emp.: 220
Distr of Heavy Construction Mining & Utility Equipment
N.A.I.C.S.: 423810
Michael M. Sill (CEO)
Russell Sheaffer (Pres)
Troy Johnson (CFO)

Subsidiaries:

Atlanta Equipment Company Inc (1)
11070 S Pipeline Rd, Euless, TX 76040
Tel.: (817) 864-0151
Web Site: http://www.trenchbox.com
Emp.: 12
Construction Machinery Mfr
N.A.I.C.S.: 333120
Corky Shelton (Gen Mgr)

Polar Parts Co. (1)
5633 W Hwy 13, Savage, MN 55378
Tel.: (952) 895-0042
Web Site: http://www.polarparts.com
Emp.: 4
Used Automotive Parts Distr
N.A.I.C.S.: 423140
J. J. Bunn (Gen Mgr)

RMS Hydraulic Services Co. (1)
12520 Quentin Ave S, Savage, MN 55378
Web Site:
http://www.rmshydraulicservices.com
Emp.: 6
Hydraulic Cylinder Mfr
N.A.I.C.S.: 333995
Rich Giese (Mgr-Ops)

RMS Rentals Company (1)
12520 Quentin Ave So Ste 100, Savage, MN 55378
Tel.: (952) 895-7033
Web Site: http://www.rmsrentals.com

Emp.: 20
Forklift Rental Services
N.A.I.C.S.: 532490
Mark Rossi (Gen Mgr)
Ken Carlson (Mgr-Svcs)
Brian Gaul (Mgr-Parts)

U.S. Shoring & Equipment Co. (1)
11070 S Pipeline Rd, Euless, TX 76040
Tel.: (817) 858-0975
Web Site:
http://www.usshoringandequipment.com
Emp.: 12
Construction Equipment Rental Services
N.A.I.C.S.: 532412
Corky Shelton (Gen Mgr)
Robert Blake (Office Mgr)

ROAD SCHOLAR TRANSPORT INC.
130 Monahan Ave, Dunmore, PA 18512
Tel.: (570) 348-1155
Web Site:
http://www.roadscholar.com
Sales Range: $10-24.9 Million
Emp.: 100
Local Trucking without Storage
N.A.I.C.S.: 484110
Jim Barrett (Co-Founder & Pres)
Debra Barrett (Co-Founder)

ROAD-MART INC.
1880 S Union Ste B, Ozark, AL 36360
Tel.: (334) 774-9937
Sales Range: Less than $1 Million
Emp.: 8
Automotive Tires
N.A.I.C.S.: 441340
William E. Hardwick (Owner)
Eddy Hardwick (Pres)
Laurie Mock (Controller)

ROADCLIPPER ENTERPRISES INC.
4006 FM 3417, Mount Pleasant, TX 75455
Tel.: (903) 572-2834
Web Site: http://www.diamondc.com
Year Founded: 1985
Flatbed Trailers Designer, Marketer & Mfr
N.A.I.C.S.: 811114
Jeffery Crabb (Co-Owner)
Kim Crabb (Co-Owner)
Ryan Cope (VP-Sls)

ROADMARK CORPORATION
900 E C St, Butner, NC 27509
Tel.: (919) 596-5005
Web Site:
http://www.roadmarkcorp.com
Sales Range: $10-24.9 Million
Emp.: 50
Highway & Street Construction
N.A.I.C.S.: 237310
David Rosenthal (CFO)
Patrick Conway (Owner & Partner)

ROADRUNNER RECORDS INC.
1290 Avenue of the Americas, New York, NY 10104
Tel.: (212) 274-7500
Web Site:
http://www.roadrunnerrecords.com
Rev.: $32,000,000
Emp.: 40
Prerecorded Records & Tapes
N.A.I.C.S.: 334610
Chris Brown (Sr Dir-Mktg)
David Bason (Dir-A&R)
Greg Dorfman (VP-ALT Promotion)
Suzi Akyuz (Sr Dir-Mktg)
Mark Abramson (VP-Promo)

ROADSHOW BMW MINI
405 N Germantown Pkwy, Cordova, TN 38018-6207
Tel.: (901) 365-2584
Web Site:
http://www.roadshowbmw.com
Year Founded: 1981
Sales Range: $10-24.9 Million
Emp.: 83
Car Whslr
N.A.I.C.S.: 441110
Randy Patton (Gen Mgr)

ROANE MEDICAL CENTER
Roane Medical Center Dr, Harriman, TN 37748
Tel.: (865) 316-1000 TN
Web Site:
http://www.roanemedical.com
Year Founded: 2008
Sales Range: $25-49.9 Million
Emp.: 350
Health Care Srvices
N.A.I.C.S.: 622110
Gaye G. Jolly (Co-Pres & Chief Admin Officer)
Jason Pilant (COO)
Carolyn Shipley (Chief Nursing Officer)
Rick Carringer (CFO)

ROANOKE ELECTRIC MEMBERSHIP
518 NC Hwy 561 W, Aulander, NC 27805
Tel.: (252) 209-2236
Web Site:
http://www.roanokeelectric.com
Sales Range: $25-49.9 Million
Emp.: 65
Distribution, Electric Power
N.A.I.C.S.: 221122
Curtis Wynn (CEO & Exec VP)
Marshall Cherry (VP-Svcs & Mktg)

ROANOKE RAPIDS SAVINGS BANK, SSB
325 Becker Dr, Roanoke Rapids, NC 27870
Tel.: (252) 537-8061
Web Site: http://www.rrsb.com
Year Founded: 1914
Sales Range: $1-9.9 Million
Emp.: 15
Federal Savings Bank
N.A.I.C.S.: 522180
Ed Jackson (Pres & CEO)

ROANOKE TRADE SERVICES INC.
1475 East Woodfield Rd Ste 500, Schaumburg, IL 60173-4903
Tel.: (847) 969-1420
Web Site:
http://www.roanoketrade.com
Rev.: $14,700,000
Emp.: 60
International Insurance
N.A.I.C.S.: 524210
Sean Walsh (Exec VP)
James L. Cahalan (Exec VP-Legal Affairs)
James Valatkas (CFO & Sr VP)
John F. Walsh (Exec VP-Grp Underwriting & Sls)
Karen Groff (Exec VP-Grp Ops & Client Svcs)
Steve Calamla (Sr VP-Surety Ops)

ROANWELL CORPORATION
2564 Park Ave, Bronx, NY 10451
Tel.: (718) 401-0288 CT
Web Site: http://www.roanwell.com
Year Founded: 1948
Sales Range: $10-24.9 Million

ROANWELL CORPORATION

Roanwell Corporation—(Continued)

Military & Commercial Communications Headsets, Handsets, Microphones & Accessories Mfr
N.A.I.C.S.: 334290
Jonathan LaBarre (Pres & COO)
Barbara C. LaBarre (CEO)
Chelly Simon (VP-Sls)

Subsidiaries:

Roanwell Corp. - Absolute Manufacturing Division (1)
24 Lomar Park Dr Ste 6F, Pepperell, MA 01463-1416
Tel.: (978) 433-0760
Web Site:
http://www.absolutemanufacturing.com
Precision Engineered Metal Components Mfr
N.A.I.C.S.: 332999

ROAR MEDIA LLC

55 Miracle Mile Ste 330, Coral Gables, FL 33134
Tel.: (305) 403-2080
Web Site: http://www.roarmedia.com
Sales Range: $1-9.9 Million
Emp.: 20
Public Relations Agency
N.A.I.C.S.: 541820
Jacques Hart (Co-Founder & CEO)
Jolie Balido (Co-Founder & Pres)
Lorraine Reigosa (Dir-Accts)

ROARK CAPITAL GROUP INC.

1180 Peachtree St NE Ste 2500, Atlanta, GA 30309
Tel.: (404) 591-5200 GA
Web Site:
http://www.roarkcapital.com
Year Founded: 2001
Privater Equity Firm
N.A.I.C.S.: 523999
Neal K. Aronson (Founder & Mng Partner)
Stephen D. Aronson (Mng Dir & Gen Counsel)
Tracy A. Haas (Treas)
Erik O. Morris (Chief Investment Officer)
David K. Lee (Principal)
Paul D. Ginsberg (Pres)
Wesley C. Lee (CFO)
Clayton D. Harmon (Mng Dir)
John P. Jordan (Principal)
Michael S. Sharkey (Mng Dir)
Timothy B. Armstrong (Mng Dir)
Sagar S. Gandhi (Principal)

Subsidiaries:

CKE, Inc. (1)
6303 Carpinteria Ave, Carpinteria, CA 93013
Tel.: (805) 745-7500
Web Site: http://www.ckr.com
Sales Range: $5-14.9 Billion
Emp.: 20,200
Holding Company; Restaurant Owner & Franchisor
N.A.I.C.S.: 551112
Andrew F. Puzder (CEO)
E. Michael Murphy (Pres & Chief Legal Officer)
Theodore Abajian (CFO & Exec VP)
Richard Buxton (Exec VP-Real Estate Dev)
Jeffrey P. Chasney (CIO & Exec VP-Strategic Plng)
John J. Dunion (Exec VP-Supply Chain Mgmt)
Brad R. Haley (CMO)
Eric Williams (COO)

Subsidiary (Domestic):

CKE Restaurants Holdings, Inc. (2)
6700 Tower Cie Ste 1000, Franklin, TN 37067 (100%)
Tel.: (805) 745-7741
Web Site: http://www.ckr.com

Sales Range: $1-4.9 Billion
Emp.: 20,200
Restaurants Operator & Franchisor
N.A.I.C.S.: 722511
John J. Dunion (Chief Supply Chain Officer)
Jeff Jenkins (CMO)
Stephen Carvelli (CIO)
Christopher Perry (Sr Mgr-Asset Protection)
Charles Jemley (CFO)
Kerry Olson (Chief Legal Officer & Gen Counsel)
Andrew Robinson (Chief HR Officer)
Chad Crawford (Chief Brand Officer)
C. Max Wetzel (CEO)
Beth Gerstenberger (Dir-Comm)

Subsidiary (Domestic):

Carl Karcher Enterprises, Inc. (3)
1325 N Anaheim Blvd, Anaheim, CA 92801 (100%)
Tel.: (805) 745-7500
Web Site: http://www.carlsjr.com
Sales Range: $25-49.9 Million
Operator of Restaurants
N.A.I.C.S.: 722513
Bradford R. Haley (CMO)
Andrew F. Puzder (CEO)

Hardee's Food Systems, Inc. (3)
100 N Broadway Ste 1200, Saint Louis, MO 63102 (100%)
Tel.: (314) 259-6200
Web Site: http://www.hardees.com
Sales Range: $1-4.9 Billion
Fast-Food Restaurant, Chain
N.A.I.C.S.: 722513
Bradford R. Haley (CMO)

Central Jersey Waste & Recycling, Inc. (1)
432 Stokes Ave, Ewing, NJ 08638
Tel.: (609) 771-8005
Web Site:
http://www.centraljerseywaste.com
Sales Range: $1-9.9 Million
Emp.: 30
Waste & Recycling Services
N.A.I.C.S.: 562219
Michael Fiumefreddo (VP)
Frank Fiumefreddo Jr. (Pres)

Divisions, Inc. (1)
300 Dave Cowens Dr, Newport, KY 41071
Tel.: (859) 448-9730
Web Site: http://www.divisionsinc.com
Facilities Support Services
N.A.I.C.S.: 561210
Gary B. Mitchell (Founder, Owner & CEO)
Kyle Murray (Co-Owner & Chief Strategy Officer)
Adam Wallace (Dir-IT)
Brain Wint (CFO)
Woodrow Richmond (Acct Coord-Natl)
Thomas Kosinski (Acct Exec-Natl)
Brett Samson (Acct Coord-Natl)
Matt Gomberg (Acct Coord-Natl)
Patrick Sellers (Acct Coord-Natl)
Richard Ross (Acct Coord-Natl)
Samuel Porter (Acct Coord-Natl)
Emily Webb (Coord-Acct Natl)
Lindsey Chapman (Mgr-Bus Analysis)

Driven Brands, Inc. (1)
440 S Church St Ste 700, Charlotte, NC 28202
Tel.: (704) 644-8101
Web Site: http://www.drivenbrands.com
Emp.: 2,400
Holding Company
N.A.I.C.S.: 551112
Jonathan Fitzpatrick (Co-Pres & CEO)
Jonathan Fitzpatrick (Co-Pres & CEO)
Danny Rivera (Pres-Meineke)
Noah Pollack (Gen Counsel & Exec VP)
Gabe Mendoza (Co-Pres & Exec VP-Distr & Quick Lube)
Jon Gaiman (Chief Dev Officer)
Blair Boggs (CMO)

Subsidiary (Domestic):

1-800-Radiator & A/C (2)
4401 Park Rd, Benicia, CA 94510
Tel.: (707) 747-7400
Web Site: http://www.1800radiator.com
Radiators & Automotive Products Distr
N.A.I.C.S.: 423120
Jay Chapman (Mgr-HR & Insurance)
Boris Berkovich (Mgr-Analytics)
Kyle Marshall (VP-Sls)
Jesse Hopkins (Dir-HR)

Boing US Holdco, Inc. (2)
6300 S Syracuse Way Ste 205, Centennial, CO 80111
Tel.: (303) 779-9009
Web Site: http://www.icwg.com
Holding Company
N.A.I.C.S.: 551112
Jonathan Booth (Deputy CEO)
Jason Price (Pres-US)
Ivona Adkins (Chief People Officer)
Brian Goodman (CTO)
Jeff Lasher (CFO)
Jeff Maize (VP-Acq)
Jean Jacquemetton (Gen Counsel)
Gabe Mendoza (Pres-North America)
Tracy Gehlan (Pres-Intl)

Subsidiary (Domestic):

Airul Enterprises, Inc. (3)
27330 Chagrin Blvd, Orange Village, OH 44122
Tel.: (216) 831-2439
Web Site: http://www.airenterprises.com
Sales Range: $1-9.9 Million
Emp.: 13
Gasoline Stations
N.A.I.C.S.: 457120

Baird Brothers Express Car Wash (3)
1313 S Vly Mills Dr, Waco, TX 76711
Tel.: (254) 295-0234
Web Site:
http://www.bairdbrothersexpress.com
Car Wash Services
N.A.I.C.S.: 811192
Bill Baird (Pres)

Subsidiary (Domestic):

CARSTAR Franchise Systems, Inc. (2)
4200 W 115th St Ste 300, Leawood, KS 66211
Tel.: (844) 906-9764
Web Site: http://www.carstar.com
Automotive Collision Repair Services
N.A.I.C.S.: 811121
Dean Fisher (COO)
Melissa Miller (VP-Ops)
Michael Macaluso (Pres-North America)
Arlo Johnson (VP-Insurance)
Grace Makoid (Sr Dir-Franchising)
Adele League (Sr Dir-Inventory Sls)
Hannah Ross (Dir-Mktg)
Sam Freeman (VP-Dev)

Econo Lube N' Tune Inc. (2)
440 S Church St Ste 700, Charlotte, NC 28202
Tel.: (704) 377-8855
Web Site: http://www.econolube.com
Auto Repair & Maintenance Services
N.A.I.C.S.: 811111

Meineke Car Care Centers, Inc. (2)
440 S Church St Ste 700, Charlotte, NC 28202
Tel.: (800) 447-3070
Web Site: http://www.meineke.com
Muffler & Brake Repair Services
N.A.I.C.S.: 811111
Danny R. Rivera (Pres)

Subsidiary (Domestic):

Walt's Auto Care Centers (3)
6310 15th Ave NW, Seattle, WA 98107
Tel.: (206) 789-7828
Web Site: http://www.waltswrench.com
Motor Vehicle Products & Services
N.A.I.C.S.: 423120

Subsidiary (Domestic):

Take 5 Oil Change, LLC (2)
2450 Severn Ave Ste 308, Metairie, LA 70001
Tel.: (504) 837-0670
Web Site: http://www.take5oilchange.com
Oil Change Service Stations Owner & Operator
N.A.I.C.S.: 811191
Pete Frey (Pres)

FOCUS Brands, Inc. (1)
200 Glenridge Point Pkwy Ste 200, Atlanta, GA 30342

U.S. PRIVATE

Tel.: (404) 255-3250
Web Site: http://www.focusbrands.com
Sales Range: $1-4.9 Billion
Food Service Franchising
N.A.I.C.S.: 551112
Steve Romaniello (Chm)
Jim Salerno (Chief Brand Officer-Carvel)
Gary Bales (Chief Strategy Officer)
Michael Dixon (CFO)
Sarah Powell (Gen Counsel, Sec & Exec VP)
Robert Manasier (Founder)
Jill Daye (COO)
Geoff Henry (Pres)
Shivram Vaideeswaran (CMO)
Jaime Denney (VP-Ops)
Jim Holthouser (CEO)
Brian Krause (Chief Dev Officer)
Tim Muir (Chief Sls Officer)
Sean Wooden (Mng Dir-Intl & VP)
Beto Guajardo (Pres-Intl)
Kerri Christian (Sr VP-Specialty Category Mktg)
Tracey Young (Chief Brand Officer-Cinnabon)
Jessica Osborne (VP-Mktg-Carvel)
Kristen Hartman (Pres-Specialty Category)

Subsidiary (Domestic):

Auntie Anne's Inc. (2)
48 - 50 W Chestnut St Ste 200, Lancaster, PA 17603
Tel.: (717) 435-1435
Web Site: http://www.auntieannes.com
Sales Range: $50-74.9 Million
Hand-Rolled Soft Pretzel Franchises
N.A.I.C.S.: 445291
Marcel Nahm (VP-Mktg)

Carvel Corporation (2)
5620 Glenridge Dr NE, Atlanta, GA 30342
Tel.: (404) 255-3250
Web Site: http://www.carvel.com
Sales Range: $50-74.9 Million
Emp.: 300
Ice Cream Mfr & Distr
N.A.I.C.S.: 311520
Lauren McGowen (Mgr-PR)
Kimberly Frazier (Mgr-Franchise Mktg)
Chris Campagna (VP-Brand Mktg)
Scott Colwell (Pres)

Cinnabon, Inc. (2)
5620 Glenridge Dr NE, Atlanta, GA 30342
Tel.: (404) 255-3250
Web Site: http://www.cinnabon.com
Sales Range: $25-49.9 Million
Emp.: 400
Bakery Products Retailer
N.A.I.C.S.: 311811
Joe Guith (Pres)
Kristen Hartman (Pres-Brand)

Jamba, Inc. (2)
3001 Dallas Pkwy Ste 140, Frisco, TX 75034
Tel.: (469) 294-9600
Web Site: http://www.jambajuice.com
Rev.: $70,926,000
Assets: $40,648,000
Liabilities: $55,222,000
Net Worth: ($14,574,000)
Earnings: ($2,742,000)
Emp.: 1,038
Fiscal Year-end: 01/02/2018
Holding Company; Natural Fruit Drink Sales
N.A.I.C.S.: 551112
Joe Thornton (COO & Sr VP)
Geoff Henry (Pres)
Jaime Denney (VP-Ops)
Shivram Vaideeswaran (Chief Mktg Officer)

Subsidiary (Domestic):

Jamba Juice Company (3)
6475 Christie Ave Ste 150, Emeryville, CA 94608
Tel.: (510) 596-0100
Web Site: http://www.jambajuice.com
Sales Range: $25-49.9 Million
Emp.: 100
Natural Juice Drink Sales
N.A.I.C.S.: 722513
Joe Thornton (COO)

Subsidiary (Domestic):

Moe's Southwest Grill, LLC (2)
2915 Peachtree Rd, Atlanta, GA 30305

COMPANIES

ROARK CAPITAL GROUP INC.

Tel.: (404) 442-8932
Web Site: http://www.moes.com
Sales Range: $250-299.9 Million
Fast-Food Franchiser
N.A.I.C.S.: 722511
Bruce Schroder *(Pres)*
Verchele Wiggins Roberts *(VP-Mktg)*
Matthew Courtoy *(Sr Mgr-Social & Digital Strategy)*
Lindsay Haynes *(Mgr-PR)*
Erik Hess *(Pres-Brand)*

Schlotzsky's, Ltd. (2)
5620 Glenridge Dr NE, Atlanta, GA 30342
Tel.: (404) 255-3250
Web Site: http://www.schlotzskys.com
Sales Range: $200-249.9 Million
Restaurant Operators
N.A.I.C.S.: 722513
Victoria Nielsen *(Sr Mgr-Social & Digital)*
Beto Guajardo *(Pres)*

Seattle's Best Coffee International (2)
5620 Glenridge Dr NE, Atlanta, GA 30342
Tel.: (404) 255-3250
Web Site: http://www.focusbrands.com
Sales Range: $50-74.9 Million
Franchisor of Coffee Bars on Military Bases & International Markets
N.A.I.C.S.: 722513
Lenore Krentz *(Chief Admin Officer & CFO)*
Mike Shattuck *(Pres)*

Fitness Connection (1)
2810 E Trinity Mills Rd, Carrollton, TX 75006
Tel.: (800) 922-7898
Web Site: http://fitnessconnection.com
Fitness & Recreational Sports Centers
N.A.I.C.S.: 713940

IMO Car Wash Group Ltd. (1)
35-37 Amersham Hill, High Wycombe, HP13 6NU, Bucks, United Kingdom
Tel.: (44) 1494 897 410
Web Site: http://www.imocarwash.com
Conveyor Car Wash Operator
N.A.I.C.S.: 811192
Jonathan Booth *(Deputy CEO)*

Subsidiary (Non-US):

IMO Autopflege GmbH (2)
Friedrich Ebert Strasse 144, Mulheim an der Ruhr, 45473, Germany
Tel.: (49) 20844 309 0
Web Site: http://www.imocarwash.com
Car Wash Operators
N.A.I.C.S.: 811192

IMO Lavage (2)
55 Chemin de la Bouyere, Marseille, 83190, France
Tel.: (33) 0147727932
Web Site: http://www.imocarwash.com
Car Wash Operators
N.A.I.C.S.: 811192

Inspire Brands, Inc. (1)
1155 Perimeter Ctr W 12th Fl, Atlanta, GA 30338
Tel.: (678) 514-4100
Web Site: http://www.inspirebrands.com
Holding Company; Multi-Brand Restaurant Operator
N.A.I.C.S.: 551112
Paul J. Brown *(CEO)*
Stephanie Sentell *(Sr VP-Ops)*
Lyle Tick *(Pres-Buffalo Wild Wings)*
Tim Murphy *(Pres/Mng Dir-Intl)*
Tim Casey *(Head-Brand-Rusty Taco)*
Nils H. Okeson *(Chief Admin Officer & Gen Counsel)*
Melissa Strait *(Chief People Officer)*
Christian Charnaux *(Chief Growth Officer)*
Greg Vojnovic *(Chief Dev Officer)*
Christopher Fuller *(Chief Comm Officer)*
Neal Aronson *(Founder)*
Selden Hunnicutt *(Coord-Corp Comm)*
Brendan Mauri *(Pres-Rusty Taco)*
Katherine D. Jaspon *(CFO)*
Jason S. Maceda *(Sr VP-Franchise Development)*

Subsidiary (Domestic):

Arby's Restaurant Group, Inc. (2)
1155 Perimeter Ctr W 9th Fl, Atlanta, GA 30338
Tel.: (678) 514-4100
Web Site: http://www.arbys.com
Holding Company; Fast Food Restaurants Operator & Franchisor
N.A.I.C.S.: 551112

Subsidiary (Non-US):

Arby's Canada, Inc. (3)
7045 Edwards Blvd Suite 304, Mississauga, L5S 1X2, ON, Canada
Tel.: (905) 672-2729
Web Site: http://www.arbys.ca
Sales Range: $10-24.9 Million
Emp.: 10
Fast Food Roast Beef Restaurant
N.A.I.C.S.: 722511

Subsidiary (Domestic):

Buffalo Wild Wings, Inc. (3)
Three Glenlake Parkway NE, Atlanta, GA 30328
Web Site: http://www.buffalowildwings.com
Holding Company; Casual Restaurant Operator & Franchisor
N.A.I.C.S.: 551112
John Bowie *(Pres-Brands)*
Lyle Tick *(Pres)*

Subsidiary (Domestic):

Dunkin' Brands Group, Inc. (2)
130 Royall St, Canton, MA 02021
Tel.: (781) 737-3000
Web Site: http://www.dunkinbrands.com
Rev.: $1,370,227,000
Assets: $3,920,024,000
Liabilities: $4,508,034,000
Net Worth: ($588,010,000)
Earnings: $242,024,000
Emp.: 1,114
Fiscal Year-end: 12/28/2019
Holding Company; Fast Food Restaurants Franchisor & Branded Food Products Licensing
N.A.I.C.S.: 551112
Karen Raskopf *(Chief Comm & Sustainability Officer)*
Scott Murphy *(Pres-Americas)*
John Varughese *(Sr VP-Intl)*
David Mann *(Chief Legal Officer & Sr VP)*
Dana Reid *(VP-Field Mktg-US)*
Jill McVicar Nelson *(VP-Mktg Strategy)*
Ryan Schaffer *(VP)*

Subsidiary (Domestic):

Dunkin' Brands, Inc. (3)
130 Royall St, Canton, MA 02021
Tel.: (781) 737-3518
Web Site: http://www.dunkinbrands.com
Sales Range: $500-549.9 Million
Emp.: 1,128
Donut, Sandwich & Ice Cream Shop Franchisor; Coffee Brand Licensing
N.A.I.C.S.: 533110
Jason S. Maceda *(Sr VP-Baskin-Robbins US,Canada)*
Nigel Travis *(Chm)*
Richard J. Emmett *(Chief Legal & HR Officer & Sr VP)*

Subsidiary (Domestic):

Dunkin' Donuts LLC (4)
130 Royall St, Canton, MA 02021
Tel.: (781) 737-3000
Web Site: http://www.dunkindonuts.com
Donut & Sandwich Shops Franchisor
N.A.I.C.S.: 533110
Nigel Travis *(Chm & CEO)*

Subsidiary (Domestic):

Baskin-Robbins LLC (5)
130 Royall St, Canton, MA 02021
Tel.: (781) 737-3000
Web Site: http://www.baskinrobbins.com
Ice Cream Shops Operator & Franchisor
N.A.I.C.S.: 722515
Jonathan Biggs *(VP-Ops-US & Canada)*

Subsidiary (Domestic):

Baskin-Robbins Franchising LLC (6)
130 Royall St, Canton, MA 02021
Tel.: (781) 737-3000
Web Site: http://www.baskinrobbins.com
Ice Cream Shop Franchisor
N.A.I.C.S.: 533110

Nigel Travis *(CEO)*

Subsidiary (Domestic):

Star Dunkin', LP (3)
3035 Ridge Rd, Rockwall, TX 75032
Tel.: (469) 314-1438
Emp.: 4
Specialty Food Store Operator
N.A.I.C.S.: 445298

Subsidiary (Domestic):

Jimmy John's LLC (2)
2212 Fox Dr, Champaign, IL 61820
Tel.: (217) 356-9900
Web Site: http://www.jimmyjohns.com
Holding Company; Sandwich Shop Franchisor & Operator
N.A.I.C.S.: 551112
James John Liautaud *(Owner & Founder)*
James North *(Pres & CEO)*
Darin Dugan *(CMO)*

Subsidiary (Domestic):

Jimmy John's Franchisor SPV, LLC (3)
2212 Fox Dr, Champaign, IL 61820
Tel.: (217) 356-9900
Web Site: http://www.jimmyjohns.com
Sandwich Shop Franchisor
N.A.I.C.S.: 533110
James North *(Pres & CEO)*
James John Liautaud *(Owner & Founder)*

Subsidiary (Domestic):

SONIC Corporation (2)
300 Johnny Bench Dr, Oklahoma City, OK 73104
Tel.: (405) 225-5000
Web Site: http://www.sonicdrivein.com
Rev.: $423,590,000
Assets: $531,134,000
Liabilities: $819,980,000
Net Worth: ($288,846,000)
Earnings: $71,205,000
Emp.: 391
Fiscal Year-end: 08/31/2018
Licensing & Operation of Drive-In Franchised Restaurants
N.A.I.C.S.: 722513
Lori Abou Habib *(VP & Chief Mktg Officer)*
Carolyn C. Cummins *(Sec & VP-Compliance)*
Paige S. Bass *(Gen Counsel, Sr VP & Asst Sec)*
Michelle E. Britten *(Chief Acctg Officer & VP)*
Christina D. Vaughan *(Pres-Sonic Restaurants, Inc.)*
Jose A. Duenas *(Chief Brand Officer & Exec VP)*
Corey F. Horsch *(CFO, Treas & VP)*
John Budd III *(Chief Strategy Officer, Chief Bus Dev Officer & Exec VP)*

Division (Domestic):

SONIC Industries, Inc. (3)
300 Johnny Bench Dr, Oklahoma City, OK 73104 (100%)
Tel.: (405) 225-5000
Web Site: http://www.sonicdrivein.com
Sales Range: $25-49.9 Million
Emp.: 220
Franchised & Partnership, Drive-through Restaurants
N.A.I.C.S.: 722513
Drew Ritger *(Sr VP-Bus Plng & Pur)*
Stephen C. Vaughn *(CFO & Exec VP)*
Paige Bass *(Gen Counsel & VP)*

Massage Envy Limited, LLC (1)
13450 N 87th St Ste 200, Scottsdale, AZ 85260
Tel.: (480) 366-4100
Web Site: http://www.massageenvy.com
Sales Range: $10-24.9 Million
Massage Therapy Clinic Operator & Franchisor
N.A.I.C.S.: 812199
Adam Jacobi *(Dir-IT Svcs)*
Elizabeth Tanardi *(Mgr-Mktg)*
George Hines *(CIO)*
Debbie Gonzalez *(Chief Brand Officer)*
Beth Stiller *(Chief Comml Officer)*
Melanie Hansen *(Gen Counsel)*

Greg Esgar *(CFO)*
Lee Knowlton *(Sr VP-Global Franchise Sls & Intl)*

Mathnasium LLC (1)
5120 W Goldleaf Cir Ste 300, Los Angeles, CA 90056-1293
Tel.: (310) 475-2222
Web Site: http://www.mathnasium.com
Learning Centers Operator
N.A.I.C.S.: 611710
Peter Markovitz *(Mgr)*
Shant Assarian *(CEO)*

McAlister's Corporation (1)
721 Avignon Dr Ste AB, Ridgeland, MS 39157
Tel.: (601) 952-1100
Web Site: http://www.mcalistersdeli.com
Sales Range: $200-249.9 Million
Deli Franchisor & Operator
N.A.I.C.S.: 722511
Peter Wright *(VP-Franchise Dev)*
Donna Josephson *(VP-Mktg)*
Jeff Sturgis *(Chief Dev Officer)*

Pet Supermarket Inc. (1)
1100 International Pkwy, Sunrise, FL 33323
Tel.: (954) 351-0834
Web Site: http://www.petsupermarket.com
Sales Range: $200-249.9 Million
Pet Supplies Retailer
N.A.I.C.S.: 459910
Diane Holtz *(CEO)*
Steve Feinberg *(VP-Mktg)*

Pet Valu Inc. (1)
130 Royal Crest Court, Markham, L3R 0A1, ON, Canada
Tel.: (905) 946-1200
Web Site: http://www.petvalu.com
Sales Range: $25-49.9 Million
Emp.: 300
Pet Food & Supply Distr
N.A.I.C.S.: 459910
Thomas H. McNeely *(CEO)*

Subsidiary (Domestic):

Pet Valu Canada, Inc. (2)
130 Royal Crest Court, Markham, L3R 0A1, ON, Canada
Tel.: (905) 946-1200
Web Site: https://www.petvalu.ca
Sales Range: $100-124.9 Million
Specialty Sale Services
N.A.I.C.S.: 459910

Subsidiary (Domestic):

Peton Distributors Inc. (3)
225 Royal Crest Court, Markham, L3R 9X6, ON, Canada
Tel.: (905) 946-1200
Web Site: http://www.petvalue.com
Sales Range: $25-49.9 Million
Pet Foods & Supplies Purchasing, Warehousing & Distributing
N.A.I.C.S.: 493190
Tom McNeely *(CEO)*

Primrose School Franchising Company (1)
3200 Windy Hill Rd SE Ste 1200 E, Atlanta, GA 30339
Tel.: (770) 529-4100
Web Site: http://www.primroseschools.com
Sales Range: $300-349.9 Million
Educational Child Care Center Franchisor
N.A.I.C.S.: 533110
Jo Kirchner *(CEO)*
Bob Benowitz *(Exec VP-Ops)*
Derek Fuller *(CFO & Sr VP-Fin)*
Paul Thaxton *(VP-Brand Mgmt)*
Bill Pierquet *(Sr VP-School Dev)*
Chris Goethe *(VP-Franchising)*
Gloria Julius *(VP-Education & Pro Dev)*
John Rosen *(VP-Real Estate & Dev)*

Roark Capital Management, LLC (1)
1180 Peachtree St NE Ste 2500, Atlanta, GA 30309
Tel.: (404) 591-5200
Web Site: http://www.roarkcapital.com
Private Equity Investment Management Firm
N.A.I.C.S.: 523999
Neal K. Aronson *(Mng Partner)*
Neal K. Aronson *(Founder & Mng Partner)*

ROARK CAPITAL GROUP INC.

U.S. PRIVATE

Roark Capital Group Inc.—(Continued)
Ezra S. Field (Co-Chief Investment Officer & Sr Mng Dir)
Erik O. Morris (Co-Chief Investment Officer & Sr Mng Dir)
David M. Wierman (Mng Dir & Head-IR)
Pritpal S. Aujla (CFO)
Stephen D. Aronson (Mng Dir & Gen Counsel)
Allison T. Feliner (Chief People Officer)
William G. Roche (Chief Compliance Officer)
Kelly M. Stone (Chief Talent Officer)
Neal K. Aronson (Mng Partner)

The ServiceMaster Company, LLC (1)
150 Peabody Pl, Memphis, TN 38103
Tel.: (901) 597-1400
Web Site: http://www.servicemaster.com
Assets: $5,135,000,000
Liabilities: $4,773,000,000
Net Worth: $362,000,000
Earnings: ($56,000,000)
Fiscal Year-end: 12/31/2014
Residential & Commercial Contract Cleaning, Landscaping, Pest Control, Inspection & Furniture Repair Services
N.A.I.C.S.: 561790
Elane B. Stock (CEO)

Subsidiary (Domestic):

AmeriSpec LLC (2)
860 Rdg Lake Blvd Fl 3, Memphis, TN 38120
Tel.: (901) 597-8500
Web Site: http://www.amerispec.com
Home Inspection Services
N.A.I.C.S.: 541350

Merry Maids Limited Partnership (2)
1661 N Shelby Oaks Dr Ste 108, Memphis, TN 38134
Tel.: (901) 290-7647
Web Site: http://www.merrymaids.com
Sales Range: $10-24.9 Million
Emp.: 100
Cleaning Serivces
N.A.I.C.S.: 561110

ServiceMaster Consumer Services Limited Partnership (2)
860 Rdg Lk Blvd, Memphis, TN 38120-9421
Tel.: (901) 766-1400
Web Site: http://www.servicemaster.com
Emp.: 2,000
Maintenance Service Of Electronic Products
N.A.I.C.S.: 561710

Subsidiary (Non-US):

ServiceMaster Ltd. (2)
ServiceMaster House Tigers Road, Tiger Road, Wigston, LE18 4WS, Leicestershire, United Kingdom
Tel.: (44) 1162759000
Web Site: http://www.servicemaster.co.uk
Sales Range: $50-74.9 Million
Emp.: 200
Professional Home & Office Cleaning Services
N.A.I.C.S.: 561720
Alan Lewin (Mng Dir)

ServiceMaster of Canada Ltd. (2)
8-60 Bristol Road East Suite 512, Mississauga, L4Z 3K8, ON, Canada
Tel.: (905) 670-0200
Web Site: https://www.servicemaster.ca
Sales Range: $25-49.9 Million
Emp.: 55
Hospitals & School Management Services & Residential/Commercial Cleaning
N.A.I.C.S.: 561720

Subsidiary (Domestic):

The Terminix International Company Limited Partnership (2)
150 Peabody Pl, Memphis, TN 38103
Tel.: (901) 597-1400
Web Site: http://www.terminix.com
Residential & Commercial Termite & Pest Control
N.A.I.C.S.: 561710

Subsidiary (Domestic):

Copesan Services Inc. (3)

W175 N 5711 Technology Dr, Menomonee Falls, WI 53051
Tel.: (262) 783-6261
Web Site: http://www.copesan.com
Disinfecting & Pest Control Services
N.A.I.C.S.: 561710
Aric Schroeder (VP-Natl Accounts)
Elizabeth Johnson (Sr Dir-Mktg)
Tara Haywood (Dir-Client Svcs)
Mike Ruland (Dir-IT)
Joe Yatta (Dir-Quality)
Steve Wolf (Sls Dir)
Jackie Trusty (Mgr-HR)

Pest Solutions, LLC (3)
8450 NW Ash St, Portland, OR 97229-6772
Tel.: (503) 895-2510
Web Site: http://www.pestsolutionsllc.com
Exterminating & Pest Control Services
N.A.I.C.S.: 561710
Eric Ufer (Founder)

Sandwich Isle Pest Solutions (3)
96-1385 Waihona St Bldg A, Pearl City, HI 96782 (100%)
Tel.: (808) 456-7716
Web Site: http://www.sandwichisle.com
Sales Range: $1-9.9 Million
Emp.: 50
Pest Control Services
N.A.I.C.S.: 561710
Michael Botha (Founder)

Subsidiary (Domestic):

Two Men & A Truck/International Inc. (2)
3400 Belle Chase Way, Lansing, MI 48911
Tel.: (517) 394-7210
Web Site: http://www.twomenandatruck.com
Rev.: $8,000,000
Emp.: 65
General Freight Trucking, Local
N.A.I.C.S.: 484110
Jon Sorber (Exec VP)
Melanie Bergeron (Pres)
Jeff Wesley (CEO)
Brig Sorber (CEO)
Jon Nobis (COO)
Mary Ellen Sheets (Founder)
Randy Shacka (Pres)

Wingstop Inc. (1)
15505 Wright Brothers Dr, Addison, TX 75001
Tel.: (972) 686-6500
Web Site: https://ir.wingstop.com
Rev.: $460,055,000
Assets: $377,825,000
Liabilities: $835,191,000
Net Worth: ($457,366,000)
Earnings: $70,175,000
Emp.: 271
Fiscal Year-end: 12/30/2023
Holding Company; Restaurant Operations
N.A.I.C.S.: 551112
Michael J. Skipworth (Pres & CEO)
Raj Kapoor (Pres-Intl & Sr VP)
Alex R. Kaleida (CFO, Principal Acctg Officer & Sr VP)
Donnie S. Upshaw (Chief People Officer & Sr VP)
Marisa J. Carona (Chief US Franchise Ops Officer & Sr VP)
Gerry McGrath (Gen Counsel, Sec & Sr VP)
Chris Fallon (CIO & Sr VP)
Melissa Cash (Chief Brand Officer & Sr VP)

Subsidiary (Domestic):

Wingstop Restaurants, Inc. (2)
5501 Lyndon B Johnson Fwy, Dallas, TX 75240
Tel.: (972) 686-6500
Web Site: http://www.wingstop.com
Restaurant Owner & Franchiser
N.A.I.C.S.: 722511
Stacy Peterson (Chief Experience Officer)
Scott McLeod (Sr VP-Ops)

Wood Structures, Inc. (1)
20 Pomerleau St Alfred Rd Business Pk, Biddeford, ME 04005
Tel.: (207) 282-7556
Wooden Trusses Mfr
N.A.I.C.S.: 321215

ROB'T J. BAGGETT INC.

759 Holcombe Ave, Mobile, AL 36606
Tel.: (251) 473-3290
Web Site: http://www.rjbaggett.com
Year Founded: 1976
Sales Range: $25-49.9 Million
Emp.: 250
Provider of Contractor Services
N.A.I.C.S.: 236210
Allan R. Crow (Treas, Sec & Office Mgr)
Charles D. Dicks Jr. (Pres)

ROB-SEE-CO

1015 N 205th St, Elkhorn, NE 68022
Tel.: (402) 218-1356
Web Site: http://www.robseeco.com
Agricultural Farming & Other Related Services
N.A.I.C.S.: 926140
Rob Robinson (CEO)

Subsidiaries:

Northstar Genetics Ltd. (1)
104 Main St, Wanamingo, MN 55983-3847
Tel.: (507) 824-2878
Web Site: http://www.northstargenetics.com
Rev.: $1,300,000
Emp.: 3
Grain & Field Bean Merchant Whslr
N.A.I.C.S.: 424510
Dan Hogstad (Pres & CEO)
Kelly Steberg (CFO)
Lyle Marcus (Product Mgr)
Brian Elliot (District Mgr-Sls)
Claude Durand (Mgr-Product Dev)
Ray Wytinck (Gen Mgr)
Sheila Heide (District Mgr-Sls)

ROBANDA INTERNATIONAL, INC.

8660 Camino Fanta SE St 8, San Diego, CA 92121
Tel.: (619) 276-7660 CA
Web Site: http://www.robanda.com
Year Founded: 1998
Sales Range: $1-9.9 Million
Emp.: 21
Mfr & Distr of Anti-Aging Skin Care Products
N.A.I.C.S.: 325620
David Lieb (Pres & CEO)
Anthony Leib (VP-Sls)

ROBAR ENTERPRISES INC.

17671 Bear Vly Rd, Hesperia, CA 92345
Tel.: (760) 244-5456
Web Site: http://www.robarenterprises.com
Year Founded: 1955
Sales Range: $50-74.9 Million
Emp.: 160
Mfr of Ready-Mixed Concrete Products
N.A.I.C.S.: 327320
Robert E. Hove (Chm)
Jonathan D. Hove (Pres)
Kevin Byrne (Controller)
Delia Escobar (Mgr-HR)

ROBB & STUCKY INTERNATIONAL

13170 S Cleveland Ave, Fort Myers, FL 33907
Tel.: (239) 415-2800 FL
Web Site: http://www.robbstuckyintl.com
Year Founded: 1915
Sales Range: $25-49.9 Million
Emp.: 100
Interior Design & Home Furnishing Services
N.A.I.C.S.: 541410
Stan Witters (Gen Mgr)
Harvey Tevah (Mgr-Sls)
Samson Kuo (Founder & Chm)
Oscar Moreno (Gen Mgr-Coral Gables)
George Swenson (Mgr-Sls-Naples Showroom)
Eric Chien (CFO & VP)
Frank D'Angelis (Gen Mgr)
Robin Hodes (Editor-Lifestyle & Design)
Mark Stuart (Dir-Creative)

ROBBIE D. WOOD INC.

1051 Old Warrior River Rd, Hueytown, AL 35023
Tel.: (205) 744-8440
Web Site: http://www.robbiedwood.com
Sales Range: $10-24.9 Million
Emp.: 140
Hazardous Waste Collection & Disposal
N.A.I.C.S.: 562211
Bruce Fallaw (Mgr-Safety)
Robbie D. Wood Jr. (Pres)

ROBBINS 8TH & WALNUT

801 Walnut St, Philadelphia, PA 19107
Tel.: (215) 925-5120
Year Founded: 1949
Sales Range: $10-24.9 Million
Emp.: 112
Jewelry Whslr
N.A.I.C.S.: 458310
Gerald Robbins (Chm)

ROBBINS AUTO PARTS, INC.

110 Washington St, Dover, NH 03820-3749
Tel.: (603) 742-2880 NH
Year Founded: 1933
Sales Range: $125-149.9 Million
Emp.: 250
Provider of Automotive Supplies & Parts
N.A.I.C.S.: 441330
Bob Weisner (Pres)
Richard Robbins (VP)
Stanley Robbins (Treas)

ROBBINS BRICK & BLOCK INC.

3862 US Hwy 221 S, Forest City, NC 28043
Tel.: (828) 245-9375
Web Site: http://www.robbinsbrickandblock.com
Sales Range: $10-24.9 Million
Emp.: 30
Brick, Except Refractory
N.A.I.C.S.: 423320
Clyde Robbins (Pres)

ROBBINS BROTHERS

6645 Topanga Canyon Blvd, Canoga Park, CA 91303
Tel.: (818) 340-3314
Web Site: http://www.robbinsbros.com
Rev.: $89,000,000
Emp.: 420
Jewelry Stores
N.A.I.C.S.: 458310
Andy Heyneman (Pres)
Moraima Alamillo (Mgr-Customer Experience)
Sarah Romanek (Coord-Pur Order)
Charles Mayrsohn (Gen Mgr)
Michael Espino (Coord-Mdse Shipping & Receiving)
Ray Golden (Gen Mgr)
Todd Carlson (Mgr-Creative)
Shirin Aliabadi (Mgr-Sls)
David Lee (Gen Mgr)

ROBBINS DIAMONDS

101 Geoffrey Dr, Newark, DE 19713
Tel.: (302) 453-4443 PA

Web Site:
http://www.robbinsdiamonds.com
Year Founded: 1937
Sales Range: $10-24.9 Million
Emp.: 100
Jewelry Sales
N.A.I.C.S.: 458310
Jason Robbins (Co-Owner)
Gordon Robbins (Co-Owner)

ROBBINS MANUFACTURING COMPANY
13001 N Nebraska Ave, Tampa, FL 33612
Tel.: (813) 971-3030 FL
Web Site:
http://www.robbinslumber.com
Year Founded: 1938
Sales Range: $75-99.9 Million
Emp.: 100
Whslr of Lumber & Provider of Lumber Mill & Wood Treating Services
N.A.I.C.S.: 321114
Greg Hellman (VP)

ROBBINS RESEARCH INTERNATIONAL
9051 Mira Mesa Blvd, San Diego, CA 92196
Tel.: (858) 535-9900
Web Site:
http://www.tonyrobbins.com
Rev.: $27,100,000
Emp.: 200
Provider of Motivational Speaking Services
N.A.I.C.S.: 513210
Alana Trax (Coord-Coaching)
Brook Bishop (Dir-Bus Mastery)
Billie Crane (Coord-Natl)

Subsidiaries:

The Anthony Robbins Company (1)
9888 Carroll Centre Rd, San Diego, CA 92126
Tel.: (858) 535-9900
Sales Range: $10-24.9 Million
Emp.: 60
Books, Publishing & Printing
N.A.I.C.S.: 513210
Sam Georges (Pres & CEO)

ROBCO, INC.
1523 Crescent Dr, Carrollton, TX 75006-3628
Tel.: (972) 242-3300
Web Site: http://www.robcoinc.com
Year Founded: 1959
Sales Range: $75-99.9 Million
Emp.: 15
Electrical Equipment Whslr
N.A.I.C.S.: 423610
Homer Rodden (Pres)
Kevin Springstead (Partner)
Ron Haynes (Engr-Sls)

ROBEKS CORPORATION
5220 Pacific Concourse Dr Ste 395, Los Angeles, CA 90045
Tel.: (310) 727-0500 CA
Web Site: http://www.robeks.com
Year Founded: 1996
Sales Range: $25-49.9 Million
Fruit Smoothie & Juice Retailer
N.A.I.C.S.: 722513
David Robertson (Chm)
Steve Davidson (Pres & CEO)

ROBELLE INDUSTRIES INC.
131 Tosca Dr, Stoughton, MA 02072-1505
Tel.: (781) 297-7422
Web Site: http://www.robelleind.com
Rev.: $12,354,539
Emp.: 50
Swimming Pool Chemicals, Equipment & Supplies

N.A.I.C.S.: 459999
Jay Hanflig (Pres)

ROBERSON MOTORS INC.
3100 Ryan Dr SE, Salem, OR 97301
Tel.: (503) 363-4117
Web Site:
http://www.robersonmotors.com
Sales Range: $25-49.9 Million
Emp.: 100
Automobiles; New & Used
N.A.I.C.S.: 441110
Michael Roberson (Owner)
Steve Freeburg (Controller)
Evan Lehman (Mgr-Svcs)
Raymond Pierce (Mgr-Fin)

ROBERT A. SHERMAN & ASSOCIATES, INC.
333 Harmon NW, Warren, OH 44483
Tel.: (330) 399-4500 OH
Web Site:
http://www.shermanexperience.com
Year Founded: 1955
Sales Range: $10-24.9 Million
Emp.: 3
N.A.I.C.S.: 541810
Jon J. Sherman (Pres)
Stacey Hotchkiss (VP-Opers & Copy Chief)
Susan Honel (Mgr-Acctg)

ROBERT ABBEY INC.
3166 Main Ave SE, Hickory, NC 28602
Tel.: (828) 322-3480
Web Site:
http://www.robertabbey.com
Rev.: $19,200,000
Emp.: 250
Residential Lighting Fixtures
N.A.I.C.S.: 335131
Ken Wilkinson (Pres & Gen Mgr)
Nancy Few (Coord-Logistics)
Joel Efird (Plant Mgr)

ROBERT B. AIKENS & ASSOCIATES, LLC
350 N Woodward Ste 300, Birmingham, MI 48009-4700
Tel.: (248) 283-1071 MI
Web Site: http://www.rbaikens.com
Year Founded: 1971
Sales Range: $1-9.9 Million
Emp.: 15
Real Estate Investment & Development Services
N.A.I.C.S.: 531390
Bruce Aikens (Vice Chm)

ROBERT B. SOLOMON HOLDING COMPANY, INC.
1940 Northwood Dr, Troy, MI 48084-5523
Tel.: (248) 362-0001 DE
Web Site: http://www.olgas.com
Year Founded: 1977
Sales Range: $50-74.9 Million
Emp.: 1,300
Eating Place
N.A.I.C.S.: 722511
Jonathan Fox (Pres)

Subsidiaries:

Olga's Kitchen Inc. (1)
2125 Butterfield Dr Ste 301N, Troy, MI 48084
Tel.: (248) 362-0001
Web Site: http://www.olgas.com
Sales Range: $10-24.9 Million
Emp.: 20
Eating Place
N.A.I.C.S.: 722511
Jonathan Fox (Pres)

ROBERT BARE ASSOCIATES

2804 N Cannon Blvd, Kannapolis, NC 28083
Tel.: (704) 938-6500
Web Site: http://www.rbalogistics.com
Rev.: $11,275,099
Emp.: 18
Freight Brokers
N.A.I.C.S.: 531130
Robert Bare (Owner)

ROBERT BERBER & SON INCORPORATED
425 Hester St, San Leandro, CA 94577-1025
Tel.: (510) 553-0444
Web Site: http://www.mirancho.com
Sales Range: $10-24.9 Million
Emp.: 170
Tortilla Mfr
N.A.I.C.S.: 311830
Tony Castillo (Asst VP-Ops)
Manuel Berber (Treas & Sec)
Carlos Oliva (Mgr-Pur)

ROBERT BOWDEN INC.
850 White Cir Ct, Marietta, GA 30061
Tel.: (770) 497-9245 GA
Web Site:
http://www.robertbowden.com
Year Founded: 1983
Sales Range: $25-49.9 Million
Emp.: 250
Millwork
N.A.I.C.S.: 423310
Steve Cole (Pres)
Robert E. Bowden (CEO)
Nick Massengill (VP-Sls & Mktg)
Greg Lucas (CFO)
Jim Turriglio (VP-Pur)
Chris Rogers (VP-Mfg)

ROBERT BUGATTO ENTERPRISES, INC.
835 Hwy 1, Bodega Bay, CA 94923
Tel.: (707) 875-2751 CA
Web Site:
http://www.bodegabayinfo.com
Year Founded: 1993
Rev.: $15,200,000
Emp.: 125
American Restaurant
N.A.I.C.S.: 722511
Eugene A. Bugatto (Owner)

ROBERT C. RHEIN INTERESTS INC.
7265 Kenwood Rd Ste 180, Cincinnati, OH 45236-4411
Tel.: (513) 891-7100 OH
Year Founded: 1982
Sales Range: $25-49.9 Million
Emp.: 15
Subdividers & Developers
N.A.I.C.S.: 237210
Robert C. Rhein (Pres)
Sharon Hopper (Office Mgr)
Jill Prior (Coord-Div)

ROBERT DIETRICK CO. INC.
9051 Technology Dr, Fishers, IN 46038
Tel.: (317) 842-1991
Web Site: http://www.rd-co.com
Year Founded: 1969
Sales Range: $10-24.9 Million
Emp.: 38
Materials Handling Machinery
N.A.I.C.S.: 423830
Robert N. Dietrick (Founder)

ROBERT E. LAMB, INC.
939 Jefferson Ave, Norristown, PA 19403-2303
Tel.: (610) 666-9200 PA
Web Site: http://www.relamb.com
Year Founded: 1917

Sales Range: $75-99.9 Million
Emp.: 60
Designer & Builder of Industrial Facilities & Office Buildings
N.A.I.C.S.: 236220
Joseph M. Sterchak (Pres)
Alfred R. Pauline (VP-Design)
John J. Peterman (VP)
Gary M. Scott (VP)

ROBERT E. LEE & ASSOCIATES, INC.
1250 Centennial Centre Blvd, Hobart, WI 54155-8995
Tel.: (920) 662-9641 WI
Web Site: http://www.releeinc.com
Year Founded: 1956
Sales Range: $25-49.9 Million
Emp.: 45
Engineering Consulting Services
N.A.I.C.S.: 541330
Mark J. Larson (Pres)
Dennis E. Reim (VP)
David K. Welsing (VP)

Subsidiaries:

NES Ecological Services (1)
4664 Golden Pond Park Ct, Oneida, WI 54155
Tel.: (920) 499-5789
Web Site: http://www.releeinc.com
Environmental Consulting Services
N.A.I.C.S.: 541620
James Havel (Mgr)

ROBERT F. HENRY TILE COMPANY
1008 Lagoon Business Loop, Montgomery, AL 36117
Tel.: (334) 269-2518
Web Site: http://www.henrytile.com
Sales Range: $50-74.9 Million
Emp.: 75
Ceramic Wall & Floor Tile
N.A.I.C.S.: 423320
Robert Henry (CEO)

ROBERT F. KENNEDY CHILDREN'S ACTION CORPS
11 Beacon St Ste 820, Boston, MA 02108
Tel.: (617) 227-4183 MA
Web Site: http://www.rfkchildren.org
Year Founded: 1970
Sales Range: $10-24.9 Million
Emp.: 439
Youth Care Services
N.A.I.C.S.: 624110
Edward P. Kelley (CEO)
Alan J. Klein (Pres)
Terence J. Shanley (Sr VP-HR)
Letitia L. Howland (VP-Organizational Capacity)
Cecilia M. Roddy (VP-Dev & External Affairs)

ROBERT FAWCETT & SON CO. INC.
1 Tyler Ct, Cambridge, MA 02140
Tel.: (617) 547-2360
Web Site: http://www.fawcettoil.com
Rev.: $11,000,000
Emp.: 45
Fuel Oil Dealers
N.A.I.C.S.: 424710
Robert R. Fawcett (Pres & Treas)

ROBERT FERRILLI, LLC
414 W State St, Media, PA 19063 PA
Web Site: http://www.figsolutions.com
Year Founded: 2002
Rev.: $2,700,000
Emp.: 26
Management Consulting Services
N.A.I.C.S.: 541611

ROBERT FERRILLI, LLC

Robert Ferrilli, LLC—(Continued)
Diane Deluca *(Dir-Bus Applications & Exec Engr-Bus Dev)*
Robert Ferrilli *(Founder & Pres)*
David Prudencio *(VP-Svcs)*

ROBERT FINVARB COMPANIES, LLC
1065 Kane Concourse Ste 201, Bay Harbor Islands, FL 33154
Tel.: (305) 866-7555   FL
Web Site:
http://www.robertfinvarbcompanies.com
Year Founded: 2002
Emp.: 3
Holding Company; Hotel Owner & Operator
N.A.I.C.S.: 551112
Robert Finvarb *(Owner & Pres)*

Subsidiaries:

Courtyard by Marriott - Miami Beach-South Beach   (1)
1530 Washington Ave, Miami Beach, FL 33139
Tel.: (305) 604-8887
Sales Range: $25-49.9 Million
Hotel Operator
N.A.I.C.S.: 721110
Nanyce Lanier *(Gen Mgr)*

Courtyard by Marriott - Miami Coconut Grove   (1)
2649 S Bayshore Dr, Miami, FL 33133-5464
Tel.: (305) 858-2500
Sales Range: $1-9.9 Million
Hotel Operator
N.A.I.C.S.: 721110
Thomas Langone *(Gen Mgr)*

ROBERT FLEEGE & PARTNERS
340 Howland Dr, Columbus, OH 43230
Tel.: (614) 270-9043
Web Site: http://www.fleege.com
Year Founded: 2000
Sales Range: Less than $1 Million
Emp.: 1
Advetising Agency
N.A.I.C.S.: 541810
Robert Fleege *(Owner & Dir-Creative)*

ROBERT FORBIS INC.
1443 Rail Head Blvd, Naples, FL 34110
Tel.: (239) 598-2000
Web Site:
http://www.premierelectric.com
Year Founded: 1988
Sales Range: $25-49.9 Million
Emp.: 250
Electrical Contractor
N.A.I.C.S.: 238210
Robert Forbis *(Owner & Pres)*

ROBERT FOX INC.
79 Main St, Mineola, NY 11501-4012
Tel.: (516) 294-8321
Web Site: http://www.foxs.com
Year Founded: 1985
Sales Range: $10-24.9 Million
Emp.: 270
Retailer of Women's Clothing
N.A.I.C.S.: 458110
Robert Fox *(Pres)*

ROBERT GIBB & SONS, INC.
2011 Great Northern Dr, Fargo, ND 58102
Tel.: (701) 282-5900   ND
Web Site: http://www.robertgibb.com
Year Founded: 1915
Sales Range: $75-99.9 Million
Emp.: 100

Plumbing Contractors; Heating & Air Conditioning Contractors; Fire Sprinkler System Installation; Sewer Line Construction; Water Main Construction
N.A.I.C.S.: 238220
Robert Gibb *(Pres)*
Greg Gibb *(VP)*

ROBERT GREEN AUTO & TRUCK, INC.
236 Bridgeville Rd, Monticello, NY 12701
Tel.: (845) 794-6161   NY
Web Site:
http://www.chevrolet.robert-green.com
Year Founded: 1968
Rev.: $23,400,000
Emp.: 72
New Car Dealers
N.A.I.C.S.: 441110
Robert Green Sr. *(Pres)*
Selma Green *(Treas & Sec)*
Robert S. Green Jr. *(VP)*

ROBERT J. BERNS ADVERTISING LTD.
2250 E Devon Ave Ste 235, Des Plaines, IL 60018
Tel.: (847) 699-9527   IL
Year Founded: 1968
Sales Range: $10-24.9 Million
Emp.: 2
N.A.I.C.S.: 541810
Mark Berns *(Owner)*
Doris Bock *(Copy Chief)*

ROBERT J. YOUNG COMPANY, LLC
809 Division St, Nashville, TN 37203-4145
Tel.: (931) 552-3473
Web Site: http://www.rjyoung.com
Rev.: $3,996,000
Emp.: 100
Office Supplies & Stationery Stores
N.A.I.C.S.: 459410
Chip Crunk *(Pres & CEO)*
Hunter McCarty *(COO)*
Bill Core *(Dir-Ops)*
Joey Lush *(Dir-IT)*
Kerry Pelham *(Dir-Sls-West)*
Mike Noffsinger *(Dir-Sls-East)*

Subsidiaries:

Computer Systems Plus Inc.   (1)
605 Sevier Ave, Knoxville, TN 37920
Tel.: (865) 573-5303
Web Site: http://www.compsysplus.com
Rev.: $3,000,000
Emp.: 20
Computer & Software Stores
N.A.I.C.S.: 449210
David Glass *(Co-Founder)*
Sarah Glass *(Co-Founder)*

Lewis Digital, Inc.   (1)
630 Capital Cir NE Ste 1, Tallahassee, FL 32301
Tel.: (850) 222-4418
Web Site: http://www.lewisdigital.net
Sales Range: $1-9.9 Million
Emp.: 15
Ret Computers/Software Computer Maintenance/Repair
N.A.I.C.S.: 449210
Alisha Turner *(Sec)*

ROBERT JAMES SALES INC.
2585 Walden Ave, Buffalo, NY 14225
Tel.: (716) 651-6000   NY
Web Site: http://www.rjsales.com
Year Founded: 1972
Sales Range: $125-149.9 Million
Emp.: 150
Distr of Stainless Steel Pipe, Valves & Fittings
N.A.I.C.S.: 423510

James Bokor *(Pres)*
Dave Simmons *(Mgr-Quality Assurance)*
Al Calderone *(Dir-Pur)*
Robert D. Glidden Jr. *(Founder)*

ROBERT KARP CONTAINER CORP
134 Garfield Ave, Jersey City, NJ 07305
Tel.: (201) 200-1151
Web Site:
http://www.robertkarpcontainer.com
Sales Range: $10-24.9 Million
Emp.: 11
Corrugated & Solid Fiber Boxes
N.A.I.C.S.: 322219
Adam Karp *(Owner)*

ROBERT KAUFMAN CO. INC.
129 W 132nd St, Los Angeles, CA 90061
Tel.: (310) 538-3482
Web Site:
http://www.robertkaufman.com
Rev.: $31,377,736
Emp.: 140
Piece Goods & Other Fabrics
N.A.I.C.S.: 424310
Arnold Kaufman *(Controller)*
Jerrold Stein *(Mgr-IT Sys)*
Eric Thomas *(VP-Ops)*
Alexandria Heath *(Dir-Mdsg)*
Tristan Heberer *(Mgr-IT)*

ROBERT L. HANSON INC.
PO Box 359, Newton, IL 62448
Tel.: (618) 783-2019
Rev.: $26,043,890
Emp.: 34
Cleaning Service
N.A.I.C.S.: 561790

ROBERT LARSON AUTOMOTIVE GROUP
7815 S Tacoma Way, Tacoma, WA 98409
Tel.: (253) 475-4816
Web Site: http://www.looklarson.com
Sales Range: $50-74.9 Million
Emp.: 75
Automobiles, New & Used
N.A.I.C.S.: 441110
Robert S. Larson *(Pres)*
Craig Noyes *(Dir-Sls)*

ROBERT LIGHTON FURNITURE, INC.
150 E 58 St Fl 3, New York, NY 10155-3450
Tel.: (212) 343-2299
Web Site:
http://www.robertlighton.com
Sales Range: Less than $1 Million
Emp.: 12
Home Furniture & Fixtures
N.A.I.C.S.: 337126
Robert Lighton *(Pres)*

ROBERT LLOYD SHEET METAL INC.
4485 Independence Hwy, Independence, OR 97351
Tel.: (503) 838-3863
Web Site: http://www.rlsm.net
Year Founded: 1982
Sheet Metal Contractors
N.A.I.C.S.: 238220
Robert Lloyd *(Pres & Project Mgr)*

ROBERT M. GOFF & ASSOCIATES
2230 Cottondale Ln Ste 1, Little Rock, AR 72202
Tel.: (501) 664-3332
Sales Range: $10-24.9 Million

U.S. PRIVATE

Emp.: 15
Owner of Hotels
N.A.I.C.S.: 721110
Wallis B. Allen *(Mng Dir)*

ROBERT M. NEFF INC.
1955 James Pkwy, Heath, OH 43056
Tel.: (740) 928-4393
Web Site: http://www.rneffinc.com
Rev.: $11,500,000
Emp.: 10
Trucking Except Local
N.A.I.C.S.: 484121
Charles Berkheimer *(Owner)*

ROBERT M. SIDES INC.
201 Mulberry St, Williamsport, PA 17701
Tel.: (570) 326-2094   PA
Web Site: http://www.rmsides.com
Year Founded: 1937
Sales Range: $10-24.9 Million
Emp.: 63
Provider of Musical Instruments
N.A.I.C.S.: 459140
Carol Doran Sides *(Owner)*
John Mu *(Mgr)*
Carolyn Myers *(Mgr-Warehouse)*
Dewey Corage *(Engr-Sound Sys)*
Richard Jensen *(Mgr-Pur, Mdsg, IT & Online Svcs)*

ROBERT MADDEN INDUSTRIES
6021 43rd St, Lubbock, TX 79407-3712
Tel.: (806) 797-4251
Web Site: http://www.rmadden.com
Year Founded: 1979
Sales Range: $25-49.9 Million
Emp.: 140
Provider of Heating & Air Conditioning Services
N.A.I.C.S.: 423730
Robert Madden *(CEO)*
Ron Madden *(Pres)*
Angie Teaff *(Mgr-Adv)*

ROBERT MANN PACKAGING, INC.
340 El Camino Real S Bldg 36, Salinas, CA 93901-4554
Tel.: (831) 789-8300   CA
Web Site: http://www.rmp.com
Year Founded: 1971
Sales Range: $10-24.9 Million
Emp.: 150
Corrugated & Solid Fiber Boxes Mfr
N.A.I.C.S.: 322211
Robert Mann *(Founder)*
Mark Comer *(CFO)*

ROBERT MCKEOWN CO. INC.
111 Chambers Brook Rd, Somerville, NJ 08876
Tel.: (908) 218-9000
Web Site:
http://www.robertmckeown.com
Rev.: $11,442,868
Emp.: 27
Insulators, Electrical
N.A.I.C.S.: 423690
Carmen Gerrone *(Gen Mgr)*
Andy Clark *(Product Mgr)*
Dawson K. McKeown *(Pres)*
Lindsey McKeown *(Product Mgr)*

ROBERT R. MCCORMICK FOUNDATION
205 N Michigan Ave Ste 4300, Chicago, IL 60601
Tel.: (312) 445-5000   IL
Web Site:
http://www.mccormickfoundation.org
Year Founded: 1989
Sales Range: $100-124.9 Million

Emp.: 47
Philanthropic Services
N.A.I.C.S.: 813211
Donald A. Cooke *(Sr VP-Philanthropy)*
Rebekah Levin *(Dir-Evaluation & Learning)*
David D. Hiller *(Pres & CEO)*
Lou Marsico *(Sr VP-Ops)*
Dennis J. FitzSimons *(Chm)*
David J. Granat *(Chief Investment Officer)*
Kim Tyler *(CFO)*

ROBERT REID WEDDING ARCHITECTS & PLANNERS, AIA, INC.
4112 W Cypress St, Tampa, FL 33607
Tel.: (813) 879-6996 FL
Web Site: http://www.rrw-architects.com
Year Founded: 1973
Sales Range: $1-9.9 Million
Emp.: 30
Architectural Services
N.A.I.C.S.: 541310
Robert R. Wedding *(Pres)*
Jose Castellanos *(VP)*
Sandra Feltner *(Dir-Ops)*

ROBERT REISER & COMPANY INC.
725 Dedham St, Canton, MA 02021-1402
Tel.: (781) 821-1290 MA
Web Site: http://www.reiser.com
Year Founded: 1966
Sales Range: $25-49.9 Million
Emp.: 150
Provider of Industrial Machinery & Equipment
N.A.I.C.S.: 423830
Roger Reiser *(Pres & CEO)*

ROBERT SKEELS & CO.
1910 E Dominguez St, Carson, CA 90810-1002
Tel.: (310) 639-7240 CA
Web Site: http://www.wylelabs.com
Year Founded: 1933
Sales Range: $1-9.9 Million
Emp.: 7
Distr of Builders Hardware & Locksmith Supplies, Including Locksets, Padlocks, Hinges, Key Blanks, Door Closers, Access Control & Panic Exit Devices
N.A.I.C.S.: 423710
Bob Lange *(Controller)*

ROBERT T. WINZINGER INC.
1704 Marne Hwy, Hainesport, NJ 08036-3640
Tel.: (609) 267-8600 NJ
Web Site: http://www.winzinger.com
Year Founded: 1960
Sales Range: $10-24.9 Million
Emp.: 66
Provider of Heavy Construction Services
N.A.I.C.S.: 237310
JoAnn Winzinger *(Pres)*
Bill Challender *(Project Mgr)*

ROBERT TALBOTT, INC.
2901 Monterey Salinas Hwy, Monterey, CA 93940-6400
Tel.: (831) 649-6000 CA
Web Site: http://www.roberttalbott.com
Year Founded: 1950
Sales Range: $10-24.9 Million
Emp.: 212
Mfr of Mens, Boys & Womens Clothing
N.A.I.C.S.: 315990
Sean Murphy *(Product Mgr-Bus Dev)*

ROBERT V. JENSEN INC.
4029 S Maple Ave, Fresno, CA 93725
Tel.: (559) 485-8210
Web Site: http://www.rvjensen.com
Sales Range: $50-74.9 Million
Emp.: 42
Petroleum Products
N.A.I.C.S.: 424720
William V. Jensen *(Pres & CEO)*
Ron King *(CFO)*
Deann Williams *(Controller)*

ROBERT W. AGEE OIL CO. INC.
19 Depot St, Sparta, TN 38583
Tel.: (931) 836-3163
Sales Range: Less than $1 Million
Emp.: 10
Petroleum Products
N.A.I.C.S.: 424720
Robert W. Agee *(Pres)*

ROBERT W. STANHOPE CO.
962 W 10th St, Azusa, CA 91702
Tel.: (626) 812-8860
Web Site: http://www.stanhopeco.com
Rev.: $14,387,113
Emp.: 30
Commercial & Office Buildings, Renovation & Repair
N.A.I.C.S.: 238990
Michael Timoney *(Pres)*
Rick Hambel *(Pres, Principal & Project Mgr)*
James McFarlane *(VP & Project Mgr)*

ROBERT WHOLEY & CO.
1711 Penn Ave, Pittsburgh, PA 15222
Tel.: (412) 391-3737
Web Site: http://www.wholey.com
Year Founded: 1912
Sales Range: $100-124.9 Million
Emp.: 50
Importer & Distributor of Fish & Seafood Products
N.A.I.C.S.: 424460
Jim Wholey *(CEO)*
Thelma Tambellini *(Gen Mgr-Retail Sls)*
John McNally *(Mgr-Seafood Retail)*

ROBERT WINNER SONS INC.
8544 SR 705, Yorkshire, OH 45388
Tel.: (419) 582-4321
Web Site: http://www.winnersmeats.com
Year Founded: 1962
Sales Range: $10-24.9 Million
Emp.: 60
Provider of Livestock Services
N.A.I.C.S.: 424520
Brian Winner *(Pres)*
Allen Winner *(VP)*

ROBERT YATES REAL ESTATE, INC.
7018 Taylorsville Rd, Fisherville, KY 40023
Tel.: (502) 477-8310
Year Founded: 1972
Sales Range: $10-24.9 Million
Emp.: 12
Real Estate Brokerage Services
N.A.I.C.S.: 531210
Robert Yates *(Partner)*

ROBERT'S HAWAII INC.
680 Iwilei Rd Ste 700, Honolulu, HI 96817-5392
Tel.: (808) 425-9861 HI
Web Site: http://www.robertshawaii.com
Year Founded: 1941
Sales Range: $1-9.9 Million
Emp.: 1,400
Local Passenger Transportation Services
N.A.I.C.S.: 487110
Aaron Kimura *(VP-Contract Mgmt)*
Gerald Hayashi *(Mgr)*
Mike Andrade *(Mgr-Trng)*
Cheryl Takakura *(Mgr-HR)*
Roy Pfund *(Pres & COO)*

Subsidiaries:

Carry-All Inc. (1)
1965 Mokumoa St, Honolulu, HI 96819-4422
Tel.: (808) 831-1570
Web Site: http://www.robertsovernighters.com
Sales Range: $10-24.9 Million
Emp.: 15
Service Providers Of Local Trucking
N.A.I.C.S.: 484220

Robert's Hawaii Cruises Inc. (1)
680 Iwilei Rd Ste 700, Honolulu, HI 96817
Tel.: (808) 523-7750
Sales Range: $10-24.9 Million
Emp.: 30
Cruises
N.A.I.C.S.: 487210

Robert's Hawaii Hotels Inc. (1)
680 Iwilei Rd Ste 700, Honolulu, HI 96817-5392
Tel.: (808) 523-7750
Web Site: http://www.robertshawaii.com
Sales Range: $10-24.9 Million
Emp.: 50
Hotels & Motels
N.A.I.C.S.: 541614

Robert's Hawaii Leasing Inc. (1)
680 Iwilei Rd Ste 700, Honolulu, HI 96817-5392
Tel.: (808) 523-7750
Web Site: http://www.robertshawaii.com
Rev.: $70,000
Emp.: 750
Providers Of Passenger Car Rental
N.A.I.C.S.: 532111

Robert's Hawaii Tours And Transportation (1)
680 Iwilei Rd Ste 700, Honolulu, HI 96817-5392
Tel.: (808) 523-7750
Web Site: http://www.robertshawaii.com
Sales Range: $25-49.9 Million
Emp.: 150
School Buses
N.A.I.C.S.: 487110

Robert's Hawaii Tours Inc. (1)
680 Iwilei Rd Ste 700, Honolulu, HI 96817-5392
Tel.: (866) 898-2519
Web Site: http://www.robertshawaii.com
Sales Range: $25-49.9 Million
Emp.: 200
Travel Agencies
N.A.I.C.S.: 561510
Susan Moye *(Mgr-Employee Rels)*
Melody Fukushima *(Dir-HR)*
Mary Hansen *(VP-HR)*

Robert's Tours & Transportation Inc. (1)
8680 Iwilei Rd Ste 700, Honolulu, HI 96817-5392
Tel.: (808) 523-7750
Web Site: http://www.robertsovernighters.com
Sales Range: $10-24.9 Million
Emp.: 50
Hawaiian Travel Services
N.A.I.C.S.: 561599

ROBERTS AIRCRAFT COMPANY
4101 Evans Ave, Cheyenne, WY 82001
Tel.: (307) 778-5700
Web Site: http://www.robertsaircraft.com
Year Founded: 1939
Sales Range: Less than $1 Million
Emp.: 6
Aircraft Sales & Leasing
N.A.I.C.S.: 532411
Kenneth C. Roberts *(Pres)*

ROBERTS CHEVROLET INC.
9617 E 350 Hwy, Raytown, MO 64133
Tel.: (816) 359-3731
Web Site: http://www.robertschevrolet.net
Rev.: $13,000,000
Emp.: 30
New Car Dealers
N.A.I.C.S.: 441110
Keith Roberts *(Pres)*
Mike Robinson *(Treas & Sec)*
Ed Roberts Jr. *(VP)*

ROBERTS CIGAR & TOBACCO COMPANY
1765 Claiborne Dr, Shreveport, LA 71103
Tel.: (318) 632-5040
Sales Range: $25-49.9 Million
Emp.: 25
Cigarettes
N.A.I.C.S.: 424940
Ruby Roberts Mazur *(Pres)*

ROBERTS COMMUNICATIONS INC.
1 N Shore Ctr 12 Federal St Ste 120, Pittsburgh, PA 15212
Tel.: (412) 535-5000 PA
Year Founded: 1989
Rev.: $18,450,000
Emp.: 14
N.A.I.C.S.: 541810
Dick Roberts *(Pres)*
Kris Pyszniak *(Controller)*
Bill Blume *(Dir-Media)*
Victor Kimmel *(Acct Mgr)*

ROBERTS COMMUNICATIONS NETWORK
4175 Cameron St Ste B10, Las Vegas, NV 89103
Tel.: (702) 227-7500
Rev.: $28,000,000
Emp.: 25
Direct Broadcast Satellite Services (Dbs)
N.A.I.C.S.: 517111
Thomas M. Roberts *(Pres & CEO)*
Paul England *(Dir-Art)*
Megan Alchowiak *(Acct Exec)*
Dan Silver *(Dir-Sls, Mktg & Bus Dev)*

ROBERTS DISTRIBUTORS INC.
255 S Meridian St, Indianapolis, IN 46225
Tel.: (317) 636-5544 IN
Web Site: http://www.robertsimaging.com
Year Founded: 1957
Sales Range: $10-24.9 Million
Emp.: 24
Provider of Imaging Products & Services
N.A.I.C.S.: 423410
Bruce Pallman *(Pres)*

ROBERTS MARKEL WEINBERG BUTLER HAILEY PC
2800 Post Oak Blvd 57th Fl, Houston, TX 77056
Tel.: (713) 840-1666 TX
Web Site: http://www.rmwbhlaw.com
Year Founded: 1981
Law firm

ROBERTS MARKEL WEINBERG BUTLER HAILEY PC

Roberts Markel Weinberg Butler Hailey PC—(Continued)
N.A.I.C.S.: 541110
Marc D. Markel (Partner)
Jeffrey D. Roberts (Partner & Atty)

ROBERTS OIL CO., INC.
408 Arizona St SE, Albuquerque, NM 87108-3749
Tel.: (505) 262-1607
Year Founded: 1959
Sales Range: $10-24.9 Million
Emp.: 80
Provider of Gasoline Services
N.A.I.C.S.: 457120
William G. Roberts (Pres)

ROBERTS OXYGEN COMPANY INC.
7564 Standish Pl Ste 100, Rockville, MD 20855-2766
Tel.: (301) 315-9090
Web Site: http://www.robertsoxygen.com
Year Founded: 1966
Sales Range: $25-49.9 Million
Emp.: 288
Distr of Compressed Gases & Welding Supplies
N.A.I.C.S.: 423450
William P. Roberts (Chm & Pres)
Fran G. Lewis (Branch Mgr)

ROBERTS PROPERTIES, INC.
450 Northridge Pkwy Ste 300, Atlanta, GA 30350
Tel.: (770) 394-6000
Web Site: https://www.robertsproperties.com
Year Founded: 1974
Sales Range: $50-74.9 Million
Holding Company; Multi-Family Housing Design, Construction, Sales & Property Management
N.A.I.C.S.: 551112
Charles S. Roberts (Pres)
Anthony W. Shurtz (CFO)

Subsidiaries:
Roberts Properties Construction, Inc. (1)
450 N Rdg Pkwy Ste 301, Atlanta, GA 30350
Tel.: (770) 394-0440
Multi-Family Dwelling For-Sale Construction
N.A.I.C.S.: 236117
Charles S. Roberts (Pres)

ROBERTS TRADING CORPORATION
5034 Grand Ridge Dr, West Des Moines, IA 50265
Tel.: (515) 283-7100
Web Site: http://www.robertsdybdahl.com
Year Founded: 1976
Sales Range: $50-74.9 Million
Emp.: 457
Provider of Lumber, Plywood & Millwork
N.A.I.C.S.: 423310
Ted Roberts (Pres)
Cyndee Johnson (Dir-Pur)

Subsidiaries:
Astro Buildings Inc. (1)
5034 Grandridge Dr W, Des Moines, IA 50365
Tel.: (515) 283-7100
Web Site: http://www.astrobuildings.com
Sales Range: $10-24.9 Million
Emp.: 5
Provider of Lumber, Plywood & Millwork
N.A.I.C.S.: 423310
Ann Menzel (VP)
John Fullerton (Gen Mgr)

Roberts & Dybdahl Inc. (1)
PO Box 1908, Des Moines, IA 50305-1908
Tel.: (515) 283-7100
Web Site: http://www.robertsdybdahl.com
Sales Range: $10-24.9 Million
Emp.: 33
Lumber, Plywood & Millwork
N.A.I.C.S.: 423310
Ted B. Roberts (Pres, CEO & Treas)

ROBERTS TRUCK CENTER, LTD.
4378 Canyon Dr, Amarillo, TX 79109
Tel.: (806) 355-9771
Web Site: https://www.robertstruck.com
Year Founded: 1999
Sales Range: $10-24.9 Million
Commercial Truck & Bus Dealerships, Leasing & Rental Centers Operator
N.A.I.C.S.: 441227
Alton McCormick (Gen Mgr)
George Ohler (Mgr-Parts)
Brian Reyes (Mgr-Lease & Rental)
Ty Williams (Mgr-Svc)

Subsidiaries:
Roberts Truck Center, Ltd. - Albuquerque (1)
1623 Aspen Ave NW, Albuquerque, NM 87104-2215
Tel.: (505) 243-7883
Web Site: https://www.robertstruck.com
Commercial Truck & Bus Dealer
N.A.I.C.S.: 441227
Todd Gohl (Mgr-Parts)

ROBERTS, J. R. CORP.
7745 Greenback Ln Ste 300, Citrus Heights, CA 95610-5866
Tel.: (916) 729-5600
Web Site: http://www.jrrobertsdeacon.com
Sales Range: $10-24.9 Million
Emp.: 15
Housing Construction Services
N.A.I.C.S.: 236117
Robert Olsen (CEO)

ROBERTS-GIBSON INC.
Hwy 51 Bypass At 115 W, Dyersburg, TN 38024
Tel.: (731) 285-4941
Sales Range: $10-24.9 Million
Emp.: 12
Franchise Owner of Petroleum Bulk Stations
N.A.I.C.S.: 424710
Jane Gibson (VP)
J. P. Roberts (VP)
Tim Gibson (Treas & Sec)
Larry W. Gibson (Owner & Pres)

ROBERTSON DEVELOPMENT INC.
2155 West Main, Alliance, OH 44601
Tel.: (330) 821-9180
Web Site: http://www.rhs1.com
Sales Range: $125-149.9 Million
Emp.: 100
Plumbing & Heating Supplies
N.A.I.C.S.: 423720
Scott Robertson (Pres)

ROBERTSON GLOBAL HEALTH SOLUTIONS CORPORATION
3555 Pierce Rd, Saginaw, MI 48604
Tel.: (989) 799-8720
Web Site: http://www.robertsonhealth.com
Sales Range: Less than $1 Million
Healthcare Software
N.A.I.C.S.: 513210
Joel C. Robertson (Founder & CEO)

ROBERTSON HEATING SUPPLY CO., INC.
2155 W Main St, Alliance, OH 44601
Tel.: (330) 821-9180
Web Site: http://www.rhs1.com
Year Founded: 1934
Sales Range: $10-24.9 Million
Emp.: 110
Plumbing & Heating Equipment Whslr
N.A.I.C.S.: 423720
E. Scott Robertson (Pres)
Tom Masterson (Mgr-Credit)

ROBERTSON SUPPLY INC.
318 6th St N, Nampa, ID 83687
Tel.: (208) 466-8907
Web Site: http://www.robertsonsupply.com
Rev.: $20,590,975
Emp.: 35
Plumbing Fittings & Supplies
N.A.I.C.S.: 423720
Richard Culley (Mgr-Comml Sls)
Thomas W. Malson Sr. (Pres)

ROBERTSON WOOD ADVERTISING
6061 S Fort Apachee Rd Ste 100, Las Vegas, NV 89148
Tel.: (702) 947-7777
Year Founded: 1977
Rev.: $21,000,000
Emp.: 20
Advetising Agency
N.A.I.C.S.: 541810
George Davey (COO)
Loralee Humphries (Controller)
Marty Wood (Partner)
Shelby Little (Media Buyer)

ROBESON HEALTH CARE CORPORATION
60 Commerce Dr, Pembroke, NC 28372
Tel.: (910) 521-2900
Web Site: http://www.rhcc1.com
Year Founded: 1985
Sales Range: $10-24.9 Million
Emp.: 221
Health Care Srvices
N.A.I.C.S.: 622110
Thomas E. Maynor (COO & Deputy CEO)
Mary Thomas-Locklear (Chief HR Officer & VP)
George Timothy Hall (Chief Behavioral Health Officer)
Bobby Charles Townsend (Chrm)
Ned A. Chavis (Treas)
Tammy Maynor (Sec)

ROBFRANKEL.COM
17645 Royce Dr W, Encino, CA 91316-3715
Tel.: (818) 990-8623
Web Site: http://www.robfrankel.com
Year Founded: 1985
Rev.: $10,000,000
Emp.: 12
N.A.I.C.S.: 541810

ROBIN HOOD SUPPLIES, INC.
301 Depot St PO Box 241, Utica, MS 39175
Tel.: (601) 885-6524
Sales Range: $1-9.9 Million
Emp.: 22
Industrial Machinery & Equipment Supplies Whslr
N.A.I.C.S.: 423830
David Hood (Sec)
Anthony K. Hood (Treas)
Royal H. Hood (VP)
Matthew Klein (Chief Program & Impact Officer)
Arnold R. Hood Jr. (Pres)

ROBIN INDUSTRIES, INC.
6500 Rockside Rd Ste 230, Independence, OH 44131
Tel.: (216) 631-7000
Web Site: http://www.robin-industries.com
Year Founded: 1947
Sales Range: $75-99.9 Million
Emp.: 700
Rubber Products Mfr
N.A.I.C.S.: 326299
Chuck Lizanich (Dir-HR)
Dave Wingett (VP & Mgr-Div)
Debbie Talbott (Dir-Pur)
Aaron Hammaker (Engr-Mfg)

ROBIN LEEDY & ASSOCIATES
118 N Bedford Rd Ste 302, Mount Kisco, NY 10549
Tel.: (914) 241-0086
Web Site: http://www.robinleedyassociates.com
Year Founded: 1986
Rev.: $15,000,000
Emp.: 11
Health Care
N.A.I.C.S.: 541820
Robin Russo (Pres)
Alyson O'Mahoney (Partner & Exec VP)
Brittany Oat (Acct Mgr & Producer)

ROBIN SHEPHERD STUDIOS, INC.
1301 Riverplace Blvd Ste 1100, Jacksonville, FL 32207-4111
Tel.: (904) 359-0981
Web Site: http://www.shepherdagency.com
Year Founded: 1984
Sales Range: $10-24.9 Million
Emp.: 65
Advertising Agencies
N.A.I.C.S.: 541810
Robin Shepherd (Founder)
Nancy Seely (Exec VP)
Mike Russel (Pres & CEO)
Kelle Stam (VP-Digital)
Tom Schifanella (Partner)
Michael Guiry (Exec VP)

Subsidiaries:
Robin Shepherd Studios, Inc. (1)
Gwinnett Commerce Ctr 3700 Crestwood Pkwy Ste 370, Duluth, GA 30096-7153
Tel.: (770) 295-2314
Web Site: http://www.trsg.net
Sales Range: $10-24.9 Million
Emp.: 20
Advertising Services
N.A.I.C.S.: 541810

ROBINETTE COMPANY
250 Blackley Rd, Bristol, TN 37620
Tel.: (423) 968-7800
Web Site: http://www.therobinetteco.com
Sales Range: $10-24.9 Million
Emp.: 300
Provider of Flexographic Printing Services
N.A.I.C.S.: 323111
Joseph R. Robinette (CEO)
Gary Hunt (VP)

ROBINS, KAPLAN, MILLER & CIRESI L.L.P.
800 LaSalle Ave Ste 2800, Minneapolis, MN 55402-2015
Tel.: (612) 349-8500
Web Site: http://www.rkmc.com
Year Founded: 1938
Emp.: 665
Law firm
N.A.I.C.S.: 541110

Andrea L. Gothing (Partner)
Michael A. Geibelson (Member-Exec Bd-Los Angeles, Silicon Valley & Mng Partner)
Steven A. Schumeister (Mng Partner, Chm-Bus Grp & Member-Exec Bd)
Richard B. Allyn (Partner)
Scott G. Johnson (Chm-Minneapolis Insurance Grp & Partner)
Steve A. Brand (Partner)
Michael A. Collyard (Chm-Ediscovery Grp & Partner)
Christopher K. Larus (Chm-Minneapolis IP & Tech Litigation Grp & Partner)
Leo F. Feeney (Partner)
Thomas L. Hamlin (Partner)
Jake M. Holdreith (Member-Exec Bd & Partner-Indus Leader, Health & Life Sciences)
Martin R. Lueck (Chm-Exec Bd & Partner)
Anne M. Lockner (Partner)
Cyrus A. Morton (Partner & Chm-Patent Office Trials Grp)
Peter A. Schmit (Chm-Personal Injury & Medical Malpractice Grp & Partner)
Ronald J. Schutz (Chm-Natl IP & Tech Litigation Grp, Member-Exec Bd & Mng Partner)
Tara D. Sutton (Chm-Mass Tort Grp, Member-Exec Bd & Partner)
K. Craig Wildfang (Chm-Antitrust & Trade Regulation Grp & Partner)
Matthew L. Woods (Partner)
Thomas C. Mahlum (Partner)
Stephen P. Safranski (Partner)
Jonathan Mutch (Partner)
Denise Rahne (Partner)
Katherine Barrett Wiik (Principal)
Melissa D'Alelio (Principal)
Matthew Frerichs (Principal)
William Reiss (Principal)
Patrick Stoneking (Principal)
H. Jeffrey Schwartz (Chm-Restructuring & Bus Bankruptcy Practice-New York & Partner)
Howard Weg (Chm-Restructuring & Bus Bankruptcy-Los Angeles & Partner)
Anthony Froio (Member-Exec Bd & Mng Partner-Boston)
Amy Churan (Partner-Los Angeles)
Breton A. Bocchieri (Partner-Los Angeles & Silicon Valley)
Jason Pfeiffer (Chm-Bus Litigation Practice Grp)
Breanna Johnson (Chief Strategy, Pricing & Legal Project Mgmt Officer)
Shonette Gaston (COO)
Leah Radtke (Mgr-Mktg)
Sharon Roberg-Perez (Principal)
Ryan Schultz (Principal)

Subsidiaries:

Robins Kaplan LLP - Los Angeles (1)
2049 Century Park E Ste 3400, Los Angeles, CA 90067
Tel.: (310) 552-0130
Web Site: http://www.robinskaplan.com
Law firm
N.A.I.C.S.: 541110
Michael A. Geibelson (Mng Partner-Los Angeles & Silicon Valley)
David E. Bocan (Partner)
Amy M. Churan (Partner)
Bernice Conn (Partner)
David Martinez (Partner)
Mark D. Passin (Partner)
Christopher S. Reeder (Partner)
David C. Veis (Partner)
William A. Webster (Partner)
Scott F. Gautier (Co-Chm-Restructuring & Bus Bankruptcy & Partner)
Howard J. Weg (Co-Chm-Restructuring & Bus Bankruptcy & Partner)
Dan J. Fielding (Dir-Admin)

James Koelzer (Partner)
Glenn Danas (Partner)
James P. Menton Jr. (Partner)

Robins, Kaplan, Miller & Ciresi L.L.P. - Atlanta (1)
1 Atlantic Ctr 1201 W Peachtree St Ste 2200, Atlanta, GA 30309-3453
Tel.: (404) 760-4300
Web Site: http://www.robinskaplan.com
Emp.: 12
Law firm
N.A.I.C.S.: 541110
A. James Anderson (Partner)
William H. Stanhope (Partner)

Robins, Kaplan, Miller & Ciresi L.L.P. - Boston (1)
800 Boylston St 25th Fl Prudential Twr, Boston, MA 02199-7080
Tel.: (617) 267-2300
Web Site: http://www.robinskaplan.com
Emp.: 35
Law firm
N.A.I.C.S.: 541110
Anthony A. Froio (Mng Partner-Boston)
William N. Erickson (Chm-Insurance & Catastrophic Loss Grp & Partner)
James S. Harrington (Partner)
Mark S. LaConte (Partner)
John N. Love (Partner)
David E. Marder (Partner)
Christopher P. Sullivan (Partner)
Jonathan Mutch (Partner)
Melissa D'Alelio (Principal)

Robins, Kaplan, Miller & Ciresi L.L.P. - Naples (1)
711 5th Ave S Ste 201, Naples, FL 34102-6628
Tel.: (239) 430-7070
Web Site: http://www.rkmc.com
Law firm
N.A.I.C.S.: 541110
Lawrence A. Farese (Partner)

Robins, Kaplan, Miller & Ciresi L.L.P. - New York (1)
399 Park Ave, New York, NY 10022-4611
Tel.: (212) 980-7400
Web Site: http://www.robinskaplan.com
Emp.: 50
Law firm
N.A.I.C.S.: 541110
Ronald J. Schutz (Chm-Exec Bd & Partner)
Jeffrey Alan Hovden (Partner)
Kellie Lerner (Co-Chm-Diversity Committee & Partner)
Hollis Salzman (Mng Partner)
Bryan J. Vogel (Partner)
Christopher K. Larus (Partner)
Steven A. Schumeister (Mng Partner)
Tara D. Sutton (Partner)

ROBINSON & BELEW INC.
240 Park Ave, Sharon, TN 38255
Tel.: (731) 456-2628
Web Site: http://www.robinsonandbelew.com
Sales Range: $10-24.9 Million
Emp.: 7
Grain Elevators
N.A.I.C.S.: 424510
Robert D. Robinson (Pres)
Keith Fowler (Bus Mgr)

ROBINSON & COLE LLP
280 Trumbull St, Hartford, CT 06103
Tel.: (860) 275-8200
Web Site: http://www.rc.com
Year Founded: 1845
Sales Range: $100-124.9 Million
Emp.: 201
Legal Advisory Services
N.A.I.C.S.: 541110
Bruce B. Barth (Partner)
Bradford S. Babbitt (Partner)
Kenneth C. Baldwin (Co-Partner)
Wystan M. Ackerman (Co-Partner)
Stephen W. Aronson (Co-Partner)
Garry C. Berman (Partner)
Patrick M. Birney (Co-Partner)
Lisa M. Boyle (Co-Partner)
Christine E. Bromberg (Partner)

Dennis C. Cavanaugh (Co-Partner)
Thomas P. Cody (Partner)
Eric C. Daniels (Partner)
Alice E. DeTora (Partner)
Natale V. Di Natale (Partner)
Brian W. Blasser (Partner)
Steven Campbell (COO)
Howard Shafer (CFO)
Frank F. Coulom Jr. (Partner)
Fernando Monteleone Jr. (CIO)

ROBINSON & MAITES, INC.
35 E Wacker Dr Ste 3500, Chicago, IL 60601-2304
Tel.: (312) 372-9333 IL
Web Site: http://www.robinsonmaites.com
Year Founded: 1960
Rev.: $24,200,000
Emp.: 25
Advetising Agency
N.A.I.C.S.: 541810
Alan Maites (Pres)
Ryan Jarol (VP & Acct Dir)
Fred Petrick (Dir-Plng)
Mike Brindley (Dir-Production)
Bob Neff (Exec Dir-Creative)

ROBINSON AVIATION (RVA) INC.
1601 NW Expy Ste 850, Oklahoma City, OK 73118
Tel.: (405) 840-3771
Web Site: http://www.rvainc.com
Year Founded: 1986
Rev.: $27,075,307
Emp.: 5
Provider of Pilot & Aviation Services
N.A.I.C.S.: 561320
Keren Williams McLendon (Pres & CEO)

Subsidiaries:

RVA Inc. (1)
3479 S Roosevelt Blvd, Key West, FL 33040
Tel.: (305) 294-2549
Sales Range: $10-24.9 Million
Pilot & Aviation Services
N.A.I.C.S.: 488190

ROBINSON CAPITAL & INVESTMENTS INC.
17314 State Hwy 249 Ste 210, Houston, TX 77064
Tel.: (713) 850-7168
Web Site: http://www.robinsoncapital.com
Sales Range: $10-24.9 Million
Emp.: 12
Land Subdividers & Developers, Commercial
N.A.I.C.S.: 237210
Michael Robinson (Pres)

ROBINSON CREATIVE INC.
Southlake Town Sq 286 Grand Ave Ste 238, Southlake, TX 76092
Tel.: (817) 748-5057
Web Site: http://www.robinsoncreativeinc.com
Year Founded: 1998
Sales Range: Less than $1 Million
Emp.: 10
Audio/Visual, Collateral, Identity Marketing, Print, Production (Print), Promotions
N.A.I.C.S.: 541810
Ben Robinson (Pres & Dir-Creative)
Sam Musso (Acct Exec)

ROBINSON ELECTRIC SUPPLY CO.
2103 B St, Meridian, MS 39307
Tel.: (601) 693-3131

Web Site: http://www.robinsonelectricsupply.com
Year Founded: 1975
Sales Range: $10-24.9 Million
Emp.: 74
Electrical Supplies
N.A.I.C.S.: 423610
Rex Gentry (Mgr-Meridian)
Windell Bridgmon (Mgr-Forest)
Debbie Bridgmon Jr. (Pres)

ROBINSON ENTERPRISES INC.
908 Rocky Mount Rd, Athens, TN 37303
Tel.: (423) 746-0061
Sales Range: $25-49.9 Million
Emp.: 100
Convenience Store
N.A.I.C.S.: 445131
David Robinson (Owner)

ROBINSON ENTERPRISES INC.
293 Lowr Grass Vly Rd, Nevada City, CA 95959
Tel.: (530) 265-5844
Web Site: http://www.robinsonenterprises.com
Rev.: $21,506,681
Emp.: 200
Logging Camps & Contractors
N.A.I.C.S.: 113310
Lowell Robinson (Pres)
Don Hoffler (Mgr-Petroleum)

ROBINSON EXPORT AND IMPORT CORPORATION
6790 Commercial Dr, Springfield, VA 22151
Tel.: (703) 256-6400
Web Site: http://www.reico.com
Year Founded: 1952
Sales Range: $25-49.9 Million
Emp.: 240
Kitchen & Bath Cabinetry Distr
N.A.I.C.S.: 423310
Laura Saddler (VP-Sls)

ROBINSON FANS, INC.
400 Robinson Dr, Zelienople, PA 16063
Tel.: (724) 452-6121 PA
Web Site: http://www.robinsonfans.com
Sales Range: $10-24.9 Million
Emp.: 200
Industrial Blowers & Fans Mfr & Distr
N.A.I.C.S.: 333413
Carl E. Staible (Pres & CEO)
Doug Bollinger (CFO)
Josh Tillotson (CIO)
Deanna Weaver (Mgr-Applications Engrg)
Kerry Courtney (Mgr-HR)

ROBINSON GAREISS LC
150 W Main St Ste 1640, Virginia Beach, VA 23462
Tel.: (757) 490-3411
Web Site: http://www.rgigc.com
Year Founded: 1997
Sales Range: $10-24.9 Million
Emp.: 22
Provider of Commercial & Office Building New Construction
N.A.I.C.S.: 236220
Drew Gareiss (Pres)

ROBINSON GRAY STEPP & LAFFITTE, LLC
1310 Gadsden St, Columbia, SC 29201
Tel.: (803) 929-1400 SC
Web Site: http://www.robinsongray.com

ROBINSON GRAY STEPP & LAFFITTE, LLC

Robinson Gray Stepp & Laffitte, LLC—(Continued)
Year Founded: 1996
Law firm
N.A.I.C.S.: 541110
Grady L. Beard (Atty)
Rebecca Laffitte (Atty)
Robin Carroll (Dir-Administration)
Kim Woodworth (Mktg Mgr)
Ashley Lamb (Mgr-HR Programs)

ROBINSON HELICOPTER COMPANY
2901 Airport Dr, Torrance, CA 90505
Tel.: (310) 539-0508　　CA
Web Site:
　http://www.robinsonheli.com
Year Founded: 1973
Sales Range: $150-199.9 Million
Emp.: 900
Mfr of Helicopters
N.A.I.C.S.: 336411
Tim Goetz (CFO)
Kurt Robinson (Pres)
Pamela Goetz (Controller)
Julie Stembridge (Mgr-Personnel)
Wayne Walden (VP-Production)

ROBINSON HOME PRODUCTS INC.
170 Lawrence Bell Dr Ste 110, Williamsville, NY 14221
Tel.: (716) 685-6300
Web Site: http://www.robinsonus.com
Year Founded: 1921
Sales Range: $75-99.9 Million
Emp.: 50
Scissors, Shears & Travel Accessories Wholesale Distr
N.A.I.C.S.: 423220
Jim Walsh (Pres)
John Fancher (CFO)
Greg Marco (Dir-Info Sys)
Rick Kivler (Mgr-Credit)
John Newman (Mgr-Customer Svc)
Laurie Licht (Mgr-Mktg)
Sharon Hadj-Chikh (VP-New Brand Dev)

ROBINSON INDUSTRIES INC.
3051 Curtis Rd, Coleman, MI 48618-0521
Tel.: (989) 465-6111
Web Site:
　http://www.robinsonind.com
Year Founded: 1949
Sales Range: $25-49.9 Million
Emp.: 270
Plastics Product Mfr
N.A.I.C.S.: 326199
Ardis V. Robinson (Co-Pres)
Ben Robinson (Pres)

ROBINSON INDUSTRIES INC.
100 NE 21st St, Miami, FL 33137
Tel.: (305) 573-8334
Sales Range: $10-24.9 Million
Emp.: 70
Highway & Street Construction
N.A.I.C.S.: 237310
Burnell D. Robinson (Pres)

ROBINSON LUMBER & EXPORT COMPANY
4000 Tchoupitoulas St, New Orleans, LA 70115-1433
Tel.: (504) 895-6377　　LA
Web Site: http://www.roblumco.com
Year Founded: 1893
Sales Range: $75-99.9 Million
Emp.: 60
Holding Company
N.A.I.C.S.: 423310
H. Ivens Robinson (Pres)
Randy Ortega (CFO)
R. Courtney Robinson (Exec VP)
Hank Marchal (Dir-European Sls)
Courtney Robinson (Mgr-Bus Dev-Pine)

Subsidiaries:
Robco Madeiras Ltda.　　(1)
R Domingos Marreiros No 109 Bairro, Umarizal, 66055 210, Belem, PA, Brazil
Tel.: (55) 91 4005 4500
Wood Products Whslr
N.A.I.C.S.: 423310

ROBINSON MANUFACTURING COMPANY INC.
798 Market St, Dayton, TN 37321-1473
Tel.: (423) 775-2212
Web Site:
　http://www.robinsonmfg.com
Year Founded: 1927
Sales Range: $25-49.9 Million
Emp.: 475
Mfr of Mens & Boys Underwear & Nightwear
N.A.I.C.S.: 315250
Richard Ferrell (CFO)

Subsidiaries:
College Concepts LLC　　(1)
2000 Riveredge Pkwy Ste 620, Atlanta, GA 30328-2909　　(100%)
Tel.: (770) 859-1420
Web Site: http://www.collegeconcepts.com
Sales Range: $10-24.9 Million
Emp.: 30
Mfr of Mens & Boys Clothing
N.A.I.C.S.: 424350
John Staton (Pres)

ROBINSON MECHANICAL CONTRACTORS INC.
2411 Walters Ln, Perryville, MO 63775
Tel.: (573) 547-8397
Web Site:
　http://www.robinsonconstruction.com
Rev.: $21,800,000
Emp.: 200
Heavy & Civil Engineering Construction
N.A.I.C.S.: 237990
Dolores Buehler (Mgr-HR)
Paul E. Findlay (VP)
Frank Robinson (Pres)
Kevin Schade (Controller)
David Monier (Mgr-Construction)
Jeff Sutterer (Mgr-Engrg)

ROBINSON METAL, INC.
1740 Eisenhower Rd, De Pere, WI 54115
Tel.: (920) 494-7411
Web Site:
　http://www.robinsonmetal.com
Rev.: $22,400,000
Emp.: 300
Sheet Metal Work Mfg
N.A.I.C.S.: 332322

ROBINSON NOBLE, INC.
Tacoma 2105 S C St, Tacoma, WA 98402
Tel.: (253) 383-1914
Web Site: http://www.robinson-noble.com
Research & Development in Biotechnology
N.A.I.C.S.: 541714
Joseph Becker (Owner)

Subsidiaries:
Cornerstone Geotechnical, Inc.　　(1)
17625 130th Ave NE C102, Woodinville, WA 98072
Tel.: (425) 488-0599
Web Site: http://www.robinson-noble.com
Geologic & Geotechnical Engineering Services
N.A.I.C.S.: 541330

ROBINSON OIL CORP.
955 Martin Ave, Santa Clara, CA 95050-2608
Tel.: (408) 327-4300
Web Site:
　http://www.rottenrobbie.com
Year Founded: 1964
Sales Range: $25-49.9 Million
Emp.: 250
Gasoline Stations
N.A.I.C.S.: 457120
Kris Kingsbury (Dir-Mktg)

ROBINSON PHARMA INC.
3330 S Harbor Blvd, Santa Ana, CA 92704
Tel.: (714) 241-0235
Web Site:
　http://www.robinsonpharma.com
Rev.: $29,693,248
Emp.: 256
Pharmaceutical Preparations
N.A.I.C.S.: 325412
Neil Shah (VP-R&D)
Brad Buchholz (VP-Sls)
Long Ho (Supvr-Production)
Ferdie Duarte (Engr-Maintenance)
Andy Truong (Mgr-Production)
Mike Choi (Mgr-Sls)
David Anderson (Supvr-Laboratory-OTC)
Kenn Israel (VP-Mktg)
Amy Grasso-Piacentino (VP-Sls)
Van Dao (Coord-Registration-Intl)
Rafi Shariff (Mgr-Pur)
Pham Henry (Mgr-QC)

ROBINSON RADIO, INC.
4991 Lake Brook Dr N Shore Commons 2 Ste 190, Glen Allen, VA 23060
Tel.: (804) 726-6400
Rev.: $35,000,000
Media Buying Services, Production, Radio, Strategic Planning/Research
N.A.I.C.S.: 541810
Buck Robinson (Pres & CEO)
Brandon Myers (VP-Ops)
Kristen Baker (VP-Media)
Sarah Mitchell (Controller & Dir-HR)
Kieran Wagner (Dir-Creative)

ROBINSON SPORTS INC.
6730 Moccasin Wallow Rd, Palmetto, FL 34221
Tel.: (941) 722-3369
Web Site: http://www.fit2run.com
Sales Range: $10-24.9 Million
Emp.: 140
Sporting Goods Stores & Fitness Centers
N.A.I.C.S.: 459110
Parks Robinson (Co-Owner)
Bill Robinson (Co-Owner & Pres)

ROBINSON SUPPLY CO. INC.
195 Broadway, Fall River, MA 02721
Tel.: (508) 675-7433
Web Site:
　http://www.robinsonsupply.com
Rev.: $19,100,000
Emp.: 50
Plumbing & Hydronic Heating Supplies
N.A.I.C.S.: 423720
Russell Robinson (Pres)
David Martin (Dir-Sls)
Stan Mickelson (Mgr-Showroom)
Joyce Kohr (Mgr-Mktg)

ROBINSON'S INDUSTRIAL GAS & EQUIPMENT CORP.
920-14 Lincoln Ave, Holbrook, NY 11741-2257
Tel.: (631) 289-1982
Web Site:
　http://www.robinsonsoxygen.com
Year Founded: 1962
Industrial & Medical Gas Distr
N.A.I.C.S.: 457210
Kevin Rubenstrunk (Mgr-Ops)
Brian Robinson (Mgr-Regional Svc & Maintenance)

ROBISON & SMITH, INC.
335 N Main St, Gloversville, NY 12078
Tel.: (518) 725-7181
Web Site: http://www.r-centerarylinenubidorms.com
Sales Range: $10-24.9 Million
Emp.: 240
Drycleaning & Laundry Services
N.A.I.C.S.: 812320
Kathi Wheatley (Plant Mgr)
Sharron Cannizzo (Reg Mgr-Svc)

ROBISON-NIERI-WHITE CONSTRUCTION
45 S Linden Ave, South San Francisco, CA 94080-6407
Tel.: (650) 737-1600
Web Site:
　http://www.rnwconstruction.com
Year Founded: 2001
Sales Range: $10-24.9 Million
Emp.: 30
Residential Remodeling Services
N.A.I.C.S.: 236118
Terry Robison (Pres)
Gale White (Owner)

ROBOCOM US, LLC
1111 Broad Hollow Rd Ste 100, Farmingdale, NY 11735
Tel.: (631) 753-2180　　DE
Web Site: http://www.robocom.com
Sales Range: $10-24.9 Million
Emp.: 30
Supply Chain Execution Software Developer & Publisher
N.A.I.C.S.: 513210
Fred Radcliffe (Pres)
Richard Adamo (VP-Customer Svcs)
Rick Register (VP)

ROBOTICS TECHNOLOGY CONSORTIUM
3025 Boardwalk, Ann Arbor, MI 48108
Tel.: (734) 995-3098　　DE
Web Site: http://www.ncms.org
Year Founded: 2009
Sales Range: $10-24.9 Million
Robotic Technology Research Services
N.A.I.C.S.: 541715
Rebecca Taylor (Sr VP)
Richard B. Jarman (Pres & CEO)
Jon Riley (Sr VP-Tech)
Rachel O'Donohue (Fin Dir)

ROBRADY, INC.
1040 Commerce Blvd N, Sarasota, FL 34243
Tel.: (941) 359-6656　　FL
Web Site: http://www.robrady.com
Year Founded: 1996
Sales Range: $10-24.9 Million
Emp.: 25
Industrial Design, Product Engineering, Graphics, Packaging, Ecommerce Design, Market Research, Brand & Retail Development, Rapid Prototyping & Production Program Management
N.A.I.C.S.: 541420
Robert Brady (Pres)

ROBROY INDUSTRIES INC.
River Rd, Verona, PA 15147
Tel.: (412) 828-2100 PA
Web Site: http://www.robroy.com
Year Founded: 1905
Emp.: 200
Non-Metallic Enclosures, Electrical Products & Components Mfr
N.A.I.C.S.: 335999
Robroy B. McIlroy (CEO)
Jeffrey Seagle (VP-Bus Dev)
Steve Voelzke (Pres-Electrical Products)
Brannon Peek (Mgr-Maintenance-Raceway Div)
Vijay Tahiliani (CFO)
Al Clavi (Engr-Sls)
Sarah Parlett (Mgr-HR-Raceway Div)
Jim Walsh (Mgr-Bus Dev-Raceway Div)
Craig Mitchell (Pres-Robroy Enclosures)
Stephanie Ellis (Dir-Mktg)

Subsidiaries:

Attabox Industrial Enclosures (1)
500 Maple St, Belding, MI 48809
Tel.: (616) 794-0700
Web Site: http://www.attabox.com
Industrial Enclosure & Electrical Accesories Mfr
N.A.I.C.S.: 335999

Duoline Technology (1)
250 W Bluebird Rd, Gilmer, TX 75645-7234
Tel.: (432) 552-9700
Web Site: http://www.oilandgasonline.com
Rev.: $12,099,090
Emp.: 15
Oil & Gas Field Machinery
N.A.I.C.S.: 333132
Peter McIlroy II (Chm & Pres)

Robroy Industries Texas Inc. (1)
US Hwy 271 & S Dean St, Gilmer, TX 75644
Tel.: (903) 843-5591
Web Site: http://www.robroy.com
Sales Range: $10-24.9 Million
Emp.: 80
Sheet Metalwork
N.A.I.C.S.: 332322
Horacio Ramirez (Mgr-Conduit Plant)
Steve Voelzke (Pres-Conduit)

Stahlin Non-Metallic Enclosures Inc. (1)
500 Maple St, Belding, MI 48809
Tel.: (616) 794-0700
Web Site: http://www.stahlin.com
Emp.: 80
Electrical Component Distr
N.A.I.C.S.: 423440
Craig Mitchell (Pres)

ROBSON COMMUNITIES, INC.
9532 E Riggs Rd, Sun Lakes, AZ 85248-7463
Tel.: (480) 895-9200 AZ
Web Site: http://www.robson.com
Year Founded: 1972
Sales Range: $800-899.9 Million
Emp.: 1,500
Retirement Community Real Estate Development Operative Builder & Sales
N.A.I.C.S.: 237210
Edward J. Robson (Founder & Chm)

Subsidiaries:

Robson Denton Development, LP. (1)
9501 Ed Robson Blvd, Denton, TX 76207
Tel.: (940) 246-2000
Web Site: http://www.robson.com
Hotel & Resort Operator
N.A.I.C.S.: 721110

ROBUCK HOMES
6131 Falls of Neuse Rd Suite 200, Raleigh, NC 27609
Tel.: (919) 876-9200
Web Site: http://www.robuckhomes.com
Year Founded: 1926
Emp.: 100
New Home Multi Family & Commercial Builder
N.A.I.C.S.: 236115
Chip Bishop (Gen Mgr)
Jessica Head (Asst Controller)
Jim Caravello (CFO)
Shannon Bottoms (Office Mgr)

ROBYN MEREDITH, INC.
460 Veterans Dr, Burlington, NJ 08016-1268
Tel.: (609) 387-1999 NJ
Year Founded: 1982
Sales Range: $10-24.9 Million
Emp.: 8
Mfr of Womens Sportswear
N.A.I.C.S.: 532490
Alan Wallace (Owner)

ROBYN, INC.
7717 W Britton Rd, Oklahoma City, OK 73132
Tel.: (405) 722-4600 OK
Web Site: http://www.robynpromo.com
Year Founded: 1990
Sales Range: $1-9.9 Million
Emp.: 26
Promotional & Printed Materials Management Services
N.A.I.C.S.: 323111
Mervyn Hackney (Pres)
Bobby Lehew (Dir-Ops)

ROC SERVICE COMPANY
191 Private Rd 1400, Bridgeport, TX 76426
Tel.: (940) 683-0159
Web Site: http://rocserviceco.com
Year Founded: 1989
Sales Range: $10-24.9 Million
Emp.: 300
Civil Engineering Services
N.A.I.C.S.: 237310
Mike Richey (Owner)

ROCH CAPITAL INC.
50 Applied Bank Blvd, Glen Mills, PA 19342
Tel.: (484) 840-9179
Web Site: https://www.rochcap.com
Emp.: 100
Investment Services
N.A.I.C.S.: 523999
Peter Abessinio (Co-Pres)
Thomas DiEmidio (Co-Pres)

ROCHDALE CORPORATION
570 Lexington Ave Fl 9, New York, NY 10022
Tel.: (212) 702-3500
Web Site: http://www.rochdale.com
Sales Range: $25-49.9 Million
Emp.: 100
Securities Brokerage & Investment Management
N.A.I.C.S.: 523150
Carl Acebes (Founder, Co-Owner & Chm)

ROCHDALE SECURITIES LLC
750 E Main St, Stamford, CT 06902
Tel.: (203) 274-9100
Web Site: http://www.rochdalesecurities.com
Year Founded: 1975
Sales Range: $1-9.9 Million
Emp.: 5
Securities Brokerage Services
N.A.I.C.S.: 523150
Daniel J. Crowley (Pres & COO)

ROCHDALE VILLAGE INC.
16965 137th Ave, Jamaica, NY 11434-4517
Tel.: (718) 276-5700 NY
Web Site: http://www.rochdalevillage.com
Year Founded: 1964
Sales Range: $50-74.9 Million
Emp.: 343
Provider of Building Management Services
N.A.I.C.S.: 531110
Clifton Stanley Diaz (Chm)
Lisa Stark (Treas)
Jean Randolph-Castro (Pres)
Joyce Williams (Sec)
Mario Turner (Second VP)
Maryam Smith (Asst Treas)

ROCHE BROS. SUPERMARKETS INC.
70 Hastings St, Wellesley, MA 02481-5439
Tel.: (781) 235-9400
Web Site: http://www.rochebros.com
Year Founded: 1952
Sales Range: $350-399.9 Million
Emp.: 2,700
Retailer of Groceries
N.A.I.C.S.: 445110
Maggie McLaughlin (Mgr-Westwood)
Artie Kroese (Mgr-Store)
Joe Curtin (Dir-Recruiting)

ROCHE CONSTRUCTORS, INC.
361 71st Ave, Greeley, CO 80634-9782
Tel.: (970) 356-3611 CO
Web Site: http://www.rocheconstructors.com
Year Founded: 1971
Sales Range: $125-149.9 Million
Emp.: 70
Provider of Contracting & Construction Services
N.A.I.C.S.: 236220
Thomas J. Roche (Pres & CEO)
Carla R. Dusin (Controller)
Sandra L. Roche (Gen Counsel & VP)
Matt Notter (CFO & VP-Fin)

Subsidiaries:

Roche Constructors Inc. - Las Vegas (1)
7680 W Sahara Ave Ste 130, Las Vegas, NV 89117
Tel.: (702) 252-3611
Web Site: http://www.rocheconstructors.com
Emp.: 30
Commercial & Institutional Building Construction
N.A.I.C.S.: 236220
Doug Olson (Reg Mgr)

ROCHELLE HOLDING COMPANY
1132 Hermitage Rd, Richmond, VA 23220
Tel.: (804) 358-2148 VA
Year Founded: 1981
Sales Range: $25-49.9 Million
Emp.: 500
Fast Food Restaurants
N.A.I.C.S.: 722513
Richard J. Ripp (Pres)
John Ripp (Controller)

ROCHESTER COLONIAL MANUFACTURING
1794 Lyell Ave, Rochester, NY 14606
Tel.: (585) 254-8191
Web Site: http://www.rochestercolonial.com
Rev.: $10,700,000
Emp.: 100
Windows & Window Parts & Trim, Wood
N.A.I.C.S.: 321911
Carolyn Weil (Controller)
Tony Monaco (CEO)

ROCHESTER ELECTRONICS INC.
16 Malcolm Hoyt Dr, Newburyport, MA 01950
Tel.: (978) 462-9332
Web Site: http://www.rocelec.com
Year Founded: 1981
Sales Range: $10-24.9 Million
Emp.: 70
Electronic Parts
N.A.I.C.S.: 423690
Curt Gerrish (Pres & CEO)
Ralph Perrotta (Controller)
Paul Gerrish (VP)
Allan Lim (Dir-Sls-Asia Pacific)
Hiroyuki Fujikawa (Dir-Sls-Japan)

ROCHESTER GIANT EAGLE
111 W Madison St, Rochester, PA 15074
Tel.: (724) 775-0551
Web Site: http://www.gianteagle.com
Sales Range: $25-49.9 Million
Emp.: 200
Retailer of Grocery Products
N.A.I.C.S.: 445110
Ken Goss (Gen Mgr)

ROCHESTER METAL PRODUCTS CORP.
616 Indiana Ave, Rochester, IN 46975
Tel.: (574) 223-3164
Web Site: http://www.rochestermetals.com
Year Founded: 1937
Sales Range: $25-49.9 Million
Emp.: 400
Gray & Ductile Iron Casting Mfr
N.A.I.C.S.: 332999
Greg Loving (Sr VP & Gen Mgr)
Tim Opar (Dir-Quality & Technical Svcs)
Richard Bean (Dir-Sls & Mktg)
Mike Slaydon (Dir-Ops)

ROCHESTER MIDLAND CORPORATION
155 Paragon Dr, Rochester, NY 14624
Tel.: (585) 336-2200 NY
Web Site: http://www.rochestermidland.com
Year Founded: 1888
Sales Range: $400-449.9 Million
Emp.: 600
Disinfectants & Soaps Mfr
N.A.I.C.S.: 325612
Liz Taylor (Mgr-Corp Mktg Comm)
Bradley Calkins (Co-CEO)
Katherine C. Lindahl (Co-CEO)

ROCHESTER PRIMARY CARE NETWORK, INC.
259 Monroe Ave Level B, Rochester, NY 14607
Tel.: (585) 325-2280 NY
Web Site: http://www.rpcn.org
Year Founded: 1986
Sales Range: $10-24.9 Million
Emp.: 123
Health Care Srvices
N.A.I.C.S.: 621610
Donald Ginsberg (Sec)
Paul Haney (Treas)
Susan Hustleby (Chm)

ROCHESTER PUBLIC LIBRARY

Rochester Primary Care Network, Inc.—(Continued)

ROCHESTER PUBLIC LIBRARY
101 2nd St SE, Rochester, MN 55904
Tel.: (507) 328-2300
Web Site: http://www.rochesterpubliclibrary.org
Year Founded: 1992
Sales Range: $10-24.9 Million
Emp.: 362
Library
N.A.I.C.S.: 519210
Patty Uttaro (Dir-Library)
Brie Harrison (Mgr-Library Fin)
Donna P. Benjamin (VP)
George T. Wolf (Sec)
John E. Lovenheim (Pres)
Richard L. Hamilton (Treas)

ROCHESTER RESORTS INC.
15951 Captiva Dr, Captiva, FL 33924
Tel.: (239) 472-5161
Web Site: http://www.tween-waters.com
Sales Range: $10-24.9 Million
Emp.: 100
Motels Resorts
N.A.I.C.S.: 721110
Antonino Lapi (CEO)
Jeff Shuff (Gen Mgr)

ROCHESTER RIVERSIDE CONVENTION CENTER
123 E Main St, Rochester, NY 14604-1619
Tel.: (585) 232-7200
Web Site: http://www.rrcc.com
Year Founded: 1985
Sales Range: $10-24.9 Million
Emp.: 477
Economic Development Services
N.A.I.C.S.: 541690
Ronald C. Beck (Dir-Ops)
David J. Carpenter (Dir-Catering Sls)
Robin A. Antill (Dir-HR)

ROCHESTER SHOE TREE COMPANY, INC.
1 Cedar Ln, Ashland, NH 03217
Tel.: (603) 968-3301
Web Site: http://www.rstco.com
Rev.: $15,000,000
Emp.: 90
All Other Miscellaneous Wood Product Manufacturing
N.A.I.C.S.: 321999
John McHugh (Controller)

ROCHEUX INTERNATIONAL INC.
220 Centennial Ave, Passaic, NJ 08854
Tel.: (732) 885-3898
Web Site: http://www.rocheux.com
Year Founded: 1996
Sales Range: $10-24.9 Million
Emp.: 100
Plastics, Materials & Basic Shapes
N.A.I.C.S.: 424610
Vanessa Wong (CEO)
Tony Chen (Mgr-Key Acct)
Vinod Warrier (Product Mgr-Flexible PVC Films)

Subsidiaries:

Rocheux International (1)
16700 Vly View Ave Ste 200, La Mirada, CA 90638-5830
Tel.: (714) 228-0788
Sales Range: $10-24.9 Million
Emp.: 10
Plastics, Materials & Basic Shapes
N.A.I.C.S.: 424610

ROCHON CORPORATION
3650 Annapolis Ln N Ste 101, Plymouth, MN 55447
Tel.: (763) 559-9393
Web Site: http://www.rochoncorp.com
Year Founded: 1982
Sales Range: $10-24.9 Million
Emp.: 21
Contractor of General, Commercial, Design & Office Building
N.A.I.C.S.: 236220
Jerry Braton (CEO)
Jeff Wellman (Exec VP)
Scott Larkin (Pres)
Nick Reynolds (VP)
Briana Fern (Project Coord-Osseo)

ROCK & WATERSCAPE SYSTEMS INC.
11 Whatney, Irvine, CA 92618-2808
Tel.: (949) 770-1936
Web Site: http://www.rockandwaterscape.com
Year Founded: 1975
Sales Range: $10-24.9 Million
Emp.: 7
Provider of Artificial Rock Work, Themed Environments & Waterfalls
N.A.I.C.S.: 561730
David A. Sinacola (Chm & CEO)

ROCK CITY MECHANICAL CO. LLC
2715 Grandview Ave, Nashville, TN 37211
Tel.: (615) 251-3045
Web Site: http://www.rcm-nashville.com
Year Founded: 1967
Sales Range: $50-74.9 Million
Emp.: 600
Mechanical Contractor Services
N.A.I.C.S.: 238220
Chris Wehby (Pres & Partner)
Clint Scott (Partner & VP)
Larry Medlen (Sr Project Mgr)
Pat Winfree (Mgr-Pre-Construction)
Eddie Franklin (Mgr-CAD)
Phil Anderson (Dir-Safety)

ROCK COMMUNICATIONS LTD.
1117 E 14th St N, Newton, IA 50208
Tel.: (641) 792-8334
Web Site: http://www.rock-com.com
Sales Range: $10-24.9 Million
Printing Services
N.A.I.C.S.: 323111
John Troen (Pres)
Curtis Cass (Gen Mgr)

ROCK CREEK STRATEGIC MARKETING
2 Wisconsin Cir Ste 1010, Chevy Chase, MD 20815
Tel.: (301) 657-0800
Web Site: http://www.rockcreeksm.com
Year Founded: 1987
Rev.: $3,500,000
Emp.: 28
Graphic Design Services
N.A.I.C.S.: 541430
Chris Lester (Principal)
David Rinaldo (COO)
Irina DaSilva (Mgr-Acctg)
Margaret Johnson (Co-Founder & Pres)
Scott Johnson (Co-Founder & Principal)
Anuj Vedak (Chief Performance Officer)
Stephanie Lemaitre (Dir-Project Mgmt)
Amanda Nguyen (Dir-Strategy)
Kat Kuhl (Dir-Tech)

Annmarie Braggs (Mgr-Customer Experience)
Emily Adams (Project Mgr)
McRae Lenahan (Project Mgr)
Jason Simko (Sr Dir-Art)
Farhana Qazi (Sr Program Mgr)

ROCK FUSCO & CONNELLY, LLC
321 N Clark St, Chicago, IL 60654
Tel.: (312) 494-1000
Web Site: http://www.rockfuscoconnelly.com
Law firm
N.A.I.C.S.: 541110
John J. Rock (Principal)
Christopher M. Novy (Principal)
James Bryan Novy (Partner)
Eileen E. Rosen (Partner)
Matthew P. Connelly (Principal)
Cory D. Anderson (Partner)
Stacy A. Benjamin (Partner)
Alec Miller (Partner)
David L. Miller (Partner)
Patrick A. Clancy (Partner)

ROCK GATE PARTNERS LLC
35 E Wacker Dr Ste 3400, Chicago, IL 60601
Tel.: (312) 283-0630
Web Site: http://www.rockgatepartners.com
Year Founded: 2006
Privater Equity Firm
N.A.I.C.S.: 523999
Kenneth L. Ali (Founder & Mng Dir)
Stephen K. Foutch (Mng Dir & Principal)

Subsidiaries:

Novus Law, LLC (1)
8700 W Bryn Mawr Ave, Chicago, IL 60631
Tel.: (773) 632-5900
Web Site: http://www.novuslaw.com
Legal Document Review, Management & Analysis
N.A.I.C.S.: 561410
Raymund Bayley (CEO)
Anad S. Dayal (VP-Global Svcs)
Lois A. Haubold (Founder)
Emily Rice Reynolds (COO)

Walpar LLC (1)
4200 Jefferson Ave SW, Birmingham, AL 35221
Tel.: (205) 925-4990
Web Site: https://www.walpar.com
Sales Range: $25-49.9 Million
Emp.: 55
Road Sign Structure Mfr
N.A.I.C.S.: 332312
Reba Brice (Office Mgr)

ROCK HILL CAPITAL GROUP, LLC
3737 Buffalo Speedway Ste 1800, Houston, TX 77098
Tel.: (713) 715-7510
Web Site: http://www.rockhillcap.com
Year Founded: 2007
Privater Equity Firm
N.A.I.C.S.: 523999
Randall B. Hale (Founder & Co-Mng Dir)
James P. Wilson (Co-Mng Dir)
Jeffery S. Chistman (Co-Mng Dir)
Trang D. Prosperie (CFO)

Subsidiaries:

Big Lake Services LLC (1)
300 N State Hwy 137, Big Lake, TX 76932
Tel.: (325) 884-2150
Oil Well Services
N.A.I.C.S.: 213112
Casey Davidson (CEO)

Subsidiary (Domestic):

Beckman Production Services, Inc. (2)
3786 Beebe Rd, Kalkaska, MI 49646
Tel.: (231) 258-9524
Web Site: http://www.beckmanproduction.com
Oil & Gas Exploration Services
N.A.I.C.S.: 213112
Dan Miller (Controller)
Kimberly Simons (Mgr-HR)
Mark Bishop (CFO, Sec & VP)
Butch Peeples (Mgr-Safety)
Rick Root (Mgr-Special Projects)
Dave Wardman (Supvr-DOT)
Dan Duguid (Supvr-DOT)

Subsidiary (Domestic):

J & R Well Service, LLC (3)
791 Ln 9, Powell, WY 82435
Tel.: (307) 754-3140
Web Site: http://www.jandrwellservice.com
Oil & Gas Exploration Services
N.A.I.C.S.: 213112
Jerry Herweyer (Pres)
Bret Hatch (Mgr-Powell Ops)

R & S Well Service, Inc. (3)
818 S 7th St, Thermopolis, WY 82443
Tel.: (307) 864-3861
Web Site: http://www.randswellservice.com
Oil & Gas Exploration Services
N.A.I.C.S.: 213112

Park Energy Services, LLC (1)
1015 N Brdwy Ave Ste 301, Oklahoma City, OK 73102
Tel.: (405) 896-3169
Web Site: http://www.parkenergyservices.com
Storage Tank Vapor Recovery Services
N.A.I.C.S.: 562991
Jonathan Warren (CFO)
Tim Knox (Pres & COO)
John Seldenrust (Chm & CEO)

Subsidiary (Domestic):

MidCon Compression, L.L.C (2)
6100 N Western Ave, Oklahoma City, OK 73118
Tel.: (405) 935-4159
Web Site: http://www.midconcompression.com
Gas Handling Equipment Distributor
N.A.I.C.S.: 811310

ROCK HILL CONCRETE
339 School St, Catasauqua, PA 18032-1832
Tel.: (610) 264-5586
Web Site: http://www.rockhillconcrete.com
Year Founded: 1947
Sales Range: $50-74.9 Million
Emp.: 50
Provider of Ready Mix Concrete
N.A.I.C.S.: 484110
Glen Buskirk (Pres)
Jeffrey Buskirk (VP)
Jay Robinson (Mgr-Sls)

ROCK HILL MECHANICAL CORP
524 Clark Ave, Saint Louis, MO 63122
Tel.: (314) 966-0600
Web Site: http://www.rhmcorp.com
Sales Range: $25-49.9 Million
Emp.: 300
Warm Air Heating & Air Conditioning Contractor
N.A.I.C.S.: 238220
Robert Schnitzer (Pres)
Stephen Chadwick (Sr Engr-Mechanical)
Sean Patterson (Sr Engr-Mechanical)
Robyn Holtgrewe (Mgr-BIM)
Jamison Bloebaum (VP-Design-Build Svcs)

ROCK ISLAND CAPITAL LLC
1415 W 22nd St Ste 1250, Oak Brook, IL 60523
Tel.: (630) 413-9136

COMPANIES

Web Site:
http://www.rockislandcapital.com
Privater Equity Firm
N.A.I.C.S.: 523999
Patrick Hartman *(Founder & Partner)*

ROCK ISLAND CORPORATION
530 Oak Ct Dr Ste 260, Memphis, TN 38117-3724
Tel.: (901) 529-5700   TN
Year Founded: 1847
Sales Range: $50-74.9 Million
Emp.: 900
Holding Company; Metal Extrusion Mfr
N.A.I.C.S.: 423710
Michael McDonnell *(Pres)*
Charlie Epperson *(VP-HR)*
Daniel R. Richards *(Treas & Sec)*
Joseph Orgill III *(Chm)*

ROCK RIVER LUMBER & GRAIN CO
5502 Lyndon Rd, Prophetstown, IL 61277
Tel.: (815) 537-5131
Web Site: http://www.rockriverag.com
Sales Range: $25-49.9 Million
Emp.: 2
Grain Elevators
N.A.I.C.S.: 424510
D. Joseph Rosengren *(Pres)*

ROCK SOLID CONSTRUCTION GROUP, INC.
1751 Mound St Ste 201, Sarasota, FL 34236
Tel.: (941) 365-1021
Web Site:
http://www.rocksolidconstructionsrq.com
Year Founded: 2005
Sales Range: $1-9.9 Million
Emp.: 10
Residential Remodeler
N.A.I.C.S.: 236118
Marjorie Broughton *(Pres)*

ROCK SOLID STABILIZATION & RECLAMATION, INC.
1001 Williams Rd, Genoa City, WI 53128
Tel.: (262) 240-4100
Web Site:
http://www.rocksolidstabilization.com
Year Founded: 2007
Sales Range: $1-9.9 Million
Road Construction Services
N.A.I.C.S.: 237310
Jonathan Pease *(Founder)*

ROCK SOLID UK LTD.
201 S Main St, Bentonville, AR 72712
Tel.: (833) 687-5368
Web Site: https://nuqleous.com
Year Founded: 2013
Software Development Services
N.A.I.C.S.: 513210
Bill Kloza *(Co-CEO)*
Garrett Levey *(Co-CEO)*

Subsidiaries:

Shiloh Technologies, LLC (1)
2003 S 52nd St Ste 1, Rogers, AR 72758
Tel.: (479) 464-4598
Web Site: https://www.shilohnext.com
Computer Parts Whslr
N.A.I.C.S.: 423430
Britt Fogg *(CEO)*
Kurt Gibbons *(COO)*

TR3 Solutions, Inc. (1)
2 Main St Ste 220, Stoneham, MA 02180
Tel.: (781) 481-0700
Web Site: https://www.tr3solutions.com
Software Package Services
N.A.I.C.S.: 513210

Dan Gallagher *(COO)*
Tom Rauh *(CEO)*

ROCK VALLEY OIL & CHEMICAL COMPANY
1911 Windsor Rd, Rockford, IL 61111
Tel.: (815) 654-2400   IL
Web Site:
http://www.rockvalleyoil.com
Year Founded: 1971
Sales Range: $10-24.9 Million
Emp.: 40
Supplier of Industrial Lubricants, Solvents & Chemicals
N.A.I.C.S.: 324191
Roger L. Schramm *(Pres)*
Jim Lang *(Mgr-Sls)*

ROCK VENTURES LLC
1050 Woodward Ave, Detroit, MI 48226-1906
Tel.: (313) 373-7700
Web Site:
http://www.rockventures.com
Year Founded: 1985
Sales Range: Less than $1 Million
Holding Company
N.A.I.C.S.: 551112
Whitney Eichinger *(VP-Comm)*
Matthew P. Cullen *(Principal)*
Howard Luckoff *(Gen Counsel)*
Matthew J. Rizik *(Chief Tax Officer)*
Daniel Gilbert *(Founder & Chm)*

ROCK WEST COMPOSITES, INC.
3392 W 8600 S Unit A, West Jordan, UT 84088-5578
Tel.: (801) 566-3402
Web Site:
http://www.rockwestcomposites.com
Carbon & Graphite Product Mfr
N.A.I.C.S.: 335991
Jim Gormican *(Pres & CEO)*

Subsidiaries:

Performance Plastics Inc. (1)
1602 Precision Park Ln, San Ysidro, CA 92173
Tel.: (619) 428-5031
Web Site: http://www.perf-plastics.com
Rev.: $6,387,040
Emp.: 80
Other Aircraft Parts & Auxiliary Equipment Mfr
N.A.I.C.S.: 336413
Lance Brean *(Mgr-HR)*
Rumiko Anan *(Controller)*
Jim Renaud *(Pres)*

ROCK-IT SAND & GRAVEL, INC.
PO Box 589, Griffin, GA 30224
Tel.: (770) 229-1160
Sales Range: $10-24.9 Million
Emp.: 30
Cargo & Freight Services
N.A.I.C.S.: 484220
Loren Guild *(CEO & CFO)*

ROCKAWAY HOME ATTENDANT SERVICES INC.
1603 Central Ave, Far Rockaway, NY 11691
Tel.: (718) 471-5800   NY
Year Founded: 1979
Sales Range: $10-24.9 Million
Emp.: 764
Home Care Services
N.A.I.C.S.: 621610

ROCKBOTTOMGOLF.COM
1250 Scottsville Rd Ste 2, Rochester, NY 14624
Tel.: (585) 436-7116
Web Site:
http://www.rockbottomgolf.com

Year Founded: 2000
Sales Range: $10-24.9 Million
Emp.: 19
Discounted Golf Gear Retailer
N.A.I.C.S.: 459110

ROCKBRIDGE GROWTH EQUITY, LLC
1 Campus Martius 1070 Woodward Ave, Detroit, MI 48226
Tel.: (313) 373-7000   MI
Web Site: http://www.rbequity.com
Privater Equity Firm
N.A.I.C.S.: 523999
Dan Gilbert *(Partner)*
Kevin Prokop *(Mng Partner)*
Steve Linden *(Partner)*
Brian M. Hermelin *(Co-Founder & Mng Partner)*
Maura Hynes *(CFO & Chief Compliance Officer)*
Ziv Weizman *(VP)*
Matthew Kearney *(Operating Partner)*

Subsidiaries:

Core Digital Media, Inc. (1)
Bluff Creek Rd, Playa Vista, CA 90094
Tel.: (310) 348-6800
Web Site: http://www.coredigitalmedia.com
Price Comparison & Lead Generation Website Publisher
N.A.I.C.S.: 519290

Subsidiary (Domestic):

Classes USA, Inc. (2)
4859 W Slauson Ave Ste 405, Los Angeles, CA 90056
Tel.: (310) 348-6800
Web Site: http://www.classesusa.com
Sales Range: $10-24.9 Million
Emp.: 200
Online Higher Education Portal
N.A.I.C.S.: 611710
Steve Krenzer *(Pres)*
Dominique Jean *(CTO)*

LowerMyBills, Inc. (2)
4859 W Slauson Ave Ste 405, Los Angeles, CA 90056
Tel.: (310) 234-0800
Web Site: http://www.lowermybills.com
Online Financial Services
N.A.I.C.S.: 519290
Steve Krenzer *(Pres)*

CurtCo Robb Media, LLC (1)
29160 Heathercliff Rd Ste 200, Malibu, CA 90265
Tel.: (310) 589-7700
Web Site: http://robbreport.com
Periodical Publishers
N.A.I.C.S.: 513120
Ilya Kurinets *(Mgr-Media Sls)*

Branch (Domestic):

Robb Report - New York (2)
475 Fifth Avenue, New York, NY 10017
Tel.: (212) 201-1111
Web Site: http://www.robbreport.com
Periodical Publishers
N.A.I.C.S.: 513120

Destination Media, Inc. (1)
255 S Old Woodward Ave Ste 200, Birmingham, MI 48009
Tel.: (248) 581-3008
Web Site: http://www.gstv.com
Sales Range: $10-24.9 Million
Emp.: 50
Gas Station Network Television Broadcasting Services
N.A.I.C.S.: 516210
Stephen Kuehn *(CFO)*
David Leider *(Pres & CEO)*

ProSites, Inc. (1)
27919 Jefferson Ave Ste 200, Temecula, CA 92590
Tel.: (951) 693-9101
Web Site: http://www.prosites.com
Medical & Dental Website Design Services
N.A.I.C.S.: 541511
Lance McCollough *(Founder & Chm)*
Ken Robinson *(CMO)*

ROCKDALE PIPELINE INC.

Dave Rutan *(CEO)*
Keith Washington *(VP-Products)*
Milton Goss *(CFO)*
Luke Wilson *(Chief Revenue Officer)*

Protect America, Inc. (1)
3800 Quick Hill Rd Bldg 1-100, Austin, TX 78728
Tel.: (512) 218-8833
Web Site: http://www.protectamerica.com
Security Systems Services; Owned by RockBridge Growth Equity LLC, Falcon Investment Advisors, LLC & Protect America, Inc.
N.A.I.C.S.: 561621
Ryan Pombrio *(VP-Bus Dev)*

Quicken Loans, Inc. (1)
20555 Victor Pkwy, Livonia, MI 48152
Tel.: (734) 805-5000
Web Site: http://www.quickenloans.com
Sales Range: $350-399.9 Million
Real Estate Financing
N.A.I.C.S.: 531390
Dan Gilbert *(Founder & Chm)*
John Fikany *(VP-Strategy)*
Jay Farner *(CEO)*
Bill Banfield *(VP-Capital Markets)*
Julie Booth *(CFO)*
Aaron Emerson *(VP-Comm)*
Linglong He *(CIO)*
Shawn Krause *(Exec VP)*
Heather Lovier *(Sr VP-Client Rels)*
Bob Walters *(Pres & COO)*
Casey Hurbis *(CMO)*

RAData, Inc. (1)
27 Ironia Rd, Flanders, NJ 07836
Tel.: (973) 927-7303
Web Site: http://www.radata.com
Rev.: $2,860,000
Emp.: 20
Testing Laboratories
N.A.I.C.S.: 541380
David Grammer *(CEO)*
Joanne Grammer *(VP & Dir-Admin)*

Title Source, Inc. (1)
1450 W Long Lk Rd Ste 400, Troy, MI 48098   (100%)
Tel.: (888) 848-5355
Web Site: http://www.titlesourceinc.com
Sales Range: $1-9.9 Million
Title Insurance Services
N.A.I.C.S.: 524127
Jeff Eisenshtadt *(CEO)*

ROCKCASTLE REGIONAL HOSPITAL AND RESPIRATORY CARE CENTER, INC.
145 Newcomb Ave, Mount Vernon, KY 40456
Tel.: (606) 256-2195   KY
Web Site:
http://www.rockcastleregional.org
Year Founded: 1957
Sales Range: $25-49.9 Million
Emp.: 620
Health Care Srvices
N.A.I.C.S.: 622110
Stephen A. Estes *(Pres & CEO)*
Conley Durham *(Dir-Pur & Matls Mgmt)*
Cheryl Mullins *(Dir-Occupational Therapy)*
Carol Bryant *(Dir-Environmental Svcs)*
Cynthia Burton *(Chief Nursing Officer)*

ROCKDALE PIPELINE INC.
1925 Old Covington Hwy SE, Conyers, GA 30013
Tel.: (770) 922-4123
Web Site:
http://www.rockdalepipeline.com
Year Founded: 1976
Sales Range: $25-49.9 Million
Emp.: 100
Water Main Construction
N.A.I.C.S.: 237110
Paul Duncan *(CEO)*
Ken Richardson *(Pres)*
Shirley Cooley *(CEO)*
John Reilly *(Controller)*

ROCKEFELLER CAPITAL MANAGEMENT

Rockefeller Capital Management—(Continued)

ROCKEFELLER CAPITAL MANAGEMENT
45 Rockefeller Plz Fl 5, New York, NY 10111
Tel.: (212) 549-5100
Web Site: http://www.rcm.rockco.com
Year Founded: 2018
Financial Services Firm
N.A.I.C.S.: 523999
Edmond N. Moriarty III *(CFO & Chief Risk Officer)*
Greg Fleming *(Pres & CEO)*

Subsidiaries:

Whitnell & Co. (1)
701 Harger Rd Ste 190, Oak Brook, IL 60523
Tel.: (630) 575-2300
Wealth Management Services
N.A.I.C.S.: 523940

ROCKET COMMUNICATIONS INC.
81 Langton St Unit 12, San Francisco, CA 94103
Tel.: (415) 863-0101
Web Site: http://www.rocketcom.com
Year Founded: 1992
Sales Range: $1-9.9 Million
Emp.: 12
Graphic Design Services
N.A.I.C.S.: 541430
Michal Anne Rogondino *(CEO & Chief Creative Officer)*
Ty Van Leuven *(Dir-Visual Design)*

ROCKET GLOBAL ACQUISITION CORP.
122 E 42nd St Unit 2105, New York, NY 10168
Tel.: (212) 277-5300 Ky
Year Founded: 2021
Investment Services
N.A.I.C.S.: 523999
Philip Wagenheim *(Chm, CEO & CFO)*

ROCKET HOMES REAL ESTATE LLC
701 Griswold St Ste 21, Detroit, MI 48226
Tel.: (888) 468-4735
Web Site: http://www.inhouserealty.com
Emp.: 25,000
Online Real Estate Services
N.A.I.C.S.: 531210
Sam Vida *(Pres & CEO)*

Subsidiaries:

ForSaleByOwner.Com, LLC, Inc. (1)
701 Griswold St Ste 21, Detroit, MI 48226
Tel.: (888) 367-7253
Web Site: http://www.forsalebyowner.com
Newspaper Publishers
N.A.I.C.S.: 513110
Damon Giglio *(Pres & CEO)*

ROCKET LAWYER INCORPORATED
220 Montgomery St Ste 917, San Francisco, CA 94104
Tel.: (877) 757-1550
Web Site: http://www.rocketlawyer.com
Year Founded: 2008
Online Legal Services
N.A.I.C.S.: 541199
Charley Moore *(Founder & CEO)*
An Tran *(VP-Tech)*
Paul Hollerbach *(CFO)*
Alon Rotem *(Gen Counsel)*
Mark Edwards *(VP & Gen Mgr-UK)*
Rob Elhardt *(VP-Product Dev)*
Paul Bussi *(VP-Sls & Customer Success)*
Santhana Parthasarathy *(Sr VP-Tech)*

ROCKET MEDIA, INC.
3335 E Baseline Rd, Gilbert, AZ 85234
Tel.: (480) 699-2579
Web Site: http://www.rocketmedia.com
Year Founded: 2003
Sales Range: $1-9.9 Million
Emp.: 20
Internet Marketing & Website Design
N.A.I.C.S.: 541613
Ben Kalkman *(Pres)*

ROCKET SCIENCE
700 Larkspur Landing Cir Ste 199, Larkspur, CA 94939
Tel.: (415) 464-8110
Web Site: http://www.rocketscience.com
Year Founded: 1996
Sales Range: $10-24.9 Million
Emp.: 10
Exhibit/Trade Shows, Media Relations, Product Placement, Public Relations, Strategic Planning/Research
N.A.I.C.S.: 541820
Mark Addison *(Chief Scientist)*
Rich Mullikin *(Head-Security Technology Practice)*
Gail Norris *(Acct Exec)*
Chris Greenfield *(Acct Exec)*

ROCKET SCIENCE CONSULTING CORP.
930 Alabama St, San Francisco, CA 94110
Tel.: (415) 651-4236
Web Site: http://www.rocketscience.is
Year Founded: 2001
Sales Range: $1-9.9 Million
Emp.: 35
It Consulting
N.A.I.C.S.: 541690
Matt McGraw *(CEO)*
Amber Carson Miller *(Engr-Mission)*
Joseph Nicoletti *(Engr-Mission)*
Sherman Cheng *(Engr-Svc Desk)*
Tim Geuy *(Mgr-IT)*
Tisha Blackburn *(Mgr-Mission Ops)*
Gerard Weese *(Engr-Mission)*
Tracy Page *(Engr-Mission)*

ROCKETCREATIVE
PO Box 71427, Phoenix, AZ 85050
Tel.: (480) 284-8144
Web Site: http://www.rocketcreative.com
Year Founded: 2004
Sales Range: $10-24.9 Million
Emp.: 2
N.A.I.C.S.: 541810
Scott Ritter *(Owner)*
Cara Mormino *(VP)*

ROCKETS PARTNER LP
1510 Polk St, Houston, TX 77002
Tel.: (713) 758-7200 DE
Web Site: http://www.nba.com
Year Founded: 1967
Emp.: 160
Professional Basketball Team & Arena Operator
N.A.I.C.S.: 711211
Tilman J. Fertitta *(Dir-Advisory)*
Les Alexander *(Owner)*
Thaddeus B. Brown *(CEO)*
John R. Croley *(VP-Corp Dev)*
Ken Sheirr *(VP-Mktg)*
Rafael Stone *(Gen Counsel)*
Gretchen Sheirr *(Pres-Bus Ops)*
Scott Manley *(VP-Ops-Arena & Asst Gen Mgr-Toyota Center)*
Joe Abercrombie *(Sr Dir-Brdcst Production & Game Presentation)*
Natalie Alvarado *(Dir-Entertainment)*
Clay Allen *(Assoc Gen Counsel)*
Chris Costa *(Dir-Ticket Svcs)*
Michael Drummond *(Mgr-Security)*
Hai Duong *(Mgr-Community Rels)*
Kristen Harper *(Dir-HR)*
Kara Infante *(Dir-Retail Ops)*
Sarah Joseph *(Dir-Community Rels)*
Dawn Keen *(Dir-Corp Partner Svcs)*
Wibnston Lin *(Dir-Strategy & Analytics)*
Nicolas Somoano *(Controller)*
Bryant Savage *(Sr Dir-Security & Guest Svcs)*
Mike Schnieders *(Dir-Events & Mktg)*
Carlos Sepulveda *(Dir-Facility Svcs)*
Hillary Thomas *(Dir-Event Ops)*
Okpara Young *(Dir-IT & Telecom)*
Julian Duncan *(Chief Mktg & Strategy Officer)*

ROCKEY & ROCKWELL ADVERTISING, INC.
1934 Old Gallows Rd, Ste 350, Vienna, VA 22182
Tel.: (703) 734-1500 VA
Web Site: http://www.rockeyrockwell.com
Year Founded: 1994
Sales Range: $10-24.9 Million
Emp.: 20
Advertising Agencies, Full Service, Media Buying Services, Public Relations
N.A.I.C.S.: 541810
Stephanie Rockey *(Owner & Pres)*

ROCKFORD BUSINESS INTERIORS INC.
211 E Riverside Dr, Austin, TX 78704-1203
Tel.: (512) 447-8056
Web Site: http://www.rockford-texas.com
Year Founded: 1991
Sales Range: $10-24.9 Million
Emp.: 120
Retail of Furniture
N.A.I.C.S.: 423210
Butch Strawbridge *(Mgr-Warehouse)*
Diane Clifton *(Mgr-Asset Mgmt & Rental)*
Mike Cameron *(Mgr-Facility Svcs Div)*
Roland Moreno *(Project Mgr-Corp Sls)*
Vicki Day *(Mgr-Customer Svc)*
Ken Beaver *(CEO)*
Kansas Sartin *(Exec VP-Architectural Solutions)*
Gary Rust *(Exec VP-Sls & Design-Austin Furniture Div)*
Amy Lopez *(Exec VP-Sls & Design-Houston Furniture Div)*

ROCKFORD CORPORATION
22845 NW Bennett St Ste 150, Hillsboro, OR 97124
Tel.: (503) 647-0224
Web Site: http://www.rockfordpipelines.com
Year Founded: 1967
Sales Range: $10-24.9 Million
Emp.: 315
Pipe Laying Construction
N.A.I.C.S.: 237110
Frank O. Welch *(Pres)*
John Murakami *(CFO)*

ROCKFORD MUTUAL INSURANCE COMPANY
527 Colman Ctr Dr, Rockford, IL 61108
Tel.: (815) 229-1500
Web Site: http://www.rockfordmutual.com
Sales Range: $25-49.9 Million
Emp.: 70
Fire, Marine & Casualty Insurance: Mutual
N.A.I.C.S.: 524126
Patrick Kennedy *(Mgr-Casualty Claim)*
Ann Krines *(Mgr-Claims)*
Tiffany Herron *(Asst Controller)*
Dina Johnson *(Controller)*
Tina Flynn *(Coord-Mktg)*
Amy Ingram *(Coord-Social Media & Comm)*
Michael Wall *(Asst VP-Underwriting)*
Lisa Ireton *(Dir-HR)*
Ann Kriens *(Dir-Claims)*
Rob Jacobson *(Pres & CEO)*

ROCKFORD OIL CORP.
1174 Manito Dr NW, Fox Island, WA 98333
Tel.: (253) 973-7135 NV
Year Founded: 2012
Oil & Gas Exploration
N.A.I.C.S.: 211120
Howard H. Bouch *(Pres, CEO, Treas & Sec)*

ROCKHEDGE HERB FARMS
2765 Rte 82, Pleasant Valley, NY 12569
Tel.: (845) 677-6726
Web Site: http://www.rockhedgeherbs.com
Year Founded: 2009
Sales Range: $1-9.9 Million
Emp.: 56
Grower & Distributor of Herbs
N.A.I.C.S.: 111219
John Alva *(Pres & CEO)*

ROCKINGHAM CONSTRUCTION CO
1211 N Main St, Harrisonburg, VA 22802
Tel.: (540) 433-1000
Sales Range: $10-24.9 Million
Emp.: 200
Electric Power Line Construction
N.A.I.C.S.: 237130
Tammy Gibson *(Office Mgr)*
Winston O. Weaver Jr. *(Pres)*

ROCKINGHAM COOPERATIVE FARM BUREAU
1040 S High St, Harrisonburg, VA 22803
Tel.: (540) 434-3856
Web Site: http://www.rockinghamcoop.com
Sales Range: $10-24.9 Million
Emp.: 170
Farm Supplies
N.A.I.C.S.: 424910
Brenda Allison *(Sec)*
Norman Wenger *(Treas)*
Joseph Lam *(VP)*
John Rosenberger *(Asst Treas & Asst Sec)*

ROCKINGHAM ELECTRICAL SUPPLY COMPANY, INC.
437 Shattuck Wy, Newington, NH 03801
Tel.: (603) 436-7731
Web Site: http://www.rockinghamelectric.com
Year Founded: 1951
Sales Range: $10-24.9 Million
Emp.: 110
Electrical Supplies Distr

N.A.I.C.S.: 423610
Sean Haight (Dir-Pur)
Tom Doyle (Exec VP)
James E. Pender Sr. (CEO)

ROCKINGHAM MUTUAL INSURANCE COMPANY
633 E Market St, Harrisonburg, VA 22801
Tel.: (540) 434-5344
Web Site:
http://www.rockinghamgroup.com
Year Founded: 1869
Sales Range: $25-49.9 Million
Emp.: 100
Fire, Marine & Casualty Insurance
N.A.I.C.S.: 524126
John Schwertfuherer (CFO)

ROCKINGHAM STEEL
2565 John Wayland Hwy, Harrisonburg, VA 22801
Tel.: (540) 433-3000
Web Site:
http://www.rockinghamsteel.com
Sales Range: $10-24.9 Million
Emp.: 35
Steel Products Mfr
N.A.I.C.S.: 332312
J. D. Sager (Mgr-Sls-Northern)
Matt Moore (VP-Bus Dev)
John Biddle (Exec VP)

Subsidiaries:

Rockingham Steel (1)
438 Kessler Mill Rd, Salem, VA 24153-4447
Tel.: (540) 433-3000
Web Site: http://www.rockinghamsteel.com
Sales Range: $10-24.9 Million
Concrete Reinforcing Steel Mfr
N.A.I.C.S.: 332312

ROCKLAND AUTO PLAZA
60 Route 304, Nanuet, NY 10954
Tel.: (845) 627-3700
Year Founded: 1981
Sales Range: $25-49.9 Million
Emp.: 55
Car Whslr
N.A.I.C.S.: 441110
Livio Odoardi (Pres)

ROCKLAND BAKERY
94 Demarest Mill Rd W, Nanuet, NY 10954
Tel.: (845) 623-5800
Web Site:
http://www.rocklandbakery.com
Year Founded: 1970
Sales Range: $25-49.9 Million
Emp.: 450
Bakery Products Mfr
N.A.I.C.S.: 311812
Phil Battaglia (Owner)
Mike Battaglia (Dir-Sls)

ROCKLAND CAPITAL, LLC
24 Waterway Ave Ste 800, The Woodlands, TX 77380-3199
Tel.: (281) 863-9000   DE
Web Site:
http://www.rocklandcapital.com
Year Founded: 2003
Privater Equity Firm
N.A.I.C.S.: 523999
Scott Harlan (Mng Partner)
Shane Litts (Partner)
Jim Maiz (Partner)
Carla Banks (VP)
Robert Rapenske (VP)
Rick Woryk (VP)
Terry E. Everett (CFO)
Joyce Tang (Controller)
Kristin Warnke (Dir-Admin)
Bill Paff (VP)
Ed Barndt (Sr VP)
Austin Peterson (VP)

Elena deLaunay (VP)
Jon Beach (Principal)
Michael J. Del Giudice (Founder)

Subsidiaries:

Beacon Power, LLC (1)
65 Middlesex Rd, Tyngsboro, MA 01879
Tel.: (978) 694-9121
Web Site: http://www.beaconpower.com
Flywheel-Based Energy Storage Systems Designer & Mfr
N.A.I.C.S.: 237130
Barry Brits (Pres & CEO)
James Arseneaux (VP-Engrg)

ROCKLAND INDUSTRIES, INC.
1601 Edison Hwy, Baltimore, MD 21213
Tel.: (410) 522-2505
Web Site: http://www.roc-lon.com
Rev.: $28,100,000
Emp.: 475
Broadwoven Fabric Finishing Mills
N.A.I.C.S.: 313310
James Beitnan (Mgr-Credit)
Mark R. Berman (Pres)
Stephen Leaderman (CFO)
Stan Fradin (Dir-Intl)

ROCKLER COMPANIES, INC.
4365 Willow Dr, Medina, MN 55340-9701
Tel.: (763) 478-8478   MN
Web Site: http://www.rockler.com
Year Founded: 1954
Sales Range: $100-124.9 Million
Emp.: 500
Hardware Catalog, Mail-Order Houses & Retailer
N.A.I.C.S.: 444140
Ann Rockler Jackson (Chm)
Diane Englund (Mgr-Category)
Steven Singer (CEO)

ROCKMAN COMPANY (U.S.A.), INC.
12011 Smith Ave, Santa Fe Springs, CA 90670
Tel.: (323) 887-7506   CA
Web Site:
http://www.rockmanusa.com
Sales Range: $10-24.9 Million
Emp.: 15
Dried Or Canned Foods
N.A.I.C.S.: 424490
Wei Fu Lin (Pres)
Vincent Luu (Gen Mgr)
Jean Pierre Lin (VP)

ROCKMONT CAPITAL PARTNERS LTD.
1290 Broadway Ste 1150, Denver, CO 80203
Tel.: (303) 839-8500
Web Site:
http://www.rockmontcapital.com
Privater Equity Firm
N.A.I.C.S.: 523940
John Pfannenstein (Founder & Mng Partner)
Stephen Deitchman (Partner)

Subsidiaries:

Brandywine Communications, Inc. (1)
1153 Warner Ave, Tustin, CA 92780
Tel.: (714) 755-1050
Web Site: http://www.brandywinecomm.com
Engineeering Services
N.A.I.C.S.: 541330
Alyona Diachenko (VP-Sls & Mktg)
Jay Krutsinger (Dir-Sls-Western Reg)
Neil Pitman (Dir-Sls-Asia)
David Wright (Dir-Sls-Europe, Middle East, Africa & Australia)

ROCKPOINT GROUP, LLC

500 Boylston St 21st Fl, Boston, MA 02116
Tel.: (617) 437-8400
Web Site: https://rockpoint.com
Sales Range: $25-49.9 Million
Emp.: 40
Real Estate Private Equity Firm
N.A.I.C.S.: 531390
William H. Walton III (Co-Founder, Co-CEO, Mng Partner & Managing Member)
Daniel Domb (Principal)
T. K. Inbody (Principal)
Keith B. Gelb (Co-Founder, Co-CEO & Mng Partner)
Spencer Raymond (Sr Mng Dir & CFO)
Hank Midgley (Principal, Head-Investor Relations & Managing Member)
Ron J. Hoyl (Sr Mng Dir, Chief Compliance Officer, Principal & Gen Counsel)
Camille Barnard (VP)
Doug Berman (VP)
Fred Borges (Sr Mng Dir)
Steve Caruso (Co-Mng Dir)
Michael Chadwick (Dir)
Steve Chen (Co-Mng Dir)
Jason Chiverton (Sr Mng Dir)
David Conte (VP)
Kaitlyn Dorka (VP)
Jennifer Dumas Hall (Co-Mng Dir)
Brendan Fullum (Co-Mng Dir)
Tom Gilbane (Pres)
Joseph Goldman (Sr Mng Dir)
Kerry Krause (VP)
Donna Linsalata (Co-Mng Dir)
Joe McNiff (Dir)
David Nulsen (Dir & Assoc Gen Counsel)
Caroline Posner (VP)
Patrick Ryan (Co-Mng Dir)
C. B. Scherer (Co-Mng Dir)
Nick Simione (VP)
Bennett Varney (Dir)

Subsidiaries:

Rockpoint Europe Limited (1)
Brookfield House 2nd Floor 44 Davies Street, London, W1K 5JA, United Kingdom
Tel.: (44) 20 70164420
Real Estate Private Equity Firm
N.A.I.C.S.: 531390

Rockpoint Group, LLC - Dallas Office (1)
Woodland Hall at Old Parkland 3953 Maple Ave Ste 300, Dallas, TX 75219
Tel.: (972) 934-0100
Web Site: http://www.rockpointgroup.com
Real Estate Private Equity Firm
N.A.I.C.S.: 531390
William H. Walton III (Pres & Mng Dir)

Rockpoint Group, LLC - San Francisco Office (1)
1 Bush St Ste 1450, San Francisco, CA 94104
Tel.: (415) 438-7920
Web Site: http://www.rockpointgroup.com
Real Estate Services
N.A.I.C.S.: 531390

ROCKPORT HOLDING COMPANY INC.
1515 E 4th St, Little Rock, AR 72202
Tel.: (501) 372-0185
Rev.: $57,000,000
Emp.: 80
Beer & Other Fermented Malt Liquors
N.A.I.C.S.: 424810
Nick Pierce (Pres)

ROCKVIEW DAIRIES INC.
7011 Stewart & Gray Rd, Downey, CA 90241
Tel.: (562) 927-5511

Web Site:
http://www.rockviewfarms.com
Rev.: $135,282,337
Emp.: 300
Dairy Products Mfr
N.A.I.C.S.: 424430
Egbert Degroot (Pres)
Joe Baladez (CFO)

ROCKVILLE FABRICS CORPORATION
99 W Hawthorne Ave Rm 302, Valley Stream, NY 11580
Tel.: (516) 561-9810   NY
Web Site:
http://www.rockvillefabrics.com
Year Founded: 1950
Sales Range: $10-24.9 Million
Emp.: 30
Household Goods Whslr & Distr
N.A.I.C.S.: 314999
Peter Levy (Pres)

Subsidiaries:

Active Quilting Div. (1)
99 W Hawthorne ave, Valley Stream, NY 11580-0049   (100%)
Tel.: (212) 563-2050
Web Site: http://www.pledy.com
Quilting for the Trade
N.A.I.C.S.: 314999

ROCKVILLE FUEL & FEED COMPANY
14901 Southlawn Ln, Rockville, MD 20850
Tel.: (301) 762-3988
Web Site:
http://www.rockvilleconcrete.com
Rev.: $12,000,000
Emp.: 90
Ready Mixed Concrete
N.A.I.C.S.: 327320
James D. Ward (Pres)

ROCKWELL PROPERTY CO.
1000 N Halsted St Ste 102, Chicago, IL 60642
Tel.: (312) 460-3300
Web Site:
http://www.rockwellproperty.com
Year Founded: 2009
Sales Range: $25-49.9 Million
Emp.: 50
Real Estate Investment Services
N.A.I.C.S.: 531390
Doug Fisher (Mng Principal)
Matt Welke (Mng Principal)
Pat Bader (Mng Principal)
Ted Thilman (Mng Principal)
Jason Fishleder (Principal & Head-Acquisitons)

ROCKWOOD BANCSHARES, INC.
219 Thresher Dr, Eureka, MO 63025
Tel.: (636) 938-9222   MO
Web Site:
http://www.rockwoodbank.com
Year Founded: 1991
Sales Range: $1-9.9 Million
Emp.: 60
State Commercial Banks
N.A.I.C.S.: 522110

Subsidiaries:

Rockwood Bank (1)
219 Thresher Dr, Eureka, MO 63025
Tel.: (636) 938-9222
Web Site: http://www.rockwoodbank.com
Sales Range: $1-9.9 Million
Commericial Banking
N.A.I.C.S.: 522110
Mark Carley (Asst VP)
Jeff Gass (CFO & Sr VP)
Joe Lunt (Pres)
Gary Smith (Sr VP)

ROCKWOOD BANCSHARES, INC.

Rockwood Bancshares, Inc.—(Continued)
Vicki Salters (Exec VP)
Jean Tucker (VP)
John Schwab (VP)
Richard Tash (VP)
Thomas J. Merle (VP)
Wally Dautenhahn (Officer-Loan)
Shelley Haney (Officer-Loan)
Christopher Smith (Officer-Loan)

ROCKWOOD CAPITAL LLC
50 California St Ste 3000, San Francisco, CA 94111
Tel.: (415) 645-4300
Web Site:
http://www.rockwoodcap.com
Year Founded: 1996
Rev.: $8,000,000,000
Emp.: 70
Real Estate Investment
N.A.I.C.S.: 531390
Peter J. Falco (Co-Founder)
Walter P. Schmidt (Sr Mng Partner)
David I. Becker (Gen Counsel & Partner)
Maysa Vahidi (Chief Compliance Officer)
David A. Streicher (Partner)
Niraj R. Shah (Partner)
Peter A. Kaye (Mng Partner)
Tyson E. Skillings (Mng Partner)
Dwight I. Arnesen (Sr Mng Dir)
Tony Larino (Partner-New York)
Joel A. Moody (Mng Dir)
Joel K. Mayer (Mng Dir)
Andrew Blanchard (Partner)
Marti Breier (Dir-Legal)
Charlie Leonard (Dir-New York)
Alexia Gottschalch (Mng Dir & Head-Client Strategy-Global)
Tara McCann (Mng Dir-New York)
Robert L. Gray Jr. (Co-Founder)

ROCKWOOD EQUITY PARTNERS, LLC
200 Park Ave Ste 420, 44122, Cleveland, OH
Tel.: (216) 342-1790   NY
Web Site:
http://www.rockwoodequity.com
Year Founded: 1999
Privater Equity Firm
N.A.I.C.S.: 523999
Brett R. Keith (Mng Partner)
H. Josef Merrill (Partner)
J. Kristin Ament (Dir-Ops)
Vince Nardy (Partner)
Kate Faust (Partner-Bus Dev)
Reed Blocksom (VP)

Subsidiaries:

AMACS Process Tower Internals (1)
14211 Industry St, Houston, TX 77053-2526
Tel.: (713) 434-0934
Web Site: http://www.amacs.com
Sales Range: $10-24.9 Million
Emp.: 100
Fabricated Mesh Products
N.A.I.C.S.: 332618
Tom Wilson (Exec VP)
Bruce E. Taylor (CEO)
Arlene Follett (Mgr-HR)
Mike Thompson (VP-Ops)

Subsidiary (Domestic):

Amistco Separation Products, Inc. (2)
23147 Highway 6, Alvin, TX 77512
Tel.: (281) 331-5956
Web Site: http://www.amistco.com
Sales Range: $1-9.9 Million
Mfr of Fabricated Metal Products Used in Separation Processes for Liquids & Gases
N.A.I.C.S.: 332618

Altimate Medical, Inc. (1)
262 W 1st St, Morton, MN 56270
Tel.: (507) 697-6393
Web Site: http://www.easystand.com

Medical Equipment Mfr & Distr
N.A.I.C.S.: 334510
Wes Ovre (Mgr-Product Dev)
Kyle Smith (Mgr-Mktg)
Andrew Gardeen (Mgr-Global Sls)

Lifeway Mobility, LLC (1)
40 Weston St Bldg 40 Site A, Hartford, CT 06120
Tel.: (860) 292-1111
Web Site: http://lifewaymobility.com
Accessibility Equipment Supplier
N.A.I.C.S.: 423450
Daniel Martin (VP)
Paul Bergantino (Pres)

Subsidiary (Domestic):

Extended Home Living Services, Inc. (2)
210 W Campus Dr Ste B, Arlington Heights, IL 60004
Tel.: (847) 318-3339
Web Site: https://www.lifewaymobility.com
Residential Remodeler
N.A.I.C.S.: 236118
Elizabeth Crandall (Pres)

Subsidiary (Domestic):

Home Mobility Solutions, Inc. (3)
5239 Thatcher Rd, Downers Grove, IL 60515-4027
Tel.: (630) 800-7800
Accessibility Solutions Provider
N.A.I.C.S.: 238990
Mike Cleary (Founder)

Medical Positioning, Inc. (1)
1717 Washington St, Kansas City, MO 64108
Tel.: (816) 474-1555
Web Site:
http://www.medicalpositioning.com
Sales Range: $1-9.9 Million
Emp.: 25
Diagnostic Imaging Beds & Tables Mfr & Sales
N.A.I.C.S.: 423450

ROCKWOOD HOLDING COMPANY INC.
200 W Madison St Fl 25, Chicago, IL 60606-3417
Tel.: (312) 750-8400
Year Founded: 1978
Rev.: $33,100,000
Fabricated Metal Products
N.A.I.C.S.: 332999

Subsidiaries:

Great Lakes Consulting Group Inc. (1)
54722 Little Flower Trl, Mishawaka, IN 46545
Tel.: (574) 287-4500
Sales Range: $10-24.9 Million
Emp.: 5
Management Consulting Services
N.A.I.C.S.: 532120

Rockwood & Co. Inc. (1)
200 W Madison St Fl 38, Chicago, IL 60606-3417 (100%)
Tel.: (312) 750-8400
Sales Range: $10-24.9 Million
Emp.: 5
Motor Vehicle Parts & Accessories
N.A.I.C.S.: 336390

ROCKWOOD HOLDINGS LIMITED PARTNERSHIP
43 Arch St, Greenwich, CT 06830-6512
Tel.: (203) 869-6734   VA
Investment Holding Company
N.A.I.C.S.: 551112
Peter O. Scannell (Founder & Mng Gen Partner)
John Lockwood (CFO)

Subsidiaries:

Rockwood Service Corporation (1)
43 Arch St, Greenwich, CT 06830
Tel.: (203) 869-6734

Web Site: http://www.rockwoodservice.com
Sales Range: $1-4.9 Billion
Emp.: 4,000
Holding Company; Non-Destructive Testing & Inspection Services
N.A.I.C.S.: 551112
Peter O. Scannell (Chm, Pres & CEO)

Subsidiary (Domestic):

Hellier NDT, Inc. (2)
1 Sparyard St, New London, CT 06320
Tel.: (860) 437-1003
Web Site: http://www.hellierndt.com
Emp.: 2
Non-Destructive Testing Training & Certification Services
N.A.I.C.S.: 611430
Ames B. Shea (Pres)

Subsidiary (Non-US):

Remote Access Technology International (2)
61 Atlantic Street, Dartmouth, B2Y 4P4, NS, Canada (100%)
Tel.: (902) 434-4405
Web Site: http://www.rat.ca
Emp.: 35
Industrial Rope Access Non-Destructive Testing, Maintenance, Repair & Standby Rescue Services
N.A.I.C.S.: 541990
Sara Primeau (Controller)

Subsidiary (Domestic):

Sperry Rail, Inc. (2)
46 Shelter Rock Rd, Danbury, CT 06810-7050
Tel.: (203) 791-4500
Web Site: http://www.sperryrail.com
Sales Range: $25-49.9 Million
Emp.: 300
Railway Non-Destructive Testing, Inspection & Engineering Services
N.A.I.C.S.: 541990
Peter O. Scannell (Chm, Pres & CEO)

ROCKY CREEK LUMBER COMPANY LLC
372 Mexboro Rd, Mexia, AL 36458
Tel.: (318) 448-0405
Web Site: http://www.royomartin.com
Sales Range: $10-24.9 Million
Emp.: 77
Lumber
N.A.I.C.S.: 423310

ROCKY MOUNT STOP & SHOP INC
4104 Sunset Ave, Rocky Mount, NC 27804
Tel.: (252) 443-9210
Sales Range: $10-24.9 Million
Emp.: 25
Convenience Store
N.A.I.C.S.: 445131
George W. Griffin (Pres)
Cindy Riddick (Office Mgr)
Pat Griffin (VP)

ROCKY MOUNTAIN AGRONOMICS INC.
1912 W Main St, Burley, ID 83318
Tel.: (208) 677-4230
Rev.: $10,000,000
Emp.: 20
Fertilizer & Fertilizer Materials
N.A.I.C.S.: 424910
Brad Bandy (Pres)

ROCKY MOUNTAIN CARE
5242 S College Dr Ste 150, Murray, UT 84123
Tel.: (801) 397-4900   UT
Web Site: http://www.rmcare.com
Year Founded: 2000
Sales Range: $10-24.9 Million
Emp.: 291
Hospice Care Services
N.A.I.C.S.: 621610
Dee R. Bangerter (Pres & Sec)

U.S. PRIVATE

ROCKY MOUNTAIN DEVELOPMENT COUNCIL
200 S Cruse, Helena, MT 59601
Tel.: (406) 447-1680   MT
Web Site: http://www.rmdc.net
Year Founded: 1966
Sales Range: $10-24.9 Million
Emp.: 280
Community Action Services
N.A.I.C.S.: 624190
Joan Anderson (Treas & Sec)
Sheilah Mevis (VP)

ROCKY MOUNTAIN ELK FOUNDATION, INC.
5705 Grant Creek Rd, Missoula, MT 59808
Tel.: (406) 523-4500   MT
Web Site: http://www.rmef.org
Year Founded: 1984
Sales Range: $25-49.9 Million
Emp.: 151
Wildlife & Habitat Conservation Services
N.A.I.C.S.: 813312
Blake Henning (Chief Conservation Officer)
David Allen (Pres & CEO)
Pete Angle (VP-Mktg Plano Synergy)
Tony Caligiuri (Pres)
Toxey Haas (Founder)
Rob Hart (VP)
Greg L'Hommedieu (VP-Store Sls & Ops)
Corey Maynard (VP-Mktg)
Bill Newton (Mng Partner)
Brad Treu (VP-Sls & Mktg)

ROCKY MOUNTAIN EXPRESS CORP
35715 Hwy 40 Bldg B, Evergreen, CO 80439
Tel.: (303) 674-8522
Web Site: http://www.rmxglobal.com
Sales Range: $10-24.9 Million
Emp.: 81
Truck Transportation Brokers
N.A.I.C.S.: 488510
William J. Henderson (CEO)
Debbie Beezley (Controller)
Tim Pepkawski (VP)

ROCKY MOUNTAIN FABRICATION INC.
1125 W 2300 N, Salt Lake City, UT 84116-1261
Tel.: (801) 596-2400
Web Site: http://www.rmf-slc.com
Year Founded: 1978
Plate Steel Structures Engineering, Fabrication & Field Erection
N.A.I.C.S.: 238120
Randy Guest (Division Mgr)
Kent Waldron (Mgr-Contracts)
John Clayton (Mgr-Engrg)
Chad Johnson (Pres & Gen Mgr)

ROCKY MOUNTAIN FIBER PLUS
33555 County Rd 37, Kiowa, CO 80117
Tel.: (303) 621-2820
Rev.: $15,200,000
Emp.: 30
Cable Television Construction
N.A.I.C.S.: 237130

ROCKY MOUNTAIN HARDWARE INC.
1020 Airport Way, Hailey, ID 83333
Tel.: (208) 788-2013
Web Site:
http://www.rockymountainhardware.com
Rev.: $25,000,000
Emp.: 75

Furniture & Other Household Hardware Mfr
N.A.I.C.S.: 332510
Mark Nickum (Owner)

ROCKY MOUNTAIN HEALTH MAINTENANCE ORGANIZATION INCORPORATED
2775 Crossroads Blvd, Grand Junction, CO 81506-8712
Tel.: (970) 244-7800
Web Site: http://www.rmhp.org
Year Founded: 1971
Emp.: 425
Health Care Insurance Brokerage
N.A.I.C.S.: 524210
Laurel Walters (COO)
Kevin R. Fitzgerald (Chief Medical Officer)

ROCKY MOUNTAIN HUMAN SERVICES
9900 E Iliff Ave, Denver, CO 80231
Tel.: (303) 636-5600
Web Site: http://www.rmhumanservices.org
Year Founded: 1991
Sales Range: $25-49.9 Million
Emp.: 347
Disability Assistance Services
N.A.I.C.S.: 624120
Nina Cruchon (Dir-Behavioral Health)
Brenda Whitlow (Dir-Svc Coordination)
Shari Repinski (Exec Dir)
John Wetherington (CFO)
Ford Allison (Chief Program Officer)
Jenny Smith (Dir-Svc Coordination)
Deanna Soulis (Dir-HR & Facilities)
Dianne Clarke (Dir-Compliance & Quality)
Amy Ross (Vice Chm)
Christine Ruggeri (Sec)
Mark Ferrandino (Treas)
Roger Schmitz (Chm)

ROCKY MOUNTAIN INSTRUMENT, INC.
106 Laser Dr, Lafayette, CO 80026
Tel.: (303) 664-5000
Web Site: http://www.rmico.com
Sales Range: $75-99.9 Million
Emp.: 100
Optical & Laser Technology Solutions
N.A.I.C.S.: 333310
Yubong Hahn (Chief Scientist & Strategist)
Steven Hahn (CEO)
Corri Klingsmith (Controller)

ROCKY MOUNTAIN LOG HOMES-CANADA, LLC
1883 US Hwy 93 S, Hamilton, MT 59840
Tel.: (406) 363-5680
Web Site: http://www.rmlh.com
Year Founded: 1974
Sales Range: $75-99.9 Million
Emp.: 100
Mfr of Log Homes
N.A.I.C.S.: 321992
James R. Schueler (Pres & CEO)
Craig Rostad (CFO & Gen Mgr)
Dave Fullerton (Mgr-Sls)
Dawn Moore (Mgr-Conceptual Design)
Klint Cleveland (Mgr-Comml Projects & Mgr-IT)
Rob Ridgway (Mgr-Sls)

ROCKY MOUNTAIN MATERIALS & ASPHALT, INC.
1910 Rand Ave, Colorado Springs, CO 80906
Tel.: (719) 473-3100
Web Site: http://www.rmmaterials.com
Year Founded: 1977
Sales Range: $25-49.9 Million
Emp.: 415
Provider of Blacktop Services
N.A.I.C.S.: 238990
Terri Burch (CFO)
Eric Bogren (VP)
Greg Schnurr-Soil (Asst VP)
J. T. Marrs (Dir-Transportation)
Rick Wallace (Mgr-Shop)
Rob Mangone (VP)
Sue Price (Controller)
Tom Smith (Gen Mgr)

ROCKY MOUNTAIN OILFIELD WAREHOUSE
414 S Elm St, Casper, WY 82601
Tel.: (307) 266-2260
Web Site: http://www.rockymountainwarehouse.com
Sales Range: $10-24.9 Million
Emp.: 42
Petroleum Industry Machinery
N.A.I.C.S.: 423830
Phillip H. Cooper (Pres)

ROCKY MOUNTAIN PIES, LLC.
250 W Crossroads Sq, Salt Lake City, UT 84115
Tel.: (801) 233-6662
Web Site: http://www.rockymountainpies.com
Sales Range: $25-49.9 Million
Emp.: 250
Dessert Pie Mfr & Whslr
N.A.I.C.S.: 311520
Sam Park (Owner)
David Park (VP-Procurement & Logistics)

ROCKY MOUNTAIN PUBLIC BROADCASTING NETWORK, INC.
1089 Bannock St, Denver, CO 80204
Tel.: (303) 892-6666
Web Site: http://www.rmpbs.org
Emp.: 70
Public Television Broadcasting Station
N.A.I.C.S.: 516120
Doug Houston (CTO)
Hubert Farbes (Chm)
Amanda Mountain (Pres & CEO)
Patricia Pacey (Vice Chm)
Jesus Salazar (Sec)
Tim Haddon (Treas)

ROCKY MOUNTAIN SANITATION, LLC
721 23 Rd, Grand Junction, CO 81505
Tel.: (970) 243-9812
Web Site: http://www.rockymountainsanitation.com
Year Founded: 1997
Sales Range: $1-9.9 Million
Emp.: 20
Solid Waste Removal Services
N.A.I.C.S.: 562111
Loren Mullen (Co-Owner)
Lisa B. Mullen (Co-Owner)

ROCKY MOUNTAIN SUPPLY INC.
350 Jackrabbit Ln, Belgrade, MT 59714
Tel.: (406) 388-4008
Web Site: http://www.rmsi.coop
Sales Range: $25-49.9 Million
Emp.: 80
Petroleum Bulk Stations
N.A.I.C.S.: 424710
Randy Whal (Controller)
Brad Gjermo (CEO)
Terry Sweeney (CFO)
Mark Rehyer (Vice Chm-Belgrade)

ROCKY ROCOCO CORPORATION
105 E Wisconsin Ave Ste 101, Oconomowoc, WI 53066
Tel.: (262) 569-5580
Web Site: http://www.rockyrococo.com
Year Founded: 1974
Sales Range: $50-74.9 Million
Emp.: 650
Franchised Pizza Restaurants
N.A.I.C.S.: 722513
Tom Hester (Pres)
Trey Hester (VP)
Kurt Kimball (Controller)

ROCKY TOP MARKETS LLC
1324 Lawnville Rd, Kingston, TN 37763-4728
Tel.: (865) 717-0700
Web Site: http://www.rockytopmarkets.com
Year Founded: 1970
Sales Range: $25-49.9 Million
Emp.: 310
Gasoline Service Stations, Convenience Stores
N.A.I.C.S.: 457120
Steve Kirkham (Pres)

ROCKY'S HARDWARE INCORPORATED
40 Island Pond Rd, Springfield, MA 01118
Tel.: (413) 781-1650
Web Site: http://www.rockys.com
Year Founded: 1926
Sales Range: $10-24.9 Million
Emp.: 400
Operators of Hardware Stores
N.A.I.C.S.: 444140
Rocco J. Falcone (Pres)
James Falcone (Founder & Chm)

ROCKYOU, INC.
305 2nd St South Tower Ste 600, San Francisco, CA 94107
Tel.: (415) 580-6400
Web Site: http://www.rockyou.com
Year Founded: 2005
Online Game Developer
N.A.I.C.S.: 541519
Lisa Marino (CEO)
Josh Grant (COO)
James Abel (Dir-Bus Dev)
Ed Zobrist (Gen Mgr-Games Div)
Mei Costello (VP-Fin & Admin)

Subsidiaries:

Gree International Inc. (1)
185 Berry St, San Francisco, CA 94107
Tel.: (415) 409-5200
Web Site: http://www.product.gree.net
Online Game Development
N.A.I.C.S.: 541519
Naoki Aoyagi (CEO)
Andrew Sheppard (COO)
Shanti Bergel (Sr VP-Bus & Corp Dev)
Yoshikazu Tanaka (Founder & Dir)

ROCS, INC.
2355 Dulles Corner Blvd Ste 650, Herndon, VA 20171
Tel.: (703) 579-6677
Web Site: http://www.rocsstaffing.com
Year Founded: 2003
Sales Range: $1-9.9 Million
Emp.: 8
Staffing & Consultancy Services
N.A.I.C.S.: 541612

Brandon Labman (Co-Founder)
Tom Moore (Co-Founder)

ROD FRASER ENTERPRISES INC.
1320 N Manzanita St, Orange, CA 92867
Tel.: (714) 633-7844
Rev.: $17,400,000
Mexican Restaurant
N.A.I.C.S.: 722511
Patricia Fraser (Pres)
Chris Sheldon (Sec)

Subsidiaries:

Young Ranch Inc. (1)
1320 N Manzanita St, Orange, CA 92867
Tel.: (714) 633-7844
Web Site: http://www.donjose.com
Rev.: $10,600,000
Emp.: 15
Liquor Stores
N.A.I.C.S.: 445320
John Hawkins (Controller)

ROD WORKS INC.
4275 Thanksgiving Way, Lehi, UT 84043-2906
Tel.: (801) 768-4178
Web Site: http://www.rodworks.com
Year Founded: 1998
Sales Range: $1-9.9 Million
Emp.: 60
Home Furnishing Merchant Whslr
N.A.I.C.S.: 423220
Mark Tuttle (Pres)
Alexis Crockett (Mgr)

ROD-L ELECTRONICS INC.
935 F Sierra Vista Ave, Mountain View, CA 94043-1701
Tel.: (650) 322-0711
Web Site: http://www.rodl.com
Year Founded: 1977
Sales Range: $10-24.9 Million
Emp.: 10
Test Equipment for Electronic & Electrical Circuits Mfr & Distr
N.A.I.C.S.: 334515
Roy Clay Sr. (Founder & Pres)

RODAN & FIELDS, LLC
60 Spear St Ste 600, San Francisco, CA 94105-1512
Tel.: (415) 273-8000
Web Site: http://www.rodanandfields.com
Year Founded: 2002
Emp.: 170
Beauty Products Mfr & Online Retailer
N.A.I.C.S.: 325620
Ralph Loura (CTO)
Chris Newman (CFO)
Lynn Emmolo (Chief Global Officer)
Kathy Fields (Co-Founder)
Amnon Rodan (Chm)
Katie Rodan (Co-Founder)
Bryan Wayda (Chief Supply & Svc Officer)
Heidi Kathleen Wissmiller (Chief Field Operating Officer)

RODATA INC.
1601 Marys Ave Ste 2G-10, Pittsburgh, PA 15215
Tel.: (412) 782-8210
Web Site: http://www.rodata.com
Sales Range: $10-24.9 Million
Emp.: 20
Prerecorded Video Discs & Tapes
N.A.I.C.S.: 449210
Tamara Slobada (Controller)
Jane Kossuth (Mgr-Inside Sls)
Joy Brobeck (Project Mgr)
Matt Smith (Acct Mgr)

RODEM INC.

Rodata Inc.—(Continued)

RODEM INC.
5095 Crookshank Rd, Cincinnati, OH 45238
Tel.: (513) 922-6140
Web Site: http://www.rodem.com
Sales Range: $10-24.9 Million
Emp.: 100
General Manufacturing Machinery
N.A.I.C.S.: 423830
Chris Diener (Pres)
Jeff Diener (Exec VP)
Karen Nickell (Mgr-Inside Sls)
Stan Pritchard (Mgr-Sls)

RODGERS BUILDERS, INC.
5701 N Sharon Amity Rd, Charlotte, NC 28215-3984
Tel.: (704) 537-6044   NC
Web Site:
   http://www.rodgersbuilders.com
Year Founded: 1963
Sales Range: $125-149.9 Million
Emp.: 260
General Contractors Services
N.A.I.C.S.: 236220
Pat Rodgers (Pres & CEO)
Ben Dellinger (CFO)
Bob Glusenkamp (Exec VP)
Steve Phifer (Exec VP)
David Page (Sr VP-Bus Dev)

RODGERS CADILLAC, INC.
8360 Kingston Pike, Knoxville, TN 37919
Tel.: (865) 539-9100
Year Founded: 1899
Sales Range: $10-24.9 Million
Emp.: 30
Car Whslr
N.A.I.C.S.: 441110
Cowan Rodgers (Pres)

RODGERS METAL CRAFT, INC.
154 Goat Rock Rd, Fortson, GA 31808
Tel.: (706) 327-4536
Web Site:
   https://rodgersmetalcraftinc.com
Rev.: $2,300,000
Emp.: 30
Fabricated Structural Metal Mfr
N.A.I.C.S.: 332312
Cindy Durga (Mgr-HR)
Gregory Rodgers (VP)

Subsidiaries:

Division 5 LLC   (1)
2650 Strawn Rd, Winston, GA 30187
Tel.: (770) 577-0355
Web Site: https://www.division5inc.com
Sales Range: $1-9.9 Million
Emp.: 20
Fabricated Structural Metal Mfr
N.A.I.C.S.: 332312
Rhonda Wylie (CFO)
Bryan E. Hill (CEO)

Subsidiary (Domestic):

Structural Steel of Carolina, LLC   (2)
1720 Vargrave St, Winston Salem, NC 27107
Tel.: (336) 725-0521
Rev.: $8,500,000
Emp.: 70
Fabricated Structural Metal Mfr
N.A.I.C.S.: 332312
Toma Ingold (Project Mgr)

RODGERS TRUCKING CO.
14327 Washington Ave, San Leandro, CA 94578
Tel.: (510) 483-7000
Web Site:
   http://www.rodgerstrucking.com
Rev.: $14,883,880
Emp.: 12

Provider of Trucking Services
N.A.I.C.S.: 484110
Frank Ghiglione (Pres)

RODHES MARKET INCORPORATED
2105 Glen Dr, Millersburg, OH 44654
Tel.: (330) 674-7075
Web Site: http://www.rodhesiga.com
Sales Range: $10-24.9 Million
Emp.: 143
Provider of Independent Supermarket
N.A.I.C.S.: 445110
Kurt A. Rodhe (Pres)

RODI AUTOMOTIVE INC.
13 Harbor Park Dr, Port Washington, NY 11050-4604
Tel.: (516) 484-9500   NY
Web Site: http://www.autobarn.com
Year Founded: 1957
Sales Range: $25-49.9 Million
Emp.: 250
Provider of Automotive Parts & Home Supply Services
N.A.I.C.S.: 441330
David Blumberg (VP)

RODI SYSTEMS CORPORATION
936 Hwy 516, Aztec, NM 87410
Tel.: (605) 334-5865
Web Site:
   http://www.rodisystems.com
Year Founded: 1995
Water Purification Equipment Mfr
N.A.I.C.S.: 221310
Stan Lueck (Pres)

RODIN INCOME TRUST, INC.
110 E 59th St, New York, NY 10022
Tel.: (212) 938-5000   MD
Web Site:
   http://www.rodinincome.com
Year Founded: 2016
Rev.: $1,850,308
Assets: $27,295,713
Liabilities: $8,670,093
Net Worth: $18,625,620
Earnings: $1,531,262
Fiscal Year-end: 12/31/21
Real Estate Investment Services
N.A.I.C.S.: 531210
John C. Griffin (CFO & Treas)
Howard W. Lutnick (Chm, Pres & CEO)

RODMAN FORD SALES INC.
52 Washington St, Foxboro, MA 02035
Tel.: (508) 543-3333
Web Site:
   http://www.rodmanford.com
Sales Range: $50-74.9 Million
Emp.: 140
Automobiles, New & Used
N.A.I.C.S.: 532111
Donald E. Rodman (Pres)
Curt Rodman (Principal-Dealer)
Mike Wagner (Mgr-Fleet & Comml Sls)
Brett Rodman (Principal-Dealer)
Sean Grover (Mgr-Svc)
Frank Winslow (Dir-Fleet)
John Hayes (Mgr-Fleet)
Kim Chubbuck (Office Mgr)
Sheryl Wagner (Mgr-Fin)

Subsidiaries:

Rodman Lincoln-Mercury Inc.   (1)
53 Washington St, Foxboro, MA 02035
Tel.: (508) 543-3333
Web Site: http://www.rodmanford.com
Sales Range: $25-49.9 Million
Automobiles, New & Used
N.A.I.C.S.: 441110
Donald E. Rodman (Pres)

RODMAN RIDE FOR KIDS
10 Lincoln Rd, Foxboro, MA 02035
Tel.: (508) 543-7892   MA
Web Site:
   http://www.rodmanforkids.org
Year Founded: 1996
Sales Range: $10-24.9 Million
Fundraising Services
N.A.I.C.S.: 813211
Don Rodman (Pres)
Tracey Goulet-Manning (Exec Dir)
Chris Small (Chm)

RODNEY D. YOUNG INSURANCE AGENCY, INC.
4445 W Ledbetter Dr, Dallas, TX 75236
Tel.: (214) 333-4002   TX
Web Site: http://www.fredloya.com
Year Founded: 1952
Sales Range: $200-249.9 Million
Emp.: 125
Insurance Agents
N.A.I.C.S.: 524210
Theo Frank (VP)
Christy Miller (Reg Mgr)
Jackie Boling (Mgr-HR)

RODON FOODS INC.
7783 Allen St, Midvale, UT 84047-7227
Tel.: (801) 566-0616
Sales Range: $10-24.9 Million
Emp.: 20
Whslr of Groceries
N.A.I.C.S.: 424410
Cory S. Rasmussen (Pres)
Thomas Brown (Mgr-IT)
Dennis Waters (Mgr-Sls)

RODROCK & ASSOCIATES INC.
12647 Hemlock St, Overland Park, KS 66213-1455
Tel.: (913) 681-2121
Web Site: http://www.rodrock.com
Sales Range: $10-24.9 Million
Emp.: 6
Residential Property Mgr
N.A.I.C.S.: 531311
Darol Rodrock (Pres)
Tom Langhofer (Gen Mgr)

RODY TRUCK CENTER OF MIAMI, INC.
10495 NW 27 Ave, Miami, FL 33147
Tel.: (305) 638-3583
Web Site: http://www.rodytrucks.com
Year Founded: 2009
Sales Range: $10-24.9 Million
Trucks & Cars Dealer
N.A.I.C.S.: 423110
Rodovaldo Gomez (Pres)

ROEBLING MANAGEMENT COMPANY, LLC
525 Vine St Ste 2205, Cincinnati, OH 45202
Tel.: (859) 445-2223
Web Site: https://roeblingcp.com
Private Equity Firm
N.A.I.C.S.: 523999
Keith Carlson (Co-Founder, CEO & Mng Dir)

Subsidiaries:

Longstreth Sporting Goods, LLC   (1)
32 Wells Rd, Parker Ford, PA 19457-0000
Tel.: (610) 495-7022
Web Site: http://www.longstreth.com
Sporting Goods Retailer
N.A.I.C.S.: 459110

ROEDER IMPLEMENT INC.
2550 Rockdale Rd, Dubuque, IA 52003

Tel.: (563) 557-1184   IA
Web Site:
   http://www.roederoutdoor.com
Sales Range: $10-24.9 Million
Emp.: 30
Providers of Agricultural Machinery & Equipment
N.A.I.C.S.: 423820
James V. Roeder (Pres & Gen Mgr)

ROEDING GROUP COMPANIES, INC.
2734 Chancellor Dr Ste 300, Covington, KY 41017
Tel.: (859) 341-0202   KY
Web Site:
   http://www.roedinginsurance.com
Year Founded: 1921
Emp.: 50
Insurance Agency & Consulting Services
N.A.I.C.S.: 524210
Stephen T. Roeding (CEO)
Sue Porter (Pres)

ROEHL TRANSPORT, INC.
1916 E 29th St, Marshfield, WI 54449
Tel.: (715) 591-3795   WI
Web Site: http://www.roehl.net
Year Founded: 1962
Sales Range: $250-299.9 Million
Emp.: 2,000
Trucking Service
N.A.I.C.S.: 484121
Richard Roehl (CEO)
Steve Wykle (VP-Fin)
John Spiros (VP-Safety & Claims Mgmt)
Phil Trierweiler (VP-Maintenance)
Tom Witt (Pres-Flatbed & Specialized Div)
Michael Hinz (Pres-Van, Refrigerated & Dedicated Div)

Subsidiaries:

Roehl Logistics, Inc.   (1)
1331 North Rd, Green Bay, WI 54313
Tel.: (866) 516-1992
Web Site: http://www.roehllogistics.com
Logistics Management Services
N.A.I.C.S.: 541614
Steve Elliott (VP)
Rob Frazier (Gen Mgr)
Jeff Scott (Mgr-Dallas)

ROERSMA & WURN BUILDERS
908 W River Ctr NE Ste A, Comstock Park, MI 49321-8990
Tel.: (616) 784-5592
Year Founded: 1986
Sales Range: $10-24.9 Million
Emp.: 20
Housing Construction Services
N.A.I.C.S.: 236117
Janet Reinke (Office Mgr)
Mark R. Wurn (Pres)

ROESCH INC.
100 N 24th St, Belleville, IL 62226
Tel.: (618) 233-2760
Web Site: http://www.roeschinc.com
Sales Range: $10-24.9 Million
Emp.: 100
Aluminum Coating of Metal Products
N.A.I.C.S.: 332812
Mike Koenigstein (Gen Mgr)
Debbie Thomas (Mgr-Sls-Ice Indus)
Debbie Voges-Schneider (Exec VP)
Hitpreet Majhail (Mgr-OEM Customer Dev)

ROESER HOUSING DEVELOPMENT CORPORATION
29700 Woodford Tehachapi Rd, Keene, CA 93531-0000
Tel.: (661) 823-6122   AZ

Year Founded: 2009
Sales Range: $1-9.9 Million
Elder Care Services
N.A.I.C.S.: 624120
Paul Park (Sec)
Paul Chavez (Pres & CEO)
Manuel Bernal (Treas)

ROETTGERS COMPANY INC.
5169 N 37th St, Milwaukee, WI 53209
Tel.: (414) 466-0890
Web Site: http://www.roettgersco.com
Rev.: $15,000,000
Emp.: 10
Convenience Store
N.A.I.C.S.: 445131
Dave Roettgers (CEO)

ROETZEL & ANDRESS
222 S Main St, Akron, OH 44308
Tel.: (330) 376-2700   OH
Web Site: http://www.ralaw.com
Year Founded: 1876
Sales Range: $75-99.9 Million
Emp.: 201
Legal Advisory Services
N.A.I.C.S.: 541110
Karen D. Adinolfi (Partner)
Jeffrey J. Farkas (CIO & Dir-Ops)
Bobbie Feigenbaum (Dir-Res & Reference)
Joseph F. Maslowski (CFO & COO)
Eric Stiles (Dir-Practice Support)
Aretta K. Bernard (Partner)
Susan S. Box (Partner)
Helen S. Carroll (Partner)
Elizabeth Nocera Davis (Partner)
Brian Tarian (Partner)
Paul Giordano (Partner & Mgr-Practice Grp-Bus Litigation)
Mazen Asbahi (Partner-Corp, Tax & Transactional Grp)
John R. Joyce (Partner-Real Estate Practice Grp)
Daniel Rohletter (Partner-Real Estate Practice Grp-Columbus)
Robert E. Blackham (Chm)
Jeffrey J. Casto (Partner-Bus & Comml Litigation Grp)
Zachary Prendergast (Partner)
Lewis W. Adkins Jr. (Mgr-Shareholder & Practice Group, Public Law, Regulatory, and Fin)
G. Frederick Compton Jr. (Partner)
John M. Coyne III (Partner)

ROFSON ASSOCIATES, INC.
3800 Brittmoore Rd, Houston, TX 77043
Tel.: (713) 975-0700   NY
Web Site: http://www.rofson.com
Year Founded: 1963
Sales Range: $10-24.9 Million
Emp.: 8
Whslr & Importer of Restaurant Equipment & Supplies
N.A.I.C.S.: 423440
Al Rofe (Owner)
Sharon Rofe (Owner)

ROGAN & ASSOCIATES, INC.
200 9th Ave N Ste 150, Safety Harbor, FL 34695
Tel.: (727) 712-3400
Web Site: http://www.roganfinancial.com
Year Founded: 1997
Rev.: $236,000,000
Emp.: 14
Portfolio Management & Financial Planning
N.A.I.C.S.: 523940
Michael Rogan (Pres)
Ed Foss (Chief Compliance Officer)
Jennifer Rogan (Mgr-Acctg & Fin)

ROGAN CORPORATION
3455 Woodhead Dr, Northbrook, IL 60062
Tel.: (847) 498-2300
Web Site: http://www.rogancorp.com
Rev.: $12,000,000
Emp.: 60
Hardware, Plastics
N.A.I.C.S.: 326199
Robert Piontek (Mgr-Quality Assurance)
Chrys Funteas (Mgr-Acctg)
Pamela Newman (Pres)

ROGER & SONS CONSTRUCTION INC.
4715 Euclid Ave, East Chicago, IN 46312
Tel.: (219) 397-8819
Web Site: http://www.rogerandsons.com
Rev.: $30,600,000
Emp.: 150
Commercial & Institutional Building Construction
N.A.I.C.S.: 236220
Rogelio Zepeda (Pres)
Nancy E. Martinez (VP)
Francisco Martinez (Project Mgr)

ROGER ARTZ
3545 Aero Ct, San Diego, CA 92123
Tel.: (858) 277-0626
Web Site: http://www.mcwe.com
Rev.: $13,300,000
Emp.: 80
Subdividers & Developers
N.A.I.C.S.: 237210
Roger Artz (Sr VP)

ROGER B. KENNEDY, INC.
1105 Kensington Park Dr, Altamonte Springs, FL 32714
Tel.: (407) 478-4500
Web Site: http://www.rbkennedy.com
Sales Range: $10-24.9 Million
Emp.: 20
Construction Services
N.A.I.C.S.: 236220
Michael Sundquist (Project Mgr)
Richard Carbone (VP)
Ron Whalen (VP)
Roger B. Kennedy Jr. (Pres)

ROGER BEASLEY MAZDA INC.
6825 Burnet Rd, Austin, TX 78757
Tel.: (512) 459-4111   TX
Web Site: http://www.rogerbeasleymazda.com
Year Founded: 1970
Sales Range: $50-74.9 Million
Emp.: 100
New & Used Car Dealers
N.A.I.C.S.: 441110
Roger Beasley (Owner & Pres)
Jim Bagan (Gen Mgr)
Terry Drake (Gen Mgr-Ops)

ROGER BURDICK AUTO SALES INC.
5885 E Circle Dr, Cicero, NY 13039
Tel.: (315) 452-1556
Web Site: http://www.driversvillage.com
Rev.: $20,900,000
Emp.: 420
Automobiles, New & Used
N.A.I.C.S.: 441110
Roger Burdick (Owner)

ROGER DEAN CHEVROLET, INC.
2235 Okeechobee Blvd, West Palm Beach, FL 33409
Tel.: (561) 683-8100

Web Site: http://www.rogerdeanchevrolet.com
Year Founded: 1961
Sales Range: $100-124.9 Million
Emp.: 125
Car Dealership
N.A.I.C.S.: 441110

ROGER MERTENS DISTRIBUTORS
119 Jaycee Dr, Jefferson City, MO 65109
Tel.: (573) 635-6419
Rev.: $19,000,000
Emp.: 10
Petroleum Bulk Stations
N.A.I.C.S.: 424710
Greg Martens (VP)

ROGER SMITH HOTELS CORP.
501 Lexington Ave, New York, NY 10017-2008
Tel.: (212) 755-1400
Web Site: http://www.rogersmith.com
Year Founded: 1929
Sales Range: $10-24.9 Million
Emp.: 85
Hotel & Restaurant Services
N.A.I.C.S.: 721110
James Knowles (Pres)

ROGER TV
1109 N Virgil Ave, Los Angeles, CA 90029
Tel.: (213) 620-1028
Web Site: http://www.roger.tv
Design, Animation & Live Action Production
N.A.I.C.S.: 512110
Terence Lee (Exec Creative Dir)
Dane Macbeth (Creative Dir)
Ken Carlson (Creative Dir)
Steve Petersen (Creative Dir)
Liz Catullo (Head-Production)
Anne Pendola (Dir-Bus Dev)

Subsidiaries:

Big Machine Design LLC   (1)
201 N Hollywood Way Ste 212, Burbank, CA 91505-3477
Tel.: (818) 841-2226
Web Site: http://www.bigmachine.net
Graphic Design Services
N.A.I.C.S.: 541430
Steve Peterson (Co-Founder & Dir)
Ken Carlson (Co-Founder & Creative Dir)

ROGER WARD INC.
17275 Green Mtn Rd, San Antonio, TX 78247
Tel.: (210) 655-8623
Web Site: http://www.wardnorthamerican.com
Rev.: $10,828,448
Emp.: 35
Household Goods Transport
N.A.I.C.S.: 484210
Kevin Ankenbauer (Pres)
Joe Harness (Mgr-HR)

ROGERS & BROWN CUSTOM BROKERS, INC.
150 W Phillips Rd Ste L, Greer, SC 29650
Tel.: (864) 879-2157
Web Site: http://www.rogers-brown.com
Sales Range: $25-49.9 Million
Emp.: 200
Customhouse Brokers
N.A.I.C.S.: 488510
Don H. Brown (Chm & CEO)
Cynthia Weaks (Dir-Acctg)
Raymond Kelley (VP-Ops)
Tanya Burton (Mgr-Air Transportation-Greer Div)
Beth Morris (Dir-Compliance)
Lori Mullins (Mgr-Houston)
Mary Jones (Mgr-Greer)
Mike McCormack (Dir-Info Sys)

Subsidiaries:

Rogers & Brown Custom Brokers, Inc. - Greer   (1)
150 W Phillips Rd Ste L, Greer, SC 29650
Tel.: (864) 879-2157
Web Site: http://www.rogers-brown.com
Sales Range: $1-9.9 Million
Emp.: 20
Freight Transportation Arrangement
N.A.I.C.S.: 488510
Cathy Jones (Mgr-Greer)
Don H. Brown (Chm & CEO)
Mary Ann Jones (Mgr-Norfolk)
Raymond Kelley (Exec VP)
Beth Morris (Dir-Compliance)
Cindy Weaks (Dir-Acctg)
Gabe McGann (VP-Ops & Fin)
Ken Bolin (Dir-Sls & Mktg)
Mark Hughes (VP-Ops & IT)
Perry Smith (Dir-Domestic Resource Allocation)
Debbie Oates (Mgr-Import-Charleston)
Don H. Brown Jr. (Pres)

ROGERS & HOLLANDS ENTERPRISES INC.
20821 Cicero Ave, Matteson, IL 60443-1201
Tel.: (708) 748-6400   IL
Web Site: http://www.rogersandhollands.com
Year Founded: 1945
Sales Range: $25-49.9 Million
Emp.: 450
Jewelry Stores
N.A.I.C.S.: 458310
Craig Stern (Pres)

Subsidiaries:

Roger Enterprises Inc.   (1)
20821 S Cicero Ave, Matteson, IL 60443
Tel.: (708) 679-7588
Sales Range: $25-49.9 Million
Emp.: 100
Jewelry Stores
N.A.I.C.S.: 458310
Alan Kadet (Owner)

ROGERS & ROGERS, INC.
2361 Hwy 86, Imperial, CA 92251
Tel.: (760) 352-2900
Web Site: http://www.rogersnissan.com
Sales Range: $10-24.9 Million
Emp.: 35
Car Whslr
N.A.I.C.S.: 441110
Leslie F. Rogers III (Pres)

ROGERS CONSTRUCTION INC.
PO Box 4810, Tualatin, OR 97062
Tel.: (503) 254-5517
Rev.: $20,469,146
Emp.: 12
Highway & Street Construction
N.A.I.C.S.: 237310
A. J. Urbanek (Pres)

ROGERS FAMILY COMPANY
1731 Aviation Blvd, Lincoln, CA 95648
Tel.: (916) 258-8000
Web Site: http://www.rogersfamilyco.com
Year Founded: 1979
Sales Range: $10-24.9 Million
Emp.: 100
Roasted Coffee & Tea Mfr & Distr

ROGERS FAMILY COMPANY — U.S. PRIVATE

Rogers Family Company—(Continued)
N.A.I.C.S.: 311920
Jon Rogers *(Pres)*
Jim Rogers *(VP)*
Bob Giacomelli *(Reg Mgr)*
Cathy Dalgliesh *(Mgr-Sls)*
Tim Albo *(Coord-Sls Project)*

ROGERS FOAM CORPORATION
20 Vernon St, Somerville, MA 02145-3647
Tel.: (617) 623-3010
Web Site: http://www.rogersfoamcorp.com
Year Founded: 1947
Sales Range: $100-124.9 Million
Emp.: 300
Provider of Plastic Foam Products
N.A.I.C.S.: 326150
David Marotta *(Pres)*
Dorthy Rogers *(CEO)*
Bill Tee *(Gen Mgr)*
Tom Linch *(Dir-Mktg & Pur)*

ROGERS FORD SALES INC.
4200 W Wall St, Midland, TX 79703
Tel.: (432) 694-8801
Web Site: http://www.rogersford.com
Rev.: $20,600,000
Emp.: 100
New & Used Car Dealers
N.A.I.C.S.: 441110
Doss Rogers *(Pres)*
Amber Locke *(Mgr-Internet Sls)*
James Strawbridge *(Mgr-Fin)*
Kelly Tucker *(Gen Mgr)*

ROGERS GRAIN INC.
5750 N Falls Clayton Rd, Covington, OH 45318
Tel.: (937) 473-2025
Web Site: http://www.rogersgrain.com
Sales Range: $10-24.9 Million
Emp.: 15
Grain Handling Services
N.A.I.C.S.: 561499
Donald L. Rogers *(Pres & CEO)*

ROGERS GROUP INC.
421 Great Circle Rd, Nashville, TN 37228-1407
Tel.: (615) 242-0585
Web Site: http://www.rogersgroupinc.com
Year Founded: 1908
Crushed Stone, Sand & Gravel, Asphalt & Highway Construction
N.A.I.C.S.: 212312
Kye Hudson *(VP-HR & Safety)*
Darin Matson *(Pres & CEO)*

ROGERS INVESTMENTS INC.
25 Carol Rd, Winchester, KY 40392
Tel.: (859) 744-3484
Sales Range: $10-24.9 Million
Emp.: 150
Soft Drinks Mfr
N.A.I.C.S.: 312111
Craig Rogers *(Pres & COO)*

ROGERS JEWELRY COMPANY
1408 10th St, Modesto, CA 95354
Tel.: (209) 578-1873
Web Site: http://www.thinkrogers.com
Sales Range: $10-24.9 Million
Emp.: 100
Jewelry, Precious Stones & Precious Metals
N.A.I.C.S.: 458310
Roger Marks *(Pres)*
Kathy Scheidt *(VP-Credit)*
Lori Arnold *(Treas & Sec)*

ROGERS MANUFACTURING CORP
801 Industrial Pkwy, West Monroe, LA 71291
Tel.: (318) 396-5700
Web Site: http://www.rogersmfg.com
Sales Range: $10-24.9 Million
Emp.: 137
Trusses; Wooden Roof
N.A.I.C.S.: 321215
Larry Rogers *(Owner)*
Carroll Hoover *(CFO)*
Derek Moody *(Pres)*

ROGERS MOTORS, INC.
2203 16th Ave, Lewiston, ID 83501
Tel.: (208) 743-5577
Web Site: http://www.rogersmotors.com
Sales Range: $10-24.9 Million
Emp.: 60
New Car Dealers
N.A.I.C.S.: 441110
Debbie Moser *(Mgr-Customer Rels)*
J. W. Nightingale *(Mgr-Sls)*
Brad Kingsley *(Mgr-Internet)*

ROGERS NORTHWEST INC.
PO Box 4810, Tualatin, OR 97062
Tel.: (503) 254-5517
Sales Range: $10-24.9 Million
Emp.: 75
Civil Engineering Services
N.A.I.C.S.: 237310
Roger Metcalf *(Treas, Sec & VP)*

ROGERS PETROLEUM INC.
1634 W 1st N St, Morristown, TN 37814-3709
Tel.: (423) 581-7460
Web Site: http://www.rogerspetro.com
Year Founded: 1980
Sales Range: $25-49.9 Million
Emp.: 250
Provider of Petroleum Services
N.A.I.C.S.: 424710
John Yeager *(Pres)*
Brent Cooper *(VP-Supply & Distr)*
Don Rogers *(Chm)*

ROGERS PETROLEUM SERVICES INCORPORATED
348 Tollage Creek, Pikeville, KY 41501
Tel.: (606) 432-1421
Web Site: http://www.rogerspetroleum.com
Rev.: $32,869,917
Emp.: 17
Petroleum Bulk Stations
N.A.I.C.S.: 424710
Jim Rogers *(VP)*

ROGERS READY MIX & MATERIALS
8128 N Walnut St, Byron, IL 61010
Tel.: (815) 234-8212
Web Site: http://www.rogersreadymix.net
Sales Range: $10-24.9 Million
Emp.: 15
Ready Mixed Concrete
N.A.I.C.S.: 327320
Robert Rogers *(VP)*
Toby Rogers *(Pres)*
Mark Jewell *(Controller)*

ROGERS SOFTWARE DEVELOPMENT, INC.
1291 Sadler Way Ste 335, Fairbanks, AK 99701
Tel.: (907) 458-1001
Web Site: http://www.rogerspos.com
Year Founded: 2001
Sales Range: $1-9.9 Million
Emp.: 23
Software Development Services
N.A.I.C.S.: 513210
Matt Rogers *(Founder & Pres)*

ROGERS STEREO INC.
525 Woodruff Rd, Greenville, SC 29607
Tel.: (864) 288-9999
Web Site: http://www.rogersstereo.com
Emp.: 50
Distribution & Wholesale of Automobile Audio Systems
N.A.I.C.S.: 334310
Michael Philyaw *(Pres)*

ROGERS SUPPLY COMPANY INC.
350 N Walnut St, Champaign, IL 61820
Tel.: (217) 356-0166
Web Site: http://www.rogerssupply.com
Rev.: $17,623,403
Emp.: 25
Refrigeration Equipment & Supplies
N.A.I.C.S.: 423740
Gerald Schmidt *(Pres)*
Kathy Kist *(Controller)*
Leah Lampton *(Mgr-Sls & Mktg)*

ROGERS-DABBS CHEVROLET, INC.
1501 W Government St, Brandon, MS 39043
Tel.: (601) 825-2277
Web Site: http://www.rogersdabbs.com
Year Founded: 1980
Sales Range: $10-24.9 Million
Emp.: 110
Car Whslr
N.A.I.C.S.: 441110
Michael Wallis *(Gen Mgr)*

ROGERS-O'BRIEN CONSTRUCTION COMPANY INC.
3901 S Lambar Bld Ste 200, Austin, TX 78704
Tel.: (512) 486-3800
Web Site: http://www.r-o.com
Year Founded: 1969
Sales Range: $25-49.9 Million
Emp.: 220
Industrial Buildings & Warehouses
N.A.I.C.S.: 236210
Patrick D. O'Brien *(Chm)*
Preston L. McAfee *(CEO)*
Mike Orr *(CFO)*
John Carver *(Sr VP)*
Paul Johnson *(Sr VP)*
Cary F. Hughes *(Sr VP)*
Ken Dunham *(VP-HR)*
Graham Merriman *(VP & Dir-Client Dev)*
Justin McAfee *(Pres-Dallas & Fort Worth)*
Leon Davis *(Dir-Client)*
Mike Dempsey *(Dir-Client)*
Joe Williams *(Dir-Tech)*
Gregg Lynch *(Pres-Houston)*
Cisco Hobbs *(Pres-Austin & San Antonio)*
Carolyn Karabinos *(Dir-Client Rels & Dev)*
Alan Najar *(Dir-Fin)*
Michael Shepherd *(CTO)*
Sung Kang *(Dir-Preconstruction)*

Subsidiaries:

RO Restoration Specialists (1)
4501 Sunbelt Dr Ste B, Addison, TX 75001 (100%)
Tel.: (214) 637-2200
Web Site: http://www.restoration-spec.com
Sales Range: $10-24.9 Million
Emp.: 13
Restoration from Fire, Water or Mold Damage
N.A.I.C.S.: 236118

ROGERSON AIRCRAFT CORPORATION
2201 Alton Pkwy, Irvine, CA 92606-5033
Tel.: (949) 660-0666
Web Site: http://www.rogerson.com
Year Founded: 1975
Sales Range: $50-74.9 Million
Emp.: 300
Aircraft Components Mfr
N.A.I.C.S.: 336413
Michael Rogerson *(Chm-Rogerson Kratos)*
Dan Solvales *(Dir-Mktg & Adv)*
Chandarin Kim *(Production Mgr)*
Fred Lucas *(VP-Ops)*
Donald Livingston *(Mgr-Quality Assurance)*

Subsidiaries:

Rogerson Aircraft Controls (1)
2201 Alton Pkwy, Irvine, CA 92606-5033
Tel.: (949) 660-0666
Web Site: http://www.rogerson.com
Sales Range: $10-24.9 Million
Emp.: 23
Mfr of Control Valves
N.A.I.C.S.: 336413
Ed Jankowski *(Gen Product Mgr)*

Rogerson Aircraft Systems (1)
2201 Alton Pkwy, Irvine, CA 92606-5033
Tel.: (949) 660-0666
Web Site: http://www.rogerson.com
Sales Range: $125-149.9 Million
Emp.: 100
Mfr of Aircraft Lavatory Systems
N.A.I.C.S.: 221122
Michael Rogerson *(CEO)*

Rogerson Kratos (1)
403 S Raymond Ave, Pasadena, CA 91105-2609
Tel.: (626) 449-3090
Web Site: http://www.rogersonkratos.com
Sales Range: $10-24.9 Million
Emp.: 100
Mfr of Aircraft Cockpit Instrumentation
N.A.I.C.S.: 334511
David Bjorum *(Coord-Shipping)*
Jim Oliver *(Dir-Ops-NCL & ITAN)*
RogersonT Rogerson *(Dir-Sls & Mktg)*
Terence Leung *(Engr-Mechanical)*
Thien Tran *(Engr-Sys)*
Richard Jimenez *(Mgr-Avionics)*
Robert Taylor *(Mgr-Avionics Sys Mktg)*
Nahin Choudhury *(Mgr-Pur)*
Brian Graves *(Mgr-Supply Chain Plng)*
Milt Pizinger *(VP)*
Robbie Nalls *(VP-Shipping)*
Kevin Agovino *(VP-Bus Mgmt)*

ROGGEN FARMERS ELEVATOR ASSOCIATION INC.
PO Box 8, Roggen, CO 80652-0008
Tel.: (303) 849-5506
Web Site: http://www.roggenfarmerselev.com
Year Founded: 1955
Sales Range: $10-24.9 Million
Emp.: 35
Farm Supply Services
N.A.I.C.S.: 424510
Keith Devoe *(Gen Mgr)*

ROHE & WRIGHT BUILDERS, INC.
3334 Richmond Ave Ste 200, Houston, TX 77098
Tel.: (713) 864-4040
Web Site: http://www.rohewright.com
Year Founded: 1999
Sales Range: $25-49.9 Million
Emp.: 10

Single-Family & Luxury Townhouse Builder
N.A.I.C.S.: 236115
Andy Suman (Mng Partner)
Chad Muir (Mng Partner)

ROHER PUBLIC RELATIONS
427 Bedford Rd Ste 380, Pleasantville, NY 10570
Tel.: (914) 741-2256
Web Site: http://www.roherpr.com
Year Founded: 1968
Sales Range: $1-9.9 Million
Emp.: 8
Public Relations Agency
N.A.I.C.S.: 541820
Richard S. Roher (Pres)
Torin C. Roher (Exec VP)

Subsidiaries:

Feintuch Communications, Inc. (1)
245 Park Ave Corner of E 46th St 39th Fl, New York, NY 10167
Tel.: (212) 808-4900
Web Site: http://www.feintuchcommunications.com
Public Relations Services
N.A.I.C.S.: 541820
Henry Feintuch (Founder & Pres)
Doug Wright (Sr Dir-Acct)
Richard L. Anderson (Sr Mng Dir)

Roher Public Relations (1)
522 SW 5th Ave 7th Fl, Portland, OR 97204
Tel.: (971) 266-8870
Web Site: http://www.roherpr.com
Sales Range: Less than $1 Million
Emp.: 3
Public Relations Agency
N.A.I.C.S.: 541820

ROHM PRODUCTS OF AMERICA
2500 Northlake Dr, Suwanee, GA 30024
Tel.: (770) 963-8440
Web Site: http://www.rohm-products.com
Year Founded: 1907
Chucking Tool Mfr
N.A.I.C.S.: 333517

Subsidiaries:

Master Work-Holding, Inc. (1)
315 Burke Dr, Morganton, NC 28655
Tel.: (828) 437-0011
Web Site: http://www.masterworkholding.com
Cutting Tool & Machine Tool Accessory Mfr
N.A.I.C.S.: 333515

ROHM SERVICES, CORP.
740 E Ave, Rochester, NY 14607
Tel.: (585) 244-0410 NY
Web Site: http://www.rohmservices.com
Year Founded: 1964
Sales Range: $1-9.9 Million
Emp.: 102
Nursing Home Services
N.A.I.C.S.: 623110
Robert W. Hurlbut (Pres & CEO)
Christine Hurlbut-Owen (VP)
Bridgett M. Reed (CFO)
Gail Brocious (Coord-Quality Care)

Subsidiaries:

The Fountains (1)
3800 N Federal Hwy, Boca Raton, FL 33431-4523
Tel.: (561) 395-7510
Nursing Home Facility
N.A.I.C.S.: 623311
Kerry Thompson (Office Mgr)

ROHN ROGERS ASSOCIATES INC.
708 3rd Ave FL 5, New York, NY 10017
Tel.: (212) 759-3800
Web Site: http://www.rohn-rogers.com
Rev.: $10,000,000
Emp.: 41
Data Processing Consultant
N.A.I.C.S.: 541512
David Denmark (Mng Dir)

ROHR-INDY MOTORS INC.
8455 US Hwy 31 S, Indianapolis, IN 46227
Tel.: (317) 887-0800
Web Site: http://www.indyhonda.com
Rev.: $65,000,000
Emp.: 68
New & Used Automobile Sales
N.A.I.C.S.: 441110
Robert V. Rohrman (Owner)
David Piercefield (Gen Mgr)
Tim Woodall (Mgr-Parts)

ROHR-LEX MOTORS INC.
1510 W Dundee Rd, Arlington Heights, IL 60004
Tel.: (847) 991-0444
Web Site: http://www.arlingtonlexus.com
Rev.: $20,300,000
Emp.: 65
New Car Dealers
N.A.I.C.S.: 441110
Robert Rohrman (Pres & Sec)

ROHRER ENTERPRISES, INC.
1515 State Rd, Duncannon, PA 17020
Tel.: (717) 957-3811 PA
Web Site: http://www.rohrerbus.com
Year Founded: 1972
Sales Range: $10-24.9 Million
Emp.: 1,200
Bus Sales
N.A.I.C.S.: 423110
John M. Schrantz (Pres)
Tahva Rohrer Wylie (VP-Bus Sls)
Howard E. Rohrer III (Founder)

ROHRERS QUARRY INC.
70 Lititz Rd, Lititz, PA 17543
Tel.: (717) 626-9760
Web Site: http://www.rohrers.com
Sales Range: $10-24.9 Million
Emp.: 100
Crushed & Broken Limestone
N.A.I.C.S.: 212312
Keith Wiegand (Mgr-Svcs)

ROHRICH AUTOMOTIVE GROUP
2020 W Liberty Ave, Pittsburgh, PA 15226
Tel.: (412) 344-6012
Year Founded: 1921
Sales Range: $25-49.9 Million
Emp.: 100
Car Whslr
N.A.I.C.S.: 441110
David A. Rohrich (Pres)
Tom A. Rohrich (VP)
Ken Goldberg (Mgr-Internet)

Subsidiaries:

Rohrich Cadillac Inc. (1)
2116 W Liberty Ave, Pittsburgh, PA 15226
Tel.: (412) 344-6000
Web Site: http://www.rohrichcadillac.com
Sales Range: $25-49.9 Million
Sales of New & Used Automobiles
N.A.I.C.S.: 441110
Jim Stimple (Mgr-PreOwned Sls)
Luanne Tramonti (Mgr-Fin)
Jim Schwartz (Mgr-Svc)
Marc Rosenstein (Mgr-Sls)
Paul Lilja (Mgr-Parts)
John Russell (Mgr-Parts Distr)
Chuck Lucci Sr. (Gen Mgr-Sls)

ROI COMMUNICATION
5274 Scotts Vly Dr, Scotts Valley, CA 95066
Tel.: (831) 430-0170 CA
Web Site: http://www.roico.com
Sales Range: $10-24.9 Million
Emp.: 109
Management Consulting Services
N.A.I.C.S.: 541618
Barbara Fagan-Smith (Founder & CEO)
Sheryl Lewis (Mng Dir)
Melanie Barna (Dir-Creative)
Linda Pederson (VP)

ROI INSTITUTE, INC.
2700 Highway 280 E Ste 180, Birmingham, AL 35223
Tel.: (205) 678-8101
Web Site: https://roiinstitute.net
Year Founded: 1992
Publishing Company
N.A.I.C.S.: 513210
Patti Phillips (CEO)

Subsidiaries:

Center For Talent Reporting, Inc (1)
2123 Cape Hatteras Ct, Windsor, CO 80550-3536
Tel.: (970) 460-0837
Web Site: http://www.centerfortalentreporting.org
Employment Placement Agencies
N.A.I.C.S.: 561311
David Vance (Exec Dir)

ROISUM ELITE SALES & MARKETING COMPANY INC.
1400 Lake Dr W, Chanhassen, MN 55317
Tel.: (952) 227-3199
Web Site: http://www.roisumelite.com
Year Founded: 1980
Rev.: $13,400,000
Emp.: 50
Food Service Agency
N.A.I.C.S.: 722310
Mike Seeger (Mgr-Sls)
Ruth Jared (Mgr-Sls-Non-Foods)
Shawn McAllister (COO & Exec VP)

ROIZIN REFINING CO. INC.
32 W 47th St Booth 15, New York, NY 10036
Tel.: (212) 391-0913
Rev.: $17,921,454
Emp.: 9
Jewelry; Precious Metal
N.A.I.C.S.: 339910

ROJO ARCHITECTURE, LLC
5701 E Hillsborough Ave Ste 1122, Tampa, FL 33610
Tel.: (813) 630-5508
Web Site: http://www.rojoarchitecture.com
Year Founded: 1998
Sales Range: $1-9.9 Million
Emp.: 10
Architectural Services
N.A.I.C.S.: 541310
Rob Glisson (Principal)

ROKK3R INC.
2121 NW 2nd Ave Unit 203, Miami, FL 33127
Tel.: (305) 259-6637 NV
Web Site: https://www.rokk3r.com
Year Founded: 1996
ROKK—(OTCBB)
Sales Range: $1-9.9 Million
Emp.: 9
Software Publisher
N.A.I.C.S.: 513210
Nabyl Charania (Chm)
Carlos Escobar (COO)
Juan Montoya (Chief Investment Officer)
Brian Sanchez (CTO)
German Montoya (Bd of Dirs, Chief Exponential Officer & Chief Exponential Officer)
Lorenzo De Leo (Mng Partner)
Emelia Ballestas (Sr Product Mgr)
Camilo Martinez (Engr-Lead)
Angela Vega (Engr-Lead)
Felipe Torres (Sr Designer)

ROKKAN
375 Hudson St Fl 14, New York, NY 10014
Tel.: (212) 835-9300
Web Site: http://www.rokkan.com
Year Founded: 1999
Sales Range: $50-74.9 Million
Emp.: 25
Interactive Agencies & Internet/Web Design
N.A.I.C.S.: 541810
John Noe (Co-Founder & CEO)
Chung Ng (Co-Founder)
Charles Bae (Co-Founder)
Bryan Le (Dir-Creative)
Brian Carley (Chief Creative Officer)
Sean Miller (Sr VP-Strategy)
Billy Veasey (Dir-Creative-Los Angeles)
Bill Carlson (Dir-Creative-Los Angeles)
Anthea Tang (VP-Client Partnership-Digital Bus)
Matthew Garcia (Chief Client Officer)
Jim Blackwelder (Chief Technical Officer)
Brian Veasey (Gen Mgr & Dir-New Bus-West Coast)
James Cockerille (Sr VP-Strategic Integration)
Kenneth Doherty (Sr VP & Dir-Acct Grp)
Scott Durday (VP & Dir-Acct)
Gina Larson (VP-HR)
Laura Mulloy (Sr VP & Exec Creative Dir)
Joe Tao (Chief Delivery Officer)

ROL MANUFACTURING OF AMERICA INC.
1255 La Quinta Dr Ste 120, Orlando, FL 32809-7740
Tel.: (407) 365-8380
Year Founded: 1977
Sales Range: $10-24.9 Million
Emp.: 115
Gaskets & Sealing Devices Mfr
N.A.I.C.S.: 339991
Michael Haller (VP)

Subsidiaries:

ROL-Tech-Fort Loramie (1)
62 Elm St, Fort Loramie, OH 45845-9307
Tel.: (937) 295-3651
Web Site: http://www.marwif.com
Sales Range: $10-24.9 Million
Emp.: 45
Mfr of Motor Vehicle Parts & Accessories
N.A.I.C.S.: 336370

ROLAND D. KELLY INFINITI INC.
155 Andover St, Danvers, MA 01923
Tel.: (978) 774-1000
Web Site: http://www.kellyauto.com
Rev.: $47,878,154
Emp.: 62
Automobiles, New & Used
N.A.I.C.S.: 441110
Brian Kelly (Pres)

ROLAND LAND INVESTMENT CO., INC.

ROLAND LAND INVESTMENT CO., INC.

Roland Land Investment Co., Inc.—(Continued)
16661 Ventura Blvd, Encino, CA 91436
Tel.: (818) 783-0744
Web Site: http://www.rolandlandinvestment.com
Sales Range: $10-24.9 Million
Emp.: 8
Real Estate Brokers & Agents
N.A.I.C.S.: 531210
George Roland (Pres)
Arabella De Leon (Gen Mgr-Sls)

ROLAND MACHINERY COMPANY INC.
816 N Dirksen Pkwy, Springfield, IL 62702-6115
Tel.: (217) 789-7711 IL
Web Site: http://www.rolandmachinery.com
Year Founded: 1994
Sales Range: $100-124.9 Million
Emp.: 200
Construction & Mining Machinery
N.A.I.C.S.: 423810
Ray Roland (CEO)
Mike Armstrong (CFO)
Bob Lovejoy (Mgr-Tech)
Phil Limper (Mgr-Parts)
Matt Roland (Pres)
Rachel Pennell (Mgr-HR)
Wally Savage (Mgr-Credit)
Melissa Brockhouse (Mgr-Sls Admin)
Jay Germann (Mgr-Used Equipment)
A. J. Perisho (Mgr-Used Equipment)
Bill McNamara (Mgr-Sls)
Zach Edwards (Mgr-Used Equipment)

ROLAND PARK-VICTOR'S MARKET INC.
6223 1/2 N Charles St, Baltimore, MD 21212
Tel.: (410) 323-3656 MD
Web Site: http://www.eddiesofrolandpark.com
Year Founded: 1953
Sales Range: $25-49.9 Million
Emp.: 250
Provider of Grocery Services
N.A.I.C.S.: 445110
Nancy Cohen (Owner, Pres & Treas)

ROLAND'S TIRE SERVICE, INC.
11 Howland Rd, Fairhaven, MA 02719
Tel.: (508) 997-4501 MA
Web Site: http://www.rolandstire.com
Sales Range: $10-24.9 Million
Emp.: 53
Automobile Tires & Tubes
N.A.I.C.S.: 423130
Charles Bourgault (Pres)

ROLL & HILL, LLC
87 34th St Unit 11, Brooklyn, NY 11232
Tel.: (718) 387-6132
Web Site: http://www.rollandhill.com
Lightning Design & Mfr
N.A.I.C.S.: 335139
Franklin Barefoot (Dir-Sls)

Subsidiaries:
Alexis Manufacturing Co. (1)
5765 Clay Ave SW, Wyoming, MI 49548
Tel.: (616) 735-3905
Web Site: http://www.alexismanufacturing.com
Office Furniture Mfr
N.A.I.C.S.: 337214
Daniel Ahlem (Mgr)

ROLL-A-SHADE
12101 Madera Way, Riverside, CA 92503
Tel.: (951) 245-5077
Web Site: http://www.rollashade.com
Year Founded: 1990
Sales Range: $1-9.9 Million
Emp.: 30
Manufactures & Installs Commercial Window Treatments
N.A.I.C.S.: 449122
Ty Pereira (Pres & CEO)
Ric Berg (Sr VP)
Kristen Fannin (Project Mgr)
Deanna McCoy (Sr Project Mgr)
Sal Silva (Mgr-Acctg)

ROLL-KRAFT, INC.
8901 Tyler Blvd, Mentor, OH 44060
Tel.: (888) 953-9400
Web Site: http://www.roll-kraft.com
Year Founded: 1963
N.A.I.C.S.:
Chuck Gehrisch (CEO)
Jacqueline Kato (CFO)
Kevin Gehrisch (VP)
Matt LaVelle (Mgr-Procurement)

Subsidiaries:
Chicago Roll Co., Inc. (1)
970 N Lombard Rd, Lombard, IL 60148
Tel.: (630) 627-8888
Web Site: http://www.roll-kraft.com
Special Die & Tool, Die Set, Jig & Fixture Mfr
N.A.I.C.S.: 333514
Jeff George (Gen Mgr-Ops)

ROLLAC SHUTTER OF TEXAS, INC.
5331 W Orange St, Pearland, TX 77581
Tel.: (281) 485-1911
Web Site: http://www.rollac.com
Year Founded: 1982
Sales Range: $10-24.9 Million
Emp.: 65
Construction Materials Whslr
N.A.I.C.S.: 423390
Eva Konrad (VP)
Stefan Poetsch (VP-Ops)
Walter Konrad (Founder & Pres)
Nohemi Cruz (Office Mgr)
Refik Demirovic (Dir-Assembly)
Suzie Sterling (Mgr-Inventory)
Philip Chavez (Asst Mgr-Warehouse)
Ross Mills (Dir-Retail Sls)
Hector D. Estrada (Mgr-Shipping)

ROLLADEN INC.
550 Ansin Blvd, Hallandale, FL 33009
Tel.: (954) 454-4114
Web Site: http://www.rolladen.com
Rev.: $13,000,000
Emp.: 150
Mfr & Sales of Metal Doors & Windows
N.A.I.C.S.: 332321
Robert Hoffman (Pres)

ROLLED ALLOYS, INC.
125 W Sterns Rd, Temperance, MI 48182-9567
Tel.: (734) 847-0561 MI
Web Site: http://www.rolledalloys.com
Sales Range: $500-549.9 Million
Emp.: 100
Stainless Steel Distr
N.A.I.C.S.: 423510
Bonnie Streeter (Mgr-Internet Svcs)
Zach Schulz (Engr-Applications)
Jason Wilson (Gen Mgr)

Subsidiaries:
Rolled Alloys (1)
4085 Thunderbird Ln, Fairfield, OH 45014
Tel.: (513) 874-2771
Web Site: http://www.rolledalloys.com
Sales Range: $25-49.9 Million
Emp.: 30
Specialty Metal Plasma Coating of Aircraft Engine Parts & Specialty Alloy Wire Distr
N.A.I.C.S.: 423510

Holding (Non-US):

Rolled Alloys Ltd. (2)
Walker Industrial Park Guide, Blackburn, BB1 2QE, Lancashire, United Kingdom (100%)
Tel.: (44) 1254582999
Web Site: http://www.neonickel.co.uk
Distribution & Sales of Specialty Metals
N.A.I.C.S.: 423510
Stephen Pollard (Mgr-Sls)

Rolled Alloys (Suzhou) Ltd. (1)
Unit 9A Modern Industrial Square No 333 Xingpu Road, Suzhou Industrial Park, Suzhou, 215126, Jiangsu, China
Tel.: (86) 512 6287 1560
Web Site: http://www.rolledalloys.cn
Sales Range: $10-24.9 Million
Emp.: 30
Ferroalloy Supplier
N.A.I.C.S.: 423510

Rolled Alloys Singapore, Ltd. (1)
61 Tuas S Ave 1, Link Place, Singapore, 637554, Singapore
Tel.: (65) 6227 2725
Web Site: http://www.rolledalloys.com.sg
Sales Range: $10-24.9 Million
Emp.: 15
Feroalloy Distr
N.A.I.C.S.: 423510
Yeo Thomas (Area Mgr-Sls)
James Lilly (Gen Mgr)

Rolled Alloys, Inc. - Los Angeles (1)
4942 W Rosecrans Ave, Hawthorne, CA 90250
Tel.: (310) 343-6000
Web Site: http://www.rolledalloys.com
Heat & Corrosion Resistant, Aerospace Titanium & Metal Alloys Mfr & Distr
N.A.I.C.S.: 331492

ROLLED STEEL PRODUCTS CORPORATION
2187 S Garfield Ave, Los Angeles, CA 90040-1805
Tel.: (323) 723-8836 CA
Web Site: http://www.rolledsteel.com
Year Founded: 1952
Sales Range: $75-99.9 Million
Emp.: 50
Distr of Steel; Flat & Strip Steel Product Service Center
N.A.I.C.S.: 423510
Steven Alperson (Pres & CEO)
Lonnie Alperson (CFO & Exec VP)
Mark Arrants (Plant Mgr)
Dennis Moslenko (Dir-MIS)
Scott Wetton (Product Mgr-Galvanized)
Lisa Schmidt (Mgr-Credit)
Nellie Romanu (Controller)
Leo Fragoso (Acct Exec)
Melanie Malloy (Acct Exec)
Marsha Wilkerson (Acct Exec)
Paul Hernandez (Mgr-Traffic)
Patti Lucero (Mgr-HR)
Ruben Olvera (Mgr-Quality Control)

Subsidiaries:
E&E Steel, Inc. (1)
2187 S Garfield Ave, Los Angeles, CA 90040-1805 (100%)
Tel.: (323) 723-0947
Sales Range: $10-24.9 Million
Emp.: 25
Steel Distributor
N.A.I.C.S.: 423510

ROLLER DERBY SKATE CORP.
311 W Edwards St, Litchfield, IL 62056
Tel.: (217) 324-3961 IL
Web Site: http://www.rollerderby.com

U.S. PRIVATE

Year Founded: 1939
Sales Range: $75-99.9 Million
Emp.: 100
Roller Skates, Ice Skates & Skateboards; Protective Equipment; Wheels & Bearings Mfr
N.A.I.C.S.: 423910
Walter Frazier (VP-Mktg)
David N. Kennedy (CFO & VP)

Subsidiaries:
TOUR HOCKEY, Inc. (1)
PO Box 930, Litchfield, IL 62056
Tel.: (217) 324-3001
Web Site: http://www.tourhockey.com
Hockey Skate Mfr
N.A.I.C.S.: 339920

ROLLER DIE & FORMING COMPANY, INC.
1172 Industrial Blvd, Louisville, KY 40219
Tel.: (502) 804-5571
Web Site: http://www.rollerdie.com
Year Founded: 1954
Emp.: 100
Standard & Custom Roll Formed Parts Mfr
N.A.I.C.S.: 332114
H. Ray Hammons (CEO)
Chris Kovacs (Exec Dir-Engrg & Technical Svcs)
Rocky Nelson (Dir-Sls)

Subsidiaries:
Pyramid Mouldings, Inc. (1)
4630 County Rd 209 S, Green Cove Springs, FL 32043-8182
Tel.: (904) 284-5611
Web Site: http://www.pyramidmouldings.com
Sales Range: $50-74.9 Million
Mfr of Roll-Formed Stainless & Carbon Steel Products for Architectural, Appliance, Luggage, Office Furniture & Other Industries
N.A.I.C.S.: 332114
William D. Munch (VP-Sls & Mktg)
Ronald Martin (Pres & CEO)

Plant (Domestic):

Pyramid Mouldings - Georgia Plant (2)
2912 Lakeview Dr, Rossville, GA 30741
Tel.: (706) 866-5111
Web Site: http://www.pyramidmouldings.com
Sales Range: $25-49.9 Million
Mfr of Roll-Formed Stainless & Carbon Steel Products for Architectural, Appliance, Automotive & Other Industries
N.A.I.C.S.: 332114

Plant (Non-US):

Pyramid Mouldings - Mexico Plant (2)
Av Epigmenio Gonzalez No 107 Zona Industrial Queretaro, Acceso 5 Seccion 3 Nave 16&17, Queretaro, 76150, Mexico
Tel.: (52) 442 217 1783
Web Site: http://www.pyramidmouldings.com
Sales Range: $25-49.9 Million
Mfr of Roll-Formed Stainless & Carbon Steel Products for Appliance, Truck & Automotive Industries
N.A.I.C.S.: 332114
Antonio Lom (Gen Mgr)

ROLLETTE OIL CO. INC.
2104 Beloit Ave, Janesville, WI 53546-3023
Tel.: (608) 754-0035 WI
Year Founded: 1995
Sales Range: $50-74.9 Million
Emp.: 60
Distr of Petroleum Products
N.A.I.C.S.: 424720
Kelly Murphy Simon (Pres & Treas)

ROLLEX CORPORATION

800 Chase Ave, Elk Grove Village, IL 60007-5605
Tel.: (847) 437-3000 IL
Web Site: http://www.rollex.com
Year Founded: 1957
Sales Range: $75-99.9 Million
Emp.: 150
Mfr of Aluminum, Vinyl & Steel Building Products
N.A.I.C.S.: 332322
John A. Foley (CFO)
Liz Meza (Mgr-Inventory Control & Traffic)
Shellie Anderson (Mgr-Mktg)
Tony Zarco (Coord-Traffic)

ROLLIN B. CHILD INCORPORATED
1820 Berkshire Ln N, Plymouth, MN 55441
Tel.: (763) 559-5531
Web Site: http://www.rbctile.com
Rev.: $10,200,000
Emp.: 155
Ceramic Wall & Floor Tile
N.A.I.C.S.: 423320
Brian Mark (Pres & CEO)
Dave Lundberg (CFO)

ROLLING HILLS AUTO PLAZA
1617 Cross St, Saint Joseph, MO 64506
Tel.: (816) 279-2711
Web Site: http://www.rollinghillsautoplaza.com
Rev.: $16,300,000
Emp.: 50
New & Used Car Dealers
N.A.I.C.S.: 441110
Adam Chadwick (Mgr-IT & Customer Rels)
Chris Smith (Gen Mgr)
Lee Hunter (Mgr-Bus)
Derek Schnepp (Mgr-Pre-Owned Sls)
Chip Frye (Mgr-Sls)

ROLLING HILLS BANK & TRUST
1307 E 7th St, Atlantic, IA 50022
Tel.: (712) 243-2244
Web Site: http://www.rollinghillsbank.com
Year Founded: 1876
Emp.: 75
Commercial Banking Services
N.A.I.C.S.: 522110
Darrell Hockenberry (Pres)

ROLLING HILLS COUNTRY CLUB
2722 W Roosevelt Blvd, Monroe, NC 28110
Tel.: (704) 289-4561 NC
Web Site: http://www.rollinghillscountryclub.org
Year Founded: 1962
Rev.: $3,155,436
Assets: $2,409,540
Liabilities: $903,022
Net Worth: $1,506,518
Earnings: ($140,889)
Emp.: 82
Fiscal Year-end: 02/28/15
Country Club
N.A.I.C.S.: 713910
Anita Nalepa-Hoskins (Mgr-Clubhouse)
Daniel Habicht (Dir-Clubhouse Maintenance)
Darren Berkman (Gen Mgr)
Debbie Laney (Controller)
Francis Di Menna (Head-Tennis Pro)
Anita Nalepa-Hoskins (Mgr-Clubhouse)
Daniel Habicht (Dir-Clubhouse Maintenance)
Darren Berkman (Gen Mgr)
Debbie Laney (Controller)
Francis Di Menna (Head-Tennis Pro)
Randy Adcock (Pres)
Jesse Milliken (VP)
Jimmy Norwood (Treas)
Butch Gilbert (Sec)
Sharon King Kilts (Dir-Membership)

ROLLING ROCK CLUB
167 CLUBHOUSE LANE, Laughlintown, PA 15655
Tel.: (724) 238-9501 PA
Year Founded: 1987
Sales Range: $10-24.9 Million
Country Club Operator
N.A.I.C.S.: 713910
Stephen J. Klee (COO)
Michael A. Dudzenski (CFO)

ROLLING SHIELD, INC.
9875 NW 79th Ave, Hialeah Gardens, FL 33016
Tel.: (305) 436-6661 FL
Web Site: http://www.rollingshield.com
Year Founded: 1993
Sales Range: $1-9.9 Million
Emp.: 32
Shutters & Awnings Mfr
N.A.I.C.S.: 332321
Jose Delgado (Pres)
Faustino Mora (Controller)

ROLLINS-PCI CONSTRUCTION COMPANY
1302 Rising Rdg Rd Ste 9, Mount Airy, MD 21771
Tel.: (301) 831-5031
Web Site: http://www.rollinspci.com
Year Founded: 1989
Sales Range: $10-24.9 Million
Emp.: 30
Commercial Builder & General Contractor
N.A.I.C.S.: 236220
Brian Abel (Dir-Special Projects)
Jason Happel (Project Mgr)

ROLLKALL TECHNOLOGIES LLC
600 E Las Colinas Blvd Ste 900, Irving, TX 75039 DE
Web Site: http://www.rollkall.com
Security System Services
N.A.I.C.S.: 561621
Steven Power (Pres)
Subsidiaries:
Cover Your Assets, LLC (1)
6324 River Frnt Dr, Harrisburg, NC 28075
Tel.: (704) 454-7685
Web Site: http://www.cyausa.com
Rev.: $1,100,000
Emp.: 13
Custom Computer Programming Services
N.A.I.C.S.: 541511
Ted Cormier (Founder)

ROLLOFFS USA INC.
8567 US Hwy 70, Mead, OK 73449
Tel.: (580) 924-6355
Web Site: http://www.rolloffs.net
Sales Range: $10-24.9 Million
Emp.: 70
Mfr of Garbage Cans & Stamped & Pressed Metal
N.A.I.C.S.: 332119
J. Danny Hankey (Pres)
John Amlin (Mgr-Production)
Ray Jean Hankey (VP)

ROLLPRINT PACKAGING PRODUCTS INC.
320 S Stewart Ave, Addison, IL 60101-3310
Tel.: (630) 628-1700 IL
Web Site: http://www.rollprint.com
Year Founded: 1983
Sales Range: $50-74.9 Million
Emp.: 150
Provider of Paper & Coated & Laminated Packaging
N.A.I.C.S.: 322220
Robert Dodrill (Chm)
Joe Miceli (VP-Mfg)
Dhuanne Dodrill (Pres)
Doug Dodrill (VP-Tech)
Dwane Hahn (VP-Sls & Mktg)
Henk Blom (Dir-Technical Svcs)
Mike Johnson (Controller)
Debra Kinder (Dir-Quality)

ROLLSTONE BANK & TRUST
780 Main St, Fitchburg, MA 01420
Tel.: (978) 345-1061
Web Site: http://www.rollstonebank.com
Sales Range: $10-24.9 Million
Emp.: 110
Federal Savings Bank
N.A.I.C.S.: 522180
Martin F. Corners (Pres & CEO)
Michael A. Olson (Chief Lending Officer)
Michael E. Montuori (Chm)
Roberta Parker (Sr VP-Retail Lending)
Arthur Feehan (COO & Exec VP)
Lori Kelly (First VP)

ROLTA AMERICAS
8720 Orion Pl Ste 100, Columbus, OH 43240
Tel.: (614) 436-9382
Web Site: http://www.rolta.com
Sales Range: $10-24.9 Million
Emp.: 30
IT Applications & Infrastructure
N.A.I.C.S.: 541519
Don Davis (CEO)
Greg Furst (Exec VP-Sls & Mktg-North America)
Subsidiaries:
Rolta Americas (1)
333 E Butterfield Rd Ste 900, Lombard, IL 60148
Tel.: (630) 960-2909
Sales Range: $10-24.9 Million
Computer Related Consulting Services
N.A.I.C.S.: 541512

ROLYN CONSTRUCTION CORPORATION
576 Frederick Ave, Rockville, MD 20852
Tel.: (301) 468-1553
Web Site: http://www.rolyncompanies.com
Sales Range: $25-49.9 Million
Emp.: 115
Commercial & Residential Restorations
N.A.I.C.S.: 236118
Ronald Bergman (CEO)

ROMAC INDUSTRIES, INC.
21919 20th Ave Ste 100, Bothell, WA 98021-4446
Tel.: (425) 951-6200 WA
Web Site: http://www.romac.com
Year Founded: 1969
Sales Range: $100-124.9 Million
Emp.: 450
Mfr of Pipe Fittings; Valves & Tools for the Water Works Industry
N.A.I.C.S.: 332919
James J. Larkin (Pres)
Kendra Hippensteel (Mgr-Inside Sls)
Kim Lance (Mgr-HR)
Ben Staley (Mgr-Inventory)
Subsidiaries:
Hays Fluid Controls (1)
114 Eason Rd, Dallas, NC 28034
Tel.: (704) 922-9565
Web Site: http://www.haysfluidcontrols.com
Sales Range: $10-24.9 Million
Emp.: 65
Flow Devices Mfr
N.A.I.C.S.: 334514
Matt Fox (Mgr-Natl OEM)
Romac Industries, Inc. - ROMAC FOUNDRY DIVISION (1)
125 Sultan Basin Rd, Sultan, WA 98294
Tel.: (425) 951-6479
Industrial Mold Mfr
N.A.I.C.S.: 333511

ROMACORP, INC.
11315 Corporate Blvd Ste 100, Orlando, FL 32817
Tel.: (877) 682-7419 DE
Web Site: http://www.tonyromas.com
Year Founded: 1972
Restaurant Operators
N.A.I.C.S.: 722511
John Brisco (Pres-Intl)
Jonathan Benjamin (VP)
Mohaimina Haque (Interim CEO)

ROMAIN BUICK INC.
7600 E Division St, Evansville, IN 47715
Tel.: (812) 479-5300
Web Site: http://www.romainbuick.com
Sales Range: $25-49.9 Million
Emp.: 80
Automobiles, New & Used
N.A.I.C.S.: 441110
Ronald D. Romain (Owner)
John Roettger (VP)

ROMAN EAGLE REHABILITATION AND HEALTH CARE CENTER, INC.
2526 N Main St, Danville, VA 24540
Tel.: (434) 836-9510 VA
Web Site: http://www.romaneagle.org
Year Founded: 1967
Sales Range: $10-24.9 Million
Emp.: 412
Disability Assistance Services
N.A.I.C.S.: 624120
Rodney G. Reynolds (Dir-Fin)
Peggy Moore (Sec)
Charlie Motley (Dir-Nursing)

ROMAN ELECTRIC COMPANY, INC.
640 S 70th St, Milwaukee, WI 53214-1631
Tel.: (414) 771-5400 WI
Web Site: http://www.romanelectric.com
Year Founded: 1929
Sales Range: $10-24.9 Million
Emp.: 120
Provider of Electrical Contracting & Telephone & Data Cabling
N.A.I.C.S.: 238210
Gabriel E. Rose (VP-Engrg)
Phillip G. Rose (Pres)
Paul E. Wild (Controller)
Susan T. Rose (Treas)

ROMAN HOLDINGS CORPORATION
824 State St, Calumet City, IL 60409
Tel.: (708) 891-0770
Sales Range: $10-24.9 Million
Emp.: 4
Adhesives
N.A.I.C.S.: 325520
Gerry Ruso (Chm)

ROMAN MANUFACTURING INC.

Roman Manufacturing Inc.—(Continued)

ROMAN MANUFACTURING INC.
861 47th St SW, Grand Rapids, MI 49509
Tel.: (616) 530-8641   MI
Web Site: http://www.romanmfg.com
Year Founded: 1968
Sales Range: $10-24.9 Million
Emp.: 100
Resistance Welders Mfr
N.A.I.C.S.: 333992
Josh Whitford *(Engr-Applications)*
Kendall Ymker *(Mgr-Engrg)*
Melissa Iden *(Mgr-HR)*
Kurt Hofman *(VP)*
Nelson F. Sanchez *(CEO)*
Ben Conner *(Engr-Design)*
Scot Reitenour *(Mgr-Inside Sls)*
Mark Siehling *(VP-Engrg)*
Chad Schondelmayer *(Dir-Mfg Ops)*
Hubert Bethlehem *(Pres)*
Don DeCorte *(VP)*
Rob Hofman *(VP-Glass & Furnace)*

ROMAN MEAL COMPANY
2101 S Tacoma Way, Tacoma, WA 98409
Tel.: (253) 475-0964   WA
Web Site: http://www.romanmeal.com
Year Founded: 1927
Sales Range: $1-9.9 Million
Emp.: 25
Whole Grain Bakery Goods, Cereals, Bakers Mixes & Other Bakery Goods Mfr & Marketer
N.A.I.C.S.: 424490
William L. Matthaei *(Chm)*
Sheri Wakeman *(CFO & VP)*
Gary Jensen *(Pres)*
Patrick Finney *(VP-New Product Innovation)*
Steve Buckholdt *(VP-Quality Assurance & Regulatory)*
Maria Cecilia O. Vicencio *(Brand Mgr)*
Peter Matthaei *(VP)*

ROMAN RESEARCH, INC.
800 Franklin St, Hanson, MA 02341-1002
Tel.: (800) 225-8652
Web Site: http://www.romanresearch.com
Year Founded: 1970
Rev.: $20,000,000
Emp.: 110
Mfr, Retailer & Mail Order of Costume Stainless Steel Hypo-Allergenic Pierced Earrings & Nickel-Free Jewelry & Watches
N.A.I.C.S.: 339910
Dale Southworth *(Pres)*

ROMAN ROOFING, INC.
805 NE 7th Ter, Cape Coral, FL 33909
Tel.: (239) 458-7663
Web Site: http://www.romanroofing.com
Year Founded: 2015
Sales Range: $10-24.9 Million
Emp.: 71
Roofing Contractor Services
N.A.I.C.S.: 238160
D. Norm *(Co-Founder & CEO)*
D. Lindsey *(Co-Founder & CFO)*
B. John *(COO)*
D. Alison *(Mgr-Scheduling)*
S. Jake *(Mgr-Crew)*

ROMAN, INC.
472 Brighton Dr, Bloomingdale, IL 60108-3100
Tel.: (630) 705-4600   IL
Web Site: http://www.roman.com
Year Founded: 1963
Sales Range: $200-249.9 Million
Emp.: 350
Whslr of Religious Articles, Collectibles, Christmas Items & Giftware
N.A.I.C.S.: 424990
Ronald T. Jedlinski *(Founder & Chm)*
Patrick J Pipp *(CFO)*
Julie Puntch *(VP-Seasonal Brands)*
Dennis Zumbahlen *(VP-Warehouse Opers)*
Diane M. Jedlinski *(Sec)*
Michael Kirby *(Special Markets Dir)*
David Lersch *(Dir-Promotional Support)*
Irene Miller *(HR Dir)*
Ralph Schiavone *(Pur Dir)*
Dan Loughman *(Pres & CEO)*

ROMANO FORD OF FAYETTEVILLE LTD.
5431 N Burdick St, Fayetteville, NY 13066
Tel.: (315) 637-4491
Web Site: http://www.romanocars.com
Sales Range: $10-24.9 Million
Emp.: 75
Car Whslr
N.A.I.C.S.: 441110
Murad Abdel *(Gen Mgr)*

ROMANO TOYOTA
6400 Basile Rowe, East Syracuse, NY 13057
Tel.: (315) 445-1070
Web Site: http://www.romanotoyota.com
Sales Range: $10-24.9 Million
Emp.: 46
Car Whslr
N.A.I.C.S.: 441110
Jim Apps *(Dir-Svc)*

ROMANOFF FLOOR COVERING
3100 Jonquil Dr, Smyrna, GA 30080
Tel.: (770) 980-1234
Web Site: http://www.romanoff-floors.com
Sales Range: $25-49.9 Million
Emp.: 150
Carpet Laying
N.A.I.C.S.: 238330
Douglas Romanoff *(Pres)*
Tom Messer *(Mgr-Production)*
Joseph Spinks *(Mgr-Info Sys)*
Valerie Clark *(Mgr-Installation)*

ROMANOFF TECHNOLOGIES OHIO LLC
1288 Research Rd, Gahanna, OH 43230
Tel.: (614) 755-4500
Web Site: http://www.romanoffgroup.cc
Rev.: $17,200,000
Emp.: 50
Provider of Voice & Data Cabling Services
N.A.I.C.S.: 516210

ROMANOW INC.
346 University Ave, Westwood, MA 02090
Tel.: (781) 320-9200
Web Site: http://www.romanowcontainer.com
Rev.: $16,300,000
Emp.: 99
Corrugated Box Mfr
N.A.I.C.S.: 322211
Ted Romanow *(Pres)*

ROMARK LABORATORIES, L.C.
3000 Bayport Dr Ste 200, Tampa, FL 33607
Tel.: (813) 282-8544
Web Site: http://www.romark.com
Year Founded: 1993
Sales Range: $10-24.9 Million
Emp.: 45
Pharmaceuticals Mfr
N.A.I.C.S.: 325412
Brian Schnieders *(CFO)*
Marc S. Ayers *(CEO & Mgr)*
Jean-Francois Rossignol *(Co-Founder & Chief Medical & Science Officer)*
Celine E. Rossignol *(COO & Exec VP)*

ROMARK LOGISTICS, INC.
822 South Ave West, Westfield, NJ 07090
Tel.: (908) 662-6337
Web Site: http://www.romarklogistics.com
Sales Range: $25-49.9 Million
Emp.: 80
Provider of Warehousing & Storage Services
N.A.I.C.S.: 493110
Roy Lebovitz *(CEO)*
Mark Lebovitz *(Pres)*
Chris Richmond *(Mgr-Ops)*

Subsidiaries:

East Coast Warehouse & Distribution Corp. (1)
1140 Polaris St, Elizabeth, NJ 07201
Tel.: (908) 351-2800
Web Site: http://www.eastcoastwarehouse.com
Warehousing & Storage Services
N.A.I.C.S.: 493110
Dan Horgan *(COO)*
Jamie Overley *(CEO)*
David Harris *(CFO)*
Bob LaMere *(CIO)*
Rich Coppola *(VP-Sls)*
Adrienne Harrison *(Sr Dir-Customs Examination Svcs)*
Rafael Varela *(Sr Dir-Warehouse Ops)*
Kevin Daly *(Chief Comml Officer)*

ROME & COMPANY
233 E Wacker Dr Apt 4011, Chicago, IL 60601-5116
Tel.: (312) 938-1013   IL
Web Site: http://www.romecreative.com
Year Founded: 1984
Sales Range: Less than $1 Million
Emp.: 8
N.A.I.C.S.: 541810
Jerry Roman *(Pres)*
Joan Novick *(Copywriter)*
Frank Stransky *(Creative Dir)*

ROMEO ENTERTAINMENT GROUP, INC.
5247 N 129th St, Omaha, NE 68164
Tel.: (402) 359-1010   NE
Web Site: http://www.romeoent.com
Year Founded: 1954
Sales Range: $10-24.9 Million
Emp.: 6
Develops & Produces Entertainment for Fairs & Festivals
N.A.I.C.S.: 561499
Bob Romeo *(Owner)*
Steve Bogdanovich *(VP & Mgr-Production)*
Harlan Burggraaf *(Accountant)*
Mindy Klein *(Dir-Mktg)*
Fran Romeo *(Pres)*

ROMEO MUSIC
14237 Inwood Rd, Dallas, TX 75244

Tel.: (972) 239-2278
Web Site: http://www.romeomusic.net
Year Founded: 2006
Sales Range: $1-9.9 Million
Emp.: 10
Digital Musical Instruments & Sound System Products
N.A.I.C.S.: 459140
Julie Romeo *(Founder)*
Peggy Morales *(Sr Mgr)*

ROMER LABS, INC.
1301 Stylemaster Dr, Union, MO 63084
Tel.: (636) 583-8600   MO
Web Site: http://www.romerlabs.com
Year Founded: 1982
Emp.: 25
Testing Laboratory
N.A.I.C.S.: 541715
Hannes Binder *(Pres & CEO)*

ROMERO GENERAL CONSTRUCTION CORPORATION
2150 N Centre City Pkwy Ste I, Escondido, CA 92026
Tel.: (760) 489-8412
Web Site: http://www.romerogc.com
Rev.: $39,000,000
Emp.: 175
Highway Street & Bridge Construction
N.A.I.C.S.: 237310

ROMERO MOTORS CORPORATION
1307 Kettering Dr, Ontario, CA 91761-2217
Tel.: (909) 390-8484
Web Site: http://www.romeromotors.com
Year Founded: 1973
Sales Range: $10-24.9 Million
Emp.: 500
New & Used Car Sales
N.A.I.C.S.: 441110
Richard J. Romero *(Pres)*

Subsidiaries:

Empire Nissan Inc. (1)
1377 Kettering Dr, Ontario, CA 91761-2217
Tel.: (909) 740-6712
Web Site: http://www.empirenissan.com
Sales of New & Used Cars
N.A.I.C.S.: 441110
Richard J. Romero *(Pres)*

ROMERO'S FOOD PRODUCTS, INCORPORATED
15155 Vly View Ave, Santa Fe Springs, CA 90670
Tel.: (562) 802-1858   CA
Web Site: http://www.romerosfood.com
Sales Range: $10-24.9 Million
Emp.: 200
Tortilla Mfr
N.A.I.C.S.: 311830
Leon S. Romero *(Co-Founder & Co-Owner)*
Raul Romero *(Co-Founder & Co-Owner)*
Robert Romero *(Co-Owner & Gen Mgr)*
Richard F. Scandaliato *(CEO)*
Alfonso Valcarcel *(Mgr-Ops)*
Jodi Lyn Johnson *(Controller)*

ROMMEL HOLDINGS INC.
PO Box 160, Fruitland, MD 21826
Tel.: (410) 749-3600
Web Site: http://www.rommelsace.com
Year Founded: 1995
Sales Range: $25-49.9 Million
Emp.: 400
Hardware Store Franchise Owner & Operator

COMPANIES
RONAN ENGINEERING COMPANY

N.A.I.C.S.: 444140
Mike Cottingham *(Pres)*
Lisa Cordrey *(Mgr-Acctg)*
Richard Livingston *(VP)*

ROMULUS INC.
4131 N 36th St, Phoenix, AZ 85018
Tel.: (602) 852-0555
Web Site: http://www.romulusinc.com
Rev.: $18,400,000
Emp.: 3,000
Family Restaurant Owner & Operator
N.A.I.C.S.: 722511
Chris Milici *(CEO)*
Ronald Randall *(Dir-Trng)*
Mark Steinmetz *(CFO)*

RON AND ANN ENTERPRISES INC.
1900 Auto Center Dr, Merced, CA 95340
Tel.: (209) 725-5050
Web Site:
http://www.ronsmithgmc.com
Sales Range: $25-49.9 Million
Emp.: 100
Automobiles; New & Used
N.A.I.C.S.: 441110
Ron Smith *(Owner)*
Ann Smith *(Sec)*

RON BOUCHARD'S AUTO SALES, INC.
500 Old Union Tpke, Lancaster, MA 01523
Tel.: (978) 345-1800
Web Site:
http://www.ronbouchardsautostores.com
Sales Range: $25-49.9 Million
Emp.: 100
New Car Retailer
N.A.I.C.S.: 441110
Ron Bouchard *(Co-Owner)*
Paula Bouchard *(Co-Owner)*
Marlin Knight *(COO)*
Jim Kane *(Dir-Svc)*
Rob Bouchard *(Mgr-Ops)*
Kendra Dickinson *(Mgr-Bus Dev)*
Alli Gabrielian *(Bus Mgr)*
John McManus *(Gen Mgr)*
Kevin Sallese *(Mgr-Sls-Honda)*
Bree Schpero *(Dir-Mktg)*
Chad Bouchard *(VP-Sls & Mktg)*
Jamie Rodiquenz *(Mgr-Honda Svc)*

RON BOWERS, INC.
85375 Highway 99 S, Eugene, OR 97405
Tel.: (541) 895-3514
Sales Range: $10-24.9 Million
Emp.: 70
Cargo & Freight Services
N.A.I.C.S.: 484220
Ronald L. Bowers *(Pres & Sec)*

RON CARTER
3005 FM 528, Alvin, TX 77511
Tel.: (281) 331-3111
Web Site: http://www.roncarter.com
Sales Range: $75-99.9 Million
Emp.: 200
New Car Retailer
N.A.I.C.S.: 441110

RON HERMAN INC.
8100 Melrose Ave, Los Angeles, CA 90046
Tel.: (323) 651-3342
Web Site: http://www.ronherman.com
Emp.: 50
Women's Clothing Store
N.A.I.C.S.: 458110

Ron Herman *(Pres)*
Jennifer Castro *(Dir-Personnel)*
Taylor Jerabek *(Mgr-Floor)*

RON JON SURF SHOP
3850 S Banana River, Cocoa Beach, FL 32931
Tel.: (321) 799-8888   FL
Web Site:
http://www.ronjonsurfshop.com
Year Founded: 1959
Beach Apparel & Accessory Store
N.A.I.C.S.: 458110
Debbie Harvey *(Pres & COO)*
Heather Lewis *(Mktg Dir)*
Subsidiaries:
R&J Advertising Inc.   (1)
3850 S Banana River Blvd, Cocoa Beach, FL 32931-3481
Tel.: (321) 799-8880
Web Site: http://www.ronjons.com
Sales Range: $10-24.9 Million
Emp.: 6
Advertising Agencies
N.A.I.C.S.: 541810
Heather Lewis *(Dir-Adv)*

RON MARHOFER CHEVROLET INC.
3423 Darrow Rd, Stow, OH 44224
Tel.: (330) 688-6644
Web Site: http://www.marhofer.com
Sales Range: $25-49.9 Million
Emp.: 290
Sales of New & Used Automobiles
N.A.I.C.S.: 532111
Ronald L. Marhofer *(Pres)*
Becky Vanaman *(Controller)*

RON NORRIS BUICK GMC
1350 S Washington Ave, Titusville, FL 32780-4250
Tel.: (321) 593-4446
Web Site:
http://www.ronnorrisbuickgmc.com
Sales Range: $25-49.9 Million
Emp.: 50
Car Whslr
N.A.I.C.S.: 441110
Ron Norris *(Pres)*

RON ROSE PRODUCTIONS LTD
1041 S Main St 3rd Fl, Royal Oak, MI 48067
Tel.: (248) 424-8400
Web Site: http://www.ronrose.com
Rev.: $13,000,000
Emp.: 35
Recording Studio & Audio Services
N.A.I.C.S.: 512240
Anita K. Lanning *(Acct Dir)*

RON SAYER'S CHRYSLER JEEP DODGE
490 Northgate Mile, Idaho Falls, ID 83401
Tel.: (208) 522-2610
Web Site:
http://www.ronsayerdodge.com
Rev.: $15,000,000
Emp.: 50
Automobiles, New & Used
N.A.I.C.S.: 441110
Rick Wallis *(Gen Mgr)*

RON SONNTAG PUBLIC RELATIONS
9406 N 107th St, Milwaukee, WI 53224
Tel.: (414) 354-0200
Web Site: http://www.rspr.com
Year Founded: 1980
Sales Range: $10-24.9 Million
Emp.: 11
Public Relations Agency

N.A.I.C.S.: 541820
Ron Sonntag *(Founder, Chm & CEO)*
Patricia Johnson *(Pres & COO)*
Dave Amoroso *(VP)*
Kandi Korth *(Office Mgr)*
Cynthia Marsh *(Dir-Editorial Svcs)*
Mark McLaughlin *(Dir-Media Rels)*

RON TIRAPELLI FORD
4355 W Jefferson St, Shorewood, IL 60404-4727
Tel.: (815) 725-3033
Web Site:
http://www.rontirapelliford.com
Sales Range: $10-24.9 Million
Emp.: 56
Car Whslr
N.A.I.C.S.: 441110
John Hanania *(Gen Mgr)*
Ron Tirapelli *(Pres)*

RON TONKIN CHEVROLET CO.
122 NE 122nd Ave, Portland, OR 97230
Tel.: (503) 255-4100
Web Site: http://www.tonkin.com
Rev.: $290,000,000
Emp.: 1,000
New & Used Car Dealers
N.A.I.C.S.: 441110
Subsidiaries:
Ron Tonkin Toyota Inc.   (1)
750 SE 122nd Ave, Portland, OR 97233
Tel.: (503) 255-0177
Web Site: http://www.tonkintoyota.com
Sales Range: $25-49.9 Million
Emp.: 36
New & Used Car Dealers
N.A.I.C.S.: 441110
Ron Tonkin *(Pres)*
Erica Sampson *(CFO)*

RON WESTPHAL CHEVROLET INC.
1425 W Ogden Ave, Aurora, IL 60543
Tel.: (630) 898-9630
Web Site:
http://www.westphalchevy.com
Sales Range: $25-49.9 Million
Emp.: 50
New Car Dealers
N.A.I.C.S.: 441110
Ronald Westphal *(Pres)*

RON WILLIAMS CONSTRUCTION INC.
3850 Hwy 90 E, Sulphur, LA 70663
Tel.: (337) 882-1238
Web Site:
http://www.rwconstruction.com
Sales Range: $10-24.9 Million
Emp.: 160
Chemical Plant & Refinery Construction
N.A.I.C.S.: 237990
Mark Ieyoub *(COO & VP)*
Billy Reeves *(Mgr-Corp HSE)*
Cheryl Luckie *(Mgr-HR)*
Jeremy Moran *(Mgr-Midstream Bus Unit)*
Al Hungerford *(Mgr-QA & QC)*
Ken Chaisson *(Mgr-Construction)*
Ray Rogers *(Mgr-Fabrication Bus Unit)*
Bryan Williams *(VP-Internal Ops)*
Ron Williams *(CFO & VP)*
Brandt Smith *(VP-Bus Dev)*

RON'S EQUIPMENT CO INC.
906 N US Hwy 287, Fort Collins, CO 80524-1385
Tel.: (970) 221-5296
Web Site:
http://www.ronsequipment.com

Farm & Garden Machinery & Equipment Merchant Whslr
N.A.I.C.S.: 423820
Ron Lonneman *(Owner)*
Subsidiaries:
Prospect Implement, Inc.   (1)
33894 Hwy 52, Keenesburg, CO 80643
Tel.: (303) 732-4321
Web Site:
http://www.prospectimplement.com
Sales Range: $1-9.9 Million
Emp.: 10
Farm & Garden Machinery & Equipment Merchant Whslr
N.A.I.C.S.: 423820
Don Altergott *(Pres)*

RON'S OIL COMPANY
580 N Central St, Coquille, OR 97423
Tel.: (541) 396-5571
Rev.: $30,200,000
Emp.: 135
Petroleum Bulk Stations
N.A.I.C.S.: 424710
Eoieli La Franchi *(Office Mgr)*

RON-SON FOODS INC.
81 Locke Ave, Swedesboro, NJ 08085
Tel.: (856) 241-7333
Web Site:
http://www.ronsonfoods.com
Sales Range: $10-24.9 Million
Groceries Distr
N.A.I.C.S.: 424490
Jim Bianco *(Owner)*

RONALD MARK ASSOCIATES INC.
1227 Central Ave, Hillside, NJ 07205
Tel.: (908) 558-0011
Web Site: http://www.ronaldmark.com
Rev.: $20,200,121
Emp.: 50
Polyvinyl Film & Sheet
N.A.I.C.S.: 326113
Leslie Satz *(CFO)*

RONALD R. WREN ADVERTISING, INC.
101 The Embarcadero Ste 130, San Francisco, CA 94105-1215
Tel.: (415) 433-1040
Year Founded: 1966
Sales Range: $1-9.9 Million
Emp.: 2
Advertising Agencies
N.A.I.C.S.: 541810
Ronald Wren *(Pres & Acct Exec)*
Jan Coakley *(VP-Fin)*

RONAN ENGINEERING COMPANY
28209 Ave Stanford, Valencia, CA 91355-3984
Tel.: (818) 883-5211
Web Site: http://www.ronan.com
Year Founded: 1959
Sales Range: $10-24.9 Million
Emp.: 175
Monitoring Equipment Mfr
N.A.I.C.S.: 334515
Subsidiaries:
Ronan Engineering Company, Measurements Division   (1)
8050 Production Dr, Florence, KY 41042
Tel.: (859) 342-8500
Web Site: http://www.ronanmeasure.com
Sales Range: $10-24.9 Million
Emp.: 30
Nuclear Measurement Instruments Mfr
N.A.I.C.S.: 334519
John Hewitson *(Owner)*
Ronan Engineering LTD.   (1)
1 Tilley Road Crowther Industrial Estate,

Ronan Engineering Company—(Continued)

Washington, NE38 0AE, Tyne & Wear,
United Kingdom
Tel.: (44) 191 416 1689
Control Panel Mfr
N.A.I.C.S.: 334419
Mike Stanley (Mgr-Sls)

RONCHETTI DISTRIBUTING CO
2621 Lakeland Blvd, Mattoon, IL 61938
Tel.: (217) 234-8200
Sales Range: $10-24.9 Million
Emp.: 18
Beer & Other Fermented Malt Liquors
N.A.I.C.S.: 424810
Robert M. Ronchetti (Pres)

RONCO COMMUNICATIONS & ELECTRONICS INC.
595 Sheridan Dr, Tonawanda, NY 14150-7850
Tel.: (716) 873-0760   NY
Web Site: http://www.ronco.net
Year Founded: 1965
Emp.: 500
Unified Communications & Networking Solutions
N.A.I.C.S.: 517121
Mark Schweizer (Exec VP-Fin)
Michael LaBella (COO)
Brian Hansen (Exec VP-Sls)
Christopher Wasp Jr. (CEO)

RONCO INVENTIONS LLC
570 Lexington Ave Fl 25, New York, NY 10022-6878
Tel.: (805) 433-1030   CA
Web Site: http://www.ronco.com
Year Founded: 1984
Sales Range: $200-249.9 Million
Emp.: 30
Household Appliances Mfr & Distr
N.A.I.C.S.: 423220
Terry Tigner (Pres & CEO)

RONCO MACHINE AND RIGGING
RR 307, Lake Winola, PA 18625
Tel.: (570) 378-2090
Rev.: $13,542,721
Emp.: 150
Paper Manufacturing Machinery
N.A.I.C.S.: 423830
Brad Reeves (Gen Mgr-Machine Div)
Steve Betts (Gen Mgr-Northern Div)
Jay Hopkins (Gen Mgr-Southern Div)
Alejandro Nash (Mgr-Pur)
Thomas Vanden Heuvel (Mgr-Southeastern Sls)
Steven T. Jenkins (Pres & CEO)
Jim DeWitt (VP)

RONELL INDUSTRIES INC.
298 Cox St, Roselle, NJ 07203
Tel.: (908) 245-5255
Web Site:
http://www.ronellmanagedservices.com
Sales Range: $25-49.9 Million
Emp.: 482
Janitorial Service, Contract Basis
N.A.I.C.S.: 561720
Ronald Globerman (Co-Pres)
Allyson Distell (CFO)
Neil Salerno (Co-Pres)

RONETCO SUPERMARKETS INC.
1070 US Hwy 46 Ste 1, Ledgewood, NJ 07852-9701
Tel.: (973) 927-8300   NJ
Web Site: http://www.shoprite.com
Year Founded: 1961
Sales Range: $100-124.9 Million
Emp.: 1,800
Grocery Stores
N.A.I.C.S.: 445110
Dominic V. Romano (Pres)
David Romano (VP)
Lisa Laureys (Supvr-Office Svcs)
Ray Stecky (Supvr-Wine & Spirits)
Gail Riker (Asst Gen Mgr-Store)
Christopher Caldarella (Mgr-Frozen Food Dept)
Ulysses Queiro (Mgr-HR)
Jonathan Harris (Coord-Catering)

RONILE, INC.
701 Orchard Ave, Rocky Mount, VA 24151-8059
Tel.: (540) 483-0261   VA
Web Site: http://www.ronile.com
Year Founded: 1984
Sales Range: $1-9.9 Million
Emp.: 250
Finishing Plants
N.A.I.C.S.: 313310
Phillip Essig (CEO)

Subsidiaries:

Bacova Guild, Ltd.   (1)
1000 Commerce Center Dr, Covington, VA 24426   (100%)
Tel.: (540) 863-2600
Web Site: http://www.bacova.com
Printed Accent Rug Printed Floor Ma & Bathroom Ensemble Mfr
N.A.I.C.S.: 314110
Brad Houff (Asst Gen Mgr)
Rick Lewis (VP-Sls)
Julie Dean (Mgr-Credit & Accts Receivable)
Kathy Fowlkes (VP-Mktg & Design)
Nick Proctor (CFO)

Branch (Domestic):

Bacova Guild, Ltd.   (2)
4035 Premier Dr, High Point, NC 27265-8048   (100%)
Tel.: (336) 841-4800
Web Site: http://www.bacova.com
Carpets & Rugs Mfr
N.A.I.C.S.: 323113

RONIN ADVERTISING GROUP
400 University Dr # 200, Coral Gables, FL 33134-7125
Tel.: (305) 858-7676
Web Site: http://www.roninadv.com
Sales Range: $10-24.9 Million
Emp.: 55
Advertising Agencies
N.A.I.C.S.: 541810
Karen Ableman (Pres)

RONIN STAFFING LLC
500 North Brand Blvd Ste 625, Glendale, CA 91203
Tel.: (818) 303-1340
Web Site: http://www.roninllc.com
Year Founded: 1999
Sales Range: $1-9.9 Million
Emp.: 120
Recruiting & Staffing Services
N.A.I.C.S.: 561311
Vivian Rutherford (CEO)

RONN MOTOR GROUP, INC.
20645 N Pima Rd Ste 140, Scottsdale, AZ 85255
Tel.: (480) 498-8989   DE
Web Site:
http://www.ronnmotorgroup.com
Year Founded: 2013
Emp.: 10
Automobile Mfr
N.A.I.C.S.: 336110
Ronal Ford (Chm & CEO)
C. G. Ryche (CMO)
Delun Wang (Sr VP-Mfg & Engrg)

RONNI NICOLE II INC.
1400 Broadway Rm 2106, New York, NY 10018
Tel.: (212) 764-1000
Rev.: $47,665,411
Emp.: 25
Women's, Junior's & Misses' Dresses
N.A.I.C.S.: 315250
Marty Pitiger (Pres)

RONNIE WATKINS FORD INC.
101 George Wallace Dr, Gadsden, AL 35903
Tel.: (256) 543-9400
Web Site:
http://www.ronniewatkinsford.com
Year Founded: 1998
Sales Range: $10-24.9 Million
Emp.: 65
Car Whslr
N.A.I.C.S.: 441110
Ronnie Watkins (Owner & Pres)
Andre Champagne (Mgr-Used Inventory)
David Sutter (Mgr-Rental)
Don Higdon (Mgr-Svc)
Eric Talbot (Mgr-Parts)
Harry Chesser (Mgr-Sls)
Jacob Vanderford (Gen Mgr)
Joey Edmondson (Mgr-Fixed Ops)
Patrick Tow (Gen Mgr-Sls)
Stoney Diggs (Mgr-Fin)
Lauren Watkins (Mgr-Internet & Mktg)

RONNING ENTERPRISES
4401 E 6th St, Sioux Falls, SD 57103
Tel.: (605) 336-6000
Web Site:
https://www.ronningcompanies.com
Sales Range: $25-49.9 Million
Emp.: 40
Subdividers & Developers
N.A.I.C.S.: 237210
Slate Ronning (Pres)

RONNINGEN RESEARCH & DEVELOPMENT CO
6700 E YZ Ave, Vicksburg, MI 49097
Tel.: (269) 649-0520   MI
Web Site:
http://www.ronningenresearch.com
Year Founded: 1966
Industrial Molds
N.A.I.C.S.: 333511
Deryl Myers (VP-Engrg)
Beth Speece (Head-Customer Svc)
Josh Velie (VP-Ops)
Nicole Mostrom (Dir-Customer Svc)
Derick Myers (Project Mgr)
Eric Swanson (Mgr-Supply Chain)

RONPAK INC.
4301 New Brunswick Ave, South Plainfield, NJ 07080
Tel.: (732) 968-8000
Web Site: http://www.ronpak.com
Sales Range: $10-24.9 Million
Emp.: 400
Bag, Wrapper & Seal Printing & Engraving
N.A.I.C.S.: 323111
Kathy Amann (Mgr-Customer Support)
Chris Sevi (VP-Sls)
James Spaanstra (Mgr-Engrg)

RONSONET BUICK-GMC TRUCK, INC.
490 E Duval St, Lake City, FL 32055
Tel.: (386) 752-2180   FL
Web Site:
http://www.ronsonetbuickgmc.com
Sales Range: $10-24.9 Million
Emp.: 22
New & Used Car Dealer
N.A.I.C.S.: 441110
Mitchell J. Ronsonet (Treas & Sec)
Vickie Harry (Mgr-Fin)
Norbie J. Ronsonet Sr. (Pres)

RONTO GROUP, INC.
3185 Horseshoe Dr S Ste 2, Naples, FL 34104
Tel.: (239) 649-6310
Web Site: http://www.ronto.com
Year Founded: 1967
Sales Range: $1-9.9 Million
Emp.: 5
Land Subdivision
N.A.I.C.S.: 237210
Anthony Solomon (Exec VP)
A. Jack Solomon (Founder & Pres)

Subsidiaries:

Twineagles Brokerage Inc   (1)
11330 Twineagles Blvd, Naples, FL 34120
Tel.: (239) 352-8000
Web Site: http://www.twineaglesonline.com
Rev.: $580,000
Emp.: 3
Real Estate Agents & Managers
N.A.I.C.S.: 531210

ROOCHI TRADERS (NY) INC.
1201 Broadway Rm 803, New York, NY 10001
Tel.: (212) 779-7555
Web Site: http://www.roochi.com
Sales Range: $25-49.9 Million
Emp.: 100
Sportswear, Men's & Boys'
N.A.I.C.S.: 424350
Neeraj Sachdeva (VP)
Vikram Sachdeva (Pres)

ROOF SYSTEMS OF VA INC.
501 Jefferson Davis Hwy, Richmond, VA 23224
Tel.: (804) 231-2875
Web Site: http://www.roofsys.com
Sales Range: $10-24.9 Million
Emp.: 135
Roofing Contractors
N.A.I.C.S.: 238160
Malcolm L. Nunn Jr. (Pres)
Josephs W. Blanks Jr. (VP)

ROOF TRUSS SUPPLY INC.
5910 234th St SE, Woodinville, WA 98072-8659
Tel.: (425) 481-0900   WA
Web Site:
http://www.rooftrusssupply.net
Year Founded: 1991
Sales Range: $50-74.9 Million
Emp.: 100
Provider of Lumber, Plywood & Millwork Services
N.A.I.C.S.: 423310
Paul Morris (CEO)

ROOFED RIGHT AMERICA, LLC
429 W Boden St., Milwaukee, WI 53207
Tel.: (414) 769-0100
Web Site:
https://www.roofedright.com
Year Founded: 2006
Commercial Roofing Contractors
N.A.I.C.S.: 238160

Subsidiaries:

Upstate Roofing & Painting, Inc.   (1)
1300 Brighton Hen Tl Rd, Rochester, NY 14623
Tel.: (585) 272-8050
Web Site:
http://www.upstateroofingandpainting.com
Sales Range: $1-9.9 Million
Emp.: 63
Roofing Contractors
N.A.I.C.S.: 238160

ROOFERS MART, INC.
7208 Weil Ave, Saint Louis, MO 63119
Tel.: (314) 968-9366   MO

COMPANIES

Web Site:
http://www.roofersmartinc.com
Year Founded: 1983
Sales Range: $10-24.9 Million
Emp.: 80
Roofing, Siding & Insulation Material Merchant Whslr
N.A.I.C.S.: 423330
Bill Vierling *(Pres)*
Mark Postawko *(VP)*
Jared Cruzen *(Partner & Reg Mgr)*
Terry Montgomery *(Partner & Mgr-Ops)*
Brent Wiley *(Sr Mgr-Sls & Partner)*
Brian Groppe *(Partner)*
Pete D'Angelo *(Partner)*
Rod Clark *(Mgr-Sls)*
Joe Licavoli *(Controller)*
Nathan Miles *(Mgr-Bridgeport)*
Kris Schriefer *(Partner)*
Jake Postawko *(Partner)*

ROOFING WHOLESALE CO., INC.
1918 W Grant St, Phoenix, AZ 85009-5933
Tel.: (602) 258-3794   AZ
Web Site: http://www.rwc.org
Year Founded: 1958
Sales Range: $200-249.9 Million
Emp.: 256
Roofing & Building Materials Sales
N.A.I.C.S.: 423330
Harley Lisherness *(Pres & CEO)*
Stephen K. Rold *(CFO & VP)*
Phil Goldie *(Mgr)*

ROOFING WHOLESALE INC.
2181 Dublin Rd, Columbus, OH 43228
Tel.: (614) 486-5376
Web Site: http://www.roofingwholesale.net
Sales Range: $10-24.9 Million
Emp.: 20
Distribution Of Roofing & Insulation
N.A.I.C.S.: 423330
Barry Ruggles *(Mgr-Albuquerque)*
Paul Binder *(Mgr-Palm Springs)*
Phil Goldie *(Mgr-Phoenix)*
Doug Lewis *(Mgr-Prescott Valley)*
Rick Knudson *(Mgr-San Bernardino)*
Duane Weston *(Mgr-San Marcos)*
Regan Anderson *(Mgr-Scottsdale)*
Mike Nicholson *(Mgr-Spring Valley)*
Mike Nelson *(Mgr-Tucson)*

ROOFSTOCK, INC.
2001 Broadway Ste 400, Oakland, CA 94612
Tel.: (800) 466-4116   DE
Web Site: http://www.roofstock.com
Year Founded: 2015
Real Estate Investment Services
N.A.I.C.S.: 531390
Gary Beasley *(Co-Founder & CEO)*
Gregor Watson *(Co-Founder & Chm)*
Andrew Schaffler *(Chief Investment Officer)*
Justin Yagerman *(Head-Capital Markets)*
Paul Briggs *(Head-Res)*

Subsidiaries:

Fidelis Asset Management, LLC   (1)
4534 Clinton St Ste 2, West Seneca, NY 14224
Web Site: http://www.rentprep.com
Sales Range: $1-9.9 Million
Emp.: 50
Real Estate Services
N.A.I.C.S.: 531210

Stessa, Inc.   (1)
4 Embarcadero Ctr Ste 1500, San Francisco, CA 94111
Tel.: (415) 985-7837
Web Site: http://www.stessa.com

Real Estate Investment Management Services
N.A.I.C.S.: 531110
Heath Silverman *(Co-Founder & CEO)*
Jonah Schwartz *(Co-Founder & CTO)*

ROOFTOP COMMUNICATIONS
2526 St Paul St, Baltimore, MD 21218
Tel.: (410) 243-5550
Web Site: http://www.rooftopcommunications.com
Year Founded: 2004
Sales Range: $10-24.9 Million
Emp.: 20
Brand Development & Integration, Direct Response Marketing, Internet/Web Design, Public Relations
N.A.I.C.S.: 541810
Barbara Brotman Kaylor *(CEO & Supvr-Acct Mgmt)*
Joseph Matos *(Dir-Creative)*
Cari Ashkin *(Asst Acct Mgr)*

ROOM & BOARD, INC.
4600 Olson Memorial Hwy, Minneapolis, MN 55422
Tel.: (763) 588-7525   MN
Web Site: http://www.roomandboard.com
Sales Range: $150-199.9 Million
Furniture & Home Furnishing Retailer
N.A.I.C.S.: 449110
John D. Gabbert *(Founder)*
Jill Byrnes *(Dir-Creative)*
Kimberly Haase Ruthenbeck *(Dir-Web Experience)*
Mary Gergen *(Gen Mgr-Delivery)*
Brenda Blank *(Mgr)*
Paul Bartlett *(Mgr-Delivery Market)*
Becky Scarcello *(Mgr-Recruitment)*

ROOM 214 INC.
3390 Valmont Rd Ste 214, Boulder, CO 80301
Tel.: (303) 444-9214
Web Site: http://www.room214.com
Year Founded: 2004
Sales Range: $1-9.9 Million
Emp.: 30
Advetising Agency
N.A.I.C.S.: 541810
James Clark *(Co-Founder)*
Jason Cormier *(Co-Founder)*
Joshua Hill *(Dir-Strategy)*
Ben Castelli *(Dir-Agency)*
Katie Evans *(Acct Dir)*
Leah Lesko *(Acct Dir)*
Maya Shaff *(Acct Dir)*
Libby Turner *(Acct Dir)*
Jen Casson *(Dir-Creative Svcs)*
Michael Kwolek *(Dir-Res)*

ROOMS TO GO, INC.
11540 Hwy 92 E, Seffner, FL 33584
Tel.: (813) 628-9724   FL
Web Site: https://www.roomstogo.com
Year Founded: 1991
Sales Range: Less than $1 Million
Emp.: 8,500
Furniture Retailers
N.A.I.C.S.: 449110
Gary Cacioppo *(Sr VP)*
Lewis Stein *(CFO)*
Linda Garcia *(VP-HR)*
Russ Rosen *(CIO)*
Janis Altshuler *(VP-Direct Mktg)*
Martha Kruse *(Sr Dir-Multicultural Mktg)*

Subsidiaries:

The Great American Home Store, Inc.   (1)
5295 Pepper Chase Dr, Southaven, MS 38671

Tel.: (662) 996-1000
Web Site: http://www.greatamericanhomestore.com
Rev.: $10,000,000
Emp.: 50
Furniture Retailer
N.A.I.C.S.: 449110
Ron Becker *(Gen Mgr)*

ROOMSTORE, INC.
12501 Patterson Ave, Richmond, VA 23233-6414
Tel.: (804) 784-7600   VA
Year Founded: 1992
Sales Range: $300-349.9 Million
Emp.: 1,452
Retail Furniture Stores
N.A.I.C.S.: 449110
Lewis M. Brubaker *(CFO & Sr VP)*
John M. Hamilton *(Sr VP-HR)*

ROOMSTORES OF PHOENIX LLC
3011 E Broadway Rd 100, Phoenix, AZ 85040
Tel.: (602) 268-1111
Web Site: http://www.arizonaroomstore.com
Sales Range: $100-124.9 Million
Emp.: 380
Furniture Store
N.A.I.C.S.: 449110
Allan Levitz *(CEO)*

ROONEY HOLDINGS, INC.
5601 S 122nd E Ave, Tulsa, OK 74146-6912
Tel.: (918) 583-6900   OK
Web Site: http://www.rooneyholdings.com
Year Founded: 1984
Sales Range: $1-4.9 Billion
Emp.: 2,625
Private Equity Firm; Industrial, Commercial & Institutional Building Construction & Electronic Components
N.A.I.C.S.: 551112
L. Francis Rooney III *(CEO)*
Rodney Stephens *(Dir-Bus Sys)*
Jeff Grippando *(Dir-IS&T Infrastructure)*

Subsidiaries:

Manhattan Construction Company   (1)
5601 S 122nd E Ave, Tulsa, OK 74146-6912   (100%)
Tel.: (918) 583-6900
Web Site: http://www.manhattanconstructiongroup.com
Sales Range: $75-99.9 Million
Emp.: 650
Industrial, Commercial & Institutional Building Construction Services
N.A.I.C.S.: 236220
Larry Rooney *(Pres)*
Jason Fuller *(VP)*
Michael Miller *(Mgr-Tampa)*

Subsidiary (Domestic):

Cantera Concrete Company   (2)
5601 S 122nd E Ave, Tulsa, OK 74146
Tel.: (918) 878-3498
Web Site: http://www.canteraconcrete.com
Concrete Placement Services
N.A.I.C.S.: 238120
Brent Dostal *(Pres)*

Division (Domestic):

Manhattan Construction Company   (2)
3705-1 Westview Dr, Naples, FL 34104
Tel.: (239) 643-6000
Web Site: http://www.manhattanconstructiongroup.com
Commercial & Residential Construction Services
N.A.I.C.S.: 236220
K. P. Pezeshkan *(VP-Mktg)*
John Reyhan *(Pres)*

Subsidiary (Domestic):

Manhattan Road & Bridge Co.   (2)
5601 S 122nd E Ave, Tulsa, OK 74146
Tel.: (918) 437-9560
Web Site: http://www.manhattanconstructiongroup.com
Sales Range: $75-99.9 Million
Emp.: 400
Bridge Construction
N.A.I.C.S.: 237310
Mike Webb *(Pres)*
Todd Saxton *(Sr VP)*
Tom Cramer II *(VP)*

Subsidiary (Domestic):

Manhattan Road & Bridge-Muskogee Office   (3)
5100 E Hancock St PO 798 74402, Muskogee, OK 74403
Tel.: (918) 683-3051
Sales Range: $25-49.9 Million
Emp.: 200
Bridge Construction
N.A.I.C.S.: 237310

OAI Electronics Inc.   (1)
6960 E 12th St, Tulsa, OK 74112
Tel.: (918) 836-9077
Web Site: http://www.oaielectronics.com
Sales Range: $50-74.9 Million
Emp.: 60
Mfr & Testing of Preprinted Circuit Boards, Cable, Wire, Harnesses & Electromechanical Assemblies
N.A.I.C.S.: 334418
Darrick Shook *(Mgr-Production Engrg)*
Bruce Clemens *(Mgr-Mktg)*

Rooney Holdings, Inc.   (1)
3705 1 Westview Dr, Naples, FL 34104
Tel.: (239) 403-0375
Sales Range: $25-49.9 Million
Emp.: 3
Commercial & Industrial Construction Services
N.A.I.C.S.: 551114
L. Francis Rooney III *(CEO)*

Rooney Insurance Agency, Inc.   (1)
5601 S 122nd E Ave, Tulsa, OK 74146
Tel.: (918) 582-0565
Web Site: http://www.rooneyinsurance.com
Sales Range: $75-99.9 Million
Emp.: 20
Business Insurance, Personal Insurance & Employee Benefits Services
N.A.I.C.S.: 524210
Jim Geisinger *(VP)*
Dana Hickman *(Mgr-Employee Benefits Dept)*

ROOP & CO.
3800 Terminal Tower 50 Public Sq, Cleveland, OH 44113
Tel.: (216) 902-3800   OH
Web Site: http://www.roopco.com
Year Founded: 1996
Sales Range: $10-24.9 Million
Emp.: 9
Public Relations & Advertising Agency
N.A.I.C.S.: 541820
James J. Roop *(Pres)*
Brad Kostka *(Sr VP)*
Lynn Dechant *(Dir-Graphic Design)*

ROOSEVELT & CROSS INC.
55 Broadway, New York, NY 10006
Tel.: (212) 344-2500
Web Site: http://www.roosevelt-cross.com
Year Founded: 1946
Sales Range: $25-49.9 Million
Emp.: 63
Bond Dealers & Brokers
N.A.I.C.S.: 523150
Dominick F. Antonelli *(Pres)*
Raymond O'Sullivan *(CFO)*

ROOSEVELT COUNTY ELECTRIC COOPERATIVE, INC.
121 N Main Ave, Portales, NM 88130

ROOSEVELT COUNTY ELECTRIC COOPERATIVE, INC.

U.S. PRIVATE

Roosevelt County Electric Cooperative, Inc.—(Continued)
Tel.: (575) 356-4491 NM
Web Site: http://www.rcec.org
Year Founded: 1940
Sales Range: $10-24.9 Million
Emp.: 54
Electric Power Distr
N.A.I.C.S.: 221122
Jerry Partin *(Gen Mgr)*

ROOSEVELT PAPER COMPANY
1 Roosevelt Dr, Mount Laurel, NJ 08054-6307
Tel.: (856) 303-4100 NJ
Web Site:
  http://www.rooseveltpaper.com
Year Founded: 1910
Sales Range: $150-199.9 Million
Emp.: 500
Printing Paper Wholesaler & Converter
N.A.I.C.S.: 322299
Ted Kosloff *(Chm & CEO)*
Eric Conine *(VP-Sls)*
David Kosloff *(Pres)*
Irving S. Kosloff *(Founder)*
Tony Janulewicz *(CFO)*

Subsidiaries:

Roosevelt Paper Company (1)
5100 W 123rd St, Alsip, IL 60803-3106
Tel.: (708) 653-5121
Web Site: http://www.rooseveltpaper.com
Sales Range: $25-49.9 Million
Emp.: 129
Writing Paper Whslr
N.A.I.C.S.: 424130
Tony Janulewicz *(CFO)*

Roosevelt Paper Company (1)
11001 Paper Blvd, Walton, KY 41094
Tel.: (859) 485-8100
Web Site: http://www.rooseveltpapaer.com
Sales Range: $25-49.9 Million
Emp.: 135
Paper & Paper Product Distr
N.A.I.C.S.: 424110

ROOSEVELT UNIVERSITY
430 S Michigan Ave, Chicago, IL 60605
Tel.: (312) 341-3500
Web Site: http://roosevelt.edu
Year Founded: 1945
Colleges & Universities
N.A.I.C.S.: 611310
James B. Connor *(Vice Chm)*
Douglas Knerr *(Provost & Exec VP)*
Miroslava Mejia Krug *(CFO & Sr VP-Fin & Admin)*
Lesley D. Slavitt *(VP-Govt Rels & University Outreach)*
Patricia Harris *(Chm)*
Paul McGuinness *(VP-Enrollment Mgmt & Student Affairs)*
Ali Malekzadeh *(Pres)*
Donald E. Jones *(VP-Institutional Advancement)*
LaDonna Long *(Chm-Govt, Law & Justice Dept)*

Subsidiaries:

Robert Morris Experiential College (1)
401 S State St, Chicago, IL 60605
Tel.: (800) 762-5960
Web Site: http://robertmorris.edu
Colleges & Universities
N.A.I.C.S.: 611310
Mablene Krueger *(Provost)*
Deborah Brodzinski *(Sr VP-Resource Admin)*
Nicole Farinella *(Sr VP-Enrollment Mgmt)*
Kathleen Suhajda *(VP-Academic Admin)*
Jaime Pena *(Coord-ETS)*
Jessica A. Acklin *(Coord-ETS)*
Angelica Castaneda *(Coord-Student)*
Carolyn M. Basley *(Dir-ETS)*
Janely Rivera *(Dir-Student Life & Housing)*
Pinkey Stewart *(Dir-Student Support Svcs)*
Catherine Lockwood *(VP-Adult Undergraduate & Graduate Education)*
Nick Jarmuz *(VP-Auxiliary Ops)*
Christine Fisher *(VP-Brand & Image)*
Ronald M. Arnold *(VP-Bus Affairs)*
Megan Smith *(VP-Extra Curricular Activities & Dir-Athletic)*
Leigh Brinson *(VP-Fin Aid)*
Nicole Skaluba *(VP-HR)*
Lisa Contreras *(VP-Info Sys)*
Danielle Naffziger *(VP-Mktg & Recruitment)*
Angela Jordan *(VP-Student Affairs)*
Nellie Phillips *(Coord-Compliance)*
Christopher B. Howard *(Pres)*
Christopher B. Howard *(Pres)*
Cornell Shelby II *(Coord-Academic)*

ROOT DESIGN COMPANY
504 Oakland Ave, Austin, TX 78703
Tel.: (512) 459-7665
Web Site:
  http://www.rootdesigncompany.com
Year Founded: 2004
Rev.: $3,500,000
Emp.: 10
Management Consulting Services
N.A.I.C.S.: 541611
Roxi Zamora *(Dir-Estate Mgmt)*
Ben Dozier *(Principal)*
Duke Cowden *(Principal)*
Connie Kelly *(Office Mgr)*

ROOTS EQUITY GROUP LLC
470 S Bedford Dr. Ste 402, Beverly Hills, CA 90212
Tel.: (323) 577-9731
Web Site:
  https://www.rootsequitygroup.com
Year Founded: 2017
Emp.: 100
Investment Management
N.A.I.C.S.: 523940

Subsidiaries:

Truss-T Structures, Inc. (1)
2100 North Pacific Highway, Woodburn, OR 97071
Tel.: (503) 981-9581
Web Site: https://www.pbsbuildings.com
Rev.: $8,666,666
Emp.: 60
Prefabricated Metal Building & Component Mfr
N.A.I.C.S.: 332311
Robert Prince *(Pres)*

ROOTS OF PEACE
990 A St Ste 402, San Rafael, CA 94901
Tel.: (415) 455-8008 CA
Web Site:
  http://www.rootsofpeace.org
Year Founded: 1999
Sales Range: $10-24.9 Million
Emp.: 25
Economic Development Services
N.A.I.C.S.: 541720
Heidi Kuhn *(Founder & CEO)*

ROPER BROTHERS LUMBER CO., INC.
130 Pocahontas St, Petersburg, VA 23803-3340
Tel.: (804) 732-9321 VA
Year Founded: 1909
Sales Range: $125-149.9 Million
Emp.: 225
Building Materials for Residential Construction
N.A.I.C.S.: 423310

ROPER BUICK GMC, INC.
808 Illinois Ave, Joplin, MO 64801
Tel.: (417) 625-5500 DE
Web Site: http://www.roperauto.com
Sales Range: $25-49.9 Million
Emp.: 170
Automobiles, New & Used
N.A.I.C.S.: 441110
Hal Roper *(Pres)*

ROPER PERSONNEL SERVICES INC.
125b Outlet Pointe Blvd, Columbia, SC 29210-5670
Tel.: (803) 798-8500
Web Site:
  http://www.roperstaffing.com
Sales Range: $10-24.9 Million
Emp.: 24
Temporary Help Service
N.A.I.C.S.: 561320
David Fuson *(Controller)*
George C. Roper III *(Pres)*

ROPER WHITNEY OF ROCKFORD INC.
2833 Huffman Blvd, Rockford, IL 61103
Tel.: (815) 962-3011
Web Site:
  http://www.roperwhitney.com
Year Founded: 1910
Rev.: $16,500,000
Emp.: 94
Sheet Metalworking Machines
N.A.I.C.S.: 333517
Greg Parkinson *(Dir-Admin & Procurement)*
Cindy Vander Waal *(Mgr-Sls)*

ROPES & GRAY LLP
Prudential Tower 800 Boylston St, Boston, MA 02199-3600
Tel.: (617) 951-7000
Web Site: https://www.ropesgray.com
Year Founded: 1865
Sales Range: $800-899.9 Million
Emp.: 1,500
Law firm
N.A.I.C.S.: 541110
R. Bradford Malt *(Chm & Partner)*
Adrienne Reynolds *(Mgr-Practice Dev)*
Louis Marani *(Supvr-Billing)*
Winston Burt *(Mgr-Litigation Tech)*
John M. Creedon *(Partner)*
Deborah Kantar Gardner *(Partner)*
Aaron Katz *(Partner)*
Peter Laybourn *(Partner)*
Michael Roh *(Partner)*
Melissa Rones *(Partner)*
Carrie Simons *(Partner)*
Martin Hall *(Partner)*
Brenda Coleman *(Partner-London)*
Maurice Allen *(Head-London)*
Thomas N. Bulleit *(Partner-Washington)*
Richard Gallagher *(Partner-Litigation Practice Grp-San Francisco)*
Ryan Murr *(Mng Partner-San Francisco)*
Harvey Cotton *(Atty)*
Patrick O'Brien *(Atty)*
Sara Lieberman *(Atty)*
Reiser Gregory *(Atty-Conflicts)*
Megan McGuire Ledeen *(Coord-Comm)*
Beth Nielsen *(Coord-HR)*
Precillia Soares *(Coord-Legal Recruiting)*
Debra Gratto *(Dir-HR)*
Jordan Sommer *(Dir-IT)*
Helen Long *(Dir-Recruiting)*
Mark Morrison *(Engr-Desktop)*
Jeremy Pires *(Engr-Network-II)*
Robyn Spanier *(Mgr-Client Intake & Conflicts Control)*
Sergey Polak *(Mgr-Enterprise Sys)*
Maria Arlotto *(Mgr-Pro Dev)*
Jennifer Saniuk *(Sr Mgr-Pro Dev)*
Georganne Mofford *(Sr Mgr-Secretarial Svcs & Trng)*
Jennifer Harris *(Partner-Global Capital Solutions & Private Credit Grp)*
David Djaha *(Mng Partner)*
Ed Sadtler *(Partner-IP Transactions)*
Jennifer Graff *(Partner-Asset Mgmt)*
Suni Sreepada *(Partner-M&A)*
Sam Badawi *(Partner-Capital Solutions & Private Credit)*
Samuel Norris *(Partner-Capital Solutions & Private Credit)*
Ryan Preston Dahl *(Partner-Bus Restructuring)*
Matthew Czyzyk *(Partner-Bus Restructuring)*
Milap Patel *(Partner)*
Patrick Dorime *(Partner)*

ROPPE CORPORATION
1602 N Union St, Fostoria, OH 44830-1958
Tel.: (419) 435-8546 DE
Web Site: http://www.roppe.com
Year Founded: 1955
Sales Range: $100-124.9 Million
Emp.: 300
Mfr of Molded & Extruded Rubber Products Including Cove Base, Stair Treads & Stair Nosings
N.A.I.C.S.: 326299
Donald P. Miller *(Chm, Pres & CEO)*
Judy R. Miller *(VP)*
Linda Schwab *(Mgr-Customer Svc)*
Doug Michelsen *(VP-Ops)*
Randy Farabee *(Dir-Mfg)*
Jana Burkett *(Mgr-HR)*
Bart Rogers *(VP-Sls & Mktg)*
Jason Lewis *(Coord-Logistics)*
Tammy Flippo *(Mgr-Accts-Natl)*
Julie Nye *(Mgr-Customer Svc Accts-Natl)*
Angie K. Welly *(Mgr-Fleet & Warehouse)*
Jim Baker *(Mgr-IT Network & Ops)*
Lisa M. Elchert *(Mgr-Pur)*
Dennis R. Roberts *(Supvr-Maintenance)*
Lawrence R. Nester Sr. *(CIO)*
Bill Moyer Jr. *(Coord-Logistics Ops & Quality Assurance)*

Subsidiaries:

Flexco Corporation (1)
1401 E Sixth St, Tuscumbia, AL 35674
Tel.: (256) 383-7474
Web Site: http://www.flexcofloors.com
Sales Range: $25-49.9 Million
Emp.: 150
Mfr & Sale of Specialized Commercial Flooring
N.A.I.C.S.: 327120
Rick Rollins *(Natl Mgr-Sls)*
Donovan Lonsway *(Dir-Indus Sls)*
Melissa Quick *(Coord-Mktg)*

ROPPEL INDUSTRIES INC.
829 Logan St, Louisville, KY 40204
Tel.: (502) 581-1004
Web Site: http://www.roppelrad.com
Sales Range: $10-24.9 Million
Emp.: 80
Automotive Supplies & Parts
N.A.I.C.S.: 423120
Kevin J. Roppel *(Pres)*
Tom Roppel *(VP)*

ROSATI WINDOWS
4200 Roberts Rd, Columbus, OH 43228
Tel.: (614) 777-4806 OH
Web Site:
  http://www.rosatiwindows.com
Year Founded: 2000
Sales Range: $250-299.9 Million
Emp.: 82

COMPANIES

Mfr & Installer of Custom Windows & Doors
N.A.I.C.S.: 332321
Cindy Seitz *(CFO)*
Dave Keplar *(Mgr-Production)*
David Lind *(Mgr-Production)*
Nicole Bunker *(Asst Controller)*

ROSBERG FOZMAN ROLANDELLI ADVERTISING
4745 Sutton Park Ct Ste 804, Jacksonville, FL 32224
Tel.: (904) 329-3797
Web Site: http://www.rfrad.com
Sales Range: $10-24.9 Million
Emp.: 5
Advetising Agency
N.A.I.C.S.: 541810
Mike Fozman *(Partner)*
Mike Rolandelli *(Partner)*
Richard Rosberg *(Partner)*

ROSCO LABORATORIES, INC.
52 Harbor View Ave, Stamford, CT 06902-5914
Tel.: (203) 708-8900   DE
Web Site: http://www.rosco.com
Year Founded: 1910
Sales Range: $75-99.9 Million
Emp.: 190
Mfr of Products Used by Theater, TV & Film Industries
N.A.I.C.S.: 333310
Stan Miller *(Chm)*
Mark Engel *(CEO)*
Andreas Dessloch *(Dir-Bus Dev-Intl)*
Donna Nicol *(Dir-Creative)*
Joanna Shapley *(Sr Acct Mgr-France & Italy)*
Huey Davis *(Mgr-Traffic)*
Stephen Spendiff *(Sr Product Mgr)*
Kees Frijters *(Pres)*
Joel Svendsen *(Mgr-Content Mktg)*
Lauren Proud *(Dir-Mktg)*
Pat Santarsiero *(Dir-HR)*

ROSCOE FINANCIAL CORPORATION
117 Cypress St, Roscoe, TX 79545
Tel.: (325) 766-3311   TX
Web Site: http://www.roscoestatebank.com
Year Founded: 1978
Sales Range: $1-9.9 Million
Emp.: 38
Bank Holding Company
N.A.I.C.S.: 551111
John W. Jay *(Pres & CEO)*
Gary Conway *(CFO)*
Kristie Fox *(Sec & VP)*

ROSCOE MOSS COMPANY
4360 Worth St, Los Angeles, CA 90063
Tel.: (323) 263-4111
Web Site: http://www.roscoemoss.com
Rev.: $11,200,000
Emp.: 102
Manufacture Water Screens & Casing
N.A.I.C.S.: 331210
Robert A. Vanvaler *(Pres)*
Gilbert Rodriguez *(Mgr)*
R. T. Van Valer *(Product Mgr)*

ROSCOR CORPORATION
1061 Feehanville Dr, Mount Prospect, IL 60056-6006
Tel.: (847) 299-8080   IL
Year Founded: 1966
Sales Range: $25-49.9 Million
Emp.: 140
Radio & T.V. Communications Equipment
N.A.I.C.S.: 334220

ROSE & ASSOCIATES LLC
2701 Beacon Ave S, Seattle, WA 98144
Tel.: (206) 323-1325
Web Site: http://www.redapple.com
Rev.: $16,000,000
Emp.: 150
Grocery Stores
N.A.I.C.S.: 445110
Lenny Rose *(Pres)*
Laura Rose *(Office Mgr)*

ROSE & SHORE
5151 Alcoa Ave, Vernon, CA 90058
Tel.: (323) 826-2144
Web Site: http://www.roseandshore.com
Year Founded: 1968
Sales Range: $10-24.9 Million
Emp.: 320
Processed Food Mfr
N.A.I.C.S.: 311615
Irwin Miller *(Pres)*
Larry Vanden Bos *(VP)*
James Craig *(VP)*

ROSE BROTHERS FURNITURE
203 Country Club Rd, Jacksonville, NC 28546
Tel.: (910) 455-4424
Web Site: http://www.rosebrothersfurniture.com
Sales Range: $10-24.9 Million
Emp.: 20
Furniture Retailer
N.A.I.C.S.: 449110
J. Travis Rose *(Chm)*

ROSE BROTHERS PAVING, INC.
Hwy 561 W Post Ofc 806, Ahoskie, NC 27910
Tel.: (252) 209-8144
Web Site: http://rosebrotherspaving.com
Rev.: $14,800,000
Emp.: 80
Highway & Street Paving Contractor Services
N.A.I.C.S.: 237310

ROSE COMMUNITY FOUNDATION
600 S Cherry St Ste 1200, Denver, CO 80246-1712
Tel.: (303) 398-7400   CO
Web Site: http://www.rcfdenver.org
Year Founded: 1995
Sales Range: $10-24.9 Million
Emp.: 34
Community Welfare Services
N.A.I.C.S.: 525120
Tish Gonzales *(Office Mgr)*
Anne Garcia *(Pres & CEO)*
Jerrold L. Glick *(Chm)*
Marci Hladik *(Dir-Ops)*
Beckett Stokes *(Dir-Comm)*
Rachel Griego *(Project Mgr)*
Kelli Rojas *(Mgr-Grants)*
Patrick Sablich *(VP-Philanthropic Svcs)*
Gretchen Lenamond *(CFO)*

ROSE CONSTRUCTION, INC.
126 Hwy 51 S, Covington, TN 38019
Tel.: (901) 476-9600   TN
Web Site: http://www.roseconstruction.biz
Sales Range: $25-49.9 Million
Emp.: 75
Prefabricated Building Erection, Industrial
N.A.I.C.S.: 236220

Paul Rose *(Pres)*
Joe Griggs *(CFO)*
Cindy Dunn *(VP-Ops)*
David Curtze *(Gen Mgr)*
Cleavette Brown *(Gen Mgr)*
Allan Rose *(Exec VP)*

ROSE DESIGN BUILD, INC.
15311 W 109 St, Lenexa, KS 66219
Tel.: (913) 782-0777   KS
Web Site: http://www.buildwithrose.com
Year Founded: 1986
Sales Range: $10-24.9 Million
Emp.: 10
Holding Company; Commercial, Institutional & Industrial Building Design & Construction Services
N.A.I.C.S.: 551112
Morgan D. Rose *(Principal)*
Christopher L. Herre *(Pres)*
Christopher R. Bell *(Sr Architect)*
Michael E. Doran *(Sr Project Mgr)*

Subsidiaries:

Rose Construction Co., Inc. (1)
15331 W 109th St, Lenexa, KS 66219
Tel.: (913) 782-0777
Web Site: http://www.buildwithrose.com
Rev.: $12,578,002
Commercial, Institutional & Industrial Building Design & Construction Services
N.A.I.C.S.: 236220
Christopher L. Herre *(Pres)*

ROSE EXTERMINATOR CO.
414 Frontage Rd, Northfield, IL 60093
Tel.: (847) 441-8300   IL
Web Site: http://www.rosepestcontrol.com
Year Founded: 1860
Exterminating & Pest Control Services
N.A.I.C.S.: 561710
Russ Ives *(Chm)*

ROSE HILL MEMORIAL PARK
3888 Workman Mill Rd, Whittier, CA 90601
Tel.: (562) 699-0921
Web Site: http://www.rosehills.com
Sales Range: $75-99.9 Million
Emp.: 600
Cemetery Subdividers & Developers
N.A.I.C.S.: 812220
Pat Monroe *(Pres)*

ROSE INTERNATIONAL INC.
16401 Swingley Ridge Rd Ste 300, Chesterfield, MO 63017
Tel.: (636) 812-4000
Web Site: http://www.roseint.com
Year Founded: 1993
Sales Range: $25-49.9 Million
Emp.: 800
Computer Consulting Services
N.A.I.C.S.: 541519
Phil Black *(VP-Contingent Workforce Svcs)*
Larry Crane *(VP-Fin)*
Teri Elder *(Dir-Govt Svcs)*

ROSE MART INC.
613 US 158 W By Pass, Henderson, NC 27537
Tel.: (252) 438-7141
Web Site: http://www.roseoilco.com
Sales Range: $10-24.9 Million
Emp.: 20
Convenience Store
N.A.I.C.S.: 445131

ROSE PARK ADVISORS LLC
200 State St, Boston, MA 02109
Tel.: (617) 849-9265

ROSE PRINTING COMPANY, INC.

Web Site: http://www.roseparkadvisors.com
Private Investment Firm
N.A.I.C.S.: 523999
Clayton Christensen *(Co-Founder)*
Matt Christensen *(Founder & Mng Partner)*
Kirk Allen *(Mng Dir)*
Aticus Peterson *(Principal)*
Jeffrey Brandon Parker *(Principal)*

Subsidiaries:

Norsk Titanium AS (1)
Flyplassveien 20, 3514, Honefoss, Norway
Tel.: (47) 97422200
Web Site: https://www.norsktitanium.com
Industrial Titanium Components Mfr
N.A.I.C.S.: 332999
Steve Littauer *(CFO)*
Gail A. Balcerzak *(Chief Legal Officer & Chief People Officer)*
Odd Terje Lium *(VP-Engineering)*
Khazeem Adesokan *(VP-Quality)*
John Andersen Jr. *(Chm)*

ROSE PARTNERS LP
380 Middlesex Ave, Carteret, NJ 07008
Tel.: (732) 541-5555
Web Site: http://www.whiterose.com
Sales Range: $250-299.9 Million
Emp.: 500
Canned Goods, Fruit, Vegetables, Seafood, Meats & Teas
N.A.I.C.S.: 424490
Steve Bokser *(Pres)*

Subsidiaries:

Di Giorgio Corporation (1)
380 Middlesex Ave, Carteret, NJ 07008-3446   (100%)
Tel.: (732) 541-5555
Web Site: http://www.whiterose.com
Wholesale Distr of Groceries
N.A.I.C.S.: 424410

Division (Domestic):

White Rose Foods (2)
380 Middlesex Ave, Carteret, NJ 07008-3446
Tel.: (732) 541-5555
Web Site: http://www.whiterose.com
Sales Range: $200-249.9 Million
Grocery Wholesale Distr
N.A.I.C.S.: 424410

Rose Trucking Corp (1)
380 Middlesex Ave, Carteret, NJ 07008
Tel.: (732) 541-5555
Web Site: http://www.whiterose.com
Rev.: $15,300,000
Emp.: 7
Groceries, General Line
N.A.I.C.S.: 424410

ROSE PAVING CO.
7300 W 100th Pl, Bridgeview, IL 60455-2414
Tel.: (708) 430-1100
Web Site: http://www.rosepaving.com
Sales Range: $25-49.9 Million
Emp.: 105
Concrete Finishing Services
N.A.I.C.S.: 238140
Ed Campbell *(Pres)*
Alan Rose *(CEO)*
Amy McGuinn *(Dir-Mktg)*

ROSE PRINTING COMPANY, INC.
2503 Jackson Bluff Rd, Tallahassee, FL 32304
Tel.: (850) 576-4151   FL
Web Site: http://www.roseprinting.com
Year Founded: 1932
Sales Range: $1-9.9 Million
Emp.: 50
Book Printing & Binding Services
N.A.I.C.S.: 323117
Charles Rosenberg *(Pres)*

ROSE'S SOUTHWEST PAPERS, INC.

U.S. PRIVATE

Rose's Southwest Papers, Inc.—(Continued)

ROSE'S SOUTHWEST PAPERS, INC.
1701 2nd St SW, Albuquerque, NM 87102
Tel.: (505) 842-0134
Web Site:
http://www.rosessouthwestpapers.com
Sales Range: $75-99.9 Million
Emp.: 250
Sanitary Paper Product Mfr
N.A.I.C.S.: 322291
Robert Espat *(Pres & CEO)*
Amir Lara *(Mgr-Mgmt Info Sys)*
Myriam Ramos *(Mgr-HR)*

ROSE-AMERICA CORPORATION
3100 S Meridian Ave, Wichita, KS 67217
Tel.: (316) 941-1100
Web Site: http://www.bmbtack.com
Rev.: $11,900,000
Emp.: 20
Equestrian Related Leather Articles
N.A.I.C.S.: 316990
Regina Kay Hanna *(Pres)*

ROSE-MARY CENTER
19350 Euclid Ave, Euclid, OH 44117
Tel.: (216) 481-4823
Web Site: http://www.rose-marycenter.com
Year Founded: 1922
Sales Range: $10-24.9 Million
Emp.: 425
Disability Assistance Services
N.A.I.C.S.: 624120
Gina Kerman *(Exec Dir)*
Victor Iacovone *(Vice Chm)*
Robert McAuley *(Chm)*

ROSEBAY INTERNATIONAL, INC.
1815 S Osprey Ave, Sarasota, FL 34239
Tel.: (941) 366-7673
Web Site: http://www.rosebay.com
Year Founded: 1991
Sales Range: $1-9.9 Million
Emp.: 75
Real Estate Broker
N.A.I.C.S.: 531210
Magdiel Rosario *(Founder & Pres)*

ROSEBRAND WIPERS INC.
4 Emerson Ln, Secaucus, NJ 07094
Tel.: (201) 809-1730
Web Site: http://www.rosebrand.com
Sales Range: $10-24.9 Million
Emp.: 200
Textiles, Woven
N.A.I.C.S.: 424310
George Jacobstein *(Pres)*
Peter Finder *(VP-Sls & Mktg)*
Bob Bertrand *(Gen Mgr)*
Tina C. Wright *(Dir-Sls & Ops-West Coast)*
Kevin Coughlin *(CFO)*

ROSEBUD MEDIA, LLC
111 N Fir St, Medford, OR 97501
Tel.: (541) 776-4411
Web Site:
http://www.rosebudmedia.com
Year Founded: 2017
Holding Company; Advertising Newspaper Publisher, Printer & Materials Distr
N.A.I.C.S.: 551112
Steven Saslow *(Owner)*

Subsidiaries:

The Mail Tribune, Inc. (1)
111 N Fir St, Medford, OR 97501
Tel.: (541) 776-4411
Web Site: http://www.mailtribune.com
Newspaper Publishing
N.A.I.C.S.: 513110
Georgie Cook *(Dir-Circulation)*

Unit (Domestic):

Ashland Daily Tidings (2)
111 N Fir St, Medford, OR 97501-2772
Tel.: (541) 776-4411
Web Site: http://www.ashlandtidings.com
Newspaper Publishers
N.A.I.C.S.: 513110
Joe Zavala *(Editor-Sports)*
Bert Etling *(Editor)*

ROSEBUD MINING COMPANY
301 Market St, Kittanning, PA 16201
Tel.: (724) 545-6222
Web Site:
http://www.rosebudmining.com
Year Founded: 1979
Bituminous Coal Underground Mining
N.A.I.C.S.: 212115
James R Barker *(VP & Sec)*
J. Clifford Forrest III *(Pres)*

ROSEBURG FOREST PRODUCTS
10599 Old Hwy 99, Dillard, OR 97432
Tel.: (541) 679-2773
Web Site: http://www.roseburg.com
Year Founded: 1936
Sales Range: $800-899.9 Million
Emp.: 3,300
Forestry; Lumber & Wood Products Distr
N.A.I.C.S.: 321212
Grady Mulberry *(Pres & CEO)*
Eric Geyer *(Dir-Strategic Bus Dev & External Affairs)*
Scott Folk *(Sr VP-Resources)*
Stuart Gray *(COO)*
Marty Daley *(CFO & Sr VP-Fin)*
Kellye Wise *(Sr VP-HR & Labor Rels)*
Tim Pruitt *(Mgr-Bus-Millwork)*

Subsidiaries:

Coos Bay Shipping Terminal (1)
PO Box 1088, Roseburg, OR 97470
Tel.: (541) 679-2773
Web Site:
http://www.coosbayshippingterminal.com
Marine Cargo Handling Services
N.A.I.C.S.: 488320
Keith Eibel *(Mgr-Chip)*

Del-Tin Fiber L.L.C. (1)
210 E Elm St, El Dorado, AR 71730
Tel.: (936) 699-1800
Web Site: http://www.deltinfiber.com
Wood Products Mfr
N.A.I.C.S.: 322219
Mike Hopkins *(Gen Mgr-Sls)*

Roseburg Forest Products Co. (1)
3660 Gateway St, Roseburg, OR 97477
Tel.: (541) 679-3311
Web Site: http://www.roseburg.com
Sales Range: $700-749.9 Million
Lumber & Wood Products Mfr
N.A.I.C.S.: 321212
Allyn C. Ford *(Pres & CEO)*

Roseburg Resources Co. (1)
10599 Old Hwy 99, Dillard, OR 97432 (100%)
Tel.: (541) 679-3311
Web Site: http://www.roseburg.com
Sales Range: $250-299.9 Million
Emp.: 140
Mfr of Lumber & Wood Products
N.A.I.C.S.: 113110
Allyn C. Ford *(CEO)*
Jeff Stuckey *(Controller)*
Steve Kilgore *(Sr VP-Solid Wood & Mktg)*
Marty Daley *(CFO & Sr VP-Fin)*
Scott Folk *(Sr VP-Resources)*

Scott Timber Co. (1)
10599 Old Hwy 99, Dillard, OR 97432 (100%)
Tel.: (541) 679-3311
Web Site: http://www.rfpco.com
Sales Range: $250-299.9 Million
Emp.: 3,000
Mfr Of Lumber & Wood Products
N.A.I.C.S.: 113310
Allyn C. Ford *(Pres)*
Jeff Stuckey *(Controller)*

ROSECOMM, INC.
80 River St Suite 4C, Hoboken, NJ 07030-5619
Tel.: (201) 656-7178
Web Site: http://www.rosecomm.com
Year Founded: 2003
Sales Range: $1-9.9 Million
Emp.: 8
Public Relations Agency
N.A.I.C.S.: 541820
Rosemary Ostmann *(Pres & CEO)*
Victoria Grantham *(Mng Dir & Sr VP)*
Tracey Cassidy *(VP)*
Lisa Trapani *(Sr VP & Dir-Editorial Svcs)*
Jennifer Leckstrom *(VP)*
Kelsey BaRoss *(Acct Exec)*
Stephanie Shaw *(Asst Acct Exec)*

ROSECRANCE, INC.
1021 N Mulford Rd, Rockford, IL 61107-3877
Tel.: (815) 391-1000
Web Site: http://www.rosecrance.org
Mental Health Services
N.A.I.C.S.: 621420
Judith Jobe *(Chief Admin Officer & Sr VP)*
David Gomel *(Pres & CEO)*
Janis Waddell *(Sr VP-Mktg)*
Thomas Wright *(Chief Medical Officer & Sr VP-Medical Affairs)*
Anne Boccignone *(VP-Comm & Dev)*
John F. Schuster *(CFO & VP)*
Kelly Epperson *(Gen Counsel & VP)*
Lisa Primm *(VP-Payer Rels)*
Paul Gilmet *(Coord-Alumni)*

Subsidiaries:

Jackson Recovery Centers, Inc. (1)
800 5th St, Sioux City, IA 51101
Tel.: (712) 234-2300
Web Site: http://rosecrancejackson.org
Addiction Treatment Services
N.A.I.C.S.: 624310
Julie Enockson *(VP-Fin)*
Kermit Dahlen *(Reg Pres)*
Annie Fridh *(VP-Ops)*
David Paulsrud *(Dir-Medical)*
Rachel Wurth *(Asst Dir-Medical)*
Ellen Nichols *(Chm)*
Marilyn Hagberg *(Treas)*
Stephanie Roth *(Vice Chm)*
Charlie Knoepfler *(Sec)*

ROSEDALE FEDERAL SAVINGS & LOAN ASSOCIATION
9616 Belair Rd, Baltimore, MD 21236
Tel.: (410) 256-5200
Web Site:
http://www.rosedalefederal.com
Year Founded: 1908
Sales Range: $10-24.9 Million
Savings Bank
N.A.I.C.S.: 522180
Matthew D. Barrett *(VP & Mgr-IT)*
Kevin M. Benson *(Pres & CEO)*
Linda A. Muffoletto *(COO, Sec & Exec VP)*
Stacey A. Rineer *(CFO, Treas & Sr VP)*
J. Edward Grant *(Chief Lending Officer & Sr VP)*
Michael Tomaszewski *(Chief Compliance Officer & Sr VP)*
Ellen M. Abrams *(Sr VP & Dir-HR)*

ROSEDALE GROUP INC.
1821 Wendell St, Dalton, GA 30721
Tel.: (706) 226-1003
Web Site:
http://www.rosedaletransport.com
Sales Range: $10-24.9 Million
Emp.: 300
Agents, Shipping
N.A.I.C.S.: 488510
Rolly W. Uloth *(Owner & Pres)*
Eva Koscielny *(CFO)*

ROSEDALE PRODUCTS INC.
3730 W Liberty Rd, Ann Arbor, MI 48103
Tel.: (734) 665-8201
Web Site:
http://www.rosedaleproducts.com
Rev.: $13,000,000
Emp.: 63
Industrial Filter Mfr
N.A.I.C.S.: 333998
Nils N. Rosaen *(Owner)*
Steven Cannaert *(Engr-Design & Welding)*
Carl Gnath *(Mgr-Warehouse)*
Dan Morosky *(VP-Sls & Mktg)*
Rodney Komaromi *(Engr)*

ROSEHILL RESOURCES INC.
16200 Park Row Ste 300, Houston, TX 77084
Tel.: (281) 675-3400
Web Site:
http://www.rosehillresources.com
Rev.: $302,283,000
Assets: $872,512,000
Liabilities: $496,370,000
Net Worth: $376,142,000
Earnings: ($23,349,000)
Emp.: 89
Fiscal Year-end: 12/31/19
Oil & Gas Exploration, Development & Production
N.A.I.C.S.: 211120
R. Craig Owen *(CFO & Sr VP)*
David L. French *(Pres & CEO)*
David Mora *(VP-Comml & Reserves)*
Jennifer Johnson *(Compliance Officer, Gen Counsel, Sec & VP)*
Gary C. Hanna *(Chm)*

ROSELAND COMMUNITY HOSPITAL
45 W 111th St, Chicago, IL 60628
Tel.: (773) 995-3000
Web Site:
http://www.roselandhospital.org
Year Founded: 1924
Sales Range: $50-74.9 Million
Emp.: 685
Healtcare Services
N.A.I.C.S.: 622110
Raul Garza *(Sec)*
Tim Egan *(Pres & CEO)*
Jeffery J. Waddy *(Vice Chm)*
Rupert M. Evans *(Chm)*

ROSELAND PARTNERS LLC
233 Canoe Brook Rd, Short Hills, NJ 07078
Tel.: (973) 218-2300
Web Site:
http://www.roselandproperty.com
Sales Range: $50-74.9 Million
Emp.: 350
Real Estate Services
N.A.I.C.S.: 531210
Bob Cappy *(CFO)*
Marshall B. Tycher *(Partner)*
Bradford R. Klatt *(Partner)*

ROSELLE PAPER CO., INC.
615 E 1st Ave, Roselle, NJ 07203-1562
Tel.: (908) 245-6758
Web Site:
http://www.rosellepaper.com

COMPANIES ROSENS DIVERSIFIED, INC.

Year Founded: 1965
Sales Range: $100-124.9 Million
Emp.: 150
Mfr of Drawing & Construction Papers, Notebooks, Stationery, Tablets, Newsprint, Packaging & Mass Merchandising Products
N.A.I.C.S.: 322230
Samuel Lefkovits (Pres)
Bernard Lefkovits (Treas)
Bella Bien (Controller)

ROSELLE SAVINGS BANK
235 Chestnut St, Roselle, NJ 07203-1217
Tel.: (908) 245-1885 NJ
Web Site:
 http://www.rosellesavings.com
Year Founded: 1889
Sales Range: $10-24.9 Million
Emp.: 39
Banking Services
N.A.I.C.S.: 522180
Jill G. Schahauser (Pres & CEO)
Cheryl McPhaul (VP)
Janice L. Ritz (Sr VP)
Detlef Felschow (COO & Exec VP)
Michael McCambridge (CFO & Sr VP)

ROSELON INDUSTRIES INC.
18 S 5th St, Quakertown, PA 18951
Tel.: (215) 536-3275
Rev.: $20,000,000
Emp.: 50
Textured Yarn
N.A.I.C.S.: 313110
Robert R. Adams (Pres)

ROSEMONT EXPOSITION SERVICES INC.
9291 W Bryn Mawr, Rosemont, IL 60018
Tel.: (847) 696-2208
Web Site:
 http://www.rosemontexpo.com
Sales Range: $10-24.9 Million
Emp.: 1,500
Renovation, Remodeling & Repairs: Industrial Buildings
N.A.I.C.S.: 812990
David D. Houston (Pres)
Christopher Stephens (Exec Dir)
Patrick Nagle (Gen Mgr-All State Arena)
Doug DuBrock (Exec Dir)
Grant Bailey (Asst Gen Mgr)
Tom Petruzzelli (Dir-Building Security)
Ben Shahriari (Mgr-Ops)

ROSEMONT PROPERTY MANAGEMENT LLC
330 Garfield St, Santa Fe, NM 87501
Tel.: (505) 992-5100 NM
Web Site:
 http://www.geminirosemont.com
Year Founded: 2003
Sales Range: $250-299.9 Million
Emp.: 135
Real Estate Agency
N.A.I.C.S.: 531210
Daniel Burrell (CEO)
Subsidiaries:
Rosemont Property Management of Texas LLC (1)
1235 N Loop W Ste 1025, Houston, TX 77008
Tel.: (713) 862-3333
Web Site: http://www.rosemontrealty.com
Rev.: $1,400,000
Emp.: 50
Real Estate Agents & Managers
N.A.I.C.S.: 531210
Mark Clarke (Mgr-Property)

ROSEMOOR FOUNDATION, INC.
117 E 70th St, New York, NY 10021
Tel.: (646) 742-2846 NY
Web Site: http://www.rosemoor.org
Year Founded: 1985
Sales Range: $10-24.9 Million
Emp.: 1
Financial Management & Consulting Support Services
N.A.I.C.S.: 611430
Maria Valdeavellano (Sec)
Jacqueline Taylor (Treas)
Maria Socrro Rodriguez (VP)
Pilar Racca (Sec)
Maria Meier (Asst Treas)

ROSEMORE INC.
1 N Charles St 22nd Fl, Baltimore, MD 21201-3759
Tel.: (410) 347-7080 MD
Web Site:
 http://www.rosemoreinc.com
Year Founded: 1999
Sales Range: $25-49.9 Million
Emp.: 40
Provider of Oil & Gas Exploration Services
N.A.I.C.S.: 213112
Frank B. Rosenberg (Co-Chm & Chief Investment Officer)
Subsidiaries:
Crown Central LLC (1)
1 N Charles St 22nd Fl, Baltimore, MD 21201-3740 (100%)
Tel.: (410) 347-7048
Web Site: http://www.crowncentral.com
Petroleum Products & Petrochemicals Refiner & Marketer
N.A.I.C.S.: 324110
Subsidiary (Domestic):
Crown Gold, Inc. (2)
PO Box 1168, Baltimore, MD 21203-1168 (100%)
Tel.: (410) 539-7400
Gold Mining
N.A.I.C.S.: 523999
FZ Corporation (2)
1 N Charles St, Baltimore, MD 21201 (100%)
Tel.: (410) 539-7400
Holding Co
N.A.I.C.S.: 445131
McMurrey Pipe Line Company (2)
425 McMurrey Dr, Tyler, TX 75702-6326
Tel.: (903) 579-3400
Pipeline Operations
N.A.I.C.S.: 486110
Gateway Gathering & Marketing Co. (1)
16430 Park 10 Pl Ste 500, Houston, TX 77084-5056
Tel.: (281) 829-3206
Web Site: http://www.gatewaygathering.net
Oil & Gas Exploration Services
N.A.I.C.S.: 213112
Rosemore Holdings Inc. (1)
1 N Charles St Ste 2400, Baltimore, MD 21201-3762
Tel.: (410) 347-7090
Sales Range: $25-49.9 Million
Emp.: 20
Holding Companies
N.A.I.C.S.: 551112

ROSEN & BRICHTA
640 N La Salle Dr Ste 555, Chicago, IL 60654
Tel.: (312) 951-1900
Year Founded: 1997
Sales Range: Less than $1 Million
Emp.: 15
Advetising Agency
N.A.I.C.S.: 541810

Jerry Rosen (CEO)
James Goldman (Exec VP & Dir-Client Svcs)
William Brichta (Pres & Chief Creative Officer)
Mark Stevens (Dir-Creative)
Eric Nardo (Dir-Interactive Strategy & Design)
Adam Lurie (Dir-Interactive Strategy & Dev)

ROSEN ASSOCIATES MANAGEMENT CORP.
33 S Service Rd, Jericho, NY 11753-1006
Tel.: (516) 333-2000 NY
Web Site: http://www.rosenmgmt.com
Year Founded: 1960
Sales Range: $75-99.9 Million
Emp.: 120
Owner, Developer & Manager of Neighborhood & Community Shopping Centers
N.A.I.C.S.: 531210
Robert A. Rosen (Founder & Chm)
David Rosen (Exec VP)
John Bernabeo (Dir-Construction)
John R. Gross (Dir-Asset Mgmt)
Kelly Crozier (Dir-Property Mgmt)
Kyle Farley (Dir-Leasing)
Maurice Dalton (Sr Project Mgr)
Rosanna Santoro (Controller)

ROSEN HOTELS & RESORTS, INC.
8990 International Dr Ste 200, Orlando, FL 32819
Tel.: (407) 996-1706 FL
Web Site:
 http://www.rosenhotels.com
Year Founded: 1974
Sales Range: $250-299.9 Million
Emp.: 4,500
Holding Company; Luxury Hotels & Resorts Owner & Operator
N.A.I.C.S.: 551112
Harris Rosen (Founder, Pres & COO)
Daniel Gutierrez (VP-Engrg & Facilities Mgmt)
Frank A. Santos (CFO & VP)
Leslie Menichini (VP-Sls & Mktg-Convention Properties)
Jim Bina (Dir-Fin)
Jonni Kimberly (Dir-HR)
Dorea Mays (Assoc Dir-HR)
Ashley Bacot (Mgr-Risk)
Ronald Ryan (Dir-Medical)
Dee Dee Baggitt (Dir-Engrg & Facilities Mgmt)
Jennifer Rice-Palmer (Dir-Guest Contact)
Kathy Marquardt (Dir-Pur)
Kenneth Aldridge Jr. (Dir-Health Svcs)
Subsidiaries:
Millennium Technology Group LLC (1)
9939 Universal Blvd, Orlando, FL 32819
Tel.: (407) 996-2399
Web Site: http://www.mtg-fl.com
Emp.: 500
Information Technology Consulting Services
N.A.I.C.S.: 541512
Josh Woods (Mgr-Tech Sls)
Robert Moncello (Sr Acct Mgr-Tech)
Jeff Hatcher (Dir-Convention Tech Sls & Mktg)
Kevin Drinan (Dir-Sls & Bus Dev)
Mark Vincent (Asst Dir-IT)
Mike Reynolds (Dir-Ops-IT)
Rosen Centre Hotel (1)
9840 International Dr, Orlando, FL 32819
Tel.: (407) 996-9840
Web Site: http://www.rosencentre.com
Luxury Hotel & Convention Hall Operator
N.A.I.C.S.: 721110

Phil Caronia (Gen Mgr)
Todd Frappier (Dir-Sls & Mktg)
Travers Johnson (Assoc Dir-Sls)
Jamie Cox (Assoc Dir-Sls)
Andrew Halsey (Mgr-Sls-Natl)
Suzanne Kennedy (Mgr-Sls-Natl)
Eliana Key (Mgr-Sls-Natl)
Julie Ryczak (Dir-Sls)
Douglas Thomas (Asst Dir-Sls)
Linda Wiman (Mgr-Sls-Natl)
Rosen Plaza Hotel (1)
9700 International Dr, Orlando, FL 32819
Tel.: (407) 996-9700
Web Site: http://www.rosenplaza.com
Sales Range: $10-24.9 Million
Emp.: 30
Hotels (except Casino Hotels) & Motels
N.A.I.C.S.: 721110
Harris Rosen (Pres & COO)
Victoria Hall (Dir-Sls & Mktg)
Gerdia Exinor (Mgr-Leisure Sls)
Jamie Cox (Assoc Dir-Sls)
Andrew Halsey (Mgr-Sls-Natl)
Patty Herder (Assoc Dir-Midwest Sls)
Suzanne Kennedy (Mgr-Sls-Natl)
Eliana Key (Mgr-Sls-Natl)
Jonathan Misiewicz (Mgr-Sls-Natl)
John Pate (Mgr-Sls-Natl)
Julie Ryczak (Assoc Dir-Sls)
Douglas Thomas (Asst Dir-Sls)
Derek Baum (Gen Mgr)
Jay Finkelstein (Asst Gen Mgr)

ROSEN MOTOR SALES
7000 Grand Ave, Gurnee, IL 60031
Tel.: (847) 856-8439
Web Site: http://www.rosenrosen.com
Rev.: $98,975,031
Emp.: 110
New & Used Car Dealers
N.A.I.C.S.: 441110
Saul Rosen (Pres)

ROSENAU BECK INC.
1310 Indus Blvd, Southampton, PA 18966
Tel.: (215) 364-1714
Sales Range: $10-24.9 Million
Emp.: 13
Girls' & Infants' Dress Sales
N.A.I.C.S.: 315250
Thomas R. Rosenau (Pres)
Cathy Polakowski (Office Mgr)

ROSENDIN ELECTRIC, INC.
880 Mabury Rd, San Jose, CA 95133-1021
Tel.: (408) 286-2800 CA
Web Site: http://www.rosendin.com
Year Founded: 1919
Sales Range: $350-399.9 Million
Emp.: 1,700
Electrical Contracting Services
N.A.I.C.S.: 238210
Tom K. Sorley (CEO)
Bill Mazzetti (Sr VP-Engrg)
Matthew Englert (Sr VP)
Angela Hart (Dir-Ops)
Joe Gross (Dir-Southeast)
Darren Salyards (Div Mgr-Virginia)
Jolsna Thomas (Mgr-Bus Dev-Texas)
James McGibney (Sr Dir-Cybersecurity & Compliance)
Tony Esteve (Mgr-Bus Dev-Mid-Atlantic Reg)
Subsidiaries:
KST Electric, Ltd. (1)
14215 Suncrest Rd, Manor, TX 78653 (100%)
Tel.: (512) 272-8841
Web Site: http://www.kstelectric.com
Sales Range: $50-74.9 Million
Emp.: 600
Electrical, Data & Communication Contractors
N.A.I.C.S.: 238210

ROSENS DIVERSIFIED, INC.

ROSENS DIVERSIFIED, INC.

Rosens Diversified, Inc.—(Continued)
1120 Lake Ave, Fairmont, MN 56031-1939
Tel.: (507) 238-6001
Web Site:
https://www.rosensdiversified.com
Year Founded: 1946
Sales Range: $1-4.9 Billion
Emp.: 4,000
Offices of Other Holding Companies
N.A.I.C.S.: 551112
Robert A. Hovde (CFO)
Dominick V. Driano Jr. (Gen Counsel & VP)

Subsidiaries:

America's Service Line, LLC (1)
1814 Elizabeth St, Green Bay, WI 54302
Tel.: (920) 430-8427
Web Site:
http://www.americasserviceline.com
Refrigerated Foodstuff Transportation Services
N.A.I.C.S.: 484230
Tom McClone (Pres)
David Picquet (Dir-Safety)

American Foods Group, LLC (1)
500 S Washington St, Green Bay, WI 54301
Tel.: (920) 437-6330
Web Site:
http://www.americanfoodsgroup.com
Sales Range: $300-349.9 Million
Emp.: 4,000
Holding Company; Beef & Pork Products Mfr & Whslr
N.A.I.C.S.: 424470
Thomas J. Rosen (CEO)
Steve Van Lannen (Exec VP-Fresh Meat Div)
Greg Benedict (Pres & COO)
Don Mehesan (Pres-Fresh Meat Div)
Ali Mohseni (VP)
Jeff Jones (VP-Sls & Mktg)
Jerry Scott (Exec VP-Fresh Meat Div)
Kevin Butler (VP-Ground Beef Sls)
Ann Kohlbeck (Mgr-Admin Svcs)
Louie Kohlbeck Jr. (VP-Boxed Beef & Trim)

Subsidiary (Domestic):

Calihan Pork Processors, Inc. (2)
1 South St, Peoria, IL 61602
Tel.: (309) 674-9175
Web Site: http://www.calihanpork.com
Bakery Products Mfr
N.A.I.C.S.: 311821
Jason Jones (Asst Gen Mgr)
Lou Landon (Co-Owner)

Cimpl's, LLC (2)
1000 Cattle Dr, Yankton, SD 57078
Tel.: (605) 665-1665
Meat Processor & Distr
N.A.I.C.S.: 311612
David Frankforter (VP-Ops)

Dakota Premium Foods, LLC (2)
425 Concord St S, South Saint Paul, MN 55075
Tel.: (651) 455-6611
Sales Range: $25-49.9 Million
Emp.: 250
Meat Processor & Distr
N.A.I.C.S.: 311612
Steve Cortinas (VP-Ops & Plant Mgr)

Gibbon Packing, LLC (2)
218 E Hwy 30, Gibbon, NE 68840
Tel.: (308) 468-5771
Web Site:
http://www.americanfoodsgroup.com
Sales Range: $75-99.9 Million
Emp.: 550
Meat Processor & Distr
N.A.I.C.S.: 311612
Rusty Oliver (VP)

Green Bay Dressed Beef, LLC (2)
544 Acme St, Green Bay, WI 54302-1807
Tel.: (920) 437-6330
Web Site:
http://www.americanfoodsgroup.com
Sales Range: $300-349.9 Million
Emp.: 1,700
Cattle Slaughtering & Beef Processing Services
N.A.I.C.S.: 311612

Long Prairie Packing LLC (2)
10 Riverside Dr, Long Prairie, MN 56347-1852
Tel.: (320) 732-2171
Sales Range: $75-99.9 Million
Emp.: 300
Cattle Slaughtering & Beef Processing Services
N.A.I.C.S.: 311612

Skylark Meats, LLC (2)
4430 S 110th St, Omaha, NE 68137
Tel.: (402) 592-0300
Web Site: http://www.skylarkmeats.com
Meat Processor, Specialty Meat Product Mfr & Distr
N.A.I.C.S.: 311612
Robert Elliott (Pres-Brands Div-American Foods Grp)

Performance Pet Products, LLC (1)
915 E Havens Ave, Mitchell, SD 57301
Tel.: (605) 990-7470
Web Site: http://www.performancepet.net
Sales Range: $10-24.9 Million
Emp.: 100
Pet Food Mfr
N.A.I.C.S.: 311111
Rob Cadenhead (VP-Sls & Mktg)
Wade Holcombe (VP-Ops)

Rosens, Inc. (1)
1120 Lake Ave, Fairmont, MN 56031-1939 (100%)
Tel.: (507) 238-4201
Sales Range: $10-24.9 Million
Emp.: 50
Fertilizer & Other Agricultural Products Distr & Services
N.A.I.C.S.: 424910
Thomas J. Rosen (Chm & CEO)
T. Kent Woodall (Dir-Mktg)
Randi Martinson (Coord-Sls)
Ken Sundblad (Mgr-Pur)
Steve Guetter (VP-Fin)

ROSENTHAL & ROSENTHAL, INC.

1370 Broadway, New York, NY 10018
Tel.: (212) 356-1400
Web Site:
http://www.rosenthalinc.com
Year Founded: 1964
Sales Range: $10-24.9 Million
Emp.: 240
Business Credit Services
N.A.I.C.S.: 522299
Peter Rosenthal (Co-Pres)
Michael Stanley (Mng Dir & Head-Factoring-East Coast)
Joshua Ceccarelli (Sr VP & Sr Acct Exec-East Coast)
Robert Martucci (Sr VP-Underwriter & Bus Dev)
Christopher Sanjenis (Sr VP)
Eric Bader (Sr VP)
Thomas Lauria (Sr VP & Portfolio Mgr)
James J. Occhiogrosso (CFO)
Eric J. Rosenthal (Chm)
Pamela Ramirez (Asst VP & Sr Acct Exec)
Ken Kleiner (Co-Pres)
Anthony Verrilli (Exec VP & Head-Credit Dept)
Joseph Pepe (Sr VP-Bus Dev)
David Bobby (VP)
Andrew Matza (VP)
Cassie Rosenthal (Sr VP)
Ying Yang (VP-Bus Dev)
Gary Norman (Exec VP & Portfolio Mgr)
Nirmala Sookiram (Sr VP & Sr Acct Exec)
Phillip Daks (VP & Acct Exec-West Coast office)
Sydnee Breuer (Exec VP & Mgr-West)
Leigh Lones (Sr VP & Sls Mgr-Southeast)
Anthony Ditirro (Sr VP & Deputy Mgr-Credit)
Ashraf Selim (CIO)
Brian Resutek (Sr VP)
Charlie Aiosa (Sr VP)
Deane Davis (Exec VP & Mgr-Acct Receivables)
Jeffrey Enoch (Exec VP-Western Reg & Portfolio Mgr)
Jennifer Draffkorn (Sr VP & Sr Acct Exec)
Joel Wolitzer (Sr VP-Bus Dev)
Kenneth Frasier (Sr VP)
Kevin Stapleton (Sr VP)
Kirk Brown (Sr VP)
Maria Contino (Sr VP-Western Reg & Mgr-Sls)
Mark Collins (Sr VP-Bus Dev)
Marty Eckstein (Sr VP-Bus Dev)
Michael Callahan (Sr VP)
Michael Cipriani (Exec VP-Bus Dev)
Paul Schuldiner (Chief Lending Officer & Exec VP)
Philippe Allard (Exec VP)
Rob Miller (Exec VP & Head-Asset Based Lending)
Robert Schnitzer (Sr VP-Bus Dev)
Dan Rogers (VP)
Peter Clement (Officer-Bus Dev-Intl Factoring & Sr VP)
Gene Walsh (Officer-Bus Dev-Atlanta & Sr VP-Atlanta)
Andrew O'Day (Officer-Bus Dev-Midwest & VP-Midwest)

ROSENTHAL CORPORATE SERVICES, INC.

1370 Broadway, New York, NY 10018
Tel.: (212) 356-1400
Web Site:
http://www.rosenthalinc.com
Year Founded: 1938
Sales Range: $10-24.9 Million
Emp.: 20
New Car Dealers
N.A.I.C.S.: 441110
Stephen J. Rosenthal (CEO)

ROSETTA TECHNOLOGIES CORP.

5912 Breckenridge Pkwy Ste B, Tampa, FL 33610
Tel.: (813) 623-6205
Web Site:
http://www.rosettatechnologies.com
Sales Range: $10-24.9 Million
Emp.: 20
Microlaser Printers Mfr & Distr
N.A.I.C.S.: 449210
Robert Hullar (Owner)
Jose Sepulveda (Mgr-Svc)

ROSEVILLE CHRYSLER PLYMOUTH JEEP INC.

25800 Gratiot Ave, Roseville, MI 48066
Tel.: (586) 859-2500
Web Site: http://www.mikeriehls.com
Year Founded: 1967
Sales Range: $75-99.9 Million
Emp.: 130
Sales of Automobiles
N.A.I.C.S.: 441110
Michael D. Riehl (Pres)
Wayne Andre (Controller)

ROSHAN TRADING INC.

2734 E 46 St, Los Angeles, CA 90058-2506
Tel.: (213) 622-9904
Web Site:
http://www.lagunafabrics.com
Rev.: $17,930,434
Emp.: 20
Mfr of Textiles
N.A.I.C.S.: 424310
Mansoor Roshan (Pres)

ROSICA STRATEGIC PUBLIC RELATIONS

2-14 Fair Lawn Ave, Fair Lawn, NJ 07410
Tel.: (201) 843-5600
Web Site: http://www.rosica.com
Year Founded: 1980
Public Relations Agency
N.A.I.C.S.: 541820
John Rosica (Pres & CEO)
Terese Kelly (VP-Media Rels)
Kathy Carliner (Sr VP-Consumer Mktg Div)

ROSIEK CONSTRUCTION CO. INC.

2000 E Lamar Blvd Ste 410, Arlington, TX 76006
Tel.: (817) 277-4342
Sales Range: $10-24.9 Million
Emp.: 6
General Contractor, Highway & Street Construction
N.A.I.C.S.: 237310
Richard D. Rosiek (Pres)
Mike Rosiek (VP)

ROSINA HOLDING, INC.

170 French Rd, Buffalo, NY 14227-2712
Tel.: (716) 668-0123
Web Site: http://www.rosina.com
Sales Range: $25-49.9 Million
Emp.: 400
Holding Company
N.A.I.C.S.: 311612
Russell Corigliano (Chrm, Pres & CEO)
Frank Corigliano (Exec VP)

Subsidiaries:

Rosina Food Products, Inc. (1)
170 French Rd, Buffalo, NY 14227-2712 (100%)
Tel.: (716) 668-0123
Web Site: http://www.rosina.com
Sales Range: $25-49.9 Million
Emp.: 300
Sales of Italian Style Foods Mfr
N.A.I.C.S.: 311612
James Corigliano (Founder)
Tom Finn (VP-Bus Dev)
Jim Whitford (Sls Mgr-Consumer Products Div)
Marcelle Smalley (Sls Mgr-Southeast-Consumer Products Div)
David Masse (Sls Mgr-Canada)
Chris Tirone (VP-Mktg & Customer Engagement)

ROSKA DIRECT

211B Progress Dr, Montgomeryville, PA 18936-9618
Tel.: (215) 699-9200
Web Site: http://www.roskadirect.com
Year Founded: 1981
Rev.: $41,000,000
Emp.: 45
Advetising Agency
N.A.I.C.S.: 541810
Jay H. Bolling (Pres & CEO)
Chuck McLeester (Sr VP-Strategic Plng)
Kurt Mueller (Chief Digital & Science Officer)

ROSKAM BAKING COMPANY INC.

4880 Corporate Exchange Blvd SE, Grand Rapids, MI 49512

COMPANIES

Tel.: (616) 574-5757
Web Site:
http://www.rothburyfarms.com
Year Founded: 1923
Emp.: 1,000
Bakery Products & Snack Foods Mfr
N.A.I.C.S.: 311812
Anthony Whyte *(Dir-Supply Chain & Logistics)*
Michael Bartikoski *(COO)*
Brett Turner *(Dir-Fin)*

ROSKAMP INSTITUTE
2040 Whitfield Ave, Sarasota, FL 34243
Tel.: (941) 752-2949
Web Site: http://www.rfdn.org
Year Founded: 1985
Sales Range: $1-9.9 Million
Emp.: 60
Brain Disease Research & Treatment
N.A.I.C.S.: 541715
Michael John Mullan *(Exec Dir)*
Fiona Crawford *(VP)*

ROSLYN SUPPLY COMPANY INC.
1587 N Easton Rd, Roslyn, PA 19001
Tel.: (215) 659-0700
Web Site:
http://www.roslynsupply.com
Sales Range: $25-49.9 Million
Emp.: 30
Roofing & Siding Materials
N.A.I.C.S.: 423330

ROSNER MANAGEMENT GROUP, LLC
3427 Jefferson Davis Hwy, Fredericksburg, VA 22408
Tel.: (540) 907-4900   VA
Web Site: http://www.rosnerauto.com
Holding Company; New & Used Car Dealerships Owner & Operator
N.A.I.C.S.: 551112
Ron Rosner *(Founder, Chm & CEO)*
Clayton Huber *(Pres)*

Subsidiaries:

RH Florida, LLC (1)
800 S Harbor City Blvd, Melbourne, FL 32901
Tel.: (321) 723-3611
Web Site: http://www.rosnerchevrolet.com
Sales Range: $10-24.9 Million
Emp.: 100
New & Used Car Dealer
N.A.I.C.S.: 441110
Mike Martinez *(Gen Mgr)*
Mike Ralston *(Mgr-Customer Rels)*

Rosner Motors, Inc. (1)
3427 Jefferson Davis Hwy, Fredericksburg, VA 22408
Tel.: (540) 907-4900
Web Site:
http://www.rosnermotorsports.com
Refurbished Sports Car Dealer
N.A.I.C.S.: 441120
Ron Rosner *(Founder, Chm & CEO)*
Clayton Huber *(Pres)*

ROSS & BARUZZINI, INC.
6 S Old Orchard, Saint Louis, MO 63119
Tel.: (314) 918-8383   MO
Web Site: http://www.rossbar.com
Year Founded: 1953
Sales Range: $1-9.9 Million
Emp.: 110
Engineering Services Architectural Services
N.A.I.C.S.: 541330
Trista Stahr *(Dir-HR)*
Michael Zoia *(VP & Dir-Aviation-North America)*
Megan Huff *(VP & Mng Principal-Macro)*
Roger Evans *(Dir-Bus Dev-Macro)*

Ihab Osman *(CTO, COO-Ops-Intl & Sr VP)*
William H. Overturf III *(Pres)*

Subsidiaries:

Cage Inc. (1)
6440 North Beltline Rd Ste 125, Irving, TX 75063
Tel.: (972) 550-1001
Web Site: http://www.cage-inc.com
Sales Range: $1-9.9 Million
Other Management Consulting Services
N.A.I.C.S.: 541618
Jeff Plant *(Pres)*

EDI, Ltd. (1)
1600 River Edge Pkwy Ste 900, Atlanta, GA 30328
Tel.: (770) 956-7000
Web Site: http://www.ediltd.com
Sales Range: $1-9.9 Million
Emp.: 23
Healthcare Software Consulting Services
N.A.I.C.S.: 541512
Donald E. Kinser *(Founder & Chm)*
Cynthia L. Cates *(VP-Fin & Admin)*
Paul Remke *(Project Dir)*
Jim P. Harrison *(Sr VP)*
Jan Stuchlik *(VP)*
Mark McComb *(Pres & CEO)*

ROSS BROTHERS CONSTRUCTION CO
7201 KY Rt 168, Catlettsburg, KY 41129
Tel.: (606) 739-5139
Sales Range: $25-49.9 Million
Emp.: 350
Industrial Buildings, New Construction
N.A.I.C.S.: 236210
John Griffiths *(Pres)*

Subsidiaries:

Robinson Excavating of Florida (1)
7201 State Route 168, Catlettsburg, KY 41129
Tel.: (606) 739-5139
Sales Range: $10-24.9 Million
Emp.: 50
Excavation Work
N.A.I.C.S.: 238910

ROSS BROTHERS CONSTRUCTION INC.
3501 Brooklake Rd NE, Salem, OR 97303
Tel.: (503) 393-5885
Web Site: http://www.allstate-construction.com
Sales Range: $10-24.9 Million
Emp.: 50
Bridge Construction
N.A.I.C.S.: 237310
Steven Tony *(VP)*

ROSS CONSOLIDATED CORP.
150 Innovation Dr, Elyria, OH 44035
Tel.: (440) 748-5800   OH
Web Site:
http://www.rossenvironmental.com
Year Founded: 1949
Rev.: $25,000,000
Emp.: 210
Holding Company for Providers of Environmental Management Services
N.A.I.C.S.: 562213
Maggie Kelch *(Mgr-Comm Rels-Ross Environmental)*
Patricia Lawson *(VP-Corp Compliance & Risk Mgmt-RES)*
Gary Vidmer *(Exec VP-Sls & Mktg-RES)*

Subsidiaries:

Ross Environmental Services, Inc. (1)
150 Innovation Dr, Elyria, OH 44035-1672
Tel.: (440) 366-2000
Web Site:
http://www.rossenvironmental.com

Sales Range: $10-24.9 Million
Emp.: 25
Hazardous & Industrial Waste Management Services
N.A.I.C.S.: 562211
Stefanie Clemens *(CFO)*
James Larson *(Pres & CEO)*

Subsidiary (Domestic):

A&D Environmental Services, Inc. (2)
2718 Uwharrie Rd, High Point, NC 27263-1680
Tel.: (336) 384-8828
Web Site: http://www.adenviro.com
Environmental Waste Cleaning & Removal Services
N.A.I.C.S.: 562998
Dan Martin *(VP-Sls & Mktg)*
Mike McClung *(VP-Transportation Div)*
Paul Butsavage *(VP-EHS & HR)*
Ron Meeks *(COO)*

Ross Incineration Services, Inc. (1)
36790 Giles Rd, Grafton, OH 44044-9125   (100%)
Tel.: (440) 748-5800
Web Site:
http://www.rossenvironmental.com
Sales Range: $25-49.9 Million
Providers of Refuse Systems
N.A.I.C.S.: 562213

Ross Transportation Services, Inc. (1)
36790 Giles Rd, Grafton, OH 44044-9125
Tel.: (440) 748-5900
Web Site:
http://www.rossenvironmental.com
Trucking Distr
N.A.I.C.S.: 484121
William E. Cromling *(Pres)*

ROSS DOWNING CHEVROLET, INC.
600 S Morrison Blvd, Hammond, LA 70403-3714
Tel.: (985) 345-1285
Web Site:
http://www.rossdowningchevrolet.com
Sales Range: $10-24.9 Million
Emp.: 80
Car Whslr
N.A.I.C.S.: 441110
Darren Blanchard *(Mgr-Svc)*
Dudley Downing *(Gen Mgr)*
Ross E. Downing *(Pres)*
Donna Ratcliff *(Office Mgr)*

ROSS EQUIPMENT INC.
7285 S 700 W, Midvale, UT 84047
Tel.: (801) 566-2437
Web Site: http://www.rossequip.com
Sales Range: $10-24.9 Million
Emp.: 30
Mining Machinery & Equipment
N.A.I.C.S.: 423810
Merrill Ross *(Pres)*

ROSS HAMMOCK RANCH, INC.
PO Box 505, Inglis, FL 34449
Tel.: (352) 447-0296
Web Site:
http://www.rosshammockranch.com
Sales Range: $1-9.9 Million
Hunting Lodge
N.A.I.C.S.: 721110
Harold R. Ross *(Founder & Pres)*

ROSS INDUSTRIES INC.
5321 Midland Rd, Midland, VA 22728
Tel.: (540) 439-3271
Web Site: http://www.rossindinc.com
Year Founded: 1968
Sales Range: $50-74.9 Million
Emp.: 140
Food Products Machinery
N.A.I.C.S.: 333241

ROSS TECHNOLOGY CORPORATION

Allen Snow *(Mgr-Quality)*
Bill Harrison *(Pkg & Tray Sealer Dev)*
Jamie Usrey *(Pres)*

ROSS INVESTMENT VENTURES
1800 Larimer St Ste 1700, Denver, CO 80202
Tel.: (303) 892-1111
Web Site:
http://www.newmarkkffr.com
Sales Range: $10-24.9 Million
Emp.: 200
Commercial & Industrial Building Operation
N.A.I.C.S.: 531120
Richard G. McClintock *(Exec VP)*
Steven K. Taniguchi *(CFO & Sr VP-Fin)*

ROSS MORTGAGE CORPORATION
27862 N Woodward Ave, Royal Oak, MI 48067
Tel.: (248) 547-4700   MI
Web Site:
http://www.rossmortgage.com
Sales Range: $10-24.9 Million
Emp.: 160
Mortgage Lending Services
N.A.I.C.S.: 522310
Tim Ross *(CEO)*
Josie Jurczak *(Coord-Loan)*
Angie Snider *(Asst Treas)*
Joni Amormino *(Asst VP)*
Betsy Corkum *(Exec VP)*
Chuck Hubbert *(Mgr-IT Support)*
Tim Pascarella *(Pres)*
Michael Fischer *(Dir-Loan Officer Acceleration & Branch Mgr)*

ROSS NETWORK INC.
27 Saint Johns Pl, Freeport, NY 11520
Tel.: (516) 223-7177
Sales Range: $25-49.9 Million
Emp.: 170
Commercial Printing, Lithographic
N.A.I.C.S.: 323111
Thomas White *(CEO)*

ROSS PALLETS INC.
913 East Walnut St, Santa Ana, CA 92701
Tel.: (714) 835-4460
Rev.: $14,600,000
Emp.: 17
Pallets, Wood
N.A.I.C.S.: 423310
Abelino Martinez *(Pres)*

ROSS REALTY INC.
1102 16th St, Central City, NE 68826-1535
Tel.: (308) 946-3852
Web Site:
http://www.rossrealtycentralcity.com
Offices of Real Estate Agents & Brokers
N.A.I.C.S.: 531210
Kim Ross *(Owner)*

ROSS SPORTSWEAR INC.
9909 S Shore Dr, Minneapolis, MN 55441
Tel.: (763) 545-9544
Sales Range: $10-24.9 Million
Emp.: 12
Screen Printing On Fabric Articles
N.A.I.C.S.: 314999
Michael J. Ross *(Pres)*

ROSS TECHNOLOGY CORPORATION
104 N Maple Ave, Leola, PA 17540-9799

ROSS TECHNOLOGY CORPORATION

U.S. PRIVATE

Ross Technology Corporation—(Continued)
Tel.: (717) 656-5600 PA
Web Site:
http://www.rosstechnology.com
Year Founded: 1962
Sales Range: $25-49.9 Million
Emp.: 144
Mfr of Steel Plates, Structural & Pallet Storage Racks & Automatic Stacking Machines
N.A.I.C.S.: 334290
Tom Crippen (Dir-Mktg)
Elmer Lapp (Mgr-Maintenance)
Steve Luscian (VP-Sls & Mktg)
Scott Espensen (Project Mgr)
Brad Hass (Project Mgr)
Bill Smith (Product Mgr)
Doug Bleecher (Plant Mgr)
Jay Otto (Pres)

ROSSER INTERNATIONAL, INC.
2 Peachtree Pointe 1555 Peachtree St NE Ste 800, Atlanta, GA 30309
Tel.: (404) 876-3800 GA
Web Site: http://www.rosser.com
Year Founded: 1946
Sales Range: $75-99.9 Million
Emp.: 75
Architectural & Engineering Services
N.A.I.C.S.: 541310
Larry Latimer (Dir-Sys Engrg)
Raymond C. Ashe (CEO)
Brenda Miller (CFO)

ROSSI'S TIRE & AUTO SERVICE
81 N Sanborn Rd, Salinas, CA 93906
Tel.: (831) 424-0011
Web Site: http://www.rossitire.com
Rev.: $10,534,182
Emp.: 50
Automotive Tires
N.A.I.C.S.: 441340
Jerry Barth (Controller)

ROSSMOYNE, INC.
3500 Ocean View Blvd, Glendale, CA 91208
Tel.: (818) 249-8397
Web Site:
http://www.rossmoyneinc.com
Year Founded: 1979
Sales Range: $10-24.9 Million
Emp.: 66
General Building Contractor Services
N.A.I.C.S.: 236116
George Pondella (Pres)

ROSWIL INC.
1878 State Hwy 125, Rogersville, MO 65742
Tel.: (417) 829-9200 MO
Web Site:
http://www.rameypricecutter.com
Year Founded: 1966
Sales Range: $25-49.9 Million
Emp.: 1,000
Grocery & Convenience Stores
N.A.I.C.S.: 445110
Erick Taylor (Pres & CEO)

ROSY BLUE INC.
529 5th Ave Fl 15, New York, NY 10017-4608
Tel.: (212) 687-8838 NY
Web Site: http://www.rosyblue.com
Year Founded: 1990
Sales Range: $150-199.9 Million
Emp.: 75
Jewelry & Precious Stones
N.A.I.C.S.: 423940
Dorus Billimoria (VP-Ops)
Dipu Mehta (Pres)
Sanjay Shah (CFO)

Subsidiaries:
Rosy Blue (India) Pvt. Ltd. (1)
Bharat Diamond Bourse F Tower FC 6017-18 Bandra Kurla Complex, Mumbai, 400 051, India
Tel.: (91) 22 6665 0000
Web Site: http://www.rosyblue.in
Jewelry & Gem Stone Whslr
N.A.I.C.S.: 423940

Rosy Blue Jewelry Inc. (1)
529 5th Ave 12th Fl, New York, NY 10017-4608 (100%)
Tel.: (212) 687-8838
Web Site: http://www.rosyblue.com
Sales Range: $10-24.9 Million
Emp.: 60
Jewelry & Precious Stones
N.A.I.C.S.: 423940
Nirad Dalal (Controller)

Rosy Blue Ltd (1)
Jewelry Mart 3rd Floor Higashi Ueno 1-10-6, Taito-ku, Tokyo, 110-0015, Japan
Tel.: (81) 3 3836 70 88
Web Site: http://www.rosyblue.com
Emp.: 30
Jewelry & Gem Stone Whslr
N.A.I.C.S.: 423940
Atul Jhaveri (Pres)

Rosy Blue NV (1)
Hoveniersstraat 53, PO Box 127, 2018, Antwerp, Belgium
Tel.: (32) 3 206 16 00
Emp.: 85
Jewelry & Gem Stone Whslr
N.A.I.C.S.: 423940
Amit Bhansali (Gen Mgr)

Rosy Blue Trading (Pty) Ltd (1)
230 Main Street Kgk House 1st Floor, Johannesburg, 2000, South Africa
Tel.: (27) 11 334 52 53
Jewelry & Gem Stone Whslr
N.A.I.C.S.: 423940

Rosyblue Hong Kong Ltd. (1)
Rm 403-4 Harbour Centre 2 8 Hok Cheung Street, Kowloon, Hung Hom, China (Hong Kong)
Tel.: (852) 2 523 9475
Web Site: http://www.rosyblue.com
Emp.: 40
Jewelry & Gem Stone Whslr
N.A.I.C.S.: 423940
Jimit Kapatia (Gen Mgr)

Rosyblue Trading LLC (1)
323 - 328 Gold Land Bldg 3rd Floor, PO Box 54303, Deira Gold Souq, Dubai, United Arab Emirates
Tel.: (971) 4 2202099
Jewelry & Gem Stone Whslr
N.A.I.C.S.: 423940
Rihen Mehta (Mng Dir)

ROTARY FORMS PRESS, INC.
835 S High St, Hillsboro, OH 45133-9602
Tel.: (937) 393-3426 MI
Web Site:
http://www.rotaryformspress.com
Year Founded: 1952
Sales Range: $75-99.9 Million
Emp.: 65
Mfr of Custom & Stock Continuous Business Forms
N.A.I.C.S.: 323111
Jon H. Cassner (Pres)
Brian Cassner (Treas & Dir-Corp Mktg)
Jerry Cochran (Supvr-Production)

Subsidiaries:
Computer Stock Forms, Inc. (1)
835 S High St, Hillsboro, OH 45133-9602
Tel.: (937) 981-7751
Web Site:
http://www.computerstockformsinc.com
Sales Range: $10-24.9 Million
Emp.: 4
Mfr of Custom & Stock Continuous Business Forms
N.A.I.C.S.: 323111

Units Sets, Inc. (1)
835 S High St, Hillsboro, OH 45133
Tel.: (937) 393-3426
Web Site: http://www.rfp.com
Sales Range: $10-24.9 Million
Emp.: 50
Mfr of Custom & Stock Continuous Business Forms
N.A.I.C.S.: 323111
Brian Cassner (Gen Mgr)

ROTARY INTERNATIONAL
1 Rotary Ctr 1560 Sherman Ave, Evanston, IL 60201-3698
Tel.: (847) 866-3000
Web Site: http://www.rotary.org
Year Founded: 1905
Sales Range: $25-49.9 Million
Emp.: 500
Humanitarian Services
N.A.I.C.S.: 813311
John Hewko (Sec)
Lori O. Carlson (CFO & Gen Mgr)
Steven Routburg (Gen Counsel)
Eric Jones (Chief Investment Officer)
Richard Kick (CIO)
Peter Iblher (Treas)

Subsidiaries:
The Rotarian Magazine (1)
One Rotary Ctr 1560 Sherman Ave, Evanston, IL 60201
Tel.: (847) 866-3000
Web Site: http://www.rotary.org
Sales Range: $1-9.9 Million
Magazine Publisher
N.A.I.C.S.: 513120
Deborah Lawrence (Dir-Design-Canada)
Janice Chambers (Sr Editor)
Marc Dukes (Coord-Adv)

ROTARY MULTIFORMS, INC.
1340 E 11 Mile Rd, Madison Heights, MI 48071
Tel.: (586) 558-7960 MI
Web Site: http://www.rmi-printing.com
Year Founded: 1982
Sales Range: $10-24.9 Million
Emp.: 9
Mfr of Manifold Business Forms
N.A.I.C.S.: 323111
Jeff Flynn (Gen Mgr)

ROTATION DYNAMICS CORP.
1101 Windham Pkwy, Darien, IL 60446
Tel.: (630) 769-9700 DE
Web Site: http://www.rotadyne.com
Year Founded: 1908
Rollers, Roll Covering & Related Products Mfr
N.A.I.C.S.: 333248
Jamin Patrick (Pres & COO)

Subsidiaries:
Advanced Graphics Technologies, Inc. (1)
942 Minters Chapel Rd, Grapevine, TX 76051-4135 (100%)
Tel.: (817) 481-8561
Sales Range: $10-24.9 Million
Emp.: 20
Chrome & Copper Plated Cylinders; Engraved Rotogravure Cylinders
N.A.I.C.S.: 332813

RotaDyne (1)
9126 Industrial Blvd, Covington, GA 30014-1473
Tel.: (770) 784-0787
Web Site: http://www.rotadyne.com
Sales Range: $25-49.9 Million
Emp.: 20
Industrial Printer Rollers, Machinery & Equipment Mfr
N.A.I.C.S.: 333248
Ed Nykiel (Gen Mgr)

ROTEC INDUSTRIES INC.
270 Industrial Dr, Hampshire, IL 60140-7902

Tel.: (630) 279-3300 DE
Web Site: http://www.rotec-usa.com
Year Founded: 1968
Sales Range: $10-24.9 Million
Emp.: 50
Conveyors & Conveying Equipment
N.A.I.C.S.: 333922
Robert F. Oury (Chm & CEO)

ROTECH HEALTHCARE, INC.
3600 Vineland Rd Ste 114, Orlando, FL 32811-6460
Tel.: (407) 822-4600 DE
Web Site: http://www.rotech.com
Year Founded: 1981
Sales Range: $450-499.9 Million
Emp.: 3,500
Home Medical Equipment & Related Products & Services; Infusion Therapy, Home Respiratory Care & Other Medical Services & Equipment Marketer & Distr
N.A.I.C.S.: 621610
Timothy C. Pigg (Pres & CEO)

Subsidiaries:
Taylor Home Health Inc. (1)
2688 Calder St, Beaumont, TX 77702-1917 (100%)
Tel.: (409) 838-9173
Web Site: http://www.rotech.com
Sales Range: $10-24.9 Million
Emp.: 10
Rental & Sales of Medical & Hospital Equipment
N.A.I.C.S.: 532283

ROTELLAS ITALIAN BAKERY INCORPORATED
6949 S 108th St, La Vista, NE 68128
Tel.: (402) 592-6600
Web Site:
http://www.rotellasbakery.com
Sales Range: $10-24.9 Million
Emp.: 300
Whslr of Bakery products
N.A.I.C.S.: 311812
Dean Jacobson (Controller)

ROTELLI PIZZA & PASTA
4755 Technology Way 1 101, Boca Raton, FL 33431
Tel.: (561) 826-0900
Web Site:
http://www.rotellipizzapasta.com
Sales Range: $50-74.9 Million
Emp.: 1,000
Italian Restaurant Operator & Franchiser
N.A.I.C.S.: 722511
Joseph Bilotti (Pres & CEO)
Joy Keller (Controller)
Iris Zayas (Dir-Mktg)
Pat Morris (COO)
Nancy Kalaty (Dir-Mktg)
Martha Guzman (Controller)

ROTEX INC.
1230 Knowlton St, Cincinnati, OH 45223
Tel.: (513) 541-1236
Web Site: http://www.rotex.com
Sales Range: $10-24.9 Million
Emp.: 400
Sifting & Screening Machines
N.A.I.C.S.: 333998
Rob Scheper (VP-Sls & Mktg)

ROTH CAPITAL PARTNERS LLC
888 San Clemente Dr, Newport Beach, CA 92660
Tel.: (949) 720-5700
Web Site: http://www.rothcp.com
Year Founded: 1984
Sales Range: $100-124.9 Million
Emp.: 200

COMPANIES

Investment Banking Services
N.A.I.C.S.: 523150
Byron Roth *(Chm)*
Gordon Roth *(CFO & COO)*
Christopher Jennings *(Mng Dir)*
Eric Rindahl *(Mng Dir)*
Aaron Gurewitz *(Mng Dir-Equity Capital Markets)*
Thomas B. Stringham *(Dir-Investment Banking)*
Joe Schimmelpfennig *(Mng Dir)*
Theodore D. Roth *(Pres)*
Jeff Martin *(Dir-Res)*
Isabel Mattson-Pain *(Dir-Mktg)*
John A. Hamel *(Mng Dir & Head-Fin Institutions Grp)*
Richard deNey *(Mng Dir & Head-Tech Investment Banking)*
Jesse Pichel *(Mng Dir-Cleantech Investment Banking)*
John Chambers *(Vice Chm)*
David T. Farina *(Mng Dir-Investment Banking)*
Adam Stormoen *(Dir-Healthcare Investment Banking)*
Eric B. Cheng *(Mng Dir & Co-Head-Healthcare Investment Banking)*
James Antonopoulos *(Mng Dir & Co-Head-Healthcare Investment Banking)*
J. Barry *(Mng Dir-Investment Banking-New York)*
Murray Huneke *(Mng Dir/Head-Consumer Investment Banking-San Francisco)*
Paul Zaffaroni *(Mng Dir & Head-Consumer Investment Banking)*
Scott Searle *(Mng Dir)*
Zegbeh Jallah *(Dir-Healthcare Res)*
Ivan Saval *(Mng Dir-AgTech Investment Banking)*
Jason Wittes *(Mng Dir)*
Sagar Sheth *(CEO)*

Subsidiaries:

MKM Partners, LLC (1)
677 Washington Blvd. Ste 510, Stamford, CT 06901
Tel.: (203) 861-9060
Web Site: http://www.mkmpartners.com
Investment Advice
N.A.I.C.S.: 523940
Michael Gallo *(Exec Dir)*

ROTH DISTRIBUTING COMPANY
742 S Broadway, Denver, CO 80209
Tel.: (303) 373-9090   **CO**
Web Site: http://www.rothliving.com
Appliance Showroom Appliance Distr
N.A.I.C.S.: 423220
John Thielen *(Pres)*

ROTH IGA FOODLINER INC.
4895 Indian School Rd NE, Salem, OR 97305
Tel.: (503) 393-7684
Web Site: http://www.roths.com
Sales Range: $10-24.9 Million
Emp.: 30
Supermarket Operator
N.A.I.C.S.: 445110
Orville N. Roth *(Founder & Chm)*
Katy Unrein *(Controller)*
Melinda Roth *(Sec)*

ROTH KASE USA, LTD.
657 2nd St, Monroe, WI 53566
Tel.: (608) 329-7666
Web Site: http://www.rothkase.com
Year Founded: 1991
Sales Range: $10-24.9 Million
Emp.: 100
Cheese; Natural & Processed
N.A.I.C.S.: 311513
Marc Druart *(Dir-Res & Dev)*
Robert Frie *(Plant Mgr)*

ROTH-ZACHRY HEATING INC.
6990 S Anderson Rd, Canby, OR 97013
Tel.: (503) 266-1249
Web Site: http://www.roth-heat.com
Year Founded: 1975
Sales Range: $10-24.9 Million
Emp.: 70
Air Conditioning System Installation Services
N.A.I.C.S.: 238220
Kory MacGregor *(Pres)*

ROTHMAN FURNITURE STORES, INC.
2101 E Terra Ln, O'Fallon, MO 63366
Tel.: (636) 978-3500
Web Site: http://www.rothmanfurniture.com
Year Founded: 1927
Sales Range: $10-24.9 Million
Furniture Retailer
N.A.I.C.S.: 449110
Bob Kershaw *(Reg Mgr-Sls)*
Jay Steinback *(Pres & CEO)*

ROTHROCK MOTOR SALES, INC.
1648 Plaza Ln, Allentown, PA 18104
Tel.: (610) 439-8485
Web Site: http://www.rothrock.com
Year Founded: 1960
Sales Range: $50-74.9 Million
Emp.: 200
Car Whslr
N.A.I.C.S.: 441110
David B. Rothrock *(Pres & CEO)*

ROTHSAY FARMERS CO-OP
215 RailRd Dr, Rothsay, MN 56579
Tel.: (218) 867-2135
Web Site: http://www.rothsaycoop.com
Sales Range: $25-49.9 Million
Emp.: 12
Grains Supplier
N.A.I.C.S.: 424510
Paul Jorgenson *(Gen Mgr)*

ROTHSTEIN CORP.
70 Olympia Ave, Woburn, MA 01801
Tel.: (781) 935-8300
Rev.: $18,700,000
Emp.: 85
Groceries & Related Products
N.A.I.C.S.: 424490
Steven A. Rothstein *(Pres)*

ROTHTEC ENGRAVING CORP.
699 Tarkiln Hill Rd, New Bedford, MA 02745
Tel.: (508) 995-4601
Web Site: http://www.rothtec.com
Year Founded: 1967
Sales Range: $10-24.9 Million
Emp.: 150
Mfr of Textile Printing Machinery
N.A.I.C.S.: 333248
Bruce Roth *(Pres)*
Fred Roth *(CEO)*

ROTO SUBARU MAZDA, INC.
1555 E Rand Rd, Arlington Heights, IL 60004-4380
Tel.: (847) 255-5700
Web Site: http://www.rotosubaru.com
Year Founded: 1954
Sales Range: $10-24.9 Million
Emp.: 69
Car Whslr
N.A.I.C.S.: 441110
Danny Napleton *(Pres)*

ROTOBLOCK CORPORATION
300 B St, Santa Rosa, CA 95401
Tel.: (707) 578-5220   **NV**
Year Founded: 2004
Sales Range: $1-9.9 Million
Emp.: 6
Engine Mfr
N.A.I.C.S.: 336310
Tony R. Collins *(VP-Corp Dev & Tech)*

ROTOLO CONSULTANTS, INC.
38001 Brownsvillage Rd, Slidell, LA 70460
Tel.: (985) 643-2427
Web Site: http://www.rotoloconsultants.com
Landscaping Services
N.A.I.C.S.: 561730
Brian Rotolo *(Comptroller)*

ROTONDA HOLDINGS INC.
4005 Cape Haze Dr, Placida, FL 33947
Tel.: (941) 697-1300
Rev.: $11,400,000
Emp.: 6
Subdividers & Developers
N.A.I.C.S.: 237210

Subsidiaries:

Cape Cave Corp. (1)
4005 Cape Haze Dr, Placida, FL 33947
Tel.: (941) 697-1300
Rev.: $9,600,000
Emp.: 2
Subdividers & Developers
N.A.I.C.S.: 237210

ROTOTECH ELECTRICAL COMPONENTS INC.
60 Woodlawn St, West Hartford, CT 06110-2326
Tel.: (317) 843-2753   **NJ**
Web Site: http://www.rototechgroup.com
Year Founded: 1982
Sales Range: $10-24.9 Million
Emp.: 1,500
Electronic Parts & Equipment Mfr
N.A.I.C.S.: 334419
Phil Fladung *(VP-Sls & Mktg)*
Jim Forte *(VP-Engrg)*

ROTOTRON CORPORATION
361 Neptune Ave, Babylon, NY 11704
Tel.: (631) 321-4400
Web Site: http://www.rototroncorp.com
Sales Range: $10-24.9 Million
Emp.: 10
Plastics Materials & Basic Shapes
N.A.I.C.S.: 424610
Joan Flaxman *(VP)*

ROTOVAC CORPORATION
17905 Bothell Everett Hwy, Mill Creek, WA 98052
Tel.: (425) 883-6746
Web Site: http://www.rotovac.com
Sales Range: $75-99.9 Million
Emp.: 20
Carpet Cleaning System Mfr
N.A.I.C.S.: 335210
Cliff Monson *(Pres)*
Adam Baird *(Mgr-Customer Svc)*

ROTTER GROUP INC.
256 Main St 2nd Fl, Huntington, NY 11743
Tel.: (631) 470-7803   **NY**
Web Site: http://www.rottergroup.com
Year Founded: 1965
Sales Range: $10-24.9 Million
Emp.: 22
Advetising Agency
N.A.I.C.S.: 541810
Steve H. Rotter *(Pres & CEO)*
Steve Stetzer *(Exec VP & Dir-Client Svcs)*

Subsidiaries:

Rotter Group Inc. (1)
2670 Solana Way, Laguna Beach, CA 92651
Tel.: (949) 715-3814
Web Site: http://www.rottergroup.com
Sales Range: $10-24.9 Million
Emp.: 5
N.A.I.C.S.: 541810
Steve Rotter *(Owner)*

ROTTINGHAUS CO. INC.
510 Gillette St, La Crosse, WI 54603
Tel.: (608) 784-2774
Web Site: http://www.rottinghaus.com
Sales Range: $25-49.9 Million
Emp.: 2,300
Sandwiches & Submarines Store Operator
N.A.I.C.S.: 722513
Peter Hansen *(Controller)*

ROTUNDA CAPITAL PARTNERS LLC
4747 Bethesda Ave Ste 1150, Bethesda, MD 20814
Tel.: (249) 482-0610
Web Site: http://www.rotundacapital.com
Year Founded: 2009
Private Investment Firm
N.A.I.C.S.: 523999
Rona Kennedy *(CFO & Chief Compliance Officer)*
John Fruehwirth *(Mng Partner)*
Dan Lipson *(Mng Partner)*
Bob Wickham *(Partner)*
Corey Whisner *(Partner)*
Ryan Aprill *(Principal)*
Nathan Bertsch *(VP-Data & Analytics)*
Emmy Frenz *(Controller)*
Brian Kim *(VP)*

Subsidiaries:

American Equipment, Inc. (1)
451 W 3440 S, Salt Lake City, UT 84115-4227
Tel.: (801) 269-0896
Web Site: http://www.amquipinc.com
Overhead Traveling Crane, Hoist & Monorail System Mfr
N.A.I.C.S.: 333923
Lori Castleton *(VP-Ops)*
Adam Zimmerman *(Pres & CEO)*

Subsidiary (Domestic):

American Scale Co. LLC (2)
7231 Cove Creek Dr, Charlotte, NC 28215
Tel.: (704) 921-4556
Web Site: https://www.americanscaleus.com
Rev.: $1,000,000
Emp.: 10
Industrial Weighting Technology Services
N.A.I.C.S.: 811490
Mike Walton *(CFO & VP)*

Division (Domestic):

Shannahan Crane & Hoist Inc. (2)
11695 Wakeside Crossing Ct, Saint Louis, MO 63146
Tel.: (314) 965-2800
Web Site: http://www.shannahancrane.com
Sales Range: $10-24.9 Million
Emp.: 20
Provider of Industrial Services
N.A.I.C.S.: 423830
Pat Brockland *(Controller)*

Amware Logistics Services, Inc. (1)
4505 Newpoint Pl, Lawrenceville, GA 30043
Tel.: (678) 377-8585
Web Site: http://www.amwarelogistics.com
Commercial Fulfillment Services
N.A.I.C.S.: 541614
Harry Drajpuch *(CEO)*
Jack Nichols *(CFO)*
Lorna Robinson *(Dir-HR)*
Duncan Thomas *(VP-Ops)*
Scott Guilmette *(VP-Bus Dev)*

ROTUNDA CAPITAL PARTNERS LLC

Rotunda Capital Partners LLC—(Continued)

Subsidiary (Domestic):

Moulton Logistics Management (2)
16620 Stagg St, Van Nuys, CA 91406
Tel.: (818) 997-1800
Web Site: http://www.moultonlogistics.com
Rev.: $11,408,676
Emp.: 250
Magazine & Newspaper Subscription Fulfillment Services
N.A.I.C.S.: 561499
Trina Spell *(Acct Mgr)*
Joel Crannell *(VP-Sls)*
Michael Cruz *(Acct Supvr-Support)*
Minerva Castro *(Supvr-Acctg)*

Bron Tapes LLC (1)
875 W Ellsworth Ave, Denver, CO 80223
Tel.: (303) 534-7387
Web Site: https://www.brontapes.com
Rev.: $58,000,000
Emp.: 46
Adhesives Tapes, Distributors & Converters
N.A.I.C.S.: 423840
Mike Shand *(CEO)*

Discount Ramps.Com, LLC (1)
760 S Indiana Ave, West Bend, WI 53095
Tel.: (262) 338-3431
Web Site: http://www.discountramps.com
Sales Range: $10-24.9 Million
Emp.: 25
Loading & Transport Items
N.A.I.C.S.: 336999
Bob Krolski *(COO)*
Larry Marmon *(CEO)*

Subsidiary (Domestic):

Heavy Duty Ramps, LLC (2)
7865 Sandy Ridge Rd, Kewaskum, WI 53040-9474
Tel.: (262) 334-5807
Web Site: http://www.hdramps.com
Aluminum Rolling, Drawing & Extruding Svcs
N.A.I.C.S.: 331318
Richard Beilstein *(Owner)*

Door Pro America, LLC (1)
14209 John Marshall Hwy, Gainesville, VA 20155
Tel.: (703) 631-0576
Web Site: http://www.doorproamerica.com
Rev.: $9,800,000
Emp.: 55
Home Center Operator
N.A.I.C.S.: 444110
Christopher Traxel *(Co-Pres)*

MacQueen Equipment, LLC (1)
1125 7th St E, Saint Paul, MN 55104
Tel.: (651) 645-5726
Web Site: http://www.macqueeneq.com
Sales Range: $1-9.9 Million
Emp.: 35
Construction And Mining Machinery
N.A.I.C.S.: 423810
Curt Steffen *(Pres)*
Mike Hawkins *(Gen Mgr)*
Heather Boston *(Controller)*
Terry Droubie *(Mgr-Svc)*
Allie Keller *(Mgr-Mktg)*
Steve Kohler *(Mgr-Parts)*
Aaron Long *(Supvr-Svc)*
Bill McCarthy *(Mgr-District Sls)*
Tyson Prahl *(Mgr-Solid Waste)*
Dan Gage *(CEO)*

Subsidiary (Domestic):

5 Alarm Fire & Safety Equipment, LLC (2)
350 Austin Cir, Delafield, WI 53018-2171
Tel.: (920) 568-1010
Web Site: http://www.5alarm.com
Rev.: $6,000,000
Emp.: 55
Fiscal Year-end: 12/31/2006
Safety & Firefighting Equipment Distr
N.A.I.C.S.: 423850

Bell Equipment Company (2)
78 Northpointe Dr, Lake Orion, MI 48359
Tel.: (248) 370-0000
Web Site: http://www.bellequip.com
Sales of Trucks, Commercial & Sanitation Equipment
N.A.I.C.S.: 423110

Steve Sauer *(Mgr-Parts)*
David Johnson *(Mgr)*
Jimmy Bell *(Pres)*

The Smart Companies, Inc. (1)
6182 Idlewild St, Fort Myers, FL 33966
Tel.: (239) 938-1000
Web Site: http://www.getsmartcompanies.com
Sales Range: $25-49.9 Million
Emp.: 110
Hurricane Shutters, Impact Windows & Doors Mfr & Installation
N.A.I.C.S.: 332321
Brian Rist *(Founder)*
John Boland *(CEO)*

Trafera, LLC (1)
2550 University Ave W Ste 315 S, Saint Paul, MN 55114
Tel.: (651) 888-7922
Web Site: http://www.trinity3.com
Warranty Services & Enterprise Products for the K-12 Education
N.A.I.C.S.: 561499
Chad Dehmlow *(Principal & Sr VP-Sls & Mktg)*
Scott Gill *(Pres & CEO)*

Subsidiary (Domestic):

AXI Education Solutions, LLC (2)
600 Deer Cross Court E, Madisonville, LA 70447
Tel.: (985) 893-0608
Web Site: http://www.axiedu.com
Computer & Computer Peripheral Equipment & Software Merchant Whslr
N.A.I.C.S.: 423430
Tyler Mallet *(Dir-Pro Dev)*
Dale Viola *(Founder)*

FireFly Computers, LLC (2)
1271 Red Fox Rd, Saint Paul, MN 55112
Tel.: (612) 564-4088
Web Site: http://www.fireflycomputers.com
Sales Range: $10-24.9 Million
Computer Hardware Distr
N.A.I.C.S.: 423690
Eli Maloley *(VP-Sls & Mktg)*
Brian Dimitroff *(Sr Mgr-Corp Dev)*
Nikki Levin *(Dir-Ops)*
Chris Mclaird *(Mgr-Technical Svcs)*
Charlie Williams *(Sr VP)*

ROUGHRIDER ELECTRIC CO-OPERATIVE, INC.

800 Highway Dr, Hazen, ND 58545-4737
Tel.: (701) 748-2293 ND
Web Site: http://www.roughriderelectric.com
Year Founded: 2008
Sales Range: $25-49.9 Million
Emp.: 63
Electric Power Distr
N.A.I.C.S.: 221122
Travis Kupper *(CFO)*
Rob Kelly *(Mgr-Engrg Svcs)*
Jason Bentz *(Mgr-Ops)*
Brad Quenette *(Dir-Member Svcs & Mktg)*
Sienna Sailer *(Mgr-HR)*
Don Franklin *(CEO & Co-Mgr)*
Bruce Darcy *(Treas)*
Chris Baumgartner *(CEO & Co-Mgr)*
Roger Kudrna *(Pres)*
Troy Sailer *(Sec)*
Darell Herman *(VP)*

ROUND HILL CLUB

33 Round Hill Club Rd, Greenwich, CT 06831-4232
Tel.: (203) 869-2350 CT
Web Site: http://www.rhclub.org
Year Founded: 1922
Sales Range: $10-24.9 Million
Emp.: 181
Social Club
N.A.I.C.S.: 813410
Leda Mejia *(Mgr-Food & Beverage Svc)*
Zoltan Toth *(Asst Mgr)*
Betty Wistrand *(Mgr-HR)*

ROUND HILL SECURITIES

PO Box 85549, San Diego, CA 92186-5549
Tel.: (925) 820-3980
Web Site: http://www.roundhill.com
Rev.: $11,700,000
Emp.: 80
Stock Brokers & Dealers
N.A.I.C.S.: 523150
Josef Forstmayr *(Mng Dir)*

ROUND ROOM LLC

525 Congressional Blvd, Carmel, IN 46032
Tel.: (765) 651-2001 IN
Web Site: http://www.roundroom.com
Holding Company; Wireless Telecommunications Industry Investment
N.A.I.C.S.: 551112
Scott Moorehead *(Pres & CEO)*
Chad Jensen *(Pres-Wireless Div)*
Katie Wiley *(Chief Strategy Officer)*

Subsidiaries:

The Cellular Connection, LLC (1)
525 Congressional Blvd, Carmel, IN 46032
Tel.: (765) 651-2001
Web Site: http://www.tccrocks.com
Emp.: 1,700
Wireless Telephone Equipment Retailer
N.A.I.C.S.: 449210
Scott Moorehead *(Pres & CEO)*

Subsidiary (Domestic):

Wireless Zone LLC (2)
795 Brook St, Rocky Hill, CT 06067
Tel.: (860) 632-9494
Web Site: http://www.wirelesszone.com
Wireless Telephones & Accessories Retailer
N.A.I.C.S.: 449210
Brian Murtari *(CTO)*
Michael Broe *(Exec VP)*
David Staszewski *(Exec VP)*
Robert G. Huelin *(VP-Legal & Compliance)*

ROUND SKY INC

848 N Rainbow Blvd Ste 326, Las Vegas, NV 89107
Tel.: (213) 537-3136
Web Site: http://www.roundsky.com
Year Founded: 2006
Sales Range: $1-9.9 Million
Emp.: 8
Lead Generation
N.A.I.C.S.: 561499
Nazar Brizinov *(CEO)*

ROUND TABLE CAPITAL MANAGEMENT, LP

120 NW 25th St Ste 203, Miami, FL 33127
Tel.: (646) 930-0930 DE
Web Site: http://www.rtcpartners.com
Year Founded: 2017
Private Investment Firm
N.A.I.C.S.: 523999
Tony Brindisi *(Founder & Mng Partner)*
Christopher Lee *(Mng Partner)*
Ashley Chang *(VP)*

Subsidiaries:

Alden Research Laboratory, Inc. (1)
30 Shrewsbury St, Holden, MA 01520-1843
Tel.: (508) 829-6000
Web Site: http://www.aldenlab.com
Hydraulic & Environmental Engineering Services
N.A.I.C.S.: 541330
Andrew E. Johansson *(Dir-Hydraulic Modeling & Consulting)*
Greg Allen *(Dir-Environmental & Engrg Svcs)*
Daniel Gessler *(Dir-Colorado Ops & VP)*
David K. Anderson *(Sr VP)*
Stuart A. Cain *(Pres)*
George E. Hecker *(CFO)*
Robert B. Campbell *(CFO)*

Duffield Associates Inc. (1)

5400 Limestone Road, Wilmington, DE 19808
Tel.: (302) 239-6634
Web Site: http://www.duffnet.com
Rev.: $9,000,000
Emp.: 120
Engineering Services
N.A.I.C.S.: 541330
Guy Marcozzi *(Pres & CEO)*
Jeffrey Bross *(Chm)*
David R. Charles *(Exec VP-Duffield Associates)*

ROUND2 COMMUNICATIONS, LLC

10866 Wilshire Blvd Ste 900, Los Angeles, CA 90024
Tel.: (310) 481-8040
Year Founded: 1993
Sales Range: $50-74.9 Million
Emp.: 28
Media Buying Agency
N.A.I.C.S.: 541830
Garfield Ricketts *(Chm & CEO)*
Isaac Brantner *(Controller)*
A. Kolcheva *(Assoc Dir-Media-Round2 Los Angeles)*

Subsidiaries:

Round2/SF (1)
101 Second St Ste 1250, San Francisco, CA 94105
Tel.: (415) 442-0680
Rev.: $20,000,000
Emp.: 5
Media Buying Services
N.A.I.C.S.: 541830
Jim Sparacino *(Media Dir)*

ROUNDBANK

200 NE 2nd St, Waseca, MN 56093
Tel.: (507) 835-4220
Web Site: http://www.roundbank.com
Year Founded: 1881
Sales Range: $10-24.9 Million
Emp.: 31
Provider of Banking Services
N.A.I.C.S.: 522110
Larry Thompson *(Pres & CEO)*
Mathias Gregor *(Chief Credit Officer)*
Christie Doe *(Mgr-Retail Sls)*
Carol Raimann *(Branch Mgr)*

ROUNDHOUSE MARKETING & PROMOTION, INC.

560 E Verona Ave, Verona, WI 53593
Tel.: (608) 497-2550
Web Site: http://www.roundhouse-marketing.com
Sales Range: $10-24.9 Million
Emp.: 20
Brand Development & Integration, Graphic Design, Point of Sale, Print, Promotions
N.A.I.C.S.: 541810
Robert Carr *(Owner)*

ROUNDPEG

1003 E 106th St, Indianapolis, IN 46280
Tel.: (317) 569-1396
Web Site: http://www.roundpeg.biz
Year Founded: 2002
Sales Range: Less than $1 Million
Emp.: 5
N.A.I.C.S.: 541810
Lorraine Ball *(Owner)*
Taylor Brough *(Dir-Creative)*
Jay Mattingly *(Dir-Mktg)*
Allison Carter *(Dir-Comm)*

ROUNDTABLE HEALTHCARE MANAGEMENT, INC.

272 E Deerpath Rd Ste 350, Lake Forest, IL 60045-3200
Tel.: (847) 739-3200 DE
Web Site: http://www.roundtablehp.com

Year Founded: 2001
Sales Range: $1-4.9 Billion
Healthcare Investment Services
N.A.I.C.S.: 523999
Joseph F. Damico (Co-Founder & Partner)
Jawwad A. Akhtar (VP)
Thomas P. Kapfer (Mng Partner)
Lester B. Knight III (Co-Founder & Partner)

Subsidiaries:

DDS Lab, LLC (1)
5440 Beaumont Ctr Blvd Ste 400, Tampa, FL 33634
Tel.: (813) 249-8800
Web Site: http://www.ddslabsolutions.com
Emp.: 80
Dental Laboratory Services
N.A.I.C.S.: 339116
Kelly Rivera (Sr VP-Sls)
Bill Warner (Mgr-Crown & Bridge)
William Braun (Pres)
Bart J. Doedens (CEO)

Endoscopy Development Company LLC (1)
14062 Riverport Dr, Maryland Heights, MO 63043
Tel.: (314) 344-4441
Web Site: http://www.edcparts.com
Commercial & Industrial Machinery & Equipment Repair & Maintenance
N.A.I.C.S.: 811310
Marcus Rosenberg (Pres)
Jeffrey Lay (Co-Founder)

Goodier Cosmetics, Inc. (1)
9019 Premier Row, Dallas, TX 75247
Tel.: (214) 630-1803
Web Site: http://www.goodiercosmetics.com
Toilet Preparation Mfr
N.A.I.C.S.: 325620
Jesus Rodriguez (Mgr-Production)

Moberg Pharma North America LLC (1)
7 E Frederick Pl, Cedar Knolls, NJ 07927
Tel.: (973) 946-7550
Pharmaceutical Preparation Mfr
N.A.I.C.S.: 325412

Renaissance Pharma Inc. (1)
370 Chemin Chambly Suite 300, Longueuil, J4H 3Z6, QC, Canada
Tel.: (514) 316-5668
Web Site: http://www.renaissanceacquisitionholdings.com
Emp.: 4
Holding Company
N.A.I.C.S.: 551112
Pierre Frechette (Pres & CEO)
Christine Woolgar (CFO & VP)
Raymond Canole (VP-Bus Dev)

Holding (Domestic):

Confab Laboratories, Inc. (2)
4355 Sir Wilfrid Laurier Blvd, Saint-Hubert, J3Y 3X3, QC, Canada
Tel.: (450) 443-6666
Web Site: http://www.confab.com
Emp.: 325
Pharmaceuticals Mfr
N.A.I.C.S.: 325412
Paul H. Johnson (COO)

Holding (US):

DPT Laboratories, Ltd. (2)
318 McCullough, San Antonio, TX 78215
Tel.: (210) 223-3281
Web Site: http://www.dptlabs.com
Sales Range: $50-74.9 Million
Pharmaceutical Development & Mfr Services
N.A.I.C.S.: 325412
Paul H. Johnson (Pres & COO)
Mark Fite (Sr VP-Ops)
Rick Bentzinger (VP-HR)
Lyle Flom (VP & Gen Mgr-San Antonio Site Ops)
Glenn Kues (Sr VP-Fin)
Nick Walp (VP-Quality Sys)
Gene Ciolfi (VP & Gen Mgr-Lakewood Site Ops)

Branch (Domestic):

DPT Lakewood, Inc. (3)
1200 Paco Way, Lakewood, NJ 08701
Tel.: (732) 367-9000
Web Site: http://www.dptlabs.com
Sales Range: $25-49.9 Million
Pharmaceutical Preparations
N.A.I.C.S.: 325412
Gene Ciolfi (VP & Gen Mgr-Lakewood Site Ops)
Mark Fite (Sr VP-Ops)
Rick Bentzinger (VP-HR)
Kuljit Bhatia (VP-Res & Dev)
Paul H. Johnson (Pres & COO)
Paul Josephs (Sr VP-Sls, Mktg & Corp Dev)
Glenn Kues (Sr VP-Fin)
Nick Walp (VP-Quality Sys)

Salter Labs (1)
100 Sycamore Rd, Arvin, CA 93203
Tel.: (661) 854-3166
Web Site: http://www.salterlabs.com
Surgical & Medical Instruments Mfr
N.A.I.C.S.: 339112
Patty Pantoja (Coord-Samples)

ROUNDTOWER TECHNOLOGIES, LLC
5905 E Galbraith Rd 3rd Fl, Cincinnati, OH 45236
Tel.: (513) 247-7900
Web Site: http://www.roundtower.com
Year Founded: 2007
Sales Range: $25-49.9 Million
Emp.: 40
Information Technology Consulting Services
N.A.I.C.S.: 541512
Stephen West (Mng Partner)
Stephen Power (Mng Partner)
Aaron Tulledge (Acct Exec)
Ben Haney (Sr Acct Mgr)
Brian Witsken (Mgr-Svcs)
David Dickmeyer (Sr Acct Exec)

ROUNDTREE AUTOMOTIVE GROUP, LLC
5307 E Mockingbird Ln Ste 975, Dallas, TX 75206
Tel.: (214) 823-3400   LA
Web Site: http://www.roundtreeautomotivegroup.com
Year Founded: 1985
Sales Range: $50-74.9 Million
Holding Company; New & Used Car Dealerships Owner & Operator
N.A.I.C.S.: 551112
Frank Stinson (Founder & Chm)
Matt Stinson (CEO)
Don Judice (CFO)
Alissa Hillhouse (Controller)
John Rowe (Dir-Corp Fixed Ops)
Stacee Story (Dir-Corp Dealership Acctg)

Subsidiaries:

Roundtree I Van Nuys, LLC (1)
5455 Van Nuys Blvd, Van Nuys, CA 91401
Tel.: (818) 782-1000
Web Site: http://www.infinitiofvannuys.com
Sales Range: $10-24.9 Million
Emp.: 75
New & Used Car Dealer
N.A.I.C.S.: 441110
Donna Williams (Gen Sls Mgr)

Roundtree N Van Nuys, LLC (1)
5425 Van Nuys Blvd, Van Nuys, CA 91401
Tel.: (818) 787-8400
Web Site: http://www.nissanofvannuys.com
Sales Range: $25-49.9 Million
Emp.: 100
New & Used Car Dealer
N.A.I.C.S.: 441110
Martin Cuevas (Gen Mgr)

ROUNDY APPAREL
179 S 1000 W, Ogden, UT 84404
Tel.: (801) 255-6665

Sales Range: $25-49.9 Million
Emp.: 200
Clothing Sales
N.A.I.C.S.: 424350
Donie Bateman (Pres)
Lori Strong (Coord)

ROUNTREE MOTORS INC.
1147 Putney Rd, Brattleboro, VT 05301
Tel.: (802) 258-2400
Web Site: http://www.brattleboroford.com
Sales Range: $25-49.9 Million
Emp.: 100
Automobiles, New & Used
N.A.I.C.S.: 441110
Paul Kause (Pres)

ROURA IRON WORKS, INC.
35355 Forton Ct, Clinton Township, MI 48035-3133
Tel.: (586) 790-6100   MI
Web Site: http://www.rouramh.com
Year Founded: 1915
Sales Range: $50-74.9 Million
Emp.: 10
Materials Handling Equipment & Self Dumping Hoppers Mfr
N.A.I.C.S.: 332322
Mike Genter (Pres)

Subsidiaries:

Roura Iron Works Inc. (1)
100 S Industrial Park Rd, Holly Springs, MS 38635-7411 (100%)
Tel.: (662) 252-1421
Web Site: http://www.rouramh.com
Self-Dumping Hopper Mfr
N.A.I.C.S.: 333924
Mike Genter (Pres)

ROUSE'S ENTERPRISES LLC
1301 St Mary Hwy, Thibodaux, LA 70301
Tel.: (985) 447-5998   LA
Web Site: http://www.rouses.com
Year Founded: 1959
Rev.: $138,222,997
Emp.: 1,200
Grocery Stores
N.A.I.C.S.: 445110
Donald J. Rouse (Pres)
Thomas Rouse (CFO)
Bob Bixenman (Dir-Maintenance & Construction)
Mike O'Shell (Dir-Center Store)

Subsidiaries:

Palco LLC (1)
1434 N Burnside Ave Ste 34, Gonzales, LA 70737
Tel.: (225) 647-3601
Supermarket & Other Grocery Store
N.A.I.C.S.: 445110

ROUSH ENTERPRISES, INC.
12447 Levan, Livonia, MI 48150-1125
Tel.: (734) 779-7006   MI
Web Site: http://www.roush.com
Year Founded: 1976
Sales Range: $450-499.9 Million
Emp.: 4,000
Holding Company; Motor Vehicle Parts Engineering, Testing & Development Services; High Performance Road Vehicles & Parts Mfr; Professional Motorsports Team Operator
N.A.I.C.S.: 551112
Jack Roush (Chm)
Evan Lyall (CEO)
Doug Smith (Pres & COO)
Jay R. Jolliffe (Gen Counsel & Sec)

Subsidiaries:

Roush Corporation (1)
4600 Roush Pl NW, Concord, NC 28027 (50%)
Tel.: (704) 720-4600
Web Site: http://www.roushfenway.com
Sales Range: $25-49.9 Million
Professional Motorsports Organization
N.A.I.C.S.: 711211
Steve Newmark (Pres)

Roush Manufacturing, Inc. (1)
12068 Market St Bldg 28, Livonia, MI 48150
Tel.: (734) 779-7028
Motor Vehicle Parts Mfr
N.A.I.C.S.: 336390

Roush Performance Products, Inc. (1)
39555 Schoolcraft Rd, Plymouth, MI 48170 (100%)
Tel.: (734) 779-7006
Web Site: http://www.roushperformance.com
Sales Range: $10-24.9 Million
Emp.: 100
High Performance Motor Vehicle & After-Market Parts Mfr
N.A.I.C.S.: 336110
Tom Siebyla (Supvr-Powertrain Engrg)
Tony Marszalek (Dir-Product & Bus Dev)

ROUSH EQUIPMENT COMPANY INC.
100 W Schrock Rd, Westerville, OH 43081
Tel.: (614) 882-1535   OH
Web Site: http://www.roushhonda.com
Year Founded: 1966
Sales Range: $50-74.9 Million
Emp.: 81
Sales of New & Used Automobiles
N.A.I.C.S.: 441110
Jeff Brindley (Gen Mgr)
Jim Erwin (Mgr-Sls-Used Cars)
Tim Fox (Mgr-Svc)
Chris Norz (Mgr-Parts)
Joe Harp (Asst Mgr-Sls-New Car)
Joe Fenstemaker (Mgr-Used Car)
Rod Williams (Mgr-Sls)

ROUSSO APPAREL GROUP INC.
525 7th Ave 22nd Fl, New York, NY 10018
Tel.: (212) 354-1890
Web Site: http://www.roussony.com
Rev.: $20,733,257
Emp.: 55
Mfr of Women's Sportswear
N.A.I.C.S.: 315250
Natalie Rousso (Chm)
William Leal (Dir-Mgmt Info Sys)
Barbara Bruk (Dir-Design)
John Singleton (Mgr-Accts Payable)
Colleen Kane (Sr Acct Exec)

ROUSSO/FISHER PUBLIC RELATIONS, INC.
5225 Wilshire Blvd Ste 718, Los Angeles, CA 90036
Tel.: (323) 933-4646
Sales Range: $10-24.9 Million
Brand Development & Integration, Media Planning, Print, Product Placement & Public Relations Services
N.A.I.C.S.: 541820
R.J. Rousso (Pres)
Carl Larsen (VP-Publicity)
Zack Tanck (Acct Exec)
Jonathan Williams (Coord-Publicity)

ROUTE 12 WASH 'N' GAS INC.
760 Milford Frenchtown Rd, Milford, NJ 08848
Tel.: (908) 996-2177
Web Site: http://www.shammyshine.com
Sales Range: $10-24.9 Million
Emp.: 150
Carwash
N.A.I.C.S.: 811192
H. Craig Stem (Pres)

Route 12 Wash 'n' Gas Inc.—(Continued)

ROUTE 2 CAPITAL PARTNERS
200 Meeting St Ste 403, Charleston, SC 29401
Tel.: (854) 529-9550
Web Site:
http://www.route2capital.com
Privater Equity Firm
N.A.I.C.S.: 523940
Scott Kester *(Partner)*
Patrick Weston *(Partner)*

ROUTE 22 HONDA
75 Route 22, Hillside, NJ 07205
Tel.: (973) 705-9300
Web Site:
http://www.route22honda.com
Year Founded: 1996
Sales Range: $25-49.9 Million
Emp.: 175
Car Whslr
N.A.I.C.S.: 441110
Alex Guzman *(Mgr-Lease Retention)*

ROUTE 22 TOYOTA
109 Route 22, Hillside, NJ 07205
Tel.: (973) 705-9400
Web Site:
http://www.route22toyota.com
Year Founded: 1989
Sales Range: $10-24.9 Million
Emp.: 80
Car Whslr
N.A.I.C.S.: 441110
Barry Rosner *(Principal)*
Alex Cancela *(Principal)*

ROUTE 23 AUTO MALL
1301 Route 23 S, Butler, NJ 07405
Tel.: (973) 838-0800
Web Site: http://www.23automall.com
Year Founded: 2000
Sales Range: $10-24.9 Million
Emp.: 69
Car Whslr
N.A.I.C.S.: 441110
Scott Barna *(Pres)*

ROVIRA BISCUIT CORPORATION
619 Avenue Cuatro Calles, Ponce, PR 00717-1901
Tel.: (787) 844-8585
Web Site:
http://www.rovirabiscuits.com
Year Founded: 1929
Sales Range: $25-49.9 Million
Emp.: 280
Crackers & Cookies Mfr
N.A.I.C.S.: 311821
Rafael L. Rovira *(Pres)*

ROW INC.
2730 SW 3rd Ave Ste 500, Miami, FL 33129
Tel.: (305) 860-0102
Web Site:
http://www.qcibritannic.com
Sales Range: $10-24.9 Million
Emp.: 7
Holding Company
N.A.I.C.S.: 213115
Enrico Freund *(Pres)*
Eduardo Portillo *(CFO)*
Subsidiaries:

QCI Britannic (1)
2730 SW 3rd Ave Ste 500, Miami, FL 33129
Tel.: (305) 860-0102
Web Site: http://www.qcibritannic.com
Trader of Nonmetallic Minerals
N.A.I.C.S.: 213115
Eduardo Portillo *(Dir-Fin)*

ROWAND MACHINERY COMPANY
6210 W Rowand Rd, Spokane, WA 99224
Tel.: (509) 838-5252
Web Site: http://www.rowand.com
Sales Range: $25-49.9 Million
Emp.: 35
Fiscal Year-end: 12/31/15
General Construction Machinery & Equipment
N.A.I.C.S.: 423810
Gordon H. Rowand *(Pres)*
David Rowand *(VP)*
Chris Dyreson *(Mgr-Parts)*

ROWE & NEWBERRY INC.
10832 SW 91st Ave, Ocala, FL 34481
Tel.: (352) 854-5915
Web Site: http://www.rowe-newberry.com
Sales Range: $10-24.9 Million
Emp.: 7
Commercial & Office Building, New Construction
N.A.I.C.S.: 236220
Jerry A. Sapp *(Exec VP)*
Phil Tyler *(Project Mgr)*
George Rowe *(Pres)*
Kirk Mason *(Treas, Sec & VP)*

ROWE ENTERPRISES INC.
700 W Wetmore Rd, Tucson, AZ 85705
Tel.: (520) 795-5565
Web Site: http://www.pretoy.com
Sales Range: $1-9.9 Million
Emp.: 200
Automobiles; New & Used
N.A.I.C.S.: 441110
Valerie Feddick *(Controller)*
John W. Rowe *(Pres)*

ROWE ENTERPRISES, INC.
9799 US Hwy 301 S, Hampton, FL 32044
Tel.: (352) 468-3306
Web Site:
http://www.roweenterprisesinc.com
Sales Range: $1-9.9 Million
Emp.: 25
Property Preservation & Real Estate Services
N.A.I.C.S.: 531390
Donna Rowe *(CFO)*
Jonathan Rowe *(VP-Field Ops)*
Shannon Rowe *(Dir-Property Preservation)*

ROWE TRUCK EQUIPMENT INC.
102 W 1st St, Otterbein, IN 47970
Tel.: (765) 583-4461
Web Site: http://www.rowetruck.com
Year Founded: 1920
Sales Range: $10-24.9 Million
Emp.: 100
Sales of Truck Equipment & Parts
N.A.I.C.S.: 441330
John C. Rowe *(Pres)*
Larry Wilcrout *(Gen Mgr)*
David Rose *(VP)*

ROWELL CHEMICAL CORPORATION
15 Salt Creek Ln Ste 205, Hinsdale, IL 60521
Tel.: (630) 920-8833
Web Site:
http://www.rowellchemical.com
Sales Range: $50-74.9 Million
Emp.: 70
Acids
N.A.I.C.S.: 424690

Terrence J. Matray *(Pres)*
Tom Harris *(Dir-Sls)*
Matt Koupal *(VP-Ops)*
John Ward *(Mgr-Customer Svcs)*

ROWERDINK INC.
211 Fuller Ave NE, Grand Rapids, MI 49503
Tel.: (616) 459-3274
Web Site: http://www.rowerdink.com
Sales Range: $25-49.9 Million
Emp.: 135
Automotive Supplies & Parts
N.A.I.C.S.: 423120
Robert Rowerdink *(VP)*
John Rowerdink *(Pres)*
Joe Frankovich *(Controller)*

ROWL, INC.
9595 Wilshire Blvd Ste 900, Beverly Hills, CA 90212
Tel.: (310) 744-6060
Web Site: http://www.rowl.com
Year Founded: 2010
Sales Range: $1-9.9 Million
Location-Based Social Networking & Mobile Advertising Applications
N.A.I.C.S.: 513210
Bill Glaser *(Founder & Pres)*
Michael Portera *(Treas)*

ROWLAND PUBLISHING, INC.
1932 Miccosukee Rd, Tallahassee, FL 32308
Tel.: (850) 878-0554
Web Site:
http://www.rowlandpublishing.com
Year Founded: 1990
Sales Range: $1-9.9 Million
Emp.: 25
Periodical Publishers
N.A.I.C.S.: 513120
Brian Rowland *(Pres & Publr)*
Larry Davidson *(Chief Content Officer)*
Daniel Vitter *(Dir-Production & Tech)*
Linda Kleindienst *(Dir-Editorial Svcs & Editor-850 Magazine)*
Dan Parisi *(Dir-New Bus Dev)*
McKenzie Burleigh *(Mgr-Mktg & Media Dev)*

ROWLEY COMPANY, LLC
230 Meek Rd, Gastonia, NC 28056
Tel.: (704) 866-0650
Web Site:
http://www.rowleycompany.com
Rev.: $5,000,000
Emp.: 25
Hardware Stores
N.A.I.C.S.: 444140
William J. Taylor *(CEO)*
Subsidiaries:

The Finial Company (1)
4030 La Reunion Pkwy, Dallas, TX 75212
Tel.: (214) 678-0805
Web Site: http://www.thefinialcompany.com
Home Furnishing Merchant Whslr
N.A.I.C.S.: 423220

ROXBURY TECHNOLOGY CORP
75 Sprague St, Hyde Park, MA 02136-2021
Tel.: (617) 524-1020
Web Site:
http://www.roxburytechnology.com
Year Founded: 1994
Sales Range: $10-24.9 Million
Emp.: 50
Computer & Software Stores
N.A.I.C.S.: 449210
Beth Williams *(Pres & CEO)*
Kemo Ceesay *(VP-Fin & Ops)*
Fabitha Harry *(Mgr)*

ROXBURY TENANTS OF HARVARD
11 New Whitney St, Boston, MA 02115
Tel.: (617) 232-4306
Web Site:
http://www.roxburytenants.org
Year Founded: 1969
Sales Range: $10-24.9 Million
Emp.: 71
Community Housing Services
N.A.I.C.S.: 624229
Moses Strassfeld *(Controller)*
Roxanne Haecker *(Dir-Program Dev)*
Ken Yanofsky *(Dir-Health & Wellness)*
LaToya Cromartie *(Mgr-Payroll)*
Karen T. Gately *(Exec Dir)*

ROXY TRADING INC.
389 N Humane Way, Pomona, CA 91768
Tel.: (626) 610-1388
Web Site: http://www.roxytrading.com
Rev.: $16,040,354
Emp.: 40
Groceries & Related Products
N.A.I.C.S.: 424490
Elvis Thang *(Pres)*

ROY D. GOODNER INC.
1949 W Elk Ave, Duncan, OK 73533-1639
Tel.: (580) 255-3357
Year Founded: 1938
Sales Range: $25-49.9 Million
Emp.: 100
Grocery Store Operator
N.A.I.C.S.: 445110
Thomas Goodner *(Pres)*
Jerry Goodson *(Dir-Oper)*

ROY E. HANSON JR. MANUFACTURING
1600 E Washington Blvd, Los Angeles, CA 90021
Tel.: (213) 747-7514
Web Site:
http://www.hansontank.com
Sales Range: $50-74.9 Million
Emp.: 85
Carbon & Stainless Steel Pressure Vessels Mfr
N.A.I.C.S.: 213112
John Goss *(CEO)*

ROY E. LADD INC.
1304 E St, Redding, CA 96001
Tel.: (530) 241-6102
Web Site:
http://www.laddconstruction.com
Sales Range: $10-24.9 Million
Emp.: 15
General Contractor, Highway & Street Construction
N.A.I.C.S.: 237310

ROY JORGENSEN ASSOCIATES, INC.
3735 Buckeystown Pike, Buckeystown, MD 21717
Tel.: (301) 831-1000
Web Site:
http://www.royjorgensen.com
Year Founded: 1961
Rev.: $70,000,000
Emp.: 90
Consulting Solutions & Implemented Contract Maintenance Services
N.A.I.C.S.: 541611
Cheryl Blackwell *(Bus Mgr)*
Natalie Brumbaugh *(Dir-Fin)*
R. Kenneth Shearin Jr. *(VP, Mgr-Engrg Manuals Grp)*

ROY MILLER FREIGHT LINES LLC

3165 E Coronado St, Anaheim, CA 92806
Tel.: (714) 632-5511
Web Site: http://www.roymiller.com
Sales Range: $10-24.9 Million
Emp.: 100
Trucking Service
N.A.I.C.S.: 484110
Lorenza Nunez *(Office Mgr)*
Wiley Miller Sr. *(Mng Partner)*

ROY O'BRIEN INC.
22201 9 Mile Rd, Saint Clair Shores, MI 48080-2910
Tel.: (586) 776-7600 MI
Web Site: http://www.royobrien.com
Year Founded: 1946
Sales Range: $100-124.9 Million
Emp.: 130
Sales of Automobiles & Trucks
N.A.I.C.S.: 441110
Mark E. O'Brien *(Chm)*
Raymond Milne *(CFO & Controller)*
John Gration *(Mgr-Collision)*
David Grout *(Dir-Bus Dev & Mktg)*
Don Holbrook *(Dir-Svc)*
Patty Borsuk *(Mgr-Rental)*
Paul Paselk *(Mgr-Fleet)*
Robb Polatka *(Mgr-Parts)*
Robert Krause *(Mgr-Inventory)*

ROY O. ELDER LUMBER COMPANY INC.
7875 Hwy 31, Opelousas, LA 70570
Tel.: (337) 942-1508
Sales Range: $10-24.9 Million
Emp.: 4
Lumber: Rough, Dressed & Finished
N.A.I.C.S.: 423310
Al Tuminello *(Owner)*

ROY O. MARTIN LUMBER COMPANY, LLC
2189 Memorial Dr, Alexandria, LA 71301-3610
Tel.: (318) 445-1973
Web Site: http://www.royomartin.com
Year Founded: 1923
Sales Range: $50-74.9 Million
Emp.: 1,100
Wood Preserving & Sawmills; Real Estate Investments
N.A.I.C.S.: 113110
Roy O. Martin III *(Pres, CEO & CFO)*
Jonathan E. Martin *(CEO)*
Joel Arnold *(Mgr-Sls)*
Bert Campbell *(Mgr-Sls)*
Joe Mackay *(VP-Plywood)*
Jesse Bolton *(CIO)*
Julia Martin Jones *(Pres)*
Adrian Schoonover *(VP-Engrg)*
Cade Young *(VP-Land & Timber)*

Subsidiaries:

Martco Ltd Partnership (1)
192 Pawnee Rd, Oakdale, LA 71463
Tel.: (318) 427-6806
Web Site: http://www.royomartin.com
Emp.: 150
Lumber Whslr
N.A.I.C.S.: 423310

ROMEX World Trade Co., L.L.C. (1)
PO Box 1110, Alexandria, LA 71309
Tel.: (318) 445-1973
Wood Products Mfr
N.A.I.C.S.: 321999

ROY SMITH COMPANY
14650 Dequindre St, Detroit, MI 48212
Tel.: (313) 883-6969 MI
Web Site: http://www.rscmain.com
Year Founded: 1924
Sales Range: $1-9.9 Million
Emp.: 35

Industrial Machinery & Equipment Whslr
N.A.I.C.S.: 423830
Peter Wong *(Pres)*

ROY'S GRAND DODGE, CHRYSLER, JEEP ON LOCUST, L.L.C.
1803 S Locust St, Grand Island, NE 68801
Tel.: (308) 384-8300
Web Site: http://www.roysgrand.com
Sales Range: $10-24.9 Million
Emp.: 49
New Car Dealers
N.A.I.C.S.: 441110
Roy Neneman *(Owner)*
Mike Corman *(Gen Mgr)*
Blake Corman *(Mgr-Gen Sls)*
Scott Dennison *(Dir-Internet)*
Mitch Hinrichs *(Mgr-Pre-Owned)*
Rick Beamon *(Mgr-Fin)*
Larry Shuppan *(Mgr-Fleet)*
Jeremy Suchanek *(Mgr-New Car)*

ROYAL AMBULANCE
14472 Wicks Blvd, San Leandro, CA 94577
Tel.: (510) 568-6005
Web Site: http://www.royalambulance.com
Sales Range: $1-9.9 Million
Emp.: 136
Ambulance Service
N.A.I.C.S.: 621910
Steve Grau *(Founder & Pres)*
Sean Young *(Mgr-Ops)*

ROYAL AMERICAN MANAGEMENT, INC.
1002 W 23rd St Ste 400, Panama City, FL 32405
Tel.: (850) 769-8981
Web Site: http://www.royalamerican.com
Year Founded: 1979
Sales Range: $10-24.9 Million
Emp.: 500
Property Management Services
N.A.I.C.S.: 531110
Kerri Toth *(Pres)*
Treana Pitts *(Mgr-Building)*
Wendi Le Mense *(VP-Compliance & Resident Rels)*

ROYAL AUTOMOTIVE
3010 Columbiana Rd, Vestavia Hills, AL 35216
Tel.: (205) 823-3100
Web Site: http://www.royalautomotive.net
Sales Range: $10-24.9 Million
Emp.: 100
Car Dealership
N.A.I.C.S.: 441110
Dave Belcherr *(Pres)*

ROYAL AUTOMOTIVE COMPANY
1901 Patrick St Plz, Charleston, WV 25312
Tel.: (304) 340-4500
Web Site: http://royalsubaruperiod.net
Year Founded: 1969
Sales Range: $10-24.9 Million
Emp.: 64
Car Whslr
N.A.I.C.S.: 441110
Kelly Smith *(Pres)*

ROYAL AUTOMOTIVE GROUP INC.
4670 N Circuit Dr, Tucson, AZ 85705
Tel.: (520) 585-5298 AL

Web Site: http://www.royaltucson.com
Year Founded: 1958
New & Used Automobiles Dealerships
N.A.I.C.S.: 441120
Paul N. Weitman *(Owner)*

ROYAL BANCSHARES, INC.
8021 Olive Blvd, Saint Louis, MO 63130
Tel.: (314) 212-1500 MO
Web Site: http://www.royalbanksofmo.com
Year Founded: 1979
Sales Range: $10-24.9 Million
Emp.: 99
Bank Holding Company
N.A.I.C.S.: 551111
Stephen A. Baden *(Pres & CEO)*
Karen J. Davis *(CFO, Exec VP & Asst Sec)*
Anthony F. Sansone Sr. *(Sec)*

Subsidiaries:

Royal Banks of Missouri (1)
8021 Olive Blvd, Saint Louis, MO 63130
Tel.: (314) 212-1500
Web Site: http://www.royalbanksofmo.com
Sales Range: $10-24.9 Million
Commericial Banking
N.A.I.C.S.: 522110
Michael S. Stevenson *(Officer-Retail Banking & Sr VP)*

ROYAL BANCSHARES, INC.
202 Main St, Elroy, WI 53929
Tel.: (608) 462-8401 WI
Web Site: http://www.royalbank-usa.com
Year Founded: 1990
Sales Range: $10-24.9 Million
Emp.: 118
Bank Holding Company
N.A.I.C.S.: 551111
Dan Ravenscroft *(Pres & CEO)*

Subsidiaries:

Royal Bank (1)
202 Main St, Elroy, WI 53929
Tel.: (608) 462-8401
Web Site: http://www.royalbank-usa.com
Sales Range: $10-24.9 Million
Commericial Banking
N.A.I.C.S.: 522110
Glenda Faull *(Exec VP)*
Dan Ravenscroft *(Pres & CEO)*
Natalie Adams *(Asst VP)*

ROYAL BEDDING COMPANY INC.
11650 Lakeside Crossing Ct, Saint Louis, MO 63146
Tel.: (314) 647-5200
Sales Range: $10-24.9 Million
Emp.: 80
Mattress Mfr
N.A.I.C.S.: 337910
Alva Moog Jr. *(Pres)*

ROYAL BRASS INC.
1470 Amherst Rd, Knoxville, TN 37950-1468
Tel.: (865) 558-0224
Web Site: http://www.royalbrassandhose.com
Sales Range: $10-24.9 Million
Emp.: 60
Industrial Supplies
N.A.I.C.S.: 423840
Robin Smithson *(Mgr-Mktg)*

ROYAL BUYING GROUP, INC.
2100 Western Court Ste 350, Lisle, IL 60532
Tel.: (630) 986-5416
Web Site: http://www.royalbuying.com

Year Founded: 1995
Sales Range: $150-199.9 Million
Emp.: 24
Inventory Management for Vendor Buying Programs
N.A.I.C.S.: 455219
Robert Juckniess *(Exec Dir)*
Robert Razowsky *(COO & Exec Dir)*
Martin Gmeiner *(CFO & Exec Dir)*
Mark Hill *(CTO & Exec Dir)*
Angela Angelilli *(Exec VP)*
William Butzloff *(CMO & Exec Dir)*

ROYAL CAR CENTER
3950 E Roosevelt Blvd, Philadelphia, PA 19124
Tel.: (215) 535-5155
Web Site: http://www.royalcarcenter.com
Year Founded: 1994
Sales Range: $10-24.9 Million
Emp.: 14
Used Car Whslr
N.A.I.C.S.: 441120
Ali Alhadad *(Owner)*
Nasim Fares *(Mgr-Bus Dev)*

ROYAL COFFEE INC.
3306 Powell St, Emeryville, CA 94608
Tel.: (510) 652-4256
Web Site: http://www.royalcoffee.com
Year Founded: 1978
Sales Range: $50-74.9 Million
Emp.: 50
Green or Roasted Coffee
N.A.I.C.S.: 424490
Robert Fulmer *(Pres)*
John Cossette *(VP)*
Sharon Shen *(Controller)*

ROYAL CONSUMER INFORMATION PRODUCTS INC.
1160 US 22, Bridgewater, NJ 08807
Tel.: (908) 864-4851
Web Site: http://www.royalsupplies.com
Year Founded: 1904
Personal Electronic Organizers, Calculators, Cash Registers & Electronic Desk Accessories, Electric Adding Machines, Electronic Printing Calculators, Office Supplies & Printers Mfr
N.A.I.C.S.: 423420
Salomon Suwalsky *(Owner, Pres & CEO)*
Todd Althoff *(VP-Mktg & Product Dev)*
David Joachim *(VP-Mktg)*

ROYAL CONTINENTAL BOX COMPANY INC.
1301 S 47th Ave, Cicero, IL 60804-1516
Tel.: (708) 656-2020 IL
Web Site: http://www.royalbox.com
Year Founded: 1922
Sales Range: $50-74.9 Million
Emp.: 250
Corrugated & Solid Fiber Boxes
N.A.I.C.S.: 322211
Robert L. McIlvaine *(Pres & CEO)*
Tim Benecke *(VP)*

Subsidiaries:

Indiana Box Corp. (1)
703 S Standard Oil Blvd, Montpelier, IN 47359-1288 (100%)
Tel.: (765) 728-2416
Web Site: http://www.royalbox.com
Sales Range: $10-24.9 Million
Emp.: 50
Mfr of Corrugated & Solid Fiber Boxes
N.A.I.C.S.: 322211
Robert L. McIlvaine *(Pres & CEO)*
Doug Holtzclaw *(VP)*

ROYAL CORINTHIAN HOMES INC.
U.S. PRIVATE

ROYAL CORINTHIAN HOMES INC.
9111 W College Pointe Dr, Fort Myers, FL 33919-5936
Tel.: (239) 437-1625
Web Site: http://www.royalcorinthianhomes.com
Year Founded: 1999
Sales Range: $1-9.9 Million
Emp.: 6
Residential Construction
N.A.I.C.S.: 236115
Jerald L. Wallace (Founder & Pres)
Glenn Cribbett (Project Mgr)
Robinson Ron (Mgr-Sls)
Jani Denison (Controller)

ROYAL CREDIT UNION
200 Riverfront Ter, Eau Claire, WI 54703
Tel.: (800) 341-9911
Web Site: http://www.rcu.org
Year Founded: 1964
Sales Range: $75-99.9 Million
Emp.: 675
Credit Union Operator
N.A.I.C.S.: 522130
Doug Olson (Chm)
Brandon Riechers (Pres & CEO)
Jennifer McHugh (Dir-Pub Affairs & Fin Education)
Holly Hermanson (Coord-Community Engagement)
Michael Dill (Chief Lending officer & Exec VP)
Pam Haller (Chief Digital Experience & Mktg Officer & Exec VP)
Nicole Frederick (Mgr-Bay Street & Woodward Avenue Offices)
Tim Sass (Mgr-New Richmond)

ROYAL CREST DAIRY INC.
350 S Pearl St, Denver, CO 80209-2020
Tel.: (303) 777-3055
Web Site: http://www.royalcrestdairy.com
Year Founded: 1927
Dairy Product Retailer
N.A.I.C.S.: 445298
Paul R. Miller (Founder & Chm)
Tim Detine (Pres)
Susan Perdue (Mgr-Admin)

ROYAL CROWN BOTTLING CO. OF WINCHESTER INC.
2927 Shawnee Dr, Winchester, VA 22601
Tel.: (540) 667-1821
Web Site: http://www.rccolawinchester.com
Rev.: $25,000,000
Emp.: 55
Bottled & Canned Soft Drinks Mfr
N.A.I.C.S.: 312111
J. Scott Bridgeforth (Owner & VP)
William Bridgeforth III (Pres)

ROYAL CROWN LEASING INC.
5408 Yadkin Rd, Fayetteville, NC 28303
Tel.: (910) 864-5778
Web Site: http://www.rentamerica.com
Sales Range: $10-24.9 Million
Emp.: 5
Consumer Goods & Equipment Rental Services
N.A.I.C.S.: 532289
Larry Tinney (Owner)

ROYAL CUP INC.
160 Cleage Dr, Birmingham, AL 35217-1461
Tel.: (205) 849-5836
Web Site: http://www.royalcupcoffee.com
Year Founded: 1896
Sales Range: $100-124.9 Million
Emp.: 530
Roasted Coffee Mfr
N.A.I.C.S.: 311920
Kevin Boughner (VP-Ops)
William Culpepper (Sr Mgr-Mktg)
Jim Collins (Mgr-Support Svcs)
Drew Dutton (Mgr-Equipment Ops)
David Wilbourn (Mgr-Office Coffee)
Bebe Goodrich (Dir-Liquid Product Innovation)
Chip Wann (Pres & CEO)
Pash Nangia (CFO)

ROYAL DOCUMENT DESTRUCTION
861 B Taylor Rd, Gahanna, OH 43230
Tel.: (614) 751-9731
Web Site: http://www.rddshred.com
Sales Range: $1-9.9 Million
Emp.: 21
Document Shredding Services
N.A.I.C.S.: 561990
Laura Daly (Partner)
Ric McPike (Mgr-Sls)
John Daly (Partner)

ROYAL FORK RESTAURANT CORP
6874 W Fairview Ave, Boise, ID 83704
Tel.: (208) 322-5600
Rev.: $14,900,000
Emp.: 30
Buffet Restaurant Operator
N.A.I.C.S.: 722513
Jerry Caven (Chm)

ROYAL FURNITURE COMPANY
122 S Main St 128, Memphis, TN 38103
Tel.: (901) 527-6407
Web Site: http://www.royalfurniture.com
Sales Range: $10-24.9 Million
Emp.: 100
Furniture Retailer
N.A.I.C.S.: 449110
Richard A. Faber (Pres)
Byron Cross (Mgr-Store)

ROYAL HAWAIIAN HERITAGE JEWELRY LTD.
1130 Bishop St, Honolulu, HI 96813
Tel.: (808) 524-4300
Rev.: $10,200,000
Emp.: 60
Jewelry, Precious Stones & Precious Metals
N.A.I.C.S.: 458310

ROYAL HAWAIIAN MOVERS, INC.
3017 Ualena St, Honolulu, HI 96819-1915
Tel.: (808) 833-1611
Web Site: http://www.royalhawaiianmovers.com
Year Founded: 1982
Sales Range: $1-9.9 Million
Emp.: 200
Goods Moving Services
N.A.I.C.S.: 484210
Edward Wong (Pres)

ROYAL HOSPITALITY CORP.
255 E Paces Ferry Rd, Atlanta, GA 30305
Tel.: (404) 239-0808
Web Site: http://www.capitalbuilding.com
Holding Company; Real Estate, Development & Food Services
N.A.I.C.S.: 551112
David Davoudpour (Founder & CEO)

Subsidiaries:

Shoney's North America Corp (1)
1717 Elm Hill Pike Ste B-1, Nashville, TN 37210
Tel.: (615) 391-5395
Web Site: http://www.shoneys.com
Sales Range: $650-699.9 Million
Emp.: 70
Restaurant Services
N.A.I.C.S.: 722511
David Davoudpour (Chm & CEO)
Kamran Habeeb (Pres)
Catherine Hite (Gen Counsel & Exec VP)
Terri Harof (Dir-Franchise Dev)
Steve Neuroth (CFO)
Gill Duff (CMO)

Division (Domestic):

Shoney's Restaurant (2)
1717 Elm Hill Pike Ste B1, Nashville, TN 37210-5701
Tel.: (615) 391-5395
Web Site: http://www.shoneys.com
Sales Range: $25-49.9 Million
Emp.: 40
Company Owned & Franchised Restaurants
N.A.I.C.S.: 722511

ROYAL IMPERIAL GROUP INC.
900 W Jackson Blvd Fl 8, Chicago, IL 60607
Tel.: (312) 738-1717
Web Site: http://www.royalimperial.com
Sales Range: $25-49.9 Million
Emp.: 5
Land Subdividers & Developers, Commercial
N.A.I.C.S.: 237210
David Tessler (CEO)
Sandy Ball (Bus Mgr)
Joshua Berger (VP)

ROYAL INDUSTRIES, INC.
1299 E Phillips Blvd, Pomona, CA 91766
Tel.: (909) 629-8565
Web Site: http://www.royalcabinets.com
Year Founded: 1983
Sales Range: $10-24.9 Million
Emp.: 250
Designs, Manufactures & Installs Cabinetry
N.A.I.C.S.: 337110
Clay Smith (Co-Founder)
Bill Roan (Co-Founder)

ROYAL INDUSTRIES, INC.
225 25th St, Brooklyn, NY 11232
Tel.: (718) 369-3046
Web Site: http://royalindustries.com
Year Founded: 1950
Vinyl Packaging & Promotional Products Mfr
N.A.I.C.S.: 326199
Ari Ruden (VP-Mktg & Mng Dir)

Subsidiaries:

DLX Industries, Inc. (1)
1970 Pitkin Ave, Brooklyn, NY 11207
Tel.: (718) 522-6630
Web Site: http://www.dlxonline.com
Business Supplies Mfr
N.A.I.C.S.: 459410

ROYAL INTER PACK CO., LTD.
475 Palmyrita Ave, Riverside, CA 92507
Tel.: (951) 787-6925
Web Site: http://www.royalinterpackusa.com
Year Founded: 2011
Sales Range: $25-49.9 Million
Plastic Package Product Mfr
N.A.I.C.S.: 326112
Visanu Chawla (Mng Dir)

ROYAL MANUFACTURING CO. INC.
516 S 25th W Ave, Tulsa, OK 74127
Tel.: (918) 587-5711
Web Site: http://www.royalmfg.com
Rev.: $15,000,000
Emp.: 50
Oils & Greases, Blending & Compounding
N.A.I.C.S.: 324191
William R. Mallory Jr. (Pres)

ROYAL MEDIA GROUP, INC.
80 Broad St Ste 1701, New York, NY 10004
Tel.: (212) 564-8972
Web Site: http://www.royalmedia.com
Data & Consulting Services
N.A.I.C.S.: 541613
J. J. Hornblass (Pres & CEO)

Subsidiaries:

Air Cargo World Magazine (1)
1080 Holcomb Bridge Rd Building 200 Ste 255, Roswell, GA 30076
Tel.: (770) 642-9170
Web Site: http://www.aircargoworld.com
Periodical Publishers
N.A.I.C.S.: 513120
Steve Prince (Pres)
Tony Tyler (CEO)
John McCurry (Editor)
Sue Addy (Mgr-Admin)
J. J. Hornblass (Publr)

ROYAL MERCANTILE TRUST CORP. OF AMERICA
10 Central Pkwy Ste 200, Stuart, FL 34994
Tel.: (772) 220-1300
Web Site: http://www.rmtc.com
Rev.: $10,000,000
Emp.: 26
Collection Agency
N.A.I.C.S.: 561440
Myron H. Gordon (Chm)

ROYAL MOORE AUTO CENTER
1380 SE River Rd, Hillsboro, OR 97123
Tel.: (503) 648-1153
Web Site: http://www.royalmoore.com
Sales Range: $10-24.9 Million
Emp.: 200
Automobiles, New & Used
N.A.I.C.S.: 441110
Maureen Springer (Comptroller)
Jennifer Moore (Mgr-Internal Affairs)
Royal D. Moore II (Owner & Pres)

Subsidiaries:

Royal Moore Buick Pontiac - GMC Truck (1)
1380 SE River Rd, Hillsboro, OR 97123
Tel.: (503) 648-1153
Web Site: http://www.royalmoore.com
Rev.: $36,614,197
Emp.: 95
Automobiles, New & Used
N.A.I.C.S.: 441110
Jennifer Moore (Mgr-Adv)
Royal D. Moore II (Pres)

ROYAL MOTOR SALES OF SAN FRANCISCO
280-285 S Van Ness Ave, San Francisco, CA 94103
Tel.: (415) 241-8100
Web Site: http://www.gotoroyalsf.com
Rev.: $28,100,000
Emp.: 50
New & Used Car Dealers
N.A.I.C.S.: 441110

COMPANIES
ROYAL TECHNOLOGIES CORPORATION

Andy Hansen *(COO)*
Mitch Kudler *(Dir-Ops)*
Daniel Torres *(Mgr-Parts)*
Luis Sanchez *(Mgr-Pre-Owned)*
Tony Rakkar *(Mgr-Body Shop)*

ROYAL NEIGHBORS OF AMERICA
230 16th St, Rock Island, IL 61201-8608
Tel.: (309) 788-4561   IL
Web Site:
http://www.royalneighbors.org
Year Founded: 1895
Sales Range: $50-74.9 Million
Emp.: 130
Life Insurance
N.A.I.C.S.: 524113
Chris Seistrup *(COO)*
Marc Schoenfeld *(CFO)*
Matt D. Mendenhall *(Dir-Philanthropy)*
Susan Kenney Cotter *(CMO)*
Cynthia Tidwell *(Pres & CEO)*

ROYAL OAK ENTERPRISES, INC.
1 Royal Oak Ave, Roswell, GA 30076-7583
Tel.: (678) 461-3200   GA
Web Site: http://www.royal-oak.com
Year Founded: 1953
Sales Range: $100-124.9 Million
Emp.: 600
Charcoal Briquettes & Activated Carbons Mfr
N.A.I.C.S.: 324199
Jim Allen *(Pres)*
Dale Elberg *(Exec VP-Sls & Mktg)*
Bob Smith *(CEO)*
Randy Beech *(VP-Ops)*

ROYAL OAK FORD, INC.
27550 Woodward Ave, Royal Oak, MI 48067-0929
Tel.: (248) 548-4100   MI
Web Site:
http://www.royaloakford.com
Sales Range: $100-124.9 Million
Emp.: 120
Sales of Automobiles
N.A.I.C.S.: 441110
Brian Brunner *(Mgr-New Inventory)*
Eddie Hall *(Pres)*
Mark Daniele *(Dir-Fixed Ops)*
Dan Lobert *(Mgr-Parts)*

ROYAL OAK INDUSTRIES INC.
39533 Woodward Ave Ste 175, Bloomfield Hills, MI 48304-5102
Tel.: (248) 340-9200   MI
Web Site: http://www.roi-1.com
Year Founded: 1985
Sales Range: $10-24.9 Million
Emp.: 300
Supplier of Industrial Machinery & Equipment
N.A.I.C.S.: 332710
Dan Carroll *(Pres & CEO)*

ROYAL OAKS NISSAN, INC.
4801 Wabash Ave, Springfield, IL 62711-7103
Tel.: (217) 787-7620
Sales Range: $10-24.9 Million
Emp.: 35
Car Whslr
N.A.I.C.S.: 441110
Robert J. Beck *(Treas & Sec)*
Brian Cox *(Gen Mgr)*
David Hahn *(Pres)*
Blair Molumby *(Gen Mgr-Sls)*

ROYAL PALMS SENIOR RESIDENCE
5121 NE 19th Ave, Fort Lauderdale, FL 33308
Tel.: (954) 491-4041
Web Site:
http://www.royalpalmsr.com
Year Founded: 1990
Lessors of Residential Buildings & Dwellings
N.A.I.C.S.: 531110
Paul Noblefranca *(Mgr)*

ROYAL PAPER BOX OF CALIFORNIA
1105 S Maple Ave, Montebello, CA 90640
Tel.: (323) 728-7041   CA
Web Site:
http://www.royalpaperbox.com
Year Founded: 1940
Sales Range: $100-124.9 Million
Emp.: 180
Mfr of Folding Paper Boxes & Displays
N.A.I.C.S.: 322212
Jim Hodges *(Pres & CEO)*

ROYAL PAPER CONVERTING INC.
711 N 17th Ave Ste 5, Phoenix, AZ 85007
Tel.: (602) 258-9007
Web Site: http://www.royalpaper.us
Rev.: $21,500,000
Emp.: 88
Towels, Napkins & Tissue Paper Products
N.A.I.C.S.: 322291
Nasser Sarraf *(Pres)*
Steve Keiper *(Mgr-Retail Sls-United States)*
John Andres *(Mgr-Electrical)*
Kim Lubbers *(Supvr-Acctg)*
Sep Dardashti *(Co-Founder)*
Bob Sarraf *(Co-Founder)*
Kevin Otero *(CEO)*
Sunil Kanuga *(COO)*
Samir Kanuga *(CFO)*

ROYAL PAPER CORPORATION
10232 Palm Dr, Santa Fe Springs, CA 90670
Tel.: (562) 903-9030
Web Site: http://www.royal-paper.com
Rev.: $12,764,513
Emp.: 70
Containers, Paper & Disposable Plastic
N.A.I.C.S.: 424130
Michael M. Rashichi *(CEO)*
Jonathan Soon *(CFO)*
Marilyn Harlow *(Mgr-Pur)*

ROYAL PAPER STOCK COMPANY INC.
1300 Norton Rd, Columbus, OH 43228-4172
Tel.: (614) 851-4714   OH
Web Site:
http://www.royalpaperstock.com
Year Founded: 1981
Sales Range: $50-74.9 Million
Emp.: 115
Paper & Waste Materials Recycler
N.A.I.C.S.: 423930
Michael Radtke *(Pres)*
Jason Radtke *(Mgr-Sls)*

ROYAL PAPERS INC.
2701 Hereford St, Saint Louis, MO 63139
Tel.: (314) 664-3900
Web Site: http://www.royalab.com
Rev.: $13,636,290
Emp.: 63
Disposable Plates; Cups; Napkins; & Eating Utensil
N.A.I.C.S.: 424130

Paul S. Passanise *(Pres)*
Jerry Farris *(Mgr-Svcs)*
Nick Kellar *(Mgr-Pur)*
Tom Steck *(Mgr-Credit)*

ROYAL PETROLEUM CORPORATION
1810 Columbia Ave Bldg 19, Folcroft, PA 19032
Tel.: (610) 586-6700
Sales Range: $10-24.9 Million
Emp.: 48
Fuel Oil
N.A.I.C.S.: 424720
Don Wenger *(Pres)*
Howard Bock *(VP)*

ROYAL PLUS ELECTRIC, INC.
9939 Jerry Mack Rd Ste 400, Ocean City, MD 21842-9293
Tel.: (410) 213-2658
Web Site:
http://www.royalpluselectric.com
Sales Range: $10-24.9 Million
Emp.: 120
Electrical Wiring Services
N.A.I.C.S.: 238210
Mark Reid Odachowski *(Owner)*

ROYAL PLUS INC.
201 Belt St, Snow Hill, MD 21863
Tel.: (410) 677-3473
Web Site: http://www.royalplus.com
Year Founded: 1983
Rev.: $25,500,000
Emp.: 100
Residential Construction
N.A.I.C.S.: 449129
Charles Lee *(Pres)*
Matt Odachowski *(Owner)*
Joel Gutierrez *(Mgr-Mktg)*

ROYAL RESOURCES PARTNERS LP
1 Allen Ctr 500 Dallas St Ste 1250, Houston, TX 77002
Tel.: (713) 874-9000   DE
Year Founded: 2014
Sales Range: $50-74.9 Million
Oil & Gas Operations
N.A.I.C.S.: 213112
Randolph Newcomer Jr. *(CEO)*

ROYAL SEAL CONSTRUCTION INC.
124 McMakin Rd, Argyle, TX 76226-8400
Tel.: (972) 539-6771
Web Site: http://www.royalseal.com
Sales Range: $10-24.9 Million
Emp.: 20
Commercial & Office Building, New Construction
N.A.I.C.S.: 236220
Martin Machek *(Mgr-IT)*

Subsidiaries:

Royal Commercial Realty Inc   (1)
124 McMakin Rd, Bartonville, TX 76226-8400
Tel.: (817) 491-6400
Web Site: http://www.royalseal.com
Emp.: 18
Real Estate Brokers & Agents
N.A.I.C.S.: 531210
Gene Colley *(Pres)*

Royal Seal Investments Inc   (1)
124 McMakin Rd, Bartonville, TX 76226-8400
Tel.: (817) 430-2700
Web Site: http://www.royalseal.com
Emp.: 50
Security Brokers & Dealers
N.A.I.C.S.: 523150
Gene Colley *(Pres & CEO)*

ROYAL SPEEDWAY, INC.
4333 E Speedway Blvd, Tucson, AZ 85712-4623
Tel.: (520) 795-0760
Web Site:
http://www.royalspeedway.com
Sales Range: $25-49.9 Million
Emp.: 170
Car Whslr
N.A.I.C.S.: 441110
Steve Lace *(Gen Mgr)*
Claire McGuire *(Principal)*
Paul Weitman *(Owner)*

ROYAL STREET CORPORATION
7620 Royal St E Ste 205, Park City, UT 84060
Tel.: (435) 649-1244
Year Founded: 1948
Sales Range: $25-49.9 Million
Emp.: 10
Provider of Hotel & Motel Services
N.A.I.C.S.: 721110
Tim Brinton *(Sr Mgr-Tax)*

Subsidiaries:

Royal Street Land Co.   (1)
7620 Royal St E Ste 205, Park City, UT 84060
Tel.: (435) 649-1244
Sales Range: $10-24.9 Million
Emp.: 9
Provider of Subdivider & Developer Services
N.A.I.C.S.: 721110

Royal Street of Utah Inc.   (1)
7620 Royal St E, Park City, UT 84060
Tel.: (435) 649-1244
Sales Range: $10-24.9 Million
Provider of Real Estate Services
N.A.I.C.S.: 721110

Starjet Air Inc.   (1)
7620 Royal St E Ste 205, Park City, UT 84060
Tel.: (435) 649-1244
Sales Range: $10-24.9 Million
Emp.: 5
Provider of Air Transportation Services
N.A.I.C.S.: 481219

ROYAL SUPPLY CO
70 Franklin Ave Ste 1, Brooklyn, NY 11205
Tel.: (718) 875-4666
Web Site: http://www.royalsupply.com
Sales Range: $10-24.9 Million
Emp.: 4
Pharmaceutical Products Distr
N.A.I.C.S.: 424210
Moses Bodek *(CEO)*

ROYAL SUPPLY CO.
1209 Lowell St, Elyria, OH 44035
Tel.: (440) 322-5411
Web Site: http://www.royalsupply.com
Sales Range: $10-24.9 Million
Emp.: 7
Industrial Machinery & Equipment
N.A.I.C.S.: 423830
Don Chargin *(Pres)*

ROYAL TECHNOLOGIES CORPORATION
3765 Quincy St, Hudsonville, MI 49426-8408
Tel.: (616) 669-3393   MI
Web Site:
http://www.royaltechnologies
corp.com
Year Founded: 1987
Sales Range: $50-74.9 Million
Emp.: 700
Plastic Materials Processor
N.A.I.C.S.: 326199
James Vanderkolk *(Pres)*
Richard Klamer *(VP)*
Scott Wilcox *(Mgr-Commodity)*
David McLaren *(Engr-Supplier Dev)*

ROYAL TECHNOLOGIES CORPORATION — U.S. PRIVATE

Royal Technologies Corporation—(Continued)
Aaron McClelland (Dir-Sls)
Bruce O'Reilly (Mgr-Pur)
Tracy Fields (Mgr-Tech)
Wendy Ahearne (Dir-HR)
Dan Vlietstra (Dir-Quality)
Michael Greko (Mgr-Production)
Steven Gerritsma (Mgr-Production)
Kimberly Buckingham (Coord-Wellness)
Marc Vander Kooi (Mgr-Process Dev)

ROYAL TIRE INC.
4021 Roosevelt Rd, Saint Cloud, MN 56301-9532
Tel.: (320) 281-4005 MN
Web Site: http://www.royaltire.com
Year Founded: 1948
Tire Dealers
N.A.I.C.S.: 423130
Paul Duininck (Founder)
Mick Pickens (Pres)
Craig Carstensen (Asst Mgr-Store)
Brad Burley (VP-Retail Ops)

ROYAL TRUCKING COMPANY
1323 N Eshman Ave, West Point, MS 39773
Tel.: (662) 494-1637
Web Site: http://www.royaltruck.com
Year Founded: 1968
Sales Range: $25-49.9 Million
Emp.: 180
Trucking Service
N.A.I.C.S.: 484121
Amy Duke (Controller)
Kenny Summerall (Supvr-Svcs)
Sherry Macon (Mgr-Ops)

ROYAL UNITED CORPORATION
65 Oxford Dr, Moonachie, NJ 07074
Tel.: (201) 869-3900 NJ
Year Founded: 1958
Sales Range: $10-24.9 Million
Emp.: 95
Distr of Hardware
N.A.I.C.S.: 423710
Steven Harrington (Mgr-Sls)
Stanley Ryman (CEO & CFO)
Michael Mathew (Controller)

ROYAL VENDORS, INC.
426 Industrial Blvd, Kearneysville, WV 25430
Tel.: (304) 728-7056
Web Site: http://www.royalvendors.com
Rev.: $11,500,000
Emp.: 1,150
Cold-Drink Vending Machines Mfr
N.A.I.C.S.: 333310
Greg Johnson (VP-Mfg)
Bruce K. Robinson (Mgr-Customer Svc)
Charity Fleming (Dir-HR)

ROYAL WINDOWS INC.
606 Fountain Pkwy, Grand Prairie, TX 75050
Tel.: (800) 872-2693
Web Site: http://www.royalwindowsinc.com
Rev.: $11,100,000
Emp.: 100
Mini Blinds
N.A.I.C.S.: 337920
Wayne Liu (Pres & CEO)
Wen Liu (Pres)
Dan Neece (Mgr-Sls-Natl)
Hien Nguyen (Product Mgr)
Kathy Phathanodom (CFO)

ROYAL WINE CORP.
65 Lefante Dr, Bayonne, NJ 07002-5024
Tel.: (718) 384-2400 NY
Web Site: http://www.royalwines.com
Year Founded: 1949
Sales Range: $10-24.9 Million
Emp.: 110
Wines, Brandy & Brandy Spirits
N.A.I.C.S.: 312130
David Herzog (Pres)
Aaron Herzog (Treas)
Douglas Simon (VP-Natl Sls-Wine & Spirits)
Charles Lynch (VP-Bus Dev-Spirits & Liqueurs)

ROYALE COMFORT SEATING INC.
PO Box 235 Hwy 16, Taylorsville, NC 28681
Tel.: (828) 632-2865
Sales Range: $10-24.9 Million
Emp.: 57
Mfr of Cushions
N.A.I.C.S.: 326199
Fred Crump (Gen Mgr)

ROYALE INTERNATIONAL COURIERS INC.
1827 42nd St, Astoria, NY 11105
Tel.: (718) 274-4999
Web Site: http://www.royalecourier.com
Rev.: $13,165,122
Emp.: 15
Air Courier Services
N.A.I.C.S.: 492110
Malcolm Shepherd (Chm & CEO)
John Conrad (Pres)

ROYALTY CARPET MILLS INC.
17111 Red Hill Ave, Irvine, CA 92614
Tel.: (949) 474-4000
Web Site: http://www.royaltycarpetmills.com
Year Founded: 1963
Sales Range: $25-49.9 Million
Emp.: 521
Mfr of Carpets
N.A.I.C.S.: 314110
Steve Piwnica (CFO)
Andrea Greenleaf (Pres & CEO)

ROYALTY FLOW INC.
1550 Larimer St 769, Denver, CO 80202 DE
Web Site: http://www.royaltyflow.com
Year Founded: 2017
Intellectual Property Management Services
N.A.I.C.S.: 523910
Jeff Schneider (CEO & CFO)
Matthew Smith (Chm)
Gary Young (Sec)

ROYCE APPAREL INC.
5800 Roy St, Kannapolis, NC 28083
Tel.: (704) 933-6000
Web Site: http://www.pressboxusa.com
Sales Range: $10-24.9 Million
Emp.: 15
Mfr & Retailer of Men's & Boy's Clothing
N.A.I.C.S.: 424350
Chip Hoke (Pres)
Farid Roy (VP-Mktg)

ROYCE ASSOCIATES
35 Carlton Ave, East Rutherford, NJ 07073
Tel.: (201) 438-5200
Web Site: http://www.royceintl.com
Rev.: $20,000,000
Emp.: 10
Industrial Organic Chemicals
N.A.I.C.S.: 325199

ROYCE GROFF OIL COMPANY
515 US Hwy 90 E, Castroville, TX 78009
Tel.: (830) 931-2135
Web Site: http://www.roycegroffoilco.com
Sales Range: $10-24.9 Million
Emp.: 30
Operator of Grocery Stores
N.A.I.C.S.: 424710

ROYCE HILL REAL ESTATE
4844 Kendall Ave, Gulfport, MS 39507-4407
Tel.: (228) 214-0014
Sales Range: $10-24.9 Million
Emp.: 2
Real Estate Manangement Services
N.A.I.C.S.: 531210
Royce Hill (Owner)

ROYCO INTERNATIONAL INC.
5380 Gulf of Mexico Dr Ste 105, Longboat Key, FL 34228
Tel.: (941) 383-5121
Web Site: http://www.roycointl.com
Rev.: $15,000,000
Emp.: 25
Food Ingredients Marketing
N.A.I.C.S.: 424490
Roy Nevans (Pres)
Roy Titterton (VP)

ROYER & SCHUTTS INC.
200 Bailey Ave Ste 300, Fort Worth, TX 76107
Tel.: (817) 332-5424
Web Site: http://www.royer-furn.com
Year Founded: 1943
Sales Range: $10-24.9 Million
Emp.: 36
Interior Decorating
N.A.I.C.S.: 541410
Tim Cox (VP)
Charles W. Royer Jr. (Pres)

ROYLE PRINTING
745 S Bird St, Sun Prairie, WI 53590
Tel.: (608) 837-5161
Web Site: http://www.royle.com
Year Founded: 1995
Sales Range: $10-24.9 Million
Emp.: 200
Commercial Printing, Lithographic
N.A.I.C.S.: 323111
Chris D. Carpenter (Owner & Pres)

ROYLE SYSTEMS GROUP
111 Bauer Dr, Oakland, NJ 07436
Tel.: (201) 644-0345 NJ
Web Site: http://www.roylesystems.com
Year Founded: 1855
Sales Range: $10-24.9 Million
Emp.: 75
Rubber & Plastics Extruders; Complete Insulating Systems for the Wire & Cable Industry
N.A.I.C.S.: 333519
John C. Ramsey (Chm)
Gregory J. Ramsey (CEO)
Peter M. Ramsey (Sr VP)
James Carbone (VP-Ops)

Subsidiaries:

Royle Extrusion Systems Pvt. Ltd. (1)
107/2 General Block MIDC Bhosari, Pune, 411026, India
Tel.: (91) 20 66129621
Web Site: http://www.roylesystems.com
Sales Range: $10-24.9 Million
Emp.: 30
Extruded Plastic Product Mfr
N.A.I.C.S.: 326199

Paulson T. Kunjukunju (Gen Mgr)

ROYS & ASSOCIATES
1603 Aviation Blvd Ste G, Redondo Beach, CA 90278
Tel.: (310) 318-8085
Web Site: http://www.roysandassoc.com
Year Founded: 2003
Sales Range: $25-49.9 Million
Emp.: 10
Executive Placement
N.A.I.C.S.: 561311
Deam Roys (CEO)

ROYTEX, INC.
16 E 34th St Fl 17, New York, NY 10016-4328
Tel.: (212) 686-3500 NY
Web Site: http://www.roytex.com
Year Founded: 1955
Sales Range: $50-74.9 Million
Emp.: 50
Sportswear Distr
N.A.I.C.S.: 424350
Dennis Mourry (CEO)
Richard Mourry (Pres)
Lori Moskowitz (Dir-Design)

ROYWELL SERVICES, INC.
4545 Dssonnett St Ste 104, Bellaire, TX 77401
Tel.: (713) 661-4747
Web Site: http://www.roywellservices.com
Year Founded: 1965
Sales Range: $10-24.9 Million
Emp.: 53
Oil & Gas Operation Services
N.A.I.C.S.: 213112
John McLain (Owner)

ROZ MARKETING GROUP A CALIFORNIA CORPORATION
11271 Ventura Blvd 612, Studio City, CA 91604
Web Site: http://www.rozstrategies.com
Year Founded: 2014
Sales Range: $1-9.9 Million
Training & Coaching Services
N.A.I.C.S.: 611699
Michael Rozbruch (Founder)
Roslyn Rozbruch (Pres)
Becky Stephens (Mgr-Client Happiness)
Ruthie Ponce (Project Mgr)

ROZALADO & CO.
6120 N Pulaski Rd, Chicago, IL 60646
Tel.: (312) 877-9127
Web Site: http://www.rozaladocleaning.com
Year Founded: 2012
Sales Range: $1-9.9 Million
Emp.: 250
Residential Cleaning Services
N.A.I.C.S.: 561720
Ricardo Regalado (Founder & CEO)
Marley Regalado (Mng Partner)
Tony Pedroza (Mng Partner)
Dominic Amoroso (Dir-Ops)
Mike Kirkpatrick (Dir-Sls & Special Svcs)

RP FUNDING, INC.
500 Winderley Pl Ste 300, Maitland, FL 32751
Tel.: (321) 397-4420
Web Site: http://www.rpfunding.com
Sales Range: $1-9.9 Million
Emp.: 70
Full Service Mortgage Lender
N.A.I.C.S.: 522310

COMPANIES

Robert Palmer *(Pres & CEO)*
Don Estell *(Sr Mgr-Loan Approval)*
Richelle Gora *(Chief Risk Officer)*
Jon Woods *(CFO)*

RP INDUSTRIES INC.
105 Reynolds Dr, Franklin, TN 37064-2926
Tel.: (615) 595-2400   TN
Web Site:
http://www.rpindustries.com
Year Founded: 1978
Sales Range: $100-124.9 Million
Emp.: 125
Nonresidential Construction
N.A.I.C.S.: 236220
Gary Parks *(CFO)*
Joseph L. Park Jr. *(Chm & Pres)*

RP LUMBER CO. INC.
514 E Vandalia St, Edwardsville, IL 62025-1855
Tel.: (618) 656-1514
Web Site: http://www.rplumber.com
Year Founded: 1977
Sales Range: $25-49.9 Million
Emp.: 900
Provider of Lumber & Other Building Materials
N.A.I.C.S.: 444110
Jeff Reno *(Mgr-Credit)*

Subsidiaries:

Kieffer Lumber Co., Inc.   (1)
703 W 9th St, Mount Carmel, IL 62863
Tel.: (618) 262-8522
Rev.: $3,354,000
Emp.: 13
Home Center Operator
N.A.I.C.S.: 444110
Duane Kieffer *(Mgr)*

Southwest Builder Supply, Inc.   (1)
204 S Fillmore St, Mount Ayr, IA 50854-1831
Tel.: (641) 464-2500
Sales Range: $1-9.9 Million
Emp.: 12
Home Center Operator
N.A.I.C.S.: 444110
Rick Fox *(Mgr)*

RP MANAGEMENT, INC.
1 E Wynnewood Rd, Wynnewood, PA 19096
Tel.: (484) 708-5100   PA
Web Site: http://www.rpmgt.com
Year Founded: 1994
Sales Range: $25-49.9 Million
Emp.: 90
Residential Real Estate Investment & Property Management Services
N.A.I.C.S.: 531390
Michelle Meehan *(VP & Controller)*
Eric Meese *(Dir-Maintenance)*
Lorinda Willner *(Mgr-Assets)*
Greg Giagnacova *(Chief Acctg Officer)*

RP MANAGEMENT, LLC
110 E 59th St 33rd Fl, New York, NY 10022
Tel.: (212) 883-0200   DE
Web Site:
http://www.royaltypharma.com
Year Founded: 1996
Sales Range: $50-74.9 Million
Emp.: 21
Pharmaceutical Intellectual Property Investment Holding Company
N.A.I.C.S.: 551112
Susannah Gray *(CFO & Exec VP)*
Alexander Kwit *(Gen Counsel & Exec VP)*
Jim Reddoch *(Exec VP & Head-Res & Investments)*
George Lloyd *(Exec VP-Investments)*
Terrance Coyne *(VP-Res & Investments)*
James S. Rielly *(VP-Fin)*
Alexander von Perfall *(VP-IR & Pub Affairs)*
Marshall Urist *(VP-Res & Investments)*
Douglas Erb *(Chief Admin Officer & Chief Compliance Officer)*
Pablo Legorreta *(CEO)*

RPA CO-OP
300 N Washigton St, Pleasant Plains, IL 62677
Tel.: (217) 626-1551
Web Site: http://www.rcmcoop.com
Sales Range: $10-24.9 Million
Emp.: 20
Grain Elevators
N.A.I.C.S.: 424510
Tom Harms *(Mgr)*

RPM ADVERTISING
222 S Morgan St, Chicago, IL 60610
Tel.: (312) 455-8600   IL
Web Site: http://www.rpmadv.com
Year Founded: 1994
Rev.: $42,000,000
Emp.: 94
Advetising Agency
N.A.I.C.S.: 541810
Mark Malin *(Pres)*
Steve Platcow *(CEO & Founding Partner)*

Subsidiaries:

RPM/Detroit   (1)
8424 Woodward Ave, Detroit, MI 48203
Tel.: (313) 873-5030
Web Site: http://www.rpmadv.com
N.A.I.C.S.: 541810
Mark Malin *(Pres)*

RPM/Las Vegas   (1)
7251 W Lake Mead Blvd Ste 300, Las Vegas, NV 89128
Tel.: (702) 562-4060
Web Site: http://www.rpmadv.com
N.A.I.C.S.: 541810
Steve Platcow *(Founding Partner & CEO)*

RPM CONSOLIDATED SERVICES, INC.
13225 Marquardt Ave, Santa Fe Springs, CA 90670-4831
Tel.: (562) 777-9510
Web Site: http://www.rpmcsi.com
Year Founded: 1985
Sales Range: $10-24.9 Million
Emp.: 110
Provider of Transportation Services
N.A.I.C.S.: 488510
Shawn Duke *(Pres)*
Chad Duke *(Gen Mgr)*
Dan Laport *(CFO)*

Subsidiaries:

Liberty Logistics Services, Inc.   (1)
6050 King Dr Unit B, Ventura, CA 93003
Tel.: (805) 204-2400
Web Site: http://www.rpmcsi.com
Logistics & Warehouse Services
N.A.I.C.S.: 541614

RPM Harbor Services, Inc.   (1)
2338 Gaylord St, Long Beach, CA 90813
Tel.: (562) 432-5060
Logistics & Warehouse Services
N.A.I.C.S.: 541614

RPM Transportation Inc.   (1)
96-1379 Waihona St, Pearl City, HI 96782
Tel.: (808) 454-8600
Web Site: http://www.rpmtrans.com
Sales Range: $10-24.9 Million
Emp.: 30
Local Trucking with Storage
N.A.I.C.S.: 484110

Royal Global Express Inc.   (1)
2586 Lane Ave N, Jacksonville, FL 32254
Tel.: (904) 786-0900
Freight Transportation Services
N.A.I.C.S.: 488510

RPM DEVELOPMENT GROUP
77 Park St, Montclair, NJ 07042
Tel.: (973) 744-5410
Web Site: http://www.rpmdev.com
Rev.: $14,688,159
Emp.: 10
Subdividers & Developers
N.A.I.C.S.: 236115
Brendan McBride *(VP-Dev)*
Steve Tancer *(Dir-Property Mgmt Ops)*
Joseph Portelli *(Asst VP-Dev)*
Mike Knab *(VP)*

RPM EQUIPMENT CO.
13317 Chrisman Rd, Houston, TX 77039-4123
Tel.: (281) 590-1494
Web Site:
http://www.wreckercapitol.com
Sales Range: $10-24.9 Million
Emp.: 8
Trucks, Tractors & Trailers: New & Used
N.A.I.C.S.: 441110
Bryan Marshall *(Pres)*

RPM MACHINERY LLC
8910 Purdue Rd Ste 665, Indianapolis, IN 46268-6268
Tel.: (616) 371-7250
Web Site:
http://www.rpmmachinery.com
Emp.: 60
Construction Machinery Retailer
N.A.I.C.S.: 423810
Troy Price *(Pres)*
Tim Williamson *(Mgr-Svc)*

RPM MANAGEMENT INC.
5112 Madison Ave Ste 201, Sacramento, CA 95841
Tel.: (916) 338-7333   CA
Web Site:
http://www.lexusofsacramento.com
Year Founded: 1977
Sales Range: $150-199.9 Million
Emp.: 250
Management Services
N.A.I.C.S.: 541611
Linda Gravelle *(Controller)*
Patrick Frink *(Pres)*
Dick Hill *(VP)*

Subsidiaries:

Lexus of Sacramento   (1)
2600 Fulton Ave, Sacramento, CA 95821   (100%)
Tel.: (916) 485-3987
Web Site:
http://www.lexusofsacramento.com
Rev.: $42,732,722
Emp.: 100
New & Used Car Dealers
N.A.I.C.S.: 441110
Christian Simon *(Gen Mgr)*
Bryon Burdette *(Mgr-Sls)*
Patrick Frink *(Pres)*
James Carpenter *(Mgr-Guest Retention)*
Mike Kennedy *(Mgr-Internet & Fleet)*
Kent Owens *(Mgr-Internet & Fleet)*
Dave Torkelsen *(Mgr-Svc)*
Ernie Wasserslaben *(Asst Mgr-Sls)*
Jameson White *(Mgr-Parts)*
Richard Williams *(Mgr-Bus Dev)*
Mike Zinda *(Dir-Fin)*

RPM MORTGAGE, INC.
3240 Stone Vly Rd W, Alamo, CA 94507
Tel.: (925) 295-9300
Web Site: http://www.rpm-mtg.com
Year Founded: 1993
Sales Range: $25-49.9 Million
Emp.: 65

Mortgage Services
N.A.I.C.S.: 522310
Julian Hebron *(Exec VP)*
Chad Baker *(Mgr-San Diego)*

RPM PIZZA INC.
15384 5th St, Gulfport, MS 39503
Tel.: (228) 832-4000
Web Site: http://www.rpmpizza.com
Sales Range: $50-74.9 Million
Emp.: 50
Pizzeria Chain
N.A.I.C.S.: 722513
Richard P. Mueller *(Chm)*

RPM STEEL INC.
PO Box 1936, Auburn, WA 98071
Tel.: (253) 939-5337
Web Site:
http://www.rpmsteelinc.com
Sales Range: $10-24.9 Million
Emp.: 35
Structural Steel Services
N.A.I.C.S.: 238190
Jeffrey Dean *(Treas & Mgr)*

RPM-RIGHT PLACE MEDIA
437 Lewis Hargett Cir Ste 130, Lexington, KY 40503
Tel.: (859) 685-3800   KY
Web Site:
http://www.rightplacemedia.com
Year Founded: 2001
Sales Range: $25-49.9 Million
Emp.: 20
Media Buying Services
N.A.I.C.S.: 541830
Joel Rapp *(Pres & CEO)*
W. C. Corbin *(CFO)*
Devin Johnson *(Sr VP & Dir-Media)*
Joey Banks *(VP & Dir-Media)*
Amy Lynne Dickinson *(Dir-Media)*
Stephanie Dowdy *(VP & Dir-Media)*
Bita Fesharaki *(Dir-Media)*
Morgan Withrow *(Supvr-Acct)*

RPMC, INC.
23975 Park Sorrento Ste 410, Calabasas, CA 91302
Tel.: (818) 222-7762
Web Site: http://www.rpmc.com
Year Founded: 1986
Sales Range: $25-49.9 Million
Emp.: 30
Sports, Entertainment & Media Services
N.A.I.C.S.: 541830
Murray Schwartz *(Founder)*
Kelly Weinberg *(Exec VP)*
Stacy Collins *(CFO)*
Von Parish *(VP-Nashville)*
Adam Salter *(Chief Strategy Officer)*
Stephen Hall *(CEO-London)*
Craig McAnsh *(Chief Creative Officer)*
Tami Rittberg *(Sr VP)*
Mariah Thompson *(Mgr-Acctg)*
Liz Owens *(VP)*
Viv Brown *(Dir-Acct)*
Steve Leary *(Mgr-Acct)*
Denise Beatty *(Sr Dir-Acct)*
Brad Mulholland *(Controller-Los Angeles)*
Karen Bell *(Sr Dir-Acct)*
Tom Robinson *(Mgr-Acct)*
Cristina Caponi *(Mgr-Acct)*
Matt Turrell *(Mgr-Fin)*
Natasha Davidson *(Dir-Acct)*
Kirsty Collins *(Sr Mgr-Acct)*
Kate Hutchings *(Sr Mgr-Acct)*
Charlie Birkin *(Mgr-Mktg)*
Megan Yeatts *(Office Mgr)*
Meghan Kane *(Coord-Acct)*
Jacqueline Bao *(Dir-Los Angeles)*
Heather Edmondson *(Dir-Los Angeles)*

RPMC, INC.

RPMC, Inc.—(Continued)

Krista Bell Mickelson *(Dir-Los Angeles)*
Pat Bilodeau *(Dir-Nashville)*
Michael Michalski *(Dir-Rio de Janeiro)*
Juliano Zappia *(Dir-Rio de Janeiro)*

Subsidiaries:

RPMC - New York (1)
560 Broadway Ste 506, New York, NY 10012
Tel.: (212) 792-8930
Web Site: http://www.rpmc.com
Emp.: 20
Promotional & Event Marketing Services
N.A.I.C.S.: 541810
Caroline Blodgett *(Office Mgr)*

RPMC Europe Ltd. (1)
167 Wardour St 2nd Fl, London, W1F 8WP, United Kingdom
Tel.: (44) 207 0256 180
Web Site: http://www.rpmc.co.uk
Sales Range: $10-24.9 Million
Emp.: 15
Promotional Services & Event Marketing
N.A.I.C.S.: 541810
Stephen Hall *(CEO)*

RPS COMPOSITES, INC.
8375 Zeigler Blvd, Mobile, AL 36608
Tel.: (800) 343-9355
Web Site: http://www.rpscomposites.com
N.A.I.C.S.:
Jeff Fraser *(CEO)*

Subsidiaries:

RPS Composites Ontario Inc. (1)
2175 Teston Road, Maple, L6A 1T3, ON, Canada
Tel.: (905) 832-8161
Web Site: http://rpscomposites.com
Mfr & Designer of Thermoplastic Products
N.A.I.C.S.: 326199

RPS PRODUCTS, INC.
281 Keyes Ave, Hampshire, IL 60140
Tel.: (847) 683-3400
Web Site: http://www.rpsproducts.com
Year Founded: 1964
Sales Range: $10-24.9 Million
Emp.: 45
Polish & Sanitation Good Mfr
N.A.I.C.S.: 325612
Richard P. Schuld *(Co-CEO)*
Dick Schuld *(Founder & Co-CEO)*

RR APPLIANCE SERVICES, INC.
8325 W 24th Ave Ste 2, Hialeah, FL 33016
Web Site: http://www.rrapplianceservices.com
Year Founded: 2008
Sales Range: $1-9.9 Million
Consumer Product & Services
N.A.I.C.S.: 532210
Audrey Ibarra *(Mgr-Parts Dept)*

RR PUBLIC RELATIONS, INC.
2220 W Dickens Ave, Chicago, IL 60647
Tel.: (773) 252-8550
Web Site: http://www.rrpublicrelations.com
Year Founded: 2003
Sales Range: Less than $1 Million
Emp.: 5
Food Service, Public Relations, Publicity/Promotions
N.A.I.C.S.: 541820
Susie Riskind Robbins *(CEO & Co-Founder)*
Peter Riskind *(Co-Founder)*

RR USA INC.
8 Creek Pkwy, Boothwyn, PA 19061
Tel.: (610) 497-0154
Web Site: http://www.rrusainc.com
Year Founded: 1985
Sales Range: $10-24.9 Million
Emp.: 25
Mfr & Distributor of Mechanical & Hydraulic Components
N.A.I.C.S.: 423840
Andrea Zanellotti *(VP-Sls)*
Hovig Kuredjian *(Area Mgr-Sls)*

RREAL TACOS SANDY SPRINGS LLC
100 6th St NE Ste 110, Atlanta, GA 30308
Tel.: (404) 458-5887
Web Site: https://rrealtacos.com
Emp.: 100
Restaurant Operators
N.A.I.C.S.: 722511
Damian Otero *(Co-Owner)*
Miguel Hernandez *(Co-Owner)*

Subsidiaries:

Zocalo L.C. (1)
187 10th St NE, Atlanta, GA 30309-4050
Tel.: (404) 424-7576
Web Site: http://www.zocalokc.com
Full-Service Restaurants
N.A.I.C.S.: 722511

RRGP SERVICES, INC.
1111 Navarro St, San Antonio, TX 78205
Tel.: (210) 828-8552
Web Site: http://www.rrgp.com
Year Founded: 1993
Sales Range: $10-24.9 Million
Emp.: 15
Computer Related Maintenance Services
N.A.I.C.S.: 541519
Gilbert Garcia *(Founder & Pres)*
Glenda Anzuaoda *(Controller)*
Paul Baca *(Dir-Info Assurance & IT)*
Efrain Contreras III *(Engr-Network-Level 2)*

RRS INC
1081 Makepono St, Honolulu, HI 96819
Tel.: (808) 847-2077
Web Site: http://www.rsihawaii.com
Sales Range: $25-49.9 Million
Emp.: 500
Roofing & Siding Materials
N.A.I.C.S.: 423330
Bob Perry Jr. *(CEO)*

RRS, INC.
621 NW 53rd St, Boca Raton, FL 33487
Tel.: (561) 893-0123
Web Site: http://www.reliablers.com
Year Founded: 1994
Sales Range: $1-9.9 Million
Emp.: 11
Disability Insurance Services
N.A.I.C.S.: 524298
Jim Franklin *(CEO)*
Joe Hughes *(Dir-Ops)*

RS EDEN
1931 W Broadway, Minneapolis, MN 55411
Tel.: (612) 287-1600   MN
Web Site: http://www.rseden.org
Year Founded: 1999
Sales Range: $10-24.9 Million
Emp.: 234
Community Action Services
N.A.I.C.S.: 624190
Dan Cain *(Pres)*
Jessie Johnson *(Dir-Asset & Property Mgmt)*
Lois Mueller *(VP-Supportive Housing)*
Amy Cushing *(Dir-Bus-RSI Labs)*
Paul Puerzer *(Pres)*

RS ENTERPRISES
PO Box 496, Gig Harbor, WA 98335
Tel.: (253) 265-8666
Year Founded: 1989
Sales Range: Less than $1 Million
Emp.: 3
N.A.I.C.S.: 541810
Russell Holster *(Dir)*

RS LEGACY CORPORATION
Mail Stop CF3-201, 300 RadioShack Cir, Fort Worth, TX 76102-1964
Tel.: (817) 415-3011   DE
Web Site: http://www.radioshack.com
Year Founded: 1919
Sales Range: $1-4.9 Billion
Emp.: 27,500
Consumer Electronics & Accessories Retailer
N.A.I.C.S.: 449210
Robert C. Donohoo *(Gen Counsel, Sec & VP)*
Michael DeFazio *(Sr VP-Store Ops)*
Marty B. Amschler *(Sr VP-Franchise)*
William Russum *(Chief Acctg Officer, VP & Controller)*
Paul Rutenis *(Chief Mdsg Officer & Sr VP)*
Janet E. Fox *(Sr VP-Global Sourcing & Product Innovation)*
Harry J. Wilson *(Chief Revitalization Officer)*
Carlin Adrianopoli *(Interim CFO)*
Nick Cannon *(Chief Creative Officer)*
Michael Tatelman *(CMO)*
Dene Rogers *(Pres & CEO)*
Robert Lavan *(Chm)*

Subsidiaries:

Antennacraft Co. (1)
1719 W Mt Pleasant St, West Burlington, IA 52655   (100%)
Tel.: (319) 758-8050
Web Site: http://www.antennacraft.net
Sales Range: $10-24.9 Million
Emp.: 50
Outdoor TV Antennas Mfr
N.A.I.C.S.: 334220
Howard Whitcomb *(Gen Mgr)*

RadioShack (HK) Ltd (1)
Ste 1407 211 World Commerce Ctr Harbor City Tsimshatsui, Kowloon, China (Hong Kong)   (100%)
Tel.: (852) 27300226
Web Site: http://www.radioshack.com
Sales Range: $10-24.9 Million
Emp.: 30
Electronic Products Trading Services
N.A.I.C.S.: 449210

RadioShack Distribution Center (1)
100 Tandy Dr, Hagerstown, MD 21740
Tel.: (240) 313-3640
Web Site: http://www.radioshack.com
Sales Range: $10-24.9 Million
Emp.: 200
Electronic Parts & Equipment Whslr
N.A.I.C.S.: 449210

RadioShack Packaging (1)
801 NE 38th St, Fort Worth, TX 76106-3732   (100%)
Tel.: (817) 415-8370
Web Site: http://www.radioshack.com
Sales Range: $25-49.9 Million
Emp.: 90
Electronics Parts & Tubes Packaging Services
N.A.I.C.S.: 561910

RadioShack Store Fixtures (1)
701 N Hampton St, Fort Worth, TX 76106-1657   (100%)
Tel.: (817) 415-1777
Web Site: http://www.radioshack.com
Sales Range: $10-24.9 Million
Emp.: 40
Store Fixture Mfr
N.A.I.C.S.: 337215

RS-UNIX
165 Page St, San Francisco, CA 94102
Tel.: (415) 397-9501
Year Founded: 1986
Sales Range: $25-49.9 Million
Emp.: 30
Computer Related Services
N.A.I.C.S.: 541519
Jeff Medeiros *(CEO)*
Keith Adams *(COO)*

RSA FILMS INC.
634 N La Peer Dr, Los Angeles, CA 90069-5602
Tel.: (310) 659-1577   DE
Web Site: http://www.rsafilms.com
Year Founded: 1986
Sales Range: $10-24.9 Million
Emp.: 40
Motion Picture & Television Advertising Commercials Producer
N.A.I.C.S.: 512110
Jules Daly *(Pres-Los Angeles)*
Dan Rosenthal *(CFO)*
Ridley Scott *(Founder)*
Jordan Scott *(Partner)*
Jake Scott *(Partner)*
Luke Scott *(CEO-Global)*

RSB SOLUTIONS, LC
6001 Savoy Dr Ste 110, Houston, TX 77036
Web Site: http://www.rsbenv.com
Year Founded: 2013
Sales Range: $1-9.9 Million
Emp.: 14
Environmental Consulting Services
N.A.I.C.S.: 541620
Sachin Butala *(CEO)*
Ralph Shaw *(Gen Mgr)*
Michael Mullins *(Branch Mgr)*
Deborah Ahlgren *(Mgr-Dept)*
Shannon Konop *(Specialist-Event Rental)*

RSC TRANSPORTATION INC.
234 Pine Barren, Pooler, GA 31322
Tel.: (912) 748-9288
Web Site: http://www.rsclogistics.com
Sales Range: $10-24.9 Million
Emp.: 55
Freight Transportation Services
N.A.I.C.S.: 484121
Stevie Canady *(Pres)*

RSD TRANSPORTATION INC.
601 Old River Rd, White River Junction, VT 05001
Tel.: (802) 295-7743
Sales Range: $10-24.9 Million
Emp.: 110
Provider of Trucking Services
N.A.I.C.S.: 484121
Richard S. Daniels *(Owner & Pres)*
Donald Hemenway *(Sec & VP)*
Scott Perrault *(Controller)*

RSG FOREST PRODUCTS INC.
985 NW 2nd St, Kalama, WA 98625-9647
Tel.: (360) 673-2825   WA
Web Site: http://www.rsgfp.com
Year Founded: 1973
Sales Range: $25-49.9 Million
Emp.: 800
Provider of Lumber Services
N.A.I.C.S.: 321113
Kirk Harrison *(Mgr-Timber)*
Duane Kraxberger *(Supvr-Electrical)*

RSI HOLDINGS INC.
28 E Court St, Greenville, SC 29601-2820

COMPANIES

Tel.: (864) 271-7171 NC
Year Founded: 1978
Sales Range: Less than $1 Million
Emp.: 2
Temporary Staffing Services
N.A.I.C.S.: 561311
Charles C. Mickel (Pres)

RSI INC.
1670 Kohlers Crossing, Kyle, TX 78640
Tel.: (512) 268-7500
Web Site: http://www.rsi-cri.com
Sales Range: $10-24.9 Million
Emp.: 20
Electronic Components
N.A.I.C.S.: 423610
Harish K. Malkani (Pres & CEO)

RSK TRANSPORT LLC
8 Poe Ct, Kendall Park, NJ 08824-1416
Tel.: (361) 500-4727
Web Site:
http://www.rsktransportllc.net
General Freight Trucking, Long-Distance, Truckload
N.A.I.C.S.: 484121
Raymond Krosnowski (Pres)

RSL FIBER SYSTEMS, LLC.
255 Pitkin St, East Hartford, CT 06108
Tel.: (860) 282-4930
Web Site:
http://www.RSLFiberSystems.com
Sales Range: $1-9.9 Million
Emp.: 14
Electric Light Mfr & Distr
N.A.I.C.S.: 237130
Giovanni P. Tomasi (CEO & CTO)
Dennis Jarvis (Mgr-Bus Dev)
Jeff McFadden (Dir-Engrg)
Thomas Maynes (Dir-DDG 1000 Program)

RSL WOODWORKING PRODUCTS CO.
3092 English Creek Ave, Egg Harbor Township, NJ 08234
Tel.: (609) 484-1600
Web Site: http://www.rslinc.com
Sales Range: $10-24.9 Million
Emp.: 45
Door Frames, Wood
N.A.I.C.S.: 321911
Ron Lewkowitz (Pres)
Kevin P. Kavanagh (VP)
Heather O'Shea (Mgr-Inside Sls)
Stephen Nixon (Mgr-Ops)

RSM ELECTRON POWER INC.
221 W Industry Ct, Deer Park, NY 11788
Tel.: (631) 586-7600
Web Site: http://www.sensitron.com
Sales Range: $10-24.9 Million
Emp.: 114
Provider of Semiconductors & Related Devices
N.A.I.C.S.: 334413
Jackie Tubbs (Controller)

RSM US LLP
1 S Wacker Dr Ste 800, Chicago, IL 60606
Tel.: (312) 384-6000 IA
Web Site: http://www.rsmus.com
Year Founded: 1926
Accounting, Auditing, Tax & Consulting Services
N.A.I.C.S.: 541211
Jeff Johannesen (Chief Strategy & Innovation Officer)
Joseph M. Adams (CEO & Mng Partner)
Rick Day (Partner & Dir-Acctg-Natl)
Doug Opheim (CFO)
Bruce Jorth (Chief Risk Officer)
Troy Cardinal (CIO)
Jackie Prillaman (Mng Partner-Raleigh)
Crystal Zhang (Partner)
Palak Singh (Sr Mgr-Lead Tax)
Jason Alexander (Principal)
Steve Kelley (Partner-Madison)
Rob Toomb (Dir-Bus Dev)
Roger Prough (Mng Partner)
Todd Pleiman (Mng Partner-Dayton)
Matt Metzig (Sr Mgr-Audit Svcs)
Andy Bosman (Principal-Natl Mktg & Sls)
Tom Ferreira (Mng Partner-Northeast Reg)
Sam Mascareno (Mng Partner-West Reg)
Kevin Prien (Mng Partner-Central Reg)
Craig Radke (Mng Partner-Southeast)
Donna Sciarappa (Mng Partner-Great Lakes)
John Jones (Dir-Risk Advisory Svcs)
John Augustin (Dir-Tech & Mgmt Consulting)
Chris Philpott (Dir-Bus Dev-Tech & Mgmt Consulting-Cincinnati & Dayton Practice)
Chris Murphy (Dir-Tech & Mgmt Consulting)
Erin Peterson (Partner)
Sarah Johnson (Partner)
Brad Partner (Partner)
Kari Henry (Partner)
Paul Short (Mng Partner-Irvine)
Bryan Marsh (Dir-Bus Dev)
Brian Berning (Partner-Tax)
Thomas Allen (Partner-Tax)
John Brackett (Partner)
Curtis White (Mgr-Tax)
Gorby Nguyen (Mgr-Valuation Svcs)
Wilson Nguyen (Mgr-Lead Tax)
Mahera Rahman (Mgr-Bus Consulting & Risk Advisory Svcs)
Alma Padilla (Mgr-Tax-Private Client Svcs Grp)
Eli Kemmerer (Partner-Transaction Advisory Svcs Practice)
Todd Albaugh (Partner)
Seth Derevensky (Principal)
Tony Spano (Principal)
Wayne Reesman (Partner)
Tommy M. Wright (Partner-Tax)
Steve Jones (Principal)
Jeremy DeSpain (Principal-Tech & Mgmt Consulting Practice)
Brad Homant (Partner-Audit-Phoenix)
Kristi Sharp (Partner-Audit)
Michael Graber (Partner-Tax-Kansas)
Robert Dunn (Partner)
Benjamin Shappell (Partner)
Kathryn Johnson (Partner)
JuliAn Coy (Principal)
Steven Marsden (Partner)
Jamie Klenieski (Partner)
Geoff Hopkins (Principal-Tech Mgmt Consulting Practice-Northeast)
Rob Casillo (Partner)
Danielle Preston (Partner)
Karen Crim (Sr Dir-Tax)
Dominic Henriques (Partner-Risk Advisory Svcs)
David Petrill (Partner-Tax)
James Rojek (Dir-Risk Advisory Svcs Grp)
Engelina Tjokro Soesilo (Mgr-Audit-Assurance Team-Houston)
Sergio De La Fe (Chm & Partner)
Gregg Kiehl (Partner)
Jerry Martin (Partner-Tax Services-Intl)
Joyce Reto (Partner-Audit Svcs)
Rob Stoettner (Partner-Audit Svcs)
Stu Taub (Partner-Audit Svcs)
Bill Gorman (COO)
Katie Lamkin (Chief HR Officer)
Sara Webber Laczo (Principal)
Gwyneth Barber (Partner-Corp Tax-Hull)
Ron Beck (Principal-Houston)
Ankit Mathur (Mgr-Audit-Assurance Practice-Houston)
Carol Warley (Partner-Tax-Private Client Practice)
F. Octavio Saenz (Dir-Transaction Advisory Svcs)
Harry Costin (Sr Mgr-Mergers & Acq)
Laura Brickey (Mktg Mgr-Houston)
Jeff Harfenist (Partner-Fin Investigations & Dispute Svcs-Houston)
Margaret Powell (Partner-Assurance-Birmingham)
Greg Hicks (Partner-Assurance-Birmingham)
Paul Popovski (Sr Mgr-Assurance)
Jason Creakbaum (Mgr-Assurance)
Danielle Gonzalez (Partner-Tax Svcs)
Charles Barley Jr. (Principal)
Charles B. Freeman II (Partner-Tax-Birmingham)

Subsidiaries:

SecureState LLC (1)
23340 Miles Rd, Cleveland, OH 44128-5493
Tel.: (216) 927-8200
Web Site: http://www.securestate.com
Sales Range: Less than $1 Million
Information Security Management Consulting Services
N.A.I.C.S.: 541690
Ken Stasiak (Owner)

Wise Consulting Associates, LLC (1)
9515 Deereco Rd Ste 610, Timonium, MD 21093
Web Site: http://www.wiseconsulting.com
Payroll Consulting Services
N.A.I.C.S.: 541214
Scott Weiss (Pres)

RSNB BANCORP
200 2nd St, Rock Springs, WY 82901
Tel.: (307) 362-8801 WY
Web Site: http://www.rsnb.com
Year Founded: 1998
Sales Range: $10-24.9 Million
Emp.: 54
Bank Holding Company
N.A.I.C.S.: 551111
Ben K. Hansen (CFO, Treas & Sec)
John W. Hay III (Chm, Pres & CEO)

Subsidiaries:

RSNB Bank (1)
200 2nd St, Rock Springs, WY 82901
Tel.: (307) 362-8801
Web Site: http://www.rsnb.com
Sales Range: $10-24.9 Million
Emp.: 60
Commericial Banking
N.A.I.C.S.: 522110
John E. Hay (Sec)
Ben Hamsen (CEO)
John W. Hay III (Chm)

RSP ARCHITECTS, LTD.
1220 Marshall St NE, Minneapolis, MN 55413-1036
Tel.: (612) 677-7100 MN
Web Site: http://www.rsparch.com
Year Founded: 1978
Rev: $5,000,000
Emp.: 425
Architectural Services
N.A.I.C.S.: 541310
Pat Parrish (Principal & Controller)

RSR DEVELOPMENT CORP.
277 North Ave Ste 200, New Rochelle, NY 10801
Tel.: (914) 774-8811 NV
Year Founded: 2011
Sales Range: $10-24.9 Million
Emp.: 1
Restaurant
N.A.I.C.S.: 722511
Rudolph Southwell (Pres, COO & Treas)
Tessle Robinson (Sec)

RSR GROUP INC.
4405 Metric Dr, Winter Park, FL 32792-6904
Tel.: (407) 677-1000 FL
Web Site: http://www.rsrgroup.com
Year Founded: 1989
Sales Range: $75-99.9 Million
Emp.: 157
Sporting Guns Whlsr & Distr
N.A.I.C.S.: 423990
Joann Weisenford (Pres)
Renee Garrett (Controller)

Subsidiaries:

RSR Group Texas Inc (1)
1010 E Ave J, Grand Prairie, TX 75050-2619
Tel.: (972) 602-3131
Web Site: http://www.rsrgroup.com
Sales Range: $10-24.9 Million
Emp.: 50
Durable Goods
N.A.I.C.S.: 423910
Bob Steger (Pres)

RSR Management Corp. (1)
4405 Metric Dr, Winter Park, FL 32792-6904
Tel.: (407) 677-1000
Web Site: http://www.rsrgroup.com
Sales Range: $10-24.9 Million
Emp.: 60
Management Services
N.A.I.C.S.: 561110
Wes Knight (Gen Mgr)

RSR Wholesale Guns Inc. (1)
4405 Metric Dr, Winter Park, FL 32792-6904
Tel.: (407) 677-1000
Web Site: http://www.rsrgroup.com
Sales Range: $10-24.9 Million
Durable Goods
N.A.I.C.S.: 423990
Bob Steger (Pres)

RSR Wholesale Guns West Inc. (1)
4878 Sparks Blvd Ste 100, Sparks, NV 89436
Tel.: (775) 827-2111
Web Site: http://www.rsrwholesale.com
Sales Range: $10-24.9 Million
Emp.: 10
Durable Goods
N.A.I.C.S.: 423990
Wes Knight (Mgr-Natl Sls)

RSR Wholesale South Inc. (1)
4405 Metric Dr, Winter Park, FL 32792-6904
Tel.: (407) 677-1000
Web Site: http://www.rsrgroup.com
Sales Range: $10-24.9 Million
Emp.: 35
Durable Goods
N.A.I.C.S.: 423990
Joanne Weisonford (VP)

RT&T GROUP, INC.
18353 U.S. Hwy 20 W, East Dubuque, IL 61025
Tel.: (815) 747-9125
Web Site:
http://www.rttenterprises.com
Year Founded: 1994
Sales Range: $10-24.9 Million
Emp.: 25
Logistics & Brokerage Transportation Services
N.A.I.C.S.: 488510
Todd Colin (Partner & Pres)
Trevor Colin (CEO & Partner)
Tiffany Suess (CFO)

RTA CABINET STORE

RTA Cabinet Store—(Continued)

RTA CABINET STORE
6 Union Hill Rd, Conshohocken, PA 19428
Tel.: (610) 337-5934
Web Site:
http://www.rtacabinetstore.com
Year Founded: 2007
Sales Range: $1-9.9 Million
Emp.: 12
Kitchen Cabinets & Bathroom Vanities
N.A.I.C.S.: 337110
Gary Nealon *(Owner)*
Liane Lauff *(Office Mgr)*

RTA FURNITURE DISTRIBUTORS
5500 Linglestown Rd, Harrisburg, PA 17112
Tel.: (717) 540-5500   DE
Web Site:
http://www.justcabinets.com
Year Founded: 1983
Sales Range: $10-24.9 Million
Emp.: 120
Distr of Unfinished Furniture
N.A.I.C.S.: 449110
Theodore Bernstein *(Pres)*

RTC HOLDINGS, L.L.C.
105 RTC Dr, Reserve, LA 70084
Tel.: (985) 536-1111
Web Site: http://www.rtconline.com
Year Founded: 1935
Telephone, Cable Television, High-speed Internet & Security Provider
N.A.I.C.S.: 517810
William Ironside *(Pres & CEO)*

Subsidiaries:

Eatelcorp Inc.   (1)
913 S Burnside Ave, Gonzales, LA 70737-4258
Tel.: (225) 621-4300
Web Site: http://www.eatel.com
Sales Range: $150-199.9 Million
Emp.: 450
Communications Services Via Wireline & Wireless Transmissions
N.A.I.C.S.: 517121
John D. Scanlan *(CEO)*
Arthur Scanlan *(Chm)*
Janet Britton *(Gen Counsel & Exec VP-HR)*
Peter Louviere *(CFO)*
Harris Miller *(Exec VP-Tech & Innovation)*
Noah Boudreaux *(Exec VP-Bus Ops)*
Josh Descant *(Pres)*
Tressy Leindecker *(Exec VP-Sls)*

Subsidiary (Domestic):

Advanced Tel, Inc.   (2)
913 S Burnside Ave, Gonzales, LA 70737-4258   **(100%)**
Tel.: (225) 621-4200
Web Site: http://www.eatel.com
Sales Range: $10-24.9 Million
Emp.: 41
Provider of Long Distance & Operator Services
N.A.I.C.S.: 517121

East Ascension Telephone Company LLC   (2)
913 S Burnside Ave, Gonzales, LA 70737-4258   **(100%)**
Tel.: (225) 621-4200
Rev.: $27,689,733
Emp.: 96
Local Telephone Exchange Carrier
N.A.I.C.S.: 517121

Eatel Construction Co., Inc.   (2)
913 S Burnside Ave, Gonzales, LA 70737-4258   **(100%)**
Tel.: (225) 621-4200
Sales Range: $25-49.9 Million
Emp.: 300
Construction of Outside Plant for Utilities
N.A.I.C.S.: 517121

SJI LLC   (2)
115 W 10th Blvd, Larose, LA 70373
Tel.: (985) 693-4567
Web Site: http://www.viscom.net
Sales Range: $25-49.9 Million
Emp.: 6
Local Telephone Communications
N.A.I.C.S.: 517121
Peter Louviere *(CFO)*

Subsidiary (Domestic):

Mobiletel Inc.   (3)
115 Tenth St, Lockport, LA 70374
Tel.: (985) 851-2355
Web Site: http://www.mobiletel.com
Cellular Telephone Services
N.A.I.C.S.: 517121

Vision Communications   (3)
165 W 10th Blvd, Larose, LA 70373
Tel.: (985) 693-4567
Sales Range: $10-24.9 Million
Local Telephone Communications
N.A.I.C.S.: 517121

RTD CONSTRUCTION, INC.
5344 9th St, Zephyrhills, FL 33542
Tel.: (813) 783-9119
Web Site:
http://www.rtdconstruction.com
Sales Range: $25-49.9 Million
Emp.: 110
Civil Engineering Services
N.A.I.C.S.: 237310
Rusty A. Haughn *(VP)*
Dannie E. Jordan *(Pres)*
Marjorie S. Jordan *(Treas & Sec)*
Tony D. Jordan *(VP)*

RTG MEDICAL
1005 E 23rd St Ste 200, Fremont, NE 68025
Web Site: http://www.rtgmedical.com
Sales Range: $1-9.9 Million
Emp.: 74
Temporary Medical Staffing Services
N.A.I.C.S.: 561320
Charlie L. Janssen *(Chm, Pres & CEO)*
Jeremy L. Guenthner *(VP-IT & Dev)*
Dave C. Guenthner *(COO & VP)*
Keli Koepke *(Gen Mgr)*

RTH MECHANICAL CONTRACTORS, INC.
99 Pine Rd, Exeter, NH 03833-6510
Tel.: (603) 772-9779
Web Site:
http://www.rthmechanicalcontractors.com
Sales Range: $10-24.9 Million
Emp.: 40
Plumbing Services
N.A.I.C.S.: 238220
Richard T. Hansell *(Owner)*

RTI LABORATORIES, INC.
31628 Glendale St, Livonia, MI 48150
Tel.: (734) 422-8000
Web Site: http://www.rtilab.com
Year Founded: 1986
Rev.: $4,300,000
Emp.: 45
Business Services
N.A.I.C.S.: 541380
Chuck O'Bryan *(Dir-Quality)*
Lloyd Kaufman *(Dir-Matls Science)*
Pat Jennings *(Mgr-Client Svcs)*
Fred Hoitash *(Dir-Environmental Sciences)*
Jerry Singh *(Pres)*

RTL NETWORKS, INC.
1391 Speer Blvd Ste 850, Denver, CO 80204
Tel.: (303) 757-3100
Web Site: http://www.rtl-networks.com
Year Founded: 2002
Sales Range: $10-24.9 Million

Emp.: 45
Computer Related Services
N.A.I.C.S.: 541512
Richard Lewis *(Owner & Pres)*
Krissy Chaney *(Mgr-Proposal)*

RTM & ASSOCIATES, INC.
650 E Algonquin Rd Ste 250, Schaumburg, IL 60173
Tel.: (847) 756-4180   IL
Web Site:
http://www.rtmassociates.com
Year Founded: 1981
Sales Range: $10-24.9 Million
Engineering & Consulting Services
N.A.I.C.S.: 541330
Ramesh Mirchandani *(Pres)*
Tony Mirchandani *(CEO)*
Doug Brewer *(Principal)*
Tracy Molloy *(Coord-Bus Svcs)*
Jim Wicker *(Principal)*
Harshida Sapra *(Project Engr)*
Jamie Diamond *(Project Engr)*
Jessica Iversen *(Project Engr)*
Scott Krieg *(Controller)*

Subsidiaries:

Concord West   (1)
3000 Youngfield St Ste 105, Wheat Ridge, CO 80215
Tel.: (720) 583-6737
Web Site: http://www.concordwest.com
Engineeering Services
N.A.I.C.S.: 541330
Douglas Sandridge *(Principal)*

Malone Finkle Eckhardt & Collins, Inc.   (1)
3333 E Battlefield Rd Ste 100, Springfield, MO 65804
Tel.: (417) 881-0020
Web Site: http://www.mfec.com
Sales Range: $1-9.9 Million
Engineeering Services
N.A.I.C.S.: 541330
Rod L. Finkle *(Grp Principal)*
Melinda Thurston *(Dir-Mktg)*

RTP COMPANY
580 E Front St, Winona, MN 55987
Tel.: (507) 454-6900
Web Site:
http://www.rtpcompany.com
Year Founded: 1923
Sales Range: $250-299.9 Million
Emp.: 850
Plastics Material & Resin Mfr
N.A.I.C.S.: 325211
Barb Marg *(Mgr-Customer Svc)*
Steve Maki *(VP-Tech)*
Joe Kluck *(Exec VP)*
Tom Cordes *(Gen Mgr-Conductive, Dir-Sls-Asia & Mgr-Sls-Europe)*
Jean Sirois *(Gen Mgr-Canada & Dir-Strategic Plng & Acquisitions)*
Jeff Kronebusch *(Mgr-Bus-Conductive)*
Eric Lee *(Mgr-Bus-Structural)*
Dave Pahl *(Mgr-Market-Automotive)*
Duncan Hogg *(Mgr-Market-Energy)*
Margaret Cox *(Mgr-Mktg Comm)*
Bob Williams *(Mgr-Sls-East)*
Collin Lee *(Mgr-Sls-Greater China)*
Chris Zakashefski *(Mgr-Sls-Midwest)*

Subsidiaries:

Alloy Polymers, Inc.   (1)
3310 Deepwater Terminal Rd, Richmond, VA 23234
Tel.: (804) 232-8000
Web Site: http://www.alloypolymers.com
Sales Range: $1-9.9 Million
Emp.: 50
Thermoplastics Compounding Mfr
N.A.I.C.S.: 325991

Subsidiary (Domestic):

Alloy Polymers Texas, LP   (2)
Hwy 287 & FM 2160, Crockett, TX 75849

U.S. PRIVATE

Tel.: (936) 544-4043
Web Site: http://alloypolymers.com
Sales Range: $1-9.9 Million
Emp.: 33
Thermoplastics Compounding Services
N.A.I.C.S.: 325991
Willis Brown *(Mgr)*

Wiman Corporation   (1)
180 Industrial Blvd, Sauk Rapids, MN 56379-0190
Tel.: (320) 259-2554
Web Site: http://www.wimancorp.com
Sales Range: $10-24.9 Million
Emp.: 60
Poly Vinyl Film & Sheet Mfr
N.A.I.C.S.: 326113

RTP CORP.
1834 SW 2nd St, Pompano Beach, FL 33069
Tel.: (954) 974-5500   FL
Web Site: http://www.rtpcorp.com
Sales Range: $75-99.9 Million
Emp.: 50
Power Supplies, Measurement & Controls
N.A.I.C.S.: 334412
Sal Provanzano *(Pres)*
Bob Luckendill *(Controller)*
Patrick Seiler *(VP-Global Safety Instrumented Sys)*

Subsidiaries:

RTP Korea Co. Ltd.   (1)
Unit 209 Migun Technoworld, 533 Yongsan-Dong Yuseong-Gu, Daejeon, 305 500, Korea (South)
Tel.:r(82) 42 863 9400
Software Development Services
N.A.I.C.S.: 541511

RTS UNIFIED COMMUNICATIONS
130 W 42nd St 3rd Fl, New York, NY 10036
Tel.: (212) 869-7144
Web Site: http://www.rtsav.com
Year Founded: 1997
Sales Range: $25-49.9 Million
Emp.: 116
Communication System Integration Services
N.A.I.C.S.: 541512
Anthony Posa *(CIO)*
Jean-Paul LaFleur *(Pres-DC Metro)*
John Vezzi *(Exec VP & Dir-Svcs)*
Robert Pepe *(Pres & COO)*
John J. Pepe *(CEO)*

RTW INVESTMENTS, LP
1350 Ave of the Americas 28th St, New York, NY 10019
Tel.: (646) 597-6984
Web Site: http://www.rtwfunds.com
Financial Services
N.A.I.C.S.: 523999
Michelle Krinke *(Dir-IR)*
Peter Fong *(Partner & Head-Company Creation)*

Subsidiaries:

RTW Biotech Opportunities Ltd.   (1)
1st Floor Royal Chambers St Julians Avenue, Saint Peter Port, GY13JX, Guernsey
Tel.: (44) 1481742642
Web Site: https://www.rtwfunds.com
Rev.: $4,170,554
Assets: $446,234,427
Liabilities: $17,211,470
Net Worth: $429,022,957
Earnings: ($4,763,209)
Fiscal Year-end: 12/31/2023
Investment Services
N.A.I.C.S.: 523999
Peter Fong *(Partner)*
Roderick Wong *(Mng Partner)*
Stephanie A. Sirota *(Partner)*
William Simpson *(Chm)*

RUAN TRANSPORTATION

COMPANIES

MANAGEMENT SYSTEMS, INC.
3200 Ruan Ctr 666 Grand Ave, Des Moines, IA 50309-2506
Tel.: (515) 245-2500   IA
Web Site: http://www.ruan.com
Year Founded: 1932
Sales Range: $700-749.9 Million
Emp.: 5,600
Local & Long Distance Commercial Freight Trucking & Storage Services
N.A.I.C.S.: 484121
John Ruan III *(Chm)*
Tara Meier *(VP-Mktg & Corp Comm)*
Roger Mason *(Sr VP-Sls)*
Marty Wadle *(Sr VP-Supply Chains Solutions)*
Lisa Gonnerman *(VP-Safety)*
Jim Cade *(VP-Fleet Svcs)*
Susan Fitzsimmons *(Gen Counsel & VP)*
Ron Hanson *(Chief Admin Officer & Sr VP)*
Dan Greteman *(CIO & VP)*
Chad Willis *(Sr VP-Ops)*
Benjamin J. McLean *(CEO)*

Subsidiaries:

Iowa Export-Import   (1)
512 Tuttle St, Des Moines, IA 50309-4618
Tel.: (515) 283-3900
Web Site: http://www.iaexim.com
Sales Range: $25-49.9 Million
Emp.: 27
Motor Vehicle Supplies & New Parts & Agricultural Equipments
N.A.I.C.S.: 423120
David Winkels *(Gen Mgr)*

RUBBER & ACCESSORIES, INC.
2120 Edgewood Dr S, Lakeland, FL 33803
Tel.: (863) 665-6115   FL
Web Site:
http://www.rubberandaccessories.com
Year Founded: 1972
Sales Range: $10-24.9 Million
Emp.: 42
Hose, Belting & Packing
N.A.I.C.S.: 423840
Buzz Hooper *(VP)*
Harry K. Robb Jr. *(Pres)*

RUBBER & SPECIALTIES INC.
5011 Commerce Park Cir, Pensacola, FL 32505
Tel.: (850) 478-9778
Web Site:
http://www.fnbhuntsvilletx.com
Rev.: $13,100,000
Emp.: 50
Rubber Goods, Wholesale Distributors
N.A.I.C.S.: 423840
Charles H. Cook *(Pres)*
Michael Lentz *(VP)*

RUBBER ASSOCIATES, INC.
1522 W Turkeyfoot Lake Rd, Barberton, OH 44203-4898
Tel.: (330) 745-2186
Web Site:
http://www.rubberassociates.com
Year Founded: 1953
Sales Range: $10-24.9 Million
Emp.: 100
Rubber Products Mfr
N.A.I.C.S.: 326299
Gene Fiocca *(CEO)*
Kris Fiocca *(Pres-Technical & Sls)*
Elmer Brueggeman *(Founder)*
Kip Fiocca *(VP)*

RUBBER CITY ARCHES, LLC
500 Grant St, Akron, OH 44311
Tel.: (330) 535-8400   OH
Year Founded: 2007
Sales Range: $10-24.9 Million
Fast-Food Restaurant Franchise Owner & Operator
N.A.I.C.S.: 722513
John C. Blickle *(Pres)*
Anne Base *(Controller)*

RUBBER ENTERPRISES INC.
2083 Reek Rd, Imlay City, MI 48444
Tel.: (810) 724-2400
Web Site:
http://www.rubberenterprises.com
Sales Range: $25-49.9 Million
Emp.: 300
Molded Rubber Products
N.A.I.C.S.: 326299
Mark Markaity *(VP-Engrg)*
Jennifer McKelvie *(Asst Controller)*

RUBBER ROLLS INC.
50 Rockwood Dr, Meadow Lands, PA 15347
Tel.: (724) 225-9240
Web Site: http://www.irpgroup.com
Year Founded: 1955
Sales Range: $10-24.9 Million
Emp.: 80
Rubber Products Mfr
N.A.I.C.S.: 326299
Chuck Ruffing *(Dir-Technical)*

RUBBERLITE INC.
2501 Guyan Ave, Huntington, WV 25703
Tel.: (304) 525-3116
Web Site: http://www.rubberlite.com
Sales Range: $25-49.9 Million
Emp.: 150
Mfr of Gaskets & Sealing Devices
N.A.I.C.S.: 339991
Ed Littlehales *(Mgr-Pur)*
Lorraine Scott *(Product Mgr)*
Cathy McMellon *(Mgr-HR)*
Paul Testani *(CFO)*

RUBEN-HOLLAND DEVELOPMENT, LLC
PO Box 11467, Bradenton, FL 34282
Tel.: (941) 953-4500
Web Site:
http://www.rubenholland.com
Sales Range: $1-9.9 Million
Emp.: 2
Commercial Development & Construction Services
N.A.I.C.S.: 237210
Roger Holland *(Owner)*

RUBENSTEIN & ZIFF, INC.
11516 K-Tel, Minnetonka, MN 55343
Tel.: (952) 854-1460   MN
Web Site:
http://www.quiltworksonline.com
Year Founded: 1974
Sales Range: $1-9.9 Million
Emp.: 10
Textiles, Woven
N.A.I.C.S.: 424310
Tom Hymanson *(Chm)*

RUBENSTEIN ASSOCIATES, INC.
Worldwide Plaza 825 8th Ave, New York, NY 10019-7416
Tel.: (212) 843-8000   NY
Web Site: http://www.rubenstein.com
Year Founded: 1954
Sales Range: $1-9.9 Million
Emp.: 200
Public Relations Agency
N.A.I.C.S.: 541820
Howard J. Rubenstein *(Founder & Chm)*
Marcia Horowitz *(Mng Dir)*
Gary Lewi *(Mng Dir)*
Steven Rubenstein *(Pres)*
Christopher Giglio *(Mng Dir)*
Peter Foley *(Exec VP & Dir-Bus Dev)*
Susan Arons *(Mng Dir)*
Iva Benson *(Exec VP)*
Christine Falvo *(COO)*
Nancy Haberman *(Exec VP)*
Suzanne Halpin *(Mng Dir)*
Talia Inbar *(Exec VP)*
Amy Jacobs *(Exec VP)*
Jamie Joyce *(Exec VP)*
Annette Juriaco *(Exec VP)*
Sandy Keenan *(Exec VP)*
Rick Matthews *(Mng Dir)*
Alice McGillion *(Mng Dir)*
Steve Murray *(Exec VP)*
Bud Perrone *(Mng Dir)*
Peter Pochna *(Exec VP)*
Deborah Raskin *(Mng Dir)*
Carolyn Sargent *(Exec VP)*
Katie Schroeder *(Exec VP)*
Patrick Smith *(Mng Dir)*
Tim Stone *(Exec VP)*
Alan Tessler *(CFO)*
Barbara Wagner *(Exec VP)*

Subsidiaries:

Rubenstein Public Relations, Inc.   (1)
1301 Avenue of the Americas, New York, NY 10019
Tel.: (212) 805-3000
Web Site: http://www.rubensteinpr.com
Emp.: 40
Public Relations Agency
N.A.I.C.S.: 541820
Richard Rubenstein *(Pres)*
Amy Delson *(VP)*
Marilyn Lopez *(Sr VP-Entertainment)*
Mitchell Breindel *(VP)*
Anu Kher *(Assoc VP)*
Dawn Rowan *(VP & Dir-Media Rels)*
Alisa Steinberg *(VP-Corp Comm)*
Gerry Casanova *(Sr VP & Dir-Client Svcs)*
Kathryn Green *(Dir-New Bus Dev)*
Michael Isaacson *(CFO)*
Christina Levin *(Acct Dir)*
Brad Taylor *(Sr VP-Entertainment)*

RUBENSTEIN'S CONTRACT CARPET, LLC
160 Cleveland St, Eugene, OR 97402
Tel.: (541) 484-1101
Web Site:
http://www.rubensteins.com
Sales Range: $25-49.9 Million
Commercial Flooring Contractor
N.A.I.C.S.: 238330
Terry Green *(Gen Mgr)*
Jay Dillon *(Coord-Labor)*
Darrell Salter *(Project Mgr)*
Kim Hurd *(Project Mgr)*
Peter Kingsbury *(Mgr)*

RUBICON ESTATE WINERY
1991 St Helena Hwy, Rutherford, CA 94573
Tel.: (707) 963-9099
Web Site:
http://www.rubiconestate.com
Sales Range: $25-49.9 Million
Emp.: 150
Winery
N.A.I.C.S.: 312130
Jay Shoemaker *(CEO)*
Gordon Wany *(CFO)*

RUBICON FINANCIAL INCORPORATED
18872 MacArthur Blvd 1st Fl, Irvine, CA 92612   DE
Web Site:
http://www.rubiconfinancial.com
Year Founded: 1986
Sales Range: $10-24.9 Million
Emp.: 24
Financial Holding Company
N.A.I.C.S.: 551112

RUBICON TECHNOLOGY PARTNERS, LLC

Joseph Mangiapane Jr. *(Chm, Pres, CEO & Sec)*

RUBICON PROFESSIONAL SERVICES
13849 Park Ctr Rd Ste A, Herndon, VA 20171
Tel.: (703) 346-5889
Web Site: http://www.rubiconps.com
Sales Range: $25-49.9 Million
Emp.: 18
Computer Facilities Management Services
N.A.I.C.S.: 518210
Bill Pirrone *(Principal)*
Eric Holzworth *(Mng Partner)*
James Dutro *(VP-Construction Svcs)*
Morris O'Riordan *(VP-Natl Construction Svcs)*

RUBICON PROGRAMS
2500 Bissell Ave, Richmond, CA 94804
Tel.: (510) 235-1516   CA
Web Site:
http://www.rubiconprograms.org
Year Founded: 1976
Sales Range: $10-24.9 Million
Emp.: 197
Job Placement Services
N.A.I.C.S.: 561311
Jane Fischberg *(CEO)*
Rob Hope *(Chief Program Officer)*
Susann Nordrum *(Treas)*
Paul Leonard *(Vice Chm)*
Kelly Dunn *(Gen Counsel)*
Virginia Davis *(Sec)*
Amit Kurlekar *(Chm)*
Roger Contreras *(CFO)*
Lisa Dyas *(Chief Dev Officer)*

RUBICON TECHNOLOGY PARTNERS, LLC
525 University Ave Ste 1325, Palo Alto, CA 94301
Tel.: (303) 872-6950   CA
Web Site: http://www.rubicontp.com
Year Founded: 2012
Privater Equity Firm
N.A.I.C.S.: 523999
Steve Carpenter *(Partner)*
Andy Gesell *(Partner-Stamford)*
Jason Winsten *(Partner)*
Alex Kleiner *(Partner)*
Dan Levy *(Principal-Stamford)*
Kirsten Porter *(Principal)*
Vincent Chao *(VP)*
Michael Fan *(VP-Stamford)*
John C. Hodge *(Partner)*

Subsidiaries:

Central Logic Inc.   (1)
100 W Towne Ridge Pkwy Ste 350, Sandy, UT 84070
Tel.: (801) 727-2340
Web Site: http://www.centrallogic.com
Developer of Patient Flow Software Enabling Hospitals & Medical Centers Improve Patient Care & Hospital Efficiencies
N.A.I.C.S.: 513210
Darin M. Vercillo *(Founder & Chief Medical Officer)*
Ryan Larsen *(Chief Customer Officer)*
Marnie Nuttall *(CFO)*
Greg Wiggins *(CTO)*
Angie Franks *(Pres & CEO)*
Maija Costello *(VP-People & Culture)*

Outmatch Inc.   (1)
1 Galleria Tower 13355 Noel Rd Ste 1500, Dallas, TX 75240
Web Site: http://www.outmatch.com
Recruitment Software Publisher
N.A.I.C.S.: 513210
Greg Morgan *(Pres & CEO)*

Subsidiary (Domestic):

Checkster, Inc.   (2)
926 Diablo Ave Ste 305, Novato, CA 94947

RUBICON TECHNOLOGY PARTNERS, LLC

Rubicon Technology Partners, LLC—(Continued)
Web Site: http://www.checkster.com
Software Publisher
N.A.I.C.S.: 513210
Littler Mendelson *(Chief Knowledge Officer)*

FurstPerson, Inc. (2)
801 N Perryville Rd Ste 2, Rockford, IL 61107
Tel.: (773) 353-8600
Web Site: http://www.furstperson.com
Software Publisher
N.A.I.C.S.: 513210
Brent Holland *(VP-Res & Consulting)*

Subsidiary (Non-US):

Harver B.V. (2)
Jollemanhof 20, Amsterdam, 1019, Netherlands
Tel.: (31) +31202400210
Web Site: https://harver.com
Software Devolopment
N.A.I.C.S.: 513210

Subsidiary (US):

Pymetrics, Inc. (3)
110 5th Ave 5th Fl, New York, NY 10011
Tel.: (646) 397-7998
Web Site: http://www.pymetrics.com
Software Publishing Services
N.A.I.C.S.: 513210
Frida Polli *(CEO)*
Mike DePuy *(CTO)*

RUBIE'S COSTUME COMPANY INC.
1 Rubie Plz, Richmond Hill, NY 11418
Tel.: (516) 326-1500 NY
Web Site: http://www.rubies.com
Year Founded: 1951
Costumes & Accessories Mfr & Dist
N.A.I.C.S.: 315250
Marc P. Beige *(CEO)*
Howard Beige *(Exec VP)*
John Clausen *(Gen Mgr)*
Giuseppe Soccodato *(CFO)*

Subsidiaries:

BuySeasons Enterprises, LLC (1)
5915 S Moorland Rd, New Berlin, WI 53151
Tel.: (262) 901-2000
Web Site: http://www.buyseasons.com
Internet Costume, Apparel & Wig Retailer
N.A.I.C.S.: 459420
Chad Olson *(CFO)*
Rick Barton *(Pres & CEO)*

Subsidiary (Domestic):

BirthdayExpress.com (2)
5915 S Moorland Rd, New Berlin, WI 53151
Tel.: (605) 271-3170
Web Site: http://www.birthdayexpress.com
Party Supplies & Costume Retailer
N.A.I.C.S.: 459420

Division (Domestic):

BuyCostumes.com (2)
16205 W Small Rd, New Berlin, WI 53151
Tel.: (605) 271-2608
Web Site: http://www.buycostumes.com
Internet Costume Retailer
N.A.I.C.S.: 315990
Rick Barton *(CEO)*

Carolina Fashions Inc. (1)
400 Von Air St, Mauldin, SC 29662
Tel.: (864) 281-0925
Sales Range: $25-49.9 Million
Emp.: 85
Apparel & Accessories
N.A.I.C.S.: 458110
Robert Watson *(Gen Mgr)*

Rubie's Deutschland GmbH (1)
Huttenstr 45-47, 51469, Bergisch Gladbach, Germany
Tel.: (49) 2202 104 0
Web Site: http://www.rubies.de
Emp.: 80
Apparel Accessory Store Operator
N.A.I.C.S.: 458110

Marc P. Beige *(Gen Mgr)*
Manuela Steiner *(Gen Mgr)*

Rubie's Masquerade Ltd (1)
Rubie's House 3-4 Moses Winter Way, Wallingford, OX10 9FE, Oxfordshire, United Kingdom
Tel.: (44) 1491 826500
Web Site: http://www.rubiesuk.com
Apparel Accessory Store Operator
N.A.I.C.S.: 458110

RUBIN POSTAER & ASSOCIATES
2525 Colorado Ave, Santa Monica, CA 90404
Tel.: (310) 394-4000 CA
Web Site: http://www.rpa.com
Year Founded: 1986
Sales Range: $150-199.9 Million
Emp.: 470
Marketing & Advertising
N.A.I.C.S.: 541810
Joe Baratelli *(Chief Creative Officer & Exec VP)*
William C. Hagelstein *(Pres & CEO)*
Pete Imwalle *(COO & Exec VP)*
Gary Paticoff *(Chief Production Officer & Sr VP)*
J. Barbush *(VP & Dir-Creative Social Media)*
Scott Westerfield *(VP & Dir-Tech)*
Mia Von Sadovszky *(Sr VP & Assoc Dir-Strategic Plng)*
Mike Margolin *(VP & Mktg Dir)*
Dave Brezinski *(Sr VP & Dir-Digital Production)*
Fern McCaffrey *(Sr VP & Dir-Acct Grp & Honda Reg Mktg)*
Isadora Chesler *(Sr VP & Dir-Video Production)*
Selena Pizarro *(Sr VP & Dir-Video Production)*

Subsidiaries:

Rubin Postaer & Associates - Atlanta Office (1)
7000 Central Pkwy Ste 1550, Atlanta, GA 30328-6060
Tel.: (770) 643-4000
Web Site: http://www.rpa.com
Emp.: 8
Advetising Agency
N.A.I.C.S.: 541810
Lisa Pilger *(VP & Dir-Local Media)*
Christina Fleming *(Mgr-Local Media-RPA Associates)*

Rubin Postaer & Associates - Chicago Office (1)
314 W Superior St Ste 400, Chicago, IL 60610-3538
Tel.: (312) 644-3636
Web Site: http://www.rpa.com
Sales Range: $10-24.9 Million
Emp.: 22
Advetising Agency
N.A.I.C.S.: 541810
Selena Chin *(Mgr-Local Media)*

Rubin Postaer & Associates - Dallas Office (1)
MacArthur Ctr II 5600 MacArthur Blvd Ste 280, Irving, TX 75038
Tel.: (972) 753-5200
Web Site: http://www.rpa.com
Emp.: 15
Advetising Agency
N.A.I.C.S.: 541810

Rubin Postaer & Associates - Denver Office (1)
3151 S Vaughn Way Ste 512, Aurora, CO 80014-3514
Tel.: (303) 337-7929
Web Site: http://www.rpa.com
Emp.: 3
Advetising Agency
N.A.I.C.S.: 541810

Rubin Postaer & Associates - Moorestown Office (1)
302 Harper Dr Ste 102, Moorestown, NJ 09057
Tel.: (856) 439-4100
Web Site: http://www.rpa.com
Emp.: 10
Advertising Agency Services
N.A.I.C.S.: 541810

Rubin Postaer & Associates - Portland Office (1)
5 Centerpointe Dr Ste 400, Lake Oswego, OR 97035
Tel.: (503) 251-5805
Web Site: http://www.rpa.com
Emp.: 10
Advetising Agency
N.A.I.C.S.: 541810
Brett Bender *(Chief Client Officer & Exec VP)*

RUBINBROWN LLP
1 N Brentwood Ste 1100, Saint Louis, MO 63105
Tel.: (314) 290-3300
Web Site: http://www.rubinbrown.com
Year Founded: 1952
Sales Range: $25-49.9 Million
Emp.: 400
Certified Public Accountants
N.A.I.C.S.: 541211
Gregory P. Osborn *(Partner-Denver & Mgr-Resident)*
Todd R. Pleimann *(Mng Partner-Kansas City)*
Michael T. Lewis *(Mng Partner-Denver)*
Bill Rooney *(Partner)*
Jeri Ann Farley *(Mgr-Tax Consulting Svcs Grp)*
Kirk Wonio *(Partner-Tax Svcs Grp)*
Nathan Croll *(Partner-Bus Advisory Svcs Grp)*
Matt Marino *(Partner)*
Glenn Goodnough *(Mng Partner-Las Vegas)*
Jeff Albach *(Partner-Assurance Svcs Grp)*
Ethan Kent *(Partner-Assurance Svcs Grp)*
John F. Herber Jr. *(Chm)*

RUBLOFF DEVELOPMENT GROUP, INC.
4949 Harrison Ave, Rockford, IL 61108-7987
Tel.: (815) 387-3110
Real Estate Development Services
N.A.I.C.S.: 531390
Mark Robinson *(Pres)*
Ronald E. Swenson *(Principal)*
Jerry H. Weber *(Principal)*

Subsidiaries:

Rubloff Jet Express, LLC (1)
4949 Harrison Ave Ste 204, Rockford, IL 61108
Tel.: (815) 387-3140
Worldwide Charter & Cargo Delivery Services
N.A.I.C.S.: 481211

RUBY COLLINS COMPANY INC.
4806 Wright Dr SE, Smyrna, GA 30082
Tel.: (770) 432-2900
Web Site: http://www.ruby-collins.com
Sales Range: $10-24.9 Million
Emp.: 130
Waste Water & Sewage Treatment Plant Construction
N.A.I.C.S.: 237110
Benjamin J. Morgan *(CEO)*
Ron Bray *(CFO, Treas & Sec)*
Michael A. Laseter *(Exec VP & Mgr-Utility Div)*
David A. Westrick *(Pres)*

U.S. PRIVATE

RUBY TUESDAY LONG ISLAND
289 Middle Country Rd, Selden, NY 11784
Tel.: (631) 732-6632
Web Site: http://www.rubytuesday-li.com
Sales Range: $10-24.9 Million
Emp.: 100
Restaurant Operators
N.A.I.C.S.: 722511
Chris Pullis *(Gen Mgr)*

RUBY TUESDAY TAMPA FRANCHISE LP
2200 E Fowler Ave, Tampa, FL 33612
Tel.: (813) 244-1965
Rev.: $16,300,000
Emp.: 5
Eating Place
N.A.I.C.S.: 722511

RUBY'S INN INC.
26 S Main St, Bryce, UT 84764
Tel.: (435) 834-5341
Web Site: http://www.rubysinn.com
Sales Range: $150-199.9 Million
Emp.: 500
American Restaurant
N.A.I.C.S.: 722511
Mondell Syrett *(Pres)*
Jean Seiler *(Dir-Event)*
Fred Syrett *(VP)*
Wester Dusk *(CEO)*

RUBY'S RESTAURANT GROUP
557 Wald, Irvine, CA 92618
Tel.: (949) 644-7829
Web Site: http://www.rubys.com
Rev.: $34,000,000
Emp.: 1,000
Restaurant
N.A.I.C.S.: 722511
Douglas Cavanaugh *(Founder & Pres)*
Ralph Kosmides *(Co-Founder)*

RUCKER & SILL LTD. INC.
14000 Carlson Pkwy, Minneapolis, MN 55441-5305
Tel.: (763) 852-2977 MN
Web Site: http://www.tileshop.com
Year Founded: 1985
Sales Range: $25-49.9 Million
Emp.: 250
Floor Covering Stores
N.A.I.C.S.: 449121
Jim Beukelman *(Controller)*

RUDCO PRODUCTS INC.
114 E Oak Rd, Vineland, NJ 08360
Tel.: (856) 691-0800
Web Site: http://www.rudco.com
Sales Range: $10-24.9 Million
Emp.: 100
Garbage Dumpster Mfr
N.A.I.C.S.: 332313
Robert A. Rudolph *(Pres)*
Michael Avis *(VP-Sls)*

RUDD CONTAINER CORPORATION
4600 S Kolin Ave, Chicago, IL 60632
Tel.: (773) 847-7600
Web Site: http://www.ruddcontainer.com
Sales Range: $10-24.9 Million
Emp.: 40
Boxes Corrugated: Made From Purchased Materials
N.A.I.C.S.: 424130
Darrell Rudd *(Chm & Pres)*
Ted Bihun *(VP)*
Lynna Cavallo *(Mgr-Design)*

COMPANIES

RUDER FINN GROUP, INC.

RUDER FINN GROUP, INC.
425 E 53rd St, New York, NY 10022-2900
Tel.: (212) 593-6400 NY
Web Site: http://www.ruderfinn.com
Year Founded: 1948
Holding Company; Public Relations & Advertising Agencies
N.A.I.C.S.: 551112
Kathy Bloomgarden (CEO)
Nick Leonard (Mng Dir-UK)
Gao Ming (Mng Dir/Sr VP-Luxury Practice-Greater China)
Atul Sharma (Mng Dir-India)
John Nolan (Chief Brand Officer)
Brian Witte (VP & Deputy Gen Mgr-Singapore)
Michael Schubert (Chief Innovation Officer)
Peggy Walsh (COO)
Ian Glover (CFO)
Tejas Totade (CTO)

Subsidiaries:

Arts & Communications Counselors (1)
301 E 57th St, New York, NY 10022-2900
Tel.: (212) 593-6475
Web Site: http://www.rf-group.com
Sales Range: $10-24.9 Million
Emp.: 300
N.A.I.C.S.: 541820
Philippa Polskin (Pres)

Comunicad, LLC (1)
1530 Wilson Blvd, Arlington, VA 22209
Tel.: (703) 807-0500
Web Site: http://www.comunicad.com
Marketing Consulting Services
N.A.I.C.S.: 541613
Carmen Marsans (Sr VP-Client Rels)
Maria Ibanez (VP-Strategic Comm & New Media)

Finn Partners, Inc. (1)
301 E 57th St 4th Fl, New York, NY 10022
Tel.: (212) 715-1600
Web Site: http://www.finnpartners.com
Sales Range: $10-24.9 Million
Emp.: 200
Public Relations Firm
N.A.I.C.S.: 541820
Jennifer Hawkins (Mng Partner-Travel)
Dan Pooley (Mng Partner)
Peter Finn (CEO)
Helen Shelton (Chief Diversity Officer-Global)
Miranda Harper (Partner)
Gil Bashe (Mng Partner & Dir-Global Health Practice)
Ovidio Torres (Partner-Natl Health Practice-Chicago)
Kristen Berry (Assoc VP-Natl Health Practice-Chicago)
Kristie Kuhl (Mng Partner-Health Practice)
Jeff Hentz (Partner-Travel & Lifestyle)
Lisa Martins (VP-Health Practice)
Christine Bock (Mng Partner)
Chantal Bowman Boyles (Mng Partner)
Jimmy Chaffin (Mng Partner)
Margaret Dunning (Mng Partner)
Anne Glauber (Mng Partner)
Dena Merriam (Mng Partner)
Amy Seigenthaler (Mng Partner)
Arielle Bernstein Pinsof (Partner-Health Practice-Chicago)
Michael Heinley (Partner)
Mina Volovitch (Sr Partner-Global Health Practice & Head-Paris)
Chantal Bowman-Boyles (Mng Partner)
Geralyn LaNeve (Grp VP-Global Health Practice)
David Shane (Deputy Mng Dir-Los Angeles & San Francisco)
Howard Solomon (Mng Partner-West Coast)
Celia Jones (CMO)
Anastasia Lopez (Partner & Head-Integration)
Kevin Jenkins (Partner-Integrated Mktg)
Noah Finn (Mng Partner)
Alicia Young (Mng Partner-Consumer Strategies)
Brooke Geller (Sr Partner-Consumer Practice-New York)
Mike DeVilling (Sr Partner-Detroit)
Scott Widmeyer (Chief Strategy Officer-Washington)
Kris Garvey Graves (Sr Partner)
Cathy Feliciano-Chon (Mng Partner)
Jeff Freedman (Mng Partner-Digital Mktg)
Diana Scott (Partner-Health Practice)
Sabrina Guttman (Head-Global Tech Practice)
Julie Walsh (Sr Partner-Global Pub Affairs)
Ryan Witherell (Mng Partner)

Subsidiary (Domestic):

ABI Marketing Public Relations (2)
301 E 57th St, New York, NY 10022
Tel.: (212) 715-1600
Web Site: http://www.abipr.com
B2B Marketing & PR Communications Agency
N.A.I.C.S.: 541820
Nicole Zampino (Partner)
Alan Isacson (Founder & CEO)
Bernard Guly (Mng Dir-EMEA)
Juliet Zhu (Mng Dir-Asia Pacific)

Branch (Non-US):

ABI Asia (3)
60 Paya Lebar Road #07-03, Paya Lebar Square, Singapore, 409051, Singapore
Tel.: (65) 68162813
Web Site: http://www.abipr.com
Public Relations Agency
N.A.I.C.S.: 541820
Juliet Zhu (Mng Dir-Asia Pacific)

ABI Europe (3)
Unit B The Cube Building 17-21 Wenlock Road, London, N1 7GT, United Kingdom
Tel.: (44) 2032177060
Web Site: http://www.abipr.com
Public Relations Agency
N.A.I.C.S.: 541820
Bernard Guly (Mng Dir)

Subsidiary (Domestic):

DVL Seigenthaler, Inc. (2)
700 12th Ave S Ste 400, Nashville, TN 37203
Tel.: (615) 244-1818
Web Site: http://www.dvlseigenthaler.com
Emp.: 450
Public Relations & Advertising Agency
N.A.I.C.S.: 541820
Beth Seigenthaler Courtney (Pres)
Ronald Roberts (CEO)
Jimmy Chaffin (Mng Partner)
Nelson Eddy (Mng Partner)
Amy Seigenthaler Pierce (Mng Partner)
Katie Seigenthaler (Mng Partner)
Katie Soltas (Acct Supvr)
Kyle Robison (Mgr-Traffic)
Tiffany Childress (Sr Acct Exec)
Nicolette Seifert (Acct Exec)
Catherina Davidson (Acct Exec)
Minh Le (Sr Acct Exec)
Stacey Nickens (Acct Supvr)
Laura Stephens (Dir-Client Svcs)

Horn Group Inc. (2)
612 Howard St 4th Fl, San Francisco, CA 94108
Tel.: (415) 905-4000
Web Site: http://www.horngroup.com
Public Relations Agency
N.A.I.C.S.: 541820
Sabrina Horn (Founder, Pres & CEO)

Branch (Domestic):

Horn Group - New York (3)
301 E 57th St, New York, NY 10022
Tel.: (646) 202-9750
Web Site: http://www.horngroup.com
Public Relations Agency
N.A.I.C.S.: 541820

Subsidiary (Domestic):

Small Army, Inc. (2)
300 Massachusetts Ave 2nd Fl, Boston, MA 02115
Tel.: (617) 450-0000
Web Site: http://www.smallarmy.net
Advertising Services
N.A.I.C.S.: 541810
Jeff Freedman (Founder & CEO)
Amy Staley (VP-Ops)

Allison Reilly (Exec VP-Relationship Mgmt & Strategy)
Chris Edwards (Exec Creative Dir)
Ashley Blais (Partner-Media & Engagement Strategy & VP)
Meghan Driscoll (Partner-Production & VP)

Planned Television Arts (1)
1110 2nd Ave, New York, NY 10022-2021
Tel.: (212) 583-2718
Web Site: http://www.plannedtvarts.com
Rev.: $9,000,000
Emp.: 40
Public Relations Agency
N.A.I.C.S.: 541820
Rick Frishman (Founder)
David Hahn (Mng Dir)
Deborah Kohan (VP & Dir-MC)
Brian Feinblum (CMO & Sr VP)
Kristin Clifford (VP & Dir-Satellite TV)
Sandy Trupp (Mng Dir-PTA-DC & PTA Politics)
Sharon Farnell (Dir-MC's Faith Div)

RF Binder Partners (1)
950 3rd Ave 7th Fl, New York, NY 10022
Tel.: (212) 994-7600
Web Site: http://www.rfbinder.com
Sales Range: $10-24.9 Million
Emp.: 4
N.A.I.C.S.: 541820
Jason Buerkle (CFO)
Amy Binder (Chm & CEO)
David Weinstock (Chief Creative Officer)
Annie Longsworth (Exec Mng Dir & Head-Impact)
Joe Fisher (Vice Chm)
Rebecca Binder (Sr Mng Dir-Strategic Initiatives)
Atalanta Rafferty (Exec Mng Dir & Head-Food, Drinks & Nutrition)
Steven Weinberg (Exec Mng Dir)
Tom Szauer (CTO)
Esther Aubry (Mng Dir-Experiential Mktg)
Craig Blakaitis (Mng Dir)
Karina Frayter (Mng Dir)
Eva Gurfein (Mng Dir & Head-LA Office)
Sarah Gwilliam (Mng Dir)
Davis MacMillan (Mng Dir)
Bonnie Taylor (Mng Dir)

Branch (Domestic):

RF Binder Partners (2)
160 Gould St Ste 115, Needham, MA 02494-2300
Tel.: (781) 455-8250
Web Site: http://www.rfbinder.com
Sales Range: $10-24.9 Million
Integrated Communications & Consulting Services
N.A.I.C.S.: 541820
Atalanta Rafferty (Exec Mng Dir & Head-Food, Drinks & Nutrition)
Jason Buerkle (CFO & Treas)
Joe Fisher (Vice Chm)
Rebecca Binder (Sr Mng Dir-Strategic Initiatives)
Steven Weinberg (Exec Mng Dir)
Amy Binder (Founder, Chm & CEO)
Bonnie Taylor (Mng Dir)
Craig Blakaitis (Mng Dir)
David Schraeder (Exec Mng Dir & Head-Corp & Fin Svcs)
David Weinstock (Chief Creative Officer)
Esther Aubry (Mng Dir-Experiential Mktg)
Eva Gurfein (Mng Dir & Head-LA Office)
Jackie Wilson (Exec Mng Dir-Strategic Initiatives)
Karina Frayter (Mng Dir)
Sarah Gwilliam (Mng Dir)
Tomas Szauer (CTO)
William McBride (Exec Mng Dir)
Will Maroni (Mng Dir & Head-Education)

Ruder Finn (1)
8 Hartum Street, PO Box 45138, Har Hotzvim, Jerusalem, 91450, Israel
Tel.: (972) 2 589 2000
Sales Range: $10-24.9 Million
Emp.: 10
N.A.I.C.S.: 541820
Glenn Jasper (Mng Dir)
Tham Kok Wing (Sr VP-Engagement & Integration-Asia Pacific)

Ruder Finn France, Sarl (1)
71 bis rue du Cardinal Lemoine, 75005, Paris, France

Tel.: (33) 1 56 81 1500
Web Site: http://www.ruderfinn.com
Sales Range: Less than $1 Million
Emp.: 13
N.A.I.C.S.: 541820

Ruder Finn Healthcare (1)
301 E 57th St, New York, NY 10022-2900
Tel.: (212) 593-6400
Web Site: http://www.ruderfinn.com
Sales Range: $25-49.9 Million
Emp.: 400
N.A.I.C.S.: 541820

Ruder Finn UK, Ltd. (1)
2nd Floor 1 Bedford Street, London, WC1A 9HG, United Kingdom
Tel.: (44) 74383050
Web Site: http://www.ruderfinn.co.uk
Sales Range: $75-99.9 Million
Emp.: 35
N.A.I.C.S.: 541820
Nick Leonard (Mng Dir)
Judith Cranford (Mng Dir)
Neil McGregor-Paterson (Head-Healthcare)

Ruder Finn West (1)
655 Commercial St, San Francisco, CA 94111
Tel.: (415) 483-7175
Web Site: http://www.ruderfinn.com
Sales Range: $10-24.9 Million
Emp.: 13
Public Relations & Communication Agency
N.A.I.C.S.: 541820
David Finn (Chm)
Scott Beaver (VP)

Ruder Finn, Inc. (1)
211 E Ontario St Ste 1600, Chicago, IL 60611-3297
Tel.: (312) 644-8600
Web Site: http://www.ruderfinn.com
Sales Range: $10-24.9 Million
Emp.: 32
Public Relations Services
N.A.I.C.S.: 541820

Subsidiary (Domestic):

SPI Group LLC (2)
165 Passaic Ave Ste 410, Fairfield, NJ 07004
Tel.: (973) 244-9191
Web Site: http://www.spigroup.com
Sales Range: $10-24.9 Million
Emp.: 16
Public Relations Agency
N.A.I.C.S.: 541820
Steve E. Goodman (Founder & CEO)
James Koppenal (Mng Dir-Digital Comm)
Sonali Munjal (Mng Dir-Application Dev)
Stacey Hajdak (Sr VP)
Dana Haase (Dir-Project Mgmt)
Heather Norian (COO)
Pam Pizzaro (Dir-Creative)
Ellen English (Mng Dir-Comm Strategy & Editorial)
Trish Nicolas (Exec VP)

Ruder Finn, Inc. (1)
1129 20th St NW Ste 200, Washington, DC 20036
Tel.: (202) 466-7800
Web Site: http://www.ruderfinn.com
Sales Range: $75-99.9 Million
Emp.: 9
N.A.I.C.S.: 541820
Sharon Keating (VP)
Jessica Berk Ross (Mng Partner)
Sabrina Guttman (Exec VP & Head-Global Tech & Innovation)
Meredith Isola (Sr VP)

The Rogers Group (1)
1875 Century Park E Ste 200, Los Angeles, CA 90067-2504
Tel.: (310) 552-6922
Web Site: http://www.finnpartners.com
Sales Range: $10-24.9 Million
Public Relations Agency
N.A.I.C.S.: 541820
Howard Solomon (Mng Partner)
Daniel Pooley (Mng Partner)
Ronald Roberts (Mng Partner)
Amy Seigenthaler (Mng Partner)

Widmeyer Communications, Inc. (1)
1129 NW 20th St Ste 200, Washington, DC 20036

RUDER FINN GROUP, INC.

U.S. PRIVATE

Ruder Finn Group, Inc.—(Continued)
Tel.: (202) 667-0901
Web Site: http://www.widmeyer.com
Sales Range: $10-24.9 Million
Emp.: 40
Public Relations Services
N.A.I.C.S.: 541820
Scott Widmeyer (Founder & Mng Partner)
Margaret Suzor Dunning (Mng Partner)
Jason F. Smith (Principal)
Jim Luetkemeyer (Sr Partner)
Barry Reicherter (Partner-Digital Strategy & Ideas)
Chad Hyett (VP)
Kristofer Eisenla (VP)
Christine Messina-Boyer (Sr Partner)
Andre Witt (VP-Ops)
Julia Gotwald (Acct Exec)
Ken Sain (Partner & Sr VP)
Stephanie Waties (Acct Exec)
Tracey Bryan (VP)
Lauren Macon (Sr Mgr-Acct)
Peter Sinn (CEO)

Branch (Domestic):

Widmeyer Communications (2)
301 E 57th St 4th Fl, New York, NY 10022
Tel.: (212) 715-1600
Web Site: http://www.widmeyer.com
Advertising Agencies Services
N.A.I.C.S.: 541810

RUDISILL ENTERPRISES, INC.
1006 Dornoch Rd, Gastonia, NC 28054
Tel.: (704) 864-2551
Sales Range: $10-24.9 Million
Emp.: 15
Alcoholic Beverage Distr
N.A.I.C.S.: 424820

RUDOLPH FOODS COMPANY
6575 Bellefontaine Rd, Lima, OH 45804-4415
Tel.: (419) 648-3611 OH
Web Site:
 http://www.rudolphfoods.com
Year Founded: 1955
Sales Range: $50-74.9 Million
Emp.: 400
Pork Rinds & Other Snack Foods Mfr
N.A.I.C.S.: 311919
Richard M. Rudolph (Pres)
Kevin Sargent (VP-Ops)

Subsidiaries:

Gaslamp Popcorn Company, LLC (1)
880 Columbia Ave Unit 6, Riverside, CA 92507
Tel.: (951) 684-6767
Web Site: http://www.rudolphfoods.com
Sales Range: $10-24.9 Million
Emp.: 40
Packaged Popcorn Mfr
N.A.I.C.S.: 311999
Rich Rudolph (Pres)

Rudolph Foods Company - Dallas Facility (1)
3660 Pipestone Rd, Dallas, TX 75212
Tel.: (214) 638-2204
Snack Food Mfr
N.A.I.C.S.: 311919

Rudolph Foods Company - Lawrenceville Facility (1)
1050 Progress Cir, Lawrenceville, GA 30043
Tel.: (770) 339-6952
Snack Food Mfr
N.A.I.C.S.: 311919

Rudolph Foods Company - New Hebron Facility (1)
607 Highway 42, Newhebron, MS 39140
Tel.: (601) 694-2230
Web Site: http://www.rudolphfoods.com
Emp.: 48
Snack Food Mfr
N.A.I.C.S.: 311919
David Lee (Plant Mgr)

Rudolph Foods Company - San Bernardino Facility (1)
1010 S Sierra Way, San Bernardino, CA 92408
Tel.: (909) 388-2202
Snack Food Mfr
N.A.I.C.S.: 311919

Whitefeather Foods Inc. (1)
13845 Cemetery Rd, Wapakoneta, OH 45895
Tel.: (419) 738-8975
Snack Food Mfr
N.A.I.C.S.: 311919

RUDY INC.
200 Hazel St, Covington, OH 45318
Tel.: (937) 473-2066 OH
Web Site: http://www.rudyinc.com
Year Founded: 1958
Sales Range: $10-24.9 Million
Emp.: 10
Marketer & Producer of Agricultural Products
N.A.I.C.S.: 424510
Robert Brian Rudy (Treas & Sec)
Robert W. Rudy Jr. (Pres)

RUDY'S MARKETS INC.
1121 NW Newport Ave, Bend, OR 97701
Tel.: (541) 382-3940
Web Site:
 http://www.newportavemarket.com
Sales Range: $10-24.9 Million
Emp.: 90
Grocery Stores, Independent
N.A.I.C.S.: 445110
Rudy Dory (Owner & Pres)

RUECKERT ADVERTISING
638 Albany Shaker Rd, Albany, NY 12211
Tel.: (518) 446-1091
Web Site:
 http://www.rueckertadvertising.com
Sales Range: Less than $1 Million
Emp.: 14
N.A.I.C.S.: 541810
Dean Rueckert (Pres)
Edward Parham (Sr Copywriter & Dir-PR)
Chris Rueckert (Acct Exec)
Tracey Simons (Dir-Creative)
Marilyn Bell (Dir-Art)
Gus Hais (Dir-Art)
Jason Rueckert (Dir-Art)
Kostas Hais (Dir-Art)
Richelle Strube (Office Mgr)

RUELCO SERVICES INC.
2063 Paxton St, Harvey, LA 70058
Tel.: (504) 340-0055
Web Site: http://www.ruelco.com
Rev: $10,250,000
Emp.: 200
Testing, Measuring, Surveying & Analysis Services
N.A.I.C.S.: 213112
Ruel R. Gober Jr. (Pres)

RUETERS RED POWER
Hwy 30 W, Grand Junction, IA 50107
Tel.: (515) 738-2571
Web Site: http://www.rueterco.com
Year Founded: 1951
Emp.: 25
Mfr of Agricultural & Construction Equipment Machinery
N.A.I.C.S.: 423820
Cecil H. Rueter (Founder)
Todd Rueter (Pres)

RUFFALO NOEL LEVITZ, LLC
1025 Kirkwood Pkwy SW, Cedar Rapids, IA 52404
Tel.: (319) 362-7483 DE
Web Site: http://www.ruffalonl.com

Year Founded: 1991
Enrollment Management & Fundraising Services
N.A.I.C.S.: 561499
Al Ruffalo (Founder)
Rob W. Ackley (VP-HR)
Lee Ann Krapfl (VP-Project Mgmt)
Will Ethridge (Chm)
Mike Evans (CFO)
Sumit Nijhawan (Pres & CEO)
Brett Frazier (Chief Customer Officer)
Renee Vaillancourt (Exec VP-Ops)
Sarah Coen (Sr VP-Consulting Svcs)
Joshua Robertson (Sr VP-Product Strategy)
Cutler Andrews (Exec VP)
Todd Abbott (Sr VP)
Robert L. Baird (Sr VP)
Chris Bingley (Sr VP)

Subsidiaries:

Converge Consulting Inc. (1)
415 12th Ave SE Ste 100, Cedar Rapids, IA 52401
Tel.: (800) 215-1456
Web Site:
 http://www.convergeconsulting.org
Website Design Services & Digital Marketing
N.A.I.C.S.: 541511
Ann Oleson (Founder & CEO)

RUFFIN COMPANIES
1522 S Florence St, Wichita, KS 67209-2634
Tel.: (316) 942-7940
Year Founded: 1982
Sales Range: $25-49.9 Million
Emp.: 300
Nonresidential Building Operators
N.A.I.C.S.: 531120
Phillip G. Ruffin (CEO)
Jenny Conner Dalrymple (Controller)
Michelle Beneke (Controller)
Kathy Khan (Controller)

RUFFLEBUTTS, INC.
4055 Corporate Dr Ste 200, Grapevine, TX 76051
Tel.: (704) 825-8811
Web Site: http://www.rufflebutts.com
Year Founded: 2007
Sales Range: $1-9.9 Million
Emp.: 11
Children's Fashion Apparel Mfr & Retailer
N.A.I.C.S.: 458110
Amber Schaub (Founder & Owner)
R. J. Manoni (Dir-E-Commerce)
Mark Schaub (Co-Owner & COO)
Alexander Navur (Coord-Retail Fulfillment)

RUGBY FARMERS UNION ELEVATOR COMPANY
105 E Dewey, Rugby, ND 58368
Tel.: (701) 776-5214 ND
Web Site:
 http://www.rugbyfarmers.com
Year Founded: 1940
Sales Range: $10-24.9 Million
Emp.: 17
Grain Elevators; Wholesale Distribution of Farm Supplies
N.A.I.C.S.: 424510
Tim McKay (Gen Mgr)
Ken Schaan (Pres)

RUGE'S AUTOMOTIVE
6882 Route 9, Rhinebeck, NY 12572
Tel.: (845) 876-7074
Web Site: http://www.rugesauto.com
Sales Range: $10-24.9 Million
Emp.: 30
Automobiles, New & Used
N.A.I.C.S.: 811111

Lewis J. Ruge (Pres)
Dave Gillmore (Gen Mgr)
John Vandenbrul (Mgr-Fin)

RUGG MANUFACTURING COMPANY
105 Newton St, Greenfield, MA 01301-3122
Tel.: (413) 773-5471 MA
Web Site: http://www.rugg.com
Year Founded: 1842
Sales Range: $1-9.9 Million
Emp.: 13
Mfr of Steel, Aluminum & Poly Snow Shovels, Scoops, Pushers & Lawn Rakes
N.A.I.C.S.: 332216
Stephen E. Peck (Pres & Treas)
Stanley S. Mellas (VP-Sls & Mktg)
Elizabeth R. Peck (VP-Acctg)

RUGGED LINER INC.
200 Universal Dr, Owosso, MI 48867-3539
Tel.: (989) 725-8354 MI
Web Site: http://www.ruggedliner.com
Year Founded: 1995
Pickup Truck Bedliners & Accessories Mfr
N.A.I.C.S.: 336390
Mike Williamson (VP)
Robert Callison (Mgr-HR)

RUGGED WEARHOUSE INC.
55 Scott Ave, Morgantown, WV 26508
Tel.: (304) 292-6965
Web Site:
 http://www.ruggedwearhouse.com
Rev: $65,483,993
Emp.: 60
Family Clothing Stores
N.A.I.C.S.: 458110
Paul Gabriel (Pres)
Ron Gabriel (VP)

RUGS AMERICA CORPORATION
242 Route 110 Broad Hollow Rd, Farmingdale, NY 11735
Tel.: (631) 843-6100
Web Site:
 http://www.rugsamericacorp.com
Rev: $10,000,000
Emp.: 8
Rug Designer & Mfr for Retailers
N.A.I.C.S.: 314110

RUHL AND RUHL REALTORS LLC
5403 Victoria Ave Ste 100, Davenport, IA 52807
Tel.: (563) 441-5200
Web Site: http://www.ruhlhomes.com
Sales Range: $10-24.9 Million
Emp.: 30
Real Estate Brokers & Agents
N.A.I.C.S.: 531210
Darcy Holle (Dir-Career Dev)
Veronica Pianca (VP-Relocation & Bus Dev)
Caroline Ruhl (CEO)
Chris Beason (Pres)

RUHL-PARR/MORAN ARCHITECTS LLC
2200 6th Ave Ste 780, Seattle, WA 98121
Tel.: (425) 999-6311 WA
Web Site: http://www.ruhl-parr.com
Sales Range: $1-9.9 Million
Emp.: 2
Commercial, Industrial & Hospitality Projects
N.A.I.C.S.: 541490
John W. Moran (Principal)

RUHLE COMPANIES, INC.
99 Wall St, Valhalla, NY 10595-1452
Tel.: (914) 761-2600 NY
Web Site: http://www.ruhle.com
Year Founded: 1991
Sales Range: $50-74.9 Million
Emp.: 55
Holding Company; Manufacturer of Transducers For Machine & Military Aerospace Industries & Numerical Controls for Machine Tools
N.A.I.C.S.: 334419
Robert E. Ruhle *(Treas, Sec & Exec VP)*

Subsidiaries:

Farrand Controls Division (1)
99 Wall St, Valhalla, NY 10595
Tel.: (914) 761-2600
Web Site: http://www.ruhle.com
Mfr of Transducers for Machine Industry/Military Aerospace Industry & Numerical Control Systems
N.A.I.C.S.: 334419
Anne Rosvold *(Supvr-Receiving & Shipping)*

RUIDOSO DOWNS RACING INC.
26225 US Hwy 70, Ruidoso Downs, NM 88346
Tel.: (575) 378-4431 NM
Web Site: http://www.btkcasino.com
Year Founded: 1946
Sales Range: $10-24.9 Million
Emp.: 230
Horse Race Track Operations
N.A.I.C.S.: 711212
R. D. Hubbard *(Owner)*

RUIZ FOOD PRODUCTS, INC.
501 S Alta Ave, Dinuba, CA 93618-2100
Tel.: (559) 591-5510 CA
Web Site: http://www.ruizfoods.com
Year Founded: 1966
Sales Range: $150-199.9 Million
Emp.: 2,600
Mfr of Frozen Mexican Foods
N.A.I.C.S.: 311412
George Turner *(VP-Pur)*

RUIZ MEXICAN FOODS INC.
1200 Marlborough Ave, Riverside, CA 92507
Tel.: (909) 947-7811
Web Site: http://www.ruizflourtortillas.com
Sales Range: $100-124.9 Million
Emp.: 150
Tortilla Producer
N.A.I.C.S.: 311830
Paul Demoss *(Controller)*

RUIZ PROTECTIVE SERVICE, INC.
2646 Andjon Dr, Dallas, TX 75220
Tel.: (214) 357-0820 TX
Web Site: http://www.ruizservices.com
Year Founded: 1983
Sales Range: $10-24.9 Million
Emp.: 600
Security Services
N.A.I.C.S.: 561612
Hector M. Ruiz *(Pres & Mgr-Sls)*
Nigel Bush *(Mgr-HR)*
Roberto Contreras *(Mgr-West Texas)*
Melissa Gumm *(Mgr-Acctg)*
Ed King *(Mgr-Trng)*
Robert Minnis *(Mgr-Federal Projects Contract)*

RUKERT TERMINALS CORPORATION
2021 S Clinton St, Baltimore, MD 21224
Tel.: (410) 276-1013
Web Site: http://www.rukert.com
Sales Range: $10-24.9 Million
Emp.: 175
General Warehousing & Storage
N.A.I.C.S.: 493110
Frank J. Olszewski *(VP)*
Jason J. Loveland *(VP-Warehousing & Admin)*
Steve W. Landess *(VP-Engrg)*
Andrew G. Nixon *(VP)*
Shaun F. Rukert *(VP-Ops)*
John L. Coulter *(Pres)*
Norman G. Rukert Jr. *(CEO)*

RULMECA CORPORATION
6508B Windmill Way, Wilmington, NC 28405
Tel.: (910) 794-9294
Web Site: http://www.rulmecacorp.com
Emp.: 100
Turbine & Turbine Generator Set Units Mfr
N.A.I.C.S.: 333611
Michael Gawinski *(Pres)*

Subsidiaries:

Rulmeca Holding Spa (1)
Via A Toscanini, 1- 24011, Alme, Italy
Tel.: (39) 0354300111
Web Site: https://www.rulmeca.com
Holding Company; Material Handling Equipment Mfr & Distr
N.A.I.C.S.: 551112

Subsidiary (US):

Douglas Manufacturing Co, Inc. (2)
300 Industrial Park Dr, Pell City, AL 35125
Tel.: (205) 884-1200
Web Site: http://www.douglasmanufacturing.com
Sales Range: $1-9.9 Million
Emp.: 40
Mfg Conveyors/Equipment
N.A.I.C.S.: 333922
Nancy Ross *(Treas & Sec)*
Charlie Grundhoefer *(Controller)*

RUMBERGER, KIRK & CALDWELL PROFESSIONAL ASSOCIATION
300 S Orange Ave Ste 1400, Orlando, FL 32801
Tel.: (407) 872-7300
Web Site: https://www.rumberger.com
Year Founded: 1978
Emp.: 200
Law firm
N.A.I.C.S.: 541110
Larry M. Roth *(Partner & Atty)*
Bud Kirk *(Founder, Partner & Atty)*
Lori J. Caldwell *(Partner & Atty)*
Francis H. Sheppard *(Mng Partner)*
J. Scott Kirk *(Partner & Atty)*
Robert H. Adams *(Partner & Atty)*
Craig A. Alexander *(Partner & Atty)*
Brian J. Baggot *(Partner & Atty)*
Michael D. Begey *(Partner & Atty)*
Sally Rogers Culley *(Partner-Admin)*
Darryl L. Gavin *(Partner & Atty)*
Daniel J. Gerber *(Partner & Atty)*
Richard A. Greenberg *(Partner & Atty)*
Jacey Kaps *(Partner & Atty)*
Lan Kennedy-Davis *(Partner)*
Rebecca Beers *(Partner)*
Chase Hattaway *(Partner)*
Carie Hall *(Partner)*
Leonard J. Dietzen III *(Partner & Atty)*

RUMBLETREE, INC.
216 Lafayette Rd, North Hampton, NH 03862
Tel.: (603) 433-6214
Web Site: http://www.rumbletree.com
Year Founded: 1990
Emp.: 10
Full-Service Agency
N.A.I.C.S.: 541810
Charlie Yeaton *(Dir-Creative)*
Jessica Kellogg *(Pres)*
Brian Beaulieu *(Dir- Creative)*
Kelley Angulo *(Dir-Client Svcs)*
Marisa Hercules *(Acct Exec)*
Becky Sullivan *(Acct Mgr)*

RUMIANO CHEESE COMPANY
511 9th St, Crescent City, CA 95531
Tel.: (707) 465-1535
Web Site: http://www.rumianocheese.com
Year Founded: 1921
Sales Range: $75-99.9 Million
Emp.: 70
Cheese Mfr
N.A.I.C.S.: 311513
Enrique Leal *(Mgr-Production)*
Tana Bachmann *(Office Mgr)*
Baird Rumiano *(Pres)*
John Rumiano *(VP)*

RUMMEL, KLEPPER & KAHL
81 W Mosher St, Baltimore, MD 21217-4243
Tel.: (410) 728-2900 MD
Web Site: http://www.rkk.com
Year Founded: 1945
Sales Range: $25-49.9 Million
Emp.: 550
Engineeering Services
N.A.I.C.S.: 541330
David W. Wallace *(Partner)*
Bob Healy *(Dir-Structures)*

RUMORS SALON & SPA
594 & 595 New Loudon Rd, Latham, NY 12110
Tel.: (518) 786-1777
Web Site: http://www.rumorsinc.com
Year Founded: 2002
Sales Range: $1-9.9 Million
Emp.: 81
Beauty Salons
N.A.I.C.S.: 812112
Marri Aviza *(Pres & CEO)*

RUMPF CORPORATION
701 Jefferson Ave, Toledo, OH 43604
Tel.: (419) 255-5005
Web Site: http://www.job1usa.com
Year Founded: 1951
Sales Range: $10-24.9 Million
Emp.: 70
Provider of Employment Services
N.A.I.C.S.: 561311
Bruce F. Rumpf *(Pres & CEO)*

RUMPKE CONSOLIDATED COMPANIES, INC.
10795 Hughes Rd, Cincinnati, OH 45251
Tel.: (513) 851-0122 OH
Web Site: http://www.rumpke.com
Year Founded: 1988
Sales Range: $300-349.9 Million
Emp.: 2,300
Holding Company; Integrated Waste Management & Recycling Services
N.A.I.C.S.: 551112
Amanda Pratt *(Dir-Corp Comm)*
Charla R. Cabe *(Dir-HR)*
Michael D. Bramkamp *(Reg VP-Northwest Market)*
Matthew J. Bauer *(Dir-Sls & Mktg)*
Richard Jay Roberts *(Dir-Engrg & Environmental Affairs)*
James E. Thaxton *(Gen Counsel & Sec)*
Stephen J. Sargent *(Dir-Recycling)*
Kevin L. Downey *(Dir-Hauling)*
Michael Puckett *(Dir-Safety)*
Jeff Rumpke *(VP-Cincinnati Market)*
Todd Rumpke *(VP-Southeast Market)*
Greg Beamer *(VP-Southern Market)*
Philip E. Wehrman *(CFO & Treas)*
Andrew M. Rumpke Sr. *(VP-Central Ohio Market)*
William J. Rumpke Sr. *(Chm)*
William J. Rumpke Jr. *(Pres & CEO)*

Subsidiaries:

Rumpke Sanitary Landfill, Inc. (1)
10795 Hughes Rd, Cincinnati, OH 45251-4523
Tel.: (513) 851-0122
Web Site: http://www.rumpke.com
Sales Range: $25-49.9 Million
Emp.: 160
Solid Waste Landfill Operator
N.A.I.C.S.: 562212
William J. Rumpke Sr. *(Pres & CEO)*

Rumpke Transporation Company, LLC (1)
10795 Hughes Rd, Cincinnati, OH 45251-4523
Tel.: (513) 851-0122
Web Site: http://www.rumpke.com
Sales Range: $75-99.9 Million
Emp.: 1,000
Waste Collection Vehicle Fleet Management, Repair & Maintenance Services
N.A.I.C.S.: 562998
William J. Rumpke Sr. *(Pres & CEO)*

Rumpke Waste, Inc. (1)
10795 Hughes Rd, Cincinnati, OH 45251-4523
Tel.: (513) 851-0122
Web Site: http://www.rumpke.com
Sales Range: $75-99.9 Million
Emp.: 60
Waste Management & Disposal Services
N.A.I.C.S.: 562998
William J. Rumpke Sr. *(Pres & CEO)*
Nick Brayton *(Mgr-Vehicle Maintenance)*
Ed Brown *(Reg Mgr-Maintenance)*
Eric Curtis *(Mgr-Ops)*
Derek Rainbolt *(Reg Mgr-Safety)*

Rumpke of Indiana, Inc. (1)
1950 Tellman Rd, Columbus, IN 47201
Tel.: (812) 372-1225
Web Site: http://www.rumpke.com
Sales Range: $25-49.9 Million
Emp.: 3
Waste Management & Recycling Services
N.A.I.C.S.: 562998
Michael T. Nelson *(Reg VP-Southern Market)*

Rumpke of Kentucky, Inc. (1)
1101 W Oak St, Louisville, KY 40210
Tel.: (502) 568-3800
Web Site: http://www.rumpke.com
Emp.: 160
Waste Management & Recycling Services
N.A.I.C.S.: 562998
Michael T. Nelson *(Reg VP-Southern Market)*

Rumpke of Ohio, Inc. (1)
10795 Hughes Rd, Cincinnati, OH 45251-4523
Tel.: (513) 851-0122
Web Site: http://www.rumpke.com
Sales Range: $100-124.9 Million
Emp.: 1,000
Waste Management & Recycling Services
N.A.I.C.S.: 562998
William J. Rumpke Sr. *(Pres & CEO)*
Charla Cabe *(Dir-HR)*

Unit (Domestic):

Rumpke Hydraulics & Machining (2)
3963 Kraus Ln, Hamilton, OH 45014
Tel.: (513) 738-0800
Web Site: http://www.rumpkehydraulics.com
Emp.: 19
Hydraulic Equipment Distr
N.A.I.C.S.: 423830
Rick Dorrel *(Gen Mgr)*

Rumpke Recycling (2)
10795 Hughes Rd, Cincinnati, OH 45251
Tel.: (800) 828-8171
Web Site: http://www.rumpkerecycling.com
Material Recycling Services

RUMPKE CONSOLIDATED COMPANIES, INC.   U.S. PRIVATE

Rumpke Consolidated Companies, Inc.—(Continued)
N.A.I.C.S.: 562920
Matt Bauer (Dir-Sls & Mktg)
Charla Cabe (Dir-HR)
Kevin Downey (Dir-Hauling)
Amanda Pratt (Dir-Corp Comm)
Mike Puckett (Dir-Safety)
Jay Roberts (Dir-Engrg & Environmental Affairs)
Jim Thaxton (Gen Counsel & Sec)
Phil Wehrman (CFO & Treas)

RUMSEY ELECTRIC COMPANY
15 Colwell Ln, Conshohocken, PA 19428-1805
Tel.: (610) 832-9000   DE
Web Site: http://www.rumsey.com
Year Founded: 1895
Sales Range: $150-199.9 Million
Emp.: 350
Wholesale Electrical Equipment & Supplies
N.A.I.C.S.: 423610
Shawn Huber (Mgr-Automation & Info Solutions)

Subsidiaries:

Relay & Power Systems   (1)
17 Colwell Ln, Conshohocken, PA 19428
Tel.: (610) 941-2900
Web Site: http://www.relaypowersystems.com
Electrical Engineering Services
N.A.I.C.S.: 541330
Tony Sleva (Mgr-Engrg & Field Svcs)
Edward Stelacio (Engr-Substation)

RUNDE CHEVROLET INC
780 Route 35 N, East Dubuque, IL 61025
Tel.: (815) 747-3011
Web Site: http://www.rundeautogroup.com
Rev.: $44,000,000
Emp.: 60
New & Used Automobiles
N.A.I.C.S.: 441110
Tim Runde (Owner)

RUNDLE-SPENCE MANUFACTURING CO
2075 S Moorland Rd, New Berlin, WI 53151
Tel.: (262) 782-3000
Web Site: http://www.rundle-spence.com
Sales Range: $10-24.9 Million
Emp.: 80
Plumbing Fittings & Supplies
N.A.I.C.S.: 423720
David E. Spence (Pres)
Rob Spence (Gen Mgr)

RUNESTONE ELECTRIC ASSOCIATION
124 7th Ave W, Alexandria, MN 56308
Tel.: (320) 762-1121
Web Site: http://www.runestoneelectric.com
Rev.: $12,059,146
Emp.: 50
Distribution, Electric Power
N.A.I.C.S.: 221122
Ronald Holm (Treas)
Sue Lundeen (Mgr-Member Svcs)
Rick Banke Jr. (CEO)

RUNNEBOHM CONSTRUCTION COMPANY INC.
144 E Rampart St, Shelbyville, IN 46176
Tel.: (317) 398-4722
Web Site: http://www.runnebohmconstruction.com
Year Founded: 1968
Sales Range: $10-24.9 Million
Emp.: 62
Provider of Commercial & Industrial Building Construction Services
N.A.I.C.S.: 236210
Nick Runnebohm (Pres)
Steve Beyer (VP)
Bob Sizemore (Controller)
Michael Runnebohm (Exec VP)

RUNNING SUPPLY INC.
911 Michigan Rd, Marshall, MN 56258
Tel.: (507) 532-9566
Web Site: http://www.runnings.com
Rev.: $32,272,498
Emp.: 181
Hardware Stores
N.A.I.C.S.: 444140
Dennis Reed (Pres)
Dan Agrrmann (COO)

RUNYON SALTZMAN & EINHORN
20 20 L St Ste100, Sacramento, CA 95814
Tel.: (916) 446-9900
Web Site: http://www.rs-e.com
Year Founded: 1960
Sales Range: $10-24.9 Million
Emp.: 56
Advertising Agencies
N.A.I.C.S.: 541810
Estelle Saltzman (Chm)
Scott Rose (Dir-Pub Affairs)
Chris Holben (Pres & Dir-PR)
Kelley Kent (Dir-Media)
Meredith Reilly (Acct Mgr)
Steve Fong (Dir-Creative)
Tina Tafoya (Dir-Production)
Vicky Lelash (Mng Dir-Southern California)
Sandy Nelson (Dir-Art)

RUNZA DRIVE-INNS OF AMERICA INC.
5931 S 58th St Ste D, Lincoln, NE 68516-3640
Tel.: (402) 423-2394   NE
Web Site: http://www.runza.com
Year Founded: 1966
Sales Range: $10-24.9 Million
Emp.: 850
Franchising Services
N.A.I.C.S.: 722513
Donald Everett Jr. (Pres)

Subsidiaries:

Runza National Inc.   (1)
5931 S 58th St Ste D, Lincoln, NE 68516-3640
Tel.: (402) 423-2394
Web Site: http://www.runza.com
Sales Range: $10-24.9 Million
Emp.: 35
Fast Food Restaurants
N.A.I.C.S.: 533110
Donald Everett Jr. (Pres)
Renee Sjulin (VP)

RUOFF MORTGAGE COMPANY, INC.
1110 E Dupont Rd, Fort Wayne, IN 46825
Tel.: (260) 497-0800
Web Site: http://www.ruoff.com
Year Founded: 1984
Sales Range: $10-24.9 Million
Emp.: 135
Real Estate Credit Services
N.A.I.C.S.: 522292
Mark K. Music (Pres & CEO)
Clint Morgan (Chief Lending Officer & Sr VP)
Diana Ringer (COO)
Jeffrey Cassetta (CFO)
Don Reber (VP & Area Mgr)
Ryan Frantz (VP & Area Mgr)
Jeff Deacon (CIO)
Sharon Baron (COO)

RUPE INVESTMENT CORPORATION
2811 McKinney Ave Ste 302, Dallas, TX 75204
Tel.: (214) 871-7521   TX
Year Founded: 1940
Sales Range: $100-124.9 Million
Emp.: 3
Provider of Investment Services
N.A.I.C.S.: 523999
Lee C. Ritchie (Pres)

Subsidiaries:

Hutton Communications Inc.   (1)
2520 Marsh Ln, Carrollton, TX 75006-2282
Tel.: (972) 417-0100
Web Site: http://www.huttoncom.com
Sales Range: $10-24.9 Million
Emp.: 130
Electronic Parts & Equipment
N.A.I.C.S.: 423690

RUPPERT LANDSCAPE, LLC
23601 Laytonsville Rd, Laytonsville, MD 20882
Tel.: (301) 482-0300
Web Site: https://www.ruppertlandscape.com
Emp.: 100
Landscaping Construction Services, Improvement & Maintenance
N.A.I.C.S.: 561730
Phil Key (CEO)

Subsidiaries:

Greenery of Charleston, LLC   (1)
489 Deanna Ln Ste A, Charleston, SC 29492
Tel.: (843) 884-0084
Web Site: http://thegreeneryinc.com
Sales Range: $1-9.9 Million
Emp.: 70
Landscaping Services
N.A.I.C.S.: 561730
Jennifer Dufenberry (Office Mgr)
Andrew Dupps (Pres)

Scott's Landscaping Inc.   (1)
110 Maple Dr, Centre Hall, PA 16828-8960
Tel.: (814) 364-2100
Web Site: http://www.scottslandscapinginc.com
Landscaping Services
N.A.I.C.S.: 561730
Scott Burk (Pres)

RUPPERT NURSERIES, INC.
23601 Laytonsville Rd, Laytonsville, MD 20882
Tel.: (301) 482-0300
Web Site: http://www.ruppertnurseries.com
Year Founded: 1990
Sales Range: $25-49.9 Million
Emp.: 600
Tree Nursery & Landscaping Services
N.A.I.C.S.: 111421
Craig A. Ruppert (CEO)
Amy Snyder (Dir-PR)
Kelly Lewis (Gen Mgr)
Ashley Miles (Mgr-Inventory)
Nick Graves (Mgr-Nursery Maintenance)

RURAL CAPITAL AREA WORKFORCE DEVELOPMENT BOARD, INC.
2701 Gattis School Rd Bldg B Ste 101, Round Rock, TX 78664
Tel.: (512) 244-7966   TX
Web Site: http://www.workforcesolutionsrca.com
Year Founded: 1996
Sales Range: $10-24.9 Million
Emp.: 89
Workforce Development Services
N.A.I.C.S.: 561311
Jenna Akridge (Dir-Contracts & Programs)
Andrew Artz (CFO)
James Satterwhite (Exec Dir)
Shannon Richter (Mgr-Contract)
Tim Rivers (Co-CFO & Controller)

RURAL ELECTRIC COOPERATIVE, INC.
N Hwy 76, Lindsay, OK 73052
Tel.: (405) 756-3104   OK
Web Site: http://www.rural-electric.com
Year Founded: 1938
Sales Range: Less than $1 Million
Emp.: 50
Distr of Electric Power
N.A.I.C.S.: 221122
Kelli Lindsey (Dir-HR)
Linda Ray (CFO)
Ed Bevers (Mgr-Ops & Engrg)
Tommy Badertscher (Pur Agent)
Dale Nye (CEO)
David Crull (Superintendent-Sys)
Megan Lawrence (Mgr-Mktg)
Brent Bacon (Treas & Sec)
Scott Christian (VP)

RURAL ELECTRIC SUPPLY COOPERATIVE INC.
2250 Pinehurst Dr, Madison, WI 53744-4430
Tel.: (608) 831-2600   WI
Web Site: http://www.resco1.com
Year Founded: 1936
Sales Range: $50-74.9 Million
Emp.: 59
Electrical Apparatus & Equipment
N.A.I.C.S.: 423610
Matt Brandrup (Pres & CEO)
Butch Akers (VP-EUSCO Div)

Subsidiaries:

Electric Utility Supply Co.   (1)
4100 30th Ave S, Moorhead, MN 56560
Tel.: (800) 346-3330
Emp.: 14
Electric Equipment Mfr
N.A.I.C.S.: 335999

RURAL MUTUAL INSURANCE COMPANY INC.
1241 John Q Hammons Dr Ste 200, Madison, WI 53717
Tel.: (608) 836-5525   WI
Web Site: http://www.ruralmutual.com
Year Founded: 1934
Fire, Marine & Casualty Insurance
N.A.I.C.S.: 524126
Peter Pelizza (Exec VP & CEO)
Dan Merk (Sr VP & Treas)

RURAL TELECOMMUNICATIONS OF AMERICA, INC.
1400 Broadfield Blvd Ste 200, Houston, TX 77084
Tel.: (281) 944-7817
Web Site: http://rta4all.com
Year Founded: 2018
Telecommunication Services[b]
N.A.I.C.S.: 517121
Donald Workman (Chm)

Subsidiaries:

TXOL Internet, Inc.   (1)
105 W Main St, Eastland, TX 76448-3014
Tel.: (254) 629-3278
Web Site: http://www.txol.net
Data Processing, Hosting & Related Services
N.A.I.C.S.: 518210
Richard Barron (Pres)

COMPANIES

RURAL TELEPHONE SERVICE CO
145 N Main St, Lenora, KS 67645
Tel.: (785) 567-4281
Web Site:
http://www.ruraltelephone.com
Sales Range: $25-49.9 Million
Emp.: 325
Local & Long Distance Telephone Communications
N.A.I.C.S.: 517121
Ron Rahjes *(Treas & Sec)*

RUSCILLI CONSTRUCTION CO. INC.
5000 Arlington Centre Blvd, Columbus, OH 43220
Tel.: (614) 876-9484 OH
Web Site: http://www.ruscilli.com
Year Founded: 1945
Rev.: $160,000,000
Emp.: 60
Industrial Buildings & Warehouses
N.A.I.C.S.: 236210
L. Jack Ruscilli *(CEO & Co-Owner)*
Bob Darrow *(VP-Sls & Mktg)*
R. Anthony Ruscilli *(Co-Owner)*
Adam Drexel *(VP-Ops)*

RUSCON CORPORATION
149 E Bay St Ste 300, Charleston, SC 29401-2104
Tel.: (843) 723-9861 SC
Web Site:
http://www.rusconconstruction.com
Year Founded: 1949
Sales Range: $75-99.9 Million
Emp.: 60
Construction & Contracting Services
N.A.I.C.S.: 236220
Robert B. Russell Jr. *(Pres)*

RUSH COMMUNICATIONS, INC.
512 7th Ave Ste 43-45, New York, NY 10018-4603
Tel.: (212) 840-9399
Web Site:
http://www.rushcommunication.com
Year Founded: 1979
Sales Range: $100-124.9 Million
Emp.: 175
Media Entertainment Company
N.A.I.C.S.: 711190
Russell Simmons *(Founder)*

RUSH HEALTH SYSTEMS INC.
1314 19th Ave, Meridian, MS 39301-4116
Tel.: (601) 483-0011 MS
Web Site:
http://www.rushhealthsystems.org
Year Founded: 1981
Sales Range: $125-149.9 Million
Emp.: 2,000
Management Services
N.A.I.C.S.: 561110
Wallace Strickland *(Chm)*
Larkin Kennedy *(Pres & CEO)*
J. H. Rush *(Founder)*

RUSH INDUSTRIES INC.
118 N Wrenn St, High Point, NC 27260
Tel.: (336) 886-7700
Web Site:
http://www.rushfurniture.com
Rev.: $150,000,000
Emp.: 6
Wood Household Furniture
N.A.I.C.S.: 337122

RUSH TRUCK CENTER
2350 Diversified Way, Orlando, FL 32804-4106
Tel.: (407) 298-1000 FL
Web Site:
http://www.truckstrucktrucks.com
Year Founded: 1936
Sales Range: $75-99.9 Million
Emp.: 100
Sales of New & Used Trucks
N.A.I.C.S.: 441110
Danny Howard *(Mgr-Svc)*

RUSH TRUCKING CORPORATION
35160 E Michigan Ave, Wayne, MI 48184-3698
Tel.: (734) 641-1711 MI
Web Site:
http://www.rushtrucking.com
Year Founded: 1984
Provider of Trucking, Automotive, Expedited Freight & Logistics Services
N.A.I.C.S.: 484110
Andra M. Rush *(Founder, Chm & CEO)*
Scott Grady *(Pres)*
Ronald Joseph *(COO)*
Daniel Piontek *(Dir-Fin & Controller)*

RUSHLAKE HOTELS USA INC.
9575 Katy Freeway Ste 490, Houston, TX 77024
Tel.: (713) 759-0790 FL
Year Founded: 1980
Sales Range: $25-49.9 Million
Emp.: 1,236
Hotels & Motels
N.A.I.C.S.: 721110
Subsidiaries:

Fiesta Inn Inc. (1)
2808 Airline Dr, Houston, TX 77009-1124 (100%)
Tel.: (713) 863-7207
Web Site: http://www.fiesta.com
Rev.: $1,200,000
Emp.: 5
Hotels & Motels
N.A.I.C.S.: 721110

RUSHMORE ELECTRIC POWER COOPERATIVE INC.
1715 Cambell St, Rapid City, SD 57701
Tel.: (605) 342-4759 SD
Web Site: http://www.rushelec.com
Year Founded: 1950
Sales Range: $25-49.9 Million
Emp.: 22
Electronic Services
N.A.I.C.S.: 221122
Victor L. Simmons *(Gen Mgr)*
Todd Eliason *(Asst Gen Mgr)*
Subsidiaries:

Rushmore Communications Inc. (1)
1715 Cambell St, Rapid City, SD 57701-3949 (100%)
Tel.: (605) 348-4940
Web Site: http://www.rushelec.com
Communications Equipment
N.A.I.C.S.: 459999

RUSK COUNTY ELECTRIC COOP
3162 State Hwy 43 E, Henderson, TX 75652
Tel.: (903) 657-4571
Web Site: http://www.rcelectric.org
Year Founded: 1937
Sales Range: $25-49.9 Million
Emp.: 70
Distribution of Electric Power
N.A.I.C.S.: 221122
Jim Latham *(Mgr-Fin & Acctg)*
Ricki Keeling *(Mgr-Svcs)*
Richard McLeon *(Gen Mgr)*

RUSKEN PACKAGING INC.
64 Walnut St NW, Cullman, AL 35055
Tel.: (256) 734-0092
Web Site: http://www.rusken.com
Sales Range: $25-49.9 Million
Emp.: 300
Storage & Packaging Products Mfr
N.A.I.C.S.: 322219
Greg Rusk *(Pres & CEO)*
John Andy Ward *(Gen Mgr)*
Joey Jackson *(VP)*

RUSMUR FLOORS, INC.
500 Sta St, Bridgeville, PA 15017
Tel.: (412) 221-6366
Web Site:
http://www.rusmurfloors.com
Year Founded: 1960
Rev.: $11,741,324
Emp.: 80
Floor Covering Retailer
N.A.I.C.S.: 449121
John Lipscak *(Mgr-Pittsburgh)*
Tom Murray *(Mgr-Bridgeville)*

RUSNAK AUTOMOTIVE GROUP
267 W Colorado Blvd, Pasadena, CA 91105
Tel.: (626) 449-2377
Web Site:
http://www.rusnakonline.com
Year Founded: 1959
Sales Range: $50-74.9 Million
Emp.: 800
Car Dealership
N.A.I.C.S.: 441110
Paul P. Rusnak *(CEO)*
Elizabeth R. Arizmendi *(VP-PR)*
Victoria Rusnak *(Pres)*

RUSNAK WESTLAKE
3832 Thousand Oaks Blvd, Westlake Village, CA 91362
Tel.: (805) 496-6500
Web Site:
http://www.audiwestlake.com
Year Founded: 1981
Sales Range: $10-24.9 Million
Emp.: 60
Car Whslr
N.A.I.C.S.: 441110
Bill Camp *(Controller-Bus)*

RUSS BASSETT CORP
8189 Byron Rd, Whittier, CA 90606
Tel.: (562) 945-2445
Web Site:
http://www.russbassett.com
Sales Range: $10-24.9 Million
Emp.: 125
Office Furniture Mfr
N.A.I.C.S.: 337214
Mike Dressendorfer *(CEO)*
Ava Rabago *(Reg Mgr-Pacific)*
Joe Malerba *(VP-Sls)*
Peter Fink *(Pres)*
Linn Steinbck *(Mgr-Production)*
Ed Toribio *(Mgr-Quality Control)*

RUSS CHEVROLET
11880 SW Pacific Hwy, Tigard, OR 97223
Tel.: (503) 639-1166
Web Site: http://russauto.com
Sales Range: $10-24.9 Million
Emp.: 88
New Car Whslr
N.A.I.C.S.: 441110
Rick Nelson *(Principal)*

RUSS DARROW GROUP, INC.
W 133 N 8569 Executive Pkwy, Menomonee Falls, WI 53051-3344
Tel.: (262) 250-9600 WI
Web Site: http://www.russdarrow.com
Sales Range: $75-99.9 Million
Emp.: 900
Automobile Dealership
N.A.I.C.S.: 441110
Colleen Kellen *(Dir-Mktg)*
Russell M. Darrow Jr. *(Pres)*
Subsidiaries:

Russ Darrow Chrysler & Jeep of Cedarburg (1)
W62 N190 Washington Ave, Cedarburg, WI 53012
Tel.: (262) 377-9600
Sales Range: $10-24.9 Million
Emp.: 80
Advertising Agencies
N.A.I.C.S.: 922120

Russ Darrow Chrysler & Jeep of Madison (1)
3502 Lancaster Dr, Madison, WI 53718
Tel.: (608) 275-7700
Web Site: http://www.russdarrow.com
Sales Range: $25-49.9 Million
Emp.: 100
Automobile Dealers
N.A.I.C.S.: 441110
Russ Darrow *(Owner)*

Russ Darrow Chrysler of Appleton (1)
2301 W College Ave, Appleton, WI 54914
Tel.: (920) 739-9411
Sales Range: $10-24.9 Million
Emp.: 30
Automobile Dealers
N.A.I.C.S.: 441110
Nancy Pietenberg *(Office Mgr)*
Mike Mechman *(Gen Mgr)*

Russ Darrow Dodge of Milwaukee (1)
W133n8569 Executive Pkwy, Menomonee Falls, WI 53051-3344
Tel.: (414) 354-8338
Web Site: http://www.russdarrow.com
Rev.: $44,200,000
Emp.: 118
New & Used Automobiles
N.A.I.C.S.: 441110

Russ Darrow Honda, Nissan & Suzuki of Milwaukee (1)
9201 W Brown Deer Rd, Milwaukee, WI 53224
Tel.: (414) 586-5400
Web Site: http://www.russdarrowgroup.com
Sales Range: $25-49.9 Million
Emp.: 120
Automobile Dealers
N.A.I.C.S.: 441110
Chad Ellis *(Gen Mgr-Honda)*

Russ Darrow Kia (1)
W133n8569 Executive Pkwy, Menomonee Falls, WI 53051-3344
Tel.: (262) 512-1500
Web Site: http://russdarrowkia.com
Automobile Dealers
N.A.I.C.S.: 441110
Bill Scheehan *(Gen Mgr)*

Russ Darrow Kia of Appleton (1)
2301 W College Ave, Appleton, WI 54914
Tel.: (920) 739-9411
Sales Range: $10-24.9 Million
Emp.: 40
Automobile Dealers
N.A.I.C.S.: 441110
Danny Johnson *(Gen Mgr)*
Russ Darrow *(Pres)*

Russ Darrow Kia of Fond du Lac (1)
416 N Rolling Meadows Dr, Fond Du Lac, WI 54937
Tel.: (920) 922-2260
Web Site: http://www.kiaoffonddulac.com
Sales Range: $10-24.9 Million
Emp.: 20
Automobile Dealers
N.A.I.C.S.: 441110
Glenn Leinen *(Gen Mgr)*

Russ Darrow Kia of Madison (1)
6525 Odana Rd, Madison, WI 53719
Tel.: (608) 275-7700
Web Site: http://www.kiaofmadison.com
Sales Range: $25-49.9 Million
Emp.: 100
Automobile Dealers

RUSS DARROW GROUP, INC.

Russ Darrow Group, Inc.—(Continued)
N.A.I.C.S.: 441110
Chad Ellis (Gen Mgr)

Russ Darrow Kia of Waukesha (1)
2141 E Moreland Blvd, Waukesha, WI 53186
Tel.: (262) 547-1761
Web Site: http://www.russdarrow.com
Sales Range: $25-49.9 Million
Emp.: 75
Automobile Dealers
N.A.I.C.S.: 441110
Josh Pepitone (Gen Mgr)

Russ Darrow Mazda of Greenfield (1)
3520 S 108th St, Greenfield, WI 53228
Tel.: (414) 329-5800
Web Site: http://www.russdarrow.com
Automobile Dealers
N.A.I.C.S.: 441110
George Boutsikakis (Gen Mgr)

Russ Darrow of West Bend (1)
2700 W Washington Ave, West Bend, WI 53095
Tel.: (262) 334-9411
Web Site: http://www.russdarrow.com
Automobile Dealers
N.A.I.C.S.: 441110

RUSS DAVIS WHOLESALE
266 4th St NE, Wadena, MN 56482-6482
Tel.: (651) 645-2720
Web Site: http://www.russdaviswholesale.com
Emp.: 100
Fresh Fruit & Vegetable Merchant Whslr
N.A.I.C.S.: 424480
Randy Graham (CFO)
Adam Gamble (Pres)
Lavonne Kucera (Head-Food Safety Quality Assurance-Processing Facilities-Twin Cit)

Subsidiaries:

Liberty Fruit Company, Inc. (1)
1247 Argentine Blvd, Kansas City, KS 66105-1508
Tel.: (913) 281-5200
Web Site: http://www.libertyfruit.com
Emp.: 100
Fresh Fruit & Vegetable Merchant Whslr
N.A.I.C.S.: 424480
Allen Caviar (Pres)

RUSS SMALE, INC.
6666 Passer Rd, Coopersburg, PA 18036
Tel.: (610) 282-1554 PA
Web Site: http://www.twcooperinsurance.com
Holding Company; Insurance Agencies & Brokerages
N.A.I.C.S.: 551112
Michael T Smale (Pres)

Subsidiaries:

T.W. Cooper Insurance, LLC (1)
6666 Passer Rd, Coopersburg, PA 18036
Tel.: (610) 282-1554
Web Site: http://www.twcooperinsurance.com
Insurance Services
N.A.I.C.S.: 524210
Michael T Smale (Pres)

RUSSCO INC.
85 Purchase St, Fall River, MA 02720
Tel.: (508) 674-5280
Web Site: http://www.russcoinc.com
Sales Range: $10-24.9 Million
Emp.: 18
Nonresidential Building Construction Services
N.A.I.C.S.: 236220

Paula Ackerson (Controller)
Steve Penick (Superintendent)
Russell Pichette Jr. (Pres)

RUSSELL & JILL HEFFNER, INC.
217 Daly Ave, Modesto, CA 95354-3901
Tel.: (209) 545-1900
Sales Range: $25-49.9 Million
Emp.: 70
Processed Meat Mfr
N.A.I.C.S.: 311611
Jill Heffner (Pres)
Russell Heffner (VP)
Diana Xavier (Office Mgr)
Gus Coutrakis (Gen Mgr)
Adam Heffner (Dir-Mktg)

RUSSELL & SMITH FORD INC.
3440 S Loop W, Houston, TX 77025
Tel.: (713) 663-4111
Web Site: http://www.russellsmith.com
Rev.: $172,541,920
Emp.: 330
Automobiles, New & Used
N.A.I.C.S.: 441110
William C. Smith (Chm)
Mark Rehkopf (VP)
Jack Carney (Gen Mgr)
Wes Blair (Dir-Ford Svc)

RUSSELL BARNETT CHRYSLER-DODGE-JEEP, INC.
2756 Decherd Blvd, Winchester, TN 37398
Tel.: (931) 967-9000
Web Site: http://www.russellbarnettchryslerdodgejeep.com
Sales Range: $10-24.9 Million
Emp.: 63
Car Whslr
N.A.I.C.S.: 441110
Russell Barnett (Co-Owner)
Rex Russell (Co-Owner)

RUSSELL BOND & CO. INC.
866 Ellicott Sq Bldg 295 Main St, Buffalo, NY 14203
Tel.: (716) 856-8220 NY
Web Site: http://www.russellbond.com
Year Founded: 1950
Sales Range: $1-9.9 Million
Emp.: 46
Insurance Services
N.A.I.C.S.: 524210
Barbara Simpson (VP)
Tony Ambrose (Asst VP)
Jeff Latke (Asst VP)
Kurt C. Bingeman (Pres)
Gary A. Hollederer (Pres)
Mark M. Palmisano (Sr VP)
Tony Kubera (Dir-Bus Dev)
Margaret J. Arnold (Asst VP & Controller)
Kim Thome (Mgr-Claims)
Paul Saccomando (Mgr-Ops)
David R. Finkelstein (VP-Distr & Programs-Chicago)
Ed Reilly (VP)
Tonya Hollederer (VP)

RUSSELL CELLULAR, INC.
5624 S Hwy FF, Republic, MO 65619
Tel.: (417) 886-7542
Web Site: http://www.russellcellular.com
Sales Range: $50-74.9 Million
Emp.: 550
Wireless Communication Services
N.A.I.C.S.: 517112

Jeff Russell (Co-Founder & Pres)
Kym Russell (Co-Founder & VP)
Darin Wray (VP-Ops)
Robert Lister (VP-Fin)

RUSSELL CHEVROLET COMPANY
6100 Landers Rd, Sherwood, AR 72117-1940
Tel.: (501) 835-8300 AR
Web Site: http://www.russellchevrolet.com
Year Founded: 1963
Sales Range: $50-74.9 Million
Emp.: 160
Retailer of New & Used Automobiles
N.A.I.C.S.: 441110
Bob Russell (Pres)
Brett Russell (Gen Mgr)

RUSSELL HERDER
100 S Fifth St Ste 2200, Minneapolis, MN 55402-1221
Tel.: (612) 455-2360
Web Site: http://www.russellherder.com
Year Founded: 1984
Sales Range: $10-24.9 Million
Emp.: 30
N.A.I.C.S.: 541810
Carol Russell (CEO)
Brian Herder (Exec Dir-Creative)
Alison Griffin (Acct Supvr-PR)

Subsidiaries:

Russell Herder (1)
315 E River Rd, Brainerd, MN 56401-3503
Tel.: (218) 829-3055
Emp.: 10
N.A.I.C.S.: 541810
Carol Russell (CEO)
Brian Herder (Partner & Exec Creative Dir)

RUSSELL LANDS INC.
2544 Willow Point Rd, Alexander City, AL 35010
Tel.: (256) 329-0835
Web Site: http://www.russelllands.com
Year Founded: 1962
Sales Range: $25-49.9 Million
Emp.: 500
Lumber & Other Building Materials
N.A.I.C.S.: 423310
Benjamin Russell (Chm)
Steve Forehand (Sec & VP)
David Sturdivant (CFO & COO)
Roger Holliday (VP)
Thomas T. Lamberth (Pres & CEO)
Carol Hope Tyler (Treas & Controller)

Subsidiaries:

Industrial Energy Inc. (1)
2544 Willow Point Rd, Alexander City, AL 35010-6218 (100%)
Tel.: (256) 329-0835
Web Site: http://www.russelllands.com
Rev.: $2,100,000
Emp.: 6
Real Estate Development
N.A.I.C.S.: 423990
Ben Russell (Chm)

RUSSELL OIL COMPANY INC.
222 Schoolhouse Rd PO Box 38, Lapine, AL 36046
Tel.: (334) 537-4315 AL
Year Founded: 1955
Sales Range: $25-49.9 Million
Emp.: 100
Petroleum Product Distr
N.A.I.C.S.: 457120
Tom Russell (Pres)

RUSSELL PETROLEUM CORPORATION

3378 Tankview Ct, Montgomery, AL 36108-1633
Tel.: (334) 834-3750 AL
Sales Range: $125-149.9 Million
Emp.: 150
Sales of Gasoline & Operator of Convenience Stores
N.A.I.C.S.: 457120
Mike Heartsill (VP)

RUSSELL REID WASTE HAULING
200 Smith St, Keasbey, NJ 08832
Tel.: (732) 225-2238
Web Site: http://www.russellreid.com
Rev.: $17,140,799
Emp.: 75
Local Trucking
N.A.I.C.S.: 484110
Mitchell Weiner (CEO)
David Dam (Exec VP)
John Nelson (Dir-Safety & Trng)

RUSSELL REYNOLDS ASSOCIATES INC.
277 Park Ave 38th Fl 10172, New York, NY 10166
Tel.: (212) 351-2000 NY
Web Site: http://www.russellreynolds.com
Year Founded: 1969
Sales Range: $10-24.9 Million
Emp.: 300
Executive Search Service
N.A.I.C.S.: 541612
Clarke Murphy (CEO)
Melanie Waters (CEO-Help for Heroes)
Bryn Parry (Founder-Help for Heroes)
Vivek Badrinath (Deputy CEO)
Paul Ottolini (CFO)
Eren Rosenfeld (Chief Human Capital Officer)
Deb Barbanel (Mng Dir)
Amy Scissons (Chief Mktg & Comm Officer)
Richard Fields (Head-Board Effectiveness Practice)
Nanaz Mohtashami (Mng Dir)

Subsidiaries:

Russell Reynolds Associates Inc. (1)
1700 New York Ave Nw Ste 400, Washington, DC 20006 (100%)
Tel.: (202) 654-7800
Web Site: http://www.russellreynolds.com
Sales Range: $10-24.9 Million
Emp.: 40
Executive Recuiting Consulting
N.A.I.C.S.: 541612
Charles A. Tribbett III (Vice Chm, Mng Dir & CEO-Advisory Grp)
Kimberly Archer (Mng Dir)
Clarke Murphy (CEO)

Russell Reynolds Associates Ltd. (1)
28 King St Almack, London, SW1Y 6QW, United Kingdom
Tel.: (44) 2078397788
Web Site: http://www.russelreynolds.com
Emp.: 200
Employment Agencies
N.A.I.C.S.: 561311
James Bichener (Dir-Fin)
Siobhan Caragher (Mng Dir-Fin Svcs Practice-UK)
Patrick Johnson (Country Mgr)

Russell Reynolds Associates, Chicago (1)
155 N Wacker Dr Ste 4100, Chicago, IL 60606-5896
Tel.: (312) 993-9696
Web Site: http://www.russellreynolds.com
Employment Agencies
N.A.I.C.S.: 541612

Russell Reynolds Associates, France (1)
21 Rue de La Pai, 75002, Paris, France (100%)

Tel.: (33) 149261300
Web Site: http://www.rusellreynolds.com
Sales Range: $10-24.9 Million
Emp.: 50
Employment Agencies
N.A.I.C.S.: 561311

Russell Reynolds Associates, Hamburg (1)
Neuer Wall 88 Palaishaus, 20354, Hamburg, Germany (100%)
Tel.: (49) 404806610
Web Site: http://www.russellreynolds.com
Emp.: 23
Employment Agencies
N.A.I.C.S.: 561311

Russell Reynolds Associates, Menlo Park (1)
260 Homer Ave Ste 202, Palo Alto, CA 94301-2777
Tel.: (650) 233-2400
Web Site: http://www.russellreynolds.com
Sales Range: $10-24.9 Million
Emp.: 50
Recruiting Employment Agencies
N.A.I.C.S.: 541612
Charles Geoly (CEO-Board Svc Practice)

RUSSELL SENIORS, LLC.
5625 S Hollywood Blvd, Las Vegas, NV 89122
Tel.: (702) 990-2390
Web Site:
 http://www.lasvegasliving.com
Year Founded: 2011
Sales Range: $10-24.9 Million
Real Estate Development Services
N.A.I.C.S.: 531190
Alan L. Molasky (Pres)

RUSSELL SIGLER INC.
9702 W Tonto St, Tolleson, AZ 85353
Tel.: (623) 388-5100 NM
Web Site: http://www.siglers.com
Year Founded: 1969
Sales Range: $200-249.9 Million
Emp.: 600
Mfr & Retailer of Heating & Air Conditioning Equipment & Heating & Air-Conditioning Supplies
N.A.I.C.S.: 423730
Robert Osborne (CFO)

RUSSELL STANDARD CORPORATION
285 Kappa Dr Ste 300, Pittsburgh, PA 15238
Tel.: (412) 449-0700 PA
Web Site:
 http://www.russellstandard.com
Year Founded: 1929
Sales Range: $50-74.9 Million
Emp.: 350
Highway & Street Construction Company
N.A.I.C.S.: 237310
Matt Johnson (Pres)
George Leach (Treas & Gen Mgr)
James R. Johnson Sr. (Chm)

RUSSELL SWINTON OATMAN DESIGN ASSOCIATES, INC.
132 Mirick Rd, Princeton, MA 01541-1111
Tel.: (978) 464-2360
Web Site:
 http://www.reproductionhouseplans.com
Year Founded: 1977
Architectural Plans for Reproduction Houses
N.A.I.C.S.: 541310
Russell S. Oatman (Pres)

RUSSELL T. BUNDY ASSOCIATES
417 E Water St, Urbana, OH 43078
Tel.: (937) 652-2151

Web Site: http://www.rtbundy.com
Sales Range: $10-24.9 Million
Emp.: 55
Bakery Equipment & Supplies
N.A.I.C.S.: 423440
Russell T. Bundy (Founder)

RUSSELL TRANSPORT, INC.
12365 Pine Springs, El Paso, TX 79928
Tel.: (915) 542-1495
Web Site:
 http://www.russelltransport.com
Year Founded: 1993
Sales Range: $10-24.9 Million
Emp.: 100
Freight Trucking Services
N.A.I.C.S.: 484121
Rami Abdeljaber (Owner)
Michael Northcut (Mgr-Ops)

RUSSELL-MOORE LUMBER INC
3116 Desiard St, Monroe, LA 71201
Tel.: (318) 325-3164
Sales Range: $10-24.9 Million
Emp.: 42
Lumber & Other Building Materials
N.A.I.C.S.: 423310
Robert E. Moore (VP)
Brian Russell (Treas)
Randy Russell (Pres & CEO)

RUSSELL-WARNER INC.
23272 Mill Creek Dr Ste 360, Laguna Hills, CA 92653
Tel.: (661) 257-9200
Web Site: http://www.rw-rotorooter.com
Year Founded: 1947
Sales Range: $10-24.9 Million
Emp.: 240
Provider of Sewer Cleaning & Rodding
N.A.I.C.S.: 562991
Linda J. McDonald (Pres)

RUSSIN LUMBER CORP
21 Leonards Dr, Montgomery, NY 12549
Tel.: (845) 457-4000
Web Site:
 http://www.russinlumber.com
Rev.: $18,000,000
Emp.: 120
Lumber, Plywood & Millwork
N.A.I.C.S.: 423310
Barry Russin (Pres)
Brent Stuart (VP)

RUSSO HARDWARE, INC.
9525 W Irving Park Rd, Schiller Park, IL 60176
Tel.: (847) 678-9525 IL
Web Site:
 http://www.russopower.com
Year Founded: 1970
Sales Range: $10-24.9 Million
Hardware Stores
N.A.I.C.S.: 444140
Eric Adams (Pres)
Joe Lobacz (Mgr-Parts)
Bob Levar (Mgr-Salt)

RUSSO'S NEW YORK PIZZERIA
5847 San Felipe Ste 1730, Houston, TX 77057
Tel.: (713) 821-1322
Web Site: http://www.nypizzeria.com
Year Founded: 1992
Sales Range: $10-24.9 Million
Emp.: 80
Italian Restaurant & Pizzeria
N.A.I.C.S.: 722511

Anthony Russo (CEO)
Alfred Naddaff (Dir-Natl Franchise Dev)
John Long (Mgr-Store)

RUST COMMUNICATIONS
301 Broadway, Cape Girardeau, MO 63701-7330
Tel.: (573) 335-6611
Web Site:
 http://www.rustcommunications.com
Year Founded: 1993
Sales Range: $25-49.9 Million
Emp.: 200
Newspaper Publishers
N.A.I.C.S.: 513110
Gary W. Rust (Chm)
Rex D. Rust (Pres)
Jon K. Rust (Publr)
Bob Miller (Editor)

Subsidiaries:

Areawide Media Inc. (1)
US Hwy 62 E, Salem, AR 72576
Tel.: (870) 895-3207
Web Site: http://www.areawidenews.com
Sales Range: $10-24.9 Million
Emp.: 29
Newspaper Printing & Distribution Services
N.A.I.C.S.: 513110
Patti Sanders (Gen Mgr)

Banner-Graphic (1)
100 N Jackson St, Greencastle, IN 46135-1240
Tel.: (765) 653-5151
Web Site: http://www.bannergraphic.com
Sales Range: $10-24.9 Million
Emp.: 30
Newspaper Publishing
N.A.I.C.S.: 513110
Daryl Taylor (Gen Mgr)

Concord Publishing House Inc. (1)
301 Broadway St, Cape Girardeau, MO 63701
Tel.: (573) 334-7100
Web Site:
 http://www.southeastmissourian.com
Sales Range: $25-49.9 Million
Emp.: 100
Multi-Color Printing & Copying Graphic Design Services
N.A.I.C.S.: 323111
Rex D. Rust (Co-Pres)

The Brazil Times (1)
100 N Meridian St, Brazil, IN 47834
Tel.: (812) 446-2216
Web Site: http://www.thebraziltimes.com
Rev.: $1,100,000
Emp.: 40
Newspaper Publishing Services
N.A.I.C.S.: 513110
Randy List (VP)

RUSTIC CANYON PARTNERS
1025 Westwood Blvd Fl 2, Los Angeles, CA 90024
Tel.: (310) 998-8000
Web Site:
 http://www.rusticcanyon.com
Year Founded: 1999
Sales Range: $10-24.9 Million
Emp.: 5
Privater Equity Firm
N.A.I.C.S.: 523999
Nate Redmond (Mng Partner)
Thomas E. Unterman (Partner)
David Travers (Partner)

RUSTIC CRUST
31 Barnstead Rd, Pittsfield, NH 03263
Tel.: (603) 435-5119
Web Site: http://www.rusticcrust.com
Year Founded: 1996
Sales Range: $10-24.9 Million
Emp.: 75
Organic Pizza Crusts, Sauce & Frozen Pizza
N.A.I.C.S.: 311824

Brad Sterl (CEO)

RUSTON INDUSTRIAL SUPPLIES, INC.
1308 Commerce St, Ruston, LA 71270
Tel.: (318) 255-6721
Year Founded: 1969
Sales Range: $10-24.9 Million
Emp.: 55
Provider of Bearings, Chains, Electrical, Fluid Power Components & Related Industrial Supplies
N.A.I.C.S.: 423840
Darrell Miller (Branch Mgr)

RUSTON PAVING CO. INC.
6216 Thompson Rd, Syracuse, NY 13206
Tel.: (315) 437-2533 NY
Web Site:
 http://www.rustonpaving.com
Year Founded: 1943
Sales Range: $10-24.9 Million
Emp.: 50
Contractor of Commercial & Industrial Paving & Site Development
N.A.I.C.S.: 237310
Don Clark (VP)
Kevin Post (Controller)
Mark Ruston (Pres & CEO)

RUSTY ECK FORD, INC.
7310 E Kellogg, Wichita, KS 67207-1608
Tel.: (316) 685-9211
Web Site:
 http://www.rustyeckford.com
Rev.: $69,700,000
Emp.: 250
New Car Dealers
N.A.I.C.S.: 441110
Leslie Eck (Owner & Pres)
Janet Cervantes (Sec)

Subsidiaries:

REE Enterprises, Inc. (1)
9203 S 145th St, Omaha, NE 68138
Tel.: (402) 896-6000
Sales Range: $75-99.9 Million
Emp.: 100
New & Used Car Dealer
N.A.I.C.S.: 441110
Vince Armijo (Gen Mgr)

RUSTY WALLIS, INC.
12277 Shiloh Rd, Dallas, TX 75228
Tel.: (214) 348-7500
Web Site:
 http://www.thehondaking.com
Rev.: $59,300,000
Emp.: 180
Owner & Operator of Car Dealerships
N.A.I.C.S.: 441110
Rusty J. Wallis (Pres)
Ronnie Robertson (Gen Mgr)

RUTHERFORD ELECTRIC MEMBERSHIP
186 Hudlow Rd, Forest City, NC 28043
Tel.: (828) 245-1621
Web Site: http://www.remc.com
Rev.: $76,216,503
Emp.: 74
Distribution, Electric Power
N.A.I.C.S.: 221122

RUTHERFORD EQUIPMENT INC.
14230 Lochridge Blvd M-P, Conyers, GA 30014
Tel.: (770) 929-1601
Web Site:
 http://www.rutherfordequipment.com
Sales Range: $10-24.9 Million
Emp.: 18

RUTHERFORD EQUIPMENT INC.

Rutherford Equipment Inc.—(Continued)
Industrial Supplies
N.A.I.C.S.: 423840
Cindy Rutherford (Mgr-Personnel)
Randy Rutherford (Chm)
Mike Rutherford (Pres)

RUTHERFORD FARMERS CO-OPERATIVE INC.
985 Middle Tennessee Blvd, Murfreesboro, TN 37130-5034
Tel.: (615) 893-6212
Web Site: http://www.rutherfordfarmerscoop.com
Year Founded: 1943
Sales Range: $100-124.9 Million
Emp.: 130
Provider Of Agricultural Services
N.A.I.C.S.: 459999
John Handersoen (Mng Dir)
Nancy Walls (Office Mgr-Credit)

RUTHMAN PUMP & ENGINEERING INC.
1212 Streng St, Cincinnati, OH 45223-2643
Tel.: (513) 559-1901
Web Site: http://www.ruthmancompanies.com
Year Founded: 1912
Pumps & Pumping Equipment Mfr
N.A.I.C.S.: 333914
Thomas R. Ruthman (Co-Owner & Pres)
Thomas G. Ruthman (Co-Owner & Exec VP)

Subsidiaries:

Gusher Pumps, Inc. (1)
22 Ruthman Dr, Dry Ridge, KY 41035-9784
Tel.: (859) 824-5001
Web Site: http://www.gusher.com
Sales Range: $10-24.9 Million
Emp.: 100
Industrial Pumps & Valve Mfr
N.A.I.C.S.: 333914
Thomas R. Ruthman (Owner & Pres)
Tim Bowen (Mgr-Assembly)
Jennifer Conrad (Mgr-Pur)
Tim McClanahan (Gen Mgr)

Division (Domestic):

Fulflo Specialties (2)
459 E Fancy St, Blanchester, OH 45107-1462
Tel.: (937) 783-2411
Web Site: http://www.fulflo.com
Sales of Hydraulic Release Valves
N.A.I.C.S.: 332919
David Locaputo (Gen Mgr-Engrg)
Jay Harding (Mgr-Order Scheduling)
William Moore (Mgr-Quality Control)

Subsidiary (Non-US):

Gusher Pumps (Shanghai) Co., Ltd. (2)
Room 4012 Polar Star Business Plaza No 913 Changlin Road, Shanghai, 200443, China
Tel.: (86) 21 26616611
Hydraulic Pump Distr
N.A.I.C.S.: 423830

RUTHRAUFF LLC
400 Locust St, McKees Rocks, PA 15136-3557
Tel.: (412) 771-6800
Web Site: http://www.ruthrauff.com
Year Founded: 1934
Sales Range: $25-49.9 Million
Emp.: 250
Provider of Mechanical Contracting, Sheet Metal & Pipe Fabrication Services
N.A.I.C.S.: 238220
John W. Sloan (Pres-Ruthrauff Svc)
Gordon Collins (VP-Engrg)

RUTLAND PLYWOOD CORP.
1 Ripley Rd, Rutland, VT 05702
Tel.: (802) 747-4000
Web Site: http://www.rutply.com
Sales Range: $10-24.9 Million
Emp.: 80
Wood Products Mfr
N.A.I.C.S.: 321211
Jack Barrett (Pres)

RUTLAND PRODUCTS CO.
38 Merchants Row, Rutland, VT 05702
Tel.: (802) 775-5519
Web Site: http://www.rutland.com
Year Founded: 1883
Sales Range: $50-74.9 Million
Emp.: 20
Stove & Fireplace Products Mfr
N.A.I.C.S.: 332510
G. Miller (CFO)
Patrick Nowick (Acct Mgr)

Subsidiaries:

Rutland Products, Inc. (1)
PO Box 1175, Jacksonville, IL 62651-1175
Tel.: (217) 245-7810
Web Site: http://www.rutland.com
Sales Range: $10-24.9 Million
Distr of Hearth & Home Maintenance Products
N.A.I.C.S.: 333414
Faith Nergenah (VP-Ops)

RUXER FORD LINCOLN MERCURY
123 Place Rd, Jasper, IN 47546
Tel.: (812) 482-1200
Web Site: http://www.ruxer.com
Sales Range: $50-74.9 Million
Emp.: 300
Sales of New & Used Cars
N.A.I.C.S.: 441110
Douglas Abbett (Owner)
Darren Mathies (Mgr-Sls)
Harry Hutton (Mgr-Sls)
Jake Bower (Mgr-Internet Sls)
Nick Abbett (Mgr-Fin)
Tim Eckstein (Mgr-Sls)
Keith Knies (Mgr-Customer Rels)
Gary Weinzapfel (Gen Mgr)

RV ACQUISITION CORP.
5547 National Tpke, Louisville, KY 40214-3725
Tel.: (502) 367-1713
Year Founded: 1986
Rev.: $32,000,000
Emp.: 225
Lumber, Plywood & Millwork
N.A.I.C.S.: 332321
Robert Russell (Pres)

RV CONNECTIONS, INC.
3926 E 15th St, Panama City, FL 32404-5883
Tel.: (850) 763-6910
Web Site: http://www.rvconnections.com
Sales Range: $10-24.9 Million
Emp.: 33
Recreational Vehicle Whslr
N.A.I.C.S.: 441210
Neal Stewart (VP)

RV PEDDLER INC
8730 Golden State Hwy, Bakersfield, CA 93308
Tel.: (661) 399-9052
Web Site: http://www.rvpeddler.net
Sales Range: $10-24.9 Million
Emp.: 85
Recreational Vehicle Dealers
N.A.I.C.S.: 441210
Anthony Morero (Pres)

RV TRADERS
2501 E Main St, Mesa, AZ 85213
Tel.: (480) 464-9724
Web Site: http://www.rv-traders.com
Year Founded: 1983
Sales Range: $10-24.9 Million
Emp.: 88
Recreational Vehicle Dealers
N.A.I.C.S.: 441210
Dallas Michaels (Mgr-Sls)

RV WORLD OF NOKOMIS INC.
2110 Tamiami Trl N, Nokomis, FL 34275
Tel.: (941) 966-2182
Web Site: http://www.rvworldinc.com
Sales Range: $25-49.9 Million
Emp.: 120
Recreational Vehicle Dealers
N.A.I.C.S.: 441210
Ed Davidson (VP & Gen Mgr)
Matt Gerzeny (VP & Gen Mgr-Sls)

RV'S NORTHWEST INC.
18919 E Broadway Ave, Greenacres, WA 99016
Tel.: (509) 891-5854
Web Site: http://www.rvsnorthwest.com
Year Founded: 1983
Sales Range: $10-24.9 Million
Emp.: 38
Motor Homes
N.A.I.C.S.: 441210
Ron Little (Pres)
Tina Little (Treas & Sec)

RVE, INC.
712 Congress Ave Ste 300, Austin, TX 78701
Tel.: (512) 480-0032
Web Site: http://www.rviplanning.com
Year Founded: 1982
Sales Range: $10-24.9 Million
Landscape Architectural Services
N.A.I.C.S.: 541320
Christopher K. Crawford (Pres)
Gene Lukow (Dir-Plng-Austin)
George Robert Richardson (Co-Founder, CEO & Principal)
Barbara Austin (Sr VP & Dir-Park Plng & Design)
Roderick A. Petschauer (CFO)
Katie Harris (Dir-Mktg)
Bob Moser (Mgr-Bus Dev-Orlando)
Ryan Seacrist (Dir-Ops-Florida)

RVM INC.
40 Rector St 17th Fl, New York, NY 10006
Tel.: (212) 693-1525
Web Site: http://www.rvminc.com
Year Founded: 1989
Sales Range: $10-24.9 Million
Emp.: 80
Electronic Discovery & Litigation Management Services
N.A.I.C.S.: 518210
Geoffrey Sherman (Dir-Tech)
Sanjay Manocha (Dir-Discovery Analytics & Review)
Greg Cancilla (Dir-Forensics)

RVOS FARM MUTUAL INSURANCE COMPANY
2301 S 37th St, Temple, TX 76504
Tel.: (254) 773-2181
Web Site: http://www.rvos.com
Rev.: $54,300,000
Emp.: 100
Direct Property & Casualty Insurance Carriers
N.A.I.C.S.: 524126
Irene Sulak (VP-Ops)
Wiley Shockley (Pres)
James Smith (Sec)
Wesley Jackson (VP-Ops)

RVP DEVELOPMENT CORPORATION
201 Ionia Ave SW, Grand Rapids, MI 49503
Tel.: (616) 988-7000
Rev.: $18,089,303
Emp.: 120
Jukebox Rental
N.A.I.C.S.: 713990
Barbara Boshoven (VP-Bus Dev)
Sharon Vander Pol (Mgr)

RW ADVERTISING, INC.
313 Canal St, Lemont, IL 60439
Tel.: (630) 257-1179
Web Site: http://www.rwadv.com
Year Founded: 2003
Sales Range: $1-9.9 Million
Emp.: 5
Advertising Agency Services
N.A.I.C.S.: 541810
Sean Ryan (Co-Founder)
Alan Woods (Co-Founder, Pres & CEO)
Heath Sorrells (Partner)

RW RHINE INC.
1124 112th St E, Tacoma, WA 98445
Tel.: (253) 537-5852
Web Site: http://www.rwrhine.com
Rev.: $11,082,000
Emp.: 25
Demolition Services
N.A.I.C.S.: 238910
Douglas S. Rhine (Pres)
Joel Simpson (VP)
Mike Lano (Superintendent)

RWB REAL ESTATE INC.
1711 Main St, Fort Myers Beach, FL 33931
Tel.: (239) 994-5049
Web Site: http://www.rwbrealestate.com
Sales Range: $1-9.9 Million
Real Estate Broker
N.A.I.C.S.: 531210
Robert W. Beasley (Owner)

RWBT INC.
220 W Ritchie Rd, Salisbury, NC 28147
Tel.: (704) 633-0311
Web Site: http://www.southeastfleetservices.com
Year Founded: 1969
Sales Range: $10-24.9 Million
Emp.: 13
Truck Leasing Services
N.A.I.C.S.: 532120
Bradley A. Bost (Pres)

RWC INC.
2105 S Euclid Ave, Bay City, MI 48706
Tel.: (989) 684-4030
Web Site: http://www.rwcinc.com
Sales Range: $25-49.9 Million
Emp.: 185
Automated Assembly Systems: Designing; Building; & Manufacturing
N.A.I.C.S.: 333519
William G. Perlberg (Pres)
Bill Beauvais (Mgr-Network)
Donald Paige (Dir-Process Innovation)
Al Glaza (Mgr-Pur)

RWC INTERNATIONAL LTD.
2202 S Central Ave, Phoenix, AZ 85004
Tel.: (602) 254-9241
Web Site: http://www.rwcinternational.com
Sales Range: $75-99.9 Million
Emp.: 100

Truck Sales & Service
N.A.I.C.S.: 423110
Robert Cunningham (Owner)
Shon Rasmussen (Acct Mgr-Fleet)

RWD TECHNOLOGIES LLC
5521 Research Pk Dr, Baltimore, MD 21228
Tel.: (410) 869-1000   MD
Web Site: http://www.rwd.com
Year Founded: 1988
Sales Range: $100-124.9 Million
Emp.: 1,200
Integrated Services to Companies in Complex Operating & High-Technology Environments
N.A.I.C.S.: 541512
Robert Deutsch (Founder & Chm)
Daniel A. Cantwell (VP)
Nancy Williams (Sr Mgr-Mktg)
Laurens MacLure Jr. (Pres & CEO)

RWM CASTERS COMPANY
1225 Isley Rd, Gastonia, NC 28053
Tel.: (704) 813-5912
Web Site: http://www.rwmcasters.com
Year Founded: 1935
Sales Range: $10-24.9 Million
Emp.: 67
Caster & Wheel Mfr
N.A.I.C.S.: 332510
Kathy Taylor (VP & Controller)
Peter Comeau (CEO)

RWP TRANSFER INC.
1313 E Phillips Blvd, Pomona, CA 91766
Tel.: (909) 868-6882
Sales Range: $10-24.9 Million
Emp.: 45
Provider of Wood Recycling Services
N.A.I.C.S.: 423990

RWR ENTERPRISES INC.
24 Greenway Plz 1209, Houston, TX 77046
Tel.: (713) 629-6681
Web Site: http://www.rwr.com
Sales Range: $25-49.9 Million
Emp.: 80
Executive Placement
N.A.I.C.S.: 541612
Joseph Richard Weiss (Pres)

RWS & ASSOCIATES ENTERTAINMENT, INC.
34-01 38th Ave Ste 302, Long Island City, NY 11101
Tel.: (212) 391-1795
Web Site: http://experiencerws.com
Year Founded: 2003
Design, Fabrication & Installation of Custom Entertainment
N.A.I.C.S.: 711310
Ryan Stana (Founder & CEO)
Broc Power (Mgr-Production-Music)
Subsidiaries:
Jack Rouse Associates, Inc.   (1)
600 Vine St Ste 1700, Cincinnati, OH 45202
Tel.: (513) 381-0055
Web Site: http://www.jackrouse.com
Emp.: 29
Architectural Services
N.A.I.C.S.: 541310
Keith James (Pres)
Dan Schultz (COO)
Shawn McCoy (VP-Mktg & Bus Dev)
Jack Rouse (Founder)
Dana Everhart (Asst Mgr-Ops)
David Ferguson (Dir-Art)
Mark Amos (Project Mgr)
Ron Bunt (VP-Production)

RWS ENTERPRISES
4335 Brambleton Ave, Roanoke, VA 24018
Tel.: (540) 774-0613
Web Site: http://www.countrycookin.com
Sales Range: $50-74.9 Million
Emp.: 700
Family Restaurants
N.A.I.C.S.: 722511
David Preston (Pres)

RWS HOLDING, LLC
2275 Half Day Rd Ste 337, Bannockburn, IL 60015
Web Site: http://www.revenuewell.com
Year Founded: 2010
Sales Range: $10-24.9 Million
Emp.: 104
Software Development Services
N.A.I.C.S.: 541511
Max Longin (Founder)
Matt Carroll (VP-Sls)
Sue Fuller (Dir-HR)
Ron Madsen (Fin Dir)
Joe Keehnast (Dir-Product Mgmt)

RX FOR FLEAS INC.
6555 NW 9th Ave Ste 412, Fort Lauderdale, FL 33309
Tel.: (954) 351-9244   FL
Web Site: http://www.fleabusters.com
Year Founded: 1987
Anti Fleas Products Mfr
N.A.I.C.S.: 325412
Robert Yarmouth (VP)

RX OPTICAL LABORATORY INC.
1700 S Park St, Kalamazoo, MI 49001
Tel.: (269) 342-5958   MI
Web Site: http://www.rxoptical.com
Year Founded: 1947
Sales Range: $10-24.9 Million
Emp.: 55
Optical Products Sales
N.A.I.C.S.: 456130
Edward Fletcher (CEO)
Steve Yonke (CFO)

RX SYSTEMS INC.
121 Point W Blvd, Saint Charles, MO 63301-4409
Tel.: (636) 925-0001   MO
Web Site: http://www.rxsystems.com
Year Founded: 1979
Sales Range: $10-24.9 Million
Emp.: 102
Industrial & Personal Service Paper
N.A.I.C.S.: 424130
Richard B. Jensen (Founder, Pres & Treas)
Walter Tate (Controller)
Dale Spires (Dir-Label Div)
Bob Tippett (VP-Plant Ops)
Eve Beye (Mgr-Ops)
Tom Peters (Plant Mgr)

RX TECHNOLOGIES CORP.
7076 Spyglass Ave, Parkland, FL 33076
Tel.: (954) 599-3672   FL
Web Site: http://www.rxtechnologies.com
Year Founded: 2008
Prescription Drug Database
N.A.I.C.S.: 513140
Michael McManus (Chm, Pres & CEO)
Shepard Doniger (CFO, VP, Treas & Sec)

RXBENEFITS, INC.
3700 Colonnade Pkwy Ste 600, Birmingham, AL 35243
Web Site: http://www.rxbenefits.com
Year Founded: 1995
Employee Benefits Solutions & Consulting Services
N.A.I.C.S.: 541612
Bryan Statham (Vice Chm)
Scott Vogel (Chief Strategy Officer)
Wendy Barnes (CEO)
Rick Jelinek (Chm)
Subsidiaries:
Confidio, LLC   (1)
502 Washington Ave Ste 450, Towson, MD 21204
Tel.: (443) 767-7200
Web Site: http://www.confidio.com
Medical Consulting Services
N.A.I.C.S.: 541611
Cory Easton (Partner)
Scott Vogel (Partner)
Sonja Quale (Chief Clinical Officer & VP-Informatics)
Cathy Addis (VP-Vendor Rels)
Jack Nelson (VP-Ops)

RXR REALTY, LLC
625 RXR Plz, Uniondale, NY 11556
Tel.: (516) 506-6000
Web Site: http://www.rxrrealty.com
Rev.: $10,000,000,000
Emp.: 170
Real Estate Operations
N.A.I.C.S.: 531390
Jason Barnett (Vice Chm & Gen Counsel)
Richard Conniff (Co-COO & Mgr-Fund)
Todd Rechler (Pres-RXR Construction & Dev & Co-COO)
David Frank (Exec VP & Asst Gen Counsel)
Frank Adipietro (Exec VP & Head-Asset Mgmt & Special Situations)
Michael McMahon (Exec VP-Portfolio Mgmt & Dir-Tax)
Tom Carey (Exec VP & Controller)
Kenneth W. Bauer (Exec VP-Leasing)
Frank Pusinelli (Exec VP-Ops-Property Mgmt & Construction)
Joanne M. Minieri (COO-Dev Svcs, Construction, and Dev-Uniondale, Manhattan & Exec VP)
William Elder (Exec VP & Mng Dir-New York)
Seth Pinsky (Exec VP, Dir-Pub Affairs & Mgr-Fund-Metro Emerging Markets)
Philip Wharton (Exec VP-Residential Dev)
Allie Barot (Chief HR Officer & Exec VP)
Scott H. Rechler (Chm & CEO)
Michael Maturo (Pres & CFO)
F. D. Rich III (Chief Admin Officer & Exec VP)

RXUSA
81 Seaview Blvd, Port Washington, NY 11050
Tel.: (516) 467-2500
Web Site: http://www.rxusa.com
Sales Range: $250-299.9 Million
Emp.: 18
Online International Pharmacy Services
N.A.I.C.S.: 456110
Robert C. Drucker (Founder, Pres & CEO)

RXVANTAGE, INC.
11810 S Bentley Ave Apt 204, Los Angeles, CA 90025
Tel.: (310) 621-4551
Web Site: http://www.rxvantage.com
Year Founded: 2007
Ambulatory Health Care Services
N.A.I.C.S.: 621999
James Dwyer (VP-Sls)
Dan Gilman (Founder & CEO)
Subsidiaries:
onPoint Oncology, Inc.   (1)
3006 Pine Trl Cir, Hudson, OH 44236
Web Site: http://www.onpointoncology.com
Health Practitioners
N.A.I.C.S.: 621399
Kerry Bradley (Principal)
Tracy Lewis (Founder & CEO)

RY TIMBER INC.
85 Mill Rd, Townsend, MT 59644
Tel.: (406) 266-3111
Web Site: http://www.rytimber.com
Year Founded: 1991
Sales Range: $25-49.9 Million
Emp.: 200
Provider of Milling Services
N.A.I.C.S.: 321113
Scott Stern (Gen Mgr)
Brian Norby (Pres)

RYAN BIGGS CLARK DAVIS, ENGINEERING & SURVEYING, P.C.
257 Ushers Rd, Clifton Park, NY 12065
Tel.: (518) 406-5506   NY
Web Site: http://www.ryanbiggs.com
Year Founded: 1973
Sales Range: $1-9.9 Million
Emp.: 40
Structural Engineering & Land Surveying Services
N.A.I.C.S.: 541330
Christopher G. Maxon (Mgr-CAD)
Jamie L. Davis (Pres & Principal)
Ann L. Clark (VP)
Jack C. Healy (Principal)
Jill M. Shorter (Mktg Dir)
Ross M. Shepherd (Mgr-IT)
Sarah Krepel (Engr-Design)
Christopher N. Latreille (Assoc Principal)
Matthew G. Yerkey (Associate Principal)
Paul A. Rouis III (Principal)
Subsidiaries:
Clark Engineering & Surveying, P.C.   (1)
20 Shaker Rd, New Lebanon, NY 12125
Tel.: (518) 794-8613
Web Site: http://www.clarkpc.com
Sales Range: $1-9.9 Million
Emp.: 10
Structural Engineering & Land Surveying Services
N.A.I.C.S.: 541330
Ann L. Clark (Principal-Structural Engrg)
Douglas Clark (Principal-Civil & Site Engrg)

RYAN COMPANIES US, INC.
533 S 3rd St Ste 100, Minneapolis, MN 55415
Tel.: (612) 492-4000   MN
Web Site: https://www.ryancompanies.com
Year Founded: 1938
Sales Range: $50-74.9 Million
Emp.: 2,000
Commercial & Institutional Building Construction
N.A.I.C.S.: 236220
Patrick G. Ryan (CEO & CEO)
David Knoll (Dir-Dev-SouthCentral)
Brian Devlin (VP-Dev-SouthEast Reg)
Todd Schell (Sr VP-Natl Indus Sector)
Rick Collins (Pres-Southwest)
Collin Barr (Pres-North Reg)
Jeff Smith (Pres-Natl)
John Gould (Dir-Architecture-Senior Living)
Connor Lewis (VP-Dev-Health Care-Southeast Reg)

RYAN COMPANIES US, INC.

U.S. PRIVATE

Ryan Companies US, Inc.—(Continued)
Tyler Wilson (VP-Real Estate Dev)
Sheila Schmidt (Dir-Healthcare Dept)
Ryan Grove (Dir-Dev)
John Strittmatter (Chm-SouthWest)
Anna Riley (Dir-Mgmt-SouthWest Reg)
Mark Schoening (Sr VP-Retail)
Anders Pesavento (VP-Capital Markets)
Geoff Eastburn (VP-Midwest)
Mike Rodriguez (VP-Architecture & Engrg)
Curt Pascoe (Dir-Dev-Great Lakes)
Josh Tracy (Mgr-Real Estate Dev)
Ed Turpin (Gen Mgr)
Mike Ryan (Pres-Ryan A+E & Sr VP)
Alena Johnson (Dir-Architecture & Healthcare)
Alisa Timm (Dir-Real Estate Mgmt-Southwest)
John DiVall (Sr VP-Real Estate Dev)
Jim Durda (Gen Mgr-City Center)
Bryce Tache (Sr Dir-Diversity & Inclusion)
Lucas Larson (Dir-Dev-Senior Living)
Mike Prefling (VP-Insights & Innovation)
Daniel Raimer (Dir-Real Estate Dev)
Jim Person (VP-Field Ops)
Jon Paul Bacariza (Dir-Architecture-Southeast)
Eric Anderson (Sr VP)
Mike Mahoney (Pres-West)
Gil Gonzalez (VP-Dev-Multifamily)
Randy Winger (Dir-Construction)
Bill Wikle (VP-Dev)
Brook Barefoot (VP-Real Estate Dev-Multifamily-Atlanta)
Cloteen Jasmin (Sr VP-Atlanta)
Brian Murray (CEO)

Subsidiaries:

Ryan Companies US, Inc. (1)
101 E Kennedy Blvd Ste 2450, Tampa, FL 33602
Tel.: (813) 204-5000
Emp.: 18
Nonresidential Construction
N.A.I.C.S.: 236220
Douglas J. Dieck (Pres)
Adam Robinson (Dir-Dev)
Mike Harryman (VP-Construction)

RYAN DODGE
1112 Missouri Ave, Bismarck, ND 58504-5294
Tel.: (701) 223-1170
Web Site:
  http://www.ryandodgebismarck.com
Sales Range: $10-24.9 Million
Emp.: 50
New Car Whslr
N.A.I.C.S.: 441110
Jory Ditsworth (Bus Mgr)

RYAN FIREPROTECTION INC.
9740 E 148th St, Noblesville, IN 46060
Tel.: (317) 770-7100 IN
Web Site: http://www.ryanfp.com
Sales Range: $25-49.9 Million
Emp.: 200
Fire Sprinkler System Installation
N.A.I.C.S.: 238220
Daniel Ryan (Pres)
Bud Gunter (Exec VP-Ops)
Mark Riffey (Exec VP-Bus Dev & Mktg)
Tim Machina (Exec VP-Sls & Estimating)
James Art (CFO)
Jerry Ryan (COO)

RYAN INCORPORATED CENTRAL
2700 E Racine St, Janesville, WI 53545
Tel.: (608) 754-2291 WI
Web Site: http://www.ryancentral.com
Year Founded: 1985
Rev.: $89,985,469
Emp.: 250
Heavy Construction
N.A.I.C.S.: 236210
Geoffrey Rankin (CFO)
Adam Ryan (Pres)
Greg Ellis (Mgr-Ops)

RYAN LAWN & TREE INC.
9120 Barton St, Overland Park, KS 66214
Web Site: http://www.ryanlawn.com
Lawn Care Services
N.A.I.C.S.: 423820
Larry Ryan (Founder)

Subsidiaries:

Simply Green Lawn Sprinklers, Inc. (1)
4301 NW Gateway, Riverside, MO 64150
Tel.: (816) 746-6817
Web Site:
  http://simplygreenlawnsprinklers.com
Sales Range: $1-9.9 Million
Emp.: 15
Landscape Lighting, Sprinkler & Lighting Designs Mfr
N.A.I.C.S.: 423820
Tony Shores (Owner)

RYAN LINCOLN MERCURY KIA
321 Baltimore Pike, Springfield, PA 19064
Tel.: (610) 544-0100 PA
Web Site:
  http://www.ryanspringfield.com
Year Founded: 1980
Sales Range: $25-49.9 Million
Emp.: 120
Sales of New & Used Automobiles
N.A.I.C.S.: 441110
Mary Ciociola (Controller)
Jim Johnson (Mgr-Svc)

RYAN PARTNERSHIP, LLC
50 Danbury Rd, Wilton, CT 06897-4448
Tel.: (203) 210-3000 CT
Year Founded: 1984
Sales Range: $100-124.9 Million
Emp.: 550
Advetising Agency
N.A.I.C.S.: 541810
Mary Perry (Pres-Ryan Wilton)

Subsidiaries:

Catapult Marketing (1)
55 Post Rd W, Westport, CT 06880
Tel.: (203) 682-4000
Rev.: $25,000,000
Emp.: 150
Advetising Agency
N.A.I.C.S.: 541810
Peter Cloutier (Pres-East)
Seth Diamond (VP-Insights)
Beth Murphy (Dir-Insights)
Margaret Lewis (Exec VP & Dir-Ops)
Shari Brickin (Exec VP & Gen Mgr)
Maura Priem (Exec VP)
Gene Tiernan (Sr VP)

Branch (Domestic):

Catapult Marketing (2)
12121 Wilshire Blvd Ste 100, Los Angeles, CA 90025-1166
Tel.: (310) 571-0804
Emp.: 35
Advetising Agency
N.A.I.C.S.: 541810

Catapult Marketing (2)
7702 E Doubletree Ranch Rd Ste 300, Scottsdale, AZ 85258
Tel.: (866) 222-2851
Advetising Agency
N.A.I.C.S.: 541810

Panavista Promotions (1)
220 E Las Colinas Blvd, Irving, TX 75039
Tel.: (469) 420-1500
Web Site: http://www.panavistapromo.com
Emp.: 10
Advetising Agency
N.A.I.C.S.: 541810
Noemi Ricalo (Pres)

RPM Connect (1)
10 S 5th St Ste 330, Minneapolis, MN 55402
Tel.: (612) 204-9790
Sales Range: $10-24.9 Million
Emp.: 50
Advetising Agency
N.A.I.C.S.: 541810

Ryan Partnership (1)
325 N LaSalle Ste 775, Chicago, IL 60654
Tel.: (312) 595-0281
Emp.: 60
Advetising Agency
N.A.I.C.S.: 541810

Ryan Partnership (1)
440 Polaris Pkwy Ste 350, Westerville, OH 43082-7262
Tel.: (614) 436-6558
Advetising Agency
N.A.I.C.S.: 541810
Jonas Phillips (Dir-Art)

Ryan Retail Zone (1)
3301 Market St Ste 203, Bentonville, AR 72758
Tel.: (479) 464-8644
Emp.: 9
Advertising Material Distribution & Other Related Services
N.A.I.C.S.: 541870
Fiona P. Dias (Principal Digital Partner)

RYAN PRINTING, INC
300 Corporate Dr Ste 6, Blauvelt, NY 10913
Tel.: (845) 535-3235
Web Site: http://www.ryanprintingny.com
Year Founded: 1992
Sales Range: $1-9.9 Million
Emp.: 18
Commercial Printing Services
N.A.I.C.S.: 323111
Al Ryan (Pres)
Marianne Rifflard (Office Mgr)
Christopher Bugeia (Mgr-Digital Prepress)

RYAN SANDERS BASEBALL, L.P.
3400 E Palm Valley Blvd, Round Rock, TX 78665-3906 TX
Year Founded: 2004
Holding Company; Professional Baseball Club Owner & Operator
N.A.I.C.S.: 551112
Jay Miller (Partner)
Eddie Maloney (Partner)
Reese Ryan (Partner)
Reid Ryan (Partner)
Brad Sanders (Partner)
Bret Sanders (Partner)
Don A. Sanders (Gen Partner)
J. J. Gotsch (Exec VP)
Lynn Nolan Ryan Jr. (Mng Partner)

Subsidiaries:

Corpus Christi Baseball Club, L.P. (1)
734 E Port Ave, Corpus Christi, TX 78401
Tel.: (361) 561-4665
Web Site:
  http://www.minorleaguebaseball.com
Sales Range: $10-24.9 Million
Emp.: 100
Professional Baseball Club
N.A.I.C.S.: 711211

Round Rock Baseball Club, L.P. (1)
3400 E Palm Valley Blvd, Round Rock, TX 78665
Tel.: (512) 255-2255

Web Site: http://www.roundrockexpress.com
Sales Range: $10-24.9 Million
Emp.: 60
Professional Baseball Club
N.A.I.C.S.: 711211
Chris Almendarez (Pres)

RYAN SEACREST ENTERPRISES, INC.
5750 Wilshire Blvd, Los Angeles, CA 90036
Tel.: (323) 954-2400 CA
Web Site:
  http://www.ryanseacrest.com
Holding Company; Entertainment Production & Marketing Services
N.A.I.C.S.: 551112
Ryan Seacrest (Founder & Owner)

Subsidiaries:

Civic Entertainment Group, LLC (1)
436 Lafayette St, New York, NY 10003
Tel.: (212) 426-7006
Web Site: http://www.cegny.com
Sales Range: $1-9.9 Million
Emp.: 45
Marketing Agency
N.A.I.C.S.: 541830
Stuart Ruderfer (Co-Founder & Co-CEO)
Parke Spencer (Pres)
David Cohn (Co-Founder & Co-CEO)
Nina Habib (Dir-Talent)
Sarah Unger (Sr VP-Cultural, Insights & Strategy)
Linda Ong (Chief Culture Officer)

Ryan Seacrest Productions, LLC (1)
5750 Wilshire Blvd, Los Angeles, CA 90036
Tel.: (323) 954-2400
Web Site: http://www.ryanseacrest.com
Cable Television Programming Production & Distribution Services
N.A.I.C.S.: 516210
Ryan Seacrest (Founder & Chm)
Eugene Young (Pres)
Rabih Gholam (Exec VP-Unscripted Programming)
Teri Kennedy (Exec VP-Dev & Original Unscripted Programming)

RYAN TRADING CORP.
2500 Westchester Ave, Purchase, NY 10577-2540
Tel.: (914) 253-6767 NY
Web Site: http://www.ryantrading.com
Year Founded: 1983
Sales Range: $10-24.9 Million
Emp.: 6
Importer of Fruit Juice Concentrates
N.A.I.C.S.: 424490
John Ryan (Pres)
Louie Goduco (Acct Exec)

RYAN, LLC
13155 Noel Rd Ste 100, Dallas, TX 75240
Tel.: (972) 934-0022 DE
Web Site: http://www.ryan.com
Year Founded: 1991
Sales Range: $350-399.9 Million
Emp.: 1,382
Tax Consulting Services
N.A.I.C.S.: 541213
George Brint Ryan (CEO, Founder & Chm)
John M. Polizzi (Principal-Client Svcs-Michigan)
Kevin S. Powell (Principal-Transaction Tax-Texas)
Albert Rex (Principal-Credits & Incentives-Massachusetts)
Lanie A. Thompson (Principal-Texas)
Michael Finnegan (Principal-Property Tax-Tennessee)
Andy Hammons (Principal-Client Svcs-Tennessee)
Susan Han (Principal-Abandoned & Unclaimed Property-California)
Kenneth M. Hartman (Principal-Property Tax-Illinois)

Alan M. Heichman (Principal-Property Tax-Illinois)
Shawn M. King (Principal-Property Tax-Illinois)
Shane Moncrief (Principal-Property Tax-Georgia)
Brendan F. Moore (Pres-Intl)
Mark A. Paolillo (Principal-Abandoned & Unclaimed Property-Massachusetts)
Clyde Seymour (Principal-Income Tax-Ontario)
Grant Smith (Principal-Tax Tech-Georgia)
James M. Trester (Principal-Client Svcs-Texas)
Melissa Munoz (Principal-Credits & Incentives Practice-New Mexico)
Alan Decker (Principal-Transaction Tax-Texas)
Brett Koch (Principal-Property Tax-Texas)
Matthew Scherer (Principal-Transaction Tax-Texas)
Nathan Bittner (Principal-Fuels & Excercise Tax Practice-Georgia)
Jennifer Ivanelli (Principal-Comml Property Tax-Illinois)
David Oldani (CFO & Sr VP)
Jon C. Sweet (Pres-Europe & Asia Pacific Ops)
Ginny B. Kissling (COO & Pres-Global)
David Douglas (Principal-Ontario)
Garry Round (Pres-Canadian Ops)
Stacey Underwood (Sr Mgr-Comm, Content, and PR)
Rebekah Gardner (Principal & Sr VP-Sls)
MaryKay Manning (Sr VP-Strategic Recruiting)
Jason Dunnachie (Principal-R&D Practice-Australia)
Gerry L. Ridgely Jr. (Vice Chm-Emerging Businesses & Exec VP)
Damon N. Chronis (Pres-Ops-U.S)
Suzanne C. den Breems (Principal)
Jon Graham (Pres-Australian Ops)
Ray Ann Cacheria (CIO & Sr VP)
Rob Foster (Principal & Sr VP-Tax as a Svc)
Brooke Keene (Chief Experience Officer & Sr VP)
Joe Mileti (Sr VP-Corp Dev)
John Smith (Chief Legal Officer, Gen Counsel & Sr VP)
Amy Tice (Chief People Officer & Sr VP)
Tim Wagner (CTO & Sr VP)
Robert Wertz (Chief Real Estate Officer & Sr VP)
Jennifer Whitten (Sr VP-Enterprise Center of Excellence)
Angela Rittgers (CMO & Sr VP)

Subsidiaries:

Economics Partners, LLC (1)
1999 Broadway Ste 4100, Denver, CO 80202-5744
Tel.: (303) 297-1260
Web Site: http://www.econpartners.com
Professional, Scientific & Technical Services
N.A.I.C.S.: 541990
Timothy Reichert (Pres)

Kurz Group, Inc. (1)
8333 Douglas Ave Ste 1370 Lb-21, Dallas, TX 75225
Tel.: (214) 696-4656
Web Site: http://www.kurzgroup.com
Activities Related to Real Estate
N.A.I.C.S.: 531390
Richard A. Kurz (Pres)

Macrostie Historic Advisors, LLC (1)
1400 16th St NW Ste 420, Washington, DC 20036
Tel.: (202) 483-2020
Web Site: http://www.macrostiehistoric.com
Professional, Scientific & Technical Services
N.A.I.C.S.: 541990
William G. MacRostie (Principal)

Morrison & Head LP (1)
4210 Spicewood Springs Rd Ste 211, Austin, TX 78759-8654
Tel.: (512) 302-5800
Web Site: http://www.morrisonandhead.com
Offices of Certified Public Accountants
N.A.I.C.S.: 541211
Chet Morrison (Partner)

Paradigm DKD Group, L.L.C. (1)
3030 N Central Ave, Phoenix, AZ 85012-2707
Tel.: (602) 393-9689
Web Site: http://www.paradigmtax.com
Law firm
N.A.I.C.S.: 541199
Matthew Fossey (Exec VP-Ops-East)

Worldwide Trade Partners, LLC (1)
601 Carlson Pkwy Ste 1050, Minneapolis, MN 55331
Tel.: (952) 955-6677
Web Site: http://www.wtpadvisors.com
Emp.: 20
Tax & Auditing Advisory Services
N.A.I.C.S.: 541213
Guy Sanschagin (Principal)
Barton Facey (Dir-UK Tax Compliance Svcs)
Kash Mansori (Dir-Transfer Pricing & Valuation Svcs)
Nancy Voth (Dir-Transfer Pricing & Valuation Svcs)
Simon Hopkins (Dir-UK Tax Advisory Svcs)

RYANS ALL-GLASS INC.
9884 Springfield Pike, Cincinnati, OH 45215
Tel.: (513) 771-4440
Web Site: http://www.ryansallglass.com
Sales Range: $10-24.9 Million
Emp.: 100
Provider of Glass Replacement & Installation Services
N.A.I.C.S.: 238150
Bruce Ryan (Pres)

RYCON CONSTRUCTION INC.
2525 Liberty Ave, Pittsburgh, PA 15222
Tel.: (412) 392-2525
Web Site: http://www.ryconinc.com
Year Founded: 1989
Sales Range: $10-24.9 Million
Emp.: 45
Nonresidential Construction Services
N.A.I.C.S.: 236220
Todd Dominick (Principal)
Brendan Madden (Project Mgr)
Nick Grguras (Project Mgr)
Ronald Demay (Controller)
Edward Szwarc (Exec VP)
Phil Linton (Sr Mgr-Preconstruction)

RYDALCH ELECTRIC INC.
250 Plymouth Ave, Salt Lake City, UT 84115
Tel.: (801) 265-1813
Web Site: http://www.rydalch-electric.com
Rev.: $12,429,744
Emp.: 105
Electrical Contractor
N.A.I.C.S.: 238210
Frank Rydalch (Pres)
Dave Gray (Project Mgr)
Joe Hancock (Project Mgr)

RYDELL CHEVROLET INC.
1325 E San Marnan Dr, Waterloo, IA 50702-4334
Tel.: (319) 234-4601
Web Site: http://www.rydellauto.com
Year Founded: 1984
Sales Range: $50-74.9 Million
Emp.: 150
Car Whslr
N.A.I.C.S.: 441110
Matt Halbur (Gen Mgr)
James Rydell (Owner)

RYDELL COMPANY INC.
2700 S Washington St, Grand Forks, ND 58201
Tel.: (701) 772-7211
Web Site: http://www.rydellcars.com
Sales Range: $150-199.9 Million
Emp.: 65
New & Used Car Dealers
N.A.I.C.S.: 441110
Wes Rydell (Pres)

Subsidiaries:

Scottsbluff Motor Company (1)
2014 E 20th Pl, Scottsbluff, NE 69361
Tel.: (308) 632-2173
Web Site: http://www.teamchev.com
Automobiles, New & Used
N.A.I.C.S.: 441110
Kent Holub (Owner & Mgr)

Sheboygan Chevrolet Cadillac (1)
3400 S Bus Dr, Sheboygan, WI 53081
Tel.: (920) 459-6840
Web Site: http://www.sheboyganauto.com
Emp.: 70
Automobiles, New & Used
N.A.I.C.S.: 441110
Randy Romanoski (Owner & Pres)

Sheboygan Chrysler Center (1)
2701 Wasshington Ave, Sheboygan, WI 53081
Tel.: (920) 459-6020
Web Site: http://www.sheboyganauto.com
Rev.: $33,067,338
Emp.: 35
Automobiles, New & Used
N.A.I.C.S.: 441110
Randy Romanoski (Pres)

RYDER MEMORIAL HOSPITAL
PO Box 859, Humacao, PR 00792
Tel.: (787) 852-0768   PR
Web Site: http://www.hryder.org
Year Founded: 1914
Sales Range: $50-74.9 Million
Emp.: 996
Health Care Srvices
N.A.I.C.S.: 622110
Edward Rivera (Pres)
Heriberto Silva (Treas)
Jess M. Reina (Sec)
Roque Lebrn (VP)
Raul Ramos Pereira (Dir-Medical)

RYE FORD INC.
1151 Post Rd, Rye, NY 10580
Tel.: (914) 967-6300
Web Site: http://www.ryesubaru.com
Rev.: $19,400,000
Emp.: 42
New & Used Car Dealers
N.A.I.C.S.: 441110
Mike Poznanski (Mgr-Sls Subaru)
Anthony Gualdino (Mgr-Sls)

RYKO PLASTIC PRODUCTS INC.
710 Palmyrita Ave Ste B, Riverside, CA 92507
Tel.: (909) 947-3000
Web Site: http://www.ryko-products.com
Rev.: $14,000,000
Emp.: 175
Mfr & Extruder of Thermoplastic Products for Doors & Windows
N.A.I.C.S.: 326199
Melvin V. Morrow (Pres)

RYNN'S LUGGAGE CORPORATION
3500 Garden Brook Dr, Farmers Branch, TX 75234
Tel.: (412) 481-6277
Web Site: http://www.netbags.com
Year Founded: 1983
Sales Range: $10-24.9 Million
Emp.: 55
Luggage Retailer
N.A.I.C.S.: 316990
Stephen Rynn (Pres)

RYNONE MANUFACTURING CORPORATION
N Thomas Ave, Sayre, PA 18840
Tel.: (570) 888-5272   DE
Web Site: http://www.rynone.com
Year Founded: 1945
Sales Range: $100-124.9 Million
Emp.: 175
Mfr of Vanities & Counter Tops
N.A.I.C.S.: 327991
Thomas E. Rynone (CEO)
William J. Rynone (Treas & Sec)
Gary Bradley (Controller)

RYONET CORP.
12303 NE 56th St, Vancouver, WA 98682
Tel.: (360) 576-7188   WA
Web Site: http://www.screenprinting.com
Year Founded: 2004
Sales Range: $10-24.9 Million
Emp.: 74
Commercial Screen Printing
N.A.I.C.S.: 323113
Ryan Moor (CEO)

RYZE CLAIM SOLUTIONS LLC
14701 Cumberland Rd Ste 300, Noblesville, IN 46060
Tel.: (317) 770-6050
Web Site: http://www.ryzeclaims.com
Claims Services Company
N.A.I.C.S.: 524291
Tony Grippa (CEO)
Alisshia Isaacs (Chief People Officer & Exec VP)

Subsidiaries:

Wimberly Claim Services (1)
9485 Regency Sq Blvd Ste 107, Jacksonville, FL 32225
Tel.: (904) 745-5471
Web Site: http://www.wimberlyclaims.com
Third Party Administration of Insurance & Pension Funds
N.A.I.C.S.: 524292
John Wimberly (CEO)

S & A HOMES INC.
2121 Old Gatesburg Rd, State College, PA 16803
Tel.: (814) 231-4780
Web Site: http://www.sahomebuilder.com
Sales Range: $10-24.9 Million
Emp.: 610
Lumber & Building Material Whslr
N.A.I.C.S.: 444110
Bob Poole (CEO)

S & B MOTELS, INC.
400 N Woodlawn St Ste 205, Wichita, KS 67208
Tel.: (316) 522-3864
Sales Range: $10-24.9 Million
Emp.: 165
Motel Owner & Operator
N.A.I.C.S.: 721110
Stanley Weilert (Owner)

S & D SPECIALTY, INC.
14546 Hawthorne Ave, Fontana, CA 92335
Tel.: (909) 350-8040   CA
Year Founded: 1987
Emp.: 50
Hydraulic Equipment Repair Services
N.A.I.C.S.: 332710

S & D SPECIALTY, INC.

S & D Specialty, Inc.—(Continued)
Dick Foster (Pres)

S & S PRECAST, INC.
840 W 25 S, Winamac, IN 46996
Tel.: (574) 946-7702
Web Site:
http://www.sandsprecast.com
Year Founded: 1993
Sales Range: $1-9.9 Million
Emp.: 20
Precast Concrete Products Mfr
N.A.I.C.S.: 327390
Richard Shinn (Dir-Ops)
Meghan Allen (Pres)
Jim Paulsen (Mgr-ReCo)

S & W CONTRACTING COMPANY INC.
952 New Salem Rd, Murfreesboro, TN 37129
Tel.: (615) 893-2511
Web Site:
http://sandwcontracting.com
Sales Range: $10-24.9 Million
Emp.: 85
Electrical Wiring Services
N.A.I.C.S.: 238210
Richie Bolin (CEO)

S AND Y INDUSTRIES, INC.
606 Industrial Rd, Winfield, KS 67156
Tel.: (620) 221-4001
Web Site:
http://www.sandyindustries.com
Year Founded: 1984
Rev.: $7,800,000
Emp.: 100
Electronic Components Mfr
N.A.I.C.S.: 334419
John Foust (CFO & VP)
Sandy Foust (Pres & CEO)
David Gaskins (Mgr-Quality)

S B BALLARD CONSTRUCTION CO.
2828 Shipps Corner Rd, Virginia Beach, VA 23453-2920
Tel.: (757) 440-5555
Web Site: http://www.sbballard.com
Year Founded: 1981
Sales Range: $100-124.9 Million
Emp.: 260
Nonresidential Construction Services
N.A.I.C.S.: 236220
Stephen B. Ballard (Pres)
Ann E. Mason (CFO)

S C S CONTRACTING, INC.
1965 Lower Roswell Rd, Marietta, GA 30068-3348
Tel.: (770) 565-7065
Year Founded: 1979
Sales Range: $10-24.9 Million
Emp.: 8
Painting & Wall Covering Installation Services
N.A.I.C.S.: 238320
Steve Sweatman (Pres)

S EDWARD INC.
229 W 36th St Fl 11, New York, NY 10018
Tel.: (212) 695-0305
Sales Range: $10-24.9 Million
Emp.: 25
Textile Converters
N.A.I.C.S.: 314999

S GROUP INC.
1928 Hau St, Honolulu, HI 96819
Tel.: (808) 456-4717
Web Site: http://www.smsihawaii.com
Year Founded: 1985
Sales Range: $10-24.9 Million
Emp.: 35
Holding Company; Residential & Commercial Construction Contracting Services
N.A.I.C.S.: 551112
Gerard Sakamoto (Pres)

Subsidiaries:

S&M Sakamoto Inc. (1)
1928 Hau St, Honolulu, HI 96819 (100%)
Tel.: (808) 456-4717
Web Site: http://www.smsihawaii.com
Sales Range: $10-24.9 Million
Emp.: 12
Commercial Construction Contracting Services
N.A.I.C.S.: 236220
Gerard Sakamoto (Chm-Board)
Dale Yoneda (Pres)

S I L INC.
PO Box 159, Alpena, SD 57312
Tel.: (605) 849-3367
Sales Range: $25-49.9 Million
Emp.: 550
Meat Product Production Services
N.A.I.C.S.: 311612
Jack Link (CEO)
Bret Ocholik (VP-Mktg)
Doug Marvel (Dir-IT)
Rick Tebee (VP)

S M RESOURCES CORPORATION
4421 Forbes Blvd Ste A, Lanham, MD 20706
Tel.: (301) 459-4424
Web Site: http://www.smrcusa.com
Year Founded: 1991
Sales Range: $1-9.9 Million
Emp.: 58
Data Processing & Computer Programming Services
N.A.I.C.S.: 518210
Neelu Modali (Pres & CEO)
Heng Gu (Project Mgr)
Kirsten Schoenfeld (Dir-HR)

S M WILSON & CO.
2185 Hampton Ave, Saint Louis, MO 63139-2904
Tel.: (314) 633-5715
Web Site: http://www.smwilson.com
Year Founded: 1932
Sales Range: $125-149.9 Million
Emp.: 300
Civil Engineering Services
N.A.I.C.S.: 237310
Michael R. Dohle (CFO)
Scott J. Wilson (CEO)
Steve Koxlien (Mgr-Quality Control)
Dan Hoffman (Project Mgr-Safety)
Jim Hoette (Dir-Indus Project Dev & Project Mgr)
Judd Presley (VP-Bus Dev)
Courtney Kinamore (Mgr-Mktg)
Tina Anthoney (Mgr-Mktg)
Debra Sheahan (Dir-Estimating)
Amanda Bohnert (Pres)
Drew Raasch (Dir-Pre-Construction)
Tom Burns (Dir-Safety)
Rachel Miller (Mgr-HR)
Jamie Berzon (Mgr-IT)
Liz Peroutka (Engr-Project)
Bill Wagner (VP)
Dan Harper (Sr VP)
Rebecca Cornatzer (Dir-HR)
Amy Berg (Pres)
Mark Patterson (CIO)
Jeff Shipp (Officer-Site Safety & Health)
Mark Cochran (COO)

S R DOOR, INC.
42 Shackelford Rd, Pataskala, OH 43062
Tel.: (740) 927-3558

Web Site:
http://www.sealritedoor.com
Year Founded: 1981
Sales Range: $10-24.9 Million
Emp.: 106
Wood Window & Door Mfr
N.A.I.C.S.: 321911
Rich Kellenberger (Gen Mgr)
Gary Kime (VP)
Bruce Landenberger (Controller)
Scott A. Miller (Pres & CEO)

S ROSE INC.
1213 Prospect Ave E, Cleveland, OH 44115
Tel.: (216) 781-8200
Web Site: http://www.srose.com
Year Founded: 1913
Sales Range: $10-24.9 Million
Emp.: 30
Distribution of Office Furniture
N.A.I.C.S.: 423210
Clark Rose (COO)
Paul Johanni (Sr VP-Sls)

S&A CUSTOM BUILT HOMES INC.
2121 Old Gatesburg Rd Ste 200, State College, PA 16803
Tel.: (814) 355-2325
Web Site:
http://www.sahomebuilder.com
Year Founded: 1968
Sales Range: $25-49.9 Million
Emp.: 610
Single-Family Housing Construction
N.A.I.C.S.: 236115
Robert E. Poole Jr. (Chm, Pres & CEO)

S&A STORES INC.
450 7th Ave Ste 701, New York, NY 10123
Tel.: (212) 244-2220
Rev.: $16,965,829
Emp.: 4
Variety Stores
N.A.I.C.S.: 455219
Marie Vera (Office Mgr)

S&B ENGINEERS & CONSTRUCTORS, LTD.
7825 Park Pl Blvd, Houston, TX 77087-4639
Tel.: (713) 845-4529
Web Site: http://www.sbec.com
Year Founded: 1967
Sales Range: $600-649.9 Million
Emp.: 5,000
Heavy Construction Services
N.A.I.C.S.: 237990
Richard L. Akin (Sr VP-Bus Dev)
Charles R. Reid (Sr VP-Engrg)
David Taylor (COO & Exec VP)
Thomas Collins (Sr VP)
Brook Brookshire (CEO)
John Parker (Sr VP-EPC & Construction)
Brad Bailey (VP-Comm & External Affairs)
Valerie Carlson (CFO & Treas)
Lindsay Burke (Dir-Comm & Mktg)

Subsidiaries:

Ford, Bacon and Davis, LLC (1)
12021 Lakeland Park Blvd, Baton Rouge, LA 70809
Tel.: (225) 292-0050
Web Site: http://www.fbd.com
Construction Engineering Services
N.A.I.C.S.: 541330
Rick Moore (Pres)
Wrightston Jackson (VP)
Walter L. Rachal (VP)
John Brabender (VP)
Michael Cruse (Sr VP-MAPPI Bus Unit)
Mark Dellinger (VP)
Jeff W. Fails (VP)

Hunter Howe (VP)
Stephen Quillin (VP)
Ray Sherman (Sr VP-Process Bus Unit)
James L. Horton Jr. (VP)

S&B Infrastructure, Ltd. (1)
3535 Sage Rd, Houston, TX 77056-7070
Tel.: (713) 845-5401
Web Site: http://www.sbinfra.com
Sales Range: $25-49.9 Million
Emp.: 3
Engineeering Services
N.A.I.C.S.: 541330
Harold R. Reddish (Pres & CEO)
Daniel O. Rios (Sr VP)

S&B Plant Services, Ltd. (1)
7825 Park Place Blvd, Houston, TX 77087
Tel.: (713) 645-4141
Web Site: http://www.sbplantservices.com
Construction Engineering Services
N.A.I.C.S.: 541330
James G. Slaughter Jr. (Chm)

S&B TECHNICAL PRODUCTS, INC.
1300 E Berry St, Fort Worth, TX 76119-3003
Tel.: (817) 923-3344
Web Site:
http://www.maloneytech.com
Year Founded: 1955
Sales Range: $50-74.9 Million
Emp.: 100
Mfr of Gaskets; Spears; Line Markers; Pipes
N.A.I.C.S.: 326299
George French (Controller)
Steve Lockard (Gen Mgr)
Brad Corbett Jr. (Pres)

Subsidiaries:

Maloney Technical Products, Inc. (1)
1300 E Berry St, Fort Worth, TX 76119 (100%)
Tel.: (817) 923-3344
Web Site: http://www.maloneytech.com
Sales Range: $10-24.9 Million
Emp.: 25
Mfr of Line Markers
N.A.I.C.S.: 326299
Steve Lockard Herst (Gen Mgr)

S&C ELECTRIC COMPANY
6601 N Ridge Blvd, Chicago, IL 60626-3904
Tel.: (773) 338-1000
Web Site: http://www.sandc.com
Year Founded: 1911
Sales Range: $350-399.9 Million
Emp.: 2,000
Switchboard Mfr
N.A.I.C.S.: 335313
John W. Estey (Chm)
Anders Sjoelin (Pres & CEO)

Subsidiaries:

S&C Electric (China) Company Ltd. (1)
181 Tai Shan Road SND, Suzhou, 215129, Jiangsu, China
Tel.: (86) 512 6665 9000
Web Site: http://www.sandc.com.cn
Sales Range: $25-49.9 Million
Emp.: 150
Power Transformer Mfr
N.A.I.C.S.: 334416
Chen Bo (Gen Mgr)

S&C Electric (Suzhou) Co. Ltd. (1)
181 Tai Shan Rd SND, Suzhou, 215129, Jiangsu, China (100%)
Tel.: (86) 51266659000
Web Site: http://www.sandc.com
Emp.: 200
Mfr of High Voltage Fuses & Switches
N.A.I.C.S.: 335313
Bo Chen (Gen Mgr)

S&C Electric Canada Ltd. (1)
90 Belfield Rd, Toronto, M9W 1G4, ON, Canada (100%)
Tel.: (416) 249-9171

Web Site: http://www.snc.com
Sales Range: $25-49.9 Million
Emp.: 300
Mfr of High Voltage Fuses & Switches
N.A.I.C.S.: 335313
Anders Hultberg *(Pres)*

S&C Electric Company-Automation Systems (1)
1135 Atlantic Ave Ste 100, Alameda, CA 94501-1176 **(100%)**
Tel.: (510) 864-9300
Web Site: http://www.sandc.com
Sales Range: $25-49.9 Million
Emp.: 75
Electric Power Distribution Automation Equipment & Systems Designer & Mfr
N.A.I.C.S.: 335314

S&C Electric Europe Ltd. (1)
Princess House Princess Way, Swansea, SA1 3LW, Wales, United Kingdom
Tel.: (44) 1792 455070
Sales Range: $10-24.9 Million
Emp.: 25
Power Transformer Mfr
N.A.I.C.S.: 334416
Andrew Jones *(Mng Dir)*
Steven Jones *(Dir-Sls)*

S&C Electric Mexicana, S. de R.L. de C.V. (1)
Dante No 36 Desp - 701 Col Anzures, 11590, Mexico, Mexico
Tel.: (52) 55 5560 3993
Web Site: http://www.sandc.com
Emp.: 176
Power Transformer Mfr
N.A.I.C.S.: 334416
Alfredo Castellanos *(Mgr-Sls)*

S&C Electric do Brasil Limitada (1)
Avenida Rui Barbosa 5525 Modulo B Sao Jose dos Pinhais, Sao Jose dos Pinhais, CEP 83045-350, Parana, Brazil
Tel.: (55) 41 3382 6481
Web Site: http://www.sandc.com.br
High Voltage Fuses & Switches Mfr
N.A.I.C.S.: 335313

S&DS MARKET INC.
858 N Plymouth Rd, Winamac, IN 46996
Tel.: (574) 946-3155
Rev.: $10,800,000
Emp.: 55
Grocery Stores, Independent
N.A.I.C.S.: 445110

S&F SUPPLIES INC.
93 Emerson Pl, Brooklyn, NY 11205
Tel.: (718) 399-3333
Web Site: http://www.sfsupplies.com
Rev.: $15,271,609
Emp.: 30
Signmaker Equipment & Supplies
N.A.I.C.S.: 423840
Joseph Sandel *(Pres)*

S&G CARPET AND MORE
4952 Almaden Exp, San Jose, CA 95118
Tel.: (408) 414-1188
Web Site: http://www.sgcarpet.com
Rev.: $27,897,708
Emp.: 40
Floor Covering Stores
N.A.I.C.S.: 449121
Doug Caskey *(Mgr)*

S&H EXPRESS, INC.
400 Mulberry St, York, PA 17403
Tel.: (717) 848-5015 PA
Web Site: http://www.sandhexpress.com
Year Founded: 1992
Sales Range: $25-49.9 Million
Emp.: 375
Freight Warehousing & Shipping Services
N.A.I.C.S.: 484121

Stephen Shellenberger *(Pres)*
Eric Evans *(VP & Dir-Maintenance)*
David Ruiz *(VP & Dir-Fin & Acctg)*
Jordan Kolb *(Exec VP)*
Subsidiaries:
Landis Express, Inc. (1)
2600/2605 Beltline Ave, Reading, PA 19605
Tel.: (610) 921-1300
Web Site: http://www.landisexpress.com
Emp.: 200
Freight Warehousing & Shipping Services
N.A.I.C.S.: 484121
Tom Detrick *(Mgr-Warehouse)*

S&H INCORPORATED
2650 Washburn Way Ste 250, Klamath Falls, OR 97603
Tel.: (541) 273-4639
Sales Range: $25-49.9 Million
Emp.: 600
Fast-Food Restaurant Owner & Operator
N.A.I.C.S.: 722513
Todd Stewart *(Pres)*
Richard Holt *(VP)*
Justin Stewart *(VP)*

S&H PACKING & SALES CO. INC.
2590 Harriet St, Los Angeles, CA 90058
Tel.: (323) 583-7588 CA
Web Site: http://www.s-hpacking.com
Year Founded: 1941
Sales Range: $25-49.9 Million
Emp.: 350
Vegetables & Melons
N.A.I.C.S.: 111219
Robert Gamble *(CFO)*
Subsidiaries:
Horwath & Co. Inc. (1)
2590 Harriett St, Los Angeles, CA 90021-1606
Tel.: (213) 627-3055
Sales Range: $10-24.9 Million
Emp.: 20
Distribute Fresh Fruits & Vegetables
N.A.I.C.S.: 111219
Royal Produce Sales Inc. (1)
2590 Harriet St, Los Angeles, CA 90058 **(100%)**
Tel.: (323) 581-7710
Web Site: http://www.s-hpacking.com
Sales Range: $10-24.9 Million
Emp.: 8
Vegetables & Melons
N.A.I.C.S.: 111219
Season Produce Co. Inc. (1)
1601 E Olympic Blvd Bays 315-318, Los Angeles, CA 90021
Tel.: (213) 689-0008
Vegetable Whslr
N.A.I.C.S.: 424480

S&J CONSTRUCTION CO. INC.
4245 166th St, Oak Forest, IL 60452
Tel.: (708) 331-1816
Rev.: $11,661,301
Emp.: 12
Bridge Construction
N.A.I.C.S.: 237310
Kenneth Regan *(Project Mgr)*

S&J REED INC.
2268 Ashland St, Ashland, OR 97520
Tel.: (541) 488-1579
Web Site: http://www.ashlandshopnkart.com
Year Founded: 1988
Sales Range: $25-49.9 Million
Emp.: 90
Independent Supermarket
N.A.I.C.S.: 445110
Steve Reed *(Owner)*
Eric Chaddock *(Mgr-Ops)*

S&J SHEET METAL SUPPLY INC.
608 E 134th St, Bronx, NY 10454
Tel.: (718) 585-2853
Web Site: http://www.sj.com
Sales Range: $10-24.9 Million
Emp.: 200
Sheet Metalwork
N.A.I.C.S.: 332322
Steven Schwartz *(Pres)*
Gary Schachne *(Controller)*

S&J VILLARI LIVESTOCK
1481 Glassboro Rd, Wenonah, NJ 08090
Tel.: (856) 468-0807
Rev.: $11,000,000
Emp.: 2
Pork Processing & Sales
N.A.I.C.S.: 424520
Sam Villari *(Partner)*
Joseph P. Villari Jr. *(Partner)*

S&K ACQUISITION CORP
317 Dewitt Ave E, Mattoon, IL 61938-3462
Tel.: (217) 258-8500 IL
Web Site: http://www.skairpower.com
Year Founded: 1987
Sales Range: $25-49.9 Million
Emp.: 60
Distr of Industrial Machinery & Equipment
N.A.I.C.S.: 423830
Don P. Portugal *(Chm & CFO)*

S&K ROOFING, SIDING & WINDOWS, INC.
5399 Enterprise St, Eldersburg, MD 21784-9363
Tel.: (410) 795-4400
Web Site: http://www.skroofing.com
Year Founded: 1980
Sales Range: $10-24.9 Million
Emp.: 24
Housing Construction Services
N.A.I.C.S.: 236117
Donald Katzenberger *(Pres)*
Charles McCurry *(Dir-Sls)*
Ray Smallwood *(Mgr-Ops)*

S&M MOVING SYSTEMS WEST INC.
2021 E Jones Ave, Phoenix, AZ 85040
Tel.: (602) 586-3200 CA
Web Site: http://www.smmoving.com
Year Founded: 1918
Sales Range: $50-74.9 Million
Emp.: 500
Provider of Trucking Services
N.A.I.C.S.: 484110
Pamela West *(Gen Mgr)*

S&M TRANSPORTATION INC
245 Jacintoport Blvd, Saraland, AL 36571
Tel.: (251) 679-3344
Web Site: http://www.smtrans.com
Sales Range: $10-24.9 Million
Emp.: 90
Trucking & Warehouse Services
N.A.I.C.S.: 484121
Jim Merritt *(Pres)*

S&ME, INC.
3201 Spring Forest Rd, Raleigh, NC 27616
Tel.: (919) 872-2660 NC
Web Site: http://www.smeinc.com
Year Founded: 1992
Sales Range: $25-49.9 Million
Emp.: 1,000
Provider of Environmental Engineering Services
N.A.I.C.S.: 541330

Bruce L. Alstaetter *(CFO & Sr VP)*
Randall Neuhaus *(Pres & CEO)*
Rosemary Thompson *(VP & Dir-HR)*
Dan Caton *(VP & Dir-Safety)*
Chris Headley *(Dir-Tech)*
Thomas J. Davis *(VP & Area Mgr-Plng & Design)*
Brian Glidewell *(VP & Area Mgr-Construction Svcs)*
Thomas P. Raymond *(VP & Area Mgr-Environmental)*
Kathleen Chambers *(Dir-Mktg)*
Emily Hancock *(Project Engr-Orlando)*
George Kramer *(Mgr-Design-South)*
Lawrence Hale *(Sr Project Mgr-Orlando)*
Byron Hinchey *(Sr Project Mgr-Water Resources)*
Ian Anderson *(Project Engr-Nashville)*
Gordon Land *(Mgr-Survey-Orlando)*
George Huddleston *(Mgr-Healthcare Grp)*
Leonard E. Arnold Jr. *(Mgr-Design Svcs South)*

S&N INC.
2505 Sturdevant St, Merrill, WI 54452
Tel.: (715) 536-6223
Rev.: $10,000,000
Emp.: 2
Sewer Line Construction
N.A.I.C.S.: 237110
Richard Schumitsch *(Pres)*

S&P COMPANY INC.
100 Shoreline Hwy Bldg B Ste 395, Mill Valley, CA 94941
Tel.: (415) 332-0550 CA
Year Founded: 1932
Sales Range: $900-999.9 Million
Emp.: 6
Holding Company
N.A.I.C.S.: 312120
Yeoryios C. Apallas *(Gen Counsel & Sec)*

S&P STEEL PRODUCTS INC.
1502 Is, Laredo, TX 78041
Tel.: (956) 726-9024
Rev.: $24,291,840
Emp.: 15
Sales of Steel Products
N.A.I.C.S.: 423510

S&S AUTOMOTIVE INC.
740 N Larch Ave, Elmhurst, IL 60126
Tel.: (630) 279-1600
Web Site: http://www.ssauto.com
Rev.: $36,000,000
Emp.: 250
Automotive Supplies & Parts
N.A.I.C.S.: 423120
Ronald L. Kushner *(Pres)*
Jim Withrow *(CFO & Controller)*

S&S BEAUTY SUPPLIES INCORPORATED
1003 Tech Dr, Milford, OH 45150
Tel.: (513) 831-3334
Web Site: http://www.ssbeautysupplies.com
Rev.: $10,000,000
Emp.: 35
Beauty Parlor Equipment & Supplies
N.A.I.C.S.: 423850
David Knapke *(Pres)*

S&S BUILDERS HARDWARE CO.
917 W Pioneer Pkwy, Peoria, IL 61615
Tel.: (309) 692-0828
Web Site: http://www.sns-co.com
Rev.: $15,000,000
Emp.: 25

S&S BUILDERS HARDWARE CO. — U.S. PRIVATE

S&S Builders Hardware Co.—(Continued)
Hardware Distr & Retailer
N.A.I.C.S.: 423710
Gary Summers *(VP)*
Susan Shay *(Project Mgr)*

S&S BUILDERS, LLC.
400 S Enterprise Ave, Gillette, WY 82717
Tel.: (307) 686-5659
Web Site: http://www.ssbuildersllc.com
Rev.: $34,200,000
Emp.: 50
Poured Concrete Foundation & Structure Contractors
N.A.I.C.S.: 238110
Jason Tystad *(Project Mgr-Civil)*
Sharon Harrod *(Mgr)*
Bryan Kaufmann *(Mgr-Safety & HR)*
Darrel Ray *(Project Mgr-Building)*
Floyd Meeks *(Project Mgr-Civil)*
Kurt Countryman *(Project Mgr-Civil)*

S&S DRYWALL INC.
202 N 27th St, San Jose, CA 95116
Tel.: (408) 294-4393
Web Site: http://www.ssdrywall.net
Rev.: $15,400,000
Emp.: 200
Drywall
N.A.I.C.S.: 238310
Gabriel Silveira *(Pres)*
Maria Silveira *(VP)*
Brian Silveira *(Mgr-Safety)*
Joe Pereira *(Mgr-Pur)*
Liz Silveira *(Mgr-Acctg)*

Subsidiaries:

S&S Drywall Installers Inc (1)
202 N 27th St, San Jose, CA 95116
Tel.: (408) 294-4393
Sales Range: $10-24.9 Million
Emp.: 1
Drywall
N.A.I.C.S.: 238310

S&S ELECTRIC CO., INC.
105 Douglas Rd E, Oldsmar, FL 34677
Tel.: (813) 855-6692
Web Site: http://www.sselectric.net
Year Founded: 1947
Sales Range: $25-49.9 Million
Emp.: 250
Provider of Electrical Contracting Services
N.A.I.C.S.: 238210
Shawn L. Smith *(Pres)*
Christopher L. Smith *(Exec VP)*
Melissa Charlton *(Dir-Bus Dev)*

S&S FIRESTONE INC.
1475 Jingle Bell Ln, Lexington, KY 40509-4113
Tel.: (859) 233-3157 KY
Web Site: http://www.sstire.com
Year Founded: 1974
Sales Range: $125-149.9 Million
Emp.: 360
Distr of Tires & Tubes
N.A.I.C.S.: 423130
Brooks Swentzel *(Pres)*
Carl Charlet *(Plant Mgr)*

S&S INDUSTRIAL MARKETING
2035 SE 10th Ave, Portland, OR 97214
Tel.: (503) 232-7092
Web Site: http://www.toolreps.com
Sales Range: $10-24.9 Million
Emp.: 6
Industrial Machinery & Equipment Whslr
N.A.I.C.S.: 423830
Terry Pucik *(Pres)*

S&S INTERNATIONAL CORP
3500 NW 79th Ave, Miami, FL 33122
Tel.: (305) 592-1181
Web Site: http://www.marmol.com
Rev.: $21,222,087
Emp.: 30
Tile & Clay Products
N.A.I.C.S.: 423320
Carlos Arche *(Mgr-Sls)*
Ernesto S. Avino Sr. *(CEO)*

S&S PETROLEUM INC.
12003 Mukilteo Speedway Ste 101, Mukilteo, WA 98275
Web Site: https://sspetro.com
Emp.: 100
Petroleum Bulk Stations & Terminals
N.A.I.C.S.: 424710

Subsidiaries:

Leathers Enterprises Inc. (1)
22300 SE Stark St, Gresham, OR 97030
Tel.: (503) 661-1244
Web Site: http://www.leathersfuels.com
Gasoline Stations with Convenience Stores
N.A.I.C.S.: 457110
Lila Leathers Fitz *(Pres & CEO)*

S&S PUBLIC RELATIONS, INC.
20 N Wacker Dr Ste 4100, Chicago, IL 60606
Tel.: (847) 955-0700 IL
Web Site: http://www.sspr.com
Year Founded: 1978
Sales Range: $10-24.9 Million
Emp.: 25
Public Relations Agency
N.A.I.C.S.: 541820
Brad Rawls *(Sr VP-Bus Dev)*

Subsidiaries:

S&S Public Relations, Inc. (1)
120 N Tejon St Ste 201, Colorado Springs, CO 80903
Tel.: (719) 634-1180
Web Site: http://www.sspr.com
Emp.: 12
Public Relations Agency
N.A.I.C.S.: 541820
Heather Kelly *(Co-Pres)*
Steve Fiore *(Dir-Bus Dev)*
Jen Grenz *(VP-Client Rels)*
Jennifer Headley *(Dir-Client Rels)*
Kelley Heider *(Dir-Social Media)*
Hanni Itah *(Dir-Client Rels)*
Jocelyn Linde *(Dir-Client Rels)*
Jo Marini *(Dir-Client Rels)*
Maggie Perry *(Dir-Client Rels)*
Brad Rawls *(Sr VP-Bus Dev)*
Mallory Snitker *(Dir-Client Rels)*

S&S SALES CORPORATION
12030 W Silver Spring Rd, Milwaukee, WI 53225-2910
Tel.: (414) 464-8550
Web Site: http://www.sssales.com
Sales Range: $75-99.9 Million
Emp.: 15
Exterior Wall Panels & Building Supplies Distr
N.A.I.C.S.: 423310
William Sprinkman *(Pres)*
Bruce L. McCain *(VP)*

S&S WORLDWIDE INC.
75 Mill St, Colchester, CT 06415
Tel.: (860) 537-3451
Web Site: http://www.ssww.com
Year Founded: 1906
Sales Range: $25-49.9 Million
Emp.: 300
Art Goods
N.A.I.C.S.: 424990
Vincent Pescosolido *(CFO)*
Adam Schwartz *(Pres)*
Marie Hughes *(Mgr-Bid & Contract)*
Chris Karam *(Mgr-Creative)*

S&T MANUFACTURING CO.
17411 E Pine St, Tulsa, OK 74116
Tel.: (918) 234-4151
Web Site: http://www.st-mfg.com
Year Founded: 1973
Sales Range: $10-24.9 Million
Emp.: 95
Fabricated Structural Metal Mfr
N.A.I.C.S.: 332312
Kenny McDaniel *(Mgr-Quality Control)*
Gary Tolbert *(Co-Owner)*

S&T OFFICE PRODUCTS, INC.
1000 Kristen Ct, Saint Paul, MN 55110
Tel.: (651) 483-4411 MN
Web Site: http://www.stoffice.com
Year Founded: 1971
Sales Range: $25-49.9 Million
Emp.: 150
Wholesale Distribution of Stationery & Office Products
N.A.I.C.S.: 424120
Frank G. Tschida *(Chm & Pres)*
Cliff Romberg *(CFO)*
Gary Sirek *(VP)*
Patrick Crowley *(VP)*

S&V INSURANCE SERVICES LLC
8850 Bender Rd, Lynden, WA 98264
Tel.: (360) 354-5988
Web Site: http://www.oltmaninsurance.com
Emp.: 15
Insurance Services
N.A.I.C.S.: 524298
Leonard Smit *(Partner)*
Denise Bergsma *(Acct Mgr)*
Ken Van Ry *(Partner)*

Subsidiaries:

Oltman Insurance Agency, Inc. (1)
2417 Meridian St Ste 102, Bellingham, WA 98225
Tel.: (360) 734-3960
Web Site: http://www.oltmaninsurance.com
Sales Range: $1-9.9 Million
Emp.: 12
Insurance Agents
N.A.I.C.S.: 524210
Ann Medina *(Partner)*
Darin DeYoung *(Partner)*

S&W CONTRACTING OF WNY, INC.
Larkin Ctr of Commerce 701 Seneca St Ste 303, Buffalo, NY 14210
Tel.: (716) 803-1167 NY
Web Site: http://www.sw-contracting.com
Year Founded: 1999
Sales Range: $1-9.9 Million
Emp.: 28
Building Construction Services
N.A.I.C.S.: 238990
Shandra Spicer *(Pres & CEO)*

S&W METAL PRODUCTS
441 County Line Rd, Gilbertsville, PA 19525
Tel.: (610) 473-2400
Web Site: http://www.swmetalproducts.com
Year Founded: 1999
Rev.: $13,800,000
Emp.: 36
Industrial Machinery & Equipment Mfr
N.A.I.C.S.: 332710
Gretchen Mohen *(Pres)*

S&W SERVICES, INC.
6057 Corporate Dr, East Syracuse, NY 13057
Tel.: (315) 655-8161 NY
Web Site: http://www.swsvcs.com
Year Founded: 1995

Sales Range: $1-9.9 Million
Emp.: 34
Construction And Petroleum Services
N.A.I.C.S.: 531190
Joel L. Swanson *(Chm)*

S-P COMPANY INC.
85 E Hylda Ave, Youngstown, OH 44507-1762
Tel.: (330) 782-5651 OH
Year Founded: 1946
Sales Range: $25-49.9 Million
Emp.: 125
Metal Stamping
N.A.I.C.S.: 332119

Subsidiaries:

C&S Land Co. (1)
400 W Railroad St Ste 2, Columbiana, OH 44408-2212
Tel.: (330) 482-0200
Web Site: http://www.compcoind.com
Sales Range: Less than $1 Million
Emp.: 2
Nonresidential Building Operators
N.A.I.C.S.: 531120
Clarence Smith *(Owner)*

Compco Holding Company Inc. (1)
400 W Railroad St, Columbiana, OH 44408
Tel.: (330) 482-0200
Web Site: http://www.compcoind.com
Sales Range: $10-24.9 Million
Emp.: 65
Holding Company
N.A.I.C.S.: 531120

Compco Land Company Inc. (1)
400 W Railroad St, Columbiana, OH 44408
Tel.: (330) 482-0200
Web Site: http://www.compcoind.com
Sales Range: $10-24.9 Million
Emp.: 20
Nonresidential Building Construction
N.A.I.C.S.: 531120
Clarence R. Smith Jr. *(Owner)*

S-T INDUSTRIES, INC.
301 Armstrong Blvd N, Saint James, MN 56081-1206
Tel.: (507) 375-3211 MN
Web Site: http://www.stindustries.com
Year Founded: 1942
Sales Range: $75-99.9 Million
Emp.: 50
Optical Comparators & Precision Measuring Tools Mfr
N.A.I.C.S.: 332216
Margaret A. Smith *(Pres & CFO)*

S-TEK INC.
26046 Broadway Ave, Cleveland, OH 44146
Tel.: (440) 439-8232
Web Site: http://www.stek-inc.com
Sales Range: $10-24.9 Million
Emp.: 6
Electrical Apparatus & Equipment
N.A.I.C.S.: 423610
David Lepore *(Pres)*

S. A. MIRO, INC.
4582 S Ulster St Pkwy Ste 300, Denver, CO 80237
Tel.: (303) 741-3737
Web Site: http://www.samiro.com
Year Founded: 1980
Sales Range: $10-24.9 Million
Emp.: 40
Engineeering Services
N.A.I.C.S.: 541330
Carol Nelson *(Mgr-Acctg)*
Dave Lewis *(Pres)*
Brad Buhler *(COO)*
Sami Miro *(CEO)*

S. ABRAHAM & SONS, INC.
4001 3 Mile Rd NW, Grand Rapids, MI 49544-1132

Tel.: (616) 453-6358   MI
Web Site: http://www.sasinc.com
Year Founded: 1927
Sales Range: $750-799.9 Million
Emp.: 1,205
Distr of Groceries, Health & Beauty Aids, Snacks, Store Supplies & Tobacco Products
N.A.I.C.S.: 424940
Jerry Abraham *(Pres)*
George Bennett *(CMO)*
George Abdoo *(VP-Sls)*

S. CARPENTER CONSTRUCTION CO.
67 Race St, Bristol, CT 06010
Tel.: (860) 589-2141
Web Site: http://www.scarpenter.com
Rev.: $19,708,322
Emp.: 35
Renovation, Remodeling & Repairs: Industrial Buildings
N.A.I.C.S.: 236220
George T. Carpenter *(Pres)*
George E. Carpenter *(VP)*
Linda Ice *(Office Mgr)*

S. F. BALLOU, INC.
3302 I Bridges St, Morehead City, NC 28557-3283
Tel.: (252) 726-0780   NC
Web Site: http://www.sfballou.com
Year Founded: 1983
Sales Range: $10-24.9 Million
Emp.: 17
Housing Construction Services
N.A.I.C.S.: 236117
Samuel Ballou Jr. *(Owner)*

S. FREEDMAN & SONS, INC.
3322 Pennsy Dr, Landover, MD 20785-1604
Tel.: (301) 322-5000   MD
Web Site: http://www.sfreedman.com
Year Founded: 1907
Sales Range: $50-74.9 Million
Emp.: 85
Provider of Industrial & Personal Service Paper, Janitorial Supplies & Restaurant Supplies
N.A.I.C.S.: 424130
Mark Freedman *(Pres)*
Barry Perlis *(Exec VP)*
Louis Sacks *(Treas & Sec)*
J.J. Thompson *(CFO)*

S. GRAHAM & ASSOCIATES
737 N Michigan Ave Ste 1050, Chicago, IL 60611
Tel.: (312) 755-8170
Web Site: http://www.stedmangraham.com
Year Founded: 1988
Sales Range: $100-124.9 Million
Emp.: 10
Business, Marketing & Corporate Training & Personnel Development Services
N.A.I.C.S.: 541613
Stedman Graham *(Founder, Chm & CEO)*

S. HOWES, INC.
25 Howard St, Silver Creek, NY 14136-1007
Tel.: (716) 934-2611
Web Site: http://www.showes.com
Year Founded: 1856
Sales Range: Less than $1 Million
Emp.: 24
Mfr & Designer of Processing Equipment
N.A.I.C.S.: 333248
Frederick Mertz *(Pres & Gen Mgr)*

S. JOSEPH & SONS
215 10th St Ste 100, Des Moines, IA 50309
Tel.: (515) 283-1961
Web Site: http://www.josephsjewelers.com
Year Founded: 1871
Sales Range: $10-24.9 Million
Emp.: 150
Owns & Operates Jewelry Stores
N.A.I.C.S.: 458310
Dean Hoffman *(Controller)*
Toby Joseph *(CEO)*

S. LICHTENBERG & CO. INC.
295 5th Ave Ste 918, New York, NY 10016
Tel.: (212) 689-4510
Web Site: http://www.lichtenberg.com
Rev.: $27,500,000
Emp.: 30
Drapery Mfr
N.A.I.C.S.: 314120
Scott Goldstein *(Pres)*
Holly Slavin *(Dir-Design)*
Scott Lichtenberg *(CEO)*

S. PARKER HARDWARE MANUFACTURING CORP.
1 Parker Dr, Englewood, NJ 07631
Tel.: (201) 569-1600
Web Site: http://www.sparker.com
Sales Range: $10-24.9 Million
Emp.: 30
Builders' Hardware
N.A.I.C.S.: 423710
Charles I. Silberman *(Pres)*
Goerge Hansen *(VP-Sls)*
Sheldon Silber *(Controller)*

S. ROTHSCHILD & CO., INC.
1407 Broadway, New York, NY 10018-4878
Tel.: (212) 354-8550   DE
Web Site: http://www.srothschild.com
Year Founded: 1960
Sales Range: $100-124.9 Million
Emp.: 250
Mfr of Women's & Children's Coats & Outerwear
N.A.I.C.S.: 315250
Mark Friedman *(Pres)*
Paul Friedman *(VP)*

Subsidiaries:

Fieldston Clothes Inc.   (1)
500 Fashion Ave, New York, NY 10018
Tel.: (212) 354-8550
Boys Clothing
N.A.I.C.S.: 315250

Larry L. Rothchild's   (1)
1407 Broadway Fl 10, New York, NY 10018-4502
Tel.: (212) 354-8550
Sales Range: $10-24.9 Million
Emp.: 75
Children's Outerwear
N.A.I.C.S.: 424350

RCM Design   (1)
1407 Broadway 10 Fl, New York, NY 10018
Tel.: (212) 354-8550
Private Label
N.A.I.C.S.: 315250
Mark Friedman *(Gen Mgr)*

RCM Manufacturing Corp.   (1)
40 County St, Fall River, MA 02723-2104
Tel.: (508) 646-2900
Sales Range: $10-24.9 Million
Emp.: 40
Girls' & Children's Outerwear
N.A.I.C.S.: 315250

River Falls Manufacturing Co. Inc.   (1)
40 County St, Fall River, MA 02723-2104
Tel.: (508) 646-2900
Sales Range: $10-24.9 Million
Emp.: 96
Knit Outerwear Mills
N.A.I.C.S.: 315120

S.A. CAMP COMPANIES
17876 Zerker Rd, Bakersfield, CA 93308
Tel.: (661) 399-4451
Web Site: http://www.sacampcompanies.com
Rev.: $13,000,000
Emp.: 60
Agricultural Machinery
N.A.I.C.S.: 423820
Don Pedersen *(Engr-Sls)*
Gerrit Otten *(Engr-Sls)*
John Reiland *(Gen Mgr)*
Josh Alvidrez *(Engr-Sls)*
James S. Camp *(Pres)*

S.A. GRAHAM COMPANY INC.
6965 US Hwy 231, Brundidge, AL 36010
Tel.: (334) 735-2362
Web Site: http://www.sagraham.com
Rev.: $12,400,000
Emp.: 50
Highway, Street & Bridge Construction
N.A.I.C.S.: 237310
Randal C. Hall *(Pres)*

S.A. MORMAN & COMPANY
1100 Gezon Pkwy SW, Grand Rapids, MI 49509
Tel.: (616) 245-0583   MI
Web Site: http://www.samorman.com
Year Founded: 1857
Sales Range: $10-24.9 Million
Emp.: 50
Supplier of Exterior Building Materials & Products
N.A.I.C.S.: 423310
Douglas M. Hoogerhyde *(Pres)*
Dave White *(Controller)*
Jennifer Cooley *(Project Mgr)*
Tom Gorman *(Mgr-Sls)*
Deidre Livingston *(Project Mgr)*
Neil Schoenherr *(Project Mgr)*

S.B. COLLINS INC.
54 Lowr Welden St, Saint Albans, VT 05478
Tel.: (802) 524-3605
Sales Range: $10-24.9 Million
Emp.: 45
Petroleum Bulk Stations
N.A.I.C.S.: 424710
Bruce Jolley *(Pres)*
Bob Clark *(Mgr-Fleet)*
Jennifer Magnant *(Mgr-Accts Payable)*

S.B. COX INC.
901 Potomac St, Richmond, VA 23231
Tel.: (804) 222-3500
Web Site: http://www.sbcoxdemolition.com
Year Founded: 1963
Sales Range: $10-24.9 Million
Emp.: 180
Site Preparation Contracting Services
N.A.I.C.S.: 238910
Mike Barr *(CFO)*

S.C. JOHNSON & SON, INC.
1525 Howe St, Racine, WI 53403-2237
Tel.: (262) 260-2440   WI
Web Site: https://www.scjohnson.com
Year Founded: 1886
Sales Range: $5-14.9 Billion
Emp.: 13,000
Polish & Other Sanitation Good Manufacturing
N.A.I.C.S.: 325612
H. Fisk Johnson *(Chm & CEO)*
Jane M. Hutterly *(Exec VP-Worldwide Corp & Environmental Affairs)*
John Rote *(VP-Mktg)*
Rudy Wilson *(Pres-Global Consumer Brands)*

Subsidiaries:

Deb Group Limited   (1)
Denby Hall Way, Derby, DE5 8JZ, Derbyshire, United Kingdom
Tel.: (44) 1773 855 100
Web Site: http://www.debgroup.com
Emp.: 250
Skin Care Products Distr
N.A.I.C.S.: 424210
Jeff Bell *(Gen Mgr)*

Subsidiary (Non-US):

Deb Australia Pty Limited   (2)
Unit 1 1 Secombe Place, 2170, Moorebank, NSW, Australia
Tel.: (61) 2 8763 1800
Web Site: http://www.debgroup.com
Skin Care Products Distr
N.A.I.C.S.: 424210

Deb Canada   (2)
42 Thompson Road West, NOE 1YO, Waterford, ON, Canada
Tel.: (519) 443-8697
Web Site: http://www.debgroup.com
Skin Care Products Distr
N.A.I.C.S.: 424210

Deb France SAS   (2)
3 a 5 rue du Pont des Halles, 94656, Rungis, Cedex, France
Tel.: (33) 1 41 80 11 30
Web Site: http://www.debgroup.com
Skin Care Products Distr
N.A.I.C.S.: 424210

Deb Group Malaysia Sdn Bhd   (2)
6th Floor Suite 16 IOI Business Park, Persiaran Puchong Jaya Selatan, Puchong, 47100, Selangor, Malaysia
Tel.: (60) 3 8064 4168
Web Site: http://www.debgroup.com
Skin Care Products Distr
N.A.I.C.S.: 424210

Deb Iberia S.L.   (2)
Paseo de Europa 11-13, San Sebastian de los Reyes, 28700, Madrid, Spain
Tel.: (34) 91 651 4870
Web Site: http://www.debgroupgroup.com
Skin Care Products Distr
N.A.I.C.S.: 424210

Deb New Zealand   (2)
PO Box 97740, Manukau, Auckland, New Zealand
Tel.: (64) 3 545 1046
Web Site: http://www.debgroup.com
Skin Care Products Distr
N.A.I.C.S.: 424210

Deb Singapore Pte. Ltd.   (2)
7 Kaki Bukit Road 1 01-10 Eunos Technolink, Singapore, 415937, Singapore
Tel.: (65) 6316 9730
Web Site: http://www.debgroup.com
Skin Care Products Distr
N.A.I.C.S.: 424210

Deb Sverige AB   (2)
Skars Led 3, 412 63, Gothenburg, Sweden
Tel.: (46) 31 16 50 50
Web Site: http://www.debgroup.com
Skin Care Products Distr
N.A.I.C.S.: 424120

Deb Swarfega A/S   (2)
Agerhatten 27B, 5220, Odense, Denmark
Tel.: (45) 6472 2400
Web Site: http://www.debgroup.com
Skin Care Products Distr
N.A.I.C.S.: 424210
Bjarne Steen Jorgensen *(Mgr-Sls)*

Deb Swarfega Norge AS   (2)
PO Box 530, 1327, Lysaker, Norway
Tel.: (47) 66 80 34 40
Web Site: http://www.debgroup.com
Skin Care Products Distr
N.A.I.C.S.: 424210

S.C. JOHNSON & SON, INC.

U.S. PRIVATE

S.C. Johnson & Son, Inc.—(Continued)

Subsidiary (US):

Deb USA, Inc. (2)
2815 Coliseum Centre Dr Ste 600, Charlotte, NC 28217
Tel.: (800) 248-7190
Web Site: http://www.debgroup.com
Skin Care Products Distr
N.A.I.C.S.: 424210
Mike Flagg (CEO-North America)

Subsidiary (Non-US):

Deb-STOKO Europe GmbH (2)
Bakerpfad 25, 47805, Krefeld, Germany
Tel.: (49) 21517380
Web Site: http://www.debgroup.com
Skin Care Products Distr
N.A.I.C.S.: 424210
Christopher Wicher (Head-Sls)
N. Matterson (Mng Dir)
J. Sitzmann (Mng Dir)
S. Gregory (Mng Dir)
Efren Carlos Wenderlich (Mgr-Comm & Designer-Web)

Deb-STOKO Europe GmbH (2)
PO Box 10 05 51, 47803, Krefeld, Germany
Tel.: (49) 215173800
Web Site: http://www.debgroup.com
Skin Care Products Distr
N.A.I.C.S.: 424210

Johnson Company, Ltd. (1)
Yamashita Cho SSK Bldg 22 Yamashita-cho Naka-ku, Yokohama, 231-0023, Japan
Tel.: (81) 456402001
Web Site: http://www.johnson.co.jp
Sales Range: $25-49.9 Million
Emp.: 629
House Cleaners & Consumer Products Sales & Mfr
N.A.I.C.S.: 325611

Johnson Financial Group, Inc. (1)
555 Main St, Racine, WI 53402-3104 (100%)
Tel.: (262) 619-2790
Web Site: http://www.johnsonbank.com
Sales Range: $150-199.9 Million
Emp.: 350
Bank Holding Company
N.A.I.C.S.: 551111
Helen P. Johnson-Leipold (Chm)
Ken Fellman (Sr VP & Mgr-Retail Banking)
Scott Sheaffer (Controller)
John J. Mau (Sr VP & Dir-Corp Credit Admin)
Jill Haupt (Sr VP & Mgr-Private Banking)
Tracy Dalton (Mgr-Wealth Fiduciary Svcs)
Daniel L. Kaminski (Head-Wealth Mgmt)
Mark Behrens (CFO & Exec VP)
Brian Andrew (Chief Investment Officer)
James Popp (Pres & CEO)
Ruth Patterson (Asst VP)
Anne Brannon (Asst VP)
Jerry Gold (Mgr-Private Banking Relationship)
Jason Gutzman (VP-Employee Benefits)
John Buresh (VP-Comml Real Estate-Southeast)
Mark Ettinger (Asst VP-Wind Point)
Jean Golla (VP)
Randy Raymond (Sr VP-Comml Insurance-Brookfield)
Joe Maier (Sr VP & Dir-Wealth Strategy)
Scott Cooney (Dir-Comml Banking)
Jon C. Donahue (Sr VP-Private Banking)
Al Araque (Sr VP & Dir-Consumer & Private Banking)
Pat Hickey (Sr VP & Dir-Wealth Svcs)

Subsidiary (Domestic):

Johnson Bank (2)
555 Main St, Racine, WI 53403-1034 (100%)
Tel.: (262) 619-2272
Web Site: http://www.johnsonbank.com
Sales Range: $75-99.9 Million
Emp.: 60
Retail & Commercial Banking Services
N.A.I.C.S.: 522180
Tom Bolger (CEO)
Peter X. Engel (Exec VP-Consumer Banking)
Gus Hernandez (Pres-Milwaukee)
Daniel Kaminski (Exec VP-Wealth)
Benjamin Pavlik (VP-Legal & Compliance & Mgr-Risk-Wealth)
Eric Johnson (Sr VP-Comml Banking-Madison)
Greg Westrich (VP-Comml Banking-Madison)
Brian Holtz (Asst VP & Mgr-Mequon)
Ron Cockle (Sr VP & Dir-Mortgage Banking Svcs)
Tracy Dalton (Sr VP & Mgr-Wealth Fiduciary Svcs)
Hope Berman-Levin (Pres-Arizona)
Mark Behrens (CFO & Exec VP)
Tom Deisinger (Sr VP-Private Banking)
Brian Andrew (Chief Investment Officer)
Michael Shlensky (Sr VP & Mgr-Retirement Plan Svcs)
Alejandra Paredes (VP & Mgr-Private Banking Relationship)
Dan Defnet (Pres)

Johnson Insurance Services, Inc. (2)
1111 Commerce Dr, Racine, WI 53406
Tel.: (262) 321-1100
Web Site: http://www.johnsonins.com
Sales Range: $1-9.9 Million
Emp.: 25
Insurance Agencies & Brokerages
N.A.I.C.S.: 524210
Michael Derdzinski (Interim Pres)
Joanne Szymaszek (Pres)
Steve Schill (Sr VP-Comml Insurance)

Monterey Benefits LLC (2)
7782 E Foxmore Lane, Scottsdale, AZ 85258 (100%)
Tel.: (612) 865-6670
Web Site: http://www.johnsonbank.com
Insurance Services
N.A.I.C.S.: 524298
Steve Grady (Exec VP)

Johnson Wax (Egypt) Co. (1)
16 El Khartoum Street, Heliopolis, Egypt (100%)
Tel.: (20) 24177072
Cleaners, Air Fresheners, Wax Products & Insecticides Mfr
N.A.I.C.S.: 325611

Johnson Wax New Zealand Limited (1)
79 Queen Street Level 8, Auckland, 121010, New Zealand (100%)
Tel.: (64) 95732850
Web Site: http://www.scjohnson.co.nz
Sales Range: $10-24.9 Million
Emp.: 20
Consumer & Commercial Products Whlslr
N.A.I.C.S.: 325611
Luisa Ortega (Gen Mgr)

Johnson Wax Nigeria Limited (1)
13/14 Abimbola St Isolo Industrial Estate, PMB 21279, Isolo, Lagos, Nigeria (100%)
Tel.: (234) 14524213
Sales Range: $25-49.9 Million
Emp.: 156
Consumer & Commercial Products
N.A.I.C.S.: 325611

Johnson Wax S.p.A. (1)
Casella Postale No 18, 20020, Milan, Italy (100%)
Tel.: (39) 0293371
Web Site: http://www.scjohnson.com
Sales Range: $25-49.9 Million
Emp.: 293
Sales of Consumer & Commercial Products
N.A.I.C.S.: 325611
Cristina Guglielmini (Dir-Mktg Svcs & Res)

Johnsons Wax (East Africa) Ltd. (1)
Panari Sky Centre, Mombassa Road, PO Box 18373, Nairobi, Kenya
Tel.: (254) 557400
Web Site: http://www.scjohnson.com
Sales Range: $10-24.9 Million
Emp.: 56
Consumer Cleaning Products
N.A.I.C.S.: 561990

Johnsons Wax De Portugal, Lda. (1)
Rua Maestro Raul Portela 1, Lagoal, Paco d'Arcos, 2760-079, Portugal (100%)
Tel.: (351) 214408130
Sales Range: $10-24.9 Million
Emp.: 90
Consumer & Commercial Products Mfr
N.A.I.C.S.: 325611

Johnsons Wax Espanola, S.A. (1)
Calle Orense 4 6 Planta, Madrid, 28020, Spain (100%)
Tel.: (34) 914565100
Web Site: http://www.johnsonwax.es
Sales Range: $10-24.9 Million
Emp.: 75
Consumer & Commercial Products Mfr
N.A.I.C.S.: 424690
Aniban Ayala (Gen Mgr)

Johnsonwax del Ecuador S.A. (1)
PO Box 09-01-874, Guayaquil, Ecuador (100%)
Tel.: (593) 4280777
Web Site: http://www.scjohnson.com
Consumer & Commercial Wax Products Mfr
N.A.I.C.S.: 325611

KAS Direct, LLC (1)
1600 Steewart Ave Ste 411, Westbury, NY 11590
Tel.: (516) 934-0539
Web Site: http://www.babyganics.com
Natural Nontoxic Product for Household Cleaning Skincare Baby Care Sun Protection & Oral & Personal Hygiene Distr
N.A.I.C.S.: 456199
Kevin Schwartz (Founder & CEO)
Keith Garber (Pres)

Korea Johnson Co., Ltd. (1)
638-13 Shinsa-dong Ssangbong Bldg 6th Fl, Kangman-ku, Seoul, 135-120, Korea (South) (100%)
Tel.: (82) 234856800
Web Site: http://www.koreajohnson.co.kr
Sales Range: $25-49.9 Million
Emp.: 152
Consumer & Commercial Products Mfr
N.A.I.C.S.: 325611

La Johnson Francaise S.A. (1)
10 rue Saint-Hilaire, BP 606, F-95310, Saint-Ouen-l'Aumone, Cedex, France (100%)
Tel.: (33) 134212121
Web Site: http://www.scjohnson.fr
Sales Range: $10-24.9 Million
Emp.: 80
Sales of Consumer & Commercial Products
N.A.I.C.S.: 424690

Norsk Johnson's Wax A/S (1)
Hvamsvingen 9 11, 2013, Skjetten, Norway (100%)
Tel.: (47) 63846070
Web Site: http://www.scjohnson.com
Sales Range: $10-24.9 Million
Emp.: 4
Consumer & Commercial Products Sales
N.A.I.C.S.: 424690

P.T. S.C. Johnson & Son (Indonesia) Ltd. (1)
Jl Pulo Lentut No 16, Kawasan Industri Pulo Gadung, Jakarta, 13920, Timur, Indonesia (100%)
Tel.: (62) 214608823
Web Site: http://www.scjohnson.co.id
Sales Range: $1-9.9 Million
Emp.: 110
Consumer Products Mfr
N.A.I.C.S.: 325611

S C Johnson & Son S.A. de C.V (1)
Arquimedes No 15, Mexico, 11580, DF, Mexico (100%)
Tel.: (52) 5552793700
Web Site: http://www.scjohnsonandson.com.mx
Sales Range: $25-49.9 Million
Emp.: 600
Consumer & Commercial Products
N.A.I.C.S.: 325611
Eduargo Ortiz (Gen Mgr)

S. C. Johnson Europe Sarl (1)
ZA La Piece 8, 1180, Rolle, Switzerland
Tel.: (41) 21 822 10 10
Web Site: http://www.scj.com
Household Cleaning Product Mfr
N.A.I.C.S.: 325612

S. C. Johnson Israel Ltd. (1)
12 Hamelacha Street New Industrial Area, Rosh Ha'Ayin, 48091, Israel
Tel.: (972) 3 9020333
Web Site: http://www.scj.com
Emp.: 6

Household Cleaning Product Mfr
N.A.I.C.S.: 325612
Ruti Salamon Goldberg (Country Mgr)

S. C. Johnson Wax Ltd. (1)
CT537 Cantonments, PO Box C537, Cantonments, Accra, Ghana (100%)
Tel.: (233) 21810193
Web Site: http://www.scj.com
Sales Range: $10-24.9 Million
Emp.: 14
Consumer & Commercial Products
N.A.I.C.S.: 325611
Doris Kwawukume (Mng Dir & Mgr-Mktg)

S. C. Johnson de Puerto Rico, Inc. (1)
Calle Resolucion 33 Ste 702 Doral Bank Plz, San Juan, PR 00920-2707
Tel.: (787) 708-6260
Household Cleaning Product Mfr
N.A.I.C.S.: 325612

S.C. Johnson & Son (Hellas) E.P.E. (1)
479 Messoghion Ave, Aghua Paraskevi, 153-43, Athens, Greece (100%)
Tel.: (30) 2106003795
Sales Range: $10-24.9 Million
Emp.: 80
Cleaning Products, Insecticides & Floor Waxes Mfr
N.A.I.C.S.: 325611

S.C. Johnson & Son Colombiana S.A, (1)
Calle 93 No 11-28 3rd Fl, Bogota, Colombia (100%)
Tel.: (57) 12576607
Sales Range: $10-24.9 Million
Emp.: 46
Consumer & Commercial Products Mfr
N.A.I.C.S.: 325611

S.C. Johnson & Son Pte. Limited (1)
24 Penjuru Rd No 03 02, 04-05 Sime Darby Centre, Singapore, 609128, Singapore (100%)
Tel.: (65) 64662666
Web Site: http://www.scjohnson.com
Sales Range: $10-24.9 Million
Emp.: 40
Consumer & Commercial Products
N.A.I.C.S.: 325611

S.C. Johnson & Son Pty. Ltd. (1)
160 Epping Rd, Lane Cove, 2066, NSW, Australia (100%)
Tel.: (61) 294289111
Web Site: http://www.scj.com
Sales Range: $10-24.9 Million
Emp.: 50
Sales of Consumer & Commercial Products
N.A.I.C.S.: 424690

S.C. Johnson & Son Taiwan, Ltd. (1)
2F 421 Fu-Jing Street, Taipei, 10588, Taiwan
Tel.: (886) 227602211
Sales Range: $10-24.9 Million
Emp.: 100
Consumer & Commercial Products
N.A.I.C.S.: 325611

S.C. Johnson & Son de Argentina S.A.I.C. (1)
Avenida Marquez 2249, 1657, Buenos Aires, Argentina (100%)
Tel.: (54) 01148418000
Web Site: http://www.johnson.com.ar
Sales Range: $25-49.9 Million
Emp.: 500
Mfr of Consumer & Commercial Products
N.A.I.C.S.: 325611

S.C. Johnson & Son de Venezuela, C.A. (1)
Apartado 70 041, Caracas, 1071-A, Venezuela (100%)
Tel.: (58) 2129504200
Sales Range: $10-24.9 Million
Emp.: 100
Consumer & Commercial Products Mfr
N.A.I.C.S.: 325611

S.C. Johnson & Son of South Africa (1)
192 Smith St, Fairland, 2195, South Africa (100%)
Tel.: (27) 1138038003

Web Site: http://www.scjohnson.com
Sales Range: $25-49.9 Million
Emp.: 168
Consumer & Commercial Products Sales
N.A.I.C.S.: 322291
Nicholas Najjar (Mng Dir)

S.C. Johnson & Son, Inc. (1)
1077 J P Rizal St, Makati, 1200, Philippines
Tel.: (63) 2 860 5200
Web Site: http://www.scjohnson.com.ph
Home Cleaning Product Mfr
N.A.I.C.S.: 325612

S.C. Johnson & Son, Inc. - Washington, DC (1)
1133 Connecticut Ave NW Ste 650, Washington, DC 20036-2507 **(100%)**
Tel.: (202) 331-1186
Sales Range: $10-24.9 Million
Emp.: 5
Sales of Consumer Cleaning Products
N.A.I.C.S.: 325612

S.C. Johnson & Son, Ltd. (1)
59 1 Suksumvit 16, Suksumvit Rd Klongtoey, Bangkok, 10110, Thailand **(100%)**
Tel.: (66) 26630888
Sales Range: $10-24.9 Million
Emp.: 53
Consumer & Commercial Products Mfr
N.A.I.C.S.: 325611

S.C. Johnson AG (1)
Riedstrasse 14, Postfach 423, 8953, Dietikon, Switzerland **(100%)**
Tel.: (41) 447443800
Sales Range: $10-24.9 Million
Emp.: 22
Seller of Consumer & Commercial Products
N.A.I.C.S.: 424690

S.C. Johnson Canada (1)
1 Webster St, Brantford, N3T 5R1, ON, Canada **(100%)**
Tel.: (519) 756-7900
Web Site: http://www.scjohnson.ca
Sales Range: $25-49.9 Million
Emp.: 385
Consumer Products Mfr
N.A.I.C.S.: 325611

S.C. Johnson Company Limited (1)
63 Pericleous St, PO Box 23874, 2021 Strovolos, Nicosia, 1687, Cyprus **(100%)**
Tel.: (357) 22421022
Web Site: http://www.scjohnson.com
Sales Range: $10-24.9 Million
Emp.: 10
Consumer & Commercial Products
N.A.I.C.S.: 561990

S.C. Johnson GmbH (1)
Mettmanner Str 25, Erkrath, 40699, Germany
Tel.: (49) 2 11 302340
Web Site: http://www.scjohnson.de
Household Cleaning Product Mfr
N.A.I.C.S.: 325612

S.C. Johnson Italy S.R.L. (1)
Dunajfka Cesta 156, Ljubljana, 1000, Slovenia
Tel.: (386) 1 5637378
Emp.: 2
Household Cleaning Product Mfr
N.A.I.C.S.: 325612
Iva Jarm (Gen Mgr)

S.C. Johnson Italy SrL Predstavnistvo (1)
Supilova 18, 11000, Belgrade, Serbia
Tel.: (381) 2750 719
Household Cleaning Product Mfr
N.A.I.C.S.: 325612

S.C. Johnson Kft. (1)
Apor Vilmos ter 6, 1124, Budapest, Hungary
Tel.: (36) 1 224 8400
Household Cleaning Product Mfr
N.A.I.C.S.: 325612

S.C. Johnson Ltd (1)
Frimley Green Rd, Camberley, GU16 7AJ, Surrey, United Kingdom **(100%)**
Tel.: (44) 1276852000
Web Site: http://www.scjohnson.co.uk
Sales Range: $25-49.9 Million
Emp.: 400
Mfr, Sales & Marketing of Consumer & Commercial Products

N.A.I.C.S.: 325611
Fisk Johnson (Chm & CEO)

S.C. Johnson Manufacturing (M) Sdn Bhd (1)
8 Jalan Hasil Kawasan Tampoi, Johor Bahru, 81200, Johor, Malaysia
Tel.: (60) 72381622
Sales Range: $25-49.9 Million
Emp.: 93
Body Care & Household Care Products Mfr
N.A.I.C.S.: 325998
Grece Luyokse (Mgr-Fin)

S.C. Johnson Scandinavia AB (1)
Norgegatan 2, 164 93, Kista, Sweden **(100%)**
Tel.: (46) 200 21 2025
Web Site: http://www.scjohnson.se
Sales Range: $10-24.9 Million
Emp.: 16
Sales of Consumer & Commercial Products
N.A.I.C.S.: 424690

S.C. Johnson Ukraine, Inc (1)
Moskovsky Ave 910 B, 04073, Kiev, Ukraine **(100%)**
Tel.: (380) 444903500
Web Site: http://www.scj.com
Sales Range: $25-49.9 Million
Emp.: 150
Detergents, Household Cleaners & Shampoo Mfr
N.A.I.C.S.: 325611

S.C. Johnson Wax Benelux N.V./S.A. (1)
Noordzone Noordkustlaan 16, B-1702, Groot-Bijgaarden, Belgium **(100%)**
Tel.: (32) 24675211
Web Site: http://www.scjohnson.be
Sales Range: $50-74.9 Million
Emp.: 40
Sales & Marketing of Consumer & Commercial Products
N.A.I.C.S.: 424690
Jean-Marc Faujour (Gen Mgr)

S.C. Johnson de Centroamerica S.A. (1)
Apartado Postal 4971, 1000, San Jose, Costa Rica **(100%)**
Tel.: (506) 22135000
Sales Range: $10-24.9 Million
Emp.: 60
Consumer & Commercial Products
N.A.I.C.S.: 325611

S.C. Johnson, Ltd. (1)
12101 24 Twr 2 metro Plz, Kwaifong, Hong Kong, China (Hong Kong) **(100%)**
Tel.: (852) 25755655
Web Site: http://www.scjohnson.co.uk
Sales Range: $10-24.9 Million
Emp.: 45
Consumer & Commercial Products
N.A.I.C.S.: 325611

SC JOHNSON AND SON CHILE LTDA. (1)
Av Del Valle No 869 Of 403 4th Floor Building Vanguard, Huechuraba, Santiago, Chile
Tel.: (56) 2 2370 5100
Sales Range: $10-24.9 Million
Emp.: 50
Home Cleaning Product Mfr
N.A.I.C.S.: 325612

SC Johnson Wax SRL (1)
Strada Plantelor nr 37A sector 2, 023972, Bucharest, Romania
Tel.: (40) 213163150
Web Site: http://www.scjohnson.ro
Emp.: 30
Home Cleaning Product Mfr
N.A.I.C.S.: 325612
Luchian Lucarazavata (Gen Mgr)

Saudi Johnson Co. Ltd. (1)
Phase 4 Industrial Area, PO Box 16339, Jeddah, 21464, Saudi Arabia
Tel.: (966) 2 637 4851
Home Cleaning Product Mfr
N.A.I.C.S.: 325612

Shanghai Johnson Ltd. (1)
932 New Jin Qiao Road, Pudong, Shanghai, 201206, China
Tel.: (86) 21 5899 4833
Home Cleaning Product Mfr

N.A.I.C.S.: 325612

S.D. DEACON CORPORATION
7745 Greenback Ln Ste 250, Citrus Heights, CA 95610
Tel.: (916) 969-0900
Web Site: http://www.deacon.com
Sales Range: $125-149.9 Million
Emp.: 500
Commercial & Office Building, New Construction
N.A.I.C.S.: 236220
Richard Smith (Pres)
Jeanine Fuller (Dir-Trng)
Brett Mykrantz (Exec VP & Gen Mgr)
Jim Day (Mgr-Safety)
Dan Leitheiser (Project Mgr & Superintendent)
Mark Whitten (Mgr-Gen Construction Div)
Brandon Nelson (Mgr-Special Projects Div)
Don Cruzon (VP)
Paul Cunha (VP)
Ben Bracelin (VP)
Anita Jain (Exec VP)
Mitch Parker (Exec VP)
Chad Snopko (Exec VP)

Subsidiaries:

S.D. DEACON CORP. OF WASHINGTON (1)
2375 130th Ave NE Ste 200, Bellevue, WA 98005
Tel.: (425) 284-4000
Construction Engineering Services
N.A.I.C.S.: 541330
Scott Lindley (Mgr-Bus Dev)
Scott Olson (Pres & Mgr-Special Projects Div)
Brian Northcott (VP)
Bill Valela (Exec VP & Gen Mgr)

S.D. Deacon Corp. (1)
901 NE Glisan St Ste 100, Portland, OR 97232
Tel.: (503) 297-8791
Web Site: http://www.deacon.com
Commercial & Office Building, New Construction
N.A.I.C.S.: 236220
Jeff Lee (Project Mgr)

S.D. IRELAND BROTHERS CORP
100 Grove St, Burlington, VT 05401
Tel.: (802) 863-6222
Web Site: http://www.sdireland.com
Sales Range: $10-24.9 Million
Emp.: 40
Site Preparation Contractor
N.A.I.C.S.: 238910
Andrew Marks (CFO)
Scott D. Ireland (Pres & CEO)

S.D. MYERS, INC.
180 South Ave, Tallmadge, OH 44278-2813
Tel.: (330) 630-7000 OH
Web Site: http://www.sdmyers.com
Year Founded: 1965
Sales Range: $25-49.9 Million
Emp.: 170
Mfr & Maintenance of Transformers
N.A.I.C.S.: 541715
Ed Muckley (CFO)
Scott Meyers (Pres)
Karen Folk (Controller)

S.D. RICHMAN SONS, INC.
2435 Wheatsheaf Ln, Philadelphia, PA 19137-1027
Tel.: (215) 535-5100 PA
Web Site:
http://www.sdrichmansons.com
Year Founded: 1901
Sales Range: $25-49.9 Million
Emp.: 40

Provider of Scrap Iron, Steel & Nonferrous Materials
N.A.I.C.S.: 423930
David Richman (Pres)
Bruce Richman (Exec VP)
Justin Comerford (Office Mgr)

S.E.E.K ARIZONA
1830 S Alma School Rd Ste 130, Mesa, AZ 85210
Tel.: (480) 902-0771
Web Site: http://www.seekarizona.org
Year Founded: 2003
Sales Range: $1-9.9 Million
Emp.: 200
Assistance Services to Children & Adults With Developmental & Behavioral Disorders
N.A.I.C.S.: 621111
Jessica L. Irwin (Founder & CEO)
Kathy Kelly (Controller)
Jenna Hamilton (Mgr-Behavior)

S.H. LEGGITT COMPANY INC.
1000 Civic Ctr Loop, San Marcos, TX 78666-9568
Tel.: (512) 396-0707 TX
Year Founded: 1945
Sales Range: $25-49.9 Million
Emp.: 100
Mfr of LPG Valves & Regulators
N.A.I.C.S.: 332911
Ross Miller (CFO)
Don C. Leggitt Sr. (Chm)

S.H.S. RESORT, LLC
105 N Bayshore Dr, Safety Harbor, FL 34695
Tel.: (727) 726-1161 FL
Web Site:
http://www.safetyharborspa.com
Year Founded: 1925
Sales Range: $75-99.9 Million
Emp.: 285
Hotel Resort & Spa Operator
N.A.I.C.S.: 721110
William E. Touloumis (Founder & CEO)

Subsidiaries:

Safety Harbor Spa Springs, Inc. (1)
105 N Bayshore Dr, Safety Harbor, FL 34695
Tel.: (727) 726-1161
Web Site: http://www.safetyharborspa.com
Sales Range: $1-9.9 Million
Health Spa & Fitness Center
N.A.I.C.S.: 713940

S.J. LOUIS CONSTRUCTION INC.
1351 Broadway St W, Rockville, MN 56369
Tel.: (320) 253-9291
Web Site: http://www.sjlouis.com
Year Founded: 1983
Sales Range: $25-49.9 Million
Emp.: 400
Constructor of Utility Projects, Grading, Water & Sewer Lines
N.A.I.C.S.: 237110
Jaime Woods (Asst Controller)
Don Meyer (CFO & VP)

S.J. SMITH CO., INC.
3707 W River Dr, Davenport, IA 52802-2411
Tel.: (563) 323-5000
Web Site: http://www.sjsmith.com
Year Founded: 1982
Sales Range: $10-24.9 Million.
Emp.: 115
Sales of Industrial Machinery & Equipment
N.A.I.C.S.: 423830
Michael Mitchell (VP-Mktg)

S.L. FUSCO INC.

S.J. Smith Co., Inc.—(Continued)

S.L. FUSCO INC.
1966 E Via Arado, Compton, CA 90220-6103
Tel.: (310) 868-1010
Web Site: http://www.slfusco.com
Year Founded: 1958
Sales Range: $10-24.9 Million
Emp.: 49
Provider of Industrial Supplies
N.A.I.C.S.: 423840
Jennifer Arndt (CFO)
Tom Burke (Dir-Ops)
Erlinda Manaois (Controller)
Jennifer Carrington (Supvr-Pur)

S.L. GILBERT COMPANY INC.
70 W Red Oak Ln, White Plains, NY 10604
Tel.: (212) 686-5145 NY
Year Founded: 1958
Sales Range: $10-24.9 Million
Emp.: 5
Provider of Mens & Boys Apparel
N.A.I.C.S.: 424350
Tom Gilbert (Pres)

S.L. WILLIAMSON COMPANY INC.
1230 River Rd, Charlottesville, VA 22902
Tel.: (434) 295-6137
Web Site: http://www.slwilliamson.com
Sales Range: $50-74.9 Million
Emp.: 125
Highway & Street Paving Contractor
N.A.I.C.S.: 237310
Shawn L. Mooney (Exec VP)
Kerri Jones (Controller & Office Mgr)
Stirling L. Williamson (Chm & CEO)
Blair K. Williamson (Pres)
Larry E. Eppard (VP)

S.M. FRANK & CO., INC.
1000 N Division St, Peekskill, NY 10566-1830
Tel.: (914) 739-3100 NY
Web Site: http://www.smfrankcoinc.com
Year Founded: 1922
Sales Range: $10-24.9 Million
Emp.: 12
Smoking Pipes & Accessories Mfr
N.A.I.C.S.: 339999
William F. Feuerbach III (Pres)

Subsidiaries:

Kaywoodie (1)
1000 N Division St, Peekskill, NY 10566-1830
Tel.: (914) 739-3100
Web Site: http://www.smfrankcoinc.com
Sales Range: $10-24.9 Million
Emp.: 10
Mfr of Smoking Pipes
N.A.I.C.S.: 339999
Bill Feuerbach III (VP-Mktg)

S.M. OSGOOD COMPANY
7550 Washington Ave S, Eden Prairie, MN 55344-3705
Tel.: (952) 937-2045
Web Site: http://www.smosgood.com
Sales Range: $50-74.9 Million
Emp.: 10
Marine Propulsion Machinery & Equipment
N.A.I.C.S.: 423860
Al Luehmann (Chm)
Tim Luehmann (Pres)
Lee Walberg (Reg Mgr-Sls)

S.N. TANNOR INC.
22202 Merrick Blvd, Springfield Gardens, NY 11413
Tel.: (718) 276-6985
Web Site: http://www.tannor.com
Sales Range: $10-24.9 Million
Emp.: 20
General Electrical Contractor
N.A.I.C.S.: 238210
Solomon Tannor (Chm)
Nassy Kasraie (Controller)
Nazir Mir (Asst VP)
Parviz Mohassel (Project Mgr-Parks)
John Denham (VP)
Evan Tannor (Pres)

S.P. KINNEY ENGINEERS, INC.
143 1st Ave, Carnegie, PA 15106-0445
Tel.: (412) 276-4600
Web Site: http://www.spkinney.com
Year Founded: 1941
Sales Range: $10-24.9 Million
Emp.: 60
Industrial Valve Mfr
N.A.I.C.S.: 332911
Craig S. Kinney (Pres)
R. Kerry Trachok (Treas)
Greg Billigen (VP-Sls)
Michael A. Majersky (Mgr-Technical Svcs)
Larry Shaffer (Supvr-Plant-VA)

S.P. RICHARDS COMPANY
4300 Wildwood Pkwy Ste 100, Atlanta, GA 30339
Tel.: (770) 436-6881 GA
Web Site: http://www.sprichards.com
Year Founded: 1848
Business Products Whslr
N.A.I.C.S.: 424120
Bryan Hall (Sr VP-Ops)
Tom C. Maley (Treas & Sr VP-Corp Dev)
Brian McGill (CIO & Sr VP)
Yancey Jones (Exec Chm)
Mike Maggio (Pres & CEO)
Jack Reagan (Exec VP)
Doug Sawyer (CFO & Sr VP)
Jim Starr (Sr VP-HR)
Nick Lomax (Sr VP-JanSan)
Stephanie Moy (Sr VP-Sls)
Brad Zwigart (VP-Ops)
Christie Pruett (VP-Info Sys)
Curt Small (VP-Mdsg)
Lindsay Eierman (VP-Supply Chain)
Kimberly Fulford (VP-Corp Sls)
Eddie Baird (VP-Furiture Sls)
Susan Lada (VP-Global Sourcing & JanSan Mdsg)
Paul Gatens (VP-Mktg)
Julie Charyna (VP-HR)

Subsidiaries:

Garland C. Norris Co. (1)
1101 Perry Rd, Apex, NC 27502
Tel.: (919) 387-1059
Web Site: http://www.gcnorris.com
Emp.: 21
Whslr & Distr of Disposables & Janitorial & Cleaning Solutions for Food Industry
N.A.I.C.S.: 423840

S.P.C. TRANSPORT
PO Box 1718, Auburn, ME 04210
Tel.: (207) 783-4200 ME
Web Site: http://www.spctran.com
Sales Range: $50-74.9 Million
Emp.: 50
Provider of Freight Transportation
N.A.I.C.S.: 484110
Tod Prawer (Pres)
Maureen Cavalero (Sr VP)
Raymond L. Giguere Jr. (Dir-Safety)

S.R. BRAY LLC
1210 N Red Gum St, Anaheim, CA 92806-1820
Tel.: (714) 765-7551
Web Site: http://www.powerplus.com

Standby & Emergency Power Specialization Services, Disaster Response & Generator Sales & Services
N.A.I.C.S.: 221118
Steve Nameroff (CFO & CIO)
Eric Heiliger (Dir-Bus Dev)
Ashby Lawson (Prod Mgr)
Mike Lang (COO)

S.R. SNODGRASS, A.C.
2009 Mackenzie Way Ste 340, Cranberry Township, PA 16066
Tel.: (724) 934-0344
Web Site: http://www.srsnodgrass.com
Year Founded: 1946
Rev.: $14,569,000
Emp.: 130
Accounting & Auditing Services
N.A.I.C.S.: 541219
Robert J. Kline (Dir-HR)
Harry E. Bertrand (Principal)

S.R. WEINER & ASSOCIATES INC.
33 Boylston St #3000, Chestnut Hill, MA 02467
Tel.: (617) 232-8900
Web Site: http://www.wsdevelopment.com
Rev.: $12,500,000
Emp.: 100
Subdividers & Developers, Nec
N.A.I.C.S.: 237210
Steven R. Weiner (Owner)
Christine B. Rocco (Dir-Leasing, Compliance & Analyst)
Robert G. Frazier (VP-Dev)
Deirdre A. Geoghegan (Treas)
Jeffrey N. Willar (Controller)
David A. Saurette (VP-Construction)
Brian T. Sciera (VP-Lifestyle Centers)
Jeremy Sclar (Pres)

Subsidiaries:

Pheasant Lane Mall Management (1)
310 Daniel Webster Hwy, Nashua, NH 03060
Tel.: (603) 888-0005
Web Site: http://www.pheasantlanemall.com
Rev.: $1,400,000
Emp.: 10
Commercial & Industrial Building Operation
N.A.I.C.S.: 541611
Vincent Cosco (Gen Mgr)
Aaron Yust (Dir-Mktg & Bus Dev)

S.S. DWECK & SONS INC.
345 Nye Ave, Irvington, NJ 07111
Tel.: (973) 375-0900 NY
Web Site: http://www.ssdweck.com
Year Founded: 1929
Sales Range: $10-24.9 Million
Emp.: 12
Homefurnishings
N.A.I.C.S.: 423220
Stephen Dweck (Pres)

S.S. LOGAN PACKING COMPANY
120 21st St, Huntington, WV 25703
Tel.: (304) 525-7625
Rev.: $24,900,000
Emp.: 65
Meat & Meat Product Merchant Whslr
N.A.I.C.S.: 424470
Nester S. Logan (Owner)
Rick Logan (CFO)
Nancy Pauley (Controller)

S.S. STEINER INC.
655 Madison Ave, New York, NY 10065-8043
Tel.: (212) 838-8900
Web Site: http://www.hopsteiner.com

Year Founded: 1845
Rev.: $40,000,000
Emp.: 20
Hops
N.A.I.C.S.: 424590

Subsidiaries:

HEG Hopfenextraktion GmbH (1)
PO Box 1113, 85126, Munchsmunster, Germany
Tel.: (49) 84027400
Production & Distribution of Hop Extracts
N.A.I.C.S.: 311930

Hops Extract Corporation of America (1)
305 N 2nd Ave, Yakima, WA 98902-2626
Tel.: (509) 248-1530
Hop Extract Distr
N.A.I.C.S.: 424490
Dave Dunhan (Mgr)

Hopsteiner Trading (Zhuhai) Co., Ltd. (1)
1503 Jiuchang Bldg 8 Haizhou Road, Zhuhai, 519015, China
Tel.: (86) 756 322 3340
Hop Extract Distr
N.A.I.C.S.: 424490

Simon H. Steiner, Hopfen, GmbH (1)
Auhofstrasse 18, 84048, Mainburg, Germany
Tel.: (49) 8751 8605 0
Web Site: http://www.hopsteiner.de
Emp.: 150
Hop Extract Distr
N.A.I.C.S.: 424490
Christof Eckel (Head-Bio Science Applications)

Steiner Hops Limited (1)
319A High Street, Epping, CM16 4DA, Essex, United Kingdom
Tel.: (44) 1992 572 331
Emp.: 6
Hop Extract Distr
N.A.I.C.S.: 424490
Trevor Roberts (Co-Mng Dir)
Russell Falconer (Co-Mng Dir)

Zatec Hop Company (1)
koleji 8/317, 161 00, Prague, Czech Republic
Tel.: (420) 220 561 474
Web Site: http://www.zhc.cz
Hop Extract Distr
N.A.I.C.S.: 424490
Jiri Sedivy (Mng Dir)
Zdenek Sokol (Dir-Comml)
Ilona Horavova (Office Mgr)
Jaroslav Blazek (Mgr-IT)
Petr Hynek (Mgr-Quality)

U.S. PRIVATE

S.S. WHITE TECHNOLOGIES INC.
8300 Sheen Dr, Saint Petersburg, FL 33709
Tel.: (727) 626-2800
Web Site: http://www.sswhite.net
Year Founded: 1844
Sales Range: $10-24.9 Million
Emp.: 125
Flexible Shaft Mfr
N.A.I.C.S.: 333613
Rahul B. Shukla (Pres & CEO)

Subsidiaries:

S S White Technologies UK Limited (1)
19 Heathfield Stacey Bushes, Milton Keynes, MK12 6HP, United Kingdom
Tel.: (44) 1908 525120
Web Site: http://www.sswhite.co.uk
Power Transmission Equipment Mfr
N.A.I.C.S.: 333613
Steve Grimes (Mng Dir)

SS White Medical Products (1)
151 Old New Brunswick Rd, Piscataway, NJ 08854
Tel.: (732) 752-8300
Web Site: http://www.sswhitemedical.com

Sales Range: $1-9.9 Million
Surgical Appliances & Supplies Mfr
N.A.I.C.S.: 339113
Rahul B. Shukla (Pres)

S.S.I. TECHNOLOGIES INC.
3200 Palmer Dr, Janesville, WI 53546-2308
Tel.: (608) 758-1500 WI
Web Site: http://www.ssitechnologies.com
Year Founded: 1982
Sales Range: $25-49.9 Million
Emp.: 1,000
Provider of Industrial Control Services
N.A.I.C.S.: 335314
David S. Baum (Pres)
Chris Lawrence (Engr-Quality)

S.S.W. MECHANICAL CONSTRUCTION, INC.
670 S Oleander Rd, Palm Springs, CA 92264-1502
Tel.: (760) 325-6007
Web Site: http://www.sswmechanical.com
Sales Range: $10-24.9 Million
Emp.: 140
Plumbing Services
N.A.I.C.S.: 238220
William Hayes (VP)

S.T. BUNN CONSTRUCTION COMPANY
1904 University Blvd, Tuscaloosa, AL 35401
Tel.: (205) 752-8195
Web Site: http://www.stbunn.com
Sales Range: $25-49.9 Million
Emp.: 170
Construction Services
N.A.I.C.S.: 236115
Guy Watkins (Mgr-Ops)

S.T. JOHNSON CO.
5160 Fulton Dr, Fairfield, CA 94534
Tel.: (510) 652-6000
Web Site: http://www.johnsonburners.com
Year Founded: 1903
Sales Range: $10-24.9 Million
Emp.: 28
Mfr of Gas, Oil & Combination Gas & Oil Burners & Control Systems For Commercial & Industrial Applications
N.A.I.C.S.: 333414
Todd Cole (Dir-Ops)
Chuck Maytum (Mgr-Pur)

S.T. WOOTEN CORPORATION
3801 Black Creek Rd SE, Wilson, NC 27893
Tel.: (252) 291-5165
Web Site: http://www.stwcorp.com
Rev.: $126,100,000
Emp.: 1,000
General Contractor, Highway & Street Construction
N.A.I.C.S.: 237310
Seth Wooten (CEO)
Ricky Vick (VP)
Seth T. Wooten (CEO)
Christopher Wooten (Pres)
Ricky Vick (VP)
Chris Wooten (CEO)

S.V.D.P. MANAGEMENT, INC.
3350 E St, San Diego, CA 92102
Tel.: (619) 446-2100 CA
Web Site: http://www.svdpv.org
Year Founded: 1992
Sales Range: $10-24.9 Million
Emp.: 177
Social Welfare & Public Relation Services
N.A.I.C.S.: 813410
Patricia Cruise (Co-Pres)

S.W. ANDERSON COMPANY, INC.
2425 Wisconsin Ave, Downers Grove, IL 60515
Tel.: (630) 964-2600 DE
Web Site: http://www.swaco.com
Year Founded: 1926
Sales Range: $10-24.9 Million
Emp.: 48
Hardware
N.A.I.C.S.: 423710

S.W. RODGERS COMPANY INC.
5816 Wellington Rd, Gainesville, VA 20155-1669
Tel.: (703) 591-8400 VA
Web Site: http://www.swrodgers.com
Year Founded: 1980
Sales Range: $50-74.9 Million
Emp.: 350
Construction & Site Preparation Services
N.A.I.C.S.: 238990
Rick Long (VP)
P. Kurtis Rodgers (Pres)
Christopher Butler (Dir-HR & Safety)

S.W.H. SUPPLY COMPANY
242 E Main St, Louisville, KY 40202
Tel.: (502) 589-9287
Web Site: http://www.swhsupply.com
Sales Range: $10-24.9 Million
Emp.: 60
Refrigeration Equipment & Supplies
N.A.I.C.S.: 423740
Robert W. Anderson Jr. (Pres)

S/R INDUSTRIES INC.
5454 Argosy Ave, Huntington Beach, CA 92649
Tel.: (714) 898-7535 CA
Web Site: http://www.beeman.com
Year Founded: 1944
Sales Range: Less than $1 Million
Emp.: 20
Mfr of Sporting & Athletic Goods
N.A.I.C.S.: 423910
Leo Thiang (Pres)

S/S/G CORPORATION
512 2nd St, Hudson, WI 54016-1549
Tel.: (715) 386-8281 WI
Web Site: http://www.ssg-autostop.com
Year Founded: 1971
Sales Range: $250-299.9 Million
Emp.: 440
Self Service Gas Station & Convenience Store
N.A.I.C.S.: 457120
Burton L. Nordstrand (Pres)
Gail Dahlstrom (VP)

S1 BIOPHARMA, INC.
7 World Trade Ctr 250 Greenwich St 46th Fl, New York, NY 10007
Tel.: (201) 283-9050 DE
Web Site: http://www.s1biopharma.com
Year Founded: 2008
Biopharmaceutical Mfr
N.A.I.C.S.: 325412
Nicolas G. Sitchon (Chm, Pres & CEO)
Robert E. Pyke (Chief Medical Officer)
John F. Kaufmann (CFO)

S2 YACHTS, INC.
725 E 40th St, Holland, MI 49423
Tel.: (616) 392-7163
Web Site: http://www.tiarayachts.com
Year Founded: 1974
Sales Range: $150-199.9 Million
Emp.: 750

Yacht Mfr
N.A.I.C.S.: 336612
Michelle Stonebrook (Mgr-IT)
David Glenn (Dir-Mktg)

S2TECH
720 Spirit 40 Park Dr, Chesterfield, MO 63005
Tel.: (636) 530-9286
Web Site: http://www.s2tech.com
Sales Range: $1-9.9 Million
Emp.: 160
Computer Software Development
N.A.I.C.S.: 541511
Dayakar Veerlapati (Pres & CEO)
Brenda Yockey (VP-Resource Mgmt)
Mike Spangler (VP-Products & Svcs)
Srinivas Tutika (Dir-Talent Acq)
Kim Stratton (Mgr-HR)
Lena Mathis (Mgr-Immigration)
Susan Cornock (Office Mgr)
Pradeep Kumar (Mgr-Delivery)
Priyankai Veerlapat (Gen Counsel)
Matt Moreau (Sr VP-Strategy & Solutions)

S3 MATCHING TECHNOLOGIES, LP
6500 River Pl Blvd Ste 306, Austin, TX 78730
Tel.: (512) 329-3245
Web Site: http://www.s3.com
Year Founded: 2003
Sales Range: $1-9.9 Million
Emp.: 34
Software Developer & Whslr
N.A.I.C.S.: 513210
Mark Davies (CEO)
John Standerfer (CTO)
Jeremy Vest (VP-Client Svcs)
Rob Olkiewicz (VP-Client Integration)
Tobin Griser (Exec. VP-Client Svcs)

S3 MEDIA INC.
1717 E 5th Ave, Tampa, FL 33605
Tel.: (813) 944-2912
Web Site: http://www.s3media.net
Sales Range: $1-9.9 Million
Emp.: 3
Advetising Agency
N.A.I.C.S.: 541810
Darian Smith (Pres)

S360S
PO Box 38809, Baltimore, MD 21231
Tel.: (410) 599-4672
Web Site: http://www.s360s.com
Sales Range: Less than $1 Million
Emp.: 7
Advetising Agency
N.A.I.C.S.: 541810
Beth Perry (Founder)

S4 INC.
209 Burlington Rd Ste 105, Bedford, MA 01730
Tel.: (781) 273-1600
Web Site: http://www.s4inc.com
Year Founded: 1996
Rev.: $16,900,000
Emp.: 100
Computer System Design Services
N.A.I.C.S.: 541512
Chandu Shah (Pres & CEO)
Steve Kerns (VP)
Eshani Shah (Mgr)
Jay Davis (Dir-Programs-Colorado Springs Reg)

S4J MANUFACTURING SERVICES, INC.
2685 NE 9th Ave, Cape Coral, FL 33909
Tel.: (239) 574-9400
Web Site: http://www.s4jmfg.com
Year Founded: 1964

Sales Range: $1-9.9 Million
Emp.: 15
Surgical & Medical Instrument Mfr
N.A.I.C.S.: 339112
Steven Gyure (Pres)
Douglas Gyure (VP)

SA PHOTONICS, INC.
120 Knowles Dr Ste A, Los Gatos, CA 95032
Tel.: (408) 376-0252 CA
Web Site: http://www.saphotonics.com
Year Founded: 2002
Sales Range: $1-9.9 Million
Emp.: 40
Design & Development of Advanced Optical Systems for Military & Commercial Clients
N.A.I.C.S.: 333310
James Coward (Founder, Pres & CEO)
Michael P. Browne (Gen Mgr-Vision Products)

SA TECHNOLOGIES, INC.
2700 Augustine Dr Ste 285, Santa Clara, CA 95054
Tel.: (408) 400-3900 DE
Web Site: http://www.satincorp.com
Year Founded: 2002
Sales Range: $10-24.9 Million
Emp.: 150
Computer Software Development
N.A.I.C.S.: 541511
Manoj Joshi (Co-Founder & CEO)
Vivek Sharma (VP-IT)

SA&E INTERNATIONAL BAG & ACCESSORIES LLC
10 W 33rd St Rm 1217, New York, NY 10001
Tel.: (212) 268-8172
Sales Range: $10-24.9 Million
Emp.: 18
Luggage Mfr
N.A.I.C.S.: 424990
Abe E. Shalam (Exec Dir)

SAAD'S HEALTHCARE SERVICES, INC.
1515 S University Blvd, Mobile, AL 36609
Tel.: (251) 380-3800 AL
Web Site: http://www.saadhealthcare.com
Year Founded: 1986
Sales Range: $75-99.9 Million
Emp.: 900
Holding Company; Healthcare Services
N.A.I.C.S.: 551112
Barbara Fultham (Pres)

Subsidiaries:

Saad's Medical Equipment Inc. (1)
1515 S University Blvd, Mobile, AL 36609 (100%)
Tel.: (251) 380-3351
Web Site: http://www.saadhealthcare.com
Rev.: $2,727,982
Emp.: 2
Medical Equipment Rental
N.A.I.C.S.: 423450
Henry Fulgham (VP-Ops)

Saad's Medical Management Inc. (1)
790 Dieux Marche, Biloxi, MS 39530-4110
Tel.: (251) 343-9600
Web Site: http://www.saadhealthcare.com
Rev.: $2,900,000
Emp.: 35
Women Healthcare Services
N.A.I.C.S.: 621610
Dorothy Dunning (Owner)

Saad's Nursing Services Inc. (1)
1515 University Blvd S, Mobile, AL 36609

Saad's Healthcare Services, Inc.—(Continued)
Tel.: (251) 380-3350
Web Site: http://www.saadshealth.com
Sales Range: $25-49.9 Million
Emp.: 150
Offices Of Health Practitioner
N.A.I.C.S.: 621399
Henry Fulgham (Owner)

SAALEX CORP.
1721 Pacific Ave Ste 180, Oxnard, CA 93033
Tel.: (805) 385-3636
Web Site: http://www.saalexsolutions.com
Year Founded: 1999
Sales Range: $1-9.9 Million
Emp.: 36
Engineeering Services
N.A.I.C.S.: 541330
Travis T. Mack (Pres)

Subsidiaries:

Network And Simulation Technologies Incorporated (1)
291 Island Dr, Middletown, RI 02842
Tel.: (401) 619-0244
Web Site: http://www.netsimco.com
Data Processing, Hosting & Related Services
N.A.I.C.S.: 518210
Michael A. Waite (Pres)

Spalding Consulting Inc. (1)
46611 Corporate Dr Ste 130, Lexington Park, MD 20653
Tel.: (301) 737-0150
Web Site: http://www.scipax.com
Sales Range: $10-24.9 Million
Emp.: 110
It Consulting
N.A.I.C.S.: 541690
Barry Spalding (Pres)
Jodi Lias (VP-Contracts)
Jake Kibler (Project Mgr)
Troy Bekel (VP)

SAAMA TECHNOLOGIES, INC.
900 E Hamilton Ave Ste 200, Campbell, CA 95008-0668
Tel.: (408) 371-1900
Web Site: http://www.saama.com
Year Founded: 1998
Sales Range: $10-24.9 Million
Emp.: 237
Computer Facilities Management Services
N.A.I.C.S.: 541513
Suresh Katta (Founder)
Vivek Sharma (CEO)
Scott Rogers (CFO)
Neelesh Sali (Mng Dir-India & Head-Europe & Asia-Pacific)
Lisa Moneymaker (CTO & Chief Product Officer)

SAAR'S INC.
32199 SR 20, Oak Harbor, WA 98277-2606
Tel.: (360) 675-3000
Web Site: http://www.saarsmarketplacefoods.com
Year Founded: 1988
Sales Range: $10-24.9 Million
Emp.: 120
Provider of Grocery Services
N.A.I.C.S.: 445110
Gregory A. Saar (Pres & CEO)
Rodney Byrd (CFO)
Mike Boyce (Mgr-Stores)

SAATVA, INC.
8 Wright St Ste 108, Westport, CT 06880
Tel.: (877) 672-2882
Web Site: http://www.saatvamattress.com
Mattress Mfr & Distr

N.A.I.C.S.: 337910
Ron Rudzin (CEO)
Ricky Joshi (CMO)
Kris Brower (CTO)
Annette Honeywell (Mgr-Exec Info)
Alex Franklyn (Gen Mgr)
Jen Pressley (Designer)
Joe McCambley (Chief Strategy Officer)

SABAH INTERNATIONAL, INC.
5925 Stoneridge Dr, Pleasanton, CA 94588
Tel.: (925) 463-0431
Web Site: http://www.sabahinternational.com
Year Founded: 1972
Fire Prevention & Asset Protection Technology Services
N.A.I.C.S.: 561621
Michele Sabah (CEO)
Matt Ramsey (Pres)

SABAL HOLDINGS INC.
200 Central Ave Ste 220, Saint Petersburg, FL 33701
Tel.: (727) 824-8700
Web Site: http://www.sabaltrust.com
Sales Range: $10-24.9 Million
Emp.: 33
Private Equity Investor
N.A.I.C.S.: 551112
Kimberly A. Early (Principal)

Subsidiaries:

Sabal Trust Company (1)
4211 W Boy Scout Blvd Ste 190, Tampa, FL 33607 (100%)
Tel.: (813) 229-2180
Web Site: http://www.sabaltrust.com
Investment Management Service
N.A.I.C.S.: 523999
Scott L. Pieper (Chief Investment Officer)
Bryant Jones (Pres)
Kathleen J. Belmonte (Principal)
Travis Brown (Principal)
Brian H. Ceras (Principal)
Kari A. Baer (Principal)
Susan Brennan (Mng Principal)

SABAL PALM BANK
5101 Fruitville Rd Ste 100, Sarasota, FL 34232
Tel.: (941) 361-1122
Web Site: http://www.sabalpalmbank.com
Year Founded: 2006
Sales Range: $1-9.9 Million
Emp.: 24
Commericial Banking
N.A.I.C.S.: 522110
David J. Froelich (CFO & Exec VP)
Richard S. Appell (Sr VP-Lending)
Kathy Collums (Sr VP-Lending)
Dee Barth (VP-Ops)
Rick Halloran (Chief Lending Officer & Exec VP)
Vicky E. (Sr VP-Compliance)
Neil D. McCurry Jr. (Pres & CEO)

SABAN CAPITAL GROUP, INC.
10100 Santa Monica Blvd, Los Angeles, CA 90067-4003
Tel.: (323) 652-6471
Web Site: http://www.saban.com
Sales Range: $25-49.9 Million
Emp.: 65
Privater Equity Firm
N.A.I.C.S.: 523999
Richard Yen (Mng Dir-Private Equity)
Haim Saban (Chm & CEO)
Niveen S. Tadros (Gen Counsel & Exec VP)
Joel Andryc (Mng Dir-Private Equity)
Caroline Banzali (Head-Global Tax)
Corinne Chong (Dir-Private Equity)
Jordan Cohen (Dir-Private Equity)

Judy Friedman (VP-Bus & Legal Affairs)
Adam Chesnoff (Pres & COO)
Philip Han (Chief Investment Officer & Exec VP)
Sumeet Jaisinghani (Mng Dir-Private Equity)

Subsidiaries:

Paul Frank Industries, Inc. (1)
270 Baker St E, Costa Mesa, CA 92626
Tel.: (714) 881-0100
Web Site: http://www.paulfrank.com
Sales Range: $25-49.9 Million
Men's & Women's Sportswear; Kids Clothing, Swimwear, Eyewear, Watches & Home Furnishings Designer & Retailer
N.A.I.C.S.: 315250

SABAS BUNCH LIMITED PARTNERSHIP
3270 N Colorado St Ste 101, Chandler, AZ 85225
Tel.: (480) 969-7122
Web Site: http://www.sabas.com
Year Founded: 1927
Sales Range: $100-124.9 Million
Emp.: 100
Quality Western Apparel
N.A.I.C.S.: 458110
Roger Saba Sr. (Pres)
Roger Saba Jr. (VP-Mktg & Sls)

SABEL INDUSTRIES INC.
749 N Ct St, Montgomery, AL 36104
Tel.: (334) 265-6771
Web Site: http://www.sabelsteel.com
Sales Range: $10-24.9 Million
Emp.: 250
Metals Service Centers & Offices
N.A.I.C.S.: 423510
Keith Sabel (COO & Exec VP)
Phillip Brown (CFO & Exec VP)
Fred Callahan (VP-Sls & Mktg)
Janet Hinton (Sec & Mgr-HR)
Steve Dunlap (Mgr-Credit)
Dicky Sanford (Treas)
Al Dozier (Mgr-Maintenance)
Paul Milton (Mgr-Pur)
Tammy Foster (Sec)

SABER ACCEPTANCE COMPANY INC.
PO Box 471823, Tulsa, OK 74147
Tel.: (918) 622-7333
Web Site: http://www.regalcars.com
Rev.: $15,000,000
Emp.: 40
Financial Services
N.A.I.C.S.: 522291
Robert Mulkey (Pres)

SABER HEALTHCARE GROUP LLC
26691 Richmond Rd, Bedford Heights, OH 44146
Tel.: (216) 292-5706
Web Site: http://www.saberhealth.com
Year Founded: 2001
Emp.: 11,000
Nursing Healthcare Facilities
N.A.I.C.S.: 623110
George S. Repchick (Pres)
Debra Pennock (Exec Dir-Clinical Svcs & Compliance)
Kelly Mutchler (Reg VP-Ops)
Glena Steele (VP-Bus Dev)

Subsidiaries:

Autumn Corporation (2)
451 N Winstead Ave, Rocky Mount, NC 27804
Tel.: (252) 443-6265
Web Site: http://www.autumncorp.com
Nursing Care Facilities
N.A.I.C.S.: 623110

Samuel M. Marsh (CFO & VP)
Gerald P. Cox (Pres)

SABER REAL ESTATE ADVISORS, LLC
80 Business Park Dr Ste 100, Armonk, NY 10504
Tel.: (914) 250-0600
Web Site: http://www.saberfund.com
Sales Range: $75-99.9 Million
Emp.: 10
Real Estate Investment Advisory Services
N.A.I.C.S.: 523999
Martin G. Berger (Mng Principal)
Michael G. Klinger (Mng Principal)

SABERT CORPORATION
2288 Main St Ext, Sayreville, NJ 08872
Web Site: http://www.sabert.com
Year Founded: 1983
Plastic Mfr
N.A.I.C.S.: 326130
Thomas Fu (VP-Innovation-Global)
Albert Salama (Founder & CEO)

Subsidiaries:

LBP Manufacturing LLC (1)
7 Alberigi Dr, Jessup, PA 18434
Tel.: (708) 329-1627
Foodservice Packaging Products Mfr & Whslr
N.A.I.C.S.: 322219
Thomas Fu (VP-Innovation-Global)

Mullinix Packages Inc. (1)
3511 Engle Rd, Fort Wayne, IN 46809-6809 (100%)
Tel.: (260) 747-3149
Web Site: http://www.mullinixpackages.com
Food & Beverage Plastics Product Mfr
N.A.I.C.S.: 326199
Gene Gentili (Pres & CEO)

SABIN METAL CORPORATION
300 Pantigo Pl Ste 102, East Hampton, NY 11937-2630
Tel.: (631) 329-1717
Web Site: http://www.sabinmetal.com
Year Founded: 1945
Sales Range: $50-74.9 Million
Emp.: 150
Precious Metals Refining Services
N.A.I.C.S.: 331492
Andrew Sabin (Owner & Pres)
Robert Hampson (VP)
Brad Cook (VP-Mktg)

SABIN ROBBINS PAPER CO.
9365 Allen Rd, West Chester, OH 45069
Tel.: (513) 874-5270
Web Site: http://www.sabinrobbins.com
Year Founded: 1884
Sales Range: $50-74.9 Million
Emp.: 260
Mfr of Paper & Allied Products
N.A.I.C.S.: 424110
Charlie Hebble (VP-Sls-Chicago & Mgr-Sls-Ohio)
Joe Tallion (Plant Mgr)
Jamie Wires (Mgr-Acctg & HR)
James Estes (VP-Ops)

SABINA FARMERS EXCHANGE INC.
292 N Howard, Sabina, OH 45169
Tel.: (937) 584-2411
Web Site: http://www.premier-services.org
Sales Range: $10-24.9 Million
Emp.: 23
Agricultural Services
N.A.I.C.S.: 424910

John Surber *(Pres)*
John Heinz *(VP)*
Mary Van Meter *(Controller)*
Corey Hoppes *(Mgr-Grain Origination)*

SABINE BANCSHARES INC.
297 Elizabeth St, Many, LA 71449
Tel.: (318) 256-7000
Web Site:
   http://www.sabinebank.com
Sales Range: $25-49.9 Million
Emp.: 320
Bank Holding Company
N.A.I.C.S.: 551111
James R. Cole Jr. *(Chm)*

Subsidiaries:

Sabine Bank Operation Center
Inc.   (1)
570 San Antonio Ave, Many, LA 71449
Tel.: (318) 256-6331
Web Site: http://www.sabinestatebank.com
Sales Range: $25-49.9 Million
Emp.: 20
Banking Services
N.A.I.C.S.: 522110
Paul Sklar *(Gen Mgr)*

Sabine State Bank & Trust
Company   (1)
297 Elizabeth St, Many, LA 71449
Tel.: (318) 256-7000
Web Site: http://www.sabinebank.com
Sales Range: $25-49.9 Million
Emp.: 100
Banking Services
N.A.I.C.S.: 522110
James R. Cole *(Chm)*
Lee H. McCann *(Pres, CEO & COO)*
John P. Godfrey *(Sr VP & Mgr-Bus Dev-Natchitoches)*
Dwayne Harper *(Sr VP & Mgr-Bus Dev-Alexandria)*

SABINE OIL & GAS HOLDINGS, INC.
1415 Louisiana St Ste 1600, Houston, TX 77002
Tel.: (832) 242-9600
Year Founded: 2019
Holding Company
N.A.I.C.S.: 551112

SABINE PASS LIQUEFACTION, LLC
700 Milam St Ste 1900, Houston, TX 77002
Tel.: (713) 375-5000   DE
Web Site: https://www.cheniere.com
Year Founded: 2010
Rev.: $9,466,000,000
Assets: $14,514,000,000
Liabilities: $13,117,000,000
Net Worth: $1,397,000,000
Earnings: $4,151,000,000
Emp.: 1,605
Fiscal Year-end: 12/31/23
Natural Gas Transmission Services
N.A.I.C.S.: 486210
Jack A. Fusco *(CEO)*
Aaron Stephenson *(Pres & Mgr)*
Zach Davis *(CFO & Mgr)*
Leonard E. Travis *(Chief Acctg Officer)*
Scott Peak *(Mgr)*

SABINE RIVER AUTHORITY OF TEXAS
12777 Hwy 87 N, Orange, TX 77632
Tel.: (409) 746-2192
Web Site: http://www.sratx.org
Year Founded: 1949
Sales Range: $25-49.9 Million
Emp.: 106
Water Supply
N.A.I.C.S.: 221310
David Montagne *(Exec VP & Gen Mgr)*

Subsidiaries:

Toledo Bend Project Joint
Operations   (1)
450 Spur 135, Burkeville, TX 75932
Tel.: (409) 565-2273
Web Site: http://www.tbpjo.org
Sales Range: $1-9.9 Million
Emp.: 22
Water Supply & Irrigation Systems
N.A.I.C.S.: 221310
Jerry Clark *(Exec VP & Gen Mgr)*

SABINE RIVER AUTHORITY, STATE OF LOUISIANA
15091 Texas Highway, Many, LA 71449
Tel.: (318) 256-4112
Water Supply
N.A.I.C.S.: 221310
James W. Pratt *(Exec Dir)*

Subsidiaries:

Toledo Bend Project Joint
Operations   (1)
450 Spur 135, Burkeville, TX 75932
Tel.: (409) 565-2273
Web Site: http://www.tbpjo.org
Sales Range: $1-9.9 Million
Emp.: 22
Water Supply & Irrigation Systems
N.A.I.C.S.: 221310
Jerry Clark *(Exec VP & Gen Mgr)*

SABINSA CORPORATION
20 Lake Dr E, Windsor, NJ 08520-5950
Tel.: (732) 777-1111
Web Site: http://www.sabinsa.com
Rev.: $18,183,760
Emp.: 33
Pharmaceuticals
N.A.I.C.S.: 424210
Muhameed Majeed *(Founder & Pres-Bus Expansion & Ops-Global)*
Shaheen Majeed *(Pres-Sabinsa Worldwide)*
Ahmed Khan *(Mgr-Sls-USA)*
N. Kalyanam *(Pres-R&D)*
Anurag Pande *(VP-Scientific Affairs)*
Asha Ramesh *(CEO)*
Madhu Subramanian *(Pres-Bus Expansion-Global & Ops)*

SABIO MOBILE, INC.
401 Wilshire Blvd 12th Fl, Santa Monica, CA 90401
Tel.: (213) 277-3647
Web Site:
   http://www.sabiomobile.com
Year Founded: 2014
Sales Range: $10-24.9 Million
Emp.: 50
Mobile Application Development Services
N.A.I.C.S.: 541511
Aziz Rahim *(CEO)*
Joe Camacho *(CMO)*
Sudha Reddy *(VP-Product Innovation)*
Jean Yap-McNamara *(Dir-Creative)*
Helen Lum *(Sr VP-Ops)*

SABLE NATURAL RESOURCES CORPORATION
12222 Merit Dr Ste 1850, Dallas, TX 75251
Tel.: (972) 770-4700   DE
Web Site: http://www.snrcorp.com
Sales Range: Less than $1 Million
Emp.: 12
Oil & Gas Exploration & Production Services
N.A.I.C.S.: 211120
Michael K. Galvis *(Chm & CEO)*
Chris Coley *(VP-Engrg & Production)*
James D. Parker *(Chief Acctg Officer)*

SABRE MARKETING
90 S Newtown St Rd Ste 10, Newtown Square, PA 19073
Tel.: (610) 353-5611
Web Site:
   http://www.sabreonline.com
Sales Range: $10-24.9 Million
Emp.: 5
N.A.I.C.S.: 541810
Elyse Sacchetti *(Project Mgr)*

SABRE YACHTS
12 Hawthorne Rd, Raymond, ME 04071
Tel.: (207) 655-3831   ME
Web Site:
   http://www.sabreyachts.com
Year Founded: 1970
Sales Range: $100-124.9 Million
Emp.: 150
Fiberglass Sailing Yachts & Motor Yachts Mfr
N.A.I.C.S.: 336612
Ed Miller *(Chm)*
Daniel Zilkha *(Pres & CEO)*
Nancy J. Basselet *(CFO)*
Bentley Collins *(VP-Sls & Mktg)*
Aaron Crawford *(Pres & COO)*
Lynn Beaudoin *(Natl Sls Mgr)*
Dave Newcomb *(Head-Engrg Dept)*
Adam Carlson *(Designer)*

SABRELINER CORPORATION
7733 Forsyth Blvd Ste 1500, Saint Louis, MO 63105-1879
Tel.: (314) 863-6880   DE
Web Site: http://www.sabreliner.com
Year Founded: 1983
Sales Range: $10-24.9 Million
Emp.: 450
Repair & Maintenance of Aircraft & Jet Engines; Aviation Logistic Support
N.A.I.C.S.: 488190
F. Holmes Lamoreux *(Chm & CEO)*
Susan Seabury Aselage *(Vice Chm, Pres, Sec, VP & Asst Treas)*
Michael McKay *(CFO, Treas & Sr VP)*
Beth Thomas *(Dir-Corp Aviation)*
D. J. Meier *(Sr VP-Govt & Subcontracting Svcs)*
Jerry Wade *(VP-Ethics & Compliance)*
Tracy Ogle *(VP-Rotary Wing Programs)*
Pat Quinn *(VP & Mgr-Govt Fixed Wing Aircraft Programs)*
Greg Fedele *(Pres)*

SACCA CORPORATION
513 Fruitvale Rd, Vacaville, CA 95688
Tel.: (707) 447-3800
Web Site: http://www.burgerking.com
Sales Range: $10-24.9 Million
Emp.: 500
Fast-Food Restaurant Owner & Operator
N.A.I.C.S.: 722513
Tina Benedict *(Partner)*

SACHEM INC.
821 E Woodward St, Austin, TX 78704
Tel.: (512) 421-4900   TX
Web Site: http://www.sacheminc.com
Year Founded: 1950
Sales Range: $10-24.9 Million
Emp.: 75
Chemical Products Mfr
N.A.I.C.S.: 325199
John Mooney *(Pres & CEO)*

Subsidiaries:

SACHEM Asia Ltd.   (1)
5 6 27 Muzuhai, Osaka, 578 0921, Japan   (100%)
Tel.: (81) 729644300
Web Site: http://sacheminc.com
Sales Range: $10-24.9 Million
Emp.: 15
Mfr of Chemical Products
N.A.I.C.S.: 325998
Tom Mooney *(Pres)*
Tomitaka Ito *(Mng Dir)*

SACHEM Europe BV   (1)
Van Voordenpark 15, 5301 KP, Zaltbommel, Netherlands   (100%)
Tel.: (31) 418682000
Web Site: http://www.sacheminc.com
Emp.: 80
Chemical Products Mfr
N.A.I.C.S.: 325998
Frank Groenen *(VP & Gen Mgr)*

SACHS ELECTRIC COMPANY
1572 Larkin Williams Rd, Fenton, MO 63026
Tel.: (636) 532-2000   MO
Web Site: http://www.sachsco.com
Year Founded: 1990
Sales Range: $100-124.9 Million
Emp.: 1,000
Electrical Construction
N.A.I.C.S.: 238210
Clayton M. Scharff *(Chm, Pres & CEO)*
C. Patrick Smallwood *(Asst VP-Pre Construction Svcs)*
Mark Ellison *(Asst VP-Safety)*
Patrick A. Kriegshauser *(CFO & Exec VP)*

Subsidiaries:

Sachs Civil Inc.   (1)
1572 Larkin Williams Rd, Fenton, MO 63026
Tel.: (636) 532-2000
Web Site: http://www.sachsco.com
Sales Range: $10-24.9 Million
Emp.: 20
Excavation Work
N.A.I.C.S.: 238910
Clayton M. Scharff *(Pres)*
Mike Parisot *(VP)*

Sachs Systems Inc.   (1)
PO Box 96, Saint Louis, MO 63166
Tel.: (636) 532-2000
Web Site: http://www.sachsco.com
Sales Range: $25-49.9 Million
Emp.: 120
Electrical Work
N.A.I.C.S.: 238210
Clayton M. Scharff *(Pres & CEO)*

SACHS HOLDING COMPANY
400 Chesterfield Ctr Ste 600, Chesterfield, MO 63017
Tel.: (636) 537-1000   IL
Web Site:
   http://www.sachsproperties.com
Year Founded: 1967
Sales Range: $75-99.9 Million
Emp.: 25
Holding Company; Real Estate Developer
N.A.I.C.S.: 551112
Jamie Marx *(Dir-Leasing)*
Ami E. Kutz *(CFO)*

Subsidiaries:

Sachs Properties   (1)
400 Chesterfield Ctr Ste 600, Chesterfield, MO 63017-4890
Tel.: (636) 537-1000
Web Site: http://www.sachsproperties.com
Sales Range: $10-24.9 Million
Emp.: 17
Real Estate Developer Owner & Manager Services
N.A.I.C.S.: 531120
Ami E. Kutz *(VP)*
Louis S. Sachs *(Founder)*

SACHS INVESTING COMPANY

SACHS INVESTING COMPANY

Sachs Investing Company—(Continued)
155 E 55th St Apt 5F, New York, NY 10022-4051
Tel.: (212) 753-3232   NY
Web Site: http://www.sachspalin.com
Year Founded: 1952
Sales Range: $50-74.9 Million
Emp.: 500
Real Estate Investment Services
N.A.I.C.S.: 531120
David Sachs (Pres & CEO)

SACHS MEDIA GROUP
114 S Duval St, Tallahassee, FL 32301
Tel.: (850) 222-1996   FL
Web Site:
  http://www.sachsmedia.com
Year Founded: 1996
Sales Range: $1-9.9 Million
Emp.: 20
Advertising Agencies
N.A.I.C.S.: 541810
Ronald L. Sachs (Founder & CEO)
Michelle Ubben (Pres & Partner)
Ryan Banfill (Head-Pub Affairs)
Lisa Garcia (Sr VP-PR)
Herbie Thiele (VP-Pub Affairs)
Vicki Johnson (Sr VP-Central Florida Ops)
Ryan Cohn (Exec VP)
Jon Peck (VP-PR)
Drew Piers (Deputy Dir-Pub Affairs)
Cheryl Stopnick (Sr VP-PR & Dir-Ops-South Florida)
Kelly Corder (Acct Mgr)
Jenn Meale Poggie (Sr Acct Mgr-Pub Affairs)
Juliet Hauser (Sr Acct Exec)

SACK LUMBER COMPANY
220 E 11th St, Crete, NE 68333
Tel.: (402) 826-2138
Web Site:
  http://www.sacklumber.doitbest.com
Sales Range: $10-24.9 Million
Emp.: 75
Building Products Sales
N.A.I.C.S.: 444110
Ronald R. Sack (Pres)
Gina Fehringer (Mgr)
Dan Silvester (Asst Gen Mgr)

SACKETT NATIONAL HOLDINGS, INC.
7373 Peak Dr, Las Vegas, NV 89128
Tel.: (702) 757-2614
Web Site:
  http://www.snhcapitalpartners.com
Year Founded: 1995
Holding Company; Private Equity Firm
N.A.I.C.S.: 551112
Jevin Sackett (CEO)
Ramya Varma (VP)
Matt Gilbreath (Mng Dir-Bus Strategy & Transformation)

Subsidiaries:

Universal Background Screening, Inc.   (1)
PO Box 5920, Scottsdale, AZ 85261-5920
Tel.: (877) 263-8033
Web Site:
  http://www.universalbackground.com
Employment & Hiring Background Services
N.A.I.C.S.: 561311
Dan Filby (CEO)

Subsidiary (Domestic):

Openonline, LLC   (2)
1650 Lake Shore Dr, Columbus, OH 43204
Tel.: (614) 481-6999
Web Site: http://www.openonline.com
Internet Service Provider
N.A.I.C.S.: 517810

Heather Browning (Exec VP)

SACO & BIDDEFORD SAVINGS INSTITUTION
252 Main St 50 Industrial Park Rd, Saco, ME 04072
Tel.: (207) 284-4591
Web Site: http://www.sbsavings.com
Sales Range: $10-24.9 Million
Emp.: 120
Banking Services
N.A.I.C.S.: 522180
Kevin P. Savage (CEO)
Robert C. Quentin (Pres, CFO & Treas)
Todd J. Rodriguez (VP & Mgr-Core Ops)
Mark R. Hodgdon (Asst VP & Mgr-Digital Banking)
Marc R. Gagnon (Chief Credit Risk & Mktg Officer & Exec VP)
Jeffrey M. Vachon (Sr VP & Dir-Bank Admin)
Michael Jean (Officer-Bus Loan & VP-Portland, Westbrook & Biddeford)
Joe Reardon (Asst VP & Mgr-Old Orchard Beach)
Diane Labrie (Sr VP & Dir-HR)
Matthew Grenier (Asst Mgr-Scarborough)
Becky Waitley (Officer-Customer Relationship-Scarborough)
Debbie Houle (Officer-Customer Relationship-Saco)
Denise McIntyre (Officer-Loan & Asst VP-Scarborough)
Dennis Dalton (Officer-Loan & Asst VP-Saco)
Eric Doyon (VP & Mgr-Bus Credit Dept-Saco)
Fran Anton (Officer-Loan & VP-Saco)
Jamie Whelan (Officer-Bus Loan & VP-Scarborough & South Portland)
Jeff St.Laurent (Officer-Loan & VP-Biddeford)
Jennifer Plourde (VP & Mgr-South Portland)
Julie Villemaire (VP & Mgr-Westbrook)
Kathleen Williamson (Officer-Customer Relationship-Saco)
Katrina Desjardins (Officer-Customer Relationship-South Portland)
Kelly Currier (Officer-Customer Relationship-Saco)
Mark Jones (Sr VP & Dir-Residential & Consumer Lending-Saco)
Patrick DeCourcey (Officer-Loan & VP-Portland & South Portland)
Phil Fearon (Sr VP & Dir-Bus Loans & Svcs-Saco)
Wanda Wilson (Officer-Customer Relationship-Old Orchard Beach)
Wayne Johnson (Officer-Loan-Portland)

SACO POLYMERS INC.
3220 Crocker Ave, Sheboygan, WI 53081
Tel.: (920) 803-0778   WI
Web Site:
  http://www.sacopolymers.com
Year Founded: 1998
Sales Range: $10-24.9 Million
Emp.: 50
Plastics Product Mfr
N.A.I.C.S.: 325991
Andrea Savonuzzi (Pres)

Subsidiaries:

AEI Compounds Limited   (1)
Sandwich Industrial Estate, Sandwich, CT13 9LY, Kent, United Kingdom   (100%)
Tel.: (44) 1304616171
Web Site: http://www.aeicompounds.com

Sales Range: $10-24.9 Million
Develops, Manufactures & Supplies Plastic Compounds
N.A.I.C.S.: 325211
Mark Shaw (Mng Dir)
Andrew Sabiston (Dir-Bus Dev)
Mike Slevin (Dir-Tech)
Evan White (Mgr-Customer Svcs)

Macromeric   (1)
1395 Danner Dr, Aurora, OH 44202
Tel.: (330) 995-1600
Web Site: http://www.macromeric.com
Emp.: 26
Thermoplastic Polymer Compounds & Additive Concentrates Mfr
N.A.I.C.S.: 325211
Beverly Jackson (Mgr-Corp Supply Chain)

SACRAMENTO EMPLOYMENT & TRAINING AGENCY
925 Del Paso Blvd, Sacramento, CA 95815-3608
Tel.: (916) 263-3800   CA
Web Site: http://www.seta.net
Year Founded: 1978
Sales Range: $25-49.9 Million
Emp.: 700
Job Training & Related Services
N.A.I.C.S.: 624310

SACRAMENTO PACKING, INC.
833 Tudor Rd, Yuba City, CA 95991
Tel.: (530) 671-4488
Web Site:
  http://www.sacramentopacking.com
Sales Range: $10-24.9 Million
Emp.: 300
Noncitrus Fruit Farming Services
N.A.I.C.S.: 111339
Jaswant Bains (CEO)

SACRAMENTO REGION COMMUNITY FOUNDATION
955 University Ave Ste A, Sacramento, CA 95825
Tel.: (916) 921-7723   CA
Web Site: http://www.sacregcf.org
Year Founded: 1983
Sales Range: $10-24.9 Million
Emp.: 16
Community Welfare Services
N.A.I.C.S.: 624190
Linda Beech Cutler (CEO)
Jim McCallum (CFO)
Shirlee Tully (CMO & Chief Dev Officer)
Winston Hom (Controller)
Kate Stille (Sec)
Martin Steiner (Vice Chm)
Donna L. Courville (Chm)
Margie Campbell (Treas)
Niva Flor (Chief Impact & Strategy Officer)

SACRED HEART COMMUNITY SERVICE
1381 S 1st St, San Jose, CA 95110
Tel.: (408) 278-2160   CA
Web Site:
  http://www.sacredheartcs.org
Year Founded: 1964
Sales Range: $10-24.9 Million
Emp.: 116
Community Care Services
N.A.I.C.S.: 624190
Poncho Guevara (Exec Dir)
Felicia Madsen (Pres)
Jorge Gonzalez (Sec)
Molly McDonald (VP)

SACRED POWER CORP.
1501 12th St NW, Albuquerque, NM 87104
Tel.: (505) 242-2292   NM
Web Site:
  http://www.sacredpower.com
Year Founded: 2001

U.S. PRIVATE

Sales Range: $10-24.9 Million
Emp.: 30
Solar Electric Services
N.A.I.C.S.: 238210

SACUNAS, INC.
835 Sir Thomas Ct, Harrisburg, PA 17109
Tel.: (717) 652-0100
Web Site: http://www.sacunas.net
Year Founded: 1990
Sales Range: $1-9.9 Million
Emp.: 10
Advetising Agency
N.A.I.C.S.: 541810
Nancy H. Sacunas (Pres & CEO)

SADCO, INC.
4552 Baldwin Ave, Montgomery, AL 36108
Tel.: (334) 288-5100   AL
Web Site: http://www.sadco-furniture.com
Year Founded: 1953
Home Appliance Distr
N.A.I.C.S.: 423620
Russell Levy (Pres)

SADDLE CREEK CORPORATION
3010 Saddle Creek Rd, Lakeland, FL 33801
Tel.: (863) 665-0966
Web Site: http://www.sclogistics.com
Sales Range: $250-299.9 Million
Emp.: 2,000
General Warehousing
N.A.I.C.S.: 493110
Scott Thornton (Chm)
Darrel Lake (VP-Admin)
Mark Cabrera (CEO)
Mike DelBovo (Pres-Transportation)
Tom Patterson (Sr VP-Warehouse Ops)
Robert Pericht (Sr VP-Warehouse Ops)
Doug Johnston (Sr VP-Customer Solutions & Ops Dev-Logistics Svcs)
Tom Collins (Dir-Mktg)
Perry Belcastro (VP-Fulfillment Svcs)
Duane Sizemore (Sr VP-Mktg & Bus Dev)
Donna Slyster (CIO)
John Erwin (VP-Transportation)
Jason Jackson (Supvr-Warehouse)
Ralph Corona (Supvr-Warehouse)
Timothy Tyson (Sr Dir-Bus Dev)
Lisa Venable (Sr Dir-Bus Dev)
Carolyn Martin (Sr Dir-Bus Dev)

SADDLEBACK ASSOCIATES INC.
27405 Puerta Real Ste 120, Mission Viejo, CA 92691
Tel.: (949) 635-1970   CA
Web Site:
  http://www.saddlebackassociates.com
Year Founded: 1987
Sales Range: $10-24.9 Million
Emp.: 7
Real Estate Investments; Owns & Operates Commercial & Industrial Buildings
N.A.I.C.S.: 531120
Raymond C. Smith (Founder & Chm)
Mark Severson (Pres)
Helen Alonso (Controller)

SADDLEBROOK HOLDINGS, INC.
5700 Saddlebrook Way, Wesley Chapel, FL 33543-4499
Tel.: (813) 973-1111
Holding Company
N.A.I.C.S.: 551112

COMPANIES

Thomas L. Dempsey *(Chm & Pres)*
Eleanor Dempsey *(Exec VP)*
Maureen Dempsey *(Exec VP)*
Diane L. Riehle *(Exec VP)*

Subsidiaries:

Saddlebrook Resorts, Inc. (1)
5700 Saddlebrook Way, Wesley Chapel, FL 33543-4499 **(100%)**
Tel.: (813) 973-1111
Web Site: http://www.saddlebrook.com
Rev.: $13,507,608
Assets: $18,805,845
Liabilities: $17,299,810
Net Worth: $1,506,035
Earnings: ($4,536,477)
Emp.: 170
Fiscal Year-end: 12/31/2020
Hotel & Resort Operator
N.A.I.C.S.: 721110
Thomas L. Dempsey *(Chm & CEO)*
Maureen Dempsey *(Pres & Asst Sec)*
Diane L. Riehle *(VP & Treas)*
Donald L. Allen *(Treas & VP)*

SADDORIS COMPANIES, INC.

400 SW Frank Phillips Blvd, Bartlesville, OK 74003
Tel.: (918) 336-6800 OK
Web Site: http://www.unitedlinen.com
Year Founded: 1996
Sales Range: $1-9.9 Million
Emp.: 125
Industrial Launderers
N.A.I.C.S.: 812332
Mat Saddoris *(Pres & CEO)*
Bob Pickle *(Mgr-Sls)*
Catherine Smith *(VP-Sls)*
Kristin Crawford *(Dir-HR)*
Rocky Denman *(VP-Ops)*
Scott Townsend *(Dir-Mktg)*

SADLER'S BAR-B-QUE SALES, LTD.

1206 N Frisco, Henderson, TX 75652
Tel.: (903) 655-7262 DE
Web Site: http://www.sadlerssmokehouse.com
Year Founded: 1948
Sales Range: $25-49.9 Million
Emp.: 300
Barbeque Chain Restaurant
N.A.I.C.S.: 722511
Harold Sadler *(Pres)*
Jason Flanagan *(CEO)*

SADOFF & RUDOY INDUSTRIES, LLP

240 W Arndt St, Fond Du Lac, WI 54935
Tel.: (920) 921-2070 WI
Web Site: http://www.sadoff.com
Year Founded: 1964
Sales Range: $200-249.9 Million
Emp.: 316
Scrap Metal Process Materials
N.A.I.C.S.: 423930
Sheldon J. Lasky *(Pres & CEO)*
Mark Lasky *(CEO)*
Mark Katz *(COO)*
Aral Eaton *(Mgr-Pur & Sls)*
Melissa Ryan *(Mgr-HR)*
Frank Villaire *(CFO)*
Bradford Lasky *(Exec VP)*
Jason Lasky *(Exec VP)*

SAE CIRCUITS COLORADO INC.

4820 N 63rd St Ste 100, Boulder, CO 80301
Tel.: (303) 530-1900
Web Site: http://www.saecircuits.com
Sales Range: $10-24.9 Million
Emp.: 62
Printed Circuit Board Mfr
N.A.I.C.S.: 334412
Steve Hodge *(Engr-Technical Sls)*

SAE INTERNATIONAL

400 Commonwealth Dr, Warrendale, PA 15096-0001
Tel.: (724) 776-4841
Web Site: http://www.sae.org
Year Founded: 1905
Sales Range: $75-99.9 Million
Mobility Engineering Services
N.A.I.C.S.: 541330
Dana M. Pless *(CFO)*
David L. Schutt *(CEO)*
Gregory L. Bradley *(Chief Legal Officer, Gen Counsel & Sec)*
Richard Wilkie *(CIO)*
Melinda Rombold *(Chief HR Officer)*
Raman Venkatesh *(COO & Exec VP)*

Subsidiaries:

SAE (India) Ltd. (1)
1/17 Ceebros Arcade 2 Fl, 3rd Cross Kasturba Nagar Adyar, Chennai, 600020, India
Tel.: (91) 4424411904
Web Site: http://www.saeindia.org
Sales Range: $10-24.9 Million
Emp.: 23
Mobility Engineering
N.A.I.C.S.: 541330
Aravind Bharadwaj *(Pres)*
Anoop Kacker *(Exec Dir-Gurgaon)*
R.K. Malhotra *(Pres)*

SAE POWER

1500 E Hamilton Ave Ste 118, Campbell, CA 95008
Tel.: (408) 808-6496
Web Site: http://www.saepower.com
Year Founded: 1963
Rev.: $14,235,345
Emp.: 1,100
Mfr of Standard, Modified Standard & Complete Custom Switch Mode Power Supplies, Magnetics & EMI/RFI Filters
N.A.I.C.S.: 334419
Allan Brown *(CTO)*
Joe Churchill *(Mgr)*

Subsidiaries:

SAE Power Company, Inc. (1)
1810 Birchmount Rd, Scarborough, M1P 2H7, ON, Canada
Tel.: (416) 298-0560
Electronic Components Mfr
N.A.I.C.S.: 334419

SAE Power Inc (1)
130 Knowles Dr Ste C, Los Gatos, CA 95032-1832
Tel.: (408) 369-2200
Rev.: $2,700,000
Emp.: 12
Electronic Parts & Equipment, Nec
N.A.I.C.S.: 334419

SAEXPLORATION HOLDINGS, INC.

1160 Dairy Ashford Rd Ste 160, Houston, TX 77079
Tel.: (281) 258-4400 DE
Web Site: http://www.saexploration.com
Year Founded: 2011
Rev.: $255,234,000
Assets: $142,215,000
Liabilities: $178,028,000
Net Worth: ($35,813,000)
Earnings: ($25,186,000)
Emp.: 981
Fiscal Year-end: 12/31/19
Seismic Data Acquisition Services to Oil & Gas Industry
N.A.I.C.S.: 541360
Darin Silvernagle *(Sr VP-Tech & Shared Svcs)*
Michael J. Faust *(Chm, Pres & CEO)*
John Simmons *(CFO & VP)*
David Rassin *(Chief Compliance Officer, Gen Counsel, Sec & VP)*
Bruce McFarlane *(VP-Land Ops)*
Mark Farine *(VP-Bus Dev & Marine Ops)*
Arturo Mendez Pardo *(VP-Ops-South America)*
Forrest Burkholder *(Exec VP-Ops)*

Subsidiaries:

SAExploration Sub, Inc. (1)
1160 Dairy Ashford Rd Ste 160, Houston, TX 77079
Tel.: (281) 258-4400
Seismic Data Acquisition Services to Oil & Gas Industry
N.A.I.C.S.: 541360

Subsidiary (Domestic):

SAExploration, Inc. (2)
8240 Sandlewood Pl Ste 102, Anchorage, AK 99507
Tel.: (907) 522-4499
Web Site: http://www.saexploration.com
Seismic Data Acquisition Services to Oil & Gas Industry
N.A.I.C.S.: 541360
Andrea Caro *(Mgr-Global HR)*

Subsidiary (Non-US):

SAExploration (Australia) Pty. Ltd. (3)
12/441 Nudgee Rd, Hendra, 4011, QLD, Australia
Tel.: (61) 732685611
Geographical Surveying Services
N.A.I.C.S.: 541360

SAExploration (Brasil) Servicos Sismicos Ltda. (3)
Av Almirante Barroso 02, Rio de Janeiro, 20031, Brazil
Tel.: (55) 2135535104
Web Site: http://www.saexploration.com
Engineering Services
N.A.I.C.S.: 541330

SAExploration (Canada) Ltd. (3)
4860-25th Street SE, Calgary, T2B 3M2, AB, Canada
Tel.: (403) 776-1950
Marketing Research & Public Opinion Polling Services
N.A.I.C.S.: 541910

SAF-GARD SAFETY SHOE CO.

2701 Patterson St, Greensboro, NC 27407
Tel.: (336) 299-1688 NC
Web Site: http://www.safgard.com
Year Founded: 1980
Emp.: 100
Shoe Stores
N.A.I.C.S.: 458210
Patrick Kubis *(Pres & CEO)*

Subsidiaries:

Michigan Industrial Shoe Co. (1)
25477 W 8 Mile Rd, Redford, MI 48240
Tel.: (313) 532-0902
Web Site: http://www.michiganshoe.com
Footwear Merchant Whslr
N.A.I.C.S.: 424340

SAFA TRUST INC.

459 Herndon Pkwy Ste 22, Herndon, VA 20170
Tel.: (703) 471-9494 DC
Year Founded: 1986
Sales Range: $10-24.9 Million
Fundraising Services
N.A.I.C.S.: 813211
Muhammad Ashraf *(Asst Sec)*
Jamal Barzinji *(Pres)*
Hisham Altalib *(Treas)*
Ahmed Totonji *(Sec)*
M. Yaqub Mirza *(VP)*

SAFARI CIRCUITS, INC.

411 Washington St, Otsego, MI 49078
Tel.: (269) 694-9471

Web Site:
http://www.safaricircuits.com
Year Founded: 1985
Sales Range: $10-24.9 Million
Emp.: 120
Contract Electronics Mfr
N.A.I.C.S.: 334419
Mike Kintz *(Pres)*
David Briggs *(Dir-Sls)*
Chris Kunze *(Acct Mgr)*
Bruce Waligora *(Acct Mgr)*
Jim Thompson *(Dir-Engrg)*

SAFAVIEH CARPETS OF ISFAHAN

40 Harbor Park Dr N, Port Washington, NY 11050
Tel.: (516) 945-1900
Web Site: http://www.safavieh.com
Rev.: $60,000,000
Emp.: 125
Rugs
N.A.I.C.S.: 423220
Arash Yaraghi *(Principal)*
John Vlahopoulos *(Mgr-Canada & Mgr-Sls-Midwest Reg)*

SAFE 1 CREDIT UNION

400 Oak St, Bakersfield, CA 93304
Tel.: (661) 327-3818 CA
Web Site: http://www.safe1.org
Year Founded: 1952
Sales Range: $10-24.9 Million
Emp.: 97
Credit Union
N.A.I.C.S.: 522130
Doug Kileen *(CEO)*
Woody Morrison *(Treas)*
Bonnie Vogt *(Vice Chm)*
Mike Reed *(Treas)*
Vernon Power *(Vice Chm)*

SAFE ALARM SYSTEMS INC.

4490 SW 64th Ave, Davie, FL 33314-3462
Tel.: (954) 791-7233 FL
Year Founded: 1975
Sales Range: $50-74.9 Million
Emp.: 12
Installation, Sales & Service of Alarms, Intercoms, CCTV & TV Systems
N.A.I.C.S.: 561621
Stuart Glickman *(Pres, CEO & CFO)*

SAFE AUTO INSURANCE GROUP, INC.

4 Easton Oval, Columbus, OH 43213
Tel.: (614) 231-0200 OH
Web Site: http://www.safeauto.com
Year Founded: 1993
Sales Range: $200-249.9 Million
Emp.: 781
Property & Casualty Insurance Holding Company
N.A.I.C.S.: 551112
Ari Deshe *(Chm & CEO)*
Jon P. Diamond *(Vice Chm & Pres)*
Tim Cahill *(Sr VP-Sls & Mktg)*

SAFE HARBOR FINANCIAL, INC.

2200 Ben Franklin Pkwy, Philadelphia, PA 19130
Tel.: (215) 568-6377 PA
Web Site:
http://www.safeharborfinancial.com
Year Founded: 1988
Rev.: $2,400,000
Emp.: 14
Insurance Agencies & Brokerages
N.A.I.C.S.: 524210

SAFE RACK, LLC

730 Electric Dr, Sumter, SC 29153
Tel.: (803) 774-7225 SC

SAFE RACK, LLC

Safe Rack, LLC—(Continued)
Web Site: http://www.saferack.com
Year Founded: 2003
Sales Range: $25-49.9 Million
Emp.: 91
Mfr Safety Equipment
N.A.I.C.S.: 423830
Fred Harmon (Co-Founder)
Rob Honeycutt (Co-Founder)
Jim Sweatt (Project Mgr)
Eric Grothaus (Dir-HR)

SAFE SPACE NYC INC.
89-74 162nd St, Jamaica, NY 11432
Tel.: (718) 526-2400 NY
Web Site:
  http://www.safespacenyc.org
Year Founded: 1919
Sales Range: $10-24.9 Million
Emp.: 371
Children & Youth Care Services
N.A.I.C.S.: 624110
Darla Pasteur (VP-Strategic Dev)
Krista Pietrangelo (Dir-Plng & Evaluation)
Elizabeth McCarthy (Pres & CEO)
Mildred Gonzalez (VP-Program Ops)
Olu Atanda-Ogunleye (Sr Dir-Community & School Svcs)

SAFE SYSTEMS, INC.
1145 Sanctuary Pkwy Ste 400, Alpharetta, GA 30009
Tel.: (770) 752-0550
Web Site:
  http://www.safesystems.com
Year Founded: 1993
Sales Range: $1-9.9 Million
Emp.: 94
Information Technology Services
N.A.I.C.S.: 518210
Darren Bridges (Pres)
Zach Duke (Exec VP-Bus Dev)
Scott Galvin (Exec VP-Technical Solutions)
Niki Neese (VP-Strategic)
Thomas Hinkel (VP-Compliance Svcs)
Brent Moore (Dir-Client Svcs)

SAFE-START, LLC
12045 34th St N, Saint Petersburg, FL 33716
Tel.: (727) 572-7731
Web Site: http://www.safe-start.com
Year Founded: 1985
Sales Range: $100-124.9 Million
Emp.: 70
Tires, Wheels & Batteries Merchant Whslr
N.A.I.C.S.: 423130
Lissette Ocasio (Controller)
Earl DeGlopper (Mgr)
Rick Aliperti (Reg Mgr)

SAFEAMERICA CREDIT UNION
6001 Gibraltar Dr, Pleasanton, CA 94588
Tel.: (925) 734-4111 CA
Web Site:
  http://www.safeamerica.com
Year Founded: 1982
Sales Range: $10-24.9 Million
Emp.: 62
Credit Union Operator
N.A.I.C.S.: 522130
Robin Hauan (VP-Mktg)
Charles Dunbar (VP-Fin)
Frank Zampella (Chm)
Carmine Perrelli (Vice Chm)
Barry Roach (COO & Exec VP)
Steven Page (VP-Digital Banking)
John Gracyalny (VP-IT)
Amrita Prasad (VP-Lending & Collections)

SAFEBUILT, INC.
3755 Precision Dr Ste 140, Loveland, CO 80538
Tel.: (970) 292-2200
Web Site: http://www.safebuilt.com
Year Founded: 1992
Rev: $10,000,000
Emp.: 67
Government Services
N.A.I.C.S.: 921190
Mike McCurdie (Pres)
David Thomsen (VP)
Scott Martin (Mgr-Bus Dev)
Karen Mack (Controller)
Steve Miller (Dir-Client Svcs-Studio)
Elizabeth Garvin (Dir-Plng-Studio)

SAFECORE, INC
One Van de Graaff Dr, Burlington, MA 01803
Tel.: (781) 272-1140
Year Founded: 2000
Rev: $5,200,000
Emp.: 16
Management Services
N.A.I.C.S.: 561110
Paul C. O'Brien (Chm)
David King (VP)
Michael Thomson (VP-Bus Dev)
Sean D. True (VP-R&D)
Peter Alex (VP-Channel Dev)
Eric Emerson (VP-Tech)
Roger L. Matus (Exec VP)

SAFEDOX, INC.
11801 Pierce St 2nd Fl, Riverside, CA 92505
Tel.: (951) 710-3090 WY
Web Site: http://www.safedox.com
Sales Range: $10-24.9 Million
Emp.: 2
Security Software
N.A.I.C.S.: 513210
Manoj Patel (Pres)
James F. Lay (Exec VP, Treas & Sec)

SAFEGUARD CHEMICAL CORPORATION
411 Wales Ave, Bronx, NY 10454-1719
Tel.: (718) 585-3170
Web Site:
  http://www.safeguardchemical.com
Year Founded: 1960
Sales Range: $10-24.9 Million
Emp.: 10
Mfr & Wholesaler of Chemicals & Insecticides
N.A.I.C.S.: 424910
Edward Pernian (Owner)

Subsidiaries:

The 707 Company (1)
411 Wales Ave, Bronx, NY 10454-1719
Tel.: (718) 585-3170
Web Site:
  http://store.safeguardchemical.com
Emp.: 25
Household, Institutional, Janitorial & Industrial Cleaning Products & Insecticide Mfr
N.A.I.C.S.: 424690
Edward Piranian (Pres)

SAFEGUARD PROPERTIES, INC.
7887 Safeguard Cir Hub Pkwy, Valley View, OH 44125
Tel.: (216) 739-2900
Web Site:
  http://www.safeguardproperties.com
Year Founded: 1990
Sales Range: $400-449.9 Million
Emp.: 655
Property Management Services
N.A.I.C.S.: 531312
Robert Klein (Founder & Chm)
Alan Jaffa (CEO)

Gregory Robinson (CFO & Exec VP)
Kellie Chambers (Asst VP-Bus Dev & IR)
Jennifer Jozity (Asst VP-Inspections, REO & Property Preservation Ops)
George Mehok (CIO)
Amitha Rao (Asst VP-Client Sys & Data Analytics)
Rick Moran (Asst VP-Application Architecture)
Michael Greenbaum (COO)
Pat Hoffman (Dir-Vendor Acct Mgmt)
Steve Meyer (Asst VP-High Risk & Hazard Claims)
Linda Erkkila (Gen Counsel & Exec VP-HR)
Tod Burkert (VP-Bus Dev)
Joe Iafigliola (VP-Vendor Mgmt)

SAFEGUARD SECURITY SERVICES INC.
8454 N 90th St, Scottsdale, AZ 85258
Tel.: (480) 609-6200
Web Site:
  http://www.safeguardsecurity.com
Year Founded: 1958
Sales Range: $10-24.9 Million
Emp.: 250
Fire Detection & Burglar Systems
N.A.I.C.S.: 561612
John R. Jennings (CEO)
Mike Bradley (Pres)

SAFEGUARD SELF STORAGE
3350 Peachtree Rd NE 17th Fl, Atlanta, GA 30326
Tel.: (866) 544-7300
Web Site: http://www.safeguardit.com
Year Founded: 1989
Rev: $11,100,000
Emp.: 180
Self Storage Services
N.A.I.C.S.: 493110
Allan J. Sweet (Pres & CEO)
Mark B. Rinder (CFO & Exec VP)
Margaret Lewis (Sr VP-HR)
Jim Goonan (Sr VP-Dev)

SAFER PRINTS INC.
1875 McCarter Hwy, Newark, NJ 07104
Tel.: (973) 482-6400
Web Site:
  http://www.safertextiles.com
Textile Mfr
N.A.I.C.S.: 561990
Albert Safer (Pres & CEO)
Niso Barokas (VP)

Subsidiaries:

Hampton Textile Printing (1)
2230 Eddie Williams Rd, Johnson City, TN 37601
Tel.: (423) 928-7247
Web Site: http://www.hamptonprints.com
Commercial Printing
N.A.I.C.S.: 323111
Tammy Ross (CEO)

Kuttner Prints Inc. (1)
1875 McCarter Hwy, Newark, NJ 07104
Tel.: (973) 482-6400
Web Site: http://www.safertextiles.com
Rev: $2,000,000
Emp.: 25
Commercial Printing, Lithographic
N.A.I.C.S.: 323111
Niso Barokas (VP)
John Honegger (Mgr-Paper Print)
John Walker (Mgr-Digital Print IT)

SAFESOFT SOLUTIONS INC.
Warner Ctr Corporate Park 20950 Warner Ctr Ln Bldg A, Woodland Hills, CA 91367
Tel.: (818) 436-3600

Web Site:
  http://www.safesoftsolutions.com
Year Founded: 2006
Sales Range: $1-9.9 Million
Emp.: 13
Business Process Outsourcing Services
N.A.I.C.S.: 561499
Aaron Kohut (Mgr)

SAFESPAN PLATFORM SYSTEMS INC.
252 Fillmore Ave, Tonawanda, NY 14150
Tel.: (716) 694-1100
Web Site: http://www.safespan.com
Sales Range: $10-24.9 Million
Emp.: 40
Steel Slab & Platform Mfr
N.A.I.C.S.: 332111
David Malcolm (VP-Sls & Mktg)
Herb Herpin (Mgr-Scaffold Ops)
Scott Krieger (Mgr-IT)
John LeViness (Project Mgr-Sls)

SAFETY & SURVIVAL SYSTEMS INTERNATIONAL LTD.
34140 Valley Center Rd, Valley Center, CA 92082
Tel.: (760) 749-6800
Web Site:
  http://www.survivalsystemsinternational.com
Lifeboat Mfr
N.A.I.C.S.: 336612
George Beatty (Pres)
Andrew Richards (CEO)

Subsidiaries:

Typhoon International Limited (1)
Limerick Road, Redcar, TS10 5JU, Cleveland, United Kingdom
Tel.: (44) 1642486104
Web Site: http://www.typhoon-int.co.uk
Drysuit Mfr
N.A.I.C.S.: 339920
James Saunders (Mgr-Ops)

SAFETY MANAGEMENT GROUP
8335 Keystone Crossing Ste 103, Indianapolis, IN 46240
Tel.: (317) 873-5064
Web Site:
  http://www.safetymanagement group.com
Year Founded: 1994
Rev: $12,600,000
Emp.: 88
Business Consulting Services
N.A.I.C.S.: 541618
Kent Burget (Pres)
Bobby Pirtle (Officer-Fin)
Craig Clark (Mgr)
Dave Schuster (Acct Mgr)
Doug Schumann (Acct Mgr)
J. Mark Steinhofer (Mgr-Special Svcs)
Jesse Brazzell (Mgr-Safety Svcs)
Mike Martin (Acct Mgr)
Randy Gieseking (Pres)
Ron Hanson (VP-Ops)

SAFETY NETACCESS, INC.
114 Gould St, Needham, MA 02494
Tel.: (617) 268-1134 MA
Web Site:
  http://www.safetynetaccess.com
Year Founded: 1999
Computer & Telecommunications Product Sales & Services
N.A.I.C.S.: 541990
Sean T. Gorman (Pres & CEO)

SAFETY SERVICES COMPANY
2626 S Roosevelt St Ste 2, Tempe, AZ 85282

COMPANIES

Web Site:
http://www.safetyservicescompany.com
Year Founded: 2003
Sales Range: $10-24.9 Million
Emp.: 214
Construction Training & Safety Materials
N.A.I.C.S.: 611430
Devon Dickinson (Founder & Pres)

SAFETY SERVICES INCORPORATED
5286 Wynn Rd, Kalamazoo, MI 49048
Tel.: (269) 382-1052   MI
Web Site:
http://www.safetyservicesinc.com
Year Founded: 1948
Sales Range: $10-24.9 Million
Emp.: 20
Distr of Safety, Health & Environmental Equipment
N.A.I.C.S.: 423840
Kathryn Bowdish (Pres)

SAFETY SHOE DISTRIBUTORS
9330 Lawndale St, Houston, TX 77012
Tel.: (713) 928-6691
Web Site:
http://www.safetyshoedist.com
Rev.: $11,400,000
Emp.: 15
Safety Footwear Distr
N.A.I.C.S.: 424340
Jack McElligott (Pres)
Bob Holmes (Gen Mgr)
Mary Kersey Goan (Office Mgr-Payables)

SAFETY STORAGE INC.
855 N 5th St, Charleston, IL 61920
Tel.: (217) 345-4422
Web Site:
http://www.safetystorage.com
Year Founded: 1986
Sales Range: $10-24.9 Million
Emp.: 38
Hazardous Material Storage Unit Mfr
N.A.I.C.S.: 332311
Janice Carter (Mgr-HR)
Kara Pearcy (Project Coord)

SAFETY TECHNOLOGY INTERNATIONAL, INC.
2306 Airport Rd, Waterford, MI 48327
Tel.: (248) 673-9898
Web Site: http://www.sti-usa.com
Year Founded: 1980
Rev.: $12,400,000
Emp.: 38
Plastics Product Mfr
N.A.I.C.S.: 326199
Brian Hodges (Mgr-Engrg)
John F. Taylor (VP)
Margie Gobler (Pres & CEO)

SAFETY VISION, LLC
6100 W Sam Houston Pkwy N, Houston, TX 77041-5113
Tel.: (713) 896-6600
Web Site:
http://www.safetyvision.com
Year Founded: 1993
Mobile Video Services
N.A.I.C.S.: 561621
Bruce Smith (Founder & CEO)
Michael Ondruch (CFO)
Heather Thomas (Acct Exec-School Bus Team-West Coast)
Clint Bryer (Mgr-School Bus Sls)
William Rieck (Mktg Dir)

Subsidiaries:
ICOP Digital, Inc.   (1)
15621 W 87th St Pkwy, Lenexa, KS 66219-1435
Tel.: (913) 338-5550
Web Site: http://icopdigital.com
Sales Range: $1-9.9 Million
Emp.: 52
Mobile Video Solutions for Law Enforcement, Military & Homeland Security Markets
N.A.I.C.S.: 561621
Mickie R. Koslofsky (CEO)
Michael Ondruch (CFO)
Mark Sahinen (VP-Sls)
Randy Wise (VP-Sls)

SAFETYCHAIN SOFTWARE, INC.
711 Grand Ave Ste 290, San Rafael, CA 94901
Tel.: (888) 235-7540
Web Site:
http://www.safetychain.com
Software Publisher
N.A.I.C.S.: 513210
Daniel Bernkopf (VP-Food Safety & Quality Assurance Applications)
Walter Smith (Co-Founder)
Barry Maxon (Co-Founder & Pres)
Roger Woehl (CTO)
Jim Wilmott (VP-Customer Delivery)
Dave Detweiler (VP-Sls)
Jill Bender (VP-Mktg & Customer Community)
Dean Brown (CEO)

Subsidiaries:
Vigilistics, Inc.   (1)
65 Enterprise Ste 300, Aliso Viejo, CA 92656
Tel.: (949) 900-8380
Web Site: http://www.vigilistics.com
Emp.: 12
Technology Solutions for Food & Beverage Industry
N.A.I.C.S.: 513210
Michael Stephens (Pres & CEO)
Greg Newman (VP-Ops)
Clara Gavriliuc (Dir-Engrg)
Pete Delgado (Dir-Sls & Customer Svc)

SAFEWARE INC.
4403 Forbes Blvd, Lanham, MD 20706
Tel.: (301) 683-1234
Web Site:
http://www.safewareinc.com
Rev.: $31,402,515
Emp.: 75
Safety Equipment Sales
N.A.I.C.S.: 423840
Edward Simons (Pres)
Keith Hyatt (CFO)
Diana Hyatt (Branch Mgr)
Jessica Faulkner (Mgr-Quality Assurance)
Doug Belden (VP-Tech)
Charles Frederick (VP-Tech)

SAFEWAY INSURANCE COMPANY
790 Pasquinelli Dr, Westmont, IL 60559
Tel.: (630) 887-8300
Web Site: http://www.safewayins.com
Sales Range: $75-99.9 Million
Emp.: 100
Automobile Insurance
N.A.I.C.S.: 524126
Robert M. Bordeman (CEO)

SAFEWAY TRANSPORTATION INC.
3499 Frontage Rd, Port Allen, LA 70767
Tel.: (225) 387-6623
Web Site:
http://www.safewaylogistics.com

Sales Range: $10-24.9 Million
Emp.: 130
Liquid Petroleum Transport Services
N.A.I.C.S.: 484230
Gregory Stewart (Pres)
Tommy Jeansonne (VP)
Reggie Melancon (Controller)

SAFFORD AUTOMOTIVE GROUP
21900 Auto World Cir, Sterling, VA 20166
Tel.: (571) 701-1911
Web Site:
https://www.saffordbrown.com
Emp.: 100
Car Dealership
N.A.I.C.S.: 441110
George Malone (Gen Mgr)

Subsidiaries:
Brown's Automotive Group Ltd   (1)
12500 Firalake Cir Ste 375, Fairfax, VA 22033
Tel.: (703) 352-5555
Web Site: http://www.brownscar.com
New & Used Automobiles Retailer
N.A.I.C.S.: 441110
Bryan Merideth (Mgr-Sls)

Subsidiary (Domestic):
Brown's Honda City   (2)
7160 Ritchie Hwy, Glen Burnie, MD 21061
Tel.: (410) 553-8014
Web Site: http://www.honda-city.com
Sales Range: $25-49.9 Million
Automobiles, New & Used
N.A.I.C.S.: 441110
Dennis White (Asst Mgr)

Brown's Richmond Volkswagen   (2)
10501 Midlothian Pike, Richmond, VA 23235
Tel.: (888) 468-5077
Web Site: https://www.brownsvw.com
Emp.: 100
New Car Dealers
N.A.I.C.S.: 441110
Robert Patterson (Pres)

Brown's Toyota   (2)
7167 Ritchie Hwy, Glen Burnie, MD 21061
Tel.: (410) 761-9000
Web Site: http://www.gbtoyota.com
Automobiles, New & Used
N.A.I.C.S.: 441110

SAFIRE REHABILITATION OF AMHERST, LLC
193 S Union Rd, Williamsville, NY 14221
Tel.: (716) 276-1900   NY
Web Site: http://www.safirecare.com
Holding Company; Elderly Nursing Care Facilities Owner & Operator
N.A.I.C.S.: 551112
Mark Smeltzer (Dir-Ops)

Subsidiaries:
Williamsville Suburban, LLC   (1)
193 S Union Rd, Williamsville, NY 14221
Tel.: (716) 276-1900
Web Site:
http://www.williamsvillesuburban.com
Sales Range: $10-24.9 Million
Emp.: 200
Nursing Care Facility Operator
N.A.I.C.S.: 623110
Karen Rizzo (Dir-Nursing)
Jennifer Stockmeyer (Dir-Social Work & Discharge Plng)
Erika Lapenna (Dir-Activities)
John Benton (Dir-Maintenance)
Nancy Rizzo (Dir-Dietary Svcs)
Jennifer Rizzo (Coord-Admissions)

SAFRA NATIONAL BANK OF NEW YORK
546 5th Ave, New York, NY 10036-5000
Tel.: (212) 704-5500   DE

SAGAMORE HOTEL

Web Site: http://www.safra.com
Year Founded: 1995
Rev.: $198,572,000
Emp.: 134
Banking Services
N.A.I.C.S.: 522110
Joseph Safra (Chm)

SAFREMA ENERGY LLC
6771 W Professional Pkwy Ste 202, Lakewood Ranch, FL 34240
Tel.: (941) 779-4161
Web Site:
http://www.safremaenergy.com
Year Founded: 2010
Emp.: 26
Water Turbine Mfr
N.A.I.C.S.: 333611
Bruno Andreis (Founder & CEO)
Jutta Kleinschmidt (Mng Partner)

Subsidiaries:
Safrema Energy Europe   (1)
Ermanno Palace 27A Bd Albert 1, MC-98000, Monaco, Monaco
Tel.: (377) 676 288 193
Water Turbine Mfr
N.A.I.C.S.: 333611

SAG HARBOR INDUSTRIES, INC.
1668 Sag Harbor Tpke, Sag Harbor, NY 11963
Tel.: (631) 725-0440   NY
Web Site:
http://www.sagharborind.com
Year Founded: 1946
Emp.: 100
Electrical Coils & Transformer Mfr
N.A.I.C.S.: 334416
Raymond Woznik (Controller)
Mary Scheerer (Pres)

Subsidiaries:
Dortonics, Inc.   (1)
1668 Bhampton Sag Harbor Tpke, Sag Harbor, NY 11963   (100%)
Tel.: (631) 725-0505
Web Site: http://www.dortronics.com
Sales Range: $10-24.9 Million
Emp.: 20
Electromagnetic Door Locks
N.A.I.C.S.: 332510
John Fitzpatrick (Pres)

SAG-AFTRA HEALTH PLAN
3601 W Olive Ave Ste 300, Burbank, CA 91505
Web Site:
https://www.sagaftraplans.org
Year Founded: 1961
Health Insurance Services
N.A.I.C.S.: 524114

SAGA ENERGY, INC.
7101 S Yale Ste 304, Tulsa, OK 74136
Tel.: (214) 960-4742   FL
Sales Range: Less than $1 Million
Emp.: 1
Petroleum Exploration
N.A.I.C.S.: 211120
J. Michael Myers (Chm, Interim Pres, CEO, & Interim CFO)
Lisa Waun (Sec)

SAGAMORE HOTEL
1671 Collins Ave, Miami Beach, FL 33139
Tel.: (305) 535-8088
Web Site:
http://www.sagamorehotel.com
Year Founded: 2001
Sales Range: $1-9.9 Million
Emp.: 75
Luxury Hotel Operator
N.A.I.C.S.: 721110

SAGAMORE HOTEL

Sagamore Hotel—(Continued)
Jonathan Eisenband *(Gen Mgr)*
John Carter *(Dir-Sls & Mktg)*
Neil Sazant *(Principal)*
Shaila Baltrons *(Supvr-Reservations)*

SAGAMORE READY MIX, LLC
9170 E 131st St, Fishers, IN 46038
Tel.: (317) 570-6201
Web Site:
http://www.sagamorereadymix.com
Year Founded: 1971
Sales Range: $10-24.9 Million
Emp.: 85
Ready Mixed Concrete
N.A.I.C.S.: 327320
Nic Babic *(Acct Mgr)*
Scott Noel *(Acct Mgr)*
Randy Tolliver *(Acct Mgr)*

SAGANTEC NORTH AMERICA
2075 Delacruz Blvd Ste 105, Santa Clara, CA 95050
Tel.: (408) 727-6290
Web Site: http://www.sagantec.com
Year Founded: 1993
Sales Range: $1-9.9 Million
Computer Software Developer
N.A.I.C.S.: 513210

SAGE ADVERTISING
1101 Flowerree St, Helena, MT 59601
Tel.: (406) 431-1031
Year Founded: 1959
Sales Range: Less than $1 Million
Emp.: 3
N.A.I.C.S.: 541810

SAGE CAPITAL LLC
8000 Maryland Ave Ste 1200, St Louis, MO 63105
Tel.: (314) 754-1118
Web Site:
https://www.sagecapitalllc.com
Emp.: 100
Investment Services
N.A.I.C.S.: 523999
Wesley Jones *(Partner)*

Subsidiaries:

Livers Bronze Co., Inc. (1)
4621 East 75th Ter, Kansas City, MO 64132
Tel.: (816) 300-2828
Web Site: http://www.liversbronze.com
Rev.: $6,666,666
Emp.: 100
Copper Foundries, except Die-Casting,
N.A.I.C.S.: 331529

SAGE COMMUNICATIONS, LLC
1651 Old Meadow Rd Ste 500, McLean, VA 22102
Tel.: (703) 748-0300 VA
Web Site: http://www.aboutsage.com
Sales Range: $1-9.9 Million
Emp.: 51
Advetising Agency
N.A.I.C.S.: 541810
Larry Rosenfeld *(Co-Founder & CEO)*
David Gorodetski *(Co-Founder, COO & Exec Creative Dir)*
Catherine Melquist *(Sr VP-Satellite Div)*
Scott Greenberg *(Dir-Non Profit & Arts)*
Ufuoma Otu *(Acct Mgr-PR)*
Omnia Elgoodah *(Coord-Digital Mktg)*
Tommy Morgan *(Acct Exec)*
Ron Lichtinger *(VP)*
Julie Murphy *(Partner)*

SAGE DINING SERVICES INC.
1402 York Rd Ste 100, Lutherville, MD 21093
Tel.: (410) 339-3950
Web Site: http://www.sagedining.com
Sales Range: $10-24.9 Million
Emp.: 2,020
Cafeteria Operator
N.A.I.C.S.: 722514
Marcel Gallo *(COO)*
Jeffrey Slack *(Dir-Food Svc)*
Colin Abernethy *(Dir-Food Svc)*
Deena Dib *(Dir-Food Svc)*
Marcus Madsen *(Dir-Tech)*
William Velez *(Acct Exec-Mid-Atlantic Reg)*
Brenden McNamee *(Acct Exec-Midwestern Reg)*
Paul Berry *(Acct Exec-Northeastern Reg)*
James Leachman *(Acct Exec-Southern Reg)*
Gary Leiderman *(Acct Exec-Western Reg)*
Anne Freedman *(Mgr-Comm)*
Mark Benfield *(VP)*
Maurice Short *(VP & Dir-Sls)*
Todd Evans *(VP-Procurement)*

SAGE ELECTRIC CORPORATION
2826 Ctr Port Cir, Pompano Beach, FL 33064
Tel.: (954) 781-9069
Web Site:
http://www.lilleyinternational.com
Rev.: $38,000,000
Emp.: 15
Noncurrent-Carrying Wiring Devices
N.A.I.C.S.: 335932

SAGE HOLDING COMPANY
3550 Cahuenga Blvd W, Los Angeles, CA 90068
Tel.: (818) 769-8100 CA
Web Site: http://www.sageauto.com
Year Founded: 1970
Sales Range: $200-249.9 Million
Emp.: 150
Holding Company; New & Used Car Dealerships
N.A.I.C.S.: 551112
Leonard Sage *(VP & Gen Mgr)*

Subsidiaries:

Glendale Nissan/Infiniti, Inc. (1)
727 S Brand Blvd, Glendale, CA 91204
Tel.: (818) 240-6000
Web Site: http://www.nissan1.com
Rev.: $33,400,000
Emp.: 40
New & Used Car Dealer
N.A.I.C.S.: 441110

Unit (Domestic):

Glendale Infiniti (2)
812 S Brand Blvd, Glendale, CA 91204
Tel.: (818) 543-5000
Web Site: http://www.glendaleinfiniti.com
New & Used Car Dealer
N.A.I.C.S.: 441110
Jay Kim *(Mgr-Fleet Sls)*

Universal City Nissan, Inc. (1)
3550 Cahuenga Blvd W, Los Angeles, CA 90068
Tel.: (818) 769-8100
Web Site:
http://www.universalcitynissan.com
Sales Range: $10-24.9 Million
Emp.: 60
New & Used Car Dealer
N.A.I.C.S.: 441110
Billie Jo Haynes *(Dir-Svc)*
Johnny Achi *(Dir-Internet Sls)*
Joseline Lopez *(Asst Mgr-Internet)*
Dennis Rivera *(Dir-Fin)*

SAGE INVESTMENT HOLDINGS
1575 Welton St Ste 300, Denver, CO 80202-4218
Tel.: (303) 595-7200 DE
Web Site:
http://www.sagehospitality.com
Year Founded: 1997
Emp.: 10
Holding Company
N.A.I.C.S.: 551112
Walter Isenberg *(Co-Founder, Pres & CEO)*
Peter Karpinski *(Co-Founder & COO-Sage Restaurant Grp)*
Michael Everett *(Chief Investment Officer)*
Lisa Donovan *(Chief People Officer)*

Subsidiaries:

Sage Hospitality Resources, LLP (1)
1575 Welton St Ste 300, Denver, CO 80202
Tel.: (303) 595-7200
Web Site: http://www.sagehospitality.com
Sales Range: $10-24.9 Million
Emp.: 84
Hotel & Resort Owner & Operator
N.A.I.C.S.: 721110
Jessica Werner *(Exec VP-Sage Studio)*
Zachary T. Neumeyer *(Chm)*
Walter L. Isenberg *(Founder, Pres & CEO)*
Kenneth Geist *(Partner & Exec VP)*
Brad A. Robinette *(Sr VP-New Bus & Transitions)*
Harris White *(CFO)*
Vincent Piro *(VP-Ops-Premier & Lifestyle)*
William Balinbin *(VP-Acq)*
John Panko *(VP-Sls & Mktg-Premier & Lifestyle Div)*
Kenneth Widmaier *(COO)*
Robert Butler *(Sr VP-Premium Branded Div)*
Lisa Donovan *(Chief People Officer)*
Jan Lucas *(VP-Premium Branded Div)*
Shane Keener *(VP-Mktg)*
Lisa Bailey *(VP-Sls & Mktg-Premier & Lifestyle Div)*
Tracie Heisterkamp *(Dir-Revenue Mgmt Div)*
Mike Case *(Gen Mgr-Denver Marriott Tech Center)*
Tobias Arff *(Gen Mgr-The Darcy Washington DC)*
Kelly McCourt *(Dir-Sls & Mktg-The Darcy Washington DC)*
Kathleen Bates *(Gen Mgr)*
Angela Blackstock *(Dir-Sls & Mktg)*
Carla Schrock *(Assoc Dir-Sls)*
Dean Stambules *(VP-Acq)*
Jason Altberger *(Chief Investment Officer)*
Ryan Kibler *(Creative Dir)*
James Hatfield III *(VP-Acq & Bus Dev)*

Division (Domestic):

Sage Restaurant Group (2)
1512 Larimer St Ste 800, Denver, CO 80202
Tel.: (303) 595-7264
Web Site:
http://www.sagerestaurantgroup.com
Restaurant Owner & Operator
N.A.I.C.S.: 722511
Peter Karpinski *(Founder & COO)*
David Marsh *(Sr VP-Ops)*
Brandon Wise *(Dir-Beverage Ops)*
Gourav Patel *(Div VP-Fin Ops)*
Michael Carr-Turnbough *(VP-Culinary)*
Meaghan Goedde *(Dir-Trng & Talent)*
Derek Lewis *(VP-Ops)*
Christina Teran *(Dir-Sls & Mktg)*

SAGE MANAGEMENT ENTERPRISE, LLC
6731 Columbia Gateway Dr Ste 150, Columbia, MD 21046
Tel.: (443) 259-9960
Web Site: http://www.sage-mgt.net
Year Founded: 2004
Sales Range: $25-49.9 Million
Emp.: 80
National Security Solutions to Federal, State & Local Government Departments
N.A.I.C.S.: 928110
Jim P. Withington *(COO & Sr VP)*
Larry Harper *(CFO & Sr VP)*

U.S. PRIVATE

Subsidiaries:

Sage Management (1)
1601 Paseo San Luis Ste 201, Sierra Vista, AZ 85635 (100%)
Tel.: (520) 458-0550
Web Site: http://www.sage-mgt.net
Emp.: 55
National Security Solutions including Atmospheric Dispersion Modeling
N.A.I.C.S.: 928110
David Tiedemann *(Gen Mgr)*

Sage Management (1)
15 Roszel Rd Ste 102, Princeton, NJ 08540 (100%)
Tel.: (609) 452-2950
Web Site: http://www.sage-mgt.net
Atmospheric Dispersion Modeling of Airborne Transport & Toxic Materials & Air Pollutants in National Security
N.A.I.C.S.: 928110

Sage Management (1)
7426 Alban Station Court Ste B200, Springfield, VA 22150 (100%)
Tel.: (703) 372-2991
Web Site: http://www.sage-mgt.net
National Security Atmospheric Dispersion Modeling
N.A.I.C.S.: 928110

SAGE PARK, INC.
725 Cool Springs Blvd Suite 245, Franklin, TN 37067
Tel.: (310) 496-1896
Web Site: http://sagepark.com
Portfolio Management
N.A.I.C.S.: 523999
Robert Joubran *(Pres & CEO)*

Subsidiaries:

Omni Directiona Boring LP (1)
1203 6 Street, Nisku, T9E 7P1, AB, Canada
Tel.: (780) 955-7794
Web Site: http://omnidirectionalboring.com
Drilling Services
N.A.I.C.S.: 213111

Subsidiary (Domestic):

Omni Directional Boring LP (2)
Unit 14 235120, Rocky View, AB T1X 0K3, AB, Canada
Tel.: (780) 955-7794
Web Site: http://omnidirectionalboring.com
Drilling Services
N.A.I.C.S.: 213111

SAGE PARTNERS, LLC
5100 W JB Hunt Dr Ste 800, Rogers, AR 72758
Tel.: (479) 443-9990
Web Site:
http://www.sagepartners.com
Emp.: 40
Real Estate Brokers & Management
N.A.I.C.S.: 531210
Brian Shaw *(CEO)*
Marshall Saviers *(Pres)*
T.J. Lefler *(Sr VP)*
Mark Saviers *(Principal)*
Grady Mathews *(VP)*
Tom Allen *(Exec VP)*

Subsidiaries:

Capital Properties, LLC (1)
212 Ctr St 800, Little Rock, AR 72201
Tel.: (501) 372-5171
Investment Services
N.A.I.C.S.: 523999

SAGE PUBLICATIONS, INC.
2455 Teller Rd, Thousand Oaks, CA 91320
Tel.: (805) 499-0721 DE
Web Site: http://www.sagepub.com
Year Founded: 1965
Sales Range: $200-249.9 Million
Emp.: 950
Journals, Books & Electronic Media Publisher
N.A.I.C.S.: 513120

COMPANIES

Sara Miller McCune *(Founder & Chm)*
Blaise R. Simqu *(Pres & CEO)*
Tracey A. Ozmina *(COO & Exec VP)*
Chris Hickok *(CFO & Exec VP)*
Mike Soules *(Pres-Corwin Press)*
Phil Denver *(CIO-Global)*
Stephen Barr *(Pres-Intl & Mng Dir-London)*
Ziyad Marar *(Deputy Mng Dir & Dir-Global Publ-London)*
Mark Hickman *(Mng Dir-Canada)*
Aziz Benmalek *(Pres-North America)*

SAGE SETTLEMENT CONSULTING, LLC
3060 Peachtree Rd NW Ste 1150, Atlanta, GA 30305
Tel.: (800) 573-8853
Web Site: http://www.sagesettlements.com
Settlement Planning Solutions
N.A.I.C.S.: 541618
Kyle Bollman *(Partner)*

Subsidiaries:

Millennium Settlements, Inc. (1)
3500 Financial Plz Fl 4, Tallahassee, FL 32312
Tel.: (850) 894-4265
Web Site: http://www.millenniumsettlements.com
Sales Range: $1-9.9 Million
Emp.: 20
Insurance Agencies & Brokerages
N.A.I.C.S.: 524210
Christopher E. Diamantis *(Pres)*

The Settlement Alliance, LLC (1)
1775 St James Pl Ste 200, Houston, TX 77056
Tel.: (713) 597-7206
Web Site: http://www.settlement-alliance.com
Financial Planning & Settlement Services
N.A.I.C.S.: 523940
Scott Freeman *(Founder & CEO)*
Jason Leiker *(Natl Dir-Sls)*

SAGE STAFFING, INC.
27441 Tourney Rd Ste 150, Valencia, CA 91355-5312
Tel.: (661) 254-4010 **CA**
Web Site: http://www.sagestaffing.com
Year Founded: 1987
Rev.: $10,000,000
Emp.: 20
Temporary Help Service
N.A.I.C.S.: 561320
Laura Kincaid *(Chm)*
Greg Kincaid *(Pres)*
Joanna Brison *(Mgr-Client Svcs)*

SAGE V FOODS, LLC
12100 Wilshire Blvd Ste 605, Los Angeles, CA 90025-7122
Tel.: (310) 820-4496 **CA**
Web Site: http://www.sagevfoods.com
Year Founded: 1992
Sales Range: $100-124.9 Million
Emp.: 10
Producer of Rice Based Ingredients for Use in Processed Foods
N.A.I.C.S.: 311212
Pete Vegas *(Owner & Pres)*
Whilma Aleman *(Controller)*

Subsidiaries:

Sage V Foods, LLC - Little Rock Plant (1)
5901 Sloane Dr, Little Rock, AR 72206
Tel.: (501) 490-0542
Web Site: http://www.sagevfoods.com
Emp.: 100
Food Products Mfr
N.A.I.C.S.: 311999

Larry Watson *(Controller)*
Bill Alkire *(Mgr-Ops)*

SAGENT AUTO, LLC
120 Dividend Dr Ste 160, Coppell, TX 75019
Web Site: http://www.sagent.net
Year Founded: 2001
Sales Range: $1-9.9 Million
Emp.: 200
Software Development Services
N.A.I.C.S.: 541511
Gordon Smith *(CEO)*

SAGENTIC WEB DESIGN
6 E Chambers St, Cleburne, TX 76031
Tel.: (817) 760-0098
Web Site: http://www.sagentic.com
Year Founded: 2003
Sales Range: $1-9.9 Million
Emp.: 10
Web Design, Graphic Design & Internet Marketing
N.A.I.C.S.: 541519
Erica Haferkamp *(Dir-Creative)*

SAGEVIEW ADVISORY GROUP LLC
1920 Main St Ste 800, Irvine, CA 92614-7227
Web Site: http://www.sageviewadvisory.com
Investment Advice
N.A.I.C.S.: 523940
Randall C. Long *(Founder & Mng Principal)*
David Anderson *(Mgr-Relationship-Southeast)*

Subsidiaries:

Horsetooth Financial LLC (1)
2708 Denver Dr, Fort Collins, CO 80525
Tel.: (970) 266-8877
Web Site: http://www.horsetoothfinancialllc.com
Real Estate Credit
N.A.I.C.S.: 522292

SAGEVIEW CAPITAL LP
245 Lytton Ave Ste 250, Palo Alto, CA 94301
Tel.: (650) 473-5400 **DE**
Web Site: http://www.sageviewcapital.com
Rev.: $1,000,000,000
Emp.: 35
Privater Equity Firm
N.A.I.C.S.: 523999
Andrew J. Campelli *(Principal)*
Sasank V. Chary *(Partner)*
Jeffrey A. Klemens *(Partner)*
Edward A. Gilhuly *(Co-Pres)*
Dino Verardo *(CFO)*
Andrew Korn *(Principal)*
Mike McClure *(Principal)*
Stu Schnabolk *(Controller)*
Scott M. Stuart *(Co-Founder & Mng Partner)*
Scott M. Stuart *(Co-Founder & Mng Partner)*

SAGEWIND CAPITAL LLC
1 Vanderbilt Ave 24th Fl, New York, NY 10017
Tel.: (646) 930-1540
Web Site: http://www.sagewindcapital.com
Year Founded: 2015
Privater Equity Firm
N.A.I.C.S.: 523999
Gerald E. Dorros *(Mng Dir)*
Steve Lefkowitz *(Founding Partner)*
Raj Kanodia *(Mng Dir)*
Brian Andruskiewicz *(CFO & Chief Compliance Officer)*

Subsidiaries:

Best Practice Associates, L.L.C. (1)
3100 Clarendon Blvd Ste 1400, Arlington, VA 22201
Tel.: (703) 229-5888
Web Site: https://triafed.com
IT Services and IT Consulting
N.A.I.C.S.: 541690
Tim Borchert *(CEO)*

Subsidiary (Domestic):

Softrams LLC (2)
161 Fort Evans Rd NE Ste 205, Leesburg, VA 20176
Tel.: (571) 918-8977
Web Site: http://www.softrams.com
Sales Range: $10-24.9 Million
Emp.: 98
Information Technology Consulting Services
N.A.I.C.S.: 541690
Atchut Kanthamani *(CEO)*
Chitra Rao *(Dir-HR)*

By Light Professional IT Services, LLC (1)
8484 Westpark Dr Ste 600, McLean, VA 22102
Tel.: (703) 224-1000
Web Site: http://www.bylight.com
Hardware & Software Engineering & Integration Services
N.A.I.C.S.: 541690
Robert Donahue *(Pres & CEO)*
Don Cole *(Principal & Sr VP-DISA)*
Mike Bowser *(Sr VP)*
John D. South *(CFO)*
Rod Phillips *(VP)*
Lucy Donahue *(Chief Strategy Officer)*
Tom Nixon *(Sr VP-Homeland Security & Law Enforcement)*
Mike Hatcher *(Chief Revenue Officer)*
Mary Harcharik *(VP-HR)*
Elissa Wylie *(VP-Talent Acq)*
Tom Ryan *(CTO-Strategic Innovation)*
Bill Sackewitz *(Sr VP-Digital Transformation)*
Erin DeCaprio *(Dir-Corp Comm)*
Amy Hansen *(Dir-Mktg)*

Subsidiary (Domestic):

Axom Technologies, LLC (2)
10010 Junction Dr Ste 201-n, Annapolis Junction, MD 20701
Tel.: (443) 283-8750
Web Site: http://www.axomtech.com
IT & Engineering Services to the Federal Government
N.A.I.C.S.: 921190
Matthew Norris *(CEO)*

Phacil, Inc. (2)
8484 Westpark Dr Ste 600, McLean, VA 22102
Tel.: (703) 526-1800
Web Site: http://www.phacil.com
Sales Range: $10-24.9 Million
Emp.: 700
Government Defense Contractor
N.A.I.C.S.: 921190
Thomas F. Shoemaker *(Chm & CEO)*
Harry J. Bartel *(Sr Mgr-Program)*

Subsidiary (Domestic):

Phacil Fort Monmouth (CECOM) Office (3)
621 Shrewsbury Ave, Shrewsbury, NJ 07702 **(100%)**
Tel.: (732) 758-1770
Web Site: http://www.phacil.com
Government Contractor
N.A.I.C.S.: 541611

Phacil-Washington, DC (3)
950 N Glebe Rd Ste 910, Arlington, VA 22203 **(100%)**
Tel.: (703) 562-4250
Web Site: http://www.phacil.com
Sales Range: $10-24.9 Million
Emp.: 45
Government Contractor
N.A.I.C.S.: 541611
Michael McDermott *(VP-Bus Dev)*

Phacil-West Coast (3)
601 California St Ste 1710, San Francisco, CA 94108 **(100%)**

SAGEWIND CAPITAL LLC

Tel.: (415) 901-1600
Web Site: http://www.phacil.com
Sales Range: $10-24.9 Million
Emp.: 25
Government Contractor
N.A.I.C.S.: 541611
Sascha Mornell *(Co-Founder & Pres)*

Subsidiary (Domestic):

Veraxx Engineering Corp. (2)
14221a Willard Rd, Chantilly, VA 20151
Tel.: (703) 961-9535
Web Site: https://www.veraxx.com
Rev.: $1,422,000
Emp.: 9
Engineeering Services
N.A.I.C.S.: 541330
Charlie Smith *(Pres)*

GCOM Software LLC (1)
24 Madison Avenue Ext, Albany, NY 12203
Tel.: (518) 869-1671
Web Site: http://www.gcomsoft.com
Sales Range: $1-9.9 Million
Emp.: 18
Custom Computer Programming Services
N.A.I.C.S.: 541511
Abid Bargeer *(CTO)*
Julie Bashant *(Mgr-Acct)*
Sunil Bhatia *(Sr VP-Staffing Solutions)*
Rahul Bhosle *(VP-Consulting Svcs)*
David Butter *(Exec VP)*
Riyaz Ladkhan *(COO)*
Marta Mosher *(Dir-HR)*
Holly Savarese *(VP-Admin Svcs)*
Kamal Bherwani *(CEO)*
Rich Harkey *(CFO)*
Jodi Huston *(Chief Admin & People Officer)*
Donna Morea *(Chm)*

Subsidiary (Domestic):

Gantech, Inc. (2)
9175 Guilford Rd Ste 101, Columbia, MD 21046
Tel.: (443) 276-4760
Web Site: http://www.gantech.net
Sales Range: $10-24.9 Million
Emp.: 150
Engineeering Services
N.A.I.C.S.: 541330
Mia Millette *(VP)*
Thomas J. Laskowski *(Pres)*

OnCore Consulting, LLC (2)
3100 Zinfandel Dr Ste 250, Rancho Cordova, CA 95670
Tel.: (916) 640-9111
Web Site: http://www.oncorellc.com
Information Technology Consulting Services
N.A.I.C.S.: 541690
Darren Tong *(Sr Mgr)*

Qlarion, Inc. (2)
12007 Sunrise Vly Dr Ste 420, Reston, VA 20191-3446
Tel.: (703) 286-2046
Web Site: http://www.qlarion.com
Custom Computer Programming Services
N.A.I.C.S.: 541511
Jake Bittner *(Pres & CEO)*

Sigma Defense Systems LLC (1)
PO Box 9261, Warner Robins, GA 31095
Tel.: (478) 256-5831
Web Site: http://www.sigdef.com
Engineeering Services
N.A.I.C.S.: 541330
Thor James *(VP)*
John Wilcox *(Chm)*
Matt Jones *(CEO)*
Edward Anderson *(VP-Maritime Strategy)*

Subsidiary (Domestic):

Electronic Warfare Associates, Inc. (2)
13873 Park Center Rd, Herndon, VA 20171
Tel.: (703) 904-5700
Web Site: https://www.ewa.com
Sales Range: $10-24.9 Million
Emp.: 1,000
Systems Engineering, Computer Related
N.A.I.C.S.: 541512
Gary Kerr *(CFO)*

Subsidiary (Domestic):

Corelis Inc. (3)

SAGEWIND CAPITAL LLC

Sagewind Capital LLC—(Continued)
Alondra Corporate Ctr 13100 Alondra Blvd,
Cerritos, CA 90703-2146
Tel.: (562) 926-6727
Web Site: http://www.corelis.com
Emp.: 30
Electronic Equipment Mfr & Distr
N.A.I.C.S.: 334419
Adam Messier (Mgr-Matls)

EWA Government Systems, Inc. (3)
13873 Park Ctr Rd Ste 500, Herndon, VA 20171
Tel.: (703) 904-5700
Web Site: http://www.ewa-gsi.com
IT Products, Cyber & Operational Technologies & Services to the U.S. Department of Defense, Other Sectors of the Federal Government & Law Enforcement Agencies
N.A.I.C.S.: 921190
Ed Tivol (VP-Cyber & Intelligence)
Brian P. Moore (Pres)

EWA Information and Infrastructure Technologies, Inc. (3)
13873 Park Ctr Rd Ste 200, Herndon, VA 20171
Tel.: (703) 478-7600
Web Site: http://www.ewa-iit.com
Systems Engineering, Computer Related
N.A.I.C.S.: 541618
John Lindquist (CEO)
Lynn Costantini (CIO)

EWA Technologies (3)
13873 Park Center Rd, Herndon, VA 20171
Tel.: (703) 904-5048
Web Site: http://www.ewatech.com
Sales Range: $10-24.9 Million
Emp.: 45
Providers of Environmental & Control Systems
N.A.I.C.S.: 541512
Brian Nix (Pres)

Subsidiary (Domestic):

Blackhawk Inc. (4)
123 Gaither Dr, Mount Laurel, NJ 08054-1701
Tel.: (856) 234-2629
Web Site: http://www.blackhawk-dsp.com
Emp.: 2
Electric Equipment Mfr
N.A.I.C.S.: 334419
Andrew Ferrari (Mgr-Sls)

Subsidiary (Domestic):

Systems Technology Associates, Inc. (3)
119 SW Maynard Rd, Cary, NC 27511
Tel.: (919) 460-0020
Software Development Services
N.A.I.C.S.: 541511

Subsidiary (Domestic):

Juno Technologies, Inc. (2)
6355 Calle Del Campanario, Rancho Santa Fe, CA 92067
Tel.: (858) 832-1251
Web Site: https://www.junotech.com
Sales Range: $1-9.9 Million
Emp.: 32
Custom Computer Programming Services
N.A.I.C.S.: 541511
Julie Ferraro (Pres)

Skience LLC (1)
580 Herndon Pkwy, Herndon, VA 20170
Tel.: (866) 754-3623
Web Site: https://skience.com
Cloud-Based Wealth Management Services
N.A.I.C.S.: 518210
Kripa Shety (Chief Admin Officer)

SAGEWORKS, INC.
5565 Centerview Dr Ste 201, Raleigh, NC 27606
Tel.: (919) 851-7474
Web Site:
    http://www.sageworksinc.com
Year Founded: 1998
Sales Range: $1-9.9 Million
Emp.: 30
Financial Analysis Tools & Private Company Information Services
N.A.I.C.S.: 561499
Brian Hamilton (Founder & Head-Product Dev)
Scott Ogle (CEO)
Jay Borkowski (VP-Corp Dev)
Sharon Hamilton (COO)
Eric Baxley (CMO)
Dominic Leali (Mgr-Product Dev)
Jay Blandford (Pres)
Monte Mauney (Dir-HR)
Nellie Vail (Dir-Fin)
Steven Martin (VP-Strategy)

SAGGEZZA INC.
200 W Madison Ste 1800, Chicago, IL 60606
Tel.: (312) 267-2929
Web Site: http://www.saggezza.com
Year Founded: 2006
Software Development Services
N.A.I.C.S.: 541511
Arvind Kapur (Co-Founder & CEO)

Subsidiaries:

Omni Resources Inc. (1)
2367 N Mayfair Rd Ste 200, Milwaukee, WI 53226
Tel.: (844) 308-0120
Web Site: http://www.omniresources.com
Sales Range: $75-99.9 Million
Emp.: 300
Provider of Information Technology Consulting Services
N.A.I.C.S.: 541511
Jeff Lang (Pres & CEO)
Marc Blazich (Dir-Natl & Strategic Accts)
Lisa Knuth (VP-Operational Excellence)

SAGINAW CONTROL & ENGINEERING INC.
95 Midland Rd, Saginaw, MI 48638
Tel.: (989) 799-6871   MI
Web Site:
    http://www.saginawcontrol.com
Year Founded: 1963
Rev.: $39,685,387
Emp.: 250
Sheet Metalwork
N.A.I.C.S.: 332322
Fred May (Pres)

SAGINAW PIPE COMPANY INC.
1980 Hwy 31 S, Saginaw, AL 35137
Tel.: (205) 664-3670
Web Site:
    http://www.saginawpipe.com
Rev.: $73,512,389
Emp.: 125
Steel Pipe & Tubing Mfr
N.A.I.C.S.: 423510
Dan Kramer (VP)
Caleb Wairegi (CFO & Treas)
Chase Wise (Pres)

SAGO NETWORKS, LLC
4465 W Gandy Blvd Ste 800, Tampa, FL 33611
Tel.: (813) 839-7242
Web Site: http://www.sagonet.com
Sales Range: $1-9.9 Million
Emp.: 50
Telecommunication Servicesb
N.A.I.C.S.: 517810
Miller Cooper (Pres)
Juju Joseph (CEO)
Laura Gibson (Mgr-Support)
Lauren Deff (Mgr-Bus)

SAGON-PHIOR
The Sawtelle Ctr 2107 Sawtelle Blvd, West Los Angeles, CA 90025
Tel.: (310) 575-4665
Web Site: http://www.sagon-phior.com
Sales Range: $25-49.9 Million
N.A.I.C.S.: 541820
Glenn Sagon (CEO & Partner)
Rio Phior (Partner & Chief Creative Officer)

Subsidiaries:

Sagon-Phior (1)
32500 Monterey Dr, Union City, CA 94587
Tel.: (510) 684-2090
Web Site: http://www.sagon-phior.com
Public Relations
N.A.I.C.S.: 541810

Sagon-Phior (1)
5 Georgia Lane, Croton on Hudson, NY 10520
Tel.: (516) 330-2066
Web Site: http://www.sagon-phior.com
Public Relations
N.A.I.C.S.: 541820

Sagon-Phior (1)
703 McKinney Ave Suite 412, Dallas, TX 75202
Tel.: (310) 966-0864
Web Site: http://www.sagon-phior.com
Public Relations
N.A.I.C.S.: 541820

SAGUS INTERNATIONAL LLC
1302 Industrial Blvd, Temple, TX 76503
Tel.: (254) 778-1811
Web Site: http://www.sagusi.com
Sales Range: $10-24.9 Million
Emp.: 400
Holding Company; School Furniture Mfr
N.A.I.C.S.: 337127
Paul St Germain (VP)

Subsidiaries:

Midwest Folding Products (1)
1500 Taylor Ave, Springfield, IL 62703
Tel.: (312) 666-3366
Web Site: http://www.midwestfolding.com
Sales Range: $10-24.9 Million
Emp.: 100
Folding Table Mfr
N.A.I.C.S.: 337214
Letty Mendez (Mgr-Table Assembly)
Derek Hostetter (VP & Gen Mgr)
Chris House (Mgr-Bus Support)
Mark Jutte (VP-Bus Dev)
Kim McBride (Chief Acctg Officer)
Charles Pineau (COO)
Greg Triplett (VP-Mktg)

SAHARA ENTERPRISES INC.
1 N Franklin St Ste 2360, Chicago, IL 60606
Tel.: (312) 782-2690
Year Founded: 1965
Sales Range: $100-124.9 Million
Emp.: 10
Investment Holding Company
N.A.I.C.S.: 212114
Tom Gahlon (Pres)
Kristin Patton (Sec)

SAHARA INC.
801 N 500 W Ste 300, Bountiful, UT 84010
Tel.: (801) 298-7724   UT
Web Site: http://www.sahara1.com
Year Founded: 1985
Rev.: $59,813,047
Emp.: 50
Management Services
N.A.I.C.S.: 541618
Thomas C. Mabey (Chm)
Allen Walters (Superintendent)
Brigham Latimer (Dir-Bus Dev)
Melissa Wallentine (COO & Sr VP)

SAHAS TECHNOLOGIES LLC
3 E 3rd St Apt 27, New York, NY 10003
Tel.: (917) 250-5870   NY
Web Site: http://www.zapaat.com
Sales Range: Less than $1 Million
Emp.: 2
Web Search Portal
N.A.I.C.S.: 519290
Syamantak Saha (CEO)

SAHLING KENWORTH INC.
2206 E Hwy 30, Kearney, NE 68847
Tel.: (308) 234-2511
Web Site:
    http://www.sahlingkenworth.com
Rev.: $26,000,000
Emp.: 45
Trucks, Tractors & Trailers: New & Used
N.A.I.C.S.: 441110
John Sahling (Pres)
Steve McNitt (Mgr-Sls)
John Hanna (Branch Mgr)
Jeff Oppliger (Mgr-Parts)
Kevin Bellows (Mgr-Svcs)
Scott Rucker (Mgr-Svc)

SAHNI ENTERPRISES
3285 Saturn Ct, Norcross, GA 30092
Tel.: (678) 421-0040
Web Site:
    http://www.sahnienterprise.com
Year Founded: 2002
Sales Range: $10-24.9 Million
Emp.: 17
Tobacco & Accessories
N.A.I.C.S.: 459991
Gary Sahni (Pres & CEO)

SAI AUTO GROUP LLC
528 S Citrus Ave, Covina, CA 91723
Tel.: (626) 967-6325
Web Site: http://www.bozzani.com
Sales Range: $25-49.9 Million
Emp.: 45
New & Used Car Dealers
N.A.I.C.S.: 441110
Greg Bozzani (Owner)

SAI PEOPLE SOLUTIONS, INC.
2313 Timber Shadows Dr Ste 200, Kingwood, TX 77339
Tel.: (281) 358-1858
Web Site: http://www.saipeople.com
Sales Range: $50-74.9 Million
Emp.: 300
Staffing & IT Services
N.A.I.C.S.: 541612
Siva P. Tayi (Pres & CEO)
Aswin Penukonda (CFO)
Amy Blackburn (Acct Mgr)

SAI SYSTEMS INTERNATIONAL, INC.
5 Research Dr, Shelton, CT 06484
Tel.: (203) 929-0790
Web Site: http://www.saisystems.com
Year Founded: 1993
Rev.: $9,700,000
Emp.: 180
Computer Programming Services
N.A.I.C.S.: 541512
Sunil Wadhwani (CFO)
Manoj Wadhwani (Pres-Saisystems Health)
Ramesh M. Wadhwani (Pres)
Don Shownkeen (Gen Mgr)
Kalyanrao Bapatla (Mgr-Project)

SAIA ELECTRIC, INC.
6175 Confidence St, Baton Rouge, LA 70806
Tel.: (225) 926-0800
Web Site: http://www.saia.net
Rev.: $12,000,000
Emp.: 80
Electrical Contractor
N.A.I.C.S.: 238210
Frank Brian (Exec VP)

SAICON CONSULTANTS, INC.
55 Corporate Woods 9300 W 110th St Ste 650, Overland Park, KS 66210
Tel.: (913) 451-1178
Web Site: http://www.saiconinc.com
Year Founded: 1998
Sales Range: $1-9.9 Million
Emp.: 100
IT Services & Consulting
N.A.I.C.S.: 541690
Swati Yelmar *(Founder & Pres)*
Ramesh S. Lokre *(CEO)*
Jason Miller *(Dir-Govt Div)*
Gary L. King *(VP-Legal)*
Dan Valia *(Sr VP)*

SAIEED CONSTRUCTION SYSTEMS
3301 Benson Dr Ste 501, Raleigh, NC 27609
Tel.: (919) 876-4772
Sales Range: $10-24.9 Million
Emp.: 50
Commercial Construction Contracting
N.A.I.C.S.: 236220

SAIF CORP.
400 High St SE, Salem, OR 97312-1000
Tel.: (503) 373-8000
Web Site: http://www.saif.com
Year Founded: 1914
Sales Range: $100-124.9 Million
Emp.: 889
Workmens Compensation Services
N.A.I.C.S.: 524113
Ken Collins *(CIO)*
Kerry Barnett *(CEO)*

SAILTHRU, INC.
160 Varick St 12th Fl, New York, NY 10013
Web Site: http://www.sailthru.com
Sales Range: $1-9.9 Million
Emp.: 60
Software Publisher
N.A.I.C.S.: 513210
Neil Capel *(Co-Founder & Chm)*
Ian White *(Co-Founder & CTO)*
Stephen Dove *(Sr VP-Product)*
Jeremy Bedford *(VP-EMEA)*
Jon Podell *(Exec VP-Worldwide Sls)*
Cassie Lancellotti-Young *(Exec VP-Customer Success)*
Rebecca Price *(Sr VP-People)*
Marty Meyer *(CFO)*

SAIN CONSTRUCTION CO.
713 Vincent St, Manchester, TN 37355-1937
Tel.: (931) 728-7644
Web Site: http://www.sainconstruction.com
Sales Range: $10-24.9 Million
Emp.: 75
Civil Engineering Services
N.A.I.C.S.: 237310
Pete Sain Jr. *(Pres)*

SAIN ENGINEERING ASSOCIATES, INC.
100 Corporate Pkwy Ste 100, Birmingham, AL 35242
Tel.: (205) 979-9966
Web Site: http://www.saineng.com
Sales Range: $10-24.9 Million
Emp.: 101
Environmental Consulting Services
N.A.I.C.S.: 541620
Stephen P. Sain *(Chm & CEO)*
Todd Billings *(Dir-Bus Dev)*
Tony Halsey *(Dir-Mktg & Comm)*
Brenda Phillips *(Pres & COO)*
Daniel Dreher *(Mgr-Energy Engrg Grp)*
Jim McCool *(Dir-Engrg)*

Bob Cooner *(Mgr-Resource Efficiency)*
Archie Puckett *(Mgr-Resource Efficiency)*
Jim Henderson *(Project Mgr-Federal Resource Efficiency Manager Program)*

SAINERGY
17705 Hale Ave Ste I5, Morgan Hill, CA 95037
Tel.: (408) 532-9800
Web Site: http://www.sainergy.net
Year Founded: 2001
Sales Range: $1-9.9 Million
Emp.: 22
IT & SAP Consulting Services
N.A.I.C.S.: 519290
Priyanka Gupta *(Pres & CEO)*

SAINT ANTHONY HOSPITAL
2875 W 19th St, Chicago, IL 60623
Tel.: (773) 484-1000
Web Site: http://www.saintanthonyhospital.org
Year Founded: 1897
Sales Range: $100-124.9 Million
Emp.: 1,019
Health Care Srvices
N.A.I.C.S.: 622110
Aileen Brooks *(Gen Counsel & VP)*
Christine Raguso *(Sr VP-Professional Svcs)*
James Sifuentes *(Sr VP-Mission & Community Dev)*
Michael Kittoe *(CFO & Exec VP)*
Bernadette O'Shea *(Chief Dev Officer & VP-Foundation)*
Stella Wolf *(Chief HR Officer & VP)*
Sherrie Spencer *(Chief Nursing Officer & VP-Patient Care)*
Mark Jennings *(CIO & VP)*
Guy A. Medaglia *(Pres & CEO)*

SAINT BENEDICT PRESS
13315 Carowinds Blvd, Charlotte, NC 28241
Tel.: (704) 731-0651
Web Site: http://www.books.benedictpress.com
Emp.: 30
Book Publishers
N.A.I.C.S.: 513130
Conor Gallagher *(VP-Publ)*
Rick Rotondi *(VP-New Bus Dev)*

Subsidiaries:
TAN Books & Publishers (1)
13315 Carowinds Blvd, Charlotte, NC 28273
Tel.: (815) 226-7777
Book Publishers
N.A.I.C.S.: 513130

Subsidiary (Domestic):
Neumann Press (2)
13315 Carowinds Blvd, Charlotte, NC 28241
Tel.: (815) 226-7770
Web Site: http://www.neumannpress.com
Book Publishers
N.A.I.C.S.: 513130
Tim McCoy *(Gen Mgr)*

SAINT CLAIR SYSTEMS, INC.
12427 31 Mile Rd, Washington, MI 48095
Tel.: (586) 336-0700
Web Site: http://www.stclairsystems.com
Year Founded: 1990
Sales Range: $1-9.9 Million
Emp.: 28
Fluid Process Control System Mfr
N.A.I.C.S.: 334513
C. Robert Gladstone *(Pres)*
Mike Bonner *(VP-Engrg & Tech)*

Subsidiaries:
Norcross Corporation (1)
255 Newtonville Ave, Newton, MA 02458
Tel.: (617) 969-7020
Web Site: http://www.viscosity.com
Sales Range: $1-9.9 Million
Emp.: 12
Instruments & Related Products Manufacturing for Measuring, Displaying & Controlling Industrial Process Variables
N.A.I.C.S.: 334513
Robert Norcross *(Pres)*
James Dulong *(Mgr-Technical Sls)*

SAINT CROIX VALLEY HARDWOODS INC.
230 Duncan St, Luck, WI 54853
Tel.: (715) 472-2131
Web Site: http://www.scvh.com
Year Founded: 1981
Sales Range: $10-24.9 Million
Emp.: 45
Provider of Lumber, Plywood & Millwork Services
N.A.I.C.S.: 423310
Julie Erickson *(Mgr-Ops)*

SAINT DOMINIC'S HOME
500 Western Hwy, Blauvelt, NY 10913
Tel.: (845) 359-3400
Web Site: http://www.stdominicshome.org
Year Founded: 1962
Sales Range: $50-74.9 Million
Emp.: 962
Developmental Disability Assistance Services
N.A.I.C.S.: 624120
Josh Scher *(CFO)*

SAINT FRANCIS HEALTH SYSTEM, INC.
6161 S Yale Ave, Tulsa, OK 74136
Tel.: (918) 494-2200
Web Site: http://www.saintfrancis.com
Year Founded: 1960
Emp.: 9,500
Health Care Association
N.A.I.C.S.: 813910
Barry Steichen *(COO & Exec VP)*
Tom Neff *(Sr VP-Strategic Plng, Corp Bus Dev)*
Jeff Sacra *(Gen Counsel & VP)*
William Schloss *(Sr VP)*
Lynn Sund *(Sr VP)*
David Weil *(Sr VP)*
Eric Schick *(CFO & Exec VP)*
Mark Frost *(Sr VP-Medical Affairs)*
Charley Trimble *(Sr VP-Ops)*
Anthony Young *(Sr VP)*
Michael Keeling *(VP)*
Jake Henry Jr. *(Pres & CEO)*

SAINT FRANCIS MEDICAL CENTER
211 Saint Francis Dr, Cape Girardeau, MO 63703
Tel.: (573) 331-3000
Web Site: http://www.sfmc.net
Year Founded: 1972
Sales Range: $400-449.9 Million
Emp.: 2,796
Health Care Srvices
N.A.I.C.S.: 622110
Marilyn K. Curtis *(VP-Pro Svcs)*
James A. Schell *(VP-Medical Affairs)*
Barbara W. Thompson *(VP-Mktg & Foundation)*
Tony A. Balsano *(VP-Fin)*
Alex Ogburn *(VP-Ambulatory Svcs)*
Jeannette Fadler *(VP-Patient Care Svcs)*
John A. Layton *(Vice Chm)*
Kevin A. Govero *(Treas & Sec)*

Clyde C. Nenninger *(Chm)*
Maryann Reese *(Pres & CEO)*
Julie Woodruff *(Chief Nursing Officer)*

SAINT JAMES HOLDING & INVESTMENT COMPANY TRUST
8 The Green Ste 4120, Dover, DE 19901
Tel.: (877) 690-9052
Web Site: https://stjameshdinvtrust.co
Year Founded: 1993
Financial Services
N.A.I.C.S.: 523999

Subsidiaries:
Victura Construction Group, Inc. (1)
13 Souder Dr, Hurst, TX 76053
Web Site: http://www.victuraconstruction.com
Sales Range: Less than $1 Million
Holding Company; Disaster Recovery & Restoration Construction
N.A.I.C.S.: 551112

SAINT JOHN ICE COMPANY
PO Box 487, Saint John, VI 00831
Tel.: (340) 693-8825
Sales Range: $50-74.9 Million
Emp.: 6
Ice Mfr
N.A.I.C.S.: 312113
Alan Johnson *(Pres)*

SAINT JOHN'S COMMUNITIES, INC.
1840 N Prospect Ave, Milwaukee, WI 53202-1975
Tel.: (414) 272-2022
Web Site: http://www.saintjohnsmilw.org
Year Founded: 1868
Sales Range: $10-24.9 Million
Emp.: 212
Elder Care Services
N.A.I.C.S.: 624120
Renee E. Anderson *(Pres & CEO-Saint John's on the Lake)*
Dan Lemminger *(Dir-Fin)*
Mary Puetzer Milliren *(Dir-Clinical Svcs)*
David C. Kuehl *(Chm)*
Stephanie Sue Stein *(Vice Chm)*
Donna Spars *(VP & Dir-LifeStreams)*

SAINT JOSEPH HOSPITAL
2700 Dolbeer St, Eureka, CA 95501-4736
Tel.: (707) 445-8121
Web Site: http://www.stjosepheureka.org
Sales Range: $125-149.9 Million
Emp.: 1,400
Hospital Management Services
N.A.I.C.S.: 622110
Kevin Klockenga *(Exec VP-Northern California)*
Roberta Luskin-Hawk *(CEO)*
William Parks *(CMO)*
David Southerland *(COO)*

Subsidiaries:
General Hospital Campus of St. Joseph Hospital (1)
2200 Harrison Ave, Eureka, CA 95501-3215
Tel.: (707) 445-5111
Sales Range: $10-24.9 Million
Emp.: 125
Healthcare Management, Consultation & Senior Living Services
N.A.I.C.S.: 621999
Joe Mark *(CEO)*

SAINT LOUIS CARDINALS, L.P.
Busch Stadium 700 Clark St, Saint Louis, MO 63102-1722

SAINT LOUIS CARDINALS, L.P.

U.S. PRIVATE

Saint Louis Cardinals, L.P.—(Continued)
Tel.: (314) 345-9600 MO
Web Site: http://www.cardinals.com
Year Founded: 1900
Sales Range: $50-74.9 Million
Emp.: 100
Professional Baseball Club
N.A.I.C.S.: 711211
Frederick O. Hanser (Principal)
Vicki Bryant (VP-Event Svcs & Mdsg)

SAINT LOUIS REGIONAL HEALTH COMMISSION
1113 Mississippi Ave Ste 113, Saint Louis, MO 63104
Tel.: (314) 446-6454 MO
Web Site: http://www.stlrhc.org
Year Founded: 2004
Sales Range: $25-49.9 Million
Emp.: 11
Health Care Srvices
N.A.I.C.S.: 622110
Angela Fleming Brown (Dir-Ops)
Latriece Kimbrough (CFO)
Dan O'Malley (Sr Mgr-Ops)
Robert Fruend Jr. (CEO)

SAINT VINCENT'S
2425 Highland Ave, Fall River, MA 02720
Tel.: (508) 679-8511 MA
Web Site: http://www.stvincentshome.org
Year Founded: 1889
Sales Range: $10-24.9 Million
Emp.: 269
Education Services
N.A.I.C.S.: 611710
Donald L. Bigwood (Dir-Medical)
Gregory A. Mathias (Vice Chm)

SAINTS CAPITAL, LLC
2020 Union St, San Francisco, CA 94123
Tel.: (415) 773-2080 DE
Web Site: http://www.saintscapital.com
Sales Range: $25-49.9 Million
Emp.: 10
Venture Capital & Private Equity Investment Firm
N.A.I.C.S.: 523999
Kenneth B. Sawyer (Co-Founder & Mng Dir)
Robert Keppler (Mng Dir & CFO)
David P. Quinlivan (Co-Founder & Mng Dir)

Subsidiaries:

Acsis, Inc. (1)
9 E Stow Rd, Marlton, NJ 08053
Tel.: (856) 489-4900
Web Site: http://www.acsisinc.com
Sales Range: $25-49.9 Million
Supply Chain Software & Services
N.A.I.C.S.: 541512
Gil Rodriguez (VP-Natl Accounts)
John J. DiPalo (Chief Strategy Officer)
Stephanie Seibel (CFO)
Jeremy Coote (CEO)

Laureate Biopharmaceutical Services, Inc. (1)
201 College Rd E, Princeton, NJ 08540
Tel.: (609) 919-3300
Web Site: http://www.lbios.com
Sales Range: $10-24.9 Million
Pharmaceutical Developer & Mfr
N.A.I.C.S.: 325412

Merisel, Inc. (1)
132 W 31st St 8th Fl, New York, NY 10001
Tel.: (212) 594-4800
Web Site: http://www.merisel.com
Rev.: $58,061,000
Assets: $32,531,000
Liabilities: $42,535,000
Net Worth: ($10,004,000)
Earnings: ($18,131,000)
Emp.: 310

Fiscal Year-end: 12/31/2012
Holding Company; Visual Communications & Brand Solutions
N.A.I.C.S.: 551112
Jeb Ball (COO & Exec VP)
Donald R. Uzzi (Chm)
Terry A. Tevis (Pres & CEO)

Subsidiary (Domestic):

Color Edge LLC (2)
132 W 31st St, New York, NY 10001
Tel.: (212) 594-4800
Web Site: http://www.coloredge.com
Visual Communication & Graphic Production Services
N.A.I.C.S.: 541430
Jeb Ball (COO & Exec VP)
Terry A. Tevis (Pres & CEO)
Sharon Koh (VP-Fin)
Lisa Frey (VP-Sls-East)
Jeff Reardon (VP-Creative Svcs)

Branch (Domestic):

Color Edge LLC - New Jersey Production Office (3)
190 Jony Dr, Carlstadt, NJ 07072
Tel.: (201) 716-5200
Web Site: http://www.coloredge.com
Emp.: 200
Visual Communication & Graphic Production Services
N.A.I.C.S.: 541430
Jeb Ball (COO & Exec VP)

Subsidiary (Domestic):

Comp 24 LLC (3)
1919 W Empire Ave, Burbank, CA 91504
Tel.: (818) 562-6676
Web Site: http://www.coloredgecomp.com
Consumer Packaging Composite Graphic Design & Printing Services
N.A.I.C.S.: 541430
Timothy Parzyck (Creative Dir)
David Esqueda (VP-Sls-Coloredge West)

SAKAR INTERNATIONAL, INC.
195 Carter Dr, Edison, NJ 08817
Tel.: (732) 248-1306
Web Site: http://www.sakar.com
Sales Range: $10-24.9 Million
Emp.: 100
Consumer Electronics Mfr
N.A.I.C.S.: 334310
Charles Saka (Founder & CEO)
Ralph Sasson (COO)
Jeff Saka (Pres)

SAL CHEMICAL CO. INC.
3036 Birch Dr, Weirton, WV 26062
Tel.: (304) 748-8200
Web Site: http://www.salchem.com
Sales Range: $10-24.9 Million
Emp.: 40
Supplier of Industrial Chemicals
N.A.I.C.S.: 424690
Steve Fenell (Pres)

SALADINO'S INC.
4397 N Golden State Blvd, Fresno, CA 93722
Tel.: (559) 271-3700 CA
Web Site: http://www.saladinos.com
Year Founded: 1947
Sales Range: $50-74.9 Million
Emp.: 410
Grocery Services
N.A.I.C.S.: 424410
Craig Saladino (Pres & Sec)
Patrick Peters (COO)
Mark Schuh (CFO)

SALAL CREDIT UNION
1515 Dexter Ave N, Seattle, WA 98109
Tel.: (206) 298-9394 WA
Web Site: http://www.salalcu.org
Year Founded: 1948
Sales Range: $25-49.9 Million
Emp.: 166
Credit Union Operator

N.A.I.C.S.: 522130
Sheryl Kirchmeier (CMO & Sr VP)
Russ Rosendal (Pres & CEO)
S. Skott Pope (Sr VP-Retail Fin Svcs)
Robert Schweigert (Chief Lending Officer & Sr VP)
Dick Woo (Chm)
Geoff Swarts (Chief Info & Risk Officer & Sr VP)
Lisa Johnson (Sec)
Randy Cloes (CFO & Sr VP)
Tara Seever (Chief HR Officer & Sr VP)

SALAMANDER INNISBROOK, LLC
36750 US Hwy 19 N, Palm Harbor, FL 34684
Tel.: (727) 942-2000
Web Site: https://www.innisbrookgolfresort.com
Year Founded: 2007
Rev.: $46,382,787
Assets: $56,215,413
Liabilities: $21,363,627
Net Worth: $34,851,786
Earnings: $8,191,959
Emp.: 292
Fiscal Year-end: 12/31/23
Resort Operator
N.A.I.C.S.: 721110
Dale Pelletier (CFO)

Subsidiaries:

Golf Host Securities, Inc. (1)
36750 US Hwy 19 N, Palm Harbor, FL 34684-1239
Tel.: (727) 942-5210
Web Site: http://www.innisbrookrealestate.com
Sales Range: $10-24.9 Million
Emp.: 4
Real Estate Broker
N.A.I.C.S.: 531210
J. Michael Williams (Mng Dir-Salamander Golf & Spa Resort)

SALAMANDER TECHNOLOGIES
122 W State St, Traverse City, MI 49684
Tel.: (231) 932-4397
Web Site: http://www.salamanderlive.com
Year Founded: 2001
Sales Range: $1-9.9 Million
Emp.: 25
First Responder Accountability, Emergency Incident Command & Mass Casualty Patient Tracking Systems Mfr
N.A.I.C.S.: 624230
Russ Miller (Co-Founder, Pres & CEO)
Rob Jones (CTO)

SALAS O'BRIEN ENGINEERS, INC.
305 S 11th St, San Jose, CA 95112
Tel.: (408) 282-1500 CA
Web Site: http://www.salasobrien.com
Year Founded: 1976
Sales Range: $25-49.9 Million
Emp.: 53
Architectural & Engineering Services
N.A.I.C.S.: 541330
Carl Salas (Co-Founder & Principal)
John Salas (Mng Principal-California Ops)
Stephen Graham (Asst VP & Controller)
Darin Anderson (Chm & CEO)
Dan O'Brien (Co-Founder & Sr Engr-Mechanical)

Jeffry Gosal (Principal & Sr Engr-Electrical)
Elana Faria (Coord-Mktg)
Yolanda Sanchez (Coord-HR)
Paul Silva (Pres & COO)
Arnold Kraakmo (Mng Principal-Washington, Montana & Los Angeles)
Brad Kalmans (Mng Principal-Texas & Louisiana)
Stan Everett (Mng Principal-Atlanta)
Michael Rabieh (Sr VP-Information Sys & Tech)
Melissa Johnson (Asst VP-Leadership & Change Mgmt)
Donald Young (Sr VP & Sr Mgr-Construction)
Douglas Diel (Principal & Architect)
Roy Goodman (Founder & Principal)
Scott A. Coward (Asst VP & Sr Project Mgr)
Eric Anest (VP-Mktg)

Subsidiaries:

I.C. Thomasson Associates, Inc. (1)
2950 Kraft Dr, Nashville, TN 37204-0527
Tel.: (615) 346-3400
Web Site: https://www.icthomasson.com
Sales Range: $100-124.9 Million
Emp.: 155
Mechanical & Electrical Consulting Engineering Services
N.A.I.C.S.: 541330
Bruce Mason (Controller)
Carolyn Martz (Dir-HR)
Kerry Rice (Mgr-Computer Sys)

Subsidiary (Domestic):

I.C. Thomasson Associates (2)
8186 Woodland Ctr Blvd, Tampa, FL 33614 (100%)
Tel.: (813) 882-4415
Web Site: http://www.icthomasson.com
Sales Range: $10-24.9 Million
Emp.: 10
Provider Of Mechanical & Electrical Consulting Engineering Services
N.A.I.C.S.: 541330

I.C. Thomasson Associates (2)
1114 Clinch Ave Ste 200, Knoxville, TN 37916 (100%)
Tel.: (865) 525-3488
Web Site: http://www.icthomasson.com
Sales Range: $10-24.9 Million
Emp.: 15
Provider of Mechanical & Electrical Consulting Engineering Services
N.A.I.C.S.: 541330

I.C. Thomasson Associates (2)
104 E Cherokee St, Brookhaven, MS 39601 (100%)
Tel.: (601) 823-0038
Web Site: http://www.icthomasson.com
Sales Range: $10-24.9 Million
Emp.: 10
Provider of Mechanical & Electrical Consulting Engineering Services
N.A.I.C.S.: 541330
Chuck Farnham (VP-Mississippi)

KDW Salas O'Brien, LLC (1)
10202 5th Ave NE Ste 300, Seattle, WA 98125
Tel.: (206) 547-1940
Web Site: http://www.salasobrien.com
Architectural & Engineering Services
N.A.I.C.S.: 541330
Arnold Kraakmo (Mng Principal-Washington, Montana & Los Angeles)
Douglas A. Diel (Principal & Sr Architect)

PCI Skanska Inc. (1)
20 NW 1st St Ste 40, Evansville, IN 47708
Tel.: (812) 425-4264
Web Site: http://www.pcidesign.com
Engineeering Services
N.A.I.C.S.: 541330
Dave King (Project Mgr)
Scott Albin (Gen Mgr)

Salas O'Brien South, LLC (1)
1255 Collier Rd, Atlanta, GA 30318
Tel.: (404) 881-5300
Web Site: http://www.salasobrien.com
Architectural & Engineering Services
N.A.I.C.S.: 541330

COMPANIES

Stan Everett *(Mng Principal)*
Tim Burnham *(Mng Principal)*
John Salas *(Mng Principal)*
Farzad Tadayon *(Mng Principal)*
Stephen Boie *(Principal & Sr Engr-Mechanical)*
David Bonaventure *(Principal & Sr Engr-Mechanical)*
Tim Brawner *(Principal & Sr Engr-Mechanical)*
Doug Carrera *(Principal-Strategic Markets)*
Kyle Cartier *(Principal & Sr Engr-Mechanical)*
Dan Clifford *(Principal & Sr Engr-Mechanical)*
Chris Cox *(Sr VP & Sr Engr-Electrical)*
Tom Evans *(Principal & Sr Engr-Electrical)*
John Floren *(Sr VP & Sr Engr-Electrical)*
Kim Gaskey *(Sr VP & Sr Engr-Plumbing)*
Keith Gassman *(Principal & Sr Engr-Electrical)*
Tim Gilbert *(Principal & Sr Engr-Mechanical)*
Sean Holder *(Principal & Sr Engr-Mechanical)*
Toby Hunt *(Principal & Sr Engr-Mechanical)*
Randy Jones *(Principal & Sr Engr-Mechanical)*

Zepnick Solutions, Inc. (1)
416 Security Blvd Ste B, Green Bay, WI 54313
Tel.: (920) 662-1682
Web Site: http://www.zepnick.com
Sales Range: $1-9.9 Million
Emp.: 20
Engineering Consultants
N.A.I.C.S.: 541330
Jody D. Zepnick *(Founder & CEO)*

SALCE CONTRACTING ASSOCIATES, INC.
335 Ferry Blvd, Stratford, CT 06615
Tel.: (203) 378-1876   CT
Web Site:
    http://www.salcecontracting.com
Year Founded: 1983
Sales Range: $10-24.9 Million
Emp.: 6
Provider of Institutional Building Construction
N.A.I.C.S.: 236220
Michael Vitello *(Pres)*

SALCO LEATHER
660 Jessie St, San Fernando, CA 91340
Tel.: (818) 365-0555
Web Site: http://www.oclas.com
Sales Range: $10-24.9 Million
Emp.: 5
Processed Leather Sales
N.A.I.C.S.: 424990
Alfredo Diana *(Pres)*
Fabian Diana *(VP)*

SALE AUTO MALL
1053 Hwy 258 N, Kinston, NC 28504
Web Site:
    http://www.saleautomall.com
Rev.: $37,500,000
Emp.: 108
New & Used Car Dealers
N.A.I.C.S.: 441110

SALEEN AUTOMOTIVE, INC.
2735 Wardlow Rd, Corona, CA 92882
Tel.: (714) 400-2121   NV
Web Site: https://www.saleen.com
Year Founded: 1984
SLNN—(OTCBB)
Sales Range: $1-9.9 Million
High-Performance Cars Designer & Mfr
N.A.I.C.S.: 336110
Stephen M. Saleen *(CEO)*

SALEM AREA VISITING NURSE ASSOCIATION
718 E 3rd St Ste A, Salem, OH 44460
Tel.: (330) 332-9986
Web Site:
    http://www.salemohiovna.com
Women Healthcare Services
N.A.I.C.S.: 621610
Sue Yoder *(Exec Dir)*

SALEM COMMUNITY HOSPITAL
1995 E State St, Salem, OH 44460
Tel.: (330) 332-1551   OH
Web Site: http://www.salemhosp.com
Year Founded: 1913
Sales Range: $100-124.9 Million
Emp.: 1,023
Health Care Srvices
N.A.I.C.S.: 622110
Mark Litalien *(Dir-Info Svcs)*
Anita Hackstedde *(Pres & CEO)*

SALEM DISTRIBUTING COMPANY INC.
5901 Gun Club Rd, Winston Salem, NC 27103
Tel.: (336) 766-1104
Web Site: http://www.salemdist.com
Year Founded: 1934
Sales Range: $25-49.9 Million
Emp.: 50
Ophthalmic Goods
N.A.I.C.S.: 423460
Ann Greco *(Mgr)*
Bill Davidson *(Acct Mgr-Flat Glass & Mirror-Salem)*
Dan Reinhart *(VP-Sls & Mktg)*

SALEM FARM SUPPLY INC.
5109 State Rte 22, Salem, NY 12865
Tel.: (518) 854-7424
Web Site:
    http://www.salemfarmsupply.com
Sales Range: $10-24.9 Million
Emp.: 30
Agricultural Construction; Lawn & Garden Equipment
N.A.I.C.S.: 423820
Philip T. Lewis *(Pres)*
Berta Lewis *(Sec)*

SALEM FIVE BANCORP
71 Washington St, Salem, MA 01970
Tel.: (978) 745-5450   MA
Web Site: http://www.salemfive.com
Year Founded: 2006
Bank Holding Company
N.A.I.C.S.: 551111
Ping Yin Chai *(Pres & CEO)*

Subsidiaries:

Salem Five Cents Savings Bank (1)
71 Washington St, Salem, MA 01970-3705
Tel.: (978) 745-5450
Web Site: http://www.salemfive.com
Savings Bank
N.A.I.C.S.: 522180

Subsidiary (Domestic):

Cape Ann Insurance, Inc. (2)
23 Dale Ave, Gloucester, MA 01930-5904
Tel.: (978) 283-7757
Web Site: http://www.salemfive.com
Insurance Related Activities
N.A.I.C.S.: 524298

SALEM GRAIN COMPANY INC.
64594 707 Ln, Salem, NE 68433
Tel.: (402) 245-5373
Web Site: http://www.salemgrain.com
Sales Range: $25-49.9 Million
Emp.: 10
Grain Purchase, Storage & Sales
N.A.I.C.S.: 424510
David Irwin *(Mgr-Elevator)*

SALEM GROUP INC.
209 Mercantile Dr, Winston Salem, NC 27105
Tel.: (336) 744-5999
Web Site:
    http://www.salemgroup.com
Year Founded: 1986
Sales Range: $10-24.9 Million
Emp.: 14
Computer & Software Sales
N.A.I.C.S.: 449210
Brian E. Heelan *(Pres)*
David A. Rosenblatt *(VP)*
John W. Millican *(VP-Solutions)*

SALEM HOLDING COMPANY
175 Charlois Blvd, Winston Salem, NC 27103
Tel.: (336) 768-6800
Web Site:
    http://www.salemleasing.com
Sales Range: $100-124.9 Million
Emp.: 60
Truck Leasing Services
N.A.I.C.S.: 532120
Thomas L. Teague *(Pres)*
Dennis Giff *(Exec VP & Gen Mgr)*
C. Stephen Dula *(CFO & Sr VP)*
Doug Chase *(Controller)*
Kenneth Langone *(CEO)*
Ken Teague *(VP-Acct Mgmt)*
Lacy Teague *(Exec VP-Sls)*

Subsidiaries:

Salem Leasing Corp. (1)
175 Charlois Blvd, Winston Salem, NC 27103
Tel.: (336) 768-6800
Web Site: http://www.salemleasing.com
Sales Range: $25-49.9 Million
Emp.: 55
Leasing of Truck Tractor & Trailers
N.A.I.C.S.: 532120
Thomas L. Teague *(Pres)*
Brian Giff *(VP-HR)*

Salem Nationallease (1)
175 Charlois Blvd, Winston Salem, NC 27103
Tel.: (336) 768-6800
Web Site: http://www.salemleasing.com
Sales Range: $100-124.9 Million
Emp.: 55
General Commodities Common Carrier & Contract Carrier
N.A.I.C.S.: 532120
Dennis Giff *(Gen Mgr)*
Douglas Chase *(Controller)*

SALEM INVESTMENT CAPITAL LLC
1355 Santa Rosa Ave, Santa Rosa, CA 95404-5424
Tel.: (707) 571-8243
Web Site: http://www.salemip.com
Commercial & Industrial Machinery & Equipment Repair & Maintenance
N.A.I.C.S.: 811310
Lance Cushing *(Mgr)*

SALEM PRINTING
5670 Shattalon Dr, Winston Salem, NC 27105
Tel.: (336) 744-9990
Web Site: http://www.esalem.net
Year Founded: 1987
Rev.: $12,400,000
Emp.: 120
Commercial Lithographic Printing
N.A.I.C.S.: 323111
Jerry Edwards *(Mgr-Sls)*
Philip Kelley Sr. *(VP)*
Philip Kelley Jr. *(Pres)*
Steve Yarbrough *(CFO)*
Tracy Brooks *(VP-Sls)*

SALEM STONE CORPORATION
PO Box 1620, Dublin, VA 24084
Tel.: (540) 674-5556   VA
Web Site:
    http://www.salemstonecorp.com

SALES BENCHMARK INDEX LLC

Year Founded: 1983
Crushed & Broken Granite
N.A.I.C.S.: 212313
Kym Kulis *(CFO)*
M. J. O'Brien Jr. *(Pres & CEO)*

SALEM TOOLS, INC.
1602 Midland Rd, Salem, VA 24153-6427
Tel.: (540) 389-0726   VA
Web Site: http://www.salemtools.com
Year Founded: 1970
Sales Range: $10-24.9 Million
Emp.: 102
Industrial Supplies
N.A.I.C.S.: 423840
William N. Powell *(Pres)*

Subsidiaries:

Regal Industries LLC (1)
4554 Poplar Level Rd, Louisville, KY 40213
Tel.: (502) 968-2991
Sales Range: $10-24.9 Million
Emp.: 4
Industrial Tools
N.A.I.C.S.: 423840

SALEM TRUCK LEASING INC.
9505 Ave D, Brooklyn, NY 11236
Tel.: (718) 649-8400
Web Site:
    http://www.truckkingintl.com
Sales Range: $25-49.9 Million
Emp.: 97
Truck Leasing Services
N.A.I.C.S.: 532120
Steven Steinberg *(Co-Pres)*
Alan Steinberg *(Co-Pres)*

SALEPOINT INC.
9909 Huennekens St Ste 205, San Diego, CA 92121
Tel.: (858) 546-9400
Web Site: http://www.salepoint.com
Year Founded: 1987
Sales Range: $10-24.9 Million
Emp.: 80
Provider of Computer Software Development Services
N.A.I.C.S.: 541511
Larry Haworth *(CEO)*
Paul Streicher *(Pres-Retail Solutions)*
Cindy Fortes *(VP-Client Svcs)*
Ken Kauffman *(VP-Software)*

SALERNO DUANE INC.
267 Broad St, Summit, NJ 07901
Tel.: (908) 277-6700
Web Site: http://www.salerno-duane.com
Sales Range: $25-49.9 Million
Emp.: 70
Sales of Automobiles
N.A.I.C.S.: 441110
Raquel Ayala *(Controller)*

SALES BENCHMARK INDEX LLC
2021 McKinney Ave Ste 550, Dallas, TX 75201
Tel.: (469) 718-1747
Web Site: https://sbigrowth.com
Business Consulting & Services
N.A.I.C.S.: 561499
Mike Hoffman *(CEO)*

Subsidiaries:

Sales Readiness Inc. (1)
8359 Amsden Rdg Dr, Minneapolis, MN 55438
Tel.: (206) 905-8756
Web Site:
    http://www.salesreadinessgroup.com
Management Consulting Services
N.A.I.C.S.: 541618

SALES DEVELOPMENT ASSOCIATES, INC.

U.S. PRIVATE

Sales Development Associates, Inc.—(Continued)

SALES DEVELOPMENT ASSOCIATES, INC.
7850 Manchester Rd, Saint Louis, MO 63143-2710
Tel.: (314) 862-8828 MO
Web Site: http://www.sdastl.com
Year Founded: 1989
Sales Range: $10-24.9 Million
Emp.: 14
N.A.I.C.S.: 541810
Patricia Biggerstaff (Pres)
Melissa Chambers (Acct Exec)
Jennifer Balossi (Controller)

SALES FOCUS INC.
2500 Wallington Way Ste 105, Marriottsville, MD 21104
Tel.: (410) 442-5600
Web Site:
http://www.salesfocusinc.com
Year Founded: 1998
Sales Range: $1-9.9 Million
Emp.: 165
Sales Management Consulting Services
N.A.I.C.S.: 541613
Tony Horwath (Founder, Pres & CEO)
David Jones (Mgr-Call Centre)
Marilyn Horwath (Dir-Comm)
C. J. Minick (Dir-Fin & HR)

SALES FORCE WON LTD.
800 N 17th Ave, Phoenix, AZ 85007
Tel.: (602) 258-1158
Web Site: http://www.sfscratch.com
Year Founded: 1995
Rev.: $11,915,296
Emp.: 30
Baked Goods & Soups Distr
N.A.I.C.S.: 424490
Rudy DePaola (Pres & CEO)

Subsidiaries:

SFS Distribution Services Inc. (1)
800 N 17th Ave, Phoenix, AZ 85007
Tel.: (602) 258-1158
Rev.: $2,530,958
Emp.: 25
Bakery Products
N.A.I.C.S.: 424420

SALES GROUP INC.
23942 Craftsman Rd, Calabasas, CA 91302
Tel.: (818) 222-0880
Web Site:
http://www.thesalesgroup.com
Sales Range: $10-24.9 Million
Emp.: 10
Communications Equipment
N.A.I.C.S.: 423690
Larry Weber (Partner)
Michael Sage (Partner)
Dana Hanford (Partner)

SALES MAX INC.
9554 7th St, Rancho Cucamonga, CA 91730
Tel.: (909) 484-2814
Web Site:
http://www.salesmaxinc.com
Sales Range: $10-24.9 Million
Emp.: 23
Groceries, General Line
N.A.I.C.S.: 424410
Frank Van Heule (Pres)

SALES OPTIMIZER LLC
2290 Lucien Way Ste 360, Maitland, FL 32751
Tel.: (407) 389-6060
Web Site:
http://www.salesoptimizer.com
Year Founded: 2003
Sales Range: $1-9.9 Million

Emp.: 51
Sales Training
N.A.I.C.S.: 611430
Nik Nikic (Founder & CEO)
Natasha Veatch (Mgr-Production)

SALES PARTNERSHIPS, INC.
9035 Wadsworth Pkwy Ste 1600, Westminster, CO 80021
Tel.: (303) 412-3181
Web Site:
http://www.salespartnerships.com
Sales Range: $1-9.9 Million
Emp.: 150
Sales Outsourcing
N.A.I.C.S.: 561311
Fred Kessler (Co-Founder & CEO)
D. Aaron Kullman (Co-Founder & VP-Ops)
Chase Scott (Dir-HR)
Paul Murphy (Dir-Bus Dev)

SALES PERFORMANCE INTERNATIONAL, LLC
6201 Fairview Rd Ste 400, Charlotte, NC 28210
Tel.: (704) 227-6500
Web Site: http://www.spisales.com
Sales Range: $1-9.9 Million
Emp.: 40
Sales Process Consulting Services
N.A.I.C.S.: 541612
Keith M. Eades (Founder & CEO)
Douglas L. Handy (CFO)
Timothy P. Sullivan (VP-Bus Dev)
Robert Kear (CTO)
James Touchstone (Dir-Learning Programs)
Brad Ansley (Dir-Life Sciences)
Dario Priolo (Chief Mktg Officer)
Steven Vantongelen (VP-Europe)

Subsidiaries:

The Complex Sale, Inc. (1)
3015 Windward Plz, Alpharetta, GA 30005
Tel.: (770) 360-9299
Web Site: http://www.complexsale.com
Emp.: 25
Marketing Consulting Services
N.A.I.C.S.: 541613
Richard Page (CEO)
David Stargel (Pres)
Liz McCune (VP-Mktg)
Jon Hauck (Sr Principal & VP)
Peter Bourke (VP-HR & Principal)
Nicholas Holbrook (Principal)
Marty Mercer (Principal)

SALES SYSTEMS LIMITED
700 Florida Ave, Portsmouth, VA 23707
Tel.: (757) 397-0763
Web Site:
http://www.salessystemsltd.com
Rev.: $15,000,000
Emp.: 34
Industrial & Military Fastener Distr
N.A.I.C.S.: 423840
William C. Creecy (Pres)

SALESFACTORY + WOODBINE, INC.
1301 Carolina St Ste 106, Greensboro, NC 27401
Tel.: (336) 324-4101 NC
Web Site:
http://www.salesfactorywoodbine.com
Year Founded: 1984
Advetising Agency
N.A.I.C.S.: 541810
Ged King (CEO-Mktg)
Peter W. Mitchell (Pres)
Matt King (Chief Creative Officer)
David Geren (Exec VP)
Vickie Canada (VP & Creative Dir)
Renee Owens (Assoc Creative Dir)

Andrew Harrison (Assoc Creative Dir)
Rachel Bowles (Acct Supvr)
Shayla Stockton (Sr Acct Exec)
Chelsea Higgins (Sr Acct Exec)
Emily Bratton (Dir-Digital Strategy)
Megan Cleworth (Dir-Digital Strategy)

SALESIFY INC.
255 Shoreline Dr Ste 145, Redwood City, CA 94065
Web Site: http://www.salesify.com
Year Founded: 2005
Sales Range: $1-9.9 Million
Emp.: 321
Customized Prospect Databases, Database Cleansing & Appends
N.A.I.C.S.: 541613
Gurdeep Singh Chimni (CEO)
Oliver Deng (CFO)

SALESLOFT, INC.
180 W Peachtree St NW Ste 600, Atlanta, GA 30309
Tel.: (770) 756-8022
Web Site: http://www.salesloft.com
Year Founded: 2011
Sales Range: $25-49.9 Million
Emp.: 320
Software Development Services
N.A.I.C.S.: 541512
David Obrand (CEO)
Randy Littleson (CMO)
Kyle Porter (Founder)
Rob Forman (Pres & COO)
Christine Kaszubski (Chief People Officer)
Sean Murray (Chief Revenue Officer)
Vincent Ooi (VP-Asia Pacific)
Nate Remmes (Exec VP-Comml Bus Unit)
Eleanor Fields (Chief Product & Engrg Officer)

SALESSTAFF, LLC
10701 Corporate Dr Ste 340, Stafford, TX 77477
Tel.: (888) 591-8022
Web Site: http://www.salesstaff.com
Year Founded: 2009
Sales Range: $1-9.9 Million
Emp.: 60
Offers Demand Generation Services to High-Tech Industries
N.A.I.C.S.: 525990
Bryan Brorsen (Pres & COO)
David Balzen (CEO)
Melanie Knight (Exec Dir-Acct Mgmt)

SALIBA CONSTRUCTION CO. INC.
1147 N Park Ave, Dothan, AL 36303
Tel.: (334) 792-9871
Web Site:
http://www.salibaconstruction.com
Sales Range: $10-24.9 Million
Emp.: 35
Commercial & Office Building, New Construction
N.A.I.C.S.: 236220
Richard Jameel Saliba (Pres)
Jane Saliba (Treas)

SALIENT PARTNERS, L.P.
4265 San Felipe St 8th Fl, Houston, TX 77027
Tel.: (713) 993-4675 TX
Web Site:
http://www.salientpartners.com
Year Founded: 1994
Rev.: $22,100,000,000
Emp.: 150
Investment Fund & Trust Management Services
N.A.I.C.S.: 523940
Gregory Allen Reid (Pres-MLP Complex-Houston)

Andrew Baird Linbeck (Co-Founder & Mng Dir)
Jeremy Lawrence Radcliffe (Pres)
Paul Axtell Bachtold (Chief Compliance Officer)
Stephen D. Strake (Mng Dir)
John E. Price (CFO)
J. Cole Dawson (Mng Dir)
David Linton (Exec VP & Head-Distr)
Michael Mithoff (Mng Dir)
Kristen Bayazitoglu (COO-Asset Mgmt)
Roz Davis (Sr VP-HR)
Jonathan DePriest (Gen Counsel & Exec VP-San Francisco)
J. Matthew Newtown (Mng Dir-Houston)
Rusty Guinn (Exec VP-Asset Mgmt-Houston)

Subsidiaries:

Salient MLP & Energy Infrastructure Fund (1)
4265 San Felipe 8th Fl, Houston, TX 77027
Tel.: (713) 993-4675
Web Site: http://www.salientpartners.com
Closed-End Investment Fund
N.A.I.C.S.: 525990
John E. Price (Mng Dir & CFO)
Ted Gardner (Mng Dir & Portfolio Mgr)
Michael Corrao (Dir-IR & Comm)
Parag Sanghani (Dir-Res)

Salient Midstream & MLP Fund (1)
4265 San Felipe Ste 800, Houston, TX 77027
Tel.: (713) 993-4675
Web Site: http://www.salientpartners.com
Sales Range: Less than $1 Million
Closed-End Investment Fund
N.A.I.C.S.: 525990
Gregory Allen Reid (Pres & CEO)

SALIENT PRODUCTS CORPORATION
1852 31st St, San Diego, CA 92102
Tel.: (206) 426-1775 NV
Year Founded: 2010
Sales Range: $10-24.9 Million
Emp.: 1
Computer Software Publisher & Sales
N.A.I.C.S.: 513210
Shehzad Peermahomed (Chm, Pres, CFO & Sec)

SALINA REGIONAL HEALTH CENTER
400 S Santa Fe Ave, Salina, KS 67401-4144
Tel.: (785) 452-7000
Web Site: http://www.srhc.com
Sales Range: $125-149.9 Million
Emp.: 1,500
General Medical & Surgical Hospitals
N.A.I.C.S.: 622110
Melinda Schmidt (Dir-Women's & Children's Svcs)
Tom Bell (Exec Dir-Govt & PR)

SALINAS VALLEY FORD
1100 Auto Center Cir, Salinas, CA 93907
Tel.: (831) 758-4444
Web Site: http://www.svford.com
Sales Range: $10-24.9 Million
Emp.: 100
Automobiles, New & Used
N.A.I.C.S.: 811121
Ron Frieberg (Pres & Principal)
Lars Frieberg (Owner & Pres)
Ken Sigala (Asst Mgr-Parts)

SALINE COUNTY MEDICAL CENTER
1 Medical Park Dr, Benton, AR 72015
Tel.: (501) 776-6000 AR
Web Site:
http://www.salinememorial.org

COMPANIES

Year Founded: 1995
Sales Range: $75-99.9 Million
Emp.: 1,146
Health Care Srvices
N.A.I.C.S.: 622110
Carla Robertson *(CFO & COO)*
Eddie Black *(Sec)*
Meredith Wineland *(Chm)*
Chris Williams *(Vice Chm)*
Jared Dixon *(Dir-Family Practice Associates)*
Nick Gann *(Sec)*
Scott Walsh *(Dir-Arkansas Bone & Joint)*
Shayna Oltmans *(Treas)*

SALISBURY MOTOR CO. INC.
700 W Innes St, Salisbury, NC 28144
Tel.: (704) 636-1341
Web Site:
http://www.salisburymotorco.com
Sales Range: $10-24.9 Million
Emp.: 29
Automobiles, New & Used
N.A.I.C.S.: 441110

SALK, INC.
119 Braintree St Ste 701, Boston, MA 02134
Tel.: (617) 782-4030   MA
Web Site: http://www.salkinc.com
Year Founded: 1950
Rev.: $2,500,000
Emp.: 30
Waterproof Protective Undergarments & Reusable Incontinence Systems Mfr
N.A.I.C.S.: 339113
Lawrence Salk *(Owner & Pres)*

SALLY CORPORATION
745 W Forsyth St, Jacksonville, FL 32204
Tel.: (904) 355-7100
Web Site: http://www.sallycorp.com
Sales Range: $10-24.9 Million
Emp.: 30
Theme Park & Attraction Animatronics
N.A.I.C.S.: 713990
John Wood *(Chm & CEO)*
William Coleman *(CFO & VP-Fin)*
Donna Gentry *(VP-Project Mgmt)*
Todd Gillrup *(VP-Ops)*
Drew Hunter *(VP-Design)*
Fitz Otis *(Mgr-Sls-Intl)*
Lauren Wood Weaver *(Dir-Mktg)*
David Jones *(Dir-Programming)*
John Stegall *(VP-Technical Svcs)*
Rich Hill *(Dir-Creative)*
Sheila Leonard *(Office Mgr)*
Greg Rodriguez *(Mgr-Customer Svc)*
Luda Budnik *(Supvr-Art)*
Ric Hostetter *(Supvr-Scenic)*
David Bishop *(COO)*

SALLY LOU FASHIONS CORPORATION
1400 Broadway Fl 6, New York, NY 10018-5300
Tel.: (212) 354-9670   NY
Year Founded: 1974
Sales Range: $25-49.9 Million
Emp.: 10
Mfr of Women's, Juniors' & Misses' Dresses
N.A.I.C.S.: 315250
Mitchell Grabow *(Pres)*

SALLYPORT COMMERCIAL FINANCE, LLC
14100 SW Fwy Ste 210, Sugar Land, TX 77478
Tel.: (832) 939-9450   DE
Web Site: https://sallyportcf.com
Financial Services
N.A.I.C.S.: 523999

SALMON RIVER MOTORS INC.
1051 S Challis St, Salmon, ID 83467-5321
Tel.: (208) 756-4211
Web Site:
http://www.salmonautodealer.com
Rev.: $24,000,000
Emp.: 30
Automobiles, New & Used
N.A.I.C.S.: 441110
Dave Hull *(Owner)*

SALO SOLUTIONS, INC.
1103 Schrock Rd Ste 101, Columbus, OH 43229
Web Site:
http://www.salosolutions.com
Information Technology Consulting Services for Healthcare Industry
N.A.I.C.S.: 541690
Tony Ott *(Pres)*

SALOMONE BROTHERS INC
17 Demarest Dr, Wayne, NJ 07470
Tel.: (973) 305-0022
Web Site: http://www.salomone.com
Sales Range: $10-24.9 Million
Emp.: 50
Service Station Construction
N.A.I.C.S.: 236220
Joseph Salomone *(Pres)*

SALON DEVELOPMENT CORP.
55 Eagle Rock Ave, East Hanover, NJ 07936
Tel.: (973) 884-2330
Rev.: $12,000,000
Emp.: 400
Owner & Operator of Hair Salons
N.A.I.C.S.: 812112
Jonathan M. Shaw *(CEO)*
Alice Ralston *(Controller)*

SALON INNOVATIONS INC.
4700 Quebec Ave North, New Hope, MN 55428
Tel.: (763) 512-5220   MN
Web Site:
http://www.saloninnovations.com
Year Founded: 1972
Sales Range: $10-24.9 Million
Emp.: 45
Distr of Beauty Parlor Equipment & Supplies
N.A.I.C.S.: 423850
Robert Todd *(Pres)*
Sam Hanson *(Controller)*

SALON PROFESSIONAL SERVICES, INC.
707 10th Ave, Belmar, NJ 07719
Web Site:
http://www.mysalonangel.com
Year Founded: 1987
Sales Range: $1-9.9 Million
Emp.: 15
Distr of Beauty Supplies
N.A.I.C.S.: 456120
Brian J. Esposito *(CEO)*

SALSBURY INDUSTRIES
1010 E 62nd St, Los Angeles, CA 90001-1598
Tel.: (323) 846-6700
Web Site: http://www.mailboxes.com
Year Founded: 1936
Sales Range: $75-99.9 Million
Emp.: 150
Postal Lock Boxes, Cubicle Tracks, Cubicle Curtains & Mailboxes Mfr & Distr
N.A.I.C.S.: 332119
John Fraher *(Chm)*
Michael Lobosso *(CFO)*
Dennis Fraher *(Owner)*
Brian P. Fraher *(VP)*
Steve Gov *(Dir-Ops)*

SALSBURY'S DODGE CITY, LLC.
9550 Airline Hwy, Baton Rouge, LA 70815-5501
Tel.: (225) 926-8800
Web Site:
http://www.salsburysdodgecity.net
Sales Range: $25-49.9 Million
Emp.: 130
Car Whslr
N.A.I.C.S.: 441110
Frank Lopinto *(Gen Mgr)*
Leah Salsbury *(Pres)*
Ray Slade *(Comptroller)*

SALT BLOCKCHAIN INC.
600 17th St Ste 2800 S, Denver, CO 80202
Tel.: (720) 457-2288   DE
Web Site:
https://www.saltlending.com
Year Founded: 2016
Emp.: 63
Financial Services
N.A.I.C.S.: 522291

SALT CREEK CAPITAL MANAGEMENT, LLC
2055 Woodside Rd Ste 250, Woodside, CA 94061
Tel.: (415) 238-4876   CA
Web Site:
http://www.saltcreekcap.com
Year Founded: 2009
Sales Range: $1-9.9 Million
Emp.: 15
Privater Equity Firm
N.A.I.C.S.: 523999
Daniel J. Phelps *(Founder & Mng Dir)*
Dan Mytels *(Mng Dir)*
W. Brad Winegar *(Mng Dir)*
Adrian LaTrace *(Partner)*
Dan Goetz *(Partner)*
J. W. Penland *(Exec Partner)*
Venugopal Shan *(Exec Partner)*
Daniel Price *(Founder)*
Chris Gorog *(Operating Partner)*
Lisa Miskinis *(Controller)*
Sterling Peloso *(Exec Partner)*
Rudy Mui *(Exec Partner)*
Mark Olivito *(Exec Partner)*
Augie DeLuca *(Exec Partner)*
Talha Ashraf *(Exec Partner)*
Ali Murdoch *(Exec Partner)*
James Knight *(Exec Partner)*
F. W. Pearce *(Exec Partner)*
Jon F. Beizer *(Operating Partner)*

Subsidiaries:

Boyd Industries, Inc. (1)
12900 44th St N, Clearwater, FL 33762
Tel.: (727) 561-9292
Web Site: http://www.boydindustries.com
Sales Range: $1-9.9 Million
Emp.: 75
Dental Equipment & Supplies Mfr & Distr
N.A.I.C.S.: 339114
Adrian LaTrace *(CEO)*
Hook Namburi *(Product Mgr)*
Kurt Schwarz *(VP-Sls)*
Tin Manezel *(Mgr-Ops)*

Griplock Systems, LLC (1)
1132 Mark Ave, Carpinteria, CA 93013
Tel.: (805) 566-0064
Web Site: http://www.griplocksystems.com
Sales Range: $1-9.9 Million
Cable Suspension Products Mfr & Marketer
N.A.I.C.S.: 332618
Hugo Napier *(Exec VP-Sls)*
Todd Hemingway *(CEO)*

King Tester Corporation (1)
308 Schell Ln, Phoenixville, PA 19460
Tel.: (610) 279-6010
Web Site: http://www.kingtester.com
Sales Range: $1-9.9 Million
Emp.: 10
Metallurgical Testing Equipment Mfr
N.A.I.C.S.: 339999
James Knight *(CEO)*

Pacific Paper (1)
8865 Utica Ave Ste A, Rancho Cucamonga, CA 91730
Tel.: (909) 476-6466
Sales Range: $1-9.9 Million
Emp.: 30
Converted Paper Product Mfr
N.A.I.C.S.: 322299
Jon Todora *(Gen Mgr)*

Tuscan Imports Inc. (1)
1305 E Palmetto St Ste B, Florence, SC 29506
Tel.: (843) 667-9101
Web Site: http://www.fontanaforniusa.com
Furniture Retailer
N.A.I.C.S.: 449110
Kirk Laing *(Founder & Pres)*

Vantage Vehicle International, Inc. (1)
1740 N Delilah St, Corona, CA 92879
Tel.: (951) 735-1200
Web Site: http://www.vantagevehicle.com
Rev.: $1,400,000
Emp.: 12
All Other Plastics Product Mfr
N.A.I.C.S.: 326199
Drew Lieberman *(CEO)*

SALT LAKE LEGAL DEFENDER ASSOCIATION
424 E 500 S Ste 300, Salt Lake City, UT 84111
Tel.: (801) 532-5444   UT
Year Founded: 1965
Sales Range: $10-24.9 Million
Emp.: 141
Law firm
N.A.I.C.S.: 541199
D. Gilbert Athay *(Chm)*
Ronald Coleman *(Vice Chm)*

SALT LAKE VALLEY BUICK GMC
3300 S 725 W, Salt Lake City, UT 84119
Tel.: (801) 265-1511
Web Site:
http://www.slvbuickgmc.com
Sales Range: $25-49.9 Million
Emp.: 60
New & Used Automobiles, Vans & Trucks
N.A.I.C.S.: 441110
Darren New *(Mgr-Svcs)*
Mike Fonger *(Dir-F&I)*

SALT RIVER ELECTRIC COOP CORP.
111 W Brashear Ave, Bardstown, KY 40004
Tel.: (502) 348-3931
Web Site: http://www.srelectric.com
Sales Range: $25-49.9 Million
Emp.: 21
Distribution, Electric Power
N.A.I.C.S.: 221122
Nicky Rapier *(VP-Dev)*
Jan Hedgepeth *(Mgr-HR)*

SALT RIVER MATERIALS GROUP
12695 N Beeline Hwy, Scottsdale, AZ 85202
Tel.: (480) 850-5757   AZ
Web Site: http://www.srmaterials.com
Year Founded: 1959
Sand, Gravel, Brick, Stone & Related Construction Materials Distr & Whslr
N.A.I.C.S.: 423320
Roger Smith Jr. *(Pres)*

SALT RIVER PROJECT

Salt River Materials Group—(Continued)

SALT RIVER PROJECT
1521 N Project Dr, Tempe, AZ 85281
Tel.: (602) 236-8833 AZ
Web Site: http://www.srpnet.com
Year Founded: 1910
Sales Range: $1-4.9 Billion
Emp.: 4,328
Power & Irrigation Services
N.A.I.C.S.: 221118
Steven J. Hulet (Treas)
John F. Sullivan (Deputy Gen Mgr)
John Hoopes (VP)
Alaina Chabrier (Assoc Gen Mgr-Mktg & Comm)
John Felty (Sec)
Mike Hummel (CEO & Gen Mgr)
David Rousseau (Pres)

SALTCHUK RESOURCES INC.
450 Alaskan Way S Ste 708, Seattle, WA 98104
Tel.: (206) 652-1111 AK
Web Site: https://www.saltchuk.com
Year Founded: 1982
Sales Range: $50-74.9 Million
Emp.: 6,600
All Other Support Activities for Transportation
N.A.I.C.S.: 488999
Steve Giese (CFO & Sr VP)
Tim Engle (Pres)
Mark N. Tabbutt (Chm)
Trevor Parris (Treas & VP)
Todd Loomer (Chief Safety Officer & Dir-Ops)
Ed Sullivan (Dir-Maintenance)
Melissa Martinez (Mgr-Payroll)
Jane Moody (Dir-Tax)
Lisa McQueen (Sr Dir-Risk Mgmt)
Colleen Rosas (Sr VP-HR)
Michelle Brown (VP-Tax)
Christopher Coakley (VP-Govt Affairs)
Shannon Girlando (VP & Controller)
Christi Harris (VP-IT)
Anne Preston (Chief Ethics Officer, Gen Counsel & Sr VP)
Paul Stevens (Mng Dir & Sr VP)
Rick Murrell (Mng Dir & Sr VP)

Subsidiaries:

AMNAV Maritime Services (1)
201 Burma Rd, Oakland, CA 94607
Tel.: (510) 834-8847
Web Site: http://www.amnav.com
Emp.: 45
Deep Sea Freight Transportation Services
N.A.I.C.S.: 483111
Brian Dobrzensky (Coord-Ops)
Ted Blanckenburg (Mgr-Sls)

Aloha Air Cargo (1)
50 Elliott St, Honolulu, HI 96819
Web Site: http://www.alohaaircargo.com
Oil Transportation Services
N.A.I.C.S.: 481212
Frank Silva (Dir-Quality & Reliability)

Alta Logistics, Inc. (1)
1407 W 31st Ave Ste 500, Anchorage, AK 99503
Tel.: (866) 961-2582
Web Site: http://www.shipalta.com
Logistics Management Consulting Services
N.A.I.C.S.: 541614

Foss Maritime Co. (1)
660 W Ewing St, Seattle, WA 98119-1529 (100%)
Tel.: (206) 281-3800
Web Site: http://www.foss.com
Sales Range: $10-24.9 Million
Emp.: 100
River & Ocean Transportation
N.A.I.C.S.: 483111
Scott Merritt (Sr VP-Ops)
Ron Costin (Mgr)
John Tirpak (VP-Bus Dev & Contract Svcs-Houston)
Jon Hie (Dir-Shipyard Ops)
Michael Minnig (Dir-Engrg)

Carl Smith (Dir-Sls & Mktg-Fleet Svcs)
Darlene Crowder (VP-HR)
Glenn K. Y. Hong (Sr VP)
Kirstin L. Sandaas (Treas)
Mike Lauer (Dir-Marine Transportation Project Svcs)
John Parrott (Pres & CEO)
Grant Johnson (VP-Health, Safety, Quality & Environment)
Jeff Horst (VP-Sls & Mktg)
Mike Welch (CFO)
Sloane Perras (Chief Ethics Officer, Gen Counsel & VP)

Division (Domestic):

Foss Maritime Co. (2)
9030 NW Saint Helens Rd, Portland, OR 97231-1127
Tel.: (503) 286-0631
Web Site: http://www.fossmaritime.com
River & Ocean Transportation
N.A.I.C.S.: 488999

Hawaiian Tug & Barge (1)
Pier 40 1331 N Nimitz Hwy, Honolulu, HI 96817
Tel.: (808) 543-9311
Web Site: http://www.htbyb.com
Sales Range: $25-49.9 Million
Emp.: 300
Cargo, Tug & Barge Operations
N.A.I.C.S.: 488320
Glenn Hong (Pres)

North Star Petroleum (1)
1177 Fairview Ave N, Seattle, WA 98109
Tel.: (206) 792-0077
Web Site: http://www.nspetroleum.com
Sales Range: $800-899.9 Million
Emp.: 900
Petroleum Distr & Marketer
N.A.I.C.S.: 424720
Brian Bogen (Pres & CEO)

Subsidiary (Domestic):

Delta Western Inc. (2)
420 L St Ste 101, Anchorage, AK 99501
Tel.: (907) 276-2688
Web Site: http://www.deltawestern.com
Petroleum & Petroleum Products Distr
N.A.I.C.S.: 424720
Norma Barco (VP & Controller)

Northern Oilfield Services, Inc. (2)
420 L St Ste 101, Anchorage, AK 99501
Tel.: (907) 659-2840
Web Site: http://www.nosi.com
Sales Range: $100-124.9 Million
Emp.: 36
Petroleum & Petroleum Products Distr
N.A.I.C.S.: 424720
Brad Osborne (Pres)
Rob Chambers (Mgr-Long Haul Trucking Div)

Overseas Shipholding Group, Inc. (1)
302 Knights Run Ave Ste 1200, Tampa, FL 33602
Tel.: (813) 209-0600
Web Site: https://www.osg.com
Rev: $466,800,000
Assets: $1,139,063,000
Liabilities: $799,378,000
Net Worth: $339,685,000
Earnings: $26,564,000
Emp.: 1,023
Fiscal Year-end: 12/31/2022
Crude Oil & Petroleum Transportation Services
N.A.I.C.S.: 483111
Samuel H. Norton (Pres & CEO)
Patrick J. O'Halloran (COO & VP)
Damon M. Mote (Chief Admin Officer & VP)
Richard L. Trueblood (CFO & VP)
Susan Allan (Gen Counsel, Sec & VP)

Subsidiary (Domestic):

Alaska Tanker Company LLC (2)
15220 NW Greenbrier Pkwy Heartwood Bldg Ste 270, Beaverton, OR 97006 (100%)
Tel.: (503) 207-0046
Web Site: https://www.aktanker.com
Emp.: 200
Freight Transportation Arrangement
N.A.I.C.S.: 488510

Clean Products International Ltd. (2)
666 3rd Ave 5th Fl, New York, NY 10017
Tel.: (212) 578-1828
Coastal Freight Transportation Services
N.A.I.C.S.: 483113

Mykonos Tanker LLC (2)
1301 Ave of the Americas, New York, NY 10017
Tel.: (212) 953-4100
Emp.: 15
Freight Transportation Services
N.A.I.C.S.: 483111

OSG America, L.P. (2)
2 Harbour Pl 302 Knights Run Ave Ste 1200, Tampa, FL 33602 (100%)
Tel.: (813) 209-0600
Sales Range: $250-299.9 Million
Emp.: 16
Marine Transportation Services
N.A.I.C.S.: 483114
Morten Arntzen (Pres & CEO)
Eric F. Smith (Chief Comml Officer)

OSG Lightering LLC (2)
10001 Woodloch Forest Dr Ste 608, The Woodlands, TX 77380
Tel.: (281) 445-5000
Crude Oil & Petroleum Transportation Services
N.A.I.C.S.: 483111
Toby King (Mgr-Comml Ops)
Melanie Matthieu (Controller)
Rajiv Mithal (Dir-Comml Dev)

Subsidiary (Non-US):

OSG Ship Management (UK) Ltd. (2)
Moreau House 116 Brompton Road, London, SW3 1JJ, United Kingdom
Tel.: (44) 2075916660
Web Site: http://www.osg.com
Sales Range: $100-124.9 Million
Emp.: 5
Freight Shipping Services
N.A.I.C.S.: 483111

OSG Ship Management Inc. (2)
Tel.: (813) 209-0600
Web Site: https://www.osg.com
Emp.: 50
Freight Transportation Arrangement
N.A.I.C.S.: 483111

OSG Ship Management, Manila Inc. (2)
102 L P Leviste Street Salcedo Village, Makati, 1227, Philippines
Tel.: (63) 23248700
Web Site: http://www.osg.com
Sales Range: $100-124.9 Million
Emp.: 70
Freight Shipping Services
N.A.I.C.S.: 483111

Petromar Limited (2)
32 Tzar Simeon 1st str, Varna, 9000, Bulgaria
Tel.: (359) 52609286
Web Site: http://www.petromar-bg.com
Emp.: 10
Crude Oil & Petroleum Transportation Services
N.A.I.C.S.: 483111
Stephen Elenski (Office Mgr)
Dimitar Simeonov (CEO)
Daniela Jordanova (Mgr-Sls)

Totem Ocean Trailer Express (1)
32001 32nd Ave S, Federal Way, WA 98001 (100%)
Tel.: (253) 449-8100
Web Site: http://www.totemocean.com
Sales Range: $25-49.9 Million
Emp.: 165
Intercoastal Freight Transportation
N.A.I.C.S.: 483113
Robert P. Magee (Chm)
Claudia Roberts (Dir-Govt Svcs)
John Parrott (Pres)
Phil Morrell (VP-Ops)
Anthony Chiarello (Pres & CEO)

Tropical Shipping & Construction Company Limited (1)
5 E 11th St, Riviera Beach, FL 33404-6902
Tel.: (561) 881-3900
Web Site: http://www.tropical.com

U.S. PRIVATE

Sales Range: $500-549.9 Million
Emp.: 1,000
Containerized Freight Shipping Distr
N.A.I.C.S.: 483111
Jorge Martinez (Gen Counsel, Secretary & VP)
Jamie Mahoney (VP-Marine & US Ops)

Young Brothers, Limited (1)
1331 N Nimitz Hwy, Honolulu, HI 96817
Tel.: (808) 543-9311
Web Site: http://www.htbyb.com
Deep Sea Freight Transportation Services
N.A.I.C.S.: 483111

SALTERMITCHELL, INC.
117 S Gadsden St, Tallahassee, FL 32301
Tel.: (850) 681-3200
Web Site: http://www.saltermitchell.com
Sales Range: $1-9.9 Million
Emp.: 30
Public Relations Agencies
N.A.I.C.S.: 541820
April Salter (Pres)
Peter Mitchell (Chm & Chief Creative Officer)
Robert Bailey (Dir-Res)
Christene Jennings (COO)
Karen Ong (Dir-Creative)

SALTMARSH CLEAVELAND & GUND CPAS
900 N 12th Ave, Pensacola, FL 32501
Tel.: (850) 435-8300
Web Site: http://www.saltmarshcpa.com
Year Founded: 1944
Sales Range: $10-24.9 Million
Emp.: 110
Certified Public Accountants
N.A.I.C.S.: 541211
Ron Jackson (Pres)
Greg Storey (Mgr-Audit)

SALTWORKS, INC.
16240 Woodinville Redmond Rd NE, Woodinville, WA 98072
Tel.: (425) 885-7258
Web Site: http://www.saltworks.us
Year Founded: 2002
Sales Range: $10-24.9 Million
Emp.: 30
Premium Grade Salts for the Wholesale, Retail & Consumer Markets
N.A.I.C.S.: 311999
Mark Zoske (CEO)
Naomi Novotny (Pres)
Kristin Brame (Controller)

SALUD INTEGRAL EN LA MONTANA, INC.
PO Box 515, Naranjito, PR 00719
Tel.: (787) 869-5900 PR
Web Site: http://www.simpr.org
Year Founded: 1974
Sales Range: $25-49.9 Million
Emp.: 450
Health Care Srvices
N.A.I.C.S.: 622110
Anabelle Torres (Dir-Ops)
Marien Vazquez (Dir-Medical)
Ada T. Torres (Dir-HR)

SALUD PARA LA GENTE
195 Aviation Way Ste 200, Watsonville, CA 95076
Tel.: (831) 728-8250 CA
Web Site: http://www.splg.org
Year Founded: 1980
Sales Range: $10-24.9 Million
Emp.: 222
Healthcare Services
N.A.I.C.S.: 622110
Dori Rose (CEO)
Faris Sabbah (Vice Chm)

Jorge Reguerin (Treas)
Tony Balistreri (CFO)
Carolyn Brown (Chief Dental Officer)

SALVA O'RENICK
1810 Cherry St, Kansas City, MO 64108
Tel.: (816) 842-6996
Web Site:
http://www.uncommonsense.com
Year Founded: 1996
Sales Range: $1-9.9 Million
Emp.: 27
Advertising Agencies
N.A.I.C.S.: 541810
Dan Salva (Co-Founder, VP & Dir-Creative)
Matt Shaw (Dir-Art)
Mark Shrout (Mng Partner)
Mark O'Renick (Co-Founder & CEO)

SALVADOR DALI MUSEUM, INC.
1 Dali Blvd, Saint Petersburg, FL 33701
Tel.: (727) 823-3767
Web Site: http://www.thedali.org
Sales Range: $10-24.9 Million
Emp.: 30
Museum & Art Gallery
N.A.I.C.S.: 712110
Hank Hine (Exec Dir)
Kathy White (Dir-Mktg)
Carol Ann Martin (CFO)

SALVADORAN AMERICAN HUMANITARIAN FOUNDATION
2050 Coral Way Ste 600, Miami, FL 33145
Tel.: (305) 860-0300   FL
Web Site: http://www.sahf.org
Year Founded: 1983
Sales Range: $10-24.9 Million
Emp.: 4
Social Advocacy Organization
N.A.I.C.S.: 813319
Loli Sangiovanni (Dir-Donor Rels)
Carlos R. Reyes (Exec Dir)

SALVADORE AUTO EXCHANGE INC.
442 W Broadway, Gardner, MA 01440
Tel.: (978) 630-2000
Web Site:
http://www.salvadoreauto.com
Sales Range: $10-24.9 Million
Emp.: 72
Used Car Sales
N.A.I.C.S.: 441120
Angelo Salvadore (Pres)

SALVADORE AUTO GROUP
442 W Broadway, Gardner, MA 01440-3110
Tel.: (978) 630-2000
Web Site:
http://www.salvadoreauto.com
Year Founded: 1990
Sales Range: $10-24.9 Million
Emp.: 68
Car Whslr
N.A.I.C.S.: 441110
Steven Salvadore (Gen Mgr)

SALVADORE TOOL & FINDINGS, INC.
24 Althea St, Providence, RI 02907-2802
Tel.: (401) 272-4100
Web Site:
http://www.salvadoretool.com
Jewelry & Silverware Mfr
N.A.I.C.S.: 339910
David Salvadore (Pres)

SALVO TECHNOLOGIES, INC.
8060 Bryan Dairy Rd, Largo, FL 33777
Tel.: (727) 544-3736
Web Site:
http://www.salvotechnologies.com
Holding Company; Security & Defense, Medical, Industrial, Semiconductor, Commercial & Science & Technology Products Mfr
N.A.I.C.S.: 551112
Hugh Garvey (Dir-Imaging & Sensing)

Subsidiaries:

Spectrecology, LLC   (1)
8060 Bryan Dairy Rd, Seminole, FL 33777
Tel.: (727) 510-6848
Web Site: http://www.spectrecology.com
Analytical Laboratory Instrument Mfr
N.A.I.C.S.: 334516
Mike Morris (Founder & Pres)

SALYER LAND COMPANY
210 Oregon Ave, Corcoran, CA 93212
Tel.: (559) 992-2131
Web Site: http://www.gemequip.com
Sales Range: $10-24.9 Million
Emp.: 6
Farm Implements
N.A.I.C.S.: 423820
Fred Salyer (Pres)
Linda Ptacek (Sec)
Steve Tompkins (VP)

SALZINGER LLC.
2 Overhill Rd Ste 400, Scarsdale, NY 10583
Tel.: (914) 358-3562
Web Site: http://www.salzinger.com
Year Founded: 2007
Sales Range: $1-9.9 Million
Emp.: 18
Business Management Consulting Services
N.A.I.C.S.: 541618
Steve Salzinger (Pres)

SAM ASH MUSIC CORPORATION
278 Duffy Ave, Hicksville, NY 11801-3605
Tel.: (516) 932-6400   NY
Web Site:
http://www.samashmusic.com
Year Founded: 1924
Sales Range: $400-449.9 Million
Emp.: 1,600
Music Instrument & Sound Equipment Retail Stores
N.A.I.C.S.: 459140
Richard S. Ash (CEO)
Howard Mendelson (Exec VP)
Mike Bentivegna (Asst Mgr-Woodworking)
Pedro Berischa (Mgr-Sls)

SAM BROUSSARD TRUCKING COMPANY INC.
2014 Jane St, New Iberia, LA 70562
Tel.: (337) 369-6011
Rev.: $10,371,606
Emp.: 7
Trucking Service
N.A.I.C.S.: 484110
Samuel S. Broussard Jr. (Pres)

SAM CLAR OFFICE FURNITURE, INC.
1221 Diamond Way, Concord, CA 94520
Tel.: (925) 602-3900   CA
Web Site: http://www.samclar.com
Year Founded: 1996
Rev.: $15,000,000
Emp.: 20

Office Furniture
N.A.I.C.S.: 449110
Jeffrey Schwartz (CEO)

SAM GALLOWAY FORD, INC.
1800 Boy Scout Dr, Fort Myers, FL 33907-2113
Tel.: (239) 936-3673
Web Site:
http://www.samgallowayford.com
Sales Range: $75-99.9 Million
Emp.: 380
Car Whslr
N.A.I.C.S.: 441110
Jerry Toney (COO)
Robert Galloway (Gen Mgr)
Sam Galloway Jr. (Pres)

SAM HOUSTON ELECTRIC CO-OPERATIVE INC.
1157 E Church St, Livingston, TX 77351-3334
Tel.: (936) 327-5711
Web Site: http://www.samhouston.net
Year Founded: 1939
Sales Range: $25-49.9 Million
Emp.: 150
Electronic Services
N.A.I.C.S.: 221118
Kyle Kuntz (CEO)
David Babcock (COO)
Charlie Palmer (Mgr-Ops)
Molly Gray (Mgr-Acctg)
Keith Stapleton (Chief Comm Officer)
Bill Townley (Mgr-Construction)
Joe Conner (CFO)

SAM HOUSTON RACE PARK LLC
7575 N Sam Houston Pkwy W, Houston, TX 77064
Tel.: (281) 807-8700
Web Site: http://www.shrp.com
Year Founded: 1994
Horse Racing Venue
N.A.I.C.S.: 711219
Andrea Young (Pres & CEO)

SAM KANE BEEF PROCESSORS, INC.
9001 Leopard St, Corpus Christi, TX 78469
Tel.: (361) 241-5000   TX
Web Site:
http://www.samkanebeef.com
Year Founded: 1949
Beef Processing Services
N.A.I.C.S.: 311611

SAM LEMAN CHRYSLER-JEEP-DODGE OF PEORIA
1801 W Pioneer Pkwy, Peoria, IL 61615-1948
Tel.: (309) 692-1801
Sales Range: $10-24.9 Million
Emp.: 65
Car Whslr
N.A.I.C.S.: 441110
Ben Leman (Owner)
Rick Pontnack (Gen Mgr)
Tom Schupp (Mgr-Ops)

SAM LEMAN CHRYSLER-PLYMOUTH-DODGE
200 E Courtland st, Morton, IL 61550
Tel.: (309) 263-2345
Web Site:
http://www.samlemanmorton.com
Rev.: $19,300,000
Emp.: 55
Automobiles, New & Used
N.A.I.C.S.: 441110
Tom Bauer (Gen Mgr-Sls)

SAM LEVITZ FURNITURE COMPANY
3430 E 36th St, Tucson, AZ 85713
Tel.: (520) 624-7443
Web Site: http://www.samlevitz.com
Sales Range: $50-74.9 Million
Emp.: 600
Furniture Retailer
N.A.I.C.S.: 449110
Sam R. Levitz (Pres)
Eric Creson (VP)
Francisco Orozco (Mgr-Inventory Control)
Stan Holmes (Mgr-Distr)

SAM LINDER, INC.
300 Auto Center Cir, Salinas, CA 93907
Tel.: (831) 424-1500
Web Site: http://www.samlinder.com
Rev.: $27,000,000
Emp.: 61
New & Used Automobile Dealer
N.A.I.C.S.: 441110
Sam Linder (Owner)
Carol Yates (Controller)

SAM M. BUTLER INC.
17900 Dana Rd, Laurinburg, NC 28352
Tel.: (704) 365-3005
Web Site:
http://www.servicethread.com
Year Founded: 1950
Sales Range: $10-24.9 Million
Emp.: 120
Fiscal Year-end: 11/30/14
Sewing Thread
N.A.I.C.S.: 424310
Jay Todd (CEO)
Neal Fournier (Mgr-Facilities & Maintenance)
Wayne Jackson (Mgr-Pur & Materials)
Eric Shippee (Mgr-Technical & R&D)
Sam M. Butler III (Chm)

SAM MEDICAL PRODUCTS
27350 SW 95th Ave Ste 3038, Wilsonville, OR 97070
Tel.: (503) 639-5474
Web Site:
http://www.sammedical.com
Year Founded: 1985
Rev.: $6,600,000
Emp.: 33
Surgical Appliance & Supplies Mfr
N.A.I.C.S.: 339113
Jan Owens (CFO)
Cherrie Scheinberg (Co-Founder)
Sam Scheinberg (Co-Founder & CEO)
Debbie Walker (Controller-HR)
Lance Hopman (Dir-R&D)

SAM MEYERS INC.
3400 Bashford Ave, Louisville, KY 40218
Tel.: (502) 459-4885
Web Site:
http://www.sammeyers.com
Rev.: $12,000,000
Emp.: 250
Dry Cleaning Services
N.A.I.C.S.: 812320
James Corbett (Pres)
Pat Corbett (Owner)

SAM PACK'S FIVE STAR FORD
1635 S I 35, Carrollton, TX 75006-7415
Tel.: (972) 242-6415
Web Site: http://www.spford.com
Year Founded: 1957
Sales Range: $25-49.9 Million
Emp.: 180
New Car Whslr
N.A.I.C.S.: 441110

SAM PACK'S FIVE STAR FORD

Sam Pack's Five Star Ford—(Continued)
Trey Russell *(Gen Mgr)*

SAM PIEVAC COMPANY INC.
13975 Monte Vista Ave, Chino, CA 91710
Tel.: (562) 404-5590
Web Site:
http://www.sampievaccompany.com
Sales Range: $10-24.9 Million
Emp.: 25
Store Fixtures
N.A.I.C.S.: 423440
Sam Scott Pievac *(Chm & CEO)*
John Meller *(Pres-SPC China)*

SAM RODGERS PROPERTIES, INC.
825 Honey Flower Loop, Bradenton, FL 34212
Tel.: (941) 896-4813   FL
Web Site:
http://www.samrodgershomes.com
Year Founded: 1991
Sales Range: $1-9.9 Million
Emp.: 20
New Single-Family Housing Construction
N.A.I.C.S.: 236115
Mary Rodgers *(Treas & Sec)*
Sam Rodgers *(Pres)*

SAM SCHWARTZ ENGINEERING D.P.C.
322 8th Ave 5th Fl, New York, NY 10001
Tel.: (212) 598-9010
Web Site:
http://www.samschwartz.com
Year Founded: 1995
Rev.: $8,300,000
Emp.: 100
Engineeering Services
N.A.I.C.S.: 541330
Amir Siddiqui *(Dir-Construction Engrg Inspection)*
Harris Schechtman *(Dir-Transit-Natl)*
Jeffrey D. Trim *(COO & Exec VP)*
Sam Schwartz *(Founder, Pres & CEO)*
Alfred Meyer *(Gen Mgr-New Jersey)*
Richard Retting *(Dir-Safety & Res & Gen Mgr-Washington)*
James R. Brown *(Principal & Dir-Environmental Plng)*
Joe Iacobucci *(Dir-Transit-Chicago)*
Michael Flynn *(Dir-City Strategies)*
Daniel Schack *(Dir-Plng)*
Jeffrey Smithline *(Dir-Traffic Engrg)*
Joan Verbon *(CFO)*
Stacey Meekins *(Principal & Dir-Transportation Plng)*
Nanette H. Bourne *(Principal)*
Frederick Wedley *(Principal & Dir-Transit & Rail-Natl)*
Greg Del Rio *(Principal & Dir-Special Projects)*

SAM SWOPE VOLKSWAGEN OF CLARKSVILLE
406 E Lewis & Clark Pkwy, Clarksville, IN 47129
Tel.: (812) 948-1541
Web Site:
http://www.samswopevolkswagen.com
Sales Range: $10-24.9 Million
Emp.: 100
Car Whslr
N.A.I.C.S.: 441110
Greg Brown *(Pres & CEO)*

SAM YODER & SON, LLC.
9387 Memory Rd, Greenwood, DE 19950
Tel.: (302) 398-4711
Web Site: http://www.samyoder.com
Year Founded: 1975
Sales Range: $10-24.9 Million
Emp.: 114
Truss Mfr
N.A.I.C.S.: 321215
Samual J. Yoder *(CEO)*

SAM, INC.
4801 SW Pkwy Bldg 2 Ste 100, Austin, TX 78735
Tel.: (512) 447-0575
Web Site: http://www.saminc.biz
Year Founded: 1970
Sales Range: $25-49.9 Million
Emp.: 700
Surveying & Mapping Services
N.A.I.C.S.: 541360

SAMARA BROTHERS LLC
34 W 33rd St Ste 1216, New York, NY 10001
Tel.: (212) 695-0210
Sales Range: $25-49.9 Million
Emp.: 35
Women's & Children's Clothing
N.A.I.C.S.: 424350
Don Gaffney *(Pres)*

SAMARITAN BEHAVIORAL HEALTH, INC.
601 Edwin C Moses Blvd Elizabeth Pl 4th Fl, Dayton, OH 45417
Tel.: (937) 734-8333   OH
Web Site: http://www.sbhihelp.org
Year Founded: 2002
Sales Range: $10-24.9 Million
Emp.: 229
Behavioral Healthcare Services
N.A.I.C.S.: 623220
Brien Dyer *(Dir-Medical)*
Beth Esposito *(Pres & CEO)*

SAMARITAN CENTER
215 N State St, Syracuse, NY 13203
Tel.: (315) 472-0650   NY
Web Site: http://www.samcenter.org
Year Founded: 1990
Sales Range: Less than $1 Million
Emp.: 8
Emergency Food Services
N.A.I.C.S.: 624210
Craig Breed *(Treas)*
Karen Belgrader *(Dir-Dev)*
Mary Beth Frey *(Exec Dir)*
Maryanne Grady *(Office Mgr)*
Craig Breed *(Treas)*
Karen Belgrader *(Dir-Dev)*
Mary Beth Frey *(Exec Dir)*
Maryanne Grady *(Office Mgr)*
Peter Derrenbacker *(Pres)*
John Sindoni *(VP)*
Stuart Wright *(Sec)*
Craig Zellar *(Treas)*
James R. Miller Jr. *(Pres)*

SAMARITAN HEALTH SERVICES, INC.
PO Box 3000, Corvallis, OR 97339-3000
Tel.: (541) 768-4773   OR
Web Site: http://www.samhealth.org
Year Founded: 1986
Sales Range: $150-199.9 Million
Emp.: 937
Health Care Srvices
N.A.I.C.S.: 622110
Daniel B. Smith *(CFO)*
Julie Manning *(VP-Dev, Mktg & PR)*
Annette Clovis *(Dir-Corp Dev)*
Doug Boysen *(Pres & CEO)*

SAMARITAN HEALTHCARE & HOSPICE
5 Eves Dr Ste 300, Marlton, NJ 08053
Tel.: (856) 596-1600   NJ
Web Site: http://www.samaritannj.org
Year Founded: 1980
Sales Range: $25-49.9 Million
Emp.: 375
Hospice Care Services
N.A.I.C.S.: 621610
Mary Ann Boccolini *(Pres & CEO)*
Stephen Goldfine *(Chief Medical Officer)*
Marjorie Ivins *(COO)*
T. Christian Rollins *(Chief Dev Officer)*
Mary M. Finn *(CFO)*
Jewelle Sutherland *(Vice Chm)*
John C. Gillespie *(Chm)*
Lee Sheilds *(Treas)*
Orsula V. Knowlton *(Sec)*
Susan Baratta *(Mgr-Clinical)*
Susan McCann *(VP-HR)*
Joanne Rosen *(VP-Mktg & Pub Affairs)*

SAMARITAN REGIONAL HEALTH SYSTEM
1025 Center St, Ashland, OH 44805
Tel.: (419) 289-0491   OH
Web Site:
http://www.uhsamaritanmedicalcenter.org
Year Founded: 1910
Sales Range: $75-99.9 Million
Emp.: 638
Health Care Srvices
N.A.I.C.S.: 622110
Phil Myers *(VP-Medical Affairs)*
Alyce Legg *(VP-Resource Dev)*
Chris Hunt *(VP-Clinical Svcs)*
Karin Schwan *(Chief Nursing Officer)*
Ron Manchester *(VP-Support Svcs)*
Danny Boggs *(Pres & CEO)*
Anne Beer *(Sec)*
Roger Snyder *(VP)*

SAMARITANS FEET INTERNATIONAL
1836 Ctr Park Dr, Charlotte, NC 28217
Tel.: (704) 341-1630   NC
Web Site:
http://www.samaritansfeet.org
Year Founded: 2003
Sales Range: $10-24.9 Million
Emp.: 21
Poor & Needy People Shoe Distribution Services
N.A.I.C.S.: 813410
Wes Cruickshank *(Dir-IT)*
Teresa Hucko *(Dir-Missions & Volunteer Rels)*
Graham Gibbs *(Dir-Dev-Corp & Donor Rels)*
Bruce Bodman *(Dir-Logistics & Supply Chain)*
Emmanuel Ohonme *(Co-Founder & Pres)*

SAMBA FEDERAL EMPLOYEE BENEFIT ASSOCIATION
11301 Old Georgetown Rd, Rockville, MD 20852
Tel.: (301) 984-1440
Web Site: http://www.sambaplans.com
Rev.: $108,479,902
Emp.: 40
Insurance Services
N.A.I.C.S.: 524210

SAMBA TV, INC.
118 King St, San Francisco, CA 94107
Tel.: (415) 400-5750   DE
Web Site: https://www.samba.tv

Year Founded: 2008
Rev.: $106,831,000
Assets: $67,973,000
Liabilities: $98,202,000
Net Worth: ($30,229,000)
Earnings: ($7,561,000)
Emp.: 262
Fiscal Year-end: 12/31/20
Software Development Services
N.A.I.C.S.: 541511
Ashwin Navin *(Co-Founder, Chm & CEO)*
Michael Farrow *(CFO)*
Alvir Navin *(Co-Founder & COO)*
Charley Lanusse *(CTO)*
Maulik Shah *(Gen Counsel)*
Tom Parsons *(Head-Client & Data Partnerships-Australia)*
Damien Tang *(Dir-Data Solutions-Australia)*
Yasmin Sanders *(Mng Dir-Australia)*

SAMBAZON, INC.
209 Avenida Fabricante Ste 200, San Clemente, CA 92672
Tel.: (949) 498-8618   CA
Web Site: http://www.sambazon.com
Year Founded: 2000
Sales Range: $10-24.9 Million
Emp.: 150
Nutraceutical Mfr
N.A.I.C.S.: 325412
Ryan Black *(Founder & CEO)*

Subsidiaries:

Sambazon Brazil   (1)
Rua Jardim Botanico 674 Sala 503, 22461 000, Rio de Janeiro, Brazil   (100%)
Tel.: (55) 2122392246
Web Site: http://www.sambazon.com.br
Sales Range: $10-24.9 Million
Emp.: 6
Exporter & Mfr of Health Supplements & Beverages
N.A.I.C.S.: 456191
Guilhernt Moraes *(Gen Mgr)*

SAMBE CONSTRUCTION COMPANY
1650 Hilton Rd, Pennsauken, NJ 08110
Tel.: (856) 663-7751
Web Site: http://www.sambe.net
Sales Range: $10-24.9 Million
Emp.: 15
Custom Builders, Non-Residential
N.A.I.C.S.: 236220
Betty Girlya *(Pres)*
Yan Girlya *(Gen Mgr)*

SAMBRAILO PACKAGING INC.
800 Walker St, Watsonville, CA 95076
Tel.: (831) 724-7581
Web Site: http://www.sambrailo.com
Sales Range: $25-49.9 Million
Emp.: 40
Plastics Materials & Basic Shapes
N.A.I.C.S.: 424610
Mark Sambrailo *(Mgr-Innovations)*
Jeff Peret *(Mgr-Logistic)*
Jennifer Evans *(Mgr-Mktg)*
Juana Ramirez *(Mgr-Sls)*
Neil Bowles *(Acct Mgr)*
Rachel Montoya *(Controller-Fin)*
Scott Gray *(Mgr-IT)*
Tom Byrne *(VP & Gen Mgr)*

SAMES MOTOR CO., INC.
6001 San Dario Ave, Laredo, TX 78041
Tel.: (956) 721-4700   TX
Web Site: http://www.samesauto.com
Year Founded: 1910
Sales Range: $125-149.9 Million
Emp.: 250
Automobiles, New & Used
N.A.I.C.S.: 441110
Laure Gutierrez *(Controller)*
Javier Gonzalez *(Dir-Fixed Ops)*

COMPANIES

Ana Rivera-Soto *(Dir-Mktg & Adv)*
Gerardo Resendez *(Dir-Used Car)*
Elsa Gobar *(Office Mgr)*
Harry E. Sames III *(Pres)*

Subsidiaries:

Sames Ford - Chorpus Christi (1)
4721 Ayers Rd, Corpus Christi, TX 78415
Tel.: (361) 851-7600
Web Site: http://www.samesfordcc.com
Sales Range: $75-99.9 Million
Emp.: 136
New & Used Car Dealer
N.A.I.C.S.: 441110
Chris Huerta *(Mgr-Sls)*

Sames Red Barn Motors (1)
620 W Slaughter Ln, Austin, TX 78748
Tel.: (512) 628-0500
Web Site: http://www.samesrbm.com
Sales Range: $10-24.9 Million
New & Used Car Dealer
N.A.I.C.S.: 441110

SAMET CORPORATION
309 Gallimore Dairy Rd, Greensboro, NC 27409-9724
Tel.: (336) 544-2600 NC
Web Site: http://www.sametcorp.com
Year Founded: 1961
Sales Range: $50-74.9 Million
Emp.: 100
Industrial Buildings & Warehouses
N.A.I.C.S.: 236220
Norman G. Samet *(Founder, Chm & Treas)*
J. Patterson *(VP-Ops)*
Derek Lanning *(Dir-Preconstruction Svcs)*
Rick Davenport *(Pres-Construction)*

SAMINCO, INC.
10030 Amberwood Rd, Fort Myers, FL 33913
Tel.: (239) 561-1561 FL
Web Site: http://www.samincoinc.com
Year Founded: 1992
Sales Range: $25-49.9 Million
Emp.: 80
High Power AC & DC Motor Control Products Mfr
N.A.I.C.S.: 335314
Bonne W. Posma *(CEO)*
Tim Grimm *(Gen Mgr-Ops)*
Philippe Maillard *(Mgr-Quality Assurance & Sys Validation Engr)*
Jon Anderson *(Mng Dir-RSA & VP-Lavallette Ops-US)*
Laura Staub *(Coord-Sls & Production)*
Rick Ferrell *(VP-Mining, Sls & Svc)*
Juan Pinzon *(VP-Intl Product Dev)*
Mervin Quirk *(Mng Dir-RSA)*

SAMMONS ENTERPRISES, INC.
5949 Sherry Ln Ste 1900, Dallas, TX 75225-8015
Tel.: (214) 210-5000 DE
Web Site: https://www.sammonsenterprises.com
Year Founded: 1938
Sales Range: $75-99.9 Million
Emp.: 6,020
Offices of Bank Holding Companies
N.A.I.C.S.: 551111
Pam Doeppe *(CFO & VP)*
Derek Claybrook *(CFO-Briggs Intl)*
Darron K. Ash *(CEO & Sr VP)*
Esfand E. Dinshaw *(Pres)*
Cheryl Gosch *(Gen Counsel, Sec & VP)*
Thomas J. Corcoran Jr. *(Chm)*

Subsidiaries:

Briggs International, Inc. (1)
10540 N Stemmons Frwy, Dallas, TX 75220
Tel.: (214) 630-0808
Web Site: https://briggssi.com
Holding Company; Materials Handling Equipment Rental, Sales & Maintenance Services
N.A.I.C.S.: 551112
Mike Winemiller *(CEO)*

Subsidiary (Non-US):

Briggs Equipment S.A. de C.V. (2)
Calle Rio San Javier No 16 Industrial de Atizapan, Atizapan, Mexico, 52940, Mexico
Tel.: (52) 55 1106 0300
Web Site: http://www.briggsequipment.com.mx
Emp.: 80
Material Handling Equipment Distr
N.A.I.C.S.: 423830
Alejandro Rocha *(Mgr)*

Briggs Equipment UK Limited (2)
Material Handling Division Orbital 7 Orbital Way, Cannock, WS11 8XW, Staffs, United Kingdom
Tel.: (44) 1543437800
Web Site: http://www.briggsequipment.co.uk
Sales Range: $300-349.9 Million
Emp.: 1,000
Material Handling Equipment Rental Sale & Maintenance Services
N.A.I.C.S.: 532490
Peter Jones *(Mng Dir)*

Division (Domestic):

Briggs Equipment UK Limited (3)
Unit G Cumbernauld Business Park, Wardlaw Road South, Cumbernauld, G67 3JZ, Glasgow, United Kingdom (100%)
Tel.: (44) 1236725061
Web Site: http://www.briggsequipment.co.uk
Sales Range: $25-49.9 Million
Emp.: 120
Lift Truck & Industrial Equipment Distributor
N.A.I.C.S.: 532490

Subsidiary (Domestic):

Briggs Equipment, Inc. (2)
10540 N Stemmons Fwy, Dallas, TX 75220-2425 (100%)
Tel.: (214) 630-0808
Web Site: http://www.briggsequipment.com
Sales Range: $150-199.9 Million
Emp.: 663
Materials Handling Equipment Rental, Sales & Maintenance Services
N.A.I.C.S.: 532490
Reid Wilson *(Dir-HR)*

Compatriot Capital, Inc. (1)
5949 Sherry Ln Ste 1900, Dallas, TX 75225 (100%)
Tel.: (214) 210-5015
Privater Equity Firm
N.A.I.C.S.: 523999
Heather Kreager *(Chm)*
Mark Van Kirk *(Pres)*

Sammons Corporation (1)
5949 Sherry Ln Ste 1900, Dallas, TX 75225
Tel.: (214) 210-5000
Web Site: http://www.sammonsenterprises.com
Sales Range: $25-49.9 Million
Emp.: 34
Business Support Services
N.A.I.C.S.: 561499
Cheryl M. Gosch *(Gen Counsel)*
Pam Doeppe *(CFO)*

Sammons Financial Group, Inc. (1)
4350 Westown Pkwy, West Des Moines, IA 50266
Tel.: (877) 586-0240
Web Site: http://www.sammonsfinancialgroup.com
Holding Company; Financial & Insurance Products & Services
N.A.I.C.S.: 551112
Esfand E. Dinshaw *(CEO)*
Kelly Coomer *(CIO & Sr VP)*
Teri Ross *(Pres-Shared Svcs)*
Amy Rider *(VP-Strategic Risk & Mortality Mgmt)*
Jeremy Bill *(VP-Product Dev)*
Jai Kuchimanchi *(CTO & VP)*
Seth Nailor *(VP-Agency Svcs)*
Mike Pietig *(VP-Annuity & Suitability Ops)*
Jackie Cockrum *(VP-Admin)*
Nick Nelson *(VP-Centralized Svcs)*
Rick King *(VP-Strategy, Change Mgmt & Continuous Process Improvement)*
Hillary Carlson *(Mgr-External Comm)*
John Melvin *(Chief Investment Officer & Sr VP)*
Susan Osweiler *(VP-Fin Strategy)*
Don Lyons *(CFO & Sr VP)*

Subsidiary (Domestic):

Beacon Capital Management, Inc. (2)
7777 Washington Village Dr Ste 280, Dayton, OH 45459
Web Site: http://www.beaconinvesting.com
Investment Advice
N.A.I.C.S.: 523940
Chris Cook *(Pres & Chief Investment Officer)*

Midland National Life Insurance Co. (2)
1 Sammons Plz, Sioux Falls, SD 57193-0001 (100%)
Tel.: (605) 335-5700
Web Site: http://www.mnlife.com
Sales Range: $500-549.9 Million
Emp.: 450
Life Insurance & Annuity Products & Services
N.A.I.C.S.: 524113
Steven C. Palmitier *(Pres & COO)*

Group (Domestic):

Sammons Annuity Group (3)
4350 Westown Pkwy, West Des Moines, IA 50266
Tel.: (877) 586-0240
Annuity Products & Services
N.A.I.C.S.: 525190
Cindy K. Reed *(Pres)*
Lori Bochner *(VP-Mktg)*
Heath Williams *(Second VP-IT & Bus Sys Officer)*
Mike Yanacheak *(Second VP-Annuity Product Dev)*
Ann Hughes *(Chief Distr Officer & VP)*

Subsidiary (Domestic):

North American Company for Life & Health Insurance (2)
525 W Van Buren St, Chicago, IL 60607
Tel.: (312) 648-7600
Web Site: http://www.nacolah.com
Life & Health Insurance Products & Services
N.A.I.C.S.: 524128
Steven C. Palmitier *(Pres & COO)*
Michael Martin *(VP-Reg Sls)*
Garth A. Garlock *(Chief Distr Officer & Sr VP)*
John Myers *(Assoc VP-Corp Comm)*
Scott Westfall-Voorvaart *(Reg VP-Sls)*

Sammons Retirement Solutions, Inc. (2)
4350 Westtown Pkwy, West Des Moines, IA 50266
Tel.: (515) 273-5694
Insurance & Financial Management Services
N.A.I.C.S.: 541611
Stacy Mercer *(Dir-Mktg & Strategic Initiatives)*

Sammons Securities Company, LLC (2)
300 Parkland Plz, Ann Arbor, MI 48103
Tel.: (734) 663-1611
Securities Brokerage & Dealing Services
N.A.I.C.S.: 523150

SAMMONS TRUCKING, INC.
3665 W Broadway St, Missoula, MT 59808-5676
Tel.: (406) 728-2600 MT
Web Site: http://www.sammonstrucking.com
Year Founded: 1976
Sales Range: $50-74.9 Million
Emp.: 90
Trucking Service
N.A.I.C.S.: 484121

Scott Palmer *(Pres)*

SAMON'S TIGER STORES INC.
2511 Monroe St NE, Albuquerque, NM 87110
Tel.: (505) 884-4615
Year Founded: 1972
Sales Range: $25-49.9 Million
Emp.: 110
Electrical Construction Materials Sales
N.A.I.C.S.: 444180
Lloyd F. Goatcher *(Pres)*
Larry Goatcher *(Sr VP)*
Jay Goatcher *(VP)*

SAMPCO INC.
651 W Washington Blvd Ste 300, Chicago, IL 60661
Tel.: (312) 346-1506
Web Site: http://www.sampcoinc.com
Year Founded: 1963
Sales Range: $10-24.9 Million
Emp.: 20
Meat Brokers
N.A.I.C.S.: 424470
Jeffrey Podell *(VP-Sls-United States)*
Leticia Abonce *(Coord-Document)*
Mary Geiersbach *(Acct Mgr)*
Jim Cunningham *(Pres-JBS Pet Product-North America)*
Pedro Beloto *(Dir-Tech Mktg)*

SAMPCO INC.
56 Downing Pkwy, Pittsfield, MA 01201
Tel.: (413) 442-4043
Web Site: http://www.sampco.com
Sales Range: $10-24.9 Million
Emp.: 125
Building Materials Marketing Samples
N.A.I.C.S.: 561499
Michael O. Ryan *(Founder)*

Subsidiaries:

Sampco of Texas, Inc. (1)
675 Grisby Way, Cedar Hill, TX 75104
Tel.: (972) 291-0017
Web Site: http://www.sampco.com
Sales Range: $10-24.9 Million
Emp.: 85
Industrial Materials Marketing Samples
N.A.I.C.S.: 423990
Joe Mcdonald *(Plant Mgr)*

Southern Sample Company (1)
1765 Hodgeville Rd, Rincon, GA 31326
Tel.: (912) 728-3179
Web Site: http://www.sampco.com
Rev.: $1,500,000
Emp.: 34
Industrial Materials Marketing Samples
N.A.I.C.S.: 327120

Vision Products Inc (1)
460 Nixon Ave Ste 100, Cheswick, PA 15024
Tel.: (724) 274-0767
Web Site: http://www.visionprod.com
Building Materials Distr
N.A.I.C.S.: 423390

SAMPSON CONSTRUCTION CO. INC.
3730 S 14th St, Lincoln, NE 68502
Tel.: (402) 434-5450
Web Site: http://www.sampson-construction.com
Sales Range: $10-24.9 Million
Emp.: 275
Industrial Building Construction
N.A.I.C.S.: 236210
John Sampson *(Pres)*
Brian Grimes *(Project Mgr)*
Joe Buelt *(Superintendent)*
Cori S. Vokoun *(VP)*

SAMPSON LUMBER CO. INC.
181 Mattakeesett St, Pembroke, MA 02359
Tel.: (781) 294-8033

SAMPSON LUMBER CO. INC.

Sampson Lumber Co. Inc.—(Continued)
Sales Range: $10-24.9 Million
Emp.: 28
Lumber & Other Building Materials Distributors
N.A.I.C.S.: 423310

SAMPSON-BLADEN OIL CO. INC.
510 Commerce St, Clinton, NC 28328
Tel.: (910) 592-4177 — NC
Web Site: http://www.sboil.com
Year Founded: 1936
Petroleum Bulk Stations & Terminals
N.A.I.C.S.: 424710
Heather Warren *(Dir-Adv & PR)*
James Spearman *(Mgr)*
Haddon Clark *(Pres)*

Subsidiaries:

Rusher Oil Co., Inc. (1)
2203 Executive Dr, Salisbury, NC 28147
Tel.: (704) 633-3211
Rev: $6,300,000
Emp.: 22
Petroleum & Petroleum Products Merchant Whslr
N.A.I.C.S.: 424720
Bob Rusher *(VP)*

SAMSARA VISION, INC.
27 Rte 202 Ste 8 & 9, Far Hills, NJ 07931
Tel.: (408) 872-9393 — DE
Web Site: https://www.samsaravision.com
Year Founded: 2015
Rev: $39,000
Assets: $3,665,000
Liabilities: $15,248,000
Net Worth: ($11,583,000)
Earnings: ($8,176,000)
Emp.: 22
Fiscal Year-end: 12/31/21
Medical Device Mfr & Distr
N.A.I.C.S.: 339112
Thomas Ruggia *(Pres & CEO)*
Joshua Fox *(CFO)*
Eli Aharoni *(VP-Research & Development & Gen Mgr)*
Mike Besserman *(VP)*

SAMSILL, INC.
5740 Hartman Rd, Fort Worth, TX 76119-6234
Tel.: (817) 536-1906 — TX
Web Site: http://www.samsill.com
Year Founded: 1953
Sales Range: $200-249.9 Million
Emp.: 350
Mfr of Plastic Products, Business Accessories, Binders & Sheet Protectors
N.A.I.C.S.: 316990
James R. Bankes *(Pres & CEO)*

SAMSON BRANDS LLC
95 Golden Hill Rd, Danbury, CT 06811
Tel.: (203) 748-9966
Web Site: http://www.samsonbrands.com
Year Founded: 1998
Sales Range: $1-9.9 Million
Emp.: 9
Juicer Appliances
N.A.I.C.S.: 335210
Brian McCrudden *(Pres)*

SAMSON ENERGY COMPANY, LLC
110 W 7th St Ste 2000, Tulsa, OK 74119
Tel.: (918) 879-0279 — DE
Web Site: http://www.samsonco.com
Year Founded: 2011
Crude Petroleum & Natural Gas Exploration & Extraction
N.A.I.C.S.: 211120
Mark Lauer *(Dir-Legal)*
Stacy Schusterman *(Chm)*
Rene Richard *(CEO)*
C. Philip Tholen *(CFO)*
Keith St. Gemme *(Sr VP-New Ventures)*
Drew S. Phillips *(VP-Acctg)*
Andy Sandberg *(VP-Deepwater GOM)*

SAMSON MANAGEMENT CORP.
97-77 Queens Blvd, Rego Park, NY 11374-3317
Tel.: (718) 830-0131
Web Site: http://www.samsonmanagement.com
Year Founded: 1964
Sales Range: $25-49.9 Million
Emp.: 300
Real Estate Sales & Management Services
N.A.I.C.S.: 531210
Nancy Caleca *(Controller)*
Nicholas Piccinini *(CFO)*

SAMTEC, INC.
520 Park E Blvd, New Albany, IN 47150
Tel.: (812) 944-6733 — IN
Web Site: https://www.samtec.com
Year Founded: 1976
Emp.: 7,500
Mfr of Electronic Connectors
N.A.I.C.S.: 334419
Lori Hillegas *(Asst Controller)*
Mark Baumann *(Mgr-Supply Chain)*
Julie Cook *(Mgr-HR)*

Subsidiaries:

Samtec Asia Pacific Pte Ltd. (1)
1 Kallang Sector 05-01/02 Kolam Ayer Industrial Park, Singapore, 349276, Singapore
Tel.: (65) 6745 5955
Web Site: http://www.samtec.com
Emp.: 30
Electronic Parts Distr
N.A.I.C.S.: 423690
Cing V. Ng *(Gen Mgr)*

Samtec France (1)
Val d Europe Park 11 Rue du Courtalin Batiment B, 77700, Magny-les-Hameaux, France
Tel.: (33) 1 60 95 06 60
Web Site: http://www.samtec.com
Emp.: 12
Electronic Parts Distr
N.A.I.C.S.: 423690

Samtec Hong Kong Limited (1)
Room 18 13/F Shatin Galleria 18-24 Shan Mei Street, Fo Tan, Sha Tin, Shatin, China (Hong Kong)
Tel.: (852) 26904858
Web Site: http://www.samtec.com
Emp.: 5
Electronic Parts Whslr
N.A.I.C.S.: 423690
Alex Yuen *(Mgr-Sls)*

Samtec Taiwan Limited (1)
10F No 182 Sec 2 Dunhua S Rd, Da-an District, Taipei, 10669, Taiwan
Tel.: (886) 2 2735 6109
Web Site: http://www.samtec.com
Electronic Parts Distr
N.A.I.C.S.: 423690

SAMUEL A. RAMIREZ & CO. INC.
61 Broadway Ste 2924, New York, NY 10006
Tel.: (212) 248-0500
Web Site: http://www.ramirezco.com
Sales Range: $10-24.9 Million
Emp.: 50
Bond Dealers & Brokers
N.A.I.C.S.: 523150
Lawrence F. Goldman *(Mng Dir)*
Dominick P. Quartuccio *(Mng Dir)*
Linda Martin *(VP)*
Ray O'Connor *(Mng Dir)*
Ted Sobel *(Head-Pub Fin)*
Alan Greco *(Mng Dir-Trading)*

SAMUEL CORALUZZO CO. INC.
1713 N Main Rd, Vineland, NJ 08360
Tel.: (856) 691-1142 — NJ
Web Site: http://www.coraluzzo.com
Year Founded: 1953
Sales Range: $10-24.9 Million
Emp.: 140
Petroleum Transport Services
N.A.I.C.S.: 484220
Michael Penza *(VP)*

SAMUEL ENGINEERING, INC.
8450 E Crescent Pkwy, Greenwood Village, CO 80111
Tel.: (303) 714-4840 — CO
Web Site: http://www.samuelengineering.com
Year Founded: 1996
Sales Range: $25-49.9 Million
Emp.: 115
Engineeering Services
N.A.I.C.S.: 541330
Claudia Samuel *(CEO)*
Robert Williams *(Chief Admin Officer)*
Everod Samuel *(Pres)*

SAMUEL GOLDWYN FILMS, LLC
9570 W Pico Blvd Ste 400, Los Angeles, CA 90035-1216
Tel.: (310) 860-3100 — CA
Web Site: http://www.samuelgoldwynfilms.com
Sales Range: $50-74.9 Million
Emp.: 10
Motion Pictures & Videos Producer & Distr
N.A.I.C.S.: 512110
Meyer Gottlieb *(Pres)*
Susan Jizba *(Controller)*
Samuel Goldwyn Jr. *(Chm & CEO)*

Subsidiaries:

Samuel Goldwyn Films, LLC - New York (1)
1133 Broadway Ste 1120, New York, NY 10010-7909
Tel.: (212) 367-9435
Web Site: http://www.samuelgoldwynfilms.com
Sales Range: $10-24.9 Million
Motion Pictures Producer & Distr
N.A.I.C.S.: 512110

SAMUEL SCOTT FINANCIAL GROUP
12651 High Bluff Ste 300, San Diego, CA 92130
Tel.: (858) 259-6070
Web Site: http://www.samuelscottfg.com
Year Founded: 2006
Sales Range: $1-9.9 Million
Emp.: 30
Financial Management & Advisory Services
N.A.I.C.S.: 523999
Katie Cortez *(Dir-Admin)*
Erica Liodice *(Dir-Mktg)*
Todd Pianin *(Sr Mng Dir)*
Russ Schreier *(Mng Dir)*
Jamie Wheat *(Dir-Ops)*

SAMUEL SHAPIRO & COMPANY INC.
1215 East Fort Ave Ste 201, Baltimore, MD 21230
Tel.: (410) 539-0540
Web Site: http://www.shapiro.com
Sales Range: $10-24.9 Million
Emp.: 70
Customhouse Brokers
N.A.I.C.S.: 488510
Margie Shapiro *(Pres & CEO)*
Robert Burdette *(VP-Strategic Dev)*
Kathy McKoy *(Mgr-Mid Atlantic Reg)*

SAMUELS GROUP, INC.
311 Financial Way Ste 300, Wausau, WI 54401-1404
Tel.: (715) 842-2222
Web Site: http://www.samuelsgroup.net
Year Founded: 1997
Sales Range: $50-74.9 Million
Emp.: 70
General Contractor & Construction Manager; Commercial, Industrial & Apartment Buildings Designer & Builder
N.A.I.C.S.: 236220
Sid Samuels *(Owner & Pres)*
Shelley Rowe *(Mgr-Mktg)*
Tim Vick *(Dir-Safety)*
Kurt Berner *(VP)*
Jennifer Guerndt *(VP-Sls & Mktg)*
Brenda Skic *(Controller)*
Jim Jasper *(Dir-Design)*
Bob Brault *(Mgr-Bus Ops)*
Michelle Theiss *(Mgr-HR)*
John Treweek *(Dir-Estimating & Pre-Construction Svcs)*
Amber Battani *(Mgr-Bus Dev)*
Len Olbrantz *(Mgr-Bus Dev)*
Dean Glatting *(Mgr-Sustainability)*
Tim Nordlund *(Mgr-Construction Ops-Wausau)*
Curt Schleicher *(Project Mgr)*
Greg Melander *(Project Mgr)*
Kelly Sampson *(Mgr-Healthcare Bus Dev)*
Lada Xiong-Vang *(Mgr-Bus Dev)*
Laura Meurette *(Project Mgr)*
Jenny Henke *(Asst Project Mgr)*
Mike Bernatz *(CFO)*

SAMY'S CAMERA INC.
431 S Fairfax Ave, Los Angeles, CA 90036-3123
Tel.: (323) 938-2420
Web Site: http://www.samyscamera.com
Year Founded: 1976
Sales Range: $10-24.9 Million
Emp.: 115
Sales of Camera & Photographic Supplies
N.A.I.C.S.: 449210
Sam Kamienowicz *(Pres & Sec)*
Ken Dethloff *(Mgr-Pasadena Pro-Digital)*
Lars Oberg *(Mgr-IT)*
Michelle Franco *(Mgr-Store)*
Mike Kampler *(Mgr-Rental)*

SAN ANTONIO CHILDREN'S MUSEUM
2800 Broadway, San Antonio, TX 78209
Tel.: (210) 212-4453 — TX
Web Site: http://www.sakids.org
Year Founded: 1992
Sales Range: $25-49.9 Million
Emp.: 118
Child Museum
N.A.I.C.S.: 712110
Vanessa Lacoss Hurd *(CEO)*

SAN ANTONIO MASONRY & TOOL SUPPLY, INC.

7480 FM 1560 N Unit 1, San Antonio, TX 78254-9564
Tel.: (210) 695-8222
Web Site: http://www.samasonry.com
Year Founded: 2000
Sales Range: $10-24.9 Million
Emp.: 65
Construction Materials Whslr
N.A.I.C.S.: 423320
Ron Isgur *(Mgr-Ops)*

SAN ANTONIO STOCK SHOW & RODEO
723 AT&T Center Pkwy, San Antonio, TX 78219
Tel.: (210) 225-5851
Web Site: http://www.sarodeo.com
Year Founded: 1948
Sales Range: $25-49.9 Million
Emp.: 326
Stock Show & Rodeo Organizer
N.A.I.C.S.: 711310
Nancy B. Loeffler *(VP)*
Joe Soules *(Chm)*
Ronnie Urbanczyk *(VP)*
Randy Vaclavik *(VP)*
Clint Swindall *(VP)*
Cody Davenport *(Pres)*
James Clingman *(VP)*
Keith Martin *(CEO & Exec Dir)*
Mark S. Colaw *(VP)*
Rusty Collier *(Sec & VP)*
Tina Altgelt Haynes *(VP)*
Patrick B. Frost *(VP)*

SAN ANTONIO WINERY & MADDALENA RESTAURANT
737 Lamar St, Los Angeles, CA 90031
Tel.: (323) 223-1401
Web Site: http://sanantoniowinery.com
Year Founded: 1917
Sales Range: $25-49.9 Million
Emp.: 150
Vineyard & Wine Mfr
N.A.I.C.S.: 111332
Santo Cambianica *(Founder)*

SAN ANTONIO ZOO
3903 N Saint Mary's St, San Antonio, TX 78212-3199
Tel.: (210) 734-7184
Web Site: http://www.sazoo.org
Year Founded: 1929
Sales Range: $10-24.9 Million
Emp.: 547
Zoo Operator
N.A.I.C.S.: 712130
J. Stephen McCusker *(Exec Dir)*
Chris Bathie *(Second VP)*
David Herrmann *(Pres)*
Frank Ruttenberg *(First VP)*
Norborne Cole *(Treas)*
William Freed *(Sec)*
Julie Gross *(VP-Dev)*

SAN BAR CONSTRUCTION CORP.
9101 Bdwy Blvd SE, Albuquerque, NM 87105
Tel.: (505) 452-8000
Web Site: http://www.sanbarcc.com
Year Founded: 1989
Sales Range: $10-24.9 Million
Emp.: 65
Highway & Street Construction
N.A.I.C.S.: 237310
David Sanchez *(Pres)*
Bob Whorton *(CFO)*

SAN BENITO SUPPLY INCORPORATED
1060 Nash Rd, Hollister, CA 95023
Tel.: (831) 637-6872
Web Site: http://www.sanbenitosupply.com
Rev.: $12,000,000
Emp.: 58
Brick, Stone & Related Material
N.A.I.C.S.: 423320
Mark Schipper *(Pres)*

SAN BERNARD ELECTRIC COOP
309 W Main St, Bellville, TX 77418
Tel.: (979) 865-3171
Web Site: http://www.sbec.org
Sales Range: $50-74.9 Million
Emp.: 120
Distribution, Electric Power
N.A.I.C.S.: 221122
Ken Wied *(Mgr-Bus Grp)*
Gus H. Miller *(Chm)*
James W. Marricle *(Pres & Gen Mgr)*
Don Roberts *(Mgr-Electrical Sys Grp)*
Robyn Lowe *(Mgr-Consumer Svcs)*
Clayton Stanford *(Dir-Engrg)*
William Peschel *(Mgr-Construction & Maintenance)*
Mike Ables *(Dir-Special Projects)*

SAN BERNARDINO MUNICIPAL WATER DEPARTMENT
1350 S E St, San Bernardino, CA 92408
Tel.: (909) 384-5141
Web Site: http://www.sbcitywater.org
Year Founded: 1905
Sales Range: $25-49.9 Million
Emp.: 250
Water Supply
N.A.I.C.S.: 221310
Stacey Aldstadt *(Gen Mgr)*

SAN CAMILLO INC.
10200 W Bluemound Rd, Wauwatosa, WI 53226
Tel.: (414) 259-6333
Web Site: http://www.stcam.com
Sales Range: $50-74.9 Million
Emp.: 400
Retirement Care, Skilled Nursing Services & Home Health Services
N.A.I.C.S.: 531110
Rick Johnson *(Pres)*

SAN DIEGO BUSINESS JOURNAL
4909 Murphy Canyon Rd Ste 200, San Diego, CA 92123
Tel.: (858) 277-6359
Web Site: http://www.sdbj.com
Sales Range: $10-24.9 Million
Emp.: 40
Publisher of Weekly Business Newspaper
N.A.I.C.S.: 513120
Mark Misiano *(Controller)*
Barbara Chodos *(Publr)*
Vik Jolly *(Editor-in-Chief)*
Stephen Adamek *(Mng Editor)*

SAN DIEGO CHARGERS FOOTBALL CO.
4020 Murphy Canyon Rd, San Diego, CA 92123
Tel.: (858) 874-4500
Web Site: http://www.chargers.com
Year Founded: 1960
Sales Range: $125-149.9 Million
Emp.: 135
Professional Football Franchise
N.A.I.C.S.: 711211
Jeanne M. Bonk *(CFO & Exec VP)*
S. Brandon Ward *(Sr Mgr-Mktg Partnerships & Brdcst Production)*
Ed McGuire *(Exec VP-Football Admin/Player Fin)*
Michael L. Dougherty *(Dir-Ticket Ops)*
Todd Poulsen *(Sr Dir-Ticket Sls & Svcs)*
Ken Derrett *(CMO & Sr VP)*
Chrystal Lee *(Mgr-Acctg)*
Dick Lewis *(Dir-Player Outreach)*
Kimberley Layton *(Dir-Pub Affairs, Corp & Community Rels)*
Dennis O'Leary *(VP-Mktg Partnerships)*
Marsha Wells *(Controller)*
Arthur Hightower *(Sr Dir-Player Engagement)*
Dean A. Spanos *(Chm)*
A. G. Spanos *(CEO & Exec VP)*
Dennis Abraham *(Dir-Pro Scouting)*
John Spanos *(Pres-Football Ops)*
Brian Duddy *(Dir-Video Ops)*
Bob Wick *(Mgr-Equipment)*
Jeremiah T. Murphy *(Exec VP)*
John Hinek *(Dir-Bus Ops)*
Chris Lee *(Sr Mgr-Corp Partnerships)*
Joel Price *(Sr Mgr-Digital)*
Tom Telesco *(Gen Mgr)*
Bill Stetson *(Dir-Security)*
Jojo Wooden *(Dir-Player Personnel)*
Nicoletta Ruhl *(Dir-Digital Media)*
Kris Moerschel *(Mgr-Ticket Ops)*
Steve Pankowski *(Sr Mgr-Ticket Sls)*
Jim Cwalinski *(Mgr-Guest Svcs)*
Bryan Cox *(Asst Dir-Pro Scouting)*
Dave Johnson *(Asst Dir-Security Gameday)*
Jason Negus *(Asst Dir-Video Ops)*
Kevin Kelly *(Dir-College Scouting)*
Quinton Owens *(Dir-Premium Seating Sls)*
Rich Alexander *(Asst Controller)*
Shirley Weinmann *(Dir-Guest Svcs)*
Michael A. Spanos *(Vice Chm)*

SAN DIEGO CITY EMPLOYEES RETIREE MEDICAL TRUST
8885 Rio San Diego Dr Ste 300, San Diego, CA 92108
Tel.: (619) 278-0021
Web Site: http://www.sdrmt.retireetrust.com
Year Founded: 2011
Sales Range: $10-24.9 Million
Health Benefit Services
N.A.I.C.S.: 525120
Michael Zucchet *(Sec)*
Debra Bevier *(Chm)*

SAN DIEGO COUNTY CREDIT UNION
6545 Sequence Dr, San Diego, CA 92121
Tel.: (858) 453-2112
Web Site: http://www.sdccu.com
Year Founded: 1938
Sales Range: $200-249.9 Million
Emp.: 958
Credit Union
N.A.I.C.S.: 522130
Teresa Halleck *(CEO)*
Laurie Levenson *(Treas & Sec)*
Dawn Martin *(Sr VP-HR)*
Valerie Kwiatkowski *(Exec VP-IT)*

SAN DIEGO COUNTY TOBACCO SECURITIZATION CORPORATION
1600 Pacific Hwy, San Diego, CA 92101
Tel.: (619) 685-2392
Year Founded: 2000
Sales Range: $25-49.9 Million
Tobacco Settlement Payment Services
N.A.I.C.S.: 541214
Daniel V. McAllister *(Chm)*
Michele Anderson *(Sec)*
Donald F. Steuer *(CFO)*
Tracy Sandoval *(CFO)*

SAN DIEGO DATA PROCESSING CORPORATION
5975 Santa Fe St, San Diego, CA 92109-1623
Tel.: (858) 581-9600
Web Site: http://www.sddpc.org
Year Founded: 1979
Sales Range: $25-49.9 Million
Emp.: 250
Government Information Technology Solutions
N.A.I.C.S.: 518210
Joyce Russell *(CFO)*

SAN DIEGO HEBREW HOMES
211 Saxony Rd, Encinitas, CA 92024
Tel.: (760) 632-0081
Web Site: http://www.seacrestvillage.org
Year Founded: 1944
Sales Range: $10-24.9 Million
Emp.: 385
Senior Living Services
N.A.I.C.S.: 623311
Robin P. Israel *(Chief Foundation Officer)*
Brad Blose *(CFO)*
Kathy Sanger *(Chief HR Officer-Seacrest Village Retirement Communities)*
Jonathan Halberg *(Chm)*
David Gilbert *(Treas)*
Jeffrey Platt *(Sec)*
Jon Schwartz *(Dir-Community Rels-Seacrest Village Retirement Communities)*
Carl Measer *(COO)*

SAN DIEGO PUBLIC LIBRARY FOUNDATION
820 E St, San Diego, CA 92101-6478
Tel.: (619) 238-6638
Web Site: http://www.supportmylibrary.org
Year Founded: 2002
Sales Range: $10-24.9 Million
Emp.: 11
Library Operator
N.A.I.C.S.: 519210
Charlie Goldberg *(Dir-Mktg)*
Gail Levin *(Vice Chm)*
Jay Hill *(CEO)*
Angelina Franco *(Mgr-Creative Svcs)*
Jeff Rowland *(Dir-Fin)*
Natalie Ganz *(Dir-Major & Planned Gifts)*
Cynthia Olmstead *(Chm)*
Wendy Urushima-Conn *(Sec)*
Steve Hermes *(Treas)*

SAN DIEGO SIGN COMPANY
3201 Lionshead Ave, Carlsbad, CA 92010
Tel.: (760) 509-4375
Web Site: http://www.sdsign.com
Year Founded: 2001
Sales Range: $10-24.9 Million
Emp.: 70
Banner & Display Stand Retailer
N.A.I.C.S.: 459999
Craig van Velzer *(Pres)*
Eric van Velzer *(CFO)*

SAN DIEGO SYMPHONY ORCHESTRA ASSOCIATION
1245 7th Ave, San Diego, CA 92101
Tel.: (619) 235-0800
Web Site: http://www.sandiegosymphony.com
Emp.: 110
Symphony Orchestra
N.A.I.C.S.: 711130
Jennifer Ringle *(Mgr-Production)*
Mark Wildman *(Head-Property Dept)*
Mariellen Oliver *(Asst Controller & Mgr-HR)*

SAN DIEGO SYMPHONY ORCHESTRA ASSOCIATION

U.S. PRIVATE

San Diego Symphony Orchestra Association—(Continued)
Robert H. Wilkins (COO)
Stephen Kougias (Dir-PR)
Seth Goldman (CFO & Chief Admin Officer)

SAN DIEGO VOLVO
5350 Kearny Mesa Rd, San Diego, CA 92111
Tel.: (858) 279-9700
Web Site: http://www.sandiegovolvo.com
Rev.: $48,600,000
Emp.: 137
New Car Dealers
N.A.I.C.S.: 441110
Wesley G. Hinkle (Founder & Owner)
Edgar Masters (Mgr-Pre-Owned Inventory)
German Soto (Mgr-Parts)
Glen Garland (Gen Mgr-Sls)
Kyle Anderson (Mgr-Sls Bus)
Leonard Buchholz (Dir-Svc)
Mary Wesloe (Mgr-Sls Bus)
Ralph Stumpp (Mgr-New Car Sls)

SAN DIEGO WORKFORCE PARTNERSHIP
3910 University Ave Fl 4, San Diego, CA 92105
Tel.: (619) 228-2900 CA
Web Site: http://www.sandiegoatwork.com
Year Founded: 1974
Sales Range: $10-24.9 Million
Emp.: 100
Non Profit Employment Agency
N.A.I.C.S.: 561311
Peter Callstrom (Pres & CEO)
Gina Charest (CFO)
David Graham (CIO & VP)
Andy Hall (Chief Program Officer & VP)
Heather Milne Barger (VP-Comm)
Cord Bailey (Dir-Youth Programs)
Jacqueline Collins (Dir-Ops)
Tina Ngo Bartel (Dir-Bus Programs & Res)

SAN DIEGO-IMPERIAL COUNTIES DEVELOPMENTAL SERVICES INC.
4355 Ruffin Rd Ste 205, San Diego, CA 92123-4308
Tel.: (858) 576-2996 CA
Web Site: http://www.sdrc.org
Year Founded: 1982
Sales Range: $50-74.9 Million
Emp.: 450
Non Profit Organization For Individual & Family Services
N.A.I.C.S.: 624120
Carlos Flores (Exec Dir)
Denise Gutirrez-Miller (Coord-Svc)
Linda Livingston (Coord-Resource)
Anthony Ferguson (Mgr-Transportation)
Lori Blair (Coord-Resource)
Erin Cuniffe (Coord-Resource)
Melissa Elliott (Coord-Resource)
John Filley (Coord-Resource)
Phil Patton (Coord-Resource)
Wanda Bardwell (Mgr-Residential Svcs)

SAN FERNANDO MARBLE & GRANITE
9803 San Fernando Rd, Pacoima, CA 91331
Tel.: (818) 897-4033 CA
Year Founded: 1994
Rev.: $10,000,000
Emp.: 9
Granite Building Stone

N.A.I.C.S.: 423320
Harold Istrin (Pres)

SAN FRANCISCO BALLET
455 Franklin St 3rd Fl, San Francisco, CA 94102
Tel.: (415) 861-5600 CA
Web Site: http://www.sfballet.org
Year Founded: 1933
Sales Range: $25-49.9 Million
Emp.: 815
Art Event Promoter
N.A.I.C.S.: 711310
Susan S. Briggs (Asst Sec)
Carl F. Pascarella (Chm)
Jennifer J. McCall (Sec)
Diane B. Wilsey (Vice Chm)

SAN FRANCISCO BASEBALL ASSOCIATES, L.P.
Oracle Park 24 Willie Mays Plz, San Francisco, CA 94107
Tel.: (415) 972-2000 CA
Web Site: http://www.sfgiants.com
Year Founded: 1992
Holding Company; Professional Baseball Club
N.A.I.C.S.: 551112
Laurence M. Baer (Pres & CEO)
Duane K. Kurisu (Owner)

Subsidiaries:
San Francisco Giants Baseball Club (1)
AT&T Park 24 Willie Mays Plaza, San Francisco, CA 94107
Tel.: (415) 972-2000
Web Site: http://sanfrancisco.giants.mlb.com
Sales Range: $25-49.9 Million
Emp.: 130
Professional Baseball Club
N.A.I.C.S.: 711211
Laurence M. Baer (Pres & CEO)
Mario Alioto (Exec VP-Bus Ops)
Jorge Costa (Sr VP-Ballpark Ops)
Jack F. Bair (Gen Counsel & Sr VP)
Brian R. Sabean (Exec VP-Baseball Ops)
Alfonso G. Felder (Exec VP-Admin)
Dick Tidrow (VP & Asst Gen Mgr-Player Personnel)
Jerry Drobny (VP-Strategic Revenue Svcs)
Craig Solomon (Dir-Season Ticket Sls)
Russ Stanley (Sr VP-Ticket Sls & Svcs)
Jason Pearl (Sr VP-Sponsorship & Bus Dev)
Valerie McGuire (Dir-Promos Event Production)
Lisa Pantages (Treas & Sr VP)
Rick Mears (VP-Guest Svcs)
Nancy Donati (VP-Creative Svcs & Visual Identity)
Fred Stanley (Dir-Player Dev)
Jeremy Shelley (VP & Asst Gen Mgr-Pro Scouting & Player Evaluation)
Jeff Tucker (VP-Ticket Sls & Premium Seating)
Faham Zakariaei (Sr Dir-Promos Special Events)
Joyce Thomas (VP-HR)
Dave Martinez (VP-Retail Ops)
Yeshayah Goldfarb (Dir-Minor League Ops & Quantitative Analysis)
Clara Ho (Dir-Baseball Personnel Admin)
Alan Lee (Sr Dir-Arizona Minor League Ops & Mgr-ML Equipment)
Matt Chisholm (Sr Dir-Media Rels)
Shana Daum (VP-Pub Affairs & Community Rels)
Sue Petersen (Exec Dir)
Matt Peterson (Sr Mgr-Bus Dev & Ticket Sls)
Nick Zanotto (Sr Mgr-New Ticket Sls)
Davin Lutes (Sr Dir-Ticket Svcs)
Rocky Koplik (VP-Client Retention & Sls Strategy)
Danny Dann (VP-Mktg & Adv)
Bonnie MacInnes (Sr Dir-Retail Ops)
John Tyler (Mgr-Video & Scoreboard Ops)
Gene Telucci (VP-Ballpark Ops)
Stephen Revetria (Sr VP & Gen Mgr)
Sara Hunt (VP)
Terri Guess (CEO)
Shane Turner (Dir-Player Dev)

Fran Weld (VP-Strategy & Dev)
Farhan Zaidi (Pres-Baseball Ops)
Staci A. Slaughter (Sr VP-Comm)
Pete Putila (Gen Mgr)

SAN FRANCISCO EQUITY PARTNERS
50 California St Ste 1320, San Francisco, CA 94111
Tel.: (415) 738-1200
Web Site: https://www.sfequitypartners.com
Privater Equity Firm
N.A.I.C.S.: 523999
Scott Potter (Mng Partner)
David Mannix (Partner)
Chris Sargent (Principal)
Hywel Robinson (Principal)

Subsidiaries:
Brazi Bites LLC (1)
11 NE Martin Luther King Jr. Blvd, Ste 303, Portland, OR 97232
Tel.: (503) 303-2272
Web Site: https://brazibites.com
Cheese Bread Mfr & Distr
N.A.I.C.S.: 311824
Junea Rocha (Co-Founder & Chief Mktg Officer)
Cameron MacMullin (Co-Founder & COO)

DGS Retail, Inc. (1)
60 Maple St Ste 100, Mansfield, MA 02048-1505
Tel.: (508) 337-2990
Web Site: http://www.dgsretail.com
Fixture & Decor Product Mfr
N.A.I.C.S.: 335131
Jon Nedland (VP-Sls)
Peter Stevens (CEO)

Subsidiary (Domestic):
RICH LTD. (2)
3809 Ocean Ranch Blvd Ste 110, Oceanside, CA 92056
Tel.: (760) 722-2300
Web Site: http://www.richltd.com
Sales Range: $10-24.9 Million
Emp.: 19
Business Products & Services
N.A.I.C.S.: 323111
Jim Hollen (Pres)

Iredale Mineral Cosmetics Ltd. (1)
50 Church St, Great Barrington, MA 01230
Tel.: (413) 644-9900
Web Site: http://www.janeiredale.com
Sales Range: $25-49.9 Million
Emp.: 60
Cosmetics Mfr & Retailer
N.A.I.C.S.: 325620

SV Labs Corporation (1)
480 Airport Blvd, Watsonville, CA 95076
Tel.: (831) 722-9526
Web Site: http://www.s-vlabs.com
Sales Range: $10-24.9 Million
Emp.: 100
Cosmetic Preparations
N.A.I.C.S.: 325620
Jeff Slaboden (Pres)
Glenn Wall (Mgr-IS)
Graham Orriss (CEO)

Subsidiary (Domestic):
Diversified Manufacturing Corporation (2)
1115 Dexter St N, Prescott, WI 54021
Tel.: (651) 458-8636
Web Site: http://www.dmcmn.com
Toilet Preparation Mfr
N.A.I.C.S.: 325620
Rishikesh Motilall (Founder)

SAN FRANCISCO FOUNDATION
1 Embarcadero Ctr Ste 1400, San Francisco, CA 94111
Tel.: (415) 733-8500 CA
Web Site: http://www.sff.org
Year Founded: 1948
Sales Range: Less than $1 Million
Emp.: 84

Grantmaking Services
N.A.I.C.S.: 813211
Ruben D. Orduna (VP-Dev & Donor)
Maria Vickroy-Peralta (Dir-Bus Dev)
Jane Sullivan (VP-Mktg & Strategic Comm)
Susan Frohlich (Controller)
Fred Blackwell (CEO)
Jen Thom (Officer-Mktg & Comm)
Sindy L. Craig (Dir-Planned Giving)
Galen Maness (Dir-HR)
Dianne Yamashiro-Omi (Officer-Community Health Program)
Lorraine Giordano (Officer-Initiative)
Yolanda Alindor (Officer-Org & Pro Dev)
Andrea Zussman (Officer-Disaster Resilience)
Ellie Rossiter (Officer-Initiative & Dir-Campaign)
Dee Dee Brantley (COO)
Terezita Romo (Officer-Arts & Culture Program)
Lisa Villarreal (Officer-Education Program)
Myra Chow (VP-Programs)
Woo Liu Ling (Dir-Mktg & Comm)
Nicole Kyauk (Dir-Donor Rels)

SAN FRANCISCO HERB & NATURAL FOOD CO.
47444 Kato Rd, Fremont, CA 94538
Tel.: (510) 770-1215
Web Site: http://www.herbspicetea.com
Year Founded: 1969
Sales Range: $50-74.9 Million
Emp.: 75
Herb, Tea & Spice Production Services
N.A.I.C.S.: 311920
Reza Faraee (Pres)
Cliff Cowing (Dir-Strategic Planning)
Craig Smith (Dir-Supply Chain)
Dawn Meenan (Mgr-Acctg)
Cheryl Petrash (Mgr-HR)
Joe Pizarro (Mgr-Content)
Ronald Roque (Mgr-Pur)

SAN FRANCISCO MARKET CORPORATION
2095 Jerrold Ave Ste 212, San Francisco, CA 94124-1628
Tel.: (415) 550-4495 CA
Web Site: http://www.sfproduce.org
Year Founded: 2012
Sales Range: $1-9.9 Million
Emp.: 850
Business Association for Retail Markets & Warehousing
N.A.I.C.S.: 813910
John Monfredini (Pres)
Helen Sause (Sec)
Larry Brucia (VP)
Lori Campbell (Treas)
Stanley Corriea Jr. (VP)

SAN FRANCISCO MUSEUM OF MODERN ART
151 3rd St, San Francisco, CA 94103
Tel.: (415) 357-4000 CA
Web Site: http://www.sfmoma.org
Year Founded: 1935
Sales Range: $200-249.9 Million
Emp.: 435
Museums
N.A.I.C.S.: 712110
Diana L. Nelson (Pres)
Mimi L. Haas (Co-Vice Chm)
Robert J. Fisher (Chm)
Dennis J. Wong (Treas & Sec)
Robin M. Wright (Co-Vice Chm)
Charles M. Collins (Co-Vice Chm)

Jennifer Northrop *(Dir-Mktg & Comm)*
Ed Lamberger *(Chief HR Officer)*
Rebecca Malkin-Chocron *(Dir-Fin)*

SAN FRANCISCO PARKING INC.
325 5th St, San Francisco, CA 94107
Tel.: (415) 495-3909
Web Site: http://www.cityparksf.com
Sales Range: $50-74.9 Million
Emp.: 30
Parking Lots
N.A.I.C.S.: 812930
Timothy K. Leonoudakis *(CEO)*
Jack Krasner *(Dir-Fin & Acctg)*

SAN FRANCISCO PARKS ALLIANCE
1663 Mission St Ste 320, San Francisco, CA 94103
Tel.: (415) 621-3260
Web Site:
  http://www.sfparksalliance.org
Year Founded: 1971
Sales Range: $10-24.9 Million
Emp.: 51
Philanthropic Services
N.A.I.C.S.: 813211
John Stoner *(Dir-Fin & Ops)*
Courtney Klinge *(Vice Chm)*
James Lazarus *(Chm)*
Meagan Demitz *(Dir-Philanthropy)*
Drew Becher *(CEO)*

SAN FRANCISCO SYMPHONY
201 Van Ness Ave, San Francisco, CA 94102
Tel.: (415) 552-8000
Web Site: http://www.sfsymphony.org
Sales Range: $50-74.9 Million
Emp.: 200
Symphony Orchestra
N.A.I.C.S.: 711130
Joyce Cron Wessling *(Mgr-Tours & Media Production)*
Michelle Consunji *(Sr Partner-HR Bus)*
Lydia I. Beebe *(Sec)*
Jennifer Franks *(Asst Dir-Events)*
Ronald Gallman *(Dir-Education & Youth Orchestra)*
Andrea Yannone *(Mgr-Programs)*
Katherine Cummins *(Mng Editor)*
Jeannette Garbarini-Walters *(Dir-Retail Ops)*
Lisa Zadek *(Dir-Plng)*
Michael Tilson Thomas *(Dir-Music)*
Julie Ambrose *(Dir-Stewardship & Donor Rels)*
Paul Delucchi *(Mgr-Repeat Performance)*
Stephen Steiner *(Dir-Gift Plng)*
Aaron Bennett *(Mgr-Bus Applications)*
Andrea Drummond *(Mgr-SFS Media)*
Casey Daliyo *(Mgr-Ops)*
Kay Anderson *(Dir-Education Programs)*
Michael Gallardo *(Mgr-Symphony Store)*
Terry Breedlove *(Mgr-Patron Svcs)*
Tim Dietrich *(Controller)*
Walter Fernandez *(Mgr-Payroll)*
David R. Strand *(VP)*
Gail L. Covington *(VP)*
Paul S. Otellini *(VP)*
Sakurako Fisher *(Pres)*
Mark C. Hanson *(CEO)*
David Chambers *(Chief Revenue & Advancement Officer)*
Liz Pesch *(CFO)*

SAN FRANCISCO TRAVEL ASSOCIATION
1 Front St Ste 2900, San Francisco, CA 94111
Tel.: (415) 974-6900
Web Site:
  http://www.sanfrancisco.travel
Year Founded: 1909
Sales Range: $25-49.9 Million
Emp.: 110
Community Economic Development Services
N.A.I.C.S.: 813410
Tina Wu *(CFO)*
Julie Van't Hul *(VP-Convention Sls)*
Nicole Rogers *(Chief Sls Officer & Exec VP)*

SAN ISABEL ELECTRIC ASSOCIATION INC
893 E Enterprise Dr, Pueblo, CO 81007
Tel.: (719) 547-2160
Web Site: http://www.siea.com
Sales Range: $10-24.9 Million
Emp.: 100
Distribution, Electric Power
N.A.I.C.S.: 221122
Dennis Astley *(COO)*

SAN JOAQUIN FIGS, INC.
3564 N Hazel Ave, Fresno, CA 93722-4912
Tel.: (559) 224-4963
Web Site: http://www.nutrafig.com
Year Founded: 1989
Sales Range: $10-24.9 Million
Emp.: 60
Fig Farming Services
N.A.I.C.S.: 111339
Keith Jura *(Pres)*
John Boylan *(Plant Mgr)*

SAN JOAQUIN GENERAL HOSPITAL
500 W Hospital Rd, French Camp, CA 95231-9693
Tel.: (209) 468-6000
Web Site: http://www.sjgeneral.org
Year Founded: 1857
Health Care Srvices
N.A.I.C.S.: 621610
David Culberson *(CEO)*
Sheela Kapre *(Chief Medical Officer)*
Belva Snyder *(Chief Nursing Officer)*
Ronald Kreutner *(CFO)*

SAN JOAQUIN HELICOPTERS INC.
1408 S Lexington St, Delano, CA 93215-9783
Tel.: (661) 725-1898
Web Site:
  http://www.sjhelicopters.com
Year Founded: 1932
Sales Range: $10-24.9 Million
Emp.: 1,000
Provider of Commercial Helicopter Travel
N.A.I.C.S.: 238210
James Josephson *(Pres)*

SAN JOAQUIN LUMBER CO.
235 W Scotts Ave, Stockton, CA 95203-9520
Tel.: (209) 465-5651
Web Site:
  http://www.sanjoaquinlumber.com
Sales Range: $10-24.9 Million
Emp.: 30
Lumber & Other Building Materials
N.A.I.C.S.: 423310
Jeff French *(Gen Mgr)*

SAN JOAQUIN REFINING CO., INC.
3129 Standard St, Bakersfield, CA 93308
Tel.: (661) 327-4257
Web Site: http://www.sjr.com
Rev.: $150,000,000
Emp.: 150
Oil Refinery
N.A.I.C.S.: 324110
Ed Starbuck *(VP-Ops)*
Kurt Hughes *(Mgr-Credit)*
Don Powell *(Mgr-Res Chemist Quality)*
Candice Neill *(Mgr-Payroll)*
Jay Phelps *(Controller)*
Jerry McKnight *(Project Mgr)*
Mark Del Papa *(VP-Supply & Distr)*
Pat Oveson *(Mgr-Refinery)*
Ryan Eberly *(Dir-Sls & Mktg-Special Products)*
Steve Hollis *(Mgr-Asphalt Mktg)*

Subsidiaries:

Tricor Refining, LLC (1)
PO Box 5877, Bakersfield, CA 93388
Tel.: (661) 393-7110
Web Site: http://www.goldenbearoil.com
Sales Range: $25-49.9 Million
Emp.: 30
Mfr of Naphthenic Oils, Extender Oils & Asphalt Products; Owned 50% by Ergon, Inc. & 50% by San Joaquin Refining Co., Inc.
N.A.I.C.S.: 424710
Jim Brownridge *(Mgr-Mktg)*
Marilyn Vallembois *(Mgr-Svcs)*
Joe Frank *(Gen Mgr)*

SAN JOAQUIN TOMATO GROWERS, INC.
PO Box 578, Crows Landing, CA 95313
Tel.: (209) 837-4721
Sales Range: $10-24.9 Million
Emp.: 10
Fruit & Vegetable Canning Services
N.A.I.C.S.: 311421
Earl Perez *(VP)*
Thomas Perez *(Pres)*
Irma Navarro *(Office Mgr)*

SAN JOSE SHARKS, LLC
525 W Santa Clara St, San Jose, CA 95113-1520
Tel.: (408) 287-7070
Web Site: http://www.sjsharks.com
Year Founded: 1990
Sales Range: $50-74.9 Million
Emp.: 100
Professional Hockey Team
N.A.I.C.S.: 711211
Jim Goddard *(Exec VP & Gen Mgr-San Jose Arena)*
Doug Bentz *(VP)*
Ken Caveney *(VP-Fin)*

SAN JOSE SURGICAL SUPPLY INC.
902 S Bascom Ave, San Jose, CA 95128-3501
Tel.: (408) 293-9033
Web Site: http://www.sjsurgical.com
Year Founded: 1968
Rev.: $25,973,855
Emp.: 135
Distr of Brand Name Pharmaceutical Supplies & Equipment
N.A.I.C.S.: 423450
Dennis J Collins *(Pres)*
Greg Guio *(Mgr-Sls)*

SAN JUAN CONSTRUCTION INC.
301 N Cascade, Montrose, CO 81401-3334
Tel.: (970) 249-6981
Web Site:
  http://www.sanjuanconstruction.com
Sales Range: $10-24.9 Million
Emp.: 47
Specialized Public Building Contractor
N.A.I.C.S.: 236220
John Theiss *(Pres & CEO)*

SAN JUAN REGIONAL MEDICAL CENTER
801 W Maple St, Farmington, NM 87401
Tel.: (505) 609-2000
Web Site:
  http://www.sanjuanregional.com
Year Founded: 1953
Sales Range: $250-299.9 Million
Emp.: 2,027
Health Care Srvices
N.A.I.C.S.: 622110
Suzanne Smith *(Chief Nursing Officer)*
Roberta Rogers *(Mgr-Mktg)*
Jeff Bourgeois *(Pres & CEO)*

SAN JUAN TRADING CO. INC.
B St Cnr C St Urb Indus, San Juan, PR 00920
Tel.: (787) 783-9300
Sales Range: $10-24.9 Million
Emp.: 38
Groceries, General Line
N.A.I.C.S.: 458110
Mariangia Locada *(Office Mgr)*
Monsy Guevarez *(Controller)*
Arthur Igartua *(VP-Sls)*
Celfo Portela *(VP-Mktg)*
Hortensia Casellas *(Pres)*

SAN LOTUS HOLDING INC.
9368 Valley Blvd Ste 202, Rosemead, CA 91770
Tel.: (626) 800-6861
Web Site:
  http://www.sanlotusholding.com
Year Founded: 2011
SLOT—(OTCBB)
Sales Range: Less than $1 Million
Emp.: 10
Investment Services
N.A.I.C.S.: 523999

SAN LUIS OBISPO COUNTY FARM SUPPLY
224 Tank Farm Rd, San Luis Obispo, CA 93401
Tel.: (805) 543-3751
Web Site:
  http://www.farmsupplyco.com
Rev.: $19,402,558
Emp.: 120
Farm Supplies
N.A.I.C.S.: 424910
Jim W. Brabeck *(CEO)*

SAN LUIS VALLEY RURAL ELECTRIC COOPERATIVE, INC.
3625 US Hwy 160 W, Monte Vista, CO 81144
Tel.: (719) 852-3538
Web Site: http://www.slvrec.com
Year Founded: 1937
Sales Range: $25-49.9 Million
Emp.: 52
Electric Power Distr
N.A.I.C.S.: 221122
Scott Wolfe *(Treas)*
Cole Wakasugi *(Sec)*
Mike Rierson *(Pres)*
Loren Howard *(CEO)*

SAN MANUEL INDIAN BINGO & CASINO
777 San Manuel Blvd, Highland, CA 92346-1763
Tel.: (909) 864-5050
Web Site: http://www.sanmanuel.com
Year Founded: 1986
Sales Range: $25-49.9 Million
Emp.: 1,300

San Manuel Indian Bingo & Casino—(Continued)
Gambling & Casino Operations
N.A.I.C.S.: 713990
Desiree Remillet *(Supvr-Mktg)*
Paul Muehter *(Mgr-Slot Sys)*
Daniel Morales *(Supvr-Mktg)*

SAN MAR CORPORATION
22833 SE Black Nugget Rd Ste 130, Issaquah, WA 98029
Tel.: (206) 727-3200   CA
Web Site: http://www.sanmar.com
Year Founded: 1962
Sales Range: $25-49.9 Million
Emp.: 1,000
Mens & Boys Clothing
N.A.I.C.S.: 424350
Dawn Cobiskey *(Acct Exec)*
Paul Harvey *(Mgr-Infrastructure & Security)*
Stephanie Huber *(Acct Exec)*

SAN MATEO COUNTY TRANSIT
1250 San Carlos Ave, San Carlos, CA 94070
Tel.: (650) 508-6200
Web Site: http://www.smcta.com
Year Founded: 1988
Sales Range: $25-49.9 Million
Emp.: 700
Local & Suburban Transit
N.A.I.C.S.: 485119
Hilda Lafebre *(Mgr-Capital Project & Environmental Plng)*
Joel Slavit *(Mgr-Programming & Monitoring)*
William Snell *(Asst Mgr-Transit Ops Trng)*
Dave Carbone *(Coord-Transportation Sys)*
Diane Shaw *(Mgr-Software Sys)*
Ilia Kay *(CFO)*
Jim Harnett *(CEO & Gen Mgr)*

SAN MATEO CREDIT UNION
575 Middlefield Rd, Redwood City, CA 94063
Tel.: (650) 363-1777   CA
Web Site: http://www.smcu.org
Year Founded: 1952
Sales Range: $50-74.9 Million
Emp.: 187
Credit Union Operator
N.A.I.C.S.: 522130
Jack Chinn *(VP-Fin)*
Donald Kneisler *(VP-Info Svcs)*
Stephen Tabler *(VP-Mktg)*

SAN MATEO FORWARDING
9220 San Mateo Dr, Laredo, TX 78045
Tel.: (956) 727-5327
Web Site: http://www.sanmateofwd.com
Freight Transportation Arrangement
N.A.I.C.S.: 488510
Jerry Tiburcio *(Mgr)*

SAN MIGUEL POWER ASSOCIATION
170 W 10th Ave, Nucla, CO 81424
Tel.: (970) 864-7311
Web Site: http://www.smpa.com
Rev.: $13,320,218
Emp.: 63
Distribution, Electric Power
N.A.I.C.S.: 221122
Bradley W. Zaporski *(CEO & Gen Mgr)*
Jim Link *(Gen Counsel)*

SAN PATRICIO ELECTRIC COOPERATIVE, INC.
402 E Sinton St, Sinton, TX 78387
Tel.: (361) 364-2220   TX
Web Site: http://www.sanpatricioelectric.org
Year Founded: 1938
Sales Range: $10-24.9 Million
Emp.: 42
Electric Power Distr
N.A.I.C.S.: 221122
Ron Hughes *(Gen Mgr)*
Tom Mayo *(Pres)*
Clyde Stewart *(Treas & Sec)*
Jim Basset *(VP)*

SAN RAMON BOAT CENTER INC.
4371 Granite Dr, Rocklin, CA 95677-2131
Tel.: (916) 415-1000
Web Site: http://www.sanramonboats.com
Sales Range: $10-24.9 Million
Emp.: 15
Boat Dealers
N.A.I.C.S.: 441222
Frank J. Warn *(Founder & Pres)*
Kathy Duprau *(Pres)*

SAN SABA PECAN, INC.
2803 W Wallace, San Saba, TX 76877
Tel.: (325) 372-5727
Web Site: http://www.sansabapecan.com
Year Founded: 1972
Sales Range: $25-49.9 Million
Emp.: 100
Roasted Nut & Peanut Butter Mfr
N.A.I.C.S.: 311911
James R. Ellis *(Dir-Sls)*
Keith Shahan *(CFO & Controller)*
R. D. Adams *(CEO)*

SAN SIMEON BY THE SOUND NURSING & REHABILITATION
61700 Route 48, Greenport, NY 11944
Tel.: (631) 477-2110   NY
Web Site: http://www.sansimeonbythesound.net
Year Founded: 2004
Sales Range: $10-24.9 Million
Emp.: 306
Nursing Care & Rehabilitation Services
N.A.I.C.S.: 623110
Myra Peskowitz *(Pres)*
Daniel Ross *(VP)*
Helen Levine *(Treas)*

SANBOR CORPORATION
6620 Grant Way, Allentown, PA 18106
Tel.: (610) 530-8500
Web Site: http://www.sanbormedical.com
Sales Range: $10-24.9 Million
Emp.: 95
Communication Wire Electronic Components
N.A.I.C.S.: 334510
Wayne Meng *(Chm)*
Antonio Boyer *(Project Mgr)*

SANBORN CHEVROLET
1210 S Cherokee Ln, Lodi, CA 95240
Tel.: (209) 334-5000
Web Site: http://www.sanbornchevrolet.com
Year Founded: 1984
Sales Range: $25-49.9 Million
Emp.: 50
Car Whslr
N.A.I.C.S.: 441110
R. Sanborn *(Pres)*
Mike Tiehm *(Gen Mgr)*

SANCHEZ ENERGY CORPORATION
1000 Main St Ste 3000, Houston, TX 77002
Tel.: (713) 783-8000   DE
Web Site: http://www.sanchezenergycorp.com
Year Founded: 2011
Rev.: $1,056,914,000
Assets: $2,819,960,000
Liabilities: $2,811,655,000
Net Worth: $8,305,000
Earnings: $85,205,000
Fiscal Year-end: 12/31/18
Crude Petroleum & Natural Gas Extraction
N.A.I.C.S.: 211120
Kirsten A. Hink *(Chief Acctg Officer & Sr VP)*
Gregory B. Kopel *(Gen Counsel & Sr VP)*
Antonio R. Sanchez III *(Pres & CEO)*

SAND BUILDING MATERIALS, INC.
11321 San Fernando Rd, San Fernando, CA 91340
Tel.: (818) 834-5400   CA
Web Site: http://www.sandbuildingmaterials.com
Year Founded: 2003
Sales Range: $1-9.9 Million
Emp.: 24
Flagstone, Masonry & Plaster Products for Construction
N.A.I.C.S.: 238140
Oscar Sandoval *(Pres)*

SAND CREEK POST & BEAM INC.
116 W 1st St, Wayne, NE 68787
Tel.: (402) 833-5600   NE
Web Site: http://www.sandcreekpostandbeam.com
Year Founded: 2004
Sales Range: $10-24.9 Million
Emp.: 75
Prefabricated Wood Buildings
N.A.I.C.S.: 321992
Jule Goeller *(CFO)*
Jack Dickinson *(CEO)*
Cal Wiechman *(Dir-Pur)*
Len Dickinson *(Pres)*

SAND DOLLAR CORPORATION
2156 N Main St, Walnut Creek, CA 94596
Tel.: (925) 935-6862
Sales Range: $10-24.9 Million
Emp.: 500
Unisex Hair Salons
N.A.I.C.S.: 812112
William L. Gore *(Pres)*
Cindy Pangrazzi *(Controller)*

SAND DOLLAR HOLDINGS INCORPORATED
1022 Bay Marina Dr Ste 106, National City, CA 91950
Tel.: (619) 477-0185   DE
Web Site: http://harvestmeat.com
Meats & Meat Products Whslr
N.A.I.C.S.: 424470

Subsidiaries:

Harvest Food Company   (1)
1000 Bay Marina Dr, National City, CA 91950
Tel.: (619) 477-0185
Web Site: http://www.harvestfooddistributors.com
Emp.: 600
Food Distr

N.A.I.C.S.: 424470
Sherwood Food Distributors, LLC   (1)
12499 Evergreen Rd, Detroit, MI 48228-1059
Tel.: (313) 659-7300
Web Site: http://www.sherwoodfoods.com
Meat Distr
N.A.I.C.S.: 424470
Alex Karp *(Founder)*

Branch (Domestic):

Sherwood Food Distributors- Cleveland Div   (2)
16625 Granite Rd, Maple Heights, OH 44137-4301
Tel.: (216) 662-8000
Web Site: http://www.sherwoodfoods.com
Wholesale Food Distr
N.A.I.C.S.: 424470
Scott Wauschek *(Dir-Pur & Mktg)*

SAND OAK CAPITAL LLC
900 3rd Ave 33rd Fl, New York, NY 10022
Tel.: (212) 317-3340
Web Site: http://www.sandoak.com
Holding Company
N.A.I.C.S.: 551112
Jeremy C. Schwimmer *(Partner)*

SAND SEED SERVICE INCORPORATED
4765 Hwy 143, Marcus, IA 51035-0648
Tel.: (712) 376-4135   IA
Web Site: http://www.sandsofiowa.com
Year Founded: 1932
Sales Range: $10-24.9 Million
Emp.: 35
Marketer of Grains
N.A.I.C.S.: 424510
Charles Sand *(Pres)*
Kathy Ogren *(Controller)*

SANDALS RESORTS INTERNATIONAL
4950 SW 72nd Ave, Miami, FL 33155-5533
Tel.: (305) 284-1300   FL
Web Site: http://www.sandals.com
Year Founded: 1981
Sales Range: $125-149.9 Million
Emp.: 300
Tourism Services
N.A.I.C.S.: 721110
Andy Blanco *(CFO)*
Jeff Clarke *(COO)*
Brett Warbrick *(VP-Brand Mktg & Partnerships)*
Adam Stewart *(Chm)*
Gebhard F. Rainer *(CEO)*
Ryan Matthew *(Dir-HR)*

SANDATA HOLDINGS, INC.
26 Harbor Park Dr, Port Washington, NY 11050-4602
Tel.: (516) 484-4400   DE
Web Site: http://www.sandata.com
Holding Company; Healthcare Industry Information Technology Services
N.A.I.C.S.: 551112
Bert E. Brodsky *(Chm)*
Harold S. Blue *(Vice Chm & CEO)*
Barbara Winner *(CTO)*

Subsidiaries:

Health Systems Solutions, Inc.   (1)
42 W 39th St 6th Fl, New York, NY 10018
Tel.: (212) 798-9400
Sales Range: $1-9.9 Million
Emp.: 89
Home Healthcare Software, Field Mobility Solutions & Professional Consulting Services
N.A.I.C.S.: 513210

Sandata Technologies, LLC. (1)
26 Harbor Park Dr, Port Washington, NY 11050-4602
Tel.: (516) 484-4400
Web Site: http://www.sandata.com
Sales Range: $10-24.9 Million
Emp.: 102
Healthcare Industry Data Processing & Programming Services
N.A.I.C.S.: 518210
Bert E. Brodsky *(Founder & Chm)*
Russ Esposito *(COO)*
Susan Cullinan *(Sr VP-Ops)*
Kenneth D. Faltischek *(COO)*
Pat Keller *(CFO)*
Denise Tocco *(Sr VP-Payer Sls)*
Tom Underwood *(CEO)*

Subsidiary (Domestic):

Interactive Financial Solutions, Inc. (2)
122 S Fulton St, Wauseon, OH 43567
Tel.: (419) 335-1280
Web Site: http://www.solanapro.com
Sales Range: $1-9.9 Million
Emp.: 14
Software Publisher
N.A.I.C.S.: 513210
Lynn Miller *(Pres)*
Doug Nafziger *(CEO)*

SANDBERG FURNITURE MANUFACTURING CO.
5685 Alcoa Ave, Los Angeles, CA 90058
Tel.: (323) 582-0711
Web Site:
　http://www.sandbergfurniture.com
Sales Range: $10-24.9 Million
Emp.: 400
Wood Bedroom Furniture
N.A.I.C.S.: 337122
Albert Sandberg *(Pres)*

SANDBRIDGE CAPITAL LLC
725 Fifth Ave 23rd Fl, New York, NY 10022
Tel.: (212) 292-7870
Web Site:
　http://www.sandbridgecap.com
Private Investment Firm
N.A.I.C.S.: 523999
Joseph M. Lamastra *(Founder & Mng Partner)*
Kenneth Suslow *(Mng Partner)*
Richard Henry *(Principal)*

SANDER SALES ENTERPRISES LTD.
580 5th Ave Rm 537, New York, NY 10036
Tel.: (212) 869-9685
Rev.: $22,457,158
Emp.: 1
Cotton Sheets, Bedding & Table Cloths Sales
N.A.I.C.S.: 449129
Eugene Sander *(Pres)*

SANDERLING VENTURES
400 S El Camino Real Ste 1200, San Mateo, CA 94402
Tel.: (650) 401-2000
Web Site: http://www.sanderling.com
Year Founded: 1987
Sales Range: $25-49.9 Million
Emp.: 16
Privater Equity Firm
N.A.I.C.S.: 523999
Robert G. McNeil *(Mng Dir)*
Timothy Mills *(Mng Dir)*
Peter McWilliams *(Mng Dir)*
Paulette Taylor *(Principal & Gen Counsel)*
Thomas Muscarella *(CFO & Principal)*
Penelope Jackson *(Controller)*
Fortune Miraflor *(Mgr-Acct)*

Michael Dixon *(Mng Dir)*
Louise Proulx *(Mng Dir)*
Fred A. Middleton *(Mng Dir)*

SANDERS BROTHERS CONSTRUCTION CO
1990 Harley St, North Charleston, SC 29406
Tel.: (843) 744-4261
Web Site:
　http://www.sandersbrothers.com
Sales Range: $10-24.9 Million
Emp.: 82
General Contractor, Highway & Street Construction
N.A.I.C.S.: 237310
Jason Cockfield *(Superintendent)*
James G. Sanders Jr. *(Founder & Chm)*

SANDERS FORD INC.
1135 Lejeune Blvd, Jacksonville, NC 28540-6333
Tel.: (910) 455-1911　NC
Web Site:
　http://www.sandersford.com
Year Founded: 1951
Sales Range: $25-49.9 Million
Emp.: 115
New & Used Car Dealers
N.A.I.C.S.: 441110
Mat C. Raymond *(Gen Mgr)*
Cliff Renchen *(Gen Mgr-Sls)*
Cassandra Humbert *(Mgr-Bus Dev)*
Jack Glover *(Mgr-Sls)*
Joe Anderson *(Bus Mgr)*
John Mooney *(Mgr-Inventory Control)*
Kevin Blake *(Mgr-Sls)*

SANDERS HYLAND CORPORATION
1640 Varner Dr, Mobile, AL 36693
Tel.: (251) 661-1952
Web Site:
　http://www.sandershyland.com
Sales Range: $10-24.9 Million
Floor Installation Services
N.A.I.C.S.: 238330
Bo McClinton *(Project Mgr)*
Jim Roberts *(Mgr-Contracts)*
Judy Booth *(Office Mgr)*

SANDERS MANUFACTURING CO., INC.
500 Industrial Park Rd Bldg L-7, Destin, FL 32541
Tel.: (850) 837-0979　FL
Web Site:
　http://www.sandersmfgco.com
Year Founded: 1977
Sales Range: $1-9.9 Million
Emp.: 13
Custom Mmachined & Molded Products Mfr
N.A.I.C.S.: 332710
Billy J. Sanders *(Pres)*

SANDERS MARKETING GROUP INC.
7721 E Uppr Rdg Dr, Pompano Beach, FL 33067
Tel.: (954) 345-5205
Rev.: $20,000,000
Emp.: 8
Miscellaneous Nondurable Goods Merchant Whslr
N.A.I.C.S.: 424990
Susan Sanders *(CEO)*

SANDERS OIL COMPANY INC.
1020 Island Rd, Columbus, MS 39701-8524
Tel.: (662) 328-2318　MS
Year Founded: 1986
Sales Range: $10-24.9 Million
Emp.: 100

Petroleum Products Sales
N.A.I.C.S.: 424710
Nancy Perkins *(Office Mgr)*
William Lee Sanders Jr. *(Pres)*

SANDERS PLUMBING SUPPLY INC.
107 E Belding St, Hot Springs, AR 71901
Tel.: (501) 321-9511
Web Site:
　http://www.sandersgallery.com
Year Founded: 1978
Sales Range: $10-24.9 Million
Emp.: 65
Plumbing Fittings & Supplies
N.A.I.C.S.: 423720
Bill E. Sanders *(Chm)*
Ed Sanders *(Pres)*
Todd Shiver *(Controller)*

SANDERSON BELLECCI, INC.
2290 Diamond Blvd, Ste 100, Concord, CA 94520
Tel.: (925) 685-4569
Engineeering Services
N.A.I.C.S.: 541330

Subsidiaries:

Coleman Engineering, Inc. (1)
1340 Blue Oaks Blvd, Roseville, CA 95678-7035
Tel.: (916) 791-1188
Web Site: http://www.coleman-eng.com
Engineeering Services
N.A.I.C.S.: 541330

Sanderson Stewart (1)
106 E Babcock St Ste C, Bozeman, MT 59715-4771
Tel.: (406) 522-9876
Web Site: http://www.sandersonstewart.com
Engineeering Services
N.A.I.C.S.: 541330
Todd Mitchell *(Mgr)*

Subsidiary (Domestic):

Bellecci & Associates, Inc. (2)
2290 Diamond Blvd Ste 100, Concord, CA 94520
Tel.: (925) 685-4561
Web Site: http://www.bellecci.com
Sales Range: $1-9.9 Million
Emp.: 12
Engineeering Services
N.A.I.C.S.: 541330
Frank C. Bellecci *(Founder, Principal, Sr Mgr & Engr-Transportation)*
Alex Fong *(Principal & Sr Mgr)*
Anoop R. Admal *(Principal & Sr Mgr)*
Charles Capp *(Principal & Sr Mgr)*
Robert E. Broestl *(Principal & Sr Mgr)*

SANDERSON FORD INC.
6400 N 51st Ave, Glendale, AZ 85301
Tel.: (623) 842-8600
Web Site:
　http://www.sandersonford.com
Sales Range: $150-199.9 Million
Emp.: 390
Retail Auto Dealership
N.A.I.C.S.: 441110
Max Sirstins *(Dir-Adv)*
Steve Wendt *(Gen Mgr)*
Neil Schrock *(Gen Mgr-Sls)*
Loren Clifton *(Mgr-New Vehicle Sls)*
Tom Collins *(Gen Mgr-Sls)*
Larry Haidek *(Mgr-Internet Sls)*
Andy Reece *(Mgr-Sls)*
Dave Tedder *(Dir-Internet)*

SANDERSON LINCOLN
2121 W Bell Rd, Phoenix, AZ 85023
Tel.: (602) 375-7500
Web Site:
　http://www.sandersonlincoln.com
Sales Range: $75-99.9 Million
Emp.: 144

New & Used Automobiles Dealer
N.A.I.C.S.: 441120
Patrick Heigl *(Mgr-Fleet & Leasing)*
Jim Landeros *(Mgr-Sls)*

SANDERSON SAFETY SUPPLY CO. INC.
1101 SE 3rd Ave, Portland, OR 97214-3343
Tel.: (503) 238-5700　OR
Web Site:
　http://www.sandersonsafety.com
Year Founded: 1989
Sales Range: $10-24.9 Million
Emp.: 110
Provider of Safety Supplies
N.A.I.C.S.: 423990
Stephen Spahr *(Pres)*
Jerry Griffin *(VP-Fin)*
Matt Hagerty *(Mgr-Construction Svcs)*
Nick Lehmann *(Mgr-Pur)*

SANDESTIN GOLF & BEACH RESORT
9300 Emerald Coast Pkwy W, Miramar Beach, FL 32550
Tel.: (850) 267-8000　FL
Web Site: http://www.sandestin.com
Sales Range: $125-149.9 Million
Resort Operator
N.A.I.C.S.: 721110
Matt Lindley *(VP-Resort Activities)*
Angela Gaff *(Mgr-Employment)*
Thomas Becnel *(Owner)*

SANDFORD OIL COMPANY, INC.
501 S US Hwy 81/287 Bus PO Box 660, Decatur, TX 76234
Tel.: (940) 627-2689　TX
Web Site: http://www.sandfordoil.com
Year Founded: 1988
Sales Range: $10-24.9 Million
Emp.: 119
Petroleum & Petroleum Products Distr
N.A.I.C.S.: 424720
R. Blake Sandford *(Pres)*

Subsidiaries:

Sandford Oil South Texas (1)
5582 Old Brownsville Rd, Corpus Christi, TX 78417
Tel.: (361) 289-7010
Web Site: http://www.sandfordoil.com
Petroleum & Petroleum Products Distr
N.A.I.C.S.: 424720
David Rivera *(Office Mgr)*

SANDHILLS PUBLISHING COMPANY
120 W Harvest Dr, Lincoln, NE 68521
Tel.: (402) 479-2181
Web Site: http://www.sandhills.com
Information Processing & Publishing Company
N.A.I.C.S.: 513199
Lindsay Kant *(Asst Mgr-Distr)*

Subsidiaries:

Equipmentfacts LLC (1)
699 US-202, Flemington, NJ 08822
Tel.: (207) 848-0739
Web Site: http://www.equipmentfacts.com
Auto Auctions
N.A.I.C.S.: 423110
Larry Garafola *(Founder & CEO)*

SANDIA BMW
6001 Pan American W Freeway NE, Albuquerque, NM 87109
Tel.: (505) 884-0066
Web Site: http://www.sandiabmw.com
Year Founded: 1986
Sales Range: $25-49.9 Million
Emp.: 150
Car Whslr

Sandia BMW—(Continued)
N.A.I.C.S.: 441110
Michael Houx (Gen Mgr)

SANDIA OFFICE SUPPLY
3831 Singer Blvd NE, Albuquerque, NM 87109
Tel.: (505) 341-4900
Web Site: http://www.sosnm.com
Year Founded: 2003
Rev.: $11,400,000
Emp.: 29
Office Supplies & Stationery Stores
N.A.I.C.S.: 459410
Lynn Long (Mgr)
Todd A. Sandoval (Pres)

SANDLAPPER SECURITIES, LLC
800 E North St 2nd Fl, Greenville, SC 29601
Tel.: (864) 679-4701
Web Site:
 http://www.sandlappersecurities.com
Year Founded: 2005
Sales Range: $1-9.9 Million
Emp.: 25
Investment Products & Services, Insurance, Annuity & Investment Banking
N.A.I.C.S.: 523999
Mark Reinstein (Pres-Retail Market Div)
Bjorn Jordan (COO)
Trevor Gordon (Founder & CEO)
Howard Davis (Pres)
Jack C. Bixler (Principal-Capital Markets Div)
Mark C. Pedersen (Mgr-Natl Accts)
Marlene Arteta (CMO)
Amy Schiera (VP-Corp Ops)
Brooke Jones (Dir-New Bus)
Raymond Sun (Mgr-Due Diligence)
Elizabeth Stevens (Sr VP-Product, Res & Mktg & Mgr-Texas)
Natalyn Klump (Specialist-Mktg)
Kenneth Bolton (Exec VP & Sls Mgr-Broker Dealer-Natl)

Subsidiaries:

Colony Park Financial Services LLC (1)
4350 Georgetown Sq Ste 757, Dunwoody, GA 30338
Tel.: (770) 886-3993
Web Site:
 http://www.colonyparkfinancial.com
Emp.: 5
Financial Services & Investment Advice
N.A.I.C.S.: 523940

SANDLER CAPITAL MANAGEMENT
711 5th Ave 15th Fl, New York, NY 10022
Tel.: (212) 754-8100 NY
Web Site: http://www.sandlercap.com
Year Founded: 1986
Rev.: $830,000,000
Emp.: 33
Investment Advisory & Alternative Asset Management Services
N.A.I.C.S.: 523940
Andrew Sandler (Mng Dir, Head-Hedge Funds & Portfolio Mgr)
Stacey Seewald (Chief Compliance Officer)
Cheryl Demaree (VP)
Michael Engelson (Controller-Fund)
Douglas Schimmel (Mng Dir & Portfolio Mgr)
Vito Menza (Mng Dir & Asst Portfolio Mgr)
Brent Benkovic (Mng Dir)
Eric Lewis (Mng Dir)
Paul Ernst (Mng Dir & CIO)
Michael Marocco (Mng Dir & Head-Private Equity)
Carese Gillespie (VP)
Eric Hsu (Mng Dir)
Matthew Kohn (Mng Dir)
Tim Marsek (Mng Dir)
Tom Molnar (Mng Dir)
Eric Stephenson (Mng Dir)
William Bianco (Mng Dir)
Steven Warshavsky (Mng Dir & CFO)
Ryan McGarrity (Asst Controller)
Benjamin Rowbotham (VP)
Justin Fitzgerald (Officer-Compliance)
Kevin Heal (Mng Dir)
R. J. Moulton (VP)

SANDLER LLC
2711 N Haskell Ave Ste 2700, Dallas, TX 75204
Tel.: (214) 257-1832 DC
Web Site: http://www.sandlerllc.com
Law firm
N.A.I.C.S.: 541110
Andrew L. Sandler (Chm & CEO)
Theresa Buenerkemper (Dir-Operational Compliance)
Marshall Mahurin (Dir-Compliance & Quality Assurance)
John Mezger (Dir-IT)
Ken Mezger (Dir-Ops)
Vicki Murphy-Gee (Exec Dir)

SANDLER PARTNERS
920 Manhattan Beach Blvd Ste 1, Manhattan Beach, CA 90266
Tel.: (310) 796-1393
Web Site:
 http://www.sandlerpartners.com
Year Founded: 2003
Sales Range: $1-9.9 Million
Emp.: 20
Telecommunications & Auditing Recovery Services
N.A.I.C.S.: 517810
Alan Sandler (Founder & Mng Partner)
Bret Masterson (Sr Partner-Bus Dev)
Marc A. Coppens (Sr Partner)
Joe Orriols (Sr Partner)
Gregory O. Welch (Sr Partner)
Steven Levine (Sr Partner)
Peter Cook (Partner)
Mark Peach (Sr VP-Sls)
Yuliya Mammadova (Controller)
Nicole Vavrek (Coord-Ops)
Gregg Madsen (Dir-Sls-Natl)
Drew Kenworthy (Mgr-Acctg)
Kirsten Ferdinandsen (Mgr-Audit & Project)
Nathan Brebner (Reg VP)
Paul Seeley (Reg VP)
Caleb Tucker (Reg VP)
Eric Beller (Sr VP-Sls & Mktg)
Tim Tucker (VP-Bus Dev)
Jennifer Griffith (Mgr-Partner Experience-Northeast)
Nick Brown (Dir-Channel-Great Lakes Reg)
Gerry Davis (VP & Engr-Sls-East)
Mark Phaneuf (Sr VP-Channel-East)
Michael Clayton (Dir-Channel-Georgia & the Carolinas)

SANDLER SYSTEMS, INC.
300 Red Brook Blvd Ste 400, Owings Mills, MD 21117
Tel.: (410) 653-1993
Web Site: http://www.sandler.com
Sales Range: $1-9.9 Million
Emp.: 24
Administrative Management & General Management Consulting Service
N.A.I.C.S.: 541611

David Mattson (Pres & CEO)
Shannon Haaf (Gen Counsel)
Margaret Jacks (Exec VP)

SANDLIN MOTORS
204-6 E 16th St, Mount Pleasant, TX 75455
Tel.: (903) 572-3656
Web Site:
 http://www.chevyhouse.com
Sales Range: $10-24.9 Million
Emp.: 40
New Car Whslr
N.A.I.C.S.: 441110
Joe Sandlin (Owner & VP)
Mark Bishop (Mgr-Fin)

SANDOVAL CRUZ COMPANY
3961 N Mission Rd, Los Angeles, CA 90031
Tel.: (323) 226-0335
Sales Range: $10-24.9 Million
Emp.: 25
Distribution Of Hardware
N.A.I.C.S.: 423710
Sandoval Cruz (CEO)

SANDOW MEDIA LLC
3651 FAU Blvd, Boca Raton, FL 33431
Tel.: (561) 961-7600 DE
Web Site: http://www.sandow.com
Year Founded: 2003
Emp.: 400
Periodical Publishers
N.A.I.C.S.: 513120
Adam I. Sandow (Founder & Chm)
Erica Holborn (CEO-Sandow Design Grp)
Cindy Allen (Chief Design Officer-Sandow Design Grp)
Bobby Bonnett (Chief Growth Officer & Exec VP-Client Strategy)

Subsidiaries:

Bellerophon Publications, Inc. (1)
205 Lexington Ave 17th Fl, New York, NY 10016
Tel.: (917) 934-9800
Web Site: http://www.metropolismag.com
Periodical Publishers
N.A.I.C.S.: 513120

Material ConneXion, Inc. (1)
101 Park Ave 4th Fl, New York, NY 10178
Tel.: (212) 842-2050
Web Site:
 http://www.materialconnexion.com
Sales Range: $10-24.9 Million
Emp.: 15
Materials Consultancy Services
N.A.I.C.S.: 541614
Tiffany Vasilchik (VP-Bus Dev)
Michele Caniato (Pres)
Gabriella Vivaldi (Mgr-Mktg & Comm)
Susan Towers (VP-Mktg & Comm)
Sarah Natkins (Dir-Mktg & Comm)

Branch (Non-US):

Material ConneXion Milano (2)
Viale Sarca 336 Edificio 16, presso Triennale Bovisa, 20126, Milan, Italy
Tel.: (39) 0286891720
Web Site:
 http://www.it.materialconnexion.com
Emp.: 10
Materials Consultancy Services
N.A.I.C.S.: 541690
Emilio Genovesi (CEO)

SANDPIPER TOO, INC.
31 Ocean Reef Dr B 100, Key Largo, FL 33037
Tel.: (305) 367-3123 FL
Web Site:
 http://www.sandpiperclothiers.com
Year Founded: 1971
Sales Range: $1-9.9 Million
Emp.: 35
Women's Clothing Store

N.A.I.C.S.: 458110
Barbara Perdue (VP)
Winifred Reynolds (Founder & Pres)

SANDRA EVANS & ASSOCIATES
3001 Bridgeway Ste K 211, Sausalito, CA 94965
Tel.: (415) 887-9230
Web Site:
 http://sandraevansandassociates.com
Year Founded: 2001
Sales Range: Less than $1 Million
Advertising & Public Relations Agency
N.A.I.C.S.: 541820
Sandra Evans (Founder & Dir-Creative)

SANDRIDGE FOOD CORPORATION
133 Commerce Dr, Medina, OH 44256-1333
Tel.: (330) 725-2348
Web Site: http://www.sandridge.com
Year Founded: 1960
Sales Range: $25-49.9 Million
Emp.: 600
Mfr of Fresh Refrigerated Prepared Foods
N.A.I.C.S.: 311991
Michael Sandridge (Sr Dir-Food Svc Dev)
Lori Kyle (Mgr-Customer Svc)
Frank Sidari (VP-Sls & New Bus Dev)
Jordan Sandridge (Co-Pres)
Dane Sandridge (Co-Pres)

Subsidiaries:

RMH Foods LLC (1)
375 Erie Ave, Morton, IL 61550
Tel.: (309) 266-1500
Web Site: http://www.rmhfoods.com
Sales Range: $10-24.9 Million
Emp.: 115
Pre-Cooked Port & Beef Entrees Sales
N.A.I.C.S.: 424470
Roger Phillis (Mgr-Sls)

Winter Gardens Quality Foods, Inc. (1)
304 Commerce St, New Oxford, PA 17350
Tel.: (717) 624-4911
Web Site: http://www.wintergardens.com
Sales Range: $10-24.9 Million
Emp.: 104
Food Preparations
N.A.I.C.S.: 311999
Ed Reichert (VP-Info Sys)
Dave Collado (VP-HR)

SANDRO CONSTRUCTION, INC.
1697 Bridge St, Rahway, NJ 07065
Tel.: (732) 388-9049 NJ
Web Site:
 http://www.sandroconstruction.com
Year Founded: 1991
Paving, Masonry & Site Contractor
N.A.I.C.S.: 237310
Joe Mallozzi (Founder, Owner & Pres)
Art Scofield (Office Mgr)

SANDS BROS AUTO SALES, INC.
501 N W End Blvd, Quakertown, PA 18951
Tel.: (215) 536-0946
Sales Range: $10-24.9 Million
Emp.: 50
Car Whslr
N.A.I.C.S.: 441110
Terry Sands (Pres)

SANDS BROTHERS ASSET MANAGEMENT LLC

15 Vly Dr, Greenwich, CT 06831
Tel.: (203) 661-7500   DE
Web Site: http://www.sandsbros.com
Year Founded: 1990
Sales Range: $25-49.9 Million
Emp.: 10
Investment Management & Advisory Services
N.A.I.C.S.: 523940
Steven B. Sands *(Co-Founder, Co-Chm, Partner & Sr Portfolio Mgr)*
Martin S. Sands *(Co-Founder, Co-Chm, Partner & Portfolio Mgr)*
Christopher Kelly *(Partner, COO & Chief Compliance Officer)*
Hugh J. Marasa Jr. *(Dir-Mktg & IR)*

Subsidiaries:

Sands Brothers & Co. Ltd.   (1)
2351 E Hallandale Beach Blvd, Hallandale, FL 33009-4851
Tel.: (954) 454-0304
Provider of Online Brokerage Services
N.A.I.C.S.: 523150

SANDS INVESTMENT GROUP, INC.
238 Mathis Ferry Rd Ste 102, Mount Pleasant, SC 29464
Web Site: http://www.signnn.com
Year Founded: 2010
Sales Range: $1-9.9 Million
Emp.: 200
Real Estate Investment Services
N.A.I.C.S.: 531210
Chris Sands *(Founder & CEO)*
Liz Sands *(COO)*
Ryan Passe *(Exec VP)*
Kim Wilton *(Dir-Mktg & Ops)*
Miranda McCurdy *(Dir-Mktg & Strategy)*

SANDS MOTOR COMPANY, INC.
5418 NW Grand Ave, Glendale, AZ 85301-4501
Tel.: (623) 931-9331   AZ
Web Site:
http://www.sandschevrolet.com
Year Founded: 1938
Sales Range: $75-99.9 Million
Emp.: 170
New & Used Automobiles Retailer
N.A.I.C.S.: 441110
Gary R. Long *(Sec & VP)*
Dan Joyce *(Dir-Svc)*
Louis Sands IV *(Pres)*

SANDSRX, LLC
4 Regency Dr, Wylie, TX 75098
Tel.: (972) 535-2020   TX
Web Site: http://www.sandsrx.com
Year Founded: 2013
Sales Range: $25-49.9 Million
Emp.: 50
Pharmaceutical Products Distr
N.A.I.C.S.: 424210
Mike Sands *(Co-Founder & CEO)*
Steve Sands *(Co-Founder & Pres)*
Mahdi Al Hallaq *(Owner)*

SANDSTONE GROUP, INC.
223 N Water St Ste 500, Milwaukee, WI 53202
Tel.: (414) 902-6700   WI
Web Site: http://www.elakeside.com
Investment Holding Company
N.A.I.C.S.: 551112
Lawrence P. Moon *(Chm)*
Terry Hoelle *(VP-Sls)*

Subsidiaries:

Alliance Products, LLC   (1)
820 Esther Ln, Murfreesboro, TN 37129-5536
Tel.: (615) 895-5333
Web Site: http://www.allianceproducts.net
Rev.: $1,200,000
Emp.: 20
Commercial Food Preparation Equipment Mfr
N.A.I.C.S.: 333241

SANDSTORM DESIGN, INC.
4619 N Ravenswood Ave Ste 300, Chicago, IL 60640
Tel.: (773) 348-4200
Web Site:
http://www.sandstormdesign.com
Year Founded: 1998
Sales Range: $1-9.9 Million
Emp.: 14
Strategic Marketing & Web Design Services
N.A.I.C.S.: 541490
Sandy Marsico *(Founder & CEO)*
Megan Culligan *(Coord-Digital)*
Janna Fiester *(Dir-Creative)*
Michael Hartman *(Dir-Tech & Usability)*
Andrea Wood *(Mng Dir)*

SANDUSCO, INC.
11012 Aurora Hudson Rd, Streetsboro, OH 44241-1629
Tel.: (330) 528-0410   OH
Web Site: http://www.arrdis.com
Year Founded: 1956
Sales Range: $25-49.9 Million
Emp.: 160
Merchandiser & Distributor of Entertainment Software Products
N.A.I.C.S.: 423990
Harry Singer *(Pres & CEO)*
Liz Jones *(Mgr-Ops)*
Jenni Hamilton *(Dir-Adv)*
Phil Singer *(Sr VP-Sls & Mktg)*

Subsidiaries:

Sandusky Distributing Company, Inc.   (1)
11012 Aurora Hudson Rd, Streetsboro, OH 44241-1629   (100%)
Tel.: (330) 528-0410
Web Site: http://www.arrdis.com
Sales Range: $10-24.9 Million
Emp.: 100
Durable Goods
N.A.I.C.S.: 423990
Harry Singer *(Pres)*

SANDUSKY CABINETS INC.
4815 Biloxi St, Millington, TN 38053
Tel.: (901) 872-6696
Web Site:
http://www.sanduskycabinets.com
Sales Range: $10-24.9 Million
Emp.: 90
Cabinetry Mfr
N.A.I.C.S.: 337126
Pete Schroder *(Reg Mgr-Mfg)*

SANDUSKY NEWSPAPERS INC.
314 W Market St, Sandusky, OH 44870
Tel.: (419) 625-5500
Web Site:
http://www.sanduskyregister.com
Sales Range: $25-49.9 Million
Emp.: 140
Newspapers
N.A.I.C.S.: 513110
Doug Phares *(Dir-Adv)*
Kevin Fraley *(Dir-Adv)*
Dudley A. White Jr. *(Chm)*

Subsidiaries:

Johnson City Press   (1)
204 W Main St, Johnson City, TN 37604-6212
Tel.: (423) 929-3111
Web Site: http://www.johnsoncitypress.com
Sales Range: $25-49.9 Million
Publisher of Newspapers
N.A.I.C.S.: 513110
Allen Moore *(Mgr-Customer Rels)*

Subsidiary (Domestic):

Lebanon Publishing Company Inc.   (2)
402 N Cumberland St, Lebanon, TN 37087-2306
Tel.: (615) 444-3952
Web Site: http://www.lebanondemocrat.com
Sales Range: $25-49.9 Million
Emp.: 35
Publisher of Newspapers
N.A.I.C.S.: 513110
Jared Felkins *(Dir-Content & Audience Dev)*

Ogden Publishing Corporation   (1)
332 S Standard Way, Ogden, UT 84404
Tel.: (801) 625-4554
Web Site: http://www.standard.net
Sales Range: $25-49.9 Million
Newspaper Publishing & Printing
N.A.I.C.S.: 513110
David Rau *(Pres)*
Jared W. Bird *(Mgr-Retail Adv)*
David H. Newman *(Mgr-Adv)*
Brad Roghaar *(Dir-Sls)*
Andy Howell *(Exec Editor)*
Vaughn Jacobsen *(Bus Mgr)*
Mark Shenefelt *(Mgr)*
Bart Wade *(Dir-Production)*
Charles Horton III *(Publr-Standard-Examiner & VP)*

SANDY HOOK YACHT SALES INC.
1410 Ocean Ave, Sea Bright, NJ 07760
Tel.: (732) 530-5500
Web Site:
http://www.sandyhookyachts.com
Sales Range: $10-24.9 Million
Emp.: 15
Boat Sales
N.A.I.C.S.: 441222
Bill Bergin *(Founder & Pres)*
Sheri Runne *(Office Mgr)*
Hank Hartmann *(Owner)*

SANDY SANSING NISSAN, INC.
5705 Pensacola Blvd, Pensacola, FL 32505-2565
Tel.: (850) 479-4700
Web Site:
http://www.sandysansingnissan.com
Year Founded: 1988
Sales Range: $10-24.9 Million
Emp.: 48
Car Whslr
N.A.I.C.S.: 441110
Kelley Manning *(Mgr-Customer Svcs)*
S. Sansing *(Pres)*

SANDYS ASSOCIATES INC.
1503 N Boeke Rd, Evansville, IN 47711
Tel.: (812) 477-5569   IN
Web Site: http://www.evansville.com
Year Founded: 1960
Sales Range: $10-24.9 Million
Emp.: 271
Fast-Food Restaurant Owner & Operator
N.A.I.C.S.: 722513
Joseph H. Harrison *(Pres)*
James Reynolds *(VP)*

SANFORD & HAWLEY, INC.
1790 Farmington Ave, Unionville, CT 06085
Tel.: (860) 673-3213   CT
Web Site: http://www.sanhaw.com
Year Founded: 1946
Sales Range: $75-99.9 Million
Emp.: 90
Sale of Building Materials; Lumber; Drywall; Hardware; Paint; Plywood; Windows; Doors; Mason Supplies & Roofing
N.A.I.C.S.: 423310
Robert P. Sanford *(Pres)*
Edmund E. Sanford *(VP-Ops)*
Frank W. Sanford *(VP-Mktg)*
Clara E. Sanford *(Sec)*

SANFORD HEALTH
1305 W 18th St, Sioux Falls, SD 57105-0401
Tel.: (605) 328-5690   SD
Web Site:
http://www.sanfordhealth.org
Sales Range: $1-4.9 Billion
Emp.: 48,622
Health Care Srvices
N.A.I.C.S.: 813910
Mark Paulson *(Vice Chm)*
Brent Teiken *(Chm)*
Cindy Morrison *(CMO)*
Paul F. Richard *(Exec VP-Sanford Fargo)*
Bill Marlette *(CFO)*
Mike Begeman *(VP-Pub Affairs)*
Kirk Zimmer *(Exec VP-Sanford Health Plan)*
Bryan Nermoe *(Exec VP-Sanford Bemidji)*
Daniel Blue *(Exec VP)*
Bill Gassen *(Pres & CEO)*
Donald Jake Jacobs *(Treas)*
Michael Lebeau *(Chief Admin Officer-Health Svcs & Sr VP)*
Nathan Peterson *(VP-Strategic Plng & Governance)*
Colleen Swank *(VP-Clinics)*
Kelly Hagen *(VP-Nursing & Clinical Svcs)*
David Shulkin *(Chief Innovation Officer)*
Micah Aberson *(Exec VP)*
Jennifer Grennan *(Chief Legal Officer)*
Allison Suttle *(Chief Medical Officer)*
Matt Hocks *(COO)*
Michael E. LeBeau *(Chief Admin Officer/VP-Health Svcs Div)*

Subsidiaries:

Maverick Air Center LLC   (1)
4201 N Maverick Pl, Sioux Falls, SD 57104-0115
Tel.: (605) 312-5680
Web Site: http://www.maverickaircenter.com
Airport Operations
N.A.I.C.S.: 488119

The Evangelical Lutheran Good Samaritan Foundation   (1)
4800 W 57th St, Sioux Falls, SD 57108
Tel.: (605) 362-3100
Web Site: http://good-sam.com
Sales Range: $1-9.9 Million
Emp.: 120
Civic & Social Organizations
N.A.I.C.S.: 813410
Joe Herdina *(VP-Fin)*
Thomas J. Kapusta *(VP-Legal, Audit & Compliance Svcs)*
Jim Krekelberg *(VP-Acctg & Controller)*
Frederick Lyons *(VP-Sls, Mktg & Comm)*
Bergen Peterson *(Chief Admin Officer & Exec VP)*
Jan Ritter *(VP-Workforce Sys)*
Tom Syverson *(COO & Exec VP)*
Grant Tribble *(CFO & Exec VP)*
Victoria Walker *(Chief Medical & Quality Officer)*
Rustan Williams *(VP-Information Svcs & Tech Sys)*
Randy Bury *(Pres & CEO)*
Gregory Johnson *(Chief Medical Officer)*

SANFORD INSTITUTION FOR SAVINGS

SANFORD INSTITUTION FOR SAVINGS

U.S. PRIVATE

Sanford Institution For Savings—(Continued)
900 Main St, Sanford, ME 04073-0472
Tel.: (207) 324-2285
Web Site: http://www.banksis.com
Year Founded: 1933
Sales Range: $25-49.9 Million
Emp.: 100
Banking Services
N.A.I.C.S.: 522180
Amanda Stacey *(Mgr-Core Admin)*
John Tanguay *(VP-Comml Lending)*
Karen Meserve *(Head-Teller)*
Kathleen MacDonald *(VP-HR)*
Patty Holman *(Mgr-Ops-Retail Lending)*
Blaine Boudreau *(CEO)*

SANFORD RESOURCES CORPORATION
9655 Hwy 18 W, Vernon, AL 35592
Tel.: (205) 695-7128
Sales Range: $25-49.9 Million
Emp.: 5
Truss Mfr
N.A.I.C.S.: 321215

Subsidiaries:

Trim Joist Corporation (1)
5146 Hwy 182 E, Columbus, MS 39702
Tel.: (662) 327-7950
Web Site: http://www.trimjoist.com
Trusses, Except Roof: Laminated Lumber
N.A.I.C.S.: 321215

SANGAM & ASSOCIATES
3435 Wilshire Blvd Ste 2880, Los Angeles, CA 90010
Tel.: (213) 252-6320 CA
Web Site: http://www.sang-am.com
Year Founded: 1995
Sales Range: $10-24.9 Million
Emp.: 15
N.A.I.C.S.: 541810
Jaime Lee *(Media Dir)*
Misun Jang *(Sr Art Dir)*
Yoon-Hee Choi *(Media Planner)*
Ray Cho *(Dir-Creative)*
Yong-cheol Kim *(Dir-Art)*
Kwi-Hee Park *(Copywriter)*
Jong-Oh Kim *(Sr Acct Exec)*
C.K. Han *(Pres)*

SANGAREE OIL COMPANY INC.
2979 Pierce St, Marianna, FL 32448
Tel.: (850) 482-5241
Rev.: $25,816,656
Emp.: 6
Petroleum Terminal
N.A.I.C.S.: 424710
Stephen A. Sangaree *(Pres)*

SANGERA BUICK, INC.
5600 Gasoline Alley Dr, Bakersfield, CA 93313-3737
Tel.: (661) 836-3737
Year Founded: 1972
Sales Range: $10-24.9 Million
Emp.: 50
Car Whslr
N.A.I.C.S.: 441110
David Bailey *(Dir-Safety)*
Damon Culbertson *(Pres)*
H. D. Sanghera *(VP)*
Melinda Tapia *(Office Mgr)*

SANGRE DE CRISTO ELECTRIC ASSOCIATION, INC.
29780 N US Highway 24, Buena Vista, CO 81211
Tel.: (719) 395-2412 CO
Web Site: http://www.myelectric.coop
Year Founded: 1940
Rev.: $19,500,443
Assets: $61,585,587
Liabilities: $39,364,679
Net Worth: $22,220,908
Earnings: $1,201,224
Emp.: 40
Fiscal Year-end: 12/31/18
Electric Power Distribution Services
N.A.I.C.S.: 221122

SANGSTER MOTORS, INC.
912 N Miller St, Wenatchee, WA 98801
Tel.: (509) 662-6134
Web Site: http://www.sangstermotors.com
Year Founded: 1989
Sales Range: $25-49.9 Million
Emp.: 44
Car Whslr
N.A.I.C.S.: 441110
Chad Sangster *(Mgr-Svc)*
Don Sangster *(Pres)*

SANI-MATIC, INC.
1915 S Stoughton Rd, Madison, WI 53716
Tel.: (608) 222-2399
Web Site: http://www.sanimatic.com
Sales Range: $10-24.9 Million
Emp.: 100
Food Product Machinery Mfr
N.A.I.C.S.: 333241
Ted Schmidt *(Engr-Product Dev)*
Aaron Zell *(Pres & CEO)*

SANIBEL CAPTIVA COMMUNITY BANK
2475 Library Way, Sanibel, FL 33957
Tel.: (239) 472-6100
Web Site: http://www.sancapbank.com
Sales Range: $10-24.9 Million
Emp.: 37
Commericial Banking
N.A.I.C.S.: 522110
Craig Albert *(Chm)*
David Carleton Hall *(CFO, COO & Exec VP)*
Tony Gropp *(Sr VP-Residential Mortgage Lending)*
David Wright *(Sr VP-Residential Mortgage Lending)*
Jennifer Briggs *(Asst Mgr-Downtown Fort Myers)*
Jonathan Ruiz *(Sr VP & Dir-IT-Winkler)*
Jill Grossenbaugh *(VP-Winkler)*
Kyle DeCicco *(Pres & CEO)*
Rudi Hamer *(VP & Mgr-Comml Relationship)*
Brian Terrell *(Chief Credit Officer & Exec VP)*

SANITY SOLUTIONS INC.
1720 S Bellaire St Ste 550, Denver, CO 80222
Tel.: (720) 570-1668
Web Site: http://www.sanitysolutions.com
Sales Range: $10-24.9 Million
Emp.: 9
Data Management Services
N.A.I.C.S.: 541513
Michael J. Gluck *(VP)*
Lisa Barrett *(Acct Exec)*

SANKO INTERNATIONAL INC.
98 Cuttermill Rd Fl 4, Great Neck, NY 11021
Tel.: (516) 829-0896
Web Site: http://www.universalmetals.us
Rev.: $11,000,000
Emp.: 19
Miscellaneous Nonferrous Products
N.A.I.C.S.: 423510
Sanjay Kochar *(Pres)*

SANNA MATTSON MACLEOD, INC.
811 W Jericho Turnpike, Smithtown, NY 11787-3232
Tel.: (631) 265-5160
Web Site: http://www.smmadvertising.com
Year Founded: 1985
Advertising Agencies
N.A.I.C.S.: 541810
Charles MacLeod *(Pres)*
Tricia Folliero *(VP-Recruitment Div)*
Judy DeBiase *(VP-Digital Dir)*
Bill Blaney *(Dir-Creative)*
Judy Bellem *(Acct Dir)*

SANO ASSOCIATES, INC.
3827 Progress Ave, Naples, FL 34104
Tel.: (239) 403-2650 FL
Web Site: http://www.category5.com
Year Founded: 1994
Sales Range: $1-9.9 Million
Emp.: 20
Metal Window & Door Mfr
N.A.I.C.S.: 332321
Jean Camposano *(Treas)*
Steve Camposano *(Pres)*

SANOMEDICS, INC.
444 Brickell Ave Ste 415, Miami, FL 33131
Tel.: (305) 433-7814 DE
Web Site: http://www.sanomedics.com
Year Founded: 1955
Sales Range: Less than $1 Million
Emp.: 3
Thermometer Mfr
N.A.I.C.S.: 339999
Gary J. O'Hara *(CTO)*
David C. Langle *(Pres, CEO, CFO & Chief Acctg Officer)*

SANOVAS, INC.
1450 N McDowell Blvd Ste 150, Petaluma, CA 94954
Tel.: (415) 729-9391 DE
Web Site: http://www.sanovas.com
Year Founded: 2010
Research & Development in Biotechnology
N.A.I.C.S.: 325412
Carlos Gonzalez *(VP-Regulatory Affairs & Quality Assurance)*

Subsidiaries:

RetinalGeniX Technologies Inc. (1)
1450 N McDowell Blvd, Petaluma, CA 94954
Tel.: (415) 578-9583
Web Site: https://retinalgenix.com
Emp.: 1
Ophthalmic Technologies Research & Development
N.A.I.C.S.: 339112

SANPULSE TECHNOLOGIES INC.
499 Washington Blvd, Jersey City, NJ 07302-3066
Tel.: (201) 536-3530
Web Site: http://www.sanpulse.com
Year Founded: 2005
Sales Range: $1-9.9 Million
Emp.: 52
Wiring Installation Contractors
N.A.I.C.S.: 238210
Gerard Lam *(Founder, Pres & CTO)*
Marie-Pierre Belanger *(VP-Product Mgmt)*

SANSEGAL SPORTSWEAR, INC.
611 W 9560 S, Sandy, UT 84070-2587
Tel.: (801) 566-3248
Year Founded: 1988
Sales Range: $10-24.9 Million
Emp.: 260
Textile Product Mill Services
N.A.I.C.S.: 314999
N. Macon Rudick *(Owner)*

SANSONE AUTO MALL
90-100 Rte 1, Avenel, NJ 07001
Tel.: (732) 815-0500 NJ
Web Site: http://www.sansoneauto.com
Year Founded: 1960
Sales Range: $125-149.9 Million
Emp.: 250
Car Dealership
N.A.I.C.S.: 441110
Paul Sandstone *(CEO)*

SANSONE GROUP LLC
120 S Central Ste 500, Saint Louis, MO 63105
Tel.: (314) 727-6664 MO
Web Site: http://www.sansonegroup.com
Year Founded: 1957
Rev.: $2,500,000,000
Emp.: 250
Real Estate Investment Development
Brokerage & Property Management Services
N.A.I.C.S.: 531390
Mike Driver *(Dir-Dev)*
Sharon A. Litteken *(Exec VP)*
Timothy J. Cherre *(Sr Exec Dir-Retail Leasing & Sls)*
James G. Sansone *(Principal)*
Douglas G. Sansone *(Principal)*
Nicholas G. Sansone *(Principal)*
Timothy G. Sansone *(Principal)*
Scott Savacool *(Dir-Ops)*
Dawn M. Owens *(Dir-Acctg & HR)*
Angie Ritz *(Controller)*
Grant Mechlin *(Mng Dir-Retail Svcs)*
Mark Kornfeld *(Mng Dir-Retail Svcs)*
Gina Danko *(Sr Dir-Residential Ops)*
Kathy Kleiman *(Sr Dir-Residential Bus Dev)*
Kathleen Mulkern *(Reg Dir-Florida)*
Samantha Gauch *(Exec Dir-Comml Property Mgmt)*
Vincent J. Bajardi *(Exec Dir-Industrial Svcs)*
Anthony F. Sansone Sr. *(Founder, Chm, CEO & Principal)*

SANTA ANA BUSINESS BANK
1666 N Main St Ste 100, Santa Ana, CA 92701
Tel.: (714) 415-1700
Commercial Banking Services
N.A.I.C.S.: 522110
Larry Sallinger *(Pres & CEO)*

SANTA BARBARA APPLIED RESEARCH INC.
2151 Alessandro Dr Ste 200, Ventura, CA 93001
Tel.: (805) 643-7081
Web Site: http://www.sbar.com
Rev.: $25,400,000
Emp.: 433
Engineeering Services
N.A.I.C.S.: 541330
Patty O'Donnell *(Mgr-HR)*

SANTA BARBARA BREWING CO.
501 State St, Santa Barbara, CA 93101
Tel.: (805) 730-1040
Web Site: http://www.sbbrewco.com
Sales Range: $10-24.9 Million
Emp.: 18
Brewery Mfr

N.A.I.C.S.: 312120
Gordon Sichi (Dir-Sls)
Eric Kelley (Owner)
Wayne Trella (Dir-Risk)

SANTA BARBARA CATERING COMPANY
1090 W 5th St Ste 5, Tempe, AZ 85281
Tel.: (480) 921-3150 AZ
Web Site:
http://www.santabarbaracatering.com
Year Founded: 1994
Sales Range: $1-9.9 Million
Emp.: 75
Catering Services
N.A.I.C.S.: 722320
Patricia Christofolo (Owner & CEO)
Lisa Tarsitano (Controller & Dir-HR)
Melissan Falcone (Mgr-Exec Event)

SANTA BARBARA NEWS-PRESS
715 Anacapa St, Santa Barbara, CA 93101-1359
Tel.: (805) 564-5200
Web Site: http://www.newspress.com
Sales Range: $75-99.9 Million
Emp.: 272
Daily Newspaper
N.A.I.C.S.: 513110
Mike McKean (Designer-Sports)
Vickie Harvey (Editor-Scene)

SANTA CLARA NUT COMPANY INC.
1590 Little Orchard St, San Jose, CA 95110
Tel.: (408) 298-2425
Sales Range: $10-24.9 Million
Emp.: 45
Nut Processing & Sales
N.A.I.C.S.: 424450
James Pusateri Jr. (Pres)

SANTA CRUZ NISSAN DODGE
1616 Soquel Ave, Santa Cruz, CA 95060
Tel.: (831) 426-5100
Web Site:
http://www.scsuperstore.com
Sales Range: $10-24.9 Million
Emp.: 65
New Car Whslr
N.A.I.C.S.: 441110
Ernest Courtright (Pres)

SANTA CRUZ SEASIDE COMPANY
400 Beach St, Santa Cruz, CA 95060
Tel.: (831) 423-5590
Web Site:
http://www.beachboardwalk.com
Rev.: $30,000,000
Emp.: 500
Amusement Park Operator
N.A.I.C.S.: 713110
Karl Rice (Pres)

SANTA ENERGY CORPORATION
154 Admiral St, Bridgeport, CT 06605-1807
Tel.: (203) 367-3661 CT
Web Site:
http://www.santaenergy.com
Year Founded: 1940
Sales Range: $25-49.9 Million
Emp.: 170
Petroleum Bulk Stations & Terminals
N.A.I.C.S.: 424710
Subsidiaries:

Inland Fuel Terminals, Inc. (1)
154 Admiral St, Bridgeport, CT 06605-1807
Tel.: (203) 367-3661
Web Site: http://www.inlandfuel.com
Sales Range: $25-49.9 Million
Emp.: 150
Petroleum Bulk Stations & Terminals
N.A.I.C.S.: 424710
Joyce Porto (VP)

Santa Buckley Energy, Inc. (1)
154 Admiral St, Bridgeport, CT 06605-1807
Tel.: (203) 336-3541
Web Site: http://www.santaenergy.com
Sales Range: $10-24.9 Million
Emp.: 9
Dealers of Gas, Diesel, Biodiesel & Jet Fuels
N.A.I.C.S.: 457210
Ed Santa (VP)

Santa Fuel, Inc. (1)
154 Admiral St, Bridgeport, CT 06605-1807
Tel.: (203) 367-3661
Web Site: http://www.santaenergy.com
Sales Range: $10-24.9 Million
Emp.: 100
Retailer of Fuels
N.A.I.C.S.: 457210
Peter S. Russell (VP & Gen Mgr)

SANTA FE COMMUNITY FOUNDATION
501 Halona St, Santa Fe, NM 87505
Tel.: (505) 988-9715 NM
Web Site: http://www.santafecf.org
Year Founded: 1981
Sales Range: $10-24.9 Million
Emp.: 22
Community Welfare Services
N.A.I.C.S.: 525120
Christa Coggins (VP-Community Philanthropy)
Sarah A. Sawtell (VP-Fin & Ops)
Rebecca Baran-Rees (Dir-Project-MoGro)
Lisa M. Enfield (Vice Chm)
Vernon Hamilton (Chm)
Diane Martinez (Sec)
Richard Moore (Treas)
Annmarie McLaughlin (Dir-Community Programs)
William Smith (Pres & CEO)

SANTA FE LEATHER CORPORATION
223 S Van Brunt St, Englewood, NJ 07631-4010
Tel.: (201) 503-0225 NY
Web Site: http://www.clava.com
Year Founded: 1996
Leather Bags & Accessories Mfr
N.A.I.C.S.: 458320
Claudio Vazquez (Founder & Pres)
Mia Hur (Creatice Dir & VP-Ops)
Kirsten Logan (VP-Sls & Mktg)

SANTA FE PETROLEUM, INC.
4011 West P Pkwy Ste 126, Plano, TX 75093
Tel.: (888) 870-7060 DE
Web Site:
http://www.sfpetroleum.com
Oil & Natural Gas Exploration Services
N.A.I.C.S.: 211120
Carl Karnes (CEO)

SANTA FE WINWATER
10244 Freeman Ave, Santa Fe Springs, CA 90670
Tel.: (562) 777-9724
Web Site:
http://www.santafewinwater.com
Sales Range: $10-24.9 Million
Emp.: 20
Plastic Pipes & Fittings Mfr
N.A.I.C.S.: 423720
Ronnie Esquer (Project Mgr)

SANTA MARIA FORD INC.
1035 E Battles Rd, Santa Maria, CA 93454
Tel.: (805) 925-2445
Web Site:
http://www.santamariaford.dealerconnection.com
Rev.: $23,800,000
Emp.: 65
New Car Dealers
N.A.I.C.S.: 441110
Eric Silver (Gen Mgr)
Dave Gullia (Dir-Fin)
Jesse Garcia (Mgr-Sls)
Joe Slaughter (Mgr-Svc)
Kurt Hale (Dir-Comml Fleet Lease & Internet Sls)

SANTA MARIA SEEDS INC.
2390 A St, Santa Maria, CA 93455
Tel.: (805) 922-5757
Web Site:
http://www.santamariaseeds.com
Sales Range: $10-24.9 Million
Emp.: 40
Vegetable & Cover Crop Seeds Distr
N.A.I.C.S.: 424910
Manuel Silva (Pres)

SANTA MARIA VALLEY HUMANE SOCIETY
1687 W Stowell Rd, Santa Maria, CA 93458
Tel.: (805) 349-3435 CA
Web Site: http://www.smvhs.org
Year Founded: 1982
Animal Welfare Services
N.A.I.C.S.: 813312
Jill Tucker (Exec Dir)
Denise Clift (Mgr-Kennel)
Bobbi Gilman (Mgr-Ops)
Claire C. Sheehy (VP)
Pam Goble (Treas)
Richard Carmody (Pres)
Wanda McDonald (Sec)
Charlotte Alexander (Exec Dir)
Doug Bouman (Dir-Ops)
Emiko Gerber (Dir-Resource Dev)
Cyndi Greer (Accountant)
Subsidiaries:

Santa Barbara Humane Society (1)
5399 Overpass Rd, Santa Barbara, CA 93111
Tel.: (805) 964-4777
Web Site: http://www.sbhumanesociety.org
Animal Welfare Services
N.A.I.C.S.: 813312
Margaret Langle (Exec Dir)

SANTA MONICA FORD COMPANY
1230 Santa Monica Blvd, Santa Monica, CA 90404-1706
Tel.: (310) 451-1588 CA
Web Site: http://www.smford.com
Year Founded: 1948
Sales Range: $75-99.9 Million
Emp.: 85
Retailer of New Automobiles
N.A.I.C.S.: 423110
Ronald Davis (Gen Mgr)
Edgar Medina (Mgr-Internet Sls)
Ernie Escobedo (Mgr-Body Shop)

SANTA MONICA SEAFOOD CO.
18531 S Broadwick St, Rancho Dominguez, CA 90220
Tel.: (310) 886-7900
Web Site:
http://www.santamonicaseafood.com
Year Founded: 1939
Fish & Seafood Mfr
N.A.I.C.S.: 424460

Herman Chiu (CFO)
Michael Cigliano (Exec VP)
Anthony Cigliano (Chm)
Roger O'Brien (Pres & CEO)

SANTA ROSA CAMPWAY, INC.
3948 Santa Rosa Ave, Santa Rosa, CA 95407
Tel.: (707) 584-4433
Web Site: http://www.campway.com
Rev.: $14,100,000
Emp.: 70
Automotive Parts & Accessories Stores
N.A.I.C.S.: 441330
Annie I. Meints (CFO, Sec & VP)
Ronald F. Meints (Pres)

SANTA ROSA CONSULTING, INC.
2555 Meridian Ste 250, Franklin, TN 37067
Tel.: (615) 807-2389
Web Site:
http://www.santarosaconsulting.com
Year Founded: 2008
Sales Range: $50-74.9 Million
Emp.: 200
Health Care Srvices
N.A.I.C.S.: 621610
Laura O'Toole (COO)
Mark Scruggs (Exec VP-Mgmt & EHR Solutions)
Mike Ragan (Chief Revenue Officer)

SANTA'S BEST CRAFT, LTD.
3750 Deerfield Rd Ste 1000, Riverwoods, IL 60015-3541
Tel.: (847) 459-3301
Web Site: http://www.santasbest.com
Sales Range: $10-24.9 Million
Emp.: 10
Christmas Tree Ornament Mfr
N.A.I.C.S.: 339999
Charles Nelson (Controller)

SANTAFE HEALTHCARE, INC.
4300 NW 89th Blvd, Gainesville, FL 32606
Tel.: (352) 372-8400
Web Site:
http://www.santafehealthcarefl.org
Sales Range: $1-4.9 Billion
Emp.: 1,900
Healtcare Services
N.A.I.C.S.: 524114
Michael P. Gallagher (Pres & CEO)
Randall L. Stuart (CFO & Sr VP)
Kay Ayers (Sr VP-Member Svcs, HR & Facilities)
Subsidiaries:

AvMed Health Plans (1)
4300 NW 89th Blvd, Gainesville, FL 32606
Tel.: (352) 372-8400
Web Site: http://www.avmed.org
Sales Range: $100-124.9 Million
Emp.: 800
Health Insurance Carrier
N.A.I.C.S.: 524114
Michael P. Gallagher (CEO)
Steven M. Ziegler (Gen Counsel & Sr VP)
Randall L. Stuart (CFO & Sr VP)
James M. Repp (Pres & COO)
Brad Bentley (Sr VP-Product Innovation)
Ann O. Wehr (CMO & Sr VP)

Haven Hospice (1)
4200 NW 90th Blvd, Gainesville, FL 32606
Tel.: (352) 378-2121
Web Site: http://www.havenhospice.org
Emp.: 250
Hospice
N.A.I.C.S.: 621610
Gayle Mattson (Pres)

SantaFe Senior Living (1)
4300 NW 89th Blvd, Gainesville, FL 32606
Tel.: (352) 372-8400
Web Site: http://www.santafehealthcarefl.org

SANTAFE HEALTHCARE, INC.

SantaFe Healthcare, Inc.—(Continued)
Senior Living Facilities
N.A.I.C.S.: 623312
Troy Hart *(Pres)*
Ramona Wilt *(Dir-Sls & Mktg)*

Subsidiary (Domestic):

The Terraces at Bonita Springs (2)
6455 S Tamiami Trl, Bonita Springs, FL 34134
Tel.: (239) 221-8907
Web Site: http://www.theterracesatbonitasprings.com
Emp.: 55
Retirement Community
N.A.I.C.S.: 623311
Sam Pal *(Dir-Sls)*
Anthony Alongi *(Exec Dir)*

SANTAFE TILE CORP.
8825 NW 95th St, Medley, FL 33178
Tel.: (305) 885-9002
Web Site: http://www.santafetile.com
Year Founded: 1993
Sales Range: $10-24.9 Million
Emp.: 8
Construction Materials Whslr
N.A.I.C.S.: 423320
Katrin Forster *(Asst Sec)*
Juan Restrepo *(Treas)*
Enrique Perea *(Sec)*
Alejandro Botero *(Pres)*
Carlos A. Uribe *(Chm)*

SANTANDER ENTERPRISES INC.
9688 SW 24th St, Miami, FL 33165
Tel.: (305) 221-8351
Sales Range: $10-24.9 Million
Emp.: 4
Supermarket Owner & Operator
N.A.I.C.S.: 445110
Aanvier Herrdra *(Gen Mgr)*

SANTANNA NATURAL GAS CORP.
7701 San Felipe Blvd Ste 200, Austin, TX 78729
Tel.: (512) 346-2500
Web Site: http://www.santannaenergyservices.com
Sales Range: $25-49.9 Million
Emp.: 48
Gases & Electricity
N.A.I.C.S.: 424720
T. Wayne Gatlin *(CEO)*

SANTARELLI & SONS OIL CO., INC.
443 Main St, Peckville, PA 18452
Tel.: (570) 489-7690
Web Site: http://www.santarelliandsonsoil.com
Emp.: 70
Heating Oil Services
N.A.I.C.S.: 333415
Fernando Santarelli *(Founder)*

Subsidiaries:

Airline Petroleum, Co. (1)
1031 Reeves St B, Dunmore, PA 18512
Tel.: (570) 945-5391
Web Site: http://www.airlinepetroleum.com
Emp.: 15
Heating Oil Services
N.A.I.C.S.: 333415
John Gentile *(VP)*

SANTARO INDUSTRIES INC.
6701 Manlius Center Rd, East Syracuse, NY 13057-2848
Tel.: (315) 463-3000
Rev.: $30,600,000
Emp.: 2
General Contractor, Highway & Street Construction
N.A.I.C.S.: 237310

Michael Santaro *(Pres)*

SANTEE PRINT WORKS, INC.
58 W 40th St, New York, NY 10018
Tel.: (212) 997-1570   SC
Web Site: http://www.santeeprint.com
Year Founded: 1949
Sales Range: $200-249.9 Million
Emp.: 500
Printing & Dyeing of Cotton Broadwoven Fabrics & Blends
N.A.I.C.S.: 313310
Martin Barocas *(Pres)*
Leon Barocas *(Treas, Sec & VP)*

Subsidiaries:

Weilwood Industries, Inc. (1)
1384 Broadway 4th Fl, New York, NY 10018-6108   (100%)
Tel.: (212) 391-2300
Web Site: http://www.exclusivelyquilters.com
Textile Converters
N.A.I.C.S.: 314999
Loretta D. Ede *(Natl Sls Mgr)*

SANTEK ENVIRONMENTAL LLC
650 25th St NW Ste 100, Cleveland, TN 37311
Tel.: (423) 303-7101
Hazardous Waste Treatment & Disposal
N.A.I.C.S.: 562211
Kenneth Higgins *(CEO)*

SANTEX TRUCK CENTER LTD.
1380 Ackerman Rd, San Antonio, TX 78219
Tel.: (210) 661-8371
Web Site: http://www.santextrucks.com
Rev: $36,500,000
Emp.: 95
Trucks, Commercial
N.A.I.C.S.: 423110
E. A. Kyrish *(Chm)*

SANTIAM DRUG INC.
4430 Franklin Blvd, Eugene, OR 97403
Tel.: (541) 726-4117
Rev.: $10,133,840
Emp.: 8
Variety Stores
N.A.I.C.S.: 455219
Michael Wolfe *(Chm)*

SANTINELLI INTERNATIONAL INC.
325 Oser Ave, Hauppauge, NY 11788
Tel.: (631) 435-3343   NY
Web Site: http://www.santinelli.com
Year Founded: 1970
Sales Range: $10-24.9 Million
Emp.: 65
Optical Goods
N.A.I.C.S.: 423490
Joseph Santinelli *(Chm)*
Gerard Santinelli *(Pres & CEO)*
Rick Clemente *(Exec VP-Sls & Svc)*
Matthew McKenna *(VP-Client Svcs)*
Franco Aluigi *(Product Mgr)*

SANTINI TRANSFER & STORAGE
8625 Lefferts Blvd, Richmond Hill, NY 11418
Tel.: (718) 507-6100
Sales Range: $10-24.9 Million
Emp.: 85
Nonresidential Construction Services
N.A.I.C.S.: 236220
Alton Rowe *(CFO)*

SANTMYER OIL CO. INC.
1055 Lincoln Way W, Wooster, OH 44691

Tel.: (330) 262-6501   OH
Web Site: http://www.scfnetwork.com
Year Founded: 1979
Sales Range: $10-24.9 Million
Emp.: 100
Provider of Petroleum Products
N.A.I.C.S.: 424720
Terry Santmyer *(Pres)*

Subsidiaries:

Santmyer Oil Co. of Ashland Inc. (1)
1011 Jacobson Ave, Ashland, OH 44805   (100%)
Tel.: (419) 289-8815
Web Site: http://www.santmyeroil.com
Petroleum Products
N.A.I.C.S.: 424720

SANTONI'S INC.
3800 E Lombard St, Baltimore, MD 21224-2400
Tel.: (410) 563-5050   MD
Web Site: http://www.santonismarket.com
Year Founded: 1930
Sales Range: $10-24.9 Million
Emp.: 150
Grocery Stores
N.A.I.C.S.: 445110
Robert N. Santoni Sr. *(Pres & CEO)*
Robert N. Santoni Jr. *(VP)*

SANTOS ENTERPRISES
5400 Alameda Ave, El Paso, TX 79905
Tel.: (915) 779-3641
Web Site: http://www.foodcityep.com
Sales Range: $125-149.9 Million
Emp.: 200
Supermarket
N.A.I.C.S.: 445110
Jose G. Santos Jr. *(Owner)*

SANWA GROWERS INC.
2801 E Hillsborough Ave, Tampa, FL 33610-4410
Tel.: (813) 642-5159   FL
Web Site: http://www.sanwagrowers.com
Year Founded: 1981
Sales Range: $75-99.9 Million
Emp.: 180
Fresh Fruits & Vegetables
N.A.I.C.S.: 424480
Tony Leung *(Pres)*
Donna Colbourne *(Mgr-HR)*
Laura Julian *(Mgr-Customer Svc)*
Wes Pinkerton *(CEO)*

SANWECO INC.
103 Beach St, Saco, ME 04072
Tel.: (207) 283-4046
Sales Range: $10-24.9 Million
Emp.: 200
Fast-Food Restaurant Owner & Operator
N.A.I.C.S.: 722513
Ronald Giles *(Pres)*
Linda Giles *(VP)*

SANWIRE CORP.
3540 W Sahara E6 135, Las Vegas, NV 89102-5816
Tel.: (805) 465-0818
Year Founded: 1997
Data Processing Services
N.A.I.C.S.: 518210
Christopher M. Whitcomb *(CEO)*

SAOTHAIR CAPITAL PARTNERS LLC
150 N Radnor Chester Rd Ste F 200, Radnor, PA 19087
Tel.: (484) 658-3100   DE
Web Site: http://www.saothair.com
Investment Services
N.A.I.C.S.: 523999

U.S. PRIVATE

Kevin Madden *(Co-Founder & Mng Partner)*

Subsidiaries:

Arandell Corporation (1)
N 82 W 13118 Leon Rd, Menomonee Falls, WI 53051-3303
Tel.: (262) 255-4400
Web Site: http://www.arandell.com
Sales Range: $150-199.9 Million
Emp.: 500
Lithography & Catalog Printing
N.A.I.C.S.: 323111
Bradley J. Hoffman *(Pres & CEO)*
Richard Kropski *(Sr VP-Logistics & Supply Chain)*
Joyce Feaster *(VP-HR)*
Steve Sanfelippo *(Sr VP-Sls & Mktg)*

SAPERE CONSULTING, INC.
103 E Main St Ste 301, Walla Walla, WA 99362
Tel.: (509) 529-7885   WA
Web Site: http://www.sapereconsulting.com
Sales Range: $1-9.9 Million
Emp.: 20
Business Management Consulting Services
N.A.I.C.S.: 541611
Jeff Smyth *(Pres)*
Kevin Miedema *(CFO)*

SAPIENT INVESTIGATIONS INC.
1810 14th St Ste 212, Santa Monica, CA 90404
Tel.: (310) 399-8200
Web Site: http://www.sapientinvestigation.com
Emp.: 10
Investigatory Services
N.A.I.C.S.: 561611
David Cogan *(Mng Dir)*

SAPORITO FINISHING COMPANY
3119 S Austin Blvd, Cicero, IL 60804
Tel.: (708) 222-5300
Web Site: http://www.saporitofinishing.com
Year Founded: 1946
Emp.: 150
Anodizing, Plating & Metal Finishing Products
N.A.I.C.S.: 332813
Jeffrey G. Logan *(Pres)*
Charles Saporito Jr. *(CEO)*

SAPP BROS PETROLEUM, INC.
9915 S 148th St, Omaha, NE 68138
Tel.: (402) 895-2202   NE
Web Site: http://www.sappbrospetro.com
Year Founded: 1980
Sales Range: $200-249.9 Million
Emp.: 250
Whslr of Petroleum Products
N.A.I.C.S.: 424720
Greg Epp *(Gen Mgr)*
Tim Kaup *(Gen Mgr)*
Virgil Jobman *(Gen Mgr)*
Chuck Swerczek *(Gen Mgr)*
Andrew Richard *(COO)*
Lee Horning *(Dir-Wholesale Ops)*
Kristen Hanes *(Gen Mgr)*
Ronnie McClendon *(Gen Mgr)*
Rod Pollard *(Gen Mgr)*
Chuck Rains *(Gen Mgr)*
Rich Sorenson *(Gen Mgr)*
Brad James *(Mgr-Fuel Delivery & Location)*
Chris Klotz *(Treas & VP)*
Ken Broz *(VP)*
Dave Freeman *(VP-Sls)*

SAPUTO DESIGN, INC.

870 Hampshire Rd Ste D, Westlake Village, CA 91361
Tel.: (805) 494-1847
Web Site: http://www.saputodesign.com
Year Founded: 1998
Sales Range: Less than $1 Million
Emp.: 10
Advetising Agency
N.A.I.C.S.: 541810
Thomas Saputo (Owner)

SARA BAY COUNTRY CLUB, INC.
7011 Willow St, Sarasota, FL 34243
Tel.: (941) 355-7658 FL
Web Site: http://www.sarabaycc.org
Year Founded: 1926
Sales Range: $1-9.9 Million
Emp.: 56
Golf Courses & Country Clubs
N.A.I.C.S.: 713910
Paul Barone (COO & Gen Mgr)
Natalie Everhart (Comptroller)
Daren King (Head-Golf Pro)
Anita Bosworth (Mgr-Dining & Event)
Dennis J. Budny Sr. (Dir-Membership Sls & Mktg)

SARABAY REAL ESTATE, INC.
7333 N Tamiami Trl, Sarasota, FL 34243
Tel.: (941) 355-7696
Web Site: http://www.sarabay.com
Year Founded: 1979
Sales Range: $1-9.9 Million
Emp.: 20
Real Estate Broker
N.A.I.C.S.: 531210
Mike Holderness (Co-Owner)

SARAH BUSH LINCOLN HEALTH CENTER
1000 Health Center Dr, Mattoon, IL 61938
Tel.: (217) 258-2525 IL
Web Site: http://www.sarahbush.org
Year Founded: 1977
Sales Range: $200-249.9 Million
Emp.: 1,891
Health Care Srvices
N.A.I.C.S.: 622110
Steve Wente (Treas)
Lyla McGuire (Sec)
Michael Smith (Chm)

SARAMAX APPAREL GROUP INC.
1372 Broadway 7th Fl, New York, NY 10018
Tel.: (212) 842-4000
Rev.: $18,100,000
Emp.: 80
Women's & Children's Lingerie & Undergarments
N.A.I.C.S.: 424350
Eddie A. Betesh (CEO)
David Anteby (Controller)
Eli Kairey (Acct Mgr)
Bill Kirby (VP)
Joanne DeLuca (VP & Mgr-Dival)
Mahalia Fox (Dir-Design)
Susan Stevens (Dir-Design)

SARASOTA 500 INC.
707 S Washington Blvd, Sarasota, FL 34236
Tel.: (941) 366-5230
Web Site: http://www.sarasotaford.com
Sales Range: $100-124.9 Million
Emp.: 160
Automobiles, New & Used
N.A.I.C.S.: 441110
Matt Buchanan (Operating Partner)
Ian Parisi (Gen Sls Mgr)

SARASOTA COUNTY PUBLIC HOSPITAL DISTRICT
1700 S Tamiami Trl, Sarasota, FL 34239
Tel.: (941) 917-9000
Web Site: http://www.smh.com
Year Founded: 1925
Sales Range: $400-449.9 Million
Emp.: 4,000
Health Care Association
N.A.I.C.S.: 813910
David Verinder (Pres & CEO)
William Woeltjen (CFO)
Jan Mauck (Chief Nursing Officer)
Lorrie Liang (COO)
James Fiorica (Chief Medical Officer)
Aurora Wong (Dir-Medical-Rehabilitation Svcs)

SARASOTA FUN MACHINES INC.
4583 Clark Rd, Sarasota, FL 34233
Tel.: (941) 925-0376
Web Site: http://www.suzukiofsarasota.com
Sales Range: $1-9.9 Million
Emp.: 10
Motorcycle, Scooter & ATV Dealership
N.A.I.C.S.: 441227
Ed Gurry (Owner)

SARASOTA MANAGEMENT AND LEASING
70 Sarsota Center Blvd, Sarasota, FL 34240
Tel.: (941) 377-8400
Web Site: http://www.sarasotamanagement.com
Sales Range: $1-9.9 Million
Residential Property Management & Leasing Services
N.A.I.C.S.: 531311
Christy Smith (Asst Mgr-Property)

SARASOTA MANATEE JEWISH HOUSING COUNCIL, INC.
1951 N Honore Ave, Sarasota, FL 34235
Tel.: (941) 337-0781
Web Site: http://www.kobernickanchin.org
Year Founded: 1988
Sales Range: $10-24.9 Million
Emp.: 305
Senior Living Services
N.A.I.C.S.: 623311
Sharon Mitchell (CFO)
John Richards (COO)
Darlene Arbeit (Exec Dir)

SARASOTA MILITARY ACADEMY, INC.
801 N Orange Ave, Sarasota, FL 34236
Tel.: (941) 926-1700 FL
Web Site: http://www.sarasotamilitaryacademy.com
Year Founded: 2002
Sales Range: $1-9.9 Million
Emp.: 50
Military School
N.A.I.C.S.: 611110
Frank S. Laudano (CFO)
Daniel P. Kennedy (CEO & Founder)

SARASOTA RARE COIN GALLERY, INC.
640 S Washington Blvd, Sarasota, FL 34236-7105
Tel.: (941) 366-2191
Web Site: http://www.sarasotacoin.com

Year Founded: 1998
Sales Range: $10-24.9 Million
Emp.: 4
Coin Supplier
N.A.I.C.S.: 423940
David Klein (Co-Owner)
Kent Gulley (Co-Owner)

SARAT FORD SALES INC.
245 Springfield St, Agawam, MA 01001
Tel.: (413) 786-0430
Web Site: http://www.saratford.com
Rev.: $30,100,000
Emp.: 81
Automobiles, New & Used
N.A.I.C.S.: 441110
John Sarat (Principal)
Aaron Coon (Mgr-Sls)
John DeLucchi (Mgr-Bus Dev)
Stephen Kocsis (Mgr-Sls)

SARATOGA HARNESS RACING INC.
342 Jefferson St, Saratoga Springs, NY 12866
Tel.: (518) 584-2110 NY
Web Site: http://www.saratogagamingandraceway.com
Year Founded: 1941
Sales Range: $200-249.9 Million
Emp.: 400
Live Harness Racing & Simulcast Wagering
N.A.I.C.S.: 711212
George Wiley (Treas)
James Hartman (COO & Exec VP)
Daniel Gerrity (Pres)
Rita Cox (Sr VP-Mktg & External Affairs)

SARATOGA HOSPITAL
211 Church St, Saratoga Springs, NY 12866
Tel.: (518) 587-3222 NY
Web Site: http://www.saratogahospital.org
Year Founded: 1891
Sales Range: $250-299.9 Million
Emp.: 2,441
Health Care Srvices
N.A.I.C.S.: 622110
Richard Falivena (Chief Medical & Physician Integration Officer & VP)
Gary Foster (CFO & VP)
John Mangona (CIO, Chief Compliance Officer & VP)
Jeffrey Methven (Chief HR Officer & VP-Ambulatory Svcs)
Kevin P. Ronayne (VP-Ops & Facilities)
Angelo G. Calbone (Pres & CEO)
Michael Lacolucci (Chm)

SARATOGA MOTORS INC.
3402 Route 9, Saratoga Springs, NY 12866
Tel.: (518) 587-9300
Web Site: http://www.saratogahonda.com
Rev.: $19,700,000
Emp.: 48
Automobiles, New & Used
N.A.I.C.S.: 441110
Timothy M. Higgins (Pres)

SARATOGA PARTNERS L.P.
535 Madison Ave 4th Fl, New York, NY 10022
Tel.: (212) 906-7800
Web Site: http://www.saratogapartners.com
Year Founded: 1984
Sales Range: $10-24.9 Million
Emp.: 20

Private Equity Investors; Independent Investment Firm
N.A.I.C.S.: 523999
Christian L. Oberbeck (Mng Partner)
Subsidiaries:

Advanced Lighting Technologies, Inc. (1)
7905 Cochran Rd Ste 300 Glenwillow, Solon, OH 44139-2814
Tel.: (440) 519-0500
Web Site: http://www.adlt.com
Sales Range: $150-199.9 Million
Emp.: 1,168
Holding Company for Metal Halide Lighting Manufacturing & Marketing Companies
N.A.I.C.S.: 551112
Shawn Toney (CEO)
John Brecker (Chm)
Subsidiary (Domestic):

APL Engineered Materials, Inc. (2)
2401 N Willow Rd, Urbana, IL 61802
Tel.: (217) 367-1340
Web Site: http://www.apl.com
Sales Range: $10-24.9 Million
Emp.: 100
Metal Halide Lighting Mfr
N.A.I.C.S.: 335131
James L. Schoolenberg (Pres)
Subsidiary (Non-US):

Advanced Lighting Technologies Asia Pte Ltd. (2)
Block 4008 Ang Mo Kio Avenue 10 No 04-06, Techplace I, Singapore, 569625, Singapore
Tel.: (65) 6844 2338
Web Site: http://www.adlt.com.sg
Emp.: 10
Lighting Equipment Mfr
N.A.I.C.S.: 335139
Francis Lee (Gen Mgr)

Advanced Lighting Technologies Australia, Inc. (2)
110 Lewis Rd, Wantirna, 3152, VIC, Australia
Tel.: (61) 398005600
Web Site: http://www.advancedlighting.com.au
Sales Range: $10-24.9 Million
Emp.: 30
Metal Halide Lighting Mfr
N.A.I.C.S.: 335131

Auer Lighting GmbH (2)
Hildesheimer Strasse 35, 37581, Bad Gandersheim, Germany
Tel.: (49) 5382 701 0
Web Site: http://www.auer-lighting.com
Sales Range: $25-49.9 Million
Emp.: 400
Lighting Component Mfr & Whslr
N.A.I.C.S.: 335139
Christoph Schuller (Member-Mgmt Bd)
Subsidiary (Domestic):

HIDirect (2)
32000 Aurora Rd, Solon, OH 44139
Tel.: (440) 542-4318
Web Site: http://www.hidirect.com
Lighting Supplier
N.A.I.C.S.: 335139
Michelle Guarino (Mgr-HR)

Venture Lighting International, Inc. (2)
32000 Aurora Rd, Solon, OH 44139
Tel.: (440) 248-3510
Web Site: http://www.venturelighting.com
Metal Halide Light Mfr
N.A.I.C.S.: 335131
Subsidiary (Non-US):

Venture Lighting Europe Ltd. (3)
Trinity Court Batchworth Island, Rickmansworth, WD3 1RT, United Kingdom
Tel.: (44) 8452302222
Web Site: http://www.venturelightingeurope.com
Sales Range: $10-24.9 Million
Emp.: 15
Metal Halide Lighting Mfr
N.A.I.C.S.: 335131
Keith Price (Mng Dir)

SARATOGA PARTNERS L.P.   U.S. PRIVATE

Saratoga Partners L.P.—(Continued)

Venture Lighting International FZE (3)
Jebel Ali Free Zone, PO Box 16994, Dubai, United Arab Emirates
Tel.: (971) 48837370
Web Site: http://www.venturelightingme.com
Sales Range: $10-24.9 Million
Emp.: 48
Metal Halide Lighting Mfr
N.A.I.C.S.: 335131
Happy Raphel (CEO)

Venture Lighting South Africa (PTY.) LTD. (3)
Unit 6 Capricorn Business Lakeshore Park Park Marina Da Gama, Cape Town, 7941, South Africa
Tel.: (27) 217090180
Web Site: http://www.venturelighting.com
Sales Range: $10-24.9 Million
Emp.: 3
Metal Halide Lighting Mfr
N.A.I.C.S.: 335131
Chris Brown (Mng Dir)

SARATOGA RESOURCES, INC.
9225 Katy Fwy Ste 100, Houston, TX 77024
Tel.: (713) 458-1560   TX
Assets: $5,689
Liabilities: $2,001,803
Net Worth: ($1,996,114)
Earnings: ($528,636)
Fiscal Year-end: 12/31/21
Oil & Gas Exploration Services
N.A.I.C.S.: 211120

SARCHIONE AUTOMOTIVE GROUP
1572 State Route 44, Randolph, OH 44265
Tel.: (91) 3303259991
Web Site: https://www.sarchione.com
Emp.: 100
Car Dealer
N.A.I.C.S.: 441110
Joe Sarchione (Principal)

Subsidiaries:

Haasz Auto Mall, LLC (1)
4886 State Route 59, Ravenna, OH 44266-8838
Tel.: (330) 296-2866
Web Site: http://www.haaszautomall.com
Automotive Repair & Maintenance
N.A.I.C.S.: 811198
Kevin Haasz (Pres)
Denise Cleavenger (Dir-Mktg)

SARDINIA CONCRETE COMPANY
1622 Mason Morrow Rd, Lebanon, OH 45036
Tel.: (513) 248-0090
Web Site: http://www.sardiniaconcrete.com
Emp.: 80
Ready Mixed Concrete
N.A.I.C.S.: 327320
Marianne Phelps (Office Mgr)
Mark Cooper (Mgr-Outside Sls)

SAREEN & ASSOCIATES, INC.
10702 Vandor Ln, Manassas, VA 20109
Tel.: (703) 366-3444
Web Site: http://www.sareentax.com
Accounting, Tax Preparation, Business Consulting & Payroll Services
N.A.I.C.S.: 541211
R. K. Cross (Pres)

SARES-REGIS GROUP
18802 Bardeen Ave, Irvine, CA 92612
Tel.: (949) 756-5959   CA
Web Site: http://www.sares-regis.com
Year Founded: 1975
Sales Range: $50-74.9 Million
Emp.: 500
Commercial & Residential Real Estate Investment, Development, Construction & Property Management Services
N.A.I.C.S.: 531390
Geoffrey L. Stack (Partner & Mng Dir)
John S. Hagestad (Sr Mng Dir)
Michael Heiken (Chief Acctg Officer)
William J. Thormahlen (Mng Dir & Principal)
Christopher Payne (Pres-Multifamily Dev)
Kenneth M. Coatsworth (Sr VP-Fin)
Julie Stewart (Dir-Client Rels)
Heather Wallace (Sr VP-Residential Mgmt)
Zoe Solsby (Dir-Corp Comm)
Sheri Druckman (VP-Bus Dev-Pacific Northwest)

Subsidiaries:

Bluffs at Highlands Ranch LLC (1)
600 W County Line Rd, Highlands Ranch, CO 80129
Tel.: (303) 791-4604
Web Site: http://www.thebluffshr.com
Sales Range: $25-49.9 Million
Emp.: 8
Multifamily Residential Property Manager
N.A.I.C.S.: 531311
Jenn Minty (Mgr)

SARGENT & LUNDY LLC
55 E Monroe St, Chicago, IL 60603-5713
Tel.: (312) 269-2000   IL
Web Site: http://www.sargentlundy.com
Year Founded: 1891
Sales Range: $250-299.9 Million
Emp.: 1,700
Provider of Engineering Consulting for Design of Nuclear & Fossil Fueled Power Generation Facilities, Transmission Lines & Related Activities for Utility & Industrial Applications
N.A.I.C.S.: 541330
John Wittenauer (Dir-IT)
Michael E. Helminski (CFO, Gen Counsel & Exec VP)
Jeff Woolley (Mgr)
Warren Vahle (Sr VP & Dir-Power Transmission)
Thomas R. White (Chm, Pres & CEO)
Ejaz Shameem (Dir-Energy Bus Consulting Grp)
Delfo Bianchini (Exec VP & Dir-Nuclear Power)
Jack Daly (Exec VP & Dir-Fossil Power)
Paula Scholl (Sr VP & Dir-Ops)

SARGENT CORPORATION
378 Bennoch Rd, Stillwater, ME 04489
Tel.: (207) 827-4435
Web Site: http://www.sargent-corp.com
Year Founded: 1926
Sales Range: $100-124.9 Million
Emp.: 400
Earthwork Construction Contracting Services
N.A.I.C.S.: 237990
Timothy Folster (VP-Ops)
Brent Hartley (CFO)

SARGENT ELECTRIC COMPANY
2767 Liberty Ave, Pittsburgh, PA 15222-4703
Tel.: (412) 391-0588   PA
Web Site: http://www.sargent.com
Year Founded: 1907
Sales Range: $100-124.9 Million
Emp.: 500
Electrical Work
N.A.I.C.S.: 238210
Tom Platt (Project Mgr)
Gary Romeo (Controller)

SARGENT TRUCKING INC.
64 Main St, Mars Hill, ME 04758
Tel.: (207) 429-8106
Web Site: http://www.sargenttrucking.com
Year Founded: 1983
Sales Range: $75-99.9 Million
Emp.: 35
Contract Haulers
N.A.I.C.S.: 484121
Joshua Tweedie (Pres)

SARGENTO FOODS INC.
1 Persnickety Pl, Plymouth, WI 53073-3544
Tel.: (920) 893-8484   WI
Web Site: http://www.sargento.com
Year Founded: 1953
Sales Range: $500-549.9 Million
Emp.: 1,300
Cheese Products Mfr
N.A.I.C.S.: 311513
Erin Price (Sr VP-Mktg)
Kris Cherukuri (VP-IT)
Vera Petrova Dickinson (VP-Food Safety & Quality)
Chris McCarthy (VP-Pricing & Demand Planning)
Holly Baumgart (VP-Strategic Planning)
Julia Klimkovich (VP-Fin Planning & Analysis)
Dennis Schweiger (VP-Treas, Corp Fin & Acctg)
Mohamed Attia (VP-Strategic Sourcing)
Brent Mann (VP-Food Safety & Quality)
Louis P. Gentine II (CEO)

Subsidiaries:

Sargento Foods Inc. (1)
460 S 8th St, Hilbert, WI 54129-0289
Web Site: http://www.sargento.com
Sales Range: $25-49.9 Million
Emp.: 100
Producer Natural Domestic & Imported Cheese Distr
N.A.I.C.S.: 445298
Sandy Howard (Gen Mgr)

Sargento Foods Inc. - Consumer Products Division (1)
One Persnickety Pl, Plymouth, WI 53073-3544 (100%)
Tel.: (920) 893-8484
Web Site: http://www.sargento.com
Sales Range: $125-149.9 Million
Packaging & Distributor of Natural Domestic & Imported Cheeses
N.A.I.C.S.: 311513
Erin Price (Dir-Mktg)
John Bottomley (Dir-Retail Mdsg)
John Arnold (Dir-Retail Sls)
Lou Gentine (Chm)
Joy Judski (Dir-Sls)
Annette Lorenz (Mgr-Sls-Natl Accts)
Lynn Webb (Mgr-Customer Bus-Natl)

Sargento Foods Inc. - Food Service Division (1)
1 Persnickety Pl, Plymouth, WI 53073 (100%)
Tel.: (920) 893-8484
Web Site: http://www.sargentofoodservice.com
Sales Range: $100-124.9 Million
Emp.: 700
Packaging & Retailer of Cheeses
N.A.I.C.S.: 311513

SARKES TARZIAN INC.
205 N College Ave 8th Fl, Bloomington, IN 47404
Tel.: (812) 332-7251
Radio & TV Broadcasting Services
N.A.I.C.S.: 516120
Thomas Tolar (Pres)
Robert W. Davis II (Sr VP-Acct & Fin)

SAROYAN LUMBER COMPANY INC.
6230 Alameda St, Huntington Park, CA 90255
Tel.: (323) 589-5704
Web Site: http://www.saroyanlumber.com
Rev.: $16,000,000
Emp.: 80
Lumber: Rough, Dressed & Finished
N.A.I.C.S.: 423310
Richard Saroyan (Pres)
Marylyne Nahery (CFO)
Tracy Perry (Mgr-Credit)

SARRACCO MECHANICAL SERVICES INC.
71 Naugatuck Dr, Naugatuck, CT 06770
Tel.: (203) 723-0935   CT
Web Site: http://www.sarracco.com
Year Founded: 1975
Sales Range: $10-24.9 Million
Emp.: 120
Mechanical Products Design & Installation Services
N.A.I.C.S.: 238220
Thomas Sarracco (Pres)
Keith Mosgrove (VP & Gen Mgr)
Yvette Wilmot (CFO & VP-Bus Dev)

SARREID, LTD.
3905 Airport Dr NW, Wilson, NC 27896
Tel.: (252) 291-1414
Web Site: http://www.sarreid.com
Year Founded: 1967
Sales Range: $10-24.9 Million
Emp.: 31
Whslr & Importer of Furniture
N.A.I.C.S.: 423210
Charles Hoffman (VP)
Theresa Watkins (Controller)
Alex Sarratt (Pres)
Charles Mauze (VP)

SARRELL DENTAL
230 E 10th St Ste 106, Anniston, AL 36207
Tel.: (256) 741-7340   AL
Web Site: http://www.sarrelldental.org
Year Founded: 2004
Sales Range: $10-24.9 Million
Emp.: 324
Children Healthcare Services
N.A.I.C.S.: 622110
Brandi Parris (Pres)
Stephen Wallace (Chief Dental Officer)
Bobby Shoulders (Dir-Athens Community)
Catherine Chappell (Mgr-Optical)
Erin Bonilla (Mgr-Insurance)
Joanna Williams (Mgr-Enterprise Ops)
John Clasen (Dir-Optometry Clinical)
Kayla Shipman (Dir-Athens Ops)
Kevin Browning (Mgr-Supply Chain)
Lauren Hunter (Mgr-Ops-Attalla)
Marlen Whitmore (Mgr-Credentialing)
Michelle Ellison (Mgr-Ops-Talladega)
Mike Woodall (Dir-Ops)
Molly Spinks (Dir-Ops)
Sally Register (Mgr-Ops-Foley)
Veronica Juan (Mgr-Operation-Pinson)

SARTELL GROUP, INC.
800 Hennepin Ave Ste 400, Minneapolis, MN 55403
Tel.: (612) 548-3100   MN

COMPANIES / SAS INSTITUTE INC.

Web Site:
http://www.sartellgroup.com
Year Founded: 1998
Sales Range: $1-9.9 Million
Emp.: 21
It Consulting
N.A.I.C.S.: 541690
Pam Sartell *(Owner & Pres)*

SARTIN LEE TRUCKING CO. INC.
RR 52, Kermit, WV 25674
Tel.: (304) 393-3300
Web Site: http://www.leesartintrk.com
Rev.: $13,945,775
Emp.: 100
Dump Truck Haulage
N.A.I.C.S.: 484220
Riley L. Sartin *(Pres)*
Maryanne Kominar *(Office Mgr)*

SARTORI COMPANY
107 N Pleasant View Rd, Plymouth, WI 53073-4948
Tel.: (920) 893-6061 WI
Web Site:
http://www.sartoricheese.com
Year Founded: 1939
Sales Range: $10-24.9 Million
Emp.: 95
Natural & Processed Cheese Mfr
N.A.I.C.S.: 311513
James C. Sartori *(Owner & CEO)*
Pat Mugan *(VP-Product Innovation)*
Bob McManus *(Dir-Sls-Natl)*

Subsidiaries:

Sartori Inspirations, LLC (1)
107 Pleasant View Rd, Plymouth, WI 53073
Tel.: (303) 410-9343
Natural & Processed Cheese Mfr
N.A.I.C.S.: 311513

Subsidiary (Domestic):

Blue Moose of Boulder, Inc. (2)
1733 Majestic Dr Ste 103, Lafayette, CO 80026
Tel.: (303) 410-9343
Web Site:
http://www.bluemooseofboulder.com
Sales Range: $10-24.9 Million
Emp.: 15
Supermarkets & Other Grocery Stores
N.A.I.C.S.: 445110
Fred Howard *(CEO)*
Victoria Hartman *(Pres)*

SARVIK CORP.
4952 S Rainbow Blvd #255, Las Vegas, NV 89118
Tel.: (702) 475-5770 NV
Year Founded: 2013
Event Organizing & Promoting
N.A.I.C.S.: 711310
Jevgeni Karamkov *(Pres, CEO, CFO, Principal Acctg Officer, Treas & Sec)*

SAS GLOBAL
21601 Mullin Ave, Warren, MI 48089
Tel.: (248) 414-4470
Web Site: http://www.sasglobal.com
Sales Range: $10-24.9 Million
Emp.: 130
Mfr of Metal Plates
N.A.I.C.S.: 332313
Rick Wark *(Pres)*
Brian Hinkle *(Gen Mgr)*

SAS INSTITUTE INC.
100 SAS Campus Dr, Cary, NC 27513-2414
Tel.: (919) 677-8000 NC
Web Site: https://www.sas.com
Year Founded: 1976
Sales Range: $1-4.9 Billion
Emp.: 12,000
Software Publisher
N.A.I.C.S.: 513210
James Goodnight *(Co-Founder & CEO)*
John Sall *(Co-Founder & Exec VP)*
Keith Collins *(CIO & Exec VP)*
John Boswell *(Chief Legal Officer & Exec VP)*
Don Parker *(CFO & Exec VP)*
Riad Gydien *(Sr VP-South & East EMEA)*
Nutapone Apiluktoyanunt *(Mng Dir-Thailand)*
Yen Yen Tan *(VP-South Asia Pacific)*
Oliver Schabenberger *(COO & CTO)*
Marvio Portela *(Head-Latin America)*
Cassio Pantaleoni *(Head-Brazil & Latin America)*
Jennifer K. Mann *(Chief HR Officer & VP)*
Wenjun Bao *(Sr Mgr-R&D-JMP Life Sciences)*

Subsidiaries:

Kamakura Corporation (1)
2222 Kalakaua Ave, Honolulu, HI 96815-2516
Tel.: (808) 791-9888
Web Site: http://www.kamakuraco.com
Custom Computer Programing Management Consulting Services
N.A.I.C.S.: 541511
Martin M. Zorn *(Pres & COO)*
Donald R. van Deventer *(Founder & Chm)*
Mark E. Slattery *(Mng Dir-Chicago-Illinois)*
Clement Ooi *(Mng Dir-Ops-Asia & Pacific & Sr VP)*
James McKeon *(Dir-Bus Solutions)*
Jim Moloney *(Mng Dir-EMEA & Dir-Sls-Global)*
Kenji Imai *(Mng Dir)*
Mark Mesler *(Mng Dir)*
Robert A. Jarrow *(Mng Dir-Res)*
Suresh Sankaran *(Mng Dir-Advisory Svcs)*
Eric Penanhoat *(Mng Dir-Boston)*

SAS Egypt LLC (1)
25A Road 84, Maadi, Cairo, 11431, Egypt
Tel.: (20) 2 23806689
Information Technology Consulting Services
N.A.I.C.S.: 541512

SAS INSTITUTE OU (1)
Narva mnt 5, Tallinn, 10117, Estonia
Tel.: (372) 6030595
Web Site: http://www.sas.com
Sales Range: $10-24.9 Million
Emp.: 6
Information Technology Consulting Services
N.A.I.C.S.: 541512
Allan Harand *(Mgr-Sls)*

SAS Institute (1)
Domaine de Gregy, Brie Comte Robert, 77257, Gregy-sur-Yerres, Cedex, France (100%)
Tel.: (33) 160621111
Web Site: http://www.sas.com
Sales Range: $25-49.9 Million
Emp.: 300
Analytics & Data Management Services & Software
N.A.I.C.S.: 334610
Jim Goodnight *(Founder & CEO)*

SAS Institute (Canada), Inc. (1)
181 Bay St Suite 2710, Toronto, M5J 2T3, ON, Canada (100%)
Tel.: (416) 363-4424
Web Site: http://www.sas.com
Sales Range: $25-49.9 Million
Emp.: 200
Software Sales
N.A.I.C.S.: 334610
Ron Reed *(VP-Sls)*

SAS Institute (India) Pvt. Ltd. (1)
Apeejay House 4th Floor 3 Dinshaw Wachha Road Churchgate, Mumbai, 400 020, India
Tel.: (91) 22 6749 2222
Sales Range: $25-49.9 Million
Emp.: 600
Information Technology Consulting Services
N.A.I.C.S.: 541512
Sudipta K. Sen *(CEO & Mng Dir)*

SAS Institute (NZ) Ltd. (1)
Level 12 89 The Terrace, PO Box 10 109, Wellington, 6011, New Zealand (100%)
Tel.: (64) 49176800
Web Site: http://www.sas.com
Sales Range: $10-24.9 Million
Emp.: 15
Software Research & Development
N.A.I.C.S.: 334610
Geoff Beynon *(Gen Mgr)*

SAS Institute (Philippines), Inc. (1)
21st Floor Equitable Bank Tower 8751 Paseo de Roxas St, 1226, Makati, Philippines (100%)
Tel.: (63) 2 792 2200
Sales Range: $10-24.9 Million
Emp.: 21
Software Solutions
N.A.I.C.S.: 423430

SAS Institute A/S (1)
Parkveien 55, PO Box 2666, Solli, 203, Oslo, Norway (100%)
Tel.: (47) 23083050
Web Site: http://www.sas.com
Sales Range: $10-24.9 Million
Emp.: 85
Software Research & Development
N.A.I.C.S.: 334610
Jim Goodnight *(CEO-SAS)*

SAS Institute A/S (1)
Kobmagergade 7 9, Copenhagen, 1150, Denmark (100%)
Tel.: (45) 70282870
Web Site: http://www.sas.com
Sales Range: $25-49.9 Million
Emp.: 300
Software Research & Development
N.A.I.C.S.: 334610
Kelt Zelnig *(Gen Mgr)*

SAS Institute AB (1)
Stora Frosunda, 169 26, Solna, Sweden (100%)
Tel.: (46) 852217000
Web Site: http://www.sas.com
Sales Range: $10-24.9 Million
Emp.: 100
Software Research & Development
N.A.I.C.S.: 334610

SAS Institute AG (1)
Richtistrasse 11, Wallisellen, 8304, Switzerland (100%)
Tel.: (41) 448057495
Web Site: http://www.sas.com
Sales Range: $10-24.9 Million
Emp.: 60
Analytics & Data Management Services & Software
N.A.I.C.S.: 334610
Susy Brunner *(Dir-HR)*

SAS Institute Australia Pty. Ltd. (1)
300 Burns Bay Rd, Private Bag No 52, Lane Cove, 2066, NSW, Australia (100%)
Tel.: (61) 294280428
Sales Range: $25-49.9 Million
Emp.: 250
Software Research & Development
N.A.I.C.S.: 334610

SAS Institute B.V. (1)
Flevolaan 69, PO Box 3053, 1270 EB, Huizen, Netherlands (100%)
Tel.: (31) 356996900
Web Site: http://www.sas.com
Sales Range: $10-24.9 Million
Emp.: 130
Software Services
N.A.I.C.S.: 334610
Edwin Petters *(Mgr-Mktg)*

SAS Institute CR, s.r.o. (1)
Na Pankraci 17-19, Prague, 140 00, Czech Republic
Tel.: (420) 261 176 310
Web Site: http://www.sas.com
Emp.: 50
Information Technology Consulting Services
N.A.I.C.S.: 541512
Hana Kvartova *(Gen Mgr)*

SAS Institute GmbH (1)
In Der Neckarhelle 162, 69118, Heidelberg, Germany (100%)
Tel.: (49) 62214150
Web Site: http://www.sas.de
Sales Range: $25-49.9 Million
Emp.: 400
Software Research & Development
N.A.I.C.S.: 334610
Wolf Lithtenftein *(Gen Mgr)*

SAS Institute Inc. (1)
111 Rockville Pike Ste 1000, Rockville, MD 20850 (100%)
Tel.: (301) 838-7030
Web Site: http://www.sas.com
Sales Range: $10-24.9 Million
Emp.: 70
Software Research & Development
N.A.I.C.S.: 541512

SAS Institute Inc. (1)
1915 NW AmberGlen Pkwy Ste 400, Beaverton, OR 97006
Tel.: (919) 677-8000
Web Site: http://www.sas.com
Sales Range: $10-24.9 Million
Emp.: 25
Computer Software Development
N.A.I.C.S.: 541511

SAS Institute Inc. - Sherman Oaks (1)
15300 Ventura Blvd Ste 523, Sherman Oaks, CA 91403
Tel.: (818) 906-7638
Web Site: http://www.sas.com
Sales Range: $75-99.9 Million
Emp.: 50
Management Consulting Services
N.A.I.C.S.: 541611
Jim Goodnight *(CEO)*

SAS Institute Japan Ltd. (1)
Roppongi Hills Mori Tower 11th Floor 6-10-1, Roppongi Minato-ku, Tokyo, 106-6111, Japan (100%)
Tel.: (81) 364343000
Sales Range: $25-49.9 Million
Emp.: 301
Software Research & Development
N.A.I.C.S.: 334610

SAS Institute Kft. (1)
Hataror ut 36, Budapest, 1122, Hungary
Tel.: (36) 1 224 2010
Sales Range: $10-24.9 Million
Emp.: 35
Information Technology Consulting Services
N.A.I.C.S.: 541512
Istvan Musza *(Mng Dir)*

SAS Institute Ltd. (1)
14 F City Plz 4 12 Taikoo Wan Rd, Taikoo Shing, China (Hong Kong) (100%)
Tel.: (852) 25684280
Web Site: http://www.sas.com
Sales Range: $10-24.9 Million
Emp.: 60
Software Research & Development
N.A.I.C.S.: 334610

SAS Institute Ltd. (1)
Unit 1801 1803 Tower E1 Oriental Plaza, No 1 East Chang An Avenue, Dong Cheng District, Beijing, 100738, China (100%)
Tel.: (86) 1059132888
Web Site: http://www.sas.com
Sales Range: $10-24.9 Million
Emp.: 45
Software Services
N.A.I.C.S.: 334610

SAS Institute Ltd. (1)
50 Northumberland Road, Ballsbridge, Dublin, Ireland
Tel.: (353) 1 613 6400
Sales Range: $10-24.9 Million
Emp.: 25
Information Technology Consulting Services
N.A.I.C.S.: 541512
John Farrelly *(Country Mgr)*

SAS Institute N.V. (1)
Kasteel De Robiano Hertenbergstraat 6, 3080, Tervuren, Belgium (100%)
Tel.: (32) 27660700
Web Site: http://www.sas.com
Sales Range: $10-24.9 Million
Emp.: 115
Software Services
N.A.I.C.S.: 334610
Geert van Peteghem *(Gen Mgr)*

SAS Institute Oy (1)
Tekniikantie 14, Espoo, 02151, Finland (100%)
Tel.: (358) 9525571

SAS INSTITUTE INC.

SAS Institute Inc.—(Continued)
Web Site: http://www.sas.com
Sales Range: $10-24.9 Million
Emp.: 60
Softwear Research & Development
N.A.I.C.S.: 334610
Johan Sandill (Country Mgr)

SAS Institute Pte. Ltd. (1)
20 Anson Road Level 8, Singapore, 079912, Singapore (100%)
Tel.: (65) 63988988
Web Site: http://www.sas.com
Sales Range: $10-24.9 Million
Emp.: 60
Software Research & Development
N.A.I.C.S.: 334610

SAS Institute S.A.U. (1)
C/ Arroyo de Valdebebas 4 Planta 4, Madrid, 28050, Spain (100%)
Tel.: (34) 912007300
Web Site: http://www.sas.com
Sales Range: $10-24.9 Million
Emp.: 100
Analytics & Data Management Services & Software
N.A.I.C.S.: 334610

SAS Institute SA (1)
3 Artemidos Str, Maroussi, 15125, Athens, Greece
Tel.: (30) 210 6898730
Web Site: http://www.sas.com
Information Technology Consulting Services
N.A.I.C.S.: 541512
Elpida Kallia (Mgr-Education & Mktg)

SAS Institute SRL (1)
Via CR Darwin 20/22, 20143, Milan, Italy (100%)
Tel.: (39) 02 8313 41
Web Site: http://www.sas.com
Sales Range: $25-49.9 Million
Emp.: 200
Software Research & Development
N.A.I.C.S.: 334610
Michela Guerra (Mgr-Mktg Comm)

SAS Institute Sdn. Bhd. (1)
Suite 6-3A Level 6 Menara CIMB Jalan Stesen Sentral 2, Kuala Lumpur Sentral, 50470, Kuala Lumpur, Malaysia (100%)
Tel.: (60) 327252288
Web Site: http://www.sas.com
Sales Range: $10-24.9 Million
Emp.: 60
Software Research & Development Mfr'
N.A.I.C.S.: 334610
Andy Zook (Sr VP-SAS Asia Pacific)

SAS Institute Taiwan Ltd. (1)
10480 3F No 10 ming Sheng East Road Sec 3, Taipei, Taiwan
Tel.: (886) 221811000
Software Services
N.A.I.C.S.: 334610

SAS Institute sarl (1)
204 Route d, Strassen, 3080, Luxembourg
Tel.: (352) 26 11 84
Sales Range: $25-49.9 Million
Emp.: 150
Information Technology Consulting Services
N.A.I.C.S.: 541512
Patrick Van Geven (Gen Mgr)

SAS Research & Development (India) Pvt. Ltd.
Level 2A & Level 3 Cybercity Tower 5 Magarpatta City, Hadapsar, Pune, 411 013, India
Tel.: (91) 20 30138888
Sales Range: $25-49.9 Million
Emp.: 450
Information Technology Consulting Services
N.A.I.C.S.: 541512
Rajnish Kumar (Sr Engr-Software)

SAS Slovakia, s.r.o. (1)
Lazaretska 12, Bratislava, 81108, Slovakia
Tel.: (421) 2 5778 0910 1
Web Site: http://www.sas.com
Sales Range: $10-24.9 Million
Emp.: 45
Information Technology Consulting Services
N.A.I.C.S.: 541512
Jozef Bencik (Mgr-Sls)

SAS Software (Thailand) Company Limited. (1)
388 Exchange Tower Building 38th Floor Unit 3803-4 Sukhumvit Road, Khlong Toei, Bangkok, 10110, Thailand
Tel.: (66) 2663 6888
Web Site: http://www.sas.com
Information Technology Consulting Services
N.A.I.C.S.: 541512

SAS Software Korea Ltd. (1)
8 10 F Daechi B D 889 11 Daechi Dong, Kangnam-ku, Seoul, 135 839, Korea (South) (100%)
Tel.: (82) 21917000
Web Site: http://www.sas.com
Sales Range: $10-24.9 Million
Emp.: 92
Software Services
N.A.I.C.S.: 334610

SAS Software, Ltd. (1)
Wittington House Henley Road, Medmenham, Marlow, SL7 2EB, Buckinghamshire, United Kingdom (100%)
Tel.: (44) 1628486933
Sales Range: $25-49.9 Million
Emp.: 400
Software Research & Development
N.A.I.C.S.: 334610
Mark Wilkinson (Mng Dir)
Stephen Kelly (COO)

SAS inSchool (1)
100 Sas Campus Dr Bldg U, Cary, NC 27513
Tel.: (919) 531-7505
Web Site: http://www.sasinschool.com
Rev: $310,000
Emp.: 77
School Curriculum Developer
N.A.I.C.S.: 513210

SASA BROTHERS, INC.
20 Scituate Ave, Johnston, RI 02919
Tel.: (401) 944-3040
Web Site: http://www.sasabrothers.com
Year Founded: 2000
Sales Range: $25-49.9 Million
Emp.: 5
Housing Construction Services
N.A.I.C.S.: 236115
Bash Sasa (Owner)

SASAKI ASSOCIATES INC.
64 Pleasant St, Watertown, MA 02472-2316
Tel.: (617) 926-3300 MA
Web Site: http://www.sasaki.com
Year Founded: 1953
Sales Range: $25-49.9 Million
Emp.: 250
Architectural Services
N.A.I.C.S.: 541310
Dennis Pieprz (Principal)
William Massey (Principal)
Tyler Patrick (Principal)
Caroline Braga (Principal)
Christine Dunn (Principal)
Fiske Crowell (Principal)
James N. Miner (CEO & Principal)
Mark Dawson (Principal & Architect-Landscape)
Pablo Savid-Buteler (Mng Principal)
Vinicius Gorgati (Principal)
Zachary Chrisco (Principal)
Ken Goulding (Principal)
Greg Havens (Principal)
Joe Hibbard (Principal & Architect-Landscape)
Lan Ying Ip (Principal)
Katia Lucic (Principal & Architect)
Fred Merrill (Principal)
Mary Anne Ocampo (Principal)
Chris Sgarzi (Principal)
Romil Sheth (Principal)
Elizabeth von Goeler (Principal)
Alan Ward (Principal)
Isabel Zempel (Principal)
Tao Zhang (Principal & Architect-Landscape)
Martin Zogran (Principal)

Subsidiaries:
Sasaki (1)
77 Geary St 4th Fl, San Francisco, CA 94108 (40%)
Tel.: (415) 776-7272
Sales Range: $25-49.9 Million
Emp.: 1
Integrated Planning, Design & Construction Services
N.A.I.C.S.: 236220

SASANI FILMS CORP.
153 W 27th St Ste 507, New York, NY 10001
Tel.: (917) 628-4828 DE
Web Site: http://www.sasanifilms.com
Year Founded: 2012
Film Production
N.A.I.C.S.: 512110
Hamid Kayani (Pres, CEO, CFO & Principal Acctg Officer)

SASCO ELECTRIC
2750 Moore Ave, Fullerton, CA 92833
Tel.: (714) 870-0217 CA
Web Site: http://www.sasco.com
Year Founded: 1968
Sales Range: $250-299.9 Million
Emp.: 1,400
General Electrical Contractor
N.A.I.C.S.: 238210
L. H. Smead (Pres)
Michelle Kwong (Dir-HR)
Eileen Allen (Controller)

Subsidiaries:
Sasco Electric (1)
148 E Brokaw Rd, San Jose, CA 95112
Tel.: (408) 970-8300
Web Site: http://www.sasco.com
Sales Range: $25-49.9 Million
Emp.: 100
Electrical Contractor
N.A.I.C.S.: 238210

Sasco Electric (1)
Pier 28 at Embarcadero 2nd Fl, San Francisco, CA 94105
Tel.: (415) 512-9158
Web Site: http://www.sasco.com
Sales Range: $25-49.9 Million
Emp.: 10
General Electrical Contractor
N.A.I.C.S.: 238210
Scott Eaton (Office Mgr)

SASCO INSURANCE SERVICES INC.
313 High St.1, Hackettstown, NJ 07840
Tel.: (908) 852-5555
Year Founded: 1984
Insurance Agencies & Brokerages
N.A.I.C.S.: 524210
Susan Seger (VP)

Subsidiaries:
Otterstedt Insurance Agency, Inc. (1)
540 Sylvan Ave Ste 1, Englewood Cliffs, NJ 07632
Tel.: (201) 227-1800
Web Site: http://www.otterstedt.com
Sales Range: $1-9.9 Million
Emp.: 80
Insurance Agencies & Brokerages
N.A.I.C.S.: 524210
Joseph C. Parisi Jr. (Pres & CEO)

SASHA HANDBAGS INC.
460 Main Ave Ste 1, Wallington, NJ 07057-1851
Tel.: (973) 470-9007
Web Site: http://www.sashahandbags.com
Rev: $12,900,000
Emp.: 47
Handbags
N.A.I.C.S.: 424350
Erol Devli (Pres)

SASID
462 Midland Rd, Janesville, WI 53546
Web Site: http://www.SASid.com
Sales Range: $1-9.9 Million
Emp.: 25
Insurance Agencies
N.A.I.C.S.: 524210
Shannon Kennedy (Pres)

SASR WORKFORCE SOLUTIONS, LLC
5400 Glenwood Ave Ste 310, Raleigh, NC 27612
Tel.: (919) 787-5571
Web Site: http://www.sasrlink.com
Year Founded: 2003
Sales Range: $10-24.9 Million
Emp.: 25
Employment Placement for the Retail Industry
N.A.I.C.S.: 561311
Patrick Henderson (Pres & CEO)
Debbie Brown (VP-Sls & Mktg)

SASSER FAMILY HOLDINGS, INC.
425 N Martingale Rd 8th Fl, Schaumburg, IL 60173 DE
Web Site: http://www.sfhsinc.com
Year Founded: 1928
Investment Holding Company
N.A.I.C.S.: 551112
Fred R. Sasser (Chm)
Jeff Walsh (CEO)
Charles Vinopal (VP-HR)
Kelly Brannon Pronek (VP-Corp Comm & Mktg)
Brock Morrison (VP-IT & Systems Strategy)
Bryan Zair (Gen Counsel, Sr VP & Asst Sec)
Brian Frizzell (Treas & VP-Corp Fin)
Susan Buchanan (CFO & Sr VP)

Subsidiaries:
Chicago Freight Car Leasing Co. (1)
425 N Martingale Rd, Schaumburg, IL 60173
Tel.: (847) 318-8000
Web Site: http://www.crdx.com
Rev: $32,000,000
Emp.: 20
Rental Of Railroad Cars
N.A.I.C.S.: 488210
Larry Abraham (Dir-Fleet Ops)
Jay Wilensky (VP-Acctg & Fin)
Paul B. Deasy (Pres)
John Cooney (VP-Fleet Ops)
Matthew Branch (Mgr-Fleet Portfolio & Mktg)
Josh Chesser (VP-Sls & Customer Support)

Union Leasing, Inc. (1)
425 N Martingale Rd 6th Fl, Schaumburg, IL 60173
Tel.: (847) 240-1500
Web Site: http://www.unionleasing.com
Automobile Leasing & Fleet Services
N.A.I.C.S.: 524210
Todd Heemsoth (Pres)
Jeff Malko (VP-Customer Experience)
Rhonda Zielinski (Sr VP-Comml Sls & Mktg)
Brad Kacsh (Sr Mgr-License & Title)
David Huizinga (VP-Ops & Bus Transformation)
Tim Cengel (Sr Mgr-Pur & Electrification)

SATCO PRODUCTS INC.
110 Heartland Blvd, Brentwood, NY 11717-8364
Tel.: (631) 243-2022
Web Site: http://www.satco.com
Year Founded: 1965
Sales Range: $10-24.9 Million
Emp.: 100
Provider of Electrical Apparatus & Equipment
N.A.I.C.S.: 423610

COMPANIES

Herbert Gildin *(CEO)*
Bill Gildin *(Pres)*
Jeff Kosberghas *(Mgr-Sls-Southeast Reg)*
Alan Karen *(Sr VP-Sls-Global)*
Pamela St. Martin *(Sr Mgr-Sls-E-Commerce)*
Ben Tuminello *(Dir-ECommerce)*

Subsidiaries:

Satco Products Inc. (1)
110 Heartland Blvd, Brentwood, NY 11717-8364
Tel.: (631) 243-2022
Web Site: http://www.satco.com
Emp.: 160
Provider of Electrical Apparatus & Equipment
N.A.I.C.S.: 423610
William Jilben *(Pres)*
Herb Jilben *(CFO)*

SATCOM RESOURCES

101 Eagle Rd Bldg 7, Avon, CO 81620-1639
Tel.: (970) 748-3094
Web Site: http://www.satcomresources.com
Year Founded: 2000
Sales Range: $10-24.9 Million
Emp.: 15
Satellite Communication Equipment Building & Installation Services
N.A.I.C.S.: 517410
Fred Pope *(Founder & CEO)*
Tom Chapman *(Mgr-Network Svcs & Sys Integration)*
Chris Weathers *(Acct Mgr-Sls)*
Jason Bastien *(Mgr-Logistics)*
John Arnot *(VP-Sls)*
Spencer Ball *(Acct Mgr)*
Marty Hijmans *(Engr-Sls)*

SATELLITE COMM SYSTEMS

2 Eaton St Ste 1000, Hampton, VA 23669
Tel.: (757) 723-0835
Web Site: http://www.sat-tel.com
Sales Range: $10-24.9 Million
Emp.: 50
Telephone Communication, Except Radio
N.A.I.C.S.: 517121
Ernie N. Hux *(CEO)*
Ernie S. Hux *(Pres)*
Renatta Hux *(Treas)*

SATELLITE HOLDINGS, INC.

750 Rittiman Rd, San Antonio, TX 78209-5500
Tel.: (210) 692-4169   TX
Web Site: http://www.satelliteholdingsinc.com
Year Founded: 2014
Holding Company; Satellite Communications & Broadcasting Services
N.A.I.C.S.: 551112
Samuel Dibrell Jr. *(Owner)*

Subsidiaries:

Orbital Media Networks, Inc. (1)
76 Inverness Dr E Ste C, Englewood, CO 80112-6770
Tel.: (303) 925-1708
Web Site:
http://www.orbitalmedianetworks.com
Emp.: 25
Satellite Communication Network Services
N.A.I.C.S.: 517410
Mike Hagans *(Pres & COO)*
Samuel Dibrell Jr. *(Pres & CEO)*

SATIC, INC.

7151 Kestrel Dr, Missoula, MT 59808
Tel.: (406) 493-1861
Web Site: http://www.saticusa.com
Year Founded: 2003
Sales Range: $1-9.9 Million

Electrical Equipments Mfr & Whslr
N.A.I.C.S.: 334515
Denis Blackstun *(CFO)*
Lynn Churchill *(CIO)*
B. D. Erickson II *(Pres)*

SATILLA RURAL ELECTRIC MEMBERSHIP CORPORATION

928 GA Hwy 32 E, Alma, GA 31510
Tel.: (912) 632-7222   GA
Web Site: http://www.satillaemc.com
Year Founded: 1937
Sales Range: $25-49.9 Million
Emp.: 140
Electricity & Electric Services
N.A.I.C.S.: 221122
Bentley Carter *(Mgr-Loss Control & Facilities)*
Jennifer Rowland *(Mgr-HR)*
David Walker *(Engr-Sys)*

SATMETRIX SYSTEMS, INC.

3 Twin Dolphin Dr Ste 225, Redwood City, CA 94065
Tel.: (650) 227-8300
Web Site: http://www.satmetrix.com
Sales Range: $25-49.9 Million
Emp.: 200
Software Publisher
N.A.I.C.S.: 513210
Laura Brooks *(VP-Innovation & Strategy)*

Subsidiaries:

Informative, Inc. (1)
950 Tower Ln Ste 500, Foster City, CA 94404-2124
Tel.: (650) 534-1010
Web Site: http://www.informative.com
Sales Range: $1-9.9 Million
Emp.: 40
Proactively Collect Critical Customer Input
N.A.I.C.S.: 517810

SATORI CAPITAL, LLC

2501 N Harwood St 20th Fl Ste 2001, Dallas, TX 75201
Tel.: (214) 390-6270
Web Site:
http://www.satoricapital.com
Private Equity Firm
N.A.I.C.S.: 523999
Sunny Vanderbeck *(Co-Founder & Mng Partner)*
Randy Eisenman *(Co-Founder & Mng Partner)*
Kern Wildenthal *(Operating Partner-Healthcare Indus)*
Willie Houston *(COO & CFO)*
Paul Schlosberg *(Operating Partner-Fin Svcs)*

Subsidiaries:

Zorch International, Inc. (1)
223 W Erie St Ste 5NW, Chicago, IL 60654
Tel.: (312) 751-8010
Web Site: http://www.zorch.com
Brand Development & Integration, Merchandising
N.A.I.C.S.: 541820
Nicole Loftus *(Founder)*

SATORY GLOBAL, LLC

1725 St NW Ste 300, Washington, DC 20006
Tel.: (202) 349-3758
Web Site: http://www.satory.com
Year Founded: 2007
Sales Range: $1-9.9 Million
Emp.: 18
Information Technology Services
N.A.I.C.S.: 541513
Anne Isaacs *(Co-Founder & CEO)*

SATTERFIELD & PONTIKES CONSTRUCTION, INC.

1100 Equit Dr Ste 100, Houston, TX 77041-4318
Tel.: (713) 996-1300
Web Site: http://www.satpon.com
Year Founded: 1989
Sales Range: $150-199.9 Million
Emp.: 400
Provider of Nonresidential Construction Services
N.A.I.C.S.: 236220
George Pontikes *(CEO)*
Sruti Nallapaneni *(Engr-BIM)*
Anjy Salinas *(Mgr-Fin)*
Denis Ducran *(Gen Counsel & VP)*
Jessica McKnight *(Coord-Estimating)*
Lee Milligan *(Superintendent)*
David Van Fleet *(VP-Industrial Market Sector)*

SATTERWHITE COMPANIES INC.

8405 HWY 259 N, Longview, TX 75605
Tel.: (903) 663-1729
Web Site: http://www.slh.net
Rev.: $20,000,000
Emp.: 35
Prefabricated Log Home Mfr
N.A.I.C.S.: 321992
Sam D. Satterwhite *(Pres)*
Travonda Satterwhite *(VP)*

SATURDAY EVENING POST SOCIETY

1100 Waterway Blvd, Indianapolis, IN 46202-2156
Tel.: (317) 634-1100   IN
Web Site:
http://www.saturdayeveningpost.com
Year Founded: 1976
Sales Range: $75-99.9 Million
Emp.: 45
Health, Medical & Literary Magazines
N.A.I.C.S.: 513120

Subsidiaries:

Children's Better Health Institute (1)
1100 Waterway Blvd, Indianapolis, IN 46202-2156
Tel.: (317) 634-1100
Web Site: http://www.cbhi.org
Sales Range: $10-24.9 Million
Publishing
N.A.I.C.S.: 513120
Joan Servaas *(Pres)*

Unit (Domestic):

Turtle Magazine for Preschool Kids (2)
1100 Waterway Blvd, Indianapolis, IN 46202
Tel.: (317) 634-1100
Publisher of Magazine for Children
N.A.I.C.S.: 531120
Bob Silvers *(VP)*

Medical Education and Research Foundation (1)
1100 Waterway Blvd, Indianapolis, IN 46202-2156   (100%)
Tel.: (317) 634-1100
Web Site: http://www.satevepost.org
Sales Range: $10-24.9 Million
Emp.: 5
Medical Newsletter Publisher
N.A.I.C.S.: 513120
Joan Servaas *(Chm)*

SATURDAY KNIGHT LTD.

4330 Winton Rd, Cincinnati, OH 45232
Tel.: (513) 641-1400
Web Site: http://www.skltd.com
Sales Range: $25-49.9 Million
Emp.: 100
Towels Mfr
N.A.I.C.S.: 314120
Diane Wiedman *(VP-Sls & Mktg)*

SATUSA CORPORATION

SATURN BUSINESS SYSTEMS INC.

228 E 45th St 5th Fl, New York, NY 10017-3303
Tel.: (212) 557-8134
Web Site: http://www.saturnb2b.com
Year Founded: 1982
Sales Range: $10-24.9 Million
Emp.: 45
Computer Integrated Design Systems
N.A.I.C.S.: 541512
Lizzette D. Pagan *(Controller)*
George Pappas *(Mgr-Sls)*
Allen Krieger *(Pres)*

SATURN CORPORATION

4701 Lydell Rd, Cheverly, MD 20781
Tel.: (301) 772-7000
Web Site: http://www.saturncorp.com
Year Founded: 1981
Sales Range: $10-24.9 Million
Emp.: 160
Data Processing Services
N.A.I.C.S.: 518210
Fielding W. Yost *(Pres)*

SATURN FREIGHT SYSTEMS INC.

561 Vlg Trace NE Bldg 13 A, Marietta, GA 30067
Tel.: (770) 952-3490
Web Site:
http://www.saturnfreight.com
Sales Range: $10-24.9 Million
Emp.: 20
Freight Forwarding
N.A.I.C.S.: 488510
Guy Stark *(Founder, Pres & CEO)*
Bill Handley *(VP)*
Michael Moore *(VP-Bus Dev)*
Jaclyn Bennett *(VP-Intl Bus Dev)*
Steve Love *(VP-Intl Bus Dev)*

SATURN OF RICHMOND, INC.

11840 Midlothian Tpke, Midlothian, VA 23294
Tel.: (888) 481-2176   VA
Web Site:
http://www.hymanbrosauto.com
Year Founded: 1946
Used Car Dealers
N.A.I.C.S.: 441110

SATURNA CAPITAL CORPORATION

1300 N State St, Bellingham, WA 98225
Tel.: (360) 734-9900   WA
Web Site: http://www.saturna.com
Year Founded: 1989
Sales Range: $25-49.9 Million
Emp.: 64
Investment Advisory Services
N.A.I.C.S.: 523940
Jane Carten *(Pres & CEO)*
Craig Churman *(VP-Product Dev)*
John Overturf *(Dir-Adv)*
Scott Klimo *(Chief Investment Officer)*
Tom Phillips *(Sec)*

SATUSA CORPORATION

5348 Vegas Dr, Las Vegas, NV 89108
Tel.: (509) 995-2433   NV
Year Founded: 2009
Rev.: $44,089
Assets: $14,825
Liabilities: $5,690
Net Worth: $9,135
Earnings: $19,541
Emp.: 1
Fiscal Year-end: 08/31/18
Test Preparation Services
N.A.I.C.S.: 611710
Kevin Nichols *(Pres, CEO, CFO, Treas & Sec)*

SAU-SEA FOODS, INC.

Sau-Sea Foods, Inc.—(Continued)

SAU-SEA FOODS, INC.
PO Box 2400, Southampton, NY 11969
Tel.: (631) 726-0270 NY
Web Site:
  http://www.sauseafoods.com
Year Founded: 1940
Sales Range: $10-24.9 Million
Emp.: 5
Shrimp Cocktails, Cocktail Sauce, Frozen Breaded Shrimp, Frozen Shrimp & Institutional Pack Cocktails Mfr & Retailer
N.A.I.C.S.: 424460
Antonio Estadella (Pres)

SAUBER MANUFACTURING CO
10 N Sauber Rd, Maple Park, IL 60151
Tel.: (630) 365-6600
Web Site: http://www.saubermfg.com
Construction & Mining Machinery
N.A.I.C.S.: 333120
Jim Sauber (Pres)
Pam Stallings (Mgr-Acctg)
Brenda Kohorst (Mgr-Acctg)
AJ Hofer (Mgr-HR)
Mike Blaser (Mgr-Mktg)

SAUCON VALLEY COUNTRY CLUB
2050 Saucon Valley Rd, Bethlehem, PA 18015
Tel.: (610) 758-7150 PA
Web Site:
  http://www.sauconvalleycc.org
Year Founded: 1920
Sales Range: $1-9.9 Million
Emp.: 493
Country Club
N.A.I.C.S.: 713910
Thomas R. Fitzmaurice (Dir-Racquet Sports)
Arden Strickland (Asst Controller)
Holly DuBois (Mgr-Catering Sls)
Jamie Siders (Dir-Banquet)
Dean Will (Mgr-Clubhouse & Dir-Food & Beverage)
Joseph Bonano (Mgr-Restaurant & Bar)
Jonathan Prostak (Asst Mgr-Banquet)
Tara Frana (Coord-Event)
Ryan Mickley (Coord-Event)
Maria Esposito (Dir-Membership)
Brad Shultz (Mgr-Food & Beverage Svcs)

SAUDER WOODWORKING CO.
502 Middle St, Archbold, OH 43502-1559
Tel.: (419) 446-2711 OH
Web Site: http://www.sauder.com
Year Founded: 1934
Sales Range: $700-749.9 Million
Emp.: 2,000
Modular Furniture, Church Furniture & Institutional Seating Mfr
N.A.I.C.S.: 337127
Kevin J. Sauder (Pres & CEO)

Subsidiaries:

Sauder Funeral Products (1)
303 West Barre Rd, Archbold, OH 43502
Web Site:
  http://www.sauderfuneralproducts.com
Sales Range: $100-124.9 Million
Wooden Furniture Mfr
N.A.I.C.S.: 321999
Kevin Sauder (Pres)

Sauder Manufacturing Company (1)
930 W Barre Rd, Archbold, OH 43502-9320
Tel.: (419) 446-9384
Web Site: http://www.saudermfg.com

Sales Range: $50-74.9 Million
Emp.: 350
Institutional Office & Church Furniture Mfr
N.A.I.C.S.: 337127
Philip Bontrager (Pres & CEO)

Sauder RTA (1)
502 Middle St, Archbold, OH 43502
Tel.: (419) 446-2711
Web Site:
  http://www.sauderwoodworking.com
Wooden Furniture Mfr
N.A.I.C.S.: 337211

SAUDI AMERICAN HOLDINGS CORP.
Weber Ctr Fort Lauderdale 3042 N Federal Hwy Ste 200, Fort Lauderdale, FL 33306
Tel.: (954) 622-9115
Software Development Services
N.A.I.C.S.: 541511
David Carruthers (Pres)

SAUGATUCK CAPITAL COMPANY
4 Armstrong Rd Ste 230, Shelton, CT 06484
Tel.: (203) 348-6669 DE
Web Site:
  http://www.saugatuckcapital.com
Year Founded: 1982
Privater Equity Firm
N.A.I.C.S.: 523999
Gary Goldberg (Mng Dir)
Stuart W. Hawley (Mng Partner)

Subsidiaries:

Femco Machine Company (1)
754 S Main St, Punxsutawney, PA 15767
Tel.: (800) 458-3445
Web Site: https://famcoservice.com
Commercial & Industrial Machinery Repair Services
N.A.I.C.S.: 811310
Dan Rondeau (Pres & CEO)

Subsidiary (Domestic):

LEME, Inc. (2)
6107 Churchman Bypass, Indianapolis, IN 46203
Tel.: (317) 788-4114
Rev.: $6,150,000
Emp.: 50
All Other Miscellaneous Fabricated Metal Product Mfr
N.A.I.C.S.: 332999
Larry Emery (Founder & Pres)

SAUK PRAIRIE HEALTHCARE
260 26th St, Prairie Du Sac, WI 53578
Tel.: (608) 643-3311 WI
Web Site:
  http://www.saukprairiehealthcare.org
Year Founded: 1956
Sales Range: $50-74.9 Million
Emp.: 575
Health Care Srvices
N.A.I.C.S.: 622110
Kenneth Carlson (VP-Plng & Bus Dev)
Carla Peck (VP-Quality & Compliance)
Dale Carlson (Treas)
Robbi Eccher Bos (VP-HR)
Roxi Maier (Sec)
Tammy Adler (Pres)
Denise Cole-Ouzounian (VP-Patient Svcs)
Shawn Lerch (CEO)

SAUL EWING ARNSTEIN & LEHR LLP
Centre Sq W 1500 Market St 38th Fl, Philadelphia, PA 19102-2186
Tel.: (215) 972-7777 DE
Web Site: http://www.saul.com

Year Founded: 1921
Sales Range: $125-149.9 Million
Emp.: 400
Law firm
N.A.I.C.S.: 541110
Steven Ziven (Mng Partner-Los Angeles)
Bruce D. Armon (Partner-Philadelphia)
David S. Antzis (Partner-Chesterbrook & Philadelphia)
Jennifer K. Peterson (Partner & COO)
Paul S. Levy (CFO)
Elizabeth Wills (Office Mgr)
Leslie K. Gross (Dir-Comm)
Leonard J. Oliveri (Dir-Info Sys)
Naomi A. Mukalian (Dir-Atty Recruiting)
Sheri M. Zachary (Dir-Career Dev)
Adam H. Isenberg (Partner-Philadelphia & New York)
Joshua S. Pasker (Partner-Philadelphia)
Joshua W. B. Richards (Partner-Philadelphia)
Barry F. Levin (Mng Partner)
April Falcon Doss (Partner)
Clarence Lee (Partner-Litigation & Insurance Practices-Washington)
Charles Kelly (Mng Partner)
William E. Manning (Mng Partner)
Wendie C. Stabler (Mng Partner)
Todd Corham (CIO)
Kelly Enache (Chief Mktg Officer)
Rebecca Abrams Sarelson (Partner)
Stephen S. Aichele (Partner)
George P. Apostolides (Partner)
Louis Archambault (Partner)
Andrea Cox (Partner)
Teresa K. D. Currier (Partner)
Steven L. Daniels (Partner)
Justin C. Danilewitz (Partner)
Gregory J. Davis (Partner)
John D. Demmy (Partner)
Michael Denberg (Partner)
Nancy Depodesta (Partner)
Cathleen M. Devlin (Partner)
Miguel Diaz De La Portilla (Partner)
Ryan L. Diclemente (Partner)
Elizabeth S. Fenton (Partner)
Franklin Zemel (Partner)
Douglas Ramler (Partner)
Kermit Nash (Partner)
Samuel Diehl (Partner)
Andrew Daly (Partner)
Nancy Burke (Partner)
Maxwell Bremer (Partner)
Stephen Eide (Partner)
Timothy W. Callahan II (Gen Counsel)
Earl Adams Jr. (Partner-Washington & Chm-Regulatory, Compliance & Govt Svcs)

Subsidiaries:

Freeman, Freeman & Smiley, LLP (1)
1888 Century Park E Ste 1900, Los Angeles, CA 90067-1723
Tel.: (310) 255-6100
Web Site: http://www.ffslaw.com
Emp.: 49
Law firm
N.A.I.C.S.: 541110
Richard E. Gilbert (Partner)
Richard D. Freeman (Partner)
Bruce M. Smiley (Partner)
Fred J. Marcus (Partner)
Glenn T. Sherman (Partner)
Sheila L. Ardalan (Dir-Bus Dev & Client Svcs)
Maureen H. Janmohamed (Paralegal)
Linda R. Kaan (Paralegal)
H. Jacob Lager (Paralegal)
Tara McKenney (Dir-Mktg)
Robert Ezra (Partner & Head-Fashion Law)

Richard A. D'Amura (Partner-Fin Svcs, Securities Regulation & Litigation practice)

SAULSBURY INDUSTRIES
2951 E Interstate 20, Odessa, TX 79766
Tel.: (432) 366-4252
Web Site: http://www.si-tx.com
Sales Range: $50-74.9 Million
Emp.: 350
Provider of Turnkey Engineering, Construction & Electrical Services
N.A.I.C.S.: 238210
Matt Saulsbury (CEO)
Jimmy Matthews (Sr VP-Ops)
Kim Combs (VP-Bus Dev)
Steve Horn (COO)
Chat York (Pres)
Jeremy Nelson (VP-Construction Svcs)
Jim Werner (VP-Construction Svcs Southwest)
Tommy Williams (VP-Electrical Svcs)
Greg Hebert (VP-Engrg-Gulf Coast)
David Dool (VP-Gulf Coast)
Marty Kunz (VP-HR)
Courtney Wardlaw (VP-Mktg & Comm)
Norman Hood (VP-Nuclear Svcs)
Ben Humphries (VP-Ops Svcs)
Dave Hedges (VP-Power)
Tom Vaughn (Sr VP-Ops-Gulf Coast)
Dennis Chismar (Sr VP-Bus Dev & Mktg)
Blake Young (Chm)

Subsidiaries:

Saulsbury Electric Co., Inc. (1)
5308 Andrews Hwy, Odessa, TX 79762
Tel.: (432) 366-3686
Web Site: http://www.si-tx.com
Rev.: $47,735,868
Emp.: 300
Provider of General Electrical Services
N.A.I.C.S.: 238210
Mark Saulsbury (VP)
Tracy Frazier (COO)
Rick Graves (CEO)
John Higgins (Chief HR Officer)
Jim Lemarr (VP-Engrg Svcs)
Jimmy Matthews (Sr VP-Ops)
Rick Rodery (CTO)
John Shefchik (VP & Gen Mgr-Southwest)
Frank A. Hunold Jr. (Gen Counsel)
Bubba Saulsbury Jr. (Sr VP-Bus Dev)

SAUNDERS BROTHERS
869 Main St Ste 900, Westbrook, ME 04092-2869
Tel.: (207) 854-2551 ME
Year Founded: 1900
Sales Range: $100-124.9 Million
Emp.: 200
Wood Dowels, Decorative Furniture Accessories & Wood Furniture Component Parts Mfr
N.A.I.C.S.: 321999

Subsidiaries:

Forest Industries, Inc. (1)
54 Fair St PO Box 66, Fryeburg, ME 04037
Tel.: (800) 343-0675
Sales Range: $10-24.9 Million
Emp.: 51
Custom Wood Turnings
N.A.I.C.S.: 321999

SAUNDERS YACHTWORKS
27075 Marina Rd, Orange Beach, AL 36561
Tel.: (251) 981-3700
Web Site:
  http://www.saundersyatch.com
Year Founded: 1959
Yacht Maintenance & Repair Services
N.A.I.C.S.: 336611
John Fitzgerald (Pres)
Bob Anderson (Mgr-Customer Svc)
Timothy Gibson (Mgr-Customer Svc)
Jeff Lowell (Mgr-Customer Svc)

David Disouryavong (Mgr-Gulf Shores Boatyard)
Jim Langley (Mgr- Gen Svc)
Randy Maddox (Mgr-Parts)
David Nunez (Mgr-Sys & Electronics)
Boyd Siegel (Mgr-Crafts)
Tim McCue (Asst Mgr-Crafts)
Murray Loper (Project Manager)
Eddie Waters (Mgr-Boatyard)
Scott Orafanello (Mgr-Svc)
Greg Lindell (Mgr-Warranty, Safety & Facilities)
Ashley Rainer (Mgr-Mktg)
Don Hancock (Mgr-IT)
Scarlett Pepperman (CFO)

SAUSE BROS. OCEAN TOWING CO. INC.
3710 NW Front Ave, Portland, OR 97210-1323
Tel.: (503) 222-1811 OR
Web Site: http://www.sause.com
Year Founded: 1947
Sales Range: $25-49.9 Million
Emp.: 405
Towing & Tugboat Services
N.A.I.C.S.: 488999
Dale Sause (Pres)
Erin McClanahan (VP-Sls & Mktg)

Subsidiaries:

Sause Bros Inc. (1)
705 N Nimitz Hwy 2nd Fl, Honolulu, HI 96817
Tel.: (808) 521-5082
Web Site: http://www.sause.com
Rev.: $80,000,000
Emp.: 80
Towing & Tugboat Service
N.A.I.C.S.: 488999

SAUSSY BURBANK, LLC.
3730 Glenlake Dr Ste 125, Charlotte, NC 28208-6841
Tel.: (704) 945-1515
Web Site: http://www.saussyburbank.com
Sales Range: $25-49.9 Million
Emp.: 40
Housing Construction Services
N.A.I.C.S.: 236117
Jim Burbank (Owner)
Brant McConkey (Mgr)
Charles Teal (CEO)
Bob Zweier (Pres)

SAV-A STEP FOOD MARTS INC.
610 W Hwy 131, Clarksville, IN 47129
Tel.: (812) 945-3096
Web Site: http://www.savastep.com
Sales Range: $10-24.9 Million
Emp.: 50
Grocery Store Owner & Operator
N.A.I.C.S.: 445110
Joseph J. Pierce (Pres)
Michael Pierce (Mgr-Ops)
Lisa Collard (Mgr-Price Book & POS)

SAV-ON DRUGS OF ARK, INC.
1014 Harkrider St, Conway, AR 72032
Tel.: (501) 327-6777 AR
Web Site: http://www.savondrugs.net
Year Founded: 1978
Drug Stores & Proprietary Stores
N.A.I.C.S.: 456110
Adra Windsor (Mgr)

SAV-ON PLATING, INC.
17 W Watkins Rd, Phoenix, AZ 85003
Tel.: (602) 252-4311 CA
Web Site: http://www.sav-onplating.com
Year Founded: 1969
Sales Range: $10-24.9 Million
Emp.: 80
Metal Electroplating Services
N.A.I.C.S.: 332813
Joseph Trimino (Owner & Pres)
Leslie Trimino (Dir)

Subsidiaries:

Sav-On Plating of Arizona Inc. (1)
17 W Watkins Rd, Phoenix, AZ 85003
Tel.: (602) 252-4311
Web Site: http://www.sav-onplating.com
Electroplating, Plating, Polishing, Anodizing & Coloring
N.A.I.C.S.: 332813
Joseph Trimino (Owner)

SAVA SENIOR CARE LLC
1 Ravinia Dr Ste 1500, Atlanta, GA 30346-2115
Tel.: (678) 443-7000 DE
Web Site: http://www.savaseniorcare.com
Year Founded: 1997
Sales Range: $1-4.9 Billion
Emp.: 35,000
Operation of Long-term Health Care Centers & Nursing Home Facilities
N.A.I.C.S.: 623110
Stefano M. Miele (Gen Counsel & Exec VP)

Subsidiaries:

Alpine Terrace (1)
746 Alpine Dr, Kerrville, TX 78028-2502
Tel.: (830) 896-2323
Web Site: http://www.savaseniorcare.com
Sales Range: $25-49.9 Million
Emp.: 45
Nursing Home Facility
N.A.I.C.S.: 623111
Debbie Martan (Mgr-Acctg)

Boulevard Manor Nursing Center (1)
2839 S Seacrest Blvd, Boynton Beach, FL 33435-7934
Tel.: (561) 732-2464
Sales Range: $50-74.9 Million
Emp.: 168
Nursing Home Facility
N.A.I.C.S.: 623311
Essie Mosley (Mgr-HR)

Hilltop Village (1)
1400 Hilltop Rd, Kerrville, TX 78028
Tel.: (830) 895-3200
Sales Range: $25-49.9 Million
Emp.: 125
Nursing Home Facility
N.A.I.C.S.: 623311
Debbie Mitchell (Mgr-Acctg)

Imperial Health Care Center (1)
900 Imperial Golf Course Blvd, Naples, FL 34110-1085
Tel.: (239) 591-4800
Sales Range: $25-49.9 Million
Emp.: 120
Nursing Home Facility
N.A.I.C.S.: 623311

Scottsdale Nursing Center (1)
3293 N Drinkwater Blvd, Scottsdale, AZ 85251-6405
Tel.: (480) 947-7443
Sales Range: $25-49.9 Million
Emp.: 83
Nursing Home Facility
N.A.I.C.S.: 623311
Brett Ottoley (Mgr)

Silver Creek Manor Nursing Center (1)
9014 Timber Path, San Antonio, TX 78250-4172
Tel.: (210) 523-2455
Web Site: http://www.savaseniorcare.com
Sales Range: $25-49.9 Million
Emp.: 105
Nursing Home Facility
N.A.I.C.S.: 623311

South Haven Manor Nursing Home (1)
1300 ESBlvd, Montgomery, AL 36116-2318
Tel.: (334) 288-0122
Web Site: http://www.savaseniorcare.com
Sales Range: $50-74.9 Million
Emp.: 150
Nursing Home Facility
N.A.I.C.S.: 623311

Southland Nursing Home (1)
500 Shivers Ter, Marion, AL 36756-3534
Tel.: (334) 683-6141
Sales Range: $10-24.9 Million
Emp.: 125
Nursing Home Facility
N.A.I.C.S.: 623311

SAVAGE & SON, INC.
3101 Yori Ave, Reno, NV 89502-4211
Tel.: (775) 828-4193
Web Site: http://www.savageandson.com
Year Founded: 1893
Sales Range: $10-24.9 Million
Emp.: 70
Plumbing Services
N.A.I.C.S.: 238220
Leonard C. Len (Pres-Savage)
Eileen Savage (Dir-Ops)
John J. Savage (Asst Dir-Ops)

SAVAGE DODGE CHRYSLER JEEP
Route 422, Robesonia, PA 19551
Tel.: (610) 693-5855
Web Site: http://www.savagechrysler.com
Sales Range: $10-24.9 Million
Emp.: 60
Car Whslr
N.A.I.C.S.: 441110
Eric Savage (Pres)

SAVAGE SERVICES CORPORATION
901 Legacy Ctr Way, Midvale, UT 84047
Tel.: (801) 944-6600 UT
Web Site: http://www.savageservices.com
Year Founded: 1946
Freight Trucking, Logistics & Supply Chain Management Services
N.A.I.C.S.: 484121
Kirk Aubry (Pres & CEO)
Kelly Flint (Gen Counsel & Exec VP)
Brad Crist (Pres-Energy & Chemical)
Jeff Kirkham (Chief People Officer & Exec VP)
Jeff Roberts (CFO & Exec VP)
Bob Knief (Pres-Agriculture)
James Hebenstreit (Vice Chm)

Subsidiaries:

Delsco Northwest, Inc. (1)
Pole Line, Roosevelt, UT 84066
Tel.: (435) 722-4236
Support Activities for Oil & Gas Operations
N.A.I.C.S.: 213112

Dupuy Storage & Forwarding LLC (1)
4300 Jourdan Rd, New Orleans, LA 70126
Tel.: (504) 245-7600
Web Site: http://www.dupuystorage.com
Rev.: $5,100,000
Emp.: 95
Warehousing & Storage Services
N.A.I.C.S.: 493190
Allan B. Colley (Pres)
Donna Loescher (Dir-Customer Svc)
Garry Luter (Dir-Ops)
Janice Smith (Dir-Fin)
Adam Miller (Controller)
Al Hernandez (VP)
Bob Olmedo (VP)
Brad Lane (Dir-Ops)
Caryn Sawyer (VP)
Curtis Watts (Mgr-Trucking)
Dana Webb (Mgr-Maintenance)
Dwayne Leon (Mgr-Bulk Facility)
Eduardo Montero (Sr Dir-Bus Dev)
Janet Colley Morse (Dir-Bus Dev)
Jay Hurckes (Mgr-Production)
Jeff Hernandez (Dir-Ops)
John Westcott (CIO)
Joseph Breiten (Mgr-Warehouse)
Keith Luter (Mgr-Ces)
Lamar Crumbliss (Mgr-Warehouse)
Michael Wright (Mgr-Silo)
Scotty Fitzgerald (Dir-Quality Sys & Regulatory Affairs)
Tom Goodman (Mgr-Warehouse)

Ft. Worth Pipe Services, LP (1)
2250 N Cresson Hwy, Cresson, TX 76035
Tel.: (817) 396-4526
Web Site: http://www.fwpipe.com
Sales Range: $10-24.9 Million
Emp.: 100
Oil & Gas Pipe Storage, Transloading, Trucking & Other Services
N.A.I.C.S.: 213112
Tony Blockley (VP)
Stacey Mosley (Ops Mgr)
Kevin Ford (Gen Mgr-Ops)

Savage Inland Marine, LLC (1)
901 Legacy Ctr Way, Midvale, UT 84047
Tel.: (985) 709-8700
Freight Trucking, Logistics & Supply Chain Management Services
N.A.I.C.S.: 484121
Mike Ellis (Exec VP-Marine Solutions)

Sunpro, Inc. (1)
7640 Whipple Ave NW, North Canton, OH 44720
Tel.: (330) 966-0910
Web Site: http://www.sunproservices.com
Electrical Contractor
N.A.I.C.S.: 238210
Jack Lewis (Gen Mgr)

SAVAL FOODS CORPORATION
6740 Dorsey Rd, Elkridge, MD 21075-8630
Tel.: (410) 379-5100 MD
Web Site: http://www.savalfoods.com
Year Founded: 1932
Sales Range: $25-49.9 Million
Emp.: 135
Full Line Food, Paper & Chemical Distributor & Processor of Meat & Pork Products
N.A.I.C.S.: 424410
Paul E. Saval (Pres & COO)
Evan Rich (Owner)

SAVANNAH BEE COMPANY INC
211 Johnny Mercer Blvd, Savannah, GA 31410
Tel.: (912) 234-0688
Web Site: http://www.savannahbee.com
Year Founded: 2002
Sales Range: $1-9.9 Million
Emp.: 14
Gourmet Honey & Organic Body Care Products Mfr
N.A.I.C.S.: 311999
Ted Dennard (Pres)

SAVANNAH DISTRIBUTING CO. INC.
2425 W Gwinnett St, Savannah, GA 31415
Tel.: (912) 233-1167
Web Site: http://www.gawine.com
Sales Range: $10-24.9 Million
Emp.: 50
Liquor Distr
N.A.I.C.S.: 424820
Henry Monsees (Pres)

SAVANNAH FOOD COMPANY, INC.
575 Industrial Rd, Savannah, TN 38372
Tel.: (731) 925-1155
Web Site: http://www.savannahclassics.com
Year Founded: 1970

SAVANNAH FOOD COMPANY, INC.

Savannah Food Company, Inc.—(Continued)
Sales Range: $10-24.9 Million
Emp.: 65
Frozen Specialty Food Mfr
N.A.I.C.S.: 311412
Paul Stodard (VP-Ops)
Lynn Austin (Dir-Production)
Thomas Gean (Dir-Pur & Inventory)
Daniel McCain (Dir-Transportation, Sanitation & Shipping)
Steve Phillips (Dir-Foodservice Sls)
Beverly Taylor (Dir-Customer Svc)
Donna Axley (Mgr-Production, Scheduler & Inventory)
J. C. Flatt (Mgr-Acctg)
Blake Johnson (Mgr-HR)
Tony Pickens (Dir-Maintenance)
Jim Sisco (VP-Sls & Mktg)
Gene Petty (Dir-Technical Svcs)
John H. Bryan III (Pres)

SAVANNAH INTERNATIONAL MOTORS
8301 White Bluff Rd, Savannah, GA 31406
Tel.: (912) 927-4741
Web Site: http://www.carvolvo.com
Year Founded: 1978
Sales Range: $25-49.9 Million
Emp.: 65
Owner & Operator of Car Dealerships
N.A.I.C.S.: 441110
Ralph Tolman (Gen Mgr)
Charles Stelling (Mgr-Parts)
Chris Elliott (Gen Mgr)

SAVANNAH RESTAURANTS CORP.
10 Mall Ct Ste A, Savannah, GA 31406
Tel.: (912) 353-9090
Web Site: http://www.savannahbk.com
Sales Range: $10-24.9 Million
Emp.: 500
Fast-Food Restaurant Owner & Operator
N.A.I.C.S.: 722513
Alex Salgueiro (Pres)
Fonda Salgueiro (Controller)

SAVANO DIRECT CAPITAL PARTNERS LLC
6 E Eager St Ste 4A, Baltimore, MD 21202
Tel.: (443) 873-3561
Web Site: http://www.brownsavano.com
Privater Equity Firm
N.A.I.C.S.: 523940
Tom Smith (Mng Partner)

SAVANT CAPITAL, LLC
190 Buckley Dr, Rockford, IL 61107
Tel.: (815) 227-0300   DE
Web Site: http://www.savantcapital.com
Rev.: $2,200,000,000
Emp.: 150
Investment Advisory & Portfolio Management Services
N.A.I.C.S.: 523940
Brent R. Brodeski (CEO & Principal)
Richard A. Bennett (COO & Principal)
David F. Barton (Dir-Advisory & Bus Dev)
Tawn M. Jacobs (Mgr-Fin Plng & Tax Svcs)
Kim S. Cady (Dir-Institutional Svcs Dept)
LaVonne L. Brown (Dir-Client Experience & Mktg)
Cindy A. Freese (Chief Compliance Officer)
Glenn Kautt (Principal)
Phil Corcoran (Mng Dir)
Stephanie Abbott (Coord-Digital Mktg Comm)
Mallory Cwynar (Coord-Accountant & Payroll)
Emily Keilback (Program Mgr-Talent Dev)
Douglas Moffitt (Chief Advisory & Dev Officer)
John Tejeck (Mgr-Bus Dev-Retirement Plan Svcs)
Katie Calagui (Chief People Officer)

Subsidiaries:

Domani Wealth, LLC   (1)
3211 N Front St Ste 201, Harrisburg, PA 17110-1342
Tel.: (717) 232-4099
Web Site: https://www.harrisburgregionalchamber.org
Estate & Wealth Transfer Planning Services
N.A.I.C.S.: 523999
Lindey Holtzman (Dir-Events)

Subsidiary (Domestic):

EHD Advisory Services, Inc.   (2)
115 E King St, Lancaster, PA 17602
Tel.: (717) 390-4336
Web Site: http://www.ehdadvisory.com
Financial Investment Activities
N.A.I.C.S.: 523999
Kenneth L. Eshleman (Pres & COO)

Green, Plagge & Shaw, Ltd.   (1)
1650 E Main St Ste 201, Saint Charles, IL 60174
Tel.: (630) 587-0193
Web Site: http://www.greenplagge.com
Emp.: 6
Portfolio Management
N.A.I.C.S.: 523940
Michael Green (Owner)

SAVANT CONSTRUCTION, INC.
13830 Mountain Ave, Chino, CA 91710
Tel.: (909) 614-4280
Web Site: http://savantconstruction.com
Sales Range: $10-24.9 Million
Emp.: 80
Nonresidential Construction Services
N.A.I.C.S.: 236220
John Aldridge (Owner)

SAVANT SYSTEMS, INC.
45 Perseverance Way, Hyannis, MA 02601
Tel.: (508) 683-2500   MA
Web Site: http://www.savant.com
Year Founded: 2005
Automation Control System Mfr
N.A.I.C.S.: 334111
Robert Madonna (Chm & CEO)
J.C. Murphy (Pres)

Subsidiaries:

Savant Technologies, LLC   (1)
1975 Noble Rd, Cleveland, OH 44112-6300
Tel.: (800) 435-4448
Web Site: http://www.gelighting.com
Light Bulb Developer, Mfr & Whslr
N.A.I.C.S.: 335139
William F. Lacey (Pres)
Bill Lacey (Pres)

SAVANTAGE SOLUTIONS INC.
1355 Piccard Dr Ste 425, Rockville, MD 20850
Tel.: (301) 258-5600
Web Site: http://www.savantage.net
Rev.: $15,000,000
Emp.: 100
Computer System Design Services
N.A.I.C.S.: 541512
Lisa R. Kazor (Pres, CEO & COO)
Kelly Moore Barnes (CFO & Treas)
Ayesha Rahman (Sr VP)
LeAnn Corcoran (Sr VP)
Wei Gu (CTO)
Raul Arze (Mgr-IT)

SAVANTIS SOLUTIONS LLC
100 Wood Ave S Ste 200, Iselin, NJ 08830
Tel.: (732) 906-3200
Web Site: http://www.savantis.com
Year Founded: 1999
Software Publisher
N.A.I.C.S.: 513210
Will Schramme (CEO)
Frank Taraschi (Sr VP-Fin & HR)
Piyush Jobanputra (Sr VP-India Ops)
Sushil Kaul (VP-Staffing)
Allan Vanderheyden (Sr VP-Solutions)

Subsidiaries:

Savantis Solutions LLC - Exton   (1)
835 Springdale Drive Ste 102, Exton, PA 19341
Tel.: (610) 590-0132
Web Site: http://www.savantis.com
Software Publisher
N.A.I.C.S.: 513210

SAVE THE CHIMPS
PO Box 12220, Fort Pierce, FL 34979
Tel.: (772) 429-0403   DC
Web Site: http://www.savethechimps.org
Year Founded: 1997
Sales Range: $10-24.9 Million
Emp.: 71
Chimpanzee Sanctuary Services
N.A.I.C.S.: 712190
Molly Polidoroff (Exec Dir)
Brian Craft (Mgr-Ops)

SAVEAROUND
31 Front St, Binghamton, NY 13905
Web Site: http://www.savearound.com
Year Founded: 2003
Sales Range: $1-9.9 Million
Emp.: 57
Group Discounts & Coupons
N.A.I.C.S.: 541890
Luke Stanton (Owner)

SAVED BY THE DRESS, INC.
1503 NW 82nd Ave, Miami, FL 33126
Tel.: (786) 299-5125
Web Site: http://www.savedbythedress.com
Year Founded: 2013
Sales Range: $10-24.9 Million
Emp.: 20
Apparel Online Retailer
N.A.I.C.S.: 458110
Bill Saedlo (Pres)

SAVEDAILY, INC.
1503 S Coast Dr Ste 330, Costa Mesa, CA 92626
Tel.: (562) 795-7500   CA
Web Site: http://www.savedaily.com
Year Founded: 1999
Sales Range: $1-9.9 Million
Emp.: 19
Holding Company; Online Mutual Fund Investment Platform Developer & Operator
N.A.I.C.S.: 551112
Jeffrey W. Mahony (Chm & Chief Architect)
Gregory D. Vacca (Pres)
Stan L. Smith (CEO)

Subsidiaries:

SaveDaily.com, Inc.   (1)
1503 S Coast Dr Ste 330, Costa Mesa, CA 92626

U.S. PRIVATE

Tel.: (562) 795-7500
Web Site: http://www.savedaily.com
Online Mutual Fund Investment Platform Developer & Operator
N.A.I.C.S.: 518210
Diann Kozlowski (Chief Compliance Officer)

SAVEONRESORTS.COM, LLC
5962 La Place Court, Carlsbad, CA 92008
Tel.: (858) 625-0630   CA
Web Site: http://www.saveonresorts.com
Year Founded: 2004
Sales Range: $1-9.9 Million
Emp.: 30
Online Discount Vacation Packages
N.A.I.C.S.: 561510
Kevin Schneider (CEO)
Elliot Springer (CEO)

SAVER SYSTEMS INC.
95 London Dr, Campbellsville, KY 42718
Tel.: (270) 465-8675
Web Site: http://www.savergroup.com
Sales Range: $10-24.9 Million
Emp.: 500
Grocery Stores
N.A.I.C.S.: 445110
Russ Slinker (CFO)
Larry Noe (Pres)

Subsidiaries:

Saver Systems of Ohio, Inc.   (1)
4908 State Route 125, Georgetown, OH 45121
Tel.: (937) 378-9300
Web Site: http://www.savergroup.com
Sales Range: $10-24.9 Million
Emp.: 30
Supermarkets & Other Grocery (except Convenience) Stores
N.A.I.C.S.: 445110
Gary Richards (Pres)

SAVERS COOPERATIVE BANK
270 Main St, Southbridge, MA 01550
Tel.: (508) 764-4329
Web Site: http://www.saversbank.com
Sales Range: $10-24.9 Million
Emp.: 102
Banking Services
N.A.I.C.S.: 522110
Joe Coderre (Pres)

SAVERS, INC.
11400 SE 6th St Ste 220, Bellevue, WA 98009
Tel.: (425) 462-1515   WA
Web Site: http://www.savers.com
Year Founded: 1954
Rev.: $39,600,000
Emp.: 150
Used Merchandise Stores
N.A.I.C.S.: 459510
Mark Walsh (CEO)

SAVEUR FOOD GROUP, LLC
6580 Allison Rd, Miami Beach, FL 33141
Tel.: (305) 864-5100
Web Site: http://www.saveurfood.com
Holding Company
N.A.I.C.S.: 551112
Paul Bensabat (Co-Pres & CEO)
Alain Bankier (Co-Pres & CFO)

Subsidiaries:

King Kold Frozen Foods, Inc.   (1)
1920 Swarthmore Ave Ste 1, Lakewood, NJ 08701
Tel.: (732) 730-2157
Web Site: http://www.kingkold.com
Sales Range: $10-24.9 Million
Emp.: 75
Frozen Food Mfr
N.A.I.C.S.: 321999

COMPANIES

SAVEWAY PETROLEUM INC.
49 S Main St, Brooklyn, CT 06234
Tel.: (860) 779-2500
Web Site:
http://www.savewaypetro.com
Sales Range: $10-24.9 Million
Emp.: 50
Fuel Oil Dealers
N.A.I.C.S.: 457210
Deb Laperle *(Mgr-Energy Risk)*
Michael Marcheterre *(Dir-Safety)*
William Hickey *(Mgr-Svcs)*

SAVI TECHNOLOGIES , INC
2775 Cruse Rd Ste 2501, Lawrenceville, GA 30044
Tel.: (770) 935-5165
Web Site: http://www.savi-tech.com
Sales Range: $1-9.9 Million
Emp.: 72
IT Staffing & Technology Solutions
N.A.I.C.S.: 561311
Ravi Prathipati *(Dir-HR)*
Scott Shaul *(Sr VP-Worldwide Sls & Svcs)*
Eric Gill *(VP-Intl Sls)*
Nanette Efird *(VP-Product Mgmt)*
Rich Carlson *(CEO)*

SAVICOM, INC.
44 Montgomery St Ste 1600, San Francisco, CA 94104
Tel.: (415) 983-0990
Web Site: http://www.savicom.net
Year Founded: 1996
Sales Range: $1-9.9 Million
Emp.: 30
Email Marketing Software & Services
N.A.I.C.S.: 513210
Steve Smith *(Chm & Chief Strategy Officer)*
Ted Bernard *(CEO)*
Ken Schmidt *(VP-Engrg & Ops)*
Patrick B. Scoggin *(VP-Worldwide Sls & Mktg)*

SAVINGS BANK MENDOCINO COUNTY
200 N School St, Ukiah, CA 95482
Tel.: (707) 462-6613
Web Site:
http://www.savingsbank.com
Rev.: $39,270,704
Emp.: 200
Banking Services
N.A.I.C.S.: 522110
Floyd Ruff *(VP)*
Stacy Starkey *(Pres)*
Scott Yandell *(CEO)*

SAVINGS BANK OF DANBURY
220 Main St, Danbury, CT 06810
Tel.: (203) 743-3849
Web Site: http://www.sbdanbury.com
Rev.: $25,093,000
Emp.: 26
Banking Services
N.A.I.C.S.: 522180
Harold C. Wibling *(Chm)*
Nicholas J. Gazetos *(Chief Lending Officer & Exec VP)*
Gary Hawley *(Vice Chm)*
Delia Espinal *(Mgr-Plumtrees Plaza)*
Savoeun Buck *(Mgr-Southbury)*
Martin G. Morgado *(Pres & CEO)*

SAVINGS BANK OF WALPOLE
68 Ames Plz Ln, Walpole, NH 03608
Tel.: (603) 756-4771
Web Site:
http://www.savingsbankofwalpole.com
Year Founded: 1875
Sales Range: $10-24.9 Million
Banking Services
N.A.I.C.S.: 522180

Tamara Richardson *(VP)*
Gregg Tewksbury *(Pres)*
Mark Bodin *(CFO & Sr VP)*
Stephen M. Bianco *(Sr VP)*
Matthew W. Guild *(VP & CIO)*
Dominic A. Perkins *(VP-Retail)*

SAVINGS OIL COMPANY INC.
447 E Main St, Tupelo, MS 38804
Tel.: (662) 842-7525
Rev.: $13,300,000
Emp.: 160
Gasoline Services
N.A.I.C.S.: 457120
Henry C. Dodge *(Pres)*
Robert B. Dodge Jr. *(VP)*

SAVITZ RESEARCH CENTER INC.
13747 Montfort Dr Ste 114, Dallas, TX 75240
Tel.: (972) 386-4050
Web Site:
http://www.savitzfieldandfocus.com
Sales Range: $10-24.9 Million
Emp.: 150
Market Analysis & Research Services
N.A.I.C.S.: 541910
Jeffrey N. Savitz *(Pres)*
Mike Kassab *(Pres-Client Svcs)*
Sandy Lewis *(Exec VP-Field Ops)*
David Ditzenberger *(VP-Client Svcs)*
Erin Jackson *(VP-Client Svcs)*
Sean Yeany *(Dir-IT Solutions)*
Mike Morgan *(Dir-Mktg Analytics)*
Paula Julian *(Dir-Qualitative Res)*

SAVIYNT, INC.
1301 E El Segundo Bl Ste D, El Segundo, CA 90245
Tel.: (310) 641-1664
Web Site: http://www.saviynt.com
Year Founded: 2010
Sales Range: $25-49.9 Million
Emp.: 300
Software Development Services
N.A.I.C.S.: 541511
Amit Saha *(CEO)*
Sachin Nayyar *(Founder & Chm)*
Yash Prakash *(COO)*
Atul Vij *(CTO)*
Vibhuti Sinha *(Chief Cloud Officer)*

SAVOIE'S SAUSAGE & FOOD PRODUCTS, INC.
1742 Hwy 742, Opelousas, LA 70570
Tel.: (337) 942-7241
Web Site:
http://www.savoiesfoods.com
Year Founded: 1949
Sales Range: $10-24.9 Million
Emp.: 75
Sausage Mfr
N.A.I.C.S.: 311612
Eula M. Savoie *(Co-Founder)*
Tom Savoie *(Co-Founder)*
Donna S. La Fleur *(Treas)*
Ronald Savoie *(VP)*
Frederick R. La Fleur *(Sec)*

SAVONA FOODS, INC.
6949 Sherman Ln, Pennsauken, NJ 08110
Tel.: (856) 662-8880 PA
Year Founded: 1990
Sales Range: $1-9.9 Million
Emp.: 40
Grocery & Related Products Merchant Whslr
N.A.I.C.S.: 424490
John Farese *(Pres & CEO)*

SAVOR STREET FOODS INC.
1 Park Plz, Wyomissing, PA 19610
Tel.: (610) 320-7800 PA
Web Site: http://www.savorstreet.com

Year Founded: 1884
Sales Range: $75-99.9 Million
Emp.: 100
Snack Food Mfr
N.A.I.C.S.: 311919
Charles T. Russo *(Opers Superintendent-Tech Supply)*
Jo Andre *(Sr Dir-Customer Svc & Logistics)*
Laura Unger *(Coord-Mktg Comm)*

SAVOURY SYSTEMS INTERNATIONAL, INC.
230 Industrial Pkwy, Branchburg, NJ 08876
Tel.: (908) 526-2524
Web Site:
http://www.savourysystems.com
Year Founded: 1997
Sales Range: $10-24.9 Million
Emp.: 18
Savory Seasonings
N.A.I.C.S.: 311942
David Adams *(Pres)*
Elizabeth Adams *(VP & Treas)*
Kevin McDermott *(Dir-Tech Sls)*
Ed Buxton *(Mgr-Product)*

SAVVY INC.
477 Congress St 5th Fl, Portland, ME 04101
Tel.: (207) 482-0637
Web Site: http://www.savvy-inc.com
Year Founded: 2000
Sales Range: Less than $1 Million
Emp.: 5
Consulting,
Government/Political/Public Affairs,
Public Relations, Publicity/Promotions
N.A.I.C.S.: 541820
Dennis Bailey *(Pres)*

SAVVY REST INC.
4414 Ivy Commons, Charlottesville, VA 22903
Tel.: (866) 856-4044
Web Site: http://www.savvyrest.com
Year Founded: 2006
Sales Range: $1-9.9 Million
Emp.: 14
Mfr of Organic Mattresses
N.A.I.C.S.: 337910
Michael Penny *(Owner)*

SAVVYPHONE, LLC
4939 Shell Stream, New Port Richey, FL 34652
Tel.: (321) 872-8891
Web Site: http://www.savvycard.com
Sales Range: $1-9.9 Million
Online Business Card System
N.A.I.C.S.: 513199
David Etheredge *(CEO)*

SAVWATT USA, INC.
475 Park Ave S 30th Fl, New York, NY 10016
Tel.: (646) 478-2676 DE
Web Site: http://www.savwatt.com
Year Founded: 2006
Sales Range: Less than $1 Million
Emp.: 20
Energy-Efficient Light Emitting Diode Lighting Products Mfr
N.A.I.C.S.: 335139
Isaac H. Sutton *(Chm, Pres, CFO, Treas & Sec)*

SAW MILL CAPITAL LLC
555 Pleasantville Rd S Bldg Ste 220, Briarcliff Manor, NY 10510
Tel.: (914) 741-1300 DE
Web Site:
http://www.sawmillcapital.com
Year Founded: 1997
Privater Equity Firm

SAWGRASS ASSET MANAGEMENT LLC

N.A.I.C.S.: 523940
Howard D. Unger *(Mng Partner)*
William M. Gerstner *(Chief Compliance Officer & Partner)*
Witold Krupinski *(Partner & Dir-Res)*
Timothy J. Nelson *(Partner)*
Scott R. Rivard *(Partner)*
Blinn M. Cirella *(CFO)*
Jason W. Mueller *(Principal & Co-Dir-Res)*
Travis C. Foltz *(Principal)*
Scott A. Vandekerkhoff *(Principal)*
Lisa Raiani *(Controller)*
Daniel J. Gregg *(VP)*
Lisa A. Rani *(Controller)*
Ray Wang *(Principal)*

Subsidiaries:

Climate Pros, LLC (1)
2190 Gladstone Ct Ste E, Glendale Heights, IL 60139
Tel.: (630) 893-8511
Web Site: https://www.climatepros.com
Refrigeration & HVAC
N.A.I.C.S.: 333415
Todd Ernest *(Founder & CEO)*

Subsidiary (Domestic):

Norfoxx Refrigeration, LLC (2)
1910 Sam Bass Rd, Round Rock, TX 78681-1904
Tel.: (512) 531-9843
Refrigeration & HVAC Services
N.A.I.C.S.: 333415
Mike Smith *(Owner)*

Nemo Tile Co., LLC (1)
48 E 21st St, New York, NY 11432
Tel.: (212) 505-0009
Web Site: http://www.nemotile.com
Brick, Stone & Related Construction Material Merchant Whslr
N.A.I.C.S.: 423320
Matt Karlin *(Pres & CEO)*

SAW SERVICE OF AMERICA INC.
8210 Industry Ave, Pico Rivera, CA 90660
Tel.: (562) 806-1801
Web Site: http://www.sawservice.com
Rev.: $10,686,491
Emp.: 22
Metal Cutting Machines & Fabricating Equipment Sales & Repair
N.A.I.C.S.: 423840

SAWBROOK STEEL CASTINGS CO.
425 Shepherd Ave, Cincinnati, OH 45215
Tel.: (513) 554-1700
Web Site:
http://www.sawbrooksteel.com
Sales Range: $10-24.9 Million
Emp.: 200
Steel Casting Products Mfr
N.A.I.C.S.: 331513
Thomas E. Kasee *(Dir-Tech)*
Krishnan Venatesan *(Pres)*

SAWGRASS ASSET MANAGEMENT LLC
1579 The Greens Way Ste 20, Jacksonville Beach, FL 32250
Tel.: (904) 493-5500
Web Site: http://www.saw-grass.com
Year Founded: 1998
Sales Range: $1-9.9 Million
Emp.: 26
Portfolio Management
N.A.I.C.S.: 523940
Andrew M. Cantor *(Principal)*
Brian K. Monroe *(Principal & Dir-Mktg & Client Svcs)*
David A. Furfine *(Partner)*
Dean McQuiddy *(Principal)*

SAWNEE ELECTRIC MEMBERSHIP CORPORATION   U.S. PRIVATE

Sawgrass Asset Management LLC—(Continued)

SAWNEE ELECTRIC MEMBERSHIP CORPORATION
543 Atlanta Hwy, Cumming, GA 30040-2701
Tel.: (770) 887-2363   GA
Web Site: http://www.sawnee.com
Year Founded: 1938
Sales Range: $250-299.9 Million
Emp.: 300
Electronic Services
N.A.I.C.S.: 221122
Michael A. Goodroe *(Pres & CEO)*

SAWSTOP, LLC
9564 SW Tualatin Rd, Tualatin, OR 97062
Tel.: (503) 570-3200
Web Site: http://www.sawstop.com
Sales Range: $10-24.9 Million
Emp.: 30
Table Saw Mfr
N.A.I.C.S.: 339999
Paul Carter *(VP-Bus Dev)*
Amber Lacombe *(Dir-Logistics)*
David Fulmer *(Mgr-IT)*

SAWTST, LLC
401 Westpark Ct Ste 100, Peachtree City, GA 30269
Tel.: (678) 870-3055
Web Site: http://www.sawtst
Sales Range: $1-9.9 Million
Emp.: 41
Computer Management Services
N.A.I.C.S.: 518210
Chris Grassmuck *(Mgr-Program)*
Douglas Conorich *(VP-IT)*
Carrie Kendrick *(VP-Security)*

SAWYER REALTY HOLDINGS LLC
1215 Chestnut St, Newton, MA 02464
Tel.: (781) 449-6650
Web Site: http://www.sawyerapts.com
Sales Range: $25-49.9 Million
Emp.: 25
Real Estate Investment & Management Services
N.A.I.C.S.: 525990
David M. Rosenberg *(CEO)*
Gary J. Gianino *(CFO)*
Gregg Clickstein *(Pres)*

SAX MOTOR COMPANY
52 21st St E, Dickinson, ND 58601-3500
Tel.: (701) 483-4411
Sales Range: $10-24.9 Million
Emp.: 34
Car Whslr
N.A.I.C.S.: 441110
Pam Kosoleky *(Owner)*

SAXON GLOBAL INC.
1320 Greenway Dr, Irving, TX 75038
Tel.: (972) 550-9346
Web Site: http://www.saxon-global.com
Year Founded: 2006
Sales Range: $1-9.9 Million
Emp.: 200
Software Development & Consulting & Staffing Services
N.A.I.C.S.: 541511
Gopi Kandukuri *(Founder & CEO)*
Sam Smith *(Sr VP)*

Subsidiaries:

Saxon Human Resources Pvt. Ltd.   (1)
Plot #13 Cyber Heights Ste 501 Road No 2
Banjara Hills, 500034, Hyderabad, Andhra Pradesh, India   **(100%)**
Tel.: (91) 40 65556628

Web Site: http://www.saxon-global.com
Staffing Solutions for International Customers
N.A.I.C.S.: 541612

SAXON-CLARK INC.
995 SR 434 North Ste 509, Altamonte Springs, FL 32714
Tel.: (407) 788-0039
Web Site: http://www.saxon-clark.com
Sales Range: $25-49.9 Million
Emp.: 18
Furniture Retailer
N.A.I.C.S.: 449110
Donald Saxon *(Pres)*
Julie Rose *(Mgr-Drapery)*

SAXONY PARTNERS LLC
1 Galleria Twr, Dallas, TX 75240
Tel.: (214) 389-7903
Web Site: http://www.saxonypartners.com
Year Founded: 2011
Sales Range: $1-9.9 Million
Emp.: 45
Management Consulting Services
N.A.I.C.S.: 541611
Brandon Horton *(Mgr-Recruiting)*
Matt Rosen *(Exec VP)*
Thomas Shaw *(Mng Dir-Consulting)*
Jeff Wilson *(Founder & CEO)*
Eric Winton *(COO)*

SAXTON HORNE ADVERTISING
9350 S 150 E Ste 950, Sandy, UT 84070
Tel.: (801) 304-1000
Web Site: http://www.saxtonhorne.com
Sales Range: $10-24.9 Million
Emp.: 7
House Agency
N.A.I.C.S.: 541810
Spencer Beckstead *(Acct Exec)*
Tina Bodrero *(Office Mgr)*
Belinda Emerson *(Dir-Media)*
Anthony Dirbeck *(Dir-Client Svcs)*
Tina Romijn *(Office Mgr)*

SAXTON PIERCE RESTAURANT CORP
8117 Preston Rd Ste 682, Dallas, TX 75225-6346
Tel.: (214) 373-3400
Web Site: http://www.thesaxtongroup.com
Sales Range: $10-24.9 Million
Emp.: 1,500
Pizzeria Owner & Operator
N.A.I.C.S.: 722511
Micheal Bambach *(Dir-IT)*
Matt Heston *(Dir-People)*
Wayne Andersen *(Reg Dir)*
Stephen Lee *(VP-Ops)*
Robert McLeod *(Reg Dir)*
Melissa Watkins *(Reg Dir)*
Adam Saxton *(VP)*
Matt Saxton *(VP)*
Amy Dickey *(Mgr-Mktg Social Media)*
Alicia Tippett *(Mgr-Recruiting)*
Gaston Lanaux IV *(Reg Dir)*

SAXTON, BRADLEY, INC
801 SW 16 St Ste 200, Renton, WA 98057
Tel.: (206) 762-7688
Web Site: http://www.saxtonbradley.com
Sales Range: $10-24.9 Million
Emp.: 50
Furniture Distr
N.A.I.C.S.: 423210

Joann Massey *(Controller)*
Dennis Purcell *(Mgr-Trng)*
Jeff Brzoska *(Project Mgr)*
Ian Sawers *(Mgr-Installation)*

SAXUM PUBLIC RELATIONS
1300 N Broadway Dr, Oklahoma City, OK 73103
Tel.: (405) 605-2003
Web Site: http://www.saxum.com
Year Founded: 2004
Sales Range: $1-9.9 Million
Emp.: 14
Public Relations Services
N.A.I.C.S.: 541820
C. Renzi Stone *(Chm & CEO)*
Debbie Schramm *(Pres)*
Lindsay Vidrine *(Sr Acct Dir)*
Houda Elyazgi *(Acct Dir)*
Lisa Lloyd *(Mng Partner-Lithos)*
Tosha Lackey *(Controller)*
Dan Martel *(Chief Creative Officer & Sr VP)*
Sara Walker *(Sr VP-HR & Ops)*
Kristi DesJarlais *(Sr VP & Gen Mgr-Houston)*
Lacey Ferguson *(Acct Coord)*
Elizabeth Byrd *(Acct Coord)*
Jeff Lowe *(Dir-Technical)*
Jenifer McAbee *(Mgr-Digital Project)*
Chelsea Watkins *(Mgr-Ops)*
Melanie Christian *(Sr Acct Dir & Gen Mgr-Tulsa)*
Kate Cunningham *(Sr Acct Exec)*
Chad Bianco *(Sr Dir-Art)*
Jessica Robbins *(Sr Dir-Art)*
Ashley Wilemon *(Sr VP-Strategy & Svc)*
Amy Pyles *(VP-Digital)*
Todd Gregory *(VP/Gen Mgr-Houston)*
Jeff Risley *(Chief Strategy Officer)*
Kim Dahlberg *(Acct Dir-Energy-Houston)*
Jennifer Monies *(Sr Dir-Pub Affairs)*
Jerryd Clinton *(Assoc Dir-Creative)*

SAYBROOK CORPORATE OPPORTUNITY FUND LP
11400 W Olympic Blvd Ste 1400, Los Angeles, CA 90064
Tel.: (310) 899-9200   CA
Web Site: http://www.saybrook.net
Year Founded: 1998
Sales Range: $1-9.9 Million
Emp.: 45
Business Support Services
N.A.I.C.S.: 561499
Jonathan Rosenthal *(Portfolio Mgr)*

Subsidiaries:

Premium Transportation Services, Inc.   (1)
18735 S Ferris Pl, Rancho Dominguez, CA 90220
Tel.: (310) 816-0260
Web Site: http://www.ttsi.com
Logistics, Warehousing & General Fright Trucking Services
N.A.I.C.S.: 484122
Victor La Rosa *(Co-Founder, Pres & CEO)*
Bill Allen *(Co-Founder, COO & Exec VP)*
Tom Franklin *(CFO & Treas)*
Scott Freeborn *(Sr VP)*
Pam Reinoehl *(Exec VP-Western Region)*
James Eakins *(Dir-IT)*
Brian Everhart *(Sr VP-Sls)*

Subsidiary (Domestic):

Marine Container Services, Inc.   (2)
802-814 Bergen St, Newark, NJ 07108
Tel.: (973) 624-5200
Web Site: http://www.mcsj.com
Sales Range: $1-9.9 Million
Emp.: 50
Trucking Except Local
N.A.I.C.S.: 484121
Joseph Noonan *(Pres)*
Bill Murphy *(Mgr-Ops)*
Linda Ponzo *(Office Mgr)*
Don White *(Mgr-Warehouse)*

Sal-Son Logistics, Inc.   (2)
888 Doremus Ave, Newark, NJ 07114
Tel.: (404) 675-0711
Web Site: http://www.salson.com
Rev.: $4,230,000
Emp.: 30
General Freight Trucking, Local
N.A.I.C.S.: 484110
Ronald Hettlick *(Mgr)*
Anthony Berritto *(Pres & CEO)*

Tri Pak, Inc.   (2)
2330 Port of Tacoma Rd, Tacoma, WA 98421
Tel.: (253) 627-8008
Sales Range: $1-9.9 Million
Emp.: 25
Marine Cargo Handling
N.A.I.C.S.: 488320
Cory Sonnen *(Pres)*
Ron Dier *(Gen Mgr)*

SAYERS GROUP LLC
825 Corporate Woods Pkwy, Vernon Hills, IL 60061-3158
Tel.: (847) 391-4040
Web Site: http://www.sayers.com
Year Founded: 1984
Computer Systems Design
N.A.I.C.S.: 541512
John Kasser *(COO)*
Alan Bibergall *(VP-Sls Enterprise IT Infrastructure)*
Chris Callahan *(Pres & CEO)*
Guhan Swaminathan *(Mng Dir)*
Chris Warfield *(Sr VP-Sls & Mktg)*
Doug Close *(VP-Engrng & Enterprise Cybersecurity)*
Vince Schuld *(VP-Sls & Comml Markets)*
Joel Grace *(VP-Engrng & Emerging Technologies)*
Jim Locke *(VP-Fin)*
Becky Holby *(Dir-HR)*

SAYLE OIL COMPANY INC.
410 W Main St, Charleston, MS 38921
Tel.: (662) 647-5802
Web Site: http://www.sayleoil.com
Sales Range: $100-124.9 Million
Emp.: 350
Gasoline Services & Products
N.A.I.C.S.: 457120
Jonathan Etheridge *(Mgr-IT)*
Isaac E. Sayle *(Pres)*
Linda Allison *(Treas)*
John G. Sayle *(Sec)*

SAYLENT TECHNOLOGIES, INC.
500 Franklin Vlg Dr Ste 204, Franklin, MA 02038
Tel.: (508) 570-2161
Web Site: http://www.saylent.com
Year Founded: 2006
Sales Range: $1-9.9 Million
Emp.: 20
Financial Software Development Services
N.A.I.C.S.: 541511
Tyson Nargassans *(Pres & CEO)*
Bill Rooney *(CFO)*
Russell J. Prettitore *(Chief Revenue Officer)*
Greg Meurer *(VP-Analytics & Pro Svcs)*
Rishi Bhatia *(CTO)*

SAYVA SOLUTIONS INC.
3636 Nobel Dr Ste 400, San Diego, CA 92122
Tel.: (858) 242-5676   CA
Web Site: http://www.sayvasolutions.com
Year Founded: 2014
Sales Range: $10-24.9 Million
Emp.: 30
Recruitment Consulting Services

COMPANIES | SBI INCORPORATED

N.A.I.C.S.: 541612
Ryan Buell *(CEO)*
John Petraglia *(CFO)*
Lauren Olen *(Dir-Ops)*
Jared Sanderson *(Mng Dir)*
Austin Kakar *(Mng Dir)*

SAZERAC COMPANY, INC.
101 Magazine St, New Orleans, LA 70130
Tel.: (504) 831-9450   LA
Web Site: https://www.sazerac.com
Year Founded: 1850
Sales Range: $1-4.9 Billion
Emp.: 5,000
Distillery & Distilled Beverage Whslr
N.A.I.C.S.: 312140
Mark Brown *(Pres, Pres, CEO & CEO)*
Kathy Thelen *(VP-HR)*
Meridith Moody *(Dir-Mktg Svcs)*
Amy Preske *(Mgr-PR)*

Subsidiaries:

A. Smith Bowman Distillery   (1)
1 Bowman Dr Ste 100, Fredericksburg, VA 22408-7318
Tel.: (540) 373-4555
Web Site: http://www.asmithbowman.com
Emp.: 5
Distilled Liquors Producer
N.A.I.C.S.: 312140
Mark Brown *(Pres & CEO)*

Monsieur Henri Wine Company   (1)
115 La Salle St Ste 2320, Chicago, IL 60603-3862
Tel.: (916) 652-3791
Web Site: http://www.monsieurhenri.com
Emp.: 15
Wine Importer
N.A.I.C.S.: 424820

SB PARTNERS
1 New Haven Ave Ste 102A, Milford, CT 06460
Tel.: (203) 283-9593   NY
Rev.: $1,221,563
Assets: $35,924,504
Liabilities: $262,598
Net Worth: $35,661,906
Earnings: $30,613,709
Fiscal Year-end: 12/31/21
Lessors of Nonresidential Buildings (except Miniwarehouses)
N.A.I.C.S.: 531120
Millie C. Cassidy *(Pres)*
Martin Cawley *(VP)*
Leland J. Roth *(Treas)*
John H. Zoeller *(CFO)*
George N. Tietjen III *(CEO)*

SB&B FOODS INC.
15681 35th St SE, Casselton, ND 58012
Tel.: (701) 347-4793
Web Site: http://www.sb-b.com
Year Founded: 1998
Sales Range: $10-24.9 Million
Emp.: 8
Agribusiness Products & Services
N.A.I.C.S.: 115210
Scott Sinner *(Mgr-Procurement)*
Todd Sinner *(Dir-Sls)*
Gene Hepper *(Controller)*
Robert Sinner *(Pres)*
Tom Bresnahan *(VP)*
Patrick Bresnahan *(VP)*

SB/RH HOLDINGS, LLC
3001 Deming Way, Middleton, WI 53562
Tel.: (608) 275-3340   DE
Web Site: http://www.spectrumbrands.com
Rev.: $2,918,799,999
Assets: $5,347,300,000
Liabilities: $2,657,600,000
Net Worth: $2,689,700,000
Earnings: $1,809,300,000
Emp.: 3,099
Fiscal Year-end: 09/30/23
Holding Company
N.A.I.C.S.: 551112
David M. Maura *(Chm & CEO)*
Jeremy W. Smeltser *(CFO & Exec VP)*
Daniel L. Karpel *(Chief Acctg Officer, VP & Controller)*
Ehsan Zargar *(Gen Counsel, Sec & Exec VP)*
Randal D. Lewis *(COO & Exec VP)*
Rebeckah Long *(Sr VP-HR-Global)*
David Albert *(Pres-Home & Personal Care Appliances)*
John Pailthorp *(Pres-Global Pet Care)*
Troy Duecker *(Pres-Home & Garden)*
Tim Goff *(Pres-Hardware & Home Improvement)*
Javier Andrade-Marin *(Pres)*

SBAR'S, INC.
14 Sbar Blvd, Moorestown, NJ 08057
Tel.: (856) 234-8220   NJ
Web Site: http://www.sbarsonline.com
Year Founded: 1952
Emp.: 100
Art & Crafts Merchandise Distr & Retailer
N.A.I.C.S.: 423920
Nick Scappa *(Mgr)*

Subsidiaries:

A.C. Moore Arts & Crafts, Inc.   (1)
130 AC Moore Dr, Berlin, NJ 08009-9500
Tel.: (856) 768-4930
Web Site: http://www.acmoore.com
Sales Range: $100-124.9 Million
Emp.: 1,449
Arts, Crafts & Floral Merchandise Retailer
N.A.I.C.S.: 459120
Joette Metzler *(VP-Supply Chain Support)*
Richard Arthur *(VP-Mktg & Adv)*
Joseph Scappa *(Exec VP, Asst Sec & Asst Treas)*
Robert Almerini *(Chief Acctg Officer & Sr VP)*
Michael Lyons *(Sr VP-Mktg)*
Frank Remillard *(VP-Ops)*
Greg Adams *(Dir-Loss Prevention)*
Anthony Piperno *(Pres & CEO)*
Pepe Pipero *(Chm)*

Subsidiary (Domestic):

Moorestown Finance, Inc.   (2)
300 Delaware Ave Ste 1200, Wilmington, DE 19801-1671
Tel.: (302) 888-2140
Sales Range: $100-124.9 Million
Business Support Services
N.A.I.C.S.: 561499

SBARRO LLC
1328 Dublin Rd, Columbus, OH 43215
Tel.: (631) 715-4100   NY
Web Site: http://www.sbarro.com
Year Founded: 1977
Sales Range: $300-349.9 Million
Emp.: 3,700
Cafeteria-Style Italian Restaurants Developer, Operator & Franchisor
N.A.I.C.S.: 722513
J. David Karam *(Chm & CEO)*
Boyd Johanson *(COO)*
Mark Inzetta *(Chief Legal Officer & Sec)*
Brian Daniels *(CFO)*
Casey Minton *(Chief Concept Officer)*
Dan March *(Sr VP)*
Werner Glass *(Sr VP-Franchise Dev-Intl)*

SBB ROOFING INC.
3310 Verdugo Rd, Los Angeles, CA 90065
Tel.: (323) 254-2888
Web Site: http://www.biltwell.com
Rev.: $19,900,000
Emp.: 180
Roofing Contractors
N.A.I.C.S.: 238160
Bruce Radenbaugh *(Pres)*

SBC ADVERTISING
333 W Nationwide Blvd, Columbus, OH 43215
Tel.: (614) 255-2333   OH
Web Site: http://www.sbcadvertising.com
Year Founded: 1969
Sales Range: $100-124.9 Million
Advertising Agencies, Business-To-Business, Collateral, High Technology, Internet/Web Design, Logo & Package Design, Media Buying Services, Public Relations, Retail
N.A.I.C.S.: 541810
Paul Hnidka *(Sr VP & Media Dir)*
Ken Brown *(VP & Acct Dir)*
Andy Knight *(Dir-Creative)*

SBCC INC
1711 Dell Ave, Campbell, CA 95008
Tel.: (408) 379-5500
Web Site: http://www.sbci.com
Year Founded: 1975
Sales Range: $200-249.9 Million
Emp.: 60
Commercial & Office Building Contractors
N.A.I.C.S.: 236220
Richard Furtado *(Pres)*
J.B. Cahoon *(Partner)*
Cameron Peach *(Partner)*

SBE ENTERTAINMENT GROUP, LLC
5900 Wilshire Blvd 30st Fl, Los Angeles, CA 90036
Tel.: (323) 655-8000
Web Site: http://www.sbe.com
Year Founded: 2002
Sales Range: $1-9.9 Million
Emp.: 70
Hospitality Services
N.A.I.C.S.: 721110
Sam Nazarian *(Founder & CEO)*
Jack Myers *(Exec VP-HR)*
Carlos Rosso *(Pres-Condominium)*
Dominique Gordon *(Office Mgr)*
Alvaro Valeriani *(Sr VP-Sls & Mktg-Global)*

SBEEG HOLDINGS, LLC
9247 Alden Dr, Beverly Hills, CA 90210
Tel.: (323) 655-8000   DE
Web Site: http://www.sbe.com
Year Founded: 2002
Holding Company; Hotels, Restaurants & Bars
N.A.I.C.S.: 551112
Sam Nazarian *(Founder, Chm & CEO)*

Subsidiaries:

Morgans Hotel Group Co. LLC   (1)
475 10th Ave 11th Fl, New York, NY 10018
Tel.: (212) 686-0300
Web Site: http://www.morganshotelgroup.com
Hotel Owner & Operator
N.A.I.C.S.: 721110

Subsidiary (Domestic):

Hudson Leaseco LLC   (2)
358 W 58th St, New York, NY 10019
Tel.: (212) 554-6000
Web Site: http://www.morganshotelgroup.com
Hotel & Motel Operator; Hotel Accomodation & Recreational Services
N.A.I.C.S.: 721110

Mondrian Los Angeles   (2)
8440 Sunset Blvd, Los Angeles, CA 90069
Tel.: (323) 650-8999
Web Site: http://www.morganshotelgroup.com
Hotels & Motels Services
N.A.I.C.S.: 721110

Shore Club South Beach   (2)
1901 Collins Ave, Miami Beach, FL 33139
Tel.: (305) 695-3100
Web Site: http://www.morganshotelgroup.com
Hotels & Motels Services
N.A.I.C.S.: 721110

The Raleigh Hotel   (1)
1775 Collins Ave, Miami Beach, FL 33139
Tel.: (305) 534-6300
Web Site: http://www.raleighhotel.com
Hotel
N.A.I.C.S.: 721110
Gilberto Garcia *(Gen Mgr)*

The Redbury Hotel   (1)
1717 Vine St, Los Angeles, CA 90028
Tel.: (323) 962-1717
Web Site: http://www.theredbury.com
Emp.: 20
Hotel
N.A.I.C.S.: 721110
John Sinclair *(Gen Mgr)*

SBG TECHNOLOGY SOLUTIONS INC.
1737 King St Ste 601, Alexandria, VA 22314
Tel.: (703) 299-9093
Web Site: http://www.sbgts.com
Year Founded: 2004
Sales Range: $10-24.9 Million
Emp.: 54
Engineering & IT Consulting
N.A.I.C.S.: 541690
Bobbie Peterson *(Head-Health Solutions)*
Lauren A. Morgan *(VP-Strategy)*
Robert Gordon *(Chief Growth Officer)*
Mike Farahbakhshian *(VP-Health Solutions)*
Bruce Dickey *(Pres & CEO)*

SBH ASSOCIATES, INC.
9120 Flint Midwest, Roswell, GA 30009
Tel.: (404) 720-5664   NV
Web Site: http://www.sbhassociatesinc.com
Year Founded: 2012
Sales Range: $1-9.9 Million
Emp.: 3
Construction Consulting & Management Services
N.A.I.C.S.: 541618
Harry A. Beecham *(Chm)*
Michael R. Beecham *(Pres & CEO)*
Brent A. Beecham *(COO, Treas, Sec & VP)*

SBH SCIENCE, INC.
4 Strathmore Rd, Natick, MA 01760
Tel.: (508) 650-6218   MA
Web Site: http://www.sbhsciences.com
Year Founded: 1998
Sales Range: $25-49.9 Million
Emp.: 15
Pharmaceutical Testing & Development Services
N.A.I.C.S.: 325412
Raphael Nir *(Pres)*

SBI INCORPORATED
8500 Valcour Ave, Saint Louis, MO 63123-2257
Tel.: (314) 615-2000   MO
Web Site: http://www.schretre.com

3559

SBI INCORPORATED

SBI Incorporated—(Continued)
Year Founded: 1976
Sales Range: $75-99.9 Million
Emp.: 500
Holding Company
N.A.I.C.S.: 551112
Carolyn Swarm *(Mgr-HR)*

Subsidiaries:

Indox Services Inc. (1)
8508 Valcour Ave, Saint Louis, MO 63123
Tel.: (314) 633-4800
Web Site: http://www.indoxservices.com
Sales Range: $25-49.9 Million
Emp.: 120
Photocopying & Duplicating Services
N.A.I.C.S.: 423490

Branch (Domestic):

Indox Services (2)
1702 Broadway, Kansas City, MO 64108
Tel.: (816) 221-2225
Web Site: http://www.indoxservices.com
Sales Range: $25-49.9 Million
Emp.: 19
Photocopying & Duplicating Services
N.A.I.C.S.: 323111

Sample Brothers Inc. (1)
8440 Valcour Ave, Saint Louis, MO 63123-2263 (100%)
Tel.: (314) 615-2020
Web Site: http://www.samplebrothers.com
Sales Range: $10-24.9 Million
Emp.: 4
Mechanical Equipment & Filtration Product Whslr
N.A.I.C.S.: 423830
Traci Kelley *(Office Mgr)*

Schroeder & Tremayne Inc. (1)
8500 Valcour Ave, Saint Louis, MO 63123
Tel.: (314) 615-2000
Web Site: http://www.schtre.com
Sales Range: $25-49.9 Million
Emp.: 150
Soap, Skin Care & Spa Product Marketer & Retailer
N.A.I.C.S.: 424990
Liz Wilmsen *(Owner)*

SBPR CORP.
3321 S Andrews Ave Ste 24, Fort Lauderdale, FL 33316
Tel.: (954) 566-1522
Web Site: http://www.sbprcorp.com
Sales Range: Less than $1 Million
Emp.: 1
Travel & Lifestyle Communications & Public Relations
N.A.I.C.S.: 541820
Stephen Bennett *(Pres)*

SBR EVENTS GROUP
235 E Irving Park Rd, Wood Dale, IL 60191
Tel.: (630) 238-8261
Web Site: http://www.sbrevents.com
Year Founded: 2016
Holding Company; Catering & Event Production Services
N.A.I.C.S.: 551112
Dave Raymond *(Owner & CEO)*
Robert Sivek *(Pres)*
Deborah Borsum *(Exec VP)*
Duce Raymond *(Dir-Culinary)*

Subsidiaries:

Sweet Baby Ray's Barbecue Wood Dale LLC (1)
249 E Irving Park Rd, Wood Dale, IL 60191
Tel.: (630) 238-8261
Web Site: http://www.sbrbbq.com
Restaurants Operator & Catering Services
N.A.I.C.S.: 722511
Dave Raymond *(Owner)*
Duce Raymond *(Partner)*

The Meetinghouse Companies, Inc. (1)
781 N Church Rd, Elmhurst, IL 60126-1413
Tel.: (630) 941-0600
Web Site: http://www.meetinghouse.com
Rev.: $3,500,000
Emp.: 32
Event Design & Production Services
N.A.I.C.S.: 561920
Deborah Borsum *(Co-Founder, Pres & CEO)*
Margarita Heinzel *(VP-Special Events)*
Noelene Wilson *(Acct Mgr)*
Robert Sivek *(Co-Founder)*

SBS ENTERPRISES INC.
6301 Imperial Dr, Waco, TX 76712
Tel.: (254) 772-6000
Web Site: http://www.spenco.com
Rev.: $20,900,000
Emp.: 120
Surgical Appliances & Supplies
N.A.I.C.S.: 339113
David McKown *(Controller)*

SBT BANCSHARES, INC.
11950 Webb Chapel Rd, Dallas, TX 75234
Tel.: (713) 681-6812   TX
Web Site: http://www.statebnk.com
Year Founded: 2004
Sales Range: $25-49.9 Million
Emp.: 42
Bank Holding Company
N.A.I.C.S.: 551111
Chandrakant B. Patel *(Founder)*
Janna B. Hayes *(Sr VP)*

Subsidiaries:

State Bank of Texas (1)
11950 Webb Chapel Rd, Dallas, TX 75234
Tel.: (972) 252-6000
Web Site: http://www.statebnk.com
Sales Range: $25-49.9 Million
Emp.: 25
Commericial Banking
N.A.I.C.S.: 522110
Chandrakant B. Patel *(Founder & CEO)*
Sushil C. Patel *(Pres)*
Rajan Patel *(VP)*
Sandesh Patel *(Sr VP-Lending)*

SC&H GROUP, LLC
910 Ridgebrook Rd, Sparks, MD 21152
Tel.: (410) 403-1500
Web Site: http://www.scandh.com
Year Founded: 1991
Sales Range: $200-249.9 Million
Emp.: 200
Management Consulting & Accounting, Advisory & Tax Services
N.A.I.C.S.: 541211
Ronald M. Causey *(Founder & CEO)*
Ed Ben *(Dir-Sls & Use Tax Practice)*
Jennifer Amato *(Principal)*
Patrick Gahagan *(Principal)*
Steve Summers *(Mgr)*
Jeff Klima *(Principal)*
Luke Sinnen *(Principal)*
Pete Ragone *(Principal)*
Dan Blake *(Principal-Microsoft Dynamics Consulting Practice)*
Mack McGee *(CMO & VP)*
Chris Helmrath *(Co-Founder & Mng Dir)*
Ed Mullin *(CTO)*
Chris College *(Mng Dir)*
Amanda Wooddell Wilhelm *(Principal)*
Angelo Poletis *(Principal)*
Chris Rossi *(Principal)*
Erin Charles *(Principal)*
Greg Tselikis *(Principal)*
Jeff Bathurst *(Dir-Tech Advisory Svcs Practice)*
Kevin O'Sullivan *(Principal)*
Lori Burghauser *(Principal)*
Matt Simons *(Principal)*
Matthew Roberson *(Principal)*
Mike Lynch *(Principal)*
Nathan DiNatale *(Principal)*
Darrin Sheetz *(Principal-Bus Performance Mgmt Consulting Practice)*
James Eaton III *(Principal-Tax)*

SCA PROMOTIONS, INC.
3030 LBJ Fwy Ste 300, Dallas, TX 75234
Tel.: (214) 860-3700   TX
Web Site: http://www.scapromotions.com
Year Founded: 1986
Sales Range: $75-99.9 Million
Emp.: 75
Sales Promotion
N.A.I.C.S.: 541810
Robert D. Hamman *(Founder & Pres)*
Tanya Mathis *(Dir-Mktg)*
Hemant Lall *(COO)*

SCAFCO CORPORATION
6200 E Main Ave, Spokane, WA 99212
Tel.: (509) 343-9000
Web Site: http://www.scafco.com
Sales Range: $1-9.9 Million
Emp.: 100
Grain Storage Systems & Steel Framing Products Mfr
N.A.I.C.S.: 493130
Lawrence B. Stone *(Pres)*
Tammy Cook *(Mgr-Acctg)*

Subsidiaries:

SCAFCO Steel Stud Manufacturing Co. (1)
2800 E Main Ave, Spokane, WA 99202
Tel.: (509) 343-9000
Web Site: http://www.scafco.com
Steel Framing Product Mfr
N.A.I.C.S.: 332999

SCAFF'S INC.
134 SE Colburn Ave, Lake City, FL 32055
Tel.: (386) 752-7344
Web Site: http://www.scaffs.com
Sales Range: $200-249.9 Million
Emp.: 340
Convenience Store Owner & Operator
N.A.I.C.S.: 445131
Carla Stall *(Mgr-Comml Fuel)*
Brian Tucker *(COO)*

SCAFFIDI MOTORS INC.
3733 Stanley St, Stevens Point, WI 54481
Tel.: (715) 344-4100
Web Site: http://www.scaffidi.com
Year Founded: 1970
Sales Range: $50-74.9 Million
Emp.: 130
Car Dealership
N.A.I.C.S.: 441110
Don Scaffidi *(Pres)*
Joel Breitzman *(Controller)*
Robert Markley *(Mgr-Heavy Truck Sls)*
Tammy Schulz *(Bus Mgr)*
Shawn Lewis *(Mgr-Used Car)*

SCALA EVENINGWEAR, INC.
209 E 32nd St, Los Angeles, CA 90011
Tel.: (323) 233-2200
Web Site: http://www.scalausa.com
Year Founded: 1985
Sales Range: $10-24.9 Million
Emp.: 25
Clothing & Accessories Whslr
N.A.I.C.S.: 424350
Beeta Grover *(Pres)*

SCALABLE SOFTWARE, INC.
11044 Research Blvd Ste D 300, Austin, TX 78753

U.S. PRIVATE

Tel.: (713) 316-4900
Web Site: http://www.scalable.com
Year Founded: 1998
Sales Range: $75-99.9 Million
Emp.: 50
Information Security Products & Services
N.A.I.C.S.: 541715
Mark Cresswell *(Pres)*
Kristin D'Alessio *(Dir-Fin & Admin)*
Bruce Aboudara *(Exec VP-Sls & Mktg)*

SCALAMANDRE, INC.
350 Wireless Blvd, Hauppauge, NY 11788
Tel.: (631) 467-8800   NY
Web Site: http://www.scalamandre.com
Year Founded: 1929
Sales Range: $200-249.9 Million
Emp.: 275
Drapery, Upholstery Fabrics, Trimmings, Wall Coverings, Rugs, Carpets & Furniture Mfr
N.A.I.C.S.: 313210
Suzanne Spina *(Dir-Ops)*
Lou Renzo *(CEO)*
Steven Stolman *(Pres)*

SCALECO MANAGEMENT LLC
6701 Carnegie Ave Suite 100, Cleveland, OH 44103
Tel.: (216) 400-6020
Web Site: https://scaleco.com
Emp.: 100
Investment Services
N.A.I.C.S.: 523999
Donnie Bedney *(Partner)*

Subsidiaries:

Safety Controls Technology, Inc. (1)
5075 Taylor Dr, Bedford Heights, OH 44128
Tel.: (216) 587-3000
Web Site: http://www.safetycontrolstech.com
Sales Range: $1-9.9 Million
Emp.: 17
Management Consulting Services
N.A.I.C.S.: 541611
Donnie Bedney *(Pres)*
Joe Ventura *(CEO)*
Jocko Vermillion *(VP)*

SCALES ADVERTISING
2303 Wycliff St, Saint Paul, MN 55114
Tel.: (651) 641-0226
Web Site: http://www.scalesadvertising.com
Year Founded: 1972
Sales Range: $10-24.9 Million
Emp.: 63
N.A.I.C.S.: 541810
Patty Schneider *(Dir-New Bus)*
Jill Gapinski *(Office Mgr)*
Holli Maines *(Dir-Mktg)*
Dan Bauer *(Sr Acct Exec)*

SCALES AIR COMPRESSOR CORP
110 Voice Rd, Carle Place, NY 11514
Tel.: (516) 248-9096
Web Site: http://www.scalesindtech.com
Sales Range: $25-49.9 Million
Emp.: 66
Compressor Mfr
N.A.I.C.S.: 423830
William Scalchunes *(Pres)*

SCALES EXPRESS INC.
121 Jordan Rd, Tifton, GA 31794
Tel.: (229) 386-8015
Rev.: $10,000,000
Emp.: 95
Trucking Service
N.A.I.C.S.: 484121

COMPANIES

Michael H. Hughes *(Pres)*

SCALEWORKS, INC.
122 E Houston St Ste 105, San Antonio, TX 78205
Tel.: (805) 966-2440
Web Site: http://www.scaleworks.com
Year Founded: 2016
Privater Equity Firm
N.A.I.C.S.: 551112
Ed Byrne *(Partner)*
Lew Moorman *(Founder & Gen Partner)*

Subsidiaries:

B7 Interactive, LLC (1)
122 East Houston St Ste 105, San Antonio, TX 78205
Tel.: (719) 594-4595
Web Site: http://www.searchspring.com
Mobile Site Search Software
N.A.I.C.S.: 513210
Peter Messana *(CEO)*

Subsidiary (Domestic):

4-Tell Inc. (2)
555 SW Oak Stt Ste 350, Portland, OR 97204
Tel.: (503) 746-9070
Web Site: http://www.4-tell.com
Software Publisher
N.A.I.C.S.: 513210
Amy Weissfeld *(Sr Dir-Bus Dev)*
Neil Lofgren *(Co-Founder & CTO)*

Subsidiary (Non-US):

Nextopia Software Corporation (2)
116 Sherbourne Street, Toronto, M5A 2R2, ON, Canada
Tel.: (416) 360-5500
Web Site: http://www.nextopia.com
Software Publisher
N.A.I.C.S.: 513210
Sanjay Arora *(Pres & CEO)*

Centage Corporation (1)
24 Prime Pkwy Ste 202, Natick, MA 01760
Tel.: (508) 948-5089
Web Site: http://www.centage.com
Software & Technology Development Services
N.A.I.C.S.: 513210
Peter Messana *(CEO)*
John Orlando *(CFO & Exec VP)*
Kamran Sassoon *(Principal)*
Jack Davidson *(Founder & CTO)*
Ram Hasson *(VP & Gen Mgr-Analytics)*
Ken Marshall *(Chm)*
Ed Gromann *(Chief Product Officer)*
Scott Jennings *(Sr VP-Sls)*
Peter Messana *(CEO)*

SCALZO GROUP
2 Stony Hill Rd, Bethel, CT 06801-1028
Tel.: (203) 205-7603
Web Site:
   http://www.scalzogroup.com
Rev.: $10,000,000
Emp.: 200
Real Estate Brokers & Agents
N.A.I.C.S.: 531210
Paul Scalzo *(Co-Founder & Pres)*
Andrea Scalzo *(Co-Founder)*

SCAN DESIGN OF FLORIDA INC.
1153 Bennett Dr, Longwood, FL 32750
Tel.: (407) 831-6633
Web Site:
   http://www.scandesign.com
Sales Range: $10-24.9 Million
Emp.: 105
Household Furniture
N.A.I.C.S.: 423210
Jesper Knudsen *(Pres)*
Cindy Patch *(Controller)*

SCAN GROUP
3800 Kilroy Airport Way Ste 100, Long Beach, CA 90806-2497
Tel.: (562) 989-5100   CA
Web Site:
   http://www.scanhealthplan.com
Year Founded: 1977
Elderly Health Maintenance Organization
N.A.I.C.S.: 813319
Sachin H. Jain *(Pres & CEO)*
Cathy Batteer *(Sr VP-Provider Integration & Partnerships)*
Janet Kornblatt *(Gen Counsel)*
Nancy J. Monk *(Chief Admin Officer)*
Linda Rosenstock *(Chm)*
Romilla Batra *(Chief Medical Officer)*
Michael Plumb *(CFO)*
Scott Weingarten *(Chief Innovation Officer)*

Subsidiaries:

SCAN Health Plan (1)
3800 Kilroy Airport Way Ste 100, Long Beach, CA 90806-2497
Tel.: (562) 989-5100
Web Site: http://www.scanhealthplan.com
Elderly Health Maintenance Organization Insurance & Care Services
N.A.I.C.S.: 524114
Sachin H. Jain *(Pres & CEO)*
Nancy J. Monk *(COO)*
Romilla Batra *(Chief Medical Officer)*
Emily Arison *(VP-HR & Facilities)*
Eve Gelb *(Sr VP-Healthcare Svcs)*
Josh Goode *(CIO)*
Sharon K. Jhawar *(Chief Pharmacy Officer)*
Moon Leung *(Chief Informatics Officer & Sr VP)*
David Milligan *(Sr VP-Natl Sls)*
Sherry Stanislaw *(Gen Mgr)*
Kathryn Qin *(VP-Actuarial Svcs)*
Linda Rosenstock *(Chm)*
Adrienne Morrell *(Sr VP-Pub, Govt & Community Affairs)*
Michael Plumb *(CFO)*

SCAN-VINO INC.
5463 Cherokee Rd, Stockton, CA 95215
Tel.: (209) 931-3570
Web Site: http://www.gocfl.com
Rev.: $36,582,741
Emp.: 70
Trucking Service
N.A.I.C.S.: 484121
Leanne Scannavino *(Owner & Pres)*

SCANDIGITAL INC.
680 Knox St Ste 150, Torrance, CA 90502
Tel.: (310) 341-0172
Web Site: http://www.scandigital.com
Year Founded: 2007
Sales Range: $1-9.9 Million
Emp.: 137
Digitizes Photos, Slides, Negatives, Home Movies, Videos & Film
N.A.I.C.S.: 812921
Anderson Schoenrock *(Co-Founder & CEO)*
Mike Mothner *(Co-Founder)*
Matthew Stone *(COO)*

SCANDRILL, INC.
11777 Katy Fwy Ste 470, Houston, TX 77079-1785
Tel.: (281) 496-5571
Web Site: http://www.scandrill.com
Year Founded: 1977
Sales Range: $50-74.9 Million
Emp.: 260
Drilling Oil & Gas Wells
N.A.I.C.S.: 213111
Luke King *(Mgr-HR)*
Torrey Mosvold *(Sr VP)*
Sami Abboud *(CFO & VP)*
Neil Pierce *(VP-Ops)*

SCANLANKEMPERBARD COMPANIES, LLC
1211 SW 5th Ave Ste 2600, Portland, OR 97204
Tel.: (503) 220-2600   OR
Web Site: http://www.skbcos.com
Year Founded: 1993
Rev.: $3,000,000,000
Emp.: 25
Real Estate Private Equity Firm
N.A.I.C.S.: 523999
Robert D. Scanlan *(Chm & CEO)*
Todd M. Gooding *(Pres)*
James V. Paul *(Principal & Exec VP-Asset Mgmt)*
Stephen T. Wong *(Sr VP-Asset Mgmt)*
George Schreck *(CFO, Chief Compliance Officer & Gen Counsel)*
Robert Riley *(Pres & CEO-Hotel Grp)*
Richard D. Morean *(Principal & Exec VP-Capital Markets)*
Adam Haber *(Principal)*
Patrick Terrell *(Principal)*

SCANLINE VFX
12910 Culver Blvd, Los Angeles, CA 90066
Tel.: (310) 827-1555
Web Site: http://www.scanlinevfx.com
Video Recording Studios
N.A.I.C.S.: 512110
Scott Miller *(COO)*
Stephan Trojansky *(Pres & Supvr)*

SCANLON AUTO GROUP
14200 S Tamiami Tr, Fort Myers, FL 33912
Tel.: (239) 433-2277
Web Site:
   http://www.scanlonauto.com
Emp.: 150
Car Dealership Owner & Operator
N.A.I.C.S.: 441110
John Scanlon *(Owner)*
Nancy Anderson *(Mgr-HR & Benefits)*

Subsidiaries:

Scanlon Lexus (1)
14200 S Tamiami Trl, Fort Myers, FL 33912
Tel.: (239) 481-9797
Web Site: http://www.lexusoffortmyers.com
Car Dealership
N.A.I.C.S.: 441110
Chris Downing *(Gen Mgr)*
William Smith *(Mgr-Sls)*
Susann Nogales *(Mgr-Bus)*
Shaun Volkmann *(Mgr-ECommerce-Sls)*
Robert Gonnelli *(Mgr-Fixed Ops)*
Denise Vaughn *(Mgr-Svc Ops)*
Darrin Fordiani *(Mgr-Parts)*
Reilly Morris *(Mgr-Bus)*

SCANTIBODIES LABORATORY INC.
9336 Abraham Way, Santee, CA 92071
Tel.: (619) 258-9300
Web Site: http://www.scltesting.com
Sales Range: $10-24.9 Million
Emp.: 270
Diagnostic Substances
N.A.I.C.S.: 325412
Thomas Cantor *(Pres & CEO)*
Andrea Hagan *(Supvr-Payroll & Fleet)*
Jeremy Garrett *(Supvr-Pur)*
Julio C. Garcia *(Supvr-IT)*
Lisa Shouse *(Supvr-Billing)*

SCAP AUTOMOTIVE
421 Tunxis Hill Rd, Fairfield, CT 06825
Tel.: (203) 384-9300
Web Site: http://www.scapauto.com
Sales Range: $10-24.9 Million
Emp.: 100
Sales of Automobiles
N.A.I.C.S.: 441110

Geza Scap *(Pres)*
Julie Scap *(VP)*

SCARBROUGH INTERNATIONAL, LTD.
10841 Ambassador Dr, Kansas City, MO 64153
Tel.: (816) 891-2400   MO
Web Site: http://www.scarbrough-intl.com
Sales Range: $10-24.9 Million
Logistics & Customs Brokerage Services
N.A.I.C.S.: 488510
Adam Hill *(Grp Pres & COO)*
Kevin Ekstrand *(VP-Sls & Mktg)*
Brad Scarbrough *(VP-Domestic Ops)*
Jeannie Scarbrough *(Co-Founder, Pres & COO)*
Kathy Shanks *(VP-HR)*
Evan Moon *(Dir-Sls)*
Amy Rice *(Mng Dir & VP)*

SCARECROW LATH & PLASTER INC.
3510 Barron Way Ste 100, Reno, NV 89511-1858
Tel.: (775) 851-8001
Year Founded: 2001
Sales Range: $10-24.9 Million
Emp.: 150
Drywall Installation Services
N.A.I.C.S.: 238310
Steven C. Crow *(Pres)*

SCARINCI HOLLENBECK, LLC
1100 Valley Brook Ave, Lyndhurst, NJ 07071-0790
Tel.: (201) 896-8660
Web Site:
   http://www.scarincihollenbeck.com
Emp.: 47
Law firm
N.A.I.C.S.: 541110
Gary J. Cucchiara *(Partner)*
Frank L. Brunetti *(Co-Partner & Atty)*
Mark K. Follender *(Partner)*
Joseph M. Donegan *(Partner)*
Joel R. Glucksman *(Co-Partner & Atty)*
Russell Ascher *(Exec Dir)*
Joel N. Kreizman *(Co-Partner)*
Fernando M. Pinguelo *(Co-Partner)*
Donald Scarinci *(Mng Partner)*
Alan Dalsass *(Partner-Corp Transactions & Bus Grp-Red Bank)*
Anthony Caruso *(Mng Partner-Red Bank)*

Subsidiaries:

Spector & Ehrenworth, P.C. (1)
30 Columbia Tpke, Florham Park, NJ 07932
Tel.: (973) 593-4800
Web Site: http://www.selawfirm.com
Law firm
N.A.I.C.S.: 541199

SCARSELLA BROS INC.
8404 S 196th St, Kent, WA 98032
Tel.: (253) 872-7173
Web Site:
   http://www.scarsellabros.com
Sales Range: $10-24.9 Million
Emp.: 200
Highway & Street Construction Contracting Services
N.A.I.C.S.: 237310
Frank Scarsella *(Pres)*
Tamarah Knapp Hancock *(Gen Counsel)*
Shelley Schmolke *(Office Mgr)*

SCC SOFT COMPUTER INC.
5400 Tech Data Dr, Clearwater, FL 33760
Tel.: (727) 789-0100

SCC SOFT COMPUTER INC.

U.S. PRIVATE

SCC Soft Computer Inc.—(Continued)
Web Site:
http://www.softcomputer.com
Year Founded: 1979
Sales Range: $125-149.9 Million
Emp.: 1,700
Laboratory & Clinical Information Systems
N.A.I.C.S.: 513210
Gilbert Hakim *(Founder & CEO)*
Jean Hakim *(Pres)*
Don Keller *(VP-Global Education & Mgr-Mktg)*

SCD INFORMATION TECHNOLOGY, LLC.
7161 Columbia Gateway Dr Ste C, Columbia, MD 21046-1798
Tel.: (410) 290-1591
Web Site: http://www.scdit.com
Year Founded: 2000
Sales Range: $1-9.9 Million
Emp.: 17
Information Technology Services
N.A.I.C.S.: 541519
Scott Surguy *(Dir-Sls & Mktg)*
Cindy Solomon *(Gen Mgr)*
Krista Matheson *(Dir-Federal Svcs Grp)*
Shaun Wilson *(Dir-Infrastructure Cabling Div)*

SCE ENVIRONMENTAL GROUP INC.
1380 Mount Cobb Rd, Lake Ariel, PA 18436
Tel.: (570) 383-4151
Web Site: http://www.scenv.com
Year Founded: 2000
Rev.: $15,700,000
Emp.: 86
Environmental Services
N.A.I.C.S.: 236220
Jody Cordaro *(Pres)*
William Bradican *(Mgr-Client & Project Coord)*
Bill Bradican *(Mgr-Client)*
Bruce Morgan *(Chief Compliance Officer)*
Nate Butler *(VP-Ops)*

SCE GROUP
500 Linwood Dr Ste 1J, Fort Lee, NJ 07024
Tel.: (201) 482-4471
Web Site:
http://www.thescegroup.com
Year Founded: 2007
Sales Range: $1-9.9 Million
Emp.: 18
Information Security Consulting
N.A.I.C.S.: 541690
Benjamin Massin *(CEO)*

SCENIC CHEVROLET
3449 Blue Ridge Blvd, West Union, SC 29691
Tel.: (864) 638-9556
Web Site:
http://www.scenicchevrolet.com
Sales Range: $10-24.9 Million
Emp.: 55
Car Dealership Owner & Operator
N.A.I.C.S.: 441110
Bobby H. Wood *(Owner & Principal)*
Kevin Jankowy *(Bus Mgr & Mgr-Fin)*
Carolina McGraw *(Mgr-Internet)*
Dave Stevens *(Mgr-Svc)*
Jereme Belmore *(Mgr-Budget Lot)*
Ron Bort *(Mgr-Detail Shop)*
April Barry *(Office Mgr)*
Kevin Thompson *(Mgr-Parts)*

SCENIC HUDSON, INC.
85 Civic Center Pl Ste 300, Poughkeepsie, NY 12601
Tel.: (845) 473-4440 NY
Web Site:
https://www.scenichudson.org
Year Founded: 1975
Sales Range: $1-9.9 Million
River Protection & Restoration Services
N.A.I.C.S.: 541620
Alexander Reese *(Vice Chm)*
Simon Roosevelt *(Co-Chm)*
Steven Rosenberg *(Sr VP)*
Sacha Spector *(Dir-Program)*
Seth McKee *(Dir-Land Conservation)*
Michael Knutson *(Sr Project Mgr-Land)*
Cari Watkins-Bates *(Asst Dir-Land Conservation)*
Rita D. Shaheen *(Dir-Parks & Community Engagement)*
Geoff Carter *(Mgr-Parks & Restoration)*
Anthony Coneski *(Project Mgr-Event & Community)*
Joseph Kiernan *(Sr Project Mgr-Parks)*
Andy Bicking *(Dir-Govt Rels & Pub Policy)*
Jason Taylor *(Assoc Dir-Comm)*
Erin Therese Riley *(Sr VP)*
Jody Harris *(Asst Dir-Dev)*
Margaret A. King *(Asst Dir-Dev)*
J. Jeffrey Anzevino *(Dir-Land Use Advocacy)*
Hayley Carlock *(Dir-Environmental Advocacy & Legal Affairs)*
Ned Sullivan *(Pres & Asst Sec)*
Jason Camporese *(Chief Fin & Ops Officer)*
Kristin Gamble *(Co-Chm)*
Richard Krupp *(Vice Chm)*
Edward B. Whitney *(Treas)*
Judah S. Kraushaar *(Asst Treas)*
Usha Wright *(Co-Sec)*
Rudolph S. Rauch III *(Co-Sec)*
Carl H. Loewenson Jr. *(Vice Chm)*

SCENIC RIVERS ENERGY COOP
231 N Sheridan St, Lancaster, WI 53813
Tel.: (608) 723-2121
Web Site: http://www.srec.coop
Sales Range: $10-24.9 Million
Emp.: 35
Electric Power Distr
N.A.I.C.S.: 221122
Steve Lucas *(CEO)*
Linda Bendorf *(CFO & Dir-Admin & Office Svcs)*

SCENIC TRAVELER RV CENTERS
3155 Scenic Rd, Slinger, WI 53086
Tel.: (262) 677-9026
Web Site: http://www.scenicrv.com
Sales Range: $10-24.9 Million
Emp.: 16
Recreational Vehicle Dealers
N.A.I.C.S.: 441210
Jeff Peterson *(VP)*

SCENIC WOOD PRODUCTS
10143 Copperhead Rd NW, Sugarcreek, OH 44681
Tel.: (330) 852-3531
Web Site:
http://www.scenicwoodproducts.com
Year Founded: 1994
Sales Range: $10-24.9 Million
Emp.: 55
Wood Container & Pallet Mfr
N.A.I.C.S.: 321920

Marty Troyer *(Pres)*
Paul Monaco *(CFO)*
Matt Stair *(Plant Mgr)*

SCENTSY, INC.
3698 E Lanark, Meridian, ID 83642
Tel.: (208) 855-0617
Web Site: http://www.scentsy.net
Year Founded: 2004
Sales Range: $150-199.9 Million
Emp.: 424
Direct-Selling Consumer & Household Products
N.A.I.C.S.: 339999
Orville Thompson *(Co-CEO)*
Heidi Thompson *(Owner & Co-CEO)*
Mark Stastny *(CMO)*
Todd Spanbauer *(Mgr-Supply Chain Procurement)*
Chuck Thompson *(Gen Mgr-North America)*
Dan Orchard *(Pres)*
Kevin Kirkpatrick *(Gen Mgr-Velata)*
Lindsay Randolph *(Chief Creative Officer)*
Reed Brimhall *(CFO)*
Richard Steel *(Chief HR Officer)*

SCEPTER HOLDINGS, INC.
301 Commerce St Ste 3200, Fort Worth, TX 76102
Tel.: (817) 332-9500 TX
Year Founded: 1994
Investment Holding Company
N.A.I.C.S.: 551112
Jeffrey Rainor *(Pres)*
Brandon Alan Teague *(VP & Dir-Trading)*

SCEPTER INC.
1485 Scepter Lane, Waverly, TN 37185
Tel.: (931) 535-3565
Web Site: http://www.scepterinc.com
Sales Range: $10-24.9 Million
Emp.: 80
Aluminum Smelting & Refining
N.A.I.C.S.: 331314
Nathan Tooley *(CFO)*
Garney Scott Jr. *(CEO)*

SCEPTER TECHNOLOGIES INC.
10045 Red Run Blvd Ste 150, Owings Mills, MD 21117
Tel.: (443) 379-4565
Web Site: http://www.sceptertech.com
Year Founded: 2008
Sales Range: $1-9.9 Million
Emp.: 90
It Consulting
N.A.I.C.S.: 541690
Srini Reddy *(Mgr-Resource)*

SCEPTRE HOSPITALITY RESOURCES
7600 E Orchard Rd Ste 230 S, Greenwood Village, CO 80111
Tel.: (303) 220-2000
Web Site:
http://www.sceptrehospitality.com
Year Founded: 1988
Sales Range: $1-9.9 Million
Emp.: 30
Hotel Booking Services
N.A.I.C.S.: 561599
Rodrigo Jimenez *(CEO)*

SCEPTRE TECHNOLOGIES INC.
16800 Gale Ave, City of Industry, CA 91745
Tel.: (626) 369-3698
Web Site: http://www.sceptre.com
Rev.: $14,200,000

Emp.: 50
Computer Peripheral Equipment
N.A.I.C.S.: 334118
Steve Liu *(Pres)*

SCF PARTNERS LTD.
600 Travis Ste 6600, Houston, TX 77002
Tel.: (713) 227-7888
Web Site:
https://www.scfpartners.com
Privater Equity Firm
N.A.I.C.S.: 551112
Garrett Jackson *(Dir)*

Subsidiaries:

DeltaValve, LLC (1)
9890 Jordan Gateway, Sandy, UT 84070
Tel.: (801) 984-1000
Web Site: https://www.deltavalve.com
Industrial Equipment Mfr
N.A.I.C.S.: 332911
Steven Seals *(CEO)*

Newpark Drilling Fluids LLC (1)
21920 Merchants Way, Katy, TX 77449
Tel.: (281) 754-8600
Sales Range: $75-99.9 Million
Emp.: 70
Drilling Fluid Products & Technical Services for Oil & Gas Industry
N.A.I.C.S.: 213111

SCHAAF CONSULTING
538 W 21st St, Houston, TX 77008-3642
Tel.: (323) 386-2336
Web Site: http://www.schaafpc.com
Sales Range: $10-24.9 Million
Emp.: 20
Affiliate Program Management Services
N.A.I.C.S.: 561499
Brook Schaaf *(Founder & Chm)*
Stephanie Harris *(Interim CEO)*
Julie Avila *(VP-Client Svcs)*

Subsidiaries:

PartnerCentric, Inc. (1)
16 W Mission St Unit M, Santa Barbara, CA 93101
Tel.: (805) 569-8750
Web Site: http://www.partnercentric.com
Advertising Agencies
N.A.I.C.S.: 541810
Dan Fink *(Dir-Affiliate Program)*
Tracie Gross *(Mgr-Affiliate)*

SCHAAKE CORPORATION
3901 Fairbanks Ave PO Box 450, Yakima, WA 98907-0450
Tel.: (509) 249-8955 WA
Year Founded: 1929
Sales Range: $50-74.9 Million
Emp.: 2
Provider Of Agricultural Services
N.A.I.C.S.: 112112
John Kincaid *(Pres & CEO)*
Tom Ringer *(Controller)*

SCHAAL HEATING & COOLING, INC.
2701 6th Ave, Des Moines, IA 50313
Tel.: (515) 212-2294 IA
Web Site:
http://www.callschaalyaall.com
Year Founded: 1956
Sales Range: $10-24.9 Million
Emp.: 47
Plumbing & Heating Contracting Services
N.A.I.C.S.: 238220
Randy Keys *(Owner)*
Jonathan Marchand *(Dir-Sls & Mktg)*
Phillip Keys *(Ops Mgr)*
Justin Riddle *(Mgr-Warehouse)*
T. J. Hodge *(Mgr-Plumbing)*

SCHADEGG MECHANICAL INC.
225 Bridgepoint Dr, South Saint Paul, MN 55075-2433
Tel.: (651) 292-9933
Web Site: http://www.schadegg-mech.com
Sales Range: $10-24.9 Million
Emp.: 90
Plumbing Services
N.A.I.C.S.: 238220
Daniel Schadegg (CEO)

SCHAEDLER/YESCO DISTRIBUTION, INC.
3982 Paxton St, Harrisburg, PA 17111
Tel.: (717) 233-1621 PA
Web Site: http://www.sydist.com
Year Founded: 1924
Electrical Supplies Distr & Whslr
N.A.I.C.S.: 423610
Jim Schaedler (CEO)
Matt Brnik (Exec VP-Sls)
John Rambler (Mgr-Indus Automation)
Joe Ritrievi (Mgr-Data Comm-Sls)
Dean Krout (VP-Mktg & Info Sys)
Chuck McLamb (Engr-Application)
Rick Nusbaum (Engr-Sys)
Kurt Suchar (VP-Sls)
Doug Sheaffer (Mgr-Outside Sls)
Dave Davis (CFO & Mgr-Pur)
Greg Schaedler (Mgr-Contractor Outside Sls)
Randy Steadman (Mgr-Corp Logistics & Inventory)
Denise Pankake (Mgr-Fin)
Deb Thomas (Mgr-HR)
Tom G. Schaedler (Mgr-IT)
Farrah Mittel (Pres)
Christine Notarfrancesco (Mgr-Mktg Comm)

Subsidiaries:

Atlantic Energy Concepts, Inc. (1)
129 Excelsior Dr, Blandon, PA 19510
Tel.: (610) 916-5013
Web Site:
   http://www.atlanticenergyconcepts.com
Facilities Services
N.A.I.C.S.: 561210
Bradley J. Salamone (Founder, Pres & Gen Mgr)

SCHAEFER AMBULANCE SERVICE
4627 Beverly Blvd, Los Angeles, CA 90004
Tel.: (323) 468-1600
Web Site:
   http://www.schaeferamb.com
Rev.: $14,500,000
Emp.: 225
Ambulance Service
N.A.I.C.S.: 621910
James Mcneal (Pres)
Linda Wilhelm (Office Mgr)
Amy Sieger (Supvr)

SCHAEFER MARINE INC.
158 Duchaine Blvd Industrial Park, New Bedford, MA 02745-1293
Tel.: (508) 995-9511 MA
Web Site:
   http://www.schaefermarine.com
Year Founded: 1965
Rev.: $7,000,000
Emp.: 65
Stamped Forgings & Marine Hardware Castings, Stainless Steel Fabrications
N.A.I.C.S.: 332510

SCHAEFER PLUMBING SUPPLY CO.
146-160 Clinton St, Buffalo, NY 14203
Tel.: (716) 853-2406
Web Site:
   http://www.schaefersupply.com
Emp.: 100
Plumbing & Hydronic Heating Supplies
N.A.I.C.S.: 423720
Mark Dietrick (Pres & Gen Mgr)
Tom Dietrick (Dir & VP-Mktg)

SCHAEFER TRANS INC.
580 Atlantic Ave, East Rockaway, NY 11518
Tel.: (516) 561-2800
Web Site:
   http://www.schaefertransinc.com
Rev.: $16,383,024
Emp.: 15
Freight Forwarding Services
N.A.I.C.S.: 488510
Paul Hoeck (Pres & CEO)
Berta Unger (VP-Export)
Felix Flaig (Mng Dir & COO)
Andre Krawentek (Mgr-South East Reg-United States)
Andy Hoeck (CFO & VP)

SCHAEFFER INDUSTRIES
1265 N Shaw Rd, Stockton, CA 95215
Tel.: (951) 681-1000
Web Site: http://www.sisteel.com
Rev.: $65,000,000
Emp.: 30
Steel Products Mfr
N.A.I.C.S.: 332111
George M. Schaeffer (Pres)
Pat Palmer (Gen Mgr)

SCHAEFFER MANUFACTURING CO
102 Barton St, Saint Louis, MO 63104
Tel.: (314) 865-4100
Web Site:
   http://www.schaefferoil.com
Sales Range: $100-124.9 Million
Emp.: 140
Oil & Grease Blending & Compounding Services
N.A.I.C.S.: 324191
Tom Herman (CEO)
Jay Shields (Pres)
Gary Johnson (VP-Sls)

SCHAFER CONDON CARTER
1029 W Madison, Chicago, IL 60607
Tel.: (312) 464-1666 IL
Web Site: http://www.sccadv.com
Year Founded: 1989
Rev.: $50,000,000
Emp.: 100
Advertising Services
N.A.I.C.S.: 541430
Tim Condon (Founder & CEO)
Greg Wenstrup (COO)
Gwen Friedow (Exec Dir-Brand Plng)
Suzanne Martineau (Exec Dir-Creative)
David Selby (Chm)
Jim Stadler (Mng Partner & Dir-Bus Dev)
Erika Bye (Dir-Digital Media)
Denny Hebson (Exec Dir-Creative)
Ron Sone (Dir-Creative)
Michael Dorich (Dir-Creative)

SCHAFER INC.
125 N Mable St, Pinconning, MI 48650
Tel.: (989) 879-2211
Web Site:
   http://www.schafershevy.com
Rev.: $21,600,000
Emp.: 50
Automobiles, New & Used
N.A.I.C.S.: 441110
Russell La Fave (Pres)

SCHAFER OIL COMPANY
9109 State Rte 66, Fort Loramie, OH 45845
Tel.: (937) 295-2801
Web Site: http://www.schaferoil.com
Rev.: $25,570,367
Emp.: 11
Fuel & Oil
N.A.I.C.S.: 424720
Tom Schafer (Pres)

SCHAFFER MECHANICAL, INC.
5420 Gulfton St, Houston, TX 77081
Tel.: (713) 669-0099
Web Site:
   http://www.hvacservicehouston.net
Year Founded: 1983
Sales Range: $25-49.9 Million
Emp.: 180
Plumbing Services
N.A.I.C.S.: 238220
Cindy Hatfield (Co-Owner)
Jack Schaffer (Co-Owner)

SCHAGRIN GAS CO.
1000 N Broad St, Middletown, DE 19709
Tel.: (302) 658-2000 DE
Web Site:
   http://www.schagringas.com
Year Founded: 1932
Sales Range: $10-24.9 Million
Emp.: 35
Bottled Propane Gas Distr
N.A.I.C.S.: 457210
Andy Lambert (VP-Ops)
Scott Aiello (Comptroller)

SCHAKRA, INC.
4004 148th Ave NE, Redmond, WA 98052 WA
Web Site: http://www.schakra.com
Year Founded: 2003
Sales Range: $1-9.9 Million
Emp.: 60
Prepackaged Software
N.A.I.C.S.: 513210
Amarendra Reddy (Founder & Pres)
Charles Prakash Dasari (VP-Engrg)

SCHALLER AUTO WORLD, INC.
1-55 Veterans Dr, New Britain, CT 06051
Tel.: (860) 223-2230
Year Founded: 1953
Sales Range: $25-49.9 Million
Emp.: 175
Car Whslr
N.A.I.C.S.: 441110
Arthur Schaller Jr. (Pres)

SCHALLER CORPORATION
49495 Gratiot Ave, Chesterfield, MI 48051
Tel.: (586) 949-6000
Web Site:
   http://www.schallergroup.com
Rev.: $63,925,048
Emp.: 110
Metal Stamping Services for Automotive Industry
N.A.I.C.S.: 332119
Arv Pikunas (VP-Mfg)
Steve Hamrick (Mgr-Mfg)
Mike Pacitti (Mgr-Quality)
Dan Gregor (Acct Mgr)

SCHALLER HARDWOOD LUMBER CO.
100 Ashcroft Rd, Poplar Bluff, MO 63901
Tel.: (573) 785-1003
Web Site:
   http://www.schallerhardwood.com
Sales Range: $10-24.9 Million
Emp.: 20
Lumber: Rough, Dressed & Finished
N.A.I.C.S.: 423310
Arthur H. Ploetze (Chm)
Denise Rowe (VP)

SCHALLER MANUFACTURING CORP.
2235 46th St, Astoria, NY 11105
Tel.: (718) 721-5480
Web Site:
   http://www.schallerweber.com
Rev.: $12,800,000
Emp.: 85
Prepared Pork Products Mfr
N.A.I.C.S.: 311612
Ralph Schaller (Pres)

SCHARF INVESTMENTS, LLC
5619 Scotts Vly Dr Ste 140, Scotts Valley, CA 95066-3453
Tel.: (831) 429-6513
Web Site:
   http://www.scharfinvestments.com
Portfolio Management
N.A.I.C.S.: 523940
Brian Krawez (Pres)

SCHAUBACH HOLDINGS INC.
1384 Ingleside Rd, Norfolk, VA 23502
Tel.: (757) 852-3300
Holding Company
N.A.I.C.S.: 551112

Subsidiaries:

Bay Disposal Inc. (1)
2224 Springfield Ave, Norfolk, VA 23523
Tel.: (757) 857-9700
Web Site: http://www.baydisposal.com
Solid Waste Collection, Disposal & Recycling
N.A.I.C.S.: 562111
Emmett Moore (District Mgr)
J. R. Pearson (VP-Ops)
Dee Crigger (Dir-Mktg & Sls)
Allison McCormick (Mgr-Customer Svc)
John Rhodes (Acct Exec)
Kerin Wimbrough (Acct Exec-Construction)
Alanda Robinson (Acct Exec)

Johns Brothers Security Inc. (1)
1384 Ingleside Rd, Norfolk, VA 23502
Tel.: (757) 852-3300
Web Site: http://www.johnsbrother.com
Security Systems Technology & Services
N.A.I.C.S.: 561621
Woody Parsons (VP-Ops & Gen Mgr-Security)
M. Dean Cribb (CFO)
Georgia Hayden (Controller)
Charles Cross (Dir-IT)
Gary Thornburg (Mgr-Svc)

SCHEAR CORPORATION
5490 Lee St, Lehigh Acres, FL 33971
Tel.: (239) 369-6323
Web Site:
   http://www.schearconstruction.com
Rev.: $38,800,000
Emp.: 250
New Multifamily Housing Construction
N.A.I.C.S.: 236116
Jeffrey G. Walls (Pres)

SCHECK MECHANICAL CORP
1 East Oak Hill Dr Ste 100, Westmont, IL 60527
Tel.: (708) 482-8100
Web Site: http://www.goscheck.com
Rev.: $33,031,055
Emp.: 18
Mechanical Contractor
N.A.I.C.S.: 238220

SCHECK MECHANICAL CORP

Scheck Mechanical Corp—(Continued)
Richard Scheck (Pres)
Kathleen Balmer (Controller)
Eric Kubina (Project Mgr)

SCHEDA ECOLOGICAL ASSOCIATES, INC.
5892 E Fowler Ave, Tampa, FL 33617
Tel.: (813) 989-9600
Web Site: http://www.scheda.com
Year Founded: 1990
Sales Range: $1-9.9 Million
Emp.: 30
Ecological Consulting Services
N.A.I.C.S.: 541620
Sandra Scheda (Pres)
Thomas Ries (Exec VP)

SCHEELS ALL SPORTS INC.
1551 45th St S, Fargo, ND 58103-3255
Tel.: (701) 232-3665
Web Site: http://www.scheelssports.com
Sales Range: $100-124.9 Million
Emp.: 175
Sports Apparel Stores
N.A.I.C.S.: 458110
Steve M. Scheel (Chm & CEO)
Fred B. Scheel (Founder)
Becky Cossette (Office Mgr)

SCHEIBEL HALASKA, INC.
735 N Water St Ste 200, Milwaukee, WI 53202
Tel.: (414) 272-6898
Year Founded: 1991
Rev.: $2,000,000
Emp.: 13
Fiscal Year-end: 12/31/06
Advetising Agency
N.A.I.C.S.: 541810
John Scheibel (CEO)
Howard Halaska (Pres, Partner & Dir-Creative)
Andy Narrai (COO)
Mary Scheibel (Owner & Principal)
Matthew Mente (Acct Exec-PR)
Elizabeth Franczyk (Acct Exec)
Allison Kubacki (Acct Coord)

SCHELL & KAMPETER, INC.
103 N Olive St, Meta, MO 65058
Tel.: (573) 229-4203
Web Site: http://www.diamondpet.com
Year Founded: 1970
Sales Range: $25-49.9 Million
Emp.: 300
Dog & Cat Food Mfr
N.A.I.C.S.: 311111
Drew Haines (Mgr-HR)
Gary Schell (CTO)
Mark Schell (Asst Gen Mgr)
Mike Kampeter (Mgr-Sls)
Andy Kampeter (Mgr-Pkg & logistics)
Tom Kampeter (Mgr-Pur)
Ken Wegman (VP-Fin)
Tim Burmeister (Mgr-Safety)
Luke Reinkemeyer (Dir-Supply Chain)
Randy Steinlage (Dir-Maintenance)

SCHENECTADY HARDWARE & ELECTRIC CO.
155 Erie Blvd, Schenectady, NY 12305
Tel.: (518) 346-2369
Web Site: http://www.sheinc.com
Rev.: $20,417,950
Emp.: 15
General Electrical Contractor
N.A.I.C.S.: 238210
Kevin Finn (VP-Ops)
Chris Spraragen (Pres & CEO)
Tom Lynch (Superintendent)

SCHENK PACKING CO. INC.
8204 288th St NW, Stanwood, WA 98292-9525
Tel.: (360) 629-3939
Web Site: http://www.schenkpacking.com
Year Founded: 1966
Sales Range: $25-49.9 Million
Emp.: 160
Meat Packing Plants
N.A.I.C.S.: 311611
Kim Tonheim (Gen Mgr)

SCHENKEL & SHULTZ INC.
111 E Wayne St Ste 555, Fort Wayne, IN 46802
Tel.: (260) 424-9080
Web Site: http://www.schenkelshultz.com
Year Founded: 1958
Sales Range: $10-24.9 Million
Emp.: 100
Architectural Services
N.A.I.C.S.: 541310
J. Thomas Chandler (Pres & CEO)
Daniel M. Tarczynski (Partner)
David J. Sholl (Partner)
J. David Torbert (Partner)
Gary F. Krueger (Partner)
Kenneth G. Dean (Partner)
Michelle M. Chandler (Partner)
Craig W. Hanson (Principal)
Daniel C. Laggan (Mng Partner)
Joseph S. Toth (Principal)
A. Ernest Straughn III (Partner)

SCHENKELBERG IMPLEMENT COMPANY
Hwy 71 N, Carroll, IA 51401
Tel.: (712) 792-1400
Web Site: http://www.schenkelbergimpco.com
Sales Range: $10-24.9 Million
Emp.: 25
Agricultural Machinery & Equipment
N.A.I.C.S.: 423820
Gary Schenkelberg (Pres)

SCHERER BROTHERS LUMBER COMPANY
9401 73rd Ave N Ste 400, Brooklyn Park, MN 55428
Tel.: (612) 379-9633
Web Site: http://www.schererbros.com
Year Founded: 1930
Sales Range: $200-249.9 Million
Emp.: 245
Lumber & Building Materials Sales
N.A.I.C.S.: 423310
Matt Higgins (Controller)
Rachael Scherer (Chm)
Paul Legrid (Gen Mgr-Arden Hills)

Subsidiaries:

Contractor Property Developers Co. (1)
3030 Centre Pointe Dr Ste 800, Roseville, MN 55113 (100%)
Tel.: (651) 556-4550
Sales Range: $10-24.9 Million
Emp.: 18
Residential Land Development & Planning
N.A.I.C.S.: 237210

SCHERER CONSTRUCTION OF WEST FLORIDA, LLC
2152 14th Cir N, Saint Petersburg, FL 33713
Tel.: (727) 321-8111
Web Site: http://www.schererconstruction.com
Year Founded: 1984
Emp.: 15
Commercial Construction Services
N.A.I.C.S.: 236220

James A. Crookston (Pres)
Douglas W. Wilcox (Pres-North Florida)

SCHERER STAFFING LLC
11001 Roosevelt Blvd N Ste 100, Saint Petersburg, FL 33716
Tel.: (727) 507-8888
Web Site: http://www.schererstaffing.com
Sales Range: $1-9.9 Million
Emp.: 16
Employment Agencies
N.A.I.C.S.: 561311
Bill Frief (Owner)

SCHERMER, INC.
12 N 12th St Ste 400, Minneapolis, MN 55403
Tel.: (612) 375-9999
Web Site: http://www.schermer.co
Sales Range: $1-9.9 Million
Emp.: 30
Advetising Agency
N.A.I.C.S.: 541810
Chris Schermer (Pres)
Scott Miller (VP & Dir-Creative)
Janelle Smith (Dir-Acct Svcs)
Jen Alstead (Dir-Agency Ops)
Maria Edwardson (Controller)
Melissa Anthony (Acct Mgr)
Dave Swanson (Assoc Dir-Creative)
Pat Petschel (VP-Acct Svcs & Strategy)
Siri Prax (Acct Dir)
Jill Howard (Acct Mgr)
Bailey Hanson (Acct Exec)
Greta Miller (Acct Coord)
Robert Nendza (VP-Experience & Engagement)
Mariann Hohe (VP-Strategy & Plng)

SCHERMERHORN BROTHERS CO.
340 Eisenhower Ln N, Lombard, IL 60148
Tel.: (630) 627-9860
Web Site: http://www.schermerhornbros.co.com
Sales Range: $10-24.9 Million
Emp.: 53
Mill Supplies
N.A.I.C.S.: 423840
Terry Duff (CFO)
Kevin Jordan (Pres)

SCHERRMAN'S IMPLEMENT & APPLIANCE
13951 Hwy 136 N, Dyersville, IA 52040
Tel.: (563) 875-2426
Web Site: http://www.scherrman.com
Year Founded: 1928
Sales Range: $10-24.9 Million
Emp.: 30
Mfr of Farm Implements
N.A.I.C.S.: 423820
Patrick William Scherrman (Pres)
Donald Scherrman (VP)

SCHEWEL FURNITURE COMPANY, INC.
1031 Main St, Lynchburg, VA 24504-1800
Tel.: (434) 522-0200
Web Site: http://www.schewels.com
Year Founded: 1897
Sales Range: $100-124.9 Million
Emp.: 800
Furniture Retailer
N.A.I.C.S.: 449110
Marc A. Schewel (Pres)
William S. Sprinkle (Treas)
Donna Schewel-Clark (Owner)
Scott Allen (Mgr-Adv)

SCHIBLEY SOLVENTS & CHEMICAL CO.
1570 Lowell St, Elyria, OH 44035
Tel.: (440) 322-1350
Web Site: http://www.schibley.com
Year Founded: 1926
Sales Range: $25-49.9 Million
Emp.: 20
Industrial Chemicals Mfr
N.A.I.C.S.: 424690
Reed Schibley (Pres)

SCHIFF ENTERPRISES
1004 New Rd, Northfield, NJ 08225
Tel.: (609) 345-8271
Year Founded: 1971
Sales Range: $50-74.9 Million
Emp.: 1,500
Gift, Novelty & Souvenir Shop
N.A.I.C.S.: 459420
Abraham Schiff (Pres)

SCHIFF FOOD PRODUCTS CO., INC.
7401 Westside Ave, North Bergen, NJ 07047-6430
Tel.: (201) 868-6800
Sales Range: $25-49.9 Million
Emp.: 40
Dried & Dehydrated Food Mfr
N.A.I.C.S.: 311423
David Deutscher (Owner)
Joseph Krausz (Chief Admin Officer)

SCHIFF'S FOOD SERVICE, INC.
7 Stauffer Industrial Pk, Taylor, PA 18517
Tel.: (570) 562-3100
Web Site: http://www.schiffs.com
Year Founded: 1969
Sales Range: $10-24.9 Million
Emp.: 80
Food Products Distr
N.A.I.C.S.: 311991
Ryan Yeager (Gen Mgr-Sls)
Paul Yeager (Plant Mgr)
John Husosky (Exec VP)
Mike Yeager (Pres)

SCHIFFMAYER PLASTICS CORP
1201 Armstrong St, Algonquin, IL 60102
Tel.: (847) 658-8140
Web Site: http://www.schiffmayerplastics.com
Rev.: $16,200,000
Emp.: 50
Thermoformed Finished Plastics Products Mfr
N.A.I.C.S.: 326199
Penny Burg (Dir-Fin)
Tina Schiffmayer (Pres)

SCHIFINO/LEE, INC.
511 W Bay St Ste 400, Tampa, FL 33606
Tel.: (813) 258-5858
Web Site: http://www.schifinolee.com
Year Founded: 1993
Sales Range: $1-9.9 Million
Emp.: 15
Advetising Agency
N.A.I.C.S.: 541810
Paola Schifino (Principal)
Ben Lee (Principal)
Nordin Benhalima (VP & Dir-Media)
Amanda Koenn (Brand Mgr-Social & Sr Acct Exec)
Chad Grandey (Sr Dir-Art)
Jon Rodriguez (Sr Dir-Art)
Kevin Byrd (Assoc Dir-Creative)
Mary Rach (Dir-Art)
Pat Floyd (Sr Dir-Digital Art)
Heather Fako Jr. (Dir-Art)

COMPANIES

SCHILDBERG CONSTRUCTION CO. INC.
108 SE 6th St, Greenfield, IA 50849
Tel.: (641) 743-2131 IA
Web Site: http://www.schildberg.com
Sales Range: $25-49.9 Million
Emp.: 250
Mining & Quarrying Construction
N.A.I.C.S.: 237990
Mark Schildberg (Pres)
Greg Schildberg (VP)
Kitty Sherer (Dir-Personnel)

SCHILKE MUSIC PRODUCTS, INC.
4520 James Pl, Melrose Park, IL 60160
Tel.: (708) 343-8858
Web Site: http://www.schilkemusic.com
Year Founded: 1956
Sales Range: $1-9.9 Million
Emp.: 35
Musical Instrument Mfr
N.A.I.C.S.: 339992
Andrew Naumann (Owner & Pres)
Elizabeth Nowak (Office Mgr)
Michael Zielinski (Dir-Sls)

Subsidiaries:
Greenhoe, Inc. (1)
4085 Lily Rd, Jackson, WI 53037-9200
Tel.: (262) 677-0460
Web Site: http://www.greenhoe.com
Musical Instrument Mfr
N.A.I.C.S.: 339992
Gary Greenhoe (Co-Founder & Pres)
Glenda Greenhoe (Co-Founder)

SCHILL LANDSCAPING & LAWN SERVICES, INC.
842 Abbe Rd, Sheffield Village, OH 44054
Tel.: (440) 949-6089 OH
Web Site: http://www.schilllandscaping.com
Year Founded: 1993
Sales Range: $10-24.9 Million
Emp.: 85
Landscaping & Lawn Care Services
N.A.I.C.S.: 541320
Jerry Schill (Co-Owner & VP)

Subsidiaries:
Grasscor Lawn & Landscapes, LLC (1)
8915 Blue Ash Rd, Blue Ash, OH 45242
Tel.: (513) 271-5296
Web Site: http://www.grasscor.com
Emp.: 100
Landscaping Services
N.A.I.C.S.: 561730
John Swisher (Acct Mgr)

SCHILLER GROUNDS CARE, INC.
1028 St Rd, Southampton, PA 18966
Tel.: (215) 357-5110
Web Site: http://www.schillergc.com
Year Founded: 2009
Sales Range: $100-124.9 Million
Emp.: 300
Lawn & Garden Power Equipment Mfr
N.A.I.C.S.: 333112
Ryan Bagwell (Reg Mgr-Sls-Rental Channels)

SCHILLER HARDWARE INC.
11525 Blankenbaker Access Dr, Louisville, KY 40299
Tel.: (502) 584-5301
Web Site: http://www.schillerhardware.com
Sales Range: $10-24.9 Million
Emp.: 80
Hardware & Door Systems Wholesaler
N.A.I.C.S.: 423710
Scott McClain (Controller)
Billy Graves (Project Mgr-Outside Sls)

SCHILLING BROS LUMBER CO., INC.
8900 Wicker Ave, Saint John, IN 46373
Tel.: (219) 365-8585
Web Site: http://www.schillinglumber.com
Year Founded: 1945
Rev.: $10,200,000
Emp.: 100
Lumber & Other Building Materials
N.A.I.C.S.: 423310
Frank E. Schilling (Pres)

SCHILLING DISTRIBUTING CO. INC.
2901 Moss St, Lafayette, LA 70501
Tel.: (337) 233-2337
Web Site: http://www.schillingdistributing.com
Sales Range: $50-74.9 Million
Emp.: 170
Beer & Other Fermented Malt Liquors
N.A.I.C.S.: 424810
Herbert E. Schilling (Owner)

SCHILLING PAPER COMPANY INC.
2435 Hauser St, La Crosse, WI 54603
Tel.: (608) 781-8100
Web Site: http://www.schillingsupply.com
Year Founded: 1904
Rev.: $25,300,000
Emp.: 36
Industrial & Personal Service Paper
N.A.I.C.S.: 424130
Chip Schilling (Pres)

SCHIMENTI CONSTRUCTION CO.
650 Danbury Rd, Ridgefield, CT 06877
Tel.: (914) 244-9100
Web Site: http://www.schimenti.com
Sales Range: $25-49.9 Million
Emp.: 125
Commercial Construction Services
N.A.I.C.S.: 236220
Matthew Schimenti (Pres)
Rob McDougal (Superintendent)
Anthony Loguercio (Dir-Ops)
Joseph Rotondo (Exec VP)
Thomas C. Madden (Dir-Corp Safety)

SCHIMMER CHEVROLET BUICK, INC.
Rt 251 S, Mendota, IL 61342-0080
Tel.: (815) 539-9343
Web Site: http://www.schimmergm.com
Year Founded: 1945
Sales Range: $10-24.9 Million
Emp.: 52
Car Whslr
N.A.I.C.S.: 441110
Jeff Schimmer (Pres)

SCHLESINGER GROUP
101 Wood Ave S Ste 501, Iselin, NJ 08830
Tel.: (732) 906-1122
Web Site: http://www.schlesingerassociates.com
Rev.: $15,600,000
Emp.: 80
Market Research
N.A.I.C.S.: 517810
Sarah B. Schlesinger (Founder)
Howard Schlesinger (Gen Counsel & Exec VP)
Jason Horine (VP-Client Dev-Online Qualitative Solutions)
Ian Ellias (CFO)
Debra Schlesinger-Hellman (Exec VP-Qualitative Solutions)
A. J. Shaw (VP-Qualitative Solutions)
Tim Holley (Dir-Specialty Panels & Recruiting)
Robert Ramirez (Sr VP-Strategic Dev-Global Mgmt Solutions Svc)
Eric Nalpas (Mng Dir-Europe)
James Sallows (Mng Dir)
Matt Campion (Exec VP)
Patty Altman (Sr VP-Strategic Dev)
Terri-Lyn Hawley (VP-Ops)
Stephenie Gordon (VP-Qualitative Solutions)
Nadine Casaletto (Dir-Global Qualitative Solutions)
Jaime Klein (VP-Talent)
Kim Johanson (VP-Recruiting-New Jersey)
Kristen Tripphahn (VP-Client Dev)
Samantha Price (VP-Global Bus Partnerships)
Sarah Longacre (VP-Client Dev)
Scott Baker (Sr VP-Acct Mgmt-Qualitative Solutions)
Stephan Lange (Mng Dir-Schmiedl Marktforschung Berlin & Frankfurt)
Ted Donnelly (VP-Client Solutions)
Heather Ashley-Collins (VP-Client Solutions)
Reed Cundiff (CEO)
Isaac Rogers (Pres)
Julie Terling (VP-Brand Mktg)

Subsidiaries:
20/20 Research Inc. (1)
2102 Cambridge Beltway Dr, Charlotte, NC 28273-3381
Tel.: (704) 587-0028
Web Site: http://www.2020research.com
Marketing Research & Public Opinion Polling
N.A.I.C.S.: 541910
Susan Brelewski (Mgr)

Marketlab Research, Inc. (1)
The Wanamaker Bldg 100 Penn Sq E Ste 1200, Philadelphia, PA 19107
Tel.: (215) 561-5500
Web Site: http://www.focuspointeglobal.com
Marketing Research Service
N.A.I.C.S.: 541910
Noel Sitzmann (Chm)
Laura Livers (CEO)
Ileen Branderbit (Exec VP-Sls)
Shawn Y. Marcellus (Sr VP-Recruiting Ops)
Kim Reale (Sr VP-Ops)
Charlotte Daley (VP-Brand Comm)
Kay Savio (VP-Client Dev & Clinical Res)

SCHLOSSMANN INVESTMENT CORP.
3450 S 108th St, Milwaukee, WI 53221
Tel.: (414) 328-3500
Web Site: http://www.schlossmannauto.com
Sales Range: $10-24.9 Million
Emp.: 50
Holding Company
N.A.I.C.S.: 551112
Michael Schlossmann (Pres)

Subsidiaries:
Schlossmann Dodge City of Milwaukee (1)
19100 W Capitol Dr, Brookfield, WI 53045
Tel.: (262) 923-8535
Web Site: http://www.1dodgecity.com
Emp.: 20
Car Dealership
N.A.I.C.S.: 441110

Mike Chesnut (Gen Mgr)

Schlossmann Imports Inc. (1)
3450 S 108th St, Milwaukee, WI 53227
Tel.: (414) 328-3500
Web Site: http://www.schlossmannimports.com
Automobiles
N.A.I.C.S.: 441110
Bradley Schlossmann (Pres)
Scott Kinkade (Controller)

Schlossmann's Dodge City Chrysler Jeep, Inc. (1)
19100 W Capitol Dr, Brookfield, WI 53045
Tel.: (262) 790-9000
Web Site: http://www.milwaukeedodgecity.com
Automobile Dealership
N.A.I.C.S.: 441110
Mike Chesnut (Gen Mgr)
Don Monte (Sls Mgr)
Tom Wendland (Sls Mgr)
Brian Hetrick (Sls Mgr)
Andrew Hetrick (Bus Mgr)
Aleks Sesum (Coord-Bus)
Brian Otto (Mgr-Parts)

SCHLUETER CO.
112 E Centerway St, Janesville, WI 53545
Tel.: (608) 755-5444
Web Site: http://www.schlueterco.com
Rev.: $15,000,000
Emp.: 35
Dairy Machinery & Equipment
N.A.I.C.S.: 423820
Bradley W. Losching (Pres)

SCHMEECKLE BROS CONSTRUCTION CO.
17168 Frontage Rd, Fort Morgan, CO 80701
Tel.: (970) 867-6664
Web Site: http://www.schmeecklebros.com
Sales Range: $10-24.9 Million
Emp.: 30
Commercial & Office Building Construction Services
N.A.I.C.S.: 236220
Wayne E. Schmeeckle (Pres)

SCHMID CONSTRUCTION INC.
1655 E Hwy 50 Ste 300, Clermont, FL 34711
Tel.: (352) 243-3720 FL
Web Site: http://www.schmidconstruction.com
Year Founded: 2002
Sales Range: $50-74.9 Million
Emp.: 40
Single-Family House Construction
N.A.I.C.S.: 236118
George Schmid (VP)
John Schmid (Pres)
Kirk Kennedy (VP-Ops)

SCHMIDT ASSOCIATES, INC.
415 Massachusetts Ave, Indianapolis, IN 46204
Tel.: (317) 263-6226
Web Site: http://www.schmidt-arch.com
Year Founded: 1976
Architectural Designing Services
N.A.I.C.S.: 541310
Sarah Hempstead (CEO & Principal)
Tom Neff (Principal)
Ron Fisher (Principal & Dir-Ops)
Anna Marie Burrell (Principal)
Wayne Schmidt (Founder)
Kyle Miller (Engr-Civil)
Julie Kost (Mktg Mgr)

Subsidiaries:
Arrasmith, Judd, Rapp, Chovan, Inc. (1)
620 S 3rd St Ste 601, Louisville, KY 40202
Tel.: (502) 581-0042

SCHMIDT ASSOCIATES, INC.

Schmidt Associates, Inc.—(Continued)
Web Site: http://www.ajrarch.com
Rev.: $3,020,000
Emp.: 20
Architectural Services
N.A.I.C.S.: 541310
John Chovan (Sec & Treas)
John Robertson (Partner)

SCHMIDT BAKING CO., INC.
7801 Fitch Ln, Baltimore, MD 21236-3916
Tel.: (410) 668-8200   MD
Web Site:
 http://www.schmidtbaking.com
Year Founded: 1886
Sales Range: $200-249.9 Million
Emp.: 638
Commercial Bakery
N.A.I.C.S.: 311812
Steve Harris (Dir-Mktg)
Rick Koester (Dir-Fin)
Sharon Crispens (Dir-HR)
Jodi Sprenkle (Branch Mgr-Sls)

SCHMIDT BUILDERS SUPPLY INC.
721 N Kansas Ave, Topeka, KS 66608
Tel.: (785) 354-1733
Rev.: $25,380,702
Emp.: 80
Building Materials Sales
N.A.I.C.S.: 423310
John Duncan (Pres)
Tim Gaggero (Mgr)

SCHMIDT DISTRIBUTORS INC.
1708 38th W PO Box 464, Spencer, IA 51301
Tel.: (712) 580-4583   IA
Year Founded: 1936
Sales Range: $10-24.9 Million
Emp.: 60
Hardware Store Owner & Operator
N.A.I.C.S.: 444140

SCHMIDT FIRE PROTECTION COMPANY, INC.
4760 Murphy Canyon Rd, San Diego, CA 92123
Tel.: (858) 279-6122
Web Site:
 http://www.schmidtfireprotection.com
Sales Range: $10-24.9 Million
Emp.: 72
Plumbing Services
N.A.I.C.S.: 238220
John E. Durso (Pres)

SCHMIDT-GOODMAN OFFICE PRODUCTS
1920 N Broadway, Rochester, MN 55906
Tel.: (507) 282-3870
Web Site:
 http://www.schmidtgoodman.com
Sales Range: $10-24.9 Million
Emp.: 45
Office Furniture
N.A.I.C.S.: 449110
Richard G. Goodman (Pres)
Bill Klepper (VP)
Karen Harlos (Controller)

SCHMIEDING ENTERPRISES INC.
2330 N Thompson St, Springdale, AR 72764-1709
Tel.: (479) 751-4517   AR
Year Founded: 1961
Sales Range: $75-99.9 Million
Emp.: 50
Producer & Retailer of Fresh Fruits & Vegetables

N.A.I.C.S.: 424480
Robbie Zimk (Treas & Sec)

SCHMIT FORD-MERCURY CORPORATION
121 N Main St, Thiensville, WI 53092
Tel.: (262) 242-1100
Web Site:
 http://www.schmitfordmerc.dealerconnection.com
Rev.: $16,000,000
Emp.: 50
New Car Dealers
N.A.I.C.S.: 441110
Thomas Schmit (Pres)
Dave Rattray (Dir-Parts & Svcs)

SCHMITT SALES INC.
2101 St Ritas Ln, Buffalo, NY 14221
Tel.: (716) 639-1500
Web Site:
 http://www.schmittsales.com
Rev.: $20,000,000
Emp.: 65
Distr of Gasoline
N.A.I.C.S.: 424720
Peter G. Glor (Pres)
Maureen Schmitt (CEO)
Michael Marong Sr (Dir-Fin)
Larry NeGron (Dir-Commission Mktg)
Mike Marong (Dir-Fin)

SCHMITT'S AUDI VOLKSWAGEN OF BUFFALO
5255 Genesee St, Bowmansville, NY 14026
Tel.: (716) 683-3343
Web Site: http://www.schmitts.com
Sales Range: $10-24.9 Million
Emp.: 45
New & Used Car Dealer
N.A.I.C.S.: 441110
Timothy U. Schmitt (Pres)
John Schmitt (VP)

SCHMITZ READY MIX INC.
5400 N 124th St, Milwaukee, WI 53225
Tel.: (414) 831-2400
Web Site: http://www.schmitzmix.com
Rev.: $10,600,000
Emp.: 50
Distribute Ready-Mixed Concrete
N.A.I.C.S.: 327320
Alan Schmitz (Pres)
Jerry Kultgen (VP)
Hal Janke (Mgr-Sls)
Jason Libka (Mgr-Quality Control)
Todd Schulz (Mgr-Supply)

SCHMUESER & ASSOCIATES INC.
1901 Railroad Ave, Rifle, CO 81650
Tel.: (970) 625-5554
Web Site: http://www.schmueser-inc.com
Sales Range: $10-24.9 Million
Emp.: 50
Industrial Constructors, Civil Engineering, Process Piping, Electrical & Instrumentation Projects
N.A.I.C.S.: 236210
Gregory Hailey (Controller)
Cindy Norris (Mgr-HR)
Blair Belnap (Project Mgr-Electrical-Grand Junction)
Bob Grimmett (Mgr-Nevada Area-Winnemucca)
Charlie Waller (Mgr-Fabrication Shop-Grand Junction)
Dave Fisher (Mgr-New Town)
Jay Thompson (Project Mgr-Winnemucca)
Jim Williams (VP-Grand Junction)
Karen Chavez (Office Mgr-Winnemucca)

Lisa Hart (Office Mgr-New Town)
Rick Jablonsky (Mgr-Equipment)
Sharon Cottrell (Office Mgr-Henderson)
Sonny LeClair (Mgr-Estimating-Grand Junction)
Stan Moore (Mgr-Henderson)
Larry R. Schmueser II (Pres)
David Masterson Sr. (Dir-Safety-Grand Junction)

Subsidiaries:

Schmueser & Associates Inc. (1)
1115 16 Rd, Fruita, CO 81521 (100%)
Tel.: (970) 858-6784
Web Site: http://www.schmueser-inc.com
Industrial Fabrication Services
N.A.I.C.S.: 332312
Jim Williams (VP)

Schmueser & Associates Inc. (1)
715 Fairgrounds Rd, Winnemucca, NV 89445 (100%)
Tel.: (775) 623-2442
Web Site: http://www.schmueser-inc.com
Industrial Constructors
N.A.I.C.S.: 236210
Bob Grimmett (Reg Mgr)

SCHNABEL ENGINEERING, INC.
9800 JEB Stuart Pkwy Ste 200, Glen Allen, VA 23059
Tel.: (804) 264-3222
Web Site: http://www.schnabel-eng.com
Emp.: 300
Engineeering Services
N.A.I.C.S.: 541330
Jim Schnabel (Founder)
Walter J. Rabe (Pres & CEO)
Dorothy Verdon (Mgr-Corp Comm)
Jeffrey Sewell (Principal)
Michael S. Quinn (Sr VP-Clifton Park)
Glen Frank (Sr VP-Seattle)
Stephen Benson (Principal & Sr Engr-Civil)

Subsidiaries:

Deere & Ault Consultants Inc. (1)
600 S Airport Rd # 205, Longmont, CO 80503
Tel.: (303) 651-1468
Web Site: http://www.deereault.com
Rev.: $1,738,000
Emp.: 45
Engineeering Services
N.A.I.C.S.: 541330
Daniel V. Ault (Pres)
Branden Effland (Engr-Water Resources)
David Swenson (Engr-Water Resources)
Christoph Goss (Principal)
Colby J. Hayden (VP)
Glen G. Church (Principal)
Mark A. McLean (VP)
Mark A. Severin (Principal)
Michael J. Ballantine (Principal)
Ray Eldridge (Principal)
Roy H. Spitzer (Principal)

SCHNABEL FOUNDATION COMPANY
45240 Business Ct Ste 250, Sterling, VA 20166
Tel.: (703) 742-0020
Web Site: http://www.schnabel.com
Rev.: $18,300,000
Emp.: 500
Shoring & Underpinning Work
N.A.I.C.S.: 238990
Kevin Cargill (Pres & CEO)
David Harris (CFO & VP)

SCHNEIDER ASSOCIATES
2 Oliver St Ste 901, Boston, MA 02109
Tel.: (617) 536-3300
Web Site:
 http://www.schneiderpr.com
Year Founded: 1980

Sales Range: $1-9.9 Million
Emp.: 23
Public Relations Agency
N.A.I.C.S.: 541820
Joan Schneider (Founder & CEO)
Phil Pennellatore (Pres)
Tom Ryan (VP-Brand Integration)
Ashley DePaolo (VP)
Don Martelli (VP & Dir-Digital Integration)
Danielle Gerard (Sr Acct Exec)
Mariela McAuley (Acct Coord)
Harrison Calato (Acct Coord)

SCHNEIDER DOWNS & CO., INC.
1 PPG Pl Ste 1700, Pittsburgh, PA 15222
Tel.: (412) 261-3644
Web Site:
 http://www.schneiderdowns.com
Year Founded: 1956
Sales Range: $25-49.9 Million
Emp.: 250
Accounting Services
N.A.I.C.S.: 541211
Rosemary Mazzeo (Mgr-Risk Advisory Svcs)
James A. Sayre (Sr Mgr-Tax Advisory Svcs)
Christopher Pascuzzi (CFO)

Subsidiaries:

Schneider Downs & Co. (1)
41 S High St Ste 2100, Columbus, OH 43215-6102
Tel.: (614) 621-4060
Web Site: http://www.sdcpa.com
Sales Range: $10-24.9 Million
Emp.: 75
Paper Production
N.A.I.C.S.: 322120
Cynthia J. Hoffman (Dir-Intl Tax Practice)
Tony Ielase (Dir-Risk Advisory Svcs)
Sarah Hoagland (Mgr-Tax Advisory Svcs)

SCHNEIDER ELECTRIC'S AGENCY
132 Fairgrounds Rd, West Kingston, RI 02892-1511
Tel.: (800) 890-4272
Web Site: http://www.apc.com
Year Founded: 1981
Sales Range: $1-9.9 Million
Emp.: 9
Brand Marketing & Promotional Events
N.A.I.C.S.: 541810
Cheryl Rapp (Sr VP-Media & Events Worldwide)
Arthur Silva (Dir-Creative & Art)
Jennifer Wendt (Dir-Media Svcs)
Laurent Vernery (Pres & CEO)
Aaron Davis (CMO & VP-Mktg)
Martin Hanna (Dir-Pub Rel)
Kristen Sisson (Global Dir-Media Svcs)

SCHNEIDER HOMES INC.
6510 S Ctr Blvd Site #1, Tukwila, WA 98188
Tel.: (206) 248-2471
Web Site:
 http://www.schneiderhomes.com
Rev.: $37,126,781
Emp.: 20
Multi-Family Dwelling Construction
N.A.I.C.S.: 236116
Joanne Coleman (Asst VP)
Ken Peckham (Dir-Project Dev)

SCHNEIDER MILLS, INC.
1430 Broadway, New York, NY 10018-3308
Tel.: (212) 768-7500   NC
Web Site:
 http://www.schneidermills.com
Year Founded: 1920
Sales Range: $100-124.9 Million

Emp.: 200
Textile Mfr
N.A.I.C.S.: 313210
Albert Schneider *(Pres)*
Mark Mincieli *(Dir-R&D)*
Will Meehan *(VP-Sls)*

Subsidiaries:

Composite Fabrics of America LLC (1)
105 Pierpoint Ln, Taylorsville, NC 28681
Tel.: (828) 632-5220
Web Site: http://www.cfamills.com
Emp.: 16
Carbon Fiber Weaving Services
N.A.I.C.S.: 313310
Matthew Mctherson *(Pres)*

SCHNEIDER'S DAIRY HOLDINGS

726 Frank St, Pittsburgh, PA 15227
Tel.: (412) 881-3525
Web Site:
http://www.schneidersdairy.com
Sales Range: $75-99.9 Million
Emp.: 150
Milk & Dairy Products Processor & Distr
N.A.I.C.S.: 311511
William Schneider Sr. *(Pres)*

Subsidiaries:

Schneider's Dairy, Inc. (1)
726 Frank St, Pittsburgh, PA 15227-1210
Tel.: (412) 881-3525
Web Site: http://www.schneidersdairy.com
Sales Range: $25-49.9 Million
Dairy Processing
N.A.I.C.S.: 311511
William D. Schneider *(Pres & VP-Ops)*

Subsidiary (Domestic):

Schneider Valley Farms Dairy (2)
1860 E 3rd St, Williamsport, PA 17701-3923 **(100%)**
Tel.: (570) 326-2021
Web Site: http://www.schneidersdairy.com
Sales Range: $25-49.9 Million
Emp.: 100
Processor & Distributor of Milk & Ice Cream Products
N.A.I.C.S.: 424430
Bob Mertz *(Gen Mgr)*

SCHNEIDERMAN'S FURNITURE, INC.

7727 Central Ave, Meadowlands, MN 55765
Tel.: (218) 427-2123 MN
Web Site:
http://www.schneidermans.com
Year Founded: 1948
Sales Range: $25-49.9 Million
Emp.: 205
Furniture Stores Owner & Operator
N.A.I.C.S.: 449110
June Morse *(Mgr-Customer Care)*

SCHNITZER WEST, LLC.

818 Stewart St Ste 700, Seattle, WA 98101
Tel.: (206) 626-3700
Web Site:
http://www.schnitzerwest.com
Sales Range: $10-24.9 Million
Emp.: 45
Commercial Real Estate Investor, Developer & Manager
N.A.I.C.S.: 525990
Dan Ivanoff *(Founder)*
Barbara Cowan *(Controller)*
Clay Blair *(Engr-Building)*
Jo Ann Williams *(Dir-Asset Ops)*
Spencer Mayes *(Mgr-Investment)*
Carolyn Stewart *(Mgr-Investment)*
Pamela Hirsch *(Mng Partner-Investment & Dev)*
Ann Klein *(Mng Partner)*

SCHOENECKERS INC.

7630 Bush Lk Rd, Minneapolis, MN 55439-2805
Tel.: (952) 835-4800 MN
Web Site:
http://www.biworldwide.com
Year Founded: 1950
Performance Improvement Company
N.A.I.C.S.: 541612
Laura Elm *(Project Mgr)*
Mark Hirschfeld *(VP)*

Subsidiaries:

Bunchball, Inc. (1)
130 East 3rd St Ste 202, Des Moines, IA 50309
Tel.: (952) 563-2999
Web Site: http://www.bunchball.com
Online Gaming Software
N.A.I.C.S.: 513210

SCHOENEMAN BROTHERS COMPANY

1801 W 50th St, Sioux Falls, SD 57105-6362
Tel.: (605) 336-2440 IA
Year Founded: 1888
Sales Range: $50-74.9 Million
Emp.: 60
Retailer of Lumber, Hardware & Building Materials
N.A.I.C.S.: 444110
Alvin C. Schoeneman *(Pres & Treas)*

SCHOEPP MOTORS INC.

3440 Tribeca Dr, Middleton, WI 53562
Tel.: (608) 831-5200
Web Site:
http://www.schoeppmotors.com
Sales Range: $10-24.9 Million
Emp.: 45
Used Car Sales & Automotive Services
N.A.I.C.S.: 441120
David Schoepp *(Pres)*
Jim Aubart *(Controller)*
Patrick Rogalla *(Mgr-Sls)*
Mark Heisig *(Mgr-Svc)*

SCHOETTLER TIRE INC.

504 NE St, Madera, CA 93638
Tel.: (559) 674-4471
Rev.: $34,000,000
Emp.: 85
Automotive Tires
N.A.I.C.S.: 441340
Thomas Schoettler *(Pres)*

SCHOFIELD MEDIA LTD.

303 E Wacker Dr 23rd Fl, Chicago, IL 60601
Tel.: (312) 236-4090
Year Founded: 2000
Sales Range: $10-24.9 Million
Emp.: 50
Publisher of Trade Publications
N.A.I.C.S.: 513120
John Krukowski *(Dir-Editorial)*
Andrew Schofield *(Founder, Chm & CEO)*

Subsidiaries:

Ideal Media LLC (1)
200 East Randolph 70th Fl, Chicago, IL 60601
Tel.: (312) 456-2822
Web Site: http://www.idealmediallc.com
Publisher of Trade Magazines
N.A.I.C.S.: 513120

Unit (Domestic):

Restaurant Business (2)
90 Broad St Ste 1506, New York, NY 10004-2291
Tel.: (646) 708-7300
Sales Range: $10-24.9 Million
Emp.: 15
Restaurant Industry Trade Magazine Publisher
N.A.I.C.S.: 513120

SCHOLAR CRAFT PRODUCTS, INC.

1 Scholar Pkwy, Birmingham, AL 35217
Tel.: (205) 841-1922 AL
Web Site:
http://www.scholarcraft.com
Year Founded: 1956
School Furniture Mfr
N.A.I.C.S.: 337127
Clint Hobbs *(Pres)*
Will Marshall *(Dir-Sls-Eastern Region)*
Bob Teigeler *(Dir-Sls-North Region)*
DeAnna Squires *(Dir-Sls-Western Region)*
Brad Snoke *(Dir-Mktg)*

SCHOLARBUYS LLC

11 W Main St Ste 202, Carpentersville, IL 60110
Web Site:
http://www.scholarbuys.com
Year Founded: 2007
Sales Range: $1-9.9 Million
Emp.: 10
Computer Peripherals for the Academic Market
N.A.I.C.S.: 423430
Bob Smith *(Co-Founder)*
Matt Ryan *(Co-Founder)*

SCHOLFIELD BROS. INC.

1333 N Greenwich Rd, Wichita, KS 67206
Tel.: (316) 648-0403
Web Site:
http://www.scholfieldbros.com
Sales Range: $50-74.9 Million
Emp.: 350
Automobiles, New & Used
N.A.I.C.S.: 441110
Steven A. Hatchett *(Pres)*

Subsidiaries:

Scholfield Lexus LLC (1)
1555 N Greenwich Rd, Wichita, KS 67207
Tel.: (316) 688-1919
Web Site: http://www.scholfieldlexus.com
Sales Range: $25-49.9 Million
Emp.: 20
Automobiles, New & Used
N.A.I.C.S.: 441110
Morgan Borrego *(Coord-Client Care Svc)*
Dan Keairns *(Mgr-Svc)*
Vy Nguyen *(Mgr-Internet Bus)*
Angelina Ortega *(Coord-Client Care Svc)*
Brittani Rohr *(Coord-Client Care Svc)*
Javier Torres *(Mgr-Lexus Parts)*
Kathy Tye *(Mgr-Bus)*
Dan Watkins *(Mgr-Client Care)*

SCHOLL FOREST INDUSTRIES INC.

6202 N Houston Rosslyn Rd, Houston, TX 77091
Tel.: (713) 329-5300 TX
Web Site:
http://www.scholllumber.com
Year Founded: 1972
Sales Range: $10-24.9 Million
Emp.: 25
Custom Builder, Lumber & Panel Composite Products
N.A.I.C.S.: 423310
Ward Scholl *(Pres & Mgr)*

SCHOLLE CORPORATION

19520 Jamboree Rd Ste 250, Irvine, CA 92612
Tel.: (949) 955-1750 NV
Web Site: http://www.scholle.com
Year Founded: 1947
Sales Range: $150-199.9 Million
Emp.: 2,000
Holding Company; Specialty Chemicals, Flexible Packaging, Metallized Plastic Films & Papers Mfr
N.A.I.C.S.: 551112
Leon P. Gianneschi *(Pres & CEO)*
William J. Scholle *(Chm)*
Chad Mueller *(CTO-Pkg Div)*
Edward Wondergem *(CFO)*

Subsidiaries:

Scholle Canada, Ltd. (1)
22000 Clark Graham, Baie-d'Urfe, H9X 4B6, QC, Canada
Tel.: (514) 457-1569
Packaging Services
N.A.I.C.S.: 561910
Ian Cadorette *(Mgr-Equipment Reliability)*

Scholle Europe France SAS (1)
Zone Industrielle, 57370, Schalbach, France
Tel.: (33) 3 87 25 73 75
Packaging Services
N.A.I.C.S.: 561910
Christophe Silas *(Gen Mgr & Mgr-FSF)*

Scholle Europe GmbH (1)
Opelstrasse 1, 68789, Sankt Leon-Rot, Germany
Tel.: (49) 6227 877 431
Web Site: http://www.scholleipn.com
Emp.: 2
Packaging Services
N.A.I.C.S.: 561910
Simon Waller *(Mng Dir)*

Scholle Europe, B.V. (1)
Minervum 7081 Industrial Area Hoogeind, 4817 ZK, Breda, Netherlands
Tel.: (31) 76 5444 500
Packaging Services
N.A.I.C.S.: 561910
Roel Seegers *(Mgr-Comml)*
Anton Oppenhuizen *(Dir-Fin)*
Gijs Geerlings *(Mgr-Bus Dev)*
Jos Fens *(Mgr-Technical Comml)*

Scholle Europe, Ltd. (1)
Unit 12A Follingsby Close Follingsby Park Wardley, Gateshead, NE10 8YG, Tyne and Wear, United Kingdom
Tel.: (44) 191 4193900
Web Site: http://www.scholle.com
Packaging Services
N.A.I.C.S.: 561910
Peter Dixon *(Plant Mgr)*

Scholle Industries, Pty, Ltd. (1)
32 Hewittson Rd, Edinburgh North, 5113, SA, Australia
Tel.: (61) 8 8255 4366
Packaging Services
N.A.I.C.S.: 561910
Erik Bosch *(Mgr-Sls)*

Scholle Packaging, Inc. (1)
200 W North Ave, Northlake, IL 60164
Tel.: (708) 562-7290
Web Site: http://www.scholle.com
Sales Range: $25-49.9 Million
Emp.: 600
Flexible Packaging Products Mfr
N.A.I.C.S.: 322220
Leon P. Gianneschi *(Pres & CEO)*
Stephen Lopiano *(Dir-Automotive Chemicals & Fluids Market Segment)*
Curt Linson *(Dir-Beverages Market Segment)*
Rick Pindur *(Dir-Equipment Engrg-Global)*

Scholle Packaging, LTDA. (1)
Av Fernando Piccinini 700 Distrito Industrial Vinhedo, Sao Paulo, 13280-000, Brazil
Tel.: (55) 19 3826 8800
Web Site: http://www.scholle.com
Emp.: 150
Packaging Services
N.A.I.C.S.: 561910
Marcelo Ribeiro *(Sr Mgr-Org Dev)*

SCHOLTEN'S EQUIPMENT INC.

8223 Guide Meridian Rd, Lynden, WA 98264
Tel.: (360) 354-4071
Web Site:
http://www.scholtensequipment.com

SCHOLTEN'S EQUIPMENT INC.

Scholten's Equipment Inc.—(Continued)
Sales Range: $10-24.9 Million
Emp.: 35
Agricultural Machinery & Equipment Sales & Service
N.A.I.C.S.: 423820
Duane Scholten *(Owner)*
Bonnie Debruin *(Office Mgr)*
Rod Hoefakker *(Mgr-Svc & Rental)*
Brent Postma *(Mgr-Parts & IT)*
Todd Wiens *(Mgr-Store)*

SCHOLZEN PRODUCTS COMPANY INC.
548 W 100 N, Hurricane, UT 84737
Tel.: (435) 635-4441
Web Site: http://www.scholzenproducts.com
Sales Range: $25-49.9 Million
Emp.: 84
Plumbing & Hydronic Heating Supplies
N.A.I.C.S.: 423720
Bruce Ballard *(Pres)*
Suzy Stanworth *(Mgr-Credit & Acctg Dept)*
Jeff Turek *(Mgr-St George)*
Keith Scholzen *(VP)*
Kelly Ashcroft *(Treas & Sec)*

SCHOMAC GROUP INC.
6418 E Tanque Verde Rd Ste 105, Tucson, AZ 85715
Tel.: (520) 577-9898
Web Site: http://www.schomacgroup.com
Sales Range: $10-24.9 Million
Emp.: 5
Subdividers & Developers
N.A.I.C.S.: 237210

SCHONFELD GROUP HOLDINGS, LLC
1 Jericho Plz, Jericho, NY 11753
Tel.: (516) 822-0202
Web Site: http://www.schonfeld.com
Year Founded: 1988
Sales Range: $25-49.9 Million
Emp.: 100
Holding Company
N.A.I.C.S.: 551112
Steven Schonfeld *(Founder & CEO)*
Andrew Fishman *(Pres)*
Mark Peckman *(Gen Counsel & Exec VP)*

Subsidiaries:

Schonfeld Securities, LLC (1)
1 Jericho Plz, Jericho, NY 11753-1680
Tel.: (516) 822-0202
Web Site: http://www.schonfeld.com
Sales Range: $800-899.9 Million
Emp.: 1,000
Security Brokers & Dealers
N.A.I.C.S.: 523150

SCHOOL APPAREL, INC.
838 Mitten Rd, Burlingame, CA 94010-1304
Tel.: (650) 827-7400 CA
Web Site: http://www.schoolapparel.com
Year Founded: 1974
Sales Range: $200-249.9 Million
Emp.: 457
Mfr of School Uniforms
N.A.I.C.S.: 315250
Jeff Cutlip *(VP-Mfg)*

SCHOOL BOX INC.
1257 Kennestone Cir, Marietta, GA 30066
Tel.: (770) 919-2232
Web Site: http://www.schoolbox.com
Rev.: $16,000,000
Emp.: 50
Education Aids, Devices & Supplies
N.A.I.C.S.: 459999
David A. Persson *(Pres)*

SCHOOL BUS SALES COMPANY
4537 Texas St, Waterloo, IA 50702
Tel.: (319) 296-1363
Web Site: http://www.sbsales.com
Rev.: $12,700,000
Emp.: 50
New & Used Automobile Whslr
N.A.I.C.S.: 423110
Charles Andrews *(Owner)*

SCHOOL HEALTH CORPORATION
865 Muirfield Dr, Hanover Park, IL 60133
Tel.: (630) 582-0024
Web Site: http://www.schoolhealth.com
Rev.: $13,800,000
Emp.: 100
Distribute Medical Equipment & Supplies
N.A.I.C.S.: 423450
Susan Rogers *(Pres)*
Rob Rogers *(VP)*
Gina Streepy *(Acct Mgr-Natl)*
Tom Wisniewski *(Mgr-Mktg)*

SCHOOL NUTRITION ASSOCIATION
120 Waterfront St Ste 300, Baltimore, MD 20745
Tel.: (301) 686-3100 VA
Web Site: http://www.schoolnutrition.org
Year Founded: 1946
Sales Range: $10-24.9 Million
Emp.: 55
School Nutrition Program Operator
N.A.I.C.S.: 611710
Marcelo Esquivel *(Dir-IT)*
Catherine Schuchart *(Sr VP-Child Nutrition & Policy)*
Jennifer Lewi *(Sr VP-Mktg)*

SCHOOL TECH SUPPLY
130a West Cochran St, Simi Valley, CA 93065
Tel.: (805) 499-2580
Web Site: http://www.stseducation-us.com
Year Founded: 2001
Sales Range: $1-9.9 Million
Emp.: 15
Technology Fund Raising Services for School Districts
N.A.I.C.S.: 611710
Marc Netka *(Pres)*
Dennis Fortner *(Mgr-Warehouse)*

SCHOOL YEAR ABROAD INC.
120 Water St Ste 310, North Andover, MA 01845
Tel.: (978) 725-6828 MA
Web Site: http://www.sya.org
Year Founded: 1965
Sales Range: $10-24.9 Million
Emp.: 47
Educational Support Services
N.A.I.C.S.: 611710
Jen Soderburg *(Mgr-Dev Sys)*
Susan McLean *(Dir-Alumni Rels & Assoc Dir-Advancement)*
Pam Eaton *(Sr Mgr-Admissions Ops)*
Aimeclaire Lambert Roche *(Vice Chm)*
Eileen Kelly-Aguirre *(Dir-Interim Resident-SYA Spain)*
Rachel Keegan Kelley *(Dir-Enrollment Mgmt & Mktg)*

Kenneth Krushel *(Chm)*
Erin Stone Ericson *(Dir-Annual Giving & Assoc Dir-Advancement)*

SCHOOL-TECH, INC.
745 State Cir, Ann Arbor, MI 48108
Tel.: (734) 761-5173 MI
Web Site: http://www.school-tech.com
Year Founded: 1954
Sales Range: $75-99.9 Million
Emp.: 60
Institutional Athletic Equipment Mfr & Distr
N.A.I.C.S.: 423910
Steve Canham *(VP)*
Don Canham Jr. *(CEO)*

Subsidiaries:

Schoolmasters (1)
745 State Cir, Ann Arbor, MI 48108-1647
Tel.: (734) 761-5173
Web Site: http://www.schoolmasters.com
Sales Range: $25-49.9 Million
Emp.: 15
Sales Of Institutional & Athletic Equipment
N.A.I.C.S.: 423910
Don Canham *(CEO)*

Wolverine Sports (1)
745 State Cir, Ann Arbor, MI 48108-1647
Tel.: (734) 761-5173
Web Site: http://www.wolverinesports.com
Sales Range: $25-49.9 Million
Emp.: 50
Sales of Institutional & Athletic Equipment
N.A.I.C.S.: 423910

SCHOOL-TO-SCHOOL INTERNATIONAL
1005 Terra Nova Blvd Ste 1, Pacifica, CA 94044
Tel.: (650) 355-6248 CA
Web Site: http://www.sts-international.org
Year Founded: 2002
Sales Range: $1-9.9 Million
Emp.: 14
Child Education & Development Services
N.A.I.C.S.: 624110
Mark Lynd *(Co-Founder & Pres)*
Candace Debnam *(Dir-Bus Dev & Organizational Strategy)*
Thomas L. Libby *(Chm)*
Jean Libby *(Vice Chm)*
Rick Annis *(Treas)*
Laura Stahl *(Sec)*

SCHOOLDUDE.COM
11000 Regency Pkwy Ste 200, Cary, NC 27518
Tel.: (919) 816-8237
Web Site: http://www.schooldude.com
Year Founded: 2000
Sales Range: $1-9.9 Million
Emp.: 200
Online Education Software Sevices
N.A.I.C.S.: 513210
Kent Hudson *(Co-Founder & CEO)*
Lee Prevost *(Co-Founder & Pres)*

SCHOOLEY MITCHELL TELECOM CONSULTANTS
15.30 Sycamore Ridge Dr, Maineville, OH 45039
Tel.: (513) 683-8881
Web Site: http://www.schooleymitchell.com
Year Founded: 1993
Sales Range: $1-9.9 Million
Emp.: 20
Telecom Consulting Services
N.A.I.C.S.: 541618
Sean Fox *(VP & Owner-Franchise)*

U.S. PRIVATE

SCHOOLS FINANCIAL CREDIT UNION
1485 Response Rd Ste 126, Sacramento, CA 95815
Tel.: (916) 569-5400 CA
Web Site: http://www.schools.org
Year Founded: 1933
Sales Range: $50-74.9 Million
Emp.: 333
Credit Union
N.A.I.C.S.: 522130
Marie B. Smith *(Co-Chm)*
Todd DeVoogd *(CFO & VP-Fin)*
Cathy Grimes *(VP-Mktg)*
Eugene J. Houghton Jr. *(Chm)*

SCHOON CONSTRUCTION INC.
1500 S 2nd St, Cherokee, IA 51012
Tel.: (712) 225-5736 IA
Web Site: http://www.schoonconstruction.com
Year Founded: 1970
Sales Range: $10-24.9 Million
Emp.: 50
Water, Sewer & Utility Line Construction
N.A.I.C.S.: 237110
LeRoy Schoon *(Pres)*
Brenda Perrin *(VP)*
Latonna Dodd *(Treas & Sec)*
Jamie Roof *(Controller)*

SCHOONER BAY REALTY INC.
1210 Del Prado Blvd S, Cape Coral, FL 33990
Tel.: (239) 997-4000
Web Site: http://www.sbrealtyinc.com
Year Founded: 1975
Emp.: 25
Real Estate Services
N.A.I.C.S.: 531390
Yeatter Yeatter *(Pres)*

SCHOTT BROTHERS, INC.
735 Rahway Ave, Union, NJ 07083
Tel.: (908) 527-0011 NY
Web Site: http://www.schottnyc.com
Year Founded: 1913
Sales Range: $100-124.9 Million
Emp.: 200
Mfr of Men's & Boys' Leather & Cloth Outerwear & Sheepskin-Lined Clothing
N.A.I.C.S.: 315250

SCHOTT DISTRIBUTING CO. INC.
6735 Hwy 14 E, Rochester, MN 55904
Tel.: (507) 289-3555
Sales Range: $10-24.9 Million
Emp.: 45
Beer Distr
N.A.I.C.S.: 424810
Bernie Schott *(Pres)*

SCHOTTENSTEIN PROPERTY GROUP, INC.
4300 E 5th Ave, Columbus, OH 43219
Tel.: (614) 445-8461 MD
Web Site: http://www.spgroup.com
Year Founded: 2010
Emp.: 65
Real Estate Investment Services
N.A.I.C.S.: 525990

SCHOTTENSTEIN STORES CORPORATION
4300 E 5th Ave, Columbus, OH 43219
Tel.: (614) 221-9200 DE
Year Founded: 1917
Sales Range: $650-699.9 Million

Emp.: 5,300
Holding Company
N.A.I.C.S.: 551112
Joseph A. Schottenstein *(Exec VP)*
Jeffrey M. Schottenstein *(VP)*
Irwin A. Bain *(Gen Counsel & VP)*
Cheryl Dennison *(Mgr-Quality Control & Field Svc)*
Ellen Evans *(Mgr-Store Plng)*
Judy Howell *(Project Mgr)*
Karen Hollins *(Supvr-Claims)*
Jay L. Schottenstein *(Chm, Pres & CEO)*
Ben Kraner *(Sr VP & Asst Sec)*

Subsidiaries:

Designer Brands, Inc. (1)
810 DSW Dr, Columbus, OH 43219
Tel.: (614) 237-7100 (93.1%)
Web Site: https://www.designerbrands.com
Rev.: $3,315,428,000
Assets: $2,009,618,000
Liabilities: $1,576,717,000
Net Worth: $432,901,000
Earnings: $162,676,000
Emp.: 14,000
Fiscal Year-end: 01/28/2023
Shoe Retail Store Owner & Operator
N.A.I.C.S.: 458210
Jay L. Schottenstein *(Chm)*
Mark A. Haley *(Sr VP & Controller)*
Doug M. Howe *(CEO)*
Laura Denk *(Pres-DSW Designer Shoe Warehouse & Exec VP)*

Subsidiary (Domestic):

DSW Shoe Warehouse, Inc. (2)
3710 Easton Market, Columbus, OH 43219-6024
Tel.: (614) 428-9030
Footwear Retailer
N.A.I.C.S.: 424340
Roger L. Rawlins *(Interim Pres)*

Subsidiary (Domestic):

Camuto LLC (3)
810 DSW Dr, Columbus, OH 43219
Tel.: (614) 237-7100
Web Site: http://www.vincecamuto.com
Holding Company; Women's Shoes & Accessories Designer, Mfr, Whslr & Online Retailer
N.A.I.C.S.: 551112

Subsidiary (Domestic):

Vincent Camuto LLC (4)
411 W Putnam Ave Ste 210, Greenwich, CT 06830
Tel.: (203) 413-7100
Web Site: http://www.vincecamuto.com
Women's Fashion Footwear Designer, Marketer & Distr
N.A.I.C.S.: 541490
Vincent Camuto *(Founder & CEO)*

Subsidiary (Domestic):

eBuys, Inc. (3)
5501 Centrepointe Dr, La Vergne, TN 37086
Tel.: (888) 272-4460
Web Site: http://www.shoemetro.com
Online Shoes & Handbags Retailer
N.A.I.C.S.: 458210
David Duong *(Founder & CEO)*

Subsidiary (Domestic):

Retail Ventures Services, Inc. (2)
4150 E 5th Ave, Columbus, OH 43219 (100%)
Tel.: (614) 238-4135
Web Site: http://www.rvi.com
Emp.: 5
Business Services
N.A.I.C.S.: 561499
Jim McGrady *(CEO)*

Kroehler Furniture Manufacturing Company, Inc. (1)
1800 Conover Blvd, Conover, NC 28613
Tel.: (828) 459-9865
Web Site: http://www.vcf.com

Sales Range: $50-74.9 Million
Emp.: 240
Mfr of Upholstered Living Room & Den Furniture, Contemporary, Traditional & Early American Sleepers & Occasional Chairs
N.A.I.C.S.: 337121
Lorraine Henicheck *(Mgr-HR)*

SCHOTTENSTEIN/BERNSTEIN CAPITAL

4300 E 5th Ave, Columbus, OH 43219-1816
Tel.: (614) 443-4080
Web Site: http://www.sbcapitalgroup.com
Sales Range: $100-124.9 Million
Emp.: 25
Merchandise Liquidators
N.A.I.C.S.: 561990
Jay L. Schottenstein *(Chm)*
Jack W. Duffy *(Controller)*
Scott Bernstein *(COO & Principal)*
Morten Kucey *(Mng Dir)*
David Bernstein *(Pres)*

SCHOUEST, BAMDAS, SOSHEA & BENMAIER, PLLC

1001 McKinney St Ste 1400, Houston, TX 77002
Tel.: (713) 588-0446 TX
Web Site: http://www.sbsblaw.com
Emp.: 80
Law firm
N.A.I.C.S.: 541110
Robert Bamdas *(Co-Founder & Partner)*
Limor BenMaier *(Co-Founder & Partner)*
John Schouest *(Co-Founder & Mng Partner)*
Brad Soshea *(Co-Founder & Partner)*

Subsidiaries:

Eastham, Watson, Dale & Forney, LLP (1)
The Niels Esperson Bldg 808 Travis Ste 1300, Houston, TX 77002-5769
Tel.: (713) 225-0905
Web Site: http://www.easthamlaw.com
Emp.: 10
Law firm
N.A.I.C.S.: 541110
Scott C. Hall *(Atty)*
Robert L. Klawetter *(Atty)*
William A. Durham *(Atty)*
Christina K. Schovajsa *(Atty)*
James T. Bailey *(Atty)*
Zachary R. Cain *(Atty)*
Ryan L. Marlatt *(Atty)*
Alejandro Mendez-Roman *(Atty)*
Thomas M. Stanley *(Atty)*

SCHOX, PLC

500 3rd St, San Francisco, CA 94107
Tel.: (888) 775-9990
Web Site: http://www.schox.com
Year Founded: 2003
Sales Range: $1-9.9 Million
Emp.: 6
Developer of Patent Portfolios for Startup Ventures
N.A.I.C.S.: 541110
Jeff Schox *(Founder & Attorney)*
Diana Lin *(VP-Patents)*

SCHRAMM, INC.

800 E Virginia Ave, West Chester, PA 19380
Tel.: (610) 696-2500
Web Site: http://www.schramminc.com
Year Founded: 1900
Sales Range: $10-24.9 Million
Emp.: 250
Hydraulic Drill Mfr
N.A.I.C.S.: 333248
Fred Slack *(VP-Bus Dev)*
John Little *(Mgr-Aftermarket-Ops)*

Greg Hillier *(Product Mgr)*
Eric Mosley *(Dir-Aftermarket)*
Jared Zabransky *(Dir-Sls-Oil & Gas)*

SCHREIBER & ROMAN, INC.

106 N Market St, Elizabethtown, PA 17022
Tel.: (717) 361-6300 PA
Year Founded: 1981
Rev.: $500,000
Emp.: 4
Fiscal Year-end: 05/31/04
Advertising Agencies, Collateral, Entertainment, Food Service, Graphic Design, Newspaper, Pharmaceutical, Point of Purchase, Production, Restaurant, Retail
N.A.I.C.S.: 541810

SCHREIBER FOODS, INC.

400 N Washington St, Green Bay, WI 54301-5137
Tel.: (920) 437-7601 WI
Web Site:
https://www.schreiberfoods.com
Year Founded: 1945
Sales Range: $1-4.9 Billion
Emp.: 10,000
Cheese Manufacturing
N.A.I.C.S.: 311513
Tom Andreoli *(CIO & Sr VP-Information Svcs)*
Chad Wiegand *(Gen Counsel, Sec & Sr VP)*
Francois Salamon *(Pres-Intl)*
Matt Mueller *(CFO & Sr VP-Fin)*
Tim Walls *(Exec VP)*
Vinith Poduval *(Sr VP-Enterprise Quality & Food Safety)*
Ron Dunford *(CEO)*

Subsidiaries:

Schreiber Foods, Inc. - Fullerton (1)
1901 Via Burton St, Fullerton, CA 92831-5341
Tel.: (714) 490-7360
Web Site: http://www.schreiberfoods.com
Sales Range: $50-74.9 Million
Emp.: 100
Dairy Products Mfr
N.A.I.C.S.: 311511

Schreiber Foods, Inc. - Shippensburg (1)
208 Dykeman Rd, Shippensburg, PA 17257
Tel.: (717) 530-5000
Web Site: http://www.schreiberfoods.com
Emp.: 1
Cream Cheese Mfr
N.A.I.C.S.: 311513
Dave Pilgert *(Plant Mgr)*

Schreiber Foods, Inc. - West Bend (1)
807 Pleasant Vly Rd, West Bend, WI 53095-9767
Tel.: (262) 675-6533
Web Site: http://www.schreiberfoods.com
Sales Range: $25-49.9 Million
Emp.: 150
Butter, Cream Cheese & Sweetened Condensed Milk Products
N.A.I.C.S.: 311512

Schreiber Mexico, S.A. de C.V. (1)
Boulevard Aeropuerto KM 10 5 Planta 3, Col San Carlos de Romo, 37320, Leon, GTO, Mexico
Tel.: (52) 477 441 3333
Sales Range: $10-24.9 Million
Emp.: 50
Cheese Mfr
N.A.I.C.S.: 311513

SCHROEDER MOVING SYSTEMS

15700 W Lincoln Ave, New Berlin, WI 53151
Tel.: (262) 784-1717
Web Site:
http://www.schroedermoving.com

Sales Range: $10-24.9 Million
Emp.: 75
Household Goods Transport
N.A.I.C.S.: 238990
John Schroeder *(Pres)*

SCHROEDER PUBLISHING COMPANY

5801 Kentucky Dam Rd, Paducah, KY 42003-9323
Tel.: (270) 898-6211
Web Site:
http://www.collectorbooks.com
Year Founded: 1974
Sales Range: $75-99.9 Million
Emp.: 65
Collector Information Publisher
N.A.I.C.S.: 513130
William T. Schroeder *(Pres & CEO)*
Rick Lloyd *(VP-Adv)*
Karen Weaver *(Mgr-Member Svc)*

Subsidiaries:

American Quilter's Society (1)
5801 Kentucky Dam Rd, Paducah, KY 42003 (100%)
Tel.: (270) 898-7903
Web Site: http://www.americanquilter.com
Sales Range: $10-24.9 Million
Emp.: 30
Publr. of Quilting Titles
N.A.I.C.S.: 513130
Meredith Schroeder *(Pres)*
Rick Lloyd *(VP)*
Bonnie K. Browning *(Exec Dir-Show)*
Lynn Loyd *(Dir-Show Dev & Sls)*
Katherine Rupp *(Mng Dir)*

Schroeder Publishing Company - Collector Books (1)
PO Box 3009, Paducah, KY 42002-3009
Tel.: (270) 898-6211
Books Publishing Services
N.A.I.C.S.: 513130

SCHROEDER-MANATEE RANCH, INC.

14400 Covenant Way, Lakewood Ranch, FL 34202
Tel.: (941) 755-6574
Web Site: http://www.smrranch.com
Sales Range: $25-49.9 Million
Emp.: 300
Land Developer; Cattle Ranching & Farming; Tree Farming
N.A.I.C.S.: 237210
Tony Chiofalo *(VP-Fin)*
Rex Jensen *(Pres & CEO)*

Subsidiaries:

Sarasota Polo Club (1)
8201 Polo Club Ln, Lakewood Ranch, FL 34240
Tel.: (941) 907-0000
Web Site: http://www.sarasotapolo.com
Sales Range: $10-24.9 Million
Polo Club
N.A.I.C.S.: 711211
Rebecca Gutierrez *(Mgr-Polo Ops)*
Robin Uihlein *(Pres)*
Nick Chavez *(Mgr-Field)*
Kristen Galvan *(Mgr-Ops)*
Dave Shurmur *(Mgr-Field)*
Sherri Sweeny *(Mgr-Events & Promos)*

SCHROEDER/LEVERINGTON INC.

Ste 200 900 American Blvd E, Minneapolis, MN 55420-1393
Tel.: (952) 835-3600
Web Site: http://www.sl-inc.com
Sales Range: $25-49.9 Million
Emp.: 6
Commercial & Office Building Contractors
N.A.I.C.S.: 236220

SCHRYVER MEDICAL SALES

SCHRYVER MEDICAL SALES

SCHRYVER MEDICAL SALES —(CONTINUED)
& MARKETING, INC.
12075 E 45th Ave Ste 600, Denver, CO 80239
Tel.: (303) 371-0073
Web Site:
http://www.schryvermedical.com
Sales Range: $25-49.9 Million
Emp.: 600
Medical Equipment & Supplies
N.A.I.C.S.: 423450
Mark Schryver *(Founder & Chm)*
Jay Schryver *(Pres)*
Arno Bergstrom *(Exec VP-Sls & Mktg)*
Dave Paison *(VP-Natl Accts)*
Jennifer Holt *(VP-Compliance)*
Doug Goetz *(CEO)*
Bruce Dakin *(Pres-Ops)*
Al Armijo *(CIO)*
Todd Hubbard *(Exec VP-Bus Dev)*
Jack Bruckner *(VP-Acctg & Fin)*

Subsidiaries:

BON Clinical Laboratories (1)
2545 S Bruce St Ste C, Henderson, NV 89169-1778
Tel.: (702) 737-5050
Web Site: http://www.bonlaboratories.com
Research & Development in Biotechnology
N.A.I.C.S.: 541714
Mike Avedissian *(Pres)*

Main Street Clinical Laboratory, Inc. (1)
1287 Main St, Southaven, MS 38671-1429
Tel.: (662) 510-5432
Web Site: http://www.mainstreetlab.com
Medical Laboratories
N.A.I.C.S.: 621511
Mark Vines *(Pres)*

Quality Mobile X Ray Services, Inc. (1)
640 Grassmere Pk Ste 116, Nashville, TN 37211
Tel.: (615) 391-4515
Web Site: http://www.qualityxray.com
Diagnostic Imaging Centers
N.A.I.C.S.: 621512
John Dunlap *(Dir-Radiology)*
Joel Herring *(CEO)*

SCHUBERT COMMUNICATIONS, INC.
112 Schubert Dr, Downingtown, PA 19335-3382
Tel.: (610) 269-2100   DE
Web Site:
http://www.schubertb2b.com
Year Founded: 1978
Sales Range: $1-9.9 Million
Emp.: 10
Advertising Agencies
N.A.I.C.S.: 541810
Joseph F. Schubert *(Founder & CEO)*
Rich Carango *(Pres & Dir-Creative)*
Peggy Schubert *(Mgr-Fin)*
Chris Henneghan *(Project Mgr-Interactive)*
Christopher D. Raymond *(VP-Interactive Svcs)*
Debbie MacKenzie *(Mgr-Production)*

SCHUCHART CORPORATION
419 3rd Ave W, Seattle, WA 98119-4001
Tel.: (206) 682-3030
Web Site: http://www.schuchart.com
Year Founded: 1988
Sales Range: $10-24.9 Million
Emp.: 75
Nonresidential Construction Services
N.A.I.C.S.: 236220
George Schuchart *(Pres)*
Ashlee Barlish *(Project Mgr)*
Carla Simpson *(Controller)*
Kevin Bakken *(Superintendent)*
Christian Geismanna *(CFO)*

Kaegan Faltys-Burr *(Project Mgr)*
Dan Rutkowski *(Partner-Indus Div)*
Jeff Tobin *(Partner-Tenant Improvement Div)*
Tyler Mjelde *(Partner-Building Div)*
Casey Schuchart *(VP-Strategy)*
Travis Harth *(Mgr-Tenant Improvement)*
Jeff Reinbold *(Mgr-Major Accts)*

SCHUCK & SONS CONSTRUCTION COMPANY, INC.
8205 N 67th Ave, Glendale, AZ 85302
Tel.: (623) 931-3661   AZ
Year Founded: 1966
Sales Range: $75-99.9 Million
Emp.: 5
Lumber & Carpentry Products Sales; Structural Wood Trusses, Doors & Door Frames Mfr
N.A.I.C.S.: 423310
Craig Steele *(Pres & CEO)*
Jeff Randall *(Mgr-Ops)*
Molly Decker *(Supvr-Fleet)*
Jill Wozniek *(Mgr-Credit)*

SCHUCO USA L.L.L.P.
240 Pane Rd, Newington, CT 06111
Tel.: (860) 666-0505
Web Site: http://www.schueco.com
Doors, Windows & Fittings, Sliding Systems & Sun Shading Systems Mfr
N.A.I.C.S.: 326199
Attila Arian *(Pres)*

SCHUETTE MOVERS
PO Box 1305, Wausau, WI 54402
Tel.: (715) 355-4500
Web Site:
http://www.schuettemovers.com
Sales Range: $10-24.9 Million
Emp.: 110
Specialty Trade Contractors
N.A.I.C.S.: 238910
Sheila Schwartz *(Principal)*

SCHUETTE STORES, INC.
17919 St Rose Rd, Breese, IL 62230
Tel.: (618) 526-7203   IL
Web Site:
http://www.onlinegrocer.com
Year Founded: 1863
Sales Range: $10-24.9 Million
Emp.: 25
Grocery Stores Owner & Operator
N.A.I.C.S.: 445110
Peter Michael Schuette *(Pres)*

SCHUKEI CHEVROLET, INC.
721 S Monroe Ave, Mason City, IA 50401
Tel.: (641) 423-5402
Web Site:
http://www.schukeichevrolet.com
Year Founded: 1964
Sales Range: $10-24.9 Million
Emp.: 55
Car Whslr
N.A.I.C.S.: 441110
Steve Schukei *(Pres)*

SCHULER BOOKS & MUSIC, INC.
2660 28th St SE, Grand Rapids, MI 49512
Tel.: (616) 942-2561
Web Site:
http://www.schulerbooks.com
Rev.: $10,800,000
Emp.: 85
Book Stores
N.A.I.C.S.: 459210
William Fehsenfeld *(Owner)*
Cecile Fehsenfeld *(Owner)*

SCHULER SHOES INC.
7835 Main St N Ste 200, Maple Grove, MN 55369
Tel.: (763) 494-0011
Web Site:
http://www.schulershoes.com
Sales Range: $10-24.9 Million
Emp.: 100
Men's Shoes
N.A.I.C.S.: 458210
John Koenig *(Controller)*
Clarissa Lund *(Coord-Mktg)*
James Dament *(Gen Mgr)*
Kari Palmer *(Dir-Mktg)*

SCHULHOF COMPANY
4701 N Arvenswood, Chicago, IL 60640
Tel.: (773) 348-1123   IL
Rev.: $12,800,000
Emp.: 24
Plumbing & Hydronic Heating Supplies
N.A.I.C.S.: 423720
James T. Cavanaugh *(Pres)*
Peter Mangione *(VP)*

SCHULL CONSTRUCTION CO.
405 1st Ave NE, Watertown, SD 57201
Tel.: (605) 886-3495
Web Site:
http://www.buildingproductsin.com
Sales Range: $10-24.9 Million
Emp.: 8
Hardware
N.A.I.C.S.: 423710
Lee E. Schull *(Pres)*

SCHULTE BUILDING SYSTEMS, INC.
17600 Badtke Rd, Hockley, TX 77447
Tel.: (281) 304-6111
Web Site: http://www.sbslp.com
Sales Range: $10-24.9 Million
Emp.: 374
Prefabricated Metal Building & Component Mfr
N.A.I.C.S.: 332311
Fred Koetting *(Pres & CEO)*
Frank Rosales *(Exec VP)*
Matt Stone *(VP-Ops)*
Donnie Humphries *(VP)*
Ronnie Peters *(VP & Controller)*
Eric Masterson *(VP-Engrg)*
Spencer Becker *(Mgr-Pur)*
Brandon Patranella *(Mgr-Corp Scheduling)*
Joe Lanning *(Plant Mgr)*
Mike Nesbitt *(Mgr-Corp Equipment)*
Ron Ambrosius *(VP-Building Sls & Mktg)*

SCHULTE CORPORATION
3100 E Kemper Rd # A, Cincinnati, OH 45241-1517
Tel.: (513) 489-9300
Web Site:
http://www.schultestorage.com
Sales Range: $25-49.9 Million
Emp.: 34
Miscellaneous Fabricated Wire Products
N.A.I.C.S.: 332618
Paul Saunders *(Mgr-Credit)*

SCHULTE, ROTH & ZABEL LLP
919 3rd Ave, New York, NY 10022-3902
Tel.: (212) 756-2000
Web Site: http://www.srz.com
Year Founded: 1969
Sales Range: $150-199.9 Million
Emp.: 600
Provider of Legal Services

U.S. PRIVATE

N.A.I.C.S.: 541110
Richard Piotrowicz *(CFO)*
Marc Weingarten *(Partner)*

SCHULTZ STEEL COMPANY
5321 Firestone Blvd, South Gate, CA 90280-3629
Tel.: (323) 564-3281
Web Site: http://www.shultzsteel.com
Year Founded: 1947
Sales Range: $100-124.9 Million
Emp.: 250
Mfr of Steel, Titanium & Other Special Metal Forgings & Rolled Rings
N.A.I.C.S.: 332112
Stephan W. Schulz *(Pres & CEO)*

SCHULTZ SURVEYING & ENGINEERING, INC.
4482 Hwy PP, Poplar Bluff, MO 63901
Tel.: (573) 686-0806   MO
Web Site:
http://www.schultzengineering.com
Year Founded: 1997
Sales Range: $1-9.9 Million
Emp.: 60
Engineeering Services
N.A.I.C.S.: 541330
Stanley J. Schultz *(Owner)*
Bari Chase *(Mgr-Matls Testing)*
David Stinson *(Dir-Engrg)*
Ronny Marshall *(Mgr-Ops & Project Mgr)*
Sammy Croy *(Comptroller)*
Jaymie Mitchell *(Mgr-Proposals)*
James Burtin *(Engr-Contract)*

SCHULTZE ASSET MANAGEMENT, LLC
800 Westchester Ave Ste S 632 Rye Brook, Purchase, NY 10573
Tel.: (914) 701-5260
Web Site: http://www.samco.net
Sales Range: $10-24.9 Million
Emp.: 10
Privater Equity Firm
N.A.I.C.S.: 523999

SCHULZE & BURCH BISCUIT COMPANY
1133 W 35th St, Chicago, IL 60609-1447
Tel.: (773) 927-6622   IL
Web Site: http://www.toastem.com
Year Founded: 1923
Sales Range: $200-249.9 Million
Emp.: 500
Mfr of Baked Goods
N.A.I.C.S.: 311812
P. Salina *(COO & Gen Mgr)*
Steve Podracky *(Mgr-Mktg)*
Joseph Adamczyk *(Supvr-Production)*
Danny Burke *(Supvr-Sanitation)*
John Roquet *(Mgr)*
Delia Ornelas *(Supvr-Production)*
James Doubek *(Supvr-Production)*

SCHUMACHER & SEILER INC.
10 W Aylesbury Rd, Lutherville Timonium, MD 21093
Tel.: (410) 561-2461
Web Site:
http://www.schumacherseiler.com
Rev.: $11,100,000
Emp.: 21
Plumbing Fittings & Supplies
N.A.I.C.S.: 423720
Russell C. Trout *(Pres & CEO)*
Jeff Sanft *(Acct Mgr)*
Mitchell Summerlin *(Acct Mgr)*

SCHUMACHER COMPANY INCORPORATED
5610 Polk St, Houston, TX 77023
Tel.: (713) 923-5548   TX

Web Site:
http://www.schumachercoinc.com
Year Founded: 1945
Sales Range: $1-9.9 Million
Emp.: 126
Electroplating & Plating
N.A.I.C.S.: 332813
Robert Gonvales *(Plant Mgr)*
James Sullivan *(COO & VP)*

SCHUMACHER DUGAN CONSTRUCTION, INC.
6355 Ctr Pk Dr, West Chester, OH 45069-3863
Tel.: (513) 777-9800 OH
Web Site: http://www.schumacher-dugan.com
Year Founded: 1964
Sales Range: $25-49.9 Million
Emp.: 100
Provider of Contracting & Construction Services
N.A.I.C.S.: 236220
Lawrence Schumacher *(Pres)*
Mark Schumacher *(VP)*
Michael Schumacher *(Project Mgr)*
Chris Wunnenberg *(Dir-Dev)*

SCHUMACHER ELEVATOR CO. INC.
1 Schumacher Way, Denver, IA 50622
Tel.: (319) 984-5676
Web Site: http://www.schumacherelevator.com
Rev.: $15,069,366
Emp.: 70
Elevators & Equipment
N.A.I.C.S.: 811490
Marvin Schumacher *(Pres)*

SCHUMACHER HOMES, INC.
2715 Wise Ave NW, Canton, OH 44708
Tel.: (330) 478-4500
Web Site:
http://www.schumacherhomes.com
Year Founded: 1992
Emp.: 500
Custom Home Builder
N.A.I.C.S.: 236117
Paul Schumacher *(Founder & CEO)*
Ryan Smith *(Gen Mgr)*

SCHUMAKER & CO. INC.
5325 S University Dr, Davie, FL 33328-5303
Tel.: (954) 846-8400
Web Site: http://www.schuco.com
Sales Range: $10-24.9 Million
Emp.: 15
Bowling Centers
N.A.I.C.S.: 713950
Joe Schumaker *(Pres)*

SCHUMANN PRINTERS, INC.
701 S Main St, Fall River, WI 53932
Tel.: (920) 484-3348
Web Site: http://www.spiweb.com
Sales Range: $10-24.9 Million
Emp.: 180
Commercial Lithographic Printing
N.A.I.C.S.: 323111
Daniel C. Schumann *(Pres)*
Mark A. Schumann *(VP)*
Arlene M. Schumann *(Treas & Sec)*

SCHUPAN & SONS, INC.
2619 Miller Rd, Kalamazoo, MI 49001
Tel.: (269) 382-0000 MI
Web Site: http://www.schupan.com
Year Founded: 1968
Recycling, Waste Materials
N.A.I.C.S.: 562920
Marc Schupan *(Pres)*
Andy Knowlton *(Corp & Treas)*

SCHUPP COMPANY, INC.
401 Pine St, Saint Louis, MO 63102-2731
Tel.: (314) 421-5200 MO
Year Founded: 1993
Sales Range: $10-24.9 Million
Emp.: 32
Advetising Agency
N.A.I.C.S.: 541810
Donna Macdonald *(Sr VP & Dir-Acct Svc)*
Linda Schumacher *(Dir-Brdcst & CIS)*
Tracy Jacobisen *(Print Production Dir)*
Jim Mayfield *(Sr VP & Exec Dir-Creative)*
Ray Ruzicka *(Sr VP & Dir-Media Svcs)*
Brian McLaughlin *(Assoc Dir-Media)*

SCHURMAN FINE PAPERS & PAPYRUS FRANCHISE CORPORATION
500 Chadbourne Rd, Fairfield, CA 94533
Tel.: (707) 428-0200
Web Site:
http://www.papyrusonline.com
Rev.: $26,000,000
Emp.: 2,000
Gift, Novelty & Souvenir Sales
N.A.I.C.S.: 424120
Dominique Schurman *(Pres)*
Laura Courtney *(Mgr-Mdse Div)*

SCHURZ COMMUNICATIONS, INC.
1301 E Douglas Rd Ste 200, Mishawaka, IN 46545
Tel.: (574) 247-7237 IN
Web Site: http://www.schurz.com
Year Founded: 1872
Holding Company; Daily Newspapers, Radio & TV Broadcasting, Cable TV & Advertising Shoppers
N.A.I.C.S.: 551112
Gesumino A. Agostino *(CFO & Sr VP)*
Brian Lynch *(Sr VP-Broadband)*
Michelle Wright *(VP-IT)*
Kent S. Johnson *(Co-Chm)*
Chris Dautel *(Dir-Strategic Plng & Corp Dev)*
James Schurz *(Co-Chm)*
Scott Schurz Jr. *(VP-People & Culture)*

Subsidiaries:

Advanced Cable Communications, Inc. (1)
12409 NW 35th St, Coral Springs, FL 33065
Tel.: (954) 753-0100
Web Site: http://www.advancedcable.net
Cable Television Operator
N.A.I.C.S.: 517111

Advocate Communications Inc. (1)
330 S 4th St, Danville, KY 40422
Tel.: (859) 236-2551
Web Site: http://www.amnews.com
Emp.: 20
Online Advocate-Messenger Services
N.A.I.C.S.: 541810
Scott Schurz *(Pres & Editor)*
Larry Hensley *(Publr)*
Ben Kleppinger *(Editor)*

Antietam Cable Television, Inc. (1)
1000 Willow Cir, Hagerstown, MD 21740
Tel.: (301) 797-5000
Web Site: http://www.antietamcable.com
Sales Range: $10-24.9 Million
Emp.: 56
Cable Television & High-Speed Internet Services
N.A.I.C.S.: 516210
Tony Heaton *(Mgr-Adv Sls)*

Long Lines, LLC (1)
501 4th St PO Box 67, Sergeant Bluff, IA 51054
Tel.: (712) 271-4000
Web Site: http://www.longlines.com
Telecommunication Servicesb
N.A.I.C.S.: 517112
Brent Olson *(Pres)*

Orbitel Holdings, LLC (1)
21116 N John Wayne Pkwy Ste B-9, Maricopa, AZ 85139
Tel.: (520) 568-8890
Web Site: http://www.orbitelcom.com
Holding Company
N.A.I.C.S.: 551112
Keith Kirkman *(CEO)*

Subsidiary (Domestic):

Orbitel Communications, LLC (2)
21116 N John Wayne Pkwy Ste B-9, Maricopa, AZ 85139
Tel.: (520) 568-8890
Web Site: http://www.orbitelcom.com
Digital Television, Internet & Telephone Services
N.A.I.C.S.: 517810

Otava, LLC (1)
825 Victors Way, Ann Arbor, MI 48108
Tel.: (877) 740-5028
Web Site: http://www.otava.com
Computer System Design Services
N.A.I.C.S.: 541512
Brad Cheedle *(CEO)*
Tom Wilten *(Pres & Gen Mgr)*
Laurel Burton *(VP-Product & Mktg)*
Cyndi Lyon *(VP-Customer Experience & Strategy)*
Kurt Schaldenbrand *(Dir-Platform Strategy & User Experience)*

Subsidiary (Domestic):

Iloka, Inc. (2)
4643 S Ulster St Ste 1200, Denver, CO 80237
Tel.: (303) 373-4444
Sales Range: $1-9.9 Million
Emp.: 63
Electrical Contractor
N.A.I.C.S.: 238210
Satish Kumar *(Pres & Treas)*

Neverfail, Inc. (2)
12400 Hwy 71 W Ste 350-407, Austin, TX 78738
Tel.: (512) 600-4300
Web Site: http://neverfail.com
Business Continuity Solutions
N.A.I.C.S.: 513210
Eric Vaughn *(Chief Revenue Officer)*
Olivier Pignault *(VP-Product Mgmt)*
Brian Hierholzer *(CEO)*
Kevin McCarthy *(CTO)*
Michele Cadd *(Chief Acctg Officer)*
Jason White *(Chief Strategy Officer)*
Joey Terrazas *(VP-Mktg)*
Scott Leslie *(Exec VP-Corp Dev)*
Kris Martel *(Chief Info Security Officer)*
Bhanu Jagasia *(VP-Audit Logic & Security)*

The New Knoxville Telephone Company (1)
301 W. S St., New Knoxville, OH 45871
Tel.: (419) 753-5000
Web Site: https://www.nktelco.com
Internet Provider Communication Services
N.A.I.C.S.: 517810

Subsidiary (Domestic):

Nktelco, Inc. (2)
301 W South St, New Knoxville, OH 45871
Tel.: (419) 753-5000
Web Site: http://www.nktelco.net
Sales Range: $1-9.9 Million
Emp.: 12
Telephone Communication, Except Radio
N.A.I.C.S.: 517810

Subsidiary (Domestic):

Hometown Cable Company, LLC (3)
305 W Main St, Coldwater, OH 45828
Tel.: (419) 678-4090
Web Site: http://www.hometowncable.net
Sales Range: Less than $1 Million
Emp.: 15
Cable & Other Subscription Programming

N.A.I.C.S.: 516210
Scott Prueter *(Principal)*

SCHUSTER COMPANY
1642 Carroll Ave, Saint Paul, MN 55104
Tel.: (651) 645-3991
Web Site: http://www.ljschuster.com
Sales Range: $10-24.9 Million
Emp.: 15
Specialty Advertising Products, Business Forms & Custom Printing Products
N.A.I.C.S.: 424120
Steve Schuster *(Pres)*

SCHUSTER ENTERPRISES INC.
3530 Macon Rd, Columbus, GA 31907
Tel.: (706) 563-3066
Sales Range: $50-74.9 Million
Emp.: 2,000
Franchise Owner of Fast-Food Restaurants
N.A.I.C.S.: 722513
Marvin R. Schuster *(Chm & CEO)*
Todd Schuster *(CEO)*
Patti Kelly *(CFO)*

SCHUTTE LUMBER COMPANY
3001 SW Blvd, Kansas City, MO 64108-3616
Tel.: (816) 753-6262 MO
Web Site:
http://www.schuttelumber.com
Year Founded: 1880
Sales Range: $75-99.9 Million
Emp.: 30
Mfr & Distributor of Hardwoods & Building Products
N.A.I.C.S.: 423310
Stacy Fyock *(CFO & Treas)*
Tommy Madina *(Mgr-Showroom)*
Michael Fuhrman *(Pres)*
John Hennes *(Mgr-Pur)*

SCHUYLKILL ENERGY RESOURCES INC.
PO Box 1200, Pottsville, PA 17901-7200
Tel.: (570) 622-5150 PA
Web Site:
http://www.readinganthracite.com
Year Founded: 1986
Sales Range: $25-49.9 Million
Emp.: 75
Electronic Services
N.A.I.C.S.: 221118
Bryan Rich *(VP)*
John W. Rich Jr. *(Chm & Pres)*

SCHUYLKILL VALLEY SPORTS
118 Industrial Dr, Pottstown, PA 19464
Tel.: (610) 327-2001
Web Site: http://www.svsports.com
Rev.: $25,251,912
Emp.: 250
Athletic Equipment & Sports Apparel Mfr
N.A.I.C.S.: 339920
Jerry Williams *(Pres)*
Phil Baumgardner *(Mgr-Mktg)*
Greg Baldwin *(VP-Mdsg)*
Laura Guest *(Mgr-HR)*

SCHWAAB INC.
11415 W Burleigh St, Milwaukee, WI 53222
Tel.: (414) 771-4150
Web Site: http://www.schwaab.com
Sales Range: $10-24.9 Million
Emp.: 200
Marking Devices & Stamping Devices

SCHWAAB INC.

Schwaab Inc.—(Continued)
N.A.I.C.S.: 339940
Douglas R. Lane (Chm)
Jeff Steggeman (VP-Sls)
Jeremiah McNeal (Pres & CEO)
Sara Wagner (VP-Sls)

Subsidiaries:

Majestic Engraving Corp. (1)
7552 N Teutonia Ave, Milwaukee, WI 53209
Tel.: (414) 351-1510
Web Site: http://www.majesticengraving.com
Rev.: $1,379,000
Emp.: 7
Metal Coating, Engraving, except Jewelry & Silverware & Allied Services to Manufacturers
N.A.I.C.S.: 332812

SCHWAN'S SHARED SERVICES, LLC
115 W College Dr, Marshall, MN 56258
Tel.: (507) 532-3274
Web Site:
http://www.schwanscompany.com
Food Production
N.A.I.C.S.: 311999
Jacob J. Berning (Pres)
Dimitrios Smyrnios (CEO)
Stacey Fowler Meittunen (Sr VP-Product Innovation & Dev)
Julie Francis (Pres-Schwan's Consumer Brands, Inc.)

Subsidiaries:

Schwan's MaMa Rosa's, LLC (1)
1910 Fair Rd, Sidney, OH 45365-8906 (100%)
Tel.: (937) 498-4511
Web Site: http://www.mama-rosas.com
Refrigerated Pizzas & Pizza Snack Products Mfr
N.A.I.C.S.: 311999
Julie Francis (Pres)

SCHWANK INC.
2 Schwank Way, Waynesboro, GA 30830-0988
Tel.: (706) 554-6191   DE
Web Site:
http://www.schwankgroup.com
Year Founded: 1882
Sales Range: $50-74.9 Million
Emp.: 5
Infrared Heaters
N.A.I.C.S.: 333414
Oliver Schwank (Mng Dir)

Subsidiaries:

Schwank (1)
2 Schwank Way, Waynesboro, GA 30830
Tel.: (877) 446-3727
Web Site: http://www.schwankusa.com
Heat Exchanger Mfr
N.A.I.C.S.: 332410

Schwank BE (1)
Titiaanstraat 49, 1000, Brussels, Belgium
Tel.: (32) 2 73 27 925
Web Site: http://www.schwank.be
Heat Exchanger Mfr
N.A.I.C.S.: 332410

Schwank BV (1)
Nijverheidsweg 5, 4104 AN, Culemborg, Netherlands
Tel.: (31) 345 513143
Web Site: http://www.schwank.nl
Emp.: 7
Heat Exchanger Mfr
N.A.I.C.S.: 332410
Oscar Schaap (Gen Mgr)

Schwank GesmbH (1)
Hetmanekgasse 1b / 3, 1230, Vienna, Austria
Tel.: (43) 1 609 1320
Web Site: http://www.schwank.at
Heating Equipment Distr
N.A.I.C.S.: 423720

Schwank GmbH (1)
Bremerhavener Strasse 43, Cologne, 50735, Germany
Tel.: (49) 221 71 76 0
Web Site: http://www.schwank.de
Sales Range: $10-24.9 Million
Heat Exchanger Mfr
N.A.I.C.S.: 332410
Oliver Schwank (Mgr)

Schwank Inc. (1)
5285 Bradco Blvd, Mississauga, L4W 2A6, ON, Canada (100%)
Tel.: (706) 554-6191
Web Site: http://www.schwankgroup.com
Sales Range: $50-74.9 Million
Infra Red Heating
N.A.I.C.S.: 333414

Schwank Ltd (1)
Suite 21 50 Churchill Square Business Centre Kings Hill, West Malling, ME19 4YU, Kent, United Kingdom
Tel.: (44) 208 641 3900
Web Site: http://www.schwank.co.uk
Sales Range: $10-24.9 Million
Emp.: 8
Heat Exchanger Mfr
N.A.I.C.S.: 332410
Steven Sherman (Mng Dir)

Schwank S.a.r.l. (1)
15 Route des Cheres, 69380, Marcilly-d'Azergues, France
Tel.: (33) 4 78 43 03 44
Web Site: http://www.schwank.fr
Heat Exchanger Mfr
N.A.I.C.S.: 332410

Schwank Srl (1)
Bd 9 Mai nr 21 bl B11/43-4462, Piatra Neamt, 610127, Romania
Tel.: (40) 233 232 411
Web Site: http://www.schwank.ro
Heat Exchanger Mfr
N.A.I.C.S.: 332410
Claudia Meftode (Gen Mgr)

SCHWARTZ BROTHERS RESTAURANTS
325 118th Ave St Ste 106, Bellevue, WA 98005
Tel.: (425) 455-3948
Web Site:
http://www.schwartzbros.com
Year Founded: 1970
Sales Range: $25-49.9 Million
Emp.: 800
Restaurant Owner & Operator
N.A.I.C.S.: 722511
Michael Schwartz (VP-Pur)
Daniel Schwartz (Dir-Sls-Schwartz Brothers Bakery)
Michael Geigle (Gen Mgr-Spazzo)
Dori Pikki (Dir-HR)

SCHWARTZ JEWELERS
6114 Hamilton Ave, Cincinnati, OH 45224
Tel.: (513) 541-5627
Web Site:
http://www.schwartzjewelers.net
Year Founded: 2007
Sales Range: $25-49.9 Million
Emp.: 13
Jewelry Retailer
N.A.I.C.S.: 458310
Martin M. Schwartz (Owner)

SCHWARTZ PUBLIC RELATIONS ASSOCIATES, INC.
30 Lincoln Plz Ste 19M, New York, NY 10023
Tel.: (212) 677-8700
Web Site: http://www.schwartzpr.com
Year Founded: 1961
Sales Range: $1-9.9 Million
Emp.: 13
Public Relations Agency
N.A.I.C.S.: 541820
Barry Schwartz (Pres)
Steven Wright-Mark (Exec VP)

SCHWARTZ VENTURES INC.
5885 N State Rte 159, Edwardsville, IL 62025
Tel.: (618) 656-5241
Sales Range: $10-24.9 Million
Emp.: 25
Telephone Communication Services
N.A.I.C.S.: 517121
Robert W. Schwartz (Pres)

SCHWARZ PAPER COMPANY
8338 Austin Ave, Morton Grove, IL 60053-3209
Tel.: (847) 966-2550   DE
Web Site: http://www.schwarz.com
Year Founded: 1907
Sales Range: $500-549.9 Million
Emp.: 850
Paper & Packaging Products; Primary Printer
N.A.I.C.S.: 424130
Bruce Barton (Sr VP-Supply Chain)
Andrew J. McKenna Jr. (Pres)

SCHWARZ PARTNERS, LP
3600 Woodview Trace Ste 300, Indianapolis, IN 46268
Tel.: (317) 290-1140
Web Site:
http://www.schwarzpartners.com
Year Founded: 1998
Holding Company
N.A.I.C.S.: 551112
Stephanie Blackman (VP & Gen Counsel)

Subsidiaries:

New-Indy Containerboard LLC (1)
5936 Perkins Rd, Oxnard, CA 93033-9044
Tel.: (805) 986-3881
Web Site: http://www.new-indy.com
Containerboard Mfr
N.A.I.C.S.: 322130
Christine Lacey (Dir-HR)
Richard Hartman (COO)

Subsidiary (Domestic):

Carolina Container Company (2)
909 Prospect St, High Point, NC 27260
Tel.: (336) 883-7146
Web Site: http://www.carolinacontainer.com
Corrugated & Solid Fiber Boxes
N.A.I.C.S.: 322211
Ron Sessions (Pres)
Rodney McSwain (Dir-HR)
Deon Griffith (Mgr-ISO)
Frank Nolley (Mgr-Customer Svc)
James Karriker (Mgr-Credit)
Randy Russell (Sls Mgr)
Susan Rogers (Coord-POP Special Project)
John Stamper (Acct Mgr)
Julie Zornes (Mgr-Design)
Brad Bible (Ops Mgr)
Brian Healy (Gen Mgr-Hickory)
Christopher Lyon (Mgr-Sustainability)
Gene Terrill (Mgr-Process Improvement)
Tony Trent (Plant Mgr)

Proactive Packaging and Display, Inc. (2)
602 S Rockefeller Ave, Ontario, CA 91761-8190
Tel.: (909) 390-5624
Web Site: http://www.proactivepkg.com
Retails Graphics Mfr
N.A.I.C.S.: 322211
Memo Gonzalez (VP-Ops)
Gary Hartog (CEO)

Shoreline Container Inc. (2)
4450 136th Ave, Holland, MI 49424
Tel.: (616) 399-2088
Web Site:
http://www.shorelinecontainer.com
Sales Range: $50-74.9 Million
Emp.: 250
Containers & Corrugated Boxes
N.A.I.C.S.: 322220
Jeff Mooney (Mgr-Production)
Tom Timmer (Mgr-Fin Div)
Kevin Houle (Plant Mgr)

U.S. PRIVATE

Thomas Deater (CFO)
Scott Bush (Mgr-Logistics)
Pat Clifford (Sr Acct Mgr)
Bob Zuker (COO)

SCHWARZSCHILD JEWELERS, INC.
11800 W Broad St Ste 1312, Richmond, VA 23233
Tel.: (804) 967-0800
Web Site:
http://www.schwarzschild.com
Year Founded: 1897
Sales Range: $10-24.9 Million
Emp.: 100
Jewelry & Related Product Distr
N.A.I.C.S.: 458310
Sam Spaulding (Gen Mgr)

SCHWEBEL BAKING CO. INC.
965 E Midlothian Blvd, Youngstown, OH 44502-2837
Tel.: (330) 783-2860   OH
Web Site: http://www.schwebels.com
Year Founded: 1906
Sales Range: $25-49.9 Million
Emp.: 1,350
Provider of Bakery Products
N.A.I.C.S.: 311812
Paul Schwebel (Exec VP)
Alyson Winick (Sr VP-Sls)
Lee Schwebel (Dir-Mktg)

Subsidiaries:

Schwebel Baking Co. of Pennsylvania Inc. (1)
4315 Walnut St, McKeesport, PA 15132-6114
Tel.: (412) 751-4080
Web Site: http://www.schwebels.com
Sales Range: $10-24.9 Million
Emp.: 30
Provider Of Bakery Product Whslr
N.A.I.C.S.: 424490

SCHWEIGER DERMATOLOGY GROUP
110 E 55th St Fl 19, New York, NY 10022
Tel.: (212) 804-6481
Web Site:
http://www.schweigerderm.com
Year Founded: 2010
Sales Range: $25-49.9 Million
Emp.: 335
Dermatology Services
N.A.I.C.S.: 621111
Eric Schweiger (CEO)

Subsidiaries:

Allergy & Asthma Care New York PLLC (1)
3016 30th Dr, Astoria, NY 11102-1855
Tel.: (508) 880-3121
Web Site: https://allergyreliefnyc.com
Offices of Physicians (except Mental Health Specialists)
N.A.I.C.S.: 621111
Clifford Bassett (Principal)

Connecticut Dermatology Group (1)
1250 Summer St Ste 201, Stamford, CT 06905-5318
Web Site: http://www.ctdermgroup.com
Offices of Physicians (except Mental Health Specialists)
N.A.I.C.S.: 621111
Maxine Conrad (Office Mgr)

Lower Manhattan Medical Associates P.C. (1)
65 Broadway Ste 1800, New York, NY 10006
Tel.: (347) 773-2955
Web Site:
http://www.morarudermatology.com
Offices of Physicians (except Mental Health Specialists)
N.A.I.C.S.: 621111
Robert A. Moraru (Founder)

COMPANIES

SCHWEITZER ENGINEERING LABORATORIES INC.
2350 NE Hopkins Ct, Pullman, WA 99163-5600
Tel.: (509) 332-1890
Web Site: http://www.selinc.com
Year Founded: 1982
Sales Range: $250-299.9 Million
Emp.: 3,000
Electricity Measurement Instruments Mfr
N.A.I.C.S.: 334515
Fernando Ayello (Reg Mgr-Sls & Mktg)
James Cheong (Mng Dir)
Dave Whitehead (CEO)
Tony Lee (Chief Res & Dev Officer)
David Costello (Chief Sls & Svcs Officer)
David Sanchez Escobedo (VP-Engrg Svcs)
Edmund O. Schweitzer III (Founder, Pres & CTO)

SCHWESERS STORES INC.
630 N Park Ave, Fremont, NE 68025
Tel.: (402) 721-1700
Web Site: http://www.schwesersstores.com
Sales Range: $10-24.9 Million
Emp.: 210
Women's Apparel Sales
N.A.I.C.S.: 458110
Robert Schweser (VP)
Tyler Smith (Pres)

SCHWING BIOSET, INC.
350 SMC Dr, Somerset, WI 54025
Tel.: (715) 247-3433   MN
Web Site: http://www.schwingbioset.com
Year Founded: 2006
Sales Range: $10-24.9 Million
Emp.: 40
Waste Water Treatment & Biosolid Material Processing Machinery Mfr, Installation & Maintenance Services
N.A.I.C.S.: 333998
Chuck Wanstrom (Dir-New Bus Dev)
Paul Katka (Mgr-Svc)
Nancy Predatsch (VP)
Tom Welch (Mgr-Sls-Southeast)
Joshua DiValentino (Sr Mgr-Sls-Western Reg)

Subsidiaries:

Custom Conveyor Corp. (1)
20550 Commerce Blvd, Rogers, MN 55374
Tel.: (763) 367-6200
Web Site: http://www.customconveyorcorp.com
Rev.: $4,431,000
Emp.: 21
Conveyor & Conveying Equipment Mfr
N.A.I.C.S.: 333922

Schwing Bioset (1)
98 Mill Plain Rd Ste 2A, Danbury, CT 06811
Tel.: (203) 744-2100
Web Site: http://www.schwingbioset.com
Waste Water Treatment & Biosolid Material Processing Machinery Mfr, Installation & Maintenance Services
N.A.I.C.S.: 333998
Nancy Predatsch (Mgr-Ops)

SCHWING ELECTRICAL SUPPLY CORP.
122 Allen Blvd, Farmingdale, NY 11735
Tel.: (631) 391-3330
Web Site: http://www.schwingelectric.com
Year Founded: 1960
Rev.: $66,500,000
Emp.: 76
Electrical Products Supplier
N.A.I.C.S.: 423610
Robert Dunigan (Owner)
John Marsich (Mgr-Warehouse)
Jack Dunigan (Treas)
Peter Schwing (Chm)

SCI CONSULTING SERVICES, INC.
7918 Jones Branch Dr Ste 600, McLean, VA 22102
Tel.: (703) 739-6600
Web Site: http://www.sciworld.com
Year Founded: 1983
Sales Range: $25-49.9 Million
Emp.: 270
IT Applications & Management Systems
N.A.I.C.S.: 541512
Lynette Spano (Pres & CEO)

SCI REAL ESTATE INVESTMENTS, LLC
11620 Wilshire Blvd 10th Fl, Los Angeles, CA 90025
Tel.: (310) 470-2600
Web Site: http://www.sciproperties.com
Sales Range: $25-49.9 Million
Emp.: 20
Commercial Real Estate Investor & Tenant-in-Common Property Manager
N.A.I.C.S.: 531390
Robert Robotti (Co-Founder)
Marc Paul (Co-Founder & Pres)
Janice Jay (Co-Founder & Principal)
Alicia Lomeli (VP-Real Estate Investments)

SCI-ROEV TEXAS PARTNERS LP
1412 Main St Ste 608, Dallas, TX 75202-4090
Tel.: (214) 742-6460
Sales Range: $25-49.9 Million
Emp.: 5
Commercial Building Operator
N.A.I.C.S.: 531120

Subsidiaries:

Akard Holdings LP (1)
1412 Main St Ste 608, Dallas, TX 75202-4090
Tel.: (214) 742-6460
Web Site: http://www.sciroev.com
Rev.: $130,000
Emp.: 3
Real Property Lessor
N.A.I.C.S.: 531190

SCI/STEELCON INC.
5071 E North Ave, Kalamazoo, MI 49048
Tel.: (269) 381-5011
Web Site: http://www.scisteelcon.com
Sales Range: $25-49.9 Million
Emp.: 150
Machine Moving & Rigging
N.A.I.C.S.: 561990
Timothy D. Russell (Pres)

SCICLONE PHARMACEUTICALS, INC.
950 Tower Ln Ste 900, Foster City, CA 94404-2125
Tel.: (650) 358-3456   DE
Web Site: http://www.sciclone.com
Sales Range: $150-199.9 Million
Emp.: 570
Pharmaceuticals Mfr
N.A.I.C.S.: 325412
Friedhelm Blobel (Pres & CEO)
Hong Zhao (CEO-Ops-China)
Lan Xie (CFO-Ops-China & VP-Fin)
Raymond A. Low (VP-Fin & Controller)
Carey Chern (Chief Compliance Officer, Gen Counsel & Sec)
Wilson W. Cheung (CFO & Sr VP-Fin)

Subsidiaries:

SCICLONE PHARMACEUTICALS HONG KONG LIMITED (1)
Room 3401A 34/F Windsor House 311 Gloucester Road, Causeway Bay, China (Hong Kong)
Tel.: (852) 25100118
Web Site: http://www.sciclone.com
Pharmaceutical Preparation Mfr
N.A.I.C.S.: 325412

SciClone Pharmaceuticals China Ltd. (1)
Room 3102 Office Tower A No 7 Dong Sanhuan Zhong Lu, Chao Yang District, Beijing, 100020, China
Tel.: (86) 10 6530 9016
Web Site: http://www.scicloneinternational.com
Sales Range: $150-199.9 Million
Pharmaceuticals Mfr
N.A.I.C.S.: 325412

SciClone Pharmaceuticals International Ltd. (1)
Rm 3401A Windsor House, 311 Gloucester Road, Causeway, Hong Kong, China (Hong Kong)
Tel.: (852) 25100118
Web Site: http://www.scicloneinternational.com
Sales Range: $150-199.9 Million
Emp.: 10
Pharmaceuticals Mfr
N.A.I.C.S.: 325412
Emil Lai (Dir-Mktg)

SCIENCE & ENGINEERING SERVICES, INC.
6992 Columbia Gateway Dr, Columbia, MD 21046
Tel.: (443) 539-0139
Web Site: http://www.sesi-md.com
Rev.: $20,629,986
Emp.: 700
Commercial Physical Research
N.A.I.C.S.: 541715
Hyo Sang Lee (Pres)
Eric Harden (Engr-Mechanical)

SCIENCE & TECHNOLOGY INTERNATIONAL
733 Bishop St Ste 3100, Honolulu, HI 96813
Tel.: (808) 540-4700
Web Site: http://www.sti-hawaii.com
Sales Range: $10-24.9 Million
Emp.: 110
Research Services
N.A.I.C.S.: 541715
Will Alameida (Sr VP)

SCIENCE KIT LLC
777 E Pk Dr, Tonawanda, NY 14150-5003
Tel.: (716) 874-6020   NY
Year Founded: 1965
Sales Range: $25-49.9 Million
Emp.: 150
Professional Equipment Sales
N.A.I.C.S.: 423490
Tom Rosenecker (VP-Mktg)

SCIENCE MUSEUM OKLAHOMA
2100 NE 52nd St, Oklahoma City, OK 73111-7107
Tel.: (405) 602-6664   OK
Web Site: http://www.sciencemuseumok.org
Year Founded: 1958
Sales Range: $10-24.9 Million
Emp.: 202
Science Museum Operator
N.A.I.C.S.: 712110

Kym Koch Thompson (Sec)
Shane Wharton (Vice Chm)
Sherry Marshall (Pres)

SCIENCE SYSTEMS & APPLICATIONS, INC.
10210 Greenbelt Rd Ste 600, Lanham, MD 20706
Tel.: (301) 867-2000
Web Site: http://www.ssaihq.com
Rev.: $77,700,000
Emp.: 250
Research & Development in the Physical Engineering & Life Sciences
N.A.I.C.S.: 541715
Om P. Bahethi (Pres)
Saraswati Bahethi (Owner, Principal, Treas & Sec)
Anoop N. Mehta (Pres)
Ron Estes (VP)
Mauricio Peredo (COO & Exec VP)
Chuck Petrilla (Dir-Bus Dev)
Robert Fleishauer (VP & Program Mgr)
Joseph Wagenhofer (VP & Program Mgr)
Linda Aguirre-Echevarria (CFO)
Robert Kasa (Mgr-Program)
Jacqueline Kendall (Chief Knowledge Officer)
Diedre Jones (Dir-HR)

SCIENCELOGIC LLC
10700 Parkridge Blvd, Reston, VA 20191
Tel.: (703) 354-1010
Web Site: http://www.sciencelogic.com
Year Founded: 2003
Rev.: $3,400,000
Emp.: 450
Information Technology Monitoring Software
N.A.I.C.S.: 513210
David Link (Founder, Chm & CEO)
Antonio Piraino (CTO)
Patrick McCoy (CFO)
Randy Jones (Sr VP-Sls)
Murali Nemani (CMO)

Subsidiaries:

AppFirst, Inc. (1)
8009 34th Ave S Suite 175, Bloomington, MN 55425   (100%)
Web Site: http://www.appfirst.com
Emp.: 50
Application Service Management Services
N.A.I.C.S.: 541511
Donn Rochette (CTO)

SCIENERGY, INC.
4100 Alpha Rd Ste 900, Dallas, TX 75244
Tel.: (972) 386-5335
Web Site: http://www.scienergy.com
Year Founded: 2007
Sales Range: $25-49.9 Million
Emp.: 160
Cloud-Based Energy Management Solutions for Building Owners & Operators
N.A.I.C.S.: 513210
Brian Bezdek (CFO & COO)
Chris Cutcliff (VP-Ops)
Richard Worth (VP-Software Engrg)
Michael Flores (VP-Sls-North America)
Brian Ratcliff (Sr VP-Enterprise Svcs)
Steve Gossett Jr. (CEO)

Subsidiaries:

Servidyne, Inc. (1)
1349 W Peachtree St Ste 1575, Atlanta, GA 30339-2929
Tel.: (470) 355-9004
Web Site: http://www.servidyne.com

SCIenergy, Inc.—(Continued)
Sales Range: $25-49.9 Million
Emp.: 97
Engineering & Technology Services in Energy, Efficiency, Demand Response, Building Maintenance Management & Building Controls
N.A.I.C.S.: 541330
Barry Abramson (Principal)
Lung-Sing Wong (Principal)

SCIENS CAPITAL MANAGEMENT LLC
667 Madison Ave, New York, NY 10065
Tel.: (212) 471-6100
Web Site: https://www.sciensam.com
Privater Equity Firm
N.A.I.C.S.: 523999

Subsidiaries:

Sciens Water Opportunities Management, LLC (1)
667 Madison Ave, New York, NY 10065
Tel.: (212) 471-6100
Web Site: https://scienswater.com
Financial Investment Services
N.A.I.C.S.: 523999
John Rigas (Chm & CEO)

Holding (Domestic):

Integrated Water Services, Inc. (2)
4001 N Valley Dr, Longmont, CO 80504
Tel.: (970) 601-5025
Web Site: https://integratedwaterservices.com
Water & Wastewater Solutions & Services
N.A.I.C.S.: 924110
Alex Buehler (Pres & CEO)

Subsidiary (Domestic):

Hi-Line Industries Ii, Inc. (3)
1208 Industrial Blvd, Brenham, TX 77833
Tel.: (979) 836-2661
Web Site: http://www.hi-lineindustries.com
Sales Range: $1-9.9 Million
Emp.: 40
Industrial Patterns
N.A.I.C.S.: 332999
Barbara McIntyre (Dir-HR)
Dennis Kocian (Pres)

KLa Systems, Inc. (3)
31 Mill St, Assonet, MA 02702
Tel.: (508) 644-5555
Web Site: http://www.klasystems.com
Rev.: $2,170,000
Emp.: 10
Hazardous Waste Treatment & Disposal
N.A.I.C.S.: 562211
Deborah Neville (Controller)
Fred Siino (Pres)

SCIENTECH, INC.
5649 Arapahoe Ave, Boulder, CO 80303-1332
Tel.: (303) 444-1361
Web Site: http://www.scientech-inc.com
Year Founded: 1968
Sales Range: $1-9.9 Million
Emp.: 16
Mfr & Marketer of Measurement Instruments, Balances, Scales & Meters
N.A.I.C.S.: 334519
Robert Serafin (Chm)
Robert Guidetti (Pres)

SCIENTIFIC BRAKE & EQUIPMENT CO.
314 W Genesee Ave, Saginaw, MI 48602
Tel.: (989) 755-4411
Web Site: http://www.scientificbrake.com
Sales Range: $10-24.9 Million
Emp.: 55
Truck Parts & Accessories
N.A.I.C.S.: 423120

John Princing (Pres)
Brad Wiechelman (Mgr-Leasing)
Bill Weber (Dir-Sls)
Stan Teliczan (Mgr-Rental)

SCIENTIFIC CERTIFICATION SYSTEMS, INC.
2000 N 2200 Powell St Ste 600, Emeryville, CA 94608
Tel.: (510) 452-8000
Web Site: http://www.scsglobalservices.com
Year Founded: 1984
Sales Range: $10-24.9 Million
Emp.: 86
Scientific Testing Services
N.A.I.C.S.: 541380
Linda Brown (Founder & Sr VP)
Scott Romito (CFO)
Tom Connelly (Dir-Art)
Sabine Daume (Dir-Sustainable Seafood-Australia)
Brendan Grady (Dir-Forest Mgmt Certification)
Aaron Maizlish (Dir-Bus Svc-Natural Resources Div)
Neil Mendenhall (Mgr-Supply Chain Svcs)
Heena Patel (Dir-Technical-Supply Chain Food Safety Audit Svcs)
Stowe Beam (VP-Environmental Certification Svcs)
Jessica Caputo (Mgr-Client Svcs-Food Safety)
Julian Eldridge (Mgr-Ops)
Vanessa Ellis (Mgr-Technical)
Bernadette Goldstein (Mgr-Sls & Mktg-Food & Agriculture)
Sarah Harris (Dir-Chain of Custody)
Keith Killpack (Mgr-Life Cycle Assessment)
Diana Kirsanova Phillips (Dir-Quality Assurance)
Stanley P. Mathuram (VP-ECS Ops & Corp Sls)
Sian Morgan (Dir-Sustainable Seafood-Americas)
Nicole Munoz (Mgr-Quality-ECS)
Brandon Nauman (Assoc Mng Dir-Food & Agriculture)
Jim Knutzon (Chm, Pres & CEO)

SCIENTIFIC COMPONENTS CORP.
13 Neptune Ave, Brooklyn, NY 11235
Tel.: (718) 934-4500
Web Site: http://www.minicircuits.com
Year Founded: 1969
Sales Range: $25-49.9 Million
Emp.: 500
Provider of RF, IF & Microwave Signal Processing Components
N.A.I.C.S.: 334419
Harvey Kaylie (Founder & Pres)
Len Rodin (Asst Controller)

SCIENTIFIC DRILLING INTERNATIONAL INC.
16701 Greenspoint Park Dr Ste 200, Houston, TX 77060
Tel.: (281) 443-3300
Web Site: http://www.scientificdrilling.com
Year Founded: 1986
Sales Range: $25-49.9 Million
Emp.: 300
Oil & Gas Well Drilling Services
N.A.I.C.S.: 213111
Philip N. Longorio (Pres & CEO)
Eric Beylier (Chief Procurement Officer & Sr VP)
Chip Abrant (Sr VP-Global Ops & Sls)
Dana Armstrong (CFO & Sr VP)

SCIENTIFIC INSTRUMENTS, INC.
4400 W Tiffany Dr, West Palm Beach, FL 33407-3225
Tel.: (561) 881-8500
Web Site: http://www.scientificinstruments.com
Year Founded: 1967
Sales Range: $1-9.9 Million
Emp.: 50
Laboratory Instrumentation & Temperature Sensing Products
N.A.I.C.S.: 334516
Leigh Ann Hoey (Owner)
Mark Sheats (Mgr-LNG Svc)
David Sheats (Engr-Application)

SCIENTIFIC MICROSCOPES INC.
1128 W Evelyn Ave, Sunnyvale, CA 94086
Tel.: (408) 739-2631
Web Site: http://www.simicroscopes.com
Sales Range: $25-49.9 Million
Emp.: 30
Microscope Distr
N.A.I.C.S.: 333310
Fred Lustig (Chm)
Bill Weldon (Controller)

SCIENTIFIC MOLDING CORPORATION
330 SMC Dr, Somerset, WI 54025
Tel.: (715) 247-3500
Web Site: http://www.smcltd.com
Sales Range: $25-49.9 Million
Emp.: 400
Injection Molding Of Plastics
N.A.I.C.S.: 326199
Chetan N. Patel (Pres)

SCIENTIFIC RESEARCH CORP.
2300 Windy Rdg Pkwy SE Ste 400 S, Atlanta, GA 30339-5665
Tel.: (770) 859-9161
Web Site: http://www.scires.com
Year Founded: 1988
Sales Range: $75-99.9 Million
Emp.: 1,500
Provider of Advanced Electronic Engineering Services
N.A.I.C.S.: 541910
Michael Watt (Pres & CEO)
Jerry Goldbaugh (VP-Contracts)

SCIENTIFIC SALES, INC.
130 Valley Ct, Oak Ridge, TN 37830
Tel.: (865) 483-9332
Web Site: http://www.scisale.com
Sales Range: $10-24.9 Million
Emp.: 20
Laboratory & Scientific Equipment Distr
N.A.I.C.S.: 423830
Vicki Dyer (Pres & CEO)
Debbie Lamb (Mgr-Ops)
Jennifer Power (Mgr-Acctg)
Matthew Calvert (Mgr-CSR)
Wendi Arnold (Mgr-Sls & Mktg)

SCIENTIFIC SUPPLIES & TECHNOLOGY INTERNATIONAL INC.
7245 NW 43rd St, Miami, FL 33166
Tel.: (305) 593-2137
Web Site: http://www.sst-intl.com
Year Founded: 1977
Sales Range: $10-24.9 Million
Emp.: 26
Medical, Dental & Hospital Equipment Whslr
N.A.I.C.S.: 423450

Peter F. Lue (Pres)
Stephen Lee (VP)
Laurel Hosang (Comptroller)

SCIENTIGO, INC.
6701 Carmel Rd Ste 205, Charlotte, NC 28226
Tel.: (704) 837-0500
Year Founded: 2003
Sales Range: Less than $1 Million
Emp.: 21
Software Solutions & Media Services
N.A.I.C.S.: 334610
Paul S. Odom (Sr VP & Chief Scientist)
Paul Griffen (VP-Channel Dev)

SCIMEDICA GROUP
20 E 2nd Ave, Conshohocken, PA 19428
Tel.: (610) 832-9955
Year Founded: 2005
Rev.: $6,500,000
Emp.: 20
Education & Training Services
N.A.I.C.S.: 611519
Dennis Zanella (Mng Partner)
Eric John (Sr VP-Market Res & Consulting)
Christopher Klemick (Mng Partner)
Ted Felix (Pres-Market Res & Consulting)

SCIMETRIKA
100 Capitola Dr Ste 106, Durham, NC 27713-4451
Tel.: (919) 354-5200
Web Site: http://www.scimetrika.com
Sales Range: $10-24.9 Million
Emp.: 100
Public Health Consulting Services
N.A.I.C.S.: 541690
Jean Orelien (Founder & CEO)

SCION INC.
21555 Mullin Ave, Warren, MI 48089
Tel.: (586) 755-4000
Web Site: http://www.scionsteel.com
Rev.: $30,000,000
Emp.: 15
Steel
N.A.I.C.S.: 423510
Carlos E. Hurches (Pres)

SCION MEDICAL TECHNOLOGIES, LLC
90 Oak St, Newton, MA 02464
Tel.: (888) 582-6211
Web Site: http://www.scionmedtech.com
Year Founded: 2011
Medical Device Mfr
N.A.I.C.S.: 339112

Subsidiaries:

BSD Medical Corporation (1)
1969 Claremont Dr, Bountiful, UT 84010
Tel.: (801) 725-4625
Emp.: 20
Heat Therapy Systems Developer, Mfr & Marketer
N.A.I.C.S.: 339112

SCM DATA INC.
30 Montgomery St Ste 1201, Jersey City, NJ 07302
Tel.: (201) 484-7644
Web Site: http://www.scmdata.com
Year Founded: 2009
Sales Range: $10-24.9 Million
Emp.: 150
Information Technology Consulting Services
N.A.I.C.S.: 541512
Ram Kambhampati (Mgr-Bus Dev)

SCO FAMILY OF SERVICES

1 Alexander Pl, Glen Cove, NY 11542
Tel.: (516) 671-1253 NY
Web Site: http://www.sco.org
Year Founded: 1898
Sales Range: $200-249.9 Million
Emp.: 4,719
Community Care Services
N.A.I.C.S.: 624190
Rose Anello (*Chief Strategy Officer*)
Johanna Richman (*CFO*)
Lee Vance (*Chm*)
Stephen Mack (*CFO*)
Bob Sherman (*Chief Admin Officer*)
Robert Sherman (*Chief Admin Officer*)
Rosemary Stein (*Chief Program Officer*)
Joseph Fatuzzo (*CIO*)
Luisa Sanchez (*Dir-Comm*)
Elyse B. Feldman (*Dir-Fin*)
Julia Jean-Francois (*Dir-Program Svcs*)
Keith M. Little (*Exec Dir*)

SCOBEE FOODS INCORPORATED
1812 Corinth St, Dallas, TX 75215-1311
Tel.: (214) 421-0898
Web Site:
  http://www.scobeefoods.com
Rev.: $18,800,000
Emp.: 70
Ready-Made Sandwich Distr
N.A.I.C.S.: 424490
Stephen A. Scobee (*Chm*)

SCOBEY MOVING & STORAGE LTD
9625 Broadway St, San Antonio, TX 78217
Tel.: (210) 828-8393
Web Site:
  http://www.scobeymovingandstorage.com
Sales Range: $10-24.9 Million
Emp.: 100
Household Goods Transport Services
N.A.I.C.S.: 484210
Russ Yeager (*CEO*)

SCOLA
21557 270th St, McClelland, IA 51548
Tel.: (712) 566-2202 IA
Web Site: http://www.scola.org
Year Founded: 1987
Sales Range: $10-24.9 Million
Emp.: 78
Educational Support Services
N.A.I.C.S.: 611710
Daniel Pike (*Mgr-Telecom*)
John Millar (*COO*)
David Karnes (*Chm*)
Francis Lajba (*Pres*)

SCOLARI'S WAREHOUSE MARKETS
255 S McCarran Blvd, Sparks, NV 89431
Tel.: (775) 331-7700
Web Site:
  http://www.scolarisclub.com
Sales Range: $150-199.9 Million
Emp.: 1,200
Supermarket Owner & Operator
N.A.I.C.S.: 445110
Joey E. Scolari (*CEO*)

SCOLDING LOCKS CORP.
1520 W Rogers Ave, Appleton, WI 54914-5007
Tel.: (920) 733-5561
Web Site:
  http://www.scoldinglocks.com
Rev.: $5,000,000
Emp.: 85
Hair Rollers & Pins & Other Hair Care Products Mfr
N.A.I.C.S.: 339993
Ben Boldt (*Pres*)

SCONCE SOLUTIONS PTE. LTD.
4645 Wyndham Ln Ste 140, Frisco, TX 75033
Tel.: (469) 325-7000
Web Site: http://www.sconce.com
Year Founded: 2001
Information Technology & Services
N.A.I.C.S.: 513210
Meyyappan Annamalai (*Founder & CEO*)
Vern Heyer (*Pres-Global Sls & Mktg*)

Subsidiaries:

Novo PLM (1)
4645 Wyndham Ln Ste 140, Frisco, TX 75033
Tel.: (469) 325-7000
Consulting & Project Implementation Services
N.A.I.C.S.: 541618
Brian Bezdek (*Mng Partner*)

SCOOP NYC
473-475 Broadway, New York, NY 10013
Tel.: (212) 925-3539
Web Site: http://www.scoopnyc.com
Sales Range: $10-24.9 Million
Emp.: 8
Ready-To-Wear & Designer Women's & Men's Apparel & Accessories
N.A.I.C.S.: 315990
Heidi Hoelzer (*VP-GMM Women's*)
Susan Davidson (*CEO*)
Kelli Swiss (*Dir-Ops*)

SCOPE EDUCATION SERVICES
100 Lawrence Ave, Smithtown, NY 11787
Tel.: (631) 360-0800 NY
Web Site: http://www.scopeonline.us
Year Founded: 1964
Sales Range: $10-24.9 Million
Emp.: 1,091
Child Development Services
N.A.I.C.S.: 624110
Patricia M. Walsh (*Dir-Fin*)
George L. Duffy III (*Exec Dir*)

SCOPE IMPORTS INC.
8020 Blankenship Dr, Houston, TX 77055-1018
Tel.: (713) 688-0077 TX
Web Site: http://www.scopeimp.com
Year Founded: 1967
Sales Range: $200-249.9 Million
Emp.: 100
Mens & Boys Clothing Mfr & Distr
N.A.I.C.S.: 424350
Wolf Finkelman (*Chm*)
Bill Meredith (*Controller*)
Alan Finkelman (*Pres*)
Steven Finkelman (*CFO*)

SCOPE SERVICES INC.
2095 Niles Rd, Saint Joseph, MI 49085-2473
Tel.: (269) 983-1554 MI
Web Site: http://www.scope-services.com
Year Founded: 1967
Sales Range: $25-49.9 Million
Emp.: 400
Provider of Employment Services
N.A.I.C.S.: 238220
Lydia Demski (*Pres*)

SCOPIA CAPITAL MANAGEMENT LP
152 W 57th St 33rd Fl, New York, NY 10019
Tel.: (212) 370-0303
Web Site: http://www.scopia.com
Year Founded: 2001
Asset Management Services
N.A.I.C.S.: 531390
Jerome J. Lande (*Mng Partner & Deputy Chief Investment Officer*)
Matt Sirovich (*Co-Founder*)
Jeremy Mindich (*Co-Founder*)

SCOPPECHIO
437 W Jefferson St, Louisville, KY 40202
Tel.: (502) 584-8787 KY
Web Site:
  http://www.scoppechio.com
Year Founded: 1987
Emp.: 170
Advetising Agency
N.A.I.C.S.: 541810
Debbie Scoppechio (*Chm*)
Toni Clem (*Pres & COO*)
Jerry Preyss (*CEO*)
Steve Leder (*Chief Creative Officer*)
Ben Williamson (*Sr Acct Exec*)

SCORE ASSOCIATION
1175 Herndon Pkwy, Herndon, VA 20170
Tel.: (703) 487-3612
Web Site: http://www.score.org
Sales Range: $10-24.9 Million
Professional Organizations
N.A.I.C.S.: 813920
John Fuqua (*Dir-Fin*)
Bridget Weston Pollack (*VP-Mktg & Comm*)
Steve Records (*VP-Field Ops*)
Chris Clark (*VP-Tech*)
Resa Kierstein (*VP-Dev*)
W. Kenneth Yancey Jr. (*CEO*)

SCORPEX, INC.
10300 W Charleston Blvd 13-160, Las Vegas, NV 89135
Tel.: (310) 891-1838
Year Founded: 1999
Waste Management Services
N.A.I.C.S.: 562998
Joseph Caywood (*CEO*)

SCORPION DESIGN LLC
3301 N Thanksgiving Way Ste 500, Lehi, UT 84043
Tel.: (866) 344-8852 CA
Web Site: http://www.scorpion.co
Year Founded: 2001
Emp.: 501
Website Design & Internet Marketing
N.A.I.C.S.: 541512
Rustin Kretz (*Founder & CEO*)
Eric R. Reuveni (*Chief Delivery Officer*)
Jamie Adams (*Chief Revenue Officer*)
Dan Bedell (*COO*)
Corey Quinn (*CMO*)
Matthew Shepherd (*CFO*)
Sarah Raphael (*Chief Org Dev Officer*)
Michael A. Sauer (*Chief Legal Officer*)
Michelle Annett (*VP-Creative Dev*)
Christine Brello (*VP-Client Mktg-Healthcare*)
Jeffrey T. Kretz (*CTO*)
Tony McGinnis (*Exec VP-Internet Mktg*)
Julia Cook (*Exec VP-Internet Mktg*)
Kevin Szypula (*Chief Adv Officer*)
Lauren Persico (*Exec VP*)
Azim Nagree (*Head-M&A*)

Subsidiaries:

MediaSmack Inc. (1)
700 Lavaca St Ste 1400, Austin, TX 78701
Tel.: (512) 960-3013
Web Site: http://www.mediasmack.com
Digital Marketing Services
N.A.I.C.S.: 541810
Zach Thompson (*Founder & CEO*)
Amanda Snowden (*Pres*)
Ola Alibaloye (*Mgr-Website Dept*)
Zain Khan (*Acct Mgr*)
Jatin Nahar (*Mgr-Website Platform*)

SCORPION PROTECTIVE COATINGS, INC.
6184 S US Hwy 231, Cloverdale, IN 46120
Tel.: (765) 653-1736
Web Site:
  http://www.scorpioncoatings.com
Year Founded: 1996
Sales Range: $1-9.9 Million
Emp.: 14
Manufactures & Wholesales Specialty Polyurethane Coatings & Window Films in Commercial Construction
N.A.I.C.S.: 326113
Clayton Tomasino (*CEO*)
Dana Mitchell (*VP-Sls*)

SCORR MARKETING
2201 Central Ave Ste A, Kearney, NE 68847-5346
Tel.: (308) 237-5567
Web Site:
  http://www.scorrmarketing.com
Sales Range: $1-9.9 Million
Emp.: 35
Fiscal Year-end: 10/31/15
Strategic & Creative Marketing Campaigns
N.A.I.C.S.: 541820
Ben Rowe (*Chief Creative Officer & SR VP*)
Cinda Orr (*CEO*)
Michael Pohl (*Dir-Digital Design*)
Ryan Larsen (*Dir-Digital Strategy*)
Krystle Buntemeyer (*Pres*)
Brook Pierce (*Dir-Creative Svcs*)
Christine Wigert (*Sr Dir-Program & Acct Svcs*)
Joanna Disley (*Dir-European*)
Lea Studer (*Sr VP-Mktg Comm*)
Stephanie Todd (*Mgr-Production*)
Dee Fuehrer (*Dir-Trade Show*)
Alyshia Samuelson (*Mgr-Program*)
Holli Kroeker (*Mgr-PR & Media*)
Cliff Echols (*Dir-Market Intelligence*)
Cherie Squires (*Sr Dir-Program Mgmt*)
Lauren Naughton (*Dir-Bus Dev*)
Ashlee Swanson (*Dir-Copy*)
Lea LaFerla (*VP-Mktg Svcs*)
Edlyn Tobias (*Mgr-Mktg Tech*)
James Wang (*Assoc Dir-Bus Dev*)
Jeremy Edwards (*VP-Strategic Bus Dev*)

SCOT FORGE COMPANY INC.
8001 Winn Rd, Spring Grove, IL 60081-9687
Tel.: (847) 587-1000
Web Site: http://www.scotforge.com
Year Founded: 1893
Sales Range: $25-49.9 Million
Emp.: 500
Provider of Iron & Steel Forgings
N.A.I.C.S.: 332111
John L. Cain (*Chm, Pres & CEO*)
Stephanie Baidinger (*Acct Mgr*)
Tony Biell (*Dir-Quality Assurance & Metallurgy*)
Ken Pedraza (*Acct Mgr*)
Chris Scheiblhofer (*Dir-Forge & Heat Treat*)

SCOT FORGE COMPANY INC.

Scot Forge Company Inc.—(Continued)
Craig Weidner *(Plant Mgr-Spring Grove)*
Harry Clayton *(Plant Mgr-Franklin Park)*
Jim Merkel *(Exec Dir-Sls & Mktg)*
Mike Dominas *(Dir-Forging Dev)*
Richard Hobday *(Plant Mgr-Clinton)*
Rob Harlan *(Dir-IT)*
Steve Brahm *(Dir-Technical Ops)*

SCOT INDUSTRIES INC.
3756 Farm Rd 250, Lone Star, TX 75668
Tel.: (903) 639-2551
Web Site: http://www.scotindustries.com
Rev.: $92,700,000
Emp.: 100
Steel
N.A.I.C.S.: 423510
Steven L. Wilmeth *(Pres)*
David Jacks *(Controller)*
Clint Mabey *(Mgr-Matls)*

SCOTCH & GULF LUMBER, LLC
1850 Conception St Rd, Mobile, AL 36633-4704
Tel.: (251) 457-6872   DE
Web Site: http://www.scotchgulf.com
Year Founded: 1972
Sales Range: $100-124.9 Million
Emp.: 205
Rough, Sawed & Planed Lumber
N.A.I.C.S.: 321113
Fred T. Stimpson *(Pres & CEO)*
William Sandy Stimpson *(Sr VP)*
James Conner *(Controller)*
Robert Mitchell Shackleford III *(Pres)*

SCOTCH PLYWOOD COMPANY OF ALABAMA
101 Main St, Fulton, AL 36446
Tel.: (334) 636-2731
Web Site: http://www.scotchplywood.com
Year Founded: 1965
Sales Range: $25-49.9 Million
Emp.: 180
Plywood Mfr & Sales
N.A.I.C.S.: 321212
Kay Harrigan Woods *(Chm)*
T. H. Onelia Jr. *(Pres)*

SCOTSCO INC.
16750 SE Kerns Ct, Milwaukie, OR 97267-9733
Tel.: (503) 653-7791   OR
Web Site: http://www.scotsco.com
Year Founded: 1971
Sales Range: $10-24.9 Million
Emp.: 28
Industrial Machinery & Equipment Sales
N.A.I.C.S.: 423830
Don Sharpe *(CFO)*
Steve Byerly *(Pres)*
Mark Boersma *(VP)*
Jon Castleman *(Dir-Sls)*
Yuriy Veytsman *(Mgr-Parts)*
Lisa Ward *(Mgr-Product Line)*
Jim Librande *(Mgr-Tech Svcs)*

SCOTT & REID GENERAL CONTRACTORS INC.
17300 Dallas Pkwy Ste 2000, Dallas, TX 75248
Tel.: (469) 374-3400
Web Site: http://www.scottandreid.com
Year Founded: 1992
Sales Range: $10-24.9 Million
Emp.: 75

Provider of Nonresidential Construction Services
N.A.I.C.S.: 236220
Christopher J. Scott *(CEO)*
Brad D. Reid *(Pres)*
Daniel Kearns *(Exec VP)*

SCOTT & WHITE HEALTH PLAN INC.
1206 W Campus Dr, Temple, TX 76502-0001
Tel.: (254) 298-3000   TX
Web Site: http://www.swhp.org
Year Founded: 1979
Sales Range: $10-24.9 Million
Emp.: 300
Health Maintenance Services
N.A.I.C.S.: 621491
Scott Dickison *(CFO)*
Jeffrey Ingrum *(CEO)*

SCOTT AND MURPHY, INC.
2335 Barren River Rd, Bowling Green, KY 42101-9483
Tel.: (270) 781-9944
Web Site: http://www.scottandmurphy.com
Industrial Building Construction
N.A.I.C.S.: 236210
Todd Matthews *(VP)*

Subsidiaries:

Hartz Construction Corp.   (1)
1855 Old Calhoun Rd, Owensboro, KY 42301
Tel.: (270) 926-6554
Web Site: http://scottmurphydaniel.com
Residential Remodeler
N.A.I.C.S.: 236118

SCOTT BRIDGE COMPANY INC.
2641 Interstate Dr, Opelika, AL 36801-1527
Tel.: (334) 749-5045
Web Site: http://www.scottbridge.com
Sales Range: $25-49.9 Million
Emp.: 250
Bridge Construction
N.A.I.C.S.: 237310
I. J. Scott *(Pres)*
William Scott *(VP)*
Charles Davis *(VP-Engrg)*
Michael Terrell *(VP)*

SCOTT BROWN MEDIA GROUP
645 Pressley Rd Ste D, Charlotte, NC 28217
Tel.: (704) 525-9775
Web Site: http://www.scottbrownmedia.com
Year Founded: 2005
Sales Range: $1-9.9 Million
Emp.: 24
Advetising Agency
N.A.I.C.S.: 541810
Rhonda Yagey *(Dir-Creative Svcs)*

SCOTT CABLE COMMUNICATIONS
42 Toledo St, Farmingdale, NY 11735
Tel.: (631) 694-7157
Web Site: http://www.scottcablecommunications.com
Sales Range: $50-74.9 Million
Emp.: 20
Radio & Television Equipment & Parts
N.A.I.C.S.: 423690
Vivian Leykamm *(Chm & Pres)*
Robert Ballas *(CEO & VP-Ops)*
Steven Ballas *(CFO)*
Scott Leykamm *(Mgr-Warehouse)*

SCOTT CITRUS MANAGEMENT, INC.
650 N Rock Rd, Fort Pierce, FL 34945
Tel.: (772) 461-7425   FL
Web Site: http://www.scottcitrus.com
Year Founded: 1990
Administrative Management & General Management Consulting Service
N.A.I.C.S.: 541611
Ken Scott *(Pres)*

SCOTT CLARK HONDA
7025 E Independence Blvd, Charlotte, NC 28227-9420
Tel.: (704) 535-4444   NC
Web Site: http://www.scottclarkhonda.com
Year Founded: 1977
Sales Range: $100-124.9 Million
Emp.: 100
Car Dealership
N.A.I.C.S.: 441110
Tony Lowder *(Mgr-Fin)*
Marcus Nicholson *(Gen Mgr-Sls)*
Justin Mann *(Dir-Fin)*
Peter Moreno *(Mgr-Fin)*
Patrick Hedrick *(Mgr-Parts)*

SCOTT COOPERATIVE ASSOCIATION
410 E 1st St, Scott City, KS 67871
Tel.: (620) 872-5823
Web Site: http://www.scottcoop.com
Sales Range: $10-24.9 Million
Emp.: 35
Grains
N.A.I.C.S.: 424510
Gary Friesen *(Gen Mgr)*
Craig Ramsey *(Treas & Sec)*
Jason Baker *(Controller & Mgr-Acctg)*

SCOTT CREDIT UNION
101 Credit Union Way, Edwardsville, IL 62025
Tel.: (618) 345-1000   IL
Web Site: http://www.scu.org
Year Founded: 1943
Sales Range: $25-49.9 Million
Emp.: 224
Credit Union
N.A.I.C.S.: 522130
Adam Koishor *(CMO)*
Donald Pierre *(Vice Chm)*
Frank Padak *(Pres & CEO)*
Pete Hostetter *(Chm)*
Wendy Erhart *(COO)*

Subsidiaries:

Tempo Bank   (1)
28 W Broadway, Trenton, IL 62293
Tel.: (618) 224-9228
Web Site: http://www.tempobank.com
Banking Services
N.A.I.C.S.: 522110
Francis J. Eversman *(Pres & COO)*
Robert J. Stroh Jr. *(Chm, CEO & CFO)*

SCOTT CRUMP TOYOTA SCION, INC.
3815 Hwy 78 E, Jasper, AL 35501
Tel.: (205) 221-3939
Web Site: http://www.scottcrumptoyota.com
Sales Range: $50-74.9 Million
Emp.: 50
New Car Dealers
N.A.I.C.S.: 441110
Scott Crump *(Owner)*

SCOTT ELECTRIC COMPANY
1000 S Main St, Greensburg, PA 15601
Tel.: (724) 834-4321
Web Site: http://www.scottelectricusa.com

U.S. PRIVATE

Year Founded: 1946
Sales Range: $25-49.9 Million
Emp.: 60
Providers of Electrical Services
N.A.I.C.S.: 423610
Samuel Scott *(Pres)*

SCOTT ENERGY CO., INC.
43 Gloucester Ave, Gloucester, MA 01930
Tel.: (978) 526-4929   MA
Web Site: http://www.scottenergyco.com
Year Founded: 1976
Sales Range: $10-24.9 Million
Fuel Oil Dealers
N.A.I.C.S.: 457210
William Scott *(Pres)*

SCOTT EQUIPMENT CO.
605 4th Ave NW, New Prague, MN 56071
Tel.: (952) 758-2591
Web Site: http://www.scottequipment.com
Sales Range: $10-24.9 Million
Emp.: 75
Chemical Machinery & Equipment
N.A.I.C.S.: 333248
Shirley Walker *(Sec)*

SCOTT EQUIPMENT COMPANY, LLC
1000 Martin Luther King, Jr Dr, Monroe, LA 71203
Tel.: (318) 388-9200   LA
Web Site: http://www.scottcompanies.com
Year Founded: 1939
Tractors & General Construction Equipment Dealer
N.A.I.C.S.: 423810
Scott Cummins *(Pres)*
Jim Bershen *(CEO)*
Bobbie W. Bordelon *(Exec VP & CFO)*
Eric Goebel *(COO)*
Curley Bordelon *(Sr VP-Div Mgr)*
Andy Beebe *(VP-Div Mgr)*

SCOTT EQUIPMENT INCORPORATED
14635 Valley Blvd, Fontana, CA 92335
Tel.: (909) 822-2200   CA
Web Site: http://www.scottequip.com
Year Founded: 1972
Sales Range: $10-24.9 Million
Emp.: 45
Construction & Agricultural Equipment, Industrial Truck & Utility Trailer Sales & Rental Services
N.A.I.C.S.: 423810
Richard N. Scott Jr. *(Pres & CEO)*

Subsidiaries:

Western Rentals Incorporated   (1)
14635 Vly Blvd, Fontana, CA 92335
Tel.: (909) 822-8008
Web Site: http://www.scottequip.com
Sales Range: $1-9.9 Million
Emp.: 20
Construction & Agricultural Equipment, Industrial Truck & Utility Trailer Rental Services
N.A.I.C.S.: 532412
Greg Scott *(VP)*

SCOTT EQUITY EXCHANGE CO.
12529 Blaine St, Scott, OH 45886
Tel.: (419) 622-6151
Web Site: http://www.scottequityexchange.com
Sales Range: $10-24.9 Million
Emp.: 9
Grain & Field Bean Whslr

N.A.I.C.S.: 424510
Jon Etzler (Gen Mgr)

SCOTT FISCHER ENTERPRISES LLC
9510 Thunder Rd, Fort Myers, FL 33913
Tel.: (239) 690-4647
Web Site: http://www.sfe-us.com
Sales Range: $75-99.9 Million
Emp.: 380
Motorcycle Dealership Owner & Operator
N.A.I.C.S.: 441227
Scott Fischer (Founder & CEO)
John Greene (Partner)
Kimberly Haskins (CFO)
Sean Delaney (Gen Mgr-Sls)
Karen Henz (Gen Mgr)
Michael Buckingham (Gen Mgr)

Subsidiaries:

Blue Ridge Harley-Davidson (1)
2002 13th Ave Dr SE, Hickory, NC 28602
Tel.: (828) 327-3030
Web Site: http://www.blueridgehd.com
Sales Range: $10-24.9 Million
Emp.: 30
Motorcycle Dealership
N.A.I.C.S.: 441227
Josh Russom (Owner & Pres)

Naples Harley-Davidson (1)
3645 Gateway Ln, Naples, FL 34109
Tel.: (239) 594-5504
Web Site: http://www.hdnaples.com
Sales Range: $10-24.9 Million
Emp.: 50
Motorcycle Dealership
N.A.I.C.S.: 441227
Scott Fischer (Owner)
Sean Delaney (Gen Mgr)
Jay Robichaud (Mgr-MotorClothes)
Sara Ancefsky (Mgr-Fin)
Jimmy Blevins (Mgr-Parts)
Ken Colts (Mgr-Fin)
Jacob Revak (Coord-Mktg)
Aaron Rodino (Mgr-Svc)
John Tabar (Gen Mgr)

Rocket Harley-Davidson (1)
15100 Hwy 20 W, Madison, AL 35756
Tel.: (256) 340-7333
Web Site: http://www.rocketharley.com
Sales Range: $10-24.9 Million
Emp.: 50
Motorcycle Dealership
N.A.I.C.S.: 441227
Seth Barron (Mgr-Sls)
Caroline Payne (Mgr-P&A)
Richard Anderson (Mgr-Svc)
Matt Todd (Mgr-Fin)
Jeff Lewis (Gen Mgr)
Aaron McAtee (Mgr-Fin)
Moe Meredith (Mgr-Mktg)

Six Bends Harley-Davidson (1)
9501 Thunder Rd, Fort Myers, FL 33913
Tel.: (239) 275-4647
Web Site: http://www.6bendshd.com
Motorcycle Dealers
N.A.I.C.S.: 441227
Nancy Hamilton (Mgr-MotorClothes)
Curtis Mckinley (Gen Mgr)
Aaron Barney (Mgr-Tech Svc)
Ryan Schell (Mgr-Parts)
Taylor Loethen (Mktg Mgr)
Suzette Crase (Accountant)

Thunderbird Harley-Davidson (1)
5000 Alameda Blvd NE, Albuquerque, NM 87113
Tel.: (505) 856-1600
Web Site: http://www.thunderbirdhd.com
Sales Range: $1-9.9 Million
Emp.: 67
Motorcycle Dealers
N.A.I.C.S.: 441227
Scott Fischer (Mgr-Acctg)
Karen Henz (Gen Mgr)
Carol Baluh-Estrada (Mgr-MotorClothes)
Dustin Hughes (Dir-Fin)
Agustin Campos (Mgr-Svc)
Darcie Conklin (Coord-Sls & Fin)
Ben Kirby (Mgr-Sls)
Hector Lozano-Garcia (Dir-Fin)
Ryan Raleigh (Gen Mgr-Sls)

SCOTT GROUP CUSTOM CARPETS, INC.
3232 Kraft Ave SE, Grand Rapids, MI 49512
Tel.: (616) 954-3200
Web Site: http://www.scottgroup.com
Custom Carpet Design & Mfr
N.A.I.C.S.: 314110
Mike Ruggeri (Pres)
Rich Ruggeri (VP)
Tim Hill (VP-Ops & Fin)

Subsidiaries:

Hokanson, Inc. (1)
5120 Woodway Dr Ste 190, Houston, TX 77056
Tel.: (713) 621-6609
Web Site: http://www.hokansoncarpet.com
Sales Range: $1-9.9 Million
Emp.: 85
Carpet & Rug Mill Services
N.A.I.C.S.: 314110
Maureen Catherwood (Pres)

SCOTT HILL ACQUISITION CORPORATION
9454 Wilshire Blvd Ste 612, Beverly Hills, CA 90212
Tel.: (310) 888-1870   DE
Year Founded: 2015
Investment Services
N.A.I.C.S.: 523999
James Cassidy (Pres & Sec)
James McKillop (VP)

SCOTT INDUSTRIAL SYSTEMS INC.
4433 Interpoint Blvd, Dayton, OH 45424-5708
Tel.: (937) 233-8146   OH
Web Site: http://www.scottindustrialsystems.com
Year Founded: 1986
Sales Range: $10-24.9 Million
Emp.: 84
Industrial Machinery & Equipment Sales
N.A.I.C.S.: 423830
Randall R. Scott (Chm)
Christina Logan (Pres)

SCOTT INDUSTRIES LLC
1573 Hwy 136 W, Henderson, KY 42420
Tel.: (270) 831-2037
Web Site: http://www.scott-mfg.com
Rev.: $29,900,000
Emp.: 100
Fiberglass Insulation
N.A.I.C.S.: 327993
T. Scott Miller (Pres)
Rocky Gamblin (Controller)

SCOTT LUMBER COMPANY
54382 National Rd, Bridgeport, OH 43912-9717
Tel.: (740) 635-2345   OH
Year Founded: 1869
Sales Range: $125-149.9 Million
Emp.: 150
Lumber, Building Materials, Hardware, Kitchen Cabinets & Plumbing Materials Mfr
N.A.I.C.S.: 423310

SCOTT M & A CORPORATION
218 W Ash St, Piqua, OH 45356
Tel.: (937) 773-7200
Web Site: http://www.scottmcdonalds.com
Sales Range: $10-24.9 Million
Emp.: 1,300
Fast-Food Restaurant, Chain
N.A.I.C.S.: 722513
Benjamin P. Scott (Pres)

SCOTT PENN, INC.
304 Yandell Ave, Canton, MS 39046-3842
Tel.: (601) 859-2666
Year Founded: 1994
Sales Range: $10-24.9 Million
Emp.: 103
Wood Products Mfr
N.A.I.C.S.: 321999
H. S. Penn (Co-Pres)
Scott Penn (Co-Pres)

SCOTT PET PRODUCTS INC.
US Hwy 41 N, Rockville, IN 47872
Tel.: (765) 569-4636
Web Site: http://www.scottpet.com
Rev.: $15,000,000
Emp.: 100
Pet Supplies
N.A.I.C.S.: 424990
Mike Bassett (CEO)
Tracey Lyons (Mgr-QC)

SCOTT PETROLEUM CORPORATION
102 Main St, Itta Bena, MS 38941
Tel.: (662) 254-9024
Web Site: http://www.scottpetroleuminc.com
Rev.: $65,930,809
Emp.: 14
Petroleum Bulk Stations & Terminals
N.A.I.C.S.: 424710
Donna Overby (Controller)

SCOTT PEYRON & ASSOCIATES, INC.
209 Main St Ste 200, Boise, ID 83702
Tel.: (208) 388-3800
Web Site: http://www.peyron.com
Emp.: 8
N.A.I.C.S.: 541820
Scott Peyron (Principal & Strategist)
Kris Lodge (Mgr-Ops)
Bryce Twitchell (Dir-Creative)
Craig Carter (Mgr-Mktg Practice Grp)

SCOTT PUBLIC RELATIONS
21201 Victory Blvd Ste 270, Canoga Park, CA 91303
Tel.: (818) 610-0270
Web Site: http://www.scottpublicrelations.com
Sales Range: $10-24.9 Million
Emp.: 12
Communications, Public Relations
N.A.I.C.S.: 541820
Joy Scott (Principal)

SCOTT RICE OFFICE INTERIORS
224 E Douglas Ave Ste 100, Wichita, KS 67202
Tel.: (316) 269-2700
Web Site: http://www.scottricewichita.com
Sales Range: $10-24.9 Million
Emp.: 18
Office Furniture
N.A.I.C.S.: 423210

SCOTT ROBINSON HONDA INC.
20340 Hawthorne Blvd, Torrance, CA 90503
Tel.: (310) 371-3521
Web Site: http://www.scottrobinson.com
Rev.: $53,200,000
Emp.: 115
Automobiles, New & Used
N.A.I.C.S.: 441110
Ernie Rivera (Mgr-Fin)

SCOTT SHERV HUMMER INCORPORATED
3333 Lehigh St, Allentown, PA 18103
Tel.: (610) 439-0347
Web Site: http://www.scottcars.com
Rev.: $51,400,000
Emp.: 130
New & Used Car Dealers
N.A.I.C.S.: 441110
Andy Scott (Pres)
Richard Salezze (Principal)

SCOTT SPECIALTIES INC.
512 M St, Belleville, KS 66935
Tel.: (785) 527-5627
Web Site: http://www.scottspecialties.com
Rev.: $16,300,000
Emp.: 115
Orthopedic Appliances
N.A.I.C.S.: 334510
Jim Mcdonald (Pres)
Timothy Wellendorf (VP-Sls & Ops)

SCOTT STREET SENIOR HOUSING COMPLEX INC
2180 Post St, San Francisco, CA 94115
Tel.: (415) 345-5060   CA
Web Site: http://www.rgplaza.org
Year Founded: 1995
Sales Range: $10-24.9 Million
Emp.: 166
Elder Care Services
N.A.I.C.S.: 623312
Amy Rassen (Dir)
Susan Koster (Exec Dir)
Corey Weiner (Dir-Food Svcs)
Iris Hudis (Dir-Community Rels)
John Fletcher (CFO)

SCOTT-CLARKS TOYOTA CITY INC.
13000 E Independence Blvd, Matthews, NC 28105
Tel.: (704) 535-1972
Web Site: http://www.scottclarkstoyota.com
Rev.: $48,800,000
Emp.: 200
Automobiles
N.A.I.C.S.: 441110
Chris Cady (Owner, Pres & Gen Mgr)

SCOTT-GROSS COMPANY, INC.
321 Venable Rd, Winchester, KY 40391
Tel.: (859) 252-7667
Web Site: http://www.scottgross.com
Year Founded: 1949
Sales Range: $10-24.9 Million
Emp.: 140
Gas & Welding Machinery & Equipment, Supplier of Bulk Liquid, Industrial & Medical Gases, Gas Mixtures & Specialty Gases & Fuel Gases Whslr
N.A.I.C.S.: 424690
Paul H. Scott (VP)
Shaw Bennett (Controller)

SCOTT-MCRAE AUTOMOTIVE GROUP INC.
Ste 200 701 Riverside Park Pl, Jacksonville, FL 32204-3339
Tel.: (904) 354-4000   FL
Web Site: http://www.scottmcraegroup.com
Year Founded: 1980
Sales Range: $50-74.9 Million
Emp.: 600
Provider of Automotive Services
N.A.I.C.S.: 441110

SCOTT-MCRAE AUTOMOTIVE GROUP INC.

Scott-McRae Automotive Group Inc.—(Continued)
Alexander Graham (Partner)
Hampton Graham (Partner)
Walter A. McRae Jr. (Chm & Partner)
Subsidiaries:

Auto Credit Investments of Georgia Inc. (1)
701 Riverside Park Pl Ste 200, Jacksonville, FL 32204-3342
Tel.: (904) 354-4000
Web Site: http://www.smag.com
Sales Range: $25-49.9 Million
Emp.: 30
Provider of Investment Services
N.A.I.C.S.: 551112

Auto Credit of Florida Inc. (1)
6255 Lake Gray Blvd 32, Jacksonville, FL 32244 (100%)
Tel.: (904) 387-9800
Sales Range: $25-49.9 Million
Emp.: 30
Provider Of Automobile Loans
N.A.I.C.S.: 522220

Auto Credit of Georgia Inc. (1)
701 Riverside Pk Pl, Jacksonville, FL 32204-3358 (100%)
Tel.: (904) 354-4000
Web Site: http://www.smag.com
Sales Range: $50-74.9 Million
Emp.: 125
Provider of Business Credit Services
N.A.I.C.S.: 522220

Duval Acura (1)
11225 Atlantic Blvd, Jacksonville, FL 32225-6506
Tel.: (904) 725-8000
Web Site: http://www.duvalacura.com
Sales Range: $25-49.9 Million
Emp.: 62
Provider of Automobile Services
N.A.I.C.S.: 441110
Kevin Snyder (Pres)
Mark Lacovara (Gen Mgr-Sls)
Bob Hubbell (Mgr-Sls)
Rafael Mejia (VP-Sls)
Eric Porter (Mgr-Sls)

Duval Motor Company Inc. (1)
1616 Cassat Ave, Jacksonville, FL 32210-1600
Tel.: (904) 387-6541
Sales Range: $25-49.9 Million
Emp.: 250
Provider of Automobile Services
N.A.I.C.S.: 441120

Duval Motors at the Avenues Inc (1)
701 Riverside Park Pl Ste 310, Jacksonville, FL 32204-3342
Tel.: (904) 354-4000
Sales Range: $10-24.9 Million
Emp.: 3
Provider of Management Services
N.A.I.C.S.: 561110

Scott-McRae Advertising Inc. (1)
701 Riverside Pk Pl Ste 100, Jacksonville, FL 32204-3343
Tel.: (904) 354-4900
Sales Range: $10-24.9 Million
Emp.: 7
Advertising, Media Buying Services
N.A.I.C.S.: 541810

Scott-McRae Investments Inc. (1)
701 Riverside Park Pl Ste 120, Jacksonville, FL 32204-3339
Tel.: (904) 354-4000
Web Site: http://www.smag.com
Sales Range: $25-49.9 Million
Emp.: 50
Investment Services
N.A.I.C.S.: 523999
William Kane (Controller)

Scott-McRae Properties Inc. (1)
Ste 120 701 Riverside Pk Pl, Jacksonville, FL 32204-3339
Tel.: (904) 354-4000
Web Site: http://www.smag.com
Sales Range: $10-24.9 Million
Emp.: 5
Provider of Nonresidential Building Services

N.A.I.C.S.: 531120

SCOTTEVEST INC.
411 6th St E, Ketchum, ID 83340
Tel.: (208) 727-6700
Web Site: http://www.scottevest.com
Year Founded: 2000
Sales Range: $1-9.9 Million
Emp.: 18
Travel Clothing
N.A.I.C.S.: 458110
Scott Jordan (Co-Owner)
Laura Jordan (Co-Owner)
Chris Dahms (Creative Dir)

SCOTTISH AMERICAN CAPITAL LLC
110W 40th St, New York, NY 10018
Tel.: (718) 906-5300
Web Site: http://www.scottishamerican.com
Sales Range: $10-24.9 Million
Private Investment Firm
N.A.I.C.S.: 523999
Subsidiaries:

Buckingham Badler Associates, Inc. (1)
2 Teleport Corporate Commons 2 Ste 105, Staten Island, NY 10311
Tel.: (718) 906-5300
Web Site: http://scottishamerican.com
Sales Range: $10-24.9 Million
Emp.: 25
Insurance Agencies & Brokerages
N.A.I.C.S.: 524210
Paul Thomson (Owner)

SCOTTISH AMERICAN INSURANCE GENERAL AGENCY, INC.
627 W College St, Grapevine, TX 76051
Tel.: (714) 550-5050
Web Site: http://www.scottishamerican.com
Year Founded: 2009
Investment Services
N.A.I.C.S.: 523999
Steven A. Cook (CFO)
Paul Thomson (Founder)
Subsidiaries:

Kaliff Insurance (1)
1250 NE Loop 410 Ste 630, San Antonio, TX 78209-1536
Tel.: (210) 829-7635
Web Site: http://www.kaliff.com
Insurance Agencies & Brokerages
N.A.I.C.S.: 524210
Mitchell Kaliff (Chm & CEO)

SCOTTO & MELCHIORRE GROUP LLC
300 Corporate Plz, Islandia, NY 11749
Tel.: (631) 481-8600
Web Site: http://www.scottomelchiorre.com
Year Founded: 2014
Sales Range: $1-9.9 Million
Emp.: 16
Financial Investment Services
N.A.I.C.S.: 523940
Gregory M. Scotto (Mng Partner)
Wesley S. Melchiorre (Partner)
Perry Colletti (Principal)
David M. Isaacs (Mgr-EA)
Diana Bertolami (Mgr-Bookkeeper)

SCOTTO'S HOLDING CORP.
40 Crossways Park Dr, Woodbury, NY 11797-2038
Tel.: (516) 333-8777
Web Site: http://www.scottobrothers.com
Year Founded: 1967

Sales Range: $25-49.9 Million
Emp.: 650
Holding Company; Restaurants
N.A.I.C.S.: 722320
Anthony Scotto (Pres & CEO)
Subsidiaries:

Carle Place Restaurant Inc. (1)
440 Old Country Rd, Carle Place, NY 11514-2122
Tel.: (516) 334-6125
Web Site: http://www.chateaubriandcaterers.com
Sales Range: $10-24.9 Million
Emp.: 150
Provider of Restaurant Services
N.A.I.C.S.: 722320

Scotto Brothers Enterprises, Inc. (1)
40 Crossways Park Dr, Woodbury, NY 11797-2038
Tel.: (516) 333-8777
Web Site: http://www.scottobros.com
Sales Range: $10-24.9 Million
Emp.: 20
Provider of Restaurant Services
N.A.I.C.S.: 722511

Scotto Brothers Westbury Restaurant Inc. (1)
1100 Jericho Tpke, Westbury, NY 11590
Tel.: (516) 333-7117
Sales Range: $10-24.9 Million
Emp.: 40
Provider of Restaurant Services
N.A.I.C.S.: 722320

Scotto Brothers Woodbury Restaurant Inc. (1)
40 Crossways Park Dr, Woodbury, NY 11797-2039
Tel.: (516) 333-8777
Web Site: http://www.scottobrothers.com
Rev.: $3,800,000
Emp.: 150
Restaurant Services
N.A.I.C.S.: 722511

SCOTTSDALE ART FACTORY LLC
7407 E Greenway Rd, Scottsdale, AZ 85260
Tel.: (480) 483-0170
Web Site: http://www.artfactory.com
Rev.: $11,500,000
Emp.: 20
Decorative Wood & Woodwork
N.A.I.C.S.: 321999

SCOTTSDALE CONVENTION & VISITORS BUREAU
4343 N Scottsdale Rd Ste 170, Scottsdale, AZ 85251
Tel.: (480) 421-1004 AZ
Web Site: http://www.experiencescottsdale.com
Year Founded: 2001
Sales Range: $10-24.9 Million
Emp.: 50
Convention & Visitor Bureau Services
N.A.I.C.S.: 561591
Rachel Pearson (VP-Community & Govt Affairs)
JoAnne Zeterberg (Dir-Creative)
Caroline Stoeckel (VP-Mktg)
Kelly Triplett (Dir-Mktg)
Genia Kehayes (VP-Fin & Admin)
Laura McMurchie (VP-Comm)
Eric Paschal (Dir-IT)
Stephanie Flick (Mgr-Natl Sls-Mid Atlantic)
Sarah Kearney (Dir-Tourism)
Tracy Jackson (Mgr-Natl Sls)
Kelli Blubaum (VP-Convention Sls & Svcs)
Kimberly Urich (Mgr-Natl Sls & Canadian Acct)
Sharon Utsunomiya (Mgr-Visitor Center)

U.S. PRIVATE

Deanne Boynton Grupp (VP-Tourism)
Shannon Johnson (Mgr-Natl Sls-Rocky Mountain)

SCOTTSDALE CULTURAL COUNCIL
7380 E 2nd St, Scottsdale, AZ 85251
Tel.: (480) 994-2787 AZ
Web Site: http://www.sccarts.org
Year Founded: 1987
Sales Range: $10-24.9 Million
Emp.: 172
Cultural Center Operator
N.A.I.C.S.: 711310
Eileen Wilson (Dir-Donor Rels)
William Kelly (Mgr-Retail)
Jason Song (Mgr-IT)
Andrew Chippindall (Chm)
Diana Smith (Vice Chm)
Jack Nydahl (Controller)
Lisa DeGroodt (Mgr-HR)
Mike Miller (Interim CEO)
Karen Churchard (Dir-Tourism & Events)
Natalie Marsh (Dir-Education & Outreach)
Stephen Baker (Dir-Mktg & Comm)

SCOTTSDALE PLAZA RESORT LLC
7400 E McCormick Pkwy 201b, Scottsdale, AZ 85258
Tel.: (480) 951-7400
Web Site: http://www.scottsdaleplaza.com
Sales Range: $25-49.9 Million
Emp.: 400
Resort Hotel
N.A.I.C.S.: 721110
John W. Dawson (Chm & CEO)
Marti Waicelunas (VP-Conference & Catering Svcs)
Jerry DePalo (Dir-Transportation)
Jim Sullivan (VP-Food & Beverage)
Sheryl Bettencourt (Dir-Mktg)
Katie Modahl (Mgr-Natl Sls)

SCOTTYS CONTRACTING & STONE LLC
2300 Barren River Rd, Bowling Green, KY 42101
Tel.: (270) 781-3998
Web Site: http://www.scottyscontracting.com
Sales Range: $50-74.9 Million
Emp.: 300
Highway & Street Paving Contractor
N.A.I.C.S.: 236210
James D. Scott (Chm)
Derek Doig (Project Mgr)

SCOTTYS FASHIONS, INC.
636 Pen Argyl St, Pen Argyl, PA 18072-1935
Tel.: (610) 863-4157
Web Site: http://www.scottysfashions.com
Rev.: $18,200,000
Emp.: 4
Women's & Juniors' Clothing
N.A.I.C.S.: 315250
Neil Scott (Pres & CEO)

SCOTWORK (NA)
400 Lanidex Plaza, Parsippany, NJ 07054-2705
Tel.: (973) 428-1991
Web Site: http://www.scotworkusa.com
Year Founded: 1975
Sales Range: $10-24.9 Million
Emp.: 200
International Negotiating Skills Training & Consultancy Services
N.A.I.C.S.: 541618
Marty Finkle (CEO)

COMPANIES

SCOVILL HOLDINGS INC.
100 Chetwynd Dr, Bryn Mawr, PA 19010
Tel.: (610) 520-7700
Rev.: $64,300,000
Emp.: 3
Aerospace Castings, Aluminum
N.A.I.C.S.: 331524
Washburn S. Oberwager *(Pres)*

SCP CONSTRUCTION, LLC
5340 W Luke Ave, Glendale, AZ 85301
Tel.: (623) 931-9131
Web Site: http://www.scpaz.com
Year Founded: 1972
Rev.: $25,300,000
Emp.: 290
Concrete Work
N.A.I.C.S.: 238110
Paul A. Stecker *(Co-Owner)*
Todd Stecker *(Pres)*
Philip Stecker *(Co-Owner)*
Doug Stecker *(Co-Owner)*

SCP WORLDWIDE
200 Park Ave 16th Fl, New York, NY 10166
Tel.: (212) 490-1414
Web Site:
    http://www.scpworldwide.net
Year Founded: 2001
Sales Range: $25-49.9 Million
Emp.: 24
Private Equity Firm; Sports, Entertainment & Media Companies
N.A.I.C.S.: 523999
Michael McCarthy *(Partner)*
Kenneth Munoz *(Partner)*
Jim Abry *(CFO)*
Subsidiaries:

Real Salt Lake (1)
9256 S State St, Sandy, UT 84070
Tel.: (801) 727-2700
Web Site: http://www.realsaltlake.com
Sales Range: $25-49.9 Million
Professional Soccer Club
N.A.I.C.S.: 711211
Elliot Fall *(Gen Mgr)*
Andy Carroll *(Chief Bus Officer)*
Canada Clawson *(Mgr-Sls)*
Dell Loy Hansen *(Owner)*
Kasia Kampf *(Accountant & Coord-Logistics)*
Craig Martin *(VP-Facility Ops & Gen Mgr)*
Tara Silcox *(CFO)*
Rob Zarkos *(Exec VP-Soccer Ops)*
Tony Beltran *(Asst Gen Mgr)*
Dan Egner *(Dir-Technical)*

St. Louis Blues Hockey Club, LLC (1)
1401 Clark Ave, Saint Louis, MO 63103-2700
Tel.: (314) 622-2500
Web Site: http://www.blues.nhl.com
Sales Range: $25-49.9 Million
Professional Hockey Franchise
N.A.I.C.S.: 711211
David W. Checketts *(Chm)*
Jennifer Nevins *(Dir-Association & Promotional Sls)*
George Pavlik *(Dir-Retail)*
Phil Siddle *(CFO & Grp VP)*
Eric Stisser *(Sr VP-Corp Sponsorship)*
Christopher Zimmerman *(Pres & CEO-Bus Ops)*
Doug Armstrong *(Pres-Hockey Ops & Gen Mgr)*
Bill Armstrong *(Dir-Amateur Scouting)*
Rob DiMaio *(Dir-Player Personnel)*
Bryan Lucas *(VP-Corp Sponsorship)*
Kevin McDonald *(Asst Gen Mgr)*
Tim Taylor *(Dir-Player Dev)*
Kevin Maxwell *(Gen Mgr-Springfield Thunderbirds)*

SCR CONSTRUCTION CO. INC.
5420 FM 2218, Richmond, TX 77469

Tel.: (281) 344-0700
Web Site:
    http://www.scrconstruction.net
Sales Range: $10-24.9 Million
Emp.: 40
General Contractor of Highway & Street Construction Services
N.A.I.C.S.: 237310
Steve Roberts *(Pres)*
Diana Itzoski *(Controller)*

SCR, INC.
8680 Sw Old Tualatin Sherwood Rd, Tualatin, OR 97062-9503
Tel.: (503) 968-1300   OR
Year Founded: 1976
Sales Range: Less than $1 Million
Emp.: 7
Whslr of Wood Products
N.A.I.C.S.: 423310
Richard Crabtree *(VP)*
Terry Crabtree *(Pres)*
Tracie Day *(Controller)*

SCRANTON EQUITY EXCHANGE INC.
12 Hamilton St Hwy 67, Scranton, ND 58653
Tel.: (701) 275-8221
Web Site:
    http://www.scrantonequity.org
Year Founded: 1914
Sales Range: $10-24.9 Million
Emp.: 45
Grain & Field Beans
N.A.I.C.S.: 424510
Renee Brown *(Office Mgr)*
Mark Kelner *(Pres)*
Mike Wedwick *(Gen Mgr)*
Dale Hande *(Mgr-Feed Dept)*
Karen Brown *(Mgr-Buffalo Feed)*
Damon Reitz *(Mgr-Agronomy)*
Donna Schaff *(Mgr-Farm & Fuel)*
Kathy Kromarek *(Mgr-Super Valu)*
Bob Susa *(Mgr-Parts)*

SCRANTON GILLETTE COMMUNICATIONS, INC.
3030 W Salt Creek Ln Ste 201, Arlington Heights, IL 60005-5025
Tel.: (847) 391-1000
Web Site:
    http://www.scrantongillette.com
Sales Range: $10-24.9 Million
Emp.: 60
Business-to-Business Communications Publisher
N.A.I.C.S.: 513120
Kevin Herda *(Dir-IT)*
Subsidiaries:

SGC Horizon LLC (1)
3030 W Salt Creek Ln Ste 201, Arlington Heights, IL 60005-5025
Tel.: (847) 391-1000
Web Site: http://www.sgchorizon.com
Magazine Publisher
N.A.I.C.S.: 513120

SCRANTON MANUFACTURING COMPANY INC.
101 State St, Scranton, IA 51462
Tel.: (712) 652-3396
Web Site:
    http://www.newwaytrucks.com
Rev.: $22,500,000
Emp.: 225
Motor Vehicle Body Mfr
N.A.I.C.S.: 336211
John McLaughlin *(CEO)*
Scott Rupiper *(Mgr-Sls-Midwest)*

SCRANTON-LACKAWANNA HUMAN DEVELOPMENT AGENCY, INC.

321 Spruce St 1st Fl, Scranton, PA 18503
Tel.: (570) 963-6836   PA
Web Site: http://www.slhda.org
Year Founded: 1965
Sales Range: $10-24.9 Million
Emp.: 396
Community Action Services
N.A.I.C.S.: 624190
Sam Ceccaci *(Exec Dir)*

SCRAP METAL SERVICES, LLC
13830 Brainard Ave, Burnham, IL 60633
Tel.: (708) 730-1400
Web Site:
    http://www.scrapmetalservices.com
Sales Range: $300-349.9 Million
Emp.: 300
Metal Scrapping Services
N.A.I.C.S.: 332811
Jeffry K. Gertler *(Co-Founder & Co-Chm)*
Ryan Johnson *(Controller)*
JoLynn Gosser *(CFO)*
Richard Gertler *(Co-Founder & Co-Chm)*
Keith Rhodes *(CFO)*
Ryan Malone *(Chief Mktg Officer)*
Wendy Webb Williams *(Chief Legal Officer)*
Craig Bahner *(CEO)*

SCRAP YOUR TRIP.COM
7111 Grand National Dr Ste 108, Orlando, FL 32819
Tel.: (407) 351-1501
Web Site:
    http://www.scrapyourtrip.com
Year Founded: 2005
Sales Range: $1-9.9 Million
Emp.: 25
Travel & Theme-Specific Scrapbook Supplies
N.A.I.C.S.: 459999
Julie E. Swatek *(Founder & Pres)*

SCREENINGONE, INC.
1860 N Avenida Republica de Cuba, Tampa, FL 33605
Web Site:
    http://www.screeningone.com
Sales Range: $1-9.9 Million
Emp.: 30
Background Screening & Applicant Tracking Software
N.A.I.C.S.: 513210
Michael Byrd *(Pres)*
Matthew Briggs *(CEO)*

SCREW CONVEYOR INDUSTRIES
700 Hoffman St, Hammond, IN 46327-1827
Tel.: (219) 931-1450   IN
Web Site:
    http://www.screwconveyor.com
Year Founded: 1932
Rev.: $20,000,000
Emp.: 300
Screw Conveyor Mfr
N.A.I.C.S.: 333922
Thomas Polka *(Sec)*
Subsidiaries:

Screw Conveyor Industries - Visalia Plant (1)
7807 Doe Ave, Visalia, CA 93291-9220
Tel.: (559) 651-2131
Conveyor Equipment Mfr
N.A.I.C.S.: 333922

Screw Conveyor Industries - Winona Plant (1)
781 Church St, Winona, MS 38967-3021
Tel.: (662) 283-3142

Conveyor Equipment Mfr
N.A.I.C.S.: 333922

SCRIBD, INC.
539 Bryant St Ste 200, San Francisco, CA 94107
Tel.: (415) 896-9890
Web Site: http://www.scribd.com
Year Founded: 2007
Emp.: 55
Digital Book Subscription Services
N.A.I.C.S.: 459210
Trip Adler *(CEO)*
Ariana Hellebuyck *(CMO)*

SCRIBEAMERICA
1200 East Las Olas Boulevard Ste 201, Fort Lauderdale, FL 33301
Tel.: (877) 488-5479
Web Site:
    http://www.scribeamerica.com
Year Founded: 2004
Sales Range: $1-9.9 Million
Emp.: 7,000
Template, Electronic & Computer Based Documentation to Hospital Emergency Rooms
N.A.I.C.S.: 622110
Michael Murphy *(CEO)*
Sarah Esquibel *(COO)*
Gary B. Glass *(Gen Counsel & Head-HR)*
Craig Newman *(Chief Strategy Officer)*

SCRIP COMPANIES
360 Veterans Pkwy Ste 115, Bolingbrook, IL 60440-4673
Tel.: (630) 771-7400
Web Site:
    http://www.scripcompanies.com
Year Founded: 1967
Sales Range: $10-24.9 Million
Emp.: 126
Massage Equipment & Supplies Distr
N.A.I.C.S.: 423450
Kray Kibler *(CFO)*
John Matusiewicz *(VP)*

SCRIP-SAFE SECURITY PRODUCTS, INC.
136 Commerce Dr, Loveland, OH 45140
Tel.: (513) 697-7789   OH
Web Site: http://www.scrip-safe.com
Year Founded: 1989
Sales Range: $10-24.9 Million
Emp.: 40
Document Preparation Services & Software Publisher
N.A.I.C.S.: 561410
Joe Orndorff *(Founder, Pres & CEO)*
Jo Anne Orndorff *(CFO)*
Mark Strickland *(Sr VP)*
Anne Thatcher *(COO)*
J. James Wager *(CIO & VP)*
Subsidiaries:

Credentials Inc. (1)
436 Frontage Rd Ste 200, Northfield, IL 60093
Tel.: (847) 716-3000
Web Site: http://www.credentials-inc.com
Electronic Document Preparation Services & Software Publisher
N.A.I.C.S.: 561410
Thomas D. McKechney *(CEO)*
J. Jeffrey Geldermann *(Pres, COO & Mgr-IT)*
Terry Reed *(Sr VP-Acct Svcs)*
John H. Weber Jr. *(Exec VP)*

SCRIPHESSCO
360 Veterans Pkwy Ste 115, Bolingbrook, IL 60440
Tel.: (309) 771-7400

SCRIPHESSCO

ScripHessco—(Continued)

Web Site:
http://www.scriphessco.com
Sales Range: $10-24.9 Million
Emp.: 55
Physician Equipment & Supplies
N.A.I.C.S.: 423910
Rob Cooper *(Pres)*
Tamala Merkel *(Head-Upholsterer)*

SCRIPPS HEALTH
10140 Campus Point Dr, San Diego, CA 92121-1513
Tel.: (858) 678-7000 CA
Web Site: http://www.scripps.org
Year Founded: 1924
Emp.: 12,779
Health Care Organization Services
N.A.I.C.S.: 813910
Richard K. Rothberger *(CFO & Exec VP)*
June Komar *(Exec VP-Strategy & Admin)*
Richard R. Sheridan *(Gen Counsel & Exec VP-HR)*
Christopher D. Van Gorder *(Pres & CEO)*
John B. Engle *(Chief Dev Officer & Sr VP)*
Shiraz M. Fagan *(COO & Exec VP)*
Richard Neale *(Chief Bus Dev & Growth Officer & Exec VP)*
Barbara Price *(CEO-Accountable Care Org & Sr VP)*
Ghazala Sharieff *(Chief Experience Officer & VP)*
James E. LaBelle *(Chief Medical Officer & Sr VP)*
Richard McKeown *(Treas & VP)*
Gerry Soderstrom *(VP)*
Bradley S. Ellis *(VP & Asst Gen Counsel)*
Loucas Koutoufidis *(VP & Controller)*
Anil Keswani *(VP-Ambulatory Care & Population Health Mgmt)*
Bruce Rainey *(VP-Construction & Facilities)*
Ed Turk *(VP-Fin Ops & Performance Improvement)*
Eric Cole *(VP-Human Capital Svcs)*
Mary Ellen Doyle *(VP-Nursing Ops)*
Mary Braunwarth *(VP-Scripps Health Foundation)*
Athena Philis-Tsimikas *(VP-Scripps Whittier Diabetes Institute)*
Carl J. Etter *(CEO-North & Sr VP)*
Tom Gammiere *(CEO-South & Sr VP)*
Lisa Thakur *(Sr VP-Ancillary Ops)*
Shawn Forrester *(Pres-Health Plan Svcs)*

Subsidiaries:

Scripps Mercy Hospital (1)
4077 5th Ave, San Diego, CA 92103 (100%)
Tel.: (619) 294-8111
Web Site: http://www.scripps.org
Emp.: 2,000
Health Care Srvices
N.A.I.C.S.: 622110
Tom Gammiere *(CEO & Sr VP)*

SCRIPTPRO LLC
5828 Reeds Rd, Mission, KS 66202-2740
Tel.: (913) 384-1008
Web Site: http://www.scriptpro.com
Year Founded: 1994
Sales Range: $10-24.9 Million
Emp.: 200
Pharmaceutical Machinery
N.A.I.C.S.: 333248
Tracy Thomas *(Exec VP & Dir-Field Ops)*
Sherry Coughlin *(Exec VP & Dir-Facilities Design)*
William J. Thomas *(COO & Exec VP)*
Claire Cunningham *(Exec VP & Dir-Customer Care)*
Jeffrey P. Knight *(VP-Software Dev)*
Christopher A. Duffy *(CIO & VP-Information Svcs)*

SCROGGS & GRIZZEL CONTRACTING, INC.
PO Box 316, Gainesville, GA 30503
Tel.: (770) 532-5000
Sales Range: $10-24.9 Million
Emp.: 75
Home Builder Services
N.A.I.C.S.: 236115
Danny Scroggs *(CEO)*
Mike Grizzel *(CFO & Sec)*
Wesley Bruce *(Project Mgr)*

SCROLLMOTION, INC.
7 Penn Plaza Ste 1112, New York, NY 10001
Tel.: (212) 608-9146
Web Site:
http://www.scrollmotion.com
Sales Range: $10-24.9 Million
Emp.: 140
Mobile Phone Application Developer
N.A.I.C.S.: 513210
Dean Furbush *(Chm)*
Josh Koppel *(Founder)*
Doug Pierce *(COO)*
Ron Kwiatkowski *(CFO)*
Davison Paull *(Gen Counsel)*
Joe Zeff *(VP & Exec Dir-Creative)*
Gregg Hano *(Chief Revenue Officer)*
Jason Gill *(VP-Bus Dev & Strategy)*
Alan Braun *(CEO)*
Dean Curtis *(Chief Revenue officer)*

SCRUB DADDY, INC.
6 Horne Dr, Folcroft, PA 19032
Tel.: (610) 583-4883
Web Site:
http://www.scrubdaddy.com
Sales Range: $10-24.9 Million
Emp.: 60
Cleaning Product Mfr
N.A.I.C.S.: 325612
Aaron Krause *(Pres)*
John O'Brien *(Mgr-Ops)*

SCRUBADUB AUTO WASH CENTERS
172 Worcester Rd, Natick, MA 01760
Tel.: (508) 650-1155
Web Site: http://www.scrubadub.com
Rev.: $14,479,160
Emp.: 10
Carwash
N.A.I.C.S.: 236220
Robert Paisner *(CEO)*
Ronald Gemellaro *(VP-Ops)*

SCRUBS & BEYOND LLC
12969 Manchester Rd, Saint Louis, MO 63131
Tel.: (314) 961-9494
Web Site:
http://www.scrubsandbeyond.com
Emp.: 1,000
Specialty Apparel Stores
N.A.I.C.S.: 458110
Kim Comer-Ross *(Dir-Mktg)*
Karla Bakersmith *(Pres & CEO)*
Ryan J. Strong *(CFO)*
Dan Schlesinger *(VP-Store Ops)*

Subsidiaries:

Life Uniform Company (1)
12969 Manchester Rd, Saint Louis, MO 63131
Tel.: (314) 824-2900
Web Site: http://www.scrubsandbeyond.com
Sales Range: $75-99.9 Million
Emp.: 80
Healthcare Apparel & Accessories Stores
N.A.I.C.S.: 458110
Karla Bakersmith *(CEO)*

SCRUFARI CONSTRUCTION CO. INC.
3925 Hyde Park Blvd, Niagara Falls, NY 14305-1701
Tel.: (716) 282-1225 DE
Year Founded: 1990
Sales Range: $75-99.9 Million
Emp.: 15
Provider of Contracting & Construction Services
N.A.I.C.S.: 236210
Gary Sankes *(Chm & Pres)*
Thomas Warda *(VP)*

SCRUGGS CONCRETE COMPANY
807 River St, Valdosta, GA 31601
Tel.: (229) 242-1170 GA
Web Site:
http://www.scruggsconcrete.com
Year Founded: 1958
Sales Range: $10-24.9 Million
Emp.: 48
Ready-Mixed Concrete Mfr
N.A.I.C.S.: 327320
Rusty Ingram *(Pres)*
Jim Scruggs *(VP)*

SCS DIRECT INC.
100 Raton Dr, Milford, CT 06461
Tel.: (203) 870-4867
Web Site:
http://www.scsdirectinc.com
Year Founded: 1998
Sales Range: $25-49.9 Million
Emp.: 40
Online Marketing Services
N.A.I.C.S.: 449110
Jason Ross *(VP-Sls)*
Howard Greenspan *(Owner & Pres)*
Jospeh Bonnassar *(Gen Counsel)*
Denise Hawkins *(Dir-PR)*
Scott Mulloy *(COO & CIO)*

SCS ENGINEERS
3900 Kilroy Airport Way Ste 100, Long Beach, CA 90806-6816
Tel.: (562) 426-9544 VA
Web Site:
http://www.scsengineers.com
Year Founded: 1970
Sales Range: $25-49.9 Million
Emp.: 757
Environmental Consulting Engineers; Solid & Hazardous Waste Management
N.A.I.C.S.: 541330
Thomas W. A. Barham *(Gen Counsel & Sr VP-Field Svcs Construction)*
Michael W. McLaughlin *(Sr VP-Environmental Svcs)*
Robert Gardner *(Sr VP)*
Daniel E. Johnson *(VP & Project Dir)*
James J. Walsh *(Pres & CEO)*
E. Thomas Conrad *(Founder, Principal & Exec VP)*
Galen Petoyan *(Sr VP & Dir-OM&M Div)*
Curtis Jang *(CFO & Sr VP)*
Nathan Eady *(VP & Project Mgr)*
Tracie Onstad Bills *(Sr Project Mgr)*
Daniel Sola *(Project Dir-Arizona & New Mexico)*
Steve Hamilton *(Sr VP & Dir-Bus Unit)*
Eddy Smith *(Sr VP-Client Success)*
Doug Doerr *(Sr VP & Dir-Bus Unit)*
Pete Carrico *(Sr VP-OM&M & Asst Dir)*
Julio Nuno *(Sr VP & Dir-Project)*

Subsidiaries:

Aquaterra Environmental Solutions, Inc. (1)
7311 W 130th St Ste 100, Overland Park, KS 66213
Tel.: (913) 681-0030
Web Site: http://www.aquaterra-env.com
Emp.: 33
Environmental Consulting Services
N.A.I.C.S.: 541620
Doug Doerr *(Co-Founder, Pres & CEO)*
Floyd Cotter *(Co-Founder, VP & COO)*

SCS ES Consultants (1)
7700 N Kendall Dr Ste 300, Miami, FL 33156
Tel.: (305) 412-8185
Web Site: http://www.scsengineers.com
Sales Range: $10-24.9 Million
Emp.: 20
Environmental Consulting Services
N.A.I.C.S.: 541620
Gina Rodriguez *(Gen Mgr)*

SCS Engineers - SCS Energy Division (1)
3900 Kilroy Airport Way Ste 100, Long Beach, CA 90806-6816
Tel.: (562) 426-9544
Web Site: http://www.scsengineers.com
Emp.: 80
Environmental Consulting Services
N.A.I.C.S.: 541620
Bob Biers *(Mgr-Energy)*

SCS Engineers - Tampa (1)
3922 Coconut Palm Dr Ste 102, Tampa, FL 33619
Tel.: (813) 621-0080
Web Site: http://www.scsengineers.com
Emp.: 50
Engineeering Services
N.A.I.C.S.: 541330
Mark Tumlin *(VP & Dir-Environ Svcs)*

SCS Engineers Korea, Ltd. (1)
Dongyang Hangang Trevelle B/D 1517, Seokyo-Dong Mapo-Gu, Seoul, Korea (South)
Tel.: (82) 2 323 3390
Environmental Consulting Services
N.A.I.C.S.: 541620

SCS Engineers of New York, PC (1)
4 Executive Blvd Ste 303, Suffern, NY 10901
Tel.: (845) 357-1510
Web Site: http://www.scsengineers.com
Sales Range: $10-24.9 Million
Emp.: 10
Environmental Consulting Services
N.A.I.C.S.: 541620
Greg McCarron *(Gen Mgr)*

SCS Field Services (1)
3900 Kilroy Airport Way Ste 100, Long Beach, CA 90806 (100%)
Tel.: (562) 426-9544
Web Site: http://www.scsengineers.com
Sales Range: $25-49.9 Million
Emp.: 640
Environmental Construction Services
N.A.I.C.S.: 541330

SCS Globex Engineering (1)
1900 NW Corporate Blvd, Boca Raton, FL 33431
Tel.: (954) 571-9200
Sales Range: $10-24.9 Million
Emp.: 24
Environmental Consulting Services
N.A.I.C.S.: 541620
Ali Khatami *(VP)*

SCS Tracer Environmental (1)
970 Los Vallecitos Blvd Ste 100, San Marcos, CA 92069
Tel.: (760) 744-9611
Web Site: http://www.scsengineers.com
Sales Range: $10-24.9 Million
Emp.: 20
Environmental Consulting Services
N.A.I.C.S.: 541620
Lee Pyle *(VP & Project Dir)*

SCST, INC.
6280 Riverdale St, San Diego, CA 92120
Tel.: (619) 280-4321 CA
Web Site: http://www.scst.com
Year Founded: 1959

Environmental & Geotechnical Engineering, Special Inspection & Facilities Consulting Services
N.A.I.C.S.: 541330
Clint Adkins *(Dir-Laboratory Svcs)*
John Kirschbaum *(Pres & COO)*
Mandy Serrano *(Dir-Mktg)*
Rik Lantz *(Dir-Environmental Svcs)*
William Earle *(Sr Project Mgr & Sr Engr)*
Royce Parker *(Sr VP-Client Svcs)*

Subsidiaries:

Talentscale, LLC (1)
31805 Temecula Pkwy Ste 204, Temecula, CA 92592
Tel.: (951) 744-0053
Web Site: http://www.talentscalellc.com
Defense & Aerospace Contractor Leasing Services
N.A.I.C.S.: 561330
Doug Poldrugo *(Co-Founder & Principal)*
Steve Santich *(Pres-Sls & Ops)*
Richard Nester *(VP-Ops-Aircraft & Facility Security Officer)*

SCULLIN OIL CO.
900 Spruce St, Sunbury, PA 17801
Tel.: (570) 286-4519
Web Site: http://www.citgo.com
Sales Range: $10-24.9 Million
Emp.: 200
Operator of Independent Convenience Stores
N.A.I.C.S.: 445131
Robert K. Scullin *(Pres)*

SCULPTZ, INC.
1150 Northbrook Dr Ste 200, Trevose, PA 19053-8443
Tel.: (215) 494-2900   DE
Web Site: http://www.silkies.com
Year Founded: 1975
Sales Range: $50-74.9 Million
Emp.: 1,108
Mfr & Sale of Women's Hosiery
N.A.I.C.S.: 315120
Sue Dudek *(Sr Dir-Global Mktg)*
Joe Toczydlowski *(Dir-Acctg)*
Phillip Lane *(Dir-Mktg)*

Subsidiaries:

US Textile Corp. (1)
1792 Silkies Blvd, Lancaster, SC 29720
Tel.: (803) 283-6800
Sales Range: $50-74.9 Million
Emp.: 350
Mfr of Womens Hosiery
N.A.I.C.S.: 315120

SCURA PARTNERS SECURITIES LLC
489 5th Ave 15th Fl, New York, NY 10017
Tel.: (212) 596-3380
Web Site: http://www.scurapartners.com
Investment Services
N.A.I.C.S.: 523940
Denis F. Kelly *(Co-Founder & Mng Partner)*
Robert J. Aiello *(Partner)*
Jerome J. Cincotta *(Partner)*
Joseph DeJulius *(Partner)*
John W. Marcus *(Partner)*
Dianne Mazzola *(Partner & Office Mgr)*
Paul V. Scura *(Founder & Mng Partner)*
Matthew D. Vertin *(Partner)*

SCURLOCK INDUSTRIES
800 W Johnson Ave, Jonesboro, AR 72401
Tel.: (870) 935-5913
Web Site:
http://www.scurlockindustries.com
Sales Range: $10-24.9 Million
Emp.: 130
Concrete Products
N.A.I.C.S.: 327390
James Scurlock *(Pres)*
Dean Massey *(CFO)*

SD MAYER & ASSOCIATES LLP
235 Montgomery St 30th Fl, San Francisco, CA 94104
Tel.: (415) 691-4040
Web Site: https://www.sdmayer.com
Accounting & Business Advisory Services
N.A.I.C.S.: 541219
Helen Johnson *(Partner)*

Subsidiaries:

Seifer, Murken, Despina, James & Teichman, ALC (1)
2135 Lombard St, San Francisco, CA 94123-2712
Tel.: (415) 749-5900
Web Site: http://www.smdjtlaw.com
Law firm
N.A.I.C.S.: 541199
Nathan James *(Partner)*

SD3IT, LLC
3703 Fir St, The Villages, FL 32163
Tel.: (202) 829-1175
Web Site: http://www.sd3it.com
Year Founded: 2014
Sales Range: $10-24.9 Million
Emp.: 12
Digital Marketing Services
N.A.I.C.S.: 541850
Dave Dimlich *(Pres)*

SDB TRADE INTERNATIONAL, LP
817 Southmore Ste 301, Houston, TX 77502
Tel.: (713) 475-0048
Web Site: http://www.sdbtrade.com
Year Founded: 2002
Rev.: $115,500,000
Emp.: 9
Wholesale Trade Agents & Brokers
N.A.I.C.S.: 425120
Dilip Bhargava *(Owner)*
Narayan Bhargava *(Mgr-Engrg)*

SDC CAPITAL PARTNERS, LLC
817 Broadway 10th Fl, New York, NY 10003
Tel.: (212) 813-6700
Web Site:
http://www.sdccapitalpartners.com
Year Founded: 2017
Private Investment Firm
N.A.I.C.S.: 523940
Todd Aaron *(Mng Partner)*
Clinton Karcher *(Principal)*
Anand Vadapalli *(Ops Partner)*

Subsidiaries:

Fatbeam LLC (1)
2065 W Riverstone Dr Ste 105, Coeur D'Alene, ID 83814
Tel.: (509) 344-1008
Web Site: http://www.fatbeam.com
Telecommunication Servicesb
N.A.I.C.S.: 517112
Bob Garner *(VP-Ops)*
Chris Jasper *(VP-Fiber Networks)*
Gregory Green *(Co-Founder & Pres)*
Shawn Swanby *(Co-Founder & Principal)*
Tammy Palm *(Dir-Sls)*
Paul Merritt *(CEO)*

SDCL EDGE ACQUISITION CORPORATION
1120 Avenue of the Americas 4th Fl, New York, NY 10036
Tel.: (212) 488-5509   Ky
Year Founded: 2021
Investment Services
N.A.I.C.S.: 523999
Jonathan Maxwell *(Chm & Co-CEO)*
Michael Feldman *(Co-CEO)*
Ned Davis *(CFO & COO)*

SDDS HOLDINGS, INC.
5018 Bristol Industrial Wy Ste 204, Buford, GA 30518
Tel.: (770) 932-8886   GA
Web Site:
http://www.sddsholdings.com
Year Founded: 1991
Logistics & Delivery Solutions
N.A.I.C.S.: 541614
Michael Gibson *(Pres)*

SDG CORPORATION
65 Water St, Norwalk, CT 06854
Tel.: (203) 866-8886
Web Site: http://www.sdgc.com
Sales Range: $10-24.9 Million
Emp.: 658
Business Consulting Services
N.A.I.C.S.: 561499
Ajay Gupta *(Pres)*
Chris Verlander *(Dir-Mktg)*
Nag Bhadravati *(Sr VP-Customer Success)*
Stacy Ochoa *(Dir-Fin)*

SDI INNOVATIONS, INC.
2880 Old US 231 S, Lafayette, IN 47909-2874
Tel.: (765) 471-8883   IN
Web Site:
http://www.sdiinnovations.com
Year Founded: 1985
Book Publisher & Educational Support Services
N.A.I.C.S.: 513130
Tim Powers *(Pres & CEO)*

Subsidiaries:

Premier Agendas, Inc. (1)
400 Sequoia Dr Ste 200, Bellingham, WA 98226
Tel.: (800) 536-2959
Web Site: http://www.premier.us
Sales Range: $10-24.9 Million
Emp.: 200
Educational Support Services
N.A.I.C.S.: 611710
Paul Taylor *(Gen Mgr)*

SDI INTERNATIONAL CORP.
1000 Corporate Dr Ste 200, Fort Lauderdale, FL 33334
Tel.: (954) 938-5400
Web Site: http://www.sdintl.com
Year Founded: 1992
Sales Range: $1-4.9 Billion
Emp.: 2,000
Business & Workforce Solutions Including Supply Chain Management, Vendor Management, General Procurement & Business Process Outsourcing Services
N.A.I.C.S.: 561499
Carmen Castillo *(Founder & Pres)*
Michael Clough *(VP)*
Brendan Curran *(Sr Dir-Natl Programs)*

SDI PRESENCE LLC
200 E Randolph Ste 3550, Chicago, IL 60601
Tel.: (312) 580-7500
Web Site:
http://www.sdipresence.com
Year Founded: 2016
Management Consulting Firm
N.A.I.C.S.: 541618
David A. Gupta *(Founder & CEO)*
Sharee Wolff *(CFO)*
Cecelia Bolden *(Chief Dev Officer)*
Dawn Gupta *(Chief Relationship Officer)*
Linda Petty *(Exec VP & Gen Counsel)*
Dawn Nash Pfeiffer *(CMO)*
Mark Raffel *(COO)*
Darin Stout *(Dir-Enterprise Sls)*
Derk Rimstidt *(Sr VP-Sls)*
Patrick Griffin *(VP-Ops-Southern California)*
Hardik Bhatt *(Pres & Chief Growth Officer)*

SDI TECHNOLOGIES, INC.
1299 Main St, Rahway, NJ 07065-5024
Tel.: (732) 574-9000   DE
Web Site:
http://www.sditechnologies.com
Year Founded: 1956
Sales Range: $50-74.9 Million
Emp.: 400
Consumer Electronics Mfr
N.A.I.C.S.: 334310
Harry Franco *(Sr VP)*
Edward Nehmad *(VP-Pur)*
Ezra S. Ashkenazi *(Pres)*
Chabetaye Chraime *(VP-Fin)*
Evan Stein *(VP-Mktg)*
Ray Siconolfi *(Controller)*

Subsidiaries:

KIDdesigns, Inc. (1)
1299 Main St, Rahway, NJ 07065
Tel.: (732) 574-9000
Web Site: http://www.kiddirect.com
Sales Range: $25-49.9 Million
Emp.: 80
Electronic Toys, Learning Aids & Child Entertainment Devices Mfr
N.A.I.C.S.: 339930
Evan Stein *(Exec VP-Mktg)*

SDII GLOBAL CORPORATION
4509 George Rd, Tampa, FL 33634
Tel.: (813) 496-9634
Web Site: http://www.sdii-global.com
Year Founded: 1989
Sales Range: $10-24.9 Million
Emp.: 115
Engineeering Services
N.A.I.C.S.: 541330
Robert J. Windschauer *(Founder & Owner)*
Jeremy Mele *(Chief Customer Officer)*
Candace Dyer *(Dir-Bus Dev)*
Catherine Carty *(Pres)*
David Mevers *(Dir-Engrg Ops)*

SDMS, INC.
333 Court St #2, Hoboken, NJ 07030
Tel.: (414) 254-6560   NV
Web Site:
http://www.satelliteedm.com
Year Founded: 2013
Music Retailer
N.A.I.C.S.: 512250
Jonathan Kadish *(COO)*
William Wong *(CEO, CFO & Principal Acctg Officer)*
Scott Richmond *(Pres)*

SDQ, LTD.
4737 County Rd 101 Ste 250, Minnetonka, MN 55345
Tel.: (952) 929-5263
Web Site: http://www.sdqltd.com
Year Founded: 1984
Sales Range: $1-9.9 Million
Emp.: 200
Janitorial Services
N.A.I.C.S.: 561720
Marie Bak *(Pres)*
Nancy Santiago *(Mgr-Mktg)*

SDR PLASTICS, INC.

SDR Plastics, Inc.—(Continued)
1 Plastics Ave, Ravenswood, WV 26164
Tel.: (304) 273-5326   WV
Web Site: http://www.starplastics.com
Rev.: $10,100,000
Emp.: 60
Recyclable Material Merchant Whslr
N.A.I.C.S.: 423930
Doug Ritchie (Pres & CEO)
Luke Schindler (Mgr-Bus Dev)

SDS INDUSTRIES INC.
10241 Norris Ave, Pacoima, CA 91331
Tel.: (818) 896-3094
Web Site:
  http://www.timelyframe.com
Rev.: $14,900,000
Emp.: 195
Window & Door Frames
N.A.I.C.S.: 332321
Robert H. Day (Pres)

SDSP INC.
972 Broadway, Chula Vista, CA 91911
Tel.: (619) 426-7377
Rev.: $11,200,000
Emp.: 11
Bond Brokers
N.A.I.C.S.: 424410
John Llano (Pres)
Anthony Valdivia (Mgr)

SDV INCORPORATED
5350 Kearny Mesa Rd, San Diego, CA 92111
Tel.: (858) 279-9700
Web Site:
  http://www.sandiegovolvo.com
Sales Range: $25-49.9 Million
Emp.: 205
Automobiles, New & Used
N.A.I.C.S.: 441110
Wes Hinkle (Pres)
Steve Hinkle (Owner & Gen Mgr)

SDV SOLUTIONS, INC.
8105 Richmond Rd Ste 205, Toano, VA 23168
Tel.: (757) 903-2068
Web Site: http://www.sdvsolutions.us
Year Founded: 2004
Sales Range: $10-24.9 Million
Emp.: 32
IT Services & Retail; Government Support
N.A.I.C.S.: 423430
Mike McMahan (Pres)
Erin Holden (VP)
Brian Brause (Mgr-Sls)
Joe Pencola (Mgr-Bus Dev)
Ron Scheil (Mgr-Acctg)
Ron Seabaugh (Dir-OCONUS Support)

SE CAPITAL, LLC
155 N Wacker Dr Ste 4250, Chicago, IL 60606
Tel.: (312) 425-1768
Web Site: http://www.secapital.com
Privater Equity Firm
N.A.I.C.S.: 523999
Brad A. Bernstein (Partner)
Jeffrey C. Kvam (Partner)
Paul O. Mulvaney (Principal)
Emily D. Reynolds (Principal)

Subsidiaries:

Eagle Adjusting Services, Inc.   (1)
14701 Cumberland Rd Ste 300, Noblesville, IN 46060-8712
Tel.: (317) 770-6050
Web Site: http://www.eagleadjusting.com

Sales Range: $1-9.9 Million
Emp.: 100
Insurance Claim Adjustment Services
N.A.I.C.S.: 524291
Judy Roach (CFO)

Transport Labor Contract/Leasing   (1)
6160 Summit Dr N Ste 500, Brooklyn Center, MN 55430
Tel.: (763) 585-7000
Web Site: http://www.tlccompanies.com
Professional Employer Organizations
N.A.I.C.S.: 561330

SEA BOX, INC.
700 Union Landing Rd, Cinnaminson, NJ 08077-2004
Tel.: (856) 303-1101
Web Site: http://www.seabox.com
Storage Container Mfr
N.A.I.C.S.: 332439
Bill Begley (Dir-Modular Hotels & Modular Housing Grp)
Jim Brennan (Pres)
Stephen Rolf (CFO)

Subsidiaries:

The Inventors Shop LLC   (1)
800 Industrial Hwy, Riverton, NJ 08077
Tel.: (856) 303-8787
Web Site: http://www.theinventorsshop.com
Sales Range: $1-9.9 Million
Emp.: 35
Special Die & Tool, Die Set, Jig & Fixture Mfr
N.A.I.C.S.: 333514
Mike Amato (Dir-Ops)
Ray Scannapieco (COO)
Tom Simons (Asst Dir-Ops)

SEA DOG BREWING COMPANY
26 Front St, Bangor, ME 04401
Tel.: (207) 947-8009
Web Site:
  http://www.seadogbrewing.com
Sales Range: $75-99.9 Million
Emp.: 105
Brewery & Restaurant Operator
N.A.I.C.S.: 312120
Tami Kennedy (Mgr-PR)
Larry Killam (Gen Mgr)
Fred Forsely (Owner & CEO)
Ann Spellman (Mgr-Svcs)

SEA ISLAND COMPANY
100 Salt Marsh, Saint Simons Island, GA 31522
Tel.: (912) 638-3611   GA
Web Site: http://www.seaisland.com
Year Founded: 1928
Sales Range: $800-899.9 Million
Emp.: 2,500
Real Estate Development, Resort & Landscape Operations
N.A.I.C.S.: 721110
Merry Tipton (Dir-Corp Comm)
William McHugh (Gen Counsel & VP)
Scott Steilen (Pres & CEO)
Vijay Singh (Mng Dir-Resort Ops)
Ella Kent (Dir-Rooms)
Dana Reitz (Dir-Spa & Fitness)

Subsidiaries:

Cloister Hotel   (1)
100 Cloister Dr, Sea Island, GA 31561
Tel.: (912) 638-3611
Web Site: http://www.cloister.com
Sales Range: $250-299.9 Million
Emp.: 1,500
Hotels & Resorts
N.A.I.C.S.: 313320
Rick Reiss (Mng Dir)

Sea Island Properties, Inc.   (1)
600 Sea Is Rd Ste 28, Saint Simons Island, GA 31522   (100%)
Tel.: (912) 638-5161
Web Site:
  http://www.seaislandproperties.com

Sales Range: $25-49.9 Million
Emp.: 25
Real Estate Developers
N.A.I.C.S.: 531120
C. Allen Brown (Sr VP)

SEA JET INDUSTRIES DE CORP.
35 Brunswick Ave, Edison, NJ 08817
Tel.: (732) 541-4800
Web Site: http://www.seajet.com
Rev.: $12,400,000
Emp.: 230
Local Trucking with Storage
N.A.I.C.S.: 493110
Ronald W. Hiemann (CEO)
Eoiseo Elis (Mgr-Ops)

SEA LION CORPORATION
PO Box 87, Hooper Bay, AK 99604
Tel.: (907) 758-4015
Web Site:
  http://www.sealioncorp.com
Year Founded: 1973
Communication Service
N.A.I.C.S.: 517810
William Naneng (Gen Mgr)

Subsidiaries:

Proto Technologies, Inc.   (1)
22808 E Appleway Ave A, Liberty Lake, WA 99019
Tel.: (509) 891-4747
Web Site: http://www.prototech.com
Premium Prototypes & Low Volume fLEXIBLE Manufacturing Services
N.A.I.C.S.: 339999
Greg Nay (VP-Ops)
Rory Nay (Pres)

SEA MIST INC.
1200 S Ocean Blvd, Myrtle Beach, SC 29577
Tel.: (843) 448-1551
Web Site: http://www.seamist.com
Rev.: $18,000,000
Emp.: 250
Owner & Operator of Resort Hotel
N.A.I.C.S.: 721110
Stephen F. Ammons (Pres)
David Meese (Controller)

SEA PAC ENGINEERING, INC.
3325 Wilshire Blvd Ste 305, Los Angeles, CA 90010
Tel.: (213) 487-6130
Web Site: http://www.seapaceng.com
Sales Range: $50-74.9 Million
Emp.: 15
Commercial & Institutional Building Construction
N.A.I.C.S.: 236220
John Lee (Pres)
Theo Kim (Controller)

SEA RAY SPORT YACHTS INC.
3201 Fairview Ave E, Seattle, WA 98102
Tel.: (206) 745-0982
Web Site:
  http://www.lakeunionsearay.com
Year Founded: 1986
Emp.: 80
Motor Boats Mfr & Distr
N.A.I.C.S.: 441222
Kevin Roggenbuck (Pres & CEO)
Mark Helgen (VP)
Jace Romine (Dir-Parts & Svc)
Josh Gilpin (Mgr-Corps Part)
Kirk Benson (Mgr-Seattle Store)

SEA RESEARCH FOUNDATION INC.
55 Coogan Blvd, Mystic, CT 06355-1997
Tel.: (860) 572-5955   CT
Web Site: http://blog.searesearch.org
Year Founded: 1977

Sales Range: $10-24.9 Million
Emp.: 426
Aquarium
N.A.I.C.S.: 712130
Denise Armstrong (CFO & Exec VP)
Tracy Romano (Exec VP-Res & Ops)
Dale Wolbrink (Dir-PR)
Andy Wood (Sr VP-External Rels)
George M. Milne (Chm)
Thomas Mosey (Treas)
Stephen M. Coan (Pres & CEO)
Steve Hazard (Sec)

SEA STAR LINE, LLC
10550 Deerwood Park Blvd Ste 509, Jacksonville, FL 32256-2809
Tel.: (904) 855-1260
Web Site: http://www.seastarline.com
Sales Range: $75-99.9 Million
Emp.: 230
Cargo Shipment Services
N.A.I.C.S.: 488510
Bob Magee (Chm & CEO)
Jim Wagstaff (VP-Ops)
Alyse Lisk (VP-Cargo Svcs)
Bill Taylor (VP-Sls-US)
Mike Nicholson (VP-Strategic Plng & Yield)
Karen Gaskill (VP-Org Dev)
Chris Willman (Dir-Natl Field Sls)

SEA STARR ANIMAL HEALTH, LLC.
1305 Kingstown Rd Ste 7, Peace Dale, RI 02879
Tel.: (401) 783-2185
Web Site: http://www.seapet.com
Year Founded: 1997
Sales Range: $100-124.9 Million
Emp.: 100
Pharmaceuticals Product Mfr
N.A.I.C.S.: 325412
Carder Starr (Pres)

SEA TOW SERVICES INTERNATIONAL INC.
700 Hummel Ave, Southold, NY 11971
Tel.: (631) 765-3660
Web Site: http://www.seatow.com
Year Founded: 1983
Sales Range: $1-9.9 Million
Emp.: 70
Navigational Services
N.A.I.C.S.: 488330
Patrizia Zanaboni (Dir-Acctg & HR)

SEA TRAIL CORPORATION
75 Clubhouse Rd, Sunset Beach, NC 28468
Tel.: (910) 287-1100
Web Site: http://www.seatrail.com
Sales Range: $10-24.9 Million
Emp.: 250
Real Estate & Golf Course Design Services
N.A.I.C.S.: 541320
Dana Hrubik (Mgr-Convention Sls)
Michael Burkley (Mgr-Mktg & IT)
Bob Lank (Dir-Facilities)
Dave Connelly (Dir-Facilities)

SEA WATCH INTERNATIONAL, LTD.
8978 Glebe Park Dr, Easton, MD 21601-7004
Tel.: (410) 822-7500   DE
Web Site: http://www.seawatch.com
Year Founded: 1978
Sales Range: $150-199.9 Million
Emp.: 500
Canned & Frozen Clam Processing
N.A.I.C.S.: 311710
Tracey Hallbauer (Dir-Mktg)
Douglas Morrow (Dir-HR)

COMPANIES

Guy Simmons (Sr VP-Mktg, Product Dev, Govt Rels & Fisheries Science)
Dan Murphy (Chief Comml Officer)
Subsidiaries:

Sea Watch International, Ltd. - Mappsville Plant (1)
13249 Lankford Hwy, Mappsville, VA 23407
Tel.: (757) 824-5651
Web Site: http://www.seawatch.com
Seafood Product Mfr
N.A.I.C.S.: 311710

SEA WIRE & CABLE INC.
451 Lanier Rd, Madison, AL 35758
Tel.: (256) 772-9616
Web Site: http://www.sea-wire.com
Rev.: $11,000,000
Emp.: 50
Electrical Apparatus & Equipment, Wiring Supplies & Related Equipment Merchant Whslr
N.A.I.C.S.: 423610
Marty Clark (Pres & COO)
Jim Duggan (Mgr-Sls-Natl)

SEA-BIRD ELECTRONICS, INC.
13431 NE 20th St, Bellevue, WA 98005-2010
Tel.: (425) 643-9866
Web Site: http://www.seabird.com
Rev.: $18,200,000
Emp.: 100
Measuring & Controlling Device Mfr
N.A.I.C.S.: 334519
Calvin Lwin (Dir-Sls)
Mike Vorkapich (Mgr-IT)
Dave Murphy (Dir-Science-Sea-Bird Scientific)
Genevieve Howell (Dir-Ops)
Judah Goldberg (Mgr-Acct-Sea-Bird Scientific)
Gary Morast (Mgr-Ops-Customer Support)
Casey Moore (Pres-Sea-Bird Scientific)
Jeff Wymore (Supvr-Svc)
David Helwig (VP-Ops-Sea-Bird Scientific)

SEA-CAP INC.
7950 Tarbay Dr, Jessup, MD 20794
Tel.: (410) 796-1177
Web Site: http://seacapinc.com
Rev.: $21,000,000
Emp.: 20
Refrigerated Products Transport
N.A.I.C.S.: 484230
Melvin Spitz (Pres)
Jason Spitz (VP)
J. Conway (Mgr-Ops)

SEA-PAC SALES COMPANY
6307 S 228th St, Kent, WA 98032
Tel.: (253) 796-3500
Rev.: $12,300,000
Emp.: 64
Home Furnishing Merchant Whslr
N.A.I.C.S.: 423220
Jar William (Pres & CEO)

SEABAY BUILDING GROUP, LLC
23575 Cabot Blvd Ste 201-202, Hayward, CA 94545
Tel.: (510) 962-8004
Web Site: http://www.seabay-group.com
Year Founded: 2013
Sales Range: $25-49.9 Million
Emp.: 25
Commercial Building Construction Services
N.A.I.C.S.: 236220
Ahbleza B. Pattison (Co-Founder & Partner)
J. Armando Martinez (Co-Founder & COO)
R. Vincent Switzer (Co-Founder & CEO)
Nate Buchman (Sr Project Mgr)
Lucas Lundin (Asst Project Mgr)

SEABOARD INDUSTRIES
185 Van Winkle Ave, Hawthorne, NJ 07507
Tel.: (973) 427-8500
Web Site: http://www.seaboard-usa.com
Rev.: $11,000,000
Emp.: 25
Swimming Pools, Equipment & Supplies
N.A.I.C.S.: 423910
Chris Rauschenbach (Pres)
Chip Rauschebach (CFO)

SEABOARD INTERNATIONAL, INC.
13815 S Freeway, Houston, TX 77047
Tel.: (713) 644-3535
Web Site: http://www.seaboardinc.com
Oil & Natural Gas Pressure Control Equipment Designer & Mfr
N.A.I.C.S.: 333132
Russell Harbison (VP-Bus Dev)

SEABOARD PRODUCE DISTRIBUTORS
601 Mountain View Ave, Oxnard, CA 93030
Tel.: (805) 486-4773
Rev.: $18,595,321
Emp.: 20
Irrigation Equipment
N.A.I.C.S.: 423820
J. Woodford Hansen (Pres)

SEABOARD SOLAR HOLDINGS, LLC
143 W St Ste C201, New Milford, CT 06776
Tel.: (860) 717-2104
Web Site: http://www.seaboardsolar.com
Holding Company
N.A.I.C.S.: 551112
Matthew Longman (Mgr)
Subsidiaries:

Seaboard Solar Operations, LLC (1)
143 W St Ste C201, New Milford, CT 06776
Tel.: (860) 717-2104
Web Site: http://www.seaboardsolar.com
Solar Power Generation & Energy Storage Installation Services
N.A.I.C.S.: 221114
Matthew G. Longman (Mgr)
Shawn Brazo (Pres)
Michael Chandler (Project Mgr)

SEABRA GROUP
574 Ferry St, Newark, NJ 07105
Tel.: (973) 491-0399
Web Site: http://www.seabragroup.com
Sales Range: $25-49.9 Million
Emp.: 150
Owner of Supermarkets
N.A.I.C.S.: 445110
Antonio Seabra (VP)
Dorinda Rodrigues (Mgr)
Subsidiaries:

A&J Seabra Supermarket (1)
440 Stafford Rd, Fall River, MA 02721-2552
Tel.: (508) 675-3240
Fruit & Vegetable Markets
N.A.I.C.S.: 445230

Triunfo Import & Export Food (1)
574 Ferry St, Newark, NJ 07105
Tel.: (973) 491-0399
Web Site: http://www.triunfofoods.com
Rev.: $31,851,556
Emp.: 100
Groceries, General Line
N.A.I.C.S.: 424410
Tony Loureiro (Gen Mgr)

SEABREEZE MANAGEMENT COMPANY, INC.
39 Argonaut Ste 100, Aliso Viejo, CA 92656
Tel.: (949) 855-1800
Web Site: http://www.seabreezemgmt.com
Year Founded: 1987
Sales Range: $1-9.9 Million
Emp.: 80
Administrative Management & General Management Consulting Service
N.A.I.C.S.: 541611
Kelly Gutierrez (Mgr-Accts Payable)
Eron Kaylor (VP-Community Mgmt)
Nancy Selby (Supvr-Fin Acctg)
Ned Heiskell (Sr VP-Ops)
Isaiah Henry (Pres & CEO)
Sharlyn Turner-Bryant (VP-HR)
Subsidiaries:

Accell Property Management Inc. (1)
23046 Avenida De La Carlota Ste 700, Laguna Hills, CA 92653
Tel.: (949) 581-4988
Web Site: http://www.accellpm.com
Nonresidential Property Managers
N.A.I.C.S.: 531312
Mark Harrison (Sr Mgr-Property)

SEABRING MARINE INDUSTRIES INC.
1579 SW 18th St, Williston, FL 32696-2477
Tel.: (352) 528-2628
Web Site: http://www.montereyboats.com
Year Founded: 1985
Sales Range: $10-24.9 Million
Emp.: 300
Boat Building & Repair Services
N.A.I.C.S.: 336612
Bobby Pita (Pres)
Jackie Owen (Coord-Dealer)

SEABROOK BROTHERS & SONS, INC.
85 Finley Rd, Seabrook, NJ 08302-3560
Tel.: (856) 455-8080
Web Site: http://www.seabrookfarms.com
Year Founded: 1977
Sales Range: $200-249.9 Million
Emp.: 325
Grows, Processes & Freezes Vegetables
N.A.I.C.S.: 311411
Brian E. Seabrook (VP-Sls)
William E. Seabrook (VP-Engrg)
Barbara Wiler (Controller)

SEABROOK HOUSE, INC.
133 Polk Ln, Seabrook, NJ 08302-5055
Tel.: (856) 455-7575
Web Site: http://www.seabrookhouse.org
Year Founded: 1973
Sales Range: $10-24.9 Million
Emp.: 280
Alcohol & Drug Rehabilitation Services
N.A.I.C.S.: 623220
Suzanne Mulrain (Dir-Healthcare Collaboratives)
Joseph N. Ranieri (Dir-Medical)
Edward Diehl (Pres)
Matthew J. Wolf (VP-Bus Ops)

SEABROOK WALLCOVERINGS, INC.
1325 Farmville Rd, Memphis, TN 38122-1002
Tel.: (901) 320-3500
Web Site: http://www.seabrookwallpaper.com
Year Founded: 1910
Sales Range: $75-99.9 Million
Emp.: 100
Whslr & Retailer of Paint & Wallpaper
N.A.I.C.S.: 424950
James H. Seabrook (Pres & CEO)
Leon Haag (Controller)
James Allen (VP-Fin)

SEACAST, INC.
6130 31st Ave NE, Marysville, WA 98271
Tel.: (360) 653-9388
Web Site: http://www.seacast.com
Year Founded: 1985
Rev.: $10,000,000
Emp.: 150
Steel Investment Casting Mfr
N.A.I.C.S.: 331512
Bert Robins (VP)
Subsidiaries:

SeaCast AIC (1)
One American Way, East Greenwich, RI 02818
Tel.: (401) 885-9555
Sales Range: $10-24.9 Million
Emp.: 50
Steel Investment Foundries
N.A.I.C.S.: 331512

SEACHEM LABORATORIES INC.
1000 Seachem Dr, Madison, GA 30650
Tel.: (706) 343-6060
Web Site: http://www.seachem.com
Year Founded: 1980
Sales Range: $1-9.9 Million
Emp.: 50
Chemicals for Maintaining Aquariums
N.A.I.C.S.: 325199
Gregory T. Morin (Co-Owner & CFO)
Doug Hill (Co-Owner, Pres & COO)
Tina Furgerson (Office Mgr)
Jim Rogers (Co-Owner & VP-Product Dev)

SEACOAST CAPITAL
55 Ferncroft Rd Ste 110, Danvers, MA 01923
Tel.: (978) 750-1300
Web Site: http://www.seacoastcapital.com
Year Founded: 1994
Privater Equity Firm
N.A.I.C.S.: 523999
Eben S. Moulton (Partner)
Thomas W. Gorman (Partner)
James T. Donelan (Principal)
Alan Rich (VP)
Phil Curatilo (CMO & Principal)
Jeffrey Holland (Partner)
Thomas Ley (Principal)
Subsidiaries:

Seacoast Capital - San Francisco (1)
1 Bush St Ste 650, San Francisco, CA 94104
Tel.: (415) 956-1400
Web Site: http://www.seacoastcapital.com
Privater Equity Firm
N.A.I.C.S.: 523999
Timothy P. Fay (Partner)
Jeffrey J. Holland (Partner)
Patrick T. Gengoux (VP)

SEACOAST COMMERCE BANK

SEACOAST COMMERCE BANK

Seacoast Commerce Bank—(Continued)
11939 Rancho Bernardo Rd Ste 200, San Diego, CA 92128
Tel.: (858) 432-7000   CA
Web Site: http://www.sccombank.com
Year Founded: 2002
Sales Range: $25-49.9 Million
Commercial Banking Services
N.A.I.C.S.: 522110
Allan W. Arendsee *(Chm)*
David H. Bartram *(COO, Sr Exec VP & Mgr-Small Bus Admin)*
Richard Visser *(Chief Credit Officer & Exec VP)*
Thomas Cheek *(VP & Mgr-Relationship)*
Scott R. Andrews *(Chief Admin Officer & Exec VP)*
Viboun Thepsoumane *(Sr VP-Austin)*
Joseph Cowles *(Sr VP)*
Dennis Vitt *(Sr VP-Small Bus Admin-St. Louis)*
Don Mercer *(Exec VP & Natl Sls Mgr-Small Bus Admin)*
Jason Hutsenpiller *(Sr VP-Salt Lake City)*
Jay Jung *(Sr VP)*
William T. Roche III *(CFO & Exec VP)*
J. Douglas Thompson Jr. *(COO & Sr VP)*
Ernesto M. Arredondo Jr. *(Chief Banking Officer)*

SEACOAST ELECTRIC COMPANY
50 Brdwy Ste 10, Hawthorne, NY 10532
Tel.: (914) 747-3870
Web Site: http://www.seacoastusa.com
Year Founded: 1991
Metal Wires, Ties, Cables & Screening
N.A.I.C.S.: 423510
David Quinn *(Pres)*

SEACOAST VOLKSWAGEN, INC.
95 Ocean Rd, Greenland, NH 03840
Tel.: (603) 436-6900
Web Site: http://www.seacoastvolkswagen.com
Sales Range: $10-24.9 Million
Emp.: 45
Car Whslr
N.A.I.C.S.: 441110
Doug Miles *(Gen Mgr)*

SEACOMP DISPLAYS, INC.
5840 S El Camino Real Ste 108, Carlsbad, CA 92008
Tel.: (760) 918-6722
Web Site: http://www.seacomp.com
Year Founded: 1997
Sales Range: $10-24.9 Million
Emp.: 20
Electronic Components Mfr
N.A.I.C.S.: 334419
Ashley Evans *(VP-Global Logistics)*

SEACORP, LLC
62 Johnny Cake Hill, Middletown, RI 02842
Tel.: (401) 847-2260
Web Site: http://www.seacorp.com
Year Founded: 1977
Sales Range: $50-74.9 Million
Emp.: 310
Government Services
N.A.I.C.S.: 921190

Brian W. Gilligan *(CEO)*
David A. Lussier *(Exec VP)*
David L. Cadorette *(Pres)*
Jason Vetovis *(VP)*

Subsidiaries:

Analysis, Design & Diagnostics, Inc.   (1)
317 W Forsyth St, Jacksonville, FL 32202
Tel.: (904) 475-0094
Web Site: http://www.adndinc.com
Systems Integration
N.A.I.C.S.: 541512
Gary M. Donoher *(Pres)*

SEACREST SERVICES, INC.
2400 Centerpark W Dr, West Palm Beach, FL 33409-6469
Tel.: (561) 697-4990   FL
Web Site: http://www.seacrestservices.com
Year Founded: 1975
Sales Range: $50-74.9 Million
Emp.: 3,000
Residential Community Association Management Services; Service Contractor
N.A.I.C.S.: 561210
Richard Fowler *(Owner)*

SEADREAM YACHT CLUB, INC.
601 Brickell Key Dr Ste 1050, Miami, FL 33131
Tel.: (305) 631-6100   FL
Web Site: http://www.seadream.com
Year Founded: 2001
Sales Range: $25-49.9 Million
Emp.: 300
Luxury Cruise Ship Operator
N.A.I.C.S.: 483112
Atle Brynestad *(Owner & CEO)*
Kris Endreson *(VP-Sls-Americas)*
Christopher Gamble *(Sr VP-Sls-Americas)*
Bob Prieto *(VP-Sls-Miami)*
John Webley *(Sls Dir-Southeast)*

SEAFARERS WELFARE PLAN INC.
5201 Auth Way, Camp Springs, MD 20746
Tel.: (301) 994-0010   MD
Web Site: http://www.seafarers.org
Year Founded: 1951
Sales Range: $50-74.9 Million
Emp.: 200
Pension Health & Welfare Funds
N.A.I.C.S.: 525120
David W. Heindel *(Treas & Sec)*
Michael Sacco *(Pres)*
Nicholas J. Marrone *(VP)*
Dean Corgey *(VP)*
Kermett Mangram *(VP-Govt Svcs)*
Tom Orzechowski *(VP)*
Augustin Tellez *(Exec VP)*
John Spadaro *(Dir-Natl)*
Joseph T. Soresi *(VP)*
Herb Perez *(VP)*

SEAFOOD PRODUCERS COOPERATIVE
2875 Roeder Ave Ste 2, Bellingham, WA 98225-2063
Tel.: (360) 733-0120
Web Site: http://www.spcsales.com
Year Founded: 1944
Sales Range: $10-24.9 Million
Emp.: 50
Retailer of Fresh & Frozen Fish
N.A.I.C.S.: 311710
Jerry Smith *(Controller)*
Thomas McLaughlin *(Pres)*
Jeff Pearson *(Asst Plant Mgr)*

SEAFOOD SALES INC.
1501 N 200th St, Shoreline, WA 98133-3301
Tel.: (206) 285-1615
Rev.: $34,000,000
Emp.: 8
Seafood Sales
N.A.I.C.S.: 424460
Terry R. Bertoson *(Pres)*
Kathy Petrazelli *(Office Mgr)*

SEAFOOD SUPPLY CO. INC.
1500 Griffin St E, Dallas, TX 75215
Tel.: (214) 565-1851
Web Site: http://www.seafoodsupplycompany.com
Sales Range: $10-24.9 Million
Emp.: 93
Seafoods
N.A.I.C.S.: 424460
Paul C. Clark *(Pres)*

SEAFORTH MINERAL & ORE CO., INC.
3690 Orange Pl Ste 495, Cleveland, OH 44122
Tel.: (216) 292-5820   OH
Web Site: http://www.seaforthinc.com
Year Founded: 1957
Sales Range: $10-24.9 Million
Emp.: 59
Processor & Distributor of Fluorspar
N.A.I.C.S.: 423520
Gary McClurg *(CEO)*
James McClurg *(Pres)*
James Temple *(Controller)*

SEAFOX BOAT COMPANY INC.
2550 Hwy 52, Moncks Corner, SC 29461
Tel.: (843) 761-6090
Web Site: http://www.seafoxboats.com
Year Founded: 1995
Sales Range: $25-49.9 Million
Emp.: 100
Mfr & Retailer of Boats
N.A.I.C.S.: 336612
Fred Renken *(Pres)*
Jeff DeBar *(Sr VP-Sls-Mktg-Quality Assurance)*

SEAFREIGHT AGENCIES INC.
9950 NW 17th St, Doral, FL 33172
Tel.: (305) 592-6060
Web Site: http://www.seafreightagencies.com
Rev.: $80,000,000
Emp.: 75
Inland Water Freight Transportation
N.A.I.C.S.: 483211
David Ross *(Exec VP)*
Roland Malins-Smith *(Pres)*

SEAGATE FOODS INC.
419 E Crossville Rd, Roswell, GA 30075
Tel.: (770) 650-9202
Year Founded: 1971
Sales Range: $10-24.9 Million
Emp.: 200
Owner of Fast-Food Restaurants
N.A.I.C.S.: 722513
Gordon Lee Cole *(Pres)*
Ed Jones *(Pres)*

SEAGULL BOOK & TAPE INC.
920 E State Rd, American Fork, UT 84003
Tel.: (801) 763-7190
Web Site: http://www.seagullbook.com
Sales Range: $10-24.9 Million
Emp.: 200
Books, Religious

N.A.I.C.S.: 459210
Guy Simmons *(VP)*
Michael Bradshaw *(CFO)*
Lee Brown *(Dir-Mdse)*
Randy Wilkes *(Mgr-IT)*

SEAGULL LIGHTING PRODUCTS INC.
301 W Washington St, Riverside, NJ 08075
Tel.: (856) 764-0500
Web Site: http://www.seagullighting.com
Sales Range: $25-49.9 Million
Emp.: 400
Residential Lighting Fixtures
N.A.I.C.S.: 335131
Matt Vollmer *(Pres)*

SEAL AFTERMARKET PRODUCTS LLC
2315 SW 32nd Ave, Pembroke Park, FL 33023
Tel.: (954) 364-2400   FL
Web Site: http://www.sealaftermarketproducts.com
Year Founded: 2009
Design, Development & Assembly of Automatic Transmission Rebuilder Kits
N.A.I.C.S.: 336350
Troy Eakins *(Pres)*
Rob Kelly *(Dir-Procurement & IT)*
Pedro Carralero *(Mgr-Production)*
Bill Fantozz *(Dir-Product Dev)*

SEAL FURNITURE SYSTEMS SAN DIEGO INC.
6720 Top Gun St, San Diego, CA 92121
Tel.: (858) 450-9960
Year Founded: 1988
Sales Range: $10-24.9 Million
Emp.: 10
Office Furniture
N.A.I.C.S.: 423210
Sherry Radcliffe *(CEO)*
William W. Radcliffe Jr. *(Owner)*

SEALAND CONTRACTORS CORP.
85 High Tech Dr, Rush, NY 14543
Tel.: (585) 359-9242
Web Site: http://www.sealandcontractors.com
Year Founded: 1977
Sales Range: $25-49.9 Million
Emp.: 150
Highway & Heavy Road & Bridge Construction
N.A.I.C.S.: 237310
Daniel Bree *(Pres)*
Robert Bree *(VP)*
George Dietz *(Controller)*

SEALAND NATURAL RESOURCES INC.
50 W Liberty St 880, Reno, NV 89501
Tel.: (702) 530-8665   NV
Web Site: http://sealandnaturalresources.com
Year Founded: 2011
Sales Range: Less than $1 Million
Investment Services
N.A.I.C.S.: 523999
Lars Aarup Poulsen *(Pres & Interim CFO)*

SEALASKA CORPORATION
1 Sealaska Plz Ste 400, Juneau, AK 99801-1245
Tel.: (907) 586-1512   AK
Web Site: http://www.sealaska.com
Year Founded: 1972
Sales Range: $75-99.9 Million

Emp.: 1,400
Holding Company; Forest Products; Natural Resource Development in Alaska; Portfolio Management; Precision Plastics; Minerals
N.A.I.C.S.: 423990
Richard Harris *(Exec VP)*
Terry Downes *(COO)*
Anthony Mallott *(Pres & CEO)*
Joseph Nelson *(Chm)*
Jaeleen Kookesh *(Gen Counsel, Sec & VP)*

Subsidiaries:

Kanaak Corporation (1)
1 Sealaska Plz Ste 400, Juneau, AK 99801
Tel.: (907) 586-1512
Plastics Product Mfr
N.A.I.C.S.: 326199

MBS Systems, LLC (1)
12325 Oracle Blvd Ste 205, Colorado Springs, CO 80921
Tel.: (719) 314-3404
Web Site: http://www.mbshome.com
Software Development Services
N.A.I.C.S.: 541511
Jon Duncan *(Pres & CEO)*

Sealaska Constructors, LLC (1)
1220 M St SE, Auburn, WA 98002
Tel.: (253) 929-1200
Web Site: http://www.seakcon.com
Construction Engineering Services
N.A.I.C.S.: 237990

Sealaska Environmental Services, LLC (1)
13810 SE Eastgate Way Ste 420, Bellevue, WA 98005-4425
Tel.: (425) 283-0630
Web Site: http://www.sealaskaenvironmental.com
Environmental Remediation Services
N.A.I.C.S.: 562910
Derik Frederiksen *(Gen Mgr)*
Anthony Mallott *(Pres & CEO)*
Peter McCormick *(Gen Mgr)*

Sealaska Global Logistics, LLC (1)
1691 Phoenix Blvd Ste 170, Atlanta, GA 30349
Tel.: (678) 884-8300
Logistics Consulting Servies
N.A.I.C.S.: 541614

Sealaska Security Holdings, LLC. (1)
1 Sealaska Plz Ste 400, Juneau, AK 99801-1245
Tel.: (907) 586-1512
Web Site: http://www.sealaska.com
Surface Land Managment Services
N.A.I.C.S.: 531390

Sealaska Timber Corporation (1)
1900 1st Ave Ste 315, Ketchikan, AK 99901-6063 (100%)
Tel.: (907) 225-9444
Sales Range: $10-24.9 Million
Emp.: 13
Harvester & Marketer of Timber
N.A.I.C.S.: 115310
Jack Beckman *(Mgr-Quality Control)*
Edward Davis *(Dir-Bus Dev)*
Jeff Eiseman *(Controller)*
Duane Woodruff *(VP-Mktg & Quality Control)*
Keli Reno *(Mgr-Acctg)*

Security Alliance of Florida, LLC (1)
8323 NW 12th St Ste 218, Miami, FL 33126
Tel.: (305) 670-6544
Web Site: http://www.securityalliancegroup.com
Emp.: 25
Security System Services
N.A.I.C.S.: 561621

Synergy Systems, Inc. (1)
13810 SE Estgate Way 42 Ste 420, Bellevue, WA 98005
Tel.: (913) 449-1765
Construction Management Services
N.A.I.C.S.: 237990
Bob Wysocki *(Gen Mgr)*

SEALCO AIR CONTROLS INC.
215 E Watkins St, Phoenix, AZ 85004-2927
Tel.: (602) 253-1007   AZ
Web Site: http://www.sealcocvp.com
Year Founded: 1997
Sales Range: $10-24.9 Million
Emp.: 50
Mfr of Motor Vehicle Parts & Accessory Services
N.A.I.C.S.: 336340
Mark Herring *(COO)*
Debbie Krakower *(CFO)*

SEALEX, INC.
8850 Moeller Dr, Harbor Springs, MI 49740
Tel.: (231) 348-5020
Web Site: http://www.sealexinc.com
Year Founded: 1992
Rev.: $2,200,000
Emp.: 9
Rubber Bands Mfr
N.A.I.C.S.: 326299
Matthias Hagen *(VP)*
Robert Hagen *(Pres)*

SEALIFT HOLDINGS INC.
68 W Main St Ste 201, Oyster Bay, NY 11771
Tel.: (516) 922-1101
Web Site: http://www.sealiftinc.com
Rev.: $94,344,000
Emp.: 2
Deep Sea Freight Transportation
N.A.I.C.S.: 483111
Alan Adler *(Pres)*

Subsidiaries:

Fortune Maritime Inc. (1)
68 W Main St, Oyster Bay, NY 11771
Tel.: (516) 922-1101
Cargo Loading & Unloading Services
N.A.I.C.S.: 488210

Remington Shipping Inc. (1)
68 W Main St, Oyster Bay, NY 11771
Tel.: (516) 922-1101
Deep Sea Freight Transportation
N.A.I.C.S.: 483111

Sealift Chemical Incorporated (1)
68 W Main St Ste 201, Oyster Bay, NY 11771
Tel.: (516) 922-1101
Web Site: http://www.sealiftinc.com
Deep Sea Freight Transportation
N.A.I.C.S.: 483111
Joann Hyatt *(Office Mgr)*

Sealift Incorporated of Delaware (1)
68 W Main St, Oyster Bay, NY 11771
Tel.: (516) 922-1000
Web Site: http://www.sealiftinc.com
Freight Transportation Services
N.A.I.C.S.: 483111

Sealift Tankships Incorporated (1)
68 W Main St Ste 201, Oyster Bay, NY 11771
Tel.: (516) 922-1101
Deep Sea Freight Transportation
N.A.I.C.S.: 483111
Alan Adler *(VP)*

Victory Maritime Inc. (1)
68 W Main St, Oyster Bay, NY 11771
Tel.: (516) 922-1101
Sales Range: $1-9.9 Million
Deep Sea Freight Transportation
N.A.I.C.S.: 483111
Alan Adler *(Pres)*

SEALING AGENTS WATERPROOFING, INC.
7412 Stinson Hartis Rd, Indian Trail, NC 28079-9694
Tel.: (704) 882-8443
Web Site: http://www.sealingagents.com
Sales Range: $10-24.9 Million
Emp.: 140
Specialty Trade Contractors
N.A.I.C.S.: 238910

Trent Hattaway *(Pres)*

SEALING DEVICES INC.
4400 Walden Ave, Lancaster, NY 14086-9716
Tel.: (716) 684-7600   NY
Web Site: http://www.sealingdevices.com
Year Founded: 1964
Sales Range: $75-99.9 Million
Emp.: 150
Mfr & Distributor of Industrial Gaskets, Seals & Sealing Materials
N.A.I.C.S.: 339991
Doug Eberhardt *(Mgr-Mktg)*

SEALING EQUIPMENT PRODUCTS COMPANY, INC.
123 Airpark Indus Rd, Alabaster, AL 35007-9598
Tel.: (205) 403-7500   AL
Web Site: http://www.sepcousa.com
Year Founded: 1985
Sales Range: $50-74.9 Million
Emp.: 110
Mfr of Gaskets, Packings & Seals
N.A.I.C.S.: 339991
Eddie Hughes *(Dir-Pur)*

SEALMASTER INDUSTRIES INC.
2520 Campbell St, Sandusky, OH 44870
Tel.: (419) 626-5470
Web Site: http://www.sealmaster.net
Rev.: $11,068,133
Emp.: 250
Paints & Paint Additives
N.A.I.C.S.: 325510
David Thorson *(Pres)*

SEALS ENTERTAINMENT CORPORATION
3340 Peachtree Rd NE Ste 1800, Atlanta, GA 30326
Tel.: (404) 222-6400   DE
Web Site: http://www.sealsentertainment.com
Holding Company; Television Broadcasting
N.A.I.C.S.: 551112
Chris Hannaford *(Exec VP-Programming & Dev)*
Warren Hansen *(Exec VP-Strategic Alliances)*
David Hollar *(Exec VP-Ops)*
Clay Phillips *(Exec VP & Controller)*
E. Lamar Seals III *(Chm & CEO)*

SEALY & SMITH FOUNDATION
2200 Market St Ste 500, Galveston, TX 77550
Tel.: (409) 762-8666   TX
Web Site: http://www.sealy-smith-foundation.org
Year Founded: 1992
Sales Range: $50-74.9 Million
Emp.: 6
Community Hospital Support Services
N.A.I.C.S.: 541611
Douglas G. Rogers *(Co-Treas & Co-Sec)*
John W. Kelso *(Pres)*
J. Fellman Seinsheimer *(VP)*
Michael C. Doherty *(Treas, Sec & Exec Dir)*
George Sealy *(Exec VP)*

SEAMAN CORPORATION
1000 Venture Blvd, Wooster, OH 44691-9358
Tel.: (330) 262-1111
Web Site: http://www.seamancorp.com
Year Founded: 1950
Sales Range: $25-49.9 Million

Emp.: 300
Broad Woven Fabric & Man-Made Fiber & Silk
N.A.I.C.S.: 313210
Richard N. Seaman *(Chm)*
Jeff Swartz *(CEO)*

SEAMAN PAPER COMPANY OF MASSACHUSETTS INC.
51 Main St, Baldwinville, MA 01436-1150
Tel.: (978) 939-2146   MA
Web Site: http://www.satinwrap.com
Year Founded: 1954
Sales Range: $100-124.9 Million
Emp.: 120
Paper Mfr
N.A.I.C.S.: 322120
George D. Jones *(Pres)*

Subsidiaries:

360 Imaging Inc. (1)
2 Concourse Pkwy Ste 140, Atlanta, GA 30328
Tel.: (404) 236-7700
Web Site: http://www.360imaging.com
Emp.: 25
Flexographic Plate Mfr
N.A.I.C.S.: 323120
Mark Palmer *(Pres & CEO)*
Yahia Megahed *(CTO)*

Dennecrepe Corporation (1)
70 Fredette St, Gardner, MA 01440
Tel.: (978) 630-8669
Sales Range: $10-24.9 Million
Emp.: 60
Mfr of Paper
N.A.I.C.S.: 322299
David Dexter *(Plant Mgr)*

Garlock Printing and Converting Inc (1)
164 Fredette St, Gardner, MA 01440-3722
Tel.: (978) 630-1028
Web Site: http://www.garlockprinting.com
Commercial Printing Services
N.A.I.C.S.: 323111
Max Omalley *(Acct Mgr-Natl)*

Seaman Paper Asia Co Ltd (1)
23rd Floor Ocean Building 80 Shanghai Street, Jordan, Kowloon, China (Hong Kong)
Tel.: (852) 2460 2028
Web Site: http://www.seamanpaperasia.com
Tape Distr
N.A.I.C.S.: 424130

SEAMATES INTERNATIONAL INC.
316 Main St, East Rutherford, NJ 07073
Tel.: (201) 896-8899
Web Site: http://www.seamates.com
Rev.: $12,388,581
Emp.: 50
Foreign Freight Forwarding
N.A.I.C.S.: 488510
Richard E. Burke *(Pres)*
Paul W. Scheuplein *(Controller)*

SEAMEN'S SOCIETY FOR CHILDREN AND FAMILIES
50 Bay St, Staten Island, NY 10301-1827
Tel.: (718) 447-7740   NY
Web Site: http://www.roots-wings.org
Year Founded: 1846
Sales Range: $10-24.9 Million
Emp.: 225
Child & Family Support Services
N.A.I.C.S.: 624190
Anna Opsha *(CFO & VP)*
Daniel Barckhaus *(Dir-Foster Care Svcs)*
Nancy Vomero *(Pres & CEO)*

SEAPAC INC.
4588 Cypress Business Park Dr, Mobile, AL 36619

SEAPAC INC.

Seapac Inc.—(Continued)
Tel.: (251) 602-1882
Web Site: http://www.seapac-inc.com
Sales Range: $10-24.9 Million
Emp.: 50
Packaging, Warehousing & Distribution Services
N.A.I.C.S.: 561910
Greg Hahn (Controller)
Don Phillips (Gen Mgr)
Larry Matthews (Gen Mgr)

SEAPORT CAPITAL, LLC
40 Fulton St 27th Fl, New York, NY 10038
Tel.: (212) 847-8900   DE
Web Site: http://www.seaportcapital.com
Year Founded: 1991
Privater Equity Firm
N.A.I.C.S.: 523999
Bill Luby (Partner)
Jim Collis (Partner)
Scott McCormack (Partner)
Howard Kaufman (CFO)
Bob Tamashunas (Partner)
Caren Dina (Controller)

Subsidiaries:

Elias Arts LLC   (1)
10 E 33rd St 4th Fl, New York, NY 10016
Tel.: (212) 807-6500
Web Site: http://www.eliasarts.com
Emp.: 15
Music & Sound Recording & Licensing Services
N.A.I.C.S.: 512240
Glenn Turell (CFO)
Katie Overcash (Head-Production)
Vicki Ordeshook (Head-Production)

Mandalay Baseball Properties, LLC   (1)
4751 Wilshire Blvd 3rd Fl, Los Angeles, CA 90010
Tel.: (323) 549-4300
Web Site: http://www.mandalay.com
Holding Company; Professional Baseball Clubs
N.A.I.C.S.: 551112
Robert Murphy (COO)
Larry Freedman (Pres-Mandalay Baseball)
James Bailey (CFO)
Eric Deutsch (Exec VP-Admin)
Gary Mayse (Exec VP-Facility Ops)
Rich Neumann (Pres-Baseball Dev)
John Deeter (VP-Fin)

Joint Venture (Domestic):

SWB Yankees, LLC   (2)
235 Montage Mountain Rd, Moosic, PA 18507   (50%)
Tel.: (570) 969-2255
Web Site: http://www.swbrailriders.com
Sales Range: $10-24.9 Million
Professional Baseball Club
N.A.I.C.S.: 711211
Kristina Knight (Dir-Corp Svcs & Special Events)
Karen Luciano (Mgr-Corp Svcs)
Rob Galdieri (Ops Mgr)
Curt Camoni (VP-Stadium Ops)
William Steiner (Dir-Gameday Ops)
Steve Horne (Dir-Field Ops)
Seth Atkinson (Dir-Ticket Ops)
Jeremy Ruby (Exec VP-Ops)
Joe Villano (Dir-Ballpark Ops)
Paul Chilek (Exec VP-Bus Ops)
Katie Beekman (VP-Mktg & Corp Svcs)
Mike Trudnak (VP-Sls)
Rob Crain (Pres & Gen Mgr)
John Sadak (Dir-Media Rels & Brdcst)

SEAPORT GLOBAL HOLDINGS LLC
360 Madison Ave 22 Fl, New York, NY 10017
Tel.: (212) 616-7700
Web Site: http://www.seaportglobal.com

Financial Advice Services; Investment Banking
N.A.I.C.S.: 523940
Edward R. Lainfiesta (Head-Equity-Sls & Trading)
Michael J. Meagher (CEO)
Michael J. Meyer (Partner & Head-Global Sls & Trading)
Stephen C. Smith (Head-Merchant Banking)
Victor K. Kurylak (COO)
Ricardo Penfold (Mng Dir)
Faisal Mian (Partner & Head--Global)
Joan Nash (Dir-Corp Affairs)

Subsidiaries:

Seaport Global Securities LLC   (1)
400 Poydras St Ste 3100, New Orleans, LA 70130
Tel.: (504) 410-8010
Web Site: http://seaportglobal.com
Financial Advice Services; Investment Banking
N.A.I.C.S.: 523940
Michael J. Meagher (Co-CEO)
Michael J. Meyer (Head-Fixed Income-Sls & Trading)
Edward R. Lainfiesta (Partner)
Stephen C. Smith (Head-Merchant Banking)
Lisa Weiss (Dir-HR)
Allen Parks (Mng Dir-Oil Field Svcs-Investment Banking Dept)
Kurt Oehlberg (Mng Dir-Mining & Metals-Investment Banking)
Chad Jennings (VP-Mining & Metals)
Margery Fischbein (Mng Dir & Head-Healthcare Investment Banking)
Bernie Colson (Mng Dir-Energy Infrastructure)
Wayne Sansiviero (Mng Dir-Energy Infrastructure)
Adam Vore (Mng Dir-New York)
Margery B. Fischbein (Mng Dir)

SEAPORT INTERNATIONAL INC.
1275 12th Ave NW Ste 13, Issaquah, WA 98027
Tel.: (425) 837-8090
Web Site: http://www.seaport-intl.com
Sales Range: $10-24.9 Million
Emp.: 5
Industrial & Personal Service Paper
N.A.I.C.S.: 424130
Jay Phillips (CEO)

SEAPORT PRODUCTS CORP.
131 7th Ave W, Kirkland, WA 98033-5301
Tel.: (425) 827-2800
Web Site: http://www.cport.net
Sales Range: $50-74.9 Million
Emp.: 8
Seafood Sales
N.A.I.C.S.: 424460
James Dresser (Chm)
Pete Swanson (Pres)
Mike Daniels (VP)
William Dresser (CEO)

SEARCE, INC.
7807 Palmer Pl Ln, Humble, TX 77346
Tel.: (281) 954-5099
Web Site: http://www.searce.com
Year Founded: 2004
Sales Range: $10-24.9 Million
Emp.: 410
Software Product Development Services
N.A.I.C.S.: 541511
Hardik Parekh (CEO)
Ami Parekh (CFO)
Mike Cary (VP)
Prabhash Ojha (VP)
Vikas Dhawan (COO)
Ekta Ganguly (Dir-Engineering)
Pradeep Pavithran (Dir-Bus Dev)

SEARCH DISCOVERY, INC.
271 17th St NW Ste 1700, Atlanta, GA 30363
Tel.: (404) 898-0430
Web Site: http://www.searchdiscovery.com
Year Founded: 2004
Sales Range: $1-9.9 Million
Emp.: 32
Search Engine Optimization & Internet Marketing
N.A.I.C.S.: 541519
Jim Neumann (Mng Dir)
Lee Blankenship (CEO)
Mike Gustafson (Pres)
Lee Isensee (Dir-Product Strategy)
Lea Pica (Dir-Data Visualization & Storytelling)
Brian Marin (Mng Dir-Europe)
Evan Bench (Mgr-Bus Intelligence-Paris)

Subsidiaries:

Alturna, LLC   (1)
259 Veterans Ln Ste 101, Doylestown, PA 18901
Tel.: (267) 870-8000
Web Site: http://www.allturna.com
Sales Range: $1-9.9 Million
Emp.: 10
Advertising Agency Services
N.A.I.C.S.: 541810
Jim Neumann (Pres)

SEARCH FOR COMMON GROUND
1601 Connecticut Ave NW Ste 200, Washington, DC 20009-2628
Tel.: (202) 265-4300   DC
Web Site: http://www.sfcg.org
Year Founded: 1982
Sales Range: $25-49.9 Million
Emp.: 81
Social Service Organization
N.A.I.C.S.: 813319
Sandra Melone (Exec VP)
Thomas Downing (CFO)
Lena Slachmuijlder (VP-Programs)
Gary Dibianco (Chm)
Matias Averbuj (COO)
Greg Houston (VP-Strategic Partnerships & Comm)
Shamil Idriss (Pres & CEO)
Lawrence Kershen (Chm)

SEARCH INC.
261 Madison Ave Fl 17th, New York, NY 10016
Tel.: (212) 808-0747   IL
Web Site: http://www.search-inc.com
Year Founded: 1969
Sales Range: $10-24.9 Million
Emp.: 417
Employment Placement Services
N.A.I.C.S.: 561311
Marc Richards (Sr VP)
Arline Panitz (Pres)
Melody Rivera (Mng Dir)
Charisse Renzi-Daus (Mgr-Admin)
Richard Adule (Mgr-Res)
Shannon Eisenberg (Mng Dir)

SEARCH INFLUENCE, LLC
935 Gravier St Ste 1300, New Orleans, LA 70112
Tel.: (504) 208-3900
Web Site: http://www.searchinfluence.com
Year Founded: 2006
Sales Range: $1-9.9 Million
Emp.: 70
Online Brokerage Services
N.A.I.C.S.: 524210
William W. Scott (Co-Founder & CEO)
Angie Scott (Co-Founder & COO)
Paula Keller French (Dir-Sls & Mktg)

Jeremy Brown (Dir-Ops)
Amy Arnold (Dir-R&D)
Erica Salm Rench (Mgr-Production)
Lynn Bergeron (Dir-Sls)

SEARCH MOJO
100 10th St NE Ste 103, Charlottesville, VA 22902
Tel.: (434) 975-6656
Web Site: http://www.marketing-mojo.com
Year Founded: 2006
Sales Range: $1-9.9 Million
Emp.: 18
Advetising Agency
N.A.I.C.S.: 541810
Janet Driscoll Miller (Pres & CEO)
Tad Miller (VP-Accts)
Adam Smith (Dir-Tech)
Jeff Driscoll (Dir-Ops)
Jenny Knizner (Dir-Mktg & Creative Svcs)
Scott Garrett (Sr Acct Exec)

SEARCH WIZARDS INC.
PO Box 191387, Atlanta, GA 31119
Tel.: (404) 846-9500
Web Site: http://www.searchwizards.net
Year Founded: 2000
Sales Range: $10-24.9 Million
Emp.: 138
Recruitment Outsourcing
N.A.I.C.S.: 561311
Leslie O'Connor (Pres & CEO)
Jackie Keniley (CFO)

SEARCHLIGHT CAPITAL PARTNERS, L.P.
745 5th Ave 26th Fl, New York, NY 10151
Tel.: (212) 293-3730
Web Site: http://www.searchlightcap.com
Year Founded: 2010
Private Investment Firm
N.A.I.C.S.: 523999
Oliver Haarmann (Partner-Founding)
Erol E. Uzumeri (Co-Founder & Partner)
Andrew S. Frey (Partner & Partner-New York)
Ralf Ackermann (Partner-New York)
Francois Dekker (Partner-New York)
Darren Glatt (Partner)
Tom Hendrick (Partner-New York)
Albert Shin (Partner-New York)
Timothy Austin (Mng Dir-New York)
Steve Colder (Mng Dir-New York)
Adam Reiss (Mng Dir-New York)
Nicolo Zanotto (Mng Dir-New York)
James Redmayne (Partner)
David G. Fuller (Operating Partner)
Ajit Pai (Partner)
Phil Bacal (Mng Dir)
Elliott Weinstein (Mng Dir)
Andrew Frey (Partner)
Eric Louis Zinterhofer (Founder & Partner)
Christopher Cruz (Partner & Mng Dir-New York)

Subsidiaries:

Care Advantage, Inc.   (1)
10041 Midlothian Turnpike, Richmond, VA 23235
Tel.: (866) 576-7089
Web Site: http://www.careadvantageinc.com
Home Health Care & Companionship Services
N.A.I.C.S.: 621610
Timothy Hanold (CEO)

Subsidiary (Domestic):

Nova Home Health Care, Inc.   (2)
2124 Jefferson Davis Hwy Ste 303B, Stafford, VA 22554-7277

COMPANIES

Tel.: (703) 865-4860
Web Site: http://www.novahhc.com
Women Healthcare Services
N.A.I.C.S.: 621610
Ali Abdi *(CEO & Gen Mgr)*

Team Nurse, Inc. (2)
3352 Halifax Rd Centerville Shopping Center, South Boston, VA 24592
Tel.: (434) 517-0050
Web Site: https://www.careadvantageinc.com
Women Healthcare Services
N.A.I.C.S.: 621610
Steve Mize *(Founder)*

Cengage Learning Holdings II, Inc. (1)
3 Ctr Plz Ste 700, Boston, MA 02108
Tel.: (513) 229-1000
Web Site: https://www.cengagegroup.com
Rev.: $1,502,700,000
Assets: $2,600,400,000
Liabilities: $2,485,700,000
Net Worth: ($389,400,000)
Earnings: ($80,900,000)
Emp.: 4,400
Fiscal Year-end: 03/31/2024
Holding Company; Library Reference & Educational Materials Publishing & Learning Solutions
N.A.I.C.S.: 551112
Michael E. Hansen *(CEO)*
Jim Chilton *(CTO)*
Darren Person *(Chief Digital Officer)*
Michael E. Hansen *(CEO)*
Bob Munro *(CFO)*
Alexander Broich *(Pres-Cengage Select & Gen Mgr-English Language Teaching & Cengage Work)*
Jeri Herman *(Chief People Officer)*
Brooke Carey *(Chief Comm Officer)*
Dawn Ehlers *(Gen Counsel)*
Morgan Wolbe *(Exec VP-Ops-Global & Chief Transformation Officer)*

Subsidiary (Domestic):

Cengage Learning, Inc. (2)
3 Ctr Plz Ste 700, Boston, MA 02108
Tel.: (513) 229-1000
Web Site: http://www.cengage.com
Library Reference & Educational Materials Publishing & Learning Solutions
N.A.I.C.S.: 513130
Michael E. Hansen *(CEO)*
Sean Chamberland *(Sr Dir-Mktg-Cengage Canada)*
Julianne Isaac *(Gen Mgr)*

Subsidiary (Domestic):

Advanced Instructional Systems, Inc. (3)
1791 Varsity Dr Ste 200, Raleigh, NC 27606
Tel.: (919) 829-8181
Web Site: https://www.webassign.com
Sales Range: $1-9.9 Million
Emp.: 25
Online Software Solutions Services
N.A.I.C.S.: 513210
Rob Simora *(CTO)*

Division (Domestic):

Cengage Higher Education (3)
20 Davis Dr, Belmont, CA 94002
Tel.: (650) 595-2350
Web Site: http://www.academic.cengage.com
Educational Book Publishing
N.A.I.C.S.: 513130

Unit (Domestic):

South-Western Cengage Learning (4)
5191 Natorp Blvd, Mason, OH 45040
Tel.: (513) 229-1000
Web Site: http://www.cengagelearning.com
Sales Range: $200-249.9 Million
Accounting, Marketing & Management Education Book Publisher
N.A.I.C.S.: 513130

Wadsworth Cengage Learning (4)
10 Davis Dr, Belmont, CA 94002-3002
Tel.: (650) 595-2350
Web Site: http://www.academic.cengage.com
Educational Software & Textbook Publisher
N.A.I.C.S.: 513130

Subsidiary (Non-US):

Cengage Learning Asia (3)
30A Kallang Place 12-06, UIC Bldg, Singapore, 339213, Singapore
Tel.: (65) 64101200
Web Site: https://www.cengageasia.com
Sales Range: $50-74.9 Million
Emp.: 70
Educational & Reference Book Publisher
N.A.I.C.S.: 513130

Cengage Learning Australia Pty. Limited (3)
80 Dorcas St Level 7, Victoria, 3205, VIC, Australia
Tel.: (61) 396854111
Web Site: http://www.cengage.com.au
Sales Range: $50-74.9 Million
Emp.: 200
Educational & Reference Book Publishing
N.A.I.C.S.: 513130
Tamara Silver *(Mgr-HR)*
Paul Petrulis *(VP-Higher Education)*
Nicole McCarten *(VP-Schools Div)*
John Durow *(Fin Dir & COO)*
Paul Brady *(Dir-Technologies)*
Nigel Matai *(Head-Production)*

Subsidiary (Domestic):

Delmar Cengage Learning (3)
5 Maxwell Dr Executive Woods, Clifton Park, NY 12065-2919
Tel.: (518) 348-2300
Web Site: http://www.cengage.com
Sales Range: $100-124.9 Million
Emp.: 294
Educational, Technical & Vocational Publishers
N.A.I.C.S.: 513130

Subsidiary (Non-US):

Gale Group Inc. (3)
Tel.: (248) 699-4253
Web Site: http://www.gale.com
Sales Range: $300-349.9 Million
Reference Book & Electronic Reference Materials Publisher
N.A.I.C.S.: 513140
Paul Gazzolo *(Sr VP & Gen Mgr)*
Brian McDonough *(Sr VP-Sls-North America)*
Terry Robinson *(Mng Dir-Intl & Sr VP)*

Division (Domestic):

Macmillan Reference USA (4)
12 Lunar Dr, Woodbridge, CT 06525-2322
Tel.: (203) 397-2600
Web Site: http://gale.cengage.com
Sales Range: $25-49.9 Million
Emp.: 55
Publisher of Academic & Professional Reference Materials, Newspapers & U.S. & Foreign Patents
N.A.I.C.S.: 513130

Subsidiary (Domestic):

Learning Objects, Inc. (3)
1528 Connecticut Ave NW, Washington, DC 20036
Tel.: (202) 265-3276
Web Site: https://www.learningobjects.com
Education Technology Software Publisher
N.A.I.C.S.: 513210

Subsidiary (Non-US):

Nelson Education Ltd. (3)
1120 Birchmount Rd, Scarborough, M1K 5G4, ON, Canada
Tel.: (416) 752-9448
Web Site: http://www.nelson.com
Sales Range: $100-124.9 Million
Education & Reference Book Publisher
N.A.I.C.S.: 513130
Steve Brown *(Pres & CEO)*
Claudine O'Donnell *(Sr VP)*
Ryan Anklesaria *(Sr VP)*

Gato Investments LP (1)
405 Lexington Ave 48th Fl, New York, NY 10151
Tel.: (212) 503-2850
Web Site: https://www.sec.gov
Investment Services
N.A.I.C.S.: 523999

Gresham House plc (1)
80 Cheapside, London, EC2V 6EE, United Kingdom
Tel.: (44) 2038376270
Web Site: https://greshamhouse.com
Rev.: $95,533,252
Assets: $299,128,797
Liabilities: $98,814,862
Net Worth: $200,313,936
Earnings: $16,562,826
Emp.: 173
Fiscal Year-end: 12/31/2021
Financial Services
N.A.I.C.S.: 541611
Anthony Dalwood *(CEO)*
Kevin Acton *(CFO)*
Andrew Hampshire *(COO & CTO)*
Graham Carter *(Dir-Investment Forestry)*
Rob Carlow *(Dir-Investment Forestry)*
Heather Fleming *(Head-Institutional Bus)*
Mike Woolley *(Head-Wholesale Retail Funds)*
Ed Simon *(Dir-Investment New Energy)*
James Braithwaite *(Controller-Fin-Housing)*
James Gilbert *(Mgr-Mktg)*
James Hendry *(Mgr-Investment-Gresham House)*
James Pendower *(Mgr-IT)*
James Sly *(Fin Dir-Housing)*
Caroline Anderson *(Fin Mgr)*
Tom Astor *(Mgr-Investment & Forestry)*
Clive Austin *(Mng Dir-VCT Portfolio)*
Peter Bachmann *(Mng Dir-Sustainable Infrastructure)*
Jamie Bakewell *(Mgr-Human Resources)*
Philip Barrow *(Sr Legal Counsel)*
Donald Beaton *(Mgr-Investment & Forestry)*
Sophie Bennion *(Mktg Mgr)*
Peter Bolton *(Dir-Investment New Energy)*
Elizabeth Brown *(Mgr-Investment Housing)*
Paul Carse *(Dir-EPC)*
Fernando Casas Garcia *(Head-Operations & Asset Mgmt New Energy)*
Mathangi Chandrasekhar *(Mgr-Investment Sustainable Infrastructure)*
Dominik Cib *(Dir-Compliance & Performance Housing)*
Natalie Clayton *(Fin Mgr-Real Assets)*
Lisa Dang *(Fin Dir)*
Claire Glennon *(Head-Institutional Sls)*
Stephen Beck *(Fin Dir-Real Assets)*
Tania Hayes *(Fin Dir-Div & COO-Strategic Equity)*
Samee Khan *(Chief Legal Officer & Sec)*
Rupert Robinson *(Mng Dir-Gresham House Asset Mgmt)*
Ben Guest *(Mng Dir-New Energy)*
Hazel Cameron *(Venture Partner & Head-Portfolio Talent)*
Geoff Lambert *(Head-Compliance)*
Andy Gibb *(Sls Dir)*
Lizzie DarBourne *(Dir-Mktg)*
Matthew Giles *(Dir-Investment Forestry)*
Trevor Blackburn *(Dir-Investment Forestry)*
Wayne Cranstone *(Dir-Investment)*
Anthony Crosbie Dawson *(Dir-Forestry & Private Clients)*
Brendan Gulston *(Dir-Investment)*
Edward Latter *(Dir-Investment Forestry)*
David Gardner *(CIO-Forestry & Dir-Investment Forestry)*
Beth Delaney *(Controller-Fin Real Assets & Sr Mgr-Fin)*
Jacqueline Kelly *(Sr Mgr-Fin)*
Gemma Richards *(Sr Mgr-Fin)*
Joe Thomas *(Dir-Investment & Housing & Mgr-Investment)*
Stephen Ramage *(Dir-Investment Forestry & Mgr-Timber Mktg)*
Lizet Nooren *(Partner-Fin Bus & Mgr-Fin-New Energy)*
Suzy Babbage *(Mgr-Investment & Renewables)*
Matthew Green *(Mgr-Investment)*
Stevie Ingamells *(Assoc Dir-Sustainable Infrastructure & Mgr-Investment)*
Adam McLean *(Assoc Dir-Forestry & Mgr-Asset-Forestry)*
Chloe Jacquet *(Mgr-Asset-New Energy)*
Henrietta Russell *(Assoc Dir-Forestry & Mgr-Asset-Forestry)*

SEARCHLIGHT CAPITAL PARTNERS, L.P.

Izzy van Romunde *(Dir-CFA Investment & Mgr-Investment-CFA)*
Carole Harris *(Dir-Investment New Energy & Asst Mgr-New Energy)*

Hyve Group plc (1)
2 Kingdom Street, London, W2 6JG, United Kingdom
Tel.: (44) 2035459400
Web Site: https://www.hyve.group
Rev.: $74,947,502
Assets: $571,476,567
Liabilities: $358,837,250
Net Worth: $212,639,318
Earnings: ($27,181,554)
Emp.: 914
Fiscal Year-end: 09/30/2021
Trade Exhibitions & Conference Organizer
N.A.I.C.S.: 561920
Andrew Beach *(CFO)*
Mark Shashoua *(CEO)*
Helen Kennedy Shamir *(Corp Counsel)*
James Warsop *(Fin Dir)*
Nikki Griffiths *(Dir)*
Marina Calero *(Head)*
Jessica Natinsky *(Dir)*
Grant Altson *(CIO)*
Rachel Brodie *(Mng Dir)*
Robert Chillman *(Mng Dir)*
Sophie Wawro *(Pres)*
Thomas Whelan *(Dir)*

Subsidiary (Non-US):

ABEC Exhibitions & Conferences Pvt. Ltd. (2)
530 Laxmi Plaza New Link Road, Laxmi Industrial Estate Andheri West, Mumbai, 400053, India
Tel.: (91) 224 286 3900
Web Site: https://www.abec.asia
Travel Arrangement Services
N.A.I.C.S.: 561599
Sumit Gandhi *(CEO & Chm)*
Manish Gandhi *(Exec Dir & COO)*

Fin-mark S.r.l. (2)
Via Pindaro 82, 00125, Rome, Italy
Tel.: (39) 065 093 1045
Web Site: https://www.finmark.it
Personal Care Product Mfr & Distr
N.A.I.C.S.: 325620

GiMA International Exhibition Group GmbH & Co. KG (2)
Schleidenstrasse 3, 22083, Hamburg, Germany
Tel.: (49) 4 023 5240
Web Site: https://www.gima.de
Sales Range: $300-349.9 Million
Emp.: 30
Organizing International Commercial Events
N.A.I.C.S.: 711310
Mathias Lauk *(Mng Dir)*

Hyve Beauty Fuarcilik AS (2)
19 Mayis Caddesi No 3 Golden Plaza Kat 7, Sisli, 34360, Istanbul, Turkiye
Tel.: (90) 212 266 7010
Web Site: https://hyvebeautyfuarcilik.com
Cosmetics Product Distr
N.A.I.C.S.: 456199

Hyve India Private Ltd. (2)
Innov8 2nd Floor 44 Regal Building Outer Circle Connaught Place, New Delhi, 110001, India
Tel.: (91) 112 644 7591
Web Site: https://india.hyve.group
Event Management Services
N.A.I.C.S.: 561920
Gordon Payne *(Reg Dir)*
Gaurav Sood *(Gen Mgr)*
Gagan Sahni *(Dir-Business Development)*

Hyve Worldwide B.V. (2)
Arthur van Schendelstraat 650, 3511 MJ, Utrecht, Netherlands
Tel.: (31) 30 700 9713
Web Site: https://www.thehyve.nl
Information Technology Services
N.A.I.C.S.: 541519
Harry Van Haaften *(CEO)*
Nivethika Mahasivam *(Project Mgr)*
Jolanda Strubel *(Mgr)*

ITE China (2)
Room1703 HongkouSOHO No 575 Wusong Road, Hongkou, Shanghai, 200030, China
Tel.: (86) 2161806789

SEARCHLIGHT CAPITAL PARTNERS, L.P.

Searchlight Capital Partners, L.P.—(Continued)
Web Site: http://eng.ite-china.com.cn
Sales Range: $50-74.9 Million
Emp.: 14
Organizer of International Trade Exhibitions, Conferences & Events
N.A.I.C.S.: 711310

ITE Eurasian Exhibitions FZ LLC (2)
Al Shatha Tower 26th Floor Office No 2613
Media City Sheikh Zayed Road, PO Box 502778, Dubai, United Arab Emirates
Tel.: (971) 4 457 2926
Web Site: https://www.ite-eurasian.com
Event Management Services
N.A.I.C.S.: 561920

ITE GULF FZ LLC (2)
Shatha Tower office 2514 Dubai Media City, PO Box 503021, Dubai, 503021, United Arab Emirates
Tel.: (971) 44332970
Web Site: http://www.ite-gulf.com
Sales Range: $50-74.9 Million
Emp.: 6
International Commercial Events Organizing Services
N.A.I.C.S.: 711310
Mehdi Ogtay Taghiyev *(Gen Mgr)*

ITE LLC Moscow (2)
3 bldg 2 Verkhnyaya Krasnoselskaya str, 107140, Moscow, Russia
Tel.: (7) 4957995585
Web Site: http://www.russia.hyve.group
Sales Range: $75-99.9 Million
Emp.: 270
Organizing International Commercial Events
N.A.I.C.S.: 711310

Subsidiary (Domestic):

ITE Moda Ltd. (2)
Lewisham Rd, The Old Town Hall, Huddersfield, HD7 5AL, West Yorkshire, United Kingdom
Tel.: (44) 1484846069
Web Site: http://www.moda-uk.co.uk
Sales Range: $25-49.9 Million
Emp.: 40
Fashion Acessories
N.A.I.C.S.: 541490
Silvia Collins *(Dir-Event)*
Jodie Goss *(Mgr-New Bus Sls)*
Luke Murphy *(Mgr-Mktg)*

Subsidiary (US):

ITE North America Inc. (2)
2500 Plaza 5 Harborside Financial Ctr, Jersey City, NJ 07311
Tel.: (201) 633-4785
Web Site: http://www.ite-northamerica.com
International Commercial Events Organizing Services
N.A.I.C.S.: 711310

Subsidiary (Non-US):

ITE Poland Sp. z o.o. (2)
Ul Niegolewskich 22/1, 60-231, Poznan, Poland
Tel.: (48) 61 662 7241
Web Site: https://iec-poland.com
Sales Range: $50-74.9 Million
Emp.: 7
Organizing International Commercial Events
N.A.I.C.S.: 711310

ITE TURKEY (2)
19 Mayis Caddesi Golden Plaza Kat 7, Golden Plz Kat 9, 34360, Istanbul, Turkiye
Tel.: (90) 2122918310
Web Site: http://www.ite-turkey.com
Sales Range: $25-49.9 Million
Emp.: 45
Organizing International Commercial Events
N.A.I.C.S.: 711310

ITE Uzbekistan (2)
3rd Floor 59A Mustakillik Avenue, Tashkent, 100000, Uzbekistan
Tel.: (998) 712051818
Web Site: http://www.iteca.uz
Sales Range: $50-74.9 Million
Emp.: 25
International Commercial Events Organizing Services
N.A.I.C.S.: 711310

ITECA ALATOO (2)
Ibrahimova Street 115 A Business Center Dordoi Plaza 6th Floor, Bishkek, Kyrgyzstan
Tel.: (996) 312 698994
Web Site: http://www.ite-exhibitions.com
Organizing International Commercial Events
N.A.I.C.S.: 711310

ITECA Kazakhstan (2)
8th floor C block World Trade Center Almaty 42 Timiryazev Str, Almaty, Kazakhstan
Tel.: (7) 727 258 3434
Web Site: https://www.iteca.kz
Organizing International Commercial Events
N.A.I.C.S.: 711310

Premier Expo (2)
4a Verkhniy Val str, Kiev, 04071, Ukraine
Tel.: (380) 444968645
Web Site: http://www.pe.com.ua
Sales Range: $50-74.9 Million
Emp.: 90
International Commercial Events Organizing Services
N.A.I.C.S.: 711310

Primexpo (2)
24 Litera A Yakubovicha St, Saint Petersburg, 190000, Russia
Tel.: (7) 8123806000
Web Site: http://www.primexpo.ru
Sales Range: $25-49.9 Million
Emp.: 50
International Commercial Events Organizing Services
N.A.I.C.S.: 711310
Irina Belova *(Mgr)*

Subsidiary (US):

Retail Meetup, LLC (2)
605 3rd Ave 26th Fl, New York, NY 10158
Tel.: (646) 598-6644
Web Site: https://staging-env.retailmeetup.com
Online Meeting Services
N.A.I.C.S.: 518210

Subsidiary (Non-US):

SIBERIAN FAIR LLC (2)
220/10 Krasny Prospekt, 630049, Novosibirsk, Russia
Tel.: (7) 3832106290
Web Site: https://sibfair.ru
Sales Range: $150-199.9 Million
Emp.: 400
Organizing International Commercial Events
N.A.I.C.S.: 711310
Sergei Tsoi *(Dir Gen)*

Latecoere SA (1)
135 Rue De Periole, BP 25211, 31079, Toulouse, Cedex 5, France (63.2%)
Tel.: (33) 561587700
Web Site: https://www.latecoere.aero
Rev.: $501,539,678
Assets: $594,660,811
Liabilities: $550,739,435
Net Worth: $43,921,376
Earnings: ($230,076,254)
Emp.: 4,764
Fiscal Year-end: 12/31/2020
Aircraft Manufacturing
N.A.I.C.S.: 336411
Pierre Gadonneix *(Chm)*
Serge Berenger *(Chief Innovation & R&T Officer)*
Chris Seherr-Thoss *(Chief M&A Officer)*
Gregoire Huttner *(Deputy CEO & Gen Mgr-Aerostructures Div)*
Thierry Mootz *(CEO & Gen Mgr-Interconnection Sys Div)*
Herve Blanchard *(Chief HR Officer)*
Michel Abaza *(CFO)*

Subsidiary (Non-US):

Avcorp Industries, Inc. (2)
10025 River Way, Delta, V4G1M7, BC, Canada
Tel.: (604) 587-4938
Web Site: http://www.avcorp.com
Rev.: $77,818,085
Assets: $80,290,872
Liabilities: $117,924,016
Net Worth: ($37,633,144)
Earnings: ($415,391)
Emp.: 488
Fiscal Year-end: 12/31/2021
Aircraft Part Mfr
N.A.I.C.S.: 336413
Amandeep Kaler *(CEO)*
Steven J. Archer *(VP-Business Development-Government Relations)*
Tony Kelsey *(Gen Mgr-Avcorp Composite Fabrication)*
Mike Elvidge *(Gen Mgr-Avcorp Structures & Integration)*

Division (Domestic):

Avior Integrated Products (3)
1001 Autoroute 440 W, Laval, QC, Canada (100%)
Tel.: (450) 629-6200
Web Site: http://www.avior.ca
Sales Range: $50-74.9 Million
Emp.: 140
Mfr of Aircraft Parts
N.A.I.C.S.: 336413
Karanjit Dulat *(VP-Engrg-Six Sigma)*
Danny Netto *(VP-Fin)*

Subsidiary (Domestic):

Comtek Advanced Structures Ltd (3)
1360 Artisans Ct, Burlington, L7L 5Y2, ON, Canada
Tel.: (905) 331-8121
Web Site: https://www.comtekadvanced.com
Sales Range: $25-49.9 Million
Emp.: 80
Aircraft Components Mfr
N.A.I.C.S.: 334511
Robin Lovell *(Pres)*

Subsidiary (Domestic):

G2METRIC (2)
40 Chemin Cazalbarbier, Launaguet, 31140, France
Tel.: (33) 5 34 27 62 90
Web Site: http://www.g2metric.com
Emp.: 35
Aviation System Mfr
N.A.I.C.S.: 334511
Nicolas Prost *(Mgr-Sls)*

Subsidiary (Non-US):

G2METRIC Limited (2)
Unit 4 Armtech Row Houndstone Business Park, Somerset, BA22 8RW, United Kingdom
Tel.: (44) 1935 472 312
Web Site: http://www.g2metric.com
Emp.: 14
Optical Measuring Instrument Whslr
N.A.I.C.S.: 423830

Subsidiary (US):

LATECOERE INC. (2)
1000 Brickell Ave Ste 641, Miami, FL 33131
Tel.: (305) 379-0676
Aerospace Engineering Services
N.A.I.C.S.: 541330

Subsidiary (Non-US):

LATECOERE Services GmbH (2)
Hein-Sass-Weg 30, 21129, Hamburg, Allemagne, Germany
Tel.: (49) 40 317 68 567
Aerospace Engineering Services
N.A.I.C.S.: 541330
Benoit Rouanet *(Gen Mgr)*

LATecis Canada Inc. (2)
3200 Autoroute Laval, Laval, H7T 2H6, QC, Canada
Tel.: (514) 600-4258
Web Site: http://www.latecoere-services.com
Emp.: 28
Aerospace Engineering Services
N.A.I.C.S.: 541330
Eric Giguere *(Mng Dir)*

LATecis UK Limited (2)
Business & Technology Centre Bessemer Drive, Stevenage, SG1 2DX, United Kingdom
Tel.: (44) 1438 791016
Web Site: http://www.latecisuk.com
Rev.: $69,780,480
Emp.: 420
Aerospace Engineering Services
N.A.I.C.S.: 541330
Scott Hancock *(Engr-Design)*

Subsidiary (Domestic):

LATelec (2)
762 Rue Max Planck-CS 57632, 31676, Labege, Cedex, France
Tel.: (33) 5 61 00 82 30
Web Site: http://www.latelec.com
Aircraft Maintenance Services
N.A.I.C.S.: 488119

Subsidiary (Non-US):

LETOV s.r.o. (2)
Beranovych 65, Prague, 199 02, Letnany, Czech Republic
Tel.: (420) 234 313 301
Web Site: http://www.llv.cz
Emp.: 670
Aircraft Mfr
N.A.I.C.S.: 336411
Tomas Rezanka *(Mgr-Quality Assurance)*

M&M Meat Shops Ltd. (1)
100-2240 Argentia Road, Mississauga, L5N 2K7, ON, Canada
Tel.: (519) 461-0171
Web Site: http://www.mmfoodmarket.com
Sales Range: $350-399.9 Million
Emp.: 100
Specialty Frozen Foods Retailer
N.A.I.C.S.: 424420

Mitel Networks Corporation (1)
350 Legget Drive, Ottawa, K2K 2W7, ON, Canada
Tel.: (613) 592-2122
Web Site: http://www.mitel.com
Rev.: $1,059,100,000
Assets: $1,630,500,000
Liabilities: $1,284,800,000
Net Worth: $345,700,000
Earnings: ($49,700,000)
Emp.: 3,820
Fiscal Year-end: 12/31/2017
Holding Company; Communications Solutions & Services
N.A.I.C.S.: 334220
Steven E. Spooner *(CFO)*
Terence H. Matthews *(Chm)*
Bob Agnes *(Pres-Mitel Products & Solutions & Exec VP)*
Luiz Domingos *(CTO & Head-Large Enterprise R&D)*
Jeremy Butt *(Sr VP-Intl)*
Jamshid Rezaei *(CIO)*
Mark Duff *(VP-Sls Engrg & Pro Svcs-Intl)*
Denise Bryant *(Dir-Distr-EMEA)*
Maria Blakeway *(VP-Customer Success)*
Mike Conlon *(VP-Channels-Global)*
Paul Riordan *(VP-Channels-Intl)*
Daniel Farrar *(Exec VP/Gen Mgr-Unified Comm-as-a-Svc Div)*
Rick Cirigliano *(Sr VP-Global Cloud Ops-Unified Comm-as-a-Svc Div)*
Billie Hartless *(Chief HR Officer)*
Tarun Loomba *(Sr VP & CEO)*
Charles-Henry Duroyon *(COO & Head-M&A)*
Todd Abbott *(Exec VP-Sls & Svcs-Global)*

Subsidiary (Non-US):

Aastra Telecom Europe A/S (2)
Roskildevej 342 B 2, 2630, Taastrup, Denmark
Tel.: (45) 43305305
Holding Company; Regional Managing Office
N.A.I.C.S.: 551112

Subsidiary (Non-US):

Mitel Communications AB (3)
Arenavagen 63, 121 77, Johanneshov, Sweden
Tel.: (46) 856867000
Web Site: http://www.mitel.se
Telecommunication Servicesb
N.A.I.C.S.: 517810
Asa Parlered *(Mgr-Pro Svcs)*

Subsidiary (Domestic):

Mitel Danmark A/S (3)
Roskildevej 342 B 2, 2630, Taastrup, Denmark
Tel.: (45) 43305305
Web Site: http://dk.mitel.com

COMPANIES

SEARCHLIGHT CAPITAL PARTNERS, L.P.

Business Communications Software & Equipment Distr
N.A.I.C.S.: 423430

Subsidiary (Non-US):

Mitel Sweden AB (3)
Arenavagen 63, 121 77, Johanneshov, Sweden
Tel.: (46) 856 867 000
Web Site: http://www.mitel.se
Sales Range: $50-74.9 Million
Emp.: 200
Telephone Communications Services & Communications Equipment & Software Mfr
N.A.I.C.S.: 517810
Claes Kolare *(Mng Dir)*

Subsidiary (Non-US):

Fernway Limited (2)
Lynda Marilyn House Mill Green, Leeds, LS12 6HE, West Yorkshire, United Kingdom
Tel.: (44) 1132045996
Web Site: http://www.fernwayltd.co.uk
Retail Market Services
N.A.I.C.S.: 455219

Mitel Belgium SA (2)
Waterranonkelstraat 2b, 1130, Brussels, Belgium
Tel.: (32) 27271811
Web Site: http://www.mitel.be
Sales Range: $25-49.9 Million
Emp.: 42
Business Communications Software & Equipment Distr
N.A.I.C.S.: 423430

Subsidiary (US):

Mitel Business Systems, Inc. (2)
1146 N Alma School Rd, Mesa, AZ 85201-3229
Tel.: (480) 961-9000
Telecommunications Equipment Repair Services
N.A.I.C.S.: 811210

Subsidiary (Non-US):

Mitel Communications Finland Ab (2)
Tekniikantie 14 Innopoli 2, 02150, Espoo, Finland
Tel.: (358) 9525 510
Business Communications Software & Equipment Distr
N.A.I.C.S.: 423430
Teuvo Havikari *(Mng Dir)*

Subsidiary (US):

Mitel Communications Inc. (2)
1 Penn Plz, New York, NY 10019
Tel.: (212) 683-4455
Telecommunication Servicesb
N.A.I.C.S.: 517810

Subsidiary (Non-US):

Mitel Communications Private Limited (2)
A- 44 and 45 4th Floor Tower - C Galaxy Business Park Sector-62, Noida, 201 309, Uttar Pradesh, India
Tel.: (91) 1204778777
Software Development Services
N.A.I.C.S.: 513210
Ramesh Sahoo *(Project Mgr)*

Mitel Deutschland GmbH (2)
Zeughofstrasse 1, 10997, Berlin, Germany
Tel.: (49) 3061040
Web Site: http://www.mitel.de
Business Communications Software & Equipment Distr
N.A.I.C.S.: 423430
Jurgen Signer *(Mng Dir)*
Graham Bevington *(Mng Dir)*
Christian Fron *(VP-DACH)*

Subsidiary (Domestic):

DeTeWe Communications GmbH (3)
Zeughofstrasse 1, 10997, Berlin, Germany
Tel.: (49) 30 47791 0
Web Site: http://www.detewe.de
Telecommunication Equipment Distr
N.A.I.C.S.: 423690
Christian Fron *(Mng Dir)*

Subsidiary (Non-US):

Mitel France SAS (2)
1 Rue Arnold Schoenberg, 78286, Guyancourt, France
Tel.: (33) 130 964 200
Web Site: http://www.mitel.fr
Business Communications Software & Equipment Distr
N.A.I.C.S.: 423430
Isabelle Seguin Kritchmar *(Acct Dir)*
Sandra Couvret *(Dir-HR)*
Pierre-Alexandre Fuhrmann *(CTO-EMEA & Deputy Gen Mgr-France)*

Mitel Incorporated Mexico S.A. de C.V. (2)
Paseo de la Reforma 250 piso 9 Col Juarez, Del Cuauhtemoc, 06600, Mexico, DF, Mexico
Tel.: (52) 5536007670
Web Site: http://mx.mitel.com
Telecommunication Servicesb
N.A.I.C.S.: 517810

Mitel Italia S.p.A. (2)
SS Padana Superiore 2/b, 20063, Cernusco sul Naviglio, MI, Italy
Tel.: (39) 02 250831
Web Site: http://it.mitel.com
Business Communications Software & Equipment Distr
N.A.I.C.S.: 423430

Mitel Lease SA (2)
Waterranonkelstraat 2b, 1130, Brussels, Belgium
Tel.: (32) 2 727 18 11
Telecommunications Equipment Leasing Services
N.A.I.C.S.: 532490

Subsidiary (US):

Mitel Leasing, Inc. (2)
885 Trademark Dr, Reno, NV 89521
Tel.: (775) 954-1288
Telecommunication Leasing Services
N.A.I.C.S.: 532490

Mitel Mobility Inc. (2)
1700 International Pkwy Ste 200, Richardson, TX 75081
Tel.: (469) 916-4393
Telecommunication Servicesb
N.A.I.C.S.: 517810
Bahram Jalalizadeh *(Exec VP)*

Subsidiary (Non-US):

Mitel Netherlands B.V. (2)
Van Deventerlaan 30-40, Utrecht, 3528 AE, Netherlands
Tel.: (31) 882356483
Software Development Services
N.A.I.C.S.: 513210

Subsidiary (US):

Mitel Netsolutions, Inc. (2)
885 Trademark Dr, Reno, NV 89521-5943
Tel.: (775) 954-1200
Web Site: http://www.mitel.com
Telecommunication Servicesb
N.A.I.C.S.: 517810

Subsidiary (Non-US):

Mitel Networks (New Zealand) Limited (2)
204 Thorndon Quay Mitel Level 4, Wellington, 6011, New Zealand
Tel.: (64) 49016339
Software Development Services
N.A.I.C.S.: 513210

Mitel Networks Asia Pacific Ltd. (2)
1 Matheson Street, Causeway Bay, 852, China (Hong Kong) (100%)
Tel.: (852) 25089780
Web Site: http://www.mitel.com
Sales Range: $25-49.9 Million
Emp.: 10
Mfr of Electronic Parts & Equipment
N.A.I.C.S.: 449210

Mitel Networks Holdings Limited (2)
Castlegate Business Park Portskewett, Caldicot, NP26 5YR, United Kingdom
Tel.: (44) 1291 430 000
Emp.: 170

Investment Management Service
N.A.I.C.S.: 523940
Graham Bevington *(Exec VP)*
Wolfram Fischer *(Sr VP-EMEA)*
David Silke *(VP-Mktg-Intl)*

Subsidiary (Domestic):

Mitel Networks Ltd. (3)
Castlegate Business Park, Monmouthshire, Caldicot, NP26 5YR, Wales, United Kingdom (100%)
Tel.: (44) 1291 430000
Web Site: http://www.mitel.com
Sales Range: $200-249.9 Million
Mfr of Electronic Parts & Equipment
N.A.I.C.S.: 335999

Subsidiary (Non-US):

LAKE Communications Limited (4)
Beech House, Greenhills Rd, Dublin, 24, Ireland
Tel.: (353) 14031000
Sales Range: $25-49.9 Million
Emp.: 50
Home Office Telecommunications Products Mfr
N.A.I.C.S.: 334210

Subsidiary (Non-US):

Mitel Networks Ltd.
Level 1 219-223 Castlereagh Street, Sydney, 2000, NSW, Australia
Tel.: (61) 290239500
Web Site: http://www.mitel.com.au
Emp.: 20
Telecommunication Software Development Services
N.A.I.C.S.: 541511

Subsidiary (Domestic):

Mitel Networks Solutions Inc (2)
135 Matheson Blvd West, Mississauga, L5R 3L1, ON, Canada
Tel.: (905) 501-4600
Telecommunication Servicesb
N.A.I.C.S.: 517810

Subsidiary (Non-US):

Mitel Networks South Africa (PTY) Limited (2)
144 Western Service Road First Floor 21A, Johannesburg, South Africa
Tel.: (27) 112752880
Software Development Services
N.A.I.C.S.: 513210

Subsidiary (US):

Mitel Networks, Inc. (2)
1146 N Alma School Rd, Mesa, AZ 85201 (100%)
Tel.: (480) 961-9000
Web Site: http://www.mitel.com
Communication Equipment Mfr
N.A.I.C.S.: 334220

Subsidiary (Non-US):

Mitel Norway AS (2)
Ostensjoveien 39/41, 0667, Oslo, Norway
Tel.: (47) 22 900 900
Web Site: http://no.mitel.com
Sales Range: $25-49.9 Million
Emp.: 15
Business Communications Software & Equipment Distr
N.A.I.C.S.: 423430
Bjorn Inge Lindhjem *(Mng Dir)*

Mitel Portugal S.A. (2)
Alfrapark - Edificio C Piso 1 Norte Estrada do Seminario 4, Alfragide, 2610-171, Amadora, Portugal
Tel.: (351) 21 472 65 00
Web Site: http://pt.mitel.com
Telecommunication Equipment Distr
N.A.I.C.S.: 423690

Mitel Schweiz AG (2)
Ziegelmattstrasse 1, 4503, Solothurn, Switzerland (100%)
Tel.: (41) 326553333
Web Site: http://www.mitel.ch
Business Communications Software & Equipment Distr

Ueli Blatter *(Mng Dir)*
Michel Eggenschwiler *(Engr-Software)*

Mitel South Africa (2)
First Floor 21A The Woodlands 144 Western Service Road, Woodmead, 2080, Sandton, South Africa
Tel.: (27) 11 275 2880
Sales Range: $25-49.9 Million
Emp.: 2
Communication Software Development Services
N.A.I.C.S.: 541511
Andy Bull *(Gen Mgr)*

Mitel South Pacific Pty. Limited (2)
219 Castlereagh St, Sydney, 2000, NSW, Australia
Tel.: (61) 290239500
Sales Range: $25-49.9 Million
Emp.: 16
Telecommunication Servicesb
N.A.I.C.S.: 517810
Frank Skiffington *(Gen Mgr)*

Mitel Spain, S.L. (2)
C/ Capitan Haya 1 Planta 17, 28020, Madrid, Spain
Tel.: (34) 915672050
Web Site: http://www.es.mitel.com
Telecommunication Servicesb
N.A.I.C.S.: 517810
Yolanda Albarracin *(Product Mgr-SME)*

Subsidiary (US):

Mitel Technologies, Inc. (2)
1146 N Alma School Rd, Mesa, AZ 85201
Tel.: (480) 449-8900
Web Site: http://www.mitel.com
Sales Range: $50-74.9 Million
Emp.: 1,900
Communication Equipment Mfr
N.A.I.C.S.: 334220

Subsidiary (Non-US):

OOO Mitel Rus (2)
Obrucheva Street 23/3, Moscow, 117630, Russia
Tel.: (7) 495 287 30 35
Web Site: http://ru.mitel.com
Sales Range: $25-49.9 Million
Emp.: 15
Business Communications Software & Equipment Distr
N.A.I.C.S.: 423430
Sergey Matrosov *(CEO)*

Subsidiary (US):

ShoreTel, Inc. (2)
960 Stewart Dr, Sunnyvale, CA 94085-3913
Tel.: (408) 331-3300
Sales Range: $350-399.9 Million
IP Telecommunications Systems
N.A.I.C.S.: 334210
Cynthia Pham Stark *(VP-Global Cloud Site Reliability Engrg & Ops)*

Subsidiary (Non-US):

ShoreTel Australia Pty. Ltd. (3)
1/441 St Kilda Rd, Melbourne, 3004, VIC, Australia (100%)
Tel.: (61) 299598000
IP Unified Communications Solutions
N.A.I.C.S.: 334290

ShoreTel UK Ltd. (3)
Inspired Easthampstead Road, Bracknell, RG12 1YQ, United Kingdom (100%)
Tel.: (44) 1344208800
IP Unified Communications Solutions
N.A.I.C.S.: 517810

Subsidiary (Non-US):

TigerTMS Limited (2)
77-79 Christchurch Road, Ringwood, BH24 1DH, United Kingdom
Tel.: (44) 1425891090
Telecommunication Servicesb
N.A.I.C.S.: 517810

Unify Software & Solutions GmbH & Co. KG (2)
Otto-Hahn-Ring 6, 81739, Munich, Germany
Tel.: (49) 8970070
Web Site: http://unify.com
Emp.: 2,000

SEARCHLIGHT CAPITAL PARTNERS, L.P.

Searchlight Capital Partners, L.P.—(Continued)
Communications Software & Services
N.A.I.C.S.: 517810

Subsidiary (Domestic):

Unify GmbH & Co. KG (3)
Mies-van-der-Rohe-Strasse 6, 80807, Munich, Germany (100%)
Tel.: (49) 8970070
Web Site: http://www.unify.com
Communications Software & Services
N.A.I.C.S.: 517810
Jon Pritchard *(CEO)*
Amy Martin *(Head-Global PR)*
Susan de Jong *(Head-Global Analyst Rels)*

NetSpend Corporation (1)
PO Box 2136, Austin, TX 78768-2136
Tel.: (512) 532-8200
Web Site: https://www.netspend.com
Sales Range: $350-399.9 Million
Emp.: 500
Debit Card Issuing
N.A.I.C.S.: 522210
Kelley Knutson *(Pres)*
Tammy Ting *(Sr VP & Gen Mgr)*
Derek Tanis *(Sr VP-Partner Channel)*
Beth Deck *(Sr VP-Fin & Acctg)*
Calvin M. Holman *(Sr VP-Information Technology)*
Diana Holgate *(Sr VP-Segment)*
Austin Smithers *(Sr VP-Compliance)*
Michael Reiff *(VP)*
Pat Vogeler *(VP-HR)*
Walt Granville *(Sr VP)*
Andrew Garner *(Sr VP & Gen Mgr)*
Brian Hobbs *(Sr VP)*
Jason Gonzalez *(Sr VP & Asst Gen Counsel)*
Rick Cox *(Sr VP-Operations)*
Shannon Johnston *(CTO)*
Walt Granville *(Sr VP)*
Andrew Garner *(Sr VP & Gen Mgr)*
Brian Hobbs *(Sr VP)*
Jason Gonzalez *(Sr VP & Asst Gen Counsel)*
Rick Cox *(Sr VP-Operations)*
Shannon Johnston *(CTO)*
Walt Granville *(Sr VP)*
Andrew Garner *(Sr VP & Gen Mgr)*
Brian Hobbs *(Sr VP)*
Jason Gonzalez *(Sr VP & Asst Gen Counsel)*
Rick Cox *(Sr VP-Operations)*
Shannon Johnston *(CTO)*
Roger D. Kidwell Jr. *(COO & Exec VP)*

Subsidiary (Domestic):

Skylight Financial, Inc. (2)
1455 Lincoln Pkwy E Ste 600, Atlanta, GA 30346
Tel.: (404) 720-2000
Web Site: http://www.skylightfinancial.com
Debit Card Issuing
N.A.I.C.S.: 522210

Opus Group AB (1)
Basargatan 10, SE-411 10, Gothenburg, Sweden (84.5%)
Tel.: (46) 317483400
Web Site: https://www.opus.global
Rev.: $289,123,548
Assets: $448,344,730
Liabilities: $344,192,423
Net Worth: $104,152,307
Earnings: ($4,050,276)
Emp.: 2,600
Fiscal Year-end: 12/31/2019
Vehicle Inspection Systems & Equipment Mfr; Vehicle Inspection Operations
N.A.I.C.S.: 336390
Andy McIntosh *(Pres-Vehicle Inspection US)*
Per Rosen *(Pres-Europe)*
Linus Brandt *(CFO & Exec VP)*
Tom Founier *(CTO)*
Alfredo R. Granai *(Pres-Latin America)*
Brain Herron *(Pres- Opus IVS)*
Francois Dekker *(Chm)*
Lothar Geilen *(CEO)*
Thomas Sanderson *(Vice Chm)*
Bjoern Rietschel *(Exec VP)*

Subsidiary (Non-US):

Autologic Diagnostics Ltd. (2)
Autologic House London Road, Wheatley,
Oxford, OX33 1JH, Oxfordshire, United Kingdom
Tel.: (44) 1865870060
Web Site: http://www.uk.autologic.com
Emp.: 150
Diagnostic Equipment Mfr
N.A.I.C.S.: 334510
Marcin Jaworski *(Head-Dev & Ops)*

Autologic Diagnostics Pty. Ltd. (2)
Suite 4 2 Compark Circuit, Mulgrave, 3170, VIC, Australia
Tel.: (61) 385617600
Web Site: http://www.au.autologic.com
Diagnostic Equipment Mfr
N.A.I.C.S.: 334510

Subsidiary (US):

Autologic Diagnostics, Inc. (2)
47 Mall Dr Ste 8, Commack, NY 11725
Tel.: (860) 392-2100
Web Site: http://www.us.autologic.com
Diagnostic Equipment Mfr
N.A.I.C.S.: 334510

Envirotest Corp. (2)
7 Kripes Rd, East Granby, CT 06026-9720
Tel.: (860) 392-2100
Vehicle Equipment Mfr
N.A.I.C.S.: 336390

FastLign LLC (2)
1410 S Acacia Ave Ste A, Fullerton, CA 92831
Tel.: (860) 392-2100
Motor Vehicle Inspection Services
N.A.I.C.S.: 811198

Gordon-Darby Systems, Inc. (2)
2410 Ampere Dr, Louisville, KY 40299
Tel.: (502) 266-5797
Web Site: http://www.gordon-darby.com
Vehicle Equipment Mfr
N.A.I.C.S.: 336390

Subsidiary (Domestic):

J&B Maskinteknik AB (2)
Backstensgatan 11 C, 431 49, Molndal, Sweden
Tel.: (46) 31 788 30 00
Web Site: http://www.jbmaskin.se
Precision Equipment Calibration Services
N.A.I.C.S.: 811210

Opus Bilprovning AB (2)
Skattegardsvagen 122, Box 118, 162 50, Vallingby, Sweden
Tel.: (46) 775500300
Web Site: http://www.bilprovning.se
Motor Vehicle Inspection Services
N.A.I.C.S.: 926150

Subsidiary (Non-US):

Opus Inspection (Pvt) Ltd. (2)
70 C-1 Gulberg III, Lahore, 54660, Pakistan
Tel.: (92) 4235754593
Vehicle Equipment Mfr
N.A.I.C.S.: 336390

Subsidiary (US):

Opus Inspection Inc. (2)
7 Kripes Rd, East Granby, CT 06026-9720
Tel.: (860) 392-2100
Web Site: http://www.opus.global
Motor Vehicle Inspection Services
N.A.I.C.S.: 811198
Andy McIntosh *(CEO)*

Subsidiary (Domestic):

Applus+ Technologies, Inc. (3)
3225 Gateway Rd Ste 450, Brookfield, WI 53045
Tel.: (312) 661-1100
Web Site: http://www.applustech.com
IT & Management Technologies
N.A.I.C.S.: 541990

Drew Technologies Inc. (3)
3915 Research Park Dr Ste 10A, Ann Arbor, MI 48108-2355
Web Site: http://www.drewtech.com
Custom Computer Programming Services
N.A.I.C.S.: 541511

Subsidiary (Domestic):

Autoenginuity LLC (4)
1819 N Rosemont, Mesa, AZ 85205
Tel.: (480) 827-8665
Web Site: http://www.autoenginuity.com
Computer Hardware Mfr
N.A.I.C.S.: 423430

Subsidiary (Non-US):

Opus Inspection SA (2)
Carcano 182 Barrio Chateu Carrera Ciudad de, Cordoba, 5003, Argentina
Tel.: (54) 3514843326
Vehicle Equipment Mfr
N.A.I.C.S.: 336390

Opus Inspection VICS Sindh (Pvt) Ltd. (2)
House No G-30/VI Sea Breeze Villas KDA Scheme 5 Clifton Block 8, Karachi, Pakistan
Tel.: (92) 2135295757
Vehicle Inspection Services
N.A.I.C.S.: 926150

Opus RS Europe S.L. (2)
Calle Gaztambide 45 Piso Bajo, 28015, Madrid, Spain
Tel.: (34) 915592868
Web Site: http://www.opusrse.com
Remote Sensor Device Component Mfr
N.A.I.C.S.: 334419

Systech Chile Ltda. (2)
Calle Andres de Fuenzalida 17 oficina 51 Region Metropolitana de, Providencia, Santiago, Chile
Tel.: (56) 998265614
Vehicle Equipment Mfr
N.A.I.C.S.: 336390

Systech Peruana SRL (2)
Carretera Panamericana Sur Km 297 2, Subtanjalla, 11000, Ica, Peru
Tel.: (51) 56223580
Vehicle Equipment Mfr
N.A.I.C.S.: 336390

TouchTunes Music Corporation (1)
850 3rd Ave Ste 15th Fl, New York, NY 10022
Tel.: (212) 991-6540
Web Site: http://www.touchtunes.com
Out-of-Home Interactive Entertainment Systems
N.A.I.C.S.: 541990
Pam Schoenfeld *(Gen Counsel & Sr VP)*
Marc Felsen *(CMO)*
Ross Honey *(Pres & CEO)*
Anthony Plesner *(CFO)*
Quentin Gallet *(CTO)*
Luke Ferro *(Exec VP-North America Sls)*

Univision Holdings, Inc. (1)
605 3rd Ave 33rd Fl, New York, NY 10158
Tel.: (212) 455-5200
Web Site: http://www.univision.com
Sales Range: $1-4.9 Billion
Holding Company; Television & Radio Broadcasting
N.A.I.C.S.: 551112
Henry G. Cisneros *(Chm)*
Sameer Dean *(Chief Digital Officer)*
Wade Davis *(CEO)*
Rafael Urbina *(Exec VP & Gen Mgr-AVOD Streaming)*

Holding (Domestic):

Univision Communications Inc. (2)
8551 NW 30th Ter, Miami, FL 33122
Tel.: (212) 455-5200
Web Site: http://corporate.univision.com
Sales Range: $1-4.9 Billion
Spanish-Language Media Holding Company
N.A.I.C.S.: 551112
Jose Valle *(Pres-Political & Advocacy Sls)*
Jorge Daboub *(Exec VP-Local Media Sls)*
Peter H. Lori *(CFO)*
Carlos Deschapelles *(Exec VP)*
Trisha Pray *(Exec VP-Sls & Client Dev)*
Roberto Ruiz *(Exec VP-Strategy & Insights)*
Jason E. Newman *(VP-Sports Sls)*
Rachel Gross *(Sr VP-Event Mktg)*
Rosemary Mercedes Beepat *(VP-Corp & Digital Comm)*
Alberto Ciurana *(Pres-Programming & Content)*
Jonathan D. Schwartz *(Chief Legal & Corp Affairs Officer)*
Hilary Dubin *(VP-Bus Dev)*
Diana Terry *(VP-Brand Dev & Corp Mktg)*
Derek Bond *(Sr VP-Production Strategy)*

U.S. PRIVATE

David Rabinowitz *(Exec VP-Brdcst Ops & Tech)*
Rosemary Mercedes *(Chief Comm Officer & Exec VP)*
Jorge Dominguez *(Sr VP-Art & Design)*
Alejandro Nieto Molina *(Sr VP & Gen Mgr-Radio)*
Jed Meyer *(Exec VP-Corp Res)*
Mark Collazo *(Mgr-Sls)*
Diego Rodriguez *(Chief Global Security Officer)*
Annie Fong *(Dir-Programmatic Ad Ops)*
Dayana Hoffman *(Dir-Sls Programmatic Revenue & Platform)*
David Katz *(VP-Programmatic Revenue Platforms & Ops & Gen Mgr)*
Silvia Garcia *(Sr VP-Media Plng & Multiplatform Strategy-Miami)*
Lourdes Diaz *(Pres-Entertainment-Los Angeles)*
Adrian Santucho *(Exec VP-Univision Studios-Miami)*
Stephen J. McGowan *(Sr VP-Corp Res)*
Danny Lowry *(VP-Radio Natl Sls)*
Christine Escobar *(VP, Gen Mgr & Dir-Sls-Austin)*
Rosemary Ravinal *(VP-Entertainment & Consumer PR-Miami)*
Steve Mandala *(Pres-Adv Sls & Mktg)*
Jack Randall *(Exec VP-Bus Dev)*
John Kozack *(Sr VP-New York Network & Digital Sls)*
Ronald Estrada *(Sr VP-Corp Social Responsibility & Community Empowerment)*
Stephen Keppel *(VP-Social Impact/Gen Mgr-Rise Up-Miami)*
Jessica Herrera-Flanigan *(Exec VP-Govt & Corp Affairs)*
Adam Shippee *(Sr VP-Corp Bus Dev & Head-IR)*
Roberto Yanez *(Sr VP/Gen Mgr-New York)*
Michael S. Mueller *(Sr VP-Bus Dev)*
Liz Blacker *(Sr VP-Branded Content Revenue)*
Lisa Valentino *(Exec VP-Revenue Innovation)*
Michael Schwimmer *(Pres-Platform Strategy & Revenue-Global)*
Wade Davis *(CEO)*
Ignacio Meyer *(Pres-Networks-US)*

Subsidiary (Domestic):

Galavision, Inc. (3)
605 3rd Ave 12th Fl, New York, NY 10158-1299
Tel.: (212) 455-5200
Web Site: http://www.unvision.com
Sales Range: $50-74.9 Million
Emp.: 320
International Network & Basic Cable Service
N.A.I.C.S.: 516210
Elidieth Stern *(Office Mgr)*
Carlos Deschapelles *(Sr VP-Sports Sls)*

Division (Domestic):

Univision Radio (3)
3102 Oak Lawn Ave Ste 215, Dallas, TX 75219-4259
Tel.: (214) 525-7700
Sales Range: $350-399.9 Million
Emp.: 55
Spanish Language Radio Broadcasting Services
N.A.I.C.S.: 516110

Unit (Domestic):

KSCA-FM (4)
655 N Central Ave Ste 2500, Glendale, CA 91203
Tel.: (818) 500-4500
Web Site: http://www.univision.com
Sales Range: $25-49.9 Million
Spanish Language Radio Programming
N.A.I.C.S.: 516110

KTNQ-AM (4)
655 N Central Ave Ste 2500, Glendale, CA 91203-1422
Tel.: (818) 500-4500
Spanish-Language Radio Broadcasting Station
N.A.I.C.S.: 516110

WADO-AM (4)
485 Madison Ave Fl 3, New York, NY 10022
Tel.: (212) 310-6000

Web Site: http://wado1280am.univision.com
Sales Range: $10-24.9 Million
Spanish Radio Broadcasting Stations
N.A.I.C.S.: 516110

Subsidiary (Domestic):

Vix, Inc. (3)
2121 Ponce de Leon Blvd Ste 800, Coral Gables, FL 33134
Tel.: (305) 476-2974
Web Site: http://www.vix.com
Publishing Services
N.A.I.C.S.: 513199
Rafael Urbina (CEO)

Subsidiary (Domestic):

Womensforum.com, Inc. (4)
444 N Michigan Ave Ste 3550, Chicago, IL 60611
Tel.: (312) 396-1800
Web Site: http://www.womensforum.com
Website Publisher
N.A.I.C.S.: 513120
Mark Kaufman (Co-Founder & CEO)
Jodi Luber (Co-Founder & Pres)

SEARCHPROS SOLUTIONS
6363 Auburn Blvd, Citrus Heights, CA 95621
Tel.: (888) 774-4737
Web Site: http://www.searchprosmp.com
Year Founded: 2005
Sales Range: $25-49.9 Million
Emp.: 713
Workforce Solutions Management Services
N.A.I.C.S.: 561311
Myla Ramos (Pres, Founder & Mng Partner)

SEARS CONTRACT, INC.
3333 Beverly Rd B6-258b, Hoffman Estates, IL 60179-0001
Tel.: (847) 286-2500
Sales Range: $25-49.9 Million
Emp.: 250
Plastering Services
N.A.I.C.S.: 238310
Shirley Bicknell (Mgr-Regulatory Complaint)
Randy McMan (Mgr)

SEARS MANUFACTURING COMPANY
1718 S Concord St, Davenport, IA 52802
Tel.: (563) 383-2800
Web Site: http://www.searsseating.com
Sales Range: $100-124.9 Million
Emp.: 600
Vehicle Furniture
N.A.I.C.S.: 336360
Jim I. Sears (CEO)

SEARS PETROLEUM & TRANSPORT CORP.
1914 Black River Blvd N, Rome, NY 13440
Tel.: (315) 337-1232 NY
Web Site: http://www.seaco.com
Year Founded: 1940
Sales Range: $10-24.9 Million
Emp.: 8
Sales & Transport of Fuel Oil
N.A.I.C.S.: 424720

SEAS INDUSTRIES INC.
1900 Empire Blvd Ste 189, Webster, NY 14580
Tel.: (585) 217-2797 WY
Year Founded: 2009
Website Owner & Operator
N.A.I.C.S.: 513199

Gabor Harsanyi (Pres, CEO, CFO & Sec)
Barry Weiner (Treas)
Nunzio J. Valerie Jr. (CFO)

SEASHORE INSURANCE & ASSOCIATION
827 Gum Branch Rd, Jacksonville, NC 28540
Tel.: (910) 455-7576
Web Site: http://www.siagroup.net
Year Founded: 1975
Rev.: $65,000,000
Emp.: 65
Insurance Agents, Brokers & Service
N.A.I.C.S.: 524210
W. Don Mills (Pres)
J. G. Rock (Treas)
Diana Evans (Exec VP)
Cliff Patterson (VP)
Crystal Smith (Acct Mgr)
Clifton Waters (VP)
Deepak Poplai (VP)
Heather Lewter (Acct Mgr)
Jane Newbern (Mgr-Underwriting)
Joan Phillips (VP)
Jyl Shirley (Acct Mgr)
Ken Hulsmann (Dir-IT)
Teri Costen (Dir-Safety & Risk Mgmt)

SEASIDE FURNITURE SHOP INC.
3301 Rte 37 E, Toms River, NJ 08753
Tel.: (732) 929-8000 NJ
Web Site: http://www.seasidefurniture.com
Year Founded: 1955
Sales Range: $10-24.9 Million
Emp.: 47
Provider of Residential Furnishings
N.A.I.C.S.: 449110
Peggy Mcgarry (VP)
Robert J. Smith (Treas)

SEASIDE UTILITIES INC.
1363 Old Hwy 52, Moncks Corner, SC 29461
Tel.: (843) 761-2007
Sales Range: $10-24.9 Million
Emp.: 80
Underground Utilities Contractor
N.A.I.C.S.: 237110
Averial D. McCoy III (Pres)

SEASPACE CORP.
13000 Gregg St Ste A, Poway, CA 92064-7151
Tel.: (858) 746-1100
Web Site: http://www.seaspace.com
Year Founded: 1982
Weather Satellite Tracking Equipment Used in Remote-Sensing Technology to Receive & Process Weather Information
N.A.I.C.S.: 334220
David Collins (Pres)

SEASPINE HOLDINGS CORPORATION
5770 Armada Dr, Carlsbad, CA 92008
Tel.: (760) 727-8399 DE
Web Site: https://www.seaspine.com
Year Founded: 2015
SPNE—(NASDAQ)
Rev.: $191,451,000
Assets: $377,267,000
Liabilities: $64,903,000
Net Worth: $312,364,000
Earnings: ($54,346,000)
Emp.: 523
Fiscal Year-end: 12/31/21
Surgical Solutions for Spinal Disorders
N.A.I.C.S.: 339113

Massimo V. Calafiore (CEO)

Subsidiaries:

SeaSpine, Inc. (1)
2302 La Mirada Dr, Vista, CA 92081
Tel.: (760) 727-8399
Web Site: http://www.seaspine.com
Sales Range: $50-74.9 Million
Emp.: 13
Medical Device Mfr
N.A.I.C.S.: 339113

SEASUCKER
6441 19th St E Bldg F, Sarasota, FL 34243
Tel.: (941) 586-2664
Web Site: http://www.seasucker.com
Year Founded: 2005
Sales Range: $1-9.9 Million
Emp.: 8
Marine Accessories, Bike Racks, Board Racks & Electronics Mounts Mfr
N.A.I.C.S.: 336999
Chuck Casagrande (Owner)

SEATER CONSTRUCTION CO. INC.
2322 Mead St, Racine, WI 53403-3337
Tel.: (262) 634-2366 WI
Web Site: http://www.cedar.com
Year Founded: 1994
Sales Range: $10-24.9 Million
Emp.: 45
Provider of Construction Services
N.A.I.C.S.: 236220

Subsidiaries:

Royale House Inc. (1)
2322 Mead St, Racine, WI 53403-3337
Tel.: (262) 637-4555
Web Site: http://www.royalehouse.com
Sales Range: $10-24.9 Million
Emp.: 5
Provider of Concrete Products
N.A.I.C.S.: 327331

SEATORQUE CONTROL SYSTEMS, LLC
2779 SE Monroe St, Stuart, FL 34997
Tel.: (772) 220-3020
Web Site: http://www.seatorque.com
Sales Range: $1-9.9 Million
Emp.: 20
Hydraulic Cylinders & Actuators Mfr for the Marine Industry
N.A.I.C.S.: 333995
Peter Srolper (Pres)
Jana Stolper (VP)

SEATRAIL GULF RESORT
211 Clubhouse Rd, Sunset Beach, NC 28468
Tel.: (910) 287-1100
Web Site: http://www.seatrail.com
Rev.: $20,400,000
Emp.: 250
Subdividers & Developers
N.A.I.C.S.: 237210
Dana Connelly (Pres)
Tom Plankers (Pres-Golf)

SEATTLE AERO LLC
8509 154th Ave NE, Redmond, WA 98050
Tel.: (425) 643-4224
Web Site: http://www.seattleaero.com
Rev.: $12,400,000
Emp.: 40
Aerospace Equipment & Supplies
N.A.I.C.S.: 423860
Riene Simpson (CFO)

SEATTLE AQUARIUM
1483 Alaskan Way Pier 59, Seattle, WA 98101
Tel.: (206) 386-4300 WA
Web Site: http://www.seattleaquarium.org
Year Founded: 1982
Sales Range: $10-24.9 Million
Emp.: 149
Marine Environmental Conservation Services
N.A.I.C.S.: 813312
C. J. Casson (Dir-Life Sciences)
David Muzia (Dir-Facilities)
Jim Wharton (Dir-Conservation & Education)
Veronica Smolen (Dir-HR)
Ryan Dean (Fin Dir & Dir-Admin)
Robert W. Davidson (Pres & CEO)
Neal Holland (Treas)
Randy J. Tinseth (Chm)
Brad Rutherford (COO)
Rick Johnson (Dir-Fin & Admin)
Babs Pinette (Dir-Mktg & Comm)

SEATTLE AUTOMOTIVE DISTRIBUTING
204 H St NW, Auburn, WA 98001
Tel.: (253) 929-2292
Web Site: http://www.seattleautomotive.com
Rev.: $15,000,000
Emp.: 99
Automotive Supplies & Parts
N.A.I.C.S.: 423120
Paul Tegantvoort (Pres)

SEATTLE BOX CO.
23400 71st Pl S, Kent, WA 98032
Tel.: (253) 854-9700
Web Site: http://www.seattlebox.com
Sales Range: $25-49.9 Million
Emp.: 125
Wooden Box Mfr
N.A.I.C.S.: 488991
Sue Kramer (Mgr-Accts Payable)
Cindy Nunley (Controller)
Robert Nist (VP-Mktg)
Mark Clarkson (Mgr-Sls)

SEATTLE CITY LIGHT
700 Fifth Ave Ste 3200, Seattle, WA 98104-5031
Tel.: (206) 684-3000 WA
Web Site: http://www.ci.seattle.wa.us
Year Founded: 1905
Sales Range: $800-899.9 Million
Emp.: 1,560
Municipal Electric Utility; Conservation Loans, Grants & Services
N.A.I.C.S.: 221122
Darwyn Anderson (Dir-HR)
Michael Mann (Interim Dir-Office Sustainability & Environ)
Julie Tobin (Office Mgr)
Jorge Carrasco (Superintendent)
Wayne Morter (Dir-Power Ops & Mktg)
Craig Smith (Dir-Conservation Resources)
Jim Baggs (Interim CEO)

SEATTLE CRAB CO.
170 W Dayton St Ste 204, Edmonds, WA 98020
Tel.: (425) 563-9200
Year Founded: 1966
Sales Range: $25-49.9 Million
Emp.: 900
Seafood Restaurants
N.A.I.C.S.: 722511
Scott Way (Exec VP)

Subsidiaries:

Skippers Inc. (1)
Ste 204 170 W Dayton St, Edmonds, WA 98020-4162

SEATTLE CRAB CO.

Seattle Crab Co.—(Continued)
Tel.: (425) 670-3393
Web Site: http://www.skippers.net
Rev.: $33,000,000
Emp.: 15
Seafood Restaurants
N.A.I.C.S.: 722511

SEATTLE FISH COMPANY
6211 E 42nd Ave, Denver, CO 80216
Tel.: (303) 329-9595
Web Site: http://www.seattlefish.com
Sales Range: $10-24.9 Million
Emp.: 105
Fish & Seafoods Whslr
N.A.I.C.S.: 424460
Edward M. Iacino (Pres)
Jason Cesario (Dir-Ops)
Hamish Walker (Dir-Pur)
Patrick Zoghby (Mgr-Corp Sls)

SEATTLE GOODWILL INDUSTRIES
1765 6th Ave S, Seattle, WA 98134
Tel.: (206) 329-1000
Web Site:
http://www.seattlegoodwill.org
Rev.: $18,710,924
Emp.: 500
Used Merchandise Stores
N.A.I.C.S.: 459510
Michael Jurich (CFO & VP)
Bert Fish (VP-Loss Prevention)
Catherine McConnell (VP-Adv)
Suzanne Ebling (VP-HR)
Daryl J. Campbell (Pres & CEO)
Barbara Nabors-Glass (VP-Job Trng & Education)
Funmi Popoola (VP-Ops)

SEATTLE GOURMET FOODS, INC.
19016 72nd Ave S, Kent, WA 98032
Tel.: (425) 656-9076
Web Site:
http://www.seattlegourmetfood.com
Year Founded: 1993
Sales Range: $25-49.9 Million
Emp.: 275
Chocolate & Cookie Mfr & Distr
N.A.I.C.S.: 311351
Mike Harris (Mgr-Distr & Logistics)
Mary Bides (Controller)
Tom Means (Gen Mgr)

SEATTLE IRON & METALS CORP.
601 S Myrtle St, Seattle, WA 98108
Tel.: (206) 682-0040
Web Site: http://www.seairon.com
Rev.: $21,000,000
Emp.: 75
Ferrous Metal Scrap & Waste
N.A.I.C.S.: 423930
Allan Sidell (Pres)
Paul Kirkman (Mgr-Safety)

SEATTLE KING COUNTY CONVENTION AND VISITORS BUREAU
701 Pike St Ste 800, Seattle, WA 98101
Tel.: (206) 461-5800 WA
Web Site: http://www.visitseattle.org
Year Founded: 1994
Sales Range: $10-24.9 Million
Emp.: 75
Convention & Visitor Bureau Services
N.A.I.C.S.: 561591
Tom Norwalk (Pres & CEO)
Chad MacKay (Chm-Fin)
Leslie Kunde (Chm)
David Blandford (VP-Comm)
Rob Hampton (Sr VP-Convention Sls & Svcs)

Keri Robinson (Vice Chm)
Kris Cromwell (VP-Fin)
Ali Daniels (VP-Mktg)

SEATTLE MARINE & FISHING SUPPLY CO.
2121 W Commodore Way, Seattle, WA 98199
Tel.: (206) 285-5010
Web Site: http://www.seamar.com
Sales Range: $10-24.9 Million
Emp.: 37
Marine Supplies
N.A.I.C.S.: 423860
Robert W. Crump (Pres)
Dan Farrow (Mgr-Net Div)

SEATTLE MARINERS BASEBALL CLUB
1250 1st Ave S, Seattle, WA 98134
Rev.: $1,600,000
Emp.: 24
Fiscal Year-end: 12/31/06
Professional Baseball Club
N.A.I.C.S.: 711211
John William Stanton (Owner)
Frederick B. Rivera (Gen Counsel, Sec & Exec VP)

SEATTLE PACIFIC INDUSTRIES, INC.
1633 Westlake Ave N Ste 300, Seattle, WA 98109
Tel.: (206) 282-8889 WA
Web Site: http://www.unionbay.com
Year Founded: 1981
Sales Range: $200-249.9 Million
Emp.: 380
Mfr, Designer & Retailer of Men's & Women's Sportswear
N.A.I.C.S.: 424350
Steve Ritchey (Pres)
Rod Leung (VP-Corp Affairs)
Gooria Lung (COO)

Subsidiaries:

Re-Union Division   (1)
1633 Westlake Ave N, Seattle, WA 98109-6214
Tel.: (206) 282-8889
Web Site: http://www.reunion.com
Sales Range: $25-49.9 Million
Emp.: 80
Mfr of Men's Sportswear
N.A.I.C.S.: 424350

Seattle Pacific Industries, Inc., Unionbay Division   (1)
1633 Westlake Ave N, Seattle, WA 98109-6214
Tel.: (206) 282-8889
Web Site: http://www.unionbay.com
Sales Range: $25-49.9 Million
Emp.: 60
Mfr of Young Mens & Young Contemporary Sportswear
N.A.I.C.S.: 424350

SEATTLE SERVICE BUREAU INC.
18912 N Creek Pkwy Ste 205, Bothell, WA 98011
Tel.: (206) 533-0877
Web Site: http://www.nsbi.net
Sales Range: $125-149.9 Million
Emp.: 100
Debt Collection Services
N.A.I.C.S.: 561440
David Conyers (CEO)

SEATTLE SUN TAN
1919 120th Ave NE, Bellevue, WA 98005
Tel.: (425) 429-7400
Web Site:
http://www.seattlesuntan.com
Year Founded: 2004
Sales Range: $10-24.9 Million

Emp.: 245
Indoor Tanning Salons
N.A.I.C.S.: 812112
Scott Swerland (Founder)
Kaela Simeona (Mgr-Store)

SEAVIEW BUICK GMC
17909 Hwy 99, Lynnwood, WA 98037
Tel.: (425) 742-1920
Web Site:
http://www.seaviewbuickgmc.com
Sales Range: $50-74.9 Million
Emp.: 94
Automobiles, New & Used
N.A.I.C.S.: 441110
Christian Olson (Pres)
Gary Danielson (Mgr-Svc)
Jim Ault (Mgr-Sls)

SEAVIEW RESOURCES INC.
270 Woodbury Dr, Sterrett, AL 35147
Tel.: (214) 329-9690 NV
Year Founded: 2012
Metal Mining
N.A.I.C.S.: 212290
Virgil Perryman (Pres, CEO, CFO, Treas & Sec)

SEAVIN, INC.
157 King St, Saint Augustine, FL 32084
Tel.: (904) 826-1594 FL
Web Site:
http://www.sansebastianwinery.com
Year Founded: 1990
Sales Range: $1-9.9 Million
Emp.: 60
Winery & Vineyards
N.A.I.C.S.: 312130
Gary Cox (Pres)

SEAWARD SERVICES INC.
22 Pearl St 3rd Fl, New Albany, IN 47150
Tel.: (954) 769-9260
Web Site:
http://www.seawardservices.com
Sales Range: $25-49.9 Million
Emp.: 135
Research & Development in the Physical, Engineering & Life Sciences
N.A.I.C.S.: 541715
David G. Henderson (Mgr-Quality Sys)
John Keever (Pres & CEO)
Nancy Wagner (Mgr-HR)

SEAWATER SEAFOOD COMPANY
1164 S W Coast Hwy Ste H, Newport, OR 97365
Tel.: (541) 574-2698
Web Site:
http://www.seawaterseafoodco.com
Year Founded: 2012
Sales Range: $1-9.9 Million
Emp.: 6
Seafood Product Distr
N.A.I.C.S.: 424460
Kathy Latimer (CFO & COO)

SEAWAY HOTELS CORPORATION
1200 Anastasia Ave, Coral Gables, FL 33134
Tel.: (305) 445-1926
Web Site:
http://www.seawaygroup.com
Sales Range: $10-24.9 Million
Emp.: 500
Hotel Owner & Operator
N.A.I.C.S.: 721110
T. Gene Prescott (CEO)

SEAWAY MANUFACTURING CORP.

U.S. PRIVATE

2250 E 33rd St, Erie, PA 16510
Tel.: (814) 898-2255
Web Site:
http://www.seawaymfg.com
Rev.: $12,903,822
Emp.: 100
Windows, Plastics
N.A.I.C.S.: 326199
Zachary McCartney (Mgr-Engrg)
Patrick Goodrich (Engr-Ops)
Jana Goodrich (Pres & CEO)

SEAWAY PLASTICS ENGINEERING, INC.
6006 Siesta Ln, Port Richey, FL 34668
Tel.: (727) 845-3235 FL
Web Site:
http://www.seawayplastics.com
Year Founded: 2003
Sales Range: $10-24.9 Million
Emp.: 120
Dies, Tools, Jigs & Fixtures Mfr
N.A.I.C.S.: 333511
Tim Smock (Founder)
Gregg Bair (Project Mgr)
John Hanke (Project Mgr)
Rocky Johnson (Mgr-Production)
Patrick Buttil (Controller)
Tom Orr (Pres & CEO)
Beth Galic (Coord-Mktg & Sls)

SEAWAY PRINTING COMPANY, INC.
1609 Western Ave, Green Bay, WI 54303
Tel.: (920) 468-1500 WI
Web Site:
http://www.seawayprinting.com
Year Founded: 1995
Sales Range: $1-9.9 Million
Emp.: 32
Commercial Printing Services
N.A.I.C.S.: 323111
Kevin Heslin (Pres)

SEAWRIGHT HOLDINGS, INC.
600 Cameron St, Alexandria, VA 22314
Tel.: (703) 340-1629 DE
Web Site:
http://www.seawrightsprings.com
Year Founded: 1999
Emp.: 1
Holding Company; Bottled Water Mfr & Distr
N.A.I.C.S.: 551112
Joel P. Sens (Chm, Pres, CEO, CFO, Treas & Sec)

SEBA BROS. FARMS, INC.
2111 E State Route Y, Cleveland, MO 64734
Tel.: (816) 618-3653
Web Site: http://www.sebabros.com
Year Founded: 1980
Sales Range: $25-49.9 Million
Agricultural Consulting Services
N.A.I.C.S.: 541690
Harold Seba (Co-Owner)
David Seba (Co-Owner)

SEBAGO BREWING CO.
PO Box 1054, Scarborough, ME 04070
Tel.: (207) 879-2537
Web Site:
http://www.sebagobrewing.com
Sales Range: $10-24.9 Million
Emp.: 121
Brewery Mfr
N.A.I.C.S.: 312120
Brian Johnson (Gen Mgr)
Tim Haines (Co-Founder & Treas)
Kai Adams (Co-Founder & VP)
Kevin Flanagan (Mgr-Floating)

Travis Ducharme *(Mgr-Kitchen)*
Jon Clegg *(Mgr-Brewer & Packaging)*
Scott Engelter *(Mgr-Kitchen)*
Anders Kjeldsen *(Mgr-Svc-Columbus)*

SEBASTIAN & ASSOCIATES, INC.
4809 Cole Ave Ste 215, Dallas, TX 75205-3581
Tel.: (214) 528-4130
Web Site: http://sebastiancg.com
Year Founded: 1977
Sales Range: $25-49.9 Million
Emp.: 41
Housing Construction Services
N.A.I.C.S.: 236117
John Sebastian *(Pres)*
Cheryl Tracy *(Controller)*

SEBASTIAN EQUIPMENT CO. INC.
1801 S Joplin Ave, Joplin, MO 64804
Tel.: (417) 623-3300
Web Site: http://www.sebastianequip.com
Rev.: $12,801,015
Emp.: 30
Industrial Machinery & Equipment
N.A.I.C.S.: 423830

SEBASTIAN HOLDINGS, INC.
537 Divison St, North Tonawanda, NY 14120
Tel.: (716) 693-6167   NY
Private Investment Firm
N.A.I.C.S.: 523999
Alexander Vik *(Owner)*

SEBRING SOFTWARE, INC.
1400 Cattlemen Rd Ste D, Sarasota, FL 34232
Tel.: (941) 377-0715   NV
Web Site: http://www.sebringsoft.com
Year Founded: 2007
Sales Range: $10-24.9 Million
Emp.: 163
Mobile Marketing Services
N.A.I.C.S.: 541613
Leif Andersen *(Pres & CEO)*
L. Michael Andersen *(VP-Ops)*
Scott A. Reynolds *(CFO & Controller)*

SECCO, INC.
1111 Primrose Ave, Camp Hill, PA 17011
Tel.: (717) 737-2142
Web Site: http://www.seccoinc.com
Year Founded: 1969
Sales Range: $10-24.9 Million
Emp.: 111
Plumbing & Air-Conditioning Contractor
N.A.I.C.S.: 238210
Barry Kindt *(Pres)*
Craig Drabenstadt *(Partner)*

SECO ARCHITECTURAL SYSTEM
2171 W Park Ct Ste E, Stone Mountain, GA 30087-3556
Tel.: (770) 469-8286
Sales Range: $10-24.9 Million
Emp.: 70
Siding Installation Services
N.A.I.C.S.: 238170
Richard Waldron *(Pres)*

SECOND CURVE CAPITAL, LLC
237 Park Ave 9th Fl, New York, NY 10017
Tel.: (646) 563-7600   DE
Web Site: http://www.secondcurve.com
Year Founded: 2000
Sales Range: $1-9.9 Million
Emp.: 6
Privater Equity Firm
N.A.I.C.S.: 523999
Thomas K. Brown *(Founder & CEO)*
Bradley Cymbol *(CFO)*

SECOND FAMILY INC.
1301 W Dumpster, Park Ridge, IL 60068
Tel.: (847) 698-3700
Web Site: http://www.bredemann.com
Year Founded: 1976
Rev.: $14,700,000
Emp.: 50
Automobiles New & Used
N.A.I.C.S.: 441110
Pete Livingston *(Controller)*
John Bredemann *(Owner & Pres)*

SECOND HARVEST OF SOUTH GEORGIA, INC.
1411 Harbin Cir, Valdosta, GA 31601
Tel.: (229) 244-2678   GA
Web Site: http://www.feedingsga.org
Year Founded: 1996
Sales Range: $25-49.9 Million
Emp.: 54
Hunger Relief Services
N.A.I.C.S.: 624210
Chet Ballard *(Chm)*
Frank Richards *(CEO)*

SECOND TO NONE, INC.
303 Detroit St Ste 1, Ann Arbor, MI 48104-1128
Tel.: (734) 302-8400   MI
Web Site: http://www.second-to-none.com
Year Founded: 1989
Sales Range: $1-9.9 Million
Emp.: 80
Mystery Shopping & Customer Experience Optimization
N.A.I.C.S.: 541910
Jeff Hall *(Founder & CEO)*
Kerry Colligan *(Mgr-Integrated Mktg)*
Tammy Lee *(Mgr-Field Ops)*
David W. Robbins *(VP-Client Svcs)*

SECRET CITY CHRYSLER DODGE JEEP
PO Box 30309, Knoxville, TN 37930
Tel.: (865) 691-4000
Sales Range: $10-24.9 Million
Emp.: 61
Car Whslr
N.A.I.C.S.: 441110
Tim Heatherly *(Mgr-Sls)*
Kenny Lane *(Owner)*

SECTEK INC.
11413 Isaac Newton Sq S, Reston, VA 20190
Tel.: (703) 435-0970
Web Site: http://www.sectek.com
Rev.: $18,000,000
Emp.: 23
Detective & Armored Car Services
N.A.I.C.S.: 561613
Douglas Daniels *(Project Mgr)*

SECTION EIGHT, INC.
4000 Warner Blvd, Burbank, CA 91522
Tel.: (818) 954-4840   CA
Motion Picture & Video Distr
N.A.I.C.S.: 512120
George Clooney *(Pres)*

SECTOR7 USA INC.
6500 River Pl Blvd Bld 2 Ste 201, Austin, TX 78730
Tel.: (512) 340-0606
Web Site: http://www.sector7.com
Year Founded: 1989
Rev.: $12,500,000
Emp.: 160
Computer Related Consulting Services
N.A.I.C.S.: 541512
Massimo Pezzini *(Res Dir)*
Blake Yeager *(COO & Sr VP)*
Mary Vaughn *(Controller)*

SECTRAN SECURITY, INC.
7633 Industry Ave, Pico Rivera, CA 90660
Tel.: (562) 948-1446   CA
Web Site: http://www.sectransecurity.com
Year Founded: 1982
Emp.: 140
Armored Car Services
N.A.I.C.S.: 561613
Fred Kunik *(Pres)*

SECURA INSURANCE COMPANY
2401 S Meml Dr, Appleton, WI 54915-1429
Tel.: (920) 739-3161   WI
Web Site: http://www.secura.net
Year Founded: 1900
Sales Range: $100-124.9 Million
Emp.: 500
Provider of Insurance Services
N.A.I.C.S.: 524126
John A. Bykowski *(Chm)*
Jeff Kargus *(CFO & VP)*
David D. Gross *(Pres & CEO)*
Harvey L. Enerson *(Reg VP)*
Garth P. Wicinsky *(Chief Admin Officer & Sr VP)*
Diana Buechel *(VP-Personal Lines Underwriting)*
Marty S. Arnold *(Chief Underwriting Officer & Sr VP)*
Shane Roh *(Reg VP)*
Steve Miller *(VP-Comml Lines Underwriting)*
Tim Heyroth *(Chief Sls Officer)*
Kevin Klestinski *(VP-Specialty Lines Underwriting)*
Tony Brecunier *(VP-Worker's Compensation Claims)*
Jennifer Haas *(VP-R&D & Trng)*
Sandra Hupfer *(VP-Casualty Claims)*
Todd Thiel *(CIO)*
Amy Dehart *(Chief Actuarial Officer & VP)*
Larry Wright *(Chief Claims Officer & VP)*
Jennifer Fisher *(VP-Property Claims)*
Carol Wedig *(VP-Continuous Improvement)*
Page Denny *(Mgr-Arizona)*
Lisa Switzer *(Mgr-Kentucky)*
Tripp Humston *(Dir-Sls)*

SECURBORATION, INC.
1050 W Nasa Blvd Ste 155, Melbourne, FL 32901
Tel.: (321) 409-5252
Web Site: http://www.securboration.com
Year Founded: 2001
Sales Range: $1-9.9 Million
Emp.: 20
Custom Computer Programming Services
N.A.I.C.S.: 541511
Bruce McQueary *(Pres)*
Arlan Sands *(Engr-Software)*
Sean Thornton *(Engr-Software)*
James Schneider *(Engr-Software-III)*
Scott White Jr. *(Engr-Software-II)*

SECURE CASH NETWORK, INC.
808 W Dallas St Ste A, Conroe, TX 77301
Tel.: (713) 357-7000
Year Founded: 2003
Rev.: $2,000,000
Emp.: 12
Commodity Contracts Dealing
N.A.I.C.S.: 523160
Nanette M. Gowan *(CFO)*
Leslie Wm Adams *(Gen Counsel & VP)*
Mark McFarlin *(Dir-Compliance)*
Luis Sandoval *(Mgr-Intl Remittance)*
Leylani Najera *(Mgr)*
Mark McCarley *(Exec VP)*
David Bloh *(COO & Exec VP)*

SECURE DESIGNS, INC.
301 N Elm St Ste 550, Greensboro, NC 27401
Tel.: (336) 232-5990
Web Site: http://www.securedesigns.com
Year Founded: 1999
Sales Range: $1-9.9 Million
Emp.: 16
Internet Security Services
N.A.I.C.S.: 518210
Larry Cecchini *(Pres & CEO)*
Ron Culler *(Founder & CTO)*
Wayne Hutchins *(CFO)*
Reeve Samson *(CIO)*
Jackie McMahon *(VP-Logistics & Admin)*

SECURE DIGITAL, INC.
2 Glenwood Ln, Huntington, NY 11743
Tel.: (631) 662-6674   NV
Emp.: 1
Digital Security Products Mfr, Marketer & Sales
N.A.I.C.S.: 334118
Peter Hodyno *(Pres, CEO, CFO, Treas & Sec)*

SECURE ENTERPRISES, LLC
1417 Sadler Rd Ste201, Fernandina Beach, FL 32034
Tel.: (954) 370-9928
Web Site: http://www.securedoor.com
Year Founded: 2003
Sales Range: $1-9.9 Million
Emp.: 4
Garage Door Brace System Mfr
N.A.I.C.S.: 332510
Jack Stumpff *(Pres)*

SECURE EXCHANGE SOLUTIONS, INC.
801 Cromwell Park Dr Ste 100, Glen Burnie, MD 21061-2539
Tel.: (410) 590-6494
Web Site: http://www.ses11.com
Year Founded: 2007
Security System Services
N.A.I.C.S.: 561621
Douglas Trotter *(Pres & CEO)*

SECURE FOUNDATION SYSTEMS, INC
5851 S Pine Ave, Ocala, FL 34480
Tel.: (352) 671-9191
Web Site: http://www.securefsi.com
Year Founded: 2007
Sales Range: $1-9.9 Million
Emp.: 41
Residential Restoration Services
N.A.I.C.S.: 236118
James Alexander *(VP)*
Ryan R. Gummer *(Owner & Pres)*
Sven Axelsson *(Gen Mgr)*

SECURE IDEAS, LLC
3412 Kori Rd, Jacksonville, FL 32257

SECURE IDEAS, LLC

Secure Ideas, LLC—(Continued)

Web Site:
http://www.secureideas.com
Year Founded: 2010
Sales Range: $1-9.9 Million
Emp.: 17
Security System Services
N.A.I.C.S.: 561621
Kevin Johnson (CEO)
Denise Johnson (Pres)
Jason Gillam (CIO)
Andrew Kates (Acct Mgr)
Greg Stanley (Coord-Security Trng)

SECURE TECHNOLOGY INTEGRATION GROUP LTD.

15 Schneider Rd, Allendale, NJ 07401
Web Site: http://www.stigroup.net
Year Founded: 1999
Sales Range: $1-9.9 Million
Emp.: 12
Information Security Services
N.A.I.C.S.: 519290
Dominic Genzano (Founder & CEO)
Jonathan Kobrick (Partner)
Richard Shinnick (Sr Partner)
David M. Gordon (Pres)

SECUREBUY, LLC

605 Crescent Blvd Ste 200, Ridgeland, MS 39157
Tel.: (408) 478-9760
Web Site: http://www.securebuy.com
Sales Range: $1-9.9 Million
Global Payment Fraud Prevention & Security Technology Software
N.A.I.C.S.: 513210
Ernie Coward (Chm & CEO)
Greg Stamatis (Founder & Pres)
James Packer (COO)
Lloyd Briggs (CTO)
Jason Napsky (Dir-Fin & Bus Dev)
Kevin Smith (Mgr-Quality Assurance & Product Testing)

SECURECOM INC.

1940 Don St Ste 100, Springfield, OR 97477-5911
Tel.: (541) 773-5740
Year Founded: 1997
Sales Range: $10-24.9 Million
Emp.: 80
Electrical Wiring Services
N.A.I.C.S.: 238210
Kevin McElwee (Pres)

SECURIAN FINANCIAL GROUP, INC.

400 Robert St N, Saint Paul, MN 55101-2098
Tel.: (651) 665-3500 DE
Web Site: https://www.securian.com
Year Founded: 1998
Rev.: $6,600,571,000
Assets: $63,138,274,000
Liabilities: $56,927,178,000
Net Worth: $6,211,096,000
Earnings: $434,800,000
Emp.: 6,400
Fiscal Year-end: 12/31/19
Holding Company; Financial & Life Insurance Products & Services
N.A.I.C.S.: 551112
Gary M. Kleist (Second VP-Investment Ops)
Warren J. Zaccaro (CFO & Exec VP)
George I. Connolly (Chief Strategy Officer)
Gary R. Christensen (Gen Counsel, Sec & Sr VP)
Bruce P. Shay (Exec VP)
Barbara A. Baumann (VP-Bus Svcs)
Robert J. Ehren (Sr VP-Bus Svcs)
Anthony J. Martins (VP-Career Distr)
Kathleen L. Pinkett (VP)
David A. Seidel (Chief Actuary & VP)
Christopher M. Hilger (Chm, Pres & CEO)
Siddharth S. Gandhi (Chief Strategy & Enterprise Tech Officer & Sr VP)
Laurence G. Cochrane (VP-Retail Product Distr)
Christopher R. Greene (Second VP-Affinity Solutions)
Julio A. Fesser (Second VP-Enterprise Facilities)
Rick L. Ayers (VP-Retirement Solutions)
Michael P. Boyle (Second VP-Law)
Kristi L. Fox (Chief Admin Officer & Exec VP)
Mark J. Geldernick (Chief Risk Officer & VP)
Susan M. Munson-Regala (VP)
Kristi J. Nelson (VP)
William M. Gould (Sr VP-Affinity Solutions)
Paul E. Rudeen (VP)
Suzette L. Huovinen (CEO-Canadian Premier & Sr VP)
Karen A. Leighton (Chief Transformation Officer & VP)
Ted J. Nistler (Treas & Sr VP)
Sean O'Connell (Chief Investment Officer)
Mark W. Sievers (Second VP)
Michael J. Webster (Second VP-Digital)
Patrick Boyd (Second VP-Enterprise Bus Dev)
Ann P. McGarry (Second VP-Mktg)
Elda Macias (Sr Dir-Customer Insights & Experience Design-Securian Fin)
Christopher B. Owens (Sr VP-Retail Life & Annuity Sls)
Becca Hagen (VP-Talent Mgmt)
Tariq Malik (Chief Diversity Officer & VP)
Kristin Ferguson (Sr VP-Individual Solutions)
Darrin Hebert (CIO & Sr VP)

Subsidiaries:

Advantus Capital Management, Inc. (1)
400 Robert St N, Saint Paul, MN 55101-2098 (100%)
Tel.: (651) 665-3826
Web Site: http://www.advantuscapital.com
Sales Range: $250-299.9 Million
Emp.: 1,500
Investment Advisory & Asset Management Services
N.A.I.C.S.: 523999
Vicki L. Bailey (VP-Investment Law)
Linda Sauber (VP & Dir-Client Strategies & Client Portfolio Mgmt Svcs)
John Messing (Sr Mgr-Relationship)
Erica Bergsland (VP & Dir-Res & Trading)
Joseph Betlej (VP & Portfolio Mgr)
Thomas Houghton (VP & Portfolio Mgr)
Jane Wyatt (VP & Portfolio Mgr)
Matthew Ketchum (VP-Institutional Sls)
Ryan Schaden (VP-Institutional Sls)
Tracy Whiteley (Mgr-Mktg)
Mike Steinert (COO, Chief Compliance Officer & Sr VP)
Sean O'Connell (Pres & CEO)

CNL Financial Corporation (1)
2960 Riverside Dr, Macon, GA 31204
Tel.: (478) 477-0400
Web Site: http://www.cnlf.com
Sales Range: $50-74.9 Million
Emp.: 100
Holding Company; Life & Accident Insurance
N.A.I.C.S.: 524113

Subsidiary (Domestic):

Cherokee National Life Insurance Co. (2)
2960 Riverside Dr, Macon, GA 31208-6097 (100%)
Tel.: (478) 477-0400
Web Site: http://www.cnlf.com
Sales Range: $75-99.9 Million
Emp.: 60
Life Insurance
N.A.I.C.S.: 525110

Enterprise Holding Corporation (1)
400 Robert St N, Saint Paul, MN 55101
Web Site: http://www.minnmutual.com
Rev.: $5,100,000
Emp.: 3
Investment Holding Companies, Except Banks
N.A.I.C.S.: 551112

Securian Financial Services, Inc. (1)
400 Robert St N, Saint Paul, MN 55101 (100%)
Tel.: (651) 665-4225
Web Site: http://www.securianfinancial.com
Sales Range: $250-299.9 Million
Emp.: 2,000
Insurance & Financial Services
N.A.I.C.S.: 524298
Patrick Kulzer (Dir-Strategic Partnerships)
Robert Senkler (CEO)
Jeffrey D. McGrath (Dir-Investment Resource Grp)

Shoemaker Financial (1)
2176 W St Ste 100, Germantown, TN 38138
Tel.: (901) 757-5757
Web Site: http://www.shoemakerfinancial.com
Rev.: $200,000
Emp.: 30
Investment Advice
N.A.I.C.S.: 523940
James Shoemaker (Pres & CEO)
Tal Goldsby (Mng Dir)
Jim Seeley (Mgr-Client Svcs & Ops)
Candida Fuller (Mgr-Corp Acctg)
Christopher Hebert (Mng Dir)
Jason Herrington (Mng Dir)
Margie McClung (CFO & VP)
Andrew McKinney (Mgr-IT)
Keith Quinn (Dir-Investments)

The Minnesota Life Insurance Company (1)
400 Robert St N, Saint Paul, MN 55101
Tel.: (651) 665-3500
Web Site: http://www.minnesotalife.com
Sales Range: $1-4.9 Billion
Emp.: 2,000
Individual & Group Life Insurance, Group Disability & Pensions; Asset Management Services
N.A.I.C.S.: 524113
Robert L. Senkler (Chm & CEO)
Mark B. Hier (VP-Comm)
Chris Owens (Dir-Natl Sls-Individual Life Insurance)

Vivid Print Solutions Inc. (1)
285 Florida St, Saint Paul, MN 55107
Tel.: (651) 665-5617
Sales Range: $1-9.9 Million
Emp.: 50
Graphic Arts & Related Design
N.A.I.C.S.: 541430

SECURIGUARD, INC.

6858 Old Dominion Dr Ste 307, McLean, VA 22101
Tel.: (703) 821-6777
Web Site: http://www.securiguardinc.com
Year Founded: 1982
Sales Range: $25-49.9 Million
Emp.: 950
Security Guard Services
N.A.I.C.S.: 561612
Patricia Marvil (Chm & CEO)
David L. Marvil (Pres)
Steve Wexler (CFO)

SECURIS

14801 Willard Rd Ste 800, Chantilly, VA 20151
Tel.: (703) 436-1967
Web Site: http://www.securis.com
Year Founded: 2003
Sales Range: $1-9.9 Million
Emp.: 23
Data Destruction Services
N.A.I.C.S.: 561499
Jeremy Farber (Founder & Pres)
Daniel Mattock (Exec VP-Sls)

SECURITAS HOLDINGS INC.

2500 Citywest Blvd # 900, Houston, TX 77042
Tel.: (713) 435-6700
Web Site: http://www.loomisfargo.com
Rev.: $85,200,000
Detective & Armored Car Services
N.A.I.C.S.: 561613

SECURITY AGENCY, INC.

202 E Water St, Decorah, IA 52101
Tel.: (563) 382-9661
Web Site: http://www.decorahbank.com
Sales Range: $25-49.9 Million
Emp.: 60
Bank Holding Company
N.A.I.C.S.: 551111
Ben Grimstad (Pres)

Subsidiaries:

Cresco Bank & Trust Company (1)
126 2nd Ave SE, Cresco, IA 52136
Tel.: (563) 547-2244
Web Site: http://www.crescobank.com
Rev.: $2,100,000
Emp.: 17
State Commercial Bank Services
N.A.I.C.S.: 522110
Donna Thomas (Pres)

Decorah Bank & Trust Company (1)
202 E Water St, Decorah, IA 52101
Tel.: (563) 382-0091
Web Site: http://www.decorahbank.com
Sales Range: $25-49.9 Million
Emp.: 52
Commericial Banking
N.A.I.C.S.: 522110
Ben Grimstad (Pres)

SECURITY ALLIANCE GROUP, LLC

8323 NW 12th St Ste 218, Miami, FL 33126
Tel.: (305) 670-6544
Web Site: http://www.securityalliancegroup.com
Year Founded: 2001
Sales Range: $10-24.9 Million
Emp.: 450
Security Officers & Services
N.A.I.C.S.: 561612
William Murphy (VP)
David Ramirez (CEO)
Carl St. Phillip (CFO & Sr VP)
Angel Rosado (Dir-Ops)

SECURITY AUTO SALES INC.

345 Merrick Rd, Amityville, NY 11701
Tel.: (631) 691-9347
Web Site: http://www.securitydodge.com
Rev.: $20,900,000
Emp.: 55
Automobiles, New & Used
N.A.I.C.S.: 441110
J. J. Vigorito (Mgr-Sls-Viper)
Gabriel Vigorito (VP)
Minka Whitlock (Mgr-IT)
Bill Hannan (Mgr-Sls-Used Car)

SECURITY BANCORP OF TENNESSEE, INC.

101 E Main St, Halls, TN 38040
Tel.: (731) 836-7515 TN
Web Site: http://www.securitybancorptn.com
Sales Range: $25-49.9 Million
Emp.: 229
Bank Holding Company
N.A.I.C.S.: 551111

COMPANIES

SECURITY FIRST INSURANCE COMPANY, INC.

Donald Hogue *(Pres)*
Nick Nunn *(Chief Investment Officer)*

Subsidiaries:

Bank of Crockett (1)
111 E Main St, Bells, TN 38006
Tel.: (731) 663-2031
Web Site: http://www.bankofcrockett.com
Sales Range: $1-9.9 Million
Emp.: 37
State Commercial Banks
N.A.I.C.S.: 522110
Donald Hogue *(Pres)*
Jermi Lambert *(VP)*

Bank of Halls (1)
101 E Main St, Halls, TN 38040
Tel.: (731) 836-7515
Web Site: http://www.bankofhalls.com
Sales Range: $1-9.9 Million
Emp.: 25
State Commercial Banks
N.A.I.C.S.: 522110
Donald Hogue *(Pres)*
Warren Nunn *(CEO)*

Gates Banking & Trust Company (1)
56 Wardlow St, Gates, TN 38037
Tel.: (731) 836-7741
Web Site: http://www.gatesbank.com
Sales Range: $1-9.9 Million
Emp.: 11
State Commercial Banks
N.A.I.C.S.: 522110
James Smith *(Pres & CEO)*
Warren Nunn *(Chm)*

Patriot Bank (1)
8376 Hwy 51 N, Millington, TN 38053
Tel.: (901) 872-2265
Web Site: http://www.patriot-bank.com
Sales Range: $10-24.9 Million
Emp.: 67
Commericial Banking
N.A.I.C.S.: 522110
Larry Jackson *(Founder & Pres)*
Charles Ennis *(Chm & CEO)*
Keith Barger *(Exec VP)*
Sandra Howard *(Officer-Corp Ops & Sr VP)*
Lori J. Osborne *(Officer-Security & VP-Corp Compliance)*
Warren Nunn *(Vice Chm)*
Bill Samisch *(Chief Credit Officer)*
Gail Johnson *(Exec VP-Tipton County)*
Larry Boyd *(Sr VP-Collierville Mortgage)*
Michelle Couch *(Sr VP)*

Security Bank (1)
120 N Mill Ave, Dyersburg, TN 38024
Tel.: (731) 287-4903
Web Site: http://www.securitybank.net
Sales Range: $1-9.9 Million
Emp.: 70
State Commercial Banks
N.A.I.C.S.: 522110
David Hayes *(Pres)*
Denise McKnight *(VP-Ops)*
Jennifer Nunley *(Exec VP & COO)*

The Bank of Jackson (1)
420 Oil Well Rd, Jackson, TN 38305
Tel.: (731) 660-8000
Web Site: http://www.bankofjackson.com
Sales Range: $1-9.9 Million
Emp.: 26
Commericial Banking
N.A.I.C.S.: 522110
Harbert Alexander *(Pres)*
David Hayes *(Vice Chm & COO)*
Gary Grisham *(Chm & CEO)*
Lisa Crews *(Sr VP)*
Tim Wilson *(Exec VP)*

SECURITY BANK
202 E 2nd St, Laurel, NE 68745
Tel.: (402) 256-3247
Web Site: http://www.mysecbank.com
Year Founded: 1928
Sales Range: $1-9.9 Million
Emp.: 38
Commericial Banking
N.A.I.C.S.: 522110
Lynn Papenhausen *(Controller)*
Charles Ebmeier *(Pres)*
Karen A. Harrington *(VP)*

SECURITY BANK & TRUST COMPANY
210 W Washington St, Paris, TN 38242
Tel.: (731) 642-6644
Web Site: http://www.securitybanktn.com
Year Founded: 1905
Sales Range: $1-9.9 Million
Emp.: 40
Commericial Banking
N.A.I.C.S.: 522110
Stephen L. Trask *(CFO & Exec VP)*
Andy Collins *(Chief Credit Officer)*
Rebecca Walker *(Sec & Sr VP)*
Cooper A. McLntosh *(Vice Chm)*
Mary Howell McLntosh Gann *(Vice Chm)*
Brian Kissell *(Sr VP)*
John Horner *(Officer-Loan & Sr VP)*
Cheryl Jones *(Officer-Admin & Loan Ops)*
Jennifer Eason *(Officer-Loan Admin)*
Jan Crockett *(Officer-Loan Admin)*
Bryant Peale *(Officer-Ops & BSA)*
Laurie Ragsdale *(Chief Acctg Officer)*
Chris Johnson *(Officer-IT)*
Kyle Brooks *(Sr VP)*
Barry P. McIntosh Jr. *(Chm, Pres & CEO)*

SECURITY BY DESIGN INC.
33262 Groesbeck Hwy, Fraser, MI 48026
Tel.: (313) 259-2700
Web Site: http://www.sbdcompanies.com
Year Founded: 2004
Sales Range: $1-9.9 Million
Emp.: 8
Security & Fire Alarm Services
N.A.I.C.S.: 561621
Jason Buckman *(Owner)*

SECURITY CARD SERVICES LLC
2653 W Oxford Loop Ste 108, Oxford, MS 38655
Tel.: (662) 281-7240
Web Site: http://securitycardservices.com
Year Founded: 1996
Sales Range: $1-9.9 Million
Emp.: 26
Payment Processing Services
N.A.I.C.S.: 522320
Joan Kuykendall *(Sr VP-Ops)*
Mike Halford *(Sr VP-Merchant Sls)*
Eric Smith *(Sr VP-Bank Sls)*
Kathi Klawitter *(COO)*

SECURITY CHECK LLC
PO Box 1211, Oxford, MS 38655
Tel.: (662) 234-0440
Web Site: http://www.payliance.com
Year Founded: 1995
Provider of Collection Services
N.A.I.C.S.: 561499
John Cullen *(CEO)*

SECURITY CHICAGO CORPORATION
190 E Delaware Pl, Chicago, IL 60611
Tel.: (312) 280-0360
Web Site: http://www.delawareplacebank.com
Year Founded: 1983
Sales Range: $10-24.9 Million
Emp.: 25
Bank Holding Company
N.A.I.C.S.: 551111
Theodore J. Aldrich *(Pres & COO)*

Subsidiaries:

Delaware Place Bank (1)
190 E Delaware Pl, Chicago, IL 60611
Tel.: (312) 280-0360
Web Site: http://www.delawareplacebank.com
Sales Range: $25-49.9 Million
Emp.: 36
State Commercial Banks
N.A.I.C.S.: 522110
Andrew T. Schmidt *(Head-Bank Ops & VP)*
Kevin Hughes *(Exec VP-Comml Lending)*
Gregory J. Miller *(Sr VP & Head-Pro Practice Grp)*
Theodore J. Aldrich *(Pres & COO)*
Bradley J. Schotanus *(Exec VP-Comml Banking)*
Mark Maltese *(Dir-Leasing Svcs)*

SECURITY COMPLIANCE ASSOCIATES LLC
2727 Ulmerton Rd Ste 310, Clearwater, FL 33762
Tel.: (727) 571-1141
Web Site: http://www.scasecurity.com
Sales Range: $1-9.9 Million
Emp.: 15
Information Security Compliance & Assessment Services
N.A.I.C.S.: 541519
James Brahm *(CEO & Mng Dir)*
Daniel Juneau *(Exec VP-Compliance Svcs)*
Rick Woods *(Dir-Sls & Mktg)*

SECURITY CORPORATION
22325 Roethel Dr, Novi, MI 48375   MI
Tel.: (248) 374-5700
Web Site: http://www.securitycorp.com
Year Founded: 1973
Sales Range: $10-24.9 Million
Emp.: 110
Fire Detection & Burglar Systems
N.A.I.C.S.: 561621
Jeff Kelly *(Mgr-Sls)*
Dan Pason *(Mgr-Installation)*
Jenifer Jason *(Mgr-Central Station & Svc)*
Robert Holloway *(Founder)*

SECURITY CREDIT SERVICES, LLC
2653 W Oxford Loop Ste 108, Oxford, MS 38655
Tel.: (662) 281-7220
Web Site: http://www.securitycreditservicesllc.com
Year Founded: 2003
Sales Range: $10-24.9 Million
Emp.: 30
Debt Acquisitions & Management Services
N.A.I.C.S.: 525990
Joan Rasberry *(COO)*
Richard Devoe *(CFO)*
Darren Price *(VP-Agency Mgmt)*
William A. Alias Jr. *(CEO)*
William A. Alias III *(Pres)*

Subsidiaries:

Security Credit Services (1)
Overlook II 2839 Paces Ferry Rd Ste 320, Atlanta, GA 30339   (100%)
Tel.: (770) 437-6151
Web Site: http://www.securitycreditservicesllc.com
Receivables, Acquisitions & Management Services
N.A.I.C.S.: 525990

SECURITY EQUIPMENT SUPPLY INC.
3435 Rider Trl, Earth City, MO 63045
Tel.: (314) 298-8930
Web Site: http://www.sesonline.com
Sales Range: $25-49.9 Million
Emp.: 100
Security Control Equipment & Systems
N.A.I.C.S.: 423690
Bob Van Dillen *(Pres & CFO)*
George Trussler *(Mgr-Ops)*
Robyn Cunningham *(Branch Mgr)*

SECURITY FEDERAL SAVINGS BANK
314 4th St, Logansport, IN 46947
Tel.: (574) 722-6261
Web Site: http://www.secfedbank.com
Year Founded: 1934
Sales Range: $10-24.9 Million
Emp.: 60
Federal Savings Bank
N.A.I.C.S.: 522180
Suzanne Chilcott *(Sr VP-Trust)*
Barb Roads *(Mgr-Trust Ops)*
Jon-Myckle Price *(Officer-Trust)*

SECURITY FINANCIAL SERVICES CORPORATION
212 W Prospect St, Durand, WI 54736
Tel.: (715) 672-4237   WI
Web Site: http://www.sfbank.com
Year Founded: 1999
Sales Range: $10-24.9 Million
Emp.: 50
Bank Holding Company
N.A.I.C.S.: 551111
Jerry M. Bauer *(Chm)*
James F. Mayo *(Pres & CEO)*
Paul Solyntjes *(CFO & Exec VP)*
Paul Rudersdorf *(Chief Banking Officer)*

Subsidiaries:

Security Financial Bank (1)
212 W Prospect St, Durand, WI 54736
Tel.: (715) 672-4237
Web Site: http://www.sfbank.com
Sales Range: $10-24.9 Million
Emp.: 80
Commercial Banking Services
N.A.I.C.S.: 522110
Paul Solyntjes *(CFO & COO)*
Curt Van Auken *(Pres-Eau Clair Market & Mgr-Bus Relationship)*
John Lisowski *(Pres-River Falls Market & Mgr-Bus Relationship)*
Mark Chilson *(Mgr-Agricultural Banking & Durand Market)*
Tammy Sinz *(Mgr-Retail Banking)*
Jenny Jereczek *(Mgr-Relationship Agricultural & Comml Banking)*
Paul Rudersdorf *(Pres & CEO)*
Deirdre Tumm *(Mgr-Customer Rels)*
Cathy Couey *(Chief Retail Officer)*

SECURITY FIRST INSURANCE COMPANY, INC.
140 S Atlantic Ste 200, Ormond Beach, FL 32176
Tel.: (877) 333-9992   FL
Web Site: http://www.securityfirstflorida.com
Year Founded: 2005
Emp.: 184
Property & Casualty Insurance Services
N.A.I.C.S.: 524126
W. Lockwood Burt *(Founer & Chm)*
Melissa Burt-DeVriese *(Pres)*
Kathy Wood *(VP-Corp Compliance)*
Werner Kruck *(COO & Dir)*
Clive Becker-Jones *(CFO, Treas & Dir)*
Ben Bomhoff *(VP-Enterprise Sys)*
Marissa Buckley *(VP-Mktg)*
Bill Coffin *(VP-Sls)*
Charlie Lowe *(VP-Claims)*
Kathie Rodier *(VP-Underwriting)*
Kerrie A. Ruland *(VP-Bus Dev & Specialty Insurance)*
Frank Molinario *(Dir-HR)*
Greg Moraski *(VP-Claims)*

SECURITY INDUSTRY SPECIALISTS, INC.

Security Industry Specialists, Inc.—(Continued)

SECURITY INDUSTRY SPECIALISTS, INC.
6071 Bristol Pkwy, Culver City, CA 90230
Web Site: http://www.sis.us
Sales Range: $25-49.9 Million
Emp.: 1,000
Security Services
N.A.I.C.S.: 561612
John Spesak (CEO)
Tom Seltz (CFO)
Jim Mulvihill (VP-Special Ops)
Dave Harville (VP-Ops)
Victor Gomes (Dir-Loss Prevention Programs)
Barry Masuda (Dir-Special Projects & Investigations)
Jerry Tidwell (Sr Dir-Security Ops)
Jeff Venturini (Dir-HR)
Holly Drew (Dir-Internal Svcs)
Danny Martinez (Dir-Secure Logistics)
Robert Bastida (Dir-Security Ops)
Chris Cesena (Dir-Security Ops)
Wayne North (Dir-Security Ops)
Scott Vermeer (Dir-Security Ops)
Lori Perry (Dir-Special Events)
Michael Kirkendall (Dir-Trng)

SECURITY LAND AND DEVELOPMENT CORPORATION
2816 Washington Rd Ste 103, Augusta, GA 30909
Tel.: (706) 736-6334
Year Founded: 1970
Rev.: $1,758,920
Assets: $11,305,171
Liabilities: $5,652,507
Net Worth: $5,652,664
Earnings: $821,412
Emp.: 5
Fiscal Year-end: 09/30/18
Real Estate Development Services
N.A.I.C.S.: 531390
T. Greenlee Flanagin (Pres, CEO & CFO)
Robert M. Flanagin (Sec)
W. Stewart Flanagin Jr. (Chm)
John C. Bell Jr. (VP)

SECURITY MUTUAL LIFE INSURANCE COMPANY OF NEW YORK
100 Court St, Binghamton, NY 13901
Tel.: (607) 723-3551
Web Site: http://www.smlny.com
Year Founded: 1886
Sales Range: $350-399.9 Million
Emp.: 350
Life Insurance & Annuity Products & Services
N.A.I.C.S.: 524113
Bruce Walter Boyea (Chm, Pres & CEO)
Daniel P. Foley (VP-Mktg & Tech)
Richard H. Shaw (VP-Retirement Plng)
Frederick L. Wortman (Chief Mktg Officer & Exec VP)
George B. Kozol (Sr VP-Mktg)
James P. Conlon (Sr VP-Agency)
James M. Lynch (VP)
Susan E. Mistretta (Officer-Privacy, Assoc Gen Counsel & VP)
Vincent J. Montelione (Sr VP-ICS, Reinsurance, Claims & Customer Rels)
Kennie Lee (Second VP-Product Dev & Actuary)
Joseph B. Sperduti (VP-Benefits Div & Svc Ops)
Susan A. Inneo (Chief Compliance Officer, Asst Gen Counsel & VP)
Heather H. Zebrowski (VP-HR)
Mary C. Ward (VP-Fin Ops)
Ronald W. Funk (Treas & VP)
Paul B. Pheffer (CFO & Exec VP)
Scott A. Sylvester (CIO & Exec VP)
Marc D. Novotney (Exec VP-Middle Market)
Christopher J. Walsh (Officer-IT Security & Second VP)
Mark A. Walker (Sr VP)
Larry E. Blanchard (VP-Mktg)
Donald J. Smith Jr. (Second VP-Grp Admin)

Subsidiaries:

SML Agency Services, Inc. (1)
100 Court St, Binghamton, NY 13901 (100%)
Tel.: (607) 723-3551
Insurance Brokerage Services
N.A.I.C.S.: 524210
James P. Conlon (Sr VP-Agency)

Security Administrators, Inc. (1)
105 Court St, Binghamton, NY 13901
Tel.: (877) 724-2464
Web Site: http://www.saiplans.com
Sales Range: $25-49.9 Million
Emp.: 6
Retirement Plan Advisory Services
N.A.I.C.S.: 524292
Dane Mitchell (Pres & COO)
Pat M. Balla (Asst VP)
Constance E. Conger (Mgr-Syracuse)

SECURITY NATIONAL AUTOMOTIVE ACCEPTANCE COMPANY, LLC
6951 Cintas Blvd, Mason, OH 45040
Tel.: (513) 459-8118
Web Site: http://www.snaac.com
Year Founded: 1986
Automobile Finance Leasing
N.A.I.C.S.: 522220
Bob Bender (VP-Credit & Compliance)
Angela Arway (VP-HR & Training)

SECURITY NATIONAL BANK
1120 S 101st St, Omaha, NE 68124
Tel.: (402) 344-7300
Web Site: http://www.snbconnect.com
Sales Range: $10-24.9 Million
Emp.: 200
Provider of Banking Services
N.A.I.C.S.: 522110
John J. Krajicek (Branch Mgr)
Jim Riha (Sr VP-Bus Banking)
Douglas Rice Rice (Chm, Pres & CEO)
Craig Mayo (Chief Credit Officer & Sr VP)

SECURITY NATIONAL CORPORATION
601 Pierce St, Sioux City, IA 51101
Tel.: (712) 277-6500
Web Site: http://www.snbonline.com
Sales Range: $50-74.9 Million
Emp.: 200
Commercial & Retail Banking
N.A.I.C.S.: 522110
Richard Waller (CEO)
Doug Rice (Pres)
Steve Corrie (COO)
Dave Hollub (Mgr-Mktg)

SECURITY NATIONAL TRUST CO., INC.
1300 Chapline St 3, Wheeling, WV 26003
Tel.: (304) 233-5215
Web Site: http://www.snt-wv.com
Trust, Fiduciary & Custody Activities
N.A.I.C.S.: 523991
Mark C. Ferrell (Pres & CEO)
H. Scott Cunningham (Chm)

Subsidiaries:

Security National Trust Co., Inc. - Lancaster (1)
100 E King St, Lancaster, PA 17602
Tel.: (717) 207-0667
Web Site: http://www.securitynationaltrust.com
Sales Range: $50-74.9 Million
Emp.: 45
Trust, Fiduciary & Custody Activities
N.A.I.C.S.: 523991
Joseph A. Myers (Sr VP)

SECURITY PACKAGING INC.
G3367 Corunna Rd, Flint, MI 48532
Tel.: (810) 235-8110
Web Site: http://www.go2northgate.com
Sales Range: $10-24.9 Million
Emp.: 160
Packaging, Processing, Warehousing & Distribution Services
N.A.I.C.S.: 322211
Rick Valley (VP)
Teresa Goggins Witt (Pres)

SECURITY SEED & CHEMICAL LLC
5217 Guthrie Hwy, Clarksville, TN 37040
Tel.: (931) 485-7333
Web Site: http://www.securityseedandchemical.com
Sales Range: $10-24.9 Million
Emp.: 100
Distribute & Wholesale Farm Supplies
N.A.I.C.S.: 424910
Barry Mayo (Partner)
Johnny Rudolph (Mgr)

SECURITY SOLUTIONS OF AMERICA
7075 US-70, 28570, Newport, NC
Tel.: (252) 648-8814
Web Site: https://www.ss-oa.com
Year Founded: 2012
Emp.: 100
Protection or Personalized Investigations Services
N.A.I.C.S.: 561612
Jim Stevens (Pres & CEO)

Subsidiaries:

Guard One Security, Inc. (1)
20 Mansell Ct E Ste 500, Roswell, GA 30076
Tel.: (470) 825-1700
Security Services
N.A.I.C.S.: 561612
Robert F. Copeland (Pres & CEO)

Subsidiary (Domestic):

Commercial Investigation & Security (2)
6142 Wilcrest Dr, Houston, TX 77072-1450
Tel.: (281) 273-1527
Web Site: http://www.cisguards.com
Security & Investigation Services
N.A.I.C.S.: 561611

SECURITY STATE BANK & TRUST
201 W Main St, Fredericksburg, TX 78624
Tel.: (830) 997-7575
Web Site: http://www.ssbtexas.com
Year Founded: 1941
Sales Range: $25-49.9 Million
Emp.: 245
Provider of Banking Services
N.A.I.C.S.: 522110
James Kemp (Chm)
Gary Stehling (Chief Lending Officer & Sr VP)
Dale Geistweidt (Officer-Loan & Sr VP)
Laurie Hartmann (Officer-HR & VP)
Linda Somerville (Officer-Mktg & VP-Kerrville)
Sonia Acosta (Officer-Admin & VP)
Stephanie Baxter (Officer-Loan Admin)
Chad Behrends (Officer-Loan Review & VP)
Brenda Burrier (Officer-Acctg & VP)
Irma Bustamante (Officer-Merchant Svcs & VP)
Rudy Cisneros (Officer-Loan & VP)
Katie DeLoof (Officer-Ops)
Jamie Duecker (Officer-Data Processing)
Suzan Gallion (CFO & Sr VP)
Randall Johnson (Officer-Trust & VP)
Dan Kemp (Sr VP)
Austin Kuhn (Officer-Credit Analyst & VP)
Caren Michel (Officer-Loan Admin & VP)
Cele Romero (Officer-Audit & VP)
Irene Sanchez (Officer-Electronic Banking)
Jacob Smith (Officer-Loan)
Cathy Straube (Officer-RE Loan Admin & VP)
Theresa Treiber (Officer-Escrow & Loan Admin)
Jill Vanderford (Officer-New Accounts & VP)

SECURITY STATE CORPORATION
1930 S Gold St, Centralia, WA 98531
Tel.: (360) 736-0763
Web Site: https://www.ssbwa.com
Year Founded: 1997
Bank Holding Company
N.A.I.C.S.: 551111

Subsidiaries:

Security State Bank (1)
1930 S Gold St, Centralia, WA 98531
Tel.: (360) 736-0763
Web Site: http://www.ssbwa.com
Sales Range: $10-24.9 Million
Emp.: 101
State Commercial Banks
N.A.I.C.S.: 522110
Dwayne Aberle (Pres)
Andy Alexander (VP)
John Alexander Jr. (Chm)

SECURITY VAULT WORKS INC.
122 Lafayette Ave, Laurel, MD 20707
Tel.: (301) 776-2577
Web Site: http://www.svwinc.com
Year Founded: 1985
Sales Range: $10-24.9 Million
Emp.: 40
Turnkey Installation & Construction Services Specifically ATMs, Vaults & Safes
N.A.I.C.S.: 238990
Tim Abell (Pres)
Linda Abell (CEO)
Denise Ingram (Controller)

SECURITY WEAVER
401 West A St Ste 2200, San Diego, CA 92101-7918
Tel.: (800) 620-4210
Web Site: http://www.securityweaver.com
Year Founded: 2004
Sales Range: $1-9.9 Million
Emp.: 40
Governance, Risk & Compliance Management (GRCM) Software Mfr
N.A.I.C.S.: 513210
Terry Hirsch (CEO)
Shailesh Maloo (COO)

Sandeep Gupta *(Co-Founder & CTO)*
Stephen DuBravac *(Exec VP-Mktg)*
Sumit Sangha *(Co-Founder, Chm & Chief Architect)*

SECURITYCLEARANCEEXPO.COM
6851 Jericho Tpke Ste 265, Syosset, NY 11791
Tel.: (516) 942-7579
Year Founded: 2002
Sales Range: $10-24.9 Million
Emp.: 25
Engineering, Event Marketing, Exhibit/Trade Shows, Government/Political/Public Affairs, Information Technology, Recruitment
N.A.I.C.S.: 541810
Kenneth Fuller *(VP-Sls)*
Jack Cohen *(CEO)*
Ryan Taliercio *(CIO)*
R.S. Kumar *(VP-Sls & Mktg)*
Michael Noonan *(VP-Fin & Chief Accountant)*

SECURITYHUNTER, INC.
7249 Ambassador Rd Windsor Mill, Windsor Mill, MD 21244
Tel.: (443) 436-0700
Web Site:
http://www.securityhunter.com
Year Founded: 1988
Sales Range: $1-9.9 Million
Emp.: 11
Security Systems
N.A.I.C.S.: 561621
Michael S. Rogers *(Founder & CEO)*
Daniel F. Prochnow *(Pres)*
Alex Elber *(CTO)*

SECURITYMETRICS, INC.
1275 W 1600 N, Orem, UT 84057
Tel.: (801) 724-9600
Web Site:
http://www.securitymetrics.com
Year Founded: 2000
Sales Range: $10-24.9 Million
Emp.: 290
Computer System Design Services
N.A.I.C.S.: 541512
Brad Caldwell *(Founder & CEO)*
Blake Stevens *(CFO)*
Wenlock Free *(VP-Bus Dev)*
Rich Running *(VP-Mktg)*
Gary Glover *(Dir-Audit)*
David Ellis *(Dir-Forensics)*
Michelle Moore *(Office Mgr)*
Russell Stay *(VP-Bus Ops)*

SECURUS PAYMENTS
7724 SE Aspen Summit Dr Ste 300, Portland, OR 97266
Tel.: (866) 649-1324
Web Site:
http://www.securuspayments.com
Year Founded: 2009
Sales Range: $1-9.9 Million
Emp.: 150
Credit & Debit Card Processing
N.A.I.C.S.: 522210
Mychol Robirds *(Pres)*
Steven Lemma *(CEO)*

SED INTERNATIONAL HOLDINGS, INC.
2150 Cedars Rd Ste 200, Lawrenceville, GA 30043
Tel.: (678) 878-2600   DE
Web Site: http://www.sedonline.com
Year Founded: 1980
Sales Range: $550-599.9 Million
Microcomputers, Computer Peripheral Equipment & Cellular Phones Distr
N.A.I.C.S.: 423430
Ronell Rivera *(Pres & Exec VP-Latin America)*
Eddie Lageyre *(Sr VP-Pur-US)*
Christopher R. Joe *(Treas, Sec & VP-Fin)*
Dan Scouler *(Chief Restructuring Officer)*
Charles Campagna *(Chief Restructuring Officer)*
Juan Orlando Bravo *(CFO)*
Carla Giussani *(VP & Gen Mgr-SED Colombia)*
Hesham M. Gad *(Chm)*

Subsidiaries:

Intermaco S.R.L.   (1)
Florida 537/71, Galeria Jardin, Buenos Aires, 1005, Argentina
Tel.: (54) 1143934471
Web Site: http://www.intermaco.com.ar
Sales Range: $50-74.9 Million
Emp.: 40
Provider of Office Equipment
N.A.I.C.S.: 459410

SED International, Inc.   (1)
3505 Newpoint Pl Ste 450, Lawrenceville, GA 30043
Tel.: (770) 491-8962
Web Site: http://www.sedonline.com
Sales Range: $150-199.9 Million
Emp.: 250
Wholesale Distributor of Computers, Computer Peripherals & Cellular Phones
N.A.I.C.S.: 423690

SED Magna (Miami), Inc.   (1)
1729 NW 84th Ave, Miami, FL 33126   (100%)
Tel.: (305) 592-0199
Web Site: http://www.sedonline.com
Sales Range: $25-49.9 Million
Emp.: 50
Provider of Computer Equipment & Cellular Telephone Equipment
N.A.I.C.S.: 423430

SEDA CONSTRUCTION COMPANY INC.
2120 Corp Sq Blvd Ste 3, Jacksonville, FL 32216-1976
Tel.: (904) 724-7800
Web Site:
http://www.sedaconstruction.com
Year Founded: 1982
Sales Range: $10-24.9 Million
Emp.: 50
Building Contracting Services
N.A.I.C.S.: 236115

SEDANO'S SUPERMARKET MANAGEMENT, INC.
3140 W 76th St, Hialeah, FL 33018
Tel.: (305) 824-1034   FL
Web Site: http://www.sedanos.com
Year Founded: 1961
Sales Range: $500-549.9 Million
Emp.: 3,000
Grocery Stores, Chain
N.A.I.C.S.: 445110
Manuel A. Herran *(Pres & CEO)*
Alfredo Guerra *(Mgr-IT)*
Daniel Valdez *(VP-Fin & Mktg)*
Javier Herran *(CMO)*

SEDCO LTD.
1281 Brummel Ave, Elk Grove Village, IL 60007
Tel.: (847) 640-6510
Web Site:
http://www.shamrockelectric.com
Sales Range: $10-24.9 Million
Emp.: 100
General Electrical Contractor
N.A.I.C.S.: 238210
Frank J. Amabile *(Pres)*

SEDGWICK COUNTY ZOO
5555 Zoo Blvd, Wichita, KS 67212-1698
Tel.: (316) 660-9453   KS
Web Site: http://www.scz.org
Year Founded: 1963
Sales Range: $10-24.9 Million
Emp.: 208
Zoo Operator
N.A.I.C.S.: 712130
Jeff Ettling *(Exec Dir)*

SEDIA BIOSCIENCES CORPORATION
4900 NE 122nd Ave, Portland, OR 97230
Tel.: (503) 459-4159
Web Site: http://www.sediabio.com
Year Founded: 2009
Medical Device & Diagnostic Services
N.A.I.C.S.: 621511
Ronald W. Mink *(Founder, Pres & Chief Science Officer)*
Roger I. Gale *(Chm & CEO)*

Subsidiaries:

Floragenex, Inc.   (1)
4640 SW Macadam Ave Ste 130D, Portland, OR 97239
Tel.: (541) 343-0747
Web Site: http://www.floragenex.com
Research & Development in Biotechnology
N.A.I.C.S.: 541714
Rick Nipper *(Pres)*
Jason Boone *(VP)*

SEDLAK MANAGEMENT CONSULTANTS, INC.
22901 Millcreek Blvd, Cleveland, OH 44122
Tel.: (216) 206-4700   OH
Web Site: http://www.jasedlak.com
Year Founded: 1958
Sales Range: $10-24.9 Million
Emp.: 45
Management Consulting Services
N.A.I.C.S.: 541618
Will O'Brien *(Pres)*

SEDONA GROUP
612 Valley View Dr, Moline, IL 61265
Tel.: (309) 797-8367
Web Site:
http://www.sedonagroup.com
Rev.: $16,500,000
Emp.: 120
Business Oriented Computer Software & Staffing Services
N.A.I.C.S.: 513210
Joe Lavin *(Dir-Risk Mgmt)*
Richard C. John Jr. *(Pres)*

SEDONA SOUL ADVENTURES, INC.
30 Kayenta Ct Ste 4, Sedona, AZ 86336
Web Site:
http://www.sedonasouladventures.com
Year Founded: 2002
Sales Range: $1-9.9 Million
Emp.: 12
Retreat Centre Operator
N.A.I.C.S.: 721214
Debra Stangl *(Founder)*

SEDULOUS CONSULTING SERVICES, LLC
18300 Quantico Gateway Dr Ste 201, Triangle, VA 22172
Tel.: (703) 630-9963
Web Site: http://www.sedulous.com
Year Founded: 2016
Management & Technical Support Consulting Services
N.A.I.C.S.: 541618
Omar Dennis *(Pres & CEO)*
James Villa *(COO & VP)*

Subsidiaries:

Infinity Support Services, Inc.   (1)
18300 Quantico Gateway Dr Ste 201, Triangle, VA 22172
Tel.: (703) 861-8245
Web Site: http://www.infinitysuppserv.com
Program Management & Technical Support Consulting Services
N.A.I.C.S.: 541611
Lindo Bradley *(Pres)*

SEE JANE RUN
2145 Keith St, San Francisco, CA 94124
Tel.: (415) 839-9393
Web Site: http://www.seejanerun.com
Year Founded: 2000
Sales Range: $1-9.9 Million
Emp.: 40
Retailer of Women's Active Apparel & Footwear
N.A.I.C.S.: 458110
Lori Shannon *(Mgr-PR)*

SEED DYNAMICS, INC.
1081-B Harkins Rd, Salinas, CA 93912
Tel.: (831) 424-1177
Web Site:
http://www.seeddynamics.com
Sales Range: $10-24.9 Million
Emp.: 39
Crop Postharvest Services
N.A.I.C.S.: 115114
Curtis Vaughan *(Gen Mgr)*
Cora Heacox *(Mgr-Customer Svc)*
Henry Rede *(Mgr-Production)*
Carol Libby *(Mgr-Res)*
Deanna Locke *(Office Mgr)*

SEED RESEARCH OF OREGON
27630 Llewellyn Rd, Corvallis, OR 97333
Tel.: (541) 757-2663
Web Site: http://www.sroseed.com
Rev.: $20,000,000
Emp.: 25
Distr of Grass Seed
N.A.I.C.S.: 424910
Bill Dunn *(Gen Mgr)*
Mike Hills *(Reg Mgr-Sls-Res)*
Lacey Briggs *(Mgr-Ops)*
Cheryl Friedel *(Mgr-Credit)*

SEEDBURO EQUIPMENT CO.
2293 S Mt Prospect Rd, Des Plaines, IL 60018-2914
Tel.: (312) 738-3700
Web Site: http://www.seedburo.com
Year Founded: 1912
Sales Range: $1-9.9 Million
Emp.: 20
Moisture Testers, Conveyors, Seed Counters, Grain Feed Seed Testing Equipment Mfr & Distr
N.A.I.C.S.: 423820
Tom Runyon *(Pres)*
Katherine A. Reading *(Officer-Export Compliance & VP-Sls)*
Cary Hall *(Treas & VP)*

SEEGARS FENCE COMPANY INC.
401 Paint Town Rd, Goldsboro, NC 27530
Tel.: (919) 735-8211
Web Site:
http://www.seegarsfence.com
Sales Range: $25-49.9 Million
Emp.: 20
Wire Fence, Gates & Accessories
N.A.I.C.S.: 423390
Wes Seegars *(Pres & CEO)*
Ben Seegars *(COO)*

SEEGER TOYOTA, INC.
12833 Olive Blvd, Saint Louis, MO 63141

SEEGER TOYOTA, INC.

Seeger Toyota, Inc.—(Continued)
Tel.: (314) 434-5000
Web Site:
http://www.seegertoyota.com
Year Founded: 1952
Sales Range: $10-24.9 Million
Emp.: 93
New Car Retailer
N.A.I.C.S.: 441110
Thomas Seeger (Owner)

SEEK CAREERS/STAFFING, INC.
1160 Opportunity Dr, Grafton, WI 53024-9596
Tel.: (262) 377-8888   WI
Web Site:
http://www.seekcareers.com
Year Founded: 1971
Sales Range: $25-49.9 Million
Emp.: 60
Staffing, Employment Placement & Professional Training Services
N.A.I.C.S.: 561320
Carol Ann Schneider (Chm & CEO)
Joel A. Schneider (Pres)
Debbie Fedel (VP-Bus Dev)
Randy E. Matter (VP-Fin)
Sara Luchsinger (VP-Ops)

SEEKING ALPHA LTD.
345 7th Ave Ste 1400, New York, NY 10001
Tel.: (212) 695-7190
Web Site:
http://www.seekingalpha.com
Year Founded: 2004
Financial Information Website
N.A.I.C.S.: 519290
David Jackson (Founder & CEO)
Avrom Gilbert (COO)
Eli Hoffmann (VP-Content)
Yosef Levenstein (VP-Harvest)
George Moriarty (VP-Content)
Katherine Divney (VP-Sls)
David Siegel (Pres)
Asi Segal (CTO)
Jason Aycock (Editor-News)
Selig Davis (VP-Audience & Mobile)

SEEKINGSITTERS INC.
3144 S Winston Ave, Tulsa, OK 74135
Tel.: (918) 749-3588
Web Site:
http://www.seekingsitters.com
Year Founded: 2004
Sales Range: $1-9.9 Million
Emp.: 4
Babysitter Referral Service
N.A.I.C.S.: 624410
Adrienne Kallweit (Founder & Owner)
Liz Pirtle (Dir-Mktg)

SEEKINS FORD LINCOLN MERCURY
1625 Seekins Ford Dr, Fairbanks, AK 99701-3170
Tel.: (907) 459-4000
Web Site: http://www.seekins.com
Year Founded: 2005
Sales Range: $75-99.9 Million
Emp.: 135
Car Whslr
N.A.I.C.S.: 441110
James Kreider (Mgr-Svc)
Aaron Seekins (Mgr-Customer Rels)
Ralph Seekins (Pres)

SEELER INDUSTRIES INC.
1 Genstar Ln, Joliet, IL 60435
Tel.: (815) 740-2640
Web Site: http://www.seeler.com
Sales Range: $10-24.9 Million
Emp.: 48
Chemicals & Allied Products
N.A.I.C.S.: 424690
Joseph Seeler (Chm & CEO)
Joe Norris (Controller)
Glenn Gibisch (Pres)

SEELYE WRIGHT KIA
3820 Stadium Dr, Kalamazoo, MI 49008
Tel.: (269) 375-3820
Sales Range: $25-49.9 Million
Emp.: 180
New Car Whslr
N.A.I.C.S.: 441110
Michael Seelye (Pres)

SEELYE-WRIGHT OF SOUTH HAVEN
10159 M 140, South Haven, MI 49090
Tel.: (269) 637-5246
Web Site:
http://www.seelyewright.com
Sales Range: $25-49.9 Million
Emp.: 60
New & Used Car Dealers
N.A.I.C.S.: 441110
Sam Oesch (Dir-Svcs)

SEEMAC INCORPORATED
11350 N Meridian St, Carmel, IN 46032-4595
Tel.: (317) 844-3995   IN
Web Site: http://www.seemac.com
Year Founded: 1971
Sales Range: $100-124.9 Million
Emp.: 20
Provider of Lumber, Plywood & Millwork Services
N.A.I.C.S.: 423310
Tom Kohlmeier (Chm)
Eddie Cantor (Sr VP)

SEEMAN HOLTZ PROPERTY & CASUALTY, LLC
301 Yamato Rd Ste 2250, Boca Raton, FL 33431
Tel.: (844) 255-6639
Web Site:
http://www.seemanholtz.com
Year Founded: 1998
Insurance Services
N.A.I.C.S.: 524126
Eric Holtz (Exec VP)

Subsidiaries:

A & J Insurance, Inc. (1)
1381 E Las Tunas Dr Ste 7, San Gabriel, CA 91776-1744
Tel.: (626) 286-3410
Web Site: http://www.anjinsurance.com
Insurance Agencies & Brokerages
N.A.I.C.S.: 524210
Adel Francis (Owner & Pres)

Dave Cutright Insurance Agency (1)
605 17th St, Vero Beach, FL 32960
Tel.: (772) 978-0900
Insurance Agencies & Brokerage Services
N.A.I.C.S.: 524210

Dickenshied Cravillion Insurance Services, Inc. (1)
1201 Enterprise Dr Ste A, De Pere, WI 54115
Tel.: (920) 336-1312
Web Site: http://www.dciwi.com
Independent Insurance Agency
N.A.I.C.S.: 441110
Dan Kassner (Branch Mgr)

National Insurance Solutions Inc. (1)
9400 Topanga Canyon Blvd Ste 201, Chatsworth, CA 91311
Tel.: (866) 647-4222
Web Site:
http://www.nationalinsurancesolution.com
Insurance Services
N.A.I.C.S.: 524210
Chris Bennett (Founder & CEO)
Kelli Schulhofer (Exec VP)

Neighbor's Insurance Advisors, Inc. (1)
1515 S Federal Hwy Ste 213, Boca Raton, FL 33432
Tel.: (561) 948-4303
Web Site: http://www.neighborsins.com
Insurance Related Activities
N.A.I.C.S.: 524298
Scott Medley (Partner)

Roth Agency Inc. (1)
301 Yamato Rd Ste 2250 A, Boca Raton, FL 33431
Tel.: (561) 451-1900
Web Site: http://www.rothagency.com
Insurance Agencies & Brokerages
N.A.I.C.S.: 524210
Steven Roth (Pres)

Schwarz Insurance, Inc. (1)
1420 N Ridge Dr, Prairie Du Sac, WI 53578
Tel.: (608) 643-3385
Web Site: http://www.schwarzins.com
Insurance Agencies & Brokerages
N.A.I.C.S.: 524210
Kathy Schwarz (Pres & CEO)
Kevin Arendt (Mgr-Risk Mgmt & Claims)
Mike Wood (Mgr-Individual Benefits)
Sheryl Loy (Dir-Mktg)

Vincent, Urban, Walker & Associates, Inc. (1)
139 S Washington St, Green Bay, WI 54301
Tel.: (920) 432-7246
Web Site: http://www.vuw4ins.com
Sales Range: $1-9.9 Million
Emp.: 18
Insurance Agents, Brokers & Related Services
N.A.I.C.S.: 524210
Cindy Hamlin (Treas)
Doug Walker (Pres)
Carol Vanlieshout (Mgr-Data Processing)

SEEMANN COMPOSITES, INC.
12481 Glascock Dr, Gulfport, MS 39503
Tel.: (228) 314-8000
Web Site:
http://www.seemanncomposite.com
Year Founded: 1987
DOD Platforms Composite Components Supplier
N.A.I.C.S.: 336992
William Seemann (CFO)

Subsidiaries:

Materials Sciences Corporation (1)
135 Rock Rd, Horsham, PA 19044,
Tel.: (215) 542-8400
Web Site: http://www.materials-sciences.com
Engineeering Services
N.A.I.C.S.: 541330
Thomas G. Cassin (Pres & CEO)

SEEVAST CORPORATION
680 Fifth Ave 10th Fl, New York, NY 10019
Tel.: (212) 710-4260
Web Site: http://www.seevast.com
Sales Range: $1-9.9 Million
Emp.: 50
Online Marketing
N.A.I.C.S.: 541613
Kent Keating (Chm)
Dave Casion (Pres & CTO)
John Edholm (VP-Affiliate Ops)
Ryan Landry (VP-Fin)
Michael Kelly (VP-Sls)

Subsidiaries:

Pulse 360 Inc. (1)
2390 N Forest Rd Ste 10, Getzville, NY 14068
Tel.: (716) 817-5000
Web Site: http://www.pulse360.com
Marketing Consulting Services
N.A.I.C.S.: 541613
Kent Keating (Chm & CEO)
Dave Casion (Pres & CTO)

SEG MEDIA GROUP INC.
12821 Commerce Lakes Dr Units 3 & 4, Fort Myers, FL 33913
Tel.: (239) 437-4367
Web Site: http://thrivefocus.com
Sales Range: $10-24.9 Million
Emp.: 11
Advetising Agency
N.A.I.C.S.: 541810
Thomas MacDonald (CEO)
Clinton Raley (VP-Mktg & Sls)
Vincent Gianduco (VP-PR & Media Plng)
Natalie Kimmel (Chief Comml Officer)
Jackie Caro (CFO)

SEGERSTROM CENTER FOR THE ARTS
600 Town Center Dr, Costa Mesa, CA 92626
Tel.: (714) 556-2121   CA
Web Site: http://www.scfta.org
Year Founded: 1973
Sales Range: $25-49.9 Million
Emp.: 571
Art Event Promoter
N.A.I.C.S.: 711310
Terrence W. Dwyer (Pres)
Roger T. Kirwan (Treas)
Sally S. Crockett (Sec)
Mark C. Perry (Chm)

SEGREST FARMS, INC.
6180 Big Bend Rd, Gibsonton, FL 33534
Tel.: (813) 677-9196
Web Site:
http://www.segrestfarms.com
Year Founded: 1961
Sales Range: $1-9.9 Million
Emp.: 115
Aquarium Fish
N.A.I.C.S.: 112511
Elwyn Segrest (Pres)

SEGUE ELECTRONICS, INC.
19210 S Vermont Ave Bldg C, Gardena, CA 90248
Tel.: (310) 643-0000
Web Site:
http://www.segueelectronics.com
Year Founded: 1997
Sales Range: $10-24.9 Million
Emp.: 20
Electronic Components Mfr
N.A.I.C.S.: 334418
Chris Chen (CEO)
Rudy Wiesinger (VP-Mktg & Sls)

SEGUIN NATURAL HAIR PRODUCTS, INC.
401 Ryland St Ste 200a, Reno, NV 89502
Tel.: (702) 738-2051   NV
Year Founded: 2014
Shampoo, Conditioner & Other Hair Care Products Mfr
N.A.I.C.S.: 325620
Danny Iandoli (Pres & Sec)

SEI ELECTRONICS INC.
2700 Wyclill Ste 14, Raleigh, NC 27607-1657
Tel.: (919) 850-9500   NC
Web Site: http://www.seielect.com
Year Founded: 1986
Sales Range: $10-24.9 Million
Emp.: 76
Electronic Resistors Retailer
N.A.I.C.S.: 334416
Jamie Mullane (COO)
Brian McCabe (Dir-Sls)
Dan Schad (VP-IT)
Joe Biernacki (VP-Ops & Quality)
Kory Schroeder (Dir-Mktg)

SEI GROUP, INC.
303 Williams Ave Ste 135, Huntsville, AL 35801
Tel.: (256) 533-0500
Web Site:
http://www.seigroupinc.com
Year Founded: 1996
Sales Range: $10-24.9 Million
Emp.: 62
Engineering, Construction & Facility Support Services
N.A.I.C.S.: 541330
Rick Coleman *(Project Mgr & Mgr-Construction)*
Michael Williams *(Engr-Mechanical)*
Bob Talianko *(VP-Engrg & Construction)*
Trent Johnson *(COO)*
Matt Hopkins *(Pres & CEO)*

Subsidiaries:

Tailored Foam of Florida, Inc. (1)
3900 Saint Johns Pkwy, Sanford, FL 32771
Tel.: (407) 332-0333
Web Site: http://www.tailoredfoaminc.com
Sales Range: $1-9.9 Million
Emp.: 40
Drywall/Insulating Contractor
N.A.I.C.S.: 238310
Jason Sander *(Pres)*
Mike Tennant *(Mgr-Sls)*

SEI INFORMATION TECHNOLOGY INC.
Ste 310 1520 Kensington Rd, Oak Brook, IL 60523-2142
Tel.: (630) 413-5050   IL
Year Founded: 1969
Sales Range: $10-24.9 Million
Emp.: 30
Provider of Computer Related Services
N.A.I.C.S.: 541512
Thomas Myers *(Mng Dir)*
Christopher M. Ciccolini *(VP-Major Accts)*
Michael Noblett *(Mng Dir-Land Side Platform Automotive Strategy)*
Geoff Obeney *(CIO)*
John R. Owings *(CFO & VP)*
Bill Fitton *(VP-Fin)*
Woody Ritchey *(CEO)*
Sharon Fletcher *(VP-HR)*
Micki Barber *(VP-Sls-Mktg)*

SEI MEETINGS AND INCENTIVES
122 W Carpenter Fwy Ste 400, Irving, TX 75039
Tel.: (972) 717-1400
Web Site: http://www.sei-mi.com
Year Founded: 1975
Rev.: $25,000,000
Emp.: 30
Meeting, Event, Travel & Incentive Services
N.A.I.C.S.: 561599
Hanna Sahliyeh *(Pres)*
Laura Gilbert *(Exec VP)*
Richard Chandler *(VP-Fin)*

SEI METALTEK
2315 Routh St, Dallas, TX 75201-3204
Tel.: (214) 953-1600   TX
Web Site:
http://www.seimetaltek.com
Year Founded: 1966
Sales Range: $75-99.9 Million
Emp.: 150
Holding Company
N.A.I.C.S.: 332613
Kevin D. Grace *(CEO)*
Hap Porter *(Pres & COO)*
Lesley Mozingo *(HR Mgr)*

Subsidiaries:

Colonial Spring Company (1)
95 Valley St, Bristol, CT 06011
Tel.: (860) 589-3231
Web Site: http://www.colonialspringco.com
Sales Range: $10-24.9 Million
Emp.: 20
Steel Spring & Metal Stamping Mfr
N.A.I.C.S.: 332613
Bill Lathrop *(Pres)*

Hardware Products, LP (1)
191 Williams St, Chelsea, MA 02150
Tel.: (617) 884-9410
Web Site: http://www.hardwareproducts.com
Sales Range: $10-24.9 Million
Emp.: 35
Spring Mfr
N.A.I.C.S.: 332613
Ted White *(Pres)*

John M. Dean Co., LLC (1)
20 Mechanics St, Putnam, CT 06260-0924
Tel.: (860) 928-7701
Web Site: http://www.jmdean.com
Hardware & Wire Product Mfr
N.A.I.C.S.: 332618
Debra Smutnick *(Gen Mgr)*

SEI MetalForms Inc. (1)
1601 Terre Colony Ct, Dallas, TX 75212
Tel.: (214) 630-0322
Web Site: http://www.seimetalforms.com
Metal Stamping Mfr
N.A.I.C.S.: 332119

Spring Engineers of Houston Ltd. (1)
9740 Tanner Rd, Houston, TX 77041-7621
Tel.: (713) 690-9488
Web Site: http://www.springhouston.com
Sales Range: $10-24.9 Million
Emp.: 85
Mechanical Springs Wire Forms, Fabrications Metal Stampings & Machinery Mfr
N.A.I.C.S.: 541330
Kevin D. Grace *(Pres & COO)*
Alfred P. West Jr. *(CEO)*

SEIDEL DIESEL GROUP
1 Seidel Ct, Bolingbrook, IL 60490
Tel.: (815) 886-9900   IL
Web Site:
http://seideldieselgroup.com
Year Founded: 1981
Diesel Fuel Injection Components Distr
N.A.I.C.S.: 423830
Paul Thoms *(Pres)*

SEIDMAN INSURANCE CONSULTANTS LLC
520 Kirkland Wy, Ste 300, Kirkland, WA 98033
Tel.: (800) 785-9340
Web Site:
https://www.seidmancg.com
Wealth Management Firm
N.A.I.C.S.: 523940

Subsidiaries:

Coldstream Capital Management, Inc. (1)
1 100th Ave NE Ste 102, Bellevue, WA 98004
Tel.: (425) 283-1600
Web Site: http://www.coldstream.com
Sales Range: $1-9.9 Million
Emp.: 22
Investment Advice
N.A.I.C.S.: 523940
Roger C. Reynolds *(Co-Founder & Mgr-Relationship)*
Howard Coleman *(Chief Investment Officer & Gen Counsel)*
David Powers *(Portfolio Mgr)*
Nina Rose *(Mgr-Relationship & Portfolio)*
Peter Beeson *(Co-Founder)*
Kevin Fitzwilson *(Mng Shareholder & Mgr-Relationship)*
Phil Platt *(COO)*
Robert Smith *(COO)*
Donna Oricchio *(CFO)*

Subsidiary (Domestic):

Rosenbaum Financial, Inc. (2)
150 SW Harrison St Ste 300, Portland, OR 97201
Tel.: (503) 296-9190
Web Site:
http://www.rosenbaumfinancial.com
Insurance Related Activities
N.A.I.C.S.: 524298
Mark Rosenbaum *(Pres & CEO)*

SEIGER GFELLER LAURIE LLP
977 Farmington Ave Ste 200, West Hartford, CT 06107
Tel.: (860) 760-8400
Web Site:
http://www.sgllawgroup.com
Year Founded: 2009
Law firm
N.A.I.C.S.: 541110
Charles Gfeller *(Partner)*

SEIGERMANS FURNITURE SHOWPLACE LLC
50 Price Pkwy, Farmingdale, NY 11735
Tel.: (631) 753-3734
Sales Range: $10-24.9 Million
Emp.: 25
Furniture Retailer
N.A.I.C.S.: 449110

SEILER INSTRUMENT AND MANUFACTURING CO. INC.
3433 Tree Ct Industrial Blvd, Saint Louis, MO 63122
Tel.: (314) 968-2282
Web Site: http://www.seilerinst.com
Sales Range: $10-24.9 Million
Emp.: 200
Optical Instruments & Lenses
N.A.I.C.S.: 333310
Pat McCoy *(CFO)*
Dane Carlson *(Mgr)*
Eric Paul Seiler Sr. *(Owner & Pres)*
Eric Seiler Jr. *(Pres)*

SEILKOP INDUSTRIES INC.
425 N Bend Rd, Cincinnati, OH 45216
Tel.: (513) 761-1035
Web Site:
http://www.epcorfoundry.com
Sales Range: $25-49.9 Million
Emp.: 75
Die Sets for Metal Stamping
N.A.I.C.S.: 333514
Kenneth Seilkop *(Pres)*
Dave Seilkop *(VP)*
Robin Vogel *(CFO)*

SEILLER WATERMAN LLC
Meidinger Tower 462 S 4th St 22nd Fl, Louisville, KY 40202
Tel.: (502) 584-7400
Web Site:
http://www.derbycitylaw.com
Year Founded: 1928
Emp.: 100
Law Firm
N.A.I.C.S.: 541110
Bill V. Seiller *(Atty)*
Joseph H. Cohen *(Atty)*
David M. Cantor *(Atty)*
Pamela M. Greenwell *(Atty)*
Alan N. Linker *(Atty)*
Christopher A. Bates *(Atty)*
John J. Bleidt *(Atty)*
Neil C. Bordy *(Atty)*
Kyle Anne Citrynell *(Atty)*
Lester I. Adams Jr. *(Atty)*

Subsidiaries:

Weber & Rose, PSC (1)
471 W Main St Ste 400, Louisville, KY 40202
Tel.: (502) 589-2200
Web Site: http://www.weberandrose.com
Emp.: 18
Law Firm
N.A.I.C.S.: 541110
Michael R. Gosnell *(Atty)*
Sharon C. Hardy *(Atty)*
Darryl W. Durham *(Atty)*
Shelton R. Weber *(Atty)*
Michael E. Lannon *(Atty)*
James M. Gary *(Atty)*
Landra Blackwell *(Atty)*
Russell Saunders *(Atty)*
Thomas J. B. Hurst *(Atty)*
R. Eric Craig *(Atty)*
Rachel Dickey *(Atty)*
James T. Lobb *(Atty)*
R. Hite Nally *(Atty)*
Brittany Griffin Smith *(Atty)*

SEILOX, LLC
170 E 9th Ave, Runnemede, NJ 08078
Tel.: (856) 939-9300   DE
Web Site: http://www.sielox.com
Year Founded: 1979
Sales Range: $10-24.9 Million
Emp.: 45
Security Video & Imaging Products Mfr
N.A.I.C.S.: 334310
Mark Isaacson *(VP-Engrg)*
Steve Casey *(CTO & Sr VP)*
Mark Evans *(VP-Mktg & Bus Dev)*
Karen G. Evans *(Pres & CEO)*

SEISMIC ENERGY PRODUCTS LP
518 Progress Way, Athens, TX 75751
Tel.: (903) 675-8571
Web Site:
http://www.sepbearings.com
Year Founded: 1972
Sales Range: $10-24.9 Million
Emp.: 65
Producer of Structural & Rail Mill Products
N.A.I.C.S.: 332312

SEISMIC EXCHANGE INC.
4805 Westway Park Blvd, Houston, TX 77041-5567
Tel.: (832) 590-5100
Web Site:
http://www.seismicexchange.com
Year Founded: 1975
Sales Range: $25-49.9 Million
Emp.: 150
Seismograph Surveys
N.A.I.C.S.: 213112
Tim Moran *(VP-3D New Ventures-New Orleans)*
Howard Patton *(VP-3D Mktg-New Orleans)*
Julie Hardie *(VP-Legal)*
Sherry Bryant *(Dir-Exec Projects)*
Jeff Lester *(VP-3D Mktg)*
Tony Traweek *(Sr Mgr-3D Data Svcs)*
Larry Tull *(VP)*
Billy Jernigan *(Dir-Tax Dept)*
Christine Russo *(Mgr-Client Svcs)*
Scott Custer *(CIO)*
George Cary III *(VP-Engrg & Plng)*
Edward R. Grady Jr. *(CFO)*

SEISMIC SOFTWARE, INC.
12390 El Camino Real, San Diego, CA 92130
Tel.: (855) 466-8748
Web Site: http://www.seismic.com
Year Founded: 2011
Sales & Marketing Software Developer
N.A.I.C.S.: 513210
J. Douglas Winter *(Co-Founder & CEO)*

SEISMIC SOFTWARE, INC.

Seismic Software, Inc.—(Continued)
Ed Calnan (Co-Founder & Chief Revenue Officer)
Marc Romano (Co-Founder & CTO)
Fred Xie (Co-Founder & Sr VP-Engrg)
Dave Myron (Sr VP-Product Mgmt)
Randy Wootton (Chief Security Officer & Pres-Percolate)
Andy Bergen (Chief Customer Officer)
John McCauley (CFO)
Craig Dunham (Gen Mgr-Fin Svcs)
Nicole McGuire (VP-People Ops)
Kevin Chew (VP-Bus & Corp Dev)
Heather Cole (VP-Market Growth)
Krish Mantipragada (Chief Product Officer)
Donna DeBerry (VP-Inclusion)
Natalie Beaulieu (Dir-Comm)
Linda Ho (Chief People Officer)
Toby Carrington (Chief Bus Officer)
Paige O'Neill (CMO)

Subsidiaries:

Percolate Industries, Inc. (1)
107 Grand St 2nd Fl, New York, NY 10013
Tel.: (646) 470-8346
Web Site: http://www.percolate.com
Software Publisher
N.A.I.C.S.: 513210
Noah Brier (Co-Founder)

The Savo Group, Ltd (1)
222 W Merchandise Mart Pl Ste 1710, Chicago, IL 60654
Tel.: (312) 506-1700
Web Site: http://www.seismic.com
Software Publisher
N.A.I.C.S.: 513210

SEITER & MILLER ADVERTISING, INC.
460 Park Ave S, New York, NY 10016
Tel.: (212) 843-9900
Web Site: http://www.seitermiller.com
Year Founded: 1990
Rev.: $50,000,000
Emp.: 25
Advetising Agency
N.A.I.C.S.: 541810
Martin Schneider (Dir-Creative)

SEITER SERVICES, LLC
590 US 42, Xenia, OH 45385
Tel.: (937) 507-3372
Web Site: http://www.seiterservices.com
Heating, Ventilation & Air Conditioning Services
N.A.I.C.S.: 238220
Chris Seiter (Co-Owner & Ops Mgr)
Sheila Seiter (Co-Owner & Fin Officer)

Subsidiaries:

Southtown Heating & Cooling, Inc. (1)
3024 Springboro W Rd, Dayton, OH 45439-1716
Tel.: (937) 298-4200
Web Site: http://www.southtownheatingcooling.com
Sales Range: $1-9.9 Million
Emp.: 26
Plumbing, Heating, Air-Conditioning, Nsk
N.A.I.C.S.: 238220
Joe Trame (Pres & Treas)
Terri L. Trame (Mgr)
Vic Brahm (Mgr-Comml Svc Sls)
Lesley Burke (Mgr-Svc)
Diane M. Bryant (Office Mgr)

SEJ SERVICES LLC
222 W Coleman Blvd, Mount Pleasant, SC 29464
Web Site: http://www.sejservices.com
Year Founded: 2011

Sales Range: $10-24.9 Million
Emp.: 165
Business Consulting Services
N.A.I.C.S.: 541611
Brandon Schneider (Co-Owner & CEO)
Chris Abel (Co-Owner & Pres)
Justin Kohl (Reg VP-Ops & Safety)
Mark Gregory (Branch Mgr)
Michael Kline (Branch Mgr)

SELA ROOFING & REMODELING
4100 Excelsior Blvd, Minneapolis, MN 55416
Tel.: (612) 823-8046
Web Site: http://www.selaroofing.com
Sales Range: $25-49.9 Million
Emp.: 110
Roofing Contractors
N.A.I.C.S.: 236118
Paz B. Sela (Pres)

SELCO COMMUNITY CREDIT UNION
PO Box 7487, Springfield, OR 97475-0487
Tel.: (541) 686-8000 OR
Web Site: http://www.selco.org
Year Founded: 1936
Sales Range: $50-74.9 Million
Emp.: 308
Financial Support Services
N.A.I.C.S.: 523999
Craig Carpenter (Sr VP-Lending)
Tiffany Washington (Sr VP-Fin)
Steve McIntire (VP-Admin)
J. Robert Newcomb (CEO & Sec)
Todd Zalk (VP-Comml Lending)

SELCO INDUSTRIES, INC.
141 Lanza Ave Bldg 10, Garfield, NJ 07026
Tel.: (973) 478-5557
Year Founded: 2003
Sales Range: $10-24.9 Million
Emp.: 26
Sanitary Paper Product Mfr
N.A.I.C.S.: 322191
Seldon Hill (Pres)
Ruby Hill (CEO)

Subsidiaries:

Gussco Manufacturing, Inc. (1)
11 Cliffside Dr, Cedar Grove, NJ 07009
Tel.: (973) 571-2316
Web Site: http://www.gussco.com
Index Cards, Indexes, File Folders & Transfer Files Mfr
N.A.I.C.S.: 322230

SELCO LLC
8909 E 21st St, Tulsa, OK 74129
Tel.: (918) 622-6100 OK
Web Site: http://www.selcotime.com
Year Founded: 1980
Sales Range: $1-9.9 Million
Emp.: 30
Jewelry, Watch, Precious Stone & Precious Metal Merchant Whslr
N.A.I.C.S.: 423940
Felice Abels (Dir-Facility)

Subsidiaries:

Belair Time Corp. (1)
1995 Swarthmore Ave, Lakewood, NJ 08701
Tel.: (732) 905-0100
Web Site: http://www.beltime.com
Jewelry, Watch, Precious Stone & Precious Metal Merchant Whslr
N.A.I.C.S.: 423940
Bill Peak (Mgr-Sls-Natl)

SELDEN'S INTERIOR FURNISHINGS, INC.

1802 62nd Ave E, Tacoma, WA 98424
Tel.: (253) 922-5700
Web Site: http://www.seldens.com
Year Founded: 1940
Sales Range: $10-24.9 Million
Emp.: 105
Furniture Retailer
N.A.I.C.S.: 449110
Scott Selden (Pres)

SELECT 1 TRANSPORT INC.
25005 Brest Rd, Taylor, MI 48180
Tel.: (734) 946-7850
Web Site: http://www.select1.com
Year Founded: 1997
Rev.: $11,876,857
Emp.: 50
Logistics & Vehicle Transportation Services
N.A.I.C.S.: 541614
Gary L. Carlson (Pres & CEO)
Patrick Evo (Gen Mgr)
Bob Allen (Mgr-Fleet)
Rick Johnson (Dir-Bus Dev)

SELECT COMMUNICATIONS, INC.
12975 16th Ave N Ste 100, Plymouth, MN 55441
Tel.: (763) 744-0900 MN
Web Site: http://www.selectcommunicationsinc.com
Year Founded: 1994
Sales Range: $10-24.9 Million
Emp.: 120
Wireless Voice & Data Services Sales
N.A.I.C.S.: 517121
Scott Alexander (Co-Owner & Co-CEO)
Rob Alexander (Co-Owner & Co-CEO)
Susan Ward (Controller)

SELECT ENGINEERING, INC.
1717 S Boulder Ave Ste 600, Tulsa, OK 74119
Tel.: (918) 592-1133
Web Site: http://www.select-engineering.com
Year Founded: 1999
Sales Range: $10-24.9 Million
Emp.: 40
Design & Engineering Services for Energy Industry
N.A.I.C.S.: 541330
Scott Hastings (Pres)

SELECT GROUP
5420 Wade Park Blvd Ste 100, Raleigh, NC 27607
Tel.: (919) 459-1400
Web Site: http://www.selectgroup.com
Year Founded: 1999
Sales Range: $25-49.9 Million
Emp.: 58
Recruitment Services
N.A.I.C.S.: 561311
Sheldon Wolitski (Founder)

SELECT INN
1025 38th St SW Ste B, Fargo, ND 58103
Tel.: (701) 282-6305
Web Site: http://www.selectinn.com
Sales Range: $10-24.9 Million
Emp.: 12
Motel, Franchised
N.A.I.C.S.: 721110
Evy Schilling (VP-Franchise Dev)

SELECT INTERNATIONAL CORP.
14 Heid Ave, Dayton, OH 45404
Tel.: (937) 233-9191
Web Site: http://www.select.org
Year Founded: 1970
Sales Range: $25-49.9 Million
Emp.: 270
Automotive Stampings
N.A.I.C.S.: 336370
Bob Whited (Founder & CEO)
John Ficklin (Mgr-Sls)
John Roppo (CFO)
Brian Shivler (COO)

Subsidiaries:

Select Engineered Products (1)
60 Heid Ave, Dayton, OH 45404
Tel.: (937) 233-9191
Web Site: http://www.selecttoolcorp.com
Rev.: $2,000,000
Emp.: 7
Automotive Stampings
N.A.I.C.S.: 336370

Select Industries Corp (1)
60 Heid Ave, Dayton, OH 45404
Tel.: (937) 233-9191
Web Site: http://www.select.org
Rev.: $47,301,358
Emp.: 115
Automotive Stampings
N.A.I.C.S.: 336370
Mark Wogoman (Pres)
Kelly Cooley (CFO)
Susan Linder (Mgr-Supply Chain)
Bob Slouffman (Sr Mgr-Acct)

SELECT MANAGEMENT HOLDINGS, INC.
1 Chagrin Highlands 2000 Auburn Dr, Cleveland, OH 44122
Tel.: (216) 464-6606
Web Site: http://www.selectrestaurants.com
Rev.: $94,400,000
Emp.: 3
Holding Company
N.A.I.C.S.: 551112
John Quagliata (Chm & CEO)

Subsidiaries:

Select Restaurants, Inc. (1)
2000 Auburn Dr Ste 410, Cleveland, OH 44122-4327
Tel.: (216) 464-6606
Web Site: http://www.selectrestaurants.com
Sales Range: $10-24.9 Million
Emp.: 13
Restaurant Services
N.A.I.C.S.: 722511
Raphael Oliver (VP-Bus Dev)

SELECT MILK PRODUCERS INC.
320 W Hermosa Dr, Artesia, NM 88210
Tel.: (575) 746-6698
Web Site: http://www.selectmilk.com
Year Founded: 1994
Sales Range: $200-249.9 Million
Emp.: 20
Dairy Products Mfr
N.A.I.C.S.: 424430
Rance Miles (CFO)
Brad Bouma (Pres)

SELECT PORTFOLIO SERVICING, INC.
PO Box 65250, Salt Lake City, UT 84165-0250 UT
Web Site: http://www.spservicing.com
Year Founded: 1989
Sales Range: $75-99.9 Million
Emp.: 500
Investment Services
N.A.I.C.S.: 522390
Matt Hollingsworth (Chm)

SELECT REALTY GROUP
5030 Medalist Ct, Oceanside, CA 92057-1946
Tel.: (760) 804-6801

Web Site:
http://www.myprocessteam.com
Activities Related to Real Estate
N.A.I.C.S.: 531390
Don Peters (VP)

SELECT REHABILITATION, LLC
2600 Compass Rd, Glenview, IL 60026
Tel.: (847) 441-5593   DE
Web Site:
http://www.selectrehab.com
Year Founded: 1998
Offices of Physical, Occupational & Speech Therapists & Audiologists
N.A.I.C.S.: 621340
Neal Deutsch (Chm & Co-Founder)
Anna Gardina Wolfe (Co-Founder & CEO)

Subsidiaries:

RehabCare Group, Inc.   (1)
680 S 4th St, Louisville, KY 40202
Tel.: (800) 545-0749
Rehabilitation Program Management Services
N.A.I.C.S.: 621498

Subsidiary (Domestic):

Clear Lake Rehabilitation Hospital, LLC   (2)
655 E Medical Center Blvd, Webster, TX 77598
Tel.: (281) 286-1500
Web Site: http://www.triumph-healthcare.com
Sales Range: $1-9.9 Million
Emp.: 180
Physiotherapist Services
N.A.I.C.S.: 621340
Barbara Franco (CFO)

Salt Lake Physical Therapy Associates, Inc.   (2)
4888 Highland Dr, Holladay, UT 84117
Tel.: (801) 264-9855
Physical Therapist Services
N.A.I.C.S.: 621340

Subsidiary (Non-US):

Tulsa Specialty Hospital, LLC   (2)
Tel.: (918) 663-8183
Sales Range: $1-9.9 Million
Emp.: 150
Specialty & Long Term Acute Care Hospitals
N.A.I.C.S.: 622310

SELECT SIRES INC.
11740 US Route 42 N, Plain City, OH 43064
Tel.: (614) 873-4683   OH
Web Site: http://www.selectsires.com
Year Founded: 1965
Artificial Insemination Services (for Livestock)
N.A.I.C.S.: 115210
David C. Thorbahn (Pres & CEO)

Subsidiaries:

Accelerated Genetics   (1)
11740 US 42 N, Plain City, OH 43064
Tel.: (614) 873-4683
Web Site: http://www.accelgen.com
Bovine Genetics & Research & Reproductive Services
N.A.I.C.S.: 115210

All West/ Select Sires, Inc.   (1)
PO Box 507, Burlington, WA 98233
Tel.: (360) 757-6093
Web Site: http://www.allwestselectsires.com
Emp.: 16
Livestock Breeding Services
N.A.I.C.S.: 115210
Jim Wells (Gen Mgr)
Jerry Lanting (Pres)

COBA / Select Sires Inc.   (1)
1224 Alton-Darby Rd, Columbus, OH 43228-9792
Tel.: (614) 878-5333
Web Site: http://www.cobaselect.com
Emp.: 15
Livestock Breeding Services
N.A.I.C.S.: 115210
Kim House (CFO)
Rex Castle (Mgr-Info Svcs)
Norman Hoff (Dir-Mktg-Southwest)
Adam Hahlen (Reg Dir-Mktg)
Rodney Wegener (Reg Dir-Mktg)
Chad Steinberger (Pres)

East Central/Select Sires   (1)
PO Box 191, Waupun, WI 53963
Tel.: (920) 324-3505
Web Site:
http://www.eastcentralselectsires.com
Sales Range: $1-9.9 Million
Livestock Breeding Services
N.A.I.C.S.: 115210
Steve Abel (Pres)
Jerome Meyer (Gen Mgr)

Minnesota/Select Sires Co-op Inc.   (1)
6601 Gregory Park Rd, Saint Cloud, MN 56301
Tel.: (320) 259-6680
Sales Range: $1-9.9 Million
Livestock Breeding Services
N.A.I.C.S.: 115210
Chris Sigurdson (Gen Mgr)

Prairie State/Select Sires   (1)
41W 394 US Hwy 20, Hampshire, IL 60140
Tel.: (847) 464-5281
Livestock Breeding Services
N.A.I.C.S.: 115210
Devin Albrecht (Gen Mgr)
Dorothy Gurke (Office Mgr)

Select Sires MidAmerica, Inc.   (1)
833 W 400 N, Logan, UT 84321
Tel.: (435) 752-2022
Emp.: 8
Livestock Breeding Services
N.A.I.C.S.: 115210
Randy Hill (Mgr)

Southeast Select Sires Inc.   (1)
3789 Old Port Royal Rd, Spring Hill, TN 37174
Tel.: (931) 489-2020
Web Site:
http://www.southeastselectsires.com
Livestock Breeding Services
N.A.I.C.S.: 115210
Tim Riley (Gen Mgr)

SELECT TEMPORARIES INC.
12700 Hillcrest Rd Ste 218, Dallas, TX 75230
Tel.: (972) 934-1888
Web Site: http://www.select-staff.com
Sales Range: $10-24.9 Million
Emp.: 12
Temporary Help Service
N.A.I.C.S.: 561320
Charles E. Tanner (Pres)

SELECTA PRODUCTS INC.
1200 E Tehachapi Blvd, Tehachapi, CA 93561-8129
Tel.: (661) 823-7050
Web Site:
http://www.selectaproductsinc.com
Year Founded: 1976
Sales Range: $10-24.9 Million
Emp.: 70
Provider of Electrical Apparatus & Equipment
N.A.I.C.S.: 423610
John Kenyon (CEO)
Craig Gossage (CFO)

SELECTED FUNERAL & LIFE INSURANCE CO.
119 Convention Blvd, Hot Springs, AR 71901
Tel.: (501) 624-2172
Web Site: http://www.sflic.net
Sales Range: $25-49.9 Million
Emp.: 100
Funeral Insurance
N.A.I.C.S.: 524113
Courtney C. Crouch Jr. (Pres & CEO)

SELECTEMP CORPORATION
1202 Gateway Loop, Springfield, OR 97477
Tel.: (541) 746-6200
Web Site: http://www.selec-temp.com
Sales Range: $10-24.9 Million
Emp.: 15
Temporary Help Service
N.A.I.C.S.: 561320
Roger Cox (CEO)

SELECTHEALTH, INC.
5381 Green St, Murray, UT 84123
Tel.: (801) 442-5000   UT
Web Site: http://www.selecthealth.org
Year Founded: 1985
Sales Range: $1-4.9 Billion
Emp.: 1,249
Health Care Srvices
N.A.I.C.S.: 622110
Robert L. White (COO & VP)
J. Murphy Winfield (CMO & VP)
Mark A. Brown (Treas & VP)
Jerry Edgington (VP)
Russ Kuze (Chief Medical Officer & VP)
Thomas Risse (CFO & VP)
Jon Larkin (Mgr-Bus & Provider Dev)
Ed Castledine (Pres-Idaho Market)
Geoffrey Swanson (Dir-Medical-New Idaho)

SELECTIVE ENTERPRISES INC.
10701 Texland Blvd, Charlotte, NC 28273
Tel.: (704) 588-3310
Web Site:
http://www.unitedsupplyco.com
Year Founded: 1962
Sales Range: $10-24.9 Million
Emp.: 160
Whslr of Drapery, Hardware & Window Blinds & Shades
N.A.I.C.S.: 337920
Micheal Metzcus (Controller)

SELECTNY L.P.
401 Broadway, New York, NY 10013-1410
Tel.: (212) 367-3560   DE
Web Site: http://www.selectny.com
Year Founded: 1993
Sales Range: $150-199.9 Million
Emp.: 50
Advetising Agency
N.A.I.C.S.: 541810
Olivier Van Doorne (Dir-Worldwide Creative)
Wolfgang Schaefer (Global Chief Strategic Officer)
Herwig Preis (Pres & CEO)
Jonathan Braaten (Mng Dir)
Fredrik Peterhoff (Exec Dir-Creative-Los Angeles)
Sara Fahim (Dir-Strategy-Los Angeles)
Suzanne Hader (Head-Digital Strategy)

Subsidiaries:

SelectNY GmbH   (1)
Hohelustchaussee 18, 20253, Hamburg, Germany
Tel.: (49) 40 45 02 19 0
Web Site: http://www.selectlp.com
Advetising Agency
N.A.I.C.S.: 541810
Annette Kunet (Mng Dir)
Herwig Preis (Pres & CEO)

Subsidiary (Domestic):

SelectNY.Berlin GmbH   (2)
Chaussee Strasse 123, Berlin, 10115, Germany
Tel.: (49) 30 34 34 630
Web Site: http://www.selectlp.com
Emp.: 45
Advetising Agency
N.A.I.C.S.: 541810

SelectNY.Koblenz GmbH   (2)
Schlossstrasse 1, Koblenz, 56068, Germany
Tel.: (49) 261 972 610
Web Site: http://www.selectny.com
Sales Range: $50-74.9 Million
Emp.: 3
Advetising Agency
N.A.I.C.S.: 541810
Gerhard Aretz (CFO & Gen Mgr)
Herwig Preis (Pres & CEO)

SelectNY.London Ltd.   (1)
1st Fl Kensington High St, London, W8 5NP, United Kingdom
Tel.: (44) 207 243 4100
Web Site: http://www.selectlp.com
Advetising Agency
N.A.I.C.S.: 541810

SelectNY.Paris   (1)
5 Pl Victoires, Esc A 7eme etage, 75009, Paris, France
Tel.: (33) 1 53 01 95 00
Web Site: http://www.selectny.com
Sales Range: Less than $1 Million
Emp.: 16
Advetising Agency
N.A.I.C.S.: 541810
Fabirice Policialla (Dir-Creative)

SELECTO PRODUCTS CO. INC.
400 Corporate Dr, Blauvelt, NY 10913
Tel.: (914) 693-1300
Web Site:
http://www.selectoperfecto.com
Sales Range: $10-24.9 Million
Emp.: 165
General Merchandise, Non-Durable
N.A.I.C.S.: 424990
Joe Brindan (Gen Mgr)

SELECTQUOTE INSURANCE SERVICES
595 Market St FL 10, San Francisco, CA 94105
Tel.: (415) 543-7338
Web Site:
http://www.selectquote.com
Sales Range: $10-24.9 Million
Emp.: 225
Provider of Life Insurance Services
N.A.I.C.S.: 524210
Charan J. Singh (Founder)
Robert Edwards (CFO & COO)

SELECTRODE INDUSTRIES INC.
230 Broadway, Huntington Station, NY 11746
Tel.: (631) 547-5470
Web Site: http://www.selectrode.com
Rev.: $20,000,000
Emp.: 40
Nonferrous Rolling & Drawing
N.A.I.C.S.: 331491
Paul Paternoster (Pres)

SELECTRON INDUSTRIAL COMPANY
901 W Walnut St, Compton, CA 90220-5109
Tel.: (310) 638-1881
Web Site:
http://www.selectroninc.com
Year Founded: 1984
Sales Range: $10-24.9 Million
Emp.: 40
Optics & Electronic Components Mfr
N.A.I.C.S.: 334419
Sam Cha (Mgr-Pur)

SELECTRONICS CORP.

Selectron Industrial Company—(Continued)

SELECTRONICS CORP.
3898 Main St, Waitsfield, VT 05673
Tel.: (802) 496-3391
Web Site: http://www.wcvt.com
Sales Range: $10-24.9 Million
Emp.: 90
Local Telephone Communications
N.A.I.C.S.: 517121
Greg Haskin *(Pres & CEO)*
Alan Jones *(Mgr)*

SELERANT CORP.
499 7th Ave 18N, New York, NY 10018
Tel.: (212) 792-8910 — NY
Web Site: http://www.selerant.com
Year Founded: 2003
Emp.: 100
Product Lifecycle Management Software Developer
N.A.I.C.S.: 513210
Carlo Colombo *(Co-Founder & CEO)*
Jacopo Colombo *(Co-Founder & CTO)*
Sunil Thomas *(COO)*

SELF ESTEEM BRANDS LLC
111 Weir Dr, Woodbury, MN 55125
Tel.: (651) 438-5000 — DE
Web Site: http://www.sebrands.com
Health, Wellness & Fitness Program Services
N.A.I.C.S.: 713940
Chuck Runyon *(Co-Founder & CEO)*
Dave Mortensen *(Co-Founder & President)*

Subsidiaries:

Anytime Fitness LLC (1)
111 Weir Dr, Woodbury, MN 55125
Tel.: (651) 438-5000
Web Site: http://www.anytimefitness.com
Sales Range: $450-499.9 Million
Emp.: 170
Health & Fitness Clubs
N.A.I.C.S.: 713940
Chuck Runyon *(Co-Founder & CEO)*
Tom Gillis *(VP-Sls)*
John Pindred *(CFO)*
Dave Mortensen *(Co-Founder)*
Stacy L. Anderson *(Pres)*
Angela Jaskolski *(Brand Pres-Waxing The City)*
Andy Thompson *(Chm-UK)*
Stuart Broster *(CEO-UK)*

Bar Method Inc. (1)
Three Embarcadero Center, Lobby Level, San Francisco, CA 94111
Tel.: (415) 956-0446
Web Site: http://www.barmethod.com
Diet & Weight Reducing Centers
N.A.I.C.S.: 812191

SELF HELP, INC.
780 W Main St, Avon, MA 02322
Tel.: (508) 588-0447 — MA
Web Site: http://www.selfhelpinc.org
Year Founded: 1965
Sales Range: $10-24.9 Million
Emp.: 277
Community Welfare Services
N.A.I.C.S.: 624190
Jonathan R. Carlson *(Exec Dir)*
Jack Bush *(Co-Pres)*
Raymond Yancy *(Co-Pres)*

SELF OPPORTUNITY, INC.
808 Office Park Cir, Lewisville, TX 75057
Tel.: (214) 222-1500
Web Site: http://www.selfopportunity.com
Year Founded: 2001
Sales Range: $1-9.9 Million
Emp.: 33
Media Buying Services
N.A.I.C.S.: 541810

Brad Holley *(VP)*

SELF SERVE LUMBER CO.
1621 S Wheeler St, Saginaw, MI 48602
Tel.: (989) 790-9510 — MI
Web Site: http://www.selfservelumber.com
Year Founded: 1933
Sales Range: $10-24.9 Million
Emp.: 135
Provider of Lumber & Other Building Materials
N.A.I.C.S.: 423310
William A. Schwannecke *(Pres)*

SELF-HELP CREDIT UNION
301 W Main St, Durham, NC 27701
Tel.: (919) 956-4400 — NC
Web Site: http://www.self-help.org
Year Founded: 1983
Sales Range: $25-49.9 Million
Credit Union Operator
N.A.I.C.S.: 522130
Tanya Branch *(Chm)*
Alan Reberg *(Sec)*
Martin Eakes *(Co-Founder & CEO)*
Kenneth Kalaher *(Pres)*
Doug Wilkerson *(Treas)*
Linda Shaw *(Exec Dir)*

SELFHELP COMMUNITY SERVICES, INC
520 8th Ave, New York, NY 10018
Tel.: (212) 971-7600 — NY
Web Site: http://www.selfhelp.net
Year Founded: 1937
Sales Range: $50-74.9 Million
Emp.: 2,003
Senior Living Services
N.A.I.C.S.: 623312
Stuart C. Kaplan *(CEO)*

SELIG ENTERPRISES INC.
1100 Spring St NW Ste 550, Atlanta, GA 30309-2857
Tel.: (404) 876-5511
Web Site: http://www.seligenterprises.com
Year Founded: 1942
Sales Range: $10-24.9 Million
Emp.: 90
Operators Of Nonresidential Buildings
N.A.I.C.S.: 531120
Bill Stogner *(Sr VP)*
Bonnie Dean *(Asst VP & Dir-Construction)*
James A. Saine *(VP-Industrial & Office Leasing)*
Ronald J. Stein *(CFO)*
Shirley A. Gouffon *(Sr VP)*
Kent Walker *(VP-Indus Properties)*
Mindy Selig *(VP-Retail Leasing)*
Joe Ann Chitty *(COO)*
Cathy Selig *(Owner)*
Matt Rendle *(Chief Investment Officer)*
Steve Baile *(COO & Exec VP)*
Chris Ahrenkiel *(Exec VP)*
Kenneth J. Clayman *(Gen Counsel, Sec & Sr VP)*
Malloy Peterson *(Sr VP)*
Steve Selig *(CEO)*
Gregory Selig Lewis *(Sr VP-Dev)*

SELIG MULTIMEDIA INC.
Northdale Plz 3903 Northdale Blvd Ste 150 W, Tampa, FL 33624
Tel.: (813) 708-1220
Web Site: http://www.seligmultimedia.com
Public Relations Agencies
N.A.I.C.S.: 541820
Glenn Selig *(Founder, Pres & CEO)*

Subsidiaries:

PR NewsChannel (1)
Northdale Plz 3903 Northdale Blvd Ste 150 W, Tampa, FL 33624
Tel.: (813) 708-1220
Web Site: http://www.prnewschannel.com
Emp.: 10
Public Relations Services
N.A.I.C.S.: 541820
Glenn Selig *(Pres & CEO)*

The Publicity Agency (1)
Northdale Plz 3903 Northdale Blvd Ste 150 W, Tampa, FL 33624
Tel.: (813) 948-7767
Web Site: http://www.thepublicityagency.com
Emp.: 6
Public Relations Agency
N.A.I.C.S.: 541820
Glenn Selig *(Pres & CEO)*

SELIGMAN & ASSOCIATES, INC.
26100 NW Hwy Ste 1913, Southfield, MI 48076
Tel.: (248) 862-8000 — DE
Web Site: http://www.seligmanassociates.com
Year Founded: 1954
Sales Range: $75-99.9 Million
Emp.: 25
Real Estate Investment Trust
N.A.I.C.S.: 531210
Scott J. Seligman *(VP)*
Stephen Thurmon *(Asst Controller)*

Subsidiaries:

Seligman Western Enterprises Limited (1)
600 Montgomery St 40th Fl, San Francisco, CA 94111
Tel.: (415) 658-2889
Web Site: http://www.seligmangroup.com
Real Estate Property Management Services
N.A.I.C.S.: 531311

SELINSGROVE MOTORS INC.
10 N Susquehanna Trl, Selinsgrove, PA 17870
Tel.: (570) 374-8131
Web Site: http://www.selinsgroveford.com
Sales Range: $10-24.9 Million
Emp.: 40
Sales of New & Used Automobiles
N.A.I.C.S.: 441110
Todd Benner *(Owner)*

SELLAND AUTO TRANSPORT INC.
615 S 96th St, Seattle, WA 98108
Tel.: (206) 767-5960
Web Site: http://www.sellandauto.com
Year Founded: 1967
Sales Range: $25-49.9 Million
Emp.: 200
Transporter of Automobiles
N.A.I.C.S.: 484230
Annita Gatlin *(Mgr-IT Logistics)*

SELLEN CONSTRUCTION COMPANY
227 Westlake Ave N, Seattle, WA 98109
Tel.: (206) 682-7770 — WA
Web Site: http://www.sellen.com
Year Founded: 1944
Sales Range: $350-399.9 Million
Emp.: 500
Provider of Contracting & Construction Services
N.A.I.C.S.: 236220
Adam Rohde *(VP, Dir-Engrg & Sr Project Mgr)*
Gerald Beltran *(Project Mgr)*

Jennifer Frey *(Mgr-Sustainability Program)*
Scott Redman *(Pres)*
Wilf Wainhouse *(COO)*
Graham Condit *(Dir-Virtual Design & Construction)*
Carrie Boettcher *(VP & Dir-Field Dev)*
Jeremiah Shakespeare *(VP, Dir-Special Projects & Sr Project Mgr)*
Todd Lee *(Exec VP & Dir-Ops-Project Mgmt)*
Dave Ratzke *(Exec VP & Dir-Ops-Preconstruction)*
Dan Barret *(Exec VP-Strategy & Corp Dev)*
Chris Angus *(Dir-Preconstruction)*
Andrew Aiken *(CFO, Sec & Exec VP)*
Andrew Donaldson *(Mgr-Field)*
Emily Blair *(Project Mgr)*
Erin Hobson *(Dir-Mktg & Comm)*
Lori Daigle *(Exec VP & Dir-Risk)*
Tim McKey *(Sr VP & Dir-Field Ops)*
Nancy Stratton *(Treas, VP & Controller)*
Jason Barnwell *(VP)*
Kate Harkess *(VP & Dir-HR)*
Randy Boettcher *(VP & Dir-Project)*
Tracy Winter *(VP & Dir-Safety)*

SELLERS BROS. INCORPORATED
4580 S Wayside, Houston, TX 77087
Tel.: (713) 640-1611
Web Site: http://www.sellersbros.com
Year Founded: 1946
Sales Range: $75-99.9 Million
Emp.: 900
Provider of Grocery Services
N.A.I.C.S.: 445110
George R. Sellers *(Pres)*
John L. Sellers *(Treas & Sec)*
Joseph L. Sellers *(VP)*

SELLERS BUICK GMC
38000 Grand River Ave, Farmington Hills, MI 48335-1508
Tel.: (248) 478-8000 — MI
Web Site: http://www.sellersgm.com
Year Founded: 1971
Sales Range: $100-124.9 Million
Emp.: 100
Sales of Automobiles & Trucks
N.A.I.C.S.: 441110
Sam Slaughter *(Pres)*
Jim Suranno *(Mgr-Parts)*

SELLERS EQUIPMENT INC.
400 N Chicago St, Salina, KS 67401
Tel.: (785) 823-6378
Web Site: http://www.sellersequipment.com
Sales Range: $10-24.9 Million
Emp.: 50
Road Construction & Maintenance Machinery
N.A.I.C.S.: 423810
David P. Sellers *(Pres)*

Subsidiaries:

Sellers Equipment Inc. (1)
400 N Chicago St, Salina, KS 67401
Tel.: (785) 823-6378
Web Site: http://www.sellersequipment.com
Rev.: $12,700,000
Emp.: 15
Road Construction & Maintenance Machinery
N.A.I.C.S.: 423810
David P. Sellers *(Pres)*

SELLERS PETROLEUM
821 S Pacific Ave, Yuma, AZ 85365-1429
Tel.: (928) 329-0777 — AZ
Web Site: http://www.sellerspetroleum.com
Year Founded: 1954

Sales Range: $10-24.9 Million
Emp.: 70
Petroleum Distr & Whslr
N.A.I.C.S.: 424720
Dave Sellers (Pres)
Thera Bratcher (Office Mgr)
Rick Reyes (Mgr-Fleet)

SELLING SOLUTIONS, INC.
3525 Piedmont Rd Bldg 5 Ste 515, Atlanta, GA 30305
Tel.: (404) 261-4966   GA
Web Site: http://www.selsol.com
Year Founded: 1983
Sales Range: $1-9.9 Million
Emp.: 10
Advetising Agency
N.A.I.C.S.: 541810
William L. Paullin (Pres)
Eric R. Mowris (VP-Bus Svcs)

SELLMARK CORP.
2201 Heritage Pkwy, Mansfield, TX 76063
Tel.: (817) 225-0310
Web Site: http://www.sellmark.net
Year Founded: 2000
Sales Range: $1-9.9 Million
Emp.: 41
Small Arms & Accessories
N.A.I.C.S.: 332994
Dianna Sellers (CEO)

SELLMORE INDUSTRIES INC.
815 Smith St, Buffalo, NY 14206
Tel.: (716) 854-1600   NY
Web Site: http://www.sellmoreind.com
Year Founded: 1957
Vinyl Window & Door Mfr & Distr
N.A.I.C.S.: 321911
Mike Kolz (Dir-Mfg)

SELLSTROM MANUFACTURING CO.
1 Sellstrom Dr, Palatine, IL 60067-6260
Tel.: (847) 358-2000   IL
Web Site: http://www.sellstrom.com
Year Founded: 1923
Sales Range: $75-99.9 Million
Emp.: 150
Protective Gear & Personal Safety Products Engineer, Mfr & Marketer
N.A.I.C.S.: 339115
David Peters (Pres & CEO)
James R. Franklin (VP-Sls & Mktg)
Lawrence Schmidt (VP-Fin)

Subsidiaries:

Sellstrom Manufacturing Co. - RTC Fall Protection Division   (1)
2050 Hammond Dr, Schaumburg, IL 60173
Tel.: (847) 358-2000
Web Site: http://www.fallprotection.com
Safety Equipment Mfr
N.A.I.C.S.: 238990
Chris Gill (Dir-Bus Dev)
David Peters (Pres & CEO)

SELLUP INC.
100 Gold St, New York, NY 10038
Tel.: (212) 863-9604   NY
Web Site: http://www.sellup.net
Email Marketing Agency
N.A.I.C.S.: 541860
Allan Levy (CEO)
Isaac Esses (Acct Exec)
Robert Varon (Coord-Sls & Outreach)
Gianna Villavicencio (Dir-Creative)
Nancy Anteby (Coord-Social Media & Mktg)

Subsidiaries:

Alchemy Worx Limited   (1)
66 Prescot Street, London, E1 8NN, United Kingdom

Tel.: (44) 207 025 2100
Web Site: http://www.alchemyworx.com
Direct Mail Advertising
N.A.I.C.S.: 541860
Dela Quist (CEO)
Michelle Casey (VP-Strategy)
Ian Deshays (Dir-Client Svcs)

Subsidiary (Non-US):

Alchemy Worx   (2)
Alchemy Worx Suite 3 Level 3 Grafton Bond Building 201 Kent St, Sydney, 2000, NSW, Australia
Tel.: (61) 2 8040 7487
Web Site: http://www.alchemyworx.com
Marketing Consulting Services
N.A.I.C.S.: 541613

Subsidiary (US):

Alchemy Worx Inc.   (2)
3355 Lenox Rd Ste 1150, Atlanta, GA 30326
Tel.: (678) 884-7452
Web Site: http://www.alchemyworx.com
Marketing Consulting Services
N.A.I.C.S.: 541613
Dela Quist (Pres)

SELMARQ
6813 Fairview Rd Ste C, Charlotte, NC 28210
Tel.: (704) 365-1455
Web Site: http://www.selmarq.com
Year Founded: 1983
Sales Range: Less than $1 Million
Emp.: 6
Advetising Agency
N.A.I.C.S.: 541810
Michele Clark (Dir-Creative)
Andrea Rothe (Office Mgr)
Jeff Rothe (Pres)

SELWAY CORPORATION
PO Box 287 Half Mile E Eastside Hwy, Stevensville, MT 59870
Tel.: (406) 777-5471
Web Site: http://www.selwaycorp.com
Year Founded: 1976
Sales Range: $10-24.9 Million
Emp.: 120
Steel Fabrication
N.A.I.C.S.: 333517
Max Downing (Pres)
Terri Nickless (Controller)

SELWAY MACHINE TOOL CO. INC.
29250 Union City Blvd, Union City, CA 94587
Tel.: (510) 487-2525
Web Site: http://www.selwaytool.com
Sales Range: $10-24.9 Million
Emp.: 37
Metalworking Machinery
N.A.I.C.S.: 423830
William Selway (Pres)

SELZER-ORNST CONSTRUCTION COMPANY LLC
6222 W State St, Milwaukee, WI 53213
Tel.: (414) 258-9900
Web Site: http://www.selzer-ornst.com
Rev.: $9,440,000
Emp.: 40
Residential Remodeler
N.A.I.C.S.: 236118
Mark N. Lemke (Mng Dir)
Matthew Tadisch (Pres & CEO)

Subsidiaries:

ABCO Building Corporation   (1)
12665 W Townsend St, Brookfield, WI 53005
Tel.: (262) 783-5300
Web Site: http://www.abcobuilding.com
Rev.: $5,192,000
Emp.: 22

Residential Remodeler
N.A.I.C.S.: 236118
Mark Jurkowski (Pres)
Brian Goodchild (Project Mgr)

SEMA EQUIPMENT, INC
11555 Hwy 60 Blvd, Wanamingo, MN 55983
Tel.: (507) 824-2256
Web Site: http://www.semaequip.com
Sales Range: $10-24.9 Million
Emp.: 18
Sales of Agricultural Machinery
N.A.I.C.S.: 423820
Tom Wozney (Gen Mgr)
Mike Apitz (Mgr-Parts)
Maggie McCall (Mgr-Mktg)
Val Boe (Office Mgr)
Kevin Schaefer (Gen Mgr-Sls)

SEMAFOR, INC.
221 Park Ave S, PMB 59081, New York, NY 10003
Tel.: (628) 888-0019   DE
Web Site: https://www.semafor.com
Year Founded: 2022
Online News Services
N.A.I.C.S.: 518210
Justin Brainerd Smith (Co-Founder & CEO)
Ben Smith (Co-Founder & Editor-in-Chief)

SEMANAL MEDIA, LLC
724 Spring St Ste 703, Los Angeles, CA 90014
Tel.: (310) 574-7100   CA
Web Site: http://www.laweekly.com
Year Founded: 2017
Holding Company; Newspaper Publisher
N.A.I.C.S.: 551112
Brian Calle (CEO & Publr)

Subsidiaries:

LA Weekly, LP   (1)
724 Spring St Ste 703, Los Angeles, CA 90014
Tel.: (310) 574-7100
Web Site: http://www.laweekly.com
Newspaper Publishers
N.A.I.C.S.: 513110
Darrick Rainey (Editor-in-Chief & Creative Dir)
Pat Connell (Dir-Circulation)
Erin Domash (COO & Assoc Publr)
Christopher Hubbert (Sls Dir)
Jorge Picado (Mgr-Production)
Susan Belair (Sr VP-Sls)
Brian Calle (CEO & Publr)

SEMANTICSPACE TECHNOLOGIES
100 Pacifica Ste 270, Irvine, CA 92618
Tel.: (949) 789-7332
Web Site: http://www.semanticspace.com
Sales Range: $25-49.9 Million
Emp.: 550
Software Developer
N.A.I.C.S.: 513210
Satya Bolli (Chm & Mng Dir)
Biju S. Nair (CFO)
Mike Hastie (CTO)
Dave Mogel (VP-Legal Affairs)

Subsidiaries:

Arsin Corp.   (1)
4800 Great America Pkwy # 425, Santa Clara, CA 95054-1228
Tel.: (408) 653-2020
Web Site: http://www.arsin.com
Rev.: $16,926,500
Emp.: 120
Integrated Software Test & Test Automation Solutions
N.A.I.C.S.: 541511
John Dusenbury (Gen Counsel)

SEMATECH, INC.
257 Fuller Rd Ste 2100, Albany, NY 12203
Tel.: (518) 649-1000   DE
Web Site: http://www.public.sematech.org
Year Founded: 1987
Sales Range: $75-99.9 Million
Emp.: 50
Chip Manufacturing Research & Development Services
N.A.I.C.S.: 541720
Ronald D. Goldblatt (Co-Pres & Co-CEO)
Jeffrey Hedrick (VP-Technical Strategy & Ops)
Satyavolu Papa Rao (Dir-Process Res & Dev)
Edward Barth (Dir-Corp Dev)
Peter DiFondi (Dir-IT & Admin)
Scott Hanson (Gen Counsel)
Stefan Wurm (Dir-Strategic Growth Initiatives)

SEMBLE, INC.
188 106th Ave NE Ste 650, Bellevue, WA 98004
Tel.: (425) 333-3333   NV
Web Site: http://www.semble.com
Year Founded: 2011
Sales Range: $10-24.9 Million
Emp.: 4
Peer-To-Community Online Lending Platform
N.A.I.C.S.: 525990
Todd Tarbert (CEO)
Chris Walcott (Pres)

SEMBLEX CORPORATION
900 N Church Rd, Elmhurst, IL 60126-1103
Tel.: (630) 833-2880
Web Site: http://www.semblex.com
Year Founded: 1968
Cold Headed Fasteners
N.A.I.C.S.: 332722
Mark Quebbeman (VP-Sls & Mktg)
Don Cunningham (Pres)

SEMI-GENERAL, INC.
54 Grenier Field Rd, Londonderry, NH 03053
Tel.: (603) 624-8311   NH
Web Site: http://www.semigen.net
Year Founded: 2009
Printed Circuit Boards Assembly & RF/Microwave Testing & Repair; Adhesives, Wire & Ribbon & Bonding Tools
N.A.I.C.S.: 423610
Jim Morgan (CEO)

Subsidiaries:

Ion Beam Milling, Inc.   (1)
850 E Industrial Park Dr, Manchester, NH 03109
Tel.: (603) 644-2326
Web Site: http://www.ionbeammilling.com
Ion Milling; Custom Circuits, Attenuators & Spiral Inductors Mfr
N.A.I.C.S.: 334419
Robert Quagan (Co-founder, Chm & Chief Engineer)
Gail Quagan (Founder & CFO)
Jim Barrett (Pres)

SEMI-TRAILER SALES & LEASING
3701 38th St S, Fargo, ND 58104
Tel.: (701) 281-9755
Web Site: http://www.semi-trailersales.net
Year Founded: 1960
Sales Range: $10-24.9 Million
Emp.: 6
Sales of Trailers for Trucks
N.A.I.C.S.: 423110

SEMI-TRAILER SALES & LEASING

Semi-Trailer Sales & Leasing—(Continued)

Dell Arneson *(Pres)*

SEMICONDUCTOR PROCESS EQUIPMENT CORPORATION
27963 Franklin Pkwy, Valencia, CA 91355
Tel.: (661) 257-0934
Web Site: http://www.team-spec.com
Sales Range: $10-24.9 Million
Emp.: 50
Semiconductor Manufacturing Machinery
N.A.I.C.S.: 333242
Arnie Gustin *(Pres)*
Kevin Mcgillivray *(VP)*

SEMIFREDDI'S, INC.
1980 N Loop Rd, Alameda, CA 94502
Tel.: (510) 596-9930
Web Site:
 http://www.semifreddis.com
Year Founded: 1900
Sales Range: $10-24.9 Million
Emp.: 120
Grocery Product Whslr
N.A.I.C.S.: 424490
Tom Frainier *(Owner, Pres & CEO)*
Wendy Brace *(Dir-Distr)*

SEMINARY RIDGE HISTORIC PRESERVATION FOUNDATION
61 Seminary Ridge, Gettysburg, PA 17325
Tel.: (717) 338-3030 PA
Web Site:
 http://www.seminaryridge.org
Year Founded: 1999
Sales Range: $1-9.9 Million
Emp.: 11
Historical Resource Preservation Services
N.A.I.C.S.: 712110
John Spangler *(Vice Chm)*
Jennifer Byers *(Co-Treas)*
Briant Bohleke *(Co-Treas)*
Emried Cole *(Chm)*
Monica Rozelle *(Sec)*
Daryl Black *(Pres-Seminary Ridge Historic Preservation Foundation)*

SEMINOLE COUNTY COALITION FOR SCHOOL READINESS, INC.
280 Hunt Park Cove Ste 1020, Lake Mary, FL 32750-7567
Tel.: (407) 960-2462 FL
Web Site:
 http://www.seminoleearlylearning.org
Year Founded: 2000
Sales Range: $10-24.9 Million
Emp.: 25
Child Development Services
N.A.I.C.S.: 624110
Cheryl Molyneaux *(Dir-Fin)*
Kerri Alberts *(Mgr-Family Svcs)*
Jennifer Grant Lessne *(Exec Dir)*
Marlyn Seda *(Dir-Ops)*
Gay DeLaughter *(Dir-Head Start)*
Mary Anne Miller *(Mgr-Provider Svc)*

SEMINOLE ELECTRIC COOPERATIVE, INC.
16313 N Dale Mabry Hwy, Tampa, FL 33618
Tel.: (813) 963-0994
Web Site: http://www.seminole-electric.com
Year Founded: 1948
Rev.: $1,083,451,000
Assets: $1,966,857,000
Liabilities: $1,577,940,000
Net Worth: $388,917,000
Earnings: $21,085,000
Emp.: 464
Fiscal Year-end: 12/31/18
Electric Power Generation
N.A.I.C.S.: 221122
Trudy S. Novak *(VP-Member Svcs & External Affairs, Asst Sec & Asst Treas)*
Steven W. Saunders *(Dir-Info Tech Svcs)*
Lisa D. Johnson *(CEO & Gen Mgr)*
Jo Ann Fuller *(CFO, Treas, VP & Asst Sec)*
James O. Woodall *(Dir-Plant Ops)*
David D. Ferrentino *(Gen Counsel & VP)*
Timothy Nasello *(Dir-Supply Mgmt)*
James Aul *(Vice Chm)*
Carrie Durden *(Vice Chm-Fin, Audit Committee & Compensation Committee)*

SEMINOLE FEED CO.
335 NE Watula Ave, Ocala, FL 34470
Tel.: (352) 732-4143
Web Site:
 http://www.seminolefeed.com
Sales Range: $10-24.9 Million
Emp.: 71
Livestock Feeds
N.A.I.C.S.: 311119
Greg Allen *(CFO)*
Richard DeSimone *(VP-Production & Logistics)*

SEMINOLE FOODS, INC
1966 Commerce Cir, Springfield, OH 45504
Tel.: (937) 521-2517
Web Site:
 http://www.seminolefoods.com
Sales Range: $1-9.9 Million
Emp.: 20
Horseradish & Specialty Sauce Mfr
N.A.I.C.S.: 311421
Wendell Christoff *(Owner)*
Mary Lerchen *(Mgr-Sls)*

SEMINOLE HOLDINGS GROUP, LLC
455 N Indian Rocks Rd, Belleair Bluffs, FL 33770
Tel.: (727) 331-8453
Web Site:
 http://www.seminolefinancialservices.com
Year Founded: 2008
Holding Company
N.A.I.C.S.: 551112
Robert J. Banks *(CEO & Principal)*
Ronald J. Campbell *(CFO & Principal)*
Chris Diaz *(Principal & Exec VP-Bus Dev)*
Tim Fetter *(Principal & Exec VP-Credit & Risk Mgmt)*
Joe Ritter *(Sr VP-Bus Dev)*

Subsidiaries:

Banks & Associates, LLC (1)
455 N Indian Rocks Rd Ste B, Belleair Bluffs, FL 33770
Tel.: (727) 331-8444
Real Estate Brokerage Services
N.A.I.C.S.: 531210

Seminole Advisory Services, LLC (1)
455 N Indian Rocks Rd Ste B, Belleair Bluffs, FL 33770
Tel.: (727) 331-8444
Web Site:
 http://www.seminolefinancialservices.com
Investment Advisory Services
N.A.I.C.S.: 523930
Robert J. Banks *(Chm & CEO)*

Seminole Capital, LLC (1)
455 N Indian Rocks Rd Ste B, Belleair Bluffs, FL 33770
Tel.: (727) 331-8444

Web Site:
 http://www.seminolefinancialservices.com
Equity Financing Services
N.A.I.C.S.: 523999

Seminole Equity Investments, LLC (1)
455 N Indian Rocks Rd Ste B, Belleair Bluffs, FL 33770
Tel.: (727) 331-8444
Web Site:
 http://www.seminolefinancialservices.com
Equity Investment Services
N.A.I.C.S.: 523999
Robert J. Banks *(Chm & CEO)*

Seminole Financial Services, LLC (1)
455 N Indian Rocks Rd Ste B, Belleair Bluffs, FL 33770
Tel.: (727) 331-8444
Web Site:
 http://www.seminolefinancialservices.com
Financial Lending & Investment Services
N.A.I.C.S.: 522310
Robert J. Banks *(CEO)*
Justin Bevens *(Mgr-Ops Support)*
Ronald J. Campbell *(Exec VP)*
Chris Diaz *(Sr VP-Renewable Energy)*
Tim Fetter *(Sr VP-Credit & Risk Mgmt)*
Susie Griffin *(VP-Servicing & Closing)*
Tony Petrisko *(VP-Asset Mgmt & Underwriting)*
Joe Ritter *(VP-Bus Dev)*
Tom Zdrodowski *(Dir-IR)*
Kris A. Dunlop *(Controller)*
Myra Peppi *(Asst Sec)*
Rana Sayegh *(Portfolio Mgr)*

Seminole Real Estate Services, LLC (1)
455 N Indian Rocks Rd Ste B, Belleair Bluffs, FL 33770
Tel.: (727) 331-8444
Real Estate Manangement Services
N.A.I.C.S.: 531312

SEMINOLE MACHINE & WELDING, INC.
9380 Ulmerton Rd Ste A, Largo, FL 33771
Tel.: (727) 586-0599 FL
Year Founded: 1979
Sales Range: $1-9.9 Million
Emp.: 25
Structural Steel Contractor
N.A.I.C.S.: 238120
Dawn Miller *(Pres)*

SEMINOLE PRECAST MANUFACTURING, INC.
PO Box 531059, Debary, FL 32753
Tel.: (386) 668-7745
Web Site:
 http://www.seminoleprecast.com
Sales Range: $10-24.9 Million
Emp.: 120
Precast Concrete Products Mfr
N.A.I.C.S.: 327390
Milton Vargas *(Mgr-Product Plng & Logistics)*
Debbie Brown *(Mgr-Cash & Credit)*
Katherine Campbell *(CFO)*
Ralph DeLeon *(Mgr-Quality Control-FL)*
L. D. Balmer *(Dir-Mktg)*
Curtis Neiswander *(Dir-Ops)*
Daniel Moody *(Gen Mgr-GA)*
Matt Silver *(Gen Mgr-Ops)*
Maureen Del Monico *(Mgr-HR)*
Mike Dukes *(Mgr-Production)*
Dathan Smith *(Plant Mgr-GA)*
Steve Griffith *(Supvr-Maintenance)*

SEMINOLE TRIBE OF FLORIDA, INC.
6300 Stirling Rd, Hollywood, FL 33024
Tel.: (954) 966-6300 FL
Web Site: http://www.semtribe.com
Year Founded: 1984

U.S. PRIVATE

Sales Range: $500-549.9 Million
Emp.: 500
American Indian Tribal Council
N.A.I.C.S.: 921150
Jim Shore *(Gen Counsel)*

Subsidiaries:

Seminole Gaming (1)
1 Seminole Way, Hollywood, FL 33314
Tel.: (954) 327-7600
Web Site: http://www.seminolehardrockhollywood.com
Sales Range: $25-49.9 Million
Emp.: 3,000
Casino & Entertainment Management Services
N.A.I.C.S.: 561110
James Allen *(CEO)*
Larry Mullin *(COO)*
Michael Volkert *(Sr VP-Slot Ops)*
Mikhail V. Gaushkin *(VP-Mktg)*
John R. Eder *(CFO)*
Timothy Burke *(Sr VP-Ops)*

Unit (Domestic):

Seminole Casino Hollywood (2)
4150 N State Rd 7, Hollywood, FL 33021
Tel.: (954) 961-3220
Web Site:
 http://www.seminoleclassiccasino.com
Sales Range: $10-24.9 Million
Casino Operator
N.A.I.C.S.: 713210

Seminole Hard Rock Entertainment, Inc. (1)
1 Seminole Way, Hollywood, FL 33314
Tel.: (954) 327-7625
Web Site: http://www.seminolehardrockhollywood.com
Sales Range: $600-649.9 Million
Casino & Entertainment Management Services
N.A.I.C.S.: 541611
Terri Lutz *(Dir-Retail Mktg)*
Frank Burga *(Dir-Bus Mktg)*
James Fair *(VP-Security & Transportation)*
William Mason *(Dir-Poker)*
Bill Wright *(Pres)*

Subsidiary (Domestic):

Hard Rock Cafe International, Inc. (2)
6050 Universal Blvd, Orlando, FL 32819
Tel.: (407) 351-7625
Web Site: https://www.hardrock.com
Sales Range: $500-549.9 Million
Emp.: 40,000
Full-Service Restaurants
N.A.I.C.S.: 722511
Jon Lucas *(COO)*
Daniel Earle *(Dir-Global Travel Indus Sls-Hard Rock Hotels & Casinos)*
Danielle Babilino *(Sr VP-Global Sls & Mktg)*

Unit (Domestic):

Hard Rock Cafe International (3)
125 Bourbon St, New Orleans, LA 70130
Tel.: (504) 529-5617
Web Site: http://www.hardrockcafe.com
Sales Range: $10-24.9 Million
Emp.: 100
Eating Place Services
N.A.I.C.S.: 722511
Joey Ledet *(Ops Mgr)*

Hard Rock Cafe International (3)
39 Pier Ste 256, San Francisco, CA 94133
Tel.: (415) 956-2013
Web Site: http://www.hardrock.com
Sales Range: $10-24.9 Million
Emp.: 120
Eating Place
N.A.I.C.S.: 722511
Jim Allen *(Chm & CEO)*
Edward Tracy *(CEO-Japan)*
Jon Lucas *(COO)*

Hard Rock Cafe International Chicago (3)
63 W Ontario St, Chicago, IL 60654
Tel.: (312) 943-5572
Web Site: http://www.hardrock.com
Sales Range: $10-24.9 Million
Emp.: 125
Eating Place

COMPANIES

N.A.I.C.S.: 722511
Darlene Maher *(Gen Mgr)*

Hard Rock Cafe International Inc. Georgia (3)
215 Peachtree St NE, Atlanta, GA 30303-1723
Tel.: (404) 688-7625
Web Site: http://www.hardrock.com
Eating Place
N.A.I.C.S.: 722511
Mike Ward *(Gen Mgr)*

Hard Rock Cafe International La Jolla (3)
909 Prospect St, La Jolla, CA 92037-4131
Tel.: (858) 454-5101
Web Site: http://www.hardrock.com
Sales Range: $10-24.9 Million
Emp.: 65
Eating Place
N.A.I.C.S.: 722511

Hard Rock Cafe International Las Vegas (3)
4455 Paradise Rd, Las Vegas, NV 89169-6574
Tel.: (702) 693-5000
Web Site: http://www.hardrockhotel.com
Sales Range: $1-9.9 Million
Full Service Theme Restaurant
N.A.I.C.S.: 722511

Hard Rock Cafe International Maui (3)
900 Frnt St, Lahaina, HI 96761-2335
Tel.: (808) 667-7400
Web Site: http://www.hardrock.com
Sales Range: $1-9.9 Million
Emp.: 60
Eating Place
N.A.I.C.S.: 722511
Brent Rumph *(Gen Mgr)*

Hard Rock Cafe International Miami (3)
401 Biscayne Blvd, Miami, FL 33132-1924
Tel.: (305) 377-3110
Web Site: http://www.hardrock.com
Rev.: $5,000,000
Emp.: 150
Eating Place
N.A.I.C.S.: 722511
Bill Tobin *(Gen Mgr)*
Prince Logan *(Gen Mgr)*

Hard Rock Cafe International New Jersey (3)
1000 Boardwalk, Atlantic City, NJ 08401-7415
Tel.: (609) 441-0007
Web Site: http://www.hardrock.com
Sales Range: $10-24.9 Million
Emp.: 150
Eating Place
N.A.I.C.S.: 722511
Todd McCann *(Gen Mgr)*

Hard Rock Cafe International New York (3)
1501 43rd St, Broadway, NY 10036
Tel.: (212) 343-3355
Web Site: http://www.hardrock.com
Sales Range: $10-24.9 Million
Emp.: 400
Eating Place
N.A.I.C.S.: 722511
Jason Petrina *(Dir-Ops)*

Hard Rock Cafe International Newport Beach (3)
Ste 100 6100 Old Park Ln, Orlando, FL 32835-2536
Tel.: (407) 445-7625
Web Site: http://www.hardrock.com
Rev.: $2,400,000
Emp.: 50
Eating Place
N.A.I.C.S.: 722511
Sharon Glees *(Dir-HR)*

Hard Rock Cafe International San Antonio (3)
111 W Crockett St, San Antonio, TX 78205-2549
Tel.: (210) 224-7625
Web Site: http://www.hardrock.com
Rev.: $4,800,000
Emp.: 150

Eating Place
N.A.I.C.S.: 722511

Hard Rock Cafe International South Carolina (3)
1322 Celebrity Cir, Myrtle Beach, SC 29577-7451
Tel.: (843) 946-0007
Web Site: http://www.hardrock.com
Sales Range: $1-9.9 Million
Eating Place
N.A.I.C.S.: 722511
Keith Stamp *(Gen Mgr)*

Hard Rock Cafe International Tennessee (3)
100 Broadway, Nashville, TN 37201-2112
Tel.: (615) 742-9900
Web Site: http://www.hardrock.com
Sales Range: $10-24.9 Million
Emp.: 110
Eating Place
N.A.I.C.S.: 722511
Don Morris *(Gen Mgr)*

Hard Rock Cafe International Texas (3)
2211 N Houston St, Dallas, TX 75219
Tel.: (469) 341-7625
Web Site: http://www.hardrock.com
Emp.: 30
Eating Place
N.A.I.C.S.: 722511
Eric Arthur *(Mgr-Sls & Mktg)*

Hard Rock Cafe International USA (3)
6050 Universal Blvd, Orlando, FL 32819
Tel.: (407) 351-5483
Web Site: http://www.hardrock.com
Sales Range: $10-24.9 Million
Emp.: 130
Hotel Operator
N.A.I.C.S.: 721120

Hard Rock Cafe International Universal City (3)
1000 Universal Studios Blvd Ste 99, Universal City, CA 91608
Tel.: (818) 853-0600
Web Site: http://www.hardrock.com
Rev.: $5,400,000
Emp.: 145
Hotel Operator
N.A.I.C.S.: 721120
Scott Brokaw *(Gen Mgr)*

Hard Rock Cafe Key West (3)
313 Duval St, Key West, FL 33040-6565
Tel.: (305) 293-0230
Web Site: http://www.hardrock.com
Rev.: $1,500,000
Emp.: 120
Eating Place
N.A.I.C.S.: 722511
Diane Eliopoulos *(Mgr-Sls)*

Hard Rock Cafe Puerto Rico (3)
253 Recinto Sur St, San Juan, PR 00901-1914
Tel.: (787) 724-7625
Web Site: http://www.hardrock.com
Rev.: $8,000,000
Emp.: 56
Eating Place
N.A.I.C.S.: 722511
Arnold Cope *(Gen Mgr)*

SEMITROPIC WATER STORAGE DISTRICT
1101 Central Ave, Wasco, CA 93280
Tel.: (661) 758-5113
Web Site: http://www.semitropic.com
Sales Range: $10-24.9 Million
Emp.: 35
Water Bank & Distr
N.A.I.C.S.: 221310
Frederick A. Wegis *(Pres-Div 7)*
Todd Tracy *(Sec-Div 6)*
Dan Waterhouse *(Treas)*

SEMLING-MENKE COMPANY INC.
605 N Ohio St, Merrill, WI 54452
Tel.: (715) 536-9411

Web Site: http://www.semcowindows.com
Rev.: $55,000,000
Emp.: 450
Window & Door Frames
N.A.I.C.S.: 237210
Eric Malm *(Gen Mgr)*
Patrick Semling *(Pres)*

SEMMELMEYER-CORBY COMPANY
5432 Highland Park Dr, Saint Louis, MO 63110
Tel.: (314) 371-4777
Web Site: http://www.semcor.net
Sales Range: $10-24.9 Million
Emp.: 27
Hose, Belting & Packing
N.A.I.C.S.: 423840
Rudolph Freedman *(Chm)*
John De Roy *(Controller)*

SEMO ELECTRICAL COOPERATIVE
1505 S Main St, Sikeston, MO 63801
Tel.: (573) 471-5821
Web Site:
http://www.semoelectric.coop
Sales Range: $10-24.9 Million
Emp.: 45
Electric Power Distr
N.A.I.C.S.: 221122

SEMO TANK/BAKER EQUIPMENT CO.
456 Semo Ln, Perryville, MO 63775
Tel.: (573) 547-8348
Web Site: http://www.semotank.com
Sales Range: $10-24.9 Million
Emp.: 40
Tank Repair
N.A.I.C.S.: 811310
Robert Baker *(Pres)*

SEMPER DEVELOPMENT LTD
821 Marquette Ave Ste 600, Minneapolis, MN 55402
Tel.: (612) 332-1500
Rev.: $75,000,000
Emp.: 9
Land Subdividers & Developers, Commercial
N.A.I.C.S.: 237210
Howard Bergerud *(Pres)*
Craig Christianson *(VP)*
John Kohler *(VP & Dir-Architecture, Engrg & Construction)*

SEMPER HOME LOANS
225 Dupont Dr, Providence, RI 02907
Tel.: (866) 330-4411
Web Site:
http://www.semperhomeloans.com
Year Founded: 2005
Sales Range: $1-9.9 Million
Emp.: 9
Mortgage Loans & Home Equity Services
N.A.I.C.S.: 522310
Matthew Sullivan *(Pres)*
Michael Securo *(Exec VP)*
Emily Murphy *(Branch Mgr)*

SEN PLEX CORPORATION
938 Kohou St, Honolulu, HI 96817
Tel.: (808) 848-0111 HI
Web Site: http://www.senplex.com
Year Founded: 1947
Rev.: $10,000,000
Emp.: 100
Commercial & Industrial Building Operation
N.A.I.C.S.: 531120

Brian Sen *(Pres)*
Norman Tada *(Exec VP)*
Erlene Matsuyama *(Treas)*
Brian Sen *(Pres)*

SENA CASES
1781 Mcgaw Ave, Irvine, CA 92614-5731
Tel.: (714) 505-8312
Web Site: http://www.senacases.com
Year Founded: 2001
Rev.: $4,500,000
Emp.: 16
Luggage & Leather Goods Stores
N.A.I.C.S.: 458320
Fevzi Oten *(Co-Owner)*
Ramsey Oten *(Co-Owner)*

SENA REIDER, INC.
99 Pacific St Ste 155D, Monterey, CA 93940-2484
Tel.: (831) 372-4961 CA
Web Site: http://www.senareider.com
Year Founded: 1980
Sales Range: $10-24.9 Million
Emp.: 12
Agriculture, Financial, Food Service, Interactive Agencies, Internet/Web Design, Leisure, Outdoor
N.A.I.C.S.: 541810
Lou Sena *(Pres)*
John Reider *(Creative Dir)*

Subsidiaries:

Sena Reider, Inc. (1)
340 Pine St Ste 503, San Francisco, CA 94104-3237
Tel.: (831) 372-4961
Emp.: 7
Full Service
N.A.I.C.S.: 541810
Lou Sena *(Pres)*
John Reider *(Creative Dir)*

SENATE CONSTRUCTION CORP.
1000 Mount Laurel Cir, Shirley, MA 01464
Tel.: (978) 425-9802
Web Site:
http://www.senateconstruction.com
Year Founded: 1990
Sales Range: $1-9.9 Million
Emp.: 10
Nonresidential Construction
N.A.I.C.S.: 236220
William Hamel *(Pres & COO)*
Juane Learnard *(Controller)*
Duncan France *(Dir-Mktg & Bus Dev)*

SENCOMMUNICATIONS, INC.
1611 Allison Woods Ln, Tampa, FL 33619-7873
Tel.: (813) 626-4404
Web Site: http://www.sencomm.com
Year Founded: 1989
Sales Range: $1-9.9 Million
Emp.: 50
Telecommunication Equipment Distr
N.A.I.C.S.: 423610
Frances Senory *(Co-Owner & Pres)*
Stacie Miller *(Co-Owner)*

SENDAYCO, LLC
1788 S Metro Pkwy, Dayton, OH 45459
Tel.: (513) 815-5329
Web Site: https://www.sendayco.com
Year Founded: 2019
Retailer Services
N.A.I.C.S.: 456199

Subsidiaries:

Reviva Labs, Inc. (1)
705 Hopkins Rd, Haddonfield, NJ 08033
Tel.: (856) 428-3885
Web Site: https://www.revivalabs.com

SENDAYCO, LLC

SenDayCo, LLC—(Continued)
Sales Range: $1-9.9 Million
Emp.: 34
Drugs & Druggists' Sundries Merchant Whslr
N.A.I.C.S.: 424210
Terry French (COO)
Ian Strassler (CEO)
Jeri Trachtman (VP-Sls)
Bobbi Jo McKenna (VP-Sls-Intl)
Jim Henry (VP-Production)
Tracey Settar (VP-Salon Dev)
Bill Levins (VP-Mktg)

SENDEREX CARGO INC.
17022 Montanero Ave Ste 6, Carson, CA 90746
Tel.: (310) 342-2900
Web Site: http://www.senderex.com
Rev.: $13,500,000
Emp.: 20
Foreign Freight Forwarding
N.A.I.C.S.: 488510
Patrick Anderson (Pres)
Larry Elsenbein (VP)
Kathy Sexton (Acct Mgr)
Donna McDaniel (Mgr-Acctg)
Ray Quiroz (Mgr-Ops)

SENDERO BUSINESS SERVICES LP
750 N Paul St Ste 700, Dallas, TX 75201
Tel.: (972) 388-5760
Web Site: http://www.senderocorp.com
Sales Range: $1-9.9 Million
Emp.: 30
Administrative Management & General Management Consulting Service
N.A.I.C.S.: 541611
Bret Farrar (CEO & Mng Partner)
Ruth Farrar (Partner)
Scott A. Miller (Chief Innovation Officer & Partner)
David Allston (Chief Bus Dev officer & Partner)
Eric McConnell (Principal)
Jeff Schar (Principal)
Kyle Berry (Principal)
Susanne Turnbo (Principal)
Wayne Tung (Partner)

SENECA BEVERAGE CORPORATION
2085 Lake Rd, Elmira, NY 14903-1856
Tel.: (607) 734-6111
Sales Range: $10-24.9 Million
Emp.: 100
Whslr of Beer & Ale
N.A.I.C.S.: 424810
John F. Potter (Pres)
Mike Meleski (Mgr-NA Div)
Jeff Franey (Brand Mgr-Specialty)

SENECA CORPORATION
4698 NE 14th St, Des Moines, IA 50313
Tel.: (515) 262-5000
Web Site: http://www.senecacompanies.com
Rev.: $35,000,000
Emp.: 350
Trailer Repair
N.A.I.C.S.: 811114
Christopher Risewick (Chm)
Phyllis Jones (CFO)
Murray Nelson (Pres)

SENECA DATA DISTRIBUTORS INC.
6040 Tarbell Rd, Syracuse, NY 13206
Tel.: (315) 433-1160
Web Site: http://www.senecadata.com
Year Founded: 1979

Sales Range: $25-49.9 Million
Emp.: 300
Computer Distributor
N.A.I.C.S.: 423430
Adolph V. Falso (Chm)
Douglas A. Falso (VP-Contract Sls)
Kevin P. Conley (CEO)

SENECA FALLS MACHINES
314 Fall St, Seneca Falls, NY 13148
Tel.: (315) 568-5804 NY
Web Site: http://www.senecafallsmachine.com
Year Founded: 1864
Custom Built, Precision Metal Working Machines Designer & Mfr
N.A.I.C.S.: 333517

SENECA FAMILY OF AGENCIES
2275 Arlington Dr, San Leandro, CA 95478
Tel.: (510) 317-1444 CA
Web Site: http://www.senecacenter.org
Year Founded: 1985
Sales Range: $75-99.9 Million
Emp.: 1,275
Child & Family Support Services
N.A.I.C.S.: 624190
Neil Gilbert (Chm)
Ken Berrick (Founder, Pres & CEO)
Janet Briggs (CFO)

SENECA FEDERAL SAVINGS & LOAN ASSOCIATION
35 Oswego St, Baldwinsville, NY 13027
Tel.: (315) 638-0233
Web Site: http://www.senecasavings.com
Sales Range: $10-24.9 Million
Emp.: 40
Federal Savings & Loan Associations
N.A.I.C.S.: 522180
Katrina Russo (Pres)
Joseph Ditale (CEO)
Vincent Fazio (CFO)
Francine Race (VP-IT)

SENECA GLOBAL FUND, L.P.
9711 Washingtonian Blvd Ste 400, Gaithersburg, MD 20878
Tel.: (240) 631-7600 DE
Year Founded: 2007
Sales Range: $1-9.9 Million
Investment Services
N.A.I.C.S.: 523999
Kenneth E. Steben (Pres)

SENECA HAWK HOLDING COMPANY INCORPORATED
11979 Southwestern Blvd, Irving, NY 14081
Tel.: (716) 261-9990
Web Site: http://www.senecahawkny.com
Rev.: $12,700,000
Emp.: 30
Petroleum Products
N.A.I.C.S.: 424720
Barry Snyder (Pres)

SENECA INVESTMENTS
16800 Westgrove Suite 100, Addison, TX 75001
Tel.: (214) 265-8686
Web Site: http://www.seninv.com
Year Founded: 1996
Sales Range: $150-199.9 Million
Emp.: 4
Real Estate Investment
N.A.I.C.S.: 531390
Warner E. Stone (Pres, Owner & CEO)

Matthew P. Stone (COO)
Jock Wise (Principal)
F. Daniel Highley (Project Mgr & Partner-Dev)

SENECA PARTNERS INC.
2 Towne Sq Ste 810, Southfield, MI 48076
Tel.: (248) 723-6650
Web Site: http://www.senecapartners.com
Secondary Market Financing
N.A.I.C.S.: 522299
Anthony W. Zambelli (Mng Dir)

Subsidiaries:

Michigan Chandelier Company, LLC (1)
20855 Telegraph Rd, Southfield, MI 48033
Tel.: (248) 353-0510
Web Site: http://www.michand.com
Lighting Fixture Distr
N.A.I.C.S.: 423610
Ken Sanders (Pres)
John Testasecca (Mgr-Sls)

SENECA PETROLEUM CO. INC.
13301 Cicero Ave, Midlothian, IL 60445
Tel.: (708) 396-1100
Sales Range: $25-49.9 Million
Emp.: 20
Asphalt Product Mfr
N.A.I.C.S.: 324110
Kevin Nelson (Mgr-Ops)
Joan Fahey (Office Mgr)
Mike Denney (Project Mgr-Ops)
Greg Lee (Exec VP)
Lisa Krueger (Mgr-Insurance, Fleet & Comm)
Owen E. Hulse Jr. (CEO)

SENECA WIRE & MANUFACTURING COMPANY
319 S Vine St, Fostoria, OH 44830-1843
Tel.: (419) 435-9261 OH
Web Site: http://www.senecawire.com
Year Founded: 1905
Sales Range: $100-124.9 Million
Emp.: 300
Mfr of Steel Wire, Industrial & Insect Screening
N.A.I.C.S.: 331222
Kevin Shumaker (CFO & VP)
Steve Wray (Pres)

SENEX EXPLOSIVES INC.
710 Millers Run Rd, Cuddy, PA 15031
Tel.: (412) 221-3218
Rev.: $17,800,000
Emp.: 50
Explosives
N.A.I.C.S.: 424690
Alex Senules III (Pres)

SENICA AIR CONDITIONING, INC.
16640 Shady Hills Rd, Spring Hill, FL 34610-6822
Tel.: (727) 856-0058
Web Site: http://www.senicaair.com
Year Founded: 1993
Sales Range: $10-24.9 Million
Emp.: 120
Plumbing Services
N.A.I.C.S.: 238220
Linnea Senica (Gen Mgr)
Daryl F. Senica (Pres)
Kevin Amick (Mgr-Svc)

SENIOR CARE GROUP INC

1240 Marbella Plaza Dr, Tampa, FL 33619
Tel.: (813) 341-2700 FL
Year Founded: 1998
Sales Range: $100-124.9 Million
Emp.: 2,107
Health Care Srvices
N.A.I.C.S.: 622110
Chudow Katherine (CFO)
Suzanne Lezell (VP-Rehabilitation)
Jacqueline Hurt (Reg VP-Ops)
R. Daniel Vaughan (Dir-Special Ops)
Stephanie Roe Papoulis (Chief Legal Officer)

SENIOR CARE, INC.
700 N Hurstbourne Pkwy Ste 200, Louisville, KY 40222
Tel.: (502) 753-6000
Web Site: http://www.elmcroft.com
Sales Range: $200-249.9 Million
Emp.: 7,000
Continuing Care Retirement Communities Operator
N.A.I.C.S.: 623311
William Patrick Mulloy II (Founder)

Subsidiaries:

Elmcroft of Florence, LP (1)
3006 Hoffmeyer Rd, Florence, SC 29501
Tel.: (843) 292-0012
Sales Range: $10-24.9 Million
Emp.: 50
Continuing Care Retirement Community Operator
N.A.I.C.S.: 623311
Melody MacGregor (Dir-Community Rels)
Rosemary Schweikart (Dir-Activity)

SENIOR CONNECTION CENTER, INC.
8928 Brittany Way, Tampa, FL 33619
Tel.: (813) 740-3888 FL
Web Site: http://www.seniorconnectioncenter.org
Year Founded: 1981
Sales Range: $1-9.9 Million
Emp.: 61
Elder Care Services
N.A.I.C.S.: 624120
Patty Suarez (Officer-Pub Info & VP-Mktg & Comm)
Charlotte K. McHenry (Pres & CEO)
Jody L. Bone (CFO)
Katie Parkinson (COO)
Kyrie-Leigh Chambliss (Mgr-Volunteer)
Christopher Reid (Mgr-HR)

SENIOR CRAFTSMAN INC.
300 Cedar Blvd Ste B6, Pittsburgh, PA 15228
Tel.: (412) 341-1977
Rev.: $15,800,000
Emp.: 20
Single-Family Home Remodeling; Additions & Repairs
N.A.I.C.S.: 236118
Jeanne Gregg (Sec)

SENIOR CREDIT INVESTMENTS, LLC
520 Madison Ave 12th Fl, New York, NY 10022
Tel.: (212) 284-3474 DE
Year Founded: 2022
Investment Management Service
N.A.I.C.S.: 523999

SENIOR FRIENDSHIP CENTERS, INC.
1888 Brother Geenen Way, Sarasota, FL 34236
Tel.: (941) 955-2122 FL
Web Site: http://www.friendshipcenters.org
Year Founded: 1973

Sales Range: $10-24.9 Million
Emp.: 200
Elder Care Services
N.A.I.C.S.: 623312
Richard Beebe *(Chm)*
Gloria Schranz *(Sec)*

SENIOR GLEANERS INC.
1951 Bell Ave, Sacramento, CA 95838
Tel.: (916) 925-3240   CA
Web Site:
http://www.seniorgleaners.org
Year Founded: 1976
Sales Range: $1-9.9 Million
Emp.: 6
Community Food Services
N.A.I.C.S.: 624210
Mark Frachiseur *(Mgr-Warehouse Ops)*
Barbara Cecil *(Treas & Dir-Fin)*
Natalie Miller *(Mgr-Grants)*

SENIOR LIFESTYLE CORPORATION
303 E Wacker Dr Ste 2400, Chicago, IL 60601
Tel.: (312) 673-4333
Web Site:
http://www.seniorlifestyle.com
Sales Range: $10-24.9 Million
Emp.: 50
Real Estate Invenstors
N.A.I.C.S.: 523999
Patrick Lee *(VP-Acq)*
Jerrold H. Frumm *(Vice Chm & Chief Investment Officer)*
Matthew Phillips *(Exec VP)*
Nancy Cutter *(VP-Dev)*
Kate DeCoursey *(VP-Fin)*
Bob Gawronski *(VP-Dev)*
Jon DeLuca *(Pres & CEO)*
Justin Robins *(Chief Admin Officer & Exec VP)*
Lisa Reed *(VP-Ops)*
Tony Aloise *(VP-Dining Svcs)*
Cherie Dupor *(Sr VP-Sls & Mktg)*
Janine Witte *(VP-Sls)*
Damon Thomas *(Reg Dir-Ops)*
Peter Kravaritis *(VP-Asset Mgmt)*

Subsidiaries:

Seasons Retirement Community   **(1)**
7300 Dearwester Dr, Cincinnati, OH 45236   **(100%)**
Tel.: (513) 984-9400
Web Site: http://www.seniorlifestyle.com
Sales Range: $10-24.9 Million
Retirement Community
N.A.I.C.S.: 623311

SENIOR LIVING INVESTMENT BROKERAGE, INC.
490 Pennsylvania Ave Ste 1, Glen Ellyn, IL 60137-4426
Tel.: (630) 858-2501
Web Site:
http://www.seniorlivingbrokerage.com
Year Founded: 1998
Rev.: $17,600,000
Emp.: 17
Real Estate
N.A.I.C.S.: 531210
Grant A. Kief *(Pres)*
Ryan Saul *(Mng Dir)*
Jeff Binder *(Mng Dir)*
Patrick Byrne *(Sr VP)*
Brad Clousing *(Sr VP)*
Jason Punzel *(Sr VP)*
Matthew Alley *(Mng Dir)*
Nicholas D. Cacciabando *(Sr VP)*
Patrick Burke *(Sr VP)*
Toby Siefert *(Sr VP)*
Tom Rusthoven *(Sr VP)*

SENIOR LIVING OPTIONS INC.
708 3rd Ave 26th Fl, New York, NY 10017
Tel.: (212) 692-9666   NY
Year Founded: 1998
Sales Range: $1-9.9 Million
Emp.: 1
Housing Assistance Services
N.A.I.C.S.: 623110
Kim Gronich *(Sec)*
Brad Hamburger *(Pres)*
John O'brien *(Treas)*

SENIOR LIVING PROPERTIES, LLC
1300 S University Dr Ste 306, Fort Worth, TX 76107
Tel.: (817) 410-7300   IN
Web Site:
http://www.seniorlivingproperties.com
Year Founded: 1998
Senior Citizen Assisted Living Facilities Owner & Operator
N.A.I.C.S.: 623311
John Stuecheli *(CFO)*
Josh Leonard *(COO)*

SENIOR MANAGEMENT ADVISORS, INC.
13770 58th St N Ste 312, Clearwater, FL 33760
Tel.: (727) 726-3980
Web Site:
http://www.seniormanagementadvisors.com
Year Founded: 2001
Sales Range: $10-24.9 Million
Emp.: 40
Senior Living Facilities Management & Operations
N.A.I.C.S.: 623311
Steven A. Piazza *(Pres)*
John J. Moschner *(Dir-Ops)*
Timothy R. Barnes *(Dir-Fin)*
Alex Lopez *(Dir-Bus Dev, Sls & Mktg)*
Scott Clark *(Dir-Renovations)*
Monique Spruill *(Asst Dir-Sls & Leasing)*
Bonnie Williamson *(Mgr-Ops)*
Scott LaBarbera *(Project Mgr)*
Mark H. Ward *(Project Mgr)*

SENIOR SERVICES OF SNOHOMISH COUNTY
11627 Airport Rd Ste B, Everett, WA 98204-8714
Tel.: (425) 355-1112   WA
Web Site: http://www.sssc.org
Year Founded: 1973
Sales Range: $10-24.9 Million
Emp.: 197
Disability Assistance Services
N.A.I.C.S.: 624120
Mary Heneghan *(Mgr-HR)*
Les Loja *(Dir-Info Sys)*
Janet Duncan *(Dir-Dev)*
Kamilia Dunsky *(Program Mgr-Mental Health)*
Ann Gifford *(Mgr-Mobility)*
James Lee *(Pres)*
Carol Wheeler *(CEO & CFO)*

SENIOR SERVICES, INC.
918 Jasper St, Kalamazoo, MI 49001
Tel.: (269) 382-0515   MI
Web Site:
http://www.seniorservices1.org
Sales Range: $10-24.9 Million
Emp.: 228
Senior Care Services
N.A.I.C.S.: 624120
Joe Pugh *(Dir-Mgmt Info Sys)*
John Grib *(Dir-Community & Clinical Svcs)*
Kathleen Kelleher *(Dir-Fund Dev)*

Tauhric Brown *(COO)*
Dan Crouch *(CFO)*
Vicki Martin *(Dir-Volunteer, Info & Accessibility Svcs)*
T. Lee Covington *(Pres)*
Jessica Hufford *(Mgr-Fund Dev)*
Michael De Ruyter *(Chm)*
Richard Kline *(CEO)*

SENIOR WESLEYAN LIVING
807 W Ave, Elyria, OH 44035
Tel.: (440) 284-9371
Web Site:
http://www.villageliving.com
Sales Range: $10-24.9 Million
Emp.: 400
Senior's Residential Care Services
N.A.I.C.S.: 623990
Swarnalatha Meyyazhagan *(Dir-Medical)*

SENIORCARE, INC.
49 Blackburn Ctr, Gloucester, MA 01930
Tel.: (978) 281-1750   MA
Web Site:
http://www.seniorcareinc.org
Year Founded: 1973
Sales Range: $10-24.9 Million
Emp.: 86
Elder Care Services
N.A.I.C.S.: 624120
Scott Trenti *(Exec Dir)*
George Winston *(VP)*
Patricia Roach *(Treas)*
Leigh Keyser *(Sec)*
Thomas Tanous *(Pres)*

SENIORS HOME CARE LLC
504 Marshall Ave, Saint Louis, MO 63119
Tel.: (314) 962-2666
Web Site:
http://www.seniorshomecare.com
Year Founded: 1987
Sales Range: $1-9.9 Million
Emp.: 188
Nursing Home Operator
N.A.I.C.S.: 621610
Kit Whittington *(Founder)*
Ryan Whittington *(Dir-Ops)*
Rebecca Pavelka *(Mgr-Admin)*
Alice Endy *(Mgr-Case)*
Wendi Bottoms *(Mgr-Recruiting)*
Ted Ryan *(Coord-Admin & Mktg)*
Diara Murphy *(Mgr-Case)*

SENNINGER PLUMBING COMPANY, INC.
5800 Kingpost Ct, Lexington, KY 40509-9424
Tel.: (859) 263-5607
Web Site:
http://www.senningerplumbing.com
Year Founded: 1953
Sales Range: $25-49.9 Million
Emp.: 190
Plumbing Services
N.A.I.C.S.: 238220
Steve Willoughby *(Mgr)*

SENSATRONICS, LLC
9020 N Capital Of Texas Hwy Ste 1-155, Austin, TX 78759-7902
Tel.: (603) 224-0167
Web Site:
http://www.sensatronics.com
Year Founded: 2001
Sales Range: $1-9.9 Million
Emp.: 13
Temperature & Environmental Monitoring Solutions
N.A.I.C.S.: 334512
Keith Wright *(Founder & CEO)*

SENSCIENT INC.
2951 Marina Bay Dr, League City, TX 77573
Tel.: (281) 639-9168
Web Site: http://www.senscient.com
Sales Range: Less than $1 Million
Emp.: 16
Gas Detection Products Mfr
N.A.I.C.S.: 334512
Kevin Dean *(Mgr-Sls-Europe)*
John Filla *(Chm)*

SENSE CORP.
2731 Sutton Blvd Ste 200, Saint Louis, MO 63143
Tel.: (314) 283-0305
Web Site: http://www.sensecorp.com
Year Founded: 1996
Sales Range: $10-24.9 Million
Emp.: 87
Business Management Software
N.A.I.C.S.: 541512
Keat Wilkins *(CEO)*

SENSEI ENTERPRISES, INC.
3975 University Dr Ste 225, Fairfax, VA 22030
Tel.: (703) 359-0700
Web Site: http://www.senseient.com
Year Founded: 1997
Computer Forensics & Information Technology Services
N.A.I.C.S.: 541199
Sharon D. Nelson *(Pres)*
John W. Simek *(VP)*
Michael Maschke *(CEO)*

SENSIA SALON, INC.
1711 Post Oak Blvd, Houston, TX 77056
Tel.: (713) 627-0070   TX
Web Site:
http://www.sensiastudio.com
Year Founded: 1990
Sales Range: $1-9.9 Million
Emp.: 16
Beauty Salon & Spa Operator
N.A.I.C.S.: 812112
Cynthia Christ Strum *(Co-Owner & VP)*
Stephen Strum *(Co-Owner & Pres)*

SENSIBA SAN FILIPPO LLP
4900 Hopyard Rd Ste 200, Pleasanton, CA 94588
Tel.: (925) 271-8700
Web Site: http://www.ssfllp.com
Accounting Services
N.A.I.C.S.: 541219
John D. Sensiba *(Mng Partner)*
Scott Anderson *(Partner-San Jose)*
Suki Mann *(Partner-Audit)*
Tim Tikalsky *(Principal)*
Jarrett Warner *(Partner)*
Santos Solano *(Partner)*
Dee Bowers *(Chief Revenue Officer)*

Subsidiaries:

Slater Moffat Associates, LLP   **(1)**
6795 N Palm Ave Ste 108, Fresno, CA 93704-1088
Tel.: (559) 437-0700
Tax Return Preparation, Forensic Accounting & Business Consulting Services
N.A.I.C.S.: 541219

SENSIBLE MICRO CORPORATION
13520 Prestige Pl, Tampa, FL 33635
Tel.: (813) 926-6700
Web Site:
http://www.sensiblemicro.com
Year Founded: 2005
Sales Range: $1-9.9 Million
Emp.: 20
Electronic Components Distr
N.A.I.C.S.: 423690
Chris Torrioni *(Pres & CEO)*
Craig Beske *(Acct Mgr)*
Mike Conran *(Acct Mgr)*

SENSIBLE MICRO CORPORATION — U.S. PRIVATE

Sensible Micro Corporation—(Continued)
Manuel Cuza *(Acct Mgr)*
Bill Meyers *(Acct Mgr)*
Ron Myers *(Sr VP)*

SENSING ENTERPRISES INC.
3425 E Thomas Rd, Phoenix, AZ 85018
Tel.: (602) 956-1991
Web Site: http://www.pruitts.com
Year Founded: 1976
Sales Range: $25-49.9 Million
Emp.: 150
Furniture Retailer
N.A.I.C.S.: 449110
Roger W. Sensing *(Pres)*
Mike Sensing *(VP)*
Joani Smit *(CFO)*

SENSIS INC.
811 Wilshire Blvd Ste 2050, Los Angeles, CA 90017
Tel.: (213) 341-0171
Web Site:
http://www.sensisagency.com
Year Founded: 1998
Sales Range: $10-24.9 Million
Emp.: 39
Advertising Services
N.A.I.C.S.: 541810
Jose Villa *(Founder & Pres)*
Javier San Miguel *(Dir-Creative Grp)*
Danny Allen *(Mng Dir, Gen Counsel-East Coast & Exec VP)*
Ken Deutsch *(Dir-Media)*
Wade Butcher *(Dir-Project Mgmt)*
Ken Yapkowitz *(Dir-Tech)*
Michelle Lavin *(Acct Dir)*
Adrianne Peschard *(Coord-Acct)*
Julie Gladnick *(Coord-Bus Dev)*
Robyn Loube *(Exec VP)*
Delmus Credle *(Dir-Strategic Plng)*
Abdi Zadeh *(Mng Dir)*
Gloria Johnson *(Mng Dir-Los Angeles & VP)*
Karla Fernandez *(Mng Dir-Texas)*
Sharon Carothers *(Mng Dir-DC)*

Subsidiaries:

Sharp & Co. (1)
794 Nelson St, Rockville, MD 20850-2049
Tel.: (301) 424-6133
Web Site: http://www.sharpandco.com
Advertising Agencies
N.A.I.C.S.: 541810
Susan Sharp *(Pres & Chief Strategy Officer)*
Mary Arzt *(CEO & Chief Creative Officer)*

SENSKE LAWN & TREE CARE, INC.
410 N Quay St, Kennewick, WA 99336
Tel.: (509) 374-5000
Web Site: http://www.senske.com
Year Founded: 1947
Lawn, Tree & Pest Control Services
N.A.I.C.S.: 561710
Chris Senske *(Pres)*
Tim Ehrhart *(COO)*
Casey Taylor *(CEO)*

Subsidiaries:

Ace of Blades LLC (1)
Coventry Cv, Springdale, AR 72764
Tel.: (479) 530-7001
Web Site: http://www.aceofbladesnwa.com
Landscaping Services
N.A.I.C.S.: 561730

Arbor-Nomics Turf, Inc. (1)
651 Langford Dr, Norcross, GA 30071
Tel.: (770) 447-6237
Web Site: https://www.arbor-nomics.com
Rev.: $4,300,000
Emp.: 52
Landscaping Services
N.A.I.C.S.: 561730

Doug Cash *(VP & Area Mgr)*
Brandon Stegal *(Mgr-Sls)*
David Sweeting *(Area Mgr)*
Dick Bare *(Pres & CEO)*

Barnes Quality Pest Control, Inc. (1)
1030 SE 3rd St Ste 6, Bend, OR 97702-2141
Tel.: (541) 389-9104
Web Site:
http://www.barnespestcontrolbend.com
Exterminating & Pest Control Services
N.A.I.C.S.: 561710

Blades of Green, Inc. (1)
4374 Solomons Island Rd, Harwood, MD 20776
Tel.: (410) 867-8873
Web Site: http://www.bladesofgreen.com
Sales Range: $1-9.9 Million
Lawn Maintenance Services
N.A.I.C.S.: 561730
Mark Leahy *(Founder & Pres)*
Brad Leahy *(VP)*

Elk Creek Lawn & Tree Care, LLC (1)
525 Violet St, Golden, CO 80401
Tel.: (303) 384-1100
Web Site: http://www.elkcreeklawn.com
Landscaping Services
N.A.I.C.S.: 561730

FIT Turf, Inc. (1)
15467 E Hinsdale Cir Unit B, Centennial, CO 80112
Tel.: (734) 223-0242
Web Site: http://www.fitturf.com
Landscaping Services
N.A.I.C.S.: 561730
Kevin Denby *(VP)*

G & G Lawn Care, Inc. (1)
201 S Bowen St, Longmont, CO 80501-5869
Tel.: (303) 772-4331
Web Site: http://www.liquilawn.com
Landscaping Services
N.A.I.C.S.: 561730

Green Mountain Lawn & Tree Care
7140 Ivy St Ste B, Commerce City, CO 80022-1989
Tel.: (303) 452-0248
Web Site:
http://www.greenmountainlawncare.com
Landscaping Services
N.A.I.C.S.: 561730
Wade Grove *(Founder & Mgr)*

National Turf Service-Clinton M. Quinn, Inc. (1)
7627 Fullerton Rd, Springfield, VA 22153-2815
Tel.:
Web Site: http://www.nationalturf.com
Landscaping Services
N.A.I.C.S.: 561730

Scientific Spray Service, Inc. (1)
423 Norpoint Way NE, Tacoma, WA 98422-3362
Tel.: (253) 927-1977
Web Site: http://www.scientificspray.com
Exterminating & Pest Control Services
N.A.I.C.S.: 561710
Gary Stark *(Pres)*

SENSOR ENTERPRISES INC.
3924 Forest Dr Ste 12, Columbia, SC 29204
Tel.: (803) 787-6647
Web Site:
http://www.sensorenterprises.com
Sales Range: $10-24.9 Million
Emp.: 900
Fast Food Restaurant Operator
N.A.I.C.S.: 722513
George Sensor *(Pres)*

SENSOR SYSTEMS, LLC
2800 Anvil St N, Saint Petersburg, FL 33710-2943
Tel.: (727) 347-2181 FL
Web Site: http://www.sensorsllc.com
Year Founded: 1998
Sales Range: $10-24.9 Million

Emp.: 120
Mfr of Potentiometers, Pressure Transducers, Encoders & Value Added Assemblies
N.A.I.C.S.: 335931
Charles Nunziata *(Gen Mgr)*
Nancy Price *(Owner & Pres)*
Janice Wickham *(Mgr-Shipping)*
Pat Grippe *(Mgr-Repair)*

SENSORS, INC.
6812 State Rd, Detroit, MI 48223-3463
Tel.: (313) 835-0044 MI
Web Site: http://www.nts.com
Year Founded: 1970
Sales Range: $75-99.9 Million
Emp.: 100
Mfr of Gas Analyzer Equipment for the Automotive Aftermarket
N.A.I.C.S.: 334513
Robert Wilson *(VP-Mktg & Sls)*

Subsidiaries:

Sensors Europe GmbH (1)
Feldheider Str 60, 40699, Erkrath, Germany
Tel.: (49) 2104 14188 0
Web Site: http://www.sensors-inc.com
Sales Range: $10-24.9 Million
Emp.: 12
Automotive Measuring Equipment Mfr
N.A.I.C.S.: 336320
Oliver Franken *(Mng Dir)*

SENTARA HEALTHCARE
6015 Poplar Hall Dr Ste 300, Norfolk, VA 23502
Tel.: (757) 455-7000
Web Site: http://www.sentara.com
Sales Range: $600-649.9 Million
Emp.: 15,000
Operates Hospital & Health Care Services
N.A.I.C.S.: 622110
Howard P. Kern *(CEO)*
Robert A. Broerman *(CFO & Sr VP)*
Megan Perry *(VP-Mergers & Affiliations)*
Michael Gentry *(COO & Sr VP)*
Becky Sawyer *(Sr VP-HR)*
David James *(Pres-Four Medical Groups & Ambulatory services)*
Dennis Matheis *(Pres & CEO)*

Subsidiaries:

Pratt Medical Center, Ltd. (1)
4900 Plank Rd, Fredericksburg, VA 22407
Tel.: (540) 786-2100
Web Site: http://www.prattmed.com
Office Of Physician
N.A.I.C.S.: 621111
Carol Kristofik *(Controller)*

SENTE MORTGAGE, INC.
Barton Oaks Plz Bldg 4 Ste 125, Austin, TX 78746
Tel.: (512) 637-9900
Web Site:
http://www.sentemortgage.com
Year Founded: 2007
Sales Range: $10-24.9 Million
Emp.: 300
Mortgage Banking Services
N.A.I.C.S.: 522310
Thomas Rhodes *(CEO)*
Dayna McElreath *(VP-Ops)*
Brian Hurd *(Mgr-Bus Dev)*
Dana Canada *(VP-Fin)*

SENTECH SERVICES, INC.
36400 Woodward Ave Ste 250, Bloomfield, MI 48304-0912
Tel.: (248) 645-1800
Web Site:
http://www.sentechservices.com
Year Founded: 1984
Sales Range: $10-24.9 Million

Emp.: 500
Placements of Skilled Trades, Industrial, Engineering, Professional & Office Personnel
N.A.I.C.S.: 561320
Kit Shults *(Acct Mgr)*

SENTEK GLOBAL INCORPORATED
2811 Nimitz Blvd, San Diego, CA 92106
Tel.: (619) 543-9550
Web Site:
http://www.sentekconsulting.com
Year Founded: 2001
Sales Range: $1-9.9 Million
Emp.: 23
Software Creator for Military Operations
N.A.I.C.S.: 334610
Eric Basu *(CEO)*
Cameron Matthews *(CTO)*

SENTINEL BROKERS CO., INC.
1045 Park Blvd, Massapequa Park, NY 11762
Tel.: (516) 541-9100
Web Site:
http://www.sentinelbrokers.com
Rev.: $1,932,000
Emp.: 6
Portfolio Management
N.A.I.C.S.: 523940
Joseph Lawless *(Owner)*

SENTINEL BUILDING SYSTEMS INC.
237 S 4th St, Albion, NE 68620
Tel.: (402) 395-5076
Web Site:
http://www.sentinelbuildings.com
Sales Range: $10-24.9 Million
Emp.: 25
Prefabricated Metal Buildings & Components
N.A.I.C.S.: 332311
Spottc Stuhlmiller *(Gen Mgr)*

SENTINEL CAPITAL PARTNERS, L.L.C.
330 Madison Ave 27th Fl, New York, NY 10017
Tel.: (212) 688-3100 DE
Web Site:
http://www.sentinelpartners.com
Year Founded: 1995
Privater Equity Firm
N.A.I.C.S.: 523999
David S. Lobel *(Co-Founder & Mng Partner)*
John F. McCormack *(Co-Founder & Sr Partner)*
Eric Bommer *(Partner)*
James D. Coady *(Partner)*
Paul F. Murphy *(Partner)*
Michael J. Fabian *(Partner)*
Joseph J. Catalano *(Mng Dir-Bus Dev)*
C. Scott Perry *(Partner)*
John C. Van Sickle *(Partner)*
Sidney J. Feltenstein *(Sr Operating Partner)*

Subsidiaries:

Captain D's, LLC (1)
921 Jefferson St, Nashville, TN 37208
Tel.: (615) 256-2263
Web Site: http://www.captainds.com
Quick Service Seafood Restaurants
N.A.I.C.S.: 722513
Michael T. Folks *(Gen Counsel & Sr VP)*
Chris Crabtree *(VP-Info Sys)*
Philip M. Greifeld *(Pres & CEO)*
Janet Duckham *(Chief Supply Chain Officer)*

COMPANIES

SENTINEL REAL ESTATE CORPORATION

Brad Reed *(Chief Dev Officer)*
Keith Davis *(CFO)*
Dawn Foster *(VP-Brand Mktg)*
Larry Jones *(VP-Construction)*
Tim Ward *(COO)*
Nancy Ward *(VP-Trng)*
Andy Castle *(VP-Ops)*
Chris Kuehn *(CMO)*
Brad Clark *(Chief Supply Chain Officer)*
Bindi Menon *(CMO)*
Robert Jones *(VP-Franchise Ops)*

Division (Domestic):

Grandy's (2)
401 E Corporate Dr, Lewisville, TX 75057
Tel.: (972) 434-9241
Web Site: http://www.grandys.com
Sales Range: $10-24.9 Million
Emp.: 20
Family Dining Restaurant Chain
N.A.I.C.S.: 722513

Controlled Products, LLC (1)
200 Howell Dr, Dalton, GA 30721
Tel.: (800) 562-4492
Web Site: http://www.cpturf.com
Turf Mfr
N.A.I.C.S.: 314110
Scott Lowrie *(Vice Chm)*
Ron Bennett *(CEO)*

Subsidiary (Domestic):

The Recreational Group LLC (2)
205 Boring Dr, Dalton, GA 30721
Tel.: (877) 881-8477
Web Site: http://www.recreationalgroup.com
Landscape Architecture Design & Consultation Services
N.A.I.C.S.: 541320
Kimberly Roos *(Chief Revenue Officer)*
Amanda Todd *(CFO)*
Ron Bennett *(CEO)*

Subsidiary (Domestic):

EasyGrass LLC (3)
14181 SW 143rd Ct, Miami, FL 33186
Tel.: (305) 234-5800
Web Site: http://www.easygrass.net
Sales Range: Less than $1 Million
Emp.: 18
Artificial Turf Products Provider
N.A.I.C.S.: 541320
Raul Martinez *(Principal)*

Swisstrax Corporation (3)
82579 Fleming Way Ste A, Indio, CA 92201-2395
Tel.: (760) 347-3330
Web Site: http://www.swisstrax.com
Floor Covering Stores
N.A.I.C.S.: 449121
Randy Nelson *(Pres)*

Turf Factory Direct LLC (3)
3843 US Hwy 41 N, Resaca, GA 30735
Tel.: (706) 260-6875
Web Site: http://www.turffactorydirect.com
Farm Machinery & Equipment Mfr
N.A.I.C.S.: 333111
Chandra Holbert *(Founder)*

Fazoli's System Management, LLC (1)
2470 Palumbo Dr, Lexington, KY 40509
Tel.: (859) 268-1668
Web Site: http://www.fazolis.com
Italian Restaurants Operator
N.A.I.C.S.: 722511
Tracy Haskins *(VP-Fin & Treasury)*
Dave Craig *(VP-HR)*
Carl Howard *(Pres & CEO)*
Rodney Lee *(CFO)*
Sam Nelson *(VP-Franchise Recruitment & Dev)*
Jonathan Quinn *(VP-Mktg)*
Donna Josephson *(CMO)*
Tom Pleiman *(VP-Ops)*
Scott Sir Louis *(VP-Strategy & Continuous Improvement)*
Steve Bailey *(Sr Dir-Franchise Sls)*
Blaine Adams *(Sr VP-Supply Chain)*
Doug Bostick *(VP-Franchise Svcs)*
Perry Pelton *(Dir-Real Estate)*
Spencer Houlihan *(VP-Fin Plng & Analysis)*
Jeff Sturgis *(Chief Dev Officer)*
Wayne Pederson *(VP-IT)*

Floral Plant Growers LLC (1)
781 N Curran Rd, Denmark, WI 54208-0790
Tel.: (920) 863-2107
Web Site: http://www.natbeauty.com
Sales Range: $25-49.9 Million
Produces, Markets & Sells Floriculture Products to Lawn & Garden Centers or Mass-Merchant Retailers
N.A.I.C.S.: 111422
Scott Lueder *(Pres)*
Kathy Pantzlaff *(Acct Mgr-Grower Ready)*

IEP Technologies, LLC (1)
417-1 S St, Marlborough, MA 01752
Tel.: (508) 485-5210
Web Site: http://www.ieptechnologies.com
Explosion Protection Services
N.A.I.C.S.: 562910
Randy Davis *(Pres & CEO)*
David Grandaw *(VP-Sls)*

Subsidiary (Non-US):

IEP Technologies GmbH (2)
Halskestrasse 32, 40880, Ratingen, Germany
Tel.: (49) 2102 5790 213
Explosion Protection Services
N.A.I.C.S.: 562910
Rudi Post *(Mng Dir)*

Marketplace Events LLC (1)
31105 Bainbridge Rd Ste 3, Solon, OH 44139
Tel.: (888) 248-9751
Web Site:
  http://www.marketplaceevents.com
Emp.: 110
Trade Show Organizer
N.A.I.C.S.: 561920
Tom Baugh *(CEO)*
Mark White *(CFO)*
Paul Schweitzer *(VP-Bus Dev)*
Sue Huff *(VP-Sls)*
Brent Keller *(VP)*
Stacey Charkow *(VP-Fin & HR)*
Lisa Kropf *(COO)*
Shelly Gepfert *(VP-Mktg)*
Ryan Rose *(VP)*
Roy Gedge *(Dir-Strategic Sys)*
Joanne Carry *(Dir-Digital Mktg)*
Arslan Ghani *(Dir-IT)*
Jill Kivett *(Reg Dir-Sponsorship)*

Mobile Communications America, Inc. (1)
100 Dunbar St Ste 304, Spartanburg, SC 29306
Tel.: (864) 529-9852
Web Site: http://www.callmc.com
Radio Solutions & Services
N.A.I.C.S.: 334290
Vince Foody *(CEO)*

Subsidiary (Domestic):

Allcomm Wireless, Inc. (2)
4116 1st Ave N, Birmingham, AL 35222
Tel.: (205) 591-8804
Web Site: http://www.allcomm.com
Sales Range: $1-9.9 Million
Emp.: 70
Radio/Television Repair Ret
Radio/Tv/Electronics
N.A.I.C.S.: 811210
Billy Hinds *(CEO)*
Mike Weathers *(Mgr-Acct)*

ComSource, Inc. (2)
41271 Concept Dr, Plymouth, MI 48170
Tel.: (248) 853-5430
Web Site: http://www.comsourcemi.com
Sales Range: $1-9.9 Million
Emp.: 31
Telecommunication Engineering Services
N.A.I.C.S.: 517810
Alan McAdams *(Treas)*

Gately Communication Company (2)
501 Industry Dr, Hampton, VA 23661-1314
Tel.: (757) 826-8210
Web Site: http://www.gately.com
Electronic Parts & Equipment Merchant Whslr
N.A.I.C.S.: 423690

Knight Security Systems, LLC (2)
11056 Shady Trl Ste 105, Dallas, TX 75229
Tel.: (214) 350-1632
Web Site: http://www.knightsecurity.com

Sales Range: $1-9.9 Million
Emp.: 22
Communication Equipment Mfr
N.A.I.C.S.: 334290
Phil Lake *(Pres & CEO)*
Christopher Hugman *(VP-Svc Innovation)*
Martin Krohn *(VP)*

Lord & Company Technologies, Inc. (2)
8809 Sudley Rd, Manassas, VA 20110-4749
Tel.: (703) 361-6009
Web Site: http://www.lordcotech.com
Automatic Environmental Control Mfr for Residential, Commercial & Appliance Use
N.A.I.C.S.: 334512

Myrtle Beach Communications, Inc. (2)
1330 Enterprise Ave, Myrtle Beach, SC 29577
Tel.: (843) 444-1199
Radio Communications & Video Surveillance Services
N.A.I.C.S.: 561621
Jon Jones *(Mgr-Sls)*

Wireless Plus, Inc. (2)
1136 Myatt Blvd, Madison, TN 37115
Tel.: (615) 333-0108
Web Site: http://www.wirelessplusinc.com
Wireless Telecommunications Carriers
N.A.I.C.S.: 517112
Mark Walker *(Owner)*

Nekoosa Coated Products LLC (1)
841 Market St, Nekoosa, WI 54457
Tel.: (715) 886-4700
Web Site: http://www.nekoosacoated.com
Emp.: 90
Industrial Machinery Mfr
N.A.I.C.S.: 333248
John Danio *(Mgr-Sls & Bus Dev-Global)*

Norsun Food Group LLC (1)
903 E 3000 N, Sugar City, ID 83448
Tel.: (208) 356-4149
Web Site: http://www.df-foods.com
Sales Range: $25-49.9 Million
Specialty Food Ingredients Distr
N.A.I.C.S.: 115114
Butch Wilson *(VP-Sls-Indus Export)*

Southern Petroleum Laboratories, Inc. (1)
24 Waterway Ave Ste 375, The Woodlands, TX 77380
Tel.: (713) 660-0901
Web Site: http://www.spl-inc.com
Testing Laboratories
N.A.I.C.S.: 541715
Brandon Pere *(CFO)*
Jeff Hibbeler *(CEO)*
Jeff Wild *(VP)*
Joe Credeur *(VP-Sls)*
Dave Curtis *(Chief Revenue Officer)*
Tim Griepp *(CTO)*
Rodrigo Bykowski *(Chief HR Officer)*

Subsidiary (Domestic):

Assured Flow Solutions LLC (2)
14090 SW Freeway Ste 300, Sugar Land, TX 77478
Tel.: (832) 500-3456
Web Site:
  http://www.assuredflowsolutionsllc.com
Engineering Services
N.A.I.C.S.: 541330
Tony Spratt *(Mng Partner)*
Tomy Golczynski *(CEO & Mng Partner)*

Atchafalaya Measurement, Inc. (2)
124 Credit Dr, Scott, LA 70583
Tel.: (337) 237-7675
Oil & Gas Operations Support Services
N.A.I.C.S.: 213112
Brandon Pere *(CFO)*

DHL Analytical, Inc (2)
2300 Double Creek Dr, Round Rock, TX 78664
Tel.: (512) 388-8222
Web Site: http://www.dhlanalytical.com
Rev.: $2,040,000
Emp.: 20
Testing Laboratories
N.A.I.C.S.: 541380
Dershing Luu *(Pres)*
John Dupont *(Gen Mgr)*

Spirit of Texas Bancshares, Inc. (1)
Tel.: (936) 521-1836
Rev.: $139,595,000
Assets: $3,266,038,000
Liabilities: $2,872,222,000
Net Worth: $393,816,000
Earnings: $42,052,000
Emp.: 363
Fiscal Year-end: 12/31/2021
Bank Holding Company
N.A.I.C.S.: 551111

TriMech Solutions, LLC (1)
4461 Cox Rd Ste 302, Glen Allen, VA 23060-3331
Tel.: (804) 257-9965
Web Site: http://www.trimech.com
Engineering & Software Solutions
N.A.I.C.S.: 541519
Angel Dieter *(Mgr-Sls-Inside)*
Kevin Zich *(Dir-Technical)*
Tom Lavinka *(CFO)*

UBEO, LLC (1)
2112 Rutland Dr Ste 140, Austin, TX 78758
Tel.: (210) 341-4431
Web Site: http://www.ubeo.com
Electronic & Precision Equipment Repair & Maintenance
N.A.I.C.S.: 811210
Jim Sheffield *(Pres & CEO)*

Subsidiary (Domestic):

Braswell Office Systems Inc. (2)
301 N Mesquite St, Corpus Christi, TX 78401
Tel.: (361) 882-4271
Web Site:
  http://www.braswellofficesystems.com
Customized Document & Office Solutions
N.A.I.C.S.: 423420

Rainmaker Document Technologies, Inc. (2)
111 Congress Ave, Austin, TX 78701-4457
Tel.: (512) 472-9911
Web Site: http://www.gorainmaker.com
Full Service Printing Solutions
N.A.I.C.S.: 323120
Kimberly Cox *(Project Mgr)*

SENTINEL ENERGY SERVICES INC.
700 Louisiana St Ste 2700, Houston, TX 77002
Tel.: (281) 407-0686 Ky
Web Site:
  http://www.sentinelenergyservices.com
Year Founded: 2017
Assets: $57,556
Liabilities: $325,512
Net Worth: ($267,956)
Earnings: ($101,621)
Emp.: 3
Fiscal Year-end: 12/31/22
Investment Services
N.A.I.C.S.: 523999
Kent Jamison *(Sec & Gen Counsel)*
Andrew F. J. Gould *(Chm)*
Gerald C. Cimador *(CFO & Chief Acctg Officer)*

SENTINEL PRODUCTS CORP.
70 Airport Rd, Hyannis, MA 02601-1802
Tel.: (508) 775-5220 NY
Year Founded: 1994
Sales Range: $10-24.9 Million
Emp.: 15
Plastic Film & Sheet Products Mfr
N.A.I.C.S.: 326113
John D. Bambara *(Pres)*
Lou Giovannone *(Controller)*

SENTINEL REAL ESTATE CORPORATION
1251 Ave of The Americas, New York, NY 10020
Tel.: (212) 408-5035

SENTINEL REAL ESTATE CORPORATION

Sentinel Real Estate Corporation—(Continued)
Web Site: http://www.sentinelcorp.com
Year Founded: 1988
Sales Range: $25-49.9 Million
Emp.: 800
Real Estate Investment Management Services
N.A.I.C.S.: 531390
John H. Streicker *(Chm)*
Mille C. Cassidy *(Pres)*
Anita Breslin *(Mng Dir)*
Martin J. Cawley *(Mng Dir)*
Leland J. Roth *(Mng Dir & CFO)*
George Tietjen *(Mng Dir)*
Michael F. Streicker *(Exec VP)*
Karen F. Hallock *(Mng Dir)*
Noel G. Belli *(Mng Dir)*
Karen Charde *(Mng Dir)*
Henry W. Haunss *(Mng Dir)*
Robert B. Kass *(Mng Dir)*
Michael J. Kenny *(Mng Dir)*
Robert Leniart *(Mng Dir)*
Brian Ritter *(Mng Dir)*
Nicholas Stein *(Mng Dir)*
Jack Granahan *(Sr VP)*
Nicholas Verano *(Sr VP)*
Max Berkelder *(Mng Dir)*
Robin L. Blauer *(Sr VP & Portfolio Mgr)*
Paul D'Elisa *(Sr VP-Statistical & Financial Analysis)*
William A. Freydberg *(Sr VP-Acquisitions & Dispositions)*
Marisa Gaedig *(Sr VP-Accounts Payable & Receivable)*
Maria Galarza-Murray *(Sr VP)*
Karen Kringel *(Sr VP)*
Connell J. Watters *(Sr VP)*
John H. Zoeller *(Sr VP)*
Scott Arden *(Mng Dir)*
Scott Barsky *(First VP)*
Robert E. Bartlett Jr. *(Mng Dir)*

SENTINEL SALES & MANAGEMENT LLC
85 E Main St, American Fork, UT 84003
Tel.: (801) 756-2919
Web Site: http://www.utahsentinelgroup.com
Year Founded: 2007
Sales Range: $10-24.9 Million
Real Estate Services
N.A.I.C.S.: 531210
Kathleen Lopez *(Pres)*
Jason Wilde *(CFO)*
William Lopez *(VP)*
Eric Blount *(CTO)*
Krista De La Rosa *(Mgr-HR & Admin)*

SENTINEL SECURITY SOLUTIONS, INC.
750B Mattie Rd, Shell Beach, CA 93449
Tel.: (805) 773-6100
Web Site: http://www.sentinelsecuritysolutions.com
Year Founded: 2009
Sales Range: $1-9.9 Million
Emp.: 16
Security System Services
N.A.I.C.S.: 561621
Justin Sherbon *(Pres & CEO)*

SENTINEL TECHNOLOGIES, INC.
2550 Warrenville Rd, Downers Grove, IL 60515-1723
Tel.: (630) 769-4343
Web Site: http://www.sentinel.com
Year Founded: 1982
Computer Hardware Maintenance Services
N.A.I.C.S.: 811210
Timothy Hill *(CFO)*
Brian Osborne *(Co-Pres & Chief Sales & Marketing Officer)*
Robert Lenartowicz *(Co-Pres & COO)*
Robert Keblusek *(CTO)*
John Elam *(Sr VP-Sls)*
Dale Owens *(Sr VP-Sls)*
Dana Jones *(VP-Ops)*
Mike Guy *(VP-Sls)*
Brad Faubion *(VP-Ops)*
Kevin Koski *(VP-Sls)*

SENTRANA INC.
1725 I St NW Ste 900, Washington, DC 20006
Tel.: (202) 507-4480 — DE
Web Site: http://www.sentrana.com
Year Founded: 2004
Rev.: $3,400,000
Emp.: 42
Custom Computer Programming Services
N.A.I.C.S.: 541511
Syeed Mansur *(CEO)*
Steven M. Washington *(Exec VP-Customer Success)*
Luis Mirantes *(Dir-Software Engrg)*
Maureen Tam *(Office Mgr)*
Justin Campbell *(Project Mgr)*
Tony Maull *(Sr VP-Sls)*
Larry Bradley *(VP-Ops)*

SENTRILLION CORPORATION
1881 Campus Commons Dr Ste 403, Reston, VA 20191
Tel.: (703) 390-5560
Web Site: http://www.sentrillion.com
Year Founded: 1990
IT & Cyber Security Solutions; Physical Security Products & Services
N.A.I.C.S.: 561621
Tim Peters *(CTO)*
Don Ofenstein *(Sr Project Mgr)*
Heather Butcher *(Mgr-Pricing & Fin)*
Katie Powers *(Co-Pres)*
Bryan Ackerman *(Gen Counsel & VP)*
Brannon Donlon *(Co-Pres)*
Daniel Dreyfus *(VP-Strategic Growth & Bus Dev)*

Subsidiaries:

LTS Corporation (1)
10 G St NE Ste 601, Washington, DC 20002
Tel.: (301) 652-2121
Web Site: http://www.ltscorporation.com
Information Technology Consulting Services
N.A.I.C.S.: 541512
Jim Bloomberg *(Pres)*

Logical Technical Services, Corp. (LTS) (1)
7250 Woodmont Ave Ste 340, Bethesda, MD 20814 (100%)
Tel.: (301) 652-2121
Web Site: http://www.ltscorporation.com
Sales Range: $1-9.9 Million
Emp.: 19
Integrated Custom Technology Security Systems to Federal & Private Sector Clients
N.A.I.C.S.: 519290

SENTRY AUTO GROUP
4100 Mystic Valley Pkwy, Medford, MA 02155
Tel.: (781) 333-3371
Web Site: http://www.sentryautogroup.com
Sales Range: $25-49.9 Million
New & Used Car Dealerships Owner & Operator
N.A.I.C.S.: 441110
Fraser Lemley *(Founder & CEO)*

Subsidiaries:

Sentry Ford Lincoln, Inc. (1)
4100 Mystic Valley Pkwy, Medford, MA 02155
Tel.: (781) 333-3371
Web Site: http://www.sentryfordauto.com
Emp.: 40
New & Used Car Dealer
N.A.I.C.S.: 441110
Fraser Lemley *(Chm & CEO)*
Christopher Lemley *(Pres)*
Anthony Capone *(VP & Controller)*
Brian McGrath *(VP & Gen Mgr)*

Sentry West, Inc. (1)
940 Boston Tpke Rte 9, Shrewsbury, MA 01545
Tel.: (508) 845-7700
Web Site: http://www.sentryautogroup.com
Sales Range: $10-24.9 Million
New & Used Car Dealer
N.A.I.C.S.: 441110
Fraser Lemley *(Chm & CEO)*
Christopher Lemley *(Pres)*
Anthony Capone *(VP & Controller)*

SENTRY CENTERS HOLDINGS LLC
366 Madison Ave 7th Fl, New York, NY 10017 — DE
Web Site: http://www.convene.com
Corporate Conference & Catering Services
N.A.I.C.S.: 722320
Christopher Kelly *(Co-Founder & Pres)*
Ryan Simonetti *(Co-Founder & CEO)*
Joyce Bromberg *(VP-Strategy & Res)*
Mark Depiero *(VP-Ops)*
Siobhan O'Leary *(VP-Human Capital Mgmt)*
Kenneth Clark *(CFO)*
James E. Higgins *(VP-Sls & Mktg)*
Alex Adelman *(Gen Mgr)*
Drew Kromm *(Dir-Pur)*
Jeremy Joseph *(Gen Mgr)*
Jonathan Wheatley *(Dir-Tech)*
Krzysztof Ozarowski *(Mgr-Svc)*
Maya Stanic *(Dir-Mktg & Brand Dev)*
Michael Shaw *(Mgr-Tech)*
Nephi Mata *(Mgr-Sls Ops)*
Stephanie Phu *(Mgr-Production)*
Stephanie Reilly *(Mgr-Svc)*

Subsidiaries:

Convene Philadelphia (1)
30 S 17th St United Plz 14th Fl Ste 1410, Philadelphia, PA 19103
Tel.: (888) 730-7307
Web Site: http://www.convene.com
Operates Network of Meeting, Event & Conference Venues
N.A.I.C.S.: 531120
Stephanie Gress *(VP-Sls)*
Norma Jean Frumento *(Dir-Acct)*
Hannah Guthrie *(Acct Mgr)*

SENTRY COMMUNICATIONS & SECURITY
60 Bethpage Rd, Hicksville, NY 11801
Tel.: (516) 822-7770 — NY
Web Site: http://www.sentryprotectsyou.com
Year Founded: 2000
Sales Range: $10-24.9 Million
Emp.: 37
Communications & Security Systems
N.A.I.C.S.: 561621
Brian Spinner *(Owner & Pres)*
Bill Roos *(Mgr-Parts & Building)*

SENTRY DETECTION INC.
47 West Street 4th Fl, New York, NY 10006
Web Site: http://www.sentrydetection.com
Sales Range: $25-49.9 Million
Emp.: 200
Safety & Security Specialization
N.A.I.C.S.: 561621

SENTRY EQUIPMENT CORP
966 Blue Ribbon Cr N, Oconomowoc, WI 53066
Tel.: (262) 567-7256
Web Site: http://www.sentry-equip.com
Sales Range: $10-24.9 Million
Emp.: 140
Process Control Instruments
N.A.I.C.S.: 334513
Brian Baker *(CEO)*
Karen Jones *(Mgr-Matls)*
Rhonda Leader *(Supvr-Acctg)*
Robert Lemke *(Reg Mgr-Inside Sls)*
Tina Timmel *(Coord-Safety & Benefits)*
Sherri McDermott *(VP-HR)*

SENTRY FORD LINCOLN, INC.
4100 Mystic Vly Pkwy, Medford, MA 02155
Tel.: (781) 395-6400 — DE
Web Site: http://www.sentrycars.com
Year Founded: 1988
Sales Range: $25-49.9 Million
Emp.: 77
New & Used Car Dealer
N.A.I.C.S.: 441110
Roland J. Walton *(Pres)*

SENTRY GROUP, INC.
900 Linden Ave, Rochester, NY 14625-2700
Tel.: (585) 381-4900 — NY
Web Site: http://www.sentrysafe.com
Year Founded: 1930
Sales Range: $150-199.9 Million
Emp.: 400
Fire & Theft Resistant Safes, Chests & Files Mfr
N.A.I.C.S.: 332999
James Brush *(CEO)*
Michael Norris *(Gen Counsel & VP-HR)*
Greg Bonsib *(Dir-Mktg)*
Mike Bauer *(CEO)*

Subsidiaries:

SentrySafe (1)
900 Linden Ave, Rochester, NY 14625-2700
Tel.: (585) 381-4900
Web Site: http://www.schwabcorp.com
Sales Range: $10-24.9 Million
Emp.: 105
Safes & Insulated Filing Cabinets Mfr
N.A.I.C.S.: 337214
Joel Murray *(Mgr-Procurement)*

SENTRY INSURANCE GROUP
1800 Northpoint Dr, Stevens Point, WI 54481
Tel.: (715) 346-6000 — WI
Web Site: http://www.sentry.com
Year Founded: 1904
Sales Range: $1-4.9 Billion
Emp.: 4,000
Insurance Holding Company
N.A.I.C.S.: 524210
Peter G. McPartland *(Chm, Pres & CEO)*

Subsidiaries:

Parker Assurance, Ltd. (1)
1800 Northpoint Dr, Stevens Point, WI 54481-1253
Tel.: (715) 346-6000
Insurance Brokerage Services
N.A.I.C.S.: 524210

Parker Centennial Assurance Company (1)
1800 North Point Dr, Stevens Point, WI 54481
Tel.: (715) 346-6000
Insurance Brokerage Services
N.A.I.C.S.: 524210

Parker Services, L.L.C. (1)
1800 Northpoint Dr, Stevens Point, WI 54481

COMPANIES

Tel.: (715) 346-7744
Fire Marine & Casualty Insurance Services
N.A.I.C.S.: 524126

Parker Stevens Agency, L.L.C. (1)
1800 Northpoint Dr, Stevens Point, WI 54481
Tel.: (715) 346-6000
Insurance Brokerage Services
N.A.I.C.S.: 524210

Peak Property and Casualty Insurance Corp. (1)
1800 North Point Dr, Stevens Point, WI 54481-1253
Tel.: (715) 346-6000
Property & Casualty Insurance Services
N.A.I.C.S.: 524126

Point Insurance Agency, LLC (1)
2000 County Rd HH, Plover, WI 54467
Tel.: (715) 544-4665
Web Site: http://www.pointagency.com
Sales Range: $25-49.9 Million
Emp.: 8
Insurance Brokerage Services
N.A.I.C.S.: 524210
Martha Garrett (Mgr-Ops)

Sentry Casualty Company (1)
1800 Northpoint Dr, Stevens Point, WI 54481-1253
Tel.: (715) 346-6000
Fire Marine & Casualty Insurance Services
N.A.I.C.S.: 524126

Sentry Insurance (1)
1800 N Point Dr, Stevens Point, WI 54481 (100%)
Tel.: (715) 346-6000
Web Site: http://www.sentry.com
Sales Range: $800-899.9 Million
Emp.: 3,800
Property & Casualty Insurance Company
N.A.I.C.S.: 524126
Jacklyn Johnson (Acct Exec-Affinity Markets)
Prathit Bondre (Assoc Dir-Architecture)
Vincent Vinnie Garth (Assoc Dir-Sls-Cycle)
Tiffany Lintz (Coord-Meeting & Travel)
Carmen Dumitrescu-Mihaly (Dir-Comml Billing)
Leanne Halder (Dir-Comml Lines Automation)
Gretchen Mattner (Dir-Compliance & Dev)
Aaron Deering (Dir-Enterprise Architecture)
Keith Imlach (Dir-IT Security Ops)
Sandy Huser (Dir-IT Sys)
Scott Cherney (Dir-IT-Data Svcs)
Joel Basala (Dir-Market Dev & Affinity Relationships)
John Ewert (Dir-Pricing & Product Dev)
Jim Clawson (Exec VP-Insurance)
Jeremy Kleifgen (Mgr-Applications Dev)
Jeff Jeske (Mgr-Change & Engr-Sys-III)
Lanaye Graser (Mgr-Claims-Disability & Life)
A. J. Hawley (Mgr-Infrastructure Ops)
Myles Hurlburt (Mgr-Infrastructure Ops)
Chad Hollenbeck (Mgr-Products Bus)
Frank Ellefson (Mgr-Products Bus & Sls-Central States)
Sam Schroeder (Project Dir-IT Office)
Mike Williams (VP)
Dan Wuest (VP-IT Comml Lines & Claims)
John Hyland (VP)
Gladys Martens (Project Mgr)
Lynn Nelson (Project Dir)
Elisha Robinson (Controller)
Jeff Willoughby (Reg Mgr)
Pete Anhalt (VP)
Leah Hermanson (Product Mgr)
Jason Mills (Product Mgr)
Peter Sampson (Product Mgr)
Rick Wittmann (CMO)
Greg Armstrong (Sr Dir-Consumer Products Claims)
Kimberly A. Bach (Sr Mgr-Claims)
Dale Bikowski (Dir-Fin Analysis & Control)
Don Broderick (Dir-Tax)
Michael Cloud (Dir-Compensation)
Tim Kelly (Sr Dir-Claims)
Kelly Kumm (Mgr-Claims)
Cheryl O'Donnell (Mgr-IT Support Center)
Chris Palmer (Assoc Dir-Sls Trng)
Shannon Schoenberg (Mgr-Meeting Svcs)
Heather Schenker (Head-Specialty)

Subsidiary (Domestic):

Dairyland Insurance Co. (2)
1800 Northpoint Dr, Stevens Point, WI 54481-1253 (100%)
Tel.: (715) 346-6000
Web Site: http://www.sentry.com
Automobile & Motorcycle Insurance
N.A.I.C.S.: 524126

Subsidiary (Domestic):

Dairyland County Mutual Insurance Co. (3)
1000 Heritage Ctr Cir, Round Rock, TX 78664-4463 (100%)
Tel.: (512) 238-3164
Sales Range: $50-74.9 Million
Emp.: 1
Insurance Company
N.A.I.C.S.: 524210

Subsidiary (Domestic):

Middlesex Insurance Co. (2)
1800 Northpoint Dr, Stevens Point, WI 54481-1253 (100%)
Tel.: (715) 346-6000
Web Site: http://www.sentry.com
Sales Range: $350-399.9 Million
Emp.: 1,000
Fire, Home, Multiple Peril & Auto Insurance
N.A.I.C.S.: 524210

Patriot General Insurance Co. (2)
Three Carlisle Rd, Westford, MA 01886-3601
Tel.: (978) 392-7000
Web Site: http://www.sentry.com
Sales Range: $50-74.9 Million
Emp.: 20
Insurance Agents, Brokers & Service
N.A.I.C.S.: 524210

Sentry Group (2)
3 Carlisle Rd, Westford, MA 01886-3601
Tel.: (978) 392-7000
Web Site: http://www.sentry.com
Sales Range: $100-124.9 Million
Emp.: 200
Insurance Services
N.A.I.C.S.: 524298

Sentry Life Insurance Company (1)
1800 Northpoint Dr, Stevens Point, WI 54481-1253 (100%)
Tel.: (715) 346-6000
Web Site: http://www.sentry.com
Sales Range: $25-49.9 Million
Emp.: 15
Life Insurance
N.A.I.C.S.: 524113
David Soyka (Mgr-Computer Ops)

Sentry Select Insurance Company (1)
1800 North Point Dr, Stevens Point, WI 54481
Tel.: (715) 346-6000
Property & Casualty Insurance Services
N.A.I.C.S.: 524126

Viking Insurance Company of Wisconsin (1)
1800 N Point Dr, Stevens Point, WI 54481
Tel.: (715) 346-6000
Insurance Brokerage Services
N.A.I.C.S.: 524126

SENTRY MANAGEMENT INC.
2180 W State Rd 434 Ste 5000, Longwood, FL 32779
Tel.: (407) 788-6700
Web Site: http://www.sentrymgt.com
Year Founded: 1975
Sales Range: $10-24.9 Million
Emp.: 500
Real Estate Management Services
N.A.I.C.S.: 531210
James W. Hart (Founder)
John Hagerty (Mgr)
Valerie Goodwin (Mgr)
Deborah Myers (Mgr)
Collin Bruner (Sr VP-Atlantic Reg)
Bradley Pomp (Pres)
Denise Tumulty (VP-Corp Mktg)
Traci Lehman (Sr VP-Midwest & South)

SENTRYCARE, INC.
106-A Ofc Park Dr, Brandon, MS 39042
Tel.: (601) 824-9010
Web Site: http://www.sentrycare.com
Holding Company; Assisted Living & Nursing Care Facilities Owner & Operator
N.A.I.C.S.: 551112
Chris H. Cheek (Pres)
Sonja S. Watkins (CFO & VP)

Subsidiaries:

Professional Rehabilitation Hospital, LLC (1)
209 Front St, Vidalia, LA 71373
Tel.: (318) 336-6500
Web Site: http://www.riverbridgela.com
Long Term Acute Care Hospital
N.A.I.C.S.: 622310
Benny Costello (CEO)
Regetta Woods (Chief Clinical Officer)
Laurie Pere (VP-Physician Rels & Education)

SEO INC.
2720 Loker Ave W Ste G, Carlsbad, CA 92010
Tel.: (760) 929-0039
Web Site: http://www.seoinc.com
Sales Range: $10-24.9 Million
Emp.: 65
Search Engine Optimization
N.A.I.C.S.: 541890
Garry Grant (Pres & CEO)

SEO ONE INC.
3948 Legacy Dr, Plano, TX 75023
Tel.: (972) 755-4592
Web Site: http://www.seoone.com
Sales Range: $10-24.9 Million
Emp.: 4
Advetising Agency
N.A.I.C.S.: 541810
Scott Booker (Pres)

SEO.COM LLC
11781 Lone Peak Pkwy Ste #100, Draper, UT 84020
Web Site: http://www.seo.com
Year Founded: 2007
Sales Range: $1-9.9 Million
Emp.: 76
Advertising Agency & Internet Marketing Planning for Search Engine Optimization
N.A.I.C.S.: 541810
Mike Mann (Founder & CEO)

SEOP
1720 E Garry St Ste 103, Santa Ana, CA 92705
Web Site: http://www.seop.com
Year Founded: 2000
Sales Range: $10-24.9 Million
Emp.: 270
Advetising Agency
N.A.I.C.S.: 541810
Rhonda Spears (Pres)

SEOUL SHIK POOM INC.
360 S Van Brunt St, Englewood, NJ 07631
Tel.: (908) 810-7230
Web Site:
http://www.seoulgrocery.com
Sales Range: $10-24.9 Million
Emp.: 100
Specialty Food Items
N.A.I.C.S.: 424490
Joong Gab Kwon (CEO)

SEP GROWTH HOLDINGS CORP.
2020 Pioneer Ct, San Mateo, CA 94403
Tel.: (650) 522-3300

SEPTODONT INC.

Year Founded: 2021
Investment Services
N.A.I.C.S.: 523999
George Kadifa (CEO)
Kyle Ryland (Chm)
Randy Randleman (CFO)

SEPARATION DYNAMICS, INC.
611 S Woods Dr, Fountain Inn, SC 29644
Tel.: (864) 862-2577
Web Site:
http://www.separationdynamics.com
Year Founded: 1986
Sales Range: $1-9.9 Million
Emp.: 16
Industrial Water Filtration
N.A.I.C.S.: 333310
Mike Presley (Pres)

SEPIALINE, INC.
221 Main St Ste 1350, San Francisco, CA 94105
Tel.: (415) 986-4900 CA
Web Site: http://www.sepialine.com
Year Founded: 1999
Sales Range: $1-9.9 Million
Emp.: 12
Custom Computer Programming Services
N.A.I.C.S.: 541511
Deanna Bradley (Sec)
Bob Paschal (Mgr-Channel Dev)
Jeremy Evans (CEO)

Subsidiaries:

Technesis, Inc. (1)
101 1st St Ste 428, Los Altos, CA 94022
Tel.: (650) 691-4700
Web Site: http://www.technesis.com
Sales Range: $1-9.9 Million
Emp.: 25
Custom Computer Programming Services, Nsk
N.A.I.C.S.: 541511
Paul Collart (Pres)

SEPRO CORPORATION
11550 North Meridian St 600, Carmel, IN 46032
Tel.: (317) 580-8282
Web Site: http://www.sepro.com
Rev.: $9,999,000
Emp.: 40
Pesticide & Other Agricultural Chemical Mfr
N.A.I.C.S.: 325320
Tyler Koschnick (Pres)

Subsidiaries:

Applied Biochemist Inc. (1)
1400 Bluegrass Lakes Pkwy, Alpharetta, GA 30004
Web Site:
http://www.appliedbiochemists.com
Pool & Spa Chemicals Mfr
N.A.I.C.S.: 325998

SEPTAGON INDUSTRIES INC.
113 E 3rd St, Sedalia, MO 65301
Tel.: (660) 827-2115
Web Site: http://www.septagon.com
Sales Range: $50-74.9 Million
Emp.: 160
Commercial & Office Buildings, Renovation & Repair
N.A.I.C.S.: 236220
David Albrecht (Treas)

SEPTODONT INC.
205 Granite Run Dr Ste 150, Lancaster, PA 17601
Tel.: (717) 286-0100
Web Site: http://www.septodont.com
Sales Range: $10-24.9 Million
Emp.: 1,200
Drugs & Drug Proprietaries
N.A.I.C.S.: 424210

SEPTODONT INC.

Septodont Inc.—(Continued)
Kent Chiu (Pres)
Paul Mondock (Sr VP-Sls & Mktg)
Subsidiaries:

TDV Dental Ltda. (1)
Rua XV de Novembro 9944, Caixa Postal 200, 89107-000, Pomerode, Santa Catarina, Brazil
Tel.: (55) 47 3395 6115
Web Site: http://www.tdv.com.br
Emp.: 80
Dental Product Mfr & Distr
N.A.I.C.S.: 339114

SEPULVEDA BUILDING MATERIALS, INC.
28092 Forbes Rd, Laguna Niguel, CA 92677
Tel.: (949) 347-2100
Web Site:
  http://www.sepulveda2.com
Rev.: $11,000,000
Emp.: 70
Lumber Plywood Millwork & Wood Panel Merchant Whslr
N.A.I.C.S.: 423310
John C. Connors (Pres)
Jason Cline (Gen Mgr)
Maietta Craig (VP)
Rick Costa (Mgr-Sls)

SEQUACHEE VALLEY ELECTRIC CO-OPERATIVE INC.
512 S Cedar Ave, South Pittsburg, TN 37380-1310
Tel.: (423) 837-8605 TN
Web Site: http://www.svalleyec.com
Year Founded: 1939
Sales Range: $25-49.9 Million
Emp.: 80
Electric Power Distr
N.A.I.C.S.: 221122
Mike Parton (VP)
Robert Matheny (Pres & CEO)

SEQUATCHIE CONCRETE SERVICE INC.
3106 Lee Hwy, Athens, TN 37380
Tel.: (423) 641-1049 TN
Web Site:
  http://www.seqconcrete.com
Year Founded: 1954
Sales Range: $25-49.9 Million
Emp.: 150
Provider of Concrete Products & Services
N.A.I.C.S.: 327331
Cindi Brooks (Mgr)
Subsidiaries:

Marion Lumber Co. Inc. (1)
E 3rd St, South Pittsburg, TN 37380
Tel.: (423) 837-7919
Sales Range: $10-24.9 Million
Emp.: 10
Provider of Lumber & other Building Materials
N.A.I.C.S.: 444110

Sequatchie Concrete Service Inc. (1)
2100 Southerland Ave, Knoxville, TN 37919 (100%)
Tel.: (865) 524-3351
Web Site:
  http://www.sequatchieconcrete.com
Sales Range: $10-24.9 Million
Emp.: 30
Provider of Building Materials
N.A.I.C.S.: 327331
Warren Strunk (Gen Mgr)

Willcan Inc. (1)
712 North Wall S, Calhoun, GA 30701
Tel.: (706) 629-0815
Web Site: http://www.basicreadymix.com
Rev.: $3,630,000
Emp.: 15
Readymix Concrete Mfr

N.A.I.C.S.: 327320
Wesley Kinard (Mgr)

SEQUEL DATA SYSTEMS, INC.
11824 Jollyville Rd Ste 400, Austin, TX 78759
Tel.: (512) 918-8841
Web Site: http://www.sequeldata.com
Year Founded: 1986
Sales Range: $25-49.9 Million
Emp.: 14
IT Solutions & Services
N.A.I.C.S.: 541512
Jennifer Luton (Mgr-Bus Dev)

SEQUEL YOUTH AND FAMILY SERVICES, LLC
1131 Eagletree Ln, Huntsville, AL 35801
Tel.: (256) 880-3339
Web Site:
  http://www.sequelyouthservices.com
Year Founded: 1999
Emp.: 1,200
Youth & Family Services
N.A.I.C.S.: 624190
John Ripley (Co-Founder & Co-Chm)
Adam Shapiro (Co-Founder & Co-Chm)
John Stupak (CEO)
Steve Gilbert (Exec VP-Mktg & Customer Dev)
Mandy Moses (Chief Program Officer & Exec VP-Ops)
Sybil Potts (CFO & Exec VP)
Bill Dean (Sr VP-Ops)

SEQUOIA CAPITAL OPERATIONS, LLC
2800 Sand Hi Rd Ste 101, Menlo Park, CA 94025
Tel.: (650) 854-3927 DE
Web Site:
  http://www.sequoiacap.com
Year Founded: 1972
Sales Range: $50-74.9 Million
Emp.: 60
Investment Services
N.A.I.C.S.: 523999
Joe Dobrenski (Partner-Human Capital)
James J. Goetz (Partner)
Piyush Gupta (Head-Strategic Dev)
Jung Son (Chief Compliance Officer)
Michael Moritz (Partner)
Carl M. Eschenbach (Gen Partner & Venture Partner)
Alfred Lin (Partner)
Subsidiaries:

MedExpress Urgent Care (1)
1751 Earl Core Rd, Morgantown, WV 26505
Tel.: (304) 225-2500
Web Site: http://www.medexpress.com
Sales Range: $150-199.9 Million
Urgent Care Clinics
N.A.I.C.S.: 621498
Bryan Stuchell (Owner)
Troy Steckler (VP-Clinical Ops)
Russ Sullivan (VP-HR)
Tim Bugin (VP-Payor Contracting & Reimbursement)

Plateno Group Co. Ltd. (1)
Plateno Group Plaza No 300 Xin Jiao Xi Road, Haizhu District, Guangzhou, Guangdong, China
Tel.: (86) 20 8911 5109
Web Site: http://www.plateno-group.com
Hotel Owner & Operator
N.A.I.C.S.: 721110
Lynn Meng (Pres & CEO-Plateno Internet Company)

Sequoia Capital China (1)
Room 3606 China Central Place Tower 3, Beijing, 100025, China
Tel.: (86) 10 844 75668
Web Site: http://www.sequoiacap.cn

Investment Services
N.A.I.C.S.: 523999
Neil Nanpeng Shen (Mng Partner)

Sequoia Capital India (1)
RMZ Millenium Thavere 11th Fl Maffy Rd, Alsoor, Bengaluru, 560 008, India
Tel.: (91) 8041245880
Web Site: http://www.sequoiacap.com
Sales Range: $25-49.9 Million
Emp.: 25
Investment Services
N.A.I.C.S.: 523999
Mohit Bhatnagar (Mng Dir)
Surendra Jain (Mng Dir)
Shailendra Singh (Mng Dir)
Sandeep Singhal (Mng Dir)
Yoav Shaked (Partner)
Rajan Anandan (Mng Dir)
Gayatri Yadav (CMO-India & Southeast Asia)
Ajey Gore (Operating Partner)
Shweta Rajpal Kohli (Head-Pub Policy)

Sequoia Capital Israel (1)
50 Ramat Yam Street Orchid Oceanus Hotel, Herzliyya, 4685150, Israel
Tel.: (972) 99579440
Web Site: http://www.sequoiacap.com
Sales Range: $25-49.9 Million
Emp.: 10
Investment Services
N.A.I.C.S.: 523999

SEQUOIA ENTERPRISES, INC.
150 W Pine St, Exeter, CA 93221-1613
Tel.: (559) 592-9455
Sales Range: $10-24.9 Million
Emp.: 70
Malt Mfr
N.A.I.C.S.: 311213
Jan Lee (Mgr)
James Wilson (Pres)

SEQUOIA EQUITIES INC.
1777 Botelho Dr Ste 300, Walnut Creek, CA 94596
Tel.: (925) 945-0900 CA
Web Site:
  http://www.elevatetosequoia.com
Year Founded: 1973
Sales Range: $10-24.9 Million
Emp.: 25
Residential Building Operator
N.A.I.C.S.: 531110
Carrie Caudill (Dir-Strategic Ops & Sr Portfolio Mgr)
Cynthia M. McSherry (Sr VP & Dir-Property Mgmt)
Subsidiaries:

Paloma Summit Apartments (1)
26371 Paloma, Foothill Ranch, CA 92610-1726
Tel.: (949) 455-2600
Web Site:
  http://www.experiencepalomasummit.com
Sales Range: $10-24.9 Million
Emp.: 5
Operator of Apartment Buildings
N.A.I.C.S.: 531110
Karen Moreno (Gen Mgr)

Seaview Summit Apartments (1)
102 Calais St, Laguna Niguel, CA 92677-5446
Tel.: (949) 499-1864
Web Site:
  http://www.seaviewsummitapts.com
Sales Range: $10-24.9 Million
Emp.: 3
Operator of Apartment Buildings
N.A.I.C.S.: 531110

SEQUOIA FINANCIAL GROUP, LLC
3500 Embassy Pkwy Ste 100, Akron, OH 44333
Tel.: (330) 375-9480
Web Site: http://www.sequoia-financial.com
Year Founded: 1991

Emp.: 88
Financial Planning & Wealth Management Services
N.A.I.C.S.: 523940
Richard J. Schiraldi (Bd of Dirs, Executives)
Hassan R. Baqar (Founder)
Tom Haught (Founder, Pres & CEO)
Subsidiaries:

Mastrapasqua Asset Management, Inc. (1)
814 Church St Ste 600, Nashville, TN 37203-3584
Tel.: (615) 244-8400
Web Site: http://www.mastrapasqua.com
Intermediation
N.A.I.C.S.: 523910

SER CAPITAL PARTNERS LLC
3 Twin Dolphin Dr., Ste 260, Redwood City, CA 94065
Tel.: (415) 873-1011
Web Site:
  https://www.sercapitalpartners.com
Year Founded: 2018
Private Equity
N.A.I.C.S.: 523940
Rahul Advani (CEO & Mng Dir)
Subsidiaries:

Charah Solutions, Inc. (1)
12601 Plantside Dr, Louisville, KY 40299
Tel.: (502) 245-1353
Web Site: https://www.charah.com
Rev.: $293,219,000
Assets: $344,107,000
Liabilities: $323,310,000
Net Worth: $20,797,000
Earnings: ($5,814,000)
Emp.: 693
Fiscal Year-end: 12/31/2021
Environmental Protection & Construction Services
N.A.I.C.S.: 541620
Nathan Boone (Chief Comml Officer & Co-Pres-Remediation & Compliance)
Rob Reynolds (VP-Byproduct & Material Sls)
Norman Divers (VP-Environmental, Health, and Safety)
Leroy Brock (Dir-Safety)
Matthew Sutton (Co-Pres & CEO)
Tony Tomljanovic (CFO & Treas)
Tia Sheppard (Head-Human Resources)
Steve Brehm (Sec & VP-Legal Affairs)

Subsidiary (Domestic):

Ash Venture LLC (2)
188 Summerfield Ct Ste 101, Roanoke, VA 24019
Web Site: http://www.ashventurellc.com
Concrete Products Mfr
N.A.I.C.S.: 327320

Avon Lake Environmental Redevelopment Group, LLC (2)
150 Avon Belden Rd, Avon Lake, OH 44012
Tel.: (440) 933-6141
Web Site: https://www.avonlake.org
Mobile Food Truck Services
N.A.I.C.S.: 722330

SCB International Holdings, LLC (2)
153 S Main St, Newtown, CT 06470
Tel.: (203) 270-1416
Web Site: http://www.scbinternational.com
Industrial Machinery & Equipment Whslr
N.A.I.C.S.: 423830
Peter E. D'Amico (Mng Dir)

SER JOBS FOR PROGRESS INC. OF SAN ANTONIO
900 N E Loop 410 Ste D124, San Antonio, TX 78209
Tel.: (210) 767-2738 TX
Web Site: http://www.serjobssa.org
Year Founded: 1967
Sales Range: $10-24.9 Million
Emp.: 402
Community Development Services
N.A.I.C.S.: 813410

COMPANIES

Linda Rivas *(Pres)*
Dianna Carmenaty *(Vice Chm)*
Christopher K. Price *(Treas)*
Jose C. Mascorro *(Sec)*
Jimmy Hasslocher *(Chm)*

SERAFINI NISSAN VOLVO
3101 Vestal Pkwy E, Vestal, NY 13850
Tel.: (607) 729-3511
Web Site:
http://www.serafiniimports.com
Year Founded: 1995
Sales Range: $10-24.9 Million
Emp.: 40
Car Whslr
N.A.I.C.S.: 441110
Nicholas Serafini *(Principal)*

SERC RELIABILITY CORPORATION
3701 Arco Corporate Dr Ste 300, Charlotte, NC 28273
Tel.: (704) 357-7372   AL
Web Site: http://www.serc1.org
Year Founded: 1970
Management Consulting Services
N.A.I.C.S.: 541618
Jason Blake *(Pres & CEO)*
Tim Ponseti *(VP-Ops)*
Holly Hawkins *(Sec, Gen Counsel & VP)*
George Krogstie *(CFO & Treas)*
Brian F. Thumm *(VP-Perfromance Improvement & Risk Mgmt)*
Melinda Montgomery *(Sr Dir-Engrg & Advanced Analytics)*
Andrew Williamson *(Dir-Reliablity Assurance)*
Stephen Brown *(Dir-Cyber & Physical Security)*
Jennifer Golynsky *(Dir-HR)*

SERC RELIABILITY CORPORATION
3701 Arco Corporate Dr Ste 300, Charlotte, NC 28273
Tel.: (704) 357-7372   AL
Web Site: http://www.serc1.org
Year Founded: 2005
Sales Range: $1-9.9 Million
Emp.: 67
Power Supply System Maintenance Services
N.A.I.C.S.: 813910
Jennifer Kelly *(Dir-Fin & Admin Svcs)*
Greg Ford *(Chm)*
Joe Spencer *(Mgr-Plng Program)*
Marion Lucas *(Treas & Sec)*
Marisa A. Sifontes *(Gen Counsel & Sec)*
Timothy Ponseti *(Vice Chm)*
August McClaine *(Mgr-Bd Rels)*
Erin Kwon *(Dir-HR)*
Linda Peavy *(Coord-Outreach)*
Gary J. Taylor *(Pres & CEO)*

SERCO MOLD INC.
2009 Wright St, La Verne, CA 91750-5812
Tel.: (626) 331-0517
Web Site: http://www.serpac.com
Rev.: $10,500,000
Emp.: 66
Injection Molding Of Plastics
N.A.I.C.S.: 326199

SERENT CAPITAL MANAGEMENT COMPANY, LLC
1 Embarcadero Ctr Ste 1680, San Francisco, CA 94111
Tel.: (415) 343-1050   DE
Web Site:
http://www.serentcapital.com
Year Founded: 2008
Privater Equity Firm

N.A.I.C.S.: 523999
Kevin Frick *(Partner)*
David Kennedy *(Partner)*
Mark Shang *(CFO)*
Lance Fenton *(Partner)*
Prital Kadakia *(Principal-Ops)*
Barry S. Obrand *(Partner-Operating)*
Jon Cheek *(Principal)*
Stewart Lynn *(Principal)*
Navid Oreizy *(VP)*
Nichole Pitzen *(VP-Human Capital)*

Subsidiaries:

Education Advanced, Inc.   (1)
2702 E 5th St Ste 372, Tyler, TX 75701
Web Site:
http://www.educationadvanced.com
Sales Range: $1-9.9 Million
Software Development Services
N.A.I.C.S.: 541511
J. Eli Crow *(CEO)*
Kelly Manlove *(COO)*
Travis Prince *(Chief Revenue Officer)*
Kenny Sikes *(CIO)*
Eric Turner *(CMO)*

Subsidiary (Domestic):

Standard For Success, LLC   (2)
10741 S County Rd 850 E, Cloverdale, IN 46120
Web Site:
http://www.standardforsuccess.com
Sales Range: $1-9.9 Million
Emp.: 10
Education Services
N.A.I.C.S.: 611110
Alan Degener *(Co-Founder & Co-CEO)*
Robbie Grimes *(Co-Founder)*
Todd Whitlock *(Co-Founder & Co-CEO)*
Patti Bostwick *(Dir-Product Support)*
Tammy Brothers *(Dir-Sls & Training)*

ICon Professional Services LLC   (1)
1065 E Hillsdale Blvd Ste 300, San Mateo, CA 94404-1689
Tel.: (650) 378-4150
Web Site: http://www.gotoicon.com
Sales Range: $10-24.9 Million
Emp.: 30
Contract Workforce Management Services
N.A.I.C.S.: 561499
Patricia Griffin *(Founder)*
Michael Soffel *(VP)*
Dana Shaw *(Pres & COO)*
Teresa Creech *(CEO)*
Catherine Chidyausiku *(Sr VP-Compliance & Legal)*
Gary Cornick *(Exec VP-Sls)*
Kimball Norup *(Sr VP-Mktg)*
Joe Russell *(CFO)*
Karen Sawyer *(Sr VP-Client Solutions)*
David Whipple *(CTO)*

Senior Dental Care LLC   (1)
8500 W 110th St, Overland Park, KS 66210
Tel.: (877) 674-1211
Dental Care Services
N.A.I.C.S.: 339116
Tony Layne *(CEO)*

Subsidiary (Domestic):

Senior Vision Services, Inc.   (2)
9239 W Ctr Rd Ste 103, Omaha, NE 68124-1900
Tel.: (402) 898-3232
Web Site:
http://www.seniorvisionservices.com
Medical Vision Care
N.A.I.C.S.: 621320
Benjamin Nelson *(Pres)*

SERETTA CONSTRUCTION INC.
2604 Clark St, Apopka, FL 32703
Tel.: (407) 290-9440
Web Site: http://www.seretta.com
Rev.: $17,500,000
Emp.: 50
Concrete Work
N.A.I.C.S.: 238110
Susan Barbery *(Controller)*
Andrew S. McPherson *(Pres)*
Christine Elias *(Dir-Mktg)*
Mike Green *(Project Mgr)*

SEREX CORPORATION
55 Victoria Rd, Youngstown, OH 44515
Tel.: (330) 792-5211   DE
Web Site:
http://www.serexvending.com
Year Founded: 1971
Sales Range: $10-24.9 Million
Emp.: 59
Merchandising Machine Operators
N.A.I.C.S.: 445132
Leonard Morris *(CFO & VP)*
Russell Hodge *(Pres)*
Greg Pastore *(VP-Sls)*
Len Morris *(Gen Mgr)*

SERFASS CONSTRUCTION COMPANY INC.
3764 Mauch Chunk Rd, Allentown, PA 18104
Tel.: (610) 769-1100
Web Site:
http://www.serfassconstruction.com
Year Founded: 1948
Sales Range: $10-24.9 Million
Emp.: 29
Construction Management, Design & General Contracting Services
N.A.I.C.S.: 236220
David Serfass *(Pres)*
Matthias Fenstermacher *(VP-Bus Dev)*
Kevin Serfass *(VP)*

Subsidiaries:

Bonsall Shafferman Architects and Space Planners, PC   (1)
3764 Mauch Chunk Rd, 18104, Allentown, PA
Tel.: (610) 866-0505
Web Site:
https://www.serfassconstruction.com
Architectural Services
N.A.I.C.S.: 541310
Frederick Bonsall *(Principal)*
Donna Spadt *(Office Mgr)*

SERFILCO, LTD.
2900 MacArthur Blvd, Northbrook, IL 60062-2005
Tel.: (847) 559-1777   IL
Web Site: http://www.serfilco.com
Year Founded: 1961
Sales Range: $25-49.9 Million
Emp.: 175
Pumps, Filtration System Product Mfr
N.A.I.C.S.: 333998
Jack H. Berg *(Pres)*

Subsidiaries:

ASM Industries Inc.   (1)
41 Industrial Cir, Lancaster, PA 17601   (100%)
Tel.: (717) 656-2161
Web Site: http://www.pacerpumps.com
Sales Range: $10-24.9 Million
Emp.: 35
Mfr of Pumps, Fittings & Injection Molding
N.A.I.C.S.: 339999

R.P. Adams Company, Inc.   (1)
225 E Park Dr, Tonawanda, NY 14150-7813
Tel.: (716) 877-2608
Web Site: http://www.rpadams.com
Sales Range: $10-24.9 Million
Emp.: 50
Air, Water & Chemical Filters, Automatic Water Strainers, Aftercoolers, Cyclone Separators, Heat Exchangers Mfr; Shell & Tube Design
N.A.I.C.S.: 333912

Serfilco International, Ltd.   (1)
Siemens Road Northbank Industrial Estate, Irlam, Manchester, M44 5AH, United Kingdom
Tel.: (44) 161 775 1910
Sales Range: $10-24.9 Million
Emp.: 18
Filter Pump Mfr.
N.A.I.C.S.: 333914

Huw Williams *(Mng Dir)*

Service Filtration Of Canada Limited.   (1)
4141 Sladeview Cres Unit 12, Mississauga, L5L 5T1, ON, Canada
Web Site: http://www.service-filtration.com
Wastewater Treatment Equipment Distr
N.A.I.C.S.: 423830

SERGENIANS FLOOR COVERINGS
3812 Kipp St, Madison, WI 53718
Tel.: (608) 273-6300
Web Site: http://www.sergenians.com
Sales Range: $10-24.9 Million
Emp.: 99
Floor Coverings
N.A.I.C.S.: 423220
James D. Garner *(CEO & Owner)*
Dave Skowen *(Controller)*
Cindy Howarth *(Mgr-Pur)*
Rich Salter *(Project Mgr-Comml)*
Jean Vogel *(Mgr-HR)*

SERIESONE, LLC
175 SW 7th St Ste 1800, Miami, FL 33130
Tel.: (844) 737-4371
Year Founded: 2013
Investment Services
N.A.I.C.S.: 523999
Michael Mildenberger *(CEO)*

Subsidiaries:

Moveix Inc.   (1)
4800 N Scottsdale Rd Ste 550, Scottsdale, AZ 85251
Tel.: (503) 536-0997
Liabilities: $57,055
Net Worth: ($57,055)
Earnings: ($39,741)
Fiscal Year-end: 12/31/2022
Electric Transportation Product Distr
N.A.I.C.S.: 423110

SERIGRAPH, INC.
3801 E Decorah Rd, West Bend, WI 53095-9597
Tel.: (262) 335-7200   DE
Web Site: http://www.serigraph.com
Year Founded: 1949
Sales Range: $100-124.9 Million
Emp.: 950
Specialty Offset & Screen Printing: Decals, Decorative Trim
N.A.I.C.S.: 323113
Jane Gottfacker *(Acct Mgr & Mgr-Customer Support)*
Linda Buntrock *(Sr VP-HR & EHS)*
Daryl Wendegatz *(Coord-New Bus Dev)*
Betsy Rettler *(Gen Mgr-Acctg)*
David Lang *(Mgr-Facility)*
Lisa Tkachuk *(Sr Acct Mgr)*
Deb Wheaton *(Sr Mgr-HR)*
Tom Gehl *(Mgr-Procurement)*
Robb Johnson *(Mgr-Quality)*
Paul Schlagenhaft *(Mgr-Value Stream)*

Subsidiaries:

Carvel Print Serigraph, Inc.   (1)
Calle 2 No 117 Fracc Benito Juarez, Parque Industrial Jurica, 76120, Queretaro, Mexico   (100%)
Tel.: (52) 4422181722
Sales Range: $10-24.9 Million
Emp.: 130
Offset & Screen Printing on Plastics & Metal Screen Printing
N.A.I.C.S.: 323111

SERLE DESIGN

Serle Design—(Continued)

SERLE DESIGN
12882 Vly View St Ste 1, Garden Grove, CA 92845-2506
Tel.: (714) 898-9229   CA
Year Founded: 1978
Sales Range: Less than $1 Million
Emp.: 5
Advetising Agency
N.A.I.C.S.: 541810
Pete Serle (Owner & Dir-Creative)

SEROKA
N17 W24222 Riverwood Dr, Waukesha, WI 53188
Tel.: (262) 523-3740   WI
Web Site: http://www.seroka.com
Year Founded: 1981
Rev.: $1,300,000
Emp.: 15
Fiscal Year-end: 12/31/06
Advetising Agency
N.A.I.C.S.: 541810
Patrick H. Seroka (Founder, Chm & CEO)
John Seroka (VP)
Amy Hansen (Dir-Client Svcs & PR)
Teri Saeed (Dir-Production)
Leslie Bonk (Sr Acct Mgr)

SERPRO INC.
220a Millwell Dr, Maryland Heights, MO 63043-2512
Tel.: (314) 209-7516
Web Site: http://serprologistics.com
Year Founded: 1983
Sales Range: $10-24.9 Million
Emp.: 14
Provider of Scheduled & On Demand Delivery Services: Local, National & International Deliveries. 1 Hour-2 Day Economy Courier Services.
N.A.I.C.S.: 561421
Doug Neuse (COO)
Paul Bunker (VP-Sls & Mktg)

SERRA AUTOMOTIVE, INC.
102 W Silver Lake Road Ste 300, Fenton, MI 48430
Tel.: (810) 694-1720   MI
Web Site: http://www.serrausa.com
Year Founded: 1973
Holding Company; Car Dealership Owner & Operator
N.A.I.C.S.: 551112
Joe Serra (Pres)
Dave Cramer (Dir-Tax)
Denny Dunfield (VP)
Matt Daugherty (CFO)
Ron Haggin (Dir-Ops)
Pete Gerosa (Dir-Acquisitions)
Dan Pratt (Dir-Internal Audit)
Jason Curie (Mgr-Ops)
Frank Odrobina (Mgr-Ops)
Scott J. Borg (Comptroller)
Cyd Sterba (Coord-Media)

Subsidiaries:

Serra Chevrolet, LLC   (1)
7850 US Hwy 64, Memphis, TN 38133-4000
Tel.: (901) 382-5644
Web Site: http://www.serrabartlett.com
New & Used Car Dealer
N.A.I.C.S.: 441110
Barry Carver (Gen Mgr)

SERRA CHEVROLET INC.
1170 Center Point Pkwy, Birmingham, AL 35215
Tel.: (205) 853-2906
Web Site: http://www.serrachevy.com
Rev.: $100,000,000
Emp.: 100
Owner & Operator of Car Dealerships
N.A.I.C.S.: 441110

Anthony Serra (Owner & Pres)
Shanon Parker (Mgr-Fin)

SERRA INTERNATIONAL INC.
75 Montgomery St Ste 300, Jersey City, NJ 07302
Tel.: (201) 860-9600
Web Site: http://www.serraintl.com
Sales Range: $10-24.9 Million
Emp.: 15
Customhouse Brokers
N.A.I.C.S.: 488510
Marshall Jhonson (Dir-HR)
Erminio Mangili (COO & Exec VP)

SERRANO ASSOCIATES, LLC
4525 Serrano Pkwy, El Dorado Hills, CA 95762
Tel.: (916) 939-4060   DE
Web Site: http://www.serranoeldorado.com
Sales Range: $75-99.9 Million
Emp.: 30
Subdividers & Developers
N.A.I.C.S.: 237210
William R. Parker (Pres)

SERTOMA CENTRE, INC.
4343 W 123rd St, Alsip, IL 60803
Tel.: (708) 371-9700   IL
Web Site: http://www.sertomacentre.org
Year Founded: 1970
Sales Range: $10-24.9 Million
Emp.: 309
Disability Assistance Services
N.A.I.C.S.: 624120
Linda Renardo (Dir-HR)
Gus van den Brink (Exec Dir)
Lynn King (Coord-Intake)
Debra Marillo (Dir-Advancement & Comm)
Glenn Bylina (Co-Pres)
Steve Foertsch (Co-Sec)
Larry Owens (Treas)
Laurel A. Quinn (Co-Sec)
Robert Straz (Co-Pres)
Frank J. Tomecek (VP)

SERVANTS INC.
3145 Lotters Dr, Jasper, IN 47546
Tel.: (812) 634-2201
Web Site: http://www.servants.com
Year Founded: 1973
Sales Range: $10-24.9 Million
Emp.: 65
Boxes Corrugated: Made From Purchased Materials
N.A.I.C.S.: 322211
Sharon Montgomery (Owner)

SERVARUSRM
12015 Lee Jackson Memorial Hwy Ste 150, Fairfax, VA 22033
Tel.: (703) 563-3900
Web Site: http://erma.servarusrm.com
Year Founded: 2005
Sales Range: $1-9.9 Million
Emp.: 52
Risk Management Software
N.A.I.C.S.: 513210
Joseph M. Zuccari (Co-Founder, Pres & CEO)
Teresa Ballantine (VP-Ops)

SERVCO FS CO-OPERATIVE
2311 Clermont St, Antigo, WI 54409
Tel.: (715) 627-4845
Sales Range: $100-124.9 Million
Emp.: 75
Agriculture
N.A.I.C.S.: 424910
Keith Watson (Asst Gen Mgr)

SERVCO PACIFIC INC.
2850 Pukoloa St Ste 300, Honolulu, HI 96819
Tel.: (808) 564-1300   HI
Web Site: http://www.servco.com
Year Founded: 1919
Sales Range: $400-449.9 Million
Emp.: 980
New Car Dealers
N.A.I.C.S.: 441110
Ryan Matsumoto (Mgr-Mktg)
Peter Hirano (Sr VP-HR)
Brian Rothe (Sr Mgr-Digital Mktg)
Ryan Trujillo (Asst Mgr-Mktg)
Sheila Bernardo (Mgr-Web Projects)
Mark H. Fukunaga (Exec Chm)

SERVER PRODUCTS INC.
3601 Pleasant Hill Rd, Richfield, WI 53076
Tel.: (262) 628-5600
Web Site: http://www.server-products.com
Sales Range: $10-24.9 Million
Emp.: 100
Commercial Cooking & Foodwarming Equipment
N.A.I.C.S.: 333310
Paul Wickesberg (Owner)
Michael Snyder (Mgr-Sls-East)
Ron Zuehlsdorf (Mgr-Sls-West)
Janet Carwell (Mgr-Sourcing)
Mike Fleming (Dir-Engrg)
Kris Falkner (Pres)

SERVERCENTRAL
209 W Jackson Blvd Ste 700, Chicago, IL 60606
Tel.: (312) 829-1111
Web Site: http://www.servercentral.com
Year Founded: 2000
Sales Range: $10-24.9 Million
Emp.: 80
Managed Data Centers
N.A.I.C.S.: 541690
Jordan Lowe (Co-Founder & CEO)
Daniel Brosk (COO)
Lew Maggio (Dir-Provisioning)
Bethany Saxton (Dir-HR)
David Heinig (CFO)
George Nelson (Dir-Managed Svcs)
Matt Arata (Dir-Ops-Bus)
Eric Dominguez (Dir-Solutions Architecture)
Joe Johnson (Mgr-IT & Officer-Compliance)
Tom Kiblin (VP-Managed Svcs)
Chris Rechtsteiner (VP-Mktg)

SERVERLIFT CORP.
17453 N 25th Ave, Phoenix, AZ 85023
Tel.: (602) 254-1557
Web Site: http://www.serverlift.com
Year Founded: 2002
Sales Range: $1-9.9 Million
Emp.: 19
Equipment for Safely Handling & Moving Computer Servers & Peripheral Data
N.A.I.C.S.: 541513
Brandon Budd (VP-Ops)

SERVERPLUS LLC
1169 S 800 E, Orem, UT 84097
Tel.: (801) 426-8283
Web Site: http://www.serverplus.com
Year Founded: 2000
Sales Range: $1-9.9 Million
Emp.: 72
Outsourced Internet Services
N.A.I.C.S.: 517121
Layne Sisk (Pres & CEO)
Bo Barrett (Mgr-Call Center)

SERVI-TEK, LLC

U.S. PRIVATE

3970 Sorrento Valley Blvd Ste 400, San Diego, CA 92121
Web Site: http://www.servi-tek.net
Year Founded: 2006
Sales Range: $1-9.9 Million
Emp.: 315
Janitorial Services
N.A.I.C.S.: 561720
Kurt G. Lester (Principal)

SERVICE ACCESS AND MANAGEMENT, INC.
19 N 6th St Ste 300, Reading, PA 19601
Tel.: (610) 236-0530   PA
Web Site: http://www.sam-inc.org
Year Founded: 1987
Sales Range: $50-74.9 Million
Emp.: 721
Health Care Srvices
N.A.I.C.S.: 622110
Mary Ann Kowalonek (COO & VP)
Nan H. Haver (Pres & CEO)
John G. Vafeas (Chm)

SERVICE ALUMINUM CORP.
3300 N Rdg Rd Ste 290, Ellicott City, MD 21043-3443
Tel.: (410) 465-3300
Web Site: http://www.servicealuminum.com
Year Founded: 1987
Sales Range: $10-24.9 Million
Emp.: 20
Provider of Scrap & Waste Materials Services
N.A.I.C.S.: 423930
Richard H. Bauer (Co-Founder & Pres)
Ed Klawansky (Co-Founder, VP & Gen Mgr)
Delvin Litman (Co-Founder, VP & Mgr-Special Accts)
Harry Neun (Controller-Maryland)
Lee Mellner (VP-Trading)
Michael Zunno (VP-Fin)

SERVICE BROADCASTING LLC
621 NW 6th St, Grand Prairie, TX 75050
Tel.: (972) 263-9911
Web Site: http://www.myk104.com
Sales Range: $25-49.9 Million
Emp.: 100
Radio Broadcasting Stations
N.A.I.C.S.: 516110
Hyman Childs (Pres)

SERVICE BY MEDALLION
411 Clyde Ave, Mountain View, CA 94043
Tel.: (650) 625-1010
Web Site: http://www.servicebymedallion.com
Year Founded: 1978
Rev.: $20,600,000
Emp.: 500
Building Maintenance Services
N.A.I.C.S.: 561720
Roland Strick Jr. (VP)
Roland H. Strick (Pres)
Maria E. Strick (Sec)

SERVICE CHAMP
180 New Britain Blvd, Chalfont, PA 18914-1832
Tel.: (215) 822-8500
Web Site: http://www.servicechamp.com
Year Founded: 1985
Sales Range: $75-99.9 Million
Emp.: 100
Retail/Franchise Auto Tune-Up Centers
N.A.I.C.S.: 423120

COMPANIES

Kirk Gustie (VP-Sls)
Rich Moore (Sr VP-Sls & Mktg-Natl)
Tom Janis (CFO)
Ken Reaves (Controller)
Mary Lou Shores (Office Mgr)
Julie Williams (Reg Mgr-Sls)

SERVICE COMMUNICATIONS INC.
10675 Willos Rd Ste 100, Redmond, WA 98052
Tel.: (425) 278-0300
Web Site:
http://www.servicecommunications.com
Year Founded: 1989
Sales Range: $10-24.9 Million
Emp.: 80
Integrated Technology Solutions Services
N.A.I.C.S.: 541513
Donald Hassard (Dir)
Andrew Hassard (VP)
Bill Garrard (Pres)

SERVICE COORDINATION, INC.
5303 Spectrum Dr Ste 1, Frederick, MD 21703
Tel.: (301) 663-8044   MD
Web Site:
http://www.servicecoord.org
Year Founded: 1989
Sales Range: $10-24.9 Million
Emp.: 383
Developmental Disability Assistance Services
N.A.I.C.S.: 624120
John Dumas (Exec Dir)
John Whittle (Assoc Exec Dir)
Carl Hildebrand (Co-Pres)
Teresa M. Berman (Co-Pres)
Tom Evans (Dir-Fin)
William V. Stack (Treas)

SERVICE CORPS OF RETIRED EXECUTIVES ASSOCIATION
1175 Herndon Pkwy Ste 900, Herndon, VA 20170
Tel.: (800) 634-0245   DC
Web Site: http://www.score.org
Year Founded: 1964
Sales Range: $10-24.9 Million
Emp.: 20
Business Associations
N.A.I.C.S.: 813910
Bridget Weston Pollack (VP-Mktg & Comm)
John Fuqua (VP-Fin)
Steve Records (VP-Field Ops)
Fred Glave (Treas)
John Campbell (Chm)
Laura Radewald (Vice Chm)
Nancy Strojny (Sec)
W. Kenneth Yancey Jr. (CEO)

SERVICE CREDIT UNION
3003 Lafayette Rd, Portsmouth, NH 03801
Tel.: (603) 422-8300   NH
Web Site: http://www.servicecu.org
Year Founded: 1957
Sales Range: $1-9.9 Million
Emp.: 820
Credit Union
N.A.I.C.S.: 522130
Joanne Whiting (Chm)
David Hanchett (Vice Chm)
Margaret Dodge (Officer-Bus Dev)
Wendy Bryant-Beswick (VP-Mktg)
Dan Clarke (Sr VP-Member Experience)
David Araujo (Pres & CEO)
Jennah Wolak (Mgr-Laconia)
Geoff Gilton (Sr VP-Tech)

May Hatem (VP-HR & Trng)
Michael Porter (VP-Ops)
Tyler Pihl (VP- Internal Audit)

SERVICE DIRECTION INC.
219 Riverdale Ave, Yonkers, NY 10705
Tel.: (914) 738-3800
Year Founded: 1952
Rev.: $10,000,000
Emp.: 65
Laundry Equipment & Supplies
N.A.I.C.S.: 423850
Steve Jagde (COO & VP)
Ronald A. Garfunkel (Pres & CEO)

SERVICE ELECTRIC CO., INC.
3716 Commercial St NE, Albuquerque, NM 87107
Tel.: (505) 345-1955   NM
Year Founded: 1971
Sales Range: $10-24.9 Million
Emp.: 99
Electrical Contractor
N.A.I.C.S.: 238210
Steve Alderete (Pres)

SERVICE EMPLOYEES INTERNATIONAL UNION
1800 Massachusetts Ave NW, Washington, DC 20036
Tel.: (202) 730-7000
Web Site: https://www.seiu.org
Year Founded: 1921
Labor Union
N.A.I.C.S.: 813930
April Verrett (Pres)
Rocio Saenz (Treas & Sec)
Joseph Bryant (Exec VP-Intl)
Neal Bisno (Exec VP)
Heather Conroy (Exec VP)
Leslie Frane (Exec VP)

SERVICE ENERGY LLC
3799 N Dupont Hwy, Dover, DE 19901
Tel.: (302) 734-7433
Web Site:
http://www.serviceenergy.com
Sales Range: $25-49.9 Million
Emp.: 64
Petroleum Products
N.A.I.C.S.: 424720
Michael Steiner (VP)

SERVICE EXPERTS LLC
3820 American Dr Ste 200, Plano, TX 75075
Tel.: (866) 397-3787
Web Site:
http://www.serviceexperts.com
Site Preparation Contractor
N.A.I.C.S.: 238910
Wayne Harrel (Gen Mgr)

Subsidiaries:

Strand Brothers Service Experts
Heating & Air Conditioning   (1)
7910 Burleson Rd, Austin, TX 78744
Tel.: (512) 596-1257
Web Site:
http://www.strandbrotherssouth.com
Site Preparation Contractor
N.A.I.C.S.: 238910
Victoria Dunkin (Branch Admin)

SERVICE FINANCIAL, LLC
PO Box 170186, Milwaukee, WI 53217-8016
Tel.: (414) 810-2011
Web Site:
http://www.servicefinancial.com
Year Founded: 1995
Sales Range: $1-9.9 Million
Emp.: 30

Comprehensive Financial Services, Asset Management, Retirement Planning & Mortgage Lending
N.A.I.C.S.: 523999

SERVICE FIRST CORPORATION
11179 Peppermill Ln, Fishers, IN 46037-9082
Tel.: (317) 845-1889
Sales Range: $25-49.9 Million
Emp.: 200
Trucking Operator & Freight Transportation Arrangement
N.A.I.C.S.: 484121

Subsidiaries:

Hiner Transport, Inc.   (1)
1350 S Jefferson St, Huntington, IN 46750
Tel.: (260) 356-8218
Sales Range: $25-49.9 Million
Trucking Operator & Freight Transportation Arrangement
N.A.I.C.S.: 484121

SERVICE FOOD MARKET INC.
321 W Lincoln Ave, Fergus Falls, MN 56537
Tel.: (218) 736-7557
Web Site:
http://www.servicefood.com
Rev.: $15,500,000
Emp.: 160
Grocery Stores, Independent
N.A.I.C.S.: 445110
Gary J. Spies (Pres)
Tim Johnson (VP)

SERVICE FOODS
4355 International Blvd Ste 150, Norcross, GA 30093
Tel.: (770) 448-5300
Web Site:
http://www.servicefoods.com
Year Founded: 1981
Sales Range: $75-99.9 Million
Emp.: 164
Online Grocer
N.A.I.C.S.: 445110
Keith Kantor (CEO)

SERVICE FOUR EQUIPMENT COMPANY, INC.
1755 N Kings Hwy, Cape Girardeau, MO 63702
Tel.: (573) 334-8362
Web Site: http://www.service4.com
Year Founded: 1984
Sales Range: $10-24.9 Million
Emp.: 50
Soap & Detergent Mfr
N.A.I.C.S.: 325611
David Bogenpohl (Gen Mgr)
Kenny James (Mgr-Warehouse)
Clay Church (Mgr-Sls)

SERVICE LIFE & CASUALTY INSURANCE CO.
6907 N Capital of Texas Hwy, Austin, TX 78731
Tel.: (512) 343-0600
Web Site: http://www.sgifs.com
Rev.: $13,500,000
Emp.: 250
Life Insurance Carrier
N.A.I.C.S.: 524113
J. Kelly Gray (Chm, Pres & CEO)
Ray Avery (VP-Mktg)

SERVICE LITHO-PRINT, INC.
50 W Fernau Ave, Oshkosh, WI 54901
Tel.: (920) 231-3060
Web Site: http://www.service-litho.com
Sales Range: $10-24.9 Million
Emp.: 48

SERVICE ORGANIZATION OF

Commercial Lithographic Printing
N.A.I.C.S.: 323111
Steven Elbing (Owner & CEO)
Steve Richard (Dir-Pur)
Scott Thoe (Pres & Treas)

SERVICE LLOYDS INSURANCE COMPANY
PO Box 26850, Austin, TX 78755
Tel.: (512) 343-0600
Web Site:
http://www.servicelloyds.com
Year Founded: 1982
Sales Range: $10-24.9 Million
Emp.: 100
Direct Life Insurance Services
N.A.I.C.S.: 524113
J. Kelly Gray (Owner, Pres & CEO)
G. Steven Collier (Dir-Underwriting)
Jan Kearbey (Dir-Mktg)
Todd Richardson (Mgr-Bus Dev-Underwriting)

SERVICE MANAGEMENT GROUP, INC.
1737 McGee St, Kansas City, MO 64108
Tel.: (816) 448-4500   MO
Web Site: http://www.smg.com
Year Founded: 1990
Sales Range: $25-49.9 Million
Emp.: 173
Transaction-Based Research for Service-Based Companies
N.A.I.C.S.: 561499
Andrew Fromm (Co-Founder & Chm)
Bill Fromm (Co-Founder)
Mary Widmer (Chief Strategic Officer)
Dennis Ehrich (CIO)
Jack Mackey (VP-Sls)
R. Louis Bellaire (Sr VP-Mobile Tech)
Chris Egan (Pres & COO)
Paul Hunt (Head-Sls-Global)
Joe Sciara (Sr VP-Brand Res)
Ken White (Chief Client Officer)
Jacqueline Mueller (VP-Client Svcs)
Mindy McEwen (VP-Client Svcs)
Paul Tiedt (VP-Client Svcs)
Todd Leach (VP-Client Svcs)
Jeff Jokerst (VP-Client Svcs & Engagement)
Shad Foos (VP-Mktg)
Jon Greenlee (VP-Sls)
Jordan Rochwick (VP-Ops)
Shannon Prato (CEO)

SERVICE MOTOR COMPANY
W 9614 Hwy 96, Dale, WI 54931
Tel.: (920) 779-4311   WI
Web Site:
http://www.servicemotor.com
Year Founded: 1916
Wholesale Distribution of Farm, Garden & Industrial Machinery & Equipment; Operation of Retail Automotive & Home Supplies Stores
N.A.I.C.S.: 425120
Jim Sommer (Pres)
Jim Haltaufderheide (Regional Mgr)
Mike Ringer (Mgr-Svc)
Kevin Posselt (Mgr-Parts)

SERVICE OIL INC.
1718 Main Ave E, West Fargo, ND 58078-2204
Tel.: (701) 277-1050   ND
Web Site: http://www.stamart.com
Year Founded: 1946
Sales Range: $25-49.9 Million
Emp.: 200
Provider of Gasoline & Grocery Services
N.A.I.C.S.: 457120
Dirk Lenthe (Owner)

SERVICE ORGANIZATION OF

SERVICE ORGANIZATION OF—(CONTINUED)

CONCHO VALLEY
2950 50th St, Lubbock, TX 79413
Tel.: (806) 791-1591   TX
Year Founded: 2010
Sales Range: $10-24.9 Million
Community Health Care Services
N.A.I.C.S.: 622110
Bryan Homer *(Chm & Pres)*
Dudley White *(Treas & Sec)*
Tim Jones *(Vice Chm & VP)*

SERVICE ORGANIZATION OF SAN ANTONIO
2950 50th St, Lubbock, TX 79413
Tel.: (806) 791-1591   TX
Year Founded: 2009
Sales Range: $10-24.9 Million
Health Care Financial Support Services
N.A.I.C.S.: 813212
John Stieby *(Chm & Pres)*
Michael Thompson *(Treas & Sec)*
Ernest Flores *(VP)*

SERVICE PACKING COMPANY-UNITED FOOD GROUP
3425 E Vernon Ave, Los Angeles, CA 90058-1811
Tel.: (323) 588-5286   CA
Year Founded: 1957
Sales Range: $100-124.9 Million
Emp.: 175
Retailer & Distributor of Meats & Meat Products
N.A.I.C.S.: 311611

SERVICE ROUNDTABLE
131 W Main St, Lewisville, TX 75057
Tel.: (817) 416-0978
Web Site:
  http://www.serviceroundtable.com
Year Founded: 2002
Sales Range: $1-9.9 Million
Emp.: 15
Internet Based Contractor Trade Group
N.A.I.C.S.: 561499
Sarah Blackhall *(Dir-Art)*
Liz Patrick *(VP-Strategic Alliances)*
Matt Michel *(CEO)*

SERVICE SELECT, INC.
16 Canal St Ste 334-349, Bristol, PA 19007
Tel.: (215) 788-3898
Web Site:
  http://www.serviceselectllc.com
Sales Range: $10-24.9 Million
Emp.: 45
Specialty Trade Contractors
N.A.I.C.S.: 238910
Robert Rorke *(Sr VP-Bus Dev)*

SERVICE SUPPLY LIMITED, INC.
1524 S Hamilton Rd, Columbus, OH 43227
Tel.: (614) 861-3681
Year Founded: 1959
Sales Range: $10-24.9 Million
Emp.: 10
Sporting & Recreation Goods
N.A.I.C.S.: 423910
Mary G. Groves *(Pres)*

SERVICE SUPPLY OF VICTORIA, INC.
101 W Mockingbird Ln, Victoria, TX 77904
Tel.: (361) 788-6220
Web Site:
  http://www.servicesupply.net
Year Founded: 1949

Sales Range: $10-24.9 Million
Emp.: 56
Plumbing & Heating Equipment Supplier & Whslr
N.A.I.C.S.: 423720
Petrina Rangnow *(Coord-Pricing)*

SERVICE SYSTEMS ASSOCIATES
4699 Marion St, Denver, CO 80216
Tel.: (303) 322-3031
Web Site: http://www.kmssa.com
Sales Range: $10-24.9 Million
Emp.: 2,000
Gift Shop
N.A.I.C.S.: 459420
Mark Schroeder *(CFO)*
Timothy L. Brantley *(COO & Sr VP)*

SERVICE TEAM INC.
6565 Interchange Rd, Lehighton, PA 18235
Tel.: (610) 377-5050
Web Site:
  http://www.countryjunction.com
Sales Range: $25-49.9 Million
Emp.: 250
Dealer of Lumber, Other Building Materials & Home Products: General Store
N.A.I.C.S.: 423310
Carl Pielmier *(VP)*
James H. Everett Jr. *(Owner & Pres)*

SERVICE TECH AV
1101 Arrow Point Dr Ste 404, Cedar Park, TX 78613
Tel.: (512) 456-2800
Web Site:
  http://www.servicetechav.com
Year Founded: 2003
Sales Range: $1-9.9 Million
Emp.: 40
Design & Install Networked & Customized AV Equipment for Homes, Offices, Recreational Vehicles & Cruise Ships
N.A.I.C.S.: 334310
Chris Pearson *(Pres)*
Kristina Pearson *(VP)*
Travis Teague *(Mgr-Tech Ops)*

SERVICE TIRE TRUCK CENTERS, INC.
2255 Ave A, Bethlehem, PA 18017-2107
Tel.: (610) 954-8473   PA
Web Site: http://www.sttc.com
Sales Range: $150-199.9 Million
Emp.: 350
Tire Retailer
N.A.I.C.S.: 811198
Ronald Bennett *(Pres)*
Katherine Propsner *(Mgr-HR)*
Howie Harding *(VP-Sls)*
Walter Dealtrey Jr. *(COO, Treas & Sec)*

SERVICE TOOL & DIE, INC.
2323 S Green St, Henderson, KY 42420
Tel.: (270) 827-9582
Web Site: http://www.servicetool.com
Year Founded: 1969
Sales Range: $10-24.9 Million
Emp.: 160
Mfr of Molds & Dies
N.A.I.C.S.: 333514
Dwight Fruit *(Pres)*
Craig Fruit *(VP)*

SERVICE TRANSFER INC.
4101 Wilcox St, Chesapeake, VA 23324
Tel.: (757) 494-1900

Web Site:
  http://www.servicetransfer.net
Rev.: $12,000,000
Emp.: 38
Local Trucking without Storage
N.A.I.C.S.: 484110
Cheryl Barrett *(Reg Mgr)*
Dwayne Paschall *(VP)*

SERVICE TRUCKING INC.
2815 W Hwy 44, Eustis, FL 32726
Tel.: (352) 357-1300
Web Site:
  http://www.servicetrucking.com
Year Founded: 1976
Sales Range: $150-199.9 Million
Emp.: 100
Long Distance Trucking
N.A.I.C.S.: 484121
Dan Baugh *(Pres)*

SERVICE WEB OFFSET CORPORATION
2500 S Dearborn St, Chicago, IL 60616-2211
Tel.: (312) 567-7000   IL
Web Site: http://www.swoc.com
Year Founded: 1939
Sales Range: $10-24.9 Million
Emp.: 50
Provider of Commercial Web Offset Color Printing
N.A.I.C.S.: 323111
John Hamilton *(Pres)*

SERVICE.COM LLC
30840 Northwestern Hwy, Farmington Hills, MI 48334
Tel.: (888) 805-0010
Web Site: http://www.service.com
Home Repair, Renovation & Maintenance Services
N.A.I.C.S.: 236118
Sandy Kronenberg *(CEO)*

SERVICEAIDE, INC.
1762 Technology Dr Ste 116, San Jose, CA 95110
Tel.: (650) 206-8988
Web Site:
  http://www.serviceaide.com
Year Founded: 2016
IT Service Mangement
N.A.I.C.S.: 541519
Wai Wong *(Founder & CEO)*
Bill Guinn *(CTO)*

Subsidiaries:

SunView Software Inc.   (1)
10210 Highland Manor Dr Ste 275, Tampa, FL 33610
Tel.: (813) 632-3600
Web Site: http://www.sunviewsoftware.com
Software Publisher
N.A.I.C.S.: 513210
Seng Sun *(CEO)*

SERVICEMASTER TOTAL RESTORATION SERVICES
5198 S Loop 340, Austin, TX 78728
Tel.: (254) 756-3560
Web Site: http://www.smtrs.com
Sales Range: $10-24.9 Million
Emp.: 4
Single-Family Home Remodeling, Additions & Repairs
N.A.I.C.S.: 238220

SERVICENET, INC.
129 King St, Northampton, MA 01060
Tel.: (413) 585-1300   MA
Web Site: http://www.servicenet.org
Year Founded: 1973
Sales Range: $25-49.9 Million
Emp.: 1,372
Behavioral Healthcare Services
N.A.I.C.S.: 621420

Abbas Hamdan *(VP-Developmental & Brain Injury Svcs)*
Susan Stubbs *(Pres & CEO)*
Karen Franklin *(VP-Outpatient Svcs)*
Jeanne Bishop *(VP-Mental Health Recovery Svcs)*

SERVICES FOR THE UNDERSERVED, INC.
463 7th Avenue, New York, NY 10018
Tel.: (212) 633-6900
Web Site: http://www.sus.org
Sales Range: $50-74.9 Million
Emp.: 1,063
Individual & Family Support Services
N.A.I.C.S.: 624190
Donna Colonna *(Pres)*
Michael Whelan *(CFO)*
Louis Cavaliere *(Exec VP-Dev & Disabilities Svcs)*
David L. Hertz *(Chief Dev Officer)*
Elaine Weinstein *(CEO)*
Terry Blackwell *(COO)*
Edward Hubbard *(Treas)*
Gareth Old *(Chm)*
James M. Donna *(Sec)*

SERVICES GROUP OF AMERICA, INC.
16100 N 71st St Ste 500, Scottsdale, AZ 85254
Tel.: (480) 927-4000   DE
Web Site: http://www.sgagroup.com
Year Founded: 1985
Sales Range: $1-4.9 Billion
Emp.: 4,200
Holding Company
N.A.I.C.S.: 551112
Peter Smith *(COO)*
Gary L. Odegard *(VP-Corp Commun)*
James Keller *(CFO)*

SERVICES GROUP, INC.
1929 Moffat Blvd, Manteca, CA 95336
Tel.: (209) 823-7641   NV
Web Site:
  http://www.kampspropane.com
Rev.: $55,636,540
Emp.: 280
Holding Company Propane Commercial & Appliance Retailer Services
N.A.I.C.S.: 551112

SERVICES TO ENHANCE POTENTIAL
2941 S Gulley Rd, Dearborn, MI 48124-3160
Tel.: (313) 278-3040   MI
Web Site: http://www.stepcentral.org
Year Founded: 1972
Sales Range: $10-24.9 Million
Emp.: 1,532
Individual Development Services
N.A.I.C.S.: 624190
Jeanna English *(Chm)*
Jeffrey McKelvey *(Vice Chm)*
Judy Hernandez *(Sec)*
Cheryl Fregolle *(Dir-Clinical & Quality Assurance)*
Riki Justice *(Mgr-Production)*
Brent Mikulski *(Pres & CEO)*
Ken G. Miller *(Mgr-Bus Svcs)*
Marcus Pugh *(Mgr-Production)*
Steve Rickerman *(Mgr-Production)*
Randy Sidebottom *(Mgr-Dream Program)*
Steve Slayton *(Dir-Resource Center)*
Brian Sullivan *(Mgr-Production)*
Phil Martinez *(Mgr-Bus Svcs)*
Christopher Cousineau *(Treas)*

SERVICETITAN, INC.
801 N Brand Blvd Ste 700, Glendale, CA 91203

Tel.: (855) 899-0970
Web Site:
http://www.servicetitan.com
Year Founded: 2012
Emp.: 147
Software Development Services
N.A.I.C.S.: 541511
Ara Mahdessian *(Co-Founder & CEO)*
Vahe Kuzoyan *(Co-Founder)*
David Burt *(CFO)*
Guy Longworth *(Chief Mktg Officer)*
Chris Trombetta *(Chief People Officer)*
Olive Huang *(Gen Counsel & Sec)*
Doug Myers *(Sr VP-Ops)*

Subsidiaries:

CUC Software Inc. (1)
1645 Ave D Ste A, Billings, MT 59102-3043
Tel.: (406) 254-9679
Web Site: http://www.cucsoft.com
Software Develoment
N.A.I.C.S.: 513210
Jack Vannoy *(Pres)*

SERVICIOS MEDICOS UNIVERSITARIOS INC
Call Box 6021, Carolina, PR 00984-6021
Tel.: (787) 757-1831 PR
Year Founded: 1998
Sales Range: $50-74.9 Million
Emp.: 675
Health Care Srvices
N.A.I.C.S.: 622110
Adelaida Fonseca Coriano *(Dir-Pharmacy)*
Jorge de Jess Rozas *(Exec Dir)*
Yolanda Quiones *(Dir-Fin)*

SERVICON SYSTEMS INC.
3965 Landmark St, Culver City, CA 90232
Tel.: (310) 204-5040
Web Site:
http://www.serviconsystems.com
Sales Range: $25-49.9 Million
Emp.: 1,000
Janitorial Service, Contract Basis
N.A.I.C.S.: 561720
Laurie Sewell *(Pres & CEO)*
Stacey Wong *(VP-Strategic Partnerships)*
Edwin Stephenson *(Mgr-District)*
Francisco Mancia *(Mgr-District)*
Hector Vasquez *(Mgr-District)*
Juan Vasquez *(Mgr-District)*
Rob Harrelson *(Chief People Officer)*
Susan Matt *(Mgr-District)*
Eugene Moorcroft *(CFO)*
Laurie Sewell *(Pres & CEO)*
Maritza Aguilar *(Head-ESG Initiative)*

SERVOMATION REFRESHMENTS INC.
7098 Cemetery Dr, Canastota, NY 13032
Tel.: (315) 875-5265
Web Site:
http://www.servomation.com
Year Founded: 2008
Sales Range: $1-9.9 Million
Emp.: 31
Refreshment & Vending Services
N.A.I.C.S.: 445132
Brian Bruno *(Founder)*

SERVPRO OF BETHLEHEM
860 N Kiowa St, Allentown, PA 18109
Tel.: (610) 838-0200
Web Site:
http://www.servprobethlehem.com
Year Founded: 1991
Sales Range: $1-9.9 Million
Emp.: 25

Remediation Services
N.A.I.C.S.: 562910
Stephen Davis *(Co-Owner)*
Dawn Davis *(Co-Owner)*

SES ADVISORS, INC.
555 E City Ave Ste 910, Bala Cynwyd, PA 19004
Tel.: (215) 508-1600
Web Site:
http://www.sesadvisors.com
Year Founded: 1987
Rev.: $8,100,000
Emp.: 29
Financial Investment Activities, Consulting & Legal Services
N.A.I.C.S.: 523999
James G. Steiker *(Chm)*
Mychelle Holloway *(Principal)*
Diane Fanelli *(Principal)*
James V. Capone *(VP-Fin & Admin)*
Michael A. Golden *(Sr VP)*
Steven R. Allison *(Sr VP)*

SES, LLC
1507 Beeson St NE, Alliance, OH 44601
Tel.: (330) 821-3322
Web Site: http://www.seseng.com
Year Founded: 1976
Sales Range: $10-24.9 Million
Emp.: 150
Custom Machinery Mfr
N.A.I.C.S.: 333998
James R. Boughton *(Owner)*
Richard Dillon *(Mgr-Tech Support)*
Nathan Lora *(Project Mgr)*
Greg Nieman *(Project Mgr)*

Subsidiaries:

Predictive Maintenance Services Group (1)
515 Morris St, Uhrichsville, OH 44683
Tel.: (740) 922-2025
Web Site: http://www.theoillab.com
Custom Machinery
N.A.I.C.S.: 541715

SES Automation Inc. (1)
1122 Finch Avenue W Unit 1, Toronto, M3J 3J5, ON, Canada
Tel.: (416) 391-1255
Industrial Equipment Mfr
N.A.I.C.S.: 333517
Leon Winitsky *(Mgr-Controls, Automation, and Software Engrg)*

SESAME WORKSHOP
1 Lincoln Plz, New York, NY 10023-7129
Tel.: (212) 595-3456
Web Site:
http://www.sesameworkshop.org
Year Founded: 1969
Sales Range: $25-49.9 Million
Emp.: 375
Producer of Children's Entertainment & Educational Television
N.A.I.C.S.: 512110
Sherrie Westin *(Pres)*
Scott Chambers *(Sr VP & Gen Mgr)*
Brown Johnson *(Exec VP & Dir-Creative)*
Steve Youngwood *(CEO)*
Joseph Salvo *(Gen Counsel & Exec VP)*
Joan Ganz Cooney *(Co-Founder)*
Daryl Mintz *(CFO)*
Samantha Maltin *(Chief Mktg Officer)*
Whit Higgins *(VP-Intl Media Distr & Bus Dev)*
Ed Wells *(Exec VP & Head-Education & Media-Global)*
Alvin Fu *(VP-China & Gen Mgr-China)*
Stefan Kastenmuller *(Gen Mgr-Europe)*

Hillary Strong *(Chief Dev Officer)*
Kim Diaz *(VP-Creative Dev)*
Wilson Stallings *(Exec VP-Creative & Production)*

SESCO ELECTRICAL SERVICES GROUP
3327 E Olive Ave, Spokane, WA 99202
Tel.: (509) 535-8500
Web Site: http://www.callsesco.com
Sales Range: $25-49.9 Million
Emp.: 200
General Electrical Contractor
N.A.I.C.S.: 811114
Colin Thompson *(CFO)*
Bruce D. Morelan Jr. *(Chm & CEO)*

Subsidiaries:

PowerCom Inc. (1)
22122 20th Ave SE Ste 152, Bothell, WA 98021
Tel.: (425) 489-8549
Web Site: http://www.callpowercom.com
Sales Range: $10-24.9 Million
Emp.: 25
Wired & Wireless Network Installation Services
N.A.I.C.S.: 238210

SESSIONS INC.
2809 Mission St, Santa Cruz, CA 95060
Tel.: (831) 461-5080
Web Site: http://www.sessions.com
Rev.: $10,000,000
Ski Jackets & Pants: Women's, Misses' & Juniors'
N.A.I.C.S.: 315250
Mark Ishimaru *(Coord-Mktg)*

SESSIONS SPECIALTY COMPANY
5090 Styers Ferry Rd, Lewisville, NC 27023
Tel.: (336) 766-2880
Web Site: http://sessionsusa.com
Sales Range: $10-24.9 Million
Emp.: 21
Druggists' Sundries, Nec
N.A.I.C.S.: 424210
Max O. Sessions *(Chm)*

SESSLER INC.
4524 Tacoma Ave, Sumner, WA 98390
Tel.: (253) 863-0660
Web Site: http://www.sesslerinc.com
Sales Range: $10-24.9 Million
Emp.: 200
Nonresidential Construction Services
N.A.I.C.S.: 236220
Jon Sessler *(Pres)*

SET CREATIVE
12 W 27Th St Fl 6, New York, NY 10001
Tel.: (646) 738-7000
Web Site: http://www.setcreative.com
Year Founded: 2009
Sales Range: $10-24.9 Million
Advertising Services
N.A.I.C.S.: 541810
Sabina Teshler *(Owner & CEO)*
Alasdair Lloyd-Jones *(Pres)*
Kurt Kujovich *(COO)*

SET ENVIRONMENTAL, INC.
450 Sumac Rd, Wheeling, IL 60090
Tel.: (847) 537-9221
Web Site: http://www.setenv.com
Sales Range: $10-24.9 Million
Emp.: 200
Hazardous Waste Transport
N.A.I.C.S.: 562112
Don Cooper *(Controller)*
Corwin Johnson *(Mgr)*

Dave DeVries *(Pres)*
Daniel A. Didier *(Dir-Compliance)*
Pamela Page Nowlin *(Mgr-Sls)*

SETA CORPORATION OF BOCA, INC.
6400 E Rogers Cir, Boca Raton, FL 33499
Tel.: (561) 994-2660 DE
Web Site:
http://www.setacorporation.com
Year Founded: 1955
Sales Range: $75-99.9 Million
Emp.: 150
Cosmetics & Perfumes, Mail Order
N.A.I.C.S.: 458310
Don Seta *(Co-Founder & Chm)*
Daniel Hyman *(CFO)*
Alicia Woloshin *(Dir-Creative)*
Dave Condon *(Mgr-Warehouse)*

SETAI HOTEL LLC
2001 Collins Ave, Miami Beach, FL 33139
Tel.: (305) 520-6000
Web Site:
http://www.thesetaihotel.com
Sales Range: $25-49.9 Million
Emp.: 350
Hotel & Resort Operator
N.A.I.C.S.: 721110
Ivan Bauza *(Dir-Sls & Mktg)*

SETHMAR TRANSPORTATION INC.
7381 W 133rd St Ste 402, Overland Park, KS 66213
Tel.: (913) 884-1244
Web Site: http://www.sethmar.com
Year Founded: 1999
Sales Range: $1-9.9 Million
Emp.: 18
Freight Transportation Services
N.A.I.C.S.: 488510
Ben Bolan *(Pres)*

SETHNESS PRODUCTS COMPANY
3422 W Touhy Ave, Lincolnwood, IL 60712
Tel.: (847) 329-2080
Web Site: http://www.sethness.com
Sales Range: $10-24.9 Million
Emp.: 90
Caramel Coloring
N.A.I.C.S.: 311930
Henry B. Sethness *(Pres)*
Mariann Serwinski *(Mgr-Customer Svc)*
Brian Sethness *(Sr Acct Exec)*

SETLIFF BROTHERS, INC.
4806 Ave C, Corpus Christi, TX 78410-4713
Tel.: (361) 241-8851 TX
Rev.: $16,800,000
Emp.: 4
Mexican Food
N.A.I.C.S.: 112112
Jerry Setliff *(Pres)*

SETON NAME PLATE COMPANY
20 Thompson Rd, Branford, CT 06405-0819
Tel.: (203) 488-8059
Web Site: http://www.seton.com
Sales Range: $100-124.9 Million
Emp.: 150
Name Plates, Labels & Identification Products Mfr; Pipe Identification Systems & Valve Marking Systems
N.A.I.C.S.: 561910

SETTE ASSOCIATES INC.

SETTE ASSOCIATES INC.

Sette Associates Inc.—(Continued)
280 Midland Ave, Saddle Brook, NJ 07663
Tel.: (201) 703-8200
Web Site: http://www.armordeck.us
Year Founded: 1984
Sales Range: $10-24.9 Million
Emp.: 50
Truck Parts & Accessories Whslr
N.A.I.C.S.: 423120
Steve Setteducati (Pres)

SETTLE MUTER ELECTRIC
711 Claycraft Rd, Columbus, OH 43230
Tel.: (614) 866-7554
Web Site: http://www.settlemuter.com
Sales Range: $10-24.9 Million
Emp.: 120
Electrical Wiring Services
N.A.I.C.S.: 238210
Mark Muter (Pres)
Minda Walker (Office Mgr)
Tom Stimmel (Project Mgr)

SETTLEMENT PLANNERS INC.
8841 Williamson Dr Ste 30, Elk Grove, CA 95624
Tel.: (916) 714-7200
Web Site: http://www.settlementplanners.com
Year Founded: 2005
Rev.: $8,200,000
Emp.: 4
Direct Insurance Carriers
N.A.I.C.S.: 524128
Richard L. Bishop (Principal)

SETTONS INTERNATIONAL FOODS, INC
85 Austin Blvd, Commack, NY 11725
Tel.: (631) 543-8090
Web Site: http://www.settonfarms.com
Year Founded: 1971
Rev.: $16,254,126
Emp.: 100
Mfr of Dried & Dehydrated Fruits
N.A.I.C.S.: 311911
Joshua Setton (Pres & CEO)
Morris Setton (VP)

SETZER FOREST PRODUCTS INC.
2555 3rd St, Sacramento, CA 95818-1100
Tel.: (916) 442-2555   CA
Web Site: http://www.setzerforest.com
Year Founded: 1927
Sales Range: $100-124.9 Million
Emp.: 280
Moldings & Veneer
N.A.I.C.S.: 321918
Carol Parlin (Controller)
Terry Dunn (Plant Mgr)

Subsidiaries:

Setzer Forest Products Inc. - OROVILLE PLANT   (1)
1980 Kusel Rd, Oroville, CA 95966
Tel.: (530) 534-8100
Emp.: 8
Wood Products Mfr
N.A.I.C.S.: 321999

SEUBERT & ASSOCIATES INSURANCE
225 N Shore Dr Ste 300, Pittsburgh, PA 15212
Tel.: (412) 734-4900
Web Site: http://www.seubert.com
Year Founded: 1973
Sales Range: $10-24.9 Million
Emp.: 80
Insurance Brokerage Services

N.A.I.C.S.: 524210
Brandon Mueller (Pres)
Kristie Lulich (Head-Comml Insurance Ops)

SEV, INC.
5 Blind Brook Ln, Rye, NY 10580
Tel.: (914) 967-0960   NV
Year Founded: 2008
Sales Range: $25-49.9 Million
Emp.: 2
Solar Panel Design Consulting, Construction Management, General Contracting Services & Support
N.A.I.C.S.: 238990
Carey G. Birmingham (CFO, Treas, Sec & VP)
David W. Mooney Jr. (Pres & CEO)

SEVA FOUNDATION
1786 5th St, Berkeley, CA 94710
Tel.: (510) 845-7382   CA
Web Site: https://www.seva.org
Year Founded: 1978
Rev.: $3,300,000
Emp.: 14
Fiscal Year-end: 12/31/06
Social Services
N.A.I.C.S.: 813319
Vaughan Acton (Sec)
Lisa Laird (Treas)
Kate Moynihan (CEO)
Claudio Privitera (Vice Chm)

SEVAN MULTI-SITE SOLUTIONS, INC.
3025 Highland Pkwy Ste 850, Downers Grove, IL 60515
Tel.: (312) 756-7778
Web Site: http://www.sevansolutions.com
Year Founded: 2011
Sales Range: $100-124.9 Million
Emp.: 437
Construction Surveying Services
N.A.I.C.S.: 541370
James Evans (Founder, Pres & CEO)
Steve Kuhn (COO-Construction Svcs & Oversees & Exec VP)
Tom Glatz (COO)
Rob Bassler (Sr VP-Ops)
Aaron Becker (CFO & Treas)
Hafsa Mahmood (VP-Mktg, Comm & DE&I)
David Hendrix (Pres-Pro Svcs)
Michelle Kretz (Sr VP-Legal)
Doug Gafney (VP-Ops)
Eric Thorsen (VP-IT)
Aaron Reisinger (Pres-Construction & Govt Svcs)
Jim Furis (Chief Experience Officer)
Timothy Kratz (VP-Ops-Civil, Zoning & Permitting)
Damian Krebsbach (VP-Ops)
Nick Peters (Sr VP-Ops)

SEVEN CROWN RESORTS INC.
8 Thomas St Ste 200, Irvine, CA 92618
Tel.: (949) 588-7100
Web Site: http://www.sevencrown.com
Sales Range: $10-24.9 Million
Emp.: 100
Houseboat Rentals
N.A.I.C.S.: 532284
John Ohanesian (Chm)
David Ohanesian (Pres)
Jackie Anderson (CFO)
Kathy Wheeler (Dir-Mktg)

SEVEN HILLS FOUNDATION
81 Hope Ave, Worcester, MA 01603
Tel.: (508) 755-2340   MA
Web Site: http://www.sevenhills.org

Year Founded: 1953
Sales Range: $125-149.9 Million
Emp.: 4,223
People Welfare Services
N.A.I.C.S.: 624190
Joseph L. Tosches (COO & Exec VP)
Kathleen M. Jordan (CEO & Exec VP)
Marilyn Lopez-Haddad (VP-HR)
William C. Stock (VP-Govt & Community Rels)
John N. Altomare (Chm)
Brian R. Forts (Vice Chm)
Melvin P. Gordon (Sec)
Robert L. Mahar (Treas)
Kathleen A. Myshrall (VP-Advancement)
Cliff R. Cabral (VP-Behavioral Health & Rhode Island)
Leslie Courtney (VP-Family Svcs)
Richard Neckes (Chief Program Officer & Sr VP)

Subsidiaries:

Youth Opportunities Upheld, Inc.   (1)
81 Plantation St, Worcester, MA 01604
Tel.: (508) 849-5600
Web Site: http://www.youinc.org
Individual & Family Support Services
N.A.I.C.S.: 624190
Paul F. Kelleher (COO)
Paula A. Aiello (CFO & VP-Admin)
Jonathan Miller (Chief Info & Compliance Officer)
Ludmilla Tonkonogy (Dir-Medical)
Ann Toomey Doane (Dir-Community Based Svcs)
Kristin Mayotte (Dir-Education & Employment Svcs)
Paul Carey (Dir-Family Support Networks)
Laura Peterson (VP-HR)
Evan Graber (Dir-Outpatient Svcs)
Elaine Waters-Daverio (Dir-Quality Mgmt)
Nathan Peterson (Dir-Residential Svcs)
David Forsberg (Pres & CEO)

SEVEN KINGS HOLDINGS, INC.
630 Maple Wood Dr, Jupiter, FL 33458
Tel.: (561) 625-9443   FL
Web Site: http://www.skholdings.com
Year Founded: 1990
Sales Range: $10-24.9 Million
Emp.: 25
Building Operators
N.A.I.C.S.: 531110
William E. Taylor (CFO)
Raymond E. Graziotto (Pres & COO)
Andree Borrows (Coord-Sys & Trng)
Kenneth A. Blair (Officer-Govt Liason & Dir-Dev & Corp)
Linda D. Searles (VP-Ops)
Patricia Kohring (Controller)
Thomas W. Sheppard (Officer-Compliance & Safety)
J. C. Solomon II (CEO & Partner)

Subsidiaries:

Euro-Suites Hotel   (1)
501 Chestnut Rdg Rd, Morgantown, WV 26505-2769   (100%)
Tel.: (304) 598-1000
Web Site: http://www.eurosuites.com
Sales Range: $10-24.9 Million
Emp.: 24
Hotel
N.A.I.C.S.: 721110
Liz Kehler (Dir-Sls)

Loggerhead Marina   (1)
5821 32nd Way S, Saint Petersburg, FL 33712
Tel.: (727) 867-2600
Web Site: http://www.loggerheadstpete.com
Marinas
N.A.I.C.S.: 713930
John Purinton (Gen Mgr)

SEVEN MILE CAPITAL PARTNERS, LLC

U.S. PRIVATE

1370 Avenue of the Americas 22nd Fl, New York, NY 10019
Tel.: (212) 207-4945   DE
Web Site: http://www.sevenmilecp.com
Year Founded: 2011
Privater Equity Firm
N.A.I.C.S.: 523999
Vincent P. Fandozzi (Mng Partner)
Derek R. Lim (Principal)
Kevin J. Kruse (Partner)

Subsidiaries:

Huron Inc.   (1)
6554 Lakeshore Rd, Lexington, MI 48450
Tel.: (810) 359-5344
Web Site: http://www.huroninc.com
Precision Machined Motor Vehicle Components Mfr
N.A.I.C.S.: 336390
Jerry Solar (Pres & CEO)
John Bowns (VP & Dir-Sls)
Rick Cook (CFO & VP)
Gerard Seidl (Dir-Ops)

Microporous Products, LLC   (1)
596 Industrial Park Rd, Piney Flats, TN 37686
Tel.: (423) 722-2038
Web Site: http://www.microporous.net
Emp.: 153
Rubber & Polyethylene Battery Separators Mfr
N.A.I.C.S.: 326299
Peter Gaugl (VP-Ops)

SEVEN NETWORKS, INC.
2100 Seaport Blvd Ste 100, Redwood City, CA 94063
Tel.: (650) 381-2500
Web Site: http://www.seven.com
Year Founded: 2000
Sales Range: $1-9.9 Million
Emp.: 74
Wireless Software for Telecommunications Carriers
N.A.I.C.S.: 513210
Bill Nguyen (Founder)
Ross Bott (Pres & CEO)
Ari Backholm (Sr VP-Analytics & Market Dev)
Michael Luna (CTO)
Tamara Steffens (Exec VP-Worldwide Field Ops)

SEVEN ONE SEVEN PARKING SERVICES, INC.
1523 N Franklin St, Tampa, FL 33602
Tel.: (813) 228-7722
Web Site: http://www.717parking.com
Sales Range: $150-199.9 Million
Emp.: 2,500
Parking Services
N.A.I.C.S.: 812930
Jason Accardi (Pres)
John Accardi (VP)
John A. Accardi Sr. (Sr VP)

SEVEN POINT EQUITY PARTNERS, LLC
36 Church Ln, Westport, CT 06880
Tel.: (203) 293-4058
Web Site: http://www.sevenpointpartners.com
Private Investment Firm
N.A.I.C.S.: 523999
Paul Nowak (Operating Partner-Medical Products)
Thomas F. Burchill (Mng Partner)
Mark L. Kammert (Partner)
Randy Iles (Operating Partner-Bldg Products)
John Keller (Operating Partner-Bldg Products)
Eric Daliere (Operating Partner-Indus Products)

COMPANIES

Medin Technologies, Inc. (1)
11 Jackson Rd, Totowa, NJ 07512
Tel.: (973) 779-2400
Web Site: http://www.medin.com
Surgical & Medical Instrument Mfr
N.A.I.C.S.: 339112

The RiteScreen Company, LLC (1)
4314 State Rte 209, Elizabethville, PA 17023-8438
Tel.: (717) 365-3400
Web Site: http://www.ritescreen.com
Sales Range: $75-99.9 Million
Emp.: 340
Door & Window Screens Mfr
N.A.I.C.S.: 332999
John Keller (COO)
Laura Wixted (Dir-HR)
Teal Gaylord (VP-HR)
Chris Yankowich (CEO)

Plant (Domestic):

RiteScreen (2)
4314 Rte 209, Elizabethville, PA 17023 (100%)
Tel.: (423) 547-1000
Emp.: 160
Window & Door Screens & Components Mfr
N.A.I.C.S.: 332999
Beth Wilder (Mgr-HR)

SEVEN SEVENTEEN CREDIT UNION, INC.
3181 Larchmont Ave NE, Warren, OH 44483
Tel.: (330) 372-8100 OH
Web Site: http://www.sscu.net
Year Founded: 1957
Sales Range: $25-49.9 Million
Emp.: 281
Credit Union
N.A.I.C.S.: 522130
Gary Soukenik (Pres)
Cheryl D'Amore (Sr VP)
Jerome McGee (Exec VP)
Michael Donadio (Sr VP)

SEVEN-UP BOTTLING COMPANY RENO
1000 Terminal Way, Reno, NV 89502
Tel.: (775) 322-3456
Web Site: http://www.7upbottling.com
Sales Range: $10-24.9 Million
Emp.: 100
Carbonated Beverages, Nonalcoholic
N.A.I.C.S.: 312111
Edward R. Frazer (Pres)

SEVENS PAINT & WALLPAPER CO.
3070 29th St SE, Grand Rapids, MI 49512
Tel.: (616) 942-2020
Web Site: http://www.sevenspaint.com
Sales Range: $10-24.9 Million
Emp.: 100
Provider of Paint & Wallpaper
N.A.I.C.S.: 444120
Mike Hanna (Dir-IT)

SEVENSON ENVIRONMENTAL SERVICES, INC.
2749 Lockport Rd, Niagara Falls, NY 14305
Tel.: (716) 284-0431 NY
Web Site: http://www.sevenson.com
Year Founded: 1977
Sales Range: $150-199.9 Million
Emp.: 500
Field Services for Remediation of Sites & Facilities Contaminated by Hazardous Materials
N.A.I.C.S.: 562910
Richard A. Elia (Exec VP)

Subsidiaries:

Sevenson Industrial Services, Inc. (1)
2749 Lockport Rd, Niagara Falls, NY 14305-2229 (100%)
Tel.: (716) 284-0431
Web Site: http://www.sevenson.com
Sales Range: $10-24.9 Million
Emp.: 100
Provides Field Services For the Remediation of Sites & Facilities Contaminated By Hazardous Materials
N.A.I.C.S.: 561720
Michael A. Elia (Pres)
Alan R. Elia Jr. (Pres & CEO)

Waste Stream Technology, Inc. (1)
302 Grote St, Buffalo, NY 14207-2442 (100%)
Tel.: (716) 876-5290
Sales Range: $10-24.9 Million
Emp.: 40
Analytical & Treatability Lab
N.A.I.C.S.: 238990
Daniel Vollmer (Dir-QA & QC)

SEVENTH POINT
4752 Euclid Rd, Virginia Beach, VA 23462-3823
Tel.: (757) 473-8152
Web Site: http://www.seventhpoint.com
Sales Range: $25-49.9 Million
Emp.: 28
Advertising Agencies
N.A.I.C.S.: 541810
Chris Calcagno (Owner & Pres)
Mike Carosi (VP-Production Ops)
Lovene Ballard (Acct Exec)

SEVENTY2 CAPITAL WEALTH MANAGEMENT LLC
7200 Wisconsin Ave Ste 903, Bethesda, MD 20814
Tel.: (301) 298-2230
Web Site: http://www.seventy2capital.com
Investment Services
N.A.I.C.S.: 523999
Troy Elser (Partner)
Thomas Fautrel (Co-Founder & Pres)
Joy Lomibao (VP-Client Relations & Founding Member)
Michael Levitsky (Partner & Dir-Investment Strategy)
Steve Otten (Sr VP)
Paul Carlson (Co-Founder & CEO)
Eric Bost (Partner)
Scott Gibson (Partner)
Linda Whittington (Partner)

SEVERN SCHOOL, INC
1185 Baltimore Annapolis Blvd, Arnold, MD 21012
Tel.: (410) 647-7700
Web Site: https://www.severnschool.com
Year Founded: 1914
Educational School
N.A.I.C.S.: 611310
Shannon Howell (Dir-Dev)
James M. Murphy (Chm)
John Stamato (Vice Chm)
Jon M. Mahan (Treas)
Jonathan Kagan (Sec)
Julian Domenech (Dir-Athletic)
Michael Glasby (Dir-Diversity, Equity, and Inclusion)
Christopher Sapienza (Dir-Fin & Bus)
Kim Slade (Dir-Enrollment, Mgmt, and Outreach)
Sidra Smith (Dir-Studies & Strategic Initiatives)

SEVERN TRENT SERVICES, INC.
220 Gibralter Rd Ste 200, Horsham, PA 19044

Tel.: (215) 646-9201 PA
Web Site: http://www.severntrentservices.com
Emp.: 40
Contract Water & Sewage Processing Management Services
N.A.I.C.S.: 238990
Stephane Bouvier (CEO)
John Freebody (CFO)
Chris Turnbull (Gen Counsel & VP)
Mark Halleman (Sr VP-Bus Dev)
Bill Malarkey (Sr VP-Strategy & Market Dev)
Shelly Azen (VP-HR)
Marnie R. Vaughan (Dir-Benefits, Compensation & HRIS)
Doug Hilton (Dir-Talent)

Subsidiaries:

Severn Trent Services, Inc. - Katy Office (1)
2002 w Grand pkway N 3100 kdteay, Houston, TX 77084-5109
Tel.: (281) 398-8211
Web Site: http://www.severntrentservices.com
Contract Water & Sewage Processing Management Services
N.A.I.C.S.: 238990

SEVERSON GROUP INCORPORATED
3601 Serpentine Dr, Los Alamitos, CA 90720
Tel.: (562) 493-3611
Web Site: http://www.mandsinc.com
Rev.: $97,522,504
Emp.: 58
Commercial & Office Building, New Construction
N.A.I.C.S.: 236220
Jonathan E. Severson (Chm)
Scott Feest (Sr VP)

Subsidiaries:

Millie & Severson Inc. (1)
3601 Serpentine Dr, Los Alamitos, CA 90720
Tel.: (562) 493-3611
Web Site: http://www.mandsinc.com
Sales Range: $25-49.9 Million
Emp.: 50
Nonresidential Construction General Contractor
N.A.I.C.S.: 236220
Jonathan E. Severson (Chm)
Brian T. Cresap (Pres)
Sandra Gutierrez (Dir-Corp Ops)

Petra Investment Company (1)
3601 Serpentine Dr, Los Alamitos, CA 90720
Tel.: (562) 493-3611
Web Site: http://www.mandsinc.com
Rev.: $250,000
Emp.: 50
Real Estate Consultant
N.A.I.C.S.: 541618
Robert Wissmann (VP)

SEVIER FARMERS COOPERATIVE
321 W Main St, Sevierville, TN 37862
Tel.: (865) 453-7101
Web Site: http://www.ourcoop.com
Sales Range: $10-24.9 Million
Emp.: 40
Retail Nurseries & Garden Stores
N.A.I.C.S.: 444240
Clint Hodges (Mgr)

SEVILLE CENTRAL MIX CORPORATION
157 Albany Ave, Freeport, NY 11520
Tel.: (516) 868-3000 NY
Year Founded: 1980
Sales Range: $10-24.9 Million
Emp.: 5
Providers of Ready-Mixed Concrete
N.A.I.C.S.: 327320

SEWART SUPPLY INC.

Peter Scalamandre (Pres)
Rocco Rossini (Controller)

SEVIROLI FOODS, INC.
301 Brook St, Garden City, NY 11530
Tel.: (516) 222-6220
Web Site: http://www.seviroli.com
Frozen Food Mfr
N.A.I.C.S.: 311412
Joseph Seviroli (Pres & CEO)

SEW WHAT, INC.
1978 E Gladwick St, Compton, CA 90220
Tel.: (310) 639-6000 CA
Web Site: http://www.sewwhatinc.com
Year Founded: 1998
Sales Range: $1-9.9 Million
Emp.: 31
Mfr of Custom Stage Curtains
N.A.I.C.S.: 459130
Adam Duckett (CFO)
Lynda Vaughn (Gen Mgr)
Megan Duckett (Pres & Mgr-Mktg)

SEW-EURODRIVE INC.
1275 Old Spartanburg Hwy, Lyman, SC 29365-1820
Tel.: (864) 439-8792 OH
Web Site: http://www.seweurodrive.com
Year Founded: 1975
Sales Range: $25-49.9 Million
Emp.: 500
Provider of Speed Changer Services
N.A.I.C.S.: 333612
Mike Thompson (Mgr-Customer Svc)
Erica Mosley (Controller)

SEWARD CO-OP GROCERY & DELI
2823 E Franklin Ave, Minneapolis, MN 55406
Tel.: (612) 338-2465
Web Site: http://www.seward.coop
Year Founded: 1972
Sales Range: $25-49.9 Million
Emp.: 209
Agricultural Cooperative Program Administration Services
N.A.I.C.S.: 926140
Leah Janus (Pres)
Joe Riemann (VP)
Sean Doyle (Gen Mgr)
Nick Seeberger (Mgr-Ops)
Liz Liddiard Wozniak (Mgr-HR)
Alex Betzenheimer (Mgr-Fin)
Travis Lusk (Mgr-Franklin Produce)
Leo Sanders (Mgr-Facilities)
Billy Williams (Mgr-Franklin Deli)
Heather Eddy (Mgr-Franklin Store)
Beau Kinstler (Mgr-IT)

SEWARD MOTOR FREIGHT, INC.
970 280th Rd, Seward, NE 68434
Tel.: (402) 643-4503
Web Site: http://www.sewardmotor.com
Year Founded: 1969
Sales Range: $10-24.9 Million
Emp.: 188
Trucking Except Local
N.A.I.C.S.: 484121
Joan Tanderup (Owner)
Ron Niemoth (Treas & Sec)
Joyce Helge (VP-Ops)
Eric H. Helge (VP-Safety)
Karla Kassik (Asst Dir-Safety)
Russ Langley (VP-Sls)
Nan McCoy (Mgr-Gen Sls)

SEWART SUPPLY INC.

SEWART SUPPLY INC.

Sewart Supply Inc.—(Continued)
7201 Hwy 182, Morgan City, LA 70380
Tel.: (985) 385-0380
Web Site: http://www.sewartsupply.com
Rev.: $22,000,000
Emp.: 24
Industrial Supplies
N.A.I.C.S.: 423840
Don Loupe (Branch Mgr-Friendswood)
Dan Templet (Branch Mgr-Harvey)
Todd Braus (Branch Mgr-Morgan City)

SEWCO INC.
1200 S Taylor St, Amarillo, TX 79101
Tel.: (806) 372-2236
Sales Range: $10-24.9 Million
Emp.: 50
Office Furniture & Office Supplies
N.A.I.C.S.: 449110
Ronald Watts (VP)
John Vanarrete (Controller)
Tommy Samson (Pres)

SEWELL CADILLAC CHEVROLET
701 Baronne St, New Orleans, LA 70113
Tel.: (504) 581-7585
Year Founded: 1986
Sales Range: $25-49.9 Million
Emp.: 120
Car Whslr
N.A.I.C.S.: 441110
Steve Schell (Gen Mgr)

SEWELL CLOTHING COMPANY INC.
115 Pacific Ave, Bremen, GA 30110
Tel.: (770) 537-2391 GA
Year Founded: 1935
Sales Range: $10-24.9 Million
Emp.: 200
Mfr of Men's & Boys' Suits
N.A.I.C.S.: 315250
Thompson Lewis (Pres)

SEWELL HARDWARE CO., INC.
1318 Mercer Ave, West Palm Beach, FL 33401
Tel.: (561) 832-7171
Web Site: http://www.sewellhardware.com
Year Founded: 1924
Sales Range: $10-24.9 Million
Emp.: 45
Retailer of Hardware
N.A.I.C.S.: 423710

SEWELL MOTOR COMPANY
3860 W NW Hwy Ste 100, Dallas, TX 75220
Tel.: (214) 902-2222 TX
Web Site: http://www.sewell.com
Year Founded: 1911
Sales Range: $125-149.9 Million
Emp.: 1,415
New & Used Car Dealerships Owner & Operator
N.A.I.C.S.: 441110
Carl J. Sewell (Gen Mgr)
Frank Jackson (Mgr-Production)
Bryan Walker (Asst Mgr-Svc)
Taylor Tullos (Asst Mgr-Svc)
Annette Starr (Controller)
Victoria Kean (Coord-Digital Mktg)
Stephen Tolerico (Dir-Mktg)
Baden Rowland (Gen Mgr)
Alyssa Noonan (Mgr-Fin)
Nick Gerlach (Mgr-Fin)
Angela Hesselgesser (Mgr-HR)
Butch Gautier (Mgr-Sls)
Danny Tyroch (Mgr-Sls)
Amy Huffman (Office Mgr)
Paul Latham (Project Mgr)
Jennifer Mercer (Asst Mgr-Credit)
Matt Redding (Asst Mgr-Parts)
Cameron Cummings (Asst Mgr-Svc)
Duren Jenkins (Asst Mgr-Svc)
Melinda Brand (Asst Mgr-Svc)
Mark Smith (COO)
Courtney Park (Coord-Special Events)
Deborah Verdinella (Dir-Fin)
Ron Mathis (Dir-Info Sys)
Chris Anderson (Dir-Mktg)
Corey Hawkins (Dir-Pre-Owned)
Jesse Gray (Dir-Pre-Owned Sls)
Klint Guerry (Gen Mgr-Plano)
Saadallah El-Jundi (Gen Mgr-Sls)
Clay Geistweidt (Mgr-Accessories)
Jason Burk (Mgr-Accessory)
Jacy Russell (Mgr-Fin)
Kalie Presti (Mgr-Fin)
Katie Tillman (Mgr-Fin)
Mallory Roberts (Mgr-Fin)
Stacy Carrington (Mgr-Fin)
Tara Hafertepe (Mgr-Fin)
Kevin Cobb (Mgr-Fixed Ops)
Joel Bruner (Mgr-Parts)
Rick Dovidio (Mgr-Parts)
Dana Waters (Mgr-Production)
Cory Nelson (Mgr-Sls)
Heath Fell (Mgr-Sls)
Ryan Leech (Mgr-Sls)
Curtis Roberson (Mgr-Svc)
Kenny Pruett (Mgr-Svc)
Russell Crader (Mgr-Vehicle Exchange)
Rodney Williams (Supvr-Warehouse)

Subsidiaries:

Sewell BMW MINI of Plano (1)
6800 Dallas Pkwy, Plano, TX 75024
Tel.: (972) 918-1100
Web Site: http://www.bmwofplano.com
Automobiles, New & Used
N.A.I.C.S.: 441110
John Kobell (Gen Mgr)
Robert Hamilton (Mgr-Svc)
David Williams (Dir-Body Shop)
Eric Maas (Owner & Principal)
John Meade (Dir-Fin)
Lon Lowery (Dir-Pre-Owned Sls)
Amanda Malchi (Mgr-Fin)
Arun Menon (Mgr-Fin)
Joe Verhey (Mgr-Fin)
Tim Walker (Mgr-Fin)
Randy Des Camp (Mgr-New Car Sls)
Randy Descamp (Mgr-New Car Sls)
Allen Holmes (Mgr-New Car Sls)

Sewell Cadillac of Dallas (1)
7310 Lemmon Ave, Dallas, TX 75209
Tel.: (214) 350-2000
Web Site: http://cadillacdallas.sewell.com
Sales Range: $100-124.9 Million
Emp.: 100
New & Used Car Dealer
N.A.I.C.S.: 441110
Benton Hodges (Mgr-Pre-Owned Sls)
Brad Morris (Mgr-Svc)
Chris Anderson (Dir-Mktg)

Sewell Ford (1)
2425 E 8th St, Odessa, TX 79761
Tel.: (432) 498-0421
Web Site: http://www.sewellford.com
Rev.: $95,000,000
Emp.: 283
Automobiles, New & Used
N.A.I.C.S.: 441110
Paul Crump (Gen Mgr)
Michael Merrill (VP-Sls)
Collin Sewell (Pres)
Jose Mendez (CFO)
Adrian Vega (Chief People Officer)

Sewell Infiniti of Dallas (1)
7110 Lemmon Ave, Dallas, TX 75209-3608
Tel.: (972) 490-4545
Web Site: http://www.sewellinfiniti-dallas.com
Sales Range: $1-9.9 Million
Emp.: 40
New & Used Car Dealer
N.A.I.C.S.: 441110
Doug Veling (Gen Mgr)

Sewell Lexus of Dallas (1)
6421 Lemmon Ave, Dallas, TX 75209
Tel.: (214) 352-8100
Web Site: http://www.sldallas.sewell.com
Sales Range: $75-99.9 Million
Emp.: 430
New & Used Car Dealer
N.A.I.C.S.: 441110
Dudley Haralson (Gen Mgr)

SEWER EQUIPMENT CO. OF AMERICA
1590 Dutch Rd, Dixon, IL 61021
Tel.: (847) 729-3316
Web Site: http://www.sewerequip.com
Sales Range: $10-24.9 Million
Emp.: 50
Sewer Cleaning Equipment
N.A.I.C.S.: 333310
Daniel J. O'Brien (Pres)
John Wichmann (CFO)

SEXTON AUTOMOTIVE GROUP
269 S Roane St, Harriman, TN 37748
Tel.: (865) 882-0833
Web Site: http://www.sextonautos.com
Rev.: $21,300,000
Emp.: 48
Sales & Service New & Used Automobiles
N.A.I.C.S.: 441110
Tim Pollitt (Gen Mgr)

SEXTON CAN CO., INC.
3101 Sexton Rd, Decatur, AL 35603
Tel.: (256) 355-5850 MA
Web Site: http://www.sextoncan.com
Year Founded: 1880
Sales Range: $75-99.9 Million
Emp.: 200
Mfr of Drawn Metal Containers
N.A.I.C.S.: 332431
Doug Baker (Mgr-Sls)

SEXTON PEST CONTROL, INC.
1401 N 29th Ave, Phoenix, AZ 85009
Tel.: (602) 942-3653 AZ
Web Site: http://www.sextonpestcontrol.com
Year Founded: 1985
Sales Range: $1-9.9 Million
Emp.: 89
Disinfecting & Pest Control Services
N.A.I.C.S.: 561710
Kent Sexton Jr. (Owner & Pres)

SEYFARTH SHAW
131 S Dearborn Ste 2400, Chicago, IL 60603-5810
Tel.: (312) 346-8000 DE
Web Site: http://www.seyfarth.com
Year Founded: 1945
Sales Range: $25-49.9 Million
Emp.: 900
Law firm
N.A.I.C.S.: 541110
Noah A. Finkel (Partner)
Blake Hornick (Partner)
Emma C. Mata (Partner)
Jesse M. Coleman (Partner)
Edward F. Fox (Partner)
John A. Lambremont (Partner)
Thomas Schramkowski (Partner)
Gordon Peery (Partner)
Gregg D. Bernhard (Partner)
David Holcombe (Sr Engr-Software-Chicago)
Heather L. Eskra (Sr Project Mgr-Legal-Chicago)
John E. Duggan (Sr Project Mgr-Legal-Chicago)
Julie A. Heine (Mgr-Legal Project)
Kyle D. Hoover (Project Mgr-Legal-Chicago)
Jeremy A. Cohen (Partner)
John D. Shire (Partner)
William B. Eck (Partner)
Gregory A. Markel (Partner-Litigation Dept-New York)
Katherine E. Perrelli (Chm-Litigation Dept & Partner)
John P. Napoli (Co-Mng Partner-New York)
Andrew S. Boutros (Partner)
Andrew R. Hough (Partner)
Kevin Young (Partner)
Andrew D. Jurczyk (CIO)
Josh Kubicki (Chief Strategy Officer)
Gregg Dulik (Partner-Litigation Dept & Construction Practice Grp-San Francisco)
Scott Lindvall (Chm-Intellectual Property Trial Practice & Partner-New York)
Steven Meier (Chm-Corp Dept)
Mark S. Albert (Partner-Corp Dept)
Cory Hirsch (Mng Partner)
Amanda Sonneborn (Mng Partner)
Dean Fanelli (Partner)
Thomas Haag (Partner)
Alison Ashford (Partner)
Arren Goldman (Partner)
Cliff Fonstein (Partner)
Cyril M. Derzie (Partner)
Daniel J. Evans (Partner)
David A. Blake (Partner)
Dean L. Fanelli (Partner)
Dennis H. Greenstein (Partner)
Jason E. Burritt (Partner)
Karen Y. Bitar (Partner)
Lester M. Bliwise (Partner)
Loren Gesinsky (Partner)
Lorie E. Almon (Co-Mng Partner-New York)
Marjorie R. Culver (Partner)
Miles M. Borden (Partner)
Paul Galligan (Partner)
Raymond C. Baldwin (Partner)
Robert L. Bodansky (Partner)
Ronald S. Gart (Partner)
Sara Beiro Farabow (Partner)
Stanley Bloch (Partner)
Stephen G. Epstein (Partner)
Thomas Galli (Partner)
Tonya M. Esposito (Partner)
Paul F. Kruger (Chm-Structured Fin Grp-Global)
John L. Telford Jr. (Partner)

Subsidiaries:

Fanelli Haag Kilger PLLC (1)
1909 K St NW Ste 1120, Washington, DC 20006
Tel.: (202) 706-7910
Web Site: http://www.fanellihaag.com
Power Boiler & Heat Exchanger Mfr
N.A.I.C.S.: 332410
Thomas Haag (Partner)

Seyfarth Shaw (UK) LLP (1)
CityPoint One Ropemaker Street, London, EC2Y 9AW, United Kingdom
Tel.: (44) 20 7763 2500
Web Site: http://www.seyfarth.com
Emp.: 20
Law firm
N.A.I.C.S.: 541199
Peter Talibart (Mng Partner)

SEYFERTH & ASSOCIATES INC.
40 Monroe Ctr NW, Grand Rapids, MI 49503
Tel.: (616) 776-3511 MI

COMPANIES

Web Site: http://www.seyferthpr.com
Year Founded: 1984
Sales Range: $10-24.9 Million
Emp.: 62
Public Relations Agency
N.A.I.C.S.: 541820
Ginny M. Seyferth *(Pres)*
Dan Spaulding *(Principal)*
Eileen McNeil *(Principal & VP-Govt Affairs)*
Michael Zalewski *(VP-Media Rels)*
Regina Daukss *(VP-Fin)*
Cynthia Domingo *(VP)*
Tyler Lecceadone *(Principal)*
Tatiana Grant *(Partner-Strategic)*

SEYMOUR MIDWEST LLC
2666 Country Club Rd, Warsaw, IN 46580
Tel.: (574) 267-7875
Web Site:
  http://www.coatings.seymourmidwest.com
Year Founded: 1990
Sales Range: $1-9.9 Million
Emp.: 25
Hand & Edge Tool Mfr
N.A.I.C.S.: 332216
Bob Vitoux *(Pres & CEO)*

Subsidiaries:

Seymour Manufacturing Co., Inc. (1)
500 N Broadway, Seymour, IN 47274
Tel.: (812) 522-2900
Web Site: http://www.seymourmfg.com
Emp.: 100
Hand Tool Mfr
N.A.I.C.S.: 332216
Randy Schubert *(Sr VP-Sls)*
Todd Sandbakken *(VP-Natl Accts)*
Dennis Park *(VP-Matls)*
Phil Miller *(VP-Mfg)*
Chuck Yeager *(Exec VP-Sls & Strategic Plng)*

Division (Domestic):

Seymour Manufacturing Link Handle Division (2)
219 Handle St, Sequatchie, TN 37374-0128
Tel.: (423) 942-5901
Web Site: http://www.seymourmfg.com
Wood Tool Handles Mfr
N.A.I.C.S.: 321999
Lewis McNeal *(Plant Mgr)*
Louis Nickel *(Plant Mgr)*

SEYMOUR N. LOGAN ASSOCIATES
29 South La Salle St Ste 705, Chicago, IL 60603
Tel.: (312) 782-6008
Web Site:
  http://www.associatedhotelsllc.com
Rev.: $12,600,000
Emp.: 10
Real Estate Managers
N.A.I.C.S.: 531210
Bryan Curry *(CFO)*
Jay D. Fishman *(Pres)*
Marti L. Robinson *(Asst VP-HR)*

SEYMOUR OF SYCAMORE, INC.
917 Crosby Ave, Sycamore, IL 60178-1343
Tel.: (815) 895-9101   IL
Web Site:
  http://www.seymourpaint.com
Year Founded: 1949
Sales Range: $75-99.9 Million
Emp.: 120
Aerosol Paint & Coatings Mfr
N.A.I.C.S.: 325510
Nancy Seymour Heatley *(CEO)*
Chris Heatley *(VP)*
Chuck Voorhies *(Mgr-Traffic)*
Dennis Kuntzelman *(Mgr-Safety)*
Jon Larson *(Plant Mgr)*

SF FIRE CREDIT UNION
3201 California St, San Francisco, CA 94118
Tel.: (415) 674-4800   CA
Web Site: http://www.sffirecu.org
Year Founded: 1951
Sales Range: $25-49.9 Million
Emp.: 161
Credit Union Operator
N.A.I.C.S.: 522130
Jennifer Ebert *(Sr VP-Fin & Admin)*
Darren Herrmann *(Pres & CEO)*
Frances E. Lee *(Sec)*
John E. Sweeney *(Chm)*

SF HOLDING CORP.
111 Center St, Little Rock, AR 72201-4402
Tel.: (501) 377-2000   AR
Web Site: http://www.stephens.com
Year Founded: 1946
Financial Holding Company; Investment Banking, Private Equity, Insurance & Wealth Management Services
N.A.I.C.S.: 551112
Warren Amerine Stephens Jr. *(Chm)*
Mark Doramus *(CFO)*
Curt Bradbury *(COO)*
Douglas H Martin *(Sr Mng Dir)*

Subsidiaries:

Stephens, Inc. (1)
111 Ctr St, Little Rock, AR 72203
Tel.: (501) 377-2000
Web Site: http://www.stephens.com
Investment Banking, Private Equity, Insurance & Wealth Management Services
N.A.I.C.S.: 523910
Douglas Howard Martin *(Sr Mng Dir)*
Warren Amerine Stephens Jr. *(Chm, Pres & CEO)*
Mary E. Kissel *(Exec VP)*
Curt Bradbury *(COO)*
Peter Gant *(Mng Dir & Head-Tech)*
Mark Christopher Doramus *(CFO)*
Joshua Long *(Mng Dir-Equity Res)*
Rachel Mondl Mayo *(Gen Counsel)*
Chris Bettina *(Sr VP)*
Matthew Marks *(Exec VP & Head-Investment Banking)*
Jason J. Fair *(Sr VP)*
Kevin Scanlon *(Exec VP & Head-Stephens Private Wealth Mgmt)*

Subsidiary (Domestic):

Stephens Capital Partners LLC (2)
111 Center St, Little Rock, AR 72201
Tel.: (501) 377-2000
Web Site: http://www.stephens.com
Privater Equity Firm
N.A.I.C.S.: 523999
Douglas Howard Martin *(Sr Mng Dir)*
Kathy Riley Bryant *(CFO)*
Robert Janes *(Mng Dir)*
Noel M. Strauss *(Mng Dir)*
Kevin W. Wilcox *(Mng Dir)*
Curt Bradbury *(COO)*
Mark Doramus *(COO)*
Richard H. Blank Jr. *(Mng Dir)*
Jackson Farrow Jr. *(Mng Dir & Gen Counsel)*

Holding (Domestic):

Vanguard Truck Centers, LLC (3)
3348 Peachtree Rd NE Tower Pl 200 Ste 1450, Atlanta, GA 30326
Tel.: (866) 216-7925
Web Site: http://www.vanguardtrucks.com
Commercial Truck Sales & Service
N.A.I.C.S.: 423110
John M. Thomas *(Exec VP-Sls)*
Tom Ewing *(Pres & CEO)*

Subsidiary (Domestic):

Nacarato Trucks, Inc. (4)
519 New Paul Rd, La Vergne, TN 37086
Tel.: (615) 280-2800
Web Site: http://www.nacaratotrucks.com
Sales Range: $100-124.9 Million
Emp.: 200
Trucks, Tractors & Trailers: New & Used
N.A.I.C.S.: 441110

Michael J. Nacarato *(CEO)*
Lloyd Baldridge *(CFO)*

Subsidiary (Domestic):

General GMC Truck Sales & Service, Inc. (5)
360 S Military Trl, West Palm Beach, FL 33415
Tel.: (561) 686-8906
Web Site: http://www.generalgmc.com
Sales Range: $1-9.9 Million
Emp.: 20
Automobile & Motor Vehicle Whslr
N.A.I.C.S.: 423110
Ron Chandler *(Mgr-Parts)*

Subsidiary (Domestic):

Vanguard Truck Center of St. Louis (4)
2350 Chouteau Ave, Saint Louis, MO 63103
Tel.: (314) 771-3180
Web Site: http://www.vanguardtrucks.com
Commercial Truck Sales & Service
N.A.I.C.S.: 423110
Kirk Slaten *(Controller)*
Mitch Casey *(Branch Mgr)*
Dan Green *(Mgr-Truck Sls & Lease)*
Sean Doyle *(Mgr-Parts)*
Bill Ripple *(Mgr-Svc)*

Holding (Domestic):

Women's Marketing, Inc. (3)
1221 Post Rd E Ste 201, Westport, CT 06880-5430
Tel.: (203) 256-0880
Web Site:
  http://www.womensmarketing.com
Emp.: 200
Marketing & Advertising Services
N.A.I.C.S.: 541613
Andrea Van Dam *(CEO)*
Kate Dillon *(Sr VP-HR & Ops)*
Eric Cowles *(Gen Mgr-Beauty)*
Brandon Heagle *(Chief Digital Officer)*
Raquel Klugman *(Sr VP-Beauty)*
Doug Bivona *(CFO)*
Marjorie Powers *(Gen Mgr-Food, Beverage & Retail)*
Rich Zeldes *(Exec VP & Mng Dir-Global Bus Dev)*
Marlea Clark *(Exec VP-Mktg & Insights)*
Kim Haley *(Exec VP-Account Strategy)*
John LaPierre *(Sr VP-Analytics & Digital Ops)*
Elissa Brown *(Media Dir)*
Anthony Vespucci *(VP-Client Svcs)*
Jenna Manula Linares *(Dir-Social Media Mktg)*
Domenica Kraus *(Sr VP-Media)*
Ann Quasarano D'Adamo *(Dir-Content)*
Lily Ray *(Dir-SEO)*
Matt Strietmeier *(Dir-Paid Search)*
Anat Rubin *(Sr VP-Adv Svcs)*
Nick Koutsopoulos *(Media Dir)*
Kathryn Pleines *(Dir-Social Strategy)*

Branch (Domestic):

Women's Marketing, Inc. - New York Office (4)
276 5th Ave Ste 407, New York, NY 10001
Tel.: (212) 673-4500
Web Site:
  http://www.womensmarketing.com
Marketing & Advertising Services
N.A.I.C.S.: 541613
Andrea Van Dam *(CEO)*

Subsidiary (Domestic):

Stephens Production Company (2)
623 Garrison Ave, Fort Smith, AR 72901
Tel.: (479) 783-4191
Natural Gas Production Services
N.A.I.C.S.: 213112

SF INVESTMENTS, INC.
799 Central Ave Ste 350, Highland Park, IL 60035
Tel.: (847) 926-5700   IL
Web Site: http://www.sfinv.com
Year Founded: 1972
Investment Management Service
N.A.I.C.S.: 523940
Daniel Shapiro *(Pres)*

SF POLICE CREDIT UNION
2550 Irving St, San Francisco, CA 94122
Tel.: (415) 564-3800   CA
Web Site: http://www.sfpcu.org
Year Founded: 1953
Sales Range: $25-49.9 Million
Emp.: 123
Credit Union
N.A.I.C.S.: 522130
Eddie Young *(Pres & CEO)*
Al Casciato *(Vice Chm)*
Michael Hebel *(Chm)*

SFA DESIGN
136 W Canon Perdido Ste 220, Santa Barbara, CA 93101
Tel.: (805) 692-1948   CA
Web Site: http://www.sfadesign.com
Year Founded: 1996
Sales Range: $25-49.9 Million
Emp.: 35
Interior Design Services
N.A.I.C.S.: 541410
Sue Firestone *(Founder & Chm)*
Kara Smith *(Pres)*
Mimi Wolfe *(Sr Project Mgr & Dir-Studio)*
Rosie Feinberg *(Principal)*

SFFI COMPANY, INC.
4383 Exchange Ave, Vernon, CA 90058-2619
Tel.: (323) 586-0000
Web Site:
  http://www.simplyfreshfruit.com
Sales Range: $25-49.9 Million
Emp.: 175
Fruit & Vegetable Canning Services
N.A.I.C.S.: 311421
Jaxon Potter *(VP)*
William T. Sander *(Pres)*
Laura Garcia *(Mgr-HR)*
Raul Moreno *(Mgr-Production)*

SFI OF TENNESSEE, L.L.C.
4768 Hungerford Rd, Memphis, TN 38118-7001
Tel.: (901) 363-1571   TN
Web Site: http://www.sfifab.com
Year Founded: 1956
Sales Range: $100-124.9 Million
Emp.: 800
Fabricated Parts for Transportation Industry
N.A.I.C.S.: 336370
Mark Baxter *(Controller)*

SFM MUTUAL INSURANCE COMPANY
3500 American Blvd W Ste 700, Bloomington, MN 55431
Tel.: (952) 838-4200
Web Site: http://www.sfmic.com
Year Founded: 1983
Rev.: $103,078,236
Emp.: 180
Insurance Services
N.A.I.C.S.: 524126
Daniel M. Janiga *(Dir-Medical)*
Michael L. Happe *(VP-Bus Dev & Mktg)*
David E. Kaiser *(CIO & VP)*
Terrence L. Miller *(Pres & CEO)*

Subsidiaries:

Barrier Free Access, Inc. (1)
1207 Frontage Rd NW, Byron, MN 55920-1386
Tel.: (507) 775-2828
Web Site: http://www.barrierfreeaccess.com
Medical, Dental & Hospital Equipment Distr
N.A.I.C.S.: 423450
Mark Stinson *(Pres & CEO)*

SFO FORECAST INC.

SFO FORECAST INC.

SFO Forecast Inc.—(Continued)
496 Jefferson St, San Francisco, CA 94109
Tel.: (415) 771-5200   CA
Web Site: http://www.sfoportco.com
Year Founded: 1991
Rev.: $13,994,797
Emp.: 45
Family Clothing Stores
N.A.I.C.S.: 458110
Arthur Hoppe *(Pres)*
Abdul Benali *(Gen Mgr-Store)*
David Berbey *(VP)*
Rhoda Berbey *(Controller)*
Arthur Hoppe *(Pres)*

SFW CAPITAL PARTNERS LLC
22 Elm Pl, Rye, NY 10580
Tel.: (914) 510-8910
Web Site: http://www.sfwcap.com
Year Founded: 2007
Emp.: 12
Privater Equity Firm
N.A.I.C.S.: 523999
Thomas P. Salice *(Co-Founder, Partner & Principal)*
Roger C. Freeman *(Partner)*
David N. Webb *(Partner)*
Ahmad Sheikh *(Partner)*
Omair Sarwar *(Principal)*
Joe Testani *(CFO & Chief Compliance Officer)*
Andrew Kane *(VP)*

Subsidiaries:

Buyers Laboratory LLC   (1)
20 Railroad Ave, Hackensack, NJ 07601
Tel.: (201) 488-0404
Web Site: http://www.buyerslab.com
Sales Range: $1-9.9 Million
Emp.: 41
Analytical Information & Services for Digital Imaging & Document Management Industry
N.A.I.C.S.: 513120
Anthony Polifrone *(Mng Dir)*
Daria Hoffman *(Mng Editor)*
Patricia Clyne *(Sr VP-Sls)*
Peter Coletto *(CFO)*
Joseph J. Douress *(COO, CMO & Chief Product Officer)*
Anthony Marchesini *(Dir-IT)*
John A. Lawler IV *(Pres & CEO)*

RDI Technologies, Inc.   (1)
10024 Investment Dr Ste 150, Knoxville, TN 37932
Tel.: (865) 256-0105
Web Site: http://www.rditechnologies.com
Sales Range: $1-9.9 Million
Emp.: 50
Technical Product Mfr
N.A.I.C.S.: 327110
Bob Wilson *(Pres)*
Jeff Hay *(CEO)*
Jenna Johns *(COO)*
Geoff Robson *(CFO)*
Mark Slemp *(VP-Software Dev)*

Subsidiary (Domestic):

Fastec Imaging Corp.   (2)
17150 Via Del Campo Ste 1, San Diego, CA 92127
Tel.: (858) 592-2342
Web Site: http://www.fastecimaging.com
Sales Range: $1-9.9 Million
Emp.: 25
Motion Picture/Video Production
N.A.I.C.S.: 512110

SG ENTERPRISES II, LLC
155-108th Ave. Ne, Ste 400,, Bellevue, WA 98004
Tel.: (425) 458-5900
Telecommunication Servicesb
N.A.I.C.S.: 517112

Subsidiaries:

Trilogy International Partners Inc.   (1)
155-108 Ave NE Ste 400, Bellevue, WA 98004
Tel.: (425) 458-5900
Web Site: https://www.trilogy-international.com
Rev.: $238,517,000
Assets: $40,640,000
Liabilities: $7,184,000
Net Worth: $33,456,000
Earnings: $433,461,000
Emp.: 7
Fiscal Year-end: 12/31/2022
Holding Company; Wireless Telecommunications Services
N.A.I.C.S.: 551112
John William Stanton *(Co-Founder & Chm)*
Scott Morris *(Gen Counsel, Sec & Sr VP)*
Erik Mickels *(CFO & Sr VP)*

Subsidiary (Domestic):

Trilogy International Partners LLC   (2)
155, 108 Ave NE Ste 400, Bellevue, WA 98004
Tel.: (425) 458-5900
Wireless Telecommunication Services
N.A.I.C.S.: 517112

Subsidiary (Non-US):

Two Degrees Mobile Limited   (2)
Symonds Street, PO Box 8355, Auckland, 1150, New Zealand   (73.17%)
Tel.: (64) 222002000
Web Site: http://www.2degreesmobile.co.nz
Telecommunication Broadband Services
N.A.I.C.S.: 517810
Christine De Lange *(Mgr-Key Acct)*

SG WHOLESALE ROOFING SUPPLIES
1101 E 6th St, Santa Ana, CA 92701
Tel.: (714) 568-1900
Web Site: http://www.sgroof.com
Sales Range: $10-24.9 Million
Emp.: 50
Roofing & Siding Materials
N.A.I.C.S.: 423330
Roger Glazer *(Pres)*
Arleen Galiati *(Mgr-Credit)*
Evy Mealey *(Branch Mgr)*

SGA GROUP, PC
100 Walnut Ave Ste 103, Clark, NJ 07066
Tel.: (732) 381-8887
Web Site: http://www.sganj.com
Year Founded: 1987
Rev.: $2,400,000
Emp.: 14
Accounting Services
N.A.I.C.S.: 541219
Thomas M. Angelo *(Mng Principal)*
Kathleen M. Clayton *(Principal)*
Anthony V. Salerno *(Pres & Principal)*
Howard Berlly *(Sec)*
Dennis Gannon *(Principal & VP)*

SGFOOTWEAR, INC.
3 University Plz Ste 400, Hackensack, NJ 07601
Tel.: (201) 342-1200
Web Site: http://www.sgfootwear.com
Sales Range: $10-24.9 Million
Emp.: 65
House Slippers
N.A.I.C.S.: 316210
Paul Kingslow *(CEO & VP)*
Elisa Gangl *(VP-Licensing & Mktg)*
Jeffrey Solomon *(Dir-Logistics)*
Peter Stern *(Acct Exec)*

SGI INC.
4334 Ardmore Ave, Fort Wayne, IN 46802
Tel.: (260) 489-1575   IN
Year Founded: 1931
Commercial Building Construction Services
N.A.I.C.S.: 236220
Jeff Graves *(Pres)*

SGS ENTERPRISES INC.
11340 Commercial Pkwy, Castroville, CA 95012
Tel.: (831) 633-3379
Web Site: http://www.asmetals.com
Sales Range: $10-24.9 Million
Emp.: 50
Automotive Wrecking For Scraps
N.A.I.C.S.: 423930
Stanley Silva Jr. *(Owner & Pres)*

Subsidiaries:

A&S Metals - Modesto   (1)
1616 Angelo Way, Modesto, CA 95358
Tel.: (209) 537-4766
Web Site: http://www.asmetals.com
Rev.: $9,100,000
Emp.: 40
Ferrous Metal Scrap & Waste
N.A.I.C.S.: 423930
Stanley G. Silva *(Pres & CEO)*
Cesar Cornejo *(Mgr)*

A&S of Castroville Inc   (1)
11340 Commercial Pkwy, Castroville, CA 95012
Tel.: (831) 633-3379
Web Site: http://www.asmetals.com
Rev.: $7,200,000
Automotive Wrecking For Scrap
N.A.I.C.S.: 423930
Stanley G. Silva Sr. *(Owner)*

SGS, LLC.
25 S Oklahoma Ave Ste 310, Oklahoma City, OK 73104
Tel.: (405) 416-8400
Year Founded: 1999
Sales Range: $10-24.9 Million
Emp.: 37
Civil Engineering Services
N.A.I.C.S.: 237310
Eddie Scott *(Pres)*

SGW INTEGRATED MARKETING COMMUNICATIONS, INC.
219 Changebridge Rd, Montville, NJ 07045-9514
Tel.: (973) 299-8000   NJ
Web Site: http://www.sgw.com
Year Founded: 1979
Advertising Agencies
N.A.I.C.S.: 541810
David F. Scelba *(CEO)*

SH WORLDWIDE, LLC
16 W Harrison St Ste 200, Seattle, WA 98119-4121
Tel.: (206) 623-2090   WA
Web Site: http://www.shworldwide.com
Sales Range: $1-9.9 Million
Emp.: 30
Site Selection, Event & Meeting Services, Online Registration & Destination Management Services
N.A.I.C.S.: 561920
Lisa Fraser *(Sr VP-Indus Rels & Special Events)*
Merrill Behnke *(Acct Exec-Natl)*
Jenny Rivera *(Acct Exec-Natl)*
Angela Evans *(Coord-Event)*
Nolan Frame *(Project Mgr)*
Rita Overton *(Mgr-Sls & Mktg)*
Sammy Scott *(Coord-Event)*
Wilhelmina Giese *(Coord-Event)*
H. S. Wright III *(Chm)*

SHACKLETON EQUITY PARTNERS LLC
501 Colorado Ave Ste 310, Santa Monica, CA 90401
Tel.: (310) 733-5658
Web Site: http://www.shackletonequity.com
Year Founded: 2008
Privater Equity Firm
N.A.I.C.S.: 523999
Mark Schelbert *(Mng Partner)*
Nick Desai *(Mng Partner)*

Subsidiaries:

Safeharbor Knowledge Solutions   (1)
302 4th St, Satsop, WA 98583
Tel.: (360) 861-8594
Web Site: http://www.safeharbor.com
Sales Range: $10-24.9 Million
Web Customer Support Solutions
N.A.I.C.S.: 561990
Heather Brix *(VP-Knowledge Mgmt Svcs)*
Comet Brower *(VP-Call Center Ops)*

SHADDOCK DEVELOPMENT CO.
2400 Dallas Pkwy Ste 510, Plano, TX 75093
Tel.: (972) 985-5505
Web Site: http://www.shaddockdev.com
Sales Range: $10-24.9 Million
Emp.: 9
Residential Subdivision Developers
N.A.I.C.S.: 237210
William Shaddock *(Pres & Partner)*
Peter H. Shaddock *(CEO & Partner)*
Patrick McMillan *(Controller)*

SHADES OF LIGHT LLC
4924 W Broad St, Richmond, VA 23230
Tel.: (804) 288-3235
Web Site: http://www.shadesoflight.com
N.A.I.C.S.:
Bryan Johnson *(CEO)*

SHADOW CONCEPTS LLC
411 W Monroe Ste 32, Austin, TX 78704
Web Site: http://www.under30experiences.com
Year Founded: 2012
Sales Range: $1-9.9 Million
Emp.: 12
Group Travel Agency Services
N.A.I.C.S.: 561510
Matt Wilson *(Co-Founder)*
Jared O' Toole *(Co-Founder)*
Eric Aguirre *(Product Dir)*
Dan Sgalia *(Sls Dir)*
Tim Gillespie *(Reg Mgr)*

SHADOW WOOD COUNTRY CLUB, INC.
22801 Oakwilde Blvd, Bonita Springs, FL 34135
Tel.: (239) 992-6000
Web Site: http://www.shadowoodcc.com
Year Founded: 1998
Sales Range: $1-9.9 Million
Emp.: 50
Country Club
N.A.I.C.S.: 713910
Danita Osborn *(Dir-Membership)*

SHADOWFAX CORPORATION
386 Pattison St, York, PA 17403
Tel.: (717) 854-7742   PA
Web Site: http://www.shadowfax.org
Year Founded: 1985
Sales Range: $10-24.9 Million
Emp.: 561
Developmental Disability Assistance Services
N.A.I.C.S.: 624120
Julie Landis *(CEO)*
Amy Brillinger *(Dir-HR)*
Theresa Linebaugh *(Dir-Fin)*
Cathy Hohenadel *(Dir-Admin)*
Mary Walter *(Dir-Residential Svcs)*

SHADOWLINE INCORPORATED
1044 Martindale Rd, Morganton, NC 28655
Tel.: (828) 437-3821

Web Site: http://www.shadowline-lingerie.com
Rev.: $15,600,000
Emp.: 320
Lingerie Mfr
N.A.I.C.S.: 315250
Chuck Myers *(VP-Admin & Fin)*
Charles Poteat *(COO)*
Judy Fisher *(Dir HR)*
Sherrod Salsbury III *(Founder)*

SHADY LANE, INC.
1235 S 24th St, Manitowoc, WI 54220
Tel.: (920) 682-8254
Web Site: http://www.shadylaneinc.com
Year Founded: 1950
Sales Range: $10-24.9 Million
Emp.: 279
Nursing Care Services
N.A.I.C.S.: 624120
Margie Meyer *(Dir-Dietary Svcs)*

SHAFER COMMERCIAL SEATING INC.
4101 E 48th Ave, Denver, CO 80216-3206
Tel.: (303) 322-7792
Web Site: http://www.shafer.com
Year Founded: 1938
Sales Range: $50-74.9 Million
Emp.: 120
Mfr of Chairs, Bar Stools, Booths, Table Tops & Bases
N.A.I.C.S.: 337127
Randall J. Shafer *(Pres)*
Richard M. Howard *(Dir-Mktg)*

SHAFER PROPERTY COMPANY INC.
3001 Knox St Ste 207, Dallas, TX 75205
Tel.: (214) 361-7778
Sales Range: $10-24.9 Million
Emp.: 20
Real Estate Agent, Commercial
N.A.I.C.S.: 531210
Steve Shafer *(Co-Pres, CEO & Principal)*
David McNeil *(Co-Pres)*

SHAFER, KLINE & WARREN, INC.
11250 Corporate Ave, Lenexa, KS 66219
Tel.: (816) 756-0444
Web Site: http://www.skw-inc.com
Rev.: $34,500,000
Emp.: 230
Architectural Services
N.A.I.C.S.: 541310
Gerald Johnson *(Exec VP)*
Ronald D. Petering *(Pres)*
Thomas Smith *(VP)*
Keith Hodges *(VP-Pipeline & Facility Design Svcs)*
Brian Johanning *(Dir-Strategic Growth)*
Greg Shelton *(CMO)*
Noelle Simmons *(Mgr-HR)*
Carey Hullinger *(Coord-HR)*

SHAFFER DISTRIBUTING COMPANY
1100 W 3rd Ave, Columbus, OH 43212
Tel.: (614) 421-6800
Web Site: http://www.shafferdistributing.com
Rev.: $16,500,000
Emp.: 58
Service Establishment Equipment Vending & Games
N.A.I.C.S.: 423850
Scott Shaffer *(VP-Sls-Columbus)*
Bill Kraft *(Pres-Columbus & Ohio)*
Chuck Ropke *(VP-Corp Svcs)*
Paul Westbrock *(CFO-Columbus & Ohio)*
Steve Shaffer *(CEO)*

SHAFFER ENTERPRISES INC.
8th Armory Rd, Clarksburg, WV 26301
Tel.: (304) 626-3064
Rev.: $23,200,000
Emp.: 50
Tobacco & Tobacco Product Merchant Whslr
N.A.I.C.S.: 424940
James S. Shaffer *(Pres)*
Martin Shaffer *(Treas & Sec)*

SHAFFNER-HEANEY ASSOCIATES INC.
2508 S Main St, South Bend, IN 46614
Tel.: (574) 232-7470
Web Site: http://www.shaffnerheaney.com
Year Founded: 1970
Sales Range: $10-24.9 Million
Emp.: 60
Interior Building Materials
N.A.I.C.S.: 423330
Fred W. Heaney *(Owner)*

SHAH & ASSOCIATES, INC.
416 N Frederick Ave, Gaithersburg, MD 20877
Tel.: (301) 926-2797
Web Site: http://www.shahpe.com
Year Founded: 1977
Sales Range: $10-24.9 Million
Emp.: 35
Engineeering Services
N.A.I.C.S.: 541330
Shreedhar Shah *(Pres & CEO)*

SHAH CAPITAL PARTNERS, LP
20380 Town Ctr Ln Ste 175, Cupertino, CA 95014
Tel.: (650) 233-4434
Web Site: http://www.shahcap.com
Emp.: 3
Investment Activities
N.A.I.C.S.: 523940
Lata Krishnan *(CFO)*

Subsidiaries:

Magellan Navigation, Inc. (1)
960 Overland Ct, San Dimas, CA 91773
Tel.: (909) 394-5000
Web Site: http://www.magellangps.com
Sales Range: $75-99.9 Million
Global Satellite Positioning, Navigation & Guidance Equipment
N.A.I.C.S.: 334511

SHAKER RECRUITMENT ADVERTISING & COMMUNICATIONS, INC.
1100 Lake St, Oak Park, IL 60301
Tel.: (708) 383-5320
Web Site: http://www.shaker.com
Year Founded: 1951
Sales Range: $50-74.9 Million
Emp.: 203
Recruitment, Advertising & Communications Services
N.A.I.C.S.: 541810
Joseph G. Shaker *(Chm & Principal)*
Catherine Shaker Breit *(Principal)*
Mike Temkin *(VP-Strategic Plng & Dev)*
Ellen Paige *(VP-Client Svcs)*
Derek Briggs *(COO)*
Jerry Digani *(VP-Health Care Div)*
Tony Lepore *(Dir-Brand Strategy)*
Denise Polanski *(Dir-Creative)*
Erin Wozniak *(VP-Sls & Accounts)*

Subsidiaries:

Shaker Recruitment Advertising & Communications, Inc. (1)
1408 N Westshore Blvd Ste 508, Tampa, FL 33607-3844
Tel.: (813) 289-1100
Web Site: http://www.shaker.com
Emp.: 7
Advertising Agency Services
N.A.I.C.S.: 541810
Joseph G. Shaker *(Chm & Principal)*
Jerry Digani *(VP-Health Care Div)*
Mike Temkin *(VP-Strategic Plng & Dev)*

SHAKESPEARE SQUARED
626 Academy Dr, Northbrook, IL 60062
Tel.: (847) 998-0535
Web Site: http://www.shakespearesquared.com
Year Founded: 2002
Sales Range: $10-24.9 Million
Emp.: 50
Educational Product Development for Publishers
N.A.I.C.S.: 611710
Jay Kleeman *(VP)*
Kathy Bretz *(Mng Editor)*
Susan Romberg *(Dir-Editorial)*

SHAKOPEE CHEVROLET-OLDSMOBILE-PONTIAC-GEO, INC.
1206 1st Ave E, Shakopee, MN 55379-1611
Tel.: (952) 445-5200
Web Site: http://www.shakopeechevrolet.com
Sales Range: $10-24.9 Million
Emp.: 36
Car Whslr
N.A.I.C.S.: 441110
Tom Frazier *(Mgr-Sls)*
George McGuire *(Principal)*
Mark Saliterman *(Owner)*
Gordy Swanson *(Dir-Svc)*
Willy Volk *(Mgr)*

SHALE-INLAND HOLDINGS LLC
6750 W Loop S Ste 520, Bellaire, TX 77401
Tel.: (855) 742-5380
Web Site: http://www.shale-inland.com
Pipes, Valves & Fittings Mfr
N.A.I.C.S.: 326122

Subsidiaries:

Flomax Products, Inc. (1)
5787 Preston Ave, Livermore, CA 94551
Tel.: (925) 449-5900
Web Site: http://www.flomax.com
Emp.: 15
Flow Control Products Mfr
N.A.I.C.S.: 423830
Jim Brannan *(Co-Founder)*

SHALEPRO ENERGY SERVICES, LLC
201 S Johnson Rd Ste 200, Houston, PA 15342
Tel.: (724) 485-7031
Web Site: http://www.shalepro.com
Energy Services & Dist
N.A.I.C.S.: 221122
Bill Johnson *(Pres & CEO)*
Kevin Johnson *(CFO)*

SHALLBETTER, INC.
3110 Progress Dr, Oshkosh, WI 54901
Tel.: (920) 232-8888
Web Site: http://www.shallbetter.com
Sales Range: $25-49.9 Million
Emp.: 80
Power Distr & Specialty Transformer Mfr
N.A.I.C.S.: 335311
Mike Bettcher *(VP)*
Corey Canniff *(VP-Fin)*

SHALLOW FORD CONSTRUCTION CO.
3513 SW HK Dodgen Loop Ste 102, Temple, TX 76502
Tel.: (254) 778-5244
Web Site: http://www.shallowford.com
Sales Range: $1-9.9 Million
Emp.: 45
Excavation & Grading, Building Construction
N.A.I.C.S.: 238910
Connie Spiegel *(Co-Owner)*
Bob Spiegel *(Co-Owner, Pres & CEO)*
Edwin Tyroch *(Controller)*
Jim Robinson *(VP & Project Mgr)*
Richard Ring *(Sr Project Mgr)*

SHALOM PARK
14800 E Belleview Dr, Aurora, CO 80015-2258
Tel.: (303) 680-5000
Web Site: http://www.shalomcares.org
Year Founded: 1984
Sales Range: $10-24.9 Million
Emp.: 342
Community Welfare Services
N.A.I.C.S.: 624190
Daniel Stenersen *(CEO)*
Gary Yourtz *(Vice Chm)*
Bruce Bendell *(Treas)*
Michael Strear *(Chm)*
Lisa Cook *(Sec)*
Marc Penner *(Pres)*

SHALTZ FLUID POWER INC.
5163 Commerce Rd, Flint, MI 48507
Tel.: (810) 732-1970
Web Site: http://www.shaltzautomation.com
Sales Range: $10-24.9 Million
Emp.: 35
Hydraulic Systems Equipment & Supplies
N.A.I.C.S.: 423830
Philip W. Shaltz *(Pres)*
Dana Jury *(VP)*

SHAMBHALA PUBLICATIONS INC.
300 Massachusetts Ave, Boston, MA 02115
Tel.: (617) 424-0030
Web Site: http://www.shambhala.com
Sales Range: $10-24.9 Million
Emp.: 20
Publisher of Books
N.A.I.C.S.: 513130
Diane McCormick *(VP-Fin)*
Nikko Odiseos *(Pres)*
Jonathan Green *(VP)*

SHAMIN HOTELS INC.
2000 Ware Bottom Spring Rd, Chester, VA 23836
Tel.: (804) 777-9000
Web Site: http://www.shaminhotels.com
Year Founded: 1982
Rev.: $18,000,000
Emp.: 50
Hotel
N.A.I.C.S.: 721110
Grayson Owen *(CFO)*
Jay Shah *(VP-Dev)*

SHAMIN HOTELS INC.

Shamin Hotels Inc.—(Continued)
Sunny Amin (Reg Dir-Ops)
Suhail Arora (Reg Dir-Ops)
Leigh P. Burke (VP-Ops)
Nick Petrone (VP-Food-Beverage)
Michael Sweeney (VP-Design & Construction)
Eileen Lamb (Dir-HR)
Mark Yardis (VP-Ops)

SHAMROCK BANCSHARES, INC.
101 N Main St, Coalgate, OK 74538
Tel.: (580) 927-2311   OK
Web Site:
  http://www.shamrockbank.com
Year Founded: 1973
Bank Holding Company
N.A.I.C.S.: 551111
Barry Edwards (Sr VP-IT)
Guy Sims (Chm, Pres & CEO)

Subsidiaries:

Shamrock Bank, N.A.   (1)
101 N Main St, Coalgate, OK 74538
Tel.: (580) 927-2311
Web Site: http://www.shamrockbank.com
Savings Bank
N.A.I.C.S.: 522180
Guy Sims (Chm, Pres & CEO)

SHAMROCK BANK OF FLORIDA
895 5th Ave S, Naples, FL 34102
Tel.: (239) 919-5199
Web Site:
  http://www.shamrockbankfl.com
Year Founded: 2007
Sales Range: $1-9.9 Million
Emp.: 13
Commericial Banking
N.A.I.C.S.: 522110
Colleen M. Kvetko (Pres & CEO)

SHAMROCK BUILDING SERVICES CORP.
PO Box 22123, Saint Petersburg, FL 33742
Tel.: (727) 585-6007
Web Site:
  http://www.shamrockclean.com
Sales Range: $25-49.9 Million
Emp.: 400
Building Maintenance Services
N.A.I.C.S.: 561720
Carl Shanahan (Pres)

SHAMROCK CABINET & FIXTURE CORP.
10201 E 65th St, Raytown, MO 64133
Tel.: (816) 737-2300
Web Site:
  http://www.shamrockcabinet.com
Year Founded: 1966
Sales Range: $10-24.9 Million
Emp.: 90
Mfr & Designer of Custom Cabinets
N.A.I.C.S.: 337110
Dan Beachner (VP)
Erik Blaney (Mgr-Sls)
William J. Price Jr. (Pres)

SHAMROCK CAPITAL ADVISORS, LLC
1100 Glendon Ave Ste 1600, Los Angeles, CA 90024
Tel.: (310) 974-6600
Web Site:
  http://www.shamrockcap.com
Privater Equity Firm
N.A.I.C.S.: 523999
William J. Wynperle (Partner)
Stephen D. Royer (Partner)
Laura Held (Partner)
Michael A. LaSalle (Partner)
Andrew J. Howard (Partner)
Patrick Russo (Partner)
Jason Sklar (Partner)
Alan H. Resnikoff (Partner)
Angelica Gallardo (Mgr-Fin)
Peter Rivera (CFO)
Timothy Bluth (VP)
Brian Barnum (Operating Partner)

Subsidiaries:

Adweek, LLC   (1)
825 8th Ave 29th Fl, New York, NY 10019
Tel.: (212) 493-4262
Web Site: http://www.adweek.com
Advertising Magazine Publisher
N.A.I.C.S.: 513120
Eleftheria Parpis (Editor-Creative)
Drew Schutte (Chief Revenue Officer)
Lisa Granatstein (Chief Content Officer)
David Griner (Dir-Digital Initiatives & Innovation)
Emily Chang (Dir-Design)
Jason D. Davis (Mgr-Digital Tech Sls)
Rob Eisenhardt (Gen Mgr-Sls & Revenue)
Liza Kalikow Kirsh (VP-Mktg)
Ariel Perallon (Mgr-Ad Ops)
Adam Remson (Gen Mgr-Sls & Revenue)
Jeffrey Rudolf (Gen Mgr)
John Sartoris (Dir-Production Grp)
Cindee Weiss (Mgr-Production)
Brian F. Martin (Chm)
Nicole Ortiz (Sr Editor)
Zoe Ruderman (Chief Content Officer)
Will Lee (CEO)
Eric Hayden Shakun (CFO)
Jenny Rooney (Chief Experience Officer)

Affiliate (Domestic):

Film Expo Group LLC   (2)
825 8th Ave 29th Fl, New York, NY 10019
Tel.: (212) 493-4147
Web Site: http://www.filmexpos.com
Film Industry Convention & Exposition Planning, Marketing & Management Services
N.A.I.C.S.: 561920

Branded Cities Network, LLC   (1)
2850 E Camelback Rd Ste 110, Phoenix, AZ 85016
Tel.: (602) 840-3000
Web Site: http://www.brandedcities.com
Marketing & Advertising Services
N.A.I.C.S.: 541890
Robert Crawford (Mng Dir-Real Estate Dev)
Steven Ellman (Chm & CEO)
Vaibhav Gupta (COO & Exec VP)
Ty Fields (Gen Counsel)
Steve Whitwell (CFO & VP)
Denise Levine (Chief Revenue Officer)
Chris McCarver (Sr VP-Real Estate & Pub Affairs)
Sam Toporek (VP-Ops)
Christoper Dow (Sr VP & Creative Dir)
Ben Martish (VP-Sls)
Shawn Taylor (VP-Tech)
Michael Galkin (Dir-Mktg & Res)

Subsidiary (Domestic):

Red Star Outdoor LLC   (2)
770 N La Salle Dr Ste 500, Chicago, IL 60654-5267
Tel.: (312) 751-9010
Web Site: http://www.redstaroutdoor.com
Marketing & Advertising Services
N.A.I.C.S.: 541850
Dean Manone (Owner)

Nth Degree Inc.   (1)
3480 Hampton Rd, Oceanside, NY 11572
Tel.: (516) 678-9880
Web Site: http://www.nthdegree.com
Rev: $5,160,000
Emp.: 15
Residential Remodeler
N.A.I.C.S.: 236118
John Yohe (Pres)
Todd Amodeo (Mgr)
Cindy Haun-Nevens (Sr Dir-Acct)
David Smith (Dir-IT Svcs)
Doug Higgins (Acct Exec)
Elise Simons (Dir-Mktg Comm)
Gary Critelli (CFO)
Kimberly Rudel (Acct Exec)
Maureen Burke (Sr Dir-Acct)
Patrick Shepherd (Acct Exec)
Sandra Braun (Dir-Accts-Natl)
Shannon Scherer (VP & Gen Mgr)

SHAMROCK CHICAGO CORP.
800 E Northwest Hwy Ste 525, Palatine, IL 60074
Tel.: (847) 701-0376
Web Site:
  http://www.shamrockchicago.com
Sales Range: $10-24.9 Million
Emp.: 65
Chemical & Allied Products Mfr & Whslr
N.A.I.C.S.: 424690
Les Kreifels (Mgr-Sls)
John F. Deamer Jr. (VP)

SHAMROCK CO.
15 Spinning Wheel Rd 110, Hinsdale, IL 60521
Tel.: (630) 655-8274
Sales Range: $50-74.9 Million
Emp.: 700
Fast-Food Restaurant, Chain
N.A.I.C.S.: 722513
Stephen C. Mcgue (Pres)

SHAMROCK CORPORATION
422 N Chimney Rock Rd, Greensboro, NC 27410-6249
Tel.: (336) 574-4200   NC
Web Site:
  http://www.shamrockwraps.com
Year Founded: 1976
Sales Range: $75-99.9 Million
Emp.: 150
Gift Wrap & Specialty Paper Packaging Products Mfr
N.A.I.C.S.: 322299
Robert Hadgraft (Pres)
Janet Pantuso (Dir-Creative Dev)
Kenneth Nelson (VP)

SHAMROCK FOODS COMPANY
3900 E Camelback Rd Ste 300, Phoenix, AZ 85018
Tel.: (602) 233-6400   AZ
Web Site:
  https://www.shamrockfoods.com
Year Founded: 1922
Sales Range: $1-4.9 Billion
Emp.: 5,600
Dairy Cattle & Milk Production
N.A.I.C.S.: 112120
Kent McClelland (Pres)
Kent Mullison (Sr VP)
Rob Baxter (CIO & VP)

Subsidiaries:

Shamrock Farms Dairy Division   (1)
2228 N Black Canyon Hwy, Phoenix, AZ 85009-2707
Tel.: (602) 272-6721
Web Site: http://www.shamrockfarms.net
Sales Range: $25-49.9 Million
Emp.: 120
Fluid Diary Product Mfr
N.A.I.C.S.: 311511
Kent McClelland (Pres & CEO)

Shamrock Foods - Arizona Foods Division   (1)
2540 N 29th Ave, Phoenix, AZ 85009
Tel.: (602) 233-6400
Web Site:
  http://www.shamrockfoodservice.com
Sales Range: $250-299.9 Million
Emp.: 2,100
Food Products Distr
N.A.I.C.S.: 424410
Larry F. Yancy (Gen Mgr & Sr VP)

Shamrock Foods - Colorado Foods Division   (1)
5199 Ivy, Commerce City, CO 80022
Tel.: (303) 289-3595
Web Site:
  http://www.shamrockfoodservice.com
Sales Range: $250-299.9 Million
Emp.: 1,000
Food Products Distr
N.A.I.C.S.: 424410

Kent Mullison (Gen Mgr)

Shamrock Foods - New Mexico Foods Division   (1)
2 Shamrock Way NW, Albuquerque, NM 87120
Tel.: (505) 345-4488
Web Site:
  http://www.shamrockfoodservice.com
Sales Range: $50-74.9 Million
Emp.: 200
Food Products Distr
N.A.I.C.S.: 424490
Thax Turner (Gen Mgr)

SHAMROCK HOLDINGS, INC.
3500 W Olive Ave Ste 700, Burbank, CA 91505
Tel.: (818) 845-4444   DE
Web Site: http://www.shamrock.com
Year Founded: 1979
Sales Range: $75-99.9 Million
Emp.: 60
Holding Company
N.A.I.C.S.: 531210
Stanley P. Gold (Pres & CEO)
George J. Buchler (Mng Dir)
Robert G. Moskowitz (Mng Dir)
Eugene I. Krieger (Vice Chm & COO)
Gregory G. Martin (CFO)
Dan Beaney (VP)

Subsidiaries:

Recorded Books, Inc.   (1)
270 Skipjack Rd, Prince Frederick, MD 20678-3410
Tel.: (410) 535-5590
Web Site: http://www.recordedbooks.com
Audio Books Retailer & Digital Content Distr
N.A.I.C.S.: 512250
Neil Tress (CFO & COO)
Tom MacIsaac (Pres & CEO)
Brian Sweany (Dir-Acq)
Patrick Deering (Dir-Mktg)
Troy Juliar (Chief Content Officer)
Ed Longo (COO)

Subsidiary (Domestic):

Tantor Media, Inc.   (2)
6 Business Park Rd, Old Saybrook, CT 06475
Tel.: (860) 395-1155
Web Site: http://www.tantor.com
Audio Books Publisher
N.A.I.C.S.: 512250
Kevin Colebank (CEO)
Kent Wilson (Dir-Fin)
Ron Formica (Dir-Acq)
Hilary Eurich (Mgr-Production)
Laura Colebank (Partner)

Shamrock Holdings of California, Inc.   (1)
4444 W Lakeside Dr, Burbank, CA 91505-4054   (100%)
Tel.: (818) 973-4200
Web Site: http://www.shamrock.com
Sales Range: $25-49.9 Million
Investment & Holding Company
N.A.I.C.S.: 531210

SHAMROCK SCIENTIFIC SPECIALTY SYSTEMS, INC.
34 Davis Dr, Bellwood, IL 60104
Tel.: (708) 547-9005
Web Site:
  http://www.shamrocklabels.com
Sales Range: $10-24.9 Million
Emp.: 100
Supplier of Blank & Pre-Printed Labels, Stock & Custom Labels
N.A.I.C.S.: 424130
Shirin Milik (Mgr-Quotations)

SHAMROCK TECHNOLOGIES INC.
Foot of Pacific St, Newark, NJ 07114
Tel.: (973) 242-2999
Web Site:
  http://www.shamrocktechnologies.com
Rev: $13,200,000

Emp.: 90
Chemical Preparations
N.A.I.C.S.: 325180
Mike Oliveri (Dir-Mktg)
Joe Shade (CFO)
Ronald Levitt (Dir-Sls-Americas)
Al Pape (Pres)

SHAN POOLS, INC.
9720 Coit Rd, Plano, TX 75025
Tel.: (469) 909-1638   TX
Web Site:
http://www.premierpoolsandspas.com
Year Founded: 2011
Sales Range: $10-24.9 Million
Emp.: 36
Swimming Pool Equipments Distr
N.A.I.C.S.: 423910
Michael Ribnikar (Owner)

SHANE DEMLER MASONRY, INC
8565 N 6400 W, Newton, UT 84327
Tel.: (435) 563-8009
Web Site:
http://www.shanedemler.com
Year Founded: 1996
Sales Range: $10-24.9 Million
Emp.: 56
Masonry Contractors
N.A.I.C.S.: 238140
Shane Demler (Pres)
Roxy Demler (Gen Mgr)

SHANER CORP.
1965 Waddle Rd, State College, PA 16803-1639
Tel.: (814) 234-4460
Web Site: http://www.shanercorp.com
Year Founded: 1983
Sales Range: $150-199.9 Million
Emp.: 2,700
Hotel & Motel Management
N.A.I.C.S.: 721110
Plato Ghinos (Pres)
Brian McMahon (VP-HR)
David Kopac (Mgr-e-Commerce)
Lisa Jacobson (VP-Sls & Mktg-Select Svc)

SHANGRI-LA
4080 Reed Rd SE Ste 150, Salem, OR 97302
Tel.: (503) 581-1732   OR
Web Site:
http://www.shangrilacorp.org
Year Founded: 1964
Sales Range: $10-24.9 Million
Emp.: 576
Disability Assistance Services
N.A.I.C.S.: 624120
Karen Rutledge (CEO)
Helen Honey (CFO)

SHANNON & WILSON, INC.
400 N 34th St Ste 100, Seattle, WA 98103-8600
Tel.: (206) 632-8020   WA
Web Site:
http://www.shannonwilson.com
Year Founded: 1954
Sales Range: $25-49.9 Million
Emp.: 300
Geotechnical & Environmental Consulting Services
N.A.I.C.S.: 541330
Gerard Buechel (Pres)
Greg Fischer (Office Mgr)
Thomas Abkemeier (VP-Saint Louis)
Meg Strong (VP)
Bob Mitchell (VP)
Monica Zidaru (Coord-Mktg-Saint Louis)

Subsidiaries:
Shannon & Wilson, Inc.   (1)
2355 Hill Rd, Fairbanks, AK 99709
Tel.: (206) 632-8020
Web Site: http://www.shannonwilson.com
Sales Range: $25-49.9 Million
Emp.: 27
Soil & Rock Testing Laboratory
N.A.I.C.S.: 115112
Christopher Darrah (Office Mgr)

SHANNON HARDWARE CO. LTD
606 Front St, Morgan City, LA 70380
Tel.: (985) 385-2700
Web Site:
http://www.shannonhardware.com
Sales Range: $10-24.9 Million
Emp.: 50
Distr of Hardware
N.A.I.C.S.: 423710
M.D. Shannon (Pres)

SHANNON HEALTH SYSTEM
120 E Harris Ave, San Angelo, TX 76903
Tel.: (325) 653-6741   TX
Web Site:
http://www.shannonhealth.com
Health Care Srvices
N.A.I.C.S.: 621999
Shane Plymell (Pres & CEO)

Subsidiaries:
Shannon Medical Center   (1)
120 E Harris Ave, San Angelo, TX 76903
Tel.: (325) 653-6741
Web Site: http://www.shannonhealth.com
General Medical & Surgical Services
N.A.I.C.S.: 622110
Shane Plymell (Pres & CEO)

SHANNON INDUSTRIAL CORPORATION
2041 Dillard Ct, Woodstock, IL 60098
Tel.: (815) 337-2349
Web Site:
http://www.shannonindustrial.com
Sales Range: $25-49.9 Million
Emp.: 15
Plastic Materials Mfr
N.A.I.C.S.: 424610
Gerald Grossi (Pres)
Donna Fairbanks (Office Mgr & Mgr-Traffic)

SHANNON PRECISION FASTENER, LLC
31600 Stephenson Hwy, Madison Heights, MI 48071
Tel.: (248) 589-9670
Web Site: http://www.shannonpf.com
Year Founded: 2004
Sales Range: $10-24.9 Million
Emp.: 250
Bolt, Nut, Screw, Rivet & Washer Mfr
N.A.I.C.S.: 332722
Glenn Purvin (VP-Sls-Engrg)
James Knight (Plant Mgr)
Robb Thompson (VP-Sls Comml)
Matt Bruce (Mgr-Quality)

SHANNON PRECISION INC.
1170 S Patton St, Xenia, OH 45385
Tel.: (937) 374-2700
Web Site: http://www.spi-connects.com
Year Founded: 1984
Military & Industrial Connectors Mfr
N.A.I.C.S.: 423690
Bill Shannon (Owner)
William J. Shannon Jr. (Pres & CEO)

SHANNON RIDGE, INC.
13888 Point Lakeview Rd, Lower Lake, CA 95457
Tel.: (707) 994-9656

Web Site:
http://www.shannonridge.com
Year Founded: 1996
Winery Services
N.A.I.C.S.: 312130
Angie Bigham (VP & Mgr-Sls-Natl)
Carol Brandt (Mgr-Acctg)
Chris Baker (COO)
Clay Shannon (Founder & Pres)
Brenda Bullington (Mgr-Sls-Western)
Charley McPherson (Mgr-Sls-Southeast)
Don Chase (CFO)
Joy Merrilees (Dir-Winemaking & Production)
Roxanne Jackson (Mgr-Mktg & PR)
Sal Spena (Mgr-Sls-Northeast)
Chip Wolf (VP-Sls)
Gary Bodine (Dir-Sls-West)
Jason Stuhmer (Dir-Sls-East)

Subsidiaries:
Steele Wines, Inc.   (1)
4350 Thomas Dr, Kelseyville, CA 95451
Tel.: (707) 279-9475
Web Site: http://www.steelewines.com
Sales Range: $1-9.9 Million
Emp.: 17
Wholesale Winery
N.A.I.C.S.: 424820

SHANOR ELECTRIC SUPPLY INC.
285 Hinman Ave, Buffalo, NY 14216
Tel.: (716) 876-0711
Web Site:
http://www.shanorelectric.com
Year Founded: 1958
Sales Range: $10-24.9 Million
Emp.: 60
Electrical Supplies & Distr
N.A.I.C.S.: 423610
Jim Shanor (VP & Gen Mgr)
Cheryl Tobin (Treas)
Nichole Shanor (Mgr-Credit)
John R. Shanor Jr. (Owner & Pres)

SHAPCO, INC.
1666 20th St Ste 100, Santa Monica, CA 90404-3818
Tel.: (310) 264-1666   CA
Year Founded: 1984
Sales Range: $75-99.9 Million
Emp.: 15
Mfr of Steel Pipe & Tubing; Real Estate
N.A.I.C.S.: 423510
Leonard Shapiro (Pres)
Steven Teller (VP)
Jerry Witkow (Gen Counsel)
Jaime Gesundheit (VP-Real Estate)
Kelly So (Mgr-HR)

Subsidiaries:
Custom Pipe & Coupling Co.   (1)
10560 Fern Ave, Stanton, CA 90680-0978
Tel.: (714) 761-8801
Web Site: http://www.custompipe.com
Sales Range: $10-24.9 Million
Fabricated Steel & Iron Pipe Mfr
N.A.I.C.S.: 332996
Tami McCarthy (CFO)

Kelly Pipe Co., LLC   (1)
11680 Bloomfield Ave, Santa Fe Springs, CA 90670-4609
Tel.: (562) 868-0456
Web Site: http://www.kellypipe.com
Sales Range: $25-49.9 Million
Steel Pipe & Tubing Distr
N.A.I.C.S.: 423510
John Wolfson (VP)
Cesar Acevedo (Mgr-Ops)
Barry Henning (Branch Mgr)
Mike Hoch (Mgr-Ops)
Nick Leech (Mgr-Ops)
Jereme Lowe (Branch Mgr)
Jim Penney (Branch Mgr)
Kevin Roberts (VP)
Carol Taylor (Gen Mgr)

Subsidiary (Domestic):
Kelly Pipe Co LLC   (2)
4710 Patrol Rd Ste E, McClellan, CA 95652-2022
Tel.: (510) 652-1710
Web Site: http://www.kellypipe.com
Sales Range: $25-49.9 Million
Emp.: 3
Pipe & Tubing, Steel
N.A.I.C.S.: 423510
Jereme Lowe (Area Mgr-Northeast)

SHAPE CORP.
1900 Hayes St, Grand Haven, MI 49417-8937
Tel.: (616) 846-8700
Web Site: http://www.shapecorp.com
Year Founded: 1974
Sales Range: $300-349.9 Million
Emp.: 1,000
Mfr of Structural Components For Automobile Industry
N.A.I.C.S.: 332322
Gary Verplank (Founder & Owner)
Peter Sturrus (Vice Chm)
Budd Brink (VP-Fin)
Bob Courrier (Pres)
Doug Peterson (VP-HR)
Mike Smith (VP)
Patrick Sullivan (Gen Mgr)
Mark White (VP)

SHAPELL INVESTMENT PROPERTIES, INC.
8383 Wilshire Blvd Ste 700, Beverly Hills, CA 90211-2406
Tel.: (323) 655-7330   DE
Year Founded: 2013
Real Estate Investment & Property Management Services
N.A.I.C.S.: 531390
William P. West (CEO)

SHAPIRO SALES COMPANY
9666 Olive Blvd Ste 500, Saint Louis, MO 63132
Tel.: (314) 381-9300
Web Site:
http://www.shapirometals.com
Sales Range: $100-124.9 Million
Emp.: 20
Ferrous Metal Scrap & Waste
N.A.I.C.S.: 423930
Bruce Shapiro (Pres & CEO)
David Lorenz (COO)
Jeff Cox (Mgr-Sls)
Rick Dobkin (Exec VP)

SHARAVSKY COMMUNICATIONS
4128 Dana Ln, Lafayette Hill, PA 19444-1320
Tel.: (610) 834-5499   PA
Web Site: http://www.sharavsky.com
Year Founded: 1993
Sales Range: $10-24.9 Million
Emp.: 7
Advertising Agencies
N.A.I.C.S.: 541810
Alan Sharavsky (Bus Dir)
Deb Censi (Dir-Productions)

SHARBELL DEVELOPMENT CORP.
1 Washington Blvd Ste 9, Robbinsville, NJ 08691
Tel.: (609) 918-2400
Web Site: http://www.sharbell.com
Year Founded: 1984
Sales Range: $75-99.9 Million
Emp.: 45
Real Estate Property Developers
N.A.I.C.S.: 236115
Thomas Troy (Sr VP)
Hannan Kalish (Pres)
Peter Weathers (VP-Fin)

SHARE CORPORATION　　　　　　　　　　　　　　　　　　　　　　　　　　　　　　　　U.S. PRIVATE

Share Corporation—(Continued)

SHARE CORPORATION
7821 N Faulkner Rd, Milwaukee, WI 53224
Tel.: (414) 355-4000
Web Site: http://www.sharecorp.com
Year Founded: 1970
Emp.: 100
Chemical Engineering Specialists
N.A.I.C.S.: 325199
Laure Des Jardins (Pres)

SHARE OUR STRENGTH
1030 15th St NW Ste 1100 W, Washington, DC 20005
Tel.: (202) 393-2925　　　　　　DC
Web Site: http://www.nokidhungry.org
Year Founded: 1984
Sales Range: $10-24.9 Million
Hunger Relief Services
N.A.I.C.S.: 624210
Debbie Shore (Founder)
Thomas Nelson (Pres & COO)
Charles Scofield (Exec VP)

SHAREBUILDERS, INC.
22484 Grosenbach Rd, Washington, IL 61571
Tel.: (309) 694-0727
Web Site: http://www.share-builders.com
Emp.: 35
Sales Management Software Developer
N.A.I.C.S.: 513210
Erin Koller (CEO)

Subsidiaries:

Efficio Solutions, Inc.　　　　　　(1)
Westerville Sq 520 S State St Ste 244B, Westerville, OH 43081
Tel.: (614) 895-9584
Web Site: http://www.efficiosolutions.com
Sales Range: $1-9.9 Million
Emp.: 14
Sales Management Software Developer
N.A.I.C.S.: 513210
David Einstein (Co-Pres)
David Everhart (Mgr-Dev)
Kitty Malone (Mgr-Customer Svc)

SHAREDLABS, INC.
6 E Bay St 4th Fl, Jacksonville, FL 32202
Tel.: (855) 208-2006　　　　　　DE
Web Site: http://www.sharedlabs.com
Year Founded: 2016
Sales Range: $10-24.9 Million
Emp.: 550
IT Services; Cloud, Security & Software Developer
N.A.I.C.S.: 518210
Jason Cory (Pres & CEO)
John Andrews (COO)
Tony Mane (CIO)
Lenny Abbott (VP-Strategy)
Michael Abrams (CFO)

Subsidiaries:

iTech US, Inc.　　　　　　　　(1)
20 Kimball Ave Ste 303 N, South Burlington, VT 05403
Tel.: (802) 383-1500
Web Site: http://www.itechus.com
Information Technology Staffing, Data Warehousing & Software Development Services
N.A.I.C.S.: 541519
Rocky Sheik (Sr Mgr)
Neil Brogan (VP-Consulting Svcs)

Subsidiary (Domestic):

SmartWorks, LLC　　　　　　(2)
55 Carter Dr Ste 107, Edison, NJ 08817
Tel.: (732) 985-8800
Web Site: http://www.smtworks.com
IT Staffing Services, Software Development & IT Training
N.A.I.C.S.: 611420

Sreenivasulu Banda (Engr-Software)

SHAREDXPERTISE MEDIA, LLC
123 S Broad St Ste 1930, Philadelphia, PA 19109
Tel.: (215) 606-9520
Web Site: http://www.sharedxpertise.com
Year Founded: 2002
Media Publication Services
N.A.I.C.S.: 513199
Elliot H. Clark (CEO)
Faye Holland (Mng Dir)
Dirk Olin (VP & Dir-Editorial)

SHARESPOST, INC.
555 Montgomery St Ste 1400, San Francisco, CA 94111
Web Site: http://www.sharespost.com
Year Founded: 2009
Emp.: 850
Private Securities Investments
N.A.I.C.S.: 523999
Greg Brogger (Founder & CEO)
Jennifer Phillips (Mng Dir)
Rohit Kulkarni (Mng Dir-Res)
John Wu (CEO-Digital Assets Grp)
Vijay Chetty (VP-Bus Dev)
Nick Grabowski (CTO)
Maureen Downey (Mng Dir-Portfolio Mgmt & New Product Dev)
Marie Jorajuria (CEO & Chief Compliance Officer)
Kevin Moss (Mng Dir-SP Investments Mgmt)
Carol L. Foster (CFO & COO)
Christian Munafo (Chief Investment Officer)
Jeff Miller (Pres & COO)

SHARETHROUGH, INC.
394 Pacific Ave 5th Fl, San Francisco, CA 94111
Tel.: (415) 644-0054
Web Site: http://www.sharethrough.com
Year Founded: 2008
Sales Range: $50-74.9 Million
Emp.: 110
Advertising Software Developer
N.A.I.C.S.: 513210
Dan Greenberg (Co-Founder & CEO)
Robert Fan (Co-Founder)
Patrick Keane (Pres)
Curt Larson (VP-Product)
John Nardone (CEO)
Tim Sims (Sr VP-Inventory Partnerships)
Dina Roman (Chief Revenue Officer)

SHARETRACKER, LLC
PO Box 20, Ashland, MO 65010　MO
Web Site: http://www.sharetracker.net
Year Founded: 2003
Telecommunications Database Marketing & Consulting Services
N.A.I.C.S.: 541613
Eric Fogle (Founder, Pres & CEO)
Ryan Verkamp (CFO)
Jerome Baccelli (CTO)
Mike Nungesser (Sr VP-Measurement Science)
Nathan Robson (Sr VP-Product Mktg)

Subsidiaries:

GeoResults, Inc.　　　　　　(1)
309 Pirkle Ferry Rd Ste 300-E, Cumming, GA 30040
Tel.: (770) 205-8111
Web Site: http://www.georesults.com
Sales Range: $1-9.9 Million
Telecommunications Database Marketing & Consulting Services
N.A.I.C.S.: 541613

James Kenny (Sr VP-Mktg & Bus Dev)
Peter R. Contreras (VP & Gen Mgr-Web Svcs)
Thomas E. Shields (Pres & CEO)
Dawn Shields (CFO & VP)
Guy Williams (VP-Info Svcs)
Mark Amato (VP-GIS)

SHARIAH CAPITAL, INC.
125 Elm St, New Canaan, CT 06840
Tel.: (203) 972-0331
Web Site: http://www.shariahcap.com
Sales Range: $1-9.9 Million
Finanacial Consulting & Investment Advisory Services
N.A.I.C.S.: 523999
Eric Meyer (Chm & CEO)

SHARK BRANDING
350 Fifth Ave Ste 6617, New York, NY 10118
Tel.: (212) 273-3379
Web Site: http://www.sharkbranding.com
Sales Range: $1-9.9 Million
Branding & Marketing Consulting
N.A.I.C.S.: 541613
Daymond John (CEO)

SHARK COMPUTERS INK.
28240 James Chaple Rd S, Holden, LA 70744
Tel.: (225) 567-1906
Sales Range: $100-124.9 Million
Computer Technology Development Services
N.A.I.C.S.: 541511
Christopher Hoyt (Owner)

SHARK INDUSTRIES, LTD.
6700 Bleck Dr, Rockford, MN 55373
Tel.: (763) 565-1900　　　　　　MN
Web Site: http://www.sharkind.com
Year Founded: 1983
Sales Range: $10-24.9 Million
Emp.: 29
Abrasives, Welding Products & Accessories Mfr
N.A.I.C.S.: 327910
Diana M. Mini (Pres)

SHARKLET TECHNOLOGIES, INC.
12635 E Montview Blvd Ste 160, Aurora, CO 80045
Tel.: (720) 859-4070
Web Site: http://www.sharklet.com
Year Founded: 2007
Medical Devices
N.A.I.C.S.: 339112
Anthony Brennan (Founder & Chm)
Liwu Zhou (CEO)
Ethan Mann (VP-Mktg & Sls)
Eric Harvey (VP-Ops)

SHARKREACH, INC.
205 Pier Ave Ste 101, Hermosa Beach, CA 90254
Web Site: http://www.sharkreach.com
Advertising Services
N.A.I.C.S.: 541810
Steve Smith (Founder & CEO)

SHARON CREDIT UNION
30 Pond St, Sharon, MA 02067
Tel.: (781) 784-7725　　　　　　MA
Web Site: http://www.sharoncu.com
Year Founded: 1956
Sales Range: $10-24.9 Million
Emp.: 99
Credit Union Operator
N.A.I.C.S.: 522130
David Cox (CFO)
Bill Beitler (COO)
James Carlson (Pres & CEO)

SHARON TOWERS
5100 Sharon Rd, Charlotte, NC 28210
Tel.: (704) 553-1670　　　　　　NC
Web Site: http://www.sharontowers.org
Year Founded: 1969
Sales Range: $10-24.9 Million
Emp.: 280
Lifecare Retirement Community Operator
N.A.I.C.S.: 623311
Anne Moffat (CEO)
Kim Flack (Dir-Dev)
Harry Lloyd (Dir-Dining Svcs)
Brad Aschenbrenner (Dir-Environmental Svcs)
Topper Amerson (Dir-Facilities Svcs)

SHARON YOUNG INC.
10367 Brockwood Rd, Dallas, TX 75238
Tel.: (214) 349-1891
Web Site: http://www.sharonyounginc.com
Sales Range: $10-24.9 Million
Emp.: 35
Women's, Junior's & Misses' Clothing
N.A.I.C.S.: 315250
Joe Mendenhall (Pres)
Ami Patel (Mgr-Logistic & QC)
Kay Fries (Dir-Sls)
Mary Garcia (Dir-IT)
Ross Morgan (VP-Ops)
Tarrah Stern (Coord-Pre-Production)
Michelle Lynch (Mgr-Customer Svc)

SHARP BROTHERS SEED COMPANY
1005 South Sycamore St, Healy, KS 67850
Tel.: (620) 398-2231
Web Site: http://www.sharpseed.com
Rev.: $12,700,000
Emp.: 30
Field, Garden & Flower Seeds
N.A.I.C.S.: 111422
Daniel Sharp (Pres)

SHARP DECISIONS INC.
1040 Ave of the Americas Rm 1700, New York, NY 10018-3771
Tel.: (212) 481-5533
Web Site: http://www.sharpdecisions.com
Year Founded: 1990
Sales Range: $10-24.9 Million
Emp.: 300
Computer Consulting Services
N.A.I.C.S.: 541512
Karen Ross (Pres & CEO)
Linda Robinson (VP-Western Reg)
Stuart Gottlieb (CFO)
Bill Cortese (Dir-Comm & Pub Affairs)

Subsidiaries:

CN TEC, Inc.　　　　　　　　(1)
4500 S Lakeshore Dr Ste 550, Tempe, AZ 85282　　　　　　　　　　(100%)
Tel.: (480) 993-0619
Web Site: http://www.cn-tec.com
Emp.: 100
IT Staffing Services
N.A.I.C.S.: 561320
Steven Byas (Pres)
Brian Beck (CEO)
Molly Gravatt (VP)

Sharp Decisions　　　　　　(1)
Central Pt 45 Beach St, London, EC2Y 8AD, United Kingdom　　　(100%)
Tel.: (44) 2078312121
Web Site: http://www.sharpdecisions.co.uk
Sales Range: $10-24.9 Million
Emp.: 60
Provider of Computer Consulting Services
N.A.I.C.S.: 541512

SHARP HOLDING CO.

95 3rd St 2nd Fl, San Francisco, CA 94103 DE
Year Founded: 2019
Holding Company
N.A.I.C.S.: 551112
Rodney Sperry *(CFO)*
Tracy Smith *(Pres, CEO, Treas & Sec)*

SHARP TRANSPORT INC.
3935 Hwy 43 N, Ethridge, TN 38456
Tel.: (931) 829-2194
Web Site:
http://www.sharptransport.com
Sales Range: $1-9.9 Million
Emp.: 120
Trucking Except Local
N.A.I.C.S.: 484121
John Sharp *(Founder)*
Allie Sharp-Schwalb *(Pres)*
Gary Shelton *(VP-Sls)*
Jonathon Molloy *(Controller)*
Ralf Maier *(Mgr-Ops)*
Angie Sharp-Ezell *(Dir-Asset Mgmt)*
Ronda Hancock *(Dir-Load Plng)*
Sam Smith *(VP-Asset Maintenance & Compliance)*

SHARPE DRY GOODS CO., INC.
200 N Broadway St, Checotah, OK 74426-2432
Tel.: (918) 473-2233 OK
Web Site:
http://www.sharpeclothing.com
Year Founded: 1913
Clothing Retailer
N.A.I.C.S.: 455110

SHARPE RESOURCES CORPORATION
3258 Mob Neck Rd, Heathsville, VA 22473
Tel.: (804) 580-8107
Year Founded: 1980
SHGP—(OTCBB)
Sales Range: Less than $1 Million
Bituminous Coal Acquiring & Developing
N.A.I.C.S.: 212115

SHARPER IMPRESSIONS PAINTING COMPANY
7801 Corporate Blvd, Plain City, OH 43064
Tel.: (614) 889-8383
Web Site:
http://www.sharperimpressionspainting.com
Year Founded: 2003
Sales Range: $1-9.9 Million
Emp.: 19
Interior & Exterior Painting Contractors
N.A.I.C.S.: 238320
Geoff Sharp *(Founder)*

SHARPRINT
4200 W Wrightwood Ave, Chicago, IL 60639
Tel.: (773) 862-9300
Web Site: http://www.sharprint.com
Sales Range: $10-24.9 Million
Emp.: 90
Commercial Screen Printing Services
N.A.I.C.S.: 323113
Kathy Hansen *(Mgr-HR & Ops)*
George Kilian *(Founder)*
Jeff Driskill *(Dir-Art)*
Angela Childs *(Mgr-Pur)*
Barbara Kudia *(Mgr-Acctg)*
Carlos Ballesteros *(Mgr-Screen Print Production)*
Samantha Ramirez *(Coord-Screen Print Production)*
Jeanette Martinez *(Mgr-Shipping & Receiving)*
Zach Corn *(Head-Sls)*
Wendy Rowman *(Supvr-Acct)*

SHARRETT INC.
10310 Auto Pl, Hagerstown, MD 21740-1430
Tel.: (301) 739-7700
Web Site: http://www.sharrett.com
Sales Range: $25-49.9 Million
Emp.: 100
New & Used Automobiles
N.A.I.C.S.: 441110
Will Perryman *(Pres)*
Paul Steiding *(Mgr-Sls-Sharrett Auto Stores)*

SHARYLAND LP
FM 1016 & S Glasscock Rd PO Box 1043, Mission, TX 78573
Tel.: (956) 585-4761 TX
Year Founded: 1973
Sales Range: $25-49.9 Million
Emp.: 449
Crop Preparation Services
N.A.I.C.S.: 111219

SHASON INC.
4940 Triggs St, Los Angeles, CA 90022-4832
Tel.: (323) 269-6666
Web Site: http://www.shasoninc.com
Rev.: $75,196,846
Emp.: 132
Woven Textiles
N.A.I.C.S.: 424310
Barok Shahery *(Pres)*
Henry Shahery *(VP)*
George Christianakis *(Mgr-Ops)*

SHASTA COMMUNITY HEALTH CENTER
1035 Placer St, Redding, CA 96001
Tel.: (530) 246-5710 CA
Web Site:
http://www.shastahealth.org
Year Founded: 1988
Sales Range: $25-49.9 Million
Emp.: 361
Community Health Care Services
N.A.I.C.S.: 621498
Sherry Caldwell *(CFO)*
Harold Carlson *(Chief Plng & Dev Officer)*
C. Dean Germano *(CEO)*
Charles Kitzman *(CIO)*
Robin Glasco *(COO)*

SHASTA HOLDINGS COMPANY
300 Steel St, Aliquippa, PA 15001-5416
Tel.: (724) 378-8280
Web Site: http://www.shastainc.com
Rev.: $24,200,000
Emp.: 60
Metal Processing Services
N.A.I.C.S.: 333998
Tom Powell *(Plant Mgr)*

Subsidiaries:

Shasta Inc. (1)
300 Steel St, Aliquippa, PA 15001-5416
Tel.: (724) 378-8280
Web Site: http://www.shastainc.com
Rev.: $20,000,000
Emp.: 6
Machine Shop, Jobbing & Repair
N.A.I.C.S.: 332710
Susan M. Oros *(Mgr-HR)*
Gary Waddell *(Mgr-Production)*
Jerry Harness *(Mgr-Sls & Quality)*
Tina M. Oros *(Office Mgr)*
Dan Rosati *(Pres)*

SHASTA INDUSTRIES INC.
3750 W Indian School Rd, Phoenix, AZ 85019
Tel.: (602) 532-3700
Web Site:
http://www.shastapools.com
Year Founded: 1968
Sales Range: $75-99.9 Million
Emp.: 575
Swimming Pool Construction & Maintenance Services
N.A.I.C.S.: 238990
Jeffrey Ast *(VP-Construction)*

SHASTA-SISKIYOU TRANSPORT
2370 Wyndham Ln, Redding, CA 96001
Tel.: (530) 241-1167
Web Site: http://www.sstoil.com
Year Founded: 1967
Sales Range: $10-24.9 Million
Emp.: 80
Provider of Fuels & Lubricants
N.A.I.C.S.: 424710
James C. Holt *(Pres)*
Paul Wellington *(VP)*
Bill Casparino *(Mgr-Mktg)*

SHATTUCK & GRUMMETT INC.
301 Seward St, Juneau, AK 99801
Tel.: (907) 586-2414
Web Site: http://www.sginc.com
Rev.: $15,000,000
Emp.: 21
Insurance Agents
N.A.I.C.S.: 524210
Stacy Grummett *(Owner)*
John Grummett *(VP)*
Teresa Young *(VP)*
Thomas Schilz *(Mgr-IT)*
Rick Shattuck *(Owner)*

SHAUB-ELLISON CO
1117 Broadway Ste 500, Tacoma, WA 98402-3508
Tel.: (253) 272-4119
Sales Range: $10-24.9 Million
Emp.: 10
Automotive Tires
N.A.I.C.S.: 441340
Steven Schaub *(Pres)*
Karen Miller *(Controller)*
Irl Rhodes *(Mgr)*

SHAVER AUTOMOTIVE GROUP, INC.
3888 E Thousand Oaks Blvd, Thousand Oaks, CA 91362
Tel.: (805) 496-7103
Web Site: http://www.shaverauto.com
Year Founded: 1987
Sales Range: $10-24.9 Million
Emp.: 70
Car Whslr
N.A.I.C.S.: 441110
Andrew Shaver *(Gen Mgr)*

SHAW & JONES MASONRY, INC.
500 Wilson Pike Cir Ste 211, Brentwood, TN 37027-3225
Tel.: (615) 373-8412
Sales Range: $10-24.9 Million
Emp.: 200
Masonry Construction Services
N.A.I.C.S.: 238140
Greg Shaw *(Owner & Mgr)*

SHAW & PETERSEN INSURANCE INC.
1313 5th St, Eureka, CA 95501
Tel.: (707) 443-0845
Web Site:
http://www.shawandpetersen.com
Sales Range: $10-24.9 Million
Emp.: 11
Insurance Agents
N.A.I.C.S.: 524210
Maurice O. Shaw Sr. *(Pres)*

SHAW & SONS INC.
829 W 17th St Ste 5, Costa Mesa, CA 92627
Tel.: (949) 642-0660
Web Site:
http://www.shawconstruction.com
Year Founded: 1948
Sales Range: $10-24.9 Million
Emp.: 85
Concrete Work
N.A.I.C.S.: 238110
Ron Shaw *(CEO)*
Paul Taylor *(CFO)*
John Wills *(Pres)*

SHAW - LUNDQUIST ASSOCIATES, INC.
2757 W Service Rd, Saint Paul, MN 55121-1230
Tel.: (651) 454-0670
Web Site:
http://www.shawlundquist.com
Sales Range: $50-74.9 Million
Emp.: 75
Nonresidential Construction Services
N.A.I.C.S.: 236220
Hoyt Shaw *(Pres)*

SHAW AREVA MOX SERVICES, LLC
Savannah River Site 730-2B, Aiken, SC 29804-7097
Tel.: (803) 819-2880
Web Site: http://www.moxproject.com
Rev.: $182,017,556
Emp.: 558
Fuel Fabrication Mfr
N.A.I.C.S.: 332999
Robert L. Jones *(VP-IT Safeguards & IT Div)*
Jim Simons *(Dir-Procurement)*
Jim Laclair *(Dir-Cost, Schedule & Estimating)*
Melissa Green *(Mgr-Contract)*
Naresh Jain *(Engr)*

SHAW BROTHERS CONSTRUCTION
511 Main St 341 Mosher Rd, Gorham, ME 04038
Tel.: (207) 839-2552
Web Site: http://www.shawbros.com
Rev.: $17,200,000
Emp.: 120
Excavation Work
N.A.I.C.S.: 238910
Jonathan E. Shaw *(Pres)*
Kevin Roy *(Supvr-Maintenance)*

SHAW CREATIONS, INC.
65 Clyde Rd Ste D, Somerset, NJ 08873-3485
Tel.: (732) 873-4343 NY
Web Site:
http://www.shawcreations.com
Year Founded: 1946
Sales Range: $75-99.9 Million
Emp.: 70
Mfr of Umbrellas
N.A.I.C.S.: 424350
Ron Rakin *(Owner)*

SHAW ELECTRIC CO.
3600 Fuller Ave, Kansas City, MO 64129
Tel.: (816) 921-0033
Web Site:
http://www.shawelectricco.com
Sales Range: $25-49.9 Million
Emp.: 140

SHAW ELECTRIC CO.

U.S. PRIVATE

Shaw Electric Co.—(Continued)
General Electrical Contractor
N.A.I.C.S.: 238210
Dick A. Shaw (CEO)

SHAW ELECTRIC CO.
22100 Telegraph Rd, Southfield, MI 48033
Tel.: (734) 425-6800
Web Site: http://www.shawelectric.com
Sales Range: $50-74.9 Million
Emp.: 75
Electrical Work
N.A.I.C.S.: 531120
David W. Kurtz (Chm)
Randy Block (VP-Project Mgmt)

SHAW ELECTRIC INC.
930 E River Dr, Davenport, IA 52803
Tel.: (563) 323-3611 IA
Web Site: http://www.shawelec.com
Year Founded: 1944
Sales Range: $10-24.9 Million
Emp.: 125
Electrical Contracting Services
N.A.I.C.S.: 238210
Donna J. Shaw (Pres)
Bob Shaw (CEO)
Steve Shaw (VP)

Subsidiaries:

IAS (1)
930 E River Dr, Davenport, IA 52803
Tel.: (563) 323-3611
Web Site: http://www.iasengineering.com
Emp.: 25
Provides Specialized System Integration Services.
N.A.I.C.S.: 423830
Ken Deering (Mgr-Div)

Light Expressions (1)
930 E River Dr, Davenport, IA 52803
Tel.: (563) 323-3611
Web Site: http://www.lightexpressions.com
Indoor & Outdoor Lighting Fixtures
N.A.I.C.S.: 335132
Donna Shaw (Pres)
Vicki Hall (Controller)
Bob Shaw Jr. (VP)

SHAW ROSS INTERNATIONAL IMPORTERS
2900 SW 400 Ave Ste 200, Miramar, FL 33027
Tel.: (954) 430-5020
Web Site: http://www.shaw-ross.com
Year Founded: 1970
Sales Range: $1-9.9 Million
Emp.: 43
Importers of Wines & Spirits
N.A.I.C.S.: 424820
Scott Jove (VP-Sls & Mktg)

SHAW STEWART LUMBER CO. INC.
645 Johnson St NE, Minneapolis, MN 55413-2535
Tel.: (651) 488-2525 WV
Web Site: http://www.shawstewartlumber.co.com
Year Founded: 1886
Sales Range: $25-49.9 Million
Emp.: 130
Lumber & Other Building Materials Retailer
N.A.I.C.S.: 444110

SHAW SUBURBAN MEDIA GROUP, INC.
7717 S State Rte 31, Crystal Lake, IL 60014
Tel.: (815) 459-4040
Web Site: http://www.shawsuburbanmedia.com
Sales Range: $10-24.9 Million
Emp.: 75
Newspaper Publishers
N.A.I.C.S.: 513110
Stacia Hahn (VP-Fin)
J. Tom Shaw (VP-Digital Media)
John Rung (Pres)

Subsidiaries:

The Daily Chronicle (1)
1586 Barber Greene Rd, Dekalb, IL 60115-7900
Tel.: (815) 756-4841
Web Site: http://www.daily-chronicle.com
Emp.: 20
Community Newspaper
N.A.I.C.S.: 513110
Brett Rowland (Editor-News)
Eric Olson (Gen Mgr)
Laura Shaw (Publr)
Kelsey Rettke (Editor)

SHAW SYSTEMS ASSOCIATES INC.
6200 Savoy Dr Ste 600, Houston, TX 77036
Tel.: (804) 272-3800
Web Site: http://www.shawsystems.com
Sales Range: $10-24.9 Million
Emp.: 80
Computer Software Development
N.A.I.C.S.: 541511
Cyndy Stone (COO)
Stephen Brannon (Dir-Bus Dev)
Chris Shaw (Sr Mgr-Ops)
Roy G. Shaw Jr. (Pres)

SHAW'S SOUTHERN BELLE FROZEN FOODS
821 Virginia St, Jacksonville, FL 32208
Tel.: (904) 765-4487
Web Site: http://www.shawsouthernbelle.com
Rev.: $12,000,000
Emp.: 150
Frozen Prepared Seafood Sales
N.A.I.C.S.: 311710
Howard Shaw (Sr Dir-Pur & Sls)
Zimmerman Joanne (VP-Fin & Controller)
Doug Mathis (Mgr-Production)

SHAWHANKINS, INC.
201 W Main St, Cartersville, GA 30120
Tel.: (770) 382-0951
Web Site: http://www.shawhankins.com
Year Founded: 1963
Sales Range: $1-9.9 Million
Emp.: 40
Insurance Agencies & Brokerage Services
N.A.I.C.S.: 524210
Randolph G. Shaw (Principal)
W. Scott Hankins (Pres & CEO)
Bart Shaw (Asst VP-Sls)
Denise Manning (Acct Mgr)
Kate Yazel (Project Mgr-Benefit Tech)

SHAWMUT EQUIPMENT COMPANY INC.
20 Tolland Tpke, Manchester, CT 06042
Tel.: (860) 643-4161
Web Site: http://www.shawmutequipment.com
Sales Range: $10-24.9 Million
Emp.: 35
Heavy Construction Equipment Rental
N.A.I.C.S.: 532412

David L. O'Connell (Pres)

SHAWMUT WOODWORKING & SUPPLY INC.
560 Harrison Ave, Boston, MA 02118
Tel.: (617) 622-7000
Web Site: http://www.shawmut.com
Year Founded: 1982
Commercial, Office & Institutional Building Contracting Services
N.A.I.C.S.: 236220
Les Hiscoe (CEO)
Tim Hurdelbrink (Dir-Construction Ops)
William Pisani (VP-Luxury Homes)
Marianne Monte (Chief People Officer)
Doug Lareau (Chief Legal Officer & VP)
Emma Van Rooyen (Chief Mktg & Strategy Officer & VP)
Randy Shelly (VP-Hospitality)
Roger Tougas (CFO & VP)
Michele Murphy (Dir-Chicago)
David A. Benson (CIO & VP)
Sharon Cadman (Sr Dir-Tri-State Institutional, Health Care & Life Sciences)
Steven Giordano (Sr Dir-Tri-State Institutional, Health Care & Life Sciences)
Ron Simoneau (VP-New England Institutional)
Greg Skalaski (VP-Retail)
Kevin Sullivan (VP- New England Institutional)
Kevin Waco (Dir-Bus Dev-Chicago)
James Down (Chm)

SHAWNEE CONSTRUCTION & ENGINEERING INC.
7701 Opportunity Dr, Fort Wayne, IN 46825
Tel.: (260) 489-1234
Web Site: http://www.shawneeconstruction.com
Sales Range: $25-49.9 Million
Emp.: 46
Commercial & Institutional Building Construction
N.A.I.C.S.: 236220
Matthew J. Schenkel (Pres & Partner)
John A. Schenkel Jr. (Owner, Partner & VP)

SHAWNEE MILLING CO., INC.
201 S Broadway Ave, Shawnee, OK 74801-8427
Tel.: (405) 273-7000 OK
Web Site: http://www.shawneemilling.com
Year Founded: 1906
Sales Range: $25-49.9 Million
Emp.: 228
Flour & Animal Feed Milling Services
N.A.I.C.S.: 311211
William L. Ford (Chm)
Robert L. Ford (Vice Chm)
Samuel J. Garlow (Exec VP)
Joseph W. Ford (Pres)
Randel W. Nusz (Exec VP)
Sarah Marchetti (Dir-Food Sls)

SHAWVER & SON, INC.
144 NE 44th St, Oklahoma City, OK 73105
Tel.: (405) 525-9451
Web Site: http://www.shawver.net
Sales Range: $25-49.9 Million
Emp.: 120
Electrical Wiring Services
N.A.I.C.S.: 238210
John W. Shawver (Pres)

SHAY OIL COMPANY, INC.
51 E 10th St, Yuma, AZ 85364-3919
Tel.: (928) 782-1828 AZ
Year Founded: 1953
Sales Range: $25-49.9 Million
Emp.: 180
Provider of Gasoline Services
N.A.I.C.S.: 457120
Daniel Shay (Pres)
John Bornt (Gen Mgr-Mktg)

SHAYCORE ENTERPRISES INC.
11235 St John Industrial Pkwy Ste 4, Jacksonville, FL 32246
Tel.: (904) 551-2592
Web Site: http://www.shaycore.com
Year Founded: 2008
Sales Range: $1-9.9 Million
Emp.: 20
Residential, Commercial & Industrial Construction
N.A.I.C.S.: 236210
William P. Kilgannon Jr. (Founder & CEO)

SHAYKIN & COMPANY
505 Park Ave Ste 1700, New York, NY 10022
Tel.: (212) 319-2800 DE
Year Founded: 1983
Sales Range: $150-199.9 Million
Emp.: 4
Investment Services
N.A.I.C.S.: 523150
Leonard Shaykin (Mng Dir)
Sandra Poole (Office Mgr)

SHAZAM, INC.
6700 Pioneer Pkwy, Johnston, IA 50131-1809
Tel.: (515) 288-2828 IA
Web Site: http://www.shazam.net
Year Founded: 1976
Sales Range: $50-74.9 Million
Emp.: 230
Data Processing & Preparation Services
N.A.I.C.S.: 518210
Dan Kramer (Exec VP-Govt & Community Affairs)
Tom Miller (Sr VP-Sls & Mng Dir-Enterprise Sls)
Richard Jenkins (Gen Counsel & Sr VP)
Paul Waltz (Pres & CEO)
Alexis Rodriguez (Head-Mktg Solutions-Global)
Amy Adkins (Gen Counsel & Exec VP)
Jace Day (Chief Client Ops Officer & Exec VP)
Scott Dobesh (CFO & Exec VP)
Terry Dooley (CIO & Exec VP)
Jackie Rolow (Chief Talent Officer & Exec VP)
Kevin Christensen (Sr VP-Market Intelligence & Data Analytics)
Clint Crain (Mng Dir-Client Retention & Growth)
David Collison (Sr VP-Application Dev)
Manish Nathwani (Sr VP-Product Dev)
Stephan Thomasee (Sr VP-IT & Security)
Cindy Smith (Sr VP-Mktg & Sls Support)
Amanda Holmgaard (Sr VP-Risk & Compliance)
Kelli Landry (Product Mgr)

Subsidiaries:

Digital Filing Solutions, Inc. (1)
5525 N MacArthur Ste 350, Irving, TX 75038

COMPANIES

Tel.: (972) 304-6300
Web Site: http://www.digitalfiling.com
Software Developer
N.A.I.C.S.: 513210
Wayne Sanderford (Pres)

SHAZDEH FASHIONS INC.
1375 Broadway, New York, NY 10018
Tel.: (212) 944-2510
Sales Range: $10-24.9 Million
Emp.: 55
Women Dresses
N.A.I.C.S.: 315250
Mansour Zar (Pres)

SHEA HOMES, LLC.
8008 Corporate Center Dr Ste 300, Charlotte, NC 28226-4489
Tel.: (704) 319-5000
Web Site:
  http://www.sheahomes.com
Year Founded: 1994
Sales Range: $10-24.9 Million
Emp.: 121
Housing Construction Services
N.A.I.C.S.: 236117
John Shea (Mng Partner)
Denise Surber (Supvr-Customer Care)
Melba Hayes (Mgr-Sls)
Jim Zimmermann (VP-Land Acq & Dev-Houston)

SHEALY'S TRUCK CENTER INC.
1340 Bluff Rd, Columbia, SC 29201
Tel.: (803) 771-0176
Web Site:
  http://www.shealytruck.com
Sales Range: $25-49.9 Million
Emp.: 75
Trucks, Tractors & Trailers: New & Used
N.A.I.C.S.: 441110
David Shealy (VP)
Bruce Shealy (Pres)

SHEAR ART SALON & SPA
13124 N Dale Mabry Hwy, Tampa, FL 33618
Tel.: (813) 968-4836
Web Site: http://www.shearart.com
Year Founded: 1986
Sales Range: $1-9.9 Million
Emp.: 50
Beauty Salon & Spa
N.A.I.C.S.: 812112
Joanne Powers (Owner & Pres)
Katie Horseman (Supvr-Front Desk)

SHEAR ENTERPRISES, LLC
12120 28th St N, Saint Petersburg, FL 33716
Tel.: (727) 540-9800
Web Site:
  http://www.shearenterprises.com
Year Founded: 2003
Sales Range: $25-49.9 Million
Emp.: 20
Intimate Apparel Mfr & Retailer
N.A.I.C.S.: 315520
Rhonda Shear (Co-Owner & Pres)
Van Fagan (Co-Owner & CEO)
Marie Crane (Dir-Mktg)

SHEARER & ASSOCIATES, INC.
4960 Corporate Dr Ste 100, Huntsville, AL 35805-6229
Tel.: (256) 830-1031   AL
Web Site:
  http://www.shearerassociates.us
Year Founded: 2000
Sales Range: $10-24.9 Million
Emp.: 23
Consulting Services for Government
N.A.I.C.S.: 541618

Frank Shearer (Owner & Pres)
Donnie Henley (Sr VP-Fin)
Dick Savage (VP-Ops)

SHEARER FARM INC.
7762 Cleveland Rd, Wooster, OH 44691
Tel.: (330) 345-9023
Web Site:
  http://www.shearerequipment.com
Sales Range: $10-24.9 Million
Emp.: 32
Agricultural Machinery & Equipment
N.A.I.C.S.: 423820
Mark Stitzlein (Partner)

SHEARMAN CORPORATION
4900 Hwy 90 E, Lake Charles, LA 70615-4037
Tel.: (337) 433-3000   LA
Web Site:
  http://www.americanpress.com
Year Founded: 1895
Sales Range: $100-124.9 Million
Emp.: 164
Publisher of Daily Newspapers
N.A.I.C.S.: 513110
Thomas B. Shearman (Pres)

SHEARSON AMERICAN REIT, INC.
1059 Redondo Dr, Los Angeles, CA 90019
Tel.: (323) 937-6563   NV
Real Estate Investment
N.A.I.C.S.: 523999
John Williams (Chm, CEO & CFO)
Richard Orcutt (Pres & Sec)

SHEBESTER BECHTEL, INC.
515 N 25th, Blackwell, OK 74631
Tel.: (580) 363-4900
Web Site:
  http://www.sbiwellservice.com
Year Founded: 1970
Sales Range: $10-24.9 Million
Emp.: 115
Support Activities for Oil & Gas Operations
N.A.I.C.S.: 213112
Chad Bechtel (Dir-Ops)

SHEBOYGAN PAINT COMPANY
1439 N 25th St, Sheboygan, WI 53081
Tel.: (920) 458-2157
Web Site: http://www.shebpaint.com
Sales Range: $10-24.9 Million
Emp.: 80
Paints & Allied Products
N.A.I.C.S.: 325510
Brock Brownrigg (CEO)
Charlie Melingoski (Pres)

SHEBOYGAN PAPER BOX CO. INC.
716 Clara Ave, Sheboygan, WI 53081
Tel.: (920) 458-8373
Web Site: http://www.spbox.com
Rev.: $15,000,000
Emp.: 90
Setup Paperboard Boxes
N.A.I.C.S.: 322219
Thomas A. Liebl (Pres)

SHEBOYGAN SYMPHONY ORCHESTRA INC.
830 N 8th St, Sheboygan, WI 53081
Tel.: (920) 452-1985
Web Site:
  http://www.sheboygansymphony.org
Year Founded: 1918
Sales Range: Less than $1 Million
Emp.: 1
Symphony Orchestra

N.A.I.C.S.: 813410

SHECKY'S MARKETING
307 Canal St #4S, New York, NY 10013
Tel.: (212) 242-2566
Web Site: http://www.sheckys.com
Sales Range: $10-24.9 Million
Emp.: 35
Consumer Marketing, Custom Publishing, Entertainment, Event Planning & Marketing, Fashion/Apparel, Product Placement
N.A.I.C.S.: 541890
Claudia Chan (Pres)
Chris Hoffman (Founder & CEO)
Jason Blake (VP-Mktg & Client Partnerships)

SHEEDY DRAYAGE CO.
1215 Michigan St, San Francisco, CA 94107
Tel.: (415) 648-7171
Web Site:
  http://www.sheedycrane.com
Sales Range: $25-49.9 Million
Emp.: 140
Cranes & Aerial Lift Equipment Rental
N.A.I.C.S.: 532412
Michael Battaini (Co-Pres)
Richard Battaini (Pres & CEO)
Peter Hogan (CFO)
Ken Bouchard (VP-Estimating)
Jim Butler (Sr VP)
Dominic DeMartini (Dir-Safety)
Cambiz Gholamshahi (Gen Mgr)
Christopher Gregori (Mgr-Engrg)
Will Whittington (Mgr-Ops)
Philip Bourgeois (Mgr-Svc-Nevada)
Darren Poythress (Mgr-Svc-Southern CA)

SHEEHAN BUICK PONTIAC GMC, INC.
2800 N Federal Hwy, Pompano Beach, FL 33064-6849
Tel.: (954) 943-2200
Web Site:
  http://www.sheehanbuickgmc.com
Year Founded: 1993
Sales Range: $25-49.9 Million
Emp.: 120
Car Whslr
N.A.I.C.S.: 441110
Mark Rindner (Mgr-Sls)
Thomas Sheehan (Pres)
Darrell Friedman (Dir-Svc & Parts)

SHEEHAN MACK SALES AND EQUIPMENT INC.
901 E 60th St N, Sioux Falls, SD 57104
Tel.: (605) 336-2000
Web Site:
  http://www.sheehanmacksales.com
Sales Range: $10-24.9 Million
Emp.: 60
Truck & Trailers Sales
N.A.I.C.S.: 423110
Bill Marketon (Controller)
Michael E. Sheehan (Owner & Pres)

SHEEHAN MOTORS INC.
926 2nd St, Cresson, PA 16630
Tel.: (814) 886-4154
Web Site: http://www.deere.com
Sales Range: $10-24.9 Million
Emp.: 35
Owner & Operator of Car Dealerships
N.A.I.C.S.: 441110
Martin Sheehan (Pres)

SHEEHY & ASSOCIATES
2297 Lexington Rd, Louisville, KY 40206-2818

SHEEHY CONSTRUCTION COMPANY

Tel.: (502) 456-9007   KY
Web Site: http://www.sheehy1.com
Year Founded: 1957
Rev.: $50,000,000
Emp.: 50
N.A.I.C.S.: 541810
Scott Kuhn (Chm & CEO)
Dave Carter (Pres & Creative Dir)
Linda Thomas (Assoc Dir-Media)

SHEEHY AUTO STORES, INC.
12701 Fair Lake Cir Ste 250, Fairfax, VA 22033-3810
Tel.: (703) 802-3480   DE
Web Site: http://www.sheehy.com
Year Founded: 1970
Automobile Dealership
N.A.I.C.S.: 441110
Brand Fowler (VP)
John Vitullo (Dir-IT)
Joe Shine (CFO)
Lisa Ziropoulos (Dir-Sls Ops)
John Adamson (COO)
Paul Tickle (Officer-Compliance)
Shawn Lumpkin (Dir-HR)
Allison Centore (Dir-Mktg)
Shaun Hicks (Gen Mgr)
Lee Holt (Gen Mgr)
Paul Larochelle (Gen Mgr)
Mike Lorton (Gen Mgr)
Frank McCarthy (Gen Mgr)
Kevin McLaughlin (Gen Mgr)
Sina Mohabat (Gen Mgr)
Dave Perrin (Gen Mgr)
Sam Wali (Gen Mgr)
Maria-Ana Robinson (VP)
Vincent A. Sheehy IV (Pres)

Subsidiaries:

Patriot Harley-Davidson, Inc.   (1)
9739 Fairfax Blvd, Fairfax, VA 22031
Tel.: (703) 352-5400
Web Site: http://www.patriothd.com
Sales Range: $1-9.9 Million
Motorcycle Dealers
N.A.I.C.S.: 441227
Keith Brooks (Sls Mgr)

Sheehy Ashland, Inc.   (1)
11450 Washington Hwy, Ashland, VA 23005   (100%)
Tel.: (804) 798-4791
Web Site: http://www.sheehyford.com
Sales Range: $25-49.9 Million
Emp.: 70
New & Used Car Dealer
N.A.I.C.S.: 441110
Kevin McLaughlin (Gen Mgr)
Travis Thomas (Mgr-Sls)
Allison Centore (Dir-Mktg)
Lisa Ziropoulos (Dir-Sls Ops)
Shawn Lumpkin (Dir-HR)
John Adamson (COO)
Scott Baker (Mgr-Fixed Ops)
Shaun Hicks (Gen Mgr)
Mike Nicoli (Gen Mgr-Sls)
Dave Perrin (Gen Mgr)
Joe Shine (CFO)
Aaron Spicer (Gen Mgr)

Sheehy Ford of Springfield, Inc.   (1)
6727 Loisdale Rd, Springfield, VA 22150   (100%)
Tel.: (703) 922-7900
Web Site: http://www.sheehy.com
Sales Range: $25-49.9 Million
Emp.: 115
New & Used Car Dealer
N.A.I.C.S.: 441110
Dave Terrin (Gen Mgr)

SHEEHY CONSTRUCTION COMPANY
360 Larpenteur Ave W Ste 200, Saint Paul, MN 55113-6782
Tel.: (651) 488-6691
Web Site:
  http://www.sheehyconstruction.com
Sales Range: $25-49.9 Million

Sheehy Construction Company—(Continued)
Emp.: 50
Nonresidential Construction Services
N.A.I.C.S.: 236220
Daniel Krause (Pres)

SHEEHY FORD OF WARRENTON
6443 Lee Hwy, Warrenton, VA 20187
Tel.: (540) 347-1234
Web Site:
http://www.sheehyfordwarrenton.com
Year Founded: 2010
Sales Range: $10-24.9 Million
Emp.: 50
Car Whslr
N.A.I.C.S.: 441110
Stephen DiDomenico (Gen Mgr)

SHEEHY WALDORF
2950 Crain Hwy, Waldorf, MD 20601
Tel.: (301) 843-5300
Web Site:
http://www.sheehyhyundaiwaldorf.com
Sales Range: $10-24.9 Million
Emp.: 48
New Car Dealers
N.A.I.C.S.: 441110
Russ Zakeri (Gen Mgr)
Calvin Jackson (Mgr-Sls)
Laura Via (Dir-Fin)
Brittany Wagner (Mgr-Customer Rels)
Jarryd Carver (Gen Mgr)
Emmanuel Jean-Francois (Gen Mgr-Sls)
Emmanuel Jean Francois (Mgr-Gen Sls)
Vincent Telli (Mgr-Parts-Columbus)
Ewing Foulks (Mgr-Sls)
Chris Cooper (Mgr-Svc)
Juan del Catillo (Mgr-Svc-Columbus)

SHEELEY ARCHITECTS, INC.
8200 College Pkwy Ste 101, Fort Myers, FL 33907
Tel.: (239) 482-2121   FL
Web Site:
http://www.sheeleyarchitects.com
Year Founded: 1992
Sales Range: $1-9.9 Million
Emp.: 8
Architectural Services
N.A.I.C.S.: 541310
Michael K. Sheeley (Pres)
Lawrence C. Byle (Controller)

SHEERTRANS SOLUTIONS, LLC
635 Trade Center Blvd, Chesterfield, MO 63005
Tel.: (314) 721-0101
Web Site: https://sheerlogistics.com
Emp.: 100
Transportation Management, Logistics & Warehousing Services
N.A.I.C.S.: 488999

Subsidiaries:

CargoBarn Inc.   (1)
4620 Jacquelyn Ave Ste 104, Fresno, CA 93722
Tel.: (559) 271-3320
Web Site: http://www.cargobarn.com
Sales Range: $1-9.9 Million
Emp.: 10
Transportation & Shipping Services
N.A.I.C.S.: 488510
Nic Walters (Mgr-Sls-Natl)
Jeremiah Fertig (Acct Mgr)
Cuinn Peters (Acct Mgr)
Abel Martin (COO)

SHEERVISION INC.
4030 Palos Verdes Dr N Ste 104, Rolling Hills Estates, CA 90274
Tel.: (310) 265-8918   DE
Web Site:
https://www.sheervision.com
Year Founded: 1999
SVSO—(OTCBB)
Sales Range: Less than $1 Million
Surgical Loupes & Headlights Mfr
N.A.I.C.S.: 339113

SHEETS & CO.
425 N Maple Dr Unit 206, Beverly Hills, CA 90210
Tel.: (310) 273-1000
Web Site: http://www.sheets.com
Sales Range: $25-49.9 Million
Emp.: 4
Bedding Sales
N.A.I.C.S.: 423220
Thomas Tanaher (Owner)

SHEETS & GRAPHIC SHEETS UNLIMITED
301 SW 27th St, Renton, WA 98055
Tel.: (425) 251-5959
Web Site:
http://www.mysticsheets.com
Rev.: $11,500,000
Emp.: 150
Corrugated & Solid Fiber Box Mfr
N.A.I.C.S.: 322211
Prescilla Hernaez (Controller)
Gordon Younger (Chm)
Mark Held (Pres)

SHEETS CONSTRUCTION INC.
1756 22nd St SE, Salem, OR 97302
Tel.: (503) 362-1164
Sales Range: $10-24.9 Million
Emp.: 20
Commercial Construction
N.A.I.C.S.: 236220
Donald E. Sheets (Chm)

SHEETS WHOLESALE INC.
430 Mill St NE, Vienna, VA 22180
Tel.: (703) 938-9110
Sales Range: $10-24.9 Million
Emp.: 15
Lumber & Plywood
N.A.I.C.S.: 423310
Russell H. Sheets (Owner)
David Sheets (Gen Mgr)
Edward Eric Belardo (Mgr)

SHEETZ, INC.
5700 6th Ave, Altoona, PA 16602
Tel.: (814) 946-3611   PA
Web Site: https://www.sheetz.com
Year Founded: 1952
Sales Range: $1-4.9 Billion
Emp.: 24,000
Gasoline Stations with Convenience Stores
N.A.I.C.S.: 457110
G. Robert Sheetz (Founder)
Ray Ryan (Exec VP-Distr Center)
Travis Sheetz (Pres & COO)
Nick Ruffner (Mgr-PR)
Ryan Sheetz (Asst VP-Brand Strategy)
Adam Sheetz (Exec VP-Ops)
Stanton R. Sheetz (Chm)

SHEFFIELD METALS INTERNATIONAL, INC.
5467 Evergreen Pkwy, Lorain, OH 44054
Tel.: (440) 934-8500
Web Site:
http://www.sheffieldmetals.com
Year Founded: 1995
Sales Range: $10-24.9 Million
Emp.: 100
Distr of Architectural Metal Products
N.A.I.C.S.: 331315

Jill Wilson (Controller)
Mike Blake (Pres)

SHEFIT OPERATING COMPANY LLC
4400 Central Pkwy, Hudsonville, MI 49426
Tel.: (616) 209-7003
Web Site: http://www.shefit.com
Year Founded: 2013
Sales Range: $1-9.9 Million
Emp.: 25
Women Apparel Distr
N.A.I.C.S.: 458110
Sara Marie (Founder)

SHEILA DONNELLY & ASSOCIATES
116 W 23rd St Ste 500, New York, NY 10011
Tel.: (212) 851-8425
Web Site:
http://www.sheiladonnelly.com
Year Founded: 1987
Rev.: $1,100,000
Emp.: 10
Fiscal Year-end: 12/31/06
Advetising Agency
N.A.I.C.S.: 541810
Leslie Kim (Sr VP)
Sheila Donnelly Theroux (Founder & Pres)
Babs Harrison (Sr VP)
Sweetie Nelson (Sr VP)
Joel Ann Rea (Dir-Special Counsel & Creative)
Joe Enos (Mktg Counsel & Sr Acct Dir-Publicist)
Brendan Donnelly (Sr Editorial Writer)
Kathy Ho (Acct Exec)
Jeong Ku Hwang (Acct Exec)
Megan Mulcahy (Acct Exec)
Aubrey McGovern (Acct Exec)

SHELBA D. JOHNSON TRUCKING, INC.
1640 Blair St, Thomasville, NC 27360-8808
Tel.: (336) 476-2000   NC
Web Site: http://www.sdjtrucking.com
Sales Range: $10-24.9 Million
Emp.: 500
Trucking Service
N.A.I.C.S.: 484121
Joe Wade (Pres)
Mike Marsh (Gen Mgr)
Kevan Johnson (Dir-Safety)
Scott Denmark (Mgr-Ops)
Diane Prim (Mgr-Claims, Shortages & Returns)

SHELBURNE CORP.
20001 Shelburne Rd, Cleveland, OH 44118
Tel.: (216) 321-9177
Rev.: $31,200,000
Industrial Vessels
N.A.I.C.S.: 332313

Subsidiaries:

Alloy Bellows & Precision
Welding   (1)
653 Miner Rd, Cleveland, OH 44143
Tel.: (440) 684-3000
Web Site: http://www.alloybellows.com
Sales Range: $1-9.9 Million
Emp.: 70
Bellows, Industrial: Metal
N.A.I.C.S.: 333998

Budzar Industries Inc.   (1)
38241 Willoughby Pkwy, Willoughby, OH 44094
Tel.: (440) 918-0505
Web Site: http://www.budzar.com
Rev.: $14,000,000
Emp.: 100
Temperature Instruments

N.A.I.C.S.: 334513
Dave Young (Pres)

SHELBY COUNTY CO-OP
2350 E State Rd 44, Shelbyville, IN 46176
Tel.: (317) 398-6655
Web Site:
http://www.shelbycountyco-op.com
Sales Range: $10-24.9 Million
Emp.: 35
Agricultural Services
N.A.I.C.S.: 457210
Denny Frey (CFO & Controller)
Randy Sprague (CFO & Controller)
Jeff Maurice (Pres)

SHELBY COUNTY STATE BANK
508 Court St, Harlan, IA 51537
Tel.: (712) 755-5112
Web Site: http://www.scsbnet.com
Year Founded: 1880
Emp.: 55
State Commercial Banks
N.A.I.C.S.: 522110
Stefanie Kramer (CFO & COO-Ops)
Janet Buman (Mgr-Mktg)
Kevin Campbell (Chm, Pres & CEO)

SHELBY GRAVEL INC.
157 E Rampart St, Shelbyville, IN 46176
Tel.: (317) 398-4485
Web Site:
http://www.shelbymaterials.com
Sales Range: $10-24.9 Million
Emp.: 30
Ready Mixed Concrete
N.A.I.C.S.: 327320
Phillip Haehl (Pres)

SHELBY MECHANICAL, INC.
1009 Broad St, Cinnaminson, NJ 08077
Tel.: (856) 665-4540
Web Site:
http://www.shelbymechanical.com
Year Founded: 2007
Sales Range: $10-24.9 Million
Emp.: 400
Plumbing, Heating & Air-Conditioning Contractors
N.A.I.C.S.: 238220
Michael P. Bray (Exec VP)
Jean Cook (Office Mgr)
Michael D. Mulligan (Exec VP)
Nancy D. Bray (CEO)

SHELBY-REID, INC.
104 W 5th St, Benton, KY 42025
Tel.: (270) 906-9275   KY
Web Site: http://www.country-chevrolet.com
Year Founded: 1994
Sales Range: $10-24.9 Million
New & Used Car Dealer
N.A.I.C.S.: 441110
Michael B. Reid (Co-Founder & Pres)
Michael Ryan Reid (Pres & Gen Mgr)
Robert W. Shelby III (Co-Founder)

SHELBYVILLE POWER, WATER, & SEWAGE SYSTEM
308 S Main St, Shelbyville, TN 37160
Tel.: (931) 684-7171
Web Site:
http://www.shelbyvillepower.com
Sales Range: $25-49.9 Million
Emp.: 82
Electric Power & Water Distr
N.A.I.C.S.: 221122
David Crowell (Gen Mgr)
Garrett Gordon (Mgr-Admin)

SHELCIDY CUSTOM REMODELING, INC.
3750 S Osprey Ave, Sarasota, FL 34239

Tel.: (941) 921-4222
Web Site: http://www.shelcidy.com
Sales Range: $1-9.9 Million
Emp.: 10
Custom Remodeler
N.A.I.C.S.: 236118
Albert Brannon (Pres)
Adam Dickerson (VP & Project Mgr)
Lupe Bowling (Mgr-Ops)

SHELCO, LLC
2320 Cascade Pointe Blvd Ste 100, Charlotte, NC 28208
Tel.: (704) 367-5600
Web Site: http://www.shelcollc.com
Year Founded: 1978
Sales Range: $250-299.9 Million
Emp.: 135
Industrial Building Construction Services
N.A.I.C.S.: 236210
D. Edwin Rose (Pres & CEO)
J. Scott Bengel (CFO, Exec VP, Treas & Sec)
Howard N. Peabody (COO, Exec VP & Asst Sec)
Gerard J. Reid (Exec VP & Asst Sec)
Barry W. Gardner (CMO & Exec VP)
Susan F. Campbell (Sr VP-Bus Admin & Asst Sec)
Earl R. Hiatt (Sr VP-Field Ops)
Daniel W. Perry (Exec VP & Asst Sec)
Chip Pope (VP-Mktg & Bus Dev)
Mark Caudill (VP-Mktg & Bus Dev-Winston-Salem)
Hunter Burnette (Sr VP-Raleigh)
James Rogers (VP-Mktg & Bus Dev)

SHELDON GROSS REALTY INC.
80 Main St Ste 420, West Orange, NJ 07052-5460
Tel.: (973) 325-6200   NJ
Web Site:
    http://www.sheldongrossrealty.com
Year Founded: 1962
Rev.: $25,000,000
Emp.: 50
Real Estate Agents & Managers
N.A.I.C.S.: 531210
Sheldon A. Gross (Pres & CEO)
Barbara Gross (Exec VP)
Marcy Gross (Project Mgr)
Robert Nathin (Sr VP)

SHELDONS OF OCEANSIDE INC.
5700 Hannum Ave, Culver City, CA 90230
Tel.: (310) 665-2100
Web Site:
    http://www.danielsjewelers.com
Rev.: $21,680,483
Emp.: 140
Jewelry; Precious Stones & Precious Metals
N.A.I.C.S.: 458310
Lawrence Sherwood (Pres)

Subsidiaries:

Sherwood Management Co. Inc.   (1)
5700 Hannum Ave, Culver City, CA 90230
Tel.: (310) 665-2100
Rev.: $15,951,397
Emp.: 125
Jewelry Stores
N.A.I.C.S.: 458310

SHELDONS' INC.
626 Ctr St, Antigo, WI 54409-2496
Tel.: (715) 623-2382   WI
Web Site: http://www.mepps.com
Year Founded: 1955
Sales Range: $50-74.9 Million
Emp.: 66
Mfr of Fishing Equipment
N.A.I.C.S.: 339920
J. M. Sheldon (Pres, CEO & COO)
Jean Luc Favre (Gen Mgr-France)
Robert M. Bender (Controller)

Subsidiaries:

Mepps SNC   (1)
840 Chemin Gheit, PO Box 09, Contes, 06390, France   (100%)
Tel.: (33) 493790707
Web Site: http://www.sheldons.com
Sales Range: $1-9.9 Million
Emp.: 50
Mfr of Recreational Fishing Lures
N.A.I.C.S.: 713940
Jean Luc Faure (Gen Mgr)

Mister Twister, L.L.C.   (1)
1401 Commerce St PO Box 996, Minden, LA 71058-0996   (100%)
Tel.: (318) 377-8818
Web Site: http://www.mistertwister.com
Rev.: $5,000,000
Emp.: 50
Mfr of Soft Plastic Recreational Fishing Lures
N.A.I.C.S.: 339920

Star Manufacturing, L.L.C.   (1)
121 Sheppard St, Minden, LA 71055-4204   (80%)
Tel.: (318) 377-1700
Sales Range: $10-24.9 Million
Emp.: 25
Mfr of Soft Plastic Recreational Fishing Lures
N.A.I.C.S.: 339920

SHELFGENIE
1642 Powers Ferry Rd SE Ste 200, Marietta, GA 30067
Tel.: (770) 618-8000
Web Site: http://www.shelfgenie.com
Year Founded: 2000
Sales Range: $1-9.9 Million
Emp.: 20
Design of Custom Shelving
N.A.I.C.S.: 337215
Allan Young (Founder & CEO)
Trudy Edenfield (COO)
Michael Sinclair (CMO)

SHELL LUMBER & HARDWARE INC.
2733 SW 27th Ave, Miami, FL 33133
Tel.: (305) 856-6401
Web Site:
    http://www.shelllumber.com
Year Founded: 1928
Sales Range: $10-24.9 Million
Emp.: 90
Hardware Retailer
N.A.I.C.S.: 444140
Jesus G. (Pres)
John Ruark (Gen Mgr)

SHELLEY ELECTRIC INC.
3619 W 29th St S, Wichita, KS 67217
Tel.: (316) 945-8311
Web Site:
    http://www.shelleyelectric.com
Sales Range: $10-24.9 Million
Emp.: 130
General Electrical Contractor
N.A.I.C.S.: 238210
Greg Rowe (CFO)
Roy Meinharet (VP)

SHELLHORN & HILL INC.
501 S Market St, Wilmington, DE 19801
Tel.: (302) 658-5293
Web Site:
    http://www.shellhornandhill.com
Rev.: $17,000,000
Emp.: 60
Petroleum Products
N.A.I.C.S.: 424720

SHELLY & SANDS INC.
3570 S River Rd, Zanesville, OH 43701
Tel.: (740) 453-0721
Web Site:
    http://www.shellyandsands.com
Rev.: $75,600,000
Emp.: 1,000
Highway & Street Paving Contractor
N.A.I.C.S.: 237310
Gerald N. Little (Pres)
Clay P. Graham (Chm)
Bryan H. Graham (Sr VP)
Doug Howell (VP-Construction)
Jerry E. Taylor (VP-Mar-Zane)
Mike W. Cline (Treas & Sec)

SHELOR MOTOR MILE
2260 Roanoke St, Christiansburg, VA 24073
Tel.: (540) 382-2981
Web Site: http://www.shelor.com
Sales Range: $25-49.9 Million
Emp.: 400
New & Used Automobiles
N.A.I.C.S.: 441110
Larry J. Shelor (Pres)
Missy Rotenberry (Controller)
Tyler Witten (Dir-Art)
Curtis Turner (Gen Mgr-Sls)
Regina Edwards (Mgr-Parts)
A. Melissa Gentry (CFO)

SHELTAIR AVIATION CENTER, LLC
1100 Lee Wagener Blvd Ste 107, Fort Lauderdale, FL 33315-3570
Web Site:
    http://www.sheltairaviation.com
Year Founded: 1963
Construction Management Services
N.A.I.C.S.: 236220
Gerald M. Holland (Founder, Chm & CEO)

Subsidiaries:

Tampa International Jet Center   (1)
4751 Jim Walter Blvd, Tampa, FL 33607-5783
Tel.: (813) 319-8000
Web Site: http://www.tampajet.com
Commercial Air, Rail & Water Transportation Equipment Rental & Leasing
N.A.I.C.S.: 532411
Phil Botana (Pres)

SHELTER CO.
4040 3rd St, San Francisco, CA 94124
Tel.: (415) 967-3630
Web Site: http://www.shelter-co.com
Year Founded: 2012
Sales Range: $1-9.9 Million
Emp.: 20
Travel & Hospitality Services
N.A.I.C.S.: 561510
Kelsey Sheofsky (Co-Founder & CEO)
Mike Sheofsky (Co-Founder & COO)
Maggie Wilson (Creative Dir)
Khaia Brogan (Head-Production)

SHELTER MUTUAL INSURANCE COMPANY
1817 W Broadway, Columbia, MO 65218-0001
Tel.: (573) 445-8441   MO
Web Site: http://www.shelterins.com
Year Founded: 1946
Sales Range: $1-4.9 Billion
Emp.: 1,800
Casualty & Life Insurance
N.A.I.C.S.: 524126
Gary Myers (Sec & Exec VP)
Rick Means (Chm)
Randa Rawlins (Pres)
Matt Moore (CEO)
Paul LaRose (Exec VP)
Stacye Smith (VP-HR Ops)

Subsidiaries:

Daniel Boone Agency, LLC   (1)
1520 Smoky Park Hwy, Candler, NC 28715
Tel.: (828) 665-0899
Web Site:
    http://www.autobrokersandconsultants.com
Used Car Dealers
N.A.I.C.S.: 441120

Haulers Insurance Company, Inc.   (1)
1101 New Hwy 7, Columbia, TN 38401
Web Site: http://www.haulersinsurance.com
Property & Casualty Insurance Services
N.A.I.C.S.: 524126

Shelter Financial Services, Inc.   (1)
305 San Anselmo Ave Ste 309, San Anselmo, CA 94960
Tel.: (415) 456-3500
Web Site: http://www.shelterfinancial.com
Automobile Finance Leasing Services
N.A.I.C.S.: 522220

SHELTER PARTNERSHIP, INC.
523 W 6th St Ste 616, Los Angeles, CA 90014-1224
Tel.: (213) 688-2188   CA
Web Site:
    http://www.shelterpartnership.org
Year Founded: 1985
Sales Range: $1-9.9 Million
Emp.: 17
Homeless People Assistance Services
N.A.I.C.S.: 624221
Ruth Schwartz (Co-Founder & Exec Dir)
Tracy Wallace (Dir-Dev)
Nicky Viola (Sr Project Mgr)
John A. DeFazio (Chm)
Kevin Sullivan (Treas)
Louise Oliver (Sec)
Rhonda Villanueva (Mgr-Distributions)

SHELTER PRODUCTS INC.
4560 SE International Way Ste 215, Milwaukie, OR 97222
Tel.: (503) 872-3600
Web Site: http://www.shelter-products.com
Year Founded: 1966
Sales Range: $50-74.9 Million
Emp.: 99
Supplier of Wood Products & Building Materials
N.A.I.C.S.: 423310
Dustin Cook (Mgr-Sls-Daphne)
Eric Heaton (Mgr-Sls-Dallas)

SHELTERING PALMS FOUNDATION INC
9045 La Fontana Blvd Ste 105, Boca Raton, FL 33434
Tel.: (561) 241-4321
Sales Range: $10-24.9 Million
Social Welfare & Public Relation Services
N.A.I.C.S.: 813410
Andrea Czarnecki (CFO)

SHELTERLOGIC CORP.
150 Callender Rd, Watertown, CT 06795
Tel.: (860) 945-6442
Web Site:
    http://www.shelterlogic.com
Year Founded: 1991
Sales Range: $10-24.9 Million
Emp.: 115
Prefabricated Metal Building & Component Mfr
N.A.I.C.S.: 332311
Jim Raymond (Pres & CEO)

SHELTERPOINT GROUP, INC.

ShelterPoint Group, Inc.—(Continued)

SHELTERPOINT GROUP, INC.
1225 Franklin Av Ste 475, Garden City, NY 11530
Tel.: (516) 829-8100   NY
Web Site:
http://www.shelterpoint.com
Year Founded: 1972
Accident & Health Insurance Services Provider
N.A.I.C.S.: 524114
John W. Baldwin *(Pres)*

Subsidiaries:

First Rehabilitation Life Insurance Co. of America Inc.   (1)
600 Northern Blvd Ste 310, Great Neck, NY 11021-5200   (100%)
Tel.: (516) 829-8100
Web Site: http://www.firstrehab.com
Sales Range: $50-74.9 Million
Accident And Health Insurance
N.A.I.C.S.: 524114
Bruce Wallach *(CFO)*

SHELTON CAPITAL MANAGEMENT
1875 Lawrence St Ste 300, Denver, CO 80202
Tel.: (800) 955-9988
Web Site: https://sheltoncap.com
Year Founded: 1985
Investment Firm
N.A.I.C.S.: 523999
Steve Rogers *(CEO)*

SHEN YUN PERFORMING ARTS INC.
140 Galley Hill Rd, Cuddebackville, NY 12729
Tel.: (845) 754-8055   NY
Web Site:
http://www.shenyunperformingarts.org
Year Founded: 2006
Sales Range: $10-24.9 Million
Emp.: 192
Art Event Organizer
N.A.I.C.S.: 711310
Xiu Guo *(CEO)*

SHENANDOAH LIFE INSURANCE COMPANY
4415 Pheasant Ridge Rd, Roanoke, VA 24014
Tel.: (540) 985-4400   VA
Web Site: http://www.shenlife.com
Year Founded: 1914
Sales Range: $150-199.9 Million
Emp.: 165
Annuity, Life & Health Insurance
N.A.I.C.S.: 524113
Paul Mistretta *(Pres & CEO)*
Marci Chrisley *(Dir-Tax & Treasury Svcs)*
Gina Hawks *(Dir-Sls Dev & Trng)*
Mark Thompson *(Dir-Tech Svcs)*

Subsidiaries:

Old Dominion Life Insurance Co.   (1)
2301 Brambleton Ave SW, Roanoke, VA 24015-4701   (100%)
Tel.: (540) 248-4400
Sales Range: $50-74.9 Million
Life Insurance
N.A.I.C.S.: 524113

SHENANDOAH MILLS, INC.
121 S Cumberland St, Lebanon, TN 37088-0369
Tel.: (615) 444-0841   TN
Web Site:
http://www.shenandoahmills.com
Sales Range: $10-24.9 Million
Emp.: 20
Mfr & Distributor of Dry Mixes
N.A.I.C.S.: 311824

Dale Nunnery *(Pres)*
Stan Edwards *(VP-Sls)*
Tom Kraus *(Plant Mgr)*

SHENANDOAH TOWER SERVICE LTD.
1617 West Beverley St, Staunton, VA 24401
Tel.: (540) 887-8000
Web Site:
http://www.shenandoahtower.com
Year Founded: 1983
Rev.: $11,328,674
Emp.: 50
Transmitting Tower Construction Services
N.A.I.C.S.: 237130
Dave Anthony *(Co-Founder)*
Angie Badles *(Controller)*
Donna Daugherty *(Dir-Opers)*

SHENANDOAH VALLEY ELECTRIC COOPERATIVE
180 Oakwood Dr, Harrisonburg, VA 22801
Tel.: (540) 434-2200   VI
Web Site: http://www.svec.coop
Year Founded: 1936
Rev.: $247,033,126
Assets: $500,191,255
Liabilities: $320,556,296
Net Worth: $179,634,959
Earnings: $15,645,166
Emp.: 234
Fiscal Year-end: 12/31/18
Electronic Services
N.A.I.C.S.: 221118
J. Michael Aulgur *(CFO & VP)*
William A. Orndoff *(Vice Chm)*
Conrad A. Helsley *(Chm)*
Jerry Dofflemyer *(Treas & Sec)*
Greg Rogers *(Pres & CEO)*
Jason Burch *(VP-Engrg)*
Tony Dean *(VP-Ops)*
Vicky Fitzgerald *(Dir-Fin & Acctg)*
Morgan Messer *(Dir-External Affairs & Comm)*
Wayne D. Hannah Jr. *(CIO & VP)*

SHENANDOAH VALLEY WESTMINSTER-CANTERBURY
300 Westminster Canterbury Dr, Winchester, VA 22603
Tel.: (540) 665-0156   VA
Web Site: http://www.svwc.org
Year Founded: 1982
Sales Range: $10-24.9 Million
Emp.: 407
Continuing Care Retirement Community Services
N.A.I.C.S.: 623311
James White *(Dir-Environmental Svcs)*
Gloria J. Shiley *(Pres & CEO)*
Duane Warnecke *(CFO)*
John Ferrulli *(Dir-IT & Security)*
Cynthia Hunter *(Dir-HR)*

SHENANGO LLC
1200 College Ave, Terre Haute, IN 47802-1400
Tel.: (812) 235-2058   IN
Web Site: http://www.shenango.com
Year Founded: 1896
Sales Range: $50-74.9 Million
Emp.: 12
Centrifugal Casting Services
N.A.I.C.S.: 331529
Bob Staley *(Gen Mgr)*

SHEPARD AUTO GROUP
181 New County Rd, Rockland, ME 04841
Tel.: (207) 594-8424
Web Site: http://shepardcars.com
Sales Range: $10-24.9 Million

Emp.: 40
New & Used Automobiles Dealer
N.A.I.C.S.: 441110
Glenn Shepard *(Pres)*
Susan Shepard *(Office Mgr)*
John Carter *(Gen Sls Mgr)*
Hayden Martz *(Mgr-Fin)*

SHEPARD EXPOSITION SERVICES INC.
1531 Carroll Dr NW, Atlanta, GA 30318-3605
Tel.: (404) 720-8600   GA
Web Site: http://www.shepardes.com
Year Founded: 1905
Sales Range: $25-49.9 Million
Emp.: 500
Business Services
N.A.I.C.S.: 561920
Carl F. Mitchell *(Chm)*
Frank Villamar *(CFO)*
Kevin Bird *(Exec VP-Sls)*
Steve Basch *(CEO)*
Steve Margos *(Exec VP-Ops)*

Subsidiaries:

Aquarian, LLC   (1)
752-C Walker Rd, Great Falls, VA 22066-2643   (100%)
Tel.: (703) 438-8838
Web Site: http://www.aquarianllc.com
Entertainment & Live Production Services
N.A.I.C.S.: 561920
Gene Lundgren *(Pres)*

SHEPARD STEEL CO. INC.
110 Meadow St, Hartford, CT 06114
Tel.: (860) 525-4446
Web Site:
http://www.shepardsteel.com
Sales Range: $25-49.9 Million
Emp.: 65
Steel Building Components Mfr
N.A.I.C.S.: 332312
Brian Ritchie *(VP)*
Jeff Parnell *(Mgr-Engrg)*
Norbert Kropiewnicki *(Project Mgr)*
Shaun Pelletier *(Project Mgr)*

SHEPARD WALTON KING INSURANCE GROUP
801 N Main St, McAllen, TX 78501
Tel.: (956) 682-2841
Web Site:
http://www.shepardwaltonking.com
Rev.: $45,000,000
Emp.: 21
Insurance Agents, Nec
N.A.I.C.S.: 524210
Robert W. Shepard *(CEO)*
Robert Walton *(Sec)*
Neal P. King *(Pres)*

SHEPARDS MOTOR
US Route Ste 1, Rockland, ME 04841
Tel.: (207) 594-8424
Web Site:
http://www.shepardcars.com
Year Founded: 1957
Sales Range: $10-24.9 Million
Emp.: 33
Car Whslr
N.A.I.C.S.: 441110
Glenn Shepard *(Pres)*

SHEPEARD COMMUNITY BLOOD CENTER
1533 Wrightsboro Rd, Augusta, GA 30904
Tel.: (706) 737-4551   GA
Web Site:
http://www.shepeardblood.org
Sales Range: $10-24.9 Million
Emp.: 121
Blood Bank
N.A.I.C.S.: 621991

Susan Dewes *(Dir-Donor Svcs)*
Sharon Johnston *(Dir-HR)*
Sally McCarty *(Dir-Technical Svcs)*
Jane Miller *(Dir-Quality Assurance)*
Pamela Rascon *(Dir-Community Resources)*

SHEPHARD'S BEACH RESORT, INC.
619 S Gulfview Blvd, Clearwater, FL 33767-2643
Tel.: (727) 442-5107
Web Site: http://www.shephards.com
Sales Range: $10-24.9 Million
Emp.: 135
Hotel, Restaurant & Bar
N.A.I.C.S.: 721110
William M. Shephard *(Owner)*

SHEPHERD CENTER, INC.
2020 Peachtree Rd NW, Atlanta, GA 30309-1465
Tel.: (404) 352-2020   GA
Web Site: http://www.shepherd.org
Year Founded: 1975
Sales Range: $150-199.9 Million
Emp.: 1,749
Health Care Srvices
N.A.I.C.S.: 622110
James H. Shepherd *(Chm)*
Gary R. Ulicny *(Pres & CEO)*
William C. Fowler *(Treas)*
Stephen B. Goot *(Sec)*

SHEPHERD CONSTRUCTION CO., INC.
1800 Briarcliff Rd NE, Atlanta, GA 30329-4008
Tel.: (404) 325-9350   GA
Year Founded: 1948
Sales Range: $200-249.9 Million
Emp.: 435
Heavy Highway Construction
N.A.I.C.S.: 237310
Stephen B. Shepherd *(Pres)*
Cecil L. Pearce *(COO)*
David Philpot *(CFO)*
William Clyde Shepherd Jr. *(Treas & Sec)*
Clyde Shepherd III *(VP)*

Subsidiaries:

Rogers Bridge Company, Inc.   (1)
1800 Briarcliff Rd NE, Atlanta, GA 30329-4008   (100%)
Tel.: (404) 325-9350
Sales Range: $10-24.9 Million
Emp.: 120
Heavy Highway Construction Services
N.A.I.C.S.: 237310
Charles H. Haney *(CEO)*
Tommy Sheperd *(Dir-PR)*
Steven Shepherd *(Pres)*

SHEPHERD'S FINANCE, LLC
13241 Bartram Park Blvd Ste 2401, Jacksonville, FL 32258
Tel.: (302) 752-2688   DE
Web Site:
https://www.shepherdsfinance.com
Year Founded: 2007
Rev.: $6,128,000
Assets: $64,834,000
Liabilities: $62,840,000
Net Worth: $1,994,000
Earnings: $2,578,000
Emp.: 19
Fiscal Year-end: 12/31/23
Commercial Lending Services
N.A.I.C.S.: 522310
Daniel M. Wallach *(CEO)*
Barbara L. Harshman *(Exec VP-Ops)*
Mark Reynolds *(Exec VP-Sls)*

SHEPPARD MULLIN RICHTER & HAMPTON LLP

COMPANIES

333 S Hope St 43rd Fl, Los Angeles, CA 90071
Tel.: (213) 620-1780
Web Site:
http://www.sheppardmullin.com
Year Founded: 1927
Sales Range: $400-449.9 Million
Emp.: 1,165
Legal Advisory Services
N.A.I.C.S.: 541110
Robert S. Beall *(Mng Partner)*
Holly Patterson *(Mgr-Intellectual Property Admin)*
Kevin M. Cloutier *(Partner)*
Lawrence C. Eppley *(Mng Partner-Chicago)*
Bradley C. Graveline *(Partner)*
Martin Bader *(Partner)*
Elizabeth S. Balfour *(Partner)*
Robert G. Copeland *(Partner)*
Domenic C. Drago *(Partner)*
Dana J. Dunwoody *(Partner)*
Paul Werner *(Partner)*
Dave Thomas *(Partner)*
Peter Carson *(Partner)*
Michael V. Solomita *(Partner)*
Craig S. Mordock *(Partner-Corp Practice Grp-Orange County)*
Katey Allen *(Partner-San Francisco)*
Jennifer Renk *(Partner-San Francisco)*
Jim Rusk *(Partner-San Francisco)*
Laura Jehl *(Partner-Bus Trial Practice)*
Colleen McDonald *(Partner)*
Adam Rosenthal *(Partner-Labor and Employment Practice Grp-Del Mar)*
Weiguo Chen *(Partner-Intellectual Property-Palo Alto)*
Thomas J. Masenga *(Partner-Real Estate, Land Use & Environmental Practice Grp)*
Jon W. Newby *(Vice Chm)*
Bijal N. Vira *(Partner-Corp & Fin Bankruptcy Practice Grps-New York)*
David J. Passey *(Partner-Tax, Employee Benefits, Trusts & Estate Practice Grp)*
Keith R. Gercken *(Partner)*
Kevin M. Ryan *(Partner-Fin & Bankruptcy Practice-Chicago)*
Aaron J. Malo *(Partner)*
Adam M. Freiman *(Partner)*
J. Barrett Marum *(Partner)*
Shannon Z. Petersen *(Partner)*
Tony K. Mou *(Partner)*
Whitney Jones Roy *(Partner)*
Michael Paddock *(Partner-Corp Practice Grp-Washington)*
Garen E. Dodge *(Partner-Labor & Employment Practice Grp-Washington)*
Robert Rhoad *(Partner-Govt Contracts, Investigations & Intl Trade Practice Grp)*
Steven Hollman *(Partner-Bus Trial Practice Grp)*
William Kane *(Partner-Complex Comml Litigation-Bus Trial Practice Grp)*
Nicholas van Aelstyn *(Partner-83 Lawyer Real Estate, Land Use & Environmental Practice)*
Amit Kalra *(Partner-Energy, Infrastructure & Project Fin)*
Laurette Petersen *(Partner)*
Andrew Ratts *(Partner)*
Christine Hourcade-Hoefliger *(Partner-Energy Grp)*
Valerie Demont *(Partner-Corp Practice Grp-New York)*
Robert D. Weber *(Partner-Bus Trial Practice Grp-Century City)*
David J. Gershon *(Partner-Corp Practice Grp-San Francisco)*
Benedict O. Kwon *(Partner-Corp Practice Grp-Orange County)*
Michael Roth *(Partner)*
Kathy Levecke *(Partner)*
Christine Clements *(Partner-Washington)*
Joseph J. LoBue *(Partner-Bus Trial Practice Grp-Washington)*
Fatema Merchant *(Partner-Washington)*
Ryan Roberts *(Partner-Washington)*
Steven Braccini *(Partner-Private Wealth & Fiduciary Litigation Practice-Palo Alto)*
Robert Masters *(Partner-Washington)*
Jonathan DeFosse *(Partner-Washington)*
Bevin Newman *(Partner-Washington)*
Stacey L. Rosenberg *(Partner-Fin & Bankruptcy Practice Grp)*
Moorari K. Shah *(Partner-Fin & Bankruptcy Practice Grp)*
David Sands *(Partner-Corp Practice Grp)*
Michael P. O'Brien *(Partner-Fin & Bankruptcy Practice Grp-Chicago)*
Leonard Lipsky *(Partner-Corp Practice Grp & Healthcare-New York)*
Soyun Park *(Partner-Tax-New York)*
Jodi Stein *(Partner-Land Use-New York)*
Ira Schulman *(Partner-Construction Litigation-New York)*
Paul Harner *(Partner-Fin & Bankruptcy-New York)*
Michael Gilbert *(Partner-Govt & Internal Investigations-New York)*
Luca Salvi *(Chm)*
Lois Durant *(Chief Diversity & Inclusion Officer)*
Brian Murphy *(CEO)*
Marisa Brutoco *(Partner-Entertainment, Tech & Adv Practice)*
Robert Brown *(COO)*

SHERATON WEST PORT INC.
900 Westport Plz, Saint Louis, MO 63146
Tel.: (314) 434-5010
Web Site:
http://www.sheratonwestport.com
Sales Range: $10-24.9 Million
Emp.: 150
Hotels & Motels
N.A.I.C.S.: 721110
Mitch Bollen *(Gen Mgr)*
Bob Oloughin *(Pres)*
Steve Oloughin *(VP)*

SHERBORNE INVESTORS MANAGEMENT LP
135 E 57th St, New York, NY 10022
Tel.: (212) 735-1000
Web Site:
http://www.sherborneinvestors.com
Investment Services
N.A.I.C.S.: 523999
Edward J. Bramson *(Founder)*

SHERBROOKE CAPITAL LLC
10 Laurel Ave Ste 130, Wellesley, MA 02481
Tel.: (617) 332-7227
Web Site:
http://www.sherbrookecapital.com
Year Founded: 1999
Emp.: 5
Privatery Equity Firm
N.A.I.C.S.: 523999
John K. Giannuzzi *(Mng Gen Partner)*

Subsidiaries:

Ciao Bella Gelato Company (1)
745 Boylston St, Boston, MA 02116
Tel.: (973) 373-1200
Web Site: http://www.ciaobellagelato.com
Sales Range: $25-49.9 Million
Ice Cream Mfr; Owned by Sherbrooke Capital LLC & Encore Consumer Capital LLC
N.A.I.C.S.: 424430
Carlos Canals *(CEO)*

SHERI-KEY
33 Sheridan Rd, Fairfield, ME 04937
Tel.: (207) 453-9313
Web Site:
http://www.sheridancorporation.com
Rev.: $28,912,705
Emp.: 8
Industrial Buildings & New Construction
N.A.I.C.S.: 236210
Douglas L. Cutchin *(Pres)*

Subsidiaries:

Sheridan Construction Corp (1)
33 Sheridan Rd, Fairfield, ME 04937
Tel.: (207) 453-9311
Web Site: http://www.sheridancorp.com
Industrial Building Services
N.A.I.C.S.: 236210
Christy Kovac *(Pres)*
Ronny Williams *(CEO)*
Chris Sheridan *(Chm)*

Sheridan Corporation (1)
33 Sheridan Rd, Fairfield, ME 04937
Tel.: (207) 453-9311
Web Site: http://www.sheridancorp.com
Sales Range: $10-24.9 Million
Commercial & Office Building, New Construction
N.A.I.C.S.: 236220
Dan Wildes *(VP)*
Brad Nelson *(Owner)*
Joseph Lewis *(Dir-Pub Works)*

SHERIDAN BROADCASTING CORPORATION
960 Penn Ave Ste 400, Pittsburgh, PA 15222
Tel.: (412) 456-4018
Year Founded: 1972
Sales Range: $10-24.9 Million
Emp.: 120
Ownership & Operation of Radio Stations
N.A.I.C.S.: 516110
Ronald R. Davenport Sr. *(Chm)*
Ronald R. Davenport Jr. *(Gen Counsel & Pres-Radio Div)*

Subsidiaries:

American Urban Radio Networks (1)
960 Penn Ave Ste 200, Pittsburgh, PA 15222-3811
Tel.: (412) 456-4000
Web Site: http://www.aurn.com
Sales Range: $1-9.9 Million
Emp.: 60
Radio Networks
N.A.I.C.S.: 516210
Ronald R. Davenport Sr. *(Chm)*
Jerry Lopes *(Pres-Program Ops & Affiliations)*
Lenore Williams *(Sr VP-Affiliate Ops & Compliance)*
Glenn Bryant *(Sr VP-Ops)*
Ty Miller *(Mgr-News & Sports)*
Brian Cook *(Mgr-Web Content)*

Division (Domestic):

American Urban Radio Networks - Chicago Sales (2)
180 N Stetson St Ste 3500, Chicago, IL 60601
Tel.: (312) 558-9090
Web Site: http://www.aurn.com
Radio Network Programming
N.A.I.C.S.: 516110
Stephen Bates *(Exec Dir-Sls)*

American Urban Radio Networks - New York Sales (2)
432 Park Ave S, New York, NY 10016
Tel.: (212) 883-2100
Web Site: http://www.aurn.com
Radio Network Programming
N.A.I.C.S.: 516110

SHERMAN & HEMSTREET, INC.

Andy Anderson *(VP-Sls-Eastern Reg)*

SBN News (1)
960 Penn Ave Ste 300, Pittsburgh, PA 15222
Tel.: (412) 456-4000
Web Site: http://www.aurn.com
Sales Range: $10-24.9 Million
Emp.: 50
Radio Network Programming
N.A.I.C.S.: 516110
Jerry Lopes *(Pres-Program Ops & Affiliates)*

SHERIDAN CAPITAL PARTNERS LLC
400 N. Michigan Ave Ste 800, Chicago, IL 60611
Tel.: (312) 548-7064
Web Site: http://www.sheridancp.com
Year Founded: 2012
Privater Equity Firm
N.A.I.C.S.: 523940
Jonathan B. Lewis *(Partner)*
Sean M. Dempsey *(Partner)*
Jessica Morris *(CFO)*
Nicholas E. Rowland *(Partner)*
Alexandra Kier *(Dir-Bus Dev)*

SHERIDAN NISSAN
114 S Dupont Hwy, New Castle, DE 19720
Tel.: (302) 326-6100
Web Site:
http://www.sheridanautogroup.com
Sales Range: $25-49.9 Million
Emp.: 75
Auto Operator & Services
N.A.I.C.S.: 441110
Joseph Sheridan *(Pres)*
Darlene White *(Controller)*
Andrew Miller *(Gen Mgr)*

SHERLAND & FARRINGTON INC.
253 W 28th St 2nd Fl, New York, NY 10001
Tel.: (212) 206-7500
Web Site: http://www.sherland.com
Rev.: $30,683,772
Emp.: 25
Carpet Laying
N.A.I.C.S.: 238330
Darren Sherland *(VP)*
Rachel Eschenasy *(Controller)*
Arthur C. Post *(Dir-Sls & Mktg)*
Ross Langhorne *(Mgr-Bus Dev)*

SHERLE WAGNER INTERNATIONAL
300 E 62nd St, New York, NY 10065
Tel.: (212) 758-3300
Web Site:
http://www.sherlewagner.com
Rev.: $18,000,000
Emp.: 35
Distr of Home Furnishings
N.A.I.C.S.: 423220
Sandra Llewellyn *(Dir-Sls-Natl)*

SHERLOQ SOLUTIONS
PO Box 972, Tampa, FL 33601-0972
Tel.: (813) 273-7700
Web Site:
http://www.sherloqsolutions.com
Year Founded: 1916
Sales Range: $10-24.9 Million
Emp.: 100
Business Assistance Services
N.A.I.C.S.: 561499
Erik Greer *(Pres)*

SHERMAN & HEMSTREET, INC.
624 Ellis St, Augusta, GA 30901
Tel.: (706) 722-8334
Web Site:
http://www.shermanandhemstreet.com

SHERMAN & HEMSTREET, INC.

Sherman & Hemstreet, Inc.—(Continued)

Year Founded: 1924
Real Estate Company
N.A.I.C.S.: 531390
Joe Edge (Pres)

Subsidiaries:

Kilpatrick & Sconyers Agency (1)
303 S Main St, Swainsboro, GA 30401-3613
Tel.: (478) 237-2291
Web Site: http://www.kilpatricksconyers.com
Offices of Real Estate Agents & Brokers
N.A.I.C.S.: 531210
Julian Sconyers (Owner)

SHERMAN AUTO RENTALS

2918 Lebanon Church Rd, Pittsburgh, PA 15122
Tel.: (412) 466-8120
Year Founded: 2012
Sales Range: $10-24.9 Million
Emp.: 40
Car Whslr
N.A.I.C.S.: 441110
Steve Sherman (Owner)

SHERMAN BROS TRUCKING

32921 Diamond Hill Dr, Harrisburg, OR 97446-9738
Tel.: (541) 995-7751
Web Site:
http://www.shermantrucking.com
Year Founded: 1969
Trucking Service
N.A.I.C.S.: 484121
Bart Sherman (Pres & CEO)
Mike Solomon (VP & Gen Mgr)
Randy Coats (Dir-Liquid Bulk Ops)
Dave Carey (Dir-Flatbed Ops)

SHERMAN COMMUNICATIONS & MARKETING

427 N Harvey Ave, Oak Park, IL 60302
Tel.: (708) 445-8598
Web Site:
http://www.shermancm.com
Sales Range: $10-24.9 Million
Emp.: 4
Advertising, Brand Development & Integration, Communications, Digital/Interactive, Email, Integrated Marketing, Media Relations, Public Relations
N.A.I.C.S.: 541820
Jason Sherman (Pres)

SHERMAN DODGE, INC.

7601 Skokie Blvd, Skokie, IL 60077-3001
Tel.: (847) 982-9500
Web Site:
http://www.shermandodge.com
Year Founded: 1986
Sales Range: $50-74.9 Million
Emp.: 105
New Car Whslr
N.A.I.C.S.: 441110
Mark Schiff (Mgr-Sls)
Alex Kocik (Gen Mgr)
Kiko Betancourt (Dir-Fin)
Matt Horn (Mgr-Sls)
Reggie Steel (Mgr-Sls)
Seba Nowak (Mgr-Sls)
Anthony Sorensen (Mgr-Fin)
Jeff Elverman (Mgr-Fin)
Maurice Bird (Mgr-Fin)
Victor Aguilar (Mgr-Fin)

SHERMAN FINANCIAL GROUP LLC

335 Madison Ave Fl 19, New York, NY 10017
Tel.: (212) 922-1616
Web Site: http://www.sfg.com

Sales Range: $50-74.9 Million
Emp.: 1,000
Financial Services
N.A.I.C.S.: 522299
Benjamin Navarro (CEO)

Subsidiaries:

Credit One Bank N.A. (1)
6801 S Cimarron Rd, Las Vegas, NV 89113
Tel.: (702) 269-1000
Web Site: http://www.creditonebank.com
Sales Range: $50-74.9 Million
Emp.: 750
National Commercial Banks
N.A.I.C.S.: 522110
Carrie Bradley (Asst Controller)

LVNV Funding, LLC (1)
625 Pilot Rd Ste 3, Las Vegas, NV 89119-4485
Tel.: (702) 692-4012
Web Site: http://www.lvnvfunding.com
Consumer Debt Purchasing Services
N.A.I.C.S.: 561440

Resurgent Capital Services, LP (1)
15 S Main St Ste 600, Greenville, SC 29601
Tel.: (864) 235-7336
Web Site: http://www.rcap.com
Sales Range: $10-24.9 Million
Emp.: 500
Credit Intermediation Services
N.A.I.C.S.: 522299

SHERMAN INTERNATIONAL CORPORATION

367 Mansfield Ave, Pittsburgh, PA 15220
Tel.: (412) 928-2880   PA
Web Site:
http://www.shermanusa.com
Year Founded: 1983
Industrial Machinery & Equipment
N.A.I.C.S.: 423830
Om Sharma (CEO)

SHERMAN V. ALLEN INC.

56 1/2 Merchants Row, Rutland, VT 05701-4413
Tel.: (802) 775-7707   VT
Year Founded: 1980
Sales Range: $10-24.9 Million
Emp.: 100
Provider of Petroleum Products
N.A.I.C.S.: 424720
Jennifer Allen (Pres)
Matt Kinsman (Controller)

SHERMAN'S BOOKS & STATIONERY, INC.

5 Commercial St, Boothbay Harbor, ME 04538
Tel.: (207) 633-7262   ME
Web Site: http://www.shermans.com
Year Founded: 1886
Sales Range: $10-24.9 Million
Books, Gifts & Stationery Stores
Owner & Operator
N.A.I.C.S.: 459210
Jeff Curtis (Owner)

Subsidiaries:

Maine Coast Book Shop, Inc. (1)
158 Main St, Damariscotta, ME 04543
Tel.: (207) 563-3207
Web Site:
http://www.mainecoastbookshop.com
Sales Range: $1-9.9 Million
Book Store & Cafe Operator
N.A.I.C.S.: 459210

SHERMAN'S PLACE INC.

1215 W Glen Ave, Peoria, IL 61614
Tel.: (309) 691-4100
Web Site:
http://www.shermaninc.com
Sales Range: $10-24.9 Million
Emp.: 90

Electrical Appliances & Home Furnishings
N.A.I.C.S.: 449210
Paul Sherman (Pres)

SHERMAN, CLAY & CO.

1111 Bayhill Dr Ste 450, San Bruno, CA 94066
Tel.: (650) 952-2300   IN
Web Site:
http://www.shermanclay.com
Year Founded: 1870
Sales Range: $25-49.9 Million
Emp.: 130
Piano Retailer
N.A.I.C.S.: 459140
Victor Richman (CFO)
Eric A. Schwartz (Co-CEO)
Michael Schwartz (Co-CEO)

SHERMAN-CARTER-BARNHART, PSC.

2405 Harrodsburg Rd, Lexington, KY 40504
Tel.: (859) 224-1351
Web Site:
http://www.scbarchitects.com
Year Founded: 1979
Rev.: $11,000,000
Emp.: 64
Architectural Services
N.A.I.C.S.: 541310
Steve Sherman (Pres)

SHERMS THUNDERBIRD MARKET

753 S Grape St, Medford, OR 97501-3627
Tel.: (541) 857-0850   OR
Web Site:
http://www.shermsmarkets.com
Year Founded: 1967
Sales Range: $200-249.9 Million
Emp.: 450
Operator of Independent Grocery Stores
N.A.I.C.S.: 445110
Sherman Olsrud (Co-Founder)
Steve Olsrud (VP)
Wanda Olsrud (Co-Founder)
Robert Ames (Gen Mgr)

SHERO ENTERPRISES INC.

424 S Industrial Blvd, Dallas, TX 75207
Tel.: (214) 744-4636
Rev.: $17,000,000
Emp.: 9
Convenience Stores, Independent
N.A.I.C.S.: 445131
Sherry Hensley (Pres)
Robert Hensley (VP)

SHERPA SOFTWARE GROUP, LP

456 Washington Ave Ste 2, Bridgeville, PA 15017
Tel.: (412) 206-0005
Web Site:
http://www.sherpasoftware.com
Sales Range: $1-9.9 Million
Emp.: 27
Email Management Software
N.A.I.C.S.: 513210
Kevin Ogrodnik (Pres)
Marta Farensbach (Dir-Product Svcs)
Rick Wilson (VP-Strategy & Solutions)
Srinivasan Balaji (VP-Product Mgmt & Dev)
Jeff Tujetsch (VP-Notes Product Dev)

SHERRIFF-GOSLIN CO.

10 Ave C, Battle Creek, MI 49015
Tel.: (269) 962-4036

U.S. PRIVATE

Web Site: http://www.sherriff-goslin.com
Sales Range: $10-24.9 Million
Emp.: 500
Roof Repair
N.A.I.C.S.: 238160
Robert C. Sherriff (Pres)
Stephen Ticknor (Exec VP)

SHERRILL FURNITURE COMPANY INC.

2405 Highland Ave NE, Hickory, NC 28601-8164
Tel.: (828) 322-2640   NC
Web Site:
http://www.sherrillfurniture.com
Year Founded: 1943
Sales Range: $50-74.9 Million
Emp.: 1,500
Upholstered Household Furniture
N.A.I.C.S.: 337121
Harold Sherrill (Pres)

Subsidiaries:

HWS Company Inc. (1)
9 Lenord Van Blvd SE, Hickory, NC 28602-8164
Tel.: (828) 322-8624
Web Site: http://www.hickorywhite.com
Rev.: $45,000,000
Emp.: 380
Upholstered Household Furniture
N.A.I.C.S.: 337121
Brian Brown (Acct Mgr)
Woody Williams (Sr VP)

SHERRY MANUFACTURING CO. INC.

3287 NW 65th St, Miami, FL 33147
Tel.: (305) 693-7000
Web Site: http://www.sherrymfg.com
Sales Range: $10-24.9 Million
Emp.: 300
Screen Printing Services; Outerwear Mfr
N.A.I.C.S.: 323113
Scott Coltune (Pres & CEO)
Denise Maresma (VP-Mktg)

SHERRY MATTHEWS ADVOCACY MARKETING

200 S Congress Ave, Austin, TX 78704-1219
Tel.: (512) 478-4397   TX
Web Site:
http://www.sherrymatthews.com
Year Founded: 1983
Rev.: $20,000,000
Emp.: 50
N.A.I.C.S.: 541810
Sherry Matthews (Pres & New Bus Contact)
Wardaleen Belvin (CFO)
Karen Purcell (Sr VP & Dir-Media)
Janet Lea (Sr VP-Acct Svcs)
Debbie LaRoche (Controller)
Charles Webre (Exec Dir-Creative)

SHERRY-LEHMANN INC.

505 Prk Ave, New York, NY 10022-8045
Tel.: (212) 838-7500   NY
Web Site: http://www.sherry-lehmann.com
Year Founded: 1934
Sales Range: $25-49.9 Million
Emp.: 70
Liquor Stores
N.A.I.C.S.: 445320
Sara Weinberg (VP-Adv)
Rudi Alibod (Controller)
Michael Yurch Jr. (Pres)

SHERWOOD CONSTRUCTION CO. INC.

3219 W May St, Wichita, KS 67213
Tel.: (316) 943-0211   KS

Web Site:
http://www.sherwoodcompanies.com
Year Founded: 1934
Heavy Highway Construction & Excavation Services
N.A.I.C.S.: 238910
Howard Sherwood *(Chm)*
Lanny Gridley *(VP & CFO)*
Rod Abbott *(Pres)*
Kurt Webber *(Dir-Talent & Org Dev)*

SHERWOOD LUMBER CORPORATION
225 Broadhollow Rd, Melville, NY 11747
Tel.: (631) 232-9191 NY
Web Site:
http://www.sherwoodlumber.com
Sales Range: $75-99.9 Million
Emp.: 100
Lumber Whslr
N.A.I.C.S.: 423310
Andrew Goodman *(Pres & CEO)*
David Gaudreau *(VP-Eastern Reg)*
Wade Hickson *(Sr VP-Sls)*
Kyle Little *(COO)*
Todd London *(Sr VP-Sls & Mktg)*
Subsidiaries:

Middle Atlantic Wholesale Lumber
Company (1)
2700 Lighthouse Point E Ste 310, Baltimore, MD 21224
Tel.: (410) 581-9300
Web Site:
http://www.middleatlanticlumber.com
Sales Range: $10-24.9 Million
Emp.: 15
Lumber, Plywood & Millwork
N.A.I.C.S.: 423310
Mary Lou Carlson *(Pres)*
Joel Winters *(VP & Gen Mgr)*

SHERWOOD OF SALISBURY
1915 N Salisbury Blvd, Salisbury, MD 21801-3305
Tel.: (410) 548-4600
Web Site:
http://www.sherwoodofsalisbury.com
Year Founded: 1988
Sales Range: $50-74.9 Million
Emp.: 200
New Car Whslr
N.A.I.C.S.: 441110
Patrick Shuey *(Gen Mgr)*

SHEW ELECTRIC, INC.
2628 River-Liberty Grove Church Rd, North Wilkesboro, NC 28659
Tel.: (336) 838-6920
Year Founded: 1997
Sales Range: $10-24.9 Million
Emp.: 14
Electronic Services
N.A.I.C.S.: 238210
Randy Shew *(Pres)*

SHEWAS, INC.
1870 Town & Country Dr Bldg D, Norco, CA 92860
Tel.: (951) 279-8100
Web Site: http://www.shewasinc.com
Year Founded: 1996
Sales Range: $1-9.9 Million
Emp.: 5
Computers & Electronics Whslr
N.A.I.C.S.: 423430
Prashant Sewa *(Pres & CEO)*

SHG HOLDINGS CORP.
201 Hindry Ave, Inglewood, CA 90301-1519
Tel.: (310) 410-4907
Web Site: http://www.zephyrtool.com
Sales Range: $1-9.9 Million
Emp.: 100
Holding Company; Handtools Mfr

N.A.I.C.S.: 551112
Bernard J. Kersulis *(Pres & CEO)*
Earl Houston *(VP-Sls & Mktg)*
Subsidiaries:

Zephyr Manufacturing Co., Inc. (1)
201 Hindry Ave, Inglewood, CA 90301-1519 (100%)
Tel.: (310) 410-4907
Web Site: http://www.zephyrtool.com
Mfr of Cutting Tools
N.A.I.C.S.: 333991
Bernard J. Kersulis *(Pres)*
Earl Houston *(Pres)*

SHGINS INSURANCE SOLUTIONS LLC
PO Box 411, Los Olivos, CA 93441-0411
Tel.: (805) 686-1148
Web Site: http://www.shgins.com
Sales Range: $10-24.9 Million
Emp.: 8
Insurance Services
N.A.I.C.S.: 524210
William Ambler *(Mgr-Sls)*

SHI INTERNATIONAL CORP.
290 Davidson Ave, Somerset, NJ 08873
Web Site: https://www.shi.com
Year Founded: 1989
Sales Range: $5-14.9 Billion
Emp.: 6,000
Computer & Computer Peripheral Equipment & Software Merchant Wholesalers
N.A.I.C.S.: 423430
Thai Lee *(Pres & CEO)*
Koguan Leo *(Founder & Chm)*
Donavan Hutchinson *(Mng Dir-SHI Corporation UK Ltd)*
Celeste Lee *(Sr VP-Intl Sls & Global Programs)*
James Prior *(CFO)*
Dave Gruver *(CTO-Modern End-User Support Strategies)*
Dwight Moore *(CIO)*
Subsidiaries:

Eastridge Technology, Inc. (1)
102 W 3rd St Ste 1250, Winston Salem, NC 27101 (100%)
Tel.: (336) 831-9800
Web Site: http://www.eastridge.net
Rev.: $1,700,000
Emp.: 17
Computer System Design Services
N.A.I.C.S.: 541512
Jennifer Miller *(CFO)*
Travis Hargett *(Pres)*
Thomas Nichols *(CTO)*
Hal Jagger *(VP & Gen Mgr)*

Locuz Enterprise Solutions Ltd. (1)
401 Krishe Sapphire Main Road, Madhapur, Hyderabad, 500 081, Telangana, India
Tel.: (91) 4045004600
Web Site: http://www.locuz.com
Information Technology Management Services
N.A.I.C.S.: 541611
Vijay Wadhi *(CEO & Mng Dir)*
Mohammad Arifuddin *(VP-Sls)*
Asit Sahoo *(CTO)*
Uttam Majumdar *(Founder & Pres-Consulting & Svcs)*

SHI Canada (1)
895 Don Mills Road One Morneau Shepell Centre Suite 200, Toronto, M3C 1W3, ON, Canada (100%)
Tel.: (888) 235-3871
Web Site: http://www.shi.ca
Software Producer
N.A.I.C.S.: 513210

SHI France (1)
1 Rond-Point Victor Hugo, 92137, Issy-les-Moulineaux, Cedex, France (100%)
Tel.: (33) 1 41 33 94 94
Web Site: http://www.shi.fr

Sales Range: $10-24.9 Million
Emp.: 1
Software Products Distr
N.A.I.C.S.: 513210

SHI Germany (1)
Feringastrasse 6 Munchen Unterfohring, Munich, 85774, Germany (100%)
Tel.: (49) 89 99 216 409
Software Developer
N.A.I.C.S.: 513210

SHI Hong Kong (1)
Ste 601 6F New World Tower, 16 18 Queen's Road, Central, China (Hong Kong) (100%)
Tel.: (852) 21533200
Web Site: http://www.shi.com
Emp.: 15
Software Products Distr
N.A.I.C.S.: 513210
Frank Cranley *(Gen Dir)*

SHI UK (1)
401 Grafton Gate Third Floor, Milton Keynes, MK9 1AQ, Bucks, United Kingdom (100%)
Tel.: (44) 1908300370
Web Site: http://www.shi.com
Software Products Distr
N.A.I.C.S.: 513210
Darren Broderick *(Gen Mgr)*

SHI Vancouver (1)
1385 W 8th Avenue Suite 610, Vancouver, V6H 3V9, BC, Canada (100%)
Tel.: (888) 744-7928
Web Site: http://www.shi.ca
Software Developer
N.A.I.C.S.: 513210
Cheryl Stookes *(Sls Dir-Reg)*

SHIBAURA TECHNOLOGY INTERNATIONAL CORP.
591 W Hamilton Ave Ste 210, Campbell, CA 95008-0521
Tel.: (408) 626-7900 CA
Web Site: http://www.shibatec.com
Year Founded: 1996
Sales Range: $10-24.9 Million
Emp.: 16
Mfr of Semiconductor Devices
N.A.I.C.S.: 423690

SHIDLER INVESTMENT COMPANY, LLC
841 Bishop St Ste 1700, Honolulu, HI 96813-4789
Tel.: (808) 531-3000 HI
Web Site: http://www.shidler.com
Year Founded: 1972
Emp.: 185
Real Estate Investment
N.A.I.C.S.: 523999
Jay H. Shidler *(Founder & Mng Partner)*
Anthony K. Talbert *(Partner-Acquisitions & Dev Investment Initiatives)*
Subsidiaries:

Waterfront A, LLC (1)
500 Ala Moana Blvd, Honolulu, HI 96813
Tel.: (808) 532-4750
Web Site:
http://www.waterfrontplaza-hawaii.com
Rev.: $1,000,000
Emp.: 1
Commercial Building Property Management & Leasing Services
N.A.I.C.S.: 531312
Steve Sullivan *(VP-Ops)*

SHIEKH LLC
4083 E Airport Dr, Ontario, CA 91761-1567
Tel.: (909) 230-6620
Web Site:
http://www.shiekhshoes.com
Year Founded: 1991
Sales Range: $25-49.9 Million
Emp.: 450

Men's, Women's & Children's Shoes Retailer
N.A.I.C.S.: 458210
Shiekh Ellahi *(Founder & Owner)*
Subsidiaries:

Karmaloop LLC (1)
334 Boylston St Ste 500, Boston, MA 02116
Tel.: (844) 625-5667
Web Site: http://www.karmaloop.com
Online Clothing Retailer
N.A.I.C.S.: 424350

SHIELD AI INC.
600 W Broadway Ste 200, San Diego, CA 92101
Tel.: (619) 719-5740
Web Site: http://www.shield.ai
Year Founded: 2015
Artificial Intelligence & Computer Software Services
N.A.I.C.S.: 541511
Ryan Tseng *(Co-Founder & CEO)*
Francois Chadwick *(CFO)*
Subsidiaries:

Heron Systems, Inc. (1)
22685 3 Notch Rd Unit B, California, MD 20619
Tel.: (301) 866-0330
Web Site: http://www.heronsystems.com
Laboratory Testing & Simulation Solution Provider
N.A.I.C.S.: 541380
Melissa Behrens *(Dir-HR)*
Don Behrens *(VP-Ops)*
Brett Darcey *(VP & Gen Mgr)*

SHIELD PACKAGING OF CALIFORNIA
99 University Rd, Canton, MA 02021
Tel.: (781) 821-0400
Web Site:
http://www.shieldpackaging.com
Sales Range: $10-24.9 Million
Emp.: 50
Packaging & Labeling Services
N.A.I.C.S.: 561910
George P. Bates *(Pres)*
Todd Johnston *(VP)*

SHIELDS ACQUISITION COMPANY
26601 W Huron River Dr, Flat Rock, MI 48134
Tel.: (734) 782-4454
Web Site: http://www.srm.com
Sales Range: $10-24.9 Million
Emp.: 500
Finishing, Metals Or Formed Products
N.A.I.C.S.: 332813
Keith King *(Pres)*

SHIELDS AUTO CENTER INC.
225 S Meyers St, Rantoul, IL 61866
Tel.: (217) 892-2155
Web Site:
http://www.shieldsautogroup.com
Sales Range: $10-24.9 Million
Emp.: 34
Automobiles, New & Used
N.A.I.C.S.: 441110
Duane Shields *(Pres)*
Lori Shields *(Controller)*

SHIELDS BUSINESS SOLUTIONS INC.
5 Twosome Dr, Moorestown, NJ 08057
Tel.: (856) 727-0227
Web Site:
http://www.shieldsbusinesssolutions.com
Year Founded: 1970
Sales Range: $10-24.9 Million
Emp.: 100

SHIELDS BUSINESS SOLUTIONS INC.

U.S. PRIVATE

Shields Business Solutions Inc.—(Continued)
Provider of Services for Adding Machines, Dictating Machines & Typewriters
N.A.I.C.S.: 423420
Bonnie Hill (Mgr-Acctg Dept)
Mark McGrath (Sr VP-Svcs Ops)
Richard Grossman (Pres & CEO)
Kristy McConnell (Mgr-Cash Room)
John McKinley (Mgr-Svcs)
Tom Raftery (VP-Cash-In-Transit)

SHIELDS FOR FAMILIES, INC.
11601 S Western, Los Angeles, CA 90047
Tel.: (323) 242-5000 CA
Web Site:
   http://www.shieldsforfamilies.org
Year Founded: 1991
Sales Range: $10-24.9 Million
Emp.: 310
Family Welfare Services
N.A.I.C.S.: 624190
Kathryn S. Icenhower (CEO)
Sara Tienda (VP-Program Dev & Quality Improvement)
Charlene K. Smith (VP-Family & Community Svcs)
Deanette Brewer (Dir-HR)
Gerald Phillips (Chm)
Xylina Bean (Pres)
Susan Haynes (Treas)
Kerry English (Vice Chm)
Donna Icenhower (Dir-Dev)
Naveen Sangwan (VP-Family & Community Svcs)
Patrick Coffin (CIO)
Renee Becraft (Dir-Clinical)
Jeffrey Perea (CFO)

SHIELDS HARPER & CO. INC.
4591 Pacheco Blvd, Martinez, CA 94553
Tel.: (510) 653-9119
Web Site:
   http://www.shieldsharper.com
Rev.: $10,500,000
Emp.: 35
Industrial Machinery & Equipment
N.A.I.C.S.: 423830
Bart Scowley (Chm & CEO)
Dave Sarginson (Pres)
Jimmy Cartmill (Mgr-Mktg & Ops)
Doug De Long (Gen Mgr-Sls)
Otto Brunnmeier (Mgr-Parts)
Greg Brown (CFO)
Todd Brennan (Mgr-Acctg & HR)
Jeff Nelson (Mgr-Customer Support)
Jennifer Nguyen (Mgr-Pur)
Tim Roth (VP-Sls)

SHIFT GLOBAL
15 E Gay St Ste 300, Columbus, OH 43215
Tel.: (614) 225-0535
Web Site: http://www.shiftglobal.com
Year Founded: 2003
Sales Range: $1-9.9 Million
Emp.: 20
Advertising Agency, Brand Development
N.A.I.C.S.: 541810
Robert Abbott (Founder)
Chris Flinders (Dir-Creative Tech)
Jim Smith (Acct Dir)

SHIFTMED, LLC
7925 Jones Branch Dr Ste 1100, McLean, VA 22102
Tel.: (800) 485-9002
Web Site: https://www.shiftmed.com
Health Care Srvices
N.A.I.C.S.: 621610
Todd Walrath (CEO)

Subsidiaries:
CareerStaff Unlimited, Inc. (1)
6363 N State Hwy 161 Ste 525, Irving, TX 75038
Tel.: (972) 812-3200
Web Site: http://www.careerstaff.com
Temporary Therapy Staff Services
N.A.I.C.S.: 623110
Ryan Taylor (VP-Ops)
Tom Miller (Sr VP-Sls & Travel Ops)

Subsidiary (Domestic):
ProCare One Nurses LLC (2)
2099 S St College Blvd Ste 260, Anaheim, CA 92806
Tel.: (888) 747-7600
Web Site: http://www.procareone.com
Sales Range: $10-24.9 Million
Emp.: 20
Nurses Staffing Agency
N.A.I.C.S.: 561311
Kim Folsom (Reg Dir)

ReadyNurse Staffing Services (2)
360 Bloomfield Ave Ste 303, Windsor, CT 06095
Web Site: http://www.readynurse.com
Emp.: 1,000
Home Health Care Staffing Professionals
N.A.I.C.S.: 621610
Chantal Desjardins (Mgr-Staffing)
David LeCours (Natl Dir)

SHILDAN USA, INC.
2047 Briggs Rd, Mount Laurel, NJ 08030
Tel.: (516) 656-0019 NY
Web Site: http://www.shildan.com
Year Founded: 1996
Sales Range: $10-24.9 Million
Emp.: 3
Rainscreens Merchandiser, Distr & Importer
N.A.I.C.S.: 455219
Moshe Steinmetz (Pres)

SHILLCRAFT, INC.
PO Box 325, Bonsall, CA 92003
Tel.: (951) 674-4307 MD
Web Site: http://www.shillcraft.com
Year Founded: 1949
Sales Range: $1-9.9 Million
Emp.: 25
Supplier of Mail Order Crafts; Latch Hook Rug Kits & Accessories
N.A.I.C.S.: 424310
Mike Gordon (CFO & VP-Fin)

SHILLINGTON BOX COMPANY LLC
3501 Tree Ct Industrial Blvd, Saint Louis, MO 63122
Tel.: (636) 225-5353
Web Site:
   http://www.shillingtonbox.com
Sales Range: $10-24.9 Million
Emp.: 90
Box Mfr
N.A.I.C.S.: 322211
Ray Deugman (Controller)

SHILO MANAGEMENT CORPORATION
11600 SW Shilo Ln, Portland, OR 97225-5995
Tel.: (503) 641-6565 OR
Web Site: http://www.shiloinns.com
Year Founded: 1974
Hospitality Services
N.A.I.C.S.: 531311
Mark S. Hemstreet (Founder & Owner-Shilo Inns)
Nikki Lederer Loveless (Asst Dir-Restaurant Ops)
Eve Drozdowski (Dir-Sls & Catering)

SHILOH CORPORATION
800 Auto Row, Post Falls, ID 83854

Tel.: (208) 773-7571
Rev.: $28,400,000
Emp.: 25
New & Used Car Dealers
N.A.I.C.S.: 441110
Mark Gibson (Owner & Pres)
Mike Fuller (Gen Mgr)
Jodi Rebman (Mgr)

SHILOH INDUSTRIES, INC.
880 Steel Dr, Valley City, OH 44280
Tel.: (330) 558-2600 DE
Web Site: http://www.shiloh.com
Year Founded: 1950
Rev.: $1,054,707,000
Assets: $651,691,000
Liabilities: $484,177,000
Net Worth: $167,514,000
Earnings: ($19,947,000)
Emp.: 3,600
Fiscal Year-end: 10/31/19
Engineered Metal Products Mfr
N.A.I.C.S.: 332119
David Dixon (Sec & VP)
Tom Luttrell (Sr VP-IT & Supply Chain & VP-Info Sys)
Brad E. Tolley (Pres & VP-Dev)
Scott Borovich (VP-Bus Dev & Tech)
Brad E. Tolley (VP-Dev)
David W. Jaeger (Mng Dir)
Eric McAlexander (VP-Ops)
Gary DeThomas (VP & Controller)
Jesse Maurer (VP-HR)
Kimberly Buhl (VP-Pur)
Tom Luttrell (VP-Info Sys)
Jim Bonebright (Sr VP-North America)
Scott P. Pepin (Sr VP-HR & EHS)
Scot S. Bowie (VP & Controller)
Cheryl Johnson (VP-Supply Chain Mgmt)
Amy Floraday (Corp Sec & VP-Legal)
Hans Vorstenbosch (VP-Europe)
John Stewart (Chm)

Subsidiaries:
Albany Chicago Company, LLC (1)
8200 100th St, Pleasant Prairie, WI 53158
Tel.: (262) 947-7600
Emp.: 300
Metal Die-Casting Services
N.A.I.C.S.: 331523

Finnveden Metal Structures AB (1)
August Barks Gata 6B, 421 32, Vastra Frolunda, Sweden
Tel.: (46) 317345900
Web Site: http://www.finnveden.co
Sales Range: $100-124.9 Million
Emp.: 400
Metal Structure Mfr
N.A.I.C.S.: 332119
Gommy Andersson (Gen Mgr)

Jefferson Blanking Inc. (1)
234 S Holland Dr, Pendergrass, GA 30567
Tel.: (706) 693-4774
Web Site: http://www.shiloh.com
Sales Range: $150-199.9 Million
Emp.: 150
Mfr of Automotive Parts
N.A.I.C.S.: 336370

Liverpool Coil Processing, Incorporated (1)
880 Steel Dr, Valley City, OH 44280
Tel.: (330) 558-2600
Web Site: http://www.shiloh.com
Sales Range: $25-49.9 Million
Emp.: 101
Receiver, Inspector, Warehouser, Processor & Deliverer of Cold Roll Galvanized Steel Coils to Automotive Companies
N.A.I.C.S.: 331110

Medina Blanking, Inc. (1)
5580 Wegman Dr, Valley City, OH 44280
Tel.: (330) 558-2300
Web Site: http://www.shiloh.com
Sales Range: $75-99.9 Million
Emp.: 250
Mfr of Machine Tool Accessories & Metal Stampings for the Automotive Industry

N.A.I.C.S.: 331513

Radar Servicious Celaya S. DE R.L. DE C.V.
Carretera Celaya-Salvatierra Km 8 5, Celaya, 38158, Mexico
Tel.: (52) 4611658612
Administrative Management Consulting Services
N.A.I.C.S.: 541611

Radar Stamping Technologies S. DE R.L. DE C.V. (1)
Carretera Celaya-Salvatierra Km 8 5 Ferropuerto Industrial Park, Celaya, 38158, Mexico
Tel.: (52) 4611658612
Industrial Machinery Mfr
N.A.I.C.S.: 333248

Sectional Stamping, Inc. (1)
350 Maple St, Wellington, OH 44090
Tel.: (440) 647-2100
Web Site: http://www.shiloh.com
Sales Range: $100-124.9 Million
Provider of Metal Stampings for the Automotive Industry
N.A.I.C.S.: 332119

Shiloh Industries (1)
7295 Haggerty Rd, Canton, MI 48187
Tel.: (734) 454-4000
Web Site: http://www.shiloh.com
Sales Range: $100-124.9 Million
Mfr of Metal Stampings for the Automotive Industry
N.A.I.C.S.: 333514

Shiloh Industries AB (1)
August Barks Gata 6 B, 40092, Vastra Frolunda, Vastra Gotaland, Sweden
Tel.: (46) 317345900
Emp.: 25
Industrial Machinery Mfr
N.A.I.C.S.: 333248

Shiloh Industries Inc., Dickson Manufacturing Division (1)
One Shiloh Dr, Dickson, TN 37055
Tel.: (615) 446-7725
Web Site: http://www.shiloh.com
Sales Range: $75-99.9 Million
Emp.: 2
Mfr of Automotive Parts
N.A.I.C.S.: 336370

Shiloh Industries Italia SRL (1)
Via Glair 41, 11029, Verres, Italy
Tel.: (39) 0125 922 111
Web Site: http://www.shiloh.com
Metal Casting Services
N.A.I.C.S.: 331523
Arianna Lachello (Dir-Sls & Bus Dev)
Paolo China-Bino (Mgr-Engrg & Tooling)

Shiloh Industries Netherlands B.V. (1)
Rijnstraat 19, 5347 KL, Oss, Netherlands
Tel.: (31) 412681444
Provider of Aluminum Foundries & High Pressure Diecasting
N.A.I.C.S.: 331524

Shiloh Internacional S.A. de C.V. (1)
Avenue Delta 2025, Parque Industrial Santa Maria, Ramos Arizpe, 25903, Coahuila, Mexico
Tel.: (52) 8444389200
Engineered Metal Product Mfr
N.A.I.C.S.: 332999

Shiloh Manufacturing Division-Liverpool (1)
880 Steel Dr, Valley City, OH 44280
Tel.: (330) 558-6400
Web Site: http://www.shiloh.com
Sales Range: $100-124.9 Million
Mfr of Metal Stampings for the Automotive Industry
N.A.I.C.S.: 332119

SHIMS BARGAIN INC.
2720 S Soto St, Los Angeles, CA 90058
Tel.: (323) 881-0099
Web Site: http://www.jcsalesweb.com
Sales Range: $50-74.9 Million
Emp.: 100
General Merchandise Sales

COMPANIES

N.A.I.C.S.: 424990
James Shim (Owner)

SHIN ENTERPRISES INC.
410 S Main St, McAllen, TX 78501
Tel.: (956) 631-6174
Sales Range: $10-24.9 Million
Emp.: 61
Perfumes
N.A.I.C.S.: 424210
John Shin (Pres)

SHINE BROS CORP.
225 10th Ave SE, Spencer, IA 51301
Tel.: (712) 262-5579
Web Site: http://www.shinebros.com
Rev: $14,400,000
Emp.: 125
Recyclable Material Merchant Whslr
N.A.I.C.S.: 423930
Dan Wycoff (Gen Mgr)
Mike Wycoff (Plant Mgr)
Toby B. Shine (Pres)
Keven Shine (Mgr-HR)
Eva Shine (Bus Mgr)

SHINE FOOD, INC.
684 Mateo St, Los Angeles, CA 90021-1325
Tel.: (213) 488-9181
Web Site: http://www.shinefoods.com
Sales Range: $10-24.9 Million
Emp.: 140
Canned Food Mfr
N.A.I.C.S.: 311422
Tracy Lee (Owner)
Bibee Shigeyoshi (Mgr-Sls)

SHINE MEDICAL TECHNOLOGIES, LLC
2555 Industrial Dr Ste 140, Monona, WI 53713
Tel.: (608) 210-1060
Web Site: http://www.shinemed.com
Year Founded: 2010
Professional Equipment & Supplies Merchant Whslr
N.A.I.C.S.: 423490
Richard Vann Bynum (COO)
Gregory Piefer (Founder & CEO)
Katrina Pitas (VP-Bus Dev)
Rod Hise (Dir-Mktg & Corp Comm)
Ross Radel (CTO)
Evan Sengbusch (Gen Mgr)

Subsidiaries:

Phoenix LLC (1)
5115 Lacy Rd, Fitchburg, WI 53711
Tel.: (608) 210-3060
Web Site: http://www.phoenixwi.com
Nuclear Technology Services
N.A.I.C.S.: 221113
Steve Books (VP-Ops)
Evan Sengbusch (Pres)

SHINETECH SOFTWARE
1 Rockefeller Plz 11th Fl, New York, NY 10020
Tel.: (917) 639-4274
Web Site:
http://www.shinetechchina.com
Year Founded: 2001
Sales Range: $10-24.9 Million
Emp.: 300
Software Development Services
N.A.I.C.S.: 541511
Jerry Zhang (Pres & Gen Mgr)
John Vanderpool (Sr VP-Global Ops)
Yanqiang Yue (COO)
Frank Zhang (VP-Europe)
Armin Roth (Dir-Western Europe)
Kati Hannula (Dir-Sls & Mktg)
John Brooks (VP-Global Delivery)

SHINGOBEE BUILDERS INC.
669 N Medina St, Loretto, MN 55357-9595
Tel.: (763) 479-1300 MN
Web Site: http://www.shingobee.com
Year Founded: 1980
Sales Range: $50-74.9 Million
Emp.: 75
Nonresidential Construction Services
N.A.I.C.S.: 236220
Keith McDonald (Pres)
Lynn Christiansen (Project Mgr)
Tony Godlewski (VP)
Nancy Samson (CFO)

SHIP SUPPLY OF FLORIDA, INC.
10800 NW 103rd St Ste 1, Miami, FL 33178
Tel.: (305) 681-7447 FL
Web Site: http://www.shipsup.com
Sales Range: $1-9.9 Million
Emp.: 25
Dedicated Services to the Maritime Industry
N.A.I.C.S.: 488510
Christian Giannakopoulos (Pres)

Subsidiaries:

Alliance Supply Management, Ltd. (1)
4551 Kennedy Commerce Dr, Houston, TX 77032-3425
Tel.: (713) 335-2500
Web Site: http://www.asmlimited.com
Sales Range: $1-9.9 Million
Emp.: 45
Transportation Equipment & Supplies to the Maritime Industry
N.A.I.C.S.: 488320
Bruce J. Margolin (Chief Commercial Officer)
Mark D. Pontiff (Exec VP & Gen Mgr)
Salim Shaikh (VP-Bus Dev & Sls)
Santino Carruba (VP-Fin)
Tommy Gooch (VP-Geophysical Sls)

Hymax, Inc. (1)
500 504 Saint Louis St, Mobile, AL 36652-2271
Tel.: (251) 432-0762
Web Site: http://www.kamilship.com
Sales Range: $1-9.9 Million
Emp.: 10
General Merchandise Stores
N.A.I.C.S.: 455219

SHIP-PAC INC.
3000 Covington Rd, Kalamazoo, MI 49001
Tel.: (269) 381-7130
Web Site: http://www.shippac.com
Sales Range: $10-24.9 Million
Emp.: 40
Provider of Packaging Services
N.A.I.C.S.: 424130
Dave Hoekstra (Mgr-Food Pkg Div)
Danna Taylor (Coord-Janitorial & Safety)

SHIPBOB, INC.
120 N Racine Ave Ste 100, Chicago, IL 60607
Web Site: http://www.shipbob.com
Year Founded: 2014
Sales Range: $25-49.9 Million
Emp.: 450
Software Development Services
N.A.I.C.S.: 541511
Kent Schofield (VP-Fin & Strategy)
Dhruv Saxena (CEO)
Divey Gulati (COO)
David Pickel (CFO)
Paul Rosen (Chief Revenue Officer)
Casey Armstong (CMO)

SHIPBUILDERS OF WISCONSIN, INC.
1811 Spring St, Manitowoc, WI 54220
Tel.: (920) 684-1600
Web Site: http://www.burgerboat.com
Year Founded: 1863
Custom Yacht Builder
N.A.I.C.S.: 336612
Cary Klager (Mgr-Svc & Warranty)
Dawn Taddy (Dir-Supply Chain)
Ron Cleveringa (VP-Sls & Mktg)
Curt Prokash (Dir-HR)

SHIPLEY ASSOCIATES
532 N 900 W, Kaysville, UT 84037-4129
Tel.: (801) 544-9787
Web Site:
http://www.shipleywins.com
Year Founded: 1972
Sales Range: $25-49.9 Million
Emp.: 75
Business Development Consulting & Training Services
N.A.I.C.S.: 541611
Steve Shipley (Chm)
Eric Gregory (Sr VP-Consulting-East Reg)
Brad Douglas (Pres & CEO)
Janae Sutton (CFO)
David Bol (Sr VP-Consulting-West Reg)
Daryl Jones (Sr VP-Bus Dev)
Larry Newman (Partner & VP)

Subsidiaries:

Shipley Limited (1)
Abbey Manor Business Centre, Preston Road, Yeovil, BA20 2EN, Somerset, United Kingdom
Tel.: (44) 1935434333
Web Site: http://www.shipleywins.co.uk
Emp.: 10
Business Development Consulting & Training Services
N.A.I.C.S.: 541611
Tony Birch (Mng Dir)

Subsidiary (Non-US):

Shipley (UK) GmbH (2)
Landsbergerstrasse 302, 80687, Munich, Germany
Tel.: (49) 8990405512
Web Site: http://www.shipleywins.co.uk
Marketing, Consulting & Customer Support Services
N.A.I.C.S.: 541611

SHIPLEY DO-NUTS FLOUR AND SUPPLY CO.
5200 N Main St, Houston, TX 77009
Tel.: (713) 869-4636
Web Site:
http://www.shipleydonuts.ws
Year Founded: 1936
Rev: $57,500,000
Emp.: 11
Bakery Products
N.A.I.C.S.: 311811
Flynn K. Dekker (CEO)
Donna Josephson (CMO)
Kerry Leo (VP-Tech)
Lawrence W. Shipley III (Pres)

SHIPLEY ENERGY COMPANY
415 Norway St, York, PA 17403-1720
Tel.: (717) 848-4100 PA
Web Site:
http://www.shipleyenergy.com
Year Founded: 1929
Sales Range: $25-49.9 Million
Emp.: 700
Producer & Retailer of Petroleum Products
N.A.I.C.S.: 457210
Richard Brandsderfer (Controller)
Brian Kottcamp (VP)
Dave Gruno (CEO)

SHIPMAN & GOODWIN
1 Constitution Plz, Hartford, CT 06103
Tel.: (860) 251-5000

SHIRTCLIFF OIL CO.

Web Site:
http://www.shipmangoodwin.com
Rev: $22,800,000
Emp.: 270
Law firm
N.A.I.C.S.: 922130
Frederick S. Gold (Partner)
Brenda A. Eckert (Partner)
Brian Clemow (Partner)
Joette Katz (Partner-Bus Litigation Practice Grp)
Alan E. Lieberman (Mng Dir)

SHIPMAN ELEVATOR COMPANY
3620 Rt 16, Shipman, IL 62685
Tel.: (618) 729-9009
Web Site:
http://www.shipmanelevator.com
Rev: $26,028,047
Emp.: 40
Corn
N.A.I.C.S.: 424510
Dean Allen (Mgr-Ops)
Bart Baker (Gen Mgr)

SHIPPERS SUPPLY COMPANY INC.
1735 W Burnett Ave, Louisville, KY 40210
Tel.: (502) 634-2800
Web Site:
http://www.shipperssupplyco.com
Rev: $30,000,000
Emp.: 45
Industrial Packaging
N.A.I.C.S.: 423840
Jeff Davis (CEO)

SHIPPERS WAREHOUSE, INC.
8901 Forney Rd, Dallas, TX 75227
Tel.: (214) 381-5050
Web Site:
http://www.shipperswarehouse.com
Emp.: 500
Warehousing & Logistics Services
N.A.I.C.S.: 493110
Ken Johnson (Pres & CEO)
Graham Swank (COO)
John Dennington (VP & Reg Mgr)
Don Cote (VP & Reg Mgr)
David Eastman (VP-Client Solutions)
Kris Hill (Mgr-Customer Svc)
Kevin West (VP-Transportation)
Nancy Landers (Controller)
Pam Ragon (CFO)
Greg Monticciolo (Mgr-Transportation-Georgia)

Subsidiaries:

Shippers Warehouse of Georgia (1)
9250 S Main St, Jonesboro, GA 30236
Tel.: (770) 603-5770
Web Site:
http://www.shipperswarehousega.com
Sales Range: $10-24.9 Million
Warehousing & Logistics Services
N.A.I.C.S.: 493110

SHIRNS PONTIAC-GMC INC.
1804 Lycoming Creek Rd, Williamsport, PA 17701
Tel.: (570) 326-1581
Web Site: http://www.shirns.com
Sales Range: $10-24.9 Million
Emp.: 15
Sales of New & Used Automobiles
N.A.I.C.S.: 441110
David M. Shirn Sr. (Pres)

SHIRTCLIFF OIL CO.
283 Western Ave, Myrtle Creek, OR 97457
Tel.: (541) 863-5268
Web Site: http://www.shirtcliffoil.com
Rev: $26,937,548
Emp.: 160

SHIRTCLIFF OIL CO.

Shirtcliff Oil Co.—(Continued)
Petroleum Bulk Stations
N.A.I.C.S.: 424710
John D. Shirtcliff (Pres)

SHIVE-HATTERY GROUP INC.
222 3rd Ave SE Ste 300, Cedar Rapids, IA 52401
Tel.: (319) 364-0227
Web Site: http://www.shive-hattery.com
Year Founded: 1895
Architecture & Engineering Firm
N.A.I.C.S.: 541310
Kyle Copelin (Dir-Public Buildings)
Nathan Hardisty (Dir-Public Infrastructure)
Tracy Longo (Dir-Higher Education & Healthcare)
Monica Sargent (Dir-Industrial)
Jeff Lewis (Dir-Comml)

Subsidiaries:

Studio 951 (1)
800 P St Ste 203, Lincoln, NE 68508
Tel.: (402) 477-1666
Planning & Architectural Services
N.A.I.C.S.: 541310
Dave Johnson (Mng Dir)

SHIVELY BROTHERS INC.
2919 S Grand Traverse St, Flint, MI 48507
Tel.: (810) 232-7401
Web Site: http://www.shivelybros.com
Year Founded: 1947
Sales Range: $10-24.9 Million
Emp.: 172
Provider of Machine Tools & Accessories
N.A.I.C.S.: 423830
Scott Shively (Pres)

SHIVELY MOTORS
801 Lincoln Way W, Chambersburg, PA 17202
Tel.: (717) 264-7134
Web Site: http://www.shivelymotors.com
Year Founded: 1939
Sales Range: $10-24.9 Million
Emp.: 35
New Car Dealers
N.A.I.C.S.: 441110
Bryan J. Burkholder (Treas & VP)
Elias J. Kymingham (Owner & Pres)

SHIVERS TRADING & OPERATING COMPANY
725 Broad St, Augusta, GA 30901-1336
Tel.: (706) 724-0851
Year Founded: 1981
Holding Company
N.A.I.C.S.: 551112
Craig S. Mitchell (Treas, Sec & Sr VP-Fin)
Delinda Fogel (CFO)
William S. Morris III (Chm)

Subsidiaries:

Millhaven Company Inc. (1)
752 Oglethorpe Trl, Sylvania, GA 30467-3705 (100%)
Tel.: (912) 829-4742
Sales Range: Less than $1 Million
Emp.: 10
Crop Preparation Services
N.A.I.C.S.: 111998
Andy Bradson (Sec)

Morris Communications Company, LLC (1)
725 Broad St, Augusta, GA 30901-1336
Tel.: (706) 823-3200
Web Site: http://www.morris.com
Books, Newspapers, Magazines & Shopping Guides Publisher; Outdoor Advertising Services; Radio Station Broadcasting Services
N.A.I.C.S.: 513110
Darrel K. Fry (Controller-Corp Acctg)
Susie Morris Baker (VP)
J. Tyler Morris (VP-Cowboy Publ Grp)
Reab Berry (Dir-Strategy & Analysis-Media Network)
Robert J. Kuhar (VP-Property & Facilities)
William S. Morris III (Chm)
William S. Morris IV (Pres & CEO)
Terry K. House Jr. (Dir-Tax & Asst Sec)

Unit (Domestic):

Alaska Star (2)
11401 Old Glenn Hwy Unit 105, Eagle River, AK 99577-7499
Tel.: (907) 694-2727
Web Site: http://www.alaskastar.com
Sales Range: $10-24.9 Million
Emp.: 10
Newspaper Publishers
N.A.I.C.S.: 513110
Evy Gebhardt (Dir-Adv)
Silvija Kasper (Acct Exec)
Ken Hanni (Acct Exec)
Suzzette Rowell (Acct Exec)

Anchorage Media Group (2)
301 Arctic Slope, Anchorage, AK 99518
Tel.: (907) 344-9622
Web Site: http://www.kbrj.com
Sales Range: $10-24.9 Million
Emp.: 4
Radio Station Owner & Operator
N.A.I.C.S.: 516110

Columbia River Media Group (2)
1124 N Miller, Wenatchee, WA 98801
Tel.: (509) 663-5186
Web Site: http://www.columbiarivermedia.com
Sales Range: $10-24.9 Million
Emp.: 20
Radio Station Owner & Operator
N.A.I.C.S.: 516110
William Morris (Pres)

Kansas Radio Networks (2)
1210 SW Executive Dr, Topeka, KS 66615
Tel.: (785) 272-3456
Web Site: http://www.radionetworks.com
Sales Range: $10-24.9 Million
Emp.: 50
Radio Broadcasting Services
N.A.I.C.S.: 516110

Unit (Domestic):

WIBW-AM (3)
1210 SW Executive Dr, Topeka, KS 66615
Tel.: (785) 228-3456
Web Site: http://www.am580wibw.com
Radio Broadcasting Services
N.A.I.C.S.: 516110

WIBW-FM (3)
1210 SW Executive Dr, Topeka, KS 66615-3850
Tel.: (785) 272-3456
Web Site: http://www.94country.com
Sales Range: $10-24.9 Million
Emp.: 45
Radio Broadcasting Services
N.A.I.C.S.: 516110
Larry Riggins (Gen Mgr)

Subsidiary (Domestic):

MCC Magazines, LLC (2)
725 Broad St, Augusta, GA 30901 (100%)
Tel.: (706) 724-0851
Holding Company; Magazines Publisher
N.A.I.C.S.: 551112
Scott Ferguson (Mgr-Circulation)

Unit (Domestic):

Alaska Journal of Commerce (3)
300 W 31st Ave, Anchorage, AK 99503
Tel.: (907) 257-4200
Web Site: http://www.alaskajournal.com
Sales Range: $10-24.9 Million
Emp.: 25
Business Magazine Publisher
N.A.I.C.S.: 513120
Ken Hanni (Acct Exec)

Subsidiary (Domestic):

Carolina Parenting, Inc. (3)
5716 Fayetteville Rd Ste 201, Durham, NC 27713
Tel.: (919) 956-2430
Web Site: http://www.carolinaparent.com
Sales Range: $1-9.9 Million
Emp.: 15
Periodical Publishers
N.A.I.C.S.: 513120
Mark Ethridge (Pres)
Wade Baker (Dir-Art)
Margaret Lucas (Dir-Bus Dev)
Melissa Stutts (Dir-Art & Digital Developmental)

Unit (Domestic):

Equine Journal (3)
83 Leicester St, North Oxford, MA 01537
Tel.: (508) 987-5886
Web Site: http://www.equinejournal.com
Magazine Publisher
N.A.I.C.S.: 513120
Elisabeth Gilbride (Gen Mgr & Exec Editor)

HorseCity.com (3)
725 Broad St, Augusta, GA 30901
Tel.: (706) 724-0851
Web Site: http://www.horsecity.com
Sales Range: $10-24.9 Million
Emp.: 4
Online Equine Magazine Publisher
N.A.I.C.S.: 513120
Dennis Faulk (Dir-Ops)

Subsidiary (Domestic):

Morris Digital Works, LLC (2)
725 Broad St, Augusta, GA 30901
Tel.: (706) 724-0851
Web Site: http://www.morrisdigitalworks.com
Tools, Technologies, Consulting & Web Development Services
N.A.I.C.S.: 541512
William S. Will (Chm & CEO)

Morris Publishing Group, LLC (2)
725 Broad St, Augusta, GA 30901 (100%)
Tel.: (706) 724-0851
Web Site: http://www.morrispublishinggroup.com
Emp.: 683
Holding Company; Newspaper, Magazine & Shopping Guide Publisher
N.A.I.C.S.: 551112
Craig S. Mitchell (Treas, Sec & Sr VP-Fin)
Steve K. Stone (Sr VP)
Derek J. May (Pres)
Richard Brashear (Gen Mgr-Main Street Digital)
Rona Johnson (Publr-Alaska)
Delinda Fogel (CFO)
William S. Morris IV (CEO)

Subsidiary (Domestic):

Echo Publishing & Printing (3)
4285 W Lake St, Pequot Lakes, MN 56472
Tel.: (218) 568-8521
Web Site: http://www.pineandlakes.com
Sales Range: $25-49.9 Million
Emp.: 7
Newspaper Publishers
N.A.I.C.S.: 513110
Pete Mohs (Publr)
Nancy Vogt (Editor)
Susie Eller (Dir-Adv)

Plant (Domestic):

Echo Publishing & Printing (4)
406 W Washington St, Brainerd, MN 56401
Tel.: (218) 587-2360
Web Site: http://www.pineandlakes.com
Sales Range: $25-49.9 Million
Newspaper Publishers
N.A.I.C.S.: 513110

Subsidiary (Domestic):

Morris Business Media, LLC (3)
725 Broad St, Augusta, GA 30901 (100%)
Tel.: (706) 823-3200
Web Site: http://www.morris.com
Print & Digital Products
N.A.I.C.S.: 334610

Unit (Domestic):

Morris Visitor Publication (2)
21200 Erwin St, Woodland Hills, CA 91367-3714
Tel.: (818) 716-7484
Web Site: http://www.wheretraveler.com
Sales Range: $10-24.9 Million
Emp.: 32
Publishers of Advertiser Supported Magazines Distributed In Hotels
N.A.I.C.S.: 513199
Ray Camberos (Dir-Art)
Teri Samuels (Dir-Art)
Linda Chase (Dir-Editorial)
Leigh Harrington (Dir-Editorial-Eastern)
Danilo Brunetti (Publr)
Laura Burkhardt (Publr)
Dane Hjort (Publr)
Charlie McNiff (Publr)
Jack Tomalis (Publr)
Andras Wiszkindenszky (Publr)
Ethan Woods (Publr)

The Columbia County News-Times (2)
4272 Washington Rd Ste 3B, Evans, GA 30809
Tel.: (706) 863-6165
Web Site: http://newstimes.augusta.com
Sales Range: $10-24.9 Million
Emp.: 5
Newspaper Publishers
N.A.I.C.S.: 513110
Suzanne Liverett (Office Mgr)

Subsidiary (Domestic):

The Globe Pequot Press, Inc. (2)
246 Goose Ln, Guilford, CT 06437
Tel.: (203) 458-4500
Web Site: http://www.globepequot.com
Travel, Outdoor & Recreation Books Publisher
N.A.I.C.S.: 513130
James Joseph (Pres)
Gail Blackhall (Dir-Subsidiary Rights)
Max Phelps (Dir-Mktg & Sls Dev-Outdoor Indus)
Jed Lyons (Publr)

Unit (Domestic):

The Hampton County Guardian (2)
306 Lee Ave, Hampton, SC 29924
Tel.: (803) 943-4645
Web Site: http://www.hamptoncountyguardian.com
Sales Range: $10-24.9 Million
Emp.: 6
Newspaper Publishers
N.A.I.C.S.: 513110

The People-Sentinel (2)
10481 Dunbarton Blvd, Barnwell, SC 29812
Tel.: (803) 259-3501
Web Site: http://www.thepeoplesentinel.com
Sales Range: $10-24.9 Million
Emp.: 10
Newspaper Publishing
N.A.I.C.S.: 513110
Laura McKenzie (Publr)
Michael Young (Editor-Sports)
Jonathan Vickery (Mng Editor)

SHIVVERS INC.
614 W English St, Corydon, IA 50060-0467
Tel.: (641) 872-1005
Web Site: http://www.shivvers.com
Year Founded: 1968
Sales Range: $75-99.9 Million
Emp.: 100
Grain Drying & Power Equipment Mfr
N.A.I.C.S.: 423820
Brenda Campbell (Sec)
Ron Raasch (CFO)
Carl Shivvers (Founder)

SHK MANAGEMENT INC.
220 W Germantown Pike, Plymouth Meeting, PA 19462
Tel.: (484) 351-2000
Web Site: http://www.korman.com
Rev: $45,000,000
Emp.: 200
Apartment Hotel Operation
N.A.I.C.S.: 581110
Brad Korman (Pres)

SHMALTZ BREWING COMPANY
6 Fairchild Sq, Clifton Park, NY 12065
Tel.: (518) 406-5430
Web Site: http://www.shmaltzbrewing.com
Year Founded: 1996
Sales Range: $1-9.9 Million
Emp.: 20
Brewery
N.A.I.C.S.: 312120
Jeremy Cowan *(Owner)*

SHO-AIR INTERNATIONAL INC.
5401 Argosy Ave, Huntington Beach, CA 92649
Tel.: (949) 476-9111
Web Site: http://www.shoair.com
Year Founded: 1986
Sales Range: $10-24.9 Million
Emp.: 65
Freight Forwarding Services
N.A.I.C.S.: 488510
Scott Tedro *(Pres)*
Kym Marmolejo *(Dir-Intl)*

SHO-DEEN INC.
17 N 1st St, Geneva, IL 60134
Tel.: (630) 232-8570
Web Site: http://www.shodeen.com
Year Founded: 1961
Sales Range: $25-49.9 Million
Emp.: 90
Holding Company; Land Development & Operative Residential & Commercial Construction Services
N.A.I.C.S.: 551112
Kent W. Shodeen *(Chm, Pres & CEO)*
Anna Harmon *(Dir-Mktg)*
Susan Trainer *(Controller)*

Subsidiaries:

Sho-Deen Construction, LLC (1)
77 N 1st St, Geneva, IL 60134-2220
Tel.: (630) 232-7883
Web Site: http://www.shodeen.com
Sales Range: $10-24.9 Million
Emp.: 30
Operative Residential & Commercial Construction Services
N.A.I.C.S.: 236117
Kent W. Shodeen *(Pres & CEO)*

SHO-ME POWER ELECTRIC COOPERATIVE INC.
301 W Jackson St, Marshfield, MO 65706-2128
Tel.: (417) 468-2615   MO
Web Site: http://www.shomepower.com
Year Founded: 1941
Sales Range: $200-249.9 Million
Emp.: 144
Electronic Services
N.A.I.C.S.: 221122
Denise Stevens *(Co-CFO)*
James D. Cottrell *(Chm)*
Jack Bybee *(Treas & Sec)*
Dan Singletary *(Vice Chm)*
John Richards *(CFO)*
Craig Thomas *(Mgr-Engrg & Transmission)*
Jeff Neas *(Mgr-Substations)*
Mark Keeling *(CTO)*
Tim Lewis *(Mgr-Member Svc & Corp Comm)*
Chris Bolick *(Mgr-Admin Svcs)*
Rebecca Gunn *(Mgr-HR)*
Peter Dawson *(Chief Compliance Officer)*

SHOALS MPE, LLC
3311 County Rd 47, Florence, AL 35630
Tel.: (256) 766-9439
Web Site: http://www.shoalsmpe.com
Mechanical, Plumbing & Electrical Services
N.A.I.C.S.: 238220
Darren Rhodes *(Pres)*

Subsidiaries:

Tim Rhodes Electric Co., Inc. (1)
707 N Broadway St, Florence, AL 35630
Tel.: (256) 766-9439
Web Site: http://www.timrhodeselectric.com
Electrical Contractor
N.A.I.C.S.: 238210

SHOALS PROVISION INC.
4144 Pkwy Dr, Florence, AL 35630
Tel.: (256) 764-1851
Web Site: http://www.shoalsprovision.com
Sales Range: $75-99.9 Million
Emp.: 20
Meat & Meat Product Merchant Whslr
N.A.I.C.S.: 424470
Ronald Pitts *(Pres)*

SHOCKOE COMMERCE GROUP, LLC.
11 S 12th St 4th Fl, Richmond, VA 23219
Tel.: (804) 343-3441
Web Site: http://www.shockoecommerce.com
Year Founded: 2008
Sales Range: $10-24.9 Million
Emp.: 20
Fitness Equipment Whslr
N.A.I.C.S.: 713940
Patrick Galleher *(CEO)*
Bobby Morris *(CFO)*
Chris Deel *(COO & CTO)*
David Mueller *(Mgr-Ops)*

SHOCO INC.
2056 E Dixon Blvd, Shelby, NC 28152
Tel.: (704) 482-7329
Web Site: http://www.shocomarine.com
Year Founded: 1958
Sales Range: $10-24.9 Million
Emp.: 9
Boats, Canoes, Watercraft & Marine Equipment Sales
N.A.I.C.S.: 423910
Dale A. Short *(Owner & Pres)*

SHOE CITY G.P. INC.
12550 Whittier Blvd, Whittier, CA 90602
Tel.: (562) 698-2400
Web Site: http://www.shoecity.com
Rev.: $12,700,000
Emp.: 50
Shoe Retailer
N.A.I.C.S.: 458210
Elsa Ibarra *(Mgr-HR)*

SHOE SHOW, INC.
2201 Trinity Church Rd, Concord, NC 28027
Tel.: (704) 782-4143   NC
Web Site: http://www.shoeshow.com
Year Founded: 1960
Sales Range: $1-4.9 Billion
Emp.: 3,800
Shoes & Accessories
N.A.I.C.S.: 424340
Robert B. Tucker *(Founder & Pres)*
Jack Van Der Poel *(CFO)*
Carolyn C. Tucker *(VP)*

SHOEMAKER CAPITAL PARTNERS LLC.
4252 N Cicero Ave, Chicago, IL 60641-1605
Tel.: (773) 427-2400
Year Founded: 1990
Sales Range: $10-24.9 Million
Emp.: 35
Housing Construction Services
N.A.I.C.S.: 236117
David J. Dubin *(Pres)*
Stuart Kantoff *(Exec VP)*

SHOEZOO.COM LLC
7721 Somerset Blvd, Paramount, CA 90723
Web Site: http://www.shoezoo.com
Year Founded: 2008
Sales Range: $1-9.9 Million
Emp.: 15
Online Shoe Store
N.A.I.C.S.: 458210
Alon Sida *(Owner)*

SHOFERS FURNITURE CO. INC.
930 S Charles St, Baltimore, MD 21230
Tel.: (410) 752-4212
Web Site: http://www.shofers.com
Sales Range: $10-24.9 Million
Emp.: 21
Furniture Retailer
N.A.I.C.S.: 449110
Herbert Shofer *(CEO)*
Jeff Lewis *(Gen Mgr)*

SHOFFEE INC.
6 Madison Rd, Fairfield, NJ 07004
Tel.: (973) 227-9001
Web Site: http://www.shoffee.com
Year Founded: 2007
Sales Range: $1-9.9 Million
Emp.: 4
Single Serve Coffee & Tea Products
N.A.I.C.S.: 311920
Judson B. Kleinman *(Owner)*

SHOGREN INDUSTRIES INC.
225 Wilshire Ave SW, Concord, NC 28025
Tel.: (704) 786-5617
Year Founded: 1977
Sales Range: $25-49.9 Million
Emp.: 400
Mfr of Hosiery
N.A.I.C.S.: 315120
Tony Shogren *(Chm)*
Richard Pollen *(Controller)*

Subsidiaries:

Shogren Hosiery Manufacturing Co., Inc. (1)
225 Wilshire Ave Southwest, Concord, NC 28025-5631   (100%)
Tel.: (704) 786-5617
Sales Range: $50-74.9 Million
Mfr of Womens Hosiery
N.A.I.C.S.: 315120

SHOGYO INTERNATIONAL CORPORATION
6851 Jericho, Syosset, NY 11791
Tel.: (516) 921-9111   NY
Web Site: http://www.shogyo.com
Year Founded: 1976
Sales Range: $150-199.9 Million
Emp.: 400
Mfr, Marketer & Retailer of Potentrometers, Miniature Lamps, Speakers, Cables Switches & Plugs
N.A.I.C.S.: 334417
H. Rubin *(Office Mgr)*
Jacob Collier *(Mgr-Matls Control)*
Jennifer Murale *(Sec)*
Robert Craig *(Controller)*

SHOKAI FAR EAST LTD.
9 Elena Ct, Cortlandt Manor, NY 10567-7012
Tel.: (914) 736-3500   NY
Web Site: http://www.shokaifareast.com
Year Founded: 1960
Sales Range: $10-24.9 Million
Emp.: 65
OEM Components Mfr
N.A.I.C.S.: 423690
Michael B. Rubin *(Pres)*
Joe Weber *(VP-Mktg)*
Ronald Sherman *(VP-Fin)*

SHONEY'S OF KNOXVILLE INC.
9720 Parkside Dr, Knoxville, TN 37922
Tel.: (865) 690-6331
Web Site: http://www.shopdinestayknoxville.com
Sales Range: $25-49.9 Million
Emp.: 26
Family Restaurants
N.A.I.C.S.: 722511
Bill Baugh *(Pres & CEO)*
Randy Mooneyham *(Mgr-Kitchen)*
Ann Smith *(Mgr-Dining Room)*
Karen Vaughn *(Mgr)*

SHONEY'S OF RICHMOND INC.
Ste 102 9816 Mayland Dr, Richmond, VA 23233-1457
Tel.: (804) 346-3414
Rev.: $21,700,000
Emp.: 15
Restaurant Operators
N.A.I.C.S.: 722511
Mark A. Sweeney *(Pres)*

SHOOK & FLETCHER INSULATION CO., INC.
4625 Vlydale Rd, Birmingham, AL 35242-4608
Tel.: (205) 991-7606   DE
Web Site: http://www.shookandfletcher.com
Year Founded: 1967
Sales Range: $25-49.9 Million
Emp.: 200
Roofing, Siding & Insulation Services
N.A.I.C.S.: 423330
Mark Damron *(Controller)*
Wayne W. Killion Jr. *(Pres)*

Subsidiaries:

National Insulation, Co. (1)
1795 Constitution Rd SE, Atlanta, GA 30316
Tel.: (404) 243-6823
Web Site: http://www.ntlinsulation.com
Sales Range: $1-9.9 Million
Emp.: 14
Roofing, Siding & Insulation Material Merchant Whslr
N.A.I.C.S.: 423330

Shook & Fletcher Insulation Co., Inc. - Atlanta Division (1)
5320 Fulton Industrial Blvd, Atlanta, GA 30336
Tel.: (770) 981-8822
Insulation Products Distr
N.A.I.C.S.: 423610
Tony Cranemore *(Gen Mgr)*

Shook & Fletcher Insulation Co., Inc. - Birmingham Division (1)
211 37th St N, Birmingham, AL 35222
Tel.: (205) 595-8441
Insulation Products Distr
N.A.I.C.S.: 423610

Shook & Fletcher Insulation Co., Inc. - Chattanooga Division (1)
5910-B Shallowford Rd, Chattanooga, TN 37421
Tel.: (423) 892-5415
Insulation Products Distr

SHOOK & FLETCHER INSULATION CO., INC.

U.S. PRIVATE

Shook & Fletcher Insulation Co., Inc.—(Continued)
N.A.I.C.S.: 423610

Shook & Fletcher Insulation Co., Inc. - Decatur Division (1)
3315 Sexton Rd, Decatur, AL 35603
Tel.: (256) 355-7011
Emp.: 6
Insulation Products Distr
N.A.I.C.S.: 423610
Scott Lynn *(Mgr-Distr)*

Shook & Fletcher Insulation Co., Inc. - Knoxville Division (1)
3420 Distribution Dr, Knoxville, TN 37914
Tel.: (865) 637-7813
Web Site: http://www.shookandfletcher.com
Insulation Products Distr
N.A.I.C.S.: 423610
Wayne Kaller *(Gen Mgr)*

Shook & Fletcher Insulation Co., Inc. - Mobile Division (1)
4651 Halls Mill Rd, Mobile, AL 36693
Tel.: (251) 478-2297
Web Site: http://www.shookandfletcher.com
Insulation Products Distr
N.A.I.C.S.: 423610

Shook & Fletcher Supply Co. of Alabama, Inc. (1)
1041 11th Ct W, Birmingham, AL 35204
Tel.: (205) 252-5157
Sales Range: $10-24.9 Million
Emp.: 5
Construction Equipment & Services
N.A.I.C.S.: 423810
Vincent Keele *(Mgr-Ops)*

SHOOK NATIONAL CORPORATION

2000 W Dorothy Ln, Moraine, OH 45439
Tel.: (937) 276-6666   OH
Web Site:
  http://www.shookconstruction.com
Year Founded: 1922
Sales Range: $75-99.9 Million
Emp.: 300
Holding Company Provides Construction Management Design-Build & Traditional General Construction Services
N.A.I.C.S.: 237210

Subsidiaries:

Shook Indiana Division (1)
7330 E 90th St Ste 2, Indianapolis, IN 46256
Tel.: (317) 849-6066
Sales Range: $25-49.9 Million
Emp.: 20
N.A.I.C.S.: 236220
Chuck Peabody *(VP)*

Shook Northern Ohio Division (1)
10245 Brecksville Rd, Brecksville, OH 44141-0020
Tel.: (440) 838-5400
Sales Range: $25-49.9 Million
Emp.: 200
Building Construction Services
N.A.I.C.S.: 236210

Shook Water Resources (1)
2000 W Dorothy Ln, Moraine, OH 45439
Tel.: (937) 276-6666
Sales Range: $25-49.9 Million
Emp.: 100
N.A.I.C.S.: 236220
Joe Mellon *(Gen Mgr)*
Ken Herr *(VP-Mktg)*

Shook, Incorporated (1)
PO Box 138806, Dayton, OH 45413-8806
Tel.: (937) 276-6666
Web Site:
  http://www.shookconstruction.comwww.shookconstruction.com
Sales Range: $125-149.9 Million
N.A.I.C.S.: 236220

SHOOK, HARDY & BACON LLP

2555 Grand Blvd, Kansas City, MO 64108
Tel.: (816) 474-6550
Web Site: http://www.shb.com
Year Founded: 1889
Sales Range: $300-349.9 Million
Emp.: 1,200
Law firm
N.A.I.C.S.: 541110
John F. Murphy *(Partner)*
Bart Eppenauer *(Mng Partner-Seattle)*
Jon R. Gray *(Partner-Kansas City)*
Mathew L. Larsen *(Partner-Kansas City)*
Lori R. Schultz *(Partner-Kansas City)*
Kristen A. Page *(Partner-Kansas City)*
Tristan L. Duncan *(Partner-Kansas City)*
Carrie A. McAtee *(Partner-Kansas City)*
Cory Fisher *(Partner-Kansas City)*
M. Katie Gates Calderon *(Partner-Kansas City)*
Mihai M. Vrasmasu *(Partner-Miami)*
Geri E. Howell *(Partner-Miami)*
Elena K. McFarland *(Partner-Kansas City)*
Micah L. Hobbs *(Partner-Kansas City)*
Nicholas N. Deutsch *(Partner-Houston)*
Kristina L. Burmeister *(Partner-Kansas City)*
Megan M. Egli *(Partner-Kansas City)*
Andrew Chang *(Partner)*
Rachael Smith *(Partner)*
Kristopher J. Verra *(Partner)*
Anthony J. Andrade *(Partner-Kansas City)*
Christopher J. Aikin *(Partner-Kansas City)*
Eric Anielak *(Partner-Kansas City)*
Hunter K. Ahern *(Partner-Houston)*
Jesse J. Camacho *(Partner-Kansas City)*
Mark D. Anstoetter *(Partner-Kansas City)*
Michael S. Cargnel *(Partner-Kansas City)*
Robert T. Adams *(Partner-Kansas City)*
Scott W. Anderson *(Partner-Tampa)*
Laura Whitmore *(Partner-Tampa)*
Buffy Mims *(Partner-Washington)*
Sharon Israel *(Partner)*
Gregory L. Fowler *(Mng Partner)*
William P. Geraghty *(Mng Partner)*
S. Kirk Ingebretsen *(Mng Partner)*
Lynn H. Murray *(Mng Partner)*
James Shepherd *(Mng Partner)*
Sean P. Wajert *(Mng Partner)*
Madeleine McDonough *(Chm)*
Jennise W. Stubbs *(Mng Partner-Houston)*
Simon J. Castley *(Mng Partner-London)*
Jennifer M. Voss *(Mng Partner-Tampa)*
Matthew Wolfe *(Partner)*
Riley Mendoza *(Partner)*
David Morehan *(Partner)*
George Ngengwe *(Partner)*
Maria Salcedo *(Partner)*
Jennifer Blues Kenyon *(Partner)*
Anne Hannah *(Partner)*
Keith Bae *(Partner)*
Devin A. Moss *(Partner)*
Erin Leffler *(Partner)*
Anna Sumner Pieschel *(Partner)*
Josh Becker *(Partner)*
Colin K. Kelly *(Mng Partner)*

SHOOTERS, INC.

601 Walnut St Ste 1050 S, Philadelphia, PA 19106
Tel.: (215) 861-0100
Web Site:
  http://www.shootersinc.com
Year Founded: 1981
Sales Range: $10-24.9 Million
Emp.: 70
Motion Picture & Video Production
N.A.I.C.S.: 512110
Bob Pyle *(VP-Engrg & Tech)*
Annie Marie Starker *(Dir-Sls)*
Justin Wineburgh *(Pres)*

SHOP EAT LIVE, INC.

423 31st St, Newport Beach, CA 92663   NV
Web Site:
  http://www.shopeatlive.com
Year Founded: 2011
Internet Shopping Services Involving Coupons, Vouchers & Local Deals
N.A.I.C.S.: 541890
Hal Sklar *(Pres, CEO, CFO, Sec & Treas)*

SHOP KWIK STORE LLC

615 S 4th St, Manhattan, KS 66502
Tel.: (785) 537-8076
Web Site:
  http://www.shopquickllc.com
Year Founded: 1993
Sales Range: $25-49.9 Million
Emp.: 130
Owner & Operator of Convenience Stores
N.A.I.C.S.: 445131
Gregory Junghans *(Pres)*

SHOP RITE INC.

115 E First St, Crowley, LA 70526-5101
Tel.: (337) 783-8696   LA
Web Site: http://www.shoprite.org
Year Founded: 1966
Sales Range: $25-49.9 Million
Emp.: 450
Convenience Store
N.A.I.C.S.: 445131
John Daniel Gielen *(Chm)*

SHOP-N-SAVE FOODS INC.

1228 Country Club Rd, Fairmont, WV 26554-2369
Tel.: (304) 366-0481
Year Founded: 1988
Sales Range: $10-24.9 Million
Emp.: 100
Grocery Services
N.A.I.C.S.: 445110
Thomas Jamieson *(Pres)*
Bruce Byers *(CFO)*

SHOPEYE, INC.

108 Flying Mist Isle, Foster City, CA 94404
Tel.: (650) 339-1077   FL
Year Founded: 2011
Retail Shopping Software
N.A.I.C.S.: 513210
Ethelinda Corpuz *(Pres, CEO, CFO, Treas & Sec)*

SHOPFORBAGS INC.

2311 Farrington, Dallas, TX 75207
Tel.: (214) 637-5300
Web Site:
  http://www.shopforbags.com
Year Founded: 2002
Sales Range: $1-9.9 Million
Emp.: 8
Fashion Apparel, Handbags, Footwear & Accessories for Women & Juniors Distr & Whslr
N.A.I.C.S.: 424350
Lisa Smith *(VP)*
Katy Messersmith *(Pres)*

SHOPJIMMY.COM, LLC

2300 W Hwy 13, Burnsville, MN 55337
Tel.: (952) 881-6492
Web Site: http://www.shopjimmy.com
Year Founded: 2007
Sales Range: $1-9.9 Million
Emp.: 53
TV Parts Distr
N.A.I.C.S.: 449210
Jimmy Vosika *(Owner)*

SHOPPAS MATERIAL HANDLING

15217 Grand River Rd, Fort Worth, TX 76155
Tel.: (817) 359-1100
Web Site: http://www.shoppas.com
Rev.: $30,356,070
Emp.: 105
Materials Handling Machinery
N.A.I.C.S.: 423830
Scott Witt *(Mgr-Aftermarket Sls)*

SHOPPING CENTER MANAGEMENT

19501 Biscayne Blvd Ste 400, Aventura, FL 33180
Tel.: (305) 937-6200
Web Site: http://www.turnberry.com
Rev.: $125,000,000
Emp.: 85
Commercial & Industrial Building Operation
N.A.I.C.S.: 531120
Anabel Llopis *(Dir-Corp Mktg & Sls)*

SHOPRITE OF BRISTOL LLC

1200 Farmington Ave, Bristol, CT 06010-4714
Tel.: (860) 584-9022
Web Site: http://www.shoprite.com
Rev.: $35,000,000
Emp.: 400
Supermarket Operator
N.A.I.C.S.: 445110
Jon Murphy *(Mgr)*
Courtney Rinaldi *(Asst Mgr-Bakery)*

SHOPSMITH, INC.

6530 Poe Ave, Dayton, OH 45414
Tel.: (937) 898-6070   OH
Web Site: http://www.shopsmith.com
Year Founded: 1972
Sales Range: $10-24.9 Million
Emp.: 95
Power Woodworking Equipment Mfr & Marketer
N.A.I.C.S.: 333243
Mark A. May *(Controller)*
Lawrence R. Jones *(VP-Ops)*

SHOPTECH SOFTWARE CORPORATION

180 Glastonbury Blvd Ste 303, Glastonbury, CT 06033
Tel.: (860) 633-0740
Web Site: http://www.shoptech.com
Year Founded: 1990
Rev.: $16,000,000
Emp.: 300
Computer Software Services
N.A.I.C.S.: 513210
Robert Lewis *(CFO)*
Todd Harris *(VP-Desktop Dev)*
George Wells *(VP-Acct Svcs)*
Angie Asher *(VP-Customer Svcs)*
Paul Ventura *(Sr VP-Mktg)*
Phillip M. Hutchinson *(Pres & CEO)*
Greg Ehemann *(Sr VP-Sls)*
Rich Ehemann *(CTO)*
Chris Coursey *(VP-Web Dev)*

SHORE CAPITAL PARTNERS, LLC

1 E Wacker Dr Ste 400, Chicago, IL 60601

COMPANIES

Tel.: (312) 348-7580
Web Site: http://www.shorecp.com
Year Founded: 2009
Emp.: 21
Healthcare Industry Private Equity Firm
N.A.I.C.S.: 523999
Ryan Kelley *(Partner)*
Mike Cooper *(Partner)*
John Hennegan *(Partner)*
Don Pierce *(Partner)*
Linda Bloom *(CFO)*
Chris Mioton *(Principal)*
Richard Boos *(Partner)*
Brad Morehead *(Partner & Head-Bus Svcs Fund)*
Justin Bentley *(Partner & Head-Capital Markets)*
Brian Tracy *(Head-IR)*
Sarah Gabriel *(Chief People Officer)*

Subsidiaries:

AA Medical Store, Inc. (1)
9830 West 190th Street Suite M, Mokena, IL 60448
Tel.: (708) 479-0062
Web Site: https://www.aamedicalstore.com
Medical & Surgical Supplies Mfr
N.A.I.C.S.: 339112
Matt Nelson *(CEO)*

Subsidiary (Domestic):

Surgical Product Solutions LLC (2)
1639 E Railroad St, Carnegie, PA 15241-0000
Tel.: (412) 564-1280
Web Site:
   http://www.surgicalproductsolutions.com
Surgical Appliance & Supplies Mfr
N.A.I.C.S.: 339113
Megan Casey *(Sr Mgr-Acq)*
Justin Tennant *(Mng Partner)*
Steven Darocy *(Mng Partner)*

SHORE CONSTRUCTION LLC
499 Powhatten Ct, Gibson, LA 70340
Tel.: (985) 868-2210
Web Site:
   http://www.shoreconstr.com
Year Founded: 2009
Sales Range: $25-49.9 Million
Emp.: 335
Supplementary Personnel For The Marine & Oilfield Industry
N.A.I.C.S.: 561320
Kristi Yates *(CEO)*

SHORE DISTRIBUTORS INC.
807 Brown St, Salisbury, MD 21804
Tel.: (410) 749-3121
Web Site: http://www.shoredist.com
Sales Range: $10-24.9 Million
Emp.: 40
Air Conditioning Equipment Distr
N.A.I.C.S.: 423730
James F. Morris *(Pres)*
Jenny Hershberger *(Controller)*

SHORE TOYOTA INC.
4236 Black Horse Pike, Mays Landing, NJ 08330
Tel.: (609) 645-2770
Web Site:
   http://www.shoretoyota.com
Year Founded: 1983
Sales Range: $10-24.9 Million
Emp.: 42
Car Whslr
N.A.I.C.S.: 441110
Mark Bruschi *(Principal)*

SHORE TRADING COMPANY
665 Union Hill Rd, Alpharetta, GA 30004
Tel.: (770) 998-0566
Sales Range: $10-24.9 Million
Emp.: 3
Fish & Seafood Whslr
N.A.I.C.S.: 424460
Martin Klausner *(CFO)*
Terri Norton *(Sec)*
Williams S. Ronald *(CEO)*

SHORE UP! INC.
520 Snow Hill Rd, Salisbury, MD 21804
Tel.: (410) 749-1142   MD
Web Site: http://www.shoreup.org
Year Founded: 1965
Sales Range: $10-24.9 Million
Emp.: 386
Community Care Services
N.A.I.C.S.: 624190
Freddy L. Mitchell *(Exec Dir)*
Tyrone Chase *(Vice Chm)*
Marlette Dixon *(Treas)*
Norma Lee Barkley *(Sec)*
Elroy Brittingham *(Chm)*

SHOREHILL CAPITAL LLC
10 S Wacker Dr Ste 3000, Chicago, IL 60606
Tel.: (312) 876-7267
Web Site:
   http://www.shorehillcapital.com
Year Founded: 2013
Privater Equity Firm
N.A.I.C.S.: 523999
Dave Hawkins *(Mng Partner)*
Brian Simmons *(Mng Partner)*
Rob Hogan *(Mng Dir)*
Charlie Denison *(Mng Dir)*
Robert Jackson *(Principal)*
Ellen Sullivan *(Mgr-Office)*

Subsidiaries:

Tribus Aerospace LLC (1)
10 S Wacker Dr Ste 3300, Chicago, IL 60606
Tel.: (312) 876-7267
Web Site: http://www.tribusaerospace.com
Machined Parts Mfr
N.A.I.C.S.: 336412

Subsidiary (Domestic):

Advanced Machining & Tooling, Inc. (2)
13535 Danielson St, Poway, CA 92064
Tel.: (858) 486-9050
Web Site: http://www.amtmfg.com
Special Dies, Tools, Jigs, And Fixtures,
N.A.I.C.S.: 333514
Tony Cerda *(Pres)*

Midwest Precision LLC (2)
34700 Lakeland Blvd, Eastlake, OH 44095-5223
Tel.: (440) 951-2333
Web Site: http://www.midwestllc.com
Precision Turned Product Mfr
N.A.I.C.S.: 332721
Russell C. Mulh *(Mgr-program)*

Precision Aerospace Corp. (2)
5300 Corporate Grove Dr Se Ste 350, Grand Rapids, MI 49507
Tel.: (616) 243-8112
Web Site: http://www.precision-aerospace.com
Machine Shops
N.A.I.C.S.: 332710
Bill Hoyer *(Pres)*
Nolan Marcus *(Dir-Mfg)*

SHORELINE BUILDERS INC.
209 E Bdwy Ste D, Vista, CA 92084
Tel.: (760) 940-6050
Web Site:
   http://www.shorelinebuilders.org
Sales Range: $10-24.9 Million
Emp.: 10
Framing Contractors
N.A.I.C.S.: 238130
Richard Bedell *(Pres)*

SHORELINE EQUITY PARTNERS, LLC
135 Professional Dr Ste 104, Ponte Vedra Beach, FL 32082
Tel.: (904) 222-6540
Web Site:
   http://shorelineequitypartners.com
Privater Equity Firm
N.A.I.C.S.: 523999
Mike Hand *(Co-Founder & Mng Partner)*
Peter Franz *(Co-Founder & Partner)*
Ian Garland *(VP)*

Subsidiaries:

Core Roofing Systems LLC (1)
1360 Union Hill Rd, Alpharetta, GA 30004
Tel.: (770) 777-6703
Web Site: http://coreroofingsystems.com
Rev.: $9,400,000
Emp.: 80
Building Finishing Contractors
N.A.I.C.S.: 238390
Steve Vicknair *(Controller)*
Chad Greene *(Sr Mgr-Acct)*
A. J. Gustavel *(Dir-Ops)*
David Hunt *(Dir-Svcs & Maintenance)*
Daniel Imboden *(VP-Florida)*
Jason Jordan *(Dir-Ops)*
Dusty Keppen *(VP-Ops)*
Todd Shannon *(VP-Florida)*

Subsidiary (Domestic):

McCurdy-Walden, Inc. (2)
5267 Commonwealth Ave, Jacksonville, FL 32254
Tel.: (904) 269-5848
Web Site: http://www.mccurdywalden.com
Roofing Contractors
N.A.I.C.S.: 238160

Dominion Paving & Sealing, Inc. (1)
18200 Hull Street Rd, Moseley, VA 23120
Tel.: (804) 739-4150
Rev.: $5,000,000
Emp.: 36
Highway, Street & Bridge Construction
N.A.I.C.S.: 237310
David Atkinson *(Pres)*
Stephen Parham *(CFO)*

Engelmans Baking Co. (1)
6185 Brook Hollow Pkwy, Norcross, GA 30071
Tel.: (770) 248-1444
Web Site: http://www.engelmansbakery.com
Rev.: $8,500,000
Emp.: 50
Commercial Bakeries
N.A.I.C.S.: 311812
Sammy Engelman *(Owner)*

Subsidiary (Domestic):

Suncoast Bakeries, Inc. (2)
2811 59th Avenue Dr E, Bradenton, FL 34203
Tel.: (941) 753-7494
Rev.: $7,154,400
Emp.: 100
Commercial Bakeries
N.A.I.C.S.: 311812
Ray Ryder *(Controller)*
Bernard J. Vroom *(Pres)*

SHORELINE FRUIT, LLC
10850 E Traverse Hwy Ste 4460, Traverse City, MI 49684
Tel.: (231) 941-4336
Web Site:
   http://www.shorelinefruit.com
Year Founded: 1986
Sales Range: $25-49.9 Million
Emp.: 180
Cherry & Dry Fruit Production & Distribution Services
N.A.I.C.S.: 111339
Tom Berg *(Dir-Mktg)*
Brian Gerberding *(Dir-Sls)*
Anne Moeller *(Controller)*
Bob Reidy *(Mgr)*
Randall B. Atwater *(Sr Mgr-Sls)*
Steve Somsel *(Mgr-Sls)*
Rob Davis *(Mgr-Retail Sls)*

SHORELINE GAS INC.

SHOREVIEW INDUSTRIES, LLC

1 Shoreline Plz Ste 2000 S, Corpus Christi, TX 78477
Tel.: (361) 888-6500   TX
Year Founded: 1985
Sales Range: $10-24.9 Million
Emp.: 12
Natural Gas Marketing
N.A.I.C.S.: 486210
Rian Grisemer *(Pres)*

SHORELINE GROUP LLC
39 Bulson Rd, New York, NY 11570
Tel.: (516) 608-6086
Web Site: http://www.casesentry.com
Rev.: $12,000,000
Emp.: 4
Custom Computer Programming Services
N.A.I.C.S.: 541511

SHORENSTEIN COMPANY, L.P.
235 Montgomery St, San Francisco, CA 94104-1714
Tel.: (415) 772-7000   CA
Web Site:
   http://www.shorenstein.com
Year Founded: 1920
Sales Range: $125-149.9 Million
Emp.: 300
Owner & Operator of Commercial Buildings
N.A.I.C.S.: 531120
Stanley E. Roualdes *(Exec VP)*
Thomas W. Hart *(Exec VP, Dir-Corp Rels & Mgr-Shorenstein Family Office)*
Douglas W. Shorenstein *(CEO)*
James A. Pierre *(Sr VP-Asset Mgmt)*
Michael D. Stanley *(Chief Admin Officer)*
Charles W. Malet *(Pres & Chief Investment Officer)*
Stuart Appley *(CTO)*
Robert S. Underhill *(Exec VP-Fund Mgmt)*
Paula M. Elliott *(Exec VP-HR)*
Mark L. McCarthy *(Mng Dir-Debt Capital Markets)*
Katie M. McGettigan *(Sr VP-Fund Mgmt)*
Jed C. Brush *(VP-Asset Mgmt)*
Tony Calabrese *(VP-Asset Mgmt)*

SHORENSTEIN HAYS-NEDERLANDER THEATRES LLC
1182 Market St Ste 200, San Francisco, CA 94102
Tel.: (415) 551-2075
Web Site: http://www.shnsf.com
Year Founded: 1977
Live Entertainment Theater Owner & Production Services
N.A.I.C.S.: 711310
Greg Holland *(CEO)*
Robert E. Nederlander *(Owner)*
David Cushing *(VP-Ticketing)*
Regina Guggenheim *(VP-Production & Theatre Ops)*
Scott Kane *(CMO)*

SHOREVIEW INDUSTRIES, LLC
222 S 9th St Ste 3300, Minneapolis, MN 55402
Tel.: (612) 436-4280   DE
Web Site: http://www.shoreview.com
Year Founded: 2002
Privater Equity Firm
N.A.I.C.S.: 523999
David J. Wakefield *(Co-Founder & Chm)*
Jeffrey A. Mudge *(Co-Founder & Mng Partner)*
Thomas D'Ovidio *(Partner)*
Scott W. Gage *(Partner)*

SHOREVIEW INDUSTRIES, LLC

ShoreView Industries, LLC—(Continued)
Brett C. Habstritt *(Partner)*
Brian Moher *(Chief Compliance Officer & VP-Fin)*
Debra Gardner *(Controller)*
Adam Reeves *(Partner)*
Monica Stone *(Chief Admin Officer)*
Peter Zimmerman *(Principal)*
Brittney Oake *(Dir-Bus Dev)*
Madeleine Shumaker *(Principal)*

Subsidiaries:

Cornerstone Foodservice Group, Inc. **(1)**
127 Ambassador Dr #147, Naperville, IL 60540
Tel.: (630) 527-8600
Web Site: http://www.cornerstonefoodservicegroup.com
Cooking Equipment Design & Mfr
N.A.I.C.S.: 333241
Kristine Holtz *(Pres & CEO)*

Subsidiary (Domestic):

Astra Manufacturing, Inc. **(2)**
127 Ambassador Dr, Ste 147, Naperville, IL 60540
Tel.: (818) 340-1800
Web Site: http://www.astramfr.com
Espresso & Cappuccino Machinery Mfr
N.A.I.C.S.: 333241
Richard Hourizadeh *(Pres)*

Crown Products, Inc. **(1)**
500 W 92nd St, Bloomington, MN 55420
Tel.: (314) 426-4500
Web Site: https://www.crowndistribution.com
Flooring Contractors
N.A.I.C.S.: 238330

Subsidiary (Domestic):

Blakely Products Company **(2)**
13891 Stephens Rd, Warren, MI 48089
Tel.: (586) 771-6600
Sales Range: $1-9.9 Million
Emp.: 28
Home Furnishing Merchant Whslr
N.A.I.C.S.: 423220
Daniel Blakely *(Pres)*
Bob Williams *(Branch Mgr)*
Carolyn Wilde *(Mgr-Credit)*
Chad Skelton *(Mgr-IT & Fin)*
Dick Welty *(Branch Mgr)*
Don Watson *(Branch Mgr)*
Houghton Lake *(Branch Mgr)*
Jeff Carter *(Branch Mgr)*
Mark Partlow *(Mgr-Ops)*
Pam Dundas *(Mgr-Pur)*
Scott Horne *(Branch Mgr)*

Cartwright Distributing, LLC **(2)**
4851 Kingston St, Denver, CO 80239-2523
Tel.: (303) 371-7950
Web Site: http://www.cartwrightdistributing.com
Home Furnishing Whslr
N.A.I.C.S.: 423220
Bill Cartwright *(Pres-Sls)*
Mike Munden *(Gen Mgr)*
Bill Kelker *(Treas & Sec-Sls)*
Terry Martin *(Accountant)*

Tri-State Wholesale Flooring, Inc. **(2)**
3900 W 34th St N, Sioux Falls, SD 57107
Tel.: (605) 336-3080
Web Site: http://www.tsf.com
Sales Range: $1-9.9 Million
Emp.: 16
Home Furnishing Merchant Whslr
N.A.I.C.S.: 423220
Joe Gaspar *(Pres)*

Walcro, Inc. **(2)**
500 W 92nd St, Bloomington, MN 55420
Tel.: (952) 884-6033
Web Site: http://www.walcro.com
Hardware Merchant Whslr
N.A.I.C.S.: 423710
Mike Belde *(Mgr-Store)*
John DeYoung *(CEO)*

Martin-Logan, Ltd. **(1)**
2101 Delaware St, Lawrence, KS 66049-3149
Tel.: (785) 749-0133
Web Site: http://www.martinlogan.com
Sales Range: $10-24.9 Million
Emp.: 30
Audio Speaker Designer & Mfr
N.A.I.C.S.: 327910
Chris Leader *(Pres)*

P&F Industries, Inc. **(1)**
445 Broadhollow Rd Ste 100, Melville, NY 11747
Tel.: (631) 694-9800
Web Site: https://www.pfina.com
Rev.: $59,041,000
Assets: $61,004,000
Liabilities: $19,048,000
Net Worth: $41,956,000
Earnings: ($1,476,000)
Emp.: 172
Fiscal Year-end: 12/31/2022
Heating Equipment & Air Powered Hand Tools & Hardware Mfr
N.A.I.C.S.: 333991

Subsidiary (Domestic):

Continental Tool Group Incorporated **(2)**
445 Broadhollow Rd Ste 100, Melville, NY 11747
Tel.: (631) 694-9800
Web Site: http://www.pfina.com
Sales Range: $125-149.9 Million
Emp.: 8
Air Powered Tools & Hardware Mfr
N.A.I.C.S.: 333991

Subsidiary (Domestic):

Hy-Tech Machine, Inc. **(3)**
25 Leonberg Rd, Pittsburgh, PA 16066
Tel.: (724) 776-6800
Web Site: http://www.hy-techinc.com
Sales Range: $25-49.9 Million
Emp.: 60
Machine Tools & Accessories Mfr
N.A.I.C.S.: 333991
Douglas Ciabotti *(Pres & COO)*

Subsidiary (Domestic):

Air Tool Service Company **(4)**
25 Leonberg Rd, Cranberry Township, PA 16066
Tel.: (440) 701-1021
Web Site: http://www.atsco.com
Sales Range: $1-9.9 Million
Emp.: 20
Pneumatic Tools & Parts Mfr & Distr
N.A.I.C.S.: 333991

Subsidiary (Domestic):

Countrywide Hardware, Inc. **(2)**
445 Broadhollow Rd Ste 100, Melville, NY 11747
Tel.: (631) 694-9800
Heating Equipment & Air Powered Hand Tool Mfr
N.A.I.C.S.: 333991

Florida Pneumatic Manufacturing Corporation **(2)**
851 Jupiter Park Ln-Unit A, Jupiter, FL 33458 **(100%)**
Tel.: (561) 744-9500
Web Site: https://www.florida-pneumatic.com
Sales Range: $50-74.9 Million
Emp.: 50
Hand Tools Mfr & Distr
N.A.I.C.S.: 333991
Bart Swank *(Pres)*

Subsidiary (Non-US):

Universal Air Tool Company Limited **(3)**
Unit 8 Lane End Industrial Park, Bucks, High Wycombe, HP14 3BY, United Kingdom
Tel.: (44) 1494883300
Web Site: https://ut-tools.com
Emp.: 5
Automobile Parts Mfr
N.A.I.C.S.: 336390
James Suckling *(Area Mgr-Sls-South)*

Subsidiary (Domestic):

Green Manufacturing, Inc. **(2)**
3985 S Fletcher Rd, Chelsea, MI 48118
Tel.: (517) 458-1500
Web Site: https://greenemfg.com
Pneumatic Hand Tools Mfr
N.A.I.C.S.: 333991

Jiffy Air Tool, Inc. **(2)**
2254 Conestoga Dr, Carson City, NV 89706-0434
Tel.: (775) 883-1072
Web Site: https://www.jiffyairtool.com
Machine Shops
N.A.I.C.S.: 332710

TMI International, LLC **(1)**
5350 Campbells Run Rd, Pittsburgh, PA 15205
Tel.: (412) 787-9750
Web Site: http://www.tmi-pvc.com
Plastic Strip Doors, PVC Products, Modular Enclosures & Dock Accessories Mfr & Distr
N.A.I.C.S.: 326199
David Rimbey *(Pres & CEO)*
Chris Cummings *(Mgr-Sls)*
Rob Hinckley *(VP-Sls & Mktg)*
Samantha North *(Dir-Global Ops)*
David Schneider *(Sr Mgr-Mktg)*

Subsidiary (Domestic):

FlexBarrier Products, LLC **(2)**
4708 S Old Peachtree Rd Ste 700, Norcross, GA 30071
Tel.: (770) 446-0054
Web Site: http://www.flexbarrier.com
Plastic Insulated Curtains, Strip Doors & Roll-Up Doors Mfr
N.A.I.C.S.: 326113

Win Plastic Extrusions, LLC **(2)**
3333 Win St, Cuyahoga Falls, OH 44223
Tel.: (330) 929-1999
Web Site: http://www.winplastics.com
Extruded Plastic Strip & Sheet Products Mfr
N.A.I.C.S.: 326130

Winzer Corporation **(1)**
4060 E Plano Pkwy, Plano, TX 75074
Tel.: (214) 341-2122
Web Site: http://www.winzer.com
Industrial & Automotive Repair Products & Support Services
N.A.I.C.S.: 423710
Rich Funkhouser *(VP-IT)*
Diane Vanderbilt *(VP)*
Kipp Bush *(VP-Mktg)*
Deborah Bynum *(Pres & CEO)*

SHOREWEST REALTORS, INC.
17450 W North Ave, Brookfield, WI 53008
Tel.: (262) 827-4111
Web Site: http://www.shorewest.com
Year Founded: 1946
Sales Range: $10-24.9 Million
Emp.: 400
Real Estate Brokerage Services
N.A.I.C.S.: 531210
Deborah Brown *(Dir-Sls-Elmbrook & Wauwatosa)*
Joe Horning *(Pres)*
Jim Young *(Dir-Sls-Mequon)*
Rick Fedor *(Dir-Sls-New Berlin)*
Tom Breitlow *(Asst Dir-Sls)*
Lauri Burkard *(Asst Dir-Sls)*
Kim Curtis *(Dir-Sls)*
Kevin Rigg *(Asst Dir-Sls-Elmbrook & Wauwatosa)*

SHOREY PUBLIC RELATIONS LLC
24 Hamilton St Suite 5A, Saratoga Springs, NY 12866
Tel.: (518) 587-1011
Web Site: http://www.shoreypr.com
Sales Range: Less than $1 Million
Emp.: 10
Communication Service
N.A.I.C.S.: 541820
Missy Shorey *(Pres & CEO)*
Jen Lynch *(Acct Exec)*

SHORR PACKAGING CORP.
800 N Commerce St, Aurora, IL 60504-7931
Tel.: (630) 978-1000
Web Site: http://www.shorr.com
Year Founded: 1922
Sales Range: $25-49.9 Million
Emp.: 150
Industrial & Retail Packaging & Supplies Distr
N.A.I.C.S.: 424990
Kevin Vrba *(CFO)*
Michael Crowley *(CIO)*
Rob Onorato *(Pres & CEO)*

Subsidiaries:

Mack Paper Co. **(1)**
340 Blackhawk Park Ave Ste 1, Rockford, IL 61104
Tel.: (815) 962-9210
Web Site: http://www.mackpaper.com
Packaging Products Mfr & Distr
N.A.I.C.S.: 322212
Steve McIntosh *(Pres)*

SHORT AND PAULK SUPPLY COMPANY
910 Main St S, Tifton, GA 31794
Tel.: (229) 382-2314
Web Site: http://www.shortpaulk.com
Rev.: $13,905,870
Emp.: 45
Lumber, Plywood & Millwork
N.A.I.C.S.: 423310
Tahl Barrett *(Controller)*

SHORT BLOCK TECHNOLOGIES, INC.
1401 N Myrtle Ave, Clearwater, FL 33755
Tel.: (727) 443-0373 FL
Web Site: http://www.shopsbt.com
Year Founded: 1997
Sales Range: $25-49.9 Million
Emp.: 350
Boat Engines & Accessories Retailer
N.A.I.C.S.: 333618
C.J. Lammers *(Pres)*
Ericka Buczkowski *(Mgr-Sls)*

SHORT ELLIOTT HENDRICKSON INC.
3535 Vadnais Ctr Dr, Saint Paul, MN 55110-5196
Tel.: (651) 490-2000 MN
Web Site: http://www.sehinc.com
Year Founded: 1927
Sales Range: $25-49.9 Million
Emp.: 750
Provider of Engineering Services
N.A.I.C.S.: 541330
Jeff Pedersen *(Principal)*
Mark Broses *(Pres-Michigan)*
Bill Kloster *(Principal)*
Cuneyt Feizoulof *(Chief Strategy & Mktg Officer)*
David Ott *(Pres & CEO)*

Subsidiaries:

SEH Design Build Inc. **(1)**
3535 Vadnais Ctr Dr, Saint Paul, MN 55110
Tel.: (651) 490-2000
Web Site: http://www.sehdb.com
Sales Range: $25-49.9 Million
Emp.: 180
Construction Services
N.A.I.C.S.: 236115
Steve Peterson *(Pres)*

SEH Technology Solutions **(1)**
100 N 6th St Ste 710C, Minneapolis, MN 55403-1515
Tel.: (612) 758-6728
Sales Range: $10-24.9 Million
Emp.: 35
Consulting Services
N.A.I.C.S.: 541690

SEH of Indiana, LLC **(1)**
9200 Calumet Ave Ste 300, Munster, IN 46321-2885

Tel.: (219) 513-2500
Construction Engineering Services
N.A.I.C.S.: 541330

SHORT RUN STAMPING CO.
925 E Linden Ave, Linden, NJ 07036
Tel.: (908) 862-1070
Web Site: http://www.shortrun.com
Rev.: $11,300,000
Emp.: 50
Metal Stamping Services
N.A.I.C.S.: 332119
Randall Speir (Pres)

SHORT'S BREWING COMPANY
121 N Bridge St, Bellaire, MI 49615
Tel.: (231) 498-2300
Web Site:
  http://www.shortsbrewing.com
Year Founded: 2002
Sales Range: $1-9.9 Million
Emp.: 40
Brewery Mfr & Pub
N.A.I.C.S.: 312120
Joe Short (CEO & Engr-Creative)
Scott Newman-Bale (Partner-Bus Dev)
Tony Hansen (Head-Brewer)
Leah Short (Owner)

SHORT'S TRAVEL MANAGEMENT, INC.
1203 W Ridgeway Ave, Waterloo, IA 50701
Tel.: (319) 433-0863
Web Site:
  http://www.shortstravel.com
Year Founded: 1946
Sales Range: $150-199.9 Million
Emp.: 95
Travel Arrangement Services
N.A.I.C.S.: 561510
David LeCompte (Pres & CEO)
David Hughes (CFO)
DeAnne Dale (Chief Sls Officer)

SHORTS MARINE INC.
32415 Long Neck Rd, Millsboro, DE 19966
Tel.: (302) 945-1200
Web Site:
  http://www.shortsmarine.com
Rev.: $13,289,943
Emp.: 52
Boat Dealers
N.A.I.C.S.: 811310
Stephen Hastings (Gen Mgr)
Jim Albrand (Dir-IT)
Randy Sharrock (Mgr-Sls)

SHORTY'S MEXICAN ROADHOUSE
1050 Bicentennial Dr, Manchester, NH 03104
Tel.: (603) 647-1050
Web Site:
  http://www.shortysmex.com
Rev.: $10,500,000
Emp.: 10
Mexican Restaurant
N.A.I.C.S.: 722513
Billy Martin (Asst Mgr)
Gordon Fogal (Gen Mgr)
Kate Gagne (Asst Mgr)
Melissa Downie (Asst Mgr)
Sean Noonan (Gen Mgr)
Tanya Barry (Gen Mgr)

SHOSHONE SILVER/GOLD MINING COMPANY
254 W Hanley Ave Ste A, Coeur D'Alene, ID 83815
Tel.: (208) 664-0620
Sales Range: Less than $1 Million

Silver & Gold Exploration, Mining & Processing
N.A.I.C.S.: 212220
Gregory Smith (Chm)

SHOTTENKIRK INC.
5031 Avenue O, Fort Madison, IA 52627
Tel.: (319) 372-6880
Web Site: http://www.shottenkirk.com
Sales Range: $75-99.9 Million
Emp.: 100
New & Used Automobiles
N.A.I.C.S.: 441110
Kim Glasgow (Controller)
Greg Shottenkirk (Pres)
Marc Luedtke (Gen Mgr)
Ben Sheedy (Gen Mgr-Sls)

SHOULTZ & ASSOCIATES ADVERTISING, INC.
2344 10th St, White Bear Lake, MN 55110-2608
Tel.: (612) 751-7359
Year Founded: 1988
Sales Range: Less than $1 Million
Emp.: 1
Business-To-Business, Collateral, Financial, High Technology, Information Technology, Media Buying Services, Print, Public Relations, Technical Advertising, Trade & Consumer Magazines
N.A.I.C.S.: 541810
Barry A. Shoultz (Pres)

SHOW IMAGING, INC.
1125 Joshua Way, Vista, CA 92081
Tel.: (760) 842-5880
Web Site:
  http://www.showimaging.com
Year Founded: 2009
Sales Range: $10-24.9 Million
Emp.: 43
Event Management Services
N.A.I.C.S.: 711310
Steven Q. Evans (Founder)

SHOW ME BREAD, INC.
PO Box 109, Camdenton, MO 65020
Tel.: (573) 346-1577
Sales Range: $25-49.9 Million
Emp.: 700
Baked Goods Mfr
N.A.I.C.S.: 311811
Greg Anderson (Pres)
Jean M. Hunot (CFO)

SHOW MEDIA
383 5th Ave 2nd Fl, New York, NY 10016
Tel.: (212) 883-8783
Web Site:
  http://www.showmedia.com
Year Founded: 2006
Sales Range: $10-24.9 Million
Emp.: 36
Media Streaming Services
N.A.I.C.S.: 518210
Laurence Hallier (Founder & CEO)
Jonathan Goodrich (COO)
Angela Chen (CFO)
Mitchell Presnick (Chm-Macau & Hong Kong)
Joshua Swinney (Coord-Mktg)
Eugenia Lau (Dir-Bus Dev)
Emily Ogden (Dir-Creative)
James Wolf (Mng Dir)
Steve Chatham (Supvr-Acct)
Ron Parkinson (VP-Ops)
Jon Lau (CTO)

SHOWA BOSTON INSTITUTE FOR LANGUAGE AND CULTURE
420 Pond St, Boston, MA 02130

Tel.: (617) 522-0080 MA
Web Site:
  http://www.showaboston.org
Year Founded: 1987
Sales Range: $1-9.9 Million
Emp.: 123
Educational Support Services
N.A.I.C.S.: 611710
Ronald H. Provost (Pres)
Koji Hirao (Chm)

SHOWALTER MOTOR COMPANY INC.
333 W Main St, Vernal, UT 84078
Tel.: (435) 789-3825
Web Site:
  http://www.showalterford.com
Sales Range: $10-24.9 Million
Emp.: 29
New & Used Car Dealers
N.A.I.C.S.: 441110
Gary Showalter (Pres)

SHOWCASE INC.
2323 Cheshire Bridge Rd NE, Atlanta, GA 30324
Tel.: (404) 325-7676
Web Site:
  http://www.showcaseinc.com
Year Founded: 1976
Sales Range: $10-24.9 Million
Emp.: 35
Selling Cameras
N.A.I.C.S.: 449210
Warren N. Steinberg (Pres)
Bob Khoury (CFO)
Kenny Chrysler (Mgr-Video Production)

SHOWCASE MOTORS INC.
1333 E Camelback Rd, Phoenix, AZ 85014
Tel.: (602) 274-3800
Web Site:
  http://www.showcasehonda.com
Sales Range: $75-99.9 Million
Emp.: 300
Sales of New & Used Automobiles
N.A.I.C.S.: 441110
Ross Erler (Gen Mgr)

SHOWCASE NEW ENGLAND INC.
67 Gail Dr, Northford, CT 06472-1308
Tel.: (203) 484-4579 CT
Web Site:
  http://www.showcasene.com
Year Founded: 1999
Sales Range: $10-24.9 Million
Emp.: 10
Catalog & Mail-Order Houses
N.A.I.C.S.: 459210
Daniel Greenhalgh (Pres)

SHOWORKS INC.
355 Douglas Rd E, Oldsmar, FL 34677
Tel.: (813) 855-9616
Web Site:
  http://www.showorksevents.com
Sales Range: $1-9.9 Million
Emp.: 7
Event Design, Floral Art & Production
N.A.I.C.S.: 541490
Stefanie Berry (Pres & CEO)
Shannon Waters (Mgr-Sls-Design)
David Rodriguez (Asst Mgr-Sls-Design)

SHOWPLACE INC.
611 Bellefontaine Ave, Marion, OH 43302
Tel.: (740) 383-6020
Web Site:
  http://www.showplaceinc.biz
Rev.: $14,318,315

Emp.: 100
Television, Furniture & Other Household Appliances Rentals
N.A.I.C.S.: 532210
Gary Ferriman (Founder, Pres & CEO)
Keith Ferriman (Mgr-Pur)

SHOWTIME CONCESSION SUPPLY INC.
200 SE 19th St, Moore, OK 73160
Tel.: (405) 895-9902
Web Site:
  http://www.showtimeconcession.com
Sales Range: $10-24.9 Million
Emp.: 5
Candy Distr
N.A.I.C.S.: 424450
John Lohman (Pres)

SHOWTIME PICTURES
729 N 1500 W, Orem, UT 84057
Tel.: (954) 527-7900
Web Site:
  http://www.showtimepictures.com
Sales Range: $10-24.9 Million
Emp.: 200
Photographic Services
N.A.I.C.S.: 541922
Kemal Arin (Pres)

SHR CONSULTING GROUP, LLC
7420 Alban Station Blvd Ste B200, Springfield, VA 22150
Tel.: (571) 297-1324
Web Site: http://www.shrgroupllc.com
Year Founded: 2012
Sales Range: $10-24.9 Million
Emp.: 61
Information Technology Consulting Services
N.A.I.C.S.: 541512
Robert Sanchious (Founder & CEO)
Randy Steiner (Pres & COO)

SHRADER & MARTINEZ CONSTRUCTION INC.
160 Dry Creek Rd, Sedona, AZ 86336-5412
Tel.: (928) 282-7554 AZ
Web Site:
  http://www.shradermartinez.com
Year Founded: 1986
Sales Range: $10-24.9 Million
Emp.: 66
Nonresidential Construction
N.A.I.C.S.: 236220
Ronald M. Martinez (Pres & Co-Owner)
Scott Shrader (Co-Owner & VP)
Michael S. Cook (CFO)

SHREVE CRUMP & LOW COMPANY
39 Newbury St, Boston, MA 02116
Tel.: (617) 267-9100
Web Site:
  http://www.shrevecrumpandlow.com
Rev.: $28,000,000
Emp.: 35
Jewelry Stores
N.A.I.C.S.: 458310
Luiza Artinian (Mgr-Customer Svc)
Andreas Winter (Mgr-Acctg)
Renee Doocey (Mgr-Inventory)

SHRINERS HOSPITALS FOR CHILDREN
2900 Rocky Point Dr, Tampa, FL 33607-1460
Tel.: (813) 281-0300
Web Site:
  http://www.shrinershospitalsforchildren.org
Year Founded: 1922
Sales Range: $500-549.9 Million

SHRINERS HOSPITALS FOR CHILDREN

Shriners Hospitals For Children—(Continued)
Emp.: 6,100
Children's Hospital Owner & Operator
N.A.I.C.S.: 622310
John McCabe *(Exec VP)*
Eugene R. D'Amore *(VP-Hospital Ops)*
Kathy A. Dean *(VP-HR)*
Scott R. Laubisch *(VP-Plng & Bus Dev)*
Laurie A. Spieler *(VP-Legal)*
Jerry G. Gantt *(Pres)*
Chris L. Smith *(First VP)*
Gary J. Bergenske *(Chm)*
Jeffrey L. Sowder *(Second VP)*
Liz Isaak *(Dir-Fiscal Svcs-St. Louis)*
Patrick C. Colbert *(Treas)*
Roger J. Robinson *(Vice Chm)*
Anna G. Small *(Chief Compliance Officer)*
Kenneth Guidera *(Chief Medical Officer)*
Sharon Russell *(VP-Fin & Acctg)*
Raymond F. Novak *(VP-Res)*
Jim L. Cain Sr. *(First VP)*

SHRINK PACKAGING SYSTEMS CORP.
15 Progress St, Edison, NJ 08820-1102
Tel.: (908) 753-2525   DE
Web Site: http://www.shrinkpackaging.com
Year Founded: 1970
Sales Range: $10-24.9 Million
Emp.: 90
Distr of Packaging Machinery
N.A.I.C.S.: 424990
Edward Schoenlank *(Mgr-Stretch Pkg Products)*

SHUBEE CUSTOMER CARE WEAR
110 Columbus W Dr, Macon, GA 31206-5294
Tel.: (478) 405-5494
Web Site: http://www.shubee.com
Year Founded: 2000
Sales Range: $1-9.9 Million
Emp.: 19
Disposable Products Mfr
N.A.I.C.S.: 326199
Tamiko Slocumb *(Office Mgr)*
Steve Stone *(Owner)*

SHUFORD MILLS LLC
447 Main St, Hudson, NC 28638
Tel.: (828) 328-2141   NC
Web Site: http://www.shufordmills.com
Year Founded: 1880
Sales Range: $150-199.9 Million
Emp.: 500
Textile Yarns & Fabrics
N.A.I.C.S.: 313110
A. Pope Shuford *(Chm)*
C. P. Davis *(Pres)*
C. Hunt Shuford Jr. *(CFO)*

SHUGART CORPORATION
34700 Pacific Coast Hwy Ste 302, Capistrano Beach, CA 92624-1350
Tel.: (949) 488-8779   DE
Year Founded: 1986
Sales Range: $50-74.9 Million
Emp.: 5
Provider of Assembly & Management Services
N.A.I.C.S.: 334111

Subsidiaries:

International Assembly Specialists, S.A. de C.V.   (1)
Circuito Siglo XXI No 1991, Parque Industrial Siglo XXI, Mexicali, 21290, Mexico
Tel.: (52) 6869050014
Web Site: http://www.ias-shugart.com
Sales Range: $10-24.9 Million
Mfr of Disk Drives, Test Equipment, Terminals & Tape Drives
N.A.I.C.S.: 334112

SHUGART ENTERPRISES LLC
221 Jones Town Rd, Winston Salem, NC 27104
Tel.: (336) 765-9661   NC
Web Site: http://www.beyshugart.com
Year Founded: 1967
Sales Range: $10-24.9 Million
Emp.: 57
Single-Family House Construction Services
N.A.I.C.S.: 236115
Brian D. Shugart *(VP)*
Grover F. Shugart Jr. *(Pres & CEO)*

SHULAR COMPANY
9475 Hwy 49, Gulfport, MS 39503
Tel.: (228) 868-1888
Web Site: http://www.shular.com
Year Founded: 1979
Sales Range: $10-24.9 Million
Emp.: 500
Hotels & Motels
N.A.I.C.S.: 721110
Michael L. Shular *(Owner)*

SHULER DISTRIBUTING COMPANY
3040 Democrat Rd, Memphis, TN 38118
Tel.: (901) 363-8770
Rev.: $15,066,113
Emp.: 7
Carpets
N.A.I.C.S.: 423220
Ted R. Shuler Sr. *(Chm)*

SHULLSBURG CREAMERY INC.
208 W Water St, Shullsburg, WI 53586-9657
Tel.: (608) 965-4485   WI
Web Site: http://www.shullsburgcreamery.com
Year Founded: 1934
Sales Range: $10-24.9 Million
Emp.: 55
Producers of Cheese Products
N.A.I.C.S.: 424430
Scott Stocker *(Pres & CEO)*

SHULTS FORD, INC.
10401 Perry Hwy, Wexford, PA 15090
Tel.: (724) 934-2388   DE
Web Site: http://www.shultsford.com
Sales Range: $25-49.9 Million
Emp.: 150
New & Used Car Dealer
N.A.I.C.S.: 441110
Richard I. Bazzy *(Owner & Pres)*
Rich Dennino *(Gen Mgr)*
Bob Saldutte *(Mgr-Used Cars)*
Dave Biggs *(Mgr-New Cars)*

Subsidiaries:

Shults Ford Lincoln-Mercury, Inc.   (1)
2871 Freeport Rd, Pittsburgh, PA 15238
Tel.: (412) 828-2300
Web Site: http://www.shultscars.com
Sales Range: $10-24.9 Million
New & Used Car Dealer
N.A.I.C.S.: 441110
Richard I. Bazzy *(Owner)*
John Jaquel *(Mgr-Svc)*
Debbie Schuessler *(Mgr-Parts)*
Miriam Brown *(Mgr-Internet)*

SHULTS MANAGEMENT GROUP, INC.
181 E Fairmont Ave, Lakewood, NY 14750
Tel.: (716) 526-0600   NY
Web Site: http://www.shultsauto.com
Year Founded: 1970
Sales Range: $100-124.9 Million
Emp.: 400
Holding Company; New & Used Car Dealer & General Automotive Repair & Maintenance Services
N.A.I.C.S.: 551112
Mike Allen *(Mgr-IT)*
Dan Crandall *(VP-Ops)*

Subsidiaries:

Ed Shults Chevrolet, Inc.   (1)
300 Fluvanna Ave, Jamestown, NY 14701
Tel.: (716) 720-9092
Web Site: http://www.shultschevy.com
Sales Range: $25-49.9 Million
Emp.: 70
New & Used Car Dealer
N.A.I.C.S.: 441110
Kevin Joslyn *(Mgr-Parts)*
Chris Baker *(Mgr-Fin)*
Cristine Brown *(Mgr-Acctg)*
Scott Ellsworth *(Mgr-New Car Sls)*
JoAnn Hoffman *(Mgr-Acctg)*
Matthew Kahm *(VP-Mktg)*
Camy Mason *(Office Mgr)*
Lenny Melice *(Gen Mgr-Sls)*
Michelle Norberg *(Mgr-Acctg)*
Chad Ramsey *(Mgr-Svc)*
Beth Tilley *(Mgr-Acctg)*

McFadden Ford, Inc.   (1)
2258 Washington St, Jamestown, NY 14701
Tel.: (716) 484-0121
Web Site: http://www.edshultsford.com
Sales Range: $25-49.9 Million
Emp.: 60
New & Used Car Dealer
N.A.I.C.S.: 441110
Erin Viemba *(Mgr-Internet Sls)*

SHULTZ DISTRIBUTING, INC.
6851 E Marginal Way S, Seattle, WA 98108
Tel.: (206) 682-8427   WA
Year Founded: 1985
Sales Range: $25-49.9 Million
Emp.: 30
Fuel Oil Dealers
N.A.I.C.S.: 457210
George Miller *(Owner)*
Martin Smith *(VP-Sls)*
Mary Deitch *(Mgr-Acctg)*

SHUR-CO, LLC
2309 Shurlock St, Yankton, SD 57078-1210
Tel.: (605) 665-6000   SD
Web Site: http://www.shurco.com
Year Founded: 1992
Tarp & Containment Systems Mfr
N.A.I.C.S.: 314910
Mike Krajewski *(VP-Agriculture Sls)*
Scot Fuhrman *(VP-Construction, Waste & Intl Sls)*
Bill Nelson *(Sls Mgr-Midwest Region)*
Jay Kuzdro *(Sls Mgr-Northeast Region)*
Lili McFarland *(Sls Mgr-Western Region)*
Chris Hilson *(Sls Mgr-Great Lakes Region)*
Steve Dolezal *(Sls Mgr-East Central Region)*
Bill Jones *(Sls Mgr-Southeast Region)*

SHURE INCORPORATED
5800 Touhy Ave, Niles, IL 60714
Tel.: (847) 866-2200   IL
Web Site: http://www.shure.com
Year Founded: 1925
Sales Range: $100-124.9 Million
Emp.: 300
Audio & Video Equipment Mfr
N.A.I.C.S.: 334310

U.S. PRIVATE

Christine Schyvinck *(Pres & CEO)*
Ray Crawford *(Sr VP-Mktg & Sls-Global)*
Mark Humrichouser *(VP-Sls Org-Americas & Asia)*
Meg Madison *(VP-HR)*
Scott Sullivan *(Assoc VP-Global Product Mgmt)*
Jamie Griffin *(VP-Ops)*
Mark Brunner *(VP)*
Sam Sabet *(CTO)*

Subsidiaries:

Shure Asia Limited   (1)
22/F 625 Kings Road, Island East, North Point, China (Hong Kong)
Tel.: (852) 2893 4290
Web Site: http://www.shureasia.com
Electric Equipment Mfr
N.A.I.C.S.: 335999

Shure Europe GmbH   (1)
Wannenacker Street 28, 74078, Heilbronn, Germany   (100%)
Tel.: (49) 713172140
Web Site: http://www.shure.de
Sales Range: $25-49.9 Million
Emp.: 50
Holding Company
N.A.I.C.S.: 551112
Markus Winkler *(Mng Dir)*

SHUTTLE PHARMACEUTICALS, INC.
1 Research Ct Ste 450, Rockville, MD 20850
Tel.: (240) 403-4212   MD
Web Site: http://www.shuttlepharma.com
Year Founded: 2012
Emp.: 6
Pharmaceuticals Product Mfr
N.A.I.C.S.: 325412
Milton Brown *(Founder & Chief Scientific Officer)*
Mira Jung *(Founder & Chief Radiation Biologist)*
Peter Dritschilo *(Pres & CFO)*
Theodore L. Phillips *(Chief Medical Officer)*
Michael J. Starkweather *(VP-Bus Dev)*

SHUTTS & BOWEN LLP
200 S Biscayne Blvd Ste 4100, Miami, FL 33131
Tel.: (305) 358-6300
Web Site: http://www.shutts.com
Year Founded: 1910
Sales Range: $125-149.9 Million
Emp.: 390
Law firm
N.A.I.C.S.: 541110
Bowman Brown *(Co-Chm-Fin Svcs Practice Grp)*
Bruce M. Boiko *(Partner)*
John W. Bustard *(Partner)*
Douglas G. Brehm *(Partner)*
George Andrews *(Partner)*
Daniel Barsky *(Partner)*
Michael J. Grindstaff *(Mng Partner)*
Daniel E. Nordby *(Partner)*
Douglas M. Kramer *(Partner)*
Charla Burchett *(Partner)*
Erik Matheney *(Partner)*
Patrick George Brugger *(Partner)*
Michelle G. Hendler *(Partner)*
Benjamin E. Wilson *(Partner)*
Osmel Cuan *(Atty-Tax & Intl Law Practice Grp)*
J. Thomas Cookson *(Partner-Corp Practice Grp)*
Rafael A. Aguilar *(Partner-Real Estate Practice Grp)*
Francis E. Rodriguez *(Chm-Tax & Intl Law Practice Grp & Mng Partner)*
Florentino Gonzalez *(Chm-Real Estate Practice Grp & Partner)*

COMPANIES

Russell P. Hintze (Partner-Tax & Intl Law Practice Grp-Orlando)
Scott G. Johnson (Sr Atty-Govt Contracts & Corp Law Practice Grp-Tampa)
Frederick B. O'Malley (COO-Miami)
Peter M. Abreu (CIO-Miami)
Bryan Wells (Co-Chm-Fin Svcs Practice Grp)
Kimberly Prior (Partner-Fin Svcs Practice Grp)
William McCullough (Partner-Corp Practice Grp)
Alfred G. Smith (Chm-Corp Practice Grp)
Deborah A. Getzoff (Partner-Tampa)
Woodrow Pollack (Partner-Tampa)
Fred Werdine (Partner-Tampa)
Jason Gonzalez (Mng Partner-Tallahassee)
Ben Gibson (Partner-Bus Litigation Practice Grp-Tallahassee)
Sara Levy (Partner-Insurance Practice Grp-Fort Lauderdale)
David Batista (Partner-Insurance Practice Grp-Fort Lauderdale)
Jack C. McElroy (Mng Partner-Firmwide)
Michael Jay Rune II (Partner)

SIANO APPLIANCE DISTRIBUTORS
5372 Pleasant View Rd, Memphis, TN 38134
Tel.: (901) 382-5833
Web Site: http://www.sianoappliances.net
Sales Range: $10-24.9 Million
Emp.: 20
Major Electrical Appliances
N.A.I.C.S.: 423620
Ralph Siano (Pres)
Steve Lawson (VP)

SIBCY CLINE, INC.
8044 Montgomery Rd, Cincinnati, OH 45236-2919
Tel.: (513) 984-4100　　OH
Web Site: http://www.sibcyclinerealtors.com
Year Founded: 1930
Sales Range: $125-149.9 Million
Emp.: 152
Real Estate Agency
N.A.I.C.S.: 531210
Robert N. Sibcy (Pres)
James Stofko (Gen Mgr)
William Borek (Treas & Sec)
Robert E. Mahoney (Sr VP)
Pamela D. Sibcy (VP-Mktg)

SIBLEY OIL COMPANY INC.
15580 Hwy 43, Russellville, AL 35653
Tel.: (256) 332-1911
Sales Range: $10-24.9 Million
Emp.: 5
Petroleum Products Sales
N.A.I.C.S.: 424720
Jim Sibley (Pres)

SIBONEY CONTRACTING CO.
1450 Central Park Blvd, West Palm Beach, FL 33401
Tel.: (561) 832-3110
Web Site: http://www.siboneycc.com
Sales Range: $10-24.9 Million
Emp.: 18
Local Trucking Services
N.A.I.C.S.: 484110
Enrique A. Tomeu (Pres)
Frank Padron (Mgr-IT)
Justo Navarro (VP)

SIBU BEAUTY
1098 E S Union Ave, Midvale, UT 84047
Web Site: http://www.sibubeauty.com
Year Founded: 2003
Sales Range: $1-9.9 Million
Emp.: 11
Beauty Products
N.A.I.C.S.: 456120
Bruce McMullin (Founder)
Stuart Hutchinson (Sr Dir-Sls & Mktg)
Ashley Jantzen (VP-Sls)

SICA FLETCHER, LLC
21 Green Ave, Amityville, NY 11701
Tel.: (516) 967-1958
Web Site: http://www.sicafletcher.com
Year Founded: 2014
Insurance Services
N.A.I.C.S.: 524298
Michael Fletcher (Mng Partner)

SICO INCORPORATED
7525 Cahill Rd, Edina, MN 55439-2738
Tel.: (952) 941-1700　　MN
Web Site: http://www.sicoinc.com
Year Founded: 1951
Sales Range: $150-199.9 Million
Emp.: 420
Mobile Folding Products Mfr; Cafeteria/Banquet Tables, Stages, Risers & Portable Dance Floors
N.A.I.C.S.: 337127
Hal Wilson (Chm)
Chris E. Wilson (CEO)
Ken Steinbauer (Pres & COO)
Pat Vanderlugt (Mgr-Adv)
Sten Andersen (Gen Mgr-Middle East)

Subsidiaries:

SICO Japan Inc. (1)
Daiwa Bldg 1F 3-10-3 Kandamisakicho, Chiyoda-ku, Tokyo, 101-0061, Japan
Tel.: (81) 332880145
Web Site: https://www.sicoinc.com
Portable Folding Product Mfr & Distr
N.A.I.C.S.: 337127

Sico Asia Pte Ltd. (1)
1 Clementi Loop 06-06 Clementi W Logis Park, Singapore, 129 808,
Singapore　　(100%)
Tel.: (65) 65000800
Web Site: http://www.sicoasia.com
Rev.: $3,000,000
Emp.: 25
Mobile Folding Space Efficient Products Mfr
N.A.I.C.S.: 339940
Ginn Cai (Acct Mgr)

Sico Europe Limited (1)
The Link Park Lympne Industrial Estate, Lympne Kent, Canterbury, CT21 4LR, United Kingdom　　(100%)
Tel.: (44) 1303 234000
Web Site: http://www.sico-europe.com
Rev.: $6,000,000
Emp.: 85
Mobile Folding Space Efficient Products Mfr
N.A.I.C.S.: 339940
Steve Mason (Gen Mgr)

Subsidiary (Non-US):

SICO Middle East JLT (LLC) (2)
Jumeirah Business Centre 1 Cluster G Building G2 Office 2307 Floor 23, PO Box 440094, Jumeirah Lake Towers, Dubai, United Arab Emirates
Tel.: (971) 4 422 8259
Web Site: http://www.sico-me.com
Sales Range: $25-49.9 Million
Emp.: 5
Hotel Furniture Whslr
N.A.I.C.S.: 423210
Graham Dimond (Gen Mgr)
Vijay Menon (Reg Mgr-Sls)
Michelle de Scally (Office Mgr)

Sico North America Inc. (1)
7525 Cahill Rd, Minneapolis, MN 55439-2738　　(100%)
Tel.: (952) 941-1700
Web Site: http://www.sicoinc.com
Sales Range: $25-49.9 Million
Emp.: 180
Furniture Mfr
N.A.I.C.S.: 337127
Chris E. Wilson (Pres-SICO Inc., & CEO-SICO-America)
Keith Dahlen (CFO-U.S.)
Pam Johnson (CFO-Intl)
Patricia van der Lugt (Dir-Mktg)

Sico South Pacific (1)
Lot 36 Craftsman Ave Unit 4 9211 Heresord, Berkeley Vale, 2261, Australia　　(100%)
Tel.: (61) 243885100
Web Site: http://www.sicosp.com.au
Rev.: $3,000,000
Emp.: 12
Mobile Folding Space Efficient Products Mfr
N.A.I.C.S.: 339940

SID HARVEY INDUSTRIES, INC.
605 Locust St, Garden City, NY 11530-6524
Tel.: (516) 745-9200　　NY
Web Site: http://www.sidharvey.com
Year Founded: 1931
Sales Range: $200-249.9 Million
Emp.: 500
HVAC Wholesale Distributor & Remanufacturer of Heating & Air Conditioning Parts
N.A.I.C.S.: 423720
Russell Tum Suden (VP)
Sidney Harvey (Pres & CEO)
Dave Harvey (Dir-Construction)
John Rynecki (VP-Sls & Mktg)

SID PATERSON ADVERTISING, INC.
650 5th Ave 23rd Fl, New York, NY 10019
Tel.: (212) 725-9600
Web Site: http://www.spadvertising.com
Year Founded: 1963
Rev.: $20,000,000
Emp.: 30
N.A.I.C.S.: 541810
Sid Paterson (Pres)
Lorenzo Concepcion (Dir-Art)
Pat Asaro (Dir-Media)
Burt Thomas (Controller)

SID PETERSON MEMORIAL HOSPITAL
551 Hill Country Dr, Kerrville, TX 78028
Tel.: (830) 896-4200　　TX
Web Site: http://www.petersonrmc.com
Year Founded: 1990
Sales Range: $75-99.9 Million
Emp.: 1,130
Health Care Srvices
N.A.I.C.S.: 622110
Gloria Olsen (Vice Chm)
Michael M. Baumann (Chm)
Sarah F. Fontenot (Vice Chm)
William R. Johnston (Vice Chm)
Robert L. Schmerbeck III (Vice Chm)

SID RICHARDSON CARBON & ENERGY LTD.
201 Main St Ste 3000, Fort Worth, TX 76102
Tel.: (817) 390-8600
Web Site: http://www.sidrich.com
Sales Range: $100-124.9 Million
Emp.: 600
Carbon Black Mfr & Marketer
N.A.I.C.S.: 325180
Gregory A. King (VP-Sls & Mktg)
Wesley Wampler (VP-R&D)

Subsidiaries:

Richardson Aviation (1)
3800 Lincoln Ave, Fort Worth, TX 76106-2729
Tel.: (817) 625-1611
Sales Range: $10-24.9 Million
Emp.: 44
Corporate FBO
N.A.I.C.S.: 488119
James Murphy (Dir-Ops & Safety)
Frank Bates (Engr-Maintenance)

SID'S CARPET BARN INC.
132 W 8th St, National City, CA 91950
Tel.: (619) 264-3000
Web Site: http://www.sidscarpet.com
Rev.: $20,883,113
Emp.: 40
Carpets
N.A.I.C.S.: 423220
Allan W. Ziman (Pres)
Don Pasquill (VP)
Chris Hadley (Gen Mgr)

SIDDALL, INC.
715 E 4th St Ste 9, Richmond, VA 23224
Tel.: (804) 788-8011　　VA
Web Site: http://www.siddall.com
Year Founded: 1975
Rev.: $18,250,196
Emp.: 6
Business-To-Business, Communications, Environmental, Financial, Public Relations, Retail, Transportation
N.A.I.C.S.: 541810
John N. Siddall (Chm)
Roberta McDonnell (COO, Sr VP & Exec Dir-Production)
Bettina Roda (VP, Controller & Dir-HR)

SIDEMARK
3312 Wooward Ave, Santa Clara, CA 95054
Tel.: (408) 490-3300
Web Site: http://www.sidemark.com
Year Founded: 1984
Emp.: 112
Office Furniture Mfr & Workplace Consulting Services
N.A.I.C.S.: 423210
Soraya Farrah (Dir)
Sandi Jacobs (Pres & CEO)
Bruce Paul (COO & Co-Owner)
Emily Ransone (Co-Owner & Principal)
Cheryl Blain (VP-Fin & Tech)
Philippe Hill (Dir-Ops)
Josh Katz (Dir-Accts)
Ann Greiner (Dir-Design)

SIDEREAL CAPITAL GROUP, LLC
450 Springfield Ave Ste 304, Summit, NJ 07901
Tel.: (973) 435-7300
Web Site: http://www.siderealcapital.com
Year Founded: 2012
Holding Company
N.A.I.C.S.: 551112
EJ Sloboda (Mng Partner)
R. Kenneth Bryant (Mng Partner)
A. Jabbar Abdi (Mng Partner)

SIDES & ASSOCIATES, INC.
222 Jefferson St Ste B, Lafayette, LA 70501-3267
Tel.: (337) 233-6473　　LA
Web Site: http://www.sides.com
Year Founded: 1976
Rev.: $6,980,000
Emp.: 20
Fiscal Year-end: 08/31/04
Consumer Marketing, Government/Political/Public Affairs
N.A.I.C.S.: 541810

SIDES & ASSOCIATES, INC.

Sides & Associates, Inc.—(Continued)
Larry Sides (Pres)
Tom Will (Sr VP-Acct Svcs)
Kathy Ashworth (Exec VP)
Bridget Mires (VP-Media)
Donny Gallagher (Art Dir-Creative Svcs-Print Production)

SIDLEY AUSTIN LLP
1 S Dearborn, Chicago, IL 60603
Tel.: (312) 853-7000 IL
Web Site: https://www.sidley.com
Year Founded: 1866
Sales Range: $900-999.9 Million
Emp.: 2,300
Law firm
N.A.I.C.S.: 541110

SIDNEY HEALTH CENTER
216 14th Ave SW, Sidney, MT 59270
Tel.: (406) 488-2100 MT
Web Site:
    http://www.sidneyhealth.org
Year Founded: 1946
Sales Range: $25-49.9 Million
Emp.: 641
Medical Care Services
N.A.I.C.S.: 622110
Matt Weber (Controller)
Tina Montgomery (CFO)
Rance Haralson (Mgr-Radiology Tech)
Linda Labatte (Mgr-Radiology Operational)

SIDOTI & COMPANY, LLC
122 E 42nd St 4th Fl, New York, NY 10168
Tel.: (212) 297-0001 DE
Web Site: http://www.sidoti.com
Year Founded: 1999
Sales Range: $25-49.9 Million
Equity Research & Investment Banking Services
N.A.I.C.S.: 541910
Peter T. Sidoti (Founder, Chm & CEO)
Marie Conway (Pres)
Gary Jacobs (Dir-Trading)

SIDRAN INC.
1050 Venture Court Ste 100, Carrollton, TX 75006
Tel.: (214) 352-7979
Web Site: http://www.sidraninc.com
Sales Range: $10-24.9 Million
Emp.: 20
Men's Clothing
N.A.I.C.S.: 315250
Roland Mizrahi (Pres)

SIEBURG INTERNATIONAL, INC.
1901 Clydesdale St, Maryville, TN 37801-3728
Tel.: (865) 982-6300
Web Site: http://www.tensilkut.com
Year Founded: 1955
Sales Range: $10-24.9 Million
Emp.: 25
Mfr of Tensile Testing Equipment
N.A.I.C.S.: 333517
Michael B. McDonald (Pres)
Margie McDonald (VP)

Subsidiaries:

Tensilkut Engineering (1)
1901 Clydesdale St, Maryville, TN 37801-3728
Tel.: (865) 982-6300
Web Site: http://www.tensilkut.com
Sales Range: $10-24.9 Million
Emp.: 5
Engineering of Machine Tools
N.A.I.C.S.: 334519

Tensilkut Intl. Corp. (1)
1901 Clydesdale St, Maryville, TN 37801
Tel.: (865) 982-6300
Web Site: http://www.tensilkut.com
Mfr of Machine Tools
N.A.I.C.S.: 334519

SIEGAL & SONS INVESTMENT LTD.
675 Washington St, Newton, MA 02458
Tel.: (617) 332-1230 MA
Web Site:
    http://www.martysfinewine.com
Year Founded: 1965
Sales Range: $10-24.9 Million
Emp.: 81
Operates Liquor Stores
N.A.I.C.S.: 445320
Martin Siegal (Pres)
Joe Lucherini (Controller)

SIEGEL OIL COMPANY
1380 Zuni St, Denver, CO 80204
Tel.: (303) 893-3211
Web Site: http://www.titanlab.com
Rev.: $20,000,000
Emp.: 35
Gasoline
N.A.I.C.S.: 424720
Donald Siegel (Pres & CEO)

SIEGERS SEED COMPANY INC.
13031 Reflections Dr, Holland, MI 49424
Tel.: (616) 786-4999
Web Site: http://www.siegers.com
Sales Range: $10-24.9 Million
Emp.: 18
Field, Garden & Flower Seeds
N.A.I.C.S.: 111422
Rick Siegers (Owner & Pres)
Jeff Siegers (VP-Sls & Mktg)

SIEMENS MANUFACTURING CO., INC.
410 W Washington St, Freeburg, IL 62243
Tel.: (618) 539-3000
Web Site:
    http://www.siemensmfg.com
Sales Range: $10-24.9 Million
Emp.: 120
Contract Electronic Assembly
N.A.I.C.S.: 335311
John F. Siemens III (Co-Founder)

SIEMER ENTERPRISES INC.
515 W Main St, Teutopolis, IL 62467
Tel.: (217) 857-3171
Web Site: http://www.siemerent.com
Sales Range: $10-24.9 Million
Emp.: 50
Bird Seed, Grass Seed & Animal Feeds Mfr & Distr
N.A.I.C.S.: 424910

SIEMER MILLING COMPANY
111 W Main St, Teutopolis, IL 62467-1201
Tel.: (217) 857-3131 IL
Web Site:
    http://www.siemermilling.com
Year Founded: 1882
Sales Range: $75-99.9 Million
Emp.: 150
Mfr of Soft Wheat Flour
N.A.I.C.S.: 311211
Richard C. Siemer (Pres)
Carl Schwinke (VP-Mdsg)
Vernon Tegeler (VP-Production)
Joyce Stock (Controller)

Subsidiaries:

Hodgson Mill, Inc. (1)
1100 Stevens Ave, Effingham, IL 62401 (100%)
Tel.: (217) 347-0105
Web Site: http://www.hodgsonmill.com
Sales Range: $10-24.9 Million
Emp.: 45
Whole Grain Mill & Mix Plant
N.A.I.C.S.: 311211
Regina Shafer (Mgr-Acctg & Fin)
Carol M. Calkins (Project Coord)

Siemer Milling Company - Hopkinsville Facility (1)
315 Quintin Ct, Hopkinsville, KY 42240
Tel.: (270) 475-9990
Flour Mfr
N.A.I.C.S.: 311211

SIENNA CORPORATION INC.
475 Horizon Dr, Suwanee, GA 30024
Tel.: (770) 408-0470
Web Site:
    http://www.siennagroup.com
Year Founded: 1995
Sales Range: $10-24.9 Million
Emp.: 100
Contract Electronics Components Mfr
N.A.I.C.S.: 334419
Bhaskar Srinivasan (Pres)
Reggie Jarvis (Supvr-Receiving Dept)
Sasa Jovanovic (Mgr-Engrg)

Subsidiaries:

Sienna ECAD Technologies Pvt. Ltd. (1)
775/A 1st & 3rd Fl 100 Feet Ring Rd, BSK 3rd Stage, Bengaluru, 560085, India (100%)
Tel.: (91) 8030410700
Web Site: http://www.siennaecad.com
Emp.: 120
Other Specialized Design Services
N.A.I.C.S.: 541490
Savita Ganjigatti (VP-Design Engrg)
C. Sivakumar (Head-Hardware Design)

SIERRA ACURA OF ALHAMBRA
1700 W Main St, Alhambra, CA 91801-1826
Tel.: (626) 284-8533
Web Site: http://www.sierraacura.com
Year Founded: 1967
Sales Range: $10-24.9 Million
Emp.: 60
New Car Whslr
N.A.I.C.S.: 441110
Lathrop T. Hoffman (Pres)
Baldwin Lopez (Mgr-Parts)
Ed Netka (Gen Mgr)

SIERRA AUTOCARS INCORPORATED
1450 S Shamrock Ave, Monrovia, CA 91016
Tel.: (626) 359-8291
Web Site: http://www.sierraauto.com
Rev.: $50,700,000
Emp.: 140
Automobiles, New & Used
N.A.I.C.S.: 441110
Peter Hoffman (Chm & Pres)
Roger Weiss (Mgr-Parts)

SIERRA BAY CONTRACTORS INC.
4021 Port Chicago Hwy, Concord, CA 94520
Tel.: (925) 671-7711 CA
Sales Range: $25-49.9 Million
Emp.: 30
Operators of Industrial Buildings & Warehouses
N.A.I.C.S.: 236220
Bob Coburn (VP)
Albert D. Seeno Jr. (Pres)

SIERRA BLANCA MOTOR CO.
300 W Hwy 70, Ruidoso, NM 88345
Tel.: (575) 257-4081 NM

U.S. PRIVATE

Web Site:
    http://www.sierrablancamotors.com
Sales Range: $25-49.9 Million
Emp.: 40
New & Used Automobiles
N.A.I.C.S.: 441110
Johnny Durham (Pres)
Ted Durham (VP)
Kurt Soagle (Dir-Parts)

SIERRA BRAVO, CORPORATION
9555 James Ave S Ste 245, Bloomington, MN 55431
Tel.: (952) 948-1211 MN
Web Site: http://www.sierra-bravo.com
Year Founded: 2003
Sales Range: $1-9.9 Million
Emp.: 450
Software Development & Technical Consulting
N.A.I.C.S.: 541511
Michael Derheim (CEO)
Michael Schmidt (VP-Software Dev)
Mark Hurlburt (Dir-Mktg)

SIERRA BULLETS LLC
1400 W Henry St, Sedalia, MO 65301
Tel.: (660) 827-6300
Web Site:
    https://www.sierrabullets.com
Year Founded: 1947
Sales Range: $1-9.9 Million
Emp.: 100
Ammunition Mfr
N.A.I.C.S.: 332992
Carroll Pilant (Mgr-Media Rels)
Mark Walker (Mgr-New Product Dev)

Subsidiaries:

Barnes Bullets, LLC (1)
38 N Frontage Rd, Mona, UT 84645
Tel.: (435) 856-1000
Web Site: http://www.barnesbullets.com
Emp.: 145
Ammunition Mfr
N.A.I.C.S.: 332992

SIERRA CENTRAL CREDIT UNION
820 Plaza Way, Yuba City, CA 95991
Tel.: (800) 222-7228 CA
Web Site:
    http://www.sierracentral.com
Year Founded: 1955
Sales Range: $25-49.9 Million
Emp.: 225
Credit Union
N.A.I.C.S.: 522130
John Cassidy (CEO)
Bob Carman (Mgr-Dev)
Desiree Manes (Sr VP-Retail Banking)
David Kelsay (Sr VP-Lending)
Stephanie Dickinson (CFO & Sr VP-Fin)

SIERRA CHEMICAL CO
2302 Larkin Cir, Sparks, NV 89431
Tel.: (775) 358-0888
Web Site:
    http://www.sierrachemsales.com
Sales Range: $10-24.9 Million
Emp.: 75
Industrial Chemicals
N.A.I.C.S.: 424690
Ron Espalin (Mgr-Customer Svc)

SIERRA CLUB
2101 Webster St Ste 1300, Oakland, CA 94612
Tel.: (415) 977-5500
Web Site: https://www.sierraclub.org
Year Founded: 1892
Sales Range: $50-74.9 Million

Social Organization & Publisher
N.A.I.C.S.: 813410
Robin Mann *(Chm-Grp Political-Southeastern PA Grp)*
Ramon Cruz *(Pres)*
Ross Macfarlane *(VP-Conservation)*
Rita Harris *(Sec)*
Mike O'Brien *(Treas)*
Patrick Murphy *(VP-Chapters, Groups & Volunteers)*
Eva Hernandez-Simmons *(Mng Dir)*
Adrienne Frazier *(CFO)*
Salena Jegede *(Chief Advancement Officer)*
Maggie Kash *(Chief Comm Officer)*
Deepa Kunapuli *(Chief Digital Officer)*
Gary Reinecke *(COO-Interim)*

SIERRA COATING TECHNOLOGIES LLC
1820 Enterprise Dr, De Pere, WI 54115
Tel.: (920) 983-8000
Web Site: http://www.sierracoating.com
Year Founded: 1997
Sales Range: $1-9.9 Million
Emp.: 20
Specialty Coating & Converting
N.A.I.C.S.: 322220
Marsha Lefko *(Mgr-HR)*
Julie Rusch *(Supvr-Pur)*
Robert Shade Jr. *(Pres)*

SIERRA CREST EQUITIES LLC
4168 Douglas Blvd Ste 200, Granite Bay, CA 95746
Tel.: (916) 773-0700
Web Site: http://www.sierracrest.com
Year Founded: 1997
Sales Range: $10-24.9 Million
Emp.: 10
Provider of Real Estate Investment Services
N.A.I.C.S.: 237210

SIERRA FOREST PRODUCTS, INC.
9000 Rd 234, Terra Bella, CA 93270
Tel.: (559) 535-4893
Year Founded: 1968
Sales Range: $10-24.9 Million
Emp.: 110
Wood Product Distr
N.A.I.C.S.: 423990
Kent Duysen *(Pres)*
Janet Garza *(Office Mgr)*
Pam Taylor *(Dir-Traffic & Dist)*
Bob Styles *(Dir-Engrg)*
Judy Hamacher *(VP)*
Glenn Duysen *(Treas & VP)*
Don Lovelady *(Dir-Personnel)*
Mike Spohn *(CFO)*
Alice Williams *(Mgr)*
David Myer *(Mgr)*

SIERRA INDUSTRIES INC.
19900 144th Ave NE, Woodinville, WA 98072
Tel.: (425) 487-5200
Web Site: http://www.sierraind.com
Year Founded: 1997
Sales Range: $25-49.9 Million
Emp.: 150
Industrial Buildings & Warehouses
N.A.I.C.S.: 236210
Roger Collins *(CEO)*
Rick Basnaw *(Pres)*
Chris Kevil *(Dir-Safety)*
Guy Blanchard *(Mgr-Ops-Oregon)*
Jarrod Cooper *(Mgr-Svcs Dept)*
Nancy Adler *(Mgr-HR)*

Subsidiaries:

Sierra Construction Company, Inc. (1)
19900 144 Ave NE, Woodinville, WA 98072
Tel.: (425) 487-5200
Web Site: http://www.sierraconstruction.com
Sales Range: $10-24.9 Million
Emp.: 50
Provider of Industrial Buildings & Warehouses
N.A.I.C.S.: 236220
Nancy Adler *(Office Mgr)*

SIERRA INSTRUMENTS INC.
5 Harris Ct Bldg L, Monterey, CA 93940
Tel.: (831) 373-0200
Web Site: http://www.sierrainstruments.com
Sales Range: $10-24.9 Million
Emp.: 70
Controllers for Process Variables
N.A.I.C.S.: 334513
John G. Olin *(Founder, Owner & CEO)*
Scott Rouse *(Product Mgr)*
Maryadine Washington *(Mgr-Mktg)*
Matthew J. Olin *(Pres)*

SIERRA INTERNATIONAL GROUP, INC.
14 Wall St 22nd Fl, New York, NY 10005
Tel.: (212) 618-1274   DE
Oil & Gas Exploration Services
N.A.I.C.S.: 211120
Hans D. Dietmann *(Pres, CEO & Mng Dir)*

SIERRA LAND GROUP INC.
801 N Brand Blvd Ste 1010, Glendale, CA 91203
Tel.: (818) 247-3681
Sales Range: $10-24.9 Million
Emp.: 12
Subdividers & Developers
N.A.I.C.S.: 237210
James Geary *(CEO)*

SIERRA MAZDA
735 E Central, Monrovia, CA 91016
Tel.: (626) 303-0077
Web Site: http://www.sierramazda.com
Sales Range: $50-74.9 Million
Emp.: 50
New & Used Car Dealers
N.A.I.C.S.: 441110
Peter Hoffman *(Pres)*

SIERRA NEVADA BREWING CO.
1075 E 20th St, Chico, CA 95928
Tel.: (530) 893-3520
Web Site: http://www.sierranevada.com
Year Founded: 1980
Sales Range: $25-49.9 Million
Emp.: 900
Brewery
N.A.I.C.S.: 312120
Ken Grossman *(Founder)*
Joe Whitney *(Chief Comml Officer)*
John Warmerdam *(Mgr-Facilities)*
Lau Ackerman *(Supvr-Ag & Landscape)*
Martin Juliano *(KY & WV)*
Gentry Power *(Mgr-Customer Experience)*
Darren Wiese *(Mgr-Sls-NW)*
Betsy Jorgensen *(Coord-Event)*
Bill Allison *(Mgr-Tech)*
Bill Rauner *(Mgr-Bus Dev)*
Blair Matlock *(Area Mgr)*
Bob Ryan *(Mgr-Bus Dev)*
Rick Callow *(Project Mgr)*
Sharon Thompson *(Supvr-Transportation)*
Hunter Sasser *(Mgr-Mktg)*
Brian Sheffield *(Supvr-Filtration)*
Jeff White *(CEO)*

SIERRA NEVADA CORPORATION
444 Salomon Cir, Sparks, NV 89434
Tel.: (775) 331-0222
Web Site: http://www.sncorp.com
Year Founded: 1963
Sales Range: $50-74.9 Million
Emp.: 2,100
Defense Electronics Engineering, Integration & Mfr
N.A.I.C.S.: 336413
Fatih Ozmen *(Co-Owner & CEO)*
Eren Ozmen *(Co-Owner & Chm)*
Dave Klingler *(Exec VP-Electronic & Information Sys)*
Jon Burgoyne *(Exec VP-ISR, Aviation & Security)*
Tim Owings *(Exec VP-Integrated Mission Sys)*
Janet Kavandi *(Exec VP-Space Sys Grp)*
Frank Peloso *(Sr VP-HR)*
Jon Piatt *(Exec VP-ISR, Aviation & Security)*
Tim Keating *(Chief Strategy Officer-Sierra Space & Sr VP-Global Govt Ops-Sierra Space)*
Tom Vice *(CEO-Sierra Space)*
Wes Collier *(VP-Proliferated Sys)*

Subsidiaries:

3S Engineering (1)
8200 E 34th St N Ste 1207, Wichita, KS 67226
Tel.: (316) 260-2258
Web Site: http://www.3s-engineering.com
Aircraft Design, Engineering & Certification Services
N.A.I.C.S.: 488190
Lori Betts *(Mgr-Bus Ops)*
Chad Harms *(Mgr-Program)*

Orbital Technologies Corp. (1)
1212 Fourier Dr, Madison, WI 53717
Tel.: (608) 827-5000
Web Site: http://www.orbitec.com
Emp.: 70
Technology Research & Development
N.A.I.C.S.: 541715
Eric Rice *(Founder)*
Paul Zamprelli *(Dir-Bus Dev)*
Ron Teeter *(Founder)*
Thomas Crabb *(Founder)*

SpaceDev Inc. (1)
13855 Stowe Dr, Poway, CA 92064-6800
Tel.: (858) 375-2000
Web Site: http://www.spacedev.com
Sales Range: $25-49.9 Million
Emp.: 173
Space Technology Systems, Subsystems, Products & Services
N.A.I.C.S.: 927110
Mark N. Sirangelo *(Chm & CEO)*
James S. Voss *(VP-Engrg)*
Charlie Hodges *(VP & Bus Team Mgr-Electromechanical Sys)*

Straight Flight, Inc. (1)
13251 E Control Tower Rd, Englewood, CO 80112
Tel.: (303) 799-8906
Web Site: http://www.straightflight.com
Aircraft Maintenance & Repair Services
N.A.I.C.S.: 488190
Ernie Smith *(Gen Mgr)*
Rob Janson *(Mgr-Parts)*
Jose Jimenez *(Dir-Maintenance)*
Harry Grinton *(Mgr-Hangar)*

SIERRA PACIFIC CONSTRUCTORS
22212 Ventura Blvd, Woodland Hills, CA 91364
Tel.: (818) 225-6000
Web Site: http://www.sierrapacificconst.com
Year Founded: 1980
Sales Range: $25-49.9 Million
Emp.: 70
Commercial Building Construction
N.A.I.C.S.: 236220

Cary Gerhardt *(Principal)*
Jeff Kitka *(VP & Sr Project Mgr)*
Joel Sullada *(VP & Sr Project Mgr)*
Ken La Spada *(Principal)*
Mark Heyer *(VP-Construction)*
Gail Eglitis *(Controller)*

SIERRA PACIFIC INDUSTRIES
19794 Riverside Ave, Anderson, CA 96007-4908
Tel.: (530) 378-8000   CA
Web Site: http://www.spi-ind.com
Sales Range: $1-4.9 Billion
Emp.: 4,000
Lumber & Wood Products Mfr & Retailer
N.A.I.C.S.: 321113
A. A. Emmerson *(Pres)*
Mark Emmerson *(CFO)*
George Emmerson *(VP-Sls & Mktg)*
Steve Gaston *(CIO)*
Tom Takach *(VP-Ops-Windows Div)*

Subsidiaries:

Sierra Pacific Windows (1)
11605 Reading Rd, Red Bluff, CA 96080
Web Site: http://www.sierrapacificwindows.com
Wood Window & Door Mfr
N.A.I.C.S.: 321911
Karen O'Connell *(Mgr-Comml Sls)*

Subsidiary (Domestic):

Westview Products, Inc. (2)
1350 SE Shelton St, Dallas, OR 97338
Tel.: (503) 623-5174
Sunrooms & Skylights Mfr
N.A.I.C.S.: 321992

SIERRA PACIFIC TURF SUPPLY
510 Salmar Ave, Campbell, CA 95008
Tel.: (408) 374-4700
Web Site: http://www.sierrapacificturf.com
Sales Range: $10-24.9 Million
Emp.: 25
Fertilizer & Fertilizer Materials
N.A.I.C.S.: 424910
Donald Naumann *(Founder & Pres)*
Becky Naumann *(VP)*

SIERRA PROPERTIES
509 Guisando de Avila Ste 200, Tampa, FL 33613
Tel.: (813) 963-5856
Web Site: http://www.sierra-properties.com
Sales Range: $10-24.9 Million
Real Estate Development
N.A.I.C.S.: 237210
J. Robert Sierra *(Chm & CEO)*
John R. Sierra *(Pres)*
Thomas Gray *(CFO & VP)*
Brent Whitley *(VP-Land Dev)*

SIERRA SELECT DISTRIBUTORS
4320 Roseville Rd, North Highlands, CA 95660
Tel.: (916) 483-9295
Web Site: http://www.sierraselect.com
Rev.: $34,359,798
Emp.: 55
Appliance Sales
N.A.I.C.S.: 423620
Dave Bill *(Mgr-IT)*
Arnie Vierra *(Mgr-Electronics Div)*
Rebecca Frye *(Mgr-Gallery)*

SIERRA TELECOMMUNICATIONS GROUP
49150 Rd 426, Oakhurst, CA 93644-8702
Tel.: (559) 683-4611

SIERRA TELECOMMUNICATIONS GROUP

Sierra Telecommunications
Group—(Continued)
Web Site: http://www.sierratel.net
Year Founded: 1975
Sales Range: $25-49.9 Million
Emp.: 250
Telephone Communication Services
N.A.I.C.S.: 517121
Harry Baker *(Pres)*

Subsidiaries:

Sierra Cellular Inc. (1)
49150 Rd 426, Oakhurst, CA 93644-8702
Tel.: (559) 658-2355
Sales Range: $10-24.9 Million
Emp.: 30
Provider of Radio & Telephone Communication Services
N.A.I.C.S.: 517121

Sierra Telephone Co. Inc. (1)
49150 Rd 426, Oakhurst, CA 93644
Tel.: (559) 683-4611
Web Site: http://www.sierratel.com
Sales Range: $25-49.9 Million
Provider of Telephone Communication Services
N.A.I.C.S.: 517121
Harry Baker *(Pres)*

SIERRA TILE SUPPLY, INC.
4155 E Speedway Blvd, Tucson, AZ 85712
Tel.: (520) 327-7324
Web Site: http://www.sierratile.com
Year Founded: 1986
Sales Range: $10-24.9 Million
Emp.: 65
Tiles Mfr
N.A.I.C.S.: 449121
Frank N. Assaf Sr. *(Pres)*

SIERRA VENTURES
2884 Sand Hill Rd Ste 100, Menlo Park, CA 94025
Tel.: (650) 854-1000   CA
Web Site:
http://www.sierraventures.com
Year Founded: 1982
Sales Range: $1-9.9 Million
Emp.: 23
Privater Equity Firm
N.A.I.C.S.: 523999
Peter C. Wendell *(Mng Dir)*
Martha A. Clarke Adamson *(CFO)*
Yunbei Yu *(Mng Dir & Venture Partner)*
Mark Fernandes *(Mng Dir)*
Tim A. Guleri *(Mng Dir)*
David Schwab *(Mng Dir)*
Steven Williams *(Mng Dir)*
Aaron Tong *(Partner)*
Jim Doehrman *(Operating Partner)*
Ayden Ye *(Principal)*
Behrooz Abdi *(Pres)*
Martin Roesch *(Co-Founder)*
Nolan Wright *(Co-Founder & CTO)*
Scott Cook *(Co-Founder)*
Scott Yara *(Co-Founder)*
Sean Knapp *(Co-Founder)*
Wayne Dai *(Co-Founder & CEO)*

SIERRA VISTA CHILD AND FAMILY SERVICES
100 Poplar Ave, Modesto, CA 95354
Tel.: (209) 523-4573   CA
Web Site:
http://www.sierravistacares.org
Year Founded: 1972
Sales Range: $10-24.9 Million
Emp.: 374
Child & Family Services
N.A.I.C.S.: 624110
John Gilfillan *(Co-CFO)*
Jeff Anderson *(Dir-Clinical)*
Judy Kindle *(CEO)*
John Sniffen *(Chm)*

Roxanna Smith *(Treas)*
Michael Grover *(Sec)*
Jean Edwards *(Co-CFO)*

SIERRA W/O WIRES, INC.
2 Robinson Plz Ste 300, Pittsburgh, PA 15205
Tel.: (412) 722-0707
Web Site:
http://www.sierraexperts.com
Year Founded: 2006
Sales Range: $1-9.9 Million
Emp.: 26
It Consulting
N.A.I.C.S.: 541690
Bruce Freshwater *(Founder, CEO & CTO)*
Stacy Freshwater *(CFO & Dir-HR)*
Aaron Brown *(Mgr-Application Dev)*
Brad Worls *(Engr-Ops)*

SIERRAPINE LIMITED
1050 Melody Ln Ste 160, Roseville, CA 95678
Tel.: (916) 772-3422   CA
Web Site: http://www.sierrapine.com
Year Founded: 1991
Sales Range: $400-449.9 Million
Emp.: 1,300
Mfr of Wood Composite Panel Products
N.A.I.C.S.: 321219
Karla Schafer *(Acct Mgr)*
Steve Mulholland *(Mgr-Sls)*
Renee Guisewite *(Mgr-Safety)*

Subsidiaries:

SierraPine - Medite Division (1)
2685 N Pacific Hwy, Medford, OR 97501-0146   (100%)
Tel.: (541) 773-2522
Web Site: http://www.sierrapine.com
Rev.: $97,956,000
Emp.: 100
Medium Density Fiber Board
N.A.I.C.S.: 321219
Troy Olivadoti *(Dir-Tech)*
Ken Cole *(Gen Mgr)*

SierraPine Limited - McKillican American - American Hardwoods Division (1)
1401 E Hadley St, Phoenix, AZ 85034
Tel.: (602) 271-4608
Wood Products Mfr
N.A.I.C.S.: 333243

SIEVEKING INC.
4636 Waldo Indus Dr, High Ridge, MO 63049
Tel.: (636) 677-4355
Web Site:
http://www.sievekinginc.com
Rev.: $29,000,000
Emp.: 23
Petroleum Products
N.A.I.C.S.: 424720
Gene Offutt *(COO)*
Darren Sieveking *(Dir-PR)*
Donnie Ballard *(VP-Ops)*

SIEVERS EQUIPMENT CO.
406 Old Rte 66, Hamel, IL 62046
Tel.: (618) 633-2622
Web Site:
http://www.sieversequipment.com
Sales Range: $25-49.9 Million
Emp.: 60
Farm & Garden Machinery
N.A.I.C.S.: 423990
Walter Sievers *(Pres)*
Garry Jim *(Pres)*

SIFIVE, INC.
1875 S Grant St Ste 600, San Mateo, CA 94402
Tel.: (415) 673-2836   DE
Web Site: https://www.sifive.com

Emp.: 100
Semiconductor Mfr
N.A.I.C.S.: 334413
Patrick W. Little *(Chm, Pres & CEO)*
Adam Dolinko *(Chief Legal Officer & Sr VP-Corp Dev)*

Subsidiaries:

Open-Silicon, Inc (1)
490 N Mccarthy Blvd, Milpitas, CA 95035
Tel.: (408) 523-1200
Web Site: http://www.open-silicon.com
Rev.: $5,600,000
Emp.: 34
Radio, Television & Other Electronics Stores
N.A.I.C.S.: 449210
Naveed Sherwani *(Pres)*
Anam Haque *(VP-Silicon Engrg)*
Mark Wright *(Sr VP-Sls & Mktg)*
Gerry Benson *(VP-Sls & Mktg)*
Hans Bouwmeester *(VP-Engrg Ops)*

SIGAL CONSTRUCTION CORPORATION
2231 Chris Dr Ste 200, Arlington, VA 22202
Tel.: (703) 302-1500   MD
Web Site: http://www.sigal.com
Year Founded: 1977
Sales Range: $75-99.9 Million
Emp.: 100
Provider of Contracting & Construction Services
N.A.I.C.S.: 236220
Gerald R. Sigal *(Founder & Pres)*
Gerard D. Heiber *(Pres)*
Mark Abbott *(Dir-Project Dev)*

SIGGINS COMPANY INC.
512 E 12th Ave, Kansas City, MO 64116
Tel.: (816) 421-7670
Web Site: http://www.siggins.com
Sales Range: $10-24.9 Million
Emp.: 20
Commercial Equipment Merchant Whslr
N.A.I.C.S.: 423440
Sandra Higman *(CEO)*
Laura Brown *(Sec)*

SIGHTLIFE
1200 6th Ave Ste 300, Seattle, WA 98101
Tel.: (206) 682-8500   WA
Web Site: http://www.sightlife.org
Year Founded: 1969
Sales Range: $10-24.9 Million
Emp.: 166
Eye Care Service
N.A.I.C.S.: 622310
Bernie Iliakis *(COO)*
Rusty Kelly *(CMO)*
Eric Schoenecker *(VP-Donor Svcs)*
Monty Montoya *(Pres & CEO)*
James Smalley *(Vice Chm)*
Melody J. Summers *(Chm)*
Kush Parikh *(Treas)*

SIGHTLINE COMMERCIAL SOLUTIONS LLC
7008 Northland Dr, Minneapolis, MN 55428
Tel.: (877) 215-7245
Web Site:
https://www.sightlinecommercial.com
Emp.: 100
Agricultural Railing Fabricator & Ornamental Metals Design & Engineering Services
N.A.I.C.S.: 332323
Laura Rygielski *(CEO)*
Michael Mendoza *(Dir-Bus Dev)*
Chad Benning *(COO)*

Subsidiaries:

Trex Commercial Products, Inc. (1)
7008 Northland Dr Ste 150, Minneapolis, MN 55428
Web Site: http://www.trexcommercial.com
Commercial Railing System Mfr
N.A.I.C.S.: 332323

SIGHTLINE HEALTH
9150 Main Ste A3, Houston, TX 77025
Tel.: (713) 589-6879
Web Site:
http://www.sightlinehealth.com
Year Founded: 2005
Sales Range: $10-24.9 Million
Emp.: 54
Advanced Cancer Treatment Programs
N.A.I.C.S.: 622110
T. J. Farnsworth *(Chm & CEO)*
Mark Montondon *(Mgr-PR)*
Tsey-Haye Pasley *(Supvr-Revenue Cycle)*
Juanita Harbin *(Controller)*
Bryan Markworth *(Dir-Tech Ops)*

SIGLER COMPANIES, INC.
3100 S Riverside Dr, Ames, IA 50010
Tel.: (515) 232-6997
Web Site: http://www.sigler.com
Holding Company; Marketing, Printing & Embroidery Services
N.A.I.C.S.: 551112
Beth Cross *(Pres & CEO)*

Subsidiaries:

Alt Studios (1)
506 3rd St Ste 200, Des Moines, IA 50309
Tel.: (515) 697-7200
Web Site: http://www.altstudios.com
Sales Range: $1-9.9 Million
Emp.: 17
Advertising Services
N.A.I.C.S.: 541810
Dawn Kuehn-Linde *(Acct Mgr)*
Dean Jessick *(Pres)*
Nicole Torstenson *(Dir-Mktg)*

SIGMA CORPORATION
700 Goldman Dr, Cream Ridge, NJ 08514-2516
Tel.: (609) 758-0800   NJ
Web Site: http://www.sigmaco.com
Year Founded: 1985
Sales Range: $200-249.9 Million
Emp.: 300
Industrial Supplies
N.A.I.C.S.: 423830
Jim McGivern *(CEO)*
Larry Rybacki *(Pres)*

SIGMA DISTRIBUTING COMPANY INCORPORATED
901 S Sabin St, Wichita, KS 67209
Tel.: (316) 943-0090
Web Site: http://www.sigmadist.com
Sales Range: $1-9.9 Million
Emp.: 30
Automobile Glass
N.A.I.C.S.: 423120
Tim Donovan *(Pres)*
Doren Rhodes *(CFO)*

SIGMA GROUP, INC.
281 State Route 79, Morganville, NJ 07751
Tel.: (732) 649-6444
Web Site:
http://www.newsigmagroup.com
Year Founded: 2007
Sales Range: $1-9.9 Million
Emp.: 25
It Consulting
N.A.I.C.S.: 541690

SIGMA PARTNERS

2105 S Bascom Ave Ste 370, Campbell, CA 95008
Tel.: (650) 853-1700
Web Site:
　http://www.sigmapartners.com
Year Founded: 1984
Venture Capital Investment Firm
N.A.I.C.S.: 523999
Wade Woodson *(Mng Dir)*
Lawrence G. Finch *(Mng Dir)*
Fahri Diner *(Mng Dir)*
Clifford L. Haas *(Mng Dir)*
Robert E. Davoli *(Mng Dir-Boston)*
John Mandile *(Mng Dir-Boston)*
Paul Flanagan *(Mng Dir-Boston)*
Gardner C. Hendrie *(Partner-Boston)*

Subsidiaries:

Sigma Prime Ventures, LLC　　(1)
20 Custom House St Ste 830, Boston, MA 02110
Tel.: (617) 330-7872
Web Site: http://www.sigmaprime.com
Venture Capital Investment Firm
N.A.I.C.S.: 523999
Robert E. Davoli *(Mng Dir)*
Jere Doyle *(Mng Dir)*
Paul Flanagan *(Mng Dir)*
John Mandile *(Mng Dir)*
John G. Simon *(Mng Dir)*
Andrea Boyer *(CFO)*

SIGMA SUPPLY INC.
824 Mid America Blvd, Hot Springs, AR 71913
Tel.: (501) 760-1511
Web Site:
　http://www.sigmasupply.com
Year Founded: 1970
Sales Range: $25-49.9 Million
Emp.: 25
Packaging Materials
N.A.I.C.S.: 424990
Banks Hamby *(Branch Mgr-Hot Springs-AR)*
Dave Ezell *(Branch Mgr-Fort Smith)*
Daniel B. Hamby Jr. *(Pres)*

SIGMA SURVEILLANCE, INC.
4040 State Hwy 121 Ste 160, Carrollton, TX 75010
Tel.: (972) 392-3635　　TX
Web Site: http://www.sts360.com
Year Founded: 2000
Sales Range: $1-9.9 Million
Emp.: 40
Security Systems Integration Services
N.A.I.C.S.: 541512
Bobby Khullar *(Pres)*
Jessica Clark *(CTO & VP)*
Jose Garza *(Dir-IT)*

SIGMABLEYZER INVESTMENT GROUP LLC
123 N Post Oak Ln Ste 410, Houston, TX 77024
Tel.: (713) 621-3111
Web Site:
　http://www.sigmableyzer.com
Year Founded: 1994
Emp.: 100
Private Equity Investment Services
N.A.I.C.S.: 523999
Michael Bleyzer *(Co-Founder, Pres, CEO & Partner)*
Lev Bleyzer *(Partner & COO)*
Valery Dema *(Partner-New Bus Dev)*
Neal Sigda *(Partner)*
Diana Smachtina *(VP & Dir-Corp Governance)*
Yuriy Davidov *(VP-Internal Controls)*
Ryan O'Malley *(Dir-IR, Buyouts & IT)*
Vadim Bodaev *(Dir-Govt Affairs-Ukraine)*
Morgan Williams *(Dir-Govt Affairs)*
Leysa Gannochenko *(Gen Counsel)*
Radu Bugica *(Mgr-Romania)*

SIGMAWAYS INC.
39737 Paseo Padre Pkwy, Fremont, CA 94538
Web Site: http://www.sigmaways.net
Year Founded: 2006
Sales Range: $1-9.9 Million
Emp.: 55
It Consulting
N.A.I.C.S.: 541690
Prakash Sadasivam *(CEO)*

SIGMUND COHN CORP.
121 S Columbus Ave, Mount Vernon, NY 10553
Tel.: (914) 664-5300　　NY
Web Site:
　http://www.sigmundcohn.com
Year Founded: 1901
Sales Range: $75-99.9 Million
Emp.: 90
Precision Metals Mfr
N.A.I.C.S.: 331491
Thomas Cohn *(Pres)*

Subsidiaries:

Pyrofuse　　(1)
121 S Columbus Ave, Mount Vernon, NY 10553-1324　　**(100%)**
Tel.: (914) 664-5300
Sales Range: $25-49.9 Million
Emp.: 75
Produces Pyrotechnic Materials
N.A.I.C.S.: 423940

Subsidiary (Domestic):

Medwire　　(2)
121 S Columbus Ave, Mount Vernon, NY 10553-1324　　**(100%)**
Tel.: (914) 664-5300
Web Site: http://www.sigmundcohn.com
Sales Range: $25-49.9 Million
Produces Medical Electrode Materials
N.A.I.C.S.: 331491
Thomas Cohn *(Pres)*

SIGN OF THE BEEFCARVER INC.
36801 Woodward Ave No 310, Birmingham, MI 48009
Tel.: (248) 645-6444
Rev.: $13,900,000
Emp.: 640
Family Restaurant Chain
N.A.I.C.S.: 722511

SIGN PARROT, LLC
6400 E Columbus Dr, Tampa, FL 33619
Tel.: (813) 612-9200
Web Site: http://www.signparrot.com
Sales Range: $1-9.9 Million
Emp.: 12
Signs & Vehicle Wraps Mfr
N.A.I.C.S.: 339950
John Webber *(Founder)*

SIGN-A-RAMA
2828 Battleground Ave, Greensboro, NC 27408
Tel.: (336) 545-1124
Web Site: http://www.signsgso.com
Year Founded: 1991
Sales Range: $1-9.9 Million
Emp.: 60
Service Sign Center
N.A.I.C.S.: 339950

SIGNAL
656 W Randolph St Ste 4W, Chicago, IL 60661
Web Site: http://www.signalhq.com
Year Founded: 2006
Sales Range: $1-9.9 Million
Emp.: 14
Software Marketing Services
N.A.I.C.S.: 449210
Jeff Judge *(Co-Founder & CEO)*
Chris Watland *(Co-Founder & Pres)*

John Sharry *(Acct Exec)*
Tim Grace *(Product Dir)*
Julian Rockwood *(Product Mgr)*
Zach Rossiter *(Coord-Social Mktg)*
Ryan Pogue *(Sr Acct Exec)*

SIGNAL LAKE MANAGEMENT LLC
606 Post Rd E Ste 667, Westport, CT 06880-4549
Tel.: (203) 454-1133　　DE
Web Site: http://www.signallake.com
Year Founded: 1998
Privater Equity Firm
N.A.I.C.S.: 523999
Bart Stuck *(Mng Dir)*

Subsidiaries:

InPhase Technologies, Inc.　　(1)
2000 Pike Rd, Longmont, CO 80501
Tel.: (720) 494-7420
Web Site: http://www.inphase-technologies.com
Sales Range: $1-9.9 Million
Emp.: 110
Holographic Data Storage System Developer
N.A.I.C.S.: 334112

SIGNAL METAL INDUSTRIES INC.
850 E Pioneer Dr, Irving, TX 75061
Tel.: (972) 438-1022
Web Site:
　http://www.signalmetal.com
Sales Range: $10-24.9 Million
Emp.: 95
Metal Products Mfr
N.A.I.C.S.: 332312
Edward Dee *(VP)*
Robert K. Robinson II *(Pres)*

SIGNAL PEAK VENTURE PARTNERS, LLC
2755 E Cottonwood Pkwy Ste 520, Salt Lake City, UT 84121
Tel.: (801) 942-8999　　DE
Web Site:
　http://www.signalpeakvc.com
Year Founded: 2011
Emp.: 12
Venture Capital Firm
N.A.I.C.S.: 523999
Scott Petty *(Mng Dir)*
Ron Heinz *(Co-Founder, Partner & Mng Dir)*
R. Brandon Tidwell *(Co-Founder & Mng Dir)*
Lisa Dunlea *(Partner-Venture)*
Phil Williams *(VP)*
Travis Heath *(CFO)*
Ben Dahl *(Mng Dir)*

Subsidiaries:

Sparxent, Inc.　　(1)
3300 Irvine Ave Ste 261, Newport Beach, CA 92660
Tel.: (949) 222-2287
Computer System Design & Installation Services
N.A.I.C.S.: 541512

Subsidiary (Domestic):

NetworkD Corp.　　(2)
3300 Irvine Ave Ste 261, Newport Beach, CA 92660
Tel.: (949) 222-2287
Sales Range: $25-49.9 Million
Systems Life-Cycle Management, Endpoint Security Management, Service Desk & IT Process Improvement Solutions
N.A.I.C.S.: 541512

SIGNAL POINT MARKETING+DESIGN
444 N Bay St, Post Falls, ID 89854
Tel.: (208) 777-8942
Web Site: http://www.signalpt.com

Year Founded: 1997
Sales Range: Less than $1 Million
Emp.: 5
Advertising Agencies
N.A.I.C.S.: 541810
Thomas Latham *(Principal)*

SIGNALSCAPE, INC.
200 Regency Forest Dr Ste 310, Cary, NC 27518
Tel.: (919) 859-4565
Web Site:
　http://www.signalscape.com
Sales Range: $1-9.9 Million
Emp.: 52
Advanced Signal Processing Solutions for Government Agencies & Businesses
N.A.I.C.S.: 513210
Jhan Vannatta *(Pres & CEO)*
Michael Kacher *(VP-Engrg)*
Sam G. Burgiss *(Dir-Products)*

SIGNALTREE MARKETING & ADVERTISING
160 Emerald St Ste 201, Keene, NH 03431
Tel.: (603) 358-5100
Sales Range: $25-49.9 Million
Emp.: 3
Advertising Agencies
N.A.I.C.S.: 541810
David Lenox *(Owner & Pres)*
Jenny Duchesneau *(Art Dir)*
Tom Bergeron *(Art Dir)*

SIGNANT HEALTH MGT LLP
785 Arbor Way, Blue Bell, PA 19422
Tel.: (267) 422-1700
Web Site:
　https://www.signanthealth.com
Pharmaceuticals Product Mfr
N.A.I.C.S.: 325412

Subsidiaries:

DSG, Inc.　　(1)
325 Technology Dr, Malvern, PA 19355
Tel.: (484) 913-0210
Web Site: http://www.dsg-us.com
Rev.: $32,100,000
Emp.: 150
Software Developer & Electronic Management Services
N.A.I.C.S.: 541519
Anthony J. Varano Jr. *(Founder & CEO)*
Elias Tharakan *(CTO)*
John McMahon *(Pres-Sls & Mktg)*
Sushma Gaonkar *(Head-HR)*

SIGNAPAY
4100 W Royal Ln Ste 150, Irving, TX 75063
Tel.: (972) 894-1139
Web Site: http://www.signapay.com
Sales Range: $10-24.9 Million
Emp.: 40
Payment Processing Services
N.A.I.C.S.: 522320
John R. Martillo *(CEO)*
Barry Ervi *(VP-Ops)*

SIGNATURE BANK OF ARKANSAS
3878 N Crossover Rd Ste 20, Fayetteville, AR 72703
Tel.: (479) 684-3700
Web Site: http://www.sbofa.com
Year Founded: 1933
Sales Range: $10-24.9 Million
Emp.: 140
Commericial Banking
N.A.I.C.S.: 522110
Gary Head *(CEO)*
Clinton Ryan *(VP)*

SIGNATURE BREADS, INC.
100 Justin Dr, Chelsea, MA 02150

SIGNATURE BREADS, INC.

Signature Breads, Inc.—(Continued)
Tel.: (617) 884-9800
Web Site:
  http://www.signaturebreads.com
Year Founded: 1981
Sales Range: $25-49.9 Million
Emp.: 250
Bakery Products Mfr
N.A.I.C.S.: 311812
Kevin Monroe *(Dir-Bus Dev)*
David Hayes *(Mgr-Sls-Northeast)*
Helga McDonald *(Mgr-Sls-Mid Atlantic)*
Kevin Helman *(Dir-Supply Chain Ops)*
Tim Konicek *(Dir-Quality & R&D)*
Courtney Jo Fraser *(Mgr-Mktg)*
Dena Domey *(Dir-Fin)*
Fabiola Salgado *(Mgr-HR)*
Levon Kurkjian *(Pres)*

SIGNATURE BUSINESS SYSTEMS, INC.
145 Talmadge Rd Ste 14, Edison, NJ 08817
Tel.: (732) 476-5900
Web Site:
  http://www.sbsgroupusa.com
Year Founded: 1996
Sales Range: $1-9.9 Million
Emp.: 39
Computer System Design Services
N.A.I.C.S.: 541512
James Bowman *(Pres & CEO)*

SIGNATURE COMMUNICATIONS
417 N Eigth St 4th Fl Ste 401, Philadelphia, PA 19123-4226
Tel.: (215) 922-3022
Web Site:
  http://www.signatureteam.com
Sales Range: $10-24.9 Million
Emp.: 12
Advertising Agencies
N.A.I.C.S.: 541810
Tony DeMarco *(CEO & Dir-Creative)*
Amy Merola *(Dir-Art)*

SIGNATURE CONTRACTING SERVICES LLC
1510 Jelmak St, Grand Prairie, TX 75050
Tel.: (214) 596-1434
Web Site: http://www.signaturellc.org
Year Founded: 2006
Sales Range: $10-24.9 Million
Emp.: 191
Commercial Construction Services
N.A.I.C.S.: 236220
Marsha Newberry *(Co-Owner & Mng Partner)*
William Propes *(Co-Owner & Partner)*
Corey Tompkins *(Co-Owner & Partner)*

SIGNATURE FOODS, INC.
73-D Enterprise Dr, Pendergrass, GA 30567
Tel.: (404) 518-0427
Web Site:
  http://www.signaturefood.com
Year Founded: 2004
Sales Range: $10-24.9 Million
Emp.: 114
Private Label & House Branded Frozen Food Mfr & Distr
N.A.I.C.S.: 424420
Tom Southworth *(Co-Founder)*
Chuck McAtee *(Co-Founder)*

SIGNATURE GENOMIC LABORATORIES, LLC
2820 N Astor St, Spokane, WA 99202
Tel.: (509) 474-6840 **WA**
Web Site:
  http://www.signaturegenomics.com
Year Founded: 2003
Sales Range: $10-24.9 Million
Emp.: 90
Diagnosis & Treatment of Chromosome Abnormalities
N.A.I.C.S.: 621511
Lisa G. Shaffer *(Pres & CEO)*
Bassem A. Bejjani *(Chief Medical Officer)*

SIGNATURE HARDWARE
2700 Crescent Springs Pike, Erlanger, KY 41017
Tel.: (859) 647-7564
Web Site:
  http://www.signaturehardware.com
Year Founded: 1999
Sales Range: $50-74.9 Million
Emp.: 158
Online Retailer of Products for Bath, Kitchen & Home
N.A.I.C.S.: 332913
Mark Morse *(VP-Mktg)*
Howard Law *(VP-Sourcing)*
Sean Fisher *(Dir-eCommerce)*

SIGNATURE HEALTHCARE LLC
12201 Bluegrass Pkwy, Louisville, KY 40299-2361
Tel.: (561) 568-7800
Web Site:
  http://www.signaturehealthcare.com
Year Founded: 2007
Sales Range: $500-549.9 Million
Emp.: 20,000
Long-Term Care & Short-Term Post Acute Rehabilitative Services
N.A.I.C.S.: 623110
John Harrison *(CFO)*
George Burkley *(Chief Strategy Officer)*
Cheri Glass *(VP-Talent Acquisition & HR)*
Rudbekia Bach *(Mgr-Ops)*
Rich Tinsley *(Chief Dev Officer)*
Kathy Owens *(Chief Nursing Officer)*
Mark Wortley *(COO)*
Kim Long *(CEO-Facility)*
Cait Crenshaw *(Coord-Digital Mktg)*
Paige Wills *(Dir-Comm)*
Kayla Darbyshire *(Coord-Digital Media)*
Robert J. Haffey *(Pres & CEO)*
Roland Rapp *(Chm)*

Subsidiaries:
Signature HealthCARE at Tower Road (1)
26 Tower Rd, Marietta, GA 30060
Tel.: (770) 422-8913
Web Site: http://shcattowerroad.com
Sales Range: $25-49.9 Million
Emp.: 200
Nursing Care Facility
N.A.I.C.S.: 623110
Loretta Barnes *(CEO)*

Signature HealthCARE of Coshocton (1)
100 S Whitewoman St, Coshocton, OH 43812
Tel.: (740) 622-1220
Web Site: http://shcofcoshocton.com
Sales Range: $1-9.9 Million
Emp.: 110
Nursing Home Facility
N.A.I.C.S.: 623110
Christopher Lofton *(CEO)*

SIGNATURE OFFSET, INC.
4900 Pearl E Cir Ste 300 E, Boulder, CO 80301
Tel.: (303) 443-3800
Web Site:
  http://www.signatureoffset.com
Year Founded: 1970
Sales Range: $25-49.9 Million
Emp.: 30
Commercial Printing Services
N.A.I.C.S.: 323111
Tom Creager *(CFO)*
Pat Henson *(Supvr-Press Room)*
Buddy Luff *(Plant Mgr)*
Cary Juvonen *(CEO)*
Brian Moser *(Dir-Ops)*
Pat Muterspaugh *(Plant Mgr)*

SIGNATURE PARTNERS, LTD.
1400 Currency St, San Antonio, TX 78219
Tel.: (210) 967-8400
Web Site:
  http://www.signaturepartnersltd.com
Year Founded: 1999
Sales Range: $10-24.9 Million
Emp.: 125
Millwork Services
N.A.I.C.S.: 321918
Robert Adams *(Co-Founder)*
Terry Mason *(Co-Founder)*

SIGNATURE SKYLIGHTS, LLC.
101 Linel Dr, Mooresville, IN 46158
Tel.: (317) 831-5314
Web Site: http://www.linel.co
Year Founded: 1974
Sales Range: $10-24.9 Million
Emp.: 80
Sheet Metal Work Mfg
N.A.I.C.S.: 332322
Robert B. Sloan *(Pres)*

SIGNATURE THEATRES LLC
135 Hutton Ranch Rd Ste 103, Kalispell, MT 59901-2141
Tel.: (925) 884-4800
Sales Range: $10-24.9 Million
Emp.: 4
Theater Building, Ownership & Operation
N.A.I.C.S.: 531120
Paige Evans *(Dir-Artistic)*

SIGNATURE TRANSPORTATION GROUP, LLC
2300 Hamilton Rd, Arlington Heights, IL 60005
Web Site: http://www.signaturetg.com
Year Founded: 2014
Sales Range: $10-24.9 Million
Emp.: 27
Travel Agency Services
N.A.I.C.S.: 561510
Sal Milazzo *(CEO)*

SIGNCASTER CORPORATION
9240 Grand Ave S, Bloomington, MN 55420
Tel.: (952) 888-9507 **MN**
Web Site:
  http://www.johnsonplastics.com
Year Founded: 1970
Plastic Engraving & Sublimation Supplies Mfr
N.A.I.C.S.: 332812
Thomas Johnson *(Co-Founder & Pres)*
Margaret Johnson *(Co-Founder & VP)*

SIGNER BUICK-CADILLAC
39639 Balentine Dr, Newark, CA 94560-5377
Tel.: (510) 226-1234
Year Founded: 1980
Sales Range: $10-24.9 Million
Emp.: 35
Car Whslr
N.A.I.C.S.: 441110
Donald R. Signer *(Pres)*

SIGNET HEALTHCARE PARTNERS, LLC
Carnegie Hall Twr 152 W 57th St 59th Fl, New York, NY 10019
Tel.: (646) 840-4990 **DE**
Web Site:
  http://www.signethealthcarepartners.com
Year Founded: 1998
Venture Capital & Private Equity; Health Finance
N.A.I.C.S.: 551112
James Gale *(Founding Partner & Mng Dir)*
Ashley Friedman *(Mng Dir)*
Nikhil Puri *(Mng Dir)*

Subsidiaries:
Moberg Pharma North America LLC (1)
7 E Frederick Pl, Cedar Knolls, NJ 07927
Tel.: (973) 946-7550
Pharmaceutical Preparation Mfr
N.A.I.C.S.: 325412

SIGNET LLC
19 North High St, Akron, OH 44308
Tel.: (330) 762-9102
Web Site: http://www.signetllc.com
Investment Firm
N.A.I.C.S.: 523999
Anthony Manna *(Chm)*
Kenneth Krismanth *(CEO & Principal)*
Kevin Williams *(Pres-Chemical Specialties Div)*
Mark Corr *(Pres & COO)*

Subsidiaries:
Kingsport Book, Inc. (1)
121 Kingsport Press Rd, Church Hill, TN 37642
Tel.: (423) 357-3433
Web Site: http://www.kingsportbook.com
Printing
N.A.I.C.S.: 323120
Fred Cooper *(CEO)*

Roswell Bookbinding Corp. (1)
2614 N 29th Ave, Phoenix, AZ 85009-1611
Tel.: (602) 272-9338
Web Site:
  http://www.roswellbookbinding.com
Tradebinding & Related Work
N.A.I.C.S.: 323120
Iris Roswell *(Founder)*
Martha Reed *(Mgr-Specialty Div)*
Jim Menke *(Mgr-Production-Trade Div)*
Michael Roswell *(Pres)*
John Dingott *(Mgr-Specialty Production Div)*

SIGNET MARITIME CORP.
1300 Post Oak Blvd Ste 600, Houston, TX 77056
Tel.: (713) 840-1100
Web Site:
  http://www.signetmaritime.com
Sales Range: $50-74.9 Million
Emp.: 300
Marine Cargo Handling
N.A.I.C.S.: 488320
J. Barry Snyder *(Pres)*
Cliff Porter *(Gen Mgr-Traffic & Bus Dev)*
Steve Key *(Mgr-Acctg)*

SIGNIANT INC.
152 Middlesex Tpke, Burlington, MA 01803
Tel.: (781) 221-4000
Web Site: http://www.signiant.com
Year Founded: 2000
Sales Range: $10-24.9 Million
Emp.: 68
Software Development Services
N.A.I.C.S.: 541511
Rick Cramer *(Sr VP-Ops-Global)*
Margaret Craig *(CEO)*
Ian Hamilton *(CTO)*
Adam Feinzig *(CFO)*
Greg Hoskin *(Mng Dir)*

SIGNIFY HEALTH LLC
4055 Valley View Ln Ste 400, Dallas, TX 75244
Tel.: (855) 984-5121 DE
Web Site: http://www.signifyhealth.com
Year Founded: 2017
Health Services
N.A.I.C.S.: 621999
Bradford Kyle Armbrester (CEO)
Kyle Armbrester (CEO)
Susan Yun (Chief People Officer)
Erin Kelly (Chief Compliance Officer, Gen Counsel & Sr VP)
Sam Pettijohn (Chief Growth Officer)
Lynn Shepherd (VP-Corp & Enterprise Comm)

SIGNO INC.
2152 Allen Blvd #3, Middleton, WI 53562
Tel.: (608) 233-3731
Rev.: $11,500,000
Emp.: 23
Grocery Stores, Independent
N.A.I.C.S.: 445110

SIGNS.COM, INC.
1550 S Gladiola St, Salt Lake City, UT 84104
Tel.: (801) 441-3400
Web Site: http://www.signs.com
Year Founded: 2012
Custom Signs & Signage Printing Services
N.A.I.C.S.: 424110
Greg Sharpless (Editor-in-Chief)
Marty McGhie (CEO)
Nelson James (Pres)
Bret Combe (Mgr-Prepress)
Madison Page (Chief Experience Officer)
Marcel Cochegrus (Dir-Graphic Design)
Travis Baker (Mgr-Print Dept)
Bryan Halladay (Production Mgr)

SIGNTALK, LLC
1673 Ocean Ave, Brooklyn, NY 11230
Tel.: (718) 559-4812
Web Site: http://www.signtalk.org
Sales Range: $1-9.9 Million
Emp.: 9
Language Interpretation Services
N.A.I.C.S.: 541930
Joseph Geliebter (Exec Dir)

SIGNTECH ELECTRICAL ADVERTISING
4444 Federal Blvd, San Diego, CA 92102
Tel.: (619) 527-6100
Web Site: http://www.signtechsandiego.com
Year Founded: 1984
Sales Range: $25-49.9 Million
Emp.: 75
Mfr & Installer of Electrical Signs
N.A.I.C.S.: 339950
David Schauer (Pres)
Kym Larsen (Mgr-HR)
Melissa Saltsgaver (Acct Exec-Sls)
Brian Espano (Dir-Design)
Jim Withrow (Dir-Safety & Trng)
Kimra Schauer (CFO)
Rick Nachtsheim (Dir-Engrg)
Randi Zeigler (Dir-Project Mgmt)
Tony Rozoff (Dir-Project Mgmt)
Art Navarro (VP-Sls)

SIGNTRONIX
1445 W Sepulveda Blvd, Torrance, CA 90501
Tel.: (310) 534-7500
Web Site: http://www.signtronix.com
Sales Range: $25-49.9 Million
Emp.: 100
Mfr of Electric Signs
N.A.I.C.S.: 339950
Kozell Boren (Founder)
Thomas Johnson (Pres)

SIGNUM GROUP, LLC
1900 The Exchange SE Bldg 200, Atlanta, GA 30339
Tel.: (770) 514-8111
Web Site: http://www.signumgroup.com
Year Founded: 1994
Sales Range: $1-9.9 Million
Scientific & Technical Consulting Services
N.A.I.C.S.: 541690
Carl Albano (CFO)
Susan Hrib (Founder & CEO)
Pratik Goradia (VP-Ops)
Malek Hamdieh (VP-Solutions Delivery)
Kerry Flading (Dir-Resources)

SIGORA SOLAR, LLC
490 Westfield Rd, Charlottesville, VA 22901
Tel.: (540) 949-6553
Web Site: http://www.sigorasolar.com
Year Founded: 2011
Sales Range: $1-9.9 Million
Emp.: 35
Solar Energy Equipment Installation Services
N.A.I.C.S.: 238210
Andy Bogdan Bindea (Founder & Pres)
Jason Paul Robert Welch (Project Mgr)
Jeff Nicholson (Dir-Dev)
Jon Proffitt (Dir-Community Programs)
Matthew Brady Allen (Project Mgr)
Logan Landry (CEO)
Ed Murray (Regl Pres)

Subsidiaries:

Aztec Solar, Inc. (1)
11370 Trade Center Dr 3, Rancho Cordova, CA 95742
Tel.: (916) 853-2700
Web Site: http://www.aztecsolar.com
Sales Range: $1-9.9 Million
Emp.: 20
Plumbing, Heating & Air-Conditioning Contractors
N.A.I.C.S.: 238220
Ed Murray (CEO)
Jack Stanger (Mgr-Acct)
Nick Frkovich (Mgr-Bus Dev)

Environmental Solar Design, Inc. (1)
11237 Magnolia Blvd, North Hollywood, CA 91601
Tel.: (818) 762-6624
Web Site: http://www.environmentalsolardesign.com
Plastering, Drywall, And Insulation, Nsk
N.A.I.C.S.: 238310
Bob Ellis (Pres)

SIGOURNEY TRACTOR & IMPLEMENT
1407 S 200th Ave, Sigourney, IA 52591
Tel.: (641) 622-3838
Web Site: http://www.sigourneytractor.com
Rev.: $9,960,000
Emp.: 20
Farm & Garden Machinery & Equipment Merchant Whslr
N.A.I.C.S.: 423820
Dave Brewer (Mgr-Parts)
Adam Bouslog (Mgr-Sls)

Subsidiaries:

Sinclair Tractor (1)
3309 Lucas St, Muscatine, IA 52761
Tel.: (563) 264-3276
Web Site: http://www.sinclairtractor.com
Sales Range: $10-24.9 Million
Emp.: 105
Farm Implements Mfr
N.A.I.C.S.: 423820
Tom Poeltler (Pres)
Pat McCrabb (COO)

SIGULER GUFF & COMPANY, LP
825 3rd Ave 10th Fl, New York, NY 10022
Tel.: (212) 332-5100
Web Site: http://www.sigulerguff.com
Year Founded: 1995
Sales Range: $10-24.9 Million
Emp.: 100
Securities Brokerage
N.A.I.C.S.: 523150
Jun Isoda (Principal & Dir-Acctg)
Jarrad Krulick (Principal & Dir-Tax)
James Gereghty (Mng Dir)
Donald P. Spencer (Mng Dir)
Clifford Yonce (Mng Dir)
Cesar Collier (Mng Dir-Sao Paulo)
Anthony Corriggio (Mng Dir)
Jason Mundt (Mng Dir-Boston)
Jonathan Wilson (Mng Dir)
Aviral Jain (Principal-Mumbai)
Bradley Bennett (Mng Dir & Head-Distressed Res)
Anthony Cusano (Mng Dir)
Douglas Loveland (Mng Dir)
Nestor Weigand (Mng Dir-London)
Angela Yang (VP-Head Fund Investing-China)
James S. Corl (Mng Dir)
Remy Kawkabani (Mng Dir & Head-EMEA)
Drew J. Guff (Founder, Mng Dir & Partner)
Matthew Brewer (Mng Dir)
Sandip Kakar (Mng Dir)
Kenneth Burns (Mng Dir & Partner)
Mark Denomme (Mng Dir-Boston)
Ralph Jaeger (Mng Dir-Boston)
David Boal (Mng Dir-London)
Florian Lahnstein (Mng Dir-London)
Kyungoh Kook (Mng Dir-Seoul)
Christopher Barbier (Principal)
Sara Bowdoin (Principal)
Scott Halper (Principal)
Kathryn Kantarian (Principal & Dir-IR)
Ilomai Kurrik (Principal-Legal & Compliance)
Neil Fowler (Principal-Legal & Compliance)
Yuebing Lu (Vice Chm-China Funds)
Aron Khurana (VP)
Fernando Arakaki (VP)
Lindsay Ingram (VP)
Vicky Hu (VP)
Scott Berger (VP & Controller)
Jacqueline Battista (VP-IR)
Meghan Conaty (VP-IR)
Lindsay Kliegman (VP-Tax)
Roman Simonov (Mng Dir)

SIIBER LLC
2602 W State Blvd, Fort Wayne, IN 46808
Tel.: (888) 788-0922
Web Site: http://www.siiber.com
Year Founded: 2009
Sales Range: $1-9.9 Million
Emp.: 9
Multiple Consumer & B2B e-Commerce Site Operations
N.A.I.C.S.: 561499
Peter Roesner (Pres & CEO)

SIITE INTERACTIVE LLC
132 E 43rd St, New York, NY 10017-4019
Tel.: (212) 481-9070
Web Site: http://www.siite.com
Sales Range: $1-9.9 Million
Digital Marketing Solutions
N.A.I.C.S.: 541810
Alan Ruthazer (Founder)

SIKICH LLP
1415 W Diehl Rd Ste 400, Naperville, IL 60563
Tel.: (630) 566-8400
Web Site: http://www.sikich.com
Year Founded: 1982
Emp.: 100
Accounting Firm
N.A.I.C.S.: 541211
Ray Beste (Partner & Officer-Tech)
Anthony Cervini (Partner-Govt Svcs)
Christopher L. Geier (CEO & Mng Partner)
Robb Zerfass (Partner-Tax)
Richard Lynch (Partner-Not For Profit & Education)
Ryan Spohn (Partner-Advisory Svcs & CFO)

Subsidiaries:

Cotton & Co. (1)
635 Slaters Ln 4th Fl, Alexandria, VA 62049-1513
Tel.: (703) 836-6701
Web Site: http://www.mcdonough-whitlow.com
Other Accounting Services
N.A.I.C.S.: 541219
David Cotton (Partner)
Steven Koons (Mng Partner)
Gary Barton (Partner-Advisory Practice)
Paul Lionikis (Dir-Outreach)

Halt Buzas & Powell Ltd. (1)
1199 N Fairfax St 10th Fl, Alexandria, VA 22314
Tel.: (703) 836-1350
Web Site: http://www.cpas4you.com
Sales Range: $1-9.9 Million
Emp.: 40
Other Accounting Services
N.A.I.C.S.: 541219
Steven Halt (Partner-Tax)
Ralitza Kamenova (Mgr)
Andy Powell (Mng Partner)
Marco Fernandes Jr. (Partner)

Scanlan & Leo, Ltd. (1)
1110 Jorie Blvd, Oak Brook, IL 60523
Tel.: (630) 990-1110
Web Site: http://www.scanlanleo.com
Public Accounting Firm
N.A.I.C.S.: 541211
James M. Curry (Mgr-Tax)

SIKORSKY FINANCIAL CREDIT UNION
1000 Oronoque Ln, Stratford, CT 06614
Tel.: (203) 377-2252 CT
Web Site: http://www.sikorskycu.org
Year Founded: 1948
Sales Range: $25-49.9 Million
Emp.: 147
Financial Support Services
N.A.I.C.S.: 523999
Janet Gyger (CIO)
Carmen C. Alvarado (Dir-Internal Audit)
Francine Platko (Sr VP-Admin & Security)
James Harper (CFO & Sr VP-Fin)
Vincent Ciambriello Jr. (Sr VP-Retail Delivery & Strategic Plng)

SIL INTERNATIONAL
7500 W Camp Wisdom Rd, Dallas, TX 75236-5629
Tel.: (972) 708-7400
Web Site: http://www.sil.org
Year Founded: 1934
Sales Range: $100-124.9 Million
Language Development Services
N.A.I.C.S.: 541720

SIL INTERNATIONAL

SIL International—(Continued)
Yuko Takata (Dir-HR Dev & Mgmt)
George F. Shultz (Sec)
Alan Conner (Dir-Global Publ Svcs)
Bill Hampton (Dir-Intl Rels)
Steve Moitozo (Chief Innovation Dev Officer)
Jeremy Nordmoe (Dir-Language & Culture Archives)
Doyle L. Peterson (Dir-Strategic Initiatives)
J. Stephen Quakenbush (Dir-Global Scripture Access Svcs)
Gary F. Simons (Chief Res Officer)
Julie A. Green (Coord-Intl Anthropology)
Doug Higby (Coord-Intl Language Tech Use)
Catherine M. B. Young (Dir-Global Language & Dev Svcs)
Curtis Wong (Dir-Mainland Asia)
Daniel Butler (Dir-SIL Eurasia)
Dick Kroneman (Coord-Intel Translation)
Ellen M. Jackson (Coord-Intl Language & Culture Learning)
Greg Henderson (Coord-Intl Vernacular Media)
Ian Hollman (Dir-Anglo-Lusophone Africa)
James W. Roberts (Dir-Americas)
John W. Eppele (Coord-Intl Language Assessment)
Karsten van Riezen (Dir-South Asia)
Michael Cahill (Coord-Intl Orthography Sevcs)
Nelis van den Berg (Dir-Francophone Africa)
Peggy Griffin Dettmer (Coord-Intl Academic Trng Programs)
Terri Chapman (Dir-Global Sign Languages Team)
Don Buhler (CFO)
Keith Robinson (Chief HR Officer-Global)
Mark Robinson (Dir-West Asia Reg)
Liz Thomson (Vice Chm)
Karel Van Der Mast (Chm)

SILBERLINE MANUFACTURING CO., INC.
130 Lincoln Dr, Tamaqua, PA 18252-0420
Tel.: (570) 668-6050 PA
Web Site: http://www.silberline.com
Year Founded: 1945
Sales Range: $100-124.9 Million
Emp.: 700
Aluminum Pigments Mfr
N.A.I.C.S.: 325130

Subsidiaries:

Silberline Asia Pacific Pte. Ltd. (1)
50 Science Park Road Suite 04-01/02 The Kendall, Singapore Science Park II, Singapore, 117406, Singapore
Tel.: (65) 6411 0170
Metallic & Mineral Pigment Mfr
N.A.I.C.S.: 325180

Silberline Brasil Limitada (1)
Rua Dr Tirso Martins 100 CJ 701, Vila Mariana, Sao Paulo, 04120-050, Brazil
Tel.: (55) 11 3562 2780
Metallic & Mineral Pigment Whslr
N.A.I.C.S.: 424950

Silberline Limited (1)
Banbeath Road, Fife, Leven, KY8 5HD, United Kingdom
Tel.: (44) 1 333 424734
Web Site: http://www.silberline.com
Metallic & Mineral Pigment Mfr
N.A.I.C.S.: 325199
Lisa Scheller (Mng Dir)

Silberline Manufacturing Co., Inc. - Silberline Manufacturing Facility (1)

Panther Vly Industrial Park 201 Dock St, Lansford, PA 18232
Tel.: (570) 645-3161
Metallic & Mineral Pigment Mfr
N.A.I.C.S.: 325180

Silberline Pigment (Suzhou) Company Limited (1)
Room 1808 Building No 6 Building C Suzhou Center SIP Suzhou, Suzhou, 215021, Jiangsu, China
Tel.: (86) 512 67333150
Metallic & Mineral Pigment Mfr
N.A.I.C.S.: 325180

Silberline Pigmentos, SRL de CV (1)
Blvd Atlixcayotl Torre Bosques II 5320-200 Reserva Territorial A, San Andres Cholula, Puebla, 72810, Mexico
Tel.: (52) 222 2252774
Metallic & Mineral Pigment Whslr
N.A.I.C.S.: 424950

Silberline Specialty Effect Pigments India Private Limited (1)
Level 8 Vibgyor Towers C-62 Block G, Bandra Kurla Complex, 4000098, Mumbai, Maharashtra, India
Tel.: (91) 704 565 7723
Metallic & Mineral Pigment Whslr
N.A.I.C.S.: 424950

SILBRICO CORPORATION
6300 River Rd, Hodgkins, IL 60525-4257
Tel.: (708) 354-3350 IL
Web Site: http://www.silbrico.com
Year Founded: 1945
Sales Range: $100-124.9 Million
Emp.: 70
Perlite Products Mfr for Lightweight Insulation
N.A.I.C.S.: 327992
Adrian Garza (Dir-IT)
Ken Scheman (Mgr-Production)

SILCO OIL COMPANY
181 E 56th Ave Ste 600, Denver, CO 80216
Tel.: (303) 292-0500
Sales Range: $100-124.9 Million
Emp.: 15
Gasoline
N.A.I.C.S.: 424720
Sue Vanderberg (Pres)
Scott Paulson (VP)
David Adams (Mgr)
Richard Miller (Mgr)
Ulrike Neitzel (Controller)

SILEX HOLDINGS, INC.
4142 S Harvard Ave Ste D3, Tulsa, OK 74135
Tel.: (918) 551-7893 OK
Web Site: http://www.silexinteriors.com
Year Founded: 2006
Sales Range: $1-9.9 Million
Emp.: 14
Holding Company; Stone Countertops, Wood Cabinets & Plumbing Fixtures Retailer
N.A.I.C.S.: 551112
Jerry J. Niblett (CEO)
Michael La Lond (CFO)
Ron Brewer (COO)

Subsidiaries:

Silex Interiors 2, LLC (1)
4142 S Harvard Ave Ste D3, Tulsa, OK 74135 (100%)
Tel.: (918) 551-7893
Web Site: http://www.silexinteriors.com
Stone Countertops, Wood Cabinets & Plumbing Fixtures Retailer
N.A.I.C.S.: 444180

SILICA APPLIANCE & ELECTRONICS
498 N Rolling Meadows Dr, Fond Du Lac, WI 54937

Tel.: (920) 929-0126
Web Site: http://www.silicaappliance.com
Rev.: $14,500,000
Emp.: 70
Household Appliance Stores
N.A.I.C.S.: 449210
Dennis Schneider (Co-Owner)
Thomas Schneider (Co-Owner & Pres)

SILICON FOREST ELECTRONICS, INC.
6204 E 18th St, Vancouver, WA 98661
Tel.: (360) 694-2000
Web Site: http://www.siliconforestelectronics.com
Sales Range: $10-24.9 Million
Emp.: 95
Contract Electronic Components Mfr
N.A.I.C.S.: 334412
Frank Nichols (Pres & CEO)
Valerie Nichols (Mgr-HR)
Jay Schmidt (Exec VP & Gen Mgr)
Kris Leistritz (Mgr-Customer Focus Team)
Rodger Teed (Mgr)
Calvin Rabe (Mgr-Ops)
Kevin Syverson (CTO)
Tom Linnemann (CFO)
Beth Bottemiller (Controller)
Terri Polette (Mgr-QA & Training)

SILICON MOUNTAIN HOLDINGS, INC.
9101 Harlan St Unit 260, Westminster, CO 80031
Tel.: (303) 938-1155 CO
Web Site: http://www.smmdirect.com
Year Founded: 1983
Sales Range: $25-49.9 Million
Emp.: 31
Holding Company; Branded Computer Memory Products, Servers & Storage Devices Marketer & Whslr
N.A.I.C.S.: 551112
Rudolph A. Cates III (Pres & CEO)

Subsidiaries:

Silicon Mountain Memory, Inc. (1)
9101 Harlan St Unit 260, Westminster, CO 80031
Tel.: (303) 938-1155
Web Site: http://www.smmdirect.com
Sales Range: $10-24.9 Million
Builds & Sells Computer Memory Products
N.A.I.C.S.: 334118

SILICON POWER CORPORATION
275 Great Vly Pkwy Ste 130, Malvern, PA 19355-1308
Tel.: (610) 407-4700
Web Site: http://www.siliconpower.com
Rev.: $16,385,000
Emp.: 28
Semiconductor Devices Mfr
N.A.I.C.S.: 334413
Harshad Mehta (Chm, Pres & CEO)
Vic Temple (Sr VP-Tech)
Robert Berta (Dir-Bus Dev)
Ajay Kogta (Dir-Sls-India)
Benson Chen (VP)

SILICON QUEST INTERNATIONAL
4425 Fortran Dr, San Jose, CA 95134-2300
Tel.: (775) 356-2155
Web Site: http://www.siliconquest.com
Rev.: $10,000,000
Emp.: 47
Semiconductors

U.S. PRIVATE

N.A.I.C.S.: 423690
Robin Richardson (Chm)
Zbigniew Radzimski (Pres)

SILICON VALLEY CONCEPTS
1460 White Oaks Rd Ste F, Campbell, CA 95008
Tel.: (888) 215-9330
Web Site: http://www.sv-concepts.com
Year Founded: 2004
Sales Range: $1-9.9 Million
Emp.: 15
Retails High-End BMW Upgrades & Accessories
N.A.I.C.S.: 441330

SILICON VALLEY MICRO-ELECTRONICS INC.
2985 Kifer Rd, Santa Clara, CA 95051-0802
Tel.: (408) 844-7100 CA
Web Site: http://www.svmi.com
Year Founded: 1990
Sales Range: $75-99.9 Million
Emp.: 50
Silicon Wafer Distr
N.A.I.C.S.: 423690
Patrick Callinan (Owner & Pres)

SILICON VALLEY SHELVING & EQUIPMENT
2144 Bering Dr, San Jose, CA 95131
Tel.: (408) 451-9500
Web Site: http://www.svseq.com
Sales Range: $25-49.9 Million
Emp.: 40
Materials Handling Machinery
N.A.I.C.S.: 423830
Wally Smith (CFO)
Mark Dewhirst (Pres)

SILICONE SPECIALTIES, INC.
2367 Glenda Lane, Dallas, TX 75229
Tel.: (972) 243-0676 OK
Web Site: http://www.ssicm.com
Year Founded: 1969
Silicone Products Mfr
N.A.I.C.S.: 811191
Duane Barnette (Owner & CEO)
John Barnett (Exec VP-Sls)
Brandon Cathey (VP-Ops)
Mark Petrikat (Mgr-Speaciality Products)
Whayland Webb (Mgr-Warehouse)
Jason Daniel (Mgr-Store)

SILKE COMMUNICATIONS, INC
680 Tyler St, Eugene, OR 97402
Tel.: (541) 687-1611
Web Site: http://www.silkecom.com
Year Founded: 1964
Sales Range: $1-9.9 Million
Radio, Television & Other Electronics Stores
N.A.I.C.S.: 449210
James D. Silke (Pres)

SILKROAD TECHNOLOGY, INC.
20 W Kinzie St Ste 1420, Chicago, IL 60654
Tel.: (866) 329-3363
Web Site: http://www.silkroad.com
Year Founded: 2005
Human Resources Software Developer
N.A.I.C.S.: 513210
Steven R. Worth (Gen Counsel & Exec VP)
Merri Bonino Chandler (CFO)
Paul O'Donnell (Chief Revenue Officer)
Lilith Christiansen (Chief Strategy & Product Officer & Sr VP)
Robert Dvorak (Pres & CEO)

COMPANIES

SILKROUTE
950 Stephenson Hwy, Troy, MI 48083
Tel.: (248) 635-5379
Web Site:
http://www.silkrouteglobal.com
Year Founded: 2008
Sales Range: $10-24.9 Million
Emp.: 48
Software Development Services
N.A.I.C.S.: 541511
Amjad Hussain *(Founder & CEO)*
Richard Corps *(Mng Dir)*
Robert Skinner *(Pres-Global Svcs)*

SILL TERHAR MOTORS, INC
150 Alter St, Broomfield, CO 80020
Tel.: (303) 469-1801
Web Site: http://www.sthmotors.com
Year Founded: 1960
Rev.: $113,000,000
Emp.: 161
New & Used Automobiles Dealer
N.A.I.C.S.: 423110
John Terhar *(Pres)*
Lis Snow *(Office Mgr)*
Dave Snow *(Gen Mgr-Sls)*
Beau Smith *(VP)*

SILLERY AND PARTNERS
10 Signal Rd, Stamford, CT 06902
Tel.: (203) 961-9993
Web Site: http://www.sillery.com
Year Founded: 1987
Sales Range: $10-24.9 Million
Emp.: 7
N.A.I.C.S.: 541810
Harrel Silverstein *(Exec VP)*
Louis Delpizzo *(Creative Dir)*

Subsidiaries:

Sillery and Partners (1)
1121 N Mills Ave, Orlando, FL 32804
Tel.: (407) 739-8875
Sales Range: Less than $1 Million
Emp.: 2
N.A.I.C.S.: 541810
Russell Sillery Jr. *(Web Designer)*

Sillery and Partners (1)
Galleria Ballotta 6, 45100, Rovigo, Italy
Tel.: (39) 0425 21136
N.A.I.C.S.: 541810
Mirco Pasqualini *(Designer-Interactive & Alternative Media)*

SILLOH INDUSTRIES INC.
124 S Florida Ave Ste 202, Babson Park, FL 33827
Tel.: (863) 215-7022
Web Site: http://www.silloh.com
Holding Company
N.A.I.C.S.: 551112
Jack Hollis *(Chm & CEO)*

Subsidiaries:

Silloh Market Research LLC (1)
PO Box 427, Babson Park, FL 33827
Tel.: (863) 669-1155
Web Site: http://www.sillohresearch.com
Market Research Services
N.A.I.C.S.: 541910

SILLS CUMMIS & GROSS P.C.
1037 Raymond Blvd, Newark, NJ 07102-5400
Tel.: (973) 643-7000
Web Site:
http://www.sillscummis.com
Year Founded: 1971
Sales Range: $75-99.9 Million
Emp.: 302
Law firm
N.A.I.C.S.: 541110
Margaret F. Black *(Atty)*
R. Max Crane *(Mng Partner)*

Brian S. Coven *(Mng Partner-New York)*
Michael B. Goldsmith *(Mng Partner-New York)*

SILOGRAM LUBRICANTS CORP.
180 W 5th St, Bayonne, NJ 07002
Tel.: (718) 467-7665
Web Site:
http://www.silogramusa.com
Sales Range: $10-24.9 Million
Emp.: 35
Lubricant Mfr
N.A.I.C.S.: 324191
Oscar Margolis *(Pres)*
Michael Mattera *(VP-Ops)*

SILOSMASHERS, INC.
2677 Prosperity Ave Ste 100, Fairfax, VA 22031
Tel.: (703) 797-5600
Web Site:
http://www.silosmashers.com
Year Founded: 1992
Sales Range: $10-24.9 Million
Emp.: 89
Management & Consulting Services
N.A.I.C.S.: 541611
Angela Drummond *(Founder & CEO)*

SILSBEE FORD LINCOLN MERCURY, INC.
1211 Hwy 96 N, Silsbee, TX 77656
Tel.: (409) 385-3724
Web Site: http://www.gitcha1.com
Year Founded: 1997
Sales Range: $10-24.9 Million
Emp.: 40
New Car Whslr
N.A.I.C.S.: 441110
Robbie Biddy *(Mgr)*
Drew Donalson *(Gen Mgr)*
Byron Leger *(Mgr-Fixed Ops)*

SILTANEN & PARTNERS
353 Coral Cir, El Segundo, CA 90245
Tel.: (310) 321-5200 CA
Web Site:
http://www.siltanenpartners.com
Year Founded: 2000
Sales Range: $10-24.9 Million
Emp.: 30
Advetising Agency
N.A.I.C.S.: 541810
Rob Siltanen *(Chm & Chief Creative Officer)*
Joe Hemp *(Dir-Creative & Partner)*
Tim Murphy *(Pres)*
Ginger Christensen *(Acct Dir)*
Anna Amador *(Acct Dir)*
Jordan Lucoff *(Assoc Dir-Bus Dev)*

SILVANIA RESOURCES INC.
1820 N Corp Lks Blvd Ste 307, Weston, FL 33326
Tel.: (954) 385-4890
Web Site:
http://www.silvaniaresources.com
Rev.: $10,092,476
Emp.: 3
Paperboard & Products
N.A.I.C.S.: 424130
Nick Thilen *(Pres)*
Fred Thilen *(VP)*

SILVAS OIL CO. INC.
3217 E Lorena Ave, Fresno, CA 93725
Tel.: (559) 233-5171
Web Site: http://www.silvasoil.com
Sales Range: $50-74.9 Million
Emp.: 90
Petroleum Distr
N.A.I.C.S.: 424720

Tim Simonsgaard *(Mgr-Mktg)*
Jan Armas *(Mgr-Credit)*
John Silvas *(VP)*
Jim Smith *(Plant Mgr)*

SILVER CLOUD INNS & HOTELS
103 118th Ave SE Ste 300, Bellevue, WA 98005
Tel.: (425) 637-9800
Web Site: http://www.silvercloud.com
Sales Range: $250-299.9 Million
Emp.: 400
Hotel Services
N.A.I.C.S.: 721110
Roberta Weymouth *(VP)*
Brian Zuber *(COO)*
Cindy Fanning *(Dir-Ops)*
Goi Holliday *(Dir-Sls)*

SILVER DINER, INC.
12276 Rockville Pike, Rockville, MD 20852-1664
Tel.: (301) 770-0333 DE
Web Site: http://www.silverdiner.com
Year Founded: 1989
Sales Range: $25-49.9 Million
Emp.: 1,100
Restaurant Operators
N.A.I.C.S.: 722511
Mark Russell *(Dir-Dev)*
Anish Singh *(Asst Controller)*
Heather Leggett *(Mgr-Catering)*
Octavio Trujillo *(Supvr-Kitchen)*
Matilde Ott *(Dir-Mktg)*
Bob Giaimo *(Founder, Pres & CEO)*

SILVER EAGLE DISTRIBUTORS LP
4609 New Hwy 90 W, San Antonio, TX 78237
Tel.: (210) 225-3044 TX
Web Site: http://www.silvereagle.com
Year Founded: 1961
Sales Range: $25-49.9 Million
Emp.: 750
Beer & Ale Distr
N.A.I.C.S.: 424810
Roxann Neumann *(VP-Corp Affairs)*
John L. Nau III *(Pres & CEO)*
James P. Limbaugh II *(VP-Sls & Mktg)*

SILVER EAGLE DISTRIBUTORS LTD.
3201 NW 72nd St, Miami, FL 33122
Tel.: (305) 230-2337
Rev.: $28,100,000
Emp.: 55
Beer & Other Fermented Malt Liquors
N.A.I.C.S.: 424810
Nody Hill *(Controller)*

SILVER FALCON MINING, INC.
1001 3rd Ave W, Bradenton, FL 34205
Tel.: (941) 761-7819 DE
Web Site:
http://www.silverfalconmining.com
Year Founded: 2007
Sales Range: Less than $1 Million
Emp.: 3
Silver Mining Services
N.A.I.C.S.: 212220
Pierre Quilliam *(Chm & CEO)*
Thomas Charles Ridenour *(CFO)*
Christian Quilliam *(COO)*
Pascale Tutt *(VP-Corp Dev)*

SILVER FOAM DISTRIBUTING CO.
3200 Cooper St, Jackson, MI 49201
Tel.: (517) 788-8108
Sales Range: $25-49.9 Million
Emp.: 2

Provider of Beer & Other Fermented Malt Liquors
N.A.I.C.S.: 424810

SILVER HILL HOSPITAL, INC.
208 Valley Rd, New Canaan, CT 06840
Tel.: (203) 966-1380 CT
Web Site:
http://www.silverhillhospital.org
Year Founded: 1934
Sales Range: $25-49.9 Million
Emp.: 381
Health Care Srvices
N.A.I.C.S.: 622110
Ellen Alliger *(Dir-Health Info Mgmt)*
Lisa Benton *(Dir-Performance Improvement & Risk Mgmt)*
Rich Juliana *(Dir-HR)*
Michael D. Groat *(Chief Clinical Officer)*
Linda Autore *(Co-Chm)*
Lance Lundberg *(Co-Chm)*
Mark J. Russ *(Chief Medical Officer)*
Andrew Gerber *(Pres & Dir-Medical)*

SILVER HORSMAN INC.
320 College Ave Ste 300, Santa Rosa, CA 95401
Tel.: (707) 524-3500
Web Site: http://www.santarosa-homes.com
Rev.: $165,000,000
Emp.: 3
Real Estate Brokers & Agents
N.A.I.C.S.: 531210
James Obrian *(Pres)*

SILVER LAKE CENTER, INC.
905 Tower Rd, Bristol, PA 19007
Tel.: (215) 785-3201 FL
Web Site:
http://www.silverlakecenter.com
Sales Range: $10-24.9 Million
Nursing Care Services
N.A.I.C.S.: 623110
Chuck Pagenhart *(Owner)*
Howard Jaffe *(Mgr)*
Martin Mersky *(Dir-Medical)*

SILVER LAKE GROUP, LLC
2775 Sand Hill Rd Ste 100, Menlo Park, CA 94025
Tel.: (650) 233-8120 DE
Web Site: http://www.silverlake.com
Year Founded: 1999
Rev.: $83,000,000,000
Emp.: 448,000
Privater Equity Firm
N.A.I.C.S.: 523999
Egon Pierre Durban *(Co-CEO)*
Audra Paterna *(Mng Dir & Head-HR)*
James M. Whitehurst *(Mng Dir)*
Glenn H. Hutchins *(Co-Founder)*
Sharon Binger *(Mng Dir, Chief Compliance Officer & Head-Litigation)*
Mike Bingle *(Vice Chm)*
Christian Lucas *(Mng Dir)*
Karen M. King *(Chief Legal Officer & Mng Dir)*
Greg Mondre *(Co-CEO & Mng Partner)*

Subsidiaries:

Endeavor Group Holdings, Inc. (1)
9601 Wilshire Blvd 3rd Fl, Beverly Hills, CA 90210 (70.9%)
Tel.: (310) 285-9000
Web Site: https://www.endeavorco.com
Rev: $5,268,137,000
Assets: $12,503,842,000
Liabilities: $9,450,349,000
Net Worth: $3,053,493,000
Earnings: $129,133,000
Emp.: 11,000
Fiscal Year-end: 12/31/2022
Holding Company
N.A.I.C.S.: 551112

SILVER LAKE GROUP, LLC

U.S. PRIVATE

Silver Lake Group, LLC—(Continued)
Seth Krauss *(Chief Admin Officer)*
Ariel Z. Emanuel *(CEO)*
Patrick Whitesell *(Chm)*
Jason Lublin *(CFO)*
Patrick Whitesell *(Exec Chm & Co-CEO)*

Subsidiary (Domestic):

Academy Hotel, LLC (2)
8110 N Academy Blvd, Colorado Springs, CO 80920
Tel.: (719) 598-5770
Web Site: https://www.theacademyhotel.com
Hotel Services
N.A.I.C.S.: 721110

Endeavor Experiences, LLC (2)
7500 Airline Dr, Minneapolis, MN 55450
Tel.: (612) 266-1470
Web Site: https://www.endeavorair.com
Airline & Aviation Services
N.A.I.C.S.: 611512
Jim Graham *(CEO)*
Phillip Underwood *(COO)*
Bill Donohue *(VP)*
Russ Elander *(VP-Operations)*

Frieze Events Inc. (2)
247 Centre St 5th Fl, New York, NY 10013
Tel.: (212) 463-7488
Magazine Publisher
N.A.I.C.S.: 513120

Subsidiary (Non-US):

Frieze Events Limited (2)
1 Surrey Street, London, WC2R 2ND, United Kingdom
Tel.: (44) 2033726111
Web Site: https://www.frieze.com
Magazine Publisher
N.A.I.C.S.: 513120
Morenike Graham-Douglas *(Sr Mgr)*

Subsidiary (Domestic):

Harry Walker Agency Inc. (2)
355 Lexington Ave Fl 21, New York, NY 10017-6603
Tel.: (646) 227-4900
Web Site: http://www.harrywalker.com
Tobacco Mfr
N.A.I.C.S.: 312230
Don Walker *(Chm)*

Subsidiary (Non-US):

IMG Media Limited (2)
566 Chiswick High Rd Bldg 6, London, W4 5HR, United Kingdom
Tel.: (44) 2082335000
Sports Organizing Services
N.A.I.C.S.: 711310

Subsidiary (Domestic):

On Location Events, LLC (2)
3375 Piedmont Rd Ste 950, Atlanta, GA 30305
Web Site: https://onlocationexp.com
Live Event Services
N.A.I.C.S.: 711310

Subsidiary (Non-US):

OpenBet Technologies Ltd. (2)
Chiswick Park Building 9 566 Chiswick High Road, London, W4 5XT, United Kingdom
Tel.: (44) 2087421600
Web Site: http://www.openbet.com
Front-End & Back-Office Software Developer
N.A.I.C.S.: 513210
Jordan E. Levin *(CEO)*
Thor Vass *(Mgr-Dev)*

Subsidiary (Domestic):

OpenBet Retail Ltd (3)
Building 6 Chiswick Park 566 Chiswick High Road, Broadford Park, London, W4 5HR, United Kingdom (100%)
Tel.: (44) 1483293900
Web Site: http://www.openbet.com
End-to-End Technology to High Street Bookmakers Solutions
N.A.I.C.S.: 513210
Jonathon Rhodes *(Dir-Ops)*

Subsidiary (Domestic):

Professional Bull Riders, LLC (2)
101 W Riverwalk, Pueblo, CO 81003
Tel.: (719) 242-2800
Web Site: https://pbr.com
Bull Riding Event Services
N.A.I.C.S.: 713990
Ty Murray *(Co-Founder)*

TKO Group Holdings, Inc. (2)
200 5th Ave 7th Fl, New York, NY 10010 (51%)
Tel.: (646) 558-8333
Web Site: https://tkogrp.com
Rev.: $1,674,968,000
Assets: $12,690,739,000
Liabilities: $3,851,787,000
Net Worth: $8,838,952,000
Earnings: ($35,227,000)
Emp.: 1,250
Fiscal Year-end: 12/31/2023
Holding Company
N.A.I.C.S.: 551112
Seth Krauss *(Chief Admin Officer & Chief Legal Officer)*
Mark Shapiro *(Pres & COO)*
Ariel Z. Emanuel *(Exec Chm & CEO)*
Andrew Schleimer *(CFO)*

Subsidiary (Domestic):

World Wrestling Entertainment, LLC (3)
707 Washington Blvd, Stamford, CT 06901
Tel.: (203) 352-8600
Web Site: https://www.wwe.com
Rev.: $1,291,523,000
Assets: $1,355,569,000
Liabilities: $838,318,000
Net Worth: $517,251,000
Earnings: $195,588,000
Emp.: 890
Fiscal Year-end: 12/31/2022
Holding Company; Sports Media & Entertainment Services
N.A.I.C.S.: 551112
Nick Khan *(CEO)*
Paul Levesque *(Chief Content Officer & Exec VP-Global Talent Strategy & Dev)*
Karen M. Mullane *(Chief Acctg Officer & Controller)*
Michelle D. Wilson *(Executives)*

Subsidiary (Domestic):

CC Reality LLC (4)
900 Bitner Rd, Park City, UT 84098
Tel.: (435) 655-6200
Web Site: http://www.ccparkcity.com
Real Estate Property Management Services
N.A.I.C.S.: 531312
Kathie Savage *(Partner & Mgr-Certified Property)*

Subsidiary (Non-US):

WWE Canada, Inc. (4)
2 Lansing Square Ste 1003, Willowdale, M2J 4P8, ON, Canada (100%)
Tel.: (416) 497-8338
Web Site: http://www.wwe.com
Sales Range: $100-124.9 Million
Wrestling & Entertainment Services
N.A.I.C.S.: 711320

WWE Germany GmbH (4)
Lothstrasse 19, 80797, Munich, Germany
Tel.: (49) 89716779818
Web Site: http://de.wwe.com
Emp.: 8
Sport Entertainment Services
N.A.I.C.S.: 711320

WWE Middle East FZ-LLC (4)
1501A Business Central Towers Dubai Media City, Dubai, United Arab Emirates
Tel.: (971) 45504300
Sports Entertainment Services
N.A.I.C.S.: 512110

Subsidiary (Domestic):

WWE Studios, Inc. (4)
12424 Wilshire Blvd Ste 1400, Los Angeles, CA 90025
Tel.: (310) 481-9370
Web Site: http://www.corporate.wwe.com
Motion Picture Production Services
N.A.I.C.S.: 512110

Subsidiary (Non-US):

World Wrestling Entertainment (International) Limited (4)
5 Jubilee Place, London, SW3 3TD, United Kingdom
Tel.: (44) 2073491740
Web Site: http://www.wwe.com
Sales Range: $10-24.9 Million
Emp.: 12
Television Program Production Services
N.A.I.C.S.: 512120

Subsidiary (Domestic):

Zuffa, LLC (3)
2960 W Sahara Ave Ste 100, Las Vegas, NV 89102
Tel.: (702) 221-4780
Web Site: http://www.ufc.com
Fighting Sports Organization
N.A.I.C.S.: 711219
Dana White *(Pres)*
Lawrence Epstein *(COO)*
Peter Stringer *(VP-Global Brands-Social Media)*
Lorenzo J. Fertitta *(Chm)*

Subsidiary (Non-US):

William Morris Endeavor Entertainment (U.K.) Limited (2)
100 New Oxford St, London, WC1A 1HB, United Kingdom
Tel.: (44) 2089298400
Media Agency Services
N.A.I.C.S.: 541840

First Advantage Corporation (1)
1 Concourse Pkwy NE Ste 200, Atlanta, GA 30328 (61.2%)
Web Site: https://fadv.com
Emp.: 5,000
Holding Company; Human Capital Screening, Verification, Safety & Compliance Technology Solutions
N.A.I.C.S.: 551112

Subsidiary (Domestic):

First Advantage Enterprise Screening Corporation (2)
100 Carillon Pkwy, Saint Petersburg, FL 33716
Tel.: (727) 214-3411
Web Site: http://www.fadv.com
Sales Range: $500-549.9 Million
Emp.: 3,000
Background Screening, Occupational Health, Employee Assessment, Recruitment & Business Tax Consulting Services
N.A.I.C.S.: 561499
Bret Jardine *(Gen Counsel & Exec VP)*
Chris Kilpatrick *(Sr VP-Global Acct Mgmt)*
Mark Parise *(CEO)*
Michael Pilnick *(Exec VP & Head-HR)*
Navin Chugh *(Exec VP-Strategic Global Sls)*
Stefano Malnati *(Chief Innovation & Tech Officer)*
Ron Douglas *(Exec VP-Global Ops)*
Terry Dwyer *(Mng Dir & Exec VP-Tax & Transportation)*
David L. Gamsey *(CFO & Exec VP)*
Nick Grecco *(Sr VP-Tech Ops)*
Joe Jaeger *(Chief Revenue Officer)*
Suzanne Mastrofski *(Exec VP-Global Clients & Strategy)*
Purushotam Savlani *(Mng Dir & Sr VP-India)*
Erik Schmit *(Mng Dir & Exec VP-Asia Pacific)*

Subsidiary (Non-US):

First Advantage Australasia Pty. Ltd. (3)
Level 1 213 Miller Street, Sydney, 2060, NSW, Australia (100%)
Tel.: (61) 290174300
Web Site: http://www.fadv.com.au
Sales Range: $75-99.9 Million
Background Screening & Risk Mitigation Services
N.A.I.C.S.: 519290
Matthew Glasner *(Mng Dir-South Asia Pacific)*
Jay Wang *(Mng Dir-North Asia Pacific)*

First Advantage Canada Inc. (3)
59 Adelaide Street E 3rd Fl Suite 300, Toronto, M5C 1K6, ON, Canada (100%)
Tel.: (416) 961-1611
Web Site: http://www.fadv.ca
Sales Range: $10-24.9 Million
Emp.: 50
Background Screening Services
N.A.I.C.S.: 561499

First Advantage Europe Ltd. (3)
2 St Johns Street, Colchester, CO2 7AA, United Kingdom (100%)
Tel.: (44) 8448243444
Web Site: http://www.fadveuropescreening.com
Sales Range: $75-99.9 Million
Emp.: 200
Employment Background Screening Services
N.A.I.C.S.: 561611
Traci Canning *(Mgr)*

Unit (Domestic):

First Advantage Investigative Services (3)
38 W 21st St 7th Fl, New York, NY 10010
Tel.: (212) 620-9700
Web Site: http://www.fadv.com
Sales Range: $10-24.9 Million
Emp.: 50
Corporate Investigative Services
N.A.I.C.S.: 561611

Subsidiary (Non-US):

First Advantage Japan K.K. (3)
ASK Building 3F 1-24-4 Ebisu, Tokyo, 150-0013, Japan (100%)
Tel.: (81) 354497373
Web Site: http://www.fadv-japan.com
Sales Range: $10-24.9 Million
Emp.: 25
Employment Screening
N.A.I.C.S.: 561499
Minako Suda *(VP-Ops)*

Subsidiary (Domestic):

First Advantage Occupational Health Services Corp. (3)
7300 Calhoun Pl, Rockville, MD 20817-7813
Tel.: (301) 571-0067
Web Site: http://www.fadv.com
Sales Range: $50-74.9 Million
Drug Screening Services
N.A.I.C.S.: 561499

Subsidiary (Non-US):

First Advantage Pte. Ltd. (3)
51 Goldhill Plaza Unit 16-05-06, Singapore, 308900, Singapore
Tel.: (65) 65343262
Sales Range: $10-24.9 Million
Emp.: 16
Background Screening & Risk Mitigation Services
N.A.I.C.S.: 519290
Vijay Vaswani *(Grp CFO-Asia Pacific)*
Matthew Glanser *(Mng Dir-Asia Pacific)*

First Advantage Pvt. Ltd. (3)
Interface 7 1st Floor Link Road, Malad, Mumbai, 400 064, India
Tel.: (91) 2240697000
Web Site: http://www.fadvasia.com
Sales Range: $75-99.9 Million
Emp.: 500
Background Screening & Risk Mitigation Services
N.A.I.C.S.: 519290
Purushotam Savlani *(Sr VP)*
Vivek Khanna *(Mng Dir)*

Unit (Domestic):

First Advantage Recruiting Solutions (3)
7999 Knue Rd Ste 400 Bldg 15, Indianapolis, IN 46250
Tel.: (317) 813-0500
Sales Range: $10-24.9 Million
Emp.: 50
Commercial Recruiting Services
N.A.I.C.S.: 541612

COMPANIES

SILVER LAKE GROUP, LLC

Angela Jennings *(Coord-Recruiting)*
Crystal Stewart *(Mgr-Client Rels)*
Janice Bhavnani *(Sr Mgr-Client Rels)*

Subsidiary (Domestic):

First Advantage Tax Consulting Services, LLC (3)
9800 Crosspoint Blvd Ste 300, Indianapolis, IN 46256 **(100%)**
Tel.: (317) 844-4242
Web Site: http://www.fadv.com
Sales Range: $75-99.9 Million
Emp.: 200
Tax Consulting Services
N.A.I.C.S.: 541618

Qualtrics International Inc. (1)
333 W River Park Dr, Provo, UT 84604
Tel.: (385) 203-4999
Web Site: https://www.qualtrics.com
Rev.: $1,458,628,000
Assets: $3,395,851,000
Liabilities: $1,491,831,000
Net Worth: $1,904,020,000
Earnings: ($1,061,478,000)
Emp.: 5,600
Fiscal Year-end: 12/31/2022
Enterprise Data Collection & Analysis Solutions
N.A.I.C.S.: 513210
Brigid Archibald *(Mng Dir-Asia Pacific & Japan)*
Zig Serafin *(CEO)*
De'Porres Brightful *(Pres-Worldwide Field Ops)*
Brian Stucki *(Pres & COO)*
Stephanie Barton *(Mng Dir)*
Abhi Ingle *(COO & Chief Bus Officer)*
Kylan Lundeen *(CMO & Chief Brand Officer)*
Bill McMurray *(Chief Revenue Officer)*

Subsidiary (Domestic):

Clarabridge, Inc. (2)
11400 Commerce Park Dr Ste 500, Reston, VA 20191
Tel.: (571) 299-1800
Web Site: http://www.clarabridge.com
Test Analytics Software Developer
N.A.I.C.S.: 334610
Sid Banerjee *(Founder, Vice Chm & Chief Strategy Officer)*
Bas Brukx *(CFO)*
Karl Knoll *(Gen Counsel)*
Ram Ramachandran *(CTO)*
Ines Thornburg *(Sr VP-Global Pro Svcs)*
Mark Bishof *(CEO)*
Sal Uslugil *(Chief Revenue Officer)*
Fabrice Martin *(Chief Product Officer)*

Subsidiary (Domestic):

Market Metrix LLC (3)
125 E Sir Francis Drake Blvd Ste 300, Larkspur, CA 94939
Tel.: (415) 721-1300
Web Site: http://www.marketmetrix.com
Emp.: 35
Marketing Research & Public Opinion Polling
N.A.I.C.S.: 541910
Robert Honeycutt *(CEO)*
Sid Banerje *(CEO)*

Silver Lake Asia Limited (1)
33/F Two IFC 8 Finance Street, Central, China (Hong Kong)
Tel.: (852) 3664 3300
Web Site: http://www.silverlake.com
Emp.: 20
Privater Equity Firm
N.A.I.C.S.: 523999
Kenneth Y. Hao *(Mng Partner)*
Germaine Sze *(Sr VP-Mktg & IR)*
Jacqueline Petts *(Head-Legal-Asia)*
Serene Nah *(Principal-Value Creation)*
Yingqi Li *(Principal-Silver Lake Partners)*
Zheng Wang *(Mng Dir-Silver Lake Partners)*

Silver Lake Europe, LLP (1)
Broadbent House 65 Grosvenor Street, London, W1K 3JH, United Kingdom
Tel.: (44) 20 3205 8400
Web Site: http://www.silverlake.com
Emp.: 25
Privater Equity Firm
N.A.I.C.S.: 523999

Simon Patterson *(Mng Dir-Silver Lake Partners)*
Simon Patterson *(Mng Dir-Silver Lake Partners)*

Silver Lake Kraftwerk Management Company, LLC (1)
2020 Pioneer Ct, San Mateo, CA 94403
Tel.: (650) 234-2570
Web Site: http://www.silverlake.com
Emp.: 20
Energy & Resource Private Equity Firm
N.A.I.C.S.: 523999
Adam Grosser *(Mng Dir & Grp Head)*
Raj Atluru *(Mng Dir)*
Bryce Lee *(Mng Dir)*
Josh Raffaelli *(Mng Dir)*
Arif Lakhani *(Principal)*
Sebastian Neelamkavil *(Principal)*

Silver Lake Management Company Sumeru, LLC (1)
2775 Sand Hill Rd Ste 100, Menlo Park, CA 94025
Tel.: (650) 233-8120
Web Site: http://www.silverlake.com
Middle Market Technology Private Equity Firm
N.A.I.C.S.: 523999
Ajay B. Shah *(Founder & Mng Partner)*
Paul Mercadante *(Mng Dir)*
Kyle Ryland *(Mng Dir)*
Hollie Moore Haynes *(Mng Dir)*
Jason Babcoke *(Principal)*
Sanjeet Mitra *(Principal)*
Randy Randleman *(Dir-Investments)*
John D. Brennan *(Mng Dir)*

Silver Lake Management, LLC (1)
2775 Sand Hill Rd Ste 100, Menlo Park, CA 94025
Tel.: (650) 233-8120
Web Site: http://www.silverlake.com
Large Cap Technology Private Equity Firm
N.A.I.C.S.: 523999
Egon Pierre Durban *(CEO, Mng Partner & Mng Dir)*
Stephen Eric Robert Evans *(Mng Dir)*
Kenneth Y. Hao *(Bd of Dirs, Executives)*
Michael J. Bingle *(Vice Chm)*
Jonathan Durham *(Mng Dir)*
Tezira Nabongo *(Partner-Talent)*
Jason Paige *(Sr VP-IT)*
Jason White *(Mng Dir)*
Audra Paterna *(Mng Dir & Head-Global HR)*
Frank Walters *(Dir-Capital Markets)*
Joerg Adams *(Mng Dir)*
Christian Avolio *(Principal)*
Brandon Barton *(Principal)*
Matthew Benson *(Mng Dir & Head-Comm)*
Carrie Braddock *(Mng Dir & Head-ESG & Impact)*
Thomas Conneely *(VP-Ops-Waterman)*
Mary Conrad *(Principal-Capital Markets)*
Brian Crews *(Mng Dir-Waterman)*
Shad Estreich *(Sr VP-Compliance)*
Daniel Gordish *(Dir-Portfolio Monitoring)*
Mark Gillett *(Mng Dir & Head-Value Creation)*
Dan Hoevel *(Sr VP-Fundraising & IR)*
Matt Kane *(VP-Comml Dev & Partnerships)*
Arian Khansari *(Principal)*
Jamie Li *(Principal)*
Bryce Lee *(Mng Dir & Head-Bus Dev & Co-Head-Fundraising & IR)*
Andrew Malcolm *(Operating Partner)*
Arun Manikundalam *(Principal)*
Courtney McLaughlin *(VP-Fundraising & IR)*
Lee E. Wittlinger *(Mng Dir)*

Joint Venture (Domestic):

A Place For Mom, Inc. (2)
701 5th Ave Ste 3200, Seattle, WA 98104
Tel.: (206) 285-4666
Web Site: http://www.aplaceformom.com
Sales Range: $50-74.9 Million
Senior Care Referral Services
N.A.I.C.S.: 624190
Lawrence Kutscher *(CEO)*
Dan Willis *(Sr VP-Partner Svcs)*
Camille Cleveland *(Gen Counsel & Sr VP)*
Ted Ellis *(CTO)*
Allen Hsieh *(CFO)*
Jennifer Mellet *(Chief Sls Officer)*
Eric Seifert *(COO)*
Scott Booker *(Pres & Chief Product Officer)*
Lawrence Kutscher *(CEO)*

Avaya Holdings Corp. (2)

350 Mt Kemble Ave, Morristown, NJ 07960
Tel.: (908) 953-6000
Web Site: https://www.avaya.com
Rev.: $2,973,000,000
Assets: $5,985,000,000
Liabilities: $5,593,000,000
Net Worth: $392,000,000
Earnings: ($13,000,000)
Emp.: 8,063
Fiscal Year-end: 09/30/2021
Holding Company; Business Communications Systems Mfr
N.A.I.C.S.: 551112
Galib Karim *(VP-Caribbean & Latin America Sls)*
Shefali Shah *(Chief Admin Officer, Gen Counsel & Exec VP)*
Fred Hayes *(Sr VP-Global Bus Ops)*
Faye Tylee *(Chief HR Officer)*
Kevin Speed *(Chief Acctg Officer, VP-Global & Controller)*
Frank Ciccone *(Sr VP-Sls-North America)*
Dennis Kozak *(Sr VP-Global Channel Sls)*
Simon Harrison *(CMO & Sr VP)*
Tony Alfano *(Sr VP-Global Svcs)*
Todd Zerbe *(Sr VP-Engrg)*
Tyler M. Chambers *(Mgr-IR & Treasury)*
Alan Masarek *(Pres & CEO)*
Becky Roof *(Interim CFO)*
Vito Carnevale *(Gen Counsel)*
Dino Beverakis *(Mng Dir-Australia & New Zealand)*
Sami Ammous *(VP-East Asia & Pacific)*
Shefali A. Shah *(Chief Admin Officer, Gen Counsel & Exec VP)*
Shefali Shah *(Chief Admin Officer, Gen Counsel & Exec VP)*
Alan B. Masarek *(Pres & CEO)*

Subsidiary (Domestic):

Avaya Inc. (3)
4655 Great American Pkwy, Santa Clara, CA 95054
Tel.: (908) 953-6000
Business Communications Systems Mfr
N.A.I.C.S.: 334210
Sanjay Pai *(Sls Dir-India)*
Frank Ciccone *(Sr VP-US Sls)*
Fred Hayes *(Sr VP-Global Bus)*
Galib Karim *(VP-Americas Intl)*
Kieran McGrath *(CFO & Sr VP)*
Ed Nalbandian *(Pres-Avaya Svcs)*
Dennis Kozak *(Sr VP-Bus Transformation)*
Chris McGugan *(Sr VP-Solutions & Tech)*
Steve Joyner *(Mng Dir-UK & Ireland)*
Ronald Rubens *(VP-Europe)*
Simon Vatcher *(Mng Dir-Australia & New Zealand)*
Sami Ammous *(VP-East Asia & Pacific)*
Bill Watkins *(Chm)*

Subsidiary (Non-US):

Avaya Australia Pty Ltd (4)
123 Epping Road, North Ryde, 2113, NSW, Australia
Tel.: (61) 1800302833
Sales Range: $50-74.9 Million
Communication Systems
N.A.I.C.S.: 334290
Peter Chidiac *(Mng Dir-Australia & New Zealand)*

Branch (Non-US):

Avaya China - Beijing Office (5)
Suite 9-12 Level 11 Tower W3 No 1 East Chang An Avenue, Dong Cheng District, Beijing, 100738, China
Tel.: (86) 1085165517
Web Site: http://www.avaya.com
Sales Range: $50-74.9 Million
Emp.: 40
Communication Systems
N.A.I.C.S.: 334290

Avaya China - Guangzhou Office (5)
Rm 6701 67/F CITIC Plz, No 233 Tian He Bei Rd, Guangzhou, China
Tel.: (86) 20 3877 1822
Web Site: http://www.avaya.com
Communication Systems
N.A.I.C.S.: 334290

Avaya China - Shanghai Office (5)
Units 01A & 06-11 7th Fl The Ctr, 989 Changle Rd, Shanghai, 200031, China
Tel.: (86) 2161206911
Web Site: http://www.avaya.com.cn

Communication Systems
N.A.I.C.S.: 334290

Subsidiary (Non-US):

Avaya Hong Kong Co. Ltd. (5)
Ste 2408 Shell Twr Times Sq 1 Matheson St, Causeway Bay, China (Hong Kong)
Tel.: (852) 31216109
Web Site: http://www.avaya-apac.com
Sales Range: $25-49.9 Million
Emp.: 45
Communication Service
N.A.I.C.S.: 334290

Branch (Non-US):

Avaya Japan (5)
Akasaka 2 Chome 17-7 Minato Ku, Tokyo, 106 8508, Japan
Tel.: (81) 0355758700
Web Site: http://www.avaya.co.jp
Sales Range: $50-74.9 Million
Communications Equipment
N.A.I.C.S.: 334290

Avaya Korea (5)
12 Fl GFC 737 Yoksam Dong, Kangnamgu, 135 984, Seoul, Korea (South)
Tel.: (82) 260074685
Web Site: http://www.avaya.co.kr
Sales Range: $50-74.9 Million
Emp.: 29
Communications Equipment
N.A.I.C.S.: 334290

Avaya Malaysia (5)
8-30-60 L 30 Twr A Jalan Bangsar Utama, Menara UQA Bangsar, No 5 Jalan Bangsar Utama 1, 59000, Kuala Lumpur, Malaysia
Tel.: (60) 320593300
Web Site: http://www.avaya.co.uk
Sales Range: $50-74.9 Million
Emp.: 30
Communications Equipment
N.A.I.C.S.: 334290

Avaya Philippines (5)
17th Fl Tower II The Enterprise Center 6766 Ayala Ave, Makati, 1226, Philippines
Tel.: (63) 28848788
Sales Range: $50-74.9 Million
Emp.: 13
Communications Equipment
N.A.I.C.S.: 334290
Ferdinand S. Macatangay *(Country Mgr)*

Avaya Singapore (5)
89 Science Pk Dr No 01 03 04 The Rutherford Block A, Singapore, 118261, Singapore
Tel.: (65) 68728599
Communications Equipment
N.A.I.C.S.: 334290
Ray Teske *(Reg Dir-Asean Ops)*
Mike Ansley *(Pres-Asia Pacific)*

Avaya Thailand (5)
Unit 6 9th Fl Wave Pl 55 Wireless Rd, Patumwan, Bangkok, 10330, Thailand
Tel.: (66) 26554791
Communications Equipment
N.A.I.C.S.: 334290

Subsidiary (Non-US):

Avaya Belgium SPRL (4)
Keizer Karellaan 576 Avenue Charles Quint, 1082, Brussels, Belgium
Tel.: (32) 27777777
Sales Range: $50-74.9 Million
Emp.: 85
Communication System Mfr
N.A.I.C.S.: 334290

Avaya Canada Corp. (4)
515 Legget Drive Tower D Suite 600, Ottawa, K2K 3G4, ON, Canada
Tel.: (905) 474-6000
Web Site: http://www.avaya.ca
Sales Range: $50-74.9 Million
Business Communication System Development Services
N.A.I.C.S.: 541511
Rejean Bourgault *(Mng Dir & Pres-Sls)*

Avaya Czech Republic (4)
Sokolovska 192/79, 186 00, Prague, Czech Republic
Tel.: (420) 222194211
Web Site: http://www.avaya.cz

SILVER LAKE GROUP, LLC

Silver Lake Group, LLC—(Continued)
Sales Range: $25-49.9 Million
Emp.: 25
Communication System Mfr
N.A.I.C.S.: 334290

Avaya France S.A. (4)
Avaya France Immeuble Ctr Park 9 Rue Maurice Mallet, Issy-les-Moulineaux, 92445, France
Tel.: (33) 140947800
Web Site: http://www.issy.avaya.com
Communication Service
N.A.I.C.S.: 517111
Olivier Djian (Mng Dir)

Avaya GmbH & Co. KG (4)
Theodor Heuss Allee 112, Frankfurt am Main, 60326, Germany
Tel.: (49) 6975050
Sales Range: $100-124.9 Million
Holding Company; Telephone Communications
N.A.I.C.S.: 551112

Subsidiary (Domestic):

Avaya Deutschland GmbH (5)
Truderinger Strase 4, 81677, Munich, Germany
Tel.: (49) 89413030
Web Site: http://www.avaya.de
Telecommunications Systems
N.A.I.C.S.: 517111
Thom Matthiessen (Chm-Mgmt Bd)
Wolfgang Zorn (Member-Mgmt Bd)
Béatrice von Brauchitsch (Mng Dir & Member-Mgmt Bd)

Subsidiary (Domestic):

Avaya Government Solutions Inc. (4)
12730 Fair Lks Cir, Fairfax, VA 22033
Tel.: (703) 653-8000
Web Site: http://www.avayagov.com
Sales Range: $200-249.9 Million
Engineering Services; Information Technology, Network Engineering
N.A.I.C.S.: 541511
Jorge Navarro (Head-Bus Dev & Exports)

Subsidiary (Non-US):

Avaya Israel (4)
Harokmim Street 26 Building D Floor 10, Holon, 5885849, Israel
Tel.: (972) 3 645 7500
Web Site: http://www.avaya.co.il
Communication Systems
N.A.I.C.S.: 517111
Tali Alkon (Mgr-Sls)

Subsidiary (Domestic):

RADVision Ltd. (5)
24 Raoul Wallenberg Street, Tel Aviv, 69719, Israel
Tel.: (972) 37679300
Web Site: http://www.radvision.com
Sales Range: $75-99.9 Million
Designs, Develops & Provides Products & Technologies for Unified Visual Communications
N.A.I.C.S.: 334220
Roberto Giamagli (Gen Mgr-Video Bus Unit)
Yair Wiener (CTO)
Pierre Hagendorf (Gen Mgr-Tech Bus Unit)

Subsidiary (Non-US):

RADVision (HK) Ltd. (6)
Suite 2901 29/F China Resources Building, 26 Harbour Road, Hong Kong, China (Hong Kong)
Tel.: (852) 3472 4388
Web Site: http://www.radvision.com
Designs, Develops & Provides Products & Technologies for Unified Visual Communications
N.A.I.C.S.: 334220

RADVision (UK) Ltd. (6)
6-9 The Square, Stockley Park, Uxbridge, UB11 1FW, United Kingdom
Tel.: (44) 203 178 8685
Designs, Develops & Provides Products & Technologies for Unified Visual Communications
N.A.I.C.S.: 334220

RADVision Communication Development (Beijing) Co. Ltd. (6)
Room 802 Capital Group Plaza No 6 Chaoyangmen Beidajie, Dongcheng District, Beijing, 100027, China
Tel.: (86) 10 65528528
Designs, Develops & Provides Products & Technologies for Unified Visual Communications
N.A.I.C.S.: 334220

RADVision France S.A.R.L. (6)
88 Avenue du General Leclerc, 92100, Boulogne-Billancourt, France
Tel.: (33) 1 55 60 51 30
Designs, Develops & Provides Products & Technologies for Unified Visual Communications
N.A.I.C.S.: 334220
Daniel Johansson (Gen Mgr-EMEA)

RADVision Japan KK (6)
Kiyotaka Bldg 3F 1-32-8 Taito, Taito-ku, Tokyo, 110-0016, Japan
Tel.: (81) 3 5816 8950
Designs, Develops & Provides Products & Technologies for Unified Visual Communications
N.A.I.C.S.: 334220

Subsidiary (Non-US):

Avaya Nederland B.V. (4)
Marconibaan 59, Nieuwegein, 3439 MR, Netherlands
Tel.: (31) 306097600
Sales Range: $50-74.9 Million
Emp.: 55
Communications Equipment
N.A.I.C.S.: 334290
Roland Geer (Dir-Fin)

Avaya UK (4)
Avaya House, Cathedral Hill, Guildford, GU27YL, United Kingdom
Tel.: (44) 1483308000
Sales Range: $50-74.9 Million
Emp.: 300
Communication Service
N.A.I.C.S.: 334290
Ioan MacRae (Mng Dir)

Branch (Domestic):

Avaya UK - Scotland Office (5)
Stewart House Porchard Way, Strathclyde Business Park, Bellshill, ML4 3HB, N Lanarkshire, United Kingdom
Tel.: (44) 1698 743 700
Web Site: http://www.avaya.com
Sales Range: $50-74.9 Million
Emp.: 20
Telecommunication Systems Sales & Administration Office
N.A.I.C.S.: 517112

Subsidiary (Domestic):

Avaya, LLC (4)
528 Zircon Way, Superior, CO 80027-4661
Tel.: (303) 354-8999
Web Site: http://www.avaya.com
Sales Range: $800-899.9 Million
Data & Network Communications
N.A.I.C.S.: 517810

Sipera Systems, Inc. (4)
1900 Firman Dr, Richardson, TX 75081
Tel.: (214) 206-3202
Web Site: http://www.sipera.com
Sales Range: $1-9.9 Million
Emp.: 17
Computer Systems Design
N.A.I.C.S.: 541512
Jim Timmer (CFO)
Chuck Pledger (VP-Channel Sls-Global)
Gil Stevens (VP-Engrg)

Joint Venture (Domestic):

Blackhawk Network Holdings, Inc. (2)
6220 Stoneridge Mall Rd, Pleasanton, CA 94582
Tel.: (925) 226-9990
Web Site: https://www.blackhawknetwork.com
Sales Range: $1-4.9 Billion
Emp.: 3,000
Other Financial Vehicles
N.A.I.C.S.: 525990
Talbott Roche (Pres & CEO)
David Tate (Sr VP-US Bus)
Joan Lockie (Chief Acctg Officer, VP & Controller)
Teri Llach (CMO)
Kirsten Richesson (Gen Counsel)
Steve Dekker (Mng Dir-Canada & Latin America)
Stewart Rigby (VP-Asia Pacific)
Owen Sagness (Gen Mgr-Achievers)
Patrick Cronin (VP-Fin Plng, Analysis & IR)
David Jones (Gen Mgr-Digital & Incentive Div)
Jonathan Kenny (Mng Dir-Europe West)
Christian Lindner (Mng Dir-Europe East)
Amie Miller (Grp VP-Ops)
Nick Samurkas (COO)
Nikhil Sathe (CTO)
Helena Mao (VP-Product Strategy-Global)
Leila Pourhashemi (CIO & VP-Tech Bus Ops)
Brett Narlinger (Head-Commerce-Global)
Cory Gaines (Chief Product Officer)
David McLaughlin (CFO)
Jay Jaffin (CMO)
Suzanne Kinner (VP-HR)

Subsidiary (Non-US):

Achievers Corp. (3)
99 Atlantic Ave Ste 700, Toronto, M6K 3J8, ON, Canada
Tel.: (888) 622-3343
Web Site: http://www.achievers.com
Electronic Financial Transaction Processing Services
N.A.I.C.S.: 522320
Jeff Cates (CEO)

Subsidiary (Domestic):

Achievers LLC (3)
PO Box 122869, Fort Worth, TX 76121
Tel.: (817) 900-9489
Emp.: 12
Electronic Financial Transaction Processing Services
N.A.I.C.S.: 522320

Subsidiary (Non-US):

Blackhawk Network (Australia) Pty Ltd. (3)
Suite 202 6a Glen Street, Milsons Point, Sydney, 2061, NSW, Australia
Tel.: (61) 294602346
Web Site: https://blackhawknetwork.com
Prepaid Payment Network Utilizing Proprietary Technology Offering Prepaid Gift, Telecom & Debit Cards In Physical & Electronic Forms
N.A.I.C.S.: 522320

Subsidiary (Domestic):

Blackhawk Network California, Inc. (3)
5918 Stoneridge Mall Rd, Pleasanton, CA 94588
Tel.: (925) 226-9990
Web Site: http://www.giftcardmall.com
Prepaid & Payments Gift Cards Network Products
N.A.I.C.S.: 522320

CashStar, Inc. (3)
25 Pearl St, Portland, ME 04101
Tel.: (207) 549-2200
Digital Gift Card Solutions
N.A.I.C.S.: 541519

DigitalGlue (3)
41601 Date St, Murrieta, CA 92562
Tel.: (949) 388-9078
Web Site: http://www.digitalglue.com
Electronic Equipment Services
N.A.I.C.S.: 423690
Tim Anderson (Co-Founder, CEO & CTO)
Sean Busby (Co-Founder & Pres)
Dave Gordon (VP-Engrg)
John McCluskey (Dir-Sls)
Jon Mott (Dir-Software Dev)
Mark Reynolds (Dir-Ops)

Subsidiary (Non-US):

GVS Gift Voucher Shop Limited (3)
Unit 2 Swords Business Park, PO Box 8942, Swords, Dublin, Ireland
Tel.: (353) 1 8708100
Web Site: http://www.giftvouchershop.com
Gift Voucher Distr
N.A.I.C.S.: 459420
Michael Dawson (Founder & CEO)

Hawk Incentives Holdings Limited (3)
Westside London Road Hemel, Hemel Hempstead, HP3 9TD, Herts, United Kingdom
Tel.: (44) 2074198100
Professional Services
N.A.I.C.S.: 561990

Subsidiary (Non-US):

Grass Roots SL (4)
Calle Alcala 54 3 Derecha, 28014, Madrid, Spain
Tel.: (34) 915218338
Web Site: http://www.grassroots.es
Employee & Customer Engagement Solutions
N.A.I.C.S.: 541910

Subsidiary (Domestic):

OmniCard, LLC (3)
680 Andersen Dr Ste 430, Pittsburgh, PA 15220
Tel.: (866) 353-4877
Electronic Financial Transaction Processing Services
N.A.I.C.S.: 522320

SVM, LP (3)
3727 Ventura Dr, Arlington Heights, IL 60004
Tel.: (877) 300-1786
Prepaid Gift Cards Distr
N.A.I.C.S.: 541611
Marshall Reavis (Founder & CEO)
Jim Speir (VP-Sls & Mktg)
Jim Leroux (Pres)

Holding (Non-US):

Cegid Group SA (2)
52 quai Paul Sedallian, 69279, Lyon, Cedex 09, France
Tel.: (33) 811884888
Web Site: http://www.cegid.com
Management Software Developer
N.A.I.C.S.: 513210
Jean-Michel Aulas (Founder & Pres)
Nathalie Echinard (Exec Dir-Retail Bus)
Pascal Houillon (CEO)

Subsidiary (US):

Cegid Corporation (3)
Rockefeller Ctr 1270 Ave of the Americas Ste 807, New York, NY 10019
Tel.: (212) 757-9038
Web Site: http://www.cegid.com
Computer Software Services
N.A.I.C.S.: 541511
Arnaud Coste (Dir-Channel & Partnership)

Subsidiary (Domestic):

Cegid U.S. (4)
2701 Loker Ave W Ste 290, Carlsbad, CA 92010
Tel.: (760) 710-4444
Web Site: http://www.cegid.com
Software Solutions for Retailers
N.A.I.C.S.: 513210
John Shackles (CEO)

Subsidiary (Non-US):

Cegid Ltd. (3)
1 Copperhouse Court, Caldecotte, Milton Keynes, MK7 8NL, United Kingdom
Tel.: (44) 1908272420
Web Site: http://www.cegid.com
Retail Software Solutions
N.A.I.C.S.: 513210

Subsidiary (Domestic):

Cemagid SAS (3)
17 rue des Vaux Pares, 3310, Sevigne, Cesso, France
Tel.: (33) 223455570
Web Site: http://www.comptanoo.com
Computer Software Services
N.A.I.C.S.: 513210

COMPANIES   SILVER LAKE GROUP, LLC

Philippe Aulnette *(Mng Dir)*

Joint Venture (Non-US):

Global Blue S.A. (2)
route de Divonne 46, CH 1260, Nyon, Switzerland
Tel.: (41) 223637740
Web Site: http://www.global-blue.com
Sales Range: $550-599.9 Million
Tax Refund Transaction Processing Services
N.A.I.C.S.: 522320
David Baxby *(CEO)*

Subsidiary (Non-US):

Global Blue (UK) Limited (3)
11th Floor GWII Great West House Great West Road, Brentford, TW8 9HU, United Kingdom
Tel.: (44) 8 707 666 789
Web Site: http://www.globalblue.com
Tax Refund Transaction Processing Services
N.A.I.C.S.: 522320
Jack Sten *(CEO)*

Joint Venture (Domestic):

GoDaddy, Inc. (2)
100 S Mill Ave Ste 1600, Tempe, AZ 85281
Tel.: (406) 760-7600
Web Site: https://www.godaddy.com
Rev.: $4,254,100,000
Assets: $7,564,900,000
Liabilities: $7,502,700,000
Net Worth: $62,200,000
Earnings: $1,374,800,000
Emp.: 6,159
Fiscal Year-end: 12/31/2023
Holding Company; Domain Name Registration Services
N.A.I.C.S.: 551112
Amanpal S. Bhutani *(CEO)*
Auguste Goldman *(Pres-Care & Svcs)*
Jared Sine *(Chief Strategy Officer & Chief Legal Officer)*
Charles Beadnall *(CTO)*
Monica Bailey *(Chief People Officer)*
Fara Howard *(CMO)*
Roger Chen *(COO)*
Nick Daddario *(Chief Acctg Officer)*
Osama Bedier *(Pres-Commerce)*
Mark D. McCaffrey *(CFO)*
Paul Nicks *(Pres-Domain Registrars & Investors)*
Laura Messerschmitt *(Pres-Intl Independents)*
Gourav Pani *(Pres-US Independents)*
Paul Bindel *(Pres-Partners)*

Subsidiary (Domestic):

GoDaddy.com, LLC (3)
14455 N Hayden Rd, Scottsdale, AZ 85260
Tel.: (480) 505-8800
Web Site: http://www.godaddy.com
Domain Name Registration Services
N.A.I.C.S.: 518210
Amanpal S. Bhutani *(CEO)*

Subsidiary (Non-US):

Host Europe Group Limited (3)
The Shipping Building Old Vinyl Factory 252-254 Blyth Road, Hayes, London, UB3 1HA, Mddx, United Kingdom
Tel.: (44) 345 450 2310
Web Site: http://www.heg.com
Domain Registrar Services
N.A.I.C.S.: 517810
Richard Winslow *(Brand Dir-123 Reg)*

Subsidiary (Domestic):

123-Reg Limited (4)
The Shipping Building Old Vinyl Factory 252-254 Blyth Road, Hayes, London, UB3 1HA, Mddx, United Kingdom
Tel.: (44) 3454502310
Web Site: https://www.123-reg.co.uk
Custom Web Hosting Services
N.A.I.C.S.: 517810
Richard Winslow *(Brand Dir)*

Subsidiary (Non-US):

Host Europe GmbH (4)
c/o WeWork Friesenplatz 4, 50672, Cologne, Germany
Tel.: (49) 22199999301
Web Site: https://www.hosteurope.de
Internet Hosting Services
N.A.I.C.S.: 518210
Claus Boyens *(Mng Dir)*
Tobias Mohr *(Mng Dir)*

Subsidiary (Domestic):

Main Street Hub Inc. (3)
600 Congress Ave Ste 1200, Austin, TX 78701
Tel.: (888) 900-0920
Online Reputation Management Services
N.A.I.C.S.: 561499

Media Temple, Inc. (3)
12655 W Jefferson Blvd Ste 400, Los Angeles, CA 90066
Tel.: (310) 841-5500
Web Site: https://www.mediatemple.net
Sales Range: $1-9.9 Million
Emp.: 225
Hosts Websites for Motion Graphic Artists, Art Directors & Broadcast & Web Design Firms
N.A.I.C.S.: 518210
Lou Kikos *(VP-Mktg)*

Outright, Inc. (3)
100 Mathilda Pl, Sunnyvale, CA 94086
Tel.: (650) 440-6352
Web Site: http://www.outright.com
Sales Range: $1-9.9 Million
Billing & Accounting Software Mfr
N.A.I.C.S.: 513210

Subsidiary (Non-US):

Special Domains Services, Inc. (3)
Tel.: (480) 505-8800
Domain Name Registration Services
N.A.I.C.S.: 541519

Subsidiary (Non-US):

Domains by Proxy, LLC (4)
Tel.: (480) 505-8800
Web Site: http://www.domainsbyproxy.com
Domain Name Registration Services
N.A.I.C.S.: 541519

Subsidiary (Domestic):

Starfield Technologies, Inc. (3)
14455 N Hayden Rd, Scottsdale, AZ 85260
Tel.: (480) 505-8825
Web Site: http://www.starfieldtech.com
Technology-Based Business Solutions Developer
N.A.I.C.S.: 541512

Wild West Domains, Inc. (3)
2150 E Warner Rd, Tempe, AZ 85284
Tel.: (480) 624-2500
Web Site: https://www.wildwestdomains.com
Domain-Related Products & Services Reseller
N.A.I.C.S.: 541519
Blake J. Irving *(CEO)*

Joint Venture (Domestic):

IMG Worldwide, Inc. (2)
200 5th Ave 7th Fl, New York, NY 10010
Tel.: (212) 489-8300
Web Site: http://www.img.com
Sales Range: $1-4.9 Billion
Media & Public Relations Agency
N.A.I.C.S.: 541830
Catherine Bennett *(Sr VP & Mng Dir-Fashion Events)*

Subsidiary (Domestic):

Fusion Marketing
6404 International Pkwy Ste 2250, Plano, TX 75093
Tel.: (469) 405-7654
Web Site: http://thisisfusion.com
Corporate & Incentive Travel Services
N.A.I.C.S.: 561520
Julie McCulloch *(Acct Dir-Performance Solutions)*
Bill Decker *(CEO)*
Caron Arnold *(Creative Dir)*
Gina Monroe *(Sr Dir-HR)*
Greg Litwicki *(Chief Creative Officer)*
Heather Heign *(Sr Mgr-Program Support)*
Pat Olds *(Assoc Dir-Creative)*
Samantha Dulle *(Acct Coord)*
Ben Loos *(Dir-Dev & Digital Experiences)*
Caroline O'keefe *(Acct Coord)*
Cam Phillips *(Mgr-Production)*
Dina Phillipi *(Dir-Technical Program Mgmt)*
Eric Schneider *(Acct Mgr)*
Jason Hackett *(Dir-Art)*
Jennifer Wubker *(Acct Dir)*
Jessen Wabeke *(Creative Dir)*
John Nolan *(Controller)*
Lisa Lawless *(Sr Mgr-Production)*
Lori Ryan *(Dir-Strategic Account & Experiential Mktg)*
Kyle Zimmerman *(Mgr-Production)*
Mike Beck *(Dir-Production)*
Nick Bommarito *(Assoc Dir-Creative)*
Lindsey Jaeger *(Acct Dir)*
Meghan Martz *(Acct Svcs Dir-Mktg)*
Michael Bischoff *(Dir-Art)*
Matthew Maddox *(Assoc Dir-Creative)*
Brad Harris *(VP-Tech)*
Nikki Spoto *(Acct Coord)*
Mike Cox *(CFO)*
Theresa Blomker *(Acct Exec)*
Rich Wells *(Dir-IT)*
Scott Gaterman *(VP-Mktg-Acct Svcs)*
Shanna Welsh *(Acct Exec)*
Zach Hollowood *(Sr Dir-Art)*
Samantha Porter *(Assoc Mgr-Production)*
Tyler Schario *(Dir-Strategy & Insights)*
Vanessa Tutka *(Dir-Art)*
Grant Stiff *(VP-Bus Dev)*
Katey Hindes *(Dir-Art)*
Melanie Flanagan *(Sr Acct Exec)*
Stephen Dennis *(VP-Bus Dev)*
Alexa Churchwell *(Sr Dir-Association Mgmt)*
Rebecca Freeman-Hoff *(Acct Dir)*
Raleigh Moore *(Acct Coord-Performance Solutions)*
Heather Baumbach *(Sr Project Mgr-Planning & Costing)*
Nicole Kramer *(Acct Dir)*
Megan May *(Project Mgr-Digital)*
Sarah Bradley *(Acct Exec)*
Maggie Halliday *(Acct Coord)*
Ashley Davis *(Mgr-Field)*
Adam Flach *(Acct Exec)*
Cara Baldwin *(Acct Coord)*
Olivia Scalise *(Acct Coord)*
Jennifer Leans *(Sr Mgr-Association)*
Caroline Scott *(Assoc Mgr)*
Kelsey Settle *(Coord-Field)*
Anne Marie Connelly *(Acct Coord)*
Megan Tillery *(Dir-Production)*
Nicole Guanlao *(Acct Exec)*
Hannah Nichols *(Acct Exec)*
Darlene Clark *(Sr VP-Sls)*
Janel Mcneal *(Coord-Accts Payable)*

Division (Domestic):

IMG College (3)
540 N Trade St, Winston Salem, NC 27101
Tel.: (336) 831-0700
Web Site: http://www.imgcollege.com
Sales Range: $75-99.9 Million
Emp.: 700
Collegiate Sports Marketing Agency
N.A.I.C.S.: 541830
Scott MacKenzie *(VP-Bus Dev & Partnership Mgmt)*
Rick Barakat *(VP-Sls Strategy & Ops)*
Tracy White *(VP-Southeast Reg)*
Jim Connelly *(Sr VP-Special Projects)*
Mark Dyer *(Sr VP)*
Tom Fletcher *(VP-West Reg)*
Andrew Giangola *(VP-Strategic Comm)*
Cameron Scholvin *(VP-Midwest Reg)*
Rex Hough *(VP-Bus Dev & Partnership Mgmt)*
Andrew Judelson *(Sr VP-Natl, Reg & Digital Sls & Mktg)*
Joe Potter *(Sr VP-Ops)*
Joe Weatherly *(CFO & VP)*
Dan Barrett *(VP-Bus Ventures)*
John Hite *(VP-Stadium Seating)*
Tim Pernetti *(Pres-Multimedia)*
Franklin Yancey *(VP-Stadium Seating)*

Branch (Non-US):

IMG Toronto (3)
175 Bloor Street East Ste 1001 South Tower, Toronto, M4W 3R8, ON, Canada
Tel.: (416) 960-5312
Web Site: http://www.img.com
Sales Range: $10-24.9 Million
Emp.: 40
Advertising & Media Services
N.A.I.C.S.: 541810
Nadean Jackson *(Office Mgr)*

Subsidiary (Domestic):

IMG Universe LLC (3)
1370 Ave of the Americas 16th Fl, New York, NY 10019
Tel.: (212) 373-4986
Web Site: http://press.missuniverse.com
Producer of the Miss Universe, Miss USA & Miss Teen USA Pageants
N.A.I.C.S.: 711320
Jackie Shahinian *(Dir-Public Rels)*

Subsidiary (Domestic):

Miss Universe, L.P. (4)
1370 Avenue of the Americas 16th Fl, New York, NY 10019 **(100%)**
Tel.: (212) 373-4999
Web Site: http://www.missuniverse.com
Producer of the Miss Universe, Miss USA & Miss Teen USA Pageants
N.A.I.C.S.: 711320

Branch (Non-US):

IMG Worldwide - Asia-Pacific Headquarters (3)
18/F East Exchange Tower 38 Leighton Rd, Causeway Bay, China (Hong Kong)
Tel.: (852) 2894 0288
Sales Range: $10-24.9 Million
Emp.: 30
Media Agency
N.A.I.C.S.: 541810
Chris Guinness *(Sr VP & Head-Asia Pacific)*

Branch (Non-US):

IMG Mumbai (4)
608 1-B/2 Western Express Highway Service Road, Bandra East, Mumbai, 400 51, India
Tel.: (91) 22 6145 5900
Web Site: http://www.img.com
Emp.: 30
Advertising & Media Services
N.A.I.C.S.: 541810
Ashu Jindal *(COO)*

Branch (Non-US):

IMG Worldwide - EMEA Headquarters (3)
Building 6 566 Chiswick High Road, Chiswick, London, W4 5HR, United Kingdom
Tel.: (44) 20 8233 5300
Web Site: http://www.img.com
Sales Range: $50-74.9 Million
Emp.: 400
Advertising & Media Services
N.A.I.C.S.: 541810
Sally Wharmby *(Mgr-Facilities)*
Kathleen Brookbanks *(Mng Dir)*
Barbara Cipolla *(CMO)*

Branch (Non-US):

IMG Barcelona (4)
VIA Augusta 200 4th Floor, 08021, Barcelona, Spain
Tel.: (34) 93 200 34 55
Web Site: http://www.img.com
Emp.: 20
Advertising & Media Services
N.A.I.C.S.: 541810
Fernando Soler *(Mng Dir)*

IMG Hungary (4)
Andrassy ut 98, 1062, Budapest, Hungary
Tel.: (36) 1 312 2406
Web Site: http://www.img.com
Advertising & Media Services
N.A.I.C.S.: 541810

IMG Middle East - Dubai (4)
Building 5 Suite 121 Gold and Diamond Park, PO Box 282339, Sheikh Zayed Rd, Dubai, United Arab Emirates
Tel.: (971) 4 408 8388
Web Site: http://www.img.com
Sales Range: $25-49.9 Million
Emp.: 10
Advertising & Media Services
N.A.I.C.S.: 541810
Greg Sproule *(Mng Dir-Middle East & North Africa)*

Branch (Domestic):

IMG Worldwide, Inc. - Cleveland (3)

SILVER LAKE GROUP, LLC

U.S. PRIVATE

Silver Lake Group, LLC—(Continued)
IMG Ctr 1360 E 9th St Ste 100, Cleveland, OH 44114
Tel.: (216) 522-1200
Web Site: http://www.imgworld.com
Holding Company; Media & Public Relations Agencies
N.A.I.C.S.: 551112

Joint Venture (Non-US):

Intelsat S.A. (2)
4 Rue Albert Borschette, Luxembourg, L-1246, Luxembourg (12%)
Tel.: (352) 27841600
Web Site: http://www.intelsat.com
Rev.: $1,913,080,000
Assets: $12,797,681,000
Liabilities: $18,712,149,000
Net Worth: $(5,914,468,000)
Earnings: $(911,664,000)
Emp.: 1,774
Fiscal Year-end: 12/31/2020
Satellite Telecommunications
N.A.I.C.S.: 517410
Michelle Bryan *(Chief Admin Officer, Gen Counsel & Exec VP)*
Michael J. DeMarco *(Chief Svcs Officer & Exec VP)*
Bruno Fromont *(CTO)*
Jean-Philippe Gillet *(Sr VP-Global Sls Network & Media)*
Samer Halawi *(Chief Comml Officer & Exec VP)*
Lisa Hammitt *(Chm)*
Jon Cobin *(Chief Strategy Officer)*
John Wade *(Pres-Comml Aviation Div)*
Gaurav Kharod *(Reg VP-Asia Pacific)*
David J. Broadbent *(Pres-Govt Solutions)*
David C. Wajsgras *(CEO)*

Joint Venture (Domestic):

LightBox (2)
9 W 57th St, New York, NY 10001
Tel.: (212) 981-5600
Holding Company
N.A.I.C.S.: 523999
Eric Frank *(CEO)*
Anthony Bisseker *(Mng Dir)*

Subsidiary (Domestic):

Digital Map Products, Inc. (3)
5201 California Ave Ste 200, Irvine, CA 92617
Tel.: (949) 333-5111
Web Site: http://www.digmap.com
Sales Range: $10-24.9 Million
Custom Platform Data Services
N.A.I.C.S.: 518210
James Skurzynski *(Founder, Pres & CEO)*
Geoff Wade *(CTO)*
Nelson Greenwood *(VP-Sls)*
Annie Schwab *(VP-Customer Success)*
Steve Stautzenbach *(VP-Product Mgmt)*
Tara Bleakley *(Dir-Data Analytics)*
Steven Cheng *(Dir-Data Dev)*
Brendan McCann *(Dir-IT)*
Diane Rettew *(Dir-HR & Talent Acq)*
Thomas R. Patterson Jr. *(COO & VP-Fin)*

Holding (Domestic):

Oak View Group, LLC (2)
11755 Wilshire Blvd. 9th Floor, Los Angeles, CA 90025
Tel.: (310) 954-4800
Web Site: https://www.oakviewgroup.com
Sports & Live Entertainment Venue Services;
N.A.I.C.S.: 711310
Tim Leiweke *(CEO)*

Subsidiary (Domestic):

Spectrum Catering (3)
27433 Robinson Rd, Conroe, TX 77385-8958
Web Site: http://www.spectrumconcessions.com
Food Service Contractors
N.A.I.C.S.: 722310
Dave Smalley *(CEO)*

Holding (Domestic):

ServiceMax, Inc. (2)
4450 Rosewood Dr Ste 200, Pleasanton, CA 94588 (90%)
Tel.: (925) 965-7859
Web Site: http://www.servicemax.com
Software & Technology Development Services
N.A.I.C.S.: 513210
Athani Krishnaprasad *(Founder & Chief Strategy Officer)*
David Milam *(Chief Mktg Officer)*
Rei Kasai *(Sr VP-Products)*
Spencer Earp *(Exec VP-EMEA & APAC)*
Takahiro Kouke *(Gen Mgr-Japan)*
Neil Barua *(CEO)*
Sophie Ames *(Chief HR Officer)*

Subsidiary (Domestic):

LiquidFrameworks, Inc. (3)
24 E Greenway Plz Ste 405, Houston, TX 77046
Tel.: (713) 552-9250
Web Site: http://www.liquidframeworks.com
Custom Computer Programming Services
N.A.I.C.S.: 541511
Travis Parigi *(Founder & CEO)*
Matt Danna *(Sr Dir-Product Strategy)*
Paul Marvin *(CFO)*
Brandon Burris *(VP-Pro Svcs)*

Holding (Non-US):

Software AG (2)
Uhlandstrasse 12, D-64297, Darmstadt, Germany (100%)
Tel.: (49) 6151923100
Web Site: https://www.softwareag.com
Rev.: $1,079,527,304
Assets: $2,551,959,853
Liabilities: $979,824,088
Net Worth: $1,572,135,765
Earnings: $(5,641,053)
Emp.: 4,482
Fiscal Year-end: 12/31/2023
Computer Software & Services
N.A.I.C.S.: 541511
Stefan Sigg *(Chief Product Officer & Member-Mgmt Bd)*
Joshua Husk *(Chief Revenue Officer)*
Benno Quade *(COO)*
Martin Biegel *(CFO)*
Toktam Khatibzadeh *(Chief HR Officer)*
Robin Colman *(Chief Strategy Officer)*

Subsidiary (Non-US):

Alfabet Saudi Arabia LLC (3)
Al Aknaz Center 3rd Floor Office No 29 Prince mohammed bin, Abdul-Aziz Road Tahliah Street 12222-7843 Olaya District, Riyadh, 11633, Saudi Arabia
Tel.: (966) 114655140
Computer Software Development Services
N.A.I.C.S.: 541512
Ahmad Salama *(VP-Sls)*

Subsidiary (US):

CONNX Solutions Inc. (3)
2039 152nd Ave NE, Redmond, WA 98052 (100%)
Tel.: (425) 519-6600
Web Site: http://www.connx.com
Rev.: $4,000,000
Emp.: 50
Data Access Software Services
N.A.I.C.S.: 541511
Larry McGhaw *(CTO & Sr VP-Engrg)*
Harpal Gill *(Sr VP-Global Alliances & Sls)*

Subsidiary (Domestic):

FACT Informationssysteme und Consulting AG (3)
Hellersbergstrasse 11, 41460, Neuss, Germany
Tel.: (49) 21317770
Web Site: http://www.fact.de
Sales Range: $25-49.9 Million
Financial Software Development Services
N.A.I.C.S.: 541511

FACT Unternehmensberatung GmbH (3)
Weissfrauenstrasse 12-16, 60311, Frankfurt am Main, Germany
Tel.: (49) 69505092420
Financial Advisory Services
N.A.I.C.S.: 523940

Subsidiary (Non-US):

FACT Unternehmensberatung Schweiz AG (3)
Forrlibuckstrasse 30, 8005, Zurich, Switzerland
Tel.: (41) 442299000
Management Consulting Services
N.A.I.C.S.: 541611

Subsidiary (Domestic):

IDS Scheer AG (3)
Altenkesseler Strasse 17, 66115, Saarbrucken, Germany
Tel.: (49) 6812100
Web Site: http://www.softwareag.com
Sales Range: $500-549.9 Million
Emp.: 480
Business Process Management Software & Consulting Solutions
N.A.I.C.S.: 513210

Subsidiary (US):

IDS Scheer Americas, Inc. (4)
565 E Swedesford Rd Ste 200, Wayne, PA 19087
Tel.: (703) 860-5050
Web Site: http://www.softwareag.com
Software Development Services
N.A.I.C.S.: 541511

Subsidiary (Non-US):

IDS Scheer Austria GmbH (4)
Guglgasse 7-9, Vienna, 1030, Austria
Tel.: (43) 1329500
Web Site: http://www.ids-scheer.at
Sales Range: $50-74.9 Million
Emp.: 105
Business Process Management Software & Consulting Solutions
N.A.I.C.S.: 513210

IDS Scheer Canada (4)
5160 Yonge Street Suite 1810, Toronto, M2N 6L9, ON, Canada
Tel.: (416) 512-6784
Business Process Management Software & Consulting Services
N.A.I.C.S.: 513210

IDS Scheer China Ltd. (4)
Room 6H Crystal Century Tower 567 Weihai Road, 200041, Shanghai, China
Tel.: (86) 2162887171
Software Development Services
N.A.I.C.S.: 541511

IDS Scheer India PVT. LTD (4)
Level One Trade Center Bandra Kurla Complex, Bandra E, 400051, Mumbai, India
Tel.: (91) 2240700159
Web Site: http://www.softwareag.com
Sales Range: $25-49.9 Million
Emp.: 10
Information Technology Consulting Services
N.A.I.C.S.: 541512

IDS Scheer Russia (4)
47A Sevastopolskiy Prospect, Moscow, 117186, Russia
Tel.: (7) 4957817781
Web Site: http://www.ids-scheer.hu
Software Development Services
N.A.I.C.S.: 541511
Sergey Cherkasov *(Gen Dir)*

IDS Scheer SDC s.r.o. (4)
Juzna Trieda 125, Kosice, 040 01, Slovakia
Tel.: (421) 557290527
Web Site: http://www.softwareag.com
Emp.: 45
Software Development Services
N.A.I.C.S.: 541511
Randy Robertson *(Mng Dir)*

IDS Scheer Saudi Arabia LLC. (4)
7109 Olaya Street Salman Bin Saedan Group Bldg 3rd Flior Office No 7, PO Box 91245, Murooj District, Riyadh, 11633, Saudi Arabia
Tel.: (966) 12298983
Web Site: http://www.softwareag.com
Software Development Services
N.A.I.C.S.: 541511

IDS Scheer Schweiz AG (4)
Thurgauerstrasse 40, 8050, Zurich, Switzerland
Tel.: (41) 589589900
Web Site: http://www.ids-scheer.ch
Sales Range: $25-49.9 Million
Emp.: 35
Business Process Management Software & Consulting Solutions
N.A.I.C.S.: 513210

IDS Scheer Singapore Pte. Ltd. (4)
Marina Boulevard Marina Bye Financial Center Power 3 Unit No 17-04, 03-03/04 Goldbell Towers, Singapore, 018982, Singapore
Tel.: (65) 64179700
Web Site: http://www.softwareag.com.sg
Sales Range: $25-49.9 Million
Emp.: 30
Business Process Management Software & Consulting Solutions
N.A.I.C.S.: 513210
Lers Bengtsson *(Mng Dir)*

IDS Scheer Sistemas de Processamento de Dados Ltda. (4)
Av Nacoes Unidas 12901 33 Andar Torre Norte Cenu, 04578 000, Sao Paulo, Brazil
Tel.: (55) 1128996600
Sales Range: $10-24.9 Million
Emp.: 5
Software Development Services
N.A.I.C.S.: 541511
Paul Vaz *(Gen Mgr)*

IDS Scheer d.o.o. (4)
Ivana Gundulica 26A, 2100, Split, Croatia
Tel.: (385) 21480600
Web Site: http://www.softwareag.com
Sales Range: $25-49.9 Million
Emp.: 6
Software Consulting Services
N.A.I.C.S.: 541512
Vedran Babik *(Mng Dir)*

IDS Scheer, d.o.o. (4)
Smartinska Cesta 152g, 1000, Ljubljana, Slovenia
Tel.: (386) 18109906
Software Development Services
N.A.I.C.S.: 541511

itelligence Slovakia, s.r.o. (4)
Prievozska 4/C Apollo BC 2 Blok D, Bratislava, 82109, Slovakia
Tel.: (421) 220911111
Web Site: http://www.itelligencegroup.com
Sales Range: $25-49.9 Million
Emp.: 30
Business Process Management Software & Consulting Solutions
N.A.I.C.S.: 541618

Subsidiary (Non-US):

PT Software AG Indonesia Operations (3)
Dbs Bank Tower 28th Floor Ciputra World One Jl Prof Dr Satrio Kav 3-5, Jakarta, 12940, Indonesia
Tel.: (62) 816950137
Computer Software Development Services
N.A.I.C.S.: 541512

Subsidiary (Domestic):

RTM Realtime Monitoring GmbH (3)
Software Center 1, 35037, Marburg, Germany
Tel.: (49) 64213048000
Web Site: http://www.realtime-monitoring.de
Event Processing Software Development Services
N.A.I.C.S.: 541511

SAG Consulting Services GmbH (3)
Uhlandstrasse 9, 64297, Darmstadt, Germany
Tel.: (49) 6151923100
Software Consulting Services
N.A.I.C.S.: 541512

SAG Deutschland GmbH (3)
Uhlandstrasse 9, 64297, Darmstadt, Germany (100%)
Tel.: (49) 6151923100
Sales Range: $150-199.9 Million
Emp.: 700
Custom Computer Programming Services
N.A.I.C.S.: 541511

SAG East GmbH (3)
Uhlandstr 12, 64297, Darmstadt, Germany

COMPANIES   SILVER LAKE GROUP, LLC

Tel.: (49) 6151920
Software Publishing Services
N.A.I.C.S.: 513210

Subsidiary (Non-US):

SAG Sales Centre Ireland Limited (3)
Bay 5 The Digital Depot Building The Digital Hub Roe Lane, Off Thomas Street, Dublin, D08 TCV4, Ireland
Tel.: (353) 15424148
Computer Software Development Services
N.A.I.C.S.: 541512

SAG Software AG Luxembourg S.A. (3)
Immeuble Laccolith 20 Rue Eugene Ruppert, 2453, Luxembourg, Luxembourg
Tel.: (352) 26493297
Computer Software Development Services
N.A.I.C.S.: 541512

SAG Software Systems AG (3)
Thurgauerstrasse 40, 8050, Zurich, Switzerland (100%)
Tel.: (41) 447459111
Web Site: http://www.softwareag.com
Sales Range: $25-49.9 Million
Emp.: 30
Software Reproducing
N.A.I.C.S.: 334610
Alain Badou *(Mng Dir)*

SAG Systems RUS Limited Liability Company (3)
2 Bldg 3 Gamsonovsky Lane, 115191, Moscow, Russia
Tel.: (7) 4957817781
Web Site: http://www.softwareag.com
Software Development Services
N.A.I.C.S.: 541511

Sede Central Software Ag Espana S.A. (3)
Ronda de la Luna 22 Tres Cantos, 28760, Madrid, Spain
Tel.: (34) 918079400
Web Site: http://www.softwareag.com
Sales Range: $75-99.9 Million
Emp.: 400
Custom Computer Programming Services
N.A.I.C.S.: 541511

Softinterest Holding AG (3)
Untermuli 9, 6302, Zug, Switzerland (100%)
Tel.: (41) 7603980
Web Site: http://www.softwareag.com
Holding Company
N.A.I.C.S.: 551112

Software AG (Asia Pacific/Singapore) Ltd. (3)
7 Temasek Blvd 30 01, Suntec Tower 1, Singapore, 38987, Singapore (100%)
Tel.: (65) 63334556
Web Site: http://www.softwareag.com
Sales Range: $25-49.9 Million
Emp.: 15
Computer Software & Services
N.A.I.C.S.: 541511

Software AG (Canada) Inc. (3)
231 Shearson Crescent Suite 101, Cambridge, N1T 1J5, ON, Canada
Tel.: (519) 624-3250
Web Site: http://www.softwareag.com
Sales Range: $25-49.9 Million
Emp.: 40
Software & IT Systems & Services
N.A.I.C.S.: 513210
David Ridout *(Reg VP & Country Mgr)*

Branch (Domestic):

Software AG Canada Corporation (4)
1250 Rene-Levesque Blvd West Suite 200, Montreal, H3B 4W8, QC, Canada
Tel.: (514) 989-3744
Sales Range: $25-49.9 Million
Emp.: 10
Custom Computer Programming Services
N.A.I.C.S.: 541511

Subsidiary (Non-US):

Software AG (Gulf) S.P.C. (3)
Office No 31 3rd Floor Building No 1269 Road No 3227 Block 332, PO Box 2154, Manama, Bahrain
Tel.: (973) 17582811
Computer Software Development Services
N.A.I.C.S.: 541512

Software AG (Israel) Ltd (3)
3B Yoni Netanyahu St, Or Yehuda, 60200, Tel Aviv, Israel (100%)
Tel.: (972) 35388333
Web Site: http://www.softwareag.com
Emp.: 100
Computer Related Services
N.A.I.C.S.: 541519

Software AG (Philippines) Inc. (3)
Unit 2202-2204 Robinsons-PCI Bank Tower, ADB Avenue cor Poveda Street O, 1603, Pasig, Philippines (100%)
Tel.: (63) 26353737
Sales Range: $25-49.9 Million
Emp.: 1
Custom Computer Programming Services
N.A.I.C.S.: 541511

Software AG (Shenzhen) Co Ltd (3)
Room 1709 Zhuoyue Bldg, 98 Fuhua Road One Futian Distr, 518033, Shenzhen, China
Tel.: (86) 75582878220
Web Site: http://www.softwareag.com
Software Reproducing
N.A.I.C.S.: 334610

Software AG (Singapore) Pte Ltd (3)
12 Marina Boulevard 17-04 Marina Bay Financial Centre Tower 3, Singapore, 018982, Singapore
Tel.: (65) 64179700
Computer Software Development Services
N.A.I.C.S.: 541512
Guo Yu *(Engr-Software)*

Software AG Argentina S.R.L. (3)
Ing Enrique Butty 275 8 Piso, Retiro, C1001, Buenos Aires, Argentina
Tel.: (54) 91144941804
Web Site: http://www.softwareag.com
Software Development Services
N.A.I.C.S.: 541511

Software AG Australia (Holdings) Pty Ltd (3)
L14 201 Miller Street, North Sydney, NSW, Australia
Tel.: (61) 294636400
Financial Management Services
N.A.I.C.S.: 523999
Stephen Keys *(Sr VP-Asia Pacific, Japan, Middle East, North Africa & Turkey)*
Sean Stephens *(Dir-Sls-Live-Asia Pacific)*
Michael Evans *(Dir-Sls-North)*
Ramesh Subramaniam *(Mgr-Pre Sls-Australia & New Zealand)*
James Wooster *(VP-Sls-Australia & New Zealand)*
Gordon Gakovic *(Mng Dir-Australia & New Zealand)*

Software AG Australia Pty Ltd. (3)
Level 4 182 Blues Point Rd, McMahons Point, 2060, NSW, Australia
Tel.: (61) 294636400
Sales Range: $50-74.9 Million
Emp.: 70
Software & Computer Systems Design
N.A.I.C.S.: 423430

Software AG Bangalore Technologies Private Ltd (3)
1st Floor Wing B Electra Exora Bussiness Park, Bengaluru, 560103, India
Tel.: (91) 8030534700
Sales Range: $75-99.9 Million
Emp.: 500
Software Development Services
N.A.I.C.S.: 541511
Padma Reddy *(Mng Dir)*

Software AG Belgium S.A. (3)
Glaverbel Terhulpensesteenweg 166/c1, 1160, Brussels, Belgium (100%)
Tel.: (32) 27770290
Web Site: http://www.softwareag.com
Sales Range: $25-49.9 Million
Emp.: 26
Computer Related Services
N.A.I.C.S.: 541519
Fabrice Van de Putte *(Dir-Sls)*

Subsidiary (Non-US):

SAG Software Systems SA (4) 40 rue Pafebruch, 8308, Capellen, Luxembourg (100%)
Tel.: (352) 29212211
Web Site: http://www.softwareag.be
Sales Range: $25-49.9 Million
Emp.: 15
Software Reproducing
N.A.I.C.S.: 334610
Marc Ten Thij *(VP-Belgium & Luxembourg)*
Mark Rhoden *(VP-Sls)*

Subsidiary (Non-US):

Software AG Bilgi Sistemleri Ticaret A.S (3)
Sasmaz Plaza Kat 9, Degirmen Yolu Sokak 34742 Kozy, 34742, Istanbul, Turkiye (100%)
Tel.: (90) 2163610506
Web Site: http://www.softwareag.com.tr
Sales Range: $25-49.9 Million
Emp.: 20
Computer & Computer Peripheral Equipment & Software Whslr
N.A.I.C.S.: 423430
Mike Saxton *(Sr VP & Gen Mgr-Middle East-Turkey)*
Ghassan Darri *(Dir-Alliance-Channel-Middle East, Turkey)*

Software AG Brasil Informatica e Servicos Ltda (3)
Av Nacoes Unidas 12 551 9 andar, Sao Paulo, 04578000, Brazil (100%)
Tel.: (55) 1134437450
Web Site: http://www.softwareag.com
Computer Storage Device Mfr
N.A.I.C.S.: 334112

Software AG Chennai Development Center India PVT Ltd (3)
5th Floor Unit 3 Pinnacle Building Ascendas It Park Taramani Road, Chennai, 600113, India
Tel.: (91) 4440927600
Web Site: http://www.softwareag.com
Software Development Services
N.A.I.C.S.: 541511

Software AG Chile S.A. (3)
La Concepcion 141, Oficina 1901-1902 Piso 19, Santiago, 7500010, Chile (100%)
Tel.: (56) 23470500
Web Site: http://www.softwareag.com
Sales Range: $25-49.9 Million
Emp.: 17
Electronic Computer Mfr
N.A.I.C.S.: 334111
Luis Hoyo *(Gen Mgr)*

Software AG China Ltd. (3)
Rm 79-80 China Life-West 5/F West Tower China Life Tower, No 16 Chaoyangmenwai Street Chaoyang District, Beijing, 100020, China
Tel.: (86) 4008428489
Computer Software Development Services
N.A.I.C.S.: 541512

Subsidiary (US):

Software AG De Puerto Rico, Inc. (3)
138 Ave Winston Churchill, San Juan, PR 00926
Tel.: (787) 232-3873
Computer Software Development Services
N.A.I.C.S.: 541512

Subsidiary (Non-US):

Software AG Development Center Bulgaria EOOD (3)
111 V Tsarigradsko shose Blvd floor 1, 1784, Sofia, Bulgaria
Tel.: (359) 29153600
Research & Development Services
N.A.I.C.S.: 541720

Software AG Development Centre Bulgaria EOOD (3)
111v Tsarigradsko Shose Blvd Walltopia Collider Activity Center Fl 1, 1784, Sofia, Bulgaria
Tel.: (359) 29153600
Web Site: http://www.softwareag.com
Software Development Services
N.A.I.C.S.: 541511

Software AG Development Centre Slovakia s.r.o. (3)
Juzna trieda 125, 040 01, Kosice, Slovakia
Tel.: (421) 557290527
Computer Software Development Services
N.A.I.C.S.: 541512

Software AG Espana S.A. (3)
Ronda De La Luna 22 Tres Cantos, 28760, Madrid, Spain
Tel.: (34) 918079400
Sales Range: $150-199.9 Million
Emp.: 600
Custom Computer Programming Services
N.A.I.C.S.: 541511
Damien Lopez *(Mng Dir)*

Software AG Espana Systemhaus S.L. (3)
Ronda De La Luna 22 Tres Cantos, 28760, Madrid, Spain (100%)
Tel.: (34) 918079400
Web Site: http://www.software.com
Sales Range: $150-199.9 Million
Emp.: 800
Custom Computer Programming Services
N.A.I.C.S.: 541511

Software AG Factoria S.A. (3)
La Concetcion 141, Oficina 1901-1902 Piso 19, Santiago, 7500010, Chile (100%)
Tel.: (56) 23470500
Web Site: http://www.softwareag.com
Sales Range: $25-49.9 Million
Emp.: 20
Computer & Computer Peripheral Equipment & Software Whslr
N.A.I.C.S.: 423430

Software AG Finland Oy. (3)
Antinkatu 3 D 7th Floor, 00100, Helsinki, Finland
Tel.: (358) 859463380
Web Site: http://www.softwareag.com
Sales Range: $25-49.9 Million
Software & Solution Services
N.A.I.C.S.: 513210

Software AG France S.A. (3)
Tour Europlaza 20 Avenue Andre Prothin, La Defense 4, 92927, Courbevoie, France
Tel.: (33) 178997000
Web Site: http://www.softwareag.com
Sales Range: $25-49.9 Million
Emp.: 90
Software & IT Systems & Services
N.A.I.C.S.: 513210
Fredrik Suchs *(Country Mgr)*

Branch (Domestic):

Software AG France S.a.r.l. (4)
Tour Europlaza 12eme etage 20 Avenue Andre Prothin, La Defense 4, 92927, Paris, Cedex, France
Tel.: (33) 1 78 99 70 00
Sales Range: $25-49.9 Million
Emp.: 24
Custom Computer Programming Services & Software Whslr
N.A.I.C.S.: 541511

Subsidiary (Non-US):

Software AG Hong Kong (3)
Room 1701-02 8 Fleming Road, Wanchai, China (Hong Kong)
Tel.: (852) 28668788
Emp.: 100
Customer Computer Programming Services & Software Whslr
N.A.I.C.S.: 541511

Software AG India Pvt Ltd. (3)
Unit No 501 Campus 1B, RMZ Ecospace Business Park, Bengaluru, 560 103, Bellandur, India
Tel.: (91) 8040104700
Web Site: http://www.softwareag.com
Software & IT Services & Systems
N.A.I.C.S.: 513210
Rajan Bhatnager *(Gen Mgr)*

Branch (Domestic):

Software AG Development Center India Private Limited (4)
Unit No 501 Campus 1B RMZ Ecospace Business Park, Bellandur, Bengaluru, 560 103, India

SILVER LAKE GROUP, LLC

U.S. PRIVATE

Silver Lake Group, LLC—(Continued)
Tel.: (91) 8040104700
Web Site: http://www.softwareag.com
Sales Range: $25-49.9 Million
Emp.: 200
Custom Computer Programming Services
N.A.I.C.S.: 541511
Padma Reddy (COO-Global R&D)

Subsidiary (Non-US):

Software AG International FZ-LLC (3)
Star Holding Building Building EIB 04 2nd Floor Office 204, Dubai Internet City, Dubai, United Arab Emirates
Tel.: (971) 45677631
Computer Software Development Services
N.A.I.C.S.: 541512
Rami Kichli (VP-Gulf & Levant)

Software AG Italia S.p.A. (3)
Via L Battistotti Sassi 11, 20133, Milan, Italy (100%)
Tel.: (39) 0221668211
Web Site: http://www.softwareag.com
Sales Range: $25-49.9 Million
Software Reproducing
N.A.I.C.S.: 334610

Software AG Korea Co., Ltd. (3)
7th Floor Korea Sanhak Foundation B/D, 1337-31 Seoch-dong Seocho-gu, Seoul, 137 070, Korea (South)
Tel.: (82) 234152900
Custom Computer Programming Services & Software Whslr
N.A.I.C.S.: 541511

Software AG Latinoamerica S.L. (3)
Ronda De La Luna 22 Tres Cantos, 28760, Madrid, Spain (100%)
Tel.: (34) 918079400
Web Site: http://www.softwareag.com
Sales Range: $150-199.9 Million
Emp.: 700
Custom Computer Programming Services
N.A.I.C.S.: 541511

Software AG Nederland B.V. (3)
Regus Teleport Towers, Kingsfordweg 151, 1043 GR, Amsterdam, Netherlands
Tel.: (31) 205814100
Web Site: http://www.softwareag.nl
Software & Computer Peripherals Whslr
N.A.I.C.S.: 423430

Software AG Nederland B.V. (3)
Loire 162 gebouw B, 2491 AL, Hague, Netherlands
Tel.: (31) 703012040
Web Site: http://www.softwareag.nl
Sales Range: $25-49.9 Million
Emp.: 49
Business Process Management Software & Consulting Services
N.A.I.C.S.: 513210
Hans Kouffeld (VP-Sales)

Software AG Nordic A/S (3)
Stamholmen 147, 2650, Hvidovre, Denmark (100%)
Tel.: (45) 43508800
Web Site: http://www.softwareag.com
Sales Range: $25-49.9 Million
Emp.: 17
Custom Computer Programming Services
N.A.I.C.S.: 541511
Camilla Emle (Mgr-Mktg)

Software AG Nordic AB (3)
Besok Kista Science Tower, Farogatan 33, 16440, Kista, Sweden (100%)
Tel.: (46) 859463380
Sales Range: $25-49.9 Million
Emp.: 20
Custom Computer Programming Services
N.A.I.C.S.: 541511
Daniel Eliasson (Dir-Sls)
Parisa Sundberg (Mgr-Mktg)

Software AG Operations Malaysia Sdn Bhd (3)
Suite 2B 22 1 Level 22 Block 2B Plaza Sentral, Jalan Stesen Sentral 5, Kuala Lumpur, 50470, Malaysia
Tel.: (60) 374902888
Web Site: http://www.softwareag.com
Sales Range: $25-49.9 Million
Emp.: 50

Custom Computer Programming Services & Software Whslr
N.A.I.C.S.: 541511
Jennifer Chiang (Office Mgr)

Software AG Polska Sp. z o.o. (3)
18 Piekna Street, 00-549, Warsaw, Poland
Tel.: (48) 223795300
Web Site: http://www.softwareag.com
Emp.: 25
Custom Computer Programming Services
N.A.I.C.S.: 541511

Software AG Portugal Alta Tecnologia Informatica Lda (3)
Campo Grande 28-1 D, Lisbon, 1700-093, Portugal (100%)
Tel.: (351) 217817530
Web Site: http://www.softwareag.com
Computer & Computer Peripheral Equipment & Software Whslr
N.A.I.C.S.: 423430
Alex Monedero (Mgr-IT)

Software AG Saudi Arabia LLC (3)
The Kingdom Ctr 28th Floor, PO Box 230888, 11321, Riyadh, Saudi Arabia (100%)
Tel.: (966) 12118022
Web Site: http://www.softwareag.com
Sales Range: $25-49.9 Million
Emp.: 20
Computer Peripheral Equipment Mfr
N.A.I.C.S.: 334118
Marco Gerazounis (Sr VP)
Bashar Yaish (VP-Gulf)

Software AG South Africa (Pty) Ltd (3)
34 Culross Main Rd, Lonehill Ext 95 Fourways, Bryanston, 2021, South Africa (100%)
Tel.: (27) 113172900
Web Site: http://www.softwareag.com
Sales Range: $25-49.9 Million
Emp.: 100
Software Reproducing
N.A.I.C.S.: 334610
Nomhle Mujakachi (Mng Partner-Pub Sector)

Software AG Sweden AB (3)
Kista Science Tower Farogatan 33, 164 51, Kista, Sweden
Tel.: (46) 859463380
Computer Software Development Services
N.A.I.C.S.: 541512
Daniel Eliasson (VP-Nordics)

Software AG UK Ltd. (3)
Locomotive Way Pride Park, Derby, DE24 8PU, United Kingdom
Tel.: (44) 1332611000
Web Site: http://www.softwareag.co.uk
Sales Range: $25-49.9 Million
Emp.: 80
Business Process Management Software & Consulting Services
N.A.I.C.S.: 513210

Division (Domestic):

Software AG UK Ltd. (4)
Barons Court, 22 The Avenue, Egham, TW20 9AB, Surrey, United Kingdom
Tel.: (44) 1784 221700
Custom Computer Programming Services & Software Whslr
N.A.I.C.S.: 541511

Software AG UK Ltd. (4)
London House London Rd, Bracknell, RG12 2UT, Berkshire, United Kingdom
Tel.: (44) 1344403800
Web Site: http://www.softwareag.com
Sales Range: $25-49.9 Million
Software & IT Systems & Services
N.A.I.C.S.: 513210

Subsidiary (Non-US):

Software AG Venezuela C.A. (3)
Av Francisco de Miranda Torre Europa Piso 9 , Oficina 903, El Rosal , 1060, Caracas, Municipio Cacao, Venezuela (100%)
Tel.: (58) 2122769211
Web Site: http://www.softwareag.com
Computer Storage Device Mfr
N.A.I.C.S.: 334112

Software AG de Panama, S.A (3)

Edificio 237 Primer Alto Calle Gerald, Paitilla, Panama (100%)
Tel.: (507) 3171322
Web Site: http://www.softwareag.com.pa
Sales Range: $25-49.9 Million
Emp.: 5
Computer System Design Services
N.A.I.C.S.: 541512

Software AG s.r.o. (3)
Na Prikope 958/25, 110 00, Prague, Czech Republic
Tel.: (420) 235517860
Web Site: http://www.softwareag.com
Sales Range: $25-49.9 Million
Emp.: 10
Software Development Services
N.A.I.C.S.: 541511

Subsidiary (US):

Software AG, Inc. (3)
11700 Plz America Dr Ste 700, Reston, VA 20191-5453 (100%)
Tel.: (703) 860-5050
Web Site: http://www.softwareagusa.com
Sales Range: $200-249.9 Million
Emp.: 800
Database Management Systems Software, Enterprise Integration Software, Applications Development & Information Center Tools Retailer
N.A.I.C.S.: 513210
Mark Edwards (CEO)
Laura McCluer (VP-Alliances & Channels)

Subsidiary (Domestic):

Software AG International Inc (4)
11700 Plaza America Dr 7th Fl, Reston, VA 20190 (100%)
Tel.: (703) 391-8191
Web Site: http://www.softwareag.com
Software Reproducing
N.A.I.C.S.: 334610
Karl-Heinz Streibich (CEO)

Software AG USA, Inc. (4)
11700 Plz America Dr Ste 700, Reston, VA 20190
Tel.: (703) 860-5050
Web Site: http://www.softwareag.com
Emp.: 200
Software Solutions for Business-to-Business Integration
N.A.I.C.S.: 541511

Subsidiary (Domestic):

Relational Networks, Inc. (5)
3211 Scott Blvd Ste 204, Sunnyvale, CA 95054
Tel.: (408) 774-9474
Web Site: http://www.longjump.com
Sales Range: $10-24.9 Million
Emp.: 20
Cloud Platform Services
N.A.I.C.S.: 541511

Software Ag Government Solutions, Inc. (5)
12950 Worldgate Dr Ste 300, Herndon, VA 20170
Tel.: (703) 949-9570
Web Site: http://www.softwareaggov.com
Software Development Services
N.A.I.C.S.: 541511
Tod Weber (Chm & CEO)
Chris Tierney (Controller)
Chris Borneman (CTO)

Terracotta, Inc. (5)
575 Florida St Ste 100, San Francisco, CA 94110
Tel.: (415) 738-4000
Web Site: http://www.terracotta.org
Sales Range: $25-49.9 Million
Emp.: 55
Software Developer
N.A.I.C.S.: 513210
Ari Zilka (Founder & CTO)

Subsidiary (Non-US):

WebMethods Australia Pty Ltd. (5)
Level 4 182 Blues Point Road McMahons Point, Sydney, 2060, NSW, Australia
Tel.: (61) 294636400
Web Site: http://www.webmethods.com

Sales Range: $10-24.9 Million
Emp.: 50
Software Development Services
N.A.I.C.S.: 541511

Subsidiary (Non-US):

Software AG, Ltd. (3)
3-12-1 Nissay Toranomon Building 12th Floor, Minato-ku, Tokyo, 1050001, Japan
Tel.: (81) 354054220
Sales Range: $25-49.9 Million
Emp.: 100
Custom Computer Programming Services & Software Whslr
N.A.I.C.S.: 541511

Software AG, S.A. de C.V. (3)
Av Volcan No 150 Ofna 415 Col, 11000, Lomas de Chapultepec, Mexico
Tel.: (52) 5541669074
Web Site: http://www.softwareag.com
Sales Range: $25-49.9 Million
Electronic Computer Mfr
N.A.I.C.S.: 334111
Gabriela Bautesta (Fin Dir)

Software GmbH Osterreich (3)
Guglgasse 7-9, 1030, Vienna, Austria (100%)
Tel.: (43) 1329500
Sales Range: $25-49.9 Million
Emp.: 40
Computer Related Services
N.A.I.C.S.: 541519
Andrea Echart (Country Mgr)

Soluciones de Integracion de Negocios S.A. (3)
Oficentro La Sabana Of 4, San Jose, Costa Rica (100%)
Tel.: (506) 2315458
Computer & Computer Peripheral Equipment & Software Whslr
N.A.I.C.S.: 423430

Subsidiary (US):

StreamSets, Inc. (3)
1875 S Grant St Ste 810, San Mateo, CA 94402
Tel.: (415) 851-1018
Web Site: https://streamsets.com
Data Integration Services
N.A.I.C.S.: 541330

Subsidiary (Non-US):

TrendMiner NV (3)
Kempische Steenweg 309/5 Corda Building 2, 3500, Hasselt, Belgium
Tel.: (32) 11263830
Web Site: https://www.trendminer.com
Computer Software Development Services
N.A.I.C.S.: 541512
Thomas Dhollander (Founder & CTO)
Joan Van de Wetering (Chief Revenue Officer)
Niels Verheijen (VP-Global Sls)
Stijn Meganck (VP-Res)
Edwin Van Dijk (VP-Mktg)

Subsidiary (US):

Zementis, Inc. (3)
3570 Carmel Mtn Rd Ste 300, San Diego, CA 92130
Tel.: (619) 330-0780
Web Site: http://www.zementis.com
Software Development Services
N.A.I.C.S.: 541511
Michael Zeller (Co-Founder & CEO)
Wendy G. Cheung (Co-Founder & COO)
David E. DeVol (Exec VP)
Alex Guazzelli (CTO)
Mark Rabkin (Dir-Bus Dev)

Subsidiary (Non-US):

itCampus (UK) Limited (3)
Heritage Business Centre Derby Road, Belper, DE56 1SW, United Kingdom
Tel.: (44) 8445899509
Web Site: http://www.elsbeth.co.uk
Software Development Services
N.A.I.C.S.: 541511
Robert Denbeigh (Mng Dir)

Subsidiary (Domestic):

itCampus Software und Systemhaus GmbH (3)

COMPANIES

SILVER POINT CAPITAL, L.P.

Nonnenstr 37, 04229, Leipzig, Germany
Tel.: (49) 34149287000
Sales Range: $25-49.9 Million
Emp.: 70
Software Development Services
N.A.I.C.S.: 541511

Joint Venture (Domestic):

SolarWinds, Inc. (2)
7171 SW Pkwy Bldg 400, Austin, TX 78735
Tel.: (512) 682-9300
Web Site: http://www.solarwinds.com
Emp.: 2,500
Corporate IT & Network Infrastructure Services
N.A.I.C.S.: 541519
Douglas G. Hibberd (Pres-Bus Ops & Exec VP)
J. Barton Kalsu (CFO & Exec VP)
Jason W. Bliss (Gen Counsel, Sec & Exec VP)
Darren Beck (CMO & Exec VP)
Joe Kim (CTO & Exec VP-Engrg)
John Pagliuca (Exec VP & Gen Mgr)
David Gardiner (Exec VP-Core IT)
Rohini Kasturi (Chief Product Officer & Exec VP)
Tim Brown (Chief Info Security Officer & VP-Security)
Andrea Webb (Chief Customer Officer & Sr VP)

Subsidiary (Domestic):

Librato, Inc. (3)
535 Mission St Ste 2100, San Francisco, CA 94105
Web Site: http://www.librato.com
Software Development Services
N.A.I.C.S.: 513210
Michelle Urban (Dir-Mktg)
Dan Stondin (Co-Founder & Dir-Design)
Nik Wekwerth (Dir-Customer Success)
Joe Ruscio (Co-Founder & CTO)
Matt Sanders (Dir-Engrg)
Mike Heffner (Co-Founder & Dir-Engrg)

Loggly, Inc. (3)
535 Mission St 14th Fl, San Francisco, CA 94101
Tel.: (512) 498-6011
Web Site: http://www.loggly.com
Software Publisher
N.A.I.C.S.: 513210
Vinh Nguyen (Principal Engr)

Subsidiary (Non-US):

Pingdom AB (3)
Kopparbergsvagen 8 5th Floor, 722 13, Vasteras, Sweden
Tel.: (46) 20889858
Web Site: http://www.pingdom.com
Website Monitoring Software Publisher
N.A.I.C.S.: 513210

SolarWinds MSP UK Ltd. (3)
The Vision Building, 20 Green Market, Dundee, DD1 4QB, United Kingdom
Tel.: (44) 1382309040
Web Site: http://www.logicnow.com
Software Services
N.A.I.C.S.: 513210
John Pagliuca (Pres)
J. P. Jauvin (Sr VP-Sls & Customer Ops)
August Wehrmann (VP-Engrg)
Mike Cullen (VP-Sls & Customer Retention)
Frank Colletti (VP-Worldwide Sls)
Leo Sanchez (VP-Worldwide Customer Support)
Mike Adler (Chief Tech & Product Officer)

Subsidiary (Domestic):

SolarWinds Worldwide, LLC (3)
7171 SW Pkwy Bldg 400, Austin, TX 78735
Tel.: (512) 682-9300
Web Site: http://www.solarwinds.com
IT Management Software Services
N.A.I.C.S.: 423210

Subsidiary (Domestic):

Weld North LLC (2)
3 Columbus Cir Ste 2405, New York, NY 10019
Tel.: (203) 413-5170
Web Site: https://www.weldnorth.com

Investment Holding Company; Digital & Software-as-a-Service Educational Products & Services
N.A.I.C.S.: 551112
Jonathan N. Grayer (CEO & Founder)
Adam Klaber (Vice Chm)
Waseem Alam (Mng Dir)

Subsidiary (Domestic):

Assessment Technology, Inc. (3)
6700 E Speedway Blvd, Tucson, AZ 85710
Tel.: (520) 323-9033
Web Site: http://www.ati-online.com
Learning & Educational Services
N.A.I.C.S.: 611710
Brian Benson (Engr-Software)
Sarah Callahan Estrada (Project Mgr)
Luke Ferris (Dir-Tech)
Kerridan Kawecki (Dir-Pro Dev)
Craig Mayhew (Dir-Field Svcs)
Scott Cunningham (Dir-Assessment & Instructional Design)

Glynlyon, Inc. (3)
300 N McKemy Ave, Chandler, AZ 85226
Tel.: (888) 881-4959
Web Site: http://www.glynlyon.com
Academic Curriculum, Learning Tools & Educational Multimedia Developer & Distr
N.A.I.C.S.: 611710
Ken Roberts (VP-Tech)

Division (Domestic):

Alpha Omega Publications (4)
804 N 2nd Ave E, Rock Rapids, IA 51246
Tel.: (800) 682-7396
Web Site: http://www.aop.com
Christian Homeschooling Curriculum Publisher
N.A.I.C.S.: 513199
Ruby Chavira (Coord-Education)

Odysseyware (4)
300 N McKemy Ave, Chandler, AZ 85226
Web Site: http://www.odysseyware.com
Online Curriculum & E-Learning Solutions Developer & Distr
N.A.I.C.S.: 513210
Matthew Given (Pres & CEO)
Charles Mallon (CFO)
Ken Roberts (VP-Tech)
David Pinkus (CTO)
Barry Swihart (Sr VP-Sls)
Josey Borman (Sr VP-Product Dev)
Kat Brown (VP-Customer Success)
Eric Dalton (Exec VP-Mktg & Consumer Div)

Subsidiary (Domestic):

Imagine Learning, LLC (3)
8860 E. Chaparral Rd, Ste 100, Scottsdale, AZ 85250
Tel.: (877) 202-0338
Web Site: https://www.imaginelearning.com
Educational Software Programming Services
N.A.I.C.S.: 541511
Joe Swenson (Pres)
John Orsanic (CFO)
Jonathan Grayer (CEO)

Subsidiary (Domestic):

Winsor Learning Inc. (4)
3001 Metro Dr Ste 480, Bloomington, MN 55425
Tel.: (800) 321-7585
Web Site: http://winsorlearning.com
Sales Range: $1-9.9 Million
Emp.: 8
Management Consulting Services
N.A.I.C.S.: 541613
Pete Joyce (Mgr)

Holding (Non-US):

ZPG Limited (2)
The Cooperage 5 Copper Row, London, SE1 2LH, United Kingdom
Tel.: (44) 2038725653
Web Site: http://www.zpg.co.uk
Digital Platform Provider
N.A.I.C.S.: 519290
Charlie Bryant (Mng Dir-Property)
Tariq Syed (Mng Dir-Comparison)

Subsidiary (Domestic):

The Printed Group Limited (3)

Q5-Quorum Business Park Benton Lane, Newcastle, NE12 8BS, United Kingdom
Tel.: (44) 1919179331
Web Site: http://www.ravensworth.co.uk
Commercial Printing Services
N.A.I.C.S.: 323111
Alison Crawford (Head-Sls)

SILVER OAK SERVICES PARTNERS, LLC
1560 Sherman Ave Ste 1200, Evanston, IL 60201
Tel.: (847) 332-0400   DE
Web Site: http://www.silveroaksp.com
Privater Equity Firm
N.A.I.C.S.: 523999
Gregory M. Barr (Mng Partner)
Linda S. Epstein (Controller)
Katie E. Perry (Chief Compliance Officer & VP-Fin)
Andrew S. Gustafson (Partner)
Bernadette R. Maida (Office Mgr)
Lynn Lipsig (VP-Investment Res)
Daniel M. Gill (Mng Partner)

Subsidiaries:

Altura Communication Solutions, LLC (1)
1540 S Lewis St, Anaheim, CA 92805
Tel.: (714) 948-8400
Web Site: http://www.alturacs.com
Sales Range: $25-49.9 Million
Emp.: 250
Corporate & Government Telecommunication Services
N.A.I.C.S.: 517121
Bob Blazek (Pres & CEO)

Commercial Cleaning Systems, Inc. (1)
1485 S Lipan St, Denver, CO 80223
Tel.: (303) 733-8997
Web Site: http://www.commercialcleaningsystems.net
Sales Range: $1-9.9 Million
Emp.: 200
Janitorial Services
N.A.I.C.S.: 561720
Jesus Guerrero (Gen Mgr)
Megan Romero (Dir-Bus Dev)
Troy Coker (CEO & Pres)

Subsidiary (Domestic):

Sparkle Maintenance, Inc. (2)
4801 Hardware Dr NE, Albuquerque, NM 87109-2019
Tel.: (505) 345-4901
Web Site: http://www.sparklemaintenance.com
Janitorial Services
N.A.I.C.S.: 561720
Carlo Lucero (Pres)

Innovative Discovery, LLC (1)
1700 N Moore St Ste 1500, Arlington, VA 22209
Tel.: (703) 875-8003
Web Site: http://www.id-edd.com
Administrative Management & General Management Consulting Service
N.A.I.C.S.: 541611
James Perkins (Chief Client Officer)
Kim Taylor (CEO)
Bryan Campbell (COO)
Ryan Lissauer (CFO)
Rachel Bloomer (VP-HR)

Subsidiary (Domestic):

Integro, Inc. (2)
88 Inverness Cir E N106, Englewood, CO 80112
Tel.: (303) 575-9300
Web Site: http://www.integro.com
Management Consulting Services
N.A.I.C.S.: 541618
Scott Burt (Pres & CEO)
Jason Brandes (Founder & VP)
John Frost (VP-Strategic Accts)
Mike Prentice (Dir-Modernization & Automation)

Integrated Oncology Network LLC (1)

104 Woodmont Blvd Ste 500, Nashville, TN 37205
Tel.: (949) 207-3111
Web Site: http://www.ion-llc.com
Freestanding Ambulatory Surgical & Emergency Centers
N.A.I.C.S.: 621493
David Crowley (Chief Acctg Officer)

Keystone Partners (1)
125 Summer St Ste 1020, Boston, MA 02110
Tel.: (617) 720-7300
Web Site:
    https://www.keystonepartners.com
All Other Personal Services
N.A.I.C.S.: 812990

Subsidiary (Domestic):

Ayers Group Inc. (2)
99 Park Ave 8th Fl, New York, NY 10016
Tel.: (212) 889-7788
Web Site: http://www.ayers.com
Sales Range: $10-24.9 Million
Emp.: 100
Placement & Recruiting Agencies
N.A.I.C.S.: 561311
Larry Fisher (VP-Bus Dev)
Liana Gordon Kahn (Exec Dir-Development)
Maurine DeJesus (Project Mgr & Mgr)

SILVER PEAK PARTNERS
621 17th St Ste 1710, Denver, CO 80202
Tel.: (303) 475-4165   CO
Web Site:
    http://www.silverpeakpartners.com
Privater Equity Firm
N.A.I.C.S.: 523999
Bill Haan (Mng Partner)
Bryan Hursh (Partner)

SILVER POINT CAPITAL, L.P.
2 Greenwich Plz 1st Fl, Greenwich, CT 06830
Tel.: (203) 542-4200
Web Site:
    http://www.silverpointcapital.com
Year Founded: 2002
Sales Range: $100-124.9 Million
Emp.: 300
Private Equity Firm; Hedge Fund Services
N.A.I.C.S.: 551112
Edward Mule (Co-Founder & Partner)
Robert O'Shea (Co-Founder & Partner)
Michael A. Gatto (Partner)

Subsidiaries:

Granite Broadcasting Corporation (1)
767 3rd Ave 34th Fl, New York, NY 10017-2023
Tel.: (212) 826-2530
Web Site: http://www.granitetv.com
Sales Range: $125-149.9 Million
Holding Company; Television Broadcasting Stations Operator
N.A.I.C.S.: 551112
Lawrence I. Wills (CFO)
Peter Markham (Chm)
Duane A. Lammers (COO)

Subsidiary (Domestic):

KBJR, Inc. (2)
246 S Lake Ave, Duluth, MN 55802
Tel.: (218) 727-8484
TV Station
N.A.I.C.S.: 516120

KOFY, Inc. (2)
2500 Marin St, San Francisco, CA 94124
Tel.: (415) 821-2020
Web Site: http://www.kofytv.com
Sales Range: $10-24.9 Million
Emp.: 32
TV Station
N.A.I.C.S.: 516120
Kemp Nichol (Pres & Gen Mgr)

SILVER POINT CAPITAL, L.P.

Silver Point Capital, L.P.—(Continued)

WEEK-TV (2)
2907 Springfield Rd, East Peoria, IL 61611
Tel.: (309) 698-2525
Web Site: http://www.week.com
Sales Range: $25-49.9 Million
Emp.: 100
TV Station
N.A.I.C.S.: 516120
Mark DeSantis (Gen Mgr)

WISE-TV, Inc. (2)
3401 Butler Rd, Fort Wayne, IN 46808
Tel.: (260) 483-0584
Web Site:
   http://www.indianasnewscenter.com
Television Broadcasting Station
N.A.I.C.S.: 516120

WTVH, LLC (2)
1030 James St, Syracuse, NY 13203
Tel.: (315) 425-5555
Sales Range: $25-49.9 Million
Emp.: 2
TV Station
N.A.I.C.S.: 516120
Kimberlin Roden (Controller)

Silver Point Capital Fund Investments LLC (1)
2 Greenwich Plz 1st Fl, Greenwich, CT 06830
Tel.: (203) 542-4200
Sales Range: $25-49.9 Million
Emp.: 50
Holding Company
N.A.I.C.S.: 551112

SILVER SHIPS, INC.
9243 Bellingrath Rd, Theodore, AL 36582-2710
Tel.: (251) 973-0000 AL
Web Site: http://www.silverships.com
Year Founded: 1985
Custom Aluminum Ships
N.A.I.C.S.: 336612
Mike McCarty (Pres & CEO)
Rebecca McCarty (VP)
Chad Gray (Mgr-Prod)

SILVER SKY CAPITAL, LTD.
14301 N 87th St Ste 301, Scottsdale, AZ 85260
Tel.: (480) 272-7290 NV
Web Site:
   http://www.silverskycapital.com
Year Founded: 2010
Sales Range: $10-24.9 Million
Emp.: 2
Health & Wellness Food & Beverage Developer
N.A.I.C.S.: 311999
Steven Paul Nickolas (Pres & CEO)

SILVER SPRINGS BOTTLED WATER CO.
2445 NW 42nd St, Ocala, FL 34475
Tel.: (352) 368-7907
Web Site: http://www.ssbwc.com
Year Founded: 1986
Sales Range: $10-24.9 Million
Emp.: 150
Bottled Water Mfr & Distr
N.A.I.C.S.: 312112
Karl E. Richmond (Chm)
David Pruett (VP-Sls)
Mike Lender (Controller)
Kane Richmond (Pres)

Subsidiaries:

Hickory Springs Water, LLC (1)
347 Old River Rd, Elloree, SC 29047
Tel.: (803) 826-6004
Web Site:
   http://www.hickoryspringswater.com
Sales Range: $1-9.9 Million
Emp.: 50
Bottled Water Mfr
N.A.I.C.S.: 312112

Rick Stewart (CEO)
Albert Withrow (Mgr-Quality)
Anne Felder (Office Mgr)
William Waters (Mgr-Production)

SILVER STAR COMMUNICATIONS
104101 Hwy 89, Freedom, WY 83120
Tel.: (307) 883-2411
Web Site: http://www.silverstar.com
Sales Range: $10-24.9 Million
Emp.: 58
Telecommunications Resellers
N.A.I.C.S.: 517121
Ron McCue (VP)
Allen R. Hoopes (Pres & CEO)

SILVER STAR PROPERTIES REIT, INC.
2909 Hillcroft Ste 420, Houston, TX 77057
Tel.: (713) 467-2222 MD
Web Site: https://silverstarreit.com
Year Founded: 2008
Rev.: $92,158,000
Assets: $505,322,000
Liabilities: $348,004,000
Net Worth: $157,318,000
Earnings: ($12,336,000)
Emp.: 162
Fiscal Year-end: 12/31/21
Real Estate Investment Trust
N.A.I.C.S.: 523999
Gerald W. Haddock (Exec Chm, Chm & Co-CEO)
David Wheeler (Pres, Co-CEO & COO)
Adrienne Collins (Gen Counsel & Sec)
Louis T. Fox III (CFO, Chief Acctg Officer, Treas & Sec)

Subsidiaries:

Hartman 400 North Belt LLC (1)
400 N Sam Houston Pkwy E, Houston, TX 77060-3548
Tel.: (281) 407-1238
Real Estate Services
N.A.I.C.S.: 531390

Hartman Cooper Street Plaza, LLC (1)
4619 - 4623 S Cooper St, Arlington, TX 76017
Tel.: (469) 249-9742
Real Estate Services
N.A.I.C.S.: 531390

Hartman Corporate Park Place LLC (1)
1333 Corporate Dr, Irving, TX 75038
Tel.: (469) 249-9742
Real Estate Services
N.A.I.C.S.: 531390

Hartman Mitchelldale Business Park, LLC (1)
5400 - 5401 Mitchelldale St, Houston, TX 77092
Tel.: (281) 407-1238
Real Estate Services
N.A.I.C.S.: 531390

Hartman Skymark Tower LLC (1)
1521 N Cooper St, Arlington, TX 76011
Tel.: (469) 249-9742
Real Estate Services
N.A.I.C.S.: 531390

Hartman Three Forest Plaza, LLC (1)
12221 Merit Dr, Dallas, TX 75215
Tel.: (469) 249-9742
Real Estate Services
N.A.I.C.S.: 531390

Hartman Westway One, LLC (1)
1707 Market Pl Blvd, Irving, TX 75063
Tel.: (469) 249-9742
Real Estate Services
N.A.I.C.S.: 531390

SILVER STATE SCHOOLS CREDIT UNION
4221 Mcleod Dr, Las Vegas, NV 89121-5215
Tel.: (702) 697-8000 NV
Web Site:
   http://www.silverstatecu.com
Year Founded: 1951
Sales Range: $25-49.9 Million
Emp.: 261
Credit Union Operator
N.A.I.C.S.: 522130
Ann Johnson (VP-HR & Trng)
Michael Randall (COO & VP)
Raymond Wilson (CFO)
Rebecca Freeman (Dir-Mktg)
James Bolin (Chief Lending Officer & VP)

SILVER SUSTAINABLE SOLUTIONS CORP.
1055 Thomas Jefferson St NW Ste 650, Washington, DC 20007
Tel.: (202) 643-9162 DE
Web Site:
   https://www.silversustainable.com
Year Founded: 2018
Assets: $868,308
Liabilities: $1,039,448
Net Worth: ($171,140)
Earnings: ($171,505)
Emp.: 3
Fiscal Year-end: 12/31/21
Investment Services
N.A.I.C.S.: 523999
Jonathan M. Silver (CEO, Co-Founder & Chm)
Michael W. Allman (Co-Founder & CFO)
Arun Majumdar (Co-Founder, CTO & Sec)
Crosby F. Fish (VP)

SILVER TOWNE LP
120 E Union City Pike, Winchester, IN 47394-8383
Tel.: (765) 584-7481 IN
Web Site: http://www.silvertowne.com
Year Founded: 1960
Sales Range: $50-74.9 Million
Emp.: 100
Sales of Silver, Coins & Jewelry
N.A.I.C.S.: 423940
Todd Hutch (Mgr-HR)
Brian Feltis (Engr-Network)
Matthew Lesher (COO)
David Hendrickson (Co-Founder & CEO)

SILVER VENTURES, INC.
303 Pearl Pkwy Ste 300, San Antonio, TX 78215
Tel.: (210) 465-5501
Year Founded: 1995
Venture Capital
N.A.I.C.S.: 523999

SILVER-LINE PLASTICS CORP.
900 Riverside Dr, Asheville, NC 28804
Tel.: (828) 252-8755
Web Site: http://www.slpipe.com
Sales Range: $10-24.9 Million
Emp.: 100
Plastic Tank Mfr
N.A.I.C.S.: 326122
Ricky Silver (Pres & CEO)

SILVERADO BUILDING MATERIALS
9297 Jackson Rd, Sacramento, CA 95826
Tel.: (916) 361-7374
Web Site:
   http://www.silveradoonline.com
Rev.: $50,000,000

Emp.: 40
Building Materials Sales
N.A.I.C.S.: 423310
Kimberly Balbuena (Office Mgr)

SILVERADO STAGES, INC.
241 Prado Rd, San Luis Obispo, CA 93401
Tel.: (805) 545-8400
Web Site:
   http://www.silveradostages.com
Year Founded: 1987
Bus Charter Services
N.A.I.C.S.: 485510
Jim Galusha (Chm)
Sharron Galusha (Pres)
Mike Watson (CMO)
Susan Schmidt (CFO)
John Langley (COO)
Aron Clark (Mgr-Fleet)
John Busskohl (CEO)
Cory Medigovich (Mgr-Digital Mktg)

Subsidiaries:

Silver State Coach, Inc. (1)
701 Fee Ana St, Placentia, CA 92870
Tel.: (714) 577-0180
Web Site: http://www.silveradostages.com
Sales Range: $1-9.9 Million
Emp.: 100
Tours, Shuttles & Private Transportation Services
N.A.I.C.S.: 561520
Anthony Fiorini (Pres)
Ricardo Cepeda (Gen Mgr)
Tina Jurkowski (Dir-Sls & Mktg)

SILVERADO SYSTEMS, INC.
771 Oak Ave Pkwy Ste 1, Folsom, CA 95630
Tel.: (916) 760-0032
Web Site: http://www.silverado.cc
Year Founded: 2003
Rev.: $2,700,000
Emp.: 3
Computer System Design Services
N.A.I.C.S.: 541512
Torrey Loomis (CEO)

SILVERBERG JEWELRY COMPANY
6730 22nd Ave N Ste E, Saint Petersburg, FL 33710
Tel.: (727) 381-2666 FL
Web Site:
   http://www.silverbergjewelry.com
Year Founded: 1998
Sales Range: $1-9.9 Million
Emp.: 35
Jewelry Stores
N.A.I.C.S.: 458310
Edward Silverberg (Pres)

SILVERCHAIR INFORMATION SYSTEMS
316 E Main St, Charlottesville, VA 22902
Tel.: (434) 296-6333
Web Site: http://www.silverchair.com
Year Founded: 1993
Sales Range: $10-24.9 Million
Emp.: 137
Periodical Publishers
N.A.I.C.S.: 513120
Bobby Jenkins (CFO & COO)
Elizabeth Willingham (Co-Founder & Exec VP)
Jake Zarnegar (Pres)
Thane Kerner (Pres & CEO)
Basia Jones (Assoc Dir-Project Mgmt)
Susan Dawson (Chief People Officer)
Joy Moore (Chief Product Officer)
Stuart Leitch (CTO)
Derek Naughton (Dir-Client Svcs & Ops)

COMPANIES

Andrew McElfresh *(Dir-Implementations)*
Craig Griffin *(Dir-Platform Roadmap)*
Evelyn Jabri *(Dir-Product Strategy)*
Zikki Munyao *(Dir-Program Mgmt Office)*
Rena Morse *(Dir-Semantics)*
Brian Hubbell *(Dir-User Experience)*
Jane McQueen *(VP-Process Mgmt)*

SILVEREDGE COOPERATIVE
39999 Hilton Rd, Edgewood, IA 52042
Tel.: (563) 928-6419
Web Site: http://www.silveredgecoop.com
Year Founded: 1931
Sales Range: $10-24.9 Million
Emp.: 29
Farm Supplies Sales
N.A.I.C.S.: 424910
Tony Hemann *(CEO & Gen Mgr)*
Grover Goldsmith *(Mgr)*
David Venteicher *(Vice Chm)*
Lynn Brunsman *(Sec & Treas)*

SILVEREDGE, LLC
4065 St Cloud Dr, Loveland, CO 80538
Tel.: (970) 800-2890
Web Site: http://pages.gosilveredge.com
Year Founded: 2007
Electronic Payment Services
N.A.I.C.S.: 522320
Ken Salazar *(Pres & CEO)*
Becky Ross *(VP-Mktg)*
Dennis Porter *(VP-Ops)*

SILVERFERN CAPITAL MANAGEMENT, LLC
599 Lexington Ave 47th Fl, New York, NY 10022
Tel.: (212) 209-8860
Web Site: http://www.silfern.com
Year Founded: 2001
Investment Management & Private Equity Firm
N.A.I.C.S.: 523999
Reeta K. Holmes *(Mng Partner)*
Clive R. Holmes *(Mng Partner)*
Edward M. Rimland *(Mng Dir)*
Andrew Isikoff *(Mng Dir)*
John R. Cattau *(Mng Dir)*
Torsten Kopke *(Mng Dir-Frankfurt)*

Subsidiaries:

Continental Bakeries B.V. (1)
Pieter Zeemanweg 17, 3316 GZ, Dordrecht, Netherlands
Tel.: (31) 786537653
Web Site: https://www.continentalbakeries.com
Sales Range: $350-399.9 Million
Emp.: 1,550
Bread, Cookie & Biscuit Mfr
N.A.I.C.S.: 311821
Ruud van Henten *(CEO)*

Gordian Medical, Inc. (1)
17595 Cartwright Rd, Irvine, CA 92614-6680
Tel.: (949) 553-0103
Web Site: http://www.amtwoundcare.com
Offices of Physicians (except Mental Health Specialists)
N.A.I.C.S.: 621111
Kathy Clark *(Office Mgr)*

Le Sueur Incorporated (1)
1409 Vine St, Le Sueur, MN 56058-1125
Tel.: (507) 665-6204
Web Site: http://www.lesueurinc.com
Sales Range: $25-49.9 Million
Emp.: 450
Provider of Industrial Products
N.A.I.C.S.: 331523
Mark Mueller *(Chm & CEO)*
Mike Jindra *(Controller)*
Dick Seidenstricker *(Pres)*

Subsidiary (Domestic):

Craft Pattern & Mold, Inc. (2)
1410 County Rd 90 Ste 3, Maple Plain, MN 55359
Tel.: (763) 479-1969
Web Site: http://www.craftpattern.com
Sales Range: $1-9.9 Million
Emp.: 30
Industrial Patterns
N.A.I.C.S.: 332999
Ben Kuehl *(Production Mgr)*
Kurt Lemke *(Mgr-Quality)*
Steve Shade *(Mgr-Project)*
Tony Cremers *(Pres & CEO)*

SILVERHAWK CAPITAL PARTNERS, LLC
140 Greenwich Ave 2nd Fl, Greenwich, CT 06830
Tel.: (203) 861-2905 DE
Web Site: http://www.silverhawkcapitalpartners.com
Year Founded: 2005
Privater Equity Firm
N.A.I.C.S.: 523999
Ted Allan Gardner *(Co-Founder & Mng Partner)*
James C. Cook *(Co-Founder & Mng Partner)*
David J. Scanlan *(Co-Founder & Mng Partner)*
Mark C. Demetree *(Co-Founder & Partner-Operating)*
Brent A. Hudson *(Chief Compliance Officer)*

Subsidiaries:

Discovery Health Record Solutions, LLC (1)
1150 Northmeadow Pkwy Ste 100, Atlanta, GA 30076
Tel.: (678) 990-5300
Healthcare Information Management Services
N.A.I.C.S.: 519290

Douglas Health Service LLC (1)
2803 Flight Safety Dr, Vero Beach, FL 32960-7911
Tel.: (772) 770-0022
Web Site: http://www.douglashs.com
Women Healthcare Services
N.A.I.C.S.: 621610
Anne M. Douglas *(Mgr)*

Elyria Foundry Company LLC (1)
120 Filbert St, Elyria, OH 44035
Tel.: (440) 322-4657
Web Site: http://www.elyriafoundry.com
Sales Range: $75-99.9 Million
Emp.: 300
Gray & Ductile Iron Castings Mfr
N.A.I.C.S.: 331511
Brian Wright *(VP-Sls & Mktg)*

Subsidiary (Domestic):

Hodge Foundry, Inc. (2)
42 Leech Rd, Greenville, PA 16125
Tel.: (724) 588-4100
Web Site: http://www.hodgefoundry.com
Sales Range: $25-49.9 Million
Emp.: 150
Gray & Ductile Iron Castings Mfr
N.A.I.C.S.: 331511

Spartan Energy Partners, LP (1)
9595 Six Pines Dr Ste 4000, The Woodlands, TX 77380
Tel.: (281) 466-3310
Web Site: http://www.spartanep.com
Gas Treating & Conditioning Services
N.A.I.C.S.: 213112

SILVERITE CONSTRUCTION CO., INC.
520 Old Country Rd W, Hicksville, NY 11801
Tel.: (516) 681-0562 NY
Web Site: http://www.silverite.com
Year Founded: 1965
Sales Range: $25-49.9 Million

Emp.: 30
Nonresidential Construction
N.A.I.C.S.: 236220
Angelo J. Silveri *(Pres)*
Jeffrey Robinson *(CFO)*
Onur Gurler *(Project Coord & Field Engr)*

SILVERLEAF ADVISORS LLC
8911 Daniels Pkwy Ste 6, Fort Myers, FL 33912
Tel.: (305) 533-1110
Web Site: http://www.silverleafad.com
Year Founded: 2008
Sales Range: $100-124.9 Million
Privater Equity Firm
N.A.I.C.S.: 523999
Douglas J. Hannah *(Founder & Mng Dir)*
Nikolaus Pongracz *(Mng Dir)*
Paul de Francisci *(Mng Dir)*
Bryan J. Davis *(Dir-Investments)*
J. Michael Morgan *(Gen Counsel)*
Michelle L. Glass *(Legal Counsel & Dir-Forclosure)*

SILVERLINING INTERIORS, INC.
2091 Broadway, New York, NY 10023
Tel.: (212) 496-7800
Web Site: http://www.silverlininginteriors.com
Year Founded: 1987
Sales Range: $10-24.9 Million
Emp.: 150
Residential Remodeler
N.A.I.C.S.: 236118
Josh Wiener *(Founder & Pres)*

SILVERMAN MCGOVERN STAFFING AND RECRUITING
284 W Exchange St, Providence, RI 02903
Tel.: (401) 632-0580
Web Site: http://www.silvermanmcgovern.com
Year Founded: 2002
Sales Range: $1-9.9 Million
Emp.: 7
Executive Search Service
N.A.I.C.S.: 561311
Patricia M. Herron *(Co-Founder)*
Faye L. Silverman *(Co-Founder)*

SILVERMAN MEDIA & MARKETING GROUP, INC.
2829 Merrick Rd Ste 115, Woodbury, NY 11770
Tel.: (516) 781-1668 NY
Year Founded: 1996
Rev.: $1,600,000
Emp.: 15
Fiscal Year-end: 12/31/06
Public Relations Services, Nsk
N.A.I.C.S.: 541820
Ira H. Silverman *(Owner, Pres & Head Coach)*

SILVERPEAK STRATEGIC PARTNERS LP
40 W 57th St 29 Fl, New York, NY 10019
Tel.: (212) 716-2000
Web Site: http://www.silverpeak.com
Year Founded: 2010
Multi-strategy Investment Platform
N.A.I.C.S.: 523999
Kaushik Amin *(Partner)*

Subsidiaries:

North Atlantic Refining Ltd. (1)
29 Pippy Pl, Saint John's, A1B 3X2, NL, Canada
Tel.: (709) 579-5831
Web Site: http://www.na-refining.nf.ca

Sales Range: $100-124.9 Million
Emp.: 750
Oil Production
N.A.I.C.S.: 324110

SILVERSCAPE TECHNOLOGIES, INC.
133 SW 130th Way, Newberry, FL 32669
Tel.: (352) 374-9657
Web Site: http://www.352media.com
Year Founded: 1997
Sales Range: $1-9.9 Million
Emp.: 70
Advertising Agencies
N.A.I.C.S.: 541810
Geoff Wilson *(Pres & CEO)*
Don Wedington *(VP-Sls)*
Caroline Blake *(COO)*
Erin Everhart *(Dir-Digital Mktg)*
Pete Bernardo *(Dir-Design)*
Jodi Higbee *(Dir-Acctg)*
Eric Cunningham *(Dir-Network Support)*
Brian Russell *(Mgr-Mktg Ops)*
Damion Wasylow *(Dir-Mktg Strategy)*
Michael Blasco *(Dir-Community Rels)*
Larry Hipp *(Dir-Software Dev)*
Evan Blake *(VP-Client Strategy)*
Chris Mann *(Dir-Quality Assurance)*
Nancy Phillips *(Office Mgr)*

SILVERSMITH MANAGEMENT, L.P.
177 Huntington Ave 25th Fl, Boston, MA 02115
Tel.: (617) 670-4300 DE
Web Site: http://www.silversmithcapital.com
Year Founded: 2015
Privater Equity Firm
N.A.I.C.S.: 523999
Todd A. MacLean *(Mng Partner)*
Marc Munfa *(Operating Partner)*
James J. Quagliaroli *(Mng Partner)*
Bryan Landerman *(Operating Partner & CTO)*
Lori Whelan *(Chief Operating Partner & CFO)*
Sri Rao *(Gen Partner)*
Brian Peterson *(Gen Partner)*
Rafael Urdaneta *(CFO)*
Kate Castle *(CMO)*
Julia Frenette *(Operating Partner)*
Jeffrey Crisan *(Mng Partner)*

Subsidiaries:

ActiveCampaign, LLC (1)
1 N Dearborn St Ste 500, Chicago, IL 60602
Tel.: (773) 360-2270
Web Site: http://www.activecampaign.com
Emp.: 75
Marketing Software & Services
N.A.I.C.S.: 541511
Jason VandeBoom *(Founder & CEO)*
Michael Rico *(Chief People Officer)*

Formstack, LLC (1)
8606 Allisonville Rd Ste 260, Indianapolis, IN 46250
Tel.: (317) 542-3125
Web Site: http://www.formstack.com
Sales Range: $10-24.9 Million
Online Form Integration Software
N.A.I.C.S.: 513210
Chris Byers *(CEO)*
Duane Hunt *(Mgr-Support)*
Ashley Walsh *(Dir-Mktg)*
Matt Taylor *(VP-Product)*
Dustin Sapp *(COO)*

Subsidiary (Domestic):

Vroman Systems Inc. (2)
5202 Washington St Ste 11, Downers Grove, IL 60515-4758
Tel.: (630) 737-1890
Web Site: http://www.formsite.com
Custom Computer Programming Services
N.A.I.C.S.: 541511

SILVERSMITH MANAGEMENT, L.P. U.S. PRIVATE

Silversmith Management, L.P.—(Continued)

Impact Radius, Inc. (1)
223 E De La Guerra St, Santa Barbara, CA 93101-2709
Tel.: (805) 324-6021
Web Site: http://www.impactradius.com
Emp.: 230
Digital Marketing Services
N.A.I.C.S.: 541890
David A. Yovanno (CEO)
Roger Kjensrud (Co-Founder & CTO)
Wade Crang (Co-Founder & VP-Ops)
Todd Crawford (Co-Founder & VP-Strategic Initiatives)
David Sendroff (CEO-Forensiq)
Adam Furness (Mng Dir-Asia Pacific)
Florian Gramshammer (Mng Dir-EMEA)
Sam Crocker (Mgr-Bus Dev)
Nina Nguyen (Engr-Sls)
Antoine Gross (Mgr-Southeast Asia)
Ayaan Mohamud (Mktg Dir-APAC)
Michael Head (Chief Partnerships Officer)
Cristy Garcia (Sr Dir-Global Programs & PR)
Per Pettersen (Co-Founder & Chief Strategy Officer)

Net Health Systems, Inc. (1)
40 24th St 1st Fl, Pittsburgh, PA 15222
Web Site: http://www.nethealth.com
Custom Computer Programming Services
N.A.I.C.S.: 541511
James J. Quagliaroli (Chm)
Patrick Colletti (Chief Innovation Officer)
Anthony Sanzo (Exec Chm)
Patrick Rooney (CFO)
Christopher Hayes (CTO)
Jason Baim (Chief Strategy Officer & Chief Corp Dev Officer)
Josh Pickus (CEO)
Christine Jones (Chief Client Officer)
Jason James (CIO)
Aaron Brandwein (Chief Revenue Officer)
Linda Kricher (Chief HR Officer)

Subsidiary (Domestic):

Casamba, LLC (2)
5210 Lewis Rd Ste 10, Agoura Hills, CA 91301
Tel.: (818) 991-9111
Web Site: http://www.casamba.net
Sales Range: $1-9.9 Million
Emp.: 16
Software Developer for Healthcare Industry
N.A.I.C.S.: 513210
Jane Moffett (Chief Product Officer)
Ronnie Amrany (Founder & Chm)
Doron Hetz (VP-Ops)
Don Moore (VP-IT Ops)
Veronica Ornelas (VP-Fin)
Will Jacobus (Sr Project Mgr)
Brian Dwyer (Chief Revenue Officer)
Billie Nutter (CEO)

Optima Healthcare Solutions, LLC (2)
4229 SW High Meadows Ave, Palm City, FL 34990
Tel.: (772) 403-1301
Web Site: http://www.optimahcs.com
Sales Range: $1-9.9 Million
Emp.: 90
Physical Therapy Software Publisher
N.A.I.C.S.: 513210
Steve Mackie (Co-Founder)
Michael Katri (Co-Founder & COO)
Ryan Katri (Co-Founder)
Aaron Brandwein (Chief Revenue Officer)
Pat Clark (Co-CFO)
Josh Pickus (CEO)
Randy Wallin (Chief Security Officer)
Jason James (CIO)
Dinesh Senanayake (Co-CFO & Gen Mgr-RCM)
Christine Jones (Chief Customer Officer)
Jeff Browning (Chief Product & Engrg Officer)

Subsidiary (Domestic):

Vantage Clinical Solutions, LLC (3)
1567 SW Chandler Ave, Bend, OR 97702
Tel.: (541) 550-7291
Revenue Cycle Management, Digital Marketing & Consulting Services
N.A.I.C.S.: 541613

Subsidiary (Domestic):

PointRight, Inc. (2)
150 CambridgePark Dr Ste 301, Cambridge, MA 02140
Tel.: (781) 457-5900
Web Site: http://www.pointright.com
Software Publisher
N.A.I.C.S.: 513210
Dean Staley (VP-Fin & Admin)
Steven Scott (CEO)
Alan Dahl (Chm)
Steven Littlehale (Chief Clinical Officer & Exec VP)
Michael Laureno (CFO)
Cesar Goulart (CFO)

Swift Prepaid Solutions, Inc. (1)
2150 E Lk Cook Rd Ste 150, Buffalo Grove, IL 60089
Tel.: (847) 325-4330
Web Site: http://www.swiftprepaid.com
Custom Prepaid Credit Cards Issuing & Support Services
N.A.I.C.S.: 522210
Juli C. Spottiswood (Chm)
Brian Levin (VP-Fin & IT)
David Josephs (CEO)

TMA Systems, LLC (1)
5100 E Skelly Dr Ste 900, Tulsa, OK 74135
Tel.: (918) 858-6600
Web Site: http://www.tmasystems.com
Sales Range: $1-9.9 Million
Emp.: 54
Computer System Design Services
N.A.I.C.S.: 541512
Dustin Taylor (Pres)
Gary R. Schaecher (Founder)
John C. Smith (Chm)
Michael Koenig (VP-Sls & Mktg)
Mark Simner (CEO)
Greg Shell (VP-Ops)
Scott Nelson (VP-Mktg)

Subsidiary (Domestic):

Eagle Technology, Inc. (2)
11019 N Towne Sq Rd, Mequon, WI 53092
Tel.: (262) 241-3845
Web Site: http://www.eaglecmms.com
Custom Computer Programming Services
N.A.I.C.S.: 541511
Harshad Shah (CEO)
Jacob Mix (Mgr-Engrg)
Harry Kohal (VP-Bus Dev)
Mark Bowling (Chief Info Security Officer)

Validity, Inc. (1)
200 Clarendon St 22nd Fl, Boston, MA 02116
Tel.: (800) 961-8205
Web Site: http://www.validity.com
Data Validation & Software Publisher
N.A.I.C.S.: 513210
Mark Briggs (Chm & CEO)
Paul Deeley (CFO)
Charlie Ungashick (CMO)
Frank Capecci (Sr VP-HR)
Barbara Cooke (Sr VP-Customer Success)
Alain Marcuse (Chief Info Security Officer)

Subsidiary (Domestic):

250ok Inc. (2)
9247 N Meridian St Ste 301, Indianapolis, IN 46260
Tel.: (317) 435-9781
Web Site: http://www.250ok.com
Email Technology & Security Solutions Services
N.A.I.C.S.: 541511
Greg Kraios (Founder & CEO)
Jeff Hansen (VP-Sls)
Paul Midgen (VP-Product)
Tim Moore (VP-Customer Solutions)

Return Path, Inc. (2)
3 Park Ave 41st Fl, New York, NY 10016
Tel.: (866) 362-4577
Web Site: http://returnpath.com
E-Mail Address Update Services
N.A.I.C.S.: 517111
Matt Blumberg (Founder)

Subsidiary (Non-US):

Return Path Australia (3)
Level 20 201 Sussex Street, Sydney, 2000, NSW, Australia
Tel.: (61) 2 9006 1591
E-Mail Address Update Service
N.A.I.C.S.: 517111

Return Path Brazil (3)
Av BrigFaria St Lima n 1690 Cj 142, 01451-001, Sao Paulo, Brazil
Tel.: (55) 11 3740 8300
E-Mail Address Update Service
N.A.I.C.S.: 517111

Return Path France (3)
171 Avenue Charles de Gaulle, 92200, Neuilly-sur-Seine, France
Tel.: (33) 1 41 43 29 80
Web Site: http://www.returnpath.com
Emp.: 15
E-Mail Address Update Service
N.A.I.C.S.: 517111

Return Path Germany (3)
Neuer Wall 80, Hamburg, 20354, Germany
Tel.: (49) 40 822 138 438
Web Site: http://www.returnpath.ge
Emp.: 6
E-Mail Address Update Service
N.A.I.C.S.: 517111
Jan Niggemann (Gen Mgr)

Return Path UK (3)
32 Wigmore Street 2nd Floor, London, W1U 2RP, United Kingdom
Tel.: (44) 845 002 0006
Web Site: http://www.returnpath.com
E-Mail Address Update Service
N.A.I.C.S.: 517111

SILVERSTREAM CAPITAL, LLC
4747 Executive Dr Ste 1010, San Diego, CA 92121
Tel.: (858) 790-5850   DE
Web Site: http://www.silverstreamcapital.com
Rev.: $1,500,000,000
Alternative Investment Firm
N.A.I.C.S.: 523999
Brett Doyle (Principal)
Matthew Simas (Mng Dir)
Anand Gowda (Mng Dir)
Patrick Cook (VP)

SILVERTECH, INC.
196 Bridge St, Manchester, NH 03104
Tel.: (603) 669-6600
Web Site: http://www.silvertech.com
Year Founded: 1996
Sales Range: $1-9.9 Million
Emp.: 50
Digital Marketing Services
N.A.I.C.S.: 541613
William Storace (Dir-Creative)
Eric Esposito (Dir-Tech)
Peggy Lindalh (Office Mgr)
Nick Soggu (Pres & CEO)
Jeff McPherson (Dir-Dev)
Erin Presseau (Mgr-Digital Strategy)

SILVERTON CONSTRUCTION COMPANY, INC.
PO Box 12629, El Paso, TX 79913-0629
Tel.: (915) 581-1138   NM
Web Site: http://silvertonc.openfos.com
Year Founded: 1978
Rev.: $20,000,000
Emp.: 55
Engineeering Services
N.A.I.C.S.: 236220

SILVERTON ENERGY, INC.
3495 Lakeside Dr Ste 107, Reno, NV 89509
Tel.: (775) 321-8224
Metal Mining Services
N.A.I.C.S.: 212290
Thannaphat Siripawinkul (Pres)

SILVERTON HEALTH
342 Fairview St, Silverton, OR 97381
Tel.: (503) 873-1500   OR
Web Site: http://www.silvertonhealth.org
Year Founded: 1918
Sales Range: $100-124.9 Million
Health Care Srvices
N.A.I.C.S.: 622110
Beth Davisson (Sec)
Darcy Ruef (Treas)
Dave Buck (Vice Chm)
Gayle Goschie (Chm)
Sarah Fronza (CEO)

SILVERTON MORTGAGE SPECIALISTS, INC.
1201 Peachtree St NE Ste 2050, Atlanta, GA 30361
Tel.: (404) 815-0291
Web Site: http://www.silvertonmortgage.com
Year Founded: 1998
Sales Range: $10-24.9 Million
Emp.: 162
Mortgage Lending Services
N.A.I.C.S.: 522310
Josh Moffitt (Pres)
Jason Strain (VP-Ops)
Susan Wingfield (Sr Mgr-Intown)
Leighton Johnson (Sr Mgr-Golden Isles)
Alesia Parker (Sr Mgr-Columbus)

SILVERWATER CAFE
237 Taylor St, Port Townsend, WA 98368
Tel.: (360) 385-6448
Web Site: http://www.silverwatercafe.com
Year Founded: 1989
Sales Range: $25-49.9 Million
Emp.: 35
Food Service
N.A.I.C.S.: 722511
Alison Hero (Co-Owner)
David Hero (Co-Owner)

SILVESTRI INVESTMENTS INC.
1215 Gessner Dr, Houston, TX 77055
Tel.: (713) 785-6272
Web Site: http://www.silvestriusa.com
Year Founded: 1955
Sales Range: $10-24.9 Million
Emp.: 25
Real Estate Services
N.A.I.C.S.: 531210
Dan Silvestri (Pres)
Jim Pheigaru (CFO)
Alice Blackburn (Mgr-Acctg)
Lisa Marek (Mgr-Property)
Stephanie Plouse (Mgr-Comml Property)
Mike Tones (Dir-Property)
Brian Hill (Gen Counsel)
Jerusha Jones (Mgr-Comml & Property)
Norma Baldit (Mgr-Property)

SILVESTRI STUDIO INC.
8125 Beach St, Los Angeles, CA 90001
Tel.: (323) 277-4420
Web Site: http://www.silvestricalifornia.com
Year Founded: 1934
Rev.: $10,196,978
Emp.: 150
Mannequins & Store Display Products Mfr
N.A.I.C.S.: 337215
Alain Levi (Pres)
Keith Barmasse (CFO)

SILVON SOFTWARE INC.
900 Oakmont Ln Ste 301, Westmont, IL 60559
Tel.: (630) 655-3313

Web Site: http://www.silvon.com
Year Founded: 1987
Sales Range: $10-24.9 Million
Emp.: 50
Computer Software Development
N.A.I.C.S.: 541511
Mike Hennel *(Pres & CEO)*
John Hughes *(Sr VP-Product Mgmt)*
Steve Morgan *(Gen Mgr-Silvon's Dev Org)*
Paul Dorsett *(VP-Pro Svcs)*
Frank C. Bunker Jr. *(VP-Pre-Sls, Strategic Customers & IT)*

Subsidiaries:

Silvon Software, Ltd. (1)
8 The Square Stockley Park, Uxbridge,
UB11 1FW, Mddx,
United Kingdom (100%)
Tel.: (44) 2031784834
Sales Range: $10-24.9 Million
Emp.: 16
Computer Software Development
N.A.I.C.S.: 541511

SIMA MARINE SALES INC.
200 Forest Dr East, Eastlake, OH
44095-1504
Tel.: (440) 269-3200 OH
Web Site:
http://www.simamarine.com
Year Founded: 1963
Sales Range: $10-24.9 Million
Emp.: 10
Sales of Boats
N.A.I.C.S.: 722511
John Sima *(Office Mgr)*

SIMAKAS COMPANY INC.
630 Route 228, Mars, PA 16046
Tel.: (724) 625-3900
Sales Range: $10-24.9 Million
Emp.: 7
Boiler Maintenance Contracting Services
N.A.I.C.S.: 238220
Lyle R. Fischer *(Pres)*

SIMCENTER ENTERPRISES, INC.
1301 Riverfront Pkwy Ste 114, Chattanooga, TN 37402-3313
Tel.: (423) 648-0395 TN
Web Site:
http://www.simcenterenterprises.com
Year Founded: 2009
Rev.: $1,488,944
Assets: $546,538
Liabilities: $186,429
Net Worth: $360,109
Earnings: $232,385
Emp.: 5
Fiscal Year-end: 06/30/14
Business Support Services
N.A.I.C.S.: 561439
Tim Walsh *(Pres)*
Allen Mccallie Attorney *(Sec)*

SIMCO ELECTRONICS
3131 Jay St Ste 100, Santa Clara,
CA 95054
Tel.: (408) 734-9750
Web Site: http://www.simco.com
Rev.: $15,100,000
Emp.: 85
Test & Measurement Instrument Calibration & Repair
N.A.I.C.S.: 541380
Bradford G. Phillips *(CFO & VP-Contracts)*
Kymberly Strack *(Mgr-Credit & Collections)*
Kenneth Cary *(Supvr-Ops)*
Brian Kenna *(CEO)*
Lee M. Kenna Jr. *(Chm)*

SIMCO SALES SERVICE OF PA INC.
101 Commerce Dr, Moorestown, NJ
08057
Tel.: (856) 813-2300 PA
Web Site: http://www.jjicc.com
Year Founded: 1929
Sales Range: $75-99.9 Million
Emp.: 320
Sales of Ice Cream & Ices
N.A.I.C.S.: 561499
Ken Schwartz *(Pres)*

SIMCONA ELECTRONICS CORP
275 Mt Read Blvd, Rochester, NY
14611
Tel.: (585) 328-3230
Web Site: http://www.simcona.com
Rev.: $40,000,000
Emp.: 50
Electronic Parts
N.A.I.C.S.: 423690
Joe Cusano *(Controller)*
Marc Iacona *(Pres)*

SIMCOTE INC.
1645 Red Rock Rd, Saint Paul, MN
55119
Tel.: (651) 735-9660
Web Site: http://www.simcote.com
Year Founded: 1978
Sales Range: $10-24.9 Million
Emp.: 40
Metals Coating Services
N.A.I.C.S.: 331110
John P. Simmet *(Pres)*
Dean Motz *(Supvr-Plant)*

SIMEUS FOODS INTERNATIONAL, INC.
812 N 5th Ave, Mansfield, TX 76063-2210
Tel.: (817) 473-1562 TX
Year Founded: 1996
Sales Range: $25-49.9 Million
Emp.: 200
Frozen Foods Including Kettle-Cooked Entrees, Sausage, Ham, Roast Beef, Breaded Meats & Cheese, Cookies & Steaks
N.A.I.C.S.: 311612

SIMFONI, INC.
450 Townsend St, San Francisco, CA
94107
Tel.: (415) 231-3691
Web Site: http://www.simfoni.com
Computer System Design Services
N.A.I.C.S.: 541512
Chirag Shah *(Chm)*

Subsidiaries:

EC Sourcing Group Inc. (1)
18 Cattano Ave, Morristown, NJ 07960
Tel.: (973) 936-9672
Web Site: http://www.ecsourcinggroup.com
Custom Computer Programming Services
N.A.I.C.S.: 541511
Andrew Caetta *(COO)*

SIMKAR CORPORATION
700 Ramona Ave, Philadelphia, PA
19120
Tel.: (215) 831-7700
Web Site: http://www.simkar.com
Rev.: $130,000,000
Emp.: 600
Fluorescent Lighting Fixtures, Commercial
N.A.I.C.S.: 335132
Phil Burch *(Dir-Mfg & Engrg)*
Yoram Weiss *(Dir-Tech & Engrg)*
Kurt Magda *(Dir-Engrg & Tech)*
Billy Hodges *(Principal)*

SIMKINS CORPORATION
2824 N 2nd St, Philadelphia, PA
19133
Tel.: (215) 739-4033
Rev.: $13,000,000
Emp.: 40
Setup Paperboard Boxes
N.A.I.C.S.: 322219
Morton Simkins *(Pres)*

SIMKINS/HARVARD FOLDING BOX COMPANY INC.
71 Linden St, Lynn, MA 01905-2048
Tel.: (781) 598-1600 MA
Web Site:
http://www.idealboxmakers.com
Year Founded: 1991
Sales Range: $25-49.9 Million
Emp.: 150
Mfr of Folding Paperboard Boxes
N.A.I.C.S.: 322212
Katie Kiley *(Mgr-Customer Svc)*

SIMMONDS RESTAURANT MANAGEMENT
11404 W Dodge Rd Ste 650, Omaha,
NE 68154
Tel.: (402) 493-2300
Rev.: $50,000,000
Emp.: 50
Fast Food Restaurant Operator
N.A.I.C.S.: 722513
Michael Simmonds *(Chm & CEO)*

SIMMONS EROSION CONTROL, INC.
6690 Steve Lee Dr, Jackson, MS
39092
Tel.: (601) 775-3305
Sales Range: $10-24.9 Million
Emp.: 50
Highway, Street & Bridge Construction Services
N.A.I.C.S.: 237310
Jenny Simmons *(Pres)*

SIMMONS FOODS, INC.
601 N Hico St, Siloam Springs, AR
72761
Tel.: (479) 524-8151
Web Site:
http://www.simmonsfoods.com
Year Founded: 1949
Sales Range: $1-4.9 Billion
Emp.: 10,000
Fresh & Frozen Poultry Products Mfr & Distr
N.A.I.C.S.: 311615
Todd Simmons *(CEO)*

Subsidiaries:

Simmons Custom Processing, Inc. (1)
1st & Dial St, Jay, OK 74346
Tel.: (918) 253-4223
Emp.: 200
Poultry Processing Services
N.A.I.C.S.: 311615
Phil Paulk *(Gen Mgr)*

Simmons Energy Solutions, Inc. (1)
PO Box 430, Decatur, AR 72722
Tel.: (479) 524-8151
Web Site:
http://www.simmonsenergysolutions.com
Propane Fuel Distr
N.A.I.C.S.: 424720

Simmons Pet Food, Inc. (1)
316 N Hico St, Siloam Springs, AR 72761
Tel.: (479) 524-8151
Sales Range: $50-74.9 Million
Emp.: 1,000
Canned Dog & Cat Foods Mfr & Distr
N.A.I.C.S.: 311615
Mark Simmons *(Chm)*
Todd Simmons *(Co-Pres & CEO)*
Jason Godsey *(Co-Pres & COO)*

Subsidiary (Domestic):

Menu Foods Midwest Corporation, Inc (2)
1400 E Logan Ave, Emporia, KS 66801
Tel.: (620) 342-1323
Pet Food Mfr
N.A.I.C.S.: 311111

Plant (Domestic):

Simmons Pet Food, Inc. - Pennsauken (2)
9130 Griffith Morgan Ln, Pennsauken, NJ 08110-3211
Tel.: (856) 662-7412
Sales Range: $50-74.9 Million
Emp.: 185
Pet Food Mfr
N.A.I.C.S.: 311111

Plant (Non-US):

Simmons Pet Food, Inc. - Streetsville (2)
8 Falconer Dr, Mississauga, L5N 1B1, ON, Canada
Tel.: (905) 826-3870
Sales Range: $100-124.9 Million
Emp.: 400
Pet Food Mfr
N.A.I.C.S.: 311111
Douglas S. Haslam *(Exec VP-Sls & Mktg)*

Simmons Prepared Foods, Inc. (1)
186 W Roller Ave, Decatur, AR 72722
Tel.: (479) 752-5000
Poultry Processing Services
N.A.I.C.S.: 311615
Todd Simmons *(CEO)*
Chip Miller *(VP-Poultry Sls)*
David Jackson *(COO)*
Joel Sappenfield *(Pres)*

SIMMONS HANLY CONROY LLP
1 Court St, Alton, IL 62002
Tel.: (618) 693-3104
Web Site:
https://www.simmonsfirm.com
Year Founded: 1999
Emp.: 275
Law firm
N.A.I.C.S.: 541199

SIMMONS IRRIGATION SUPPLY INC.
526 Sidneys Rd, Walterboro, SC
29488
Tel.: (843) 538-5566
Web Site:
http://www.simmonsirrigation.com
Rev.: $11,984,362
Emp.: 40
Irrigation Equipment
N.A.I.C.S.: 423820
Ray E. McLin *(VP & Gen Mgr)*
Marion R. Simmons III *(Pres & CEO)*

SIMMONS-BOARDMAN PUBLISHING CORP.
345 Hudson St 12 Fl, New York, NY
10014-4502
Tel.: (212) 620-7200 DE
Web Site:
http://www.simmonsboardman.com
Year Founded: 1928
Sales Range: $10-24.9 Million
Emp.: 75
Publisher of Industrial & Trade Magazines
N.A.I.C.S.: 513120
Arthur J. McGinnis *(Chm & Pres)*
Allen Morrell *(Controller)*
Wendy Williams *(Dir-Art)*
Jane Poterala *(Dir-Conference)*

Subsidiaries:

Railway Educational Bureau (1)
1809 Capitol Ave, Omaha, NE 68102-4905
Tel.: (402) 346-4300
Web Site: http://www.transalert.com

SIMMONS-BOARDMAN PUBLISHING CORP.

U.S. PRIVATE

Simmons-Boardman Publishing Corp.—(Continued)
Sales Range: $10-24.9 Million
Emp.: 15
Mechanical & Maintenance Training for the Railroad Industry Through Correspondence Trade School Utilizing Text & Video
N.A.I.C.S.: 513120

SIMMONS-ROCKWELL, INC.
784 County Rd 64, Elmira, NY 14903
Tel.: (607) 796-5555
Web Site: http://www.simmons-rockwell.com
Sales Range: $25-49.9 Million
Emp.: 250
New & Used Automobiles
N.A.I.C.S.: 441110
Brian Barrett (Owner)

SIMMS CHEVROLET COMPANY INC.
4220 W Vienna Rd, Clio, MI 48420
Tel.: (810) 686-1700
Web Site: http://www.simmschevrolet.com
Sales Range: $10-24.9 Million
Emp.: 35
Car Whslr
N.A.I.C.S.: 441110
Bruce M. Simms (Pres)

SIMMS LUMBER CO. INC.
1150 Fort Worth Hwy, Weatherford, TX 76086
Tel.: (817) 594-2788
Web Site: http://www.simmslumber.com
Sales Range: $10-24.9 Million
Emp.: 50
Lumber, Plywood & Millwork
N.A.I.C.S.: 423310
Keith Kirk (VP)
John T. Simms III (Pres)

SIMON & ARRINGTON INC.
6215 Brookshire Ter, Fort Myers, FL 33912-4239
Tel.: (305) 718-0630
Web Site: http://www.s-a.us
Rev.: $18,000,000
Emp.: 27
IT Products, Services & Solutions
N.A.I.C.S.: 513210

SIMON CONTRACTORS INC.
1103 Old Town Ln Ste 201 A, Cheyenne, WY 82009
Tel.: (307) 635-9005
Web Site: http://www.simoncontractors.com
Rev.: $88,900,000
Emp.: 180
Highway Street & Bridge Construction
N.A.I.C.S.: 287310
Arnaud Chabenat (CFO & VP)

SIMON HOLDINGS LLC
24501 Ecorse Rd, Taylor, MI 48180
Tel.: (313) 292-5500
Year Founded: 1985
Sales Range: $900-999.9 Million
Holding Company
N.A.I.C.S.: 551112
Sam Simon (Chm & CEO)
David Barnes (Exec VP & Gen Counsel)

Subsidiaries:

Atlas Oil Company (1)
24501 Ecorse Rd, Taylor, MI 48180
Tel.: (313) 292-5500
Web Site: http://www.atlasoil.com
Sales Range: $125-149.9 Million
Emp.: 120
Petroleum Products
N.A.I.C.S.: 424720

Sam Simon (Chm & CEO)
Michael Evans (Exec VP)
Robert Kenyon (Pres)
Edwin Herbert (Chief Admin Officer, Gen Counsel & Exec VP)
Faiz Simon (VP-Real Estate)
Joseph Rivera (VP-Acctg)
Satish Kalala (CEO)
Gene McDougald (VP-Oil Field Svcs)
Jitesh Shah (VP-IT)
Michael Fahy (COO)
Tom Jones (VP-Transportation)
Paul Barnard (Mgr-Emergency Ops)
Jake Leatherman (VP- Wholesale & Real Estate)
Gerry King (VP-EHS, Risk & HR)
Dawn Thompson (Dir-HR)
Mark Kryska (VP-Tech)
Rocio Cabrera (Dir-Procurement)

SIMON PEARCE US INC.
109 Park Rd, Windsor, VT 05089
Tel.: (802) 674-6280
Web Site: http://www.simonpearceglass.com
Sales Range: $25-49.9 Million
Emp.: 350
Glass Furnishings & Accessories Mfr & Sales
N.A.I.C.S.: 327212
Simon Pearce (Pres)
Laura Pillsbury (VP-Ops)
Nelson Duranceau (Mgr-Customer Rels)

SIMON ROOFING AND SHEET METAL CORP.
70 Karago Ave, Youngstown, OH 44512-5949
Tel.: (330) 629-7663   OH
Web Site: http://www.simonroofing.com
Year Founded: 1900
Sales Range: $100-124.9 Million
Emp.: 1,000
Provider of Roofing, Siding & Sheetmetal Work
N.A.I.C.S.: 238160
Alex Simon (Owner)
Rocco Augustine (VP)
Danielle Aschoff (Coord-Bus Dev-Nashville)
James Simon Jr. (Owner)

SIMON WORLDWIDE, INC.
18952 Macarthur Blvd, Irvine, CA 92612
Tel.: (949) 251-4660
Advertising Services
N.A.I.C.S.: 541810
Gregory Mays (CEO)

SIMONCOMPUTING, INC.
5350 Shawnee Rd Ste 200, Alexandria, VA 22312
Tel.: (703) 914-5454
Web Site: http://www.simoncomputing.com
Year Founded: 2002
Rev.: $4,800,000
Emp.: 40
Custom Computer Programming Services
N.A.I.C.S.: 541511
Simon Woo (VP)
Danaiya Woo (Pres)
Lat Siriwong (Engr-Software)

SIMONDS-SHIELDS-THEIS GRAIN CO.
4800 Main St Ste 328, Kansas City, MO 64112-2517
Tel.: (816) 561-4155   MO
Year Founded: 1884
Sales Range: $150-199.9 Million
Emp.: 8
Commodities Trading
N.A.I.C.S.: 523999

SIMONINI BUILDERS
501 E Morehead St Ste 4, Charlotte, NC 28202-2630
Tel.: (704) 358-9940
Web Site: http://www.simonini.com
Year Founded: 1996
Sales Range: $200-249.9 Million
Emp.: 60
Residential Construction
N.A.I.C.S.: 236117
Alan C. Simonini (Co-Owner, Pres & Chief Creative Officer)
William E. Saint (CFO)
Ray A. Killian Jr. (Co-Owner & CEO)

SIMONIZ USA, INC.
201 Boston Tpke, Bolton, CT 06043-7203
Tel.: (860) 646-0172   CT
Web Site: http://www.simonizusa.com
Year Founded: 1997
Sales Range: $75-99.9 Million
Emp.: 60
Automobile Care Product Mfr
N.A.I.C.S.: 325612
William Gorra (Pres)
Mark Kershan (CEO)

Subsidiaries:

Washing Equipment Technologies, Inc. (1)
691 Phillips Rd, Webster, NY 14580
Tel.: (585) 265-1140
Web Site: http://www.simonizprofessional.com
Sales Range: $1-9.9 Million
Emp.: 20
Car Washing Equipment
N.A.I.C.S.: 423850

SIMONS HARDWARE & BATH, INC.
421 3rd Ave, New York, NY 10016
Tel.: (212) 532-9220
Web Site: http://www.simonshardwareandbath.com
Sales Range: $10-24.9 Million
Emp.: 65
Hardware & Plumbing Supplies Sales
N.A.I.C.S.: 444140
Alison Murray (Pres)
Oscar Bayon (Mgr-Hardware Sls)

SIMONS MICHELSON ZIEVE, INC.
900 Wilshire Dr Ste 102, Troy, MI 48084-1634
Tel.: (248) 362-4242   MI
Web Site: http://www.smz.com
Year Founded: 1929
Sales Range: $50-74.9 Million
Emp.: 50
Advertising Agencies
N.A.I.C.S.: 541810
James A. Michelson (Chm)
Kathleen Finley (Sr VP & Dir-Print Production)
Joel Bienenfeld (VP & Dir-Brdcst Production)
Debbie Michelson (Exec VP & Grp Acct Dir)
Amy Klein (Dir-Media Plng)
Gary Wolfson (Exec VP & Chief Creative Officer)
Brianna M. Wilkinson (Assoc Dir-Media)
Pam Renusch (Exec VP & Grp Acct Dir)

SIMONS SUPPLY CO. INC.
821 Cambridge St, Fall River, MA 02721
Tel.: (508) 679-6431   MA
Web Site: http://www.simonsupply.com
Year Founded: 1933

Sales Range: $10-24.9 Million
Emp.: 48
Plumbing & Hydronic Heating Supplies Distr
N.A.I.C.S.: 423720
Lloyd O. Felder (Pres)
Fred Selder (VP)

SIMONSON CONSTRUCTION SERVICES, INC.
2112 Troy Rd, Ashland, OH 44805
Tel.: (419) 281-8299
Web Site: http://www.simonsonconstruction.com
Sales Range: $10-24.9 Million
Emp.: 72
Nonresidential Construction Services
N.A.I.C.S.: 236220
Melinda Mendenhall (Comptroller)
Daniel R. Moore (Pres)
Jay Myers (VP)
Robert M. Simonson (Founder)
Dan Smith (VP)
Eric A. Gillett (CEO)
Dave Wurster (Owner)

SIMONSON PROPERTIES COMPANY
2455 12th St SE, Saint Cloud, MN 56304
Tel.: (320) 252-9385
Web Site: http://www.simonson-lumber.com
Sales Range: $25-49.9 Million
Emp.: 11
Millwork & Lumber
N.A.I.C.S.: 444110
Richard F. Hobbs (Owner)

SIMPAK INTERNATIONAL, LLC
2107 Production Dr, Louisville, KY 40299
Tel.: (502) 671-8250
Web Site: http://www.simpakinternational.com
Year Founded: 2004
Sales Range: $1-9.9 Million
Emp.: 25
Packaging Products Mfr
N.A.I.C.S.: 488991
Michael Lyons (Pres)
Nick Hettich (Dir-Sls & Mktg)
Steve Witt (Plant Mgr)

SIMPLE MANAGEMENT GROUP, INC.
625 Main St Ste 27, Windermere, FL 34786
Tel.: (321) 424-5919   DE
Web Site: https://www.simplemanagementgroup.com
Year Founded: 2009
Emp.: 100
Financial Services
N.A.I.C.S.: 523999
John Thedford (Chm & CEO)

Subsidiaries:

FFI Holdings, Inc. (1)
1085 W Morse Blvd, Winter Park, FL 32789
Tel.: (407) 478-7296
Web Site: http://lafamiliapawn.com
Emp.: 100
Holding Company
N.A.I.C.S.: 551112
Lawrence Kahlden (Pres & CEO)

Subsidiary (Domestic):

La Familia Pawn & Jewelry (2)
1085 W Morse Blvd Ste 200, Winter Park, FL 32789
Tel.: (407) 478-7296
Web Site: http://www.lafamiliapawn.com
Rev.: $26,000,000
Pawn Shop
N.A.I.C.S.: 459510
Wilton A. Whitcomb (CFO)

COMPANIES

SIMPLE PRODUCTS CORPORATION
9314 S 370 W, Sandy, UT 84070
Tel.: (801) 553-8886   NV
Web Site:
http://www.simpleproductscorp.com
Year Founded: 2003
Sales Range: $10-24.9 Million
Emp.: 14
General Merchandise Business Development, Mfr & Distr
N.A.I.C.S.: 561499
Brian Christensen *(Chm, Pres, CEO, CFO & Principal Acctg Officer)*
Craig J. Carlston *(Treas)*
Kevin Alsop *(Sec)*
Scott Carlston *(Controller)*

SIMPLE SUGARS
PO Box 11273, Pittsburgh, PA 15238
Tel.: (888) 819-8994
Web Site:
http://simplesugars.myshopify.com
Sales Range: $1-9.9 Million
Emp.: 24
Skin Care Products
N.A.I.C.S.: 325620
Lani Lazzari *(Founder)*

SIMPLEHEALTH, INC.
228 Park Ave S Ste 20627, New York, NY 10003
Web Site:
https://www.simplehealth.com
Emp.: 100
Health, Wellness & Fitness Services
N.A.I.C.S.: 621399
Subsidiaries:

Emme Inc.   (1)
22782 Courtland Park Dr, Ashburn, VA 20148-5600
Tel.: (808) 947-6677
Web Site: http://www.emmeinc.com
General Freight Trucking, Local
N.A.I.C.S.: 484110
Gail Llanos *(Owner)*

SIMPLERAY, LLC
705 Raymond Ave Ste 220, Saint Paul, MN 55114
Tel.: (800) 952-3235
Web Site: http://www.simpleray.com
Year Founded: 2007
Sales Range: $1-9.9 Million
Emp.: 2
Designs, Installs & Retails Photovoltaic Solar Panels & Related Components
N.A.I.C.S.: 221114
Geoff Stenrick *(Pres)*
Rachael Zola *(COO)*

SIMPLESIGNAL, INC.
34232 Pacific Coast Hwy Ste E, Dana Point, CA 92629
Tel.: (949) 487-3333   CA
Web Site:
http://www.simplesignal.com
Year Founded: 2004
Sales Range: $1-9.9 Million
Emp.: 27
Telecommunication Servicesb
N.A.I.C.S.: 517810
Michael Sterl *(VP)*
Ujjval Karihaloo *(CTO)*

SIMPLETIRE, LLC
5 Neshaminy Interplex Dr Ste 101, Trevose, PA 19053-6974
Web Site: http://www.simpletire.com
Year Founded: 2012
Sales Range: $250-299.9 Million
Emp.: 56
Online Shopping Services
N.A.I.C.S.: 441340

Andy Chalofsky *(Co-Founder)*
Josh Chalofsky *(Co-Founder & COO)*
Kenny Pratt *(Co-Founder & CTO)*
Chris Vitale *(VP-Tech)*
Thomas Ganey *(Sr VP-Ops)*
Karthik Iyer *(Pres & CEO)*
Subsidiaries:

Sonsio, LLC   (1)
5630 Ward Rd, Arvada, CO 80002-1310
Tel.: (303) 736-1111
Web Site: http://www.sonsio.com
Sales Range: $1-9.9 Million
Emp.: 100
Direct Insurance Services
N.A.I.C.S.: 524128
William R. Jones *(Founder)*

SIMPLEVIEW, INC.
8950 N Oracle Rd, Tucson, AZ 85704
Tel.: (520) 575-1151   AZ
Web Site:
http://www.simpleviewinc.com
Year Founded: 2005
Sales Range: $10-24.9 Million
Emp.: 200
Advertising & Marketing Software Developer & Support Services
N.A.I.C.S.: 513210
Ryan George *(Co-Founder & CEO)*
Bill Simpson *(Co-Founder & CTO)*
Rich Reasons *(Pres)*
Scott Wood *(COO)*
Rolf Senstad *(Gen Mgr-Europe)*
Anthony Bocquentin *(Pres-Barberstock)*
Christian Ortlepp *(Dir-Europe, Middle East & Africa)*
Caroline Dawson *(Mgr-Bus Dev-Europe)*

SIMPLEX HEALTHCARE, INC.
6840 Carothers Parkway Ste 600, Franklin, TN 37067
Tel.: (615) 226-2221
Web Site:
http://www.simplexhealthcare.com
Year Founded: 2007
Sales Range: $150-199.9 Million
Emp.: 291
Mail Delivery of Medical & Diabetic Supplies
N.A.I.C.S.: 325412
Ellen Hitt *(VP-HR)*

SIMPLEX INDUSTRIES INC
Keyser Industrial Park 1 Simplex Dr, Scranton, PA 18504
Tel.: (570) 346-5113   PA
Web Site:
http://www.simplexhomes.com
Year Founded: 1971
Sales Range: $150-199.9 Million
Emp.: 400
Prefabricated Wood Buildings & Modulars Mfr
N.A.I.C.S.: 321992
David Boniello *(VP)*
Patrick A. Fricchione Jr. *(Pres & CEO)*
Subsidiaries:

Cornerstone Building Solutions, Inc.   (1)
PO Box 218, Chinchilla, PA 18410
Tel.: (570) 983-0340
Web Site:
http://www.cornerstonebuildingsolutions.com
Residential & Commercial Building Construction Services
N.A.I.C.S.: 236220
Dave Boniello *(VP)*
Mark Hoffa *(Dir-Construction Svcs)*
Patrick Fricchione Jr. *(Pres & CEO)*

Simplex Construction Co. Inc.   (1)
One Simplex Dr, Scranton, PA 18504   (100%)

Tel.: (570) 346-5113
Web Site: http://www.simplexhomes.com
Emp.: 250
Modular Home Set-up; General Construction Services
N.A.I.C.S.: 321992
Patrick Fricchione *(COO)*

SIMPLICITY CONSULTING, INC
11250 Kirkland Way Ste 203, Kirkland, WA 98033
Tel.: (425) 968-2492
Web Site:
http://www.simplicityconsulting.com
Sales Range: $10-24.9 Million
Emp.: 300
Business Consulting Services
N.A.I.C.S.: 541618
Lisa Hufford *(Founder & CEO)*
Carrie Morris *(Dir-Employee Engagement)*
Stephanie Chacharon *(Dir-Mktg)*

SIMPLICITY FINANCIAL MARKETING HOLDINGS INC.
86 Summit Ave, Ste 303, Summit, NJ 07901
Tel.: (860) 724-4511   DE
Web Site:
http://simplicitymarketing.com
Life Insurance, Annuities & Other Financial Products Brokerage Services
N.A.I.C.S.: 524210
Diana Greenberg *(Partner)*
Bruce Donaldson *(Pres & CEO)*
Subsidiaries:

Dressander BHC Inc.   (1)
400 E Diehl Rd Ste 400, Naperville, IL 60563
Tel.: (630) 717-6668
Web Site: http://www.dbhc.com
Annuities Brokerage Services
N.A.I.C.S.: 524210
Cam Dressander *(Sr VP)*
Mike Dressander *(Pres)*
Barbara G. Frederickson *(COO)*
Carla Urbaszewski *(CMO)*
David McDaniel *(CMO-West Coast)*
Dave Vick *(Sr VP-Bus Dev)*

Financial Security Associates, Inc.   (1)
4820 6 Forks Rd, Raleigh, NC 27609
Tel.: (919) 981-0333
Web Site: http://www.fsa4life.com
Rev: $1,400,000
Emp.: 12
Insurance Agencies & Brokerages
N.A.I.C.S.: 524210
Paige Blair *(VP)*
Sherry Mobley *(VP)*

Imeriti, Inc.   (1)
4134 Deegan Ct Ste 300, Monticello, MN 55362
Web Site: http://www.imeriti.com
Insurance Related Activities
N.A.I.C.S.: 524298
Jacob Stern *(Chm & CEO)*
Brian Schneier *(Pres)*
Nathan Zuidema *(CFO & COO)*
Ed Prewitt *(CMO)*

Jurs Montgomery Brokerage, LLC   (1)
1175 Pittsford-Victor Rd Ste 110, Pittsford, NY 14534
Tel.: (585) 203-1206
Web Site: http://www.jursmontgomery.com
Insurance Services
N.A.I.C.S.: 524210
Justin Jurs *(Mng Partner)*
Chris Ronshagen *(Partner & Exec VP)*
Rose-Anne Cesternino *(Mgr-Sls)*
Richard Gursky *(Mgr-Sls)*
Stephanie L. Travis *(Mgr-New Bus)*
Joseph Moore *(Mgr-Sls)*

M3 Financial, Inc.   (1)
427 Naubuc Ave Ste 102, Glastonbury, CT 06033
Tel.: (860) 734-1600
Web Site: http://www.m3financial.nyc

SIMPLIMATIC ENGINEERING HOLDINGS LLC

Insurance Annuities Broker
N.A.I.C.S.: 524210
Jarrod Fisher *(Sls Dir-Natl)*
Michael Bartolotta *(Mng Principal)*
Remy Bartolotta *(Dir-Bus Dev)*

Oxbow Marketing Company   (1)
3053 Nationwide Pkwy, Brunswick, OH 44212-2361
Tel.: (330) 273-4870
Web Site: http://www.oxbowmkt.com
Insurance Related Activities
N.A.I.C.S.: 524299
Robert Daugherty *(Pres)*

Simplicity Group Holdings   (1)
86 Summit Ave, Ste 303, Summit, NJ 07901
Tel.: (860) 724-4511
Web Site:
http://www.simplicitygroupholdings.com
Holding Company
N.A.I.C.S.: 551112
Heather Peck *(Exec VP-HR)*
Bruce Donaldson *(Pres & CEO)*
Alex Timeus *(Dir-Comm)*
Denielle Webb *(VP)*

Total Financial & Insurance Services, LLC   (1)
11835 W Olympic Blvd Ste 600, Los Angeles, CA 90067
Tel.: (310) 477-7500
Web Site:
http://www.totalfinancialinsurance.com
General Insurance Services
N.A.I.C.S.: 524113
Diana Greenberg *(Pres)*
Seth Moses *(Dir-Annuities)*

SIMPLICITY GROUP
2250 W Ctr St, Springville, UT 84663
Tel.: (801) 623-6974
Web Site: http://www.simplx.com
Year Founded: 2002
Rev.: $5,200,000
Emp.: 40
Computer Programming Services
N.A.I.C.S.: 541511
Brian G. Farr *(Mng Dir-2Go Entertainment)*
Amanda Jensen *(Office Mgr-Accounts)*
Henry P. Ferreyra *(Div Mgr-2Go Entertainment)*
Carly Shimmin *(Mgr-Customer Svcs)*
Sean Howard *(Mgr-Ops)*
Riley Griffin *(Dir-Bus Coaching)*
Cooper Corless *(Sls Mgr-Intl)*
K. Michael Benson *(Dir-Tech & Dev)*
Adam K. Wilkinson *(CEO)*
Aaron Davies *(Dir-Sls Trng)*

SIMPLIFI, INC.
3601 Hulen St Ste 102, Columbus, OH 43215
Tel.: (817) 737-1700
Web Site: http://www.simplifieso.com
Sales Range: $25-49.9 Million
Emp.: 18
Third-Party Administrator of Health Plan Benefits
N.A.I.C.S.: 524292
Rodney Napier *(CMO)*
Subsidiaries:

CBCA Administrators, Inc.   (1)
3601 Hulen St Ste 102, Fort Worth, TX 76107-6877
Tel.: (817) 737-1804
Web Site: http://www.cbca.com
Sales Range: $125-149.9 Million
Third-Party Administrator of Health Plan Benefits
N.A.I.C.S.: 524292

SIMPLIMATIC ENGINEERING HOLDINGS LLC
1046 W London Park Dr, Forest, VA 24551
Tel.: (434) 385-9181
Web Site: http://www.simplimatic.com
Year Founded: 1965

3667

Simplimatic Engineering Holdings LLC—(Continued)
Sales Range: $10-24.9 Million
industrial Machinery Mfr & Whslr
N.A.I.C.S.: 423830
Thomas Dinardo *(Pres & CEO)*

SIMPLION TECHNOLOGIES INC.
1525 McCarthy Blvd Ste 228, Milpitas, CA 95035
Tel.: (408) 935-8686
Web Site: http://www.simplion.com
Year Founded: 2004
Sales Range: $1-9.9 Million
Emp.: 114
It Consulting
N.A.I.C.S.: 541990
Dhiraj Sharma *(CEO)*

SIMPLURIS, INC.
3176 Pullman St, Costa Mesa, CA 92626
Tel.: (714) 824-8590
Web Site: http://www.simpluris.com
Year Founded: 2007
Sales Range: $1-9.9 Million
Emp.: 60
Administrative Support for Class Action Settlements
N.A.I.C.S.: 541199
Zach Hoffman *(Co-Founder & CTO)*
Troy Hoffman *(Co-Founder)*
Angela Hansen *(Dir-Disbursement)*
Denise Islas *(Mgr-Quality Assurance)*
Nick Castro *(Mgr-Claims)*
Krista Tittle *(Co-Founder & Mgr-Case)*
Kevin Lee *(Pres & CEO)*

SIMPLY COLOR LAB INC.
1479 Exeter Rd, Akron, OH 44306
Tel.: (877) 803-6366
Web Site:
 http://www.simplycolorlab.com
Year Founded: 2005
Sales Range: $1-9.9 Million
Emp.: 55
Photograph to Canvas Online Retailer
N.A.I.C.S.: 541921
Adam Fried *(CEO)*

SIMPLY DENTAL MANAGEMENT, INC.
87 Elm St, Hopkinton, MA 01748
Tel.: (508) 293-1446
Web Site:
 http://www.simplydentalmanagement.com
Year Founded: 2005
Sales Range: $10-24.9 Million
Emp.: 240
Dental Care Services
N.A.I.C.S.: 621399
Sam Alkhoury *(Founder)*

SIMPLY FASHION STORES LTD.
2500 Crestwood Blvd, Birmingham, AL 35210-2095
Tel.: (205) 951-1700
Web Site:
 http://www.simplyfashions.com
Year Founded: 1991
Sales Range: $100-124.9 Million
Emp.: 1,500
Women's Clothing Sales
N.A.I.C.S.: 458110
Mark Smith *(CFO)*
Mark Barstein *(Exec VP & Mgr-Mdsg)*
Kathy Hymer *(VP-Mdsg)*

SIMPLY NUC, INC.
495 Round Rock W Dr, Round Rock, TX 78681
Tel.: (512) 766-0401
Web Site: http://www.simplynuc.co
Year Founded: 2015
Sales Range: $10-24.9 Million
Emp.: 44
Computer Hardware Distr
N.A.I.C.S.: 423430
Aaron Rowsell *(Founder & CEO)*

SIMPLYGLOBO INC
130 E Hill St, Villa Park, IL 60181
Tel.: (888) 751-4951
Web Site:
 http://www.simplyglobo.com
Year Founded: 2008
Sales Range: $1-9.9 Million
Emp.: 12
Office Equipment Mfr, Distr & Designer
N.A.I.C.S.: 423420
James Yu *(Pres & CEO)*

SIMPSON & MCCRADY LLC
310-330 Grant St Ste 1320, Pittsburgh, PA 15219-2207
Tel.: (412) 261-2222
Web Site:
 http://www.simpsonmccrady.com
Year Founded: 1985
Sales Range: $1-9.9 Million
Insurance Agents
N.A.I.C.S.: 524210
Colvin McCrady *(Principal)*
Stefanie Cellitti *(Asst Controller)*
Kim Shadley *(Dir-Fin & Ops)*
Susan Campbell *(VP-Client Svc & Admin)*
Joe Hohman *(Dir-Bus Dev & Mktg)*
S. Clayton Saftner *(COO & Principal)*
William H. Simpson *(Acct Exec)*
Rick Farmer *(Acct Exec)*

SIMPSON CONSTRUCTION COMPANY, INC.
178 Durkee Rd, Cleveland, TN 37323
Tel.: (423) 472-4553
Web Site:
 http://www.simpsonconst.net
Year Founded: 1962
Rev.: $16,000,000
Emp.: 175
Bridge Construction
N.A.I.C.S.: 237310
Claude Simpson *(Pres)*

SIMPSON CONSTRUCTION MATERIALS
PO Box 250, Valley Park, MO 63088
Tel.: (636) 343-4944
Web Site:
 http://www.simpsoncompany.com
Sales Range: $10-24.9 Million
Emp.: 10
Sand, Gravel & Limestone Processor
N.A.I.C.S.: 324121
Mark Simpson *(Pres)*
J. C. Webb *(Mgr-Quality Control)*

SIMPSON CONSTRUCTION SERVICES, INC.
1831 S Anna St, Wichita, KS 67209-2897
Tel.: (316) 942-3206
Web Site:
 http://www.simpsonconst.com
Year Founded: 1984
Sales Range: $25-49.9 Million
Emp.: 48
Nonresidential Construction Services
N.A.I.C.S.: 236220
W. Gregg Oblinger *(Gen Mgr)*
Robert Simpson *(Owner)*
Chad Buresh *(VP-Ops)*

SIMPSON ELECTRIC COMPANY
520 Simpson Ave, Lac Du Flambeau, WI 54538
Tel.: (715) 588-3311
Web Site:
 http://www.simpsonelectric.com
Year Founded: 1936
Sales Range: $150-199.9 Million
Emp.: 60
Mfr of Analog & Digital Test Instrumentation & Panel Meters
N.A.I.C.S.: 334220
Jon Schmitz *(Gen Mgr)*

SIMPSON GUMPERTZ & HEGER INC.
41 Seyon St Ste 500, Waltham, MA 02453
Tel.: (781) 907-9214
Web Site: http://www.sgh.com
Year Founded: 1956
Sales Range: $150-199.9 Million
Emp.: 400
Consulting Engineers; Design of Buildings & Building Envelopes; Mechanical Structures & Infrastructures; Technical & Material Sciences
N.A.I.C.S.: 541330
Thomas A. Schwartz *(Principal-Consulting)*
Jason P. Heroux *(VP-Bus Dev)*
Julianne C. Nevins *(VP-HR)*
Ronald O. Hamburger *(Sr Principal & Head-Structural Engrg-Western)*
Paul L. Kelley *(Sr Principal & Head-Structural Engrg-Eastern)*
Jeffry Ceruti *(Sr Principal)*
Kenneth A. Klein *(Sr Principal & Head-Building Tech-Western)*
Matthew Daw *(Sr Principal)*
James Parker *(CEO)*
David Gonzalez *(Sr Principal)*
Niklas Vigener *(CTO)*
Derrick Watkins *(Principal)*
Frederic Grant *(Head-EMI-South California)*

SIMPSON HOUSE
2101 Belmont Ave, Philadelphia, PA 19131-1628
Tel.: (215) 878-3600
Web Site:
 http://www.simpsonhouse.org
Year Founded: 1865
Sales Range: $10-24.9 Million
Emp.: 331
Continuing Care Retirement Community Operator
N.A.I.C.S.: 623311
James Koniszewski *(CFO)*
Toni McClay *(COO)*

SIMPSON HOUSING LIMITED PARTNERSHIP
8110 E Union Ave Ste 200, Denver, CO 80237
Tel.: (303) 283-4100
Web Site:
 http://www.simpsonproperty group.com
Year Founded: 1995
Rev.: $316,696,000
Emp.: 1,200
Multi-Family Property Management & Development
N.A.I.C.S.: 531390
J. Robert Love *(CEO)*
Donald Mabry *(Chief Dev Officer)*
Michael Casper *(CIO & VP-IT)*
Adrienne Robinson *(VP-People Svcs)*
Stephen R. Bair *(Sr VP-Construction)*
Kyle Lucas *(Mgr-Community)*
Karen Simons *(Exec VP-Fin & Admin)*

Subsidiaries:

Simpson Property Group, LP (1)

8110 E Union Ave Ste 200, Denver, CO 80237
Tel.: (303) 283-4100
Web Site:
 http://www.simpsonpropertygroup.com
Sales Range: $10-24.9 Million
Emp.: 75
Operator of Apartment Buildings
N.A.I.C.S.: 531110
Todd S. Pope *(Pres)*
Kailey Norelius *(Dir-Mktg-West Coast)*

SIMPSON HOUSING SOLUTIONS, LLC
330 W Victoria St, Gardena, CA 90248-3527
Tel.: (562) 256-2000
Sales Range: $75-99.9 Million
Emp.: 80
Home Remodeling, Real Estate & Other Related Services
N.A.I.C.S.: 236118
Thomas Erickson *(Sr VP-Acq)*
Martha Lennig *(Office Mgr)*

SIMPSON INVESTMENT COMPANY
400 Simpson Ave, McCleary, WA 98557
Tel.: (360) 495-3291
Year Founded: 1890
Sales Range: $400-449.9 Million
Emp.: 2,839
Holding Company; Wood Door Mfr & Distr
N.A.I.C.S.: 551112
Colin Moseley *(Chm & CEO)*
Allen F. Trinkwald *(Pres)*

Subsidiaries:

Simpson Door Company (1)
400 Simpson Ave, McCleary, WA 98557
Tel.: (360) 495-3291
Web Site: http://www.simpsondoor.com
Sales Range: $25-49.9 Million
Emp.: 250
Mfr of Doors
N.A.I.C.S.: 321911
Brad Loveless *(Mgr-Mktg & Product Dev)*
Phil Steklenski *(VP & Gen Mgr)*

SIMPSON OF MARYLAND, INC.
7476 Candlewood Rd, Hanover, MD 21076-3108
Tel.: (410) 525-0152
Web Site:
 http://www.simpsonofmd.com
Sales Range: $10-24.9 Million
Emp.: 125
Nonresidential Construction Services
N.A.I.C.S.: 236220
Dennis Patrick *(Pres)*

SIMPSON PLASTERING LLC
PO Box 321275, Birmingham, AL 35232
Tel.: (205) 994-2801
Web Site:
 http://www.simpsonplastering.com
Year Founded: 1948
Sales Range: $1-9.9 Million
Emp.: 50
Plastering
N.A.I.C.S.: 238390
Richard Riley *(Pres)*
Michael Kennedy *(COO)*
Seth White *(Mgr-Waterproofing Div)*
Woody Kennedy *(Project Mgr-Wetwall Div)*
Ronny Harden *(Project Mgr)*
Rodney Chambers *(Project Mgr)*

SIMPSON THACHER & BARTLETT LLP
425 Lexington Ave, New York, NY 10017-3954

Tel.: (212) 455-2000
Web Site: https://www.stblaw.com
Year Founded: 1884
Sales Range: $900-999.9 Million
Emp.: 1,500
Law Firm
N.A.I.C.S.: 541110
Maripat Alpuche *(Partner)*
Ryan R. Bekkerus *(Partner)*
Thomas H. Bell *(Partner)*
Joshua Ford Bonnie *(Partner)*
Brian E. Chisling *(Partner)*
Edward J. H. Chung *(Partner)*
Elizabeth A. Cooper *(Partner)*
Barrie B. Covit *(Partner)*
John J. Creed *(Partner)*
S. Todd Crider *(Partner)*
James D. Cross *(Partner)*
M. Breen Haire *(Partner)*
Robert Rabalais *(Partner)*
Jeffrey H. Knox *(Partner)*
David Azarkh *(Partner)*
Carol Daniel *(Partner)*
Susannah Geltman *(Partner)*
Brian Gluck *(Partner)*
Jonathan Lindabury *(Partner)*
Wheatly MacNamara *(Partner)*
Sebastian Tiller *(Partner)*
Jessica Tuchinsky *(Partner)*
Paul Curnin *(Co-Head-Litigation Dept)*
Jonathan K. Youngwood *(Co-Head-Litigation Dept)*
Michael Hersch *(Exec Dir)*
Lee Meyerson *(Head-Fin Institutions Practice)*
Michael Wolitzer *(Head-Investment Funds Practice)*
David W. Blass *(Partner-Investment Funds Practice- Washington)*
Edie R. Jennings *(Chief HR & Office Admin Officer)*
Brooke E. Cucinella *(Partner-Litigation)*
Stephen M. Cutler *(Partner-Litigation)*
Kathryn King Sudol *(Co-Head-Merger & Acq-Global)*
Stephen M. Cutler *(Partner-Litigation)*

SIMS BROTHERS INC.
1011 S Prospect St, Marion, OH 43302
Tel.: (740) 387-9041   OH
Web Site: http://www.simsbros.com
Year Founded: 1920
Sales Range: $10-24.9 Million
Emp.: 55
Iron & Steel Products Mfr
N.A.I.C.S.: 423510
Stan Casey *(Controller)*
Garrett Tracey *(COO/Chief Comml Officer-Recycling)*
Scott Knowles *(CEO)*

SIMS BUICK -GMC- TRUCK INC.
3100 Elm Rd NE, Warren, OH 44483
Tel.: (330) 372-3500
Sales Range: $10-24.9 Million
Emp.: 54
Car Whslr
N.A.I.C.S.: 441110
Vito Maggio *(Gen Mgr-Sls)*
William R. Sims *(Pres)*

SIMS CRANE & EQUIPMENT COMPANY
1219 N US Hwy 301, Tampa, FL 33619
Tel.: (813) 626-8102
Web Site: http://www.simscrane.com
Sales Range: $50-74.9 Million
Emp.: 325
Cranes & Aerial Lift Equipment Rental Services
N.A.I.C.S.: 532412

Steve Stodghill *(Pres)*
George Suarez *(Dir-HR)*
Kurt Kuffermann *(VP & Gen Mgr-Ops)*
Mark A. Hollister *(VP-Bus Dev)*
Bob Berry *(Dir-Safety)*
Kelly Johnston *(Office Mgr)*
Erika Sims *(VP-Sls)*
David Wessin *(Dir-Safety-South Florida)*
Rick DeCarlo *(Sr Mgr-Bus Affairs)*
Ryan Camp *(VP-Corp Svcs)*
Art Gilfus *(Mgr-Orlando)*
Deborah Garringer *(CFO)*
Bill Titus *(Gen Mgr-West Palm Beach)*
Dean Sims II *(VP-Mktg)*

SIMS IMPORT INC.
1615 S Goldenrod Rd, Burlington, WA 98233
Tel.: (360) 757-7467
Web Site: http://www.simshonda.com
Sales Range: $10-24.9 Million
Emp.: 30
Car Dealership
N.A.I.C.S.: 441110
Vern Sims *(Owner)*

SIMS-LOHMAN, INC.
6325 Este Ave, Cincinnati, OH 45232
Tel.: (513) 651-3510   OH
Web Site: http://www.sims-lohman.com
Year Founded: 1971
Cabinetry & Granite Countertops Distr
N.A.I.C.S.: 337110
John Beiersdorfer *(CEO)*
Steve Steinman *(Chm)*
Joe Kline *(Pres)*
Jason Sigl *(CFO)*
Mark Hausfeld *(VP-Fin)*

Subsidiaries:

Canton Cut Stone Co. Inc.   (1)
6570 Promway Ave NW, Canton, OH 44720
Tel.: (330) 456-8408
Web Site: https://cts.sims-lohman.com
Cut Stone & Cut Stone Product Mfr
N.A.I.C.S.: 327991

SIMSBURY ASSOCIATES INC.
14 Storrs Ave, Braintree, MA 02184
Tel.: (781) 849-7722
Rev.: $13,000,000
Emp.: 15
Apartment Building Operator
N.A.I.C.S.: 531110
Bill Giovannucci *(VP-Dev)*

SIMSCROFT-ECHO FARMS INC.
2 Farms Village Rd, Simsbury, CT 06070
Tel.: (860) 651-0231
Web Site: http://www.simscroft.com
Rev.: $15,000,000
Emp.: 75
Excavation Work
N.A.I.C.S.: 238910
Michael A. Girard *(Pres)*

SIMVENTIONSM INC.
100 Riverside Pkwy Ste 123, Fredericksburg, VA 22406
Tel.: (540) 372-7727
Web Site: http://www.simventions.net
Year Founded: 2000
Sales Range: $10-24.9 Million
Emp.: 200
Software Engineering Services
N.A.I.C.S.: 541511
Larry Root *(CEO)*
Paul Gustavson *(CTO)*
George Hughes *(Pres)*
Bob Duffy *(VP-Bus Dev)*

Mary Beth Roberts *(VP-HR, Facilities & Security)*
Herb Kaler *(Sr VP)*
Joe Caliri *(COO)*
Paul Gatanis *(CIO)*
Jake Johnson *(VP)*
Jason Doering *(VP)*
Jennifer Conway *(Controller)*
John Kvartunas *(VP)*
Matt Wilson *(VP)*
Megan Shepherd *(VP)*
Robert Fidler *(VP)*
Steve Goss *(CFO)*

SINAI HEALTH SYSTEM
California Ave at 15th St, Chicago, IL 60608
Tel.: (773) 542-2000
Web Site: http://www.sinai.org
Sales Range: $400-449.9 Million
Hospital Operator
N.A.I.C.S.: 622110
Charles Weis *(CFO & Exec VP)*
Donnica Austin *(Chief Integrity Officer & Asst VP)*
Aaron Austin *(VP-HR)*
Debra G. Wesley *(Founder & Pres)*
Loren F. Chandler *(COO & Exec VP)*
Mark Multach *(Chief Medical Officer)*
Rachel Dvorken *(Gen Counsel & Exec VP)*
Roberta Rakove *(Sr VP-Govt & Pub Affairs)*
Tanvir Mangat *(Chief Strategy Officer)*
Gary Newton *(Pres & CEO)*
Joan E. Sproul *(Chief Admin Officer & Exec VP-Fin)*

SINCA INDUSTRIES, INC.
1001 E Eisenhower Ave, Hoskins, NE 68702-1247
Tel.: (402) 371-1400
Year Founded: 1993
Mfr of Industrial Equipment
N.A.I.C.S.: 333111

Subsidiaries:

Apache Industries, Inc.   (1)
202 S Main St PO Box 238, Hoskins, NE 68740
Tel.: (402) 371-1400
Boat, Bus & Dog Carrier Mfr
N.A.I.C.S.: 441222

Henke Machine - Buffalo Equipment   (1)
1001 E Eisenhower Ave, Norfolk, NE 68601-3513
Tel.: (402) 562-0014
Sales Range: $10-24.9 Million
Emp.: 63
Agricultural Equipment
N.A.I.C.S.: 333111

SINCLAIR ELEVATOR INC.
327 46th Sinclair Ave, Parkersburg, IA 50665
Tel.: (319) 346-1954   IA
Sales Range: $10-24.9 Million
Emp.: 24
Grains & Agricultural Supplies Distr
N.A.I.C.S.: 424510
Roger A. Baker *(Owner & Pres)*

SINCLAIR INSURANCE GROUP INC.
35 Thorpe Ave Ste 200, Wallingford, CT 06492-5914
Tel.: (203) 265-0996
Web Site: http://www.sinclair-insurance.com
Rev.: $85,000,000
Emp.: 29
Insurance Agents & Brokers
N.A.I.C.S.: 523999
David Sinclair *(Pres)*

SINCLAIR PRINTING COMPANY
4005 Whiteside St, Los Angeles, CA 90063-1616
Tel.: (323) 264-4000   CA
Web Site: http://www.sinclairprinting.com
Year Founded: 1929
Sales Range: $25-49.9 Million
Emp.: 120
Provider of Printing Services
N.A.I.C.S.: 323111
Robert J. Sinclair *(Pres)*
Dan Sinclair *(VP-Sls)*
Armine Khachaturian *(Controller)*

SINCLAIR RESEARCH CENTER, LLC
562 State Rd DD, Auxvasse, MO 65231
Tel.: (573) 387-4400
Web Site: http://www.sinclairresearch.com
Year Founded: 1965
Sales Range: $10-24.9 Million
Emp.: 200
Laboratory Research Services
N.A.I.C.S.: 621511
Guy F. Bouchard *(CEO)*
Mark Crane *(VP-Bus Dev)*
Mark Lane *(Dir-Bus Dev)*
Gary Jacobson *(Pres & CFO)*

SINCLAIR WELL PRODUCTS INC.
10602 Midway Ave, Cerritos, CA 90703
Tel.: (562) 403-3559
Web Site: http://www.sinclairwellproducts.com
Year Founded: 1987
Sales Range: $25-49.9 Million
Emp.: 15
Well Drilling Equipment Whslr
N.A.I.C.S.: 423810
Renan Listi *(Pres)*
Stewart Dunham *(Gen Mgr-Sls)*

SINCO INC.
750 Pleasant St, Belmont, MA 02478
Tel.: (617) 484-8212
Web Site: http://www.sinco-inc.com
Sales Range: $10-24.9 Million
Emp.: 68
Bond Brokers
N.A.I.C.S.: 424410
Robert Snyder *(Pres)*
Scott Richmond *(CFO)*
Paul Dembling *(Pres)*

SING BROTHERS INC.
3121 N Oak St Ext, Valdosta, GA 31602-1055
Tel.: (229) 242-4882   GA
Web Site: http://www.singbros.com
Year Founded: 1972
Sales Range: $25-49.9 Million
Emp.: 85
Gasoline Service Stations
N.A.I.C.S.: 457120
Joe P. Singletary Jr. *(Exec Officer)*
Joe Singletary III *(Pres)*

SINGAPORE RESOURCES, INC.
176 E Main St Ste 6, Westborough, MA 01581
Tel.: (508) 366-7676
Web Site: http://www.singapore-resources.com
Sales Range: $10-24.9 Million
Emp.: 675
Electronic & Medical Device Mfr
N.A.I.C.S.: 423610
Stephen Barker *(Pres & Treas)*
Clotilde Didomenico *(Sec)*

SINGER EQUIPMENT COMPANY
150 S Twin Vly Rd, Elverson, PA 19520-9328
Tel.: (610) 929-8000 PA
Web Site: http://www.singerequipment.com
Year Founded: 1918
Sales Range: $25-49.9 Million
Emp.: 175
Food Service Equipment & Supplies
N.A.I.C.S.: 423440

Subsidiaries:

Kittredge Equipment Co. Inc. (1)
100 Bowles Rd, Agawam, MA 01001
Tel.: (413) 304-4100
Web Site: http://www.kittredgeequipment.com
Sales Range: $10-24.9 Million
Emp.: 50
Wholesale Dealer of Commercial Cooking & Food Service Equipment
N.A.I.C.S.: 423440
Wendy Webber (Pres)

SINGER LEWAK GREENBAUM & GOLDSTEIN
10960 Wilshire Blvd Ste 700, Los Angeles, CA 90024-3710
Tel.: (310) 477-3924
Web Site: http://www.slgg.com
Rev.: $20,000,000
Emp.: 300
Certified Public Accountants
N.A.I.C.S.: 541211
Sally Aubury (Partner)

SINGER TRAVEL
18 Commerce Dr, Wyomissing, PA 19610
Tel.: (610) 378-1610
Web Site: http://www.singertravel.com
Year Founded: 1983
Sales Range: $1-9.9 Million
Emp.: 10
Travel Agency
N.A.I.C.S.: 561510
Helene G. Singer (Pres)

SINGH DEVELOPMENT CO. LTD.
7125 Orchard Lake Rd Ste 200, West Bloomfield, MI 48322
Tel.: (248) 865-1600
Web Site: http://www.singhweb.com
Rev.: $20,000,000
Emp.: 35
Multi-Family Dwelling Construction Services
N.A.I.C.S.: 236116
Darshan S. Grewal (Pres)
Gurmale S. Grewal (CEO)

SINGING BEACH CLUB INC.
Beach St, Manchester, MA 01944-0000
Tel.: (978) 526-4965 MA
Year Founded: 1943
Social Club
N.A.I.C.S.: 813410
Ronald Skates (Pres)

SINGING RIVER ELECTRIC POWER ASSOCIATION
11187 Old Hwy 63 S, Lucedale, MS 39452
Tel.: (601) 947-4211
Web Site: http://www.singingriver.com
Rev.: $81,828,174
Emp.: 250
Electric Power Distribution
N.A.I.C.S.: 221122
Buck Williams (Mgr-Risk)

SINGLE PATH
905 Parkview Blvd, Lombard, IL 60148
Tel.: (630) 812-2300
Web Site: http://www.singlepath.com
Year Founded: 2003
Rev.: $8,200,000
Emp.: 30
Telecommunication Servicesb
N.A.I.C.S.: 541990
Marty Jensen (Project Mgr)
Laura Staron (Office Mgr)

SINGLE SOURCE PACKAGING CO. LLC.
5505 W 74th St, Indianapolis, IN 46268
Tel.: (317) 290-1140
Rev.: $38,700,000
Emp.: 270
Paper Mills
N.A.I.C.S.: 322120
Jack Schwarz (Mgr)

SINGLE SOURCE ROOFING CORP
24 Summit Park Dr, Pittsburgh, PA 15275-1110
Tel.: (412) 249-6800
Web Site: http://www.singlesourceroofing.com
Sales Range: $10-24.9 Million
Emp.: 60
Roofing
N.A.I.C.S.: 326299
Gary Kassem (Pres)

SINGLE STOP USA
1825 Park Ave Ste 503, New York, NY 10035
Tel.: (212) 480-2870 NY
Web Site: http://www.singlestopusa.org
Year Founded: 2007
Sales Range: $10-24.9 Million
Emp.: 55
Social Welfare & Public Relation Services
N.A.I.C.S.: 813410
Michael Lumpp (CTO)
Cathryn McAleavey (Chief Fin & Admin Officer)
Angela Dorn (COO & Gen Counsel)

SINGLER-ERNSTER INC.
6950 Burnett St, Sebastopol, CA 95472
Tel.: (707) 823-0574
Web Site: http://www.singlerfamilyrestaurants.com
Sales Range: $10-24.9 Million
Emp.: 15
Pizzeria Chain
N.A.I.C.S.: 722513
Peter A. Singler (Chm)
Kimberly Ambrosino (CFO)

SINGLETON & PARTNERS, LTD.
1337 W 10th St, Cleveland, OH 44113
Tel.: (216) 344-9966
Web Site: http://www.singletonpartners.com
Sales Range: Less than $1 Million
Emp.: 20
Advetising Agency
N.A.I.C.S.: 541810
Renee Singleton (Pres & CEO)
Joyce Brown (VP & Dir-Mktg Div)
Elizabeth Radivoyevitch (Dir-Creative)
Janda Singleton-Johnson (VP & Dir-Social Mktg Div)
Jeane Holley (Mgr-Mktg Comm)

SINGLETON MARINE GROUP
5529 Lanier Island Pkwy, Buford, GA 30518
Tel.: (770) 741-2514
Web Site: http://www.singletonmarine.com
Year Founded: 2006
Holding Company; Boat Dealerships & Marinas Owner & Operator
N.A.I.C.S.: 551112
Austin Singleton (Pres)
Scott Cunningham (Mng Partner)
Ryan Ervin (Bus Mgr)
Philip Austin Singleton Jr. (Founder)
Anthony M. Aisquith (Mng Partner)

Subsidiaries:

Phil Dill Boats, Inc. (1)
1520 N Stemmons Fwy, Lewisville, TX 75067
Tel.: (972) 436-3581
Web Site: http://www.phildillboats.com
Sales Range: $10-24.9 Million
Emp.: 40
Boat Dealers
N.A.I.C.S.: 441222
Pat LaRocco (Mgr-Acctg)
John McCroskey (Gen Mgr)

Singleton Marine Group - Blue Creek Marina at Lake Martin (1)
7280 Hwy 49 S, Dadeville, AL 36853
Tel.: (256) 825-8888
Web Site: http://www.singletonmarinegroup.com
Sales Range: $1-9.9 Million
Emp.: 30
Boat Dealer & Marina
N.A.I.C.S.: 441222
Billy Smith (Mgr)

Singleton Marine Group Yacht Center at Holiday Marina (1)
6900 Lanier Islands Pkwy, Buford, GA 30518
Tel.: (770) 614-6655
Web Site: http://www.singletonmarinegroup.com
Sales Range: $1-9.9 Million
Emp.: 25
Boat Dealer & Marina Operator
N.A.I.C.S.: 441222
Michael Sachs (Pres)

Singleton Marine Group of Atlanta (1)
5529 Lanier Islands Pkwy, Buford, GA 30518
Tel.: (770) 831-8898
Web Site: http://www.singletonmarinegroup.com
Sales Range: $10-24.9 Million
Emp.: 20
Boat Dealers
N.A.I.C.S.: 441222
Austin Singleton (Pres)

SINGULEX, INC.
1650 Harbor Pkwy Ste 200, Alameda, CA 94502
Tel.: (510) 995-9000 DE
Web Site: http://www.singulex.com
Year Founded: 1997
Sales Range: $10-24.9 Million
Emp.: 177
Medical Products Researcher & Developer
N.A.I.C.S.: 621511
Guido Baechler (Pres & CEO)
Jeffrey Bishop (VP-R&D)
Peter Heseltine (Chief Medical Officer)
Jessica McCarthy (VP-Global Mktg & Comm)

SINTON DAIRY FOODS COMPANY L.L.C.
3801 Sinton Rd, Colorado Springs, CO 80907-5036
Tel.: (719) 633-3821 CO
Web Site: http://www.sintondairy.com
Year Founded: 1987
Sales Range: $25-49.9 Million
Emp.: 369
Milk Producer
N.A.I.C.S.: 311511
Randy Furstenau (Mgr-Mktg)
Mike Maloney (Product Mgr)
Amanda Moore (Mgr-Quality Assurance)

SINU, INC.
285 W Bdwy Ste 410, New York, NY 10013
Tel.: (212) 380-1230
Web Site: http://www.sinu.com
Sales Range: $1-9.9 Million
Emp.: 25
Information Technology Consulting Services
N.A.I.C.S.: 541512
Larry Velez (Founder & CTO)
John Christie (COO)

SINUATE MEDIA, LLC.
105 W 39th St Ste 216, Baltimore, MD 21201
Tel.: (443) 992-4682
Web Site: http://www.sinuatemedia.com
Sales Range: Less than $1 Million
Emp.: 6
Corporate Communications, Event Planning & Marketing, Exhibit/Trade Shows, Guerilla Marketing, Internet/Web Design, Mobile Marketing, Nonprofit/Social Marketing, Podcasting, Viral/Buzz/Word of Mouth
N.A.I.C.S.: 541810
Leah Messina (Founder & CEO)
Molly McConnell Guthrie (Acct Exec)
Melissa Macchiavelli (Acct Mgr)

SION POWER CORPORATION
9040 S Rita Rd 20900 E Zira RD, Tucson, AZ 85756
Tel.: (520) 799-7500
Web Site: http://www.sionpower.com
Year Founded: 1988
Sales Range: $125-149.9 Million
Electrochemical Energy Storage Systems
N.A.I.C.S.: 541715
John Kopera (VP-Comml Ops)
Tracy E. Kelley (CEO)
Leo Guthart (Chm)
Jeff Britt (VP-Ops)

SIONIX CORPORATION
914 Westwood Blvd Box 801, Los Angeles, CA 90024
Tel.: (704) 971-8400 NV
Web Site: http://www.sionix.com
Year Founded: 1996
Water Management & Treatment Systems Designer, Developer & Marketer
N.A.I.C.S.: 221310
Henry W. Sullivan (Chm & CEO)
Rex Crick (COO)
Mark J. Hayes (Chief Science Officer & VP-Technical Svcs)

SIOUNI & ZAR CORP.
49 W 37th St Fl 10, New York, NY 10018-0180
Tel.: (212) 704-9603
Web Site: http://www.dannyandnicole.com
Year Founded: 1984
Sales Range: $10-24.9 Million
Emp.: 55
Women's, Misses' & Juniors' Dresses Mfr & Distr
N.A.I.C.S.: 315250
Ken Prizeman (CFO)

SIOUX AUTOMATION CENTER INC.

877 1st Ave NW, Sioux Center, IA 51250
Tel.: (712) 722-1488   IA
Web Site:
   http://www.siouxautomation.com
Year Founded: 1951
Sales Range: $10-24.9 Million
Emp.: 100
Whslr of Farm & Garden Machinery
N.A.I.C.S.: 423820
Ron Hulshof *(Pres)*
Dan Hicks *(Mgr-Info Sys)*

SIOUX CITY FORD LINCOLN
3601 Singing Hills Blvd, Sioux City, IA 51106-5161
Tel.: (712) 277-8420
Web Site:
   http://www.siouxcityford.com
Sales Range: $25-49.9 Million
Emp.: 57
Car Dealership
N.A.I.C.S.: 441110
Rob Brooks *(Owner)*
Dan Bubb *(Mgr-Parts)*
Jay Menke *(Mgr-Sls)*
Scott Sterling *(Mgr-Gen Sls)*
Jim Caylor *(Mgr-Svcs)*
Brad Lindgren *(Mgr-Pre-Owned Sls)*
Doug Engle *(Mgr-Fin & Insurance)*
Rick Quintana *(Mgr-Collision Center)*
Roxanne Flammang *(Controller & Office Mgr)*
Sam Burrish *(Mgr-Mktg & Dev)*

SIOUX CITY FOUNDRY CO.
801 Division St, Sioux City, IA 51105-2644
Tel.: (712) 252-4181   IA
Web Site:
   http://www.siouxcityfoundry.com
Year Founded: 1871
Sales Range: $25-49.9 Million
Emp.: 250
Steel Production Services
N.A.I.C.S.: 423510
Doug DeStigter *(Mgr-Structural Fabrication)*
Rachel Arneson *(Coord-Mktg)*

SIOUX CITY TRUCK SALES INCORPORATED
2601 Voyager Ave, Sioux City, IA 51111
Tel.: (712) 255-1121   IA
Web Site: http://www.pbtruck.com
Year Founded: 1969
Sales Range: $50-74.9 Million
Emp.: 20
Trucks, Tractors & Trailers Sales
N.A.I.C.S.: 441110
Brad Wilson *(Pres)*
Eric Madsen *(Dir-Parts)*

SIOUX FALLS CHRISTIAN SCHOOLS
6120 S Charger Cir, Sioux Falls, SD 57108
Tel.: (605) 334-1422   SD
Web Site:
   http://www.siouxfallschristian.org
Year Founded: 2003
Sales Range: $10-24.9 Million
Emp.: 41
Educational Support Services
N.A.I.C.S.: 611710
Audra Eide *(Sec)*

SIOUX FALLS CONSTRUCTION COMPANY
800 S 7th Ave, Sioux Falls, SD 57104-5123
Tel.: (605) 336-1640   SD
Web Site: http://www.sfconst.com
Year Founded: 1910
Sales Range: $75-99.9 Million
Emp.: 55
Provider of Contracting & Construction Services
N.A.I.C.S.: 236220
David F. Fleck *(Chm)*
Randy Knecht *(CFO)*
Thomas Wilson *(VP)*
Brad Goldstine *(VP)*
Marilyn Bergeson *(VP-Ops)*
Jay D. Rasmussen *(Project Mgr)*

SIOUX FALLS FORD INC.
4901 W 21sy St, Sioux Falls, SD 57106
Tel.: (605) 361-0361
Web Site:
   http://www.siouxfallsford.com
Sales Range: $100-124.9 Million
Emp.: 200
New & Used Automobiles
N.A.I.C.S.: 441110
Randall J. Nehring *(Owner & Pres)*
Tim Hilber *(Controller)*
Bill Heim *(Mgr-Sls)*
Steve Remund *(Mgr-Sls)*

SIOUX HONEY ASSOCIATION
301 Lewis Blvd, Sioux City, IA 51101-2237
Tel.: (712) 258-0638   IA
Web Site: http://www.suebee.com
Year Founded: 1921
Sales Range: $75-99.9 Million
Emp.: 100
Honey Processor
N.A.I.C.S.: 424490
Vic Lund *(VP-Fin & Acctg)*
Dave Allibon *(Pres & CEO)*
Renee Nissen *(Dir-Mgmt Info Sys)*

SIOUX MANUFACTURING CORP.
1115 Dekotah Dr, Fort Totten, ND 58335
Tel.: (701) 766-4211   ND
Web Site:
   http://www.siouxmanufacturing.com
Year Founded: 1973
Sales Range: $100-124.9 Million
Emp.: 93
Mfr of Composite Molded Components & Metal Structures
N.A.I.C.S.: 336992
Carl McKay *(Pres & CEO)*

SIOUX STEEL COMPANY
196 1/2 E 6th St, Sioux Falls, SD 57104-5929
Tel.: (605) 336-1750   SD
Web Site: http://www.siouxsteel.com
Year Founded: 1918
Sales Range: $75-99.9 Million
Emp.: 200
Livestock Equipment, Grain Handling Equipment & Front End Loaders for Tractors Mfr
N.A.I.C.S.: 333111
Phillip Rysdon *(Chm)*
Scott Rysdon *(CEO & VP)*

Subsidiaries:

Koyker Mfg. Co.   (1)
200 N Cleveland St, Lennox, SD 57039
Tel.: (605) 647-2811
Web Site: http://www.koykermfg.com
Sales Range: $25-49.9 Million
Emp.: 110
Mfr of Front-End Loaders & Attachments
N.A.I.C.S.: 333111

SIOUX VALLEY ENERGY
47092 S Dakota Hwy 34, Colman, SD 57017
Tel.: (605) 534-3535   SD
Web Site: http://www.sve.com
Year Founded: 1940
Sales Range: $150-199.5 Million
Emp.: 100
Electrical Power Co-op
N.A.I.C.S.: 221122
Don Marker *(Gen Mgr)*
Betty VanDerWerff *(Dir-Fin)*
Janice Bobendrier *(Sec)*
Carrie Law *(Mgr-Mktg)*

Subsidiaries:

Sioux Valley Rural Television   (1)
47088 SD Hwy 34, Colman, SD 57017
Tel.: (605) 534-3241
Web Site: http://www.svwireless.com
Sales Range: $25-49.9 Million
Emp.: 10
Rural Television
N.A.I.C.S.: 221122

Sioux Valley Wireless   (1)
47092 SD Hwy 34, Colman, SD 57017
Tel.: (605) 534-3241
Web Site: http://www.svtv.com
Wireless Internet Service Provider
N.A.I.C.S.: 517112
Betty VanDerWerff *(Dir-Fin & Acctg)*

SIOUX VALLEY-SOUTHWESTERN ELECTRIC COOPERATIVE, INC.
47092 SD Highway 34, Colman, SD 57017
Tel.: (605) 534-3535   SD
Web Site:
   http://www.siouxvalleyenergy.com
Year Founded: 1939
Rev.: $83,091,840
Assets: $250,156,148
Liabilities: $160,929,044
Net Worth: $89,227,104
Earnings: $10,332,679
Emp.: 97
Fiscal Year-end: 12/31/18
Electric Power Distribution Services
N.A.I.C.S.: 221122
Betty VanderWerff *(Dir-Fin & Acctg)*
Debra Biever *(Dir-Customer & Employee Rels)*
Tim McCarthy *(CEO & Gen Mgr)*
Ted Smith *(Dir-Engrg & Ops)*
Arlyn Zylstra *(Treas)*
Rodney DeMent *(Pres)*
Carrie Vugteveen *(Dir-PR)*

SIOUXLAND ENERGY COOPERATIVE
3890 Garfield Ave, Sioux Center, IA 51250
Tel.: (712) 722-4904
Web Site:
   https://www.siouxlandenergy.com
Sales Range: $1-9.9 Million
Emp.: 25
Wet Corn Milling Services
N.A.I.C.S.: 311221
Darrell Vermeer *(Pres)*
Todd Popken *(VP)*
Jim Wagner *(Sec)*
Jeff Altena *(Controller & Dir-Ops)*
Jeff Larson *(Mgr-Plant)*
Steve Westra *(Mgr-Lab)*
Tom Miller *(Mgr-Commodity)*
Leah Holverson *(Office Mgr)*
Doug Opheim *(Mgr-Environment, Health & Safety)*
Shane Rasset *(Plant Mgr)*
Will Adler *(Mgr-Environmental, Health, and Safety)*
Tim Reinert *(Mgr-Maintenance)*
Wayne Schuller *(Ops Mgr)*
Kyle Kubesh *(Mgr-Lab)*
Derrick Postma *(Mgr-Co Products)*
Jessica Buyert *(Accountant-Staff)*

SIOUXLAND ETHANOL, LLC.
1501 Knox Blvd, Jackson, NE 68743
Tel.: (402) 632-2676
Web Site:
   http://www.siouxlandethanol.com
Year Founded: 2004
Sales Range: $10-24.9 Million
Emp.: 33
Ethyl Alcohol Mfr
N.A.I.C.S.: 325193
Chuck Hofland *(Gen Mgr)*
Mark Rolfes *(CFO)*
Carla Glass *(Mgr-Acctg)*
Susan Bostwick *(Mgr-Commodities)*
Samantha King *(Office Mgr)*
Mark Jenkins *(Plant Mgr)*
Pat Baker *(Plant Mgr)*
Pam Miller *(Chm)*
Shennen Saltzman *(Vice Chm)*
Tom Lynch *(Sec)*
Bruce Malcom *(Mgr-Maintenance)*

SIPCO SERVICES INC.
38 C Willson Rd, Humble, TX 77338
Tel.: (281) 878-3100
Rev.: $21,719,000
Emp.: 275
Industrial Painting
N.A.I.C.S.: 238320
Eric Stolz *(Pres)*

SIPI METALS CORP.
1720 N Elston Ave, Chicago, IL 60642-1579
Tel.: (773) 276-0070   IL
Web Site: http://www.sipicorp.com
Year Founded: 1932
Scrap Precious Metal Recovery
N.A.I.C.S.: 423510
Marion A. Cameron *(CEO)*
Len Stack *(Exec VP)*
Joris Coopmans *(Sr VP-Ops)*
Arlene McKitterick *(CFO)*
Eric Dorn *(Sr VP & Gen Mgr)*

Subsidiaries:

Belmont Technology Remarketing   (1)
Davy House Davy Ave The Quadrant, Birchwood Park, Warrington, WA36SW, Cheshire, United Kingdom
Tel.: (44) 925242000
Web Site: http://www.belmont-trading.com
Sales of Used Computers
N.A.I.C.S.: 541512

Subsidiary (Domestic):

Datec Technologies, Ltd.   (2)
1 Byreho Pl, W Byreho Industrial Est, Kilwinning, KA136LD, United Kingdom   **(100%)**
Tel.: (44) 001294556581
Web Site: http://www.datectech.co.uk
Sales of Used Computers
N.A.I.C.S.: 541512
Douglas Noris *(Mng Dir)*

SIQUIS, LTD.
1340 Smith Ave Ste 300, Baltimore, MD 21209-3797
Tel.: (410) 323-4800   MD
Web Site: http://www.siquis.com
Year Founded: 1986
Rev.: $56,000,000
Emp.: 50
Brand Development, Broadcast, Business-To-Business, Collateral, Corporate Identity, Direct Marketing, Interactive Agencies, Internet/Web Design, Media Buying Services, Print, Strategic Planning
N.A.I.C.S.: 541810
Anita Kaplan *(Pres)*
Moira DiJulio *(VP-Direct Response)*
Marc Rosenstein *(CFO & VP)*
Debbie Norris *(Dir-Media)*

SIRCHIE FINGERPRINT LABS
100 Hunter Pl, Youngsville, NC 27596
Tel.: (919) 554-2244

SIRCHIE FINGERPRINT LABS

U.S. PRIVATE

Sirchie Fingerprint Labs—(Continued)
Web Site: http://www.sirchie.com
Rev.: $16,000,000
Emp.: 105
Detection Apparatus,
Electronic/Magnetic Field &
Light/Heat
N.A.I.C.S.: 334511
Jim Gocke (VP)

Subsidiaries:

Premier Crown Corp. (1)
100 Hunter Pl, Youngsville, NC 27596
Tel.: (919) 554-2244
Unsupported Plastics Profile Shape Mfr
N.A.I.C.S.: 326121

SIRINA FIRE PROTECTION CORP.
151 Herricks Rd, Garden City Park, NY 11040
Tel.: (516) 942-0400
Web Site: http://www.sirinafire.com
Sales Range: $10-24.9 Million
Emp.: 80
Fire Sprinkler System Installation
N.A.I.C.S.: 238220
Christopher Allen (Controller)
Michael Warttinger (Exec VP)
Timothy Olsen (Engr-Sprinkler)

SIRIS CAPITAL GROUP, LLC
601 Lexington Ave 59th Fl, New York, NY 10022
Tel.: (212) 231-0095   DE
Web Site: http://www.siriscapital.com
Year Founded: 2011
Privater Equity Firm
N.A.I.C.S.: 523999
John A. C. Swainson (Exec Partner)
Jeffrey M. Hendren (Co-Founder & Mng Dir)
Elias Mendoza (COO, Partner & Sr Mng Dir)
Philip Lo (Mng Dir-IR)
Jerry Stapp (Principal)
Dominick Golio (Dir-Special Projects)
Ciara Roche (Mng Dir-Compliance & Ops)
Ian Silverman (CFO)
Daniel Goetz (VP)
Michael Hulslander (Mng Dir)
Daniel M. Moloney (Partner-Exec)
Merle Gilmore (Partner-Exec)
Daniel Moloney (Partner-Exec)
Theodore Schell (Partner-Exec)
Steven Spencer (Chief Compliance Officer, Gen Counsel, Partner & Sr Mng Dir)
Jonathan Liva (Controller)
Himanshu Sekhar (Sr Mgr-Strategy & Bus Dev)
Stephen Catera (VP)
Sandeep Guleria (VP)
Tyler Sipprelle (VP)
Hina Patel (Office Mgr)
Sherwyn Williams (Mgr-IT & Cybersecurity)
Robert M. Aquilina (Partner-Exec)
Hilton Romanski (Partner & Sr Mng Dir)
Frank Augustus Baker (Co-Founder & Mng Partner)
Joe Cozzolino (Partner)
Roderick K. Randall (Exec Partner)
Peter E. Berger (Mng Dir)
Hubert de Pesquidoux (Partner-Exec)

Subsidiaries:

Constant Contact, Inc. (1)
Reservoir Pl 1601 Trapelo Rd, Waltham, MA 02451
Tel.: (781) 472-8100
Web Site: http://www.constantcontact.com
Web-Based Services for E-Mail Marketing Campaigns
N.A.I.C.S.: 561499

Jonathan Kateman (Gen Mgr)

Digital River, Inc. (1)
10380 Bren Rd W, Minnetonka, MN 55343
Tel.: (952) 253-1234
Web Site: http://www.digitalriver.com
Sales Range: $350-399.9 Million
Outsourcing Services for Web Commerce & Online Marketing Solutions
N.A.I.C.S.: 541613
Kristin McKensie (Assoc Dir-Corp Comm)
Gerri Dyrek (Grp VP-Corp Comm)
Scott Scazafavo (Sr VP-Product Mgmt)
David Woolenberg (Sr VP-Global Sls-Digital Commerce)
Rob Hines (Sr VP-Global Sls & Field Mktg)
Hayden Reed (Gen Mgr & Sr VP-Digital River World Payments)
Joydeep Haldar (Sr VP-Professional Services & Strategic Alliances)
Stewart Sagastume (Sr VP-Microsoft & Global Account Expansion)
Ian Holsman (Sr VP-Dev & Engrg)
Kathy Tompt (VP-Enterprise Ops)
KT Lindberger-Schmidt (Chief HR Officer & Gen Counsel)
Jason Nyhus (VP-Global Mktg & Comm)
John Cullinane (Dir-Product Strategy)
Eric Moen (Mgr-Strategic Mktg)
Christopher Bernander (CFO)
Adam Coyle (CEO)
Natalie Wires (Dir-Corp Comm)
Ted Rogers (CMO)
Theodore R. Cahall Jr. (COO & Exec VP)

Subsidiary (Domestic):

CustomCD, Inc. (2)
7725 Washington Ave S, Minneapolis, MN 55439
Tel.: (952) 500-9845
Web Site: http://www.customcd.com
On Demand Printing Solution Provider
N.A.I.C.S.: 323111

Subsidiary (Non-US):

Digital River GmbH (2)
Scheidtweilerstrasse 4, Cologne, 50933, Germany
Tel.: (49) 221310880
Web Site: http://www.digitalriver.com
E-Business & Marketing Management Services
N.A.I.C.S.: 541613
John Strosahl (VP)

Digital River Ireland Limited (2)
Unit 153 Shannon Free Zone West, Shannon, Clare, Ireland
Tel.: (353) 61230000
Web Site: http://www.digitalriver.com
Online & E-Marketing Solutions Provider
N.A.I.C.S.: 541613

Digital River Online Games (2)
Mariahilferstrasse 50/2/11, Entrance Kirchengasse 1, Vienna, 1070, Austria
Tel.: (43) 123622970
Web Site: http://www.digitalriver.com
Monetizing Online Games Software Developer
N.A.I.C.S.: 513210
Daniel Petri (Mng Dir)
Thomas Stagl (Dir-Tech)

Subsidiary (Domestic):

Fireclick, Inc. (2)
2355 Northside Dr Ste B-250, San Diego, CA 92108
Tel.: (952) 253-1234
Web Site: http://www.fireclick.com
Web Experience Management Solutions
N.A.I.C.S.: 518210
Xavier Casanova (Founder)

JourneyEd.com, Inc. (2)
80 E McDermott Dr, Allen, TX 75002
Tel.: (469) 429-2380
Web Site: http://www.journeyed.com
Educational Software Distr
N.A.I.C.S.: 449210

Electronics For Imaging, Inc. (1)
6750 Dumbarton Cir, Fremont, CA 94555
Tel.: (650) 357-3500
Web Site: http://www.efi.com
Rev.: $1,015,021,000
Assets: $1,499,034,000
Liabilities: $772,926,000
Net Worth: $726,108,000

Earnings: ($971,000)
Emp.: 3,400
Fiscal Year-end: 12/31/2018
Printing & Prepress Management Software
N.A.I.C.S.: 334118
Paul Cripps (VP-Sls & Ops-EMEA)
Frank Mallozzi (Chief Revenue Officer)
Marc D. Olin (COO)
Toby Weiss (Sr VP & Gen Mgr-Fiery Bus Unit)
Scott Schinlever (COO-Inkjet Bus-Global)
Alex K. Grab (Chief Legal Officer)
Gabriel Matsliach (Sr VP & Gen Mgr-Productivity Software)
Patrick Morrissey (VP-Sls-Americas)
Samir Gulve (Mng Dir-India & VP-Engrg)
Roy Douglass (Chief Bus Dev Officer)
Bernie Lepore (VP-Partner Alliance)
Paul Sexton (Chief HR Officer)
Jill Norris (CIO)
Jeff Jacobson (Chrm & CEO)
Grant Fitz (CFO)

Subsidiary (Non-US):

EFI (Canada), Inc. (2)
121 Granton Drive Unit 14, Richmond Hill, L4B 3N4, ON, Canada
Tel.: (905) 882-2500
Emp.: 30
Printer & Ink Product Mfr
N.A.I.C.S.: 322230
Micah Kornberg (VP)

EFI Belgium BVBA (2)
Ikaroslaan 9, Zaventem, 1930, Belgium
Tel.: (32) 27499420
Emp.: 44
Printing & Prepress Management Software Services
N.A.I.C.S.: 541511

EFI Brazil Ltda. (2)
Alameda Santos 6 Andar Paraiso, Sao Paulo, 01418-000, SP, Brazil
Tel.: (55) 132663263
Sales Range: $10-24.9 Million
Emp.: 8
Imaging & Printing Products Mfr
N.A.I.C.S.: 333248

EFI Cretaprint S.L. (2)
Pol Ind Supoi-8 Carrer del Ibers 54, 12550, Almazora, Castellon, Spain
Tel.: (34) 902118996
Imaging & Printing Products Mfr
N.A.I.C.S.: 333248

EFI Cretaprint, S.L. (2)
Calle dels Ibers Pol Industrial Supoi 8 54 - Apdo De Correos N 93, Almassora, 12550, Castellon de la Plana, Spain
Tel.: (34) 964340264
Computer Terminal & Other Peripheral Device Mfr
N.A.I.C.S.: 334118

EFI K.K. (2)
Shinjuku Oak Tower 14th Fl 6-8-1, Nishi Shinjuku, Tokyo, 163-6014, Japan
Tel.: (81) 333443123
Web Site: http://www.efi.co.jp
Sales Range: $25-49.9 Million
Emp.: 45
Imaging & Printing Products Mfr
N.A.I.C.S.: 333248

Electronics For Imaging AB (2)
Frosundaviks Alle 15, 169 70, Solna, Sweden
Tel.: (46) 86552620
Web Site: http://www.efi.se
Sales Range: $10-24.9 Million
Emp.: 1
Imaging & Printing Products Mfr
N.A.I.C.S.: 333248
John Dekker (Pres)

Electronics For Imaging Australia Pty. Ltd. (2)
Office 1F 24 Macquarie Street, Teneriffe, Brisbane, 4005, QLD, Australia
Tel.: (61) 7 3625 9200
Web Site: http://www.efi.com
Sales Range: $125-149.9 Million
Emp.: 20
Imagine & Printing Products Mfr
N.A.I.C.S.: 333248
Kathy Mitchell (Dir-Ops)

Electronics For Imaging India Private Limited (2)
Kalyani Platina 4th Floor Block I No 24 EPIP Zone Phase II White Field, Bengaluru, 560 066, India
Tel.: (91) 8067681000
Web Site: http://www.efi.com
Sales Range: $150-199.9 Million
Emp.: 500
Printer & Ink Product Mfr
N.A.I.C.S.: 325910
Steve Green (VP-Sls-Asia Pacific)
Samir Gulve (Mng Dir)

Electronics For Imaging Korea Co., Ltd. (2)
13th Floor Kyobo Tower B 1303-22 Seochodong, Seocho-gu, Seoul, 137-070, Korea (South)
Tel.: (82) 2 6463 8488
Sales Range: $125-149.9 Million
Mfr of Imaging & Printing Products
N.A.I.C.S.: 333248

Branch (Domestic):

Electronics For Imaging, Inc. - Arizona (2)
17250 N Hartford Dr Ste 101, Scottsdale, AZ 85255
Tel.: (480) 538-5800
Web Site: http://www.efi.com
Sales Range: $25-49.9 Million
Emp.: 500
Printing Products Mfr
N.A.I.C.S.: 333248

Electronics For Imaging, Inc. - Georgia (2)
4955 Avalon Rdg Pkwy Ste 300, Norcross, GA 30071
Tel.: (770) 448-9008
Web Site: http://www.efi.com
Sales Range: $10-24.9 Million
Emp.: 55
Designs Digital Document Processing Systems
N.A.I.C.S.: 541511

Electronics For Imaging, Inc. - Inkjet Solutions (2)
1 Vutek Pl, Meredith, NH 03253
Tel.: (603) 279-6800
Web Site: http://www.efi.com
Sales Range: $125-149.9 Million
Emp.: 275
Printer Mfr
N.A.I.C.S.: 333248

Electronics For Imaging, Inc. - Lebanon (2)
5 Commerce Ave, West Lebanon, NH 03784
Tel.: (603) 443-8400
Web Site: http://www.efi.com
Sales Range: $25-49.9 Million
Emp.: 40
Software Providers for the Graphic Arts Industry
N.A.I.C.S.: 423830

Electronics For Imaging, Inc. - Massachusetts (2)
9 Aldrin Rd, Plymouth, MA 02360
Tel.: (603) 298-2490
Sales Range: $150-199.9 Million
Software Solutions for the Printing Industry
N.A.I.C.S.: 423830

Electronics For Imaging, Inc. - Pittsburgh (2)
40 24th St 1st Fl, Pittsburgh, PA 15222
Tel.: (412) 456-1141
Web Site: http://www.efi.com
Sales Range: $25-49.9 Million
Emp.: 60
Printing Technology
N.A.I.C.S.: 323111
Marc D. Olin (CFO)

Subsidiary (Non-US):

Electronics for Imaging B.V. (2)
Tupolevlaan 65-75, Schiphol-Rijk, 1119 PA, Amsterdam, Netherlands (100%)
Tel.: (31) 206588000

COMPANIES

SIRIS CAPITAL GROUP, LLC

Web Site: http://www.efi.com
Sales Range: $25-49.9 Million
Emp.: 45
Imaging & Printing Products Distr
N.A.I.C.S.: 333248

Electronics for Imaging GmbH (2)
Kaiserswerther Str 115, 40880, Ratingen,
Germany
Tel.: (49) 2102 745 4100
Web Site: http://www.efi.com
Sales Range: $10-24.9 Million
Emp.: 80
Printing Equipment Mfr
N.A.I.C.S.: 333248
Georg Hollenbach *(Mng Dir)*

**Electronics for Imaging Italia
SRL** (2)
Via Saccardo 9, 20134, Milan, Italy
Tel.: (39) 0236595850
Web Site: http://www.efi.com
Imaging & Printing Products Supplier
N.A.I.C.S.: 333248

**Electronics for Imaging Japan
YK** (2)
Shinjuku Oak Tower 14 Fl 6-8-1 Nishi Shin-juku, Shinjuku-ku, Tokyo, 163-6014, Japan
Tel.: (81) 333443123
Web Site: http://www.efi.co.jp
Printing Machinery & Ink Mfr
N.A.I.C.S.: 325910

Electronics for Imaging United Kingdom Limited (2)
Midland House 26 North Station Road,
Colchester, CO1 1RB, United Kingdom
Tel.: (44) 1246298000
Sales Range: $25-49.9 Million
Emp.: 20
Printing Machinery & Printing Ink Mfr
N.A.I.C.S.: 325910
Guy Gecht *(CEO)*

Escada Innovations Ltd. (2)
C4di Queen Street, East Yorkshire, Hull,
HU1 1UU, United Kingdom
Tel.: (44) 1723624463
Web Site: http://www.escadasystems.com
Printing Equipment Mfr & Software Developer
N.A.I.C.S.: 333248
Mike Reed *(Dir-EFI Escada)*

Mart BV (2)
Eschpark 5-7, 7131 TG, Lichtenvoorde,
Netherlands
Tel.: (31) 544396600
Computer Terminal & Other Peripheral Device Mfr
N.A.I.C.S.: 334118

Reggiani Macchine S.P.A. (2)
Via Zanica 17/o, PO Box 41, Grassobbio,
24050, BG, Italy
Tel.: (39) 0353844511
Printing & Prepress Management Software
Services
N.A.I.C.S.: 541511
Mauro Parisi *(Mgr-Automation)*

Subsidiary (Domestic):

Streamline Development, LLC (2)
6750 Dumbarton Cir, Fremont, CA 94555
Tel.: (415) 499-3355
Web Site:
   http://www.streamlinesolutions.com
Sales Range: $25-49.9 Million
Emp.: 50
Printing Software Developer
N.A.I.C.S.: 513210

Subsidiary (Non-US):

alpagraph team GmbH (2)
Im Teelbruch 130 Alphahaus, 45219, Essen,
Germany
Tel.: (49) 492054105300
Web Site: http://www.alphagraph.com
Sales Range: $25-49.9 Million
Emp.: 30
Computer Software Development Services
N.A.I.C.S.: 541511

Endurance International Group Holdings, Inc. (1)
10 Corporate Dr Ste 3000, Burlington, MA
01803
Tel.: (781) 852-3200
Web Site: http://www.endurance.com
Rev.: $1,113,278,000
Assets: $2,584,086,000
Liabilities: $2,387,132,000
Net Worth: $196,954,000
Earnings: ($12,347,000)
Emp.: 3,762
Fiscal Year-end: 12/31/2019
Holding Company; Internet Hosting & Back-End Technologies Support Services
N.A.I.C.S.: 551112
David C. Bryson *(Chief Legal Officer-Endurance International Group)*
Tom Aurelio *(Chief HR Officer-Endurance International Group)*
Christine Timmins Barry *(COO-Web Presence Brands)*
Timothy R. Oakes *(Chief Acctg Officer)*
James C. Neary *(Chm)*
Jeffrey H. Fox *(Pres & CEO)*
Allen M. Chaves Jr. *(CTO-Endurance International Group)*

Subsidiary (Domestic):

Bluehost Inc. (2)
1958 S 950 E, Provo, UT 84606
Tel.: (801) 765-9400
Web Site: http://www.bluehost.com
Internet Hosting Services
N.A.I.C.S.: 518210

FastDomain Inc. (2)
1958 S 950 E, Provo, UT 84606
Tel.: (801) 765-9400
Web Site: http://www.fastdomain.com
Internet Hosting Services
N.A.I.C.S.: 518210
Marc Montagner *(CFO)*
James Grierson *(VP-Bus Dev)*
David Bryson *(Chief Legal Officer)*
Hari Ravichandran *(CEO)*
Katie Forsgren *(Mgr-Affiliate)*

HostGator.com LLC (2)
11251 NW Fwy Ste 400, Houston, TX
77092
Tel.: (713) 574-5287
Web Site: http://www.hostgator.com
Internet Hosting Services
N.A.I.C.S.: 518210

Newfold Digital Inc. (2)
5335 Gate Pkwy, Jacksonville, FL 32256
Web Site: https://newfold.com
Data Processing, Hosting & Related Services
N.A.I.C.S.: 518210
Sharon T. Rowlands *(Pres & CEO)*

Subsidiary (Domestic):

MarkMonitor Inc. (3)
50 California St Ste 200, San Francisco, CA
94111
Tel.: (415) 278-8400
Web Site: http://www.markmonitor.com
Domain Management Services
N.A.I.C.S.: 541511

Subsidiary (Domestic):

**The Endurance International Group,
Inc.** (2)
10 Corporate Dr, Burlington, MA 01803
Tel.: (781) 852-3200
Web Site: http://www.endurance.com
Sales Range: $400-449.9 Million
Internet Hosting & Back-End Technologies
Support Services
N.A.I.C.S.: 541519
Hari K. Ravichandran *(Founder & CEO)*
Katherine J. Andreasen *(Chief Admin Officer)*
Jean McCarthy *(Sr VP-Mktg)*
David C. Bryson *(Chief Legal Officer)*
James C. Neary *(Chm)*
Mitchell Haber *(Sr VP-Partnerships-Global)*

Equiniti Group PLC (1)
Sutherland House Russell Way, Crawley,
RH10 1UH, West Sussex, United Kingdom
Tel.: (44) 207 469 1902
Web Site: http://www.equiniti.com
Rev.: $640,572,296
Assets: $1,404,561,340
Liabilities: $701,941,240
Net Worth: $702,620,100
Earnings: ($1,493,492)
Emp.: 5,254
Fiscal Year-end: 12/31/2020
Holding Company; Business Support Services
N.A.I.C.S.: 551112
John Stier *(CFO)*
Kathy Cong *(Sec)*
Mark Churley *(Mng Dir-Eqpay)*
Lina Brown *(Chief Comml Officer)*
Adam Green *(Chief Risk Officer)*
Amy Madden *(Chief Customer Officer)*
James Brown *(Dir-Corp Dev)*
Paul Matthews *(CEO-Boardroom)*
Todd May *(CEO-US)*
Kevin O'Connor *(CIO)*
Enrique Sacau *(CEO-EQ Digital)*
Duncan Watson *(CEO-EQ Paymaster)*
Thera Prins *(COO & CEO-EQ Invest)*
Andrew Stephenson *(Chief People Officer)*
Paul Lynam *(CEO)*

Subsidiary (Domestic):

Aquila Group Holdings Limited (2)
Aquila House 35 London Rd, Redhill, RH1
1NJ, Surrey, United Kingdom
Tel.: (44) 1737859859
Web Site: http://www.aquilauk.co.uk
Sales Range: $10-24.9 Million
Emp.: 137
Pension & Financial Management Software
N.A.I.C.S.: 334610
Finlay Ross *(Chm)*
David E. Ackroyd *(CEO)*

Equiniti 360 Clinical Limited (2)
Sutherland House Russell Way, Crawley,
RH10 1UH, United Kingdom
Tel.: (44) 3451801405
Web Site: http://www.equiniti360clinical.com
Healthcare Services
N.A.I.C.S.: 621999
Tim Cresswell *(Mgr-Svc Support)*

Equiniti Data Limited (2)
Elder House St Georges Business Park
Brooklands Road, Weybridge, KT13 0TS,
Surrey, United Kingdom
Tel.: (44) 3335779077
Web Site: http://www.equinitidata.co.uk
Software Services
N.A.I.C.S.: 541511

Equiniti Gateway Limited (2)
Elder House Unit 3 St Georges Business
Park Brooklands Road, Weybridge, KT13
0TS, United Kingdom
Tel.: (44) 1903894375
Software Services
N.A.I.C.S.: 541511

Subsidiary (Non-US):

Equiniti India (Private) Limited (2)
Block 10 8th floor DLF IT Park 1/124 Mt
Poonamalle High Road, Ramapuram, Chennai, 600 089, Tamil Nadu, India
Tel.: (91) 4442889800
Web Site: http://www.equiniti-india.com
IT Management Outsourcing & Consulting
Services
N.A.I.C.S.: 541511
Chandrasekar Kesavan *(Head-Admin,
Health & Safety)*
Srinivasan Veeraraghavan *(Head-Fin)*
P. K. Manikandan *(Head-Learning Dev)*
Sam Halford *(Mng Dir)*
Ashok Shunmugavel *(Gen Mgr)*

Equiniti KYC Solutions B.V. (2)
Danzigerkade 23B, 1013 AP, Amsterdam,
Netherlands
Tel.: (31) 840036600
Web Site: http://www.equiniti-kyc.com
Software Services
N.A.I.C.S.: 541511
Matt Caesar-Gordon *(Mgr-Sls Ops)*

Subsidiary (Domestic):

Equiniti Limited (2)
Aspect House Spencer Road, Lancing,
BN99 6DA, West Sussex, United Kingdom
Tel.: (44) 121 415 7082
Web Site: http://www.equiniti.com
Business Support Services
N.A.I.C.S.: 561499

MyCSP Limited (2)
Park Square Bird Hall Lane, Cheadle, SK3
0XN, United Kingdom
Tel.: (44) 3001236666
Web Site: http://www.mycsp.co.uk
Emp.: 340
Pension Training & Education Services
N.A.I.C.S.: 611710

Toplevel Computing Limited (2)
500 Stonehouse Park, Stonehouse, GL10
3UT, Gloucestershire, United Kingdom
Tel.: (44) 1453852700
Web Site: http://www.equiniti-toplevel.com
Software Services
N.A.I.C.S.: 541511
Phil Webb *(Mng Dir)*

Mavenir Systems, Inc. (1)
1700 International Pkwy, Richardson, TX
75081
Tel.: (469) 916-4393
Web Site: http://www.mavenir.com
Network-Based Messaging, Converged Billing & IP Communications Services
N.A.I.C.S.: 541512
Hubert de Pesquidoux *(Chm)*
Roy S. Luria *(Gen Counsel, Sec & Exec VP)*
Pardeep Kohli *(Pres & CEO)*
Terry Hungle *(CFO & Exec VP)*
Stefano Cantarelli *(CMO & Exec VP)*
Mike Voigt *(Chief HR Officer & Sr VP)*
Bejoy Pankajakshan *(Chief Tech & Strategy Officer)*
John Baker *(Sr VP-Bus Dev)*
Brandon Larson *(Sr VP & Gen Mgr-Multimedia Bus Unit)*
Ramnik Kamo *(CIO & Exec VP-Ops)*
Guillaume Le Mener *(Sr VP & Gen Mgr-Enterprise Bus Unit)*
Vishant Vora *(Pres-Global Customer Ops & Managed Svcs)*
Jorgen Nilsson *(Pres-Enterprise Connect Solutions)*

Subsidiary (Non-US):

Mavenir (NZ) Limited (2)
Level 22 205 Queen Street, Auckland,
1010, New Zealand
Tel.: (64) 93666890
Software Development Services
N.A.I.C.S.: 541511

Mavenir Australasia Pty Ltd. (2)
Ground Floor Suite 1 12 Julius Avenue,
North Ryde, 2113, NSW, Australia
Tel.: (61) 298059000
Software Development Services
N.A.I.C.S.: 541511

Mavenir Spain SL (2)
Office 16 No 1 de Alcobendas, Madrid,
Spain
Tel.: (34) 915561199
Software Development Services
N.A.I.C.S.: 541511

Premiere Global Services, Inc. (1)
300 Lakeview Parkway Ste 300, Alpharetta,
GA 30009
Tel.: (404) 262-8400
Sales Range: $550-599.9 Million
Holding Company; Conferencing & Collaboration Servicses
N.A.I.C.S.: 551112
Hubert de Pesquidoux *(Chm)*
Boland T. Jones *(Founder)*
Sean O'Brien *(Pres-Strategic Initiatives & Chief Strategy Officer)*
Theodore P. Schrafft *(Pres & CEO)*
Michele Dobnikar *(Exec VP-Customer Care)*
Alison Sheehan *(Sr VP-HR)*
Kevin McAdams *(CFO)*
June McCarthy *(Exec VP-Mktg)*
Patrick Harper *(CTO)*
Warren Neuburger *(Chief Information Officer & Exec VP-Ops)*
Michele Nelson *(Exec VP-Gen Counsel & Sec)*

Subsidiary (Non-US):

**Enterprise Care Teleconferencing
(Asia) Pty Ltd.** (2)
Level 2 409 St Kilda Road, Melbourne,

SIRIS CAPITAL GROUP, LLC

Siris Capital Group, LLC—(Continued)

3004, VIC, Australia
Tel.: (61) 85926284
Web Site: http://www.ect.com.au
Teleconferencing Technology Services
N.A.I.C.S.: 541512

Premiere Conferencing (Japan), Inc. (2)
1-21-2 Shinkawa, Chuo-ku, Tokyo, 104-0033, Japan
Tel.: (81) 345609600
Teleconferencing Technology Services
N.A.I.C.S.: 561499

Premiere Conferencing (UK) Limited (2)
17 Godliman Street, London, EC4V 5BD, United Kingdom
Tel.: (44) 2070265970
Web Site: http://uk.pgi.com
Teleconferencing Technology Services
N.A.I.C.S.: 561499

Premiere Conferencing E.U.R.L. (2)
Saint-Lazare 26-28 rue de Londres, Paris, 75009, France
Tel.: (33) 156698150
Tele Conferencing Services
N.A.I.C.S.: 561499

Premiere Conferencing GmbH (2)
Hanauer Landstrasse 182a, 60314, Frankfurt am Main, Germany
Tel.: (49) 69506037600
Tele Conferencing Services
N.A.I.C.S.: 561499

Premiere Conferencing Pte. Ltd. (2)
300 Beach Road 1401, Singapore, 199555, Singapore
Tel.: (65) 64195999
Tele Conferencing Services
N.A.I.C.S.: 561499

Premiere Conferencing Pty Limited (2)
35 Clarence Street, Sydney, 2000, NSW, Australia
Tel.: (61) 293388800
Teleconferencing Technology Services
N.A.I.C.S.: 541512

Premiere Global Services Denmark APS (2)
Arne Jacobsens Alle 7, 2300, Copenhagen, Denmark
Tel.: (45) 78787878
Tele Conferencing Services
N.A.I.C.S.: 561499

Premiere Global Services Italy Srl (2)
Via Monte di Pieta 21, 20121, Milan, Italy
Tel.: (39) 0236269656
Tele Conferencing Services
N.A.I.C.S.: 561499
Paola Tigrati *(Mgr-Regus Centre)*

Premiere Global Services Korea Ltd. (2)
1401 Seoul Forest IT Castle Bldg 130 Gwangnaru-ro, Seongdong-gu, Seoul, 04788, Korea (South)
Tel.: (82) 260030300
Tele Conferencing Services
N.A.I.C.S.: 561499

Premiere Global Services Sweden AB (2)
Vegagatan 14 plan 4, Stockholm, 113 29, Sweden
Tel.: (46) 854591170
Tele Conferencing Services
N.A.I.C.S.: 561499

Premiere Global Services Switzerland GmbH (2)
Wagistrasse 21, Schlieren, 8952, Zurich, Switzerland
Tel.: (41) 447554488
Tele Conferencing Services
N.A.I.C.S.: 561499

Subsidiary (Domestic):

Premiere Global Services, Inc. - Colorado Springs (2)
2424 Garden of the Gods, Colorado Springs, CO 80919
Tel.: (719) 578-0700
Tele Conferencing Services
N.A.I.C.S.: 561499
Dennis Choo *(Mng Dir)*

Premiere Global Services, Inc.-Kansas (2)
18103 W 106th St Ste 200, Olathe, KS 66061
Tel.: (913) 661-0700
Conference Calling Services
N.A.I.C.S.: 517810

TalkPoint Holdings, L.L.C. (2)
100 William St Fl 8, New York, NY 10038
Tel.: (866) 323-8660
Web Site: http://www.talkpoint.com
Webcasting Solutions
N.A.I.C.S.: 513210
Mike Vitale *(CTO)*
Steve Rubin *(VP-Channel Sls)*
Andrew Denlow *(VP-Global Enterprise Sls)*
Marissa Gonzalez *(Dir-Event Productions)*
Daniel Engvoldstas *(VP-Enrgr-Sls)*
Matt Mantione *(VP-Enrg)*
Manish Shah *(Dir-Software Dev)*
Alicia Morici *(Dir-Product & User Experience)*
Nicole Paolillo-Cennamo *(Mgr-Acctg)*
Stephane Barnatt *(Head-Bus Dev-EMEA)*
Ju-Kyung Lee *(Mgr-APAC-Sls)*

Subsidiary (Non-US):

TalkPoint EMEA (3)
First Floor 1 Poultry, London, EC2R 8JR, United Kingdom
Tel.: (44) 20 3021 3100
Webcasting Solutions
N.A.I.C.S.: 513210

Subsidiary (Domestic):

iMeet Central (2)
87 N Raymond Ave Fl 6, Pasadena, CA 91103
Tel.: (626) 689-4420
Web Site: http://www.imeetcentral.com
Management Software Services
N.A.I.C.S.: 513210
Alan Bryan *(VP-IT & Ops-Web)*

Stratus Technologies Group, S.A. (1)
123 Avenue de X Septembre, L-2551, Luxembourg, Luxembourg (56.5%)
Holding Company
N.A.I.C.S.: 551112

Holding (Non-US):

Stratus Technologies International S.a.r.l. (2)
Ilmmeuble Challenge 92 81 Avenue Francois Arago, Nanterre, Paris, 92017, France (72%)
Tel.: (33) 141203737
Web Site: http://www.stratus.com
Sales Range: $250-299.9 Million
Emp.: 796
Holding Company
N.A.I.C.S.: 551112
Robert C. Laufer *(CFO & Sr VP-Fin)*

Subsidiary (Non-US):

Icopal Hispania S.L. (3)
Entenza 332-334, 08029, Barcelona, Spain
Tel.: (34) 933636022
Web Site: http://www.siplast.es
Sales Range: $25-49.9 Million
Emp.: 5
Waterproofing Mfr
N.A.I.C.S.: 324122
Fabien Remaut *(Gen Mgr)*

Stratus Technologies Bermuda Ltd. (3)
Cumberland House 9th Floor 1 Victoria Street, Hamilton, HM 11, Bermuda
Tel.: (441) 2954630
Web Site: http://www.stratus.com
Holding Company
N.A.I.C.S.: 551112
David C. Laurello *(Pres & CEO)*

Travelport Worldwide Limited (1)
Axis One Axis Park, Langley, SL3 8AG,
Berks, United Kingdom
Tel.: (44) 1753 288000
Web Site: http://www.travelport.com
Rev.: $2,551,064,000
Assets: $2,929,057,000
Liabilities: $3,081,415,000
Net Worth: ($152,358,000)
Earnings: $72,628,000
Emp.: 3,700
Fiscal Year-end: 12/31/2018
Travel Commerce Marketplace
N.A.I.C.S.: 561599
Erika Moore *(VP & Gen Mgr-Sls)*
Matthew Minetola *(CIO & Exec VP)*
Stephen Shurrock *(Chief Comml Officer & Exec VP)*
Bernard L. Bot *(CFO)*
Mark Meehan *(Mng Dir-Asia Pacific, Middle East and Africa)*
Simon Ferguson *(Pres/Mng Dir-Americas)*
Margaret K. Cassidy *(Gen Counsel & Exec VP)*
Fiona Shanley *(Chief Customer & Mktg Officer)*
Nick Dagg *(Sr VP-Global Agency Sls)*
Jason Clarke *(Head-Travel Partners)*
Damian Hickey *(Head-Air Travel Partners-Global)*
Antonios Basoukeas *(Chief Acctg Officer)*
Simon Gros *(Interim Chief HR Officer & Grp VP-Industry Affairs)*

Subsidiary (Non-US):

Galileo Deutschland GmbH (2)
Lyoner Strasse 15, Niederrad, 60528, Frankfurt, Germany
Tel.: (49) 692273670
Online Travel Support Services
N.A.I.C.S.: 561510

Locomote IP Pty. Ltd. (2)
42 Barkly Street, Saint Kilda, 3182, VIC, Australia
Tel.: (61) 1300652802
Web Site: http://www.locomote.com
Online Travel Support Services
N.A.I.C.S.: 561510

Locomote Technologies Trading Pty. Ltd. (2)
42 Barkly Street, Saint Kilda, 3182, VIC, Australia
Tel.: (61) 412552164
Emp.: 5
Computer Programming Services
N.A.I.C.S.: 541511

Southern Cross Distribution Systems Pty Limited (2)
35 Grafton Street Level 6, Bondi Junction, 2022, NSW, Australia
Tel.: (61) 293914000
Software Publisher
N.A.I.C.S.: 513210

Travelport Digital Limited (2)
1 Cumberland Place Fenian Street, Dublin, D02 FF20, Ireland
Tel.: (353) 14853452
Web Site: http://digital.travelport.com
Online Travel Support Services
N.A.I.C.S.: 561510

Subsidiary (US):

Travelport Inc. (2)
300 Galleria Pkwy, Atlanta, GA 30339
Tel.: (770) 563-7400
Web Site: http://www.travelport.com
Rev.: $2,076,000,000
Assets: $3,088,000,000
Liabilities: $4,399,000,000
Net Worth: ($1,311,000,000)
Earnings: ($189,000,000)
Emp.: 3,500
Fiscal Year-end: 12/31/2013
Online Travel Tools & Services
N.A.I.C.S.: 561599
John A. C. Swainson *(Exec Chm)*
Ming Foong *(Mng Dir-Asia)*
Mark Meehan *(Mng Dir-Asia Pacific, Middle East & Africa)*
Robert Bailey *(Chief Strategy Officer)*
Greg Webb *(CEO)*
Nick Bray *(CFO)*

Subsidiary (Domestic):

Galileo International, LLC (3)
400 Interpace Pkwy Bldg A, Parsippany, NJ 07054
Tel.: (973) 939-1000
Web Site: http://www.galileo.com
Sales Range: $550-599.9 Million
Emp.: 3,300
Electronic Global Travel Distribution Services
N.A.I.C.S.: 541512

Subsidiary (Non-US):

Galileo Ireland Ltd. (4)
Palmerston House Fenian Street, Dublin, Ireland
Tel.: (353) 6020444
Web Site: http://www.galileo.com
Sales Range: $10-24.9 Million
Emp.: 38
Electronic Global Travel Distribution Services
N.A.I.C.S.: 541512

Subsidiary (Domestic):

Travelport GDS (3)
300 Galleria Pkwy, Atlanta, GA 30339
Tel.: (770) 563-7400
Web Site: http://www.travelport.com
Sales Range: $125-149.9 Million
Emp.: 600
Travel Maps & Technologies
N.A.I.C.S.: 561599

Subsidiary (Non-US):

Worldspan Services Ltd. (4)
242 Bath Road Axis House, Hayes, UB3 5AY, Middlesex, United Kingdom
Tel.: (44) 2087451900
Web Site: http://www.worldspan.com
Sales Range: $75-99.9 Million
N.A.I.C.S.: 561499

Subsidiary (US):

Travelport, LP (2)
300 Galleria Pkwy, Atlanta, GA 30339
Tel.: (770) 563-7400
Online Travel Support Services
N.A.I.C.S.: 561510
Majid Nazir *(VP-IR)*
David A. Lauderdale *(CTO & Sr VP-Technical Ops)*
Jeffrey C. Smith *(Gen Counsel, Sec & Sr VP-HR)*

Subsidiary (Non-US):

travel-IT GmbH & Co. KG (2)
Solinger Strasse 16, 45481, Mulheim an der Ruhr, Germany
Tel.: (49) 2083099660
Web Site: http://www.travel-it.de
Online Travel Support Services
N.A.I.C.S.: 561510

U.S. TelePacific Corp. (1)
515 S Flower St Fl 47, Los Angeles, CA 90071
Tel.: (213) 213-3000
Web Site: http://www.tpx.com
Local & Long-Distance Phone Services
N.A.I.C.S.: 517121
Richard A. Jalkut *(Pres & CEO)*
Timothy J. Medina *(CFO & Exec VP)*
Josephine Young *(Sr VP-IT)*
Dick Jalkut *(Chm, Pres & CEO)*
David Zahn *(Sr VP-Mktg)*

Subsidiary (Domestic):

DSCI, LLC (2)
303 Wyman St Ste 350, Waltham, MA 02451
Tel.: (781) 862-8300
Web Site: http://www.dscicorp.com
Telecommunications Resellers
N.A.I.C.S.: 517121
James Maloney *(Sr VP-Sls)*
Sean Dandley *(Pres-East)*
Timothy J. Medina *(CFO & Exec VP)*
Russ Shipley *(Exec VP-Wholesale & Network Svcs)*
David Zahn *(Sr VP-Mktg)*
Josephine Young *(Sr VP-IT)*
Rob Madore *(Sr VP-Ops, Admin & Facilities)*
Ken Bisnoff *(Sr VP-Strategic Opportunities)*
Michael James *(Sr VP-Customer Experience)*

COMPANIES

Chris Pelley *(Pres-Texas)*
Andrew Paretti *(Pres-California & Nevada)*
Michael Dyer *(Dir)*
Scott Rogers *(Dir)*
Kim Harrison *(VP)*
Joe Cozzolino *(Chm)*
Ken McMahon *(Sr VP-Customer Success)*
Lynne Pincek *(Sr VP-Sls)*
Dan Solito *(Sr VP-Sls Ops)*
Ashley Arbuckle *(Chief Product Officer)*
Aditi Dravid *(Gen Counsel & Sec)*
Mark Roberts *(CMO)*
Patti Key *(Chief Revenue Officer)*
Richard Mace *(CEO)*
Stacy Conrad *(Sr VP-Channel Sls)*

O1 Communications, Inc. (2)
4359 Town Center Blvd Ste 217, El Dorado Hills, CA 95762
Tel.: (916) 554-2100
Web Site: http://www.o1.com
Sales Range: $10-24.9 Million
Emp.: 40
Telecommunication Servicesb
N.A.I.C.S.: 517810
Brad Jenkins *(CEO)*
Max Seely *(Sr VP)*
Jim Beausoleil *(CFO)*

Web.com Group, Inc. (1)
5335 Gate Pkwy, Jacksonville, FL 32256
Tel.: (904) 680-6600
Web Site: http://www.web.com
Website Development, Marketing & Consulting Services
N.A.I.C.S.: 541519
Rob Solomon *(Chief Customer Officer)*
Deb Myers *(Chief People Officer)*
Christina Clohecy *(CFO)*
Michael Bouchet *(CIO)*
Chris Ortbals *(Chief Product Officer)*
Ted Schremp *(CMO)*

Subsidiary (Non-US):

Acquisio Inc. (2)
6300 Auteuil Suite 300, Brossard, J4Z 3P2, QC, Canada
Tel.: (450) 465-2631
Web Site: https://www.acquisio.com
Search Engine Marketing Software
N.A.I.C.S.: 513210
Richard Couture *(Co-Founder & CTO)*
Pierre-Luc Dupont *(VP-Tech)*
Jason MacDonald *(VP)*

Enable Media Limited (2)
Scoot House 19 Falcon Court, Preston Farm Industrial Estate, Stockton-on-Tees, TS18 3TU, United Kingdom
Tel.: (44) 1642881088
Business Directory Publishing Services
N.A.I.C.S.: 513199

Subsidiary (Domestic):

Leads.com (2)
10021 Balls Ford Rd Ste 200, Manassas, VA 20109-2666
Tel.: (703) 257-2852
Web Site: http://www.leads.com
Sales Range: $10-24.9 Million
Emp.: 50
Web Design, Search Platforms & Tracking Solutions
N.A.I.C.S.: 541512

NameJet, LLC (2)
5808 Lake Washington Blvd Ste 300, Kirkland, WA 98033
Tel.: (425) 974-4687
Web Site: http://www.namejet.com
Data Processing & Hosting Services
N.A.I.C.S.: 518210

Register.com, Inc. (2)
575 8th Ave 8th Fl, New York, NY 10018
Tel.: (902) 749-2762
Web Site: http://www.register.com
Sales Range: $100-124.9 Million
Emp.: 489
Domain Name Registration Service
N.A.I.C.S.: 541990
David L. Brown *(Pres)*

SnapNames Web.com, LLC (2)
12808 Gran Bay Pkwy W, Jacksonville, FL 32258
Tel.: (570) 708-8760
Web Site: http://www.snapnames.com

Sales Range: $25-49.9 Million
Emp.: 21
Resells Expired & Deleted Internet Domain Names Through Online Auctions
N.A.I.C.S.: 513140

Solid Cactus Inc. (2)
106 S Lehigh St, Wilkes Barre, PA 18702
Tel.: (570) 706-7150
Web Site: http://www.solidcactus.com
Sales Range: $1-9.9 Million
Emp.: 100
E-Commerce Website Design, Marketing & Consulting Services
N.A.I.C.S.: 541519
Miguel Younger *(VP-Ops)*
Cathy Kolcun *(Bus Mgr)*
Lisa Kramer *(Mgr-Sls Ops)*
Michal Dwojewski *(Mgr-Traffic)*
Alicia Magda *(Mgr-Internet Mktg)*
Jeff Stolarcyk *(Mgr-Affiliate Mktg)*
Michelle Johnson *(Mgr-Email Mktg)*
Greg Kosicki *(Sr Dir-Call Center Ops)*
Katrina Domkowski *(Mgr-Call Center Ops)*

TLDS, LLC (2)
113 E Fulton St, Gloversville, NY 12078-3222
Tel.: (518) 725-7475
Website Development, Marketing & Consulting Services
N.A.I.C.S.: 541519

Subsidiary (Non-US):

Touch Local Limited (2)
16th Floor 89 Albert Embankment, London, SE1 7TP, United Kingdom
Tel.: (44) 2078404300
Web Site: http://www.touchlocal.com
Business Directory Publishing Services
N.A.I.C.S.: 513199

Web.com Canada, Inc. (2)
128 Wellington Street West 205, Barrie, L4N 8J6, ON, Canada
Tel.: (705) 792-1961
Web Site: http://www.web.com
Website Development, Marketing & Consulting Services
N.A.I.C.S.: 541519

Subsidiary (Domestic):

Web.com Holding Company, Inc. (2)
12808 Gran Bay Pkwy W, Jacksonville, FL 32258
Tel.: (904) 680-6600
Web Site: http://www.web.com
Website Development, Marketing & Consulting Services
N.A.I.C.S.: 541519

Web.com, Inc. (2)
Marquis 1 Tower 245 Peachtree Ctr Ave NE Ste 2000, Atlanta, GA 30303
Tel.: (404) 966-5255
Web Site: http://www.web.com
Rev.: $49,140,000
Emp.: 290
Web & Application Hosting Services
N.A.I.C.S.: 518210
Roseann Duran *(Chief People Officer)*
David L. Brown *(Chm, Pres & CEO)*
Matthew McClure *(Chief Legal Officer & Sec)*

Yodle Web.com, Inc. (2)
330 W 34th St 16th Fl, New York, NY 10001
Web Site: http://www.yodle.com
Cloud-Based Marketing Automation Solutions
N.A.I.C.S.: 541810
John Berkowitz *(Co-Founder)*
Nathaniel Stevens *(Co-Founder)*
Ben Rubenstein *(Co-Founder)*
Kartik Hosangar *(Co-Founder)*

SIRIUS SOLUTIONS LLC
1233 Westloop S Ste 1800, Houston, TX 77027
Tel.: (713) 888-0488
Web Site: http://www.sirsol.com
Sales Range: $25-49.9 Million
Emp.: 168
Accounting & Financial Services for Energy Industry
N.A.I.C.S.: 561499

Kristi Chickering *(CEO)*
Jessica Harris *(Dir-Supply Chain Practice-Dallas)*
Randall Grogan *(Mng Dir-Tech Svcs)*

SIRSAI MULTI SOURCING
Nine Lake Bellview Dr Ste 118, Bellevue, WA 98005
Tel.: (425) 533-2158
Web Site: http://www.sirsai.com
Year Founded: 2001
Sales Range: $1-9.9 Million
Emp.: 174
Global Business Consulting, Outsourcing & Technology Services
N.A.I.C.S.: 541618
Vijay Gunturu *(Mng Dir)*

SIRSIDYNIX CORPORATION
3300 N Ashton Blvd Ste 500, Lehi, UT 84043
Tel.: (800) 223-5200
Web Site: http://www.sirsidynix.com
Sales Range: $75-99.9 Million
Library Systems Vendor
N.A.I.C.S.: 541511
Berit Nelson *(VP-Library Rels)*
Thomas Gates *(VP-Mktg)*
Bill Davison *(CEO)*
Brad Whittle *(VP-Global Sls)*
Eric Keith *(VP-Mktg & Strategic Alliances)*
Jim Wilson *(Founder & VP)*
Tim Hyde *(VP-Prof Svcs)*
Sheridan Richey *(VP-Product Dev)*
Ranny Lacanienta *(Dir-Academic Product Strategy)*
Rick Branham *(VP-Global Accts & Alliances)*
Scott Wheelhouse *(Sr VP-Ops)*
Scott Askew *(Sec & Gen Counsel)*
Barbara Pacut *(VP-Sls & Ops)*
David King *(VP-New Accts)*
John Martin *(VP-Fin)*
Chris Harris *(VP-Sls)*

Subsidiaries:

EOS International (1)
2292 Faraday Ave, Carlsbad, CA 92008-7208
Tel.: (760) 431-8400
Web Site: http://www.eosintl.com
Sales Range: $1-9.9 Million
Software Development Services
N.A.I.C.S.: 541511
Jeff Goodwin *(VP-Product Dev)*
Jeff Smith *(VP-Client Svcs)*
Salvatore Provenza *(VP-Sls & Mktg)*
Ken Bonney *(Dir-Sls)*

SirsiDynix Corporation (1)
400 W 5050 N, Provo, UT 84604-5650
Tel.: (314) 432-1100
Sales Range: $25-49.9 Million
Emp.: 205
Application Software Developer & Marketer
N.A.I.C.S.: 541512

Subsidiary (Non-US):

SirsiDynix (2)
180 Northfield Drive West Suite 4 1st Floor, Waterloo, N2L 0C7, ON, Canada (100%)
Web Site: http://www.sirsidynix.com
Sales Range: $25-49.9 Million
Emp.: 8
Develops, Markets & Supports Application Software
N.A.I.C.S.: 541511

SISBARRO DEALERSHIPS
425 W Boutz Rd, Las Cruces, NM 88005-3191
Tel.: (575) 524-7707   NM
Web Site: http://www.sisbarro.com
Year Founded: 1948
Sales Range: $10-24.9 Million
Emp.: 75
Automobile Dealership
N.A.I.C.S.: 441110

Louis F. Sisbarro *(Pres & CEO)*
Jeanette Yoke *(Comptroller)*
Dan Sisbarro *(Gen Mgr)*

SISCO ENTERPRISES INC.
500 W E Ave, Chico, CA 95926
Tel.: (530) 895-8330
Sales Range: $10-24.9 Million
Emp.: 10
Pizzeria Operator
N.A.I.C.S.: 722513
Frank Sisco *(Pres)*
Alan Sisco *(VP)*
Rich Lougee *(Controller)*

SISENCE INC.
1359 Broadway 4th Fl, New York, NY 10018
Tel.: (646) 432-1507
Web Site: http://www.sisense.com
Year Founded: 2004
Software Publisher
N.A.I.C.S.: 513210
Amir Orad *(CEO)*
Aviad Harell *(Co-Founder & COO)*
Guy Boyango *(Co-Founder & CTO)*

SISK AUTO MALL
4599 Fort Campbell Blvd, Hopkinsville, KY 42240
Tel.: (270) 885-9900
Web Site: http://www.siskautomall.com
Year Founded: 1945
Sales Range: $10-24.9 Million
Emp.: 50
New Car Whslr
N.A.I.C.S.: 441110
Wilson Sisk *(Owner)*

SISKIYOU FOREST PRODUCTS
6275 Hwy 27, Anderson, CA 96007
Tel.: (530) 378-6980
Web Site: http://www.siskiyouforestproducts.com
Sales Range: $10-24.9 Million
Emp.: 80
Millwork Mfr
N.A.I.C.S.: 321918
Bill Duchi *(VP)*
Aaron Duchi *(Controller)*
Fred M. Duchi Jr. *(Owner)*

SISKIYOU TELEPHONE CO.
30 Telco Way, Etna, CA 96027
Tel.: (530) 467-6000
Web Site: http://www.sisqtel.net
Sales Range: $10-24.9 Million
Emp.: 50
Provider of Telephone Communication Services
N.A.I.C.S.: 517121
Jim Lowers *(Pres & CEO)*
Rod Hendricks *(VP)*

SISSETON-WAHPETON SIOUX TRIBE
100 Veterans Memorial Dr, Sisseton, SD 57262
Tel.: (605) 698-3911
Web Site: http://www.dakotasioux.com
Sales Range: $10-24.9 Million
Emp.: 240
Card & Game Services
N.A.I.C.S.: 713990
Greg Benidt *(CFO)*

SISSY'S LOG CABIN, INC.
2319 S Camden Rd, Pine Bluff, AR 71603-3637
Tel.: (870) 879-3040
Web Site: http://www.sissyslogcabin.com
Sales Range: $10-24.9 Million

SISSY'S LOG CABIN, INC.

Sissy's Log Cabin, Inc.—(Continued)
Emp.: 100
Jewelry Whslr
N.A.I.C.S.: 458310
Sissy Jones (Founder & CEO)
Murphy Jones (Treas & Sec)
Bill Jones (Pres)
Kim Rieve (CFO)
Lamar McCubbin (Reg Mgr)

SISTERS OF MERCY HEALTH SYSTEM
14528 S Outer 40 Ste 100, Chesterfield, MO 63017
Tel.: (314) 579-6100
Web Site: http://www.mercy.net
Year Founded: 1986
Emp.: 40,000
Health Care Services Organization
N.A.I.C.S.: 813910
Lynn Britton (Pres & CEO)
Jolene Goedken (Sr VP)
Michael McCurry (COO & Exec VP)
Shannon Sock (CFO & Exec VP-Strategy)
Patrick McCruden (VP-Mission Integration)
Philip Wheeler (Gen Counsel & Sr VP)
Brian O'Toole (Sr VP-Mission & Ethics)
Vance B. Moore (Pres-ROi)
Jon Vitiello (Sr VP-Fin)
Cynthia Mercer (Chief Admin Officer & Sr VP)
Donn Sorensen (Exec VP-Ops)
Linda Knodel (Chief Nursing Officer & Sr VP)
Tony Krawat (Chief Compliance Officer & Sr VP)

Subsidiaries:

St. John's Mercy Health Care (1)
14528 S Outer Forty Dr Ste 100, Chesterfield, MO 63017
Tel.: (314) 628-3868
Web Site: http://www.stjohnsmercy.org
Sales Range: $500-549.9 Million
Healthcare Services
N.A.I.C.S.: 622110

SISU HEALTHCARE IT SOLUTIONS, LLC
5 W 1st St Ste 200, Duluth, MN 55802
Tel.: (218) 529-7900
Web Site: http://www.sisusolutions.com
Year Founded: 2001
Sales Range: $1-9.9 Million
Emp.: 80
It Consulting
N.A.I.C.S.: 541690
Chris Meyer (Dir-Cloud Svcs)
Jodi Nelson (VP-Healthcare Applications)
Mark Sandvick (Dir-Meaningful Use)
Scott Anderson (VP-Applications)
Kris Olberg (COO & CIO)
Kevin Boerboom (CFO & Controller)
Jon Forsman (Dir-MEDITECH Practice)
Hilary McCausland (Dir-HR)
Jeff Burton (Dir-Security)
Mike Delfs (Chm)
John Fossum (Vice Chm)
Rick Breuer (Treas & Sec)
Erika Running (VP-Analytics)
Ariel Avestruz (Sr Acct Mgr)

SIT INVESTMENT ASSOCIATES, INC
3300 IDS Center 80 S 8th St, Minneapolis, MN 55402
Tel.: (612) 332-3223
Web Site: http://www.sitinvest.com
Year Founded: 1981
Sales Range: $50-74.9 Million
Emp.: 100
Provider of Investment Services
N.A.I.C.S.: 523940
Peter L. Mitchelson (Vice Chm)
Roger J. Sit (Co-Pres, CEO & Chief Investment Officer-Global)
Ronald D. Sit (VP)
Kent L. Johnson (Sr VP & Portfolio Mgr)
Robert W. Sit (VP)
David A. Brown (VP, Dir-Client Svcs & Portfolio Mgr)
Bryce A. Doty (Sr VP & Sr Portfolio Mgr)
Michael C. Brilley (Pres)
Robert B. Harrigan (VP-Mktg)
Mark H. Book (VP & Mgr)
Paul J. Jungquist (VP & Sr Portfolio Mgr-Fixed Income)

SITCO IMPORTING CO.
4041 Hadley Rd Ste H, South Plainfield, NJ 07080
Tel.: (908) 754-4004
Web Site: http://www.sitcoimporting.com
Sales Range: $10-24.9 Million
Emp.: 25
China
N.A.I.C.S.: 423220
Morris Sitt (Pres)

SITE ENGINEERING INC.
545 Kaaahi St, Honolulu, HI 96817
Tel.: (808) 841-8883
Sales Range: $25-49.9 Million
Emp.: 40
Site Preparation Contractor
N.A.I.C.S.: 238910
Jaroslaw Jurek (VP)
Kenneth Nakamura (Exec VP)
Michael Masutani (Pres)

SITE OIL COMPANY OF MISSOURI
7751 Carondelet Ave Ste 202, Saint Louis, MO 63105-3340
Tel.: (314) 725-4321 MO
Year Founded: 1925
Sales Range: $75-99.9 Million
Emp.: 6
Operator of Gasoline Stations & Convenience Stores
N.A.I.C.S.: 457120
Alvin Siteman (Pres)
Chris Kemph (VP-Mktg)
Eldon Schoeber (Treas, Sec & VP)
Scott Scharfenberg (Mgr-HR)

SITE ORGANIC, LLC
14488 Old Stage Rd, Lenoir City, TN 37772-5494
Tel.: (865) 329-6192 DE
Web Site: http://www.ministrybrands.com
Year Founded: 2012
Software Developer & Publisher
N.A.I.C.S.: 513210
Daniel Simmons (Mng Dir)

Subsidiaries:

ParishSOFT LLC (1)
3767 Ranchero Dr Ste 100, Ann Arbor, MI 48108-2770
Tel.: (734) 205-1000
Web Site: http://www.parishsoft.com
Sales Range: $1-9.9 Million
Emp.: 35
Custom Computer Programming Services
N.A.I.C.S.: 541511
Timothy J. Sember (VP & Gen Mgr)
Mike Cusick (VP-Sls & Mktg)

SITE PERSONNEL SERVICES INC.
N 92 W 17420 Appleton Ave Ste 200, Menomonee Falls, WI 53051
Tel.: (262) 345-9933
Web Site: http://www.sitepersonnel.com
Year Founded: 1988
Sales Range: $25-49.9 Million
Emp.: 100
Engineering, Technical & IT Recruiting Services
N.A.I.C.S.: 561320
Chip Holmes (VP)
Mike Rose (Mgr-Engrg Svcs)

SITE WORK SPECIALISTS INC.
803 Industrial Ave, Rapid City, SD 57702
Tel.: (605) 355-0933
Web Site: http://www.siteworkinc.com
Year Founded: 2000
Sales Range: $10-24.9 Million
Emp.: 60
Specialty Trade Contractors
N.A.I.C.S.: 238910
James Skull (Pres)

SITEK MARKETING & COMMUNICATIONS
704 Westbrooke Terrace Dr, Ballwin, MO 63021
Tel.: (636) 861-0509
Year Founded: 1999
Sales Range: Less than $1 Million
Emp.: 5
N.A.I.C.S.: 541810
Tim Sitek (Pres)

SITELINES, INC.
4512 Manchester Ave Ste 300, Saint Louis, MO 63110
Tel.: (314) 534-4513 MO
Web Site: http://www.sitelinesinc.com
Year Founded: 2000
Sales Range: $10-24.9 Million
Emp.: 10
General Contractor; Commercial, Institutional & Industrial Construction
N.A.I.C.S.: 236220
Kelly Kenter (Pres)
Vince Winkelmann (VP)

SITESPECT, INC.
10 Milk St Ste 820, Boston, MA 02108
Tel.: (617) 859-1900
Web Site: http://www.sitespect.com
Year Founded: 2004
Sales Range: $25-49.9 Million
Software Developer
N.A.I.C.S.: 513210
Eric J. Hansen (Co-Founder, CTO & Exec VP)
Larry Epstein (Co-Founder & COO)
Ara Pongratz (VP-Customer Ops & Success)
Patricia Foye (CMO)
Patrick Romich (CEO)
Justin Bougher (VP-Product)
Bill Cunningham (VP-Sls)
Mike Laureno (CFO)
Jon Fraser (VP-Global Sls)

Subsidiaries:

SiteSpect Europe (1)
De Corridor 27, 3621 ZA, Breukelen, Netherlands
Tel.: (31) 208 202 082
Software Developer
N.A.I.C.S.: 513210

SiteSpect Germany (1)
Kolosseumstr 1a, 80469, Munich, Germany
Tel.: (49) 89 94003007
Software Developer
N.A.I.C.S.: 513210

SiteSpect UK (1)
90 Long Acre Covent Garden, London, WC2E 9RZ, United Kingdom
Tel.: (44) 203 652 0161
Software Developer
N.A.I.C.S.: 513210

SITEWIRE
740 S Mill Ave Ste 210, Tempe, AZ 85281
Tel.: (480) 731-4884
Web Site: http://www.sitewire.net
Year Founded: 1999
Sales Range: $1-9.9 Million
Emp.: 50
Advetising Agency
N.A.I.C.S.: 541810
Bret Giles (Co-Founder & Pres)
Margie Traylor (Co-Founder & CEO)
Sandy Catour (COO & CFO)
Rick Snailun (Creative Dir)
Joyce Clark (Controller)
Gloria Medina (Office Mgr)

SITEWIT CORP.
5201 W Kennedy Blvd 500, Tampa, FL 33609
Tel.: (813) 279-8888
Web Site: http://www.sitewit.com
Year Founded: 2010
Sales Range: $1-9.9 Million
Internet Traffic Quality Tracking Software
N.A.I.C.S.: 513210
Ricardo Lasa (Co-Founder & CEO)
Don Berndt (Co-Founder)
Stacey Schott (Controller-Fin)
Jesse Baynard (VP-Engrg)

SITEWORX, INC.
11480 Commerce Park Dr 5 Fl Ste 500, Reston, VA 20191
Tel.: (703) 964-1700
Web Site: http://www.siteworx.com
Year Founded: 2002
Sales Range: $300-349.9 Million
Emp.: 68
Web Design & Application Development Services
N.A.I.C.S.: 541519
Savani Tatake (Dir-Analytics)
Liz Duggan (Dir-e-Commerce)
Malek Tayara (Mng Partner)
Chuck Gahun (VP-Experience Mgmt)
Gregg Wyland (VP-Alliances & Partners)
Randy Higgins (VP-Digital Mktg)
Andrew Walker (CEO)

SITNASUAK NATIVE CORP.
214 Front St 2nd Fl, Nome, AK 99762
Tel.: (907) 387-1200 AK
Web Site: http://www.snc.org
Year Founded: 1971
Emp.: 1,500
Holding Company
N.A.I.C.S.: 551112
Robert Evans (Chm)
Bobbi Quintavell (Pres & CEO)
Cameron Piscoya (Dir-HR)
Tom Delamater (CFO)
Ukallaysaaq Tom Okleasik (VP-Corp Affairs)
Holly Poydack (VP-Corp Admin)
Jason Evans (Treas)
Helen C. Bell (Sec)
Mark Allred (Vice Chm)
Louis H. Green Jr. (Vice Chm)

SITRICK & CO.
1840 Century Park E Ste 800, Los Angeles, CA 90067
Tel.: (310) 788-2850
Web Site: http://www.sitrick.com
Sales Range: $50-74.9 Million
Emp.: 50
Public Relations Firm

N.A.I.C.S.: 541820
Brian Glicklich *(Chm-Digital Practice)*
Matthew Fern *(Dir-Media & Analytics-Digital Practice)*

SITTERLE HOMES
2015 Evans Rd Ste 100, San Antonio, TX 78258
Tel.: (210) 494-9192
Web Site:
http://www.sitterlehomes.com
Year Founded: 1973
Sales Range: $25-49.9 Million
Emp.: 30
Housing Construction Services
N.A.I.C.S.: 236117
Frank Sitterle Jr. *(Pres)*

SITTERS ETC.
216 Centerview Dr Bldg 7 Ste 180, Brentwood, TN 37027
Tel.: (615) 373-3133
Web Site: http://www.sittersetc.com
Sales Range: $1-9.9 Million
Emp.: 275
Non-Medical in Home Care Services for the Elderly
N.A.I.C.S.: 621999
Beau Brothers *(Founder & Pres)*

SITTON BUICK GMC SAAB
2640 Laurens Rd, Greenville, SC 29607
Tel.: (864) 288-5600
Web Site: http://www.sittongm.com
Rev.: $55,754,776
Emp.: 75
New & Used Car Dealers
N.A.I.C.S.: 441110
Jim Coward *(VP)*
Carol Cocher *(Controller)*
J. Henry Sitton III *(Pres)*

SITTON MOTOR LINES, INC.
4586 Hwy 43, Joplin, MO 64804-8801
Tel.: (417) 782-2600   MO
Web Site: http://www.sitm.com
Year Founded: 1979
Sales Range: $75-99.9 Million
Emp.: 650
Trucking Service
N.A.I.C.S.: 484121
Richard Sitton *(Pres & CEO)*
David Allgood *(VP-Risk Mgmt)*
Brad Storrs *(Dir-Sls)*
Stan Edens *(VP-Maintenance)*

SITV INC.
700 N Central Ave Ste 600, Glendale, CA 91203
Tel.: (323) 256-8900
Web Site: http://www.mynuvotv.com
Latino Cable Television Network
N.A.I.C.S.: 516120
Michael Schwimmer *(CEO)*
Craig Geller *(Sr VP-Adv Sls)*
Bill Hilary *(Pres)*

SITV, INC.
3030 Andrita St, Los Angeles, CA 90065
Tel.: (323) 256-8900
Year Founded: 2004
Sales Range: $1-9.9 Million
Emp.: 75
Television Broadcasting
N.A.I.C.S.: 516120
Micheal Schwimmer *(CEO)*
Abilia Barraza *(Acct Exec)*
Adriana Sbardellati *(Mgr-Ops)*
Bill Lopez *(Dir-Sls)*
Carmen Santiago *(Dir-Sls)*
Darrell Monroe *(Dir-Traffic)*
Kim Capria *(Dir-Sls)*

Maria Perez-Brown *(VP-Programming)*
Mark Turner *(Dir-Sls)*
Mike Roggero *(COO & CFO)*
Tracey McCormack *(VP-Sls)*

Subsidiaries:

FUSE Networks LLC   (1)
11 Penn Plz 17th Fl, New York, NY 10001
Tel.: (212) 324-3400
Web Site: http://www.fuse.tv
Music Television Network
N.A.I.C.S.: 516210
Jason Miller *(Sr VP-Adv Sls)*
Karen Ramspacher *(VP-Res)*
Sal LoCurto *(Sr VP-Dev)*
Donna Wolfe *(VP-Production)*

SIU CREDIT UNION
395 N Giant City Rd, Carbondale, IL 62902
Tel.: (618) 457-3595   IL
Web Site: http://www.siucu.org
Year Founded: 1938
Sales Range: $10-24.9 Million
Emp.: 123
Credit Union
N.A.I.C.S.: 522130
Mike Lantrip *(Pres & CEO)*
Stacy Callahan *(VP-Lending)*
Erica Panky *(Exec VP)*

SIVALLS, INC.
2200 E 2nd St, Odessa, TX 79761-4910
Tel.: (432) 337-3571   TX
Web Site: http://www.sivalls.com
Year Founded: 1947
Sales Range: $75-99.9 Million
Emp.: 160
Mfr of Oil & Gas Process Equipment
N.A.I.C.S.: 332313
Richard Sivalls *(Pres & CEO)*
I. R. Nolen *(CFO)*
Jack A. Zuerker *(Exec VP)*
Danny Brister *(Sr VP)*
Jim Bradley *(VP-Engrg)*

Subsidiaries:

Sivalls, Inc. - Brownwood Manufacturing Plant   (1)
2300 Dickman Rd, Brownwood, TX 76801
Tel.: (325) 643-3621
Emp.: 25
Oil & Gas Surface Production Equipment Mfr
N.A.I.C.S.: 333132
Clayton Kuykendall *(Mgr)*

Sivalls, Inc. - Pampa Manufacturing Plant   (1)
Hwy 60 S, Pampa, TX 79065
Tel.: (806) 665-7111
Oil & Gas Surface Production Equipment Mfr
N.A.I.C.S.: 333132

SIVYER STEEL CORPORATION
225 33rd St, Bettendorf, IA 52722-6403
Tel.: (563) 355-1811   IA
Web Site: http://www.sivyersteel.com
Year Founded: 1909
Sales Range: $75-99.9 Million
Emp.: 400
Alloy Steel Castings
N.A.I.C.S.: 331513
Keith D. Kramer *(Pres)*
Joe Drolshagen *(Dir-Sls)*
Cathy Meinsma *(CFO)*
Mike Baxley *(CEO)*

Subsidiaries:

Sivyer Steel Corporation Riverside Products Div.   (1)
225 33rd St, Bettendorf, IA 52722-6403   (100%)
Tel.: (563) 355-1811

Web Site: http://www.riversidespooner.com
Sales Range: $25-49.9 Million
Emp.: 150
Steel Engineering & Research Services
N.A.I.C.S.: 331513

SIWEL CONSULTING INC.
213 W 35th St Ste 12 W, New York, NY 10001
Tel.: (212) 691-9326
Web Site: http://www.siwel.com
Year Founded: 1992
Sales Range: $10-24.9 Million
Emp.: 60
Value-Added Resellers & Computer Systems
N.A.I.C.S.: 541512
Lewis W. Johnson *(Pres)*
Frank Venezia *(VP)*
Allison Mason *(Acct Mgr-Inside Sls)*

SIX ROBBLEES INC.
11010 Pacific Hwy S Tukwila Intl Blvd, Seattle, WA 98168
Tel.: (206) 767-7970   WA
Web Site: http://www.sixrobblees.com
Year Founded: 1987
Sales Range: $10-24.9 Million
Emp.: 70
Provider of Truck Parts & Accessories
N.A.I.C.S.: 423120
Richard Metcaf *(Controller)*

SIX.02 BIOSERVICES, LLC
5119 Pegasus Ct Ste M-P, Frederick, MD 21704
Tel.: (929) 602-1023
Web Site: http://www.six02bio.com
Year Founded: 2018
N.A.I.C.S.:
Michael Keefe *(Partner)*
David Hicks *(Partner)*
Michael Keefe *(Partner)*

Subsidiaries:

Kemp Proteins, LLC   (1)
5119 Pegasus Ct Ste M-P, Frederick, MD 21704
Tel.: (240) 629-8924
Web Site: http://www.kempproteins.com
Chemicals Mfr
N.A.I.C.S.: 325414
Michael Keefe *(CEO)*
David Hicks *(COO & Head-Quality)*
April Birch *(Mgr-Project)*
Carter Mitchell *(Chief Scientific Officer)*
Chris Kemp *(Founder)*

SIX88 SOLUTIONS, INC.
1877 Broadway Ste 703, Boulder, CO 80302
Tel.: (303) 449-5285   CO
Web Site:
http://www.shipcompliant.com
Year Founded: 2006
Sales Range: $1-9.9 Million
Emp.: 60
Web-Based Compliant Software Tools to Wine & Spirits Suppliers
N.A.I.C.S.: 513210
Jason Eckenroth *(Founder & Pres)*
Jeff Carroll *(VP-Strategy & Compliance)*
Pawel Smolarkiewicz *(CTO)*

SIXTEENTH STREET COMMUNITY HEALTH CENTER
1337 S Cesar E Chavez Dr, Milwaukee, WI 53204
Tel.: (414) 672-6220   WI
Web Site: http://www.sschc.org
Year Founded: 1971
Sales Range: $25-49.9 Million
Emp.: 366
Community Health Care Services
N.A.I.C.S.: 621498

John Bartkowski *(Co-Pres & CEO)*
Rick Walters *(Co-Pres)*
Tom Gazzana *(VP)*
Laura J. Arnow *(Treas)*
Juan Ruiz *(Sec)*

SIXTH AVENUE ELECTRONICS, INC.
22 US Hwy 22 W, Somerset, NJ 08812
Tel.: (973) 467-3905   NY
Web Site: http://www.6ave.com
Year Founded: 1984
Sales Range: $200-249.9 Million
Emp.: 340
Consumer Electronics Retailer
N.A.I.C.S.: 449210
Michael Temiv *(Pres)*

SIXTH STREET LENDING PARTNERS
2100 McKinney Ave Ste 1500, Dallas, TX 75201
Tel.: (469) 621-3001   DE
Web Site:
https://www.sixthstreet.com
Year Founded: 2022
Rev.: $246,073,000
Assets: $3,138,265,000
Liabilities: $1,321,198,000
Net Worth: $1,817,067,000
Earnings: $128,279,000
Fiscal Year-end: 12/31/23
Investment Management Service
N.A.I.C.S.: 523999

SIXTH STREET PARTNERS LLC
345 California St Ste 3300, San Francisco, CA 94104
Tel.: (415) 743-1500
Web Site: http://www.sixthstreet.com
Year Founded: 2009
Investment Services
N.A.I.C.S.: 523999
Oliver Zhang *(VP)*
Jessica Weldon *(VP)*
Chris Despain *(VP)*
Alan Waxman *(Founder & CEO)*
Michael McGinn *(Partner & Head-Growth)*
R. Martin Chavez *(Vice Chm & Partner)*

Subsidiaries:

Grupo FerroAtlantica, S.A.U.   (1)
Paseo de la Castellana 259D 45th & 49th Floors, Torre Espacio, 28046, Madrid, Spain
Tel.: (34) 91 590 3219
Holding Company; Ferroalloys Mfr
N.A.I.C.S.: 551112
Clara Ines Cerdan Molina *(Gen Counsel & Sec)*

Subsidiary (Domestic):

FerroAtlantica, S.A.U.   (2)
Paseo de la Castellana 259D 49th Floor, Torre Espacio, 28046, Madrid, Spain
Tel.: (34) 91 590 3219
Web Site: http://www.ferroatlantica.es
Ferroally Mfr; Hydroelectric Power Plants Operator
N.A.I.C.S.: 331110

Legends Hospitality, LLC   (1)
61 Broadway Ste 2400, New York, NY 10006   (51%)
Tel.: (212) 317-3200
Web Site: http://www.legends.net
Hospitality & Merchandising Services
N.A.I.C.S.: 541618
Paula Perez *(Mgr)*
Shervin Mirhashemi *(Pres & CEO)*

Pushpay Holdings Limited   (1)
Vero Centre Level 19 48 Shortland Street,

SIXTH STREET PARTNERS LLC

Sixth Street Partners LLC—(Continued)
Auckland, 1010, New Zealand
Tel.: (64) 800995045
Web Site: https://www.pushpay.com
Rev.: $202,841,000
Assets: $261,338,000
Liabilities: $99,093,000
Net Worth: $162,245,000
Earnings: $33,403,000
Emp.: 564
Fiscal Year-end: 03/31/2022
Software Development Services
N.A.I.C.S.: 541511
Aaron Senneff (CTO)
Molly Matthews (CEO)
Burt Chao (CFO)

Subsidiary (US):

Resi Media LLC (2)
3409 N Central Expwy Ste 201, Plano, TX 75023
Web Site: https://resi.io
Video Streaming Platform Developer & Marketer
N.A.I.C.S.: 541511
Collin Jones (Pres)

ZipZap Processing Incorporated (2)
18300 Redmond Way Ste 130, Redmond, WA 98052-3937
Tel.: (844) 947-9277
Web Site: http://zipzapprocessing.com
Credit Card Processing Services
N.A.I.C.S.: 522320

SIXTHMAN, LLC
1040 Blvd SE Ste J, Atlanta, GA 30312
Tel.: (404) 523-3111
Web Site: http://www.sixthman.net
Sales Range: $10-24.9 Million
Emp.: 17
Tour & Travel Agency Services
N.A.I.C.S.: 561520
Andy Levine (Pres)
Carlee Thomas (Coord-SPARK)
Joy Todaro (Dir-Guest Svcs)
Jeff Cuellar (VP-Partnerships)
Anthony Diaz (CEO)

SIZEMORE GROUP
1700 Commerce Dr NW, Atlanta, GA 30318
Tel.: (404) 605-0690
Web Site: http://www.sizemoregroup.com
Year Founded: 1971
Sales Range: $10-24.9 Million
Emp.: 13
Detective & Armored Car Services
N.A.I.C.S.: 561621
Michael M. Sizemore (Founding Principal)
Thomas Sayre (CFO & Principal)
Bill De St. Aubin (Principal)
Crystal Callwood (Mgr-Mktg)

Subsidiaries:

Sizemore Personnel Inc. (1)
1369 Reynolds St, Augusta, GA 30901-1046
Tel.: (706) 736-1456
Web Site: http://www.sizemoreinc.com
Emp.: 300
Provider of Employment Agency Services
N.A.I.C.S.: 561621
Preston Sizemore (Office Mgr)

SIZZLER USA, INC.
5801 Sepulveda Blvd, Culver City, CA 90230
Tel.: (310) 398-6111 DE
Web Site: http://www.sizzler.com
Year Founded: 1958
Sales Range: $350-399.9 Million
Restaurant Franchisor & Operator
N.A.I.C.S.: 722511
Kerry Kramp (CEO)

SIZZLING PLATTER LLC
348 E 6400 S Ste 200, Murray, UT 84107
Tel.: (801) 268-3400 UT
Web Site: http://www.splat.com
Year Founded: 1963
Sales Range: $25-49.9 Million
Emp.: 2,000
Restaurant Management
N.A.I.C.S.: 722511
Ted Morton (Pres)
Mark Howe (VP-Ops)
Jonathan K. Shulkin (Chm)

SJ AMOROSO CONSTRUCTION CO.
390 Bridge Pkwy, Redwood City, CA 94065
Tel.: (650) 654-1900
Web Site: http://www.sjamoroso.com
Rev.: $233,547,310
Emp.: 330
Commercial & Office Building Contractors
N.A.I.C.S.: 236220
Dana McManus (CEO)
Maria Gannon (Coord-Insurance)
Dean Ramsay (Project Mgr)

SJ COMMUNICATIONS
25251 Paseo De Alicia Ste 200, Los Angeles, CA 92653
Tel.: (818) 881-3889
Web Site: http://www.sjcommunications.com
Sales Range: $10-24.9 Million
Emp.: 10
Advetising Agency
N.A.I.C.S.: 541810
Jenny Loffill (Acct Mgr-Digital)
Krysty O'Quinn Ronchetti (Owner)

SJ FUEL CO., INC.
601 Union St, Brooklyn, NY 11215
Tel.: (718) 855-6060
Web Site: http://www.sjfuelco.com
Year Founded: 1935
Sales Range: $75-99.9 Million
Fuel Oil Dealers
N.A.I.C.S.: 457210
Constantine D'Arco (Pres)
Peter D'Arco (VP)

SJ MANAGEMENT COMPANY OF SYRACUSE INC.
301 Prospect Ave, Syracuse, NY 13203
Tel.: (315) 448-5889 NY
Year Founded: 2009
Sales Range: $1-9.9 Million
Charitable Services
N.A.I.C.S.: 813211
Mary W. Brown (VP)

SJA INC.
10303 Channel Rd, Lakeside, CA 92040
Tel.: (619) 443-3891
Web Site: http://www.andersondrilling.com
Year Founded: 1945
Sales Range: $50-74.9 Million
Emp.: 70
Core Drilling & Cutting
N.A.I.C.S.: 238990
Dan Cadenhead (Pres)
Jason Bellow (CFO)

SJC INC.
703 W Park St, Cayuga, IN 47928
Tel.: (765) 492-3345 IA
Year Founded: 1968
Sales Range: $100-124.9 Million
Emp.: 25
Provider of Gasoline Services
N.A.I.C.S.: 457120
Pat Crowder (Controller)

SJH DISTRIBUTING INC.
503 Washington Ave, Jermyn, PA 18433
Tel.: (570) 876-5220
Rev.: $28,000,000
Emp.: 70
Tobacco Products Distr
N.A.I.C.S.: 424940
Stanley Hallowich (Pres)

SJI, INC.
1918 Innerbelt Business Center Dr, Saint Louis, MO 63114
Tel.: (314) 336-1700
Web Site: http://www.sji-inc.com
Year Founded: 1988
Sales Range: $1-9.9 Million
Emp.: 10
Sales Promotion
N.A.I.C.S.: 541810
Beth Wood (VP-Promo & Events)

Subsidiaries:

SJI Fulfillment (1)
155 Weldon Pkwy Ste 110, Maryland Heights, MO 63043
Tel.: (314) 336-1700
Sales Range: Less than $1 Million
Emp.: 5
Sales Promotion
N.A.I.C.S.: 541810

SJL BROADCAST MANAGEMENT CORP.
1482 E Valley Rd Ste 712, Santa Barbara, CA 93108
Tel.: (805) 687-9278 MT
Year Founded: 1984
Sales Range: $25-49.9 Million
Emp.: 200
Holding Company; Television Broadcasting Stations Owner & Operator
N.A.I.C.S.: 551112
George D. Lilly (Chm & CEO)
Wade O'Hagan (CFO)
Brian Lilly (COO & Pres)
Peter Veto (Exec VP-West)

Subsidiaries:

WTVG, Inc. (1)
4247 Dorr St, Toledo, OH 43607-2134
Tel.: (419) 531-1313
Web Site: http://www.13abc.com
Sales Range: $10-24.9 Million
Emp.: 120
Television Broadcasting Station
N.A.I.C.S.: 516120
Justin Feldkamp (Dir-Sports)

SJOSTROM & SONS INC.
1129 Harrison Ave, Rockford, IL 61104
Tel.: (815) 226-0330
Web Site: http://www.sjostromconstruction.com
Sales Range: $10-24.9 Million
Emp.: 80
Commercial & Office Building, New Construction
N.A.I.C.S.: 236220
Joel G. Sjostrom (Chm)

SK CAPITAL PARTNERS, LP
400 Park Ave 18th Fl, New York, NY 10022
Tel.: (212) 826-2700 DE
Web Site: http://www.skcapitalpartners.com
Year Founded: 2007
Rev.: $7,800,000,000
Privater Equity Firm
N.A.I.C.S.: 523999
Barry B. Siadat (Co-Founder & Mng Dir)
Aaron C. Davenport (Mng Dir)
Jamshid Keynejad (Co-Founder & Mng Dir)

Randall S. Dearth (Sr Dir)
Jerry Truzzolino (CFO)
Jack Norris (Mng Dir)
Edward Donkor (Principal)
Simon Dowker (Dir-Bus Dev)
Barry Penney (Mng Dir)
James Marden (Mng Dir)
Jared Kramer (VP)
Jayesh Taunk (VP)
Stephen d'Incelli (Mng Dir)
Steven Schmedlin (Dir-Fin & Transition Mgmt)
Kate Ghirardi (Controller)
Cecilia Pulmano (Office Mgr)
Chris Redding (Dir-Talent Mgmt)
Mario Toukan (Mng Dir)
Jennifer Cattier (Chief Compliance Officer & Gen Counsel)
Richard Jackson (Mng Dir & Head-Capital Markets)

Subsidiaries:

Addivant USA, LLC (1)
199 Benson Rd, Middlebury, CT 06762
Tel.: (203) 573-2259
Web Site: http://www.addivant.com
Stabilizer Chemical Products Mfr & Distr
N.A.I.C.S.: 325998

Apotex Pharmaceutical Holdings Inc. (1)
150 Signet Dr, Toronto, M9L 1T9, ON, Canada
Tel.: (800) 268-4623
Web Site: https://www.apotex.com
Emp.: 100
Holding Company
N.A.I.C.S.: 551112
Aaron C. Davenport (Chm)
Allan Oberman (Pres & CEO)

Subsidiary (Domestic):

Apotex Inc. (2)
150 Signet Drive, Toronto, M9L 1T9, ON, Canada
Tel.: (800) 268-4623
Web Site: http://www1.apotex.com
Pharmaceuticals Mfr
N.A.I.C.S.: 325412
Bernard C. Sherman (Founder)
Peter Hardwick (Chief Comml Officer & Exec VP)
Jordan Berman (VP)
Joanne Campbell (VP-Global talent Mgmt)
Steven Liberty (Exec VP)
Kevin Zive (Gen Counsel, VP & Head-Intellectual Property)
Kiran Krishnan (Sr VP-Regulatory Affairs)
Pradeep Sanghvi (Exec VP-Global R&D)
Andrew McNicoll (Sr VP-Global Quality & Compliance)

Subsidiary (US):

Apotex Corp. (3)
2400 N Commerce Pkwy Ste 400, Weston, FL 33326
Tel.: (800) 706-5575
Web Site: http://www.apotex.com
Biopharmaceutical Research & Development Services
N.A.I.C.S.: 541715
Beth Hamilton (VP)

Subsidiary (Non-US):

Apotex Ilac San.Tic.Ltd.Sti. (3)
Mithatpasa cad Hurriyet Apt 44 20, Yenisehir, Ankara, 06410, Turkiye
Tel.: (90) 3124356944
Pharmaceutical Products Distr
N.A.I.C.S.: 424210

Apotex NZ Ltd (3)
32 Hillside Road, Glenfield, 0627, Auckland, New Zealand
Tel.: (64) 94442073
Web Site: http://www.apotex.com
Pharmaceutical Product Mfr & Distr
N.A.I.C.S.: 325411
Colin Robertson (Mng Dir)

Apotex Netherlands BV (3)
Bio Science Park Archimedesweg 2, 2333 CN, Leiden, Netherlands
Tel.: (31) 715243100

COMPANIES

SK CAPITAL PARTNERS, LP

Web Site: http://www.apotex.com
Pharmaceutical Products Distr
N.A.I.C.S.: 424210
Ben Haneveld (Mng Dir)

Apotex Nicaragua, S.A. (3)
Hospital Bautista 1c al Oeste 1c al Sur, Managua, Nicaragua
Tel.: (505) 22494602
Pharmaceutical Products Distr
N.A.I.C.S.: 424210

Apotex Panama, S.A. (3)
Via Fdez de Cdba Y Via Espana, Panama, Panama
Tel.: (507) 2296400
Pharmaceutical Products Distr
N.A.I.C.S.: 424210

Apotex Pty Ltd. (3)
Level 3 16 Giffnock Ave, Macquarie Park, 2113, NSW, Australia
Tel.: (61) 288778333
Web Site: http://www.apotex.com.au
Sales Range: $50-74.9 Million
Emp.: 100
Pharmaceuticals Marketing & Sales
N.A.I.C.S.: 424210
Roger Millichamp (Mng Dir)

Apotex Research Private Limited. (3)
Plot No 1 & 2 Bommasandra Industrial Area 4th Phase Jigani Link Road, Bengaluru, 560099, India
Tel.: (91) 8022891014
Web Site: http://www.apotex.com
Biopharmaceutical Research & Development Services
N.A.I.C.S.: 541715
Sanjay Kapadia (Head-Quality, Regulatory Affairs & Site)

Archroma Management GmbH (1)
Neuhofstrasse 11, 4153, Reinach, Switzerland
Tel.: (41) 617163401
Web Site: http://www.archroma.com
Coating & Specialty Chemicals Mfr & Distr
N.A.I.C.S.: 325998
Alexander Wessels (Vice Chm)
Roland Waibel (CFO)
Hans Lourens (Gen Counsel)
Stephan Sielaff (COO)
Heike van de Kerkhof (CEO)

Subsidiary (Non-US):

Archroma Pakistan Ltd. (2)
Plot 1-A/1 Sector 20 Korangi Industrial Area, Karachi, Pakistan (75%)
Tel.: (92) 2135123261
Web Site: https://www.archroma.com.pk
Rev.: $123,951,544
Assets: $72,617,557
Liabilities: $57,224,418
Net Worth: $15,393,139
Earnings: $4,419,560
Emp.: 253
Fiscal Year-end: 09/30/2023
Dye & Paint Mfr
N.A.I.C.S.: 325130
Irfan Chawala (CFO)
Rahim Mujtaba (CEO)

Subsidiary (US):

Archroma U.S., Inc. (2)
5435 77 Ctr Dr, Charlotte, NC 28217
Tel.: (704) 395-6569
Web Site: http://www.archroma.com
Dyes Distr
N.A.I.C.S.: 424690
Andres Lotz (Pres)

Aristech Acrylics LLC (1)
7350 Empire Dr, Florence, KY 41042 (100%)
Tel.: (859) 283-1501
Web Site: http://www.aristechacrylics.com
Sales Range: $75-99.9 Million
Emp.: 400
Acrylic Sheet Mfr
N.A.I.C.S.: 325211

Unit (Domestic):

Aristech Acrylics LLC - Avonite Surfaces (2)
1945 Hwy 304, Belen, NM 87002-7354
Tel.: (505) 864-3800

Web Site: http://www.avonitesurfaces.com
Sales Range: $10-24.9 Million
Emp.: 56
Acrylic Sheet Mfr
N.A.I.C.S.: 325211

Ascend Performance Materials LLC (1)
1010 Travis Ste 900, Houston, TX 77002
Tel.: (888) 927-2363
Web Site: http://www.ascendmaterials.com
Rev.: $1,800,000,000
Emp.: 3,000
Nylon Product Mfr
N.A.I.C.S.: 314999
Barry B. Siadat (Chm)
Phil McDivitt (Pres & CEO)
Kevin Bartol (CFO)
Vikram Gopal (VP-Tech-Nylon)
Jim Hull (VP-Nylon Ops)
Finlay Morrison (VP-Specialty Chemicals)
Andrew Ralston (Gen Counsel & VP)

Canlak Coatings, Inc (1)
1999 Elizabeth St, North Brunswick, NJ 08902
Tel.: (732) 821-3200
Web Site: https://canlak.com
Chemical Coatings Mfr
N.A.I.C.S.: 325510

Subsidiary (Domestic):

US Coatings, LLC (2)
260 Baldwin Rd, Satsuma, AL 36572
Tel.: (251) 445-2388
Web Site: http://www.uscoatingsinc.com
Highway, Street & Bridge Construction Services
N.A.I.C.S.: 237310

Deltech LLC (1)
11911 Scenic Hwy, Baton Rouge, LA 70807
Tel.: (225) 775-0150
Web Site: https://www.deltechcorp.com
Resins & Polymers Mfr
N.A.I.C.S.: 325991
Don Rutherford (VP & Gen Mgr)
Jesse Zeringue (Pres & CEO)

Subsidiary (Domestic):

Deltech Polymers Corporation (2)
1250 S Union St, Troy, OH 45373
Tel.: (937) 335-5286
Web Site: http://www.deltechcorp.com
Polymers Mfr
N.A.I.C.S.: 326199

Deltech Resin Co. (2)
49 Rutherford St, Newark, NJ 07105
Tel.: (973) 589-0880
Web Site: http://www.deltechresins.com
Sales Range: $1-9.9 Million
Emp.: 35
Plastics Material & Resin Mfr
N.A.I.C.S.: 325211

StanChem, Inc. (2)
401 Berlin St, East Berlin, CT 06023-1127
Tel.: (860) 828-0571
Web Site: http://www.stanchem-inc.com
Fire Retardant Paints & Fire Proofing Coatings, Latex Polymers & Specialty Coatings Mfr
N.A.I.C.S.: 325998
Carl J. Sullivan (Dir-Polymer Products Mktg & Sls)
Paul Stenson (Pres & CEO)
Steve McGuff (COO)
Michael Foley (Chm)

Division (Domestic):

Albi Manufacturing (3)
401 Berlin St, East Berlin, CT 06023-1127
Tel.: (860) 828-0571
Web Site: http://www.albi.com
Emp.: 100
Mfr of Fire Retardant Paints & Fire Proofing Coatings, Latex Polymers & Specialty Coatings
N.A.I.C.S.: 325998
Daryl Orlich (VP-Sls-East)

Subsidiary (Domestic):

Albi Protective Coatings (3)
401 Berlin St, East Berlin, CT 06023
Tel.: (860) 985-3138

Fireproofing, Intumescent Paints & Specialty Protective Coatings Mfr
N.A.I.C.S.: 325510

Subsidiary (Domestic):

Hawthorne Paint Company, Inc. (4)
66 5th Ave, Hawthorne, NJ 07506
Tel.: (973) 423-2335
Petrochemical Mfr
N.A.I.C.S.: 325110
Murray Greene (CEO)

Florachem Corporation (1)
5209 San Jose Blvd, Jacksonville, FL 32207
Tel.: (904) 733-5759
Web Site: http://www.florachem.com
Sales Range: $10-24.9 Million
Emp.: 6
Supplier & Sales of Raw Materials for the Flavor, Fragrance, Consumer & Industrial Product Industries
N.A.I.C.S.: 424690
Steven M. McAlister (Founder & CEO)
Craig Hood (Dir-Bus-Performance Products)

Lacerta Group, Inc. (1)
360 Forbes Blvd, Mansfield, MA 02048
Tel.: (508) 339-3312
Web Site: http://www.lacerta.com
Rev.: $9,400,000
Emp.: 102
All Other Plastics Product Mfr
N.A.I.C.S.: 326199
Ali R. Lotfi (Owner)
Denise L. Lotfi (Treas)

Luxium Solutions, LLC (1)
17900 Great Lakes Pwy, Hiram, OH 44234
Tel.: (440) 834-5600
Web Site: https://luxiumsolutions.com
Radiation Detection, Baggage Scanning & Other Navigation Instrument Mfr & Distr
N.A.I.C.S.: 334511

Subsidiary (Domestic):

Inrad Optics, Inc. (2)
181 Legrand Ave, Northvale, NJ 07647
Tel.: (201) 767-1910
Web Site: https://www.inradoptics.com
Rev.: $10,631,032
Assets: $9,098,939
Liabilities: $5,431,147
Net Worth: $3,667,792
Earnings: $152,575
Emp.: 59
Fiscal Year-end: 12/31/2022
Optical Components & Laser System Devices & Instrumentation
N.A.I.C.S.: 333310
Thomas Caughey (VP-R&D)
Amy Eskilson (Pres & CEO)
George Murray (VP-Sls & Mktg)
Theresa A. Balog (CFO, Treas & Sec)

Division (Domestic):

Inrad Optics, Inc. (3)
6455 Parkland Dr, Sarasota, FL 34243
Tel.: (941) 753-8707
Web Site: http://www.inradoptics.com
Optical Components & Laser System Devices & Instrumentation
N.A.I.C.S.: 333310

Subsidiary (Domestic):

Plx, Inc. (2)
40 W Jefryn Blvd, Deer Park, NY 11729
Tel.: (631) 586-4190
Web Site: http://www.plxinc.com
Sales Range: $1-9.9 Million
Emp.: 34
Optical Instruments And Lenses
N.A.I.C.S.: 333310
Jack Lipkins (Pres)
Irina Shats (Engr-Opto Mechanical Design)
Itai Vishnia (CEO)

Noramco, Inc. (1)
500 Swedes Landing Rd, Wilmington, DE 19801
Tel.: (302) 652-3840
Web Site: http://www.noramco.com
Pharmaceutical Ingredient Mfr
N.A.I.C.S.: 325412
Chris Close (CFO)
Charlie Enzinger (VP-Integrated Supply Chain)

Bill Grubb (VP-Bus Dev & Innovation)
John Daly (Sr Dir-API External Mfg & Tech Transfer)

Phoenix Aromas & Essential Oils, Inc. (1)
375 Chestnut St 355, Norwood, NJ 07648
Tel.: (201) 784-6100
Web Site: http://www.phoenixaromas.com
Sales Range: $1-9.9 Million
Emp.: 15
Chemicals And Allied Products, Nec
N.A.I.C.S.: 424690
Anna Rivero (First VP)

SI Group, Inc. (1)
2750 Ball Gown Rd, Schenectady, NY 12309
Tel.: (518) 370-4200
Web Site: http://www.siigroup.com
Sales Range: $400-449.9 Million
Emp.: 2,200
Insulating Varnishes, Magnet Wire Enamels, Coatings & Alkylphenols Mfr
N.A.I.C.S.: 325110
Paul Tilley (Sr VP-North America & Global Key Accts)
David A. Bradley (Pres & CEO)
Stephen Haller (Sr VP-Strategy & New Bus Dev)
Emmanuel Hess (VP-Asia Pacific)
Philip Ingham (Sr VP-Strategy & New Bus Dev)
Deborah Patterson (VP-Global HR)
Tara Morgan (Mgr-Global PR & Comm)
Christopher Cornille (VP-Supply Chain Svcs)
Thomas J. Masterson (Gen Counsel & VP)
Brooke A. Manrique (VP-HR & Comm)
David A. Bradley (Pres & CEO)
Mike Perez (Mgr-Talent Acq)
Pankaj Chadha (Exec Dir-Center-Led Procurement)
Omar Irani (Dir-Strategic Markets-Rubber)
John Whitney (Sr Mgr-Center of Competency-Rubber Tech)
David Bradley (Pres & CEO)
Rustom Jilla (CFO & Sr VP)
Terry Walsh (Sr VP-Ops)

Subsidiary (Non-US):

SI Group - Bethune SAS (2)
1111 Avenue George Washington, 62404, Bethune, Cedex, France
Tel.: (33) 3 21 68 67 67
Web Site: http://www.sigroup.com
Sales Range: $10-24.9 Million
Emp.: 100
Industrial Chemicals Mfr
N.A.I.C.S.: 325998
Xavier Moutarde (Gen Mgr)

SI Group - Singapore Ptd. Ltd (2)
18 Banyan Avenue Jurong Island, Singapore, 627720, Singapore
Tel.: (65) 6506 2900
Sales Range: $10-24.9 Million
Emp.: 30
Industrial Chemicals Mfr
N.A.I.C.S.: 325998
Jennifer Chiu (Mgr-Ops)

Plant (Non-US):

SI Group Crios - Jundiai - Plant 2 (2)
Rua Wilhelm Winter 80 - Distrito Industrial, 13213-000, Jundiai, Brazil
Tel.: (55) 11 3308 5900
Industrial Chemicals Mfr
N.A.I.C.S.: 325998

SI Group Crios - Rio Claro - Plant 1 (2)
Avenida Brasil 4500 - Distrito Industrial, 13505-600, Rio Claro, Brazil
Tel.: (55) 19 3535 6700
Web Site: http://www.siigroup.com
Sales Range: $25-49.9 Million
Emp.: 300
Industrial Chemicals Mfr
N.A.I.C.S.: 325998
Luis Degaspari (Mgr-Supply Chain)

Subsidiary (Non-US):

SI Group India Ltd (2)
1003-1006 10th Fl Arcadia 195 NCPA Marg, Nariman Point, Mumbai, 400 021, India

SK CAPITAL PARTNERS, LP

SK Capital Partners, LP—(Continued)
Tel.: (91) 2222024224
Web Site: http://www.herdillia.com
Sales Range: $10-24.9 Million
Emp.: 45
Petrochemical Producer
N.A.I.C.S.: 325110

Unit (Domestic):

SI Group - India Limited - Lote Unit (3)
Plot No D-1/3 M I D C Lote Parshuram, Tal Khed Dist, Ratnagiri, 415722, Maharashtra, India
Tel.: (91) 2356272246
Web Site: http://www.siigroup.com
Sales Range: $10-24.9 Million
Industrial Chemicals Mfr
N.A.I.C.S.: 325998
Pankaj Chadha (Sr Dir-Asia Pacific)

SI Group - India Limited - Navi Mumbai Unit (3)
Thane-Belapur Road Opp Juinagar Railway Station, Turbhe, Mumbai, 400 705, India
Tel.: (91) 22 6673 2000
Industrial Chemicals Mfr
N.A.I.C.S.: 325998

SI Group - India Limited - Ranjangaon Unit (3)
E-89 MIDC Ranjangaon Nagar Road Taluka Shirur, Pune, 412 220, India
Tel.: (91) 2138 670407
Industrial Chemicals Mfr
N.A.I.C.S.: 325998

SI Group - India Limited - Rasal Unit (3)
Post-Pali Pali-Khopoli Road, Tal Sudhagad Dist Raigad, 410 205, Rasal, Maharashtra, India
Tel.: (91) 2142 242669
Industrial Chemicals Mfr
N.A.I.C.S.: 325998

Subsidiary (Non-US):

SI Group South Africa (Pty) Ltd (2)
45/47 Potgieter Street Alrode, Alberton, 1451, Gauteng, South Africa
Tel.: (27) 11 864 4608
Sales Range: $10-24.9 Million
Emp.: 70
Chemical Intermediates Mfr
N.A.I.C.S.: 325998
Philip Ingham (VP)

SI Group-Switzerland (2)
Kastelliweg 7, Pratteln, 4133, Switzerland (100%)
Tel.: (41) 618258111
Sales Range: $25-49.9 Million
Emp.: 140
Mfr of Alyklated Phenols, Cresols & Xylenols
N.A.I.C.S.: 325211
Philip Ingham (Gen Mgr)

SI-Group - Shanghai Co, Ltd. (2)
26D Cross Region Plaza No 899 Lingling Road, Shanghai, 200030, China
Tel.: (86) 21 64271122
Industrial Chemicals Mfr
N.A.I.C.S.: 325998

Schenectady Australia Pty. Ltd. (2)
72 Christie St, Saint Marys, 2760, NSW, Australia (100%)
Tel.: (61) 296239044
Web Site: http://www.siigroup.com
Sales Range: $10-24.9 Million
Emp.: 15
Mfr of Varnishes
N.A.I.C.S.: 325510
Walter Hockar (Gen Mgr)

Schenectady Brasil Limitada (2)
Rodovia Edgard Maximo Zambotto km 79, Atibaia, 12940 972, Sao Paulo, SP, Brazil
Tel.: (55) 56607381
Mfr of Varnishes
N.A.I.C.S.: 325510

Schenectady Europe, S.A. (2)
916 Ave George Washington, PO Box 237, 62404, Bethune, France (100%)
Tel.: (33) 321686761
Web Site: http://www.schenectady.sas.com

Sales Range: $10-24.9 Million
Emp.: 120
Mfr of Varnishes
N.A.I.C.S.: 325510

Schenectady Mexico, S.A. de C.V. (2)
Col Aragon Deleg Gustavo A Madero, PO Box 118014, 7530, Mexico, Mexico (100%)
Tel.: (52) 5557145282
Web Site: http://www.smx.com.mx
Sales Range: $10-24.9 Million
Emp.: 70
Mfr of Varnishes
N.A.I.C.S.: 325510

Si Group Korea Ltd. (2)
308 Namsan Lotte Castle Iris 35 Sogong-ro, Jung-gu, Seoul, Korea (South)
Tel.: (82) 2 6937 8900
Web Site: http://www.siigroup.com
Sales Range: $10-24.9 Million
Emp.: 20
Industrial Chemicals Mfr
N.A.I.C.S.: 325998
Jinsub Shin (Mng Dir)

TPC Group Inc. (1)
500 Dallas St Ste 1000, Houston, TX 77002
Tel.: (713) 627-7474
Web Site: http://www.tpcgrp.com
Emp.: 525
Petrochemical Mfr
N.A.I.C.S.: 325110
Charles W. Graham (Sr VP-Comml)
Ed Dineen (Chm & CEO)
Courtney Ruth (VP-Reliability & Capital Project Mgmt)
Peter Dumoulin (Sr VP-HR)
Dan Valenzuela (CFO & VP)
Patrick Hurt (Gen Counsel & VP)
Adrian Jacobsen (VP-Corp Dev-Fuels & Strategic Raw Materials)
Dona Burke (VP-Supply Chain)

Subsidiary (Domestic):

Port Neches Fuels, LLC (2)
2102 Spur 136, Port Neches, TX 77651
Tel.: (713) 627-7474
Web Site: http://www.tpcgrp.com
Petrochemical Mfr
N.A.I.C.S.: 325110
Ed Dineen (CEO)

Texas Butylene Chemical Corporation (2)
3524 Cities Service Highway, Westlake, LA 70669
Tel.: (337) 882-1380
Web Site: http://www.tbcgroup.com
Emp.: 3
Petrochemical Mfr
N.A.I.C.S.: 325110

Tasmanian Alkaloids Pty. Ltd. (1)
160 Birralee Rd, Westbury, 7303, TAS, Australia
Tel.: (61) 363935202
Web Site: http://www.tasalk.com.au
Sales Range: $75-99.9 Million
Emp.: 230
Pharmaceutical Ingredient Mfr
N.A.I.C.S.: 325411
Douglas Blackaby (Mng Dir)
Colin Ralph (Gen Mgr)
Ian Jones (CFO)
Iziar Iriondo (Dir-Quality Ops)
Sam Bailey (Dir-Scientific Affairs)
Les Baxter (Dir-Agricultural R&D)
John Kearns (Dir-Logistics & Procurement)

Techmer Engineered Solutions, LLC (1)
1 Quality Cir, Clinton, TN 37716
Tel.: (865) 425-2121
Web Site: http://www.techmeres.com
Custom Plastic Compounds Mfr
N.A.I.C.S.: 325991
Tom Drye (Mng Dir)
John Manuck (Chm & CEO)

Subsidiary (Domestic):

TP Composites, Inc. (2)
8 Crozerville Rd, Aston, PA 19014
Tel.: (610) 358-9001

Sales Range: $1-9.9 Million
Emp.: 50
Engineered Plastics Mfr
N.A.I.C.S.: 326199
John Manuck (Owner)

Tilley Chemical Co., Inc. (1)
501 Chesapeake Park Plz, Baltimore, MD 21220-4203
Tel.: (410) 574-4500
Web Site: http://www.tilleychem.com
Chemical & Allied Products Merchant Whslr
N.A.I.C.S.: 424690
John Tilley (Pres)

Tri-Tex co inc (1)
1001 Boulevard Industriel, Saint-Eustache, J7R 6C3, QC, Canada
Tel.: (450) 974-1001
Web Site: https://www.tritex.com
Chemical Products Mfr
N.A.I.C.S.: 325998
Naim Laham (Pres & CEO)

Subsidiary (Non-US):

Trichromatic Mexico S.DE R.L. (2)
19 SUR No 3540, 72410, Puebla, Mexico
Tel.: (52) 2222403189
Chemical Products Distr
N.A.I.C.S.: 424690

Trichromatic Misr (2)
Area A2 East of Land 10-04, 10th of Ramadan City, Egypt
Tel.: (20) 2015411485
Web Site: http://www.trichromatic-eg.com
Chemical Products Distr
N.A.I.C.S.: 424690

Subsidiary (US):

Trichromatic West Inc. (2)
6070 Rickenbacker Rd, Commerce, CA 90040-3030
Tel.: (323) 722-0123
Chemical Products Distr
N.A.I.C.S.: 424690

United States Mineral Products Company (1)
41 Furnace St, Stanhope, NJ 07874
Tel.: (973) 347-1200
Web Site: http://www.cafco.com
Sales Range: $50-74.9 Million
Emp.: 90
Mineral Wool Insulation Products Mfr
N.A.I.C.S.: 327993
Scott Schwartz (CEO)

Wavelength Pharmaceuticals Ltd. (1)
Ofer Park Brosh Building 4th floor, POB 3158, 94 Shlomo Shmeltzer Road, Petah Tikva, 4970602, Israel
Tel.: (972) 3 577 3880
Web Site: http://www.wavelengthpharma.com
Active Pharmaceutical Ingredients Mfr
N.A.I.C.S.: 325412
Aaron C. Davenport (Chm)
Iftach Seri (CEO)
Tami Cohen (CFO)
Benzion Dolitzky (VP-R&D)
Sarah Isaacs (VP-Quality & RA)
Ilan Avni (VP-Bus Dev, Mktg & IP)
Liat Mayan (Head-HR)

Subsidiary (US):

Wavelength Enterprises, Inc. (2)
1700 Rte 23 N Ste 130 1st Fl, Parsippany, NJ 07470
Tel.: (973) 987-3030
Web Site: http://www.wavelengthpharma.com
Pharmaceuticals Mfr
N.A.I.C.S.: 325412

SK HAND TOOL, LLC
1600 S Prairie Dr, Sycamore, IL 60178
Tel.: (800) 822-5575
Web Site: http://www.sktools.com
Hand Tools Designer & Mfr
N.A.I.C.S.: 332216
Keith Kladder (Dir-Mktg)

SK INTERNATIONAL, INC.

2300 Pilot Knob Rd, Mendota Heights, MN 55120
Tel.: (651) 681-7362
Sales Range: $25-49.9 Million
Pet Food Mfr
N.A.I.C.S.: 311111
David Kutoff (CEO)

SK+G ADVERTISING
8912 Spanish Ridge Ave, Las Vegas, NV 89148
Tel.: (702) 478-4000
Web Site: http://www.skgadv.com
Year Founded: 1999
Sales Range: $75-99.9 Million
Emp.: 120
Advertising Agencies
N.A.I.C.S.: 541810
Kim Nasuta (Dir-HR)

SK3 GROUP, INC.
80 SW 8th St Ste 2000, Miami, FL 33130
Tel.: (305) 423-7114
Web Site: http://www.medicalgreens.com
Medical Cannabis Licensing, Management & Logistic Svcs
N.A.I.C.S.: 424210
Kevin Allyn (Chm)
Michael Choo (Dir-Ops)
Roy Laughlin (Dir-Media Rels)
Jeffrey Benz (Gen Counsel, Exec VP-Bus, Legal & Govt Affairs)
Artemus Mayor (Pres & CEO)

SKAG-WAY DISCOUNT DEPARTMENT STORES INC.
620 State St, Grand Island, NE 68801-3552
Tel.: (308) 384-8222
Web Site: http://www.skagwaystores.com
Year Founded: 1959
Sales Range: $50-74.9 Million
Emp.: 500
Provider of Grocery Services
N.A.I.C.S.: 445110
Jim Goodman (VP)
William C. Martin (Pres & Treas)

SKAGFIELD CORPORATION
270 Crossway Rd, Tallahassee, FL 32305
Tel.: (850) 878-1144
Web Site: http://www.skandiawf.com
Sales Range: $25-49.9 Million
Emp.: 180
Window Blinds
N.A.I.C.S.: 337920
Hilmar O. Skagfield (Pres & CEO)
Bill Hughes (Controller)

SKAGGS COMPANIES, INC.
3828 S Main St, Salt Lake City, UT 84115-4426
Tel.: (801) 261-4400
Web Site: http://www.skaggscompanies.com
Year Founded: 1977
Sales Range: $10-24.9 Million
Emp.: 100
Mfr of Communication Systems & Equipment
N.A.I.C.S.: 423490
Don L. Skaggs (Pres)
Patricia Shiramizu (CFO)

SKAGGS-WALSH, INC.
11902 23rd Ave, College Point, NY 11356-2506
Tel.: (718) 353-7000
Web Site: http://www.skaggswalsh.alo.com
Year Founded: 1966
Sales Range: $10-24.9 Million

Emp.: 70
Dealers of Fuel Oil
N.A.I.C.S.: 457210
Allison Heaney *(Pres)*

SKAGIT FARMERS SUPPLY
1276 S Burlington Blvd, Burlington, WA 98233
Tel.: (360) 757-6053
Web Site: http://www.skagitfarmers.com
Sales Range: $25-49.9 Million
Emp.: 145
Farm Supplies
N.A.I.C.S.: 424910
Rick Gauger *(Mgr-Freeland)*
Danica Lisle-Crawley *(Mgr-Mount Vernon)*
Verlin Leedy *(Mgr-Oak Harbor)*
Larry Pipkin *(Mgr-Stanwood)*
Ryan Nootenboom *(Mgr-Energy)*

SKAGIT RIVER BREWERY
404 S 3rd St, Mount Vernon, WA 98273
Tel.: (425) 320-7231
Web Site: http://www.skagitbrew.com
Sales Range: $25-49.9 Million
Emp.: 32
Brewery Mfr
N.A.I.C.S.: 312120
Eric Lint *(Pres & Dir-Ops)*
Mike Armstrong *(Head-Brewer)*
Don Tapley *(Owner)*
Ken Okese *(Mgr-Used Car)*

SKAJAQUODA GROUP INC.
1001 Society Dr, Claymont, DE 19703
Tel.: (302) 504-4448   DE
Web Site:
  http://www.skajaquoda.com
Sales Range: $1-9.9 Million
Emp.: 1
Investment Advisory Services
N.A.I.C.S.: 523940
Einar Agustsson *(CEO)*
Agust Agustsson *(VP)*

SKAN, INC.
101 Jefferson Dr 1st Fl, Menlo Park, CA 94025
Tel.: (415) 687-4607
Web Site: https://www.skan.ai
Year Founded: 2018
Software Development Services
N.A.I.C.S.: 541511

SKAR AUDIO, INC.
5424 W Crenshaw St, Tampa, FL 33634   DE
Web Site: http://www.skaraudio.com
Year Founded: 2012
Sales Range: $10-24.9 Million
Emp.: 11
Audio Product Mfr
N.A.I.C.S.: 334310
Kevin Schlenker *(Founder & CEO)*
Matthew Kimball *(Sr VP)*
Ryan Schlenker *(VP)*
Jordan Alexander *(VP-Customer Svc)*
Devin De Armas *(VP-Photography & Media)*

SKATENATION PLUS
4350 Pouncey Tract Rd, Glen Allen, VA 23060-5830
Tel.: (804) 364-1477
Web Site: http://richmondskating.com
Membership Sports & Recreation Clubs
N.A.I.C.S.: 713940
Lea Rizer *(Dir-Skating)*

SKB CORPORATION
434 W Levers Pl, Orange, CA 92867
Tel.: (714) 637-1252
Web Site: http://www.skbcases.com
Year Founded: 1977
Rev.: $40,000,000
Emp.: 100
Cases, Plastics
N.A.I.C.S.: 326199
Steven Kottman *(Founder & CEO)*
Brian Torres *(Dir-Creative)*
Dave Sanderson *(Pres)*

SKC ENTERPRISES INC.
10929 Page Ave, Saint Louis, MO 63132
Tel.: (618) 242-8448
Web Site: http://shoprentone.com
Rev.: $14,158,959
Emp.: 125
Quality Merchandise Rentals
N.A.I.C.S.: 532289
Larry Carrico *(CEO)*
Trent Agin *(Pres)*
Mark Williams *(VP-Sls & Mktg)*

SKC INC.
863 Valley View Rd, Eighty Four, PA 15330-9613
Tel.: (724) 941-9701
Web Site: http://www.skcinc.com
Year Founded: 1962
Air Sampling Equipment Distr
N.A.I.C.S.: 423490
Daniel Guild *(Chm)*
Subsidiaries:

SKC Gulf Coast, Inc.   (1)
9827 Whithorn Dr, Houston, TX 77095
Tel.: (281) 859-8050
Web Site: http://www.skcgulfcoast.com
Sales Range: $1-9.9 Million
Emp.: 12
Air Sampling Equipment Distr
N.A.I.C.S.: 423490
Roy McCullough *(VP-Sls & Mktg)*

SKC-West, Inc.   (1)
2380 E Walnut Ave, Fullerton, CA 92831
Tel.: (714) 992-2780
Web Site: http://www.skcwest.com
Emp.: 20
Air Sampling Equipment Distr
N.A.I.C.S.: 423490
Carolyn Crum *(Office Mgr)*

SKCO INVESTMENTS CORP.
7354 Airport Blvd, Mobile, AL 36608
Tel.: (251) 343-4488
Web Site:
  http://www.skcoautomotive.com
Year Founded: 1999
Sales Range: $10-24.9 Million
Emp.: 45
Used Car Dealers
N.A.I.C.S.: 441120
Syed S. Kabir *(Pres)*

SKE MIDWESTERN INC.
1111 Westrac Dr Ste 206, Fargo, ND 58103
Tel.: (701) 232-3775
Web Site:
  http://www.skemidwestern.com
Sales Range: $10-24.9 Million
Emp.: 3
Grains Distr
N.A.I.C.S.: 424510
Todd Swenson *(CFO)*

SKENDER CONSTRUCTION
200 W Madison Ste 1300, Chicago, IL 60606-3454
Tel.: (312) 781-0265
Web Site: http://www.skender.com
Year Founded: 1955
Sales Range: $75-99.9 Million
Emp.: 65
Nonresidential Construction Services
N.A.I.C.S.: 236220
Joseph C. Skender *(Pres)*
Luke DeTolve *(Sr Superintendent)*
John Estes *(Dir-Field Ops)*
Dan Stefka *(Mgr-Field Ops)*
Bobby Lucchesi *(Sr Superintendent)*
Mike Hester *(Sr Superintendent)*
Stacy Laughlin *(Controller)*
Tom Behringer *(Sr Superintendent)*
John Kozielek *(Superintendent)*
Harris Menos *(Superintendent-Healthcare)*
Dan Ulbricht *(VP)*
Todd Andrlik *(VP-Mktg)*
Afshan Barshan *(Partner & Exec VP)*
Clay Edwards *(Partner & VP)*
Andy MacGregor *(Partner & Exec VP)*
Brett Opie *(VP)*
Tim Swanson *(Chief Design Officer)*
Kevin Bredeson *(CTO)*
Matt Baker *(Sr Superintendent)*
Dan Polito *(Dir-Ops-Northern California)*
Angela Spadoni *(Dir-Residential Architecture)*
Dan Conley *(Dir-Mfg Ops)*
Mike Mulrooney *(Dir-Engrg)*
Michelle Levy *(Acct Mgr-Strategic)*
Jeff Janicke *(Partner & VP)*
Brian Bukowski *(Partner)*
Joe Pecoraro *(Partner)*
Brian Simons *(Partner)*
Pete Conlin *(Dir-Field Ops)*
Jeff Krause *(Dir-Field Ops)*
Brian Ribordy *(Dir-Field Ops)*
Dan Torres *(Dir-Safety)*

SKEPTON CONSTRUCTION, INC.
3481 Finland Rd, Pennsburg, PA 18073
Tel.: (215) 679-7147
Web Site:
  http://www.skeptonconstruction.com
Year Founded: 1976
Sales Range: $50-74.9 Million
Emp.: 50
General Construction Services, Construction Management & Pre-Engineered Metal Buildings
N.A.I.C.S.: 236220
Kevin B. Frantz *(Pres & COO)*
Roger L. Perose *(VP-Project Dev)*
Robert J. Perose *(VP-Project Mgmt)*
Michael Mould *(Project Mgr)*
J. E. Berkowitz *(Pres)*
Dennis J. Wheeler Jr. *(Controller)*

SKH MANAGEMENT CO. INC.
813 Lititz Pike, Lititz, PA 17543-8629
Tel.: (717) 626-4771   PA
Web Site: http://www.skh.com
Year Founded: 1932
Sales Range: $200-249.9 Million
Emp.: 1,100
Supplier of Produce, Grocery, Bakery Goods, Seafood, Meat, Deli, Gardening Supplies & Home Accents
N.A.I.C.S.: 424410
Donovan Oberholtzer *(CFO)*
Subsidiaries:

Stauffers of Kissel Hill   (1)
1850 Oregon Pike, Lancaster, PA 17601-6402
Tel.: (717) 569-2688
Web Site: http://www.skh.com
Sales Range: $25-49.9 Million
Emp.: 92
Grocery Stores
N.A.I.C.S.: 445110
Justin Shiffer *(Asst Mgr-Bakery)*

Stauffers of Kissel Hill   (1)
51 Gettysburg Pike, Mechanicsburg, PA 17055
Tel.: (717) 766-7993
Web Site: http://www.skh.com
Sales Range: $25-49.9 Million
Emp.: 150
Nursery Stock, Seeds & Bulbs
N.A.I.C.S.: 444240
John Snyder Jr. *(Mgr-BtoB)*

Stauffers of Rohrerstown Inc.   (1)
301 Rohrerstown Rd, Lancaster, PA 17603-2232
Tel.: (717) 397-4718
Web Site: http://www.skh.com
Sales Range: $25-49.9 Million
Emp.: 110
Grocery Stores, Nurseries & Green Houses
N.A.I.C.S.: 445110

SKI CHALET INC.
2704 Columbia Pike, Arlington, VA 22044
Tel.: (703) 521-1700
Web Site: http://www.sunandski.com
Year Founded: 1969
Sales Range: $10-24.9 Million
Emp.: 100
Retailer of Skiing, Snowboarding, Skating & Kayaking Equipment
N.A.I.C.S.: 423910
Bryan Sasste *(Mgr)*

SKI HI ENTERPRISES LTD.
2943 Stuart Dr, Fort Worth, TX 76104-6766
Tel.: (817) 429-7520
Web Site: http://www.skihi.com
Year Founded: 1981
Sales Range: $25-49.9 Million
Emp.: 250
Provider of Plumbing, Heating & Air-Conditioning Services
N.A.I.C.S.: 238220
Richard Skipper *(Founder & CEO)*
Coy Skipper *(Exec VP)*
Don McCallum *(Sr VP)*
Subsidiaries:

Ski Hi Mechanical Services Inc.   (1)
2943 Stuart Dr, Fort Worth, TX 76104-6766
Tel.: (817) 923-0292
Web Site: http://www.skihi.com
Sales Range: $25-49.9 Million
Emp.: 200
Provider of Help Supply Services
N.A.I.C.S.: 561320
Lisa Breshears *(Dir-HR)*

SKIDAWAY HEALTH AND LIVING SERVICES, INC.
95 Skidaway Island Park Rd, Savannah, GA 31411
Tel.: (912) 598-3601   GA
Year Founded: 1999
Sales Range: $10-24.9 Million
Elder Care Services
N.A.I.C.S.: 623312
Amanda Elliott *(Exec Dir)*
Beau Sanders *(CFO & VP)*
Kirby Mason *(Sec)*
Wallace Smith *(Pres & CEO)*

SKIDMORE OWINGS & MERRILL LLP
224 S Michigan Ave Ste 1000, Chicago, IL 60604
Tel.: (312) 554-9090   IL
Web Site: http://www.som.com
Year Founded: 1936
Sales Range: $75-99.9 Million
Emp.: 1,000
Provider of Architectural Services
N.A.I.C.S.: 541310
Kent Jackson *(Partner-Design)*
Leo Chow *(Partner-Design)*
Michael Duncan *(Dir-Design)*
Eric Keune *(Dir-Design)*
Jose Luis Palacios *(Dir-Design)*
Scott Duncan *(Partner)*
Paul Danna *(Dir-Design)*

SKIDMORE OWINGS & MERRILL LLP

Skidmore Owings & Merrill LLP—(Continued)
Jaime Velez (Dir-Interior Design)
Mark Sarkisian (Partner-Structural & Seismic Engrg)
Charles Besjak (Dir-Structural Engrg)
Luke Leung (Dir-Sustainable Engrg)
Keith Boswell (Partner-Technical)
Daniel R. Ringelstein (Dir-Urban Design & Plng)
Ellen Lou (Dir-Urban Design & Plng)
Thomas Behr (Mng Partner)
Jonathan Stein (Mng Partner)
Brant E. Coletta (Mng Partner)
Laura Ettelman (Mng Partner)
Xuan Fu (Mng Partner)
Christopher McCready (Officer-Strategic)
Mark Igou (Mng Dir)
Kenneth A. Lewis (Mng Partner)
Michael Mann (Mng Dir)
Anthony Vacchione (Mng Partner)
Gene Schnair (Partner-Consulting)
Gary Haney (Partner-Design)
Craig W. Hartman (Sr Partner-Consulting Design)
Brian Lee (Partner-Design)
Carrie Byles (Partner)
Nicole Dosso (Dir-Technical Grp-New York)
David Horos (Partner-Design)
Thomas Hussey (Dir-Urban Design & Plng)
Michael Lingertat (Mng Dir)
Eric Long (Dir-Structural Engrg)
Adam Semel (Mng Partner)
Jed Zimmerman (Mng Dir-Los Angeles)
Larry Chien (Mng Dir-San Francisco)
Peter Kindel (Dir-Urban Design & Plng-San Francisco)
Mark Nagis (Dir-Design)

SKIER'S CHOICE INC.
1717 Henry G Ln St, Maryville, TN 37801
Tel.: (865) 983-9924
Web Site: http://www.skierschoice.com
Sales Range: $350-399.9 Million
Emp.: 355
Power Boat Mfr
N.A.I.C.S.: 336612
Rick Tinker (Pres)
Mike Shirley (Mgr-Engrg)
Matt Brown (Mgr-Product Dev-Supra)
Amy Mauzy (Mgr-Mktg)

SKIL-TECH, INC.
5111 Green Vly Rd, Oshkosh, WI 54903
Tel.: (920) 231-9000
Web Site: http://www.skil-tech.com
Rev.: $11,200,000
Emp.: 175
Management Consulting Services
N.A.I.C.S.: 541618
Cindy Johnson (VP)
Rudy Iglewski (Pres)

SKILCRAFT LLC.
5184 Limaburg Rd, Burlington, KY 41005
Tel.: (859) 371-0799
Web Site: http://www.skilcraft.com
Year Founded: 1965
Sales Range: $10-24.9 Million
Emp.: 72
Sheet Metal Work Mfg
N.A.I.C.S.: 332322
Colin Stith (Mgr-Aerospace Ops)

SKILLS OF CENTRAL PENNSYLVANIA, INC.
341 Science Park Rd, State College, PA 16803
Tel.: (814) 238-3245 PA
Web Site: http://www.skillsofcentralpa.org
Year Founded: 1960
Sales Range: $25-49.9 Million
Emp.: 1,464
Disability Assistance Services
N.A.I.C.S.: 624120
Becky Aungst (CEO)
Cathy McFee (Reg VP)
Shawn Cupec (CIO)
Elia Ofiesh (VP & Controller)
Ann Stacey (Chm)
Wendy Pardee (Pres)
Justin Beigle (VP-Reg)
Pennie Spalding (VP-Reg)
Robin Weirich (VP-Reg)
Todd Deffenbaugh (CFO)
Lorie L. Smith (Sr Dir-HR)
Val Barner (COO)
Mary Kay Fultz (VP-Centre, Lycoming, Clinton, Huntingdon, Mifflin & Juniata)
Andrew Bollinger (Sr Dir-Quality & Compliance)

SKILLS, INC.
PO Box 65, Saint Albans, ME 04971
Tel.: (207) 938-4615 ME
Web Site: http://www.skillsinc.net
Year Founded: 1961
Sales Range: $10-24.9 Million
Emp.: 492
Intellectual Disability Assistance Services
N.A.I.C.S.: 623210

SKILLSET GROUP, LLC
3631 S Harbor Blvd Ste 130, Santa Ana, CA 92704
Web Site: http://www.skillsetgroup.com
Year Founded: 2013
Sales Range: $10-24.9 Million
Emp.: 740
Staff Requirement Services
N.A.I.C.S.: 561311
Clint Armstrong (Co-Founder & CEO)
Steve Vierra (Co-Founder & COO)
Jose Baca (CMO)
Steve K. Coppola (Dir-Specialty Projects)

SKILLSNET, INC.
310 W Jefferson, Waxahachie, TX 75165
Tel.: (972) 923-2950
Web Site: http://www.skillsnet.com
Year Founded: 1997
Sales Range: $10-24.9 Million
Emp.: 6
Creates Web-based Software
N.A.I.C.S.: 513210
Michael L. Brown (Founder & CEO)

SKILLSTORM, INC.
6414 NW 5th Way, Fort Lauderdale, FL 33309
Tel.: (954) 566-4647
Web Site: http://www.skillstorm.com
Year Founded: 2002
Sales Range: $25-49.9 Million
Emp.: 450
Information Technology, Engineering, Consulting, Intelligence Solutions, Global Telecommunications & Logistics Solutions to Federal, State & Local Agencies
N.A.I.C.S.: 541690
Paul Moura (Pres)
Dan Grace (Exec VP-Operational Svcs)

SKILSTAF INC.
860 Airport Dr PO Box 729, Alexander City, AL 35011
Tel.: (256) 234-6208
Sales Range: $200-249.9 Million
Emp.: 5,000
Employee Leasing Services
N.A.I.C.S.: 561330
Wayne Stark (Pres)
Crystal Dunn (Controller)

SKINNER TRANSFER CORP.
2020 E Main St, Reedsburg, WI 53959
Tel.: (608) 524-2326
Web Site: http://www.skinnertransfer.com
Year Founded: 1932
Sales Range: $10-24.9 Million
Emp.: 160
Provider of Hauling Services
N.A.I.C.S.: 484121
Evelyn Skinner (CEO)

SKINNYCORP L.L.C.
1260 W Madison St, Chicago, IL 60607-1933
Tel.: (773) 878-3557
Web Site: http://www.threadless.com
Sales Range: $25-49.9 Million
Emp.: 60
E-Commerce & Internet Website Owner & Operator; Apparel Mfr & Sls
N.A.I.C.S.: 315990
Tom Ryan (CEO)

SKINOVATION PHARMACEUTICAL INCORPORATED
2157 S Lincoln St, Salt Lake City, UT 84106
Tel.: (801) 323-2395
Year Founded: 1988
Assets: $16,234
Liabilities: $463,435
Net Worth: ($447,201)
Earnings: ($35,866)
Fiscal Year-end: 12/31/23
Investment Services
N.A.I.C.S.: 523999
Hugo Rodier (Pres, CEO & CFO)
M. Jeanne Ball (Treas & Sec)

SKINSMART DERMATOLOGY
5911 N Honore Ave Ste 210, Sarasota, FL 34243
Tel.: (941) 308-7546
Web Site: http://www.sarasotadermatologist.com
Year Founded: 2005
Sales Range: $1-9.9 Million
Emp.: 20
Dermatology Services
N.A.I.C.S.: 621111
Elizabeth F. Callahan (Founder)
Ronald Allbee (Mgr-Practice Dev)

SKINSTORE.COM
11344 Coloma Rd Ste 725, Gold River, CA 95670
Tel.: (916) 475-1464
Web Site: http://www.skinstore.com
Year Founded: 1998
Sales Range: $10-24.9 Million
Emp.: 38
Health & Beauty Products Retailer
N.A.I.C.S.: 456120
Christina Bertolino (Sr Mgr-Buying)
Jeff Askenas (VP)
Julie Hinkson (Coord-Mdsg)

SKIP CONVERSE, INC.
318 Jones St, Pineville, LA 71360
Tel.: (318) 445-7196
Web Site: http://www.skipconverse.com
Sales Range: $10-24.9 Million
Emp.: 60
General Contracting Services

N.A.I.C.S.: 236220
Cathleen Ingles (Treas, Sec & Office Mgr)
Carl Riche (VP)
Richard Sanders (Project Mgr)
Randy Deloach (VP)
Doug Franks (Project Mgr)
Bobby Bowen (Mgr-Warehouse)

SKIP-A-LONG FAMILY AND COMMUNITY SERVICES
4210 44th Ave, Moline, IL 61265
Tel.: (309) 764-3724 IL
Web Site: http://www.salfcs.org
Year Founded: 1970
Sales Range: $10-24.9 Million
Emp.: 245
Community Care Services
N.A.I.C.S.: 624190
Malia Owens (Dir-The Home Child Care Network)
Marcy Mendenhall (Pres & CEO)

SKIPPER BUDS OF ILLINOIS INC.
215 N Point Dr, Winthrop Harbor, IL 60096
Tel.: (847) 872-3200
Web Site: http://www.skipperbuds.com
Rev.: $21,000,000
Emp.: 320
Commercial & Industrial Machinery & Equipment Repair & Maintenance
N.A.I.C.S.: 811310
Mike Pretasky (Pres)
Blair Desrochers (Mgr-Accessories)
Glenn Pollock (Dir-IT)

SKIPPING STONE, INC.
83 Pine St Ste 101 W, Peabody, MA 01960
Tel.: (978) 717-6100 DE
Web Site: http://www.skippingstone.com
Year Founded: 1996
Sales Range: $10-24.9 Million
Emp.: 15
Consulting & Technology Services
N.A.I.C.S.: 541618
Peter Weigand (Chm & CEO)
Greg Lander (Pres)
Steve Hinton (Principal & VP-Ops & Capacity Center)
John P. W. Brown (Partner)
Ross Malme (Partner)
Shuichi Kishida (Pres-Skipping Stone-Japan)

SKIRBALL CULTURAL CENTER
2701 N Sepulveda Blvd, Los Angeles, CA 90049
Tel.: (310) 440-4500 CA
Web Site: http://www.skirball.org
Year Founded: 1995
Sales Range: $10-24.9 Million
Emp.: 363
Cultural Center Operator
N.A.I.C.S.: 711310
Kathryn Girard (Exec VP)
Arthur H. Bilger (Vice Chm)
Jessie Kornberg (Pres & CEO)

SKIVA INTERNATIONAL INC.
1407 Broadway Fl 5, New York, NY 10018
Tel.: (212) 736-9520
Web Site: http://www.skiva.com
Rev.: $14,000,000
Emp.: 50
Women's & Children's Sportswear
N.A.I.C.S.: 424350
Albert Chehebar (Pres)
Zackery Wertenmer (CFO)

Indraneel Basu *(Sr Mgr)*
Len Camacho *(Controller)*
Bruce Resch *(Dir-Ops)*

SKLAR CORPORATION
889 S Matlack St, West Chester, PA 19382-4971
Tel.: (610) 756-7888
Web Site: http://www.sklarcorp.com
Year Founded: 1892
Surgical Instruments Mfr & Distr
N.A.I.C.S.: 339112
Kamran Sarwar *(Acct Mgr)*

SKM GROUP
6350 Transit Rd, Depew, NY 14043
Tel.: (716) 989-3200
Year Founded: 1986
Rev.: $13,000,000
Emp.: 25
Full Service
N.A.I.C.S.: 541810
Susan Kerrigan-Meany *(Pres)*
Micky Farber *(Sr VP-Direct Mktg & Ops)*
Ellen Peinkofer *(CFO)*
Bryan LeFauve *(COO)*
Pamela McDowell *(Acct Supvr)*
Andrea D'Angelo *(Acct Exec)*
Steve Fazio *(Dir-Art)*
Rob Murphy *(Dir-Creative)*
Lauren Cius *(Assoc Dir-Creative)*
Michael Brown *(Sr Dir-Art)*
Mike Mathis *(Chief Creative Officer)*
Jason Hughes *(Dir-Creative)*
Victoria Jayes *(Acct Supvr)*
Jeff Schaefer *(Dir-Integrated Services)*
Laura McFeely *(Acct Exec)*
Jonathan Koziol *(Mgr-Traffic)*
Tara Erwin *(Mgr-PR)*
Julie Desmond Schechter *(Acct Dir-Direct Mktg)*
Ira Kantor *(Acct Exec)*
Mary Usen *(Sr Mgr-Production)*
Diane Warner *(Dir-Media)*
Angela Twentyfive *(Mgr-Acctg)*
Lisa Dojnik *(Dir-Art)*
Erin Doherty *(Sr Mgr-Interactive Project)*
Ashley Lewis *(Acct Supvr)*
Katie Johnson *(Acct Exec)*
Kimberly McCarthy *(Sr Acct Exec)*
Theresa Siconolfi *(Mgr-Production)*
Amanda Waggoner *(Acct Exec)*
Samantha Maroney *(Acct Exec)*
Jamie Garcia *(Dir-Art)*
James Gillan *(Mgr-Strategic Branding)*
Jillian Fiorella *(Acct Supvr)*
Michael Downey *(Dir-Art)*

SKM MEDIA CORP.
6001 Broken Sound Pkwy NW Ste 510, Boca Raton, FL 33487
Tel.: (561) 404-1040
Web Site: http://www.skmmediagroup.com
Sales Range: $1-9.9 Million
Emp.: 15
Data, Direct Mail Fulfillment, Email Marketing, Social Media Marketing & Management, Internet Lead Generation & Consultation
N.A.I.C.S.: 541613
Steven L. Moreno *(Co-Founder & CEO)*
Howard Minsky *(Co-Founder & Pres)*
John R. Lesnik *(Sec)*

SKODA, MINOTTI & CO., CERTIFIED PUBLIC ACCOUNTANTS
6685 Beta Dr, Mayfield Village, OH 44143
Tel.: (440) 449-6800

Web Site: http://www.skodaminotti.com
Year Founded: 1980
Certified Public Accountants
N.A.I.C.S.: 541211
Michael L. Minotti *(Pres)*
Gregory J. Skoda *(Co-Founder & Chm)*
Daniel Golish *(Partner-Atlanta)*
Heidi Hoyt *(Mng Dir-Professional Staffing)*
Marilea Campomizzi *(Principal-Acctg & Auditing Dept)*
Gerald M. Appel *(Partner-Cleveland)*
Robert M. Barkett *(Partner Emeritus-Cleveland)*
Randall P. Bosley *(Principal-Cleveland)*
Patrick T. Carney *(Partner-Cleveland)*
Joseph Compton *(Principal-Cleveland)*
Robert E. Coode *(Partner-Cleveland)*
Alyson Fieldman *(CMO-Cleveland)*
Amy J. Gibson *(Principal-Cleveland)*
Theodore R. Ginsburg *(Principal-Cleveland)*
Danielle B. Gisondo *(Partner-Cleveland)*
Bob Goricki *(Dir-Digital Mktg)*
Steven H. Gross *(Partner-Cleveland)*
Cindy Spitz *(Sr Dir-Content)*
Laura Rohde *(Dir-HR Cleveland)*
Dawn M. Minotas *(Mng Dir- Small Bus Svcs)*

SKOGMAN CONSTRUCTION COMPANY OF IOWA INC.
411 1st Ave SE Ste 400, Cedar Rapids, IA 52401-1318
Tel.: (319) 363-8285
Web Site: http://www.skogmanhomes.com
Year Founded: 1947
Sales Range: $25-49.9 Million
Emp.: 182
Provider of Construction Services
N.A.I.C.S.: 236115
Richard Siders *(Treas)*

Subsidiaries:

Midwest Development Co. Inc. (1)
411 1st Ave SE Ste 410, Cedar Rapids, IA 52401-1318 (100%)
Tel.: (319) 363-8285
Web Site: http://www.skogman.com
Sales Range: $25-49.9 Million
Emp.: 4
Provider of Holding Services
N.A.I.C.S.: 551112

Midwest Home Distributors Inc. (1)
411 1st Ave SE, Cedar Rapids, IA 52401-1318
Tel.: (319) 363-8285
Web Site: http://www.skogman.com
Sales Range: $10-24.9 Million
Emp.: 1
Mfr of Home Furnishings
N.A.I.C.S.: 423220
Kyle D. Skogman *(Pres)*

Skogman Ralston & Carlson Inc. (1)
1110 Dina Ct Ste B, Hiawatha, IA 52233
Tel.: (319) 366-6288
Web Site: http://www.skogmanins.com
Sales Range: $25-49.9 Million
Emp.: 16
Provider of Insurance Services
N.A.I.C.S.: 524126
Chad Sneby *(VP)*
Holly Ranney *(Mgr-Comml Lines Acct)*
Kurt Feller *(Mgr-Comml Lines Acct)*

Skogman Realty Co. Inc. (1)
411 1st Ave Se Ste 500, Cedar Rapids, IA 52401 (100%)
Tel.: (319) 366-6427
Web Site: http://www.skogman.com
Sales Range: $10-24.9 Million
Emp.: 75
Provider of Real Estate Services

N.A.I.C.S.: 531210
Rick Skogman *(Founder)*
Chris Skogman *(Pres)*

SKOKIE VALLEY BEVERAGE COMPANY
199 Shepard Ave, Wheeling, IL 60090-6021
Tel.: (847) 541-1500
Web Site: http://www.svbco.com
Year Founded: 1946
Sales Range: $75-99.9 Million
Emp.: 80
Beverages Whslr
N.A.I.C.S.: 424810
Anton T. Schirmang *(Sr VP)*
Kenneth C. Schirmang *(Pres)*

SKOLNIK INDUSTRIES INC.
4900 S Kilbourn Ave, Chicago, IL 60632
Tel.: (773) 735-0700
Web Site: http://www.skolnik.com
Sales Range: $10-24.9 Million
Emp.: 75
Mfr Of Metal Barrels, Drums & Pails
N.A.I.C.S.: 332439
Howard Z. Skolnik *(Pres & CEO)*
Ed Elins *(CFO)*
Tom Kreiniker *(VP-Fin)*
W. Dean Ricker *(VP-Sls & Mktg)*

SKOOKUM SERVICES, LLC
4525 Auto Center Way, Bremerton, WA 98312
Tel.: (360) 475-0756
Web Site: http://www.skookum.org
Year Founded: 1988
Sales Range: $75-99.9 Million
Emp.: 1,240
Disability Assistance Services
N.A.I.C.S.: 624120
Jeff Dolven *(Pres & CEO)*
Scott Bell *(COO & VP)*

SKOWHEGAN SAVINGS BANK
13 Elm St, Skowhegan, ME 04976
Tel.: (207) 474-9511
Web Site: http://www.skowsavings.com
Rev.: $16,623,327
Emp.: 55
State Commercial Banks
N.A.I.C.S.: 522110
John C. Witherspoon *(Pres & CEO)*
Nanook Tuefferd *(Mgr-Bingham & Jackman)*
Meghan Loubier *(Branch Mgr)*
Renee Hawthorne *(Branch Mgr-II)*
Angel Quick *(Branch Mgr-II)*
Richard St. Pierre *(CFO & Sr VP)*
Christopher C. Farmer *(VP)*
Dan Tilton *(Sr VP-Sls & Customer Rels)*
Roger Gifford *(Chm)*
Barbara Cotta *(COO & Sr VP)*
Barry Martin *(Sr VP-HR)*
David Cyr *(Exec VP)*
Steve Thomas *(Sr VP)*
Vicki Alward *(Chief Risk Officer & Sr VP)*

SKS, INC.
1730 Mission Rd, Escondido, CA 92029
Tel.: (858) 566-0830
Web Site: http://www.sksoil.com
Year Founded: 1965
Sales Range: $25-49.9 Million
Emp.: 69
Petroleum Product Distr
N.A.I.C.S.: 424720
Eric D. Kroesche *(Chm)*
Michele Pascoe *(CFO)*
Newell Bowden *(Mgr-Ops)*

SKSW ADVERTISING
1255 W 15th St Ste 800, Plano, TX 75075
Tel.: (972) 424-3000
Web Site: http://www.sksw.com
Year Founded: 1996
Sales Range: $10-24.9 Million
Emp.: 13
N.A.I.C.S.: 541810
Janice Krueger *(Partner)*
Bill Krueger *(Dir-New Bus Dev)*
Eric Brule *(Dir-Art)*
Katrina Davis *(Dir-Print Production)*
Amanda Mathis *(Office Mgr)*
David Hadeler *(Partner)*

SKULLS UNLIMITED INTERNATIONAL, INC.
10313 S Sunnylane Rd, Oklahoma City, OK 73160
Tel.: (405) 794-9300
Web Site: http://www.skullsunlimited.com
Year Founded: 1986
Sales Range: $1-9.9 Million
Emp.: 20
Osteological Specimens Supplier
N.A.I.C.S.: 423450
Jay Villemarette *(Co-Owner & Pres)*
Kim Villemarette *(Co-Owner)*
Eric Humhries *(Supvr-Production)*
Allyson Cameron *(Mgr-Inventory & Custom Cleaning)*
Lacey Johnson *(Mgr-Shipping)*
Michelle Hayer *(Office Mgr)*
Josh Villemarette *(Coord-Admin)*
Jaron Villemarette *(Mgr-Retail)*

SKUTTLE INDOOR AIR QUALITY PRODUCTS
101 Margaret St, Marietta, OH 45750-9052
Tel.: (740) 373-9169
Web Site: http://www.skuttle.com
Year Founded: 1917
Sales Range: $1-9.9 Million
Emp.: 30
Mfr of Whole-House Humidifiers, Air Cleaners & Make-up Air Controls
N.A.I.C.S.: 335210

SKY ADVERTISING, INC.
14 E 33 St 8th Fl, New York, NY 10016
Tel.: (212) 677-2500
Web Site: http://www.skyad.com
Year Founded: 1989
Sales Range: $10-24.9 Million
Emp.: 15
N.A.I.C.S.: 541810
Janine Jones *(Exec VP-Fin)*
Jimmy Cintron *(VP-Ops)*
Alan Gladstone *(Sr VP)*
Phil Kaminowitz *(Sr VP)*

Subsidiaries:

Sky Advertising-Chicago (1)
159 N Marion St Ste 292, Oak Park, IL 60301-1032
Tel.: (708) 707-2070
Web Site: http://www.skyad.com
N.A.I.C.S.: 541810
Perry Edward Perez *(Sr Acct Exec)*
Bill Steely *(Pres & CEO)*
Jimmy Cintron *(VP-Ops)*

SKY BIRD TRAVEL & TOUR INC.
24701 Swanson Rd, Southfield, MI 48033
Tel.: (248) 372-4800
Web Site: http://www.skybirdtravel.com
Year Founded: 1976
Sales Range: $100-124.9 Million
Emp.: 100

SKY BIRD TRAVEL & TOUR INC.

Sky Bird Travel & Tour Inc.—(Continued)
Travel Agencies
N.A.I.C.S.: 561510
Arvind V. Shah (Chm)

SKY COMPUTERS, INC.
27 Industrial Ave, Chelmsford, MA 01824
Tel.: (978) 250-2420
Web Site:
http://www.skycomputers.com
Year Founded: 1980
Sales Range: $400-449.9 Million
Emp.: 50
Processor Mfr & Services for Military, Homeland Security & Industrial Inspection
N.A.I.C.S.: 334412
Henry Shean (Pres)

SKY COUNTRY TRANSPORTATION SERVICE
895 State Farm Rd, Boone, NC 28607
Tel.: (828) 268-2655
Web Site:
http://www.skycountryinc.com
Year Founded: 1995
Sales Range: $10-24.9 Million
Emp.: 4
Truck Transportation Brokers
N.A.I.C.S.: 488510
Ken Younger (Pres & CEO)

SKY HELICOPTERS, INC.
Garland/DFW Heliport 2559 S Jupiter Rd, Garland, TX 75041
Tel.: (214) 349-7000   TX
Web Site:
http://www.skyhelicopters.com
Year Founded: 1992
Sales Range: $1-9.9 Million
Emp.: 10
Helicopter Operations & Flight Training
N.A.I.C.S.: 488119
Connie Pyatt (VP)

SKY HIGH FOR ST. JUDE INC.
1819 W Pinhook Ste 103, Lafayette, LA 70501-4756
Tel.: (337) 889-3347   LA
Web Site:
http://www.skyhighshoot.org
Year Founded: 2007
Sales Range: $1-9.9 Million
Fundraising Organization
N.A.I.C.S.: 813211
Jessy Deardurff (Dir-Ops)
Brittany Hebert (Founder & Pres)
Christl Mahfouz (VP)
Marla Ratzlaff (Sec)
Jenifer Tule Ham (Treas)
Chris Connard (CEO-Extreme Energy Svcs)

SKY HIGH UNLIMITED INC.
1375 E Washington Blvd, Los Angeles, CA 90021
Tel.: (213) 749-3388
Rev.: $11,955,979
Emp.: 10
Men's & Boys' Sportswear & Work Clothing
N.A.I.C.S.: 424350
Michael Isaacson (CEO)
Mei Mae (Controller)

SKY ISLAND CAPITAL LLC
2301 Cedar Springs Rd 450, Dallas, TX 75201
Tel.: (817) 948-1534
Web Site:
http://www.skyislandcap.com
Year Founded: 2018
Investment Services
N.A.I.C.S.: 523999
Jack Waterstreet (Mng Partner)

Subsidiaries:

Material Sciences Corporation   (1)
6855 Commerce Blvd, Canton, MI 48187
Tel.: (734) 207-4444
Web Site:
http://www.materialsciencescorp.com
Engineered Materials, Coated Steel & Electro-Galvanized Steel Products Mfr
N.A.I.C.S.: 332812
Patrick Murley (CEO)
Leslie Boyle-Zickuhr (Dir-Pur)
Brian Quick (Mgr-Strategic Acct)
Brian Robb (Mgr-Strategic Acct)
James Todd (CFO)
Joel Turak (Mgr-Strategic Acct)
Mike Cocanig (Exec VP-Ops)
Bill Stapleton (Sr VP-Sls-Elk Grove Village)
Kevin McCallum (COO)
Paul Pirko (VP-Sls-Electrogalvanized Products)
Marty Scott (Dir-Sls-Walbridge)
Alex Davies (Dir-Sls-Toronto)
Jeff Howard (Corp Controller)
Dominick Wojewnik (Dir-IT Svcs)
Nancy Topp (Mgr-Supply Chain)
Tim O'Connor (Mgr-Strategic Acct)
Tony Shillingford (Mgr-Strategic Acct)
Alain Lavalliere (Mgr-Strategic Acct)
Mike Nellich (Mgr-Strategic Acct)
Allan Garrett (VP-Bus Dev)

Subsidiary (Domestic):

Material Sciences Corporation - Ohio Facility   (2)
30610 E Bdwy St, Walbridge, OH 43465
Tel.: (419) 666-6130
Web Site:
http://www.materialsciencescorp.com
Steel Coating Services
N.A.I.C.S.: 332812
Jeff Ramsey (Ops Mgr)
Marty Scott (Dir-Sls)
Andrea Taylor (Mgr-Inside Sls)

Subsidiary (Non-US):

Material Sciences Corporation - Toronto Facility   (2)
1430 Martin Grove Road, Rexdale, M9W 4Y1, ON, Canada
Tel.: (416) 743-7980
Web Site: http://www.metalkoting.com
Emp.: 165
Galvanized, Painted & Printed Steel & Aluminum Coil Mfr
N.A.I.C.S.: 332812
Kevin McCallum (COO)

Pacific Paper Tube, Inc.   (1)
1025 98th Ave, Oakland, CA 94603
Tel.: (510) 562-8823
Web Site: http://www.pacificpapertube.com
Sales Range: $1-9.9 Million
Emp.: 90
Fiber Can, Tube, Drum & Similar Products Mfr
N.A.I.C.S.: 322219
Casey Wallace (VP)

Polished Metals Ltd Inc.   (1)
487 Hillside Ave, Hillside, NJ 07205-7111
Tel.: (908) 688-1188
Web Site: http://www.polishedmetals.com
Nonferrous Metal Foundries
N.A.I.C.S.: 331529
Malcolm Tamuzza (Pres)

Subsidiary (Domestic):

Pride Metal Polishing, Inc.   (2)
10822 Saint Louis Dr, El Monte, CA 91731
Tel.: (626) 350-1326
Sales Range: $1-9.9 Million
Emp.: 19
Plating And Polishing
N.A.I.C.S.: 332813
Rod Lowell (Pres)

SKY LOGISTICS AND DISTRIBUTION
4001 32nd St N, Fargo, ND 58102
Tel.: (701) 298-0349
Web Site:
http://www.skylogistics.com
Sales Range: $10-24.9 Million
Emp.: 43
Truck Transportation Brokers
N.A.I.C.S.: 488510
Robert Nelson (Pres)
Mike Volk (Gen Mgr)

SKY RANCH
24657 CR 448, Van, TX 75790
Tel.: (903) 266-3300   TX
Web Site: http://www.skyranch.org
Year Founded: 1955
Sales Range: $10-24.9 Million
Emp.: 712
Christian Camp Operator
N.A.I.C.S.: 611699
D'Anne Behee (Sr Dir-Admin)
Linda Spragins Paulk (Pres & CEO)
Emily Hubbard (Sec)

SKY TELECOM TPC
10376 E Colonial Dr Ste 135, Orlando, FL 32817
Tel.: (407) 382-7888
Web Site:
http://www.thephonecards.com
Sales Range: $100-124.9 Million
Emp.: 200
Long Distance Telephone Services
N.A.I.C.S.: 517121
Pradip Patel (Pres)

SKYAUCTION.COM, INC.
501 Madison Ave, New York, NY 10022-5602
Tel.: (212) 486-1250
Web Site: http://www.skyauction.com
Year Founded: 1999
Sales Range: $10-24.9 Million
Emp.: 20
Online Auction for Airline Flights
N.A.I.C.S.: 561510
Salvatore Esposito (Co-Founder & COO)
Michael Hering (Co-Founder, Pres & CEO)
Tilly M. Bachmann (Dir-Sls & Svcs)
DeeDee Flagg (Dir-Creative)

SKYBRIDGE AMERICAS, INC.
310 4th Ave S Ste 5010 Unit 92077, Minneapolis, MN 55415
Tel.: (763) 477-7600
Web Site:
http://www.skybridgeamericas.com
Multi-Channel & Product Fulfillment Solutions
N.A.I.C.S.: 541613
Keith Schwartz (Pres-Customer Fulfillment & Digital Svcs)
Mark Morris (Chm & Principal)
Andrew Bosko (CEO)
Bobby Matthews (Sr VP-Sls & Mktg)

Subsidiaries:

Alive Companies, Inc.   (1)
13098 George Weber Dr Ste 300, Rogers, MN 55374
Tel.: (952) 960-3670
Web Site: http://www.alivefulfillment.com
E-Commerce, Internet Marketing & Fulfillment Solutions
N.A.I.C.S.: 541890
Matt Rogers (Pres)

SKYBRIDGE CAPITAL
527 Madison Ave 16th Fl, New York, NY 10022
Tel.: (212) 485-3100
Web Site:
http://www.skybridgecapital.com
Year Founded: 2005
Rev.: $12,000,000,000
Privater Equity Firm
N.A.I.C.S.: 523999

U.S. PRIVATE

Ray Nolte (Co-Chief Investment Officer)
Anthony Scaramucci (Founder & Mng Partner)
Tatiana Segal (Mng Dir & Head-Risk Mgmt)
Brett Messing (Pres, COO & Co-Chief Investment Officer)

SKYBRIDGE RESOURCES, LLC
1715 N Westshore Blvd Ste 320, Tampa, FL 33607
Tel.: (813) 579-1220
Web Site:
http://www.skybridgeresources.com
Year Founded: 2005
Sales Range: $10-24.9 Million
Emp.: 275
Employment Services
N.A.I.C.S.: 561311
Randy Bahlow (Pres)

SKYCREST ENTERPRISES INC.
448 Redcliff Dr Ste 210, Redding, CA 96002
Tel.: (530) 241-3600
Web Site:
http://www.cousingarys.com
Rev.: $23,400,000
Emp.: 7
Mobile Home Dealers
N.A.I.C.S.: 459930

SKYE ASSOCIATES LLC
7529 Standish Ste 100, Rockville, MD 20855
Tel.: (301) 656-6463
Web Site:
http://www.skyeassociatesllc.com
Year Founded: 2006
Sales Range: $1-9.9 Million
Emp.: 29
Web Design & E-Commerce Technology
N.A.I.C.S.: 541690
Adam Hanin (Owner)
Austin Thomas (Dir-Simply Soles)
Lauren Lynch (Dir-PR & Acct Mgr)
Meg Taylor (Acct Mgr)

SKYHORSE PUBLISHING CO., INC.
555 Eighth Ave Ste 903, New York, NY 10018
Tel.: (212) 643-6816
Web Site:
http://www.skyhorsepublishing.com
Rev.: $1,484,000
Emp.: 12
Book Publishers
N.A.I.C.S.: 513130
Abigail Gehring (Mng Editor)
Sarah Fox (Mgr)
Tony Lyons (Pres & Publr)
Mark Gompertz (Grp Dir-Editorial)

Subsidiaries:

REGNERY PUBLISHING, INC.   (1)
300 New Jersey Ave NW Ste 500, Washington, DC 20001-2253
Tel.: (202) 216-0600
Web Site: http://www.regnery.com
Book Publishers
N.A.I.C.S.: 513130
Marjory Grant Ross (Pres & Publr)
Harry W. Crocker (VP & Exec Editor)

SKYKNIGHT CAPITAL LLC
One Letterman Dr Bldg C Ste 3-950, San Francisco, CA 94129
Tel.: (415) 914-0788
Web Site:
http://www.skyknightcapital.com
Privater Equity Firm
N.A.I.C.S.: 523999

COMPANIES — SKYLINE TELEPHONE MEMBERSHIP CORPORATION

Matthew Ebbel (Mng Partner)
Subsidiaries:

STR Mechanical, LLC (1)
PO Box 681507, Charlotte, NC 28216-2411
Tel.: (704) 536-5335
Web Site: https://strmechanical.com
Emp.: 50
Full Service Commercial HVAC Contractor
N.A.I.C.S.: 238220

Subsidiary (Domestic):

Technical Services, Inc. (2)
825 Greenbriar Cir Ste A, Chesapeake, VA 23320-5992
Tel.: (757) 548-5889
Web Site: http://www.technicalsvcs.com
Electrical Contractor
N.A.I.C.S.: 238210

Vendor Credentialing Service LLC (1)
315 Capitol St Ste 100, Houston, TX 77002
Tel.: (281) 863-9500
Web Site: http://www.symplr.com
Healthcare Credentialing & Compliance Services
N.A.I.C.S.: 561499
Tres Thompson (CFO & COO)
Jason Rupert (Chief Sls Officer)
B. J. Schaknowski (CEO)
Brian Fugere (Chief Product Officer)
Kristin Russel (CMO)

Subsidiary (Domestic):

API Healthcare Corporation (2)
1550 Innovation Way, Hartford, WI 53027
Tel.: (262) 673-6815
Web Site: http://www.apihealthcare.com
Sales Range: $75-99.9 Million
Emp.: 350
Healthcare Business Management Software & Services
N.A.I.C.S.: 513210

Subsidiary (Domestic):

API Healthcare Corporation - San Diego (3)
9276 Scranton Rd Ste 400, San Diego, CA 92121
Tel.: (262) 673-6815
Web Site: http://www.apihealthcare.com
Sales Range: $10-24.9 Million
Emp.: 50
Healthcare Staffing Solutions
N.A.I.C.S.: 561311

Subsidiary (Domestic):

Res-Q Healthcare Systems, Inc. (4)
9276 Scranton Rd Ste 400, San Diego, CA 92121
Tel.: (858) 882-8500
Sales Range: $1-9.9 Million
Management Consulting Services
N.A.I.C.S.: 541618
Michael Meisel (Pres & CEO)

Subsidiary (Domestic):

CBR Associates Inc. (2)
1415 Broad St, Durham, NC 27705-3534
Tel.: (919) 286-1326
Web Site: http://www.cbrassociates.com
Healthcare Credentialing Solutions
N.A.I.C.S.: 513210
Brenda Sorrell (CEO)

HealthcareSource HR, Inc. (2)
100 Sylvan Rd Ste 100, Woburn, MA 01801
Tel.: (781) 368-1033
Web Site: http://www.healthcaresource.com
Healtcare Services
N.A.I.C.S.: 621999
J. P. Fingado (Pres)
Kerry Unflat (VP-Talent Mgmt)
David Wilkins (CMO)
Gabe Camera (CFO)
Bob Zurek (CTO & Sr VP)
Chris Martins (Mgr-Product Mktg)
Lisa Frank (Sr Mgr-Product Mktg)
Norma Gaffin (Sr Mgr-Content Mktg)
Kelli Rice (Dir-Mktg Insight)
Sarah Joyce (VP-Client Ops)
Katherine Shuman (Chief Sls Officer)
Patrick McDonough (CTO)
Michael Grossi (CEO)

ISG Group LLC (2)
61 Split Brook Rd, Nashua, NH 03060
Tel.: (603) 888-0542
Web Site: http://www.intellisoftgroup.com
Medical Credentialing, Provider Enrollment & Contract Management Software Publisher & Whslr
N.A.I.C.S.: 513210
Mike Melville (Grp CEO)
Mitch Martin (Pres)
Mike Aha (Dir-Dev)
Karen Roy (Dir-Ops)
Marcia Wessell (Dir-Mktg Comm)

Medkinetics, LLC (2)
124 1st Ave S Ste 200, Franklin, TN 37064-6326
Tel.: (615) 599-1627
Healthcare Credentialing & Compliance Services
N.A.I.C.S.: 561499
Jim Cox (Pres)

TractManager, Inc. (2)
2711 N Haskell #1450, Dallas, TX 75204
Tel.: (423) 267-9300
Web Site: http://www.tractmanager.com
Contract Management Services
N.A.I.C.S.: 561499
Donald Deieso (Chm)
Trace Devanny (CEO)
Sandra L. Taylor (CFO)
Patrick Flynn (Chief Product Officer)
Kimberly Hartsfield (Chief Date Officer)

Subsidiary (Domestic):

MD Buyline, Inc. (3)
5910 N Cntrl Expy, Dallas, TX 75206
Tel.: (214) 891-6700
Web Site: http://www.mdbuyline.com
Sales Range: $1-9.9 Million
Information Network Service For High-Tech Medical Electronic Products & Provides Information On Information Systems Industry
N.A.I.C.S.: 513199
Lyle Ellerbach (VP)
Kevin Hodges (Dir-Ops)
Eric Slimp (Mgr-Purchased Svcs)
Katie Regan (Mgr-Clinical Publ)
Nicole Hodges (VP-Ops)
Peter Stelling (Gen Mgr-Purchased Svcs)

SKYLAND AUTOMOTIVE, INC.
255 Smoky Park Hwy, Asheville, NC 28806
Tel.: (828) 667-5213
Web Site: http://www.skylandautomotive.com
Sales Range: $25-49.9 Million
Emp.: 70
Car Whslr
N.A.I.C.S.: 441110
John Parker (Pres & CEO)

SKYLINE ADVANCED TECHNOLOGY SERVICES
490 Division St, Campbell, CA 95008
Tel.: (408) 370-1200
Web Site: http://www.skylineats.com
Sales Range: $25-49.9 Million
Emp.: 25
Computer Training, Professional Services & Hardware Sales
N.A.I.C.S.: 423430
Carol Mauldin (Pres)
Nancy Smith (CFO)
Michael Mauldin (Chm & CEO)
Mike Capace (VP-Education)
Roger Robert (Dir-Tech Svcs)

SKYLINE CHILI, INC.
4180 Thunderbird Ln, Fairfield, OH 45014
Tel.: (513) 874-1188 OH
Web Site: http://www.skylinechili.com
Year Founded: 1949
Sales Range: $25-49.9 Million
Emp.: 700
Quick Service Restaurants Owner, Operator, Developer & Franchiser
N.A.I.C.S.: 722511

Charlie L. Harnist (VP-Grocery Sls)
Jim Konves (VP-Grocery)

SKYLINE COMMERCIAL INTERIORS
731 Sansome St 4th Fl, San Francisco, CA 94111
Tel.: (415) 908-1020
Web Site: http://www.skylineconstruction.build
Sales Range: $25-49.9 Million
Emp.: 75
Commercial & Office Buildings, Renovation & Repair
N.A.I.C.S.: 236220
David Hayes (CEO)
Howard Fish (VP)

SKYLINE CONNECTIONS INC.
242 W 36th St Fl 5, New York, NY 10018
Tel.: (212) 947-3897 NY
Web Site: http://www.skylineconnections.com
Year Founded: 1997
Sales Range: $10-24.9 Million
Emp.: 22
Sales of Brand Name Computers
N.A.I.C.S.: 423430
Rodney Evans (CEO)
Jim Brewington (VP)

SKYLINE CREDIT RIDE INC.
5229 35th St, Long Island City, NY 11101-3205
Tel.: (718) 482-8585
Web Site: http://www.skylineride.com
Year Founded: 1977
Sales Range: $10-24.9 Million
Emp.: 800
Provider of Local Passenger Transportation Services
N.A.I.C.S.: 485320
Jalal Ehrari (Pres)
Mercedes Balladares (VP & Gen Mgr-Sls & Mktg)
Preston Clement (Dir-Mktg)
Edward Goldsmith (VP-Sls & Mktg)
Patricio Martinez (Mgr)
Magaly Troncoso (Sec)
Fernando Rojas (Chm-Comm)
Allice Shield (Controller)

Subsidiaries:

Skyline Funding Inc. (1)
5229 35th St, Long Island City, NY 11101-3205
Tel.: (718) 482-8585
Web Site: http://www.skylineride.com
Provider of Personal Credit Institution Services
N.A.I.C.S.: 561499
James Orozco (VP)

SKYLINE DFW EXHIBITS & EVENTS
900 Ave S, Grand Prairie, TX 75050
Tel.: (972) 522-0500
Web Site: http://www.dfwexhibits.com
Sales Range: $1-9.9 Million
Emp.: 24
Event Organizing Services
N.A.I.C.S.: 711310
Jeff Meisner (Pres & CEO)
Ally Walker (Project Coord)
Charles Shannon Dickerson (Supvr-Warehouse)
Erin Clute (Coord-Project)
Frank Garcia (Dir-Ops)
Jimmy Soares (Mgr-Warehouse)
Kelly Brady (Supvr-Event Svcs)

SKYLINE DISPLAYS INC.
3355 Discovery Rd, Eagan, MN 55121
Tel.: (651) 234-6000

Web Site: http://www.skyline.com
Year Founded: 1980
Sales Range: $10-24.9 Million
Emp.: 300
Mfr of Signs & Advertising Specialties
N.A.I.C.S.: 339950
Jeff Meyer (CFO)
Brian Schmoll (Supvr-Production & Sr Engr-Mfg)

Subsidiaries:

Skyline Exhibits (1)
3355 Discovery Rd, Saint Paul, MN 55121-2098
Tel.: (651) 234-6000
Web Site: http://www.skyline.com
Trade Shows & Exhibit Organizers
N.A.I.C.S.: 561920
Bill Dierberger (Pres)
Tim Brengman (VP-Ops)
Elaine Prickel (Sr Dir-HR)
Dave Bouquet (VP-Sls & New Bus Dev)
Mark Gomilla (Gen Mgr-Svc Center-Chicago)
Brian Falati (Mgr-Svc Center-Las Vegas)

Skyline Exhibits of Los Angeles Inc. (1)
10318 Santa Fe Springs Rd, Santa Fe Springs, CA 90670-3734
Tel.: (562) 944-1677
Web Site: http://www.skyline.com
Trade Shows & Exhibit Organizers
N.A.I.C.S.: 561920
Jeff Johnson (Owner & CEO)

Skyservice, Inc. (1)
3355 Discovery Rd, Eagan, MN 55121 (100%)
Tel.: (651) 234-6000
Web Site: http://www.skyserviceairlines.com
Provider of Equipment Rental Services
N.A.I.C.S.: 339950

SKYLINE EQUITIES REALTY, LLC
800 Brickell Ave Ste 201, Miami, FL 33131
Tel.: (305) 285-7272
Web Site: http://www.skylineequitiesrealty.com
Real Estate Services
N.A.I.C.S.: 531210
Evangeline Gouletas (Chm & CEO)

SKYLINE PROPERTIES
2099 Market St, San Francisco, CA 94114
Tel.: (415) 861-1111
Sales Range: $25-49.9 Million
Emp.: 10
Real Estate Managers
N.A.I.C.S.: 531210
Eileen Wong (Controller)
Daniel Shirazi (Sr Dir-Sls)

SKYLINE SALES INC.
2510 Commercial St SE, Salem, OR 97302
Tel.: (503) 581-2411
Web Site: http://www.skylineford.net
Rev.: $65,000,000
Emp.: 130
New & Used Automobiles
N.A.I.C.S.: 441110
Jim Donofrio (Owner)

SKYLINE TELEPHONE MEMBERSHIP CORPORATION
1200 NC Hwy 194 N, West Jefferson, NC 28694
Tel.: (336) 877-3111
Web Site: http://www.skyline.org
Year Founded: 1951
Sales Range: $75-99.9 Million
Emp.: 130
Provider of Local Telephone Communication Services
N.A.I.C.S.: 517121

SKYLINE TELEPHONE MEMBERSHIP CORPORATION

U.S. PRIVATE

Skyline Telephone Membership Corporation—(Continued)
R. C. Mitchell *(Pres)*
Jimmy Blevins *(CEO)*
Cindy Rothstein *(Exec Dir-Fin)*
Kim Shepherd *(Exec Dir-Customer Ops)*
Robbie Farmer *(Exec Dir-Engrg Ops)*
Molly Gambill *(Asst Treas & Asst Sec)*
Edward Hinson *(Exec Dir-Competitive Ops)*
D. C. Smith *(Treas)*
Joseph McNeil *(VP)*

SKYLINK TRAVEL
980 Avenue of the Americas Ste 401, New York, NY 10018
Tel.: (212) 380-2438
Web Site: http://www.skylinkus.com
Rev.: $35,000,000
Emp.: 15
Travel & Transportation Consolidator
N.A.I.C.S.: 561599
Arti Singh *(Mgr-Mktg & E-Commerce)*

SKYMARK REAL ESTATE INVESTMENTS
1400 E Oakland Park Blvd Ste 103, Fort Lauderdale, FL 33334
Tel.: (954) 567-5161
Web Site: http://www.skymarkinvestment.com
Rev.: $450,000,000
Real Estate Investment & Development Consulting Services
N.A.I.C.S.: 531390
Stanley Markofsky *(Chm & Pres)*
Brent Markofsky *(VP-Bus Dev, Land Acq & Sls)*
Matthew Markofsky *(CFO & VP-Contracts & Entitlements)*
Jarrod Markofsky *(VP-Product Dev, Construction & Sls)*

SKYPORT COMPANIES LLC
2601 S Quebec St Apt 6, Denver, CO 80231
Tel.: (303) 317-9000
Rev.: $12,000,000
Emp.: 10
Concessionaire
N.A.I.C.S.: 722513

SKYRUN BRECKENRIDGE, LLC
118 S Ridge St Unit 4, Breckenridge, CO 80424
Tel.: (970) 300-1815
Web Site: http://www.breckenridge.skyrun.com
Year Founded: 2009
Sales Range: $1-9.9 Million
Emp.: 13
Rental Booking Services
N.A.I.C.S.: 561599
Mike McGoff *(Co-Owner)*
Anna McGoff *(Co-Owner)*
Jessica Kingston *(Dir-Ops)*
Heidi Sheldon *(Gen Mgr)*

SKYRUN VACATION RENTALS, LLC
737 29th St, Boulder, CO 80303
Tel.: (970) 660-4422
Web Site: http://www.skyrun.com
Year Founded: 2008
Sales Range: $10-24.9 Million
Emp.: 98
Property Management Services
N.A.I.C.S.: 531311
Barry Cox *(Founder & CEO)*

SKYTYPERS, INC.
10650 San Sicily St, Las Vegas, NV 89141
Web Site: http://www.skytypers.com
Year Founded: 2004
Sales Range: $1-9.9 Million
Publicity/Promotions, Sales Promotion, Sponsorship & Sports Marketing
N.A.I.C.S.: 541810
Greg Stinis *(CEO & Squadron Commander)*
Stephen Stinis *(Pres)*

SKYVIEW CAPITAL, LLC
2000 Avenue of the Stars Ste 810N, 90067, Los Angeles, CA
Tel.: (310) 273-6000   DE
Web Site: http://www.skyviewcapital.com
Year Founded: 2005
Private Equity Firm Services
N.A.I.C.S.: 523999
Alex R. Soltani *(Founder, Chm & CEO)*
Jeffrey H. White *(Sr VP-Bus Dev)*
Christopher Aye *(Head-Mergers & Acquisition)*
Rod Stoddard *(Sr VP-Portfolio Ops-Century City)*
Darryl Smith *(Pres-Portfolio Ops-Global)*
Rick Bigelow *(Sr VP-Portfolio Ops)*
Jim Hall *(Gen Counsel & Sr VP)*
Matt Thompson *(Sr VP-Portfolio Ops)*
Shrikar Kasturi *(Sr VP-Mergers & Acquisition)*
Dean Estrada *(Sr VP-Capital Markets)*

Subsidiaries:

Continuum Global Solutions, LLC   (1)
3824 Cedar Springs Rd #801-1678, 75219, Dallas, TX
Tel.: (222) 232-5794
Web Site: http://www.continuumgbl.com
Customer Care Services & Call Centers
N.A.I.C.S.: 561499
Michael L. Flodin *(CEO)*
Wesley OBrien *(COO)*
Dawn Lynch *(Chief HR Officer)*
Scott Kendall *(CFO)*
Jaimie Bean *(CTO)*

Subsidiary (Domestic):

Faneuil, Inc.   (2)
2 Eaton St Ste 1002, Hampton, VA 23669
Tel.: (757) 722-3235
Web Site: https://faneuil.com
Emp.: 5,500
Multi-Channel Contact Center Solutions
N.A.I.C.S.: 561499
Anna McNider Van Buren *(Pres & CEO)*
Tarsha Leherr *(Exec VP-Bus Solutions)*
Alden Eldredge *(Gen Counsel & Exec VP-Admin)*
Arlin Ohmes *(Exec VP-Tech Ops & Solutions Engrg)*
Steve Czirjak *(Co-CFO)*
Nick Mannella *(Chief Revenue Officer)*
Nanette Harrell *(Sr VP-Transportation & Digital Principal)*
Lee Harris *(Principal-Customer Care Ops & Sr VP-Govt & Pub Utilities)*
Michael Bassetti *(Co-CFO)*
Michael Stann *(COO)*

King Teleservices LLC   (2)
140 58th St Ste 7E, Brooklyn, NY 11220
Tel.: (718) 361-4100
Wired Telecommunications Carriers
N.A.I.C.S.: 517111

Digital Lumens, Inc.   (1)
374 Congress St 6th Fl, Boston, MA 02210
Tel.: (617) 723-1200
Web Site: http://www.digitallumens.com
Led Based Lighting System Mfr
N.A.I.C.S.: 334413
Brian Bernstein *(CEO)*

NewNet Communication Technologies, LLC   (1)
700EButterfield Rd Ste350, Lombard, IL 60148
Tel.: (224) 795-5200
Web Site: http://www.newnet.com
Sales Range: $10-24.9 Million
Telecommunications & Information Technologies Integration Software & Support Services
N.A.I.C.S.: 541511
Jim Hall *(Gen Counsel)*
Angie Batterson *(VP)*
T. K. Cheung *(Pres)*
Mike Nikzad *(COO)*
Krishna Viswanadham *(Pres & Chief Strategy Officer)*
Mike Nikzad *(COO)*

SchoolKidz.com, LLC   (1)
900 S Ste 200, Woodridge, IL 60517
Tel.: (630) 739-5000
Web Site: http://www.schoolkidz.com
School Supplies & Services
N.A.I.C.S.: 459410

SKYVIEW OWNERS CORPORATION
5701 Arlington Ave, Bronx, NY 10471
Tel.: (718) 549-7036   NY
Web Site: http://www.skyviewonthehudson.com
Year Founded: 1986
Sales Range: $10-24.9 Million
Emp.: 52
Apartment Building Operator
N.A.I.C.S.: 531110
Brian McCarthy *(Pres)*

SKYWALKER COMMUNICATION INC.
1700 W Terra Ln, O'Fallon, MO 63366-7534
Tel.: (636) 272-8025
Web Site: http://www.skywalker.com
Year Founded: 1980
Sales Range: $10-24.9 Million
Emp.: 25
Sales of Satellite Products, Consumer Electronics, Computers & Parts
N.A.I.C.S.: 423690
Diana Humburd *(Acct Mgr)*
Dick Prescott *(Branch Mgr)*
Jamie Trentacoste *(Branch Mgr)*

SKYWARD INC.
5233 Coye Dr, Stevens Point, WI 54481
Tel.: (715) 341-9406
Web Site: http://www.skyward.com
Rev.: $10,259,348
Emp.: 392
Computer Software Development
N.A.I.C.S.: 541511
James R. King *(Chm)*
Scott Glinski *(Pres)*
Cliff King *(CEO)*

SKYWAY CAPITAL PARTNERS, LLC
100 N Tampa St Ste 3550, Tampa, FL 33602
Tel.: (813) 318-9600
Web Site: http://www.skywaycapital.com
Emp.: 7
Privater Equity Firm
N.A.I.C.S.: 523999
Scott N. Feuer *(Co-Founder)*
Bryan L. Crino *(Co-Founder & Pres)*
Joseph Passero *(VP)*
Kyle Schroeder *(VP)*

Subsidiaries:

Skyway Advisors, LLC   (1)
100 N Tampa St Ste 3550, Tampa, FL 33602
Tel.: (813) 318-9600
Web Site: http://www.skywaycapital.com
Investment Advisory & Banking Services
N.A.I.C.S.: 523940

Scott N. Feuer *(CEO)*
Bryan L. Crino *(Pres)*

SKYWAY TECHNOLOGY GROUP, INC.
5014 Tampa W Blvd, Tampa, FL 33634
Tel.: (813) 249-0101   FL
Web Site: http://www.stg.biz
Year Founded: 1995
Sales Range: $1-9.9 Million
Emp.: 30
Office Equipment Distr
N.A.I.C.S.: 423420
Byron J. Norrie Jr. *(Pres & CEO)*

SKYWORKS LLC
100 Thielman Dr, Buffalo, NY 14206
Web Site: http://www.skyworksllc.com
Commercial & Industrial Machinery & Equipment Rental & Leasing
N.A.I.C.S.: 532490
Jim Dennison *(Mgr-Credit)*

Subsidiaries:

Gold Coast Hi-Lift, Inc.   (1)
2910 Stirling Rd, Hollywood, FL 33020
Tel.: (954) 920-5438
Web Site: http://www.goldcoasthilift.com
Sales Range: $1-9.9 Million
Emp.: 15
Heavy Construction Equipment Rental Services
N.A.I.C.S.: 532412

SKYWORKS TECHNOLOGIES, INC.
177 Gatzmer Ave, Jamesburg, NJ 08831-1356
Tel.: (201) 457-1000   NJ
Web Site: http://www.skyworks.com
Year Founded: 1995
Rev.: $7,600,000
Emp.: 38
Fiscal Year-end: 12/31/06
Computers, Peripherals & Software Developer
N.A.I.C.S.: 541810

SLACK & CO. CONTRACTING, INC.
10622 S Main St, Houston, TX 77025
Tel.: (713) 838-7300
Web Site: http://www.slackandco.com
Year Founded: 1992
Sales Range: $10-24.9 Million
Emp.: 150
Construction Engineering Services
N.A.I.C.S.: 237310
Jim Slack *(Owner)*
John Benton *(Mgr-Ops)*
Adam Ryan *(Dir-Project Mgmt)*

SLACK & COMPANY, LLC
233 N Michigan Ave Ste 3050, Chicago, IL 60601
Tel.: (312) 970-5800
Web Site: http://www.slackandcompany.com
Year Founded: 1988
Integrated Marketing Communications
N.A.I.C.S.: 561499
Gary Slack *(CEO)*
Ron Klingensmith *(Exec VP, Chief Creative Officer & Partner)*
Kelley Fead *(Exec VP & Partner)*
Gayle Novak *(Exec VP, Dir-Client Svcs & Partner)*
K. Rich Dettmer *(Exec VP, Dir-Digital Strategy & Partner)*
Terry McDermott *(VP & Dir-Media)*
Matt Finizio *(VP & Dir-Creative)*
Mike Ritt *(VP & Dir-Associate Creative)*
Monika Jentsch *(Mgr-Employee Experience)*

COMPANIES

SLACK AND COMPANY, LLC
233 N Michigan Ave Ste 3050, Chicago, IL 60601
Tel.: (312) 970-5800
Web Site:
http://www.slackandcompany.com
Year Founded: 1987
Sales Range: $1-9.9 Million
Emp.: 52
Marketing/Communications
N.A.I.C.S.: 541613
Gary L. Slack *(Chm & Chief Experience Officer)*
Ron Klingensmith *(Chief Creative Officer, Partner & Exec VP)*
K. Rich Dettmer *(Partner, Exec VP & Dir-Digital Strategy)*
Terrance McDermott *(VP & Dir-Media)*
Gayle Novak *(Partner, Exec VP & Dir-Acct & Client Svcs)*
Matt Finizio *(VP & Creative Dir)*
Mike Ritt *(VP & Creative Dir)*
Kelly Fead *(Partner & Exec VP)*

SLACK CHEMICAL CO. INC.
465 S Clinton St, Carthage, NY 13619
Tel.: (315) 493-0430
Web Site: http://www.slackchem.com
Rev.: $15,007,128
Emp.: 63
Chemicals & Allied Products
N.A.I.C.S.: 424690
Robert R. Sturtz *(Pres)*
Derrik Davis *(Gen Mgr)*
Jeff Patrie *(Mgr-Sls)*
Tom Williams *(Dir-Transportation & Security)*

SLADE GORTON & CO. INC.
225 Southampton St, Boston, MA 02118
Tel.: (617) 442-5800
Web Site:
http://www.sladegorton.com
Rev.: $26,000,000
Emp.: 125
Fresh Fish Sales
N.A.I.C.S.: 424460
Kimberly Gorton *(Pres & CEO)*
Michael C. Gorton Sr. *(Chm)*
Mike Gorton Jr. *(VP-Sls-Foodservice)*

SLAKEY BROTHERS INC.
2215 Kausen Dr Ste 2, Elk Grove, CA 95758-7115
Tel.: (916) 330-6100   CA
Web Site: http://www.slakey.com
Year Founded: 1939
Sales Range: $200-249.9 Million
Emp.: 110
Heating & Air Conditioning Equipment Whslr
N.A.I.C.S.: 423730
Richard Batt *(Branch Mgr)*

Subsidiaries:

Plumbing n' Things, Inc.   (1)
1620 Industrial Way, Redwood City, CA 94063
Tel.: (650) 363-7333
Web Site: http://www.plumbingnthings.com
Rev.: $11,769,796
Emp.: 10
Plumbing & Hydronic Heating Supplies
N.A.I.C.S.: 238220

The Plumbery Inc.   (1)
4467 Granite Dr, Rocklin, CA 95677-2144   (100%)
Tel.: (916) 315-8700
Web Site: http://www.plumbery.com
Sales Range: $10-24.9 Million
Emp.: 6
Provider of Plumbing Equipment & Supplies
N.A.I.C.S.: 423720
Frank Nisonger *(Pres)*

SLANE HOSIERY MILLS, INC.
313 S Centennial St, High Point, NC 27260-6753
Tel.: (336) 883-4136   NC
Web Site:
http://www.slanehosiery.com
Year Founded: 1928
Sales Range: $100-124.9 Million
Emp.: 250
Mfr of Hosiery
N.A.I.C.S.: 315120
Gloria Overby *(Controller)*
Rose Faircloth *(Mgr-Production)*
Cobb Bush *(Pres & COO)*

SLANT/FIN CORPORATION
100 Forest Dr, Greenvale, NY 11548
Tel.: (516) 484-2610   NY
Web Site: http://www.slantfin.com
Year Founded: 1949
Sales Range: $150-199.9 Million
Emp.: 600
Climate Control Equipment & Device & Optical Instrument Mfr
N.A.I.C.S.: 333414
Melvin Dubin *(Founder)*
Adam Dubin *(Chm)*

Subsidiaries:

Slant/Fin, Ltd/Ltee.   (1)
400 Ambassador Dr, Mississauga, L5T 2J3, ON, Canada
Tel.: (905) 677-8400
Web Site: http://www.slantfin.ca
Heating Equipment Mfr
N.A.I.C.S.: 333414

SLASH PINE ELECTRIC MEMBERSHIP CORPORATION
794 W Dame Ave, Homerville, GA 31634
Tel.: (912) 487-5201   GA
Web Site:
http://www.slashpineemc.com
Year Founded: 1940
Sales Range: $10-24.9 Million
Emp.: 9
Electric Power Distr
N.A.I.C.S.: 221122
J. Timothy Register *(Gen Mgr)*
Mary Bennett *(Coord-Youth Tour)*

SLATE CAPITAL GROUP LLC
The Latrobe Bldg 2 East Read St 3rd Fl, Baltimore, MD 21202
Tel.: (410) 560-3572
Web Site: https://www.slatecap.com
Year Founded: 2004
Privater Equity Firm
N.A.I.C.S.: 523999
Erik Ginsberg *(Co-Founder & Partner)*
Rick Corcoran *(Co-Founder & Partner)*

Subsidiaries:

Cumberland Diversified Metals, Inc.   (1)
4925 Pointe Pkwy, Cleveland, OH 44128
Tel.: (216) 595-9222
Web Site:
http://www.cumberlandmetals.com
Sales Range: $1-9.9 Million
Emp.: 12
Metal Service Centers & Other Metal Merchant Whslr
N.A.I.C.S.: 423510
Steven Goodman *(Pres)*

First Source, LLC   (1)
3612 La Grange Pkwy, Toano, VA 23168
Tel.: (757) 566-5360
Web Site: http://www.first-source.com
Specialty Food, Mixed Treats & Confectionery Distr
N.A.I.C.S.: 445292
Rod Hogan *(CFO)*
Christy Benoit *(Mgr-Sls-Inside & Customer Svc)*
Nanette Ross *(Mgr-Pur)*
Loretta Manning *(Mgr-Credit)*
Tammy Varble *(Mgr-Ops)*
Judy Mecham *(Dir-Mktg)*
Kelley Parkes *(Dir-IT-VA & TN Ops)*
Paul Fryling *(Mgr-Pricing)*
Dave Guldner *(Dir-Mktg)*
Rachel Morgan *(Supvr-Customer Svc)*

Subsidiary (Domestic):

First Source, LLC - Tennessee   (2)
675 Maddox Simpson Pkwy, Lebanon, TN 37090
Tel.: (615) 443-2066
Web Site: http://www.wythewill.com
Confectionery Mfr
N.A.I.C.S.: 424450
Chuck Farrow *(Mgr-Ops)*
Judy Proffitt *(Office Mgr)*

Subsidiary (Domestic):

Clark Gum Company   (3)
1100 Military Rd, Buffalo, NY 14217-2514
Tel.: (716) 877-0800
Sales Range: $10-24.9 Million
Emp.: 50
Mfr of Gum & Candy
N.A.I.C.S.: 424450
Chris Tzetzo *(VP)*

O'Donnell Metal Deck, LLC   (1)
6724 Binder Ln., Elkridge, MD 21075
Tel.: (844) 838-2969
Web Site: https://odonnellmetaldeck.com
Cmmercial Construction Industry
N.A.I.C.S.: 236220

Subsidiary (Domestic):

Tombari Structural Products, Inc.   (2)
1501 N Howard St, Spokane, WA 99201
Tel.: (509) 327-2780
Sales Range: $1-9.9 Million
Emp.: 13
Construction Material Merchant Whslr
N.A.I.C.S.: 423390

SLATE GROUP
6024 45th St, Lubbock, TX 79407
Tel.: (806) 794-7752
Web Site: http://www.slategroup.com
Year Founded: 1985
Sales Range: $25-49.9 Million
Emp.: 200
Digital, Display Graphics & Offset Printing Solutions, Graphic Design & Mailing Services
N.A.I.C.S.: 323111
Marc Hayes *(Pres & CFO)*
Don Denny *(VP-Sls & Owner)*
Rico Vega *(Dir-Creative Svcs)*
Steve Witt *(Mgr-Production)*

SLATE ROCK SAFETY LLC
755 W Smith Rd Unit C, Medina, OH 44256
Web Site:
http://www.slaterocksafety.com
Year Founded: 2007
Sales Range: $1-9.9 Million
Emp.: 11
Flame Resistant Clothing
N.A.I.C.S.: 458110
Heidi Sweeney *(Partner)*
Kim Wilson *(Partner)*
Chad Wilson *(Partner)*

SLATER CONTROLS, INC.
2511 S Country Rd 1257, Midland, TX 79706
Tel.: (432) 563-2002
Web Site:
http://www.slatercontrols.com
Sales Range: $10-24.9 Million
Emp.: 25
Electric & Pnuematic Industrial Control Distr
N.A.I.C.S.: 423830
Brian Carter *(Mgr-Sls)*

SLATER DYE WORKS INC.

SLAY INDUSTRIES INC.

700 School St, Pawtucket, RI 02860
Tel.: (401) 725-1730
Sales Range: $10-24.9 Million
Emp.: 175
Bleaching Cotton Broadwoven Fabrics
N.A.I.C.S.: 313310

SLAUGHTER GROUP
2336b 20th Ave S, Birmingham, AL 35223-1006
Tel.: (205) 871-9020   AL
Year Founded: 1980
Rev.: $30,000,000
Emp.: 25
Brand Development, Graphic Design
N.A.I.C.S.: 541810
Terry D. Slaughter *(Owner)*
John D. Carpenter *(Exec VP-Brand Dev)*
David Webb *(Designer)*
Ruby Traylor *(Controller)*
Natalie Asman *(Acct Dir)*

SLAVONIC BENEVOLENT ORDER OF THE STATE OF TEXAS
520 N Main St, Temple, TX 76501
Tel.: (254) 773-1575   TX
Web Site: http://www.spjst.org
Year Founded: 1897
Sales Range: Less than $1 Million
Emp.: 21
Fire Insurance Services
N.A.I.C.S.: 524113
Brian Vanicek *(Pres)*
Leonard Mikeska *(Treas & Sec)*
Clifton Coufal *(VP)*
Melanie Zavodny *(Dir-Comm)*

SLAY INDUSTRIES INC.
1441 Hampton Ave, Saint Louis, MO 63139-9904
Tel.: (314) 647-7529
Web Site: http://www.slay.com
Year Founded: 1920
Sales Range: $50-74.9 Million
Emp.: 800
Freight & Local Trucking
N.A.I.C.S.: 484110

Subsidiaries:

GJ Leasing Company Inc.   (1)
1441 Hampton Ave, Saint Louis, MO 63139
Tel.: (314) 647-7529
Rev.: $2,500,000
Emp.: 26
Loading Vessels
N.A.I.C.S.: 488320

Industrial Marketing Inc.   (1)
1441 Hampton Ave, Saint Louis, MO 63139
Tel.: (314) 647-7529
Rev.: $1,100,000
Emp.: 50
Financial Management For Business
N.A.I.C.S.: 561110

JS Leasing Company Inc.   (1)
1441 Hampton Ave, Saint Louis, MO 63139
Tel.: (314) 647-7529
Rev.: $100,000,000
Emp.: 20
Equipment Rental & Leasing, Nec
N.A.I.C.S.: 532490

SI Warehousing Company Inc.   (1)
16643 Jacintoport Blvd, Houston, TX 77015
Tel.: (281) 452-9000
Rev.: $48,000
Emp.: 40
General Warehousing & Storage
N.A.I.C.S.: 493110
Chuck Jaoude *(VP)*

Slay Transportation Co Inc   (1)
1100 N 1st St, East Saint Louis, IL 62201
Tel.: (618) 874-7529
Web Site: http://www.slay.com
Sales Range: $10-24.9 Million
Emp.: 15
Trucking Except Local

SLAY INDUSTRIES INC.   U.S. PRIVATE

Slay Industries Inc.—(Continued)
N.A.I.C.S.: 484121
Eugene P. Slay (Chm)

SLAY STEEL, INC.
6215 5th St, Meridian, MS 39307
Tel.: (601) 483-3911
Web Site: http://www.slaysteel.com
Year Founded: 1984
Sales Range: $10-24.9 Million
Emp.: 51
Metal Service Centers & Other Metal Whslr
N.A.I.C.S.: 423510
Greg Slay (VP)

SLAYDEN PLUMBING & HEATING, INC.
1998 Richardson Hwy, North Pole, AK 99705
Tel.: (907) 488-3359
Web Site:
  http://www.slaydenplumbing.biz
Year Founded: 1979
Sales Range: $10-24.9 Million
Plumbing Contractor
N.A.I.C.S.: 238220
Dana Shriner (Mgr-Acctg)

SLAYMAKER RESTAURANT GROUP INC.
404 E 4500 S Ste A12, Salt Lake City, UT 84107
Tel.: (801) 261-3700
Year Founded: 1976
Sales Range: $25-49.9 Million
Emp.: 1,700
Restaurant Operators
N.A.I.C.S.: 722511
Scott Slaymaker (CEO)
Eric Slaymaker (Pres-Wingers)

SLEDD CO.
100 E Cove Ext, Wheeling, WV 26003
Tel.: (304) 243-1820
Web Site: http://www.sleddco.com
Rev.: $84,100,000
Emp.: 200
Tobacco & Tobacco Product Merchant Whslr
N.A.I.C.S.: 424940
Jay DeSantis (Dir-Sls)

SLEEP WELL INC.
14300 S Main St, Gardena, CA 90248-1900
Tel.: (310) 608-6838
Web Site: http://www.sitnsleep.com
Rev.: $50,000,000
Emp.: 170
Mattresses
N.A.I.C.S.: 449110
Lawrence Miller (Pres)
Nelson Bercier (Principal)
David Muro (CFO)

SLEEPERS IN SEATTLE
4741 California Ave SW, Seattle, WA 98116
Tel.: (206) 932-8500
Web Site:
  http://www.sleepersinseattle.com
Year Founded: 1991
Sales Range: $1-9.9 Million
Emp.: 11
Sleeper Sofas
N.A.I.C.S.: 449110
David Feldhammer (Dir-Ops)

SLEEPMED INC
200 Corp Pl Ste 5B, Peabody, MA 01960-3840
Tel.: (978) 536-7400
Web Site: http://www.sleepmed.md
Year Founded: 1999
Sales Range: $10-24.9 Million
Emp.: 100
Mfr, Designer & Developer of Ambulatory EEG & Sleep Monitoring Services
N.A.I.C.S.: 621511
Richard K. Bogan (Chief Medical Officer)
Greg Poulos (CIO & CTO)
Sean Heyniger (Pres & CEO)
Jack Fiedor (CFO & COO)

Subsidiaries:

SleepMed Inc. - Sleep Therapy Services Operations Center (1)
60 Chastain Ctr Blvd Ste 66, Kennesaw, GA 30144
Tel.: (770) 592-5544
Web Site: http://www.sleepmedinc.com
Sleep Wellness Programs & Services
N.A.I.C.S.: 621511

SLEEPSAFE BEDS, LLC
3629 Reed Creek Dr, Bassett, VA 24055-5882
Tel.: (276) 627-0088
Web Site:
  http://www.sleepsafebed.com
Year Founded: 2000
Sales Range: $1-9.9 Million
Wood Household Furniture Mfr
N.A.I.C.S.: 337122
Gregg Weinschreider (Co-Founder & Pres)
Casey Collins (Office Mgr)
Dave Janczuk (Mgr-Production)

SLETTEN CONSTRUCTION INC.
1000 25th St N, Great Falls, MT 59401
Tel.: (406) 761-7920
Web Site:
  http://www.slettencompanies.com
Year Founded: 1928
Sales Range: $10-24.9 Million
Emp.: 40
Commercial & Office Building, New Construction
N.A.I.C.S.: 236220
Erik Sletten (Pres & CEO)
Steve Garness (Mgr-Shop)
Dane Carter (VP & Mgr-Building Div-Las Vegas)
Tony Ewalt (Sr VP)
Ron Hagen (Mgr-Idaho)
Dallin Wayment (Gen Counsel, Treas & Sec)
Shawn Warner (Sr VP & Mgr-Wyoming Div)

Subsidiaries:

Sletten Construction Boise (1)
6202 W Gowen Rd, Boise, ID 83709
Tel.: (208) 658-9888
Web Site: http://www.slettencompanies.com
Commercial & Office Building Construction
N.A.I.C.S.: 236220
Ron Hagen (Mgr-Idaho)

Sletten Construction Phoenix (1)
2501 E University, Phoenix, AZ 85034
Tel.: (602) 273-1474
Web Site: http://www.slettencompanies.com
Commercial & Office Building Construction
N.A.I.C.S.: 236220
Sandra Richardson (Mgr-Mktg)

Sletten Construction of Nevada, Inc. (1)
5825 S Polaris Ave, Las Vegas, NV 89118
Tel.: (702) 739-8770
Web Site: http://www.sletteninc.com
Commercial & Office Buildings, Renovation & Repair
N.A.I.C.S.: 236220
Erik Sletten (Pres & CEO)
Dane Carter (VP & Mgr-Building Div)
Tony Ewalt (VP & Mgr-Corrections Div)

Sletten Construction of Wyoming, Inc. (1)
3225 Big Horn Ave, Cody, WY 82414
Tel.: (307) 527-6515
Web Site: http://www.slettencompanies.com
Commercial & Office Building Construction
N.A.I.C.S.: 236220
Shawn Warner (Sr VP & Mgr-Wyoming)

SLI GROUP INC.
10200 Katy Fwy, Houston, TX 77043
Tel.: (713) 465-4650
Web Site: http://www.sligroup.com
Sales Range: $10-24.9 Million
Emp.: 100
Commercial & Office Buildings, Renovation & Repair
N.A.I.C.S.: 236220
Sarah Lucksinger (CEO)
Scott Hollingsworth (Pres)
Chris Adams (VP)
Dorough Rick (Mgr-Construction)
Sue Riebschlager (Dir-Design)
Travis Dorough (Superintendent)

Subsidiaries:

SLI Construction Inc. (1)
10200 Katy Fwy, Houston, TX 77043
Tel.: (713) 465-4650
Web Site: http://www.thesligroup.com
Sales Range: $10-24.9 Million
Emp.: 50
Commercial & Office Building Construction
N.A.I.C.S.: 236220
Sarah Lucksinger (Chm)
Chris Adams (Dir-Mktg)
Scott Hollingsworth (Pres)

SLI Design Inc. (1)
10200 Katy Fwy, Houston, TX 77043
Tel.: (713) 465-4650
Web Site: http://www.thesligroup.com
Sales Range: $10-24.9 Million
Emp.: 54
Architectural Services
N.A.I.C.S.: 541310
Sarah Lucksinger (CEO)
Scott Hollingsworth (Pres)

SLI SYSTEMS, INC.
Metro Plaza 101 Metro Dr Ste 230, San Jose, CA 95110-2738
Tel.: (408) 777-6010
Web Site: http://www.sli-systems.com
Year Founded: 2001
Rev.: $32,035,000
Emp.: 200
Fiscal Year-end: 06/30/18
Software Publisher
N.A.I.C.S.: 513210
Shaun Ryan (Co-Founder)
Wayne Munro (Co-Founder & CTO)
Blair Cassidy (Chief Product Officer)
Rod Garrett (CFO)
Michael Grantham (Co-Founder & CIO)
Greg Cross (Chm)
Steven E. Marder (Co-Founder)
Chris Brennan (CEO & Mng Dir)
Martin Onofrio (Chief Revenue Officer)
Gary Schaumburg (VP-Customer Success)
Chris Brubaker (CMO)
Carter Perez (Chief Revenue Officer)
Cherl Winterberg (CMO)

Subsidiaries:

SLI Systems, Inc. (1)
101 Finsbury Pavement, London, EC2A 1RS, United Kingdom
Tel.: (44) 203 217 0321
Web Site: http://www.sli-systems.co.uk
Emp.: 20
Software Publisher
N.A.I.C.S.: 513210
Carter Perez (Chief Revenue Officer)
Cheri Winterberg (CMO)

SLICK WILLIE'S FAMILY POOL HALL
6222 Richmond Ave Ste 500, Houston, TX 77057
Tel.: (713) 978-7390
Web Site: http://www.slickw.com
Rev.: $13,900,000
Emp.: 8
Recreational Services
N.A.I.C.S.: 713940
Edmond Mah (Pres)

SLIDEMATIC INDUSTRIES INC.
4520 W Addison St, Chicago, IL 60641
Tel.: (773) 545-4213
Web Site:
  http://www.slidematicproducts.com
Sales Range: $10-24.9 Million
Emp.: 91
Manufacture Slides & Metal Stampings & Bolts, Nuts, Rivets & Washers
N.A.I.C.S.: 332722
David L. Magnuson (Chm)

SLIFER SMITH & FRAMPTON
90 Benchmark Rd St 106, Avon, CO 81620
Tel.: (970) 845-2000
Web Site: http://www.slifer.net
Sales Range: $25-49.9 Million
Emp.: 120
Real Estate Brokers & Agents
N.A.I.C.S.: 531210
Jim Flaum (Pres-Real Estate)
Julie Bergsten (VP-Fin & Ops)
Jeff Moore (VP)
Shawna Topor (VP-Mktg)
John Pfeiffer (VP-Sls & Broker Dev-Real Estate-Summit & Eagle)
Eric Burgund (Coord-Mktg)
Harry Frampton (Founder & Partner)
Jason Cole (Dir-Ops)
Rod Slifer (Founder & Partner)
Sara Roberts (Dir-Online Media)
Tori Lord (Coord-Mktg)

SLIM CHICKENS DEVELOPMENT CO.
1088 E Millsap Rd, Fayetteville, AR 72703
Tel.: (479) 935-4444
Web Site:
  http://www.slimchickens.com
Year Founded: 2003
Sales Range: $1-9.9 Million
Emp.: 5,000
Restaurant Operators
N.A.I.C.S.: 721110
Jackie Lobdell (Dir-Franchise Dev)

SLIM-FAST NUTRITIONAL FOOD LLC.
2000 Hwy 51 N, Covington, TN 38019-2009
Tel.: (320) 329-8305
Sales Range: $25-49.9 Million
Emp.: 270
Convenience Foods Mfr
N.A.I.C.S.: 311991
Edward L. Steinberg (Pres)
Martin Sears (Exec VP)

SLINGER MANUFACTURING CO., INC.
760 Hilldale Rd, Slinger, WI 53086
Tel.: (262) 644-5256
Web Site: http://www.slingermfg.com
Year Founded: 1944
Sales Range: $25-49.9 Million
Emp.: 60
Iron Cylinder Liners Mfr
N.A.I.C.S.: 331511
Charles H. Buchert (Exec VP-Sls)
Steven T. Holtan (Pres & Treas)

SLINGSHOT SEO

8900 Keystone Crossing Ste 100, Indianapolis, IN 46240
Tel.: (317) 575-8852
Web Site:
http://www.slingshotseo.com
Sales Range: $1-9.9 Million
Emp.: 54
Search Engine Optimization Services
N.A.I.C.S.: 541511
Aaron Aders *(Co-Founder & Chief Strategy Officer)*
Jay Love *(CEO)*
Paul Davison *(Dir-Client Success)*
Jeff Rothe *(Sr Mgr-Client Success)*
Kim Greuel *(Mgr-Client Success)*
Trisha Barton *(Mgr-Client Success)*
Marty Muse *(Mgr-Client Success)*
Phillip Golobish *(Mgr-Search Media)*
Leah Beatty *(Mgr-Social Media Networkers)*
Austin Cobb *(Mgr-Social Media Networkers)*
Brian O'Neal *(VP-Dev)*
Abbe Yale *(Product Mgr)*
Daren Tomey *(Sr VP-Corp Dev)*

SLINGSHOT, LLC
208 N Market St Ste 500, Dallas, TX 75202
Tel.: (214) 634-4411
Web Site: http://www.slingshotllc.com
Year Founded: 1995
Sales Range: $25-49.9 Million
Emp.: 100
Advetising Agency
N.A.I.C.S.: 541810
Owen Hannay *(Founder, Chm & CEO)*
David Young *(Pres & COO)*
Paul W. Flowers *(Sr VP-Acct Svc)*
Susan Levine *(VP & Exec Dir-Creative)*
Braden Bickle *(Dir-Creative)*
Charlotte H. Carter *(VP-Media & Comm Plng)*
Chris Hawthorn *(Dir-HR)*
Danielle Johnson *(Acct Dir)*
Clay Coleman *(Assoc Dir-Creative)*
Karen Stanton *(CFO)*
Brandi Shiver Vess *(Controller)*
Julia Heath *(Dir-Art)*
Jody Morris *(Dir-Infrastructure)*
Aaron Fickes *(Dir-IT Dev)*
Tony Balmer *(VP & Dir-Acct Mgmt)*
Kristy Ladner *(VP-Digital Presence)*

SLITERS
55 Somers Rd, Somers, MT 59932
Tel.: (406) 857-3306
Web Site: http://www.sliters.com
Sales Range: $25-49.9 Million
Emp.: 54
Lumber & Other Building Materials
N.A.I.C.S.: 423310
Tom Sliter *(Owner)*

SLM FACILITY SOLUTIONS NATIONWIDE
5000 Commerce Dr, Green Lane, PA 18054
Web Site: http://www.slmwaste.com
Year Founded: 1988
Sales Range: $25-49.9 Million
Emp.: 45
Facility Maintenance & Waste Removal
N.A.I.C.S.: 562998
Susan Daywitt *(CEO)*

SLOAN EQUIPMENT SALES CO. INC.
1677 Tuckerstown Rd, Dresher, PA 19025-1320
Tel.: (215) 784-0771
Sales Range: $10-24.9 Million
Emp.: 2

Manufacturers Representatives For Environmental Systems & Water Treatments
N.A.I.C.S.: 423830
Louis Sloan *(Pres)*

SLOAN FINANCIAL GROUP, LLC
1474 Hwy 55 E Ste 500, Clover, SC 29710
Tel.: (803) 222-2892
Web Site:
http://www.sloanfinancial.net
Financial Planning, Tax Preparation & Insurance Products & Services
N.A.I.C.S.: 525990
Angela D. Sloan *(Founder & CEO)*
Carl Sloan *(CFO & COO)*
Katie Spearman *(VP-Fin Svcs)*
Nancy Truesdale *(Dir-Mktg)*

SLOAN FORD
415 W Lincoln Hwy, Exton, PA 19341
Tel.: (610) 363-2870
Web Site: http://www.sloanford.com
Sales Range: $10-24.9 Million
Emp.: 40
Car Whslr
N.A.I.C.S.: 441110
Steve Patterson *(Owner)*

SLOAN MIYASATO INC.
2 Henry Adams St Ste 207, San Francisco, CA 94103
Tel.: (415) 431-1465
Web Site: http://www.sloanm.com
Rev.: $10,206,088
Emp.: 29
Homefurnishings
N.A.I.C.S.: 423220
Tommy Talbot *(Principal)*
Susan Carr *(Principal)*

SLOAN VALVE COMPANY
10500 Seymour Ave, Franklin Park, IL 60131
Tel.: (847) 671-4300   IL
Web Site: http://www.sloanvalve.com
Year Founded: 1906
Sales Range: $125-149.9 Million
Emp.: 750
Plumbing Systems, Hand Dryers, Wall Paneling, Vacuum Breakers & Non-Ferrous Brass Coatings Mfr & Whslr
N.A.I.C.S.: 332919
Kirk Allen *(Pres & CEO)*
Steve Connaughton *(Mgr-Product Line)*
Parthiv Amin *(VP-Mktg)*

Subsidiaries:

Program Water Technologies   (1)
10500 Seymour Ave, Franklin Park, IL 60131-1212   (100%)
Tel.: (847) 671-4300
Sales Range: $25-49.9 Million
Emp.: 200
Electric Prison Control Systems
N.A.I.C.S.: 332919
Steve Connaughton *(Product Mgr)*

Sloan Flushmate   (1)
30075 Research Dr, New Hudson, MI 48165
Tel.: (248) 446-5300
Web Site: http://www.flushmate.com
Sales Range: $10-24.9 Million
Emp.: 95
Export Sales of Valve Products
N.A.I.C.S.: 332919
Paul DeBoo *(Mgr-Sls)*

Sloan Valve Company - Arichell Technologies Division   (1)
55 Border St, Newton, MA 02465
Tel.: (617) 796-9001
Bathroom Accessory Mfr & Distr
N.A.I.C.S.: 423220

Sloan Valve Company, Foundry Div.   (1)
2719 Business Hwy, Augusta, AR 72006
Tel.: (870) 347-2501
Web Site: http://www.sloanvalve.com
Sales Range: $25-49.9 Million
Emp.: 150
Nonferrous Brass Castings
N.A.I.C.S.: 332919
Robert Beard *(Dir-Ops)*
Chuck Allen *(Pres)*

Sloan Valve Water Technologies (Suzhou) Co., Ltd   (1)
China Torch Road Suzhou New District, 215009, Suzhou, Jiangsu, China
Tel.: (86) 512 68 438 068
Web Site: http://www.sloan.com.cn
Sales Range: $10-24.9 Million
Emp.: 70
Plumbing Fixture Mfr
N.A.I.C.S.: 327110

Sloan de Mexico. S. de R.L. de C.V.   (1)
Carretera a Los Pinos Km 1 Ramos Arizpe, Ramos Arizpe, 25900, Coahuila, Mexico
Tel.: (52) 844 488 0669
Web Site: http://www.sloanvalve.com
Emp.: 45
Bathroom Accessory Mfr & Distr
N.A.I.C.S.: 423220
Hector Marroquin *(Dir-Sls)*

SLOANE TOYOTA OF GLENSIDE
503 N Easton Rd, Glenside, PA 19038
Tel.: (215) 885-5400
Web Site:
http://www.sloanetoyota.com
Sales Range: $125-149.9 Million
Emp.: 400
Sales of New & Used Cars
N.A.I.C.S.: 441110
Greg Pilong *(Gen Mgr)*

SLOAT GARDEN CENTER INC.
420 Coloma St, Sausalito, CA 94965
Tel.: (415) 332-0657
Web Site:
http://www.sloatgardens.com
Rev.: $16,205,851
Emp.: 20
Retail Nurseries & Garden Stores
N.A.I.C.S.: 444240
Dave Straus *(Owner)*
Daryl Quijano *(Mgr-Acctg)*
Molly Congdon *(Mgr-Sls)*

SLOMIN'S INC.
125 Lauman Ln, Hicksville, NY 11801-6522
Tel.: (516) 932-7000   NY
Web Site: http://www.slomins.com
Year Founded: 1942
Sales Range: $25-49.9 Million
Emp.: 850
Fuel Oil Dealers; Alarm Systems & Air Conditioning Systems
N.A.I.C.S.: 457210
Ira Salzman *(Chm & Pres)*
Adam Handelman *(VP)*
Edward Lane *(Mgr-Customer Sls)*
Dave McKenney *(CFO)*
Joel Liss *(VP)*
Frank Fiorillo *(Gen Mgr)*
Doron Jaget *(CIO & CTO)*
David Olsen *(Gen Mgr)*
Mike Alfiero *(VP-Ops)*
Robert Napoli *(VP-Bus Dev)*
Ron Sposito *(VP-IT)*

SLONE PONTIAC BUICK GMC TRUCK INC.
406 E Lewis & Clark Blvd, Clarksville, IN 47129
Tel.: (812) 218-5210
Sales Range: $10-24.9 Million
Emp.: 75

Car Whslr
N.A.I.C.S.: 441110
Dan Bates *(Gen Mgr & VP)*
Dick Swope *(Pres & CEO)*

SLOVAK AMERICAN CHARITABLE ASSOCIATION
3615-3521 16th St, Zion, IL 60099
Tel.: (847) 746-2147   IL
Web Site:
http://www.rollinghillscampus.org
Year Founded: 1915
Sales Range: $10-24.9 Million
Emp.: 309
Assisted Living Services
N.A.I.C.S.: 623110
James Stefo Sr. *(CEO & Exec Dir)*

SLOVENE NATIONAL BENEFIT SOCIETY
247 W Allegheny Rd, Imperial, PA 15126
Tel.: (724) 695-1100
Web Site: http://www.snpj.com
Year Founded: 1904
Sales Range: $25-49.9 Million
Emp.: 20
Fraternal Life Insurance Organization
N.A.I.C.S.: 524113
Joseph C. Evanish *(Pres)*
Ruth Wright *(Office Mgr)*
Karen Pintar *(Sec)*

SLOWBOY RACING, INC.
1830 Oakland Ave Unit 125, Indiana, PA 15701
Tel.: (724) 349-8417
Web Site:
http://www.slowboyracing.com
Year Founded: 2002
Sales Range: $1-9.9 Million
Emp.: 20
Aftermarket Motors Mfr & Sales for Racing
N.A.I.C.S.: 811198
Michael Huml *(Founder & CEO)*

SLP PERFORMANCE PARTS, INC.
1501 Industrial Way, Toms River, NJ 08755
Tel.: (732) 240-3696
Web Site: http://www.slponline.com
Rev.: $26,690,919
Emp.: 50
Automobile Assembly, Including Specialty Automobiles
N.A.I.C.S.: 441130
Christopher Cuzzocrea *(Dir-Network Ops)*

SLR CONTRACTING & SERVICE COMPANY, INC.
260 Michigan Ave, Buffalo, NY 14203
Tel.: (716) 896-8148
Web Site:
http://www.slrcontracting.com
Year Founded: 1996
Sales Range: $10-24.9 Million
Emp.: 20
Construction Services
N.A.I.C.S.: 236220
Sundra L. Ryce *(Pres & CEO)*

SLUMBERLAND INC.
3060 Centerville Rd, Saint Paul, MN 55117-1105
Tel.: (651) 482-7500   MN
Web Site:
http://www.slumberland.com
Year Founded: 1967
Sales Range: $100-124.9 Million
Emp.: 1,200
Retail Home Furnishings
N.A.I.C.S.: 449110
Kenneth R. Larson *(Owner & CEO)*

SLURRY PAVERS INC.

Slurry Pavers Inc.—(Continued)

SLURRY PAVERS INC.
1277 Mountain Rd, Glen Allen, VA 23060
Tel.: (804) 264-0707
Web Site: http://www.slurrypavers.com
Sales Range: $25-49.9 Million
Emp.: 125
Highway & Street Paving Contractor
N.A.I.C.S.: 237310
Frederick Dabney (VP)
David Stowell (Mgr-Sls)
Douglas Wiedeman (Mgr-Pavement Plng)
Larry Roberts (Division Mgr)

SLY, INC.
8300 Dow Cir, Strongsville, OH 44136
Tel.: (440) 891-3200
Web Site: http://www.slyinc.com
Year Founded: 1874
Sales Range: $10-24.9 Million
Emp.: 75
Mfr of Dust Collectors, Wet Scrubbers & Bulk Loadout Equipment
N.A.I.C.S.: 333413
Bill Kurz (VP)
Steve Ragan (Pres)
Lisa Rutkai (Mgr-Aftermarket Acct)
Dwayne Sanders (Mgr-Scrubber Product)

SM&A CORPORATION
4695 MacArthur Ct 8th Fl, Newport Beach, CA 92660-1882
Tel.: (949) 975-1550
Web Site: http://www.smawins.com
Year Founded: 1982
Sales Range: $75-99.9 Million
Emp.: 400
Proposal Management & High-End Contract Support Services
N.A.I.C.S.: 541612
Ted Casner (Sr VP-Strategic Accts)
Ajay Patel (Pres & CEO)
Jacque Keats (COO)
Alan Berman (VP-Recruiting)

Subsidiaries:

SM&A (1)
One Fountain Square 11911 Freedom Dr Ste 500, Reston, VA 20190
Tel.: (571) 299-4250
Web Site: http://www.smawins.com
Sales Range: $25-49.9 Million
Emp.: 250
Proposal Consulting Management Services
N.A.I.C.S.: 541611
Elena Yaroshin (Dir-Competitive Assessments)
Basil Soutos (Sr Mgr-EVM Ops-Washington)
Alan Berman (VP-Recruiting)
Ken Bruder (Sr VP-New Product Dev)
Ted Casner (Sr VP-Strategic Accts)
Jacque Keats (Exec VP-Sls & Ops)
Maureen Murphy (VP-HR)
Ajay Patel (Pres & CEO)
Raashi Quattlebaum (Sr VP-Program & Technical Mgmt)

SM&A-West (1)
184001 Karman Ave Ste 500, Irvine, CA 92612
Tel.: (949) 975-1550
Sales Range: $25-49.9 Million
Emp.: 250
Provider of Proposal Consulting Management Services
N.A.I.C.S.: 541611

SMA SOLUTIONS
3946 Glade Valley Dr, Kingwood, TX 77339
Tel.: (281) 446-5000
Web Site: http://www.smasolutions.it
Year Founded: 1980
Sales Range: $10-24.9 Million
Emp.: 73
Software Development Services
N.A.I.C.S.: 541511
Michael W. Taylor (CEO)

SMAIL LINCOLN MERCURY MAZDA
Rte 30 E, Greensburg, PA 15601
Tel.: (724) 837-4210
Web Site: http://www.smailauto.com
Year Founded: 1956
Sales Range: $10-24.9 Million
Emp.: 50
Car Whslr
N.A.I.C.S.: 441110
C. Bud Smail (Pres)

SMALL BUSINESS TRANSPORTATION
57 S Michigan Ave, Valparaiso, IN 46383
Tel.: (219) 947-3000
Web Site: http://www.freight101.com
Sales Range: $10-24.9 Million
Emp.: 25
Long Haul Trucking
N.A.I.C.S.: 484121
Joseph Wilson (Pres)
Felix Diaz (VP)

SMALL DOG ELECTRONICS
1673 Main St, Waitsfield, VT 05673
Tel.: (802) 496-7171
Web Site: http://www.smalldog.com
Year Founded: 1994
Sales Range: $10-24.9 Million
Emp.: 40
Computer Reseller
N.A.I.C.S.: 423430
Don Mayer (CEO)
Hapy Mayer (CFO & COO)
Rob Amon (Mgr-Bus Solutions)
Morgan Aldridge (Dir-IT & Dev)
Raul De Arriz (Mgr-Govt Solutions)
Tyler Bolduc (Mgr-HR)
Joe Lytton (Mgr-Retail)
Patrick McCormack (Mgr-Store-Retail)
Will Frascella (Product Mgr)

SMALL MINE DEVELOPMENT LLC
967 E Park Ctr Blvd Ste 396, Boise, ID 83706
Tel.: (208) 338-8880
Web Site: http://www.undergroundmining.com
Year Founded: 1982
Sales Range: $100-124.9 Million
Emp.: 480
Underground Mine Development Services
N.A.I.C.S.: 213114
Keith Jones (Gen Mgr)

SMALL NEWSPAPER GROUP INC.
8 Dearborn Sq, Kankakee, IL 60901-0632
Tel.: (815) 937-3300
Web Site: http://www.sngnews.com
Year Founded: 1983
Sales Range: $25-49.9 Million
Emp.: 150
Newspaper Services
N.A.I.C.S.: 513110
Len R. Small (Pres)
Joe Lacaeyse (VP-Fin)
Brenda Montgomery (Dir-HR)
Cynthia Liptak (Dir-Fin)

Subsidiaries:

Kankakee Daily Journal Company LLC (1)
8 Dearborn Sq, Kankakee, IL 60901-3909

Tel.: (815) 937-3300
Web Site: http://www.daily-journal.com
Sales Range: $10-24.9 Million
Emp.: 100
Provider of Newspaper Services
N.A.I.C.S.: 513110
Rob Small (Pres & CEO)

Ottawa Publishing Co., LLC (1)
110 W Jefferson St, Ottawa, IL 61350-5010 (100%)
Tel.: (815) 433-2000
Web Site: http://www.mywebtimes.com
Sales Range: $10-24.9 Million
Emp.: 100
Provider of Newspaper Services
N.A.I.C.S.: 513110
Cindy Liptak (Bus Mgr)

Pacific Palisades Post Inc. (1)
881 Alma Real Dr Ste 213, Pacific Palisades, CA 90272-3618
Tel.: (310) 454-1321
Web Site: http://www.palipost.com
Sales Range: $10-24.9 Million
Emp.: 30
Newspaper Services
N.A.I.C.S.: 513110

The Times Inc. (1)
110 W Jefferson St, Ottawa, IL 61350
Tel.: (815) 433-2000
Web Site: http://www.mywebtimes.com
Sales Range: $10-24.9 Million
Emp.: 60
Provider of Newspaper Services
N.A.I.C.S.: 513110
John Newby (Gen Mgr)
Dan Goetz (Publr)

SMALL PARTS, INC.
600 Humphrey St, Logansport, IN 46947-4949
Tel.: (574) 753-6323
Web Site: http://www.smallpartsinc.com
Year Founded: 1958
Sales Range: $150-199.9 Million
Emp.: 500
Custom & Pressed Stampings
N.A.I.C.S.: 332313
Clay T. Barnes (CEO)
Michael H. Winings (Sec & VP-HR)
Tony Firmani (CFO)
C. J. Rozzi (VP-Engrg)

SMALL WORLD TRADING CO, INC.
90 Windward Way, San Rafael, CA 94901
Tel.: (415) 945-1900
Web Site: http://www.eoproducts.com
Year Founded: 1991
Sales Range: $1-9.9 Million
Emp.: 33
Toilet Preparation Mfr
N.A.I.C.S.: 325620
Susan Black (Pres & CEO)

SMALL WORLD VACATIONS, INC.
998 Harrison St, Washington Township, NJ 07676
Tel.: (201) 263-0363
Web Site: http://www.smallworldvacations.com
Year Founded: 1999
Sales Range: $1-9.9 Million
Emp.: 7
Travel & Tour Agency Services
N.A.I.C.S.: 561520
Susan Pisaturo (Owner)
Thomas Pisaturo (VP)

SMALLBIZPROS, INC.
160 Hawthorne Park, Athens, GA 30606
Tel.: (706) 548-1040
Web Site: http://www.a-toast-to-you.com
Year Founded: 1966

Sales Range: $1-9.9 Million
Emp.: 25
Tax Consultation, Financial Reporting, Payroll Services & Consulting Services for Small Businesses
N.A.I.C.S.: 541219
Steve Rafsky (Chm & CEO)
Dan Sautner (Co-Vice Chm)
Roger Harris (Pres & COO)
Brian Austin (Co-Vice Chm & Head-Canadian Ops)
Gary Hendershot (CFO & VP)

SMALLEY & COMPANY INC.
861 S Jason St, Denver, CO 80223-2817
Tel.: (303) 777-3435
Web Site: http://www.smalleyandcompany.com
Year Founded: 1967
Sales Range: $10-24.9 Million
Emp.: 70
Coatings & Waterproofing Whslr
N.A.I.C.S.: 424690
Bruce E. Coy (Pres)
Joseph Coy (VP)

SMALLEY STEEL RING COMPANY
555 Oakwood Rd, Lake Zurich, IL 60047
Tel.: (847) 719-5900
Web Site: http://www.smalley.com
Year Founded: 1918
Sales Range: $10-24.9 Million
Emp.: 110
Industrial Retaining Rings, Snap Rings, Wave Springs & Compression Springs Mfr
N.A.I.C.S.: 332613
Ken Massett (Dir-Mktg)
Mark Greenhill (VP)

SMALLS ELECTRICAL CONSTRUCTION, INC.
Bklyn Navy Yard 63 Flushing Ave Unit 338 Bldg 3 Ste 1107, Brooklyn, NY 11205
Tel.: (718) 254-0009
Web Site: http://www.smallselectrical.com
Year Founded: 1997
Sales Range: $10-24.9 Million
Emp.: 77
Electrical Contracting Services
N.A.I.C.S.: 238210
Jeffrey Smalls (Pres & CEO)
Ingrid Callender (Sec)
Jonathan Acosta (Project Mgr)
Karey Hall (Office Mgr & Mgr-HR)

SMARDAN-HATCHER COMPANY
14009 Halldale Ave, Gardena, CA 90249
Tel.: (310) 532-5260
Web Site: http://www.smardan.com
Year Founded: 1930
Sales Range: $25-49.9 Million
Emp.: 200
Heating Equipment (Hydronic) & Plumbing Equipment Distr
N.A.I.C.S.: 423720
Rick Leoff (VP-Pur & Sls)
Randy Benton (VP-Ops)

SMARR EMC
2100 E Exchange Pl, Tucker, GA 30084
Tel.: (770) 270-7958
Year Founded: 1998
Sales Range: $25-49.9 Million
Eletric Power Generation Services
N.A.I.C.S.: 335311

COMPANIES / SMARTDATA ENTERPRISES INC.

Anne F. Appleby (CFO)
Patricia N. Nash (Sec)
Ronnie Lee (Pres & CEO)

SMART AUTOMATION SYSTEMS
950 S Rochester Rd, Rochester Hills, MI 48307
Tel.: (248) 651-5911
Web Site: http://www.sanyo-machine.com
Rev.: $15,000,000
Emp.: 20
Spot Welding Apparatus, Electric
N.A.I.C.S.: 333992
Masatake Horiba (Pres & CEO)

SMART BEAR SOFTWARE, INC.
450 Artisan Way, Somerville, MA 02145
Tel.: (617) 684-2600
Web Site: http://www.smartbear.com
Software Development Services
N.A.I.C.S.: 541511
Anne Scanlon (Chief People Officer)
Bryce Chicoyne (COO)
Christian Wright (Pres & Chief Product Officer)
Cynthia Gumbert (CMO)
Frank Roe (CEO)
Lou DiFruscio (Chief Revenue Officer)
Ben Watkins (Controller)
Christine Purpura (Sr VP-Info Sys)
Joanna Schloss (VP-Product Mktg)
Greg Nicastro (Exec VP/Gen Mgr-Products & Tech)
Maureen Plowman (Sr VP-Brand)
Christine Whichard (Chief Info Security Officer)
Shital Whitmore (CFO)

SMART CARPET, INC.
1913 Atlantic Ave Ste R4, Manasquan, NJ 08736-1039
Tel.: (732) 899-9840
Web Site: http://www.smartcarpet.com
Year Founded: 1995
Sales Range: $25-49.9 Million
Emp.: 75
Carpet & Flooring Sales through Mobile Van Showrooms
N.A.I.C.S.: 449121
Jim Hickey (Controller)
Ken Lewis (Mgr-Pur)

SMART CHEVROLET CO.
515 W 5th Ave, Pine Bluff, AR 71611
Tel.: (870) 534-8122
Web Site: http://www.smartdrive.com
Sales Range: $50-74.9 Million
Emp.: 55
New & Used Automobiles
N.A.I.C.S.: 441110
Roger L. Smart (Pres)
Rodney Cooper (Mgr-Fin)
Michael Betts (Mgr-Sls)

SMART DESTINATIONS, INC.
85 Merrimac St Ste 200, Boston, MA 02114
Tel.: (617) 671-1001
Web Site: http://www.smartdestinations.com
Year Founded: 2003
Sales Range: $10-24.9 Million
Emp.: 34
Sightseeing Admission Passes Supplier
N.A.I.C.S.: 561599
Matt Higgins (CTO)
Rob Cartwright (CFO)

SMART FINANCIAL CREDIT UNION
6051 North Course Dr, Houston, TX 77072
Tel.: (713) 850-1600   TX
Web Site: http://www.smartcu.org
Rev.: $42,826,819
Assets: $687,422,982
Liabilities: $15,815,578
Net Worth: $671,607,404
Earnings: $4,546,311
Fiscal Year-end: 12/31/18
Credit Union Operator
N.A.I.C.S.: 522130
Tricia Smith (VP-Lending Svcs)
Angela Aguirre (VP-Lending Sls)
Michael O'Neill (Chm)
Tammie Moore (Treas)
Darcy Stephens (Chief People Officer)
Sean Price (Sr VP-Support Ops)
Chris Conway (VP-Svc Solutions)
Michael Davis (VP-Credit)
Cynthia Galindo (VP-Support Ops)
Jeremy Huddleston (VP-IT)
Shana Scott (VP-Relationship Dev)

SMART IMS
103 Morgan Ln Ste 104, Plainsboro, NJ 08536
Tel.: (609) 955-3030
Web Site: http://www.smartims.com
Year Founded: 1999
Sales Range: $10-24.9 Million
Emp.: 210
Infrastructure Management & Support Services
N.A.I.C.S.: 541618
Amar Reddy (CEO)
Nagesh Gouravaram (COO)
Venkat Ramana Gajula (Mgr-Resource)
Imran Ali (Mgr-Resource)

Subsidiaries:

Capricorn Systems, Inc.   (1)
3569 Habersham Bldg K, Tucker, GA 30084-4009
Tel.: (678) 514-1080
Web Site: http://www.capricornsys.com
Sales Range: $10-24.9 Million
Emp.: 120
Computer Integrated Systems Design
N.A.I.C.S.: 541511
Ed Guillory (VP-Govt Solutions)

SMART LEASING INC.
502 Gordon Dr, Exton, PA 19341
Tel.: (610) 594-0900
Web Site: http://www.smartbusinesscredit.com
Sales Range: $10-24.9 Million
Emp.: 5
Loan Broker
N.A.I.C.S.: 522310
Jim Guarino (Pres & CEO)

SMART PARTS INC.
100 Station St, Loyalhanna, PA 15661
Tel.: (724) 520-8690
Web Site: http://www.smartparts.com
Year Founded: 1989
Paintball Guns
N.A.I.C.S.: 423910
James Bonelli (Mgr-Ops)

SMART ROOFS SOLAR, INC.
618 Main St, Monroe, CT 06468
Web Site: http://www.smartroofsct.com
Year Founded: 2013
Sales Range: $1-9.9 Million
Emp.: 14
Solar Energy Equipment Distr
N.A.I.C.S.: 423690
Joe Chenoweth (CEO)

SMART SOURCE OF GEORGIA, LLC
7270 McGinnis Ferry Rd, Suwanee, GA 30024
Tel.: (770) 449-6300   DE
Web Site: http://www.smartsourcellc.com
Year Founded: 2003
Business Process Outsourcing & Printing Services
N.A.I.C.S.: 323111
Joe D'Amore (VP-Sls)
Thomas D'Agostino Jr. (CEO)

Subsidiaries:

Financial & Office Systems, Inc.   (1)
2660 Holcomb Bridge Rd, Alpharetta, GA 30022
Tel.: (770) 986-7410
Web Site: http://www.netbankstore.com
Print, Promotional & Cash Management Supplies
N.A.I.C.S.: 423490
Glenn Mueller (Owner)

Grandflow, Inc.   (1)
135 Lindbergh Ave Ste D, Livermore, CA 94551
Tel.: (925) 443-0855
Web Site: http://www.grandflow.com
Sales Range: $1-9.9 Million
Emp.: 14
Document Management & Printing Services
N.A.I.C.S.: 561410
Carl Rusca (Founder)
John Rusca (CFO)
Matt Rusca (Pres)
Tom Allen (COO & CTO)

SMART START, INC.
4850 Plaza Dr, Irving, TX 75063
Tel.: (972) 621-0252   TX
Web Site: http://www.smartstartinc.com
Year Founded: 1993
Sales Range: $10-24.9 Million
Emp.: 80
Mfr of Ignition Interlock Devices
N.A.I.C.S.: 441330
Jim Ballard (Vice Chm)
Daryl Grimes (Dir-Distr Ops)
Justin McCord (Dir-Franchise)
Milton Reveles (Mgr-Supply Chain)
Sandy Hudson (Mgr-Acctg)
Mark Mazan (Dir-Field Ops)
Thomas Allison (Dir-IT)
Abram Garcia (Dir-Ops)
Domingo Rodriguez (Mgr-Distr)
Matt Strausz (CEO)
Brandy Anderson Nannini (VP-Govt Affairs)

SMART TUITION
10 Woodbridge Center Suite 200, Woodbridge, NJ 07095
Tel.: (888) 868-8828
Web Site: http://www.smarttuition.com
Year Founded: 1988
Sales Range: $10-24.9 Million
Emp.: 125
Developer of Cloud-Based Monthly Tuition Services for Private & Parochial Schools
N.A.I.C.S.: 513210
John Cook (COO)
Ted Kalomiris (Exec VP-Sls)
Mark Ullman (Chm)
Matt Knapp (Pres & CEO)
Jordan Schwartz (CTO)
Amy Hammond (Sr VP)
Ben Heroux (Sr VP)
Catherine Blades (Sr VP-Strategic Initiatives)
Joe Fortini (Sr VP-Acct Mgmt)
Matt Thomas (Exec VP-Grp Sls)
Nathan Foreman (Sr VP & Dir-Sls-Eastern Region)
Tanya Thorsen-Masingil (Sr VP)

Xavier Sanchez (Sr VP-Ops)
Rebecca Fallon (VP-Client Success)
James Klossek (VP-Acct Mgmt)
Beth Riccardi (VP-Acct Mgmt)
Michael Vanpatten (VP-Fin)

SMART WIRES INC.
3292 Whipple Road, Union City, CA 94587
Tel.: (415) 800-5555
Web Site: http://www.smartwires.com
Year Founded: 2010
Sales Range: $1-9.9 Million
Emp.: 200
Eletric Power Generation Services
N.A.I.C.S.: 221111
Peter Wells (CEO)
Evan Geisert (CFO)
Michael Walsh (Chief Comml officer)
Haroon Inam (CTO)
Shannon Ross (Chief People Officer)

SMARTBASE SOLUTIONS LLC
18322 Minnetonka Blvd Ste A, Wayzata, MN 55391
Tel.: (952) 767-9900
Web Site: http://www.smartbasesolutions.com
All Other Support Services
N.A.I.C.S.: 561990
Kris Lynch (CEO)

SMARTBOX COMPANY
8188 Baymeadows Way W, Jacksonville, FL 32256
Tel.: (904) 739-9100
Web Site: http://www.smartboxcompany.com
Health Snack Vending Machines
N.A.I.C.S.: 445132
Brandon Stallings (CEO)

SMARTBUG OPERATING LLC
2618 San Miguel Dr Ste 216, Newport Beach, CA 92660
Tel.: (949) 236-6448   CA
Web Site: http://www.smartbugmedia.com
Year Founded: 2008
Sales Range: $1-9.9 Million
Media Marketing Services
N.A.I.C.S.: 541840
Mark Kelly (VP)
Ryan Malone (Founder)
Jen Spencer (CEO)

Subsidiaries:

Chair 10 Marketing, Inc.   (1)
4241 21st Ave W Ste 202, Seattle, WA 98199
Tel.: (206) 529-4310
Web Site: http://www.chair10marketing.com
Sales Range: $1-9.9 Million
Emp.: 21
Digital Marketing Services
N.A.I.C.S.: 541810
Mark Kelly (Founder, Pres & CEO)

SMARTCEO PUBLISHING
2700 Lighthouse Point E Ste 220A, Baltimore, MD 21224
Tel.: (410) 342-9510
Web Site: http://www.smartceo.com
Year Founded: 2001
Rev.: $2,500,000
Emp.: 33
Media Services
N.A.I.C.S.: 541830

SMARTDATA ENTERPRISES INC.
11740 San Pablo Ave Ste 204 Del Norte Pl, El Cerrito, CA 94530
Tel.: (650) 330-1958
Web Site: http://www.smartdatainc.com
Year Founded: 1996

smartData Enterprises Inc.—(Continued)
Contract Software Development Services
N.A.I.C.S.: 513210
Sanjai Tiwari (Chm)
Ajay Tewari (CEO)

Subsidiaries:

smartData Enterprises (India) Ltd. (1)
E-37 Phase-VIII Industrial Area, Mohali, 160071, Punjab, India
Tel.: (91) 172 4060000
Contract Software Development Services
N.A.I.C.S.: 513210

SMARTDRAW.COM
9909 Mira Mesa Blvd Ste 300, San Diego, CA 92131
Tel.: (858) 225-3300 CA
Web Site: http://www.smartdraw.com
Year Founded: 1994
Sales Range: $10-24.9 Million
Emp.: 40
Prepackaged Software Services
N.A.I.C.S.: 513210
Paul Stannard (Founder & CEO)
J. Anthony Patterson (COO)

SMARTDRIVE SYSTEMS, INC.
9276 Scranton Rd Ste 500, San Diego, CA 92121
Tel.: (858) 225-5550
Web Site: http://www.smartdrive.net
Year Founded: 2004
Sales Range: $25-49.9 Million
Emp.: 400
Fleet Management & Safety Solutions
N.A.I.C.S.: 541512
Dan Lehman (VP-Corp Dev)
Jason Palmer (Pres)
Dave Vucina (Chm)
Mark Freitas (VP-Product Mgmt)
Slaven Sljivar (VP-Hardware & Analytics)
Michael J. Baker (VP-Worldwide Sls)
Andy Deninger (VP-Engrg)
Wendy Wyatt (VP-Client Svcs)
Shawn Swaney (VP-Fin)
Melissa Purcell (VP-Mktg)
Dave Muller (VP-Infrastructure Dev & Delivery)
Aidan Rowsome (VP-EMEA)
Ray Ghanbari (CTO)
Steve Mitgang (CEO)

SMARTEDGE
4 Peuquet Pkwy, Tonawanda, NY 14150
Tel.: (716) 693-7290
Web Site: http://www.bcsco.com
Year Founded: 1988
Rev.: $19,600,000
Emp.: 100
Thermostats
N.A.I.C.S.: 423730
Robert Klein (Gen Mgr)
Scott Drabek (VP & Partner)
Joe Kelly (Project Mgr)
Michelle Gerace (Dir-Ops)

SMARTER MORTGAGES
4725 Lakehurst Ct # 400, Dublin, OH 43016
Tel.: (614) 768-1148
Web Site: http://www.smartermortgages.com
Year Founded: 2005
Sales Range: $10-24.9 Million
Emp.: 65
Financial Mortgage Services
N.A.I.C.S.: 522310
Brian Folwarczny (COO)
David Eckert (Sr Mgr-Mortgage)
Debbie Foley (VP)

SMARTER SECURITY, INC.
110 Wild Basin Rd Ste 200, Austin, TX 78746
Tel.: (512) 328-7277 TX
Web Site: http://www.smartersecurity.com
Year Founded: 2002
Sales Range: $10-24.9 Million
Emp.: 15
Security Systems & Services
N.A.I.C.S.: 561621
Jeffrey Brown (CEO)
Danielle Ebner (Mgr-Sls-Northeast)
David Dolmanet (CFO)
Kirsten Matetich (VP-Mktg)

SMARTHEALTH INC.
3400 E McDowell Rd, Phoenix, AZ 85008
Tel.: (602) 225-9090 AZ
Web Site: http://www.smartpractice.com
Year Founded: 1972
Sales Range: $25-49.9 Million
Emp.: 360
Provider of Health Care Industry Services
N.A.I.C.S.: 423450
Curt Hamann (Co-Owner, Pres, CEO & Dir-Medical)
Beth Hamann (Co-Owner & VP)

Subsidiaries:

SmartPractice.com (1)
3400 E McDowell Rd, Phoenix, AZ 85008-7899
Tel.: (602) 225-0595
Web Site: http://www.smartpractice.com
Sales Range: $50-74.9 Million
Emp.: 350
Distr of Online Medical Supplies
N.A.I.C.S.: 423450
Karen Burk (Mgr-Mktg)
Matthew Faulhaber (Dir-Mktg-Pet Care Products)

SMARTHOUSE INTEGRATION, LLC
1385 5th St, Sarasota, FL 34236
Tel.: (941) 404-4470
Web Site: http://www.smarthouseintegration.com
Year Founded: 1997
Sales Range: $1-9.9 Million
Emp.: 5
Audio & Video Equipment Systems Installation, Design & Sales
N.A.I.C.S.: 238210
Mark van den Broek (Founder & Pres)

SMARTIT STAFFING INC.
1 Indiana Sq Ste 2350, Indianapolis, IN 46204
Tel.: (317) 634-0211
Web Site: http://www.smartitstaffing.com
Year Founded: 2005
Sales Range: $1-9.9 Million
Emp.: 200
IT Staffing
N.A.I.C.S.: 561311
Karen Cooper (Pres)
Regina Lyons (Principal)
Paul Rothwell (COO)

SMARTLING, INC.
1375 Broadway 14th Fl, New York, NY 10018
Tel.: (347) 204-5225
Web Site: http://www.smartling.com
Year Founded: 2009
Emp.: 51
Website Development Services
N.A.I.C.S.: 541511

Jack Welde (Founder)
Matt DeLoca (VP-Channels & Alliances)
Olga Beregovaya (VP-Machine Translation & Artificial Intelligence)
Andrew Saxe (VP-Product)
Chris Masino (Sr VP-Worldwide Sls)
Kevin Cohn (Sr VP-Ops)
Annette Obermeier (VP-Mktg)
Adrian K. Cohn (Dir-Comm)
Gavin Grimes (VP-Language Svcs)
Bryan Murphy (CEO)

Subsidiaries:

VerbalizeIt, Inc. (1)
79 Madison Ave 2nd Fl, New York, NY 10016
Web Site: http://www.verbalizeit.com
Software Publisher
N.A.I.C.S.: 513210
Kunal Sarda (Co-Founder & COO)
Ryan Frankel (Co-Founder & CEO)
Minjeong Lee (Mgr-Ops)

SMARTLITE
4800 N Federal Hwy Ste 200A, Boca Raton, FL 33431
Tel.: (561) 416-0220
Web Site: http://www.smartliteusa.com
Year Founded: 2002
Sales Range: Less than $1 Million
Emp.: 18
N.A.I.C.S.: 541810
Eric Fernon (VP-Mktg & Mall Dev)
Paul Lauro (CEO & VP-Sls)
Mayra Lugo (COO)

SMARTPHONE EXPERTS LLC
3151 E Thomas St, Inverness, FL 34453
Tel.: (352) 400-4400
Web Site: http://www.smartphoneexperts.com
Year Founded: 2002
Sales Range: $10-24.9 Million
Emp.: 23
Smartphone Accessories Online Retailer & Mfr
N.A.I.C.S.: 334210
Marcus Adolfsson (Founder & CEO)
Diana Kingree (Sr VP-Commerce)
Andrew Carton (Pres)
Kevin Michaluk (Chief Media Officer)
James Falconer (Mgr-Community)
Phil Nickinson (Mng Editor)

SMARTPITCH VENTURES, LLC
3057 Nutley St Ste 531, Fairfax, VA 22031
Tel.: (703) 848-5078 VA
Web Site: http://www.smartpitchventures.com
Year Founded: 2019
Venture Capital & Private Equity Firm
N.A.I.C.S.: 523999
Gautam Chandra (Co-Founder & Mng Dir)
Sanjiv Mahan (Co-Founder & Mng Dir)

Subsidiaries:

Impact Power Solutions, LLC (1)
2670 Patton Rd, Roseville, MN 55113
Tel.: (651) 789-5305
Web Site: http://www.ips-solar.com
Rev.: $3,976,000
Emp.: 8
Power System Installation Services
N.A.I.C.S.: 238210
Jamie Borell (Pres)
Ralph Jacobson (Chief Innovation Officer)
Eric Pasi (Chief Dev Officer)

SMARTPRICE SALES & MARKETING INC.
651 Landwehr Rd, Northbrook, IL 60062
Tel.: (847) 637-8390
Web Site: http://www.smartpricesales.com
Year Founded: 2002
Sales Range: $1-9.9 Million
Emp.: 7
Marketing Sales Solutions
N.A.I.C.S.: 561499
Jim Nazarowski (COO & VP)

SMARTREVENUE, INC.
263 Tresser Blvd 9th Fl, Stamford, CT 06901
Tel.: (203) 733-9156
Web Site: http://www.smartrevenue.com
Year Founded: 2000
Rev.: $6,700,000
Emp.: 481
Business Products & Services
N.A.I.C.S.: 541910
Jon Keesey (VP-Field Ops & Ethnographic Resources)
Braxton Haulcy (VP-Bus Dev & New Opportunities)
John Dranow (CEO)
Dard Neuman (Pres-Insights)
Candace Adams (Pres-Global Retail Strategy)
Jennifer Heuss (VP-Ethnographic Insights-Global)
Seema Rizvi (VP-Mktg)

SMARTS TRUCK & TRAILER EQUIPMENT
4730 Washington Blvd, Beaumont, TX 77707
Tel.: (409) 842-5110
Web Site: http://www.smartstruck.com
Sales Range: $10-24.9 Million
Emp.: 45
Truck Parts & Accessories
N.A.I.C.S.: 423120
Donald J. Smart (Pres)

SMARTSAT, INC.
8222 118th Ave Ste 600, Largo, FL 33773
Tel.: (727) 535-6880 FL
Web Site: http://www.smartsat.com
Year Founded: 1994
Sales Range: $1-9.9 Million
Emp.: 10
Satellite Communications & Consulting
N.A.I.C.S.: 517410
Heidi Akers (CFO & VP)
David Akers (Pres & CEO)

SMARTSIGN.COM LLC
300 Cadman Plaza W Ste 1303, Brooklyn, NY 11201
Tel.: (718) 889-3700
Web Site: http://www.smartsign.com
Year Founded: 2006
Sales Range: $10-24.9 Million
Emp.: 75
Signs, Tags, Mats & Labels Mfr & Distr
N.A.I.C.S.: 339950
Blair Brewster (Pres)

SMARTSOFT INTERNATIONAL, INC.
5050 Research Code Ste 100, Suwanee, GA 30024
Tel.: (770) 368-0208 GA
Web Site: http://www.smartsoftus.com
Year Founded: 1997
Sales Range: $10-24.9 Million
Emp.: 650
Consultancy & Customized Enhancements using SAP Technologies
N.A.I.C.S.: 541690

COMPANIES

Shanthi Murugadass *(Co-Founder & Pres)*
Murugadass Krishnan *(Co-Founder, CEO & VP)*

SMARTWARE GROUP
PO Box 188, Center Harbor, NH 03226
Tel.: (603) 574-4520
Web Site:
http://www.bigfootcmms.com
Year Founded: 2002
Sales Range: $1-9.9 Million
Emp.: 20
Preventive Maintenance Software
N.A.I.C.S.: 513210
Dave Peelstrom *(Co-Founder & Partner)*
Paul Lachance *(Co-Founder & Partner)*
Marc Bromberg *(Partner)*

SMB RESTAURANTS LLC
4571 Columbus St, Virginia Beach, VA 23462
Tel.: (757) 490-0650
Sales Range: $10-24.9 Million
Emp.: 8
Fast Food Restaurant Operator
N.A.I.C.S.: 722513
Karen Fry *(Mgr)*

SMBOLOGY, INC.
1916 Baldwin St, Houston, TX 77002
Tel.: (713) 739-7774
Web Site: http://www.smbology.com
Year Founded: 2003
Rev.: $2,400,000
Emp.: 20
Advertising Services
N.A.I.C.S.: 541810
Justin Singer *(Founder & Pres)*
Wayne Washburn *(COO)*
Caylee Rose *(Dir-Mktg)*

SMC COMPANIES
PO Box 250, Upland, CA 91786
Tel.: (909) 982-8933
Sales Range: $10-24.9 Million
Emp.: 50
Holding Company; Industrial Services
N.A.I.C.S.: 551112
Allyn Scheu *(Pres)*

Subsidiaries:

Scheu Steel Supply Company (1)
8830 Vineyard Ave, Rancho Cucamonga, CA 91730
Tel.: (909) 982-1325
Steel
N.A.I.C.S.: 423510
Leland C. Scheu *(Chm)*
Alan Scheu *(CEO)*

SMC ELECTRICAL PRODUCTS INC.
6072 Ohio River Rd, Huntington, WV 25702
Tel.: (304) 736-8933
Web Site:
http://www.smcelectrical.com
Year Founded: 1973
Sales Range: $1-9.9 Million
Emp.: 100
Electric Control Panels Mfr
N.A.I.C.S.: 335313
Greg Sanders *(Pres)*

SMC ENTERTAINMENT INC.
3210 21st St, San Francisco, CA 94110
Tel.: (415) 282-4466
Web Site: http://www.smc-entertainment.com
Recorded Music Operations
N.A.I.C.S.: 512290

Ralph Tashjian *(Co-Chm & Co-CEO)*
Rick Bjorklund *(Co-Chm & Co-CEO)*
Neil Mavis *(CTO)*

SMD, INC.
1 Oilfield, Irvine, CA 92618
Tel.: (949) 470-7700
Web Site: http://www.smdinc.com
Emp.: 30
Cable Assembly & Wire Harness Mfr
N.A.I.C.S.: 335921
Rich Unruh *(Pres)*

SME INDUSTRIES INC.
5801 W Wells Park Rd, West Jordan, UT 84081
Tel.: (801) 280-0711
Web Site: http://www.smesteel.com
Year Founded: 1977
Sales Range: $25-49.9 Million
Emp.: 1,300
Steel Building Components Mfr
N.A.I.C.S.: 332312
Jerry C. Moyes *(Chm)*

Subsidiaries:

CoreBrace, LLC (1)
5789 W Wells Park Rd, West Jordan, UT 84081
Tel.: (801) 280-0701
Web Site: http://www.corebrace.com
Emp.: 20
Industrial Research & Development Services
N.A.I.C.S.: 541715
Dieter Klohn *(Pres)*

Southwest Stair Inc (1)
10211 El Mirage Rd, El Mirage, AZ 85335
Tel.: (623) 536-1640
Structural Steel Mfr & Distr
N.A.I.C.S.: 332312
Jose Angel Mendoza *(Mgr-Shipping)*

Southwest Steel, LLC (1)
280 Sunpac Ave, Henderson, NV 89011
Tel.: (702) 320-4900
Web Site: http://www.sws-steel.com
Sales Range: $25-49.9 Million
Emp.: 80
Building Contracting Services
N.A.I.C.S.: 238120
Phil Helm *(Pres)*
Christian Klink *(Sr VP-Sls & Mktg)*

SMEAD MANUFACTURING COMPANY
600 Smead Blvd, Hastings, MN 55033-2200
Tel.: (651) 437-4111   MN
Web Site: http://www.smead.com
Year Founded: 1906
Sales Range: $550-599.9 Million
Paper Filing Supplies & Records Management Software Mfr & Distr
N.A.I.C.S.: 322299
Dale Olson *(VP-Fin & Admin)*
Casey Avent *(Pres)*

Subsidiaries:

S&W Manufacturing (1)
1901 N Irby St, Florence, SC 29501
Tel.: (843) 662-8324
Web Site: http://www.smead.com
Sales Range: $25-49.9 Million
Emp.: 120
Office Supplies Mfr
N.A.I.C.S.: 322230
Sharon Avent *(CEO)*

Smead Europe BV (1)
Postbus 14, Hoogezand, Netherlands
Tel.: (31) 598329880
Web Site: http://www.smead-europe.com
Sales Range: $25-49.9 Million
Emp.: 230
Document Management & Organizational Products
N.A.I.C.S.: 337214

SMEE BUILDERS INC.

444 N Prospect St Ste A, Porterville, CA 93257-1931
Tel.: (559) 788-0525
Web Site:
http://www.smeebuilders.com
Sales Range: $10-24.9 Million
Emp.: 20
Housing Construction Services
N.A.I.C.S.: 236117
Gary Smee *(Pres)*

SMETZERS TIRE CENTER INC.
352 W Liberty St, Wooster, OH 44691
Tel.: (330) 264-9901   OH
Web Site:
http://www.smetzerstirecenter.michelindealers.com
Year Founded: 1964
Sales Range: $10-24.9 Million
Emp.: 80
Automotive Parts & Services
N.A.I.C.S.: 423130
Dana Brooks *(Controller)*

SMF INC.
1550 Industrial Park Ln, Minonk, IL 61760
Tel.: (309) 432-2586
Web Site: http://www.smf-inc.com
Sales Range: $25-49.9 Million
Emp.: 230
Fabricated Structural Metal
N.A.I.C.S.: 332312
Brian Brown *(Pres)*
Paul Harrison *(CFO)*
Ken Baur *(Mgr-Quality)*
Stacy Zehr *(Mgr-HR & Benefits)*
George Parks *(Engr-Mfg Process)*

SMILE BUSINESS PRODUCTS INC.
4525 Auburn Blvd, Sacramento, CA 95841-4202
Tel.: (916) 485-4748
Year Founded: 1997
Sales Range: $10-24.9 Million
Emp.: 85
Radio & Electronic Product Whslr
N.A.I.C.S.: 441330
Patti Cutler *(Mgr)*
Joe Reeves *(Pres & CEO)*

SMILEBUILDERZ
1685 Crown Ave, Lancaster, PA 17601
Tel.: (717) 481-7645
Web Site:
http://www.smilebuilderz.com
Year Founded: 2006
Sales Range: $1-9.9 Million
Emp.: 150
Oral Health Care & Orthodontia Services
N.A.I.C.S.: 339116
Anthony P. Skiadas *(Founder & CEO)*
Jim Bournelis *(Dir-Urgent Dental Care)*
Christi Binder *(Mgr-Talent)*
Jared Shaw *(Dir-HR)*

SMITH
321 Arch St, Fayetteville, NC 28301
Tel.: (910) 222-5071   NC
Year Founded: 1973
Rev.: $25,000,000
Emp.: 30
Advetising Agency
N.A.I.C.S.: 541810
Gary T. Smith *(Pres & CEO)*
Cynthia Harlan *(Dir-Media)*
Petra Bobbitt *(Sr Dir-Art)*
Lauren Burgoing *(Acct Mgr)*

Subsidiaries:

SMITH (1)

2033 Wood St Ste 210, Sarasota, FL 34237
Tel.: (941) 955-7094
N.A.I.C.S.: 541810
Lauren Bourgoing *(VP-Florida)*
Sarah Mapelli *(Mgr-Pub Rel)*
Kelley Yatco *(Acct Exec)*

SMITH & ASSOCIATES REAL ESTATE
3801 Bay to Bay Blvd, Tampa, FL 33629
Tel.: (813) 839-3800
Web Site:
http://www.smithandassociates.com
Sales Range: $25-49.9 Million
Emp.: 229
Real Estate Broker
N.A.I.C.S.: 531210
Robert P. Glaser *(Pres & CEO)*
Nikki Phillips *(VP-Real Estate)*
Doug Swain *(Dir-Career Dev)*
Tracey Strube *(VP-Real Estate)*

SMITH & CARSON
400 N Rdg Rd Ste 500, Atlanta, GA 30350
Tel.: (770) 350-2550
Web Site:
http://www.smithcarson.com
Sales Range: $10-24.9 Million
Emp.: 45
Insurance Claim Adjustment Services
N.A.I.C.S.: 524291
Shannon Barrett *(COO)*
Larry W. Carson *(Owner, Pres & CEO)*
James B. Johnson *(Exec VP)*
Allison Oliver *(Mgr-Client)*

SMITH & COFFMAN INCORPORATED
Hwy 37 N and Star St, Clarksville, TX 75426
Tel.: (903) 427-2711   TX
Year Founded: 1980
Sales Range: $10-24.9 Million
Emp.: 25
Gasoline Service Stations, Convenience Stores
N.A.I.C.S.: 457120
Wendell Reeder *(Pres)*

SMITH & COMPANY INC.
2400 South Federal Hwy Ste 210, Stuart, FL 34994
Tel.: (772) 223-0037
Web Site: http://www.smithcoinc.net
Sales Range: $50-74.9 Million
Emp.: 15
Land Preparation Construction
N.A.I.C.S.: 236210
Stephen W. Smith *(Pres)*

SMITH & DE SHIELDS INC.
165 NW 20th St, Boca Raton, FL 33431
Tel.: (561) 395-0808
Web Site:
http://www.smithanddeshields.com
Rev.: $19,987,237
Emp.: 55
Metals Service Centers & Offices
N.A.I.C.S.: 423510
Britt Zappia *(Mgr-Credit)*
Carl Allen *(Mgr-Hardware)*
Dan Wright *(Mgr-Sls)*

SMITH & EDWARDS COMPANY
3936 N Hwy 126, Ogden, UT 84404-9604
Tel.: (801) 731-1120
Web Site:
http://www.smithandedwards.com
Year Founded: 1947
Sales Range: $10-24.9 Million
Emp.: 150
Apparel Whslr
N.A.I.C.S.: 424350

Smith & Edwards Company—(Continued)
Kelly Parke *(Acct Mgr)*

SMITH & GRAY
16573 Conneaut Lake Rd, Meadville, PA 16335
Tel.: (814) 724-8245
Web Site: http://www.smithgray.com
Sales Range: $10-24.9 Million
Emp.: 30
Car Whslr
N.A.I.C.S.: 441110
Richard T *(Pres)*

SMITH & JONES
76 Main St, Sturbridge, MA 01566-1260
Tel.: (508) 347-7793
Web Site: http://www.smithnjones.com
Year Founded: 1995
Sales Range: Less than $1 Million
Emp.: 10
Advetising Agency
N.A.I.C.S.: 541810
Jean Giguere *(Founder, Partner & Dir-Accts)*
Christine Tieri *(Founder, Partner & Dir-Creative)*
Derek Beahn *(Acct Mgr)*
Brian Harris *(Mgr-Interactive)*
Anne Renaud-Jones *(Mgr-Fin)*
Jennifer Day *(Acct Coord)*

SMITH & KEENE ELECTRIC SERVICE, INC.
833 Live Oak Dr, Chesapeake, VA 23320
Tel.: (757) 420-1231
Web Site: http://www.smithandkeene.com
Year Founded: 1947
Sales Range: $50-74.9 Million
Emp.: 350
Provider of Heating, Air Conditioning & Plumbing Contracting Services
N.A.I.C.S.: 238210
Steven Wilson *(VP)*
Gary Smith *(VP)*
Bonnie Mohr *(Controller)*

SMITH & PICKLE CONSTRUCTION, INC.
13415 N Santa Fe Ave, Oklahoma City, OK 73114
Tel.: (405) 755-7624
Sales Range: $10-24.9 Million
Emp.: 80
Civil Engineering Services
N.A.I.C.S.: 237310
Sam Smith *(Owner)*

SMITH & SCHAEFER INC.
3035 Reading Rd, Cincinnati, OH 45206
Tel.: (513) 221-8182
Web Site: http://www.smith-schaefer.com
Sales Range: $10-24.9 Million
Emp.: 40
Hospital Equipment & Furniture
N.A.I.C.S.: 423450
Tom Stollenwerk *(Pres)*

SMITH & WHITFIELD OILS INC.
169 W Main, Camden, TN 38320
Tel.: (731) 584-8436
Sales Range: $10-24.9 Million
Emp.: 12
Petroleum Bulk Stations
N.A.I.C.S.: 424710
H. Ray Smith *(Pres & Owner)*
Christi Odom *(Gen Mgr)*

SMITH BROTHERS FARMS, INC.
26401 79th Ave S, Kent, WA 98032-7262
Tel.: (253) 852-1000
Web Site: http://www.smithbrothersfarms.com
Year Founded: 1920
Sales Range: $75-99.9 Million
Emp.: 68
Provider of Milk
N.A.I.C.S.: 311511
Scott Highland *(Pres)*
David Dorn *(CFO & COO)*
Gary Cassano *(Mgr-Route & Distr)*
Ron Garceau *(Mgr-Direct Sls)*
Sean Flaherty *(Mgr-Mktg)*

SMITH BROTHERS INSURANCE, LLC
68 National Dr, Glastonbury, CT 06033
Tel.: (860) 652-3235
Web Site: http://www.smithbrothersusa.com
Year Founded: 1971
Insurance Services
N.A.I.C.S.: 524298
James B. Nelson *(Principal & Dir-Surety)*
Joseph B. Smith *(Pres, CEO & Principal)*
Bill Wittman *(Principal & Dir-Large Comml Lines)*
Chris Komanetsky *(Principal & Dir-Client Experience)*
Dave Soule *(Principal)*
Donald C. Poulin *(Principal & Dir-Employee Benefits)*
Jared Carillo *(Principal & Dir-Foundation Accts PL/SCL)*
Kimberley S. Connolly *(Principal & Exec VP-Fin, Tech & Data Strategy)*
Michael Dunn *(Principal, Gen Counsel & VP)*
Patty Manke *(CFO)*
Carolyn Ahern *(Dir-Quality)*

SMITH BROTHERS OF BERNE INC.
356 Monroe St, Berne, IN 46711
Tel.: (260) 589-2131
Web Site: http://www.smithbrothersfurniture.com
Sales Range: $10-24.9 Million
Emp.: 200
Household Furniture Mfr
N.A.I.C.S.: 337126
Steven Lehman *(Pres)*
Derek Augsburger *(Mgr-Network)*
Eric Schmitz *(Mgr-Quality)*

SMITH CHEVROLET COMPANY INC.
3477 S Piner Dr, Idaho Falls, ID 83402
Tel.: (208) 522-9800
Web Site: http://www.smithgroup.com
Sales Range: $25-49.9 Million
Emp.: 145
Automobiles, New & Used
N.A.I.C.S.: 441110
Jim Bringman *(Gen Mgr)*
Brian McLean *(Mgr-Bus)*
Cannon Smith *(Gen Mgr)*
Cody Saxton *(Mgr-Comml)*
Denys Hansen *(Mgr-Comml)*
Frank Sykes *(Gen Mgr-Sls)*
Geremy Earl *(Mgr-Bus)*
Jared Nickel *(Mgr-Bus)*
Jared Sloan *(Mgr-Floor)*
John Giannini *(Mgr-Svc)*
Sem Cruz *(Mgr-Bus)*
Jesse Lovato *(Mgr-Comml)*
Jake Welker *(Mgr-Sls)*

SMITH COMPANIES OF LEXINGTON
720 W Ctr St, Lexington, NC 27292
Tel.: (336) 243-2772
Web Site: http://www.gaultchevrolet.com
Sales Range: $10-24.9 Million
Emp.: 28
Lumber & Other Building Materials
N.A.I.C.S.: 423310
Jerry F. Smith *(Pres)*
Steve Smith *(Vp)*

SMITH DAIRY PRODUCTS COMPANY INC.
1381 Dairy Ln, Orrville, OH 44667
Tel.: (330) 683-8710
Web Site: http://www.smithdairy.com
Year Founded: 1909
Sales Range: $25-49.9 Million
Emp.: 575
Milk Producer
N.A.I.C.S.: 311511
Brian DeFelice *(VP-Sls)*

Subsidiaries:

Wayne Dairy Products, Inc. (1)
1590 NW 11th St, Richmond, IN 47374-1404
Tel.: (765) 935-7521
Sales Range: $10-24.9 Million
Emp.: 110
Milk Producer
N.A.I.C.S.: 311511

SMITH DRAY LINE & STORAGE CO.
320 Frontage Rd, Greenville, SC 29611
Tel.: (864) 269-3696
Web Site: http://www.smithdray.com
Sales Range: $25-49.9 Million
Emp.: 75
Transport Household Goods
N.A.I.C.S.: 484210
Sam Turrentine *(CEO)*
Scot Singletary *(VP-Sls)*
W. Newton Turrentine Sr. *(Pres)*

SMITH ELECTRIC VEHICLES CORP.
12200 NW Ambassador Dr Ste 326, Kansas City, MO 64163
Tel.: (816) 464-0508
Web Site: http://www.smithelectric.com
Sales Range: $25-49.9 Million
Emp.: 300
Electric Commercial Vehicles Mfr & Whslr
N.A.I.C.S.: 336120
Paul R. Geist *(CFO)*
Robin J. Mackie *(Founder)*
Jacques D. Schira *(VP-Legal & Comml Affairs & Gen Counsel)*

Subsidiaries:

Smith Electric Vehicles Europe Limited (1)
Future Technology Centre Barmston Court Nissan Way, Sunderland, SR5 3NY, Tyne & Wear, United Kingdom (100%)
Tel.: (44) 845 077 9077
Web Site: http://www.smithelectric.com
Emp.: 40
Electric Commercial Vehicles Mfr & Whslr
N.A.I.C.S.: 336120
Geoffrey E. Allison *(Mng Dir)*
David Graham *(Mgr-Production)*

SMITH ELLIOTT KEARNS & COMPANY, LLC
19405 Emerald Sq Ste 1400, Hagerstown, MD 21742
Tel.: (301) 733-5020
Web Site: http://www.sek.com
Year Founded: 1963
Public Accounting Firm
N.A.I.C.S.: 541211
Susan M. Smith *(Mgr)*

Subsidiaries:

Klingler & Associates PC (1)
1156 Walnut Bottom Rd Ste 2, Carlisle, PA 17015-9130
Tel.: (717) 243-2536
Accounting Firm
N.A.I.C.S.: 541211

SMITH FEIKE MINTON, INC.
2333 Rombach Ave, Wilmington, OH 45177
Tel.: (937) 382-2546
Web Site: http://www.sfminsurance.com
Year Founded: 1966
Sales Range: $10-24.9 Million
Emp.: 23
Insurance Brokerage Services
N.A.I.C.S.: 524210
Brian Smith *(Pres)*
Kent Vandervort *(VP)*
John Luttrell *(VP)*
Julie Butcher *(Controller)*

SMITH FIRE SYSTEMS INC.
1106 54th Ave E, Tacoma, WA 98424
Tel.: (253) 926-1880
Web Site: http://www.smithfire.com
Sales Range: $10-24.9 Million
Emp.: 85
Fire Sprinkler System Installation Services
N.A.I.C.S.: 238220
Brandy Smith *(Pres)*

SMITH FLOORING INC
1501 W Hwy 60, Mountain View, MO 65548
Tel.: (417) 934-2291
Web Site: http://www.smithflooring.com
Rev.: $15,000,000
Emp.: 100
Flooring, Hardwood
N.A.I.C.S.: 321918
Van Kent Smith *(Chm)*
John Smith *(Pres)*

SMITH FROZEN FOODS, INC.
101 Depot St, Weston, OR 97886-0068
Tel.: (541) 566-3515
Web Site: http://www.smithfrozenfoods.com
Year Founded: 1919
Sales Range: $400-449.9 Million
Emp.: 1,000
Processing of Frozen Peas, Lima & Green Beans, Corn, Carrots, Mixed Vegetables
N.A.I.C.S.: 311411
Sharon L. Smith *(Owner)*
Gary Crowder *(Pres & CFO)*
Ken Porter *(Dir-Bus Dev)*
Gordon H. Smith *(Chm)*
Mike Downs *(Treas)*

Subsidiaries:

Brittany Farming Co. (1)
1116 N Columbia St, Milton Freewater, OR 97862-7606
Tel.: (541) 938-7695
Sales Range: $10-24.9 Million
Emp.: 100
Crop Harvesting & Farm Management Services
N.A.I.C.S.: 115116
Gary Crowder *(Gen Mgr)*

Garrett Packing Co. (1)
11 NW 4th Ave, Milton Freewater, OR 97862-1901
Tel.: (541) 938-3325
Packaged Frozen Food Mfr
N.A.I.C.S.: 311412

Smith Food Sales, Inc. (1)
302 SW 16th St, Pendleton, OR 97801
Tel.: (541) 276-3711
Web Site: http://www.smithfrozenfoods.com
Sales Range: $25-49.9 Million
Emp.: 300
Packaged Frozen Food Distr
N.A.I.C.S.: 424420
Gary Crowder (Pres)

SMITH GARDENS, INC.
4164 Meridian St Ste 400, Bellingham, WA 98226
Tel.: (360) 733-4671
Web Site:
http://www.smithgardens.com
Sales Range: $10-24.9 Million
Emp.: 550
Nursery & Tree Production Services
N.A.I.C.S.: 111421
Harry Smith (Pres)

SMITH HANLEY ASSOCIATES INC.
107 John St, Southport, CT 06890
Tel.: (203) 319-4300   CT
Web Site:
http://www.smithhanley.com
Year Founded: 1980
Sales Range: $25-49.9 Million
Emp.: 40
Executive Recruitment Placement Services
N.A.I.C.S.: 541612
Tracey Gmoser (Mng Dir-Pharmaceutical)
Jacque Paige (Mng Dir-Mktg)
Linda Burtch (Mng Dir-Mktg)
Thomas A. Hanley Jr. (Pres & CEO)

SMITH HAVEN CORP.
827 Jericho Tpke, Saint James, NY 11780
Tel.: (631) 724-4070
Web Site:
http://www.smithhavenmitsubishi.com
Sales Range: $10-24.9 Million
Emp.: 50
Car Whslr
N.A.I.C.S.: 441110
Dennis Aberle (Mgr)

SMITH IMPLEMENTS INC.
1929 E Main St, Greenfield, IN 46140
Tel.: (317) 462-5585
Web Site:
http://www.smithimplements.com
Rev.: $23,567,721
Emp.: 250
Farm Equipment & Supplies
N.A.I.C.S.: 459999
Wade Whipple (Dir-Sls-AG)
Darren Barker (Dir-Sls-Turf & CWP)
Matt Eldridge (Dir-Aftermarket Sls)
Mike Smith (Mgr-Svc)
Steve Rayburn (Mgr-Svc)
Jeff Browning (Mgr-Parts-Columbus)

SMITH IRONWORKS INC.
5285 Hwy 114, Lyerly, GA 30730
Tel.: (706) 895-3311
Web Site: http://www.smith-ironworks.com
Rev.: $10,576,676
Emp.: 40
Fabricated Structural Metal
N.A.I.C.S.: 332312
Daryl Smith (Owner)

SMITH MANAGEMENT CO., INC.
708 N Ashley Rdg Loop Ste 109, Shreveport, LA 71106
Tel.: (318) 861-1994   LA
Sales Range: $125-149.9 Million
Emp.: 60
Motels Management & Development
N.A.I.C.S.: 531110
Harrison W. Smith (Pres)

SMITH MOORE LLP
300 N Greene St Ste 1400, Greensboro, NC 27401-2171
Tel.: (336) 378-5200   NC
Web Site:
http://www.smithmoorelaw.com
Year Founded: 1986
Sales Range: $25-49.9 Million
Emp.: 400
Law firm
N.A.I.C.S.: 541110
Skip Long (Dir-Fin)
Steve Earp (Partner)
Robert R. Marcus (Partner)
Doug Walker (COO)

SMITH MOTORS, INC.
6405 Indianapolis Blvd, Hammond, IN 46320-2875
Tel.: (219) 845-4000   IN
Web Site:
http://www.smithchevyusa.com
Sales Range: $100-124.9 Million
Emp.: 62
Sales of New & Used Automobiles
N.A.I.C.S.: 441110
J. Timothy Roper (VP)
Samantha Roper (VP)

SMITH OFFICE & COMPUTER SUPPLY
1009 S 21st Ave, Hollywood, FL 33020
Tel.: (954) 922-4811
Web Site:
http://www.smithofficesupply.com
Rev.: $15,000,000
Emp.: 32
Stationery & Office Supplies Merchant Whslr
N.A.I.C.S.: 424120
David Levy (Pres)
Robert Weinstein (Treas)
Bruce Kahn (Mgr-Bids & Contracts)

SMITH OFFICE EQUIPMENT INC.
50 Creasy Ct, Lafayette, IN 47904
Tel.: (765) 447-3171
Web Site: http://www.smithop.com
Rev.: $11,000,000
Emp.: 42
Retailer of Office Furniture
N.A.I.C.S.: 449110
Daniel B. Smith (Pres & CEO)

SMITH OIL CORPORATION
2120 16th St, Rockford, IL 61104
Tel.: (815) 229-8100   IL
Web Site:
http://www.smithoilrockford.com
Rev.: $14,000,000
Emp.: 15
Petroleum Whslr
N.A.I.C.S.: 424710
Roger Breeland (Pres)

SMITH PACKING CO. INC.
PO Box 520, Utica, NY 13503-0520
Tel.: (315) 732-5125
Web Site:
http://www.smithpacking.com
Sales Range: $10-24.9 Million
Emp.: 55
Meat Packaging & Sales
N.A.I.C.S.: 424470
Eric Smith (Pres)

SMITH PETROLEUM INC.
6415 Hwy 49 N, Hattiesburg, MS 39401
Tel.: (601) 264-7596
Sales Range: $10-24.9 Million
Emp.: 6
Oil & Gas Distr
N.A.I.C.S.: 424710
D. Michael Smith (Pres)
Subsidiaries:
Mississippi Oil Inc. (1)
6415 Hwy 49 N, Hattiesburg, MS 39401
Tel.: (601) 264-7596
Sales Range: $10-24.9 Million
Gas Station & Convenience Store Operator
N.A.I.C.S.: 445131

SMITH PHILLIPS BUILDING SUPPLY
603 E 17th St, Winston Salem, NC 27105
Tel.: (336) 722-8167
Web Site: http://www.smithphillips.net
Year Founded: 1880
Sales Range: $10-24.9 Million
Emp.: 50
Lumber & Other Building Materials Mfr
N.A.I.C.S.: 423310
Mickey Boles (Pres & CEO)

SMITH PIPE & SUPPLY INC.
3011 Agoura Rd Ste A, Westlake Village, CA 91361
Tel.: (805) 498-6744
Web Site:
http://www.smithpipesupply.com
Rev.: $14,900,000
Emp.: 20
Irrigation Equipment
N.A.I.C.S.: 423820

SMITH POWER PRODUCTS INC.
PO Box 27527, Salt Lake City, UT 84127-0527
Tel.: (801) 415-5000   DE
Web Site:
http://www.smithpowerproducts.com
Year Founded: 1991
Sales Range: $10-24.9 Million
Emp.: 200
General Automotive Repair Services
N.A.I.C.S.: 336350
Michael Smith (Pres)
Brent Sandberg (CFO & VP)

SMITH PROTECTIVE SERVICES INC.
4440 Beltway Dr, Addison, TX 75001
Tel.: (972) 960-7644
Web Site:
http://www.smithprotective.com
Sales Range: $10-24.9 Million
Emp.: 2,000
Protective & Security Services
N.A.I.C.S.: 561612
Chris Sonderhouse (Reg Mgr)

SMITH PUMP COMPANY INC.
301 M & B Industrial Dr, Waco, TX 76712
Tel.: (254) 776-0377
Web Site: http://www.smithpump.com
Sales Range: $10-24.9 Million
Emp.: 80
Industrial Water Pumps Mfr
N.A.I.C.S.: 423830
L. Granger Smith (Pres)

SMITH READY MIX INC.
251 W Lincoln Way, Valparaiso, IN 46383
Tel.: (219) 462-3191
Web Site:
http://www.smithreadymix.com
Sales Range: $10-24.9 Million
Emp.: 50
Ready Mixed Concrete
N.A.I.C.S.: 327320
Douglas Smith (Pres)
Dave Mestrich (Mgr-Ops)

SMITH ROGERS OIL CO. INC.
3725 E Hwy 76, Mullins, SC 29574
Tel.: (843) 464-9577
Web Site:
http://www.corporate.exxonmobil.com
Rev.: $30,888,112
Emp.: 11
Petroleum Bulk Stations
N.A.I.C.S.: 424710

SMITH SCHAFER AND ASSOCIATES, LTD.
220 S Broadway Ste 102, Rochester, MN 55904
Tel.: (507) 288-3277
Web Site:
http://www.smithschafer.com
Offices of Certified Public Accountants
N.A.I.C.S.: 541211
Steve Staats (COO & CFO)
Subsidiaries:
Blanski Peter Kronlage & Zach, P.A. (1)
7500 Olson Memorial Hwy Ste 200, Golden Valley, MN 55427
Tel.: (763) 546-7635
Web Site: http://www.bpkz.com
Emp.: 28
Accounting Services
N.A.I.C.S.: 541219
Nathan Agre (Mgr)
Brandon Dunigan (Mgr)
Timothy Jewell (Mgr)
Arlis Esnough (Mgr)
Michelle Gates (Dir-Mktg)

SMITH SECKMAN REID INC.
2995 Sidco Dr, Nashville, TN 37204
Tel.: (615) 383-1113
Web Site: http://www.ssr-inc.com
Year Founded: 1968
Sales Range: $75-99.9 Million
Emp.: 500
Engineering & Consulting Services
N.A.I.C.S.: 541330
Clark Denson (Engr-Building Performance)
Eric Sheffer (Principal)
Mike Bernard (Principal)
Rusty Ross (Principal)
Aaron Whitten (Sr Engr-Mechanical)
Charles Alexander (Principal)

SMITH SERVICES, INC.
1306 29th St, Vero Beach, FL 32960
Tel.: (772) 589-7666   FL
Web Site: http://www.smith-hvac.com
Year Founded: 1975
Full-service Heating & Air Conditioning Company
N.A.I.C.S.: 333415
Michael Brown (Dir)
Frances Brown (Pres)
Davide Deblasio (Ops Mgr-Warehouse)
Kristine Deblasio (VP)
Michael Geary (Mgr-Ops & Svc)

SMITH SYSTEM PINION, LLC
600 Jefferson St Ste 1400, Lafayette, LA 70501
Tel.: (337) 769-9608   DE
Web Site:
http://www.pinioncourseware.com
Year Founded: 2018
Compliance, Training & Information Management Software Developer & Publisher
N.A.I.C.S.: 513210

SMITH SYSTEM PINION, LLC

Smith System Pinion, LLC—(Continued)
Robert Supple (Gen Mgr)
Julie Langwell (Ops Mgr)
Paul Williams (Bus Mgr)
Aimee Speyrer (Coord-Production)

SMITH TEMPORARIES, INC.
1200 Summit Ave Ste 518, Fort Worth, TX 76102
Tel.: (817) 332-5882
Web Site: http://www.cornerstonestaff.com
Sales Range: $10-24.9 Million
Emp.: 947
Temporary Staffing Services
N.A.I.C.S.: 561311
Stephen Michael Smith (Pres)

SMITH TRACTOR CO. INC.
3834 Hwy 4, Jay, FL 32565
Tel.: (850) 675-4505
Web Site: http://www.smithtractorco.com
Sales Range: $10-24.9 Million
Emp.: 50
Tractor Sales
N.A.I.C.S.: 423820
Ricky Smith (VP)
Shonna Nowling (Sec)

SMITH TURF & IRRIGATION CO.
4355 Golf Acres Dr, Charlotte, NC 28208
Tel.: (704) 393-8873
Web Site: http://www.smithturf.com
Year Founded: 1925
Sales Range: $50-74.9 Million
Emp.: 300
Turf & Irrigation Equipment
N.A.I.C.S.: 423820
Quay Youngblood (CFO)
Steve Smith (Pres)
Anna-Lindsay Yarbrough (Exec VP)
Wayne B. Smith Jr. (Chm)

SMITH WALKER DESIGN
19625 62nd Ave S Ste C 109, Kent, WA 98032
Tel.: (253) 872-2111
Sales Range: Less than $1 Million
Emp.: 6
N.A.I.C.S.: 541810
Robin Walker (Partner & Dir-Art)
Jeffrey Smith (Pres & Dir-Creative)

SMITH'S GREENHOUSES, INC.
4940 Seymour Hwy, Wichita Falls, TX 76310
Tel.: (940) 692-7100
Web Site: http://www.smithsgardentown.com
Year Founded: 1940
Nursery & Tree Production
N.A.I.C.S.: 111421

Subsidiaries:

Pitts Sand & Gravel, Inc. (1)
6007 Seymour Hwy, Wichita Falls, TX 76310
Tel.: (940) 689-9600
Web Site: http://www.pittsstoneyard.com
Emp.: 22
Brick, Stone & Related Construction Material Merchant Whslr
N.A.I.C.S.: 423820

SMITH, BRYAN & MYERS INC.
311 E Park Ave, Tallahassee, FL 32301
Tel.: (850) 224-5081
Web Site: http://www.smithbryanandmyers.com
Sales Range: $1-9.9 Million
Emp.: 7
Governmental & Political Consulting Services
N.A.I.C.S.: 541618
Matt Bryan (Pres & Co-Partner)
Jeff Hartley (Co-Partner & VP)
David Daniel (VP)
Andrea B. Reilly (Gen Counsel)

SMITH, GAMBRELL & RUSSELL
Promenade 1230 Peachtree St NE Ste 3100, Atlanta, GA 30309
Tel.: (404) 815-3500
Web Site: http://www.sgrlaw.com
Year Founded: 1893
Emp.: 200
Law firm
N.A.I.C.S.: 541110
Robert I. Paller (Partner)
Rodney G. Fulton (Chief HR Officer)
Matthew Warenzak (Partner-Intellectual Property Practice)
Peter Crofton (Partner-Construction Law Practice)
Alan Jacobs (Partner-Corp Practice)
Eric Balber (Partner-Real Estate Practice)
Roger Juan Maldonado (Partner-Litigation Practice)
Michael Manzi (Partner-Real Estate Practice)
Todd Pickard (Partner-Real Estate Practice)
Robin Silberzweig (Partner-Real Estate Practice)
John Van Der Tuin (Partner-Litigation Practice)
Yash Dave (Partner-Litigation Practice)

Subsidiaries:

Smith, Gambrell & Russell, LLP (1)
1230 Peachtree St NE Ste 3100, Atlanta, GA 30309-3592
Tel.: (404) 815-3500
Web Site: http://www.sgrlaw.com
Emp.: 165
Law firm
N.A.I.C.S.: 922130
Christopher P. McDaniel (CIO & Chief Investment Officer)
Lee Watts (Dir-Mktg & Bus Dev)
Eugene Bryant (Partner)
Julie Sebastian (Partner)
Joseph C. Mandarino (Partner)
Bruce McDonald (Partner-Trademark & Intellectual Property Litigation Grp)
Michael P. Regan (Partner)
John F. Weeks IV (Partner)

SMITH, GRAHAM & COMPANY INVESTMENT ADVISORS, LP.
6900 JPMorgan Chase Tower 600 Travis St, Houston, TX 77002
Tel.: (713) 227-1100
Web Site: http://www.smithgraham.com
Year Founded: 1990
Sales Range: $1-9.9 Million
Emp.: 26
Investment Advice Services
N.A.I.C.S.: 523940
Jamie G. House (Vice Chm & COO)
Lynda Leslie (Sr VP & Dir-Client & Consultant Svcs)
Peter A. Heine (Sr Mgr-Portfolio)
Nirmal Singh (Sr VP & Sr Portfolio Mgr)
George Onisiforou (VP & Assoc Portfolio Mgr)
John Scott (VP)
Michael Kravitz (Asst VP)
Gerald B. Smith (Founder & Chm)
William G. Charcalis (Mng Dir & Head-Equity Investments)
Stephen Marciano (Sr VP & Mgr-Portfolio)
Lynda Dibari (Sr VP & Dir-Fixed Income Client & Consultant Svcs)
Mark Dube (Chief Compliance Officer & Sr VP)
Lorenzo Newsome Jr. (Chief Investment Officer)

SMITH, KAPLAN, ALLEN & REYNOLDS, INC.
111 S 108th Ave, Omaha, NE 68154-2699
Tel.: (402) 330-0110
Year Founded: 1949
Rev.: $25,000,000
Emp.: 36
Advertising Agencies, Full Service
N.A.I.C.S.: 541810
H. Wayne Smith (CEO & Partner)
Joleen Smith David (Pres, Partner & Dir-Creative)
La Von Eby (Partner, Exec VP-Corp & Media Svcs)
Mike Duman (Partner & Dir-Creative)
Mike Collins (Partner & Sr VP-Acct Svcs)
Greg Ahrens (Partner & Dir-Creative)
Mel David (Acct Exec)
Todd Sanning (Partner & VP-Acct Svcs)
Mark Carpenter (Partner, Creative Strategist & Sr Copywriter)

SMITH, PHILLIPS & DI PIETRO
1440 N 16th Ave, Yakima, WA 98902
Tel.: (509) 248-1760
Year Founded: 1932
Rev.: $3,600,000
Emp.: 6
Fiscal Year-end: 12/31/03
N.A.I.C.S.: 541810
Robert W. Phillips (Acct Mgr, Agency Partner, & Dir-Creative)
Rhonda Karnitz (Office Mgr-Acctg & Media Buying)
Trina Nixon (Dir-Art & Designer)
Darcie Hanratty (Mgr-Traffic)
Robert Di Pietro Jr. (Partner, Dir-Creative & Acct Mgr)

SMITH-CAIRNS FORD INC.
900 Central Park Ave, Yonkers, NY 10704
Tel.: (914) 377-8100
Web Site: http://www.smithcairns.com
Year Founded: 1972
Sales Range: $75-99.9 Million
Emp.: 90
Sales of New & Used Automobiles
N.A.I.C.S.: 441110
Dwight McGuirk (Owner)
Christine Tintino (Controller)

SMITH-EDWARDS-DUNLAP COMPANY
2867 E Allegheny Ave, Philadelphia, PA 19134-5903
Tel.: (215) 425-8800
Web Site: http://www.sed.com
Sales Range: $10-24.9 Million
Emp.: 120
Provider of Commercial Letterpress Printing, Typesetting, Binding, Direct Mail Services & Publishing
N.A.I.C.S.: 323111
Wayne Collins (VP-Mfg)
Paul Favorite (Mgr-Sls)
Sheryl Bendheim (VP-Ops)
Jonathan Shapiro (Pres)

SMITH-EMERY COMPANY
781 E Washington Blvd, Los Angeles, CA 90021-3043
Tel.: (213) 749-3411
Web Site: http://www.smithemery.com
Year Founded: 1904
Sales Range: $100-124.9 Million
Emp.: 300
Provider of Construction-Related Testing & Inspection
N.A.I.C.S.: 541715
James E. Partridge (Pres)
Azmat Imam (Mgr-QA)

SMITH-GRAY ELECTRIC CO. INC.
1508 Cusseta Rd, Columbus, GA 31901
Tel.: (706) 322-2569
Web Site: http://www.smithgrayelectric.com
Sales Range: $10-24.9 Million
Emp.: 150
General Electrical Contractor
N.A.I.C.S.: 238210
Dorothy Bergquist (Chm)
Paul Gray (Pres)

SMITH/JUNGER/WELLMAN
920 Abbot Kinney Blvd, Venice, CA 90291-3311
Tel.: (310) 392-8625
Year Founded: 1978
Sales Range: Less than $1 Million
Emp.: 6
Advertising Agency
N.A.I.C.S.: 541810
Susan Qualls (Dir-Art)
Doug Smith (Dir-Creative)
Courtney Skelton (Controller)
Stacy Watkins (VP-Acct Svcs)
Andrew Wellman (CEO)

SMITHAHN CO., INC.
836 E North St, Bethlehem, PA 18017
Tel.: (610) 866-4461
Web Site: http://www.smithahn.com
Rev.: $4,000,000
Emp.: 100
All Other Specialty Trade Contractors
N.A.I.C.S.: 238990
James Hahn (Pres)
Craig Smith (Pres & CEO)
Nick Cenci (VP)

SMITHBILT INDUSTRIES INC.
1061 Hwy 92, Auburndale, FL 33823
Tel.: (863) 665-3767
Web Site: http://www.smithbilt.com
Year Founded: 1982
Sales Range: $10-24.9 Million
Prefabricated Metal Building Mfr.
N.A.I.C.S.: 332311
Jeanette K. Smith (Treas & Sec)

SMITHBUCKLIN CORPORATION
330 N Wabash Ave, Chicago, IL 60611
Tel.: (312) 644-6610
Web Site: http://www.smithbucklin.com
Year Founded: 1949
Association Management Services
N.A.I.C.S.: 561499
David Schulte (CMO & Sr VP)
Michael E. Silverman (Chief Legal Officer & Sr VP-Specialized Ops)
Colette Huzinec (Chief HR Officer & Sr VP)
David Schmahl (CEO-Healthcare & Scientific Indus Practice & Exec VP)
Michael L. Payne (Exec VP)
Carol McGury (Exec VP-Event & Education Svcs)
Ellen Brislin (CFO & Exec VP)
Tom Myers (VP-Sls Svcs)
Stephanie Yanecek (Sr VP-Mktg & Comm Svcs & Mng Dir-Information)

COMPANIES

Brian Teague *(VP-Fin Mgmt & Acctg Svcs)*
Scott Johnston *(VP-IT Svcs)*
Leslie Thornton *(Pres & VP-Outsourced Svcs)*
James McNeil *(CEO-Bus & Trade Indus Practice & Exec VP)*
Matt Sanderson *(Pres & CEO)*

Subsidiaries:

Courtesy Associates (1)
2025 M St NW Ste 800, Washington, DC 20036
Tel.: (202) 331-2000
Web Site: http://www.courtesyassociates.com
Conference & Event Planning Services
N.A.I.C.S.: 561920
Leslie Thornton *(Pres)*
Brian Aiken *(CFO)*
Carla Battle *(Dir-Meetings & Events)*
Stacey Chattman *(Dir-Ops)*
Susan Dolibois *(Dir-Govt Programs)*
Alison Frisch *(Dir-Bids & Proposals)*
Lauren Deaton *(Dir-Strategic Acct)*
Donna Johnson *(Dir-Strategic Acct)*

Global Inventures, Inc. (1)
Bishop Ranch 6 2400 Camino Ramon Ste 375, San Ramon, CA 94583
Tel.: (925) 275-6690
Web Site: http://www.inventures.com
Sales Range: $1-9.9 Million
Emp.: 25
Collaborative Business Alliance Management Services
N.A.I.C.S.: 561499
Deepak Kamlani *(Founder & CEO)*
Darrell Garner *(VP-Relationship Mgmt)*
Lory Yeakle *(VP-Ops & Client Svcs)*
Steve Crumb *(VP & Exec Dir)*
John Ehrig *(Exec Dir)*
Stan Moyer *(VP & Exec Dir)*
Kevin Schader *(VP & Exec Dir)*

Information, Inc. (1)
6707 Democracy Blvd, Bethesda, MD 20817
Tel.: (301) 215-4688
Web Site: http://www.infoinc.com
Emp.: 25
Association Newsletter & Supplier Directory Publisher
N.A.I.C.S.: 513199
James McNeil *(Pres & Publr)*

SDI Travel & Incentives (1)
330N Wabash Ave, Chicago, IL 60611
Tel.: (312) 644-6610
Web Site: http://www.sditravel.com
Event Management, Travel & Incentives Services
N.A.I.C.S.: 561599
Scott Dillion *(Pres)*

Tech Image (1)
330 N Wabash Ave, Chicago, IL 60611
Tel.: (312) 673-5444
Web Site: http://www.techimage.com
Emp.: 10
Public Relations Agency
N.A.I.C.S.: 541820
Michael A. Monahan *(Pres)*
Mary Beth Nevulis *(Mgr-Content)*

The France Foundation (1)
10 Vista Dr Ste 100, Old Lyme, CT 06371
Tel.: (860) 434-1650
Web Site: http://www.francefoundation.com
Emp.: 15
Multidisciplinary Accredited Education Services
N.A.I.C.S.: 611710
Stacy Miller *(Pres)*

The Townsend Group, Inc. (1)
2025 M St NW Ste 800, Washington, DC 20036
Tel.: (202) 367-1245
Web Site: http://www.townsend-group.com
Sales Range: $1-9.9 Million
Emp.: 14
Advertising, Sponsorship & Trade Show Sales Services
N.A.I.C.S.: 541890
Holly Townsend *(Pres)*

SMITHCO ENGINEERING INC.

6312 S 39th W Ave, Tulsa, OK 74132-1237
Tel.: (918) 446-4406
Web Site: http://www.smithco-eng.com
Year Founded: 1982
Sales Range: $10-24.9 Million
Emp.: 150
Industrial Products Mfr
N.A.I.C.S.: 333415
Tom Montgomery *(Mgr-Parts & Svcs)*
Gary Mourton *(CFO)*
Dave Block *(Pres)*

SMITHCO, INC.

34 W Ave, Wayne, PA 19087
Tel.: (610) 688-4009
Web Site: http://www.smithco.com
Year Founded: 1967
Rev.: $11,000,000
Emp.: 8
Mfr of Turf Maintenance Machinery
N.A.I.C.S.: 423820
Donald H. Smith *(Pres)*
Ted Smith *(Founder)*
Bill Kenney *(VP)*

SMITHERS-OASIS COMPANY

295 South Water St Ste 201, Kent, OH 44240
Tel.: (330) 945-5100
Web Site: http://www.smithersoasis.com
Sales Range: $50-74.9 Million
Emp.: 17
Floral Foam Products
N.A.I.C.S.: 326150
Robin Kilbride *(Pres & COO)*
James M. Stull *(CFO)*
Larry White *(VP-Tech)*

Subsidiaries:

Floralife Inc. (1)
751 Thunderbolt Dr, Walterboro, SC 29488
Tel.: (843) 538-3839
Web Site: http://www.floralife.com
Sales Range: $10-24.9 Million
Emp.: 30
Water Treating Compounds & Flower Foods
N.A.I.C.S.: 325998
Jim Daly *(VP-Ops)*

Oasis Floralife Central Europe GmbH (1)
Salm-Reifferscheidt-Allee 31, 41540, Dormagen, Germany
Tel.: (49) 21334793590
Floral Product Distr
N.A.I.C.S.: 424930
Reinier van Groeningen *(Acct Mgr)*

Oasis Floralife Colombia Ltda. (1)
Siberia Manzana B lote 4 Parque Industrial La Argelia, Kilometro 2 Via Funza, Cundinamarca, Colombia
Tel.: (57) 1 826 3028
Floral Product Distr
N.A.I.C.S.: 424930

Smithers-Oasis Adria d.o.o. (1)
Gradac 136, Gradac, 8332, Metlika, Slovenia
Tel.: (386) 7 3052262
Floral Product Distr
N.A.I.C.S.: 424930

Smithers-Oasis Australia Pty Ltd (1)
PO Box 183, Quambatook, 3540, VIC, Australia
Tel.: (61) 3 54 57 1460
Floral Product Distr
N.A.I.C.S.: 424930

Smithers-Oasis Belgium N.V. (1)
Europark 1 087, 3530, Houthalen, Belgium
Tel.: (32) 11600860
Floral Product Distr
N.A.I.C.S.: 424930

Smithers-Oasis France Sarl (1)
20 rue de Labaroche, 67100, Strasbourg, France
Tel.: (33) 3 88 39 98 99
Floral Product Distr
N.A.I.C.S.: 424930

Smithers-Oasis Germany GmbH (1)
Robert-Bosch Strasse 2, 67269, Grunstadt, Germany
Tel.: (49) 6 359 8004 0
Web Site: http://www.oasisfloral.de
Emp.: 130
Floral Product Distr
N.A.I.C.S.: 424930
Wolfgang Zipperer *(Gen Mgr)*

Smithers-Oasis Iberica, S.L. (1)
C/Galileo Galilei parcela n 48, 46520, Sagunto, Spain
Tel.: (34) 96 265 0603
Floral Product Distr
N.A.I.C.S.: 424930

Smithers-Oasis India Pvt. Ltd. (1)
Plot No 10 M I D C, Taloja, Navi Mumbai, 410 208, India
Tel.: (91) 22 2741 2471
Web Site: http://www.oasisfloral.com
Emp.: 40
Floral Product Distr
N.A.I.C.S.: 424930
Bipin Nerurkar *(Gen Mgr)*

Smithers-Oasis Japan Co., Ltd. (1)
3rd Floor TN Building 4-39-6 Honcho, Nakano-ku, Tokyo, 164-0012, Japan
Tel.: (81) 3 5385 7300
Floral Product Distr
N.A.I.C.S.: 424930

Smithers-Oasis Korea Co., Ltd. (1)
196-4 Yongjeong-ri Epchang-myun, Seobuk-ku, Cheonan, 331-824, Chungnam, Korea (South)
Tel.: (82) 41 582 8000
Web Site: http://www.smithersoasis.com
Floral Product Distr
N.A.I.C.S.: 424930

Smithers-Oasis Malaysia Sdn Bhd (1)
7 & 8 Jalan Kempas 7 Kawasan Industri Ringan, Sungai Petani, 8000, Kedah, Malaysia
Tel.: (60) 4 431 8198
Web Site: http://www.oasisfloral.com.my
Emp.: 100
Floral Product Distr
N.A.I.C.S.: 424930

Smithers-Oasis North America (1)
919 Marvin St, Kent, OH 44240
Tel.: (330) 673-5831
Floral Product Mfr
N.A.I.C.S.: 339999

Smithers-Oasis U.K. Ltd. (1)
Crowther Road Crowther Industrial Estate, Tyne & Wear, Washington, NE38 0AQ, United Kingdom
Tel.: (44) 1 91 417 5595
Floral Product Distr
N.A.I.C.S.: 424930

Smithers-Oasis de Mexico S.A. de C.V. (1)
Ave Movimiento Obrero 227, Col La Fama, Santa Catarina, 66100, Mexico
Tel.: (52) 81 8336 1245
Web Site: http://www.oasisfloral.mx
Emp.: 100
Floral Product Distr
N.A.I.C.S.: 424930
Francisco Salinas *(Gen Mgr)*

SMITHGIFFORD

106 W Jefferson St, Falls Church, VA 22046
Tel.: (703) 532-5992
Web Site: http://www.smithgifford.com
Year Founded: 2002
Rev.: $20,000,000
Emp.: 10
N.A.I.C.S.: 541810
Matt Smith *(CEO)*
Bruce Gifford *(Dir-Creative)*
Karen Riordan *(Pres)*
Colleen Fauerbach *(Acct Supvr)*
Alexander Biles *(Jr Dir-Art)*
Brad Klein *(Asst Acct Mgr)*
Dawn Hall *(Asst Acct Mgr)*
Anja Ohmert *(Dir-Art)*

SMITHGROUP COMPANIES, INC.

SMITHGROUP COMPANIES, INC.

500 Griswold St Ste 1700, Detroit, MI 48226
Tel.: (313) 983-3600   MI
Web Site: http://www.smithgroup.com
Year Founded: 1853
Emp.: 1,300
Holding Company; Architectural, Engineering, Planning, Construction, Land Development & Management Services
N.A.I.C.S.: 551112
Russell Sykes *(Mng Partner)*
Michael Medici *(Pres & Mng Partner)*
Carl Roehling *(Principal-Strategic Plng)*
Susan Arneson *(VP & Dir-Corp Mktg & Comm)*
Edward Dodge *(Dir-HR)*
Bart F. Stasa *(Gen Counsel)*
Troy Thompson *(Mng Partner)*
Kathleen Hudson-Beitz *(VP & Dir-Bus Dev)*
Kristen Harrison *(Dir-Bus Dev)*
Paul Leef *(VP)*
Steve Schonberger *(Principal)*
Frank Markley *(Principal)*
Wayne Barger *(Dir-Health Practice)*
Christopher Meigel *(Sr Project Mgr)*
Walter Marks II *(Principal-Dallas)*

Subsidiaries:

SmithGroup, Inc. (1)
500 Griswold St Ste 1700, Detroit, MI 48226
Tel.: (313) 983-3600
Web Site: http://www.smithgroupjjr.com
Architectural, Engineering, Planning, Construction, Land Development & Management Services
N.A.I.C.S.: 541310
Russell Sykes *(Mng Partner)*
Michael Medici *(Pres & Mng Partner)*
Carl Roehling *(Principal-Strategic Plng)*
Troy Thompson *(Mng Partner)*
Kathleen Hudson-Beitz *(VP & Dir-Bus Dev)*
Wayne Barger *(VP & Dir-Health Practice-Global)*

Branch (Domestic):

SmithGroup, Inc. - Chicago (2)
35 E Wacker Ste 2200, Chicago, IL 60601
Tel.: (312) 641-0770
Web Site: http://www.smithgroup.com
Emp.: 50
Building Architects
N.A.I.C.S.: 541320
Andy Vazzano *(Sr VP)*
Matt Dumich *(Principal)*
Susanne Buchberger *(Dir-Bus Dev)*

SmithGroup, Inc. - Madison (2)
44 E Mifflin St Ste 500, Madison, WI 53703
Tel.: (608) 251-1177
Web Site: http://www.smithgroupjjr.com
Emp.: 25
Landscape Architecture
N.A.I.C.S.: 541320

SmithGroup, Inc. - Phoenix (2)
455 N 3rd St, Phoenix, AZ 85004-1009
Tel.: (602) 265-2200
Web Site: http://www.smithgroup.com
Emp.: 100
Architect Design And Engineering Services
N.A.I.C.S.: 541310
Mike Medici *(Pres & Mng Partner)*
Anne Bilsbarrow *(Principal & Dir-Plng)*
Adam Denmark *(Principal-Science & Tech Practice Strategist & Dir-Lab Plng)*

SmithGroup, Inc. - San Francisco (2)
301 Battery St 7th Fl, San Francisco, CA 94111
Tel.: (415) 227-0100
Web Site: http://www.smithgroupjjr.com
Emp.: 100
Architectural Services
N.A.I.C.S.: 541310
Bill Diefenbach *(Head-Design-Res Facilities)*

SMITHGROUP COMPANIES, INC.

U.S. PRIVATE

SmithGroup Companies, Inc.—(Continued)
Steven L. Cohen (VP & Dir-Ops)
Bonnie Khang-Keating (Office Dir)
Rosa Sheng (Principal)
Bill Higgins (Principal)

SmithGroup, Inc. - Washington, DC (2)
1700 New York Ave NW Ste 100, Washington, DC 20006-5428
Tel.: (202) 842-2100
Web Site: http://www.smithgroupjjr.com
Architecture, Engineering, Interiors & Project Planning Services
N.A.I.C.S.: 541310
John Harriman (VP-Mechanical Engrg)
Sally Lee (Principal & Dir-Bus Dev)
Robert Bull (Principal & Dir-Ops)
Roxanne Malek (VP)
Chris Purdy (VP & Dir-Higher Education)
Sven Shockey (VP & Dir-Corp Design)
Jason Stangland (Principal & Dir-Waterfront Practice)

SMITHSONIAN MAGAZINE
600 Maryland Ave SW Ste 6001
MRC 513, Washington, DC 20024
Tel.: (202) 633-6090 DC
Web Site:
    http://www.smithsonianmag.com
Year Founded: 1970
Sales Range: $75-99.9 Million
Emp.: 100
Magazine Publisher
N.A.I.C.S.: 513120
Thomas Ott (Pres)
Alan Chu (Gen Mgr)
Lisa Dunham (Dir-Consumer Mktg)
Maria G. Keehan (Dir-Art)
Kathleen M. Burke (Editor)
T. A. Frail (Editor)
Jeanne Maglaty (Editor)
Arik Gabbai (Editor)
Beth Py-Lieberman (Editor-Digital-Museums)
Debra Rosenberg (Dir-Editorial Ops)
Erik K. Washam (Assoc Dir-Art)
Heather Palmateer (Designer)
Jennie Rothenberg Gritz (Editor)
Tiffany Y. Ates (Coord-Art Svcs)

SMITHTOWN NISSAN INC.
535 Middle Country Rd, Saint James, NY 11780
Tel.: (631) 361-9696 NY
Web Site:
    http://www.smithtownnissan.com
Rev.: $38,200,000
Emp.: 79
New & Used Car Dealer
N.A.I.C.S.: 441110
Joseph Oscar Rubio (Owner)
Joanna Pryde (Mgr-Acctg)

SMITHVILLE TELEPHONE COMPANY INCORPORATED
1600 W Temperance St, Ellettsville, IN 47429
Tel.: (812) 876-2211
Web Site: http://www.smithville.net
Sales Range: $50-74.9 Million
Emp.: 300
Local Telephone Communications
N.A.I.C.S.: 517121
Darby McCarty (CEO)
Cullen McCarty (VP)
Dave Brodin (COO)
Wilson Smith (CFO)
Nicole Plunkett (VP-Comml Sls)

SMITTY'S SUPPLY INC.
63399 Hwy 51 PO Box 530, Roseland, LA 70456
Tel.: (985) 748-3007
Web Site: http://www.smittysinc.net
Year Founded: 1969
Sales Range: $25-49.9 Million
Emp.: 140
Distr of Automotive Parts & Supplies
N.A.I.C.S.: 423120
David Smith (Co-Owner)

Subsidiaries:

Smitty's Supply (1)
6720 Sippel St, Shreveport, LA 71106
Tel.: (318) 219-2628
Petroleum, Lubricating Oils & Specialty Products Distr
N.A.I.C.S.: 424720

SMIZER PERRY
68 Pepperbox Rd, Waterford, CT 06385-3512
Tel.: (860) 437-8877
Web Site:
    http://www.smizerperry.com
Sales Range: Less than $1 Million
Emp.: 6
N.A.I.C.S.: 541810
Karl Smizer (Owner & Dir-Creative)
Tina Clare (Dir-Bus Devel)

SMK IMAGING, LLC
8 Westchester Plz Ste 112, Elmsford, NY 10523
Tel.: (914) 592-6100 NY
Web Site:
    https://imageworkscorporation.com
Year Founded: 2013
Medical Imaging Equipment Mfr & Whslr
N.A.I.C.S.: 334510

Subsidiaries:

Health Sciences Corporation (1)
8 Westchester Plz Ste 112, Elmsford, NY 10523
Tel.: (914) 592-6100
Medical Imaging Equipment & Systems Mfr
N.A.I.C.S.: 334510
David Vozick (Chm & CEO)

Subsidiary (Domestic):

Dent-X Corporation (2)
250 Clearbrook Rd, Elmsford, NY 10523-1315 (100%)
Tel.: (914) 592-6665
Web Site: http://www.dent-x.com
N.A.I.C.S.: 334517
Elise Nissen (CFO & Exec VP-Fin)
Cathy Helwig (Mgr-Customer Svc)
Marc Irving (Head-Production)
Jim Johnson (Dir-Engrg)
Scott Joanes (Mgr-Intl Sls)

SMOG 'N GO, LLC
8034 Orchard Loop, Elk Grove, CA 95624
Tel.: (916) 760-4200
Web Site: http://www.smogngo.com
Year Founded: 1988
Sales Range: $1-9.9 Million
Emp.: 20
Auto Smog Inspection Services
N.A.I.C.S.: 811114
Jack Williams (Owner)

SMOKEFREE INNOTEC, INC.
2300 W Sahara Ave Ste E-6, Las Vegas, NV 89102
Electronic Cigarette Mfr & Distr
N.A.I.C.S.: 312230
George Roth (Pres & CEO)

SMOKER CRAFT INC.
68143 Clunette St, New Paris, IN 46553
Tel.: (574) 831-2103 IN
Web Site:
    http://www.smokercraft.com
Year Founded: 1964
Sales Range: $25-49.9 Million
Emp.: 450
Boatbuilding & Repairing
N.A.I.C.S.: 336612

SMOKEWOOD FOODS
PO Box 3966, Fullerton, CA 92834
Tel.: (714) 634-4221
Web Site:
    http://www.smokewoodfoods.com
Year Founded: 1948
Sales Range: $75-99.9 Million
Emp.: 5
Edible Bowl & Shell Mfr
N.A.I.C.S.: 311830
Van K. Reese (VP-Sls)
Dave Schindele (Owner)

SMOKIN' JOES TOBACCO SHOP, INC.
952 Wilkes Barre Township Blvd, Wilkes Barre, PA 18702
Tel.: (570) 704-4223 PA
Web Site: http://www.gotojoes.com
Sales Range: $10-24.9 Million
Emp.: 45
Tobacco & Tobacco Products Sales
N.A.I.C.S.: 459991
Richard Prezelski (Pres)

SMOKY JENNINGS CHEVROLET
152 N Main St, Palmyra, IL 62674-5865
Tel.: (217) 436-2414
Sales Range: $10-24.9 Million
Emp.: 41
Car Whslr
N.A.I.C.S.: 441110
Rick Thoroman (Gen Mgr)

SMOKY MOUNTAIN KNIFE WORKS INC.
2320 Winfield Dunn Pkwy, Sevierville, TN 37876-0557
Tel.: (865) 453-5871 TN
Web Site: http://www.smkw.com
Year Founded: 1974
Sales Range: $25-49.9 Million
Emp.: 200
Catalog & Mail-Order Houses
N.A.I.C.S.: 449129
Kevin G. Pipes (Pres)
Donna Lutjens (VP)
Tammy Sims (Supvr-Etching)
Doug Stone (VP-Retail Ops)
Gail Clevenger (Dir-Art)

SMOKY SYSTEMS, LLC
804 Estates Dr Ste 100, Aptos, CA 95003
Tel.: (831) 685-3031
Holding Company; Meats & Fish Products
N.A.I.C.S.: 551112
Edward C. Feintech (Pres & CEO)

SMOLKER BARTLETT SCHLOSSER LOEB & HINDS, P.A.
100 N Tampa St Ste 2050, Tampa, FL 33602
Tel.: (813) 223-3888
Web Site:
    http://www.smolkerbartlett.com
Sales Range: $1-9.9 Million
Emp.: 70
Law Firm
N.A.I.C.S.: 541110
Jay J. Bartlett (Atty)
David Smolker (Atty)
Jon P. Tasso (Atty)
Shannon Sheppard (Atty)
Ethan J. Loeb (Atty)
Jeffrey L. Hinds (Atty)

SMOTHER'S MOTORS
2881 Corby Ave, Santa Rosa, CA 95407-7878
Tel.: (707) 542-4810
Web Site:
    http://www.smothers europeanvolvo.com
Sales Range: $10-24.9 Million
Emp.: 58
New Car Whslr
N.A.I.C.S.: 441110
Brian Velyvis (Principal)

SMP ASSET MANAGEMENT, LLC
1865 Palmer Ave, Larchmont, NY 10538
Tel.: (914) 833-0875
Web Site: http://www.smplp.com
Year Founded: 1982
Rev.: $49,000,000
Emp.: 6
Individuals & Institutional Investors Services
N.A.I.C.S.: 523940
Lawrence J. Goldstein (Principal)

SMR HOLDINGS, LLC
613 Bond St, Statesville, NC 28677
Tel.: (704) 873-8878
Web Site: http://www.smr-worldwide.com
Year Founded: 2014
Sales Range: $25-49.9 Million
Emp.: 76
Information Technology Services
N.A.I.C.S.: 541512
Shelly Li (CEO)

SMR RESEARCH CORP.
1 Edgeview Dr Ste 3B, Hackettstown, NJ 07840-2160
Tel.: (908) 852-7677
Web Site:
    https://www.smrresearch.com
Year Founded: 1984
Internet Publishing & Broadcasting & Web Search Portals
N.A.I.C.S.: 516210
Stuart Feldstein (Pres)

SMS ASSIST LLC
6 W Hubbard St 8th Fl, Chicago, IL 60654
Tel.: (888) 258-2109
Web Site: http://www.sms-assist.com
Rev.: $56,000,000
Emp.: 70
Janitorial Services
N.A.I.C.S.: 561720
Michael Rothman (Founder & Chm)
Michael L. McMath (VP-Client Svcs)
Matt Renner (Chief Revenue Officer)
Jianqing Zhao (CIO)
Dave Sweitzer (Sr VP-Sls)
Richard Cusack (VP-Compliance)
Andrew Boron (VP-Risk Mgmt)
John Martin (VP-Sls)
James Cusack (VP-Strategic Ops)
Lauren Glandt (VP-Trng)
Taylor Rhodes (CEO)
Alexander Rothman (Chief Product Officer)
Alex Bezdek (VP-Strategy, Pricing & Analytics)
Guy Edasis (VP-Mktg)
Jason Moos (VP-Fin)
Josh Lessack (VP-Ops-Facility Svcs)
Marc Shiffman (Pres & CFO)
Mike Travalini (Pres-Residential)
Richard Wender (VP-Strategic Acct Ops)
Shannon Kenny (VP-Ops)
Shawn Rouse (VP-Ops)
Becky Lowe (Chief HR Officer)
Jodi Navta (Chief Mktg Officer)

SMS DATA PRODUCTS GROUP INCORPORATED
1751 Pinnacle Dr Ste 1200, McLean, VA 22102

COMPANIES

Tel.: (703) 288-8100
Web Site: http://www.sms.com
Sales Range: $10-24.9 Million
Emp.: 230
CD-Rom Towers & Services
N.A.I.C.S.: 423430
Melanie Shipley (Officer-Facility Security & VP-HR)
Juan Hernandez (Pres)
John Ladd (COO)
Luis Laranjeira (Exec VP)
Juan Morales (CFO)
Neil Belden (Gen Counsel)
Thomas Kupiec (Chief Information Security Officer)

SMS HOLDINGS CORPORATION
7135 Charlotte Pike Ste 100, Nashville, TN 37209
Tel.: (615) 399-1839
Web Site:
  http://www.smsholdings.com
Year Founded: 1988
Sales Range: $300-349.9 Million
Emp.: 12,600
Investment Holding Company
N.A.I.C.S.: 551112
Keith Wolken (Chm & CEO)
Hiram Cox (Chief Admin Officer & Exec VP)
Jim Burnett (Chief Dev Officer & Exec VP)

Subsidiaries:

FirstLine Transportation Security, Inc. (1)
7135 Charlotte Pike Ste 100, Nashville, TN 37209
Tel.: (615) 399-1839
Web Site: http://www.firstlinets.com
Security Guard Services
N.A.I.C.S.: 561612

Mydatt Services, Inc. (1)
640 S 4th St Ste 110, Louisville, KY 40202
Tel.: (502) 749-1551
Web Site: http://www.blockbyblock.com
Security Guards & Patrol Services
N.A.I.C.S.: 561612
Jeremy Curran (Pres)

Service Management Systems, Inc. (1)
7135 Charlotte Pike Ste 100, Nashville, TN 37209
Tel.: (615) 399-1839
Web Site: http://www.smsholdings.com
Sales Range: $25-49.9 Million
Emp.: 17,000
Building Cleaning Services
N.A.I.C.S.: 561720
Keith Wolken (Chm, CEO & COO)
Glenn Bowron (VP & Controller)
Michael Wein (Pres)
Matt Houston (Asst Dir)

SMS MEMORY MODULE ASSEMBLY, INC.
2254 Trade Center Way, Naples, FL 34109
Tel.: (239) 596-2254
Web Site:
  http://www.smsassembly.com
Sales Range: $1-9.9 Million
Emp.: 10
Computer Memory Modules Distr
N.A.I.C.S.: 423430
Jeff Bittner (Founder & Pres)

SMSC ENTERPRISES
2400 Mystic Lake Blvd, Prior Lake, MN 55372
Tel.: (952) 445-9000
Web Site: http://www.mysticlake.com
Year Founded: 1981
Sales Range: $350-399.9 Million
Emp.: 4,000
Casino Operator
N.A.I.C.S.: 713290

Steven Son (CEO)

SMUGGLERS' NOTCH INVESTMENT CO.
4323 Vt Route 108 S, Jeffersonville, VT 05464-9537
Tel.: (802) 644-8851   VT
Web Site: http://www.smuggs.com
Year Founded: 1996
Sales Range: $50-74.9 Million
Emp.: 1,000
Real Estate Investment Trust; Family Resort Owner & Operator
N.A.I.C.S.: 525990
William P. Stritzler (Owner & Mng Dir)
Steve L. Clokey (VP-Market Mgmt)
Keith R. Glover (VP-Consumer Experience)
Lisa M. Howe (Pres)

Subsidiaries:

Smugglers' Notch Management Company Ltd. (1)
4323 Vermont Rte 108 S, Smugglers Notch, VT 05464
Tel.: (802) 644-8851
Web Site: http://www.smuggs.com
Resort Management
N.A.I.C.S.: 531390
William P. Stritzler (Owner & Mng Dir)

SMUGMUG, INC.
67 E Evelyn Ave Ste 200, Mountain View, CA 94041
Tel.: (650) 265-0396
Web Site: http://www.smugmug.com
Year Founded: 2002
Digital Photography Services
N.A.I.C.S.: 812921
Don Macaskill (CEO)

Subsidiaries:

Ludicorp Research & Development Ltd. (1)
390 Fremont St, San Francisco, CA 94105
Tel.: (408) 349-3300
Web Site: http://www.flickr.com
Internet Photo-Posting Site
N.A.I.C.S.: 513199
Don MacAskill (CEO)

SMULEKOFF FURNITURE COMPANY INC
97 3rd Ave SE, Cedar Rapids, IA 52401
Tel.: (319) 362-2181
Web Site: http://www.smulekoffs.com
Sales Range: $10-24.9 Million
Emp.: 90
Retail Home Furnishings
N.A.I.C.S.: 449110

SMY MEDIA, INC.
625 N Michigan Ave Ste 525, Chicago, IL 60611
Tel.: (312) 621-9600   IL
Web Site: http://www.smymedia.com
Year Founded: 1969
Sales Range: $25-49.9 Million
Emp.: 12
Media Buying Services
N.A.I.C.S.: 541830
Virginia L. Shirley (Founder, Chm & CEO)
Gerry Grant (Exec VP-Sls & Acct Svcs)
Karen P. Sheridan (Exec VP)

SMYTH AUTOMOTIVE INC.
4275 Mount Carmel Tobasco Rd, Cincinnati, OH 45244
Tel.: (513) 528-2800
Web Site:
  http://www.smythautomotive.com
Sales Range: $10-24.9 Million
Emp.: 87
Automotive Supplies & Parts

N.A.I.C.S.: 423120
Holly Leitz (Dir-HR)
Jeff Dunn (Mgr)

SMYTH COMPANIES, INC.
1085 Snelling Ave N, Saint Paul, MN 55108-2705
Tel.: (651) 646-4544   MN
Web Site: http://www.smythco.com
Year Founded: 1877
Sales Range: $150-199.9 Million
Emp.: 500
Mfr of Labels & Packaging Products
N.A.I.C.S.: 322299
John Hickey (CEO)
David Baumgardner (CFO)
Scott Fisher (Pres)
William Hickey III (COO)

SNAGAJOB.COM, INC.
4851 Lk Brook Dr, Glen Allen, VA 23060
Tel.: (804) 236-9934
Web Site: http://www.snagajob.com
Sales Range: $10-24.9 Million
Emp.: 250
Employment Website Operator
N.A.I.C.S.: 513140
Peter Harrison (CEO)

SNAK KING CORP.
16150 E Stephens St, City of Industry, CA 91745
Tel.: (626) 336-7711
Web Site: http://www.snakking.com
Sales Range: $50-74.9 Million
Emp.: 350
Snack Food Mfr
N.A.I.C.S.: 311919
Barry C. Levin (Chm & CEO)
Vesna Kelley (CFO)

Subsidiaries:

C.J. Vitner Co. (1)
4202 W 45th St, Chicago, IL 60660
Tel.: (773) 523-7900
Web Site: http://www.snakking.com
Sales Range: $50-74.9 Million
Snack Foods
N.A.I.C.S.: 311919
William A. Vitner (CEO)

SNAKE RIVER SUGAR CO.
1951 S Satrun Way Ste 100, Boise, ID 83709
Tel.: (208) 383-6500   OR
Web Site: http://www.srcoop.com
Year Founded: 1994
Sales Range: $600-649.9 Million
Emp.: 1,500
Sugar Beet Mfr & Distr
N.A.I.C.S.: 551112
Wayne P. Neeley (CFO, VP & Controller)
Scott Blickenstaff (Gen Counsel & Sec)
John McCreedy (CEO)

Subsidiaries:

Amalgamated Sugar Co. (1)
138 W Karcher Rd, Nampa, ID 83687
Tel.: (208) 466-3541
Web Site: http://www.srcoop.com
Sales Range: $75-99.9 Million
Emp.: 400
Beet Sugar Processor
N.A.I.C.S.: 311313
Scott Blickenstaff (Gen Counsel & Sec)
Jessica Anderson (Mgr-Pub Affairs)

Amalgamated Sugar Co. (1)
2320 Orchard E, Twin Falls, ID 83301 (100%)
Tel.: (208) 733-4104
Web Site:
  http://www.amalgamatedsugar.com
Sales Range: $50-74.9 Million
Emp.: 300
Beet Sugar Processor

N.A.I.C.S.: 311313
Joe Huff (Chief Bus Dev Officer & Exec VP)
Duane Grant (Chm)

Amalgamated Sugar Co. (1)
105 E Main St, Nyssa, OR 97913-0266 (100%)
Tel.: (541) 372-2277
Web Site: http://www.srcoop.com
Sales Range: $25-49.9 Million
Emp.: 100
Beet Sugar Processor
N.A.I.C.S.: 311313

SNAKY CREEK ENTERPRISES, LLC
1815 23rd Ave N, Fargo, ND 58102-1047
Tel.: (701) 235-5478   MN
Web Site: http://www.spectrum-aeromed.com
Year Founded: 1991
Sales Range: $1-9.9 Million
Emp.: 26
Medical Equipment Distr
N.A.I.C.S.: 423450
Horst Heinicke (VP-Intl Sls)
Chad Kost (COO)
Dean Atchison (CEO)

SNAP ADVANCES
136 E S Temple Ste 2420, Salt Lake City, UT 84111
Tel.: (516) 247-1909
Web Site:
  http://www.snapadvances.com
Year Founded: 2009
Sales Range: $10-24.9 Million
Emp.: 40
Financial Services
N.A.I.C.S.: 523999
Mike Landau (Pres)
Matthew Hawkins (CEO)
Terri Hatch (Mgr)

SNAP AGENCY, INC.
725 Florida Ave S, Minneapolis, MN 55426
Tel.: (763) 703-1597   MN
Web Site:
  http://www.snapagency.com
Year Founded: 2010
Sales Range: $1-9.9 Million
Emp.: 28
Digital Marketing Services
N.A.I.C.S.: 541810
George Lee (CEO)
Spenser Baldwin (Pres)
Josh Kennedy (VP)
Chelsey Maas (Creative Dir)
Abby Herman (Dir-Strategy)

SNAP CONTRACTING CORPORATION
2043 W Pembroke Ave, Hampton, VA 23661
Tel.: (757) 245-0036
Year Founded: 1983
Sales Range: $10-24.9 Million
Emp.: 50
Commercial & Office Building Construction Services
N.A.I.C.S.: 236220
John Saafi (Owner)

SNAP FITNESS, INC.
2411 Galpin Ct Ste 110, Chanhassen, MN 55317
Tel.: (952) 474-5422
Web Site:
  http://www.snapfitness.com
Year Founded: 2003
Sales Range: $25-49.9 Million
Emp.: 2,000
Fitness Center Operator

SNAP FITNESS, INC.

Snap Fitness, Inc.—(Continued)
N.A.I.C.S.: 713940
Peter Taunton (Founder)
Ali McElroy (Gen Counsel)

SNAP INSTALL, INC.
7001 E Fish Lake Rd Ste 200, Maple Grove, MN 55311 — PA
Web Site: http://www.snap-install.com
Year Founded: 2011
Sales Range: $1-9.9 Million
Emp.: 33
Integration System Installation Services
N.A.I.C.S.: 541512
Travis Peterson (Pres & CEO)
Tony Green (VP-Bus Dev)
Jamin Johnson (VP-Ops)
Greg Peckham (Dir-Tech)
Nicole McCarty (Dir-Admin)

SNAP, INC.
4080 Lafayette Center Dr Ste 340, Chantilly, VA 20151 — VA
Tel.: (703) 393-6400
Web Site: http://www.snapinc.net
Year Founded: 1998
Information Technology Consulting Services
N.A.I.C.S.: 541512
Bruce Adams (Chief Strategy Officer)
Craig Park (VP-Federal Market Sector)
Rajiv Jain (CIO)
Janak Thadani (CFO)
Paul J. Masters (COO)
Matt Salmon (Comml Dir)
Navneet Gupta (Founder, Pres & CEO)

SNAPFINGER, INC.
3025 Windward Plaza Ste 150, Alpharetta, GA 30005
Tel.: (678) 739-4650
Web Site: http://www.snapfinger.com
Year Founded: 2004
Sales Range: $1-9.9 Million
Emp.: 25
Online & Mobile Food Ordering Services
N.A.I.C.S.: 722330
James Garrett (Founder & CEO)

SNAPPING SHOALS ELECTRIC MEMBERSHIP CORP.
14750 Brown Bridge Rd, Covington, GA 30016
Tel.: (770) 786-3484
Web Site: http://www.ssemc.com
Year Founded: 1936
Sales Range: $75-99.9 Million
Emp.: 240
Distribution of Electric Power
N.A.I.C.S.: 221122
Anthony Norton (Chm)
Ruby Woods (Treas & Sec)
Walter Johnson (Vice Chm)

SNAVELY DEVELOPMENT COMPANY
7139 Pine St, Chagrin Falls, OH 44022
Tel.: (440) 585-9091 — OH
Web Site: http://www.snavely.com
Real Estate Development & Building Construction
N.A.I.C.S.: 236115
Polly Snavely (VP-Mktg)
Brad Lohan (VP-Fin & Admin)
Bill Porter (VP-Field Ops)
Greg Osborne (VP-Project Mgmt)
Lisa Swan (Asst Controller)
Victor Epelbaum (Controller)

Zoe Adams (Mktg Dir-Property Company)
Andrew Costello (Superintendent)
Dave Cyr (Project Engr)
Spencer Diedrich (Project Engr)
Pete Dougherty (Superintendent)
Ryan Nagel (Mgr-Dev)
Ira Young (Dir-Fin & Controller)
Pete Snavely Sr. (Pres)
Pete Snavely Jr. (VP-Dev)

SNB HOLDINGS, INC.
220 E Lawrence Harris Hwy, Slocomb, AL 36375
Tel.: (334) 886-2367 — DE
Web Site: http://www.friendbank.net
Year Founded: 1999
Sales Range: $1-9.9 Million
Emp.: 45
Bank Holding Company
N.A.I.C.S.: 551111
Hope Harris Johnson (Chm, Pres & CEO)

Subsidiaries:

Friend Bank (1)
220 E Lawrence Harris Hwy, Slocomb, AL 36375
Tel.: (334) 886-2367
Web Site: http://www.friendbank.net
Sales Range: $1-9.9 Million
Emp.: 40
Commericial Banking
N.A.I.C.S.: 522110
Hope Harris Johnson (Chm & CEO)
Ken Grimes (Pres-Slocomb Market)
Joseph Johnson (Pres-Dothan Market)
Randall Meeks (Pres-Geneva Market)
David Bailey (Pres-Hartford Market)
Dan Hale (Pres-Dale County Market)

SNC SQUARED
706 W 26th St, Joplin, MO 64804
Tel.: (417) 622-0933
Web Site: http://www.sncsquared.com
Year Founded: 1998
Sales Range: $1-9.9 Million
Emp.: 10
Information Technology Services
N.A.I.C.S.: 541512
John Motazedi (CEO)

SNEDEKER OIL COMPANY INC.
709 E Walnut St, Lewistown, PA 17044
Tel.: (717) 248-2665
Web Site: http://www.snedoil.com
Sales Range: $10-24.9 Million
Emp.: 13
Petroleum Products Sales
N.A.I.C.S.: 457210
Randy Conklin (CFO)
Fred Ciecierski (Mgr-Svc)
Scott Sherwood (Pres)
Ron Miller (VP-Stores & Wholesale Transport Dept)

SNELL & WILMER LLP
1 Arizona Ctr 400 E Van Buren St Ste 1900, Phoenix, AZ 85004
Tel.: (602) 382-6000
Web Site: http://www.swlaw.com
Year Founded: 1938
Sales Range: $200-249.9 Million
Emp.: 415
Law firm
N.A.I.C.S.: 541110
John J. Bouma (Partner)
Andy Halaby (Partner)
Patrick Fowler (Partner-Phoenix)
Brent W. Nelson (Partner)
Charles Giddings (Partner)
Greg Marshall (Partner)
Joe Adams (Partner)
Joel Hoxie (Partner)

Marvin Swift (Partner)
Steven Jerome (Partner)
Marek Bute (Partner)
Justin Carley (Partner)
Joy L. Isaacs (Atty)
Damon Ashcraft (Partner)
Matthew Feeney (Chm)
Ketan Vakil (Chm-Intellectual Property Grp, Partner-Admin-Orange County)
Bill O'Hare (Sr Partner-Comml Litigation)
Jason Brinkley (Partner)
Dan Wittenberg (Partner)
Don Martin (Partner-Real Estate-Las Vegas)

SNELL SERVICES INC.
2220 W Frnt St, North Platte, NE 69101
Tel.: (308) 532-6870
Web Site: http://www.snellservices.com
Sales Range: $10-24.9 Million
Emp.: 95
Mechanical Contractor
N.A.I.C.S.: 238220
Dave Morman (Pres)

SNIDER ADVISORS
222 W Las Colinas Blvd Ste 543E, Irving, TX 75039
Web Site: http://www.snideradvisors.com
Year Founded: 2002
Rev.: $2,800,000
Emp.: 20
Financial Services
N.A.I.C.S.: 522320
Jim Hughes (CFO)

SNIDER FLEET SOLUTIONS
200 E Meadowview Rd, Greensboro, NC 27406-4521
Tel.: (336) 691-5480 — NC
Web Site: http://www.sniderfleet.com
Year Founded: 1987
Sales Range: $50-74.9 Million
Emp.: 850
Tire Retreader & Wholesaler
N.A.I.C.S.: 441340
Bill Riordon (VP-Special Projects)
Floyd Allen (VP-Natl Accts)
Marty Herndon (COO & Exec VP)
John K. Snider (Pres & CEO)
Russ Hunt (Sr VP)
Sean Baird (VP-Ops)
Keith Allen (Dir-Sls & Mktg)

SNIKIDDY LLC
2505 Walnut St, Boulder, CO 80302
Tel.: (303) 444-4405
Web Site: http://www.snikiddy.com
Year Founded: 2007
Sales Range: $1-9.9 Million
Emp.: 11
All Natural Snacks
N.A.I.C.S.: 311919
Mary Owings Schulman (Founder)

SNL DISTRIBUTION INC.
244 Goodwin Crest Dr Ste 100, Birmingham, AL 35209
Tel.: (205) 943-0010
Web Site: http://www.snldoc.com
Rev.: $22,000,000
Emp.: 2
Local Trucking without Storage
N.A.I.C.S.: 484121

SNODGRASS & SONS CONSTRUCTION CO., INC.
2700 S George Washington Blvd, Wichita, KS 67210-1520
Tel.: (316) 687-3110

U.S. PRIVATE

Web Site: http://www.snodgrassconstruction.com
Year Founded: 1948
Sales Range: $10-24.9 Million
Emp.: 75
Structural Steel & Precast Concrete Contracting Services
N.A.I.C.S.: 238120
David L. Snodgrass (Pres)
Perry Hilt (Project Mgr)
Steve Slusher (VP)
James Snodgrass (Chm)
Aaron Snodgras (Sec)

SNOHOMISH COUNTY PUBLIC UTILITY DISTRICT
2320 California St, Everett, WA 98201
Tel.: (425) 783-1000
Web Site: http://www.snopud.com
Year Founded: 1946
Sales Range: $350-399.9 Million
Emp.: 900
Electronic Services
N.A.I.C.S.: 221118
Glenn McPherson (Treas & Asst Gen Mgr)
Steve Klein (Gen Mgr)
Jim West (Asst Gen Mgr)
Benjamin Beberness (CIO)
Kristi Treckeme (Dir-Employee Resources)

SNOKIST GROWERS CO-OP
2506 Ter Hts Dr, Yakima, WA 98901
Tel.: (509) 453-5631 — WA
Web Site: http://www.snokist.com
Year Founded: 1903
Sales Range: $200-249.9 Million
Emp.: 700
Marketing of Fresh Fruits, Marketing & Processing of Canned Fruits
N.A.I.C.S.: 311421
Jim Bradley (Mgr-HR)

SNOLINE EXPRESS, INC.
1130 Orchard Loop Rd, Troy, ID 83871
Tel.: (208) 835-4981 — ID
Sales Range: $1-9.9 Million
Refrigerated Freight Transportation Services
N.A.I.C.S.: 484230
Eva Lou C. Diebel (Pres)

SNOOGOO CORP.
7150 E Camelback Rd Ste 444, Scottsdale, AZ 85251
Year Founded: 2010
Information Online Services
N.A.I.C.S.: 519290
Robert Egeland (Pres & COO)
Terry W. Neild (CEO)

SNOW AND JONES INC.
85 Accord Park Dr, Norwell, MA 02061
Tel.: (781) 878-3312
Web Site: http://www.snowandjones.com
Sales Range: $10-24.9 Million
Emp.: 50
Plumbing & Hydronic Heating Supplies
N.A.I.C.S.: 423720
Daniel Jones (Pres)

SNOW KING RESORT, INC.
400 E Snow King Ave, Jackson, WY 83001
Tel.: (307) 733-5200 — WY
Web Site: http://www.snowking.com
Year Founded: 1976
Sales Range: $75-99.9 Million
Emp.: 200
Ski Resort

N.A.I.C.S.: 721110
Dana Ahrensberg (Gen Mgr)
Erik Dombroski (Dir-Sls & Mktg)
Jeff Young (Gen Mgr)
Teresa Holden (Dir-Sls & Mktg)
David Kingston (Gen Mgr)
Gregg Fracassa (Gen Mgr)
Andy Blair (Fin Dir)

SNOW PEAK CAPITAL, LLC
1900 9th St Ste #210, Boulder, CO 80302
Tel.: (720) 909-3406
Web Site:
https://www.snowpeakcapital.com
Year Founded: 2019
Holding Company
N.A.I.C.S.: 551112
Steven C. Yager (Mng Partner)
Anthony Chirikos (Partner)

Subsidiaries:

Dalco Nonwovens, LLC (1)
2050 Evergreen Dr NE, Conover, NC 28613
Tel.: (828) 459-2577
Nonwoven Fabric Mill Services
N.A.I.C.S.: 313230
Mark Evans (Pres & CEO)
Joy Evans (Controller)
Jeff Bennett (Mgr-Sls)
Joe Jessmer (Mgr-Shipping)
Karl Ashworth (Mgr-Production)
Melissa Hedger (Mgr-Pur)
Scott Greenwood (Gen Mgr)
Susan Josey (Mgr-Acctg)
Joey Duncan (CEO)

Sandy Alexander, Inc. (1)
200 Entin Rd, Clifton, NJ 07014
Tel.: (973) 470-8100
Web Site: http://www.sandyinc.com
Graphic Communications Mfr & Printer
N.A.I.C.S.: 323111
Michael Graff (Pres)
Peter Stillo (Sr VP-Sls)
Joe Brocato (Exec VP-Sls)
Tim Fisher (CTO & Exec VP)

SNOWBIRD CORPORATION
Hwy 210, Snowbird, UT 84092
Tel.: (801) 933-2222
Web Site: http://www.snowbird.com
Sales Range: $25-49.9 Million
Emp.: 1,000
Ski Lodge
N.A.I.C.S.: 236117
Richard D. Bass (Owner)
Bob Vonar (Pres)
Simon Diggin (Mgr-Sls)
Brain Brown (Asst Dir-PR)

SNS LOGISTICS, INC.
2463 Lloyd Rd, Jacksonville, FL 32254
Tel.: (904) 378-2544
Web Site: http://www.sns-logistics.com
Year Founded: 2006
Sales Range: $1-9.9 Million
Emp.: 23
Warehousing, Freight Consolidation & Management Cartage, Distribution, Long & Short-term Storage
N.A.I.C.S.: 488510
Cary Simon (Co-Founder)
Nedret Cunningham (Co-Founder)

SNS MARKETING
400 Red Brook Blvd Ste 310, Owings Mills, MD 21117
Tel.: (410) 527-1800   MD
Web Site:
http://www.snsmarketing.com
Year Founded: 1976
Rev.: $42,000,000
Emp.: 25
Advetising Agency
N.A.I.C.S.: 541810

Don Mahaney (CEO)
Brenda Shawley (Pres)
Dave Dobyski (Sr Dir-Art)
John Ballard (VP-Acct Plng)
Robert W. Maczis (Chief Creative Officer)
Holly S. Ballard (VP-Client Svcs)
Patricia Kielholtz (Sr Dir-Art)
Tom Daniel (VP & Dir-Creative)
Mark Kennedy (VP-Partner Dev)

SNTECH, INC.
1702 E Highland Ave Ste 400, Phoenix, AZ 85016
Tel.: (480) 776-0500
Web Site: http://www.sntech.com
Sales Range: $10-24.9 Million
Emp.: 100
Electric Motor Mfr
N.A.I.C.S.: 335312
Shannon Bard (CEO)
Jordan Bass (Mgr-Bus Dev)

SNTIAL TECHNOLOGIES, INC.
125 Ainslie Ct, Westmont, IL 60559
Tel.: (630) 452-4735
Web Site: http://www.sntialtech.com
Year Founded: 2001
Rev.: $2,400,000
Emp.: 15
Business Support Services
N.A.I.C.S.: 561499
Reena Singh (VP-Admin)
Sandeep Nain (Principal)

SNUGZ USA INC
1901 S 5070 W, Salt Lake City, UT 84104-4729
Web Site: http://www.SnugZUSA.com
Year Founded: 1989
Sales Range: $10-24.9 Million
Emp.: 210
Promotional Products
N.A.I.C.S.: 333310
Brandon Mackay (Owner)

SNVC, L.C.
12150 Monument Dr Ste 510, Fairfax, VA 22033
Tel.: (703) 952-7682   VA
Web Site: http://www.snvc.com
Year Founded: 1998
Sales Range: $10-24.9 Million
Emp.: 105
Project Management, System Analysis & Network Design
N.A.I.C.S.: 541512
Tom DeWitt (Pres & CEO)
Beth Miller-Herholtz (Chief Strategy Officer)

SNYDER AUTO WORKS INC.
4695 Campbells Run Rd, Pittsburgh, PA 15205
Tel.: (412) 787-0666
Sales Range: $10-24.9 Million
Emp.: 26
Automotive Services
N.A.I.C.S.: 457120
Don Snyder (Pres)

SNYDER CHEVROLET OLDSMOBILE, INC.
524 N Perry St, Napoleon, OH 43545
Tel.: (419) 599-1015
Web Site:
http://www.snyderchevrolet.com
Sales Range: $10-24.9 Million
Emp.: 32
Car Whslr
N.A.I.C.S.: 441110
Bill Snyder (Owner)

SNYDER CONCRETE PRODUCTS INC.
2301 W Dorothy Ln, Dayton, OH 45439
Tel.: (937) 299-7388
Web Site:
http://www.snyderonline.com
Year Founded: 1949
Sales Range: $10-24.9 Million
Emp.: 50
Bricks Mfr
N.A.I.C.S.: 423320
Lee E. Snyder (Pres)
Mark Snyder (VP)

SNYDER CORP.
6 Fountain Plz, Buffalo, NY 14202
Tel.: (716) 332-4233
Web Site: http://www.snydercorp.com
Year Founded: 1958
Sales Range: $10-24.9 Million
Emp.: 25
Land Subdividers & Developers
N.A.I.C.S.: 237210
Barbara Roedel (VP-Admin)
Paul L. Snyder (Founder & Chm)
Kathy Snyder Egan (Exec VP-Sls)
Sandra Snyder Schoellkopf (Exec VP-Mktg)
Paul L. Snyder III (CEO)

SNYDER ENVIRONMENTAL, INC.
7031 Dewafelbakker Ln, North Little Rock, AR 72213   AR
Web Site:
http://www.snyderenvironmental.com
Year Founded: 2001
Sales Range: $1-9.9 Million
Emp.: 114
Remediation Services
N.A.I.C.S.: 562910
Joe Carter (CEO)
Shelly Martin (Dir-HR)

SNYDER GROUP INCORPORATED
1 Selleck St 3F, Norwalk, CT 06855
Tel.: (203) 852-1101
Web Site:
http://www.snydergroupinc.com
Year Founded: 1995
Sales Range: $10-24.9 Million
Emp.: 10
N.A.I.C.S.: 541810
David Synder (Pres)

SNYDER INTERNATIONAL BREWING GROUP LLC
1940 E 6th St Ste 200, Cleveland, OH 44114-2239
Tel.: (216) 619-7424
Year Founded: 1999
Sales Range: $10-24.9 Million
Emp.: 181
Brewery Mfr
N.A.I.C.S.: 312120
Dave Snyder (Chm & Partner)
Jim Gerhig (CFO)
Christopher Livingston (Pres & Partner)

SNYDER LANGSTON LP
17962 Cowan, Irvine, CA 92614
Tel.: (949) 863-9200
Web Site:
http://www.snyderlangston.com
Year Founded: 1959
Sales Range: $200-249.9 Million
Emp.: 110
Real Estate & Construction Services
N.A.I.C.S.: 236220
Jason Rich (Project Mgr)
John F. Rochford (Pres & COO)
Gary Campanaro (CFO)

SNYDER PAPER CORPORATION
250 26th St Dr SE, Hickory, NC 28602-1456
Tel.: (828) 328-2501
Web Site:
http://www.snyderpaper.com
Year Founded: 1946
Sales Range: $50-74.9 Million
Emp.: 355
Provider of Paper
N.A.I.C.S.: 424990
Larry Kahill (COO & Exec VP)
Gary Franklin (Treas)
Harry Niekamp (Mgr-Pur)
Peter Gravely (Mgr-Sys)
Wilson Eddie (VP)
Tim Beach (Supvr-Shipping)

SNYDER ROOFING & SHEETMETAL INC.
12650 SW Hall Blvd, Tigard, OR 97223-6243
Tel.: (503) 620-5252   OR
Web Site:
http://www.snyderroofing.com
Year Founded: 1922
Sales Range: $25-49.9 Million
Emp.: 250
Roofing & Sheetmetal Work
N.A.I.C.S.: 238160
Ron Newton (Pres)

SNYDER, CROMPTON & ASSOCIATES, INC.
3411 Silverside Rd Ste 202, Wilmington, DE 19810-4803
Tel.: (302) 478-6030
Web Site:
http://www.scaconstructs.com
Year Founded: 1954
Sales Range: $10-24.9 Million
Emp.: 60
General Contracting Services
N.A.I.C.S.: 236220
Jeni Albany (Mgr-HR)

SNYDER-DIAMOND
1399 Olympic Blvd, Santa Monica, CA 90404-3730
Tel.: (310) 450-1000   CA
Web Site:
http://www.snyderdiamond.com
Year Founded: 1949
Sales Range: $10-24.9 Million
Emp.: 110
Plumbing Fixtures & Supplies, Appliances, Decorative Hardware & Kitchen Appliances Sales
N.A.I.C.S.: 459999
Adam Litberg (Mgr-Store-Santa Monica)
Brian Cousens (Mgr-Store-Pasadena)
Jose Marcial (Mgr-Store-North Hollywood)

SO ACCURATE GROUP INC.
3100 47th Ave Ste 5a, Long Island City, NY 11101-3068
Tel.: (212) 465-8082
Web Site: http://www.soaccurate.com
Sales Range: $75-99.9 Million
Emp.: 25
Precious Metals
N.A.I.C.S.: 423940
Sam Trencher (Pres)
Lawrence Wilson (VP)

SO CALIFORNIA VENTURES LTD.
1101 Richfield Rd, Placentia, CA 92870-6790
Tel.: (714) 572-8555
Sales Range: $10-24.9 Million
Emp.: 80
Civil Engineering Services
N.A.I.C.S.: 236220

SO CALIFORNIA VENTURES LTD.

So California Ventures Ltd.—(Continued)
Bradley Fisher (Branch Mgr)
John T. Palazzo (Pres)

SO DO IT, LLC
13561 SW Bayshore Dr Ste 3000,
Traverse City, MI 49684
Tel.: (231) 922-9977
Web Site: http://www.oneupweb.com
Year Founded: 2000
Sales Range: $10-24.9 Million
Emp.: 35
Advetising Agency
N.A.I.C.S.: 541810

SO OTHERS MIGHT EAT
71 O St NW, Washington, DC 20001
Tel.: (202) 797-8806   DC
Web Site: http://www.some.org
Year Founded: 1970
Sales Range: $25-49.9 Million
Emp.: 417
Poor & Homeless People Assistance Services
N.A.I.C.S.: 624221
Ralph F. Boyd Jr. (Pres & CEO)
Richard Gerlach (Exec Dir)
Suzanne Bond (Chief Admin Officer)
Ann Chauvin (Chief Clinical Officer)
Linda Parisi (Chief Dev Officer)
Mary Catherine Guiler (Sec)
Jason E. Geno (Vice Chm)
Michele Durbin (Treas)
Mary Bader (Chm)

SOAPROJECTS, INC.
495 N Whisman Rd Ste 100, Mountain View, CA 94043
Tel.: (650) 960-9900
Web Site:
   http://www.soaprojects.com
Year Founded: 2004
Sales Range: $1-9.9 Million
Emp.: 200
Crisis Management Services
N.A.I.C.S.: 541618
Manpreet Grover (CEO & Partner)
Manav Singh (Founder & Partner)
Yuko Wakasugi (Partner-Technical Acctg)
Kaushik Raha (Partner-Risk Advisory & Forensic Svcs)
Robert Strasser (Partner-Internal Audit & SOX)
Miguel Martin (Sr Dir-IT Compliance & Advisory)

Subsidiaries:

Alchemy Search Partners, Inc.   (1)
1735 N 1st St Ste 308, San Jose, CA 95112
Tel.: (408) 487-8700
Web Site: http://www.alchemysearch.com
Rev.: $1,200,000
Emp.: 13
Professional Direct Hire & Consulting Services
N.A.I.C.S.: 541612

SOAR COMMUNICATIONS
PO Box 581138, Salt Lake City, UT 84158
Tel.: (801) 656-0472
Web Site: http://www.soarcomm.com
Year Founded: 2004
Sales Range: Less than $1 Million
Emp.: 3
Collateral, Communications, Financial, Graphic Design, Local Marketing, Media Relations, Outdoor, Sales Promotion, Sports Marketing, Strategic Planning/Research
N.A.I.C.S.: 541810
Chip Smith (Pres)
Maura Lansford (Acct Exec)

SOAVE ENTERPRISES, LLC
3400 E Lafayette, Detroit, MI 48207
Tel.: (313) 567-7000   MI
Web Site: http://www.soave.com
Year Founded: 1961
Sales Range: Less than $1 Million
Scrap Metal Processing Recycling & Environmental Distr
N.A.I.C.S.: 551112
Michael L. Piesko (CFO & VP)
Yale Levin (Exec VP)
Richard T. Brockhaus (Treas & Sr VP)
Timothy J. Bley (Dir-Tax)
Marcia K. Moss (Dir-HR)
Bryant M. Frank (Sec)
Nico Schultz (Sr VP-Real Estate)
Darlene Soave (Founder)
Anthony L. Soave (Pres & CEO)

Subsidiaries:

Ferrous Processing & Trading Co.   (1)
3400 E Lafayette, Detroit, MI 48207
Tel.: (313) 567-9710
Web Site: http://www.ferrousprocessing.com
Sales Range: $10-24.9 Million
Emp.: 90
Metal Scrap Processing
N.A.I.C.S.: 423930
Steve Benacquisto (Sr Exec VP)
Howard Sherman (Chm)
Dave Dobronos (Pres & CEO)
Joanie Streicher (CFO)
Rob Bakotich (Exec VP-Pur & Sls)

Subsidiary (Domestic):

FPT Canton, LLC   (2)
1514 Maple Ave NE, Canton, OH 44705
Tel.: (330) 456-9649
Web Site: http://www.fptscrap.com
Metal Recycling Services
N.A.I.C.S.: 562920

FPT Cleveland, LLC   (2)
8550 Aetna Rd, Cleveland, OH 44105
Tel.: (216) 441-3800
Web Site: http://www.fptscrap.com
Metal Recycling Services
N.A.I.C.S.: 562920

FPT Ft. Myers, LLC   (2)
3750 Veronica Shoemaker Blvd, Fort Myers, FL 33196
Tel.: (239) 332-1997
Industrial Supplies Whslr
N.A.I.C.S.: 423840

FPT Pontiac Division, LLC   (2)
500 Collier Rd, Pontiac, MI 48340
Tel.: (248) 335-8141
Metal Recycling Services
N.A.I.C.S.: 562920

FPT Schlafer Division, LLC   (2)
1950 Medbury Ave, Detroit, MI 48211
Tel.: (313) 925-8200
Sales Range: $1-9.9 Million
Metal Recycling Services
N.A.I.C.S.: 562920

Plant (Domestic):

Ferrous Processing & Trading Co. - FPT Ft Lauderdale/Sunrise Recycling Facility   (2)
700 NW 21st Ter, Fort Lauderdale, FL 33311
Tel.: (954) 791-2844
Metal Recycling Services
N.A.I.C.S.: 562920
Jesus Martin (Gen Mgr)

Ferrous Processing & Trading Co. - FPT Wyoming Ave. Facility   (2)
3651 Wyoming Ave, Dearborn, MI 48126
Tel.: (313) 582-2911
Web Site: http://www.fptscrap.com
Metal Recycling Services
N.A.I.C.S.: 562920

Subsidiary (Non-US):

Zalev Brothers Company   (2)
100 Grand Marais Road East, Windsor, N9A 6N5, ON, Canada

Tel.: (519) 966-0620
Web Site: http://www.fptscrap.com
Metal Recycling Services
N.A.I.C.S.: 562920
Rachael Gaulitieri (Mng Dir)

Soave Hydroponics Company   (1)
1400 Road 3, Kingsville, N9Y 2E9, ON, Canada
Tel.: (519) 322-2000
Web Site: http://www.soave.com
Emp.: 200
Electric Power Distribution Services
N.A.I.C.S.: 221122
Guido Vanhethos (Gen Mgr)

Division (Domestic):

Soave Hydroponics Company - Great Northern Seedlings Division   (2)
1400 Rd 3 East, Kingsville, N9Y 2E5, ON, Canada
Tel.: (519) 322-2000
Web Site: http://www.soaveag.com
Seed Production Services
N.A.I.C.S.: 111219

SOB STABLES, INC.
205 Ave Del Mar Ste 974, San Clemente, CA 92674
Tel.: (949) 461-1471   DE
Year Founded: 2012
Thoroughbred Horse Racing
N.A.I.C.S.: 112920
Joseph Wade (Pres, CEO, CFO & Principal Acctg Officer)

SOBC CORP.
55 Madison Ave Ste 400, Morristown, NJ 07960
Tel.: (215) 805-0272   DE
Web Site: http://www.sobccorp.com
Year Founded: 2014
Reinsurance Services
N.A.I.C.S.: 524130
Stephanie Mocatta (CEO)

Subsidiaries:

SOBC DARAG Holdings Ltd.   (1)
8200 Beckett Park Dr Ste 201, West Chester, OH 45069
Tel.: (513) 889-5663
Web Site: http://sobcdarag.com
Run-Off Acquisition & Management Solutions
N.A.I.C.S.: 561499
Stephanie Mocatta (CEO)
Brian Johnston (CFO)

SOBEL CO.
2385 NW Executive Ctr Dr Ste 370, Boca Raton, FL 33431
Tel.: (561) 994-3434   MI
Web Site: http://www.sobelco.com
Year Founded: 1958
Sales Range: $1-9.9 Million
Emp.: 20
Commercial, Retail & Residential Real Estate Development, Construction, Leasing, Management & Ownership
N.A.I.C.S.: 236220
Jeffrey E. Sobel (Pres)
Samuel R. Sobel (Chm)
Carol G. DeMare (CFO)
Tirso San Jose (VP-Residential Dev)

SOBEL WESTEX
2670 S Western Ave, Las Vegas, NV 89109
Tel.: (702) 735-4973
Web Site:
   http://www.sobelwestex.com
Sales Range: $25-49.9 Million
Emp.: 45
Distr Of Table Linen
N.A.I.C.S.: 423220
Carlos Fabrri (CFO)
Walter Teleaz (CEO)
Nathan Bennett (Dir-Info Sys & Tech)

U.S. PRIVATE

SOBRAN, INC.
4401 Dayton Xenia Rd, Dayton, OH 45432
Tel.: (937) 426-0696
Web Site: http://www.sobran-inc.com
Year Founded: 1987
Sales Range: $50-74.9 Million
Emp.: 800
Biomedical, Engineering, Logistics & Hazard-Protection Services
N.A.I.C.S.: 541690
Gregory Kelly (Sr VP-Biomedical Res Svcs)
Amos L. Otis (Founder, Pres & CEO)
Robert Williams (VP-Corp Svcs)
Will Hobbs (VP-Fairfax)

SOCAL HARVEST, INC.
6755 Mira Mesa Blvd Ste 123 Rm 187, San Diego, CA 92121
Tel.: (858) 999-5818   WY
Web Site: http://www.so-calharvest.com
Year Founded: 2017
Assets: $2,484
Liabilities: $98,183
Net Worth: ($95,699)
Earnings: ($74,077)
Emp.: 1
Fiscal Year-end: 12/31/19
Fruit Farming Services
N.A.I.C.S.: 111419
Mark Botsford (Founder, Pres, CEO, CFO, Treas & Sec)

SOCI, INC.
225 Broadway Ste 600, San Diego, CA 92101
Tel.: (858) 225-4110
Web Site: http://www.meetsoci.com
Year Founded: 2012
Marketing Platform
N.A.I.C.S.: 541890
Afif Khoury (Founder & CEO)
Falk Gottlob (Chief Product Officer)

Subsidiaries:

Brandify, Inc.   (1)
5101 E La Palma Ave Ste 107, Anaheim, CA 92807
Tel.: (714) 660-4870
Web Site: http://www.brandify.com
Computer Related Services
N.A.I.C.S.: 541519
Manish Patel (Founder & CEO)

Subsidiary (Domestic):

Hyperlocal Industries LLC   (2)
115 S 35th St, Boulder, CO 80305-5434
Tel.: (917) 545-7774
Web Site: http://www.streetfightmag.com
Internet Publishing & Broadcasting & Web Search Portals
N.A.I.C.S.: 516210
Anne Marie Stephen (Pres)

SOCIAL CAPITAL HEDOSOPHIA HOLDINGS CORP. IV
506 Santa Cruz Ave Ste 300, Menlo Park, CA 94025
Tel.: (650) 521-9007   Ky
Year Founded: 2020
IPOD—(NYSE)
Rev.: $27,491,008
Assets: $460,393,603
Liabilities: $51,316,949
Net Worth: ($50,979,185)
Earnings: $24,899,397
Fiscal Year-end: 12/31/21
Investment Holding Company
N.A.I.C.S.: 551112
Chamath Palihapitiya (Chm & CEO)

SOCIAL CAPITAL HEDOSOPHIA HOLDINGS CORP. VI
506 Santa Cruz Ave Ste 300, Menlo Park, CA 94025

Tel.: (650) 521-9007   Ky
Year Founded: 2020
IPOF—(NYSE)
Rev.: $1,762,810,000
Assets: $19,007,675,000
Liabilities: $13,479,199,000
Net Worth: $5,528,476,000
Earnings: ($320,407,000)
Emp.: 4,200
Fiscal Year-end: 12/31/22
Investment Holding Company
N.A.I.C.S.: 551112
Chamath Palihapitiya *(Chm & CEO)*

SOCIAL CONCERN COMMUNITY DEVELOPMENT CORP
22618 Merrick Blvd, Laurelton, NY 11413
Tel.: (718) 978-7776   NY
Year Founded: 1980
Sales Range: $10-24.9 Million
Emp.: 737
Home Care Services
N.A.I.C.S.: 621610
Charlene Jordan *(Program Dir)*

SOCIAL CUBE INC.
515 S Flower St Ste 3600, Los Angeles, CA 90071
Tel.: (213) 236-3657   DE
Year Founded: 1989
Sales Range: $1-9.9 Million
Emp.: 2
Holding Company; Social Gaming & Social Networking Services
N.A.I.C.S.: 551112
Byung Jin Kim *(Chm & CEO)*
Jonathan Lee *(CFO)*

SOCIAL INTEREST SOLUTIONS
3841 N Fwy Blvd Ste 210, Sacramento, CA 95834
Tel.: (510) 834-1300   CA
Web Site: http://www.socialinterest.org
Year Founded: 2006
Sales Range: $10-24.9 Million
Emp.: 61
Healthcare & Social Welfare Software Publishing Services
N.A.I.C.S.: 513210
Deanne Wertin *(COO)*
John Caterham *(CEO)*
Kelly Guthner *(CIO)*

SOCIAL MEDIA VENTURES, INC.
471 N Broadway Ste 207, Jericho, NY 11753
Tel.: (516) 204-4843
Year Founded: 1998
Emp.: 1
Online Advertising Services
N.A.I.C.S.: 541890
Robert A. Thayer *(Chm, Pres, CEO & CFO)*

SOCIAL SOLUTIONS GLOBAL INC.
425 Williams Ct Ste 100, Baltimore, MD 21220
Tel.: (443) 460-3417
Web Site: http://www.socialsolutions.com
Human & Socail Services Software Distr
N.A.I.C.S.: 423430
Nikhil Kumar *(COO)*
Ken Saunders *(CFO)*
Jon Bahl *(Chief Revenue Officer)*
Sean Ramsey *(VP-Product Mgmt)*
Heather Smith *(VP-Mktg)*
Erin Mulligan Nelson *(CEO)*

Subsidiaries:

Community Techknowledge, Inc. (1)
9442 Capital of Texas Hwy N Bldg 1 Ste 200, Austin, TX 78759
Tel.: (512) 345-9090
Web Site: http://www.communitytech.net
Sales Range: $1-9.9 Million
Emp.: 25
Custom Computer Programming Services
N.A.I.C.S.: 541511
Kathy Englehardt-Cronk *(Founder & CEO)*
Alison Urban *(COO)*
Justin Bouldin *(CTO)*
Rosie Marshall *(VP-Quality Assurance & Transition)*
Seychelle Martinez *(Dir-Software Implementations)*
Shelly Johnson *(Dir-Ongoing Support & Retention)*
Derek Hansen *(Dir-Strategic Partnerships & Community Engagement)*
Jessica Eichler *(Dir-Mission Solutions)*

SOCIAL SPARKLING WINE, LLC
333 W North Ave Ste 380, Chicago, IL 60610
Tel.: (312) 550-2000
Web Site: http://www.socialsparklingwine.com
Year Founded: 2013
Sales Range: $1-9.9 Million
Emp.: 9
Winery Product Distr
N.A.I.C.S.: 445320
Leah Caplanis *(Founder & CEO)*

SOCIAL STUDIES SCHOOL SERVICE
10200 Jefferson Blvd Box 802, Culver City, CA 90232
Tel.: (310) 839-2436   CA
Web Site: http://www.socialstudies.com
Year Founded: 1967
Emp.: 100
Supplemental Learning Materials Publisher & Whslr
N.A.I.C.S.: 513199
David Weiner *(CEO)*
Eytan Bernstein *(Mgr-Active Class Room)*

Subsidiaries:

Nystrom Education (1)
10200 Jefferson Blvd, Culver City, CA 90232
Tel.: (310) 839-2436
Web Site: http://www.nystromeducation.com
Sales Range: $10-24.9 Million
Emp.: 70
Maps, Globes & Other Supplemental Learning Materials Publisher, Mfr & Whslr
N.A.I.C.S.: 513199
David Weiner *(CEO)*

SOCIALCOM INC.
13468 Beach Ave, Marina Del Rey, CA 90292
Tel.: (310) 289-4477
Web Site: http://www.audiencex.com
Year Founded: 2014
Sales Range: $10-24.9 Million
Emp.: 80
Digital Marketing Services
N.A.I.C.S.: 541810
Reeve Benaron *(Co-Founder & CEO)*
Jason Wulfsohn *(Co-Founder & COO)*
Brian Ko *(Chief Comml Officer)*
Ryan Carhart *(CFO)*
Candice Driscoll *(Chief People Officer)*

SOCIALFLY LLC
231 W 29th St Ste 702, New York, NY 10001
Tel.: (917) 300-8298

Web Site: http://www.socialflyny.com
Year Founded: 2012
Sales Range: $1-9.9 Million
Emp.: 30
Media Advertising Services
N.A.I.C.S.: 541840
Courtney Spritzer *(Co-Founder & Co-CEO)*
Stephanie Abrams Cartin *(Co-Founder & Co-CEO)*

SOCIALRADIUS
3277 E Warm Springs Rd Ste 200, Las Vegas, NV 89120
Tel.: (702) 410-7818
Web Site: http://www.socialradius.com
Year Founded: 2007
Sales Range: $1-9.9 Million
Emp.: 15
Marketing & Public Relation Services
N.A.I.C.S.: 541820

SOCIALTEXT, INC.
558 Waverly St, Palo Alto, CA 94301
Tel.: (650) 323-0800
Web Site: http://www.socialtext.com
Year Founded: 2003
Sales Range: $1-9.9 Million
Emp.: 25
Software Publisher
N.A.I.C.S.: 513210
Stephen Turner *(Sr VP & Gen Mgr)*

SOCIETY AWARDS
3718 Northern Blvd Ste 516, Long Island City, NY 11101
Tel.: (646) 290-7448
Web Site: http://www.societyawards.com
Year Founded: 2007
Sales Range: $1-9.9 Million
Emp.: 8
Mfr of Custom Awards, Sculptures & Recognition Products
N.A.I.C.S.: 332999
David Moritz *(CEO)*
Larry Maloney *(COO)*

SOCIETY BRANDS, INC.
3033 Whipple Ave NW,, Canton, OH 44718
Tel.: (330) 354-8530
Web Site: https://www.societybrands.com
Year Founded: 2020
Software Publisher
N.A.I.C.S.: 513210
Michael Sirpilla *(Co-Founder & CEO)*

Subsidiaries:

Primal Life Organics, LLC (1)
405 Rothrock Rd Ste 105, Copley, OH 44321
Tel.: (800) 942-0178
Web Site: http://www.primallifeorganics.com
Sales Range: $1-9.9 Million
Emp.: 25
Skin Care Product Mfr
N.A.I.C.S.: 325620

SOCIETY FOR LEUKOCYTE BIOLOGY
9650 Rockville Pike, Bethesda, MD 20814
Tel.: (301) 634-7814   NJ
Web Site: http://www.leukocytebiology.org
Year Founded: 1971
Sales Range: $1-9.9 Million
Medical Professional Association
N.A.I.C.S.: 813920
Ann Richmond *(Pres)*
Mary Dinauer *(Treas)*

SOCIETY FOR NEUROSCIENCE
1121 14th St NW Ste 1010, Washington, DC 20005
Tel.: (202) 962-4000   DC
Web Site: http://www.sfn.org
Year Founded: 1969
Sales Range: $25-49.9 Million
Emp.: 118
Neuroscience Professional Organization
N.A.I.C.S.: 813920
Marty Saggese *(Exec Dir)*
Betsy S. Schultz *(Mgr-Facilities)*
Stuart Wales *(Mgr-HR)*
Marcia Leach *(Mgr-Sls & Mktg)*
Steven E. Hyman *(Pres)*

SOCIETY FOR SCIENCE & THE PUBLIC
1719 N St NW, Washington, DC 20036
Tel.: (202) 785-2255   DE
Web Site: http://www.societyforscience.org
Year Founded: 1921
Rev.: $31,991,156
Assets: $102,112,945
Liabilities: $12,488,259
Net Worth: $89,624,686
Earnings: $2,401,060
Fiscal Year-end: 12/31/21
Scientific Research Services
N.A.I.C.S.: 541715
Maya Ajmera *(Pres, CEO & Publr-Science News)*
Mary Sue Coleman *(Chm)*
Paul J. Maddon *(Sec)*
Erin Otwell *(Dir-Design)*
James C. Moore *(CTO)*
Kathlene Collins *(CMO)*
Stephen Egts *(Chief Design Officer)*
Michele Glidden *(Chief Program Officer)*
Gayle Kansagor *(Chief Comm Officer)*
Bruce Makous *(Chief Advancement Officer)*
Martin Chalfie *(Vice Chm)*
Karen Shelley *(Dir-Strategic Partnerships)*
Shannon Giorgianni *(Mgr-Institutional Giving & Special Projects)*
Dan Reznikov *(CFO)*
Nancy Shute *(Editor-in-Chief)*
Ed Maxwell *(Fin Dir)*
Eman Ahmed *(Mgr-Acctg)*
Eric Olson *(Dir-Annual Giving & Membership)*
Lisa Russell-Mina *(Dir-Major Gifts)*
Carole Russo *(Dir-Grants Admin)*
Michele Brenner *(Mgr-Dev Ops)*
Aparna Paul *(Comm Mgr)*
Eric Nguyen *(Mgr-Social Media)*
Nancy Baden Moulding *(Mgr-Design Ops)*
Tzeitel Fetter *(Dir-Events)*
Pratham Patkar *(Dir-IT)*
Krystal Robinson *(Mgr-Database Dev)*
Tracy Lee *(Dir-Digital Products)*
Daryl Anderson *(Dir-Media Sls)*
John Pierce *(Mgr-Mktg Automation)*
Caitlin Sullivan *(Dir-Outreach & Equity Programs)*
Allison Hewlett Stifel *(Dir-Regeneron Science Talent Search)*
Anna Rhymes *(Mgr-Program-Science News)*
Elizabeth Quill *(Editor-Special Projects)*
Macon Morehouse *(Dir-News)*
Kate Travis *(Dir-Digital)*

SOCIETY FOR THE PROTECTION OF NEW HAMPSHIRE FORESTS

SOCIETY FOR THE PROTECTION OF NEW HAMPSHIRE FORESTS — U.S. PRIVATE

Society for the Protection of New Hampshire Forests—(Continued)
54 Portsmouth St, Concord, NH 03301
Tel.: (603) 224-9945 NH
Web Site: http://www.forestsociety.org
Year Founded: 1901
Rev.: $10,497,544
Assets: $86,780,226
Liabilities: $786,427
Net Worth: $85,993,799
Earnings: $3,027,163
Fiscal Year-end: 04/30/18
Forest Protection & Conservation Services
N.A.I.C.S.: 813312
Jack Savage (VP-Comm & Outreach)
Will Abbott (VP-Policy & Reservation Stewardship)
Susanne Kibler-Hacker (VP-Dev)
Denise Vaillancourt (VP-Fin)
Deanna Howard (Chm)
Jane A. Difley (Pres)
Diane Forbes (Sr Dir-Dev)
Margaret Liszka (Dir-Membership)
Brenda Charpentier (Mgr-Comm)
Nigel Manley (Dir-North Country Property)
Carleen Quinn (Mgr-Retail & Events)
Reagan Bissonnette (Dir-Easement Stewardship)
Brian Hotz (VP-Land Conservation)
Tom Howe (Sr Dir-Land Conservation)
Carrie Deegan (Mgr-Volunteer & Community Engagement)
Ryan Young (Mgr-Strategic Projects)
Jenn Seredejko (Coord-Land Steward)
Rita Carroll (Coord-Policy & Reservation Stewardship)
Matt Leahy (Mgr-Policy)
Allan Krygeris (VP-Dev)

SOCIETY INSURANCE
150 Camelot Dr, Fond Du Lac, WI 54936-1029
Tel.: (920) 922-1220 WI
Web Site: http://www.societyinsurance.com
Year Founded: 1915
Sales Range: $50-74.9 Million
Emp.: 250
Workers Compensation, Commercial Packages & Commercial Auto Insurance
N.A.I.C.S.: 524126
Bill Bunzel (VP-Property)
Jim Putzer (Mgr-Workers Compensation Claims)
Mike Rosenau (Dir-Risk Control)
Tracy Schneider (Mgr-Claims)

SOCIETY OF BEHAVIORAL MEDICINE
555 E Wells St Ste 1100, Milwaukee, WI 53202-3823
Tel.: (414) 918-3156 NY
Web Site: http://www.sbm.org
Year Founded: 1979
Sales Range: $1-9.9 Million
Healthcare Professional Association
N.A.I.C.S.: 813920
Lindsay Bullock (Sr Mgr-Media & Member Comm)
Kevin S. Masters (Editor-Annals of Behavioral Medicine)
Erin Trimmer (Mgr-Meetings)
Marian L. Fitzgibbon (Pres)
Michael A. Diefenbach (Treas & Sec)
Tara Withington (Partner-Consulting)
Johanna Moss (Program Mgr)

SOCIETY OF EXPLORATION GEOPHYSICISTS
8801 S Yale Ave Ste 500, Tulsa, OK 74137-3575
Tel.: (918) 497-5500 OK
Web Site: http://www.seg.org
Year Founded: 1930
Sales Range: $10-24.9 Million
Emp.: 91
Geophysics Promotion Services
N.A.I.C.S.: 541715
Dana Falletti (Dir-Fin)
Don W. Steeples (Pres)
Jie Zhang (Second VP)
Mauricio Dino Sacchi (Editor)
Alison W. Small (Treas)
Dorsey Morrow (Sec)
John Holloway Bradford (Pres)

SOCIETY OF MANUFACTURING ENGINEERS
1 SME Dr, Dearborn, MI 48128-2408
Tel.: (313) 271-1500
Web Site: http://www.sme.org
Year Founded: 1969
Sales Range: $75-99.9 Million
Emp.: 140
Mfr Engineering Society; Publisher of Magazine; Promotion of Trade Related Events
N.A.I.C.S.: 813920
Steve Prahalis (COO)
Sandra Bouckley (Interim CEO)

SOCIETY OF PHOTO-OPTICAL INSTRUMENTATION ENGINEERS
1000 20th St, Bellingham, WA 98225-6705
Tel.: (360) 676-3290 WA
Web Site: http://www.spie.org
Year Founded: 1955
Sales Range: $25-49.9 Million
Emp.: 188
Instrumentation Engineer Association
N.A.I.C.S.: 813920
Toyohiko Yatagai (Pres)
Glenn D. Boreman (VP)
Kent Rochford (CEO)

SOCIUS MARKETING INC.
2701 N Rocky Point Dr Ste 410, Tampa, FL 33607
Tel.: (813) 282-8300
Web Site: http://www.sociusmarketing.com
Year Founded: 2006
Sales Range: $1-9.9 Million
Emp.: 2,100
Search Engine Optimization, Web Design, Marketing & Advertising Services
N.A.I.C.S.: 541890
William Harper (Co-Owner & CEO)
Chris Behan (Co-Owner, Pres & Chief Optimization Officer)
Bob Ford (Co-Owner & COO)
Stacy Behan (Co-Owner, Pres & Chief Optimization Officer)
Daniel Murphy (Owner)

SOCKET HOLDINGS CORP.
2703 Clark Ln, Columbia, MO 65202
Tel.: (573) 817-0000 MO
Web Site: http://www.socket.net
Year Founded: 1994
Sales Range: $10-24.9 Million
Emp.: 94
Telephone & Internet Service
N.A.I.C.S.: 517810
George Pfenenger (Co-Founder, Co-Owner & CEO)
Chris Force (Dir-Fin & Acctg)
Dave Sill (Mgr-IT)
Carson Coffman (Co-Founder & Co-Owner)

SOCO GROUP INC.
5962 Priestly Dr, Carlsbad, CA 92008-8812
Tel.: (858) 627-0440
Web Site: http://www.thesocogroup.com
Sales Range: $125-149.9 Million
Emp.: 175
Petroleum Product Distr
N.A.I.C.S.: 424720
Keith Skeans (VP-Retail)
Paul Olivier (CEO)
Toby Taitano (CFO)
Angus McDonald (Pres)
Rick Boatman (Chief Distr Officer)
Nick Sanden (VP-Retail & Dealer Ops)
Ron Lamb (COO)
Tobi Garber (Mgr-Retail)
Walt Bragg (Mgr-Territory)
Ed Laurino (Mgr-Territory)
Bob Miller (Plant Mgr-Casa Grande)
Robert Rivera (Plant Mgr-El Centro)
Scott Keller (Plant Mgr-Escondido)
Analiza Pitts (Plant Mgr-Indio)
Deanna Sylvester (Plant Mgr-Perris)
Kayla Torres (Plant Mgr-QC & LA)
Doug Robinson (VP-Sls)
Matt Davis (VP-Supply & Trading)

SOCORRO ELECTRIC COOPERATIVE
215 Manzanares Ave, Socorro, NM 87801
Tel.: (575) 835-0560
Web Site: http://www.socorroelectric.com
Emp.: 30
Electric Power Distr
N.A.I.C.S.: 221122
David Wade (VP)
Leo Cordova (Sec & Treas)
Eileen Latasa (Dir-HR)
Anne Dorough (Pres)

SOCOTHERM LABARGE
817 Shields St, Channelview, TX 77530
Tel.: (713) 378-7200
Sales Range: $10-24.9 Million
Emp.: 150
Construction Engineering Services
N.A.I.C.S.: 237310
Heather Frenza (Principal)

SODREL TRUCK LINES INC.
1 Sodrel Dr, Jeffersonville, IN 47129
Tel.: (812) 282-7941
Web Site: http://www.sodreltrucklines.com
Sales Range: $300-349.9 Million
Emp.: 150
Contract Haulers
N.A.I.C.S.: 484121
Noah Sodrel (Pres)
John Mayberry (Dir-Ops)

SOEHNLEN PIPING COMPANY
1400 W Main St, Louisville, OH 44641
Tel.: (330) 875-5513
Rev.: $10,600,000
Emp.: 40
Plumbing Contractor
N.A.I.C.S.: 238220
Gene Sitford (Chm)

SOELLINGEN ADVISORY GROUP, INC.
777 S Flagler Dr Ste 800, West Palm Beach, FL 33401
Tel.: (561) 214-4832 FL
Web Site: http://www.soellingen.com
Year Founded: 2013
Sales Range: Less than $1 Million
Business Advisory & Consulting Services
N.A.I.C.S.: 541611
David James Haig (CEO)
Raymond Skaff (Exec VP-Corp Comm & Mktg)
Nelson Riis (VP-Govt & Strategic Rels)
William D. Webb Jr. (CFO)

SOFIE BIOSCIENCES, INC.
6160 Bristol Pkwy, Culver City, CA 90230
Tel.: (310) 215-3159
Web Site: http://www.sofiebio.com
Research & Development in Biotechnology
N.A.I.C.S.: 541714
Patrick Phelps (Pres & CEO)
Melissa Moore (CTO)
Philipp Czernin (Chief Revenue Officer)
Ajit Singh (Chm)

SOFINNOVA VENTURES, INC.
3000 Sand Hill Rd Bldg 4 Ste 250, Menlo Park, CA 94025-7075
Tel.: (650) 681-8420
Web Site: http://www.sofinnova.com
Year Founded: 1974
Sales Range: $1-4.9 Billion
Emp.: 240
Venture Capital Firm
N.A.I.C.S.: 523999
Nathalie Auber (CFO & Partner)
Hooman Shahlavi (Partner & Gen Counsel)
Alfred Yue (Dir-Fin)
Lars G. Ekman (Partner)
Tina Giangiacomo-Yogya (Coord-Events)
Lesley Weber (Mgr-San Diego)
Tiffany Davis (Office Mgr)
Anand Mehra (Executives)
Charlotte Shropshire (Chief Compliance Officer)
James Brody (COO & Chief Compliance Officer)
Alan B. Colowick (Gen Partner)
James I. Healy (Gen Partner)
Michael F. Powell (Gen Partner)

Subsidiaries:

Xceive Corporation (1)
3900 Freedom Cir, Santa Clara, CA 95054
Tel.: (408) 486-5610
Rev.: $10,000,000
Emp.: 10
Radio & Television Broadcasting & Wireless Communications Equipment Mfr
N.A.I.C.S.: 334220

SOFT COMPUTER CONSULTANTS INC.
5400 Tech Data Dr, Clearwater, FL 33760
Tel.: (727) 789-0100 FL
Web Site: http://www.softcomputer.com
Year Founded: 1979
Sales Range: $25-49.9 Million
Emp.: 450
Integrated Clinical Laboratory Systems Information
N.A.I.C.S.: 541512
Gilbert Hakim (Founder & CEO)
Jean Hakim (Pres)

SOFT LANDING LABS LTD
747 Church Rd, Elmhurst, IL 60126
Tel.: (630) 424-0030
Web Site: http://www.softlandinglabs.com
Sales Range: $1-9.9 Million
Testing Laboratory
N.A.I.C.S.: 541380

A. Fahmy (CEO)
Farrah Tunk (CMO)
Kareem Fahmy (COO)
Ning Liu (Dir-Lab)
Kate Odallo (CFO)

SOFT TECH CONSULTING INC.
4229 Lafayette Ctr Dr Ste 1700, Chantilly, VA 20151
Tel.: (703) 348-1673
Web Site: http://www.softtechconsulting.com
Year Founded: 1996
Sales Range: $1-9.9 Million
Emp.: 100
Project Management & Software Development
N.A.I.C.S.: 513210
Christine Do (Founder & CEO)

SOFTEC SOLUTIONS, INC.
384 Inverness Pkwy Ste 211, Englewood, CO 80112
Tel.: (303) 662-1010
Web Site: http://www.softecinc.com
Year Founded: 1996
Sales Range: $10-24.9 Million
Emp.: 70
IT Consulting & Outsourcing Solutions
N.A.I.C.S.: 519290
Joseph Oltmann (Chm & CEO)
Stephanie Tolman (Mgr-HR)

SOFTEON, INC.
11700 Plz America Dr Ste 910, Herndon, VA 20190
Web Site: http://www.softeon.com
Software Publisher
N.A.I.C.S.: 513210
Gana Govind (Pres)

Subsidiaries:

GetUsROI LLC (1)
148 Westlake Pt, Montgomery, TX 77356
Tel.: (262) 264-0477
Web Site: http://www.getusroi.com
Sales Range: $1-9.9 Million
Software Development Services
N.A.I.C.S.: 541511
Mark Fralick (Pres)
Jalil Malik (Mgr-Ops)

SOFTERWARE, INC.
132 Welsh Rd Ste 140, Horsham, PA 19044
Tel.: (215) 628-0400
Web Site: http://www.softerware.com
Year Founded: 1982
Rev.: $18,100,000
Emp.: 140
Computer Programming Services
N.A.I.C.S.: 541511
Douglas Schoenberg (CEO)
Nathan Relles (Pres)
Michael Bronder (Mng Dir & VP-Computer Resources)

SOFTMAN PRODUCTS COMPANY, LLC
13470 Washington Blvd, Marina Del Rey, CA 90292
Tel.: (310) 305-3644
Web Site: http://www.buycheapsoftware.com
Year Founded: 1997
Sales Range: $10-24.9 Million
Emp.: 15
Computer Products Online Retailer
N.A.I.C.S.: 449210
Jonathan Dracup (CEO)
Brent Robinson (CFO)

SOFTNICE
5050 Tilghman St Ste 115, Allentown, PA 18104
Tel.: (610) 871-0400
Web Site: http://www.softnice.com
Year Founded: 2001
Sales Range: $1-9.9 Million
Emp.: 190
Staffing & Technical Support
N.A.I.C.S.: 561311
Zafar Shaikh (COO)
Robin Daniel (Mgr-Recruitment)

SOFTPRINT HOLDINGS, INC.
100 Carlson Rd, Rochester, NY 14610
Tel.: (585) 662-7810
Holding Company
N.A.I.C.S.: 551112
John M Lacagnina (CEO)

SOFTSOL RESOURCES
42808 Christy St Ste 100, Fremont, CA 94538
Tel.: (510) 824-2000
Web Site: http://www.softsol.com
Year Founded: 1993
Developer of Computer Software
N.A.I.C.S.: 541511
Srini Madala (Founder)
Robert Hersh (CFO)
R. K. Ghanta (VP-Consulting Svcs)

SOFTURA, INC
23570 Haggerty Rd, Farmington Hills, MI 48335
Tel.: (248) 344-2100
Web Site: http://www.softura.com
Year Founded: 1997
Sales Range: $1-9.9 Million
Emp.: 100
Custom Computer Programming Services
N.A.I.C.S.: 541511
Mark Murphy (CEO)
Mary Little (Office Mgr)
Swami Nathan (VP-Sls & Mktg)

SOFTWARE & INFORMATION INDUSTRY ASSOCIATION, INC.
1090 Vermont Ave NW 6th Fl, Washington, DC 20005
Tel.: (202) 289-7442
Web Site: http://www.siia.net
Emp.: 50
Government Relations, Business Development, Corporate Education & Intellectual Property Protection Services
N.A.I.C.S.: 561499
Ken Wasch (Pres)
Tom Davin (Mng Dir & Sr VP)
Tom Meldrum (VP-Fin & Admin)
Mark MacCarthy (VP-Pub Policy)
Eric Fredell (VP-Membership)
David LeDuc (Sr Dir-Pub Policy)
Heather Cejovic (Dir-Sponsorships & Recruitment)
Geri FitzGerald (Dir-Mktg & Strategic Svcs)
Anika King (Dir-Events & Sponsor Rels)
Carl Schonander (Sr Dir-Intl Policy)
Emily Ruf (Sr Dir-Mktg & Events)
Hope Wilkes (Mgr-Comm)
Jennifer Baranowski (Dir-Award)
Liz Martin (Sr Dir-Art & Comm)
Michael Marchesano (Mng Dir)
Nick Merritt (Dir-FISD Programs)
Ronn Levine (Dir-Editorial)
Tim Tyre (Dir-Internet Anti-Piracy)
Meg Hargreaves (Chm)

Subsidiaries:

American Business Media (1)
675 3rd Ave Ste 2200, New York, NY 10017-5704
Tel.: (212) 661-6360
Web Site: http://www.abmassociation.com

Sales Range: $10-24.9 Million
Emp.: 16
Specialized Business Publications
N.A.I.C.S.: 813910
Matthew Kinsman (VP-Content & Programming)
Heather Cejovic (Dir-Sponsorships & Recruitment)
Geri FitzGerald (Dir-Mktg & Strategic Svcs)

SOFTWARE DIVERSIFIED SERVICES
1322 81st Ave NE, Spring Lake Park, MN 55432
Tel.: (763) 571-9000
Web Site: http://www.sdsusa.com
Year Founded: 1981
Sales Range: $75-99.9 Million
Emp.: 20
Developer of Prepackaged Computer Software
N.A.I.C.S.: 513210
John Lampi (Pres)
James Lampi (VP-Sls & Mktg)

SOFTWARE FOLKS, INC.
50 Bridge St, Metuchen, NJ 08840
Tel.: (609) 945-1859
Web Site: http://www.softwarefolks.com
Year Founded: 1999
Sales Range: $10-24.9 Million
Emp.: 350
Custom Computer Programming
N.A.I.C.S.: 541511
Rohit Mahajan (Pres & CEO)

SOFTWARE GALAXY SYSTEMS, LLC
4390 Rte 1 N Ste 210, Princeton, NJ 08540
Tel.: (609) 919-1133
Web Site: http://www.sgsconsulting.com
Year Founded: 1997
Sales Range: $10-24.9 Million
Emp.: 70
Information Technology Consulting, Training & Outsourcing Services
N.A.I.C.S.: 541690
Ganesh Balan (Principal)
Srini Vengad (Principal)

SOFTWARE INFORMATION SYSTEMS
165 Barr St, Lexington, KY 40507
Tel.: (859) 977-4747
Web Site: http://www.capsonic.com
Sales Range: $25-49.9 Million
Emp.: 130
Custom Computer Programming Services
N.A.I.C.S.: 423430
Steve Sigg (CEO)
Patrick Cashman (Dir-Mktg)
Chris Sigg (CFO)

SOFTWARE MANAGEMENT CONSULTANTS INC.
500 N Brand Blvd Ste 1100, Glendale, CA 91203-3942
Tel.: (818) 240-3177
Web Site: http://www.smci.com
Year Founded: 1976
Rev.: $28,717,000
Emp.: 260
Computer Related Services & Consulting Services
N.A.I.C.S.: 541512
Spencer L. Karpf (Pres & CEO)

SOFTWARE PACKAGING ASSOCIATES INC
401 Milford Pkwy, Milford, OH 45150
Tel.: (513) 733-8800
Web Site: http://www.softpack.com
Year Founded: 1986

Sales Range: $10-24.9 Million
Emp.: 53
Packaging Of Software
N.A.I.C.S.: 423430
William O'Brian (Pres)

SOFTWARE PARADIGMS INTERNATIONAL GROUP LLC
5 Concourse Pkwy Ne Ste 500, Atlanta, GA 30328-6101
Tel.: (404) 582-6020
Web Site: http://www.spi.com
Year Founded: 1994
Sales Range: $10-24.9 Million
Emp.: 580
Computer System Design Services
N.A.I.C.S.: 541512
Sophie Mookerji (Chm)
Jeff Meaux (Sr VP-Svcs)
S. V. Krishnan (COO)
Jamilia Smith (Gen Counsel)
Sreedhar Kajeepeta (Head-Products, Solutions & Tech-Global)
Girish Karunakaran (Pres-Eurasia)
Steve Taylor (Sr VP-Product Delivery)
Britt Fogg (Sr VP-Product Ops)
Kurt Gibbons (Sr VP-Products & Solution Sls)
David Cochenour (VP & Head-HR-Global)
Robert Barronton (VP-Client Rels)
Tim Hill (VP-Infrastructure Svcs)
Alejandra Sosa (VP-Ops)
Almaz Nanjappa (Sr VP-Innovation Labs)
Andres Angelani (CEO)
Bret Cunningham (Sr VP-Digital Consulting)
Christopher Walton (VP-Guilds)
Jason Elkin (VP-Talent Acquisition)
John Stossel (VP-Solutions)
Laurentiu Russo (Founder & CTO)
Snjezana Cvoro-Begovic (Chief Partnerships Officer)
Tom Delbrook (CFO-Global & Head-Legal Svcs)

SOFTWARE PROFESSIONALS INCORPORATED
1029 Long Prairie Rd Ste A, Flower Mound, TX 75022-4344
Tel.: (972) 518-0198
Web Site: http://www.spius.net
Sales Range: $10-24.9 Million
Emp.: 175
Systems Integration & Custom Software Development
N.A.I.C.S.: 541511
Reena Batra (Pres)

SOFTWARE TECHNICAL SERVICES
105 Noble Ct, Alpharetta, GA 30005
Tel.: (678) 254-1000
Rev.: $19,738,435
Emp.: 26
System Software Development Services
N.A.I.C.S.: 541512
Pundi Narasimham (Pres)
Ruby Ruby (Pres-IT Staffing)
Suja Suja (VP-IT Staffing)

SOFTWARE TRANSFORMATIONS, INC.
16901 N Dallas Pkwy Ste 103, Addison, TX 75001
Tel.: (972) 746-4114
Web Site: http://www.softtrans.net
Sales Range: $1-9.9 Million
Emp.: 78
Custom Application Development Services
N.A.I.C.S.: 541511
Venkat Sri (Owner)

SOFTWARENOLOGY, LLC

Softwarenology, LLC—(Continued)

SOFTWARENOLOGY, LLC
4522 Executive Dr Ste 202, Naples, FL 34119
Tel.: (305) 741-5507
Web Site:
http://www.softwarenology.com
Sales Range: $1-9.9 Million
Software Developer
N.A.I.C.S.: 513210
Marcos Quiros (CEO)
Jasan Alvarez (Chief Product Officer)
Emilio Baez (Pres)

SOFTWAREPUNDITS, INC.
20 Burlington Mall Rd, Burlington, MA 01803
Tel.: (781) 229-6655
Rev.: $15,653,000
Emp.: 71
Computer Related Consulting Services
N.A.I.C.S.: 541512
Deepu Suresh (Mgr-Bus Dev)
Jogesh Nair (Mgr-Bus Dev)

SOG INTERNATIONAL, INC.
240 Harmon Ave, Lebanon, OH 45036
Tel.: (513) 932-8148 OH
Web Site:
http://www.southernohiogun.com
Year Founded: 1918
Sales Range: $75-99.9 Million
Emp.: 7
Firearm Sales
N.A.I.C.S.: 423910
Richard Herdtner (Pres)

SOHNEN ENTERPRISES INC.
8945 Vice Rd, Santa Fe Springs, CA 90670-2618
Tel.: (562) 946-3531
Web Site: http://www.sohnen.com
Year Founded: 1973
Sales Range: $25-49.9 Million
Emp.: 550
Radio & Television Repair Services
N.A.I.C.S.: 811210
Bryan Chase (Controller)

SOICHER MARIN OF FLORIDA LLC
7245 16th St E Ste 110, Sarasota, FL 34243
Tel.: (941) 308-7500 CA
Web Site: http://www.soicher-marin.com
Year Founded: 1959
Sales Range: $1-9.9 Million
Emp.: 37
Commercial Art & Wall Decor
N.A.I.C.S.: 459920
Jennifer Balest (VP-Sls)

SOIL & MATERIALS ENGINEERS, INC.
The Kramer Bldg 43980 Plymouth Oaks Blvd, Plymouth, MI 48170-2584
Tel.: (734) 454-9900 MI
Web Site: http://www.sme-usa.com
Year Founded: 1964
Sales Range: $25-49.9 Million
Emp.: 250
Geosciences, Materials & Environmental Consultancy Services
N.A.I.C.S.: 541620
Kenneth W. Kramer (Founder)
Mark K. Kramer (CEO)
Michael S. Meddock (Mgr-Columbus)
Robert C. Rabeler (Sr VP)
Andrew J. Emmert (CFO & Sr VP)
Chuck A. Gemayel (COO & Sr VP)

Subsidiaries:

EDP Geosciences (1)
9375 Chillicothe Rd, Kirtland, OH 44094-8501
Tel.: (440) 256-6500
Sales Range: $1-9.9 Million
Emp.: 50
Geosciences & Environmental Consulting Services
N.A.I.C.S.: 541620
John E. Dingeldein (VP)
Anthony L. Jarem (Principal)
Joseph W. Petraus (VP)

SOIL WATER SNOW, LLC
1379 W 3300 South, Salt Lake City, UT 84119
Tel.: (801) 972-8725 UT
Web Site: http://www.plazacycle.com
Rev.: $30,000,000
Emp.: 60
Motorcycle Dealers
N.A.I.C.S.: 441227
Claude Hicken (Pres)
Greg Seguel (Gen Mgr)

SOKOL & COMPANY
5315 Dansher Rd, Countryside, IL 60525-3101
Tel.: (708) 482-8250 IL
Web Site: http://www.solofoods.com
Year Founded: 1895
Sales Range: $75-99.9 Million
Emp.: 50
Cake, Pastry & Dessert Fillings, Fruit Glazes, Ice Cream Toppings, Crunches & Almond Paste
N.A.I.C.S.: 311999
Ralph Pirritano (COO & Exec VP)
Eva Karnezis (Mgr-Mktg)
Pat Rochan (Controller)
Shawn M. Sullivan (CEO)
Tim Novak (Chm)
John Pimpo (VP-Ingredients, Sls & Mktg)
Lauren Davis (VP-Fin & Strategy)

SOL CARE SERVICES, INC.
PO Box 1419, Pharr, TX 78577-1419
Tel.: (956) 787-7030 TX
Web Site:
http://www.solcareservices.com
Year Founded: 1990
Sales Range: $10-24.9 Million
Emp.: 32
Child & Adult Care Services
N.A.I.C.S.: 624210
Clemencia Cuellar (Exec Dir)
Magdalena Gonzalez-Paniagua (Dir-Fin)

SOL SYSTEMS
1718 Connecticut Ave NW Third Floor, Washington, DC 20009
Tel.: (202) 349-2085
Web Site: http://www.solsystems.com
Year Founded: 2008
Sales Range: $1-9.9 Million
Emp.: 40
Renewable Energy & Project Financing
N.A.I.C.S.: 221118
Yuri Horwitz (Co-Founder & CEO)
George Ashton (Co-Founder & Pres)
Leslie Barkemeyer (Deputy Gen Counsel)
Andrew Gilligan (Sr Dir-Investments)
Colin Murchie (Sr Dir-Customer Energy Svcs)
Sara Rafalson (Dir-Policy & New Markets)
James Machulak (Dir-Asset Mgmt)
Jason Cimpl (Sr Dir-Trading)
Joe Song (Sr Dir-Investment Analysis)
Liz Barentzen (Chief Culture Officer)
Dan Yonkin (VP-Fin)

Elizabeth Weir (COO)
Scott Day (CTO)
Michael Woods (Gen Counsel)
Chip Hoagland (CFO & Treas)

SOL'S PIPE & STEEL INC.
4951 Transport Dr, Monroe, LA 71203
Tel.: (318) 387-2242
Web Site:
http://www.solspipeandsteel.com
Rev.: $17,000,000
Emp.: 60
Steel Pipes Mfr & Whslr
N.A.I.C.S.: 423510
Jackie Rosenberg (Pres)

SOLACE CAPITAL PARTNERS, LLC
11111 Santa Monica Blvd Ste 1275, Los Angeles, CA 90025
Tel.: (310) 919-5401
Web Site: http://www.solacecap.com
Privater Equity Firm
N.A.I.C.S.: 523999
Vincent J. Cebula (Co-Founder)
Christopher S. Brothers (Mng Partner)
Brian Moody (Mng Dir & Operating Partner)
Tom Beatty (CEO)
Naeem Arastu (Mng Dir)
Hilary Adams (Principal-IR)
Xavuier Corzo (Principal, Chief Admin Officer & Chief Compliance Officer)
Tracy Chow (VP)
Depa Makhija (VP-Acctg & Fin)
Andrew Morris (Principal)
Brett G. Wyard (Mng Partner)

Subsidiaries:

CST Industries, Inc. (1)
903 E104th St Ste 900, Kansas City, MO 64131
Tel.: (913) 621-3700
Web Site: http://www.cstindustries.com
Metal Storage Tanks
N.A.I.C.S.: 332420
Brad Barkley (VP-Global Ops)
Tim Carpenter (Pres & CEO)
Tom Dedonder (VP-Construction & Svcs)
Greg Hentschel (VP-Global Engrg)
Jim Hickey (CFO)
Matt Gregg (VP)
Erik Carson (VP-Global Sls)
Jonathan Starmach (VP-HR)

Division (Non-US):

CST Industries (Manufacturing Facility), Inc. - UK (2)
Cotes Park Lane, Cotes Park Industrial Estate, Alfreton, DE55 4NJ, Derbyshire, United Kingdom
Tel.: (44) 1773835321
Web Site: http://www.cstindustries.com
Storage Tank Repairs & Maintenance
N.A.I.C.S.: 332420

Subsidiary (Domestic):

CST Manufacturing Facility Conroe (CST Covers) (2)
498 N Loop 336 E, Conroe, TX 77301
Tel.: (713) 290-9944
Web Site: http://www.cstindustries.com
Fabricated Structural Metal Design & Mfr
N.A.I.C.S.: 332312

Division (Domestic):

DeKalb Manufacturing Facility (CST Storage) (2)
345 Harvestore Dr, Dekalb, IL 60115
Tel.: (815) 756-1551
Web Site: http://www.cstindustries.com
Storage Structure Erection & Manufacture
N.A.I.C.S.: 332420

Fabcon Precast LLC (1)
6111 W Hwy 13, Savage, MN 55378-1298
Tel.: (952) 890-4444
Web Site: http://www.fabcon-usa.com

Panels & Sections; Pre-Cast Concrete Products Mfr & Distr
N.A.I.C.S.: 327390
Mark Hansen (VP-Reconstruction Svcs)
Jim Houtman (VP-Sls & Mktg)
Jeffrey Prewitt (COO)
Mark Pederson (CFO)
Kim Capel (VP-Technical Svcs)
John Allgaier (VP-Bus Dev & Supply Chain)
Tony Secton (Production Mgr)
Abby School (Coord-Field)
Linda Whitmore (Dir-Admin)
Adam Leuthner (Asst Project Mgr)
Jake Rubash (Engr-Mfg)
Justin Ofsthun (Mgr-Environmental Health & Safety)
Cody Lang (Engr-Corp Materials)
Mitul Desai (Project Engr)
Mike Rafi (CEO)

Division (Domestic):

Kerkstra Precast, Inc. (2)
3373 Busch Dr, Grandville, MI 49418
Tel.: (616) 224-6176
Web Site: http://www.kerkstra.com
Sales Range: $10-24.9 Million
Emp.: 150
Precast Concrete Building & Infrastructure Products Mfr
N.A.I.C.S.: 238120
Greg Kerkstra (Pres & CEO)
Steve Haskill (Dir-Estimating & Project Mgmt)
Lynn Zylman (Sr Project Mgr)
Andy Eustice (Project Mgr)
Scott Brower (Project Mgr)
Scott Bosscher (Mgr-CAD)
Scott Woodard (Plant Mgr)
Ray Simmons (Mgr-Yard)
James Morgan (Mgr-Specialty Production)
Lisa DeRoo (Mgr-HR)
Amy Bronkema (Engr-Structural)
John Kaashoek (Engr-Structural)
Kurt DeKock (Dir-Ops)
Nathan Krause (Engr-Structural)
Phil Holtrop (CFO)
Susan Rollins (Dir-Quality, Safety & Lean)
Zach Morrison (Engr-Structural)

Sun Mountain Sports Inc. (1)
301 N First St W, Missoula, MT 59802-3625
Tel.: (406) 728-9224
Web Site: http://www.sunmountain.com
Sales Range: $25-49.9 Million
Emp.: 400
Supplier of Sporting & Athletic Goods
N.A.I.C.S.: 339920
Ed Kowaphek (Mgr-Sls)
Blake Ludwig (Controller)
Mark Heydon (VP-Outerwear)
Vincent Chong (Mgr-IT)
Ping Lin (Dir-Outsourcing & Supply Chain Mgmt)

SOLAI & CAMERON INC.
3410 W Van Buren, Chicago, IL 60624
Tel.: (773) 506-2720
Web Site: http://www.solcam.com
Year Founded: 1994
Custom Computer Programming Services
N.A.I.C.S.: 541511
Mallar Solai (Pres)

SOLANA ENVIRONMENTAL ASSOCIATES INC.
503 S 57th St, Tampa, FL 33619
Tel.: (813) 621-2872
Web Site: http://www.solana-env.com
Sales Range: $1-9.9 Million
N.A.I.C.S.:
Valerie R. Coton (Founder & Pres)

SOLANO COUNTY COMMUNITY HOUSING CORPORATION
1049 Union Ave Ste A, Fairfield, CA 94533
Tel.: (707) 422-5919 CA
Year Founded: 1993
Sales Range: $10-24.9 Million

Home Rental Services
N.A.I.C.S.: 624190
Dennis McCray (Exec Dir)

SOLAR ART WINDOW FILM, INC.
9301 Research Dr, Irvine, CA 92618
Tel.: (949) 770-8969   CA
Web Site: http://www.solarart.com
Year Founded: 1985
Sales Range: $1-9.9 Million
Emp.: 61
Commercial Building Window Film Installation Services
N.A.I.C.S.: 238990
Matthew Darienzo (Pres & CEO)
Michelle Benyamini (Mgr-Ops-Los Angeles)
Dawn Baggs (Dir-Ops)
Brian Lagestee (COO)

Subsidiaries:

American Window Film Inc   (1)
21 Cocasset St, Foxboro, MA 02035
Tel.: (508) 549-0300
Web Site:
   http://www.americanwindowfilm.com
Rev.: $1,200,000
Emp.: 12
Commercial & Institutional Building Construction
N.A.I.C.S.: 236220
James N. Maloof (VP-Sls)
Peter Davey (Pres)
James S. Davey (VP-Ops)

Amersol, Inc.   (1)
9750 Skillman St, Dallas, TX 75243
Tel.: (214) 503-9977
Web Site: http://www.amersol.com
Sales Range: $1-9.9 Million
Emp.: 14
Lumber, Plywood, Millwork & Wood Panel Merchant Whslr
N.A.I.C.S.: 423310
Rick Dietel (Pres)

Metro Tint   (1)
7014 N 27th Ave Ste 1, Phoenix, AZ 85051-8411
Tel.: (602) 589-5385
Web Site: http://www.metrotint.com
Other Building Material Dealers
N.A.I.C.S.: 444180

Royal Window Films, Inc.   (1)
1425 N Central Park Ave, Anaheim, CA 92805
Tel.: (714) 535-6676
Web Site: http://www.royalwindowfilms.com
Emp.: 10
Window Film Installation Services
N.A.I.C.S.: 238990
John Henderson (VP-Sls)

The Brower Glass Tinting Company   (1)
245 SW 41st St 11-A, Renton, WA 98057
Tel.: (425) 251-6849
Web Site: http://www.tintandgraphics.com
Sales Range: $1-9.9 Million
Emp.: 12
Glass & Glazing Contractors
N.A.I.C.S.: 238150
Richard Sorrells (Pres)

Window Solutions, Inc.   (1)
1161 Chess Dr Ste C, Foster City, CA 94404
Tel.: (650) 349-2499
Web Site: http://www.windowsolutions.com
Sales Range: $1-9.9 Million
Emp.: 15
Window Installation Services
N.A.I.C.S.: 238990
Paul Murphy (VP-Sls)

SOLAR ATMOSPHERES, INC.
1983 Clearview Rd, Souderton, PA 18964-0476
Tel.: (215) 721-1502
Web Site: http://www.solaratm.com
Year Founded: 2000
Sales Range: $10-24.9 Million
Emp.: 75
Metal Heat Treating Services
N.A.I.C.S.: 332811
William R. Jones (Founder & CEO)
Roger A. Jones (Pres)
Robert S. Sandora (VP-Ops)
Robert Hill (Pres-Solar Atmospheres)
Mike Moffit (VP-Ops-California)

Subsidiaries:

Vac-Met, Inc.   (1)
7236 Murthum Ave, Warren, MI 48092
Tel.: (586) 264-8100
Web Site: http://www.vac-met.com
Sales Range: $1-9.9 Million
Emp.: 20
Metal Heat Treating Services
N.A.I.C.S.: 332811

SOLAR FUNDING SOLUTIONS CORP.
142 Island Way Ste 252, Clearwater Beach, FL 33767
Tel.: (727) 667-9424   FL
Year Founded: 2007
Sales Range: $10-24.9 Million
Emp.: 1
Solar Installation Products & Solutions
N.A.I.C.S.: 238210
Michael J. Daniels (Chm, Pres, CEO & CFO)

SOLAR INDUSTRIES INC.
6151 S Tucson Blvd, Tucson, AZ 85706
Tel.: (520) 519-8258   AZ
Web Site:
   http://www.solarindustriesinc.com
Year Founded: 1976
Sales Range: $10-24.9 Million
Emp.: 25
Mfr of Interior Lighting
N.A.I.C.S.: 327211
Jennifer Burns (CEO)
Kent Vella (VP-Waste & Recycle)

SOLAR INNOVATIONS, INC.
31 Roberts Rd, Pine Grove, PA 17963
Tel.: (570) 915-1500
Web Site:
   http://www.solarinnovations.com
Year Founded: 1998
Sales Range: $10-24.9 Million
Emp.: 128
Residential Glass Enclosure Mfr & Distr
N.A.I.C.S.: 327211
Greg Header (Pres)
Darren Coder (VP-Installation)
Meghan Dagle (Engr-Design)
Andreja Rocknage (Project Coord)

SOLAR LIBERTY
6500 Sheridan Dr Ste 120, Buffalo, NY 14221
Tel.: (716) 634-3780
Web Site: http://www.solarliberty.com
Year Founded: 2003
Sales Range: $10-24.9 Million
Emp.: 21
Solar Electric Systems
N.A.I.C.S.: 221114
Adam Rizzo (Co-Founder)
Nathan Rizzo (Co-Founder)
Jun Zha (Engr-Mechanical)
Michael Prinzi (Project Mgr)
Lance Lombardo (Engr-Electrical)
Paul Lavoie (Gen Counsel)

SOLAR SOLUTIONS & DISTRIBUTION, LLC.
8450 E Crescent Pkwy Ste 350, Greenwood Village, CO 80111
Tel.: (303) 948-6300
Web Site: http://www.soldist.com
Year Founded: 2009
Sales Range: $10-24.9 Million
Emp.: 32
Air Conditioning System Installation Services
N.A.I.C.S.: 238220
Michael Pyle (Owner)

SOLAR SOURCES, INC.
6755 Gray Rd, Indianapolis, IN 46237
Tel.: (317) 788-0084   IN
Sales Range: $75-99.9 Million
Emp.: 300
Coal Mining Services
N.A.I.C.S.: 212114
Felson Bowman (Chm & CEO)
Sergio Guerrero (Mgr-IT)

SOLAR SUPPLY, INC.
1212 12th St, Lake Charles, LA 70601-6376
Tel.: (337) 310-1000   LA
Web Site: http://www.solarsupply.us
Year Founded: 1954
Sales Range: $25-49.9 Million
Emp.: 185
Wholesale Refrigeration & Heating
N.A.I.C.S.: 423730
Ronald R. Dingler (Chm & Pres)
Charlotte D. Guillory (Sec)
Charmaine D. Yelverton (VP)

Subsidiaries:

Solar Supply of Houston Inc.   (1)
1212 12th St, Lake Charles, LA 70601-6376
Tel.: (337) 310-1000
Sales Range: $25-49.9 Million
Refrigeration Equipment & Supplies
N.A.I.C.S.: 423730

Solar Supply of Lafayette Inc.   (1)
1212 12th St, Lake Charles, LA 70601-6376   (100%)
Tel.: (337) 310-1000
Web Site: http://www.solarsupply.us
Sales Range: $10-24.9 Million
Emp.: 20
Heating & Air Conditioning Equipment Distr
N.A.I.C.S.: 423730

Solar Supply of Lake Charles Inc.   (1)
1212 12th St, Lake Charles, LA 70601-6376
Tel.: (337) 310-1000
Web Site: http://www.ut.com
Sales Range: $10-24.9 Million
Emp.: 20
Warm Air Heating & Air Conditioning
N.A.I.C.S.: 423730

Solar Supply of Louisiana Inc.   (1)
1212 12th St, Lake Charles, LA 70601-6376
Tel.: (337) 310-1000
Web Site: http://www.solarsupply.com
Sales Range: $25-49.9 Million
Warm Air Heating & Air Conditioning
N.A.I.C.S.: 423730
Ron Dingler (Owner)

SOLAR SYSTEMS & PERIPHERALS
8134 304th Ave SE Bldg 3, Preston, WA 98050
Tel.: (425) 222-7588
Web Site:
   http://www.solarsystems.com
Year Founded: 1992
Sales Range: $10-24.9 Million
Emp.: 24
Computers, Peripherals & Software Sales
N.A.I.C.S.: 423430
E. Paul Cooke (CEO)

SOLAR UNIVERSE INC.
1152 Stealth St, Livermore, CA 94551
Tel.: (925) 455-4700
Web Site:
   http://www.solaruniverse.com
Year Founded: 2008
Sales Range: $25-49.9 Million
Emp.: 250
Solar Electric System Installation Services
N.A.I.C.S.: 238220
Joseph Bono (Founder)
Stephen M. Schmidt (Gen Counsel, Sec & VP-Corp Dev)
Elton Hart (VP-Sls)
Michael Mahre (COO)
Mahesh Mansukhani (CEO)
Daniel Rubin (Chief Revenue Officer & Sr VP-REPOWER)
Joseph Barghouthi (Dir-Channel Dev)
Aamir Khan (Dir-Enablement)
Josh Schlipp (VP-Franchise Bus Mgmt)

SOLAR VELOCITY
3300 Highland Pkwy Ste 260, Smyrna, GA 30082
Tel.: (404) 978-2240
Web Site:
   http://www.solarvelocity.com
Year Founded: 1999
Sales Range: $10-24.9 Million
Emp.: 12
Advetising Agency
N.A.I.C.S.: 541810
Jason Swenk (Co-Founder & CEO)
Kirby J. Winters (Co-Founder & COO)
Mike Hunt (Dir-Mktg)

SOLAR WIND ENERGY, INC.
1997 Annapolis Exchange Pkwy Ste 300, Annapolis, MD 21401
Tel.: (410) 972-4713
Web Site:
   http://www.solarwindenergytower.com
Year Founded: 2010
Wind Electric Power Generation Services
N.A.I.C.S.: 221115
Ronald W. Pickett (Chm, Pres & CEO)

SOLARAY CORPORATION
761 Ahua St, Honolulu, HI 96819
Tel.: (808) 523-0711
Web Site: http://www.solarsupply.com
Year Founded: 1975
Sales Range: $10-24.9 Million
Emp.: 23
Solar Heating Equipment & Panels
N.A.I.C.S.: 333414
Richard R. Reed (Pres)

Subsidiaries:

Pacific Liquid and Air Systems   (1)
761 Ahua St, Honolulu, HI 96819
Tel.: (808) 523-0711
Web Site: http://www.pacificliquid.com
Sales Range: $10-24.9 Million
Emp.: 7
Distr of Pumps, Electric Motors, Motor Controls & Pump Accessories
N.A.I.C.S.: 423830
Brad Whitten (Gen Mgr)

SunEarth, Inc.   (1)
8425 Almeria Ave, Fontana, CA 92335
Tel.: (909) 434-3100
Web Site: http://www.sunearthinc.com
Sales Range: $10-24.9 Million
Mfr of Solar Thermal Collectors, Systems & Ancillary Equipment
N.A.I.C.S.: 333414

SOLARIS POWER CELLS, INC.
3111 E Tahquitz Way, Palm Springs, CA 92262
Tel.: (760) 600-5272   NV
Web Site:
   http://www.solarispowercells.com
Year Founded: 2007
Sales Range: Less than $1 Million

SOLARIS POWER CELLS, INC.   U.S. PRIVATE

Solaris Power Cells, Inc.—(Continued)
Renewable Energy Storage Device Mfr
N.A.I.C.S.: 335910
Steve Lawrence (COO)

SOLARITY CREDIT UNION
PO Box 2922, Yakima, WA 98907
Tel.: (509) 248-1720   WA
Web Site: http://www.solaritycu.org
Year Founded: 1951
Sales Range: $10-24.9 Million
Emp.: 167
Credit Union Operator
N.A.I.C.S.: 522130
Mina Worthington (Pres & CEO)
Chad Ritchie (CIO)
Gene DeLuca (VP-New Market Dev)

SOLARONE SOLUTIONS, INC.
220 Reservoir St Ste 19, Needham, MA 02494
Tel.: (339) 225-4530
Web Site: http://www.solarone.net
Year Founded: 2004
Solar Outdoor Lighting Equipment Mfr
N.A.I.C.S.: 335139
Moneer Azzam (Pres & CEO)
Ilze Greene (Dir-Sls & Mktg)

Subsidiaries:

Inovus Solar, Inc.   (1)
3380 W Americana Ter Ste 230, Boise, ID 83706-2554
Tel.: (208) 908-0627
Web Site: http://www.inovussolar.com
Solar Outdoor Lighting Equipment Mfr
N.A.I.C.S.: 335139
Bruce Eastman (COO & Dir)
Doug Stewart (CEO)
Clay Young (Co-Founder & Chm)
Kent Walker (VP-Mfg)
Mary Givens (Dir)
David E. Gonzalez (VP-Solutions)

SOLARTECH UNIVERSAL CORP.
150 Motor Pkwy, Hauppauge, NY 11788
Tel.: (631) 485-5800
Web Site: http://www.solartechuniversal.com
Sales Range: $1-9.9 Million
Solar Panel Mfr
N.A.I.C.S.: 333414
Louis Koster (Mng Partner)
Boris Rosenstein (Mng Partner)

SOLARUS
440 E Grand Ave, Wisconsin Rapids, WI 54494
Tel.: (715) 421-8111
Web Site: http://www.solarus.net
Sales Range: $25-49.9 Million
Emp.: 125
Local Telephone Communications
N.A.I.C.S.: 517121
Doug Wenzlaff (CEO)
Jerry Johnson (Controller)
Delbert Gear (VP)
Dave Miller (Chm)
Jim Timmerman (Pres)

SOLARX EYEWEAR LLC
4210 Foltz Industrial Pkwy, Strongsville, OH 44149
Tel.: (866) 298-0433
Web Site: http://www.solarxeyewear.com
Eyewear Mfr
N.A.I.C.S.: 333310

SOLBERG MANUFACTURING INC.
1151 Ardmore Ave, Itasca, IL 60143
Tel.: (630) 616-4400
Web Site: http://www.solbergmfg.com
Year Founded: 1968
Sales Range: $10-24.9 Million
Emp.: 95
Mfr of Filters & Silencers
N.A.I.C.S.: 333413
Tor Solberg (Pres)
Dave Wells (Mgr-Quality Assurance)
Charles H. Solberg Sr. (Founder & Chm)

SOLCO PLUMBING SUPPLY INC.
413 Liberty Ave, Brooklyn, NY 11207-3004
Tel.: (718) 345-1900
Web Site: http://www.solco.com
Year Founded: 1975
Sales Range: $10-24.9 Million
Emp.: 100
Plumbing Fixtures, Equipment & Supplies
N.A.I.C.S.: 423720
Stuart Baker (Pres)
Stanford Weiner (VP)
Lesley Ober (VP)
Steve Miller (CFO)

SOLE SOURCE CAPITAL LLC
1299 Ocean Ave Ste 410, Santa Monica, CA 90401
Tel.: (310) 844-1800
Web Site: http://solesourcecapital.com
Year Founded: 2016
Privater Equity Firm
N.A.I.C.S.: 523999
David Fredston (Founder & CEO)
Scott Sussman (Partner-M&A)
Dewey Turner (Pres-Portfolio Ops & Partner)

Subsidiaries:

Chef's Choice Produce Co.   (1)
395 Commercial St, San Jose, CA 95112
Tel.: (408) 213-3880
Web Site: http://www.chefschoiceproduce.com
Fresh Fruit & Vegetable Merchant Whslr
N.A.I.C.S.: 424480
Candie Thompson (Principal)

Dallas Plastics Corporation   (1)
924 Dalworth Dr, Mesquite, TX 75149
Tel.: (972) 289-5500
Web Site: http://www.dallasplastics.com
Plastic Mfr
N.A.I.C.S.: 326111
Kevin Piere (CEO)

Subsidiary (Domestic):

Hi-De Liners, LLC   (2)
131 W Main St, Orange, MA 01364
Tel.: (978) 544-7801
Web Site: http://www.hideliners.com
Paper, except Newsprint, Mills
N.A.I.C.S.: 322120
Donna Horne (VP)
William Horne (Pres)

Peak Technologies, Inc.   (1)
10330 Old Columbia Rd, Columbia, MD 21046
Tel.: (480) 092-6921
Web Site: https://www.peaktech.com
Sales Range: $150-199.9 Million
Emp.: 500
Automatic Identification & Data Collection Equipment & Systems, Enterprise Mobility Solutions & Support Services
N.A.I.C.S.: 333248
Ross M. Young (Chm)
Michele Adams (CFO)
Tim Wills (CMO)
Juliann Larimer (Chm)
Brad Tracy (Sr VP-Sls-North America)
Jim Polcaro (CIO)
Janet Johnson (Sr Dir-Mktg)

Subsidiary (Domestic):

Bar Code Direct, Inc.   (2)
41 N Main St, North Grafton, MA 01536
Tel.: (508) 839-1600
Web Site: http://www.barcodedirect.com
Sales Range: $1-9.9 Million
Emp.: 10
Barcode & Label Software Distr
N.A.I.C.S.: 423430
Derek Frost (Dir-Sls)

DBK Concepts Inc.   (2)
12905 SW 129th Ave, Miami, FL 33186
Tel.: (305) 596-7226
Web Site: http://www.dbk.com
Computer Repair Services
N.A.I.C.S.: 811210
Daniel Katz (Founder & CEO)
Louis Barroso (Pres)
Eric Katz (Exec VP-Ops)
Rene Rodriguez (VP-Tech Svcs)

Graphic Label, Inc.   (2)
110 S 2nd Ave, Yakima, WA 98902
Tel.: (509) 457-1833
Web Site: http://www.graphiclabel.com
Sales Range: $1-9.9 Million
Emp.: 10
Stationery & Office Supplies Merchant Whslr
N.A.I.C.S.: 424120

Inovity, Inc.   (2)
5775 Peachtree Dunwoody Rd Ste D-550, Atlanta, GA 30342
Tel.: (678) 904-9040
Web Site: http://www.inovity.com
Rev.: $2,300,000
Emp.: 21
Computer System Design Services
N.A.I.C.S.: 541512
Steven T. George (Exec VP)
Jack A. Tinsley Jr. (Pres)

Subsidiary (Domestic):

ADC Integrated Systems, Inc.   (3)
1180 Vickery Ln Ste 101, Cordova, TN 38016-0629
Tel.: (901) 327-9946
Web Site: http://www.adcisi.com
Computer Related Services
N.A.I.C.S.: 541519
Robert F. Cooper (Pres)

Subsidiary (Domestic):

Manage Mobility, LLC   (2)
2555 Marconi Dr Ste 100, Alpharetta, GA 30005
Tel.: (678) 578-4040
Web Site: http://www.managemobility.com
Wireless & Telecom Consulting Solutions
N.A.I.C.S.: 517112
Mike McGuire (Pres)
David McMinn (VP-Ops)
Stacy Chisum (VP-Bus Dev)

North Coast Technical Sales, Inc.   (2)
8251 Mayfield Rd Ste 105, Chesterland, OH 44026
Tel.: (440) 729-7540
Web Site: http://www.nctechsales.com
Sales Range: $1-9.9 Million
Emp.: 10
Electronic Parts And Equipment, Nec, Nsk
N.A.I.C.S.: 423690
Dave Sexton (CEO)

Division (Domestic):

Peak-Catalyst   (2)
6009 Williams Rd, Norcross, GA 30093
Tel.: (770) 837-0427
Web Site: http://www.peak-catalyst.com
Sales Range: $50-74.9 Million
Supply Chain Management Software Mfr
N.A.I.C.S.: 513210

Subsidiary (Domestic):

Ryzex Inc.   (2)
4600 Ryzex Way, Bellingham, WA 98226-7691
Tel.: (360) 715-2000
Web Site: http://www.ryzex.com
Sales Range: $10-24.9 Million
Emp.: 200
Automated Data Collection Hardware & Software Products
N.A.I.C.S.: 541519

Telpar, Inc.   (2)
121 Broadway Ste 201, Dover, NH 03820
Tel.: (603) 750-7237
Web Site: http://www.telpar.com
Commercial Printers Mfr & Whslr
N.A.I.C.S.: 333248
Vicki L. Pillsbury (Grp VP-Mfg & Logistics)

Supply Chain Services, LLC   (1)
7800 Third St N Ste 920, Oakdale, MN 55128
Tel.: (651) 430-8044
Web Site: http://supplychainservices.com
Computer Integrated Systems Design, Nsk
N.A.I.C.S.: 541512
Chip Emery (CEO)
Andy Berry (Dir-IT)
Dave Green (CEO)
Jared Hamann (Mgr-Warehouse)
Jon Danforth (Dir-Sls)
Lori Johnson (Accountant)
Mike Biedermann (Mgr-Media)
Nhut Doan (VP-Sls)
Randy Gallatin (CFO)
Rebecca Kwiatkowski (Coord-Sls & Mktg)
William Gleason (Accountant)

Subsidiary (Domestic):

Coridian Technologies Inc.   (2)
8140 Mallory Ct, Chanhassen, MN 55317
Tel.: (952) 361-9980
Web Site: http://www.coridian.com
Rev.: $9,000,000
Emp.: 12
Computer & Computer Peripheral Equipment & Software Merchant Whslr
N.A.I.C.S.: 423430
Mike Cleary (Pres)
Tony Maetzold (Acct Mgr)
Patrick Geraghty (VP-Sls & Mktg-Chanhassen)

Dasco Systems, Inc.   (2)
10370 Flanders St NE, Minneapolis, MN 55449
Tel.: (763) 574-2275
Web Site: http://www.dascolabel.com
Commercial Printing
N.A.I.C.S.: 323111

Miles Data Technologies, LLC   (2)
N7 W22081 Johnson Dr, Waukesha, WI 53186
Tel.: (262) 522-6700
Web Site: http://www.milesdata.com
Rev.: $10,000,000
Emp.: 13
Computer System Design Services
N.A.I.C.S.: 541512
Robert W. Ladd (Exec VP)

Trade Supplies, LLC   (1)
5625 Firestone Blvd, South Gate, CA 90280
Tel.: (323) 581-3250
Web Site: http://www.tradesuppliesinc.com
Packaging, Janitorial Supplies & Foodservice Disposable Items Distr
N.A.I.C.S.: 424310
Jeremy Shapiro (Pres & CEO)
Lindsey Shapiro Lamb (Exec Dir-Client Svcs)

SOLEM & ASSOCIATES
1 Daniel Burnham Ct Ste 315c, San Francisco, CA 94109-0465
Tel.: (415) 788-7788   CA
Year Founded: 1977
Rev.: $1,200,000
Emp.: 12
Fiscal Year-end: 12/31/06
Communications, Crisis Communications, Government/Political/Public Affairs, Graphic Design, Media Relations, Production, Strategic Planning/Research
N.A.I.C.S.: 541810
Don Solem (Pres)
Anne B. Solem (Counsel)
Jon Kaufman (Exec VP-Corp Affairs)
Anne Jeffrey (Sr VP)
Dave Hyams (Sr VP-Media Rels)
Chris Nishimura (Acct Coord)

SOLENTUS
241 18th St Ste 405, Arlington, VA 22202

Tel.: (571) 970-6862
Web Site: http://www.solentus.com
Year Founded: 2005
Sales Range: $10-24.9 Million
Emp.: 32
Management Consulting Services
N.A.I.C.S.: 541618
Son Tran (Gen Mgr)

SOLEO COMMUNICATIONS, INC.
300 WillowBrook Dr, Fairport, NY 14450-4222
Tel.: (585) 641-4300
Web Site: http://www.soleo.com
Year Founded: 2002
Sales Range: $10-24.9 Million
Emp.: 85
Telecommunication Servicesb
N.A.I.C.S.: 517810
Daniel Gallagher (Co-Founder & CEO)
Michael Thorpe (CTO)
Robert Deming (VP-Product Mgmt)
James Sonnick (Co-Founder & Sr VP-Strategic Accts)
Peter Juroe (CFO & Treas)
Johnna McCooey (VP-Digital Media Svcs)
Cathy Tobin (Gen Counsel)
Ken McManus (Dir-Sls-North America Reg)
Bucky Buchanan (Acct Mgr-Intl)

SOLERAN, INC.
7400 W 132nd St, Overland Park, KS 66213
Tel.: (913) 647-5900
Web Site: http://www.soleran.com
Year Founded: 1999
Sales Range: $25-49.9 Million
Emp.: 200
Technology for Web-Based Business Applications
N.A.I.C.S.: 513210
Greg Truitt (Owner, Co-Founder & Partner)
Grady Hawley (Co-Founder, Pres & CEO)

Subsidiaries:

eSalesTrack (1)
7400 W 132nd St Ste 140, Overland Park, KS 66213 (100%)
Tel.: (913) 647-5900
Web Site: http://www.esalestrack.com
Cloud Based CRM Solutions
N.A.I.C.S.: 513210
Greg Truitt (Partner)

SOLES ELECTRIC COMPANY INC.
1552 Tulip Ln, Fairmont, WV 26554
Tel.: (304) 363-2058
Sales Range: $10-24.9 Million
Emp.: 70
Provider of Electric Motor Repairs
N.A.I.C.S.: 811310

SOLES4SOULS
319 Martingale Dr, Old Hickory, TN 37138
Tel.: (615) 391-5723 AK
Web Site: http://www.soles4souls.org
Year Founded: 2006
Sales Range: $10-24.9 Million
Emp.: 62
Community Care Services
N.A.I.C.S.: 624190
Les Ward (CFO)
Buddy Teaster (CEO)
David Graben (COO)
CeCe McCormick-Moore (Dir-Corp Engagement)

SOLID EARTH, INC.
113 Clinton Ave W, Huntsville, AL 35801-4922
Tel.: (256) 536-0606
Web Site: http://www.solidearth.com
Year Founded: 1998
Sales Range: $1-9.9 Million
Emp.: 11
Real Estate Technology Services
N.A.I.C.S.: 531390
Kai Chan (Co-Founder & Dir-Product Dev)
Robert S. Moore (Co-Founder & Chm)
Bill Fowler (Mktg Dir-Client Support Trng)

SOLID MARKETING INC.
270 Spagnoli Rd, Melville, NY 11747
Tel.: (516) 384-4000
Rev.: $17,000,000
Emp.: 7
Electronic Parts & Equipment Distr
N.A.I.C.S.: 423690
Jagmohan Wadhwa (Pres)

SOLID STATE DEVICES, INC.
14701 Firestone Blvd, La Mirada, CA 90638-5918
Tel.: (562) 404-4474 CA
Web Site: http://www.ssdi-power.com
Year Founded: 1967
Sales Range: $50-74.9 Million
Emp.: 75
Mfr of Semiconductor Circuit Networks
N.A.I.C.S.: 334413
Arnold N. Applebaum (Chm, Pres & CEO)
Ileana Branzai (Engr-Quality)
Crystal Hayashida (Mgr-HR)
Eli Dexter (Engr-Mechanical)
David Guy (Dir-Engrg)
Rosa Lopez (Coord-Matl Control)
Jedd Bennett (Controller)

SOLID STATE EQUIPMENT LLC
185 Gibraltar Rd, Horsham, PA 19044
Tel.: (215) 328-0700
Web Site: http://www.ssecusa.com
Sales Range: $25-49.9 Million
Emp.: 65
Semiconductor Machinery Mfr
N.A.I.C.S.: 333242
Shanye Hudson (VP-IR)

SOLID STATE INC.
46 Farrand St, Bloomfield, NJ 07003
Tel.: (973) 429-8700
Web Site: http://www.solidstateinc.com
Year Founded: 1972
Sales Range: $10-24.9 Million
Emp.: 65
Electronic Components Distr
N.A.I.C.S.: 423690
Andrew Licari (Owner & Pres)
Anne Bocchino (Mgr-Sls)
Anne Boochino (Mgr-Sls)

SOLID STATE MEASUREMENTS INC.
47 Manning Rd, Billerica, MA 01821-3925
Tel.: (412) 787-0620
Web Site: http://www.ssm-inc.com
Year Founded: 1970
Sales Range: $10-24.9 Million
Emp.: 33
Mfr Test Equipment Used In The Semiconductors Industry
N.A.I.C.S.: 334515

SOLID SURFACES, INC.
10909 Metronome Dr, Houston, TX 77043
Tel.: (713) 935-0352 TX
Year Founded: 1995
Sales Range: $1-9.9 Million
Emp.: 14
Lumber, Plywood, Millwork & Wood Panel Merchant Whslr
N.A.I.C.S.: 423310
Robert Cook (Admin)

SOLIDARITY CONTRACTING LLC.
10100 W Sam Houston Pkwy S Ste 340, Houston, TX 77099
Tel.: (281) 495-6777
Web Site: http://www.solidaritycontracting.com
Year Founded: 2008
Sales Range: $25-49.9 Million
Emp.: 17
Design, Engineering, Contracting & Project Management Services
N.A.I.C.S.: 236220
Deniz Cevik (Owner)

SOLIGENT HOLDINGS INC.
1400 N McDowell Blvd Ste 201, Petaluma, CA 94952
Tel.: (707) 992-3100
Web Site: http://www.soligent.net
Year Founded: 1979
Emp.: 100
Solar Electric & Thermal Systems Distr & System Integrator
N.A.I.C.S.: 221118
Jonathan Doochin (CEO)
Eric Von DerMehden (VP-Fin)
Austin Blackmon (VP-Ops)
Ken Lima (Head-Sls)

SOLIS WOMEN'S HEALTH, INC.
15601 Dallas Pkwy Ste 500, Addison, TX 75001
Web Site: http://www.solismammo.com
Diagnostic Imaging Centers
N.A.I.C.S.: 621512
James Polfreman (CEO)
Ted Bucknam (COO)
Jolene Varney (CFO)
Duleep Wickramanayake (CIO)
Rob Polisky (Gen Counsel)
Michael Bennett (Chief Dev Officer)

Subsidiaries:

Breast Diagnostics of North Texas, PA (1)
300 Miron Dr, Southlake, TX 76092-7861
Tel.: (817) 749-2000
Web Site: http://www.breastdiagnostics.net
Diagnostic Imaging Centers
N.A.I.C.S.: 621512
Ravi Venugopal (Pres)

SOLITAIRE HOMES, INC.
7605 Nickles Rd, Duncan, OK 73533
Tel.: (580) 252-6060
Web Site: http://www.solitairehomes.com
Year Founded: 1965
Sales Range: $100-124.9 Million
Emp.: 1,500
Mfr & Retailer of Mobile Homes
N.A.I.C.S.: 459930
Jerry J. Elliott (Chm)
Matthew Leitner (Controller)
D.J. Hogstad (Pres)

Subsidiaries:

Elliott Homes Inc. (1)
7605 Nickles Rd, Duncan, OK 73533
Tel.: (580) 252-6060
Rev.: $30,060,178
Emp.: 235
Mobile Home Sales

N.A.I.C.S.: 321991

SOLIX, INC.
30 Lanidex Plaza W, Parsippany, NJ 07054
Tel.: (973) 581-6700
Web Site: http://www.solixinc.com
Year Founded: 2000
Sales Range: $75-99.9 Million
Emp.: 500
Business Process Outsourcing Services
N.A.I.C.S.: 711410
Jack Miller (Pres & CEO)
Bill Ingersoll (CIO & Sr VP)
Eric Storey (Chief Sls Officer & Sr VP)

SOLMAC INC.
1975 Wehrle Dr Ste 130, Williamsville, NY 14221
Tel.: (716) 630-7061
Web Site: http://www.solmac.com
Year Founded: 2005
Sales Range: $1-9.9 Million
Emp.: 10
Computer Numerical Control Machining Services
N.A.I.C.S.: 541519
Borris Soldo (Pres)

SOLOFLEX, INC.
1281 NE 25 Th Ave Ste I, Hillsboro, OR 97124
Tel.: (503) 640-8891 OR
Web Site: http://www.soloflex.com
Sales Range: $50-74.9 Million
Emp.: 25
Mfr of Weightlifting Machines
N.A.I.C.S.: 339920
Jerry Wilson (CEO)

SOLOMON BUILDERS, INC.
4539 Trousdale Dr, Nashville, TN 37204-4513
Tel.: (615) 333-9369
Web Site: http://www.solomonbuilders.com
Sales Range: $10-24.9 Million
Emp.: 87
Nonresidential Construction Services
N.A.I.C.S.: 236220
Bob Edwards (Pres)

SOLOMON CHEVROLET CADILLAC
4886 Montgomery Hwy, Dothan, AL 36303-1557
Tel.: (334) 793-3444
Web Site: http://www.solomonchevroletcadillac.com
Sales Range: $25-49.9 Million
Emp.: 61
Car Whslr
N.A.I.C.S.: 441110
Tony Clark (Owner & Mgr)

SOLOMON FRIEDMAN ADVERTISING LLC
40900 Woodward Ave Ste 300, Bloomfield Hills, MI 48304-2256
Tel.: (248) 540-0660 MI
Web Site: http://www.realintegrated.com
Year Founded: 1954
Sales Range: $1-9.9 Million
Emp.: 35
Advetising Agency
N.A.I.C.S.: 541810
Dean A. Friedman (CEO)
Susan Schumacher (VP-Integrated Media)
Lisa Anderson (CFO & Exec VP)
Crystal Ratledge Ceo (Dir-Acct Svcs)
John Ozdych (Pres & Creative Dir)

SOLOMON HOMES, INC. U.S. PRIVATE

Solomon Friedman Advertising LLC—(Continued)

SOLOMON HOMES, INC.
1758 Mileground Rd, Morgantown, WV 26505
Tel.: (304) 292-8969
Web Site:
   http://www.seeamericanhomes.com
Rev.: $10,319,581
Emp.: 57
Mobile Home Dealers
N.A.I.C.S.: 459930
Holly Glenn (Mgr-Sls & Mktg)

SOLOMON MCCOWN & COMPANY, INC.
177 Milk St Ste 610, Boston, MA 02109
Tel.: (617) 695-9555
Web Site:
   http://www.solomonmccown.com
Year Founded: 2003
Sales Range: $1-9.9 Million
Emp.: 20
Public Relations
N.A.I.C.S.: 541820
Helene Solomon (CEO)
Ashley McCown (Pres)
T. J. Winick (VP)
Bill Stein (CFO)
Michelle Mastrobattista (VP-Digital Comm)
Jonathan Pappas (VP)
Travis Small (Sr VP)

SOLOMON-PAGE GROUP LLC
260 Madison Ave Fl 3, New York, NY 10016
Tel.: (212) 403-6100   DE
Web Site: https://solomonpage.com
Year Founded: 1993
Sales Range: $50-74.9 Million
Emp.: 260
Provider of Temporary & Permanent Employment Services
N.A.I.C.S.: 561311
Lloyd B. Solomon (Co-Founder & Mng Dir)
Scott Page (Co-Founder & Mng Dir)
Eric M. Davis (CFO & VP-Fin)
Jacob Navon (Head-Asset Mgmt-Global)
David Trevena (Dir-Asset Mgmt)
Marc Gouran (Founder/Gen Mgr-Healthcare & Life Sciences Div)

Subsidiaries:

E.A. Hughes & Co., Inc.   (1)
200 Madison Ave, New York, NY 10016
Tel.: (212) 689-4600
Web Site: http://www.eahughes.com
Professional, Scientific & Technical Services
N.A.I.C.S.: 541990
Elaine Hughes (Founder & CEO)

SOLOMONEDWARDSGROUP, LLC
1255 Drummers Ln, Wayne, PA 19087
Tel.: (610) 902-0440
Web Site:
   http://www.solomonedwards.com
Professional Services
N.A.I.C.S.: 561499
Edward Baumstein (Founder & Chm)
John Moerman (Mng Partner-Philadelphia)
Lito Abiva (Dir-IT)
Candace Caley (Mng Partner-Banking & Fin Svcs)
Mark Gaydos (VP-Mktg)
Margaret Wolford (Sr VP-Resource Mgmt Office)
Scott Balestrier (CEO)

Subsidiaries:

M Squared Consulting, Inc.   (1)
111 Sutter St Ste 900, San Francisco, CA 94104-4545
Tel.: (415) 391-1038
Web Site: http://www.msquared.com
Sales Range: $10-24.9 Million
Human Resource Consulting Services
N.A.I.C.S.: 541612
Dirk Sodestrom (Mng Partner)
Maureen Kasper (Principal-Bus Transformation)
Bob Camilo (Dir-Bus Consulting)
Peter Wright (Partner-Delivery)
Edward S. Baumstein (Founder, Pres & CEO)

OpenGate Consulting, Inc.   (1)
1006 W 9th Ave, King of Prussia, PA 19406-1206
Tel.: (610) 296-3200
Web Site: http://www.opengate.com
All Other Support Services
N.A.I.C.S.: 561990

QUAD, a SolomonEdwards
Company   (1)
1255 Drummers Lane Ste 200, Wayne, PA 19087
Tel.: (610) 687-6441
Web Site: http://www.quad656.com
Human Resources & Executive Search Consulting Services
N.A.I.C.S.: 541612
Randi Goltz (Co-Founder & Principal)
Lori Marcus (Co-Founder & Principal)

SOLORO GOLD
2681 Chateu Clermont St, Henderson, NV 89044
Tel.: (888) 357-2435   NV
Web Site: http://www.sologogold.com
Year Founded: 2005
Gold Mining
N.A.I.C.S.: 212220
Denis D. Corin (CEO)

SOLPAC INC.
2424 Congress St, San Diego, CA 92110
Tel.: (619) 296-6247
Web Site:
   http://www.soltekpacific.com
Rev.: $156,350,336
Emp.: 500
Commercial & Office Building
N.A.I.C.S.: 236220
Steve Thompson (CEO)
Cathy Young (Controller)

SOLSBURY HILL LLC
5805 E 39th Ave, Denver, CO 80207
Tel.: (303) 295-1777
Web Site:
   http://www.dbcirrigation.com
Sales Range: $25-49.9 Million
Emp.: 100
Irrigation Systems & Products Distr
N.A.I.C.S.: 423850
John Alderman (Owner & Pres)
Alan Tanaka (CFO)

SOLSTICE BENEFITS, INC.
PO Box 19199, Plantation, FL 33318
Tel.: (954) 476-1182
Web Site:
   http://www.solsticebenefits.com
Year Founded: 1998
Sales Range: $10-24.9 Million
Emp.: 85
Dental, Vision & Life Insurance Carrier
N.A.I.C.S.: 524114
Carlos Ferrera (COO)
Alissa Gavrilescu (Dir-Mktg)
Stacey Brocatto-McManus (Dir-Provider Rels)
Brian Correia (Dir-Bus Dev)
Ellen deClaire (Dir-HR)
Tammy Eveslage (Dir-Project Mgmt & Quality Compliance)

SOLSTICE MARKETING CORP.
107 Spring St, New York, NY 10012-3807
Tel.: (212) 219-3940
Sunglass Distr
N.A.I.C.S.: 423460
Pang T. (Mgr)

Subsidiaries:

Solstice Marketing Concepts, LLC   (1)
404 5th Ave 2nd Fl, New York, NY 10022
Tel.: (646) 348-6100
Web Site: http://www.solsticestores.com
Sun Glasses Retailer
N.A.I.C.S.: 456130
Jan Michel (VP-Retail)

SOLSTICE MOBILE
111 N Canal 5th Fl, Chicago, IL 60606
Tel.: (312) 265-6010
Web Site: http://www.solstice-mobile.com
Year Founded: 2001
Sales Range: $10-24.9 Million
Emp.: 300
Mobile Strategy & IT Development
N.A.I.C.S.: 541519
J. Schwan (Founder & CEO)
Dan Kardatzke (CFO)
Marisa Mann (COO)

SOLSTICE PLANNING AND ARCHITECTURE
1900 Main St Ste 202, Sarasota, FL 34236
Tel.: (941) 365-5721
Web Site: http://www.solstice-pa.com
Architectural Services
N.A.I.C.S.: 541310
Jonathan Parks (Sr Principal)
Selma Goker Wilson (Architect)

SOLSTICE SLEEP PRODUCTS, INC.
2652 Fisher Rd Unit A, Columbus, OH 43204
Tel.: (614) 279-8850   OH
Web Site: http://solsticesleep.com
Year Founded: 2009
Mattress Sales
N.A.I.C.S.: 449129
Kevin Sisson (COO)

Subsidiaries:

Jamison Bedding, Inc.   (1)
5301 Virginia Way Ste 100, Brentwood, TN 37027-7542
Tel.: (615) 794-1883
Web Site: http://www.jamisonbedding.com
Sales Range: $25-49.9 Million
Emp.: 100
Mfr Bedding Products
N.A.I.C.S.: 337910

SOLTEK PACIFIC
2424 Congress St Ste A, San Diego, CA 92110
Tel.: (619) 296-6247
Web Site:
   http://www.soltekpacific.com
Year Founded: 1974
Sales Range: $200-249.9 Million
Emp.: 235
Nonresidential Construction Services
N.A.I.C.S.: 236220
Steve Thompson (Pres)
Mike Jovin (Superintendent)
Larry Richie (Pres)
Casey Young (Project Mgr)

SOLTYS SCHNITZLER SCHIRMER LLC
718 Main St, Boonton, NJ 07005
Tel.: (973) 257-5533
Web Site:
   http://www.thes3agency.com
Year Founded: 2001
Sales Range: $200-249.9 Million
Emp.: 25
Advertising Services
N.A.I.C.S.: 541810
Denise Blasevick (Pres)
Adam Schnitzler (Chief Creative Officer)

SOLU TECHNOLOGY PARTNERS
7647 Main St Fishers, Victor, NY 14564
Tel.: (585) 625-2600
Web Site:
   http://www.solutechnology.com
Information Technology Employment Placement Services
N.A.I.C.S.: 561311
Jerry Jewell (COO)

Subsidiaries:

Solu Technology Partners - Phoenix
Office   (1)
9380 E Bahia Dr Ste A202, Scottsdale, AZ 85260
Tel.: (480) 948-9322
Web Site: http://www.solutechnology.com
Sales Range: $10-24.9 Million
Emp.: 50
Information Technology Employment Placement Services
N.A.I.C.S.: 561311
John O'Brien (VP-Reg)

SOLUGENIX CORP.
601 Valencia Ave Ste 260, Brea, CA 92823
Web Site: http://www.solugenix.com
Year Founded: 2005
Computer Related Services, Nec, Nsk
N.A.I.C.S.: 541512
Shashi Jasphi (Pres & CEO)
Damola Akinola (VP-Consulting Svcs)
Jemma David (VP-Enterprise Support Svcs)
Suneetha Menon (VP-Prof Svcs)
Ramki Venkatraman (VP-Tech & Dev Svcs)
Andrea Butz (Dir-HR)
Srihari Atluri (Dir)
Rich Mewes (Dir-Enterprise Support Svcs)
Chin Pyun (Mgr-Talent Acq)
Crystal Kolosick (Mgr-Mktg)

Subsidiaries:

SEI LLC   (1)
701 Demers Ave, Grand Forks, ND 58201
Tel.: (701) 317-7583
Web Site: http://www.seillc.com
Call Center Services
N.A.I.C.S.: 561499
Brian Haan (CTO & Chief Security Officer)
Kristi Gappert (Mgr-Retail Support Acct)
Christine Antonelli (Pres)
Rob Gappert (Mgr-Ops)
Dan Sundquist (Dir-Ops Sys)
Nicole Pigeon (Mgr-Ops)

SOLUTION BEACON LLC
14419 Greenwood Ave N Ste 332, Seattle, WA 98133
Tel.: (206) 366-6606
Web Site:
   http://www.solutionbeacon.com
Sales Range: $10-24.9 Million
Emp.: 50
Computer System Design Services
N.A.I.C.S.: 541512
Craig Hobson (Pres)

SOLUTION IT INC.
120 Presidential Way Ste 340, Woburn, MA 01801
Tel.: (781) 503-1700
Web Site: http://www.solutionit.com

COMPANIES

SOMERSET CAPITAL GROUP, LTD.

Year Founded: 2007
Sales Range: $1-9.9 Million
Emp.: 70
IT Staffing & Consulting
N.A.I.C.S.: 541690
Atish Rastogi *(Pres & CEO)*
Chuck Rice *(Mgr-Sls)*
Morgan Miller *(Acct Coord)*
Gowridhar Saragadam *(Acct Mgr)*

SOLUTION STREET, LLC.
427-B Carlisle Dr, Herndon, VA 20170
Tel.: (703) 657-0511
Web Site: http://www.solutionstreet.com
Year Founded: 2002
Sales Range: $1-9.9 Million
Emp.: 14
Software Consulting Services
N.A.I.C.S.: 541512
Arthur Frankel *(Mng Partner)*
Joel Nylund *(Mng Partner)*
Susan Campbell *(Engr-QA-Software)*

SOLUTIONHEALTH
360 Route 101 Unit 8, Bedford, NH 03110
Tel.: (603) 663-2090   NH
Web Site: http://www.solutionhealth.org
Health Care Srvices
N.A.I.C.S.: 621610
Sherry Hausmann *(Pres & CEO)*

SOLUTIONPOINT INTERNATIONAL INC.
415 Madison Ave 11th Fl, New York, NY 10017
Tel.: (917) 748-5517
Web Site: http://www.solutionpoint-intl.com
Intermediation
N.A.I.C.S.: 523910
Jon Walklin *(Dir-Tech Dev)*

SOLUTIONS BY DESIGN, INC.
451 Clovis Ave Ste 130, Clovis, CA 93612
Tel.: (559) 436-8380   CA
Web Site: http://www.solutionsbydesign.com
Year Founded: 1985
Sales Range: $1-9.9 Million
Emp.: 18
Advertising Agencies
N.A.I.C.S.: 541810
William A. Poss *(Founder, Pres & CEO)*

SOLUTIONS-IES, INC.
1101 Nowell Rd, Raleigh, NC 27607
Tel.: (919) 873-1060
Web Site: http://www.solutions-ies.com
Year Founded: 1999
Sales Range: $1-9.9 Million
Emp.: 27
Environmental Consulting Services
N.A.I.C.S.: 541620
Ann Borden *(Pres)*
M. Tony Lieberman *(Mgr-Bioremediation Program)*
Robert C. Borden *(Principal-Engrg)*

SOLUTIONS-II INCORPORATED
8822 S Ridgeline Blvd Ste 117, Littleton, CO 80129
Tel.: (303) 796-8393
Web Site: http://www.solutions-ii.com
Year Founded: 1992
Sales Range: $10-24.9 Million
Emp.: 50
Computer Related Consulting Services

N.A.I.C.S.: 541512
David W. Stone *(Exec VP)*
Scott Neher *(Controller)*
Todd Bowling *(Pres & CEO)*

SOLUTIONSET LLC
2100 Geng Rd Ste 105, Palo Alto, CA 94303-3307
Tel.: (650) 328-3900
Web Site: http://www.solutionset.com
Year Founded: 2002
Sales Range: $10-24.9 Million
Emp.: 100
Web Design & Development, Branding & Online Marketing & IT Services
N.A.I.C.S.: 541490
Libby DeMeo *(Partner & Mgr-Projects)*
Robert Balmaseda *(Sr VP)*
Jeff Haggin *(Vice Chm)*

Subsidiaries:

SolutionSet   (1)
85 2nd St, San Francisco, CA 94105   (100%)
Tel.: (415) 777-3800
Web Site: http://www.solutionset.com
Sales Range: $10-24.9 Million
Emp.: 90
Web Design & Development, Branding & Online Marketing
N.A.I.C.S.: 541613
Lisa Henderson *(Mng Dir-Client Svcs)*
Wayne Townsend *(Mng Dir-Digital Channel Delivery)*

SOLVANG LUTHERAN HOME, INC.
636 Atterdag Rd, Solvang, CA 93463
Tel.: (805) 688-3263   CA
Web Site: http://www.peoplewhocare.com
Year Founded: 1956
Sales Range: $10-24.9 Million
Emp.: 138
Retirement Care Services
N.A.I.C.S.: 623311
David Pedersen *(VP)*
Judith Greer *(Sec)*
Verva Enoch *(Treas)*
Carol Anders *(Pres)*

SOLVCHEM, INC.
4704 Shank Rd, Pearland, TX 77581
Tel.: (281) 485-5377
Web Site: http://www.solvchem.com
Rev.: $55,000,000
Emp.: 43
Chemical & Allied Products Merchant Whslr
N.A.I.C.S.: 424690
Gabriel Baizan *(Chm)*
Jean-Pierre Baizan *(Pres)*
Katia Baizan *(Mgr-Svcs)*
Michaela Murry *(Mgr-HR)*

SOLVE ADVISORS INC.
265 Sunrise Hwy Ste 45, Rockville Centre, NY 11570
Tel.: (646) 699-5041
Web Site: http://www.solveadvisors.com
Emp.: 100
Professional, Scientific & Technical Services
N.A.I.C.S.: 541990
Adam Prather *(Principal & Head-Bus Dev)*

Subsidiaries:

Advantage Data Inc.   (1)
1 Federal St Ste 25, Boston, MA 02110-2012
Tel.: (617) 261-9700
Web Site: http://www.advantagedata.com
Rev.: $6,200,000
Emp.: 19
Computer Software Services

N.A.I.C.S.: 513210
Rene Robert *(Pres)*
Sourav Srimal *(Head-Ops)*
David Chau *(Mgr-IT)*

Lumesis, Inc.   (1)
1 Atlantic St 3rd Fl, Stamford, CT 06901
Tel.: (203) 274-8611
Web Site: http://www.lumesis.com
Software & Data Services
N.A.I.C.S.: 541511
Gregg L. Bienstock *(Founder & CEO)*
Joshua Laurito *(Founder)*
Timothy J. Stevens *(Co-Founder, Pres & COO)*
Vincent Aubrun *(CTO & VP-Engrg)*
Steve McLaughlin *(Mng Dir-Bus Dev)*
Stacey Virzi *(Dir-Client Svcs)*
Philip D. Moyer *(Chm)*
Heidi Leonard *(Dir-Bus Dev)*
K. Justin Coombs *(Dir-Data Product Mgmt)*
L. K. Tan *(Dir-Fin)*
Mark Harries *(Mng Dir-Bus Dev)*
Michael C. Craft *(Mng Dir-Credit)*
Pete M. Newman *(Mng Dir-Bus Dev)*
Sue Childs *(Dir-Mktg)*

SOLVE IT, INC.
200 Union Blvd Ste 115, Lakewood, CO 80228
Tel.: (720) 981-3712
Web Site: http://www.solveit.us
Sales Range: $1-9.9 Million
Emp.: 16
Technology Management Services
N.A.I.C.S.: 541690
Garrett Bucker *(Founder & Pres)*
Rick Roundy *(Dir-Bus Dev)*
Lance i *(Dir-Svcs)*
Sean Smith *(Exec Dir-Creative/Partner-Minneapolis)*

SOLVEGY, INC.
1601 Elm St Fl 33, Dallas, TX 75201
Tel.: (202) 670-5179
Web Site: http://www.solvegy.com
Year Founded: 2014
Sales Range: $1-9.9 Million
Emp.: 6
Information Technology Services
N.A.I.C.S.: 541512
Dipesh Patel *(Founder)*

SOLVIX SOLUTIONS, LLC
701 A Route 73 S Ste 425, Marlton, NJ 08053
Tel.: (856) 324-4100
Web Site: http://www.solvixsolutions.com
Year Founded: 2013
Sales Range: $10-24.9 Million
Emp.: 10
Technology Product Mfr
N.A.I.C.S.: 339999
Stacey Rock *(Pres)*
Tony Rock *(VP)*
Kyle Sellers *(Sls Mgr)*
Bill Monetti *(Acct Mgr)*

SOLX, INC.
230 Second Ave Ste 120, Waltham, MA 02451
Tel.: (781) 609-2016
Web Site: http://www.solx.com
Year Founded: 2000
Sales Range: $100-124.9 Million
Emp.: 5
Glaucoma Products
N.A.I.C.S.: 333310
Howard Kim *(Dir-Clinical Affairs & Bus Dev)*
Patrick H. King *(VP-Sls & Mktg)*
Abraham Massouda *(Dir-Ops & Quality)*
Beth McHallam *(Dir-Fin & Admin)*

SOMA NETWORKS, INC.
650 Townsend St Ste 305, San Francisco, CA 94103

Tel.: (415) 882-6500
Web Site: http://www.somanetworks.com
Year Founded: 1998
Sales Range: $25-49.9 Million
Emp.: 250
Provider of Wireless Communication Systems
N.A.I.C.S.: 517112
Yatish Pathak *(Founder & CEO)*
R. Douglas Kneebone *(Gen Counsel & Sr VP)*

SOMERA CAPITAL MANAGEMENT, LLC
115 W Canon Perdido St, Santa Barbara, CA 93101
Tel.: (805) 681-0144   CA
Web Site: http://www.someracapital.com
Year Founded: 1994
Sales Range: $1-4.9 Billion
Private Equity Real Estate Investment Trust
N.A.I.C.S.: 525990
Steven H. Firestone *(Founder & Chm)*
David A. Brown *(Sr Mng Partner)*
Julie Lubin *(Exec VP-Fin)*
Jake Farver *(VP)*
Chris Hahs *(CFO)*

Subsidiaries:

Quorum Hotels & Resorts, Ltd.   (1)
5429 LBJ Freeway Ste 65, Dallas, TX 75240
Tel.: (972) 458-7265
Web Site: http://www.quorumhotels.com
Sales Range: $1-9.9 Million
Emp.: 60
Administrative Management & General Management Consulting Service
N.A.I.C.S.: 541611
Gary Levine *(VP-Food & Beverage Ops)*
Jean Hungerford *(Sr VP-Mktg & Rooms Ops)*
Pam MacRae *(VP-HR)*
Ted Mosley *(Pres, COO & Principal)*
Tony Farris *(Chm, CEO & Principal)*
Melissa Stillwell *(Dir-Revenue Mgmt)*
Rex Stewart *(CFO)*
Rob Drawbridge *(Principal & Exec VP-Asset Mgmt)*
Walter Peseski *(Dir-Dev)*

SOMERSET BUICK-GMC, INC.
1850 W Maple Rd, Troy, MI 48084-7104
Tel.: (248) 643-8600   MI
Web Site: http://www.somersetbuickgmc.com
Sales Range: $100-124.9 Million
Emp.: 72
Sales of Automobiles
N.A.I.C.S.: 441110
John Fowler *(Pres)*
Jim Bechtell *(Gen Mgr-Sls)*
Duane Jelley *(Mgr-Fin)*

SOMERSET CAPITAL GROUP, LTD.
612 Wheelers Farms Rd, Milford, CT 06461
Tel.: (203) 701-5100   CT
Web Site: http://www.somersetcapital.com
Year Founded: 1984
Sales Range: $50-74.9 Million
Emp.: 55
Computer Rental & Custom Business Equipment Leasing Services
N.A.I.C.S.: 532420
Evan M. Bokor *(Pres & CEO)*
Mark A Fiorentino *(COO & Exec VP)*
Adam K. Simon *(Exec VP-Sls)*
Brian Stearney *(Exec VP-Indirect Ops Grp)*

SOMERSET CAPITAL GROUP, LTD.   U.S. PRIVATE

Somerset Capital Group, Ltd.—(Continued)
Andrew G. Cotter (CIO & Exec VP)
Evan M. Bokor (Pres & CEO)
George Rieber (Exec VP-Somerset Equipment Sls)
Mark A. Fiorentino (COO & Exec VP)
Steven R. Norris (Exec VP-Somerset Tech Sls)
Brian K. Stearney (Exec VP-Indirect Ops Grp)
Andrew G. Cotter (CIO & Exec VP)
George Rieber (Exec VP-Somerset Equipment Sls)
Steven R. Norris (Exec VP-Somerset Tech Sls)

SOMERSET HOUSE PUBLISHING INC.
29366 McKinnon Rd, Fulshear, TX 77441
Tel.: (800) 444-2540   TX
Web Site:
  http://www.somersetfineart.com
Year Founded: 1972
Art Copy & Poster Publishing
N.A.I.C.S.: 513199
Larry Smith (Owner)

SOMERSET INDUSTRIES INC.
68 Harrison St, Gloversville, NY 12078
Tel.: (518) 773-7383
Sales Range: $10-24.9 Million
Emp.: 60
Lace & Warp Knit Fabric Mills
N.A.I.C.S.: 313240
Mo Akhawala (Plant Mgr)

SOMERSET SAVINGS BANK, SLA
220 W Union Ave, Bound Brook, NJ 08805
Tel.: (732) 560-1700   NJ
Web Site:
  http://www.somersetsavings.com
Year Founded: 1887
Sales Range: $25-49.9 Million
Emp.: 100
Savings Institutions
N.A.I.C.S.: 522180
David M. Prugh (Chm & CEO)
Stephen P. Zecca (VP)
Christopher Pribula (Sr VP-Ops)

Subsidiaries:
Somerset Consumer Service Corp.   (1)
220 W Union Ave, Bound Brook, NJ 08805-1335
Tel.: (732) 560-1700
Sales Range: $25-49.9 Million
Emp.: 17
Insurance Agents, Brokers & Service
N.A.I.C.S.: 524210
Donald Rheinhard (VP-Mktg)

SOMERSET SPORTART
1651 SE 195th Terr, Morriston, FL 32668
Tel.: (352) 528-4763
Web Site:
  http://www.somersetsportart.com
Year Founded: 1988
Sales Range: Less than $1 Million
Emp.: 3
Advetising Agency
N.A.I.C.S.: 541810
Susan Benson (CEO)

SOMERSET TRUST CO.
151 W Main St, Somerset, PA 15501
Tel.: (814) 443-9200
Web Site:
  http://www.somersettrust.com
Sales Range: $10-24.9 Million
Emp.: 300

Banking Services
N.A.I.C.S.: 522110
G. Henry Cook (Chm & CEO)
Mike Whipkey (Officer-Compliance & VP)
Thomas J. Cook (Pres)

SOMERSET WOOD PRODUCTS, CO.
10 Johnson Dr, Raritan, NJ 08869
Tel.: (908) 526-0030   NJ
Web Site:
  http://www.somersetwood.net
Year Founded: 1977
Sales Range: $1-9.9 Million
Emp.: 20
Millwork (including Flooring)
N.A.I.C.S.: 321918
Lester Bloch (Pres)

SOMERVILLE BANCORP.
197 S Main St, Somerville, OH 45064
Tel.: (513) 726-6471   OH
Web Site:
  http://www.somervillebank.net
Year Founded: 2017
Bank Holding Company
N.A.I.C.S.: 551111
Paul E. Taylor (Pres)

Subsidiaries:
Somerville Bank   (1)
197 S Main St, Somerville, OH 45064
Tel.: (513) 726-6471
Web Site: http://www.somervillebank.net
Sales Range: $1-9.9 Million
Emp.: 47
Commericial Banking
N.A.I.C.S.: 522110
David Ulrich (Chief Lending Officer & Sr VP)
Paul Gene Taylor (Pres & CEO)

SOMMER METALCRAFT CORPORATION
315 Poston Dr, Crawfordsville, IN 47933
Tel.: (765) 362-6200   IN
Web Site:
  http://www.sommermetalcraft.com
Year Founded: 1908
Sales Range: $50-74.9 Million
Emp.: 115
Mfr of Wire Forms & Welded Wire Assembly
N.A.I.C.S.: 332618
Scott Sommer (Pres)

Subsidiaries:
SMC South   (1)
1955 McMillan St, Auburn, AL 36832-4206
Tel.: (334) 887-6200
Sales Range: $10-24.9 Million
Wire Fabricator
N.A.I.C.S.: 332618

SOMNIO SOLUTIONS INC.
11305 4 Points Dr Bldg 2 Ste 200, Austin, TX 78726
Tel.: (512) 493-9800   TX
Web Site: http://www.somnio.com
Year Founded: 2003
Sales Range: $1-9.9 Million
Emp.: 25
Digital Marketing Consulting Services
N.A.I.C.S.: 541613
Harold Valderas (CEO)
Scott Killingsworth (CFO)
Layne Hedrick (VP-Client Delivery)
Kim Potter (Controller)
Christina Silva (Mgr-Quality Assurance)
Steve Meier (Dir-Sls & Mktg)
Henry Medrano (Dir-Creative)
Raquel Chandler (Mgr-Talent)

Jacob Golding (VP-Strategy)
Garrett Goeters (COO)
Curtis Cummings (VP-Client Engagement)

SOMOS, INC.
2 Tower Ctr Blvd 20th Fl, East Brunswick, NJ 08816
Tel.: (844) 439-7666
Web Site: http://www.somos.com
Data Processing, Hosting & Related Services
N.A.I.C.S.: 518210
Gina Perini (CEO)
Karthik Yajurvedi (VP-Engrg)
Sri Ramachandran (CTO & Sr VP)

Subsidiaries:
XConnect Global Networks Ltd.   (1)
Cooper House 316 Regents Park Road, London, N3 2JX, United Kingdom
Tel.: (44) 20 8371 4800
Web Site: http://www.xconnect.net
Sales Range: $10-24.9 Million
Emp.: 50
IP Interconnect Services
N.A.I.C.S.: 517810
Eli Katz (Founder & CEO)
Neil Cohen (Dir-Fin)
Myer Luknar (Dir-IT)
Ohad Finkelstein (Chm)

Subsidiary (US):
Xconnect Americas, Inc.   (2)
649 Route 206 Unit 9 Ste 103, Hillsborough, NJ 08844
Tel.: (908) 547-0910
Telecommunication Servicesb
N.A.I.C.S.: 517810

Subsidiary (Non-US):
Xconnect Global Networks (Israel) Ltd   (2)
Hagan Hatechnologi, Jerusalem, Israel
Tel.: (972) 26218000
Telecommunication Servicesb
N.A.I.C.S.: 517810

SONA MOBILE HOLDINGS, CORP.
10100 W Charleston Blvd Ste 160, Las Vegas, NV 89135
Tel.: (702) 243-7662
Year Founded: 2004
Software Development Services
N.A.I.C.S.: 541511
John Bush (Pres & CEO)

SONACARE MEDICAL, LLC
10130 Perimeter Pkwy Ste 250, Charlotte, NC 28216
Tel.: (888) 874-4384   DE
Web Site:
  http://www.sonacaremedical.com
Year Founded: 2004
Sales Range: $10-24.9 Million
Emp.: 63
Sonic & Ultrasound Medical Equipment Developer, Mfr & Whslr
N.A.I.C.S.: 334510
Mark Carol (Chief Dev Officer)
Narenda Sanghvi (Chief Scientific Officer)
Mark Schoenberg (Chief Medical Officer)
Hrishikesh Gadagkar (VP-R&D & Mfg)
Alex Gonzalez (VP-Intl Ops)
Thomas Mendell (Chm)
Stefan Parker (CFO)
Kevin Alverson (VP-Sls)
Neal Sangani (VP-Fin)
Stephen R. Puckett Sr. (Founder)

SONAG COMPANY, INC.
5510 W Florist Ave, Milwaukee, WI 53218
Tel.: (414) 393-9911   WI

Web Site: http://www.sonag.com
Sales Range: $25-49.9 Million
Emp.: 20
Commercial & Office Building Construction
N.A.I.C.S.: 236220
Brian Ganos (Chm, Pres & CEO)

Subsidiaries:
Sonag Ready Mix, LLC   (1)
N59 W14909 Bobolink Ave, Menomonee Falls, WI 53051
Tel.: (262) 252-9911
Web Site: http://www.sonagconcrete.com
Sales Range: $10-24.9 Million
Readymix Concrete Mfr
N.A.I.C.S.: 327320
Brian Ganos (Chm & CEO)
Nick Rivecca (Pres)

SONALYSTS, INC.
215 Pkwy N, Waterford, CT 06385-1209
Tel.: (860) 442-4355   CT
Web Site: http://www.sonalysts.com
Year Founded: 1973
Sales Range: $25-49.9 Million
Emp.: 275
Provider of Engineering Services
N.A.I.C.S.: 541330
Stephen Freitas (Dir-Creative)
Mike Hewitt (Exec VP)
Suzanne Lemon (Mgr-AR)

SONANT SYSTEMS, INC.
6520 Salt Creek Ave, Apollo Beach, FL 33572
Tel.: (321) 200-0142   NV
Year Founded: 2010
Sales Range: Less than $1 Million
Social Networking Applications & Website Operator
N.A.I.C.S.: 513210
Enzo Taddei (CEO & CFO)

SONCO WORLDWIDE, INC.
5000 Windom Rd, Bladensburg, MD 20710
Tel.: (301) 779-1111   MD
Web Site: http://www.soncoww.com
Year Founded: 1976
Sales Range: $10-24.9 Million
Emp.: 100
Mfr of Chain Link Fencing
N.A.I.C.S.: 331222
Stephen Greer (Chm & CEO)

SONDERMIND, INC.
1738 Wynkoop Street Ste 303, Denver, CO 80210
Tel.: (844) 256-8915
Web Site:
  https://www.sondermind.com
Emp.: 100
Healtcare Services
N.A.I.C.S.: 621999
Mark Frank (Co-Founder & CEO)

SONEL TEST & MEASUREMENT, INC.
3350 Scott Blvd Bldg 55 Unit 1 Santa, Santa Clara, CA 95054
Tel.: (408) 898-2215   DE
Web Site: http://www.SonelTest.com
High-Quality Electrical & Telecommunication Application Measuring Instrument
N.A.I.C.S.: 334515
Peter Pawlik (Dir-Sls)
Spiros Georgiadis (Chief Comml Officer & Exec VP)

SONETTE, INC.
350 Karin Ln, Hicksville, NY 11801
Tel.: (516) 932-8800   NY
Sales Range: $50-74.9 Million
Emp.: 500

COMPANIES

Baseball Hats & Head Wear
N.A.I.C.S.: 424350
Byung T. Cho (Pres)
Paul Parks (VP)

SONGTRADR, INC.
2701 Ocean Park Blvd #220, Santa Monica, CA 90405
Tel.: (424) 744-8190
Web Site: https://www.songtradr.com
Year Founded: 2014
Music Industry
N.A.I.C.S.: 512230
Paul Wiltshire (CEO)

Subsidiaries:

7digital Group PLC (1)
LABS Hawley Lock 1 Water Lane, 9-12 Water Lane, London, NW1 8NZ, United Kingdom
Tel.: (44) 2070997777
Web Site: https://www.7digital.com
Rev.: $9,140,171
Assets: $2,449,327
Liabilities: $10,711,053
Net Worth: ($8,261,726)
Earnings: ($5,320,905)
Emp.: 51
Fiscal Year-end: 12/31/2021
Radio Content & Broadcast Data Software Supplier
N.A.I.C.S.: 516210
Simon Cole (CEO)
Matthew Honey (CFO)
Pete Downton (Deputy CEO)
Donald G. Cruickshank (Chm)

Subsidiary (Domestic):

Smooth Operations (Productions) Limited (2)
PO Box 18, Dobcross, Oldham, OL3 5FS, United Kingdom
Tel.: (44) 1457873752
Web Site: http://www.smoothoperations.com
Sales Range: $25-49.9 Million
Emp.: 15
Radio & TV Mfr
N.A.I.C.S.: 334220
John Leonard (Mng Dir)
Stuart Maconie (Mgr)

SONIC FINANCIAL CORPORATION
5401 E Independence Blvd, Charlotte, NC 28212
Tel.: (704) 532-3306
Financial Services
N.A.I.C.S.: 523999
B. Scott Smith (Co-Owner)
Michael Hodge (CFO & VP)
David Smith (CEO)

Subsidiaries:

Speedway Motorsports, LLC (1)
5401 E Independence Blvd, Charlotte, NC 28212 (100%)
Tel.: (704) 538-3318
Web Site: http://www.speedwaymotorsports.com
Holding Company; Motorsports Racetrack Owner & Operator
N.A.I.C.S.: 551112
O. Bruton Smith (Chm)
Marcus G. Smith (Pres & CEO)
William R. Brooks (Vice Chm, Treas & VP)
B. Scott Smith (Co-Owner)
Michael Hodge (CFO, Exec VP & Asst Treas)
David Bruton Smith (Co-Owner)
Jessica Fickenscher (Chief Experience Officer)
Cynthia Jacobson (Sr VP-HR)
Donald Hawk (Chief Racing Dev Officer)
Mike Burch (Chief Strategy Officer)
Geoff Ulrich (Sr VP-Consumer Strategy)
Jill Gregory (Exec VP/Gen Mgr-Sonoma Raceway)
Kevin Camper (Chief Sls Officer)
J. Cary Tharrington IV (Gen Counsel & Sr VP)

Subsidiary (Domestic):

600 Racing Inc. (2)
5245 Hwy 49 S, Harrisburg, NC 28075-8476 (100%)
Tel.: (704) 455-3896
Web Site: http://www.600racing.com
Sales Range: $10-24.9 Million
Emp.: 43
Mfr & Distributor of Legends Cars & Bandolero Cars
N.A.I.C.S.: 339930

Atlanta Motor Speedway, Inc. (2)
PO Box 500, Hampton, GA 30228
Tel.: (770) 707-7904
Web Site: http://www.atlantamotorspeedway.com
Sales Range: $10-24.9 Million
Emp.: 75
Motorsports Facility & Motorsports Promotion & Entertainment Events
N.A.I.C.S.: 711212
Mike Bruner (VP-Fin)
Ed Clark (Pres)
Sheila Summey (Asst Controller)
Rebecca Reid (Dir-Ticket Ops)
Jake Mullins (VP-Bus Dev)
Dustin Bixby (VP-Mktg & Promo)
Brandon Hutchison (Exec VP & Gen Mgr)

Bristol Motor Speedway (2)
151 Speedway Blvd, Bristol, TN 37620 (100%)
Tel.: (423) 989-6900
Web Site: http://www.bristolmotorspeedway.com
Sales Range: $10-24.9 Million
Emp.: 72
Promotion of Motorsports & Entertainment Events
N.A.I.C.S.: 711212
DeDe Hash (VP-Security & Asset Mgmt)
Jack Cocklin (Mgr-Dragway Ops)
Scott Hatcher (VP-Ops & Dev)
Gail Hulse (Dir-Fan Initiatives)
Tanyua Kerns (VP-Events)
Ben Trout (Sr Dir-Customer Rels)
Julie Bennett (Gen Counsel & VP)
Becky Cox (VP-Comm)
Greg Harvey (VP-Sls)
Marty Denton (VP-Fin)
Adam Rust (VP-Pur & Tech)
Drew Bedard (VP-Brand & Consumer Mktg)
Jennifer Payne (Sr Dir-HR)
Billy Kerns (Sr Dir-Ops)
Landon Owen (Dir-Sls-Ticket)
Brandon Cross (Dir-Bristol Dragway)
Anthony Vestal (Dir-Comm)
Daniel Warren (Mgr-Camping)
Chris Lawyer (Mgr-Comm)

Charlotte Motor Speedway, LLC (2)
5555 Concord Pkwy, Concord, NC 28027-0600 (100%)
Tel.: (704) 455-3200
Web Site: http://www.charlottemotorspeedway.com
Sales Range: $50-74.9 Million
Emp.: 200
Motorsports Racetrack Operator
N.A.I.C.S.: 711212
O. Bruton Smith (Chm & Co-CEO)
Marcus G. Smith (Co-CEO)
Greg Walter (Exec VP & Gen Mgr)

Dover Motorsports, Inc. (2)
1131 N Dupont Hwy, Dover, DE 19901
Tel.: (302) 883-6500
Web Site: http://www.dovermotorsports.com
Rev.: $38,543,000
Assets: $87,546,000
Liabilities: $18,519,000
Net Worth: $69,027,000
Earnings: $7,482,000
Emp.: 52
Fiscal Year-end: 12/31/2020
Holding Company; Motorsports Racetracks Operator & Events Promoter
N.A.I.C.S.: 551112
Thomas G. Wintermantel (Treas, Sec & VP)

Subsidiary (Domestic):

Dover International Speedway, Inc. (3)
1131 N Dupont Hwy, Dover, DE 19901
Tel.: (302) 883-6500
Web Site: http://www.doverspeedway.com
Sales Range: $25-49.9 Million
Motorsports Racetrack Operator & Events Promoter

N.A.I.C.S.: 711212
Denis L. McGlynn (Pres & CEO)

Nashville Speedway, USA, Inc. (3)
4847-F McCrary Rd, Lebanon, TN 37090-7875
Tel.: (615) 994-4465
Web Site: http://www.nashvillesuperspeedway.com
Sales Range: $10-24.9 Million
Race Track Services
N.A.I.C.S.: 711212

Subsidiary (Domestic):

Kentucky Raceway, LLC (2)
1 Speedway Dr, Sparta, KY 41086
Tel.: (859) 578-2300
Web Site: http://www.kentuckyspeedway.com
Motorsports Racetrack Operator
N.A.I.C.S.: 711212
Tim Bray (Dir-Comm)

Las Vegas Motor Speedway (2)
7000 Las Vegas Blvd, North Las Vegas, NV 89115
Tel.: (702) 644-4444
Web Site: http://www.lvms.com
Sales Range: $25-49.9 Million
Emp.: 50
Racetrack Operator
N.A.I.C.S.: 711212
R. Christopher Powell (Pres & Gen Mgr)

Subsidiary (Domestic):

Nevada Speedway, LLC (3)
17623 S 1700 Rd, Nevada, MO 64772-8992
Tel.: (417) 667-5859
Web Site: http://www.nevadaspeedway1.com
Motorsports Racetrack Operator
N.A.I.C.S.: 711212
O. Bruton Smith (Chm)
Chris Powell (Pres & Gen Mgr)
Tim Richter (Mgr-Racing Ops-Short Tracks)
Bill Soard (VP-Fin)
Kevin Camper (Sr VP-Sls & Mktg)
David Stetzer (VP-Ops)
Bud Hertig (Dir-Emergency Svcs)
Bobby McKenna (Dir-Facility Ops)
Jeff Motley (VP-PR)

Speedway Funding, LLC (3)
2215 Renaissance Dr Ste B, Las Vegas, NV 89119
Tel.: (702) 932-4906
Mortgage Loan Brokerage Services
N.A.I.C.S.: 522299

Subsidiary (Domestic):

New Hampshire Motor Speedway, Inc. (2)
1122 Route 106 N, Loudon, NH 03307
Tel.: (603) 783-4931
Web Site: http://www.nhms.com
Racing Track Operator
N.A.I.C.S.: 711212
O. Bruton Smith (Chm)
Marcus G. Smith (CEO)
Tom Blanchette (Dir-Ops)
David McGrath (Gen Mgr)
Kristen Lestock (Dir-Comm)
Shannon Stephens (Mgr-Comm)

Oil-Chem Research Corporation (2)
6800 W 73rd St, Bedford Park, IL 60638
Tel.: (708) 728-0028
Emp.: 4
Lubricants & Engine Oil Mfr & Whslr
N.A.I.C.S.: 325998

SMISC Holdings, Inc. (2)
5239 ZMAX Blvd, Harrisburg, NC 28075
Tel.: (704) 455-9453
Emp.: 75
Freight Transportation Services
N.A.I.C.S.: 484110
Bruton Smith (Owner)

Speedway Sonoma LLC (2)
29355 Arnold Dr, Sonoma, CA 95476
Tel.: (707) 938-8448
Web Site: http://www.infineonraceway.com
Sales Range: $10-24.9 Million
Emp.: 40
Motorsports Racetrack
N.A.I.C.S.: 711212

SONICS & MATERIALS, INC.

O. Bruton Smith (Chm)
Steve Page (Pres & Gen Mgr)
Diana Brennan (VP-Mktg & PR)
Georgia Seipel (Mgr-Drag Racing)

Texas Motor Speedway (2)
3545 Lone Star Cir, Fort Worth, TX 76177 (100%)
Tel.: (817) 215-8500
Web Site: http://www.texasmotorspeedway.com
Sales Range: $25-49.9 Million
Emp.: 130
Promotion of Motorsports & Entertainment Events
N.A.I.C.S.: 711212
O. Bruton Smith (Chm)
Eddie Gossage (Pres)
Travis Gafford (Sr Dir-Ticket Sls, Svc & Ops)

SONIC MANAGEMENT
2528 Sam Houston Ave, Huntsville, TX 77340
Tel.: (936) 291-0338
Web Site: http://www.sonicfood.com
Sales Range: $10-24.9 Million
Emp.: 100
Restaurant Operators
N.A.I.C.S.: 722513
Ken Watford (Pres)
Kim Hamilton (CFO)

SONIC MERRITTED GROUP
750 N 17th St, Las Cruces, NM 88005
Tel.: (575) 524-8998
Sales Range: $10-24.9 Million
Emp.: 5,000
Sonic Drive-In Franchise Management
N.A.I.C.S.: 722513
Bobby J. Merritt (Pres)

SONIC PROMOS
435-E E Diamond Ave, Gaithersburg, MD 20877
Tel.: (301) 869-7800
Web Site: http://www.sonicpromos.com
Year Founded: 1997
Sales Range: $1-9.9 Million
Emp.: 10
Advetising Agency
N.A.I.C.S.: 541810
Seth Weiner (Pres)
Mallory Scott (Mgr-Mktg)
Debbie Bostin (Mgr-Production)
Marsha Glazer (Dir-Strategic Accts)
Lindsay Hixson (Mgr-Brand)
Casey Szesze (Mgr-Fulfillment & Office)
Julianne Weiner (COO)

SONICS & MATERIALS, INC.
53 Church Hill Rd, Newtown, CT 06470-1614
Tel.: (203) 270-4600 DE
Web Site: http://www.sonics.com
Year Founded: 1969
Sales Range: $1-9.9 Million
Emp.: 58
Ultrasonic Welding & Cutting Devices Mfr
N.A.I.C.S.: 335999
Robert Soloff (Pres & CEO)
Lauren Soloff (Sec & VP-Legal Affairs-Investor Relations)
Brian Gourley (Sls Mgr-Welding Product Line-North America)
Lois Baiad (Mgr-Sls Admin)
Jeff Warner (Mgr-Svc)
Michael Donaty (Product Mgr-Vibra-Cell)
Bruce Green (Mgr-Tech Support)

Subsidiaries:

Sonics & Materials, Inc.-European Office (1)

SONICS & MATERIALS, INC.

U.S. PRIVATE

Sonics & Materials, Inc.—(Continued)

13 Rue Pedra Fontaine, CH 1217, Meyrin, Geneva, Switzerland **(100%)**
Tel.: (41) 223641520
Web Site:
http://www.euro.sonicsandmaterials.ch
Provider of Ultrasonic Biotechnology Devices & Vibration Welders
N.A.I.C.S.: 334519

Ultra Sonic Seal Inc. (1)
53 Churchill Rd, Newtown, CT 06470-3015
Tel.: (610) 497-5150
Web Site: http://www.ultrasonicseal.com
Ultra Sonic Plastic Welding Equipment
N.A.I.C.S.: 423840

SONICS, INC.
890 N McCarthy Blvd Ste 200, Milpitas, CA 95035
Tel.: (408) 457-2800 **DE**
Web Site: http://www.sonicsinc.com
Sales Range: $10-24.9 Million
Emp.: 75
Semiconductor Devices & Related Products Mfr
N.A.I.C.S.: 334413
Grant A. Pierce *(Chm, Pres & CEO)*
Martin M. Kovacich *(CFO)*
Drew E. Wingard *(CTO)*
Hayssam Balach *(VP-Global Sls)*
Marcelle Loveday *(VP-Major Accts)*
Randy Smith *(VP-Mktg)*

SONIFI SOLUTIONS, INC.
3900 W Innovation St, Sioux Falls, SD 57107-7002
Tel.: (605) 988-1000 **DE**
Web Site: http://www.sonifi.com
Year Founded: 1980
Sales Range: $350-399.9 Million
Emp.: 840
End-to-End Interactive Content & Connectivity Solutions for the Hospitality & Healthcare Industries
N.A.I.C.S.: 517111
Thomas M. McAdaragh *(Sr VP-Ops)*
Thomas W. Storey *(Pres-Hospitality)*
John Chang *(CFO)*
Ahmad Ouri *(CEO)*
Joel Zdepski *(CTO)*
Tommy Moreno *(Sr VP-Change Mgmt Grp)*
Nick Clessuras *(Sr VP-Sls)*
Tracy Geist *(Sr VP-Product)*
Kara Heermans *(VP-User Experience & Product Mgmt)*
Mark Dyer *(Sr VP-Sls-SONIFI Health)*
Roy Kosuge *(Gen Mgr-SONIFI Health)*

Subsidiaries:

LodgeNet StayOnline Inc. (1)
120 Interstate North Pkwy Ste 160, Atlanta, GA 30339
Tel.: (770) 933-0600
Web Site: http://www.stayonline.net
Sales Range: $100-124.9 Million
Hospitality & Lodging High-Speed Internet Solutions
N.A.I.C.S.: 517810

SONJU TWO HARBORS LLC
893 Phoenix Dr, Two Harbors, MN 55616
Tel.: (218) 834-2181
Web Site: http://www.sonju.com
Rev.: $45,000,000
Emp.: 70
New & Used Automobiles
N.A.I.C.S.: 441110
Terry Johnson *(Pres)*

SONNAX INDUSTRIES, INC.
1 Automatic Dr, Bellows Falls, VT 05101
Tel.: (802) 463-9722
Web Site: http://www.sonnax.com

Year Founded: 1978
Rev.: $15,800,000
Emp.: 200
Automatic Transmissions & Related Products Mfr
N.A.I.C.S.: 336350
Steve Jaussaud *(VP-Sls)*
Bob Warnke *(VP-Tech Dev)*
Joe Lombardi *(Mgr-Sls-Intl)*
Tommy Harmon *(Pres & CEO)*

SONNEBORN, LLC
600 Parsippany Rd Ste 100, Parsippany, NJ 07054
Web Site: http://www.sonneborn.com
Year Founded: 1903
Industrial Organic Chemicals Mfr
N.A.I.C.S.: 325199
Luther Jones *(VP)*
Gregg Kam *(CFO)*

Subsidiaries:

Sonneborn Refined Products B.V. (1)
Mainhavenweg 6, 1043 AL, Amsterdam, Netherlands
Tel.: (31) 206117475
Web Site: https://www.sonneborn.com
Emp.: 200
Specialty Chemicals Mfr
N.A.I.C.S.: 325998

SONNEN AUDI VOLKSWAGEN
740 Francisco Blvd W, San Rafael, CA 94901-3927
Tel.: (415) 460-4100
Web Site: http://www.sonnen.com
Year Founded: 1987
Sales Range: $25-49.9 Million
Emp.: 175
Car Whslr
N.A.I.C.S.: 441110
Peter Sonnen *(Pres)*

SONNENALP PROPERTIES INC.
20 Vail Rd, Vail, CO 81657
Tel.: (970) 476-5656
Web Site: http://www.sonnenalp.com
Year Founded: 1919
Sales Range: $1-9.9 Million
Emp.: 250
Resort Hotel
N.A.I.C.S.: 721110
Johannes Faessler *(Owner)*
John Mills *(Controller)*

Subsidiaries:

Sonnenalp Real Estate (1)
242 E Meadow Dr Ste D, Vail, CO 81657
Tel.: (970) 477-5300
Web Site:
http://www.sonnenalprealestate.com
Real Estate
N.A.I.C.S.: 721110
Joni White Taylor *(Owner & Pres)*

SONNHALTER
633 W Bagley Rd Ste 4, Berea, OH 44017-1356
Tel.: (440) 234-1812 **OH**
Web Site: http://www.sonnhalter.com
Year Founded: 1977
Sales Range: $1-9.9 Million
Emp.: 8
Advertising Agencies
N.A.I.C.S.: 541810
Matt Sonnhalter *(Architect-Vision)*
Sandra Bucher *(Engr-Media)*

SONNY CANNON AUTO PLAZA INC.
220 W Doolin Ave, Blackwell, OK 74631
Tel.: (580) 363-0322
Web Site:
http://sonnycannonautosales.com

Sales Range: $10-24.9 Million
Emp.: 25
Sells & Services New & Used Cars
N.A.I.C.S.: 441110
William Cannon *(Pres)*

SONNY'S ENTERPRISES INC.
5605 Hiatus Rd, Tamarac, FL 33321
Tel.: (954) 467-1203
Web Site: http://www.sonnysdirect.com
Year Founded: 1978
Rev.: $59,000,000
Emp.: 138
Conveyorized Carwach Machinery Distr
N.A.I.C.S.: 423830
Paul Fazio *(CEO)*
Ron Lick *(Dir-Equipment Sls)*
Melanie Marino *(Mgr-HR)*
Anthony Analetto *(Pres-Tunnel Equipment)*
John Reeves *(COO)*

SONNY'S FRANCHISE COMPANY INC.
201 N New York Ave 3rd Fl, Winter Park, FL 32789
Tel.: (407) 660-8888
Web Site: http://www.sonnysbbq.com
Year Founded: 1968
Sales Range: $200-249.9 Million
Emp.: 115
Barbecue Restaurant
N.A.I.C.S.: 722511
Robert Yarmuth *(CEO)*

SONNY'S REAL PIT BAR-B-QUE
1720 US Hwy 1 S, Saint Augustine, FL 32084-6016
Tel.: (904) 824-3220 **FL**
Web Site: http://www.sonnysbbq.com
Year Founded: 1968
Sales Range: $250-299.9 Million
Emp.: 6,435
Family Restaurant Owner & Operator
N.A.I.C.S.: 722511
Richard Irvin *(Gen Mgr)*

SONNYS HOME CENTER INC.
3090 E Main St, Canon City, CO 81212
Tel.: (719) 275-1544
Web Site:
http://www.acehardware.com
Rev.: $11,922,388
Emp.: 80
Plumbing Fittings & Supplies
N.A.I.C.S.: 423720

SONOMA BRANDS LLC
117 W Napa St Ste C, Sonoma, CA 95476
Tel.: (707) 656-2015 **DE**
Web Site:
http://www.sonomabrands.com
Year Founded: 2015
Privater Equity Firm
N.A.I.C.S.: 523999
Jonathan Sebastiani *(Founder)*
Jon Sebastiani *(Founder & Mng Partner)*
Brian Nicholson *(Mng Dir)*
Kevin Murphy *(Mng Dir)*

Subsidiaries:

Krave Pure Foods, Inc. (1)
500 W 5th St Ste 900, Austin, TX 78701
Tel.: (707) 939-9176
Web Site: http://www.kravejerky.com
Sales Range: $100-124.9 Million
Emp.: 40
Food Products Mfr
N.A.I.C.S.: 311412

SONOMA PARTNERS, LLC

525 W Monroe St Ste 500, Chicago, IL 60661
Tel.: (312) 627-0700
Web Site:
http://www.sonomapartners.com
Year Founded: 2001
Sales Range: $10-24.9 Million
Emp.: 150
Computer System Design Services
N.A.I.C.S.: 541512
James J. Steger *(Mgr)*

SONORAN AIR INC.
2225 W Whispering Wind Dr Ste 108, Phoenix, AZ 85085
Tel.: (623) 581-9555
Web Site: http://www.sonoranair.com
Sales Range: $25-49.9 Million
Emp.: 350
Plumbing Services
N.A.I.C.S.: 238220
Keith Laizure *(Mgr)*
Christine Marotta *(Mgr-Customer Svcs)*

SONORAN ROOFING INC.
4161 Citrus Ave, Rocklin, CA 95677
Tel.: (916) 624-1080
Web Site:
http://www.sonoranroofing.com
Sales Range: $10-24.9 Million
Emp.: 120
Roofing Contractors
N.A.I.C.S.: 238160
John R. Daly *(Pres)*

SONS ACURA
7060 Jonesboro Rd, Morrow, GA 30260
Tel.: (770) 968-5252
Web Site: http://www.sonsacura.com
Sales Range: $100-124.9 Million
Emp.: 250
New Car Dealers
N.A.I.C.S.: 441110
Freddy Felton *(Gen Mgr)*
Ginger Balch *(Office Mgr)*

SONSRAY, INC.
23935 Madison St, Torrance, CA 90505
Tel.: (323) 319-1900 **CA**
Web Site: http://www.sonsray.com
Year Founded: 2014
Holding Company; Construction Machinery Distr & Rental Services; Commercial Vehicle Fleet management Services
N.A.I.C.S.: 551112
Matthew Hoelscher *(Owner & Pres)*
Mark Hicken *(CFO)*

Subsidiaries:

Sonsray Machinery, LLC (1)
23935 Madison St, Torrance, CA 90505
Tel.: (323) 319-1900
Web Site: http://www.sonsraymachinery.com
Construction Equipment Distr & Rental Services
N.A.I.C.S.: 423810
Patrick Fisher *(VP)*

TK Services, Inc. (1)
23935 Madison St, Torrance, CA 90505
Web Site: http://www.tksvinc.com
Commercial Vehicle Fleet Management Services
N.A.I.C.S.: 811111
Alan Grenier *(VP)*

SONSTEGARD FOODS COMPANY
5005 S Bur Oak Pl, Sioux Falls, SD 57108
Tel.: (605) 338-4642
Web Site: http://www.sonstegard.com
Year Founded: 1972
Sales Range: $75-99.9 Million

COMPANIES
SOROS FUND MANAGEMENT LLC

Emp.: 5
Poultry & Poultry Products
N.A.I.C.S.: 424440
Philip Sonstegard *(Pres)*
Subsidiaries:

Sonstegard Foods of Georgia (1)
5005 S Bur Oak Pl, Sioux Falls, SD 57108
Tel.: (770) 534-5644
Web Site: http://www.sonstegard.com
Eggs, Processed Frozen
N.A.I.C.S.: 311999

SOONER BOLT & SUPPLY INC.
1843 N 106th E Ave, Tulsa, OK 74116-1510
Tel.: (918) 836-7756
Web Site: http://www.sbsindustries.com
Year Founded: 1976
Sales Range: $10-24.9 Million
Emp.: 75
Wholesale of Hardware Supplies
N.A.I.C.S.: 423710
Jeff Greer *(Controller)*

SOONER COOPERATIVE INC.
301 E Oklahoma St, Okeene, OK 73763
Tel.: (580) 822-4423
Sales Range: $10-24.9 Million
Emp.: 16
Grain Elevators
N.A.I.C.S.: 424510
Lois Seelke *(Office Mgr)*

SOONER EQUIPMENT & LEASING, INC.
20213 E Admiral Pl, Catoosa, OK 74015
Tel.: (918) 266-2000
Web Site: http://www.soonertrucksales.com
Year Founded: 1985
Sales Range: $10-24.9 Million
Emp.: 9
Motor Vehicle Supplies & New Parts Whslr
N.A.I.C.S.: 423120
George Cornelison *(Owner)*

SOONER LIFT INC.
3401 S Purdue St, Oklahoma City, OK 73179
Tel.: (405) 682-1400
Web Site: http://www.soonerlift.com
Sales Range: $10-24.9 Million
Emp.: 50
Industrial Machinery & Equipment
N.A.I.C.S.: 423830
Jeff McIver *(Pres)*
Calvin Woods *(Mgr-Parts)*

SOONER SOUTHWEST BANK-SHARES, INC.
1751 E 71st St, Tulsa, OK 74136
Tel.: (918) 496-4242   OK
Year Founded: 1986
Sales Range: $10-24.9 Million
Emp.: 90
Bank Holding Company
N.A.I.C.S.: 551111
Robert B. Krumme *(Pres & CEO)*
Deborah Krumme *(Sec)*
Subsidiaries:

Community Bank (1)
104 S Main St, Bristow, OK 74010
Tel.: (918) 367-3343
Web Site: http://www.cbbristow.com
Sales Range: $1-9.9 Million
Emp.: 23
Commericial Banking
N.A.I.C.S.: 522110
W. David Roberts *(Pres & CEO)*
Rob Smith *(Chief Loan Officer & Sr VP)*

First National Bank (1)
400 E 1st St, Heavener, OK 74937
Tel.: (918) 653-3200
Web Site: http://www.okfnb.com
Sales Range: $1-9.9 Million
Emp.: 39
Commericial Banking
N.A.I.C.S.: 522110
Mark A. Caldwell *(Pres & CEO)*
Chris Ward *(Chief Lending Officer & Exec VP)*
Dana L. Scott *(VP)*
Eddie J. Freeman *(Sr VP)*

Security First National Bank of Hugo (1)
100 S Broadway, Hugo, OK 74743
Tel.: (580) 326-9641
Web Site: http://www.sfnb.net
Sales Range: $1-9.9 Million
Emp.: 37
Commericial Banking
N.A.I.C.S.: 522110
Mike Brewer *(Pres & CEO)*
Ronnie Golden *(Exec VP & Loan Officer)*
Shane Spillman *(Sec & VP)*
Verna Sue Butler *(VP & Asst Sec)*
Michael Melton *(VP & Secrecy/CRA Officer)*

SOPARK CORP.
3300 S Pk Ave, Buffalo, NY 14218
Tel.: (716) 822-0434
Web Site: http://www.sopark.com
Sales Range: $10-24.9 Million
Emp.: 98
Contract Electronic Services
N.A.I.C.S.: 334412
John Kasperek *(Controller)*
Darren Denzel *(Supvr-Production)*
Joseph Miano *(Mgr-Sls)*
Keith Calhoun *(Mgr-Sls)*
Clinton R. Wyckoff III *(Pres)*

SOPHIRIS BIO INC.
1258 Prospect St, La Jolla, CA 92037
Tel.: (858) 777-1760   BC
SPHS—(OTCBB)
Sales Range: $1-9.9 Million
Pharmaceutical Mfr, Researcher & Developer
N.A.I.C.S.: 541715
Kim Stevenson *(Office Mgr)*

SOPHLOGIC GLOBAL, LLC
8374 Market St Ste 133, Bradenton, FL 34202
Tel.: (941) 932-8570   DE
Web Site: http://www.sophlogic.com
Year Founded: 2004
Sales Range: $10-24.9 Million
Emp.: 20
IT & Life Sciences Staffing
N.A.I.C.S.: 561311
Michael Bovaird *(Pres)*

SOR, INC.
14685 W 105th St, Lenexa, KS 66215-2003
Tel.: (913) 888-2630   KS
Web Site: http://www.sorinc.com
Year Founded: 1956
Sales Range: $100-124.9 Million
Emp.: 175
Pressure & Temperature Switches; Level & Flow Switches Mfr
N.A.I.C.S.: 335314
Mike Waters *(CEO)*
Tom Geissler *(Mgr-Sls-Western Reg)*
Ted Johnson *(Dir-Global Temperature Sls)*
Srinivasan Seetharaman *(Mgr-Sls-Asia & Pacific Rim)*
Zhao Xu *(Mgr-Sls-China)*
Michelle Scott *(Mgr-Sls-Europe, Africa & CIS)*
Romy Mathew *(Mgr-Sls-Middle East)*
Subsidiaries:

SOR (Europe) Ltd. (1)
Farren Court cowfold, Horsham, RH13 8BP, West Sussex, United Kingdom (100%)
Tel.: (44) 1403864000
Web Site: http://www.sorinc.com
Sales Range: $25-49.9 Million
Emp.: 4
Provider of Controlling Devices
N.A.I.C.S.: 334519

SORCE PROPERTIES INC.
414 Essex St, Hackensack, NJ 07601-1265
Tel.: (201) 488-4000
Web Site: http://www.sorce.com
Year Founded: 1983
Sales Range: $10-24.9 Million
Emp.: 20
Real Estate Agency Services
N.A.I.C.S.: 531210
Santo Sorce *(Pres)*

SORDONI CONSTRUCTION SERVICES, INC.
45 Owen St, Forty Fort, PA 18704-4305
Tel.: (570) 287-3161   PA
Web Site: http://www.sordoni.com
Year Founded: 1910
Sales Range: $10-24.9 Million
Emp.: 125
Commercial Construction & General Contractor Services
N.A.I.C.S.: 238990
William E. Sordoni *(Pres & CEO)*
Kimberly Fanning *(Controller)*
Jennifer Pocius Davis *(Dir-Design & Dev)*
Timothy C. O'Shea *(Chief Bus Officer)*
Todd D. Rothermel *(COO & Corp Counsel)*
Subsidiaries:

Sordoni Construction Co. (1)
1 Pluckemin Way, Bedminster, NJ 07921
Tel.: (908) 879-1130
Web Site: http://www.sordoniconstruction.com
Construction & Project Management
N.A.I.C.S.: 236220
Michael J. Healy *(Chm, Co-Pres & Co-CEO)*
Matthew T. Lorenzo *(Co-Pres & Co-CEO)*
Seth H. Levy *(COO & Exec VP)*
Leo Kushner *(CFO)*
Frank A. Bostjancic Jr. *(Dir-Corp Safety)*

SORENSEN FLEXIBLE BENEFITS, LTD.
318 Plum St, Red Wing, MN 55066
Tel.: (651) 388-7104   MN
Web Site: http://www.sorensenbenefits.com
Year Founded: 1989
Sales Range: $1-9.9 Million
Emp.: 10
Insurance Agencies & Brokerages
N.A.I.C.S.: 524210

SORENSON CAPITAL PARTNERS
3400 N Ashton Blvd Ste 400, Lehi, UT 84043
Tel.: (801) 407-8400
Web Site: http://www.sorensoncapital.com
Year Founded: 2003
Sales Range: $25-49.9 Million
Emp.: 30
Privater Equity Firm
N.A.I.C.S.: 523999
Tim Layton *(Founder & Mng Dir)*
Ron Mika *(Founder & Mng Partner)*
Mark Ludwig *(Mng Dir)*
Brian Dunn *(CFO)*
Donald Blohm *(Partner-Operating)*
Peter Sturgeon *(Mng Dir)*
LeGrand Lewis *(Mng Dir)*
Luke Sorenson *(Mng Dir)*
Matt Marsh *(Mng Dir)*
Bert Roberts *(Mng Dir)*
Brady Broadbent *(Principal)*
Tom Pierce *(VP-Fin & Tax)*
Len Blackwell *(Mng Dir-Portfolio Ops)*
Ken Elefant *(Mng Dir)*
Rob Rueckert *(Mng Dir)*
Subsidiaries:

Mity Enterprises, Inc. (1)
1301 W 400 N, Orem, UT 84057-4442
Tel.: (801) 224-0589
Web Site: http://www.mitylite.com
Sales Range: $50-74.9 Million
Commercial Furniture Mfr
N.A.I.C.S.: 337214
Gregory D. Dye *(VP-HR)*
Brandon Ross *(VP-Sls & Mktg)*

Subsidiary (Non-US):

Broda Enterprises, Inc. (2)
560 Bingemans Centre Drive, Kitchener, N2B 3X9, ON, Canada
Tel.: (519) 746-8080
Web Site: http://www.brodaseating.com
Sales Range: $25-49.9 Million
Geriatric Medical & Special Need Seating Mfr
N.A.I.C.S.: 337127
Tricia Boudrea *(Mgr-Mktg)*

SORENSON TRANSPORTATION CO
632 NW California St, Chehalis, WA 98532
Tel.: (360) 748-8877
Web Site: http://www.sorensontransport.com
Sales Range: $10-24.9 Million
Emp.: 108
Refrigerated Products Transport
N.A.I.C.S.: 484230
Darrell E. Sorenson *(Pres)*

SORG DODGE INC.
1811 Elkhart Rd, Goshen, IN 46526-1111
Tel.: (574) 533-8605
Web Site: http://www.sorgdodge.net
Sales Range: $10-24.9 Million
Emp.: 23
New Car Whslr
N.A.I.C.S.: 441110
Dennis L *(Pres)*

SOROS FUND MANAGEMENT LLC
250 West 55th St Fl 29, New York, NY 10019
Tel.: (212) 872-1054
Investment Services
N.A.I.C.S.: 523999
Subsidiaries:

Vice Media LLC (1)
90 N 11th St, Brooklyn, NY 11211
Tel.: (718) 599-3101
Web Site: http://www.vice.com
Sales Range: $150-199.9 Million
Emp.: 750
Magazine & Internet Publishing
N.A.I.C.S.: 513120
Shane Smith *(Co-Founder)*
Suroosh Alvi *(Co-Founder)*
Andrew Creighton *(Co-Pres)*
Eddy Moretti *(Pres-Programming)*
James Schwab *(Co-Pres)*
Alex Miller *(Dir-Creative-EMEA-Viceland)*
Nick Weidenfeld *(Pres-Programming)*
Cristian Jofre *(Dir-Creative-Viceland Intl)*
Guy Slattery *(Gen Mgr-Viceland)*
Ciel Hunter *(Head-Content)*
James Rosenstock *(Chief Corp Dev Officer & Pres-Viceland Intl)*
Tom Punch *(Chief Comml & Creative Officer)*
Mimi Turner *(Sr VP-Strategy-UK)*
Matt O'Mara *(Mng Dir-UK)*

SOROS FUND MANAGEMENT LLC

U.S. PRIVATE

Soros Fund Management LLC—(Continued)
Sam Bergen *(Exec Dir-Creative-West Coast)*
Nicolas Bonard *(CEO-France)*
Benjamin Lassale *(Gen Mgr)*
Tammy Smulders *(Pres-Fashion Grp)*
Matt Elek *(CEO-EMEA)*
Nilesh Zaveri *(CFO/COO-Asia Pacific)*
Hosi Simon *(CEO-Asia Pacific)*
Lucy Delacherois-Day *(Dir-Comml-Fashion Grp)*
Dominique Delport *(Chief Revenue Officer & Pres-Intl)*
Rohit Tugnait *(Comml Dir-India)*
Samira Kanwar *(Head-Content-Asia Pacific)*
Susie Banikarim *(Exec VP & Head-Newsgathering-Global-Vice News)*
Daisy Auger-Dominguez *(Chief People Officer)*
Jannat Gargi *(VP & Head-Documentaries-Vice Studios)*
Danny Gabai *(Exec VP & Head-Vice Studios-US)*
Nadja Bellan-White *(CMO-Global)*
Jonathan Bing *(Chief Comm Officer)*

Subsidiary (Domestic):

Carrot Creative LLC (2)
55 Washington St Ste 900, Brooklyn, NY 11201
Tel.: (718) 395-7934
Web Site: http://www.carrot.is
Emp.: 70
Advetising Agency
N.A.I.C.S.: 541810
Mike Germano *(Co-Founder & CEO)*
Chris Petescia *(Co-Founder & Chief Experience Officer)*
Kyle MacDonald *(CTO)*
Tim Nolan *(Chief Creative Officer)*

Subsidiary (Non-US):

Pulse Films Limited (2)
17 Hanbury Street, London, E1 6QR, United Kingdom
Tel.: (44) 20 7426 5700
Web Site: http://www.pulsefilms.co.uk
Motion Picture Production Services
N.A.I.C.S.: 512110
Thomas Benski *(Co-Founder & CEO)*
Marisa Clifford *(Co-founder & CEO-Europe)*
Davud Karbassioun *(Pres-Commercials & Branded Entertainment)*
Jade Maxwell *(Head-HR)*
Rik Green *(Head-Music Videos)*
Julia Nottingham *(Head-Documentary)*
Emma Cooper *(Pres-Global)*
Jon Alwen *(Sr VP-Non-Fiction TV-UK)*
Nelesh Dhand *(Head-Dev-Global)*
Bianca Gavin *(Head-Production-Scripted Television & Film)*
Jamie Hall *(COO-Scripted Television & Film)*

Subsidiary (Domestic):

Refinery 29, Inc. (2)
225 Broadway 23rd Fl, New York, NY 10007
Tel.: (212) 966-3110
Web Site: http://www.refinery29.com
Sales Range: $1-9.9 Million
Emp.: 59
Fashion, Beauty & Entertainment Website
N.A.I.C.S.: 519290
George Mitchell *(VP-Bus Affairs & Ops)*
Jenny Gorenstein *(Dir-Fashion)*
Kirsty Hathaway *(Creative Dir-Europe)*
Kristin Cardwell *(VP-Strategy & Bus Dev-Intl)*
Nina Joyce *(Dir-PR-Europe)*
Kate Ward *(Sr VP & Head-Intl)*
Simone Oliver *(Editor-in-Chief)*

SORRENTO CAPITAL, INC.
3161 Michelson Dr Ste 900, Irvine, CA 92612
Tel.: (949) 943-1110
Year Founded: 2001
Sales Range: $25-49.9 Million
Emp.: 428
Financial Services
N.A.I.C.S.: 522320
Robert Knohl *(Co-Founder & CEO)*
Dana Keith *(Co-Founder & Pres)*
Greg Hebner *(COO & Pres-MOS Grp)*
Julia Sohn *(VP-HR)*
Tyler Aldous *(CFO)*
Steven A. Ozonian *(Chm)*

SORRISO TECHNOLOGIES, INC.
40 Nagog Park, Acton, MA 01720
Tel.: (978) 635-3900
Web Site: http://www.sorrisotech.com
Year Founded: 1996
Rev.: $3,900,000
Emp.: 25
Prepackaged Software Services
N.A.I.C.S.: 513210
John A. Kowalonek *(Pres)*

SORRY ROBOTS LLC
1202 Grant Ave Ste D, Novato, CA 94945
Tel.: (650) 877-2874
Web Site: http://www.gir.co
Year Founded: 2012
Sales Range: $1-9.9 Million
Emp.: 13
Kitchen Accessory Mfr & Distr
N.A.I.C.S.: 337110
Samantha Rose *(Founder)*

SOS CORPORATION
331 W St, Milford, MA 01757
Tel.: (508) 473-0466
Web Site: http://www.soscorp.net
Sales Range: $10-24.9 Million
Emp.: 15
Construction Site Cleanup
N.A.I.C.S.: 238990
Brent Oldfield *(VP)*
Jarrod Mahimtura *(Project Mgr-Safety & Coord-SOS Special Projects)*
Charlie Bjornson *(Project Mgr)*

SOS HYDRATION INC.
1265 Bramwood Pl Unit 6, Longmont, CO 80501
Tel.: (303) 834-9170   NV
Web Site: https://www.soshydration.com
Year Founded: 2013
Rev.: $1,782,632
Assets: $1,529,955
Liabilities: $1,177,292
Net Worth: $352,663
Earnings: ($1,748,446)
Emp.: 12
Fiscal Year-end: 12/31/20
Hydration Drink Mfr
N.A.I.C.S.: 312112
James Mayo *(Pres, CEO, Co-Founder & Sec)*
Victor Andrade *(CFO)*
Blanca Lizaola-Mayo *(Co-Founder)*
Thomas Mayo *(Co-Founder)*

SOS INTERNATIONAL LLC
1881 Campus Commons Dr Ste 500, Reston, VA 20191
Tel.: (703) 391-9680   DE
Web Site: http://www.sosi.com
Year Founded: 1989
Defense, Intelligence & Government Services
N.A.I.C.S.: 561621
Julian Setian *(Pres & CEO)*
Nayna Diehl *(Assoc Gen Counsel)*
John Avalos *(COO)*
Dan Robinson *(VP-Bus Dev)*
Kevin Henderson *(Chief Growth Officer)*
Jennifer Diamond Haber *(VP-Comm)*
Kyle Fox *(CTO)*
Andrew Bream *(VP-IT)*

Subsidiaries:

SOS International Ltd. (1)
1881 Campus Commons Dr Ste 500, Reston, VA 20191
Tel.: (703) 391-9680
Web Site: http://www.sosi.com
Government Services
N.A.I.C.S.: 921190
Mike Franz *(VP-Bus Dev)*

Vykin Corporation (1)
400 N Ashley Dr Ste 1440, Tampa, FL 33602
Tel.: (888) 809-0025
Web Site: http://www.vykincorp.com
Data Processing, Hosting & Related Services
N.A.I.C.S.: 518210
Leisha Griffin *(Pres)*
Phillip Galinshi *(Dir-IT)*

SOS OF TAMPA BAY, INC.
18562 US Hwy 19 N, Clearwater, FL 33764
Tel.: (727) 571-1000
Web Site: http://www.sos.co
Sales Range: $1-9.9 Million
Office Equipment Distr
N.A.I.C.S.: 423420
Tom Generaldi *(Pres)*

SOTEL SYSTEMS, LLC
2465 Centerline Industrial Dr, Maryland Heights, MO 63043
Tel.: (866) 467-6835
Web Site: http://www.sotelsystems.com
Telecom Repair Sevices
N.A.I.C.S.: 517810
Jimx Goebel *(Pres & CEO)*

SOTERA WIRELESS, INC.
10020 Huennekens St, San Diego, CA 92121
Tel.: (858) 427-4620
Web Site: http://www.soterawireless.com
Developer & Marketer of Medical Devices for Monitoring Vital Signs
N.A.I.C.S.: 339112
Tom Watlington *(CEO)*
Charlie Alvarez *(Sr VP-Sls & Mktg)*
Benjamin Kanter *(Chief Medical Officer)*
James Moon *(CTO)*
Jim Welch *(Exec VP-Product Dev & Customer Fulfillment)*

Subsidiaries:

Reflectance Medical, Inc. (1)
116 Flanders Rd Ste 1000, Westborough, MA 01581-1072
Tel.: (508) 366-4700
Web Site: http://www.reflectancemedical.com
Electromedical & Electrotherapeutic Apparatus Mfr
N.A.I.C.S.: 334510
Babs Soller *(Pres & CEO)*

SOTIS BUSINESS EQUIPMENT LTD.
52C N Main St, Marlboro, NJ 07746
Tel.: (212) 227-9838
Web Site: http://www.sotis.com
Sales Range: $10-24.9 Million
Emp.: 20
Office Equipment Sales
N.A.I.C.S.: 423420
Mike Caraba *(Pres)*

SOTTO INTERNATIONAL, INC.
1214 E 33rd St, Tulsa, OK 74105
Tel.: (918) 894-3487   OK
Web Site: http://www.sottointernational.com
Year Founded: 2001
Sales Range: $10-24.9 Million
Emp.: 122
Health Care Srvices
N.A.I.C.S.: 622110
Roger A. Bruhn *(CEO)*
Ed Gungor *(Founder & Pres)*

SOUCY INDUSTRIES INC.
5 Dick Tracy Dr, Pelham, NH 03076
Tel.: (603) 883-4500
Web Site: http://www.soucyindustries.com
Sales Range: $10-24.9 Million
Emp.: 20
Architectural Metalwork
N.A.I.C.S.: 332323
William Soucy *(Pres)*
Brian Allison *(Controller)*

SOUDAN METALS COMPANY INC.
319 W 40th Pl, Chicago, IL 60609
Tel.: (773) 548-7600
Web Site: http://www.soudanmetals.com
Year Founded: 1968
Sales Range: $10-24.9 Million
Emp.: 120
Steel
N.A.I.C.S.: 423510
Tom Soudan Jr. *(Pres)*

SOUDRONIC, LTD.
465 N State Rd, Briarcliff Manor, NY 10510-1468
Tel.: (914) 941-4808   NY
Web Site: http://www.soudronic.com
Year Founded: 1972
Sales Range: $50-74.9 Million
Emp.: 200
Industrial Machinery & Equipment
N.A.I.C.S.: 423830
Jakob Guyer *(CEO)*
Kirk Samy *(Mgr-Technical)*

SOUERS CONSTRUCTION INC.
1500 Coors Blvd NW Ste B, Albuquerque, NM 87121-1100
Tel.: (505) 836-4917   NM
Year Founded: 1995
Sales Range: $10-24.9 Million
Emp.: 1
Single-Family Housing Construction
N.A.I.C.S.: 236115
Arlond Souer *(Pres)*

SOUL BIOTECHNOLOGY CORPORATION
234 E Beech St, Long Beach, NY 11561
Tel.: (516) 544-2812   NV
Web Site: http://www.adorbskids.com
Year Founded: 2017
Rev.: $102
Assets: $9,499
Liabilities: $143,180
Net Worth: ($133,681)
Earnings: ($45,798)
Emp.: 1
Fiscal Year-end: 12/31/21
Children's Clothing Mfr
N.A.I.C.S.: 315990
Rebecca Jill Lazar *(Pres, CEO, CFO, Treas & Sec)*
David Lazar *(Pres, CEO & CFO)*

Subsidiaries:

MySpray Therapeutics Inc. (1)
125 Railway Ave E, PO Box 2149, Canora, S0A0L0, SK, Canada
Web Site: https://myspray.ca
Health Care Product Mfr & Distr
N.A.I.C.S.: 325620

SOUL COMMUNITY PLANET, INC.
741 S Coast Hwy, Laguna Beach, CA 92651
Tel.: (714) 423-4394   DE

COMPANIES

Web Site: https://scphotel.com
Year Founded: 2018
Hospitality Services
N.A.I.C.S.: 721110
Ken Cruse *(Founder & CEO)*

Subsidiaries:

Albion River Inn, Inc. (1)
3790 N Highway 1, Albion, CA 95410
Tel.: (707) 937-1919
Web Site: http://www.albionriverinn.com
Sales Range: $1-9.9 Million
Emp.: 90
Hotel Services
N.A.I.C.S.: 721110
Peter Wells *(Pres)*

SOULCYCLE INC.
609 Greenwich St, New York, NY 10014
Tel.: (212) 876-7685 DE
Web Site: http://www.soul-cycle.com
Year Founded: 2006
Sales Range: $100-124.9 Million
Emp.: 1,237
Fitness Services
N.A.I.C.S.: 713940
Harvey J. Spevak *(Chm)*
Stephen Nason *(Mgr-Field Mktg)*
Julie J. Rice *(Co-Founder)*
Carolyn Chiang Rosebrough *(VP & Head-PR & Comm)*
Gregory Gittrich *(Sr VP-Digital Media)*
Laurel Pinson *(VP-Content)*
Angela Bowers *(Sr Dir-Casting & Creative Dev)*
Sunder Reddy *(CFO)*
Evelyn Webster *(CEO)*

SOUND COMMUNICATIONS, INC.
149 W 36th St 11th Fl, New York, NY 10018
Tel.: (212) 489-1122 NY
Web Site: http://www.scommunications.com
Year Founded: 1987
Sales Range: $25-49.9 Million
Emp.: 15
Media Buying Services
N.A.I.C.S.: 541810
Steven Sackler *(Pres)*
Jill Sackler Souto *(Dir-Media)*
Louise Pucciarelli *(Dir-Media & Sr Media Buyer)*
John Sadowski *(Mgr-Bus Devel)*
Jack Bloom *(Dir-Creative)*
Scott Semaya *(Dir-Brdcst & Sr Media Buyer)*

SOUND CREDIT UNION
1331 Broadway, Tacoma, WA 98402
Tel.: (253) 383-2016
Web Site: http://www.soundcu.com
Year Founded: 1940
Rev.: $71,543,216
Assets: $1,840,108,777
Liabilities: $1,617,166,989
Net Worth: $222,941,788
Earnings: $18,940,061
Fiscal Year-end: 12/31/19
Credit Union
N.A.I.C.S.: 522130
David J. Wasson *(Chm)*
Shelley R. Coleman *(Vice Chm)*
John H. Bauder *(Treas & Sec)*
Wendy Cleveland *(COO & Sr VP)*
Charlene Henson *(Chief Retail Officer & Sr VP)*
Don L. Clark Jr. *(Pres & CEO)*

Subsidiaries:

MilePost Credit Union (1)
3633 Pacific Ave, Tacoma, WA 98418
Tel.: (253) 474-9000
Rev.: $3,400,000
Emp.: 22
Fiscal Year-end: 12/31/2006
Credit Union
N.A.I.C.S.: 522130

SOUND ENGINEERING, INC.
12933 Farmington Rd, Livonia, MI 48150
Tel.: (734) 522-2910
Web Site: http://www.soundeng.com
Year Founded: 1973
Sales Range: $10-24.9 Million
Emp.: 78
Sound Equipment Specialization
N.A.I.C.S.: 541690
Charles Schwab *(Pres)*
Michael Kellers *(Controller)*

SOUND FORD, INC.
101 SW Grady Way, Renton, WA 98057
Tel.: (425) 235-1000 DE
Web Site: http://www.soundford.com
Year Founded: 1973
Sales Range: $75-99.9 Million
Emp.: 200
New Car Dealers
N.A.I.C.S.: 441110
Leo Vickers *(Mgr-Parts)*
Adam Larson *(Gen Mgr-Sls)*
Jason Larkin *(Asst Mgr-Parts)*
Randy Parrott *(Asst Mgr-Svc)*
Travis Snyder *(Mgr-Svc)*
Kwok Yau *(Sls Mgr)*

SOUND GLASS SALES, INC.
5501 75th St W, Tacoma, WA 98499
Tel.: (425) 264-0395
Web Site: http://soundglass.com
Sales Range: $10-24.9 Million
Emp.: 82
Glass & Glazing Work Services
N.A.I.C.S.: 238150

SOUND MENTAL HEALTH
1600 E Olive St, Seattle, WA 98122
Tel.: (206) 302-2200 WA
Web Site: http://www.smh.org
Year Founded: 1967
Sales Range: $25-49.9 Million
Emp.: 625
Behavioral Healthcare Services
N.A.I.C.S.: 623220
Paul Eisenhauer *(CFO)*
Mary Bartels *(Dir-Medical)*
Susan Bean *(Chief Dev Officer)*

SOUND PARTNERS, LLC
1507 E Ash St, Goldsboro, NC 27532
Tel.: (919) 736-3866
Web Site: https://www.sound-partners.com
Emp.: 100
Financial Services
N.A.I.C.S.: 523999

SOUND POINT CAPITAL MANAGEMENT, LP
375 Park Ave 33rd Fl, New York, NY 10152
Tel.: (212) 895-2280 DE
Web Site: http://www.soundpointcap.com
Year Founded: 2008
Investment Management Service
N.A.I.C.S.: 523940
Stephen Ketchum *(Founder & Mng Partner)*
David Grill *(Head-Strategy)*

Subsidiaries:

Assured Investment Management LLC (1)
1633 Broadway 25th Fl, New York, NY 10019
Tel.: (212) 905-3900
Web Site: http://www.assuredinvestmentmanagement.com
Financial Investment Services
N.A.I.C.S.: 523999
David Buzen *(CEO & Chief Investment Officer)*
Evan Boulukos *(Head-Municipal Bonds)*
Brandon Cahill *(Head-CLOs)*
Robert De Veer *(Chief Risk Officer)*

SOUND SEAL, INC.
50 Hp Almgren Dr, Agawam, MA 01001-2971
Tel.: (413) 789-1770
Web Site: http://www.soundseal.com
Year Founded: 1978
Pressed, Blown Glass & Glassware Mfr
N.A.I.C.S.: 327212
Max Fischer *(Mgr-Bus Dev)*

Subsidiaries:

Lamvin, Inc. (1)
4675 North Ave, Oceanside, CA 92056
Tel.: (760) 806-6400
Web Site: http://www.lamvin.com
Mineral Wool
N.A.I.C.S.: 541310
David Castellanos *(Pres)*

SOUND SHORE MEDICAL CENTER OF WESTCHESTER
16 Guion Pl, New Rochelle, NY 10801
Tel.: (917) 816-3561 NY
Year Founded: 1940
Sales Range: $125-149.9 Million
Emp.: 1,556
Health Care Srvices
N.A.I.C.S.: 622110
John R. Spicer *(Pres & CEO)*
Clark E. Walter *(Gen Counsel & Sr VP)*
Madhu Rangraj *(Dir-Medical)*

SOUND TELECOM
1131 Poplar Pl S, Seattle, WA 98144
Tel.: (206) 774-3100
Web Site: http://www.sound-tele.com
Year Founded: 1986
Sales Range: $1-9.9 Million
Emp.: 72
Telephone Answering Services
N.A.I.C.S.: 561421
Diana Barlow *(Mgr-Billing, Credit & Collections)*

SOUND VIDEO SOLUTIONS, INC.
1720 Military Rd, Buffalo, NY 14217
Tel.: (716) 684-8700 NY
Web Site: http://www.svsny.com
Year Founded: 2002
Sales Range: $10-24.9 Million
Emp.: 25
Mfr & Distr of Portable AV Systems
N.A.I.C.S.: 334310
Doug Smith *(Pres)*
Dena Keller *(CEO)*

SOUNDCONNECT, LLC
1 Batterymarch Park Ste 104, Quincy, MA 02169
Tel.: (888) 827-4462
Web Site: http://www.sound-connect.com
Year Founded: 2004
Sales Range: $1-9.9 Million
Emp.: 15
Multi-Feature Hosted Audio Conferencing, Web Conferencing, Webcasting & Video Conferencing for Businesses
N.A.I.C.S.: 517810
Tom Sullivan *(Pres)*
Shaun Chambers *(Founder & CEO)*
Beth Peters *(Dir-Customer Svc)*
Jessica Ferro *(Dir-Fin & Ops)*

SOURCE CAPITAL, LLC

SOUNDCORE CAPITAL PARTNERS, LLC
489 Fifth Ave Fl 20, New York, NY 10017
Tel.: (212) 812-1180 DE
Web Site: http://www.soundcorecap.com
Year Founded: 2015
Privater Equity Firm
N.A.I.C.S.: 523999
Jarrett R. Turner *(Founder & Mng Partner)*
Art Zuckerman *(Partner, CFO, Chief Compliance Officer & Head-Portfolio Ops)*
Erik W. Emmett *(Principal & Head-Deal Origination)*
Feliks Zarotsky *(Mng Partner)*
Frank Mancuso *(VP)*
Jillian Freeman *(Controller)*
John Gabler *(VP)*
George Rolfs *(VP)*

Subsidiaries:

Alloy Wheel Repair Specialist, Inc. (1)
3100 Meadlock Bridge Rd Ste 305, Norcross, GA 30071
Tel.: (770) 903-1236
Web Site: http://www.awrswheelrepair.com
Emp.: 28
Automotive Alloy Wheel Repair Shops Operator & Franchisor
N.A.I.C.S.: 811198
Thomas Morris *(Founder)*
Rob Wheeley *(CEO)*

SOUNDEXCHANGE, INC.
733 10th St NW 10th Fl, Washington, DC 20001
Tel.: (202) 640-5858 DE
Web Site: http://www.soundexchange.com
Year Founded: 2003
Sales Range: $25-49.9 Million
Emp.: 134
Musical Royalty Collection & Distribution Services
N.A.I.C.S.: 512230
Barry LeVine *(VP-Indus Rels)*
Jonathan Bender *(COO)*
Scott Day *(CTO)*
Michael Huppe *(Pres & CEO)*
Richard Conlon *(Chief Corp Dev Officer)*
Anjula Singha *(CFO & Exec VP)*
Esther-Mireya Tejeda *(Chief Mktg & Comm Officer)*
Paul Gills *(VP-Publr Svcs)*
Tim Dadson *(Gen Counsel)*
Brieanne Jackson *(Deputy Gen Counsel)*

SOURCE CAPITAL, LLC
74 14th St Ste 2700, Atlanta, GA 30309
Tel.: (866) 949-1381
Web Site: http://www.source-cap.com
Year Founded: 2002
Privater Equity Firm
N.A.I.C.S.: 523999
Thomas S. Harbin *(Mng Partner)*
Katherine Harbin Clammer *(Mng Dir)*
Benjamin S. Emmons *(Mng Dir)*
Thomas van der Meulen *(Partner-Operating)*

Subsidiaries:

BlueAlly Technology Solutions, LLC (1)
1225 Crescent Green Ste 115, Cary, NC 27518
Tel.: (888) 768-2060
Web Site: http://www.blueally.com
Information Technology Products & Services
N.A.I.C.S.: 519290
Vijay Tanamala *(Founder & Chm)*
George Barkley *(CEO)*

SOURCE CAPITAL, LLC

Source Capital, LLC—(Continued)

Subsidiary (Domestic):

B2B Technologies, LLC (2)
1776 Peachtree St NW Ste 540 North Twr,
Atlanta, GA 30309
Tel.: (404) 892-1500
Web Site: http://www.b2btech.com
Sales Range: $1-9.9 Million
Emp.: 20
E-Commerce Engines, Intranet Portals &
Data Warehouse Builder
N.A.I.C.S.: 541519
Frank Fuerst (Pres)
Cherie Knight-Batey (Project Mgr)

Chesapeake Netcraftsmen, LLC (2)
1290 Bay Dale Dr, Arnold, MD 21012
Tel.: (410) 757-3050
Web Site: http://www.netcraftsmen.net
Data Processing, Hosting & Related Services
N.A.I.C.S.: 518210
Noel Mistichelli (Treas)
Paul H. Mauritz (Pres & CEO)

N2grate Government Technology Solutions, LLC (2)
9111 Edmonston Rd, Ste 303, Greenbelt,
MD 20770
Tel.: (202) 810-0122
Web Site: http://www.n2grate.com
Sales Range: $25-49.9 Million
Information Technology Consulting Services
N.A.I.C.S.: 541512
Steve Halligan (Co-Founder, Pres & COO)
Jack Farley (Co-Founder)

Virtual Graffiti, Inc. (2)
9979 Muirlands Blvd, Irvine, CA 92618
Tel.: (949) 870-3500
Web Site: http://www.virtualgraffiti.com
Sales Range: $10-24.9 Million
Emp.: 27
Information Technology Services
N.A.I.C.S.: 519290
Hillel Sackstein (Pres & CEO)
Ryan Lipschitz (VP-Engrg)
Michael Ellison (VP-Sls)
Howard Sackstein (VP-Mktg)
Jamie Ellison (VP-Digital)
Joel Newman (VP-Bus Dev)

Pickaway Plains Ambulance Service, Inc. (1)
1950 Stoneridge Dr, Circleville, OH 43113
Tel.: (740) 474-7787
Web Site: http://www.procareoh.com
Sales Range: $1-9.9 Million
Ambulance Transportation Services
N.A.I.C.S.: 621910
Ryan Little (Pres & CEO)

Pinnacle Central Company, Inc. (1)
103 Bryan St, Jacksonville, FL 32202
Tel.: (904) 354-5746
Web Site: http://www.pinnaclecentral.com
Sales Range: $1-9.9 Million
Emp.: 22
Motor & Generator Mfr
N.A.I.C.S.: 335312
Stephen Archibald (Pres)
Joe Fisher (Mgr-Svc)

Precision Boilers, Inc. (1)
5727 Superior Dr, Morristown, TN 37814-1075
Tel.: (423) 587-9390
Web Site: http://www.precisionboilers.com
Sales Range: $25-49.9 Million
Gas Boilers, Electric & Gas Hot Water
Heaters Mfr
N.A.I.C.S.: 332410

Preferred Technology Systems, LLC. (1)
9160 E Bahia Dr, Scottsdale, AZ 85260
Tel.: (480) 257-2600
Web Site: http://www.ptisecurity.com
Communication Equipment Mfr
N.A.I.C.S.: 334290
Franklin Young (CEO)
Jeff Flowers (COO)
Richard Dotson (CFO)
Thomas Brooks (VP-Sls)

SOURCE COMMUNICATIONS

433 Hackensack Ave, Hackensack,
NJ 07601-6319
Tel.: (201) 343-5222
Web Site: http://www.sourcead.com
Year Founded: 1984
Sales Range: $100-124.9 Million
Emp.: 50
Advertising Agencies
N.A.I.C.S.: 541810
Lawrence Rothstein (Pres)
Dennis Koye (Partner & Exec Dir-Creative)
Marcia Wasser (CMO & Exec VP)
Janine Perkal (VP & Acct Dir)
Rich Degni (VP & Dir-Creative)
Erica Hayman (VP & Acct Dir)
Jason Bacharach (VP & Acct Dir)
Amy Ehrlich (VP & Acct Dir)

Subsidiaries:

Source Communications (1)
2592 Coronado Pl, Vista, CA 92081
Tel.: (858) 655-7465
Emp.: 5
N.A.I.C.S.: 541810
Janine Perkal (Acct Dir)

SOURCE MANAGEMENT INC.

13350 W 43rd Dr Ave Ste 370 C,
Wheat Ridge, CO 80403
Tel.: (303) 964-8100
Web Site: http://www.sourcemgmt.com
Sales Range: $10-24.9 Million
Emp.: 45
Stationery & Office Supplies
N.A.I.C.S.: 493190
John C. Givens (Pres)

SOURCE OFFICE & TECHNOLOGY

13350 W 43rd Dr, Golden, CO 80403
Tel.: (303) 964-8100
Web Site: http://www.sourceot.com
Year Founded: 1990
Sales Range: $25-49.9 Million
Emp.: 126
Office Products
N.A.I.C.S.: 459410
John Givens (CEO)
Ken Larson (Pres & COO)
Rick Allen (Reg VP-Sls)

SOURCE ONE DISTRIBUTORS, INC.

3280 Fairlane Farms Rd, Wellington,
FL 33414-8793
Tel.: (561) 296-0520   FL
Web Site:
    http://www.buysourceone.com
Year Founded: 2003
Sales Range: $25-49.9 Million
Emp.: 20
Distribution, Logistics, Operational
Support, Tactical Equipment & Other
Services for Military
N.A.I.C.S.: 423990
Ray Wood (Dir-Sls)

SOURCE ONE MANAGEMENT, INC.

1125 17th St Ste 2300, Denver, CO
80202-2018
Tel.: (303) 832-8600   CO
Web Site: http://www.sourceone.com
Year Founded: 1985
Sales Range: $10-24.9 Million
Emp.: 250
Integrated Business Solutions
N.A.I.C.S.: 561439
Salvador Gomez (Owner, Pres & CEO)
Ruth McKinney (COO & Exec VP)
Alan Bill (CFO)
John Crossley (Mgr-IT)

SOURCE ONE MEDICAL MANAGEMENT

2 Carnegie Rd, Lawrenceville, NJ
08648
Tel.: (609) 482-3080
Web Site:
    http://www.source1med.com
Sales Range: $10-24.9 Million
Emp.: 10
Temporary Help Service
N.A.I.C.S.: 561320
James S. Radvany (Pres)
Ruth Harris (Mng Partner)

SOURCE ONE STAFFING LLC

5312 Irwindale Ave Ste 1H, Irwindale,
CA 91706
Tel.: (626) 337-0560
Web Site: http://www.s1staffing.com
Year Founded: 1995
Sales Range: $10-24.9 Million
Emp.: 58
Temporary Help Service
N.A.I.C.S.: 561320
Paulina Kuroki (CFO)
Claudia Daley (Mgr-Sls)

SOURCE OUTDOOR CORP.

11451 NW 36th Ave, Miami, FL
33167
Tel.: (800) 260-4512
Web Site:
    http://www.sourceoutdoor.net
Year Founded: 2009
Sales Range: $10-24.9 Million
Emp.: 70
Outdoor Furniture Mfr
N.A.I.C.S.: 337126
Gerald Shvartsman (CEO)
Jim Levine (COO)

SOURCE PHOTONICS, INC.

8521 Fallbrook Ave Ste 200, Canoga
Park, CA 91304
Tel.: (818) 773-9044   DE
Web Site:
    http://www.sourcephotonics.com
Year Founded: 1988
Fiber Optic Components & Subsystems Designer, Developer & Mfr
N.A.I.C.S.: 335921
Hari Krishnamurthy (CFO & Exec VP)

SOURCE RECOVERY COMPANY INC.

1070 Applecross Dr, Roswell, GA
30075
Tel.: (770) 667-5043
Web Site: http://www.source-recovery.com
Sales Range: $10-24.9 Million
Emp.: 3
Computer Consultants
N.A.I.C.S.: 541512
Jim Rahm (Mng Dir)

SOURCE ROCK, INC.

6528 E 101st St Ste 380, Tulsa, OK
74133
Web Site:
    http://www.sourcerockinc.com
Year Founded: 2010
Investment Services
N.A.I.C.S.: 523999

SOURCE SELECT GROUP, LLC

1715 N Westshore Blvd Ste 445,
Tampa, FL 33607
Tel.: (813) 507-8191
Web Site:
    http://www.sourceselectgroup.com
Sales Range: $1-9.9 Million
Emp.: 7
Employment Placement Agency
N.A.I.C.S.: 561311

Angie Short (CEO)

SOURCE TWO SPARES INC.

1818 Memorial Dr Ste 201, Houston,
TX 77007
Tel.: (281) 449-1100   TX
Web Site:
    http://www.sourceonespares.com
Year Founded: 1997
Sales Range: $50-74.9 Million
Emp.: 20
Mfr of Aircraft Engines & Engine
Parts
N.A.I.C.S.: 423860
Seth Hall (Co-Founder & Pres)

SOURCEBOOKS, INC.

1935 Brookdale Road Ste 139, Naperville, IL 60563
Tel.: (630) 961-3900
Web Site:
    http://www.sourcebooks.com
Books Printing
N.A.I.C.S.: 323117
Dominique Raccah (CEO)
Eliza Swift (Sr Editor-Fire & Jabberwocky)

SOURCEMANTRA INC

295 Durham Ave Ste 201, South
Plainfield, NJ 07080
Tel.: (908) 444-8940
Web Site:
    http://www.sourcemantra.com
Year Founded: 2007
Sales Range: $1-9.9 Million
Emp.: 30
Information Technology Consulting
Services
N.A.I.C.S.: 541512
Shridhar Dandu (Founder & CEO)

SOURCENET DISTRIBUTION, INC.

51 Monroe St Ste 1101, Rockville,
MD 20850
Tel.: (240) 778-1790
Web Site: http://www.sourcenet.org
Sales Range: $25-49.9 Million
Emp.: 18
Computer Peripherals & Software
Products
N.A.I.C.S.: 423430

SOURCENTRA, INC.

150 Speen St, Framingham, MA
01701
Tel.: (508) 405-2605   MA
Web Site: http://www.sourcentra.com
Year Founded: 1995
Sales Range: $25-49.9 Million
Emp.: 22
Custom Packaging Materials & Services
N.A.I.C.S.: 561910
Daniel C. Gonyea (CEO)

SOURCEONE GLOBAL PARTNERS LLC

400 West Erie St Ste 200, Chicago,
IL 60654
Tel.: (312) 321-8222
Web Site: http://www.source-1-global.com
Sales Range: $10-24.9 Million
Emp.: 25
Drugs & Druggists' Sundries Merchant Whslr
N.A.I.C.S.: 424210
Jesse Lopez (Founder & CEO)
Andrew Halpner (VP-Science, Innovation & Tech)

SOURCEPASS, INC.

81 Larkfield Rd E, Northport, NY
11731

Tel.: (877) 678-8080
Web Site: https://sourcepass.com
Year Founded: 2001
Emp.: 100
Software Publisher
N.A.I.C.S.: 513210
Daniel Johnson (Sr VP-Western US)
Chuck Canton (Founder & CEO)

Subsidiaries:

Infinity Computer Systems, Inc. (1)
340 E 80th St Ste 8C, New York, NY 10075
Tel.: (212) 995-5466
Web Site: http://www.infinityusa.com
Sales Range: $1-9.9 Million
Emp.: 20
Computer System Design Services
N.A.I.C.S.: 541512

Machinelogic, LLC (1)
4 Inverness Ct E Ste 300, Englewood, CO 80112
Tel.: (303) 217-7001
Web Site: http://www.machinelogic.com
Sales Range: $1-9.9 Million
Information Technology Consulting Services
N.A.I.C.S.: 541512
Daniel Johnson (CEO)
Peter Hoang (Dir-Bus Dev)
Chris Kasten (Dir-Technical Svcs)
Corey Eberly (Dir-Talent Svcs)
Nathan Taylor (Engr-Cloud)
Greg Hegarty (Mgr-Svc Desk)
Ken Fisk (Mgr-Ops)

Super-Server, LLC (1)
707 E Main St Ste 1425, Richmond, VA 23219-2807
Tel.: (804) 342-1200
Web Site: http://www.proxios.com
IT Consulting Services
N.A.I.C.S.: 541618

SOURCETOAD, LLC
2901 W Busch Blvd Ste 1018, Tampa, FL 33618
Web Site: http://www.sourcetoad.com
Year Founded: 2008
Sales Range: $1-9.9 Million
Emp.: 20
Software Development Services
N.A.I.C.S.: 541511
Greg Ross-Munro (Founder & CEO)
Justin Weber (Partner & CTO)
Nick DeMelas (Partner & Dir-Projects)

SOURCEWISE
2115 The Alameda, San Jose, CA 95126
Tel.: (408) 350-3200 CA
Web Site: http://www.mysourcewise.com
Year Founded: 1974
Sales Range: $10-24.9 Million
Emp.: 138
Elder Care Services
N.A.I.C.S.: 623312
Stephen M. Schmoll (CEO)
Manuel Altamirano (COO)
Kimberly Marlar (CFO)
Bea Robinson-Mendez (Second VP)
Michal Mendoza (Pres)
Jeff Tepper (First VP)
Mitsu Kumagai (Treas)

SOURCING INTERESTS GROUP (SIG)
6 N 2nd St Ste 202, Fernandina Beach, FL 32034
Tel.: (904) 310-9560
Web Site: http://www.sig.org
Year Founded: 1991
Sales Range: $1-9.9 Million
Emp.: 22
Membership Organization Offering Leadership & Networking Services
N.A.I.C.S.: 561312
Sarah Holliman (Chief Mktg Officer)
Geoff Talbot (VP-Member Svcs Grp)

Mary Zampino (Dir-Global Sourcing Intelligence)
Snehal Sindhvad (Dir-Member Programs)
Mark Pollack (Chief Strategy Officer)

SOURIS RIVER COOPERATIVE
8674 City Rd 20, Newburg, ND 58762
Tel.: (701) 272-6179
Web Site: http://www.sourisrivercooperative.com
Sales Range: $75-99.9 Million
Emp.: 40
Grain Elevators
N.A.I.C.S.: 424510
Cameron Erickson (Gen Mgr)
Mike Hall (Pres)
Kelly Thorenson (Chm)

SOUTH ALABAMA BRICK COMPANY
230 Ross Clark Cir, Dothan, AL 36303
Tel.: (334) 794-4173
Web Site: http://www.southalabamabrick.com
Year Founded: 1990
Sales Range: $10-24.9 Million
Emp.: 90
Distr of Bricks
N.A.I.C.S.: 423310
William C. Thompson (Pres)

SOUTH ALABAMA ELECTRIC COOPERATIVE
PO Box 449, Troy, AL 36081
Tel.: (334) 566-2060 AL
Web Site: http://www.southaec.com
Year Founded: 1937
Sales Range: $25-49.9 Million
Electric Power Distr Cooperative
N.A.I.C.S.: 221122
Mark Hill (Office Mgr)
Ronald Wade (Mgr-Engrg)
David Bailey (Gen Mgr)
James Shaver (Pres)

SOUTH ALABAMA GAS
714 W Frnt St, Evergreen, AL 36401
Tel.: (251) 578-2740
Web Site: http://www.southalabamagas.org
Sales Range: $25-49.9 Million
Emp.: 86
Natural Gas Distribution
N.A.I.C.S.: 221210
Mark Burgess (CEO)
Wayne Caylor (Dir-Propane Ops)

SOUTH AMERICAN RESTAURANTS CORP.
PO Box 360597, San Juan, PR 00936-0597
Tel.: (787) 788-8811
Web Site: http://www.shurchspr.com
Rev.: $21,700,000
Fast Food Restaurants & Stands
N.A.I.C.S.: 722513
Juan Antonio Larrea (Pres)

SOUTH ARKANSAS YOUTH, SERVICES, INC.
128 N Washington, Magnolia, AR 71753
Tel.: (870) 234-6550
Web Site: http://www.saysyouth.org
Sales Range: $10-24.9 Million
Emp.: 445
Youth Care Services
N.A.I.C.S.: 624110
Larry Lundeen (VP)
Byron Thomason (Treas)
Robert Burns (Sec)
Jerry Walsh (Exec Dir)

SOUTH ATLANTIC FOREST PRODUCTS INC.
15010 Abercorn St, Savannah, GA 31419
Tel.: (912) 925-1100
Web Site: http://www.gasterlumber.com
Sales Range: $10-24.9 Million
Emp.: 48
Retailer of Lumber & Other Building Materials
N.A.I.C.S.: 423310
Raymond Gaster (Pres)

SOUTH ATLANTIC LLC
1907 S 17th St Ste 2A, Wilmington, NC 28401
Tel.: (910) 332-1900
Web Site: http://www.southatlanticllc.com
Sales Range: $10-24.9 Million
Emp.: 10
Iron & Steel Galvanizing Services
N.A.I.C.S.: 332812
Cary Peterson (Pres)
Kim Seidner (Asst Mgr-Fin)

SOUTH ATLANTIC PACKAGING CORP.
3932 Westpoint Blvd, Winston Salem, NC 27103
Tel.: (336) 774-3122
Web Site: http://www.southatlanticpackaging.com
Rev.: $2,000,000
Emp.: 15
Contract Packaging for Food & Beverage Industries
N.A.I.C.S.: 561910
Steve Burns (VP-Ops)

Subsidiaries:

ProStar Packaging Inc. (1)
1000 Armand Hammer Blvd, Pottstown, PA 19464 (100%)
Tel.: (610) 326-4601
Web Site: http://www.prostarpackaging.com
Packaging & Labeling Services
N.A.I.C.S.: 561910
Jim Cash (Dir-Ops)
Clinton Van Zyverden (VP)

SOUTH ATLANTIC TRANSPORTATION CORPORATION
170 Sunport Ln Ste 800, Orlando, FL 32809
Tel.: (407) 859-1730
Web Site: http://www.thearrasgroup.com
Year Founded: 2000
Sales Range: $10-24.9 Million
Emp.: 5
Electrical Apparatus & Equipment Whslr
N.A.I.C.S.: 423610
Danny Arnold (Pres & Engr-Electrical & Sls)
Jim Moxon (Office Mgr)

SOUTH BANKING COMPANY
501 W 12th St, Alma, GA 31510
Tel.: (912) 632-8631
Web Site: http://www.aebalma.com
Sales Range: $10-24.9 Million
Emp.: 30
State Commercial Banks
N.A.I.C.S.: 522110

Subsidiaries:

Alma Exchange Bank & Trust (1)
501 W 12th St, Alma, GA 31510
Tel.: (912) 632-8631
Web Site: http://www.aebalma.com
Rev.: $3,900,000
Emp.: 130
State Commercial Banks
N.A.I.C.S.: 522110

Olivia Bennett (Chm)
Lawrence Bennett (Pres)

SOUTH BARNES DEVELOPMENT CO.
1256 S Barnes Ave, Springfield, MO 65804-0406
Tel.: (417) 881-4820 MO
Year Founded: 1971
Sales Range: $10-24.9 Million
Emp.: 130
Nonresidential Real Estate Development & Construction
N.A.I.C.S.: 237210
Martin W. McGehee (CFO, Treas & Sec)
Jerry L. Hackleman (Sr VP)
Randall A. Ganz (Pres & CEO)

Subsidiaries:

DeWitt & Associates, Inc. (1)
1256 S Barnes Ave, Springfield, MO 65804
Tel.: (417) 881-4820
Web Site: http://www.dewittassociates.com
Commercial & Institutional Building Construction Contractor
N.A.I.C.S.: 236220
Randall A. Ganz (Pres & CEO)
Martin W. McGehee (CFO)

SOUTH BAY CABLE CORP.
54125 Maranatha Dr, Idyllwild, CA 92549
Tel.: (951) 659-2183
Web Site: http://www.southbaycable.com
Rev.: $11,800,000
Emp.: 75
Nonferrous Wiredrawing & Insulating; Specialized Cable
N.A.I.C.S.: 332618
Bill Tell (Engr-Sls)
Oscar Lehuede (Mgr-Engrg)
Gary Brown (Mgr-Sls)

SOUTH BAY CIRCUITS INC.
99 N McKemy Ave, Chandler, AZ 85226-3447
Tel.: (480) 940-3125 CA
Web Site: http://www.sbcinc.com
Year Founded: 1981
Sales Range: $10-24.9 Million
Emp.: 270
Printed Circuit Boards
N.A.I.C.S.: 334412
Randy Langston (VP-Sls)
Phil Vazquez (Dir-Ops)

SOUTH BAY LEXUS
24777 Crenshaw Blvd, Torrance, CA 90505-5308
Tel.: (310) 325-9999
Web Site: http://www.southbaylexus.com
Year Founded: 2009
Sales Range: $10-24.9 Million
Emp.: 63
New Car Whslr
N.A.I.C.S.: 441110
Leonard Knott (VP)

SOUTH BAY MOTORS LLC
20550 Hawthorne Blvd, Torrance, CA 90503
Tel.: (310) 939-7470
Web Site: http://www.pacific-audi.com
Rev.: $30,400,000
Emp.: 58
Automobiles, New & Used
N.A.I.C.S.: 441110
Michael Sullivan (DP Mgr)

SOUTH BAY WORKFORCE INVESTMENT BOARD
11539 Hawthorne Blvd, Hawthorne, CA 90250

SOUTH BAY WORKFORCE INVESTMENT BOARD

South Bay Workforce Investment Board—(Continued)
Tel.: (310) 970-7700   CA
Web Site: http://www.sbwib.org
Year Founded: 2000
Sales Range: $10-24.9 Million
Emp.: 99
Employment & Placement Services
N.A.I.C.S.: 561311
James Carradine *(Mgr-Procurement)*
Catherine Blaylock *(Mgr-Contracts)*
Jan Vogel *(Exec Dir)*

SOUTH BOSTON COMMUNITY HEALTH CENTER
409 W Broadway, Boston, MA 02127
Tel.: (617) 269-7500   MA
Web Site: http://www.sbchc.org
Year Founded: 1979
Sales Range: $10-24.9 Million
Emp.: 198
Community Health Care Services
N.A.I.C.S.: 622110
Akin Ogungbadero *(CFO)*
Mary O'Hara *(VP)*
Nisha Thakrar *(Dir-Medical)*

SOUTH BROWARD HOSPITAL DISTRICT
3501 Johnson St, Hollywood, FL 33021
Tel.: (954) 987-2000   FL
Web Site: http://www.mhs.net
Year Founded: 1953
Rev.: $2,148,017,000
Assets: $3,731,665,000
Liabilities: $1,484,615,000
Net Worth: $2,247,050,000
Earnings: $165,547,000
Emp.: 7,000
Fiscal Year-end: 04/30/19
Public Health Care Services
N.A.I.C.S.: 622110
Matthew Muhart *(Chief Admin Officer & Exec VP)*
Forest Blanton *(Co-CIO & Sr VP)*
David Smith *(CFO & Sr VP)*
Nina Beauchesne *(Exec VP-East Ops)*
Leah A. Carpenter *(CEO-Memorial Hospital West)*
Mark Doyle *(Pres/CEO-Holy Cross Health)*
Grisel Fernandez-Bravo *(CEO-Memorial Hospital Miramar)*
Maggie Hansen *(Sr VP)*
C. Kennon Hetlage *(Exec VP-West Ops)*
Kevin R. Janser *(Chief Dev Officer & Sr VP)*
Kimarie Stratos *(Chief Privacy Officer, Gen Counsel & Sr VP)*
Margie Vargas *(Chief HR Officer & Sr VP)*
Douglas A. Zaren *(CEO-Memorial Reg Hospital South)*
Peter Powers *(CEO-Memorial Reg Hospital)*
Caitlin Stella *(CEO-Joe DiMaggio Children's Hospital & Pediatric Svcs)*
Frank Rainer *(Gen Counsel & Sr VP)*
Jeffrey Sturman *(Co-CIO & Sr VP)*
Marc L. Napp *(Chief Medical Officer & Sr VP)*
Aurelio M. Fernandez III *(Pres & CEO)*

Subsidiaries:

Memorial Regional Hospital South   (1)
3600 Washington St, Hollywood, FL 33021
Tel.: (954) 518-5200
Web Site: http://www.mhs.net
Sales Range: $25-49.9 Million
Emp.: 720
Hospital Services

N.A.I.C.S.: 622110
Doug Zaren *(CEO)*

SOUTH CAROLINA AQUARIUM
100 Aquarium Wharf, Charleston, SC 29401
Tel.: (843) 577-3474   SC
Web Site: https://scaquarium.org
Year Founded: 1992
Sales Range: $1-9.9 Million
Emp.: 76
Botanical/Zoological Garden
N.A.I.C.S.: 712130
Kevin Mills *(Pres & CEO)*
J. Donald Higgins *(Treas)*
Albert George *(Dir-Conservation)*
Brian Brasher *(Dir-Capital Projects & Facilities)*
Brian Thill *(Dir-Education)*
Courtenay Speir *(Dir-Advancement)*
Kevin Kampwerth *(Dir-Mktg & Creative)*
Mike Mistler *(Dir-Fin)*
Paul Nunez *(Dir-HR)*
Rachel Kalisperis *(Dir-Husbandry)*
Jason Oddo *(CFO)*
Amie Yam-Babinchak *(CMO)*
Barrett Christie *(Dir-Animal Care)*
Lauren McDaniel *(Dir-Guest Svcs)*
Sara McDonald *(Dir-Conservation)*
Jamie Torres *(Dir-Veterinary Care)*

SOUTH CAROLINA DEPARTMENT OF TRANSPORTATION
955 Park St, Columbia, SC 29202
Tel.: (803) 737-1302
Web Site: http://www.scdot.org
Sales Range: $900-999.9 Million
Emp.: 5,000
Highway & Street Maintenance
N.A.I.C.S.: 926120
Robert J. St. Onge *(Sec-Transportation)*
Michael Queen *(Engr-Dist 6 Matls)*
Greg Shaw *(Engr-District 4 Traffic)*
Andrew Johnson *(Engr-State Pavement Design)*
George Radler *(Engr-Traffic Mgmt)*
Wilson Elgin *(Mgr-Design)*
James Teeter *(Mgr-Roadway Inventory)*
Henry Clay Middleton *(Mgr-Verification Lab)*
Andrew Egan *(Engr-Traffic)*
Dipak Patel *(Dir-Tech Application)*
Diane Lackey *(Mgr-Programs-State Wide)*

SOUTH CAROLINA FARM BUREAU MUTUAL INSURANCE COMPANY
724 Knox Abbott Dr, Cayce, SC 29033-3340
Tel.: (803) 796-6700   SC
Web Site: http://www.scfbins.com
Year Founded: 1955
Sales Range: $50-74.9 Million
Emp.: 250
Provider of Insurance Services
N.A.I.C.S.: 524126
Lee Wilkins *(VP-Sls)*
Marty Sauls *(Mgr-Agency-Beaufort)*

SOUTH CAROLINA FIRST STEPS TO SCHOOL READINESS
1300 Sumter St Ste 100, Columbia, SC 29201
Tel.: (803) 734-0479   SC
Web Site: http://www.scfirststeps.org
Year Founded: 1999
Sales Range: $1-9.9 Million
Emp.: 90
Child Care & Development Services
N.A.I.C.S.: 624410

Russell Brown *(Dir-Fin & Audit)*
Mary Anne Mathews *(Dir-Parenting Programs)*
Beverly Mills *(Mgr-Fiscal)*
Debbie Robertson *(Chief Partnership Officer)*
Julia-Ellen Davis *(Dir-Interim)*
Molly Spearman *(Superintendent-Education)*
Judith Aughtry *(Chm-Fin & Admin)*
Ken Wingate *(Chm)*

SOUTH CAROLINA MANUFACTURING EXTENSION PARTNERSHIP
250 Berryhill Rd Ste 512, Columbia, SC 29210
Tel.: (803) 252-6976
Web Site: http://www.scmep.org
Sales Range: $10-24.9 Million
Emp.: 20
Mfr Consultants
N.A.I.C.S.: 541611
Chris Rauch *(VP-Greenville Reg)*
Stacy Smith *(Mgr-Fin)*

SOUTH CAROLINA PHILHARMONIC ASSOCIATION INC.
721 Lady St Ste B, Columbia, SC 29201
Tel.: (803) 771-7937
Web Site: http://www.scphilharmonic.com
Emp.: 100
Symphony Orchestra
N.A.I.C.S.: 711130
Judith Lawrence *(Mgr-Youth Orchestra)*
Jason Rapp *(Dir-Comm & Audience Svcs)*
Robin Hallyburton *(Dir-Dev)*
Ashley Horvat *(Dir-Personnel)*
John L. Hunsinger II *(Mgr-Production & Stage)*

SOUTH CAROLINA PUBLIC SERVICE AUTHORITY
1 Riverwood Dr, Moncks Corner, SC 29461-2998
Tel.: (843) 761-8000
Web Site: http://www.santeecooper.com
Year Founded: 1934
Sales Range: $1-4.9 Billion
Emp.: 1,850
Electric Power & Water Supply Services Administration Organization
N.A.I.C.S.: 926130
William A. Finn *(First Vice Chm)*
Marc R. Tye *(COO & Exec VP)*
Jeffrey D. Armfield *(CFO & Sr VP)*
Mollie Gore *(Dir-Corp Comm)*
James E. Brogdon Jr. *(Pres-Interim & CEO)*
W. Leighton Lord III *(Chm)*

SOUTH CAROLINA RESEARCH AUTHORITY
1000 Catawba St, Columbia, SC 29201-5706
Tel.: (803) 799-4070   SC
Web Site: http://www.scra.org
Year Founded: 1983
Sales Range: $10-24.9 Million
Emp.: 120
Research Services
N.A.I.C.S.: 541720
Cole Dudley *(Dir-Indus Programs)*
James P. Clements *(Pres)*
Douglas MacIntyre *(CEO)*
Keith Y. Shah *(Mng Dir & Chief Strategy Officer)*

SOUTH CAROLINA STATE PORTS AUTHORITY

176 Concord St, Charleston, SC 29401
Tel.: (843) 723-8651
Web Site: http://www.port-of-charleston.com
Year Founded: 1947
Sales Range: $75-99.9 Million
Emp.: 469
Provider of Marine Cargo Handling Services
N.A.I.C.S.: 488310
Byron D. Miller *(Dir-Sls & Mktg Admin)*
Paul G. McClintock *(Sr VP-Sls & Mktg)*
Kurt D. Grindstaff *(Treas)*
Pamela P. Lackey *(Chm)*
Willie E. Jeffries *(Sec)*
Robert R. Mozdean *(Sr VP-HR)*
Stanley R. Van Ostran *(Sr VP-Fin & Admin)*
Jordi Yarborough *(Sr VP-External Affairs)*
James I. Newsome III *(Pres & CEO)*

SOUTH CENTRAL ARKANSAS ELECTRIC COOPERATIVE, INC.
4818 Hwy 8 W, Arkadelphia, AR 71923
Tel.: (870) 246-6701   AR
Web Site: http://www.scaec.com
Year Founded: 1940
Sales Range: $10-24.9 Million
Electric Cooperative
N.A.I.C.S.: 221122
Leslie Holloway *(Mgr-Consumer Svcs)*
Randy Duncan *(Mgr-Ops)*
Stanley Beck *(Engr-Staking)*
Elton Buck *(Treas & Sec)*
Kevin Brownlee *(CEO)*
Brian Kirksey *(Pres)*
Danny Buck *(VP)*
Melissa Jones *(Mgr-IT)*

SOUTH CENTRAL CO-OP
Hwy 4 S, Fairfax, MN 55332
Tel.: (507) 426-8263   MN
Web Site: http://www.scgemn.com
Year Founded: 1906
Sales Range: $75-99.9 Million
Emp.: 50
Distr of Grains & Farm Supplies
N.A.I.C.S.: 424510
Gene Lutteke *(Gen Mgr)*

SOUTH CENTRAL COMMUNICATIONS CORPORATION
20 NW 3rd St, Evansville, IN 47708
Tel.: (812) 463-7950   IN
Web Site: http://www.southcentralcommunications.net
Year Founded: 1946
Sales Range: $25-49.9 Million
Emp.: 300
Radio Broadcasting Stations
N.A.I.C.S.: 516110
John D. Engelbrecht *(Chm, Pres & CEO)*
Robert Shirel *(CFO, Treas & Sec)*
Tim Hulsing *(Gen Mgr)*

SOUTH CENTRAL COMPANY INC.
3055 State St, Columbus, IN 47201
Tel.: (812) 376-3343
Web Site: http://www.southcentralco.com
Sales Range: $10-24.9 Million
Emp.: 50
Plumbing Heating Air Conditioning
N.A.I.C.S.: 423730
William E. Sasse *(Pres)*

SOUTH CENTRAL CONNECTICUT REGIONAL WATER AUTHORITY INC.
90 Sargent Dr, New Haven, CT 06511-5966
Tel.: (203) 562-4020
Web Site: http://www.rwater.com
Year Founded: 1864
Sales Range: $75-99.9 Million
Emp.: 270
Water Treatment & Distribution Services
N.A.I.C.S.: 221310
Jean Zanella Dyer (VP-Svc Delivery)
James J. Flynn (VP-Ops)
Rochelle Kowalski (VP & Controller)
Kevin J. Curseaden (Treas & Sec)
Mark Levine (Sec)
Richard W. Albrecht (Treas)
Jeanine F. Reckdenwald (Sr VP-Employee Svc)
Edward O. Norris III (VP-Asst Mgmt)

SOUTH CENTRAL COOP
2120 Osceola Ave, Chariton, IA 50049
Tel.: (641) 774-2135
Web Site: http://www.sccoop.com
Sales Range: $10-24.9 Million
Emp.: 17
Distribution of Feed Grains
N.A.I.C.S.: 424510
Don Brown (Mgr)
Lyla Stephenson (Office Mgr)

SOUTH CENTRAL FS INC.
1800 Hillsboro Rd, Vandalia, IL 62471-3240
Tel.: (618) 283-0789
Web Site: http://www.southcentralfs.com
Year Founded: 1993
Sales Range: $10-24.9 Million
Emp.: 70
Provider of Agricultural Supplies
N.A.I.C.S.: 459999
Byron Sikma (CEO)

SOUTH CENTRAL GRAIN CO-OPERATIVE
122 Main Ave W, Napoleon, ND 58561-7025
Tel.: (701) 754-2573
Web Site: http://www.southcentralgrain.com
Year Founded: 1914
Sales Range: $10-24.9 Million
Emp.: 25
Provider of Farm Supplies
N.A.I.C.S.: 424510
Jeff Mehl (Gen Mgr)

SOUTH CENTRAL HUMAN RESOURCE AGENCY
1437 Winchester Hwy, Fayetteville, TN 37334
Tel.: (931) 433-7182
Web Site: http://www.schra.us
Year Founded: 1975
Sales Range: $10-24.9 Million
Emp.: 610
Community Welfare Services
N.A.I.C.S.: 624190
Lisa Williams (Asst Dir-Fiscal Ops)
James Coy Anderson (Exec Dir)
James H. Reynolds (Dir-Fiscal Ops)
Cindy Miles (Dir-Community Svcs)
Judy McLeod (Dir-Community Corrections)
David Pennington (Vice Chm)
Peggy Bevels (Vice Chm)
Wallace Cartwright (Sec)
Donna Brazier (Dir-Nutrition & In-Home Care)
Scarlet Patterson (Dir-HR)
Janet Vanzant (Chm)
Bobbie Cox (Dir-Foster Grandparent & RSVP)
Pamela Morris (Dir-Title V Older Worker)
Patsy Freeman (Sec)

SOUTH CENTRAL INDIANA RURAL ELECTRIC MEMBERSHIP CORPORATION
300 Morton Ave, Martinsville, IN 46151
Tel.: (765) 342-3344
Web Site: http://www.sciremc.com
Year Founded: 1939
Emp.: 130
Electric Industry Support Services
N.A.I.C.S.: 813910
Marilou Idland (VP-HR)
Jack Hubband (VP-Engrg)
Kate Frank (CFO)
Bruce Hamlin (Chm)
James Tanneberger (Pres & CEO)

SOUTH CENTRAL POWER COMPANY INC.
2780 Coonpath Rd NE, Lancaster, OH 43130-9343
Tel.: (740) 653-4422
Web Site: http://www.southcentralpower.com
Year Founded: 1936
Sales Range: $200-249.9 Million
Emp.: 234
Provider of Electric Services
N.A.I.C.S.: 221122
Kenneth Davis (Chm)
Richard Poling (Vice Chm)
James Evans (Treas)
Harold E. Cooper (Asst Treas)
Thomas Lamb (Sec)
Lawrence Kobi (Asst Sec)
Alan Gabriel (Asst Sec)
Rick Lemonds (Pres & CEO)
Cathy Bitler (VP-Admin)
Susan Everly (VP-HR)
James Meyers (VP-Ops)
Rebecca Witt (CFO)

SOUTH CENTRAL RURAL TELEPHONE
1399 Happy Valley Rd, Glasgow, KY 42141
Tel.: (270) 678-2111
Web Site: http://www.scrtc.com
Rev.: $19,973,353
Emp.: 125
Local Telephone Communications
N.A.I.C.S.: 517121
David Davis (Gen Mgr)

SOUTH CENTRAL SERVICE COMPANY
405 S Banker, Effingham, IL 62401-3754
Tel.: (217) 342-9231
Web Site: http://www.southcentralfs.com
Sales Range: $75-99.9 Million
Emp.: 100
Retailer of Grain, Agricultural Supplies, Petroleum, Feed & Seed, Fertilizer, Chemicals, Livestock & Farm Equipment
N.A.I.C.S.: 424510
Byron Sikma (CEO)
Gerald Witges (Mgr-Mktg)
Joe Meinhart (CFO)

SOUTH CENTRAL UTAH TELEPHONE ASSOCIATION, INC.
45 N 100 W, Escalante, UT 84726
Tel.: (435) 826-4211
Web Site: http://www.socen.com
Year Founded: 1953
Sales Range: $10-24.9 Million
Emp.: 102
Telephone Service Provider
N.A.I.C.S.: 517111
Alan Torgersen (Dir-Sls & Svc)
Duncan Reed (Mgr-Outside Plant)
Michael East (Pres & CEO)
Kerry Alvey (VP-Ops)
Blake Keller (Dir-Mktg)
Luke Geddes (Dir-Non Regulated Ops)
Marc McLemore (Mgr-Acctg)
Troy Brian (Mgr-Inside Plant)
Lance Goulding (Mgr-Construction & Engrg)
Ronda Barney (Dir-Human Svcs)
Craig Laub (Vice Chm)

SOUTH CHESTER TUBE COMPANY
210 N Brinton Lake Rd, Concordville, PA 19331
Tel.: (610) 459-4000
Web Site: http://ww.southco.com
Holding Company
N.A.I.C.S.: 551112
Brian McNeill (Pres)

Subsidiaries:

Southco, Inc. (1)
210 N Brinton Lake Rd, Concordville, PA 19331
Tel.: (610) 459-4000
Web Site: http://www.southco.com
Sales Range: $350-399.9 Million
Emp.: 1,500
Latching Systems & Hardware Mfr & Designer
N.A.I.C.S.: 339993
David Montgomery (Treas)
Ray Canzanese (VP)
Michael McPhilmy (VP-HR)
Jay Lu (Mng Dir-Asia Pacific)
Thomas Mehler (Pres)
Joaquin Tam (Gen Mgr-Greater China)

Subsidiary (Domestic):

CounterBalance Corporation (2)
1025 Louis Dr, Warminster, PA 18974
Tel.: (215) 957-9260
Web Site: http://www.cbal.com
Sales Range: $1-9.9 Million
Emp.: 35
Electro-Mechanical Equipment Mfr & Distr
N.A.I.C.S.: 334419
Greg Fosbenner (Mgr-Engrg)
Angela Michetti (Office Mgr)

SOUTH COAST CONSTRUCTION SERVICES
3235 Fuqua St, Houston, TX 77047
Tel.: (713) 222-2308
Web Site: http://www.sccsi.net
Rev.: $37,400,000
Emp.: 50
Commercial & Office Buildings, Renovation & Repair
N.A.I.C.S.: 236220
Russell York (Pres)

SOUTH COAST PLAZA
3333 Bristol St, Costa Mesa, CA 92626
Tel.: (714) 435-2000
Web Site: http://www.southcoastplaza.com
Rev.: $14,400,000
Emp.: 300
Shopping Centers Operator
N.A.I.C.S.: 455219
Henry Segerstrom (Partner)
Debra Gunn Downing (Exec Dir-Mktg)
Karl Schuler (Asst Dir-Security)
Ramon Mateo (Supvr-Security)
Robert C. Thomas (Mgr-Construction)
Sarah Kruer (Dir-Tourism Dev)
Barney Page (Dir-Real Estate)
Debra Downing (Exec Dir-Mktg)

SOUTH COAST SUPPLY COMPANY
20702 Hempstead Rd Ste 100, Houston, TX 77065
Tel.: (713) 688-7721
Web Site: http://www.southcoastsupply.com
Year Founded: 1972
Sales Range: $1-9.9 Million
Emp.: 20
Industrial Supplies Distr
N.A.I.C.S.: 423840
Bill Cox (Exec VP)

SOUTH COAST TERMINALS LP
7402 Wallisville Rd, Houston, TX 77020-3595
Tel.: (713) 672-2401
Web Site: http://www.scterm.com
Sales Range: $10-24.9 Million
Emp.: 102
Oils & Greases, Blending & Compounding
N.A.I.C.S.: 324191
Artie McFerrin (Owner)
Robin Martin (Plant Mgr)
J. J. Griffin (Mgr-Sls & Admin)
Lester Young (Mgr-Lab)

SOUTH COAST WATER DISTRICT
31592 W St, Laguna Beach, CA 92651
Tel.: (949) 499-4555
Web Site: http://www.scwd.org
Year Founded: 1932
Sales Range: $10-24.9 Million
Emp.: 72
Water & Waste Water Management Services
N.A.I.C.S.: 221310
Ernie Garcia (Supvr-Collections Sys)
Andrew Brunhart (Gen Mgr)
Wayne Rayfield (Pres)
Joe McDivitt (COO)
Sonja Morgan (Officer-Pub Information)

SOUTH COASTAL BANK
279 Union St, Rockland, MA 02370
Tel.: (781) 878-5252
Web Site: http://www.southcoastalbank.com
Sales Range: $10-24.9 Million
Emp.: 21
Banking Services
N.A.I.C.S.: 522180
Michael Pang (VP-Credit Admin & Mgr)
Paula Clough (Asst VP-Fin Dept)
Timothy Rhuda (Officer-Comml Banking)
Debra Wooley (Controller)
Steven Owens (CFO, COO & Treas)
Daniel Bosley (Chm)
Noelle M. Pandell (Sec)
Pamela Art (Vice Chm)

SOUTH CONE HOME, INC.
7770 Girard Ave, La Jolla, CA 92037
Tel.: (619) 536-1110
Web Site: http://www.southconefurniture.com
Year Founded: 1988
Furniture Mfr & Whslr
N.A.I.C.S.: 423210
Mario I. Scolari (Pres)

SOUTH CYPRESS
2818 Government Blvd, Mobile, AL 36606
Tel.: (800) 891-2623
Web Site: http://www.southcypress.com
Year Founded: 1952

South Cypress—(Continued)
Sales Range: $1-9.9 Million
Emp.: 6
Online Flooring Retailer
N.A.I.C.S.: 327120
Mickey Goneke (Pres)

SOUTH DADE AUTOMOTIVE INC.
2875 N W 77th Ave, Miami, FL 33122
Tel.: (305) 718-6664
Web Site: http://www.sdatire.com
Rev.: $16,786,590
Emp.: 20
Automobile Tires & Tubes
N.A.I.C.S.: 423130
Jorge I. Pola (Pres)
Dilna Llorente (Mgr-Program)

SOUTH DADE ELECTRICAL SUPPLY
13100 SW 87th Ave, Miami, FL 33176
Tel.: (305) 238-7131
Web Site: http://www.south-dade.com
Rev.: $16,928,278
Emp.: 44
Electrical Supplies
N.A.I.C.S.: 423610
Don C. Elliott (CEO & Treas)
Ted McClure (Mgr-Ops)
Marina Elliott (Mgr-Credit)

SOUTH DADE NEWS, INC.
205 N Flagler Ave, Homestead, FL 33030-6110
Tel.: (305) 245-2311
Web Site: http://www.southdadenewsleader.com
Year Founded: 1912
Sales Range: $1-9.9 Million
Newspaper Publishers
N.A.I.C.S.: 513110
Dale L. Machesic (Publr)
Ann E. Machesic (Mng Editor)

SOUTH DAKOTA BANCSHARES, INC.
420 S Pierre St, Pierre, SD 57501
Tel.: (605) 224-7391
Web Site: http://www.bankwest-sd.com
Year Founded: 1975
Sales Range: $50-74.9 Million
Emp.: 338
Bank Holding Company
N.A.I.C.S.: 551111
Rebecca J. Burke (VP-Strategic Initiatives-BankWest)
Charles H. Burke III (Chm, Pres & CEO)

Subsidiaries:
BankWest, Inc. (1)
420 S Pierre St, Pierre, SD 57501
Tel.: (605) 224-7391
Web Site: http://www.bankwest-sd.com
Sales Range: $50-74.9 Million
Commericial Banking
N.A.I.C.S.: 522110
Rebecca J. Burke (VP-Strategic Initiatives)
Robert J. Burke (Mgr-Fraud Risk)
Charles H. Burke III (Chm, Pres & CEO)

SOUTH DAKOTA SOYBEAN PROCESSORS, LLC
100 Caspian Ave, Volga, SD 57071
Tel.: (605) 627-9240
Web Site: https://www.sdsbp.com
Rev.: $721,532,329
Assets: $311,196,770
Liabilities: $147,658,094
Net Worth: $163,538,676
Earnings: $67,464,101
Emp.: 6
Fiscal Year-end: 12/31/22
Soybean Processing & Whslr
N.A.I.C.S.: 311224
Thomas J. Kersting (CEO)
Mark Hyde (CFO)

SOUTH DAKOTA STATE UNIVERSITY FOUNDATION
823 Medary Ave, Brookings, SD 57006
Tel.: (605) 697-7475 SD
Web Site: https://www.sdsufoundation.org
Year Founded: 1940
Rev.: $1,200,000
Emp.: 50
Fiscal Year-end: 12/31/06
Business Services
N.A.I.C.S.: 561990
Al Bahe (Dir-Dev-College of Nursing)
Andrew Wenthe (Assoc VP-Dev)
Carolyn Poss (Assoc VP-Philanthropic Fulfillment)
Don Linn (Dir-Dev-College of Natural Sciences)
Erin Glidden (Assoc VP-Pipeline Strategy)
Holly Tilton Byrne (Assoc VP-HR)
Jillian Baldini (Program Mgr-Scholarship)
Keith Mahlum (VP-Dev)
Keli Books (Assoc VP-Philanthropy)
Lisa Bergmann (Dir-Data Integrity & Acq)

SOUTH DAKOTA WHEAT GROWERS ASSOCIATION
908 Lamont St S, Aberdeen, SD 57401
Tel.: (605) 225-5500
Web Site: http://www.sdwg.com
Sales Range: $300-349.9 Million
Emp.: 250
Grain Elevators
N.A.I.C.S.: 424510
Chris Pearson (CEO)

Subsidiaries:
MZB Technologies, LLC (1)
11 8th Ave SE, Watertown, SD 57201
Tel.: (605) 882-4214
Web Site: http://www.mzbtech.com
Agronomy Consulting Services
N.A.I.C.S.: 541690
Wade Marzahn (Mgr-Agronomy Trng)
Nick Waite (Mgr-Mapping Center)

South Dakota Wheat Growers (1)
1 S Commercial Ave, Saint Lawrence, SD 57373
Tel.: (605) 853-2728
Web Site: http://www.sdwg.com
Sales Range: $25-49.9 Million
Emp.: 17
Grain Supply Services
N.A.I.C.S.: 424510
Randy Bertsch (Mgr-Location)

SOUTH DAVIS COMMUNITY HOSPITAL
401 S 400 E, Bountiful, UT 84010
Tel.: (801) 295-2361 UT
Web Site: http://www.sdch.com
Year Founded: 1976
Sales Range: $1-9.9 Million
Emp.: 863
Health Care Srvices
N.A.I.C.S.: 622110
David A. Bland (CEO)
Daniel J. Foster (CFO)

SOUTH DELTA PLANNING & DEVELOPMENT DISTRICT, INC.
124 South Broadway St, Greenville, MS 38702-1776
Tel.: (662) 378-3831 MS
Web Site: http://www.southdeltapdd.com
Year Founded: 1976
Sales Range: $10-24.9 Million
Emp.: 59
Community Development Services
N.A.I.C.S.: 624190
Willie F. Brown (Treas & Sec)
Edgar Donahoe (VP)
J. Y. Trice (Pres)

SOUTH EAST AREA HEALTH EDUCATION CENTER
2511 Delaney Ave, Wilmington, NC 28403
Tel.: (910) 343-0161 NC
Web Site: http://www.seahec.net
Sales Range: $25-49.9 Million
Emp.: 156
Health Care Srvices
N.A.I.C.S.: 813920
William O. McMillan (Treas)
Larry Reinhart (Vice Chm)
Fred Michael (Chm)
Joe Pino (Pres & CEO)
Donna Flake (Dir-Library)

SOUTH FEATHER WATER & POWER AGENCY
2310 Oro Quincy Hwy, Oroville, CA 95966
Tel.: (530) 533-4578
Web Site: http://www.southfeather.com
Sales Range: $10-24.9 Million
Emp.: 60
Water & Electric Power Services
N.A.I.C.S.: 221118
Michael Glaze (Gen Mgr)
Steve Wong (Mgr-Fin)

SOUTH FLORIDA BAKERY, INC.
14159 SW 144th St, Miami, FL 33186-5539
Tel.: (305) 256-1777
Sales Range: $10-24.9 Million
Emp.: 120
Commercial Bakery Services
N.A.I.C.S.: 311812
Carmen Bernardo (Treas)
Sharon Luchsinger (Office Mgr)
Lourdes Bernardo (Owner)
Rick Bernardo (COO & Sec)

SOUTH FLORIDA MEDIA GROUP, LLC
5830 Coral Ridge Dr Ste 240, Coral Springs, FL 33076
Tel.: (800) 779-3526
Sales Range: $10-24.9 Million
Emp.: 35
Local Newspaper & Magazine Publisher
N.A.I.C.S.: 513110

Subsidiaries:
Welcome Wagon International, Inc. (1)
5830 Coral Ridge Dr Ste 240, Coral Springs, FL 33076
Tel.: (800) 779-3526
Web Site: http://www.welcomewagon.com
Sales Range: $10-24.9 Million
Advertising, Public Relations & Sales Promotions, Mover Programs, Newly-Wed Programs & Baby Programs
N.A.I.C.S.: 541860
Steve Goodman (Pres & COO)

SOUTH FLORIDA PBS, INC.
14901 NE 20th Ave, Miami, FL 33181
Tel.: (305) 949-8321 FL
Web Site: http://www.wpbt2.org
Year Founded: 1953
Public Television Broadcasting Station

N.A.I.C.S.: 516120
Delores Sukhdeo (CEO)
Laurie S. Silvers (Co-Chm)
Michele Kessler (Co-Chm)
Pamela Olmo (Chief Admin Officer)
Thomasina Caporella (Vice Chm)
Bernie Friedman (Sec)
David C. Prather (Treas)

SOUTH GATE ENGINEERING, LLC.
13477 Yorba Ave, Chino, CA 91710
Tel.: (909) 628-2779
Web Site: http://www.southgateengineering.com
Sales Range: $10-24.9 Million
Emp.: 115
Plate Work Mfr
N.A.I.C.S.: 332313
William Paolino (Gen Mgr)
Jeff Weiser (Mgr-Engrg)
Scott Rosier (Engr-Sls)
Corey Althouse (Engr-Sls)
William DelValle (Engr-Sls)

SOUTH GEORGIA PECAN COMPANY INC.
309 S Lee St, Valdosta, GA 31601-5723
Tel.: (229) 244-1321
Web Site: http://www.georgiapecan.com
Year Founded: 1913
Sales Range: $25-49.9 Million
Emp.: 150
Provider of Pecans & Snacks
N.A.I.C.S.: 311919
Jim P. Worn (Owner)
Ed Crane (Owner)

SOUTH HILLS HONDA
3663 Washington Rd, McMurray, PA 15317
Tel.: (724) 941-9100
Web Site: http://www.southhillshonda.com
New Car Dealers
N.A.I.C.S.: 441110
Gregory Norton (Owner & Pres)

SOUTH IOWA MUNICIPAL ELECTRIC COOPERATIVE ASSOCIATION
111 S Chestnut St, Lamoni, IA 50140
Tel.: (641) 784-6911 IA
Year Founded: 1967
Sales Range: $10-24.9 Million
Electricity Association
N.A.I.C.S.: 813910
David Ferris (VP)
Doug Christensen (Sec)
Emil Segebart (Treas)
Duane Armstead (Chief Admin Officer)

SOUTH JERSEY CHILDCARE CORP.
116 Grand St, Iselin, NJ 08830
Tel.: (732) 481-1270
Web Site: http://www.lightbridgeacademy.com
Year Founded: 1997
Sales Range: $50-74.9 Million
Emp.: 1,286
Consumer Product Services
N.A.I.C.S.: 532289
Mark Mele (Sr VP-Franchise Sls)
Brenda Febbo (CMO)

SOUTH JERSEY MARINA INC.
1231 Route 109, Cape May, NJ 08204
Tel.: (609) 884-0177
Web Site: http://www.sjmarina.com
Rev.: $49,937,663
Emp.: 17

Motor Boat Dealers
N.A.I.C.S.: 441222
Richard Weber (Pres)

SOUTH JERSEY PORT CORPORATION
2nd & Beckette St, Camden, NJ 08103
Tel.: (856) 541-8500
Web Site:
http://www.southjerseyport.com
Sales Range: $10-24.9 Million
Emp.: 150
Waterfront Terminal Operation
N.A.I.C.S.: 488320
Patrick Abusi (Treas)
Kevin Castagnola (Exec Dir)
Athina Efelis (Mgr-Billing)
Steven Bell (Mgr-Warehouse)

SOUTH KENTUCKY RURAL ELECTRIC CO-OPERATIVE CORPORATION
200 Electric Ave, Somerset, KY 42501
Tel.: (606) 678-4121
Web Site: http://www.skrecc.com
Year Founded: 1938
Rev: $131,378,166
Assets: $309,924,100
Liabilities: $172,177,316
Net Worth: $137,746,784
Earnings: $7,178,908
Emp.: 145
Fiscal Year-end: 12/31/18
Electric Power Services
N.A.I.C.S.: 221118
Lee Coffee (Co-Treas & Co-Sec)
Cathy Crew Epperson (Vice Chm)
Greg Beard (Co-Treas & Co-Sec)

SOUTH LUBES INC.
1890 Kingsley Ave Ste 104, Orange Park, FL 32073
Tel.: (904) 276-3598
Web Site:
http://www.jiffylubesoutheast.com
Sales Range: $1-4.9 Billion
Emp.: 20
Automotive Lubrication Service
N.A.I.C.S.: 811191
Dwain Sanders (VP-Fin & Treas)
Louis W. Huntley (Pres)
Jeff Grant (Dir-Trng)

SOUTH MIAMI PHARMACY
6050 S Dixie Hwy, Miami, FL 33143
Tel.: (305) 668-6150
Web Site:
http://www.southmiamipharmacy.com
Year Founded: 2003
Rev: $9,400,000
Emp.: 20
Pharmacies & Drug Stores
N.A.I.C.S.: 456110
Armando Batista (Owner)
Brian Brito (VP)
Marco Salgado (Gen Mgr)

SOUTH MIDDLESEX OPPORTUNITY COUNCIL, INC.
7 Bishop St, Framingham, MA 01702
Tel.: (508) 872-4853
Web Site: http://www.smoc.org
Year Founded: 1965
Sales Range: $50-74.9 Million
Emp.: 873
Day Care Services
N.A.I.C.S.: 623990
Bruce Hulme (Pres)
James T. Cuddy (Exec Dir)
Jeffrey Fishman (VP)
Jerry Desilets (Dir-Policy, Plng & Community Rels)

SOUTH MILL MUSHROOMS SALES, INC.
649 W S St, Kennett Square, PA 19348
Tel.: (610) 444-4800
Web Site: http://www.southmill.com
Year Founded: 2017
Compost Producer & Mushroom Growers
N.A.I.C.S.: 111411
Jessica Weil (Brand Comm Mgr)

Subsidiaries:

The Mushroom Company (1)
902 Woods Rd, Cambridge, MD 21613
Tel.: (410) 221-8971
Web Site:
http://www.themushroomcompany.com
Prepared Sauces Mfr
N.A.I.C.S.: 311941
Dennis Newhard (Pres & Gen Mgr)

SOUTH MISSISSIPPI ELECTRIC & POWER ASSOCIATION
7037 Hwy 49 N, Hattiesburg, MS 39402
Tel.: (601) 268-2083
Web Site: http://www.smepa.coop
Sales Range: $25-49.9 Million
Emp.: 280
Generation, Electric Power
N.A.I.C.S.: 221118
Jim Compton (CEO & Gen Mgr)
Joey Ward (Dir-Environmental Affairs & Fuels)
Greg Chancellor (Plant Mgr)
Henry Martin (Engr-Results)
Bobby Vinson (Controller)
Ray Haley (CFO)
Ron Repsher (Engr-Generation Plng)

SOUTH MOTOR COMPANY OF DADE COUNTY
16165 S Dixie Hwy, Miami, FL 33157
Tel.: (305) 238-0900
Web Site:
http://www.southmotors.com
Sales Range: $100-124.9 Million
Emp.: 1,000
Owner & Operator of Car Dealerships
N.A.I.C.S.: 441110
Charles Dascal (Chm)
Miguel Villamanan (Pres)
John Hilton (CFO)
Ileana Salotr (Controller)

Subsidiaries:

South Motors Infiniti (1)
16915 S Dixie Hwy, Miami, FL 33157
Tel.: (305) 256-2000
Web Site: http://www.southinfiniti.com
Rev: $57,000,000
Emp.: 50
Automobiles, New & Used
N.A.I.C.S.: 441110
Charles Dascal (Owner & Chm)

SOUTH OAK DODGE, INC.
4550 Lincoln Hwy, Matteson, IL 60443-2314
Tel.: (708) 747-7950
Web Site: http://www.southoak.com
Year Founded: 1988
Sales Range: $10-24.9 Million
Emp.: 70
Car Whslr
N.A.I.C.S.: 441110
Dennis Guest (Pres)
Mark Hester (Gen Mgr-Sls)
Jonathan Jefferies (Dir-Svc)

SOUTH OTTUMWA SAVINGS BANK
320 Church St, Ottumwa, IA 52501
Tel.: (641) 682-7541
Web Site: http://www.sosb-ia.com
Sales Range: $10-24.9 Million
Emp.: 60
Banking Services
N.A.I.C.S.: 522110
Suzanne Morrison (Sr VP & Dir-Mktg)

SOUTH PARK CORPORATION
1019 Concord St N, South Saint Paul, MN 55075
Tel.: (651) 455-4510
Web Site: http://www.spcbrass.com
Year Founded: 1932
Sales Range: $1-9.9 Million
Emp.: 10
Miscellaneous General Purpose Machinery Mfr
N.A.I.C.S.: 333998
Curtis Kemp (Pres)

Subsidiaries:

FlameFighter Corporation (1)
208 Industrial Blvd, Waconia, MN 55387
Tel.: (763) 762-3440
Web Site: http://www.flamefighter.com
Cosmetics, Beauty Supplies & Perfume Stores
N.A.I.C.S.: 456120
Steven Peterson (CEO)

SOUTH PARK MOTOR LINES INC.
9850 Havana St, Henderson, CO 80640
Tel.: (303) 534-6376
Web Site: http://www.casttrans.com
Rev: $10,705,743
Emp.: 110
Heavy Machinery Transport
N.A.I.C.S.: 484110
Richard A. Eshe (Owner & Pres)
Al Wetsch (Controller)

SOUTH PLAINS BIOMEDICAL SERVICES, INC.
4315 Ironton Ave Unit C, Lubbock, TX 79407
Tel.: (800) 713-2396
Web Site: http://www.spbs.com
Year Founded: 1985
Electronic & Precision Equipment Repair & Maintenance
N.A.I.C.S.: 811210

SOUTH PLAINS ELECTRIC COOPERATIVE
4727 S Loop 289 Ste 200, Lubbock, TX 79424-3215
Tel.: (806) 775-7732
Web Site: http://www.spec.coop
Year Founded: 1937
Sales Range: $25-49.9 Million
Emp.: 140
Electronic Services
N.A.I.C.S.: 221122
James Driver (Exec VP & Gen Mgr)
Ronnie Rucker (CFO)
Tommy Joines (Pres)

SOUTH PUGET INTERTRIBAL PLANNING AGENCY
3104 Old Olympic Hwy, Shelton, WA 98584
Tel.: (360) 426-3990
Web Site: http://www.spipa.org
Year Founded: 1976
Sales Range: $10-24.9 Million
Emp.: 133
Community Welfare Services
N.A.I.C.S.: 624190
Zelma McCloud (Co-Founder)
Mel Youckton (Co-Founder)
Bill Smith (Co-Founder & Exec Dir)
Dan Gleason (Chm)

SOUTH RIVER ELECTRIC MEMBERSHIP CORPORATION
17494 US Hwy 421 S, Dunn, NC 28334
Tel.: (910) 892-8071
Web Site: http://www.sremc.com
Sales Range: $50-74.9 Million
Emp.: 103
Distribution, Electric Power
N.A.I.C.S.: 221122
Buddy G. Creed (CEO & Exec VP)
Carlton Martin (Treas)
Kelly Harrington (VP)
Catherine Dell (Mgr-Member Svcs)

SOUTH SEAS CYCLE EXCHANGE INC.
3149 N Nimitz Hwy, Honolulu, HI 96819
Tel.: (808) 836-1144
Web Site: http://www.warrendist.com
Sales Range: $10-24.9 Million
Emp.: 22
Motorcycle Dealers
N.A.I.C.S.: 441227
Steven Spiegel (Owner)

SOUTH SHORE ASSOCIATION FOR INDEPENDENT LIVING, INC.
1976 Grand Ave, Baldwin, NY 11510
Tel.: (516) 855-1800
Web Site: http://www.sailservices.org
Year Founded: 1982
Sales Range: $10-24.9 Million
Psychiatric Healthcare Services
N.A.I.C.S.: 621420
Noelle Palazzo (Controller)
Michael Scott (Mgr-Facilities)
Marjorie Vezer (Exec Dir)
Anita Namdar (Coord-Properties)
Larry Skutelsky (Coord-Purchasing)
Jennifer Sauchelli (Coord-Svc)
Brian Cohen (Dir-Assoc)

SOUTH SHORE COMMUNITY ACTION COUNCIL, INC.
71 Arc Obery St, Plymouth, MA 02360
Tel.: (508) 747-7575
Web Site: http://www.sscac.org
Year Founded: 1965
Sales Range: $10-24.9 Million
Emp.: 171
Community Action Services
N.A.I.C.S.: 624190
Jennifer Swinhart (Dir-Early Education)
Jack Cocio (Dir-Fiscal)
Stephen Salwak (Dir-Transportation)
Charlie Schena (Treas)
Dan Shannon (Pres)
Sandie Grauds (Sec)
Jim Stewart (VP)

SOUTH SHORE FORD INC.
110 S Shore Rd, Marmora, NJ 08223
Tel.: (609) 390-9000
Rev: $29,700,000
Emp.: 80
Automobiles, New & Used
N.A.I.C.S.: 441110

SOUTH SHORE HOSPITAL
8012 S Crandon Ave, Chicago, IL 60617
Tel.: (773) 356-5000
Web Site:
http://www.southshorehospital.com
Year Founded: 1976
Sales Range: $25-49.9 Million
Emp.: 657
Health Care Srvices
N.A.I.C.S.: 622110
Helen Wiersma (Asst Sec)
Scott Spencer (CFO & Asst Treas)
Milicia Lukac (Mgr-Nurse)
Vera Ray (Dir-Lab)

SOUTH SHORE MOTORS CORP

South Shore Motors Corp—(Continued)

SOUTH SHORE MOTORS CORP
5686 Sunrise Hwy, Sayville, NY 11782
Tel.: (631) 589-4800
Web Site: http://www.sayvillefordgiant.com
Rev.: $62,900,000
Emp.: 155
Automobiles, New & Used
N.A.I.C.S.: 441110
Clifford Korade (VP & Mgr-Fleet)
Jim Smith (Mgr-Parts)
Michael Oswalt (Bus Dir)
Lisa Pavesi (Mgr-Comml Truck)
Tim Granito (Mgr-Pre-Owned Sls)
Neil J. Spare Jr. (Chm)

SOUTH SHORE SAVINGS BANK
1530 Main St, South Weymouth, MA 02190-1310
Tel.: (781) 337-7800
Web Site: http://www.sssb.com
Year Founded: 1868
Sales Range: $50-74.9 Million
Emp.: 200
Provider of Banking Services
N.A.I.C.S.: 522180
Nobo Sircar (CFO & Exec VP)
Heather Wilson (Asst VP)
Jeff Viall (Portfolio Mgr)
John Mannion (VP & Mgr-Small Bus Dev)
Joseph McPhee (Mgr-Comml Relationship)
Michael R. Healy (Officer-Comml Loan & Sr VP)
Michael Wilcox (Officer-Bus Dev)
Richard Testa (VP & Officer-Retail Bank)
Thomas Gillen (Officer-Comml Lending & VP)
Pamela J. O'Leary (COO, CTO & Exec VP)

SOUTH SHORE TRANSPORTATION CO.
4010 Columbus Ave, Sandusky, OH 44870
Tel.: (419) 626-6267
Web Site: http://www.sshoretrans.com
Sales Range: $10-24.9 Million
Emp.: 8
Contract Haulers
N.A.I.C.S.: 484121
Peter H. Hanley (Chm)
Cole Hanley (Pres)
Craig Wysocki (VP)

SOUTH SIDE CONTROL SUPPLY CO.
488 N Milwaukee Ave, Chicago, IL 60654
Tel.: (312) 226-4900
Web Site: http://www.southsidecontrol.com
Sales Range: $1-9.9 Million
Emp.: 40
Distr of Warm Air Heating Equipment & Supplies
N.A.I.C.S.: 423730
Lenord Kasper (VP)
Joe Bucaro (Exec VP & Gen Mgr)
Cliff Spyrka (Engr-Sls Application)

SOUTH TAHOE PUBLIC UTILITY DISTRICT
1275 Meadow Crest Dr, South Lake Tahoe, CA 96150
Tel.: (530) 544-6474
Web Site: http://www.stpud.us
Year Founded: 1950
Sales Range: $10-24.9 Million
Emp.: 110
Sewage Treatment Facility Services
N.A.I.C.S.: 221320
Kelly Sheehan (VP)
Richard Solbrig (Gen Mgr)
Paul Hughes (CFO)

SOUTH TEXAS ELECTRIC CO-OPERATIVE, INC.
2849 Farm Rd, Nursery, TX 77976
Tel.: (361) 575-6491   TX
Web Site: http://www.stec.org
Sales Range: $300-349.9 Million
Emp.: 227
Electric Power Distr
N.A.I.C.S.: 221122
Michael Packard (Gen Mgr)

SOUTH TEXAS LONE STAR DRYWALL
370 N Eureka Ave, Columbus, OH 43204
Tel.: (614) 351-8201
Sales Range: $10-24.9 Million
Emp.: 150
Drywall Construction
N.A.I.C.S.: 238310
James Tribbie (Pres)
Jack Gordon (VP-Ops)
Brent Allen (VP-Sls)
Kirk Iler (Controller)

SOUTH VILLAGE FORD
2840 Washington Rd, McMurray, PA 15317
Tel.: (724) 941-5040
Year Founded: 1934
Sales Range: $25-49.9 Million
Emp.: 78
Car Whslr
N.A.I.C.S.: 441110
Ronald Charapp (Pres)

SOUTH WEYMOUTH DODGE
577 Columbian St, South Weymouth, MA 02190
Tel.: (781) 331-8300
Year Founded: 1993
Sales Range: $10-24.9 Million
Emp.: 35
Car Whslr
N.A.I.C.S.: 441110
Roy Serrentino (Pres)

SOUTHARD COMMUNICATIONS
1011 John St, New York, NY 10038
Tel.: (212) 777-2220
Web Site: http://www.southardinc.com
Year Founded: 1994
Sales Range: $10-24.9 Million
Emp.: 15
Public Relations Agency
N.A.I.C.S.: 541820
Bill Southard (Founder & CEO)
Kelley DeVincentis (VP)
Brandon Thomas (Sr Acct Dir)

SOUTHBAY TOYOTA
18416 S Western Ave, Gardena, CA 90248
Tel.: (310) 323-7800
Web Site: http://www.southbaytoyota.com
Sales Range: $25-49.9 Million
Emp.: 141
New & Used Car Dealer
N.A.I.C.S.: 441110
Bill Coyne (VP & Gen Mgr)
Ryan Clements (Gen Mgr-Sls)
Mike Pike (Mgr-Sls)
Bill Raho (Mgr-Sls)
Jeff Vance (Mgr-Used Car)
Steve Coyne (Mgr-Sls)
David Flores (Mgr-Fin)
Tina Frodge (Mgr-Fleet)
Yuki Ochiai (Mgr-Japanese Fleet)
Carlos Santiago (Head-Svc Porter)
Ali Shah (Mgr-Fin)
Cheri Urias (Mgr-Customer Rels)
Filberto Vasquez (Mgr-Sls Porter)
Benjamin Onubah (Mgr-Fin)
Eduardo Rojas (Mgr-Fin)
John Matsubayashi (Mgr-Parts)
Ricky Lemoli (Dir-Parts & Svc)

SOUTHCO DISTRIBUTING COMPANY
2201 S John St, Goldsboro, NC 27530-8139
Tel.: (919) 735-8012   NC
Web Site: http://www.southcodistributing.com
Year Founded: 1981
Sales Range: $200-249.9 Million
Emp.: 240
Whslr of Cigarettes, Confectionery, Notions, Dry Goods, Novelties, Snack Foods, Health & Beauty Aids & Groceries
N.A.I.C.S.: 424940
Sherwin Herring (CEO)
Mel Fairchild (Exec VP-Sls)
Frank French (Mgr-IT)
Scott Barry (Mgr-Ops)
Tammy Stokes (Dir-MIS)
Max Stevens (Dir-Transportation)
Sonny Wooten (Pres)
Gerald Jones (Dir-HR)
Wendy Whitfield (Dir-Programs)

SOUTHCOMM, INC.
210 12th Ave S. Ste 100, Nashville, TN 37203
Tel.: (615) 244-7989   TN
Web Site: http://www.southcomm.com
Emp.: 72
Holding Company; Newspaper, Periodical & Specialty Publication Publisher
N.A.I.C.S.: 551112
Patrick Rains (Exec VP)
Jennifer Wilberschied (Editor-Printing News Grp)
Kelley Holmes (Grp Publr)
Bob Mahoney (CFO)
Ed Nichols (VP-Events)
Eric Kammerzelt (VP-Tech)

Subsidiaries:

SouthComm Communications, Inc. (1)
210 12th Ave S Ste 100, Nashville, TN 37203
Tel.: (615) 244-7989
Web Site: http://www.southcomm.com
Niche Newspaper & Periodical Publisher
N.A.I.C.S.: 513110
Chris Ferrell (CEO)
Patrick Min (CFO)
Eric Norwood (COO)
Susan Torregrossa (CMO)
Matt Locke (CTO)
Patrick Rains (Dir-Content & Online Dev)

Subsidiary (Domestic):

Creative Loafing Atlanta, Inc. (2)
115 MLK Jr Dr SW Ste 301, Atlanta, GA 30303
Tel.: (404) 688-5623
Web Site: http://www.clatl.com
Emp.: 40
Newspaper Publishers
N.A.I.C.S.: 513110
Sharry Smith (Publr)
Debbie Michaud (Editor-in-Chief)
Kartrina Thomas (Mgr-Ops)
Leigh Anne Anderson (Dir-Market Dev)
Alicia Carter (Mng Editor)
Deborah Eason (Founder)
Thomas Wheatley (Editor-News)

Creative Loafing Tampa, LLC (2)
1911 N 13th St Ste W200, Tampa, FL 33605
Tel.: (813) 739-4800
Web Site: http://www.cltampa.com
Emp.: 25
Newspaper Publishers
N.A.I.C.S.: 513110
James Howard (Publr)
David Warner (Editor-in-Chief)
Leilani Polk (Editor-Music)
Joran Oppelt (Dir-Mktg & Promos)
Marsha Smoot (Mgr-Credit)
London Fajkus (Mgr-Ops)
Chris Madalena (Dir-Adv)
Chris Ferrell (CEO)
Ron Jiranek (COO)
Julio Ramos (Dir-Creative)
Mark Bartel (Exec VP-Local Publ)
Blair Johnson (COO)
Kelly Knaggs (Mgr-Ops)
Todd Patton (Controller)
Curt Pordes (VP-Production Ops)
Stephanie Stein (Mgr-HR)
Ed Tearman (CFO)

SOUTHDATA, INC.
201 Technology Ln, Mount Airy, NC 27030
Tel.: (336) 719-5000
Web Site: http://www.southdata.com
Year Founded: 1985
Sales Range: $10-24.9 Million
Emp.: 129
Document Management Services
N.A.I.C.S.: 518210
Chelsey Seidel (Mgr-Mktg)
Terry Simpson (Mgr-Production)
Tim Fleming (Supvr-Tech Support)
Kenny Meredith (CFO)
John Springthorpe III (Pres)

SOUTHEAST ALABAMA GAS DISTRICT
715 Martin Luther King Jr Expy, Andalusia, AL 36420
Tel.: (334) 222-4177   AL
Web Site: http://www.seagd.net
Year Founded: 1952
Sales Range: $50-74.9 Million
Emp.: 75
Distr of Natural Gas
N.A.I.C.S.: 221210
J. Gregory Henderson (Pres & CEO)
Royce Sightler (Dir-Ops)
Lex Colquett (Dir-Corp Svcs)
Shannon Gooden (Mgr-Comm)

SOUTHEAST ALASKA REGIONAL HEALTH CONSORTIUM
3100 Channel Dr Ste 300, Juneau, AK 99801
Tel.: (907) 463-4000   AK
Web Site: https://searhc.org
Year Founded: 1975
Emp.: 100
Health Care Srvices
N.A.I.C.S.: 621999

Subsidiaries:

Juneau Physical Therapy, A Professional Corporation (1)
2841 Riverside Dr, Juneau, AK 99801
Tel.: (907) 789-4165
Web Site: http://www.juneauphysicaltherapy.com
Offices of Physical, Occupational & Speech Therapists & Audiologists
N.A.I.C.S.: 621340
Sharon Buis (VP)

SOUTHEAST ALASKA SMOKED SALMON CO., INC.
550 S Franklin St, Juneau, AK 99801
Tel.: (907) 463-4617
Web Site: http://www.takustore.com
Sales Range: $10-24.9 Million
Emp.: 45

COMPANIES

SOUTHEAST BANCSHARES, INC.
101 W Main St, Chanute, KS 66720
Tel.: (620) 431-1400
Year Founded: 1994
Sales Range: $10-24.9 Million
Emp.: 50
Bank Holding Company
N.A.I.C.S.: 551111
Mike Aylward *(VP)*

Subsidiaries:

Bank of Commerce (1)
101 W Main St, Chanute, KS 66720
Tel.: (620) 431-1400
Web Site: http://www.boc-ks.com
Retail & Commercial Banking
N.A.I.C.S.: 522110
Mark Lair *(Pres)*

First Neodesha Bank (1)
524 Main St, Neodesha, KS 66757
Tel.: (620) 325-2632
Web Site:
  http://www.firstneodeshabank.com
Rev.: $2,200,000
Emp.: 17
State Commercial Banks
N.A.I.C.S.: 522110
Casey Lair *(Pres)*

SOUTHEAST BEVERAGE COMPANY
771 W Union St, Athens, OH 45701
Tel.: (740) 593-3353
Web Site:
  http://www.southeastbeverage.com
Year Founded: 1950
Rev.: $10,000,000
Emp.: 47
Whslr & Distr of Beer & Other Fermented Malt Liquors
N.A.I.C.S.: 424810
Eric Emmert *(Mgr-Sls)*

SOUTHEAST BRONX NEIGHBORHOOD CENTERS, INC.
955 Tinton Ave, Bronx, NY 10456
Tel.: (718) 542-2727 NY
Web Site: http://www.sebnc.org
Year Founded: 1971
Sales Range: $10-24.9 Million
Emp.: 197
Community Care Services
N.A.I.C.S.: 624190
Clyde Thompson *(Dir-Community Affairs, Trng & Employment)*
Sheron Gayle *(CFO)*

SOUTHEAST COLORADO POWER ASSOCIATION
901 W 3rd St PO Box 521, La Junta, CO 81050
Tel.: (719) 384-2551
Web Site: http://www.secpa.com
Year Founded: 1937
Sales Range: $25-49.9 Million
Emp.: 49
Electric Power Distribution
N.A.I.C.S.: 221122
Randy Phillips *(Pres)*
Kevin Brandon *(CTO)*
Jack Johnston *(CEO)*
Bill Cochell *(COO)*
Scott Larsen *(CFO)*
Kevin Karney *(VP)*
Lawrence Brase *(Sec & Treas)*
Angela Bamber *(Chief HR Officer)*
Telly Stanger *(Chief Member Svc Officer)*
Rob Thayer *(Chief Mktg Officer)*

SOUTHEAST COMMUNITY WORK CENTER, INC.
181 Lincoln St, Depew, NY 14043
Tel.: (716) 683-7100 NY
Web Site: http://www.southeast-works.org
Year Founded: 1974
Sales Range: $10-24.9 Million
Emp.: 354
Developmental Disability Assistance Services
N.A.I.C.S.: 624120
JoAnne Hudecki *(Pres)*
Marc Shatkin *(Treas)*
Melinda DuBois *(Sec)*
Kevin Brzezinski *(VP)*

SOUTHEAST CONSTRUCTION PRODUCTS, INC.
11029 E Weaver Ave, South El Monte, CA 91733
Tel.: (626) 443-9333
Web Site:
  http://www.southeastproducts.com
Sales Range: $10-24.9 Million
Emp.: 90
Distribute Concrete Building Products
N.A.I.C.S.: 459999
Robert Lewis *(Pres)*
Bryan Trestrial *(VP)*

SOUTHEAST COOPERATIVE SERVICE CO.
32876 Hwy 25 S, Advance, MO 63730
Tel.: (573) 722-3522
Rev.: $15,696,633
Emp.: 20
Farm Supplies
N.A.I.C.S.: 424910
John Bishop *(Gen Mgr)*

SOUTHEAST DIESEL CORP.
5820 NW 84th Ave, Miami, FL 33166-3313
Tel.: (305) 592-9745
Web Site:
  http://www.tradewindspower.com
Year Founded: 1978
Sales Range: $25-49.9 Million
Emp.: 100
Holding Company
N.A.I.C.S.: 551112
Alex Colon *(CFO-Miami)*
Diego Aleaga D. J. *(Coord-Sls Support-Miami)*
Daniel Santos *(Supvr-Traffic)*
Jeff Beard *(Gen Mgr-Miami)*
Jorge Rodriguez *(Engr-Sls-Intl-Miami)*
Juan Monreal *(Dir-Sls-Intl-Miami)*
Leonor Balsera *(Mgr-Fin-Miami)*
Mike Braswell *(Mgr-Pur-Miami)*
Pete Kappesser *(Mgr-Svc-Sebring)*
Thomas Tracy III *(Pres)*

Subsidiaries:

Perkins Power Corp. (1)
55 Industrial Loop N, Orange Park, FL 32073 (100%)
Tel.: (904) 278-9919
Web Site: http://www.perkinspower.com
Sales Range: $10-24.9 Million
Emp.: 16
Provider of Motor Vehicle Supplies & New Parts
N.A.I.C.S.: 423830
Chuck Scott *(Gen Mgr)*
Jerry Rose *(Mgr-Engrg)*

Tradewinds Power Corp. (1)
5820 NW 84th Ave, Miami, FL 33166-3313
Tel.: (305) 592-9745
Web Site: http://www.tradewindspower.com
Sales Range: $10-24.9 Million
Emp.: 79
Motors & Generator Mfr
N.A.I.C.S.: 335312
Charlie Smith *(CFO)*
Frances Aybar *(Dir-HR)*
Mike Braswell *(Dir-Pur & Logistics)*
James Ohare *(Mgr-Engrg)*
Daniel Santos *(Mgr-Export)*

Leonor Balsera *(Mgr-Fin)*
Jeff Beard *(Gen Mgr)*
Tom Tracy *(Owner)*
Juan Monreal *(Dir-Intl Sls)*
Pete Kappesser *(Mgr-Svc)*

SOUTHEAST FARMERS ELEVATORS COOP
32702 479th Ave, Elk Point, SD 57025
Tel.: (605) 966-5474
Web Site:
  http://www.southeastfarmers.com
Sales Range: $25-49.9 Million
Emp.: 20
Grain Elevators
N.A.I.C.S.: 424510
Douglas Hanson *(Pres)*
Don Truhe *(Gen Mgr)*

SOUTHEAST FINANCIAL CREDIT UNION
220 S Royal Oaks Blvd, Franklin, TN 37064
Tel.: (615) 465-5400 TN
Web Site:
  http://www.southeastfinancial.org
Rev.: $23,932,041
Assets: $368,415,688
Liabilities: $4,352,450
Net Worth: $364,063,238
Earnings: $1,065,863
Emp.: 211
Fiscal Year-end: 12/31/18
Credit Union Operator
N.A.I.C.S.: 522130
Jeff Dahlstrom *(Pres)*
John Jacoway *(CEO)*

SOUTHEAST FLORIDA BEHAVIORAL HEALTH NETWORK, INC.
140 Intracoastal Pointe Dr Ste 211, Jupiter, FL 33477-5096
Tel.: (561) 203-2485 FL
Web Site: http://www.sefbhn.org
Year Founded: 2010
Sales Range: $25-49.9 Million
Behavioral Health Services
N.A.I.C.S.: 623210
Ann M. Berner *(CEO)*
Becky Walker *(Dir-Network Mgmt)*
Jill Sorensen *(Dir-Wraparound Fidelity)*
Ed Harper *(Dir-IT)*
Cheri Sheffer *(Treas)*
John Fowler *(Vice Chm)*
Larry Rein *(Sec)*

SOUTHEAST FOOD SERVICES CORP
9041 Executive Park Dr # 300, Knoxville, TN 37923
Tel.: (865) 691-1393
Web Site:
  http://www.wenburgerknoxville.com
Sales Range: $10-24.9 Million
Emp.: 29
Fast Food Restaurant Operator
N.A.I.C.S.: 722513
Mike Cardinal *(Pres)*

SOUTHEAST FOODS DISTRIBUTION
3261 Ext Way, Miramar, FL 33025
Tel.: (305) 652-4622
Web Site: http://www.seff.com
Year Founded: 1958
Sales Range: $25-49.9 Million
Emp.: 500
Frozen Specialty Food Mfr
N.A.I.C.S.: 311412
Richard A. Bauer *(Pres & CEO)*
Marc Goodman *(CFO)*

Danny Payne *(VP-Warehouse Ops)*
Timothy Martis *(VP-Procurement)*
Isabel Morejon *(Dir-HR)*

SOUTHEAST FROZEN FOODS COMPANY LP
18770 NE 6 Ave, Miami, FL 33179-3916
Tel.: (305) 652-4622 DE
Web Site: http://www.seff.com
Year Founded: 1991
Sales Range: $650-699.9 Million
Emp.: 650
Packaged Frozen Food Distr
N.A.I.C.S.: 424420
Rich Bauer *(Pres & CEO)*
Danny Payne *(VP-Ops)*
Marc Goodman *(CFO)*

SOUTHEAST HARLEY-DAVIDSON, INC.
23105 Aurora Rd, Bedford Heights, OH 44146
Tel.: (440) 439-5300 OH
Web Site:
  http://www.southeastharley.com
Year Founded: 1948
Sales Range: $100-124.9 Million
Emp.: 112
Sales of Motorcycles
N.A.I.C.S.: 441227

SOUTHEAST INDUSTRIAL EQUIPMENT, INC.
12200 Stillcreek Rd, Charlotte, NC 28273-5483
Tel.: (704) 399-9700 NC
Web Site: http://www.sielift.com
Year Founded: 1994
Sales Range: $10-24.9 Million
Emp.: 200
Industrial & Construction Machinery
N.A.I.C.S.: 333120
Cory Thorne *(Pres)*
Blake Loftin *(Mgr-Major Accts)*
Ed Harris *(Reg Mgr-Sls)*
Bill Mouille *(Acct Mgr)*
Lauren Hunke *(Coord-Mktg)*
Greg Snipes *(VP-Sls)*

SOUTHEAST KANSAS COMMUNITY ACTION PROGRAM, INC.
401 N Sinnet St, Girard, KS 66743
Tel.: (620) 724-8204 KS
Web Site: http://www.sek-cap.com
Year Founded: 1966
Sales Range: $10-24.9 Million
Emp.: 290
Anti-Poverty Advocacy Services
N.A.I.C.S.: 813319
Joanie Burke *(Asst Dir-Early Childhood Svcs)*
Steve Lohr *(Exec Dir)*

SOUTHEAST KANSAS EDUCATION SERVICE CENTER, INC.
947 W 47 Hwy, Girard, KS 66743-2347
Tel.: (620) 724-6281
Web Site: http://www.greenbush.org
Year Founded: 1976
Sales Range: $25-49.9 Million
Emp.: 420
School & Educational Services
N.A.I.C.S.: 611699
John Staton *(CFO)*
Russ Wilcox *(Coord-Procurement Mktg)*
Misty Burke *(Dir-Prevention & Wellness)*
Randy Corns *(COO)*

SOUTHEAST KANSAS INDE-

SOUTHEAST KANSAS INDE

SOUTHEAST KANSAS INDE—(CONTINUED)

PENDENT LIVING RESOURCE CENTER, INC.
1801 Main St, Parsons, KS 67357
Tel.: (620) 421-5502   KS
Web Site: http://www.skilonline.com
Year Founded: 1992
Sales Range: $25-49.9 Million
Emp.: 2,152
Disability Assistance Services
N.A.I.C.S.: 623210
John Kazmierski (Chm)

SOUTHEAST LAND CONSULTANTS, INC.
550 N Reo St Ste 104, Tampa, FL 33609
Tel.: (813) 875-5263
Web Site:
http://www.southeastlandconsultants.com
Sales Range: $1-9.9 Million
Land Brokers
N.A.I.C.S.: 531390
David Berner (Pres)
Bill Short (VP)

SOUTHEAST LINEN ASSOCIATES, INC.
315 Shawnee North Dr Ste 350, Suwanee, GA 30024
Tel.: (678) 546-6687
Web Site:
http://www.southeastlinen.com
Sales Range: $10-24.9 Million
Emp.: 150
Linen Supply
N.A.I.C.S.: 812331
Jim Krupansky (Pres)
Earl Delbridge (Gen Mgr)

SOUTHEAST MEDIA, INC.
1720 Townhurst Dr, Houston, TX 77043
Tel.: (713) 676-1661   TX
Web Site: http://www.semtx.com
Year Founded: 1994
Sales Range: $1-9.9 Million
Emp.: 49
Commercial Printing
N.A.I.C.S.: 823111
Cheryl Parnell (VP-Sls)
Gregg Parnell (Pres & CEO)
Rick Baker (Plant Mgr)

SOUTHEAST MENTAL HEALTH CENTER
3810 Winchester Rd, Memphis, TN 38181-0720
Tel.: (901) 369-1469   TN
Web Site: http://www.semhcinc.com
Year Founded: 1973
Sales Range: $10-24.9 Million
Emp.: 204
Behavioral Healthcare Services
N.A.I.C.S.: 623220
Kyle Hataway (CFO)
Gene Lawrence (Exec Dir)

SOUTHEAST MILK, INC.
1950 SE Hwy 484, Belleview, FL 34420
Tel.: (352) 245-2437   FL
Web Site:
http://www.southeastmilk.org
Year Founded: 1998
Sales Range: $10-24.9 Million
Emp.: 300
Dairy Cooperative
N.A.I.C.S.: 112120
Cheryl Pfeil (Mgr-Risk)
Henry Bruns (Mgr-Traffic)
Ray Hodge (Dir-Govt Affairs)
Ruth Ann Athey (Mgr-Corp Payroll)

Shana Wooten (Mgr-Milk Procurement)
Steve Kennedy (Dir-Transportation)
Subsidiaries:

Flagship Atlanta Dairy LLC   (1)
777 Memorial Dr SE, Atlanta, GA 30316-1186
Tel.: (404) 688-2671
Dairy Cooperative
N.A.I.C.S.: 311511

Sunshine State Dairy Farms   (1)
3304 Sydney Rd, Plant City, FL 33566-1181
Tel.: (813) 754-1847
Dairy Products Mfr
N.A.I.C.S.: 311520
Paul Bikowitz (CEO)

SOUTHEAST MISSOURI HOSPITAL ASSOCIATION
1701 Lacey St, Cape Girardeau, MO 63701
Tel.: (573) 334-4822
Web Site: http://www.sehealth.org
Year Founded: 1928
Sales Range: $800-899.9 Million
Emp.: 2,348
Hospital Services
N.A.I.C.S.: 622110
Dan Berry (VP-Legal Affairs)
Judy Aslin (Chief Nursing Officer & VP)
Kenneth W. Bateman (Pres & CEO)
Mike Nichols (CIO)
Erin Pfeifer (VP-HR)
Steven Haas (CFO)
Maria Sudak (COO)
Frank M. Kinder (Chm)
Steve Green (Vice Chm)
Charles Kruse (Sec)
Stanley Crader (Treas)
Subsidiaries:

Dexter Hospital LLC   (1)
1200 N One Mile Rd, Dexter, MO 63841   (100%)
Tel.: (573) 624-5566
Web Site: http://www.sehealth.org
Sales Range: $10-24.9 Million
Emp.: 200
Hospital Operator
N.A.I.C.S.: 622110
Amy Ellinghouse (Dir-Mktg)

SOUTHEAST PERSONNEL LEASING, INC.
2739 US Hwy 19, Holiday, FL 34691
Tel.: (727) 938-5562   FL
Web Site:
http://www.southeastpersonnel.com
Year Founded: 1986
Sales Range: $1-4.9 Billion
Emp.: 300
Payroll, Workers' Compensation & Benefits Solutions
N.A.I.C.S.: 561330
John Porreca (Pres & Owner)
Jacki Phelps (Supvr-Acctg)
Steve Caldwell (Dir-Sls)
Phyllis Harvey (Supvr-Sls Support)

SOUTHEAST POWER SYSTEMS OF ORLANDO, INC.
4220 N Orange Blossom Trl, Orlando, FL 32804
Tel.: (407) 293-7971
Web Site: http://www.se-power.com
Sales Range: $10-24.9 Million
Emp.: 54
Truck Supplies & Parts
N.A.I.C.S.: 423120
Paul Anningson (CEO)
Subsidiaries:

Southeast Power Systems of Tampa   (1)

4220 N Orange Blossom Trl, Orlando, FL 32804
Tel.: (407) 293-7971
Web Site:
http://spsdiesel-com.3dcartstores.com
Rev: $3,500,000
Emp.: 25
Diesel Engine Repair Automotive
N.A.I.C.S.: 811111
Jim Smith (Pres)

SOUTHEAST QUADRANT MOBILE CRITICAL CARE UNIT INC.
2527 Baird Rd, Penfield, NY 14526
Tel.: (585) 218-0026   NY
Web Site:
http://www.southeastquadrantmccu.org
Year Founded: 1976
Sales Range: $1-9.9 Million
Emp.: 73
Health Care Srvices
N.A.I.C.S.: 621111
Rick Van Den Berge (Sec)
William Stumbo (Pres)
Gary Hart (Treas)
Hugh Franklin (VP)

SOUTHEAST RESTORATION GROUP
120 Mtn Brook Dr, Canton, GA 30115
Tel.: (770) 345-3500
Web Site:
http://www.southeastrestoration.com
Sales Range: $10-24.9 Million
Emp.: 100
Commercial & Residential Restoration Services
N.A.I.C.S.: 236118
Ben Looper (Pres & CEO)
Jeremy Swafford (Controller-Fin)
Trent Lane (Project Mgr)
Keith Newberry (Project Mgr)
Brian Taylor (Project Mgr)
Kyle Sears (Mgr-Production)
Jill Marden (Office Mgr-HR)
Keally Webb (Mgr-Ops)
Ghani Massoud (Project Mgr)
Truett Scales (Project Mgr)
Scott Gold (Project Mgr)

SOUTHEAST SPREADING COMPANY
13650 Fiddlesticks Blvd Ste 202-336, Fort Myers, FL 33912
Tel.: (239) 437-7463
Web Site:
http://www.southeastspreading.com
Year Founded: 2000
Sales Range: $1-9.9 Million
Emp.: 15
Soil Preparation Services
N.A.I.C.S.: 115112
Shane Shirey (Pres)

SOUTHEAST TEXAS CLASSIC AUTOMOTIVE
1000 Interstate 10 N, Beaumont, TX 77702
Tel.: (409) 892-6696
Sales Range: $100-124.9 Million
Emp.: 400
Automobiles, New & Used
N.A.I.C.S.: 441110
Ken Ruddy (Pres)
Subsidiaries:

Beaumont Motor Co.   (1)
3855 Eastex Fwy, Beaumont, TX 77706
Tel.: (409) 892-5050
Web Site: http://www.classicbeaumont.com
Sales Range: $25-49.9 Million
Emp.: 300
Automobiles, New & Used
N.A.I.C.S.: 441110
Bryan Case (Gen Mgr)

Classic-Tyler Motors Inc.   (1)
1717 W SW Loop 323, Tyler, TX 75701
Tel.: (903) 579-0655
Web Site: http://www.classictoyotatyler.com
Rev: $103,958,896
Emp.: 157
New & Used Car Dealers
N.A.I.C.S.: 441110

Eastex Dodge of Beaumont Inc.   (1)
3855 Eastex Fwy, Beaumont, TX 77706
Tel.: (409) 898-1212
Web Site: http://www.setclassic.com
Rev: $37,200,000
Emp.: 120
New & Used Car Dealers
N.A.I.C.S.: 441110

Twin City Motors Inc.   (1)
10549 Memorial Blvd, Port Arthur, TX 77640
Tel.: (409) 727-2779
Web Site: http://www.twincitymotors.com
Sales Range: $25-49.9 Million
Emp.: 100
New & Used Car Dealers
N.A.I.C.S.: 441110
Gaynell Delaney (Controller)

SOUTHEAST TEXAS INDUSTRIES
Hwy 96 S, Buna, TX 77612
Tel.: (409) 994-3570
Web Site: http://www.setxind.com
Sales Range: $75-99.9 Million
Emp.: 1,000
Pipe Fabricating
N.A.I.C.S.: 332312
Paul Spence (Pres)
James Parshley (CFO)
Richard Purkey Jr. (VP)

SOUTHEAST TEXAS WORKFORCE DEVELOPMENT BOARD
304 Pearl St Ste 300, Beaumont, TX 77701
Tel.: (409) 719-4750   TX
Web Site: http://www.setworks.org
Sales Range: $10-24.9 Million
Workforce Development Services
N.A.I.C.S.: 561311
Marilyn A. Smith (Exec Dir)

SOUTHEAST TRAVEL SERVICES USA CO. LTD.
3545 El Camino Real, Palo Alto, CA 94306
Tel.: (415) 956-6688
Web Site:
http://www.usachinatour.com
Year Founded: 1997
Sales Range: Less than $1 Million
Emp.: 30
Provider of Travel Services
N.A.I.C.S.: 561510
David Mei (Pres)

SOUTHEAST UNITED DAIRY INDUSTRY ASSOCIATION, INC.
5340 W Fayetteville Rd, Atlanta, GA 30349
Tel.: (770) 996-6085   KY
Web Site:
http://www.southeastdairy.org
Year Founded: 1971
Sales Range: $10-24.9 Million
Emp.: 57
Dairy Industry Association
N.A.I.C.S.: 541690
Anne Cain (Dir-Comm)
Barbara Sims (Dir-Fin & Admin)
Bob Midles (Dir-Indus Rels)
Mark Farmer (Partner-Rels & Dir-Mktg)
Molly Szymanski (Dir-School Health & Wellness)
Douglas Ackerman (Gen Mgr)

SOUTHEAST WOOD TREATING INC.
3077 Carter Hill Rd, Montgomery, AL 36111
Tel.: (334) 269-9663
Sales Range: $25-49.9 Million
Wood Preservation Services
N.A.I.C.S.: 321114
Donald King (Controller)
Stinson Slawson (VP)
Guice Slawson Sr. (Pres)

SOUTHEAST, INC.
16 W Long St, Columbus, OH 43215
Tel.: (614) 225-0990 OH
Web Site:
  http://www.southeastinc.com
Year Founded: 1978
Sales Range: $10-24.9 Million
Emp.: 451
Fiscal Year-end: 06/30/15
Behavioral Healthcare Services
N.A.I.C.S.: 623220
Bill Lee (CEO)
Sandy Stephenson (Dir-Healthcare)
Steve Atwood (CFO)
Wendy Williams (Chief Compliance Officer)

SOUTHEASTERN ALUMINUM PRODUCTS, INC.
4925 Bulls Bay Hwy, Jacksonville, FL 32219
Tel.: (904) 781-8200
Web Site:
  http://www.southeasternalumi num.com
Sales Range: $10-24.9 Million
Emp.: 100
Mfr of Bath Enclosures & Mirror Closet Doors
N.A.I.C.S.: 332321
Jeff Dowd (VP-Sls)
Thomas Pierson (Coord-Production)
Scott Witt (CFO)
Patrick Dussinger (Pres)

SOUTHEASTERN ASSET MANAGEMENT, INC.
6410 Poplar Ave Ste 900, Memphis, TN 38119
Tel.: (901) 761-2474 TN
Web Site:
  http://www.southeasternasset.com
Year Founded: 1975
Investment Advisory & Portfolio Management Services
N.A.I.C.S.: 523940
William Reid Sanders (Founder)
O. Mason Hawkins (Chm, CEO & Principal)
G. Staley Cates (Pres)
Ross Glotzbach (Principal)
Lowry H. Howell (Principal)
Lee B. Harper (Principal)
Gary Wilson (Principal & Portfolio Mgr-Client)
Deborah L. Craddock (Principal)
Steve Fracchia (COO & Principal)
Andrew R. McCarroll (Principal & Gen Counsel)
Mike Wittke (Chief Compliance Officer)
Josh Shores (Principal)
Ken Siazon (Principal)
Manish Sharma (Principal)
Scott Cobb (Principal)
W. Douglas Schrank (Principal & Head-Trading)
Brandon Arrindell (Sr Analyst)
Jim Barton Jr. (Principal & Head-Portfolio Risk Mgmt)

Subsidiaries:

Southeastern Asset Management International (UK) Ltd. (1)
3rd Floor 7 Savile Row, London, W1S 3PE, United Kingdom
Tel.: (44) 20 7479 4200
Web Site: http://www.longleafpartners.com
Emp.: 6
Investment Advisory & Portfolio Management Services
N.A.I.C.S.: 523940
Scott Cobb (Principal)
Josh Shores (Principal)
Gwin G. Myerberg (Portfolio Mgr-Client)

SOUTHEASTERN AUTOMOTIVE WAREHOUSE
460 Decatur St SE, Atlanta, GA 30312
Tel.: (404) 523-5591
Web Site:
  http://www.sawpartsplus.com
Rev.: $15,700,000
Emp.: 100
Motor Vehicle Supplies & New Parts
N.A.I.C.S.: 423120
W. D. Ward (Pres)
Patty Claton (VP & Controller)
Robbie Wright (Gen Mgr)

SOUTHEASTERN BANCORP, INC.
223 Varner Ave, Greeleyville, SC 29056
Tel.: (843) 426-2161 SC
Web Site: http://www.bog1.com
Year Founded: 1988
Sales Range: $1-9.9 Million
Emp.: 20
Bank Holding Company
N.A.I.C.S.: 551111
Bobby Jonte (Pres & CEO)

Subsidiaries:

Bank of Greeleyville (1)
223 Varner Ave, Greeleyville, SC 29056
Tel.: (843) 426-2161
Web Site: http://www.bog1.com
Sales Range: $1-9.9 Million
Commericial Banking
N.A.I.C.S.: 522110
Scott Williamson (Exec VP)
Bobby Jonte (Pres & CEO)

SOUTHEASTERN BANCORP, INC.
611 E College St, Dickson, TN 37055
Tel.: (615) 446-2822 TN
Web Site: http://www.ffbtn.com
Year Founded: 1995
Sales Range: $10-24.9 Million
Bank Holding Company
N.A.I.C.S.: 551111
Anthony T. Moore (Pres & CEO)

Subsidiaries:

First Federal Bank (1)
611 E College St, Dickson, TN 37055
Tel.: (615) 446-2822
Web Site: http://www.ffbtn.com
Sales Range: $10-24.9 Million
Emp.: 135
Federal Savings Bank
N.A.I.C.S.: 522180
Anthony T. Moore (Pres & CEO)
Lorene Halliburton (VP & Branch Mgr-Dickson)
Nancy Murphy (VP & Mgr-Loans)
Lisa Bowers (Sr VP)

SOUTHEASTERN COMMUNITY & FAMILY SERVICES, INC.
405 N Elm St PO Box 1025, Lumberton, NC 28358
Tel.: (910) 277-3500 NC
Web Site: http://www.scfsnc.org
Year Founded: 1964
Sales Range: $10-24.9 Million
Community Development Services
N.A.I.C.S.: 813319
Tonie Brite (Dir-Headstart)
Davian Joy Ellison (Chm)
Gwendolyn Chavis (Asst Treas)
Jason King (Vice Chm)
John Ferguson (Treas)
Linda McLaughlin (Co-Sec)
Ericka J. Whitaker (CEO)
Kim Clark (Dir-Programs)
Tamara Monroe (Dir-HR)
Cynthia Demery (Treas)
Dorene Evans (Co-Sec)

SOUTHEASTERN COMPUTER CONSULTANTS, INC.
3 Hillcrest Dr Ste A201, Frederick, MD 21703
Tel.: (301) 695-5311
Web Site: http://www.scci-tx-inc.com
Sales Range: $1-9.9 Million
Emp.: 8
Computer Software Systems Analysis & Design
N.A.I.C.S.: 541511
Angela Koeimola (Office Mgr)

SOUTHEASTERN CONSTRUCTION & MAINTENANCE, INC.
1150 Pebbledale Rd, Mulberry, FL 33860
Tel.: (863) 428-1511 FL
Web Site:
  http://www.southeasternconst.com
Sales Range: $10-24.9 Million
Emp.: 170
Industrial Plant Construction
N.A.I.C.S.: 237990
Steve Howell (VP)

SOUTHEASTERN CONTAINER INC.
1250 Sand Hill Rd, Enka, NC 28728
Tel.: (828) 667-0101 NC
Web Site:
  http://www.southeasterned.com
Year Founded: 1982
Sales Range: $600-649.9 Million
Emp.: 775
Provider of Plastic Bottles
N.A.I.C.S.: 326160
Tom Francis (Pres)
Michelle Yanik (VP-Mfg Svcs)
Kevin Young (Mgr-HR)
Michael Ramos (CFO)
Merel Johnson (Engr-Sys)

SOUTHEASTERN DATA COOPERATIVE
100 Ashford Ctr N Ste 500, Atlanta, GA 30338
Tel.: (770) 414-8400
Web Site: http://www.sedata.com
Year Founded: 1971
Sales Range: $50-74.9 Million
Emp.: 300
Billing & Bookkeeping Service
N.A.I.C.S.: 541219

SOUTHEASTERN ELECTRICAL DISTRIBUTORS INC.
280 Fire Forest Way, Greenville, SC 29607
Tel.: (864) 233-7484
Web Site:
  http://www.southeasterned.com
Sales Range: $25-49.9 Million
Emp.: 55
Electrical Services & Equipment
N.A.I.C.S.: 423610
Paul Hodges (Pres)

SOUTHEASTERN ENERGY CORP.
180 Hunter Loop Rd, Montgomery, AL 36108
Tel.: (334) 265-2501
Sales Range: $25-49.9 Million
Emp.: 16
Petroleum Bulk Stations & Terminals
N.A.I.C.S.: 424710
Jack R. Pitts (Pres)
Thomas Pitts (VP)
Trish Fountain (Mgr-HR)

SOUTHEASTERN EQUIPMENT & SUPPLY, INC.
1919 Old Dunbar Rd, West Columbia, SC 29172
Tel.: (803) 252-0100 SC
Web Site:
  http://www.southeasternequip ment.net
Year Founded: 2001
Sales Range: $1-9.9 Million
Emp.: 23
Professional Floor Cleaning Services
N.A.I.C.S.: 332813
Lee Martin (Pres)

SOUTHEASTERN EQUIPMENT CO., INC.
10874 E Pike Rd, Cambridge, OH 43725-9615
Tel.: (740) 432-6303 OH
Web Site:
  http://www.southeasternequip.com
Year Founded: 1957
Sales Range: $100-124.9 Million
Emp.: 220
Construction Equipment Sales & Rental Services
N.A.I.C.S.: 423810
William L. Baker (Founder & Chm)
Johnny Taylor (Mgr-Parts-Brilliant)
Mike Hinton (CFO)
Thor Hess (Exec VP)
Heath Watton (VP)
Mickey Gourley (Pres)
Chris Kurz (Mgr-North Canton)

SOUTHEASTERN EXTRUSION & TOOL, INC.
510 Staples Dr, Florence, AL 35630
Tel.: (256) 766-6421 AL
Web Site: http://www.set-tool.com
Year Founded: 1971
Sales Range: $10-24.9 Million
Emp.: 140
Extrusion Tooling Services
N.A.I.C.S.: 331318
John Moody (Co-Owner)
Garry L. Barnes (Co-Owner)
Paul Fickbohm (Controller)
Jack Gregory (Gen Mgr-Tooling & Tech)
Wilbur Craven (Dir-Sls & Engrg)
Joe Hanback (Mgr-Engrg)

SOUTHEASTERN FARMERS COOPERATIVE
2615 Blue Springs Rd SE, Cleveland, TN 37311
Tel.: (423) 472-3239
Web Site: http://www.sefcoop.com
Year Founded: 1947
Sales Range: $10-24.9 Million
Emp.: 40
Feed & Farm Supplier
N.A.I.C.S.: 424910
Darrell Clark (Gen Mgr & Treas)
John Moore (Pres)
Marvin Weaver (VP)
David Hannah (Sec)

SOUTHEASTERN FINANCIAL INC.
1300 McFarland Blvd NE Ste 100, Tuscaloosa, AL 35406
Tel.: (205) 391-6700 DE
Web Site: http://www.1stfed.com
Year Founded: 1988
Sales Range: $25-49.9 Million
Emp.: 80
Bank Holding Company

SOUTHEASTERN FINANCIAL INC.

Southeastern Financial Inc.—(Continued)
N.A.I.C.S.: 551111
Charles Wolbach Jr. (Pres)

Subsidiaries:

First Federal Bank, A FSB (1)
1300 McFarland Blvd NE Ste 100, Tuscaloosa, AL 35406-2282
Tel.: (205) 391-6700
Web Site: http://www.1stfed.com
Sales Range: $50-74.9 Million
Emp.: 60
Federal Savings Bank
N.A.I.C.S.: 522180
Charles Wolbach Jr. (Pres)

SOUTHEASTERN FREIGHT LINES, INC.

420 Davega Dr, Lexington, SC 29073
Tel.: (803) 794-7300   SC
Web Site: http://www.sefl.com
Year Founded: 1950
Sales Range: $700-749.9 Million
Emp.: 6,000
Freight Trucking Services
N.A.I.C.S.: 484121
Mike Heaton (Sr VP-Sls & Mktg)
Keith Heaton (Sr VP)
David Turner (Reg VP-Ops)
Brian Schulz (Reg VP-Ops)
Austin Winters (Mgr-Svc Center-Huntsville)
Rob Smith (Reg VP-Ops)
Dan Poteat (Mgr-Svc Center-Baton Rouge)
Seth Fetzer (Reg VP-Ops)
Jacob Smith (Mgr-Svc Center-Shreveport)
Reed Doster (Mgr-Svc Center-Monroe)
Scott Lackie (Mgr-Svc Center-Louisville)
Kim Shore (VP-Ops-Southeastern)
Nick Crawford (Mgr-Svc Center-West Palm Beach)
Marty Cox (Mgr-Svc Center)
Richard Slater (VP-HR)
Bill Blatnik (Mgr-Svc Center-Kinston)
Taylor Wray (Mgr-Svc Center-Charlotte)
Kim Sore (Reg VP)
John Toombs (Mgr-Svc Center-New Orleans)
Matt Smith (VP-Ops-Reg)
Mark Coggin (Mgr-Svcs Center-Montgomery)
Dale White (Mgr-Svc Center-Wichita Falls)
William Wolfe (Mgr-Svc Center-South Charlotte)
Patrick Mackey (Mgr-Svc Center-Jackson & Mississippi)
Bryan Hale (Mgr-Svc Center-Nashville)
John Fuentes (Mgr-Svc Center-Mobile)
Zach Vincent (Mgr-Svc Center-Knoxville)
Paul Riddle (Dir-Sls Support & Dev)
Sherri Bane (VP-Fin)
Shannon Mangrum (Mgr-Svc Center-Lubbock)
Tommy Jones (Mgr-Svc Center-Norfolk)
Richard Bogan (Sr VP-HR)
Michelle Tate (Dir-HR)
Chad Smith (Mgr-Svc Center-San Antonio)
Todd Dilworth (Mgr-Svc Center-Jackson)
Josh Logue (Mgr-Svc Center-Monroe)
Andy Johnson (Mgr-Svc Center-Fort Smith)
Jim Jones (Reg VP-Ops)
Blake Potter (Mgr-Svc Center-Dalton)
Wade Lovejoy (Mgr-Svc Center-Tri-Cities)
Matt Andra (Mgr-Svc Center-Mobile-Alabama)
Mark Schwarzmueller (Reg VP-Ops)
W. T. Cassels Jr. (Chm)
Russell J. Burleson Jr. (Sr VP-Fin)
W. T. Cassels III (Pres)

SOUTHEASTERN ILLINOIS ELECTRIC CO-OPERATIVE INC.

Hwy 142 S, Eldorado, IL 62930
Tel.: (618) 273-2611   IL
Web Site: http://www.seiec.com
Year Founded: 1938
Sales Range: $25-49.9 Million
Emp.: 85
Provider of Electric Services
N.A.I.C.S.: 221122
Dustin Tripp (Pres & CEO)

SOUTHEASTERN INDUSTRIAL CONSTRUCTION COMPANY INC.

180 Commerce Dr, Pelham, AL 35124
Tel.: (205) 663-1024
Rev.: $20,900,000
Emp.: 50
Commercial & Institutional Building Construction
N.A.I.C.S.: 236220
Nancy Weems (Gen Mgr)
R.W. Roper (Pres)
Lida Moore (Sec)

SOUTHEASTERN INSTALLATION, INC.

207 Cedar Ln Dr, Lexington, NC 27292
Tel.: (336) 357-7146
Web Site: http://www.siidrykilns.com
Emp.: 60
Kilns, Lumber
N.A.I.C.S.: 333248
Paul D. Mathews (Chm)
Paula Turlington (VP)
Mack Carrick (Dir-Pur)

SOUTHEASTERN INTERNATIONAL SALES

9800 Reeves Rd, Tampa, FL 33619
Tel.: (813) 626-3191
Rev.: $13,000,000
Emp.: 150
Wire Fence, Gates & Accessories
N.A.I.C.S.: 423390

SOUTHEASTERN KIDNEY COUNCIL, INC.

1000 St Albans Dr Ste 270, Raleigh, NC 27609
Tel.: (919) 855-0882   NC
Web Site: http://www.esrdnetwork6.org
Year Founded: 1988
Sales Range: $1-9.9 Million
Emp.: 25
Fiscal Year-end: 06/30/15
Dialysis Center Operator
N.A.I.C.S.: 621492
Barry Freedman (Chm)

SOUTHEASTERN MANUFACTURERS AGENTS, INC.

3020 Amwiler Rd, Atlanta, GA 30360
Tel.: (770) 246-0111
Web Site: http://www.semareps.com
Rev.: $18,000,000
Emp.: 10
Food Industry Machinery
N.A.I.C.S.: 423830
Peter A. Cabrelli (Pres)
Richard Filitor (Gen Mgr)

SOUTHEASTERN MEDEQUIP, INC.

905 N 3rd St, Jacksonville Beach, FL 32250-7152
Tel.: (904) 246-0333   FL
Year Founded: 1973
Sales Range: $75-99.9 Million
Emp.: 3
Supplier of Medical Equipment to At-Home Patients
N.A.I.C.S.: 532283
Sheri Fogg-Parkinson (VP)
F.W. Fogg Sr. (Pres & CEO)
William Fogg III (Treas)

Subsidiaries:

Naturally You (1)
905 3rd St N, Jacksonville Beach, FL 32250-7152 (100%)
Tel.: (904) 246-0333
Emp.: 5
Boutique For Women With Mastectomies
N.A.I.C.S.: 456199
Sheri F. Parkinson (Pres)

SOUTHEASTERN OIL CO. INC.

160 Twitchell Rd, Dothan, AL 36303
Tel.: (334) 792-3136
Web Site: http://www.southeasternoil.com
Sales Range: $10-24.9 Million
Emp.: 15
Petroleum Bulk Stations
N.A.I.C.S.: 424710
Lee M. Brennan (Pres)

SOUTHEASTERN PAPER GROUP, INC.

50 Old Blackstock Rd, Spartanburg, SC 29301
Tel.: (864) 574-0440
Web Site: http://www.sepapergroup.com
Year Founded: 1969
Disposable Paper Products, Packaging & Janitorial & Sanitation Supplies
N.A.I.C.S.: 424130
Will Green (VP-Ops)
Christin Nelson (Mgr-Customer Svc)
E. Lewis Miller Sr. (Founder)
E. Lewis Miller Jr. (Pres)

SOUTHEASTERN PAPERBOARD INC.

100 S Harris Rd, Piedmont, SC 29673
Tel.: (864) 277-7353   GA
Web Site: http://www.southeasternpaperboard.com
Year Founded: 1979
Sales Range: $10-24.9 Million
Emp.: 100
Supplier of Corrugated Converted Paper Products
N.A.I.C.S.: 322130
Lou Scola (CFO)
Richard Beerman (Acct Mgr)
Tiffany F. Brooks (Mgr-Customer Svc)

Subsidiaries:

Southeastern Paperboard Inc. (1)
509 Old Griffin Rd, Piedmont, SC 29673-9376
Tel.: (864) 299-1904
Web Site: http://www.southeasternpaperboard.com
Sales Range: $10-24.9 Million
Provider of Paperboard Services
N.A.I.C.S.: 322130
Michael Ward (VP)

SOUTHEASTERN PENNSYLVANIA TRANSPORTATION AUTHORITY

1234 Market St, Philadelphia, PA 19107-3721
Tel.: (215) 580-4000   PA
Web Site: http://www.septa.org
Year Founded: 1963
Sales Range: $400-449.9 Million
Emp.: 12,000
Passenger Transportation Services
N.A.I.C.S.: 485119
Elizabeth M. Grant (Sec)
Jeff Knueppel (Deputy Gen Mgr)
Carol R. Looby (Sec)
Thomas E. Babcock (Vice Chm)
Pasquale T. Deon Sr. (Chm)
Robert Lund Jr. (Asst Gen Mgr-Engrg, Maintenance & Construction)

SOUTHEASTERN PETROLEUM CO., INC.

PO Box 1667, Richton, MS 39476
Tel.: (601) 788-6766
Rev.: $13,700,000
Emp.: 70
Petroleum Bulk Station & Service Station
N.A.I.C.S.: 424710
Billy Bowen (Pres)
Faye Bowen (Sec-Engrg & Fin)

SOUTHEASTERN POLE SALES, INC.

113 Industrial Park Dr, Cumming, GA 30040
Tel.: (770) 205-9007
Sales Range: $10-24.9 Million
Emp.: 8
Electrical Apparatus & Equipment Whslr
N.A.I.C.S.: 423610
David Kelvington (CEO)
Tom Dekle (CFO)
Craig Carrow (Sec)

SOUTHEASTERN PRINTING COMPANY INC.

3601 SE Dixie Hwy, Stuart, FL 34997
Tel.: (772) 287-2141
Web Site: http://www.seprint.com
Year Founded: 1924
Full Service Commercial Printing
N.A.I.C.S.: 323111
Don Mader (Owner, Pres & CEO)

Subsidiaries:

Bluewater Editions (1)
4665 SE Dixie Hwy, Port Salerno, FL 34997
Tel.: (772) 286-0484
Web Site: http://www.blueweatereditions.com
Sales Range: $10-24.9 Million
Emp.: 5
Fine Art Printing Services
N.A.I.C.S.: 541922
Jason Leonard (Gen Mgr)

SEP Communications, LLC (1)
1100 Holland Dr, Boca Raton, FL 33487
Tel.: (561) 998-0870
Digital & Sheetfed Printing Services
N.A.I.C.S.: 323111

SOUTHEASTERN PUBLIC SERVICE AUTHORITY

723 Woodlake Dr, Chesapeake, VA 23320
Tel.: (757) 420-4700
Web Site: http://www.spsa.com
Year Founded: 1985
Rev.: $84,941,249
Emp.: 155
Solid Waste Disposal Service
N.A.I.C.S.: 236210
Rowland Taylor (Exec Dir-Fin, Construction, Ops & Maintenance)
Morley Woodall (Chm)
C. W. McCoy (Vice Chm)
John Keifer (Chm)

SOUTHEASTERN REALTY GROUP INC.

933 Lee Rd Ste 400, Orlando, FL 32810-5537

Tel.: (407) 629-6660 FL
Web Site:
   http://www.southeasternrealty.com
Year Founded: 1978
Sales Range: $75-99.9 Million
Emp.: 20
Provider of Real Estate Services
N.A.I.C.S.: 531120
Al Clark (Sr VP)
Jean Roye (Controller)
Bryan Johnson (CEO)

SOUTHEASTERN SALON SUPPLIERS, INC.
627 Market St, Zanesville, OH 43701
Tel.: (740) 453-1917
Web Site: http://www.sesalon.com
Year Founded: 1980
Sales Range: $10-24.9 Million
Emp.: 47
Whslr & Distributor of Beauty Parlor Equipment & Supplies
N.A.I.C.S.: 423850
Connie Warren (Pres)
Jim Elkin (Controller)
Mike Lang (CEO)
Jay Hunt (Dir-MIS)
Sherry Smith (MIS Dir)

SOUTHEASTERN SUPPLY CO. INC.
1345 Sadlier Cir S Dr, Indianapolis, IN 46239
Tel.: (317) 359-9551 IN
Web Site:
   http://www.southeasternsupply.com
Year Founded: 1956
Sales Range: $10-24.9 Million
Emp.: 50
Building Materials Sales
N.A.I.C.S.: 423310
Vince Kenny (Pres)

SOUTHEASTERN TELECOM INC.
500 Royal Pkwy, Nashville, TN 37214-3683
Tel.: (615) 874-6000 TN
Web Site: http://www.setelecom.com
Year Founded: 1974
Sales Range: $25-49.9 Million
Emp.: 275
Telecommunications, PBX/Key Telephone Systems & Voicemail
N.A.I.C.S.: 238210
Casi McClure (Mgr-Inside Sls)
Brian Jones (CEO)
Greg Wass (Chief Admin Officer)
Rick Apple (COO)

Subsidiaries:

Southeastern Telecom (1)
817 Timber Creek Dr, Cordova, TN 38018-6357 (100%)
Tel.: (901) 332-0990
Web Site: http://www.setelecom.com
Rev.: $2,100,000
Emp.: 5
Electrical Work
N.A.I.C.S.: 238210
John W. Haley (Chm)

Southeastern Telecom of Knoxville Inc. (1)
1001 Data Lane Ste108, Knoxville, TN 37932
Tel.: (865) 584-7777
Web Site: http://www.setelecom.com
Sales Range: $10-24.9 Million
Emp.: 30
Electrical Work
N.A.I.C.S.: 238210
Rick Apple (COO)
Rich Fricke (VP-Fin)
Brian Jones (CEO)
Chris Murphy (VP-Engrg)
Greg Wass (Chief Admin Officer)

SOUTHERN AG CARRIERS, INC.
3422 Sylvester Rd, Albany, GA 31703
Tel.: (229) 434-4950 GA
Web Site: http://www.sou-ag.com
Year Founded: 1990
Sales Range: $75-99.9 Million
Emp.: 254
Provider of Trucking Services
N.A.I.C.S.: 484121
Henry H. Griffin (Pres & CEO)
Todd Griffin (VP-Ops)
Michael Jenkins (Controller)

SOUTHERN AGRICULTURAL INSECTICIDES, INC.
7600 Bayshore Rd, Palmetto, FL 34221-8363
Tel.: (941) 722-3285 FL
Web Site: http://www.southernag.com
Year Founded: 1930
Sales Range: $25-49.9 Million
Emp.: 86
Agricultural Chemicals; Agricultural & Household Pesticides
N.A.I.C.S.: 424910
William E. Diem (VP)
Linda L. Diem (Treas & Sec)
Darrin Diem (Mgr-Mktg)

Subsidiaries:

Southern Agricultural Insecticides (1)
511 Maple St, Hendersonville, NC 28792 (100%)
Tel.: (828) 692-2233
Web Site: http://www.southernag.com
Sales Range: $25-49.9 Million
Emp.: 20
Agricultural & Household Pesticides
N.A.I.C.S.: 424910

Southern Agricultural Insecticides (1)
395 Brook Hallow Dr, Boone, NC 28607-0085
Tel.: (828) 264-8843
Web Site: http://www.southernag.com
Sales Range: $25-49.9 Million
Emp.: 15
Agricultural & Household Pesticides
N.A.I.C.S.: 424910
Mike Presnell (Plant Mgr)

SOUTHERN AIR, INC.
2655 Lakeside Dr, Lynchburg, VA 24501-6944
Tel.: (434) 385-6200 VA
Web Site: http://www.southern-air.com
Year Founded: 1946
Sales Range: $75-99.9 Million
Emp.: 780
Commercial, Industrial & Institutional Plumbing, Electrical, Heating, Ventilation & Air Conditioning Contractor Services
N.A.I.C.S.: 238220
Paul Denham (Pres)
Charles T. Cardwell (VP-Svc)
Greg A. Graham (VP-Mechanical Construction)
William E. Maddox (VP-Electrical)
Lester B. Wilkinson (VP-Bus Dev)
Sierria Carvajal (Dir-Emp Dev)
Robert W. Burrill Jr. (CFO, Treas & Sec)

SOUTHERN ALUMINUM FINISHING CO. INC.
1581 Huber St NW, Atlanta, GA 30318-3781
Tel.: (404) 355-1560 GA
Web Site: http://www.saf.com
Year Founded: 1946
Sales Range: $100-124.9 Million
Emp.: 120
Aluminum Finishing Services
N.A.I.C.S.: 423510

Carol Long (Office Mgr)
Todd Hamilton (Gen Mgr-Atlanta)
Eliza Evans (Project Mgr)
Sam Heier (Gen Mgr)
Corey Faciane (Mgr-Product)
Zac Adams (Project Mgr)
Angela Krasley (Project Mgr)
Luke Lynam (Project Mgr)
Stephen Powell (Project Mgr)
Dave Merwitz (COO)
John Menghini (Exec VP-Sls & Mktg)
Allison Schultz (Pres & CEO)
John B. McClatchey Sr. (Mgr-Sls)

SOUTHERN ASSOCIATION OF COLLEGES & SCHOOLS COMMISSION ON COLLEGES
1866 Southern Ln, Decatur, GA 30033
Tel.: (404) 679-4500 GA
Web Site: http://www.sacscoc.org
Year Founded: 2008
Sales Range: $1-9.9 Million
Emp.: 62
College Association
N.A.I.C.S.: 813910
Donna Barrett (Dir-Institutional Fin)
Carol S. Hollins (Dir-Institutional Support)
Belle S. Wheelan (Pres)
Sarah Armstrong (Dir-Substantive Change)
Crystal A. Baird (VP)
Mary P. Kirk (VP)
Steven M. Sheeley (Sr VP)

SOUTHERN AUTO SALES INC.
161 S Main St, East Windsor, CT 06088
Tel.: (860) 292-7500
Web Site: http://www.saa.com
Sales Range: $125-149.9 Million
Emp.: 500
Automobile Auction
N.A.I.C.S.: 423110
Lawrence G. Tribble Jr. (Chm)

SOUTHERN AUTO TRANSPORT SERVICES, INC.
411 43rd St E, Palmetto, FL 34221
Tel.: (941) 722-3326 FL
Web Site:
   http://www.southernautotransport.com
Year Founded: 1993
Sales Range: $1-9.9 Million
Emp.: 5
Automotive Transportation Services
N.A.I.C.S.: 484230
Allen J. Morrell (VP)
Keith B. Morrell (Pres)

SOUTHERN BANCORP, INC.
601 Main St, Arkadelphia, AR 71923
Tel.: (870) 246-5811
Web Site:
   http://www.banksouthern.com
Year Founded: 1988
Sales Range: $25-49.9 Million
Emp.: 275
Bank Holding Company
N.A.I.C.S.: 551111
Andrea Parnell (Sr VP-HR)
Darrin L. Williams (CEO)
Christopher W. Wewers (CFO)
Wendy Von Kanel (Pres-Phillips)
Glendell Jones Jr. (Chm)

Subsidiaries:

Southern Bancorp Bank (1)
601 Main St, Arkadelphia, AR 71923
Tel.: (870) 246-5811
Web Site: http://www.banksouthern.com
Sales Range: $1-9.9 Million
Emp.: 38
Banking & Financial Services

N.A.I.C.S.: 522110
Sherman Tate (Chm)
John T. Olaimey (Pres & CEO)
Darryl Swinton (Dir-Housing & Economic Dev Weatherization)

SOUTHERN BELLE DAIRY CO. INC.
607 Bourne Ave, Somerset, KY 42501-1919
Tel.: (606) 679-1131 KY
Web Site:
   http://www.southernbelledairy.com
Year Founded: 1951
Sales Range: $125-149.9 Million
Emp.: 240
Producer, Sales & Distributor of Packaged Milk, Milk Products, Ice Cream Mixes & Related Products
N.A.I.C.S.: 424430
Mike Chandler (Pres)
Kevin Randolph (Plant Mgr)
Carol Robinson (Dir-Mgmt Info Sys)

SOUTHERN BEVERAGE CO. INC.
1939 Davis Johnson Dr, Richland, MS 39218-8406
Tel.: (601) 969-5550 MS
Web Site:
   http://www.southernbeverage.com
Year Founded: 1972
Rev.: $12,100,000
Emp.: 125
Beer & Ale Distr
N.A.I.C.S.: 424810
Theo P. Costas (Owner, Pres & Gen Mgr)
Sam Goad (Dir-IT)

SOUTHERN BEVERAGE PACKERS, INC.
6341 Natures Way, Appling, GA 30814-4141
Tel.: (706) 541-9222 GA
Web Site:
   http://www.southernbev.com
Year Founded: 1984
Sales Range: $10-24.9 Million
Emp.: 22
Bottled Water & Soft Drinks Mfr
N.A.I.C.S.: 312112
David M. Byrd (Pres & Plant Mgr)
Steven Byrd (Exec VP)
Cindy Slover (Dir-Acctg)
Ralph Montigny (Dir-Mfg Ops)

SOUTHERN CALIFORNIA HOUSING DEVELOPMENT CORP.
9421 Haven Ave, Rancho Cucamonga, CA 91730
Tel.: (909) 483-2444
Web Site: http://www.nationalcore.org
Sales Range: $10-24.9 Million
Emp.: 350
Subdividers & Developers
N.A.I.C.S.: 237210
Jeff Burum (Founder, Owner & Chm)

SOUTHERN CALIFORNIA MATERIAL HANDLING
12393 Slauson Ave, Whittier, CA 90606
Tel.: (562) 949-1000
Web Site: http://www.scmh.com
Rev.: $43,400,000
Emp.: 220
Materials Handling Machinery
N.A.I.C.S.: 423830
Jermaine Ratcliffe (Mgr-IT)
Tony Edgar (Mgr-Parts)
Kathryn Keck (Mgr-Acct)
Cindy Bautista (Controller)
Alfred Gallegos (Controller)
Angela Fuller (Mgr-Warehouse Sys)

SOUTHERN CALIFORNIA REGIONAL RAIL AUTHORITY

Southern California Regional Rail Authority—(Continued)

SOUTHERN CALIFORNIA REGIONAL RAIL AUTHORITY
1 Gateway Plz Fl 12, Los Angeles, CA 90012
Tel.: (213) 452-0200
Web Site: http://www.metrolinktrains.com
Year Founded: 1991
Sales Range: $150-199.9 Million
Emp.: 240
Local & Suburban Transit Services
N.A.I.C.S.: 485112
Daryl Busch *(Vice Chm)*
Janelle Strohmyer *(Dir-HR)*
Donald O. Del Rio *(Gen Counsel)*
Patricia Torres Bruno *(Chief Admin Officer)*
Andrew Kotyuk *(Chm)*
Art Leahy *(CEO)*
Elissa Konove *(Deputy CEO)*
Ronnie Campbell *(CFO)*
Kimberly Yu *(COO)*

SOUTHERN CALIFORNIA SECTION OF THE PGA OF AMERICA
3333 Concours St Bldg 2 Ste 2100, Ontario, CA 91764
Tel.: (951) 845-4653
Web Site: http://www.scpga.com
Sales Range: $10-24.9 Million
Emp.: 18
Sports Clubs, Managers & Promoters
N.A.I.C.S.: 561499
Tom Adiss *(Pres)*

SOUTHERN CALIFORNIA SOUND IMAGE, INC.
2425 Auto Park Way, Escondido, CA 92029
Tel.: (760) 737-3900   CA
Web Site: http://www.sound-image.com
Year Founded: 1971
Sales Range: $10-24.9 Million
Emp.: 45
Communications Specialization
N.A.I.C.S.: 238210
Ralph Wadner *(CFO)*
Jeff Oliver *(Dir-Pur)*
Rob Mailman *(Mgr-Touring Ops)*
Laurence Italia *(VP-Integration Div)*
Bob Delson *(Project Mgr)*
Dave Paviol *(Dir-Ops)*
Jeff Schmitz *(Dir-Engrg)*
Jerry Fleury *(Project Mgr)*
Mike Fay *(Gen Mgr-Integration)*
Mike Martin *(Sr Project Mgr)*

SOUTHERN CHAMPION CONSTRUCTION
1939 B Parker Ct, Stone Mountain, GA 30087
Tel.: (770) 736-9222
Web Site: http://www.southernchampion.com
Sales Range: $10-24.9 Million
Emp.: 50
Industrial Plant Construction
N.A.I.C.S.: 562991
Alan O'Neal *(Project Manager)*
Matt Broom *(Pres)*
Tommy Terry *(VP)*
Sheri Broom *(Treas & Sec)*
Matt Deal *(Project Manager)*

SOUTHERN CHAMPION TRAY CO. INC.
220 Compress St, Chattanooga, TN 37405
Tel.: (423) 756-5121   TN
Web Site: http://www.sctray.com
Year Founded: 1948

Sales Range: $25-49.9 Million
Emp.: 450
Mfr of Paperboard Boxes & Labels
N.A.I.C.S.: 322212
Charles M. Zeiser *(Chm)*
John Zeiser *(Pres & CEO)*
Anne Hooser *(Coord-Natl Accts & Sls)*
Jonathan Pappas *(Mgr-Safety & Quality)*

Subsidiaries:

Honeymoon Paper Products, Inc. (1)
7100 Dixie Hwy, Fairfield, OH 45014
Tel.: (513) 755-7200
Web Site: http://www.honeymoonpaper.com
Sales Range: $1-9.9 Million
Emp.: 70
Converted Paper Product Mfr
N.A.I.C.S.: 322299
Kevin Gorsuch *(VP)*

SOUTHERN CHUTE, INC.
3772 SW 30th Ave, Fort Lauderdale, FL 33312
Tel.: (954) 584-2257
Web Site: http://www.southernchute.com
Sales Range: $1-9.9 Million
Emp.: 11
Trash Chutes, Laundry Chutes & Dryer Riser Repair & Maintenance
N.A.I.C.S.: 811310
Chet Ribner *(Pres)*

SOUTHERN COAL CORPORATION
106 Lockheed Dr, Beaver, WV 25813
Tel.: (304) 252-1074
Coal Mining
N.A.I.C.S.: 212114
Steve Ball *(VP & Gen Counsel)*
Steve Sarver *(VP-Sls)*
James C. Justice II *(Pres & CEO)*
James C. Justice III *(Exec VP)*

Subsidiaries:

A&G Coal Corporation (1)
6250 Hurricane Rd, Wise, VA 24293
Tel.: (276) 328-3421
Sales Range: $25-49.9 Million
Emp.: 40
Coal Mining
N.A.I.C.S.: 212114

SOUTHERN COLOR NORTH AMERICA INC.
7 Swisher Dr, Cartersville, GA 30120
Tel.: (770) 386-4766
Web Site: http://www.southerncolor.com
Sales Range: $10-24.9 Million
Emp.: 120
Colors & Pigments Manufacturing
N.A.I.C.S.: 424950
Carlton Johnson *(Pres)*

SOUTHERN COMMUNITY NEWSPAPERS INC.
PO Box 603, Lawrenceville, GA 30046
Tel.: (770) 963-9205
Web Site: http://www.southerncommunitynewspapers.com
Sales Range: $25-49.9 Million
Emp.: 400
Newspaper Publishers
N.A.I.C.S.: 513110
Mike Gebhart *(COO & Exec VP)*
Mark Miekle *(CFO & Exec VP)*
Bob McCray *(VP-Sls & Mktg)*
Tina Pethel *(Controller)*

Subsidiaries:

Gwinnett Daily Post (1)

725 Old Norcross Rd, Lawrenceville, GA 30046
Tel.: (770) 963-9205
Web Site: http://www.gwinnettdailypost.com
Sales Range: $25-49.9 Million
Emp.: 100
Newspaper Publishers
N.A.I.C.S.: 513110
J. K. Murphy *(VP-Content)*
Todd Cline *(Editor)*
Johanna Pearse *(Gen Mgr-Sls)*
Thom Bell *(Sr VP-Circulation & Facilities)*
Jason Braverman *(Mgr-Web Ops)*
Josalyn Gibson *(Dir-HR)*
Donnie Ikpa *(Mgr-Digital Ops)*
Janet McCray *(Dir-Major Accts & Digital Sls)*
Tina Pethel *(Controller)*
Nicole Puckett *(Editor-Graphics)*

The Albany Herald Publishing Co. (1)
126 N Washington St, Albany, GA 31701-2552
Tel.: (229) 888-9300
Web Site: http://www.albanyherald.com
Rev.: $10,200,000
Emp.: 150
Daily Newspaper Publisher
N.A.I.C.S.: 513110
Danny Carter *(Mng Editor)*
Ken Boler *(Gen Mgr)*

SOUTHERN COMPONENTS, INC.
114 Old Runway Rd, Tupelo, MS 38801
Tel.: (662) 844-7884
Web Site: http://www.fibrecraft.net
Year Founded: 2000
Sales Range: $10-24.9 Million
Emp.: 55
Cellulosic Organic Fiber Mfr
N.A.I.C.S.: 325199
Robert Dexter *(Owner)*
Angel Nanney *(Office Mgr)*
Terry Medlin *(Mgr-Quality)*
Larry Duvall *(Mgr-Maintenance Svcs)*

SOUTHERN COMPUTER WAREHOUSE
1395 S Marietta Pkwy SE Bldg 300 Ste 106, Marietta, GA 30062
Tel.: (770) 579-8927
Web Site: http://www.gotoscw.com
Sales Range: $10-24.9 Million
Emp.: 16
Computers, Peripherals & Software
N.A.I.C.S.: 423430
Sam Brown *(Dir-IT)*
Valerie State *(Mgr-Sls)*
Joseph E. Gabriel III *(Pres)*

SOUTHERN CONCRETE CONSTRUCTION CO.
733 Liberty Expy, Albany, GA 31705
Tel.: (229) 434-4754
Sales Range: $50-74.9 Million
Emp.: 159
Bridge Construction
N.A.I.C.S.: 237310
Billy Willis *(CEO)*

SOUTHERN CONCRETE PRODUCTS INC.
266 E Church St E 412 Hwy, Lexington, TN 38351
Tel.: (731) 968-2537
Web Site: http://www.southernconcrete.com
Sales Range: $50-74.9 Million
Emp.: 200
Concrete Products
N.A.I.C.S.: 327331
Richard Odle *(Pres)*
Mason Peters *(Mgr-Production)*
Ross Armstrong *(Mgr-Quality Control)*
Tuffy Craig *(Gen Mgr)*

SOUTHERN CONNECTION

U.S. PRIVATE

SEAFOOD, INC.
4884 Crisfield Hwy, Crisfield, MD 21817
Tel.: (410) 968-3367
Web Site: http://www.crabsandseafood.com
Rev.: $10,000,000
Emp.: 15
Seafoods
N.A.I.C.S.: 424460
James Patrick Reese Jr. *(Pres)*

SOUTHERN CONTROLS, INC.
3511 Wetumpka Hwy, Montgomery, AL 36110-2751
Tel.: (334) 277-5030   AL
Web Site: http://www.southerncontrols.com
Year Founded: 1974
Sales Range: $10-24.9 Million
Emp.: 71
Mfr of Electrical Apparatus & Equipment
N.A.I.C.S.: 423610
Joe Davis *(Owner & CEO)*
Dan Hill *(Branch Mgr)*
David Barnes *(Mgr-Sls)*
Shannon Flores *(Controller)*
Glen Helms *(Mgr-Engrg)*
William Spear *(VP)*
Charlie Ferrall *(Engr-Application)*
David Harp *(Engr-Application)*
Scott Davis *(VP)*

SOUTHERN COUNTIES OIL CO.
1800 W Katella Ave Ste 400, Orange, CA 92867
Tel.: (714) 744-7140   CA
Web Site: http://www.scfuels.com
Year Founded: 1930
Sales Range: $10-24.9 Million
Emp.: 120
Petroleum Product Distr
N.A.I.C.S.: 424710
Frank P. Greinke *(Chm)*
Patrick W. Barnecut *(Pres-Unbranded Wholesale)*
Robert W. Bollar *(Gen Counsel)*
Steven Greinke *(CEO)*
Barbara J. Francis *(VP-HR)*
R. Clint Mercer *(Pres-Branded Wholesale)*
Ed Wondergem *(CFO)*
David Larimer *(COO)*
Derek Bettencourt *(Pres-Cardlock)*
Angus McDonald *(Pres-SC Comml)*
Ed Holloran *(Pres-Comml Svcs)*

Subsidiaries:

Canyon State Oil Company Inc. (1)
2640 N 31st Ave, Phoenix, AZ 85009
Tel.: (602) 269-7981
Web Site: http://www.canyonstateoil.com
Petroleum Distr
N.A.I.C.S.: 424720
Dave Kirby *(Dir-Ops)*

SOUTHERN CRAFTED HOMES, INC.
3840 Land O Lakes Blvd, Land O Lakes, FL 34639
Tel.: (813) 909-9644   FL
Web Site: http://www.southerncraftedhomes.com
Year Founded: 1990
Sales Range: $10-24.9 Million
Emp.: 30
New Single-Family Housing Construction
N.A.I.C.S.: 236115
Kurt Hull *(Pres)*
Jim Deitch *(COO)*

SOUTHERN CROSS AVIATION INC.

COMPANIES

SOUTHERN FOODS, INC.

1120 NW 51st Ct, Fort Lauderdale, FL 33309
Tel.: (954) 377-0320
Web Site: http://www.scross.com
Sales Range: $10-24.9 Million
Emp.: 35
Aircraft Dealers
N.A.I.C.S.: 541990
Fred Guido (Owner)

SOUTHERN CROSS CONTRACTING, INC.
389 Interstate Blvd, Sarasota, FL 34240
Tel.: (941) 927-1919 FL
Web Site:
http://www.sccsarasota.com
Year Founded: 1988
Sales Range: $1-9.9 Million
Emp.: 12
Commercial & Institutional Building Construction
N.A.I.C.S.: 236220
John M. Proctor (CEO)
Jeffrey Morgenstern (Project Mgr)

SOUTHERN DATA STORAGE, INC.
4532 W Kennedy Blvd Ste 118, Tampa, FL 33609-2539
Tel.: (813) 655-3282
Web Site: http://www.southerndatastorage.com
Sales Range: $1-9.9 Million
Data Storage Services
N.A.I.C.S.: 334112
Mark Hall (Pres)

SOUTHERN DISTRIBUTING CO. INC.
220 Guadalupe St, Laredo, TX 78040
Tel.: (956) 723-2968
Web Site:
http://www.southernlaredo.com
Sales Range: $10-24.9 Million
Emp.: 60
Beer & Other Fermented Malt Liquors
N.A.I.C.S.: 424810
Drew Claes (Controller)
Guillermo F. Trevino (Pres)

SOUTHERN DIVERSIFIED TECHNOLOGIES
130 N 2nd St, Brookhaven, MS 39601
Tel.: (601) 823-9440
Web Site: http://www.sdt-1.com
Year Founded: 1993
Sales Range: $25-49.9 Million
Emp.: 200
Electrical Contractor
N.A.I.C.S.: 238210
Kirk Smith (VP)
Charlie Smith (CEO)
R. Bruce Day (VP-Ops)
Amanda Stewart (Mgr-Real Estate)
Richard Johnson (CFO)
James Ezell (Pres)

SOUTHERN EAGLE DISTRIBUTING, INC.
5300 Glades Cutoff Rd, Fort Pierce, FL 34981
Tel.: (772) 461-8644 MO
Web Site:
http://www.southerneagledist.com
Year Founded: 1984
Sales Range: $25-49.9 Million
Beer Distr
N.A.I.C.S.: 424810
Peter W. Busch (Owner)
Philip E. Busch (Pres)
Paul Trabulsy (CFO)
Gerry Hoeffner (VP-HR)
Dane Jones (VP)
Willie Roundtree (Dir-Ops)
Brandon Smith (Dir-Delivery & Logistics)
Gerrit Topp (Dir-Delivery & Logistics)
Steve Butala (Mgr-Mechanic)

SOUTHERN EAGLE DISTRIBUTING, LLC
1600 Charleston Regional Pkwy, Charleston, SC 29492
Tel.: (843) 388-6800 GA
Web Site: http://sc.soeagle.net
Year Founded: 1907
Sales Range: $25-49.9 Million
Emp.: 150
Beer Distr
N.A.I.C.S.: 424810
William J. Dorminy Jr. (Pres)

SOUTHERN ELECTRONICS SUPPLY
1909 Tulane Ave, New Orleans, LA 70112
Tel.: (504) 524-2343
Web Site:
http://www.southernele.com
Rev.: $12,000,000
Emp.: 40
Electronic Parts
N.A.I.C.S.: 423690
Elmira Schadler Perrin (CEO)
Iggie Perrin (VP)

SOUTHERN EQUIPMENT CO. INC.
3610 Bush St, Raleigh, NC 27609-7511
Tel.: (919) 790-1520 NC
Web Site: http://www.rmcc.com
Year Founded: 1976
Sales Range: $25-49.9 Million
Emp.: 850
Provider of Concrete
N.A.I.C.S.: 327320
Pete Scavone (Mgr-Charlotte Reg)
Robert Scott (Mgr-Columbia Div)
Chris Johnson (Mgr-Eastern NC Div)
Quinn Vaughan (Mgr-Eastern NC Div)
Bruce Creech (Mgr-I-95 Corridor VA to SC Div)
Jeff Robertson (Mgr-I-95 Corridor VA to SC Div)
Duane Allen (Mgr-Pee Dee Div)
Mellisa Swanson (Mgr-Sls-Central)
Steve Alexander (Mgr-Sls-Charleston Reg)
Lyman Austin (Mgr-Sls-Raleigh & Durham)
Kenneth Combs (Mgr-Triad Reg)
Wayne Bracey (Mgr-Virginia Reg)
Joey Allen (Mgr-Wilmington Div)

SOUTHERN EQUIPMENT CORPORATION
1401 US 301 N, Tampa, FL 33619
Tel.: (813) 251-1839
Web Site: http://www.southern-eq.com
Year Founded: 1952
Sales Range: $10-24.9 Million
Emp.: 100
Warm Air Heating & Air Conditioning Contractor
N.A.I.C.S.: 238220
Bryan Berry (Pres)
Adrian Cornellier (Mgr-Fleet)
Terry Manrique (Mgr-Svcs)

SOUTHERN ERECTORS INCORPORATED
6540 W 9th Mile Rd, Pensacola, FL 32526
Tel.: (850) 944-0013
Web Site: http://www.sei-group.com
Year Founded: 1973
Sales Range: $10-24.9 Million
Emp.: 175
Structural Steel Erection
N.A.I.C.S.: 238120

SOUTHERN FARM BUREAU CASUALTY INSURANCE COMPANY
1800 E County Line Rd Ste 400, Ridgeland, MS 39158
Tel.: (601) 957-7777 MS
Web Site: http://www.sfbcic.com
Year Founded: 1947
Sales Range: $1-4.9 Billion
Emp.: 1,900
Property & Casualty Insurance
N.A.I.C.S.: 524126
Ronald Anderson (Pres)
Rod A. Moore (CEO & Exec VP)
Robert Garratt (Pres)
Dennis Griffin (Treas & VP)
Steve Ingram (Sec & VP-Legal)
Wayne Lee (VP)
David Moore (Sr VP)

Subsidiaries:

Florida Farm Bureau Casualty Insurance Company, Main Office (1)
5700 SW 34th St, Gainesville, FL 32608-5300 (100%)
Tel.: (352) 378-1321
Web Site: http://www.floridafarmbureau.com
Sales Range: $10-24.9 Million
Emp.: 250
Property & Casualty Insurance
N.A.I.C.S.: 524210
John Hoblick (Pres)
Bill Courtney (CEO & VP)

Louisiana Farm Bureau Casualty Insurance Company (1)
9516 Airline Hwy, Baton Rouge, LA 70815-5501 (100%)
Tel.: (225) 922-6200
Web Site: http://www.lafarmbureau.com
Sales Range: $50-74.9 Million
Emp.: 200
Property & Casualty Insurance
N.A.I.C.S.: 524210
Blaine Briggs (CFO & Exec VP)

Mississippi Farm Bureau Casualty Insurance Company (1)
6311 Ridgewood Rd, Jackson, MS 39211 (100%)
Tel.: (601) 957-3200
Web Site: http://www.msfbins.com
Sales Range: $25-49.9 Million
Emp.: 320
Providers of Property & Casualty Insurance
N.A.I.C.S.: 813910
Jack William (VP)

SOUTHERN FARM BUREAU LIFE INSURANCE CO. INC.
1401 Livingston Ln, Jackson, MS 39213-8004
Tel.: (601) 981-7422 MS
Web Site: http://www.sfbli.com
Year Founded: 1946
Sales Range: $100-124.9 Million
Emp.: 619
Life Insurance
N.A.I.C.S.: 524113
Billy Sims (VP-HR)
Joey Stroble (CEO & Exec VP)
Randy Veach (Chm & Pres)

SOUTHERN FASTENING SYSTEMS, INC.
635 Fairgrounds Rd, Muscle Shoals, AL 35661-3598
Tel.: (256) 381-3628 DE
Web Site:
http://www.southernfastening.com
Year Founded: 1986
Sales Range: $75-99.9 Million
Emp.: 260
Fastener System Sales
N.A.I.C.S.: 423840
Jim Whitley (Pres)

SOUTHERN FIDELITY INSURANCE CO.
2255 Killearn Center Blvd, Tallahassee, FL 32309
Tel.: (850) 521-3080
Web Site:
http://www.southernfidelityins.com
Sales Range: $100-124.9 Million
Emp.: 150
Property & Casualty Insurance Services
N.A.I.C.S.: 524126
James A. Graganella (Pres & CEO)

SOUTHERN FIDELITY MORTGAGE
4730 S Fort Apache Rd Ste 100, Las Vegas, NV 89147
Web Site:
http://www.gosouthernfidelity.com
Sales Range: $1-9.9 Million
Emp.: 70
Mortgage Services
N.A.I.C.S.: 522310
Rowe Nelson (COO)

SOUTHERN FILM EXTRUDERS INC.
2319 English Rd, High Point, NC 27262-1487
Tel.: (336) 885-8091 NC
Web Site:
http://www.southernfilm.com
Year Founded: 1965
Sales Range: $10-24.9 Million
Emp.: 145
Retail Film & Sheet Packaging Mfr
N.A.I.C.S.: 326113
Angelo Walters (Mgr-Customer Svc)

SOUTHERN FILTER MEDIA LLC
2735 Kanasita Dr, Hixson, TN 37343
Tel.: (423) 698-8988
Web Site:
http://www.southernfiltermedia.com
Sales Range: $10-24.9 Million
Emp.: 100
Mfr of Industrial General Line Filters
N.A.I.C.S.: 333998
Charles Poe (Pres & CEO)
Mark Mullins (Mgr-Inventory & Pur)

SOUTHERN FLORAL CO.
1313 W 20th St, Houston, TX 77008
Tel.: (713) 880-1300
Web Site: http://www.sofloco.com
Rev.: $22,800,000
Emp.: 70
Flowers, Fresh
N.A.I.C.S.: 424930
Robert H. Weatherford (CEO)

SOUTHERN FOOD PARK INCORPORATED
1105 E Broadway, Sparta, IL 62286
Tel.: (618) 443-4329
Rev.: $20,000,000
Emp.: 10
Convenience Store
N.A.I.C.S.: 445131
Mary Lou Boight (Controller)

SOUTHERN FOODS, INC.
402 Commerce Ct, Goldsboro, NC 27530
Tel.: (919) 778-3000 NC
Web Site: http://www.pdco.com
Year Founded: 1954
Sales Range: $200-249.9 Million
Emp.: 480
Retailer & Distr of Meat Products & Food Items
N.A.I.C.S.: 424470

SOUTHERN FOODS, INC.

Southern Foods, Inc.—(Continued)
Malcolm Sullivan (Owner)
Laurence Willard (VP-Food Svc)
Paul Amburn (Reg Mgr-Sls)
Sue James (VP-Admin)
Subsidiaries:
Southern Foods, Inc. - Home Division (1)
3500 Old Battleground Rd, Greensboro, NC 27410-2420
Tel.: (336) 545-3800
Web Site: http://www.southernfoods.com
Provider of Food Delivery Services
N.A.I.C.S.: 424470

SOUTHERN FOODSERVICE MANAGEMENT INC.
500 Office Park Dr Ste 210, Birmingham, AL 35223-2441
Tel.: (205) 871-8000   DE
Web Site: http://www.southernfoodservice.com
Year Founded: 1951
Sales Range: $50-74.9 Million
Emp.: 1,200
Foodservice Management Services
N.A.I.C.S.: 722514
Floyd C. Liles (Chm)
Laura Laird (Mgr-HR)
Walter T. Berry Jr. (Exec VP)

SOUTHERN FREIGHT INC.
99 University Ave SW, Atlanta, GA 30315
Tel.: (404) 688-0002
Web Site: http://southernfreight.com
Sales Range: $25-49.9 Million
Emp.: 300
Provider of Trucking Services
N.A.I.C.S.: 532120
Steve Robertson (Sr VP)
Larry Barker (VP)
Robert J. Fauls Jr. (Founder & Pres)

SOUTHERN FS, INC.
2002 E Maine, Marion, IL 62959
Tel.: (618) 993-2833
Web Site: http://www.southernfs.com
Sales Range: $100-124.9 Million
Emp.: 120
Farm Supplies
N.A.I.C.S.: 424510
Rolo Burnett (Pres)
Mark Eddleman (Treas)

SOUTHERN FULFILLMENT SERVICES
1650 90th Ave, Vero Beach, FL 32966
Tel.: (772) 226-3500   FL
Web Site: http://www.southernfulfillment.com
Year Founded: 1947
Sales Range: $10-24.9 Million
Emp.: 100
Catalog & Mail Order Fruit Services
N.A.I.C.S.: 445230
Don Wright (Pres)
Alex Brown (Pres)

SOUTHERN FURNITURE COMPANY OF CONOVER INC.
1099 2nd Ave Pl SE, Conover, NC 28613-2165
Tel.: (828) 464-0311   NC
Web Site: http://www.southernfurniture.net
Year Founded: 1926
Upholstered Household Furniture Mfr
N.A.I.C.S.: 337121
Jerome W. Bolick (VP)
Trent Wright (Pres)
Linda B. Bolick (Sec)

SOUTHERN GAS & FUELS INC.
9585 Hwy 78, Ladson, SC 29456
Tel.: (843) 797-2311
Rev.: $37,947,312
Emp.: 20
Diesel Fuel Supplier
N.A.I.C.S.: 424720
Michael A. Kocak (Pres)

SOUTHERN GROUT & MORTARS INC.
1502 SW 2nd Pl, Pompano Beach, FL 33069
Tel.: (954) 943-2288
Web Site: http://www.sgm.cc
Sales Range: $10-24.9 Million
Emp.: 100
Adhesives Mfr & Distr
N.A.I.C.S.: 325520
Ron Picou (Founder & CEO)

SOUTHERN HERITAGE BANK
1201 4th St, Jonesville, LA 71343
Tel.: (318) 339-8505
Web Site: http://www.shbnet.com
Year Founded: 1972
Rev.: $10,278,647
Emp.: 110
Retail & Commercial Banking
N.A.I.C.S.: 522110
Kenneth Wood (Exec VP)
Denise Holmes (Asst VP-Jackson Saint Loan Dept)
Johnny Snow (VP)
Robert Alexander (Sr VP)
Paul Funderburk (VP)
Tom Watkins (Sr VP)
Steve Ledbetter (Pres & COO)

SOUTHERN HIGHLANDS COMMUNITY MENTAL HEALTH CENTER
200 12th St Ext, Princeton, WV 24740
Tel.: (304) 425-9541   WV
Web Site: http://www.shcmhc.com
Year Founded: 1950
Sales Range: $10-24.9 Million
Emp.: 473
Behavioral Healthcare Services
N.A.I.C.S.: 623220
Judy L. Akers (CEO)

SOUTHERN HOBBY SUPPLY INC.
211 Ellery Ct, Nashville, TN 37214
Tel.: (615) 366-5858
Web Site: http://www.southernhobby.com
Sales Range: $10-24.9 Million
Emp.: 20
Toys & Hobby Goods & Supplies
N.A.I.C.S.: 423920
James Austin (Pres)
Chris Austin (VP)

SOUTHERN HOME & RANCH CENTER
1110 N Park St, Carrollton, GA 30117
Tel.: (770) 832-0114
Web Site: http://www.southernhomeandranch.com
Sales Range: $10-24.9 Million
Emp.: 50
Retailer of Lumber & Other Building Materials
N.A.I.C.S.: 423310
Frank Cuda (Gen Mgr)

SOUTHERN HOSPITALITY AUTO GROUP OF VIRGINIA
1414 S Military Hwy, Chesapeake, VA 23320

Tel.: (757) 424-4600
Web Site: http://www.drivingsouthern.com
Holding Company; New & Used Car Dealerships Owner & Operator
N.A.I.C.S.: 551112
Doug Keffer (Mgr-Sls)
John Twohig (Mgr-Inventory & Sys)
Tom Johnson (Dir-IT)
William R. Shepherd Jr. (Pres)
Subsidiaries:
Greenbrier Chrysler-Jeep (1)
1414 S Military Hwy, Chesapeake, VA 23320
Tel.: (757) 424-4600
Web Site: http://www.drivingsouthern.com
Sales Range: $25-49.9 Million
Emp.: 150
New & Used Car Dealer
N.A.I.C.S.: 441110
Mike King (CFO)
Jimmy Moore (Exec VP)
William R. Shepherd Jr. (Pres)

SOUTHERN ILLINOIS HEALTHCARE FOUNDATION
2041 Goose Lake Rd, Sauget, IL 62206
Tel.: (618) 332-0694   IL
Web Site: http://www.sihf.org
Year Founded: 1985
Sales Range: $50-74.9 Million
Emp.: 600
Health Care Srvices
N.A.I.C.S.: 622110
Larry McCulley (Pres & CEO)
Leslie O'Connor (Dir-Fin)
Lucy Smith (Sec)
Vicky Eden (Asst Sec)
Richard Sinclair (Treas)
Willie B. Nelson (Chm)
Ethel Manager (Vice Chm)
Sara Duguay (Dir-Provider Rels)
Joe Jansen (VP)
Patrice Howard (VP-Admin)

SOUTHERN ILLINOIS POWER COOP
11543 Lk of Egypt Rd, Marion, IL 62959
Tel.: (618) 964-1448
Web Site: http://www.sipower.org
Sales Range: $50-74.9 Million
Emp.: 100
Generation, Electric Power
N.A.I.C.S.: 221118
Stefanie Oxford (CFO)
John Rembold (Supvr-Sys)
Robert Conn (Mgr-Asset)
Jeffrey Jones (Engr-Electrical)
Ashley McCuan (Mgr-Sys)
Don Gulley (Pres)
Alvis Lanton (Coord-Compliance & Trng)
Bill Hutchison (VP)

SOUTHERN IMPERIAL INC.
1400 Eddy Ave, Rockford, IL 61103
Tel.: (815) 877-7041
Web Site: http://www.southernimperial.com
Sales Range: $10-24.9 Million
Emp.: 175
Screw Eyes & Hooks
N.A.I.C.S.: 332722
Nate Adrian (Project Mgr)
Dale Carroll (Dir-Ops)
Steven Vandemore (Pres & CEO)
Dennis Kahous (Coord-EDI & PC Tech)

SOUTHERN INSURANCE UNDERWRITERS INC.
4500 Mansell Rd, Alpharetta, GA 30022
Tel.: (678) 498-4500   GA

U.S. PRIVATE

Web Site: http://www.siuins.com
Year Founded: 1964
Sales Range: $50-74.9 Million
Emp.: 140
Provider of Insurance Services
N.A.I.C.S.: 524210
Hugh T. Nelson (Sr VP-Alternative Insurance Svcs)
Rick Sheppard (VP-Admin)
Lee Cox (VP & Mgr-Acctg)
John M. Schoerner (Mgr-Pro Lines Practice)
Dene Schoerner (Chief Underwriting Officer)
Wesley C. Duesenberg Jr. (CEO)
John W. Lamay Jr. (CFO & Pres-SIUPREM, Inc.)
Wesley C. Duesenberg III (Pres)

SOUTHERN IONICS, INC.
201 Commerce St, West Point, MS 39773
Tel.: (662) 494-3055
Web Site: http://www.southernionics.com
Year Founded: 1980
Sales Range: $25-49.9 Million
Emp.: 245
Mfr of Specialty & Intermediate Inorganic Chemicals
N.A.I.C.S.: 325180
Steve Mitchener (VP)
Kristy Todd (Mgr-Corp Admin)
Deena McIntyre (Controller)
Milton O. Sundbeck Jr. (Pres)

SOUTHERN JET INC.
6301 Porter Rd Ste 5, Sarasota, FL 34240
Tel.: (954) 495-7101
Web Site: http://www.southernjet.com
Sales Range: $1-9.9 Million
Emp.: 9
Chartered Passenger Air Transportation
N.A.I.C.S.: 481211
Steve White (Pres)
Thomas Hood (Mng Partner & Dir-Ops)
Jerod Davis (CEO)
Eric Sanchez (Dir-Sls)

SOUTHERN LEATHER COMPANY
677 Phelan Ave, Memphis, TN 38126-4005
Tel.: (901) 774-0400   TN
Web Site: http://www.southernleatherco
Year Founded: 1912
Sales Range: $10-24.9 Million
Emp.: 25
Shoe Repair Supplies Sales
N.A.I.C.S.: 458210
L. S. Cardosi (VP-Ops)
Harry Loewenberg (Pres)

SOUTHERN LITHOPLATE INC.
105 Jeffrey Way, Youngsville, NC 27596
Tel.: (919) 556-9400
Web Site: http://www.slp.com
Rev.: $27,600,000
Emp.: 130
Lithographic Plates
N.A.I.C.S.: 323120
Edward A. Casson (Chm & CEO)
Steve Mattingly (Sr VP-Sls & Mktg)

SOUTHERN LOCK & SUPPLY CO.
10910 Endeavor Way, Largo, FL 33777
Tel.: (727) 541-5536
Web Site: http://www.southernlock.com
Sales Range: $10-24.9 Million

Emp.: 45
Locksmith Equipment & Supplies
N.A.I.C.S.: 423850
Pete Auseklis (VP)

SOUTHERN LUMBER & MILLWORK CORP.
2031 King St Ext, Charleston, SC 29405-9419
Tel.: (843) 744-6281 SC
Web Site: http://www.southernlumbermillwork.com
Year Founded: 1940
Sales Range: $10-24.9 Million
Emp.: 60
Wholesale & Retail Lumber, Custom Made Doors & Windows; Custom Millwork Building Materials
N.A.I.C.S.: 444110
Joyce A. Shuler (CEO-Fin Ops)
Randall Benderson (Mgr-Production Div)
David Baldauf (Owner)
Rex Burgher (CEO-Mfg Ops)

SOUTHERN MAINE HEALTH CARE
1 Medical Center Dr, Biddeford, ME 04005
Tel.: (207) 283-7000 ME
Web Site: http://www.smhc.org
Year Founded: 1899
Sales Range: $200-249.9 Million
Emp.: 2,601
Health Care Srvices
N.A.I.C.S.: 622110
Bernard Gaines (Chm)
Merilee Perkins (Sec)
Michael Albaum (Chief Medical Officer & Sr VP)
George Hissong Jr. (Vice Chm)

SOUTHERN MANAGEMENT CORPORATION
324 SW 16th St, Belle Glade, FL 33430-2824
Tel.: (561) 996-6581 FL
Year Founded: 1977
Sales Range: $25-49.9 Million
Emp.: 650
Restaurant Operators
N.A.I.C.S.: 722513
Juvenal Vlanco (District Mgr)

SOUTHERN MANUFACTURING TECHNOLOGIES, INC.
5910 Johns Rd, Tampa, FL 33634
Tel.: (813) 888-8151 FL
Web Site: http://www.smt-tampa.com
Year Founded: 1983
Sales Range: $10-24.9 Million
Emp.: 110
Machine Shops
N.A.I.C.S.: 332710
Roy Sweatman (Pres)
Dale Lynn (Plant Mgr)
Bill Schuler (Mgr-Quality & Environment)
Glenn Lagrange (Mgr-Pur)
Al Card (Mgr-Continuous Improvement)
John Mills (Mgr-Sls)

SOUTHERN MARKETING AFFILIATES, INC.
2623 Commerce Dr, Jonesboro, AR 72401
Tel.: (870) 935-3291 AR
Web Site: http://www.smalink.com
Year Founded: 1964
Sales Range: $10-24.9 Million
Emp.: 31
Farm Equipment Parts & Supplies Distr
N.A.I.C.S.: 423820
Rodger Hurt (Pres)
Jane Mote (CFO & Controller)
William B. Hurt Jr. (Chm)

Subsidiaries:

Southern Marketing Affiliates of the Southwest, Inc. (1)
4000 E State Hwy 31, Corsicana, TX 75109
Tel.: (903) 874-4840
Web Site: http://www.smalink.com
Sales Range: $10-24.9 Million
Emp.: 20
Farm Equipment Parts & Supplies Distr
N.A.I.C.S.: 423820
Rodger Hurt Jr. (Pres)

SOUTHERN MARYLAND ELECTRIC COOPERATIVE INC.
15035 Burnt Store Rd, Hughesville, MD 20637
Tel.: (301) 274-3111 MD
Web Site: http://www.smeco.coop
Year Founded: 1937
Sales Range: $75-99.9 Million
Emp.: 440
Electronic Services
N.A.I.C.S.: 221121
Austin Joseph Slater Jr. (Pres & CEO)
Kenneth M. Capps (COO & Sr VP-Engrg & Ops)
Mark A. MacDougall (Gen Counsel & Sr VP-External Affairs)
Joseph Trentacosta (CIO & Sr VP-Info & Customer Svcs)
Kenneth L. Dyson (Treas & Sec)
Sonja M. Cox (CFO & Sr VP-Fin, Economic & Employee Svcs)
Joseph V. Stone Jr. (Chm)

SOUTHERN MARYLAND TRI-COUNTY COMMUNITY ACTION COMMITTEE, INC.
8377 Old Leonardtown Rd, Hughesville, MD 20637
Tel.: (301) 475-5574 MD
Web Site: http://www.smtccac.org
Year Founded: 1965
Sales Range: $1-9.9 Million
Emp.: 173
Community Action Services
N.A.I.C.S.: 624190
Swynice Hawkins (Co-Pres)
Anita Bratcher-Butler (Sec)
Michael E. Young (Co-Pres)
Ernest E. Dow (Chm)
Rush Cox Jr. (CFO)

SOUTHERN MATERIALS COMPANY
3358 E Division St, Springfield, MO 65802
Tel.: (417) 865-2822 MO
Web Site: http://www.southernmaterials.com
Year Founded: 1948
Sales Range: $10-24.9 Million
Emp.: 13
Plumbing Supplies Distr
N.A.I.C.S.: 423720
Bill Squires (Sec & Office Mgr)
Steve Squires (Pres)

Subsidiaries:

SMC Electric Supply (1)
509 Washington Ave, Springfield, MO 65801
Tel.: (417) 865-2825
Web Site: http://www.smcelectric.com
Sales Range: $10-24.9 Million
Emp.: 45
Electrical Hardware Supplier
N.A.I.C.S.: 423610
John Squires (Pres)

SOUTHERN MEDICAL HEALTH SYSTEMS INC.
3719 Dauphin St, Mobile, AL 36608-1246
Tel.: (251) 344-9630 DE
Web Site: http://www.springhillmedicalcenter.com
Year Founded: 1986
Sales Range: $75-99.9 Million
Emp.: 1,400
Management of Health Care Services
N.A.I.C.S.: 541611
Celia A. Wallace (Owner & CEO)

Subsidiaries:

Springhill Health Services Inc. (1)
3632 Dauphin St, Mobile, AL 36608-1247
Tel.: (251) 460-5280
Sales Range: $10-24.9 Million
Emp.: 25
Management of Health Services
N.A.I.C.S.: 561110
Theresa Hilton (Office Mgr)

Springhill Hospitals, Inc. (1)
3719 Dauphin St, Mobile, AL 36608 (100%)
Tel.: (251) 344-9630
Web Site: http://www.springhillmedicalcenter.com
Emp.: 2,000
General Medical & Surgical Hospitals
N.A.I.C.S.: 622110
Julio Garcia (Dir-Center)
Jeff St Clair (Pres & CEO)

Springhill Medical Complex Inc. (1)
3719 Dauphin St, Mobile, AL 36608-1753
Tel.: (251) 460-5220
Web Site: http://www.springhillmedical.com
Sales Range: $25-49.9 Million
Emp.: 850
Management of Health Services
N.A.I.C.S.: 541611
Jeff St. Clair (Pres)

SOUTHERN METALS CO INC.
111 N Raleigh Ave, Sheffield, AL 35660
Tel.: (256) 383-3261
Rev.: $10,700,000
Emp.: 125
Aluminum Extruded Product Mfr
N.A.I.C.S.: 331318
M.D. Bedford (VP)
J.D. Dill (Pres)
Elton H. Darby (Treas & Sec)

SOUTHERN MINNESOTA BEET SUGAR COOPERATIVE
83550 County Rd 21 PO Box 500, Renville, MN 56284
Tel.: (320) 329-8305 MN
Web Site: http://www.smbsc.com
Year Founded: 1972
Sales Range: $200-249.9 Million
Emp.: 320
Beet Sugar, Pulp & Molasses Mfr
N.A.I.C.S.: 311313
Ron Bailey (Controller)
Paul Sorenson (Dir-Info Sys)
Thomas McDonnell (Engr-Software)
Carol Maurice (Mgr-HR)
Kevin Zimmer (Dir-Pur)
Brandy Fischer (Dir-Safety)
Steve Domm (CEO)

Subsidiaries:

Holly Seed, LLC. (1)
1967 W 5th St, Sheridan, WY 82801
Tel.: (307) 672-8997
Web Site: http://www.hollyseed.com
Sugar Beet Mfr
N.A.I.C.S.: 111971
Mark Law (Gen Mgr-Seed Ops)

Midwest Agri-Commodities (1)
999 5th Ave Ste 500, San Rafael, CA 94901
Tel.: (415) 259-2720
Web Site: http://www.mwagri.com
Sales Range: $250-299.9 Million
Emp.: 60
Sugar Beet Pulp, Molasses & Raffinates Whslr
N.A.I.C.S.: 424490
Jim Eichenberger (Pres)
Tim Klovstad (Mgr-Natl Sls)
Roger Roslund (Mgr-Sls)
Kevin Christensen (VP-Fin)

Spreckels Sugar Company, Inc. (1)
395 W Keystone Rd, Brawley, CA 92227
Tel.: (760) 344-3110
Web Site: http://www.spreckelssugar.com
Beet Sugar Mfr
N.A.I.C.S.: 311313

SOUTHERN MISSOURI CONTAINER PACKAGING GROUP
900 N Belcrest Ave, Springfield, MO 65802-2513
Tel.: (417) 831-2685 MO
Web Site: http://www.smcpackaging.com
Year Founded: 1972
Sales Range: $100-124.9 Million
Emp.: 300
Mfr of Corrugated Boxes
N.A.I.C.S.: 322211
Mark McNay (Sr VP & Gen Mgr)
Tom VanHooser (Sr VP & Gen Mgr)
Pat Myers (Mgr-Customer Svc)
David Dodge (Mgr-Pkg Sys)
Jeff Woods (Mgr-Sls)
Brad Tabor (Gen Mgr)
Gary Robinson (Mgr-Sls)
Vern Bennett (Gen Mgr)

Subsidiaries:

Arrowhead Containers Inc. (1)
4330 Clary Blvd, Kansas City, MO 64130-2329 (100%)
Tel.: (816) 861-8050
Web Site: http://www.smcpackaging.com
Sales Range: $10-24.9 Million
Emp.: 60
Custom & Stock Corrugated Box Mfr
N.A.I.C.S.: 322211
Vern Bennett (VP & Gen Mgr)
Debbie Uehling (Mgr-Customer Svc)
Ross Ausburn (Founder)
Kevin Ausburn (Chm & CEO)
Donna Johnson (Mgr-HR)
Mark McNay (Sr VP & Gen Mgr)
Pat Myers (Mgr-Customer Svc)
Bryan Vote (Mgr-Accts-Natl)
Chris White (Mgr-Production)

Sooner Packaging, Inc. (1)
4477 S 70thE Ave Bldg 3 Ste A, Tulsa, OK 74145
Tel.: (918) 621-4300
Web Site: http://www.fmcpackaging.com
Packaging Products Mfr
N.A.I.C.S.: 322212
Gary Robinson (Mgr-Sls)

Wonder State Box Co. (1)
584 Commerce Rd, Conway, AR 72032 (100%)
Tel.: (501) 327-8777
Sales Range: $10-24.9 Million
Emp.: 50
Corrugated Boxes
N.A.I.C.S.: 322211
Brad Tabor (Gen Mgr)

SOUTHERN MOTOR CARRIERS ASSOCIATION, INC.
500 Westpark Dr, Peachtree City, GA 30269
Tel.: (770) 486-5800 GA
Web Site: http://www.smc3.com
Year Founded: 1935
Sales Range: $10-24.9 Million
Emp.: 105
Motorcoach Association
N.A.I.C.S.: 813920
Danny B. Slaton (Exec VP-Bus & Product Dev)
Andrew Flusher (CEO)

SOUTHERN MOTORS HONDA

SOUTHERN MOTORS HONDA

Southern Motors Honda—(Continued)
10300 Abercorn St, Savannah, GA 31406
Tel.: (912) 927-0700
Web Site:
  http://www.southernmotorshonda.net
Sales Range: $10-24.9 Million
Emp.: 80
Car Dealership
N.A.I.C.S.: 441110
Danny Kaminsky (Co-Owner)
Myron Kaminsky (Co-Owner)
Ross Kaminsky (Co-Owner & Gen Mgr)
Brad Strauss (Mgr-Sls)
Angela Henderson (Mgr-Parts)
Ron Barnes (Mgr-Sls & Compliance)
Kerri Balser (Dir-Bus Dev)
Kevin Rutland (Mgr-Bus)
Jenna Booth (Mgr-Sls)
Amanda Arkwood (Mgr-Svc-Columbus)
Billie Kersey (Mgr-Svc-Columbus)
Daniel Newman (Mgr-Svc-Columbus)
Darryl Smith (Mgr-Svc-Columbus)
Keith Coner (Mgr-Svc)
Ruark Brown (Comptroller)

SOUTHERN MULTIFOODS INC.

101 E Cherokee St, Jacksonville, TX 75766
Tel.: (903) 586-1524
Web Site: http://www.smi-tex.com
Sales Range: $25-49.9 Million
Emp.: 1,600
Mexican Restaurant
N.A.I.C.S.: 722511
Larry K. Durrett (Pres)
Robert Cudd (CFO)
Shoundra Walter (Dir-Corp Acctg)

SOUTHERN NATIONAL BANKS, INC.

29 N Eglin Pkwy, Fort Walton Beach, FL 32548
Tel.: (850) 796-2000 FL
Web Site: http://www.fnbt.com
Year Founded: 1997
Sales Range: $10-24.9 Million
Emp.: 103
Bank Holding Company
N.A.I.C.S.: 551111
John J. Tringas (Chm & CEO)

Subsidiaries:

FNBT Bank (1)
29 N Eglin Pkwy, Fort Walton Beach, FL 32548
Tel.: (850) 796-2000
Web Site: http://www.fnbt.com
Assets: $377,000,000
Emp.: 77
Commercial Banking & Lending Services
N.A.I.C.S.: 522110
John J. Tringas (Chm & CEO)
French Brown (Sr VP-Comml Lending)
Tracy Hodgins-Lott (Exec VP-Bank & Branch Ops)
Joanie Dudas (VP-Deposit Ops)
James Tucker (CIO)
Joanne Wallace (Exec VP-HR)
Skip Rainer (Sr VP-Comml Lending)
J. Larry Beasley Sr. (Vice Chm, Pres & COO)

SOUTHERN NEVADA CONSERVANCY

6755 W Charleston Blvd Ste D, Las Vegas, NV 89146
Tel.: (702) 258-7757 NV
Year Founded: 1988
Rev.: $127,656
Assets: $477,985
Liabilities: $43,055
Net Worth: $434,930
Earnings: $127,656
Emp.: 23
Fiscal Year-end: 09/30/14
Environmental Conservation Services
N.A.I.C.S.: 813312
Helen Barrett (CFO)
Blaine Benedict (Exec Dir)
Helen Mortenson (Sec)
John Mowbray (VP)
Lewis Wallenmeyer (Treas)
Steve Stallworth (VP)

SOUTHERN NEVADA HARLEY-DAVIDSON SALES, INC.

5191 S Las Vegas Blvd, Las Vegas, NV 89119
Tel.: (702) 431-8500
Web Site: http://www.lvhd.com
Sales Range: $25-49.9 Million
Emp.: 250
Motorcycle Dealers
N.A.I.C.S.: 441227
Don Andress (Pres)
Tim Cashman (Owner)

SOUTHERN NEWSPAPERS INC.

5701 Woodway Dr Ste 131, Houston, TX 77057-1589
Tel.: (713) 266-5481
Web Site: http://www.sninews.com
Rev.: $28,800,000
Emp.: 25
Newspapers, Publishing & Printing
N.A.I.C.S.: 513110
Ruby Barrow (Treas & Dir-Acctg)
Jason Keever (VP)
Jackie Zimmerman (Publr-The Lufkin Daily News)
Leonard Woolsey (Pres)

SOUTHERN OAK INSURANCE COMPANY

1300 Sawgrass Corp Pkwy Ste 300, Sunrise, FL 33323
Tel.: (904) 353-4000 FL
Web Site:
  http://www.southernoakins.com
Year Founded: 2004
Property & Casualty Insurance Services
N.A.I.C.S.: 524126
Tony A. Loughman (Pres & CEO)
Daniel M. Kutzer (CFO)
Kimberly A. Chaney (VP-Underwriting)
Ronald E. Natherson Jr. (COO)

SOUTHERN OIL CO. INC.

501 Main St, Hattiesburg, MS 39401
Tel.: (601) 582-5455 MS
Year Founded: 1983
Sales Range: $10-24.9 Million
Emp.: 100
Producer of Petroleum Products
N.A.I.C.S.: 445110
Mitchell Morris (Pres)

SOUTHERN OIL COMPANY INC.

1500 Holland Rd, Suffolk, VA 23434
Tel.: (757) 539-2374
Sales Range: $10-24.9 Million
Emp.: 35
Convenience Store
N.A.I.C.S.: 445131
David L. Holland (Pres)

SOUTHERN OREGON SANITATION INC.

1381 Redwood Ave, Grants Pass, OR 97527
Tel.: (541) 479-5335
Web Site:
  http://www.sosanitation.com
Year Founded: 1946
Sales Range: $1-9.9 Million
Waste Management Services
N.A.I.C.S.: 562998
Patrick D. Fahey (Coord-Governmental Affairs)
Karin Callahan (Controller)

SOUTHERN PAN SERVICES COMPANY

2385 Lithonia Indus, Lithonia, GA 30058
Tel.: (678) 301-2400
Web Site:
  http://www.southernpan.com
Sales Range: $50-74.9 Million
Emp.: 30
Concrete Work
N.A.I.C.S.: 238110
David Tamplin (Project Mgr)
Eswar Burra (Mgr-Engrg-PE)
Jim Kelly (VP)
Patrick Marchman (Dir-Safety)

Subsidiaries:

MST & Associates Inc. (1)
PO Box 82757, Conyers, GA 30013
Tel.: (678) 750-0880
Rev.: $2,900,000
Emp.: 17
Floor Washing & Polishing Machines, Commercial
N.A.I.C.S.: 333310

SOUTHERN PEANUT CO. INC.

Hwy 87, Dublin, NC 28332
Tel.: (910) 862-2136
Web Site:
  http://www.southernpeanutcompany.com
Year Founded: 1946
Sales Range: $10-24.9 Million
Emp.: 15
Peanut Shelling Mill Operations
N.A.I.C.S.: 424590

SOUTHERN PINE ELECTRIC CO-OPERATIVE INC.

2134 S Blvd, Brewton, AL 36426-7164
Tel.: (251) 867-5415 ALT
Web Site:
  http://www.southernpine.org
Year Founded: 1938
Sales Range: $25-49.9 Million
Emp.: 100
Electronic Services
N.A.I.C.S.: 221122
Vince Johnson (CEO & Gen Mgr-Economic Dev & Key Acct)
Jason Jackson (Office Mgr)
Raymond Wiggins (Mgr-Safety & Environmental)
Dwight Maloy (Vice Chm)
Aaron White (Treas & Sec)

SOUTHERN PIPE & SUPPLY CO., INC.

4330 Hwy 39 N, Meridian, MS 39301
Tel.: (8-5) 3-5178 DE
Web Site:
  http://www.southernpipe.com
Year Founded: 1938
Sales Range: $125-149.9 Million
Emp.: 680
Plumbing & Heating Supplies Whslr & Distr
N.A.I.C.S.: 423720
Ernie Cottrill (Mgr-Compliane Lease & Risk)
Ron Black (Dir-HR)
Jay Davidson (Pres)
Marc Ransier (CFO)
Josh Cottrill (System Administrator)

Subsidiaries:

Steinhouse Supply Co Inc (1)
24 Andrew T Whittemore St, Nashville, TN 37210
Tel.: (615) 254-1612
Rev.: $4,300,000
Emp.: 25
Plumbing & Heating Equipment & Supplies, Hydronics, Merchant Whslr
N.A.I.C.S.: 423720

SOUTHERN PIPE, INC.

135 Random Dr, New London, NC 28127
Tel.: (704) 463-5202
Web Site: http://www.southern-pipe.com
Year Founded: 1998
Sales Range: $10-24.9 Million
Emp.: 80
Plastics Pipe & Pipe Fitting Mfr
N.A.I.C.S.: 326122
Bryan Mitchell (Pres & CEO)
Kevin Mitchell (Mgr-Natl Sls)
Patricia J. Mitchell (Owner)

SOUTHERN PIPING COMPANY

1908 Baldree Rd, Wilson, NC 27893
Tel.: (252) 291-1561
Web Site:
  http://www.southernpiping.com
Year Founded: 1965
Sales Range: $10-24.9 Million
Emp.: 120
Mechanical Contractor
N.A.I.C.S.: 238220
Chris Williford (Pres)
Stout Sharber (VP & Mgr-Raleigh)
Larry Bissette (CFO & Exec VP)
Arthur Crocker (Mgr-Wilmington)
Estie McCullough (VP-HR & Client Rels)

SOUTHERN POWER & CONTROLS CORP.

8918 Sabal Industrial Blvd, Tampa, FL 33619
Tel.: (813) 620-2700 FL
Web Site:
  http://www.southernpower.net
Year Founded: 1994
Sales Range: $10-24.9 Million
Emp.: 85
Electrical Contractor
N.A.I.C.S.: 238210
William Barry (Founder & CEO)
Andy Nechtem (Dir-Ops)
Renee Barry (Controller)

SOUTHERN PRESTIGE INDUSTRIES, INC.

113 Hatfield Rd, Statesville, NC 28625
Tel.: (704) 872-9524
Web Site:
  http://www.southernprestige.com
Year Founded: 1979
Sales Range: $1-9.9 Million
Emp.: 74
Machine Shop Operator
N.A.I.C.S.: 332710
Cynthia Kress (Dir-HR)
Cordia L. Wilson (VP)

SOUTHERN PRODUCE DISTRIBUTORS, INC.

111 W Center St N, Faison, NC 28341
Tel.: (910) 267-0011
Web Site: http://www.southern-produce.com
Year Founded: 1942
Sales Range: $75-99.9 Million
Emp.: 100
Seed Potato Production Services
N.A.I.C.S.: 111211
Stewart Precythe (Pres & CEO)
Brenda Oglesby (Mgr-Sls & Mktg)

SOUTHERN PUBLIC POWER DISTRICT

4550 W Husker Hwy, Grand Island, NE 68803
Tel.: (308) 384-2350
Web Site: http://www.southernpd.com
Sales Range: $25-49.9 Million
Emp.: 91
Electronic Services
N.A.I.C.S.: 221118
Neal Niedfeldt *(Pres & CEO)*
Craig Paro *(Mgr-Info Sys)*
Scott Welk *(Mgr-Customer Svcs)*
Brad Kool *(Mgr-Fin)*

SOUTHERN REFRIGERATION CORP.
3140 Shenandoah Ave NW, Roanoke, VA 24017-4938
Tel.: (540) 342-3493
Web Site:
http://www.southernrefcorp.com
Sales Range: $10-24.9 Million
Emp.: 50
Warm Air Heating Equipment & Supplies
N.A.I.C.S.: 423730
Richard Bell *(Product Mgr-TSA)*
Tracy Moore *(Product Mgr-TSA)*
Tommy Ross *(VP-Sls)*
Johnny Eanes *(Product Mgr)*

SOUTHERN RESIDENTIAL INSTALLATIONS LLC
704 McKnight Industrial Blvd, Augusta, GA 30907
Tel.: (706) 868-8118
Web Site:
http://southernresidentialinstallations.com
Residential Housing Interior Design & Installation Services
N.A.I.C.S.: 236118
Jeff Casswell *(CFO & Partner)*
Subsidiaries:
SRI-Cutter's Insulation Inc. (1)
618 Greenwood Rd W, Columbia, SC 29210
Tel.: (803) 791-0055
Web Site: http://www.cuttersinsulation.com
Residential Remodeler
N.A.I.C.S.: 236118
S. Craig Cutter *(Dir-Sls & Mktg)*

SOUTHERN REWINDING & SALES
5277 Chumar Dr, Fortson, GA 31904
Tel.: (706) 317-5545
Web Site:
http://www.southernrewinding.com
Year Founded: 1986
Sales Range: $1-9.9 Million
Emp.: 50
Electric Equipment & Wiring Merchant Whslr
N.A.I.C.S.: 238210
Michael Phillips *(Sr VP & Sls Mgr)*
Wayne Eunice *(Mgr-Inside Sls)*

SOUTHERN SECURITIES LTD.
3200 Northline Ave Ste 140, Greensboro, NC 27408
Tel.: (336) 292-7641
Rev.: $10,000,000
Emp.: 3
Printing Paper
N.A.I.C.S.: 424110
Robert Worth *(Pres)*

SOUTHERN SHELL FISH CO. INC.
501 Destrehan Ave, Harvey, LA 70058-2737
Tel.: (504) 341-5631
Year Founded: 1988
Sales Range: $1-9.9 Million
Emp.: 8
Shrimp, Oysters & Crabmeat Preparer
N.A.I.C.S.: 311710

SOUTHERN SIDING COMPANY INC.
11636 Industriplex Blvd, Baton Rouge, LA 70809
Tel.: (225) 924-6666
Rev.: $12,400,000
Emp.: 50
Siding Contractors
N.A.I.C.S.: 238170
Tanweer Bhatti *(Pres)*

SOUTHERN STAFFING INC.
712 W Taylor St, Griffin, GA 30223
Tel.: (770) 227-9103
Web Site:
http://www.expresspros.com
Rev.: $15,000,000
Emp.: 4
Employment Agencies
N.A.I.C.S.: 561311
Don A. King *(Owner)*

SOUTHERN STAIRCASE INCORPORATED
6025 Shiloh Rd Ste E, Alpharetta, GA 30005
Tel.: (770) 888-7333
Web Site:
http://www.southernstaircase.com
Sales Range: $25-49.9 Million
Emp.: 100
Millwork
N.A.I.C.S.: 321918
Randy Scott *(Pres)*
Don Wagner *(VP-Natl Sls)*
Mike Hanagriff *(Mgr-Ops)*

SOUTHERN STANDARD CARTONS, INC.
2415 Plantside Dr, Louisville, KY 40299
Tel.: (502) 491-2760
Web Site:
http://www.thestandardgroup.com
Year Founded: 1965
Sales Range: $10-24.9 Million
Emp.: 130
Folding Paperboard Boxes & Printing Cartons
N.A.I.C.S.: 322212
Steven Levkoff *(Founder)*

SOUTHERN STATES BDM, LLC
2511 Wake Forest Rd, Raleigh, NC 27609
Tel.: (919) 839-7481 NC
Web Site:
http://www.southernstate.com
Sales Range: $100-124.9 Million
Emp.: 185
New & Used Auto Sales
N.A.I.C.S.: 441110
Jeff Dunn *(Pres)*

SOUTHERN STATES COOPERATIVE, INC.
6606 W Broad St, Richmond, VA 23230-1717
Tel.: (804) 281-1000 VA
Web Site:
http://www.southernstates.com
Year Founded: 1923
Sales Range: $1-4.9 Billion
Emp.: 3,959
Wholesale & Retail Feed, Pet Food, Fertilizer, Seed, Petroleum, Farm, Home & Garden Supplies; Livestock, Grain, Cotton & Peanut Marketing
N.A.I.C.S.: 311119
Curry Roberts *(Chm)*

SOUTHERN STATES MARKETING INC.
5304 Estate Ln, Plano, TX 75094
Tel.: (214) 432-0309 TX
Web Site: http://www.ssminc.com
Year Founded: 1999
Sales Range: $75-99.9 Million
Emp.: 9
Electronic Component Parts
N.A.I.C.S.: 423690
Joseph Morgan *(Pres)*
Chip Morgan *(Mgr-Mktg & Sls)*

SOUTHERN STRIPING SOLUTIONS, LLC
6089 Janes Ln, Naples, FL 34109
Tel.: (239) 591-5902
Web Site:
http://www.southfloridamilling.com
Year Founded: 2009
Sales Range: $10-24.9 Million
Emp.: 116
Construction Services
N.A.I.C.S.: 237310
David Teets *(CFO)*

SOUTHERN SYSTEMS, INC.
4101 Viscount Ave, Memphis, TN 38118
Tel.: (901) 362-7340
Web Site:
http://www.ssiconveyors.com
Year Founded: 1968
Sales Range: $25-49.9 Million
Custom Conveyor Systems, Electrical Controls & Automation Equipment Mfr
N.A.I.C.S.: 333922
Leon Linton *(Chm)*
Craig Steffey *(VP-Sls)*
David Nordwall *(CFO)*

SOUTHERN THEATRES, LLC
935 Gravier St Ste 1200, New Orleans, LA 70112
Tel.: (504) 297-1133
Web Site:
http://www.thegrandtheatre.com
Year Founded: 2002
Sales Range: $10-24.9 Million
Emp.: 25
Theater Operator
N.A.I.C.S.: 711110
George Solomon *(Chm)*
Trent Hickman *(Mng Dir-Veronis Suhler Stevenson)*
Jeffrey Stevenson *(Mng Partner-Veronis Suhler Stevenson)*

SOUTHERN TIER INSULATIONS INC.
3150 Buckingham Rd, Endwell, NY 13760
Tel.: (607) 754-6464 NY
Web Site:
http://www.stinsulations.com
Year Founded: 1978
Sales Range: $10-24.9 Million
Emp.: 65
Insulation of Pipes & Boilers
N.A.I.C.S.: 238990

SOUTHERN TILE DISTRIBUTORS, INC.
4590 Vlg Ave, Norfolk, VA 23502
Tel.: (757) 855-8041
Web Site:
http://www.southerntile.com
Sales Range: $10-24.9 Million
Emp.: 32
Floor Coverings
N.A.I.C.S.: 423220
Jeff Black *(Pres)*
Daryl Mitchell *(Dir-Ops)*

SOUTHERN TIRE MART, LLC
800 Hwy 98, Columbia, MS 39429
Tel.: (601) 424-3200 MS
Web Site: http://www.stmtires.com
Year Founded: 1973
Emp.: 5,000
Tire Dealerships Operator
N.A.I.C.S.: 441340
Jim Duff *(Pres)*
Subsidiaries:
Friend Tire Company (1)
11 Industrial Dr, Monett, MO 65708
Web Site: http://www.friendtire.com
Emp.: 100
Tire Distr
N.A.I.C.S.: 423130
Don Isbell *(Pres)*
Robert Roller *(VP-Sls)*
Lance Isbell *(VP-Ops)*

SOUTHERN TRUST MORTGAGE, LLC
4433 Corporation Ln Ste 300, Virginia Beach, VA 23462
Tel.: (757) 518-0700 VA
Web Site:
http://www.southerntrust.com
Year Founded: 1998
Mortgage Lending Services
N.A.I.C.S.: 522292
Jerry Flowers *(Founder & Chm)*
Robert O'Bday *(Sr VP/Mgr-Charlotte)*
Jack Lane *(Pres)*
Ritchie Love *(Reg Sls Mgr)*
Clayton Hicks *(Sr VP & Reg Mgr)*
Steven Shriner *(CFO)*
Tuck Reed *(CEO)*

SOUTHERN TRUST SECURITIES HOLDING CORP.
145 Almeria Ave, Coral Gables, FL 33134
Tel.: (305) 446-4800 FL
Web Site: http://www.stshc.com
Year Founded: 1998
Sales Range: $1-9.9 Million
Emp.: 24
Financial Holding Company
N.A.I.C.S.: 551112
Kirby Pascus *(VP)*
Frank P. Dunbar *(Controller)*

SOUTHERN WEAVING COMPANY
1005 W Bramlett Rd, Greenville, SC 29611
Tel.: (864) 233-1635
Web Site:
http://www.southernweaving.com
Year Founded: 1924
Sales Range: $25-49.9 Million
Emp.: 200
Supplier of Webbing & Woven Fabrics
N.A.I.C.S.: 313220
Ron Mohling *(CEO)*
Curtiss Burdette *(Dir-New Product Dev)*
Tommy Lee *(Acct Mgr-Sls)*

SOUTHERN WHOLESALE FLOORING CO.
955 B Cobb Place Blvd, Kennesaw, GA 30144
Tel.: (770) 514-7110
Web Site: http://www.swfloor.com
Year Founded: 1952
Sales Range: $10-24.9 Million
Emp.: 45
Floor Coverings
N.A.I.C.S.: 423220
Charles Kilgore *(Pres)*
Delinda Kilgore *(VP)*

SOUTHFIELD CAPITAL ADVISORS, LLC

SOUTHFIELD CAPITAL ADVISORS, LLC

Southfield Capital Advisors, LLC—(Continued)

140 Greenwich Ave 4th Fl, Greenwich, CT 06830
Tel.: (203) 813-4100
Web Site:
http://www.southfieldcapital.com
Privater Equity Firm
N.A.I.C.S.: 523999
Andy Levinson (Founder & Mng Partner)
Andy Cook (Partner)
Heb James (Partner)
Tim Lewis (Partner)
Brandon Pinderhughes (Principal)
Chris Grambling (Principal)
Jonathan Goldstein (CFO)
Elysia Pawlowicz (Ops Mgr-Ops)
Josh Sylvan (VP)

Subsidiaries:

Alba Wheels Up International, Inc. (1)
1 E Lincoln Ave, Valley Stream, NY 11580
Tel.: (718) 276-3000
Web Site: http://www.albawheelsup.com
Sales Range: $25-49.9 Million
Emp.: 100
Custom House Broker & International Freight Forwarding Services
N.A.I.C.S.: 488510
Salvatore J. Stile (Pres)
Damien Stile (CEO)
Yoav Millet (CFO)

Subsidiary (Domestic):

Alba Wheels Up International, Inc. (2)
1 E Lincoln Ave, Valley Stream, NY 11582
Tel.: (718) 276-3000
Web Site: http://www.albawheels.com
Sales Range: $10-24.9 Million
Emp.: 35
International Freight Forwarding Services
N.A.I.C.S.: 488510
Damien Stile (COO)
Salvhure J. Stile II (Pres)

Alba Wheels Up International, Inc. (2)
4005 NW 114th Ave Ste 25, Miami, FL 33178
Tel.: (305) 499-9994
Web Site: http://www.albawheelsup.com
Sales Range: $10-24.9 Million
Emp.: 4
Custom House Broker & International Freight Forwarder Distr
N.A.I.C.S.: 488510
Salvatore J. Stile II (Pres)

V T Mancusi, Inc. (2)
700 Rockaway Tpke Ste 303, Lawrence, NY 11559
Tel.: (516) 371-5666
Sales Range: $1-9.9 Million
Emp.: 12
Freight Transportation Arrangement
N.A.I.C.S.: 488510
Tom Mancusi (Pres)

American Refrigeration Company, LLC (1)
500 Research Dr, Wilmington, MA 01887
Tel.: (978) 474-4000
Web Site: http://arc.cool
Rev.: $4,300,000
Emp.: 30
Site Preparation Contractor
N.A.I.C.S.: 238910
Michael G. Sirois (CEO)
Tim Mason (Project Engr)
Bill Fleming (Pres)

Subsidiary (Domestic):

Capitol Engineering Co. (2)
151 California St, Newton, MA 02458
Tel.: (617) 965-2020
Web Site: http://capitol-eng.com
Rev.: $1,300,000
Emp.: 12
Site Preparation Contractor
N.A.I.C.S.: 238910
William T. Chaisson (CEO)
Barbara Altman (Office Mgr)

Cooling & Heating Specialists, Inc. (2)
151a California St, Newton, MA 02458
Tel.: (617) 244-0203
Web Site: http://www.chsinc.net
Rev.: $3,650,000
Emp.: 25
Site Preparation Contractor
N.A.I.C.S.: 238910

Ntiva, Inc. (1)
7900 Westpark Dr Ste A100, McLean, VA 22102
Tel.: (703) 891-0131
Web Site: http://www.ntiva.com
Information Technology Solutions
N.A.I.C.S.: 518210
Steven J. Freidkin (CEO)
David Rossell (Officer-Security)
Holly Dowden (VP-Mktg)
Jim Wilson (Pres & COO)
Mark Gilbreth (CFO)
Jerry Craig (Chief Information Security Officer)
Kevin Doyle (Chief Client Officer)
Michelle Brockney (VP-Ops)
Kelly Wolkomir (VP-People)
Steve Banke (VP-Transformation)
Christopher Vollmond-Carstens (VP-Corp Dev)

Subsidiary (Domestic):

3Points, LLC (2)
801 Oak Creek Dr, Lombard, IL 60148
Tel.: (708) 491-0300
Web Site: http://www.3points.com
Custom Computer Programming Services
N.A.I.C.S.: 541511

MXOtech, Inc. (2)
1101 W Adams St Ste A, Chicago, IL 60607
Tel.: (312) 313-4887
Web Site: http://www.mxotech.com
Sales Range: $1-9.9 Million
Emp.:
Information Technology Consulting Services
N.A.I.C.S.: 541512
Joanna Sobran (Pres & CEO)
George Mirov (Mgr-Client Svcs)
Bartlomiej Barcewicz (Dir-IT)
Steve Feldman (CFO)
Sean Blair (CTO)
William Orellana (Mgr-Svc)

Middleground Technologies LLC (2)
5105 Tollview Rd Ste 160, Rolling Meadows, IL 60008-3728
Web Site: http://www.mgtechweb.com
Computer System Design Services
N.A.I.C.S.: 541512
Rj Josh (Dir-Ops)

Network Alliance, Inc. (2)
7900 Westpark Dr Ste A100, McLean, VA 22102
Tel.: (703) 891-0131
Web Site: http://www.networkalliance.com
Hosted Desktop & VoIP, IT Support & Cloud Services
N.A.I.C.S.: 541512

RC&E, LLC (1)
2309 Chester St, Fort Worth, TX 76103
Tel.: (817) 348-0600
Web Site: https://rcenh3.com
Rev.: $3,500,000
Emp.: 29
Fiscal Year-end: 12/31/2006
Whol Refrigeration Equipment/Supplies
N.A.I.C.S.: 423740

Security Services Holdings, LLC (1)
90 Town Ctr St Ste 202, Daleville, VA 24083
Tel.: (866) 403-9630
Web Site: http://www.protossecurity.com
Security Services
N.A.I.C.S.: 561612
Shannon Janney (Controller)
Nathaniel Shaw (CEO)

Subsidiary (Domestic):

Mulligan Security Corp. (2)
2 Penn Plaza, New York, NY 10121
Tel.: (212) 563-0500
Web Site: http://www.mulligansecurity.com
Armored Car Services
N.A.I.C.S.: 561613

Kevin Mulligan (Founder & Pres)
John LaBarbera (Dir-Ops)

TFS, Ltd. (1)
7050 Spring Meadows Dr W, Holland, OH 43528
Tel.: (419) 868-8853
Web Site: http://www.tfsglobal.com
Fleet Management Services
N.A.I.C.S.: 561210
Brent Parent (CEO)
Michael Quimby (Pres)
Todd Roberts (COO)

Subsidiary (Domestic):

Curlin, Inc. (2)
6001 E Columbus Dr, Tampa, FL 33619
Tel.: (813) 626-4173
Web Site: http://www.curlin.com
Industrial Machinery & Equipment Merchant Whslr
N.A.I.C.S.: 423830
Elaine Eaton (Mgr-Svc)
Jeremy Chapman (VP)

SOUTHFIELD CHRYSLER JEEP

28100 Telegraph Rd, Southfield, MI 48034
Tel.: (248) 354-2950
Web Site:
http://www.southfieldchrysler.com
Rev.: $109,000,000
Emp.: 140
Automobiles, New & Used
N.A.I.C.S.: 441110
Daniel L. Frost (Owner & Pres)
Gary Wood (VP & Owner)
Paul Steel (VP-Sls & Mktg)
Wendy Schultz (VP-HR & Investor Svcs)

SOUTHFIRST BANCSHARES, INC.

126 N Norton Ave, Sylacauga, AL 35150
Tel.: (256) 245-4365   DE
Web Site: http://www.southfirst.com
Year Founded: 1951
Bank Holding Company
N.A.I.C.S.: 551111
Randall L. Fields (Pres & CEO)
Rick Taylor (CFO)

SOUTHFRESH AQUACULTURE

1792 N Mcfarland Blvd Ste B, Tuscaloosa, AL 35406
Tel.: (662) 513-5484
Web Site: http://www.southfresh.com
Year Founded: 1987
Sales Range: $50-74.9 Million
Emp.: 225
Fresh Catfish Processing Services
N.A.I.C.S.: 311710
Rivers Myres (Pres)
Mark Lamb (Pres)

SOUTHGATE FORD INC.

16501 Fort St, Southgate, MI 48195-1403
Tel.: (734) 282-3636   MI
Web Site:
http://www.southgateford.net
Year Founded: 1983
Sales Range: $125-149.9 Million
Emp.: 155
New & Used Automobile Retailer
N.A.I.C.S.: 441110
Jim Jurcak (Gen Mgr)
Ken Short (Mgr-Fin)
Walter J. Oben Jr. (Owner)

Subsidiaries:

Southgate Lincoln (1)
16800 Fort St, Southgate, MI 48195-1424
Tel.: (734) 285-8800
Web Site: http://www.southgatelincoln.com

Sales Range: $25-49.9 Million
Emp.: 100
Car Dealership
N.A.I.C.S.: 441110
John C. Majewski (Mgr-New Car Sls)
Shawn Hale (Gen Mgr)
Scott Gutekunst (Mgr-Parts)

SOUTHGATE TIMBER CO. INC.

11 Central Industrial Rd, Purvis, MS 39475
Tel.: (601) 794-2797
Year Founded: 1982
Sales Range: $10-24.9 Million
Emp.: 19
Whslr of Timber Products
N.A.I.C.S.: 423990
Glen Harron (VP)

SOUTHLAKE EQUITY GROUP LLC

1121 S Carroll Ave Ste 230, Southlake, TX 76092
Tel.: (817) 328-3600
Web Site:
http://www.southlakeequity.com
Year Founded: 2007
Sales Range: $10-24.9 Million
Emp.: 5
Privater Equity Firm
N.A.I.C.S.: 523999
Thomas C. Keene (Co-Founder & Mng Dir)
David A. Spuria (Partner & Gen Counsel)
Douglas D. Wheat (Co-Founder)
Doug Clark (CFO)

SOUTHLAKE FOOD MART

2210 W Southlake Blvd, Southlake, TX 76092
Tel.: (817) 481-0282
Sales Range: $10-24.9 Million
Emp.: 3
Convenience Store
N.A.I.C.S.: 445110
Leeann Hoang (Mgr)

SOUTHLAND CREDIT UNION

10701 Los Alamitos Blvd, Los Alamitos, CA 90720
Tel.: (562) 862-6831
Web Site: http://www.southlandcu.org
Sales Range: $25-49.9 Million
Credit Union
N.A.I.C.S.: 522130
Walter Finnigan (Chm)
Annie Perez (Vice Chm)
Angie Avery (Treas & Sec)
Ferris R. Foster (Pres & CEO)
Thomas G. Lent (CFO & Exec VP)
Rene M. LeJay (COO & Sr VP)
Curt A. Bannock (CIO & VP)
Matthew P. Herrick (VP-Sls & Mktg)
Patty Jiminez (VP-Lending)
Cynthia E. Smolinski (VP-HR)
Bertrand Villavert (VP & Controller)

Subsidiaries:

Harbor Credit Union (1)
510 W Carson St, Carson, CA 90745
Tel.: (310) 816-0440
Web Site: http://www.southlandcu.org
Federal Credit Unions
N.A.I.C.S.: 522130

SOUTHLAND IMPORTS, INC.

6000 S Lindbergh Blvd, Saint Louis, MO 63123
Tel.: (314) 892-8200   MO
Web Site: http://www.suntrupvw.com
Year Founded: 1957
New & Used Car Dealerships Owner & Operator
N.A.I.C.S.: 441110
Donald J. Suntrup Jr. (Pres & CEO)

COMPANIES / SOUTHSIDE ELECTRIC COOPERATIVE INC.

Subsidiaries:

Suntrup Buick-Pontiac-GMC Truck, Inc. (1)
4200 N Service Rd, Saint Peters, MO 63376-6464
Tel.: (636) 284-2668
Web Site: http://www.suntrupbuickgmc.com
Sales Range: $10-24.9 Million
Emp.: 68
New & Used Car Dealer
N.A.I.C.S.: 441110
Ken Klein (Gen Mgr)
Perry Gambino (Dir-Parts & Svc)
Eric Trigg (Mgr-Preowned Internet)

Suntrup Ford Kirkwood (1)
10340 Manchester Rd, Kirkwood, MO 63122-1521
Tel.: (314) 822-9300
Web Site: http://www.suntrupfordkirkwood.com
Sales Range: $25-49.9 Million
Emp.: 47
New & Used Car Dealer
N.A.I.C.S.: 441110
Tom Dietz (Mgr-Internet Sls)
Kirk Latta (Gen Mgr)
Eric Proemsey (Mgr-Pre-Owned Sls)
Alma Gantney (Controller)
Gerry Andracsek (Mgr-Parts)
Collette Carnahan (Mgr-Svc)
Dave Gibson (Mgr-Fin)
Kevin Ruzicka (Mgr-Fleet)

Suntrup Volkswagen (1)
6000 S Lindbergh Blvd, Saint Louis, MO 63123
Tel.: (314) 892-8200
Web Site: http://www.suntrupvw.com
Sales Range: $10-24.9 Million
New & Used Car Dealer
N.A.I.C.S.: 441110

W.C. Motor Company, Inc. (1)
14410 Manchester Rd, Ballwin, MO 63011
Tel.: (636) 227-8303
Web Site: http://www.wcvolvo.com
Sales Range: $10-24.9 Million
Emp.: 60
New & Used Car Dealer
N.A.I.C.S.: 441110
Chris Suntrup (Pres)
Steve Lynch (Gen Mgr)

SOUTHLAND INDUSTRIES
7390 Lincoln Way, Garden Grove, CA 92841
Tel.: (949) 440-5000   CA
Web Site: http://www.southlandind.com
Year Founded: 1949
Sales Range: $450-499.9 Million
Emp.: 1,000
Heating & Air Conditioning Contractors
N.A.I.C.S.: 238220
Ted Lynch (CEO)
Kevin J. Coghlan (CFO)
Lisa Hoffman Starr (Chief HR Officer)
Anthony Roner (VP-Southland Energy)
Joe Cvetas (Exec VP-Southland Energy)
Dan Navarrete (VP-Mktg & Comm)
Brian Boutte (Chief Comml Officer)

Subsidiaries:

Southland Industries-Mid-Atlantic Division (1)
22340 Dreseen St Ste 177, Dulles, VA 20166   (100%)
Tel.: (703) 834-5570
Web Site: http://www.southlandindustries.com
Sales Range: $50-74.9 Million
Emp.: 100
N.A.I.C.S.: 238210

Southland Industries-Northern California Division (1)
33225 Western Ave, Union City, CA 94587
Tel.: (510) 477-3300
Web Site: http://www.southlandind.com
Sales Range: $25-49.9 Million
Emp.: 350
Mechanical Contractor
N.A.I.C.S.: 238220
Rick Blavier (Pres)

Southland Industries-Southern California Division (1)
12131 Western Ave, Garden Grove, CA 92841
Tel.: (714) 901-5800
Web Site: http://www.southlandindustries.com
Sales Range: $25-49.9 Million
Emp.: 100
Providers of Building Construction Services
N.A.I.C.S.: 238220

Southland Industries-Southwest Division (1)
4765 Cameron St, Las Vegas, NV 89103-5205
Tel.: (702) 736-4041
Web Site: http://www.southlandind.com
Sales Range: $25-49.9 Million
Emp.: 250
Mechanical Contractor
N.A.I.C.S.: 238220

The Brandt Companies, LLC (1)
1728 Briercroft Ct, Carrollton, TX 75006
Tel.: (972) 395-6000
Web Site: http://www.brandt-companies.com
Plumbing, Heating & Air-Conditioning Contractors
N.A.I.C.S.: 238220
Barry Moore (Pres & CEO)
Mark Zilbermann (Chm)
Steve Hayes (Exec VP & Gen Mgr-North Texas)
Mike Arthurs (CFO & Exec VP)
Kelly Carr (Exec VP & Gen Counsel)
John Zelman (Exec VP-Power & Energy)
Curtis Harbour (Exec VP & Gen Mgr-Houston)

Subsidiary (Domestic):

Hilbig Services Inc. (2)
5910 Fm 1863, Bulverde, TX 78163
Tel.: (830) 438-3030
Web Site: http://www.hilbigservices.com
Rev.: $7,300,000
Emp.: 50
Site Preparation Contractor
N.A.I.C.S.: 238910
Russell Tschoerner (Mgr-Parts)

Magnum Technical Services, Inc. (2)
24 Commercial Pl, Schertz, TX 78154
Tel.: (210) 658-5351
Web Site: http://www.magnumengineering.com
Engineering & Controls Services
N.A.I.C.S.: 541330

SOUTHLAND LIGHTING SALES, INC.
1219 Warren Hall Ln, Atlanta, GA 30319
Tel.: (404) 252-1044
Sales Range: $10-24.9 Million
Emp.: 7
Electrical Apparatus & Equipment Whslr
N.A.I.C.S.: 423610
James G. Smith (CFO & Sec)
Robert M. Smith (CEO)

SOUTHLAND PLUMBING SUPPLY INC.
2321 N Arnoult Rd, Metairie, LA 70001
Tel.: (504) 835-8411
Web Site: http://southlandplumbingsupplymetairie.com
Year Founded: 1968
Sales Range: $10-24.9 Million
Emp.: 40
Whslr & Retailer of Plumbing & Hydronic Heating Supplies
N.A.I.C.S.: 423720
Joey Togade (Gen Mgr)

SOUTHLAND PRINTING CO., INC.
213 Airport Dr, Shreveport, LA 71137-7263
Tel.: (318) 221-8662
Web Site: http://www.southlandprinting.com
Rev.: $8,594,000
Emp.: 65
Other Commercial Printing
N.A.I.C.S.: 323111
John Manno (Pres & CEO)
Carlos Cockerham (Mgr-IT)
Olen Ashby (Gen Mgr)
Donna Faulkner (Office Mgr)
Noemi Garcia (Coord-Acct)
Brady Lewis (Mgr-Prepress)
Charles McHenry (Mgr-Sls Acct)
Robert Saucedo (Mgr-Pressroom)
Richard Smith (Mgr-HR)
Dale Spoor (Mgr-Production)
Mitch Timmons (Controller)

SOUTHLAND TECHNOLOGY, INC.
8053 Vickers St, San Diego, CA 92111
Tel.: (858) 694-0932
Web Site: http://www.southlandtechnology.com
Sales Range: $10-24.9 Million
Emp.: 30
Computer & Computer Peripheral Equipment & Software Merchant Whslr
N.A.I.C.S.: 423430
Robert Pedigo (Pres)
Grace Pedigo (COO)
Ben Keepper (CTO)

SOUTHLAND TRANSPORTATION CO.
7925 Hwy 601 N, Boonville, NC 27011
Tel.: (336) 367-4767
Web Site: http://www.southlandtransportation.com
Sales Range: $10-24.9 Million
Emp.: 180
Contract Haulers
N.A.I.C.S.: 484121
R. J. Cummings (Pres)
Bobby Stanley (VP)

SOUTHMINSTER
8919 Park Rd, Charlotte, NC 28210
Tel.: (704) 551-6800   NC
Web Site: http://www.southminster.org
Year Founded: 1984
Sales Range: $25-49.9 Million
Emp.: 395
Retirement Community Operator
N.A.I.C.S.: 623311
David Lacy (Pres & Exec Dir)
Kenda Laughey (CFO)
Stewart Wiley (Dir-Sls & Mktg)
Salem Suber (Dir-Dining Svcs)
Mary Cooper (Dir-Health & Wellness)
Lisa McClellan (Dir-HR)

SOUTHPAW SPORTS & ENTERTAINMENT, INC.
13859 Diplomat Dr Ste 150, Farmers Branch, TX 75234
Tel.: (469) 299-4111
Web Site: http://www.southpawlive.com
Digital Signage & Large Screen LED Video Systems Services
N.A.I.C.S.: 335139
Garry Waldrum (Founder & Chm)
Kevin Kelley (Pres & CEO)
George Pappas (COO)

Subsidiaries:

D3 LED, LLC (1)
11370 Sunrise Park Dr, Rancho Cordova, CA 95742-6596
Tel.: (916) 669-7408
Web Site: http://www.d3led.com
Lighting Equipment Mfr
N.A.I.C.S.: 335139
David Neale (Dir-Europe)

SOUTHPOINT RISK ADVISORS LLC
395 S Main St, Ashland City, TN 37015
Tel.: (615) 792-3500
Web Site: http://www.southpointriskadvisors.com
Year Founded: 1986
Full-service Independent Insurance Agency
N.A.I.C.S.: 524210
David B. Aldridge (COO, CFO & VP-Geny Insurance)

SOUTHPORT FINANCIAL CORPORATION
2507 Post Rd, Southport, CT 06890-1259
Tel.: (203) 255-3434   CT
Web Site: http://www.southprop.com
Multifamily Residential Real Estate Investment, Property Management & Leasing Services
N.A.I.C.S.: 531311
Elisha Packer Wilbur (Pres)
Dennis G. Boyd (CEO)
Gary R. Hediger (Dir-Property Mgmt)
James R. Willis (Dir-Acq)
Jeffrey T. Lombardo (Dir-IR)
Diana Bell (VP & Reg Mgr-Property)
Ginger Comer (VP & Reg Mgr-Property)

SOUTHRIDGE TECHNOLOGY GRP, LLC.
246 Federal Rd Unit B12, Brookfield, CT 06804
Tel.: (203) 431-8324
Web Site: http://www.southridgetech.com
Sales Range: $1-9.9 Million
Emp.: 15
Information Technology Services
N.A.I.C.S.: 518210
Joe Garzi (Founder & Pres)
Jonathan Gibney (VP-Ops)

SOUTHSIDE DODGE SALES INC.
7740 NE Loop 820, Fort Worth, TX 76180
Tel.: (817) 276-7700
Web Site: http://www.allensamuelsdodge.com
Sales Range: $50-74.9 Million
Emp.: 140
Automobiles, New & Used
N.A.I.C.S.: 441110
Allen Samuels (Chm)

SOUTHSIDE ELECTRIC COOPERATIVE INC.
2000 W Virginia Ave, Crewe, VA 23930
Tel.: (434) 645-7721   DE
Year Founded: 1936
Sales Range: $50-74.9 Million
Emp.: 170
Electronic Services
N.A.I.C.S.: 221118
Allan Sharrett (Dir-Comm & PR)
Carol Hutchinson (Coord-Trng)
George Felts (Mgr-Engrg & Ops Svcs)

SOUTHSIDE ELECTRIC COOPERATIVE INC.
U.S. PRIVATE

Southside Electric Cooperative Inc.—(Continued)
Graham Fowlkes *(Supvr-Staking)*
Jean Morris *(Mgr-HR)*
Jeffrey Edwards *(Pres & CEO)*

SOUTHSIDE IMPORTS INC.
3300 Washington Rd, Augusta, GA 30907
Tel.: (706) 854-1000
Web Site:
http://www.sunbeltnissan.com
Rev.: $44,754,116
Emp.: 40
Automobiles, New & Used
N.A.I.C.S.: 441110
Janelle M. Watson *(Pres)*
Mike Watson *(CFO)*

SOUTHSIDE MEDICAL CENTER INC.
1046 Ridge Ave SW, Atlanta, GA 30315
Tel.: (404) 688-1350 GA
Web Site:
http://www.southsidemedical.net
Year Founded: 1970
Sales Range: $10-24.9 Million
Emp.: 288
Health Care Srvices
N.A.I.C.S.: 622110
Janis Ware *(Chm)*
Billy Mathis *(Treas)*
Melvin Preston *(Vice Chm)*
Greg Taylor *(Sec)*

SOUTHSIDE TIRE CO. INC.
N 2453 US Hwy 45 S, Antigo, WI 54409
Tel.: (715) 627-4858
Web Site:
http://www.southsidetire.com
Year Founded: 1967
Sales Range: $100-124.9 Million
Emp.: 100
Retailer of Tires
N.A.I.C.S.: 423130
Tim Husnick *(Pres)*
Craig Husnick *(VP)*

SOUTHWARK METAL MANUFACTURING COMPANY
2800 Red Lion Rd, Philadelphia, PA 19114
Tel.: (215) 735-3401 PA
Web Site:
http://www.southwarkmetal.com
Year Founded: 1946
Sales Range: $10-24.9 Million
Emp.: 350
Mfr of Sheet Metal Products, Galvanized Ducts & Fittings for Heaters & Air Conditioners
N.A.I.C.S.: 332322
William D. Spiegel *(Pres)*
Martin L. Seidman *(Treas)*
Gary J. Spiegel *(Sec)*

Subsidiaries:

Southwark Metal Manufacturing Company - Greenville Division (1)
255 Bessie Rd Hwy 86, Piedmont, SC 29673
Tel.: (864) 845-4929
Web Site: http://www.southwarkmetal.com
Sheet Metal Work Mfg
N.A.I.C.S.: 332322
Scebe Lankford *(Plant Mgr)*

Southwark Metal Manufacturing Company - Idaho Division (1)
4002 Skyway St, Caldwell, ID 83605
Tel.: (208) 402-2125
Sheet Metal Work Mfg
N.A.I.C.S.: 332322

Southwark Metal Manufacturing Company - Indianapolis Division (1)
10401 E 59th St, Indianapolis, IN 46320
Tel.: (317) 823-5300
Web Site: http://www.southwarkmetal.com
Emp.: 150
Sheet Metal Work Mfg
N.A.I.C.S.: 332322
Terry Mulder *(Plant Mgr)*

Southwark Metal Manufacturing Company - Mississippi Division (1)
8680 Stanton Rd, Southaven, MS 38671
Tel.: (662) 393-3010
Sheet Metal Work Mfg
N.A.I.C.S.: 332322

Southwark Metal Manufacturing Company - Nebraska Division (1)
2073 N Rademakers Way, Fremont, NE 68025
Tel.: (402) 753-9290
Sheet Metal Work Mfg
N.A.I.C.S.: 332322

SOUTHWAY FORD INC.
7979 IH 35 S, San Antonio, TX 78224
Tel.: (210) 922-2222
Web Site:
http://www.southwayford.com
Sales Range: $25-49.9 Million
Emp.: 160
Automobiles, New & Used
N.A.I.C.S.: 441110
Cindy Frazier *(Mgr-HR)*
Paul Edwards *(Dir-Fin)*

SOUTHWEST ADMINISTRATORS INC.
1000 S Fremont Ave Bldg 9A W, Alhambra, CA 91803-8839
Tel.: (626) 284-4792 CA
Year Founded: 1950
Sales Range: $50-74.9 Million
Emp.: 300
Third Party Administrators of Pension, Health & Welfare Funds
N.A.I.C.S.: 525110
Lenei Ishmael *(CFO)*
Toni Todd-Roberts *(Pres)*

SOUTHWEST ARCHITECTURAL BUILDERS, INC.
3826 N 3rd St, Phoenix, AZ 85012-2022
Tel.: (602) 235-9200
Web Site: http://www.sab-arizona.com
Year Founded: 1986
Sales Range: $10-24.9 Million
Emp.: 33
Commercial Building Construction
N.A.I.C.S.: 236220
Joe Hitzel *(Pres)*
Frank Sandstedt *(Project Mgr)*
Tom Newman *(Project Mgr)*
Sheila Gardner *(Project Mgr)*
Louis Burgdorf *(Project Mgr)*
Tanja Fusco *(Project Mgr)*
Eric Jankowsky *(Project Mgr)*

SOUTHWEST ARKANSAS DEVELOPMENT COUNCIL
3902 Sanderson Ln, Texarkana, AR 71854
Tel.: (870) 773-0819 AR
Web Site: http://www.swadc.com
Year Founded: 1969
Sales Range: $10-24.9 Million
Emp.: 499
Community Care Services
N.A.I.C.S.: 561990
Sandra Patterson *(Exec Dir)*
Vickie Vital *(Dir-Transportation)*

SOUTHWEST ARKANSAS ELECTRIC COOPERATIVE CORPORATION
2904E 9th St, Texarkana, AR 71854-5873
Tel.: (870) 772-2743 AR
Web Site: http://www.swrea.com
Year Founded: 1937
Sales Range: $25-49.9 Million
Emp.: 80
Electronic Services
N.A.I.C.S.: 221122
Wayne Whitaker *(Pres & Gen Mgr)*
George Wall *(Mgr-Ops & Engrg)*

SOUTHWEST BAKING CO.
600 Phil Gramm Blvd, Bryan, TX 77807
Tel.: (979) 778-6600
Sales Range: $10-24.9 Million
Emp.: 190
Baked Products Producer
N.A.I.C.S.: 311812
Willie Dairy *(Mgr-Transportation)*
Buddy King *(Plant Mgr)*

SOUTHWEST BAKING COMPANY, LLC.
9604 W Buckeye Rd, Tolleson, AZ 85353-9141
Tel.: (602) 229-8164
Sales Range: $25-49.9 Million
Emp.: 2
Bakery Products Mfr
N.A.I.C.S.: 311812
Robert Wroblewski *(Plant Engr)*

SOUTHWEST BANCSHARES, INC.
1900 NE Loop 410, San Antonio, TX 78213
Tel.: (210) 807-5500 TX
Web Site:
http://www.texaspartners.bank
Year Founded: 2007
Sales Range: $25-49.9 Million
Bank Holding Company
N.A.I.C.S.: 551111
Brent R. Given *(Pres/CEO-Bank)*
J. Bruce Bugg Jr. *(Chm, Pres & CEO)*
Brent R. Given *(Pres/CEO-Bank)*

Subsidiaries:

Texas Partners Bank (1)
1900 NW Loop 410, San Antonio, TX 78213 (100%)
Tel.: (210) 807-5500
Web Site:
http://www.texaspartnersbank.com
Sales Range: $25-49.9 Million
Emp.: 150
Commericial Banking
N.A.I.C.S.: 522110
Brent R. Given *(Pres & CEO)*
J. Bruce Bugg Jr. *(Chm)*
Amy Sondergeld *(CFO & Exec VP)*
Andrew Reid *(Chief Credit Officer & Exec VP)*
Alan C. Smith *(Exec VP-Specialty Fin Grp)*
Rob Glenn *(Exec VP-Comml Banking)*
Tom Moreno *(COO & Exec VP)*
Patricia Wilson *(Exec VP-HR)*
Brandi C. Vitier *(Exec VP-Private Banking, Comml & Bus Div)*
Steve Villarreal *(Sr VP-Bus Banking)*
Amanda McChesney *(Sr VP & Mgr-Private Banking Relationship)*
Angie Lewis *(VP & Mgr-Bus Banking Relationship)*
Alan Kramer *(Exec VP & Mgr-Comml Banking)*
Angelica Palm *(Sr VP & Dir-Mktg & Comm)*
J. Bruce Bugg Jr. *(Chm)*

Subsidiary (Domestic):

The Bank of San Antonio Insurance Group, Inc. (2)
1900 NW Loop 410 Ste 200, San Antonio, TX 78213
Tel.: (210) 822-1571
Web Site:
http://www.thebankofsainsurance.com
Insurance Agency & Administration Services
N.A.I.C.S.: 524210

Michael Grossman *(Pres)*

Division (Domestic):

Luhn-McCain Insurance Agency, Ltd. (3)
8000 W Ih 10 Ste 1145, San Antonio, TX 78230
Tel.: (210) 822-1571
Web Site: http://www.luhn-mccain.com
Sales Range: $1-9.9 Million
Insurance Agents
N.A.I.C.S.: 524210
Marietta McCain *(Gen Mgr)*

SOUTHWEST BUSINESS CORPORATION
9311 San Pedro Ste 600, San Antonio, TX 78216
Tel.: (210) 525-1241
Web Site: http://www.swbc.com
Sales Range: $25-49.9 Million
Emp.: 1,000
Insurance Brokers
N.A.I.C.S.: 524210
Gary Dudley *(Co-Founder & Pres)*
Charlie Amato *(Co-Founder & Chm)*
Karen Meriwether *(CFO)*
Joy Larson *(CEO-Insurance Svcs)*

Subsidiaries:

Equi-Trax Asset Solutions LP. (1)
14 E Carrillo St Ste B, Santa Barbara, CA 93101
Tel.: (805) 683-4411
Web Site: http://www.equi-trax.com
Real Estate & Asset Management Services
N.A.I.C.S.: 523940
Guy Taylor *(CEO)*
Brad Gustavson *(Mgr-Ops)*
Antonio Rosales *(Coord-Acct)*
Mark Weisgerber *(COO & Mgr-Ops)*

SOUTHWEST CASINO CORP.
2001 Killebrew Dr Ste 306, Minneapolis, MN 55425
Tel.: (952) 853-9990
Year Founded: 2002
Casino Management Services
N.A.I.C.S.: 713210
Jim Druck *(Founder & CEO)*

SOUTHWEST COMMUNITY HEALTH CENTER, INC.
968 Fairfield Ave, Bridgeport, CT 06605
Tel.: (203) 330-6000 CT
Web Site: http://www.swchc.org
Year Founded: 1976
Sales Range: $10-24.9 Million
Emp.: 238
Health Care Srvices
N.A.I.C.S.: 622110
Thomas J. Krause *(COO)*
Nancy Wiltse *(Chief Behavioral Health Officer)*
Dimitri Hrisovulos *(CFO)*
Scott Burrows *(Chief HR Officer)*
Dara Richard *(Chief Medical Officer)*

SOUTHWEST CONTRACTORS, INC.
3235 Unicorn Rd, Bakersfield, CA 93308-5716
Tel.: (661) 588-0484
Web Site:
http://www.swcontractors.net
Year Founded: 1985
Sales Range: $10-24.9 Million
Emp.: 130
Water, Sew & Utility Contracting Services
N.A.I.C.S.: 237110
Floyd Bowman *(Pres)*

SOUTHWEST CONVENIENCE STORES LLC
PO Box 711, Odessa, TX 79760-0711

Tel.: (432) 362-7356   TX
Year Founded: 1995
Sales Range: $125-149.9 Million
Emp.: 1,500
Provider of Grocery Services
N.A.I.C.S.: 445131
Yossi Lipman *(CEO)*
DeAnne Patman *(Mgr-License & Permit)*

SOUTHWEST EDUCATIONAL DEVELOPMENT LABORATORY
4700 Mueller Blvd, Austin, TX 78723
Tel.: (512) 476-6861   TX
Web Site: http://www.sedl.org
Year Founded: 1966
Sales Range: $10-24.9 Million
Emp.: 91
Educational Support Services
N.A.I.C.S.: 611710
Michael Vaden-Kiernan *(Dir-Res & Evaluation)*
Beth Howard-Brown *(Program Mgr)*
Stuart Ferguson *(CFO)*
R. Victoria Dimock *(Chief Program Officer)*
Joe Cook *(Sec)*
Linda Villarreal *(Chm)*
Wesley A. Hoover *(Pres & CEO)*

SOUTHWEST ELECTRIC CO. INC.
2617 South Agnew Ave, Oklahoma City, OK 73108-6227
Tel.: (405) 869-1100
Web Site: http://www.swelectric.com
Year Founded: 1946
Sales Range: $25-49.9 Million
Emp.: 240
Armature Rewinding Services; Transformers Mfr; Motor & Generator Repairs
N.A.I.C.S.: 811310
Roy Townsdin *(Chm)*
John Maravich *(CFO)*

SOUTHWEST ELECTRIC CO-OPERATIVE, INC.
1023 S Springfield Ave, Bolivar, MO 65613
Tel.: (417) 326-5244   MO
Web Site: http://www.swec.org
Year Founded: 1939
Sales Range: $50-74.9 Million
Emp.: 82
Electric Power Distribution Services
N.A.I.C.S.: 221122
Leslie Cantrell *(Mgr-Fin & Acctg)*
Jason Carver *(Mgr-Engrg)*
James Ashworth *(CEO & Gen Mgr)*
Brent Gamble *(Mgr-Office Svcs & Risk Mgmt)*
Ted Zeugin *(Mgr-Member Svcs & Comm)*
Gary Stiles *(Mgr-Ops)*
Rick Condren *(Mgr-IT)*

SOUTHWEST FLORIDA CABLE CONSTRUCTION, INC.
4261 James St Ste Unit2, Port Charlotte, FL 33980
Tel.: (941) 624-0804   FL
Year Founded: 1995
Sales Range: $1-9.9 Million
Emp.: 37
Power & Communication Line & Related Structures Construction
N.A.I.C.S.: 237130
Kevin Williams *(Pres)*

SOUTHWEST FLORIDA FRANCHISES INC.
6011 E 31st St, Bradenton, FL 34203
Tel.: (941) 751-5879
Sales Range: $1-9.9 Million
Emp.: 80
Commercial Laundry Services
N.A.I.C.S.: 812310
Rick Rone *(Pres)*

SOUTHWEST FLORIDA INSURANCE ASSOCIATES, INC.
8695 College Pkwy Ste 2080, Fort Myers, FL 33919
Tel.: (239) 489-1212
Web Site: http://www.swflinsurance.com
Year Founded: 1982
Sales Range: $1-9.9 Million
Emp.: 20
Insurance Agencies
N.A.I.C.S.: 524210
Robert H. Whitlock *(Owner)*

SOUTHWEST FORD INC.
3000 Fort Worth Hwy, Weatherford, TX 76087
Tel.: (817) 596-5700
Web Site: http://www.southwestautogroup.com
Rev.: $37,400,000
Emp.: 115
Automobiles, New & Used
N.A.I.C.S.: 441110
Charles Gilchrist *(Owner & CEO)*
Kevin Barbour *(Acct Mgr-Comml)*

SOUTHWEST FREIGHT INC.
9005 Spikewood, Houston, TX 77078
Tel.: (713) 633-8889
Web Site: http://www.southwestfreight.com
Sales Range: $10-24.9 Million
Emp.: 70
Trucking Except Local
N.A.I.C.S.: 484121
Michael E. Johnson *(Pres)*
Ernie McDonald *(VP)*
Kimberly Kimmi *(Acct Mgr-Export Dept)*
Debby Seals *(Supvr-Yard II)*

SOUTHWEST FUNDING L.P.
13150 Coit Rd Ste 100, Dallas, TX 75240
Tel.: (214) 221-5215
Web Site: http://www.southwestfunding.com
Rev.: $13,200,000
Emp.: 63
Mortgage Banker
N.A.I.C.S.: 522310

SOUTHWEST GEORGIA COMMUNITY ACTION COUNCIL, INC.
912 1st Ave SE, Moultrie, GA 31776-3728
Tel.: (229) 985-3610   GA
Web Site: http://www.swgacac.com
Year Founded: 1965
Sales Range: $25-49.9 Million
Emp.: 1,012
Community Welfare Services
N.A.I.C.S.: 624190
Raimond Burley *(Chm)*
Myrtis Mulkey Ndawula *(CEO)*
Elizabeth Hylick *(Vice Chm)*
Jimmy Burch *(Sec)*

SOUTHWEST GEORGIA OIL CO., INC.
1711 E Shotwell St, Bainbridge, GA 39819
Tel.: (229) 246-1553   GA
Web Site: http://www.inland-stores.com
Year Founded: 1959
Sales Range: $100-124.9 Million
Emp.: 350
Provider of Convenience Store Gasoline Services
N.A.I.C.S.: 457120
Aaron Goodman *(VP-Ops)*
Glennie C. Bench *(VP-Fin)*
Cindy Doodan *(Controller)*
Mike Harrell *(Pres)*

SOUTHWEST HEALTH CENTER
1400 Eastside Rd, Platteville, WI 53818
Tel.: (608) 348-2331   WI
Web Site: http://www.southwesthealth.org
Year Founded: 1981
Sales Range: $25-49.9 Million
Emp.: 451
Health Care Srvices
N.A.I.C.S.: 622110
Dan Rohrbach *(CEO)*

SOUTHWEST HEALTH SYSTEM, INC.
1311 N Mildred Rd, Cortez, CO 81321
Tel.: (970) 565-6666   CO
Web Site: http://www.swhealth.org
Year Founded: 1996
Sales Range: $25-49.9 Million
Emp.: 465
Health Care Srvices
N.A.I.C.S.: 622110
Liz Sellers *(CEO-Interim & Chief Clinical Officer)*
Jodi Harris *(Dir-Rehabilitation Svcs)*
Dennis Keown *(Dir-Emergency Svcs)*
Travis B. Parker *(Dir-HR)*
Kim Jaeger *(Mgr-Practice)*
Anthony G. Sudduth *(Interim CEO)*
Paul Deshayes *(Chm)*
Kerri White *(Interim Chief Nursing Officer & Dir-Surgical Svcs)*
Shelle Zachary *(Interim Chief Ambulatory Svcs Officer & Dir-Medical Staff Svcs)*
Sam Radke *(Interim CFO)*

SOUTHWEST HEALTHCARE SERVICES
802 2nd St NW, Bowman, ND 58623
Tel.: (701) 523-3226   ND
Web Site: http://www.swhealthcare.net
Year Founded: 2000
Sales Range: $10-24.9 Million
Emp.: 241
Health Care Srvices
N.A.I.C.S.: 622110
Sasha Ruggles *(CFO)*
Gary Brennan *(Pres)*
John Osse *(Interim CEO)*

SOUTHWEST HIDE COMPANY
250 S Beechwood, Boise, ID 83709
Tel.: (208) 378-8000
Sales Range: $10-24.9 Million
Emp.: 14
Cattle Hide Processing & Sales
N.A.I.C.S.: 316110

SOUTHWEST INTERNATIONAL TRUCKS, INC.
3722 Irving Blvd, Dallas, TX 75247
Tel.: (214) 638-4685
Web Site: http://www.southwesttrucks.com
Rev.: $126,000,000
Emp.: 200
Sales & Service of Trucks
N.A.I.C.S.: 441110
Bobbette Manes *(Office Mgr)*
David Cobb *(Coord-Mobile Repair)*
Holly Luck *(Dir-Acctg & Leasing Svcs)*
Chuck McGrath *(Bus Mgr)*
Teresa Hutchason *(Coord-Sls)*

SOUTHWEST IOWA RENEWABLE ENERGY, LLC
10868 189th St, Council Bluffs, IA 51503
Tel.: (712) 366-0392   IA
Web Site: https://www.sireethanol.com
Year Founded: 2005
Rev.: $302,820,000
Assets: $156,426,000
Liabilities: $82,038,000
Net Worth: $74,388,000
Earnings: $8,584,000
Emp.: 62
Fiscal Year-end: 09/30/21
Ethanol, Grains & Corn Syrup Processor & Distr
N.A.I.C.S.: 213112
Michael D. Jerke *(Pres & CEO)*
Karol D. King *(Chm)*
Ann Reis *(CFO, Chief Acctg Officer, Controller & Asst Sec)*
Theodore V. Bauer *(Bd of Dirs, Treas & Sec)*
Ben Parsley *(Dir-Operations)*
Kristan Barta *(Dir-Commodities)*

SOUTHWEST KEY PROGRAMS
6002 Jain Ln, Austin, TX 78721
Tel.: (512) 462-2181   TX
Web Site: http://www.swkey.org
Year Founded: 1987
Sales Range: $150-199.9 Million
Emp.: 2,643
Youth & Family Welfare Services
N.A.I.C.S.: 624190
Joella L. Brooks *(Interim CEO)*
Juan Sanchez *(Founder)*
Jennifer Nelson *(VP-Community Engagement)*
Melody Chung *(CFO)*
Anselmo Villarreal *(Treas)*
Orlando Martinez *(Chm)*
Rachel Luna *(Gen Counsel)*
Rosa Santis *(Sec)*

SOUTHWEST LANDCOM
1715 S University Dr, Nacogdoches, TX 75961
Tel.: (936) 560-1000
Sales Range: $50-74.9 Million
Emp.: 3
Excavation & Grading Building Construction
N.A.I.C.S.: 531120
Jack Raines *(Pres & CFO)*

SOUTHWEST LOUISIANA ELECTRIC MEMBERSHIP CORPORATION
3420 NE Evangeline Thruway, Lafayette, LA 70507-2554
Tel.: (337) 896-5384
Web Site: http://www.slemco.com
Year Founded: 1937
Sales Range: $200-249.9 Million
Electric Power Distr
N.A.I.C.S.: 221122
Glenn Tamporello *(CEO & Gen Mgr)*
Jim Laque *(Dir-Engrg & Ops)*
Katherine Domingue *(CFO)*
Bryan G. Leonards Sr. *(Treas & Sec)*
Joseph David Simon Jr. *(Pres)*

SOUTHWEST LOUISIANA HOSPITAL ASSOCIATION
1701 Oak Park Blvd, Lake Charles, LA 70601
Tel.: (337) 494-3000   LA

SOUTHWEST LOUISIANA HOSPITAL ASSOCIATION / U.S. PRIVATE

Southwest Louisiana Hospital Association—(Continued)
Web Site: http://www.lcmh.com
Year Founded: 1952
Sales Range: $200-249.9 Million
Emp.: 2,578
Health Care Srvices
N.A.I.C.S.: 622110
Larry M. Graham *(Pres & CEO)*
Kathleen DeRouen *(Sr VP-Mktg)*
Denise Emerson Rau *(Chm)*
Anna Cazes *(COO & Sr VP)*
Todd A. Delahoussaye *(Sr VP-Specialty & Physician Svcs)*
Brian Kirk *(VP-Fin)*
Leif Pedersen *(Sr VP-Philanthropy)*
Robert Prehn *(VP-Specialty Svc)*
Jason Rashall *(VP-Bus Dev)*
Charles P. Whitson *(Sr VP-Fin)*

SOUTHWEST MATERIAL HANDLING INC.
3725 Nobel Ct, Mira Loma, CA 91752
Tel.: (951) 763-8868   CA
Web Site: http://www.swmhinc.com
Year Founded: 1989
Material Handling Services
N.A.I.C.S.: 423830
Marc Mateus *(Mgr-Natl Accts)*
Brad Christman *(VP-Sys & Sls)*
Cyndi Bowne *(Head-Munchkin)*
Rick Ventura *(Mgr-Svc)*

SOUTHWEST MEDIA GROUP, LLC
1717 Main St 40th Fl, Dallas, TX 75201
Tel.: (214) 561-5678   TN
Web Site: http://www.swmediagroup.com
Year Founded: 1995
Advertising & Media Buying Agency
N.A.I.C.S.: 541810
Bob Nichol *(CEO)*
Kurt Schweitzer *(Dir-Grp Plng)*
Kim Kohler *(Chief Rel Officer)*
Melissa Wolf *(Grp Dir-Buying Ops)*
Eric Schaefer *(Pres)*
Debbie Bridgewater *(Dir-Fin)*
Ryan Ward *(Dir-Grp Plng)*
April Cook *(Dir-Talent & Dev)*
Todd Unruh *(Head-Innovation)*

SOUTHWEST MEDICAL CENTER
PO Box 1340, Liberal, KS 67905
Tel.: (620) 624-1651   KS
Web Site: http://www.swmedcenter.com
Year Founded: 1963
Sales Range: $25-49.9 Million
Emp.: 460
Health Care Srvices
N.A.I.C.S.: 622110
Jo L. Harrison *(VP-Patient Care Svcs)*
Bill Ermann *(Pres & CEO)*

SOUTHWEST MERIDIAN CORP.
2000 Magnolia Dr, Pasadena, TX 77503
Tel.: (713) 477-0475
Rev.: $10,000,000
Emp.: 11
Building Fireproofing Services
N.A.I.C.S.: 238990
Robert M. Ferguson *(Pres)*

SOUTHWEST METAL FINISHING
2445 S Calhoun Rd, New Berlin, WI 53151
Tel.: (262) 784-1919
Web Site: http://www.swmetalfinishing.com
Sales Range: $10-24.9 Million
Emp.: 200
Metal Finishing Services
N.A.I.C.S.: 332813
Tom Kallenberger *(Mgr-Customer Compliance)*
Scott Power *(Mgr-Maintenance & Facilities)*
Mary Trauernicht *(Mgr-IT)*
Philip Gould *(VP-Sls & Product Dev)*

SOUTHWEST MICROWAVE INC.
9055 S McKemy St, Tempe, AZ 85284
Tel.: (480) 783-0201
Web Site: http://www.southwestmicrowave.com
Rev.: $14,737,771
Emp.: 105
Designs, Mfr, Markets Electronic Perimeter Intrusion Detection Systems & Wireless CCTV Transmission Systems
N.A.I.C.S.: 334220
Richard McCormick *(Chm & CEO)*
Bob Kirkaldie *(Dir-Mktg)*
Diana Vuong *(Mgr-Mktg Comm)*
Michelle Roe *(Pres)*
Maira Zanrosso *(Dir-Sls & Mktg)*
John Gilbert *(Mgr-East)*

SOUTHWEST MISSISSIPPI ELECTRIC POWER ASSOCIATION
18671 Highway 61, Lorman, MS 39096
Tel.: (601) 437-3611   MS
Web Site: http://www.southwestepa.com
Year Founded: 1937
Sales Range: $50-74.9 Million
Electric Power Distr
N.A.I.C.S.: 221122
Kevin Bonds *(Gen Mgr)*
John Brady *(Asst Sec)*
Randy Woolley *(VP)*
W. Bruce Lewis *(Atty)*
Frank Wilson *(Sec)*
Billy Key Smith *(Pres)*
Kevin Cotten *(Mgr-Ops)*
Virgil Scott *(Office Mgr)*
Jeff Mac Segrest *(Supvr-Right-of-Way)*
Paula Clune *(Supvr-Customer Accts & Billing)*
Stephanie Knotts *(Sec)*

SOUTHWEST MISSOURI BANK
300 W 3rd St, Carthage, MO 64836
Tel.: (417) 358-9331
Web Site: http://www.smbonline.com
Sales Range: $25-49.9 Million
Emp.: 200
State Commercial Banks
N.A.I.C.S.: 522110
Garry Denney *(CEO)*
Gayle Tuck *(Dir-HR)*
Steve Koelkebeck *(Pres)*
David Russell *(Controller)*

SOUTHWEST OHIO REGIONAL TRANSIT AUTHORITY
602 Main St Gweyne Bldg Ste 1100, Cincinnati, OH 45202-1116
Tel.: (513) 621-9450
Web Site: http://www.go-metro.com
Sales Range: $25-49.9 Million
Emp.: 970
Bus Line Operations
N.A.I.C.S.: 485113

Sallie L. Hilvers *(VP-External Comm)*
Mary Beth Moning *(VP-Strategic Mgmt)*
William J. Desmond *(VP-Legal Svcs)*
Darryl Haley *(Interim CEO)*
Demarcus Peters *(Dir-Diversity)*
Brandy Jones *(Dir-External Affairs)*
David Riposo *(CFO)*
Kreg Keesee *(Chm)*
Alyson Beridon *(Vice Chm)*

SOUTHWEST PAPER COMPANY INC.
3930 Bridgeport Cir, Wichita, KS 67219
Tel.: (316) 838-7755
Web Site: http://www.swpaper.com
Sales Range: $25-49.9 Million
Emp.: 80
Industrial & Personal Service Paper
N.A.I.C.S.: 424130
Eric D. Tangeman *(Pres & CEO)*
Curt D. Clanton *(CFO)*

SOUTHWEST PET PRODUCTS INC.
330 S 75th Ave, Phoenix, AZ 85043
Tel.: (623) 936-1941   AZ
Year Founded: 1980
Sales Range: $10-24.9 Million
Emp.: 40
Pet Food Mfr
N.A.I.C.S.: 311111
John Benken *(Pres)*

SOUTHWEST PLASTIC BINDING COMPANY
109 Millwell Ct, Maryland Heights, MO 63043
Tel.: (314) 739-4400
Web Site: http://www.swbindinglaminating.com
Year Founded: 1966
Sales Range: $10-24.9 Million
Emp.: 120
Bookbinding Machinery & Supplies Mfr & Sales
N.A.I.C.S.: 323120
Mark J. Mercer *(Sr VP)*
Carol Thompson *(Controller)*
Michael Mercer *(Sr VP)*

SOUTHWEST POWER POOL INC.
201 Worthen Dr, Little Rock, AR 72223
Tel.: (501) 664-0146
Web Site: http://www.spp.org
Year Founded: 1941
Sales Range: $300-349.9 Million
Emp.: 450
Commercial Nonphysical Research
N.A.I.C.S.: 541715
Barbara Sugg *(Pres & CEO)*
Bruce Rew *(VP-Ops)*
Kevin Perry *(Dir-Critical Infrastructure Protection)*
Lanny Nickell *(VP-Engrg)*
James E. Eckelberger *(Chm)*
Paul Suskie *(Gen Counsel & Exec VP-Regulatory Policy)*
Emily Pennel *(Coord-Outreach & Standards)*
Deborah Currie *(Mgr-Regulatory Interface & Process Improvement)*
Keith Collins *(Exec Dir-Market Monitoring Unit)*
Terry Rhoades *(Mgr-Project Mgmt)*
Kara Fornstrom *(Dir-State Regulatory Policy)*

SOUTHWEST PRECISION PRINTERS, L.P.
1055 Conrad Sauer Dr, Houston, TX 77043
Tel.: (713) 777-3333
Web Site: http://www.swpp.com
Year Founded: 1975
Commercial Printing Services
N.A.I.C.S.: 323111
Tim Tully *(Founder & CEO)*
Mohammed Khan *(Dir-Pur)*
Rick Nussle *(VP-Sls)*
Jeff Glover *(Pres)*
Tod Tully *(VP)*
Karl Kluetz *(VP-Ops)*
Bobbie King *(Controller)*
Jeff Perkins *(Mgr-Production)*
Paula Benson *(Mgr-HR)*

SOUTHWEST PRODUCTS CORPORATION
11690 N 132nd Ave, Surprise, AZ 85379
Tel.: (602) 269-3581
Web Site: http://www.southwestproducts.com
Rev.: $20,000,000
Emp.: 100
Truck & Tractor Truck Assembly
N.A.I.C.S.: 336120

SOUTHWEST PROFESSIONAL VEHICLES
3910 E Overton Rd, Dallas, TX 75216
Tel.: (214) 371-3474
Web Site: http://www.spvinc.com
Sales Range: $10-24.9 Million
Emp.: 25
Automobiles & Other Motor Vehicles
N.A.I.C.S.: 423110
Jerry Altom *(Gen Mgr)*

SOUTHWEST PUBLIC POWER DISTRICT
221 N Main St, Palisade, NE 69040
Tel.: (308) 285-3295
Web Site: http://www.swppd.com
Sales Range: $10-24.9 Million
Emp.: 30
Electronic Services
N.A.I.C.S.: 221118
Bob Romine *(Pres)*

SOUTHWEST REGIONAL REPRESENTATIVES, INC.
4117 Visa Rd Ste B, Pasadena, TX 77504
Tel.: (713) 910-4420
Web Site: http://swregionalreps.com
Sales Range: $10-24.9 Million
Emp.: 5
Lawn & Garden Machinery & Equipment, Animal Health Products & Hardware Distr
N.A.I.C.S.: 423820
Trey Kendrick *(Pres)*

SOUTHWEST RESEARCH INSTITUTE
6220 Culebra Rd PO Drawer 28510, San Antonio, TX 78238-5166
Tel.: (210) 684-5111   TX
Web Site: http://www.swri.org
Year Founded: 1947
Sales Range: $1-9.9 Million
Emp.: 2,574
Commercial Physical Research & Development Services
N.A.I.C.S.: 541715
Walter D. Downing *(Exec VP)*
Ricardo Romo *(Chm)*
Milton B. Lee *(Vice Chm)*
Beth Ann Rafferty *(CFO, Sec & VP-Fin)*
Michael G. MacNaughton *(VP-Chemistry & Chemical Engrg)*
Danny M. Deffenbaugh *(VP-Mechanical Engrg)*

COMPANIES — SOUTHWESTERN MOTOR TRANSPORT INCORPORATED

James L. Burch *(VP-Space Science & Engrg)*
John W. McLeod *(Gen Counsel & VP-Legal & Patent Office)*
Linda M. Boehme *(Treas & Asst Sec)*
Steven D. Marty *(VP-Fuels & Lubricants Res)*
C. Nils Smith *(VP-Signal Exploitation & Geolocation)*
Paul D. Easley *(VP-Facilities & Gen Svcs)*
Mary Massey *(VP-Applied Power)*
Daniel Stewart *(VP-Engine, Emissions & Vehicle Res)*
Kenneth H. Bennett Jr. *(VP-Applied Physics)*

SOUTHWEST SOLUTIONS GROUP
2535-B E State Hwy 121 Ste 110, Addison, TX 75050
Tel.: (972) 250-1970
Web Site: http://www.southwestsolutions.com
Year Founded: 1969
Rev.: $30,100,000
Emp.: 75
Furniture Merchant Whslr
N.A.I.C.S.: 423210
Raymond Streight *(Pres)*
Craig Crock *(VP)*
Randy Brant *(VP)*
Jo Molen *(Mgr-HR)*

SOUTHWEST STEEL FABRICATORS, INC.
2520 Scheidt Ln, Bonner Springs, KS 66012
Tel.: (913) 422-5500
Web Site: http://www.southweststeelfab.com
Rev.: $7,300,000
Emp.: 75
Fabricated Structural Metal Mfr
N.A.I.C.S.: 332312
Craig Nelsen *(Pres)*
Richard Teahan *(Chm)*
Robert Dill *(Exec VP)*

SOUTHWEST TENNESSEE ELECTRIC MEMBERSHIP CORP.
1009 E Main St, Brownsville, TN 38012-2652
Tel.: (731) 772-1322 TN
Web Site: http://www.stemc.com
Year Founded: 1936
Sales Range: $200-249.9 Million
Emp.: 127
Provider of Electric Services
N.A.I.C.S.: 221122
Kevin Murphey *(Pres)*
Billy Gordon *(VP-Engrg)*

SOUTHWEST TEXAS ELECTRIC CO-OP
101 E Gillis St, Eldorado, TX 76936
Tel.: (325) 853-2544
Web Site: http://www.swtec.com
Rev.: $11,038,694
Emp.: 42
Electric Power Distr
N.A.I.C.S.: 221122
William B. Whitten *(Gen Mgr)*

SOUTHWEST TEXAS EQUIPMENT DISTRIBUTORS INC.
1126 S Saint Marys St, San Antonio, TX 78210
Tel.: (210) 354-0691
Web Site: http://www.swted.com
Sales Range: $10-24.9 Million
Emp.: 100
Ice Making Machines
N.A.I.C.S.: 423740

Sherry Kruciak *(VP)*
John Triplet *(CFO)*
A. J. Lewis III *(Owner)*

SOUTHWEST TRADERS INCORPORATED
27711 Diaz Rd 27565, Temecula, CA 92590
Tel.: (951) 699-7800 CA
Web Site: http://www.southwesttraders.com
Year Founded: 1977
Individual Restaurant Operator
N.A.I.C.S.: 722513
Lynne Bredemeier *(CFO)*
Shawn Lee *(Sr VP-Bus Dev)*
Stephanie Eisenhower *(Mgr-HR)*
Ken Smith *(Founder & CEO)*
Terry Walsh *(Pres)*

SOUTHWEST TRADING COMPANY
3575 S Decatur Blvd, Las Vegas, NV 89103
Tel.: (702) 253-7062
Sales Range: $10-24.9 Million
Emp.: 12
Tile Sales
N.A.I.C.S.: 423320
Lynda C. Fleming *(Partner)*
Rick Regano *(Gen Mgr)*

SOUTHWEST TRAILERS AND EQUIPMENT LLC
10400 W Reno Ave, Oklahoma City, OK 73127
Tel.: (405) 943-9851
Web Site: http://www.swtrailer.com
Sales Range: $10-24.9 Million
Emp.: 50
Trailers For Trucks, New & Used Dealer & Service Department
N.A.I.C.S.: 441110
Mark Kopf *(Controller)*
Kristi Sunderland *(Mgr-HR)*
Jay Baker *(Mgr-Svc)*

SOUTHWEST TRAILS
19203 S Figueroa St, Gardena, CA 90248
Tel.: (310) 538-5730
Web Site: http://www.southwesttrails.com
Sales Range: $10-24.9 Million
Emp.: 86
Petroleum Hauling
N.A.I.C.S.: 484220
Thomas P. Donaldson *(Owner & Pres)*
Ray Ormond *(Supvr-Safety)*

SOUTHWEST TRANSPLANT ALLIANCE, INC.
5489 Blair Rd, Dallas, TX 75231
Tel.: (214) 522-0255 TX
Web Site: http://www.organ.org
Year Founded: 1975
Sales Range: $25-49.9 Million
Emp.: 170
Organ & Tissue Donation Services
N.A.I.C.S.: 621991
Patricia Niles *(Pres & CEO)*
Jo Ann Arias *(VP-HR)*
Steve Peterson *(Dir-IT)*
Geoffrey Funk *(Assoc Dir-Medical)*
Chad Ezzell *(VP-Clinical Svcs)*
Katie Whitton *(Dir-PR)*
Sam Davis *(VP-Client Svcs)*
Faith Borunda *(Dir-El Paso)*
Sandi Lemons *(COO)*
Kirsten Gappelberg *(VP-Mktg Comm & Foundation Rels)*

SOUTHWESTERN BANCORP, INC.
1208 S Main St, Boerne, TX 78006
Tel.: (830) 249-3955 TX
Web Site: http://www.texasheritagebank.com
Year Founded: 1980
Sales Range: $1-9.9 Million
Emp.: 36
Bank Holding Company
N.A.I.C.S.: 551111
Steven S. Mack *(Pres & CEO)*
Robert Valdez *(CFO)*

Subsidiaries:

Texas Heritage Bank (1)
1208 S Main St, Boerne, TX 78006
Tel.: (830) 249-3955
Web Site: http://www.texasheritagebank.com
Sales Range: $1-9.9 Million
Commericial Banking
N.A.I.C.S.: 522110
Steven S. Mack *(Pres & CEO)*
David A. Estes *(Sr VP-Comml Lending)*
Robert Valdez *(CFO)*

SOUTHWESTERN COMMUNITY SERVICES, INC.
63 Community Way, Keene, NH 03431-0603
Tel.: (603) 352-7512 NH
Web Site: http://www.scshelps.org
Year Founded: 1965
Sales Range: $10-24.9 Million
Emp.: 188
Community Action Services
N.A.I.C.S.: 624190
James Stitham *(Dir-Facilities & Property Mgmt)*
John Manning *(CEO)*
Keith Thibault *(Chief Dev Officer-Admin)*
Meg Freeman *(CFO-Admin)*
Scott Croteau *(Vice Chm)*
Elaine Amer *(Treas)*
Diane Lucas Plotczyk *(Dir-IT & Comm Svcs)*
Paula McQuillan *(Dir-HR)*
Kevin Watterson *(Pres)*
Tina Roy *(Chief Admin Officer)*
Bagdat Caglar *(Dir-Child Dev Svcs)*
Sarah Burke *(Program Dir)*
Terra Rogers *(Dir-Energy & Employment Programs)*
Beth Daniels *(COO-Admin)*

SOUTHWESTERN ELECTRIC CO-OPERATIVE INC.
525 US Route 40, Greenville, IL 62246
Tel.: (618) 664-1025 IL
Web Site: http://www.sweci.com
Year Founded: 1939
Sales Range: $25-49.9 Million
Emp.: 80
Provider of Electric Services
N.A.I.C.S.: 221122
Joe Richardson *(VP-Comm)*
Alan G. Libbra *(Pres)*
Richard M. Gusewelle *(VP)*
Ann M. Schwarm *(Pres)*
Michael Barns *(Dir-Art)*
Thaddius Intravaia *(Dir-IT)*
Bobby Williams *(CEO)*

Subsidiaries:

Propane Plus Inc. (1)
Rural Rte 2 Box 372-B, Mulberry Grove, IL 62262
Tel.: (618) 283-0852
Web Site: http://www.propaneplus.coop
Sales Range: $25-49.9 Million
Emp.: 10
Sale of Propane Gas
N.A.I.C.S.: 221118

SOUTHWESTERN ELECTRICAL COMPANY INC.
1638 E 1st St, Wichita, KS 67214-4161
Tel.: (316) 263-1264
Web Site: http://www.sw-electric.com
Rev.: $10,000,000
Emp.: 120
Electrical Contractor
N.A.I.C.S.: 238210
Dick Drake *(VP)*
Don Sage *(Mgr-Project Mgmt)*
Carl Amrine *(Treas)*
Doug Cunningham *(Mgr-Svc Dept)*

SOUTHWESTERN FINANCIAL CORPORATION
1835 S Extension Rd, Mesa, AZ 85210
Tel.: (480) 730-4920 AZ
Web Site: http://www.mahoneygroup.com
Sales Range: $25-49.9 Million
Emp.: 250
Insurance Brokerage Services
N.A.I.C.S.: 524210
Glendon D. Nelson *(Chm & CEO)*
Steven R. Goble *(Pres)*
Michael J. Mesenbrink *(Treas & Sec)*
Leon B. Byrd Jr. *(Sr VP)*

SOUTHWESTERN ILLINOIS HEALTH FACILITIES, INC.
6800 State Route 162, Maryville, IL 62062
Tel.: (618) 391-6400 IL
Year Founded: 1977
Sales Range: $150-199.9 Million
Emp.: 1,305
Health Care Srvices
N.A.I.C.S.: 622110
Keith Page *(Pres & CEO)*
Michael Marshall *(CFO & VP-Fin)*
Lynn Fromm *(Dir-Pharmacy)*
Kathleen Parks *(Dir-Admin-Rehab)*
Lisa Klaustermeier *(Chief Nursing Officer)*

SOUTHWESTERN INDUSTRIES, INC.
2615 Homestead Pl, Rancho Dominguez, CA 90220-9066
Tel.: (310) 608-4422 CA
Web Site: http://www.southwesternindustries.com
Year Founded: 1951
Sales Range: $150-199.9 Million
Emp.: 175
Machine Tools Designer, Mfr & Whslr
N.A.I.C.S.: 333517
Richard W. Leonhard *(CEO)*
Tom Copeland *(VP-Ops)*
Stephen F. Pinto *(Pres)*
Robert Page *(Engr-Motion Control)*
Christopher Lee *(Mgr-Supply Chain)*

SOUTHWESTERN IRRIGATED COTTON GROWERS ASSOCIATION INC.
3500 Doniphan Dr, El Paso, TX 79922
Tel.: (915) 581-5441
Sales Range: $50-74.9 Million
Emp.: 42
Cotton Marketing & Sales
N.A.I.C.S.: 424590

SOUTHWESTERN MOTOR TRANSPORT INCORPORATED
4600 Goldfield, San Antonio, TX 78218
Tel.: (210) 662-2390
Web Site: http://www.smtl.com
Sales Range: $75-99.9 Million
Emp.: 600
Trucking Service
N.A.I.C.S.: 484121

SOUTHWESTERN MOTOR TRANSPORT INCORPORATED   U.S. PRIVATE

Southwestern Motor Transport Incorporated—(Continued)
Rick Eller (Sr VP)
Roy J. Gilbert Jr. (Chm)

SOUTHWESTERN PETROLEUM CORPORATION
534 N Main St, Fort Worth, TX 76164
Tel.: (817) 332-2336 TX
Web Site: http://www.swepcousa.com
Year Founded: 1933
Sales Range: $75-99.9 Million
Emp.: 50
Industrial Lubricants, Protective Coatings, Paints & Chemical Products
N.A.I.C.S.: 324122
Robert C. Dickerson (Pres)

Subsidiaries:

NV Southwestern Petroleum Europe, SA (1)
Industrieweg 6, 2390, Malle, Oostmalle, Belgium
Tel.: (32) 3 3123141
Web Site: http://www.swepcousa.com
Sales Range: $25-49.9 Million
Emp.: 2
Building Maintenance & Roofing Product Mfr
N.A.I.C.S.: 324122
Art Dickerson (Gen Mgr)

Southwestern Petroleum Canada Ltd. (1)
87 W Dr, Brampton, L60 2J6, ON, Canada
Tel.: (905) 457-0511
Web Site: http://www.swepco.usa.com
Sales Range: $10-24.9 Million
Emp.: 2
Industrial Lubricants, Protective Coatings, Paints & Chemical Products
N.A.I.C.S.: 324191

SOUTHWESTERN PROPERTY CORP.
5613 DTC Pkwy Ste 810, Greenwood Village, CO 80111
Tel.: (720) 881-2900
Web Site: http://www.swinvest.com
Year Founded: 2009
Real Estate Development & Multifamily Housing Construction Management Services
N.A.I.C.S.: 237210
Mark D. Campbell (Founder & Pres)
Eli Henrie (CFO)
Thomas Oldenburg (VP-Dev & Construction)
Joseph Pelham (VP-Acquisitons)

SOUTHWESTERN SECURITY SERVICES
505 E Washington St, Brownsville, TX 78520
Tel.: (956) 546-4141
Web Site: http://www.swssinc.com
Rev.: $16,299,124
Emp.: 10
Security & Private Investigation Services
N.A.I.C.S.: 561611
Jesus Morales (Chm & Owner)

SOUTHWESTERN STATIONERY & BANK SUPPLY, INC.
4500 N Santa Fe Ave, Oklahoma City, OK 73118-7902
Tel.: (405) 525-9411
Web Site: http://www.southwesternok.com
Sales Range: $10-24.9 Million
Emp.: 60
Lithographic Commercial Printing
N.A.I.C.S.: 323111
Bob Allee (Pres)
Dick Robberson (VP-Sls-Southwestern)
Don Miles (Mgr-Production)

SOUTHWESTERN SUPPLIERS, INC.
6815 E 14th Ave, Tampa, FL 33619-2917
Tel.: (813) 626-2193 FL
Web Site: http://www.sowes.com
Year Founded: 1959
Building Materials Whslr & Distr & Rebar Fabrication
N.A.I.C.S.: 423320
Martin Koch (Chm)
Rob Webb (Pres)

SOUTHWICK CLOTHING LLC
25 Computer Dr, Haverhill, MA 01832
Tel.: (978) 686-3833
Web Site: http://www.southwick.com
Year Founded: 1929
Clothes for Men Mfr
N.A.I.C.S.: 315250

SOUTHWICK INC.
2400 Shattuck Ave, Berkeley, CA 94704
Tel.: (510) 845-2530
Web Site: http://www.toyotaofberkeley.com
Rev.: $40,000,000
Emp.: 82
Car Dealership Owner & Operator
N.A.I.C.S.: 441110
Timothy Southwick Sr. (Pres)

SOUTHWIND MANUFACTURING
415 Cypress Rd, Ocala, FL 34472
Tel.: (352) 687-1999
Web Site: http://www.southwindmfg.com
Sales Range: $10-24.9 Million
Emp.: 30
Urethane & Foam Product Mfr
N.A.I.C.S.: 326150
Dave Berkley (COO)
Roger Walters (Plant Mgr)
Colleen Winchester (Mgr-Pur)
Denise Tinline (Office Mgr)

SOUTHWIRE COMPANY, LLC
1 Southwire Dr, Carrollton, GA 30119
Tel.: (770) 832-4242 GA
Web Site: https://www.southwire.com
Year Founded: 1950
Sales Range: $1-4.9 Billion
Emp.: 8,500
Other Aluminum Rolling, Drawing & Extruding
N.A.I.C.S.: 331318
Will Berry (Sr VP-SCR & Intl)
Charlie Murrah (Exec VP-Power Sys & Solutions)
Jeff Herrin (Sr VP-Mktg-Sustainability, Environmental, Health & Quality)
Gary Leftwich (Dir-Corp Comm)
Norman Adkins (Chief Comml Officer & Exec VP)
Phil Tuggle (Sr VP-Construction Sls & Channels)
Rebecca Cranford (Sr VP-Mfg Construction Sys & Solutions)
Winn Wise (Exec VP-OEM & Industrial)
Rich Stinson (Pres & CEO)
Marc Hall (VP-In Vehicle Sls)
Bobby Raatz (Dir-Sls, Mobile Power & Electrical Safety)
Mike Conway (Mgr-Outside Sls)

Subsidiaries:

Coleman Cable, Inc. (1)
1530 Shields Dr, Waukegan, IL 60085
Tel.: (847) 672-2300
Web Site: http://www.colemancable.com
Sales Range: $900-999.9 Million
Emp.: 1,726
Electronic Wire & Cable Products Developer, Mfr & Distr
N.A.I.C.S.: 332618
Dale Plautz (Dir-Corp Pur)
Wayne Kowalski (VP-Specialty Products)
Warren Schade (VP-Sls)
Kathy Jo Van (Exec VP-Distr Grp)
Kenneth A. McAllister (Exec VP-Distr Grp)
J. Kurt Hennelly (Exec VP-Ops)
Michael A. Frigo (Exec VP-OEM Grp)
Tony Gabriel (Dir-Engrg)
Gene Wethington (Mgr-Mdsg)
Howard Strauss (VP-Wire & Cable)
Philip K. Metz (VP-Sls & Mktg-Indus Products)
Cristina Ayi (Dir-Mktg & Ops-Canada)
Jane Hearing (Dir-Sourced Products)
John Suarez (Dir-Retail Mktg-North America)
Sarah MacRae (Mgr-Acct-Canada-Natl)
Eric Penne (Mgr-Acct-Automotive-Natl)
Gord Underwood (VP-Sls & Mktg-Canada)
Scott Hagen (Dir-Product Dev & Assembled Products)

Plant (Domestic):

Coleman Cable, Inc. - Bremen (2)
1115 W North St, Bremen, IN 46506
Tel.: (574) 546-5115
Web Site: http://www.colemancable.com
Sales Range: $150-199.9 Million
Emp.: 200
Copper Wires Mfr
N.A.I.C.S.: 331420
Rhonda Rogers (Mgr-New Bus)

Subsidiary (Domestic):

Technology Research Corporation (2)
4525 140th Ave N Ste 900, Clearwater, FL 33762
Tel.: (727) 535-0572
Web Site: http://www.trci.net
Sales Range: $25-49.9 Million
Emp.: 529
Portable Electrical Safety Products Designer, Mfr & Marketer; Power Monitoring & Control Equipment Supplier
N.A.I.C.S.: 423610
Richard C. O'Neal (VP-Comml Sls & Mktg)
J. Bradley Freeman (VP-Ops)
Gary Yetman (Pres & CEO)

Subsidiary (Domestic):

Patco Electronics, Inc. (3)
1855 Shepard Dr, Titusville, FL 32780
Tel.: (321) 268-0205
Web Site: http://www.patcoelectronics.com
Sales Range: $1-9.9 Million
Emp.: 15
Battery Management Equipment Mfr
N.A.I.C.S.: 335999
Roger Boatman (Pres)

Subsidiary (Non-US):

TRC Honduras S.A. de C.V. (3)
Segundo Anillo Periferico 20-27 Calle S.E. San Jose, 3973, San Pedro Sula, Cortes, Honduras (100%)
Tel.: (504) 5540096
Web Site: http://www.trci.net
Sales Range: $100-124.9 Million
Emp.: 335
Portable Electrical Safety Products Mfr
N.A.I.C.S.: 335999
Hamze M. Moussa (Pres & Gen Mgr)

Subsidiary (Domestic):

Watteredge LLC (2)
567 Miller Rd, Avon Lake, OH 44012-2304
Tel.: (440) 933-6110
Web Site: http://www.watteredge.com
Sales Range: $25-49.9 Million
Emp.: 80
Electrical Accessories & Equipment Mfr & Marketer
N.A.I.C.S.: 335999
Bob LaRussa (VP-Mktg)
Ben Gontarz (Mgr-Engrg)
Dennis Marquard (Mgr-Quality)
John Jeffreys (Gen Mgr & Mgr-Pur)
Sharon Call (Mgr-Credit)
Mark Amsden (Mgr-Inside Sls & Customer Svc)
Erhard Redeker (Gen Mgr)

Construction Electrical Products, LLC
7800 Las Positas Rd, Livermore, CA 94551
Tel.: (925) 828-9420
Web Site: http://www.cepnow.com
Power, Distribution & Specialty Transformer Mfr
N.A.I.C.S.: 335311
Scott Hess (Dir-Mfg)

Novinium, Inc. (1)
22820 Russell Rd, Kent, WA 98032
Tel.: (253) 395-0200
Web Site: http://www.novinium.com
Sales Range: $10-24.9 Million
Emp.: 300
Cable Rejuvenation Products & Services
N.A.I.C.S.: 561499
Glen Bertini (Founder, Chm, Pres & CEO)
Mark Newton (VP-Engrg)
Jon Engman (CFO)
Kevin Laux (Engr-Mechanical)
Michael Pines (Engr-Mechanical)
Branko Horvat (Dir-New Product Dev)
Peter Christman (VP-IT)

Seatek Company Inc. (1)
392 Pacific St, Stamford, CT 06902
Tel.: (203) 324-0067
Web Site: http://www.seatekco.com
Rev.: $1,800,000
Emp.: 19
Vitreous China, Fine Earthenware & Other Pottery Product Mfr
N.A.I.C.S.: 327110

Southwire Canada Company (1)
5769 Main Street, Stouffville, L4A 2T1, ON, Canada
Tel.: (905) 640-4333
Web Site: http://www.southwire.ca
Sales Range: $25-49.9 Million
Emp.: 200
Mfr of Industrial Components, Performance Chemicals & Fiber Optics
N.A.I.C.S.: 335921
Tim King (Pres)

Sumner Manufacturing Co., Inc. (1)
7514 Alabonson Rd, Houston, TX 77088
Tel.: (281) 999-6900
Web Site: http://www.sumner.com
Rev.: $6,666,666
Emp.: 75
Overhead Traveling Crane, Hoist & Monorail System Mfr
N.A.I.C.S.: 333923

SOUTHWOOD FURNITURE CORP.
2860 Nathan St, Hickory, NC 28602
Tel.: (828) 465-1776
Web Site: http://www.southwoodfurn.com
Year Founded: 1973
Sales Range: $10-24.9 Million
Emp.: 40
Household Furniture Mfr
N.A.I.C.S.: 337121
Diann Rooker (Mgr-IT)

SOUTHWORTH COMPANY INC.
265 Main St, Agawam, MA 01001-1822
Tel.: (413) 789-1200 MA
Web Site: http://www.southworth.com
Year Founded: 1839
Sales Range: $25-49.9 Million
Emp.: 150
Paper Mills
N.A.I.C.S.: 322120
David C. Southworth (Pres)

SOUTHWORTH INTERNATIONAL GROUP INC.
11 Gray Rd, Falmouth, ME 04105
Tel.: (207) 878-0700 ME
Web Site: http://www.southworthproducts.com
Year Founded: 1986
Sales Range: $100-124.9 Million
Emp.: 80

Ergonomic Materials Handling Equipment Mfr for Vertical Lifting & Work Positioning
N.A.I.C.S.: 333924
Subsidiaries:

Southworth Products Corp. (1)
11 Gray Rd, Falmouth, ME 04105
Tel.: (207) 878-0700
Web Site:
http://www.southworthproducts.com
Rev.: $10,000,000
Emp.: 70
Tables, Lift: Hydraulic
N.A.I.C.S.: 333924

SOUTHWORTH-MILTON INC.
100 Quarry Dr, Milford, MA 01757-1729
Tel.: (508) 634-3400   NH
Web Site: http://www.miltoncat.com
Year Founded: 1960
Sales Range: $50-74.9 Million
Emp.: 900
Construction & Mining Machinery
N.A.I.C.S.: 532412
Jack W. Milton (Owner)
Christopher Milton (Pres)
Steve Boyd (CFO)
Subsidiaries:

Milton Cat (1)
294 Ainsley Dr, Syracuse, NY 13210
Tel.: (315) 703-7042
Web Site: http://www.miltoncat.com
Sales Range: $25-49.9 Million
Emp.: 200
Construction & Mining Equipment Whslr
N.A.I.C.S.: 423810
Ruth Leach (Controller)
George S. Deptula (Sec)
Cris Milton (Pres & CEO)
Michael Dickerson (Mgr-Power Sys Sls-NY)

SOVEREIGN CONSULTING INC.
111A N Gold Dr, Robbinsville, NJ 08691
Tel.: (609) 326-1500
Web Site: http://www.sovcon.com
Year Founded: 1999
Sales Range: $25-49.9 Million
Emp.: 170
Environmental Support Services
N.A.I.C.S.: 541620
Richie Atkinson (Project Mgr)
Cathy Ames (Asst Controller)
Jorge Montoy (Engr-Environmental)
Julie Ciabattoni (Mgr-Billing)
Kristen Bebout (Project Mgr)
Michael Hanlon (Mgr-Bus Dev)
Nancy Smith (Mgr-Health & Safety)
Ellyn Brixius (Project Mgr)

SOVEREIGN DISTRIBUTORS INC.
651 Rte 72 E, Manahawkin, NJ 08050
Tel.: (609) 978-9700
Web Site:
http://www.avaloncarpettile.com
Rev.: $19,717,433
Emp.: 220
Floor Covering Stores
N.A.I.C.S.: 449121
John P. Millar (Pres)

SOVEREIGN GROUP INTERNATIONAL
517 US Hwy 1 S Ste 3100, Iselin, NJ 08830
Tel.: (732) 750-2300
Web Site:
http://www.sovereignins.com
Rev.: $20,000,000
Emp.: 20
Insurance Agents
N.A.I.C.S.: 524210

William F. Lynch (Pres)
Iryna Paratsa (Office Mgr)

SOVEREIGN LENDING GROUP, INC.
18400 Von Karman Ste 550, Irvine, CA 92612
Web Site:
htttp://www.slgmortgage.com
Year Founded: 2005
Sales Range: $1-9.9 Million
Emp.: 50
Mortgage Refinancing, Home Equity Loans & Debt Consolidation
N.A.I.C.S.: 522310
Joseph Pirro (Principal)
Dan Holtz (CEO)
Allison Wapato (VP-Processing)

SOVEREIGN VOLKSWAGEN LLC.
340 W Old Country Rd, Hicksville, NY 11801
Tel.: (516) 942-7300
Sales Range: $10-24.9 Million
Emp.: 43
Car Whslr
N.A.I.C.S.: 441110
Josh Lever (Owner)

SOVRANO LLC
5912 Balcones Dr, Austin, TX 78731-4202
Tel.: (512) 459-2222   DE
Investment Holding Company
N.A.I.C.S.: 551112
Michael Poates (Pres)
Subsidiaries:

Mr. Gatti's, L.P. (1)
PO Box 470726, Fort Worth, TX 76147
Tel.: (816) 546-3500
Web Site: http://www.gattispizza.com
Sales Range: $125-149.9 Million
Pizza Restaurants & Arcades Operator & Franchisor
N.A.I.C.S.: 722513
Michael Poates (Pres)

SOVRN HOLDINGS, INC.
1101 W Grove St Ste 201, Boise, ID 83702-5124
Tel.: (208) 345-6064
Web Site:
http://www.sovrncreative.com
Motion Picture & Video Production
N.A.I.C.S.: 512110
Philip McLain (Partner)
Todd Siegler (COO)
Walter Knapp (CEO)
Subsidiaries:

VigLink, Inc. (1)
333 Bush St Fl 22 Ste 2200, San Francisco, CA 94104
Tel.: (888) 828-8492
Web Site: http://www.viglink.com
Software Publisher
N.A.I.C.S.: 513210
Oliver Roup (CEO)
Steven Hartman (VP-Mktg)
Josh Jaffe (VP-Bus Dev)
William Johnson (VP-Ops)
Siavash Amirrezvani (Engr-Staff Software)
Emily Schmuhl (Mgr-Customer Success)
Hanna Fritzinger (Mgr-Mktg)
Cody Pape (Mgr-Network Quality)
Leah Salloway (Mgr-Publr Svcs)
Brian Braunlich (Product Mgr)
Marianne Lontoc (Sr Mgr-Mktg)
Prakash Chandra (VP-Engrg)
Mike Campbell (VP-Product)

Subsidiary (Domestic):

LinkSmart, Inc. (2)
1805 11th St Unit C, Boulder, CO 80302
Tel.: (303) 668-8277
Web Site: http://www.linksmart.com

Sales Range: $1-9.9 Million
Software Publisher
N.A.I.C.S.: 513210
Daniel Weiss (VP-Product)
Pete Sheinbaum (Founder & CEO)
Emmanuel Puentes (CTO)

SOWELL & CO., INC.
1601 Elm St Ste 3500, Dallas, TX 75201-7277
Tel.: (214) 871-3320
Web Site: http://www.sowellco.com
Sales Range: $50-74.9 Million
Emp.: 50
Management Investment Company
N.A.I.C.S.: 523999
James E. Sowell (Principal)
Keith D. Martin (CFO & Principal)
Steven E. Smathers (Principal)
Subsidiaries:

Apache Enterprises, Inc. (1)
2985 Red Hawk Dr, Grand Prairie, TX 75052
Tel.: (972) 641-0835
Web Site: http://www.apache-enterprises.com
Sales Range: $1-9.9 Million
Aircraft Part Mfr
N.A.I.C.S.: 336413

Vantex Commercial Property Group (1)
9920 W Sam Houston Pkwy S Ste 405, Houston, TX 77099
Tel.: (713) 780-4300
Web Site: http://www.vantexcpg.com
Sales Range: $50-74.9 Million
Emp.: 10
Real Estate Services
N.A.I.C.S.: 531210

SP IMAGES LLC
1000 Franklin Vlg Dr Ste 304, Franklin, MA 02038
Tel.: (508) 530-3225
Web Site: http://www.spimages.com
Sports & Entertainment Products Distr & Marketer
N.A.I.C.S.: 424990
John Capuano (VP)
Justin Abreu (Acct Mgr)
John Baumann (Natl Acct Mgr)
Darren Danielson (Natl Acct Mgr)
Joseph Each (VP-Sls)
Bob Jones (Mgr-eCommerce)
Chris Koch (Mgr-Pur)
Owen Marmaduke (COO)
April McClung (Coord-Ground Freight)
Julia O'Dell (Mgr-Acctg)
Michelle Owens (Gen Mgr)
Aaron Shetler (Ops Mgr)
Matt Williams (Natl Acct Mgr)
Ellen Samon (Mgr-Credit)

SPA PARTS PLUS
7175 E 2nd St Ste B, Prescott Valley, AZ 86314
Tel.: (928) 775-5058
Web Site: http://www.spaparts.com
Year Founded: 1986
Sales Range: $10-24.9 Million
Emp.: 15
Sales of Spa Equipment & Supplies
N.A.I.C.S.: 423910
Barry W. Knickerbocker (Co-Founder & CEO)
Paulette Knickerbocker (Co-Founder)

SPAAN TECH, INC.
311 S Wacker Dr Ste 2400, Chicago, IL 60606
Tel.: (312) 277-8800
Web Site: http://www.spaantech.com
Year Founded: 1998
Sales Range: $10-24.9 Million
Emp.: 65
Construction & Design Services

N.A.I.C.S.: 236220
Smita N. Shah (Founder & CEO)
David Viglielmo (Coord-Tech & Project Mgr-IT)
Frank Bressendorf (Dir-Facilities)
Erik Johnson (Engr-Civil)
Steve Shelus (Mgr-Engrg)

SPACE & ASSET MANAGEMENT INC.
3680 Wyse Rd, Dayton, OH 45414
Tel.: (937) 918-1000
Web Site: http://www.elementsiv.com
Sales Range: $1-9.9 Million
Emp.: 48
Whslr of Furniture
N.A.I.C.S.: 423210
Mark William (Pres & CEO & Gen Mgr)

SPACE ADVENTURES LTD.
8245 Boone Blvd Ste 570, Vienna, VA 22182
Tel.: (703) 524-7172
Web Site:
http://www.spaceadventures.com
Year Founded: 1998
Sales Range: $1-9.9 Million
Emp.: 19
Space Flight Simulation Services
N.A.I.C.S.: 713990
Peter H. Diamandis (Co-Vice Chm)

SPACE AGE FUEL INC.
15525 SE Formor St, Gresham, OR 97015
Tel.: (503) 665-5693
Web Site:
http://www.spaceagefuel.com
Rev.: $16,100,000
Emp.: 150
Gasoline
N.A.I.C.S.: 424720
Trey Brunton (Mgr-Retail)
Sonja Parks (Asst Controller)
Terese Schopf Tyler (Controller)

SPACE AGE SERVICES, INC.
2625 Keystone Rd Unit #5, Tarpon Springs, FL 34688
Tel.: (813) 925-3880   FL
Web Site: http://www.saeweb.com
Year Founded: 1996
Sales Range: $1-9.9 Million
Emp.: 15
Custom Computer Programming Services
N.A.I.C.S.: 541511
Richard Vanderwiede (Pres)

SPACE CENTER INC.
2501 Rosegate, Saint Paul, MN 55113
Tel.: (651) 604-4200
Web Site:
http://www.spacecenterinc.com
Sales Range: $50-74.9 Million
Emp.: 250
Real Estate Managers
N.A.I.C.S.: 531210

SPACE COAST BUSINESS, LLC
5131 Industry Dr Ste 107, Melbourne, FL 32940
Tel.: (321) 622-5986
Web Site:
http://www.scbmarketing.com
Year Founded: 2006
Sales Range: $1-9.9 Million
Emp.: 19
Multimedia Marketing Agency Services
N.A.I.C.S.: 541613
Jeff Piersall (Founder & CEO)

SPACE EXPLORATION TECHNOLOGIES CORP.   U.S. PRIVATE

Space Coast Business, LLC—(Continued)

SPACE EXPLORATION TECHNOLOGIES CORP.
1 Rocket Rd, Hawthorne, CA 90250
Tel.: (310) 363-6000
Web Site: https://www.spacex.com
Year Founded: 2002
Emp.: 12,000
Guided Missile & Space Vehicle Manufacturing
N.A.I.C.S.: 336414
Bret Johnsen *(CFO)*
Dex Torricke-Barton *(Sr Dir-Comm)*
Gwynne E. Shotwell *(Pres & COO)*

Subsidiaries:

Pioneer Aerospace Corporation   (1)
45 S Satellite Rd Ste 2, South Windsor, CT 06074
Tel.: (860) 528-0092
Other Aircraft Parts & Auxiliary Equipment Mfr
N.A.I.C.S.: 336413

SPACE FITTERS INC.
44 Baker Hollow Rd, Windsor, CT 06095
Tel.: (860) 683-9053
Web Site: http://www.sfiservices.com
Rev.: $15,461,364
Emp.: 50
Computer Related Consulting Services
N.A.I.C.S.: 541512

SPACE NEEDLE CORPORATION
400 Broad St, Seattle, WA 98109
Tel.: (206) 905-2100
Web Site:
   http://www.spaceneedle.com
Sales Range: $10-24.9 Million
Emp.: 700
Restaurant & Tourist Attraction Operator
N.A.I.C.S.: 722511
David Mandapat *(Mgr-Mktg)*
Nate Wilkinson *(Partner)*
Karen Olson *(VP-Mktg)*

SPACE VECTOR CORPORATION
9174 Deering Ave, Chatsworth, CA 91311-5801
Tel.: (818) 734-2600
Web Site:
   http://www.spacevector.com
Year Founded: 1969
Sales Range: $25-49.9 Million
Emp.: 45
Government & Military Aerospace Launch Vehicles & Services
N.A.I.C.S.: 336414
Eric Grabow *(Pres)*
Frank Bednarik *(Dir-Ops)*
Diana Colton *(Mgr-HR)*
Scott Higgins *(VP-Engrg)*

SPACE-CRAFT MANUFACTURING, INC.
300 East St, New Haven, CT 06511
Tel.: (203) 781-8020
Web Site: http://www.space-craft.com
Year Founded: 1970
Sales Range: $10-24.9 Million
Emp.: 40
Precision Machine Shop Focusing on Aerospace Industry
N.A.I.C.S.: 332710
Victor Pavlick *(VP-Sls)*
Don Clark *(VP-Engrg)*
Kathleen Williams *(Mgr-Shipping)*

SPACEBOUND, INC.
280 Opportunity Way, Avon, OH 44050
Tel.: (440) 355-8008
Web Site:
   http://www.spacebound.com
Year Founded: 1986
Sales Range: $10-24.9 Million
Emp.: 28
Software Mfr
N.A.I.C.S.: 423430
Patricia A. Miller *(CEO & CFO)*
Anthony Saliba *(Partner & CIO)*
Jacquelyne Diab *(Product Mgr)*
Kate Walker *(Dir-Sls-Govt Div)*

SPACEMAKERS INC.
PO Box 11104, Norfolk, VA 23517
Tel.: (757) 640-8100
Web Site:
   http://www.spacemakers.net
Year Founded: 1986
Sales Range: $100-124.9 Million
Emp.: 15
Commercial & Office Building Contracting Services
N.A.I.C.S.: 236220
Bjorn W. Marshall *(Pres)*
Jackie Evans *(Controller)*

SPACESAVER STORAGE SOLUTIONS LLC
10040 Whitesel Rd Ste 107, Ashland, VA 23005
Tel.: (804) 798-3701
Web Site:
   http://www.spacesaverva.com
Year Founded: 2007
Sales Range: $1-9.9 Million
Emp.: 20
Shelving & Storage Systems
N.A.I.C.S.: 337215
David Craig *(Owner)*

SPACETIME, INC.
35 E Wacker Dr Ste 3100, Chicago, IL 60601-2307
Tel.: (312) 425-0800
Web Site:
   http://www.spacetimemedia.com
Year Founded: 1994
Sales Range: $25-49.9 Million
Emp.: 16
Media Buying Services
N.A.I.C.S.: 541810
Robin Lampert *(Pres)*
Susanna Avila *(Mgr-Acctg)*

SPACEWORKS ENTERPRISES, INC.
1040 Crown Pointe Pkwy Ste 950, Atlanta, GA 30338-4741
Tel.: (770) 379-8000
Web Site: http://www.sei.aero
Year Founded: 2000
Sales Range: $1-9.9 Million
Emp.: 15
Aerospace Engineering Design Services
N.A.I.C.S.: 541330
John R. Olds *(Co-Founder & CEO)*
Melinda S. Olds *(Co-Founder & CFO)*
John E. Bradford *(Pres-SpaceWorks Engrg)*

SPADONE ALFA SELF LUBRICATING PRODUCTS, LLC
PO Box 411, Westport, CT 06851-4411
Tel.: (800) 959-2529
Web Site: http://www.spadone-alfa.com
Self Lubricating Bearings, Pillow Blocks & Flange Units Mfr
N.A.I.C.S.: 332991

SPAEQUIP, INC.
211 Wapoo Ave, Calistoga, CA 94515
Tel.: (707) 737-1100
Web Site: http://www.spaequip.com
Year Founded: 1987
Rev.: $15,400,000
Emp.: 35
Medical & Hospital Equipment Supplies Merchant Whslr
N.A.I.C.S.: 423450
Ed Johnson *(VP)*
Kitty Gray *(Controller)*
Philippe Therene *(Sec)*
Polly Johnson *(VP)*

SPAFINDER, INC.
257 Park Ave S 10th Fl, New York, NY 10010
Tel.: (212) 924-6800
Web Site: http://www.spafinder.com
Year Founded: 1996
Sales Range: $50-74.9 Million
Emp.: 150
Spa, Travel & Marketing Services
Connecting Consumers Via Publishing, Internet & Corporate Incentive Programs
N.A.I.C.S.: 513120
Pete Ellis *(Chm & CEO)*
Susie Ellis *(Pres)*
Neil Kurlander *(Chief Admin Officer & Gen Counsel)*
Steve Kane *(Chief Revenue Officer)*
Michael Muller *(Sr VP-Fin)*
Elaine D'Farley *(Editor-in-Chief-Spafinder Wellness 365)*
Dave Walters *(CTO)*
Peter Manice *(Partner-Dev & VP)*

Subsidiaries:

Spafinder Wellness UK, Ltd.   (1)
Unit 208 Screenworks 22, Highbury Grove, London, N5 2ER, United Kingdom
Tel.: (44) 8701216066
Web Site: http://www.spafinder.co.uk
Spa, Travel & Marketing Services
N.A.I.C.S.: 541890
Pete Ellis *(Chm & CEO)*

SPAHN & ROSE LUMBER CO., INC.
2175 Southpark Ct, Dubuque, IA 52004-0149
Tel.: (563) 582-3606   IA
Web Site:
   http://www.spahnandrose.com
Year Founded: 1904
Sales Range: $25-49.9 Million
Emp.: 239
Building Material Sales
N.A.I.C.S.: 444110
John P. Hannan *(CEO)*
R. E. Gansen *(VP-Fin)*
K. L. Funke *(VP-Ops)*
David C. Davis *(Pres)*
John Cook *(VP)*

Subsidiaries:

Still Lumber Co. Inc.   (1)
1515 Old Covington Rd NE, Conyers, GA 30013
Tel.: (770) 483-8022
Web Site: http://www.stilllumber.com
Rev.: $1,200,000
Emp.: 11
Lumber, Plywood, Millwork & Wood Panel Merchant Whslr
N.A.I.C.S.: 423310

SPALDING AUTOMOTIVE INC.
4529 Adams Cir, Bensalem, PA 19020
Tel.: (215) 638-3334
Web Site:
   http://www.spaldingautomotive.com
Sales Range: $10-24.9 Million
Emp.: 100
Sale of Motor Vehicle Parts & Accessories
N.A.I.C.S.: 336390
Wes Kuehnle *(Pres)*

SPALDING DEDECKER ASSOCIATES, INC.
905 South Blvd E, Rochester Hills, MI 48307
Tel.: (248) 844-5400   MI
Web Site: http://www.sda-eng.com
Year Founded: 1954
Sales Range: $10-24.9 Million
Emp.: 125
Engineering, Surveying & Architectural Services
N.A.I.C.S.: 541330
Mike F. H. DeDecker *(VP & Sr Project Mgr-Survey)*
George Platz *(Chm & Dir-Surveying)*
Steve Benedettini *(Pres & CFO)*
Catherine M. DeDecker *(VP & Mgr-Mktg)*
Cheryl L. Gregory *(VP & Sr Project Mgr-Transportation)*
Thomas J. Sovel *(VP & Sr Project Mgr-Land Dev)*
Ted Meadows *(Mgr-Construction Engrg Project)*
David Richmond *(Mgr-Municipal Project)*
Keith Sirois *(Mgr-Survey Project)*
Philip A. Rasor Jr. *(VP & Dir-Engrg)*

SPAN CONSTRUCTION & ENGINEERING INC
1841 Howard Rd, Madera, CA 93637
Tel.: (559) 661-1111
Web Site:
   http://www.spanconstruction.com
Sales Range: $125-149.9 Million
Emp.: 85
Commercial & Office Buildings, Prefabricated Erection
N.A.I.C.S.: 236220
Firoz Mohamed Husein *(Pres)*
Mark A. Reynolds *(Mgr-Bus Dev)*

SPANDEX USA INC.
1857 Walnut St, Allentown, PA 18104
Tel.: (610) 434-9889
Web Site:
   http://www.clarksystems.com
Sales Range: $10-24.9 Million
Emp.: 25
Computer Software
N.A.I.C.S.: 423430
Charles J. Kelly *(Pres)*
Charles Kelly Sr. *(VP)*

SPANG & COMPANY
110 Delta Dr, Pittsburgh, PA 15238-2811
Tel.: (412) 963-9363   PA
Web Site: http://www.spang.com
Year Founded: 1894
Sales Range: $150-199.9 Million
Emp.: 500
Mfr of Electric Components, Switchgear & Switchboard Apparatus; Specialty Metals Distribution & Specialty Transformers; Toys & Games
N.A.I.C.S.: 334412
Lynne Ellis *(VP-HR)*
Kevin R. McKnight *(VP-Fin)*
William Glass *(Mgr-Sls)*
Robert A. Rath Jr. *(VP)*

Subsidiaries:

Magnetics   (1)
110 Delta Dr, Pittsburgh, PA 15238 (100%)
Tel.: (412) 696-1333
Web Site: http://www.mag-inc.com
Sales Range: $10-24.9 Million
Emp.: 60
Mfr of a Broad Range of Magnetic Cores
N.A.I.C.S.: 333511
Richard Durham *(Controller)*

Plant (Domestic):

Spang & Company-Booneville Plant   (2)

3070 Hwy Ten E, Booneville, AR 72927
Tel.: (479) 675-4800 **(100%)**
Web Site: http://www.spangpower.com
Mfr of Magnetic Cores
N.A.I.C.S.: 334419

Spang Power Electronics (1)
PO Box 457, Sandy Lake, PA 16145-0457 **(100%)**
Tel.: (724) 376-7515
Web Site: http://www.spangpower.com
Sales Range: $10-24.9 Million
Emp.: 35
Produces AC & DC Power Supplies & Transformers, Drive Systems & Power Systems
N.A.I.C.S.: 334610
Robert Smith *(Pres)*
Christopher M. McCormick *(VP-Bus Dev)*
Eric Corry *(VP-Sls & Mktg)*

SPANGLER CANDY COMPANY
400 N Portland St, Bryan, OH 43506-1200
Tel.: (419) 636-4221 **OH**
Web Site: http://www.spanglercandy.com
Year Founded: 1906
Sales Range: $200-249.9 Million
Emp.: 500
Mfr of Candy
N.A.I.C.S.: 311340
Jim Knight *(VP-ECommerce & IT)*
Dean L. Spangler *(Chm)*
Evan S. Brock *(Dir-Mktg)*
Kirkland B. Vashaw *(CEO)*
Stephen S. Kerr *(VP-Mfg)*
William G. Martin *(Pres)*

SPANGLER COMPANIES, INC.
1110 E Morehead St, Charlotte, NC 28204-2815
Tel.: (704) 372-4500 **NC**
Year Founded: 1966
Investment Holding Company
N.A.I.C.S.: 551112
William D. Cornwell Jr. *(Pres)*

Subsidiaries:

National Gypsum Services Company (1)
2001 Rexford Rd, Charlotte, NC 28211
Tel.: (704) 365-7300
Web Site: http://www.nationalgypsum.com
Emp.: 2,400
Drywall & Other Gypsum Products Mfr
N.A.I.C.S.: 327420
Thomas C. Nelson *(Pres)*
Lori Hudson *(CFO)*
Laura E. Budzichowski *(Sec)*
Richard G. Parkhurst *(Treas)*

Subsidiary (Domestic):

ProForm Finishing Products, LLC (2)
2001 Rexford Rd, Charlotte, NC 28211
Tel.: (704) 365-7300
Web Site: http://www.proformfinishing.com
Gypsum Finishing Products Mfr
N.A.I.C.S.: 327420
John King *(Mgr)*

Spangler Properties, LLC (1)
1110 E Morehead St, Charlotte, NC 28204-2815
Tel.: (704) 372-4500
Real Estate Investment & Development
N.A.I.C.S.: 531390

SPANGLES INC.
437 N Hillside St, Wichita, KS 67214
Tel.: (316) 685-8817
Web Site: http://www.spanglesinc.com
Sales Range: $10-24.9 Million
Emp.: 450
Fast Food Restaurants & Stands
N.A.I.C.S.: 722513

Craig Steven *(Pres)*
Dale Steven *(VP)*
David Dooman *(CFO)*

SPANISH COVE HOUSING AUTHORITY
11 Palm St, Yukon, OK 73099
Tel.: (405) 354-1901 **OK**
Web Site: http://www.spanishcove.com
Year Founded: 1998
Sales Range: $1-9.9 Million
Emp.: 240
Lifecare Retirement Community Operator
N.A.I.C.S.: 623311
Larry Taylor *(Vice Chm)*
Don Blose *(CEO)*

SPANISH TRAILS ASSOCIATES LP
6767 W Tropicana Ave 2nd Fl, Las Vegas, NV 89103
Tel.: (702) 367-1733
Sales Range: $10-24.9 Million
Emp.: 84
New Construction, Single-Family Houses
N.A.I.C.S.: 236115
Lynn Wilcox *(Mgr-HR)*

SPANOS BARBER JESSE & CO.
2001 N Main St Ste 650, Walnut Creek, CA 94596
Tel.: (415) 848-1990
Web Site: http://www.sbjcap.com
Private Investment Firm
N.A.I.C.S.: 523999
Gus Spanos *(Mng Dir)*
Tom Barber *(Mng Dir)*
Bill Jesse *(Mng Dir)*
Matt Cole *(Mng Dir)*
Ben Landis *(Mng Dir)*
Porter Hall *(VP)*
Patrick Muller *(VP)*
Tara Genstiil *(CFO)*
Stela Nevada *(Controller)*
Ashley Gonzales *(Mgr-Office)*

Subsidiaries:

Central Lake Armor Express, Inc. (1)
7915 Cameron St, Central Lake, MI 49622
Tel.: (231) 544-6090
Web Site: http://www.armorexpress.com
Body Armor Mfr
N.A.I.C.S.: 331110
James R. Henderson *(CEO)*
Matt Davis *(Chm)*
Brian Murphy *(Mgr-Saves Progham)*
Tom Thebes *(CFO)*
Glenn Wiener *(Chief Strategy Officer)*
Lushana Offutt *(Sr VP-Govt Ops)*
Frank Cappo *(Vp-Sls)*
James Mays *(Dir-Plant Ops)*
Jonathan MacNeil *(Dir-Ballistics Research & Dev)*
Filipe Placucci *(Dir- Carrier Research & Dev)*
Deniese Miranda *(Sr VP-HR)*
Jermey Graham *(Reg Dir-Sls)*
Mike Lee *(Reg Dir-Sls)*
David Jones *(Dir-Federal Sls)*
Steve Murphy *(Dir-Product Line)*
Frank Flores *(Dir-Intl Sls)*

Subsidiary (Domestic):

KDH Defense Systems, Inc. (2)
750 Fieldcrest Rd, Eden, NC 27288
Tel.: (336) 635-4158
Web Site: http://www.armorexpress.com
Apparels Mfr
N.A.I.C.S.: 315990
Jim Henderson *(CEO)*

SPARBOE FARMS
23577 Hwy 22, Litchfield, MN 55355
Tel.: (320) 593-9600 **MN**
Web Site: http://www.sparboe.com

Year Founded: 1954
Sales Range: $10-24.9 Million
Emp.: 140
Egg Producer & Egg Products
N.A.I.C.S.: 112310
Ken Zakman *(Controller)*
Beth Sehnell *(Pres)*
Sadie Ludowese *(Coord-Logistics)*
Kevin Kieke *(Dir-Engrg)*
Kristy Vossen *(Gen Mgr-Acctg)*
Lee Murphy *(Mgr-Credit)*
Nita Nurmi *(Mgr-HR, Safety & Benefits)*
Dan Amundson *(Dir-Processing)*

SPARC HOLDING COMPANY
6593 Merchant Pl, Warrenton, VA 20187
Tel.: (540) 351-5121
Web Site: https://www.sparcresearch.com
Emp.: 100
Holding Company
N.A.I.C.S.: 551112
Patrick Hewitt *(CEO)*

Subsidiaries:

SPARC Research LLC (1)
6593 Merchant Pl, Warrenton, VA 20187
Tel.: (540) 351-5121
Web Site: https://www.sparcresearch.com
Aerospace Engineering Services
N.A.I.C.S.: 334511

Subsidiary (Domestic):

Design Integrated Technology, Inc. (2)
100 E Franklin St, Warrenton, VA 20186
Tel.: (540) 349-9425
Web Site: http://www.ditusa.com
Rev.: $7,552,000
Emp.: 8
Other Miscellaneous Durable Goods Merchant Whslr
N.A.I.C.S.: 423990

SPARC, LLC
2387 Clements Ferry Rd, Charleston, SC 29492
Tel.: (843) 471-1231
Web Site: http://www.sparcedge.com
Year Founded: 2009
Sales Range: $10-24.9 Million
Emp.: 160
Software Engineering Services
N.A.I.C.S.: 541511
Bob Williams *(CTO)*
Eric Bowman *(Chm & Pres)*
Elizabeth Buske *(CEO)*

SPARCO.COM
7089 Ryburn Dr, Millington, TN 38053-6200
Tel.: (901) 872-2272
Web Site: http://www.sparco.com
Year Founded: 1997
Sales Range: $25-49.9 Million
Emp.: 24
Computer Software Publishers & Developers
N.A.I.C.S.: 449210
Soo-Tsong Lim *(Pres)*
Mubashir Cheema *(VP)*

SPARE TIME INC.
11344 Coloma Rd Ste 350, Gold River, CA 95670
Tel.: (916) 859-5910
Web Site: http://www.sparetimeclubs.com
Year Founded: 1972
Sales Range: $50-74.9 Million
Emp.: 1,500
Racquetball Club, Membership
N.A.I.C.S.: 713940
Dan Lopez *(Mgr-Corp Facilities)*

SPARK
1 W Broad St Suite 1000, Bethlehem, PA 18018
Tel.: (484) 821-0920
Web Site: http://www.sparkcreatives.com
Year Founded: 2004
Sales Range: $10-24.9 Million
Emp.: 16
Advertising, Local Marketing, Media Relations, Public Relations
N.A.I.C.S.: 541810
Michael Drabenstott *(Principal)*

SPARK
2309 W Platt St, Tampa, FL 33609-3343
Tel.: (813) 253-0300
Web Site: http://www.spark.us
Year Founded: 2001
Sales Range: $1-9.9 Million
Emp.: 30
Advertising, Brand Development & Integration
N.A.I.C.S.: 541810
Michael Peters *(Founder)*
Gordon Weller *(Dir-Creative)*
Dylan Melcher *(Dir-Photography)*
Amanda Eichmann *(Mgr-Brand)*
Joe Guerra *(Editor)*
Lauren Williams *(Coord-Ops)*
Nicole Luistro *(Mgr-Community)*
Patrick Guyer *(Editor)*
Tiffany Ballas *(Mgr-Brand)*

Subsidiaries:

SPARK STUDIOS (1)
2309 W Platt St, Tampa, FL 33609
Tel.: (813) 253-0300
Web Site: http://www.sparkstudios.tv
Post-Ppoduction, Video Production, Visual Effects, Motion Graphics, Broadcast Production, Retouching & Still Photography
N.A.I.C.S.: 512110

SPARK.ORANGE, LLC
304 S Franklin St Ste 201, Syracuse, NY 13202
Tel.: (315) 552-0520 **NY**
Web Site: http://www.sparkorange.net
Year Founded: 2013
Sales Range: $1-9.9 Million
Emp.: 21
Business Management Consulting Services
N.A.I.C.S.: 541611
Derek Vargas *(Co-Founder)*
Aliza Seeber *(Co-Founder)*

SPARKFACTOR DESIGN
344 Addison Ave, Palo Alto, CA 94301
Tel.: (650) 327-3006
Web Site: http://www.sparkfactordesign.com
Year Founded: 2001
Rev.: $3,900,000
Emp.: 15
Business Services
N.A.I.C.S.: 541990
Claudia Truesdell *(Founder)*
Abraham Farag *(CEO)*
Laura Gingher *(COO)*
Mike Lohse *(Dir-Engrg)*

SPARKFUN ELECTRONICS
6175 Longbow Dr Ste 200, Boulder, CO 80301
Tel.: (303) 284-0979
Web Site: http://www.sparkfun.com
Year Founded: 2003
Sales Range: $25-49.9 Million
Emp.: 135
Online Marketing Services
N.A.I.C.S.: 449210

SparkFun Electronics—(Continued)
Chris Taylor *(Project Mgr)*
Matt Bolton *(Dir-Production)*
Mike Albrecht *(Mgr-Desktop Ops)*
Nathan Seidle *(Founder & CEO)*

SPARKHOUND, INC.
11207 Proverbs Ave, Baton Rouge, LA 70816
Tel.: (225) 216-1500
Web Site:
http://www.sparkhound.com
Year Founded: 1998
Sales Range: $10-24.9 Million
Emp.: 151
Information Technology Services
N.A.I.C.S.: 541512
Shawn Usher *(Pres & CEO)*
Patrick Thompson *(COO)*
Noah Boudreaux *(Chief Admin Officer)*
Tommy Mann *(Gen Mgr-Houston)*
Melissa Lambert *(Dir-Mktg)*
Kevin McDonald *(Sr VP)*
Dave Baxter *(VP-Sls-Louisiana)*
Richard Morehouse *(Sr Project Mgr-Consultant)*
Kyle Collins *(Dir-Bus Dev)*
Craig Hays *(Mng Dir-Infrastructure)*

SPARKLE MAINTENANCE, INC.
5827 4th St NW, Espanola, NM 87107
Tel.: (505) 345-5501
Web Site:
http://www.sparklecorp.com
Year Founded: 1964
Sales Range: $10-24.9 Million
Cleaning Service Contractor
N.A.I.C.S.: 561720
Carlo Lucero *(Pres)*
Bette Wilson *(Controller)*
Paul Lucero *(VP & Gen Mgr)*
Linda McCaffrey *(Mgr-HR & Safety)*
Jerry Lineweaver *(Mgr-Ops)*
Gabriel Sedillo *(Mgr-Area)*
Janis Pettus *(Mgr-Quality)*
Kathryn Rodriguez *(Mgr-Area)*
Virginia Quezada *(Mgr-Area)*

SPARKLE POWER INC.
48502 Kato Rd, Fremont, CA 94538
Tel.: (408) 519-8888
Web Site:
http://www.sparklepower.com
Sales Range: $10-24.9 Million
Emp.: 25
Computers, Peripherals & Software
N.A.I.C.S.: 423430
Wen Jang *(Pres)*
David Hwing *(Owner)*

SPARKLE, LLC
111 Princess St, Wilmington, NC 28401
Tel.: (910) 763-4669
Year Founded: 2004
Holding Company
N.A.I.C.S.: 458310
Alan M. Zimmer *(Pres & CEO)*

SPARKPR
2 Bryant St Ste 100, San Francisco, CA 94105
Tel.: (415) 962-8200
Web Site: http://www.sparkpr.com
Sales Range: $10-24.9 Million
Emp.: 30
Public Relation Agency Services
N.A.I.C.S.: 541820
Alan Soucy *(CEO)*
Diane Schreiber *(Sr Mng Dir)*
Tim Turpin *(Gen Mgr)*

Jay Kolbe *(Mng Dir-Digital Ad & Mktg)*
Donna Burke *(Co-Founder & Mng Partner)*
Walter Kuhn *(Dir-Creative)*
Marco Iannucci *(Dir-Strategy)*
Matt Marquess *(Dir-Talent)*
Nicole Bestard *(Mng Dir)*
Cameron McPherson *(VP-Fin)*
Jeff Koo *(VP)*
Mary Magnani *(VP)*

SPARRER SAUSAGE COMPANY, INC.
4325 W Ogden Ave, Chicago, IL 60623
Tel.: (773) 762-3334
Year Founded: 1935
Sales Range: $25-49.9 Million
Emp.: 120
Sausage Mfr
N.A.I.C.S.: 311612
Robert Rodgers *(Mgr-Acctg)*
Chris Hetherman *(VP)*
Brian Graves *(Co-Pres & CEO)*
Mary Morgan *(Mgr-Acctg)*
Carmen Munoz *(Mgr-HR)*
Matt Duffy *(Co-Pres)*
Patrick Silva *(Plant Mgr)*
Betty Deweese *(Product Mgr)*
Angie Sanchez *(Supvr-Quality Control)*
Noemi Diaz *(Mgr-Facilities Ops)*

SPARTA CHEVROLET, INC.
8955 Sparta Ave NW, Sparta, MI 49345
Tel.: (616) 887-1791
Web Site:
http://www.spartachevy.com
Sales Range: $10-24.9 Million
Emp.: 35
Car Whslr
N.A.I.C.S.: 441110
Dave Vanderhyde Jr. *(Gen Mgr)*

SPARTA COOPERATIVE SERVICES
325 Hemstock Dr, Sparta, WI 54656
Tel.: (608) 269-2255
Web Site: http://www.spartacoop.com
Year Founded: 1997
Sales Range: $25-49.9 Million
Emp.: 43
Agricultural Services
N.A.I.C.S.: 424510
Mona Kenyon *(Office Mgr)*
Bruce Towns *(Gen Mgr)*

SPARTA ECUMENICAL COUNCIL ON SENIOR CITIZEN HOUSING INC.
39 Trapasso Dr, Sparta, NJ 07871
Tel.: (973) 729-4311
Web Site:
http://www.knowllproperties.org
Year Founded: 1978
Sales Range: $1-9.9 Million
Emp.: 16
Low Income People Housing Services
N.A.I.C.S.: 624229
Lisa Reidinger *(Mgr-Property)*

SPARTACUS ACQUISITION CORPORATION
6470 E Johns Crossing Ste 490, Duluth, GA 30097
Tel.: (770) 305-6434
Year Founded: 2020
Investment Services
N.A.I.C.S.: 523999
Igor Volshteyn *(CFO)*
Peter D. Aquino *(Chm)*

SPARTAN AUTOMATIC RETAILERS
3761 Lamar Ave, Memphis, TN 38118-3706
Tel.: (901) 365-2611
Sales Range: $75-99.9 Million
Emp.: 35
Vending Services
N.A.I.C.S.: 445132
Timothy E. Jackson *(Owner)*

SPARTAN AUTOS INCORPORATED
5701 S Pennsylvania Ave, Lansing, MI 48911
Tel.: (517) 394-6000
Web Site:
http://www.spartanmotormall.com
Sales Range: $50-74.9 Million
Emp.: 100
Automobiles, New & Used
N.A.I.C.S.: 441110
Rosario Criscuolo *(Pres)*
Mark Shuert *(Controller)*

SPARTAN CHEMICAL CO. INC.
1110 Spartan Dr, Maumee, OH 43537
Tel.: (419) 531-5551
Web Site:
http://www.spartanchemical.com
Sales Range: $100-124.9 Million
Emp.: 169
Polishes & Sanitation Goods
N.A.I.C.S.: 325612
John Willis Swigart *(Pres)*
J.P. Little *(Mgr-Info & Sls Tech)*

SPARTAN DISTRIBUTORS INC.
487 W Division St, Sparta, MI 49345-1046
Tel.: (616) 887-7301
Web Site: http://www.spartandist.com
Year Founded: 1947
Sales Range: $75-99.9 Million
Emp.: 100
Golf Course Cutting & Irrigation Equipment & Machinery Distr
N.A.I.C.S.: 423820
Dawn Johnson *(Chm & Pres)*
Bruce Johnson *(CFO)*
Fritz Middleton *(Mgr-Golf Car Div)*
John Andrus *(Mgr-Irrigation Svc & Golf Sls)*

SPARTAN GOLD LTD.
13591 N Scottsdale Rd Ste 233, Scottsdale, AZ 85260
Tel.: (480) 391-7400
Year Founded: 2007
Gold Exploration Services
N.A.I.C.S.: 212220
Mick Gavrilovic *(COO)*

SPARTAN INDUSTRIAL INC.
3896 Laniell St, Detroit, MI 48211
Tel.: (313) 846-5400
Web Site:
http://www.spartanindustrial.com
Rev: $12,000,000
Emp.: 40
Industrial Machinery & Equipment Repair
N.A.I.C.S.: 811210
Terry Hawkins *(Pres & CEO)*

SPARTAN LIGHT METAL PRODUCTS
510 E McClurken Ave, Sparta, IL 62286
Tel.: (618) 443-4346
Web Site: http://www.spartanlmp.com
Sales Range: $10-24.9 Million
Emp.: 700
Aluminum Die-Castings
N.A.I.C.S.: 331523

Don Jubel *(Pres)*
Kevin Monahan *(VP-Fin)*

SPARTAN SCHOOL OF AERONAUTICS
8820 E Pine St, Tulsa, OK 74115-5802
Tel.: (918) 836-6886
Web Site: http://www.spartan.edu
Year Founded: 1928
Sales Range: $75-99.9 Million
Emp.: 300
Aviation Related Courses
N.A.I.C.S.: 611519
Damon Bowling *(VP-Mktg)*

SPARTAN SHOPS INC.
1125 N 7th St, San Carlos, CA 95112
Tel.: (408) 924-1900
Web Site:
http://www.spartanshops.com
Sales Range: $10-24.9 Million
Emp.: 510
Contract Food Services
N.A.I.C.S.: 722310
Jeff Pauley *(Dir-Dining Svcs)*
Phil Chiaramonte *(Sr Dir-Retail Svcs)*
Adam Filipp *(Coord-Sustainability)*

SPARTANBURG FOREST PRODUCTS INC.
1431 Hwy 101 S, Greer, SC 29651-6731
Tel.: (864) 699-3100
Web Site:
http://www.spartanburgforestproducts.com
Year Founded: 1978
Sales Range: $10-24.9 Million
Emp.: 25
Lumber & Building Materials Sales
N.A.I.C.S.: 423310
Stephen W. Michael *(Pres & CEO)*
Angela Bishop *(Controller)*
Mike Paspore *(VP)*

SPARTANBURG MEAT PROCESSING CO., INC.
3003 N Blackstock Rd, Spartanburg, SC 29301
Tel.: (864) 574-1225
Web Site: http://www.eatbbqribs.com
Year Founded: 1999
Sales Range: $10-24.9 Million
Emp.: 52
Processed Chicken, Pork & Beef Mfr
N.A.I.C.S.: 311611
Joanne Laboundy *(Pres)*
Travis Smith *(Gen Mgr)*
Tommy Coggins *(Mgr-Maintenance)*
Anthony Wells *(Coord-Quality Assurance & Safety)*
John Lepore *(Exec VP)*
Josi Santia *(VP-Admin)*
Paul Harper *(CFO)*
Sukha Matharu *(VP-General Freight Ops)*

SPARTANBURG REGIONAL HEALTH SERVICES DISTRICT, INC.
101 E Wood St, Spartanburg, SC 29303
Tel.: (864) 560-6000
Web Site:
http://www.spartanburgregional.com
Year Founded: 1995
Emp.: 6,500
Holding Company; Hospital & Health Care Services Operator
N.A.I.C.S.: 551112
Byrd Miller *(Chm)*
Bruce Holstien *(Pres & CEO)*
Mark Aycock *(COO)*

COMPANIES

Subsidiaries:

Mary Black Health System LLC (1)
1700 Skylyn Dr, Spartanburg, SC 29307
Tel.: (864) 573-3000
Web Site:
   http://www.maryblackhealthsystem.com
Hospital Operator & Specialty Healthcare Services
N.A.I.C.S.: 622110
Parkes Coggins *(VP-Hospital Integration)*
Cody Butts *(Pres-Interim-Cherokee Medical Center)*
Brett English *(CFO)*
Howard C. Bean *(Chief Medical Officer)*
Chanda Flynn *(Chief Nursing Officer)*

Subsidiary (Domestic):

Gaffney HMA, Inc. (2)
1530 N Limestone St, Gaffney, SC 29340-4742
Tel.: (864) 487-1659
Web Site:
   https://www.maryblackhealthsystem.com
Sales Range: $50-74.9 Million
Hospital Services
N.A.I.C.S.: 622110
Joshua Self *(CEO)*
Christine Poplawski *(CFO)*
Mychelle Ross *(Chief Nursing Officer)*

Spartanburg Medical Center (1)
101 E Wood St, Spartanburg, SC 29303
Tel.: (864) 560-6000
Web Site:
   http://www.spartanburgregional.com
Hospital Operator
N.A.I.C.S.: 622110

The Spartanburg Regional Healthcare System Foundation (1)
101 E Wood St, Spartanburg, SC 29303
Tel.: (864) 560-6727
Medical Grantmaking Foundation
N.A.I.C.S.: 813219
Bruce Holstien *(Pres & CEO)*

SPARTANBURG WATER SYSTEM
200 Commerce St, Spartanburg, SC 29304
Tel.: (864) 583-7361
Web Site:
   http://www.spartanburgwater.org
Year Founded: 1887
Sales Range: $10-24.9 Million
Emp.: 175
Water Supply
N.A.I.C.S.: 221310
Sue G. Schneider *(CEO)*
G. Newton Pressley *(CFO)*
Kevin Brown *(Dir-IT)*
Remsen Parrish *(Mgr-Purchasing)*
David Ledbetter *(Mgr-Collection Sys)*
Angie Price *(Mgr-Construction Asset Dept-Collection & Distr Dept)*
Ronnie Champion *(Dir-Water Collection & Distr)*
Ron O'Neill *(Mgr-Reservoir)*
Steven Robertson *(Mgr-Engrg Projects)*
Gene Jackson *(Officer-Capital Projects)*
Robert Walden *(COO)*

SPATIAL NETWORKS, INC.
18167 US Hwy 19N Ste 240, Clearwater, FL 33764
Tel.: (727) 538-0545
Web Site:
   http://www.spatialnetworks.com
Year Founded: 2000
Sales Range: $1-9.9 Million
Emp.: 35
Data Processing & Related Services
N.A.I.C.S.: 518210
Anthony Quartararo *(Pres & CEO)*

SPATZ CENTERS INC.
14 N Peoria St Suite 3F, Chicago, IL 60607-2646
Tel.: (312) 733-4033
Web Site:
   http://www.spatzcenters.com
Real Estate Development & Management Services
N.A.I.C.S.: 531120
Wendy Spatz *(VP-Design)*

SPAULDING BRICK COMPANY INC.
5 Lopez Rd, Wilmington, MA 01887
Tel.: (401) 467-2220
Web Site:
   http://www.spauldingbrick.com
Sales Range: $10-24.9 Million
Emp.: 27
Bricks Mfr
N.A.I.C.S.: 423320
Ralph Watson *(Controller)*
Ralph Lawson *(Treas)*

SPAULDING COMPOSITES, INC.
55 Nadeau Dr, Rochester, NH 03867-4637
Tel.: (603) 332-0555 NH
Web Site:
   http://www.spauldingcom.com
Year Founded: 1873
Sales Range: $10-24.9 Million
Emp.: 125
Mfr of Laminated Plastics, Plate & Sheet Products
N.A.I.C.S.: 326130
Miranda Harmon *(Mgr-Inside Sls)*
Kenneth Otto *(Pres & CEO)*
Peggy Grainger *(Mgr-Cust Svcs)*
Chris Smith *(Exec VP-Engrg)*

SPAULDING DECON, LLC
3615 E 7th Ave, Tampa, FL 33605
Tel.: (813) 298-7122
Web Site:
   http://www.spauldingdecon.com
Year Founded: 2005
Sales Range: $1-9.9 Million
Crime Scene Cleanup, Decontamination, Disinfection, Hoarding Cleanup, Restoration & Property Preservation Services; Crime Victim Services
N.A.I.C.S.: 561740
Laura Spaulding *(Owner & Pres)*
Juaniti Smith *(Mgr-Ops)*

SPAW GLASS HOLDING LP
9331 Corp Dr, Selma, TX 78154
Tel.: (210) 651-9000
Web Site: http://www.spawglass.com
Year Founded: 1953
Sales Range: $200-249.9 Million
Emp.: 300
Nonresidential Construction
N.A.I.C.S.: 236220
Fred D. Raley *(Chm & CEO)*

Subsidiaries:

Spaw Glass Construction Corp. (1)
13800 W Rd, Houston, TX 77041
Tel.: (281) 970-5300
Web Site: http://www.spawglass.com
Rev.: $216,250,129
Emp.: 130
Commercial & Office Building Contractors
N.A.I.C.S.: 236220
Michael Emmons *(COO)*
Kelly Fox *(Mgr-Bus Dev)*
Brandon Meyers *(Pres-Houston)*

Spaw Glass Contractors Inc. (1)
9331 Corporate Dr, Schertz, TX 78154
Tel.: (956) 412-9880
Web Site: http://www.spawglass.com
Rev.: $117,036,829
Emp.: 120
Commercial & Office Building Contractors
N.A.I.C.S.: 236220
Fred D. Raley *(Chm & CEO)*
Chuck Calvin *(Pres)*

SPAWN IDEAS, INC.
510 L St Ste 100, Anchorage, AK 99501
Tel.: (907) 274-9553 AK
Web Site: http://www.spawnak.com
Year Founded: 1975
Sales Range: $10-24.9 Million
Advetising Agency
N.A.I.C.S.: 541810
Karen King *(Pres & CEO)*
Kathy Norford *(VP & Dir-Media)*
Susanne Izo *(Office Mgr)*
Charles Leshan *(Dir-Production)*
April Cook *(Dir-Project Mgmt & Assoc Dir-Acct Svc)*
Mike Weed *(VP & Creative Dir)*

SPCA INTERNATIONAL, INC.
PO Box 8682, New York, NY 10001
Tel.: (888) 690-7722 DE
Web Site: http://www.spcai.org
Year Founded: 2006
Sales Range: $10-24.9 Million
Emp.: 5
Animal Welfare Services
N.A.I.C.S.: 812910
J. D. Winston *(Exec Dir)*

SPEAKERBUS, INC.
1 Chase Manhattan Plz Ste 3901, New York, NY 10005-1416
Tel.: (646) 289-4724
Web Site:
   http://www.speakerbus.com
Emp.: 100
Audio & Video Equipment Mfr
N.A.I.C.S.: 334310
Dave Hurford *(VP-Global Channel Mgmt)*
Roy Williamson *(Global Head-Sls & Mktg)*

Subsidiaries:

Imarket Communications Inc. (1)
675 Line Road, Aberdeen, NJ 07747
Tel.: (732) 765-9100
Web Site:
   http://www.imarketcommunications.com
Rev.: $1,665,000
Emp.: 5
Wired Telecommunications Carriers
N.A.I.C.S.: 517111
Dennis Costello *(Pres & CEO)*

SPEAKMAN COMPANY
400 Anchor Mill Rd Twin Spans Business Park, New Castle, DE 19720
Tel.: (302) 764-7100 DE
Web Site:
   http://www.speakmancompany.com
Year Founded: 1869
Sales Range: $75-99.9 Million
Emp.: 110
Mfr of Showers, Brass Plumbing, Decorative Brass Plumbing Fittings & Safety Equipment
N.A.I.C.S.: 332913
Tara Scanzillo *(Dir-Sls)*

SPEAKS OIL CO. INC.
121 Dekalb St, Camden, SC 29020
Tel.: (803) 432-3501
Rev.: $10,036,701
Emp.: 9
Petroleum Products Sales
N.A.I.C.S.: 424720
John R. Speaks *(Pres)*

SPEAR MARKETING GROUP LLC
1630 N Main St Ste 200, Walnut Creek, CA 94596
Tel.: (925) 891-9050
Web Site:
   http://www.spearmarketing.com
Sales Range: $1-9.9 Million
Emp.: 26

SPEARHALL ADVERTISING & PUBLIC RELATIONS

Advetising Agency
N.A.I.C.S.: 541810
Howard J. Sewell *(Pres)*
Matt Randolph *(CEO)*
Tom Meriam *(VP-Bus Dev)*
Tracy Ciampi *(Dir-Client Svcs)*
Gilda Raczkowski *(Dir-Creative)*
Laura McInerney *(Dir-Art)*
Dan Reed *(Dir-Mktg Automation)*

SPEAR PHYSICAL THERAPY, PLLC.
120 E 56th St, New York, NY 10022
Tel.: (212) 759-2211
Web Site:
   http://www.spearcenter.com
Sales Range: $1-9.9 Million
Emp.: 23
Physical Therapy Center Operator
N.A.I.C.S.: 621340
Ryan Kitzen *(Dir-Clinical)*
Dan Siciliano *(Co-Founder & Co-Pres)*
Dan Rootenberg *(Co-Founder & Co-Pres)*

SPEAR USA LLC
5510 Courseview Dr, Mason, OH 45040
Tel.: (513) 459-1100
Web Site: http://www.spearlabel.com
Sales Range: $400-449.9 Million
Emp.: 400
Film Pressure-Sensitive Labeling Systems
N.A.I.C.S.: 323111
Michael Henry *(CFO)*
Rick Spear *(CEO)*
Randy Spear *(Pres)*

Subsidiaries:

SPEARsystem Packaging Africa (Pty) Ltd (1)
Bantry Park 41 Jansen Road Jet Park, Boksburg, 1469, South Africa
Tel.: (27) 11 323 3600
Packaging & Labeling Services
N.A.I.C.S.: 561910

Spear USA LLC (1)
48 Powers St, Milford, NH 03055
Tel.: (603) 673-6400
Web Site: http://www.spearlabel.com
Rev.: $9,500,000
Emp.: 81
Labels (Unprinted), Gummed: Made From Purchased Materials
N.A.I.C.S.: 322220

Spear USA LLC (1)
801 Alfred Thun Rd, Clarksville, TN 37040
Tel.: (931) 920-9000
Web Site: http://www.spearsystem.com
Sales Range: $50-74.9 Million
Emp.: 200
Supplier of Film Pressure-Sensitive Labeling Systems
N.A.I.C.S.: 323111
Jeff Feldman *(Dir-Ops)*

Spearsystem Packaging Asia Pte Ltd. (1)
65 Fernhill Road, Singapore, 259120, Singapore
Tel.: (65) 6520 5371
Packaging & Labeling Services
N.A.I.C.S.: 561910

SPEARHALL ADVERTISING & PUBLIC RELATIONS
9740 Appaloosa Rd Ste 250, San Diego, CA 92131
Tel.: (858) 586-1202
Web Site: http://www.spearhall.com
Year Founded: 1980
Sales Range: Less than $1 Million
Emp.: 2
N.A.I.C.S.: 541810

Spearhall Advertising & Public Relations—(Continued)

Shelly Hall (Pres)
Melissa Holden (Acct Mgr)
Gina Mancini (Dir-Creative)
Michael Nesbit (VP-Special Events)
Stephanie Prebis (Acct Coord)

SPEARMAN BANCSHARES, INC.

PO Box 337, Spearman, TX 79081
Tel.: (806) 659-5544 TX
Web Site: http://www.fnbspearman.com
Year Founded: 1990
Sales Range: $50-74.9 Million
Emp.: 35
Bank Holding Company
N.A.I.C.S.: 551111
Ginger Pittman (Sr VP)

Subsidiaries:

First National Bank (1)
729 W 7th St, Spearman, TX 79081
Tel.: (806) 659-5544
Web Site: http://www.fnbspearman.com
Retail & Commercial Banking
N.A.I.C.S.: 522180
Bill D. Pittman (Chm & CEO)
Tindle Ramon (CFO & Sr VP)
Ginger Pittman (Sr VP)
Brian Gillispie (Pres)
Bret Burgin (Exec VP)

SPEARMC CONSULTING

400 Spear St Ste 221, San Francisco, CA 94105
Web Site: http://www.spearmc.com
Year Founded: 2004
Sales Range: $1-9.9 Million
Emp.: 15
It Consulting
N.A.I.C.S.: 541690
Marcus Bode (Founder & Principal)

SPEARS MANUFACTURING COMPANY

15853 Olden St, Sylmar, CA 91342
Tel.: (818) 364-1611
Web Site: http://www.spearsmfg.com
Year Founded: 1969
Sales Range: $25-49.9 Million
Emp.: 134
Injection Molded Finished Plastics Product Mfr
N.A.I.C.S.: 326199
Wayne Spears (Pres)
Greg Newell (Mgr-Warehouse Ops)
Paul Feng (VP-IT)
Dennis Littleford (Controller)

Subsidiaries:

Coastline Plastics L.L.C. (1)
86334 Coastline Dr, Yulee, FL 32097-3355
Tel.: (904) 225-5950
Web Site: http://www.coastlineplastics.com
Sales Range: $10-24.9 Million
Emp.: 30
Pipe Couplings, Fittings, Valves, Accessories & Tools Mfr
N.A.I.C.S.: 325211
Steve Clark (Mgr-Natl Sls)

SPECHT ELECTRIC CO. INC.

3212 Wilgus Ave, Sheboygan, WI 53081
Tel.: (920) 457-7321
Web Site: http://www.spechtelectric.com
Sales Range: $10-24.9 Million
Emp.: 45
General Electrical Contractor
N.A.I.C.S.: 238210
Gene Specht (Pres)
Scott Specht (Controller)

SPECIAL DISTRICT SERVICES, INC.

The Oaks Ctr 2501A Burns Rd, Palm Beach Gardens, FL 33410
Tel.: (561) 630-4922
Web Site: http://www.sdsinc.org
Year Founded: 1993
Sales Range: $1-9.9 Million
Emp.: 20
Financial Management Services
N.A.I.C.S.: 541611
Peter L. Pimentel (Chm)
Todd Wodraska (Pres)

SPECIAL FLEET SERVICE INC.

875 Waterman Dr, Harrisonburg, VA 22802
Tel.: (540) 434-4488
Web Site: http://www.specialfleet.com
Rev.: $10,000,000
Emp.: 54
Derrick Building, Repairing & Dismantling
N.A.I.C.S.: 237120
M. Gregory Weaver (Pres)

SPECIAL METALS INC.

6406 S Eastern Ave, Oklahoma City, OK 73149
Tel.: (405) 677-7700
Web Site: http://www.specialmetalsinc.com
Sales Range: $10-24.9 Million
Emp.: 30
Metal Products
N.A.I.C.S.: 423510
Mike Potts (Pres)

SPECIAL MOLD ENGINEERING INC.

1900 Production Dr, Rochester Hills, MI 48309
Tel.: (248) 652-6600
Web Site: http://www.specialmold.com
Rev.: $11,415,167
Emp.: 65
Industrial Molds
N.A.I.C.S.: 333511
Marta J. MacDonald (Pres)
Eddie Elliott (Mgr-Ops)
Dan Doll (Mgr-Quality Control)
Marta MacDonald (Pres)
Dina DeWeese (Treas & Sec)
Keith MacDonald (VP-Estimating)
David MacDonald (VP-Mfg)
Darin MacDonald (VP-Pur)

SPECIAL OPERATIONS GROUP INC.

526 Railroad St, Corona, CA 92882
Tel.: (951) 279-3300
Rev.: $18,400,000
Emp.: 12
Bus Ticket Offices
N.A.I.C.S.: 561599

SPECIAL OPERATIONS SOLUTIONS LLC

8070 Georgia Ave Ste 309, Silver Spring, MD 20910
Tel.: (706) 307-0532
Web Site: http://www.specopsolutions.com
Year Founded: 2007
Sales Range: $1-9.9 Million
Emp.: 27
Technical Staffing
N.A.I.C.S.: 541690
Manan Patel (Founder & Pres)

SPECIAL OPERATIONS WARRIOR FOUNDATION, INC.

1137 Marbella Plaza Dr, Tampa, FL 33619
Tel.: (813) 805-9400 FL
Web Site: http://www.specialops.org
Year Founded: 1980
Rev.: $16,447,060
Assets: $123,600,321
Liabilities: $47,044,991
Net Worth: $76,555,330
Earnings: ($7,192,570)
Emp.: 14
Fiscal Year-end: 12/31/18
Grantmaking Services
N.A.I.C.S.: 813211
Thomas D. Deitz (Coord-Dev)
Thomas Arthur (Sec)
Edie Rosenthal (Sr Dir-Programs)
David Redmond (Treas)
Sean J. Corrigan (Exec VP)
Denise Anderson (Deputy Dir-Scholarships & Family Outreach)
Angel C. Mason (Dir-Resources)
Lisa Henson (Mgr-Acctg)
Gary Aquino (Mgr-Admin)
Greg Von Schottenstein (Dir-Dev)
Brooke Hardy (Mgr-Corp Rels)
Alex Gordon (Coord-Event)
Clayton M. Hutmacher (Pres & CEO)
Raymond Thomas III (Chm)

SPECIAL PRODUCT COMPANY

8540 Hedge Ln Ter, Lenexa, KS 66227-3200
Tel.: (913) 491-8088 DE
Web Site: http://www.spc.net
Year Founded: 1988
Sales Range: $10-24.9 Million
Emp.: 30
Indoor & Outdoor Telecommunication & Electronic Equipment Enclosure & Cabinet Mfr
N.A.I.C.S.: 332439
Jerry Garrett (Pres & CEO)

SPECIAL PRODUCTS & MANUFACTURING, INC.

2625 Discovery Blvd, Rockwall, TX 75032
Tel.: (972) 771-8851
Web Site: http://www.spmfg.com
Rev.: $18,000,000
Emp.: 160
Sheet Metalwork
N.A.I.C.S.: 332322
Rob Grand-Lienard (CEO)
James Morris (CTO)

SPECIAL RISKS FACILITIES INC.

38555 Mound Rd Ste 100, Sterling Heights, MI 48310
Tel.: (586) 795-8200
Web Site: http://www.specialrisksinc.com
Year Founded: 1972
Sales Range: $25-49.9 Million
Emp.: 35
Insurance Services
N.A.I.C.S.: 524210
Randy Kaszeta (Exec VP)
Jack Klebba (Pres)

SPECIAL SERVICE FOR GROUPS

905 E 8th St, Los Angeles, CA 90021
Tel.: (213) 553-1800 CA
Web Site: http://www.ssg.org
Year Founded: 1952
Sales Range: $25-49.9 Million
Emp.: 727
Community Care Services
N.A.I.C.S.: 624190
Dianna Malak-Lopez (Dir-Strategic Dev & Partnerships)
Antonia Diaz (Mgr-HR)
Naomi Kageyama (Dir-Special Projects)
Herbert K. Hatanaka (Sec & Exec Dir)
Hayley Levy (Dir-Admin)

SPECIAL T'S, INC.

20325 N 51st Ave Bldg 9, Glendale, CA 85308-5674
Tel.: (623) 551-1990
Web Site: http://www.specialts.net
Year Founded: 1993
Sales Range: $1-9.9 Million
Emp.: 15
Advertising Services
N.A.I.C.S.: 541890
Matt Denicola (VP)
Jeff Bleich (Pres)

SPECIALISTS IN UROLOGY, PA

990 Tamiami Trl N, Naples, FL 34102
Tel.: (239) 434-6300
Web Site: http://www.specialistsinurology.com
Year Founded: 1991
Sales Range: $10-24.9 Million
Emp.: 300
Urology Services
N.A.I.C.S.: 621111
William Figlesthaler (Mng Partner)

SPECIALISTS MARKETING SERVICES, INC.

777 Terrace Ave Ste 401, Hasbrouck Heights, NJ 07604
Tel.: (201) 865-5800
Web Site: http://www.sms-inc.com
Year Founded: 1987
Sales Range: $10-24.9 Million
Emp.: 120
Direct Mail Advertising & Marketing Services
N.A.I.C.S.: 541860
Lon Mandel (Pres & CEO)
Robin B. Neal (Exec VP-List Mgmt & Insert Media)
Cyndi Lee (Sr VP-List Mgmt Sls & Strategic Dev)
Amy L. Lyons (Sr VP-Mktg)
Susan Giampietro (Exec VP-List Brokerage)
Peter Candito (Exec VP-B2B Grp)
Randi Morris (Exec VP-Interactive Div)
Tom Walsh (Exec VP-Data)
James L. Orleman (Sr Dir-IT)
Nora J. Bush (CFO)
Nicole Jason (Dir-HR)
Kim Fitzgerald (VP-List Brokerage)
Bruce Sherman (CTO)
Dave Thornbury (Co-CEO)
Fran Sharkey (CMO)

SPECIALIZED AUTOMATION SERVICES, LLC.

3165 Pipe Ct, Grand Junction, CO 81504-6237
Tel.: (970) 241-4175
Web Site: http://www.sas-llc.net
Year Founded: 2004
Sales Range: $10-24.9 Million
Emp.: 100
Industrial Equipment Whsr
N.A.I.C.S.: 423830
Jared R. Roberts (VP)
Derek Bernal (Mgr-Procurement)

SPECIALIZED BICYCLE COMPONENTS

15130 Concord Cir, Morgan Hill, CA 95037
Tel.: (408) 779-6229
Web Site: http://www.specialized.com
Year Founded: 1974
Sales Range: $200-249.9 Million
Emp.: 200

COMPANIES

Bicycles & Related Parts
N.A.I.C.S.: 336991
Mike Sinyard *(Founder & CEO)*

SPECIALIZED LEASING, INC.
9004 Dutton Dr, Twinsburg, OH 44087
Tel.: (330) 425-2715   OH
Year Founded: 1993
Rev.: $1,500,000
Emp.: 11
Fiscal Year-end: 12/31/10
Surgical Equipment
N.A.I.C.S.: 339112

SPECIALIZED MEDIA SERVICES, INC.
741 Kenilworth Ave Ste 204, Charlotte, NC 28204
Tel.: (704) 333-3111   NC
Web Site: http://www.specializedmedia.net
Year Founded: 1982
Sales Range: $10-24.9 Million
Emp.: 10
Media Buying Services
N.A.I.C.S.: 541830
Darlene S. Jones *(Pres)*
Mark Loyd *(Dir-Traffic)*

SPECIALIZED TRANSPORTATION SERVICE
225 Sam Griffins Rd 37167, Smyrna, TN 37167
Tel.: (615) 742-9944
Web Site: http://www.shipsts.com
Sales Range: $10-24.9 Million
Emp.: 125
Long Haul Trucking
N.A.I.C.S.: 484121
Tim Britt *(Gen Mgr)*
Ramsey Hassan *(Owner)*
Stevie Embree *(Dir-IT)*

SPECIALTY A/C PRODUCTS INC.
310 Soquel Way, Sunnyvale, CA 94085
Tel.: (408) 481-3611
Sales Range: $25-49.9 Million
Emp.: 100
Electrical Heating Equipment
N.A.I.C.S.: 423730
Donald Druyanoff *(Pres)*
Michael Wood *(CFO)*
Jim Jonas *(Exec VP)*
Santina Adams *(Mgr-Safety)*
Kathleen Backenson *(Dir-Mktg)*
Steve Butt *(Mgr)*
Tracey Burns *(Mgr-HR-Orlando)*
Mike Carey *(Mgr)*
Lisa Chupak *(Mgr-Safety-Wisconsin)*
Kevin Colbert *(Mgr-Sls-Madison)*
Paul Davignon *(Mgr)*
Ken Eggers *(Mgr-Indirect Sls-Tucson)*
Peg Fillenwarth *(Dir-Trng & Mktg-San Francisco)*
Mark Halderson *(Ops Mgr-THC Controls Offices)*
Jeff Hassell *(Mgr)*
John Kelley *(Mgr-Sls)*
Ryan Meinholz *(Mgr-Natl Accts)*
John Holland *(Controller)*
Ron LeVee *(Mgr-Svc)*
Tom Nastro *(Dir-Bus Dev-Boston)*
Dave Shaw *(Mgr-Contractor Sls)*

SPECIALTY ADHESIVES, INC.
3835 Viscount Ave Ste 5, Memphis, TN 38118
Tel.: (901) 794-8556
Web Site: http://www.specialtyadhesivesinc.com
Year Founded: 1988
Sales Range: $10-24.9 Million
Emp.: 50
Adhesive Mfr
N.A.I.C.S.: 325520
Larry Myrick *(Pres)*
John C. Dunavant *(VP)*
Tim Myrick *(Mgr-Sls-Natl)*
Connie Lesley *(Office Mgr)*
Mark Cox *(Gen Mgr-North Central)*
Kenneth Patton *(Gen Mgr-Texas Sls)*
Vince Lauria *(Dir-Technical Svc)*
Eddie Burton *(Mgr-Coatings & Paint Sls)*
Mellisa Bryant *(Mgr-Logistics)*
Don Berlin *(Mgr-Northeast)*
Steve Breeding *(Mgr-Ops)*
Larry Clarke *(Mgr-Ops & Facilities)*
Leslie Williams *(Mgr-Pur & AP)*

SPECIALTY BAKERS, INC.
450 S State Rd, Marysville, PA 17053-1012
Tel.: (717) 957-2131
Web Site: http://www.sbiladyfingers.com
Year Founded: 1901
Sales Range: $100-124.9 Million
Emp.: 300
Baking Products Supplier
N.A.I.C.S.: 311812
John L. Piotrowski *(Owner, Pres & CEO)*
Charles Smith *(Dir-Logistics)*
Jerry Look *(Controller)*
Karen Swinnerton *(Mgr-Customer Svc & Sls Support)*
James Graham *(Mgr-Distr)*

SPECIALTY BOTTLE LLC
3434 4th Ave S, Seattle, WA 98134
Tel.: (206) 382-1100
Web Site: http://www.specialtybottle.com
Year Founded: 1998
Sales Range: $1-9.9 Million
Emp.: 20
Glass, Plastic & Metal Bottles, Jars & Containers Mfr
N.A.I.C.S.: 327213
Scott Eskenazi *(Founder)*

SPECIALTY BUILDING PRODUCTS, INC.
2160 Satellite Blvd Ste 450, Duluth, GA 30097
Tel.: (678) 474-4577   DE
Web Site: https://www.specialtybuildingproducts.com
Year Founded: 2020
Rev.: $1,670,070,000
Assets: $1,030,826,000
Liabilities: $947,423,000
Net Worth: $83,403,000
Earnings: $18,019,000
Emp.: 2,653
Fiscal Year-end: 01/03/20
Holding Company
N.A.I.C.S.: 551112
Jeffery McLendon *(Pres & CEO)*
Ronald Stroud *(CFO)*
Bryan Lovingood *(COO)*
Carl McKenzie *(Chief Comml Officer)*
Christopher Gerhard *(Exec VP)*

SPECIALTY BUILDING PRODUCTS, LLC
2160 Satellite Blvd Ste 450, Duluth, GA 30097
Tel.: (678) 474-4577
Web Site: http://www.specialtybuildingproducts.com
Holding Company
N.A.I.C.S.: 551112
Jeff McLendon *(Pres & CEO)*

Subsidiaries:

US Lumber Group Inc.   (1)
2160 Satellite Blvd Ste 450, Duluth, GA 30097
Tel.: (678) 474-4577
Web Site: http://www.uslumber.com
Specialty Building Materials Distr
N.A.I.C.S.: 423310
Dan Wagoner *(Mgr-Sls)*
Ashley Kay *(Reg Mgr)*

Subsidiary (Domestic):

Mid-State Lumber Corp.   (2)
200 Industrial Pkwy, Somerville, NJ 08876
Tel.: (908) 725-4900
Web Site: http://www.midstatelumber.com
Rev.: $72,000,000
Emp.: 60
Lumber: Rough, Dressed & Finished
N.A.I.C.S.: 423310
Gary Bernstein *(Pres)*
Maria Eugenia Hall *(Mgr-Inventory Control)*
Liz Ryan *(Mgr-Mktg)*
Paul Burnham *(Dir-Sls-New England)*

Midwest Lumber Minnesota, Inc.   (2)
1720 Twr Dr, Stillwater, MN 55082
Tel.: (651) 439-5051
Web Site: http://www.midwestlumberinc.com
Building Product Mfr
N.A.I.C.S.: 423390

Subsidiary (Non-US):

Moulure Alexandria Moulding Inc.   (2)
20352 Power Dam Road, Alexandria, K0C 1AO, ON, Canada
Tel.: (613) 525-2784
Web Site: http://www.alexandriamoulding.com
Sales Range: $75-99.9 Million
Emp.: 725
Door & Mouldings Mfr
N.A.I.C.S.: 321911
Andre Cholette *(Pres)*

Subsidiary (Domestic):

Royal Woodworking Co. Limited   (3)
60 Industrial Road, Bradford, L3Z 3G7, ON, Canada
Tel.: (905) 727-2755
Web Site: http://www.royalwoodworking.com
Rev.: $11,477,344
Emp.: 55
Wood Mouldings Mfr
N.A.I.C.S.: 321999

SPECIALTY COATING & LAMINATING LLC
10351 Verdon Rd, Doswell, VA 23047
Tel.: (804) 876-3135   DE
Web Site: http://www.specoat.com
Poly-Extrusion & Aqueous-Coated Paper & Paperboards Mfr
N.A.I.C.S.: 322219
Geoff Baldwin *(Pres & CEO)*

SPECIALTY CONSTRUCTION MANAGEMENT, INC.
1314 8th St Nw, Washington, DC 20001-4206
Tel.: (202) 832-7250
Web Site: http://www.specialtyconstruction.net
Rev.: $21,700,000
Emp.: 56
Commercial & Institutional Building Construction
N.A.I.C.S.: 236220
Christy Figueroa *(VP)*
Joginder Kaur *(Pres)*

SPECIALTY ENGINE COMPONENTS L.L.C.
25940 Northline Rd, Taylor, MI 48180
Tel.: (734) 955-6500
Web Site: http://www.wathomas.com
Year Founded: 1996
Sales Range: $10-24.9 Million
Emp.: 11
Carburetors, Pistons, Piston Rings & Valves Supplier
N.A.I.C.S.: 336310
Mike Akwitz *(Plant Mgr)*

SPECIALTY ENTERPRISES CO., INC.
6858 E Acco St, Commerce, CA 90040-1902
Tel.: (323) 726-9721
Web Site: http://www.seco-ind.com
Sales Range: $10-24.9 Million
Emp.: 120
Plastics Foam Products
N.A.I.C.S.: 335210
Charles De Heras *(Pres)*

SPECIALTY FEEDS, INC.
2301 Latham St, Memphis, TN 38109
Tel.: (901) 774-9080
Web Site: http://www.specialty-feeds.com
Year Founded: 1960
Sales Range: $10-24.9 Million
Emp.: 30
Dog & Cat Food Mfr
N.A.I.C.S.: 311111
Charles Coscia *(CFO)*
Joseph J. Coscia *(Treas & Sec)*
Chuck Harland *(Dir-Pur)*

SPECIALTY FOOD ASSOCIATION, INC.
136 Madison Ave 12th Fl, New York, NY 10016
Tel.: (212) 482-6440   NY
Web Site: http://www.specialtyfood.com
Year Founded: 1952
Sales Range: $25-49.9 Million
Emp.: 55
Specialty Foods Trade Association
N.A.I.C.S.: 813910
Chris Crocker *(Sr VP-Content & Media)*
Ron Tanner *(VP-Philanthropy & Govt & Indus Rels)*
Michael Tuccillo *(Treas & VP-Acctg)*
Matt Nielsen *(Vice Chm)*
Becky Renfro Borbolla *(Chm)*
Trish Pohanka *(Sec)*
Todd Rubin *(Dir-Board)*
Ric Camacho *(Chief Tech & Digital Officer)*
Bill Lynch *(Interim Pres)*
Lisa Stefanoff *(Chief Membership Officer)*
Albert Straus *(Founder & CEO)*
William W. Booker III *(Officer-Fin)*

SPECIALTY GRANULES INC.
13424 Pennsylvania Ave Ste 303, Hagerstown, MD 21742
Tel.: (301) 733-4000
Web Site: http://www.specialtygranules.com
Year Founded: 1965
Sales Range: $25-49.9 Million
Emp.: 220
Mineral Granules for Roofing & Other Industries
N.A.I.C.S.: 213115
Wade Kemp *(VP & Gen Mgr)*
Ken Walton *(Pres)*

Subsidiaries:

Specialty Granules Inc.   (1)
1 Hillcrest Dr, Annapolis, MO 63620
Tel.: (573) 598-4235
Web Site: http://www.specialtygranules.com
Sales Range: $25-49.9 Million
Emp.: 175
Mineral Products Mfr
N.A.I.C.S.: 327992
Ken Walton *(Pres)*

SPECIALTY GRAPHIC IMAG-

SPECIALTY GRAPHIC IMAG—(CONTINUED)

ING ASSOCIATION
10015 Main St, Fairfax, VA 22031
Tel.: (703) 385-1335
Web Site: http://www.sgia.org
Year Founded: 1948
Screen & Digital Printing Community
N.A.I.C.S.: 323113
Ford Bowers *(Pres & CEO)*

Subsidiaries:

North American Publishing Co. (1)
1500 Spring Garden St Ste 1200, Philadelphia, PA 19130
Tel.: (215) 238-5300
Web Site: http://www.napco.com
Business, Professional & Consumer Magazine Publisher
N.A.I.C.S.: 513120
Irvin J. Borowsky *(Chm)*
Bob Gibbons *(Sr VP)*
Dave Leskusky *(Pres)*
Nichole Stella *(Pres & Chief Risk Officer-Promotional Products & Nonprofit)*
Mark J. Subers *(Pres & Chief Risk Officer-Printing, Packaging & Publishing)*
Chris Lyons *(Pres & Chief Risk Officer-Mktg & Retail)*
Ben Felix *(Pres & Chief Risk Officer-Consumer Tech)*
Travis Colla *(VP-Fin)*
Jeanne Scully *(VP-HR)*
Thomas Perkins *(VP-IT)*
Patty Perkins *(VP-Mktg & Audience Dev)*
Valerie Tickle *(VP-Audience Dev & Data Intelligence)*
Ambrose Crenshaw *(Dir-Digital)*
John Gelety *(Dir-Video Svcs)*
Nathan Safran *(Dir-Res)*
Julie Lamond *(Mgr-Design Dept)*
Matthew T. Gresge *(CEO)*

SPECIALTY HOLDINGS CORP.
2000 Friedensburg Rd, Reading, PA 19606
Tel.: (610) 779-1357
Web Site: http://www.specialtydesign.com
Rev.: $10,000,000
Emp.: 2
Machine Shop, Jobbing & Repair
N.A.I.C.S.: 332710
Craig Knabb *(Pres & CFO)*

Subsidiaries:

Specialty Design & Manufacturing Co. (1)
2000 Friedensburg Rd, Reading, PA 19606
Tel.: (610) 779-1357
Web Site: http://www.specialtydesign.com
Sales Range: $1-9.9 Million
Machine Shop, Jobbing & Repair
N.A.I.C.S.: 332710
Craig A Knabb *(Pres)*

SPECIALTY INDUSTRIES, INC.
175 Walnut St, Red Lion, PA 17356-2523
Tel.: (717) 246-1661 PA
Web Site: http://www.specialtyindustries.com
Year Founded: 1972
Sales Range: $100-124.9 Million
Emp.: 250
Corrugated Packaging Material Mfr
N.A.I.C.S.: 322211
Carl W. Cheek *(Chm & CEO)*
Ronald L. Mckinney *(VP-Sls)*
John Forrey *(Pres & CFO)*

Subsidiaries:

Krafcor Unlimited (1)
6301 Seaforth St, Baltimore, MD 21224
Tel.: (410) 633-4320
Web Site: http://www.specialtyindustries.com
Sales Range: $10-24.9 Million
Emp.: 50
Making Cardboards Corrugated Sheets
N.A.I.C.S.: 322211

Christina Pyle *(Office Mgr)*
Robert Rehak *(Gen Mgr)*

SPECIALTY INTERIORS INC.
2652 Crescent Springs Pk, Covington, KY 41017
Tel.: (859) 331-2696
Web Site: http://www.siohio.com
Year Founded: 1985
Rev.: $33,200,000
Emp.: 300
Interior Construction & Design Services
N.A.I.C.S.: 238310
Jeff Wollnitzek *(Pres)*

Subsidiaries:

Spectrum Interiors Tennesee Inc. (1)
201 Rosa Helmsway, Franklin, TN 37067
Tel.: (859) 331-2696
Web Site: http://www.spectruminteriors.com
Rev.: $10,700,000
Emp.: 175
Drywall Subcontractor
N.A.I.C.S.: 238310

SPECIALTY LIGHTING INC.
35 Industrial Park Rd No 10, Centerbrook, CT 06409
Tel.: (860) 767-0110
Web Site: http://www.sslighting.com
Sales Range: $10-24.9 Million
Emp.: 40
Lighting Fixtures
N.A.I.C.S.: 423610
Paula Donnelly *(VP)*

SPECIALTY MANUFACTURERS, INC.
2410 Executive Dr, Indianapolis, IN 46241
Tel.: (317) 241-1111
Web Site: http://www.spcmfg.com
Year Founded: 1958
Sales Range: $25-49.9 Million
Emp.: 235
Plastic Injection Molder
N.A.I.C.S.: 326199
Don Lucas *(CFO)*

Subsidiaries:

Apollo Plastics Corp. (1)
5333 N Elston Ave, Chicago, IL 60630-1667
Tel.: (773) 282-9222
Web Site: http://www.spcmfg.com
Sales Range: $10-24.9 Million
Emp.: 60
All Other Plastics Product Mfr
N.A.I.C.S.: 326199
Alberto Silva *(Pres)*

D&M Tool Corporation (1)
699 Washboard Rd, Springville, IN 47462
Tel.: (812) 279-8882
Emp.: 25
Tool & Die Mfr
N.A.I.C.S.: 333514
Bill Maddox *(VP)*
Tim Deckard *(Pres)*

PRD Inc. (1)
747 Washboard Rd, Springville, IN 47462
Tel.: (812) 279-8885
Web Site: http://www.prd-inc.com
Rev.: $9,300,000
Emp.: 150
Injection Molded Finished Plastics Product Mfr
N.A.I.C.S.: 326199

SPECIALTY MANUFACTURING CO.
5858 Centerville Rd, Saint Paul, MN 55127
Tel.: (651) 653-0599
Web Site: http://www.specialtymfg.com
Year Founded: 1900
Rev.: $29,000,000
Emp.: 75

Machining, Stamping, Injection Molding & Assembly Services; Valves & Dental Components Mfr
N.A.I.C.S.: 333511
Daniel McKeown *(Pres)*
Heidi Sandberg McKeown *(Chm)*
Kent Burner *(VP)*
Daniel McKeown *(Pres)*
David Kafka *(Plant Mgr)*
Jill Prahm *(Mgr-Ops)*

SPECIALTY MATERIALS, INC.
1449 Middlesex St, Lowell, MA 01851
Tel.: (978) 322-1900
Web Site: http://www.specmaterials.com
Year Founded: 2001
Sales Range: $10-24.9 Million
Emp.: 74
Cellulosic Organic Fiber Mfr
N.A.I.C.S.: 325199
Monte Treasure *(Pres)*

SPECIALTY MERCHANDISE CORPORATION
4119 Guardian St, Simi Valley, CA 93063
Tel.: (805) 578-5500 CA
Web Site: http://www.smartlivingcompany.com
Year Founded: 1948
Sales Range: $25-49.9 Million
Emp.: 300
Consumer Goods Mail Order Services
N.A.I.C.S.: 455219
Mark Schelbert *(Pres & CEO)*
Tom Kelly *(Dir-HR)*
Jessica Perry *(Supvr-Sls & Svc)*

SPECIALTY METALS CORPORATION
8300 S 206th St, Kent, WA 98032
Tel.: (253) 872-8000
Web Site: http://www.specialtymetalscorp.com
Sales Range: $10-24.9 Million
Emp.: 46
Metal Service Centers & Other Metal Merchant Whslr
N.A.I.C.S.: 423510
Doug Johnson *(Mgr)*
Theresa Nelson *(VP)*
James Stice Jr. *(Pres)*

SPECIALTY PIPING CORP.
1230 S Meadville Rd, Davisville, WV 26142
Tel.: (304) 424-5347
Web Site: http://www.specialtypiping.com
Sales Range: $10-24.9 Million
Emp.: 50
Commercial & Institutional Building Construction
N.A.I.C.S.: 236220
David Romine *(VP)*
Michael L. Romine *(Pres & Treas)*

SPECIALTY POLYMERS INC.
2475 Progress Way, Woodburn, OR 97017
Tel.: (503) 981-7523
Web Site: http://www.specpoly.com
Year Founded: 1969
Sales Range: $10-24.9 Million
Emp.: 75
Plastics Materials & Resins
N.A.I.C.S.: 325211
Sheryl Southwell *(Pres)*
Steve Reiser *(VP-Sls & Mktg)*
Aaron Hughes *(Dir-Ops)*

SPECIALTY RENTAL TOOLS & SUPPLY, INC.
1600 E Hwy 6 Ste 418, Alvin, TX 77511
Tel.: (281) 331-1800
Web Site: http://www.stsrental.com
Rev.: $10,000,000
Emp.: 30
Oil Field Machinery & Equipment
N.A.I.C.S.: 333132
Charles Helms *(Pres)*
Chris Crage *(Pres)*

SPECIALTY RESTAURANT GROUP LLC
150 W Church Ave, Maryville, TN 37801
Tel.: (865) 273-1394
Sales Range: $100-124.9 Million
Emp.: 15
Restaurant Operators
N.A.I.C.S.: 722511

SPECIALTY RESTAURANTS CORPORATION
8191 E Kaiser Blvd, Anaheim, CA 92808-2214
Tel.: (714) 279-6100
Web Site: http://www.specialtyrestaurants.com
Year Founded: 1958
Operator of Restaurants
N.A.I.C.S.: 722511
John Tallichet *(CEO)*
Chelsea Madden *(Natl Dir-Special Events)*
Charles Ochoa *(CFO)*
Heather Arcos *(Mgr-Payroll)*

SPECIALTY RESTORATION OF TEXAS
6906 Old McGregor Rd, Waco, TX 76712
Tel.: (254) 776-0441
Web Site: http://www.specialtyrestorationoftexas.com
Rev.: $11,300,000
Emp.: 100
Construction & Renovation Services
N.A.I.C.S.: 236118
Brian Ford *(Sr VP-Ops)*
Stuart Redding *(Exec VP)*
Wayne Redding *(Pres)*

SPECIALTY RETAIL VENTURES LLC
6411 Burleson Rd, Austin, TX 78744
Tel.: (512) 386-7220
Web Site: http://www.calendarclub.com
Year Founded: 1993
Sales Range: $1-9.9 Million
Emp.: 200
Holding Company
N.A.I.C.S.: 551112
Marc Winkelman *(CEO)*
Paul Hoffman *(COO)*
Jim Hull *(CFO)*

Subsidiaries:

Calendar Club LLC (1)
6411 Burleson Rd, Austin, TX 78744
Tel.: (512) 386-7220
Web Site: http://www.calendars.com
Whslr of Wall Calendars, Desk Calendars & Engagement Calendars
N.A.I.C.S.: 459410
Mike Hejny *(Exec VP-Mdsg & Store Ops)*
Dwight Duggins *(Mgr)*
Abel Mireles *(VP-IS & Distr)*
Jennifer Schubert *(VP-Mdsg)*

SPECIALTY STEEL TREATING INC.
34501 Commerce Rd, Fraser, MI 48026
Tel.: (586) 293-5355
Web Site: http://www.sstfraser.com

COMPANIES

SPECTRATEK TECHNOLOGIES INC.

SPECIALTY STRIP & OSCILLATING, INC.
Year Founded: 1956
Rev: $20,000,000
Emp.: 130
Provider of Metal Heat Treating Services
N.A.I.C.S.: 332811
Mark Sosnowski (VP)

SPECIALTY STRIP & OSCILLATING, INC.
1262 Standard Ave, Masury, OH 44438
Tel.: (330) 448-2228
Web Site:
http://www.specialtystrip.com
Year Founded: 1994
Sales Range: $10-24.9 Million
Emp.: 15
Metal Slit Coils Whslr
N.A.I.C.S.: 333519
Adam von Philp (VP)
Thomas M. von Philp (Pres)
Shawn Upshir (Plant Mgr)
Lana Hixson (Office Mgr)

SPECIALTY TOOL, INC.
6925 Trafalgar St, Fort Wayne, IN 46803
Tel.: (260) 493-6351
Web Site:
http://www.specialtytool.com
Year Founded: 1985
Machine Tools & Accessories Whslr
N.A.I.C.S.: 423830
Tom Martin (Pres)
Dick Gibson (Sec)
Dan Cartell (CEO)

SPECIALTY'S CAFE AND BAKERY
115 Sansome St Ste 300, San Francisco, CA 94104
Tel.: (415) 362-2052
Web Site: http://www.specialtys.com
Year Founded: 1987
Sales Range: $10-24.9 Million
Emp.: 80
Cafe & Bakery Services
N.A.I.C.S.: 722511
Craig Saxton (Founder)
Brenda Natera (Mgr-Closing Shift)
Loretta Malone (Gen Mgr)

SPECIFIC MEDIA INC.
4 Park Plz Ste 1500, Irvine, CA 92614
Tel.: (949) 861-8888
Web Site:
http://www.specificmedia.com
Year Founded: 1999
Advetising Agency
N.A.I.C.S.: 541810
Tim Vanderhook (Pres & CEO)
Chris Vanderhook (Founder & COO)
Jon Schulz (CMO)
Fabrizio Blanco (CTO)
Larry Madden (CTO)
Jeff Collins (Chief Revenue Officer)
Linh Chung (CIO)

Subsidiaries:

Broadband Enterprises, Inc. (1)
245 Fifth Ave 21st Fl, New York, NY 10016
Tel.: (212) 889-1537
Rev: $25,300,000
Emp.: 55
Business Support Services
N.A.I.C.S.: 561499

MySpace, LLC (1)
407 N Maple Dr, Beverly Hills, CA 90210 (100%)
Tel.: (310) 969-7400
Web Site: http://www.myspace.com
Sales Range: $50-74.9 Million
Emp.: 200
Online Social Networking Services Website Developer & Hosting Services

N.A.I.C.S.: 518210
Mitchell Pavao (VP-Product & Tech)
Brett Woitunski (VP-Product & Design)
Alex Chan (Dir-Front End Engrg)
Ron Nielsen (Gen Mgr)

SPECIFIED SYSTEMS INC.
5007 SE Rio Ct, Ankeny, IA 50021
Tel.: (515) 309-2000
Web Site:
http://www.specifiedsystems.net
Sales Range: $10-24.9 Million
Emp.: 9
Plumbing & Hydronic Heating Supplies
N.A.I.C.S.: 423720
Jeff Reichart (Partner)

SPECS FAMILY PARTNERS LTD.
2410 Smith St, Houston, TX 77006
Tel.: (713) 526-8787
Web Site:
http://www.specsonline.com
Rev: $100,000,000
Emp.: 500
Hard Liquor
N.A.I.C.S.: 445320
John Rydman (Owner & Pres)
Bob Heisler (CFO)
Mike Sanford (Dir-Property Dev)

SPECTOR & ASSOCIATES, INC.
85 Broad St, New York, NY 10004
Tel.: (212) 943-5858
Web Site: http://www.spectorpr.com
Year Founded: 1991
Sales Range: $1-9.9 Million
Emp.: 18
Public Relations, Digital Strategies & Integrated Marketing
N.A.I.C.S.: 541820
Barry Spector (Co-Founder, Dir-Creative & Exec VP)
Shelley Spector (Pres & Co-Founder)

SPECTRA GROUP LTD.
4 Brayton Ct, Commack, NY 11725
Tel.: (631) 499-3100
Web Site:
http://www.spectragraphic.com
Year Founded: 1983
Sales Range: $25-49.9 Million
Emp.: 75
Commercial Art & Graphic Design Services
N.A.I.C.S.: 541430
Nolan J. Meredith (Pres)

Subsidiaries:

Spectragraphic New England (1)
407 R Mystic Ave Ste 36C, Medford, MA 02155
Tel.: (617) 737-3575
Web Site: http://www.spectragraphic.com
Rev: $2,100,000
Emp.: 20
Color Separations, For Printing
N.A.I.C.S.: 323120
Nolan Meredith (Pres)

SPECTRA INNOVATIONS INC.
1141 Ringwood Ct, San Jose, CA 95131
Tel.: (408) 954-8474
Web Site: http://www.spectraus.com
Year Founded: 1989
Sales Range: $10-24.9 Million
Emp.: 50
Computers, Peripherals & Software
N.A.I.C.S.: 423430
Prasad Mamidanna (CEO)

SPECTRA LOGIC CORPORATION
6285 Lookout Rd, Boulder, CO 80301

Tel.: (303) 449-6400
Web Site:
http://www.spectralogic.com
Year Founded: 1979
Sales Range: $10-24.9 Million
Emp.: 250
Data Conversion Equipment
N.A.I.C.S.: 334118
Nathan C. Thompson (CEO)
Matthew T. Starr (CTO)
Brett Huston (Gen Counsel & VP-HR)
Jeff Biley (VP-Community Affairs)
Brian Grainger (Chief Sls Officer)
Bruce Kornfeld (CMO)
Brian Rome (Co-CFO)
Jon Benson (VP & Gen Mgr-Emerging Markets)
Roberto Bigliani (VP-Svc Ops-Worldwide)
Steve van Engen (COO)
Barry A. Rudolph (Co-CEO)
Jim Tholen (Co-CFO)
Jennifer K. Hopkins (Co-CEO)

SPECTRA METAL SALES INC.
6104 Boat Rock Blvd SW, Atlanta, GA 30336-2706
Tel.: (404) 344-0455
Web Site:
http://www.spectrametals.net
Year Founded: 1988
Sales Range: $50-74.9 Million
Emp.: 200
Gutters & Roofing Material & Products Mfr; Aluminum Fabricating Services
N.A.I.C.S.: 423510
Bernie Grahs (VP-Fin & Controller)
Andy Snell (Pres)
Johnny Tatonetti (Mgr-Sls)
Keith Herron (Mgr-Sls-Natl)

SPECTRA360, INC.
1700 Broadway 4th Fl, Burlingame, CA 94010
Web Site: http://www.spectra360.com
Year Founded: 2013
Sales Range: $10-24.9 Million
Emp.: 481
Management Consulting Services
N.A.I.C.S.: 711410
Andrew Bergen (Pres & CEO)
Brian Browning (COO)
Wendy Sanders (VP-Talent Acquisition)
Nick Pecchenino (VP-Fin)
Jen Lacap (VP-Major Accounts)

SPECTRAFORCE TECHNOLOGIES INC.
5511 Capital Ctr Dr Ste 340, Raleigh, NC 27606
Tel.: (919) 233-4466
Web Site:
http://www.spectraforce.com
Sales Range: $25-49.9 Million
Emp.: 637
Information Technology Consulting & Staffing Services
N.A.I.C.S.: 541512
Amit Singh (Pres & CEO)
Kamalesh Nayudu (COO-Asia Pacific)
Madhu Modugu (COO)

SPECTRAL DYNAMICS, INC.
2199 Zanker Rd, San Jose, CA 95131-2012
Tel.: (408) 678-3500
Web Site:
http://www.spectraldynamics.com
Year Founded: 1984
Sales Range: $50-74.9 Million
Emp.: 35
Mfr of Data Acquisition Instrumentation

N.A.I.C.S.: 334515
Steward Blackhous (Pres)
John Arbuckle (Dir-Ops)
Michelle Eisenbruck (Controller)
Stewart Slykhous (Pres)

Subsidiaries:

SD Germany GmbH (1)
Peter-Henlein-Str 24, 85540, Haar, Germany
Tel.: (49) 89 4623600
Emp.: 5
Electronic Equipment Whslr
N.A.I.C.S.: 423690
Rainer Konstandt (Gen Mgr)

Spectral Dynamics (UK) Ltd. (1)
Fulling Mill Fulling Mill Lane, Welwyn, AL6 9NP, Herts, United Kingdom
Tel.: (44) 1438 716626
Web Site: http://www.spectraldynamics.fr
Electronic Equipment Whslr
N.A.I.C.S.: 423690

SPECTRAL ENTERPRISES, INC.
11288 US Hwy 31, Grand Haven, MI 49417-9665
Tel.: (616) 846-8450
Web Site:
http://www.northlandexpresstransport.com
Year Founded: 1972
Sales Range: $10-24.9 Million
Emp.: 30
Freight Transportation Services
N.A.I.C.S.: 484121
Edward Wiers (CFO)
Todd Bustard (Pres & CEO)

Subsidiaries:

Bremer Authentic Ingredients (1)
420 100th Ave, Zeeland, MI 49464
Tel.: (616) 772-9100
Sales Range: $1-9.9 Million
Food Ingredients Whslr
N.A.I.C.S.: 424490
Tim Malefyt (Gen Mgr)
Brent Post (Mgr-Logistics)
Todd Gifford (Mgr-Sls)

SPECTRANETIX, INC.
845 Stewart Sr Ste B, Sunnyvale, CA 94085
Tel.: (408) 982-9057
Web Site:
http://www.spectranetix.com
Radio, Television Broadcasting & Wireless Communications Equipment Mfr
N.A.I.C.S.: 334220
Bret Banfield (VP-Engrg)

SPECTRASERV INC.
75 Jacobus Ave, Kearny, NJ 07032
Tel.: (973) 589-0277
Web Site:
http://www.spectraserv.com
Year Founded: 1961
Sales Range: $10-24.9 Million
Emp.: 110
Refuse Collection & Disposal Services
N.A.I.C.S.: 237110
Steven A. Townsend (Pres & CEO)
Francis Senske (Sr VP-Tech Svcs)
John Wengryn (Sr VP-Ops)
Steve Kulcsar (VP)

SPECTRATEK TECHNOLOGIES INC.
5405 Jandy Pl, Los Angeles, CA 90066
Tel.: (310) 822-2400
Web Site: http://www.spectratek.net
Sales Range: $10-24.9 Million
Emp.: 30

SPECTRATEK TECHNOLOGIES INC.

U.S. PRIVATE

Spectratek Technologies Inc.—(Continued)
Offset Printing
N.A.I.C.S.: 323111
Michael Foster (Chm)
Michael Wanlass (Founder, Pres & CEO)
Terry Conway (COO)

SPECTRO LUME INC.
373 E Rte 46 W Ste 230, Fairfield, NJ 07004
Tel.: (973) 882-5555
Web Site:
http://www.spectrolume.com
Year Founded: 1957
Sales Range: $100-124.9 Million
Emp.: 30
Lighting Fixtures Supplier
N.A.I.C.S.: 335132
Gary Bender (VP-Sls)

SPECTRONICS CORPORATION
956 Brush Hollow Rd, Westbury, NY 11590-1731
Tel.: (516) 333-4840   NY
Web Site: http://www.spectroline.com
Year Founded: 1955
Sales Range: $100-124.9 Million
Emp.: 200
Ultraviolet Light Sources, X-Ray Cassettes, Laboratory Instruments, Banking, Security, Air Conditioning & Refrigeration & Vehicle/Industrial Leak Detectors
N.A.I.C.S.: 335132
Jonathan Cooper (Pres)
Daniel Cooper (Sls Mgr-Acct)
Limin Chen (VP-Mfg & Special Projects)
Michael C. Fleming (Dir-Product Mgmt)
Daniel Tristan (Mgr-Sls-Latin America & Asia-Pacific)
Debra Hammond (Mgr-Global Customer Svc)
Fred Silverman (CFO)

Subsidiaries:

Tracer Products   (1)
956 Brush Hollow Rd, Westbury, NY 11590-1731   (100%)
Tel.: (516) 333-1254
Web Site: http://www.tracerline.com
Sales Range: $10-24.9 Million
Emp.: 31
Mfr of Auto Leak Detection Lamps, Dyes & Kits Using UV-Fluorescent Technology
N.A.I.C.S.: 335132

SPECTRUM BUSINESS SOLUTIONS, LLC
3 Hutton Centre Dr Ste 600, Santa Ana, CA 92707
Tel.: (714) 285-4848   CA
Web Site:
http://www.spectrumadvantage.com
Year Founded: 2001
Sales Range: $10-24.9 Million
Emp.: 20
Electronic Payment Processing Services
N.A.I.C.S.: 525990
Marco Leardini (Pres & CEO)

SPECTRUM CAPITAL ENTERPRISES, INC.
241 Main St 5th Floor, Buffalo, NY 14203
Tel.: (716) 854-1994   DE
Investment Holding Company
N.A.I.C.S.: 551112
Lee Hess (Chm)
Thomas C. Hunt (CEO)

SPECTRUM CHEMICAL MANUFACTURING CORPORATION
769 Jersey Ave, New Brunswick, NJ 08901-3605
Tel.: (732) 214-1300
Web Site:
http://www.spectrumchemical.com
Chemicals Mfr
N.A.I.C.S.: 325998
Russell Kneipp (Pres & CEO)
Randy Burg (Co-Chm)
Paul Burg (Founder & Co-Chm)
Jobe Dubbs (VP-Mktg)

Subsidiaries:

Spectrum Chemicals & Laboratory Products, Inc.   (1)
14422 S San Pedro St, Gardena, CA 90248-2027
Tel.: (310) 516-8000
Web Site: http://www.spectrumchemical.com
Sales Range: $25-49.9 Million
Emp.: 280
Laboratory & Research Chemicals & Laboratory Equipment & Supplies Mfr & Distr
N.A.I.C.S.: 325998

SPECTRUM CLUBS INC.
15759 San Pedro Ave, San Antonio, TX 78232
Tel.: (210) 490-1980
Web Site:
http://www.spectrumclubs.com
Rev.: $34,000,000
Emp.: 20
Health Club
N.A.I.C.S.: 713940
Mark Hyatt (Dir-Sls)

SPECTRUM COMM. INC.
1 Compass Way Ste 300, Newport News, VA 23606-4486
Tel.: (757) 224-7500
Web Site: http://www.sptrm.com
Year Founded: 1999
Sales Range: $25-49.9 Million
Emp.: 280
Communications, Intelligence-Gathering, Surveillance & Reconnaissance Services for the Department of Defense
N.A.I.C.S.: 921190
Jeffrey D. Wassmer (Chm & CEO)
Michael A. Nickerson (VP & Dir-Bus Portfolio)
Serdar Gokcen (VP-Bus Dev)
Ken Briggs (VP & Dir-Bus Portfolio)
William K. Stulb (Pres & COO)
Anthoney E. Stoney I (Vice Chm)

SPECTRUM COMMUNICATIONS CABLING SERVICES, INC.
226 N Lincoln Ave, Corona, CA 92882
Tel.: (951) 371-0549
Web Site:
http://www.spectrumccsi.com
Year Founded: 1985
Sales Range: $400-449.9 Million
Emp.: 130
Provider of Network Services Including Consulting, Network Design, Installation & Maintenance
N.A.I.C.S.: 517810
Sherry Rivera (Pres)

SPECTRUM CONTRACTING, INC.
3705-2 Westview Dr, Naples, FL 34104
Tel.: (239) 643-2772   FL
Web Site: http://www.scifla.com
Year Founded: 1993
Sales Range: $10-24.9 Million
Emp.: 125
Painting & Wall Covering Contractor
N.A.I.C.S.: 238320

Robert D. Valentine (Exec VP)
Terry Wilson (Sr VP)
John B. C. Schallert (Pres)

SPECTRUM DIRECT INSURANCE SERVICES, INC.
26023 Acero Ste 100, Mission Viejo, CA 92691
Tel.: (949) 600-7900
Web Site:
http://www.spectrumdirect.com
Year Founded: 2001
Rev.: $10,300,000
Emp.: 30
Insurance Agencies & Brokerages
N.A.I.C.S.: 524210
Christopher B. Snyder (Pres)
Seymour Alter (Pres)
Shannon Steele (Mgr-Acctg & Fin)

SPECTRUM EQUITY INVESTORS, L.P.
1 International Pl 35th Fl, Boston, MA 02110
Tel.: (617) 464-4600   DE
Web Site:
http://www.spectrumequity.com
Year Founded: 1994
Privater Equity Firm
N.A.I.C.S.: 523999
Michael Farrell (Mng Dir)
Benjamin C. Spero (Mng Dir)
Julia Huo Chen (VP)
Bill Collatos (Co-Founder)
John Connolly (Principal)
Ronan Cunningham (Mng Dir)
Coley Florance (Head-Talent)
Adam Gassin (VP)
Jeff Haywood (Mng Dir)
Pete Jensen (Mng Dir)

Subsidiaries:

Mortgagebot LLC   (1)
1000 W Donges Bay Rd Ste 200, Mequon, WI 53092
Sales Range: $10-24.9 Million
Internet Mortgage Lending Services
N.A.I.C.S.: 522310

Verisys Corp.   (1)
1001 N Fairfax St, Alexandria, VA 22314-1797
Tel.: (888) 837-4797
Web Site: http://www.verisys.com
Healthcare Technology Services
N.A.I.C.S.: 541519
Amy Roberson (VP-Ops)
Jamie A. Harper (COO)
John P. Benson (Founder & CEO)
Jennifer Gillespie (Officer-Compliance)
Chris Stabile (CFO)
Dustin Faultner (Dir-HR)
Srini Chillara (CTO)

SPECTRUM FOOD SERVICE, INC.
8 Halfmoon Exec Pk Dr, Clifton Park, NY 12065-5630
Tel.: (518) 373-3810
Web Site:
http://www.foodservicebroker.com
Year Founded: 1950
Sales Range: $10-24.9 Million
Emp.: 50
General Line Groceries
N.A.I.C.S.: 424410
Glenn Oliver (VP)

SPECTRUM GAMING GROUP
1201 New Rd Ste 308, Linwood, NJ 08221
Tel.: (609) 926-5100
Web Site:
http://www.spectrumgaming.com
Year Founded: 1993
Sales Range: $1-9.9 Million
Emp.: 11
International Gaming Consultancy

N.A.I.C.S.: 541618
Fredric E. Gushin (Mng Dir)
Michael J. Pollock (Mng Dir)
Francisco Nolla (VP-Bus Dev-Latin America)
Liliana Costa (VP-Latin America)
Asaka Ishiyama (Sr VP-Japan)
Matthew Roob (Sr VP-Fin Analysis)
Richard Doss (Coord-Mktg & Events)

SPECTRUM GLASS COMPANY INC.
24105 Sno-Woodinville Rd, Woodinville, WA 98072
Tel.: (425) 483-6699
Web Site:
http://www.spectrumglass.com
Sales Range: $75-99.9 Million
Emp.: 100
Specialty Glass Product Mfr
N.A.I.C.S.: 327215
Monica Pillay (Engr-Chemical & Glass)

SPECTRUM HEALTH CONTINUING CARE GROUP, INC.
100 Michigan ST NE, Grand Rapids, MI 49503
Tel.: (616) 391-5700
Web Site:
http://www.spectrumhealth.org
Year Founded: 1995
Nursing Care Facilities
N.A.I.C.S.: 623110
Roger Jansen (Chief Strategy Officer & Sr VP-Bus Dev)
Pamela Ries (Chief HR Officer & Sr VP)
Tina Freese Decker (Pres & CEO)

Subsidiaries:

Priority Health Managed Benefits, Inc.   (1)
1231 E Beltline Ave NE, Grand Rapids, MI 49525-4501
Tel.: (616) 942-0954
Web Site: http://www.priorityhealth.com
Healtcare Services
N.A.I.C.S.: 621999
Praveen Thadani (Pres)
Michael Sytsma (CFO)
Megan Schmidt (Sr VP-Employer Solutions)
Shannon Wilson (VP-Populations Health & Health Equity)

SPECTRUM HEALTH SYSTEMS
10 Mechanic St Ste 302, Worcester, MA 01608
Tel.: (508) 792-5400   MA
Web Site:
http://www.spectrumhealthsystems.org
Year Founded: 1971
Sales Range: $50-74.9 Million
Emp.: 1,389
Mental Health & Substance Abuse Treatment Services
N.A.I.C.S.: 623220
Jeffrey Baxter (CMO)
Kurt A. Isaacson (Pres & CEO)
Sherry Ellis (COO)

SPECTRUM IMAGING TECHNOLOGIES, INC.
5900 Gateway Blvd E, El Paso, TX 79905
Tel.: (915) 781-2000   TX
Web Site:
http://www.spectrumistechnology.com
Year Founded: 1911
Sales Range: $10-24.9 Million
Office Equipment Whslr
N.A.I.C.S.: 423420
Joan Plesant (VP)

SPECTRUM INDUSTRIES, INC.

700 Wealthy St SW, Grand Rapids, MI 49504
Tel.: (616) 451-0784 MI
Web Site:
http://www.spectrumindustries.com
Sales Range: $75-99.9 Million
Emp.: 110
Mfr of Industrial Paints
N.A.I.C.S.: 332812
Kevin Bassett *(Co-Pres)*
Subsidiaries:
Spectrum Industries, Inc. - Decorative Finishes Division (1)
13 McConnell St SW, Grand Rapids, MI 49503-5126
Tel.: (616) 451-4599
Emp.: 100
Hydrographic Coating Services
N.A.I.C.S.: 332813
Robert Wilder *(VP-Engrg)*

SPECTRUM INDUSTRIES, INC.
1600 Johnson St, Chippewa Falls, WI 54729-1468
Tel.: (715) 723-6750 WI
Web Site:
http://www.spectrumfurniture.com
Year Founded: 1968
Sales Range: $75-99.9 Million
Emp.: 190
Mfr of Wood Furniture
N.A.I.C.S.: 337127
David Hancock *(CEO)*
Dean White *(Plant Mgr)*
David See *(Controller)*

SPECTRUM INTERNATIONAL CORPORATION
1100 S Kimball Ave, Southlake, TX 76092
Tel.: (817) 329-6647
Web Site: http://www.specialized.net
Sales Range: $50-74.9 Million
Emp.: 50
Electronic Parts & Equipment
N.A.I.C.S.: 423690
Pete W. Smith Jr. *(Pres)*

SPECTRUM MARKETING, INC.
48 Jackson Dr, Stony Point, NY 10980
Tel.: (212) 244-4915 NY
Web Site:
http://www.spectrummktg.com
Year Founded: 1971
Sales Range: $10-24.9 Million
Emp.: 6
Advertising & Public Relations Services
N.A.I.C.S.: 541810
Keith R. Albert *(Pres)*
Rhea Albert *(VP-Media)*

SPECTRUM SALES INC.
6800 W 107th St Ste 200, Overland Park, KS 66212
Tel.: (913) 648-6811
Web Site:
http://www.spectrumsales.net
Rev.: $32,000,000
Emp.: 13
Electronic Parts
N.A.I.C.S.: 423690
James Burton *(CEO & VP)*
Patrick Powell *(Pres)*
Bill Nutt *(Engr-Sls)*

SPECTRUM SOLUTIONS L.L.C.
12248 Lone Peak Pkwy #106, Draper, UT 84020
Tel.: (801) 569-0465
Web Site:
https://spectrumsolution.com
Laboratory Services & Clinical Testing
N.A.I.C.S.: 621511

Subsidiaries:
Microarrays, Inc. (1)
601 Genome Way Ste 3300, Huntsville, AL 35806-2915
Tel.: (256) 327-0544
Web Site: http://www.microarrays.com
Biological Products
N.A.I.C.S.: 325414

SPECTRUM SYSTEMS, INC.
11325 Random Hills Rd Ste 600, Fairfax, VA 22030-0987
Tel.: (703) 591-7400
Web Site: http://www.spectrum-systems.com
Year Founded: 1986
Sales Range: $25-49.9 Million
Emp.: 32
Computer System Integration Services
N.A.I.C.S.: 541512
Jason Wallace *(Acct Mgr)*
Martin Burke *(Exec VP)*
Lauren Gardner *(Acct Mgr-Federal)*
James Ratliff *(CTO)*

SPECTRUM TECHNOLOGIES, INC.
3600 Thayer Ct, Aurora, IL 60504
Tel.: (815) 436-4440 IL
Web Site:
http://www.specmeters.com
Year Founded: 1987
Sales Range: $1-9.9 Million
Agricultural Measuring Equipment Mfr & Distr
N.A.I.C.S.: 334519
Mike Thurow *(Founder & Pres)*
David Lau *(Dir-Bus Dev-Asia)*
Martin Roeder *(Mgr-Intl Sls)*
Beth Randall *(Mgr-Customer Expectations)*
Franca Perez *(Coord-Sls-Domestic)*
Loyd Bowman *(Acct Mgr-Turf-Natl)*
Ralph George *(Dir-Sls-Europe, Middle East & Africa)*

SPECTRUM TECHNOLOGIES, INC.
8320 Hedge Lane Terrace, Shawnee Mission, KS 66227
Tel.: (314) 423-2311 MO
Web Site: http://www.skccom.com
Year Founded: 1991
Emp.: 250
Enterprise Communications Equipment Merchant Whslr
N.A.I.C.S.: 423690
Tray Vedock *(Pres & CEO)*
Jill Phillips *(CMO)*
Jennifer Lowe *(CFO)*
Kelli Herr *(VP-Ops)*
Jeff Holton *(CTO)*

SPECTRUM TECHNOLOGY, INC.
8004 Castleway Dr, Indianapolis, IN 46250
Tel.: (317) 596-3650 IN
Web Site: http://www.spectrumti.com
Year Founded: 2013
Sales Range: $10-24.9 Million
Emp.: 40
Information Technology Support Services
N.A.I.C.S.: 541519
Tony Schafer *(Pres & CEO)*
Rob Glass *(Head-Technical Svcs)*
Damon Richards *(Head-Mktg)*
Tom Penno *(COO)*

SPECTRUM TRANSPORTATION
PO Box 43583, Atlanta, GA 30336
Tel.: (678) 904-5660

Web Site:
http://www.spectrumlogistics.com
Year Founded: 2002
Sales Range: $1-9.9 Million
Emp.: 35
Transportation & Logistics Solutions
N.A.I.C.S.: 488510
Brian Sweeney *(Pres & Partner)*

SPECTRUMDNA, INC.
1781 Sidewinder Dr Ste 201, Park City, UT 84068
Tel.: (435) 658-1349 DE
Web Site:
http://www.spectrumdna.com
Year Founded: 2006
Sales Range: Less than $1 Million
Emp.: 8
Social Media Software & Mobile Applications
N.A.I.C.S.: 513210
James A. Banister *(Chm)*
Parrish B. Ketchmark *(Pres & CEO)*

SPECULATIVE PRODUCT DESIGN, LLC
177 Bovet Rd Ste 200, San Mateo, CA 94402
Tel.: (650) 462-2040
Web Site:
http://www.speckproducts.com
Year Founded: 1996
Sales Range: $10-24.9 Million
Emp.: 25
Electronic & Cell Phone Accessories Designer & Mfr
N.A.I.C.S.: 334419
Jarret Weis *(Sr Mgr-Engrg)*

SPEE-DEE DELIVERY SERVICE INC.
4101 Clearwater Rd, Saint Cloud, MN 56301-9635
Tel.: (320) 251-6697
Web Site:
http://www.speedeedelivery.com
Year Founded: 1978
Sales Range: $75-99.9 Million
Emp.: 1,400
Overnight Delivery Services
N.A.I.C.S.: 484110
Don Weeres *(Pres)*
Michael Eichten *(Mgr-HR)*
Craig Heurung *(Mgr-Sls)*

SPEED FAB-CRETE
1150 E Kennedale Pkwy, Fort Worth, TX 76060
Tel.: (817) 478-1137
Web Site: http://www.speedfab-crete.com
Year Founded: 1951
Sales Range: $25-49.9 Million
Emp.: 125
Commercial & Institutional Building Construction Services
N.A.I.C.S.: 236220
Dave Bloxom Jr. *(Principal)*

SPEED LUBE LLC
408 Johnson St, Pocahontas, IL 62275
Tel.: (618) 669-2333
Web Site: http://www.speedlube.com
Sales Range: $10-24.9 Million
Emp.: 250
Automotive Services
N.A.I.C.S.: 811191
Steve Dugan *(Owner)*

SPEED-O-TACH, INC.
4090 Pike Ln, Concord, CA 94520
Tel.: (925) 691-4090
Web Site:
http://www.sotelectronics.com
Year Founded: 1976

Sales Range: $10-24.9 Million
Emp.: 20
Radio & Television Repair Services
N.A.I.C.S.: 811114
Richard D. Fripp II *(Pres)*

SPEEDIMPEX USA INC.
3502 48th Ave, Long Island City, NY 11101-2421
Tel.: (718) 392-7477
Web Site:
http://www.speedimpex.com
Year Founded: 1962
Sales Range: $10-24.9 Million
Emp.: 65
Distr of Foreign Language Newspapers & Magazines
N.A.I.C.S.: 424920
Stefano Sciubba *(Pres & CEO)*
Greg Allen *(Branch Mgr)*
Jennifer DiMaggio *(Acct Exec)*
Pedro Pena *(Comptroller)*
Jay Pandya *(Mgr-Los Angeles)*
Adriana Azar *(Mgr-San Francisco)*

SPEEDLING INCORPORATED
4447 Old US Hwy 41, Ruskin, FL 33570
Tel.: (813) 645-3221 FL
Web Site: http://www.speedling.com
Year Founded: 1968
Sales Range: $100-124.9 Million
Emp.: 250
Mfr of Expanded Polystyrene Products; Distr of Horticultural Products; Transplant Grower of Vegetables, Herbs & Tobacco; Ornamental Nurseries
N.A.I.C.S.: 111422
Greg Davis *(Pres & CEO)*

Subsidiaries:

Speedling Incorporated-Alamo Transplants Division (1)
1 Mile S Alamo Rd, Alamo, TX 78516 (100%)
Tel.: (956) 787-1911
Web Site: http://www.speedling.com
Sales Range: $10-24.9 Million
Emp.: 12
Greenhouse Production Nursery Services
N.A.I.C.S.: 111419

Speedling Incorporated-Bushnell Division (1)
2722 SE 60th Ave, Bushnell, FL 33513-8746 (100%)
Tel.: (352) 793-6715
Sales Range: $10-24.9 Million
Emp.: 50
Crop Cultivation Services
N.A.I.C.S.: 111419
Mark Worley *(Mgr-East Coast Div)*

Speedling, Incorporated (1)
199 Crawley Gap Rd, Blairsville, GA 30512-6344
Tel.: (706) 745-7057
Web Site: http://www.speedling.com
Sales Range: $25-49.9 Million
Emp.: 15
Greenhouse Nursery Facility
N.A.I.C.S.: 424930
Mark Worley *(Mgr-East Coast Div)*

Speedling, Incorporated (1)
1040 N Thompson Ave, Nipomo, CA 93444-9494 (100%)
Tel.: (805) 489-8500
Web Site: http://www.speedling.com
Sales Range: $10-24.9 Million
Emp.: 35
Greenhouse Production Nursery Services
N.A.I.C.S.: 111419
Lynn Leube *(Office Mgr)*

Speedling, Incorporated-San Juan Bautista Nursery (1)
2640 San Juan Hwy, San Juan Bautista, CA 95045-9783 (100%)
Tel.: (831) 623-4432
Web Site: http://www.speedling.com

SPEEDLING INCORPORATED

Speedling Incorporated—(Continued)
Sales Range: $10-24.9 Million
Emp.: 20
Greenhouse Nursery Facility
N.A.I.C.S.: 111219

Speedling, Incorporated-Sun City Nursery Division (1)
PO Box 7129, Sun City, FL 33586-7129 (100%)
Tel.: (813) 645-3284
Web Site: http://www.speedling.com
Sales Range: $10-24.9 Million
Emp.: 100
Greenhouse Nursery Facility
N.A.I.C.S.: 111421
Mark Worley *(Mgr-Nursery)*
Greg Davis *(Pres & CEO)*

SPEEDMARK TRANSPORTATION INC.
1525 Adrian Rd, Burlingame, CA 94010
Tel.: (650) 259-9181
Web Site: http://www.speedmark.com
Year Founded: 1971
Sales Range: $10-24.9 Million
Emp.: 28
Global Logistics & Transportation Services
N.A.I.C.S.: 488510
Anthony Tsou *(Pres)*
David Liu *(Controller)*
Lian Pan *(CFO)*

SPEEDRACK PRODUCTS GROUP, LTD.
7903 Venture Ave NW, Sparta, MI 49345-9309
Tel.: (616) 887-0002 MI
Web Site: http://www.speedrack.net
Year Founded: 1989
Sales Range: $25-49.9 Million
Emp.: 300
Supplier of Pallet Racking & Storage Systems
N.A.I.C.S.: 332322
Ron Ducharme *(CEO & Dir-Fin)*
Brad Wells *(Mgr-Scheduling & Plng)*
Greg Dunneback *(Mgr-Inside Sls & Estimating)*
Eric Quist *(VP-Mfg)*
James Johnson *(Pres)*
Mike Roney *(VP-Engrg)*
John Loose *(Reg Mgr-Sls)*

SPEEDTECH INTERNATIONAL, INC.
2410 Norwood Ct, Racine, WI 53403
Tel.: (262) 635-9393
Web Site: http://www.speedtechinternational.com
Year Founded: 1996
Fastener Mfr
N.A.I.C.S.: 339993
Chris Karnowski *(Pres)*

Subsidiaries:

Toleeto Fasteners International, Inc. (1)
1580 Jayken Way, Chula Vista, CA 91911
Web Site: http://www.cord-lox.com
Sales Range: $1-9.9 Million
Emp.: 26
Fastener, Button, Needle & Pin Mfr
N.A.I.C.S.: 339993
David Deavenport *(Pres)*

SPEEDY Q MARKETS
2799 Wadhams Rd, Port Huron, MI 48060
Tel.: (810) 982-9700
Web Site: http://www.speedyqmarkets.com
Sales Range: $25-49.9 Million
Emp.: 15
Convenience Store
N.A.I.C.S.: 445131
Craig A. Lawrence *(Pres)*

SPELL CAPITAL PARTNERS, LLC
222 S Ninth St Ste 2880, Minneapolis, MN 55402
Tel.: (612) 371-9650 MN
Web Site: http://www.spellcapital.com
Year Founded: 1988
Sales Range: Less than $1 Million
Emp.: 18
Privater Equity Firm
N.A.I.C.S.: 523999
William H. Spell *(Founder & Pres)*
James W. Rikkers *(Sr Mng Dir)*
Andrea R. Nelson *(CFO & COO)*
Toni L. Sierakowski *(Mgr-Acctg)*
Harry Spell *(Mng Dir)*
Heather Pribyl *(Controller)*
Kelli Hoversten *(VP-Admin)*
Sarah Richens *(Office Mgr)*

Subsidiaries:

Griplock Systems, LLC (1)
1132 Mark Ave, Carpinteria, CA 93013
Tel.: (805) 566-0064
Web Site: http://www.griplocksystems.com
Sales Range: $1-9.9 Million
Cable Suspension Products Mfr & Marketer
N.A.I.C.S.: 332999
Hugo Napier *(Exec VP-Sls)*
Todd Hemingway *(CEO)*

Norshield Security Products LLC (1)
3232 Mobile Hwy, Montgomery, AL 36108
Tel.: (334) 551-0650
Web Site: http://www.norshield.net
Sales Range: $10-24.9 Million
Mfr & Supplier of Ballistic, Attack & Blast Resistant Products
N.A.I.C.S.: 332311
Barry White *(Pres & CEO)*
John Wood *(Mgr-Sls & Mktg)*

Premier Precision Group LLC (1)
260 Plymouth Ave N, Minneapolis, MN 55411
Tel.: (612) 288-0231
Web Site: http://www.premierprecision.com
Sales Range: $75-99.9 Million
Fabricated Metal Component Mfr
N.A.I.C.S.: 332999
Chris May *(Dir-Engrg)*
Dan Ortloff *(Dir-Fin & Admin)*

Subsidiary (Domestic):

Falls Fabricating, Inc. (2)
5091 Hilltop Ave N, Lake Elmo, MN 55042
Tel.: (320) 632-2322
Web Site: http://www.fallsfab.com
Sales Range: $25-49.9 Million
Sheet Metal Work Mfg
N.A.I.C.S.: 332322

Plant (Domestic):

Premier Precision Group - RDS Facility (2)
3 Putnam Rd, Newport, NH 03773
Tel.: (603) 863-4131
Web Site: http://www.rdmachineandtool.com
Sales Range: $25-49.9 Million
Fabricated Metal Products Mfr
N.A.I.C.S.: 332999
Becky Speir *(Controller)*

VPI Acquisition Corp. (1)
1 Viking St, Corry, PA 16407
Tel.: (814) 664-8671
Web Site: http://www.vikingplastics.com
Sales Range: $10-24.9 Million
Holding Company
N.A.I.C.S.: 551112
Kelly Goodsel *(Pres & CEO)*
Marty Radock *(Sr Project Mgr)*
Rob Prindle *(Mgr-IT)*
Cathy Pitts *(Controller)*
Bob Senz *(Dir-Quality)*
Thomas D. Valentine *(Dir-Sls & Mktg)*

SPELLBINDERS PAPER ARTS LLC
1125 W Pinnacle Peak Rd Bldg 3 Ste 124, Phoenix, AZ 85027
Tel.: (602) 385-7700
Web Site: http://www.spellbinderspaperarts.com
Year Founded: 2003
Sales Range: $1-9.9 Million
Emp.: 10
Equipment & Supplies for Crafts
N.A.I.C.S.: 339940
Stacey Caron *(Pres)*
Jeff Caron *(CEO)*
Joe Hall *(Dir-Ops)*

SPELLMAN BRADY & COMPANY
8251 Maryland Ave, Saint Louis, MO 63105
Tel.: (314) 862-0070
Web Site: http://www.spellmanbrady.com
Year Founded: 1991
Rev.: $10,100,000
Emp.: 21
Interior Design Services
N.A.I.C.S.: 541410
Diana Spellman *(Pres)*
Michael Frisch *(Mgr)*
Marcia Ludwig *(Project Mgr-Acct Mgmt, Project Logistics & Oversight)*
Robyn Gaynor *(Dir-Contract Markets)*
Alicia Nicolay *(Dir-Senior Living)*
Melissa Keeney *(Dir-Senior Living)*
Monica Stefek *(Dir-Mktg)*
Michelle Hamilton *(Dir-Bus Dev)*

SPELLMAN HARDWOODS INC.
4645 N 43rd Ave, Phoenix, AZ 85031
Tel.: (602) 272-2313
Web Site: http://www.spellmanhardwoods.com
Sales Range: $25-49.9 Million
Emp.: 45
Lumber: Rough, Dressed & Finished
N.A.I.C.S.: 423310
James W. Spellman *(CEO)*
Chip Spellman *(Pres)*
Mary Yeager *(Treas)*

SPELLMAN HIGH VOLTAGE ELECTRONICS CORPORATION
475 Wireless Blvd, Hauppauge, NY 11788-3951
Tel.: (631) 630-3000 NY
Web Site: http://www.spellmanhv.com
Year Founded: 1947
Sales Range: $10-24.9 Million
Emp.: 130
Direct Current High Voltage Power Supply Systems Mfr
N.A.I.C.S.: 335999
Loren Skeist *(Pres)*

Subsidiaries:

Spellman High Voltage Electronics Corp. - Valhalla (1)
1 Commerce Park, Valhalla, NY 10595
Tel.: (914) 686-3600
Web Site: http://www.spellmanhv.com
Direct Current High Voltage Power Supply Systems Mfr
N.A.I.C.S.: 335999
Dave Burgess *(Gen Mgr)*

SPELNA, INC.
225 Industrial Ct, Fredericksburg, VA 22408-2420
Tel.: (540) 898-1524
Web Site: http://spelnabcb.com
Year Founded: 1977
Sales Range: $75-99.9 Million
Emp.: 3
Management Consulting Services
N.A.I.C.S.: 531120
Olivier Jacqueau *(Pres-BCB)*
John Bufalari *(Gen Mgr & Mgr-HR)*

Subsidiaries:

American Unic Corp. (1)
PO Box 3375, Fredericksburg, VA 22402
Tel.: (540) 898-0720
Mobile Automotive Lifts-Distribution & Sales
N.A.I.C.S.: 423830

SPELZON CORP.
5348 Vegas Dr, Las Vegas, NV 89108
Tel.: (702) 751-8467 NV
Year Founded: 2014
Mobile Game Developer
N.A.I.C.S.: 513210
Arthur Parrik *(Pres, Treas & Sec)*

SPENCE, MARSTON, BUNCH, MORRIS & CO.
250 N Belcher Rd Ste 100, Clearwater, FL 33765
Tel.: (727) 441-6829
Web Site: http://www.spencemarston.com
Year Founded: 1971
Sales Range: $1-9.9 Million
Emp.: 28
Accounting Services
N.A.I.C.S.: 541219
Stephen M. Bunch *(Partner)*
Bruce Taylor *(Mng Dir)*
F. Gordon Spoor *(Principal)*
Robert Riley *(Mng Dir)*
Tom Whiteman *(Principal)*
Richard B. Franz III *(Partner)*
W. Gordon Spoor II *(Partner)*

SPENCE/BANKS INC.
700 N 1st St, Terre Haute, IN 47807
Tel.: (812) 232-3475 IN
Web Site: http://www.spencebanks.com
Year Founded: 1982
Sales Range: $10-24.9 Million
Emp.: 14
Provider of Heating Oil
N.A.I.C.S.: 457210
Melissa Drake *(Office Mgr & Mgr-Credit)*
Tom Holt *(Dir-Safety)*

SPENCER CAPITAL HOLDINGS, LTD.
140 E 45th St 28th Fl, New York, NY 10017
Tel.: (646) 546-5078
Web Site: http://www.spencercapital.com
Year Founded: 2000
Investment Services
N.A.I.C.S.: 523999
Kenneth H. Shubin Stein *(Chm & CEO)*
Stephen Roseman *(Pres)*

Subsidiaries:

SouthWest Dealers Services, Inc. (1)
18 Bunsen, Irvine, CA 92618
Tel.: (800) 395-5277
Web Site: http://www.swds.net
Sales Range: $100-124.9 Million
Car Dealership Support Services
N.A.I.C.S.: 561499
Eric Hamann *(CEO)*
Craig Cleaver *(VP)*

SPENCER COMPANIES INC.
120 Woodson St NW, Huntsville, AL 35801-5521
Tel.: (256) 533-1150 AL
Web Site: http://www.spencercos.com
Year Founded: 1923
Sales Range: $100-124.9 Million
Emp.: 240

Wholesale & Retail Gasoline; Convenience Stores
N.A.I.C.S.: 424720
Sarah S. Chappell (VP & Dir)
Gary Tucker (CFO)
Irv Bell (Mgr-Environment)
Jennifer Hereford (Mgr-HR)
Bruce Waldon (Mgr-Bulk Plant & Dispatching)
J. Spencer (Pres & CEO)
Joe Putman (Dir-Retail Ops)
Mike King (Mgr-Svc Dept)

SPENCER DISTRIBUTING LP
2210 Hwy 155 N, Palestine, TX 75803
Tel.: (903) 729-8886
Year Founded: 1975
Sales Range: $100-124.9 Million
Emp.: 13
Gasoline Whslr & Distr
N.A.I.C.S.: 424720
Jerry Spencer (Owner)
Darren Mackie (Gen Mgr)

SPENCER FABRICATIONS, INC.
29511 County Rd 561, Tavares, FL 32778
Tel.: (352) 343-0014   FL
Web Site: http://www.spenfab.com
Year Founded: 1994
Sales Range: $1-9.9 Million
Emp.: 25
Plate Work Mfr
N.A.I.C.S.: 332313
Greg Leonard (Co-Owner)
Kawal Persaud (Co-Owner)

SPENCER FANE LLP
1000 Walnut St Ste 1400, Kansas City, MO 64106-2140
Tel.: (816) 474-8100
Web Site:
  http://www.spencerfane.com
Emp.: 101
Law Firm
N.A.I.C.S.: 541110
Samuel Alba (Atty)
John E. Gates (Atty)
Michael R. Carlston (Atty)
Russell W. Baker (Co-Partner)
Scott E. Blakesley (Co-Partner)
Andrew C. Brought (Co-Partner)
Kristen H. Dekker (Co-Partner)
David Schatz (Co-Partner)
Kelly A. Campbell (Co-Partner)
Bruce E. Cavitt (Co-Partner)
Gardiner B. Davis (Co-Partner)
Michael F. Delaney (Co-Partner)
Kyle L. Elliott (Co-Partner)
Scot Seabaugh (Co-Partner)
Jason Hawkins (Office Managing Partner-Utah)

Subsidiaries:

Bone McAllester Norton PLLC   (1)
Nashville City Ctr 511 Union St Ste 1600, Nashville, TN 37219-1733
Tel.: (615) 238-6300
Web Site: http://www.bonelaw.com
Law Firm
N.A.I.C.S.: 541110
Trace Blankenship (Gen Counsel & Atty)
Charles W. Bone (Founder, Chm & Atty)
Charles Robert Bone (Pres & CEO)
Anne Sumpter Arney (Atty)
David M. Anthony (Atty)
Deron Peak (Dir-Tech)
Samar S. Ali (Atty)
Richard J. Nickels (Atty)
Andrea P. Perry (Atty)
Olatayo O. Atanda (Atty)
George J. Phillips (Atty)
Robert D. Pinson (Atty)
Sharon O. Jacobs (Atty)
Kristie Putman (Paralegal & Atty)

Paul W. Kruse (Atty)
Alex Little (Atty)
Colten Jones (Atty-Hendersonville)
Courtney Lutz (Atty)

Pahl & McCay A Professional Corporation   (1)
225 W Santa Clara St Ste 1500, San Jose, CA 95113-1752
Tel.: (408) 286-5100
Web Site: http://www.pahl-mccay.com
Emp.: 12
Law Firm
N.A.I.C.S.: 541110
Stephen D. Pahl (Chm & Sr Partner)
Karen Kubala McCay (Mng Partner & Atty)
Catherine Schlomann Robertson (Partner & Atty)
Fenn C. Horton III (Partner & Atty)

Snow, Christensen & Martineau, P.C.   (1)
10 Exchange Pl 11th Fl, Salt Lake City, UT 84145
Tel.: (801) 521-9000
Web Site: http://www.scmlaw.com
Emp.: 52
Law Firm
N.A.I.C.S.: 541110
Max D. Wheeler (Atty)
Kim R. Wilson (Atty)

SPENCER INDUSTRIES INC.
902 Buffaloville Rd, Dale, IN 47523
Tel.: (812) 937-4561
Web Site:
  http://www.spencerindustries.com
Sales Range: $10-24.9 Million
Emp.: 300
Thermoformed Finished Plastics Products
N.A.I.C.S.: 326199
Tom Messmer (Pres)
Brian Gehlhausen (Mgr-Engrg)
Jason Hedinger (Supvr-Maintenance)
Nate Schuler (Mgr-Bus Dev)

SPENCER MAC CORPORATION
26864 Watauga Rd, Abingdon, VA 24211
Tel.: (276) 676-2376   VA
Year Founded: 1980
Sales Range: $10-24.9 Million
Holding Company; Overhead Crane & Underground Mining Equipment Mfr
N.A.I.C.S.: 551112
Eric Miller (Co-Owner & Pres-Damascus)
Jim Marianski (Co-Owner)

Subsidiaries:

Damascus Equipment, LLC   (1)
26864 Watauga Rd, Abingdon, VA 24211
Tel.: (276) 676-2376
Web Site: http://www.damascuscorp.com
Sales Range: $1-9.9 Million
Emp.: 25
Mining Machinery & Equipment Mfr
N.A.I.C.S.: 333131
Eric Miller (Pres)
Leno Rainero (VP-Sls)
Richard Mullins (Sr VP-Ops)

Platnick Steel & Engineering, Inc.   (1)
269 Saint Clairs Crossing, Bluefield, VA 24605
Tel.: (276) 322-5477
Web Site: http://www.platnick.net
Sales Range: $1-9.9 Million
Emp.: 25
Overhead Cranes & Structural Steel Products Mfr
N.A.I.C.S.: 333923
Brad Ayers (Pres)
Barry Davidson (Mgr-Ops & Coord-Projects)

SPENCER OIL COMPANY
16410 Common Rd, Roseville, MI 48066
Tel.: (586) 775-5022

Web Site:
  http://www.spenceroilcompany.com
Year Founded: 1962
Sales Range: $25-49.9 Million
Emp.: 20
Fuel Oil Dealers
N.A.I.C.S.: 457210
Tom Spencer (Pres)
Suzanne Zehel (Controller)
James Spencer (Principal)

SPENCER QUARRIES, INC.
25341 430th Ave, Spencer, SD 57374
Tel.: (605) 246-2344
Web Site:
  http://www.spencerquarriesinc.com
Sales Range: $10-24.9 Million
Emp.: 40
Broken Stone Mining Services
N.A.I.C.S.: 212319
Todd Waldera (Gen Mgr)

SPENCER REED GROUP, LLC
5700 W 112th St Ste 110, Overland Park, KS 66211
Tel.: (913) 663-4400   KS
Web Site:
  http://www.spencerreed.com
Year Founded: 1990
Employment Placement & Staffing Services
N.A.I.C.S.: 561311
William T. Solon (CEO)
Janine Bedora (Mgr-Div)
Joy Davis (Asst Mgr)
Jackie Middleton (Mgr-Direct Hire)

SPENCER SAVINGS BANK, SLA
611 River Dr, Elmwood Park, NJ 07407
Tel.: (201) 703-3800   NJ
Web Site:
  http://www.spencersavings.com
Year Founded: 1939
Sales Range: $75-99.9 Million
Emp.: 240
Banking Services
N.A.I.C.S.: 522180
Jose B. Guerrero (Chm, Pres & CEO)
John C. Duncan (Chief Lending Officer & Exec VP)
Jonathan Shachov (VP & Dir-IT)
Mercedes M. Pedrick (VP-Mortgage Originations)
Michael P. Irslinger (VP-Retail Banking)
George Celetano (Sr VP & Dir-Retail Banking)
Paul Pearce (Treas & VP)

SPENCER TECHNOLOGIES INC.
102 Otif St, Northborough, MA 01532
Tel.: (508) 595-9496
Web Site:
  http://www.spencertech.com
Sales Range: $25-49.9 Million
Emp.: 150
Installer of Fiber Optic Cable
N.A.I.C.S.: 238210
Jennifer Patterson (Project Mgr)
Yaquira Sanchez (Dir-Field Ops)
Roger Fortin (Project Mgr)

SPENCER TRASK & CO.
1700 E Putnam Ave Ste 306, Old Greenwich, CT 06870
Tel.: (212) 326-9200
Web Site:
  http://www.spencertraskco.com
Rev.: $21,500,000
Emp.: 45
Security Brokers & Dealers
N.A.I.C.S.: 523150

Kevin Kimberlin (Chm)

Subsidiaries:

Spencer Trask Ventures, Inc.   (1)
1700 E Putnam Ave Ste 306, Old Greenwich, CT 06870
Tel.: (212) 326-9200
Web Site: http://www.spencertraskco.com
Rev.: $10,000,000
Emp.: 30
Security Brokers & Dealers
N.A.I.C.S.: 523150

Stolle Milk Biologics Inc.   (1)
4735 Devitt Dr, West Chester, OH 45246
Tel.: (513) 489-7997
Web Site: http://www.smbimilk.com
Rev.: $3,000,000
Emp.: 3
Powdered Milk
N.A.I.C.S.: 311514

SPENCER'S AIR CONDITIONING & APPLIANCE
115 W 1st Ave, Mesa, AZ 85210
Tel.: (480) 833-3072   AZ
Web Site: http://www.spencerstv.com
Year Founded: 1973
Sales Range: $25-49.9 Million
Electric Household Appliances
N.A.I.C.S.: 449210
Richard Biederbeck (Pres)

SPENCO MEDICAL CORPORATION
6301 Imperial Dr, Waco, TX 76712
Tel.: (254) 772-6000   TX
Web Site: http://www.spenco.com
Year Founded: 1967
Sales Range: $150-199.9 Million
Emp.: 520
Personal Care Products Mfr, Whslr & Online Retailer
N.A.I.C.S.: 316210
Steven B. Smith (Pres & CEO)

SPENDSMART NETWORKS, INC.
805 Aerovista Pkwy Ste 205, San Luis Obispo, CA 93401   DE
Web Site:
  http://www.spendsmartinc.com
Year Founded: 1990
SSPC—(OTCBB)
Sales Range: $1-9.9 Million
Payment Solutions Developer
N.A.I.C.S.: 561499
Isaac Blech (Vice Chm)
Jerold Howard Rubinstein (Chm)
Geoff Chaney (VP-Masterminds Svcs)
Louis Camassa (VP-Product Dev)
Brian Olson (VP-Engrg)
Brett Schnell (Interim CEO & CFO)

SPENUZZA BROTHERS INC.
1128 Sherborn St, Corona, CA 92879
Tel.: (951) 281-1830
Web Site:
  http://www.imperialrange.com
Sales Range: $25-49.9 Million
Emp.: 100
Cooking Equipment, Commercial
N.A.I.C.S.: 333310
Matt Wise (Gen Mgr)
Peter Spenuzza Jr. (Pres)

SPERBER LANDSCAPE COS. LLC
30700 Russell Ranch Rd Ste 120, Westlake, CA 91362
Tel.: (310) 579-6154
Web Site:
  https://sperbercompanies.com
Year Founded: 1949
Emp.: 100
Commercial Services
N.A.I.C.S.: 236220

SPERBER LANDSCAPE COS. LLC

Sperber Landscape Cos. LLC—(Continued)

Subsidiaries:

Pro-Qual Industries, LLC, (1)
411 W Orion St, Tempe, AZ 85283
Tel.: (480) 456-0608
Web Site:
  http://www.proquallandscaping.com
Sales Range: $1-9.9 Million
Emp.: 85
Lawn & Garden Services
N.A.I.C.S.: 561730
Warren Wheat (Pres)

SPERIDIAN TECHNOLOGIES, LLC

2400 Louisiana Blvd Bldg 3, Albuquerque, NM 87110
Tel.: (505) 217-3725
Web Site: http://www.speridian.com
Year Founded: 2003
Sales Range: $10-24.9 Million
Emp.: 600
Custom Computer Programming Services
N.A.I.C.S.: 541511
Girish Panicker (CEO)
Ashith Vahab (Sr Mgr-RMG/Staffing)
K. P. Hari (CFO & Mng Partner)
Ali Hasan (COO)
Girish Nair (Chief Comml Officer)
Satish Ganta (Exec VP & Head-Ops-India)

Subsidiaries:

Ingenuity Consulting Partners, Inc. (1)
410 SE 3rd St Bldg B Suite 102, Lees Summit, MO 64063
Tel.: (816) 272-8145
Web Site:
  http://www.ingenuityconsulting.com
Business & Technology Consulting Services
N.A.I.C.S.: 541690
Brenda Riggs (CEO & Sr VP-Bus Dev)
Edie Dozier (COO & Sr VP-HR)

Speridian Technologies LLC
Office No 105 Pinnacle Building Al Barsha First Shaikh Zayed Road, Dubai, United Arab Emirates
Tel.: (971) 4 392 7366
Web Site: http://www.speridian.com
IT Consulting & Various Technology Services
N.A.I.C.S.: 541690
David Madhan (VP-Reg Sls)
Khurram Rasheed (Practice Mgr)

Speridian Technologies Pvt Ltd (1)
Technopark Campus G2 Thejaswini, 695 581, Trivandrum, India
Tel.: (91) 471 270 0525
Web Site: http://www.speridian.com
IT Consulting & Technology Services
N.A.I.C.S.: 541690
Satish Ganta (Exec VP)
Chandra Vempati (Exec VP)

Speridian Technologies Pvt Ltd (1)
Embassy Signet Cessna Business Park 13/1 Kadubeesanahalli Varthur, Hubli New Horizon College Outer Ring Road, Bengaluru, 560 103, Marathahalli, India
Tel.: (91) 806 703 8100
Web Site: http://www.speridian.com
IT Consulting & Technology Services
N.A.I.C.S.: 541690
Chandra Vempati (Head-Ops & Sr VP)

Xelleration, LLC (1)
2042 Bus Cntr Dr 203, Irvine, CA 92612
Tel.: (949) 417-2024
Web Site: http://www.xelleration.com
Sales Range: $1-9.9 Million
Emp.: 25
Management Consulting Services
N.A.I.C.S.: 541611
Dilshad Khaleeque (Principal)

SPERRY & RICE LLC

9146 US 52, Brookville, IN 47012
Tel.: (765) 647-4141
Web Site: http://www.sperryrice.com
Year Founded: 1946
Extruded Rubber & Plastic Mfr
N.A.I.C.S.: 326299
Tom Sander (CFO)
Randy Dobbs (Pres & CEO)

SPERRY UNION STORE, INC.

11721 Locust St, Sperry, IA 52650
Tel.: (319) 985-2169 IA
Web Site:
  http://www.sperryunionstore.com
Year Founded: 1927
Sales Range: $10-24.9 Million
Emp.: 14
Feed & Grain Whslr
N.A.I.C.S.: 424510
Donald Thie (Pres)

SPERRY VAN NESS INTERNATIONAL CORP.

18881 Von Karman Ave Ste 800, Irvine, CA 92612
Tel.: (949) 278-6224
Web Site: http://www.svn.com
Year Founded: 2001
Sales Range: $1-9.9 Million
Emp.: 72
Real Estate Broker
N.A.I.C.S.: 531210
Mark Van Ness (Founder)
George Slusser (Chief Growth Officer)
Denise Mills (CFO)
Karen Hurd (Mgr-Sls-Franchise Dev)
Diane Danielson (COO)
Solomon Poretsky (Exec VP-Org Dev)
Marc Seinfeld (VP-Natl Franchise Sls & Dev)
Rosa Thomas (VP-Fin & Acctg)
Xavier Mufraggi (CEO)
Tim Spillane (Pres)

SPETNER ASSOCIATES, INC.

8630 Delmar Blvd Ste 100, Saint Louis, MO 63124
Tel.: (314) 997-5700 MO
Web Site: http://www.spetner.com
Year Founded: 1986
Rev.: $1,300,000
Emp.: 13
Fiscal Year-end: 12/31/06
Insurance Agents
N.A.I.C.S.: 524210

SPEX CLOTHING COMPANY INC.

6801 Westside Ave, North Bergen, NJ 07047
Tel.: (201) 854-8690
Year Founded: 1991
Sales Range: $10-24.9 Million
Emp.: 22
Women's & Children's Sportswear & Swimsuits
N.A.I.C.S.: 424350
Sunil Mahtani (CEO)

SPEYSIDE EQUITY LLC

24 Frank Lloyd Wright Dr Ste H3225, Ann Arbor, MI 48105
Tel.: (212) 994-0308 DE
Web Site:
  http://www.speysideequity.com
Year Founded: 2004
Privater Equity Firm
N.A.I.C.S.: 523999
Kevin Daugherty (Mng Dir)
Jeffrey Stone (Mng Dir)
Robert Sylvester (Mng Dir)

Subsidiaries:

Ashland Foundry & Machine Works, LLC (1)
500 E Center St, Ashland, PA 17921
Tel.: (570) 875-6100
Web Site:
  http://www.ashlandfoundrymachineworks.com
Steel & Alloy Castings Mfr
N.A.I.C.S.: 332111

Craftsman Custom Metals LLC (1)
3838 N River Rd, Schiller Park, IL 60176
Tel.: (847) 655-0040
Web Site: http://www.ccm.com
Sheet Metal Stampings Mfr
N.A.I.C.S.: 332322
Julio Gesklin (Pres & CEO)
Eric Siegal (VP-Sls)
Jack Brewer (Qty Mgr)
Evelio Almanza (Dir-Cell Ops)
Renee Adam (Mgr-Pur)
Roman Kramarz (Mgr-Engrng)

Dalton Corporation (1)
1900 E Jefferson St, Warsaw, IN 46580
Tel.: (574) 267-8111
Web Site: http://www.daltoncorporation.com
Sales Range: $50-74.9 Million
Iron Casting Mfr
N.A.I.C.S.: 331511
Jeffrey Stone (Pres)

Plant (Domestic):

Dalton Corporation - Stryker Plant (2)
310 Ellis St, Stryker, OH 43557
Tel.: (574) 371-5210
Web Site: http://www.daltoncorporation.com
Metal Machining Services
N.A.I.C.S.: 332710

Opta Group LLC (1)
300 Corporate Prkwy-118N, Amherst, NY 14226
Tel.: (716) 446-8888
Web Site: https://optagroupllc.com
Chemical Wholesale Distributors
N.A.I.C.S.: 424690

Subsidiary (Domestic):

Anker Industries (2)
938 Larimer Ave, Turtle Creek, PA 15145
Tel.: (412) 823-3695
Rev.: $5,412,000
Emp.: 25
Clay Refractory Mfr
N.A.I.C.S.: 327120
John Klatko (Controller)

Nuflux LLC (2)
2395 Ohio 5, Cortland, OH 44410
Tel.: (330) 399-1122
Web Site: http://www.nuflux.com
Chemicals Mfr
N.A.I.C.S.: 325180

SPF NORTH AMERICA, INC.

5300 Hwy 25 N, Hodges, SC 29653-9673
Tel.: (864) 374-3239
Web Site: http://www.spf-diana.com
Sales Range: $25-49.9 Million
Emp.: 168
Dog & Cat Food Mfr
N.A.I.C.S.: 311111
Judy Gehler (Mgr-HR)
Jamilla Walcott (Mgr-Mktg)
Robert L. Wills (Pres)

SPFS INC.

1309 Briaryville Rd No 201, Madison, TN 37115
Tel.: (615) 860-2592
Sales Range: $25-49.9 Million
Emp.: 500
Seafood Shack
N.A.I.C.S.: 722511
David Simmons (Pres)
Mike Tidwell (CFO)

Subsidiaries:

SP Delta Foods Inc. (1)
1309 Briaryville Rd Ste 201, Madison, TN 37115
Tel.: (615) 860-2592
Rev.: $340,000
Emp.: 14
Fast-Food Restaurant, Independent
N.A.I.C.S.: 722513

SPG SOLAR INC.

1039 N McDowell Blvd Ste B, Petaluma, CA 94954
Tel.: (415) 883-7657
Web Site: http://www.spgsolar.com
Sales Range: $50-74.9 Million
Emp.: 155
Solar Power System Design & Installation Services
N.A.I.C.S.: 238990
Dan Thompson (Founder & Chm)
Lin Johnson (Gen Counsel & VP)
Douglas May (CEO)
John Tomaszewski (Sr VP-Ops, Customer Svc & Warranty)
Soren Jensen (Dir-Engrg)

SPGL ACQUISITION CORPORATION

222 Berkeley St 18th Fl, Boston, MA 02116
Tel.: (617) 824-1000 Ky
Year Founded: 2021
Investment Services
N.A.I.C.S.: 523999
Jihye Whang Rosenband (CEO)
Chuck Bland (CFO)
John Ocampo (Chm)

SPHERION OF LIMA INC.

216 N Elizabeth St, Lima, OH 45801
Tel.: (419) 227-0113
Rev.: $40,736,633
Emp.: 30
Temporary Help Service
N.A.I.C.S.: 561320
Robert Schulte (Pres)

SPI LIGHTING INC.

10400 N Enterprise Dr, Mequon, WI 53092
Tel.: (262) 242-1420
Web Site: http://www.spilighting.com
Sales Range: $10-24.9 Million
Emp.: 150
Sales of Commercial Lighting Fixtures
N.A.I.C.S.: 335132
Angelina Atterberry (VP-Sls)
Jeff Buntrock (Mgr-Production)
Ed Murray (Mgr-Ops)
Kathleen Brehm (VP-Ops)
Joe Clark (Mgr-Inside Sls)

SPICEOLOGY, INC.

715 E Sprague Ave Ste 115, Spokane, WA 99202
Tel.: (509) 241-3040 WA
Web Site: http://www.spiceology.com
Year Founded: 2013
Sales Range: $1-9.9 Million
Emp.: 49
Food & Beverage Product Distr
N.A.I.C.S.: 445298
Pete Taylor (Founder)

SPIES CORPORATION

312 9th Ave SE Ste A, Watertown, SD 57201
Tel.: (605) 882-0464
Sales Range: $10-24.9 Million
Emp.: 120
Owner of Convenience Stores
N.A.I.C.S.: 445131
James Spies (Pres)

SPIGEL PROPERTIES INC.

70 NE Loop 410 Ste 185, San Antonio, TX 78216-5888
Tel.: (210) 349-3636 TX
Year Founded: 1980
Sales Range: $10-24.9 Million
Emp.: 8
Real Estate Services
N.A.I.C.S.: 531120

Stanley Spigel *(Pres)*
Rachael Hurst *(Sr Mgr-Property)*
David Weil *(Partner-Leasing Property, Mgmt, Acq & Dispositions)*
Tatiana Gaston *(Office Mgr)*
Erica Gold *(Reg Mgr-Property)*

SPIKE ADVERTISING INC.
27 Kilburn St, Burlington, VT 05401
Tel.: (802) 951-1700
Year Founded: 1998
Sales Range: $10-24.9 Million
Emp.: 10
N.A.I.C.S.: 541810
Ken Millman *(Pres)*
Ren Chase *(Dir-Art)*
Pat Sears *(CEO & Gen Mgr)*
Mat Wilcox *(Copywriter & Producer-Creative)*
Becca Padden *(Dir-Art)*
Peter Foytho *(Dir-Creative & Dir-Art)*

SPIKER COMMUNICATIONS, INC.
3200 Brooks St, Missoula, MT 59801
Tel.: (406) 721-0785
Web Site:
http://www.spikercomm.com
Year Founded: 1983
Sales Range: $10-24.9 Million
Emp.: 10
Advetising Agency
N.A.I.C.S.: 541810
John Wes Spiker *(Pres & Partner)*
Chris Spiker *(VP)*
Anita Cleland *(Mgr-Production)*

SPILLER FURNITURE COMPANY
5605 McFarland Blvd, Northport, AL 35476
Tel.: (205) 333-2000
Web Site:
http://www.spillerfurniture.com
Year Founded: 1948
Rev.: $12,000,000
Emp.: 150
Owner & Operator of Furniture Stores
N.A.I.C.S.: 449110
Shane Spiller *(Owner & Pres)*
David Williams *(VP)*

SPIN RECRUITMENT ADVERTISING
712 Bancroft Rd Ste 521, Walnut Creek, CA 94598
Tel.: (925) 944-6060
Web Site:
http://www.spinrecruitment.com
Sales Range: $10-24.9 Million
Emp.: 8
N.A.I.C.S.: 541810
Traci Dondanville *(Owner)*
Stephanie Fong *(VP)*

SPINAL ELEMENTS HOLDINGS, INC.
3115 Melrose Dr Ste 200, Carlsbad, CA 92010   DE
Year Founded: 2016
Rev.: $95,916,000
Assets: $105,921,000
Liabilities: $227,609,000
Net Worth: ($121,688,000)
Earnings: ($51,420,000)
Emp.: 120
Fiscal Year-end: 12/31/19
Holding Company
N.A.I.C.S.: 551112
Jason Blain *(Pres & CEO)*

SPINDLETOP CAPITAL MANAGEMENT LLC
7000 N Mopac Expy Ste 315, Austin, TX 78731
Tel.: (512) 961-4633
Web Site:
http://spindletopcapital.com
Year Founded: 2011
Investment Services
N.A.I.C.S.: 523940
Evan Melrose *(Founder & Mng Dir)*
Subsidiaries:

Tricity Pain Associates PA   (1)
110 Stone Oak Pkwy, San Antonio, TX 78258
Tel.: (844) 789-7246
Web Site: https://tricitypainassociates.com
Pain Management Care, Physical Medicine & Rehabilitation Services
N.A.I.C.S.: 621999
Urfan Dar *(Founder & CEO)*

SPINDUSTRY INTERACTIVE, INC.
1370 NW 114th St Ste 300, Des Moines, IA 50325
Tel.: (515) 225-0920
Web Site: http://www.spindustry.com
Year Founded: 1996
Sales Range: Less than $1 Million
Emp.: 25
Information Technology Services
N.A.I.C.S.: 541519
Stephen Fry *(Co-Founder & COO)*
Michael Bird *(Co-Founder & Pres)*

SPINE & SPORT
201 Bussines Park Dr Ste 202, Rincon, GA 31326
Tel.: (912) 826-3797
Web Site: http://www.spinesport.org
Year Founded: 2004
Sales Range: $1-9.9 Million
Emp.: 97
Physical Therapy, Personal Training & Weight Management Programs
N.A.I.C.S.: 621340
Jacques L. Beauchamp *(Co-Founder)*
Eric C. Bull *(Co-Founder)*
Bobby Goldner *(Deputy VP-Ops)*
Melissa Fender *(VP-Admin)*
Brian Walker *(Mgr-Personnel)*
Christy Wayde *(Mgr)*
Jessica Shea *(Mgr-Comm)*

SPINEEX, INC.
4046 Clipper Court, Fremont, CA 94538
Tel.: (510) 573-1093   DE
Web Site: http://www.spineexinc.com
Year Founded: 2017
Emp.: 14
Medical Device Mfr & Distr
N.A.I.C.S.: 339113
Roy Chin *(Chm & CEO)*
Andrew Rogers *(Pres & Sec)*
Robyn-Burrows Ownbey *(CTO)*
Christie Wang *(Pres-Global Bus)*
Eric Blossey *(Chief Comml Officer)*

SPINIELLO COMPANIES
354 Eisenhower Pkwy, Livingston, NJ 07039
Tel.: (973) 808-8383
Web Site: http://www.spiniello.com
Rev.: $56,429,718
Emp.: 400
Water, Sewer & Utility Lines
N.A.I.C.S.: 237110
Pat Solinine *(Pres)*
Art Caprio *(Mgr-Ops)*
Caprice Bynes *(Coord-Payroll)*
Deb Schoonover *(Mgr-Acctg)*
Jose Alpizar *(Mgr-Safety)*
William Peters *(CIO)*
April Amico *(Controller)*

SPINK SHREVES GALLERIES, INC.
3100 Monticello Ave, Dallas, TX 75205
Tel.: (972) 788-2100
Web Site: http://www.shreves.com
Sales Range: $10-24.9 Million
Emp.: 6
Auction Gallery
N.A.I.C.S.: 459999

SPINNAKER CONSULTING GROUP LLC
8000 Franklin Farms Dr Ste 100, Richmond, VA 23229
Tel.: (804) 510-0768
Web Site:
http://www.spinnakerconsultinggroup.com
Year Founded: 2012
Sales Range: $1-9.9 Million
Emp.: 30
Business Management Consulting Services
N.A.I.C.S.: 541611
Shawn Sweeney *(Founder & Mng Partner)*
Chris Landrum *(Principal)*
Brett Ludden *(Principal)*
Scott Hamilton *(Head-Svc Delivery)*
Paige Wolk *(Dir-Ops)*

SPINNAKER MANAGEMENT GROUP, LLC
900 Threadneedle St Ste 450, Houston, TX 77079
Tel.: (720) 457-5500
Web Site:
http://www.spinnakermgmt.com
Year Founded: 2002
Consulting Services
N.A.I.C.S.: 541611
Robert Benson *(Founder & Mng Principal)*
John Sharkey *(Sr VP)*
Jeff Jorgensen *(Sr VP)*
Subsidiaries:

Plan4Demand Solutions, Inc.   (1)
1501 Reedsdale St, Pittsburgh, PA 15233
Tel.: (412) 733-5000
Supply Chain Planning & Consulting Solutions
N.A.I.C.S.: 541614

Spinnaker Support, LLC   (1)
5445 DTC Pkwy Ste 850, Greenwood Village, CO 80111
Tel.: (720) 457-5500
Web Site: http://www.spinnakersupport.com
Sales Range: $25-49.9 Million
Emp.: 250
IT Support & Consulting
N.A.I.C.S.: 541519
Matt Stava *(CEO)*
Kurt Moydell *(VP-Sls-Americas)*
Mark Kreutz *(VP-Global Support Svcs)*
Shawn Du Plessis *(VP-SAP Global Support Svcs)*
Jessica Vahey *(Dir-Resource Ops)*
Bob Harland *(VP-Oracle Global Support Svcs)*
Devan Brua *(VP-Compliance & Risk)*
Lee Mashburn *(VP-Mktg)*
Nigel Pullan *(VP-Sls-EMEA)*
Iain Saunderson *(CTO)*
James R. Nollsch *(CFO)*

SPIRATEX COMPANY INC.
6333 Cogswell St, Romulus, MI 48174
Tel.: (734) 722-0100
Web Site: http://www.spiratex.com
Rev.: $14,844,379
Emp.: 80
Plastics Processing
N.A.I.C.S.: 326199
Garry Markle *(Pres)*

SPIRE CAPITAL PARTNERS, LLC
1500 Broadway Ste 1811, New York, NY 10036-4052
Tel.: (212) 218-5454
Web Site:
http://www.spirecapital.com
Year Founded: 2000
Rev.: $600,000,000
Emp.: 12
Privater Equity Firm
N.A.I.C.S.: 523999
Bruce M. Hernandez *(Partner)*
Donald E. Stewart *(CFO & Chief Compliance Officer)*
Sean C. White *(Partner)*
David K. Schaible *(Partner)*
Karl Rodger *(VP)*
Linda B. Barish *(Chief Admin Officer)*
Anthony D. Cassano *(Partner)*
Andrew J. Armstrong Jr. *(Partner)*
Subsidiaries:

Dynamic Quest, Inc.   (1)
4821 Koger Blvd, Greensboro, NC 27407
Tel.: (336) 370-0555
Web Site: http://www.dynamicquest.com
Rev.: $3,510,000
Emp.: 11
Wired Telecommunications Carriers
N.A.I.C.S.: 517111
Javeir Gomez *(CEO)*
Willie Lash *(COO)*
Jen Wong *(Founder)*

Subsidiary (Domestic):

Nexxtep Technology Services, Inc.   (2)
3354 Greystone Way, Valdosta, GA 31605
Tel.: (229) 671-1513
Web Site: http://ncare.com
Rev.: $1,500,000
Emp.: 17
Custom Computer Programming Services
N.A.I.C.S.: 541511
Ryan Williams *(VP-Bus Dev)*
Paul Nichols *(Pres & CEO)*
Stuart Avera *(CTO)*
Richard Baker *(Acct Mgr)*
Robert McMichen *(Mgr-Svc)*
Anne Shenton *(Dir-Mktg)*
Bart Shiver *(Mgr-Logistics)*
James Gillis *(Gen Mgr)*
Linda Exum *(Office Mgr)*
Roger Horton *(Gen Mgr)*

Southern Data Solutions, Inc.   (2)
12655 Edison Dr Ste 100, Alpharetta, GA 30005
Tel.: (678) 872-7380
Web Site: http://www.therightmsp.com
Instrument Mfr
N.A.I.C.S.: 334515
Jeff Davis *(Pres)*

SPIRE CORPORATION
1 Patriots Park, Bedford, MA 01730-2396
Tel.: (781) 275-6000   MA
Web Site: http://www.spirecorp.com
Year Founded: 1969
Sales Range: $10-24.9 Million
Emp.: 82
Solar Energy Manufacturing Equipment & Solar Systems, Biomedical Devices & Optoelectronic Components Developer, Mfr & Marketer
N.A.I.C.S.: 334413
Rodger W. LaFavre *(Pres & CEO)*

SPIRE INVESTMENT PARTNERS LLC
7901 Jones Branch Dr, McLean, VA 22102
Tel.: (703) 748-5800
Web Site: http://www.spireip.com
Year Founded: 1997
Sales Range: $10-24.9 Million
Emp.: 25
Wealth Management Services
N.A.I.C.S.: 523940

SPIRE INVESTMENT PARTNERS LLC
U.S. PRIVATE

Spire Investment Partners LLC—(Continued)
David Blisk (CEO)
Paul T. Murphy (Exec VP & Mng Dir)
Dianne Nolin (First VP)
Steven Donald (VP)

SPIRES RESTAURANTS INC.
1411 N Batavia St Ste 101, Orange, CA 92867-3526
Tel.: (714) 997-9780 — CA
Web Site: http://www.spires-restaurants.com
Year Founded: 1965
Sales Range: $125-149.9 Million
Emp.: 350
Operator of Chain of Restaurants
N.A.I.C.S.: 722511
Catherine Haretakis (Pres)

SPIRIT & SANZONE DISTRIBUTING CO.
6495 Fly Rd, East Syracuse, NY 13057
Tel.: (315) 463-6103
Web Site: http://www.spiritandsanzone.com
Sales Range: $10-24.9 Million
Emp.: 106
Beer & Other Fermented Malt Liquors
N.A.I.C.S.: 424810
Francis S. Sanzone (Pres)

SPIRIT CHRYSLER JEEP
4611 Avenue Q, Lubbock, TX 79412
Tel.: (806) 747-4461
Web Site: http://www.spiritauto.com
Sales Range: $10-24.9 Million
Emp.: 44
Automobiles, New & Used
N.A.I.C.S.: 441110
John Bures (Mgr-Parts)
Rustin Johnson (Mgr-Fin)

SPIRIT FORD INC.
4402 N Ann Arbor Rd, Dundee, MI 48131
Tel.: (734) 529-5521
Web Site: http://www.spiritford.com
Sales Range: $25-49.9 Million
Emp.: 37
Sales of New & Used Cars
N.A.I.C.S.: 441110
Bill Colovos (Gen Mgr-Sls)

SPIRIT INTERNATIONAL INC.
2620 Regatta Dr Ste 102, Las Vegas, NV 89128
Tel.: (702) 359-0881 — NV
Year Founded: 2014
Sales Range: Less than $1 Million
Alcoholic Beverage Distr
N.A.I.C.S.: 424820
Zur Dadon (Pres, CEO, CFO, Treas & Sec)

SPIRIT MTA REIT
2727 N Harwood St Ste 300, Dallas, TX 75201
Tel.: (972) 476-1409 — MD
Web Site: http://www.spiritmastertrust.com
Rev.: $246,307,000
Assets: $2,305,649,000
Liabilities: $2,596,720,000
Net Worth: ($291,071,000)
Earnings: ($229,513,000)
Fiscal Year-end: 12/31/18
Real Estate Investment Services
N.A.I.C.S.: 531210
Ricardo Rodriguez (Pres, CEO, CFO & Treas)

SPIRITE INDUSTRIES, INC.
150 S Dean St, Englewood, NJ 07631-3514
Tel.: (201) 871-4910 — NY
Web Site: http://www.spirite.com
Year Founded: 1892
Sales Range: $75-99.9 Million
Emp.: 50
Mfr of Womens Undergarments
N.A.I.C.S.: 315250
Gary H. Kronfeld (CEO)

SPIRITRUST LUTHERAN
1050 Pennsylvania Ave, York, PA 17404
Tel.: (717) 854-3971 — PA
Web Site: http://www.spiritrustlutheran.org
Year Founded: 1951
Lifecare Retirement Community Operator
N.A.I.C.S.: 623311
Carol Hess (VP-HR)
Angela L. Dohrman (COO-Senior Living & Sr VP)
K. Weidner (Dir-Clinical Excellence)
Glenn Miller (Pres-SpiriTrust Lutheran Foundation & VP-External Rels)
Revena Rossi (CFO & VP-Support Svcs)
Terry Shade (Pres-Life, VP-Community Health Svcs & Exec Dir-Home Care & Hospic)
Kimberly Alvarez (Dir-Dev)
Crystal L. Hull (Dir-Comm & Public Rels)
Tiffany Jones (Dir-Accts Receivable & Reimbursement)
Lindsay Marchant (Controller)
Joseph Sabold (Dir-Facilities Mgmt & Construction)
Melissa Williams (Dir-Senior Living Sls & Mktg)
Robert L. Rundle Jr. (Pres & CEO)

SPIRK BROTHERS INC.
8052 William Penn Hwy, Easton, PA 18045
Tel.: (610) 867-3008
Web Site: http://www.spirkbrothers.com
Year Founded: 1985
Sales Range: $1-9.9 Million
Emp.: 25
Full-Service Construction & Project Management
N.A.I.C.S.: 236220
David M. Spirk (Founder)

SPIRO & ASSOCIATES MARKETING, ADVERTISING & PUBLIC RELATIONS
12651 Mcgregor Blvd Ste 402, Fort Myers, FL 33919-4489
Tel.: (239) 481-5511
Web Site: http://www.spiroandassociates.com
Year Founded: 1988
Sales Range: $10-24.9 Million
Emp.: 12
N.A.I.C.S.: 541810
Christopher T. Spiro (CEO)
Steve J. Martin (VP & Dir-Creative)
Mark Heidman (Dir-Art)
Jessica S. Barton (Acct Exec-PR)
Jackie Burke (Acct Exec)
Gail Gubelman (Dir-Art)
Melodie Hagopian (Mgr-Traffic & Production)

SPIROL INTERNATIONAL CORPORATION
30 Rock Ave, Danielson, CT 06239-1425
Tel.: (860) 774-8571 — CT
Web Site: http://www.spirol.com
Year Founded: 1948
Sales Range: $150-199.9 Million
Emp.: 500
Bolt, Nut, Screw, Rivet & Washer Mfr
N.A.I.C.S.: 332722
Jeffrey F. Koehl (Pres)
Christopher Jeznach (Mgr-Automotive Sls-US)

Subsidiaries:

Ascutney Metal Products (1)
2637 US Rt 5 N, Windsor, VT 05089-9723
Tel.: (802) 674-6721
Web Site: http://www.spirolascutney.com
Sales Range: $10-24.9 Million
Emp.: 15
Mfr of Milled Brass Nuts & Screw Machine Products
N.A.I.C.S.: 332710
Jeffrey F. Koehl (Chm & CEO)

Spirol Industries, Ltd. (1)
17 Princewood Road, Corby, NN17 4ET, Northants, United Kingdom (100%)
Tel.: (44) 1536444800
Web Site: http://www.spirol.com
Sales Range: $10-24.9 Million
Emp.: 40
Industrial Fastener Assembly Equipment Mfr
N.A.I.C.S.: 339993

Spirol Industries, Ltd. (1)
3103 St Etienne Blvd, Windsor, N8W 5B1, ON, Canada (100%)
Tel.: (519) 974-3334
Web Site: http://www.spirolcanada.com
Sales Range: $10-24.9 Million
Emp.: 35
Mfr of Industrial Fasteners, Stampings & Assembly Equipment
N.A.I.C.S.: 339993
Thomas Buchta (Pres)

Spirol International Corporation - Stow (1)
321 Remington Rd, Stow, OH 44224-4915 (100%)
Tel.: (330) 920-3655
Web Site: http://www.spirol.com
Sales Range: $10-24.9 Million
Emp.: 88
Metal Stamping Mfr
N.A.I.C.S.: 332119
Tom Butorac (Mgr-Mfg)
Ken Hagan (Mgr-Mfg)

Spirol SAS (1)
Cite de I Automobile ZAC Croix Blandin 18 Rue Lena Bernstein, 51100, Reims, France (100%)
Tel.: (33) 326363142
Web Site: http://www.spirol.com
Sales Range: $10-24.9 Million
Emp.: 13
Industrial Fastener Mfr
N.A.I.C.S.: 339993

Spirol West, Inc. (1)
1950 Compton Ave Unit 111, Corona, CA 92881-6471 (100%)
Tel.: (951) 273-5900
Web Site: http://www.spirol.com
Sales Range: $10-24.9 Million
Emp.: 9
Sales Office
N.A.I.C.S.: 332119
Kevin Prokopchuk (Office Mgr)

SPIRTAS WRECKING CO. INC.
951 Skinker Pkwy, Saint Louis, MO 63112-1413
Tel.: (314) 862-9800
Web Site: http://www.spirtas.com
Year Founded: 1954
Sales Range: $10-24.9 Million
Emp.: 70
Wrecking Services
N.A.I.C.S.: 238910
Arnold Spirtas (Pres)

SPITFIRE GROUP, LLC
905 W 124th Ave Ste 220, Westminster, CO 80234
Tel.: (303) 485-1880
Web Site: http://www.spitfiregroup.com
Year Founded: 2004
Sales Range: $1-9.9 Million
Emp.: 40
Technology Consulting Services
N.A.I.C.S.: 541690
Doug Gregory (Dir-Practice)
Michael Byrne (Dir-Practice)
Michael Stratton (Mgr-Technical Solutions)
Cindy Knowlton (Mng Partner & Dir-Institutional Mktg Denver Investments)

SPITZER CHEVROLET COMPANY
7111 Sunset Strip Ave NW, Canton, OH 44720
Tel.: (330) 499-3353
Web Site: http://www.spitzerchevrolet.com
Sales Range: $10-24.9 Million
Emp.: 40
Car Whslr
N.A.I.C.S.: 441110
Chris Jung (Gen Mgr)

SPITZER CHEVY NORTHFIELD
333 E Aurora Rd, Northfield, OH 44067
Tel.: (330) 467-4141
Web Site: http://www.spitzerchevyeast.com
Sales Range: $10-24.9 Million
Emp.: 70
Car Whslr
N.A.I.C.S.: 441110
Bob Oakes (Treas)
Alan Spitzer (Pres)
Larry Ward (Dir-Ops)

SPITZER MANAGEMENT, INC.
150 E Bridge St, Elyria, OH 44035
Tel.: (440) 323-4671 — OH
Web Site: http://www.spitzer.com
Year Founded: 1904
Sales Range: $800-899.9 Million
Emp.: 600
Holding Company; Car Dealerships, Marinas & Golf Courses Owner & Operator
N.A.I.C.S.: 551112
Alan Spitzer (Chm & CEO)
Cathy Schuster (Dir-Real Estate)

Subsidiaries:

Spitzer Autoworld Homestead, Inc. (1)
30101 S Dixie Hwy, Homestead, FL 33033
Tel.: (305) 248-5880
Web Site: http://www.autoworldchryslerdodgejeepram.com
Rev.: $10,700,000
Emp.: 10
New & Used Car Dealer
N.A.I.C.S.: 441110
Alan Spitzer (Pres)

SPIVEY ENTERPRISES INC.
6148 Brookshire Blvd F, Charlotte, NC 28216
Tel.: (704) 399-4802
Web Site: http://www.quikshoppe.com
Sales Range: $10-24.9 Million
Emp.: 20
Convenience Store Operator
N.A.I.C.S.: 445131
Patsy Costantino-Spivey (VP)
Constance Mayhew (VP)
Bob Small (Dir-Ops)
Robert C. Spivey Jr. (Pres)

SPIVEY UTILITY CONSTRUCTION CO. INC.
13338 Interlaken Rd, Odessa, FL 33556
Tel.: (813) 926-8846
Web Site: http://www.spiveyutility.com

Sales Range: $25-49.9 Million
Emp.: 180
Power & Communication Line & Related Structures Construction
N.A.I.C.S.: 237130
Colette Lazar *(Treas & Sec)*
Tim Spivey *(VP-Boring Ops)*
Danny Spivey *(VP-Ops)*
Jim Spivey *(VP-Ops)*
Steve Spivey *(VP-Fleet)*
David Lazar *(Dir-Safety)*

Subsidiaries:

Florida Directional Boring Equipment & Supplies, Inc. (1)
13338 Interlaken Rd, Odessa, FL 33556
Tel.: (813) 926-3698
Web Site: http://www.floridadirectional.com
Sales Range: $1-9.9 Million
Emp.: 34
Construction, Mining & Forestry Machinery & Equipment Rental & Leasing
N.A.I.C.S.: 532412

SPL ASSOCIATES INC.
100 Ave D, Williston, VT 05495-0759
Tel.: (802) 864-9831 VT
Web Site:
http://www.blodgettsupply.com
Year Founded: 1986
Sales Range: $25-49.9 Million
Emp.: 70
Holding Company; Plumbing & Heating Supplies, Electrical Appliances & Industrial Freezers
N.A.I.C.S.: 551112
Samuel E. Levin *(Pres)*

Subsidiaries:

Blodgett Supply Co. Inc. (1)
100 Ave D, Williston, VT 05495-9704
Tel.: (802) 864-9831
Web Site: http://www.blodgettsupply.com
Sales Range: $10-24.9 Million
Emp.: 30
Distribution Of Plumbing, Heating, Electrical Appliances & Television
N.A.I.C.S.: 423620

SPLASH CAR WASH, INC.
472 Wheelers Farms Rd Ste 304, Milford, CT 06461
Tel.: (203) 324-5400 DE
Web Site:
https://splashcarwashes.com
Emp.: 100
Car Washing Services
N.A.I.C.S.: 811192
Mark Curtis *(CEO)*

Subsidiaries:

4 Seasons Car Wash (1)
7795 Oswego Rd, Liverpool, NY 13090
Tel.: (419) 236-6869
Web Site: https://www.welovecleancars.com
Car Washes
N.A.I.C.S.: 811192

SPLASH MEDIA LP
5048 Addison Cir, Addison, TX 75001
Tel.: (972) 392-6700
Web Site:
http://www.splashmedia.com
Sales Range: $1-9.9 Million
Emp.: 70
Social Media Marketing
N.A.I.C.S.: 541890
John Dankovchik *(Owner & CEO)*
Linda Randall *(Dir-Admin & Recruiting)*
Derek McIntyre *(Mng Dir-Digital Media)*
Dolph Fun *(Dir-Innovation)*
Dennis Wilson *(Dir-Production Svcs)*
Rob Howe *(Dir-Strategic Insight)*
Carrie Pinkley *(Dir-Strategic Plng)*
Brian Shelton *(Dir-Video Ops)*
Sean Clayton *(Mng Dir-Paid Media)*
Eve Mayer *(Chief Mktg Officer)*

SPLASH PRODUCTS INC.
1380 Corporate Ctr Curve Ste 200, Eagan, MN 55121-1202
Tel.: (651) 454-4100
Web Site:
http://www.splashwash.com
Year Founded: 1959
Sales Range: $25-49.9 Million
Emp.: 150
Polish & Sanitation Good Mfr
N.A.I.C.S.: 325612
Elliott Badzin *(Pres)*

SPLASHLIGHT LLC
75 Varick St, New York, NY 10013
Tel.: (212) 268-7247
Web Site: http://www.splashlight.com
Year Founded: 2002
Visual Content Creator
N.A.I.C.S.: 512110
James Ingram *(CEO)*

Subsidiaries:

Telmar Group Inc. (1)
711 3rd Ave 15th Fl, New York, NY 10017
Tel.: (212) 725-3000
Web Site: http://www.telmar.com
Sales Range: $10-24.9 Million
Emp.: 300
Supplier of Information Services & Software Solutions
N.A.I.C.S.: 513210
Stanley P. Federman *(Chm & CEO)*
Susan Lanzetta *(COO)*
Corey V. Panno *(Pres)*
Anna Fountas *(Pres-Americas)*
Jenny Jones *(VP-Bus Dev & Client Svcs-Canada)*

Subsidiary (Non-US):

Telmar (Asia) Ltd. (2)
Room 1506-07 Olympia Plaza 255 King's Road, North Point, China (Hong Kong)
Tel.: (852) 2811 8566
Web Site: http://www.telmar.hk
Emp.: 3
Advetising Agency
N.A.I.C.S.: 541810
Jennifer Daniel *(Gen Mgr)*

Telmar Communications Limited (2)
43-45 Dorset Street, London, NW1 U7N, United Kingdom
Tel.: (44) 2074672599
Web Site: http://www.telmar.co.uk
Sales Range: $10-24.9 Million
Emp.: 25
Advertising Media Information Services
N.A.I.C.S.: 519290
Gary Mosson *(Country Mgr)*

Telmar HMS Ltd. (2)
36 King Street East 4th Floor Toronto, Toronto, M5C 3B2, ON, Canada
Tel.: (416) 487-2111
Web Site: http://www.ca.telmar.com
Sales Range: $10-24.9 Million
Emp.: 3
Medical Information Services
N.A.I.C.S.: 519290
C. Panno *(Gen Mgr)*

Subsidiary (Domestic):

Telmar Information Services Corp. (2)
711 3rd Ave 15th Fl, New York, NY 10017
Tel.: (212) 725-3000
Web Site: http://www.telmar.com
Emp.: 25
Advertising Media Information Services
N.A.I.C.S.: 519290
Vicky De Sousa *(VP-Client Svcs)*
Stanley Federman *(Chm & CEO)*

Subsidiary (Non-US):

Telmar International Inc. (2)
Level 12 1 Pacific Highway, North Sydney, 2060, NSW, Australia
Tel.: (61) 2 9959 9618
Web Site: http://www.telmarpacific.com.au
Advetising Agency
N.A.I.C.S.: 541810

Telmar Media Systems (Pty) Limited (2)
The Woodlands Western Service Road, Woodmead, Johannesburg, South Africa
Tel.: (27) 0118044489
Web Site: http://www.telmar.com
Sales Range: $10-24.9 Million
Emp.: 100
Advertising Media Information Services
N.A.I.C.S.: 519290
Jennifer Daniel *(Mng Dir)*
Marcia Swart *(Deputy Mng Dir)*

Telmar Peaktime B.V. (2)
Strawinskylaan 3051 3rd floor, 1077 ZX, Amsterdam, Netherlands
Tel.: (31) 20 301 2423
Web Site: http://www.telmar.nl
Advetising Agency
N.A.I.C.S.: 541810

Telmar Peaktime S.A.S. (2)
15 place de la Republique, 75003, Paris, France
Tel.: (33) 0172890300
Web Site: http://www.telmarpeaktime.com
Sales Range: $10-24.9 Million
Emp.: 15
Medical Information Services
N.A.I.C.S.: 519290
Mathew Floirat *(Gen Mgr)*

Telmar Polska Sp zoo (2)
ul Dzikiej Roxy 19/2, 05-509, Jozefoslaw, Poland
Tel.: (48) 601223486
Web Site: http://www.pl.telmar.com
Advertising Media Information Services
N.A.I.C.S.: 519290

Telmar Software (Shanghai) Ltd. (2)
Room 1212 Chunshenjiang Building 400 Zhejiang Zhong Road, Shanghai, 200001, China
Tel.: (86) 21 6351 9409
Web Site: http://www.telmar.com
Advetising Agency
N.A.I.C.S.: 541810

Telmar-Het Media Instituut BV (2)
Weerdestein 21, 1083 GA, Amsterdam, Netherlands
Tel.: (31) 206440770
Web Site: http://www.nl.telmar.com
Sales Range: $10-24.9 Million
Emp.: 4
Advertising Media Information Services
N.A.I.C.S.: 519290

SPLENDOR DESIGN GROUP, INC.
50 Broad St Ste 1, Red Bank, NJ 07701
Tel.: (732) 295-1551
Web Site: http://www.splendordesign.com
Marketing & Advertising Services
N.A.I.C.S.: 541890
Adam Taylor *(Owner & CEO)*
Jay Sharfstein *(Creative Dir)*
Michelle Fulton *(Art Dir)*
Chris Brignola *(Creative Dir)*
Alexandra Venier *(VP)*

Subsidiaries:

Filter Advertising LLC (1)
160 Pearl St 2nd Fl, New York, NY 10005
Tel.: (212) 248-3028
Web Site: http://filteradvertising.com
Sales Range: $10-24.9 Million
Emp.: 12
N.A.I.C.S.: 541810

SPLICE COMMUNICATIONS
4040 Campbell Ave Ste 120, Menlo Park, CA 94025
Tel.: (650) 577-2304 CA
Web Site:
http://www.splicetelecom.com
Year Founded: 2002
Sales Range: $10-24.9 Million
Emp.: 16
VOIP Telecommunications Systems
N.A.I.C.S.: 517112
Andrew Coan *(Founder, Pres & CEO)*
Scott Bischoff *(CFO)*
Eileen Warner *(Dir-Svc Ops & Carrier Rels)*
Natalia Rowland *(Dir-Pricing & Carrier Dev)*

SPOHN RANCH, INC.
6824 S Centinela Ave, Culver, CA 90230
Tel.: (626) 330-5803 CA
Web Site:
http://www.spohnranch.com
Year Founded: 1992
Sales Range: $1-9.9 Million
Emp.: 50
Skate Park Construction & Management
N.A.I.C.S.: 711320
Aaron Spohn *(Pres)*

SPOKANE FOOD SERVICES, INC.
3123 E Bridgeport Ave, Spokane, WA 99217
Tel.: (509) 489-5531 WA
Web Site:
http://www.mcdspokane.com
Sales Range: $10-24.9 Million
Emp.: 800
Franchise Fast-Food Restaurants Owner & Operator
N.A.I.C.S.: 722513
Chris Weber *(Controller)*
Kari Rose *(Supvr-Mktg)*
Mark Ray Sr. *(Chm, Pres & CEO)*

SPOKANE HARDWARE SUPPLY, INC.
2001 E Trent, Spokane, WA 99220
Tel.: (509) 535-1663
Web Site: http://www.spokane-hardware.com
Rev.: $15,900,000
Emp.: 34
Hardware Merchant Whslr
N.A.I.C.S.: 423710
Rick Reinbold *(VP)*
Stephen J. Northrop *(Owner & Pres)*
Charlie Iverson *(Mgr)*
Stephanie Willer *(Mgr-Mktg-Internet Sls)*

SPOKANE INDUSTRIES INC.
3808 N Sullivan Rd Bldg 1, Spokane, WA 99216
Tel.: (509) 924-0440
Web Site:
http://www.spokaneindustries.com
Sales Range: $10-24.9 Million
Emp.: 250
Alloy Steel Castings
N.A.I.C.S.: 331513
Robert G. Tenold *(Chm)*
Ken Vorhees *(CFO)*
Pam Axel *(Coord-Production)*
Kevin Garasky *(Mgr-Reg Sls)*
Ed Kaczmarek *(Gen Mgr-Castings)*
Greg Tenold *(Pres)*
Nate Batson *(Gen Mgr-Metal Products)*
Tracei Scofield *(Dir-HR)*
Tyrus Tenold *(Pres-Castings)*

SPOKANE INTERNATIONAL AIRPORT
9000 W Airport Dr, Spokane, WA 99224
Tel.: (509) 455-6455
Web Site:
http://www.spokaneairports.net
Sales Range: $25-49.9 Million
Emp.: 111
Airport Services

SPOKANE INTERNATIONAL AIRPORT   U.S. PRIVATE

Spokane International Airport—(Continued)
N.A.I.C.S.: 488119
Lawrence J. Krauter (CEO)
Collins Sprague (Sec)
Max Kuney (Vice Chm)
Kelly Fukai (Mgr- Public & External Affairs)

SPOKANE SEED COMPANY
6015 E Alki Ave, Spokane, WA 99212
Tel.: (509) 535-3671
Web Site: http://www.spokaneseed.com
Sales Range: $10-24.9 Million
Emp.: 50
Dry Pea & Bean Farming
N.A.I.C.S.: 111130
Andrew Fontaine (VP-Sls)
Peter Johnstone (Pres & CEO)
Charlie Shrope (VP-Procurement)
Jim Groth (Mgr-Production)
John Zamora (Coord-Quality Sys)
Amanda Taylor (Coord-Traffic)
Tom Organ (Plant Mgr-Colfax)

SPOKANE SYMPHONY ORCHESTRA
1001 W Sprague Ave, Spokane, WA 99201
Tel.: (509) 624-1200
Web Site: http://www.spokanesymphony.org
Year Founded: 1945
Emp.: 100
Symphony Orchestra
N.A.I.C.S.: 711130
Charles Karschney (Mgr-Production)
Kat Langenheim (Dir-Major Gifts & Planned Giving)
Jennifer Hicks (Dir-Dev)
Daniel Cotter (Gen Mgr)
Carolyn Gooley (Sec)
Lorrie Scott (Pres)
Michael Ebinger (VP)
Russ Lee (Treas)
Bruce Bodden (Principal)
Emily Browne (Principal)
John Marshall (Principal)
Larry Jess (Principal)
Leonard Byrne (Principal)
Lynne Feller-Marshall (Principal)
Ross Holcombe (Principal)

SPOKANE TEACHERS CREDIT UNION
106 W Nora Ave, Spokane, WA 99205-4845
Tel.: (509) 326-1954   WA
Web Site: http://www.stcu.org
Year Founded: 1934
Sales Range: $75-99.9 Million
Emp.: 567
Credit Union Operator
N.A.I.C.S.: 522130
Tom Johnson (Pres & CEO)
Keith Connolly (VP-Retail Svc Delivery)
Brandy Schloss (Reg Mgr-Moran Prairie, South & Cheney)
Lisa Chitwood (Reg Mgr-South Valley, Valley & Liberty Lake)
Tracy Ballard (Dir-HR)
Amanda Kirk (Mgr-Coeur d'Alene)
Eli Brown (Mgr-South Hill)

SPOKANE TELEVISION INC.
500 W Boone Ave, Spokane, WA 99201
Tel.: (509) 324-4000
Web Site: http://www.kxly.com
Sales Range: $10-24.9 Million
Emp.: 235
Television Broadcasting
N.A.I.C.S.: 516120

Elizabeth M. Burns (Pres)
Teddy Gibbon (VP)
John B. Murphy (Treas & Sec)
Brian Paul (Gen Mgr)
Wendy Peter (Office Mgr)
Robert Cole Jr. (Controller)

SPOKANE UNITED METHODIST HOMES
2903 E 25th Ave, Spokane, WA 99223
Tel.: (509) 536-6650
Web Site: http://www.rockwoodretirement.org
Sales Range: $10-24.9 Million
Emp.: 175
Retirement Hotel Operation
N.A.I.C.S.: 531110
Allan Curryer (Pres & CEO)
James Maxwell (CFO)
Jaak Juhkentaal (VP-Ops)

SPOONER HEALTH SYSTEM
819 Ash St, Spooner, WI 54801
Tel.: (715) 635-2111   WI
Web Site: http://www.spoonerhealthsystem.com
Year Founded: 1955
Sales Range: $10-24.9 Million
Community Health Care Services
N.A.I.C.S.: 621498
Michael Schafer (CEO)
Rebecca Busch (CFO)
Cindy Rouzer (Dir-HR)
Clint Miller (Dir-Patient Care Svcs)

SPOROCO INC.
92 H & S Dr, Selinsgrove, PA 17870
Tel.: (570) 374-8116
Web Site: http://www.sporoco.com
Sales Range: $10-24.9 Million
Emp.: 25
Manufactured Housing
N.A.I.C.S.: 423310
Pat Oberlin (Owner)

SPORT & HEALTH CLUBS, L.C.
1760 Old Meadow Rd Ste 300, McLean, VA 22102-4330
Tel.: (703) 556-6556   VA
Web Site: http://www.sportandhealth.com
Year Founded: 1980
Sales Range: $75-99.9 Million
Emp.: 1,900
Gym & Fitness Centers Operator
N.A.I.C.S.: 713940
Scott Thomas (CFO)
Mark Fisher (CEO)
John Galiani (Co-Chm)
Kirk Galiani (Co-Chm)

SPORT & SPINE REHAB
9300 Livingston Rd Suite 100, Fort Washington, MD 20744
Tel.: (301) 203-6734
Web Site: http://www.ssrehab.com
Year Founded: 1994
Sales Range: $1-9.9 Million
Emp.: 65
Back, Neck & Spine Therapy & Rehabilitation
N.A.I.C.S.: 621111
Jay S. Greenstein (CEO)

SPORT CHEVROLET CO. INC.
3101 Automobile Blvd, Silver Spring, MD 20904
Tel.: (301) 890-6000
Web Site: http://www.sportchevrolet.com
Year Founded: 1968
Sales Range: $75-99.9 Million
Emp.: 200

Owner & Operator of Car Dealerships
N.A.I.C.S.: 441110
Robert H. Fogarty (Pres)
Gerry Ryan (Gen Mgr-Sls)
Gary Bowring (Treas & Controller)

SPORT CLIPS, INC.
110 Briarwood Dr, Georgetown, TX 78628-2490
Tel.: (512) 869-1201   TX
Web Site: http://www.sportclips.com
Year Founded: 1993
Sales Range: $10-24.9 Million
Emp.: 62
Barber Shops Owner & Franchisor
N.A.I.C.S.: 812111
Gordon B. Logan (Founder & CEO)
Jean Booth (VP-Market Dev)
Greg Smith (VP-Real Estate)
Mark Kartarik (Pres)
Edward Logan (COO)
Mike Runyan (Chief Talent Officer)

SPORT HALEY HOLDINGS, INC.
10367 Brockwood Rd, Dallas, TX 75238
Tel.: (303) 320-8800   CO
Web Site: http://www.sporthaley.com
Year Founded: 1992
Sales Range: $10-24.9 Million
Mid-Priced & Premium-Priced Golf Sportswear for Women
N.A.I.C.S.: 339920
Catherine B. Blair (Pres & Creative Dir)
Samuel A. Kidston (Chm & Interim CEO)
Steven M. Jones (COO)
Cheryl L. Ellis (Treas & VP-Fin)

Subsidiaries:

Chromcraft Revington, Inc.   (1)
1330 Win Hentschel Blvd Ste 250, West Lafayette, IN 47906
Tel.: (765) 807-2640
Web Site: http://www.chromcraft-revington.com
Sales Range: $50-74.9 Million
Emp.: 275
Designer, Manufacturer & Sales of Residential & Commercial Furniture
N.A.I.C.S.: 337122
Myron D. Hamas (Sec & VP-Fin)
James M. La Neve (CFO, Fin Officer, Acctg Officer & VP)
Jeffrey Sockol (Chief Restructuring Officer)

Subsidiary (Domestic):

CRI Capital Corporation   (2)
1330 Win Hentschel Blvd Ste 250, West Lafayette, IN 47906
Tel.: (765) 807-2640
Business Services
N.A.I.C.S.: 812990

Chromcraft Corporation   (2)
1 Quality Ln, Senatobia, MS 38668   (100%)
Tel.: (662) 562-8203
Web Site: http://www.chromcraftcorp.com
Mfr of Casual Dining Room Furniture, Contract Seating & Office Furniture
N.A.I.C.S.: 337122

Peters-Revington Corp.   (2)
1100 N Washington St, Delphi, IN 46923-9479   (100%)
Tel.: (765) 564-2586
Web Site: http://www.peters-revington.com
Mfr of Wood Occasional Tables & Wall Units, Curio Cabinets & Home Office Furniture
N.A.I.C.S.: 337122

SPORT OBERMEYER LTD.
115 Aspen Airport Business Ctr, Aspen, CO 81611
Tel.: (970) 925-5060   CO
Web Site: http://www.obermeyer.com
Year Founded: 1947

Sales Range: $150-199.9 Million
Emp.: 40
Ski Parkas, Sweaters, Suits & Accessories Mfr & Whslr
N.A.I.C.S.: 315250
Klaus Obermeyer (Founder & CEO)
Biege Jones (Dir-Internal Art)
Gregory Bannister (COO)

SPORT SEASONS LP
539 Cool Springs Blvd Ste 120, Franklin, TN 37067
Tel.: (615) 778-1638
Web Site: http://www.sport-seasons.com
Sales Range: $10-24.9 Million
Emp.: 50
Sporting Good & Bicycles Sales
N.A.I.C.S.: 459110
Doug Beam (Founder & Owner)

SPORT STIX INC.
18101 Von Karman Ave 140-121, Irvine, CA 92612
Tel.: (949) 825-7786   NV
Web Site: http://www.sportstixusa.com
Year Founded: 2012
Sports Drink Powder Mfr & Distr
N.A.I.C.S.: 311999
Charles Todd (Pres & CEO)

SPORTIF USA INC.
1415 Greg St Ste 101, Sparks, NV 89431
Tel.: (775) 359-6400
Web Site: http://www.sportif.com
Year Founded: 1965
Sales Range: $10-24.9 Million
Emp.: 20
Men's & Women's Clothing
N.A.I.C.S.: 424350
John E. Kirsch (Pres & CEO)
Tom Williamson (VP-Sls & Mktg)
Janet Weaver (Mgr-Acctg)
Jim Hulse (VP-Fin & Ops)
Mike Youngblood (Dir-IT & Ops)

SPORTO CORP.
65 Sprague St Ste 1, Boston, MA 02136-2062
Tel.: (617) 364-3001   MA
Web Site: http://www.sporto.net
Year Founded: 1926
Sales Range: $75-99.9 Million
Emp.: 26
Women's Winter Boots Mfr
N.A.I.C.S.: 315210
David Brilliant (Pres & CEO)
Noreen Brilliant (VP-Operations & Mktg Dir)
Karen Kennedy (Dir-HR)
James Kiely (Controller)

SPORTS & EXHIBITION AUTHORITY OF PITTSBURGH & ALLEGHENY COUNTY
171 10th St 2nd Fl, Pittsburgh, PA 15222
Tel.: (412) 393-0200
Web Site: http://www.pgh-sea.com
Year Founded: 1954
Sales Range: $25-49.9 Million
Emp.: 12
Urban Sports Facility, Parking Garage & Infrastructure Development & Property Lessor Organization
N.A.I.C.S.: 925120
Mary Conturo (Exec Dir)
Rosanne Casciato (CFO)
Wayne Fontana (Chm)
Anthony J. Ross (Treas)
Michael F. Dunleavy (Vice Chm)
Steve Morrison (Dir-Info Sys)
Rifat Qureshi (Mgr-Dev)
Taylor Blice (Dir-Fin & Coord-ADA)

COMPANIES

Jhason Dixon *(Accountant)*
Maura Lawson *(Accountant)*
Jill Weimer *(Treas)*
Sala Udin *(Sec)*
Subsidiaries:

Pittsburgh Arena Operating LP (1)
1001 5th Ave, Pittsburgh, PA 15219
Tel.: (412) 642-1800
Web Site:
  http://www.consolenergycenter.com
Sales Range: $25-49.9 Million
Sports & Entertainment Arena Operator
N.A.I.C.S.: 711310
Kevin Hart *(VP & Controller)*

SPORTS AFIELD, INC.
15621 Chemical Ln Ste B, Huntington Beach, CA 92644
Tel.: (714) 373-4910
Web Site:
  http://www.sportsafield.com
Sales Range: $10-24.9 Million
Emp.: 30
Hunting & Fishing Magazines
N.A.I.C.S.: 513199
Ludo Wurfbain *(Owner)*
Diana Rupp *(Editor-in-Chief)*

SPORTS AND IMPORTS, INC.
8133 Hog Neck Rd, Pasadena, MD 21122
Tel.: (410) 360-8600   MD
Web Site:
  http://www.sportsandimportsonline.com
Sales Range: $10-24.9 Million
Emp.: 15
Used Car Dealerships Owner & Operator
N.A.I.C.S.: 441120
Jimmy Hill *(VP)*
Gustav S. Kurtz Jr. *(Pres)*

SPORTS CAR CLUB OF AMERICA
Bldg 300 B St, Topeka, KS 66619
Tel.: (785) 357-7222
Web Site: http://www.scca.org
Rev.: $12,438,846
Emp.: 50
Publisher of Magazines
N.A.I.C.S.: 513120
Lee Hill *(Chm)*
Michael Cobb *(Pres & CEO)*

SPORTS ENDEAVORS INC.
431 US Hwy 70a E, Hillsborough, NC 27278-9912
Tel.: (919) 644-6800
Web Site:
  http://www.sportsendeavors.com
Year Founded: 1984
Sales Range: $10-24.9 Million
Emp.: 400
Fitness & Sporting Goods, Mail Order
N.A.I.C.S.: 459110
Mike Moylan *(Founder)*
Brendan Moylan *(COO)*

SPORTS FIELD HOLDINGS, INC.
1020 Cedar Ave Ste 230, Saint Charles, IL 60174
Tel.: (978) 914-7570   NV
Web Site: http://www.firstform.com
Year Founded: 2011
SFHI—(OTCBB)
Sales Range: $1-9.9 Million
Emp.: 7
Athletic Facilities & Sports Complexes Engineering, Designing Constructing & Construction Management
N.A.I.C.S.: 236220

SPORTS HUMANITARIAN GROUP INC.
49 W 27th St Ste 930, New York, NY 10001
Tel.: (646) 649-8280   NY
Web Site: http://www.righttoplay.com
Year Founded: 1999
Sales Range: $1-9.9 Million
Emp.: 20
Youth Development Services
N.A.I.C.S.: 624110
Karen Scanlan *(VP-HR)*
Dennis Lepholtz *(CFO)*
Johann Olav Koss *(Founder)*
Rob MacLellan *(Chm)*
David Danylewich *(VP-Strategy & Systems)*
Katrin Imhof *(Dir-East & Southern Africa)*
Lori Smith *(Dir-Canada)*
Sherine Ibrahim *(VP-Middle East & Asia Programs)*
Carl L. Liederman *(Founder & CEO)*

SPORTS IMAGE INC.
9059 Springboro Pike, Miamisburg, OH 45342
Tel.: (937) 704-9670
Web Site:
  http://www.sportimageinc.com
Sales Range: $1-9.9 Million
Sports Marketing & Event Management Services
N.A.I.C.S.: 541613
Eric Horstman *(Pres & CEO)*
Bill Horstman *(VP & Dir-Corp Projects)*
Renee Dabbas *(Dir-Fin)*

SPORTS UNLIMITED, INC.
346 Godshall Dr, Harleysville, PA 19438
Tel.: (610) 825-6368
Web Site:
  http://www.sportsunlimitedinc.com
Year Founded: 1983
Sales Range: $1-9.9 Million
Emp.: 50
Internet Sporting Goods Retailer
N.A.I.C.S.: 423910
Don Ball *(Pres)*
David Neff *(CFO)*

SPORTS ZONE INC.
5851 Ammendale Rd, Beltsville, MD 20705
Tel.: (301) 527-9100
Rev.: $27,720,001
Emp.: 50
Retailer of Athletic Gear & Footwear
N.A.I.C.S.: 458210
Michael Syag *(Pres)*

SPORTSHOE CENTER, INC.
10 Main St, Kennebunk, ME 04043
Tel.: (207) 985-4966
Web Site: http://sportshoecenter.com
Retailer of Shoes
N.A.I.C.S.: 458210
Marc Brunelle *(Pres)*
Pam Salvas *(Mgr-Credit)*

SPORTSMAN SUPPLY INC.
2219 Hitzert Ct, Fenton, MO 63026
Tel.: (636) 600-9301   MO
Web Site:
  http://www.sportsmanssupplyinc.com
Year Founded: 1968
Sporting Goods Whslr
N.A.I.C.S.: 423910
Troy Nogoske *(Pres)*
Greg Heider *(VP)*

SPORTSMEDIA TECHNOLOGY CORP.
3511 University Dr, Durham, NC 27707
Tel.: (919) 493-9390
Web Site: http://www.smt.com
Year Founded: 1988
Rev.: $5,700,000
Emp.: 160
Custom Computer Programming Services
N.A.I.C.S.: 541511
Gerard J. Hall *(Founder & CEO)*
Jay Abraham *(Chief Revenue Officer)*
Kirk Brown *(COO)*
Robbie Louthan *(Sr VP-Bus Dev)*
Ron Harnek *(Pres-Operating Div-Jacksonville)*
Subsidiaries:

Sportvision, Inc. (1)
4619 N Ravenswood Suite 304, Chicago, IL 60640   (100%)
Tel.: (773) 293-4300
Web Site: http://www.sportvision.com
Emp.: 80
Online Sports Data Content & Enhancements for Sports Broadcasts & Applications
N.A.I.C.S.: 516120
Hank Adams *(CEO)*
Mike Jakob *(Pres & COO)*
Jeff Jonas *(Exec VP & Gen Mgr)*

SPORTSMEMORABLIA.COM, LLC
15701 SW 29th St, Miramar, FL 33027
Tel.: (800) 689-2001
Web Site:
  http://www.sportsmemorabilia.com
Year Founded: 2006
Sales Range: $10-24.9 Million
Emp.: 32
Sports Memorabilia Online Retailer & Authenticator
N.A.I.C.S.: 458110
Stefan Tesoriero *(CEO)*
Michael Gallucci *(VP-Ops)*
Keith Zimmerman *(CTO)*
Cassandra Wesch *(VP-Mktg)*
Andres Yepez *(Mgr-Mktg)*

SPORTSTRUST ADVISORS, LLC
3340 Peachtree Rd NE 16th Fl, Atlanta, GA 30326
Tel.: (404) 842-7800   TN
Web Site: http://www.sportstrust.com
Sales Range: $1-9.9 Million
Emp.: 8
Athlete Representative Agency
N.A.I.C.S.: 711410
Bill Johnson *(Pres)*
Chandra Vitale *(COO)*
Randi Chapman *(VP-Mktg)*
Julia Lauria *(Dir-Mktg)*
Ben Setas *(Dir-Client Dev)*
Patrick Fain Dye Jr. *(Founder & CEO)*

SPORTSWEAR STORE INC.
136 Howard, Framingham, MA 01702-8311
Tel.: (508) 872-4888   MA
Year Founded: 1951
Sales Range: $25-49.9 Million
Emp.: 450
Sewing, Needlework & Piece Goods
N.A.I.C.S.: 459130
Robert Weitzler *(Mng Dir)*
Tom Kennard *(Controller)*
Ronald Isaacson *(Sec)*
Alec Vezina *(CEO)*

SPOT BEHAVIOR MEDIA, LLC
6001 Broken Sound Pky NW Ste 510, Boca Raton, FL 33487
Tel.: (954) 218-1532
Web Site:
  http://www.spotbehavior.com

SPOTLIGHT INNOVATION INC.

Year Founded: 2006
Rev.: $18,200,000
Emp.: 26
Advetising Agency
N.A.I.C.S.: 541810
Wendy Slosberg *(Pres-Bus Dev)*
Brad Freesman *(Sls)*
Linda Didonato *(Dir-Pub Rels)*

SPOT COOLERS INC.
661 Commerce St, Burr Ridge, IL 60527
Tel.: (630) 655-8610
Web Site: http://www.spot-coolers.com
Year Founded: 1986
Sales Range: $10-24.9 Million
Emp.: 75
Sales of Air Conditioning Appliances
N.A.I.C.S.: 423620
Kenneth Swanson *(Gen Mgr)*

SPOT FREIGHT, INC.
141 S Meridian St, Indianapolis, IN 46204
Tel.: (317) 635-6207
Web Site:
  http://www.spotmyfreight.com
Year Founded: 2009
Sales Range: $10-24.9 Million
Emp.: 90
Logistics Consulting Servies
N.A.I.C.S.: 541614
Andy Schenck *(Owner)*
Andrew Krop *(CFO)*

SPOTHERO, INC.
125 S Clark St, Chicago, IL 60603
Tel.: (844) 324-7768   DE
Web Site: http://www.spothero.com
Year Founded: 2011
Emp.: 167
On-Demand Parking Mobile Application & Website for Parking Services
N.A.I.C.S.: 513210
Mark Lawrence *(Co-Founder & CEO)*
Larry Kiss *(Co-Founder & Chief Architect Officer)*
Elan Mosbacher *(Sr VP-Strategy & Ops)*
Tim Maloney *(Head-Strategic Partnerships)*
Tiffany Voltz *(Chief People Officer)*
Adam Zilberbaum *(Sr VP-Tech Tools & Partnership)*
Matt Sullivan *(VP-Sls)*
Kevin Sherlock *(Head-Legal)*
Varvara Alva *(CFO)*
Eric Brooke *(CTO)*
Matt DiBari *(Chief Product Officer)*
Subsidiaries:

Parking Panda Corp. (1)
3422 Fait Ave, Baltimore, MD 21230
Tel.: (800) 232-6415
Web Site: http://www.parkingpanda.com
Mobile Applications for Parking Services
N.A.I.C.S.: 513210
Adam Zilberbaum *(Founder & CEO)*

SPOTLIGHT ADVERTISING
4 Dennis McHugh Ct, Tappan, NY 10983
Tel.: (845) 398-1717
Year Founded: 2005
Sales Range: Less than $1 Million
Emp.: 1
Advetising Agency
N.A.I.C.S.: 541810
Susan Camus *(CEO)*

SPOTLIGHT INNOVATION INC.
6750 Westown Pkwy Ste 200-226, West Des Moines, IA 50266
Tel.: (515) 274-9087   NV
Web Site:
  https://www.spotlightinnovation.com
Year Founded: 2006
STLT—(OTCBB)

SPOTLIGHT INNOVATION INC.

Spotlight Innovation Inc.—(Continued)
Sales Range: Less than $1 Million
Emp.: 4
Healthcare Investment Services
N.A.I.C.S.: 523999
David Hostelley (CFO)

Subsidiaries:

Memcine Pharmaceuticals (1)
2500 Crosspark Rd Ste E110, Coralville, IA 52240-2304
Tel.: (319) 471-7803
Web Site: http://www.memcine.com
Research & Development in Biotechnology
N.A.I.C.S.: 541714
Kathleen Ho (CEO)

SPOTLIGHT TICKET MANAGEMENT, INC.
26635 Agoura Rd Ste 200, Calabasas, CA 91302
Web Site:
http://www.ticketmanager.com
Year Founded: 2007
Sales Range: $1-9.9 Million
Emp.: 27
Software Development Services
N.A.I.C.S.: 541511
Matt Lewis (Mgr-Bus Dev)
Tony Knopp (Co-Founder & CEO)

Subsidiaries:

Sports Systems Services, Inc. (1)
2015 Jones Rd, Fort Lee, NJ 07024
Tel.: (201) 429-9270
Web Site: http://www.sportssystems.com
Computer Services
N.A.I.C.S.: 541690
James Daigle (CEO)
Will Thomas (VP-Bus Dev)
Barb Hyde (COO)
John Scott (CTO)
Rick Dameron (VP-Mktg)
Brian Binette (VP-Mktg)
David Grim (VP-Mktg)
Jim Daigle (Founder & Pres)

SPOUTING ROCK FINANCIAL PARTNERS LLC
925 W Lancaster Ave Ste 250, Bryn Mawr, PA 19010
Tel.: (610) 788-2128
Web Site: http://spoutingrock.us
Year Founded: 2018
Merchant Banking Services
N.A.I.C.S.: 525990
Andrew Smith (CEO)

Subsidiaries:

Spouting Rock Alternative Credit, LLC (1)
925 W Lancaster Ave Ste 250, Bryn Mawr, PA 19010
Tel.: (610) 788-2128
Financial Services
N.A.I.C.S.: 523999
Jeff Haas (Pres)
Peter Faigl (Chief Investment Officer)

Spouting Rock Asset Management LLC (1)
925 W Lancaster Ave Ste 250, Bryn Mawr, PA 19010
Tel.: (610) 788-2128
Investment Services
N.A.I.C.S.: 523999
Marc Brookman (CEO)

Subsidiary (Domestic):

Old Hill Partners Inc (2)
1120 Post Rd, Darien, CT 06820
Tel.: (203) 656-3004
Web Site: http://www.oldhill.com
Rev.: $2,800,000
Emp.: 20
Investment Banking & Securities Dealing
N.A.I.C.S.: 523150
Jeffrey Haas (COO & Portfolio Mgr)

SPP MANAGEMENT SERVICES, LLC
300 S Tryon St Ste 1210, Charlotte, NC 28202
Tel.: (704) 654-3400   DE
Web Site:
http://www.summitparkllc.com
Privater Equity Firm
N.A.I.C.S.: 523999
Bob Calton (Co-Founder & Partner)
Jim Johnson (Co-Founder & Partner)
Chris Cotton (Operating Partner-Fin & Principal)
Rachel Hannon (Principal-Bus Dev & IR)
Matt Magan (Principal)
Michael York (Principal)
Corey Millette (Controller)
Janell Niebuhr (Ops Mgr-Admin)

Subsidiaries:

Arkive Information Management LLC (1)
6751 Discovery Blvd, Mableton, GA 30126-4647
Tel.: (678) 888-9139
Web Site: http://www.myarkive.com
Document Storage, Destruction & Digital Data Services
N.A.I.C.S.: 493190
Justin Ririe (CEO)
Ben Nicholson (CFO)
David Gonce (VP-Sls & Mktg)

Freedom Electronics LLC (1)
2205 May Ct NW, Kennesaw, GA 30144
Tel.: (770) 792-8888
Web Site:
http://www.freedomelectronics.com
Electronic Components Mfr
N.A.I.C.S.: 334419
Rod Smith (Co-Founder & CEO)
John Slocum (Co-Founder)

SPR INC.
233 S Wacker Dr Ste 3500, Chicago, IL 60606-6383
Tel.: (312) 756-1760
Web Site: http://www.spr.com
Year Founded: 1973
IT Solutions
N.A.I.C.S.: 541512
Robert M. Figliulo (CEO)
Douglas F. Rossier (Pres)
Matthew T. Mead (CTO)
Jeff Shurts (Exec VP-Delivery)
Patrick Ryan (Exec VP-Sls)
Bob Moore (Exec VP-Delivery)
William Heintz (Exec VP-Ops)
Tom Ryan (Exec VP)
Mark Sami (VP-Enterprise Architecture)
Naresh Koka (VP-Alliances)
Mike Beaudin (VP-Project Mgmt Svcs)
Justin Rodenbostel (VP-Delivery)
Rebecca Butman (Dir-Mktg)

SPRADLEY BARR FORD LINCOLN OF GREELEY INC.
4901 W 29th St, Greeley, CO 80634
Tel.: (970) 506-3600
Web Site:
http://www.spradleybarrgreeley.com
Year Founded: 2007
Sales Range: $50-74.9 Million
Emp.: 60
Car Whslr
N.A.I.C.S.: 441110
Bill Henershot (Mng Partner)

SPRADLEY CHEVROLET-HYUNDAI
2146 W US Hwy 50, Pueblo, CO 81008-1619
Tel.: (719) 544-8162
Web Site: http://www.spradley.com
Year Founded: 1980

Sales Range: $10-24.9 Million
Emp.: 103
New Car Whslr
N.A.I.C.S.: 441110
Philip Gama (Gen Mgr)

SPRAGUE PEST SOLUTIONS, INC.
2725 Pacific Ave, Tacoma, WA 98402
Tel.: (253) 272-4400
Web Site:
http://www.spraguepest.com
Rev.: $1,663,300
Emp.: 25
Exterminating & Pest Control Services
N.A.I.C.S.: 561710
Alfred Treleven (CEO)
Joann Carlson (CFO)
Ross Treleven (VP-Ops)
Jeff Miller (COO)
Larry Treleven (Exec VP)

Subsidiaries:

TMC Pest Management, Inc. (1)
186 Quantico Ave Ste A, Bakersfield, CA 93307-3072
Tel.: (661) 322-5015
Web Site: http://www.tmcpest.com
Exterminating & Pest Control Services
N.A.I.C.S.: 561710
Jeff McCaa (Pres)

SPRAGUES' ROCK & SAND CO.
230 Longden Ave, Irwindale, CA 91706
Tel.: (626) 445-2125
Web Site:
http://www.srmconcrete.com
Year Founded: 1927
Sales Range: $10-24.9 Million
Emp.: 50
Mfr of Ready-Mixed Concrete
N.A.I.C.S.: 327320
Steve Toland (Gen Mgr)

SPRAY EQUIPMENT & SERVICE CENTER, INC.
311 Pattie St, Wichita, KS 67211
Tel.: (316) 264-4349
Web Site:
http://www.sprayequipment.com
Year Founded: 1969
Sales Range: $25-49.9 Million
Emp.: 81
Manufacturers' Representative for Industrial Paint Spray Equipment
N.A.I.C.S.: 423830
Mark Hammar (Pres)
Carl Goossen (CFO)
Corey Huelskamp (VP)

Subsidiaries:

Finishline Technologies, Inc. (1)
4412 N Long Rd, Columbus, IN 47203
Tel.: (812) 372-3493
Web Site: http://www.flt-inc.com
Sales Range: $1-9.9 Million
Hardware Mfr
N.A.I.C.S.: 332510
John D. Cord (Pres)
Gwen B. Cord (CEO)

SPRAY SYSTEMS ARIZONA INC.
2202 W Medtronic Way Ste 108, Tempe, AZ 85281-5107
Tel.: (480) 967-8300
Web Site:
http://www.spraysystemseri.com
Rev.: $12,000,000
Emp.: 60
Asbestos Removal & Encapsulation
N.A.I.C.S.: 562910

Chris Boyles (Founder, Owner & Pres)
Karen Boyles (VP)

Subsidiaries:

Environmental Response Inc. (1)
2202 W Medtronic Way Ste 108, Tempe, AZ 85281
Tel.: (480) 967-2802
Web Site:
http://www.environmentalresponseinc.com
Rev.: $4,200,000
Emp.: 40
Hazardous Waste Collection & Disposal Services
N.A.I.C.S.: 562211
Chris Boyles (Founder & Owner)

SPRAYING SYSTEMS CO.
North Ave at Schmale Rd, Wheaton, IL 60188
Tel.: (630) 665-5000   IL
Web Site: http://www.spray.com
Year Founded: 1937
Sales Range: $450-499.9 Million
Emp.: 1,000
Spray Nozzles & Spray Guns Mfr
N.A.I.C.S.: 423830
James E. Bramsen (CEO)
Martin Hynes (VP-Fin)
Frank Bramsen (Dir-Indus Sls, Adv & Mktg-US)

Subsidiaries:

Spraying Systems Deutschland GmbH (1)
Grobmoorkehre 1, 21079, Hamburg, Germany   (100%)
Tel.: (49) 407660010
Web Site: http://www.spray.de
Sales Range: $25-49.9 Million
Emp.: 110
Mfr & Sales of Spray Nozzles
N.A.I.C.S.: 326199
Raoul Winne (Mng Dir)

Spraying Systems Japan Co. Ltd. (1)
5-25 Sasei Gotanda Bldg, Schinagawa Ku, Tokyo, 141 0022, Japan   (100%)
Tel.: (81) 334456031
Web Site: http://www.spray.co.jp
Sales Range: $25-49.9 Million
Emp.: 30
Mfr & Sales of Spray Nozzles
N.A.I.C.S.: 326199

SPREADSHIRT, INC.
186 S St 1st fl, Boston, MA 02111
Web Site: http://www.spreadshirt.com
Sales Range: $1-9.9 Million
Emp.: 300
Cloth Design & Service
N.A.I.C.S.: 458110
Philip Rooke (CEO)
Tobias Schaugg (CFO)
Jurgen Gauger (COO)
Hugo Smoter (Chief Comml Officer)

SPRECHER BREWING COMPANY, LLC
701 W Glendale Ave, Glendale, WI 53209
Tel.: (414) 964-7837   WI
Web Site:
http://www.sprecherbrewery.com
Year Founded: 1985
Sales Range: $1-9.9 Million
Emp.: 50
European-Style Beer & Gourmet Sodas Brewery
N.A.I.C.S.: 312120
Sharad Chadha (CEO)
Jeff Hamilton (Pres)
Andy Nunemaker (Chm)
Jim Kanter (Sls Mgr)

Subsidiaries:

Chameleon Brewing (1)
701 W Glendale Ave, Glendale, WI 53209

Tel.: (414) 964-7837
Beer Mfr
N.A.I.C.S.: 312120

SPREEN, INC.
25050 Redlands Blvd, Loma Linda, CA 92354
Tel.: (909) 328-6141 CA
Web Site:
  http://www.spreenhonda.com
Year Founded: 1984
New & Used Car Dealer
N.A.I.C.S.: 441110
Jim Schultz *(Mgr-Svc)*
Jeffrey Spreen *(Gen Mgr)*
Janet Hoefler *(Mgr-Bus)*
John Awabdy *(Gen Sls Mgr)*
Steve Dockery *(Mgr-Parts)*

SPRIG ELECTRIC CO.
1860 S 10th St, San Jose, CA 95112-4108
Tel.: (408) 298-3134
Web Site:
  http://www.sprigelectric.com
Sales Range: $25-49.9 Million
Emp.: 250
Electrical Wiring Services
N.A.I.C.S.: 238210
Mike Jurewicz *(COO)*
Chris Zimmer *(Mgr-Facilities Svcs & Energy Solutions Div)*
Mark Mandarelli *(Pres & CIO)*
Rob Valderrama *(Chief Project Delivery Officer)*
Matt Nelson *(Chief Project Mgmt Officer)*
Rick Clinton *(Exec VP)*
Tim Martin *(VP-Low Voltage Sys)*
Clint Ramsey *(CFO)*
Hossein Tofangsazan *(Chief Revenue Officer)*
Pepper Snyder *(Chm & CEO)*
Laura Lacomble *(Chief People Officer)*

SPRING BANCORP, INC.
3400 Wabash Ave, Springfield, IL 62711
Tel.: (217) 529-5555 IL
Web Site:
  http://www.bankwithbos.com
Year Founded: 1987
Sales Range: $25-49.9 Million
Emp.: 180
Bank Holding Company
N.A.I.C.S.: 551111
Lynn Bandy *(COO)*

Subsidiaries:

Bank of Springfield (1)
3400 W Wabash, Springfield, IL 62711
Tel.: (217) 529-5555
Web Site: http://www.bankwithbos.com
Sales Range: $25-49.9 Million
Retail & Commercial Banking
N.A.I.C.S.: 522110
Tom Marantz *(Chm & CEO)*
Jerry Sheley *(VP)*
Jason Knoedler *(VP)*

SPRING CITY ELECTRICAL MFG. CO., INC
1 S Main St, Spring City, PA 19475
Tel.: (610) 948-4000
Web Site: http://www.springcity.com
Year Founded: 1843
Sales Range: $10-24.9 Million
Outdoor Lighting Equipment Mfr
N.A.I.C.S.: 335139
Alan Brink *(Pres)*

SPRING ENGINEERING, INC.
3014 US Hwy 19, Holiday, FL 34691
Tel.: (727) 938-1516 FL
Web Site:
  http://www.springengineeringinc.com
Year Founded: 1988
Sales Range: $1-9.9 Million
Emp.: 30
Architectural Services
N.A.I.C.S.: 541310
Richard M. Bekesh *(Pres & COO)*
Steve Bergwall *(Project Mgr)*

SPRING METRICS, INC.
211 N Church St, Durham, NC 27701
Tel.: (800) 799-9304
Web Site:
  http://www.springmetrics.com
Sales Range: $1-9.9 Million
Software Publisher
N.A.I.C.S.: 513210
Peter Bourne *(CEO)*
Scott Lacy *(Mgr-Customer Experience)*
Shawn Williams *(Mgr-Sls)*

SPRING MOUNTAIN ADVENTURE CORP.
757 Spring Mount Rd, Spring Mountain, PA 19478
Tel.: (610) 287-7900
Web Site:
  http://www.springmountainadventures.com
Year Founded: 1996
Rev.: $8,100,000
Emp.: 150
Ski Resort; Sports & Recreation Instruction
N.A.I.C.S.: 713920
Richard Buckman *(Co-Owner)*
Gayle Buckman *(Co-Owner)*
Jennifer B. Brown *(Sec & Treas)*

SPRING TOLLMAN COMPANY, INC.
91 Enterprise Dr, Bristol, CT 06010-7472
Tel.: (860) 583-1326
Web Site:
  http://www.tollmanspring.com
Year Founded: 1945
Sales Range: $10-24.9 Million
Emp.: 90
Spring & Slide Stamping Mfr
N.A.I.C.S.: 332613
Rick Zink *(Co-Pres)*

SPRING VENTURE GROUP, LLC
120 W 12th St Ste 1700, Kansas City, MO 64105
Tel.: (816) 888-7900
Web Site:
  http://www.springventuregroup.com
Year Founded: 2009
Sales Range: $50-74.9 Million
Emp.: 410
Insurance Advisory Services
N.A.I.C.S.: 524298
Chris Giuliani *(CEO)*
Jeffery Anderson *(Founder & Chief Sls Officer)*
Virginia Picotte *(Exec VP-Compliance)*
Johnny Hilgers *(Exec VP-Bus Analytics)*
Scott Campbell *(Exec VP-Fin)*
John Griggs *(Exec VP-Ops)*
Grant Eckert *(CMO)*

SPRING WORKS UTAH
976 W 850 S, Woods Cross, UT 84087
Tel.: (801) 298-0113
Web Site:
  http://www.springworksutah.com

Year Founded: 2002
Rev.: $2,200,000
Emp.: 20
Coiled Flat Springs Mfr
N.A.I.C.S.: 332613
Eli Mongeon *(Gen Mgr)*

SPRING, O'BRIEN & CO. INC.
50 W 23rd St Fl 11, New York, NY 10010-5205
Tel.: (212) 620-7100 NY
Year Founded: 1982
Rev.: $32,500,000
Emp.: 40
Business-To-Business, Financial, Interactive Agencies, Real Estate, Technical Advertising, Travel & Tourism
N.A.I.C.S.: 541810
Chris Spring *(Pres)*
Sharon Fischer *(CFO)*
Robert Steward *(Exec VP & Dir-Creative)*
David M. Kleinman *(Exec VP)*
Jim Campbell *(Dir-Media)*
Colm Lynch *(Sr VP & Acct Dir)*
John T. Mulqueen *(Dir-Editorial)*
Nora Brossard *(Dir-Editorial & Sr Acct Supvr)*
Martin Elder *(Mgr-Media Rels)*
Diane Elliot *(Acct Exec)*
Ulku Ulrucar *(Acct Exec)*
Michael Goode *(Sr Dir-Art & Mgr-Studio)*
Marty Holland *(Acct Supvr)*
Bruce Jonas *(Dir-Creative)*
Lauren Kaufman *(VP)*
Linda Larrymore *(Mgr-Acctg)*
Kit McCracken *(Assoc Dir-Creative)*
Yin Moy *(Dir-Art)*
Beth Leri *(Acct Supvr)*

SPRING-GREEN LAWN CARE CORPORATION
11909 S Spaulding School Dr, Plainfield, IL 60585
Tel.: (815) 436-8777 DE
Web Site: http://www.spring-green.com
Year Founded: 1977
Sales Range: $50-74.9 Million
Emp.: 21
Lawn & Tree Care Services
N.A.I.C.S.: 561730
James Young *(COO)*
Brian Kish *(VP-Bus Intelligence)*
Marilyn Darin *(Mgr-Acctg)*
R. J. Krone *(Dir-Ops)*
Paul McDonald *(Dir-IT)*
Gillian Hrycyk *(Dir-Mktg)*
Lena Bogan *(Mgr-Brand Consistency)*
Gwen Pothier-Ward *(Mgr-Call Center)*
Brad Johnson *(VP-Franchise Ops)*

SPRINGAHEAD
525 2nd St, San Francisco, CA 94107
Tel.: (415) 931-9500
Web Site:
  http://www.springahead.com
Year Founded: 2008
Sales Range: $1-9.9 Million
Emp.: 19
Time & Expense Tracking Software
N.A.I.C.S.: 513210
Brad Pirtle *(Founder)*
Chris Farrell *(CEO)*

SPRINGBOARD
6910 E Chauncey Ln Ste 120, Phoenix, AZ 85054
Tel.: (623) 516-8001
Web Site:
  http://www.springboardhealthcare.com
Year Founded: 2002

Sales Range: $100-124.9 Million
Emp.: 150
Travel Staffing for Hospitals
N.A.I.C.S.: 561311
Gavin Hays *(CEO)*

SPRINGBOARD CAPITAL, LLC
11512 Lake Mead Ave Bldg 100, Jacksonville, FL 32256
Tel.: (904) 432-3358
Web Site:
  http://www.springboardcapllc.com
Privater Equity Firm
N.A.I.C.S.: 523999
Alan W. Rossiter *(Pres)*

Subsidiaries:

IxReveal, Inc. (1)
3100 University Blvd S Ste 240, Jacksonville, FL 32216
Tel.: (904) 421-7388
Web Site: http://www.ureveal.com
Sales Range: $1-9.9 Million
Emp.: 9
Software Publisher
N.A.I.C.S.: 513210
Charles A. Clarkson *(Chm & CEO)*
Ren Mohan *(Founder & CTO)*

SPRINGBOARD COMMUNICATIONS
17 N Main St, Marlboro, NJ 07746
Tel.: (732) 863-1900
Web Site:
  http://www.springboardpr.com
Year Founded: 1995
Sales Range: $10-24.9 Million
Emp.: 10
Public Relations Agency
N.A.I.C.S.: 541820
Domenick Cilea *(Pres)*
Shannon Gotthelf Cortina *(Acct Supvr)*
Mark Tordik *(Acct Exec)*
Joseph Mindo *(Acct Exec)*

SPRINGBOARD NONPROFIT CONSUMER CREDIT MANAGEMENT, INC.
4351 Latham St, Riverside, CA 92501
Tel.: (951) 779-7724 CA
Web Site: http://www.credit.org
Year Founded: 1974
Sales Range: $25-49.9 Million
Emp.: 159
Consumer Credit Management Services
N.A.I.C.S.: 561450
Ken Lentz *(Dir-IT)*
Todd Emerson *(Pres & CEO)*
Justin Waller *(Sr Mgr-IT)*
Marlisa Hodgin *(CFO)*
Aaron Horvath *(Exec VP)*

SPRINGBOX, LTD.
708 Colorado St, Austin, TX 78701-3217
Tel.: (512) 391-0065 TX
Web Site: http://www.springbox.com
Year Founded: 2004
Sales Range: $25-49.9 Million
Emp.: 60
Advetising Agency
N.A.I.C.S.: 541810
Megan Coffey *(Chief Creative Officer)*
Angie Gette *(Dir-Strategy & Analytics)*
Maria Seaver *(Chief Experience Officer)*
Kate Thomas *(Dir-Content Strategy)*
Tom West *(Chm)*
John John *(CEO)*
Paul Boomgaart *(CTO)*

SPRINGBROOK
105 Campus Dr, Oneonta, NY 13820
Tel.: (607) 286-7171 NY

SPRINGBROOK

U.S. PRIVATE

Springbrook—(Continued)

Web Site:
http://www.springbrookny.org
Year Founded: 1941
Sales Range: $25-49.9 Million
Emp.: 1,409
Developmental Disability Assistance Services
N.A.I.C.S.: 623210
Christopher Hulbert *(Dir-HR)*
Patricia Kennedy *(CEO)*
Tom Ford *(Dir-Facilities)*
Peter van der Riet *(Vice Chm)*
Thomas O. Maggs *(Chm)*
Seth Haight *(COO)*
William Mirabito *(Treas)*
Gerald Pondolfino *(Sec)*
Wade Harman *(CFO)*
Robert Vogel *(Officer-Corp Compliance & Dir-Quality Assurance)*

SPRINGDALE TRACTOR COMPANY INC.
6160 W Sunset Ave, Springdale, AR 72764
Tel.: (479) 361-2513
Web Site:
http://www.springdaletractor.com
Sales Range: $10-24.9 Million
Emp.: 25
Retailer of Agricultural Machinery & Equipment
N.A.I.C.S.: 441120
Gene Baker *(Owner)*
Donna Baker *(VP)*
Alvin Huck *(Mgr-Parts)*

SPRINGFIELD AUTO SUPPLY INC.
1241 W Columbia St, Springfield, OH 45504
Tel.: (937) 325-6272
Rev.: $10,700,000
Emp.: 35
Automotive Supplies & Parts
N.A.I.C.S.: 423120
James R. Pullins *(Pres)*

SPRINGFIELD ELECTRIC SUPPLY COMPANY
700 N 9th St, Springfield, IL 62702
Tel.: (217) 788-2100
Web Site:
http://www.springfieldelectric.com
Year Founded: 1912
Sales Range: $100-124.9 Million
Emp.: 250
Electrical Supply Distr
N.A.I.C.S.: 423610
Todd Emerson *(Pres)*
W. R. Schnirring *(Owner)*
Bill Schnirring *(CEO)*
Dan Dungan *(Sr VP-Indus Mktg & Sls)*
Chris Scarbrough *(Sr VP)*
Amy Byers *(VP-Operational Svcs)*

SPRINGFIELD HYUNDAI
754 Baltimore Pike, Springfield, PA 19064
Tel.: (610) 690-4604
Web Site:
http://www.springfieldhyundai.com
Sales Range: $125-149.9 Million
Emp.: 170
Automobiles, New & Used
N.A.I.C.S.: 441110
Chris Bernicker *(Gen Mgr)*
Danielle Bizzari *(Mgr-Fin)*
Gary Segal *(Mgr-Fin)*
Debbie Damico *(Office Mgr)*

SPRINGFIELD PEPSI COLA BOTTLING CO. INC.
1937 E Cook St, Springfield, IL 62703
Tel.: (217) 522-8841
Sales Range: $10-24.9 Million
Emp.: 85
Soft Drink Bottling Services
N.A.I.C.S.: 312111
John Faloon *(Pres)*
Mark Wanless *(Mgr-On-Premise Sls)*

SPRINGFIELD URBAN LEAGUE, INC.
100 N 11th St, Springfield, IL 62703
Tel.: (217) 789-0830
Web Site: http://www.springfieldul.org
Year Founded: 1926
Sales Range: $10-24.9 Million
Emp.: 422
Community Welfare Services
N.A.I.C.S.: 624190
Lillie Jasper *(COO)*

SPRINGFIELD UTILITY BOARD INC.
PO Box 300, Springfield, OR 97477-0077
Tel.: (541) 746-8451
Web Site: http://www.subutil.com
Year Founded: 1950
Sales Range: $25-49.9 Million
Emp.: 135
Provider of Electric & Other Services
N.A.I.C.S.: 221118
Ted L. Johnson *(Chm)*
Sanjeev King *(Mgr-Electrical Engrg)*
Amy Chinitz *(Coord-Drinking Water Source Protection)*
Brenda Slaughter *(Mgr-Customer Svc)*
Michael Warren *(Mgr-Safety & Environmental)*

SPRINGFIELD WATER & SEWER COMMISSION
250 M St Ext, Agawam, MA 01101
Tel.: (413) 787-6060
Web Site:
http://www.waterandsewer.org
Year Founded: 1996
Sales Range: $25-49.9 Million
Emp.: 240
Supplier of Water
N.A.I.C.S.: 221310
William E. Leonard *(Chm)*
Tony Basile *(CFO)*

SPRINGFIELD WIRE INC.
100 Moody St, Ludlow, MA 01056-1269
Tel.: (413) 385-0115
Web Site: http://www.springfield-wire.com
Sales Range: $50-74.9 Million
Emp.: 1,500
Heating Units for Electric Appliances
N.A.I.C.S.: 335210
Robert Strempek *(Dir-Tech)*
Richard Rossi *(Controller)*

SPRINGHILL MEDICAL SERVICES, INC.
2001 Doctors Dr, Springhill, LA 71075
Tel.: (318) 539-1000
Web Site: http://www.smccare.com
Year Founded: 2000
Sales Range: $10-24.9 Million
Emp.: 251
Health Care Srvices
N.A.I.C.S.: 622110
Vincent Sedminik *(CEO)*

SPRINGMOOR LIFE CARE RETIREMENT COMMUNITY
1500 Sawmill Rd, Raleigh, NC 27615
Tel.: (919) 848-7000
Web Site: http://www.springmoor.org
Year Founded: 1983
Sales Range: $1-9.9 Million

Lifecare Retirement Community Operator
N.A.I.C.S.: 623311
David W. Ammons *(CEO)*
Allison Rouse *(Dir-Sales & Mktg)*
Amanda Cottle *(Coord-Mktg)*
Susan Gardner *(Mgr-Office)*
Brandon Hair *(Exec Dir)*

SPRINGPOINT SENIOR LIVING
4814 Outlook Dr Ste 201, Wall Township, NJ 07753
Tel.: (800) 222-0609
Web Site:
http://www.springpointsl.org
Year Founded: 1997
Sales Range: $10-24.9 Million
Emp.: 125
Community Welfare Services
N.A.I.C.S.: 525120
Pamela I. Smith *(Sr VP-Strategy & Mktg)*
Anthony A. Argondizza *(Pres & CEO)*
John J. McSorley *(Chm)*
David L. Woodward *(COO & Sr VP)*
Michael Oakes *(Sr VP)*
John Harz *(Sr VP-HR)*
Matthew Runyan *(CIO & VP-IT)*

SPRINGPOINT TECHNOLOGIES
4765 E 91st St Ste 100, Tulsa, OK 74137
Tel.: (918) 584-3300
Web Site:
http://www.myspringpoint.com
Year Founded: 2003
Sales Range: $1-9.9 Million
Emp.: 14
Information Technology Consulting & Staffing Services
N.A.I.C.S.: 541512
Travis Short *(Pres)*
Andrew Watts *(Mgr-Network Ops Center)*

SPRINGS FABRICATION, INC.
850 Aeroplaza Dr, Colorado Springs, CO 80916-4000
Tel.: (719) 596-8830
Web Site: http://www.springsfab.com
Year Founded: 1986
Sales Range: $25-49.9 Million
Emp.: 250
Plate Work Mfr
N.A.I.C.S.: 332420
Tom Neppl *(Pres & CEO)*

Subsidiaries:

Springs Fabrication, Inc. - Advanced Technology Group (1)
1150 W 120th Ave Ste 400, Broomfield, CO 80234
Tel.: (303) 438-1570
Web Site: http://www.springsfabatg.com
Sales Range: $10-24.9 Million
Emp.: 65
Custom Containment System Mfr
N.A.I.C.S.: 334516
John Bailey *(Engr)*

SPRINGS GLOBAL, INC.
205 N White St, Fort Mill, SC 29716-0070
Tel.: (803) 547-1500
Web Site: http://www.springs.com
Year Founded: 1887
Sales Range: $1-4.9 Billion
Emp.: 19,500
Finished Fabrics, Home Furnishings & Window Treatments
N.A.I.C.S.: 313210
Tom O'Connor *(Pres)*
Harvey Simon *(Pres-Private Label Bus Unit)*
Josue Christiano Gomes da Silva *(Chm & CEO)*

Subsidiaries:

Charles D. Owen Mfg. Co. (1)
875 Warren Wilson Rd, Swannanoa, NC 28778
Tel.: (828) 298-6802
Rev.: $38,200,000
Emp.: 500
Mfr of Blankets & Throws
N.A.I.C.S.: 313210

Springs Global Participacoes S.A. (1)
Bairro Planalto Avenida Magalhaes Pinto 4000, 39840-166, Montes Claros, Minas Gerais, Brazil (50%)
Tel.: (55) 553832157777
Mfr of Linens, Rugs, Pillows & Window Treatments
N.A.I.C.S.: 313210

Subsidiary (US):

Springs Global US, Inc. (2)
205 N White St PO Box 70, Fort Mill, SC 29715
Tel.: (803) 547-3775
Web Site: http://www.springs.com
Sales Range: $650-699.9 Million
Emp.: 100
Mfr of Home Furnishing Products
N.A.I.C.S.: 313210
Janice Louttit *(Mgr-Trade Payables)*
Brian Chiles *(Mgr-Indus Engrg, Trade Compliance & Transportation)*

Subsidiary (Domestic):

Espacio LLC (3)
7913 McPherson Rd Ste 106, Laredo, TX 78045
Tel.: (956) 791-7183
Web Site: http://www.espaciosonline.com
Office Furniture Whslr
N.A.I.C.S.: 423210
Debra McLennan *(Mgr-Ops)*

Division (Non-US):

Springs Canada, Ltd. (3)
110 Matherson Blvd W Ste 200, Mississauga, L5R 3T4, ON, Canada (100%)
Tel.: (905) 890-4994
Sales Range: $10-24.9 Million
Emp.: 70
Marketing of Bed & Bath Products
N.A.I.C.S.: 449129

Springs de Mexico, S.A. de C.V. (3)
Carretera Acambaro Jerecuaro No 19, Acambaro Guanajuato, CP 38610, Mexico, Mexico (100%)
Tel.: (52) 4171727711
Sales Range: $25-49.9 Million
Finished Fabrics, Home Furnishings & Window Treatments Mfr
N.A.I.C.S.: 314910

Subsidiary (Domestic):

Warbird Corporation (3)
1105 N Market St, Wilmington, DE 19801
Tel.: (302) 427-9903
Holding Company
N.A.I.C.S.: 551112

Springs Global, Inc.- Bath Fashions Division (1)
205 N White St, Fort Mill, SC 29716-0070
Tel.: (803) 547-1500
Web Site: http://www.springs.com
Sales Range: $125-149.9 Million
Emp.: 1,200
Premium Bed & Bath Products Targeted to the Middle & Upper Range of the Market
N.A.I.C.S.: 313210

SPRINGTREE FARM GROUP
12618 Fellowship Way, North Potomac, MD 20878-4756
Tel.: (301) 272-7359
Sales Range: $10-24.9 Million
Emp.: 13
Processed Meat Mfr
N.A.I.C.S.: 311611
Paul Robinson *(Principal)*

SPRINT INDUSTRIAL HOLDINGS LLC

5300 Memorial Dr Ste 270, Houston, TX 77007
Tel.: (713) 426-4196 DE
Web Site: http://sprintindustrial.com
Holding Company
N.A.I.C.S.: 551111
Sandy Scott (Pres & CEO)

Subsidiaries:

Sprint Industrial Services, LLC (1)
5300 Moyle Dr, Houston, TX 77007
Tel.: (713) 426-4196
Web Site: http://www.sprintsafety.com
Sales Range: $1-9.9 Million
Emp.: 50
Support Activities for Oil & Gas Operations
N.A.I.C.S.: 213112
Fred Hamilton (Mgr-Sls-Pub Sector)

SPRINT OIL COMPANY
469 N Maple St, Orleans, IN 47452
Tel.: (812) 865-2240
Rev.: $18,884,853
Emp.: 9
Convenience Store
N.A.I.C.S.: 445131
Rick L. Richardson (Pres)

SPRINTZ FURNITURE SHOWROOM INC.
325 White Bridge Rd, Nashville, TN 37209
Tel.: (615) 352-5912
Web Site: http://www.sprintz.com
Rev.: $14,200,000
Emp.: 125
Owner & Operator of Furniture Stores
N.A.I.C.S.: 449110
David Hammond (Gen Mgr)

SPRUCE CREEK DEVELOPMENT CO. OF OCALA
9880 SE 176th, Summerfield, FL 34491
Tel.: (352) 347-3700
Web Site:
    http://www.sprucecreekonline.com
Sales Range: $10-24.9 Million
Emp.: 67
Single-Family Housing Construction
N.A.I.C.S.: 236115
Harvey D. Erp (Pres)
Brenda J. Erp (Sec)

SPRUCE PRIVATE INVESTORS LLC
1 Stamford Plz 263 Tresser Blvd 15th Fl, Stamford, CT 06901
Tel.: (203) 428-2600 DE
Web Site:
    http://www.spruceinvest.com
Year Founded: 2001
Sales Range: $25-49.9 Million
Emp.: 20
Asset Management & Investment Services
N.A.I.C.S.: 523940
John Bailey (Founder & CEO)
Robert Bastone (COO & Chief Compliance Officer)
Scott Ogur (Mng Dir & CFO)

SPS COMPANIES INC.
6363 State Hwy 7, Saint Louis Park, MN 55416-2346
Tel.: (952) 929-1377 MN
Web Site:
    http://www.spscompanies.com
Year Founded: 1989
Sales Range: $25-49.9 Million
Emp.: 220
Provider of Plumbing Fixtures, Equipment & Supplies
N.A.I.C.S.: 423720
Bill Weber (CFO & Controller)
Matt Crocker (CEO)

SPS CORPORATION
3502 Independence Dr, Fort Wayne, IN 46808
Tel.: (260) 482-3702
Web Site:
    http://www.spscorporation.com
Year Founded: 1982
Rev.: $16,961,441
Emp.: 25
Siding Contractors
N.A.I.C.S.: 238170
Chris Craney (Controller)

Subsidiaries:

SPS Corporation, Curtain Wall Division (1)
1100 Perry Rd, Apex, NC 27502
Tel.: (919) 367-8885
Web Site: http://www.spscorp.com
Sales Range: $25-49.9 Million
Siding Contractors
N.A.I.C.S.: 238160
Mike Russo (Pres)

SPS Corporation, Retrofit Division (1)
1229 Perry Rd Ste 108, Apex, NC 27502
Tel.: (919) 367-8885
Sales Range: $25-49.9 Million
Siding Contractors
N.A.I.C.S.: 238160

SPS INDUSTRIAL INC.
283 Cranes Roost Blvd Ste 111, Altamonte Springs, FL 32701
Tel.: (321) 251-8156
Web Site:
    http://www.spsindustrial.com
Year Founded: 2004
Sales Range: $1-9.9 Million
Emp.: 8
Industrial Supply
N.A.I.C.S.: 532490
Steve Sarno (Owner)
Leslee Burdette (Dir-Ops)

SPS STUDIOS, INC.
2905 Wilderness Pl, Boulder, CO 80301-5402
Tel.: (303) 449-0536 CO
Web Site: http://www.sps.com
Year Founded: 1971
Greeting Cards, Poetry Books & Stationery Publisher & Distr
N.A.I.C.S.: 513191
Susan Polis Schutz (Co-Founder)
Stephen Schutz (Co-Founder)

SPT LABTECH LIMITED
1 Kendall Sq Ste B2303, Cambridge, MA 02139-1594
Tel.: (617) 494-9794
Web Site: http://www.ttplabtech.com
Scientific & Technical Consulting Services
N.A.I.C.S.: 541690
Ben Schenker (Mgr)
David Newble (Mng Dir)
Jas Sangera (Founder & Chm)

Subsidiaries:

Biomicrolab, Inc. (1)
2500 Dean Lesher Dr Ste A, Concord, CA 94520
Tel.: (925) 689-2055
Web Site: http://www.biomicrolab.com
Sales Range: $1-9.9 Million
Emp.: 25
Scales And Balances, Except Laboratory
N.A.I.C.S.: 333998
David Miller (Pres)
William Hess (VP)

SPUDNIK EQUIPMENT COMPANY
584 W 100 N, Blackfoot, ID 83221
Tel.: (208) 785-0480
Web Site: http://www.spudnik.us
Rev.: $24,561,000
Emp.: 170
Potato Diggers, Harvesters & Planters
N.A.I.C.S.: 333111
Kevin Smyer (Mgr-Shop-Heyburn)
Robert Griffeth (Mgr-Shop-Presque Isle)
Rainer Borgmann (CEO)

SPURLIN INDUSTRIES INC.
625 Main St, Palmetto, GA 30268
Tel.: (770) 463-1644
Web Site:
    http://www.spurlinindustries.com
Rev.: $13,100,000
Emp.: 80
Bath Tubs, Laundry Tubs & Showers Mfr
N.A.I.C.S.: 326191
Todd Spurlin (Pres)

SPURLINO MATERIALS, LLC
4000 Oxford State Rd, Middletown, OH 45044
Tel.: (513) 422-6677
Web Site: http://www.spurlino.net
Year Founded: 2000
Rev.: $14,300,000
Emp.: 100
Construction Materials Mfr & Distr
N.A.I.C.S.: 333120
Jim Spurlino (Pres & CEO)
Jeff Raussen (Dir-Sls & Mktg)
Rick Baumgartner (Controller)

SPURLOCK SCRAP INC.
138 Hwy 231 N Byp, Troy, AL 36081
Tel.: (334) 566-2886
Web Site:
    http://www.spurlockscrap.com
Rev.: $50,000,000
Emp.: 10
Ferrous Metal Scrap & Waste
N.A.I.C.S.: 423930
Jerry Spurlock Jr. (Pres)

SPURR CHEVROLET INC & COURTESY PONTIAC-GMC
6325 Brockport-Spencerport Rd, Brockport, NY 14420
Tel.: (585) 637-3999
Web Site:
    http://www.spurrdealerships.com
Year Founded: 2001
Sales Range: $10-24.9 Million
Emp.: 55
Car Whslr
N.A.I.C.S.: 441110
Richard Spurr (Pres)
Randy Spurr (Owner)

SPURRIER CHEMICAL COMPANIES, INC.
1200 E Central Ave, Wichita, KS 67214
Tel.: (316) 265-9491 KS
Web Site:
    http://www.spurrierchemical.com
Year Founded: 1932
Sales Range: $10-24.9 Million
Emp.: 45
Mfr of Cleaning Products
N.A.I.C.S.: 325199
Robert Spurrier (Pres)
Donald Ryel (Sr VP)
Marcia Ryel (VP-Ops)
Tony D. Stefano (Controller)

SPURS SPORTS & ENTERTAINMENT
1 AT&T Ctr, San Antonio, TX 78219
Tel.: (210) 444-5731
Web Site: http://www.spurs.com
Sales Range: $75-99.9 Million
Emp.: 350
Holding Company; Professional Basketball Team & Sports Arena Owner & Operator
N.A.I.C.S.: 551112
Frank Miceli (Sr VP-Sls & Franchise Bus Ops)
Lori Warren (Exec VP)
Tim Salier (VP-Franchise Sls & Ops)
Tammy Turner (VP-HR & Corp Admin)
Mike Malo (VP-Mktg & Branding)
Julianna Hawn Holt (Chm)
R. C. Buford (CEO)
Brian Wright (Gen Mgr)
Bobby Perez (Exec VP)
Brandon Gayle (Exec VP-Revenue, Brand & Comm)

Subsidiaries:

San Antonio Spurs, LLC (1)
1 At AT&T Center Pkwy, San Antonio, TX 78219
Tel.: (210) 444-5000
Professional Basketball Franchise
N.A.I.C.S.: 711211
Gregg Popovich (Pres-Spurs Basketball)
Joe Clark (VP-Ticket Sls & Svcs)
Rick A. Pych (Pres)
R. C. Buford (Pres-Sports Franchises)
Frank Miceli (Sr VP-Sls & Franchise Bus Ops)
Tim Salier (VP-Franchise Sls & Ops)
Tammy Turner (VP-HR & Corp Admin)
Lori Warren (Sr VP-Corp Fin & Strategy)

SPURWINK SERVICES INCORPORATED
901 Washington Ave Ste 100, Portland, ME 04103
Tel.: (207) 871-1200 ME
Web Site: http://www.spurwink.org
Behavioral Health Services
N.A.I.C.S.: 621420
Eric Meyer (Pres & CEO)
Daniel M. Bonner (COO)
Amy Cohan (VP-Outpatient & Community Svcs)
Al Durgin (VP-CQI & Outcomes)
Kristen Farnham (VP-Dev)
Kane Loukas (VP-Childrens Residential & Education Svcs)
John McAnuff (CFO)
Jonathan Normand (VP-Educational Svcs)
Mary Celia O'Neil (VP-HR & Pro Dev)
Alistair Y. Raymond (Chm)
Theresa A. Kelly (Vice Chm)

Subsidiaries:

Tri-County Mental Health Services (1)
1155 Lisbon St, Lewiston, ME 04240
Tel.: (207) 647-5629
Sales Range: $1-9.9 Million
Emp.: 40
Outpatient Health Care Services
N.A.I.C.S.: 621498

SQA SERVICES, INC.
550 Silver Spur Rd 3rd Fl, Rolling Hills Estates, CA 90275
Tel.: (310) 802-4442
Web Site:
    http://www.sqaservices.com
Year Founded: 1995
Rev.: $16,500,000
Emp.: 350
Business Products & Services
N.A.I.C.S.: 561499
Jim McKay (Founder & Chm)
Mike McKay (Founder, Pres & CEO)
Gerard Pearce (Exec VP)
Debbie Trutanich (Office Mgr)

SQUADHELP, INC.
3333 Beverly Rd EC-155A, Hoffman Estates, IL 60179
Tel.: (847) 620-0070

SQUADHELP, INC.

Squadhelp, Inc.—(Continued)
Web Site: http://www.squadhelp.com
Year Founded: 2011
Sales Range: $1-9.9 Million
Business Management Consulting Services
N.A.I.C.S.: 541611
Darpan Munjal *(Founder & CEO)*
Grant Polachek *(Dir-Mktg & Ops)*
Jonathan Bautista *(Mgr-Customer Svc)*

SQUAN CONSTRUCTION SERVICES LLC
329 Harold Ave, Englewood, NJ 07631
Tel.: (201) 408-5111
Web Site: http://www.squan.com
Year Founded: 2008
Engineeering Services
N.A.I.C.S.: 541330
Keith Pennachio *(Chief Strategy Officer)*
Duane W. Albro *(Chm)*
Glenn Weber *(CFO)*
Nick White *(Pres-Wireless)*
Ken Stabler *(Pres-Fiber)*
Carolyn Hardwick *(Pres-Engrg)*
Beth Martindale *(VP-Engrg)*
Rob Feiler *(Pres & COO)*
Chris Roach *(CEO)*

Subsidiaries:

Strong Tower Communications, LLC   (1)
4462 Bretton Ct Ste 8, Acworth, GA 30101
Tel.: (678) 398-9338
Web Site:
  http://www.strongtowercommunications.com
Wired Telecommunications Carriers
N.A.I.C.S.: 517111
Joshua Ward *(Pres)*
Sam Tincher *(Dir-Ops)*

SQUAR MILNER LLP
18500 Von Karman Ave 10 Fl, Irvine, CA 92612
Tel.: (949) 222-2999
Web Site:
  http://www.squarmilner.com
Accounting & Auditing Services, Business Consulting & Tax Planning, Preparation & Review Services
N.A.I.C.S.: 541211
Stephen P. Milner *(Mng Partner)*
Scharrell Jackson *(COO,CFO & Partner)*
Adam Bullock *(Partner)*
David W. Cortney *(Partner)*
Richard E. Evans *(Partner)*
Katherine Gough *(Partner)*
Ahmed Hamdy *(Partner)*
Kenneth M. Kasianovitz *(Partner)*
Michael H. Lorber *(Partner)*
Ernest D. Miranda *(Partner)*
Kristi D. Oates *(Partner)*
Laurence D. Smetana *(Partner)*
Keith Troutman *(Partner)*
Craig A. Weaver *(Partner)*
Ronald R. Williamson *(Partner)*

SQUARE DEAL BUILDING SUPPLY
7670 19 Mile Rd, Sterling Heights, MI 48314
Tel.: (586) 731-3670
Web Site: http://www.square-deal.com
Rev.: $11,500,000
Emp.: 60
Building Materials Whslr
N.A.I.C.S.: 423390
Joe Meza *(Mgr-Wyoming)*
Marshall Brown *(Mgr-Sterling Heights)*

SQUARE MILE CAPITAL MANAGEMENT LLC
350 Park Ave, New York, NY 10022
Tel.: (212) 605-1000   DE
Web Site:
  http://www.squaremilecapital.com
Emp.: 22
Real Estate Investment & Asset Management Services
N.A.I.C.S.: 531390
Jeffrey B. Citrin *(Bd of Dirs, Executives)*
Elliot Rattner *(Mng Dir-Investments)*
Daniel M. Kasell *(Mng Dir & Chief Legal Officer)*
Brad Cohen *(Sr Mng Dir-Investments)*
Craig H. Solomon *(Co-Founder & CEO)*
Laurie Golub *(Sr Mng Dir & COO)*
Vivian Chang *(Principal-Fin Admin)*
Eric Cohen *(Principal-Investments)*
Jesse Goepel *(Mng Dir-Investments)*
Nolan Hecht *(Sr Mng Dir-Investments)*
Jeong Gu Lee *(VP-Investments)*
Angela Lin *(VP-Investments)*
Beth Newman *(Principal)*
Charles Ochman *(Mng Dir-Asset Mgmt)*
Sean Reimer *(Principal-Investments)*
Deborah Schiavo *(Mng Dir-Loan Ops)*
Jason J. Tighe *(Mng Dir-Fin & Reporting)*
Jeffrey F. Fastov *(Sr Mng Dir-Credit Strategies)*
Michael Lavipour *(Mng Dir-Investments)*
Samir Tejpaul *(Principal-Investments)*
Tom Burns *(Principal-Investments)*

SQUARE ONE
1095 Main St 2nd Fl, Springfield, MA 01103
Tel.: (413) 732-5183   MA
Web Site: http://www.sdn.org
Year Founded: 1883
Sales Range: $1-9.9 Million
Emp.: 263
Child Care Services
N.A.I.C.S.: 624110
William Sullivan *(Chm)*
Joanne Denver *(Treas)*
Joan Kagan *(Pres & CEO)*
Dawn Forbes DiStefano *(Exec VP)*

SQUARE ONE ARMORING SERVICES CO.
12370 SW 130th St, Miami, FL 33186
Tel.: (305) 477-1109
Web Site: http://www.sq1armor.com
Rev.: $15,800,000
Emp.: 70
Automobile Mfr
N.A.I.C.S.: 336110
Allan Velazquez *(Mgr-Sls)*
Martin Cardenal *(VP)*

SQUARE ONE MARKETING
1993 Albany Ave, West Hartford, CT 06117
Tel.: (860) 232-7300
Web Site: http://www.squareone-marketing.com
Year Founded: 2003
Rev.: $2,000,000
Emp.: 2
Fiscal Year-end: 12/31/04
N.A.I.C.S.: 541810
David Riley *(Pres & Dir-Creative)*

SQUARE ONE, INC.
1801 N Lamar Ste 300, Dallas, TX 75202
Tel.: (214) 749-1111
Web Site: http://www.sq1agency.com

Year Founded: 1995
Rev.: $186,000,000
Emp.: 90
Advetising Agency
N.A.I.C.S.: 541810
Casey Carey *(CMO)*
Ian Little *(Mgr-Mktg)*
Neil Patel *(Co-Founder)*

SQUARE ROOT, INC.
508 Oakland Ave, Austin, TX 78703
Tel.: (512) 693-9232
Web Site: http://www.square-root.com
Year Founded: 2006
Sales Range: $1-9.9 Million
Emp.: 17
Software Product Development Services
N.A.I.C.S.: 541511
Chris Taylor *(Founder & CEO)*
Sarah Gerichten *(Dir-Mktg)*
Fred Smith *(Chief Revenue Officer)*
Sarah Kampman *(VP-Product)*
Ranjini Chandirakanthan *(CFO & VP-Bus Dev)*

SQUARE-H BRANDS INC.
2731 S Soto St, Los Angeles, CA 90058
Tel.: (323) 267-4600   CA
Web Site: http://www.sqhb.com
Year Founded: 1995
Sales Range: $25-49.9 Million
Emp.: 150
Provider of Sausages & Prepared Meat Products
N.A.I.C.S.: 311612
Henry Haskell *(Pres)*
Bill Parke *(Mgr-Quality Assurance)*
Kirk Kolden *(Dir-Sls)*

Subsidiaries:

Bill Bailey Meat Packing Co Inc.   (1)
2731 S Soto St, Los Angeles, CA 90058   (100%)
Tel.: (323) 267-4600
Web Site: http://www.sqhb.com
Provider of Meat Packing Services
N.A.I.C.S.: 311611
Henry Haskell *(Pres)*
Bill Hannigan *(Controller)*

SQUIRE BOONE CAVERNS INCORPORATED
PO Box 711, New Albany, IN 47151
Tel.: (812) 941-5900
Web Site:
  http://www.squireboonecaverns.com
Rev.: $22,400,000
Emp.: 100
Souvenirs
N.A.I.C.S.: 423990
W. Rick Conway *(Pres)*
Jim Hudson *(CFO)*

SQUIRE CORRUGATED CONTAINER CORP.
111 Somogyi Ct, South Plainfield, NJ 07067
Tel.: (908) 862-9111
Sales Range: $10-24.9 Million
Emp.: 100
Corrugated & Solid Fiber Boxes Mfr
N.A.I.C.S.: 322211
James Beneroff *(CFO & VP)*

SQUIRE PATTON BOGGS (US) LLP
4900 Key Tower 127 Public Sq, Cleveland, OH 44114-1304
Tel.: (216) 479-8500   OH
Web Site:
  http://www.squirepattonboggs.com
Year Founded: 1890
Sales Range: $75-99.9 Million
Emp.: 1,500

Law Firm
N.A.I.C.S.: 541110
Rodney Earl Slater *(Executives)*
Stephen P. Anway *(Partner)*
David S. Goodman *(Co-Mng Partner)*
Stacy D. Ballin *(Partner)*
Mark J. Ruehlmann *(Chm & Global CEO)*
Linda Pfatteicher *(Partner-San Francisco)*
Kimberly J. Donovan *(Partner)*
Jeffrey R. Wahl *(Partner)*
Traci L. Martinez *(Partner)*
Gregory R. Daniels *(Partner)*
Tamara Fraizer *(Partner-Palo Alto)*
Michele L. Connell *(Co-Mng Partner)*
Coates Lear *(Principal)*
Allison M. Binkley *(Principal)*
Jason Daniel Joffe *(Partner)*
John W. Hutchinson *(Partner)*
Matthew S. Bailey *(Partner)*
Jason Sampson *(Principal)*
Stacy H. Krumin *(Partner)*
Gregory Davis *(Principal-Phoenix)*
Stephen Owens *(Partner-Phoenix)*
Kelly Singer *(Partner-Restructuring & Insolvency Grp-Natl)*
Edward Steiner *(Partner)*
Elias J. Hayek *(Partner-Global Hospitality & Leisure Practice Grp)*
Pedro Hernandez *(Partner-Miami)*
Thomas Wilson *(Mng Partner-Dubai)*
Shane Wilson *(Partner-Pub & Infrastructure Fin Practice Grp-Dubai)*
Matthew Yarbrough *(Partner-Dallas)*
Michael S. Forshey *(Mng Partner-Dallas)*
Nick Bell *(Partner-Fin Svcs)*
D. Zachary Adams *(Partner)*
Antoine Adeline *(Partner)*
Stephan Adell *(Partner)*
Jose E. Aguilar Shea *(Partner)*
Awilda M. Alcantara-Bourdier *(Partner)*
John Alderton *(Partner)*
David W. Alexander *(Partner)*
Robin Baillie *(Partner)*
Gassan A. Baloul *(Partner)*
Amanda K. Banton *(Partner)*
Denis C. Barat *(Partner)*
Rosa Barcelo *(Partner)*
Mark Barker *(Partner)*
James Barratt *(Partner)*
Brain A. Cabianca *(Partner)*
Ryan K. Callender *(Partner)*
Victoria Camfield *(Partner)*
Robin B. Campbell *(Partner)*
Antonio Canadas *(Partner)*
Jeremy Cape *(Partner)*
Aengus H. Carr *(Partner)*
Scott J. Carr *(Partner)*
Jaime R. Daddona *(Partner)*
John Danahy *(Partner)*
Jonathan Jones *(Mng Partner-Europe)*
Cipriano S. Beredo III *(Partner)*
Allen A. Kacenjar Jr. *(Partner)*

Subsidiaries:

Squire Patton Boggs (US) LLP - Washington, DC   (1)
2550 M St NW, Washington, DC 20037
Tel.: (202) 457-6000
Emp.: 350
Law Firm
N.A.I.C.S.: 541110
Edward J. Newberry *(Mng Partner)*
Mitchell R. Berger *(Chm-Litigation Dept & Partner)*
Jeff Cole *(Partner & Chm-Bus Dept)*
Jeffrey L. Turner *(Partner & Chm-Pub Policy/Admin & Regulatory Dept)*
Thomas M. Keane *(CMO & Chief Bus Dev Officer)*
Donald V. Moorehead *(Partner & Chm-Private Investment Funds Grp)*
Laura F. Laemmle-Weidenfeld *(Partner)*

Larry A. Makel *(Partner)*
Kevin McCarthy *(Dir-Pur & Procurement)*
Russell Hill *(Partner)*
Monika Kuschewsky *(Partner-Data Privacy & Cybersecurity-Belgium)*
Sabine Pittrof *(Partner-Frankfurt)*
John Bartrum *(Partner)*
Tara Swaminatha *(Partner-Data Privacy & Cybersecurity Practice)*
Squire Patton Boggs *(Principal-Fin Svcs Practice)*
Deirdre Johnson *(Partner-Litigation Practice Grp)*
Paul Kalish *(Partner-Litigation Practice Grp)*
Jefferson P. VanderWolk *(Partner-Tax Strategy & Benefits Practice)*
Christopher Giaimo *(Partner)*
Jeffrey Rothleder *(Partner)*
Benjamin Beaton *(Partner & Co-Chm-Appellate Practice)*
Lauren Kuley *(Partner & Co-Chm-Appellate Practice)*
Claiborne Porter *(Partner-Govt Investigations & White Collar Practice)*

SR PERROTT INC.
4 N Perrott Dr, Ormond Beach, FL 32174
Tel.: (386) 672-2275
Web Site: http://www.srperrott.com
Rev.: $19,500,000
Emp.: 70
Beer & Other Fermented Malt Liquors
N.A.I.C.S.: 424810
Michele Connors *(Pres)*
Gary Conners *(Exec VP-Ops)*
Lori Hobdy *(Controller)*
Mark Champagne *(Mgr-Warehouse)*

SRAM INTERNATIONAL CORPORATION
1000 W Fulton Market 4th Fl, Chicago, IL 60607
Tel.: (312) 664-8800   DE
Web Site: http://www.sram.com
Year Founded: 2011
Emp.: 150
Holding Company
N.A.I.C.S.: 551112
Michael R. Herr *(VP-Fin)*
Stanley R. Day Jr. *(Pres)*
David Zimberoff *(VP-Mktg)*
Ken Lousberg *(COO)*
Marcus Schneider *(Dir-Bus Dev-E-MTB & E-mobility)*
Ron Ritzler *(VP-Product Dev)*

Subsidiaries:

SRAM - Taiwan   (1)
1598 8 Chung Shan Rd, Shenkang Shiang, Taichung, 42941, Taiwan
Tel.: (886) 425613678
Web Site: http://www.sram.com
Sales Range: $50-74.9 Million
Emp.: 500
Bicycle Parts Mfr
N.A.I.C.S.: 336991

SRAM, LLC   (1)
1333 N Kingsbury St Ste 4, Chicago, IL 60642
Tel.: (312) 664-8800
Web Site: http://www.sram.com
Sales Range: $500-549.9 Million
Bicycle Components Mfr
N.A.I.C.S.: 336991
Michael R. Herr *(VP-Fin)*
Frederick K.W. Day *(Exec VP)*
Jeffrey M. Shupe *(COO)*
Stanley R. Day Jr. *(Pres)*
John Nedeau *(VP-Global Sls)*
Brian Benzer *(VP-Corp Dev)*
Michael D. Mercuri *(VP-Product)*
Tim Smith *(VP-Engrg)*
Jeff Winterkorn *(VP-Ops-Asia)*

Unit (Domestic):

SRAM, LLC - Colorado Development Center   (2)
1610 Garden Of The Gods Rd, Colorado Springs, CO 80907-3418
Tel.: (719) 278-7469

Web Site: http://www.sram.com
Sales Range: $50-74.9 Million
Emp.: 35
Mfr, Designer & Marketer of High Performance Bicycle Suspension Products
N.A.I.C.S.: 336991

SRAMPORT - Transmissoes Mechanicas, Lda.   (1)
Antonio Sergio No 15, PO Box 8150, Coimbra, 3025041, Portugal   (100%)
Tel.: (351) 239499050
Web Site: http://www.sram.com
Sales Range: $10-24.9 Million
Emp.: 120
Radio & Television Transmission
N.A.I.C.S.: 334220
Joao Pires *(Gen Mgr)*

SRC CORP.
4215 S 500 W, Salt Lake City, UT 84123
Tel.: (801) 268-4500   UT
Web Site: http://www.steveregan.com
Year Founded: 1936
Animal Health Products, Pesticides & Other Agricultural Supplies Mfr
N.A.I.C.S.: 424910
Steve M. Harmsen *(Pres)*

SRC HOLDINGS CORPORATION
531 S Union Ave, Springfield, MO 65802
Tel.: (417) 862-4510   MO
Web Site:
  http://www.srcholdings.com
Year Founded: 1983
Sales Range: $10-24.9 Million
Emp.: 20
Internal Combustion Engines
N.A.I.C.S.: 333618
Jack P. Stack *(CEO)*

Subsidiaries:

Ciona Technologies LLC   (1)
3001 E Division St, Springfield, MO 65802
Tel.: (417) 893-2686
Web Site: http://www.cionatech.com
Electronic Components Mfr
N.A.I.C.S.: 334419
Jo Miles *(CFO)*
Mike Finan *(Gen Mgr)*
Brad Lawrence *(Dir-Sls & Mktg)*
Jo MacDonnell *(CFO)*

Great Game of Business Inc.   (1)
3055 E Division St, Springfield, MO 65802-2410   (100%)
Tel.: (417) 831-7706
Web Site: http://www.greatgame.com
Sales Range: $10-24.9 Million
Emp.: 10
Management Consulting Services
N.A.I.C.S.: 541611
Jack P. Stack *(Pres)*
Richard Armstrong *(Pres)*
Kim Brown *(Controller)*
Ken Cook *(Dir-Sls & Mktg)*
Tiffany Montileone *(Dir-Fin & Admin)*
Cassie Potts *(Coord-Events)*
Kristi Stringer *(Coord-Conference)*
Lizzie Vaughn *(Coord-Admin)*

NewStream Enterprises, LLC.   (1)
1925 E Chestnut Expy, Springfield, MO 65802
Tel.: (417) 831-3112
Web Site: http://www.newstreaming.com
Supply Chain Management Services
N.A.I.C.S.: 561990
Tom Bates *(Dir-Strategic Plng)*

SRC Automotive, Inc.   (1)
4431 W Calhoun St, Springfield, MO 65802
Tel.: (417) 829-2400
Web Site: http://www.srcautomotive.com
Gas Engine Mfr
N.A.I.C.S.: 336310
Anne Lund *(Coord-Toolcrib)*

SRC Electrical LLC   (1)
2720 N Commerce Dr, Springfield, MO 65803
Tel.: (417) 862-1110

Web Site: http://www.srcelectrical.com
Electrical Equipment Whslr
N.A.I.C.S.: 423610
Steven Huffman *(Mgr-Supply Chain)*
Philip Lueckenotto *(Mgr-Engrg)*
Lou Mustari *(Mgr-Quality)*
Jeremy Dodd *(Dir-Ops)*
Matt Wardle *(Dir-Sls & Engrg)*
Tim Stack *(Gen Mgr)*
Erin Wibbenmeyer *(Mgr-HR)*

SRC Logistics, Inc.   (1)
2065 E Pythian, Springfield, MO 65802-1000
Tel.: (417) 863-6166
Web Site: http://www.srclogisticinc.com
Sales Range: Less than $1 Million
Emp.: 70
Public & Contract Warehousing, Fulfillment Services, Distribution, Reverse Logistics & Custom Software Services
N.A.I.C.S.: 493110
Tim Stack *(Gen Mgr)*
Todd Choate *(Dir-Sls & Mktg)*

SRC Power Systems   (1)
4727 E Kearney St, Springfield, MO 65803
Tel.: (417) 885-8080
Web Site: http://www.srcreman.com
Motor Vehicle Parts & Accessories
N.A.I.C.S.: 336390
Kevin Snider *(Gen Mgr)*
Erin Wibbenmeyer *(Mgr-HR)*

SRC Power Systems Inc.   (1)
2707 N Farm Rd 123, Springfield, MO 65803
Tel.: (417) 885-8080
Web Site: http://srcpowersystems.com
Sales Range: $10-24.9 Million
Designer & Manufacturer of Motors & Generators
N.A.I.C.S.: 335312

Springfield Remanufacturing Corp. Heavy Duty Div   (1)
650 N Broadview Pl, Springfield, MO 65802-1099   (100%)
Tel.: (417) 862-3501
Web Site: http://www.srcreman.com
Internal Combustion Engines
N.A.I.C.S.: 333618

SRC, INC.
7502 Round Pond Rd, North Syracuse, NY 13212
Tel.: (315) 452-8000   NY
Web Site: http://www.srcinc.com
Year Founded: 1957
Emp.: 100
Defense, Environment & Intelligence Research & Development Services
N.A.I.C.S.: 541715
Paul G. Tremont *(Pres & CEO)*
Philip Fazio *(CFO & Exec VP)*
Kevin Hair *(COO)*
Mary L. Snyder *(Gen Counsel & Exec VP)*
James F. Holland *(Exec VP-Enterprise Svcs)*
Ronald Hayward *(Sr VP-Radars & Sensors)*
Joseph T. Lauko *(Sr VP-Electronic Warfare)*
James L. Daniels *(VP-Intl Bus)*
David C. Lyons *(VP-Technical Svcs)*
Andrea V. Masten *(VP-Bus Dev)*
Anthony O. Stewart *(VP-Corp Quality)*
Donald L. Kerrick *(Chm)*
Judy Lewis *(VP-Strategy)*
Thomas Triscari Jr. *(Vice Chm)*

Subsidiaries:

SRC International, Inc.   (1)
7502 Round Pond Rd, North Syracuse, NY 13212
Tel.: (315) 452-8000
Holding Company; Electronic Warfare Intelligence Production & Reprogramming Services
N.A.I.C.S.: 551112
Joseph T. Lauko *(Exec Dir)*
Kevin Hair *(Chm)*

SRC Ventures, Inc.   (1)
7502 Round Pond Rd, North Syracuse, NY 13212
Tel.: (315) 452-8000
Holding Company; Defense, Environment & Intelligence Research & Development Services
N.A.I.C.S.: 551112
Paul G. Tremont *(Chm, Pres & CEO)*
Mary Pat Hartnett *(Pres-SRCTec & Sec)*

Subsidiary (Domestic):

SRC Commercial Holdings, Inc.   (2)
7502 Round Pond Rd, North Syracuse, NY 13212
Tel.: (315) 452-8000
Holding Company; Point-of-Need Food Safety Testing & Analysis Services
N.A.I.C.S.: 551112
Paul G. Tremont *(Chm, Pres & CEO)*
Timothy Moshier *(Pres-Acumen Detection)*

Subsidiary (Domestic):

Acumen Detection, LLC   (3)
6274 Running Rdg Rd, North Syracuse, NY 13212
Web Site: http://www.acumendetection.com
Bio Technology Services
N.A.I.C.S.: 541990
Timothy Moshier *(Pres)*

Subsidiary (Domestic):

SRCTec, LLC   (2)
5801 E Taft Rd, North Syracuse, NY 13212
Tel.: (315) 452-8700
Web Site: http://www.srcinc.com
Military Electromechanical & Life Cycle Management Products Mfr
N.A.I.C.S.: 334419
Mary Pat Hartnett *(Pres)*

SRECO-FLEXIBLE INCORPORATED
140 Washington St, El Segundo, CA 90245-4321
Tel.: (310) 606-9009
Web Site:
  http://www.srecoflexible.com
Sales Range: $25-49.9 Million
Emp.: 20
Sewer Cleaning Equipment
N.A.I.C.S.: 333310
Wendy Mackett *(Office Mgr)*
Mark C. Goss *(Pres & CEO)*
Jon Gotchis *(Mgr-Intl Sls)*
Bob Cox *(Mgr-Machine Ops & Bid)*

SRI FIRE SPRINKLER CORP.
1060 Central Ave, Albany, NY 12205
Tel.: (518) 459-2776
Web Site:
  http://www.srifiresprinkler.com
Sales Range: $10-24.9 Million
Emp.: 20
Fire Sprinkler System Installation
N.A.I.C.S.: 238220
Donald A. Deluca *(Pres)*

SRI INTERNATIONAL
333 Ravenswood Ave, Menlo Park, CA 94025-3453
Tel.: (650) 859-2000   CA
Web Site: http://www.sri.com
Year Founded: 1946
Sales Range: $200-249.9 Million
Emp.: 2,500
Research & Development Services
N.A.I.C.S.: 541715
William Mark *(Pres-Info & Computing Sciences)*
Michael Page *(Sr VP-Shared Svcs)*
Manish Kothari *(Pres-SRI Ventures)*
Eric Pearson *(VP-Special Programs)*
Scott Seaton *(Pres-Advanced Tech & Sys Div)*
Robert A. Brown *(Dir-Security & Survivability)*
Greg Kovacs *(CTO)*
Erin Andre *(Chief People Officer)*

SRI INTERNATIONAL

SRI International—(Continued)
Joe Broz *(VP-Advanced Science-ATSD)*
Peter Marcotullio *(VP-Comml R&D)*
Steve Perna *(Pres-Integrated Sys & Solutions)*
Rick Laird *(Project Mgr)*
Stephanie DeFino *(CFO)*
Ian M. Colrain *(Pres-SRI Biosciences)*

Subsidiaries:

Sarnoff Corporation (1)
201 Washington Rd, Princeton, NJ 08540-5300 (100%)
Tel.: (609) 734-2000
Web Site: http://www.sarnoff.com
Sales Range: $25-49.9 Million
Emp.: 400
Vision, Video & Semiconductor Technology
N.A.I.C.S.: 541715
Mark Clifton *(VP-Products & Svcs)*

SRI TELECOM
18405 E Petroleum Dr, Baton Rouge, LA 70809
Tel.: (225) 201-9676
Web Site: http://www.sritelecom.net
Year Founded: 1999
Rev.: $13,400,000
Emp.: 128
Electrical Contractor
N.A.I.C.S.: 238210
Elizabeth Greer *(Mgr)*
Shane M. Breaux *(Pres)*

SRIRAMA ASSOCIATES LLC
515 Madison Ave Ste 880, New York, NY 10022
Tel.: (813) 601-3533
Investment Services
N.A.I.C.S.: 523999

SRIVEN SYSTEMS, INC.
560 Broadhollow Rd Ste 311, Melville, NY 11747
Tel.: (631) 393-0300 NY
Web Site: http://www.srivensys.com
Year Founded: 1999
Sales Range: $10-24.9 Million
Emp.: 100
High Technology Outsourcing Solutions
N.A.I.C.S.: 541512
Rita Pasham *(Mgr-HR)*
Nida Ali *(Mgr-Payroll)*

SRO HOUSING CORPORATION
1055 W 7th St Ste 3250, Los Angeles, CA 90017
Tel.: (213) 229-9640 CA
Web Site: http://www.srohousing.org
Year Founded: 1984
Sales Range: $10-24.9 Million
Emp.: 234
Community Housing Assistance Services
N.A.I.C.S.: 624229
Steven Van Zile *(Dir-Property Mgmt & Facilities)*
Anita U. Nelson *(CEO)*
Ervin Munro *(Dir-Social Svcs)*
Joseph Corcoran *(Dir-Plng & Housing Dev)*
Alton Wright *(Vice Chm)*

SRP ENVIRONMENTAL LLC
348 Aero Dr, Shreveport, LA 71107
Tel.: (318) 222-2364
Web Site: http://www.srpenvironmental.com
Year Founded: 1996
Sales Range: $1-9.9 Million
Emp.: 22
Ponseti Clubfoot Brace Mfr
N.A.I.C.S.: 339113

Keith Sampson *(Pres & CEO)*
Joel Barron *(Project Mgr)*
Jacob N. Colson *(Dir-Large Loss & Catastrophe Response)*
Kevin G. Hunter *(Sr Project Mgr)*
Rick Laird *(Project Mgr)*
Robert W. Storment *(Mgr-Health & Safety)*

SRS CORE LLC
286 S Main St Ste 400, Alpharetta, GA 30009
Web Site: http://www.srscore.com
Year Founded: 2008
Sales Range: $1-9.9 Million
Emp.: 20
Real Estate Consulting Service
N.A.I.C.S.: 531390
Jeff Lyon *(Dir-Ops)*

SRS ENGINEERING, INC.
41610 Date St Ste 107, Murrieta, CA 92562
Tel.: (951) 526-2239
Web Site: http://www.srsengineering.com
Year Founded: 1985
Sales Range: $1-9.9 Million
Emp.: 31
Mfr of Industrial Process Equipment for Biodiesel Plants
N.A.I.C.S.: 333248
Clayton Hawranik *(Pres & CEO)*

SRS, INC.
131 Saundersville Rd Ste 210, Hendersonville, TN 37075
Tel.: (615) 230-2966
Web Site: http://www.srsincorp.com
Year Founded: 2001
Sales Range: $10-24.9 Million
Emp.: 121
Engineeering Services
N.A.I.C.S.: 236210
Talmadge Dewayne Scott *(Co-Founder, Pres & CEO)*
Joseph L. Shaw *(Co-Founder & VP-Ops)*
Monte A. Edwards *(Exec VP-Mktg & Bus Dev)*
Vincent E. Malone *(Dir-Safety, Risk & Compliance)*
Bobby Reed *(Co-Founder & VP-Construction)*

SRSSOFT
155 Chestnut Ridge Rd, Montvale, NJ 07645
Tel.: (201) 802-1300
Web Site: http://www.srssoft.com
Year Founded: 1998
Sales Range: $10-24.9 Million
Emp.: 100
Hybrid Electronic Medical Records (EMR) Management Software
N.A.I.C.S.: 541511
Lynn Scheps *(VP-Govt Affairs & Consulting Svcs)*
Michael Earley *(VP-Bus Dev)*
Scott Ciccarelli *(CEO)*
Khal Rai *(Sr VP-Dev & Ops)*
Rob Wilkinson *(Acct Exec)*
Ed Gould *(CFO)*
Helene Kaiden *(Chief Acctg Officer & VP-Fin)*
Lyndsey Scott *(Dir-Sls)*
Tennis Smith *(VP-HR)*
Diane Beatini *(VP-Sls)*

SRT COMMUNICATIONS INC.
3615 N Broadway, Minot, ND 58703
Tel.: (701) 858-1200
Web Site: http://www.srt.com
Rev.: $36,447,494
Emp.: 200
Local Telephone Communications

N.A.I.C.S.: 517121
Steven Lysne *(CEO & Gen Mgr)*
John A. Reiser *(COO & Asst Gen Mgr)*
Perry Erdmann *(CFO)*

SRT SOLUTIONS INC.
206 S Fifth Ave, Ann Arbor, MI 48104
Tel.: (734) 929-3211
Web Site: http://www.srtsolutions.com
Sales Range: $1-9.9 Million
Emp.: 17
Software Services
N.A.I.C.S.: 513210
Bill Wagner *(Co-Founder & CEO)*
Dianne Marsh *(Co-Founder & Pres)*
Jill Bornemeier *(Project Mgr)*
Kerry Colligan *(VP-Ops & Mktg)*
Lisa Zuber *(Office Mgr)*

SRVS
3971 Knight Arnold Rd, Memphis, TN 38118
Tel.: (901) 869-7787 TN
Web Site: http://www.srvs.org
Year Founded: 1970
Sales Range: $25-49.9 Million
Emp.: 1,256
Disability Assistance Services
N.A.I.C.S.: 624120
Laura Tumminello *(Chm)*
Carol Snowden Morris *(Sec)*
Thomas Sullivan *(Treas)*

SRW INDUSTRIES CORPORATION
500 Capital Dr, Lake Zurich, IL 60047
Tel.: (847) 550-1800
Sales Range: $10-24.9 Million
Emp.: 10
Medical & Hospital Equipment
N.A.I.C.S.: 423450
Marry Rybacki *(Pres)*

SRW PRODUCTS
32020 126th St, Princeton, MN 55371
Tel.: (763) 389-2722
Web Site: http://www.srwproducts.com
Year Founded: 1989
Sales Range: $10-24.9 Million
Emp.: 22
Farm & Garden Machinery & Equipment Whslr
N.A.I.C.S.: 423820
Sandi Nelson *(Mgr-Mktg)*

SS VENTURES II INC.
207 N Poindexter St, Elizabeth City, NC 27909
Tel.: (252) 338-9111
Rev.: $75,000,000
Emp.: 2
Loan Broker
N.A.I.C.S.: 522310
John Smith *(Pres)*

SS&KH CORPORATION
4606 Convoy St, San Diego, CA 92111
Tel.: (858) 279-6862
Web Site: http://www.sandiegoautofinders.com
Rev.: $17,000,000
Emp.: 7
Automobiles, Used Cars Only
N.A.I.C.S.: 441120
Siamaj Salami *(Pres)*

SSARIS ADVISORS, LLC
Wilton Corp Ctr Courtside Bldg Ste 2C 187 Danbury Rd, Wilton, CT 06987
Tel.: (203) 328-7200 CT
Web Site: http://www.ssaris.com

Year Founded: 2001
Investment Advisory Services
N.A.I.C.S.: 523940
Mark Rosenberg *(Chm)*
Peter A. Hinrichs *(CFO & Chief Admin Officer)*

SSB COMMUNITY BANCORP MHC
176 Main St, Spencer, MA 01562
Tel.: (508) 885-5313 MA
Year Founded: 2007
Sales Range: $25-49.9 Million
Mutual Savings Bank Holding Company
N.A.I.C.S.: 551111
K. Michael Robbins *(Chm & CEO)*
Todd M. Tallman *(Pres & Treas)*

Subsidiaries:

SSB Community Bancorp Inc. (1)
176 Main St, Spencer, MA 01562
Tel.: (508) 885-5313
Bank Holding Company
N.A.I.C.S.: 551111
Todd M. Tallman *(Pres & Treas)*
K. Michael Robbins *(Chm & CEO)*

Subsidiary (Domestic):

Southbridge Savings Bank (2)
253-257 Main St, Southbridge, MA 01550
Tel.: (508) 765-9103
Web Site: http://www.southbridgesavingsbank.com
Sales Range: $10-24.9 Million
Emp.: 111
Mutual Savings Bank
N.A.I.C.S.: 522180
Todd M. Tallman *(Pres & CEO)*
Anthony M. Detarando *(Vice Chm)*
Susan E. Keough *(VP-Compliance & Security)*
Thomas E. Dufresne *(CTO & Sr VP)*
Susan A. Gunnell *(COO & Exec VP)*
John Q. Colognesi *(Pres)*
Brian M. Chandley *(Sr VP-Comml Lending & Svcs)*
Patrick M. Harvey *(Asst VP & Sr Branch Mgr)*
Scott Auen *(Sr VP-Retail Lending)*
Jason D. Main *(Sr VP-Investment Svcs)*
Scott M. Dungey *(VP & Controller)*

Spencer Savings Bank (2)
176 Main St, Spencer, MA 01562
Tel.: (508) 885-5313
Web Site: http://www.spencerbankonline.com
Sales Range: $10-24.9 Million
Mutual Savings Bank
N.A.I.C.S.: 522180
K. Michael Robbins *(Pres & CEO)*
Priscilla L. Berthiaume *(VP)*
Jerry Shpak *(VP-Investment)*
Randal D. Webber *(Sr VP)*
Michael J. Quink *(Sr VP & Mgr-Comml Div)*
Lynne M. Esposito *(VP & Mgr-Mortgage Div)*
Marianne Hosford *(VP-Personnel)*
Douglas R. Schmeling *(VP)*

SSDC SERVICES CORP.
28125 Cabot Dr Ste 201, Novi, MI 48377
Tel.: (248) 344-4444
Web Site: http://www.ssdcservices.com
Social Security Disability Insurance Services
N.A.I.C.S.: 524298
Craig Horton *(Pres & CEO)*
Dick Lewis *(Chm)*

SSF INC.
1400 S Dan Gurney Dr, Santa Ana, CA 92705
Tel.: (714) 560-6950
Web Site: http://www.volvo-oc.com
Sales Range: $10-24.9 Million
Emp.: 60
Car Dealership

COMPANIES

N.A.I.C.S.: 441110
James Speck *(Pres)*
Delores Bos *(Controller)*
Mike Nernst *(VP)*
Leanne Conkling *(Office Mgr)*

SSI (U.S.) INC.
353 N Clark Ste 2400, Chicago, IL 60654
Tel.: (312) 822-0088   DE
Web Site: http://www.spencerstuart.com
Year Founded: 1956
Sales Range: $25-49.9 Million
Emp.: 390
Employment Agencies
N.A.I.C.S.: 541612
Ben Williams *(CEO)*

Subsidiaries:

Cambria Consulting Inc.   (1)
50 Milk St Fl 16, Boston, MA 02109-5002
Tel.: (617) 523-7500
Web Site: http://www.cambriaconsulting.com
Administrative Management & General Management Consulting Service
N.A.I.C.S.: 541611
Ellen Kumata *(Mng Partner)*
George Klemp *(Partner)*
Scott Simpson *(CTO & Partner)*

SSI INCORPORATED
2817 Yuma St, Fort Smith, AR 72901-8778
Tel.: (479) 646-2901   AR
Web Site: http://www.ssigc.com
Year Founded: 1969
Sales Range: $25-49.9 Million
Emp.: 75
Construction Services
N.A.I.C.S.: 236220
Leo Anhalt *(Co-Owner, Pres & Gen Mgr)*
Ken Hart *(VP)*
Steve Maestri *(VP-Fin)*
Greg Nally *(Dir-Ops)*
Brian Byrd *(Project Mgr)*
Jimmy Carson *(Project Mgr)*
Wes Coats *(Project Mgr)*
Justin Wisdom *(VP-Bus Dev)*

SSI SERVICES, LLC
308 S State Ave, Indianapolis, IN 46201
Tel.: (317) 269-2120
Web Site: http://www.ssiweb.com
Year Founded: 1978
Sales Range: $10-24.9 Million
Emp.: 15
Asbestos Removal & Encapsulation
N.A.I.C.S.: 562910
Jerome D. Weaver *(CEO)*
Ed Cockerill *(CFO)*
David Weaver *(Controller)*

SSI TECHNOLOGIES
1027 Waterwood Pkwy, Edmond, OK 73034
Tel.: (405) 359-6000
Web Site: http://www.ssicards.com
Sales Range: $10-24.9 Million
Emp.: 50
Plastic Retail, Identification & Other Data Cards & Products Mfr
N.A.I.C.S.: 326199
Ron E. Goade *(Founder & Pres)*
Lasaundra Kendall *(Mgr-HR)*
McFarlin Tammy *(Acct Mgr)*

SSM HEALTH CARE CORPORATION
10101 Woodfield Ln, Saint Louis, MO 63132
Tel.: (314) 994-7800   MO
Web Site: http://www.ssmhc.com
Year Founded: 1872
Sales Range: $1-4.9 Billion
Emp.: 25,800
Non-Profit Healthcare Organization; Hospital & Nursing Care Facilities Owner & Operator
N.A.I.C.S.: 813212
Kris A. Zimmer *(Sr VP-Fin)*
Kevin Johnson *(Chief Medical Officer-Hospital Ops & VP-Sys)*
Paula J. Friedman *(Sr VP-Strategic Dev)*
Chris Howard *(Pres-Hospital Ops & Exec VP)*
Maggie Fowler *(Chief Nursing Officer & Sr VP-Sys)*
Michael Panicola *(Sr VP-Mission, Legal & Govt Affairs)*
Shane Peng *(Pres-Physicians & Ambulatory Svcs)*
Damond Boatwright *(Pres-Hospital Ops)*
Thomas Ahr *(VP-Sys-Talent)*
Laura Smith Kaiser *(Pres & CEO)*
Steve Little *(COO)*
Sony Jacob *(CIO)*
Trevor Sawallish *(VP-Reg Medical Grp Ops)*

Subsidiaries:

Dean Health Systems, Inc.   (1)
1808 W Beltline Hwy, Madison, WI 53713
Tel.: (608) 250-1075
Web Site: http://www.deancare.com
Multi-Specialty Clinic Owner & Operator; Insurance Services
N.A.I.C.S.: 621111
Stewart Watson *(Pres & CEO)*

Subsidiary (Domestic):

Navitus Health Solutions, LLC   (2)
999 Fourier Dr Ste 301, Madison, WI 53717
Tel.: (608) 827-7100
Web Site: http://www.navitus.com
Sales Range: $1-9.9 Million
Emp.: 110
Management Consulting Services
N.A.I.C.S.: 541611
Diana Gibson Pace *(Sr VP-Sls)*
David Fields *(Pres & CEO)*
Shayna Schulz *(COO)*
Ken Goodnight *(Chief Transformation & Digital Officer)*
Richard Stephens *(Vice Chm)*
Laura Kaiser *(Chm)*

Subsidiary (Domestic):

Lumicera Health Services LLC   (3)
310 Integrity Dr, Madison, WI 53717
Tel.: (855) 847-3553
Pharmaceutical Care Services
N.A.I.C.S.: 325412
Sharon Faust *(VP)*

SSM INDUSTRIES INC.
3401 Grand Ave, Pittsburgh, PA 15225-2225
Tel.: (412) 777-5100   PA
Web Site: http://www.ssmi.biz
Year Founded: 1989
Sales Range: $10-24.9 Million
Emp.: 280
Plumbing, Heating & Air-Conditioning
N.A.I.C.S.: 332312
Tom Szymczak *(Owner & Pres)*
Larry Gorman *(Owner, Treas & Sec)*
Gary Mihlfried *(Mgr-Ops)*
Bob Birch *(Superintendent)*
Jay Davis *(Mgr-Ops)*
Ken Lintelman *(Mgr-Ops)*
Ron Schnell *(Mgr-Ops)*
Mark Saucier *(Mgr-Power Div)*
Leo Monaghan *(Owner & Pres)*

SSMB PACIFIC HOLDING COMPANY, INC.
1755 Adams Ave, San Leandro, CA 94577
Tel.: (510) 836-6100   CA
Web Site: http://www.norcalkw.com
Year Founded: 1999
Sales Range: $50-74.9 Million
Emp.: 60
Holding Company
N.A.I.C.S.: 551112
Harry Mamizuka *(Pres)*
Jill Pringle *(Mgr-Credit)*
Alex Turan *(Controller)*

Subsidiaries:

NorCal Kenworth - Anderson   (1)
20769 Industry Rd, Anderson, CA 96007
Tel.: (530) 222-1212
Web Site: http://www.norcalkw.com
Sales Range: $10-24.9 Million
Emp.: 30
Automobile & Other Motor Vehicle Sales & Service
N.A.I.C.S.: 423110
Tom Bertolino *(Gen Mgr)*

NorCal Kenworth - Sacramento   (1)
707 Display Way, Sacramento, CA 95838
Tel.: (916) 371-3372
Web Site: http://www.norcalw.com
Sales Range: $10-24.9 Million
Emp.: 30
Heavy & Medium Duty Truck Dealership
N.A.I.C.S.: 423110
Tom Bertolino *(Owner)*

NorCal Kenworth - San Leandro   (1)
1755 Adams Ave, San Leandro, CA 94577
Tel.: (510) 836-6100
Web Site: http://www.bayareakw.com
Sales Range: $10-24.9 Million
Emp.: 54
Heavy Duty Truck Sales Service & Spares
N.A.I.C.S.: 423110
Harry Mamizuka *(Pres)*
Larry Orosco *(Mgr-Parts)*

SSOE GROUP
1001 Madison Ave, Toledo, OH 43604
Tel.: (419) 255-3830
Web Site: http://www.ssoe.com
Year Founded: 1948
Sales Range: $75-99.9 Million
Emp.: 1,000
Architectural, Engineering, Environmental Analyses & Property Survey Services
N.A.I.C.S.: 541310
James Jaros *(CFO & Sr VP)*

Subsidiaries:

Integrated Engineering Services   (1)
70 Saratoga Ave 200, Santa Clara, CA 95051
Tel.: (408) 321-0810
Web Site: http://www.intengr.com
Rev: $1,896,000
Emp.: 12
Engineeering Services
N.A.I.C.S.: 541330
Jeffery Tarter *(Co-Founder & Principal)*
Rizik Michael *(Co-Founder & Principal)*

Stevens & Wilkinson, Inc.   (1)
100 Peachtree St NW Ste 2500, Atlanta, GA 30303
Tel.: (404) 522-8888
Web Site: http://www.stevens-wilkinson.com
Holding Company; Architectural, Engineering & Interior Design Services
N.A.I.C.S.: 551112
Ronald V. Stang *(Chm & Principal)*
T. Ashby Gressette *(Pres, Principal & Dir-Architecture)*
Guido Alvarez *(Sr Engr-Electrical)*
Shayla Merritt *(Sr Coord-Mktg)*
Judy Laval *(Dir-Office Svcs)*
Vincent Lafitte *(Mgr-HR)*
Barry Kahler *(Sr Project Mgr-3D Revit Production)*
Janice Wittschiebe *(Principal & VP)*
Aaron Noyes *(Sr Engr-Structural)*
Richard Boler *(Controller & Asst VP)*

Subsidiary (Domestic):

Stevens & Wilkinson GA, Inc.   (2)
100 Peachtree St NW Ste 2500, Atlanta, GA 30303   (100%)
Tel.: (404) 522-8888
Web Site: http://www.stevens-wilkinson.com
Architectural, Engineering & Interior Design Services
N.A.I.C.S.: 541310
Bill Clark *(Pres)*
Ken Daenecke *(Principal, Sr VP & Dir-Electrical Engrg)*
John Abbott *(Principal & VP)*
Kirk Marchisen *(Principal & VP)*
Steve Faulk *(VP & Engr-Plumbing & Fire Protection)*
Andrea King *(Coord-Mktg)*
Jae Chong *(VP & Architect)*
Judy Laval *(Dir-Office Svcs)*
Janice Wittschiebe *(Sr VP)*
Keith Branham *(Principal, Sr VP & Dir-Engrg)*
Lee Morris *(Exec VP)*
Patrick Laster *(Designer-Mechanical)*
Richard Boler *(Assoc VP & Controller)*
Shayla Merritt *(Coord-Mktg)*

Stevens & Wilkinson SC, Inc.   (2)
1501 Main St Ste 730, Columbia, SC 29201
Tel.: (803) 765-0320
Web Site: http://www.stevens-wilkinson.com
Architectural, Engineering & Interior Design Services
N.A.I.C.S.: 541310
Bobby Lyles *(Chm & Principal)*
Bill Fleming *(VP & Architect)*
Keith Branham *(Principal, Sr VP & Dir-Engrg)*
Richard Boler *(Controller & Assoc VP)*
Vincent Lafitte *(Mgr-HR)*
Shayla Merritt *(Assoc Mgr-Mktg & Comm)*

SSP FITTINGS CORP.
8250 Boyle Pkwy, Twinsburg, OH 44087-2200
Tel.: (330) 425-4250
Web Site: http://www.my-ssp-usa.com
Year Founded: 1926
Sales Range: $10-24.9 Million
Emp.: 150
Metal Valve & Pipe Fitting Mfr
N.A.I.C.S.: 332919
Jeffrey E. King *(CEO)*
David B. King *(COO)*

SSP INDUSTRIAL GROUP, INC.
1290 New Cut Rd, Spartanburg, SC 29303
Tel.: (864) 699-3200   NV
Web Site: http://www.ssprod.com
Year Founded: 1997
Sales Range: $25-49.9 Million
Emp.: 600
Automotive Stamping Mfr
N.A.I.C.S.: 336370
Bryan Bickimer *(Pres)*
Mark Hamlin Jr. *(Owner & Pres-Reserve Grp)*

Subsidiaries:

Sharpsville Container Corporation   (1)
600 Main St, Sharpsville, PA 16150-2058
Tel.: (724) 962-1100
Web Site: http://www.sharpsvillecontainer.com
Sales Range: $10-24.9 Million
Emp.: 47
Fabricated Plate Work
N.A.I.C.S.: 332420

SSS DEVELOPMENT INC.
1317 W Washington, Pittsfield, IL 62363
Tel.: (217) 285-5558
Web Site: http://www.jiffistop.com
Sales Range: $10-24.9 Million
Emp.: 150
Convenience Store
N.A.I.C.S.: 445131
C. Keith Smith *(Pres)*
David Smith *(VP)*
John Schoenherr *(Treas & Sec)*
Richard Sun *(Executives)*

SST ENERGY CORPORATION

SST Energy Corporation—(Continued)

SST ENERGY CORPORATION
8901 W Yellowstone Hwy, Casper, WY 82604
Tel.: (307) 235-3529
Web Site: http://www.sstenergy.com
Rev.: $23,970,506
Emp.: 20
Drilling Oil & Gas Wells
N.A.I.C.S.: 213111
Paul Miao *(Pres)*
Jeff Wilmetti *(Mgr-Pur)*
Nancy Shogren *(Supvr-AR & AP)*

SSW PARTNERS LP
152 W 57th St 36th Fl, New York, NY 10019
Web Site: https://sswpartners.com
Year Founded: 2021
Emp.: 100
Investment Services
N.A.I.C.S.: 523999
Eric Stuart Schwartz *(Partner)*

Subsidiaries:

Veoneer, Inc.   (1)
Box 13089, SE-103 02, Stockholm, Sweden
Tel.: (46) 852776281
Web Site: https://www.veoneer.com
Rev.: $1,657,000,000
Assets: $1,750,000,000
Liabilities: $897,000,000
Net Worth: $853,000,000
Earnings: ($385,000,000)
Emp.: 7,099
Fiscal Year-end: 12/31/2021
Automotive Safety Electronic Product Mfr & Distr
N.A.I.C.S.: 334419
Lars Sjobring *(Gen Counsel, Sec & Exec VP-Legal Affairs)*
Thomas Jonsson *(Exec VP-Comm & IR)*
Art Blanchford *(Exec VP-Sls & Bus Dev)*
Steve Rode *(Exec VP-Ops)*
Ray Pekar *(CFO & Exec VP-Fin)*
Per Skytt *(Exec VP-Technical Competence Centers)*
Mikael Landberg *(Exec VP-HR)*
Christer Lundstrom *(Exec VP-Quality)*
Matthias Bieler *(Exec VP-Bus Unit-Europe)*
Christine Rankin *(Principal Acctg Officer & Sr VP-Corp Control)*
Jacob Svanberg *(CEO)*
Eric Swanson *(Gen Counsel, Sec & Exec VP-Legal Affairs)*
Scott Brawner *(Sr VP-Customer Areas)*
Hakan Soderlund *(Sr VP-Sourcing)*
Stuart Klapper *(Sr VP-Thermal Product Area)*
Chris Van Dan Elzen *(Exec VP-Product Area Radar)*
Christoph Schmickler *(Exec VP-ADAS ECU & Integration Product Area)*
Steven Jenkins *(CTO & Exec VP-Product Area Active Safety Integration)*

ST. CLAIR DARDEN HEALTH SYSTEM
20531 Darden Rd, South Bend, IN 46637
Tel.: (574) 272-0100   IN
Web Site: http://www.healthwin.org
Year Founded: 1994
Sales Range: $10-24.9 Million
Emp.: 297
Health Care Srvices
N.A.I.C.S.: 622110
Kristin Everett *(Dir-Admissions & Mktg)*
Jeannine Groot *(Dir-HR)*
Debra Kimbrell *(Chief Clinical Officer)*
Larry Waltz *(Dir-Rehabilitation Svcs)*

ST. HENRY TILE CO. INC.
281 W Washington St, Saint Henry, OH 45883
Tel.: (419) 678-4168
Web Site: http://www.sthenrytileco.com
Sales Range: $10-24.9 Million
Emp.: 90
Ready Mixed Concrete
N.A.I.C.S.: 327320
Robert Homan *(Pres)*
Mike Homan *(Mgr-Wayne Builders Supply)*

ST. JOHN OF GOD RETIREMENT AND CARE CENTER
2468 S St Andrews Pl, Los Angeles, CA 90018
Tel.: (323) 731-0641   CA
Web Site: http://www.stjohnofgodseniors.org
Year Founded: 1942
Sales Range: $10-24.9 Million
Emp.: 411
Retirement Care Services
N.A.I.C.S.: 623311
Santiago Lopez *(Pres & CEO)*
Stephen de la Rosa *(Chm)*

ST. JOSEPH'S REHABILITATION & RESIDENCE
1133 Washington Ave, Portland, ME 04103
Tel.: (207) 797-0600   ME
Year Founded: 1972
Sales Range: $10-24.9 Million
Emp.: 266
Elder Care Services
N.A.I.C.S.: 623312
Yvette Ramirez *(Mgr-Fiscal Svcs)*

ST. LOUIS BOILER SUPPLY, INC.
617 Hanley Industrial Ct, Saint Louis, MO 63144
Tel.: (314) 962-9242
Web Site: http://www.stlboiler.com
Year Founded: 1989
Sales Range: $10-24.9 Million
Emp.: 16
Plumbing & Heating Equipment Whslr
N.A.I.C.S.: 423720
Anne Eisele *(Office Mgr)*

ST. LOUIS MUNICIPAL FINANCE CORPORATION
1200 Market St 212 City Hall, Saint Louis, MO 63103   MO
Year Founded: 1991
Sales Range: $10-24.9 Million
Financial Support Services
N.A.I.C.S.: 541611
Candice T. Gordon *(Pres)*

ST. LOUIS RIVERPORT HOLDING COMPANY, INC.
7501 Wisconsin Ave Ste 200, Bethesda, MD 20814
Tel.: (240) 482-2900   MD
Year Founded: 1995
Sales Range: $10-24.9 Million
Real Estate Services
N.A.I.C.S.: 531390
H. James Darcey *(Treas)*

ST. NICHOLAS HUMAN SUPPORT CORPORATION
2 Kingsland Ave 2nd Fl, Brooklyn, NY 11211
Tel.: (718) 388-5454   NY
Year Founded: 1979
Sales Range: $125-149.9 Million
Emp.: 1,381
Elder Care Services
N.A.I.C.S.: 624120
Mary Ciorciari McAuliff *(Dir-Home Care)*
Michael Rochford *(Exec Dir)*
Cindy Ross *(Dir-Fin)*

ST. PAPER, LLC
106 E Central Ave, Oconto Falls, WI 54154
Tel.: (920) 846-3411
Web Site: http://www.stpaperllc.com
Sales Range: $1-9.9 Million
Emp.: 29
Tissue, Napkin & Paper Towel Mfr
N.A.I.C.S.: 322291
Bill Culek *(VP & Gen Mgr)*

ST. ALEXIUS MEDICAL CENTER
900 E Broadway Ave, Bismarck, ND 58501
Tel.: (701) 530-7000   ND
Web Site: http://www.st.alexius.org
Year Founded: 1905
Sales Range: $250-299.9 Million
Emp.: 2,646
Health Care Services
N.A.I.C.S.: 622110
Shiraz Hyder *(VP-Medical Affairs)*

ST. ANDREWS COUNTRY CLUB, INC.
17557 Claridge Oval W, Boca Raton, FL 33496
Tel.: (561) 451-4900   FL
Web Site: http://www.standrewscc.com
Year Founded: 1982
Sales Range: $10-24.9 Million
Country Club
N.A.I.C.S.: 713910
Paul Clivio *(Dir-Golf)*
Patricia Sorensen *(CFO)*
Aaron Krickstein *(Dir-Tennis)*
Alice Newman Friedman *(Sec & Exec VP)*
Joseph Wasch *(Exec VP)*
Michael Goldman *(Treas & VP)*
Ron Gallatin *(Pres)*
Rick Dente *(COO & Gen Mgr)*

ST. ANN'S HOME, INC.
100A Haverhill St, Methuen, MA 01844
Tel.: (978) 682-5276   MA
Web Site: http://www.st.annshome.org
Year Founded: 1955
Sales Range: $10-24.9 Million
Emp.: 360
Residential Program Services
N.A.I.C.S.: 623220
Beth Liao *(Dir-Medical)*
J. Bryan Hehir *(Treas)*
John Rice *(Dir-Dev)*

ST. ANNE'S CREDIT UNION
286 Oliver St, Fall River, MA 02724-2998
Tel.: (508) 324-7300   MA
Web Site: http://www.stannes.com
Year Founded: 1935
Sales Range: $25-49.9 Million
Emp.: 223
Credit Union Operator
N.A.I.C.S.: 522130
Richard N. Beaulieu *(VP-Ops)*
Michelle Marcos *(VP-HR)*
Eileen M. Danahey *(Pres & CEO)*
Peter Panaggio *(CFO)*
Karen Skinner *(VP-Compliance & Deposit Ops)*
Robin Levesque *(VP-Branch Admin)*
Richard Kane *(VP-Comml Risk)*
Luisa Rochester *(VP-Residential Lending)*
William Bouchard *(Chm)*
John Ledwidge *(Vice Chm)*
Carlos A. DaCunha *(Chief Lending Officer & Sr VP)*

ST. ANNE'S MATERNITY HOME
155 N Occidental Blvd, Los Angeles, CA 90026
Tel.: (213) 381-2931   CA
Web Site: http://www.stannes.org
Year Founded: 1908
Sales Range: $10-24.9 Million
Maternity Healthcare Services
N.A.I.C.S.: 622110
Joe Hou *(Admin)*
Brian W. Matthews *(Treas)*
Veronica Arteaga *(VP-Housing Programs)*
Carlos Tobar *(Dir-Quality Assurance)*
Claire Veroda *(Dir-Comm & Mktg)*
Maryam Sesay *(Dir-Residential Treatment Program)*
Correnda Perkins *(VP-Community-Based Programs)*

ST. ANNE'S RETIREMENT COMMUNITY, INC.
3952 Columbia Ave, Columbia, PA 17512-1715
Tel.: (717) 285-5443   PA
Web Site: http://www.stannesretirementcommunity.com
Year Founded: 1977
Sales Range: $10-24.9 Million
Emp.: 344
Retirement Community Operator
N.A.I.C.S.: 623311
Michele J. Bard *(CFO)*
Mary Turnbaugh *(Pres)*
Donald Nikolaus *(Sec)*
James Kendig *(Treas)*
Jon Farrell *(Chm)*
Kevin M. Kraft Sr. *(Vice Chm)*

ST. ANTHONY REGIONAL HOSPITAL & NURSING HOME
311 S Clark St, Carroll, IA 51401
Tel.: (712) 792-3581   IA
Web Site: http://www.stanthonyhospital.org
Year Founded: 1905
Sales Range: $50-74.9 Million
Emp.: 739
Health Care Srvices
N.A.I.C.S.: 622110
John Munson *(CFO)*
Gary P. Riedmann *(Pres & CEO)*
Edward H. Smith Jr. *(VP)*

ST. ANTHONY'S MEDICAL CENTER
10010 Kennerly Rd, Saint Louis, MO 63128
Tel.: (314) 525-1000   MO
Web Site: http://www.stanthonysmedcenter.com
Year Founded: 1971
Sales Range: $400-449.9 Million
Emp.: 5,070
Health Care Srvices
N.A.I.C.S.: 622110
Carol Ellis *(VP-Nursing)*
Russ Schroeder *(Chief Nursing Officer)*
Laura Frame *(VP-Risk Mgmt)*
Kadi Montez *(VP-Information Svcs)*

ST. BARNABAS INC.
5850 Meridian Rd, Gibsonia, PA 15044
Tel.: (724) 443-0700
Web Site: http://www.stbarnabashealthsystem.com
Year Founded: 1900
Sales Range: $50-74.9 Million
Emp.: 600
Health Care Community
N.A.I.C.S.: 531110
William V. Day *(Pres)*
Douglas W. Day *(Sr VP)*
Karen Tabacchi *(Pres-Clinical Svcs)*

ST. BARTH PROPERTIES, INC.
693 E Central St Ste 201, Franklin, MA 02038
Tel.: (508) 528-7727
Web Site: http://www.stbarth.com
Year Founded: 1989
Sales Range: $1-9.9 Million
Emp.: 8
Real Estate Services
N.A.I.C.S.: 531390
Tom Smyth (VP)
Kathryn Schlitzer (Dir-Client Svcs)

ST. BERNARDS HEALTHCARE, INC.
225 E Jackson, Jonesboro, AR 72401
Tel.: (870) 207-4100
Web Site: http://www.stbernards.info
Year Founded: 1997
Sales Range: $10-24.9 Million
Emp.: 148
Health Care Srvices
N.A.I.C.S.: 622110
Chris Barber (Pres & CEO)
Lillian Marie Reiter (Chm)
Dana Housley (Coord-Volunteer)
Kelli Merryman (Office Mgr)
John Lieblong (VP-Physician Svcs)
Leo Baltz (Chm)
Marilyn M. Hummelstein (Pres)
Kila Owens (Mgr-Media Rels)

ST. CHARLES GLASS & GLAZING, INC.
166 Enterprise Dr, Wentzville, MO 63385-5571
Tel.: (636) 332-5339
Web Site: http://www.stcharlesglass.com
Sales Range: $10-24.9 Million
Emp.: 65
Glass & Glazing Work Services
N.A.I.C.S.: 238150
Daryn Weatherman (Owner)
Daryn Weathernman (Pres)

ST. CHRISTOPHER'S, INC.
71 S Broadway, Dobbs Ferry, NY 10522
Tel.: (914) 693-3030
Web Site: http://www.sc1881.org
Year Founded: 1885
Sales Range: $10-24.9 Million
Emp.: 409
Child & Family Care Services
N.A.I.C.S.: 623210
Horace Turnbull (COO)
Dara Caputo (Dir-Mental Health)

ST. CLAIR APPAREL, INC.
3975 William Richardson Dr, South Bend, IN 46628
Tel.: (574) 243-0591
Web Site: http://www.stclairapparel.com
Sales Range: $10-24.9 Million
Emp.: 15
Customized Promotional Apparel Designer & Retailer
N.A.I.C.S.: 315990
David St. Clair (VP)
Steve St. Clair (Pres & CEO)
Matthew St. Clair (Mgr-Ops)

ST. CLAIR DIE CASTING, LLC
225 St Clair Indus Pk, Saint Clair, MO 63077-3052
Tel.: (636) 629-2550
Web Site: http://www.stclairdiecasting.com
Year Founded: 1967
Sales Range: $10-24.9 Million
Emp.: 68
Nonferrous Foundries
N.A.I.C.S.: 331529

John Graves (Pres)
Tracy Cox (Mgr)
Jeff Van Dixhorn (VP-Ops)

ST. CLAIR FOODS
3100 Bellbrook Dr, Memphis, TN 38116
Tel.: (901) 396-8680
Web Site: http://www.stclair.com
Year Founded: 1976
Sales Range: $10-24.9 Million
Emp.: 125
Salad, Pasta & Sauce Mfr
N.A.I.C.S.: 311991
Brian Edmonds (VP-Ops)
Dennis Spence (Plant Mgr)
Angela Griffith (Acct Exec-Reg)
Kevin Vorderlandwehr (Acct Exec-Reg)
Oscar H. Edmonds III (Pres & CEO)

ST. CLAIR SERVICE CO.
1036 S Green Mount Rd, Belleville, IL 62220
Tel.: (618) 233-1248
Web Site: http://www.stclairfs.com
Sales Range: $25-49.9 Million
Emp.: 50
Farm Supplies
N.A.I.C.S.: 424910
Jim Milleville (Gen Mgr)
David Maurer (Sec)

ST. CLAIRE GROUP
716 Adams St Ste C, Carmel, IN 46032
Tel.: (317) 816-8810
Year Founded: 1992
Rev.: $18,000,000
Emp.: 11
N.A.I.C.S.: 541810
Bob St. Claire (Pres)
Rhonda Hibbert (Mgr-Bus)
Ken Honeywell (Creative Dir)
Curt Chuvalas (Creative Dir)
Ken Haupt (Sr VP)

ST. CLAIRE PLASTICS CO.
30855 Teton Pl, Chesterfield, MI 48047
Tel.: (586) 598-9930
Web Site: http://www.scplastics.com
Sales Range: $10-24.9 Million
Emp.: 160
Plastic Injection Molding Services
N.A.I.C.S.: 326199
Connie Plantinga (Controller)
Will Lianos (CEO)
Tony Plantia (VP)

ST. CLOUD CAPITAL, LLC
10866 Wilshire Blvd Ste 1450, Los Angeles, CA 90024
Tel.: (310) 475-2700
Web Site: http://www.stcloudcapital.com
Year Founded: 2001
Privater Equity Firm
N.A.I.C.S.: 523999
Benjamin Hom (Mng Partner)
Kacy Rozelle (Mng Partner)
Robert Lautz (Mng Partner)
Jeremy May (Principal)
Matt Smith (VP)
Brian Chow (VP)
James Hays (CFO & Chief Compliance Officer)

ST. CLOUD TOYOTA INC.
418 2nd St S, Waite Park, MN 56387
Tel.: (320) 253-2581
Web Site: http://www.stcloudtoyota.com
Sales Range: $50-74.9 Million
Emp.: 40
Automobiles, New & Used

N.A.I.C.S.: 441110
Mike J. Dockendorf (Pres)
Jack Dockendorf (VP)

ST. CLOUD TRUCK SALES INC.
701 15th Ave SE, Saint Cloud, MN 56304
Tel.: (320) 251-0931
Web Site: http://www.stcloudtruck.com
Rev.: $28,656,114
Emp.: 94
Trucks, Commercial
N.A.I.C.S.: 423110
Pat Miller (CFO)
Duane Wittowski (Mgr-Sls)

ST. CROIX PRESS, INC.
1185 S Knowles Ave, New Richmond, WI 54017-1739
Tel.: (715) 246-5811
Web Site: http://www.stcroixpress.com
Year Founded: 1971
Sales Range: $10-24.9 Million
Emp.: 85
Periodical Printing
N.A.I.C.S.: 323111
Edward A. Monette (Founder & Pres)
Mike Monette (VP & Gen Mgr)

ST. CROIX TREE SERVICE, INC.
675 Grupe St, Roberts, WI 54023
Tel.: (715) 749-3475
Web Site: http://www.stcroixtreeservice.com
Tree Care & Removal Services
N.A.I.C.S.: 561730
Dennis Ullom (Pres & CEO)

ST. EDWARD HOME
3131 Smith Rd, Fairlawn, OH 44333
Tel.: (330) 666-1183
Web Site: http://www.vased.org
Year Founded: 1970
Sales Range: $10-24.9 Million
Emp.: 284
Elder Care Services
N.A.I.C.S.: 623312
John Hennelly (Pres & CEO)
Kathleen Franey (Dir-Health Svcs)
Elizabeth Weinhold (CFO & VP-Fin)

ST. GEORGE WAREHOUSE TRUCKING OF CALIFORNIA
1650 S Central Ave, Compton, CA 90220
Tel.: (310) 764-4395
Web Site: http://www.stgusa.com
Sales Range: $25-49.9 Million
Emp.: 197
General Warehousing Services
N.A.I.C.S.: 493110
Anthony Fortunato (Founder & CEO)

Subsidiaries:

St. George Warehouse Trucking of Texas Inc. (1)
4035 Underwood Rd ste 200, Pasadena, TX 77507
Tel.: (281) 474-5700
Web Site: http://www.stgusa.com
Rev.: $4,067,163
Emp.: 20
General Warehousing & Storage
N.A.I.C.S.: 493110
Dave Graglia (VP)

ST. GILES-THE TUSCANY HOTEL
120-130 E 39th St, New York, NY 10016
Tel.: (212) 686-1600

Web Site: http://www.tuscany.stgilesnewyork.com
Rev.: $10,800,000
Emp.: 142
Hotel
N.A.I.C.S.: 721110
Chris Swaim (Gen Mgr)

ST. JAMES INSURANCE GROUP, INC.
6675 Westwood Blvd Ste 360, Orlando, FL 32821
Tel.: (407) 248-1554
Web Site: http://www.stjamesinsurance.com
Year Founded: 1984
Insurance Program Management Services
N.A.I.C.S.: 524292
James McCahill (Chm)
Robert Lucas (Pres)
Edward Falzarano (CFO)
Dave Stricker (Exec VP)
Jonathan Mertz (VP & Dir-Mktg)

ST. JOE PETROLEUM CO.
2520 S 2nd St, Saint Joseph, MO 64503
Tel.: (816) 279-0770
Web Site: http://www.stjoepetroleum.com
Rev.: $23,000,000
Emp.: 45
Owner & Operator of Convenience Stores; Wholesaler & Retailer of Petroleum Products
N.A.I.C.S.: 445131
Ronald Backman Jr. (Pres)

ST. JOHN & PARTNERS
1301 Riverplace Blvd Ste 200, Jacksonville, FL 32207
Tel.: (904) 281-2500
Web Site: http://www.sjp.com
Year Founded: 1984
Rev.: $120,000,000
Emp.: 85
Advertising Services
N.A.I.C.S.: 541810
Dan St. John (Chm & CEO)
Shawn Parks (Assoc Dir-Media)
Shane Santiago (VP & Dir-Digital)
Melanie Brodsky (Asst Mgr-PR)
Josh Poag (Copywriter)

ST. JOHN HEALTH SYSTEM INC.
1923 S Utica Ave, Tulsa, OK 74104
Tel.: (918) 744-2345
Web Site: http://www.sjhealthsystem.com
Year Founded: 1926
Sales Range: $900-999.9 Million
Emp.: 7,500
Medical Devices
N.A.I.C.S.: 622110
Lex Anderson (CFO)
William Allred (Dir-Medical)
Cheena Pazzo (Dir-Community Rels)
David Pynn (CEO)
Bob Sullivan (Chm)

Subsidiaries:

Utica Services Inc. (1)
1923 S Utica Ave, Tulsa, OK 74104
Tel.: (918) 744-2965
Web Site: http://www.sjhealthsystem.com
Rev.: $14,100,000
Emp.: 250
Nonresidential Building Operators
N.A.I.C.S.: 531312

ST. JOHN HOLDINGS INC.
320 King Of Prussia Rd, Radnor, PA 19087-4440
Tel.: (610) 964-8702
Year Founded: 1985

ST. JOHN HOLDINGS INC.

St. John Holdings Inc.—(Continued)

Sales Range: $25-49.9 Million
Emp.: 4
Provider of Investment Services
N.A.I.C.S.: 523150
Michael Quigg (Pres & CEO)
John Greenebaum (Sr VP-Dev)

Subsidiaries:
Lake Oswego Holdings Inc. (1)
320 King Of Prussia Rd, Radnor, PA
19087-4440 (100%)
Tel.: (610) 964-8702
Provider of Loan Services
N.A.I.C.S.: 522310

Security Guard Inc. (1)
1142 E Chestnut Ave Ste A, Vineland, NJ
08360-5449
Tel.: (856) 691-5555
Web Site: http://www.tri-countysecuritynj.com
Sales Range: $25-49.9 Million
Provider of Detective & Armored Car Services
N.A.I.C.S.: 561612

ST. JOHN NISSAN 7198
5001 S Broadway, Englewood, CO 80113
Tel.: (303) 762-9922
Web Site:
http://www.larrymillernissan.com
Car Dealer
N.A.I.C.S.: 441110
Bill Byerly (Gen Mgr)

ST. JOSEPH COUNTY HIGHWAY DEPARTMENT
4141 Lathrop St, South Bend, IN 46628
Tel.: (574) 235-7800
Web Site:
http://www.stjosephcountyindiana.com
Rev.: $11,000,000
Emp.: 90
Highway, Street & Bridge Construction
N.A.I.C.S.: 237310
Andrew Hayes (Project Mgr)

ST. JOSEPH MANOR HEALTH CARE INC.
215 Thatcher St, Brockton, MA 02302
Tel.: (508) 583-5834 MA
Web Site: http://www.sjmbrockton.org
Year Founded: 1975
Sales Range: $10-24.9 Million
Emp.: 305
Health Care Srvices
N.A.I.C.S.: 622110
Aisha Bonny (Chm)
Paul Arenburg (Vice Chm)

ST. JOSEPH'S CENTER
2010 Adams Ave, Scranton, PA 18509
Tel.: (570) 342-8379 PA
Web Site:
http://www.stjosephcenter.org
Year Founded: 1927
Sales Range: $1-9.9 Million
Emp.: 758
Intellectual & Developmental Disability Assistance Services
N.A.I.C.S.: 623210
Kristine A. Holmes (Pres)
Patricia Tetreault (VP)
Maryalice Jacquinot (Exec Dir)
Joseph J. Corcoran (Sec)
Kimberly Abda-Santarsiero (Treas)

ST. JOSEPH'S/CANDLER
5353 Reynolds St, Savannah, GA 31405
Tel.: (912) 819-6000 GA
Web Site: http://www.sjchs.org
Year Founded: 1996
Sales Range: $10-24.9 Million
Health Care Srvices
N.A.I.C.S.: 622110
Paul P. Hinchey (Pres & CEO)
William E. Johnston (Chm)

ST. JOSEPH, INC.
4205 Carmel Mountain Dr, McKinney, TX 75070
Tel.: (469) 534-8088 CO
Web Site: http://www.stjosephinc.com
Year Founded: 1999
Recruitment Services
N.A.I.C.S.: 561311
Gerald McIlhargey (Pres & CEO)
Kenneth L. Johnson (Treas & Sec)
Donal Kent Ford (Pres & CEO)

ST. JUDE CHILDREN'S RESEARCH HOSPITAL
262 Danny Thomas Pl, Memphis, TN 38105-2729
Tel.: (901) 495-3300
Web Site: http://www.stjude.org
Sales Range: $75-99.9 Million
Emp.: 3,759
Pediatric Childrens Cancer Research
N.A.I.C.S.: 541720
George P. Shadroui (Chief Strategy Officer)
Dana Bottenfield (VP-HR)
Keith Perry (CIO)
Barry Whyte (VP-Comm & PR)
Carlos Rodriguez-Galindo (Dir-Outreach Program-Intl)
Pat Keel (CFO)
Danny Thomas (Founder)
Tangie Thomas (VP-Clinical Trials Ops)
Denise Roe (VP-Clinical Research Regulatory & Quality Mgmt)
Leena Munjal (Chief Strategy Officer)
Richard C. Shadyac Jr. (Pres & CEO)
Dave Lew (Sr VP-Strategic Mktg)
Albert Crews (VP-New Ventures)
Jennifer Hart (VP-Direct Mktg)

ST. LANDRY HOMESTEAD FEDERAL SAVINGS BANK
235 N Court St, Opelousas, LA 70570
Tel.: (337) 948-3033
Web Site:
http://www.stlandryhomestead.com
Sales Range: $250-299.9 Million
Emp.: 50
Banking Commercial Services
N.A.I.C.S.: 522110
Joe Zanco (Pres & CEO)
Jacques L. J. Bourque (CFO)
Jutta A. Codori (Sr Administrative Officer)

ST. LAWRENCE HOMES INC.
7200 Falls of Neuse Rd, Raleigh, NC 27615-5384
Tel.: (919) 676-8980 NC
Year Founded: 1989
Sales Range: $10-24.9 Million
Emp.: 15
Single-Family Housing Construction
N.A.I.C.S.: 236115
Robert Ohmann (Pres)
Larry Holt (VP-Remodeling)
Marybeth Sewell (Controller)
Debbie Conaway (Mgr-Resource)

ST. LAWRENCE-LEWIS BOCES
40 W Main St, Canton, NY 13617-3504
Tel.: (315) 386-4504 NY
Web Site: http://www.sllboces.org
Year Founded: 1952

Sales Range: $25-49.9 Million
Emp.: 600
Vocational School
N.A.I.C.S.: 611519
Rachelle Romoda (Supvr-Instructional Res)
Patricia Fisher (Supvr-Instructional Tech & Model Schools)
Susan Bouchey (Supvr-Special Education)
Lisa McKeel (Supvr-Instructional Res)

ST. LOUIS ARC, INC.
1177 N Warson Rd, Saint Louis, MO 63132
Tel.: (314) 569-2211 MO
Web Site: http://www.slarc.org
Year Founded: 1956
Sales Range: $10-24.9 Million
Emp.: 640
Developmental Disability Assistance Services
N.A.I.C.S.: 623210
Scott Monette (Chm)
Shaughnessy H. Daniels (VP-Community Support)
Jennifer Adams (Dir-Dev)
Andrea Bringardner (Mgr-Special Events)
Kathleen Schue (Dir-Comm & PR)
Tim Bradbury (VP-Comprehensive Svcs)
John Taylor (VP-Advancement)
Kathy Tisone (CFO & VP-Ops)

ST. LOUIS AREA FOODBANK, INC.
70 Corporate Woods Dr, Bridgeton, MO 63044
Tel.: (314) 292-6262 MO
Web Site: http://www.stlfoodbank.org
Year Founded: 1980
Sales Range: $50-74.9 Million
Emp.: 53
Community Food Services
N.A.I.C.S.: 624210
David Froeckmann (Mgr-Logistics)
Frank Finnegan (Pres & CEO)
Ryan Farmer (Dir-Comm)
Matt Dace (Sr VP)
Verletta Cole (VP-Dev)
Ben Spirk (VP-Fin)
Scott Frick (Chm)
John Long (Sec)
Mike Pugh (Vice Chm)
Lenora Gooden (VP-Product Sourcing)
Tim Reeves (Vice Chm)

ST. LOUIS BRIDGE CONSTRUCTION CO.
655 Landmark Dr, Arnold, MO 63010
Tel.: (636) 296-3300
Web Site: http://www.stlbridge.com
Year Founded: 1972
Bridge Construction
N.A.I.C.S.: 237310
Janet Webb (Sr VP)
William Johnson (Pres)

ST. LOUIS METRO ELECTRIC SUPPLY
6801 Hoffman Ave, Saint Louis, MO 63139
Tel.: (314) 645-5656
Web Site:
http://www.metrolightingcenters.com
Sales Range: $10-24.9 Million
Emp.: 150
Distr Of Electrical Supplies & Lighting
N.A.I.C.S.: 423610
William A. Frisella (Pres)
Jerry Salisbury (Controller)
Matt Gagnepain (Gen Mgr)

ST. LOUIS PARKING COMPANY INC.
505 N 7th Firststar Ste 2405, Saint Louis, MO 63101
Tel.: (314) 241-7777
Web Site:
http://www.stlouisparking.com
Sales Range: $10-24.9 Million
Emp.: 15
Garage & Parking Lot Operator
N.A.I.C.S.: 812930
Jack E. Pohrer (Founder)
Karen Barton (Dir-Community Dev)
John Stark (Dir-Richfield Community Dev)
Jacqueline Larson (Mgr-Comm)

ST. LOUIS PIPE & SUPPLY, INC.
17740 Edison Ave, Chesterfield, MO 63005
Tel.: (636) 391-2500
Web Site:
http://www.stlpipesupply.com
Year Founded: 1987
Sales Range: $10-24.9 Million
Emp.: 9
Metal Service Whslr
N.A.I.C.S.: 423510
Gary Walshauser (Pres & CEO)
Tim Walshauser (VP)
Morgan Kuhn (Branch Mgr-Denver)

ST. LOUIS TELECOMMUNICATIONS
4940 Delmar Blvd, Saint Louis, MO 63108
Tel.: (314) 361-4331
Rev.: $10,000,000
Cable & Other Pay Television Services
N.A.I.C.S.: 516210

ST. LUCIE BATTERY & TIRE INC.
5500 Orange Ave, Fort Pierce, FL 34947
Tel.: (772) 461-1746
Web Site: http://www.slbt.com
Year Founded: 1970
Sales Range: $25-49.9 Million
Emp.: 100
Sales & Services of Tires & Batteries
N.A.I.C.S.: 423120
Joseph G. Miller (Pres)

ST. LUKE'S CATARACT & LASER INSTITUTE
43309 US Hwy 19 N, Tarpon Springs, FL 34689
Tel.: (727) 938-2020
Web Site: http://www.stlukeseye.com
Year Founded: 1997
Sales Range: $10-24.9 Million
Emp.: 280
Surgical Centers
N.A.I.C.S.: 622110
James Gills (Founder)
Kim Newby (Dir-Bus Svcs)
Linda Austin (Mgr-HR)
Jon Nedry (Dir-Mktg)

ST. LUKE'S FREE MEDICAL CLINIC
162 N Dean St, Spartanburg, SC 29302
Tel.: (864) 542-2273 SC
Web Site: http://www.slfmc.org
Year Founded: 1992
Sales Range: $10-24.9 Million
Emp.: 17
Healtcare Services
N.A.I.C.S.: 622110
Becky Hoover (Mgr-Clinical Ops)
Daniel McKinney (Treas)

George Bass *(Dir-Medical)*
Jada McAbee *(Chm)*
Mary Jane Jennings *(Sec)*

ST. LUKE'S HEALTH NETWORK, INC.
801 Ostrum St, Bethlehem, PA 18015
Tel.: (484) 526-4000   PA
Web Site: http://www.slhn.org
Year Founded: 1872
Non-Profit Regional Hospital & Healthcare Organization
N.A.I.C.S.: 813920
Samuel Kennedy *(Dir-Corp Comm)*

Subsidiaries:

St. Luke's Physician Group, Inc.   (1)
801 Ostrum St, Bethlehem, PA 18015
Tel.: (866) 785-8537
Web Site: http://www.slhn.org
Health Care Services
N.A.I.C.S.: 621999
Michael Owsinski *(Dir-Reg)*

Subsidiary (Domestic):

Dublin Internal Medicine PC   (2)
161 N Main St, Dublin, PA 18917-2107
Tel.: (267) 985-5090
Web Site: http://www.dublininternal.com
All Other Miscellaneous Ambulatory Health Care Services
N.A.I.C.S.: 621999
Beth Humphreys *(Mgr)*

ST. LUKE'S HOSPITAL
232 S Woods Mill Rd, Chesterfield, MO 63017
Tel.: (314) 434-1500
Web Site: http://www.stlukes-stl.com
Year Founded: 1866
General Medical & Surgical Hospital
N.A.I.C.S.: 622110
Scott H. Johnson *(CFO & Sr VP)*
Jon Bettale *(VP-Surgical & Ambulatory Svcs)*
Marth Fleischmann *(VP-Fin)*
Jan Hess *(VP-Pro & Admin Svcs)*
Ronald Leidenfrost *(Chm-Heart & Vascular Institute)*
Sharon Mertzlufft *(VP/Exec Dir-Dev)*
Don Miller *(VP-Facility & Support Svcs)*
Janette Taaffe *(VP-HR)*
Diane Ray *(COO, Chief Nursing Officer & Sr VP-Network)*
Gary Olson *(Interim Pres & Interim CEO)*
David Loving *(Pres)*

Subsidiaries:

St. Luke's Des Peres Hospital   (1)
2345 Dougherty Ferry Rd, Saint Louis, MO 63122
Tel.: (314) 966-9100
Web Site: http://www.stlukes-stl.com
General Hospital Services
N.A.I.C.S.: 622110

ST. MARGARET'S AT MERCY
3525 Bienville St, New Orleans, LA 70119
Tel.: (504) 279-6414   LA
Web Site:
http://www.stmargaretsno.org
Year Founded: 1931
Sales Range: $10-24.9 Million
Emp.: 258
Elder Care Services
N.A.I.C.S.: 623312
Alec Lundeberg *(COO)*
Michael Gilman *(Dir-Dev)*
Larry Stansberry *(CEO)*
Lori Jefferson *(Chief Clinical Officer)*
Kiwana Keller *(Dir-Activities)*
Angela Jackson *(Dir-Nursing)*

ST. MARY'S BANK
200 McGregor St, Manchester, NH 03102
Tel.: (603) 669-4600   NH
Web Site:
http://www.stmarysbank.com
Year Founded: 1908
Sales Range: $25-49.9 Million
Emp.: 239
Credit Union Operator
N.A.I.C.S.: 522130
Judi Window *(Coord-Community Outreach)*
Michael Beck *(VP-Wealth Mgmt-Fin Svcs Program-Credit Union)*
Jack Cleary *(VP & Dir-IT)*
Ronald H. Covey Jr. *(CEO)*

ST. MARY'S CREDIT UNION
46 Lizotte Dr, Marlborough, MA 01752
Tel.: (508) 490-8000   MA
Web Site: http://www.stmaryscu.org
Year Founded: 1913
Sales Range: $10-24.9 Million
Financial Support Services
N.A.I.C.S.: 522130
Thomas F. Seymour *(Exec VP-Lending)*
Anthony J. Battista *(VP-Mktg)*
James Petkewich *(Sr VP-Retail Svcs)*
Gerard P. Richer *(Chm)*
Larissa C. Thurston *(CFO & COO)*
Nabil M. Farooq *(Sr VP & Sr Comml Lending Officer)*
Christopher J. Mancini *(Sr VP-Tech)*
Sherrie L. LeBoeuf *(Sr VP-HR)*
Sarah A. Day *(VP)*
Armand A. Fernandez *(VP)*
Christine G. Monteiro *(VP & Mgr-Market)*

ST. MARY'S HEALTH CARE SYSTEM
1230 Baxter St, Athens, GA 30606-3791
Tel.: (706) 389-3000   GA
Web Site:
http://www.stmarysathens.org
Year Founded: 1938
Sales Range: $75-99.9 Million
Health Care Srvices
N.A.I.C.S.: 622110
Terri Sartain *(Mgr-Medical Staff Svcs)*
Bob Snipes *(Chm)*
Don McKenna *(Pres & CEO)*
Jean Chin *(Vice Chm)*
Titus Gambrell *(Chief Nursing Officer & VP)*

ST. MARY'S/WESTSIDE FOOD BANK ALLIANCE
2831 N 31st Ave, Phoenix, AZ 85009
Tel.: (602) 242-3663
Web Site:
http://www.firstfoodbank.org
Sales Range: $50-74.9 Million
Emp.: 175
Special Warehousing & Storage Services
N.A.I.C.S.: 493190
John Demetra *(Chm)*
Marc Isaacs *(Vice Chm)*
Susan Wain *(Sec)*
Nicki Schillhahn-Amos *(Treas)*
Tom Kertis *(Pres & CEO)*
Sarah Stuckey *(CFO)*

ST. MORITZ SECURITY SERVICES, INC.
4600 Clairton Blvd, Pittsburgh, PA 15236
Tel.: (412) 885-3144
Web Site: http://www.smssi.com
Year Founded: 1982
Sales Range: $10-24.9 Million
Security Guard Services
N.A.I.C.S.: 561612
Philip St. Moritz *(Owner & CEO)*
Brian Fiscus *(CFO)*
Mark Sheratsky *(VP)*
Kevin Smith *(Pres)*
Bob Buckley *(VP-Loss Prevention & Escort Svcs)*
Nick Boelens *(VP-Admin)*

ST. PATRICK CENTER
800 N Tucker Blvd, Saint Louis, MO 63101
Tel.: (314) 802-0700   MO
Web Site:
http://www.stpatrickcenter.org
Year Founded: 1982
Sales Range: $10-24.9 Million
Emp.: 160
Community Housing Services
N.A.I.C.S.: 624229
Bryan Graiff *(Treas)*
Patrick M. Quinn *(Pres)*
Laurie Phillips *(CEO)*

ST. PATRICK'S MANOR SKILLED NURSING AND SHORT TERM REHABILITATION CENTER
863 Central St, Framingham, MA 01701
Tel.: (508) 879-8000   MA
Web Site:
http://www.stpatricksmanor.org
Year Founded: 1953
Sales Range: $25-49.9 Million
Emp.: 485
Rehabilitation & Nursing Care Services
N.A.I.C.S.: 623110
Maureen McDonough *(Treas)*
David Hines *(CFO)*
Jodi Oiumette *(Sec)*
Suzanne Wasylak *(Dir-Nurses)*

ST. PATRICK'S RESIDENCE
1400 Brookdale Rd, Naperville, IL 60563
Tel.: (630) 416-6565   IL
Web Site:
http://www.stpatricksresidence.org
Year Founded: 1965
Sales Range: $10-24.9 Million
Emp.: 351
Nursing Care & Rehabilitation Services
N.A.I.C.S.: 623110
Maria Therese *(Dir-Vocations)*

ST. PATRICKS HOME
66 Van Cortlandt Park S, Bronx, NY 10463
Tel.: (718) 519-2800   NY
Web Site:
http://www.stpatrickshome.org
Year Founded: 1931
Sales Range: $25-49.9 Million
Emp.: 380
Elder Care Services
N.A.I.C.S.: 624120
Juan Ruiz *(Fin Dir)*
Kevin Patricia *(Co-Treas)*
Mary Lou De Maio *(Dir-Rehabilitation)*
Ludine Ferdinand *(Dir-Nursing)*
Elizabeth Dunleavy *(Sec)*

ST. PETER'S HEALTH PARTNERS
315 S Manning Blvd, Albany, NY 12208
Tel.: (518) 525-1111   NY
Web Site: http://www.sphp.com
Year Founded: 2012
Sales Range: $75-99.9 Million
Emp.: 12,500
Medical Association
N.A.I.C.S.: 813920
Donald G. Martin *(CEO)*
Paul Gordon *(CFO)*
Thomas Lawrence *(Chief Medical Officer)*
Michael S. Finegan *(Pres-Acute Care)*
James Keel Reed *(Pres & CEO)*

ST. ROMAIN OIL CO. INC.
293 Industrial Blvd, Mansura, LA 71350
Tel.: (314) 240-9494
Web Site: http://www.stromainoil.com
Sales Range: $25-49.9 Million
Emp.: 25
Petroleum Products
N.A.I.C.S.: 424720
Laura Fisher *(Controller)*
Annie Gauthier *(CFO)*
Mike St. Romain *(Mgr-Wholesale)*
Nick St. Romain *(COO)*
Sondra St. Romain *(VP)*
Amanda Norred *(Dir-HR)*
Todd St. Romain *(CEO)*

ST. VINCENT DE PAUL OF SEATTLE/KING COUNTY
5950 4th Ave S, Seattle, WA 98108
Tel.: (206) 767-9975   WA
Web Site: http://www.svdpseattle.org
Year Founded: 1922
Sales Range: $10-24.9 Million
Emp.: 190
Poor & Needy People Assistance Services
N.A.I.C.S.: 813319
Jim McFarland *(Dir-Mktg & Comm)*
Ned Delmore *(Exec Dir)*
Donna Whitford *(Dir-Dev)*
Eddie Roldan *(Dir-Fin)*
John Morford *(Pres)*
Mary Ann Curran *(Second VP)*
Richard Muhlebach *(First VP)*

ST. VINCENT DE PAUL SOCIETY OF LANE COUNTY, INC.
2890 Chad Dr, Eugene, OR 97408
Tel.: (541) 687-5820   OR
Web Site: http://www.svdp.us
Year Founded: 1953
Sales Range: $10-24.9 Million
Emp.: 616
Community Action Services
N.A.I.C.S.: 624190
Carol Belmer *(Dir-Personnel)*
Kristen Karle *(Dir-Housing Dev)*
Terry McDonald *(Exec Dir)*
Leisha Wallace *(Gen Mgr-Stores)*
Anne M. Williams *(Mgr-Housing Programs)*
Louise Westling *(Chm)*
Virgil Heidecker *(Sec)*
Ken Corricello *(Vice Chm)*

ST. VINCENT DE PAUL VILLAGE, INC.
1501 Imperial Ave, San Diego, CA 92101
Tel.: (619) 233-8500   CA
Web Site: http://www.svdpv.org
Year Founded: 1992
Sales Range: $10-24.9 Million
Emp.: 370
Community Housing Services
N.A.I.C.S.: 624190
Patricia Cruise *(Pres & CEO)*
Kathi Bradshaw *(Dir-Residential Svcs)*
Julie DeDe *(Dir-Social Svcs)*
Edward Hershey *(Dir-Support Svcs)*
Sonya Thomas *(Coord-Special Events)*

ST. VINCENT HOSPITAL

St. Vincent Hospital—(Continued)
455 St Michaels Dr, Santa Fe, NM 87505
Tel.: (505) 913-3361 NM
Web Site: http://www.stvin.org
Year Founded: 1967
Sales Range: $300-349.9 Million
Emp.: 2,527
Health Care Srvices
N.A.I.C.S.: 622110
Margo Dittrich (VP-Corp Compliance)
Bob Moon (CFO)
Jason Adams (COO)
Kathy Armijo Etre (VP-Community Health)
John Beeson (Chief Medical Officer)
Christopher Clark (Pres)
Lillian J. Montoya (Chief Admin Officer)

ST.NICKS ALLIANCE
2 Kingsland Ave 1st Fl, Brooklyn, NY 11211
Tel.: (718) 388-5454 NY
Web Site: http://www.stnicksalliance.org
Year Founded: 1975
Sales Range: $10-24.9 Million
Emp.: 285
Community Development Services
N.A.I.C.S.: 624190
Michael F. Rochford (Exec Dir)
Mary Ciorciari (Dir-Elder Care)
Frank Lang (Dir-Housing)
Cindy Ross (Dir-Fin & Admin)
Philip J. Waldvogel (Sec)
Paul Pallotta (VP)
Joseph K. Robles (Chm)
John D'Arienzo (Treas)
Larry Rothchild (Mng Dir)

STA INTERNATIONAL INC.
1400 Old Country Rd Ste 411, Westbury, NY 11590-5119
Tel.: (516) 997-2400
Web Site: http://www.stacollect.com
Year Founded: 1955
Sales Range: $50-74.9 Million
Emp.: 138
Financial Services
N.A.I.C.S.: 561440
Colin Thomas (Mng Dir-UK)
Jeffrey Tulchin (Pres)
Kate Zhang (CFO)
Steven Tulchin (Sr VP)
Walter Lockhart (COO)

Subsidiaries:
Asset Source International, Inc. (1)
1400 Old Country Rd Ste 411, Westbury, NY 11590-5119
Tel.: (516) 997-2400
Web Site: http://www.assetsource.com
Sales Range: $10-24.9 Million
Emp.: 100
Legal Investigative Services
N.A.I.C.S.: 561611

STAAB CONSTRUCTION CORPORATION
1800 Laemle Ave, Marshfield, WI 54449
Tel.: (715) 387-8429
Web Site: http://www.staabco.com
Sales Range: $25-49.9 Million
Emp.: 85
Water & Sewer Line & Related Structures Construction
N.A.I.C.S.: 237110
Aaron E. Staab (Founder)
Jeffrey Graves (Treas)
Kevin Leick (VP)

STABILUS
36225 Mound Rd, Sterling Heights, MI 48310
Tel.: (586) 977-2950
Web Site: http://www.stabilus.com
Emp.: 100
Furniture Merchant Whslr
N.A.I.C.S.: 423210
Mark Wilhelms (CFO)

Subsidiaries:
DESTACO (1)
15 Corporate Dr, Auburn Hills, MI 48326
Tel.: (248) 836-6700
Robotic Tooling & Flexible Industrial Automation Solutions
N.A.I.C.S.: 333995

Subsidiary (Domestic):
CPI Products, Inc. (2)
500 N Spring St, Port Washington, WI 53074 (100%)
Tel.: (877) 756-2388
Web Site: http://www.cpiproducts.com
Plastic Fabrication Product Mfr
N.A.I.C.S.: 332312

Central Research Laboratories (2)
3965 Pepin Ave, Red Wing, MN 55066
Tel.: (651) 385-2142
Web Site: https://crlsolutions.com
Sales Range: $25-49.9 Million
Emp.: 55
Remote Handling of Toxic & Dangerous Materials
N.A.I.C.S.: 562211

Subsidiary (Non-US):
De-Sta-Co (Asia) Company, Limited (2)
Chalongkrung Road, Kwaeng Lamplatiew Khet Ladkrabang, Bangkok, 10520, Thailand
Tel.: (66) 232608126
Sales Range: $25-49.9 Million
Emp.: 4
Material Handling Tools Mfr
N.A.I.C.S.: 333515

Subsidiary (Non-US):
DE-STA-CO Shanghai Co., Ltd. (3)
Room 1802 Building A IBC 391 Guiping Road, Xuhui District, Shanghai, 200233, China
Tel.: (86) 2124112600
Web Site: http://www.destaco.com
Machine Component Mfr
N.A.I.C.S.: 333414

Subsidiary (Non-US):
De-Sta-Co Europe GmbH (2)
Hiroshimastrasse 2, 61440, Oberursel, Germany
Tel.: (49) 61717050
Machine Tools Mfr
N.A.I.C.S.: 333515

Subsidiary (Non-US):
DE-STA-CO Benelux B.V. (3)
Amsteldijk 173, 1422 XZ, Uithoorn, Netherlands
Tel.: (31) 297285332
Web Site: http://www.destaco.com
Sales Range: $10-24.9 Million
Machine Tools Mfr
N.A.I.C.S.: 333515

Subsidiary (Domestic):
Industrial Motion Control, LLC (2)
1444 S Wolf Rd, Wheeling, IL 60090
Tel.: (847) 459-5200
Motion Control Component Mfr
N.A.I.C.S.: 333613

STACEY ENTERPRISES INC.
3768 Pacific Ave, Ogden, UT 84405-1617
Tel.: (801) 621-6210 UT
Web Site: http://www.staceygc.com
Year Founded: 1983
Sales Range: $10-24.9 Million
Emp.: 15
Nonresidential Construction
N.A.I.C.S.: 236220

Scott R. Dixon (Pres)
Kevin M. Gleaves (Project Mgr & Dir-Safety)
John J. Kearns (VP & Project Mgr)
Erin Smith (Office Mgr)

STACEY MOVING & STORAGE, INC.
9825 Cincinnati Dayton Rd, West Chester, OH 45069-3825
Tel.: (513) 759-5900 OH
Web Site: http://www.staceymayflower.com
Year Founded: 1876
Provider of Trucking Services
N.A.I.C.S.: 484121
Stephen Sabatolo (Pres)

STACEY SMITH ENTERPRISES
300 Crescent Ct, Dallas, TX 75201
Tel.: (214) 756-6050
Sales Range: $10-24.9 Million
Emp.: 3
Convenience Store
N.A.I.C.S.: 445131
Stacey Smith (Partner)

STACK ELECTRONICS
100 W Main St, Babylon, NY 11702
Tel.: (631) 321-6086
Web Site: http://www.stackelectronics.com
Sales Range: $10-24.9 Million
Emp.: 100
Mfr of Terminal Boards
N.A.I.C.S.: 335932
Steve Patsis (Pres)

Subsidiaries:
Micro Control Manufacturing Inc. (1)
190 Rodeo Dr, Brentwood, NY 11717
Tel.: (631) 321-7539
Web Site: http://www.stackny.com
Rev.: $19,700,000
Emp.: 90
Panelboards
N.A.I.C.S.: 423610
Steve Patsis (Mgr)

Stack Electronics Ltd (1)
Unit 2304 23/F Nanyang Plaza No 57 Hung To Road, Kowloon, Kwun Tong, China (Hong Kong)
Tel.: (852) 2790 8979
Electronic Components Mfr
N.A.I.C.S.: 334419

STACK-ON PRODUCTS CO. INC.
1360 N Old Rand Rd, Wauconda, IL 60084-9763
Tel.: (847) 526-1611
Web Site: http://www.stack-on.com
Year Founded: 1972
Home Safes, Gun Security Products, Garage Storage & Organizational Structures Mfr & Distr
N.A.I.C.S.: 332119
Kevin Collins (Natl Sls Mgr)

STACKHOUSE BENSINGER INC.
330 Revere Blvd, Sinking Spring, PA 19608
Tel.: (610) 777-8000
Web Site: http://www.stseinc.com
Year Founded: 1998
Sales Range: $1-9.9 Million
Emp.: 20
Engineeering Services
N.A.I.C.S.: 541330
Robert P. Stackhouse (Pres)

STADIUM INTERNATIONAL TRUCKS INC.
105 7th N St, Liverpool, NY 13088-5215
Tel.: (315) 475-8471 NY
Web Site: http://www.stadiumtrucks.com
Year Founded: 1982
Sales Range: $25-49.9 Million
Emp.: 75
New & Used Truck Dealers
N.A.I.C.S.: 441227
John T. Paradis (Pres)
Gary Devennie (Treas & Sec)
Art Ives (Dir-Svc)
Jeff Devennie (Mgr-New Trucks)
Brian Devennie (Mgr-Ops)
Lindsay Baker (Controller)
Angela Pursati (Mgr-HR)

STADIUM TOYOTA SCION
5088 N Dale Mabry Hwy, Tampa, FL 33614
Tel.: (813) 872-4881
Web Site: http://www.stadiumtoyota.com
Sales Range: $25-49.9 Million
Emp.: 179
New Car Retailer
N.A.I.C.S.: 441110
Steve Couey (VP)
Tim Couey (Gen Mgr)
Rocky Santa Cruz (Dir-New Car)
Paul Vallot (Mgr-New Car Sls)
Rob Sabine (Mgr-Pre-Owned Sls)
Will Byrd (Dir-Fin)
Jason Hunter (Mgr-Fin)
Jose Lodeiro (Mgr-Sls)
Vince Lovasco (Mgr-Pre-Owned Sls)
Alice Morales (Office Mgr)
Marco Calo (Mgr-Collision)
Scott Rashleigh (Mgr-Parts)

STADIUMRED GROUP
40 Wall St 58th Fl, New York, NY 10005
Tel.: (212) 804-7878
Web Site: http://www.stadiumred.com
Year Founded: 2007
Holding Company
N.A.I.C.S.: 551112
Debbie Kaplan (Chief Strategy Officer)
George Bennett (Chief Growth Officer)
Claude Zdanow (Founder & CEO)

Subsidiaries:
Mediakix, LLC (1)
2218 Main St Unit 201, Santa Monica, CA 90405
Tel.: (310) 450-1999
Web Site: http://www.mediakix.com
Marketing Research Service
N.A.I.C.S.: 541910
Evan Asano (Founder)

STAFAST PRODUCTS INC.
505 Lakeshore Blvd, Painesville, OH 44077
Tel.: (440) 357-5546
Web Site: http://www.stafast.com
Year Founded: 1958
Rev.: $24,000,000
Emp.: 60
Distr of Industrial Fasteners, Nuts, Bolts & Screws
N.A.I.C.S.: 423840
Donald Selle (Pres)
Joan Selle (Treas)
Diane McNabb (Sec-Sls)
Kirk Hedger (Mgr-Ops)

STAFF FORCE INC.
419 Mason Park Blvd, Katy, TX 77450-1707
Tel.: (281) 492-6044 TX
Web Site: http://www.staff-force.com
Year Founded: 1989
Sales Range: $10-24.9 Million
Emp.: 120
Temporary Staffing Services

N.A.I.C.S.: 561320
Glenn Van Dusen (Controller)
Jennifer Lee (Mgr-HR)
Dennis Steger (Reg Mgr-Risk)
Haley Mallette (Mgr-Sls)
Russell Potocki (VP)
Jennifer Ortega (Mgr-Ops-Houston Area)

STAFF OF LIFE NATURAL FOODS MARKET
1266 Soquel Ave, Santa Cruz, CA 95062
Tel.: (831) 423-8632
Web Site: http://www.staffoflifemarket.com
Year Founded: 1969
Sales Range: $10-24.9 Million
Emp.: 90
Food Supplement Distr
N.A.I.C.S.: 456191
Richard Josephson (Owner)

STAFF ON SITE, INC.
1514 15th St, Rockford, IL 61108
Tel.: (815) 397-7667
Web Site: http://www.staffonsite.com
Sales Range: $10-24.9 Million
Emp.: 150
Temporary Help Service
N.A.I.C.S.: 561320
Carol Oliveira (Pres)

STAFF PRO INC.
15272 Newsboy Cir, Huntington Beach, CA 92649-1202
Tel.: (562) 596-5949
Web Site: http://www.staffpro.com
Sales Range: $10-24.9 Million
Emp.: 2,000
Security System Services
N.A.I.C.S.: 561621
Cory Meredith (Pres)
Todd Browneller (Mgr-Northern California Branch)
Blake Meredith (Dir-Trng & Dev)
Curtis Garrett (Gen Mgr-Los Angeles & Orange County)
Chuck Rogers (Dir-Bus Dev)
Mark Williams (Mgr-Security-Spokane)
Pete Wachob (CFO)
Mike Reichert (Sr Dir-Ops & Mgr-Northwest Branch)

Subsidiaries:

Staff Pro Services Inc. (1)
675 Convention Way, San Diego, CA 92101
Tel.: (619) 544-1774
Web Site: http://www.staffpro.com
Detective & Armored Car Services
N.A.I.C.S.: 561613

STAFFBUILDERSHR, LLC
116 S Tennessee Ave Ste 110, Lakeland, FL 33801
Tel.: (863) 701-8690
Web Site: http://www.staffbuildershr.com
Sales Range: $1-9.9 Million
Emp.: 7
Temporary Help Service
N.A.I.C.S.: 561320
Johnnie Ford (CEO)

STAFFING ASSOCIATES INC.
350 E St John St, Spartanburg, SC 29302
Tel.: (864) 542-0039
Web Site: http://www.staffingassociates.com
Sales Range: $10-24.9 Million
Emp.: 16
Temporary Staffing Services
N.A.I.C.S.: 561320

Nancy Parker (Mgr-Ops)
Jill Horton (Acct Mgr)
Lisa Hawkins (Acct Mgr)

STAFFING SERVICES LLC
4316 S St, Lakewood, CA 90712
Tel.: (562) 272-6844
Web Site: http://www.staffingllc.com
Rev.: $19,000,000
Emp.: 12
Placement Agencies
N.A.I.C.S.: 561311

STAFFING TECHNOLOGIES, LLC
221 Roswell St Ste 200, Alpharetta, GA 30009
Tel.: (678) 338-2040
Web Site: http://www.staffingtechnologies.com
Year Founded: 1994
Sales Range: $25-49.9 Million
Emp.: 350
Computer System Design Services
N.A.I.C.S.: 541512
Jim McNabb (Pres)

STAFFLOGIX CORPORATION
1751 W Diehl Rd Ste 300, Naperville, IL 60563-4800
Tel.: (630) 596-0319
Year Founded: 1998
Rev.: $53,000,000
Emp.: 1,200
Computer System Design Services
N.A.I.C.S.: 541512
Andrew Zimmerman (Reg Mgr)
Thomas Callahan (Mgr-Bus Svcs)

STAFFORD & COMPANY INSURANCE LTD.
1168 County St, Somerset, MA 02726
Tel.: (508) 675-7404
Web Site: http://www.stafford-insurance.com
Insurance Related Activities
N.A.I.C.S.: 524298
Mary Lou Miranda (Mgr-Personal Risk)

STAFFORD CONSTRUCTION COMPANY, L.L.C.
9396 Florida Blvd, Walker, LA 70785
Tel.: (225) 665-8460
Sales Range: $10-24.9 Million
Emp.: 10
Commercial & Institutional Building Construction Services
N.A.I.C.S.: 236220
Lynwood Hall Stafford (Mgr)

STAFFORD COUNTY FLOUR MILLS CO
108 S Church St, Hudson, KS 67545
Tel.: (620) 458-4121
Web Site: http://www.hudsoncream.com
Rev.: $16,862,779
Emp.: 30
Flour & Other Grain Mill Products
N.A.I.C.S.: 311211
Reuel Foot (Pres)

STAFFORD DEVELOPMENT COMPANY
1821 US Hwy 82 W, Tifton, GA 31793
Tel.: (229) 382-4400
Year Founded: 1960
Construction Equipment Retail, Parts & Services
N.A.I.C.S.: 423810
Kevin Belflower (Pres & CEO)
Tim Tomberlin (VP & Sls Mgr)

STAFFORD OIL CO. INC.
231 Ct St, Laconia, NH 03246
Tel.: (603) 524-1480
Web Site: http://www.staffordoil.com
Sales Range: $10-24.9 Million
Emp.: 40
Fuel Oil Dealers
N.A.I.C.S.: 457210
Charles D. Stafford (Pres)
Brenda Williams (Mgr-HR)

STAFFORD-SMITH INC.
3414 S Burdick St, Kalamazoo, MI 49001
Tel.: (269) 343-1240
Web Site: http://www.staffordsmith.com
Year Founded: 1945
Sales Range: $50-74.9 Million
Emp.: 75
Commercial Cooking & Food Service Equipment
N.A.I.C.S.: 423440
David J. Stafford (Pres)
Don Conrad (Reg Mgr)

STAFFWORKS GROUP
20505 W 12 Mile Rd, Southfield, MI 48076
Tel.: (248) 416-1150
Web Site: http://www.staffworksgroup.com
Year Founded: 1996
Sales Range: $10-24.9 Million
Emp.: 850
Employment Placement Agency
N.A.I.C.S.: 561311
L. William Brann (CEO)
Kristin Moran (Mgr-Facility & HR)

STAG-PARKWAY, INC.
7095 Tradewater Pkwy, Atlanta, GA 30336
Tel.: (404) 349-1918
Web Site: http://www.stagparkway.com
Year Founded: 1968
Sales Range: $25-49.9 Million
Emp.: 280
Distr of RV Parts & Accessories
N.A.I.C.S.: 423120
Brad Patton (Controller)
Martin Street (Pres & CEO)
Bob Barra (Sr VP-Sls)
Laura Mallary (Mgr-Sls-Northeastern Reg)

STAGE 1 VENTURES, LLC
890 Winter St Ste 208, Waltham, MA 02451
Tel.: (781) 772-1010
Web Site: http://www.stage1ventures.com
Privater Equity Firm
N.A.I.C.S.: 523940
David William Baum (Mng Dir)

Subsidiaries:

Pure Auto LLC (1)
1447 Peachtree St NE #900, Atlanta, GA 30309
Web Site: http://www.PureCars.com
Sales Range: $1-9.9 Million
Emp.: 81
Advertising & Marketing Services
N.A.I.C.S.: 541810
Jeremy Anspach (Founder & Chm)
Don DeLillo (CFO)
Sam Mylrea (CEO)
Mac White (Dir-Dev)
Adam Phillips (Chief Product Officer & Chief Strategy Officer)
Jeff Ranalli (Chief Revenue Officer)

STAGE 2 NETWORKS
70 W 40th St 7th Fl, New York, NY 10018
Tel.: (212) 497-8000

Web Site: http://www.stage2networks.com
Year Founded: 2004
Sales Range: $1-9.9 Million
Emp.: 21
Telecommunication Servicesb
N.A.I.C.S.: 517810
Joseph P. Gillette (Founder & CEO)
Tom Faherty (CTO)
Matthew Kessler (VP-Sls Engrg)
Joseph Reynolds (VP-Fin)
Laura Hobbs (Dir-Svc Delivery)
Eleni Toumazatos (Controller)
Louis Hayner (COO)

STAGE 4 SOLUTIONS, INC.
4701 Patrick Henry Dr Bldg 19, Santa Clara, CA 95054
Tel.: (408) 868-9739
Web Site: http://stage4solutions.com
Year Founded: 2001
Sales Range: $1-9.9 Million
Emp.: 26
Marketing Solutions & Services
N.A.I.C.S.: 541613
Jane Rayskaya (Mgr-Accts & Ops)
Niti Agrawal (Pres)

STAGE EQUITY PARTNERS, LLC
5215 Old Orchard Rd Ste 625, Skokie, IL 60077
Tel.: (847) 410-1090
Web Site: http://www.stageequity.com
Sales Range: $1-9.9 Million
Real Estate Investment Services
N.A.I.C.S.: 523999
Brian Howard (Founder & Pres)
Russell Brenner (Partner)

STAGE FRONT PRESENTATION SYSTEMS
6 Southern Oaks Dr, Savannah, GA 31405
Tel.: (912) 236-1345
Web Site: http://www.sfps.net
Year Founded: 1978
Sales Range: $10-24.9 Million
Emp.: 84
Audio Visual System Design & Installation Services
N.A.I.C.S.: 334310
Steve Stephens (Pres)
Scott Stephens (Sr VP-Quality Control)
Mike Reynolds (VP-Engrg)

STAGECOACH COFFEE, INC.
31 Pioneer St Ste 2, Cooperstown, NY 13326
Tel.: (607) 547-6229
Web Site: http://www.stagecoachcoffee.com
Year Founded: 1993
Sales Range: $25-49.9 Million
Emp.: 50
Roasted Coffee Mfr & Distr
N.A.I.C.S.: 311920
Christopher Grady (Owner)
Matty Grady (Owner)
Roderick Torrence (Partner)
Robin Torrence (Owner)

STAGER ENTERPRISES INC.
296 Sonman Rd, Portage, PA 15946
Tel.: (814) 736-4430
Year Founded: 1976
Sales Range: $10-24.9 Million
Emp.: 50
Country Store Operator
N.A.I.C.S.: 455219
Philip Stager (Pres)

STAGESTEP INC.

STAGESTEP INC.

Stagestep Inc.—(Continued)
Ste 4 4701 Bath St, Philadelphia, PA 19137-2235
Tel.: (215) 636-9000
Web Site: http://www.stagestep.com
Year Founded: 1969
Sales Range: $50-74.9 Million
Emp.: 20
Specialty Flooring Products Dealer
N.A.I.C.S.: 449121
F. Randolph Swartz *(Pres & CEO)*
Sandi Brandon *(Controller)*
Sam Jamison *(Mgr-Ops)*

STAHL'S INC.
20600 Stephens St, Saint Clair Shores, MI 48080-1084
Tel.: (586) 772-6161
Web Site: http://www.stahls.com
Year Founded: 1977
Sales Range: $100-124.9 Million
Emp.: 650
Fabricated Textile Products Mfr
N.A.I.C.S.: 314999
Ted Stahl *(Pres & CEO)*
Josh Ellsworth *(VP-Sls)*
Jon Deimel *(CFO)*

STAHL-MEYER FOODS, INC.
2071 Lemoine Ave Ste 202, Fort Lee, NJ 07024
Tel.: (201) 242-5500
Web Site: http://www.stahlmeyer.com
Year Founded: 1836
Sales Range: $50-74.9 Million
Emp.: 225
Meat Processing, Packaging & Distr
N.A.I.C.S.: 311612
Guillermo Gonzalez *(Pres & CEO)*

STAINLESS SPECIALISTS INC.
T7441 Steel Ln, Wausau, WI 54403
Tel.: (715) 675-4155
Web Site: http://www.stainlessspecialists.com
Sales Range: $10-24.9 Million
Emp.: 200
Sheet Metalwork
N.A.I.C.S.: 238390
Roger Prochnow *(Pres)*
Helen Prochnow *(VP)*
Tim Mielke *(Project Mgr)*
Rick Riemer *(Project Mgr)*
Mike Slattery *(Mgr-Ops & Project Mgr)*
Kati Waldburger *(Coord-Mktg)*
Jim Kavanagh *(Mgr-Sls)*

STAINLESS STEEL MIDWEST LLC
2615 Hwy 146 E, La Grange, KY 40031
Tel.: (502) 805-1120
Web Site: https://ssmw.us
Stainless Steel & Alloy Scrap Metals Recycling Services
N.A.I.C.S.: 562920
Steve Jones *(Pres)*

Subsidiaries:

Allied Alloys LP (1)
6767 Kirbyville St, Houston, TX 77033
Tel.: (713) 643-6966
Web Site: http://www.alliedalloys.com
Metal Recycling & Metals Management Services
N.A.I.C.S.: 423930
Mukesh Turakhia *(VP)*
Nidhi Turakhia *(CEO)*

STAINLESS SYSTEMS INC.
300 E 4th Ave, South Hutchinson, KS 67505-1228
Tel.: (620) 663-4346
Web Site: http://www.sssystems.com
Sales Range: $10-24.9 Million

Emp.: 10
Food Products Machinery
N.A.I.C.S.: 333241
Gregory Roepka *(Pres)*

STAJAC INDUSTRIES, INC.
3710 Corporex Park Dr Ste 100, Tampa, FL 33619
Tel.: (813) 870-0340 FL
Web Site:
http://www.excellenceindustries.com
Year Founded: 1991
Sales Range: $10-24.9 Million
Emp.: 13
Commercial Refrigeration
N.A.I.C.S.: 333415
Howard Noskowicz *(CEO)*
Dell Dahl *(Pres)*
Joe Parrino *(VP-Ops)*
Mike Moses *(CFO)*

STAKE CENTER LOCATING INC.
2920 W Directors Row, Salt Lake City, UT 84104
Tel.: (801) 841-1063
Web Site: http://www.sctrl.com
Year Founded: 1998
Sales Range: $10-24.9 Million
Emp.: 280
Underground Pipelines & Utility Infrastructure
N.A.I.C.S.: 237990
Chuck Schvanebeldt *(CEO)*

STAKMORE, INC.
30 Elm St, Owego, NY 13827-1314
Tel.: (607) 687-1616 NY
Web Site: http://www.stakmore.com
Year Founded: 1922
Sales Range: $50-74.9 Million
Emp.: 38
Mfr of Folding Furniture
N.A.I.C.S.: 337122
Eric P. Niermeyer *(Owner)*

STALELIFE STUDIOS
1730 W Huron St Unit 1, Chicago, IL 60622
Tel.: (312) 602-9601
Year Founded: 2006
Sales Range: Less than $1 Million
Emp.: 1
Advetising Agency
N.A.I.C.S.: 541810

STALEY COMMUNICATION, INC.
2 22nd St Ste 902, Wheeling, WV 26003-3826
Tel.: (304) 233-8780
Web Site: http://www.staleycom.com
Rev.: $13,700,000
Emp.: 85
Electronic Parts & Equipment Merchant Whslr
N.A.I.C.S.: 423690
Paul Staley *(Dir-Mktg)*

STALEY INC.
3400 J E Davis Dr, Little Rock, AR 72209
Tel.: (501) 565-9675
Web Site: http://www.staleyinc.com
Year Founded: 1951
Sales Range: $10-24.9 Million
Emp.: 320
Provider of Voice, Data & Video Wiring Contracting Services
N.A.I.C.S.: 238210
Ed Staley *(Pres & CEO)*
Gary Serrell *(Pres)*

STALKUP'S RV SUPERSTORE, INC.

501 W Yellowstone Hwy, Casper, WY 82601
Tel.: (307) 577-9350
Web Site: http://www.stalkupsrv.com
Sales Range: $10-24.9 Million
Emp.: 18
Recreational Vehicle Whslr
N.A.I.C.S.: 441210
Amie Stalkup *(VP)*

STALLINGS BROTHERS INC.
11471 Finch Ave, Middlesex, NC 27557
Tel.: (252) 235-3367
Web Site: http://www.sbh-nc.com
Sales Range: $25-49.9 Million
Emp.: 66
Gasoline
N.A.I.C.S.: 424720
Jeff Stallings *(Pres)*
Kathy Pitte *(Office Mgr)*

STALLION OILFIELD SERVICES, LTD.
950 Corbindale Rd Ste 300, Houston, TX 77024
Tel.: (713) 528-5544 DE
Web Site:
http://www.stallionoilfield.com
Year Founded: 2002
Oil Production Wellsite Support & Construction Logistics Services
N.A.I.C.S.: 213111
David C. Mannon *(CEO & Pres)*
Mark Margavio *(Sr VP & CFO)*
Brian D. Baird *(Sr VP, Gen Counsel & Sec)*
Stephen Thorness *(Sr VP & Chief Admin Officer)*
Jason Lu *(VP & CIO)*

STALLION, INC.
36-08 34th St, Long Island City, NY 11106-1930
Tel.: (212) 290-2510 NY
Luxury Apparel Mfr
N.A.I.C.S.: 315250
John Georgiades *(Co-Owner & CEO)*
Peter Georgiades *(Co-Owner)*

Subsidiaries:

J. Mendel, Inc. (1)
463 7th Ave, New York, NY 10018
Tel.: (212) 968-6260
Web Site: http://www.jmendel.com
Sales Range: $25-49.9 Million
Women's Clothing Mfr
N.A.I.C.S.: 315250
Malika A. Jordan *(Asst Mgr-Ops)*
Marc Durie *(CEO)*
Sue Yeung *(Coord-Production)*
Susan Romano *(VP-Fur Production)*
Eddie Ramah *(Mgr-Costing)*
Mary Nugent *(Mgr-Retail Fur Production)*
Sarai Lugo *(Mgr-Wholesale Production)*
Holly Henderson-Smith *(VP-Adv)*
Gilles Mendel *(Chief Creative Officer)*
Edward W. Meredith *(CFO)*
Tara Connaughton *(VP-Comm-Global)*
Jodi Riesenberg *(VP-Mdsg & Retail)*
Alexander Dymek IV *(Dir-Fur Dev)*

STALLWORTH & JOHNSON INC.
17010 Hwy 4, Minter, AL 36761
Tel.: (334) 872-4852 AL
Year Founded: 1976
Sales Range: $10-24.9 Million
Emp.: 5
Wood Processing Services
N.A.I.C.S.: 113310
John L. Stallworth *(Pres)*

STAMATS
615 5th St SE, Cedar Rapids, IA 52406-1888
Tel.: (319) 364-6167 IA
Web Site: http://www.stamats.com

Year Founded: 1923
Rev.: $15,000,000
Emp.: 125
Fiscal Year-end: 12/31/04
Advertising Agencies, Brand Development, Consulting, Direct Marketing, Education, Internet/Web Design, Recruitment
N.A.I.C.S.: 541810
Peter S. Stamats *(CEO)*
William S. Stamats *(Exec VP)*
Marcy Bader *(VP-Production)*
Robert A. Sevier *(Sr VP-Strategy)*
Pegi Anton *(Sr VP-Client Svcs)*
Marilyn Osweiler *(Sr VP-Consulting)*
Chuck Reed *(Sr VP-Client Svcs)*
Becky Morehouse *(VP-Client Svcs)*
Ann Oleson *(Dir-Consulting)*
Lynne Calloway *(Principal Mgr-Project Comm)*
Jennifer Shaddox *(Mgr-Acct)*
Sabra Fiala *(Dir-Strategic Mktg)*
Kathryn Edwards *(VP-Bus Dev)*

STAMBAUGH'S AIR SERVICE, INC.
1000 Jetport Rd, Brunswick, GA 31525
Tel.: (912) 265-7244
Web Site:
http://www.stambaughaviation.com
Sales Range: $10-24.9 Million
Emp.: 100
Aircraft & Heavy Equipment Repair Services
N.A.I.C.S.: 811310
Mark R. Stambaugh Sr. *(Pres)*

Subsidiaries:

Stambaugh Aviation, Inc. (1)
1000 Jetport Rd, Brunswick, GA 31525
Tel.: (912) 265-7244
Web Site:
http://www.stambaughaviation.com
Aviation Services
N.A.I.C.S.: 811310
Scott Stambaugh *(Pres)*

STAMCO INDUSTRIES INC.
26650 Lakeland Blvd, Euclid, OH 44132-2644
Tel.: (216) 731-9333 OH
Web Site: http://www.stamcoind.com
Year Founded: 1983
Sales Range: $50-74.9 Million
Emp.: 50
Mfr of Metal Stampings for Automotive & General Industries
N.A.I.C.S.: 336370
William E. Sopko *(Pres)*
Leroy Richards *(Mgr-Sls & Comml)*

STAMFORD FORD LINCOLN, LLC
212 Magee Ave, Stamford, CT 06902
Tel.: (203) 357-0357
Web Site:
http://www.stamfordmotors.com
Sales Range: $25-49.9 Million
Emp.: 55
Car Dealership Owner & Operator
N.A.I.C.S.: 441110
Dominic Franchella *(Principal)*
Gus Gournaris *(Gen Mgr-Sls)*
Tom Zvon *(Gen Mgr)*
Christopher Febbraio *(Mgr-Internet)*
Tony Siciliano *(Mgr-Fin)*
Andres Cadena *(Mgr-Fin)*
Miles Mobuis *(Mgr-Leasing)*
Ed Dickan *(Mgr-Parts)*
Eric Munnilal *(Mgr-Svc)*
Neil Avellino *(Mgr-Pre-Owned)*

STAMFORD HEALTH SYSTEM INC.

COMPANIES

30 Shelbourne Rd, Stamford, CT 06904
Tel.: (203) 276-1000
Web Site: http://www.stamhealth.org
Sales Range: $450-499.9 Million
Emp.: 1,900
Health Care Srvices
N.A.I.C.S.: 561110
Darryl McCormick *(Sr VP-Talent & Culture)*
Arun Nandi *(Chm-Dept Of Emergency Medicine-Lower Fairfield)*

STAMM INTERNATIONAL CORPORATION
PO Box 1929, Fort Lee, NJ 07024
Tel.: (201) 947-1700
Web Site: http://www.stamminternational.com
Sales Range: $75-99.9 Million
Emp.: 600
Holding Company; Manufacturer & Distributor of Heating & Air Conditioning Equipment
N.A.I.C.S.: 333414
Marilyn Stamm *(CFO)*

STAMMEN INSURANCE GROUP, LLC
115 S Main St, Celina, OH 45822
Tel.: (419) 586-7500   OH
Web Site: https://stammeninsurance.com
Year Founded: 1919
Rev.: $1,800,000
Emp.: 23
Fiscal Year-end: 12/31/09
Insurance Agencies & Brokerages
N.A.I.C.S.: 524210

STAMPIN UP INC.
12907 S 3600 W, Riverton, UT 84065
Tel.: (801) 257-5400
Web Site: http://www.stampinup.com
Rev.: $99,000,000
Emp.: 500
Embossing Seals & Hand Stamps
N.A.I.C.S.: 339940
Scott Nielsen *(CFO)*

STAN & LOU ADVERTISING
504 W 9th St, Houston, TX 77007
Tel.: (713) 683-8000
Web Site: http://www.stanandlou.com
Year Founded: 1988
Sales Range: $10-24.9 Million
Emp.: 10
N.A.I.C.S.: 541810
Lou Congelio *(Pres & Chief Creative Officer)*
Scott Brinkmeyer *(Assoc Dir-Creative)*
Sarah Springer *(Acct Exec)*
Alfred Anderson *(Controller)*
Kate Wiggins *(Acct Coord)*
Brandy Beverly *(Acct Exec)*

STAN HOUSTON EQUIPMENT CO.
501 S Marion Rd, Sioux Falls, SD 57106
Tel.: (605) 336-3727
Web Site: http://www.stanhouston.com
Sales Range: $10-24.9 Million
Emp.: 53
General Construction Supplies & Equipment
N.A.I.C.S.: 423810
Ken Mazourek *(Mgr-Equipment)*
Bryce Strasser *(Asst Mgr-Woodworking)*
Brent Thoelke *(Gen Mgr)*
Scott Flint *(Mgr-Rental)*
Charlie Keeley *(Mgr-Store)*
Stacey Larson *(Mgr-Store)*
Mark Petrich *(Mgr-Svc)*
Fred Richards *(Mgr-Woodworking)*

STAN JOHNSON COMPANY
6120 S Yale Ave Ste 813, Tulsa, OK 74136
Tel.: (918) 494-2690
Web Site: http://www.stanjohnsonco.com
Sales Range: $1-9.9 Million
Emp.: 100
Single-Tenant Net Lease Services
N.A.I.C.S.: 531390
Stan L. Johnson *(CEO)*
Harold Briggs *(Exec Mng Dir-Tulsa)*
Jeffrey W. Cox *(COO)*
Lanie Rea *(Dir-Res)*
Mark Hellwig *(Mng Dir-Chicago)*
Amar Goli *(Assoc Dir-Los Angeles)*
Andrew Peeples *(Dir-Houston)*
Andrew Ragsdale *(Assoc Dir-Tulsa)*
Andy Gatchell *(Assoc Dir-Chicago)*
Anne Perrault *(Assoc Dir-Tulsa)*
Brad Moulder *(Dir-Tulsa)*
Brandon Duff *(Dir-Chicago)*
Brett Butler *(Sr Dir-Houston)*
Brian Corriston *(Assoc Dir-Houston)*
Albert Muller *(Assoc Dir-Houston)*
Susan Harris *(Assoc Dir-San Francisco)*
Matt Lipson *(Assoc Dir-West Coast)*
Brad Feller *(Mng Dir)*

STAN KING CHEVROLET
333 Brookhaven St, Brookhaven, MS 39602
Tel.: (601) 833-4961
Web Site: http://www.stankinggmsuperstore.com
Year Founded: 1997
Sales Range: $10-24.9 Million
Emp.: 42
Car Whslr
N.A.I.C.S.: 441110

STAN KOCH & SONS TRUCKING
4200 Dahlberg Dr Golden Vly, Minneapolis, MN 55422
Tel.: (763) 302-5400
Web Site: http://www.kochcompanies.com
Sales Range: $75-99.9 Million
Emp.: 5,000
Trucking Except Local
N.A.I.C.S.: 484121
Dave Koch *(Co-Owner)*
Randy Koch *(Co-Owner)*

Subsidiaries:

GW Transportation Services   (1)
710 Johnson Dr, Delano, MN 55328
Tel.: (763) 972-6116
Web Site: http://www.gwtransportationservices.com
Rev.: $5,500,000
Emp.: 7
Foreign Freight Forwarding
N.A.I.C.S.: 488510
Lance Wetter *(Gen Mgr)*

STAN MCNABB
2000 N Jackson St, Tullahoma, TN 37388-2206
Tel.: (931) 455-3451
Web Site: http://www.stanmcnabb.com
Sales Range: $25-49.9 Million
Emp.: 48
Car Whslr
N.A.I.C.S.: 441110
Terry Jones *(Office Mgr)*
Trent McNabb *(Gen Mgr)*
Stan McNabb *(Owner)*

STAN STONER, INC.
PO Box 428, Enid, OK 73702
Tel.: (580) 234-4159   OK
Year Founded: 1970
Rev.: $1,000,000
Emp.: 2
Fiscal Year-end: 07/31/02
N.A.I.C.S.: 541810
Stanley R. Stoner *(Pres)*
Bobbie Stoner *(Sec & VP)*

STAN'S - LPS MIDWEST
1375 S Eastwood Dr, Woodstock, IL 60098
Tel.: (815) 338-0549
Web Site: http://www.stans.com
Year Founded: 1960
Emp.: 30
Printer & Copier Repair Services
N.A.I.C.S.: 811210
Stanley J. Steadman *(Founder)*
Mark Steadman *(Pres)*

Subsidiaries:

Stateline Copy Products, Inc.   (1)
16050 Woodmint Ln, South Beloit, IL 61080
Tel.: (815) 389-9295
Web Site: http://www.statelinecopy.com
Sales Range: $1-9.9 Million
Emp.: 15
Office Supplies & Associated Business Solutions
N.A.I.C.S.: 459410
Dick Miller *(Co-Founder & Pres)*
Bonnie Miller *(Co-Founder)*

STAN'S CONTRACTING INC.
99-1280 Waiua Pl, Aiea, HI 96701
Tel.: (808) 484-4400
Sales Range: $10-24.9 Million
Emp.: 28
Commercial & Office Buildings, Renovation & Repair
N.A.I.C.S.: 236220
Warren Shioi *(Pres)*
Doreen Shioi *(Sec & VP)*

STANBEE COMPANY, INC.
70 Broad St, Carlstadt, NJ 07072-2006
Tel.: (201) 933-9666   NJ
Web Site: http://www.stanbee.com
Year Founded: 1947
Sales Range: $75-99.9 Million
Emp.: 20
Mfr of Shoe Components
N.A.I.C.S.: 316210
Michael Berkson *(Pres)*
Robert J. Dalla Riva *(VP & Controller)*
Bruce Goldberg *(Dir-Tech Svcs)*
Yasser Trisatriya *(Mgr-Sls-Stanbee Asia Limited)*
Leo Provencher *(Mgr-Tech-Asia)*

Subsidiaries:

Stanbee Asia, Ltd.   (1)
700/273 Moo 1 Amata Nakorn Industrial Estate Tambol Bankao, Amphur Panthong, Chon Buri, 20160, Thailand
Tel.: (66) 3846 5621
Sales Range: $10-24.9 Million
Shoe Mfr & Distr
N.A.I.C.S.: 316210

STANCO METAL PRODUCTS, INC.
2101 168th Ave, Grand Haven, MI 49417-9396
Tel.: (616) 842-5000   MI
Web Site: http://www.stancometal.com
Year Founded: 1917
Sales Range: $75-99.9 Million
Emp.: 100
Mfr of Auto Hardware, Bathroom Fixtures, Reflector Pans for Electric & Gas Stoves & Splatter Shields
N.A.I.C.S.: 336370
Regis Eller *(Mgr-Customer Satisfaction)*

STAND ENERGY CORPORATION
1077 Celestial St Ste 110, Cincinnati, OH 45202-1629
Tel.: (513) 621-1113   OH
Web Site: http://www.stand-energy.com
Year Founded: 1984
Sales Range: $25-49.9 Million
Emp.: 25
Provider of Natural Gas Services
N.A.I.C.S.: 221118
Matthew Toebben *(Chm)*
Judith Phillips *(Co-Founder)*
Mark Ward *(VP-Regulatory Affairs)*

STAND FAST PACKAGING PRODUCTS INC.
710 Kimberly Dr, Carol Stream, IL 60188
Tel.: (630) 600-0900
Web Site: http://www.standfastpkg.com
Sales Range: $10-24.9 Million
Emp.: 60
Corrugated Box Mfr
N.A.I.C.S.: 322211
Keith Carman *(Exec VP)*
John S. Carman Sr. *(CEO)*
John S. Carman Jr. *(VP-Ops)*

STANDALE LUMBER & SUPPLY CO. INC.
4046 Lk Michigan Dr NW, Grand Rapids, MI 49534
Tel.: (616) 453-8201   MI
Web Site: http://www.standalelumber.com
Year Founded: 1952
Sales Range: $10-24.9 Million
Emp.: 130
Lumber & Other Building Materials
N.A.I.C.S.: 423310
Kenneth E. Holtvluwer *(Owner)*
Keith Walker *(Gen Counsel)*

Subsidiaries:

Standale Home Center   (1)
4100 Lake Michigan Dr NW, Grand Rapids, MI 49534
Tel.: (616) 453-8207
Web Site: http://www.standalelumber.com
Door & Window Distr
N.A.I.C.S.: 423310

STANDARD AIR & LITE CORPORATION
2406 Woodmere Dr, Pittsburgh, PA 15205-1839
Tel.: (412) 920-6505   PA
Web Site: http://www.stdair.com
Year Founded: 1977
Sales Range: $25-49.9 Million
Emp.: 60
Provider of Heating & Air Conditioning Services
N.A.I.C.S.: 423730
Chris Belculfine *(Mgr-Residential Sls)*
Jay Wade *(Engr-Carrier Sls)*

STANDARD APPLIANCE INC.
5240 SE 82nd Ave, Portland, OR 97266-4804
Tel.: (503) 777-3377   OR
Web Site: http://www.standardtvandappliance.com
Year Founded: 1949
Sales Range: $25-49.9 Million
Emp.: 117
Household Appliance Stores
N.A.I.C.S.: 449210
Ed Hilger *(Mgr-Ops)*
Scott Sandie *(Mgr-HR)*

STANDARD BEVERAGE CORPORATION

Standard Beverage Corporation—(Continued)

STANDARD BEVERAGE CORPORATION
2416 E 37th St N, Wichita, KS 67219
Tel.: (316) 838-7707
Web Site:
http://standardbeverage.com
Sales Range: $75-99.9 Million
Emp.: 185
Wine & Distilled Beverages
N.A.I.C.S.: 424820
Roger Fowler (VP)

STANDARD BUILDERS SUPPLY INC.
220 W 2700 S, Salt Lake City, UT 84115
Tel.: (801) 487-7731
Year Founded: 1971
Sales Range: $10-24.9 Million
Emp.: 90
Lumber, Plywood & Millwork
N.A.I.C.S.: 423310
Michael S. Hansen (Pres)
Jim Ridd (VP)

STANDARD BUSINESS SERVICES
640 Magazine St, New Orleans, LA 70130
Tel.: (504) 524-6131
Web Site:
http://www.coffeeservice.com
Year Founded: 1935
Sales Range: $25-49.9 Million
Emp.: 6
Promotional Events & Public Relations
N.A.I.C.S.: 541810
Sarah Camnetar (Mgr-Mktg)

STANDARD CHANGE-MAKERS INC.
3130 N Mitthoeffer Rd, Indianapolis, IN 46235
Tel.: (317) 899-6966
Web Site:
http://www.standardchange.com
Sales Range: $10-24.9 Million
Emp.: 75
Change Making Machines
N.A.I.C.S.: 333310
Mike Hassfurder (CFO)
James R. McNutt (Pres & CEO)
John Doyle (VP)
Tonya Duff (Mgr-Parts)

STANDARD COMPANIES INC.
2601 S Archer Ave, Chicago, IL 60608-5913
Tel.: (312) 225-2777
Web Site:
http://www.thestandardcompanies.com
Year Founded: 1917
Sales Range: $10-24.9 Million
Emp.: 20
Janitorial Supplies Distr
N.A.I.C.S.: 423850
Michelle Ruvola (VP)
George Bonomo (Sec)

STANDARD CONCRETE PRODUCTS INC.
945 Broadway, Columbus, GA 31901
Tel.: (706) 322-3274
Web Site:
http://www.standardconcrete.net
Year Founded: 1890
Sales Range: $150-199.9 Million
Emp.: 400
Highways; Bridges; Dams; Locks; Powerhouse Construction
N.A.I.C.S.: 327390

Mason H. Lampton (Chm)
Fred Dodelin (CFO)

STANDARD CONSTRUCTION COMPANY, INC.
7434 Raleigh La Grange Rd, Cordova, TN 38018
Tel.: (901) 754-5181
Web Site: http://www.stdconst.com
Rev.: $22,000,000
Emp.: 190
Provider of Highway & Street Paving Contracting Services
N.A.I.C.S.: 237310
Clifton S. Hunt (Pres)
Beth Henderson (Controller)

STANDARD DISTRIBUTING CO. INC.
100 S Mews Dr, New Castle, DE 19720
Tel.: (302) 655-5511
Web Site: http://www.standardde.com
Sales Range: $25-49.9 Million
Emp.: 140
Winery
N.A.I.C.S.: 424820
Bob Green (Supvr-On Premise Sls)
Michael P. Fusca (Mgr-Ops)
David Ford (Mgr-Sls)
Wayne Brzoska (Supvr-Sls)
Mark Tigani (Mgr-Warehouse-Dover)
Joe Dewson (Asst Mgr-Mktg)
Steven D. Tigani (VP)
John Gazzerro (Mgr-Mdsg)
Tim Schuler (Mgr-Mktg)
Matt Kelly (Mgr-Off Premise)
Pam Fallers (Mgr-Pur Dept)
Jim Dawson (Mgr-Special Events)
Mike Tielleman (Mgr-Warehouse)
Victor Mattia (Supvr-Craft Div)

STANDARD DRYWALL INC.
9902 Channel Rd, Lakeside, CA 92040
Tel.: (619) 443-7034
Web Site:
http://www.standarddrywall.com
Year Founded: 1983
Sales Range: $10-24.9 Million
Emp.: 1,200
Drywall & Construction Projects
N.A.I.C.S.: 238310
Robert E. Caya (Pres & CEO)
Ed Capparelli (VP)
Jeff Miller (COO)
Alicyn Taylor (CFO)
Robert A. Caya (Exec VP)

STANDARD DUPLICATING MACHINES CORPORATION
10 Connector Rd, Andover, MA 01810-5927
Tel.: (978) 470-1920   MA
Web Site: http://www.sdmc.com
Year Founded: 1910
Sales Range: $75-99.9 Million
Emp.: 65
Duplicating Machines, Collators, Binders, Bookletmakers, Cutters, Folders, Numberers, Joggers, Staplers & Associated Supplies Mfr
N.A.I.C.S.: 423420
Douglas E. Reny (VP-Ops)
Steven Reny (Pres)
Mark Hunt (Dir-Mktg-Standard Finishing Sys)

Subsidiaries:

Standard Duplicating Machines Corporation - Standard Business Systems Division   (1)
10 Connector Rd, Andover, MA 01810
Tel.: (877) 202-2260
Web Site: http://www.sdmc.com

Sales Range: $25-49.9 Million
Emp.: 60
Industrial Machinery & Equipment Distr
N.A.I.C.S.: 423830
Rick Campaiola (Mgr-Logistics)

STANDARD ELECTRIC COMPANY
2650 Trautner Dr, Saginaw, MI 48604
Tel.: (989) 497-2100   MI
Web Site:
http://www.standardelectricco.com
Year Founded: 1929
Sales Range: $100-124.9 Million
Emp.: 60
Electrical Apparatus & Equipment
N.A.I.C.S.: 423610
William Gray (Pres)
Richard Green (Mgr-Gaylord)

STANDARD ELECTRIC SUPPLY CO. INC.
222 N Emmber Ln, Milwaukee, WI 53233
Tel.: (414) 272-8100   WI
Web Site: http://www.sescowi.com
Year Founded: 1919
Sales Range: $10-24.9 Million
Emp.: 60
Electrical Apparatus & Equipment
N.A.I.C.S.: 423610
Larry Stern (Pres)
Mike Harvey (VP-Sls & Mktg)
Cassie Petty (VP-HR)
Tom Poehlmann (Controller)
Tom Zymanek (VP-Supply Chain Mgmt)

Subsidiaries:

Standard Electric Supply Co.   (1)
1055 Stevenson Ct, Roselle, IL 60172
Tel.: (630) 860-0236
Web Site:
http://www.standardelectricsupply.com
Electrical Apparatus & Equipment Distribution
N.A.I.C.S.: 423610
Larry Stern (Pres)

STANDARD FREIGHT, LLC
16814 N Eldridge Pkwy Ste B, Tomball, TX 77377
Web Site: http://www.standard-freight.com
Year Founded: 2014
Sales Range: $10-24.9 Million
Freight Transportation Services
N.A.I.C.S.: 488510
Case Craycraft (Partner)

STANDARD FURNITURE MANUFACTURING COMPANY INC.
801 S US Hwy 31, Bay Minette, AL 36507-2811
Tel.: (251) 937-6741   AL
Web Site: http://www.standard-furniture.com
Year Founded: 1946
Sales Range: $25-49.9 Million
Emp.: 900
Mfr of Wood Household Furniture
N.A.I.C.S.: 337122
Billy Hodgson (Chm)
Tim Ussery (Pres)
Todd Evans (CEO)
Van Bui (Pres-I.F.M. Asia)
Mark Gosnell (Pres-Albany Furniture)

STANDARD FUSEE CORPORATION
28320 Saint Michaels Rd, Easton, MD 21601
Tel.: (410) 822-0318
Web Site:
http://www.orionsignals.com
Rev.: $24,000,000

Emp.: 55
Mfr of Automotive & Railway Flares (Fusees)
N.A.I.C.S.: 325998
Dave Stiffler (CFO)
Jay McLaughlin (Pres)

STANDARD GENERAL LP
767 5th Ave 12th Fl, New York, NY 10153
Tel.: (212) 257-4701   DE
Web Site:
http://www.standardgenerallp.com
Year Founded: 2007
Private Equity & Investment Firm
N.A.I.C.S.: 523999
Soohyung Kim (Founder, Mng Partner, Partner & Chief Investment Officer)
Soo Kim (Mng Partner & Chief Investment Officer)
Joseph Mause (CFO)
Gail Steiner (Partner, Chief Compliance Officer & Gen Counsel)

Subsidiaries:

General Wireless Operations Inc.   (1)
801 NE 38TH St, Fort Worth, TX 76106-3732
Tel.: (800) 843-7422
Radio, Television & Other Electronics Stores
N.A.I.C.S.: 449210

Standard Media Group LLC   (1)
3102 W End Ave Ste 400, Nashville, TN 37203
Web Site: http://www.standardmedia.com
Television Stations & Digital Media Services
N.A.I.C.S.: 516120
Stan Knott (COO)
Andrew C. Carington (Chief Legal Officer)
Deborah A. McDermott (CEO)

WLNE-TV   (1)
10 Orms St, Providence, RI 02904
Tel.: (401) 453-8000
Web Site: http://www.abc6.com
Television Station
N.A.I.C.S.: 516120
Anne Marie Menard (Mgr-Bus)
Nicole Moye (Dir-News)
Cindy Walsh (Gen Mgr-Sls)
Ken Bell (Dir-ABC6 Sports)
Cristina Antonio (Mgr-Bus)
Bill Lancaster (Sls Mgr-Local)
Kathy Douglass (Mgr-Traffic)
Don Curtin (Dir-Brdcst Ops)
Brian Egan (Dir-Promo)

STANDARD HOMEOPATHIC COMPANY
154 W 131st St, Los Angeles, CA 90061
Tel.: (310) 768-0700
Web Site: http://www.hylands.com
Rev.: $11,815,100
Emp.: 70
Pharmaceutical Preparations
N.A.I.C.S.: 325412
Les Hamilton (VP-Sls)
Sharon Faustina (Controller)
Richard Walton (Dir-Facilities & Engrg)
Robert Loya (Mgr-Validation)

STANDARD HORSE NAIL COMPANY, LLC
1415 5th Ave, New Brighton, PA 15066
Tel.: (724) 846-4660
Web Site: https://www.stanho.com
Precision Products Manufacturing
N.A.I.C.S.: 332721

Subsidiaries:

Precision Kidd Steel Co. Inc.   (1)
1 Quality Way, Aliquippa, PA 15001-2459
Tel.: (724) 378-7670
Web Site: http://www.precisionkidd.com
Sales Range: $25-49.9 Million
Emp.: 70
Mfr Cold Finishing, Steel Shapes
N.A.I.C.S.: 331221

COMPANIES

STANDARD INDUSTRIES HOLDINGS INC.

Dom Lea *(Pres)*
Joel Ruckert *(Mgr-Quality Sys)*

STANDARD IMAGING, INC.
3120 Deming Way, Middleton, WI 53562-1461
Tel.: (608) 831-0025   WI
Web Site:
  http://www.standardimaging.com
Year Founded: 1989
Sales Range: $10-24.9 Million
Emp.: 60
Medical Instrument Mfr
N.A.I.C.S.: 334519
Ed Neumueller *(Founder, Pres & CEO)*
Ray Riddle *(Chief Regulatory Officer)*
Eric DeWerd *(Pres)*
Diane Washa *(Dir-Mktg)*
Dan Schmidt *(Dir-Engrg)*
Myles Sommerfeldt *(Dir-Sys)*
Jeff Manion *(Dir-Software)*
John Mabis *(Dir-Production)*
Kathy Wulff *(Dir-Admin)*
Carmen Crook *(Dir-HR)*

STANDARD INDUSTRIES HOLDINGS INC.
9 W 57th St 47th Fl, New York, NY 10019
Tel.: (212) 821-1600
Web Site:
  https://www.standardindustries.com
Year Founded: 1886
Emp.: 20,000
Offices of Other Holding Companies
N.A.I.C.S.: 551112
David Millstone *(Co-CEO)*
David Winter *(Co-CEO)*

Subsidiaries:

W. R. Grace & Co.-Conn   (1)
7500 Grace Dr, Columbia, MD 21044-4098
Tel.: (410) 531-4000
Web Site: http://www.grace.com
Rev.: $1,729,800,000
Assets: $3,765,500,000
Liabilities: $3,531,000,000
Net Worth: $234,500,000
Earnings: $1,800,000
Emp.: 4,000
Fiscal Year-end: 12/31/2020
Specialty Chemicals Mfr
N.A.I.C.S.: 325998
Laura Schwinn *(Pres-Specialty Catalysts)*
Sandra Wisniewski *(Pres-Grace Materials Technologies)*
Bhavesh V. Patel *(CEO)*

Subsidiary (Non-US):

Alltech Applied Science B.V.   (2)
Hooilaan 1, Breda, 4816 EM, Netherlands
Tel.: (31) 765717576
Chromatography Products Mfr & Distr
N.A.I.C.S.: 325998

Alltech France S.A.R.L.   (2)
ZA La Papillonniere Rue Charles Amand, 14500, Vire, France
Tel.: (33) 261220001
Web Site: http://www.alltech.com
Health Sector & Animal Nutrition Distr
N.A.I.C.S.: 456191

Alltech Grom GmbH   (2)
In der Hollerhecke 1, 67545, Worms, Germany
Tel.: (49) 745794930
Web Site:
  http://www.discoverysciences.com
Construction Product Mfr & Distr
N.A.I.C.S.: 333120

Alltech Italia S.R.L.   (2)
Via Giuseppe Parini 1, 40033, Casalecchio di Reno, Italy
Tel.: (39) 051434987
Web Site: http://www.alltech.com
Construction Products Mfr & Distr
N.A.I.C.S.: 333120

Subsidiary (Domestic):

Darex Puerto Rico, Inc.   (2)
7500 Grace Dr, Columbia, MD 21044-4009
Tel.: (410) 531-4000
Sales Range: $250-299.9 Million
Emp.: 520
Mfr Chemicals
N.A.I.C.S.: 325180

Subsidiary (Non-US):

Darex UK Limited   (2)
Cromwell Road, Saint Neots, PE19 2ER, Cambridgeshire, United Kingdom
Tel.: (44) 1480324453
Construction Chemicals Mfr
N.A.I.C.S.: 238110

Subsidiary (Domestic):

De Neef Construction Chemicals (US) Inc.   (2)
5610 Brystone Dr, Houston, TX 77041
Tel.: (713) 896-0123
Web Site: http://www.deneef.com
Construction Chemicals Mfr
N.A.I.C.S.: 238110

Subsidiary (Non-US):

De Neef Construction Chemicals NV   (2)
Industriepark 8, 2220, Heist-op-den-Berg, Belgium
Tel.: (32) 15257461
Web Site: http://www.dncp.be
Sales Range: $25-49.9 Million
Emp.: 35
Construction Chemicals Mfr
N.A.I.C.S.: 238110

De Neef Deutschland GmbH   (2)
Hohestrasse 7, 44139, Dortmund, Germany
Tel.: (49) 231550060
Construction Chemicals Mfr
N.A.I.C.S.: 238110

De Neef France S.A.R.L.   (2)
86 Avenue Du Chateau, Saint-Ouen-l'Aumone, 95310, France
Tel.: (33) 130375600
Web Site: http://www.grace.com
Emp.: 100
Construction Chemicals Mfr
N.A.I.C.S.: 238110
Jean-Michel Caron *(Mng Dir)*

De Neef Scandanavia AB   (2)
Bergaalle 1 25452, 424 57, Helsingborg, Sweden
Tel.: (46) 313300590
Web Site: http://www.deneef.se
Construction Chemicals Mfr
N.A.I.C.S.: 238110

De Neef Scandinavia AB   (2)
Langavallsgatan 15, 424 57, Gunnilse, Sweden
Tel.: (46) 313300590
Web Site: http://www.deneef.se
Catalyst & Packaging Material Mfg
N.A.I.C.S.: 326112

De Neef Technologies S.L.   (2)
Pol Ind El Pedregar - C/ Progres s/n nave 9 y 10, Montmelo, 08160, Barcelona, Spain
Tel.: (34) 935444554
Construction Chemicals Mfr
N.A.I.C.S.: 238110

Grace (New Zealand) Limited   (2)
26 Mohuia Crescent, Elsdon, Porirua, New Zealand
Tel.: (64) 42382048
Specialty Chemicals Mfr
N.A.I.C.S.: 325998

Grace Argentina S.A.   (2)
Primera Junta 570 1878, Quilmes, Buenos Aires, Argentina
Tel.: (54) 1142295303
Web Site: http://www.grace.com
Sales Range: $300-349.9 Million
Emp.: 42
Container Sealants & Application Equipment; Flexible Packaging Materials & Equipment, Specialty Construction Materials
N.A.I.C.S.: 424690
Claugio Garcia Madeo *(Pres)*

Grace Australia Pty. Ltd.   (2)
40 Scanlon Dr, Epping, 3076, VIC, Australia   **(100%)**
Tel.: (61) 384016300
Web Site: http://www.grace.com.au
Sales Range: $10-24.9 Million
Emp.: 57
Mfr & Distributor of Absorbents, Sealants, Specialty Construction Materials & Admixtures
N.A.I.C.S.: 325520

Grace Bauprodukte GmbH   (2)
Pyrmonter Strasse 56, Lugde, 32676, Germany
Tel.: (49) 528177040
Web Site:
  http://www.de.graceconstruction.com
Construction Products Mfr & Distr
N.A.I.C.S.: 333120

Grace Brasil Ltda.   (2)
Rua Albion 229 An 10 Cj 104 Lapa, Sao Paulo, 05077-130, SP, Brazil   **(100%)**
Tel.: (55) 1131332700
Web Site: http://www.grace.com
Cement & Concrete Chemicals, Container Sealants & Compound Application Equipment, Flexible Packaging Materials & Equipment, Micronized Silicas & Silica Gel
N.A.I.C.S.: 424690

Grace Canada, Inc.   (2)
294 Clements Rd W, Ajax, L1S 3C6, ON, Canada   **(100%)**
Tel.: (905) 683-8561
Web Site: http://www.graceconstruction.com
Sales Range: $25-49.9 Million
Emp.: 75
Construction Products, Container & Chemical Specialties, Petroleum Catalysts, Packaging Materials & Equipment
N.A.I.C.S.: 325520

Grace Catalyst AB   (2)
Industrivagen, 444 32, Stenungsund, Sweden
Tel.: (46) 303351000
Web Site: http://grace.com
Specialty Chemicals Mfr
N.A.I.C.S.: 325998

Grace Catalyst AB   (2)
Industrivagen, Stenungsund, 444 32, Sweden
Tel.: (46) 303351000
Web Site: http://www.grace.com
Absorbents Distr
N.A.I.C.S.: 325998

Grace China Ltd.   (2)
19th Floor K Wah Center 1010 Huai Hai Zhong Road, Loeoli Tao, Shanghai, 200031, China   **(100%)**
Tel.: (86) 2131582888
Web Site: http://www.grace.com
Sales Range: $10-24.9 Million
Emp.: 50
Mfr of Container Sealants, Construction Products, Packaging Materials & Specialty Chemicals
N.A.I.C.S.: 322230

Grace Colombia S.A.   (2)
Calle 17a No 69-39, Zone Industrial Montevideo, Bogota, 617, Colombia
Tel.: (57) 14251600
Web Site: http://www.grace.com
Absorbents; Container Sealants; Compound Application Equipment; Flexible Packaging Materials; Micronized Silicas; Industrial Water Treatment Chemicals & Services
N.A.I.C.S.: 325998

Division (Domestic):

Grace Construction Products   (2)
62 Whittemore Ave, Cambridge, MA 02140
Tel.: (617) 876-1400
Web Site: http://www.graceconstruction.com
Sales Range: $1-4.9 Billion
Emp.: 400
Specialty Construction Chemicals & Materials Mfr & Distr
N.A.I.C.S.: 325998

Subsidiary (Domestic):

Halex Corporation   (3)
4200 E Santa Ana St, Ontario, CA 91761

Tel.: (909) 622-3537
Web Site: http://www.halexcorp.com
Saw Blade & Handtool Manufacturing
N.A.I.C.S.: 332216

Subsidiary (Non-US):

Grace Construction Products N.V.   (2)
Rudy Vermeersch Lodewijk de Raetlaan 15, 8870, Izegem, Belgium
Tel.: (32) 51335959
Web Site: http://www.graceconstruction.be
Emp.: 3
Construction Product Mfr
N.A.I.C.S.: 333120

Grace Construction Products S.A.   (2)
En Budron E9, 1052, Le Mont-sur-Lausanne, Switzerland
Tel.: (41) 216528585
Web Site: http://www.batidoc.ch
Construction Product Mfr & Distr
N.A.I.C.S.: 333120

Grace Container, S. A. de C. V.   (2)
Av Isidro Fabela S/N, Parque Industrial, 52600, Santiago Tianguistenco, Mexico
Tel.: (52) 7222761300
Investment Management Service
N.A.I.C.S.: 551112

Grace Darex GmbH   (2)
Erlengang 31, Norderstedt, 22844, Germany
Tel.: (49) 4052601100
Web Site: http://www.gracedarex.com
Packaged Food & Beverage Mfr
N.A.I.C.S.: 311423

Division (Domestic):

Grace Davison   (2)
7500 Grace Dr, Columbia, MD 21044
Tel.: (410) 531-4000
Web Site: http://www.grace.com
Sales Range: $250-299.9 Million
Emp.: 700
Specialty Chemicals, Materials & Formulation Technologies Mfr & Distr
N.A.I.C.S.: 325998

Plant (Domestic):

Grace Davison - Curtis Bay (Baltimore) Plant   (3)
5500 Chemical Rd, Baltimore, MD 21226
Tel.: (410) 355-9400
Web Site: http://www.grace.com
Sales Range: $125-149.9 Million
Emp.: 530
Specialty Chemicals, Materials & Formulation Technologies Mfr
N.A.I.C.S.: 325998
John Kimmel *(Dir-Ops)*

Unit (Domestic):

Grace Davison Discovery Sciences   (3)
2051 Waukegan Rd, Deerfield, IL 60015
Tel.: (847) 948-8600
Web Site:
  http://www.discoverysciences.com
Sales Range: $50-74.9 Million
Emp.: 250
Analytical Instruments Supplier
N.A.I.C.S.: 334516

Subsidiary (Non-US):

Casa Cientifica   (4)
Cra 27A 49A-41, Bogota, DC, Colombia
Tel.: (57) 13126310
Web Site: http://www.casacientifica.com
Sales Range: $10-24.9 Million
Emp.: 25
Laboratory Systems Integration & Consulting Services
N.A.I.C.S.: 541990

Unit (Domestic):

Grace Davison Discovery Sciences   (3)
17434 Mojave St, Hesperia, CA 92345
Tel.: (760) 244-6107
Web Site: http://www.grace.com

STANDARD INDUSTRIES HOLDINGS INC.   U.S. PRIVATE

Standard Industries Holdings Inc.—(Continued)
Sales Range: $10-24.9 Million
Emp.: 13
Silica Amorphous
N.A.I.C.S.: 325180

Subsidiary (Non-US):

W. R. Grace Limited (3)
Oak Park Business Centre Alington Road,
Little Barford, Saint Neots, PE19 6WL,
Cambs, United Kingdom (100%)
Tel.: (44) 1480324430
Web Site: http://www.grace.com
Sales Range: $10-24.9 Million
Emp.: 4
Sales of Micronized Silicas, Molecular Sieves & Silica Gel Absorbents
N.A.I.C.S.: 325180

Subsidiary (Non-US):

Grace Davison (Proprietary) Limited (2)
Corner Mill & Iscor Street, Bellville, 7530,
Cape Province, South Africa
Tel.: (27) 219517011
Web Site: http://www.grace.com
Emp.: 46
Specialty Chemicals Mfr
N.A.I.C.S.: 325998

Grace Germany GmbH (2)
In Der Hollerhecke 1, Worms, 67545, Germany
Tel.: (49) 624140300
Catalyst & Packaging Material Mfr
N.A.I.C.S.: 326112

Grace GmbH & Co. KG (2)
In der Hollerhecke 1, Worms, 67545, Germany
Tel.: (49) 624140300
Catalyst & Packaging Material Mfr
N.A.I.C.S.: 326112

Subsidiary (Domestic):

Grace H-G, Inc. (2)
7500 Grace Dr, Columbia, MD 21044
Tel.: (410) 531-4000
Sales Range: $10-24.9 Million
Emp.: 3
Chemical Company
N.A.I.C.S.: 325180

Subsidiary (Non-US):

Grace Hellas E.P.E. (2)
64 Ave Kifissias Maroussi, Kalithea, 15125,
Athens, Greece (100%)
Tel.: (30) 2109231404
Web Site: http://www.grace.com
Sales Range: $10-24.9 Million
Emp.: 5
Sales of Containers Sealing Compounds & Application Equipment, Lacquers & Other Metal Packaging Products, Flexible Packaging
N.A.I.C.S.: 325520

Grace Holdings, S.A. de C.V. (2)
Av Isidro Fabela S N Parque Industrale,
Santiago Tianguistenco, 52600, Mexico
Tel.: (52) 7222761300
Holding Company
N.A.I.C.S.: 551112

Grace Italy S.r.l. (2)
Via Trento 7, Passirana Di Rho, 20017, Milan, Italy
Tel.: (39) 029314881
Electric Equipment Mfr
N.A.I.C.S.: 335999
Ignazio Catucci (Mgr-Global Mktg)

Grace Japan K.K. (2)
100 Kaneda, Atsugi, 243-0807, Kanagawa,
Japan
Tel.: (81) 462258800
Web Site: http://www.grace.com
Sales Range: $10-24.9 Million
Emp.: 50
Flexible Plastic Packaging
N.A.I.C.S.: 322220

Grace Japan Kabushiki Kaisha (2)
100 Kaneda, Atsugi, 243-0807, Kanagawa,
Japan
Tel.: (81) 462258824

Catalyst & Packaging Material Mfr
N.A.I.C.S.: 326112

Grace Netherlands B.V. (2)
Amstelveenseweg 760, 1081 JK, Amsterdam, Netherlands
Tel.: (31) 205043800
Emp.: 10
Catalyst & Packaging Material Mfr
N.A.I.C.S.: 326112

Subsidiary (Domestic):

Grace PAR Corporation (2)
7500 Grace Dr, Columbia, MD 21044-4009
Tel.: (410) 531-4000
Sales Range: $10-24.9 Million
Emp.: 59
Mfr of Chemicals
N.A.I.C.S.: 325180

Subsidiary (Non-US):

Grace Products (Singapore) Private Limited (2)
390 Orchard Road 15-02/03 Palais Renaissance, Singapore, 238871, Singapore
Tel.: (65) 63314188
Web Site: http://grace.com
Container Sealants & Compound Application Equipment, Water Treatment Products & Services, Construction Products Mfr
N.A.I.C.S.: 325520

Grace Silica GmbH (2)
Kreuzauer Str 46, 52355, Duren, Germany
Tel.: (49) 242140370
Web Site: http://grace.com
Specialty Chemicals Mfr
N.A.I.C.S.: 325998

Grace Sp. z o.o. (2)
Ul Szczepanowski 10/2, Poznan, 60541,
Poland
Tel.: (48) 618439292
Web Site: http://www.grace.com
Sales Range: $25-49.9 Million
Emp.: 35
Specialty Chemicals Mfr
N.A.I.C.S.: 325998

Grace Trading (Shanghai) Co., Ltd. (2)
K Wah Center 1010 Huai Hai Zhong Road
19th Floor, Shanghai, 200031, China
Tel.: (86) 2133258288
Web Site: http://www.grace-china.com.cn
Construction Products Mfr & Distr
N.A.I.C.S.: 333120

Subsidiary (Domestic):

Rive Technology Inc (2)
1 Deer Park Dr Ste A, Monmouth Junction,
NJ 08852
Tel.: (732) 329-4463
Other Metal Valve & Pipe Fitting Mfr
N.A.I.C.S.: 332919

Subsidiary (Non-US):

W. R. Grace (Hong Kong) Ltd. (2)
Units 1001-3 10/F AXA Centre 151 Gloucester Road, Wanchai, China (Hong Kong)
Tel.: (852) 25902828
Web Site: http://www.grace.com
Construction & Specialty Chemicals, Container Sealants & Application Equipment,
Flexible Packaging Materials & Equipment,
Absorbents, Catalysts, Concrete Admixtures, Water Treatment Chemicals
N.A.I.C.S.: 325998

W. R. Grace (Malaysia) Sdn. Bhd. (2)
Lot 7 Lorong Cj 1 1a Off Jalan Balakong
Cheras Jaya, Cheras, 43200, Malaysia (100%)
Tel.: (60) 390746133
Web Site: http://www.graceconstruction.com
Sales Range: $10-24.9 Million
Emp.: 25
Construction Products
N.A.I.C.S.: 237110

W. R. Grace (Panama) S.A. (2)
Local No 4 Flex No 2 Andrews Boulevard & Stauffer Avenue, Antigua Base Aerea de Howard P, Panama, Panama
Tel.: (507) 3011846

Sales Range: $25-49.9 Million
Emp.: 8
Specialty Chemicals Mfr
N.A.I.C.S.: 325998

W. R. Grace (Philippines), Inc. (2)
Silangang Canlubang Industrial Park,
Canlubang Calamba, Laguna, 4028,
Philippines (100%)
Tel.: (63) 495497373
Web Site: http://www.grace.com
Sales Range: $1-9.9 Million
Emp.: 50
Construction & Specialty Chemicals, Container Sealants & Application Equipment,
Flexible Packaging Materials & Equipment
N.A.I.C.S.: 325520

W. R. Grace (Thailand) Ltd. (2)
253 2 Bangpoo Industrial Estate Sukhumvit
Rd KM 34, Samut Prakan, 10280, Thailand (100%)
Tel.: (66) 27094470
Web Site: http://www.grace.com
Sales Range: $10-24.9 Million
Emp.: 30
Specialty Chemicals, Container Sealants & Application Equipment, Flexible Packaging Materials & Equipment, Lacquers
N.A.I.C.S.: 325998

W. R. Grace Argentina S.A. (2)
Primera Junta 570, Quilmes, 1878, Buenos Aires, Argentina
Tel.: (54) 1142295303
Chemical Products Distr
N.A.I.C.S.: 424690
Enrique Tomas Kenny (Mgr-Comml-Reg)

W. R. Grace Brasil Industria e Comercio de Produtos Quimicos Ltda. (2)
Av Parana 4690 Cajuru do Sul Rua 2, Sorocaba, 18105-000, Brazil
Tel.: (55) 1531414100
Chemical Products Mfr
N.A.I.C.S.: 325998
Wagner C. Pereira (Dir-HR-Latin America)

W. R. Grace Canada Corp. (2)
42 Rue Fabre, Salaberry-de-Valleyfield, J6S 4K7, QC, Canada
Tel.: (450) 373-4224
Chemical Products Mfr
N.A.I.C.S.: 325998
Patrick Tanguay (Dir-Ops)

Subsidiary (Domestic):

W. R. Grace Capital Corporation (2)
7500 Grace Dr, Columbia, MD 21044-4009
Tel.: (410) 531-4000
Web Site: http://www.grace.com
Sales Range: $400-449.9 Million
Emp.: 600
Distribution of Chemicals
N.A.I.C.S.: 424690

Subsidiary (Non-US):

W. R. Grace Holdings, S.A. de C.V. (2)
Av Isidro Fabela S/N Col Parque Industrial
Santiago Tianguistenco, Fraccionamiento
Industrial, 52600, Mexico, Mexico (100%)
Tel.: (52) 7222761386
Web Site: http://www.graceholdings.com
Sales Range: $25-49.9 Million
Emp.: 100
Container Sealants & Application Equipment, Flexible Packaging Materials & Equipment, Micronized Silicas, Absorbents
N.A.I.C.S.: 325520

W. R. Grace Italiana S.p.A. (2)
Via Trento 7, Passirana di Rho, 20017, Milan, Italy (100%)
Tel.: (39) 02935371
Web Site: http://www.grace.com
Sales Range: $300-349.9 Million
Dispersants; Flexible Packaging Materials; Petroleum Fluid Cracking & Industrial Catalysts; Micronized Silicas; Molecular Sieves
N.A.I.C.S.: 325222

W. R. Grace Korea Inc. (2)
14 Fl G Square Tower, Anyang, 010-310,
Gyeonggi-Do, Korea (South)
Tel.: (82) 313408401
Inorganic Chemical Mfr

N.A.I.C.S.: 325180
S. J. Hwang (Gen Mgr-Sls)

W. R. Grace S.A. (2)
33 Rte de Gallardon, Epernon, 28234, France (100%)
Tel.: (33) 237188762
Sales Range: $75-99.9 Million
Emp.: 180
Adhesive Mfr
N.A.I.C.S.: 325520
Gerard Blond (Pres)
Thierry Pizol (Mgr-Customer Svc)

W. R. Grace Vietnam Company Limited (2)
Lot B14 Section B Street 12 National Highway 22 Xuan Thoi Son Ward, Hoc Mon District, Ho Chi Minh City, Vietnam
Tel.: (84) 87106168
Web Site: http://www.vn.graceconstruction.com
Specialty Chemicals Mfr
N.A.I.C.S.: 325998

STANDARD IRON & WIRE WORKS INC.
524 Pine St, Monticello, MN 55362-8916
Tel.: (763) 295-8700   MN
Web Site: http://www.std-iron.com
Year Founded: 1930
Sales Range: $10-24.9 Million
Emp.: 300
Sheet Metalwork
N.A.I.C.S.: 332322
Richard Demeules (Pres & CEO)
Brent Curtis (Project Mgr)
Dan Welter (Mgr-IT)

Subsidiaries:

Helgesen Industries Inc. (1)
7261 Hwy 60, Hartford, WI 53027
Tel.: (262) 709-4444
Web Site: http://www.helgesen.com
Sales Range: $25-49.9 Million
Emp.: 350
Standard & Custom Tanks Mfr
N.A.I.C.S.: 332420
Ann Schmid (Engr-Mfg)
Charles Dubey (Dir-Intl Bus)
James Grover (Engr-Mfg)
Ryan O'Connor (Engr-Advanced Dev)
Aaron Fralish (Engr-Mfg)
Brad Lynn (Engr-Mfg)
Todd Gruszynski (Mgr-Bus Dev)
Tom Marshall (Pres)

STANDARD LABORATORIES INC.
147 11th Ave Ste 100, South Charleston, WV 25303-1114
Tel.: (304) 744-6800   WV
Web Site:
  http://www.standardlabs.com
Year Founded: 1972
Sales Range: $25-49.9 Million
Emp.: 500
Testing Services
N.A.I.C.S.: 541715
Rick Flesher (Pres & CEO)
Todd Stallard (Dir-Sls & Mktg)
Allan Seaman (Dir-Technical Svcs)

Subsidiaries:

Precision Samplers Inc. (1)
147 11th Ave Ste 200, South Charleston, WV 25303-1114
Tel.: (304) 744-5534
Web Site: http://www.precisionsamplers.com
Sales Range: $10-24.9 Million
Emp.: 12
Coal Measuring & Controlling Services
N.A.I.C.S.: 334519
Greg Pendergrass (Mgr)

STANDARD MANAGEMENT COMPANY
5901 W Century Blvd Ste 1010, Los Angeles, CA 90045
Tel.: (310) 410-2300

Web Site:
http://www.standardmanagement.com
Year Founded: 1961
Rev.: $11,000,000
Emp.: 523
Real Estate Services
N.A.I.C.S.: 522299
Robert E. Fleischer *(VP-Construction & Capital Projects)*
Sonia Carrillo *(VP-Admin)*
Samuel K. Freshman *(Founder & Chm)*
Nelson You *(Assoc Dir-Acq)*
Michael Schoellhammer *(Dir-Acq & Lending)*
Nancy Kresek *(Sr VP & Controller)*
Kari Horii *(VP-Residential Ops)*

STANDARD MANUFACTURING CO., INC.
750 2nd Ave, Troy, NY 12182
Tel.: (518) 235-2200   NY
Web Site:
http://www.sportsmasterapparel.com
Year Founded: 1922
Sales Range: $200-249.9 Million
Emp.: 600
Mfr of Men's & Boys' Outerwear
N.A.I.C.S.: 315250
George H. Arakelian *(Pres)*
Dorothy J. Arakelian *(Treas & Sec)*
David Arakelian *(Dir-Sls & Mktg)*
Subsidiaries:

Caribbean Outerwear Corp.   (1)
Juan Martin Ind Pk HC 3, Yabucoa, PR 00767-9801
Tel.: (787) 893-2260
Sales Range: $10-24.9 Million
Emp.: 65
Men's & Boys Clothing
N.A.I.C.S.: 315210

STANDARD MEAT COMPANY
5105 Investment Dr, Dallas, TX 75236
Tel.: (214) 561-0561
Web Site:
http://www.standardmeat.com
Year Founded: 1935
Sales Range: $10-24.9 Million
Emp.: 80
Sausage Mfr
N.A.I.C.S.: 311612
Manny Gonzales *(VP-Bus Dev)*
Greg Hall *(VP)*
Greg Hollingsworth *(Mgr-Process & Capital Project)*
Cecilia Montalvo-Silburn *(Dir-HR)*
Troy Richardson *(CFO)*
David McKee *(Dir-Innovation & Process Improvement)*
Shane Kolle *(Dir-Quality Assurance)*
Cheney Garza *(Mgr-Customer Svc)*
Scott Boleman *(VP-Ops)*
Ben Rosenthal *(Pres & CEO)*
Tom Allen *(COO)*
Subsidiaries:

Syracuse's Sausage Company   (1)
903 N Hwy 156, Ponder, TX 76259
Tel.: (940) 479-2700
Web Site: http://www.syracusesausage.com
Sales Range: $10-24.9 Million
Emp.: 70
Processed Meat Mfr
N.A.I.C.S.: 311612
Anthony Musacchio *(VP-Sls & Mktg)*

STANDARD MERCHANDISING CO.
1125 Wright Ave, Camden, NJ 08103
Tel.: (856) 964-9700
Web Site:
http://www.standardmerchandisingco.com
Year Founded: 1922
Sales Range: $10-24.9 Million
Emp.: 79
Mfr Sporting & Athletic Goods
N.A.I.C.S.: 339920
Jeff Tarnoff *(Pres)*
Dawn Hillen *(Office Mgr)*

STANDARD MOBILE, INC.
16870 Valley View Ave, La Mirada, CA 90638
Tel.: (714) 228-9002   DE
Sales Range: $25-49.9 Million
Cellular Phones & VoIP Telecommunications Equipment Distr & Sales
N.A.I.C.S.: 517121
Hyung Gyu Choi *(Pres, CEO & CFO)*

STANDARD MORTGAGE CORPORATION
701 Poydras St 300 Plz, New Orleans, LA 70139
Tel.: (504) 569-3788
Web Site: http://www.stanmor.com
Year Founded: 1925
Sales Range: $25-49.9 Million
Emp.: 150
Mortgage Banking Services
N.A.I.C.S.: 522292
Kasey Sartin *(Loan Officer)*
Emily Henricks *(Loan Officer)*

STANDARD NUTRITION COMPANY
11824 Arbor St, Omaha, NE 68144
Tel.: (402) 393-3198
Web Site:
http://www.standardnutrition.com
Sales Range: $25-49.9 Million
Emp.: 15
Feed Concentrates
N.A.I.C.S.: 311119
Bill Dyer *(Pres)*
Jed Brown *(CFO)*
Craig Anderson *(Reg Mgr)*
Skip Osgood *(Reg Mgr)*

STANDARD OFFICE SUPPLY
35 Sheridan St NW, Washington, DC 20011
Tel.: (202) 829-4820
Web Site:
http://www.standardofficesupply.com
Rev.: $15,100,000
Emp.: 36
Supplies & Stationery Stores
N.A.I.C.S.: 459410
Milton D. Morris *(Pres & CEO)*
Vaselia Thomas *(Mgr-Pur)*
Merrillie D. Morris *(Sr VP & Gen Mgr)*
Marcia D. Morris *(VP-Bus Dev)*

STANDARD OFFICE SYSTEMS ATLANTIC INC.
2475 Meadowbrook Pkwy Ste A, Duluth, GA 30096
Tel.: (770) 449-9100
Web Site:
http://www.soscanhelp.com
Sales Range: $10-24.9 Million
Emp.: 125
Photocopy Machines
N.A.I.C.S.: 484210
S. Bryan Ammons *(Pres)*
Andy Koehler *(CFO)*

STANDARD OFFSET PRINTING CO.
433-435 Pearl St, Reading, PA 19602
Tel.: (610) 375-6174
Web Site:
http://www.standardgroup.com
Sales Range: $50-74.9 Million
Emp.: 80
Commercial Printing, Lithographic
N.A.I.C.S.: 323111

Charlotte B. Cooper *(Pres)*

STANDARD PAINT & WALLPAPER
409 W Yakima Ave, Yakima, WA 98902
Tel.: (509) 453-3171
Web Site:
http://www.standardpaintandcarpet.com
Year Founded: 1954
Sales Range: $10-24.9 Million
Emp.: 50
Distr of Paints & Painting Products
N.A.I.C.S.: 444120
Richard W. Myers *(Pres)*
Chris Hunt *(Mgr-West)*
Charmin Louis *(Mgr-Adv)*

STANDARD PARTS CORPORATION
168 140th St S, Tacoma, WA 98444
Tel.: (253) 531-5763
Web Site: http://www.spc-napa.com
Sales Range: $10-24.9 Million
Emp.: 50
Automotive Supplies & Parts
N.A.I.C.S.: 423120
Richard B. Davis *(Pres)*

STANDARD PLUMBING & HEATING CO.
435 Walnut Ave SE, Canton, OH 44702
Tel.: (330) 453-9191   OH
Web Site:
http://www.standardpandh.com
Year Founded: 1912
Sales Range: $10-24.9 Million
Emp.: 60
Plumbing Contracting Services
N.A.I.C.S.: 238220
Dave Grabowsky *(Pres)*

STANDARD PLUMBING SUPPLY COMPANY, INC.
9150 S 300 W, Sandy, UT 84070
Tel.: (801) 255-7145   UT
Web Site:
http://www.standardplumbing.com
Year Founded: 1952
Sales Range: $75-99.9 Million
Emp.: 500
Plumbing & Hydronic Heating Equipment & Supplies Retailer & Whslr
N.A.I.C.S.: 423720
Richard N. Reese *(Pres)*
Matt Freeman *(Dir-Natl Sls & Distr)*
Joel Gray *(Dir-Supply Chain)*
Matt Larsen *(Dir-Store Ops & Sls)*
Diane Magario *(Dir-Showrooms & Mktg)*

STANDARD PROCESS INC.
1200 W Royal Lee Dr, Palmyra, WI 53156
Tel.: (262) 495-2122
Web Site:
http://www.standardprocess.com
Rev.: $11,800,000
Emp.: 200
Food Supplement Stores
N.A.I.C.S.: 456191
Charles C. DuBois *(CEO)*
Lorre Pietenpol *(Sr Mgr-Natl Sls)*
Chandrika Karanam *(Sr Mgr-IT Project)*
Royal Lee *(Founder)*
John P. Troup *(Pres)*
Deb Morgan *(VP-Sls & Mktg)*
Brian Hall *(Dir-Sls & Bus Dev)*

STANDARD REFRIGERATION CO. INC.
Barrio Quebiada Arenas Kilometer 24

PR1 Camino Mangual, San Juan, PR 00725
Tel.: (787) 789-1000
Web Site: http://www.standardpr.com
Sales Range: $10-24.9 Million
Emp.: 145
Mechanical Contractor
N.A.I.C.S.: 238220
Joaquin Acevedo *(VP)*
Aixa Navarro *(Sec)*
Juan Quintana *(Pres)*

STANDARD RESTAURANT EQUIPMENT COMPANY
3500 SW Temple, Salt Lake City, UT 84115-4408   UT
Web Site:
http://www.standardrestaurant.com
Sales Range: $25-49.9 Million
Emp.: 250
Mfr & Retailer of Restaurant Equipment & Janitorial Supplies
N.A.I.C.S.: 423440
Ellery Kingston *(Pres)*
Del Kingston *(CFO)*
Edmund Gustafson *(Dir-Mktg)*

STANDARD SAFETY EQUIPMENT CO.
1407 Ridgeview Dr, McHenry, IL 60050
Tel.: (815) 363-8565
Year Founded: 1921
Sales Range: $75-99.9 Million
Emp.: 50
Mfr of Personal Safety Equipment & Protective Clothing
N.A.I.C.S.: 315250
Scott R. Olson *(Chm, Pres & CEO)*
Steve Medves *(Exec VP)*
Cindy Burger *(VP-Admin)*

STANDARD SALES CO. INC.
4800 E 42nd St Ste 400, Odessa, TX 79762
Tel.: (432) 367-7662
Web Site:
http://www.standardsalescompany.com
Sales Range: $75-99.9 Million
Emp.: 14
Beer & Other Fermented Malt Liquors
N.A.I.C.S.: 424810
Frank Deaderick *(Pres)*

STANDARD STRUCTURES INC.
5900 Pruitt Ave, Windsor, CA 95492-8767
Tel.: (707) 836-8100   CA
Web Site:
http://www.standardstructures.com
Year Founded: 1947
Sales Range: $50-74.9 Million
Emp.: 325
Structural Wood Services
N.A.I.C.S.: 321215

STANDARD SUPPLY & DISTRIBUTING CO. INC.
1431 Regal Rd, Dallas, TX 75247
Tel.: (214) 630-7800
Web Site:
http://www.standardsupplyhvac.com
Sales Range: $25-49.9 Million
Emp.: 100
Warm Air Heating & Air Conditioning
N.A.I.C.S.: 423730
Lance Malone *(Pres)*

STANDARD TECHNOLOGY INC.
5201 Leesburg Pike Ste 1400, Falls Church, VA 22041
Tel.: (703) 379-2500
Web Site: http://www.stic2.com
Year Founded: 1985
Rev.: $18,900,000
Emp.: 25

STANDARD TECHNOLOGY INC.   U.S. PRIVATE

Standard Technology Inc.—(Continued)
Provider of Technology & Management Consulting Services
N.A.I.C.S.: 541512
Kathryn C. Turner *(Chm, Pres & CEO)*

STANDARD TEXTILE CO., INC.
1 Knollcrest Dr, Cincinnati, OH 45237
Tel.: (513) 761-9255   OH
Web Site:
   http://www.standardtextile.com
Year Founded: 1940
Sales Range: $450-499.9 Million
Emp.: 1,100
Health Care Textiles & Apparel Mfr & Distr
N.A.I.C.S.: 315250
Gary Heiman *(Chm & CEO)*
Norman Frankel *(VP-Sls & Mktg)*
Lisa Seitz *(VP-Hospitality Product Mgmt)*
Marty Glassmeyer *(VP-Hospitality Sls & Ops)*
Katy Butcher *(Dir-Product Line Strategy & Project Mgmt)*
Rebecca Mackert *(Dir-Inside Sls & Client Svcs)*
Jonathan Simon *(Exec VP-Global Growth & Strategy)*
Alex Heiman *(Pres)*
Judy Sroufe *(VP-Brand Mgmt & Comm)*

Subsidiaries:

Standard Textile bvba   (1)
Latem Business Park Xavier Decocklaan 72, 9831, Sint-Martens-Latem, Belgium
Tel.: (32) 9 381 5151
Web Site: http://www.standardtextile.com
Sales Range: $10-24.9 Million
Emp.: 9
Linen Product Mfr
N.A.I.C.S.: 314120
Ignace Vandenberghe *(Gen Mgr)*

STANDARD TILE DISTRIBUTORS OF NEW HAVEN INC.
105 Hamilton St, New Haven, CT 06511
Tel.: (203) 777-3637
Web Site: http://www.tileamerica.com
Rev.: $10,000,000
Emp.: 30
Whslr & Retailer of Ceramic Wall & Floor Tile
N.A.I.C.S.: 423320
Brian Knies *(Pres)*

STANDARD TRANSPORTATION SERVICES, INC.
1801 Roosevelt Ave, Joplin, MO 64801
Tel.: (417) 782-1990
Web Site:
   http://www.standardtransinc.com
Year Founded: 1984
Sales Range: $10-24.9 Million
Emp.: 70
Domestic Freight Forwarding; Over the Road Trucking & Warehousing
N.A.I.C.S.: 488510
Todd Stout *(Owner)*
John Claybrook *(Dir-Brokerage)*
Kathy Doss *(Dir-Safety & Compliance)*
J. D. McArthur *(Gen Mgr)*
Stan Hughes *(Mgr-Warehouse)*
Jeff Weston *(Mgr-Warehouse)*
Ja'Mes Ammons *(Mgr-Warehouse)*
Lois Metz *(Coord-Warehouse)*

STANDARD TUBE SALES CORPORATION
90 Bartlett St, Marlborough, MA 01752
Tel.: (508) 481-7100
Web Site:
   http://www.standardtube.com
Rev.: $18,900,000
Emp.: 26
Metal Tubing
N.A.I.C.S.: 423510
Jeffrey Maloney *(Controller)*

STANDARD WIRE & CABLE CO.
2050 E Vista Bella Way, Rancho Dominguez, CA 90220
Tel.: (310) 609-1811   CA
Web Site: http://www.standard-wire.com
Year Founded: 1945
Sales Range: $10-24.9 Million
Emp.: 40
Electrical & Electronic Wires, Fiber Optic Cables, Cables & Cords Mfr & Distr
N.A.I.C.S.: 335929
Dick Hampikian *(Chm)*
Russ Skrable *(Pres)*
Bruce Haft *(Mgr-Info Svcs)*
Jerry Gaither *(VP-Ops)*
Bud Gardner *(VP-Sls & Mktg)*
Art Skorka *(Controller)*

Subsidiaries:

Standard Wire & Cable Co.   (1)
3120 W Thomas Rd Ste 801, Phoenix, AZ 85017-5300
Tel.: (602) 269-2501
Web Site: http://www.std-wire.com
Electric Cable & Wire
N.A.I.C.S.: 335929
Bob Maughan *(Gen Mgr)*

STANDARD-KNAPP, INC.
63 Pickering St, Portland, CT 06480-1860
Tel.: (860) 342-1100   CT
Web Site: http://www.standard-knapp.com
Year Founded: 1890
Sales Range: $50-74.9 Million
Emp.: 65
Mfr of Automatic Packaging Equipment
N.A.I.C.S.: 333993
Robert L. Reynolds *(VP-Mfg)*
Mike Weaver *(Pres & CEO)*

STANDARD-TAYLOR INDUSTRIES, INC.
516 N McDonough St, Montgomery, AL 36104
Tel.: (334) 834-3000
Web Site:
   http://www.standardtaylor.com
Sales Range: $10-24.9 Million
Emp.: 30
Roofing Contractors
N.A.I.C.S.: 551112
Kristine Minteo *(CFO)*

STANDING PARTNERSHIP
1610 Des Pers Rd Ste 200, Saint Louis, MO 63131
Tel.: (314) 469-3500
Web Site:
   http://www.standingpartnership.com
Year Founded: 1991
Sales Range: $1-9.9 Million
Emp.: 23
Public Relations Agency
N.A.I.C.S.: 541820
Melissa Lackey *(Pres & CEO)*
Julie Steininger *(Partner & Sr VP)*
Ashlyn Brewer *(VP)*

Subsidiaries:

Standing Partnership   (1)
3445 Seminole Trl Ste 196, Charlottesville, VA 22911
Tel.: (434) 973-0645
Public Relations Agency
N.A.I.C.S.: 541820

STANDISH MILLING COMPANY
1331 W Cedar St, Standish, MI 48658
Tel.: (989) 846-6911
Web Site: http://standishmilling.com
Sales Range: $10-24.9 Million
Emp.: 50
Grain Processing & Sales
N.A.I.C.S.: 424510
Jim Mitrzyk *(Pres)*

STANDLEY'S SYSTEMS, INC
528 W Iowa, Chickasha, OK 73018
Tel.: (405) 224-0819
Web Site: http://www.standleys.com
Year Founded: 1934
Rev.: $15,500,000
Emp.: 70
Photocopiers Distr
N.A.I.C.S.: 333310
Jayna Braden Anderson *(Sr VP-Sls)*
Richmond Logan *(Acct Mgr-Govt)*
Tim Elliott *(Owner)*

STANDRIDGE COLOR CORPORATION
1196 E Hightower Trl, Social Circle, GA 30025
Tel.: (770) 464-3362   GA
Web Site:
   http://www.standridgecolor.com
Sales Range: $50-74.9 Million
Emp.: 265
Mfr of Color Concentrates from Organic & Inorganic Pigments; Custom Compound Work
N.A.I.C.S.: 325130
Mable Standridge *(Exec VP)*

STANDRIDGE EQUIPMENT CO., INC.
627 N 16th St, Chickasha, OK 73018
Tel.: (405) 224-4411
Web Site:
   http://www.standridgeequipment.com
Sales Range: $10-24.9 Million
Emp.: 40
Retailer of Tractors
N.A.I.C.S.: 423820
Tom Adams *(Gen Mgr)*
Red Skelton *(Pres)*
Jane Wayne *(Treas & Sec)*

STANFORD HOTELS CORPORATION
433 California St Fl 7, San Francisco, CA 94104-2016
Tel.: (415) 398-3333   CA
Web Site:
   http://www.stanfordhotels.com
Year Founded: 1995
Sales Range: $10-24.9 Million
Emp.: 30
Hotel Operator
N.A.I.C.S.: 721110
Lawrence Lui *(Pres)*
James E. M. Evans *(CFO & Exec VP)*
Linda Simpson *(VP-Sls & Mktg)*
Scott Kammeyer *(Mgr-E-Commerce Sls)*

Subsidiaries:

L'Enfant DC Hotel LLC   (1)
480 L'Enfant Plz SW, Washington, DC 20024-2114
Tel.: (202) 484-1000
Web Site: http://www.lenfantplazahotel.com
Luxury Hotel Operator
N.A.I.C.S.: 721110
Will Gibbs *(Sr VP)*

STANFORD LUMBER COMPANY INC.
2001 Rte 286, Pittsburgh, PA 15239
Tel.: (724) 327-6800   PA
Web Site:
   http://www.stanfordhome.com
Year Founded: 1954
Sales Range: $10-24.9 Million
Emp.: 80
Home Center Operator
N.A.I.C.S.: 444110
Carl T. Piekarski *(Co-Owner)*
Susie Reese *(Co-Owner)*

STANGER INDUSTRIES
4900 Lawn Ave, Kansas City, MO 64130
Tel.: (816) 861-2800
Web Site: http://www.stangerinc.com
Year Founded: 1981
Sales Range: $10-24.9 Million
Emp.: 60
Nonresidential Construction Services
N.A.I.C.S.: 236220
Greg E. Stanger *(Pres)*

STANION WHOLESALE ELECTRIC CO. INC.
812 S Main St, Pratt, KS 67124
Tel.: (620) 672-5678
Web Site: http://www.stanion.com
Sales Range: $75-99.9 Million
Emp.: 235
Electrical Supplies
N.A.I.C.S.: 423610
William Keller *(Pres)*
Ron Harms *(Mgr)*

STANISLAUS FARM SUPPLY COMPANY
624 E Service Rd, Modesto, CA 95358
Tel.: (209) 538-7070
Web Site:
   http://www.stanislausfarmsupply.com
Sales Range: $10-24.9 Million
Emp.: 61
Fertilizer & Fertilizer Materials
N.A.I.C.S.: 424910
Louise Bettencourt *(Office Mgr)*
Joey Gonsalves *(Coord-Seed & Feed Sls)*

STANLEY AUTOMOTIVE ENTERPRISES, INC.
3915 Lemmon Ave Ste 300, Dallas, TX 75219-3773
Tel.: (214) 219-4040
Web Site:
   http://www.stanleyautogroup.com
New Car Dealership
N.A.I.C.S.: 441110
Gaines Stanley *(Owner)*
Lori Morris *(Dir-Ops)*

Subsidiaries:

Stanley Ford - McGregor   (1)
1280 E McGregor Dr, McGregor, TX 76657
Tel.: (254) 840-2868
Web Site: http://www.stanleymcgregor.net
Sales Range: $1-9.9 Million
Emp.: 29
New Car Dealers
N.A.I.C.S.: 441110
Gaines Stanley *(Owner)*

STANLEY CONSULTANTS CO.
225 Iowa Ave, Muscatine, IA 52761
Tel.: (563) 264-6600   IA
Web Site:
   http://www.stanleygroup.com
Year Founded: 1913
Sales Range: $100-124.9 Million
Emp.: 1,750
Holding Company; Engineering, Environmental & Construction Services

N.A.I.C.S.: 551112
Gayle Roberts (Chm)
Ken Cable (Chief Strategy Officer & VP)
Marvinetta Hartwig (VP)
Michael Hunzinger (COO)
Helmut Steudel (VP)
Jesse Cabrera (Mgr-Bus Dev)
Kate Harris (CEO)
Doug Cowin (Mgr-Bus Dev)
Scott Hartford (VP)
Kate Despinoy (Mgr-Client Svc-Water Market)
Mike Rothberg (VP)
John Guilfoyle (Dir-Tech & Innovation)
Stuart Crenshaw (Chief Legal Officer & Sec)
Jennifer Wozniak (Chief Comm Officer)

Subsidiaries:

Stanley Consultants (Engineers), P.S.C. (1)
St 1 Metro 6 Ste 301, Guaynabo, PR 00968
Tel.: (787) 774-0290
Sales Range: $10-24.9 Million
Emp.: 3
Engineering Consulting Services
N.A.I.C.S.: 541330
John Downes (Office Mgr)

Stanley Consultants Inc (1)
2658 Crosspark Rd Ste 100, Coralville, IA 52241 (100%)
Tel.: (319) 626-3990
Web Site: http://www.stanleyconsultants.com
Sales Range: $10-24.9 Million
Emp.: 18
Environmental Consulting Services
N.A.I.C.S.: 541611
Richard C. Smith (Treas)
Mike Hunzinger (COO)

Stanley Consultants India Private Limited (1)
Unit No 405 A & B Rectangle 1 4th Floor Saket, New Delhi, 110017, India
Tel.: (91) 112 956 5322
Web Site: http://www.scipl.com
Sales Range: $10-24.9 Million
Emp.: 25
Engineeering Services
N.A.I.C.S.: 541330
Arun Prasad (Mng Dir)

Stanley Design-Build, Inc. (1)
225 Iowa Ave Stanley Bldg, Muscatine, IA 52761 (100%)
Tel.: (563) 264-6254
Web Site: http://www.stanleyconsultants.com
Sales Range: $10-24.9 Million
Emp.: 280
Construction Services
N.A.I.C.S.: 541618
Gregs G. Thomopulos (Pres)
Steven J. Allchin (Treas)

STANLEY MACHINING & TOOL CORPORATION

425 Maple Ave, Carpentersville, IL 60110
Tel.: (847) 426-4560
Web Site: http://www.stanleymachining.com
Year Founded: 1966
Sales Range: $10-24.9 Million
Emp.: 94
Mfr of Machine Parts
N.A.I.C.S.: 332710
Stanley Trzaska (Chm)
Krystyna Trzaska (Pres)
Barbara Colletier (VP & Controller)

STANLEY MARTIN COMPANIES INC.

No 200 11111 Sunset Hills Rd, Reston, VA 20190-5339
Tel.: (703) 715-7800
Web Site: http://www.stanleymartin.com
Year Founded: 1966
Rev.: $36,000,000
Emp.: 150
Provider of Single-Family House Construction Services
N.A.I.C.S.: 236115
Steven B. Alloy (Pres)
Fred Hetzel (VP-Land Acq)
Lauri Payson (VP-Mktg)

STANLEY MILLER CONSTRUCTION CO.

2250 Howenstine Dr SE, East Sparta, OH 44626-9538
Tel.: (330) 484-2229 OH
Web Site: http://stanleymillerconstruction.com
Nonresidential Construction
N.A.I.C.S.: 236220
Brian Sudduth (Sr VP)

STANLEY NISSAN INC.

2610 S Cushman St, Fairbanks, AK 99701
Tel.: (907) 452-1701
Web Site: http://www.stanleynissan.com
Year Founded: 1997
Sales Range: $10-24.9 Million
Emp.: 71
New Car Whslr
N.A.I.C.S.: 441110
Mel Stanley (Owner & Pres)

STANLEY STEEMER INTERNATIONAL, INC.

5800 Innovation Dr, Dublin, OH 43016
Tel.: (614) 764-2007 OH
Web Site: http://www.stanleysteemer.com
Year Founded: 1947
Sales Range: $250-299.9 Million
Emp.: 1,800
Carpet & Upholstery Cleaning & Related Services
N.A.I.C.S.: 561740
Wesley Bates (CEO)
Mark Bunner (CFO & VP)
Philip P. Ryser (Gen Counsel & Exec VP)

Subsidiaries:

Stanley Steemer Atlanta (1)
3730 Honeysuckle Ln, Atlanta, GA 30340
Tel.: (770) 451-3035
Web Site: http://www.stanleysteemer.com
Sales Range: Less than $1 Million
Emp.: 110
Residential & Commercial Cleaning Services, Flooring Sales & Installation & Water Damage Restoration
N.A.I.C.S.: 561740
Barry Goldberger (CFO)

Stanley Steemer of Charleston (1)
7890 Dorchester Rd, Charleston, SC 29418
Tel.: (843) 552-4090
Web Site: http://www.stanleysteemer.com
Rev.: $135,388,579
Emp.: 25
Carpet & Furniture Cleaning On Location
N.A.I.C.S.: 561740
David Floyd (Pres)

STANLEY STEPHENS CO. INC.

2565 Pearl Buck Rd, Bristol, PA 19007
Tel.: (215) 788-1515
Web Site: http://www.sstfloor.com
Year Founded: 1977
Sales Range: $50-74.9 Million
Emp.: 25
Floor Coverings
N.A.I.C.S.: 423220
Stephen Seidman (Pres)
Kevin Mays (Sr VP)

STANLEY STREET TREATMENT & RESOURCES

386 Stanley St, Fall River, MA 02720
Tel.: (508) 679-5222 MA
Web Site: http://www.sstar.org
Year Founded: 1977
Sales Range: $10-24.9 Million
Emp.: 392
Substance Abuse Rehabilitation & Mental Health Care Services
N.A.I.C.S.: 623220
Sandy DeGaetano (Dir-Program)
Michael Aguiar (Dir-BOLD Youth Program)
Lisa Garcia (Dir-Program)
Linda Coutinho (Dir-HR)
Patricia Emsellem (COO)
Nancy E. Paull (CEO)
Richard Barnett (Coord-Driver Alcohol Education Program)
Robin Quinterno (Dir-Program-Ambulatory Behavioral Health Svcs)
Diane Gouveia (Dir-Program-Birth)
Dale Brown (Dir-Program-Womens Center)
Timothy Comeaux (Mgr-Clinic)
Maggie Carr (Dir-Program-Dual Diagnosis Svcs)
Robert Hitt (Dir-Project Aware)

STANLEY TOTAL LIVING CENTER, INC.

514 Old Mount Holly Rd, Stanley, NC 28164
Tel.: (704) 263-1986 NC
Web Site: http://www.stanleytotallivingcenter.org
Year Founded: 1984
Sales Range: $10-24.9 Million
Emp.: 223
Retirement Community Operator
N.A.I.C.S.: 623311
Mike Dixon (CFO & Treas)
Ron Ensley (Pres)

STANMAR INC.

321 Commonwealth Rd Ste 201, Wayland, MA 01778
Tel.: (508) 310-9922 MA
Web Site: http://www.stanmar-inc.com
Year Founded: 1965
Sales Range: $10-24.9 Million
Emp.: 65
Provider of Heavy Construction Services
N.A.I.C.S.: 236210
Susan Thompson (Dir-Mktg)
Nancy Sooper (CFO & VP)
Jerry Burke (Dir-Plng)
Irene Barney (Office Mgr)
Oliver Snider (VP-Bus Dev)
Christine Jones (Mgr-Mktg)
Ralph Agostinelli (Sr Project Mgr)

STANSFIELD VENDING INC.

3172 Berlin Dr, La Crosse, WI 54601
Tel.: (608) 782-7181
Web Site: http://www.stansfieldvending.com
Sales Range: $10-24.9 Million
Emp.: 210
Vending
N.A.I.C.S.: 445132
Janet Stansfield Hess (Pres)

STANTON COMMUNICATIONS, INC.

1150 Connecticut Ave NW Ste 810, Washington, DC 20036
Tel.: (202) 223-4933
Web Site: http://www.stantoncomm.com
Year Founded: 1989
Sales Range: $1-9.9 Million
Emp.: 15
Public Relations Agency
N.A.I.C.S.: 541820
Peter V. Stanton (CEO)
Lori Russo (Pres)
Jeff Urbanchuk (Acct Mgr)
Abbey Race (Acct Exec)

Subsidiaries:

Stanton Communications Inc. (1)
300 E Lombard St Ste 1440, Baltimore, MD 21202
Tel.: (410) 727-6855
Web Site: http://www.stantoncomm.com
Emp.: 3
Public Relations Agency
N.A.I.C.S.: 541820
Lori Russo (Pres)
Amy Bowman (Acct Mgr)

Stanton Communications Inc. (1)
45 Rockefeller Plz Ste 2000, New York, NY 10111
Tel.: (212) 616-3601
Web Site: http://www.stantoncomm.com
Public Relations Agency
N.A.I.C.S.: 541820
Peter V. Stanton (CEO)

STAP INC.

370 N Morgan St, Chicago, IL 60607
Tel.: (312) 421-3737
Web Site: http://www.foxdeluxefoods.com
Rev.: $12,300,000
Emp.: 45
Packaged Frozen Food Merchant Whslr
N.A.I.C.S.: 424420
Fred Samano (Mgr)
Bassam S. Samano (Pres)

STAPLE COTTON COOPERATIVE ASSOCIATION

214 W Market St, Greenwood, MS 38930
Tel.: (662) 453-6231 TN
Web Site: http://www.staplcotn.com
Year Founded: 1921
Sales Range: $1-4.9 Billion
Emp.: 230
Marketer of Cotton; Cooperative for Cotton Farmers; Provider of Agricultural Financing
N.A.I.C.S.: 424590
Kenneth E. Downs (Gen Counsel & Sec)
Mike Moffatt (CFO & VP)
Thomas E. Dillard (COO & VP)
Hank Reichle (Pres & CEO)
Frederick Barrier (VP-Sls)
Russell Robertson (VP-HR)
Crawford A. Tatum (Dir-Economic Res)
Mike P. Sturdivant III (Chm)

Subsidiaries:

Staple Cotton Cooperative Association/Itta Bena (1)
PO Box 547, Greenwood, MS 38935-0547
Tel.: (662) 254-6344
Web Site: http://www.staplcotn.com
Cotton Storage
N.A.I.C.S.: 424590

Staple Cotton Discount Corporation (1)
PO Box 547, Greenwood, MS 38935-0547 (100%)
Tel.: (662) 453-6231
Web Site: http://www.staplcotn.com
Sales Range: $50-74.9 Million
Emp.: 80
Agricultural Lending
N.A.I.C.S.: 522299
Tom Dillard (COO & VP)
Conner Caffey (Officer-Loan)

STAPLE STREET CAPITAL LLC

STAPLE STREET CAPITAL LLC

U.S. PRIVATE

Staple Street Capital LLC—(Continued)
1290 Avenue of the Americas 10th Fl,
New York, NY 10104
Tel.: (212) 613-3100
Web Site:
  http://www.staplestreetcapital.com
Privater Equity Firm
N.A.I.C.S.: 523999
Stephen D. Owens (Mng Dir)
Hootan Yaghoobzadeh (Mng Dir)
Andre Ohnona (Principal)
Jeffrey D. Hyslop (Principal)
Rashid Lattouf (Principal)
Steve Burgermeister (Chief Compliance Officer & Controller)

Subsidiaries:

Ironline Compression Limited
Partnership   (1)
700 15 Ave, Nisku, T9E 7S2, AB,
Canada   (100%)
Tel.: (780) 955-0700
Web Site: https://www.ironline.com
Sales Range: $50-74.9 Million
Emp.: 100
Natural Gas Contract Compression Services
N.A.I.C.S.: 423830
Tim Kelley (Pres & CEO)

STAPLES OIL CO. INC.
866 1st Ave N, Windom, MN 56101
Tel.: (507) 831-4450
Rev.: $18,185,720
Emp.: 10
Petroleum Bulk Stations
N.A.I.C.S.: 424710
Allan J. Staples (Pres)

STAR & CRESCENT BOAT COMPANY
990 N Harbor Dr, San Diego, CA 92101
Tel.: (619) 234-4111
Rev.: $10,000,000
Emp.: 100
Excursion Boat Operators
N.A.I.C.S.: 487210
George Palermo (Pres)
Karen Spencer (Controller)

STAR BRONZE COMPANY, INC.
803 S Mahoning Ave, Alliance, OH 44601-3233
Tel.: (330) 823-1550   OH
Year Founded: 1932
Sales Range: $10-24.9 Million
Emp.: 15
Consumer Paint Sundry Products Mfr
N.A.I.C.S.: 325510
Brian Miller (CEO & Treas)

STAR BUICK GMC
326 E Market St, Leesburg, VA 20176
Tel.: (703) 840-1079
Web Site: http://www.starcars.com
Sales Range: $10-24.9 Million
Emp.: 43
New Car Retailer
N.A.I.C.S.: 441110
Jeff Smith (Mgr-Svc)
Tom Gibbs (Mgr-Sls)
Frank All (Mgr-Sls)
Jill Anderson (Office Mgr)
Judy Ronning (Comptroller)

STAR COLLABORATIVE
18120 46th Ave N, Plymouth, MN 55446
Tel.: (763) 355-4145
Web Site:
  http://www.starcollaborative.com
Year Founded: 2009
Sales Range: $10-24.9 Million
Emp.: 10

Staffing & Consulting
N.A.I.C.S.: 561311
Ed Lefkow (Pres)
Dan Olson (Co-Founder & VP)
Casandra Noyes (VP-Bus Dev)
Danielle Shumilovsky (Mgr-Ops & Vendor)
Jade Jahner (Dir-Talent & Recruiting)
Sara Kittridge (Project Mgr-Candidate Rels)

STAR CUTTER COMPANY
23461 Industrial Park Dr, Farmington Hills, MI 48335-2855
Tel.: (248) 474-8200   MI
Web Site: http://www.starcutter.com
Year Founded: 1927
Sales Range: $50-74.9 Million
Emp.: 500
Mfr of Metal Cutting Tools
N.A.I.C.S.: 333515
Bradley L. Lawton (Pres)
Lapo Vivereloi (VP-Fin)

Subsidiaries:

H.B. Carbide Company   (1)
4210 Doyle Dr, Lewiston, MI 49756
Tel.: (989) 786-4223
Web Site: http://www.hbcarbide.com
Cutting Tool Mfr
N.A.I.C.S.: 333515
Jeff Kleven (Plant Mgr)

Star Cutter Company - Elk Rapids
Engineering Division   (1)
210 Industrial Park Dr, Elk Rapids, MI 49629
Tel.: (231) 264-5661
Web Site: http://www.starcutter.com
Emp.: 50
Cutting Tool Mfr
N.A.I.C.S.: 333515
Jason Walter (Gen Mgr)

Star SU Federal de Mexico S.A. de
C.V   (1)
ACCESO V Nave 20 No 115-A Desarrollo La Montana, 2000 Seccion III, Queretaro, 46150, Mexico
Tel.: (52) 442 217 34 45
Web Site: http://www.su.com
Emp.: 25
Cutting Tool Mfr
N.A.I.C.S.: 333515
Eredh Roderiguez (Gen Mgr)

Star-SU LLC.   (1)
5200 Prairie Stone Pkwy Ste 100, Hoffman Estates, IL 60192
Tel.: (847) 649-1450
Web Site: http://www.star-su.com
Sales Range: $10-24.9 Million
Emp.: 40
Machine Tool & Precision Cutting Tool Mfr
N.A.I.C.S.: 333517
David Goodfellow (Pres)
Bruce Cowley (Reg Mgr-Sls)

Tru Tech Systems Inc.   (1)
24550 N. River Road, Mt. Clemens, MI 48043
Tel.: (586) 469-2700
Web Site: http://www.trutechsystems.com
Surgical & Medical Instrument Mfr
N.A.I.C.S.: 339112
Brian Gehrke (Mgr-Engrg)

STAR DISTRIBUTION SYSTEMS INC.
2302 Henderson Way, Plant City, FL 33563-7904
Tel.: (813) 659-1002
Web Site:
  http://www.stardistribution.us
Year Founded: 1931
Emp.: 200
Refrigerated Warehousing & Storage
N.A.I.C.S.: 493120
David Mattioli (Exec VP)
Larry W. Jiminez (Pres & CEO)
Debbie Vaillant (VP-Admin)
Pete Brainard (Dir-Safety)

STAR DODGE CHRYSLER JEEP HYUNDAI
5101 S 1st St, Abilene, TX 79605-1334
Tel.: (325) 698-2222
Web Site: http://www.stardodge.net
Sales Range: $10-24.9 Million
Emp.: 65
New Car Whslr
N.A.I.C.S.: 441110
Mike Dunnahoo (Owner)
Mike Byrom (Mgr-Svc)

STAR ENERGY INTERNATIONAL CORPORATION
4315 South Dr, Houston, TX 77053
Tel.: (832) 269-8899
Web Site: http://www.istarenergy.com
Energy Investment Holding Company
N.A.I.C.S.: 551112
Linhua Guan (Chm)
Xiaochun Jin (CEO & Partner)
Bin Gong (Partner)

STAR EQUIPMENT, LTD.
1401 2nd Ave, Des Moines, IA 50314
Tel.: (515) 283-2215
Web Site: http://www.starequip.com
Year Founded: 1968
Sales Range: $10-24.9 Million
Emp.: 60
General Construction Machinery & Equipment
N.A.I.C.S.: 423810
Bruce Bowman (Co-Owner & Pres)
Brett Bowman (VP & Mgr-Svcs)
Brad Bowman (Co-Owner & VP)

STAR EXHIBITS & ENVIRONMENTS, INC.
6688 93rd Ave N, Minneapolis, MN 55445-1714
Tel.: (763) 561-4655
Web Site: https://engagestar.com
Year Founded: 1993
Emp.: 1,294
Services Related to Advertising
N.A.I.C.S.: 541890

Subsidiaries:

Exhibit Edge Inc.   (1)
4315-A Walney Rd, Chantilly, VA 20151
Tel.: (703) 230-0000
Web Site: https://www.exhibitedge.com
Sales Range: $1-9.9 Million
Emp.: 15
Support Services
N.A.I.C.S.: 561990

STAR FISHERIES INC.
2206 Signal Pl, San Pedro, CA 90731
Tel.: (310) 832-8395
Web Site:
  http://www.starfisheries.com
Rev.: $14,000,000
Emp.: 100
Fish & Seafoods
N.A.I.C.S.: 424460
Anthony DiMaggio (Pres)
Boyd Horan (Gen Mgr)
Neal Smith (Controller)
Melissa Castagnloa (Mgr)

STAR FOOD PRODUCTS, INC.
727 S Spring St, Burlington, NC 27216
Tel.: (336) 227-4079   NC
Web Site:
  http://www.starfoodproducts.com
Year Founded: 1963
Sales Range: $75-99.9 Million
Emp.: 78
Mfr & Wholesale Distribution of Sausage & Other Prepared, Smoked & Cured Meats
N.A.I.C.S.: 424470

George L. Bell (Chm)
Norman Mabry (Pres)
Joyce Abbott (CFO)

STAR FORD
1101 S Brand Blvd, Glendale, CA 91204
Tel.: (818) 956-0977
Web Site: http://www.starford.com
Rev.: $86,244,296
Emp.: 250
New & Used Car Dealers
N.A.I.C.S.: 441110
Moe Khan (Mgr-Internet Sls)
Alex Tamez (Gen Mgr)
Angela Chavez (Mgr-Internet Sls)
Mike Nickeloff (Mgr-Comml Fleet Sls)
Tim Wilkins (Mgr-Fleet)

STAR FURNITURE COMPANY
PO Box 4010, Clarksburg, WV 26302
Tel.: (304) 624-8444
Web Site:
  http://www.starfurniturewv.com
Sales Range: $25-49.9 Million
Emp.: 100
Furniture Retailer
N.A.I.C.S.: 449110
William C. Spurlock III (Treas & Sec)

STAR GRAPHICS, INC.
4785 Eastex Fwy, Beaumont, TX 77706
Tel.: (409) 892-0671   TX
Web Site:
  http://www.stargraphicsinc.com
Year Founded: 1982
Sales Range: $10-24.9 Million
Emp.: 45
Copiers & Business Machines
N.A.I.C.S.: 423420
Keith Watts (VP-Svcs)
Sally Lamb (Mgr-Parts)

STAR HEADLIGHT AND LANTERN CO., INC.
455 Rochester St, Avon, NY 14414
Tel.: (585) 226-9500
Web Site: http://www.star1889.com
Sales Range: $10-24.9 Million
Emp.: 250
Railroad Signaling Devices
N.A.I.C.S.: 334290
Chris Jacobs (Pres)
John Green (Asst VP & Gen Mgr)

STAR INDUSTRIES INC.
130 Lakeside Ave Ste 200, Seattle, WA 98122
Tel.: (206) 328-1600
Year Founded: 1998
Sales Range: $50-74.9 Million
Emp.: 1
Provider of Leasing Services of Heavy Construction Equipment
N.A.I.C.S.: 532412
Leigh W. Rabel (Owner & Pres)
John B. Rabel (VP)
William E. Rabel (Sec)

STAR INDUSTRIES INC.
425 Underhill Blvd, Syosset, NY 11791
Tel.: (516) 921-9300   NY
Web Site: http://www.star-indust.com
Year Founded: 1934
Sales Range: $75-99.9 Million
Emp.: 20
Importer of Liquor
N.A.I.C.S.: 424810
Martin Silver (Pres & CEO)
Phyllis Valenti (Exec VP)

STAR INTERNATIONAL, INC.
250 S Kings Hwy, Texarkana, TX 75501

Tel.: (903) 832-5044
Web Site: http://www.starintl.net
Sales Range: $10-24.9 Million
Emp.: 24
Industrial Machinery & Equipment Whslr
N.A.I.C.S.: 423830
Lee Ann Burke *(Mgr-Acctg & Accts Receivable)*
Scott Martin *(Gen Mgr)*

STAR LUMBER & SUPPLY COMPANY, INC.
325 S W St, Wichita, KS 67213-2105
Tel.: (316) 942-2221 KS
Web Site: http://www.starlumber.com
Year Founded: 1939
Sales Range: $100-124.9 Million
Emp.: 380
Lumber & Other Building Materials Mfr & Retailer
N.A.I.C.S.: 423310
Roger Voge *(Exec VP)*

Subsidiaries:

Perfection Structural Components LLC (1)
1666 S Saint Clair St, Wichita, KS 67213
Tel.: (316) 942-8361
Web Site: http://www.perfectionstructural.com
Emp.: 30
Construction Materials Distr
N.A.I.C.S.: 423390
Dan Zimmerman *(Pres)*

STAR MEDIA NETWORK
5290 Overpass Rd Ste 103, Santa Barbara, CA 93111
Tel.: (805) 730-1108
Web Site: http://www.starmedianetwork.com
Year Founded: 1999
Sales Range: $1-9.9 Million
Emp.: 10
Direct Response Advertising Agency
N.A.I.C.S.: 541810
Joshua Hyman *(Pres)*

STAR MULTI CARE SERVICES INC.
115 Broadhollow Rd Ste 275, Melville, NY 11747-4990
Tel.: (631) 423-6689 NY
Web Site: http://www.extendedfamilycare.com
Year Founded: 1938
Sales Range: $10-24.9 Million
Emp.: 53
Healthcare Personnel Staffing
N.A.I.C.S.: 561311
Stephen Sternbach *(Chm, Pres & CEO)*
Lawrence A. Muenz *(Gen Counsel)*
David Schoenberg *(Dir-Fin)*

Subsidiaries:

Star Multi Care Services of Florida, Inc (1)
2221 N University Dr Ste C, Pembroke Pines, FL 33024
Tel.: (954) 962-0926
Web Site: http://www.starmulticare-florida.com
Emp.: 5
Health Care Srvices
N.A.I.C.S.: 621999
Claudia Lobo *(Mgr)*

STAR NURSERY INC.
125 Cassia Way, Henderson, NV 89014
Tel.: (702) 568-2000 NV
Web Site: http://www.starnursery.com
Year Founded: 1983
Sales Range: $25-49.9 Million
Emp.: 150
Plant Nursery

N.A.I.C.S.: 459310
Craig Keough *(Pres)*
Cindi Thornton *(Coord-Freight)*
David Natoli *(Office Mgr-Warehouse)*
Bobbie Jo Parslow *(Mgr-Credit)*

STAR OF INDIA FASHIONS, INC.
1038 W Southern Ave, Tempe, AZ 85282-4514
Tel.: (480) 968-6195 AZ
Web Site: http://www.soifashions.net
Year Founded: 1969
Sales Range: $10-24.9 Million
Emp.: 65
Women's, Children's & Infants' Clothing & Accessories
N.A.I.C.S.: 424350
Avtar C. Verma *(Pres)*

STAR OF THE WEST MILLING CO.
121 E Tuscola St, Frankenmuth, MI 48734
Tel.: (989) 652-9971 MI
Web Site: http://www.starofthewest.com
Year Founded: 1870
Sales Range: $100-124.9 Million
Emp.: 230
Mfr of Flour
N.A.I.C.S.: 311211
Art Loeffler *(Pres)*
Roy Krauss *(Plant Mgr)*
Francois Lachance *(Plant Mgr)*
Alan McTaggart *(Plant Mgr)*
Mary Homrich *(Office Mgr)*
Anne Stesny *(Office Mgr)*
Candi Stahly *(Office Mgr)*
Jacob Hecht *(Mgr-Plant Food)*
Keith Martus *(Mgr-Sls)*
Ron Hecht *(Plant Mgr)*

STAR ONE CREDIT UNION
1080 Enterprise Way Ste 150, Sunnyvale, CA 94089
Tel.: (408) 543-5202 CA
Web Site: http://www.starone.org
Year Founded: 1956
Sales Range: $150-199.9 Million
Emp.: 193
Credit Union
N.A.I.C.S.: 522130
Richard A. Heldebrant *(Pres & CEO)*
Kevin Collins *(Sr VP-Loan Svcs)*
Brian Ross *(Exec VP-Fin & Admin)*
Richard Aubrey *(Co-Treas)*
Gary Rodrigues *(Exec VP-Ops)*
Koji Fukumoto *(VP-Audit)*
Russ McAlpine *(VP-Info Systems)*
Chris Beer *(Sr Mgr-Info Systems)*
Sandy Moix *(VP-Branch Svcs)*
Ann Sebastian *(VP & Controller)*
Regina Rutledge *(VP-HR)*
Joe Fagenstrom *(VP-Mktg)*
Margarete Mucker *(VP-Remote Svcs)*

STAR PAVING CO.
3109 Love Rd SW, Albuquerque, NM 87195
Tel.: (505) 877-0380
Web Site: http://www.starpaving.com
Year Founded: 1956
Sales Range: $25-49.9 Million
Concrete & Asphalt Paving
N.A.I.C.S.: 237310
Joe M. Cruz *(Pres)*
Dick Rowles *(Project Mgr)*
Michael Zamora *(Controller)*

STAR READY MIX INC.
Rd 189 KM Barrio Navarro, Gurabo, PR 00778
Tel.: (787) 258-8111
Web Site: http://www.starreadymixpr.com

Sales Range: $10-24.9 Million
Emp.: 50
Ready Mixed Concrete
N.A.I.C.S.: 327320
Victor M. Diaz *(Pres)*
Victor Diaz Maldonado *(VP)*

STAR SALES & DISTRIBUTING
29 Commerce Way, Woburn, MA 01801
Tel.: (781) 933-8830
Web Site: http://www.starsales.com
Sales Range: $25-49.9 Million
Emp.: 60
Hardware
N.A.I.C.S.: 423710
Robert F. Ryan *(Pres & CEO)*
Margit E. Star *(COO)*
Steven S. Serowik *(VP)*
Dennis Arsenault *(Mgr-Pur)*
Annmarie Petersen *(Dir-MIS)*

STAR SALES CO., INC.
1803 N Central St, Knoxville, TN 37917-5412
Tel.: (865) 524-0771 TN
Web Site: http://www.starsalescompany.com
Year Founded: 1988
Sales Range: $75-99.9 Million
Emp.: 90
Wholesale Distributor of Notions, Druggists Sundries, Toys, Florists' Supplies, Artificial Flowers & Automotive Supplies
N.A.I.C.S.: 424990
Neil Foster *(Pres & CEO)*

STAR STAINLESS SCREW CO.
30 W End Rd, Totowa, NJ 07512
Tel.: (973) 256-2300
Rev.: $58,200,000
Emp.: 100
Hardware
N.A.I.C.S.: 423710
Bill Fivehouse *(Office Mgr)*
Bruce Wheeler *(Pres)*
Susan Raab Denicola *(CIO & Dir-IT)*

STAR TELEPHONE MEMBERSHIP CORP.
3900 US Hwy 421 N, Clinton, NC 28328
Tel.: (910) 564-4194
Web Site: http://www.stmc.net
Year Founded: 1959
Sales Range: $10-24.9 Million
Emp.: 150
Telecommunication Servicesb
N.A.I.C.S.: 517121
Robert G. Hester *(Pres)*
Kenneth Melvin *(Engr-OSP Distr)*
Tim Butler *(Engr-Broadband)*
Jeffrey Shipp *(Mgr-Community Rels)*
Jeffrey Allen Nethercutt *(Asst Gen Mgr)*
Lyman Horne *(Exec VP & Gen Mgr)*

Subsidiaries:

InterStar Communications, Inc. (1)
3900 Hwy 421 N, Clinton, NC 28328
Tel.: (910) 564-4638
Web Site: http://www.intrstar.net
Provider of Internet Access to Home & Residential Customers
N.A.I.C.S.: 517810
Kelly Rackley *(Mgr-Accts)*

StarVision, Inc. (1)
3900 US Hwy 421 N, Clinton, NC 28328
Tel.: (910) 564-7888
Web Site: http://www.starvisions.tv
Sales Range: $10-24.9 Million
Emp.: 16
Provider of Cable Television Programming
N.A.I.C.S.: 516210

STAR TRIBUNE MEDIA COMPANY LLC
650 3rd Ave S Ste 1300, Minneapolis, MN 55488
Tel.: (612) 673-4000 DE
Web Site: http://www.startribunecompany.com
Year Founded: 2009
Holding Company; Newspaper, Directory & Advertising Materials Publisher
N.A.I.C.S.: 551112
Michael J. Klingensmith *(CEO & Publr)*
Chuck Brown *(CFO & Sr VP)*
Randy Lebedoff *(Gen Counsel & Sr VP)*
Kevin Desmond *(Sr VP-Ops)*
Rene Sanchez *(Sr VP & Editor)*
Jim Bernard *(Sr VP-Digital)*
Steve Yaeger *(Chief Mktg Officer & VP)*
Arden Dickey *(Sr VP-Circulation)*
Paul Kasbohm *(Chief Revenue Officer)*
Christine Phelps *(Sr VP-HR)*

Subsidiaries:

The Star Tribune Company (1)
425 Portland Ave S, Minneapolis, MN 55488
Tel.: (612) 673-4000
Web Site: http://www.startribune.com
Emp.: 1,000
Newspaper Publishers
N.A.I.C.S.: 513110
Paul Kasbohm *(Chief Revenue Officer & Sr VP)*
Scott Gillespie *(Editor-Editorial Pages)*
Rene Sanchez *(Sr VP & Editor)*
Suki Dardarian *(VP)*
Michael J. Klingensmith *(CEO & Publr)*
Jim Bernard *(Sr VP-Digital)*
Kevin Desmond *(Sr VP-Ops)*
Adrienne Sirany *(Sr VP-HR)*
Randy Lebedoff *(Gen Counsel & Sr VP)*
Steve Yaeger *(CMO & VP)*
Arden Dickey *(Sr VP-Circulation)*
Brian Kennett *(VP-Digital Adv Sls)*
Kyndell Harkness *(Mng Editor-Asst-Diversity & Community)*
Thom Kupper *(Mng Editor-Asst-News)*
Courtnay Kim *(Mng Editor-Asst-Bus News)*

STAR WERKS INC.
1237 Capitol Dr, Addison, IL 60101
Tel.: (630) 628-0880
Web Site: http://www.starwerk-inc.com
Rev.: $15,000,000
Emp.: 15
Electronic Parts & Equipment
N.A.I.C.S.: 423690
James Giusto *(Pres)*
Brian Harrigan *(Engr-Electrical)*

STAR WEST SATELLITE INC.
580 Pronghorn Dr, Bozeman, MT 59718
Web Site: http://www.starwestsatellite.net
Sales Range: $350-399.9 Million
Emp.: 25
Satellite Dish Sales
N.A.I.C.S.: 517410
Pete Sobrepena *(Pres)*

Subsidiaries:

Star West Satellite (1)
2200 N Elder St, Nampa, ID 83687
Tel.: (208) 467-6365
Rev.: $840,000
Emp.: 12
Antennas, Satellite Dish
N.A.I.C.S.: 516210

Star West Satellite (1)
6009 W Seltice Way, Post Falls, ID 83854
Tel.: (208) 457-0766
Cable & Other Pay Television Services
N.A.I.C.S.: 516120

STAR-GLO INDUSTRIES LLC — U.S. PRIVATE

Star-Glo Industries LLC—(Continued)

STAR-GLO INDUSTRIES LLC
2 Carlton Ave, East Rutherford, NJ 07073
Tel.: (201) 939-6162
Web Site: http://www.starglo.com
Rev.: $14,694,984
Emp.: 150
Molded Rubber Products
N.A.I.C.S.: 326299
Anthony G. Olivieri (Pres)
Dennis Azzolina (Sr VP)
Himan Patel (Dir-Tech)

STAR-USA LLC
5001 Mayfield Rd Ste 220, Cleveland, OH 44124-2609
Tel.: (216) 691-7827
Web Site: http://www.star-usa.net
Sales Range: Less than $1 Million
Emp.: 8
Translation Services
N.A.I.C.S.: 541930
Alan Horvath (Mng Dir)

STARBAND COMMUNICATIONS INC.
1750 Old Meadow Rd - 7th Fl, McLean, VA 22102-4302
Tel.: (703) 287-3000
Rev.: $12,000,000
Emp.: 150
Internet Service Provider
N.A.I.C.S.: 459999
Andreas M. Georghiou (CEO)
Jill Robins (Dir-Mkg)

STARBOARD MOTORS INC.
701 Washington Ave, Cloquet, MN 55720
Tel.: (218) 879-4668
Web Site: http://www.okcloquet.com
Sales Range: $10-24.9 Million
Emp.: 37
Automobiles, New & Used
N.A.I.C.S.: 441110
Peter Nelson (Pres & Gen Mgr)
Trudy Okerman (Controller)

STARBOARD VALUE LP
777 3rd Ave 18th Fl, New York, NY 10017
Tel.: (212) 845-7977
Web Site: http://www.starboardvalue.com
Year Founded: 2002
Sales Range: $75-99.9 Million
Emp.: 28
Investment Advisory & Hedge Fund Management Services
N.A.I.C.S.: 523940
Peter Alexander Feld (Head-Research & Portfolio Mgr)
Kevin Marlin (CFO & Chief Compliance Officer)
Jeffrey Chad Smith (CEO)
Jonathan Sagal (Partner)
Gavin T. Molinelli (Partner)

STARC SYSTEMS, INC.
166 Orion St, Brunswick, ME 04011   DE
Web Site: http://www.starcsystems.com
Year Founded: 2015
Sales Range: $1-9.9 Million
Emp.: 39
Building Panel Mfr
N.A.I.C.S.: 326199
Timothy Hebert (Founder & Chm)
Chris Vickers (Pres & CEO)
Bruce Bickford (VP-Product Dev)
Jonathan Thomas (Sr VP-Sls)
Chris MacKenzie (VP-Bus Dev)

STARCHTECH, INC.
720 Florida Ave, Minneapolis, MN 55426
Tel.: (763) 545-5400
Web Site: http://www.starchtech.com
Year Founded: 1996
Sales Range: $10-24.9 Million
Emp.: 20
Mfr of Biodegradable Packing Peanuts
N.A.I.C.S.: 488991
Edward Boehmer (CEO)
Denise Pech (Dir-Mktg & Acct Mgmt-North Central United States)

STARCO IMPEX INC.
2710 S 11th St, Beaumont, TX 77701
Tel.: (409) 840-9601
Web Site: http://www.starcoimpex.com
Sales Range: $10-24.9 Million
Emp.: 35
Sales of Store Merchandise to Wholesalers
N.A.I.C.S.: 424990
Mohammad Tahir Javed (Pres)
Jennifer Trull (Office Mgr)
Nasir Jamal (VP-Sls)
Mohammed Danishmund (CFO)

STARCON INC.
2100 Ellis Rd, New Lenox, IL 60451
Tel.: (815) 478-4615
Web Site: http://www.starconinternational.com
Year Founded: 1983
Sales Range: $25-49.9 Million
Emp.: 2,200
Mechanical Contractor
N.A.I.C.S.: 238220
Reggie Williams (Reg Mgr)

STARCREST PRODUCTS OF CALIFORNIA
19465 Brennan Ave, Perris, CA 92599-1000
Tel.: (951) 943-2011   DE
Web Site: http://www.starcrest.com
Year Founded: 1971
Sales Range: $400-449.9 Million
Emp.: 1,700
Mail-Order Houses
N.A.I.C.S.: 455110
T. M. Calandra (Owner & CEO)
Michael E. Donnelly (Pres)
Diann Bowman (Mgr-Order Fulfillment & Order Entry)
Shawn Trew (Mgr-Facilities)
Erika Alexander (Supvr-Recruiting)

Subsidiaries:

Handsome Rewards   (1)
19465 Brennan Ave, Perris, CA 92599
Tel.: (951) 943-2011
Web Site: http://www.handsomerewards.com
Sales Range: $50-74.9 Million
Emp.: 720
Mail Order House Distr
N.A.I.C.S.: 541860
T.M. Calandra (CEO)
M. Donnelly (Pres)

Signatures   (1)
3660 Brennan Ave, Perris, CA 92571
Tel.: (951) 943-2011
Sales Range: $125-149.9 Million
Emp.: 1,001
Mail-Order Houses
N.A.I.C.S.: 516210

Starcrest of California   (1)
19465 Brennan Ave, Perris, CA 92599-1000
Tel.: (951) 943-2011
Web Site: http://www.starcrest.com
Sales Range: $50-74.9 Million
Emp.: 750
Mail-Order Houses
N.A.I.C.S.: 444180
T. M. Calandra (CEO)
M. Donnelly (Pres)

STARDUST TRANSPORTATION
8604 Allsnville Rd Ste 207, Indianapolis, IN 46250
Tel.: (317) 915-2000
Web Site: http://www.stardusttransport.com
Year Founded: 2000
Rev.: $5,500,000
Emp.: 42
Specialized Freight, Trucking & Long-Distance
N.A.I.C.S.: 484230
Tom Harris (Owner & Pres)

STARENSIER INC.
PO Box 737, Byfield, MA 01922
Tel.: (978) 462-7311
Web Site: http://www.cosmofabric.net
Year Founded: 1903
Rev.: $16,629,784
Emp.: 10
Mfr of Textiles
N.A.I.C.S.: 313310
Richard N. Van Dernoot (Chm)
Josh Van Dernoot (Pres)

STARFLOWER ESSENTIALS ORGANIC SKIN CARE
411 S Pineapple Ave, Sarasota, FL 34236
Tel.: (941) 554-4292
Web Site: http://www.starflower.com
Year Founded: 1994
Sales Range: $1-9.9 Million
Skin Care Product Mfr
N.A.I.C.S.: 325620
Cherylyn Van Kirk (Founder & CEO)

STARGATE INDUSTRIES LLC
810 Parish St, Pittsburgh, PA 15222
Tel.: (412) 316-7800
Web Site: http://www.expedient.com
Year Founded: 1994
Sales Range: $50-74.9 Million
Emp.: 75
Provider of Residential & Internet Connectivity, Application Development, Datacenter Services, It Staffing & Web Development & Hosting
N.A.I.C.S.: 517810
Bryan K. Smith (VP-Sls)

STARGATE TELECOM INC.
3614 Meridian St, Bellingham, WA 98225
Tel.: (360) 738-4664
Rev.: $12,000,000
Emp.: 100
Communications Specialization
N.A.I.C.S.: 238210
Shaun Liu (CEO)

STARGEL OFFICE SYSTEMS, INC.
4700 Blalock RD, Houston, TX 77041
Tel.: (713) 461-5382
Web Site: http://www.stargel.com
Year Founded: 1987
Emp.: 100
Office Equipment Whslr
N.A.I.C.S.: 423420
Jack Stargel (Founder & CEO)
Tyson Stargel (Co-Pres)
Slade Stargel (Co-Pres)

Subsidiaries:

Round Rock Copier, LLC   (1)
1101 Egger Ave, Round Rock, TX 78664-3058
Tel.: (512) 388-0731
Emp.: 100
Computer & Office Machine Repair & Maintenance
N.A.I.C.S.: 811210

STARIZON, INC.
31 River Overlook Ct, Keystone, CO 80435
Tel.: (970) 262-2123
Web Site: http://www.starizon.org
Sales Range: $1-9.9 Million
Emp.: 13
Business Management & Reorganization Services
N.A.I.C.S.: 561499
Gary Adamson (Chief Experience Officer)
Leigh Adamson (Chief Dev Officer)

STARK & ROTH, INC.
735 N Water St Ste 790, Milwaukee, WI 53202
Tel.: (414) 294-7000   WI
Web Site: http://www.starkinvestments.com
Year Founded: 1993
Sales Range: $25-49.9 Million
Emp.: 100
Private Investment Firm
N.A.I.C.S.: 523999
Michael Roth (Founder, Principal & Head-Bus Dev)
Donald Bobbs (Principal & Sr Portfolio Mgr-Credit)
Troy Holmes (Principal)
Brian Jay Stark (CEO & CIO)
Rob Barnard (Deputy CIO & Sr Portfolio Mgr-Fundamental Strategies)

STARK AUTOMOTIVE GROUP
1423 US Hwy 51, Stoughton, WI 53589
Tel.: (608) 873-5661
Web Site: http://www.starkauto.com
Year Founded: 1956
Sales Range: $10-24.9 Million
Emp.: 40
Car Whslr
N.A.I.C.S.: 441110
Don Dillman (Mgr-Svc)
William J. Hoile (CFO & VP)
Bill Stark (Pres)

STARK BANK GROUP LTD.
1207 Central Ave, Fort Dodge, IA 50501
Tel.: (515) 573-2154
Web Site: http://www.bankfirstamerican.com
Sales Range: $50-74.9 Million
Emp.: 200
Bank Holding Company
N.A.I.C.S.: 551111
Thomas Schnurr (Pres & CEO)
Linda Donner (VP-IT)

Subsidiaries:

First America Bank   (1)
4040 Gulf Shore Blvd N, Naples, FL 34103
Tel.: (239) 403-0076
Web Site: http://www.firstamericanbank.com
Sales Range: $25-49.9 Million
Emp.: 20
Banking Services
N.A.I.C.S.: 522110
Jhon Fisher (Pres)

STARK BROTHERS NURSERIES & ORCHARDS CO.
20947 Hwy 54 W, Louisiana, MO 63353
Tel.: (573) 754-5111   IL
Web Site: http://www.starkbros.com
Year Founded: 1816
Sales Range: $75-99.9 Million
Emp.: 150
Whslr of Fruit Trees & Ornamental Plants
N.A.I.C.S.: 111421

STARK CARPET CORPORATION

D&D Bldg 979 3rd Ave Fl 11, New York, NY 10022
Tel.: (212) 752-9000
Web Site: http://www.starkcarpet.com
Sales Range: $100-124.9 Million
Emp.: 150
Carpet Sales
N.A.I.C.S.: 423220
Peter Karp *(Controller)*
Sylvana Carlucci *(Mgr-Wall Coverings)*
Joe Nehls *(Supvr-Import)*
Nyan Gabriel *(Dir-Mktg & Bus Dev)*
Richard Zolt *(VP-Sls & Mktg)*

STARK COMMUNITY FOUNDATION, INC.
400 Market Ave N Ste 200, Canton, OH 44702
Tel.: (330) 454-3426 OH
Web Site: http://www.starkcf.org
Year Founded: 1963
Sales Range: $10-24.9 Million
Emp.: 14
Fundraising Services
N.A.I.C.S.: 813211
Mark Samolczyk *(Pres & CEO)*
Amy Krebs *(Dir-Grants & Community Initiatives)*
Stephanie Boka *(Accountant)*
Marilyn Thomas Jones *(Dir-Community Engagement)*
Bridgette Neisel *(VP-Advancement)*

STARK EXCAVATING INC.
1805 W Washington St, Bloomington, IL 61701
Tel.: (309) 828-5034
Web Site: http://www.starkcompanies.com
Rev.: $48,955,773
Emp.: 300
Highway & Street Construction
N.A.I.C.S.: 237310
Gary W. Masso *(CFO)*
Ila Slagell *(Sec & Controller)*
Lou Huff *(Superintendent-Concrete)*
Patti Bornder *(Coord-Accts Receivable)*
Travis Templin *(Project Mgr)*
Brad Jameson *(Project Mgr)*
Chris Tolson *(Mgr-Estimating)*

STARK SERVICES
12444 Victory Blvd 3rd Fl Ste 300, North Hollywood, CA 91606-3173
Tel.: (818) 985-2003 CA
Web Site: http://www.starkservices.com
Year Founded: 1972
Sales Range: $1-9.9 Million
Emp.: 75
Subscription Fulfillment & Circulation Management Services
N.A.I.C.S.: 518210
Maricel Zabel *(Pres)*
Carl David *(VP-Mktg)*
Richard Magana *(Acct Mgr)*

STARK TALENT
10713 RM 620 N Ste 424, Austin, TX 78726
Tel.: (512) 329-8100
Web Site: http://www.starktalent.com
Sales Range: $10-24.9 Million
Emp.: 31
Hightech Staffing Agency
N.A.I.C.S.: 561320
Nancy Miller *(Owner)*
Marianne Metzner *(Pres)*
Jimmy Goolsby *(Acct Mgr)*

STARKE COUNTY FARM BUREAU COOPERATIVE ASSOCIATION
4 W Plymouth St, Hamlet, IN 46532
Tel.: (574) 867-2411
Web Site: http://www.starkecountycoop.com
Sales Range: $75-99.9 Million
Emp.: 32
Grain Elevators
N.A.I.C.S.: 424510
Virgil Brown *(Gen Mgr)*
Mike Shireman *(Controller)*

STARKEY LABORATORIES, INC.
6700 Washington Ave S, Eden Prairie, MN 55344
Tel.: (952) 941-6401 MN
Web Site: http://www.starkey.com
Year Founded: 1967
Sales Range: $250-299.9 Million
Emp.: 3,300
Customized Hearing Aids Mfr
N.A.I.C.S.: 334510
William F. Austin *(Founder)*
Thomas Victorian *(Dir-Continuation Engrg)*
Brandon Sawalich *(Pres & CEO)*
Lisa Richard *(VP-Sls & Customer Rels)*
Phil Lyons *(Sr VP-Ops-Intl)*
Steve Richards *(Exec VP-Sls-North American)*
Pete Salmi *(VP-Product Dev)*

STARKEY, INC.
4500 W Maple St, Wichita, KS 67209
Tel.: (316) 942-4221 KS
Web Site: http://www.starkey.org
Year Founded: 1955
Sales Range: $10-24.9 Million
Emp.: 488
Developmental Disability Assistance Services
N.A.I.C.S.: 623210
Lori Marceau *(Sec)*
Mark Koch *(VP)*
Lenore Warne *(Controller)*
Doug Long *(Dir-Facilities & Transportation)*
Angeline Anderson *(Asst Dir-Community Living)*
Don Wiesner *(CFO)*
Crystal Porter *(Supvr-Trng & Dev)*
Colin McKenney *(CEO)*
Kris Macy *(COO)*
Jamie Opat *(Dir-Comm)*
Dana Salinas *(Dir-HR)*
Christian Lehr *(Treas)*
Ryan Hiekes *(Dir-Dev)*

STARKWEATHER & SHEPLEY INSURANCE BROKERAGE, INC.
60 Catamore Blvd, East Providence, RI 02914
Tel.: (401) 435-3600
Web Site: http://www.starkweathershepley.com
Year Founded: 1879
Property & Casualty Insurance Agent
N.A.I.C.S.: 524210
Peter Plumb *(COO & Exec VP)*
Larry Keefe *(Chm & CEO)*
Stefan Petrella *(Sr VP)*
Sean Cottrell *(Sr VP)*

Subsidiaries:

Paolino Insurance Agency, Inc. (1)
100 Westminster St 17th Fl, Providence, RI 02903
Tel.: (401) 421-2588
Web Site: http://www.paolinoinsurance.com
Insurance Agency & Brokerage Services
N.A.I.C.S.: 524210
Anthony J. Paolino Jr. *(VP)*
Gregory A. Paolino Jr. *(Principal)*

STARLIGHT INTERNATIONAL LTD, LP
80 Garden Ct Ste 100, Monterey, CA 93940
Tel.: (831) 373-4800
Web Site: http://www.starlightonline.com
Year Founded: 1978
Health & Dietetic Food Stores
N.A.I.C.S.: 456191
Steven M. Goldberg *(Founder & Pres)*

STARMARK INTERNATIONAL, INC.
210 S Andrews Ave, Fort Lauderdale, FL 33301
Tel.: (954) 874-9000
Web Site: http://www.starmark.com
Year Founded: 1992
Sales Range: $25-49.9 Million
Emp.: 55
Advertising Agencies
N.A.I.C.S.: 541810
Peggy Nordeen *(Founder & CEO)*
Brett Circe *(Chief Interactive Officer)*
Jacqui Hartnett *(Pres)*

STARMARK MANAGEMENT HOLDINGS LLC
6140 Greenwood Plz Blvd, Greenwood Village, CO 80111-4803
Tel.: (303) 866-0800
Web Site: http://www.wellbridge.com
Rev.: $120,100,000
Emp.: 75
Holding Company: Membership Sports & Recreation Clubs
N.A.I.C.S.: 551112
Ed Williams *(Pres)*

Subsidiaries:

Kingwood Athletic Club Inc. (1)
22000 Northpark Dr, Kingwood, TX 77339-3803
Tel.: (281) 358-7765
Web Site: http://www.kingwood.com
Rev.: $2,412,817
Emp.: 25
Athletic Club & Gymnasiums, Membership
N.A.I.C.S.: 713940

Wellbridge Club Management Inc. (1)
6140 Greenwood Plaza Blvd, Greenwood Village, CO 80111
Tel.: (303) 866-0800
Web Site: http://www.wellbridge.com
Rev.: $790,000
Emp.: 60
Health Club
N.A.I.C.S.: 713940
Ed Williams *(Pres & CEO)*

STARMOUNT LIFE INSURANCE COMPANY
8485 Goodwood Blvd, Baton Rouge, LA 70806
Tel.: (225) 926-2888
Web Site: http://www.starmountlife.com
Year Founded: 1983
Rev.: $47,400,000
Emp.: 141
Direct Life Insurance Carrier Services
N.A.I.C.S.: 524113
Donna Sternberg *(Exec VP)*
Jeff Wild *(CFO)*
Hans Sternberg *(Chm)*
Erich Sternberg *(Pres)*

STARPOINT
700 S 8th St, Canon City, CO 81212
Tel.: (719) 275-1616 CO
Web Site: http://www.starpointco.com
Year Founded: 1972
Sales Range: $10-24.9 Million
Emp.: 411
Disability Assistance Services
N.A.I.C.S.: 624120
Claudia Stevens *(Chief Admin Officer)*
Robert Lovegrove *(CFO)*
Yvonne Bustos *(Dir-Adult Svcs)*
Marilyn Core *(Dir-Adult Svcs)*
Annette Nimmo *(Sec)*
Janet Trujillo *(Chm)*
Katy Grether *(Vice Chm)*
Robert Arnold *(CEO)*
Susan Williams *(Treas)*
Bonnie Stumph *(Dir-Adult Svcs)*
Bryana Marsicano *(Dir-Case Mgmt)*
Jana Butler *(Dir-Fin)*
Bill Davis *(Dir-Chaffee County)*
Coleen Abeyta *(Dir-Denver)*
Ron Hinkle *(Dir-Foundation)*

STARPOINT GENERAL CORPORATION
102 Montauk Blvd, East Hampton, NY 11937
Tel.: (631) 604-1039 NV
Year Founded: 2013
Corporate Advisory Services
N.A.I.C.S.: 541618
David Cohen *(Pres, CEO, CFO, Treas & Sec)*

STARR TINCUP
1412 W. Magnolia Ste 200, Fort Worth, TX 76104
Tel.: (817) 204-0401
Rev.: $12,000,000
Emp.: 17
N.A.I.C.S.: 541810
Jennifer Greenway *(Dir-Traffic & Production)*

STARR TRANSIT CO. INC.
2531 E State St Ext, Trenton, NJ 08619
Tel.: (609) 587-0626
Web Site: http://www.starrtours.com
Rev.: $15,000,000
Emp.: 150
Bus Charter Service, Except Local
N.A.I.C.S.: 485510
Allen Glickman *(CEO)*

STARRCO COMPANY INC.
11700 Fairgrove Industrial Blvd, Maryland Heights, MO 63043-3436
Tel.: (800) 325-4259
Web Site: http://www.starrco.com
Year Founded: 1965
Portable Buildings, Pre-engineered Modular Office Systems, Mezzanines & Exterior Portable Buildings Mfr
N.A.I.C.S.: 332311
Bryan Carey *(Pres)*
Daryl Carlson *(VP-Engrng)*
Dave Cox *(VP)*

STARRETT CORPORATION
1279 Delmar Loop, Brooklyn, NY 11239
Tel.: (718) 642-7000
Web Site: http://starrettcorp.com
Year Founded: 1922
Construction & Real Estate
N.A.I.C.S.: 237210
Paul Khan *(Dir-Asset Mgmt)*

Subsidiaries:

Grenadier Realty Corp. (1)
1230 Pennsylvania Ave, Brooklyn, NY 11239
Tel.: (718) 642-8700
Sales Range: $25-49.9 Million
Emp.: 200
Real Estate Agents & Managers
N.A.I.C.S.: 531210
Felice L. Michetti *(Chm)*
Ben Torres *(Asst Dir-IT)*

STARREZ INC.

STARREZ INC.

Starrez Inc.—(Continued)
6100 Greenwood Plz Blvd, Greenwood Village, CO 80111
Web Site: http://www.starrez.com
Computer System Design Services
N.A.I.C.S.: 541512
William Quarta (VP-Pro Svcs)

Subsidiaries:

Residential Management Systems (1)
7701 Six Forks Rd 120, Raleigh, NC 27615
Tel.: (919) 845-9004
Web Site: http://www.rms-inc.com
Rev.: $3,925,000
Emp.: 25
Custom Computer Programming Services
N.A.I.C.S.: 541511
Graham Banister (Pres)

STARRFOAM MANUFACTURING INC.
3220 Ave F, Arlington, TX 76011
Tel.: (817) 654-4688
Web Site: http://www.starrfoam.com
Sales Range: $200-249.9 Million
Emp.: 40
Mfr of Polystyrene Resins
N.A.I.C.S.: 325211

STARRTECH INTERACTIVE
1003 Bishop St Pauahi Tower 9th Fl, Honolulu, HI 96813
Tel.: (808) 544-3099
Year Founded: 1987
Sales Range: Less than $1 Million
Emp.: 4
Asian Market, Audio/Visual, Bilingual Marketing, Communications, Entertainment, Event Marketing, Full Service, Investor Relations, Leisure, Public Relations, Publicity/Promotions, Travel & Tourism
N.A.I.C.S.: 541820
Mei Jeanne Wagner (VP)

START TREATMENT & RECOVERY CENTERS
937 Fulton Street, Brooklyn, NY 11238
Tel.: (718) 260-2953 NY
Web Site: http://www.startny.org
Year Founded: 1969
Sales Range: $25-49.9 Million
Alcoholism Addiction Recovery Services
N.A.I.C.S.: 624190
Sudhakar Duvoor (CFO)
Regina Phillips Tabon (COO)
Clewert Sylvester (Dir-Res & Evaluation)
Lawrence S. Brown Jr. (CEO)

START TRUCKING, INC.
4811 N McCarty St, Houston, TX 77013
Tel.: (713) 674-4411 TX
Web Site: http://www.start-trucking.com
Year Founded: 1985
Sales Range: $10-24.9 Million
Emp.: 25
General Freight Trucking Services
N.A.I.C.S.: 484110
Tony Bruton (Dir-Safety)

START.IO, INC
584 Broadway St 12th Fl Ste 1206, New York, NY 10012
Tel.: (212) 600-8221 DE
Web Site: https://www.start.io
Year Founded: 2010
Advertising Services
N.A.I.C.S.: 541810

Gil Dudkiewicz (Co-Founder & CEO)
Ran Avidan (Co-Founder & CTO)
Omri Barnes (CMO)
Shira Hoffer (VP-HR)

STARTECH.COM USA LLP
2315 Creekside Pkwy Ste 300, Lockbourne, OH 43137
Tel.: (519) 455-9425
Web Site: http://www.StarTech.com
Sales Range: $25-49.9 Million
Emp.: 160
Hardware Services
N.A.I.C.S.: 444140
Paul Seed (Co-Founder, Pres & CEO)
Ken Kalopsis (Co-Founder)

STARTEK, INC.
4610 S Ulster St Ste 150, Denver, CO 80237
Tel.: (303) 262-4500 DE
Web Site: https://www.startek.com
Year Founded: 1987
SRT—(NYSE)
Rev.: $385,074,000
Assets: $626,043,000
Liabilities: $374,477,000
Net Worth: $251,566,000
Earnings: ($2,259,000)
Emp.: 33,000
Fiscal Year-end: 12/31/22
Business Process Optimization Services
N.A.I.C.S.: 561499
Surender Mohan Gupta (Chief People Officer-Global)
Abhinandan Jain (Chief Digital Officer)
Gurpal Singh (COO)
Murali Ramachandran (CIO)

Subsidiaries:

Aegis BPO Services Australia Holdings Pty. Ltd. (1)
Level 6 15 William Street, Melbourne, 3000, VIC, Australia
Tel.: (61) 392565000
Business Outsourcing Services
N.A.I.C.S.: 541611
Simon Clenick (Mgr-IT Ops)

Aegis Peru S.A.C (1)
Jr Camana 851 Cercado de Lima, Lima, 15106, Peru
Tel.: (51) 17070830
Business Outsourcing Services
N.A.I.C.S.: 541611

Aegis Services Lanka Private Limited (1)
No 135 Union Place 02, Colombo, 00700, Sri Lanka
Tel.: (94) 114810001
Business Outsourcing Services
N.A.I.C.S.: 541611
M. Ruzaick (VP-Bus Dev)

Collection Center, Inc. (1)
PO Box 1057, Bismarck, ND 58502-1057
Tel.: (701) 258-7734
Web Site: http://www.collectioncenterinc.com
Pharmaceutical Products Distr
N.A.I.C.S.: 424210

Contact Center Company (1)
Al Narjes Commercial and Administrative Complex Abu Bakr Road, Riyadh, 11427, Saudi Arabia (51%)
Tel.: (966) 118255888
Web Site: http://www.ccc.net.sa
Emp.: 4,000
Business Outsourcing Services
N.A.I.C.S.: 541611
Aditya Anand (Sr VP-Ops & Transitions)

StarTek Canada Services, Ltd. (1)
1400 Vincent Massy Drive, Cornwall, K6J 5N4, ON, Canada
Tel.: (613) 937-7000
Web Site: http://www.startek.com

Sales Range: $150-199.9 Million
Emp.: 650
Outsourcing Services
N.A.I.C.S.: 561499

StarTek Health Services, Inc. (1)
Carrara Pl 4th Fl Ste 485 6200 S Syracuse Way, Greenwood Village, CO 80111
Tel.: (303) 262-4500
Web Site: http://www.startekhealth.com
Pharmaceutical Products Distr
N.A.I.C.S.: 424210

Startek Australia Pty Ltd (1)
Level 1, 15 William Street, Melbourne, 3000, VIC, Australia
Tel.: (61) 392565000
Web Site: http://www.aegiscareers.com.au
Business Process Outsourcing Services
N.A.I.C.S.: 541611

STARTEL CORPORATION
16 Goodyear B-125, Irvine, CA 92618-3760
Tel.: (949) 863-8700
Web Site: http://www.startelcorp.com
Year Founded: 1980
Call Center Voice, Data & Networking Solution Services
N.A.I.C.S.: 518210
Dan Xu (Dir-R&D)
Brian Stewart (CEO)
Margaret Lally (Sr Dir-Ops & Technical Svcs)
Pat Kalik (Dir-Customer Svc)
Steve Newell (Dir-Sls)
Alan Hartmann (Dir-Software Dev)
Jim Graham (Dir-Special Ops)

STARTENGINE CROWDFUNDING, INC.
4100 W Alameda Ave 3rd Fl, Burbank, CA 91505
Web Site: https://www.startengine.com
Year Founded: 2014
Rev.: $24,360,685
Assets: $31,498,978
Liabilities: $4,760,713
Net Worth: $26,738,265
Earnings: ($7,935,178)
Emp.: 82
Fiscal Year-end: 12/31/22
Equity Crowdfunding
N.A.I.C.S.: 523999

Subsidiaries:

SeedInvest, LLC (1)
447 Broadway Ste 2, New York, NY 10013
Tel.: (917) 445-0020
Web Site: http://www.seedinvest.com
Business Support Services
N.A.I.C.S.: 561499
Ryan M. Feit (Co-Founder & CEO)

STARTRAK PRODUCTS, INC.
102 Morris Ave, Boonton, NJ 07950-2443
Tel.: (732) 236-4507 NJ
Web Site: http://www.startrakinc.com
Railcar Tracking & Monitoring Systems Mfr
N.A.I.C.S.: 561621
Thomas A. Robinson (Co-Founder & Exec VP)
E. Kevin Dahill (Pres)

STARTUP HEALTH HOLDINGS, INC.
85 Broad St, New York, NY 10004
Web Site: http://www.startuphealth.com
Healthcare Services
N.A.I.C.S.: 456199
Steven Kein (CEO)

STARVAGGI INDUSTRIES, INC.
401 Pennsylvania Ave, Weirton, WV 26062

Tel.: (304) 748-1400
Web Site: http://www.starvaggi.com
Rev.: $13,000,000
Emp.: 100
Readymix Concrete Mfr
N.A.I.C.S.: 327320
James Obrien (Treas & VP)
Donald R. Donell (Pres)
Michael Wehr (Sec)

STARVING STUDENTS MOVING COMPANY
1850 Sawtelle Blvd Ste 300, Los Angeles, CA 90025
Tel.: (310) 235-6683 CA
Web Site: http://www.ssmovers.com
Year Founded: 1973
Sales Range: $350-399.9 Million
Emp.: 1,000
Provider of Moving Services
N.A.I.C.S.: 484210
Ethan Margalith (Founder & Chm)

STARWEAR INC.
1384 Broadway Ste 1606, New York, NY 10018
Tel.: (212) 971-0003
Web Site: http://www.starwear.com
Year Founded: 1983
Sales Range: $10-24.9 Million
Emp.: 10
Retailer of Women's & Children's Sportswear
N.A.I.C.S.: 424350
Albert Antebi (Pres)

STARWOOD CAPITAL GROUP GLOBAL I, LLC
591 W Putnam Ave, Greenwich, CT 06830
Tel.: (203) 422-7700 CT
Web Site: http://www.starwoodcapital.com
Year Founded: 1991
Sales Range: $450-499.9 Million
Emp.: 535
Real Estate Investment Firm
N.A.I.C.S.: 523999
Mark Mach (VP)
Lenore Warne (Compliance Officer)
Doug Long (CIO)
Angelina Anderson (Chief Strategy Officer-CVG)
Drew Wiesenfeld (Mng Dir)
Christal Porter (Mng Dir)
Colin McKinstry (Mng Dir)
Jamie Orcel (Dir-Comm)
Jamie Massy (COO)
Gary W. Masso (CFO)
Lou Hull (Managing Dir)
Fred Fretz (Mng Dir)
Jerry Silvey (Vice Chm & CFO)
Jeffrey G. Dishner (Pres & COO)
Arash Azarbarzin (Pres-SH Grp)
Christopher D. Graham (Sr Mng Dir & Head--Global)
Mark Deason (Mng Dir & Head-Asset Mgmt)
Sean Harris (Mng Dir)
Kevin Lee (Mng Dir & Head-Real Estate-Asia Pacific)
James Fogarty (VP-Hong Kong)
Cody Bradshaw (Head-Intl Hotels)
John P. McCarthy Jr. (Mng Dir)

Subsidiaries:

CA Immobilien Anlagen AG (1)
Mechelgasse 1, 1030, Vienna, Austria (58.8%)
Tel.: (43) 15325907
Web Site: https://www.caimmo.com
Rev.: $247,186,698
Assets: $6,594,508,383
Liabilities: $3,270,799,739
Net Worth: $3,323,708,644
Earnings: $440,420,781
Emp.: 414
Fiscal Year-end: 12/31/2019
Commercial Real Estate Investment, Development & Property Management
N.A.I.C.S.: 531390
Uwe Frerichs (Head-Engrg)
Ralf Schneider (Head-Dev)
Gregor Drexler (Head-Asset Mgmt)
Dmitry Mints (Deputy Chm-Supervisory Bd)
Susanne Steinbock (Head-Corp Comm)
Frank Nickel (CEO & Chm-Mgmt Bd)
Matthias Schmidt (Head-Dev-Germany)
Markus Kuttner (Head-Asset Mgmt)

Subsidiary (Domestic):

CA Immo Asset Management GmbH (2)

COMPANIES

Rennweg 16 Eingang Mechel Alley 1, 1030, Vienna, Austria
Tel.: (43) 15325907
Web Site: http://www.caimmoag.com
Sales Range: $25-49.9 Million
Emp.: 100
Business Management Services
N.A.I.C.S.: 541618
Bruno Ettenauer (Gen Mgr)

CA Immo BIP Liegenschaftsverwaltung GmbH (2)
Mechelgasse 1, 1030, Vienna, Austria
Tel.: (43) 15325907
Sales Range: $50-74.9 Million
Emp.: 65
Alcoholic Beverages Whslr
N.A.I.C.S.: 424810

Subsidiary (Non-US):

CA Immo Czech Republic (2)
Karolinska 661/4, 186 00, Prague, Czech Republic
Tel.: (420) 233 109 328
Web Site: http://www.caimmo.com
Investment Property Management Services
N.A.I.C.S.: 523940
Alois Vyleta Mrics (Head)

CA Immo Deutschland GmbH (2)
Europa Allee 22, 60327, Frankfurt am Main, Germany
Tel.: (49) 6976806718
Web Site: http://www.caimmo.com
Sales Range: $25-49.9 Million
Emp.: 100
Business Management Services
N.A.I.C.S.: 541618
Gregor Drexler (Mng Dir-Asset Mgmt)
Bruno Ettenauer (CEO)
Florian Nowotny (Member-Mgmt Bd)
Ralf Schneider (Member-Mgmt Bd)
Matthias Tripp (CFO)

CA Immo Deutschland GmbH (2)
Klaus-Mann Platz 1, Munich, 80636, Germany
Tel.: (49) 89 545 48530
Web Site: http://www.caimmo.com
Emp.: 70
Asset Management Services
N.A.I.C.S.: 525990
Gregor Drexler (Mng Dir)
Tobias Jauch (Gen Mgr)

Subsidiary (Domestic):

CA Immo Galleria Liegenschaftsverwaltung GmbH (2)
Mechel Alley 1, Vienna, 1030, Austria
Tel.: (43) 15325907
Web Site: http://www.caimmoag.com
Sales Range: $25-49.9 Million
Emp.: 100
Housing Construction Services
N.A.I.C.S.: 236117
Frank Nicole (Mgr)

Subsidiary (Non-US):

CA Immo Real Estate Management Hungary Kft. (2)
Rakoczi ut 70-72, 1074, Budapest, Hungary
Tel.: (36) 1 501 28 00
Web Site: http://www.caimmo.com
Real Estate Management Services
N.A.I.C.S.: 531390
Ede Gulyas (Mng Dir)

CA Immo Real Estate Management Poland Sp. z o.o. (2)
Ul Emilii Plater 53, 00-113, Warsaw, Poland
Tel.: (48) 22 540 6540
Web Site: http://www.caimmo.com
Emp.: 20
Real Estate Management Services
N.A.I.C.S.: 531390
Andrzej Mikolajczyk (Mng Dir)

CA Immo Real Estate Management Romania SRL (2)
Bdul Lascar Catargiu Nr 47-53 Europe House Etaj 5, 010665, Bucharest, Romania
Tel.: (40) 21 300 17 02
Web Site: http://www.caimmo.com
Real Estate Management Services
N.A.I.C.S.: 531390
Marian Roman (Co-Mng Dir)
Christoph Buchgraber (Co-Mng Dir)

Subsidiary (Domestic):

CA Immo Rennweg 16 GmbH (2)
Mechelgasse 1, 1030, Vienna, Austria
Tel.: (43) 15325907
Web Site: http://www.caimoag.com
Emp.: 60
Investment Management Service
N.A.I.C.S.: 541618
Bruno Ettenauer (CEO)

CA Immobilien Anlagen Beteiligungs GmbH (2)
Freyung 3 2 11, Vienna, 1030, Austria
Tel.: (43) 15325907
Web Site: http://www.caimmoag.com
Sales Range: $25-49.9 Million
Emp.: 70
Investment Management Service
N.A.I.C.S.: 541618
Frank Nickel (Mng Dir)

CA Immobilien Anlagen Beteiligungs GmbH & Co Finanzierungs OEG (2)
Mechel Alley 1, Vienna, 1030, Austria
Tel.: (43) 15325907
Web Site: http://www.caimmo.com
Sales Range: $25-49.9 Million
Emp.: 100
Business Management Services
N.A.I.C.S.: 541618
Florian Nowotny (CFO)

Europolis AG (2)
Kohlmarkt 8-10, 1010, Vienna, Austria
Tel.: (43) 13197200
Web Site: http://www.europolis.com
Sales Range: $50-74.9 Million
Emp.: 30
Real Estate Investment & Asset Management
N.A.I.C.S.: 523999
Thomas Kurzmann (COO)

SQUARE S Holding GmbH (2)
Mechelgasse 1, Vienna, Austria
Tel.: (43) 15325907
Web Site: http://www.caemmoat.com
Emp.: 70
Investment Management Service
N.A.I.C.S.: 541618
Nickel Frank (Gen Mgr)

Subsidiary (Non-US):

TM Immo d.o.o (2)
Djordja Stanojevic 14, 11070, Belgrade, Serbia
Tel.: (381) 113189120
Sales Range: $25-49.9 Million
Emp.: 6
Business Management Services
N.A.I.C.S.: 541618

VIADOR GmbH (2)
Hedderichstr 55-57, 60594, Frankfurt am Main, Germany
Tel.: (49) 69606270
Web Site: http://www.viador.eu
Real Estate Management Services
N.A.I.C.S.: 531390

omniCon Verwaltungs GmbH (2)
Hedderichstrasse 55-57, 60594, Frankfurt am Main, Germany
Tel.: (49) 6103 3001610
Chemical & Rubber Products Mfr
N.A.I.C.S.: 325212

omniPro Gesellschaft fur Projektmanagement mbH (2)
Im Steingrund 8, Dreieich, Germany
Tel.: (49) 61033001610
Web Site: http://www.omnipro.de
Business Management Services
N.A.I.C.S.: 541618

Extended Stay America, Inc. (1)
11525 N Community House Rd Ste 100, Charlotte, NC 28277 (50%)
Tel.: (980) 345-1600
Web Site: http://www.esa.com
Rev.: $1,042,316,000
Assets: $4,089,149,000
Liabilities: $2,951,706,000
Net Worth: $1,137,443,000
Earnings: $23,267,000
Emp.: 4,200
Fiscal Year-end: 12/31/2020
Home Management Services
N.A.I.C.S.: 721110
Howard J. Weissman (Chief Acctg Officer & Controller)

Subsidiary (Domestic):

ESH Hospitality, Inc. (2)
11525 N Community House Rd Ste 100, Charlotte, NC 28277
Tel.: (980) 345-1600
Web Site: http://www.esa.com
Rev.: $562,809,000
Assets: $3,951,117,000
Liabilities: $2,855,835,000
Net Worth: $1,095,282,000
Earnings: $175,868,000
Emp.: 4,199
Fiscal Year-end: 12/31/2020
Real Estate Investment Services
N.A.I.C.S.: 523999
Howard J. Weissman (Chief Acctg Officer & Controller)
Douglas G. Geoga (Chm)
David A. Clarkson (CFO)
Bruce N. Haase (Pres & CEO)
Christopher N. Dekle (Gen Counsel & Sec)
Judi Bikulege (Chief Investment Officer)

RDI REIT P.L.C. (1)
33 Regent Street, London, SW1Y 4NB, United Kingdom (100%)
Tel.: (44) 2078110100
Web Site: http://www.rdireit.com
Rev.: $122,634,600
Assets: $1,934,610,000
Liabilities: $960,091,200
Net Worth: $974,518,800
Earnings: ($98,107,680)
Emp.: 238
Fiscal Year-end: 08/31/2019
Property Investment Trust
N.A.I.C.S.: 525990
Lisa Hibberd (Sec)
Darryl Kohler (Mgr-Grp Dev)
Adrian Horsburgh (Dir-Property)
Michelle Daniels (Head-Mktg-Grp)
Sarah Jones (Head-Comml Asset Mgmt)
Matthew Baddeley (Head-Retail Asset Mgmt-UK)

Subsidiary (Non-US):

Justizzentrum in Halle Wichford & Co. KG (2)
Aachener Strasse 1053-1055, 50858, Cologne, Nordrhein-Westfalen, Germany
Tel.: (49) 221489010
Real Estate Property Management Services
N.A.I.C.S.: 531210

Justizzentrum in Halle Wichford Verwaltungsgesellschaft mbH (2)
Max-Pechstein-Str 54, Cologne, 50858, Nordrhein-Westfalen, Germany
Tel.: (49) 2212808829
Real Estate Property Management Services
N.A.I.C.S.: 531210

Societe du Louvre SA (1)
10 Ave De Friedland, 75008, Paris, France
Tel.: (33) 145645000
Web Site: http://www.societedulouvre.com
Holding Company
N.A.I.C.S.: 721110
Jeffrey G. Dishner (Mng Dir)

Unit (Non-US):

Golden Tulip Warsaw Centre Hotel (2)
Ul Towarowa 2, 00811, Warsaw, Poland
Tel.: (48) 225827500
Web Site: http://www.goldentulipwarsawcentre.com
Hotel Operations
N.A.I.C.S.: 721110

Premiere Classe Hotel (2)
ul Towarowa 2, 00-811, Warsaw, Poland
Tel.: (48) 226240800
Web Site: http://www.premiere-classe-warszawa.pl
Sales Range: $25-49.9 Million
Emp.: 200
Hotels & Motels
N.A.I.C.S.: 721110
Wojciech Debski (Mng Dir)

Starwood Capital Europe Advisers, LLP (1)

STARWOOD REAL ESTATE INCOME TRUST, INC.

1 Eagle Place 2nd Floor, London, SW1Y 6AF, United Kingdom
Tel.: (44) 2070163650
Web Site: http://www.starwoodcapital.com
Sales Range: $25-49.9 Million
Emp.: 25
Investment Management Service
N.A.I.C.S.: 523940
Samantha Hancock (Office Mgr)

Starwood Capital Group European Sarl (1)
3 Rue Mozart 2166, 2668, Luxembourg, Luxembourg
Tel.: (352) 26645120
Web Site: http://www.starwoodcapital.com
Sales Range: $25-49.9 Million
Emp.: 12
Investment Management Service
N.A.I.C.S.: 523940
Thierry Drinka (Gen Mgr)

Starwood Real Estate Securities, LLC (1)
591 W Putnam Ave, Greenwich, CT 06830
Tel.: (203) 422-7740
Web Site: http://www.starwoodsecurities.com
Real Estate Investment Management Services
N.A.I.C.S.: 523940

STARWOOD REAL ESTATE INCOME TRUST, INC.
2340 Collins Ave, Miami Beach, FL 33139
Tel.: (305) 695-5500 MD
Web Site: https://www.starwoodnav.reit
Year Founded: 2017
Rev.: $1,579,348,000
Assets: $26,764,853,000
Liabilities: $16,619,062,000
Net Worth: $10,145,791,000
Earnings: ($65,708,000)
Fiscal Year-end: 12/31/22
Real Estate Investment Services
N.A.I.C.S.: 531210
Christopher D. Graham (Pres)
Mark Deason (Head-Asset & Portfolio Mgmt)
Sean Harris (CEO)
John P. McCarthy Jr. (Vice Chm)
Matthew S. Guttin (Chief Compliance Officer-Starwood Capital Grp)
Barry S. Sternlicht (Bd of Dirs, Executives)

Subsidiaries:

2350 Harper House, L.L.C. (1)
2350 Sawmill Pl Blvd, Columbus, OH 43235
Tel.: (614) 953-5933
Web Site: http://www.harperhousecolumbus.com
Real Estate Services
N.A.I.C.S.: 531210

2390 Graham Park, L.L.C. (1)
2390 Harper Isabelle, Columbus, OH 43235
Tel.: (614) 502-5854
Web Site: http://www.grahamparkcolumbus.com
Real Estate Services
N.A.I.C.S.: 531210

250 High Street, L.L.C. (1)
250 S High St, Columbus, OH 43215
Tel.: (380) 228-7773
Web Site: https://www.250high.com
Real Estate Services
N.A.I.C.S.: 531210

600 Goodale, L.L.C. (1)
600 W Goodale St, Columbus, OH 43215
Tel.: (380) 228-5557
Web Site: https://www.600goodale.com
Real Estate Services
N.A.I.C.S.: 531210

80 on the Commons, L.L.C. (1)
80 E Rich St, Columbus, OH 43215
Tel.: (380) 388-4308
Web Site: https://www.80onthecommons.com
Real Estate Services

STARWOOD REAL ESTATE INCOME TRUST, INC.

U.S. PRIVATE

Starwood Real Estate Income Trust, Inc.—(Continued)
N.A.I.C.S.: 531210

801 Polaris Holdings, L.L.C. (1)
801 Polaris Pkwy, Columbus, OH 43240
Tel.: (380) 228-5541
Web Site: https://www.801polaris.com
Real Estate Services
N.A.I.C.S.: 531210

SREIT Camri Green Apartments, L.L.C. (1)
3820 Losco Rd, Jacksonville, FL 32257
Tel.: (904) 468-6449
Web Site: http://www.camrigreen.com
Real Estate Services
N.A.I.C.S.: 531210

SREIT Columbia Hills, L.L.C. (1)
1002 S Frederick St, Arlington, VA 22204
Tel.: (571) 517-2871
Web Site: https://www.columbiahillsarlington.com
Real Estate Services
N.A.I.C.S.: 531210

SREIT Courtney Manor, L.L.C. (1)
5620 Collins Rd, Jacksonville, FL 32244
Tel.: (904) 531-0741
Web Site: https://www.courtneymanorfl.com
Real Estate Services
N.A.I.C.S.: 531210

SREIT Creekside at Bellemeade, L.P. (1)
2350 Bellemeade St, High Point, NC 27263
Tel.: (336) 656-2378
Web Site: https://www.creeksideatbellemeade.com
Real Estate Services
N.A.I.C.S.: 531210

SREIT Dominion Pines, L.L.C. (1)
529 Pine Valley Run, Chesapeake, VA 23320
Tel.: (757) 997-1937
Web Site: https://www.dominionpinesapts.com
Real Estate Services
N.A.I.C.S.: 531210

SREIT Falcon Pointe, L.P. (1)
915 Cole Ave, Rosenberg, TX 77471
Tel.: (281) 603-4591
Web Site: http://www.falconpointeapts.com
Real Estate Services
N.A.I.C.S.: 531210

SREIT Falcon Trace, L.L.C. (1)
1635 Peregrine Falcons Way, Orlando, FL 32837
Tel.: (407) 612-2650
Web Site: https://www.falcontraceapts.com
Real Estate Services
N.A.I.C.S.: 531210

SREIT Griffin Scottsdale, L.L.C. (1)
3234 N Scottsdale Rd, Scottsdale, AZ 85251
Tel.: (480) 900-1603
Web Site: https://www.thegriffinscottsdale.com
Real Estate Services
N.A.I.C.S.: 531210

SREIT Hatteras Sound, L.L.C. (1)
13000 Island Bay Cir, Sanford, FL 32771
Tel.: (407) 805-1757
Web Site: https://www.hatterassound.com
Real Estate Services
N.A.I.C.S.: 531210

SREIT Holly Cove Apartments, L.L.C. (1)
1745 Wells Rd, Orange Park, FL 32073
Tel.: (904) 468-6487
Web Site: https://www.hollycovefl.com
Real Estate Services
N.A.I.C.S.: 531210

SREIT Las Villas De Kino, L.L.C. (1)
5515 S Forgeus Ave, Tucson, AZ 85706
Tel.: (520) 462-7852
Web Site: https://www.lasvillasdekinoapts.com
Real Estate Services
N.A.I.C.S.: 531210

SREIT Las Villas de Leon, L.P. (1)
6611 W Commerce St, San Antonio, TX 78227
Tel.: (726) 200-4511
Web Site: https://www.lasvillasdeleon.com
Real Estate Services
N.A.I.C.S.: 531210

SREIT Leigh Meadows Apartments, L.L.C. (1)
4320 Sunbeam Rd, Jacksonville, FL 32257
Tel.: (904) 468-6492
Web Site: https://www.leighmeadows.com
Real Estate Services
N.A.I.C.S.: 531210

SREIT Lexington Club, L.L.C. (1)
6885 20th St, Vero Beach, FL 32966
Tel.: (772) 209-3781
Web Site: http://www.lexingtonclubatvero.com
Real Estate Services
N.A.I.C.S.: 531210

SREIT Madelyn Oaks, L.L.C. (1)
5710 Lenox Ave, Jacksonville, FL 32205
Tel.: (904) 447-1299
Web Site: https://www.madelynoaksfl.com
Real Estate Services
N.A.I.C.S.: 531210

SREIT Overlook at Simms Creek, L.P. (1)
4730 Archean Way, Raleigh, NC 27616
Tel.: (919) 584-9752
Web Site: https://www.overlookeatsimmscreek.com
Real Estate Services
N.A.I.C.S.: 531210

SREIT Patriots Pointe, L.P. (1)
3699 Patriots Pointe Dr, Concord, NC 28025
Tel.: (704) 285-1894
Web Site: https://www.patriotspointeliving.com
Real Estate Services
N.A.I.C.S.: 531210

SREIT Ponce Harbor, L.L.C. (1)
225 Ponce Harbor Dr, Saint Augustine, FL 32086
Tel.: (904) 447-2269
Web Site: https://www.ponceharbor.com
Real Estate Services
N.A.I.C.S.: 531210

SREIT Reserves at Arboretum, L.L.C. (1)
5000 Reserve Way, Newport News, VA 23602
Tel.: (757) 350-8452
Web Site: https://www.reservesatarboretum-apts.com
Real Estate Services
N.A.I.C.S.: 531210

SREIT River Park Place, L.L.C. (1)
700 3Rd Cir, Vero Beach, FL 32962
Tel.: (772) 362-2997
Web Site: https://www.riverpark-apts.com
Real Estate Services
N.A.I.C.S.: 531210

SREIT River Reach, L.L.C. (1)
1628 River Reach Dr, Orlando, FL 32828
Tel.: (407) 512-9479
Web Site: https://www.riverreachorlando.com
Real Estate Services
N.A.I.C.S.: 531210

SREIT Soldiers Ridge, L.L.C. (1)
11201 Soldiers Ridge Cir, Manassas, VA 20109
Tel.: (571) 339-0311
Web Site: https://www.soldiersridge.com
Real Estate Services
N.A.I.C.S.: 531210

SREIT South Maine Commons, L.L.C. (1)
8981 Wood Drift Cir, Manassas, VA 20110
Tel.: (571) 339-0226
Web Site: https://www.southmaincommons.com
Real Estate Services
N.A.I.C.S.: 531210

SREIT Spinnaker Reach, L.L.C. (1)
3875 San Pablo Rd S, Jacksonville, FL 32224
Tel.: (904) 447-2179
Web Site: https://www.spinnakerreachapts.com
Real Estate Services
N.A.I.C.S.: 531210

SREIT Sterling Crest, L.L.C. (1)
7001 Silber Rd, Arlington, TX 76017
Tel.: (817) 478-7994
Web Site: https://www.sterlingcrestarlington.com
Real Estate Services
N.A.I.C.S.: 531210

SREIT Stone Creek, L.P. (1)
11344 Coloma Rd Ste 542, Gold River, CA 95670
Tel.: (916) 638-7916
Web Site: https://www.stonecreekpm.com
Real Estate Services
N.A.I.C.S.: 531210
Chris Ryan (Owner & Mgr-Property)

SREIT Thomas Chase Apartments, L.L.C. (1)
4901 Sunbeam Rd, Jacksonville, FL 32257
Tel.: (904) 560-5287
Web Site: http://www.thomaschasefl.com
Real Estate Services
N.A.I.C.S.: 531210

SREIT Vista Haven, L.L.C. (1)
4100 Geranium Ln, Sanford, FL 32771
Tel.: (407) 588-9119
Web Site: https://www.vistahavenapts.com
Real Estate Services
N.A.I.C.S.: 531210

SREIT-Coastal Partners, L.P. (1)
700 N Green St Ste 202, Chicago, IL 60642
Tel.: (312) 481-6200
Web Site: https://www.coastalpartners.net
Real Estate Services
N.A.I.C.S.: 531210
Brett Baumgarten (CEO)
Brett Keeshin (Pres)
Tom Ott (VP-Midwest)
Greg Sukenik (VP-Fin)
Sheryl Peven (Acct Mgr)

STASCO MECHANICAL CONTRACTORS
1391 Cobb Pkwy N, Marietta, GA 30062
Tel.: (770) 422-7118
Web Site: http://www.stasco-mech.com
Sales Range: $10-24.9 Million
Emp.: 48
Plumbing Contractor
N.A.I.C.S.: 238220
Amanda Krok (Pres)
Rex Pace (Mgr-Warehouse)

STASH FINANCIAL, INC.
500 7th Ave 8th Fl, New York, NY 10018   DE
Web Site: http://www.stash.com
Online Investment, Wealth Management & Financial Advisory Data Services
N.A.I.C.S.: 522320
Edward Robinson (Co-Founder & Pres)
Brandon Krieg (Co-Founder & CEO)
Dale Sperling (CMO)
Giff Carter (Chief Revenue Officer)
Gloria Basem (Chief People Officer)
Sudev Balakrishnan (Chief Product Officer)
Meredith Smith (Gen Counsel)
Kimberley Meehan (Chief Customer Officer)
Chidi Achara (Chief Creative Officer)
Cliff Hazelton (CTO)
Adriel Lares (CFO)

STASZAK COMMUNICATIONS
16462 Martincoit Rd, Poway, CA 92064
Tel.: (858) 674-7409   CA
Web Site: http://www.staszakcom.com
Year Founded: 2002
Sales Range: Less than $1 Million
Emp.: 2
Advertising Agencies, Consulting, Full Service, Recruitment
N.A.I.C.S.: 541810
Teresa Staszak (Owner)

STAT NURSING SERVICES INC.
2740 Van Ness Ave Ste 210, San Francisco, CA 94109
Tel.: (415) 673-9791
Web Site: http://www.statrn.com
Sales Range: $10-24.9 Million
Emp.: 10
Nurses' Registry
N.A.I.C.S.: 561311
Mark Deal (Mgr-Ops)

STATCO ENGINEERING & FABRICATORS INC.
7595 Reynolds Cir, Huntington Beach, CA 92647
Tel.: (714) 375-6300
Web Site: http://www.statco-engineering.com
Year Founded: 1982
Sales Range: $10-24.9 Million
Emp.: 115
Engineeering Services
N.A.I.C.S.: 423830

STATE AUTOMOBILE MUTUAL INSURANCE COMPANY
518 E Broad St, Columbus, OH 43215
Tel.: (614) 464-5000   OH
Web Site: http://www.stateauto.com
Year Founded: 1921
Sales Range: $1-4.9 Billion
Emp.: 2,000
Property & Casualty Insurance
N.A.I.C.S.: 524126
John M. Petrucci (Sr VP-Customer Svc)
Douglas E. Allen (VP & Dir-IT)
Steven E. English (CFO & Sr VP)
Michael E. LaRocco (Pres & CEO)

Subsidiaries:

A.M. Best Company (1)
Ambest Rd, Oldwick, NJ 08858
Tel.: (908) 439-2200
Web Site: http://www.ambest.com
Insurance Brokerage Services
N.A.I.C.S.: 524210
Larry Mayewski (CEO & Chm)
Lee McDonald (Grp VP-Comm)
Jim Fowler (Mgr-Bus Dev-Rating Svcs)
Susanna Lam (Mng Dir-A.M. Best Asia-Pacific, Ltd)
Steven Fan (Dir-Market Dev-North Asia-A.M. Best Asia-Pacific Ltd.)
David Teo (Dir-Market Dev-South East Asia-A.M. Best Asia-Pacific Ltd.)
William Mills (Dir-Market Dev-EMEA)
Nick Charteris-Black (Mng Dir-Market Dev-European, Middle East & Africa)
Yvette Essen (Dir-Res & Comm)
Scott Ryrie (Dir-Comml-Asia Pacific)
Edem Kuenyehia (Dir-Market Dev & Comm)
Jim Peavy (Asst VP-PR)
Andrea Keenan (Chief Strategy Officer & Exec VP)
Alfonso Novelo (Sr Dir-Analysis)
Matt Mosher (COO & Exec VP)
Riccardo Ciccozzi (Dir-Market Dev-Europe)
Richard Banks (Dir-Indus Res-European, Middle East & Africa)
Carlos De la Torre (Mng Dir-Ops-AM Best Latin America, SA de CV)
Christopher Sharkey (Assoc Dir-PR)

American Compensation Insurance Company (1)
8500 Normandale Lake Blvd Ste 1400, Bloomington, MN 55437
Tel.: (952) 893-0403
Insurance Brokerage Services

COMPANIES

N.A.I.C.S.: 524210

Bloomington Compensation Insurance Company (1)
8500 Normandale Lk Blvd, Bloomington, MN 55437-3813
Tel.: (952) 893-0403
Insurance Brokerage Services
N.A.I.C.S.: 524210

Meridian Citizens Mutual Insurance Company (1)
2955 N Meridian St, Indianapolis, IN 46206
Tel.: (614) 464-5000
Property & Casualty Insurance Services
N.A.I.C.S.: 524298

Plaza Insurance Company (1)
700 W 47th St Ste 350, Kansas City, MO 64112
Tel.: (816) 412-2860
Property & Casualty Insurance Services
N.A.I.C.S.: 524126

Rockhill Holding Company (1)
700 W 47th St Ste 350, Kansas City, MO 64112
Tel.: (816) 412-2801
Web Site: http://www.rhkc.com
Insurance Holding Company
N.A.I.C.S.: 551112
Colin Mayo (Chief Property Officer & Sr VP)
Doug Goode (COO)
Jerry W. Brumfield (VP & Assoc Gen Counsel)
Jack Abney (VP-Environmental-Environmental Underwriting Unit)

Subsidiary (Domestic):

RTW, Inc. (2)
8500 Normandale Lake Blvd Ste 1400, Bloomington, MN 55437
Tel.: (952) 893-0403
Web Site: http://www.rtwi.com
Sales Range: $50-74.9 Million
Emp.: 168
Integrated Disability & Worker Productivity Solution Services
N.A.I.C.S.: 524126
Nathan Nelson (Dir-Sls)

Rockhill Insurance Company (2)
700 W 47th St Ste 350, Kansas City, MO 64112
Tel.: (816) 412-2801
Web Site: http://www.rhkc.com
Property & Casualty Insurance Services
N.A.I.C.S.: 524126
Philip R. Cole (VP-Underwriting & Compliance)
Jerry W. Brumfield (VP & Assoc Gen Counsel)
Christine Triche (Asst VP-Midwest)
Michael Klima (Dir-Underwriting)
Dave Dietz (VP & Dir-Comml Lines)
Andy Draper (Dir & Actuary)
Doug Goode (COO)
Shad Oliver (Dir-Bus Dev)

State Auto Financial Corporation (1)
518 E Broad St, Columbus, OH 43215-3976
Tel.: (614) 464-5000
Web Site: https://www.stateauto.com
Rev.: $1,482,400,000
Assets: $3,102,500,000
Liabilities: $2,092,500,000
Net Worth: $1,010,000,000
Earnings: $13,100,000
Emp.: 2,025
Fiscal Year-end: 12/31/2020
Property & Casualty Insurance Services
N.A.I.C.S.: 525190

Subsidiary (Domestic):

518 Property Management and Leasing, LLC (2)
518 E Broad St, Columbus, OH 43215-3901
Tel.: (614) 464-5000
Property Management Services
N.A.I.C.S.: 531120

State Auto Property and Casualty Insurance Company (2)
1300 Woodland Ave, West Des Moines, IA 50265
Tel.: (515) 223-9438
Property & Casualty Insurance Services
N.A.I.C.S.: 524126

State Auto Insurance Company (1)
2955 N Meridian St, Indianapolis, IN 46208-4714 (64%)
Tel.: (317) 931-7000
Web Site: http://www.stateauto.com
Sales Range: $100-124.9 Million
Emp.: 400
Regional Holding Company Engaged in the Property & Casualty Insurance Business
N.A.I.C.S.: 524126
Steven E. English (CFO & Sr VP)
Mike Larocco (Pres & CEO)
Elise Spriggs (Sr VP-Assoc & External Rels)
Greg Tacchetti (CIO, Chief Strategy Officer & Sr VP)
Jason Berkey (Sr VP-Personal Lines)
Kim Garland (Mng Dir-State Auto Labs & Exec VP-Comml Lines)
Melissa Centers (Gen Counsel, Sec & Sr VP)
Paul Stachura (Chief Claims & Risk Engrg Officer & Sr VP)

State Auto P & C (1)
518 E Broad St, Columbus, OH 43215
Tel.: (614) 464-5000
Web Site: http://www.stateauto.com
Sales Range: $125-149.9 Million
Emp.: 700
Property & Casualty Insurance
N.A.I.C.S.: 524126

STATE BANK & TRUST COMPANY
147 S Railroad Ave PO Box 319, Brookhaven, MS 39601
Tel.: (601) 833-4451
Web Site: http://www.statebank1898.com
Rev.: $10,099,000
Emp.: 50
Banking Services
N.A.I.C.S.: 522110
Jamie Rogers (VP-Deposit Ops)
Jason Hultgren (Sr VP & Mgr-Mortgage Production)
J. Thomas Wiley Jr. (CEO)

STATE BANK OF COUNTRYSIDE INC.
6734 Joliet Rd, Countryside, IL 60525-4577
Tel.: (708) 485-3100
Web Site: http://www.bankcountryside.com
Year Founded: 1975
Sales Range: $50-74.9 Million
Emp.: 50
Banking Services
N.A.I.C.S.: 522110
John D. Wheeler (Pres & CEO)

STATE BANK OF LINCOLN CORP.
508 Broadway, Lincoln, IL 62656
Tel.: (217) 735-5551
Web Site: http://www.sblincoln.com
Sales Range: $10-24.9 Million
Emp.: 100
Banking Services
N.A.I.C.S.: 522110
Steven Aughenbaugh (Pres)
David Irwin (Sr VP)
Rodney Meyer (Asst VP)
Gail Nunnery (VP)

STATE BANK OF SOUTHERN UTAH
377 N Main St, Cedar City, UT 84721-8472
Tel.: (435) 586-9456
Web Site: http://www.sbsu.com
Sales Range: $10-24.9 Million
Emp.: 138
Provider of Banking Services
N.A.I.C.S.: 522110

John Westwood (CFO)
Brandon Condie (VP-Comml Loans)
Clint Penrod (Asst VP & Mgr-Credit Svcs)
Dean Woodbury (VP & Mgr)
DeLynn Barton (Exec VP)
Joey Garrett (First VP)
Jon Ashdown (Sr VP-IT)
Trevor Andersen (Sr VP)
Tyler Brown (Sr VP-Mktg)
Joey Bleak (Dir-HR)

STATE BANKSHARES, INC.
3100 13th Ave SW, Fargo, ND 58103
Tel.: (701) 298-1500 ND
Web Site: http://www.bellbanks.com
Year Founded: 1989
Sales Range: $150-199.9 Million
Bank Holding Company
N.A.I.C.S.: 551111

Subsidiaries:

Bell State Bank & Trust (1)
3100 13th Ave SW, Fargo, ND 58103
Tel.: (701) 298-1500
Web Site: http://www.bellbanks.com
Sales Range: $150-199.9 Million
Commericial Banking
N.A.I.C.S.: 522110

Division (Domestic):

Bell Mortgage (2)
5500 Wayzata Blvd Ste 300, Minneapolis, MN 55416
Tel.: (952) 591-1880
Web Site: http://www.bellbanks.com
Emp.: 200
Mortgage Lending Services
N.A.I.C.S.: 522292
Michael Solberg (Pres)

STATE BEAUTY SUPPLY OF ST. LOUIS
2351 Millpark Dr, Maryland Heights, MO 63043
Tel.: (324) 423-9599
Web Site: http://www.statebeautystl.com
Year Founded: 1967
Sales Range: $10-24.9 Million
Emp.: 65
Professional Salon & Stylist Product Whslr
N.A.I.C.S.: 812112
Bud Goellner (Co-Owner)
Mike Goellner (Co-Owner)
Abby Goellner (Coord-Education & Mktg)
Sarah Blase (Mgr-HR & Payroll & Admin-Report)

STATE CENTER FINANCIAL, INC.
109 W Main St, State Center, IA 50247
Tel.: (641) 483-2505 IA
Web Site: http://www.centralstatebankia.com
Year Founded: 1979
Sales Range: $1-9.9 Million
Bank Holding Company
N.A.I.C.S.: 551111
Brian Disney (Pres)

Subsidiaries:

Central State Bank (1)
109 W Main St, State Center, IA 50247-7769
Tel.: (641) 483-2505
Web Site: http://www.centralstatebankia.com
Sales Range: $10-24.9 Million
Emp.: 28
Commericial Banking
N.A.I.C.S.: 522110
Brian Disney (Pres)
Kevin Geis (Sr VP & Mgr-Lending)
Chris Brinkmeyer (Chief Credit Officer & Sr VP)

Julie Riley (Mgr-Acctg)
Lori Ash (Mgr-IT)
Stephanie Smith (Officer-Comml Loan & Asst VP)

STATE CENTRAL BANK
612 1st St, Bonaparte, IA 52620
Tel.: (319) 592-3372
Web Site: http://www.statecentralbank.com
Year Founded: 1858
Sales Range: $1-9.9 Million
Emp.: 23
Commericial Banking
N.A.I.C.S.: 522110
W. Tyler Logan (Pres & CEO)

STATE EMPLOYEES CREDIT UNION
813 St Michaels Dr, Santa Fe, NM 87505
Tel.: (505) 983-7328 NM
Web Site: http://www.secunm.org
Year Founded: 1958
Sales Range: $1-9.9 Million
Credit Union
N.A.I.C.S.: 522130
Harold K. Dixon (Pres & CEO)
Mark Sadowski (CFO)

STATE EMPLOYEES CREDIT UNION OF MARYLAND, INC.
PO Box 23896, Baltimore, MD 21298
Tel.: (410) 487-7328 MD
Web Site: http://www.secumd.org
Year Founded: 1951
Sales Range: $125-149.9 Million
Emp.: 699
Credit Union
N.A.I.C.S.: 522130
Roderic Flowers (VP-HR)
Margaret Young (VP-Mktg)
Michael Gordy (COO & Exec VP)
Steven Arbaugh (CFO & VP-Fin)
Mark Reger (Chm)
Dave Sweiderk (Pres & CEO)

STATE EMPLOYEES' CREDIT UNION
PO Box 29606, Raleigh, NC 27626-0606
Tel.: (919) 857-2150
Web Site: http://www.ncsecu.org
Sales Range: $800-899.9 Million
Credit Union
N.A.I.C.S.: 522130
Bob Brinson (Chm)
Leigh Brady (COO)
Jama Campbell (Exec Dir)
Jim Hayes (Pres & CEO)
Sandra Jones (Sr VP-Member Comm)
Josh Bomba (Chief IT Officer)

STATE EQUIPMENT INC.
560 Goff Mtn Rd, Cross Lanes, WV 25313
Tel.: (304) 776-4405
Web Site: http://www.stateequipment.com
Year Founded: 1986
Sales Range: $10-24.9 Million
Emp.: 50
General Construction Machinery & Equipment
N.A.I.C.S.: 423810
Terry Lamm (Pres)
Eddie Rowan Jr. (Gen Mgr)

STATE FARM MUTUAL AUTOMOBILE INSURANCE COMPANY
1 State Farm Plz, Bloomington, IL 61710
Tel.: (309) 766-2311 IL
Web Site: http://www.statefarm.com

STATE FARM MUTUAL AUTOMOBILE INSURANCE COMPANY — U.S. PRIVATE

State Farm Mutual Automobile Insurance Company—(Continued)

Year Founded: 1922
Rev.: $43,426,000,000
Assets: $159,865,000,000
Liabilities: $59,112,000,000
Net Worth: $100,753,000,000
Earnings: $6,350,000,000
Emp.: 68,000
Fiscal Year-end: 12/31/18
Automobile & Fire Insurance; Mutual Funds, Banking & Financial Service Products
N.A.I.C.S.: 524126
Michael Leon Tipsord *(Chm, Pres & CEO)*
Fawad Ahmad *(Chief Digital Officer & Sr VP)*

Subsidiaries:

Gainsco, Inc. (1)
3333 Lee Pkwy Ste 1200, Dallas, TX 75219-5134
Tel.: (972) 629-4400
Web Site: http://www.gainsco.com
Holding Company; Insurance Services
N.A.I.C.S.: 524126
Daniel J. Coots *(CFO)*
Terence J. Lynch *(CIO & Sr VP-Investments)*

Subsidiary (Domestic):

Gainsco Service Corp. (2)
3333 Lee Pkwy Ste 1200, Dallas, TX 75219-9023
Tel.: (866) 424-6726
Web Site: http://www.gainscoinc.com
Insurance Services
N.A.I.C.S.: 524298

Lalance Financial Group, Inc. (2)
9675 Nw 117th Ave Ste 400, Medley, FL 33178-1232
Tel.: (305) 552-1027
Sales Range: $10-24.9 Million
Emp.: 100
Insurance Services
N.A.I.C.S.: 524298

State Farm Annuity & Life Insurance Co. (1)
2702 Ireland Grove Rd, Bloomington, IL 61709
Tel.: (877) 543-3619
Life Insurance Carrier
N.A.I.C.S.: 524113
Edward Barry Rust Jr. *(Chm & CEO)*

State Farm Bank, F.S.B. (1)
1 State Farm Plz, Bloomington, IL 61710
Financial Banking Services
N.A.I.C.S.: 522110
Brian Lewand *(CFO)*

State Farm Fire & Casualty Co. (1)
1 State Farm Plz, Bloomington, IL 61710-4300 **(100%)**
Tel.: (309) 766-2311
Sales Range: $1-4.9 Billion
Emp.: 7,000
Property Insurance
N.A.I.C.S.: 524126
Edward Barry Rust Jr. *(CEO)*

State Farm Florida Insurance Company (1)
7401 Cypress Gardens Blvd, Winter Haven, FL 33888-0001 **(100%)**
Tel.: (863) 318-3000
Sales Range: $250-299.9 Million
Emp.: 2,000
Property Insurance
N.A.I.C.S.: 524126
Chris Neal *(Mgr-Pub Affairs)*

State Farm General Insurance Company (1)
1 State Farm Plz, Bloomington, IL 61710
Tel.: (309) 766-2311
Property Insurance Services
N.A.I.C.S.: 524126
Edward Barry Rust Jr. *(Chm & CEO)*

State Farm Indemnity Company (1)
300 Kimball Dr, Parsippany, NJ 07054
Tel.: (973) 739-5000

Sales Range: $100-124.9 Million
Emp.: 800
Automobile Insurance
N.A.I.C.S.: 524210

Subsidiary (Domestic):

State Farm Guaranty Insurance Company (2)
1220 Route 46, Parsippany, NJ 07054-2122
Tel.: (973) 334-5111
Automobile Insurance Services
N.A.I.C.S.: 524128

State Farm Insurance Co. (1)
17301 Preston Rd, Dallas, TX 75252-5727 **(100%)**
Tel.: (512) 918-4000
Sales Range: $100-124.9 Million
Emp.: 1,600
Providers Of Casualty Insurance Services
N.A.I.C.S.: 541110
Krys Iwanicki *(Mgr-HR)*

Subsidiary (Domestic):

State Farm Lloyds, Inc. (2)
17301 Preston Rd, Dallas, TX 75252-5727 **(100%)**
Tel.: (512) 918-4000
Property Insurance Services
N.A.I.C.S.: 524128
Edward Barry Rust Jr. *(Chm & CEO)*

State Farm Insurance Co. (1)
1 State Farm Plz, Bloomington, IL 61710 **(100%)**
Tel.: (309) 763-1000
Sales Range: $800-899.9 Million
Emp.: 4,007
Life Insurance
N.A.I.C.S.: 524291

State Farm Investment Management Corp. (1)
3 State Farm Plz, Bloomington, IL 61791-0001
Tel.: (800) 447-0740
Investment Management Service
N.A.I.C.S.: 523940

State Farm Life & Accident Assurance Co. (1)
1 State Farm Plz, Bloomington, IL 61710-0001
Tel.: (309) 766-2311
Fire Insurance Services
N.A.I.C.S.: 524113
Chad Hatten *(Acct Mgr)*

Top Layer Reinsurance Ltd. (1)
Renaissance House, 12 Crow Lane, Pembroke, HM 19, Bermuda
Tel.: (441) 2954513
Web Site: http://www.renre.com
Sales Range: $75-99.9 Million
Emp.: 130
Reinsurance Services; Joint Venture Renaissance Reinsurance (50%) & State Farm Mutual Automobile Insurance Company (50%)
N.A.I.C.S.: 524130
David A. Eklund *(Pres)*

STATE FISH COMPANY INC.

2194 Signal Pl, San Pedro, CA 90731-7225
Tel.: (310) 832-2633 CA
Web Site: http://www.statefish.com
Year Founded: 1946
Sales Range: $25-49.9 Million
Emp.: 250
Fish & Seafood
N.A.I.C.S.: 311710
Patrick Downs *(Mgr-Facility Maintenance)*
Humberto Arakaki *(Mgr-Production)*
Sandy Snider *(Mgr-Acctg)*
Vanessa DeLuca *(Pres)*
Janet Esposito *(Owner)*

STATE FUND MUTUAL INSURANCE CO.

3500 American Blvd W Ste 700, Bloomington, MN 55431
Tel.: (952) 838-4200

Web Site: http://www.sfmic.com
Year Founded: 1983
Sales Range: $100-124.9 Million
Emp.: 180
Workers Compensation Insurance
N.A.I.C.S.: 524126
Terrence L. Miller *(Pres & CEO)*
David E. Kaiser *(Founder, Pres, CIO & Sr VP)*
M. Scott Brener *(Gen Counsel & Sr VP)*
Michael L. Happe *(CMO, Pres-SFM Risk Solutions & Sr VP)*
Steven T. Sandilla *(Sr VP-Strategic Bus Ops)*
Kent D. Dixon *(Vice Chm)*
Chris Anderson *(Controller & Dir-Fin Reporting)*
Amanda Aponte *(Chief Risk Officer & VP)*
Robert S. Mars III *(Chm)*

Subsidiaries:

CompCost Inc. (1)
3500 American Blvd W Ste 700, Minneapolis, MN 55431
Tel.: (952) 838-4200
Sales Range: $1-9.9 Million
Insurance Claims Processing
N.A.I.C.S.: 524292

SFM Systems Inc. (1)
3500 American Blvd W Ste 700, Minneapolis, MN 55431
Tel.: (952) 838-4200
Web Site: http://www.sfmic.com
Prepackaged Software
N.A.I.C.S.: 513210

STATE GAS & OIL, LLC

1540 Martin St, State College, PA 16803
Tel.: (814) 237-4355 PA
Web Site: http://www.stategasandoil.com
Year Founded: 1986
Sales Range: $75-99.9 Million
Emp.: 6
Distr of Home Heating Oil
N.A.I.C.S.: 424720
James Martin *(Pres)*

STATE INDUSTRIAL PRODUCTS CORPORATION

5915 Landerbrook Dr Ste 300, Mayfield Heights, OH 44124
Tel.: (216) 861-7114 OH
Web Site: http://www.stateindustrial.com
Year Founded: 1911
Sales Range: $10-24.9 Million
Emp.: 1,300
Cleaning Product Mfr
N.A.I.C.S.: 325611
Brian Limbert *(Pres & COO)*

Subsidiaries:

State Chemical Sales Company International Inc. (1)
Royal Indl Park Bldg M Local Ste 5 Carr 869 KM 1 5 Palmas, Catano, PR 00962-4607
Tel.: (787) 275-3180
Rev.: $240,000
Emp.: 39
Provider of Chemical Products
N.A.I.C.S.: 424690
Carlos Concepcion *(Branch Mgr)*

State Cleaning Solutions (1)
5915 Landerbrook Dr Ste 300, Mayfield Heights, OH 44124
Tel.: (866) 727-5477
Web Site: http://www.statecleaningsolutions.com
Emp.: 200
Cleaning Product Distr
N.A.I.C.S.: 424690
Pat Darling *(Mgr-Sls-District)*

State Contract Manufacturing (1)

383 N High St, Hebron, OH 43025
Tel.: (740) 929-1100
Web Site: http://www.statecontractmfg.com
Chemical Products Mfr
N.A.I.C.S.: 325998

STATE INDUSTRIES, LLC

500 Tennessee Waltz Pkwy, Ashland City, TN 37015
Tel.: (615) 792-4371 TN
Web Site: http://www.statewaterheaters.com
Year Founded: 1946
Hot Water Heaters; Household
N.A.I.C.S.: 335220
Ajita G. Rajendra *(Pres)*

STATE NARROW FABRICS INC.

2902 Borden Ave, Long Island City, NY 11101-6817
Tel.: (718) 392-8787
Web Site: http://www.statenarrow.com
Year Founded: 1979
Sales Range: $10-24.9 Million
Emp.: 25
Narrow Fabric Mills
N.A.I.C.S.: 313220
Al Lebensfeld *(VP)*

STATE OF FRANKLIN HEALTHCARE ASSOCIATES PLLC

2528 Wesley St Ste 2, Johnson City, TN 37601
Tel.: (423) 794-2435
Web Site: http://www.sofha.net
Offices of Physicians (except Mental Health Specialists)
N.A.I.C.S.: 621111
Vicki Moody *(Officer)*

STATE OF NEW YORK MORTGAGE AGENCY

641 Lexington Ave Fl 4, New York, NY 10022
Tel.: (212) 688-4000
Web Site: http://www.nyshcr.org
Sales Range: $300-349.9 Million
Emp.: 300
Bond & Mortgage Companies
N.A.I.C.S.: 522292
Edwin Bonilla *(Sr VP-IT)*
Gerald Lubin *(Asst Treas)*
Roger Harry *(Asst VP-Multifamily Fin)*
Gail A. Davis-Kresge *(Asst VP & Mgr-Relationship)*

STATE SERVICE CO. INC.

1062 Harbor 2 Bishop Rd, Ingleside, TX 78362
Tel.: (361) 776-7399
Web Site: http://www.stateservice.com
Sales Range: $10-24.9 Million
Emp.: 80
Dams, Waterways, Docks & Other Marine Construction
N.A.I.C.S.: 236210
Russell Little *(Pres)*
Jeff Little *(VP)*

STATE SERVICES ORGANIZATION, INC.

444 N Capitol St NW Ste 237, Washington, DC 20001
Tel.: (202) 624-5490 DC
Web Site: http://www.sso.org
Year Founded: 2001
Sales Range: $10-24.9 Million
Emp.: 21,000
Business Center Operator
N.A.I.C.S.: 813410
Charles Walton *(Mgr-Library)*
Val Ogora *(Sr Mgr-Logistic)*

COMPANIES

Wendy Shapiro *(Mgr-Ops)*
Stephen Roberts *(Exec Dir)*
Towanna Gates *(Sr Mgr-Logistics)*
Audrey Williams *(Controller)*
Fabio Andrade Jr. *(CIO)*

STATE STEEL SUPPLY CO
208 Court St, Sioux City, IA 51101
Tel.: (712) 277-4000
Web Site: http://www.statesteel.com
Sales Range: $75-99.9 Million
Emp.: 300
Steel
N.A.I.C.S.: 423510
Jack Bernstein *(Pres)*
Greg Yaeger *(Mgr-Sls)*
David Bernstein *(VP)*

STATE STREET CAPITAL REALTY, LLC
250 Civic Center Dr Ste 500, Columbus, OH 43215
Tel.: (614) 228-5331   OH
Web Site: http://www.castoinfo.com
Sales Range: $10-24.9 Million
Emp.: 100
Real Estate Development
N.A.I.C.S.: 531120
Frank S. Benson *(Partner)*
Paul G. Lukeman *(Partner & Head-Retail Dev)*
Stephen E. Dutton *(Partner)*
Linda Swearingen *(Exec VP-Asset Mgmt Div)*
Brett Hutchens *(Partner-Retail Dev-Southeastern US)*
C. H. Waterman *(VP & Dir-Legal)*
Don M. Casto III *(Partner)*

Subsidiaries:

Eastbay Equities Inc.   (1)
191 W Nationwide Blvd, Columbus, OH 43215
Tel.: (614) 228-5331
Web Site: http://www.castoinfo.com
Real Estate Services
N.A.I.C.S.: 531390

STATE TEACHERS RETIREMENT SYSTEM OF OHIO
275 E Broad St, Columbus, OH 43215-3703
Tel.: (614) 227-4090   OH
Web Site: http://www.strsoh.org
Year Founded: 1919
Sales Range: $100-124.9 Million
Emp.: 670
Pension & Financial Services
N.A.I.C.S.: 525110
Sandra L. Knoesel *(Chief Benefits Officer & Deputy Exec Dir-Member Benefits)*
Andrew J. Marfurt *(Dir-HR)*
William J. Neville *(Gen Counsel)*
Gregory A. Taylor *(Dir-IT)*
John D. Morrow *(CIO & Deputy Exec Dir-Investments)*
Marla E. Bump *(Dir-Governmental Rels)*
Michael J. Nehf *(Exec Dir)*
Nicholas J. Treneff *(Dir-Comm Svcs)*
Paul M. Snyder *(CFO & Deputy Exec Dir-Fin)*

STATE TOOL & MANUFACTURING CO.
1650 E Empire Ave, Benton Harbor, MI 49022
Tel.: (269) 927-3153
Web Site: http://www.statetool.com
Year Founded: 1953
Rev.: $10,400,000
Emp.: 40
Sockets, Electric
N.A.I.C.S.: 335931

Manroe Raschke *(Pres & Gen Mgr)*
Doug Christy *(VP-Sls Engrg)*

STATE UTILITY CONTRACTORS INC.
4417 Old Charlotte Hwy, Monroe, NC 28110
Tel.: (704) 289-6400
Web Site: http://www.sucontractors.com
Year Founded: 1985
Sales Range: $25-49.9 Million
Emp.: 125
Water Main Construction
N.A.I.C.S.: 237110
Bill Norwood *(Chm)*
Ron Brown *(Pres)*

Subsidiaries:

State Building Group, Inc.   (1)
4417 Old Charlotte Hwy, Monroe, NC 28110-7335
Tel.: (704) 289-4523
Web Site: http://www.statebuildinggroupinc.com
Construction Engineering Services
N.A.I.C.S.: 541330
Bill Vibbert *(Project Mgr)*

STATE VOLUNTEER MUTUAL INSURANCE CO.
101 Westpark Dr, Brentwood, TN 37027
Tel.: (615) 377-1999   TN
Web Site: http://www.svmic.com
Year Founded: 1975
Sales Range: $75-99.9 Million
Emp.: 120
Provider of Property & Casualty Insurance
N.A.I.C.S.: 524126
James W. Howell *(Sr VP)*
James E. Smith *(Sr VP)*

STATELINE COOPERATIVE INC.
120 E Walnut St, Burt, IA 50522
Tel.: (515) 924-3555   IA
Web Site: http://www.statelinecoop.com
Year Founded: 1996
Sales Range: $10-24.9 Million
Emp.: 150
Provider of Farm Supply Sevices
N.A.I.C.S.: 424910
Renee Pals *(Controller)*
Steve Gangestad *(Mgr-Ops)*
Steve Vaske *(Mgr-Ops)*

STATEN ISLAND BOAT SALES INC.
222 Mansion Ave, Staten Island, NY 10308
Tel.: (718) 984-7676
Web Site: http://www.siboats.com
Rev.: $45,000,000
Emp.: 40
Motor Boat Dealers
N.A.I.C.S.: 441222
Frank Bongiorno *(Pres & CEO)*
Jackie Kuhfahl *(Controller)*
Peter Hoffman *(Mgr-Customer Svc)*

STATEN ISLAND MENTAL HEALTH SOCIETY, INC.
669 Castleton Ave, Staten Island, NY 10301-2028
Tel.: (718) 442-2225   NY
Web Site: http://www.simhs.org
Year Founded: 1954
Sales Range: $10-24.9 Million
Emp.: 296
Child Mental Health Care Services
N.A.I.C.S.: 623220
Carmen Chisvette *(VP-Facility)*
Fern A. Zagor *(Pres & CEO)*

Anthony Defazio *(Treas)*
Elizabeth Palagiano *(Sec)*
John Tapinis *(Chm)*

STATEN ISLAND NISSAN
1220 Hylan Blvd, Staten Island, NY 10305
Tel.: (718) 447-3800
Web Site: http://www.sinissan.com
Sales Range: $25-49.9 Million
Emp.: 103
Car Whslr
N.A.I.C.S.: 441110
Peter S. Folino *(Pres)*
Scott Reback *(CEO)*

STATES UNLIMITED
300 N Breckenridge Ave, Breckenridge, TX 76424-3506
Tel.: (254) 559-3355   TX
Year Founded: 1984
Sales Range: $125-149.9 Million
Emp.: 65
Oil & Gas Production & Operators
N.A.I.C.S.: 211120
Fred F. Deuser *(CEO)*
John H. Connally *(Pres & CFO)*
E. Bruce Street *(Partner)*
Eileen Speer *(Dir-Payroll)*

Subsidiaries:

Breck Operating Corp.   (1)
300 N Breckenridge Ave, Breckenridge, TX 76424-3506   (100%)
Tel.: (254) 559-3355
Web Site: http://www.breckop.com
Sales Range: $25-49.9 Million
Emp.: 40
Oil & Gas Producing Services
N.A.I.C.S.: 211120
Barbra J. Beene *(Sec)*
Wayne Christian *(Pres)*

STATESERV MEDICAL, LLC
1201 S Alma School Rd Ste 4000, Mesa, AZ 85210
Tel.: (480) 966-9730   AZ
Web Site: http://www.stateserv.com
Year Founded: 2004
Hospice Care Market Durable Medical Equipment Benefit Management Services
N.A.I.C.S.: 423450
Anthony R. Perre *(Co-Founder & Chm)*
Paul DiCosmo *(Co-Founder & CEO)*
Chris Roode *(COO)*

Subsidiaries:

Network Medical, LLC   (1)
2625 2nd Ave N, Birmingham, AL 35203
Tel.: (205) 440-4459
Web Site: http://www.hospicelink.com
Hospice Care Market Durable Medical Equipment Benefit Management Services
N.A.I.C.S.: 423450
Patrick Kent *(COO)*
Steve Potier *(Sr VP-Network Ops)*
Tim Callahan *(Sr VP-Sls)*

STATEWIDE DISASTER RESTORATION, INC.
22310 Telegraph Rd, Southfield, MI 48033
Tel.: (248) 353-9500   MI
Web Site: http://www.statewidedisaster.com
Year Founded: 1994
Sales Range: $25-49.9 Million
Emp.: 68
Disaster Recovery Repair & Restoration
N.A.I.C.S.: 238990
Jeff Levine *(VP-Bus Dev)*

STATEWIDE MORTGAGE, LLC
10221 Linn Station Rd, Louisville, KY 40223

STATON WHOLESALE INC.

Tel.: (502) 585-5626   KY
Web Site: http://www.statewidemortgage.com
Year Founded: 2001
Emp.: 40
Mortgage Brokerage Services
N.A.I.C.S.: 522310
Keith Swisher *(Pres)*

STATEWIDE TIRE DISTRIBUTORS
2085 Wagner St, Vandalia, IL 62471
Tel.: (618) 283-1102
Web Site: http://www.statewidetire.com
Rev.: $11,368,489
Emp.: 15
Distr of Tires & Tubes
N.A.I.C.S.: 423130
Roger Cornelius *(Pres)*

STATEWOOD INCORPORATED
514 Salmon Brook St, Granby, CT 06035
Tel.: (860) 653-7241
Web Site: http://www.statelineoil.net
Sales Range: $10-24.9 Million
Emp.: 75
Provider of Petroleum Products
N.A.I.C.S.: 457210
Bill Spanswick *(Mgr-Svc)*
Michael B. Guarco Sr. *(Pres)*

STATEX PETROLEUM I, L.P.
PO Box 797545, Dallas, TX 75379
Tel.: (972) 869-2800   CA
Sales Range: $100-124.9 Million
Emp.: 7
Explorer & Developer of Oil & Natural Gas Properties
N.A.I.C.S.: 211120
Dhar Carman *(Mgr)*

STATICWORX, INC
124 Watertown St, Watertown, MA 02472
Tel.: (617) 923-2000
Web Site: http://www.staticworx.com
Sales Range: $1-9.9 Million
Emp.: 6
Flooring Contractors
N.A.I.C.S.: 238330
David H. Long *(Pres & CEO)*

STATLINK SYSTEMS LLC
3320 Park Ave, Memphis, TN 38111
Tel.: (901) 454-4790
Web Site: http://www.statlinksystems.com
Year Founded: 2007
Sales Range: $1-9.9 Million
Emp.: 14
Business Process & Database Management Software
N.A.I.C.S.: 513210
Dana Capocaccia *(Pres & CEO)*

STATMON TECHNOLOGIES CORP.
3000 Lakeside Dr Ste 300 S, Bannockburn, IL 60015
Tel.: (847) 604-5366   NV
Web Site: http://www.statmon.com
Year Founded: 1978
Sales Range: $1-9.9 Million
Emp.: 12
Wireless & Fiber Infrastructure Network Management Solutions
N.A.I.C.S.: 517112
Geoffrey P. Talbot *(Co-Founder, Chm & CEO)*
Peter J. Upfold *(Co-Founder & CTO)*
Ken Dillard *(Exec VP-Global Sls & Mktg)*

STATON WHOLESALE INC.

STATON WHOLESALE INC.

Staton Wholesale Inc.—(Continued)
14275 Welch Rd, Dallas, TX 75244
Tel.: (972) 448-3000
Web Site:
 http://www.statononline.com
Sales Range: $10-24.9 Million
Emp.: 70
Mfr of Clothing
N.A.I.C.S.: 424350
Edward Staton (Chm)
Bruce McKinley (Mgr-Freight)
Chris Petrilla (Controller)

STATRAD
13915 Danielson St Ste 200, Poway, CA 92064
Web Site: http://www.statrad.com
Sales Range: $1-9.9 Million
Emp.: 39
Teleradiology Services
N.A.I.C.S.: 519290
Vincent G. Lobdell (CEO)
Philippe Raffy (VP-Data Sciences & Clinical Dev)
Chris Hafey (CTO)

STAUB METALS CORPORATION
7747 Rosecrans Ave, Paramount, CA 90723-1425
Tel.: (562) 602-2200
Web Site:
 http://www.staubmetals.com
Year Founded: 1980
Sales Range: $10-24.9 Million
Emp.: 130
Provider of Metals Services
N.A.I.C.S.: 423510
Kenneth L. Staub (Pres & CEO)
Jim Pelletier (COO)
Walt Binggeli (Gen Mgr-Sls)

STAUCH VETROMILE & MITCHELL ADVERTISING, INC.
2 Charles St 3rd Fl N, Providence, RI 02904
Tel.: (401) 490-9700
Web Site:
 http://www.svmmarcom.com
Year Founded: 1971
Sales Range: $1-9.9 Million
Emp.: 16
Advertising & Public Relations Agency
N.A.I.C.S.: 541810
Julian Peters (VP-Creative)
Rachelle Costa (Admin Dir)
Robert W. Vetromile (Pres & Partner)
Laura Nelson (Dir-Pub Rels)
Cari Thorpe (Controller)
Jennifer O'Shea (Partner & VP-Client Svcs)
Jill Colna (Dir-Pub Rels)

STAUFF CORPORATION
7 William Demarest Pl, Waldwick, NJ 07463
Tel.: (201) 444-7800
Web Site: http://www.stauff.com
Year Founded: 1972
Rev.: $18,000,000
Emp.: 50
Liquid Automation Machinery & Equipment
N.A.I.C.S.: 333998
Knut Menshen (Chm)
Glen Behrens (Mgr-Pur)
Jeff Behling (Pres & CEO)

STAUFFER GLOVE & SAFETY
361 E 6th St, Red Hill, PA 18076-1118
Tel.: (215) 679-4446
Web Site:
 http://www.stauffersafety.com
Year Founded: 1955

Sales Range: $50-74.9 Million
Emp.: 100
Industrial Hand Protection, Safety Equipment & Personal Body Protection Distr
N.A.I.C.S.: 424350
Jeffrey R. Stauffer (VP)
George Wainwright (Controller)
John Gillespie (Acct Mgr)
Doug Angle (Mgr-Customer Svc)
Steve Barnes (Mgr-Natl Contracts)

STAUNTON CAPITAL, INC.
3406-E W Wendover Ave, Greensboro, NC 27407-1527
Tel.: (336) 855-9992
Year Founded: 1989
Sales Range: $10-24.9 Million
Emp.: 172
Bearing Mfr
N.A.I.C.S.: 332991
James E. Hooper (Pres & CEO)

STAVE ISLAND LTD. PARTNERSHIP
135 W Lakeshore Dr, Colchester, VT 05446
Tel.: (802) 863-6376
Sales Range: $10-24.9 Million
Emp.: 150
Holding Company: Investments
N.A.I.C.S.: 551112
Dawn Hazlett (Pres)

Subsidiaries:

Hazelett Strip-Casting Corp. (1)
135 W Lakeshore Dr, Colchester, VT 05446
Tel.: (802) 863-6376
Web Site: http://www.hazelett.com
Sales Range: $10-24.9 Million
Emp.: 140
Designs, Manufactures, Installs & Services Twin-belt Continuous Casting Machines
N.A.I.C.S.: 551112
David Hazelett (Pres)

STAVOLA CONTRACTING CO. INC.
175 Drift Rd, Tinton Falls, NJ 07724
Tel.: (732) 542-2328
Web Site: http://www.stavola.com
Sales Range: $25-49.9 Million
Emp.: 70
General Contractor, Highway & Street Construction
N.A.I.C.S.: 237310
John Stavola (Pres)
Richard Stavola (VP)
Jules Cattie (CFO)

STAVROS CENTER FOR INDEPENDENT LIVING, INC.
210 Old Farm Rd, Amherst, MA 01002
Tel.: (413) 256-0473
Web Site: http://www.stavros.org
Year Founded: 1974
Sales Range: $10-24.9 Million
Emp.: 176
Disability Assistance Services
N.A.I.C.S.: 624120
Nancy Bazanchuk (VP)
Glenn Hartmann (Pres)
Donna M. Bliznak (Treas)

STAY-GREEN, INC.
26415 Summit Cir, Santa Clarita, CA 91350
Tel.: (800) 741-9150
Web Site: http://www.staygreen.com
Year Founded: 1970
Sales Range: $1-9.9 Million
Emp.: 170
Lawn And Garden Services
N.A.I.C.S.: 561730

Charlene Angelo (Founder)
Steven Seely (COO)
Chris Angelo (Pres & CEO)

Subsidiaries:

Emerald Landscape Services, Inc. (1)
1041 N Kemp St, Anaheim, CA 92801
Tel.: (714) 993-9006
Sales Range: $1-9.9 Million
Emp.: 70
Landscaping Services
N.A.I.C.S.: 561730

STAYSAFE RESEARCH SYSTEMS LTD.
8746 112th St, Richmond Hill, NY 11418
Tel.: (718) 849-0671
Rev.: $92,000,000
Emp.: 170
Cigarettes
N.A.I.C.S.: 561611
Peter Grinenko (Pres)

STAYWELL HEALTH CARE, INC.
80 Phoenix Ave, Waterbury, CT 06702
Tel.: (203) 756-8021
Web Site:
 http://www.staywellhealth.org
Year Founded: 1992
Sales Range: $10-24.9 Million
Emp.: 155
Health Care Srvices
N.A.I.C.S.: 622110
Amit Patel (Dir-Dental)
Dorothy Smith (Mgr-Billing)
Lule Tracey (CFO)
Sunil D'Cunha (Dir-Medical)
Christine Bianchi (Dir-Community Programs, Grants & Dev)
Beverly Lyons (Dir-Behavioral & Mental Health Svcs)
Donald Thompson (Pres & CEO)
Janet Ciarleglio (Mgr-Driggs School-Based Health Center)
Naga Yalamanchilli (Dir-IT)
Heather A. Garofalo (Coord-Grant Mgmt)
Rubina Ramirez (Coord-Dental)

STC ASSOCIATES
210 5th Ave 2nd Fl, New York, NY 10010
Tel.: (212) 725-1900
Web Site:
 http://www.stcassociates.com
Year Founded: 1992
Sales Range: $1-9.9 Million
Emp.: 25
Public Relations Agency
N.A.I.C.S.: 541820
Laurent Bourscheidt (Exec Dir-Creative)
Jorge Quintans (VP-New Media & Tech)
Carolyn Robertson (VP-Mktg)

STC GROUP INC.
10 Basil Sawyer Dr, Hampton, VA 23666
Tel.: (757) 766-5800
Web Site: http://www.stcnet.com
Rev.: $16,000,000
Emp.: 60
Commercial Physical Research
N.A.I.C.S.: 541715
Paul Try (Sr VP, Dir & Mgr)

Subsidiaries:

Science and Technology Corp. (1)
10 Basil Sawyer Dr, Hampton, VA 23666
Tel.: (757) 766-5800
Web Site: http://www.stcnet.com
Commercial Physical Research

N.A.I.C.S.: 541715

STEADFAST BRAND, INC.
PO Box 540263, Orlando, FL 32854
Tel.: (407) 985-2817
Web Site:
 http://www.steadfastbrand.com
Sales Range: $10-24.9 Million
Apparel & Other Accessories Mfr & Online Retailer
N.A.I.C.S.: 315990
Chris Collins (Owner)

STEADFAST COMPANIES
18100 Von Karman Ave Ste 500, Irvine, CA 92612
Tel.: (949) 852-0700
Web Site:
 http://www.steadfastcompanies.com
Year Founded: 1994
Holding Company; Real Estate Investment, Development & Portfolio Management Services
N.A.I.C.S.: 551112
Rodney F. Emery (Chm & CEO)
Ella Shaw Neyland (Pres)
Dinesh K. Davar (CFO)
Ana Marie del Rio (Chief Legal Officer & Chief Admin Officer)
Phillip Meserve (Pres & CEO-Capital Markets Grp)
Christopher M. Hilbert (Pres)
Luis H. Garcia (Mng Dir)
Robert M. Murray (Mng Dir)
Richard D. Gann (Chief Products Officer)
Jason Grovert (CIO)

Subsidiaries:

Steadfast Income REIT, Inc. (1)
18100 Von Karman Ave Ste 500, Irvine, CA 92612
Tel.: (949) 852-0700
Web Site: http://www.steadfastreits.com
Rev.: $141,988,859
Assets: $1,019,657,998
Liabilities: $728,896,664
Net Worth: $290,761,334
Earnings: $89,083,552
Fiscal Year-end: 12/31/2018
Real Estate Investment Services
N.A.I.C.S.: 523999
Rodney F. Emery (Chm & CEO)
Kevin J. Keating (CFO & Treas)

Steadfast Properties & Development, Inc. (1)
18100 Von Karman Ave Ste 500, Irvine, CA 92612
Tel.: (949) 852-0700
Web Site:
 http://www.steadfastcompanies.com
Real Estate Investment, Development & Portfolio Management Services
N.A.I.C.S.: 531390
Rodney F. Emery (Chm & CEO)
Ella Shaw Neyland (Pres)

Subsidiary (Domestic):

Steadfast Capital Markets Group, LLC (2)
18100 Von Karman Ave Ste 500, Irvine, CA 92612
Tel.: (949) 852-0700
Web Site: http://www.steadfastcmg.com
Real Estate Investment & Portfolio Management Services
N.A.I.C.S.: 531390
Phillip Meserve (Pres & CEO)
Steve Skytte (Chief Compliance Officer)
Gary Davi (CIO)
Angela Barbera (Sr VP-Natl Accts)

STEAL NETWORK, LLC.
2181 California Ave Ste 400, Salt Lake City, UT 84104
Tel.: (801) 210-0304
Web Site:
 http://www.stealnetwork.com
Year Founded: 2008

Sales Range: $10-24.9 Million
Emp.: 71
Online Marketing Services
N.A.I.C.S.: 459999
Melanie Comadena *(Controller)*
Marco Rodriguez *(Sr Engr-Software)*

STEALTH-ISS GROUP INC.
4601 N Fairfax Dr Ste 1200, Arlington, VA 22203
Web Site: http://www.stealth-iss.com
Year Founded: 2002
Sales Range: $1-9.9 Million
Emp.: 55
Cyber Security Consulting Services
N.A.I.C.S.: 541690
Dasha Deckwerth *(Founder & Pres)*
Robert Davies *(CEO)*
Robert Goodrich *(VP-Federal BD)*

STEALTHCOM SOLUTIONS INC.
9475 Briar Village Point Ste 316, Colorado Springs, CO 80920
Tel.: (719) 359-5410
Web Site: http://www.stealthcom.com
Year Founded: 2006
Sales Range: $1-9.9 Million
Emp.: 9
Design & Installation of Cabling Infrastructure for Networks
N.A.I.C.S.: 335921
Jason Aguilar *(Owner & Pres)*
Buddy Kitzmiller *(VP-Ops)*

STEAM & CONTROL SYSTEMS, INC.
2805 Riverside Dr, Chattanooga, TN 37406
Tel.: (423) 624-1727
Web Site: http://www.scsenergy.com
Year Founded: 1993
Sales Range: $10-24.9 Million
Emp.: 100
Air Conditioning System Installation Services
N.A.I.C.S.: 238220
Gail Brown *(Controller)*
W. Perry Smith III *(Pres)*

STEAMBOAT MOTORS, L.L.C.
2310 Lincoln Ave, Steamboat Springs, CO 80487
Tel.: (970) 879-8880
Web Site: http://www.steamboatmotors.com
Sales Range: $10-24.9 Million
Emp.: 39
New & Used Car Dealer
N.A.I.C.S.: 441110
John Centner *(Gen Mgr)*
Lee Williams *(Bus Dir)*
Tom Kleman *(Mgr-Rental)*
John Wilkinson *(Bus Dir)*

STEARNS ELECTRIC ASSOCIATION
900 E Kraft Dr, Melrose, MN 56352
Tel.: (320) 256-4241
Web Site: http://www.stearnselectric.org
Sales Range: $10-24.9 Million
Emp.: 60
Distribution, Electric Power
N.A.I.C.S.: 221122
Steve Notch *(Sec & Treas)*
Randy Rothstein *(Pres)*
Harlan Jopp *(VP)*

STEARNS FINANCIAL SERVICES, INC.
4191 2nd St S, Saint Cloud, MN 56301
Tel.: (320) 253-6607 MN
Web Site:
http://www.stearnsbank.com
Year Founded: 1912
Sales Range: $125-149.9 Million
Bank Holding Company
N.A.I.C.S.: 551111
Norman C. Skalicky *(Chm & Co-CEO)*
Matt Geist *(CFO)*
Harley Vestrum *(Chief Risk Officer)*
Greg Misterman *(Chief Credit Officer)*
Steve Domine *(Pres-MN Community Banking & Sr VP-Natl Lending)*
Pam Bjerke *(Chief HR Officer)*
Rory Bidinger *(CMO)*
Josh Hofer *(Chief Risk & Information Security Officer)*
Theresa Tschumperlin *(COO)*
Ann Erickson *(Chief Compliance & Audit Officer)*
Heather Plumski *(CFO & Chief Strategy Officer)*

Subsidiaries:

Stearns Bank Holdingford N.A. (1)
580 Main St, Holdingford, MN 56340
Tel.: (320) 746-2261
Web Site: http://www.stearnsbank.com
Sales Range: $1-9.9 Million
Emp.: 4
Federal Savings Bank
N.A.I.C.S.: 522180

Stearns Bank N.A. (1)
4191 2nd St S, Saint Cloud, MN 56301-3761
Tel.: (320) 253-6607
Web Site: http://www.stearnsbank.com
Sales Range: $50-74.9 Million
Emp.: 70
Federal Savings Bank
N.A.I.C.S.: 522180
Norman C. Skalicky *(Chm)*
Thomas Zernick *(Pres-Market-Florida)*
Steve Domine *(Sr VP & Gen Mgr-Stearns Equipment Fin)*
Matt Geist *(CFO)*
Daryn Lecy *(VP-Ops-Stearns Equipment Fin)*
Greg Misterman *(Chief Credit Officer)*
Kelly Skalicky *(Pres & CEO)*
Harley Vestrum *(COO & Chief Risk Officer)*

Stearns Bank Upsala N.A. (1)
105 S Main St, Upsala, MN 56384
Tel.: (320) 573-2111
Web Site: http://www.stearnsbank.com
Sales Range: $1-9.9 Million
Federal Savings Bank
N.A.I.C.S.: 522180

STEARNS PACKAGING CORPORATION
4200 Sycamore Ave, Madison, WI 53704-0216
Tel.: (608) 246-5150
Web Site: http://www.stearnspkg.com
Year Founded: 1951
Sales Range: $10-24.9 Million
Emp.: 46
Specialty Chemical Product Mfr
N.A.I.C.S.: 325998
Bill Bestmann *(VP-Sls & Mktg)*
Colleen Heiser *(Mgr-Traffic)*
Jeff Hanson *(Mgr-Pur)*
John B. Everitt *(Pres)*
Jim Peterson *(Mgr-Dairy Product)*
Craig Koerner *(Coord-Quality Control)*

STEARNS PRODUCTS INC.
2131 Word Ave, Simi Valley, CA 93065
Tel.: (805) 582-2710
Web Site: http://www.dermae.net
Sales Range: $1-9.9 Million
Emp.: 25
Beauty Care Products
N.A.I.C.S.: 325620
David Stearn *(Pres)*
Linda Miles *(VP)*
Susan Morehart *(Dir-Sls & Mktg)*
Jennifer Norman *(VP-Mktg)*
Barbara Roll *(VP-Mktg)*

STEBBINS ENGINEERING & MANUFACTURING COMPANY
363 Eastern Blvd, Watertown, NY 13601-3140
Tel.: (315) 782-3000 NY
Web Site:
http://www.stebbinseng.com
Year Founded: 1884
Sales Range: $125-149.9 Million
Emp.: 1,500
Mfr & Install Reinforced Tile & Linings
N.A.I.C.S.: 238990
A. E. Calligaris *(Chm, Pres & CEO)*
Robert J. Storms *(Sr VP)*
Ken Sturge *(Treas)*
Anthony M. Marra *(VP-Construction)*
Dave Honan *(VP-Engrg)*

Subsidiaries:

Stebbins Engineering & Manufacturing Co. - Port Allen (1)
4831 N River Rd, Port Allen, LA 70767-3854 (100%)
Tel.: (225) 343-6671
Sales Range: $25-49.9 Million
Emp.: 200
Mfr & Installation of Reinforced Tile & Linings
N.A.I.C.S.: 238990

Stebbins Engineering & Manufacturing Co. - Seattle (1)
Ste 201 4707 NE Minnehaha St, Vancouver, WA 98661-1858 (100%)
Tel.: (206) 365-2111
Sales Range: $10-24.9 Million
Emp.: 2
Mfr & Installation of Reinforced Tile & Linings
N.A.I.C.S.: 238990

STEBBINS ENTERPRISES INC.
1359 Hooksett Rd, Hooksett, NH 03106
Tel.: (603) 623-8811
Web Site: http://www.proconinc.com
Sales Range: $125-149.9 Million
Emp.: 150
Commercial & Office Building, New Construction Large Scale Residential
N.A.I.C.S.: 236220
Dan Dal Pra *(Sr VP)*
Bruce Desmarais *(CFO)*

STEDMAN MACHINE COMPANY
129 Franklin St, Aurora, IN 47001
Tel.: (812) 926-0038
Web Site: http://www.stedman-machine.com
Year Founded: 1834
Sales Range: $50-74.9 Million
Emp.: 70
Mfr of Crushing Machinery
N.A.I.C.S.: 333131
Dennis Gilmour *(Pres)*

STEED CONSTRUCTION, INC.
1250 E Iron Eagle Dr No 200, Eagle, ID 83616
Tel.: (208) 378-7300
Web Site:
http://www.steedconstruction.com
Year Founded: 1988
Commercial & Institutional Building Construction
N.A.I.C.S.: 236220
Randy S. Steed *(Pres & CEO)*
Scott J. Raymes *(COO & Exec VP)*
Scott A. Steed *(VP-Utah)*
Thomas Cervino *(CFO)*
Chris Steed *(Officer-Compliance & Project Mgr)*
Kevin Raymes *(Project Mgr)*

STEED TIMBER CO. INC.
78797 Hwy 77 N, Lincoln, AL 35096
Tel.: (205) 763-7761
Web Site:
http://www.steedtimber.com
Sales Range: $10-24.9 Million
Emp.: 5
Timber Products, Rough
N.A.I.C.S.: 423990
Garett Walker Steed *(VP)*

STEEL & ALLOY UTILITY PRODUCTS, INC.
110 Ohio Ave, McDonald, OH 44437
Tel.: (330) 530-2220 OH
Web Site: http://www.steelalloy.com
Year Founded: 1946
Sales Range: $10-24.9 Million
Emp.: 75
Custom Steel & Alloy Fabrication & Machining Services
N.A.I.C.S.: 332999
Nathan Gallo *(Co-Owner, Pres & CEO)*
Nick Gallo *(Co-Owner & VP)*

STEEL & MACHINERY TRANSPORTATION
3680 179th St, Hammond, IN 46323
Tel.: (219) 845-5858
Web Site:
http://www.steelmachinerytransport.com
Rev.: $11,032,708
Emp.: 20
Heavy Hauling
N.A.I.C.S.: 484121
John R. Riley *(Pres)*

STEEL & PIPE SUPPLY COMPANY INC.
555 Poyntz Ave, Manhattan, KS 66502-6085
Tel.: (785) 587-5100 KS
Web Site: http://www.spsci.com
Year Founded: 1933
Sales Range: $10-24.9 Million
Emp.: 425
Metals, Service Centers & Offices
N.A.I.C.S.: 423510
Dennis A. Mullin *(CEO)*
Derk Dagline *(CFO)*
Julie Byrom *(Acct Mgr)*
Connie Casper *(VP-Sls)*
Jerry Peavy *(Pres)*

STEEL & PIPES INC.
Km 27 9 HM 5 RR 1, Caguas, PR 00725
Tel.: (787) 747-9415
Web Site:
http://www.steelandpipes.com
Sales Range: $25-49.9 Million
Emp.: 56
Steel
N.A.I.C.S.: 423510
Felipe Vidal Cos *(CEO)*
Felipe Figueroa *(Pres)*
Alberto Vidal *(VP)*

STEEL BRANDING
6414 Bee Cave Rd Ste B, Austin, TX 78746
Tel.: (800) 681-8809
Web Site:
http://www.steelbranding.com
Sales Range: $1-9.9 Million
Emp.: 26
Advertising Agencies
N.A.I.C.S.: 541810
Kristen Cutshall *(CEO & Partner)*
Denise Waid *(Partner & Dir-Creative)*
Amy Bailey *(Partner & VP-PR)*
Nada Saidi Smith *(Dir-Interactive)*
Nancy George *(Grp Acct Dir)*

STEEL CITY CORPORATION
1000 Hedstrom Dr, Ashland, OH 44805
Tel.: (330) 792-7663

STEEL CITY CORPORATION

Steel City Corporation—(Continued)
Web Site: http://www.scity.com
Rev.: $42,838,802
Emp.: 15
Injection Molding Of Plastics
N.A.I.C.S.: 326199
Kenneth Fibus *(Pres)*
Jim Smith *(Mgr-Natl Sls)*

STEEL CURTAIN INDUSTRIES, LLC
2039 Peck Hollow Rd, Rogersville, MO 65742
Tel.: (417) 869-5954
Web Site: http://www.sportsland.com
Year Founded: 1996
Sales Range: $1-9.9 Million
Emp.: 15
Mfr of Tonneau Covers & Fiberglass Covers for Pickups
N.A.I.C.S.: 423120
Steve Brallier *(Pres)*
Alesia Traiteur *(Controller)*

STEEL ENCOUNTERS INC.
525 E 300 S, Salt Lake City, UT 84102-4001
Tel.: (801) 322-4701
Web Site: http://www.steelencounters.com
Year Founded: 1985
Sales Range: $25-49.9 Million
Emp.: 150
Provider of Metals Services
N.A.I.C.S.: 423510
Dennis Peterson *(Exec VP & Div Mgr)*
Dan Painter *(Mgr-Engrg)*
Pam Foote *(Mgr-Sls)*
Miriam Stone *(Office Mgr)*
Peter Hatton *(Gen Mgr)*
Dan Tibbitts *(CFO)*

STEEL ETC., LLP
1408 52nd St N, Great Falls, MT 59405
Tel.: (406) 761-4848
Web Site: http://www.steeletc.com
Sales Range: $10-24.9 Million
Emp.: 50
Wholesale Distributor of Hardware, Steel, Warehouse Products, Automotive & Industrial Power Transmission Products
N.A.I.C.S.: 423710
James Filipowicz *(Owner & Gen Mgr)*

STEEL KING INDUSTRIES INC.
2700 Chamber St, Stevens Point, WI 54481-4856
Tel.: (715) 341-3120
Web Site: http://www.steelking.com
Year Founded: 1970
Sales Range: $25-49.9 Million
Emp.: 350
Fabricated Structural Metal
N.A.I.C.S.: 332312
Jay Anderson *(Pres)*
Steve Krueger *(Plant Mgr)*

STEEL PIER CAPITAL ADVISORS LLC
750 Lexington Ave 22nd Fl, New York, NY 10022
Tel.: (212) 994-9861
Web Site: http://www.steelpiercap.com
Privater Equity Firm
N.A.I.C.S.: 523999
Michael L. Clofine *(Pres & CEO)*
Veronica Cavanagh *(VP-Ops)*
Gene Z. Salkind *(Partner)*
David Kovacs *(Partner)*
Edward L. Storm *(Partner)*
John Pavia *(Partner)*
Steven Sjoblad *(Partner)*

STEEL SERVICE CORPORATION
2260 Flowood Dr, Jackson, MS 39232
Tel.: (601) 939-9222
Web Site: http://www.steelservice.com
Year Founded: 1969
Sales Range: $10-24.9 Million
Emp.: 200
Provider of Steel Contracting Services
N.A.I.C.S.: 332312
Terry Cruse *(Mgr-Branch)*
John Oxley *(VP-Pur)*
Skip Mitchell *(Mgr-QA & QC)*
Stewart Heard *(CFO)*
James Simonson *(COO & Exec VP)*

STEEL SERVICES INCORPORATED
9800 Mayland Dr, Richmond, VA 23233
Tel.: (804) 673-3810
Web Site: http://www.steelservicesinc.com
Rev.: $35,331,037
Emp.: 11
Metals Service Centers & Offices
N.A.I.C.S.: 423510
Thomas J. Starke *(Chm & CEO)*
Josh Starke *(Mgr-Ops)*

STEEL STORAGE SYSTEMS, INC.
6301 Dexter St, Commerce City, CO 80022-3122
Tel.: (303) 287-0291
Web Site: http://www.steelstorage.com
Year Founded: 1964
Mfr of Storage & Material Handling Equipment
N.A.I.C.S.: 333922
Brian McCallin *(Pres)*
Tim Costello *(Mgr-Sls)*
Jim Ulrich *(Mgr-Sls)*

STEEL SUMMIT OHIO
11150 Southland Rd, Cincinnati, OH 45240-3202
Tel.: (513) 825-8550
Web Site: http://www.steelsummit.com
Year Founded: 1990
Sales Range: $100-124.9 Million
Emp.: 42
Metals Service Centers & Offices
N.A.I.C.S.: 423510
Hiroki Nakajima *(Pres)*

STEEL TESTING LABORATORY
51100 Pontiac Trl, Wixom, MI 48393
Tel.: (313) 921-2000
Web Site: http://www.steeltestinglab.com
Steel Testing Services
N.A.I.C.S.: 541380

STEEL WAREHOUSE OF WISCONSIN, INC.
2722 W Tucker Dr, South Bend, IN 46624
Tel.: (800) 348-2529
Web Site: http://www.steelwarehouse.com
Year Founded: 1973
Metal Service Centers & Other Metal Merchant Whslr
N.A.I.C.S.: 423510

Subsidiaries:

Siegal Steel Company (1)
4747 S Kedzie Ave, Chicago, IL 60632
Tel.: (773) 927-7600

Web Site: http://www.siegalsteel.com
Metal Service Centers & Other Metal Merchant Whslr
N.A.I.C.S.: 423510

STEEL, LLC
405 N Clarendon Ave, Scottdale, GA 30079
Tel.: (404) 292-7373
Web Site: http://www.steelincga.com
Year Founded: 1947
Sales Range: $1-9.9 Million
Emp.: 100
Structural Steel
N.A.I.C.S.: 332312
Claudia Grey *(Mgr-HR)*
Robb Merritt *(VP-Fin)*
Scott Godfrey *(Pres)*
Marvin Brown *(Exec VP)*
Daniel Smith *(Mgr-Ops)*
Rob Williams *(Dir-Engrg)*
Adam Andris *(VP-Sls)*
Gabe Tilley *(VP-Estimating)*

STEELBRO INTERNATIONAL CO. INC.
26 Pleasant Ln, Oyster Bay, NY 11771
Tel.: (516) 922-8002
Web Site: http://www.steelbrousa.com
Sales Range: $10-24.9 Million
Emp.: 6
Nonferrous Metals Scrap
N.A.I.C.S.: 423930
Andy Goenka *(Pres)*

STEELCELL OF NORTH AMERICA, INC.
510 Industrial Park Rd, Baldwin, GA 30511
Tel.: (706) 778-9615
Web Site: http://www.steelcell.com
Year Founded: 2001
Rev.: $26,100,000
Emp.: 45
Commercial Institutional Building Construction
N.A.I.C.S.: 236220
Mike Smith *(Pres & CEO)*
Ray Handte *(COO & VP)*
Jim Strange *(Mgr-Engrg)*
Christy Ivester *(Office Mgr)*

STEELCLOUD LLC
20110 Ashbrook Pl Ste 270, Ashburn, VA 20147
Tel.: (703) 674-5500
Web Site: http://www.steelcloud.com
Year Founded: 1987
Sales Range: $1-9.9 Million
Emp.: 10
Mobility Computing Appliance Solutions Mfr
N.A.I.C.S.: 334118
Kenneth A. Merlau *(Chm)*
Steven Snyder *(CFO)*

STEELE CREEK CAPITAL CORPORATION
210 S College St Ste 1690, Charlotte, NC 28244
Tel.: (704) 343-6011
Year Founded: 2020
Rev.: $8,350,000
Assets: $151,170,000
Liabilities: $100,795,000
Net Worth: $50,375,000
Earnings: $3,076,000
Fiscal Year-end: 12/31/22
Investment Services
N.A.I.C.S.: 523940
Douglas Applegate Jr. *(CFO)*
Glenn Duffy *(Pres, CEO & Chief Investment Officer)*
Christopher Ryan *(Chm & Treas)*

STEELE HOLDINGS, INC.
102 W Front St, Arp, TX 75750
Tel.: (903) 593-1803
Web Site: http://www.asbtx.com
Year Founded: 2010
Sales Range: $10-24.9 Million
Emp.: 71
Bank Holding Company
N.A.I.C.S.: 551111
Brandon Steele *(Chm, Pres & CEO)*
Kelly Sanders *(Pres/CEO-American State Bank)*
Kyle Williams *(Dir-Dev & Construction)*

Subsidiaries:

American State Bank (1)
102 Front St Drawer 100, Arp, TX 75750
Tel.: (903) 859-1100
Web Site: http://www.asbtx.com
Sales Range: $10-24.9 Million
Retail & Commercial Banking
N.A.I.C.S.: 522110
Brandon Steele *(Chm)*
Kelly Sanders *(Pres & CEO)*
John Falls *(Exec VP & Controller)*
Robert Hampton *(Chief Credit Officer & Exec VP)*
Terri Maus *(Chief Mktg Officer)*

STEELE+
2500 Northwinds Pkwy Ste 190, Atlanta, GA 30009
Tel.: (770) 772-3600
Web Site: http://www.steeleplus.com
Year Founded: 2003
Sales Range: $10-24.9 Million
Emp.: 9
N.A.I.C.S.: 541810
Christopher Steele *(CEO)*
Scott Coleman *(Pres)*
Scott Estep *(Exec VP & Dir-Media)*
Donna McKinley *(Dir-Production)*
John Kendall *(Dir-Creative)*

STEELER INC.
10023 Maritn Luther King Jr Way S, Seattle, WA 98178
Tel.: (206) 725-2500
Web Site: http://www.steeler.com
Sales Range: $25-49.9 Million
Emp.: 90
Studs & Joists, Sheet Metal
N.A.I.C.S.: 332322
Matt Surowiecki *(Founder & Pres)*
Michael Dollard *(Controller)*
Christina Vargas *(Mgr-Credit)*
Jerry Ward *(Mgr-Traffic & Transportation)*

STEELFAB INC.
8623 Old Dowd Rd, Charlotte, NC 28214
Tel.: (704) 394-5376
Web Site: http://www.steelfab-inc.com
Sales Range: $25-49.9 Million
Emp.: 500
Provider of Structural Steel Fabrication for Buildings
N.A.I.C.S.: 332312
Scott Edgar *(Mgr-Detailing-SC)*
Stuart R. Sherrill *(Pres-Alabama)*
William Pulyer *(VP-Engrg-North Carolina)*
Dimitri Mavropoulos *(VP-Project Mgmt-North Carolina)*
Jeff Tucker *(VP-Project Mgmt-North Carolina)*
Dwane Burkhart *(VP-Pur-North Carolina)*

COMPANIES

Russell Barngrover *(Exec VP & Plant Mgr)*
Drew Harper *(VP-Sls)*
Collin Hughes *(VP-Engrg)*
Greg Sain *(VP-Project Mgmt)*
Craig Sherrill *(VP)*
R. Glenn Sherrill Jr. *(Pres)*

Subsidiaries:

Steelfab Inc. of Alabama (1)
5448 Spadling Dr Bldg 200, Norcross, GA 30092-3606
Tel.: (770) 248-0075
Web Site: http://www.steelfab-inc.com
Sales Range: $10-24.9 Million
Emp.: 29
Provider of Metals Service Centers & Offices
N.A.I.C.S.: 423510
Stuart Sherrill *(Pres)*
Robert Bready *(VP)*
Sam Boykin *(VP-Sls)*
Cindy Strain *(VP-Pur)*
Bill Zanow *(VP-Project Mgmt)*

Steelfab Inc. of South Carolina (1)
1220 Steel Rd, Florence, SC 29506-4141
Tel.: (843) 664-1811
Web Site: http://www.steelfab-inc.com
Sales Range: $10-24.9 Million
Emp.: 80
Structural Steel Fabrication for Buildings
N.A.I.C.S.: 332312
Rob Rutherford *(Pres)*

Steelfab Inc. of Virginia (1)
5105 Bur Oak Cir Ste 100, Raleigh, NC 27612-3160
Tel.: (919) 828-9545
Web Site: http://www.steelfab-inc.com
Sales Range: $10-24.9 Million
Emp.: 50
Provider of Structural Steel Fabrication for Buildings
N.A.I.C.S.: 332312
Rob Burlington *(Pres)*

STEELFAB TEXAS, INC.
301 S. McDonald St, McKinney, TX 75069
Tel.: (972) 562-7720 TX
Web Site: http://www.steelfab-inc.com
Year Founded: 1978
Fabricated Structural Metal
N.A.I.C.S.: 332312
David Garrett *(Pres)*
Josh Dellinger *(VP)*
Chris Walsh *(VP-Mktg)*
Jill Thompson *(Head-HR)*

STEELMAN-DUFF INC.
1490 Fair St, Clarkston, WA 99403
Tel.: (509) 758-3357
Year Founded: 1950
Sales Range: $10-24.9 Million
Emp.: 5
Contractor of Highway & Street Construction
N.A.I.C.S.: 237310
Hyrum L. Cox *(Pres)*

STEELMART, INC.
3476 Lawrenceville Hwy, Tucker, GA 30084
Tel.: (770) 416-6999
Web Site: http://www.steelmartatlanta.com
Year Founded: 1993
Rev.: $9,800,000
Emp.: 35
Construction Services
N.A.I.C.S.: 238170
Brian Satisky *(Principal)*
Paul Carling *(Principal)*
Ashley Morris *(Office Mgr-Credit)*

STEELMASTER BUILDINGS, INC.
1023 Laskin Rd Ste 109, Virginia Beach, VA 23451
Tel.: (757) 422-6800
Web Site: http://www.steelmasterusa.com
Year Founded: 1982
Sales Range: $10-24.9 Million
Emp.: 90
Whslr & Retailer of Prefabricated Steel Buildings
N.A.I.C.S.: 444180
Rhae Adams *(Chm)*
Karen Willis *(Controller)*

STEELPOINT CAPITAL PARTNERS, LP
2081 Faraday Ave, Carlsbad, CA 92008
Tel.: (858) 764-8700 DE
Web Site: http://www.steelpointcp.com
Private Investment Firm
N.A.I.C.S.: 523999
Jim Caccavo *(Founder & Mng Partner)*
Tim Broadhead *(Mng Dir & CFO)*
Jim Sullivan *(Partner-Operating)*
Kristy Hepfer *(Controller)*

STEELRIVER INFRASTRUCTURE PARTNERS LP
1 Letterman Dr Bldg 5th Fl, San Francisco, CA 94129
Tel.: (415) 291-2200
Web Site: http://www.steelriverpartners.com
Sales Range: $25-49.9 Million
Equity Investment Management Firm
N.A.I.C.S.: 523940
Chris Kinney *(CEO)*
Michael J. Cyrus *(COO)*

Subsidiaries:

Peoples Natural Gas Company, LLC (1)
375 N Shore Dr Ste 600, Pittsburgh, PA 15212
Tel.: (412) 244-2626
Web Site: http://www.peoples-gas.com
Rev.: $786,719,000
Natural Gas Distribution
N.A.I.C.S.: 221210

Subsidiary (Domestic):

Peoples TWP LLC (2)
205 N Main St, Butler, PA 16001
Tel.: (724) 287-2751
Web Site: http://www.peoplestwp.com
Sales Range: $150-199.9 Million
Natural Gas Distribution
N.A.I.C.S.: 221210

STEEN MACEK PAPER CO. INC.
3224 Market St, Green Bay, WI 54304-5614
Tel.: (920) 336-0070 WI
Web Site: http://www.smacek.com
Year Founded: 1975
Sales Range: $10-24.9 Million
Emp.: 45
Printing & Writing Paper
N.A.I.C.S.: 424110
Phil Milazzo *(Gen Mgr)*

STEEPLETON TIRE CO.
777 S Lauderdale St, Memphis, TN 38126
Tel.: (901) 774-6440 TN
Web Site: http://www.steepletontire.com
Year Founded: 1945
Sales Range: $10-24.9 Million
Emp.: 50
Tire Recapping
N.A.I.C.S.: 811198
Patrick Steepleton *(Pres)*

STEERE HOUSE
100 Borden St, Providence, RI 02903
Tel.: (401) 454-7970 RI
Web Site: http://www.steerehouse.org
Year Founded: 1874
Sales Range: $10-24.9 Million
Emp.: 193
Nursing Care Services
N.A.I.C.S.: 623110
Julie Richard *(Exec Dir)*
Aman Nanda *(Dir-Medical)*
Nadia Mujahid *(Dir-Medical)*
Dianne Bourget *(Dir-Fin)*
Nicole Plante *(Dir-Nursing)*
Gina Williamson *(Dir-Activities)*
Jill M. Fallon *(Dir-Fund Dev)*

STEET-PONTE FORD
5074 Commercial Dr, Yorkville, NY 13495
Tel.: (315) 736-3381
Web Site: http://www.steet-ponteford.com
Sales Range: $10-24.9 Million
Emp.: 42
Owner & Operator of Car Dealerships
N.A.I.C.S.: 441110
Joe Steet *(Owner)*
Steve Ponte *(Co-Owner)*

STEFAN SYDOR OPTICS, INC.
31 Jet View Dr, Rochester, NY 14624
Tel.: (585) 271-7300
Web Site: http://www.sydor.com
Year Founded: 1964
Sales Range: $10-24.9 Million
Emp.: 60
Precision Optical Components Mfr
N.A.I.C.S.: 333310
James M. Sydor *(Owner & Pres)*
Carol Corey *(Engr-Sls)*
Sam Ezzezew *(Mgr-Production)*

STEFFES CORPORATION
3050 Hwy 22 N, Dickinson, ND 58601
Tel.: (701) 483-5400
Web Site: http://www.steffes.com
Sales Range: $75-99.9 Million
Emp.: 140
Mfr of Industrial Products
N.A.I.C.S.: 332322
Paul Steffes *(Chm)*
Joe Rothschiller *(Pres & COO)*
Al Takle *(Mgr-Sls-Natl)*
Dennis Jarrett *(Project Coord-Special)*
Jim Deichert *(Mgr-Mktg)*
Peter Rackov *(CFO & VP-Bus Excellence)*

STEIN + PARTNERS BRAND ACTIVATION
432 Park Ave S, New York, NY 10016-8013
Tel.: (212) 213-1112
Web Site: http://www.steinias.com
Sales Range: $10-24.9 Million
Emp.: 100
Advetising Agency
N.A.I.C.S.: 541810
Tom Stein *(Chm & Chief Client Officer)*
Marianne Moore *(Chief Strategy Officer)*
Ted Kohnen *(CMO)*
Susan Guerrero *(VP & Dir-Acct Svcs)*
Michael Ruby *(VP & Exec Dir-Creative)*
Daniel Santos *(Dir-Creative Svcs)*
Rebecca Falk *(Acct Dir-Global)*
Rob Morrice *(CEO)*
Shirelle Pexton *(Dir-China)*
Craig Duxbury *(Dir-Client Svcs)*
Paul Myerscough *(Dir-Content)*
Reuben Webb *(Dir-Creative)*

STEIN INDUSTRIES, INC.

Tim Ramundo *(Dir-Creative)*
Stephane Munier *(Dir-France)*
Charlotte Forshaw *(Dir-Global Acct)*
Sam Jordan *(VP-Global Accts)*

Subsidiaries:

IAS Smarts Limited (1)
Clarence Mill Clarence Road, Bollington, Prestbury, SK10 5JZ, Cheshire, United Kingdom
Tel.: (44) 1625578578
Web Site: http://www.steinias.com
Advetising Agency
N.A.I.C.S.: 541810
Paul Myerscough *(Dir-PR)*
Rob Morrice *(Mng Dir)*

STEIN BROS INC.
16102 N Hwy 41, Rathdrum, ID 83858
Tel.: (208) 687-0767
Web Site: http://www.steinsmarket.com
Sales Range: $25-49.9 Million
Emp.: 150
Supermarket
N.A.I.C.S.: 445110

STEIN FIBERS LTD.
4 Computer Dr W Ste 200, Albany, NY 12205-1623
Tel.: (518) 489-5700 NY
Web Site: http://www.steinfibers.com
Year Founded: 1976
Sales Range: $10-24.9 Million
Emp.: 25
Piece Goods & Notions Fibers
N.A.I.C.S.: 424310
Peter J. Spitalny *(Pres)*
Tom Cesarano *(Controller)*
Chip Stein *(VP)*

STEIN GARDEN CENTERS, INC.
5400 S 27th St, Milwaukee, WI 53221
Tel.: (414) 761-5404 WI
Web Site: http://www.steingg.com
Year Founded: 1946
Sales Range: $50-74.9 Million
Emp.: 1,000
Owner & Operator of Retail Nurseries & Garden Stores
N.A.I.C.S.: 444240
Bob Young *(CEO)*

STEIN INDUSTRIES, INC.
7153 Northland Dr N, Brooklyn Park, MN 55428
Tel.: (763) 504-3500
Web Site: http://www.stein-industries.com
Year Founded: 1907
Sales Range: $25-49.9 Million
Emp.: 140
Holding Company; Electronics Products, Store Fixtures & Retail Display Products Distr
N.A.I.C.S.: 551112
Michael Stein *(Chm)*
Tom Meyers *(CEO)*
Terry Kraus *(Dir-HR)*

Subsidiaries:

Carlson JPM Store Fixtures (1)
7147 Northland Dr N, Brooklyn Park, MN 55428
Tel.: (763) 504-3822
Web Site: http://www.carlson-store-fixtures.com
Retail Display, Store Fixtures, Signage & Accessories Mfr & Distr
N.A.I.C.S.: 423710
Nancy Houle *(Mgr-Pur)*
Eric Ramberg *(Mgr-Sls)*
Todd Potter *(Dir-Engrg)*
Letty Robinson *(Mgr-Mktg)*

E-Switch, Inc. (1)

STEIN INDUSTRIES, INC.

U.S. PRIVATE

Stein Industries, Inc.—(Continued)

7153 Northland Dr N, Brooklyn Park, MN 55428
Tel.: (763) 504-3525
Web Site: http://www.e-switch.com
Emp.: 50
Electro-Mechanical Switches Mfr & Distr
N.A.I.C.S.: 423610
Rebecca Hauptman *(Mgr-Mktg)*
Rick Nelson *(Mgr-Sls-Natl)*
Larry Ness Jr. *(Mgr-Sls-Inside)*

STEIN INVESTMENT GROUP

5607 Glenridge Dr Ste 200, Atlanta, GA 30342
Tel.: (678) 892-6963
Web Site: http://www.steininvest.com
Emp.: 100
Retail, Office, Self-Storage, Multifamily & Residential Real Estate Investment
N.A.I.C.S.: 523999
Adam Sauer *(Principal)*

STEIN MART, INC.

1200 Riverpl Blvd, Jacksonville, FL 32207
Tel.: (904) 346-1500   FL
Web Site: http://www.steinmart.com
Year Founded: 1908
Rev.: $1,236,473,000
Assets: $765,514,000
Liabilities: $733,576,000
Net Worth: $31,938,000
Earnings: ($10,463,000)
Emp.: 9,000
Fiscal Year-end: 02/01/20
Department Stores
N.A.I.C.S.: 458110
Glori Katz *(Sr VP-Mktg & Adv)*
Steven Jay Horowitz *(Sr VP-Strategy & Dev)*
MaryAnne Morin *(Pres)*
E. Chantelle Quick *(Chief Acctg Officer, Sr VP & Controller)*
Sharon Hart *(CIO & Sr VP)*
John Hegedus *(Sr VP-Stores)*
Linda L. Tasseff *(Dir-IR)*
Robert Devine *(Chief Legal Officer & Sr VP)*
Nick Swetonic *(Sr VP-Plng & Allocation)*

Subsidiaries:

Stein Mart Buying Corp.   (1)
1200 Riverplace Blvd, Jacksonville, FL 32207
Tel.: (904) 346-1500
Department Stores
N.A.I.C.S.: 455110

Stein Mart Inc. (Alabama)   (1)
5275 Hwy 280, Birmingham, AL 35242
Tel.: (205) 991-0458
Web Site: http://www.steinmart.com
Sales Range: $100-124.9 Million
Department Stores
N.A.I.C.S.: 458110

Stein Mart, Inc. (California)   (1)
13031 Peyton Dr, Chino Hills, CA 91709
Tel.: (909) 465-9221
Sales Range: $100-124.9 Million
Department Stores
N.A.I.C.S.: 458110

Stein Mart, Inc. (Florida)   (1)
9831 Glades Rd, Boca Raton, FL 33434
Tel.: (561) 482-3696
Web Site: http://www.steinmart.com
Sales Range: $100-124.9 Million
Department Stores
N.A.I.C.S.: 458110

Stein Mart, Inc. (North Carolina)   (1)
848 Merrimon Ave, Asheville, NC 28804
Tel.: (828) 253-9962
Web Site: http://www.steinmart.com
Sales Range: $125-149.9 Million
Emp.: 100
Department Stores
N.A.I.C.S.: 458110

Stein Mart, Inc. (South Carolina)   (1)
101 Verdae Blvd, Greenville, SC 29607
Tel.: (864) 288-7691
Sales Range: $100-124.9 Million
Department Stores
N.A.I.C.S.: 458110
Kiim Cox *(Gen Mgr)*

Stein Mart, Inc. (Tennessee)   (1)
2020 Gunbarrel Rd, Chattanooga, TN 37421
Tel.: (423) 510-9601
Sales Range: $100-124.9 Million
Department Stores
N.A.I.C.S.: 458110

Stein Mart, Inc. (Texas)   (1)
290 Meyerland Plz, Houston, TX 77096
Tel.: (713) 665-6000
Sales Range: $100-124.9 Million
Department Stores
N.A.I.C.S.: 458110

STEIN ROGAN + PARTNERS

432 Park Ave S, New York, NY 10016-8013
Tel.: (212) 213-1112   NY
Web Site: http://www.steinrogan.com
Year Founded: 1984
Rev.: $25,000,000
Emp.: 40
Advetising Agency
N.A.I.C.S.: 541810
Thomas Stein *(Pres & CEO)*
Marianne Moore *(Partner & Chief Strategy Officer)*
Barrie Rubinstein *(Dir-Bus Dev)*
Susan Guerrero *(VP & Dir-Acct Svcs)*
Daniel Santos *(Dir-Production Svcs)*
Ted Kohnen *(VP-Interactive Mktg)*
John Battistini *(Dir-Interactive Svcs)*
Michael Ruby *(Dir-Creative)*

STEIN SEAL COMPANY

1500 Industrial Blvd, Kulpsville, PA 19443
Tel.: (215) 256-0201
Web Site: http://www.steinseal.com
Rev.: $19,500,000
Emp.: 190
Aircraft Engines & Engine Parts
N.A.I.C.S.: 339991
Richard Ramseyer *(Mgr-Mfg Engrg)*
Donna Broughan *(Mgr-HR)*
Gary Schuler *(Plant Mgr-Mfg)*

STEINER ELECTRIC COMPANY

1250 Touhy Ave, Elk Grove Village, IL 60007-5302
Tel.: (847) 228-0400   IL
Web Site: http://www.steinerelectric.com
Year Founded: 1916
Sales Range: $200-249.9 Million
Emp.: 368
Distr of Electrical & Electronic Supplies
N.A.I.C.S.: 423610
Richard Kerman *(Pres & COO)*

Subsidiaries:

Steiner Electric Company - Chicago   (1)
2415 W 19th St, Chicago, IL 60608-2448   (100%)
Tel.: (312) 421-7220
Web Site: http://www.steinerelectric.com
Aelectronic Supplies Distr & 24 Hour Motor Repair Service
N.A.I.C.S.: 423610

STEINER EQUITIES GROUP LLC

75 Eisenhower Pkwy, Roseland, NJ 07068
Tel.: (973) 228-5800
Web Site: http://www.steinereq.com
Year Founded: 1907
Sales Range: $550-599.9 Million

Emp.: 205
Commercial Real Estate Development Services
N.A.I.C.S.: 531390
David S. Steiner *(Chm & Pres)*

Subsidiaries:

Eponymous Associates LLC   (1)
15 Washington Ave, Brooklyn, NY 11205
Tel.: (718) 858-1600
Web Site: http://www.steinerstudios.com
Sales Range: $10-24.9 Million
Emp.: 100
Management Services
N.A.I.C.S.: 541611
Douglas C. Steiner *(Chm)*

Subsidiary (Domestic):

Steiner Studios LLC   (2)
Brooklyn Navy Yard 15 Washington Ave, Brooklyn, NY 11205
Tel.: (718) 858-1600
Web Site: http://www.steinerstudios.com
Production Studios
N.A.I.C.S.: 512110
Douglas C. Steiner *(Chm)*
John Eddey *(VP)*
Daniel S. Moore *(CIO)*

STEINGOLD VOLVO

766 Broadway, Pawtucket, RI 02861
Tel.: (401) 723-4700
Web Site: http://www.steingold.com
Year Founded: 1935
Sales Range: $10-24.9 Million
Emp.: 30
Car Whslr
N.A.I.C.S.: 441110
Manny Bernardo *(Owner)*

STEINHAFEL'S INC.

W 231 N 1013 Hwy County F, Waukesha, WI 53186-1502
Tel.: (262) 436-4600   WI
Web Site: http://www.steinhafels.com
Year Founded: 1960
Sales Range: $25-49.9 Million
Emp.: 500
Furniture Stores
N.A.I.C.S.: 531120
Adam Werni *(Mgr-Warehouse)*
Karen Lukomski *(Coord-Clearance Center)*
Kevin Polaski *(Mgr-Corp Svc)*
Mike Bujak *(Mgr-Inventory Control)*
Pam Ceccato *(Dir-Adv & Creative)*
Andrea Kokott *(Mgr-HR)*
Brian Fisher *(Mgr-Warehouse)*
Jeff Tennyson *(Mgr-Bedding Ops)*
John Haas *(Mgr-Distr)*
Fred Schweinert *(Dir-Stores)*

STEINHAGEN OIL COMPANY, INC.

3850 Interstate Hwy 10 S, Beaumont, TX 77705
Tel.: (409) 727-5680
Sales Range: $10-24.9 Million
Emp.: 26
Owner of Convenience Stores
N.A.I.C.S.: 445131
Craig Hill *(Pres)*

Subsidiaries:

Darby Gas & Oil Co., Inc.   (1)
1601 Brinkman Dr, Port Arthur, TX 77642-2804
Tel.: (409) 983-6015
Petroleum Products & Services
N.A.I.C.S.: 441330

STEINKAMP WAREHOUSES, INC.

1000 N Main St, Huntingburg, IN 47542
Tel.: (812) 683-3860   IN
Sales Range: $10-24.9 Million
Emp.: 33

Lumber Whslr & Building Materials Retailer
N.A.I.C.S.: 423310
Scott A. Steinkamp *(Pres)*

STEINREICH COMMUNICATIONS, LLC

2125 Center Ave, Fort Lee, NJ 07024
Tel.: (201) 498-1600
Web Site: http://www.scompr.com
Year Founded: 2002
Emp.: 15
Consumer Goods, Fashion/Apparel, Financial, Health Care, Nonprofit/Social Marketing, Retail, Travel & Tourism
N.A.I.C.S.: 541810
Stan Steinreich *(CEO)*
Ariella Steinreich *(VP)*
Ellyn Small *(Sr VP)*
John Jones *(Sr Acct Dir-Fashion Practice)*
Kristi Delahanty *(Dir-Consumer Practice Grp)*
Joshua Lavine *(Acct Mgr-Jewish & Israel)*
Monica Edwards *(Sr VP & Head-Lifestyle Brands Practice)*

Subsidiaries:

McNeill Communications Group Inc.   (1)
202 Neal Pl, High Point, NC 27262
Tel.: (336) 884-8700
Web Site: http://www.mcneillcommunications.com
Sales Range: Less than $1 Million
Public Relations Agencies
N.A.I.C.S.: 541820
Karen McNeill-Harris *(CEO)*
Kristin Hawkins *(VP)*

STEINWALL INC.

1759 116th Ave NW, Coon Rapids, MN 55448
Tel.: (763) 767-7060   MN
Web Site: http://www.steinwall.com
Year Founded: 1965
Sales Range: $10-24.9 Million
Emp.: 104
Plastics Product Mfr
N.A.I.C.S.: 326199
Maureen Steinwall *(Pres)*
Jeremy Dworshak *(Engr-Sls)*
Heidi Allen *(Coord-Quality & ISO)*
Bob Evans *(Mgr-Scheduling & Pur)*
Jake Nelson *(Engr-R&D)*
Luke Buerkley *(Engr-Quality)*
Rick Gunderman *(Project Mgr)*
Scott Denker *(Engr-Quality)*
Shaun Meehan *(Project Mgr)*

STEINWAY CHILD AND FAMILY SERVICES, INC.

22-15 43rd Ave, Long Island City, NY 11101-3852
Tel.: (718) 389-5100   NY
Web Site: http://www.steinway.org
Year Founded: 1973
Sales Range: $10-24.9 Million
Emp.: 289
Behavioral Healthcare Services
N.A.I.C.S.: 621420
Mary D. Redd *(Pres & CEO)*
Lewis E. Duckett *(VP-Fin & Admin)*
Jannett Taylor *(Dir-Admin Support Svcs)*
Pasquale DePetris *(COO & VP)*
Tommy Allen *(Dir-Fin)*

STEINWAY MUSICAL INSTRUMENTS HOLDINGS, INC.

1 Steinway Pl, Astoria, NY 11105
Tel.: (718) 721-2600   DE
Year Founded: 2021
Rev.: $538,350,000
Assets: $646,050,000

Liabilities: $275,654,000
Net Worth: $370,396,000
Earnings: $59,263,000
Emp.: 619
Fiscal Year-end: 12/31/21
Holding Company
N.A.I.C.S.: 551112
Benjamin Steiner (Pres & CEO)
Maia Moutopoulos (CFO)
Eric Feidner (CTO & Chief Innovation Officer)

STEINY & COMPANY, INC.
12907 E Garvey Ave, Baldwin Park, CA 91706
Tel.: (626) 338-9923　　CA
Web Site: http://www.steinyco.com
Year Founded: 1953
Sales Range: $200-249.9 Million
Emp.: 400
Electrical Contractor
N.A.I.C.S.: 238210
Susan Steiny (Pres)
Jack Steiny (Chm)
Vincent P. Mauch (CFO)

Subsidiaries:

Computer Service Company　　(1)
12907 E Garvey, Baldwin Park, CA 91706
Tel.: (909) 738-1444
Sales Range: $25-49.9 Million
Emp.: 40
Mfr of Trafic Signals
N.A.I.C.S.: 334290

Steiny & Company Inc.　　(1)
221 N Ardmore Ave, Los Angeles, CA 90004-4503
Tel.: (213) 382-2331
Web Site: http://www.steinyco.com
Sales Range: $25-49.9 Million
Emp.: 300
Electrical Work
N.A.I.C.S.: 238210
Susan Steiny (Pres)
Jack O. Steiny (Chm)

STELAR INC.
10 S Riverside Plz Ste 1040, Chicago, IL 60606-3768
Tel.: (312) 707-9600　　IL
Year Founded: 1858
Sales Range: $10-24.9 Million
Emp.: 55
Retailer of Furniture, Carpets, Rugs & Household Appliances
N.A.I.C.S.: 449110
Stephen M. Ehrlichman (Pres)
Michael Coombs (Controller)

STELLA & CHEWY'S
2842 S 5th Ct, Milwaukee, WI 53207
Tel.: (888) 477-8977
Web Site:
　http://www.stellaandchewys.com
Year Founded: 2003
Sales Range: $10-24.9 Million
Emp.: 80
Mfr & Distr of All-Natural Raw, Frozen & Freeze-dried Pet Foods & Treats
N.A.I.C.S.: 311111
Marie Moody (Founder & Chm)
Lloyd Parks (Dir-Ops)
Gregg Coccari (CEO)
Mark Sapir (CMO)

STELLA & DOT LLC
1000 Cherry Ave Ste 300, San Bruno, CA 94066
Tel.: (800) 920-5893　　CA
Web Site: http://www.stelladot.com
Year Founded: 2004
Sales Range: $25-49.9 Million
Emp.: 50
Direct Seller of Jewelry for Adults & Children
N.A.I.C.S.: 339910

Jessica Herrin (Founder & CEO)
Blythe Harris (Chief Creative Officer)
Michael Lohner (Chm)
Dana Bloom (VP & Gen Mgr)
Danielle Redner (VP-Trng)
Dina Hooker (VP-Plng)
Evan Price (CFO)
Neil Markey (CIO)

STELLA MARIS INC.
2300 Dulaney Vly Rd, Timonium, MD 21093
Tel.: (410) 252-4500　　MD
Web Site:
　http://www.stellamarisinc.com
Year Founded: 1953
Sales Range: $100-124.9 Million
Emp.: 800
Provider of Long Term Health Care & Independent Living Facilities
N.A.I.C.S.: 531190
Jerome Bowen (COO)
Fredric S. Sirkis (Chief Medical Officer)
Crystal Hickey (VP-HR)
M. Karen McNally (Chief Admin Officer)
Stephen Stinnette (CFO & Sr VP-Fin)
Susan Gragel (Pres)
Daniel Lettenberger-Klein (Exec Dir)

STELLA ORTON HOME CARE AGENCY
3155 Amboy Rd, Staten Island, NY 10306
Tel.: (718) 987-4300　　NY
Year Founded: 1982
Sales Range: $25-49.9 Million
Emp.: 1,392
Elder Care Services
N.A.I.C.S.: 623312
Bella Dulitsky (Exec Dir)
James Simmon (Dir-Fin)

STELLA POINT CAPITAL, LP
444 Madison Ave 25th Fl, New York, NY 10022
Tel.: (212) 235-0200
Web Site: http://stellapoint.com
Year Founded: 2013
Holding Company
N.A.I.C.S.: 551112
Howard Weiss (COO & CFO)

Subsidiaries:

Autoagent Data Solutions, LLC　　(1)
433 Plz Real, Ste 275, Boca Raton, FL 33432
Tel.: (877) 932-8478
Web Site: https://www.autoagent.com
Information Technology & Services
N.A.I.C.S.: 513210
Niko Spyridonos (Founder & CEO)

Subsidiary (Domestic):

Municipay, LLC　　(2)
22 Free St 403, Portland, ME 04101
Web Site: http://www.municipay.com
Sales Range: $1-9.9 Million
Emp.: 50
Online Payment Services
N.A.I.C.S.: 522320
Jamie Nonni (CEO)

STELLAR DEVELOPMENT, INC.
59 Sarasota Center Blvd, Sarasota, FL 34240
Tel.: (941) 907-9577
Web Site: http://www.stellargc.com
Year Founded: 1999
Sales Range: $1-9.9 Million
Industrial, Commercial, Retail, Multi-family & Single Family Construction Services
N.A.I.C.S.: 236210

Maurice Opstal (Pres)
Brian Ellis (Dir-Ops)

Subsidiaries:

Interstellar, Inc.　　(1)
292 Ivy St., Unit E,, San Francisco, CA 94102
Tel.: (805) 441-8312
Web Site: https://interstellar.com
Software Devolepment
N.A.I.C.S.: 513210
Mike Kennedy (CEO)

STELLAR DISTRIBUTION LLC
2000 Dogwood Dr SE, Conyers, GA 30013
Tel.: (770) 918-6131
Web Site: http://www.jrtruck.com
Year Founded: 1999
Sales Range: $1-9.9 Million
Emp.: 50
Truck Equipment & Parts
N.A.I.C.S.: 441330
Scott Wilson (Pres)

STELLAR INDUSTRIAL SUPPLY LLC
711 E11th St, Tacoma, WA 98421
Tel.: (253) 383-2700
Web Site:
　http://www.stellarindustrial.com
Sales Range: $25-49.9 Million
Emp.: 90
Industrial Supplies
N.A.I.C.S.: 423840
Tim Daly (VP-Fin)
John S. Wiborg (Pres)
Ken Wentworth (Dir-Sls)
Molly Langdon (VP-Customer Experience)
Dina McClees (Controller)
John Diaz (VP-Sls & Bus Dev-SE)
Phil Canipe (VP-Sls & Bus Dev-SW)
Jim Chamberlin (VP-Supply Chain Mgmt)
Rene Savage (VP-Tech Solutions)
Brian Bassett (VP-Value Added Svcs)

Subsidiaries:

IMC Supply Company　　(1)
3310 Commercial Pkwy, Memphis, TN 38116
Tel.: (901) 345-6001
Web Site: https://imcsupply.com
Rev.: $2,200,000
Emp.: 10
Business to Business Electronic Markets
N.A.I.C.S.: 425120
Mark Hill (Pres)

STELLAR INDUSTRIES INC.
190 State St, Garner, IA 50438
Tel.: (641) 923-3741　　MI
Web Site: http://www.stellar-industries.com
Year Founded: 1989
Sales Range: $10-24.9 Million
Emp.: 190
Welding Apparatus
N.A.I.C.S.: 333248
Kirk Uhlenhopp (Reg Mgr-Sls)
Steve Schnieders (VP-Ops)
Jim Fisk (Dir-Ops-Garner & Kanawha Facilities)
Jason Vertin (Asst Product Mgr-Inside Sls-American Eagle Accessories Grp Div-Ha)
Karl Bauer (Mgr-Mfg)

Subsidiaries:

Elliott Machine Works, Inc.　　(1)
1351 Saint Freese Works Pl East, Galion, OH 44833
Tel.: (800) 299-4012
Web Site: http://www.elliottmachine.com
Rev.: $4,666,666
Emp.: 70
Machine Shops
N.A.I.C.S.: 332710

Brad Ekin (VP-Mfg)
Kim Legge (Mgr-HR)
Joel Callis (Engr)

STELLAR IT SOLUTIONS, INC.
9210 Corporate Blvd, Suite 390, Rockville, MD 20850
Tel.: (240) 774-0001　　MD
Web Site: http://www.stellarit.com
Year Founded: 1997
Information Technology & Services
N.A.I.C.S.: 541511
Dipak Thakker (Pres & CEO)

Subsidiaries:

StanSource Inc.　　(1)
22375 Broderick Dr Ste 135, Dulles, VA 20166
Tel.: (703) 879-3450
Web Site: http://www.stansource.com
It Consulting
N.A.I.C.S.: 541690

STELLAR IT SOLUTIONS, LLC
3056 Castro Vly Blvd, Castro Valley, CA 94546-5510
Tel.: (510) 881-8265
Web Site:
　http://www.stellaritsolutions.com
All Other Support Services
N.A.I.C.S.: 561990
Gino Bossetto (Owner)

STELLAR MANAGEMENT GROUP, INC.
412 Georgia Ave Ste 300, Chattanooga, TN 37403-1853
Tel.: (423) 265-7090
Web Site: http://www.vincitgroup.com
Rev.: $23,000,000
Emp.: 3,500
Garbage Disposals
N.A.I.C.S.: 423620

STELLAR RECOVERY, INC.
4500 Salisbury Rd Ste 105, Jacksonville, FL 32216
Tel.: (904) 738-6939
Web Site:
　http://www.stellarrecoveryinc.com
Sales Range: $10-24.9 Million
Emp.: 150
Debt Collection
N.A.I.C.S.: 561440
Liza Akley (COO)
Garrett Schanck (CEO)
Keith Jones (CMO)
Kim Harvey (Dir-Client Svcs)
Albert Rodriguez (Dir-Collections)
Valle Martin (Dir-Compliance)
Hayden Miller (Mgr-Ops)

STELLAR SOLUTIONS INC.
250 Cambridge Ave Ste 204, Palo Alto, CA 94306
Tel.: (650) 473-9866
Web Site:
　http://www.stellarsolutions.com
Year Founded: 1995
Sales Range: $25-49.9 Million
Emp.: 130
Engineeering Services
N.A.I.C.S.: 541330
Kevin Ford (CFO)
Janet Grondin (CEO)
Melissa Ferrell (VP-Comml Programs)
Michael Hollis Jr. (VP-Civil Sector)
Agns Lahure-Lecompte (Dir-Stellar Solutions Aerospace France)
Celeste Volz Ford (Founder & Chm)

STELLAR STRUCTURES LLC
PO Box 4489, Spanaway, WA 98387
Tel.: (253) 891-2400
Web Site:
　http://www.stellarstructures.com

STELLAR STRUCTURES LLC

Stellar Structures LLC—(Continued)
Sales Range: $10-24.9 Million
Emp.: 25
Mfr of Roof Structures
N.A.I.C.S.: 423330
Linda Glenn *(Mgr-Ops)*

STELLEX CAPITAL MANAGEMENT LP
900 Third Ave 25th Fl, New York, NY 10022
Tel.: (212) 710-2323
Web Site:
  https://www.stellexcapital.com
Privater Equity Firm
N.A.I.C.S.: 523999
Ray Whiteman *(Mng Partner)*
Michael Stewart *(Mng Partner)*
Mark Alter *(Mng Dir)*
Karthik Achar *(Partner)*
Tony Braddock *(CFO)*
Michael Livanos *(Mng Dir)*
David Waxman *(Mng Dir)*
Shankar Kiru *(Mng Dir)*

Subsidiaries:

Armada Parent, Inc. (1)
7884 Spanish Fort Blvd, Spanish Fort, AL 36527
Tel.: (251) 626-3625
Holding Company
N.A.I.C.S.: 551112
Bob Doran *(Sr VP-Admin)*

Subsidiary (Domestic):

Advanced Marine Preservation, LLC (2)
1841 Wambolt St, Jacksonville, FL 32202
Tel.: (619) 846-0214
Web Site: https://gotoamp.com
Marine Preservation Services
N.A.I.C.S.: 488390
Karen K. Webb *(Mgr-HR)*

International Marine & Industrial Applicators, LLC (2)
7884 Spanish Fort Blvd, Spanish Fort, AL 36577
Tel.: (251) 626-3625
Web Site: http://www.imiallc.com
Water Transportation Support
N.A.I.C.S.: 488390
Bob Doran *(VP-Risk, QA & Estimating)*
Yehuda Chakoff *(Pres)*
Joe Rella *(VP-HR, Strategic & Production Plng)*
Mike Hoods *(VP-Trades)*
Jonathan Thompson *(Gen Mgr-Structural Div)*
Michael Keenan Jr. *(CEO)*

Subsidiary (Domestic):

Main Industries, Inc. (3)
107 E St, Hampton, VA 23661
Tel.: (757) 380-0180
Web Site: http://www.mainindustries.com
Rev.: $10,100,000
Emp.: 160
Ship Repairing, Marine & Industrial Contractor
N.A.I.C.S.: 488390
Meredith Challoner *(VP)*

Custom Glass Solutions, LLC (1)
12688 State Route 67, Upper Sandusky, OH 43351
Tel.: (419) 294-4921
Glass Mfr
N.A.I.C.S.: 238150
Matthew J. Dietrich *(CEO)*

Subsidiary (Domestic):

North American Specialty Glass LLC (2)
2175 Kumry Rd, Trumbauersville, PA 18970
Tel.: (215) 536-0333
Web Site: http://www.naspecialtyglass.com
Strengthened or Reinforced Glass Mfr
N.A.I.C.S.: 327215
Mark Koder *(Sls Mgr-Armored)*
Laura Klee *(Mgr-HR)*

Danielle Willing *(Mgr-Customer Svc Inside Sls)*
Elaine DeVito *(Program Mgr)*
John Gamble *(Mgr-Engrg)*
Dan Craig *(Gen Mgr)*
David Smith *(Mgr-Sls & Program)*

Custom Made Meals LLC (1)
5575 Logan St, Denver, CO 80216-1757
Tel.: (303) 227-4993
Web Site:
  http://www.custommademeals.com
Emp.: 500
Meat & Meat Product Merchant Whslr
N.A.I.C.S.: 423140
Matt Barnes *(Gen Mgr)*
Doug Burris *(CEO)*

Fenix Parent LLC (1)
860 Airport Fwy Ste 701, Hurst, TX 76054
Tel.: (817) 760-4570
Web Site: https://www.fenixparts.com
Holding Company; Used Motor Vehicle Parts Reclamation Services & Sales
N.A.I.C.S.: 551112
Jeremiah Johnson *(Gen Mgr-Indianapolis)*
Bill Stevens *(CEO)*

Subsidiary (Domestic):

A & P Auto Parts, Inc. (2)
8572 Brewerton Rd, Cicero, NY 13039
Tel.: (315) 699-2728
Web Site: http://www.apautoparts.com
Sales Range: $1-9.9 Million
Emp.: 38
Automotive Parts & Accessories Stores
N.A.I.C.S.: 441330
Kathleen Abold *(Treas & Sec)*

Brothers Auto Salvage Yard, Inc. (2)
1000 S Kitley Ave, Indianapolis, IN 46203-2623
Tel.: (317) 352-1681
Web Site: http://www.brothersauto.com
Sales Range: $1-9.9 Million
Emp.: 28
Automobile Part Recycling Services
N.A.I.C.S.: 423140
Branden Ashburn *(Mgr-Sls)*

Butler Auto Sales and Parts, Inc. (2)
584 McSwain D, Forest City, NC 28043
Tel.: (828) 245-3686
Web Site: http://www.butlerautoparts.net
Automotive Accessory Distr
N.A.I.C.S.: 441330
Heath Bridges *(Acct Mgr-Sls)*

Don's Automotive Mall, Inc. (2)
216 Colesville Rd, Binghamton, NY 13904
Tel.: (607) 775-1542
Web Site: http://www.donsauto.com
Used Motor Vehicle Parts Reclamation Services & Sales
N.A.I.C.S.: 423140

Eiss Brothers, Inc. (2)
28250 NY State Rte 37, Watertown, NY 13601
Tel.: (315) 629-4370
Web Site: http://www.eissbrothers.com
Used Motor Vehicle Parts Reclamation Services & Sales
N.A.I.C.S.: 423140

F.A.P'S INC. (2)
8111 Rawsonville Rd, Belleville, MI 48111-8111
Web Site: http://www.foxautoparts.com
Recyclable Material Merchant Whslr
N.A.I.C.S.: 423930
Eric Hammond *(Mgr-Inventory)*

Gary's U-Pull-It, Inc. (2)
230 Colesville Rd, Binghamton, NY 13904-3904
Tel.: (607) 775-1900
Web Site: http://www.garysupullit.com
Used Motor Vehicle Parts Sales
N.A.I.C.S.: 423140

Green Oak Investments LLC (2)
12270 New Kings Rd, Jacksonville, FL 32219
Tel.: (904) 765-4242
Web Site: http://www.goautorecycling.com
Used Motor Vehicle Parts Reclamation Services & Sales
N.A.I.C.S.: 423140

Horseheads Automotive Recycling, Inc. (2)
1592 Sears Rd, Elmira, NY 14903
Tel.: (607) 739-3851
Web Site:
  http://www.horseheadspickapart.com
Used Motor Vehicle Parts Sales
N.A.I.C.S.: 423140

Jerry Brown, Ltd. (2)
26 Lower Warren St, Queensbury, NY 12804
Tel.: (518) 798-8141
Web Site: http://www.jbap.com
Used Motor Vehicle Parts Reclamation Services & Sales
N.A.I.C.S.: 423140

Leesville Auto Wreckers, Inc. (2)
186 Leesville Ave, Rahway, NJ 07065
Tel.: (732) 388-0783
Web Site: http://www.leesvilleauto.com
Used Motor Vehicle Parts Reclamation Services & Sales
N.A.I.C.S.: 423140

Ocean County Auto Wreckers, Inc. (2)
176 Atlantic City Blvd Rte 9, Bayville, NJ 08721
Tel.: (732) 349-0332
Web Site: http://www.cosmosautoparts.com
Used Motor Vehicle Parts Recycling Services
N.A.I.C.S.: 423140

Standard Auto Wreckers, Inc. (2)
3800 Highland Ave, Niagara Falls, NY 14305
Tel.: (716) 282-8212
Web Site:
  http://www.standardautowreckers.com
Used Motor Vehicle Parts Reclamation Mfr & Distr
N.A.I.C.S.: 423140

Tri-City Auto Salvage Inc. (2)
3848 Burlington Rd, Greensboro, NC 27405
Tel.: (336) 375-5871
Web Site: http://www.tricityautosalvage.com
Automotive Accessory Distr
N.A.I.C.S.: 441330

U-Pull U-Save Auto Parts (2)
7030 Myers Road,. East Syracuse, NY 13057
Tel.: (315) 656-7533
Web Site: https://upullusavecny.com
Automotive Recycle Services
N.A.I.C.S.: 811114

University Auto Recyclers, Inc. (2)
709 Massachusetts Ave, Pensacola, FL 32505
Tel.: (850) 435-2983
Web Site:
  http://www.pensacolaautosalvage.com
Rev.: $2,400,000
Emp.: 18
Furniture Merchant Whslr
N.A.I.C.S.: 423210
Bobby R. Minchew *(Pres)*

G2 Web Services, Inc. (1)
1750 112th Ave NE Ste C101, Bellevue, WA 98004
Tel.: (425) 749-4040
Web Site: http://www.g2webservices.com
Sales Range: $10-24.9 Million
Emp.: 90
Information Technology Security Services
N.A.I.C.S.: 541512
Ed Barton *(Pres & COO)*
Gunawan Herri *(CIO & VP-Tech)*
Rob Leach *(Exec VP)*
David Landis *(VP-Global Sls)*
Karina Sinclair *(VP-Ops)*
Sophia Chen *(Dir-Asia Pacific)*
Keith Groves *(Dir- Europe, Middle East & Africa)*
Robert Caldwell *(Co-Founder & Co-Partner)*
Kevin Omiliak *(Co-Founder & Co-Partner)*

Grammer Industries Inc. (1)
6320 E State St, Columbus, IN 47201
Tel.: (812) 579-5655
Web Site:
  http://www.grammerindustries.com
Trucking Service
N.A.I.C.S.: 484121

Amanda Morrison *(Sr VP-Process Improvement & Ammonia Dev)*
Mike Rees *(CFO)*
James Winton *(COO)*
Patrick Maher *(Chief Comml Officer)*
Angela Branchi *(Sr VP-Strategic Growth & Bus Dev)*
Dawn Kutruff *(VP-HR)*
Chad Hall *(VP-Safety & Risk)*
Brett Veness *(Controller)*

Joy Global Conveyors Inc. (1)
438 Industrial Dr, Winfield, AL 35594
Tel.: (205) 487-6492
Industrial Equipment Mfr & Distr
N.A.I.C.S.: 333922

Paragon Metals (1)
14120 Ballantyne Corporate Pl Ste 460, Charlotte, NC 28277
Tel.: (980) 235-1400
Web Site: http://www.paragonmetals.com
Sales Range: $10-24.9 Million
Emp.: 300
Iron Foundry Services
N.A.I.C.S.: 331511
David Smith *(VP-Pur & Logistics)*

Vigor Industrial LLC (1)
5555 N Channel Ave, Portland, OR 97217
Tel.: (503) 247-1777
Web Site: http://www.vigor.net
Sales Range: $25-49.9 Million
Emp.: 350
Holding Company; Ship Building & Repairing Services
N.A.I.C.S.: 551112
Greg Lind *(Dir-Estimating)*
Thomas Hickman *(VP-Sls & Mktg-Complex Fabrication)*

Subsidiary (Domestic):

Cascade General Inc. (2)
5555 N Channel Ave, Portland, OR 97217-7655
Tel.: (503) 247-1777
Web Site: http://www.vigor.net
Sales Range: $25-49.9 Million
Emp.: 250
Shipbuilding & Repairing
N.A.I.C.S.: 336611
Frank J. Foti *(CEO)*

Everett Shipyard, Inc. (2)
2730 Federal Ave, Everett, WA 98201
Tel.: (425) 259-0137
Web Site: http://www.everettship.com
Sales Range: $10-24.9 Million
Emp.: 40
Shipyard
N.A.I.C.S.: 336611

Marine Hydraulics International, Inc. (2)
543 E Indian River Rd, Norfolk, VA 23523
Tel.: (757) 545-6400
Web Site: http://www.mhi-shiprepair.com
Emp.: 500
Military Ship Repair, Overhaul & Conversion Services
N.A.I.C.S.: 336611
Thomas Epley *(Pres & CEO)*
Rolland Long *(Dir-Estimating)*
Chris Ceglio *(Dir-Comml Mktg)*

Marine Industries Northwest, Inc. (2)
313 East F St, Tacoma, WA 98421
Tel.: (253) 627-9136
Web Site: http://vigorindustrial.com
Sales Range: $10-24.9 Million
Emp.: 50
Shipbuilding & Repairing
N.A.I.C.S.: 336611
Mark Donahue *(Gen Mgr)*

Vigor Alaska Ship & Drydock Inc. (2)
3801 Tongass Ave, Ketchikan, AK 99901
Tel.: (907) 225-7199
Emp.: 200
Ship Building & Repair Services
N.A.I.C.S.: 336611
Mike Tearson *(Gen Mgr)*

Vigor Machine LLC (2)
5926 N Basin Ave, Portland, OR 97217
Tel.: (503) 283-2795
Ship Building & Repair Services
N.A.I.C.S.: 336611

Vigor Marine LLC (2)

3410 Terminal Ave, Everett, WA 98201
Tel.: (425) 259-1230
Marine Engineering Services
N.A.I.C.S.: 541330
Dave Byers (Dir-Project Mgmt)

Vigor Shipyards (2)
1801 16th Ave SW Harbor Island, Seattle, WA 98134-1017
Tel.: (206) 623-1635
Web Site: http://www.vigor.net
Ship Building & Repairing
N.A.I.C.S.: 336611
Frank J. Foti (CEO)
Bruce A. Dummer (CFO)
Spiro Risvas (Dir-Special Projects-Ship Repair Facilities)
John Lockwood (Dir-Mktg & Bus Dev)
David A. Whitcomb (COO)

Subsidiary (Non-US):

Vigor Works LLC (2)
5555 N Channel Ave., Portland, 97217, OR, Afghanistan
Tel.: (503) 247-1777
Web Site: https://vigor.net
Sales Range: $10-24.9 Million
Emp.: 200
Fiscal Year-end: 12/31/2014
Steel Fabrication & Manufacturing Services
N.A.I.C.S.: 332312
Tae Rhee (Gen Counsel & Sec)
Frank Collins (Sr VP-Govt & Pub Affairs)
Dawn Cartwright (VP-HR Svcs & Risk Mgmt)
Chris Palmer (VP-Fabrication)
Adam L. Beck (Pres-Alaska & Exec VP-Ship Repair)
Steve Zogas (CFO)
Jim Marcotuli (CEO)

STELLUS CAPITAL MANAGEMENT, LLC
4400 Post Oak Pkwy Ste 2200, Houston, TX 77027
Tel.: (713) 292-5400
Web Site:
  http://www.stelluscapital.com
Rev.: $1,500,000,000
Investment Management Service
N.A.I.C.S.: 523940
Joshua T. Davis (Partner)
Robert T. Ladd (Mng Partner)
Dean A. D'Angelo (Partner)
W. Todd Huskinson (Partner, CFO & Chief Compliance Officer)
Bill Haverland (Principal)
Casey Carroll (VP-IR)
Ryan Hughes (Mng Dir & Head-IR)
Zachary Roberson (VP & Dir-High Net Worth IR)

Subsidiaries:

Stellus Capital Investment Corporation (1)
4400 Post Oak Pkwy Ste 2200, Houston, TX 77027
Tel.: (713) 292-5400
Web Site: http://www.stelluscapital.com
Rev.: $105,847,568
Assets: $908,086,328
Liabilities: $588,146,540
Net Worth: $319,939,788
Earnings: $42,210,577
Fiscal Year-end: 12/31/2023
Closed-End Investment Fund
N.A.I.C.S.: 525990
Robert T. Ladd (Chm, Pres & CEO)
W. Todd Huskinson (CFO, Chief Compliance Officer, Treas & Sec)

STEMACO USA, INC.
230 N Main St, Hudson, OH 44236-2826
Tel.: (330) 342-3375
Web Site: http://www.stemacos.com
Sales Range: $10-24.9 Million
Emp.: 4
Chemical Product Whslr
N.A.I.C.S.: 424690
Barbara Holord (Pres)

STEMCYTE, INC.
1589 W Industrial Park St, Covina, CA 91722
Tel.: (626) 646-2500
Web Site: http://www.stemcyte.com
Year Founded: 1997
Sales Range: $10-24.9 Million
Emp.: 270
Umbilical Cord Blood Collection & Storage Services
N.A.I.C.S.: 621511
Kenneth J. Giacin (Chm)
Lawrence D. Petz (Chief Medical Officer)
Robert Chow (Founder)
Jonas Wang (Pres & CEO)
Charles Lu (COO)

STEMGENT, INC.
51 Moulton Street, Cambridge, MA 02139
Tel.: (617) 245-0000
Web Site: http://www.stemgent.com
Year Founded: 2008
Sales Range: $10-24.9 Million
Emp.: 100
Stem Cell Research Services
N.A.I.C.S.: 541715

Subsidiaries:

Asterand Inc. (1)
440 Burroughs TechOne Ste 501, Detroit, MI 48202
Tel.: (313) 263-0960
Sales Range: $10-24.9 Million
Emp.: 51
Human Tissue Research Services
N.A.I.C.S.: 541715

STEMILT GROWERS INC.
123 Ohme Garden Rd, Wenatchee, WA 98801
Tel.: (509) 663-1451   WA
Web Site: http://www.stemilt.com
Year Founded: 1964
Sales Range: $25-49.9 Million
Emp.: 600
Crop Preparation Services for Market
N.A.I.C.S.: 115114
Mike Taylor (VP-Sls & Mktg)
West Mathison (Pres)
Tate Mathison (Dir-Sls)
Dennis Howell (Dir-Plng)
Brianna Shales (Dir-Mktg)

STEMTECH INTERNATIONAL, INC.
151 Calle Iglesia, San Clemente, CA 92672
Tel.: (949) 542-8600
Web Site: http://www.stemtech.com
Year Founded: 2005
Sales Range: $50-74.9 Million
Emp.: 143
Biotechnology Development Services
N.A.I.C.S.: 541714
Christian Drapeau (Chief Science Officer)
Andy Goodwin (Dir-Sls & Mktg)
Jonathan Lester (Sr VP-Intl Bus Dev)
John W. Meyer (COO)
Don Karn (VP-Products Div)
Errol C. Lester (Dir-North American Food Support)
Jonathan Lim (VP-Asian Markets)
Heather Livingston (VP-Global Product Training & Sports Mktg)
Paola Mazzoni (VP-Product Training & Dev)
George Tashjian (Dir-Global IT)
Anil Singh (VP-Fin & Global Controller)
Christian Tricoche (Mng Dir-Western Europe)
Royston Knowles (Mng Dir-African Markets)
Darryl V. Green (Chm)
Victoria Rudman (CFO)
Charles Arnold (Chm & CEO)
David Casanova (Pres-Global Sls & Mktg)
Ray C. Carter Jr. (Founder)

STENCOR COMPANY, LLC
4555 N Jackson, Jacksonville, TX 75766
Tel.: (903) 586-0914
Web Site: http://www.stencor.com
Year Founded: 2009
Contract Manufacturing Services
N.A.I.C.S.: 541330
Kenneth W. Brimmer (CEO)

STENERSON BROS LUMBER COMPANY
1702 1st Ave N, Moorhead, MN 56560
Tel.: (218) 233-3437
Web Site:
  http://www.stenersonlumber.com
Sales Range: $25-49.9 Million
Emp.: 80
Lumber & Other Building Materials
N.A.I.C.S.: 423310
Leslie G. Stenerson (Pres)

STENSTROM COMPANIES LTD.
2420 20th St, Rockford, IL 61104
Tel.: (815) 398-2420
Web Site: http://www.rstenstrom.com
Year Founded: 1953
Rev.: $22,971,214
Emp.: 35
Industrial Buildings, New Construction
N.A.I.C.S.: 236210
Robert W. Stenstrom (Chm & CEO)

Subsidiaries:

Stenstrom Excavation & Blacktop Group (1)
2422 Ctr St, Rockford, IL 61108
Tel.: (815) 398-3478
Web Site: http://www.rstenstrom.com
Construction Services Related to Concrete
N.A.I.C.S.: 237110

Stenstrom General Contractor-Design Build Group (1)
2420 20th St, Rockford, IL 61104
Tel.: (815) 398-2420
Web Site: http://www.rstenstrom.com
Sales Range: $10-24.9 Million
Emp.: 15
Commercial & Office Building, New Construction
N.A.I.C.S.: 236220

Stenstrom Petroleum Services (1)
2422 Center St, Rockford, IL 61108
Tel.: (815) 398-3478
Web Site: http://www.rstenstrom.com
Rev.: $4,692,552
Emp.: 15
Service Station Equipment Installation, Maint & Repair Mfr
N.A.I.C.S.: 238990

Stenstrom Sand & Gravel Group (1)
12905 N 2nd St, Roscoe, IL 61073
Tel.: (815) 398-3478
Brick, Stone & Related Material
N.A.I.C.S.: 423320
Dave Sockness (Pres)

STENTEN'S GOLF CART ACCESSORIES, INC.
2785 Commerce Pkwy, North Port, FL 34289
Tel.: (941) 378-3993
Web Site: http://www.stenten.com
Sales Range: $1-9.9 Million
Emp.: 15
Golf Cart Accessories Distr
N.A.I.C.S.: 423120
Marilyn G. Stenten (Pres)

STEP BY STEP, INC.
744 Kidder St, Wilkes Barre, PA 18702
Tel.: (570) 829-3477   PA
Web Site:
  http://www.stepbystepusa.com
Year Founded: 1977
Sales Range: $50-74.9 Million
Emp.: 1,636
Disability Assistance Services
N.A.I.C.S.: 624120
Michael Kasenchak (CFO & VP-Fin)
Edith Hennebaul (VP-HR)
Bill Fromel (Chm)
Denise Cavenaugh (VP-Ops-Western)
Edward Coleman (VP-Ops-Southeast)
Janet Romero (VP-Ops-Lehigh Valley)
Meg Lukaszewski (VP-Ops-Northeast)
Michael Bernatovich (Interim Pres & Interim CEO)

STEP UP FOR STUDENTS, INC.
337 S Plant Ave, Tampa, FL 33606
Tel.: (904) 352-2246   FL
Web Site:
  http://www.stepupforstudents.org
Year Founded: 2000
Rev.: $708,029,489
Assets: $589,394,333
Liabilities: $75,690,706
Net Worth: $513,703,627
Emp.: 66
Fiscal Year-end: 06/30/18
Educational Support Services
N.A.I.C.S.: 611710
Debra Woerner (Exec VP-Dev)
Glen Gilzean (VP-Family & Community Affairs)
Doug Tuthill (Pres)
Scott Massey (CIO)
Alissa Randall (CMO & VP-Advancement)
Anne White (COO)
Carol Thomas (VP)
John Kirtley (Chm)
Jon East (VP-Policy & Pub Affairs)
Amanda Lopez (Chief Mktg Officer & VP-Advancement)
Cheryl Audas (Officer-Dev)
David Bryant (Officer-Dev)
Diana Allan (Officer-Dev)
Jaclyn Kilpatrick (Officer-Dev)
Joe Pfountz (CFO)
Karen Cordy (Officer-Dev)
Karis Turner (Officer-Dev)
Megan Gulick (Officer-Dev)
Renae Sweeney (Officer-Dev)
Wendy J. Woolley (Officer-Dev)

STEPHAN & BRADY, INC.
1850 Hoffman St, Madison, WI 53704-2541
Tel.: (608) 241-4141   WI
Web Site:
  http://www.stephanbrady.com
Year Founded: 1952
Sales Range: $10-24.9 Million
Emp.: 40
Advertising Agencies
N.A.I.C.S.: 541810
George Whitely (Pres & CEO)
Edie Devine (Supvr-Digital Production)
Emily Shea (Partner, VP & Exec Dir-Creative)
Laura Krogstad (Dir-Media)
Travis Biechele (VP-PR & Dir-Social Media)
Paul Clark (VP, Controller & Dir-HR)
Ryan Werner (VP & Creative Dir)
Jena Vuylsteke Williamson (VP & Dir-Acct)

STEPHAN, COLE & ASSOCIATES, LLC

Stephan, Cole & Associates, LLC—(Continued)

STEPHAN, COLE & ASSOCIATES, LLC
4560 Via Royale Ste 2, Fort Myers, FL 33919
Tel.: (239) 936-4041
Web Site: http://www.stephan-cole.com
Sales Range: $10-24.9 Million
Real Estate Appraisals, Professional Assistance, Research, Analysis & Consulting
N.A.I.C.S.: 531320
Bruce A. Stephan *(Founder)*

STEPHANIE ODEGARD COLLECTION
200 Lexington Ave Ste 1209, New York, NY 10016
Tel.: (212) 545-0205
Web Site: http://www.stephanieodegard.com
Rev.: $10,000,000
Emp.: 20
Carpets, Wall Hangings, Tapestries & Furniture
N.A.I.C.S.: 423220
Stephanie Odegard *(Pres)*

STEPHANIE TIRE CORP.
20213 NE 16th Pl, Miami, FL 33179
Tel.: (305) 652-2200
Web Site: http://www.stephanietires.com
Sales Range: $10-24.9 Million
Emp.: 7
Automobile Tires & Tubes
N.A.I.C.S.: 423130
Isaac Dargoltz *(Pres)*
Amparito Dargoltz *(VP)*

STEPHEN GOULD CORPORATION
35 S Jefferson Rd, Whippany, NJ 07981-1034
Tel.: (973) 428-1510 NJ
Web Site: http://www.stephengould.com
Year Founded: 1939
Sales Range: $500-549.9 Million
Emp.: 500
Customized Packaging Mfr, Product Fulfillment, JIT Warehouse Functions & CAD Design Service Solutions
N.A.I.C.S.: 561910
Michael Golden *(CEO)*
John Golden *(Exec VP)*
Anthony Lupo *(CFO)*
Justin Golden *(Pres)*

Subsidiaries:

Gould Midwest, Inc. (1)
110 Tduke Ct, Saint Charles, MO 63301
Tel.: (636) 724-4747
Web Site: http://www.stephengould.com
Sales Range: $10-24.9 Million
Emp.: 6
Sales & Marketing Office
N.A.I.C.S.: 424130
Mike Petrosino *(Mgr-Sls)*

Gould Paper of Florida, Inc. (1)
1101 N Keller Rd, Orlando, FL 32810
Tel.: (407) 875-1808
Web Site: http://www.stephengould.com
Sales Range: $10-24.9 Million
Emp.: 14
Sales & Marketing Office For Packaging Materials
N.A.I.C.S.: 424130

Gould Paper of Florida, Inc. (1)
5132 Tampa W Blvd, Tampa, FL 33634
Tel.: (813) 886-8460
Web Site: http://www.stephengould.com
Sales Range: $10-24.9 Million
Emp.: 10
Packaging Services
N.A.I.C.S.: 424130

Gould Southern (1)
2940 Old Norcross Rd, Duluth, GA 30096-7628
Tel.: (770) 921-1111
Web Site: http://www.gouldsouthern.com
Sales Range: $10-24.9 Million
Emp.: 25
Packaging Sales & Marketing
N.A.I.C.S.: 333993
Bob Sherman *(Mgr-Sls)*
Lisa Davis *(Office Mgr)*

Stephen Gould Corp
45541 Northport Loop W, Fremont, CA 94538-6458
Tel.: (510) 770-3500
Web Site: http://www.stephengould.com
Sales Range: $10-24.9 Million
Emp.: 50
Sales & Marketing Office
N.A.I.C.S.: 424130
Don Wallunas *(Gen Mgr)*

Stephen Gould Paper Co., Inc. (1)
35 S Jefferson Rd, Whippany, NJ 07981
Tel.: (973) 428-1500
Sales Range: $10-24.9 Million
Emp.: 100
Sales & Marketing Office
N.A.I.C.S.: 326150
Micheal Goldel *(CEO)*

Stephen Gould of Alabama, Inc. (1)
4960 Corporate Dr Nw Ste 130-G, Huntsville, AL 35805-6215
Tel.: (201) 837-1700
N.A.I.C.S.: 322211

Stephen Gould of Arizona, Inc. (1)
1555 W University Dr Ste 101, Tempe, AZ 85281
Tel.: (480) 968-1900
Web Site: http://www.stephengould.com
Sales & Marketing Office
N.A.I.C.S.: 315250

Stephen Gould of Carolina, Inc. (1)
598 Airport Blvd Ste 1200, Morrisville, NC 27560
Tel.: (919) 547-3700
Web Site: http://www.stephengouldpromos.com
Sales Range: $10-24.9 Million
Emp.: 2
Sales & Marketing Office
N.A.I.C.S.: 424130
John Golden *(Pres)*
Ian Sunshine *(Mgr-Sls)*

Stephen Gould of Carolina, Inc./Charlotte Div. (1)
13315 Carowinds Blvd, Charlotte, NC 28273-7700
Tel.: (704) 587-6100
Web Site: http://www.gouldcharlotte.com
Sales Range: $10-24.9 Million
Emp.: 18
Sales & Marketing Office
N.A.I.C.S.: 424130
Michael Golden *(Pres)*

Stephen Gould of Colorado, Inc. (1)
12150 E Briarwood St, Centennial, CO 80112
Tel.: (303) 662-1900
Sales Range: $10-24.9 Million
Emp.: 5
Sales & Marketing Office
N.A.I.C.S.: 238220

Stephen Gould of Connecticut Corp. (1)
360 New Haven Ave, Milford, CT 06460
Tel.: (203) 306-5210
Web Site: http://www.stephengould.com
Sales Range: $10-24.9 Million
Emp.: 12
Sales & Marketing Office
N.A.I.C.S.: 424130
Lesa Timlin *(Office Mgr)*

Stephen Gould of Illinois, Inc. (1)
225 Spring Lake Dr, Itasca, IL 60143
Tel.: (630) 510-7900
Web Site: http://www.stephengould.com
Sales Range: $10-24.9 Million
Emp.: 25
Sales & Marketing Office
N.A.I.C.S.: 424130

Stephen Gould of Indiana, Inc. (1)
8351 NW Blvd Ste 100, Indianapolis, IN 46278 (100%)
Tel.: (317) 802-6200
Web Site: http://www.stephengould.com
Sales Range: $10-24.9 Million
Emp.: 16
Sales & Marketing Office
N.A.I.C.S.: 424130
Don Hildebrandt *(Reg Mgr)*
Eric Snyder *(Sr Mgr-Acct)*
Mike McMahon *(Mgr-Sls)*
Nick Kraft *(Mgr-Acct)*

Stephen Gould of Maryland, Inc. (1)
20111 Century Blvd, Germantown, MD 20874
Tel.: (301) 528-8700
Sales Range: $10-24.9 Million
Emp.: 20
Sales & Marketing Office
N.A.I.C.S.: 424130
Eric Zimmerman *(Office Mgr)*

Stephen Gould of Michigan, Inc. (1)
700 Welch Rd, Commerce Township, MI 48390
Tel.: (973) 428-1500
Web Site: http://www.stephengould.com
Sales Range: $10-24.9 Million
Emp.: 100
Sales & Marketing Office
N.A.I.C.S.: 424130
Micheal Golden *(Pres)*

Stephen Gould of New England, Inc. (1)
30 Commerce Way, Tewksbury, MA 01876-1766
Tel.: (978) 851-2500
Web Site: http://www.stephengould.com
Sales Range: $10-24.9 Million
Emp.: 45
Sales & Marketing Office
N.A.I.C.S.: 424130
Ted Vitas *(VP-Sls)*

Stephen Gould of Ohio, Corp. (1)
4350 Renaissance Pkwy, Cleveland, OH 44128-5797
Tel.: (216) 292-3500
Web Site: http://www.stephengould.com
Sales Range: $10-24.9 Million
Emp.: 14
Sales & Marketing Distr
N.A.I.C.S.: 424130
Alan H. Malcolm *(Mgr-Sls)*

Stephen Gould of Ohio, Corp. (1)
10816 Kenwood Rd, Cincinnati, OH 45242-4709 (100%)
Tel.: (513) 793-1010
Web Site: http://www.stephengould.com
Sales Range: $10-24.9 Million
Emp.: 15
Sales & Marketing Office
N.A.I.C.S.: 424130

Stephen Gould of Pennsylvania Corp. (1)
310 Horizon Dr, Robbinsville, NJ 08691
Tel.: (609) 890-4646
Web Site: http://www.stephengould.com
Sales Range: $10-24.9 Million
Emp.: 750
Sales & Marketing Office
N.A.I.C.S.: 488991
Michael Golden *(Owner & Pres)*
Tom O'Hare *(Gen Mgr)*

Stephen Gould of Puerto Rico, Inc. (1)
PO Box 4985 PMB 294, Caguas, PR 00725 (100%)
Tel.: (787) 745-5206
Web Site: http://www.stephengould.com
Sales Range: $10-24.9 Million
Emp.: 1
Sales & Marketing Office
N.A.I.C.S.: 561910

Stephen Gould of Rochester (1)
145 Sullys Trl Ste 5, Pittsford, NY 14534
Tel.: (585) 586-1150
Web Site: http://www.stephengould.com
Sales Range: $10-24.9 Million
Emp.: 3
Sales & Marketing Office
N.A.I.C.S.: 541512

Michael Golden *(Pres)*

Stephen Gould of Tennessee, Inc. (1)
11029 Terrapin Station Ln, Knoxville, TN 37932
Tel.: (865) 777-3600
Web Site: http://www.stephengould.com
Sales Range: $10-24.9 Million
Emp.: 5
Sales & Marketing Office
N.A.I.C.S.: 424130
Todd Fisher *(Mgr-Sls)*
Christain Tuggle *(Office Mgr)*

Stephen Gould of Texas, Inc. (1)
16420 Midway Rd, Addison, TX 75001
Tel.: (972) 447-0099
Web Site: http://www.stephengould.com
Sales Range: $10-24.9 Million
Emp.: 30
Sales & Marketing Office
N.A.I.C.S.: 424130
Michael Golden *(Pres)*

Stephen Gould, Inc./LA (1)
10940 Wilshire Blvd Ste 950, Los Angeles, CA 90024
Tel.: (310) 338-9050
Web Site: http://www.stephengould.com
Sales Range: $10-24.9 Million
Emp.: 15
Providing Packaging Services
N.A.I.C.S.: 424130
Michael Golden *(CEO)*

The Stephen Gould Corporation (1)
1491 Route 52, Fishkill, NY 12524-1606
Tel.: (845) 896-7800
Web Site: http://www.gouldny.com
Sales Range: $10-24.9 Million
Emp.: 9
Sales & Marketing Office
N.A.I.C.S.: 424130
Rick Beckerman *(Gen Mgr)*

STEPHEN GROSS & SONS INC.
255259 Campbell Dr, Hamilton, OH 45011
Tel.: (513) 863-5161
Sales Range: $10-24.9 Million
Emp.: 25
Commercial & Office Building, New Construction
N.A.I.C.S.: 236220
Stephen J. Gross *(Pres)*

STEPHEN IMPORTS INC.
465 6th St, San Francisco, CA 94103
Tel.: (415) 777-9996
Sales Range: $10-24.9 Million
Emp.: 4
Telephone Equipment
N.A.I.C.S.: 423690
Benjamin Ku *(Pres)*

STEPHEN PONTIAC-CADILLAC, INC.
1097 Farmington Ave Ste 6, Bristol, CT 06010
Tel.: (860) 583-3325
Year Founded: 1957
Sales Range: $25-49.9 Million
Emp.: 180
Car Whslr
N.A.I.C.S.: 441110
Stephen Barberino *(Pres)*

STEPHEN WADE AUTO CENTER
150 W Hilton Dr, Saint George, UT 84770
Tel.: (435) 628-5201
Web Site: http://www.stephenwade.com
Sales Range: $50-74.9 Million
Emp.: 250

New & Used Car Dealerships Owner & Operator
N.A.I.C.S.: 441110
Stephen W. Wade *(Pres & CEO)*
Brad Fawson *(Dir-e-Commerce)*

STEPHENS & ASSOCIATES ADVERTISING, INC.
7400 W 132nd St Ste 100, Overland Park, KS 66213
Tel.: (913) 661-0910 KS
Year Founded: 1980
Sales Range: $10-24.9 Million
Emp.: 30
Agriculture, Business-To-Business
N.A.I.C.S.: 541810
Chuck Stephens *(CEO)*
Carol Stewart *(Production Mgr)*
Ray Huss *(Mgr-IR)*
Scott Kane *(Sr Art Dir)*
Jennifer Brocker *(Chief Creative Officer)*
Kathy Binkley *(Media Dir)*
Erin Evans *(Dir-Medical Comm)*
Boo Larsen *(Dir-Client Svcs)*
Patricia Thomblison *(Dir-Medical)*
Ted Glickman *(Dir-PR)*
Patrick Sweet *(CFO)*
Lori Sirotiak *(Mgr-Traffic)*
Jason Landrum *(Acct Exec)*
Lisa Siebert *(Acct Supvr)*
Tara Stewart *(Acct Dir)*
Brenda Andersen *(Chief Strategy Officer)*

STEPHENS & SMITH CONSTRUCTION CO. INC
1542 S 1st St, Lincoln, NE 68502
Tel.: (402) 475-8087
Web Site:
 http://www.stephensandsmith.com
Sales Range: $10-24.9 Million
Emp.: 175
Concrete Work
N.A.I.C.S.: 238110
Ryan Good *(VP-Specialty Products)*
Lance Jordan *(Chm-Omaha Foundations)*
Brett Richert *(VP-Lincoln Foundations)*
Steve Willis *(CEO)*
Carroll Smith *(Office Mgr)*
Bob Irwin *(VP-Flatwork & Decorative Concrete)*
Denise Kobza *(Controller)*
Gary Ebert *(VP-Comml Flatwork)*

STEPHENS FLOOR COVERING CO. INC.
2606 Rock Hill Industrial Ct, Saint Louis, MO 63144-2140
Tel.: (314) 918-9696
Sales Range: $10-24.9 Million
Emp.: 50
Floor Laying & Floor Work
N.A.I.C.S.: 238330
Mike Wood *(VP)*
Chris Meadows *(Sec)*

STEPHENS MEDIA GROUP MANAGEMENT, LLC
2448 E 81st St Ste 5500, Tulsa, OK 74137
Tel.: (918) 492-2660
Web Site: http://www.kxoj.com
Sales Range: $25-49.9 Million
Emp.: 20
Radio Holding Company
N.A.I.C.S.: 551112
David Stephens *(Gen Mgr)*

Subsidiaries:

KXOJ Inc. (1)
2448 E 81st St Ste 5500, Tulsa, OK 74137
Tel.: (918) 492-2660
Web Site: http://www.kxoj.com
Radio Station Operator
N.A.I.C.S.: 516110
David Stephens *(Gen Mgr)*

Stephens Media Group-Watertown, LLC (1)
134 Mullin St, Watertown, NY 13601
Tel.: (315) 788-0790
Sales Range: $25-49.9 Million
Radio Stations
N.A.I.C.S.: 516110
Glenn Curry *(Gen Mgr)*

STEPHENS PIPE & STEEL INC.
2225 E Hwy 619, Russell Springs, KY 42642-7928
Tel.: (270) 866-3331 KY
Web Site: http://www.spsfence.com
Year Founded: 1974
Sales Range: $50-74.9 Million
Emp.: 500
Mfr Steel Fences
N.A.I.C.S.: 423510
Terry Stephens *(Pres)*
Ted Eysenbach Sr. *(Gen Mgr)*

STEPHENSON EQUIPMENT, INC.
7201 Paxton St, Harrisburg, PA 17111-5126
Tel.: (717) 564-3434 PA
Web Site:
 http://www.stephensonequipment.com
Year Founded: 1957
Sales Range: $50-74.9 Million
Emp.: 110
General Construction Equipment & Machinery; Masonry Equipment & Supplies; Cranes; Heavy Construction Equipment Rental & Repair
N.A.I.C.S.: 811210
Robert M. Criste *(CFO & VP)*
Dennis Heller *(Pres)*
Gary Allegrucci *(Mgr-Parts)*

Subsidiaries:

Service Supply Corporation (1)
5885 Grayson Rd, Harrisburg, PA 17111-5126 (100%)
Tel.: (717) 564-7781
Web Site: http://www.servicesupplycorp.com
Sales Range: $10-24.9 Million
Emp.: 12
New & Used Small Contractor Equipment Sales, Service, Rentals, Parts & Supplies
N.A.I.C.S.: 811210

STEPHENSON GROUP
37 Hollow Brook Rd, Califon, NJ 07830
Tel.: (908) 439-3660
Web Site:
 http://www.stephensongroup.com
Year Founded: 1987
Rev.: $4,200,000
Emp.: 42
Public Relations Agency
N.A.I.C.S.: 541820
Jeff Adleman *(Exec VP-Corp Mktg)*
Emma Lintner *(Sls Mgr-Ingredients Div)*
Paul Pickering *(Mgr-Bus Dev)*
Shaun Warrington *(Mgr-Bus Dev)*
Jamie Bentley *(CEO)*

Subsidiaries:

Stephenson Group (1)
1575 Spinnaker Dr Ste 105B-167, Ventura, CA 93001
Tel.: (805) 772-1200
Web Site: http://www.stephensongroup.com
Sales Range: $10-24.9 Million
Emp.: 18
N.A.I.C.S.: 541820

STEPHENSON LUMBER COMPANY, INC.
6267 State Route 9, Chestertown, NY 12817
Tel.: (518) 494-2471 NY
Web Site:
 http://www.stephensonlumber.com
Year Founded: 1985
Sales Range: $10-24.9 Million
Emp.: 40
Lumber Whslr
N.A.I.C.S.: 423310
Larry Stephenson *(Pres & Treas)*

STEPHENSON MARKETING COOPERATIVE, INC.
W 505 S Dr, Stephenson, MI 49887
Tel.: (906) 753-2207
Web Site: http://www.smccoop.com
Sales Range: $10-24.9 Million
Emp.: 33
Farm Supplies Whslr
N.A.I.C.S.: 424910
Jessie Betters *(CEO)*

STEPHENSON MILLWORK CO. INC.
210 Harper St NE, Wilson, NC 27893
Tel.: (252) 237-1141
Web Site: http://www.smcinc.com
Sales Range: $10-24.9 Million
Emp.: 80
Architectural Millwork
N.A.I.C.S.: 321918
Randy Turner *(CFO)*
Ken Dietel *(Project Mgr)*
Russ Stephenson *(CEO)*
Lee Stephenson III *(Pres)*

STEPHENSON NATIONAL BANK & TRUST
1820 Hall Ave, Marinette, WI 54143
Tel.: (715) 732-1732
Web Site: http://www.snbt.com
Rev.: $11,103,000
Emp.: 56
National Commercial Banks
N.A.I.C.S.: 522110
Dan Peterson *(Pres)*

STEPHENSON OIL CO., INC.
7676 Charles Page Blvd, Tulsa, OK 74127-7158
Tel.: (918) 245-0287 OK
Year Founded: 1956
Sales Range: $1-9.9 Million
Emp.: 50
Convenience Store
N.A.I.C.S.: 445131
Betty Stephenson *(CFO)*

STEPHENSON PRINTING, INC.
5731 General Washington Dr, Alexandria, VA 22312-2490
Tel.: (703) 642-9000 DE
Web Site:
 http://www.stephensonprinting.com
Year Founded: 1959
Sales Range: $25-49.9 Million
Emp.: 40
Sheetfed & Web Lithography & Color Separation Services
N.A.I.C.S.: 323111
G.W. Stephenson *(Pres)*
Sandy Stephenson *(VP-Admin)*

STEPHENSON WHOLESALE COMPANY INC.
230 S 22nd Ave, Durant, OK 74701
Tel.: (580) 920-0110 OK
Web Site: http://www.inwsupply.com
Year Founded: 1969
Sales Range: $400-449.9 Million
Emp.: 360
Supplier of Tobacco & Confectionery Products
N.A.I.C.S.: 424940
Jerry Wheatley *(CFO)*
Richard Dunham *(VP-Ops)*
Dawn Laxson *(VP-Admin)*
Zack Harris *(Coord-Mktg & Pur)*
Carter Adair *(Dir-Sls)*
Steven Potts *(Mgr-Customer Svc)*
Tommy Bertrand *(Mgr-Retail Programs)*
Tony Rose *(Mgr-Sls)*
Mitch Taylor *(Mgr-Sls)*
Randy West *(Mgr-Sls)*
Nathan Williams *(Mgr-Transportation)*
Becky Spellmann *(VP-Pur & Mktg)*

STEPHERSON INCORPORATED
4744 Spottswood Ave, Memphis, TN 38117
Tel.: (901) 683-6861
Web Site:
 http://www.superlofoods.com
Sales Range: $10-24.9 Million
Emp.: 75
Independent Supermarket
N.A.I.C.S.: 445110
Tommy Rodgers *(Gen Mgr)*

STEPSTONE GROUP LP
450 Lexington Ave 31st FL, New York, NY 10017
Tel.: (212) 351-6100 DE
Web Site:
 http://www.stepstoneglobal.com
Private Equity & Real Estate Investment Firm
N.A.I.C.S.: 523999
Jose Fernandez *(Partner-New York & Co-COO)*
Monte M. Brem *(Partner)*
Thomas Bradley *(Partner)*
Darren M. Friedman *(Partner-New York)*
Jason Ment *(COO & Partner)*
Johnny Randel *(CFO & Partner)*
Kate Budiselik *(Principal)*
Bruna Riotto *(VP-Sao Paulo)*
Ian Aaker *(Principal)*
John Anthony Coelho *(Partner)*
Josh Cleveland *(Partner)*
Lindsay Creedon *(Partner)*
Michael Elio *(Partner)*
Margaret McKnight *(Partner-Real Estate Grp)*
Scott W. Hart *(CEO)*
Michael I. McCabe *(Partner)*
Mark T. Maruszewski *(Partner-New York)*
Thomas Keck *(Partner)*
David Y. Park *(Chief Acctg Officer)*
Darren M. Friedman *(Partner)*

Subsidiaries:

PetSmart, Inc. (1)
19601 N 27th Ave, Phoenix, AZ 85027
Tel.: (623) 587-2025
Web Site: https://www.petsmart.com
Sales Range: $5-14.9 Billion
Emp.: 50,000
Pet & Pet Supplies Retailers
N.A.I.C.S.: 459910
Raymond Svider *(Chm)*
Erick Goldberg *(Sr VP-HR)*
Chris McCurdy *(Sr VP-Supply Chain)*
Brian Amkraut *(Exec VP-Store Ops, Svcs, Supply Chain & Real Estate)*
Gregg Scanlon *(Sr VP-Store Ops & Svcs)*
Jerrod Johnson *(Dir-Global Investigations & Corp Security)*
Robert Seaser *(Mgr-Brand Risk Investigations & Intelligence)*
Joshua Kanter *(Exec VP-Mktg & Customer Experience)*
Erin Gray *(Sr Mgr-Corp Comm)*
J. K. Symancyk *(Pres & CEO)*
Meredith Plaxco *(Sr Dir-Loss Prevention & Safety)*
Jackie Goebbel *(Mgr-Safety & Loss Prevention)*

STEPSTONE GROUP LP

StepStone Group LP—(Continued)
Alan Schnaid *(CFO & Exec VP-Fin, IT & Strategy)*
Jim Persinger *(Sr VP-MP&A)*
Lacey Bundy *(Gen Counsel, Sec & Sr VP)*
Michael Sapp *(Sr VP-Buying)*
Paul Hunt *(Sr VP-Sourcing & Product Dev)*
Deborah Gonzalez *(VP-Merchandising Mktg)*
Joanne Dwyer *(VP-Corp Social Responsibility & Sustainability)*
Rob Litt *(VP-Corp Comm & PR)*
Paulette R. Dodson *(Gen Counsel & Sec)*

Subsidiary (Domestic):

Chewy, Inc. (2)
7700 W Sunrise Blvd, Plantation, FL 33322
Tel.: (786) 320-7111
Web Site: https://www.chewy.com
Rev.: $11,147,720,000
Assets: $3,186,851,000
Liabilities: $2,676,607,000
Net Worth: $510,244,000
Earnings: $39,580,000
Emp.: 18,100
Fiscal Year-end: 01/28/2024
Animal Food Distr
N.A.I.C.S.: 459910
Raymond Svider *(Chm)*
Satish Mehta *(CTO)*
Sumit Singh *(CEO)*
William G. Billings *(Chief Acctg Officer)*
David W. Reeder *(CFO)*

StepStone Group Real Estate LP (1)
450 Lexington Ave 31st Fl, New York, NY 10017
Tel.: (212) 351-6100
Web Site: http://www.stepstoneglobal.com
Real Estate & Investment Services
N.A.I.C.S.: 531390
Jay Morgan *(Partner)*
Alex Abrams *(Mng Dir)*
Jeremy Cobin *(VP)*
Dev Subhash *(Partner)*
Dami Alade *(VP)*
Josh Cleveland *(Partner)*
Kieran Farrelly *(Partner)*
Christopher Georgeson *(Dir-Luxembourg)*
Jeff Giller *(Partner)*
Drew Iandanza *(VP)*

Subsidiary (Domestic):

Courtland Partners Ltd. (2)
127 Public Square Ste 5050, Cleveland, OH 44114
Tel.: (216) 522-0330
Web Site: http://www.stepstoneglobal.com
Activities Related to Real Estate
N.A.I.C.S.: 531390

STEPSTONE, INC.
13238 S Figueroa St, Los Angeles, CA 90061
Tel.: (310) 327-7474 CA
Web Site:
  http://www.stepstoneinc.com
Year Founded: 1963
Sales Range: $10-24.9 Million
Precast Concrete Products Mfr & Whslr
N.A.I.C.S.: 327331
Monte M. Brem *(Co-Founder)*
Brian Harris *(Pres)*

STEPTOE & JOHNSON LLP
1330 Connecticut Ave NW, Washington, DC 20036
Tel.: (202) 429-3000
Web Site: http://www.steptoe.com
Year Founded: 1945
Sales Range: $350-399.9 Million
Emp.: 1,001
Legal Advisory Services
N.A.I.C.S.: 541110
Michael J. Allan *(Partner-New York)*
Thomas M. Barba *(Partner)*
Stewart A. Baker *(Partner)*
Filiberto Agusti *(Partner)*
Tom Best *(Partner)*
Timothy C. Bickham *(Partner)*
Steven H. Brose *(Partner)*
John Caracappa *(Partner)*
Betty Jo Christian *(Partner)*
John Molenda *(Partner)*
Paul Hurst *(Partner)*
Sarah Gordon *(Partner)*
Kendall Enyard *(Partner)*
Matthew Kulkin *(Partner)*
Micah Green *(Partner)*
Carolyn Walsh *(Partner)*
Pablo Bentes *(Mng Dir-Intl Trade & Investment)*
Amanda Varma *(Partner)*
Jennifer Key *(Partner)*
Alan Bayless Feldman *(Partner)*
Shehzad Hasan *(Partner)*
Paul K. Charlton *(Partner-Phoenix)*
Allison Nyholm *(Dir-Govt Affairs & Public Policy)*
Dane Jaques *(Partner)*
Ruth Madrigal *(Partner-Tax Grp)*
Joe Caldwell *(Partner)*
Jody Cummings *(Partner)*
Brian Egan *(Partner)*
Jon Sallet *(Partner)*
Brad Anwyll *(Partner-Tax Grp)*
Kelly Eberspecher *(Partner)*
Tery Gonsalves *(Partner)*
Jeff Beatrice *(Partner)*
Catherine Cockerham *(Partner)*
Will Drake *(Partner)*
Leah Quadrino *(Partner)*
Gwen Renigar *(Vice Chm)*
George Callas *(Mng Dir-Govt Affairs, Pub Policy & Tax Groups)*
Sara Pikofsky *(Partner-ERISA Litigation Practice)*
Peter Denton *(Partner-Transportation Grp)*
Will Turner *(Partner-Chicago)*
Teddy Baldwin *(Partner)*
Joan Baughan *(Partner-Global Food Contact Matls Practice)*
Adie Olson *(Partner-Govt Affairs & Pub Policy Grp-Chicago)*
Stacie Hartman *(Chm-Fin Svcs Grp-Chicago)*
Damon Kalt *(Partner)*
Jessica Hoffmann *(COO)*

STEREN ELECTRONICS INTERNATIONAL LLC
6920 Carroll Rd Ste 100, San Diego, CA 92121
Tel.: (858) 546-5000 CA
Web Site: http://www.sterenusa.com
Year Founded: 1956
Electronic Components Distr
N.A.I.C.S.: 423690
Alexander Cohen *(COO)*
Javier Garcia Hinojosa *(VP)*

STERILITE CORPORATION
30 Scales Ln, Townsend, MA 01469-1010
Tel.: (978) 597-1100 MA
Web Site: http://www.sterilite.com
Year Founded: 1939
Sales Range: $25-49.9 Million
Emp.: 650
Mfr of Plastic Kitchenware, Tableware, Houseware & Storage Products
N.A.I.C.S.: 326199
Richard Ahern *(VP-Mktg)*
John Cassidy *(VP-Sls)*
Jeff Difonte *(Controller)*
Richard G. Murphy *(VP-HR)*
Keith D. Boissoneau *(VP-Fin)*

STERKS SUPER FOODS INC.
6527 Columbia Ave, Hammond, IN 46320
Tel.: (219) 933-3600
Rev.: $73,000,000
Emp.: 100
Independent Supermarket
N.A.I.C.S.: 445110

Joe Kolova *(Pres)*
Glenn Jacobson *(Controller)*

STERLING ACCEPTANCE CORP.
1 Melvin Ave, Annapolis, MD 21401
Tel.: (410) 268-1545
Web Site:
  http://www.sterlingacceptance.com
Sales Range: $25-49.9 Million
Emp.: 10
Short-Term Business Credit Services
N.A.I.C.S.: 522299
Dave Trostle *(VP)*
Robin Cottmeyer *(Dir-Ops)*

STERLING ADVERTISING CO.
461 Cochran Rd Ste 139, Pittsburgh, PA 15228
Tel.: (412) 260-4592
Year Founded: 2007
Sales Range: $10-24.9 Million
Emp.: 7
N.A.I.C.S.: 541810
Claire Devereux Thompson *(Pres)*

STERLING AMERICAN PROPERTY INC.
111 Great Neck Rd Ste 408, Great Neck, NY 11021
Tel.: (516) 773-3800
Web Site:
  http://www.sterlingamerican.com
Year Founded: 1991
Rev.: $4,500,000,000
Emp.: 200
Real Estate Investment Services
N.A.I.C.S.: 523999
Michael Katz *(Co-CEO-American Funds & Sr Exec VP)*
Richard A. Wilpon *(Co-CEO-American Funds & Sr Exec VP)*
Thomas Osterman *(Officer-Acquisition & Exec VP)*
Mark Peskin *(CFO)*
Gregory P. Nero *(Gen Counsel)*
Tarak Patolia *(Chief Investment Officer & Officer-Acquisition)*
Gregory A. Katz *(Officer-Acquisition & Sr VP)*
Robert Bergman *(Sr VP)*
James E. Seiler *(Sr VP)*
Thomas A. Dolan *(Sr VP)*
Matt Harvey *(VP)*
Jeffrey S. Wilpon *(Exec VP)*
Eric S. Saretsky *(Dir-Construction)*
Daniel G. Rosenberg *(Controller)*
Joseph D. Hyman *(Treas)*
Anthony Sferrazza *(Dir-Fin-Real Estate)*
Rajiv Bhalla *(Sr Mgr-Tax)*
Fred Wilpon *(Co-Founder & Chm)*
Saul B. Katz *(Co-Founder & Pres)*
Todd M. Katz *(Officer-Acquisition & VP)*

STERLING AVIATION, INC.
5480 S Howell Ave, Milwaukee, WI 53207
Tel.: (414) 744-1300
Web Site:
  http://www.sterlingaviation.com
Rev.: $11,157,226
Emp.: 50
Charter Air Transportation Services
N.A.I.C.S.: 481211
Roger Banaszak *(VP-Mktg & Sls)*
Chris Mayer *(Dir-Ops)*
Kurt Schlamer *(Dir-Maintenance)*

STERLING BANCSHARES, INC.
1100 Sterling Dr, Poplar Bluff, MO 63901
Tel.: (573) 778-3333 MO
Year Founded: 2003

U.S. PRIVATE

Sales Range: $25-49.9 Million
Emp.: 140
Bank Holding Company
N.A.I.C.S.: 551111
Kenneth E. Poteet *(Chm, Pres & CEO)*
Scott E. Spencer *(Pres-Banking)*
Kelly Williams *(CFO)*

Subsidiaries:

Sterling Bank (1)
1100 Sterling Dr, Poplar Bluff, MO 63901
Tel.: (573) 778-3333
Web Site: http://www.sterbank.com
Sales Range: $25-49.9 Million
Emp.: 54
Commericial Banking
N.A.I.C.S.: 522110
Kenneth E. Poteet *(Founder, Chm & CEO)*
Scott E. Spencer *(Vice Chm & Pres)*
Jim Duncan *(Exec VP)*
McLane Poteet *(Sr VP)*
Corey Poteet *(VP)*
Ellen Hope *(VP)*
Brenda Brown *(Sec)*
Dan Campbell *(CMO)*

STERLING BOILER & MECHANICAL INC.
1420 Kimber Ln, Evansville, IN 47715
Tel.: (812) 479-5447
Web Site:
  http://www.sterlingboiler.com
Sales Range: $150-199.9 Million
Emp.: 800
Plumbing Services
N.A.I.C.S.: 238220
Daniel Felker *(Pres)*
John Vinitski *(Dir-Ops)*
Gary Roberts *(Dir-Quality Control)*
Stephanie A. Freiwald *(Gen Counsel)*

STERLING BUSINESS FORMS INC.
5300 Crater Lake Ave, Central Point, OR 97502
Tel.: (541) 779-3173
Web Site: http://www.sbsnet.com
Sales Range: $25-49.9 Million
Emp.: 180
Mfr of Manifold Business Forms
N.A.I.C.S.: 323111
Michael W. Jackson *(Chm)*
Dave Goodnature *(VP)*
David Pollock *(Mgr-Graphics & Pre-Press)*
Bob Howes *(Mgr-Production)*
Justin Dack *(Mgr-IT)*
Kelley Mankins *(Mgr-Customer Svc)*

STERLING COMMERCIAL CREDIT
10559 Citation Dr Ste 204, Brighton, MI 48116
Tel.: (810) 229-2601
Web Site:
  http://www.sterlingcommercialcredit.com
Year Founded: 2004
Sales Range: $1-9.9 Million
Emp.: 20
Financial Services
N.A.I.C.S.: 523999
Brian Jenks *(Pres)*
Edwin Small *(CEO)*
Greg L. Boller *(COO)*

STERLING COMMUNICATIONS
750 University Ave Ste 100, Los Gatos, CA 95032
Tel.: (408) 395-5500
Web Site: http://www.sterlingpr.com
Sales Range: $25-49.9 Million
Emp.: 25
Public Relations Agency
N.A.I.C.S.: 541820
Marianne O'Connor *(CEO)*

STERLING COMPUTERS
1508 Square Turn Blvd, Norfolk, NE 68701
Tel.: (402) 379-1030
Web Site: http://www.sterlingcomputers.com
Rev.: $200,000
Emp.: 120
Computer & Software Stores
N.A.I.C.S.: 449210
Jennifer Deitloff *(CFO)*
Jean Marie Moore *(CEO)*
Brad Moore *(Pres & CEO)*
Darrell Moore *(Sr VP-Corp Dev)*
Jeff Moore *(Sr VP-Bus Dev & Contracts)*
Stan Lupkes *(VP-Svcs)*
Steve Van Ginkel *(VP-Bus Dev & Partner Alliances)*
Tim McCabe *(VP-Sls)*

Subsidiaries:

BlueSpace Software Corp (1)
6300 Bridgepoint Pkwy Ste 1-450, Austin, TX 78730-5103
Tel.: (512) 366-3940
Web Site: http://www.bluespace.com
Software Publisher
N.A.I.C.S.: 513210
Pat Motola *(Pres & CEO)*
Christine Mallory *(CFO & VP-Fin & Admin)*

STERLING CONSTRUCTION COMPANY
3158 Baron Ln, Rifle, CO 81650
Tel.: (970) 625-8606
Sales Range: $10-24.9 Million
Emp.: 5
Oil & Gas Pipeline Construction
N.A.I.C.S.: 237110
Pat Atsimpson *(Pres)*

STERLING CORPORATION
263 Industrial Ave E, Lowell, MA 01852
Tel.: (978) 667-0044
Sales Range: $10-24.9 Million
Emp.: 80
Local Trucking with Storage
N.A.I.C.S.: 424490
Brian J. Fishkin *(Pres)*
Bill Dastou *(Mgr-Ops)*
Owen Stokes *(Mgr-Bus Dev & Mktg)*
John Woodbury *(Sr Acct Exec)*
Tom Smart *(Project Mgr)*

STERLING CUT GLASS COMPANY, INC.
3233 Mineola Pike, Erlanger, KY 41018-1027
Tel.: (859) 283-2333 KY
Web Site: http://www.sterlingcutglass.com
Year Founded: 1902
Sales Range: $10-24.9 Million
Emp.: 80
Mfr of Etched & Cut Glassware
N.A.I.C.S.: 423220
Michael W. Dyas *(Pres)*
Leslie Dyas *(Exec VP)*
Stu Wagner *(Controller)*

STERLING ELECTRIC, INC.
7997 Allison Ave, Indianapolis, IN 46268
Tel.: (317) 872-0471 CA
Web Site: http://www.sterlingelectric.com
Year Founded: 1927
Sales Range: $50-74.9 Million
Emp.: 40
Motor Mfr
N.A.I.C.S.: 335312
Walter Mashburn *(Pres & COO)*
Bryan Moeller *(VP-Engrg)*

STERLING ENGINEERING, INC.
Two Westbrook Corporate Centre Ste 300, Elmhurst, IL 60154
Tel.: (630) 993-3400
Web Site: http://www.sterling-engineering.com
Year Founded: 1969
Sales Range: $25-49.9 Million
Emp.: 1,098
Recruitment Services
N.A.I.C.S.: 561311
Rama Kavaliauskas *(Pres)*
Paul Russo *(VP)*
Greg Simutis *(VP)*
Michael Sury *(VP-Sls)*
Tim Silkaitis *(VP-Fin)*
Steve Waszkowiak *(Mgr-Engrg)*

STERLING EQUITIES, INC.
4 World Trade Ctr 150 Greenwich St, New York, NY 10007
Tel.: (212) 485-4400
Web Site: http://www.sterlingequities.com
Year Founded: 1972
Emp.: 200
Commercial Real Estate & Private Equity Investment Firm
N.A.I.C.S.: 525990
Saul B. Katz *(Co-Founder & Pres)*
Fred Wilpon *(Co-Founder & Chm)*
Michael Katz *(Sr Partner)*
Richard A. Wilpon *(Sr Partner)*
David M. Katz *(Partner)*
Thomas Osterman *(Partner)*
Jeffrey S. Wilpon *(COO-New York Mets & Partner)*
Gregory A. Katz *(Partner)*
Mark Peskin *(CFO)*
Gregory P. Nero *(Gen Counsel)*
Tarak Patolia *(Chief Investment Officer)*
Richard T. Browne *(Mng Partner-Sterling Project Dev Grp)*
Scott A. Wilpon *(Partner)*
Todd M. Katz *(Partner)*
Bruce N. Wilpon *(Partner)*

Subsidiaries:

Sterling Entertainment Enterprises, LLC (1)
150 Greenwich St, New York, NY 10007
Tel.: (212) 485-4800
Sales Range: $50-74.9 Million
Emp.: 150
Holding Company
N.A.I.C.S.: 551112
Saul B. Katz *(Chm)*

Joint Venture (Domestic):

SportsNet New York, LLC (2)
1271 Avenue of the Americas Fl 16, New York, NY 10020
Tel.: (212) 485-4800
Web Site: http://www.sny.tv
Regional Sports Cable Network Operator
N.A.I.C.S.: 516210
Steve Raab *(Pres)*
Gary Morgenstern *(VP-Programming)*
Scott Weinfeld *(CFO & Sr VP-Fin & Admin)*

Sterling Mets, L.P. (1)
Citi Field 126th St & Roosevelt Ave, Flushing, NY 11368-1699
Tel.: (718) 507-8499
Web Site: http://www.mets.com
Sales Range: $200-249.9 Million
Professional Baseball Club
N.A.I.C.S.: 711211
Saul B. Katz *(Pres & Partner)*
Fred Wilpon *(Chm & CEO)*
Michael Katz *(Partner)*
Richard A. Wilpon *(Partner)*
David M. Katz *(Partner)*
Jeff Wilpon *(COO & Partner)*
David Cohen *(Gen Counsel & Exec VP)*
Mark Peskin *(CFO)*
David Newman *(Sr VP-Mktg & Comm)*
Jay Horwitz *(VP-Media Rels)*

Leonard Labita *(VP & Controller)*
Robert Kasdon *(VP-Security)*
Mike Landeen *(Sr VP-Venue Svcs & Ops)*
Tom Osterman *(Partner)*
Marvin Tepper *(Partner)*
John Ricco *(Sr VP)*
Neal Kaplan *(VP & Deputy Gen Counsel)*
Lou DePaoli *(Chief Revenue Officer & Exec VP)*
Wes Engram *(VP-Corp Partnership Sls & Svcs)*
Chris Zaber *(VP-Ticket Sls & Svcs)*
Chaim Bloom *(Gen Mgr)*

STERLING FEDERAL BANK FSB
110 E 4th St, Sterling, IL 61081
Tel.: (815) 626-0614
Web Site: http://www.sterlingfederal.com
Rev.: $21,522,000
Emp.: 200
Federal Savings & Loan Associations
N.A.I.C.S.: 522180
Rita Smith *(Controller)*
Kate Lich *(Sec)*

STERLING FURNITURE CO
3194 Gateway Loop, Springfield, OR 97477
Tel.: (541) 726-6221
Web Site: http://www.mjacobsfamilyofstores.com
Sales Range: Less than $1 Million
Emp.: 20
Furniture Retailer
N.A.I.C.S.: 449110
Michael Schwartz *(Chm)*

STERLING GLOBAL OPERATIONS, INC.
2229 Old Hwy 95, Lenoir City, TN 37771
Tel.: (865) 988-6063
Web Site: http://www.sterlinggo.com
Sales Range: $250-299.9 Million
Emp.: 3,500
Weapons Management Services
N.A.I.C.S.: 541611
Matt Kaye *(Pres & CEO)*
Erik Quist *(Gen Counsel)*
David Johnson *(VP-Strategis Dev & Ops-Washington)*
Steven Hile *(CFO)*

STERLING HEIGHTS DODGE, INC.
40111 Van Dyke Ave, Sterling Heights, MI 48313-3730
Tel.: (586) 939-3900 MI
Web Site: http://www.sterlingheightsdodge.com
Year Founded: 1946
Sales Range: $100-124.9 Million
Emp.: 75
Retailer of New & Used Automobiles
N.A.I.C.S.: 441110
Anthony J. Viviano *(Pres)*
Philip Viviano *(VP)*
Cathie Fital *(Controller)*

STERLING HOLDINGS INC.
9549 Koger Blvd Ste 102, Saint Petersburg, FL 33701
Tel.: (727) 894-7978
Rev.: $15,400,000
Emp.: 3
Life Insurance
N.A.I.C.S.: 524113

STERLING HOUSING LLC
3411 Richmond Ave Ste 200, Houston, TX 77046
Tel.: (832) 209-1200

Web Site: http://www.sterlinghousing.com
Rev.: $24,736,000
Emp.: 200
Apartment Building Operator
N.A.I.C.S.: 531110
Jack Dinerstein *(CEO)*

STERLING INTERNATIONAL INC.
3808 N Sullivan Rd Bldg 16, Spokane, WA 99216
Tel.: (509) 926-6766 WA
Web Site: http://www.rescue.com
Year Founded: 1982
Insect Traps & Attractants & All-natural Insect Repellent Mfr
N.A.I.C.S.: 561710
Rod Schneidmiller *(Founder & Pres)*
Gerry Simpson *(VP-Ops)*
Jim Oxley *(VP-Sls)*
Paul Crooks *(Mgr-Ops)*

STERLING INVESTMENT PARTNERS, L.P.
285 Riverside Ave Ste 300, Westport, CT 06880-4806
Tel.: (203) 226-8711 DE
Web Site: http://www.sterlinglp.com
Year Founded: 1991
Privater Equity Firm
N.A.I.C.S.: 523999
Michael A. Barr *(Partner)*
Charles W. Santoro *(Co-Founder & Mng Partner)*
William M. Macey *(Co-Founder & Mng Partner)*
Douglas L. Newhouse *(Co-Founder & Mng Partner)*
Amy L. Weisman *(Dir-Bus Dev)*
Joseph Gault *(Principal)*
James W. Soldano *(Partner)*
David H. Kahn *(Mng Dir-Bus Dev)*
Audrey L. Hertzel *(Office Mgr)*
William P. Russell Jr. *(Partner)*
B. Benjamin Baldanza *(Operating Partner)*

Subsidiaries:

Fairway Group Holdings Corp. (1)
2284 12th Ave, New York, NY 10027
Tel.: (646) 616-8000
Web Site: http://www.fiarwaymarket.com
Rev.: $797,555,000
Assets: $359,136,000
Liabilities: $381,739,000
Net Worth: ($22,603,000)
Earnings: ($46,534,000)
Emp.: 900
Fiscal Year-end: 03/29/2015
Holding Company; Food & Alcoholic Beverage Retailer
N.A.I.C.S.: 551112
Charles W. Santoro *(Chm)*
Nathalie Augustin *(Gen Counsel, Sec & Sr VP)*
Aaron J. Fleishaker *(Sr VP-Real Estate & Dev)*
Kevin McDonnell *(Pres & COO)*
Brian Riesenburger *(Chief Mdsg Officer & Sr VP)*
Larry Santoro *(Chief Admin Officer & Exec VP)*
Peter Romano *(VP-Produce)*
Dorothy M. Carlow *(Chief Mdsg Officer & Exec VP)*

Subsidiary (Domestic):

Fairway Market, Inc. (2)
2127 Broadway 74th St, New York, NY 10023
Tel.: (212) 595-1888
Web Site: http://www.fairwaymarket.com
Sales Range: $550-599.9 Million
Grocery Stores
N.A.I.C.S.: 445110
Abel Porter *(CEO)*

Markon, Inc. (1)
400 S Maple Ave Ste 230, Falls Church, VA 22046

STERLING INVESTMENT PARTNERS, L.P.

U.S. PRIVATE

Sterling Investment Partners, L.P.—(Continued)
Tel.: (703) 884-0030
Web Site: http://www.markonsolutions.com
Sales Range: $10-24.9 Million
Emp.: 76
Business Management Consulting Services
N.A.I.C.S.: 541611
Matthew J. Dean (Pres & CEO)
Leigh Valudes (VP)
Ray Carney (VP-Client Delivery)
Drew Thompson (VP-Ops)
Kyle Werking (VP)
Steve Genn (VP)

Subsidiary (Domestic):

Advanced Systems Engineering Corporation (2)
12030 Sunrise Valley Dr Ste 325, Reston, VA 20191
Tel.: (703) 942-5821
Web Site: http://www.asec-usa.com
Sales Range: $10-24.9 Million
Emp.: 90
Engineeering Services
N.A.I.C.S.: 541330
Lynn R. Wallace (CEO)
Jeffrey A. Wallace (Pres)
Joel L. Henson (COO & Sr VP)
Anita M. Hohman (CFO & VP)

Integrate IT (2)
4309 Kenwyn Ct, Annandale, VA 22003-3658
Tel.: (703) 425-1757
Web Site: http://www.integrateit.net
General Management Consulting Services
N.A.I.C.S.: 541611

Verdantas LLC (1)
6397 Emerald Pkwy Ste 200, Dublin, OH 43016
Tel.: (614) 793-8777
Web Site: https://www.verdantas.com
Sales Range: $25-49.9 Million
Emp.: 170
Project Development, Engineering & Consulting Services
N.A.I.C.S.: 541330
Craig A. Kasper (Exec VP)
Eric H. Wilburn (Principal)
Terry Reynolds (VP-Mktg & Comm)
Jesse Kropelnicki (CEO)
Alyson Hanson (VP-Strategic Comm)
Ashraf Jahangir (Chief Strategy Officer)

Subsidiary (Domestic):

Borton-Lawson Engineering, Inc. (2)
3897 Adler Pl, Bethlehem, PA 18017
Tel.: (484) 821-0470
Web Site: http://www.borton-lawson.com
Sales Range: $1-9.9 Million
Emp.: 35
Engineeering Services
N.A.I.C.S.: 541330
Frank Joanlanne (Pres)
Donald R. Spencer (VP)
Christopher D. McCue (VP-Oil & Gas)
Lucinda Boardwine (Mgr-Mktg)

Division (Domestic):

Hull & Associates, Inc. - Brownfields Division (2)
4770 Duke Dr Ste 300, Mason, OH 45040
Tel.: (513) 459-9677
Web Site: http://www.hullinc.com
Site Remediation, Project Development & Engineering Services
N.A.I.C.S.: 541330
Brad S. White (VP)

Subsidiary (Domestic):

JM Sorge, Inc. (2)
57 4th St, Somerville, NJ 08876
Tel.: (908) 218-0066
Web Site: http://www.jmsorge.com
Environmental Consulting
N.A.I.C.S.: 541690
John Kopceuch (Dir-Admin Svcs & HR-Foley, Inc.)

Jobes, Henderson & Associates, Inc. (2)
59 Grant St, Newark, OH 43055
Tel.: (740) 344-5451
Web Site: http://www.jobeshenderson.com

Sales Range: $1-9.9 Million
Emp.: 35
Civil Engineering & Land Surveying Services
N.A.I.C.S.: 541330
Jim Roberts (Pres & CEO)
Jeremy Van Ostran (Sr VP)
Susan Derwacter (Dir-Pub Works)
Justin Lowe (Dir-Land Dev)
Scott Haines (Project Mgr)
Amanda Spencer (Project Mgr)
Ben Russell (Engr-Bridge)
Brad Olinger (Engr-Project)
Cameron Smith (Engr-Project)
Sam Eppley (Engr-Project)
Tyler Eppley (Engr-Project)

Lewandowski Engineers (2)
234 N Erie St, Toledo, OH 43624-1608
Tel.: (419) 255-4111
Web Site: http://www.lewandowskieng.com
Engineeering Services
N.A.I.C.S.: 541330
Matt Lewandowski (Owner)

Peterson Brustad Inc. (2)
1180 Iron Point Rd, Folsom, CA 95630
Tel.: (916) 608-2212
Web Site: http://www.pbiengineering.com
Rev.: $3,000,000
Emp.: 8
Architectural Services
N.A.I.C.S.: 541310
David Peterson (Principal)
Mike Rossiter (Project Mgr)
Chris Fritz (Project Mgr)
Austin Peterson (Project Mgr)
Karl Brustad (Principal)

STERLING LUMBER & INVESTMENT CO.
9101 Harlan St Unit 300, Westminster, CO 80031-2927
Tel.: (303) 427-9661 CO
Web Site: http://www.sterlinglbr.com
Year Founded: 1909
Sales Range: $75-99.9 Million
Emp.: 100
Retailer of Lumber & Other Building Materials
N.A.I.C.S.: 423310
Duane Jakober (Mgr-Acctg)

STERLING LUMBER COMPANY
3415 W 127th St, Blue Island, IL 60406
Tel.: (708) 388-2223
Web Site: http://www.sterlinglumber.com
Sales Range: $10-24.9 Million
Emp.: 60
Lumber, Plywood, Millwork & Wood Panel Whslr
N.A.I.C.S.: 423310
Cooper Sterling (VP-Pur & Ops)
Carter Sterling (CEO)
Christian Sterling (VP-Internal Ops)
Carson Sterling (VP-Market Res)
Brad Zenner (Gen Mgr-Ops)
Jay Bailey (Reg Mgr-Sls)
James McKenney (Mgr-Sawmill)
Shane Green (Pres)

STERLING ORGANIZATION
340 Royal Poinciana Way Ste 316, Palm Beach, FL 33480
Tel.: (561) 835-1810
Web Site: http://www.sterlingorganization.com
Sales Range: $75-99.9 Million
Emp.: 40
Private Equity Real Estate Firm
N.A.I.C.S.: 523999
Brian D. Kosoy (CEO & Mng Principal)
Gregory S. Moross (Founder & Pres)
Craig Mueller (Sr Mng Dir-Ops)
Michael McCarthy (Mng Dir-Investments)

Adam L. Munder (Chief Mktg Officer & Principal)
Robert Vreeland (Dir-Leasing)
Adrian Jimenez (VP-Leasing)
Ed Senenman (Sr Mng Dir)
Rob Meeks (Dir-Mid Atlantic)
Brian T. Ferguson (VP-Fin)
Dustin Hicks (VP-Dev & Construction)
Peggy Wei (Mng Dir)
David Milgram (VP-Investments-Southeast)
Michael J. Horne (Dir-Midwest)
Jonathan Mendis (Sr VP-Investments-Western)
Karen Lynch (VP-Lease Admin)
Scott Schry (Sr VP-West)
D. J. Belock (CFO)
Joe Dykstra (Pres-Sterling Logistics Properties)
Bob Dake (COO-Retail)

STERLING PAPER CO.
2155 Castor Ave, Philadelphia, PA 19134-2704
Tel.: (215) 744-5350 PA
Year Founded: 1972
Sales Range: $1-9.9 Million
Emp.: 60
Mfr of Paperboard Cartons, Pails, Plates & Specialties
N.A.I.C.S.: 322212
Martin Stein (Pres)
Suzanne S. Faigen (VP)
Joyce Silver (Controller)

STERLING PAPER COMPANY
1845 Progress Ave, Columbus, OH 43207
Tel.: (614) 443-0303
Web Site: http://www.sterling-paper.com
Sales Range: $25-49.9 Million
Emp.: 70
Whslr of Printing Paper
N.A.I.C.S.: 424110
Mike Duncan (Dir-IT)

STERLING PARTNERS
401 N Michigan Ave Ste 3300, Chicago, IL 60611
Tel.: (312) 465-7000
Web Site: http://www.sterlingpartners.com
Year Founded: 1983
Private Equity Firm
N.A.I.C.S.: 523999
R. Christopher Hoehn-Saric (Co-Founder & Mng Dir)
Steven M. Taslitz (Co-Founder & Sr Mng Dir)
Jeffrey Elburn (Mng Dir & CFO)
M. Avi Epstein (Mng Dir)
Rick Elfman (Mng Dir)
Michael Gershenzon (VP)
Whitney Krutulis (VP)
Doug Becker (Co-Founder & Mng Dir)
Jeffrey Keith (Operating Partner)

Subsidiaries:

Keypath Education International Inc. (1)
1501 E Woodfield Rd Ste 204N, Schaumburg, IL 60173 (100%)
Tel.: (224) 419-7988
Web Site: https://www.keypathedu.com
Rev.: $124,168,000
Assets: $82,880,000
Liabilities: $28,248,000
Net Worth: $54,632,000
Earnings: ($19,705,000)
Emp.: 745
Fiscal Year-end: 06/30/2023
Educational Support Services
N.A.I.C.S.: 611710

Sterling Partners - Chicago Office (1)

401 N Michigan Ave Ste 3300, Chicago, IL 60611
Tel.: (312) 465-7000
Web Site: http://www.sterlingpartners.com
Sales Range: $200-249.9 Million
Privater Equity Firm
N.A.I.C.S.: 523999
Merrick M. Elfman (Mng Dir)
Jason Rosenberg (Mng Dir)
Shoshana M. Vernick (Mng Dir)
M. Avi Epstein (Mng Dir)
Renee Berghoff (Dir-Events)
Kiley Taslitz Anderson (Co-Founder & Mng Dir)
Amsey Bai (Ops Mgr)
Eric Becker (Co-Founder)
Michael Brown (VP)
Lara Compton (Dir-Platform Mktg)
Shawn Domanic (VP)
Jeffrey Izenman (Mng Dir-Strategic Dev & Sterling Partners Equity Advisors)
Lauren Kaiser (Mgr-IT)
Timothy A. Knight (Dir-Ops)
Stacey Lager (VP)
Kelsey Lawrie (VP-Talent)
Sam Leibovitz (VP)
John A. Schattenfield (Head-Distr)
Roberta Schwartz (Mgr-Client Relationship)
Brian Schwartz (Principal)
Kevin Silverman (Chief Investment Officer & Portfolio Mgr)
Stefan Weitz (Co-Founder & Mng Dir)
Lauren Yeager (Assoc Gen Counsel)
Desmond Werthman (Pres-Quantitative Investments)

Holding (Non-US):

Conversant Intellectual Property Management Incorporated (2)
515 Legget Drive Suite 100, Ottawa, K2K 3G4, ON, Canada
Tel.: (613) 576-3000
Web Site: https://www.mosaid.com
Sales Range: $25-49.9 Million
Semiconductors & Data Systems Mfr
N.A.I.C.S.: 334413
Boris Teksler (Pres & CEO)

Subsidiary (Non-US):

Conversant IP Japan K.K. (3)
Compass Offices 7/F Toranomon 40 MT Bldg 5-13-1 Toranomon, Minato-ku, Tokyo, Japan (100%)
Tel.: (81) 3 4530 9821
Web Site: http://www.conversantip.com
Sales Range: Less than $1 Million
Emp.: 2
Mfr of Semiconductors & Data Systems
N.A.I.C.S.: 334413
Hiroyuki Takahori (Gen Mgr)

Holding (Domestic):

DeAngelo Brothers Inc. (2)
100 N Conahan Dr, Hazleton, PA 18201
Tel.: (570) 459-1114
Web Site: http://www.dbiservices.com
Infrastructure Maintenance, Management & Operational Services; Facilities Management
N.A.I.C.S.: 541330
Joseph Ferguson (Gen Counsel)
Michael McRae (CEO)
Niel Markey (Chief Comml Officer)
Jon Mezlo (Chief Transformation Officer)
Diane Newmier (Chief HR Officer)

Subsidiary (Domestic):

Digital Traffic Systems, Inc. (3)
11056 Air Park Rd, Ashland, VA 23005
Tel.: (804) 381-5100
Web Site: http://www.digitaltrafficsystems.com
Intelligent Transportation Systems & Traffic Data Collection Solutions & Services
N.A.I.C.S.: 488490
Peter Keen (Pres)

Reforestation Services, Inc. (3)
PO Box 3197, Salem, OR 97302
Tel.: (503) 362-8322
Web Site: http://www.dbiservices.com

Forestry Services
N.A.I.C.S.: 115310
Ann Cecil *(Mgr-Accts-Hyrail)*
Stan Rogers *(Project Mgr-Hyrail)*

Holding (Domestic):

Educate, Inc. (2)
1001 Fleet St, Baltimore, MD 21202
Tel.: (410) 843-6200
Web Site: http://www.educate-inc.com
Sales Range: $350-399.9 Million
Holding Company; Supplemental Education Services
N.A.I.C.S.: 551112
Jeffrey H. Cohen *(Pres/CEO-Sylvan Learning)*
C. Alan Schroeder *(Chief Legal Officer, Gen Counsel & Sec)*
Carol Vallone *(CEO-Educate Online)*

Subsidiary (Domestic):

Educate Online, Inc. (3)
99 Conifer Hill Dr, Danvers, MA 01923
Tel.: (978) 624-7000
Web Site: http://www.educate-online.com
Online Educational Support Services
N.A.I.C.S.: 611710
Carol Vallone *(CEO)*
Dave Dupre *(CTO)*
William Rieders *(COO)*
Chris Wheedleton *(Sr VP-Bus Dev-K-12)*
Lisa Philpott *(VP-Mktg)*
Folline Cullen *(CFO)*

Sylvan Learning, Inc. (3)
1001 Fleet St 9th Fl, Baltimore, MD 21202
Tel.: (410) 843-6200
Web Site: http://www.sylvanlearning.com
Tutoring & Educational Support Services
N.A.I.C.S.: 611691
Jeffrey H. Cohen *(Pres & CEO)*
John McAuliffe *(CFO)*
Sasha Shultz *(Chief People Officer)*

STERLING PIPE & TUBE INC.
5335 Enterprise Blvd, Toledo, OH 43612
Tel.: (419) 729-9756
Web Site:
http://www.sterlingpipeandtube.com
Year Founded: 1987
Sales Range: $50-74.9 Million
Emp.: 150
Electric Welded Tubing & Pipe Mfr
N.A.I.C.S.: 331210
Fred Shelar *(Pres)*
Bill Kuhlman *(Dir-Mktg)*
Dennis Krout *(VP-Sls & Admin)*
Chris Rowe *(Controller)*

STERLING PONTIAC BUICK GMC INC.
205 N Earl Rudder Fwy, Bryan, TX 77803
Tel.: (979) 846-5555
Web Site:
http://www.sterlingautogroup.net
Sales Range: $50-74.9 Million
Emp.: 100
New & Used Car Dealers
N.A.I.C.S.: 441110
Manuel Gonzalez *(Pres)*
Steven Nolet *(Gen Mgr-Sls)*
Tom Pais *(Controller)*

STERLING REAL ESTATE TRUST
4340 18th Ave S Ste 200, Fargo, ND 58103
Tel.: (701) 353-2720   ND
Web Site: https://www.smftrust.com
Year Founded: 2002
Rev.: $135,060,000
Assets: $888,723,000
Liabilities: $565,257,000
Net Worth: $323,466,000
Earnings: $8,921,000
Fiscal Year-end: 12/31/22
Real Estate Investment Services
N.A.I.C.S.: 531210

Barry L. Schmeiss *(Chief Investment Officer-Sterling Multifamily Trust)*
Michael Carlson *(Gen Counsel & Sec)*
Kenneth P. Regan *(CEO)*

Subsidiaries:

Sterling Quail Creek, LLC (1)
Quail Creek Apartments 1450 W Lark St, Springfield, MO 65810
Tel.: (417) 886-6800
Web Site: https://www.quailcreekapartmenthomes.com
Flooring Installation Services
N.A.I.C.S.: 238330

STERLING REALTY ORGANIZATION CO.
600 106th Ave NE Ste 200, Bellevue, WA 98004
Tel.: (425) 455-8100
Web Site:
http://www.sterlingrealty.com
Year Founded: 1943
Sales Range: $10-24.9 Million
Emp.: 20
Provider of Real Estate Management & Development Services
N.A.I.C.S.: 531190

STERLING RICE GROUP
1801 13th St Ste 400, Boulder, CO 80302
Tel.: (303) 381-6400
Web Site: http://www.srg.com
Year Founded: 1984
Emp.: 125
Advertising Agencies, Brand Development, Communications, Consulting, Financial, Food Service, Full Service, Graphic Design, Planning & Consultation
N.A.I.C.S.: 541810
Michael Rice *(Mng Partner)*
John Cooke *(Partner & Mng Dir)*
Ed Rzasa *(Mng Partner)*
Tim Shanahan *(Mng Partner)*
Jay Waddell *(Partner & Mng Dir)*
Mike Walters *(Mng Partner)*
Brad Derthick *(Dir-Res)*
Susan Peck *(Partner & Dir-Media)*
Rob Heider *(Dir-Creative)*
Chip Hisle *(Assoc Dir-Creative)*
John Grubb *(Mng Partner)*
Cathryn Olchowy *(Partner)*
Jennifer Jones *(Mng Dir & Dir-Design Strategy)*
Al Banisch *(Partner & Mng Dir)*
Dan Burak *(Mng Dir)*
Laura Slavec *(Acct Dir)*
Lobelia Buckner *(Sr Acct Mgr)*
Kate McQuail *(Sr Copywriter)*
Jill Holmstrom *(Dir-Innovation)*
Surf Melendez *(Sr Dir-Art)*
Wade Paschall *(Dir-Creative)*
Tim Streeb *(Mng Dir-Mktg & PR)*
Elizabeth Moskow *(Dir-Culinary)*
Kevin Appel *(Dir-Culinary)*
Matt Bromley *(Mng Dir & Partner)*
Eric Friedman *(Grp Acct Dir)*
Robyn Zimmer *(Dir-Media)*
Cindy Judge *(Pres)*
Adam Wohl *(Exec Dir-Creative)*

STERLING SERVICE INC.
8071 S Broadway Ste C, Littleton, CO 80122
Tel.: (303) 820-4500
Web Site:
http://www.sterlingserv.com
Year Founded: 1976
Automotive Repair Services
N.A.I.C.S.: 811111
John Bradley *(Owner)*

STERLING SPRING LLC

5432 W 54th St, Chicago, IL 60638
Tel.: (773) 582-6464
Web Site:
http://www.sterlingspring.com
Rev.: $12,830,301
Emp.: 63
Wire Springs
N.A.I.C.S.: 332613
Tony Massaro *(Controller)*
Ignacio Fresas *(Mgr-Quality)*
Mike Malesky *(Acct Mgr)*

STERLING SUPPLY CO. INC.
1535 Baltimore Ave, Kansas City, MO 64108
Tel.: (816) 472-0999
Web Site: http://www.sterling-inc.com
Rev.: $23,000,000
Emp.: 50
Gifts & Novelties
N.A.I.C.S.: 424990
Lawrence Weiner *(Owner)*
Jeff Gesser *(CFO)*

Subsidiaries:

Nathan Weiner & Associates Inc. (1)
1535 Baltimore Ave, Kansas City, MO 64108-1301
Tel.: (816) 474-9830
Web Site: http://www.sterling-inc.com
Sales Range: $10-24.9 Million
Provider of Nondurable Goods
N.A.I.C.S.: 424990

STERLITECH CORPORATION
22027 70th Ave S, Kent, WA 98032-1911
Tel.: (253) 437-0844
Web Site: http://www.sterlitech.com
Sales Range: $1-9.9 Million
Emp.: 13
Laboratory Filtration Product Mfr & Distr
N.A.I.C.S.: 334516
Mark Spatz *(Pres)*
Jason Struthers *(Engr-Application & Tech Support)*
Kristina Shahbazian *(Engr-Applications)*

STERN & STERN INDUSTRIES INC.
188 Chacher St, New York, NY 10017-4201
Tel.: (212) 972-4040   NY
Web Site:
http://www.sternandstern.com
Year Founded: 1889
Sales Range: $75-99.9 Million
Emp.: 96
Industrial Fabrics Mfr
N.A.I.C.S.: 313210
Peter B. Thornton *(Chm & Pres)*
Stanley Cone *(VP-Mfg)*
Lee Kessler *(Sec & Controller)*

STERN CARDIOVASCULAR FOUNDATION
8060 Wolf River Blvd, Germantown, TN 38138
Tel.: (901) 271-1000   TN
Web Site: http://www.sterncardio.com
Year Founded: 2010
Sales Range: $25-49.9 Million
Health Care Srvices
N.A.I.C.S.: 622110
Melissa Reaves *(CFO)*
Sharon Goldstein *(Dir-Comm & PR)*
Gregory M. Duckett *(Sec)*
Debbie Eddlestone *(CEO)*

STERN OIL COMPANY INC.
27923 US Hwy 81, Freeman, SD 57029
Tel.: (605) 925-7999
Web Site: http://www.sternoil.com
Sales Range: $10-24.9 Million

Emp.: 45
Sale Diesel Fuel
N.A.I.C.S.: 424720
Gillas J. Stern *(Pres)*
Peg Waltner *(Controller)*

STERN STRATEGY GROUP
186 Wood Ave S Ste 300, Iselin, NJ 08830
Tel.: (908) 276-4344
Web Site:
http://www.sternstrategy.com
Year Founded: 1985
Emp.: 28
Public Relations Agency
N.A.I.C.S.: 541820
Susan Stern *(Founder & Pres)*
Ned Ward *(Sr VP)*
Daniel R. Stern *(Mng Dir)*
Tara Baumgarten *(Sr VP)*
Joan Bosisio *(Sr VP)*

Subsidiaries:

Stern + Associates (1)
Two Canal Park SE 560, Cambridge, MA 02141
Tel.: (908) 276-4344
Emp.: 20
Public Relations Agency
N.A.I.C.S.: 541820

STERNBERG CHRYSLER PLYMOUTH
1781 S US Hwy 231, Jasper, IN 47546
Tel.: (812) 482-5125   IN
Web Site: http://www.sternbergs.com
Year Founded: 1952
Sales Range: $25-49.9 Million
Emp.: 125
Sales of New & Used Cars
N.A.I.C.S.: 441110
Derek Sternberg *(Principal)*

STEUART INVESTMENT COMPANY
5454 Wisconsin Ave Ste 1600, Chevy Chase, MD 20815-6906
Tel.: (301) 951-2700   DE
Web Site: http://www.steuart.com
Year Founded: 1953
Sales Range: $75-99.9 Million
Emp.: 20
Provider of Real Estate Services
N.A.I.C.S.: 531120
Michael B. Goheen *(CFO)*
Guy T. Steuart II *(Chm)*
John R. Clark III *(Pres)*

Subsidiaries:

Steuart-Kret Homes (1)
4518 Printers Ct, White Plains, MD 20695
Tel.: (301) 870-5603
Web Site: http://www.skhomes.com
Building Construction Services
N.A.I.C.S.: 236220
George Kemp *(Mgr-Punch Out)*

STEUBEN FOODS INC.
1150 Maple Rd, Elma, NY 14059
Tel.: (716) 655-4000
Web Site:
http://www.steubenfoods.com
Year Founded: 1985
Producer of Canned Specialties & Dairy Products
N.A.I.C.S.: 311999
Jeff Sokal *(Sr VP-Bus Dev)*
Julie Senko *(Exec VP-HR)*
Frank V. Balon *(Exec VP-Chief Legal & Fin Officer)*

STEVE BARRY BUICK INC.
16000 Detroit Ave, Lakewood, OH 44107
Tel.: (216) 221-7000   OH

STEVE BARRY BUICK INC.

Steve Barry Buick Inc.—(Continued)
Web Site:
http://www.stevebarrybuick.com
Year Founded: 1903
Sales Range: $10-24.9 Million
Emp.: 29
Provider of New & Used Automobiles
N.A.I.C.S.: 441110
Steve Barry (Gen Mgr)
Bruce Barry (Mgr-Fin)

STEVE CASEY MOTORS INC.
4100 Youngfield St, Wheat Ridge, CO 80033
Tel.: (303) 422-2001
Web Site:
http://www.rvfourseasons.com
Sales Range: $25-49.9 Million
Emp.: 80
Recreational Vehicle Dealers
N.A.I.C.S.: 441210
Joe Birkemeyer (Mgr)

STEVE CONNOLLY SEAFOODS CO
34 Newmarket Sq, Boston, MA 02118-2601
Tel.: (617) 427-7700
Web Site:
http://www.steveconnollyseafood.com
Sales Range: $25-49.9 Million
Emp.: 70
Wholesaler; Processor of Fish & Seafoods
N.A.I.C.S.: 424460
David Coombs (VP-Sls)
Stephen H. Connolly Jr. (Chm & CEO)

STEVE COURY BUICK PONTIAC GMC
6101 E Coury Dr, Camp Verde, AZ 86322
Tel.: (928) 567-3399
Web Site: http://www.stevecoury.com
Sales Range: $10-24.9 Million
Emp.: 52
Automobiles, New & Used
N.A.I.C.S.: 441110
Steve Coury (Pres)

STEVE DEYOUNG'S BIG TOP MARKET
3630 Clyde Park Ave SW, Wyoming, MI 49509-4024
Tel.: (616) 534-9671
Rev.: $23,000,000
Emp.: 85
Independent Supermarket
N.A.I.C.S.: 445110
Steve DeYoung (Pres)

STEVE FOLEY CADILLAC
100 Skokie Blvd, Northbrook, IL 60062-1610
Tel.: (847) 564-4090
Web Site: http://www.stevefoley.com
Sales Range: $75-99.9 Million
Emp.: 100
Sales of New & Used Automobiles
N.A.I.C.S.: 532111
Ed Rodriguez (Dir-Svcs)

STEVE HENDERSON LOGGING INC.
1702 21st St Ste 104, Lewiston, ID 83501
Tel.: (208) 746-1627
Year Founded: 1972
Sales Range: $1-9.9 Million
Emp.: 14
Logging Camps & Contractors
N.A.I.C.S.: 113310
Steve Henderson (Owner & Pres)

STEVE HOPKINS INC.
2499 Auto Mall Pkwy, Fairfield, CA 94533-5850
Tel.: (877) 466-9808
Web Site:
http://www.stevehopkinshonda.com
Sales Range: $25-49.9 Million
Emp.: 65
Car Whslr
N.A.I.C.S.: 441110
Steven E. Hopkins (Pres)

STEVE PADIS JEWELRY PLUS ENTERPRISES
101 Utah St Ste 201, San Francisco, CA 94103
Tel.: (415) 626-8288
Web Site: http://www.padisgems.com
Sales Range: $10-24.9 Million
Emp.: 40
Jewelry & Precious Stones
N.A.I.C.S.: 423940
Steve Padis (Pres)

STEVE PLATZ REALTY INC.
3736 Boardman Canfield Rd Ste 3, Canfield, OH 44406
Tel.: (330) 757-4889
Web Site:
http://www.platzrealtygroup.com
Real Estate & Property Development Services
N.A.I.C.S.: 531210
Steve Platz (Pres & CEO)

Subsidiaries:

Kutlick Realty, LLC   (1)
6995 Appleridge Cir, Youngstown, OH 44512
Tel.: (330) 965-6500
Web Site: http://www.kutlickrealtyllc.com
Offices of Real Estate Agents & Brokers
N.A.I.C.S.: 531210
Bill Kutlick (Pres)

STEVE SELVIN ASSOCIATE INC
207 Union St, Hackensack, NJ 07601-4225
Tel.: (201) 488-3332   NJ
Web Site:
http://www.newworldsales.com
Year Founded: 1978
Sales Range: $75-99.9 Million
Emp.: 51
Mens & Boys Clothing
N.A.I.C.S.: 424350
Steve Selvin (Pres & CEO)

STEVE SHANNON TIRE COMPANY
920 Millville Rd, Bloomsburg, PA 17815
Tel.: (570) 387-6387
Web Site:
http://www.steveshannon.com
Sales Range: $10-24.9 Million
Emp.: 130
Mfr of Tires & Tubes
N.A.I.C.S.: 423130
Lance Danilowicz (Mgr)
Steven H. Shannon (Founder, Owner, Pres & CEO)

STEVE WARD & ASSOCIATES INC.
7330 Cockrell Bend, Nashville, TN 37209
Tel.: (615) 350-7310
Web Site: http://www.swainc.com
Sales Range: $10-24.9 Million
Emp.: 50
Manufacture Millwork
N.A.I.C.S.: 321918

Stephen W. Ward (Pres)
Scott Easter (Mgr-Millwork General)
Jeff Anthony (Mgr-Health Care Div)

STEVE WHITE MOTORS, INC.
3470 US Hwy 70 SW, Hickory, NC 28658
Tel.: (828) 464-3458
Web Site:
http://www.stevewhitemotors.net
Sales Range: $10-24.9 Million
Emp.: 45
Car Whslr
N.A.I.C.S.: 441110
Robert Baxa (Principal)
Ramona Ervin (Office Mgr)
Marc Hatchel (Principal)
Tim Potter (Principal)
Gary Sullivan (Gen Mgr)
R. Chandler White (VP)
Steve White Jr. (Pres)

STEVE'S CHEVROLET OF CHOWCHILL, LLC.
1 Auto Park Pl, Chowchilla, CA 93610-9375
Tel.: (559) 665-3701
Web Site:
http://www.steveschevroletchowchilla.com
Sales Range: $10-24.9 Million
Emp.: 22
Car Whslr
N.A.I.C.S.: 441110
Wayne Chapman (Gen Mgr)
Brett V. Steves (Pres)

STEVE'S EQUIPMENT SERVICE, INC.
1400 Powis Rd, West Chicago, IL 60185
Tel.: (630) 231-4840
Web Site: http://www.sesequip.com
Year Founded: 1968
Sales Range: $10-24.9 Million
Emp.: 40
Sales & Rental of General Construction Machinery & Equipment
N.A.I.C.S.: 423810
Steve L. Martines (Pres)

STEVEN DOUGLAS ASSOCIATES, INC.
1301 International Pkwy Ste 510, Sunrise, FL 33323
Tel.: (954) 385-8595   FL
Web Site:
http://www.stevendouglas.com
Year Founded: 1984
Employment Agency
N.A.I.C.S.: 541612
Steven Sadaka (Founder & Chm)
Matt Shore (CEO)
Mark Viner (Pres-Interim Resources)
Steve Kalisher (Exec VP)
Karen Melby (VP-Minneapolis)
Julie Zorn (VP-Fin Svcs Search)
Ross Cohen (Mgr-Fin & Acctg Search)
Carol Stewart (Dir-Client Svc)
Elizabeth Jacobs (Exec VP)
Jonathan Bolton (Sr VP-New York)
Dan Hafetz (Sr VP-Interim Resources)
Jamie Javorsky (Sr VP-Tech South Florida)
Sylvia Alvarez (CFO)
Tammy L. Curtis (Mng Dir-Interim Resources)
Don Zinn (VP-Exec Search)
John Gramer (VP-Exec Search-Princeton)
Kirk Bukowski (VP-Exec Search-Boston)
Bradley Swisher (Mng Dir-Tech Search-San Diego)

Angelica Chadwick (Head-Tech Search Practice-Central Florida)
Craig Lewis (Sr VP-Interim Resources Division)
Vivian Gonzalez-Padilla (Mng Dir-Search Div)

Subsidiaries:

Tallience LLC   (1)
123 NW 13th St, Boca Raton, FL 33432
Tel.: (954) 229-1070
Web Site: http://www.tallience.com
Staffing, Recruiting & Consulting Services
N.A.I.C.S.: 561311
Tim Baron (Mng Partner)

STEVEN ENGINEERING, INC.
230 Ryan Way, South San Francisco, CA 94080
Tel.: (650) 588-9200
Web Site:
http://www.stevenengineering.com
Year Founded: 1975
Sales Range: $10-24.9 Million
Emp.: 100
Industrial Controls & Components Distr
N.A.I.C.S.: 423690
Scott A. Wolfgram (Mgr-Contract Mfg)
Thomas J. Fletcher (Mgr-Technical Svcs)
Carrie Casillas (Mgr-HR)
Paul E. Burk III (VP-Mktg)

STEVEN LABEL CORPORATION
11926 Burke St, Santa Fe Springs, CA 90670
Tel.: (562) 698-9971
Web Site:
http://www.stevenlabel.com
Rev.: $14,992,453
Emp.: 100
Letterpress Printing
N.A.I.C.S.: 323111
Steve Stong (Pres)
Lane McGinnis (VP-Ops)
Randy Santos (Controller)
Rob Henderson (Plant Mgr)

STEVEN MOTOR GROUP
11028 W Kellogg St, Wichita, KS 67209
Tel.: (316) 773-2002
Web Site:
http://www.stevenmotors.com
Sales Range: $10-24.9 Million
Emp.: 100
Car Whslr
N.A.I.C.S.: 441110
Regan Hunt (Mgr-Sls)

STEVEN ROBERTS ORIGINAL DESSERTS LLC.
2780 Tower Rd, Aurora, CO 80011
Tel.: (303) 375-9925
Web Site:
http://www.originaldesserts.com
Sales Range: $75-99.9 Million
Emp.: 850
Frozen Dessert Mfr & Distr
N.A.I.C.S.: 311813
Charles Kosmont (Owner)
Paula Karabell (Dir-Innovation & Dev)

STEVEN TOYOTA SCION
2970 S Main St, Harrisonburg, VA 22801
Tel.: (540) 434-1400
Web Site:
http://www.steventoyota.com
Sales Range: $10-24.9 Million
Emp.: 100
Car Whslr
N.A.I.C.S.: 441110
Andria Jackson (COO)
Steven D. Sodikoff (Pres)

STEVEN WALKER COMMUNITIES, INC
7111 Indiana Ave Ste 300, Riverside, CA 92504-4557
Tel.: (951) 784-0840
Sales Range: $10-24.9 Million
Emp.: 25
Subdividers & Developers
N.A.I.C.S.: 237210
Steve Berzansky (Pres)

STEVEN WINTER ASSOCIATES, INC.
61 Washington St, Norwalk, CT 06854
Tel.: (203) 857-0200
Web Site: http://www.swinter.com
Year Founded: 1972
Emp.: 130
Architectural Services
N.A.I.C.S.: 541310
Steven Winter (Founder & Chm)
Maureen Mahle (Mng Dir-Sustainable Housing Svcs)
Andrea Foss (Dir-Sustainability Svcs)
Cynthia Gardstein (Sr VP)
Dianne Griffiths (Exec VP)
Marc Zuluaga (VP & Dir-Multifamily Energy Svcs)
Paula Zimin (Dir-Simulation Svcs)
Peter A. Stratton (Sr VP & Dir-Accessibility Compliance & Consulting Grp)
Ryan Merkin (VP & Dir-Multifamily Energy Svcs)
William Zoeller (Sr VP)

Subsidiaries:

Everyday Green LLC (1)
1877 Ingleside Ter NW, Washington, DC 20010-1009
Tel.: (202) 640-1058
Web Site: http://www.everydaygreendc.com
Building Science Consulting Services
N.A.I.C.S.: 541310
Andrea Foss (Founder & Mng Partner)

STEVENS & STEVENS BUSINESS RECORDS MANAGEMENT, INC.
11515 53rd St N, Clearwater, FL 33760
Tel.: (727) 573-3900 FL
Web Site: http://www.ssbrm.com
Year Founded: 1994
Sales Range: $1-9.9 Million
Emp.: 60
Business Records Storage & Management Services
N.A.I.C.S.: 493190
R. Marshall Stevens (Pres)

STEVENS ADVERTISING
190 Monroe Ave NW Ste 200, Grand Rapids, MI 49503
Tel.: (616) 942-2801
Web Site: http://www.stevensinc.com
Year Founded: 1921
Sales Range: $10-24.9 Million
Emp.: 10
N.A.I.C.S.: 541810
Mike Muller (Exec VP)
Allen Crater (Pres)
Jenna Von Wagner (Acct Exec)
Elaine Oberland (CFO)
Charla Proctor (Sr Dir-Art)
Diane Rivard (Dir-Media)
Ken Avink (Dir-Creative)
Lisa Decker (Acct Exec)
Becky Stencel (Mgr-Project)

STEVENS AVIATION INC.
600 Delaware St, Greenville, SC 29605
Tel.: (864) 879-6000
Web Site: http://www.stevensaviation.com
Sales Range: $100-124.9 Million
Emp.: 35
Aircraft Cleaning & Janitorial Service
N.A.I.C.S.: 561720
Thomas C. Foley (Chm)
Neal McGrail (COO)
Jim Williams (VP)
Ryan Cothran (Gen Mgr)
Thomas D. Grunbeck (VP-Sls & Mktg)
Paul Witt (Exec VP-Ops)
Randy Smith (VP-Mobile Maintenance Svcs)

STEVENS COMMUNICATIONS INC.
11 S La Salle St Ste 2155, Chicago, IL 60603-1337
Tel.: (312) 895-5200
Web Site: http://www.stevenscom.com
Sales Range: $10-24.9 Million
Emp.: 10
Call Center Applications & Consulting Services
N.A.I.C.S.: 423690
Steven David Kaiser (CEO)

STEVENS COMMUNITY MEDICAL CENTER
400 E 1st St, Morris, MN 56267
Tel.: (320) 589-1313 MN
Web Site: http://www.scmcinc.org
Year Founded: 1984
Sales Range: $25-49.9 Million
Emp.: 369
Healthcare Services
N.A.I.C.S.: 622110
Kerrie Mcevilly (Dir-Fin)

STEVENS CONSTRUCTION CORP
PO Box 7726, Madison, WI 53707
Tel.: (608) 222-5100
Web Site: http://www.stevensconstruction.com
Rev.: $71,381,336
Emp.: 90
Commercial & Office Building, New Construction
N.A.I.C.S.: 236220
David Torkelson (Sr Mgr-Preconstruction)
Mark Rudnicki (CEO & Treas)
Geoffrey Vine (Pres)
Brian Wagner (VP-Preconstruction Svcs)
Michelle Rose (Dir-Bus Dev)

STEVENS CONSTRUCTION, INC.
6208 Whiskey Creek Dr, Fort Myers, FL 33919
Tel.: (239) 936-9006 FL
Web Site: http://www.stevensconstructioninc.com
Year Founded: 2003
Sales Range: $10-24.9 Million
Emp.: 19
Commercial Construction
N.A.I.C.S.: 236220
Mark Stevens (Founder)
Troy Hernly (VP-Central Florida)
Terri Sobeck (Controller)

STEVENS CREEK QUARRY INC.
12100 Stevens Canyon Rd, Cupertino, CA 95014
Tel.: (408) 253-2512
Web Site: http://www.scqinc.com
Year Founded: 1954
Sales Range: $50-74.9 Million
Emp.: 110
Provider of Highway & Street Construction Services
N.A.I.C.S.: 237310
Richard Voss (Pres)
Jose Gonzalez (Mgr-Equipment)

STEVENS CREEK VOLKSWAGEN
4490 Stevens Creek Blvd, San Jose, CA 95129
Tel.: (408) 492-1200
Web Site: http://www.scvw.com
Sales Range: $75-99.9 Million
Emp.: 60
New & Used Car Dealers
N.A.I.C.S.: 441110
Mike Gabbani (Gen Mgr-Sls)

STEVENS ENGINEERS & CONSTRUCTORS
7850 Freeway Cir Ste 100, Cleveland, OH 44130
Tel.: (440) 234-7888 OH
Web Site: http://www.stevensec.com
Year Founded: 1970
Sales Range: $50-74.9 Million
Emp.: 500
Industrial Buildings & Warehouses
N.A.I.C.S.: 236210
Vicki Anderson (Treas)
John Roberts (Coord-Mechanical)
Chet Seroka (Gen Mgr-Cleveland & Ops)
Eric Mays (Project Mgr)
Paul Stroz (Dir-Capital Projects)

Subsidiaries:

Continental Design & Management Group Inc. (1)
150 Technology Dr, Canonsburg, PA 15317-9563
Tel.: (724) 873-1200
Sales Range: $10-24.9 Million
Emp.: 100
Engineeering Services
N.A.I.C.S.: 541330

STEVENS GROUP, INC.
527 W Morley Dr, Saginaw, MI 48601
Tel.: (989) 755-3000 MI
Web Site: http://www.stevensworldwide.com
Year Founded: 1905
Emp.: 500
Trucking Service
N.A.I.C.S.: 484210
Lindsey Stevens Eggers (Pres & COO)
Joe Biskner (Exec VP)
Jan Price (VP-Human Relations)
Roger Wise (VP-Sls & Mktg)
Nicole Fox (Controller)
Morrison Stevens Sr. (Chm & CEO)
Morrie Stevens Jr. (VP-Comml Agency Div)

Subsidiaries:

Ace Van Lines Inc. (1)
527 W Morley Dr, Saginaw, MI 48601
Tel.: (989) 755-3000
Web Site: http://www.acevanlines.com
Sales Range: $10-24.9 Million
Emp.: 110
Provider of Trucking Services
N.A.I.C.S.: 484210
Morrison Stevens (Pres)
Gicget Keeser (Controller)

Advantage Forwarders Inc. (1)
527 W Morley Dr, Saginaw, MI 48601
Tel.: (989) 755-3000
Sales Range: $10-24.9 Million
Emp.: 110
Trucking Service
N.A.I.C.S.: 484210
Morrison Stevens (Pres)

Burnham World Forwarders Inc. (1)
527 W Morley Dr, Saginaw, MI 48601
Tel.: (989) 755-3000
Web Site: http://www.stevensworldwide.com
Sales Range: $25-49.9 Million
Provider of Trucking Services
N.A.I.C.S.: 484210

JS Financial Services Co., Inc. (1)
527 W Morley Dr, Saginaw, MI 48601
Tel.: (989) 755-3000
Web Site: http://www.svlonline.com
Sales Range: $25-49.9 Million
Provider of Bookkeeping Services
N.A.I.C.S.: 541219
Joe Biskner (Pres)

Patriot Forwarders Inc. (1)
527 W Morley Dr, Saginaw, MI 48601
Tel.: (989) 755-3000
Web Site: http://www.stevensworldwide.com
Sales Range: $10-24.9 Million
Emp.: 110
Provider of Trucking Services
N.A.I.C.S.: 484210
Jo Biskner (VP)

Stevens Forwarders Inc. (1)
527 W Morley Dr, Saginaw, MI 48601
Tel.: (989) 755-3000
Web Site: http://www.stevensworldwide.com
Sales Range: $10-24.9 Million
Emp.: 115
Provider of Trucking Services
N.A.I.C.S.: 488510
Morrison Stevens (Owner)

Stevens Transportation Co. Inc. (1)
527 W Morley Dr, Saginaw, MI 48601 (100%)
Tel.: (989) 755-3000
Web Site: http://www.stevensworldwide.com
Sales Range: $25-49.9 Million
Provider of Trucking Services
N.A.I.C.S.: 484210
Joe Stevens (Pres)

Stevens Van Lines Inc. (1)
527 W Morley Dr, Saginaw, MI 48601
Tel.: (989) 755-3000
Web Site: http://www.stevensworldwide.com
Sales Range: $10-24.9 Million
Emp.: 130
Provider of Trucking Services
N.A.I.C.S.: 484210
Morrison Stevens (Pres & CEO)

STEVENS INDUSTRIES, INC.
704 W Main St, Teutopolis, IL 62467-1212
Tel.: (217) 857-7100
Web Site: http://www.stevensind.com
Year Founded: 1956
Laminated Panels, Furniture & Cabinets Mfr
N.A.I.C.S.: 337211
Todd Wegman (Pres)
Mike Gibson (VP-Sls & Mktg)
Amanda Emmerich (Coord-Mktg)

Subsidiaries:

LSI Corporation of America, Inc. (1)
704 West Main Street Teutopolis, Effingham, IL 62467
Tel.: (763) 559-4664
Web Site: http://www.lsi-casework.com
Laminate Casework Systems & Related Products Mfr
N.A.I.C.S.: 337127

STEVENS KOENIG REPORTING
700 17th St Ste 1750, Denver, CO 80202
Tel.: (303) 988-8470
Web Site: http://www.skreporting.com
Emp.: 10
Court Reporting Service
N.A.I.C.S.: 561492
Judy Stevens (Pres)

Subsidiaries:

Avery Woods Reporting Service (1)
455 Sherman St Ste 250, Denver, CO 80203-4409
Tel.: (303) 825-6119

Stevens Koenig Reporting—(Continued)

Web Site: http://www.averywoods.net
Court Reporting & Stenotype Services
N.A.I.C.S.: 561492
Bonnie Nikolas (Office Mgr)

STEVENS MARINE INC.
9180 SW Burnham St, Tigard, OR 97223
Tel.: (503) 620-7023
Web Site:
http://www.stevensmarine.com
Year Founded: 1971
Sales Range: $10-24.9 Million
Emp.: 50
Marine Supplies
N.A.I.C.S.: 441222
Paul Mayer (Pres)
Dan Gruss (Controller)

STEVENS OFFICE INTERIORS
6804 Manlius Ctr Rd E, Syracuse, NY 13057
Tel.: (315) 472-2955
Web Site:
http://www.stevensinteriors.com
Sales Range: $10-24.9 Million
Emp.: 34
Furniture & Related Product Distr
N.A.I.C.S.: 449110
Ralph Placito (Sr Acct Mgr)
Maugeri Tom (Owner)

STEVENS STRATEGIC COMMUNICATIONS, INC.
Gemini Towers, Ste 500, 1991 Crocker Rd, Westlake, OH 44115-1900
Tel.: (440) 617-0100
Web Site:
http://www.stevensstrategic.com
Year Founded: 1973
Sales Range: $10-24.9 Million
Emp.: 12
Advetising Agency
N.A.I.C.S.: 541810
Edward M. Stevens (Chm & CEO)
Sally Stevens (Exec VP)
Julie Osborne (VP)
Anne Pillot (Dir-Art)
David Walker (Pres)

STEVENS TRANSPORT INC.
9757 Military Pkwy, Dallas, TX 75227-4805
Tel.: (972) 289-1611
Web Site:
http://www.stevenstransport.com
Year Founded: 1969
Sales Range: $25-49.9 Million
Emp.: 3,500
Trucking Except Local
N.A.I.C.S.: 484121
Steven L. Aaron (Chm & CEO)
Audie Delgado (Mgr-Svc)
Scott Sparr (Dir-Fuel)
Robert Solimani (VP-Ops)
Todd Aaron (Vice Chm)
Bennett Aaron (VP-Contractor Div)

STEVENS' CYCLE SALES INC.
3636 S Huron Rd, Bay City, MI 48706
Tel.: (989) 684-9872
Web Site:
http://www.stevenscycle.com
Rev.: $11,000,000
Emp.: 35
Retailer of Snowmobiles
N.A.I.C.S.: 441227
William A. Stevens Sr. (Pres)

STEVENSON THE COLOR COMPANY
535 Wilmer Ave, Cincinnati, OH 45226
Tel.: (513) 321-7500
Web Site:
http://www.stevensoncolor.com
Sales Range: $10-24.9 Million
Emp.: 190
Color Printing Services
N.A.I.C.S.: 323120
Andrew Stevenson (VP)
Tom Stevenson (Pres & CEO)

STEVES & SONS, INC.
203 Humble St, San Antonio, TX 78225
Tel.: (210) 924-5111
Web Site:
http://www.stevesdoors.com
Year Founded: 1866
Sales Range: $150-199.9 Million
Emp.: 400
Mfr of Doors & Frames
N.A.I.C.S.: 321911
Sam Steves (Pres & COO)
Edward Galt Steves (CEO)
Chris Metaldoors (Chm)

STEVES CHEVROLET-BUICK, INC.
PO Box 575, Oakdale, CA 95361
Tel.: (209) 847-2261
Web Site:
http://www.steveschevroletbuick.com
Sales Range: $10-24.9 Million
Emp.: 45
Car Whslr
N.A.I.C.S.: 441110
Brett Steves (Gen Mgr & VP)
Jeff Steves (Pres)

STEVINSON AUTOMOTIVE INC.
1726 Cole Blvd Ste 300, Lakewood, CO 80401
Tel.: (303) 232-2006
Web Site:
http://www.stevinsonauto.com
Year Founded: 1962
Rev.: $148,900,000
Emp.: 600
New & Used Car Dealers
N.A.I.C.S.: 441110
Kent P. Stevinson (Pres & CEO)

Subsidiaries:
Denver West Leasing (1)
1546 Cole Blvd, Lakewood, CO 80401
Tel.: (303) 232-8100
Rev.: $390,000
Emp.: 3
Passenger Car Leasing
N.A.I.C.S.: 532490

Stevinson Chevrolet-West Inc (1)
15000 W Colefax Ave, Lakewood, CO 80401
Tel.: (303) 279-3311
Web Site:
http://www.stevinsonautomotive.com
Emp.: 70
Automobiles, New & Used
N.A.I.C.S.: 441110
Kent E. Stevinson (Pres & CEO)

Stevinson Imports Inc (1)
5500 S Broadway, Littleton, CO 80121
Tel.: (303) 794-3550
Web Site: http://www.stevinsonimports.com
Emp.: 85
Automobiles, New & Used
N.A.I.C.S.: 441110
Kent Stevenson (Owner)

Stevinson Lexus of Lakewood (1)
801 Indiana St, Lakewood, CO 80401
Tel.: (303) 277-9339
Web Site:
http://www.stevinsonlexusoflakewood.com
Automobile Dealers
N.A.I.C.S.: 441120
April Floyd (Asst Mgr-Svc)
Dwaine Croft (Mgr-Svc)
Derek Puckett (Mgr-New Sls)
Jerry Amaya (Mgr-Sls)
Pete Souvall (Mgr-Fin)
William Johnson (Gen Mgr)

Stevinson Toyota East Scion Inc. (1)
444 S Havana St, Aurora, CO 80012
Tel.: (303) 340-2170
Web Site:
http://www.stevinsonstoyotaeast.com
Automobiles, New & Used
N.A.I.C.S.: 441110
Kent Stevinson (Pres)

Stevinson Toyota-West Inc (1)
780 Indiana St, Lakewood, CO 80401
Tel.: (303) 277-0550
Web Site: http://www.stevinsonauto.com
Automobiles, New & Used
N.A.I.C.S.: 441210

STEVVA CORPORATION
112 N Curry St, Carson City, NV 89703
Tel.: (775) 321-8225
Web Site:
http://www.homierecipes.com
Year Founded: 2012
Emp.: 1
Recipe Website
N.A.I.C.S.: 513199

STEW HANSEN HYUNDAI
11344 Hickman Rd, Des Moines, IA 50325
Tel.: (515) 253-3000
Web Site:
http://www.stewhansenhyundai.com
Year Founded: 2011
Sales Range: $125-149.9 Million
Emp.: 175
Car Whslr
N.A.I.C.S.: 441110
Daniel Boettcher (Gen Mgr)
Tracy Crowell (Office Mgr)

STEW LEONARD'S
100 Westport Ave, Norwalk, CT 06851-3915
Tel.: (203) 847-7214
Web Site:
http://www.stewleonards.com
Year Founded: 1969
Sales Range: $125-149.9 Million
Emp.: 2,000
Grocery Stores
N.A.I.C.S.: 445110
Vince Summa (CFO & Exec VP)
Doug Hempstead (Dir-Ops)
Meghan Bell (VP-PR)
Stew Leonard Jr. (Pres & CEO)

STEWARD CONSTRUCTION SERVICES, LLC
4249 Diplomacy Dr, Columbus, OH 43228
Tel.: (614) 679-2721
Web Site: http://www.steward-construction.com
Year Founded: 2014
Sales Range: $10-24.9 Million
Emp.: 9
Construction Services
N.A.I.C.S.: 236220
Rob Steward (Owner)

STEWARD HEALTH CARE SYSTEM LLC
1900 N Pearl St Ste 2400, Dallas, TX 75201
Tel.: (469) 341-8800
Web Site: http://www.steward.org
Year Founded: 2010
Emp.: 40,000
Hospital Management Services
N.A.I.C.S.: 622110
Ralph de la Torre (Chm & CEO)
Mark Rich (Pres)
Brian Carty (CMO)
Nadine Delicata (COO-Malta)
John Bezzina (Dir-HR-Malta)
Lindsay Smelser (VP-Mktg)
Joseph Weinstein (Chief Medical Officer)
Herb Holtz (Gen Counsel & Exec VP)
John Doyle (CFO)
John Polanowicz (COO)
Julie Berry (CIO)
Karren Murray (Chief Compliance Officer & Sr VP)
Patrick Lombardo (Exec VP-HR)
Laura Tortorella (Exec VP-Ops)
Armin Ernst (Pres-Steward Health Care Intl)
Ruben Jose King-Shaw Jr. (Chief Strategy - Officer-Steward Health Care Network & Pres-)

Subsidiaries:
Odessa Regional Medical Center (1)
520 E 6th St, Odessa, TX 79761
Tel.: (432) 582-8000
Web Site:
http://www.odessaregionalmedicalcenter.org
Emp.: 700
General Medical & Surgical Hospitals
N.A.I.C.S.: 622110
Stacey L. Brown (CEO)

Steward Easton Hospital, Inc. (1)
250 S 21st St, Easton, PA 18042-3892
Tel.: (610) 250-4000
Web Site: http://www.easton-hospital.org
Hospital Operator
N.A.I.C.S.: 622110
Linda Grass (Pres)
Tom Muller (Chm)

Steward Hillside Rehabilitation Hospital, Inc. (1)
8747 Squires Ln NE, Warren, OH 44484
Tel.: (330) 841-3700
Web Site:
http://www.hillsiderehabhospital.org
Rehabilitation Specialty Hospital Operator
N.A.I.C.S.: 622310

Steward Melbourne Hospital, Inc. (1)
250 N Wickham Rd, Melbourne, FL 32935-8625
Tel.: (321) 752-1200
Web Site: http://www.melbourneregional.org
Medical Devices
N.A.I.C.S.: 622110
Ron Gicca (Pres)
Daniel St. Armand (Chief Nursing Officer)
JoDee Alverson (Chief Quality Officer)

Steward Rockledge Hospital, Inc. (1)
110 Longwood Ave, Rockledge, FL 32955-2828
Tel.: (321) 636-2211
Web Site: http://www.rockledgeregional.org
Medical Devices
N.A.I.C.S.: 622110
Andy Romine (Pres)
Mary Sue Zinsmeister (Chief Nursing Officer)
Dale Armour (CFO)
ALison Patterson (Chief Quality Officer)

Steward Sebastian River Medical Center, Inc. (1)
13695 US Hwy 1, Sebastian, FL 32958
Tel.: (772) 589-3186
Web Site:
http://www.sebastianrivermedical.org
Hospital Services
N.A.I.C.S.: 622110
Kelly Enriquez (Pres)

Steward Sharon Regional Health System, Inc. (1)
740 E State St, Sharon, PA 16146-3328
Tel.: (724) 983-3911
Web Site:
http://www.sharonregionalmedical.org
Health Care Srvices
N.A.I.C.S.: 622110
Karen Winner Sed (Chm)
David L. D'Amore (Vice Chm)
Joseph G. Hugar (Sec)

Steward Trumbull Memorial Hospital, Inc. (1)

1350 E Market St, Warren, OH 44482
Tel.: (330) 841-9011
Web Site: http://www.trumbullregional.org
Health Care Srvices
N.A.I.C.S.: 622110
Ron Bierman (Pres)

Youngstown Ohio Physician Services Company, LLC (1)
500 Gypsy Ln, Youngstown, OH 44504-1315
Tel.: (404) 849-1774
Web Site: http://www.healthcare4ppl.com
Health Care Srvices
N.A.I.C.S.: 622110

STEWARD MARKETING, LLC
9595 Six Pines Ste 8210, The Woodlands, TX 77380
Tel.: (832) 955-1056
Web Site:
http://www.stewardmarketing.com
Year Founded: 2002
Rev.: $10,000,000
Emp.: 11
Advetising Agency
N.A.I.C.S.: 541810
James P. Alexander (Pres & CEO)
Bart Darling (Dir-Creative)

STEWARD PARTNERS GLOBAL ADVISORY, LLC
4949 Meadows Rd Ste 400, Lake Oswego, OR 97035
Tel.: (971) 353-9700
Web Site:
http://www.stewardpartnersis.com
Investment Services
N.A.I.C.S.: 523999
Mohan Gurupackiam (CIO)
Scott Baines (Partner & Sr VP)
Eric Field (Partner & Pres-West Coast Div)
Hy Saporta (Pres & COO)

Subsidiaries:

Steward Partners Investment Solutions, LLC (1)
1 SW Columbia St Ste 300, Portland, OR 97258 (100%)
Tel.: (503) 226-7000
Web Site:
http://www.umpquainvestments.com
Sales Range: $100-124.9 Million
Emp.: 70
Securities Brokers & Financial Advisors
N.A.I.C.S.: 523150
Jennifer Adelblue (Asst VP & Specialist-Acctg)
Jeani Winterbourne (Pres & COO)
J. Eric Field (CEO)
Sherrie Kerr (VP & Dir-Ops & Supervision)
Steven Chang (Chief Compliance Officer)
Tera Brown (VP & Mgr-Admin)
Ryan Brown (Asst VP & Ops Mgr)
Scott D. Baines (Sr VP-Investments)
David R. Balk (First VP-Investments)
Douglas P. Eikenberry (First VP-Investments)
Mark Hwee (First VP-Investments)
Brian Joelson (First VP-Investments)
Jeffrey D. Kantor (Sr VP-Investments)
Bill McShane (Sr VP-Investments)
Donald F. Murray (VP-Investments)
Tinh T. Nguyen (First VP-Investments)
Duane J. Rodewald (Sr VP-Investments)
Kevin G. Sahli (Sr VP-Investments)
David Stockton (VP-Investments)

STEWARD STEEL INC.
US Hwy 62 E, Sikeston, MO 63801
Tel.: (573) 471-2121
Web Site:
http://www.stewardsteel.com
Rev.: $16,000,000
Emp.: 100
Mfr of Steel
N.A.I.C.S.: 423510
Timothy Buchheit (Mgr-HR)

STEWART & TATE, INC.
950 Smile Way, York, PA 17404
Tel.: (410) 642-9166
Web Site:
http://www.stewartandtate.com
Sales Range: $25-49.9 Million
Emp.: 350
Highway & Street Construction
N.A.I.C.S.: 237310
Timothy R. Tate (Pres)
John L. Kerchner (Exec VP-Building Div)
Ron Koncar (VP-Indus Div)

Subsidiaries:

Henry H. Lewis Contractors LLC (1)
55 Gwynns Mill Ct, Owings Mills, MD 21117-3511 (100%)
Tel.: (410) 356-4200
Web Site: http://www.lewis-contractors.com
Sales Range: $10-24.9 Million
Emp.: 60
Construction Services
N.A.I.C.S.: 236220
Tyler Tate (Pres)

Riley Welding & Fabricating LLC (1)
234 Poplar St, Hanover, PA 17331
Tel.: (717) 637-6014
Web Site: http://www.rileywelding.com
Sales Range: $1-9.9 Million
Emp.: 15
Metal Welding, Fabrication & Repair Services
N.A.I.C.S.: 423510
Ron Orndorft (Mgr-Production)
Josh Barnhart (Mgr-Production)

STEWART BROS INC.
2480 Pleasantdale Rd, Atlanta, GA 30340
Tel.: (770) 447-5810
Web Site:
http://www.stewartbrotherspaving.com
Sales Range: $10-24.9 Million
Emp.: 10
Highway & Street Construction
N.A.I.C.S.: 237310
William Stewart (VP)
Scurry Laws (CFO)
Donald B. Stewart Jr. (Pres)

STEWART BUILDERS LTD
16575 Village Dr, Houston, TX 77040
Tel.: (713) 983-8002
Web Site:
http://www.keystoneconcrete.com
Sales Range: $100-124.9 Million
Emp.: 850
Concrete
N.A.I.C.S.: 238110
Donald G. Stewart (Pres)

STEWART C MILLER & CO. INC.
3440 Kossuth St, Lafayette, IN 47905
Tel.: (765) 447-8803
Web Site: http://www.scmiller.com
Rev.: $20,100,000
Emp.: 35
Accident & Health Insurance
N.A.I.C.S.: 524298
Stewart Miller (Pres)

STEWART CAPITAL PARTNERS LLC
6385 Old Shady Oak Rd Ste 270, Minneapolis, MN 55344
Tel.: (952) 835-7100
Web Site:
http://www.stewartcapitalpartners.com
Year Founded: 2006
Private Equity Firm Services
N.A.I.C.S.: 523999
Stewart R. Stender (Founder & Mng Partner)

Subsidiaries:

TC/American Crane Company (1)
11110 Industrial Cir NW Ste A, Elk River, MN 55330
Tel.: (763) 497-7000
Web Site: http://www.tcamerican.com
Cranes & Monorail Systems Designer, Mfr & Whslr
N.A.I.C.S.: 333923
Jeff Palkovich (CEO)

STEWART CORPORATION
130 E Wilson Bridge Rd Ste 150, Worthington, OH 43085
Tel.: (614) 891-4942
Web Site: http://www.trnj.com
Year Founded: 1969
Rev.: $20,104,677
Emp.: 30
Foreign Freight Forwarding
N.A.I.C.S.: 488510
Mark Stewart (Pres)

STEWART FILMSCREEN CORPORATION
1161 W Sepulveda Blvd, Torrance, CA 90502-2754
Tel.: (310) 784-5300
Web Site: http://www.stewartfilm.com
Sales Range: $25-49.9 Million
Emp.: 200
Projection Screen Mfr
N.A.I.C.S.: 334310
Patrick H. Stewart (CEO)
Diana Ha (Mgr-Ops)
Mark Robinson (VP-Tech)
Victoria Ferrari (Mgr-Reg Sls)
Stephanie Hunter (Mgr-Sls-Central Reg)
Zach Hurvitz (Mgr-Natl AV Consultant)
Grant Stewart (Pres)

Subsidiaries:

Stewart Filmscreen Corporation - Ohio (1)
3919 Bach Buxton Rd, Amelia, OH 45102
Tel.: (513) 753-0800
Web Site: http://www.stewartfilm.com
Sales Range: $10-24.9 Million
Emp.: 20
Projection Screen Mfr
N.A.I.C.S.: 334310
Grant Stewart (Owner)

STEWART GRAIN CO. INC.
8217 W 300 N, Williamsport, IN 47993
Tel.: (765) 986-2254
Web Site:
http://www.stewartgrain.com
Year Founded: 1922
Sales Range: $1-9.9 Million
Emp.: 9
Grains
N.A.I.C.S.: 424510
Burton E. Etchison (Pres)

STEWART MANAGEMENT GROUP INC.
20844 Harper Ave Ste 100, Harper Woods, MI 48225
Tel.: (734) 427-6200
Web Site: http://www.stewartmg.com
Rev.: $72,900,000
Emp.: 110
Automobiles, New & Used
N.A.I.C.S.: 441110
Craig Hale (Treas)

STEWART P. WILSON INC.
2050 State Rte 14, Montour Falls, NY 14865
Tel.: (607) 535-6532
Web Site:
http://www.stewartpwilsoninc.com
Rev.: $14,300,000

Emp.: 20
Petroleum Products
N.A.I.C.S.: 424720
Thomas G. Wade (Pres)
Diane Bond (Office Mgr)

STEWART SENTER INC.
333 Baldwin Rd, Hempstead, NY 11550
Tel.: (516) 486-7500
Web Site:
http://www.tennisplanning.com
Sales Range: $10-24.9 Million
Emp.: 75
Tennis Court Construction
N.A.I.C.S.: 236210
Stewart Senter (Pres)

STEWART STAINLESS SUPPLY INC.
3660 Swiftwater Park Dr, Suwanee, GA 30024
Tel.: (770) 925-0075
Web Site:
http://www.stewartstainless.com
Year Founded: 1982
Sales Range: $25-49.9 Million
Emp.: 100
Stainless Steel Distr
N.A.I.C.S.: 423510
Butch Stewart (Pres)
Tim Stewart (Gen Mgr)
Gordon Stone (Mgr-Sls)
Andy Johnston (Mgr)
Duane Humphries (Branch Mgr)
Maston Stewart (Branch Mgr)

STEWART'S SHOPS CORPORATION
2907 Route 9, Ballston Spa, NY 12020
Tel.: (518) 581-1200
Web Site:
http://www.stewartsshops.com
Year Founded: 1950
Sales Range: $1-4.9 Billion
Emp.: 2,990
Ice Cream & Dairy Products Mfr; Operator of Retail Convenience Stores
N.A.I.C.S.: 445131
Gary C. Dake (Pres)
Maria D'Amelia (Mgr-Mktg)
James Norton (VP)

STEWART'S SLEEP CENTER INC.
11750 S Cleveland Ave, Fort Myers, FL 33907
Tel.: (239) 275-3968
Web Site:
http://www.matterbrothersfurniture.com
Sales Range: $25-49.9 Million
Emp.: 150
Furniture Retailer
N.A.I.C.S.: 449110
Gary Matter (VP)
John Matter (Pres)

STEWART'S FOOD STORE INC.
102 Hwy 332, Brazoria, TX 77422
Tel.: (979) 798-2600
Rev.: $13,600,000
Emp.: 85
Grocery Stores
N.A.I.C.S.: 445110
Bubba Fink (Pres)

STEWART'S PRIVATE BLEND FOODS INC.
4110 W Wrightwood Ave, Chicago, IL 60639-2127
Tel.: (773) 489-2500
Web Site: http://www.stewarts.com
Year Founded: 1913

STEWART'S PRIVATE BLEND FOODS INC.

Stewart's Private Blend Foods Inc.—Continued
Sales Range: $1-9.9 Million
Emp.: 55
Coffee, Tea & Allied Foods Mfr
N.A.I.C.S.: 311920
Robert Stewart (Pres)
Bob Tomkins (Dir-Mktg)
Elita Pagan (Comptroller)

STEWART'S PROCESSING CORP
2907 RR 9, Ballston Spa, NY 12020
Tel.: (518) 581-1000
Web Site: http://www.stewartsshops.com
Sales Range: $25-49.9 Million
Emp.: 50
Fluid Milk
N.A.I.C.S.: 311511
Gary C. Dake (Pres)
Jim Norton (Controller)

STGI INC.
99 Canal Center Plz Ste 500, Alexandria, VA 22314
Tel.: (703) 578-6030
Web Site: http://www.stginternational.com
Sales Range: $25-49.9 Million
Emp.: 800
Business Management & Technical Services
N.A.I.C.S.: 561499
Michelle S. Lee (Pres & CEO)
Jeff Bell (COO & VP-Fin)

STHEALTH CAPITAL INVESTMENT CORP.
680 5th Ave 21st Fl, New York, NY 10019
Tel.: (212) 601-2769
Web Site: http://www.sthealthcapital.com
Year Founded: 2014
Rev.: $30,040
Assets: $3,140,160
Liabilities: $554,685
Net Worth: $2,585,475
Earnings: ($1,304,224)
Fiscal Year-end: 12/31/20
Investment Services
N.A.I.C.S.: 523999
Derek R. Taller (Chief Investment Officer)
Jeffrey Davi (Chm)

STI ELECTRONICS, INC.
261 Palmer Rd, Madison, AL 35758
Tel.: (256) 461-9191
Web Site: http://www.stielectronicsinc.com
Year Founded: 1982
Rev.: $14,200,000
Emp.: 50
Industrial Machinery Whslr
N.A.I.C.S.: 423830
David E. Raby (Pres)
Mary E. Raby (CFO)
Mark McMeen (VP)
Diana Bradford (VP-Ops & Trng Resources)
Kelli King (Mgr-Inside Sls)

STI OPTRONICS, INC.
2755 Northup Way, Bellevue, WA 98004-1403
Tel.: (425) 827-0460
Web Site: http://www.stioptronics.com
Year Founded: 1969
Sales Range: $50-74.9 Million
Emp.: 10
Government Contract Laser Research & Development
N.A.I.C.S.: 541715

Wayne D. Kimura (VP)
William Thayer III (Pres)

STICKLER CONSTRUCTION LLC
4401 Grand Cir, Crestwood, KY 40014
Tel.: (502) 233-7616
Web Site: http://www.sticklerllc.com
Home Remodeling & Renovation Services
N.A.I.C.S.: 236118
Joel Stickler (Owner)

STIDHAM TRUCKING INC.
321 Payne Ln, Yreka, CA 96097
Tel.: (530) 842-4161
Web Site: http://www.stidhamtrucking.com
Year Founded: 1963
Sales Range: $10-24.9 Million
Emp.: 150
Provider of Transportation Services
N.A.I.C.S.: 484121
Larry L. Stidham (Owner)
Mike Jones (Dir Gen)

STIEGLER, WELLS, BRUNSWICK & ROTH, INC.
3865 Adler Pl, Bethlehem, PA 18017-9000
Tel.: (610) 866-0611
Web Site: http://www.swbrinc.com
Year Founded: 1969
Sales Range: $1-9.9 Million
Emp.: 22
Advertising Agencies
N.A.I.C.S.: 541810
Ernie R. Stiegler (CEO)
Donna R. Sinko (VP-Production)
Henry R. Raab (VP-PR)
Scott Friedman (Pres & COO)
Debbie Drake (VP-Comm Plng)
Tom Doerfler (Co-Dir-Creative)
Donna Kopes (Office Mgr-Svcs)
Patti Merlo (Asst Controller)
Tony Susi (Assoc Dir-Art)
Mike Walbert (Dir-Strategic Comm)

STILES CORPORATION
301 E Las Olas Blvd, Fort Lauderdale, FL 33301-2295
Tel.: (954) 627-9300
Web Site: http://www.stiles.com
Year Founded: 1951
Sales Range: $75-99.9 Million
Emp.: 240
Office, Industrial & Retail Projects; Mixed-use Residential Construction; Real Estate Brokers; Landscaping Contractors; Architectural Services; Property Management
N.A.I.C.S.: 236210
Terry W. Stiles (Chm & Co-CEO)
Douglas Eagon (Pres)
Stephen R. Palmer (COO)
Robert Esposito (CFO)
Rocco Ferrera (Chief Investment Officer)
Kenneth Stiles (Co-CEO)
Robert Breslau (Chief Dev Officer)
Chris Rotolo (Pres-Property Mgmt)
Jeff Peal (Pres-Architectural Grp)
Timothy Moore (Pres-Construction)
Paul Marko (Pres-Realty)
Jeff McDonough (Pres-Stiles Residential Grp)
Mike Carpenter (VP)
Madelayne Garcia (Sr VP)
Brad Rabinowitz (VP-IT)
Lourdes Vidal (VP-Risk Mgmt)
Adrienne Zalkind (VP-Mktg)

STILES TRUCK LINE INC.
1901 Jasmine Dr, Pasadena, TX 77503

Tel.: (713) 472-0861
Web Site: http://www.stilestruckline.com
Sales Range: $25-49.9 Million
Emp.: 115
Heavy Hauling
N.A.I.C.S.: 484121
Kurt Stiles (Pres)

STILL WATERS DESIGN/BUILD GROUP
8551 Boatclub RD Ste 121-114, Fort Worth, TX 76179
Tel.: (817) 236-2090
Web Site: http://www.stillwatersinc.com
Year Founded: 1985
Sales Range: Less than $1 Million
Emp.: 4
Commercial & Residential Construction Services
N.A.I.C.S.: 238990
Gary Martinec (Co-Founder, VP & Dir-Field Ops)
Dinah Martinec (Co-Founder & Pres)
Brian Leggett (Dir-Project Mgmt)

STILLMAN BANCCORP N.A.
101 E Main St, Stillman Valley, IL 61084
Tel.: (815) 645-2266
Web Site: http://www.stillmanbank.com
Sales Range: $10-24.9 Million
Emp.: 101
Bank Holding Company
N.A.I.C.S.: 522110
Gary L. Rhodes (Chm & CEO)
Martin Larson (Pres)
Marilyn Janes (Supvr-Collateral)
Sherri Hayes (VP)
Jill Wheelock (Mgr-Mktg)

Subsidiaries:

Stillman Bank (1)
101 E Main St, Stillman Valley, IL 61084
Tel.: (815) 645-2266
Web Site: http://www.stillmanbank.com
Sales Range: $25-49.9 Million
Emp.: 35
Provider of Banking Services
N.A.I.C.S.: 522110
Martin Larson (Pres)

STILLWATER DESIGNS & AUDIO
3100 N Husband St, Stillwater, OK 74075
Tel.: (405) 624-8510
Web Site: http://www.kicker.com
Rev.: $13,200,000
Emp.: 200
Speaker Systems
N.A.I.C.S.: 334310
Steve M. Irby (Founder & Pres)
Bill Doering (Mgr-Electronic)
Diane Elliott Dyer (Mgr-HR)
Randy Davis (Mgr-Sls-Eastern Reg)

STILLWATER MILLING COMPANY INC.
512 E 6th Ave, Stillwater, OK 74074-3600
Tel.: (405) 372-3445
Web Site: http://www.stillwatermill.com
Year Founded: 1891
Sales Range: $25-49.9 Million
Emp.: 160
Mfr of Prepared Feeds
N.A.I.C.S.: 311119
David Fairbank (Pres)

STILLWELL ENTERPRISES, INC.
PO Box 635, Sylva, NC 28779
Tel.: (828) 586-6424

Sales Range: $10-24.9 Million
Emp.: 85
Utility Contracting Services
N.A.I.C.S.: 237110
Richard Stillwell (Pres)
Warren Stillwell (Sec)
George Stillwell (Treas)
William Stillwell (VP)

STILLWELL HANSEN INC.
3 Fernwood Ave, Edison, NJ 08837
Tel.: (732) 225-7474
Web Site: http://www.stillwell-hansen.com
Sales Range: $10-24.9 Million
Emp.: 60
Heating Equipment (Hydronic) & Air Conditioning
N.A.I.C.S.: 423720
Gordon Stillwell (Founder)
Carol Stillwell (Pres & CEO)
Christopher Post (Acct Mgr)
Chuck Hofmann (Acct Mgr)
Neal Pabst (Acct Mgr)
Len Giuliano (Acct Mgr)
Joe Mastropaolo (Acct Mgr)
Glenn Pabst (VP)
Keith Driscoll (Mgr-Sls)
Ken Pienkowski (Mgr-Parts)

STIMSON LUMBER COMPANY
520 SW Yamhill St Ste 700, Portland, OR 97204-1330
Tel.: (503) 222-1676
Web Site: http://www.stimsonlumber.com
Year Founded: 1931
Sales Range: $200-249.9 Million
Emp.: 2,000
Sawmills & Planing Mills
N.A.I.C.S.: 321113
Andrew Miller (Pres & CEO)
Greg Baumgardner (CTO)

Subsidiaries:

Stim-Air Inc. (1)
520 SW Yamhill St Ste 700, Portland, OR 97204-1326
Tel.: (503) 222-1676
Web Site: http://www.stimson.com
Sales Range: $1-9.9 Million
Equipment Rental & Leasing
N.A.I.C.S.: 532411
Andrew Miller (Pres)

Stimson Lumber Tillamook (1)
5900 Moffet Rd, Tillamook, OR 97141-9621
Tel.: (503) 842-4007
Web Site: http://www.stimsonlumber.com
Sales Range: $10-24.9 Million
Emp.: 120
Soft & Hardwood Lumber, Wood Products & By-Products
N.A.I.C.S.: 321113

STIMULANT
180 Capp St Ste 6, San Francisco, CA 94110
Tel.: (415) 255-7081
Web Site: http://www.stimulant.io
Year Founded: 2007
Sales Range: $1-9.9 Million
Emp.: 10
Grid Based Music Sequencing Software
N.A.I.C.S.: 513210
Darren David (Founder & CEO)
Jules Konig (Dir-Art)
Mark Coleran (Exec Dir-Creative)

STINE INC.
1509 S Huntington St, Sulphur, LA 70663
Tel.: (337) 527-0121
Web Site: http://www.stinelumber.com
Year Founded: 1945
Sales Range: $25-49.9 Million

COMPANIES

Emp.: 415
Producer of Lumber & Other Building Materials
N.A.I.C.S.: 423310
Dennis Stine *(Pres)*
Tim Stine *(CFO)*

Subsidiaries:

Stine & Lumber Inc. (1)
130 Wheelock St, Alexandria, LA 71301-7101
Tel.: (318) 442-7781
Web Site: http://www.stinelumber.com
Sales Range: $10-24.9 Million
Emp.: 20
Producer of Lumber & other Building Materials
N.A.I.C.S.: 423310

STINE LUMBER COMPANY
2950 Ruth St, Sulphur, LA 70663
Tel.: (337) 527-0121
Web Site: http://www.stinehome.com
Year Founded: 1954
Sales Range: $150-199.9 Million
Emp.: 750
Lumber & Building Material Whslr
N.A.I.C.S.: 444110
Jay Stine *(Bus Mgr)*
Tim Stine *(Comptroller)*
Dennis Stine *(Pres)*
David Stine *(VP)*

STINE SEED COMPANY
22555 Laredo Trl, Adel, IA 50003
Tel.: (515) 677-2605
Web Site: http://www.stineseed.com
Sales Range: $10-24.9 Million
Emp.: 15
Seeds & Bulbs
N.A.I.C.S.: 424910
Harry H. Stine *(Owner)*
Jerry Reckland *(CFO)*
Myron Stine *(VP-Sls)*
Jeff Anderson *(Dir-Sls-West)*

STING ALARM INC.
7120 Rafael Rdg Way, Las Vegas, NV 89119
Tel.: (702) 737-8464
Web Site: http://www.stingalarm.com
Year Founded: 2003
Sales Range: $1-9.9 Million
Emp.: 46
Security Alarm & Surveillance Systems
N.A.I.C.S.: 561621
Jonathan Fine *(Founder)*
Jon Perry *(Owner & Sr VP)*
Bob Gasner *(Gen Mgr)*
John Potter *(Mgr-Pur)*

STINKER STORES, INC.
3184 Elder St, Boise, ID 83705
Tel.: (208) 375-0942
Web Site: http://www.stinker.com
Year Founded: 1936
Supermarkets & Other Grocery, except Convenience, Stores
N.A.I.C.S.: 445110
Charley Jones *(Pres & Owner)*
Nancy Jones *(Owner & VP)*

Subsidiaries:

J.H. Kaspar Oil Co. (1)
305 16th St, Rawlins, WY 82301
Tel.: (800) 279-3748
Lubricants & Heating Oil Dealers
N.A.I.C.S.: 457210

Sav-O-Mat, Inc. (1)
7268 S Tucson Way, Englewood, CO 80112
Tel.: (303) 744-1711
Sales Range: $1-9.9 Million
Emp.: 42
Gasoline Stations
N.A.I.C.S.: 457120

STINSON LEONARD STREET LLP
7700 Forsyth Blvd Ste 1100, Saint Louis, MO 63105
Tel.: (314) 863-0800   MO
Web Site: http://www.stinson.com
Year Founded: 1995
Law firm
N.A.I.C.S.: 541110
Vaughan Butts *(Chief Risk Officer & CIO)*
Mark D. Hinderks *(Mng Partner)*
Allison M. Murdock *(Deputy Mng Partner)*
Shawn L. Adams *(COO)*
Emily Dalbec *(CFO)*
Ann Jenrette-Thomas *(Chief Diversity & Inclusion Officer)*
Heidi Burton *(Chief HR Officer)*

Subsidiaries:

Stinson Leonard Street LLP - Minneapolis (1)
50 S 6th St Ste 2600, Minneapolis, MN 55402
Tel.: (612) 335-1500
Web Site: http://www.stinsonleonard.com
Emp.: 200
Law firm
N.A.I.C.S.: 541110
Lowell V. Stortz *(Partner)*
Vaughan Butts *(Chief Risk Officer)*
Jill Weber *(CMO & Chief Bus Dev Officer)*
Ruth A. Rivard *(Partner)*
Heidi Burton *(Chief HR Officer)*
Jeremy Estenson *(Dir-Govt Rels)*
Bree Johnson *(Dir-Value Pricing & Legal Project Mgmt)*
Lynda Moore *(Chief Dev Officer & Chief Atty Recruiting Officer)*
Ann Jenrette-Thomas *(Chief Diversity & Inclusion Officer)*
Joel E. Abrahamson *(Partner)*
Kadee J. Anderson *(Partner)*
Phillip J. Ashfield *(Partner)*
David D. Axtell *(Partner)*
James J. Bertrand *(Partner)*
Douglas R. Boettge *(Partner)*
Traci V. Bransford *(Partner)*
James G. Bullard *(Partner)*
Jeffrey P. Cairns *(Partner)*
Edwin H. Caldie *(Partner)*
Donald T. Campbell *(Partner)*
Dominic J. Cecere *(Partner)*
Kevin D. Conneely *(Partner)*
Amy B. Conway *(Partner)*
Anne P. Cotter *(Partner)*
Benjamin J. Court *(Partner)*
David R. Crosby *(Partner)*
Andrew W. Davis *(Partner)*
Eileen M. Day *(Partner)*
Katherine E. Devlaminck *(Partner)*
Robert F. Devolve *(Partner)*
Tracey Holmes Donesky *(Partner)*
Christine Eid *(Partner)*
Nathan E. Endrud *(Partner)*
Jason Engelhart *(Partner)*
Mary P. Foarde *(Partner)*
Mary P. Foarde *(Partner)*

STIR ADVERTISING & INTEGRATED MARKETING
252 E Highland Ave, Milwaukee, WI 53202
Tel.: (414) 278-0040
Web Site: http://www.stirstuff.com
Year Founded: 2000
Sales Range: $10-24.9 Million
Emp.: 22
Advertising Agencies
N.A.I.C.S.: 541810
Brian Bennett *(Owner-Strategic Plng)*

STIRISTA, LLC
16414 San Pedro Ave Ste 150, San Antonio, TX 78232
Tel.: (210) 293-0029
Web Site: http://www.stirista.com
Year Founded: 2009
Sales Range: $1-9.9 Million
Advertising & Marketing Services

N.A.I.C.S.: 541810
Richard Zimmer *(VP-Brands & Creative)*
Ajay Gupta *(CEO)*
Brian Wool *(Chief Revenue Officer)*
David Bailey *(VP-Sls)*
Candice Cochran Gupta *(VP)*
Jane Diane Hasse *(Dir-HR)*
Anthony Lucia *(CTO)*

Subsidiaries:

Customer Portfolios, LLC (1)
306 Northern Ave, Boston, MA 02210
Tel.: (617) 224-9501
Web Site: http://www.customerportfolios.com
Rev.: $2,600,000
Emp.: 10
Administrative Management & General Management Consulting Service
N.A.I.C.S.: 541611
Augie Maccurrach *(CEO & Founder)*

ZDI Images & Motion Inc. (1)
121 W Oak Street, Amityville, NY 11701
Tel.: (631) 667-5595
Web Site: http://www.zdidesigngroup.com
Computer System Design Services
N.A.I.C.S.: 541512

STIRLING HOTELS & RESORTS, INC.
14185 Dallas Pkwy Ste 1200, Dallas, TX 75254
Tel.: (972) 490-9600   MD
Year Founded: 2023
Resort Operator
N.A.I.C.S.: 721120

STIVERS SUBARU
1950 Orion Dr, Decatur, GA 30033-4307
Tel.: (404) 248-1888
Web Site: http://www.stiversatlantasubaru.com
Sales Range: $10-24.9 Million
Emp.: 25
Car Whslr
N.A.I.C.S.: 441110

STIVERS TEMPORARY PERSONNEL INC.
200 W Monroe St Ste 1300, Chicago, IL 60606-5008
Tel.: (312) 558-3550   IL
Web Site: http://www.stivers.com
Year Founded: 1945
Sales Range: $10-24.9 Million
Emp.: 60
Provider of Staffing Services
N.A.I.C.S.: 561320
Sue Berry *(CFO)*

STM AUTOMOTIVE
3410 Pacheco Blvd, Martinez, CA 94553
Tel.: (925) 372-4890
Web Site: http://www.spauto.com
Rev.: $11,900,000
Emp.: 31
Automotive Supplies & Parts
N.A.I.C.S.: 423120
Lynn Morales *(Office Mgr)*

STM INDUSTRIES, INC.
1712 8th St Dr SE, Hickory, NC 28602
Tel.: (828) 325-2700
Year Founded: 1996
Sales Range: $200-249.9 Million
Emp.: 800
Holding Company; Adhesive Tape Mfr
N.A.I.C.S.: 551112
A. Pope Shuford *(Pres)*
Stephen Shuford *(Vice Chm)*

Subsidiaries:

Shurtape Technologies, LLC (1)

1712 8th St Dr SE, Hickory, NC 28602
Tel.: (828) 322-2700
Web Site: http://www.shurtapetech.com
Emp.: 1,500
Adhesive Including Tape Mfr
N.A.I.C.S.: 325520
Kevin Stamets *(VP-Industrial Mktg-Industrial Grp)*
Bill Kahl *(Exec VP-Mktg)*
Vuk Trivanovic *(CEO)*

Subsidiary (Domestic):

Shurtape Specialty Coating, LLC (2)
29 Industrial Park Rd, New Hartford, CT 06057
Tel.: (860) 738-2600
Web Site: http://www.syntacusa.com
Emp.: 50
Specialty Adhesive Coated Products Mfr
N.A.I.C.S.: 325520
Stephen Shuford *(CEO)*

STO BUILDING GROUP INC.
330 W 34th St, New York, NY 10001
Tel.: (212) 481-6100   DE
Web Site: https://stobuildinggroup.com
Year Founded: 2016
Emp.: 4,789
Holding Company; Construction Services
N.A.I.C.S.: 551112
Eugene Peter White *(Exec VP-Client Rels)*
John White Jr. *(COO-Structure Tone)*
James K. Donaghy *(Chm)*
Robert W. Mullen *(CEO)*
Rebecca Leonardis *(Sr VP-Mktg & Comm)*
Greg Dunkle *(COO)*
Terrence Robbins *(CIO & Sr VP)*
Brett Phillips *(CFO)*

Subsidiaries:

L.F. Driscoll Company LLC (1)
9 Presidential Blvd, Bala Cynwyd, PA 19004-1003
Tel.: (610) 668-0950
Web Site: http://www.lfdriscoll.com
Sales Range: $25-49.9 Million
Emp.: 230
Contracting & Construction Services
N.A.I.C.S.: 236220
Robert Miller *(Exec VP)*
Frank M. Stulb *(Pres)*
Michael F. Delaney *(Exec VP-Estimating & Pur)*
Al Fazzini *(Dir-Mktg)*
Ken J. Innella *(VP)*
Al Fazzini *(Dir-Mktg)*
John J. Donnelly *(CEO)*
John DeFazio *(VP)*
Thomas McDonald *(VP)*

Layton Construction Company, LLC (1)
9090 S Sandy Pkwy, Sandy, UT 84070-6409
Tel.: (801) 568-9090
Web Site: http://www.laytonconstruction.com
Sales Range: $50-74.9 Million
Emp.: 850
Nonresidential Construction
N.A.I.C.S.: 236210
David S. Layton *(Pres & CEO)*
Jeff Beecher *(VP)*
Alan Rindlisbacher *(Dir-Mktg)*
Trevor Ford *(Coord-Safety)*
Penny Dennis *(Mgr-Bus Dev & Preconstruction-Boise)*
Chris Bardan *(VP)*
Roy Catalani *(VP-Bus Dev)*
Thomas Smith *(Dir-Bus Dev-South California)*
John Thornton *(Exec VP-South California)*

Pavarini Construction Co. Inc. (1)
8174 W 26th Ave, Hialeah, FL 33016
Tel.: (954) 903-3700
Web Site: http://www.pavarini.com
Sales Range: $25-49.9 Million
Emp.: 300
Residential & Commercial Construction Services

STO BUILDING GROUP INC.

U.S. PRIVATE

STO Building Group Inc.—(Continued)
N.A.I.C.S.: 236117

Division (Domestic):

Pavarini Construction Co. Inc.-Stamford (2)
30 Oak St 3rd Fl, Stamford, CT 06905 **(100%)**
Tel.: (203) 327-0100
Web Site: http://www.pavarini.com
Sales Range: $25-49.9 Million
Emp.: 75
Residential & Commercial Construction Services
N.A.I.C.S.: 236220
James Hurley (Pres)

Pavarini McGovern LLC (1)
770 Broadway Fl 10, New York, NY 10003-9553
Tel.: (212) 907-0900
Web Site: http://www.pavarinimcgovern.com
Sales Range: $10-24.9 Million
Emp.: 25
Supplies a Broad Range of Construction Services for New Buildings in Residential, Commercial, Healthcare, Hospitality & Science & Technology Markets
N.A.I.C.S.: 236220
Alexander V. Bergo (VP-Bus Dev)
Marie Lombardo (Coord-HR)
William Frederick (Exec VP)
Patrick Pagano (Project Mgr)
Gregory Smalling (Project Mgr)
Eric McGovern (Pres & CEO)

Structure Tone, LLC (1)
330 W 34th St, New York, NY 10001
Tel.: (212) 481-6100
Web Site: http://www.structuretone.com
Commercial & Residential Construction
N.A.I.C.S.: 236220
John White Jr. (COO)
Joseph Cribbin (Pres-Southwest)
Michael Neary (Pres)
Joseph Cribbin (Pres-Southwest)
Stacey Dackson (VP & Dir-Special Projects)
Dan Finnegan (Exec VP)
Eugene Peter White (Exec VP-Client Rels)
Scott Corneby (Exec VP)
Michael Neary (Pres)

Subsidiary (Non-US):

S&techs (Hong Kong) Limited (2)
23F Chinachem Johnston Plaza, 178 186 Johnston Road, Wanchai, China (Hong Kong)
Tel.: (852) 21470158
Web Site: https://s-techs.com
Residential & Commercial Construction Services
N.A.I.C.S.: 236220

Subsidiary (Non-US):

S&techs (Japan) Limited (3)
2-20-5Mishuku Setagaya-ko, Tokyo, Japan
Tel.: (81) 3 3795 0887
Industrial Building Construction Services
N.A.I.C.S.: 236210

S&techs (Taiwan) Limited (3)
4F No 107-4 Fu Shing 1st Road, Kaohsiung, Taiwan
Tel.: (886) 7 235 4762
Industrial Building Construction Services
N.A.I.C.S.: 236210

Subsidiary (Non-US):

Structure Tone Limited (2)
1 Kingram Place, Dublin, Ireland
Tel.: (353) 14793245
Web Site: http://www.structuretone.com
Sales Range: $10-24.9 Million
Emp.: 20
Commercial Construction
N.A.I.C.S.: 236220
Dean Manning (Mng Dir)
James Reidy (Mng Dir & Grp Mng Dir-Intl)

Division (Domestic):

Structure Tone Southwest (2)
4550 Post Oak Pl Dr Ste 335, Houston, TX 77027
Tel.: (713) 650-6420
Web Site: http://www.constructors.com

New & Interior Fit-Out Construction Services
N.A.I.C.S.: 236220
Joseph Cribbin (Pres)
Lane Anderson (VP-Mission Critical)
Nicholas Dwyer (Dir-Bus Dev)
Chris Talley (VP-Reg)
Jody Reed (Dir-Ops & Interiors)
Scott Rugen (Acct Exec)
Matt Cunningham (Acct Exec)
Jeffrey Brown (Dir-Bus Dev)
Tala Matchett (VP-Bus Dev)
Brent Jordan (Acct Exec)
Brett Skyllingstad (Dir-Bus Dev & Technical Svcs)
Eric Hage (VP-Dallas)
Greg Francis (VP-Healthcare-Dallas)
Ben Martin (Dir-Ops-San Antonio)
Tim Glenn (Reg VP-Houston)
Fred Noblett III (VP-Austin)

Subsidiary (Non-US):

Structure Tone UK (2)
77 Gracechurch Street, London, EC3V 0AS, United Kingdom
Tel.: (44) 2072047000
Web Site: http://www.structuretone.co.uk
Sales Range: $10-24.9 Million
Emp.: 100
Commercial & Refurbishing Contractors
N.A.I.C.S.: 236220
Dean Manning (Mng Dir)

Subsidiary (Domestic):

Structure Tone, Inc. (2)
330 W 34th St, New York, NY 10001
Tel.: (212) 481-6100
Web Site: http://www.structuretone.com
Sales Range: $1-4.9 Billion
Emp.: 1,450
General Contracting, Design & Construction Services
N.A.I.C.S.: 236210
Scott Corneby (Exec VP)

Subsidiary (Domestic):

Structure Tone Inc.-Hamilton (3)
300 American Metro Blvd Ste 210, Hamilton, NJ 08619 **(100%)**
Tel.: (609) 588-0362
Web Site: http://www.structuretone.com
Sales Range: $10-24.9 Million
Emp.: 45
Construction Services
N.A.I.C.S.: 236220

Structure Tone Inc.-Philadelphia (3)
1500 Walnut St Ste 1410, Philadelphia, PA 19102 **(100%)**
Tel.: (215) 563-7875
Web Site: http://www.structuretone.com
Sales Range: $10-24.9 Million
Emp.: 35
Commercial Construction Services
N.A.I.C.S.: 236220
Nicole Marker (Dir-Bus Dev)
Luke Thomas (Acct Exec)
Stephen Dennis (Mgr-Estimating)

Structure Tone, Inc. (3)
2300 Clarendon Blvd Ste 900, Arlington, VA 22201 **(100%)**
Tel.: (703) 526-1240
Web Site: http://www.structuretone.com
Sales Range: $10-24.9 Million
Emp.: 50
Interior & Base Building Construction & Renovation
N.A.I.C.S.: 236220

Structure Tone, Inc. (3)
1050 Wall St W, Lyndhurst, NJ 07071 **(100%)**
Tel.: (201) 896-1606
Web Site: http://www.structuretone.com
Property Development & Construction Services
N.A.I.C.S.: 236220

Structure Tone, Inc. - Boston (3)
711 Atlantic Ave 2nd Fl, Boston, MA 02111
Tel.: (617) 348-2800
Web Site: http://www.structuretone.com
Sales Range: $200-249.9 Million
Emp.: 100
Construction Management Services
N.A.I.C.S.: 236220

Kristin Poulin (VP-Bus Dev)
David Kempton (Reg VP)
Michael Ryan (VP-Ops)

STO CORPORATION
3800 Camp Creek Pkwy Bldg 1400 S 120, Atlanta, GA 30331
Web Site: http://www.stocorp.com
Sales Range: $10-24.9 Million
Emp.: 95
Cladding & Coating
N.A.I.C.S.: 325510
Michael Sweeney (Mgr-Media)

STOCK & OPTION SOLUTIONS, INC.
910 Campisi Way Ste 2 E, Campbell, CA 95008
Tel.: (408) 979-8700 CA
Web Site: http://www.sos-team.com
Year Founded: 1999
Sales Range: $1-9.9 Million
Emp.: 80
Stock Plan Management & Consulting
N.A.I.C.S.: 541611
Scott McDonald (Dir-Sls & Mktg)
Elizabeth Dodge (VP-Product Mgmt)
Steve Gaylord (CTO)
Andrea Best (Mng Dir-People Solutions)

STOCK BUILDING SUPPLY
4501 Burleson Rd, Austin, TX 78744
Tel.: (512) 444-3172 TX
Web Site: http://www.stockbuildingsupply.com
Year Founded: 1883
Sales Range: $200-249.9 Million
Emp.: 450
Lumber & Building Materials Sales; Building Contractors
N.A.I.C.S.: 423310
Cassandra Fields (Mgr-Pur)
Jim Marasco (Mgr-Premium Window Sls)
Carol Sierra (Office Mgr)

Subsidiaries:

K&A Lumber Company Inc. (1)
1001 W Mowry Dr, Homestead, FL 33030
Tel.: (305) 245-5311
Sales Range: $125-149.9 Million
Emp.: 140
Whslr of Lumber & Rebar
N.A.I.C.S.: 423310

STOCK DEVELOPMENT, LLC
2647 Professional Cir Ste 1201, Naples, FL 34119
Tel.: (239) 592-7344
Web Site: http://www.stockdevelopment.com
Year Founded: 2001
Sales Range: $250-299.9 Million
Emp.: 190
Land Subdivision & Home Builder
N.A.I.C.S.: 237210
K. C. Stock (Chm)
Brian Stock (CEO)
Claudine Leger-Wetzel (VP-Sls & Mktg)

Subsidiaries:

Noble Title & Trust (1)
2647 Professional Cir Ste 1203, Naples, FL 34119
Tel.: (239) 449-4000
Web Site: http://www.nobletitleandtrust.com
Emp.: 11
Title Insurance
N.A.I.C.S.: 524127
Ronnie Evans (Pres)

Stock Construction
2639 Professional Cir Ste 1201, Naples, FL 34119
Tel.: (239) 592-7344
Web Site: http://www.stockdevelopment.com

Residential Construction
N.A.I.C.S.: 236115
Bob Imig (Pres-Construction)

Stock Financial (1)
2639 Professional Cir Ste 105, Naples, FL 34119
Tel.: (239) 449-3700
Emp.: 50
Mortgage Financing
N.A.I.C.S.: 522310
Erica Lolli (Pres)

STOCK TRANSPORT INC.
10037 Faust Rd, Lebanon, IL 62254
Tel.: (618) 537-8440
Web Site: http://www.stocktransportinc.com
Sales Range: $10-24.9 Million
Emp.: 179
Trucking Except Local
N.A.I.C.S.: 484121
Robert Stock (Pres)

STOCK USA EXECUTION SERVICES INC
1717 Rte 6, Carmel, NY 10512
Tel.: (845) 531-2631
Web Site: http://www.stockusainvest.com
Year Founded: 1999
Sales Range: $10-24.9 Million
Emp.: 8
Online Futures Trading
N.A.I.C.S.: 425120
Mark Jordon (Principal)
Craig Manderson (Pres & CEO)

STOCKADE BUILDINGS INC.
1543 State Hwy 91, Oran, MO 63771
Tel.: (573) 262-3593
Web Site: http://www.stockadebuildings inc.com
Rev.: $11,100,000
Emp.: 60
Nonresidential Construction
N.A.I.C.S.: 236220
Stephen Keith (Mgr-Sls-Natl)

STOCKADE COMPANIES, INC.
1611 Chisholm Trail Ste 210, Round Rock, TX 78681
Tel.: (620) 669-9372
Web Site: http://www.stockadecompanies.com
Sales Range: $10-24.9 Million
Emp.: 20
Family Restaurant Operator
N.A.I.C.S.: 722511
Vincent Runco (CEO)

STOCKCROSS FINANCIAL SERVICES, INC
9464 Wilshire Blvd, Beverly Hills, CA 90212
Tel.: (310) 385-0948
Web Site: http://www.stockcross.com
Year Founded: 1971
Investment Advisory, Securities Brokerage & Wealth Management Services
N.A.I.C.S.: 523940
Andrew H. Reich (Chm)
Kamyar Kashfi (Mng Dir-Investments)

STOCKELL CONSULTING INC.
15400 S Outer Forty, Chesterfield, MO 63017
Tel.: (636) 537-9100
Web Site: http://www.stockell.com
Rev.: $14,000,000
Emp.: 80
Computer System Design Services
N.A.I.C.S.: 541512
Richard Brian Stockell (Pres)

COMPANIES

Subsidiaries:

Lindenberg Technologies LLC (1)
701 Emerson Rd Ste 300, Saint Louis, MO 63141
Tel.: (314) 997-5858
Sales Range: $10-24.9 Million
Emp.: 41
Computer System Design Services
N.A.I.C.S.: 541512

STOCKHAM CONSTRUCTION, INC.
475 Portal St Ste F, Cotati, CA 94931-3006
Tel.: (707) 664-0945
Web Site: http://www.stockhamconstruction.com
Sales Range: $10-24.9 Million
Emp.: 120
Carpentry Services
N.A.I.C.S.: 238350
Boyd Stockham *(Owner)*

STOCKLAND GRAIN COMPANY INC.
100 Oak St, Stockland, IL 60967
Tel.: (815) 682-4211
Web Site: http://www.stockland.com
Rev.: $20,000,000
Emp.: 15
Grain & Field Bean Merchant Whslr
N.A.I.C.S.: 424510
Tim Metzinger *(VP)*
Leonard J. Metzinger *(Pres)*

STOCKMAN FINANCIAL CORP.
700 Main St, Miles City, MT 59301
Tel.: (406) 234-8420 MT
Web Site: http://www.stockmanbank.com
Year Founded: 1980
Sales Range: $100-124.9 Million
Emp.: 360
State Commercial Banks
N.A.I.C.S.: 522110
William Coffee *(Vice Chm & Exec VP)*
Dave Zoanni *(Pres)*
Paul Roble *(CTO)*

Subsidiaries:

Stockman Asset Management, Inc. (1)
402 N Broadway, Billings, MT 59101-2507
Tel.: (406) 655-3960
Investment Management Service
N.A.I.C.S.: 523940
Brenda Hittmeier *(Portfolio Mgr)*
Eric George *(Portfolio Mgr)*
Jennifer Hemphill *(Chief Compliance Officer & Portfolio Mgr)*
Karyn Sigler *(Portfolio Mgr)*
Ron O'Donnell *(Portfolio Mgr)*

Stockman Bank of Montana (1)
700 Main St, Miles City, MT 59301-0250
Tel.: (406) 234-8420
Web Site: http://www.stockmanbank.com
Sales Range: $50-74.9 Million
Emp.: 90
Provider of Commercial Banking Services
N.A.I.C.S.: 522110
Bill Coffee *(CEO)*

Stockman Insurance Inc. (1)
700 Mian St, Miles City, MT 59301
Tel.: (406) 234-8485
Web Site: http://www.stockmanbank.com
Sales Range: Less than $1 Million
Emp.: 15
Providers of Insurance Services
N.A.I.C.S.: 522110

STOCKMAN OIL COMPANY
1138 Reynolds Ave, Greenwood, SC 29649
Tel.: (864) 223-8486
Web Site: http://www.stockmanoil.com
Year Founded: 1932
Sales Range: $10-24.9 Million
Emp.: 30
Distr of Petroleum Products
N.A.I.C.S.: 424720
Chip Stockman *(Pres)*
Donna Turner *(Controller)*

STOCKMANS BANK
3421 N Main St, Altus, OK 73521
Tel.: (580) 477-2222
Web Site: http://www.stockmansbank.com
Year Founded: 1910
Commericial Banking
N.A.I.C.S.: 522110
Mark Pritschet *(VP-Credit Administration)*

STOCKMENS FINANCIAL CORPORATION
805 5th St, Rapid City, SD 57701
Tel.: (605) 399-2740 NE
Bank Holding Company
N.A.I.C.S.: 551111
Gregory A. Hunter *(Pres & CEO)*

Subsidiaries:

Security First Bank (1)
5505 Red Rock Ln, Lincoln, NE 68516
Tel.: (402) 323-8045
Web Site: http://www.security1stbank.com
Sales Range: $1-9.9 Million
Emp.: 24
Commericial Banking
N.A.I.C.S.: 522110

STOCKNER'S NURSERY, INC.
15474 Pouncey Tract Rd, Rockville, VA 23146
Tel.: (804) 749-4407
Web Site: http://www.stockners.com
Sales Range: $1-9.9 Million
Emp.: 75
Landscaping Services
N.A.I.C.S.: 561730
Dean Stockner *(Acct Mgr)*
Daniel Stockner *(VP-HR)*

STOCKTON 12 AUTOMOTIVE, INC.
10860 S Auto Mall Dr, Sandy, UT 84070-4174
Tel.: (801) 553-5100
Web Site: http://www.stockton12honda.com
Sales Range: $10-24.9 Million
Emp.: 50
Car Whslr
N.A.I.C.S.: 441110
Greg Miller *(Pres)*
Shane Parrish *(Gen Mgr)*
John Stockton *(Owner)*

STOCKTON OIL COMPANY
1607 4th Ave N, Billings, MT 59101
Tel.: (406) 245-6376
Web Site: http://www.stocktonoilbillings.com
Rev.: $51,379,216
Emp.: 193
Petroleum Bulk Stations
N.A.I.C.S.: 424710
Mykel Stockton *(Pres)*

STOCKTON TELECOMMUNICATIONS
6106 Jefferson St, Albuquerque, NM 87109
Tel.: (505) 255-0404
Web Site: http://www.stocktel.com
Sales Range: $10-24.9 Million
Emp.: 113
Communications Specialization
N.A.I.C.S.: 238210
Judy Stockton *(Pres)*
William Stockton *(CEO)*

STODDARD BAPTIST GLOBAL CARE, INC.
2601 18th St NW, Washington, DC 20018
Tel.: (202) 541-6270 DC
Web Site: http://www.wcasdc.org
Year Founded: 2010
Sales Range: $10-24.9 Million
Emp.: 565
Community Health Care Services
N.A.I.C.S.: 621498
Keisha M. Clark *(Dir-Dev)*
Linda Robinson *(Dir-Clinical)*

STODDARD NLA, LLC
190 Alpha Park, Highland Heights, OH 44143
Tel.: (440) 869-9890
Web Site: http://www.stoddard.com
Year Founded: 1957
Car Whslr
N.A.I.C.S.: 441110
Bruce Schwartz *(Pres)*
Mark Taylor *(Mgr-Mktg & Product)*
Per Schroeder *(Mktg Mgr-Digital)*
Mark Jelenic *(Mgr-Warehouse)*
Pete Yanda *(Sls Mgr)*

STODOLA-MAAS CONSTRUCTION INC.
195 Trowbridge Dr, Fond Du Lac, WI 54936
Tel.: (920) 923-6086
Rev.: $13,000,000
Emp.: 50
Commercial & Office Building, New Construction
N.A.I.C.S.: 236220
Jerry Stodola *(Pres)*

STOEL RIVES LLP
760 SW 9Th Ave Swe 3000, Portland, OR 97204
Tel.: (503) 224-3380
Web Site: http://www.stoel.com
Year Founded: 1907
Sales Range: $200-249.9 Million
Emp.: 550
Legal Advisory Services
N.A.I.C.S.: 541110
Steven W. Abel *(Partner)*
Paul S. Angello *(Partner)*
Bethany A. Bacci *(Partner)*
Gary R. Barnum *(Partner)*
Todd A. Bauman *(Partner)*
Brenda K. Baumgart *(Partner)*
Barbara A. Brainard *(Partner)*
Jason M. Brauser *(Partner)*
Jennie L. Bricker *(Partner)*
Michael R. Campbell *(Partner)*
Stuart Chestler *(Partner)*
William L. Clydesdale *(Partner)*
Greg D. Corbin *(Partner)*
Aaron C. Courtney *(Partner)*
Barbara D. Craig *(Partner)*
Jerry R. Fish *(Partner)*
Brad S. Daniels *(Partner)*
Adam H. Dittman *(Partner)*
Amy Edwards *(Partner)*
Jason Morgan *(Partner)*
Wendy S. Goffe *(Partner-Seattle)*
Jason Johns *(Partner)*
Tina M. Grovier *(Mng Partner-Anchorage)*
Christopher Pooser *(Mng Partner-Boise)*
Scott F. Young *(Mng Partner-Salt Lake City)*
Bradley F. Tellam *(Chief Admin Officer)*
Bob Van Brocklin *(Mng Partner)*
Jill L. King *(Chief Lawyer Dev Officer)*
Laura Rosenbaum *(Partner)*
Oren Haker *(Partner)*
Brian Nese *(Partner)*
Aric Jarrett *(Partner)*
Devin McComb *(Partner)*
Matthew R. Wilmot *(Partner)*
Sylvia Arostegui *(Partner)*
Ryan Wood *(Partner)*
Connor Olson *(Assoc Atty)*
Cheryl Musselman *(Atty)*
Jim Torgerson *(Mng Partner-Firm Wide)*
Andrea Thompson *(Partner)*
Eric Martin *(Partner)*
Reilley Keating *(Partner)*
Michael Sherman *(Partner)*
Richard P. Bonnifield *(Partner-Energy Practice Grp-Washington)*
Geoffrey B. Tichenor *(Partner)*
Jonathan M. Cohen *(Partner)*
Krista K. McIntyre *(Partner)*
Louis A. Ferreira *(Partner)*
J. Mark Morford *(Partner)*
Martin K. Banks *(Partner)*
Serena S. Carlsen *(Partner)*
Tamara L. Boeck *(Partner)*
Thomas A. Ellison *(Partner)*
Thomas R. Wood *(Partner)*
Sam Gardiner *(Partner-Corp Practice Grp)*
Oliver A. Thoenen *(Mgr-PR)*
Kelly Roberts *(Dir-Litigation Tech Support)*
Vanessa Soriano Power *(Mng Partner-Seattle)*
Alfredo Villanueva *(Partner)*
Chad T. Marriott *(Partner)*
Kirk B. Maag *(Partner)*
B. John Casey *(Partner)*
Saskia de Boer *(Partner)*
Steven J. Boender *(Partner)*
Jasmine Trillos-Decarie *(Chief Bus Dev Officer)*
Kevin D. Burnett *(Partner-Corporate Grp)*
Brant J. Norquist *(Partner)*
Todd L. Friedman *(Partner)*
Bryan Hawkins *(Partner)*
J. Anthony Girolami *(Partner)*
Jeffrey Nielson *(Atty-Real Estate & Construction Grp-Boise)*
Bruce J. McNeil *(Partner-Employee Benefits Grp-Seattle)*
Rachel Hoffman Cox *(Partner)*
Joseph Nussbaum *(Partner)*
Bart Reed *(Partner)*
Andrew J. Pieper *(Partner)*
Robert R. Teel *(Partner)*
Elijah Watkins *(Partner)*
Adam Coady *(Partner-Real Estate, Dev & Construction Grp)*
Alexandra Kleeman *(Partner-Environmental, Land Use & Natural Resources Grp)*
Nathan Luce *(Partner-Real Estate, Dev & Construction Grp)*
Kate Mathews *(Atty-Seattle)*
Crystal Chase *(Partner)*
Susan Beckert Bock *(Partner)*
Heather Stewart *(Partner)*
Kristin Russell *(Partner)*

STOELTING CO.
620 Wheat Ln, Wood Dale, IL 60191-1164
Tel.: (630) 860-9700
Web Site: http://www.stoeltingco.com
Year Founded: 1886
Sales Range: $1-9.9 Million
Emp.: 30
Developer of Psychological & Physiological Apparatus & Tests, Educational Tests, Lie Detectors, Bio-Feedback Instruments & Employee Screening Materials
N.A.I.C.S.: 334516

STOELTING CO.

Stoelting Co.—(Continued)
Mark A. Cochran (Pres)
Jamie Martin (VP)
Rory Geoghegan (Mng Dir-Europe)
Susan Labuschagne (Mgr-Office Support)

STOHLMAN AND ROGERS INC.
427 14th St, Marysville, CA 95901
Tel.: (530) 743-9661
Web Site: http://www.fuel-card.com
Sales Range: $25-49.9 Million
Emp.: 14
Petroleum Bulk Stations
N.A.I.C.S.: 424710
Theron Rogers (Pres)

STOHLMAN AUTOMOTIVE FAMILY
8433 Leesburg Pike, Tysons Corner, VA 22182
Tel.: (703) 893-2990
Web Site: http://www.stohlman-vw.com
Year Founded: 1970
Sales Range: $50-74.9 Million
Emp.: 120
New Car Retailer
N.A.I.C.S.: 441110
Michael Rusnak (Gen Mgr)
Cathy Stohlman (Pres)
Jaime Dent (Gen Mgr-Sls)
Tom Guzulaitis (Dir-Internet)
Hue Beasley (Bus Mgr)
Michael Bolourian (Bus Mgr)
Hesham Kamal (Bus Mgr)
Manhee Lee (Dir-Fin)
Joe Lishman (Dir-Sls)
Pierre Ndiaye (Mgr-Pre-Owned)
Debbie Perkins (Mgr-Svc)
Erick Ponce (Asst Mgr-Parts)
Dave Prowitt (Dir-Parts)

STOIC HOLDINGS LLC
3879 Tennyson St, Denver, Colorado
Tel.: (303) 539-3036
Web Site: https://www.stoicholdings.com
Privater Equity Firm
N.A.I.C.S.: 523999

Subsidiaries:

Accredited Home Elevator, Inc. (1)
127 S Main St, Barnegat, NJ 08005
Tel.: (609) 660-8100
Web Site: https://www.accelevator.com
Home Elevator Mfr & Maintenance Services
N.A.I.C.S.: 333921
Michael Gurzo (CEO)
Scott Wallace Sr. (Founder)
Scott Wallace Jr. (Principal)

Subsidiary (Domestic):

Sunrise Elevator Co., Inc. (2)
433 Plaza Dr, Tarpon Springs, FL 34689
Tel.: (727) 934-8280
Web Site: https://sunriseelevatorco.com
Sales Range: $1-9.9 Million
Emp.: 15
Building Equipment Contractors
N.A.I.C.S.: 238290
Edith Slater (Treas)

STOKERS TENDEREX FARMS INC.
1725 Dixie Hwy, Louisville, KY 40210
Tel.: (502) 775-6700
Web Site: http://www.stokersinc.com
Rev.: $12,074,663
Emp.: 34
Groceries & Related Products
N.A.I.C.S.: 424490
Mike Mcallister (CFO & Treas)
Daniel E. Patterson Sr. (Chm)

STOKES & SPIEHLER INC.
No 100 110 Rue Jean Lafitte, Lafayette, LA 70508-3108
Tel.: (337) 233-6871
Web Site: http://www.stokesandspiehler.com
Rev.: $15,000,000
Emp.: 100
Oil Consultants
N.A.I.C.S.: 213112
Bruce M. Jordan (Pres)
Jacqueline Broussard (CFO & Treas)
George W. Stokes (Exec VP)
John S. Long (Sr VP & Gen Mgr)
Tony Shell (VP-Sls & Mktg)
Blair LeBlanc (VP-Offshore Ops)
Russ Bellard (VP-Onshore Ops)
Donnie Busscher (Mgr-Engrg)

STOKES AUTOMOTIVE, INC.
8650 Rivers Ave, North Charleston, SC 29406
Tel.: (843) 572-4700   SC
Web Site: http://www.stokesautomotive.com
Sales Range: $50-74.9 Million
Emp.: 65
New & Used Car Dealerships Owner & Operator
N.A.I.C.S.: 441110
Yomi Soyebo (Mgr-Fin)
William E. Stokes Sr. (Pres)

Subsidiaries:

Stokes Brown Toyota of Hilton Head (1)
100 Fording Island Rd, Bluffton, SC 29910
Tel.: (843) 815-4444
Web Site: http://www.stokesbrowntoyotahiltonhead.com
Sales Range: $25-49.9 Million
Emp.: 70
New & Used Car Dealer
N.A.I.C.S.: 441110
J. J. Stokes (Owner)

Stokes-Craven Automotive (1)
2601 Paxville Hwy, Manning, SC 29102
Tel.: (803) 433-5400
Web Site: http://www.stokescraven.com
Sales Range: $10-24.9 Million
Emp.: 50
New & Used Car Dealer
N.A.I.C.S.: 441110

STOKES CHEVROLET, INC.
86 Peach Tower Rd, Clanton, AL 35045
Tel.: (205) 755-3700   AL
Web Site: http://www.stokeschevrolet.com
Year Founded: 1954
Sales Range: $10-24.9 Million
Emp.: 42
Car Whslr
N.A.I.C.S.: 441110
Kirk A. Stokes (Owner)

STOKES DISTRIBUTING CO. INC.
12 Stokes Dr, Hattiesburg, MS 39401
Tel.: (601) 545-3121
Web Site: http://www.stokesdistributing.com
Sales Range: $10-24.9 Million
Emp.: 35
Beer & Other Fermented Malt Liquors
N.A.I.C.S.: 424810
Sparky Walker (Pres)
Tommy Stokes (VP)

STOKES ELECTRIC COMPANY
1701 McCalla Ave, Knoxville, TN 37915
Tel.: (865) 525-0351
Web Site: http://www.stokeselectriccompany.com
Sales Range: $25-49.9 Million
Emp.: 55
Electrical Apparatus & Equipment
N.A.I.C.S.: 423610
Sherry Reed (Mgr-Warehouse)

STOKES MECHANICAL CONTRACTORS INC
2001 7th Ave N, Lake Worth, FL 33461
Tel.: (561) 582-3589
Web Site: http://www.stokes.com
Sales Range: $10-24.9 Million
Emp.: 30
Warm Air Heating & Air Conditioning Contractor
N.A.I.C.S.: 238220
Susan C. Stokes (Pres & CEO)
Evan C. Stokes (Founder)

STOLL KEENON OGDEN PLLC
500 W Jefferson St 2000 PNC Plz, Louisville, KY 40202-2828
Tel.: (502) 333-6000
Web Site: http://www.skofirm.com
Year Founded: 1897
Law Firm
N.A.I.C.S.: 541110
Douglas C. Ballantine (Atty)
James D. Allen (Atty)
John T. Ballantine (Atty)
Culver Halliday (Atty)
David H. Thomason (Atty)
W. Gregory King (Atty)
D. Randall Gibson (Atty)
Richard Griffith (Atty)
Stacy Kula (Atty)
Thomas E. Rutledge (Atty)
Thomas M. Williams (Atty)
Justin Clark (Owner)
Lea Goff (Owner)
Adam M. Back (Atty)
Shannon Bishop Arvin (Atty)
Charles R. Baesler Jr. (Atty)

STOLLER INTERNATIONAL INC.
15521 E 1830 N Rd, Pontiac, IL 61764
Tel.: (815) 844-6197
Web Site: http://www.stollerinternational.com
Sales Range: $10-24.9 Million
Emp.: 20
Agricultural Machinery & Equipment
N.A.I.C.S.: 423820
Clark Stoller (Pres)
Lynn Stoller (VP)
Mike Billington (Controller)

STOLLER WHOLESALE WINE & SPIRITS
3325 Mount Prospect Rd, Franklin Park, IL 60131
Tel.: (847) 957-1200
Web Site: http://www.stollerwholesale.com
Sales Range: $10-24.9 Million
Emp.: 50
Distr of Alcoholic Beverages
N.A.I.C.S.: 424820
Randy Stoller (Pres)
Larry Stoller (Sr VP-Fin & Admin)

STOLTENBERG CONSULTING, INC.
5815 Library Rd, Bethel Park, PA 15102
Tel.: (412) 854-5688
Web Site: http://www.stoltenberg.com
Year Founded: 1995
Rev.: $7,100,000
Emp.: 100
Computer System Design Services
N.A.I.C.S.: 541512
Sheri Stoltenberg (Pres & CEO)
Shane Pilcher (VP)

Daniel O'Connor (VP-Clinical Practice)
Mark Hess (Sr VP)

STOLTZ MARKETING GROUP
615 W Main St 2nd Fl, Boise, ID 83702
Tel.: (208) 388-0766
Web Site: http://www.stoltzgroup.com
Year Founded: 1996
Rev.: $15,000,000
Emp.: 15
Advetising Agency
N.A.I.C.S.: 541810
Ken Stoltz (Pres)
Kate Holgate (VP)
Jill Coles (Mgr-Production & Media)
Ward Duft (CEO & Dir-Creative)
Jay Bowen (Sr Acct Dir)
Jill Watterson (COO & Dir-Client Svcs)
Adie Bartron (Sr Acct Mgr)
Mitch Kuhn (Sr Art Dir)
Katherine Johnson (Dir-Brand Strategy)
Tracy Hitchcock (Dir-Bus Dev)

STONE & COMPANY
PO Box 776, Connellsville, PA 15425-0776
Tel.: (724) 628-2200
Web Site: http://www.stoneconcrete.com
Rev.: $20,616,390
Emp.: 17
Ready-Mixed Concrete Products & Services
N.A.I.C.S.: 327320
Mark W. Stone (Co-Pres)
Greg Stone (Co-Pres)

STONE & SIMONS ADVERTISING
24245 Northwestern Hwy, Southfield, MI 48075-2573
Tel.: (248) 562-7276   MI
Web Site: http://www.stonesimons.com
Year Founded: 1956
Rev.: $65,000,000
Emp.: 25
Advetising Agency
N.A.I.C.S.: 541810
Charles G. Stone (Chm)
Ken Palczynski (VP-Graphic Svcs)
Marian Szczepanek (Brdcst Production Mgr)
Joseph Koch (Acct Exec)

STONE ARCH CAPITAL, LLC
800 Nicollet Mall Ste 1150, Minneapolis, MN 55402
Tel.: (612) 317-2980
Web Site: http://www.stonearchcapital.com
Year Founded: 2003
Sales Range: $25-49.9 Million
Emp.: 10
Privater Equity Firm
N.A.I.C.S.: 523999
Charles B. Lannin (Partner)
F. Clayton Miller (Partner)
Kelly J. Horner (CFO & Chief Compliance Officer)
Kasey T. Sime (VP)

STONE BELT FREIGHT LINES INC.
101 W Dillman Rd, Bloomington, IN 47403
Tel.: (812) 247-2332
Web Site: http://www.stonebeltfreight.com
Sales Range: $100-124.9 Million
Emp.: 70
Local Trucking without Storage

STONE CANYON INDUSTRIES, LLC

N.A.I.C.S.: 484110
Ted Benckart *(Owner & Pres)*

STONE BREWING CO.
1999 Citracado Pkwy, Escondido, CA 92029
Tel.: (760) 471-4999
Web Site: http://www.stonebrew.com
Year Founded: 1996
Rev.: $36,900,000
Emp.: 251
Beer Mfr
N.A.I.C.S.: 312120
Greg Koch *(Co-Founder & Chm)*
Steve Wagner *(Co-Founder & Interim CEO)*

STONE BRIDGE CELLARS, INC.
200 Taplin Rd, Saint Helena, CA 94574-9601
Tel.: (707) 963-2745   CA
Web Site: http://www.jpvwines.com
Year Founded: 1981
Rev.: $19,200,000
Emp.: 250
Wines, Brandy & Brandy Spirits
N.A.I.C.S.: 312130
William Phelps *(Chm)*
Robert Boyd *(CFO & VP)*
Sam Burton *(VP & Dir-Ops)*

STONE CANYON INDUSTRIES, LLC
1875 Century Park E Ste 320, Los Angeles, CA 90067
Tel.: (424) 316-2061   DE
Web Site: http://www.stonecanyonllc.com
Emp.: 10,000
Holding Company
N.A.I.C.S.: 551112
Adam Cohn *(Co-CEO)*
Michael Neumann *(Pres)*
Sascha Kaeser *(Sr VP)*
Shawn Malleck *(Sr VP)*
Andrew K. Hirsch *(Gen Counsel)*
Kenneth M. Roessler *(CEO-SCI Pkg)*
Bill Kiefer *(CEO-SCI Rail)*
Mark Cox *(Sr VP)*
James H. Fordyce *(Co-CEO)*
Michael C. Salvator *(COO)*

Subsidiaries:

A. Stucki Company   (1)
900 Commerce Dr Ste 906, Moon Township, PA 15108
Tel.: (412) 771-7300
Web Site: http://www.stucki.com
Sales Range: $25-49.9 Million
Emp.: 18
Freight Railroad Stabilizer Mfr
N.A.I.C.S.: 336510

Subsidiary (Domestic):

American Industries, Inc   (2)
American Way, Sharon, PA 16146
Tel.: (724) 981-4100
Railroad Rolling Stock Mfr
N.A.I.C.S.: 336510

Independent Draft Gear Co.   (2)
1000 Martin Luther King Jr Blvd, Farrell, PA 16121
Tel.: (724) 981-2251
Emp.: 14
Railroad Rolling Stock Mfr
N.A.I.C.S.: 336510
Adam Hunyadi *(Gen Mgr)*

Salco Products Inc.   (2)
1385 101st St Ste A, Lemont, IL 60439
Tel.: (630) 783-2570
Web Site: http://www.salcoproducts.com
Provider of Railroad Equipment
N.A.I.C.S.: 336510
Dave A. Oestermeyer *(Pres)*
Jackie Stevenson *(Coord-Inventory Svc)*
Edwin Luper *(Acct Mgr)*
Brian Putnam *(VP-Product Mgmt)*
Terry Weaver *(Mgr-IT)*
Craig Leighton *(Mgr-CAD)*
Chuck Simpson *(Dir-Supply Chain)*
Tom DeLafosse *(VP-Engrg & Technical Consulting Svcs)*

Subsidiary (Non-US):

Stucki De Mexico S De Rl De C.V.   (2)
Av Los Andes No 200 Fracc Coyoacan, 64510, Monterrey, Nuevo Leon, Mexico
Tel.: (52) 8180077300
Web Site: http://www.stuckidemexico.com
Railroad Rolling Stock Mfr
N.A.I.C.S.: 336510

Stucki Do Brasil Ltda   (2)
Rua Dr Guilherme Bannitz 90-5, Sao Paulo, 04532-060, Brazil
Tel.: (55) 1138424630
Rail Transportation Services
N.A.I.C.S.: 488210

BWAY Corporation   (1)
8607 Roberts Dr Ste 250, Atlanta, GA 30350-2230
Tel.: (770) 645-4800
Web Site: http://www.bwaycorp.com
Holding Company; Metal & Plastic Container Mfr
N.A.I.C.S.: 551112
Kenneth M. Roessler *(Pres & CEO)*
Leslie L. Bradshaw *(Exec VP-Pur & Logistics)*
Michael A. Noel *(Exec VP-Sls & Mktg)*
Dennis M. Kitchen *(VP-HR)*
Jeffery W. Sprick *(VP & Controller)*
Richard D. Turek *(VP-Metal Ops)*
Michael G. Bero *(VP-Comml Sls)*
Michael C. Sheppard *(VP-Strategic Accts & Distr)*
John G. Becker *(VP-Plastic Ops)*
Tarek Maguid *(COO & Exec VP)*
Donald W. Pearson *(CFO & Exec VP)*
Nathan J. Spang *(VP-Fin, Plng & Analysis)*
William D. Waller *(VP-Engrg & Technical Svcs)*
Fernando C. Graf *(VP-IT)*
Bruno Couteille *(VP-HR)*
John Thiersch *(VP-Enrg & Technical Svcs)*
Greg Hutchison *(VP-Plastic Ops)*

Plant (Domestic):

BWAY Corp. - Cincinnati Plant   (2)
8200 Broadwell Rd, Cincinnati, OH 45244
Tel.: (513) 388-2200
Web Site: http://www.bwaycorp.com
Aerosol Can Mfr
N.A.I.C.S.: 332431

BWAY Corp. - Elk Grove Village Plant   (2)
1350 Arthur Ave, Elk Grove Village, IL 60007-5707
Tel.: (847) 956-0750
Web Site: http://www.bwaycorp.com
Rigid Plastic Shipping & Packaging Containers Mfr
N.A.I.C.S.: 326199

BWAY Corp. - LaGrange Plant   (2)
1603 Orchard Hill Rd, LaGrange, GA 30240
Tel.: (706) 885-1772
Web Site: http://www.bwaycorp.com
Sales Range: $50-74.9 Million
Emp.: 75
Rigid Plastic Shipping & Packaging Containers Mfr
N.A.I.C.S.: 326199
Adam Worsley *(Plant Mgr)*

Plant (Non-US):

BWAY Corp. - Langley Plant   (2)
5850 272nd Street, Langley, V4W 3Z1, BC, Canada
Tel.: (604) 857-1177
Web Site: http://www.bwaycorp.com
Rigid Plastic Shipping & Packaging Containers Mfr
N.A.I.C.S.: 326199

Plant (Domestic):

BWAY Corp. - Mansfield Plant   (2)
1501 E Dallas St, Mansfield, TX 76063-2405
Tel.: (817) 473-0259
Web Site: http://www.mauserpackaging.com
Rigid Plastic Shipping & Packaging Containers Mfr
N.A.I.C.S.: 326199

Plant (Non-US):

BWAY Corp. - Oakville Plant   (2)
2240 Wyecroft Road, Oakville, L6L 6M1, ON, Canada
Tel.: (905) 827-9340
Web Site: http://www.bwaycorp.com
Rigid Plastic Shipping & Packaging Containers Mfr
N.A.I.C.S.: 326199

BWAY Corp. - Springhill Plant   (2)
29 Memorial Crescent, Springhill, B0M 1X0, NS, Canada
Tel.: (902) 597-3787
Web Site: http://www.bwaycorp.com
Rigid Plastic Shipping & Packaging Containers Mfr
N.A.I.C.S.: 326199
David Mac Donald *(Plant Mgr)*

Plant (Domestic):

BWAY Corp. - Trenton Plant   (2)
6 Litho Rd, Trenton, NJ 08638
Tel.: (732) 997-4050
Web Site: http://www.bwaycorp.com
Metals Service Center
N.A.I.C.S.: 423510

BWAY Corp. - York Plant   (2)
599 Davies Dr, York, PA 17402
Tel.: (717) 840-2100
Web Site: http://www.bwaycorp.com
Metal Container Mfr
N.A.I.C.S.: 332431

Subsidiary (Domestic):

Industrial Container Services, LLC   (2)
2600 Maitland Ctr Pkway, Maitland, FL 32751
Tel.: (407) 930-4182
Web Site: http://www.iconserv.com
Emp.: 1,700
Reusable Container Products & Services
N.A.I.C.S.: 322219
Gerald Butler *(COO)*
Kurt Richardson *(CMO)*
Charles Veniez *(Pres & CEO)*
Alan Johansen *(CFO)*

Unit (Domestic):

ICS Cargo Clean   (3)
820 State Ave, Cincinnati, OH 45204
Tel.: (513) 921-8811
Web Site: http://www.iconserv.com
Sales Range: $25-49.9 Million
Emp.: 30
Holding Company; Steel, Fiber & Plastic Drum Mfr & Refurbisher
N.A.I.C.S.: 551112
John Steven *(Mgr-Div)*

Branch (Domestic):

Industrial Container Services, LLC - Cincinnati 26   (3)
837 Depot St, Cincinnati, OH 45204
Tel.: (513) 251-8683
Web Site: http://www.iconserv.com
Sales Range: $50-74.9 Million
Emp.: 24
Steel, Fiber & Plastic Drum Mfr & Refurbisher
N.A.I.C.S.: 322219

Industrial Container Services, LLC - Columbus   (3)
1385 Blatt Blvd, Gahanna, OH 43230
Tel.: (614) 864-1900
Web Site: http://www.iconserv.com
Sales Range: $50-74.9 Million
Steel, Fiber & Plastic Drum Mfr & Refurbisher
N.A.I.C.S.: 322219

Industrial Container Services, LLC - Denver   (3)
640 Baseline Rd, Brighton, CO 80601-6663
Tel.: (303) 659-5095
Web Site: http://www.iconserv.com
Reusable Container Products & Services
N.A.I.C.S.: 322219

Industrial Container Services, LLC - Louisville   (3)
405 Industry Rd, Louisville, KY 40208
Tel.: (502) 637-5428
Web Site: http://www.iconserv.com
Sales Range: $75-99.9 Million
Steel, Fiber & Plastic Drum Mfr & Refurbisher
N.A.I.C.S.: 322219
Dan Wheeler *(VP-Ops & Sls)*

Industrial Container Services, LLC - Orlando   (3)
6191 Jones Ave, Zellwood, FL 32798
Tel.: (407) 889-5500
Web Site: http://www.iconserv.com
Sales Range: $25-49.9 Million
Reusable Container Products & Services
N.A.I.C.S.: 322219

Subsidiary (Non-US):

Mauser Group N.V.   (2)
Souvereinstraat 1, 4903 RH, Oosterhout, Netherlands
Tel.: (31) 162 483 700
Web Site: http://www.mausergroup.com
Holding Company; Rigid Packaging Products Mfr
N.A.I.C.S.: 551112
Siegfried Weber *(Sr VP-Global Sls & Mktg)*
Michael Steubing *(Pres/CEO-Intl)*
Glenn Frommer *(Pres/CEO-North America)*
Ricardo Goldenberg *(Pres/CEO-NCG)*

Subsidiary (US):

Mauser Packaging Solutions   (3)
1515 W 22nd St Ste 1100, Oak Brook, IL 60523
Tel.: (630) 203-4100
Web Site: https://mauserpackaging.com
Packaging & Containers Mfr
N.A.I.C.S.: 561910

Subsidiary (Domestic):

Consolidated Container Company LLC   (4)
109 27th Ave NE, Minneapolis, MN 55418-2716
Tel.: (612) 781-0923
Web Site: http://www.containerexperts.com
Container Products & Services
N.A.I.C.S.: 322219
William B. Dworsky *(Co-Founder & CEO)*

Subsidiary (Non-US):

Mauser-Werke GmbH   (3)
Schildgesstrasse 71-163, 50321, Bruhl, Germany
Tel.: (49) 2232781000
Web Site: http://www.mausergroup.com
Emp.: 5,600
Industrial Packaging Materials Mfr
N.A.I.C.S.: 332439
Bjoern Kreiter *(Mng Dir)*
Ricardo Goldenberg *(Pres/CEO-NCG)*
Glenn Frommer *(Pres/CEO-North America)*
Siegfried Weber *(Sr VP-Global Sls & Mktg)*
Michael Steubing *(Mng Dir, Pres-Intl & CEO-Intl)*

Subsidiary (US):

MAUSER USA, LLC   (4)
Tower 2 Ctr Blvd 20th Fl, East Brunswick, NJ 08816
Tel.: (732) 353-7101
Web Site: http://www.mausergroup.com
Industrial Packaging Materials Mfr
N.A.I.C.S.: 326199
Glenn Frommer *(Pres/CEO-Mauser North America)*

Subsidiary (US):

NCG-ERC, LLC   (3)
Woodward Ave 1101, Charlotte, NC 28206
Tel.: (704) 358-6700
Web Site: http://www.nationalcontainer.com
Industrial Packaging Materials Mfr
N.A.I.C.S.: 326199
Peter Suttoni *(Pres)*

Kissner Group Holdings LP   (1)
148 Manitou Dr Suite 301, Kitchener, N2C 1L3, ON, Canada

STONE CANYON INDUSTRIES, LLC

U.S. PRIVATE

Stone Canyon Industries, LLC—(Continued)
Tel.: (519) 279-4860
Web Site: http://www.kissner.com
Chemical Distr
N.A.I.C.S.: 424690

Subsidiary (US):

The Detroit Salt Company (2)
12841 Sanders St, Detroit, MI 48217
Tel.: (313) 841-5144
Web Site: http://www.detroitsalt.com
Sales Range: $50-74.9 Million
Emp.: 43
Salt Mining
N.A.I.C.S.: 212319

STONE CAPITAL GROUP INC.
1780 Green Bay Rd Ste 202, Highland Park, IL 60035
Tel.: (847) 266-6700
Rev.: $16,100,000
Emp.: 80
Futures Brokers & Dealers, Commodity
N.A.I.C.S.: 523160

STONE CREEK FURNITURE INC.
200 S Kyrene Rd, Chandler, AZ 85226
Tel.: (602) 458-9800
Web Site:
  http://www.stonecreekfurniture.com
Sales Range: $10-24.9 Million
Emp.: 100
Furniture Mfr
N.A.I.C.S.: 337211
Ronald Jones (Pres)

STONE GLACIER, INC.
608 W Griffin Dr Unit A, Bozeman, MT 59715
Tel.: (406) 404-0641
Web Site:
  http://www.stoneglacier.com
Year Founded: 2012
Sales Range: $1-9.9 Million
Emp.: 7
Trekking Equipment Mfr
N.A.I.C.S.: 314910
Kurt Racicot (Founder & Owner)
Jeff Sposito (Pres & CEO)
Lyle Hebel (Mktg Dir)
Peter Muennich (Sls Mgr)
Colby Adamek (Ops Mgr)

STONE HILL WINERY
1110 Stone Hill Hwy, Hermann, MO 65041
Tel.: (573) 486-3479
Web Site:
  http://www.stonehillwinery.com
Year Founded: 1847
Sales Range: $10-24.9 Million
Emp.: 100
Wine Mfr
N.A.I.C.S.: 312130
Jonathan Held (VP & Gen Mgr)
Thomas Held (Second VP & Dir-Fin)
Nick Pehle (Mgr-Vineyard)

STONE MARKETING INTERNATIONAL
6437 N Burlington Dr, Houston, TX 77092-1108
Tel.: (713) 956-1616
Web Site:
  http://www.stonemarketingintl.com
Rev.: $10,000,000
Emp.: 33
Brick, Stone & Related Material
N.A.I.C.S.: 423320
George Frisbie (Pres)
Dawn Romagnoly (Gen Mgr)

STONE MOTORS INC.
622 W 1st St, Julesburg, CO 80737
Tel.: (970) 474-3391
Web Site:
  http://www.stonemotors.com
Sales Range: $10-24.9 Million
Emp.: 10
Automobiles; New & Used
N.A.I.C.S.: 441110
Joyce Macht (Office Mgr)

STONE POINT CAPITAL LLC
20 Horseneck Ln, Greenwich, CT 06830
Tel.: (203) 862-2900 DE
Web Site: http://www.stonepoint.com
Privater Equity Firm
N.A.I.C.S.: 523999
James R. Matthews (Mng Dir)
Charles Arthur Davis (Co-CEO)
Darran A. Baird (Mng Dir)
Kurt E. Bolin (Mng Dir)
Christopher M. Doody (Executives)
Michael D. Gregorich (Mng Dir)
Fayez S. Muhtadie (Mng Dir)
William J. Santaniello (Controller & Dir)
Eric L. Rosenzweig (Mng Dir)
Dhruv Sarna (Mng Dir)
Agha S. Khan (Mng Dir)
Meryl Deborah Hartzband (Partner)
Scott J. Bronner (Mng Dir)
David J. Wermuth (Mng Dir & Gen Counsel)
James D. Carey (Co-CEO)
Nicolas D. Zerbib (Mng Dir)

Subsidiaries:

Alliant Insurance Services, Inc. (1)
18100 Von Karman Ave 10th Fl, Irvine, CA 92612
Tel.: (949) 756-0271
Web Site: http://www.alliant.com
Commercial & Specialty Insurance & Financial Services
N.A.I.C.S.: 524210
Thomas W. Corbett (Chm & CEO)
Peter Arkley (Pres-Retail Property & Casualty)
Michael S. Liebowitz (Pres, CEO, Mng Dir & Exec VP)
Diana Kiehl (Chief Admin Officer)
Daniel Howell (Sr Exec VP-Pub Entity)
Peter Carpenter (COO)
Sean McConlogue (Pres-Alliant Underwriting Solutions)
Michael Cusack (Exec VP & Mng Dir-Alliant Specialty)
Ilene Anders (CFO)
Bob Bennetsen (Sr Mng Dir & Exec VP)
Ralph Hurst (Pres-Natl Brokerage Grp)
Kevin Overbey (Pres-Alliant Employee Benefits)
Nick Kopinga (VP-Corp Mktg & Comm)
Karey Vaught (Mng Dir & Exec VP)
Tim McGinnis (Sr VP-Construction Svcs Grp)
Mike Honeycutt (Sr VP-Pub Entity)
David Wightman (Sr VP)
Adam R. Walter (VP)
James Fraser (Sr VP-Employee Benefits)
Doug Bixby (Sr VP)
Rich Leavitt (Sr VP)
James Crystal (Vice Chm)
Lilian Vanvieldt (Chief Diversity, Equity & Inclusion Officer)
Charles Cook (Exec VP-Employee Benefits Grp)
Charles Cook (Exec VP)
Javin Overbey (Pres-Alliant Employee Benefits)
Pete Kranz (Sr VP-Alliant Specialty)
Madeline Currie (Asst VP)
Edward Stewart (Sr VP)
Seamus Breen (VP-Employee Benefits-Global)
Phil Toughey (VP-Employee Benefits Grp)
Robert Treacy (Sr VP-Employee Benefits Grp-Austin)
Bev Gregory (Sr VP-Employee Benefits Grp)
Sarah Rizzo (VP-Employee Benefits Grp-Kansas City)
Frank Verdi (VP-Employee Benefits Grp)
Megan Ford (Comm Mgr)
Joe Marsh (Sr VP-Hilo)
Jared Pelissier (Sr VP & Mng Dir-Alliant Specialty)
Cherrise Howard (VP-Employee Benefits Grp)
Dan Bjornlie (VP-Employee Benefits Grp)
Greg Martens (Exec VP-Alliant Employee Benefits)
Jennifer Carl (VP)
Paul Malone (Sr VP-Americas)
Greg Sanford (VP-Americas)
Dan Berry (Exec VP-Alliant M&A)

Subsidiary (Domestic):

Alliant Insurance Services Houston LLC (2)
5847 San Felipe St Ste 2750, Houston, TX 77056-3265
Tel.: (832) 485-4000
Web Site: http://www.alliantinsurance.com
Sales Range: $50-74.9 Million
Emp.: 100
Specialty Insurance Services
N.A.I.C.S.: 524126
Freddie Nutt (Exec VP)
Dan Burton (Sr VP-Surety)
Rob Schanen (Pres-Employee Benefits)
Jo Ann Barnard (VP)
Lee D. Snelgrove (Sr VP)
Marc Halvorsen (First VP)
Rhesa Boulton (First VP)
Ted Dimitry (VP-Energy & Marine Grp)
Jessie Guerrero (Sr VP-Energy & Marine)

Alliant Specialty Insurance Services, Inc. (2)
1301 Dove St Ste 200, Newport Beach, CA 92660
Tel.: (949) 756-0271
Web Site: http://www.alliantinsurance.com
Insurance Services
N.A.I.C.S.: 524210
Tom Corbett (Chm & CEO)
Sherrie Aldrich (Dir-Education)
Greg Zimmer (Pres)
Sean McConlogue (Pres-Alliant Specialty Insurance Services)
Peter Carpenter (COO)
Ilene Anders (CFO)
Ralph Hurst (Pres-Natl Brokerage Grp)
Diana Kiehl (Chief Admin Officer)
Bob Bennetsen (Exec VP & Sr Mng Dir-Alliant Americas)
Kevin Overbey (Sr VP & Sr Mng Dir-Employee Benefits Grp)
James W Cystal (Vice Chm-Alliant Insurance Svcs)

Alliant/Mesirow Insurance Services (2)
353 N Clark St, Chicago, IL 60654
Tel.: (312) 595-6200
Web Site: http://www.alliant.com
Insurance Brokerage Services
N.A.I.C.S.: 524210
Brian Diedrich (Mng Dir & Exec VP-Employee Benefits)
Dana Mikstay (Exec VP-Life & Disability)
Mary Gould (Sr VP-Personal Lines)
Maureen Flood (Sr VP-Structured Settlements)
Jacquelyn Norstrom (Sr VP-Surety)

Andre-Romberg Insurance Agency, Inc. (2)
818 W Riverside Ste 800, Spokane, WA 99201
Tel.: (509) 624-3291
Web Site: http://andre-romberg.agentform.com
Sales Range: $1-9.9 Million
Emp.: 15
Insurance Agents
N.A.I.C.S.: 524210
Kenneth Kurt (First VP)
Ed Barker (VP)

Broken Arrow Insurance Agency, Inc. (2)
2720 N Hemlock Ct Ste A, Broken Arrow, OK 74012
Tel.: (918) 258-6681
Web Site: http://www.arrow-group.com
Sales Range: $1-9.9 Million
Emp.: 11
Insurance Agencies & Brokerages
N.A.I.C.S.: 524210

CLS Partners (2)
3600 N Capital of Texas Hwy Bldg B Ste 200, Austin, TX 78746
Tel.: (512) 306-9300
Insurance Agencies & Brokerages
N.A.I.C.S.: 524210
Clint Scott (Pres & CEO)

Confie Seguros Insurance Services, Inc. (2)
7711 Center Ave Ste 200, 92647, Huntington Beach, CA
Tel.: (714) 252-2500
Web Site: http://www.confie.com
Consumer Insurance Brokerage Services
N.A.I.C.S.: 551112
Darrin Silveria (Chief Sls Officer)

Subsidiary (Domestic):

Baja Auto Insurance (3)
6500 International Pkwy Ste 1500, Plano, TX 75093
Tel.: (214) 398-2252
Web Site:
  http://www.bajaautoinsurance.com
Insurance Agencies & Brokerages
N.A.I.C.S.: 524210
Aziz Noorani (CEO)

Best Rate Insurance Agency, Inc. (3)
3361 Cottage Hill Rd, Mobile, AL 36606-2712
Tel.: (251) 478-3331
Insurance Agencies & Brokerages
N.A.I.C.S.: 524210

CW Baker Insurance Agency, Inc. (3)
53 Walnut St, Lockport, NY 14095
Tel.: (716) 433-2690
Web Site: http://www.cwbaker.com
Sales Range: $1-9.9 Million
Emp.: 15
Insurance Services
N.A.I.C.S.: 524210
Timothy J. Smith (Pres)

Confie Holding II Co. (3)
7711 Ctr Ave Ste 200, Huntington Beach, CA 92647
Tel.: (714) 252-2500
Web Site: https://www.confie.com
Insurance Services
N.A.I.C.S.: 524298
Cesar M. Soriano (CEO)

Subsidiary (Domestic):

Acceptance Insurance Agency of Tennessee, Inc. (4)
247 N Calderwood St, Alcoa, TN 37701
Tel.: (865) 970-2034
Web Site:
  http://www.acceptanceinsurance.com
Insurance Agencies & Brokerages Services
N.A.I.C.S.: 524210

Estrella Insurance Inc. (4)
3750 W Flagler St, Miami, FL 33134-1602
Tel.: (305) 443-2829
Web Site: http://www.estrellainsurance.com
Sales Range: $25-49.9 Million
Emp.: 130
Provider of Insurance Products & Services
N.A.I.C.S.: 524210
Nicolas Estrella (Founder & Pres)
Yesenia Flores (Co-Owner)
Raysa Pino (Co-Owner)
Rosa Oller (Co-Owner & Mgr)

Southern Harvest Insurance Agency Inc. (4)
1515 S 7th St, 31015, Cordele, GA
Tel.: (229) 228-7475
Web Site: https://www.southernharvestinsurance.com
Insurance Agencies & Brokerages
N.A.I.C.S.: 524210

Subsidiary (Domestic):

Duane Sammons Insurance Center, Inc. (3)
1414 Broadway, Bellingham, WA 98225-3041
Tel.: (360) 647-0090
Web Site: http://www.duanesammons.com
Insurance Agencies & Brokerages

COMPANIES — STONE POINT CAPITAL LLC

N.A.I.C.S.: 524210
Duane Sammons (Pres)

Freeway Insurance Services Inc. (3)
1715 E Katella Ave Ste C, Orange, CA 92867
Tel.: (888) 259-9992
Web Site: http://www.freewayinsurance.com
Sales Range: $10-24.9 Million
Insurance Services
N.A.I.C.S.: 524210

Lockwood Agency, Inc. (3)
617 N Main St, Jamestown, NY 14701 (100%)
Tel.: (716) 664-3110
Web Site: http://www.lockwoodagency.com
Emp.: 3
Insurance Agencies & Brokerages
N.A.I.C.S.: 524210
Mark Lockwood (Pres)
David Lockwood (VP)
Sue Kent (Office Mgr & Sr CSR)

Most Insurance Agency (3)
801 N Armenia Ave, Tampa, FL 33609
Tel.: (813) 347-5555
Web Site: http://www.mostins.com
Insurance Management Services
N.A.I.C.S.: 524298
Nora Sanchez (Acct Mgr)
Bob Most (Founder)
Eric Most (VP)

Realty Support Services, Inc. (3)
PO Box 15206, Santa Ana, CA 92735
Tel.: (714) 558-8041
Web Site: https://www.calins.com
Insurance Agencies & Brokerages
N.A.I.C.S.: 524210

Subsidiary (Domestic):

Wm K Lyons Agency, Inc. (4)
2100 F St Ste 200, Bakersfield, CA 93301
Tel.: (661) 327-9731
Web Site: http://www.wmklyons.com
Insurance Agencies & Brokerages
N.A.I.C.S.: 524210
Patricia Solis (Acct Mgr-Personal Lines)
Heidi Dickson (Acct Mgr-Comml Lines)

Subsidiary (Domestic):

Seguros sin Barreras Insurance Agency, Inc. (3)
6380 Wilshire Blvd Ste 1400, Los Angeles, CA 90048
Tel.: (323) 782-7400
Web Site: http://www.segurossinbarreras.com
Insurance Agent & Broker Services
N.A.I.C.S.: 524210
Janet Mendez (Mgr-Corp Affairs)

Stonewood Insurance Services, Inc. (3)
2701 Citrus Rd Ste A, Rancho Cordova, CA 95742
Tel.: (800) 396-1485
Web Site: http://www.stonewoodinsurance.com
Insurance Agent/Broker
N.A.I.C.S.: 524210

Survival Insurance, Inc. (3)
6380 Wilshire Blvd Ste 1400, Los Angeles, CA 90048
Tel.: (800) 870-4838
Web Site: http://www.survivalinsurance.com
Sales Range: $150-199.9 Million
Insurance Services
N.A.I.C.S.: 524210

Vern Fonk Insurance, Inc. (3)
23830 Pacific Hwy S Ste 104, Kent, WA 98032
Tel.: (253) 943-2212
Web Site: http://www.vernfonk.com
Sales Range: $1-9.9 Million
Emp.: 5
Insurance Agents, Brokers & Service
N.A.I.C.S.: 524210

Subsidiary (Domestic):

Degginger, McIntosh & Associates, Inc. (2)
3977 Harbour Pointe Blvd SW, Mukilteo, WA 98275
Tel.: (206) 232-6000

Insurance Related Activities
N.A.I.C.S.: 524298

FJC & Associates, Inc. (2)
14 Church Hill Rd Ste B6, Newtown, CT 06470
Tel.: (203) 364-1092
Web Site: http://www.fjcpensions.com
Retirement Plan Design & Administration Services
N.A.I.C.S.: 525110
Karen Colavito (Office Mgr)

Farmin Rothrock & Parrott, Inc. (2)
2110 N Washington, Spokane, WA 99205-4702 (100%)
Tel.: (509) 323-3232
Web Site: http://www.frpins.com
Emp.: 100
Insurance Services
N.A.I.C.S.: 524210

Frank Crystal & Co. Inc. (2)
32 Old Slip, New York, NY 10005
Tel.: (212) 344-2444
Web Site: http://www.crystalco.com
Insurance Brokers
N.A.I.C.S.: 524210
Jonathan Crystal (Exec VP & Mng Dir)
Robert Amendola (Exec Mng Dir)
Michael S. Grant (Exec Mng Dir)
Lou Roca (Exec Mng Dir)
Jonathan Gilbert (Sr Mng Dir-Mergers & Acq)
Janis Garone (Mng Dir-Ops & Corp Client Svcs)
James W. Crystal (Chm & CEO)

Fred Daniel & Sons, Inc. (2)
5727 S Lewis Ste 420, Tulsa, OK 74105
Tel.: (918) 582-8206
Insurance Agencies & Brokerages
N.A.I.C.S.: 524210

Group Insurance, Incorporated of Louisiana (2)
3636 S Sherwood Forest Blvd Ste 111, Baton Rouge, LA 70816
Tel.: (225) 293-1770
Web Site: http://www.groupinsuranceinc.com
Sales Range: $150-199.9 Million
Emp.: 10
Medical Insurance Brokerage; Accident & Health
N.A.I.C.S.: 524210
Dan Jumonville (Chm & Pres)
Carla Jumonville (Sec)
Phyllis Chambers (Dir-Pur)
Eric Harrington (COO)

Subsidiary (Domestic):

Insurance Services of America Inc. (3)
3636 S Sherwood Forest Blvd Ste 370, Baton Rouge, LA 70816
Tel.: (225) 292-3222
Web Site: http://www.insuranceservicesofamerica.com
Emp.: 5
General Insurance Services
N.A.I.C.S.: 524210

Seniors Advisory Services Inc. (3)
3636 S Sherwood Forest Blvd Ste 370, Baton Rouge, LA 70816
Tel.: (225) 293-0013
Web Site: http://www.seniorsadvisoryservices.com
Emp.: 1
General Insurance Services
N.A.I.C.S.: 524210

Subsidiary (Domestic):

Hecht & Hecht Insurance Agency, Inc. (2)
425 NE Hancock St, Portland, OR 97212
Tel.: (503) 542-1130
Web Site: http://www.hechtins.com
Insurance Agencies & Brokerages
N.A.I.C.S.: 524210
Larry Hecht (Pres)
Philip Brus (Mgr)
Joel Ankerich (Mgr-Acct)
Ann Cole (Mgr-Acct)
Lena Overmyer (Mgr-Acct)
Samantha Peschka (Mgr-Acct)

Subsidiary (Non-US):

INVISION Benefit, Inc. (2)
Tel.: (847) 428-9200
Insurance Related Activities
N.A.I.C.S.: 524298
Mark Castillo (Owner)

Subsidiary (Domestic):

Mary Roach Insurance Agency, Inc. (2)
7395 N Palm Bluffs Ave Ste 103, Fresno, CA 93711
Tel.: (559) 437-0550
Web Site: http://www.mricrop.com
Group Insurance Services
N.A.I.C.S.: 524210
Mary Roach (Founder & Pres)

Mcanally Wilkins LLC (2)
11116 W CR-127, Odessa, TX 79765
Tel.: (214) 205-2423
Web Site: http://www.mcanallywilkins.com
Insurance Agencies & Brokerages
N.A.I.C.S.: 524210
Christophe McAnally (Owner)

North County Insurance (2)
570 Rancheros Dr Ste 100, San Marcos, CA 92069
Tel.: (760) 745-9511
Web Site: http://www.northcountyinsurance.com
Insurance Agencies & Brokerages
N.A.I.C.S.: 524210
John Giamanco (Pres)

Preferred Concepts, LLC (2)
14 Wall St 18th Fl, New York, NY 10005
Tel.: (646) 218-3278
Web Site: http://www.preferredconcepts.com
Sales Range: $1-9.9 Million
Emp.: 50
Insurance Agencies & Brokerages
N.A.I.C.S.: 524210
Stuart Farber (Chm & CEO)
Catherine R. Pipitone (Exec VP & Dir-Customer Svcs-Underwriting Div)
Joseph Chamberlain (Sr VP & Mgr-Underwriting Ops)
Maura Fields-Ryan (VP-Preferred Underwriting)
Robert Lynch (Sr VP-Preferred Underwriting)
Robert Rodia (Sr VP-Comml Accts-Preferred Underwriting Unit)
Shawn K. Young (VP-Preferred Underwriting)
David Palchik (VP-Preferred Underwriting)
Michael S. Ryan (COO)
Francesca D'Angelo (Sr Exec VP-Underwriting)

Subsidiary (Domestic):

Metro Insurance Services, Inc. (3)
100 Morris Ave Ste 201, Springfield, NJ 07081
Tel.: (973) 467-4467
Web Site: http://www.metroins.com
Insurance Agent/Broker
N.A.I.C.S.: 524210

Subsidiary (Domestic):

Seafax, Inc. (2)
62 US Route 1, Cumberland Foreside, ME 04110
Tel.: (207) 773-3533
Web Site: http://www.seafax.com
Rev.: $6,500,000
Emp.: 58
Credit Bureaus
N.A.I.C.S.: 561450
Anne Ollmann (VP-Engrg)
David B. Weatherbie (Principal & Treas)
George Babeu (Principal)
Sheldon Hamilton (VP-Sls & Mktg)
Frank Martino (Sr VP-Credit Svcs, Consulting & Client Relationships)
James M. Bonnvie (Pres)
Mike DeLuca (Principal)
Richard Kelly (VP-Collections & Risk Mgmt Svcs)

Senior Market Sales, Inc. (2)
8420 W Dodge Rd 5th Fl, Omaha, NE 68114
Tel.: (402) 397-3311

Web Site: http://www.seniormarketsales.com
Emp.: 300
Insurance & Financial Services
N.A.I.C.S.: 524298
Jim Summers (Pres)
Milton M. Kleinberg (CEO)
Dan C. Drennen (Dir-Intl Benefits & Travel Insurance)
Dwane McFerrin (VP-Medicare Solutions)

Subsidiary (Domestic):

Agency Services of Arkansas, Inc. (3)
11807 Hinson Rd, Little Rock, AR 72212
Tel.: (501) 224-7739
Web Site: http://www.theasagroup.com
Sales Range: $1-9.9 Million
Emp.: 12
Insurance Agencies & Brokerages
N.A.I.C.S.: 524210
Walter Ramsey (Pres)

Subsidiary (Domestic):

TCOR Insurance Management, Ltd. (2)
1421 Hanz Dr, New Braunfels, TX 78130
Tel.: (830) 387-7019
Web Site: http://www.tcormanagement.com
Commercial Insurance Services
N.A.I.C.S.: 524210
Ross Dubney (Office Mgr)
Brannon Brooke (Partner)
Cory Brooke (Partner)
Rick Dudney (Mng Partner)

The Arlen Group, Inc. (2)
2121 N California Blvd Ste 1000, Walnut Creek, CA 94596
Tel.: (925) 287-7200
Web Site: http://www.arlengroup.com
Sales Range: $25-49.9 Million
Emp.: 40
Employee Benefit Solutions
N.A.I.C.S.: 513210
Bret Goodman (Co-Founder & VP)
Roger Arlen (Co-Founder & CEO)

West Coast Insurance Services, Inc. (2)
916 Main St, Vancouver, WA 98660-3136
Tel.: (360) 695-3301
Web Site: http://www.biggsinsurance.com
Sales Range: $1-9.9 Million
Emp.: 35
Insurance Agencies & Brokerages
N.A.I.C.S.: 524210
Rich Biggs (Pres)

Whitboy, Inc. (2)
21 Cedar Ave, Fair Haven, NJ 07704-3264
Tel.: (732) 747-0800
Web Site: http://www.boyntonandboynton.com
Insurance Agencies & Brokerages
N.A.I.C.S.: 524210
Jay Lynch (Pres)
Ronald Gillaspie (COO & Exec VP)
Jim Woods (VP-Benefits)
John Bisbee (VP)
John Forrester (VP)
John Lambert (VP-Sls)
Kevin J. Byrne (VP-Boynton Healthcare)
Scott Hershkowitz (VP)
Steven Przybylski (Asst VP)
Don Warren (Mgr-Mktg)

AmTrust Financial Services, Inc. (1)
59 Maiden Ln 2nd Fl, New York, NY 10038
Tel.: (212) 220-7120
Web Site: https://amtrustfinancial.com
Sales Range: $5-14.9 Billion
Emp.: 6,063
Insurance Agencies & Brokerages
N.A.I.C.S.: 524210
Barry Dov Zyskind (Chm & CEO)
Stephen B. Ungar (Gen Counsel, Sec & Sr VP)
David H. Saks (Chief Legal Officer & Exec VP)
Adam Karkowsky (Pres)
Zachary Wolf (Exec VP-Strategic Dev & M&A)
Chaya M. Cooperberg (Chief People & Comm Officer & Exec VP)
J. Daniel Hickey (Grp Chief Underwriting Officer)

STONE POINT CAPITAL LLC

Stone Point Capital LLC—(Continued)

William Waddell-Dudley (Co-Head-Accident & Health)
Jahangez Chaudhery (Co-Head-Accident & Health)
Julian Griffiths (Exec VP-Underwriting)
Chris Coyne (Head-Ops)
Christopher Foy (Exec VP & Head-Comml Property & Casualty-North America)
Peter Dewey (Exec VP & Head-Intl)
Jeff Fenster (Head-North America Specialty Risk & Exec VP)
Todd Jaeger (CIO & Exec VP)
Andrew Morgan (Chief Claims Officer & Exec VP)
Daniel Hargraves (Exec VP & Head-Litigation)
Daniel Pacicco (CFO & Exec VP)
Steve Jennings (Sr VP-Underwriting)
Jeff Duncan (Exec VP-Comml Lines)
Hunter Hoffmann (CMO)

Subsidiary (Domestic):

ARI Casualty Company (2)
133 Franklin Corner Rd, Lawrenceville, NJ 08648
Tel.: (609) 882-7500
Property & Casualty Insurance Services
N.A.I.C.S.: 524210

AmCom Insurance Services, Inc. (2)
1655 Grant St Ste 700, Concord, CA 94520
Tel.: (925) 288-6780
Web Site: http://www.amcomins.com
Emp.: 120
Insurance Services
N.A.I.C.S.: 524298
David R. Hall (COO)

AmTrust Agriculture Insurance Services, LLC (2)
11300 Tomahawk Creek Pkwy Ste 300, Leawood, KS 66211
Tel.: (844) 350-2767
Agricultural Insurance Services
N.A.I.C.S.: 524126
Mark Raymie (Pres)

Subsidiary (Non-US):

AmTrust Central Bureau of Services Ltd. (2)
1 Minster North 4th Floor Mincing Lane, London, EC3R 7AA, United Kingdom
Tel.: (44) 2072806000
Property & Casualty Insurance Services
N.A.I.C.S.: 524210

AmTrust Claims Management SrL. (2)
Via Giovanni Porzio Snc, Naples, 80143, Italy
Tel.: (39) 0810168501
Insurance Services
N.A.I.C.S.: 524298

AmTrust Corporate Member Limited (2)
1 Great Tower Street, London, EC3R 5AA, United Kingdom
Tel.: (44) 2076968099
Insurance Management Services
N.A.I.C.S.: 524298

AmTrust Gestion Bolivia S.R.L. (2)
Torre de Negocios Oficina P-11 Sur Calle lo Cedros esquina Av, Las Ramblas Manzana 24 de la U V 58, Santa Cruz, Bolivia
Tel.: (591) 33888827
Casualty Insurance Services
N.A.I.C.S.: 524126

AmTrust Gestion Paraguay S.A. (2)
World Trade Center WTC Tower I - Floor 18 Aviadores del Chaco 2050, Asuncion, Paraguay
Tel.: (595) 974903013
Casualty Insurance Services
N.A.I.C.S.: 524126

AmTrust Gestion Peru S.A.C. (2)
Av Jorge Basadre 860 - 870 San Isidro, Lima, Peru
Tel.: (51) 16527241
Casualty Insurance Services
N.A.I.C.S.: 524126

AmTrust Insurance Luxembourg S.A. (2)
21 Rue Leon Laval, 3372, Leudelange, Luxembourg
Tel.: (352) 286755
Emp.: 5
Insurance Services
N.A.I.C.S.: 524298
Benjamin Bourseau (Gen Mgr)

AmTrust Insurance Services Norway AS (2)
Hakon VIIs Gate 6, 0161, Oslo, Norway
Tel.: (47) 40481888
Web Site: http://www.aisn.no
Insurance Brokerage Services
N.A.I.C.S.: 524210

Subsidiary (Domestic):

AmTrust International Insurance Ltd. (2)
59 Maiden Ln, New York, NY 10038
Tel.: (212) 220-7120
Web Site: http://www.amtrustgroup.com
Sales Range: $75-99.9 Million
Insurance Services
N.A.I.C.S.: 524210

Subsidiary (Non-US):

AmTrust Europe Ltd. (3)
Market Square House, St James's Street, Nottingham, NG1 6FG, United Kingdom
Tel.: (44) 115 941 1022
Web Site: http://www.amtrustinternational.com
Property & Casualty Insurance Services
N.A.I.C.S.: 524126

Subsidiary (Domestic):

AmTrust Europe Legal, Ltd. (4)
10Th Market Square House St James s Street Nottinghamshire, Nottingham, NG1 6FG, United Kingdom
Tel.: (44) 1159348983
Web Site: http://www.amtrustinternational.com
Emp.: 130
Insurance Services
N.A.I.C.S.: 524298
Denise Johnson (Dir-Mktg)

Subsidiary (Non-US):

AmTrust International Underwriters Limited (4)
40 Westland Row, Dublin, 2, Ireland
Tel.: (353) 1775 2900
Web Site: http://www.amtrusteurope.com
Sales Range: $1-9.9 Million
Emp.: 50
Insurance Services
N.A.I.C.S.: 524298

AmTrust Nordic AB (4)
Grev Turegatan 14, 114 46, Stockholm, Sweden (100%)
Tel.: (46) 8 4403 800
Web Site: http://www.amtrustinternational.com
Insurance Services
N.A.I.C.S.: 524298

Subsidiary (Domestic):

AmTrust North America, Inc. (2)
59 Maiden Ln, New York, NY 10038
Tel.: (212) 220-7120
Web Site: http://www.amtrustfinancial.com
Sales Range: $75-99.9 Million
Emp.: 50
Insurance Services
N.A.I.C.S.: 524210

Subsidiary (Domestic):

AmTrust North America (3)
4455 Lyndon B Johnson Freeway Ste 700, Dallas, TX 75244
Tel.: (214) 360-8000
Sales Range: $125-149.9 Million
Small Business Insurance Services
N.A.I.C.S.: 524128
Curtis P. Haag (Gen Mgr)

AmTrust North America of Florida, Inc. (3)
903 NW 65th St, Boca Raton, FL 33487
Tel.: (561) 962-9300
Web Site: http://www.amtrustfinancial.com
Insurance Services

N.A.I.C.S.: 524298

AmTrust Underwriters, Inc. (3)
500 Enterprise Dr Ste 3C, Rocky Hill, CT 06067
Tel.: (800) 215-7265
Web Site: http://www.amtrustgroup.com
Insurance Brokerage Services
N.A.I.C.S.: 524210

Subsidiary (Non-US):

AmTrust Re Aries S.A. (2)
412F Route d Esch, 1470, Luxembourg, Luxembourg
Tel.: (352) 2469531
Insurance Management Services
N.A.I.C.S.: 524298

AmTrust Underwriting Limited (2)
1 Great Tower Street, London, EC3R 5AA, United Kingdom
Tel.: (44) 2030036969
Web Site: http://www.amtrustunderwriting.com
Insurance Management Services
N.A.I.C.S.: 524292

AmTrust at Lloyd's Limited (2)
1 Great Tower Street, London, EC3R 5AA, United Kingdom
Tel.: (44) 2030036800
Web Site: http://www.amtrustatlloyds.com
Emp.: 1,590
Insurance Services
N.A.I.C.S.: 524298
Mike Sibthorpe (Dir-Underwriting)

Subsidiary (Domestic):

AmVenture Insurance Agency, Inc. (2)
PO Box 6208, Cleveland, OH 44101-1208
Tel.: (844) 508-6547
Web Site: http://amventure.com
Disability Insurance Services
N.A.I.C.S.: 524126

Subsidiary (Non-US):

Arc Legal Assistance Limited (2)
The Gatehouse Lodge Park Lodge Lane, Colchester, CO4 5NE, United Kingdom
Tel.: (44) 3447709000
Web Site: http://www.arclegal.co.uk
Insurance Agency Services
N.A.I.C.S.: 524298
Helen Withers (CEO)
James Waddy (Mgr-Comml Dev)
Rebecca Conway (Dir-Claims & Ops)
Peter Harvey (Head-Bus)

Subsidiary (Domestic):

Associated Industries Insurance Company, Inc. (2)
PO Box 812319, Boca Raton, FL 33481-2319
Tel.: (561) 962-9300
Insurance Agency & Brokerage Services
N.A.I.C.S.: 524210
Kerry Heitz (CFO & Treas)

Automotive Assurance Group, LLC (2)
236 Canal Blvd Unit 1, Ponte Vedra Beach, FL 32082
Tel.: (844) 242-6626
Web Site: http://www.automotiveassurance.com
Insurance Consulting Services
N.A.I.C.S.: 524210
Nick DAmico (Pres)
Ashley Coots (VP-Sls)
Christine Tyrrell (VP-Ops)

Builders & Tradesmen's Insurance Services, Inc. (2)
6610 Sierra College Blvd, Rocklin, CA 95677
Tel.: (916) 772-9200
Web Site: http://my.btsinc.com
Emp.: 100
Insurance Services
N.A.I.C.S.: 524298
Paul Hohlbein (Exec VP-Mktg)
Jeff Hohlbein (Gen Counsel)
Lisa Erickson (Exec VP-Admin)

Builders Insurance Services, LLC (2)

U.S. PRIVATE

5 Centerpointe Ste 350, Lake Oswego, OR 97035
Tel.: (503) 431-2381
Web Site: http://www.insurancebis.com
Insurance Services
N.A.I.C.S.: 524298
Steve Gaines (Pres)
Todd Nelson (Sr VP)
Brandy Florence (Mgr-OR, MT & WY)
Bill Litwin (Mgr-WA & ID Territory)
Sally Steindorf (Sr VP & Mgr-Underwriting)

Subsidiary (Non-US):

Car Care Plan Limited (2)
Jubilee House 5 Mid Point Business Park, Thornbury, Bradford, BD3 7AG, West Yorkshire, United Kingdom
Tel.: (44) 3445738000
Web Site: http://www.carcareplan.com
Vehicle Insurance Services
N.A.I.C.S.: 524298
Tim Heavisides (Grp CEO)
Paul Newton (COO)
Simon Wright (CFO)
Mike Cowling (Head-Sls-Non Mfg Sls)
Philip Morrison (Head-Corp Sls)
Richard Hornby (Head-Sls Dev)

Collegiate Management Services Limited (2)
18 Mansell Street, London, E1 8FE, United Kingdom
Tel.: (44) 2074593456
Web Site: http://www.collegiate.co.uk
Insurance Carrier Services
N.A.I.C.S.: 524126
Salin Talavdekar (Controller-Financial)

Composite Assistance Limited (2)
Suffolk House Trade Street, Cardiff, CF10 5DT, United Kingdom
Tel.: (44) 8714237417
Web Site: http://compositeassistance.co.uk
Insurance Services
N.A.I.C.S.: 524298

Composite Legal Expenses Limited (2)
18 Park Place, Cardiff, CF10 3DQ, United Kingdom
Tel.: (44) 2920222033
Web Site: http://www.composite-legal.com
Insurance Services
N.A.I.C.S.: 524298
Tim Mullin (Head-Bus Dev)
David Gilchrist (Head-Underwriting)
Alan Walters (Gen Mgr)
Andrew Kenyon (Mgr-Claims)
Michael Jenkins (Head-Legal Advice Centre)

Composite Legal Services Limited (2)
Suffolk House Trade Street, Cardiff, CF10 5DT, United Kingdom
Tel.: (44) 8714235240
General Insurance Services
N.A.I.C.S.: 524210

Subsidiary (Domestic):

Contractor Managing General Insurance Agency, Inc. (2)
20335 Ventura Blvd Ste 426, Woodland Hills, CA 91364-2458
Web Site: http://www.cmgia.com
Insurance Agencies & Brokerages
N.A.I.C.S.: 524210
Chilo Crane (Mgr)

CorePointe Insurance Company (2)
401 S Old Woodward Ave Ste 300, Birmingham, MI 48009
Tel.: (800) 782-9164
Web Site: http://www.corepointeinsurance.com
Automotive Property & Casualty Insurance Services
N.A.I.C.S.: 524126

Subsidiary (Domestic):

CorePointe Insurance Agency, Inc. (3)
401 S Old Woodward Ave Ste 300, Birmingham, MI 48009
Tel.: (734) 456-5486
Web Site: http://corepointeinsurance.com
Insurance Services

COMPANIES — STONE POINT CAPITAL LLC

N.A.I.C.S.: 524298

Subsidiary (Non-US):

Dent Wizard Ventures Limited (2)
Dunton Park, Sutton Coldfield, B76 9EB, Warwickshire, United Kingdom
Tel.: (44) 1675470267
Web Site: http://www.dentwizard.co.uk
Automobile Insurance Services
N.A.I.C.S.: 524126
Richard Hornby *(Mng Dir)*

Dore Underwriting Services Limited (2)
1 Great Tower Street, London, EC3R 5AA, United Kingdom
Tel.: (44) 2071521319
Web Site: http://www.agdore.com
Insurance Management Services
N.A.I.C.S.: 524298
Siobhan Davies *(Deputy Mgr-Claims)*
Dominic Frost *(Head-Special Lines)*
David Siddle *(Mgr-Claims)*

Finagra Group Limited (2)
The Loom Suite 3 3 14 Gower s Walk, London, E1 8PY, United Kingdom
Tel.: (44) 2070639300
Web Site: http://finagragroup.com
Coffee Merchant Whslr
N.A.I.C.S.: 424490
David Margulies *(Chm)*
Ogi Krsmanovic *(Head-Mktg)*
Michael Murungi *(Mng Dir)*
Ho Huu Dung *(Gen Mgr)*

Subsidiary (Domestic):

First Atlantic Title Insurance Corp. (2)
611 Lynnhaven Pkwy Ste 200, Virginia Beach, VA 23452-7335
Tel.: (757) 431-8900
Web Site: http://www.firstatlantictitlegroup.com
Insurance Management Services
N.A.I.C.S.: 524298

First Nationwide Title Agency LLC (2)
220 E 42nd St, New York, NY 10017
Tel.: (212) 499-0100
Web Site: http://www.firstnationwidetitle.com
Insurance Agency Services
N.A.I.C.S.: 524210
Steven Napolitano *(Pres & CEO)*
Steven Laforgia *(Exec VP)*
Michael Antonucci *(Sls Mgr)*
Bernadette Cuevas *(Mng Dir)*
Elizabeth Joyce *(Exec VP)*

First Nationwide Title Agency of Texas, LLC (2)
600 Congress Ave 14th Fl, Austin, TX 78701
Tel.: (512) 808-4120
Insurance Agency Services
N.A.I.C.S.: 524210

First Nonprofit Companies, Inc. (2)
233 N Michigan Ave Ste 1000, Chicago, IL 60601
Tel.: (312) 239-8385
Web Site: http://www.firstnonprofitcompanies.com
Property Insurance Services
N.A.I.C.S.: 524298
Cruz Mendez *(Asst Dir-Sls & Mktg)*

First Nonprofit Insurance Company (2)
1 S Wacker Dr Ste 2380, Chicago, IL 60606
Tel.: (312) 715-3010
Web Site: http://www.firstnonprofit.com
Property Insurance Services
N.A.I.C.S.: 524298
Christopher Finkley *(VP-Ops-Insurance)*
Steven R. Wellbank *(VP-Property & Casualty Claims)*
Robert White *(Pres)*
Richard J. Dacey *(CFO & Sr VP)*
Trish Shanahan *(VP-Nonprofit Rels)*
Deb Zborowski *(VP-Reg Ops & Programs)*
Joe Poretto *(VP-Sls & Mktg)*
Philip R. Warth Jr. *(CEO)*

Subsidiary (Non-US):

GMAC International Insurance Services Limited (2)
Gmac House 35-39 Castle Street, High Wycombe, HP13 6RN, United Kingdom
Tel.: (44) 1494470721
Insurance Management Services
N.A.I.C.S.: 524298

Gadget Repair Solutions Limited (2)
Unit 19 & 20 Roach View Business Park Millhead Way, Millhead Way, Rochford, SS4 1LB, Essex, United Kingdom
Tel.: (44) 3713322088
Web Site: http://www.gadgetrepairsolutions.com
Emp.: 50
Electronics Repair Services
N.A.I.C.S.: 811210
Anthony Calton *(Dir-Intl Dev)*
Andrew Shelton *(Dir-Ops)*
Stuart Barclay *(Mng Dir)*

Subsidiary (Domestic):

I.G.I. Underwriting Agency, Inc. (2)
59 Maiden Ln, New York, NY 10038-4502
Tel.: (212) 220-7120
Insurance Brokerage Services
N.A.I.C.S.: 524210

Subsidiary (Non-US):

Motors Insurance Company Limited (2)
Jubilee House 5 Mid Point Business Park, Thornbury, Bradford, BD3 7AG, West Yorkshire, United Kingdom
Tel.: (44) 3445736256
Web Site: http://www.motors-insurance.co.uk
Insurance Management Services
N.A.I.C.S.: 524291
Tim Heavisides *(Grp CEO)*
Paul Newton *(COO)*
Simon Wright *(CFO)*
Gary Whitelam *(Mng Dir-Car Care Plan Insurance)*
Mark Holley *(Head-Underwriting)*
Dave Kelly *(Head-Actuarial)*

Nationale Waarborg B.V. (2)
Dukatenburg 88A, 3437, Nieuwegein, Netherlands
Tel.: (31) 302205546
Web Site: http://nationalewaarborg.nl
Insurance Carrier Services
N.A.I.C.S.: 524126

Subsidiary (Domestic):

Northcoast Warranty Services, Inc. (2)
Maxine Nugent 8995 Westside Pkwy, Alpharetta, GA 30009
Tel.: (817) 585-6337
Insurance Services
N.A.I.C.S.: 524298

OwnerGUARD Corporation (2)
1785 Hancock St Ste 100, San Diego, CA 92110-2051
Tel.: (619) 228-0100
Web Site: http://www.ownerguard.com
Insurance & Financial Services
N.A.I.C.S.: 524210

PDP Group, Incorporated (2)
10909 McCormick Rd, Hunt Valley, MD 21031
Tel.: (410) 584-1651
Web Site: http://www.pdpgroupinc.com
Insurance Agency Services
N.A.I.C.S.: 524210
John Yarbrough *(Dir-Bus Dev)*

PDP Holdings, Inc. (2)
102 Woodmont Blvd Ste 350, Nashville, TN 37205
Tel.: (866) 737-3611
Web Site: http://www.pdpholdings.com
Surgical & Medical Instrument Mfr
N.A.I.C.S.: 339112

Subsidiary (Non-US):

PT Tecprotec (2)
The H Tower Floor 12A-Unit E Jalan HR Rasuna Said Kav 20, Kuningan, Indonesia
Tel.: (62) 2129533296
Insurance Management Services
N.A.I.C.S.: 524298

Primero Seguros, S.A. de C.V. (2)
Cerro de la Silla 919, Monterrey, 64060, CP, Mexico
Tel.: (52) 8180480500
Web Site: http://www.primeroseguros.com
Insurance Services
N.A.I.C.S.: 524298
Alejandro Gonzalez-Davila *(Pres)*

Subsidiary (Domestic):

Risk Services, LLC (2)
1605 Main St Ste 800, Sarasota, FL 34236
Tel.: (941) 955-0793
Web Site: http://www.riskservcos.com
Insurance Services
N.A.I.C.S.: 524298
Michael T. Rogers *(Chm & CEO)*
Troy Winch *(VP)*

Subsidiary (Domestic):

Risk Services-Vermont, Inc. (3)
58 E View Ln Ste 2, Barre, VT 05641
Tel.: (802) 223-2200
Insurance Brokerage Services
N.A.I.C.S.: 524210

Subsidiary (Domestic):

Rochdale Insurance Company (2)
59 Maiden Ln 6th Fl, New York, NY 10038
Tel.: (212) 220-7120
Insurance Brokerage Services
N.A.I.C.S.: 524210

Sequoia Insurance Company (2)
31 Upper Ragsdale Dr, Monterey, CA 93940
Tel.: (831) 333-9880
Insurance Services
N.A.I.C.S.: 524298

TMI Solutions, LLC (2)
360 Market Pl, Roswell, GA 30075
Tel.: (404) 566-4920
Web Site: http://www.tmisolutions.org
Software Protection Development Services
N.A.I.C.S.: 541511
Tom Manger *(Mng Partner)*
Karen Johnson *(VP-Client & Employee Rels)*
Virgil Ruff *(VP-Ops)*
Will Hendrick *(VP-Bus Dev)*
Theresa Maddox *(Mgr-Admin & Facilities)*

Subsidiary (Non-US):

Tecprotec Asia Private Limited (2)
301 3rd Floor Echo House Vishweshwar Colony Off Aarey Road, Mumbai, 400063, Maharashtra, India
Tel.: (91) 2265309200
Insurance Management Services
N.A.I.C.S.: 524298

Tecprotec Sdn Bhd (2)
308B Phileo Damansara Ii Jalan 16/11 Off Jalan Damansara, 46350, Petaling Jaya, Malaysia
Tel.: (60) 379549141
Web Site: http://www1.tecprotec.com.my
Insurance Management Services
N.A.I.C.S.: 524298
Merk Simmons *(Gen Mgr)*

Therium Capital Management Limited (2)
11 Staple Inn, London, WC1V 7QV, United Kingdom
Tel.: (44) 2033273460
Web Site: http://www.therium.com
Insurance Services
N.A.I.C.S.: 524298
Martin Middleton *(Controller-Fin)*
Jo Mepham *(Mgr-Ops)*

Subsidiary (Domestic):

Therium Inc. (2)
1460 BRdway, New York, NY 10036
Tel.: (212) 951-0570
Property & Casualty Insurance Services
N.A.I.C.S.: 524210
Neil Purslow *(Founder & Chief Investment Officer)*

Total Program Management, LLC (2)
4175 Veterans Memorial Hwy Ste 306, Ronkonkoma, NY 11779
Tel.: (888) 773-2238
Web Site: http://tpmrisk.com
Insurance Agency Services
N.A.I.C.S.: 524210

Unified Grocers Insurance Services (2)
874 S Vlg Oaks Dr, Covina, CA 91724
Tel.: (626) 915-1951
Web Site: http://www.unifiedgrocers.com
Insurance Services
N.A.I.C.S.: 524298
Leon G. Bergmann *(Exec VP-Sls & Procurement)*
Daniel J. Murphy *(Exec VP-Fresh Programs & Mfg)*
Christine Neal *(CFO, Treas & Exec VP)*
Dick W. Gonzales *(Chief HR Officer & Sr VP)*
Robert M. Ling Jr. *(Pres & CEO)*

Vista Surety Insurance Solutions, LLC (2)
17771 Cowan Ste 100, Irvine, CA 92614
Tel.: (949) 263-3440
Web Site: http://www.vistasurety.com
Insurance Services
N.A.I.C.S.: 524298
Kevin Jackson *(Mgr)*
Harry Crowell *(Chm)*
Sam Zaza *(Pres)*

Warrantech Corporation (2)
2200 Hwy 121, Bedford, TX 76021
Tel.: (817) 785-6601
Web Site: http://www.warrantech.com
Sales Range: $100-124.9 Million
Emp.: 349
Automotive Warranty Services
N.A.I.C.S.: 524128
Jeanine M. Folz *(Sr VP)*
Laurence Tutt *(COO & Sr VP-IT)*
Thomas J. Fontanetta *(Sr VP-Sys Dev)*
John Sauers *(VP-Field Ops)*
Shaun Hickson *(Pres-Consumer Product Svcs)*

Subsidiary (Domestic):

Warrantech Automotive, Inc. (3)
PO Box 1179, Bedford, TX 76095
Tel.: (800) 723-1154
Web Site: http://www.wtechauto.com
Sales Range: $100-124.9 Million
Vehicle Service Contract Services
N.A.I.C.S.: 532111

Warrantech Consumer Product Services Group (3)
2200 Hwy 121, Bedford, TX 76021
Tel.: (817) 785-6601
Web Site: http://www.warrantech.com
Sales Range: $50-74.9 Million
Emp.: 100
Extended Insurance Services
N.A.I.C.S.: 524128

Warrantech Direct, Inc. (3)
2200 Hwy 121, Bedford, TX 76021
Tel.: (817) 785-6601
Web Site: http://www.warrantech.com
Sales Range: $125-149.9 Million
Service Plan Marketing
N.A.I.C.S.: 524128

Warrantech Home Service Company (3)
2200 Hwy 121 Ste 100, Bedford, TX 76021
Tel.: (800) 342-5349
Web Site: http://www.warrantech.com
Insurance Brokerage Services
N.A.I.C.S.: 524210

Subsidiary (Domestic):

Warranty Solutions Management Corporation (2)
7125 W Jefferson Ave Ste 200, Lakewood, CO 80235
Tel.: (303) 987-5500
Web Site: http://www.warrantysolutions.com
Vehicle Service Contracts, Automotive Finance & Insurance Products & Services
N.A.I.C.S.: 524126
Adam Pope *(Pres)*

Beeline.com, Inc. (1)
12724 Gran Bay Pkwy W Ste 200, Jacksonville, FL 32258
Tel.: (904) 527-5700
Web Site: http://www.beeline.com
Emp.: 500

STONE POINT CAPITAL LLC

Stone Point Capital LLC—(Continued)
Vendor Management Systems & Workforce Management Solutions
N.A.I.C.S.: 513210
Doug Leeby *(CEO)*
Autumn Vaupel *(COO)*
Colleen Tiner *(Sr VP-Product Mgmt)*
Ron Litton *(Exec VP-Global Sls)*
Manuel Roger *(Sr VP-EMEA Markets & Ops)*
Sherri Hammons *(CTO)*
Barry Capoot *(CFO)*
Brian Hoffmeyer *(VP-Mktg Strategies)*
Elijah Bradshaw *(Mgr-HR)*
Jessica Ashcraft *(VP-Mktg)*
Michael Schiappa *(Chief Procurement Officer)*

Subsidiary (Domestic):

Employer Services Corporation (2)
20 Pineview Dr, Buffalo, NY 14228
Tel.: (716) 691-4455
Web Site: http://www.myesc.com
Emp.: 50
Recruitment Process Outsourcing Services
N.A.I.C.S.: 561330
Greg M. Bauer *(Founder & Pres)*
Joanne M. Bauer *(Exec VP-Community Dev)*
Linda M. Doran *(Exec VP-Fin & Acctg)*
Liz Warren *(Exec VP-HR)*
Jan Owczarczak *(VP-Bus Dev)*
Kim M. Bartolotti *(Exec VP-Strategic Ops)*
Michael Cichon *(Engr-Technical Support-IT Dept)*
Rachael Brown *(Dir-Bus Dev)*
Lindsay Jones *(Mgr-Benefits & Customer Onboarding)*
Cheryl Somers *(Mgr-Payroll)*
Carol Vosburgh *(Mgr-Acctg)*
Bill Warren *(Asst Mgr-Benefits)*
Jillian Suttell *(Controller)*

CoreLogic, Inc. (1)
40 Pacifica, Irvine, CA 92618
Tel.: (949) 214-1000
Web Site: http://www.corelogic.com
Rev.: $1,642,375,000
Assets: $4,283,222,000
Liabilities: $3,559,960,000
Net Worth: $723,262,000
Earnings: $301,355,000
Emp.: 5,300
Fiscal Year-end: 12/31/2020
Consumer, Financial & Property Information Services
N.A.I.C.S.: 519290
James L. Balas *(CFO)*
Patrick L. Dodd *(Pres, CEO, COO & Chief Growth Officer)*
Bob Frosell *(CIO)*
Aaron Henry *(Chief Legal Officer & Sec)*
Devi Mateti *(Pres-Enterprise Entity Solutions)*
Waqas Cheema *(Chief Transformation Officer)*
Lisa Claes *(Mng Dir-Intl)*
WeiLing Jang *(CMO)*

Subsidiary (Non-US):

ACN 108 719 197 PTY LTD (2)
L 1 1100 Waymouth St, Adelaide, 5000, SA, Australia
Tel.: (61) 413491415
Emp.: 4
Real Estate Services
N.A.I.C.S.: 237210

ADL SOFTWARE PTY LTD (2)
PO Box 364, Wilston, Brisbane, 4051, QLD, Australia
Tel.: (61) 733671982
Web Site: http://www.adlsoftware.com
Software Development Services
N.A.I.C.S.: 541512

Subsidiary (Domestic):

Breakaway Holdings, LLC (2)
14100 Parke-Long Ct Ste G, Chantilly, VA 20151
Tel.: (703) 953-3866
Web Site: http://www.homevisit.com
Marketing Services
N.A.I.C.S.: 541613
Greg Trzaska *(Founder)*

CDS Business Mapping, LLC (2)
100 Riverview Ctr Ste 150, Middletown, CT 06457
Tel.: (617) 737-4444
Web Site: http://www.riskmeter.com
Digital Mapping Sales & Solutions
N.A.I.C.S.: 541370

Subsidiary (Non-US):

CORELOGIC NZ LIMITED (2)
Level 2 275 Cuba St, Wellington, 6011, New Zealand
Tel.: (64) 49156000
Web Site: http://www.corelogic.co.nz
Property Information & Geospatial Solution Provider
N.A.I.C.S.: 531990
Nick Goodall *(Head-Res)*
Tom Coad *(Head-Product)*
Paul White *(Head-SME)*

Cordell Information Pty Ltd (2)
Level 10 10 Help Street, Chatswood, 2067, NSW, Australia
Tel.: (61) 299345555
Web Site: http://www.cordellconnect.com.au
Emp.: 160
Engineeering Services
N.A.I.C.S.: 541330

Subsidiary (Domestic):

CoreLogic Background Data, LLC (2)
3001 Hackberry Rd, Irving, TX 75063
Tel.: (866) 234-4455
Real Estate Services
N.A.I.C.S.: 531390

CoreLogic Credco LLC (2)
12395 1st American Way, Poway, CA 92064
Tel.: (619) 938-7012
Web Site: http://www.credco.com
Sales Range: $25-49.9 Million
Emp.: 100
Credit Reporting Services
N.A.I.C.S.: 561450

CoreLogic Flood Services, LLC (2)
11902 Burnet Rd, Austin, TX 78758
Tel.: (512) 834-9595
Web Site: http://www.floodcert.com
Sales Range: $100-124.9 Million
Emp.: 400
Flood Insurance Coverage
N.A.I.C.S.: 524298

CoreLogic National Background Data, LLC (2)
PO Box 772277, Ocala, FL 34477-2277
Tel.: (352) 629-9904
Web Site: http://www.nationalbackgrounddata.com
Sales Range: $50-74.9 Million
Criminal History Database Information Services
N.A.I.C.S.: 513140

CoreLogic REO Asset Management (2)
40 Pacifica Ste 900, Irvine, CA 92618
Tel.: (949) 214-1000
Web Site: http://www.corelogic.com
Sales Range: $300-349.9 Million
Asset Disposition & Real Estate Management Services
N.A.I.C.S.: 531210

CoreLogic Rental Property Solutions, LLC (2)
PO Box 509124, San Diego, CA 92150
Tel.: (888) 333-2413
Real Estate Services
N.A.I.C.S.: 531390

Subsidiary (Non-US):

CoreLogic SARL (2)
7 Rue Drouot, 75009, Paris, France
Tel.: (33) 144790101
Software Development Services
N.A.I.C.S.: 541512
Michel Voronkoff *(Mgr-Europe Modelling)*

Subsidiary (Domestic):

CoreLogic SafeRent, LLC (2)
11140 Rockville Pike, Rockville, MD 20852-3106
Tel.: (301) 881-3400
Web Site: http://www.fadvsaferent.com
Sales Range: $25-49.9 Million
Emp.: 100
Multifamily Housing Resident Screening Services
N.A.I.C.S.: 561611

Division (Domestic):

Jenark Business Systems, Inc. (3)
7300 Westmore Rd Ste 3, Rockville, MD 20850
Tel.: (301) 840-6292
Web Site: http://www.jenark.com
Sales Range: $100-124.9 Million
Property Management Software Developer
N.A.I.C.S.: 513210

Subsidiary (Non-US):

CoreLogic Solutions Limited (2)
6th Floor South Tower 26 Elmfield Road, Bromley, BR1 1WA, Kent, United Kingdom
Tel.: (44) 2082281288
Web Site: http://www.corelogicsolutions.co.uk
Sales Range: Less than $1 Million
Emp.: 10
Automated Real Estate Valuation Products
N.A.I.C.S.: 531390

Subsidiary (Domestic):

CoreLogic Solutions, LLC (2)
40 Pacifica Ste 900, Irvine, CA 92618
Tel.: (949) 214-1000
Web Site: http://www.corelogic.com
Real Estate Investment Services
N.A.I.C.S.: 525990

CoreLogic Tax Collection Services, LLC (2)
1 CoreLogic Dr Bldg 4, Westlake, TX 76262
Tel.: (877) 442-2797
Real Estate Services
N.A.I.C.S.: 237210

CoreLogic Transportation Services (2)
94 Acoma Blvd S Ste 101, Lake Havasu City, AZ 86403
Tel.: (928) 680-9449
Web Site: http://www.fadvtransportation.com
Sales Range: $900-999.9 Million
Trucking Industry Credit Information Services
N.A.I.C.S.: 519290

Subsidiary (Non-US):

CoreLogic UK Limited (2)
Fore 2 2 Huskisson Way, Shirley, Solihull, B90 4SS, United Kingdom
Tel.: (44) 3331231414
Web Site: http://www.corelogic.uk
Residential Estate Management Services
N.A.I.C.S.: 531390
Jim Driver *(Mng Dir)*
David Driver *(Comml Dir)*
Mark Blackwell *(COO)*

Subsidiary (Domestic):

CoreLogic Valuation Services, LLC (2)
12395 1st American Way, Poway, CA 92064
Tel.: (619) 938-7078
Web Site: http://www.appraisals.com
Sales Range: $150-199.9 Million
Emp.: 185
Electronic Valuation Solutions for the Real Estate Industry
N.A.I.C.S.: 531320

CoreLogic Valuation Solutions, Inc. (2)
3256 Shetland Rd, Beavercreek, OH 45434
Tel.: (937) 671-1745
Real Estate Services
N.A.I.C.S.: 531390

DataQuick Information Systems, Inc. (2)
9530 Towne Centre Dr, San Diego, CA 92121
Tel.: (858) 597-3100

Web Site: http://www.dataquick.com
Real Estate Information Services
N.A.I.C.S.: 519290

Subsidiary (Domestic):

DataQuick Title LLC (3)
5700 Smetana Dr Ste 300, Minnetonka, MN 55343
Tel.: (952) 933-8804
Web Site: http://www.dataquicktitle.com
Title Insurance Products & Services
N.A.I.C.S.: 524127

Subsidiary (Non-US):

ECMK Limited (2)
Fore 2 2 Huskisson Way, Shirley, Solihull, B90 4SS, United Kingdom
Tel.: (44) 3331231418
Web Site: http://www.ecmk.co.uk
Accreditation Training Services
N.A.I.C.S.: 611519
Joe Mellon *(Dir-Comml)*
Stephen Farrow *(Mgr-Accreditation Scheme)*
Rob Cartwright *(Product Dir-Energy Solutions)*

Subsidiary (Domestic):

FNC, Inc. (2)
1214 Ofc Park Dr, Oxford, MS 38655
Tel.: (662) 236-2020
Web Site: http://www.fncinc.com
Real Estate Collateral Information Software Publisher
N.A.I.C.S.: 513210
Greg Dennis *(Exec VP-Ops)*
Michael Mitchell *(Chief Strategy Officer & Dir-Bus Dev)*
Kimberly Taylor *(Dir-Support Ops)*
Gwen Knight *(Mgr-Customer Support)*
Pat Brown *(Mgr-Contracts & Reporting)*
Bethany Cooper *(Partner-HR Bus & Coord-Corp Recruitment & Talent)*

Finiti Group, LLC (2)
7090 Samuel Morse Dr, Columbia, MD 21046-3442
Tel.: (443) 259-1000
Real Estate Investment Services
N.A.I.C.S.: 525990

Subsidiary (Non-US):

Intersect (2)
30 Adelaide St E, Toronto, M5C 3G8, ON, Canada
Tel.: (416) 924-2784
Web Site: http://www.weareintersect.com
Mobile Application Development Services
N.A.I.C.S.: 541511

Subsidiary (Domestic):

Location Inc. Group Corporation (2)
120 Front St Ste 420, Worcester, MA 01608
Tel.: (508) 753-8029
Web Site: http://locationinc.com
Risk Management Software Development Services
N.A.I.C.S.: 541511
Andrew Schiller *(Chm & CEO)*
Andy Couture *(VP-Sls)*
Chris Kokkinos *(VP-Product Dev)*
Paul Gallagher *(Dir-Mktg)*

Marshall & Swift/Boeckh, LLC (2)
10001 W Innovation Dr Ste 102, Milwaukee, WI 53226
Tel.: (262) 780-2800
Web Site: http://www.msbinfo.com
Sales Range: $25-49.9 Million
Emp.: 350
Residential & Commercial Property Valuation Products & Services
N.A.I.C.S.: 531390

Mercury Network, LLC (2)
501D NE 122nd St, Oklahoma City, OK 73114
Tel.: (405) 300-1450
Web Site: http://www.mercuryvmp.com
Management Software Provider
N.A.I.C.S.: 513210

Subsidiary (Domestic):

Platinum Data Solutions, Inc. (3)

COMPANIES — STONE POINT CAPITAL LLC

12 Journey Ste 200, Aliso Viejo, CA 92656-5335
Tel.: (888) 794-0455
Web Site: http://www.platdata.com
Business Services Technology Providers
N.A.I.C.S.: 561499

Subsidiary (Domestic):

National Tax Search, LLC (2)
130 S Jefferson St Ste 300, Chicago, IL 60601
Tel.: (800) 426-7466
Web Site: http://www.nationaltaxsearch.com
Real Estate Consulting Service
N.A.I.C.S.: 531210

Next Gear Solutions, LLC (2)
304 Heritage Dr Ste 2, Oxford, MS 38655
Tel.: (866) 769-7855
Web Site: http://www.nextgearsolutions.com
Restoration Company Consulting Services & Management Software
N.A.I.C.S.: 513210

Subsidiary (Domestic):

Accurence, Inc. (3)
305 S Arthur Ave, Louisville, CO 80027
Tel.: (303) 500-5799
Web Site: http://www.accurence.com
Smart Property Insurance Services
N.A.I.C.S.: 513210

Subsidiary (Non-US):

REALTOR.COM.AU PTY LTD (2)
L 21 2 Market St, Sydney, 2000, NSW, Australia
Tel.: (61) 731149999
Web Site: http://www.corelogic.com.au
Emp.: 300
Real Estate Services
N.A.I.C.S.: 531210

Subsidiary (Domestic):

RELS, LLC (2)
8009 34th Ave S Ste 1300, Minneapolis, MN 55425
Tel.: (952) 933-8804
Real Estate Asset Valuation & Appraisal Services
N.A.I.C.S.: 531320

RES Direct, LLC (2)
8009 34th Ave S Ste 500, Bloomington, MN 55425-1616
Tel.: (952) 876-4300
Real Estate Investment Services
N.A.I.C.S.: 525990

Subsidiary (Non-US):

RP DATA NEW ZEALAND LIMITED (2)
Level 2 275 Cuba Street, PO Box 4072, Wellington, 6140, New Zealand
Tel.: (64) 800355355
Web Site: http://www.rpnz.co.nz
Real Estate Information Provider
N.A.I.C.S.: 531390

RP DATA VALUATION SERVICES PTY LTD (2)
Burwood Road 529, Hawthorn East, Melbourne, 3122, VIC, Australia
Tel.: (61) 388033199
Information Management Services
N.A.I.C.S.: 513199

RP Data Limited (2)
6 Eagleview Place, Eagle Farm, 4009, QLD, Australia
Tel.: (61) 731149999
Web Site: http://www.rpdata.com
Sales Range: $50-74.9 Million
Emp.: 350
Online Real Estate Information Services
N.A.I.C.S.: 531390

Subsidiary (Domestic):

Symbility Solutions Corp. (2)
Ste 200 100 Country Club Dr, Hendersonville, TN 37075
Risk Management Software Development Services
N.A.I.C.S.: 541511
Jeff Brinkman *(Sr VP-Client Dev)*

Subsidiary (Non-US):

Symbility Solutions GmbH (2)
Stammheimer Strasse 10, 70806, Kornwestheim, Germany
Tel.: (49) 621232010
Risk Management Software Development Services
N.A.I.C.S.: 541511

Symbility Solutions Limited (2)
The Old Stables Home Farm Cams Hall Estate, Fareham, PO16 8UT, Hampshire, United Kingdom
Tel.: (44) 3303801282
Risk Management Software Development Services
N.A.I.C.S.: 541511
Michael Porter *(Sr VP-Intl Markets)*

Symbility Solutions, Inc. (2)
30 Adelaide St E Ste 500, Toronto, M5C 3G8, ON, Canada
Tel.: (647) 775-8600
Web Site: https://www.symbilitysolutions.com
Rev.: $25,513,981
Assets: $30,247,319
Liabilities: $6,846,691
Net Worth: $23,400,628
Earnings: ($76,473)
Emp.: 174
Fiscal Year-end: 12/31/2017
Software Development Services
N.A.I.C.S.: 513210

Subsidiary (Domestic):

Automated Benefits Inc. (3)
111 Peter Street Suite 901, Toronto, M5V 2H1, ON, Canada
Tel.: (416) 359-9339
Web Site: http://www.adjudicare.com
Health & Dental Claim Software Development Services
N.A.I.C.S.: 541511

Symbility Solutions Inc. (3)
30 Adelaide E Suite 500, Toronto, M5C 3G8, ON, Canada
Tel.: (866) 796-2454
Web Site: http://www.symbilitysolutions.com
Insurance Software Development Services
N.A.I.C.S.: 541511

Subsidiary (Domestic):

a la mode, Inc. (2)
3705 West Memorial 402, Salt Lake City, UT 73134
Tel.: (405) 359-6587
Web Site: http://www.alamode.com
Real Estate Software
N.A.I.C.S.: 513210

Subsidiary (Non-US):

eTech Solutions Limited (2)
Fore 2 2 Huskisson Way Shirley, Solihull, B90 4SS, United Kingdom
Tel.: (44) 3331231414
Web Site: http://www.etech.net
Emp.: 120
Real Estate Services
N.A.I.C.S.: 531390

Credit Infonet Group, Inc. (1)
4540 Honeywell Ct, Dayton, OH 45424-5760
Tel.: (937) 235-8900
Web Site: http://www.cingroup.com
Law firm
N.A.I.C.S.: 541110
Susan Berry *(CEO)*

Eliassen Group, LLC (1)
55 Walkers Brook Dr 6th Fl, Reading, MA 01867
Tel.: (800) 354-2773
Web Site: http://www.eliassen.com
IT Staffing Services; Data Management & Technical, Consulting & Training Services for Bio-Pharma & Medical Device Industries
N.A.I.C.S.: 561311
Anthony Valente *(CFO)*
Mike McBrierty *(Exec VP)*
Peggy Murphy *(Sr VP)*
Scott Cordeiro *(Exec VP-Pro Svcs)*
Mark Biscoe *(Pres)*
Jonathan Mann *(Gen Counsel & VP)*
Thomas Hart *(COO)*
Greg Coir *(Exec VP)*
Joe Ventura *(Chief People Officer)*
Kris Kurcoba *(VP-Mid Atlantic Region)*
Tom Renda *(VP-New England Reg)*
Chad Durden *(VP-Southwest Region)*
Todd Butler *(VP-Sls & Bus Dev)*
Heather Jordan *(VP-HR)*
Josh Nazarian *(Chief Bus Dev Officer)*
Sandra G. Callahan *(VP-Mktg)*
Melissa Brenner *(Exec VP-Integrations & Ops Strategy)*
Sally Bauer *(Sr VP-Cloud Svcs)*
Michael Lane *(Sr VP-Risk Mgmt & Bus Optimization)*
Robert Conder *(Reg VP-Southeast)*
David MacKeen Jr. *(CEO)*

Subsidiary (Domestic):

Ferguson Consulting Inc. (2)
1350 Timberlk Mnr Pkwy, Chesterfield, MO 63017
Tel.: (636) 728-4401
Web Site: http://www.fergusonconsultinginc.com
Emp.: 57
Custom Computer Programming Services
N.A.I.C.S.: 541511
Susan Ferguson *(Pres & CEO)*

Foothills Consulting Group, Inc. (2)
101 S 1st St Ste 405, Burbank, CA 91502
Tel.: (818) 845-1525
Web Site: http://www.foothillscg.com
Sales Range: $1-9.9 Million
Emp.: 36
Management Consulting Services
N.A.I.C.S.: 541618
Philip Ashworth *(VP-Ops-Los Angeles)*

Principle Solutions Group, LLC (2)
5 Concourse Pkwy Ste 2700, Atlanta, GA 30328
Tel.: (770) 399-4500
Web Site: http://www.eliassen.com
IT Staffing & Consulting Services
N.A.I.C.S.: 561320
Addy Schilling *(Office Mgr)*
Patti Vetter *(Mgr-Acct)*
Heather Jordan *(Dir-HR)*
Kelly Meadows *(Dir-Recruiting)*
Erin Gilley *(Sr Acct Mgr)*
Corali Nogueras *(Sr Acct Mgr)*
Corey West *(Sr Acct Mgr)*
Todd Butler *(VP-Sls & Bus Dev)*

Project One Inc. (2)
450 Fashion Ave Ste 1701, New York, NY 10123-1701
Tel.: (212) 268-5800
Web Site: http://www.project1.com
Technology Consulting & Staffing Services
N.A.I.C.S.: 541512
Gary S. Zander *(Founder, Pres & CEO)*

Safenet Consulting, LLC (2)
5810 Baker Rd, Minnetonka, MN 55343
Tel.: (952) 930-3636
Web Site: http://www.safenetconsulting.com
Rev.: $11,300,000
Emp.: 75
Computer Software Systems Analysis & Design
N.A.I.C.S.: 541511
Martin Miller *(Pres)*
Bob Purdy *(CEO)*
Angela Savasta *(Mgr-Bus Dev)*
Cortney Ihde *(Mgr-Mktg & Bus Dev)*
Brad Zepecki *(Mng Partner)*
Michael Fox *(Dir-Project Svcs)*
Ryan Bennett *(Mng Dir)*

The Armada Group, Inc. (2)
325 Soquel Ave Ste A, Santa Cruz, CA 95062
Web Site: http://www.thearmadagroup.com
Software Publisher
N.A.I.C.S.: 513210
Lisa Y. Sullivan *(VP-Client Rels)*

The Evanston Group, LLC (2)
1 S Wacker Dr Ste 2130, Chicago, IL 60606
Tel.: (847) 424-1020
Web Site: http://www.evanstongroup.com
Sales Range: $10-24.9 Million
Emp.: 11
Information Technology Consulting Services
N.A.I.C.S.: 541512
Kay Anderson *(Pres & CEO)*
Michael Anderson *(Co-Pres & COO)*
Tamara McKnight *(VP-Fin & Ops)*

VIA Technical, LLC (2)
591 Camino De La Reina Ste 929, San Diego, CA 92108
Tel.: (619) 704-1400
Web Site: http://www.via-technical.com
Sales Range: $1-9.9 Million
Human Resource Consulting Services
N.A.I.C.S.: 541612
Natalie Viani *(Owner & CEO)*
Amy Balko *(Office Mgr)*

Enlyte Group, LLC (1)
9771 Clairemont Mesa Blvd Ste A, San Diego, CA 92124
Tel.: (866) 389-2069
Web Site: https://www.enlyte.com
Clinical Software; Other Casualty Claims Management & Case Management Services
N.A.I.C.S.: 513210

Subsidiary (Domestic):

Mitchell International, Inc. (2)
6220 Greenwich Dr, San Diego, CA 92122
Tel.: (858) 368-7000
Web Site: http://www.mitchell.com
Information Retrieval Services
N.A.I.C.S.: 517810
Erez Nir *(Exec VP & CTO)*
Debbie Day *(Exec VP & Gen Mgr-Auto Physical Damage Bus Unit)*
Dave Torrence *(Exec VP & Gen Mgr-Pharmacy Solutions, Strategy & Corp Dev)*
M. G. Kristian *(Exec VP-People & Workplace)*
Stephanie Kroon *(Gen Counsel, Sec & Sr VP)*
Norman Brown *(Exec VP & CFO)*
Steve Laudermilch *(Exec VP-Casualty Solutions Grp & Gen Mgr-Casualty Solutions Grp)*

Subsidiary (Domestic):

Fairpay Solutions, Inc. (3)
14295 Midway Rd Ste 300, Addison, TX 75001
Tel.: (972) 715-8000
Sales Range: $1-9.9 Million
Emp.: 75
Insurance Claims Management Services
N.A.I.C.S.: 524292
Chad Birckelbaw *(Pres & CEO)*
Mark Castellanet *(Exec VP-Sls & Bus Dev)*
Dionne Lacey-Artis *(Exec VP-Sls & Acct Mgmt)*

GENEX Services, LLC (3)
440 E Swedesford Rd Ste 1000, Wayne, PA 19087
Tel.: (610) 964-5100
Web Site: http://www.genexservices.com
Managed Care Services & Solutions
N.A.I.C.S.: 541611
Delphia B. Frisch *(COO & Exec VP)*
Ronald J. Skrocki *(Sr VP-Product Mgmt & Dev)*
Joe Weitzman *(CIO & Sr VP)*
Tim Howard *(Sr VP-Field Case Mgmt)*
Brandon Patch *(CFO & Sr VP)*

Subsidiary (Domestic):

Alpha Review Corporation (4)
1933 N Meacham Rd Ste 300, Schaumburg, IL 60173
Tel.: (630) 305-8108
Web Site: http://www.alphareview.com
Medical Bill Auditing Specialists
N.A.I.C.S.: 541219

Subsidiary (Non-US):

GENEX Services of Canada, Inc. (4)
9 6975 Meadowvale Town Centre Circle Suite 411, Mississauga, L5N 2V7, ON, Canada
Tel.: (905) 817-9730
Web Site: http://www.genexservices.com
Managed Care Services; Health Management Solutions
N.A.I.C.S.: 541618

Subsidiary (Domestic):

M Hayes & Associates, LLC (4)
225 International Circle Ste 201, Hunt Valley, MD 21030
Tel.: (410) 628-4050

STONE POINT CAPITAL LLC

U.S. PRIVATE

Stone Point Capital LLC—(Continued)
Insurance Services
N.A.I.C.S.: 524298

Objective Medical Assessments Corporation (4)
401 2nd Ave S Ste 110, Seattle, WA 98104 (100%)
Tel.: (206) 324-6622
Web Site: http://www.omacinc.com
Medical Information Claims Related Decisions
N.A.I.C.S.: 524114
Steffen Nelson (Pres)

Options & Choices, Inc. (4)
10700 E Geddes Ave Ste 200, Englewood, CO 80112
Tel.: (303) 967-9611
Web Site: http://optis.com
Integrated Information Systems
N.A.I.C.S.: 541511
Bryan Stonecipher (CEO)
Mike Quast (Dir-Client Ops)
John-Alex Bailey (Dir-SIs)
Andy Kersh (Dir-Data Analytics)
Teddy Corn (Dir-Tech)

Subsidiary (Domestic):

PMOA, Inc. (3)
676 University Blvd, Mobile, AL 36609
Tel.: (800) 486-8792
Web Site: http://www.pmoainc.com
Pharmacy Benefit Management Solutions Provider
N.A.I.C.S.: 541618

Focus Financial Partners Inc. (1)
875 3rd Ave 28th Fl, New York, NY 10022
Tel.: (646) 519-2456
Web Site: https://focusfinancialpartners.com
Rev.: $2,143,321,000
Assets: $4,866,754,000
Liabilities: $3,563,459,000
Net Worth: $1,303,295,000
Earnings: $91,784,000
Emp.: 5,000
Fiscal Year-end: 12/31/2022
Holding Company; Investment Advisory & Wealth Management Services
N.A.I.C.S.: 551112
Ruediger Adolf (Co-Founder, Chm & CEO)
James Shanahan (CFO)
Rajini Sundar Kodialam (Co-Founder & COO)
Leonard R. Chang (Co-Founder, Sr Mng Dir & Head-M&A)

Subsidiary (Domestic):

Focus Financial Partners, LLC (2)
875 3rd Ave 28 Fl, New York, NY 10022
Tel.: (646) 519-2456
Web Site: https://www.focusfinancialpartners.com
Sales Range: $1-4.9 Billion
Investment Advisory & Wealth Management Services
N.A.I.C.S.: 523940
Ruediger Adolf (Co-Founder, Chm & CEO)
James Shanahan (CFO)
Leonard R. Chang (Co-Founder & Sr Mng Dir)
Faizan Tukdi (VP & Asoc Gen Counsel)
Rajini Kodialam (COO)
Eric Amar (Mng Dir)
Travis Danysh (Mng Dir)
Pradeep Jayaraman (Mng Dir)
Sukanya Kuruganti (Mng Dir)
Timothy Connor (VP)
Alexander Gleeson (VP)
Brian Gracia (VP)
Tony Khalilov (VP)
Peter Lydon (VP)
Alec Pickering (VP)
Jack Spitsin (VP)

Subsidiary (Domestic):

BFSG, LLC (3)
2040 Main St Ste 720, Irvine, CA 92614
Tel.: (949) 955-2552
Web Site: https://www.bfsg.com
Investment Consulting & Wealth Management Services
N.A.I.C.S.: 523940
Christopher Rowey (Principal)
Michael Allbee (Chief Compliance Officer)

Subsidiary (Domestic):

Pacwest Financial Management, Inc. (4)
1643 E Bethany Home Rd, Phoenix, AZ 85016
Tel.: (888) 997-8882
Web Site: http://www.pacwestfn.com
Investment Consulting Services
N.A.I.C.S.: 523940

Subsidiary (Domestic):

Bridgewater Wealth & Financial Management LLC (3)
7475 Wisconsin Ave Ste 600, Bethesda, MD 20814
Tel.: (301) 656-1200
Web Site: http://www.bridgewaterwealth.com
Wealth Management Services
N.A.I.C.S.: 523940
Ron Rubin (CEO & Mng Partner)
Jessica Brede (CFO & Partner)
Steve Schuler (Chief Investment Officer & Partner)
Nina Mitchell (Partner & Sr Wealth Advisor)
Wayne Zussman (Partner & Sr Wealth Advisor)
Kim Allred (Chief Compliance Officer & Dir-Client Svcs)
Jane DiNardo (Dir-Human Capital)

Buckingham Asset Management, LLC (3)
8182 Maryland Ave Ste 500, Saint Louis, MO 63105
Tel.: (314) 725-0455
Web Site: http://www.buckinghamassetmanagement.com
Emp.: 400
Investment Advisory & Management Services
N.A.I.C.S.: 523940

Subsidiary (Domestic):

Buckingham Strategic Partners, LLC (4)
8182 Maryland Ave Ste 500, Saint Louis, MO 63105
Tel.: (314) 725-0455
Web Site: https://www.buckinghamstrategicpartners.com
Investment Advisory Services
N.A.I.C.S.: 523940
Jared Kizer (Chief Investment Officer)
Alex Potts (Pres)
Adam Birenbaum (CEO)
Kristen Donovan (Dir-Retirement Solutions)
Mike Clinton (Chief Bus Officer)
Steven Atkinson (Mng Dir)
Howard Lee (Mng Dir-Svc, Trading & Ops)
Cynthia Chu (VP-Advisor Svcs)
Amy Michaelson (Dir-Trading)

Subsidiary (Domestic):

Connectus Group LLC (3)
875 3rd Ave 28th Fl, New York, NY 10022
Tel.: (646) 560-4000
Financial Services
N.A.I.C.S.: 523999

Crestwood Advisors Group, LLC (3)
1 Liberty Square, Suite 500, Boston, MA 02109
Tel.: (617) 523-8880
Web Site: https://www.crestwoodadvisors.com
Emp.: 100
Investment Advice
N.A.I.C.S.: 523940
J. Michael Costello (Mng Partner)
Michael Eckton (CEO & Mng Partner)

Subsidiary (Domestic):

Crestwood Advisors LLC (4)
50 Federal St, Boston, MA 02110
Tel.: (617) 523-8880
Web Site: http://www.crestwoodadvisors.com
Rev.: $1,000,000
Emp.: 9
Portfolio Management
N.A.I.C.S.: 523940

Michael Eckton (CEO, Mng Partner & Portfolio Mgr)
John W. Morris (Mng Partner & Mgr-Wealth)
Michelle Herd (Mgr-Relationship)
Roy Treible (Chief Compliance Officer, Partner & Mng Dir-Client Svc & Ops)
Alyson L. Nickse (Mgr-Rels)
Leah R. Sciabarrasi (Pres)

Endurance Wealth Management, Inc. (4)
121 N Main St, Providence, RI 02903-1309
Tel.: (401) 854-0993
Web Site: http://www.endurancewealth.com
Offices of Real Estate Agents & Brokers
N.A.I.C.S.: 531210
J. Michael Costello (Founder)
John J. Webber (Dir-Res)

Subsidiary (Domestic):

Douglas C Lane & Associates, Inc. (4)
885 2nd Ave 42nd Fl, New York, NY 10017
Tel.: (212) 262-7670
Web Site: https://www.dclainc.com
Emp.: 33
Investment Advice
N.A.I.C.S.: 523940
Douglas C. Lane (Co-Founder, Partner & Portfolio Mgr)

Fort Pitt Capital Group, Inc. (3)
680 Anderson Dr, Pittsburgh, PA 15220
Tel.: (412) 921-1822
Web Site: http://www.fortpittcapital.com
Portfolio Management
N.A.I.C.S.: 523940
Charlie Smith (Partner & Chief Investment Officer)

Jones Barclay Boston (3)
1718 Gaylord St, Denver, CO 80206
Web Site: http://www.jb2.net
Investment Advice
N.A.I.C.S.: 523940
Lynda Hanshaw (Gen Mgr)

Kovitz Investment Group, LLC (3)
71 S Wacker Dr Ste 1860, Chicago, IL 60606
Tel.: (312) 334-7300
Web Site: https://www.kovitz.com
Rev.: $3,600,000
Emp.: 30
Portfolio Management
N.A.I.C.S.: 523940
Jonathan A. Shapiro (Co-Founder, Principal & Portfolio Mgr)
Joel D. Hirsh (Principal & Portfolio Mgr)
Marc S. Brenner (Co-Founder, Pres & Principal)
Mitch A. Kovitz (Co-Founder, Principal & Portfolio Mgr)
Mark C. Rosland (Principal)
Bruce A. Weininger (Principal)
Edward W. Edens (Principal)
Leonard S. Gryn (Principal)
Theodore J. Rupp (Principal)
Robert A. Contreras (Principal & Gen Counsel)
Patrick B. Wiese (CIO & Principal)
Harold Gianopulos Jr. (Principal)

Subsidiary (Domestic):

Northern Capital Management, LLC (4)
8000 Excelsior Dr Ste 201, Madison, WI 53717-1914
Tel.: (608) 831-8018
Web Site: http://www.norcap.com
Sales Range: $150-199.9 Million
Emp.: 10
Investment & Asset Management Services
N.A.I.C.S.: 523940
Stephen L. Hawk (Chm & CEO)
Daniel T. Murphy (Pres & Chief Investment Officer)
Paul A. Perry (Dir-Acct Mgmt)

Subsidiary (Domestic):

Patton Albertson & Miller Group, LLC (3)
3340 Peachtree Rd NE Ste 2320, Atlanta, GA 30326
Tel.: (404) 917-2727
Web Site: http://www.pattonalbertsonmiller.com

Financial Investment Activities
N.A.I.C.S.: 523999
James B. Patton (Co-Founder & CEO)
J. Marc Albertson (Co-Founder & Dir-Client Svcs)
Jennifer McCarthy (Partner)
Julia A. Davis (Partner)
R. David Maloy Jr. (Partner)

Telemus Capital Partners, LLC (3)
2 Towne Sq Ste 800, Southfield, MI 48076
Tel.: (248) 827-1800
Web Site: http://www.telemus.com
Sales Range: $1-4.9 Billion
Emp.: 25
Investment Advisory Services
N.A.I.C.S.: 523940
Gary Ran (Chm, CEO & Partner)
Robert J. Schlagheck (CFO)
Andrew Bass (Mng Dir & Chief Wealth Officer)
Eric C. Oppenheim (COO, Gen Counsel & Mng Dir)
Joshua S. Levine (Partner)
Mary Bakhaus (Partner & Sr Portfolio Mgr)
Thomas E. Uber (Portfolio Mgr-Municipal Bonds)
James M. Housler (Partner)
Matthew Espinosa (Mgr-Portfolio Acctg)
Lloyd A. Perlmutter (COO)
David Post (Chief Investment Officer)
Lyle Mathew Wolberg (Partner)

The Colony Group, LLC (3)
2 Atlantic Ave, Boston, MA 02110
Tel.: (617) 723-8200
Web Site: http://www.thecolonygroup.com
Sales Range: $25-49.9 Million
Emp.: 140
Wealth Management Services
N.A.I.C.S.: 523940
Michael J. Nathanson (Chm, Pres & CEO)
Stephen T. Sadler (Mng Dir)
Elisabeth L. Talbot (Mng Dir)
Brian W. Katz (Chief Investment Officer & Pres-Colony Investment Mgmt)
Seth P. Hieken (Exec VP & Dir-Proprietary Strategies)
Stephen R. Stelljes (Pres-Client Svcs)
Cheryl L. Wilkinson (Exec VP)
Gina K. Bradley (COO & Gen Counsel)
Vincent J. Gratch (Chief Compliance Officer)
Robert J. Glovsky (Vice Chm)
Cary P. Geller (Mng Dir)
Amy C. McMaster (Dir-Investment Svcs)
Denise M. Duffy (VP)
Erin H. Manganello (VP)
Jay A. Lupica (Sr VP)
Jeffrey T. Craig (VP)
Nan Vlad (Sr VP)
Ted Schiela (Sr VP)
Terri A. Feeney (CFO)
Faith A. Hill (Deputy Chief Compliance Officer)
Robert H. Schundler (VP & Dir-Res)
Jonathan Thrun (VP & Dir-Fixed Income)
John C. White (Chief Admin Officer)
Andrew J. Wig (VP & Dir-Equity Portfolios)
Robert Kohl (Principal & VP)
Alexander I. Hock (Principal & VP)
Ian Barclay (Mng Dir-Rocky Mountain)
Tim Delay (Officer-Bus Dev)
Jennifer Geoghegan (Chief Strategy Officer)
Max Haspel (Mng Dir & Principal)
Matthew C. Ilteris (Principal & VP)
Craig S. Jones (Mng Dir-Rocky Mountain)
Jeremy K. Kuhlen (Principal & VP)

Vestor Capital, LLC (3)
10 S Riverside Plz Ste 1400, Chicago, IL 60606
Tel.: (312) 641-2400
Web Site: https://www.vestorcapital.com
Investment Advisory Services
N.A.I.C.S.: 523999
Martin Buehler (Partner)

Freepoint Commodities LLC (1)
599 W Putnam Ave, Greenwich, CT 06830
Tel.: (203) 542-6000
Web Site: http://www.freepoint.com
Sales Range: $100-124.9 Million
Commodity Trading & Marketing Services
N.A.I.C.S.: 523160
Frank Gallipoli (Pres)
Rob Feilbogen (COO)
Michael Beck (Exec VP)
Daniel Hecht (Gen Counsel)

COMPANIES

STONE POINT CAPITAL LLC

Sheldon Pang (Vice Chm)
David A. Messer (CEO)

Grace Hill, LLC (1)
15 S Main St Ste 500, Greenville, SC 29601
Web Site: http://www.gracehill.com
Educational Support Services
N.A.I.C.S.: 611710
Christi Dobbins (Dir-Validate Success)
Robert Gettys (VP-Bus Dev)
Kendall Pretzer (COO)
Adam Kaufman (Sr VP-Mktg)
Mark Piening (Sr VP-Sls)
Keely Leonard (Mgr-PR)

Subsidiary (Domestic):

Elizabeth Moreland Consulting, Inc. (2)
956 Carlisle Rd, Chipley, FL 32428-4359
Tel.: (850) 415-3430
Web Site: http://www.taxcredit.com
Tax Preparation Services
N.A.I.C.S.: 541213
Elizabeth Moreland (Pres)

Kingsley Associates, Inc. (2)
44 Montgomery St Ste 1430, San Francisco, CA 94104
Tel.: (415) 777-1140
Web Site: http://www.kingsleyassociates.com
Administrative Management & General Management Consulting Service
N.A.I.C.S.: 541611
John Falco (Principal)
A. J. Rao (COO)
Brandon Campen (Exec VP-Ops)
Lisa Green (VP)
Steve Kingsley (Pres)

HireRight Holdings Corporation (1)
100 Centerview Dr Ste 300, Nashville, TN 37214
Tel.: (615) 320-9800
Web Site: https://www.hireright.com
Rev.: $806,668,000
Assets: $1,605,747,000
Liabilities: $1,037,429,000
Net Worth: $568,318,000
Earnings: $144,574,000
Emp.: 3,078
Fiscal Year-end: 12/31/2022
Holding Company
N.A.I.C.S.: 551112
Guy Abramo (Pres & CEO)
Thomas Spaeth (CFO)
Mark Dzialga (Chm)
Laurie Blanton (Chief Acctg Officer & Sr VP)

Subsidiary (Domestic):

Dexter Group Holdings LLC (2)
2900 Industrial Pkwy E, Elkhart, IN 46516
Tel.: (574) 295-7888
Web Site: https://www.dextergroup.com
Trailer Parts Mfr & Distr
N.A.I.C.S.: 336212

Fingerprint Solutions, LLC (2)
917 Chapin Rd, Chapin, SC 29036
Web Site: https://www.fingerprintsolutions.com
Background Check Services
N.A.I.C.S.: 561611

Subsidiary (Non-US):

HireRight AU Pty Ltd (2)
PO Box 40, Boolaroo, Lake Macquarie, 2284, NSW, Australia
Tel.: (61) 240230603
Background Check Services
N.A.I.C.S.: 561611

HireRight Background Screening India LLP (2)
Unit No 13 - 16 Level 7 Innovator Building ITPB Whitefield Main Rd, Bengaluru, 560066, India
Tel.: (91) 2249054399
Human Resouce Services
N.A.I.C.S.: 541612

HireRight UK Holding Limited (2)
15 Westferry Circus Canary Wharf, London, E14 4HD, United Kingdom
Tel.: (44) 2077672400
Human Resouce Services
N.A.I.C.S.: 541612

Home Point Capital LP (1)
1194 Oak Valley Dr Ste 80, Ann Arbor, MI 48108
Web Site: http://www.homepointfinancial.com
Private Investment Firm
N.A.I.C.S.: 523999
William Newman (CEO)

Pre-Paid Legal Services, Inc. (1)
1 Pre-Paid Way, Ada, OK 74820-5605
Tel.: (580) 436-1234
Web Site: http://www.legalshield.com
Legal Service Membership Plans
N.A.I.C.S.: 541199
Steve Williamson (Interim CFO)
Clark Burton (Mgr-Middle Tennessee)
Don Thompson (Pres-Network Div)
Martine Girotto (Pres-Canada)
Cara Whitley (CMO)
Hollon Kohtz (Dir-Publicity)
Stefan Pepe (Chm)

Rialto Capital Management, LLC (1)
790 NW 107th Ave Ste 400, Miami, FL 33172
Tel.: (305) 485-2077
Web Site: http://www.rialtocapital.com
Real Estate Investment Management Services
N.A.I.C.S.: 525990
Jay Mantz (Pres)
Illeanne Rukes (Sr VP-HR)
Liat Heller (Chief Compliance Officer & Gen Counsel)
Jeffrey Krasnoff (CEO)
Cory Olson (COO)
Joseph Bachosky (Mng Dir & Co-Head-Investment Mgmt)
Joshua Cromer (Mng Dir & Co-Head-Investment Mgmt)

Safe-Guard Products International, LLC (1)
2 Concourse Pkwy Ste 500, Atlanta, GA 30328
Web Site: http://www.safe-guardproducts.com
Financial & Insurance Services for Automotive Aftermarket Industry
N.A.I.C.S.: 524298
Jeffrey Koenig (CFO)
Randy Barkowitz (CEO)

Situs Holdings, LLC (1)
5065 Westheimer Rd Ste 700E, Houston, TX 77056
Tel.: (713) 328-4400
Web Site: http://www.situs.com
Holding Company; Financial & Real Estate Consulting, Lending & Managing Services
N.A.I.C.S.: 551112
Steven J. Powel (CEO)
Nick Rudenstine (Pres & COO)
Dave Declark (CFO)

Subsidiary (Domestic):

American Mortgage Consultants, Inc. (2)
630 3rd Ave Ste 1601, New York, NY 10017 (100%)
Tel.: (212) 247-5782
Web Site: http://www.amcfirst.com
Mortgage Consulting Services
N.A.I.C.S.: 541618

Subsidiary (Domestic):

Meridian Asset Services, LLC (3)
780 94th Ave N Ste 102, Saint Petersburg, FL 33702
Tel.: (727) 497-4650
Asset Management & Mortgage Services
N.A.I.C.S.: 525990

Subsidiary (Domestic):

Situs Group LLC (2)
5065 Westheimer Ste 700 E, Houston, TX 77056
Tel.: (713) 328-4400
Web Site: http://www.situs.com
Sales Range: $25-49.9 Million
Emp.: 125
Financial & Real Estate Consulting, Lending & Managing Services
N.A.I.C.S.: 541611

Lori Hadley (Mng Dir-Consulting Solutions)
Nick Rudenstine (Pres & COO)
Steven J. Powell (CEO)
Deina Arteaga (CFO)
Cecilia Panozzo (CMO)
James Watson (CIO)
Steven Bean (Exec Mng Dir-US Advisory & Bus Dev)
Warren Friend (Exec Mng Dir & Head-Product Strategy & Strategic Client Dev)
Zenobia Tambuvala (Exec Mng Dir-Structured Solutions & Head-Trng & Quality Control)
John Weaver (Exec Mng Dir-Strategic Platforms & Assets Under Mgmt)
George Wisniewski (Exec Mng Dir-Primary/Special Servicing)
Danielle Karpf (Head-HR-Global)
Tom Lawrence (Dir-Risk & Compliance)
Adriana Boudreaux (Asst Gen Counsel)
Dave DeClark (CFO)
Kenneth Riggs Jr. (Pres-Real Estate Res Corporation)

Subsidiary (Non-US):

Situs International Limited (2)
34th Floor 25 Canada Square, Canary Wharf, London, E14 5LB, United Kingdom
Tel.: (44) 2070716100
Web Site: http://www.situs.com
Investment Advisory Services
N.A.I.C.S.: 523940
Chip Good (Mng Dir)
Andrew Phillips (Mng Dir)

Subsidiary (Domestic):

Situs Europe Limited (3)
34th Floor 25 Canada Square, Canary Wharf, London, E14 5LB, United Kingdom
Tel.: (44) 20 7071 6100
Web Site: http://www.situs.com
Emp.: 50
Investment Advisory, Financial & Real Estate Consulting Services
N.A.I.C.S.: 525990
Cecilia Panozzo (CMO-US & Europe)
Chip Good (Mng Dir)
Cristina Tomas (Head-HR)

Subsidiary (Domestic):

SitusAMC Holdings Corporation (2)
150 E 52nd St Ste 4002, New York, NY 10022
Tel.: (212) 294-1300
Web Site: http://www.situs.com
Sales Range: $1-9.9 Million
Emp.: 40
Financial & Real Estate Consulting, Lending & Managing Services
N.A.I.C.S.: 551112
Andrew Phillips (Mng Dir)
Michael Franco (CEO)
Stanley Street (Vice Chm-SitusAMC Technologies)
Garry P. Herdler (CFO)
Andy Garrett (Head-Mktg)

Subsidiary (Domestic):

Street Resource Group, Inc. (3)
100 Bull St Ste 200, Savannah, GA 31401-3305
Tel.: (770) 390-3000
Web Site: http://www.streetresourcegroup.com
Administrative Management & General Management Consulting Service
N.A.I.C.S.: 541611
Stanley Street (Founder & CEO)

Tivity Health, Inc. (1)
Tel.: (615) 614-4929
Web Site: https://www.tivityhealth.com
Rev.: $481,252,000
Assets: $598,541,000
Liabilities: $479,634,000
Net Worth: $118,907,000
Earnings: $104,914,000
Emp.: 380
Fiscal Year-end: 12/31/2021
Comprehensive Care & Disease Management Services for Health Plans & Hospitals
N.A.I.C.S.: 524114
Ryan M. Wagers (Chief Acctg Officer & Controller)
Jill Meyer (VP-PR)

Stacey Santo (Chief Experience & Innovation Officer)
Ray Bilbao (Chief Legal Officer & Sec)
Jessica Erb (Chief Growth Officer)
Chris Morrison (Chief Admin Officer)
Caroline Khalil (COO)
Beth Cooper (CTO)
Natasha Deckmann (Chief Transformation Officer)
Hill Ferguson (Pres & CEO)
Kent Griffin (Chief Product Officer)

Subsidiary (Domestic):

American Healthways Services, Inc. (2)
3841 Green Hills Village Dr, Nashville, TN 37215-2691 (100%)
Tel.: (615) 665-1122
Sales Range: $50-74.9 Million
Emp.: 370
Health Care Srvices
N.A.I.C.S.: 621493

CareSteps.com (2)
701 Close Springs Blvd, Franklin, TN 37067 (100%)
Tel.: (615) 665-1122
Sales Range: $200-249.9 Million
Emp.: 750
Health Care Srvices
N.A.I.C.S.: 621410

Division (Domestic):

Healthways Health Support (2)
9280 S Kyrene Rd Ste 107, Tempe, AZ 85284
Tel.: (480) 783-9555
Sales Range: $125-149.9 Million
Healthcare Management
N.A.I.C.S.: 621399

Subsidiary (Domestic):

Healthways Wholehealth Networks, Inc. (3)
21251 Ridgetop Cir Ste 150, Sterling, VA 20166
Tel.: (800) 274-7526
Web Site: http://www.wholehealthpro.com
Health Benefit Management Services
N.A.I.C.S.: 621999

Subsidiary (Non-US):

Healthways International, GmbH (2)
Kurfurstendamm 30, 10719, Berlin, Germany
Tel.: (49) 30886200140
Web Site: http://www.healthways.de
Comprehensive Care & Disease Management Services for Health Planning Services
N.A.I.C.S.: 524114

Truist Insurance Holdings, Inc. (1)
301 College St Ste 208, Asheville, NC 28801
Tel.: (828) 225-2044
Web Site: http://www.truistinsurance.com
Holding Company
N.A.I.C.S.: 551112
Wes Dasher (Pres)
Kenya Odoms (Chief Talent Officer)
Kedar Bryan (Chief Mktg & Comm Officer)
Mike Clark (Chief Risk Officer)
Amanda Martin (Chief Admin Officer)
Andrea Holder (CFO)
Matt Spriggs (CIO)
Tammy Stringer (Gen Counsel)
Todd Wartchow (Exec VP-Business Development-Strategy)
Henry Wright (Officer)
Kedar Bryan (Chief Mktg & Comm Officer)
Mike Clark (Chief Risk Officer)
Amanda Martin (Chief Admin Officer)
Andrea Holder (CFO)
Matt Spriggs (CIO)
Tammy Stringer (Gen Counsel)
Todd Wartchow (Exec VP-Business Development-Strategy)
Henry Wright (Officer)
John Howard (Chm & CEO)

Subsidiary (Domestic):

8121 Insurance Management, Inc. (2)
2201 Cantu Ct Ste 102, Sarasota, FL 34232

STONE POINT CAPITAL LLC

Stone Point Capital LLC—(Continued)
Tel.: (941) 377-4842
Sales Range: $1-9.9 Million
Emp.: 10
Direct Property & Casualty Insurance Carriers
N.A.I.C.S.: 524126
Alex Hahn (CEO)

BB&T Insurance Services, Inc. (2)
4309 Emperor Blvd Ste 300, Durham, NC 27703
Tel.: (919) 281-4500
Sales Range: $75-99.9 Million
Insurance Services
N.A.I.C.S.: 524210
Wes Dasher (Pres-Insurance-Mid,Atlantic Reg)
Mike Arnaud (Sr VP)
Randy McGann (Sr VP-Employee Benefits)
Read Davis (CEO)
Renee Keen (CFO)
Robert Drew (Pres-Insurance-South Reg)
Patrick Dessauer (Pres-Insurance-West Reg)
Steve Aldrich (Mng Dir)
Southgate Jones III (Chief Sls Exec Officer)

Subsidiary (Domestic):

AmRisc, LP
20405 State Hwy Ste 430, Houston, TX 77070
Tel.: (281) 257-6700
Web Site: http://www.amrisc.com
Underwriting Services
N.A.I.C.S.: 561499

Unit (Domestic):

BB&T - J. Rolfe Davis Insurance (3)
850 Concourse Pkwy S Ste 200, Maitland, FL 32751-6145
Tel.: (407) 691-9600
Web Site: http://insurance.bbt.com
Sales Range: $1-9.9 Million
Emp.: 45
Insurance Agents
N.A.I.C.S.: 524210

BB&T - J.V. Arthur (3)
112 N Loudoun St, Winchester, VA 22601-3310
Tel.: (540) 662-3865
Web Site: http://www.insurance.bbt.com
Sales Range: $1-9.9 Million
Emp.: 40
Insurance Agents
N.A.I.C.S.: 524210

BB&T - John Burnham Insurance Services (3)
750 B St Ste 2400, San Diego, CA 92101-2476
Tel.: (619) 525-2807
Web Site: http://www.insurance.bbt.com
Sales Range: $10-24.9 Million
Emp.: 75
Insurance Agents
N.A.I.C.S.: 524210

BB&T Insurance Services, Inc. - Burkey Risk Services (3)
1661 Sandspur Rd, Maitland, FL 32751
Tel.: (407) 682-1122
Web Site: http://insurance.bbt.com
Sales Range: $1-9.9 Million
Emp.: 9
Insurance Agents
N.A.I.C.S.: 524210

BB&T Insurance Services, Inc. - Frederick Underwriters (3)
5280 Corporate Dr Ste 250A, Frederick, MD 21703-2852
Tel.: (301) 662-1147
Sales Range: $1-9.9 Million
Emp.: 60
Insurance Underwriting Services
N.A.I.C.S.: 524298

BB&T Insurance Services, Inc. - TCFG (3)
47 Airpark Ct, Greenville, SC 29607
Tel.: (864) 297-4444
Sales Range: $1-9.9 Million
Emp.: 105
Insurance Agencies & Brokerages
N.A.I.C.S.: 524210

Thomas Parrish (VP)
Donald M. Harris (Sr VP)

Subsidiary (Domestic):

Liberty Benefit Insurance Services, Inc. (3)
5446 Thornwood Dr Ste 200, San Jose, CA 95123
Tel.: (408) 360-0300
Sales Range: $25-49.9 Million
Emp.: 48
Insurance Services
N.A.I.C.S.: 524210

Subsidiary (Domestic):

Constellation Affiliated Partners LLC (2)
667 Madison Ave 16th Fl, New York, NY 10065
Tel.: (212) 235-1000
Insurance Services
N.A.I.C.S.: 524298
Bill Goldstein (CEO)

Holding (Domestic):

Coastal Insurance Underwriters, Inc. (3)
816 Hwy A1A Ste 206, Ponte Vedra Beach, FL 32082
Tel.: (904) 285-7683
Web Site: http://www.ciuins.com
Insurance Services
N.A.I.C.S.: 524298
Charles Bushong (Pres & CEO)
Faye Leto (COO & VP)
Sim Bridges (VP-Underwriting)
Kimberly Bushong Petrillo (VP)
Michele T. Ortiz (Dir-Underwriting)

Subsidiary (Domestic):

Cybercom International Corp. (4)
232 Canal Blvd, Ponte Vedra Beach, FL 32082-3744
Tel.: (904) 517-5610
Web Site: http://www.cybercom-intl.com
Business to Business Electronic Markets
N.A.I.C.S.: 425120
Erez Wolf (Owner)

Subsidiary (Domestic):

Kensington Vanguard National Land Services, LLC (2)
39 W 37th St 3rd Fl, New York, NY 10018
Tel.: (212) 532-8686
Web Site: http://www.kvnational.com
Insurance Agencies
N.A.I.C.S.: 524210
Brian M. Cooper (Co-CEO)
Jarett Fein (Co-CEO)

Subsidiary (Domestic):

GRS Title Services, LLC (3)
901 E Byrd St Suite 1100, Richmond, VA 23219
Tel.: (804) 486-9465
Web Site: http://www.grs-global.com
Insurance Services
N.A.I.C.S.: 524127
Stephen W. Francis (Dir)

Subsidiary (Domestic):

Wellington Insurance Group, Inc. (2)
6801 Calmont Ave, Fort Worth, TX 76116
Tel.: (817) 732-2111
Web Site:
  http://www.wellingtoninsgroup.com
Holding Company
N.A.I.C.S.: 551112
Paul R. Poston (Pres & CEO)

STONE POINT CREDIT CORPORATION
20 Horseneck Ln, Greenwich, CT 06830
Tel.: (203) 862-2900   DE
Web Site:
  https://www.stonepoint.com
Year Founded: 2020
Rev.: $129,949,996
Assets: $1,744,124,451
Liabilities: $926,938,862

Net Worth: $817,185,589
Earnings: $64,916,038
Fiscal Year-end: 12/31/22
Investment Management Service
N.A.I.C.S.: 523940
Scott J. Bronner (Pres)
David J. Wermuth (Chm)

STONE POINTE, LLC
55 S Main St Ste 335, Naperville, IL 60540
Tel.: (630) 696-4175
Web Site:
  https://stonepointeinvest.com
Emp.: 100
Investment Services
N.A.I.C.S.: 523999

STONE RIVER CAPITAL PARTNERS, LLC
261 E Maple Rd, Birmingham, MI 48009
Tel.: (248) 203-9840   MI
Web Site:
  http://www.stonerivercap.com
Year Founded: 2011
Investment Advisory & Private Equity Firm
N.A.I.C.S.: 523999
Guy W. Boitos (Partner)
Alex G. Markus (Partner)

Subsidiaries:

Burtek Enterprises, Inc. (1)
50325 Patricia St, Chesterfield, MI 48051
Tel.: (586) 421-8000
Web Site: http://www.burtekenterprises.com
Design, Production, Testing & Integration of Complex Systems & Applications for Mobile Military Ground Vehicles, Radar Platforms & Other Defense Systems
N.A.I.C.S.: 541519
Jeff Daniel (Pres & CEO)

Subsidiary (Domestic):

Votaw Precision Technologies, Inc. (2)
13153 Lakeland Rd, Santa Fe Springs, CA 90670
Tel.: (562) 944-0661
Web Site: http://www.votaw.com
Precision Components, Fixtures & Tools Designer & Mfr
N.A.I.C.S.: 333514
Art Montes (Mgr-Program)
Art Talavera (Mgr-Mfg)
Scott Merrell (Mgr-Quality Assurance)
Scott Wallace (Pres)
Mike Carlson (Mgr-Program)
Daniel Telles (Mgr-Program)
Mike Petriccione (Dir-Sls & Mktg)
L. Wood Bullock (Controller)

Fabco Automotive Corporation (1)
151 Lawrence Dr, Livermore, CA 94551-5126
Tel.: (925) 454-9500
Web Site: http://www.fabcoautomotive.com
Sales Range: $25-49.9 Million
Automotive Parts Mfr & Supplier
N.A.I.C.S.: 336390
Al Sunderland (Pres)
Mark Reitz (VP-Engrg)

Subsidiary (Domestic):

R. Cushman & Associates, Inc. (2)
32840 W 8 Mile Rd 12623 Newburgh, Livonia, MI 48150
Tel.: (248) 477-9900
Web Site: http://www.rcushman.com
Drive Train & Power Transmission Design & Production
N.A.I.C.S.: 336350
Kevin Krause (Mgr-Quality)

STONE TRANSPORT INC.
3495 Hack Rd, Saginaw, MI 48601-9256
Tel.: (989) 754-4788   MI
Web Site:
  http://www.stonetransport.com

Year Founded: 1978
Sales Range: $25-49.9 Million
Emp.: 330
Provider of Trucking Services
N.A.I.C.S.: 484121
Dean Darby (Pres)
Steve Anderson (CFO)

STONE WARD
225 E Markham St Ste 450, Little Rock, AR 72201-1629
Tel.: (501) 375-3003   AR
Web Site: http://www.stoneward.com
Year Founded: 1984
Rev.: $19,000,000
Emp.: 45
Advetising Agency
N.A.I.C.S.: 541810
Millie Ward (Pres)
Brenda Fowler (Dir-Print Production)
John Rogers (CFO)
Brenda Scisson (Dir-Pub Rels)
Tommy Walker (Dir-Brdcst Production)
Kyle Floyd (Assoc Dir-Creative & Dir-Design)
Tom Lillig (Dir-Acct Mgmt)
Jason Marlin (Dir-Digital Strategy)
Emily Reeves (Dir-Acct Mgmt-Res)
Bill Brookshire (Sr Dir-Art)
Angie Morgan (Acct Mgr)
Kandace Gerber (Dir-Art)
Millie Ward (Pres)
Emily Brosius (Mgr-Community)
Maeghen Carter (Assoc Acct Exec-PR)
Larry Stone (Chm & Exec Dir-Creative)

STONE WHEEL INC.
7675 S Quincy St, Willowbrook, IL 60527
Tel.: (630) 325-7200
Web Site:
  http://www.stonewheel.com
Year Founded: 1912
Sales Range: $10-24.9 Million
Automotive Supplies & Parts Distr
N.A.I.C.S.: 423120
Raymond P. Renehan (Chm & Pres)
Charles Staines (Mgr-Sls)
Fred Tarpley (Mgr-Sls-WI)
Nick Hamersly (Asst Mgr)
Steve Duray (Controller)
Thomas Hernandez (Mgr)

STONE'S, INC.
601 Calhoun St, Bainbridge, GA 39817
Tel.: (229) 246-2929
Web Site:
  http://www.stoneshomecenter.com
Year Founded: 1959
Sales Range: $100-124.9 Million
Emp.: 180
Other Building Material Retailer
N.A.I.C.S.: 444180
David White (Mgr-Store)
Charles Brock (Asst Mgr)
George Davis (Mgr-Floor)

STONE-GOFF PARTNERS, LLC
900 3rd Ave 33rd Fl, New York, NY 10022
Tel.: (212) 308-2058   DE
Web Site: http://www.stonegoff.com
Privater Equity Firm
N.A.I.C.S.: 523999
Laurens M. Goff (Co-Founder & Mng Partner)
Hannah Stone Craven (Co-Founder & Mng Partner)
Jin Kim (Principal)

Subsidiaries:

The Greene Turtle Franchising Corporation (1)

COMPANIES

7550 Teague Rd Ste 113, Hanover, MD 21076-1339
Tel.: (443) 366-4298
Web Site: http://www.thegreenturtle.com
Full-Service Restaurant & Bar Franchisor & Operator
N.A.I.C.S.: 722511
J. Michael Sanford (Vice Chm)
Robert J. Barry Jr. (Pres & CEO)

STONEAGE, INC.
466 S Skylane Dr, Durango, CO 81303
Tel.: (970) 259-2869
Web Site:
http://www.stoneagetools.com
Year Founded: 1980
Sales Range: $10-24.9 Million
Emp.: 65
High Pressure Industrial Waterblast Tools Mfr
N.A.I.C.S.: 333310
Jerry Zink (Co-Founder)
John Wolgamott (Co-Founder & Pres)
Kerry Petranek (CEO)

STONEBRIDGE
15301 Spectrum Dr Ste 400, Addison, TX 75001
Tel.: (972) 404-9755   TX
Web Site: http://www.sbti.com
Year Founded: 1985
Sales Range: $10-24.9 Million
Emp.: 80
Computer Integrated Systems Design
N.A.I.C.S.: 541512
James Ivy (Founder & CEO)
Sharon Anthamatten (CFO)
Dale Young (Dir-Practice)

STONEBRIDGE PARTNERS, LLC
81 Main St, White Plains, NY 10606
Tel.: (914) 682-2700   DE
Web Site:
http://www.stonebridgepartners.com
Year Founded: 1986
Privater Equity Firm
N.A.I.C.S.: 523999
Michael S. Bruno (Mng Partner)
Greg Goulette (Partner-Ops)
William G. Connors (Mng Dir)
Stephen A. Hanna (Mng Dir)
Andrew W. Magyar (CFO & COO)
Daniel P. Murphy (Partner-Ops)
Daniel W. Fulham (Partner-Ops)
John L. Thomson (Chm-Investment)
Michael A. Steinbeck (Partner-Ops)
David R. Schopp (Operating Partner)

Subsidiaries:

ADI American Distributors LLC (1)
2 Emery Ave, Randolph, NJ 07869
Tel.: (973) 328-1181
Web Site: http://www.americandistr.com
Sales Range: $10-24.9 Million
Electronic Parts & Equipment Mfr
N.A.I.C.S.: 423690
David Beck (Pres & CEO)
David Kasner (VP-Sls & Mktg)
Michele Almeida (VP-Sls & Mktg)
Bart Mallory (VP-Quality)

BrandFX Body Company (1)
2800 Golden Triangle Blvd, Fort Worth, TX 76177
Tel.: (817) 431-1131
Web Site: http://www.brandfxbody.com
Motor Vehicle Body Mfr
N.A.I.C.S.: 336211
Carla Anglin (VP-Sls & Mktg)

Cast-Crete USA, LLC (1)
6324 County Rd 579, Seffner, FL 33584
Tel.: (813) 621-4641
Web Site: http://www.castcrete.com
Precast Terrazzo & Concrete Products Mfr
N.A.I.C.S.: 327390
Dan Cheney (CFO)

STONEBRIDGE REALTY ADVISORS, INC.
4949 S Niagara St Ste 300, Denver, CO 80237
Tel.: (303) 785-3100   CO
Web Site:
http://www.stonebridgecompanies.com
Year Founded: 1991
Sales Range: $250-299.9 Million
Emp.: 2,500
Holding Company; Franchise Hotels Owner & Operator
N.A.I.C.S.: 551112
Navin C. Dimond (Founder, Pres & CEO)
Jim Luchars (Chief Investment Officer)
Howard Pollack (Gen Counsel)
Scott McChesney (Sr VP-Acquisition & Dev)
J. B. Bettinger (VP-HR)
Matt Friend (VP-Risk Mgmt)
David Chin (VP-IT)
Tommy Nigro (VP-Real Estate)
Steve Johnson (VP-IT)
Stephani Johnson (Mgr-Revenue)
Phillip Dixon (Gen Mgr-Courtyard Glenwood Springs)
Jeff Jones (Gen Mgr-Hampton Denver West Golden)
Trey O'Shields (CFO)
Tom Sprankle (Reg VP-Ops)
Kellee Amerman (Dir-Benefits & Total Rewards)
Kristin Spivey (Dir-Design)
Salvatore Acquilato (VP-Design & Construction)
Judy Blattert (VP-Sls & Mktg)
Jane Gomez (VP-Hotel Ops)

Subsidiaries:

Best Western - Denver International Airport (1)
7020 Tower Rd, Denver, CO 80249
Tel.: (303) 373-1600
Sales Range: $1-9.9 Million
Emp.: 45
Hotel Operator
N.A.I.C.S.: 721110
George Farmakis (Gen Mgr)

Brisbane Lodging, L.P. (1)
5000 Sierra Point Pkwy, Brisbane, CA 94005
Tel.: (415) 467-4400
Web Site: http://www.sbcos.com
Sales Range: $1-9.9 Million
Emp.: 75
Luxury Hotel Operator
N.A.I.C.S.: 721110

Hampton Inn & Suites - Cherry Creek (1)
4150 E Kentucky Ave, Denver, CO 80246
Tel.: (303) 692-1800
Web Site: http://www.sbcos.com
Sales Range: $1-9.9 Million
Emp.: 34
Hotel Operator
N.A.I.C.S.: 721110
Yon Meyers (Mgr)
Blake Williams (Mgr-Sls Grp)

Hampton Inn - Foothill Ranch (1)
27102 Towne Centre Dr, Foothill Ranch, CA 92610
Tel.: (949) 597-8700
Web Site:
http://www.hamptoninn3.hilton.com
Sales Range: $1-9.9 Million
Emp.: 25
Hotel Operator
N.A.I.C.S.: 721110
Alfredo Sanedrin (Gen Mgr)

Hampton Inn - Lakewood (1)
137 Union Blvd, Lakewood, CO 80228
Tel.: (303) 969-9900
Web Site:
http://www.denverwestfederalcenter.hamptoninn.com

Sales Range: $1-9.9 Million
Emp.: 35
Hotel Operator
N.A.I.C.S.: 721110
Celia Sellers (Gen Mgr)
Sam Karabeo (Gen Mgr)

Hilton Garden Inn - Anchorage (1)
4555 Union Sq Dr, Anchorage, AK 99503
Tel.: (907) 562-9000
Web Site: http://www.sbcos.com
Sales Range: $1-9.9 Million
Emp.: 45
Luxury Hotel Operator
N.A.I.C.S.: 721110

Hilton Garden Inn - Cherry Creek (1)
600 S Colorado Blvd, Denver, CO 80246
Tel.: (303) 754-9800
Sales Range: $10-24.9 Million
Emp.: 65
Luxury Hotel Operator
N.A.I.C.S.: 721110
Eric Hautzenrader (Gen Mgr)

Hilton Garden Inn - Garden Grove (1)
11777 Harbor Blvd, Garden Grove, CA 92840
Tel.: (714) 703-9100
Web Site: http://www.anaheimhgi.com
Sales Range: $1-9.9 Million
Emp.: 70
Luxury Hotel Operator
N.A.I.C.S.: 721110
Mitchel Hershman (Gen Mgr)

Holiday Inn Express - Denver International Airport (1)
6910 Tower Rd, Denver, CO 80249
Tel.: (303) 373-4100
Web Site: http://www.sbcos.com
Sales Range: $1-9.9 Million
Emp.: 20
Hotel Operator
N.A.I.C.S.: 721110
Manuela O'Brien (Gen Mgr)

Homewood Suites - Anchorage (1)
101 W 48th Ave, Anchorage, AK 99503
Tel.: (907) 762-7000
Web Site: http://www.sbcos.com
Sales Range: $1-9.9 Million
Emp.: 50
Hotel Operator
N.A.I.C.S.: 721110
Tracey Morgan (Gen Mgr)

West Coast Lodging, L.P. (1)
12005 Harbor Blvd, Garden Grove, CA 92840
Tel.: (714) 740-1800
Web Site: http://www.homewoodsuites.com
Sales Range: $1-9.9 Million
Emp.: 45
Hotel Operator
N.A.I.C.S.: 721110
Kevin Escoto (Gen Mgr)

STONEBROOKE ENGINEERING, INC.
12279 Nicollet Ave, Burnsville, MN 55337
Tel.: (952) 402-9202
Web Site:
http://www.stonebrookeengineering.com
Year Founded: 2003
Sales Range: $1-9.9 Million
Emp.: 50
Construction Services
N.A.I.C.S.: 236116
Tim Arvidson (CEO)

STONEBURNER COMPANIES, LLC
495 Bayfront Pl, Naples, FL 34102
Tel.: (239) 649-8700
Web Site:
http://www.stoneburnercompanies.com
Sales Range: $1-9.9 Million
Emp.: 2

STONECALIBRE, LLC

Real Estate Development & Investment Services
N.A.I.C.S.: 237210
Kevin L. Stoneburner (Founder & Pres)

STONECALIBRE, LLC
2049 Century Park E Ste 2550, Los Angeles, CA 90067
Tel.: (310) 774-0014
Web Site:
http://www.stonecalibre.com
Year Founded: 2012
Privater Equity Firm
N.A.I.C.S.: 523999
Brian M. Wall (Founder & CEO)

Subsidiaries:

Alpha-Tec Systems, Inc. (1)
1311 SE Cardinal Court Ste 170, Vancouver, WA 98683
Tel.: (360) 260-2779
Web Site: http://www.alphatecsystems.com
Medicinal & Botanical Mfr
N.A.I.C.S.: 325411

Applied Voice & Speech Technologies, Inc. (1)
20000 North Creek Pkwy Ste 200, Bothell, WA 98011
Web Site: http://www.avst.com
Telecommunication Servicesb
N.A.I.C.S.: 517810

Calibre Scientific, Inc (1)
6201 Trust Dr, Holland, OH 43528
Tel.: (211) 5672970358
Web Site: https://calibrescientific.com
Biotechnology Research
N.A.I.C.S.: 541714
Ben Travis (CEO)

Subsidiary (Domestic):

Anatrace Products, LLC (2)
434 W Dussel Dr, Maumee, OH 43537-1685
Web Site: http://www.anatrace.com
High Purity Detergents & Synthetic Lipids Developer, Mfr & Distr
N.A.I.C.S.: 325998
Ben Travis (Pres & CEO)

Subsidiary (Non-US):

Molecular Dimensions Ltd. (3)
Unit 6 Goodwin Business Park Willie Snaith Road, Newmarket, CB8 7SQ, Suffolk, United Kingdom
Tel.: (44) 1638561051
Web Site:
http://www.moleculardimensions.com
Modern Screens, Reagents, Other Consumables & Instrumentation Mfr
N.A.I.C.S.: 334516
Tony Savill (Founder & Mng Dir)

Subsidiary (US):

Molecular Dimensions Inc. (4)
849 Sunshine Ln, Altamonte Springs, FL 32714-3901
Tel.: (407) 886-6901
Web Site:
http://www.moleculardimensions.com
Modern Screens, Reagents, Other Consumables & Instrumentation Mfr
N.A.I.C.S.: 334516
Tony Savill (Founder & Mng Dir)

Subsidiary (Non-US):

Camlab, Ltd. (2)
Unit 24 Norman Way Industrial Estate Over, Cambridge, CB24 5WE, United Kingdom
Tel.: (44) 1954233110
Web Site: https://www.camlab.co.uk
Emp.: 100
Scientific Equipment, Chemicals, Labware & Other Laboratory Supplies Distr
N.A.I.C.S.: 423450
William Mason (Chm)

Subsidiary (Domestic):

Greenwood Products, Inc. (2)
253 Wagner St, Middlesex, NJ 08846
Tel.: (732) 469-7200

STONECALIBRE, LLC

U.S. PRIVATE

StoneCalibre, LLC—(Continued)
Web Site: http://www.greenwoodprod.com
Sales Range: $1-9.9 Million
Emp.: 11
Miscellaneous Durable Goods Merchant Whslr
N.A.I.C.S.: 423990
Floyd Graham (Mgr-Production)
John Scala (Mgr-Sls)

Edge Biosystems, Inc. (1)
201 Perry Pkwy Ste 5, Gaithersburg, MD 20877
Tel.: (301) 990-2685
Web Site: http://www.edgebio.com
DNA Sequencing Preparation & Clean-up Products Mfr & Distr
N.A.I.C.S.: 334516
John Seed (Founder, Pres & CTO)
Matthew Lorence (Exec VP-Mktg & Sls)

Source Technologies Holdings, LLC (1)
4205 B Westinghouse Commons Dr, Charlotte, NC 28273
Tel.: (704) 522-8500
Web Site: http://www.sourcetech.com
Sales Range: $50-74.9 Million
Emp.: 40
Holding Company; Printing Equipment Mfr & Distr
N.A.I.C.S.: 551112
Keith Hamilton (CEO)
Boyce White (Dir-Ops)
Kevin Forrester (Sr VP-Sls)
Mike Drury (CFO)
Suzi McNicholas (VP-Mktg)
Tim Baker (CTO & Exec VP)
Kevin Kennedy (Dir-Engrg & Solutions Delivery)
Summer Cline (VP-Fin)

Subsidiary (Domestic):

Source Technologies, LLC (2)
4205B Westinghouse Commons Dr, Charlotte, NC 28273
Tel.: (704) 522-8500
Web Site: http://www.sourcetech.com
Sales Range: $50-74.9 Million
Printing Equipment Mfr & Distr
N.A.I.C.S.: 333248
Keith Hamilton (Pres & CEO)
Tim Baker (CTO & Exec VP)
Mike Drury (CFO)
Boyce White (Dir-Ops)

Ventraq Corporation (1)
9707 Key W Ave Ste 202, Rockville, MD 20850
Tel.: (301) 721-3010
Web Site: http://www.netplustms.com
Telecommunications Network & Mobility Management Software & Services
N.A.I.C.S.: 541511
Ben Gray (VP)
Dave Garman (Dir-Engrg)
James Gilmour (Dir-Mobility Solutions)
Joe Mulick (Dir-Program Mgmt)

Subsidiary (Domestic):

Amtel, Inc. (2)
900 Lafayette St Ste 506, Santa Clara, CA 95050-4967
Tel.: (408) 615-0522
Web Site: http://www.amtelnet.com
Mobile Telecommunications Security & Data Protection Software & Services
N.A.I.C.S.: 541511
Pankaj Gupta (Pres)

STONECOURT CAPITAL LP
10 E 53rd St 13th Fl, New York, NY 10022
Tel.: (212) 430-2200   DE
Web Site:
  http://www.stonecourtlp.com
Private Investment Firm
N.A.I.C.S.: 523999
Lance Hirt (Mng Partner)

Subsidiaries:

365 Services LLC (1)
200 Connecticut Ave Ste 5A, Norwalk, CT 06854
Tel.: (415) 901-5700

Web Site: http://www.365datacenters.com
Data Center Solutions
N.A.I.C.S.: 518210
Bob DeSantis (CEO)
Jason Kiser (VP-Ops)
Jason Katz (Chief Admin Officer & VP)
Jeff Slapp (VP-Cloud Svcs & Support)
Robert Allison (Dir-Bus Dev)
James Ashton (Dir-Network Engrg)
Tony Franchi (Sr VP-Sls & Mktg)
Nelson A. Weinstein (Chief Acctg Officer & VP-Fin)
Stephen Klenert (Sr VP-Customer Solutions & Implementation)
James Cornman (CTO)
Steve Oakie (Sr VP-Sls & Mktg)

Subsidiary (Domestic):

Atlantic Metro Communications, Inc. (2)
4 Century Dr Ste 102, Parsippany, NJ 07054
Tel.: (212) 792-9950
Web Site: http://www.atlanticmetro.net
Sales Range: $1-9.9 Million
Emp.: 19
Telecommunication Servicesb
N.A.I.C.S.: 517810
Matthew Lombardi (CEO)
Roy A. Ceccato (CFO)
Darius Milani (VP-Solutions Engrg)
Timothy P. Ray (Gen Counsel)

Subsidiary (Domestic):

InfoRelay Online Systems, Inc. (3)
13873 Park Ctr Rd Ste 75, Herndon, VA 20171
Tel.: (703) 485-4600
Web Site: http://www.inforelay.com
Information Technology Consulting Services
N.A.I.C.S.: 541512
Matthew Lombardi (CEO)
Roy A. Ceccato (CFO)
Stephen Klenert (Co-Founder & Chief Strategy Officer)
James Cornman (Co-Founder & CTO)
Russ Weiss (Co-Founder & CIO)
Darius Milani (VP-Solutions Engrg)
Steve Oakie (VP-Sls & Mktg)
Timothy P. Ray (Gen Counsel)

STONECREEK CAPITAL, INC.
18500 Von Karman Ave Ste 590, Irvine, CA 92612
Tel.: (949) 752-4580
Web Site:
  http://www.stonecreekcapital.com
Year Founded: 1992
Privater Equity Firm
N.A.I.C.S.: 523999
Drew H. Adams (Pres)
Bruce N. Lipian (Mng Dir)
David M. Sincich (VP)

STONECREST AT DOUBLE OAK MOUNTAIN
1 Stonecrest Dr, Birmingham, AL 35242
Tel.: (334) 821-0928
Year Founded: 1997
Sales Range: $25-49.9 Million
Emp.: 50
Civil Engineering Services
N.A.I.C.S.: 237310
Kellie Ezell (Mgr)
Michael V. Shannon (Gen Partner)

STONECUTTER MILLS CORP.
230 Spindale St, Spindale, NC 28160
Tel.: (828) 286-2341   NC
Web Site:
  http://www.stonecuttermills.com
Year Founded: 1920
Sales Range: $75-99.9 Million
Emp.: 6
Industrial Park Manager
N.A.I.C.S.: 531312
James R. Cowan (CEO)

Subsidiaries:

Henson Timber Products Corp. (1)

177 Duke St, Forest City, NC 28043
Tel.: (828) 245-4241
Web Site:
  http://www.hensonbuildingmaterials.com
Sales Range: $10-24.9 Million
Emp.: 25
Building Products & Hardware Services
N.A.I.C.S.: 444110
Dan Honeycutt (Mgr-Store)

STONEEAGLE F&I, INC.
3400 N. Central Expy, Ste #110, Richardson, TX 75080   DE
Web Site: http://www.stoneeagle.com
F&I Product Solutions
N.A.I.C.S.: 541519
Cindy Allen (CEO)
Damar Christopher (COO)

Subsidiaries:

StoneEagle, Inc. (1)
111 W Spring Vly Rd Ste 100, Richardson, TX 75081-4016
Tel.: (972) 934-1751
Web Site: http://www.stoneeagle.com
Information Services
N.A.I.C.S.: 519290
Brent Allen (Founder & COO)
Bobby Allen (Chm)
Cindy Allen (CEO)

STONEHAM BANK
80 Montvale Ave, Stoneham, MA 02180
Tel.: (781) 438-0430
Web Site:
  http://www.stonehambank.com
Year Founded: 1887
Sales Range: $50-74.9 Million
Emp.: 70
Federal Savings Institutions
N.A.I.C.S.: 522180
Janice Houghton (Chm)
Anna Dinis (Sr VP-Ops)
Michael Rubinov (Asst Mgr-Billerica)
Michael Connelly (Officer-Loan & Exec VP)
Shane Bellavance (Sr VP-Residential Lending)
Paul Totino (Pres)
Edward F. Doherty Jr. (CEO)

STONEHAM MOTOR CO. INC.
185 Main St, Stoneham, MA 02180
Tel.: (781) 438-0490   MA
Web Site:
  http://www.stonehamford.net
Year Founded: 1986
Sales Range: $25-49.9 Million
Emp.: 40
Sales of New & Used Automobiles
N.A.I.C.S.: 441110
Bill Pollack (Mgr-Sls)
George Benn (Mgr-Fin)
Doug Prentice (Mgr-Sls)

STONEHENGE CAPITAL CORP.
450 Laurel St, Baton Rouge, LA 70801
Tel.: (225) 408-3000
Web Site:
  http://www.stonehengecapital.com
Rev.: $6,230,000
Emp.: 10
Commodity Contracts Dealing
N.A.I.C.S.: 523160
Thomas J. Adamek (Pres & Mng Dir)
Gordon LeBlanc (Mng Dir)
C. Patrick McConnell (VP-Tax Credit Svcs)
Will Owens (Mng Dir)
L'Quentus Thomas (Sr Mng Dir)
Anna Kathryn Barber (VP)
Barry G. Gowdy (Mng Dir)
David B. Webber (Mng Dir)
Jeffrey A. Ralston (VP)

John P. Witten (Mng Dir & Gen Counsel)
Jonathan M. Crawford (VP)
Matthew S. Orr (VP)
Matthew L. Whalen (VP)
Taylor B. Mayeux (VP)
Richard Allen (Dir-Strategic Initiatives-Tax Credit Svcs)

Subsidiaries:

Stonehenge Growth Equity Partners (1)
707 W Azeele St, Tampa, FL 33606
Tel.: (813) 223-9335
Web Site:
  http://www.stonehengegrowthequity.com
Rev.: $80,000,000
Emp.: 4
Venture Capital
N.A.I.C.S.: 523999
Steven Lux (Mng Partner)
Brian Model (Mng Partner)
Travis Milks (Partner)

STONEHENGE PARTNERS, INC.
191 W Nationwide Blvd Ste 600, Columbus, OH 43215
Tel.: (614) 246-2500
Web Site:
  http://www.stonehengepartners.com
Year Founded: 1999
Sales Range: $25-49.9 Million
Emp.: 15
Privater Equity Firm
N.A.I.C.S.: 523999
Michael J. Endres (Partner & Principal)
David R. Meuse (Principal)
Stephen E. Kimpel (Mng Partner)
Thomas R. Utgard (Mng Partner)
B. Michael Affinito (Mng Dir & CFO)
Michael D. Arguelles (Mng Dir)
Andrew F. Bohutinsky (Mng Partner)
Keith A. Bishop (Mng Dir)

STONELEIGH RECOVERY ASSOCIATES LLC
810 Springer Dr, Lombard, IL 60148
Tel.: (630) 812-2820
Web Site:
  http://www.stoneleighrecoveryassociates.com
Year Founded: 2007
Credit Card Collection Services
N.A.I.C.S.: 561440
Mark Savoie (VP-Bus Dev)
Ronni Majewski (VP-Ops)
Steven Fuernstahl (Pres)

STONEPEAK PARTNERS L.P.
55 Hudson Yards 550 W 34th St 48th Fl, New York, NY 10001
Tel.: (212) 907-5100
Web Site:
  http://www.stonepeakpartners.com
Year Founded: 2011
Privater Equity Firm
N.A.I.C.S.: 523999
Michael Dorrell (Co-Founder, Chm & CEO)
Trent Vichie (Co-Founder & Vice Chm)
Jack Howell (Co-Pres)
Luke Taylor (Co-Pres)
Peter Bruce (Sr Mng Dir, CFO & COO)
Steve Mlynar (Chief Acctg Officer & Principal)
Adrienne Saunders (Sr Mng Dir & Gen Counsel & Chief Compliance Officer)
Saira Khan (Deputy Gen Counsel)
Michael Allison (Sr Mng Dir)
Brian McMullen (Sr Mng Dir)
Brenden Woods (Mng Dir)
Daniel Schmitz (Mng Dir)

COMPANIES
STONEPEAK PARTNERS L.P.

George Watts *(Mng Dir)*
Cyrus Gentry *(Mng Dir & Head-Comm-Europe)*
Ryan Roberge *(Mng Dir)*
Michael Turner *(Principal)*
James Wyper *(Sr Mng Dir)*
Michael Bricker *(Principal)*
Petros Lekkakis *(VP)*
Ben Judson *(VP)*
Chris Partridge *(VP)*
Andrew Thomas *(Principal)*
Regina Jakobson *(Controller)*
Olga Vaynerman *(Controller-Fund)*
James Cork *(VP-Corp Dev)*
Joni Sciascia *(Head-Admin)*
Peng Li *(Principal)*
Bill Fathers *(Sr Operating Partner)*
Denis Hughes *(Sr Operating Partner)*
Jeffry Myers *(Sr Operating Partner)*
Ken desGarennes *(Sr Operating Partner)*
Daniel Wong *(Sr Mng Dir & Head-Europe)*

Subsidiaries:

Astound Broadband, LLC (1)
215 Mason Cir, Concord, CA 94520-1203
Web Site: http://www.astound.net
Data Processing, Hosting & Related Services
N.A.I.C.S.: 518210
Frank Freitas *(Mgr-Right of Access)*

Division (Domestic):

Grande Communications Networks LLC (2)
401 Carlson Cir, San Marcos, TX 78666
Tel.: (512) 878-4600
Web Site: http://www.mygrande.com
Telecommunications; Broadband Network Services for Cable Television, Telephone & Internet
N.A.I.C.S.: 517810
C. Matthew Rohre *(Sr VP-Ops & Gen Mgr)*
Lamar Horton *(VP-Network Ops & Engrg)*
Tracy Brutcher *(VP-HR)*
Dawn Blydenburgh *(VP-Customer Care)*
Jerry L. Horne *(VP-Field Ops)*
James Jordan *(VP-Network Svcs)*
Mark Chauvette *(VP-Fin)*
Charles Dixon *(VP-Mktg)*

Subsidiary (Domestic):

RCN Telecom Services, LLC (2)
650 College Rd E Ste 3100, Princeton, NJ 08540
Tel.: (703) 434-8200
Web Site: http://www.rcn.com
Telephone & Cable Services
N.A.I.C.S.: 517111
Jim Holanda *(CEO)*
Doug Guthrie *(Sr VP/Gen Mgr-New York)*
Tori Faulkenberry *(Sr VP-Customer Care)*
Michael McPhillips *(VP-Bus Solutions-Central)*
Sanford Ames *(Sr VP/Gen Mgr-Pennsylvania & Washington, D.C.)*
Chris Fenger *(COO)*

Subsidiary (Domestic):

Starpower Communications, LLC (3)
10th St NE Ste 3734, Washington, DC 20017
Tel.: (800) 746-4726
Telephone Communication Services
N.A.I.C.S.: 517810

Subsidiary (Domestic):

WaveDivision Holdings, LLC (2)
401 Kirkland Parkplace Ctr Ste 500, Kirkland, WA 98033 **(68.75%)**
Tel.: (425) 576-8200
Web Site: http://www.wavebroadband.com
Holding Company; Telecommunications Services
N.A.I.C.S.: 551112
Chris Fenger *(COO)*

Subsidiary (Domestic):

Digital West Networks, Inc. (3)
1998 Santa Barbara Ave #200, San Luis Obispo, CA 93401
Tel.: (805) 548-8000
Web Site: http://www.digitalwest.com
Computer Network Management Services
N.A.I.C.S.: 541512
Meg McCall *(Dir-Mktg)*
Ron Brown *(VP-Ops)*
Sandra Davis *(CFO)*
Tim Williams *(Founder & CEO)*
Michael Boyer *(COO)*
Sharon Durant *(Mgr-Mktg & Comm)*
Logan Johnson *(Mgr-Ops)*

Cologix, Inc. (1)
225 E 16th Ave, Denver, CO 80203
Tel.: (855) 265-6449
Web Site: http://www.cologix.com
Network Interconnection Services & Colocation Services
N.A.I.C.S.: 517810
Val Milshtein *(CIO & Sr VP-Network Svcs)*
Matthew Spencer *(CTO)*
Bill Fathers *(Chm)*
Laura Ortman *(CEO)*
Dawn Smith *(Pres)*
Rachel Stack *(CFO)*
Chris Heinrich *(Chief Revenue Officer)*

ExteNet Systems, Inc. (1)
3030 Warrenville Rd Ste 340, Lisle, IL 60532
Tel.: (630) 505-3800
Web Site: http://www.extenetsystems.com
Emp.: 118
Telecommunications Infrastructure Design, Construction & Operation
N.A.I.C.S.: 237130
Ross W. Manire *(Founder)*
Eric Lekacz *(Exec VP-Bus Dev & Strategy)*
Tormod Larsen *(CTO & VP)*
Tim Ayers *(VP-Global Svcs)*
H. Anthony Lehv *(Gen Counsel & Sr VP)*
Andrew G. Chavez *(Sr VP-Sls & Mktg)*
Monnie McGaffigan *(Chief Revenue Officer)*
Richard J. Coyle Jr. *(Pres & CEO)*

Subsidiary (Domestic):

Hudson Fiber Network (2)
17 N Ste 120, Paramus, NJ 07652
Tel.: (201) 575-4420
Web Site: http://www.HudsonFiber.com
Sales Range: $10-24.9 Million
Emp.: 13
Telecommunication Servicesb
N.A.I.C.S.: 517810
Brett Diamond *(CEO)*
Keith Muller *(COO)*
Robert Hagan *(CFO)*
Jeff Robator *(VP-Ops)*
Kevin Errity *(Sr VP-Sls)*
Tina A. Davis *(Gen Counsel)*

Fleet Equipment LLC. (1)
2505 Farrisview Blvd, Memphis, TN 38118
Tel.: (901) 332-3381
Web Site: https://www.fleetequip.com
Sales Range: $10-24.9 Million
Emp.: 38
New Car Dealers
N.A.I.C.S.: 441110
Woody Welch *(Chm)*
Mark Welch *(Pres)*
George Hough *(CEO)*
Jay Luther *(VP-Sls)*

Seapeak LLC (1)
4th Floor Belvedere Building 69 Pitts Bay Road, Hamilton, HM 08, Bermuda
Tel.: (441) 2982530
Web Site: https://www.seapeak.com
Rev.: $726,791,000
Assets: $5,661,601,000
Liabilities: $2,984,522,000
Net Worth: $2,677,079,000
Earnings: $317,716,000
Emp.: 2,897
Fiscal Year-end: 12/31/2023
Natural Gas Transportation
N.A.I.C.S.: 483111

TRAC Intermodal LLC (1)
750 College Rd E, Princeton, NJ 08540 **(98.42%)**
Tel.: (609) 452-8900
Web Site: http://www.tracintermodal.com
Rev.: $669,203,000
Assets: $1,845,851,000
Liabilities: $1,296,628,000
Net Worth: $549,223,000
Earnings: $19,925,000
Emp.: 700
Fiscal Year-end: 12/31/2016
Holding Company; Intermodal Transportation Equipment Leasing Services
N.A.I.C.S.: 551112
Chris Annese *(CFO & Exec VP)*
Gregg Carpene *(Chief Legal Officer, Sec & Exec VP)*
Val T. Noel *(COO & Exec VP)*
James Bowe *(Chief Comml Officer & Sr VP)*
Kevin Snyder *(CTO & Exec VP)*
Daniel Walsh *(Pres & CEO)*

Subsidiary (Domestic):

TRAC Interstar LLC (2)
500 Meijer Dr Ste 300, Florence, KY 41042
Tel.: (470) 484-2935
Web Site: http://www.fyxfleet.com
Fleet Emergency Breakdown Repair Services
N.A.I.C.S.: 811198

Textainer Group Holdings Limited (1)
Century House 16 Par-la-Ville Road, Hamilton, HM 08, Bermuda
Tel.: (441) 2962500
Web Site: https://www.textainer.com
Rev.: $810,014,000
Assets: $7,613,234,000
Liabilities: $5,616,945,000
Net Worth: $1,996,289,000
Earnings: $289,549,000
Emp.: 162
Fiscal Year-end: 12/31/2022
Marine Containers Leasing Services
N.A.I.C.S.: 488320
Michael Samsel *(Reg VP-EMEA)*
Adam Hopkin *(Sec)*
Joaquim Figueira *(VP-Ops & Procurement)*
Philippe Wendling *(Sr VP-Mktg)*
Giancarlo Gennaro *(VP-Fin)*
Cannia Lo *(VP-External Reporting & Consolidation)*
Philip Anderson *(VP)*

Subsidiary (Non-US):

Containerpool (2)
Suite 702 Walker House 161 Walker Street, Sydney, 2060, NSW, Australia
Tel.: (61) 299226677
Web Site: http://www.textainer.com
Sales Range: $50-74.9 Million
Emp.: 3
Agent for Textainer Marine Containers
N.A.I.C.S.: 532411

Port Klang (2)
Suite 9 05 Level 6 Menara Trend Intan Millennium Sq, Taman Intan Klang, 41300, Kuala Lumpur, Selangor, Malaysia
Tel.: (60) 333426752
Web Site: http://www.textainer.com
Marine Cargo Services
N.A.I.C.S.: 532411
Chong Wing Peng *(Area Mgr)*

Sealite Shipping Co., Ltd. (2)
116 94 95 SSP Tower 2 25th Fl Na Ranong Rd Klontoey, 10110, Bangkok, Thailand
Tel.: (66) 26974555
Web Site: http://www.sealitegroup.co.th
Sales Range: $50-74.9 Million
Emp.: 100
Marine Shipping Agent for Textainer
N.A.I.C.S.: 532411

TEM (H.K.) Limited (2)
Unit A 4/F Winbase Centre 208 Queen's Road, Central, Sheung Wan, China (Hong Kong)
Tel.: (852) 25439339
Web Site: http://www.textainer.com
Sales Range: $50-74.9 Million
Emp.: 4
Marine Container Agent for Textainer
N.A.I.C.S.: 532411
William Chan *(Dir-Mktg)*

TEM Agencies cc (2)
268A Florida Rd Morningside, Durban, 4001, South Africa
Tel.: (27) 313138620
Web Site: http://www.textainer.com
Sales Range: $50-74.9 Million
Emp.: 5
Agent for Textainer & Marketing Operations
N.A.I.C.S.: 532411
David Attenborough *(Dir-Mktg & Resale)*

TEM Equipment Management GmbH (2)
Kattrepelsbruecke 1, Hamburg, Germany
Tel.: (49) 4030200010
Web Site: http://www.textainer.com
Emp.: 5
Agent for Textainer & Marketing Operations
N.A.I.C.S.: 423860

Textainer Equipment (2)
Room 704 No 58 Chang Liu Rd, Zendai Cube Edifice, 200135, Shanghai, PRC, China
Tel.: (86) 2168540808
Web Site: http://www.textainer.com
Emp.: 12
Marketing & Operations of Marine Container Shipping
N.A.I.C.S.: 532411
Charles Li *(Dir-Mktg)*

Subsidiary (US):

Textainer Equipment Management (2)
1 University Plz Ste 500, Hackensack, NJ 07601 **(100%)**
Tel.: (201) 498-7268
Web Site: http://www.textainer.com
Sales Range: $25-49.9 Million
Emp.: 15
Marine Container Leasing & Marketing Operations
N.A.I.C.S.: 532411

Textainer Equipment Management (U.S.) Limited (2)
650 California St 16th Fl, San Francisco, CA 94108 **(100%)**
Tel.: (415) 434-0551
Web Site: http://www.textainer.com
Sales Range: $50-74.9 Million
Emp.: 70
Marine Container Leasing to International Shipping Lines
N.A.I.C.S.: 532411
John Simmons *(VP)*

Subsidiary (Non-US):

Textainer Equipment Resale (2)
Textainer House 82 Coombe Road, New Malden, KT3 4QS, Surrey, United Kingdom **(100%)**
Tel.: (44) 2089428488
Web Site: http://www.textainer.com
Sales Range: $25-49.9 Million
Emp.: 14
Equipment Resale on Marine Containers
N.A.I.C.S.: 483111
Paola Gaggioli *(Area Mgr-South Europe)*

Textainer Japan Limited (2)
5F Nisso No 8 Bldg, 2 3 19 Kitasaiwai Nishi ku, Yokohama, 220 0004, Kanagawa, Japan
Tel.: (81) 455346130
Web Site: http://www.textainer.com
Sales Range: $50-74.9 Million
Emp.: 4
Marketing & Marine Container Operations Agent
N.A.I.C.S.: 532411

Worldlink Corporation (2)
8F No 477 1 Sec 2 Tiding Blvd, Nei Hu Tech Park, Taipei, 114, ROC, Taiwan
Tel.: (886) 226275510
Web Site: http://www.textainer.com
Sales Range: $50-74.9 Million
Emp.: 4
Marine Container Agent for Textainer
N.A.I.C.S.: 532411

Xplornet Communications Inc. (1)
300 Lockhart Mill Road, PO Box 9060, Woodstock, E7M 6B5, NB, Canada
Tel.: (506) 328-8853
Web Site: http://www.xplornet.com
Rural Broadband Services Throughout Canada
N.A.I.C.S.: 517111
Allison Lenehan *(Pres & CEO)*

STONEPEAK PARTNERS L.P.   U.S. PRIVATE

Stonepeak Partners L.P.—(Continued)

euNetworks Group Limited (1)
15 Worship Stree, London, EC2A 2DT, England, United Kingdom
Tel.: (44) 42097521300
Web Site: http://www.eunetworks.com
Internet Connectivity Services
N.A.I.C.S.: 517111
Gary Jordan (COO)
Richard Taylor (Gen Counsel)
Brady Rafuse (Chm)
Andrew Weddell (Sr VP-Sls)
Andrew Field (Gp Dir-Fin)
Kevin Dean (CMO)
Paula Cogan (CEO)
Matt Winward (SR VP-Content & Infrastructure)
Katherine Alexakis (CFO)

Subsidiary (Non-US):

euNetworks B.V. (2)
Paul van Vlissingenstraat 16, 1096 BK, Amsterdam, Netherlands
Tel.: (31) 20 354 8080
Web Site: http://www.eunetworks.com
Fiber Networks & Communications Infrastructure & Networking Solutions Services
N.A.I.C.S.: 517810
Vincent Kroes (Dir-Acct)

Subsidiary (Domestic):

euNetworks Fiber UK Limited (2)
15 Worship Street, London, EC2A 2DT, United Kingdom
Tel.: (44) 20 7952 1300
Web Site: http://www.eunetworks.com
Fiber Networks & Communications Infrastructure & Networking Solutions Services
N.A.I.C.S.: 517810
Brady Rafuse (CEO & Dir)

Subsidiary (Non-US):

euNetworks GmbH (2)
Theodor-Heuss-Allee 112, 60486, Frankfurt, Germany
Tel.: (49) 69 90554 0
Web Site: http://www.eunetworks.com
Internet Connectivity Services
N.A.I.C.S.: 517810
Myriam Buchheister (Mng Dir)

euNetworks Ireland - Private Fiber Limited (2)
Unit 1 2050 Orchard Avenue Citywest Business Campus, Dublin, 24, Ireland
Tel.: (353) 16521200
Web Site: http://www.eunetworks.com
Internet Connectivity Services
N.A.I.C.S.: 517810

STONER & CO., INC.
121 Boston Post Rd, Sudbury, MA 01776-2405
Tel.: (978) 443-7514
Year Founded: 1981
Sales Range: $10-24.9 Million
Emp.: 6
Provider of Business Services
N.A.I.C.S.: 561990

STONER BUNTING ADVERTISING
322 N Arch St Fl 1, Lancaster, PA 17603-2991
Tel.: (717) 291-1491   PA
Web Site:
http://www.stonerbunting.com
Year Founded: 1984
Rev.: $35,000,000
Emp.: 30
Advetising Agency
N.A.I.C.S.: 541810
Jim Roosa (Mng Acct Dir)
Dan Nguyen (Pres & Creative Dir)
Dave Loose (Grp Acct Dir)
Pam Hoffmaster (Acct Supvr-Gift Card Grp)
Allison Schiding (Assoc Dir-Creative)
Christine Vulgaris (CFO)

Tiffany Anderson (Acct Exec)
Patrick Kirchner (Assoc Dir-Content)
Cheryl Shinton (Mng Dir)

STONER ELECTRIC INC.
1904 SE Ochoco St, Milwaukie, OR 97222
Tel.: (503) 462-6500
Web Site:
http://www.stonergroup.com
Sales Range: $10-24.9 Million
Emp.: 111
Electrical Work
N.A.I.C.S.: 238210
Lenny Weiss (Mgr-Ops)
Mike Falconer (Pres)
Paul Miller (Mgr-Document Control)
Jon Karp (VP)
Mark Scott (Co-Pres)

STONER INC.
1070 Robert Fulton Hwy, Quarryville, PA 17566
Tel.: (717) 786-7355
Web Site:
http://www.stonersolutions.com
Rev.: $10,200,000
Emp.: 45
Lubricating Oils
N.A.I.C.S.: 324191
Jon Farrell (Controller & Mgr-IT)

STONERISE HEALTHCARE LLC
700 Chappell Rd, Charleston, WV 25304
Tel.: (304) 343-1950
Web Site:
http://www.stonerisehealthcare.com
Year Founded: 2009
Emp.: 450
Nursing Facility Services
N.A.I.C.S.: 623110
David H. Gardner (Dir-Strategy)
Deanna Hunley (Dir-Fin Ops)
Shannon Dunlap (Chief Compliance Officer)
Sonia Bailey-Bibson (Sr Dir)
Larry Pack (Mng Dir)

Subsidiaries:

River Oaks (1)
100 Pkwy Dr, Clarksburg, WV 26301
Tel.: (304) 624-6401
Web Site:
http://www.stonerisehealthcare.com
Nursing Care Facilities
N.A.I.C.S.: 623110
Janean Oliverio (Dir-Admissions)

STONES TOWN & COUNTRY MOTORS
615 S Hwy 191, Rexburg, ID 83440
Tel.: (208) 356-9366
Web Site: http://www.stonescars.com
Sales Range: $10-24.9 Million
Emp.: 25
Automobiles, New & Used
N.A.I.C.S.: 441110
Ray Loveland (Pres)
Blake Loveland (CFO)

STONESTREET & STONESTREET
821 Lakeshore Dr, Auburn, IN 46706
Tel.: (260) 925-3618
Sales Range: $25-49.9 Million
Emp.: 8
Gasoline
N.A.I.C.S.: 424720

STONEWALL CONTRACTING CORP
109-15 14th Ave, College Point, NY 11356
Tel.: (718) 460-3300

Web Site: http://www.sccnyc.com
Sales Range: $10-24.9 Million
Emp.: 10
Industrial Buildings & Warehouses
N.A.I.C.S.: 236220
Danny Sawh (Pres)
Lynn Narain (Treas)

STONEWAY ROOFING SUPPLY
19020 Hwy 99, Lynnwood, WA 98036
Tel.: (206) 632-7820   WA
Web Site:
http://www.stonewayroofing.com
Year Founded: 1924
Rev.: $16,000,000
Emp.: 12
Roofing Supplies Retailer & Contractor
N.A.I.C.S.: 423330
Johnny Shi (Branch Mgr)

STONEY ROAD PRODUCTION INC.
409 Santa Monica Blvd # 2, Santa Monica, CA 90401
Tel.: (310) 394-5022
Sales Range: $10-24.9 Million
Emp.: 20
Motion Picture Production
N.A.I.C.S.: 512110
Troy Putney (VP)

STONINGTON FERTILIZER INC.
1707 E 1800 N Rd, Stonington, IL 62567
Tel.: (217) 325-3281
Sales Range: $10-24.9 Million
Emp.: 15
Fertilizer & Fertilizer Materials
N.A.I.C.S.: 424910
Tom Bollinger (Pres)

STONITE COIL CORPORATION
476 Route 156, Trenton, NJ 08620
Tel.: (609) 585-6600
Web Site: http://www.stonitecoil.com
Sales Range: $10-24.9 Million
Emp.: 24
Electronic Coils & Transformers
N.A.I.C.S.: 334416
William G. Engel (Pres)
Sandra Marritt (Mgr-Admin)
Hank Delgado (Mgr-Electrical Engrg)

STONY POINT GROUP, INC.
2 Town Sq Blvd Ste 310, Asheville, NC 28803
Tel.: (828) 210-8120   DE
Web Site: http://www.stonypoint.com
Year Founded: 1995
Rev.: $2,395,378
Emp.: 5
Private Equity Investment & Asset Management Services
N.A.I.C.S.: 523999
Kenneth Glass (Owner)
Bernard Stanek (Pres & CEO)

Subsidiaries:

Turbine Engine Components Technologies Corp. (1)
1211 Old Albany Rd, Thomasville, GA 31792
Tel.: (229) 228-8910
Sales Range: $150-199.9 Million
Mfr of Fan Blades, Vanes & Structural Components
N.A.I.C.S.: 333611
Robert S. Cohen (Pres & CEO)
Doug Cochran (Mgr-Major Acct)
Anthony Ratica (Pres-TECT Power)

Division (Domestic):

TECT Aerospace (2)
5545 N Mill Heights Dr, Park City, KS 67219
Tel.: (316) 529-5000

Sales Range: $25-49.9 Million
Sheet Metal Fabrication Services for Aerospace Industry
N.A.I.C.S.: 336371
Colin Strain (VP-Sls & Mktg)

Unit (Domestic):

TECT Aerospace (3)
1515 75th St SW, Everett, WA 98203
Tel.: (425) 353-8080
Web Site: http://www.tectaero.com
Sales Range: $10-24.9 Million
Fabricated Sheet metal Mfr
N.A.I.C.S.: 336413
William McCormick (Vice Chm)
Rick Rosenjack (Pres)

STOOL & DINETTE FACTORY INC.
4848 E Cactus Rd, Scottsdale, AZ 85254
Tel.: (623) 879-6555
Web Site:
http://www.azstoolanddinette.com
Sales Range: $10-24.9 Million
Emp.: 24
Furniture Retailer
N.A.I.C.S.: 449110
Kenneth Felder (Pres)

STOOPS AUTOMOTIVE GROUP, INC.
4055 W Clara Ln, Muncie, IN 47304
Tel.: (765) 288-1903
Web Site: http://www.stoopsauto.com
Year Founded: 1988
Sales Range: $10-24.9 Million
Emp.: 65
Automotive Part Repair & Maintenance Services
N.A.I.C.S.: 811121
John Frigge (CFO)
Henry Fallis (Bus Mgr)

Subsidiaries:

Stoops Buick, Inc. (1)
1251 Quaker Blvd, Plainfield, IN 46168
Tel.: (317) 839-7771
Web Site: http://www.stoopsbuickgmc.com
New & Used Car Dealer
N.A.I.C.S.: 441110
Jim Meyers (Gen Mgr)
Kellie Stocking (Dir-Svc)
Jeff Shorter (Mgr-Parts)
Jim Jarvis (Sls Mgr)
Ed Booth (Mgr-Fleet)
Mike Johnson (Mgr-Collision Dept)
Barbara Rady (Dir-Ecommerce & Mktg)

STOOPS FREIGHTLINER QUALITY TRAILER
1851 W Thompson Rd, Indianapolis, IN 46217
Tel.: (317) 788-1533
Web Site: http://www.stoops.com
Year Founded: 1987
Sales Range: $450-499.9 Million
Emp.: 500
Truck Distr
N.A.I.C.S.: 441110
David Bibler (Mgr-Fin-Indianapolis)
Mark Hall (Gen Mgr-Trailers Sls-Indianapolis)
David Shane (Mgr-Fixed Ops-Indianapolis)
Stan Eisenhooth (Gen Mgr-Anderson)

Subsidiaries:

Stoops Nationalease Inc (1)
1631 W Thompson Rd Ste A, Indianapolis, IN 46217
Tel.: (317) 788-1533
Web Site: http://www.stoopsfreightliner.com
Sales Range: $1-9.9 Million
Emp.: 12
Truck Leasing, Without Drivers
N.A.I.C.S.: 532120

COMPANIES

STORAGE & TRANSPORTATION CO., INC.
27050 Wick Rd, Taylor, MI 48180-3015
Tel.: (313) 292-2120 MI
Web Site: http://www.hazentransport.com
Year Founded: 1988
Sales Range: $10-24.9 Million
Emp.: 113
Local Trucking & Storage Services
N.A.I.C.S.: 484110
Richard F. Palmer (Pres)

Subsidiaries:

Hazen Transport Inc. (1)
27050 Wick Rd, Taylor, MI 48180-1841
Tel.: (313) 292-4061
Web Site: http://www.hazentransport.com
Sales Range: $10-24.9 Million
Emp.: 65
Provider of Local Trucking & Car Hauling Services
N.A.I.C.S.: 484110
Marcos Sanchez (Reg Mgr)
John R. Peczynski (Gen Mgr)
Tom Welland (CFO)
Richard Palmer Jr. (Pres)

Division (Domestic):

Executive Courier, Inc. (2)
120 Ottley Dr NE, Atlanta, GA 30324
Tel.: (404) 249-9000
Web Site: http://www.executivecourier.com
Courier, Expedited Freight & Cartage, Logistics & Transactional Warehousing & Distr Services
N.A.I.C.S.: 561499
Vince Hill (Office Mgr)

STORAGE SYSTEMS MIDWEST
N 16 W 23430 Stone Ridge Dr, Waukesha, WI 53188
Tel.: (262) 650-7700
Web Site: http://www.ssmidwest.com
Rev.: $13,000,000
Emp.: 55
Store Fixtures
N.A.I.C.S.: 423440
Randy Safranek (Pres)
Bill Brush (VP)
Lyn Lasneski (Project Mgr)

STORCENTRIC, INC.
1289 Anvilwood Ave, Sunnyvale, CA 94089
Tel.: (408) 427-8488 DE
Web Site: http://www.storcentric.com
Software Publisher
N.A.I.C.S.: 513210
Mihir Shah (Founder & CEO)
John P. Coughlan (CFO)
Read Fenner (VP-Global Sls)
Samina Subedar (VP-Mktg & Comm)
Dave Bartizal (VP-Busi Infrastructure & Solutions)

Subsidiaries:

Drobo, Inc. (1)
2540 Mission College Blvd, Santa Clara, CA 95054
Tel.: (408) 454-4200
Web Site: http://www.drobo.com
Data Storage & Data Protection Devices Mfr
N.A.I.C.S.: 334112
Brian Lazara (VP-Engrg)
John Westfield (CFO)
Mihir H. Shah (CEO)

Retrospect, Inc. (1)
1547 Palos Verdes Mall Ste 155, Walnut Creek, CA 94597
Tel.: (925) 476-1030
Web Site: http://www.retrospect.com
Software Publisher
N.A.I.C.S.: 513210

STORD, INC.
817 W Peachtree St NW Ste 200, Atlanta, GA 30308
Tel.: (678) 735-4772 DE
Web Site: http://www.stord.com
Supply Chain Solutions Services
N.A.I.C.S.: 513210
Sean Henry (Co-Founder & CEO)
Jacob Boudreau (Co-Founder & CTO)
Doug King (VP-Transportation)
Dan Klenkar (VP-Sls)
Tom Barone (Pres & Chief Comml Officer)
Steve Swan (COO)
Mark Satisky (Interim CFO)
Shyam Sundar (VP-Engrg)
Bradley Weill (VP-Product)
Sara Feulner (VP-People)
Mario Paganini (VP-Mktg)
Austin Pauls (VP-Fin)

Subsidiaries:

Fulfillment Works, LLC (1)
297 State St Bldg 1, North Haven, CT 06473
Web Site: http://www.fulfillmentworks.com
General Warehousing & Storage Services
N.A.I.C.S.: 493110
Amy Cooper (CEO)

STORE KRAFT MANUFACTURING CO
500 Irving St, Beatrice, NE 68310
Tel.: (402) 223-2348
Web Site: http://www.storekraft.com
Sales Range: $25-49.9 Million
Emp.: 200
Fixtures, Store: Except Wood
N.A.I.C.S.: 337126
Guy Peters (VP-Bus Opportunities)
Bob Reed (Controller)
Gary Schacht (Pres)

STORE SUPPLY WAREHOUSE, LLC.
12955 Enterprise Way, Bridgeton, MO 63044
Tel.: (314) 427-8887
Web Site: http://www.storesupply.com
Year Founded: 1994
Sales Range: $10-24.9 Million
Emp.: 68
Commercial Equipment Whslr
N.A.I.C.S.: 423440
John McMahon (Mgr-Credit)
Matthew Wohlstadter (Owner)

STOREFRONT FOR ART & ARCHITECTURE
97 Kenmare St, New York, NY 10012
Tel.: (212) 431-5795 NY
Web Site: http://www.storefrontnews.org
Year Founded: 1992
Rev.: $1,459,889
Assets: $1,080,504
Liabilities: $46,724
Net Worth: $10,331,780
Earnings: $272,320
Emp.: 6
Fiscal Year-end: 05/31/14
Arts Promotion Services
N.A.I.C.S.: 711310
Max Lauter (Mgr-Gallery & Coord-Project)
Eva Franch Gilabert (Exec Dir)

STORER EQUIPMENT COMPANY LTD.
504 W 67th St, Shreveport, LA 71106
Tel.: (318) 865-1466
Web Site: http://www.storerservices.com
Year Founded: 1959
Sales Range: $10-24.9 Million

Emp.: 80
Electrical Heating Equipment Sales
N.A.I.C.S.: 423730
Craig Storer (Chm)

STOREY-KENWORTHY COMPANY
1333 Ohio St, Des Moines, IA 50314
Tel.: (515) 288-3243
Web Site: http://www.storeykenworthy.com
Year Founded: 1933
Sales Range: $25-49.9 Million
Emp.: 140
Provider of Office Furniture
N.A.I.C.S.: 423210
David Kenworthy (Pres)
Jim Muller (Controller)

STORIS INC.
400 Valley Rd, Mount Arlington, NJ 07856
Tel.: (973) 601-8200
Web Site: http://www.storis.com
Rev.: $11,200,000
Emp.: 105
Computer Software Writing Services
N.A.I.C.S.: 541511
Donald J. Surdoval (Pres & CEO)
Doug Culmone (COO)

STORK AVENUE, INC.
2441 Bellevue Avenue, Daytona Beach, FL 32114
Tel.: (305) 669-4878
Sales Range: $1-9.9 Million
Emp.: 35
Mail Order of Birth Announcements & Invitations
N.A.I.C.S.: 323111
Wayne Mergenthal (VP)
Rita Valdes (CFO)
Robert J. Hunter Jr. (Pres)

STORK H & E TURBO BLADING
334 Comfort Rd, Ithaca, NY 14850
Tel.: (607) 277-4968
Web Site: http://www.he-machinery.com
Year Founded: 1976
Sales Range: $10-24.9 Million
Emp.: 170
Aircraft Turbine Mfr
N.A.I.C.S.: 336412
Ben te Beek (Controller)
Brian Meyers (Mgr-Production)
James Garrison (Supvr-Cutter Grind)
Debbie Chadwick (Mgr-HR)

STORM INDUSTRIES, INC.
23223 Normandie Ave, Torrance, CA 90501-5050
Tel.: (310) 534-5232
Web Site: http://www.stormind.com
Year Founded: 1932
Sales Range: $10-24.9 Million
Emp.: 120
Administrative, Strategic & Financial Services to Manufacturing, Residential Builders & Real Estate Businesses
N.A.I.C.S.: 541611
Tom Grzywacz (Pres)
Jeff Mattox (VP-Construction)
Hammond Michael (VP)
Rose Buscemi (Controller)

Subsidiaries:

Storm Manufacturing Group, Inc. (1)
23201 Normandie Ave, Torrance, CA 90501
Tel.: (310) 326-8287
Web Site: http://www.storm-manufacturing.com
Mfr of Engineered Products for Irrigation, Water Drilling & Compressed Air Industries
N.A.I.C.S.: 332911

Kate Sixel (Mgr-Customer Svc)
Brian Babb (Pres)

Storm-Western Development Corp. (1)
23223 Normandie Ave, Torrance, CA 90501-5050
Tel.: (310) 534-5232
Web Site: http://www.stormdevelopment.com
Sales Range: $10-24.9 Million
Emp.: 15
Mfr of Subdividers & Developers
N.A.I.C.S.: 237210

STORM SMART BUILDING SYSTEMS, INC.
6182 Idlewild St, Fort Myers, FL 33912
Tel.: (239) 938-1000
Web Site: http://www.stormsmart.com
Year Founded: 1996
Sales Range: $10-24.9 Million
Emp.: 110
Hurricane Protection Products Mfr
N.A.I.C.S.: 332321
Mike Killeen (Mgr-Ops)
Parker Bradtmiller (Dir-IT)
Diane Rist (Mgr-Acctg)
Hilda Provost (Mgr-Installation Scheduling)
Cliff Rice (Mgr-Pur)
Phil Miller (Mgr-Floor Production)
Ezequiel Ortiz (CFO)

STORM VULCAN MATTONI
2225 Burbank St, Dallas, TX 75235-3124
Tel.: (214) 637-1430 TX
Web Site: http://www.stormvulcan.com
Sales Range: $50-74.9 Million
Emp.: 16
Automotive Engine Rebuilding Equipment Mfr
N.A.I.C.S.: 333310
Richie Mattoni (CEO)
Terry Wagner (VP-Ops)

STORMANS INC.
1932 4th Ave E, Olympia, WA 98506
Tel.: (360) 754-2203
Web Site: http://www.stormans.com
Rev.: $12,800,000
Emp.: 8
Grocery Stores, Chain
N.A.I.C.S.: 445110
Kenneth R. Stormans (Pres)
Tim Thielen (Coord-Pricing)
Trevor Dewispelaere (Supvr-Produce)
Charelle Foege (VP)
Carly Marie Brettmann (Mgr-Mktg)

STORMS MOTORS, INC.
691 County Rd 39, Southampton, NY 11968
Tel.: (631) 283-1600
Web Site: http://www.stormsmotors.net
Sales Range: $10-24.9 Million
Emp.: 40
Car Whslr
N.A.I.C.S.: 441110
Stuart Schoener (VP & Gen Mgr)

STORR OFFICE ENVIRONMENTS, INC.
10800 World Trade Blvd, Raleigh, NC 27617
Tel.: (919) 313-3700 NC
Web Site: http://www.storr.com
Sales Range: $25-49.9 Million
Emp.: 200
Office Furniture Whslr
N.A.I.C.S.: 423210
Bob Schanz (Pres)
Scott Bosman (Gen Mgr)

3831

STORR OFFICE ENVIRONMENTS, INC.

Storr Office Environments, Inc.—(Continued)
Michael McMyne (VP-Ops)
Hunter Mason (CFO)
Tom Vande Guchte (CEO)
Subsidiaries:

Storr Office Environments of Florida, Inc. (1)
5112 W Linebaugh Ave, Tampa, FL 33624 (100%)
Tel.: (813) 418-3300
Web Site: http://www.storr.com
Sales Range: $10-24.9 Million
Emp.: 50
Office Furniture Whslr
N.A.I.C.S.: 423210

STORR TRACTOR CO.
3191 US Hwy 22, Branchburg, NJ 08876
Tel.: (908) 722-9830
Web Site: http://www.storrtractor.com
Sales Range: $25-49.9 Million
Emp.: 100
Provider of Irrigation Equipment
N.A.I.C.S.: 423820
David Dietz (Mgr-Svc)

STORY CONSTRUCTION CO
300 S Bell Ave, Ames, IA 50010
Tel.: (515) 232-4358
Web Site: http://www.storycon.com
Sales Range: $50-74.9 Million
Emp.: 180
Commercial & Office Building, New Construction
N.A.I.C.S.: 236220
Mike Espeset (Pres)
Brian Haessig (Project Mgr)

STORY DISTRIBUTING CO.
300 E Griffin Dr, Bozeman, MT 59715
Tel.: (406) 587-0702
Web Site: http://www.storydist.com
Rev: $20,000,000
Emp.: 60
Petroleum Bulk Stations
N.A.I.C.S.: 424710
Douglas A. Alexander (Pres)
Dan Alexander (VP)

STORY HOUSE PRODUCTION, INC.
2233 Wisconsin Ave NW Ste 240, Washington, DC 20007
Tel.: (202) 342-1373
Web Site: http://www.storyhousepro.com
Year Founded: 1999
Sales Range: $1-9.9 Million
Emp.: 11
Television & Motion Picture Production Services
N.A.I.C.S.: 512110
Andreas Gutzeit (Chief Creative Officer & Gen Mgr)
Carsten Oblaender (VP & Gen Mgr)
Robert Preuss (CFO)
Subsidiaries:

STORY HOUSE Productions GmbH (1)
Michael kirchstrasse 17&18, Berlin, 10179, Germany
Tel.: (49) 302809310
Web Site: http://www.storyhousepro.com
Television & Motion Picture Production Services
N.A.I.C.S.: 512110
Andreas Gutzeit (Co-Pres)
Carsten Oblaender (Co-Pres)

STORYBOOK COTTAGE DAY-CARE CENTER, LLC
375 County Rd 2104, Daingerfield, TX 75638-4963
Tel.: (903) 645-4791 TX
Year Founded: 2016
Sales Range: $1-9.9 Million
Child Day Care Services
N.A.I.C.S.: 624410
Valerie J. Epnett (Owner)

STOTT & DAVIS MOTOR EXPRESS
15 Garfield St, Auburn, NY 13021
Tel.: (315) 253-8431
Web Site: http://www.stottanddavis.com
Sales Range: $10-24.9 Million
Emp.: 50
Trucking Except Local
N.A.I.C.S.: 488510
Peter Marsh (Pres)

STOUGHTON TRAILERS, INC.
416 S Academy St, Stoughton, WI 53589-0606
Tel.: (608) 873-2500 WI
Web Site: http://www.stoughton-trailers.com
Year Founded: 1961
Sales Range: $350-399.9 Million
Emp.: 1,200
Truck Trailer Mfr
N.A.I.C.S.: 336212
Donald D. Wahlin (CEO)
Mike Fontaine (Controller)
Bob Wahlin (Pres & CEO)
H. Dean Lindquist (Dir-Sls Network)
Bill Hasz (Dir-Sls-Dealer Network)
Luke McMaster (VP-Sls & Mktg)

STOUT RISIUS ROSS, INC.
150 W 2nd St Ste 400, Royal Oak, MI 48067
Tel.: (248) 208-8800 MI
Web Site: http://www.stout.com
Year Founded: 1991
Financial Advisory & Management Consulting Services
N.A.I.C.S.: 523940
Craige L. Stout (CEO)
Mark J. Melancon (Mng Dir-Chicago)
Andrew Fargason (Mng Dir-Atlanta)
Michael Amacker (Mng Dir-Atlanta)
Steve Sahara (Dir-Chicago)
Loretta Cross (Mng Dir-Houston)
Simon Heaton (Chief Sr Talent Officer)
Jeffrey S. Shippy (Dir-Investment Banking Grp-Los Angeles)
Ronak P. Shah (Dir-Valuation Advisory Grp-Houston)
Ryan N. Sutherland (Dir-Valuation Advisory Grp-Chicago)
Carsten Hoffmann (Mng Dir-Valuation Advisory Grp & Head-Irvine)
John Calcagnini (Mng Dir-Healthcare Practice-Investment Banking Grp-Los Angeles)
Nick Jachim (Mng Dir & Head-Investment Banking-Chicago)
Christine D. Jaroszewicz (Chief HR Officer)
Jeff Risius (Head-Client Svc)
Ryan D. Thies (COO)
Daniel Broadhurst (Mng Dir)

STOUT ROOFING INC.
9705 Washburn Rd, Downey, CA 90241
Tel.: (562) 923-6775
Web Site: http://www.stoutroofing.com
Sales Range: $1-9.9 Million
Emp.: 20
Roofing Contractors
N.A.I.C.S.: 238160
Ray De Brouwer (Pres & CEO)

STOVESAND AUTO GROUP
3476 Park Ave, Paducah, KY 42001

Tel.: (270) 444-0011
Web Site: http://www.buyfromlarry.com
Sales Range: $50-74.9 Million
Emp.: 80
New & Used Car Dealerships Owner & Operator
N.A.I.C.S.: 441110
Larry Stovesand (Owner & Pres)

STOWASSER BUICK GMC, INC.
600 E Betteravia Rd, Santa Maria, CA 93456
Tel.: (805) 925-9565
Web Site: http://www.stowassergmc.com
Year Founded: 1949
Sales Range: $10-24.9 Million
Emp.: 35
Car Whslr
N.A.I.C.S.: 441110
Robert Stowasser Jr. (Pres)

STOWE AREA ASSOCIATION AGENCY
51 Main St, Stowe, VT 05672
Tel.: (802) 253-7321
Web Site: http://www.gostowe.com
Year Founded: 1972
Sales Range: $1-9.9 Million
Emp.: 12
Co-op Advertising, Magazines, Newspaper, Restaurant, Retail, Travel & Tourism
N.A.I.C.S.: 541810
Ed Stahl (Exec Dir)
John Walsh (Coord-Mktg)
Sharon Harper (Dir-Mktg)

STOWE-PHARR MILLS, INC.
100 Main St, McAdenville, NC 28101-9700
Tel.: (704) 824-3551 NC
Web Site: http://www.pharryarns.com
Year Founded: 1939
Sales Range: $200-249.9 Million
Emp.: 3,004
Mfr of Textile Yarns
N.A.I.C.S.: 313110
William Carstarphen (Pres)
Greg Peeler (Treas & Asst Sec)
Subsidiaries:

Stowe-Pharr Mills, Inc. - Pharr Polomar Plant (1)
6781 8th St, Buena Park, CA 90620
Tel.: (714) 522-4811
Textile Products Mfr
N.A.I.C.S.: 314999

STOWERS FURNITURE COMPANIES LTD
210 W Rector St, San Antonio, TX 78216
Tel.: (210) 342-9411
Web Site: http://www.stowersfurniture.com
Sales Range: $10-24.9 Million
Emp.: 40
Furniture Retailer
N.A.I.C.S.: 449110
Walter Harrell Spears (Pres)
Johnathan Spears (Gen Mgr)
Melinda Nunn (Coord-Display)

STOWERS MACHINERY CORP
6301 Old Rutledge Pike, Knoxville, TN 37924
Tel.: (865) 546-1414
Web Site: http://www.stowerscat.com
Sales Range: $100-124.9 Million
Emp.: 337
Distr & Maintenance Of Road Construction Equipment
N.A.I.C.S.: 423810

Mike Holman (Controller)
Chad Jones (Coord-Rental)
Howard Kirkland (VP)
Matt Kirkpatrick (Mgr-Sls-Power Sys Div)
Eddie Collins (Mgr-Admin Sls)

STOWERS RESOURCE MANAGEMENT, INC.
1000 E 50th St, Kansas City, MO 64110
Tel.: (816) 926-4000 DE
Web Site: http://www.stowers.org
Year Founded: 2005
Sales Range: $200-249.9 Million
Emp.: 137
Molecular Biology Research Services
N.A.I.C.S.: 541715
Abby Freeman (VP-Admin)
Richard Brown (Chm, Pres & CEO)
David A. Welte (Gen Counsel & Exec VP)
Roderick L. Sturgeon (CFO & Exec VP)
James E. Stowers III (Owner)

STP INVESTMENT SERVICES
158 Gay St, West Chester, PA 19380
Tel.: (610) 363-5684
Web Site: http://www.stpis.com
Emp.: 40
Investment & Business Services
N.A.I.C.S.: 561499
Dan Schlossberg (Exec VP-Client Svc & Bus Dev)
Patrick Murray (Pres & CEO)
Keith Bradley (COO)
Chris Sallemi (CTO & Head-Software Dev)
Subsidiaries:

Financial Control Systems, Inc. (1)
6 Dickinson Dr Ste 214, Chadds Ford, PA 19317
Tel.: (610) 358-2400
Web Site: http://www.fcsinc.us
Rev: $2,300,000
Emp.: 17
Investment & Accounting Software Services
N.A.I.C.S.: 523999

STRADA CAPITAL, CORP.
23046 Avenida De La Carlota Ste 350, Laguna Hills, CA 92653
Tel.: (949) 789-8850
Web Site: http://www.stradacapital.com
Year Founded: 1999
Sales Range: $10-24.9 Million
Emp.: 35
Equiment Financing
N.A.I.C.S.: 525990
Melissa Fisher (VP-Credit)
Calvin Nicholson (Acct Exec)
Carlos Cestero (COO)

STRADA SERVICES, LLC
3400 St Johns Pkwy, Sanford, FL 32771
Tel.: (866) 434-2218
Web Site: https://stradaservices.com
Full Service Electrical, Security & Air Conditioning Contracting Company
N.A.I.C.S.:
Joe Strada (Pres & CEO)
Subsidiaries:

L & M Electric, Inc. (1)
2260 Hewatt Rd, Snellville, GA 30039
Tel.: (770) 978-2300
Web Site: https://www.lmelectricinc.com
Residential Electric, Air conditioning, Security & Smart Home Installation & Maintenance Services
N.A.I.C.S.: 238210
Michael Lever (Treas)
Roger Lee (Co-Founder)
John Mezzles (Co-Founder)

STRAIGHT ARROW PRODUCTS, INC.
2020 Highland Ave, Bethlehem, PA 18020
Tel.: (610) 882-9606
Web Site:
http://www.straightarrowinc.com
Sales Range: $1-9.9 Million
Emp.: 35
Hair Care & Skin Care Products Mfr
N.A.I.C.S.: 325412
Devon Katzev *(Pres)*
Ed Kline *(VP-Sls & Mktg)*

STRAIGHT NORTH LLC
1001 W 31st St Ste 100, Downers Grove, IL 60515
Tel.: (630) 366-8150
Web Site:
http://www.straightnorth.com
Sales Range: $1-9.9 Million
Emp.: 55
Advetising Agency
N.A.I.C.S.: 541810
Kevin C. Duffy *(Pres & Chief Creative Officer)*
Tammy Barry *(Dir-HR)*
David M. Duerr *(Chm & CEO)*
Joseph T. Cahill *(Chief Strategy Officer)*
Aaron A. Wittersheim *(COO)*
Ian J. Stevenson *(VP-Sls)*
Brad Shorr *(Dir-Content Strategy)*
Matthew J. Cannon *(Dir-Web Svcs)*
Frank Fornaris *(VP-Fin)*
Matt Lane *(Mgr-Bus Dev)*
Tom Ploch *(Mgr-Sls)*
Carolyn Goettsch *(Dir-Client Svcs)*
April Reynolds *(Acct Mgr)*
Ann Rickerman-Hambry *(Sr Project Mgr)*
Sara Rowles *(Acct Mgr)*
Joshua Schmidt *(Dir-Client Svcs)*
Jess Stewart *(Acct Mgr)*

STRAINRITE INC.
65 1st Flight Dr, Auburn, ME 04210
Tel.: (207) 777-3100
Web Site: http://www.strainrite.com
Sales Range: $10-24.9 Million
Emp.: 80
Industrial Filter Mfr
N.A.I.C.S.: 333998
Jana Lapoint *(Chm)*
Allen Lapoint *(Pres)*

STRAIT & LAMP LUMBER CO. INC.
269 National Rd SE, Hebron, OH 43025-9578
Tel.: (740) 928-4501   OH
Web Site:
http://www.straitandlamp.com
Year Founded: 1977
Sales Range: $50-74.9 Million
Emp.: 150
Lumber, Plywood & Millwork
N.A.I.C.S.: 423310
Wilbur C. Strait Jr. *(Owner, Chm & Pres)*

Subsidiaries:

Dublin Millwork Co. Inc.   (1)
7575 Fishel Dr S, Dublin, OH 43016
Tel.: (614) 889-7776
Web Site: http://www.dublinmillwork.com
Rev.: $6,300,000
Emp.: 50
Wood Molding Distr
N.A.I.C.S.: 423310
Bryan Sonner *(Gen Mgr)*

Fifth Avenue Lumber Co., Inc.   (1)
479 E 5th Ave, Columbus, OH 43201-2876
Tel.: (614) 294-0068
Rev.: $10,300,000
Emp.: 25
Sales of Lumber & Other Building Materials

Linworth Lumber Inc.   (1)
2310 West Dublin Granville Rd, Columbus, OH 43085
Tel.: (614) 885-9543
Web Site: http://www.straitandlamp.com
Sales Range: $10-24.9 Million
Emp.: 24
Lumber, Plywood & Millwork
N.A.I.C.S.: 423310
John Sobolewski *(Gen Mgr)*

S & L Contracting Inc.   (1)
269 National Rd SE, Hebron, OH 43025-9578
Tel.: (740) 928-4501   (100%)
Web Site:
http://www.straitlumber.doitbest.com
Sales Range: Less than $1 Million
Emp.: 30
Housing Construction Services
N.A.I.C.S.: 236115
Cindi Osborn *(Controller)*

STRAIT LANE CAPITAL PARTNERS, LLC
4448 W Lovers Ln, Dallas, TX 75209
Tel.: (469) 466-9472
Web Site:
http://www.straitlanecapital.com
Privater Equity Firm
N.A.I.C.S.: 523999
Mark King *(Chm)*

STRAITS CORPORATION
1424 Straits Dr, Bay City, MI 48706
Tel.: (989) 684-5088   MI
Year Founded: 1953
Sales Range: $10-24.9 Million
Emp.: 12
Railroads, Line-Haul Operating
N.A.I.C.S.: 482111
Charles Pinkerton *(Pres)*
Charles A. Pinkerton III *(Pres)*

STRAND ASSOCIATES, INC.
910 W Wingra Dr, Madison, WI 53715
Tel.: (608) 251-4843
Web Site: http://www.strand.com
Rev.: $21,500,000
Emp.: 340
Engineeering Services
N.A.I.C.S.: 541330
Philip Budde *(Pres & COO)*

STRAND BOOK STORE INC.
828 Broadway, New York, NY 10003
Tel.: (212) 473-1452
Web Site:
http://www.strandbooks.com
Year Founded: 1927
Rev.: $15,000,000
Emp.: 200
Owner & Operator of Used Book Stores
N.A.I.C.S.: 459510
Fred Bass *(Co-Owner)*
Tris Miller *(Mgr-Library)*

STRANG CORPORATION
8905 Lake Ave, Cleveland, OH 44102
Tel.: (216) 961-6767
Web Site: http://www.strangcorp.com
Year Founded: 1942
Sales Range: $150-199.9 Million
Emp.: 3,500
Hospitality Services
N.A.I.C.S.: 722511
Peter Strang *(Exec VP)*
Donald W. Strang Jr. *(Chm)*

STRANGE'S FLORIST & GREENHOUSES
3313 Mechanicsville Pike, Richmond, VA 23223-1726
Tel.: (804) 321-2200
Web Site: http://www.stranges.com
Sales Range: $10-24.9 Million
Emp.: 100
Online Flowers & Floral Arrangements Retailer
N.A.I.C.S.: 459310
Cary T. Gouldin *(Sec & VP)*
William J. Gouldin Jr. *(Pres & CEO)*

STRAPACK INC.
33508 Central Ave, Union City, CA 94587
Tel.: (510) 475-6000
Web Site: http://www.strapack.com
Rev.: $12,218,152
Emp.: 13
Packaging Machinery & Equipment
N.A.I.C.S.: 423830
Keisho Yamamoto *(Pres)*
Sergey Moroz *(Asst Mgr)*

STRASBURGER & PRICE, LLP
901 Main St Ste 6000, Dallas, TX 75202
Tel.: (214) 651-4300
Web Site: http://www.strasburger.com
Year Founded: 1939
Sales Range: $75-99.9 Million
Emp.: 201
Legal Advisory Services
N.A.I.C.S.: 541110
Jules S. Brenner *(Partner-Energy, Oil & Gas, Corp & Securities)*
Diana J. Bearden *(Partner-Fin Svcs & Real Estate)*
Alison J. Cross *(Partner-Fin Svcs & Real Estate)*
Allan C. Wisk *(Partner-Fin Svcs)*
Annie J. Jacobs *(Partner-Comml, Products Litigation & Transportation & Logistics)*
Ashley T. Kisner *(Partner-Comml Fiduciary Litigation, Real Estate & Retail)*
Brian G. Hamilton *(Partner-Healthcare, Food Drug & Device Law)*
Carol Glendenning *(Partner-Corp Securities, Energy Oil & Gas)*
Charles M. Hosch *(Partner-Comml Litigation, Franchise & Distr)*
Christopher R. Ward *(Partner-Construction, Fidelity, Insurance Counsel & Logistics)*
Courtney Jones Kieffer *(Partner-Comml Litigation & Environmental)*
Daniel L. Butcher *(Partner-Distr, Retail & Tax)*
David N. Kitner *(Partner-Comml Litigation & Pro Liability)*
Robert K. Sugg *(Partner-Real Estate, Bus Reorganization & Bankruptcy)*
Jeremy Kell *(Partner)*
Brad Oxford *(Partner)*
Martin E. Thornthwaite *(Partner & Atty)*
Debra Gatison Hatter *(Partner)*
Sujata Ajmera *(Partner)*
Anita Kerin *(Partner)*
Corinne Smith *(Partner)*
Mark Andrews *(Partner-Securities, Food Drug, Device Law & Transportation)*
Taylor S. Boone *(Partner-Estate Plng Trust, Probate & Fiduciary Litigation)*
Tom Anson *(Partner-Appellate, Comml Litigation, Energy Oil & Land Use)*

STRASBURGER ENTERPRISES, INC.
7 N 5th St, Temple, TX 76501
Tel.: (254) 778-3547   TX
Web Site: http://www.strasburger.net
Year Founded: 1974
Real Estate, Farming & Ranching, Insurance & Banking
N.A.I.C.S.: 531390
H. Tommy Strasburger *(CEO)*
Roy Strasburger *(Pres)*

STRAT-O-MATIC MEDIA, LLC
42 Railroad Ave, Glen Head, NY 11545
Tel.: (516) 671-6566   NY
Web Site: http://www.strat-o-matic.com
Year Founded: 1962
Emp.: 115
Fantasy Sports Games Producer
N.A.I.C.S.: 459120
Harold Richman *(Pres & Founder)*

STRATA CORPORATION
1600 N 48th St, Grand Forks, ND 58203
Tel.: (701) 746-7491
Web Site: http://www.strata-corp.com
Sales Range: $25-49.9 Million
Emp.: 700
Highway & Street Construction
N.A.I.C.S.: 237310
James Bradshaw *(Pres)*
Henry Hauge *(Engr-Tech Svcs)*
Jay Evans *(Reg Mgr)*
Mike Martin *(Mgr-Aggregate Safety)*

STRATA GRAPHICS, INC.
5166 Campus Dr, Plymouth Meeting, PA 19462
Tel.: (610) 941-6100
Web Site: http://www.gostrata.com
Rev.: $4,100,000
Emp.: 43
Commercial Lithographic Printing
N.A.I.C.S.: 323111
Jeff Sammak *(Pres)*

Subsidiaries:

Movad, LLC   (1)
801 Bristol Pike, Bensalem, PA 19020-6361
Tel.: (215) 638-2679
Web Site: http://www.movadcorp.com
Printing
N.A.I.C.S.: 323120
Joan McCloskey *(Pres)*

STRATA MARKETING, INC.
30 W Monroe St Ste 1900, Chicago, IL 60603
Tel.: (312) 222-1555
Web Site: http://www.stratag.com
Year Founded: 1984
Sales Range: $10-24.9 Million
Emp.: 100
Software Development & Marketing Research Services
N.A.I.C.S.: 513210
Mike McHugh *(VP-Media Sls & Electronic Delivery)*
David Drucker *(VP & Mgr-Agency Svcs)*
Joy Baer *(Pres)*
Paul Levy *(VP-Custom Dev)*
Tom Gombas *(VP-Cable Products)*
Michael Latulippe *(Sr VP-Fin & Admin)*
Peter Nason *(VP-Contracts & Mktg)*
Francine L. Olson *(VP-Major Accts-Cable)*
Michael Dehler *(VP-Technical Infrastructure)*
David Prager *(VP-e-Bus Solutions & Program Mgmt)*

STRATACACHE INC.
2 Emmet St Ste 200, Dayton, OH 45405
Tel.: (937) 224-0485
Web Site:
http://www.stratacache.com
Rev.: $4,000,000
Emp.: 30
Computer System Design Services

STRATACACHE INC.

Stratacache Inc.—(Continued)
N.A.I.C.S.: 541512
Chris Riegel (CEO)
Chuck Gose (VP-Corp Comm)
Jeff Griffin (Exec VP-Retail Media Networks)
Erkki Rajamaki (Dir-Bus Dev-Canada)
Subsidiaries:

Real Digital Media LLC (1)
5959 Cattlemen Ln, Sarasota, FL 34232
Tel.: (941) 951-0130
Web Site: http://www.realdigitalmedia.com
Digital Signage Software
N.A.I.C.S.: 513210
Ken Goldberg (CEO)
Michael Baron (Pres)
Kevin Spaeth (VP-Sls)
Jason Broom (VP-Mktg)
John Moons (VP-Dev)

Scala, Inc. (1)
7 Great Valley Pkwy Ste 300, Malvern, PA 19355
Tel.: (610) 363-3350
Web Site: http://www.scala.com
Custom Computer Programming Services
N.A.I.C.S.: 541511
Daniel Rubenstein (Dir-Fin Sls)
Stefan Menger (VP-Advanced Analytics)
Rune Halvorsen (Chm)
Harry Horn (Gen Mgr-EMEA)
Joe Sullivan (COO)
Manish Kumar (Mng Dir-Asiapacific Ops & Sr VP)

STRATASHOPS LLC
2001 W Franklin, Elkhart, IN 46516
Web Site:
http://www.stratashops.com
Year Founded: 2008
Sales Range: $1-9.9 Million
Emp.: 8
Outdoor Furniture
N.A.I.C.S.: 449110
John Webber (Founder & Pres)

STRATE WELDING SUPPLY CO. INC.
101 Comet Ave, Buffalo, NY 14216
Tel.: (716) 873-3660
Web Site:
http://www.strateweldingsupply.com
Year Founded: 1949
Rev.: $18,400,000
Emp.: 85
Cylinders, Bulk Compressed Gases & Cryogenic Storage Products Distr
N.A.I.C.S.: 423830
Frank Russell Strate (Chm)

STRATEGAS RESEARCH PARTNERS, LLC
52 Vanderbilt Ave 8th Fl, New York, NY 10017
Tel.: (212) 497-2731
Web Site: http://www.strategasrp.com
Emp.: 60
Macro Research, Advisory & Capital Markets Services
N.A.I.C.S.: 523940
Donald J. Rissmiller (Dir-Res)
Jason Trennert (Chm & Mng Partner)
Nicholas Bohnsack (COO)
Dan Clifton (Partner & Head-Washington Office)
Subsidiaries:

Encima Global LLC (1)
645 Madison Ave 5th Fl, New York, NY 10022
Tel.: (212) 876-4400
Web Site: http://www.encimaglobal.com
Economic & Market Research for Institutional Investors
N.A.I.C.S.: 541910
David R. Malpass (Pres)
Adrienne Hepworth (Dir-Mktg)

STRATEGEX, INC.
20 S Clark St Ste 2400, Chicago, IL 60603
Tel.: (312) 551-0505
Web Site: http://www.strategex.com
Year Founded: 1993
Sales Range: $1-9.9 Million
Emp.: 30
Market Research & Consulting Services
N.A.I.C.S.: 541611
Peter Philippi (Founder & CEO)
Richard Dodge (VP)
Tom Taber (VP)
Joe Hahn (VP)
Michael Underwood (VP)
Mark Curran (VP)

STRATEGIC AMERICA
6600 Westown Pkwy Ste 100, West Des Moines, IA 50266-7708
Tel.: (888) 898-6400
Web Site:
http://www.strategicamerica.com
Year Founded: 1980
Sales Range: $50-74.9 Million
Emp.: 100
Advetising Agency
N.A.I.C.S.: 541810
John Schreurs (CEO)
Bruce Ganzer (Principal & VP-Creative)
Carrie Thomson (Dir-Medical)
Bryce Thomson (Principal & VP-Client Svcs)
Nathan Johnson (Principal & VP-Mktg Svcs)
Carolyn Hikiji (Dir-Media)
Marilyn Cox (Dir-HR)
Troy Wells (CFO & VP)
Dave Miglin (Principal & VP-Interactive Svcs)
Lisa Holtorf (Principal & VP-Ops & Integration)

STRATEGIC ANALYSIS INC.
475 Wilson Blvd Ste 200, Arlington, VA 22203
Tel.: (703) 527-5410
Web Site: http://www.sainc.com
Year Founded: 1986
Rev.: $15,616,877
Emp.: 120
Commercial Physical Research
N.A.I.C.S.: 541715
Alice Burgess (COO)
Roger Alex (VP-Program Mgmt & Analysis)
Greg Fischer (VP-Defense Science & Tech Svcs)
Brian James (VP-Energy Analysis Svcs)
Roger Nicholas (CFO & Exec VP)
Barbara Smith (VP-Conference Svcs)
Diane M. Smith (Gen Counsel & Exec VP)
Ted Stump (VP-Advanced Concepts & IT)

STRATEGIC AR
10800 Farley St Ste 165, Overland Park, KS 66210
Tel.: (913) 744-3360
Web Site: http://www.strategicar.com
Year Founded: 2006
Sales Range: $1-9.9 Million
Emp.: 12
Patient Billing & Collection
N.A.I.C.S.: 561440
Salil Talauliker (CTO)

STRATEGIC ASSET MANAGEMENT GROUP ADVISORS, INC.
6451 North Federal Hwy Ste 409, Fort Lauderdale, FL 33308
Tel.: (954) 473-1110
Web Site: http://www.1samgroup.com
Year Founded: 1998
Investment Management & Advisory Services
N.A.I.C.S.: 523940
Robert Oden (Mng Partner)
Andrew Oden (CFO)

STRATEGIC ASSET MANAGEMENT, INC.
25 New Britain Ave, Unionville, CT 06085
Tel.: (860) 675-0439
Web Site: http://www.samicorp.com
Year Founded: 1996
Rev.: $10,523,786
Emp.: 15
Management Consulting Services
N.A.I.C.S.: 541611
S. Bradley Peterson (CEO)
Mark Broussard (Pres & COO)
Dave Army (Sr VP-Ops)
Kent Johnson (Sr VP-North America)

STRATEGIC BUSINESS SYSTEMS, INC.
5180 Parkstone Dr Ste 110, Chantilly, VA 20151
Tel.: (703) 639-4681
Web Site: http://www.sbsplanet.com
Year Founded: 2000
Information Technology Infrastructure Design, Integration & Consulting Services
N.A.I.C.S.: 541512

STRATEGIC CAPITAL HOLDINGS, LLC
10 Terrace Rd, Ladera Ranch, CA 92694
Tel.: (949) 429-6600
Web Site:
http://www.strategicreit.com
Holding Company; Storage Facilities Real Estate Investment & Property Management Services
N.A.I.C.S.: 551112
H. Michael Schwartz (CEO)
James L. Berg (Gen Counsel)
Subsidiaries:

SmartStop Asset Management, LLC (1)
10 Ter Rd, Ladera Ranch, CA 92694
Web Site: http://www.strategicreit.com
Real Estate Investment Fund Management Services
N.A.I.C.S.: 523940
Paula Mathews (Exec VP)
H. Michael Schwartz (CEO)
Subsidiary (Domestic):

Strategic Student & Senior Housing Trust, Inc. (2)
19900 MacArthur Blvd Ste 250, Irvine, CA 92612
Web Site: https://www.strategicreit.com
Rev.: $34,430,834
Assets: $210,454,098
Liabilities: $200,613,909
Net Worth: $9,840,189
Earnings: ($534,244)
Fiscal Year-end: 12/31/2022
Real Estate Investment Services
N.A.I.C.S.: 531210
Matt F. Lopez (CFO, Treas & Sec)
John Strockis (Pres & Chief Investment Officer)
John D. Strockis (CEO)
H. Michael Schwartz (Chm)
James L. Berg (Sec)

SmartStop Self Storage REIT, Inc. (1)
10 Terrace Rd, Ladera Ranch, CA 92694
Tel.: (949) 429-6600
Web Site:
https://investors.smartstopselfstorage.com
Rev.: $232,991,744

Assets: $1,895,640,725
Liabilities: $1,399,777,813
Net Worth: $495,862,912
Earnings: ($2,745,698)
Emp.: 500
Fiscal Year-end: 12/31/2023
Real Estate Investment Trust
N.A.I.C.S.: 523999
H. Michael Schwartz (Founder, Chm & CEO)
James R. Barry (CFO & Treas)
Joe Robinson (COO)
Nicholas M. Look (Gen Counsel)
David Corak (VP-Finance)
Michael Terjung (Chief Acctg Officer)

STRATEGIC COMMUNICATIONS, LLC.
310 Evergreen Rd, Louisville, KY 40243
Tel.: (502) 493-7234
Web Site:
http://www.yourstrategic.com
Year Founded: 1994
Sales Range: $25-49.9 Million
Emp.: 40
IT Services & Infrastructure Capabilities
N.A.I.C.S.: 519290
Stella Kathy Mills (Pres)
Karli Neutz (Coord-Svc)
Paige Reh (Mgr-HR)
Fred Devoid (Dir-Svcs)
Christopher Payne (Reg Acct Mgr)

STRATEGIC CONSULTING SOLUTIONS, INC.
109A Jefferson Ave, Oak Ridge, TN 37830
Tel.: (865) 220-0051
Web Site:
http://www.scsconsults.com
Year Founded: 2004
Sales Range: $1-9.9 Million
Emp.: 23
Accounting Software Services
N.A.I.C.S.: 541219
Laura Davis (Founder & Pres)
David Norris (Dir-Ops)

STRATEGIC DATA SYSTEMS
7777 Alvarado Rd Ste 920, La Mesa, CA 91941
Tel.: (619) 697-0025
Web Site:
http://www.sdatasystems.com
Year Founded: 1993
Sales Range: $10-24.9 Million
Emp.: 125
Information Technology Services to Government & Private Industry
N.A.I.C.S.: 517810
Andrew J. Toth (VP-Enterprise Solutions)

STRATEGIC DECISIONS GROUP INTERNATIONAL LLC
951 Mariners Island Ste 307, San Mateo, CA 94404
Tel.: (650) 475-4400
Web Site: http://www.sdg.com
Management Consulting Services
N.A.I.C.S.: 541618
Sandra J. Wrobel (Partner & Mng Dir)
Carl Spetzler (Founder, Chm & CEO)
Mary Lea Kirven (Mng Dir & HR Officer)
Mark Seidler (Partner, Mng Dir & Head-European Ops)
Steven Tani (Partner)
Mazen A. Skaf (Partner & Mng Dir)
Naoki Shimoda (Partner & Mng Dir)
Hannah Winter (Partner & Mng Dir)
Craig H. Shaffer (Partner & Mng Dir)

STRATEGIC DIGITAL SERVICES INC.

318 N Monroe St Ste 2, Tallahassee, FL 32301
Tel.: (850) 792-4186
Year Founded: 2014
Sales Range: $1-9.9 Million
Emp.: 7
Digital Advertising Services
N.A.I.C.S.: 541850
Matt Farrar *(Co-Founder)*
Joe Clements *(Co-Founder)*
Rebecca Romero *(VP-Clients Rels)*
Nipa Eason *(Creative Dir)*
Sara Holland *(Mgr-Bus Ops)*

STRATEGIC FEEDBACK INC.
47 E Chicago Ave Ste 310, Naperville, IL 60540
Tel.: (630) 527-9780
Web Site: http://www.satisfyd.com
Year Founded: 1998
Sales Range: $1-9.9 Million
Emp.: 8
Customer Satisfaction Tools
N.A.I.C.S.: 541690
Leigh Condon *(Co-Founder)*
Ryan Condon *(Co-Founder)*
Erick Blake *(Project Mgr)*

STRATEGIC FOCUS
36083 Soapberry, Fremont, CA 94536
Tel.: (408) 568-3993   CA
Web Site:
  http://www.strategicfocus.com
Year Founded: 1986
Sales Range: Less than $1 Million
Emp.: 14
Business Strategy Consulting & Software Evaluation
N.A.I.C.S.: 541512
Jay Prakash *(Pres)*

STRATEGIC FUNDRAISING, INC.
7591 9th St N, Saint Paul, MN 55128
Tel.: (651) 649-0404
Web Site:
  http://www.strategicfundraising.com
Year Founded: 1991
Rev.: $26,100,000
Emp.: 723
Analytics & Advanced Technology
N.A.I.C.S.: 927110
Jeremy London *(Mgr-Comm)*
Eric Johnson *(VP-Bus Dev)*
Jennifer Coufal *(Dir-Bus Dev-Tallmadge)*

STRATEGIC GOVERNMENT RESOURCES INC.
PO Box 1642, Keller, TX 76244
Tel.: (817) 337-8581
Web Site: https://www.governmentresource.com
Year Founded: 1999
Recruitment Services
N.A.I.C.S.: 561311

STRATEGIC INDUSTRIES, LLC
26 Main St Ste 200, Chatham, NJ 07928-2425
Tel.: (732) 512-0195
Year Founded: 2000
Sales Range: $200-249.9 Million
Aircraft Engines & Components Mfr
N.A.I.C.S.: 336412

STRATEGIC INVESTMENTS & HOLDING INC.
50 Fountain Plz Ste 1350, Buffalo, NY 14202-1725
Tel.: (716) 857-6000   DE
Web Site: http://www.sihi.net
Year Founded: 1991
Sales Range: $10-24.9 Million
Emp.: 9
Provider of Investment Services
N.A.I.C.S.: 541611
Gary M. Brost *(Principal)*
Subsidiaries:
General Housing Inc.   (1)
2255 Industrial Blvd, Waycross, GA 31503-6969
Tel.: (912) 285-5068
Mobile Home Mfr
N.A.I.C.S.: 321991

STRATEGIC MEDIA, INC.
2857 Executive Dr Ste 120, Clearwater, FL 33762-5584
Tel.: (727) 531-7622
Web Site: http://www.strategic-media-inc.com
Year Founded: 1995
Sales Range: $1-9.9 Million
Emp.: 20
Advetising Agency
N.A.I.C.S.: 541810
Chuck Nelms *(Pres)*
Michael Finegold *(Dir-Ops)*
Lauri Ravenna *(Mgr-Bus Dev)*
Samantha Rolfe *(Mgr-Social Media)*
Lucine Colignon *(Mgr-Social Media)*

STRATEGIC MICRO SYSTEMS OF NJ, LLC.
120 Littleton Rd, Parsippany, NJ 07054
Tel.: (973) 628-0099
Web Site: http://www.stmicro.net
Year Founded: 2001
Rev.: $2,100,000
Emp.: 14
Computer Related Services
N.A.I.C.S.: 541512
Ted Passalacqua *(Founder & Pres)*
Aaron Perry *(Dir-Bus Dev)*

STRATEGIC MOBILITY GROUP
1201 Wiley Rd Ste 120, Schaumburg, IL 60173
Tel.: (847) 995-1010
Web Site:
  http://www.strategicmobility.com
Year Founded: 2002
Sales Range: $10-24.9 Million
Emp.: 16
It Consulting
N.A.I.C.S.: 541690
Michael Grudecki *(VP-Mktg & Inside Sls)*
Eric Holmes *(VP-Sls)*
Nancy Gorski *(Founder, Pres & CEO)*
Nico Genet *(Dir-Natl Accounts)*
Stacie Lamprecht *(Dir-HR)*
Maria DiNicola *(CFO)*
Christine Pearson *(Mgr-Ops)*

STRATEGIC NURSE STAFFING, INC.
60 Knickerbocker Ave, Bohemia, NY 11716   NY
Year Founded: 2005
Sales Range: $10-24.9 Million
Emp.: 109
Healthcare Staffing Services
N.A.I.C.S.: 561311
Rob Simmons *(Founder, Owner, Pres & CEO)*
Teresa Mann *(Chief Nursing Officer)*

STRATEGIC PUBLICATIONS, LLC
75 Boxwood Ln, Cheektowaga, NY 14225
Tel.: (716) 668-5223   DE
Sales Range: $25-49.9 Million
Emp.: 400
Community Newspapers Publisher
N.A.I.C.S.: 513110
Bernard Bradpiece *(Pres & CEO)*
Subsidiaries:
Metro Group, Inc.   (1)
75 Boxwood Ln, Cheektowaga, NY 14227-2707
Tel.: (716) 668-5223
Web Site: http://www.metrogroupwny.com
Sales Range: $10-24.9 Million
Emp.: 110
Publisher of Shopper & Community Newspapers
N.A.I.C.S.: 513110

STRATEGIC REALTY CAPITAL, LLC
1411 5th St Ste 406, Santa Monica, CA 90401
Tel.: (310) 566-1320
Web Site:
  http://www.strategicrealtycapital.com
Private Equity Real Estate Firm
N.A.I.C.S.: 523999
Charles Hill *(Co-Founder & Mng Dir)*
Eddie Lorin *(Co-Founder & Mng Dir)*
Greg Salyers *(Partner)*
Andy Park *(Partner)*
Howard Song *(Dir-Asset Mgmt)*

STRATEGIC REALTY TRUST, INC.
550 W Adams St Ste 200, Chicago, IL 60661
Tel.: (312) 878-4860   MD
Web Site: https://www.srtreit.com
Year Founded: 2008
Rev.: $2,787,000
Assets: $35,748,000
Liabilities: $18,602,000
Net Worth: $17,146,000
Earnings: ($11,545,000)
Fiscal Year-end: 12/31/22
Retail Properties Investment Services
N.A.I.C.S.: 523999
Todd Allan Spitzer *(Chm)*
Ryan Hess *(CFO, Chief Acctg Officer & Treas)*
Domenic Lanni *(COO)*
Domenic Lanni *(CEO)*

STRATEGIC RETAIL ADVISORS, INC.
405 Cochituate Rd Ste 301, Framingham, MA 01701
Tel.: (508) 405-1918
Web Site: http://www.sraretail.com
Year Founded: 2001
Sales Range: $1-9.9 Million
Emp.: 15
Commercial Real Estate Services
N.A.I.C.S.: 531390
Peter M. Belsito *(Founder & Pres)*
Steve Ferris *(Principal)*
Jonathan Lapat *(Principal)*

STRATEGIC RISK SOLUTIONS INC.
2352 Main St Ste204, Concord, MA 01742
Tel.: (781) 487-9800
Web Site:
  http://www.strategicrisks.com
Year Founded: 1993
Sales Range: $25-49.9 Million
Emp.: 50
Provider of Insurance Services
N.A.I.C.S.: 541611
J. Brady Young *(Pres & CEO)*
Andrew Berry *(Mng Dir & COO)*
Michael O'Malley *(Mng Dir)*
Andrew Hupman *(Dir-Ops)*
Matthew Charleson *(COO-Fund Svcs & ILS)*
Subsidiaries:
Strategic Risk Solutions Inc.   (1)
Pearman Bldg 3rd Fl 3 Gorham Rd, Hamilton, Bermuda
Tel.: (441) 2925939
Sales Range: $25-49.9 Million
Emp.: 8
Provider of Insurance Services
N.A.I.C.S.: 524298

STRATEGIC STAFFING SOLUTIONS INC.
645 Griswold St Ste 2900, Detroit, MI 48226-4206
Tel.: (313) 965-1110
Web Site:
  http://www.strategicstaff.com
Year Founded: 1982
Sales Range: $500-549.9 Million
Emp.: 610
Information Technology Services
N.A.I.C.S.: 541512
Cynthia J. Pasky *(Founder, Pres & CEO)*
David Fox *(VP)*
Colonel Ken Huxley *(VP-Talent Acq)*
Jeff Nelson *(Exec VP)*
Ed Mannino *(CFO)*

STRATEGIC SYSTEMS & TECHNOLOGY CORPORATION
3325 Paddocks Pkwy Ste 250, Suwanee, GA 30024
Tel.: (678) 389-7200
Web Site: http://www.sstid.com
Year Founded: 1999
Sales Range: $10-24.9 Million
Emp.: 35
Computer Software Development Services
N.A.I.C.S.: 541511
Richard Bissonnette *(Owner)*
David Bissonette *(Exec VP)*

STRATEGIC SYSTEMS, INC.
485 Metro Pl S Ste 270, Dublin, OH 43017
Tel.: (614) 717-4774
Web Site: http://www.strsi.com
Sales Range: $10-24.9 Million
Emp.: 140
Software Development & Information Technology Staffing Services
N.A.I.C.S.: 541511
Steve Rugg *(VP-Sls)*

STRATEGIC TELECOM SOLUTIONS
8894 Spanish Rdg Ave, Las Vegas, NV 89148
Tel.: (702) 363-8127
Web Site:
  http://www.strategictelecom.com
Year Founded: 2004
Sales Range: $1-9.9 Million
Emp.: 28
Wireless Telecommunication Services
N.A.I.C.S.: 517112
Joey Marlow *(Pres & CEO)*
Lori Chura *(CFO)*
Vito Centofanti *(VP-Sls)*

STRATEGIC VALUE PARTNERS, LLC
100 W Putnam Ave, Greenwich, CT 06830
Tel.: (203) 618-3500   DE
Web Site: http://www.svpglobal.com
Year Founded: 2001
Emp.: 60
Privater Equity Firm
N.A.I.C.S.: 523999
David Geenberg *(Head-Investment-North America)*
Victor Khosla *(Co-Founder & Chief Investment Officer)*
Daniel Y. Han *(Mng Dir-Investment-US)*
Jason Clarke *(Mng Dir-Investment)*
H. J. Woltery *(Mng Dir-Investment)*

STRATEGIC VALUE PARTNERS, LLC

U.S. PRIVATE

Strategic Value Partners, LLC—(Continued)

Edward Kelly *(COO)*
Jean-Louis Lelogeais *(Co-Founder & Sr Mng Dir)*
Michael Hewett *(Mng Dir-IR-Global)*
Carter Weil *(Mng Dir)*
Chris Jackson *(Mng Dir)*
John Brantl *(Mng Dir)*
Jumbo Tanaka *(Mng Dir)*
Ranji Nagaswami *(Mng Dir & Chief Strategy & Comml Officer)*
Brian Himot *(Mng Dir & Head-Structured Capital)*

Subsidiaries:

GSE Holding, Inc. **(1)**
19103 Gundle Rd, Houston, TX 77073
Tel.: (281) 443-8564
Web Site: http://www.gseworld.com
Rev: $417,652,000
Assets: $266,152,000
Liabilities: $246,256,000
Net Worth: $19,896,000
Earnings: ($84,526,000)
Emp.: 643
Fiscal Year-end: 12/31/2013
Holding Company; Geosynthetic Lining Products Mfr & Distr
N.A.I.C.S.: 551112
Peter R. McCourt *(Pres-Intl)*
Jeffery D. Nigh *(Exec VP-Global Ops)*
Edward Zimmel *(VP-Engrg)*
Daniel C. Storey *(CFO & Sr VP)*

IPC Systems, Inc. **(1)**
Harborside Financial Plz 10 32nd St 15th Fl, Jersey City, NJ 07311 **(100%)**
Tel.: (201) 253-2000
Web Site: http://www.ipc.com
Communications Technology & Network Services
N.A.I.C.S.: 541512
Michael Speranza *(Sr VP-Corp Strategy & Mktg)*
David Brown *(Mng Dir-Fin Markets Network & Sr VP)*
Ben Chrnelich *(CFO)*
Don Henderson *(Sr VP-Product & Customer Success)*
Mike Jerich *(Sr VP & Head-Sls & Mktg-Global)*
Adam Bozek *(Gen Counsel & Sr VP)*

Subsidiary (Non-US):

IPC Information Systems Ltd. **(2)**
Tower House 67 73 Worship Street, London, EC2A 2DZ, United Kingdom
Tel.: (44) 2079797200
Web Site: http://www.ipc.com
Voice Over IP Technology & Integrated Network Management Services
N.A.I.C.S.: 541512

Kleopatra Holdings 2 S.C.A. **(1)**
46A Avenue J F Kennedy, L-1855, Luxembourg, Luxembourg
Tel.: (352) 26 428 1
Holding Company; Rigid Plastic Film Mfr
N.A.I.C.S.: 551112

Subsidiary (Non-US):

Klockner Pentaplast GmbH **(2)**
Industriestrasse 3-5, 56401, Heiligenroth, Germany
Tel.: (49) 26029150
Web Site: http://www.kpfilms.com
Sales Range: $1-4.9 Billion
Emp.: 800
Plastic Film & Sheet Mfr
N.A.I.C.S.: 326113

Subsidiary (Non-US):

Klockner Pentaplast Ltd. **(3)**
33 Fern Close Pen-y-Fan Industrial Estate, Crumlin, Gwent, NP11 3EH, United Kingdom
Tel.: (44) 1495241800
Web Site: http://www.kpfilms.com
Sales Range: $50-74.9 Million
Plastic Film & Sheet Mfr
N.A.I.C.S.: 326113
Giles Peacock *(VP-Packaging & Speciality Bus Units)*

Subsidiary (Domestic):

LINPAC Group Limited **(4)**
Wakefield Road, Featherstone, Pontefract, WF7 5DE, West Yorkshire, United Kingdom
Tel.: (44) 1977 692 111
Web Site: http://www.linpacpackaging.com
Sales Range: $900-999.9 Million
Emp.: 2,500
Holding Company; Plastic Packaging, Container & Film Products Mfr & Distr
N.A.I.C.S.: 551112
John A. Jones *(Dir-HR & HSSHEQ)*
Helene Roberts *(Dir-Mktg & Innovation)*
Simon Joseph *(Gen Counsel & Sec)*
Mark Lewis *(Dir-Supply Chain & Dev)*

Subsidiary (Domestic):

LINPAC Packaging Limited **(5)**
Wakefield Road, Featherstone, Pontefract, WF7 5DE, W Yorkshire, United Kingdom
Tel.: (44) 1977 692111
Web Site: http://www.linpacpackaging.com
Emp.: 400
Plastic Moulded Food Packaging Products Mfr & Distr
N.A.I.C.S.: 326199
Bart Stubbe *(VP-Pur & IT)*
John A. Jones *(Dir-HR & HSSHEQ)*
Adam Barnett *(Mng Dir-Northern Europe)*
Louise Glover *(Mgr-Comml-UK)*
Helene Roberts *(Dir-Mktg & Innovation)*
Andrew Copson *(Mng Dir-UK, Middle East & Australia)*
Ricardo Cabeza *(Mng Dir-Southern Europe & VP)*

Subsidiary (Non-US):

LINPAC Packaging (Changzhou) Co., Ltd. **(6)**
No 16 Fengqi Road Wujin High-Tech Industrial Development Zone, Changzhou, Jiangsu, China
Tel.: (86) 519 862 226 88
Packaging Product Distr
N.A.I.C.S.: 424610

LINPAC Packaging AS **(6)**
Kucukyali is merkezi C Blok No 4, Kucukyali, 34852, Istanbul, Turkiye
Tel.: (90) 216 519 9240
Packaging Product Distr
N.A.I.C.S.: 423840

LINPAC Packaging Australia Pty Ltd **(6)**
28 Distribution Drive, Truganina, 3029, VIC, Australia
Tel.: (61) 39219 4300
Web Site: http://www.linpac.com
Emp.: 80
Packaging Products Mfr & Distr
N.A.I.C.S.: 424610
Peter Di Gioia *(Gen Mgr)*

LINPAC Packaging BV **(6)**
Saturnus 4-11 Industrial Area IBF, 8448 CC, Heerenveen, Netherlands
Tel.: (31) 513 657 120
Packaging Product Distr
N.A.I.C.S.: 424610
Patrick Hilger *(Sls Mgr-Benelux)*

LINPAC Packaging GmbH **(6)**
Deltastrasse 1, 27721, Ritterhude, Germany
Tel.: (49) 4292 9910
Plastic Packaging Products Mfr & Distr
N.A.I.C.S.: 326199

Subsidiary (Domestic):

LINPAC Packaging Rigid GmbH **(7)**
Am Bahnhof Oegeln 3, 15848, Beeskow, Germany
Tel.: (49) 3366 4120
Web Site: http://www.linpac.com
Plastic Packaging Products Mfr & Distr
N.A.I.C.S.: 326199

Subsidiary (Non-US):

LINPAC Packaging Hungaria Kft **(6)**
Depo, 2045, Torokbalint, Hungary
Tel.: (36) 23 330626
Plastic Packaging Product Distr
N.A.I.C.S.: 424610

LINPAC Packaging Infia Italy S.r.l. **(6)**
Via Caduti de Via Fani 85, 47032, Bertinoro, Forli-Cesena, Italy
Tel.: (39) 0543 466 511
Plastic Packaging Product Distr
N.A.I.C.S.: 424610

LINPAC Packaging Pontivy SAS **(6)**
Parc d'Activites de Kerguilloten, 56920, Noyal-Pontivy, France
Tel.: (33) 2 97 28 70 70
Web Site: http://www.linpac.com
Emp.: 400
Plastic Packaging Product Distr
N.A.I.C.S.: 326112
Laurent Bouffandeau *(Mng Dir)*

LINPAC Packaging Pravia, S.A. **(6)**
Vegafriosa La Calzada, 33128, Pravia, Asturias, Spain
Tel.: (34) 98 582 3501
Emp.: 450
Plastic Packaging Product Distr
N.A.I.C.S.: 424610
Ana Fernandez *(Dir-Innovation)*
Jose Queipo *(Dir-Comml)*
Ana Borras Cardona *(Mgr-Retail Mktg-Southern Europe)*

LINPAC Packaging Production SP z.o.o. **(6)**
Bukowice 39, 56-120, Brzeg Dolny, Poland
Tel.: (48) 713 191 207
Plastic Packaging Products Mfr & Distr
N.A.I.C.S.: 326112
Marcin Rutkowski *(Sls Dir-Central Europe & Turkey)*
Piotr Krzyzynski *(Dir-Fin-Northern Europe)*

LINPAC Packaging Romania S.R.L. **(6)**
Traian Vlua Street No 208, 400397, Cluj Napoca, Romania
Tel.: (40) 2 642 74135
Web Site: http://www.linpac.com
Plastic Packaging Product Distr
N.A.I.C.S.: 424610

LINPAC Packaging Russia OOO **(6)**
Feodosiyskaya 1 bld 16, 11721, Moscow, Russia
Tel.: (7) 495 565 3914
Plastic Packaging Products Mfr & Distr
N.A.I.C.S.: 326112
Lyudmila Timofeeva *(Controller)*

LINPAC Packaging Scandinavia **(6)**
Tune Parkvej 5, 4030, Tune, Denmark
Tel.: (45) 3693 2692
Plastic Packaging Product Distr
N.A.I.C.S.: 424610
Lars Leth *(Sls Mgr-Scandinavia)*

LINPAC Packaging Spol. s.r.o. **(6)**
Cerna Silnice 1457, 295 01, Mnichovo Hradiste, Czech Republic
Tel.: (420) 326 770 416
Plastic Packaging Product Distr
N.A.I.C.S.: 424610

LINPAC Packaging Verona Srl **(6)**
Via Monte Pastello 40, 37057, San Giovanni Lupatoto, 37057, VR, Italy
Tel.: (39) 045 92 16 411
Plastic Packaging Product Distr
N.A.I.C.S.: 424610

LINPAC Packaging sro **(6)**
Vasinova 61, 949 01, Nitra, Slovakia
Tel.: (421) 37 7729 198
Plastic Packaging Product Distr
N.A.I.C.S.: 424610

OVARPACK - Embalagens S.A. **(6)**
Z Ind de Ovar Rua De Cabo Verde, 3881-902, Ovar, Portugal
Tel.: (351) 256 579 170
Plastic Packaging Product Distr
N.A.I.C.S.: 424610
Ricardo Ferreira *(Mgr-Supply Chain)*

Subsidiary (US):

Klockner Pentaplast of America, Inc. **(3)**
3585 Klockner Rd, Gordonsville, VA 22942-0500
Tel.: (540) 832-3600
Web Site: http://www.kpfilms.com
Sales Range: $150-199.9 Million
Plastic Film & Sheet Mfr
N.A.I.C.S.: 326113

Michael F. Tubridy *(Pres & COO)*
Bob Matkovich *(Treas & Mgr)*

Subsidiary (Non-US):

Kloeckner Pentaplast (Shanghai) Co., Ltd. **(3)**
Room 2505 25/F Platinum Building 233 TaiCang Rd LuWan District, Shanghai, 200020, China
Tel.: (86) 21 6089 9009
Plastic Film & Sheet Mfr
N.A.I.C.S.: 326113

NextMedia Group, Inc. **(1)**
6312 S Fiddlers Green Cir Ste 205 E, Englewood, CO 80111-4927
Tel.: (303) 694-9118
Web Site: http://www.nextmediagroup.net
Sales Range: $10-24.9 Million
Radio & Interactive Media Advertising
N.A.I.C.S.: 541810

STRATEGICCLAIM

18 Terry Ave, Burlington, MA 01803
Tel.: (888) 262-2345
Web Site:
  http://www.strategicclaim.com
Sales Range: Less than $1 Million
Claim Engagement Services
N.A.I.C.S.: 524126

STRATEGIES, A MARKETING COMMUNICATIONS CORPORATION

13681 Newport Ave Ste 8 Ste 616, Tustin, CA 92780
Tel.: (714) 957-8880 **CA**
Web Site:
  http://www.strategiesadpr.com
Year Founded: 1991
Sales Range: Less than $1 Million
Emp.: 8
Advetising Agency
N.A.I.C.S.: 541810
Tara Stoutenborough *(Principal)*
Linda White *(Principal)*
Deborah Jones *(Acct Svcs Dir)*
Lindsay Thompson *(Acct Exec)*

STRATEGIS

12 Welch Ave Ste 7, Stoughton, MA 02072
Tel.: (781) 297-9200
Web Site:
  http://www.strategisadv.com
Year Founded: 1999
Sales Range: $10-24.9 Million
Emp.: 8
Advertising Agencies
N.A.I.C.S.: 541810
George Irish *(Pres & CEO)*
Dolores Gonsalves *(CFO)*
Akeem Mason *(Dir-Creative)*
Chris Harrington *(CTO)*
Lindsay Borgen *(Mgr-Acct)*
Michelle Whipple *(Mgr-Acct)*

STRATEGY COMMUNICATIONS

5480 Baltimore Dr Ste 101, La Mesa, CA 91942
Tel.: (619) 713-0622
Web Site:
  http://www.scpublicrelations.com
Sales Range: Less than $1 Million
Emp.: 2
Public Relations
N.A.I.C.S.: 541820
Amy Lewis *(Principal)*

STRATES ENTERPRISES INC.

10600 Orange Ave, Orlando, FL 32824
Tel.: (407) 855-4330
Web Site: http://www.strates.com
Sales Range: $10-24.9 Million
Emp.: 10
Carnival Operation

N.A.I.C.S.: 713990
Susan Magid (Pres)
E. James Strates (Mgr)

Subsidiaries:

Strates Holding Corp (1)
10600 Orange Ave, Orlando, FL 32824
Tel.: (407) 855-4330
Web Site: http://www.strates.com
Rev.: $200,000
Emp.: 5
Equipment Rental & Leasing
N.A.I.C.S.: 532490
James E. Strates (Pres)
E. Jay Strates (Dir-Fin & Admin)

STRATFORD BANCSHARES, INC.
307 Weber St, Stratford, WI 54484
Tel.: (715) 687-2411   WI
Web Site:
http://www.partnersbankwi.com
Year Founded: 1985
Sales Range: $1-9.9 Million
Emp.: 35
Bank Holding Company
N.A.I.C.S.: 551111
Jeffery J. Lappe (Pres)
Martin P. Reinhart (CEO)
Todd Toppen (CFO)

Subsidiaries:

Partners Bank of Wisconsin (1)
907 N Central Ave, Marshfield, WI 54449
Tel.: (715) 384-4005
Web Site: http://www.partnersbankwi.com
Sales Range: $1-9.9 Million
Commericial Banking
N.A.I.C.S.: 522110
Martin P. Reinhart (CEO)
Thomas H. Henseler (Sr VP-Loans)
Kathy R. Meidl (VP-HR)
Jeffery J. Lappe (Pres)
Todd Toppen (CFO)
Adam Brubaker (COO)
Sara Wenzel (Sec & Asst VP)
Monty Wiggins (VP-Downtown Helena)

STRATFORD HOMES LP
402 S Weber Ave, Stratford, WI 54484
Tel.: (715) 687-3133
Web Site:
http://www.stratfordhomes.com
Rev.: $23,000,000
Emp.: 150
Modular Homes, Prefabricated, Wood
N.A.I.C.S.: 321992
Aaron Lang (Engr-Comml Modular)

STRATHAM TIRE INC.
355 Rte 125, Brentwood, NH 03833-6611
Tel.: (603) 679-2232
Web Site:
http://www.strathamtire.com
Sales Range: $10-24.9 Million
Emp.: 25
Retailer of Automobile Tires & Tubes
N.A.I.C.S.: 423310
Denise Littlefield (Mgr-Ops)
Jason Eide (Mgr)
Mark Hanson (Mgr-Svcs)

STRATIVIA LLC
1401 Mercantile Ln Ste 501, Largo, MD 20774
Tel.: (301) 362-6555
Web Site: http://www.strativia.com
Year Founded: 2007
Sales Range: $10-24.9 Million
Emp.: 152
Consulting Services
N.A.I.C.S.: 541618
Kenneth Kelly (Pres & CEO)

STRATMAR RETAIL SERVICES
109 Willett Ave, Port Chester, NY 10573-4232
Web Site: http://www.stratmar.com
Year Founded: 1969
Sales Range: $1-9.9 Million
Emp.: 650
Advetising Agency
N.A.I.C.S.: 541810
Dan Ailloni-Charas (Chm)
Ethan Charas (Pres & CEO)

STRATTAM CAPITAL, LLC
111 Congress Ave Ste 1140, Austin, TX 78701
Tel.: (512) 829-3949   DE
Web Site: http://www.strattam.com
Year Founded: 2013
Emp.: 100
Privater Equity Firm
N.A.I.C.S.: 523999
Kimberley Kasper (CMO)
Bob Morse (Co-Founder & Mng Partner)
Adrian Polak (Co-Founder & Partner)
Ray Villareal (Partner)
Hilary Fleischer (Principal)

Subsidiaries:

Acendre Pty. Ltd. (1)
Level 3 600 Victoria Street, Richmond, 3121, VIC, Australia
Tel.: (61) 1800 642 638
Web Site: https://hireroad.com
Talent Management Software Solutions
N.A.I.C.S.: 513210
Otto Berkes (CEO)
Larry Fichter (CFO)
Mac Mirchandani (Chief Product Officer)
Dawn McAvoy (VP-Mktg-Global)
Liam Ackland (Mng Dir-Asia Pacific)
Corey Epperly (Head-Sls-North America & United Kingdom)
Janine Nieuwoudt (VP-HR-Global)

Subsidiary (US):

Interactive Communications Solutions Group, Inc. (2)
8221 Ritchie Hwy Ste 303, Pasadena, MD 21122
Tel.: (410) 975-9440
Web Site: http://www.icslearninggroup.com
Custom Computer Programming Services
N.A.I.C.S.: 541511

Action Title Research, LLC (1)
519 S Broad St, Glen Rock, NJ 07452
Tel.: (201) 531-1663
Web Site: http://www.actiontitleresearch.com
Property Information Services Company
N.A.I.C.S.: 541191

Subsidiary (Domestic):

Eastland Title Service LLC (2)
200 Sullivan Ave Ste 3, South Windsor, CT 06074-1953
Tel.: (860) 436-4047
Web Site:
http://www.eastlandtitleservices.com
Offices of Real Estate Agents & Brokers
N.A.I.C.S.: 531210
Phillip Apter (Pres)

MHC Software LLC (1)
12000 Portland Ave S Ste 230, Burnsville, MN 55337
Web Site: http://www.mhcsoftwareinc.com
Document Management Software Services
N.A.I.C.S.: 513210
Dawn Watz (Chief People Officer)
Gina Armada (CEO)
Erik Gilder (Chief Growth Officer)
Dan Ward (CTO)
Trevor Young (VP-Strategy)
Aaron Stenhaug (VP-Fin)
John Shields (Chm)

Subsidiary (Domestic):

Vanguard Systems, Inc. (2)
2901 Dutton Mill Rd Ste 220, Aston, PA 19014
Tel.: (800) 445-1418
Custom Computer Programming Services
N.A.I.C.S.: 541511

STRATTON & BRATT LANDSCAPES, LLC
754 W 700 S, Pleasant Grove, UT 84062
Tel.: (801) 785-8011
Web Site:
http://www.strattonandbratt.com
Rev.: $6,000,000
Emp.: 25
Landscaping Services
N.A.I.C.S.: 561730
Zack Stratton (CEO)

Subsidiaries:

Elite Grounds, L.C. (1)
754 W 700 S, Pleasant Grove, UT 84062
Tel.: (801) 785-5973
Web Site: http://www.elitegrounds.com
Landscaping Services
N.A.I.C.S.: 561730

STRATTON EQUITY CO-OPERATIVE COMPANY INC.
98 Colorado Ave, Stratton, CO 80836
Tel.: (719) 348-5326
Web Site:
http://www.strattoncoop.com
Year Founded: 1915
Sales Range: $10-24.9 Million
Emp.: 80
Retail Grain & Field Beans
N.A.I.C.S.: 424510
Daniel Salger (CEO)
Nikki Witzel (Mgr-Credit)

STRATUS BUILDING SOLUTIONS
1861 Craig Rd, Saint Louis, MO 63146
Tel.: (314) 731-2000
Web Site:
http://www.stratusbuildingsolutions.com
Sales Range: $100-124.9 Million
Emp.: 11
Building Construction Services
N.A.I.C.S.: 236115
Dennis Jarrett (CEO)
Rob Lancit (VP-Franchise Dev)
Doug Flaig (Pres)
Maureen DiStefano (VP-Ops)

STRAUB DISTRIBUTING CO. LTD
2701 Dow Ave, Tustin, CA 92780-7209
Tel.: (714) 247-7300
Web Site:
http://www.straubdistributing.com
Rev.: $78,400,000
Emp.: 310
Beer & Other Fermented Malt Liquors
N.A.I.C.S.: 424810
Mark E. Danner (Pres & CEO)
Rick Sweeney (Gen Mgr)

STRAUB MOTORS, INC.
400 Highway 35, Keyport, NJ 07735
Tel.: (732) 264-4000
Web Site:
http://www.straubmotors.com
Year Founded: 1948
Sales Range: $10-24.9 Million
Emp.: 60
Car Whslr
N.A.I.C.S.: 441110
Charles F. Straub III (Gen Mgr)

STRAUBE CENTER LLC
1 Straube Ctr Blvd, Pennington, NJ 08534
Tel.: (609) 737-3322   NJ
Web Site:
http://www.straubecenter.com
Sales Range: $50-74.9 Million
Emp.: 6

Holding Company; Office Rentals
N.A.I.C.S.: 561110
Nancy Scarpiello (CEO)
Elizabeth Klein (Asst Gen Mgr)
Alison Sim Lin Chan (Controller)
William Lea (Mgr-Facilities)

STRAUSS MEDIA STRATEGIES, INC.
National Press Bldg Ste 1163 529 14th St NW, Washington, DC 20045
Tel.: (202) 638-0200
Web Site:
http://www.straussradio.com
Sales Range: $25-49.9 Million
Emp.: 13
Public Relations, Radio
N.A.I.C.S.: 541820
Matthew Lawrence (Sr Acct Exec)
Richard Strauss (Founder & Pres)
Raul Martinez (Acct Dir)
Benny Martinez (Sr Acct Exec)
Howard Davis (Mng Dir)

Subsidiaries:

Strauss Media Strategies, Inc. (1)
262 W 38th St Ste 803, New York, NY 10018
Tel.: (212) 302-1234
Web Site: http://www.straussradio.com
Sales Range: $10-24.9 Million
Public Relations, Communications, Consulting & Strategy Services
N.A.I.C.S.: 541820
Raul Martinez (Acct Dir)
Zach Seidenberg (Sr Acct Mgr)
Mark Edwards (Acct Mgr)

STRAUSS VEAL FEEDS INC.
600 Strauss Provimi Rd, North Manchester, IN 46962
Tel.: (260) 982-8611
Web Site:
http://www.straussfeeds.com
Rev.: $15,300,000
Emp.: 35
Livestock Liquid Feed Mfr
N.A.I.C.S.: 311119
Garen Bushong (Controller)

Subsidiaries:

Strauss Feeds (1)
W7507 Provimi Rd, Watertown, WI 53098
Tel.: (920) 261-7882
Web Site: http://www.straussfeeds.com
Sales Range: $10-24.9 Million
Dry Livestock Feed Mfr
N.A.I.C.S.: 311119
David Grant (Pres)
Dan Catherman (Dir-Tech Svcs)
Trina Adkins (Mgr-Ops-Orders)

STRAUSSER INSURANCE AGENCY, INC.
PO Box 484, Hamburg, PA 19526
Tel.: (610) 562-2048
Web Site:
http://www.strausserins.com
Insurance Agencies & Brokerages
N.A.I.C.S.: 524210
Denise Specht (Owner)

STRAW HAT RESTAURANTS, INC.
18 Crow Canyon Ct Ste 200, San Ramon, CA 94583-1669
Tel.: (925) 837-3400   CA
Web Site:
http://www.strawhatpizza.com
Year Founded: 1959
Pizza Restaurants Franchiser & Operator
N.A.I.C.S.: 722513

STRAWSER PAVING CO., INC.
1595 Frank Rd, Columbus, OH 43223
Tel.: (614) 276-5501

STRAWSER PAVING CO., INC.

Strawser Paving Co., Inc.—(Continued)
Web Site:
http://www.strawserconstruction.com
Sales Range: $10-24.9 Million
Emp.: 8
Highway & Street Construction Services
N.A.I.C.S.: 237310
Michael Buckingham (Pres)

STREACKER TRACTOR SALES INC.
1400 N 5th St, Fremont, OH 43420
Tel.: (419) 334-9775
Web Site: http://www.streacker.com
Sales Range: $10-24.9 Million
Emp.: 22
Farm Equipment
N.A.I.C.S.: 444230
Marsha Rutherford (Office Mgr)

STREAM COMPANIES
255 Great Valley Pkwy Ste 150, Malvern, PA 19355
Tel.: (610) 644-8637
Web Site:
http://www.streamcompanies.com
Year Founded: 1997
Sales Range: $1-9.9 Million
Emp.: 25
Advetising Agency
N.A.I.C.S.: 541810
Jason Brennan (Co-Founder)
David Regn (Co-Founder & CEO)
Brian Baker (Chief Client Officer, Partner & Exec VP)
Brendan Reily (Acct Dir)
Bill Parlaman (Chief Digital Officer)
Subi Ghosh (Exec VP-Strategic Partnerships)
Jordan Richards (Chm)
David Mazzoni (Chief Creative Officer)
Rich Harrisson (Exec VP-Agency Ops)

STREAM REALTY PARTNERS, L.P.
2200 Ross Ave 54th Fl, Dallas, TX 75201
Tel.: (214) 267-0400
Web Site:
http://www.streamrealty.com
Year Founded: 1996
Sales Range: $10-24.9 Million
Emp.: 272
Leases & Manages Industrial, Retail & Office Properties
N.A.I.C.S.: 531312
Jason Moser (Partner & Sr VP)
Lee Belland (Co-Founder & Mng Partner)
Chris Jackson (Mng Partner-Dallas)
Tim O. Terrell (Partner & Exec VP)
Paul R. Moser (Co-Mng Partner-Stream Data Centers)
Brad Fricks (Sr VP)
Ryan Bishop (Mng Dir-Office)
Paul Coonrod (Mng Dir & Partner)
Adam Jackson (Mng Dir & Partner)
Liz Sheff (COO)
Sam Owen (VP)
Will Nichols (Partner)
Brad Philp (Mng Dir)
Ramsey March (Partner)
Ryan Boozer (Sr VP-Industrial Div)
Sara Terry (VP)
Caitlyn Ryan (VP-Investments)
Matteson Hamilton (Mng Dir-Industrial)
Liam Stagg (Sr Mgr-Construction)
J. J. Leonard (Mng Dir)
Tom Bahn (Sr VP)
Demian Salmon (Sr VP-Land Div)

Victoria Knudson (Exec VP-Property Mgmt-Chicago)
John Huff (Mng Dir-Healthcare)
Mica Hopkins (Dir-Property Mgmt-Fort Worth)
Chad Smith (VP)
Hunter Jones (VP)
Alex Mather (Mng Dir-Chicago)
Dan Harris (Mng Dir)

STREAMLIGHT INC.
30 Eagleville Rd, Eagleville, PA 19403
Tel.: (610) 631-0600
Web Site: http://www.streamlight.com
Year Founded: 1973
Sales Range: $75-99.9 Million
Emp.: 270
Mfr of Portable Lighting Equipment
N.A.I.C.S.: 335139
Edward Tasca (Controller)
Michael F. Dineen (VP-Sls & Mktg)
Philippe Marzin (Mgr-Europe)

STREAMLINE CAPITAL, INC.
3342 International Park Dr, Atlanta, GA 30316
Tel.: (678) 904-6591
Web Site: http://www.apyron.com
Sales Range: $10-24.9 Million
Emp.: 4
Private Investment Firm
N.A.I.C.S.: 523999

Subsidiaries:

Apyron Technologies, Inc. (1)
3342 International Park Dr, Atlanta, GA 30316
Tel.: (678) 904-6591
Web Site: http://www.apyron.com
Sales Range: Less than $1 Million
Developer & Mfr of Chemical Absorbents & Antimicrobial Products
N.A.I.C.S.: 325998
Leslie J. Story (Pres & COO)
Wei-Chih Chen (Chm & CEO)
John A. Reade (CFO)

STREAMLINE DEFENSE, LLC
100 N Tampa St Ste 2125, Tampa, FL 33602
Tel.: (813) 774-3477
Web Site:
http://www.streamlinedefense.com
Year Founded: 2007
Sales Range: $1-9.9 Million
Emp.: 60
Intelligence, Operations, Knowledge Management & IT Services for Defense & Intelligence Communities
N.A.I.C.S.: 541618
Terrell Martin (Pres)

STREAMLINE ENVIRONMENTAL, INC.
1821 Sahlman Dr Ste B, Tampa, FL 33605
Tel.: (813) 258-5561
Web Site:
http://www.streamlineenv.com
Sales Range: $1-9.9 Million
Emp.: 15
Environmental Consulting Services
N.A.I.C.S.: 541620
Craig R. Smith (Pres)
Michael J. Roose (VP)
Lawrence McClure (Project Mgr)
Jereme H. Willis (Project Mgr)
Lee T. Ford (VP)

STREAMLINE TECHNICAL SERVICES, INC.
2711 Oakmont Dr, Round Rock, TX 78665
Tel.: (512) 244-0007
Web Site: http://www.sts-us.net
Year Founded: 2001

Sales Range: $1-9.9 Million
Emp.: 81
Computer Equipment Repair Services
N.A.I.C.S.: 811210
John Sanny (VP-Engrg & IT)
Tom Lintner (Pres)
Lynn Bennett (Pres)
Dave Cunningham (Program Mgr)
Dave Jespersen (Chm)

STREAMLINEVENTS INC.
6005 Shellmound Ste 200, Emeryville, CA 94608
Tel.: (510) 463-6000
Web Site:
http://www.streamlinevents.com
Year Founded: 2002
Sales Range: $10-24.9 Million
Emp.: 55
Event Planning Services
N.A.I.C.S.: 561920
Kevin Kinsella (VP)
Sarah Murphy (Mgr-HR)
Alison Gill (Mgr-Sls)

STREAMWORKS LLC
3770 Dunlap St N, Arden Hills, MN 55112
Web Site:
http://www.streamworksmn.com
Year Founded: 2013
Marketing Communications & Consulting Services
N.A.I.C.S.: 541870
Joe Klohn (COO)
Tony Zirnhelt (Pres)
Molly Bleymeyer (VP-Bus Dev)
Mike Gilbert (VP-Resource Mgmt)
Bill Hedahl (VP)
Andrea Quandt (VP-Data Svcs)
Bill Bell (VP-Sls & Client Rels)
Bree Conover (Acct Mgr)
Gail Hawk (Sr Acct Mgr)
Jill Carty (Acct Mgr)
Karen Johnson (Sr Acct Mgr)
Krissy Cameron (Sr Acct Mgr)
Laura Jarrett (Sr Acct Mgr)
Mitch Porter (VP-Sls & Estimating)
Steve Doyscher (VP-Integrated Mktg)
Tara Johnson (Acct Mgr)

STREATOR INDUSTRIAL HANDLING, INC.
1705 N Shabbona St, Streator, IL 61364
Tel.: (815) 672-0551
Web Site:
http://www.streatordependable.com
Sales Range: $10-24.9 Million
Emp.: 100
Material Handling Equipment Mfr & Distr
N.A.I.C.S.: 423440
Chris Walker (Plant Mgr)

STRECK LABORATORIES INC.
7002 S 109th St, La Vista, NE 68128
Tel.: (402) 333-1982
Web Site: http://www.streck.com
Year Founded: 1971
Sales Range: $25-49.9 Million
Emp.: 300
Diagnostic Substances
N.A.I.C.S.: 325412
Connie Ryan (Pres)
Jodi Gnader (Dir-Sls)
John Noble (VP-Ops)
Mike Morgan (CFO & Chief Admin Officer)
Joey Patterson (Dir-HR)
Wendy Royalty (Dir-Quality)
Steve Bullock (Exec VP)
Rob Owen (Gen Counsel)

STREET CANCE MARKETING COMMUNICATIONS

234 W Florida St, Milwaukee, WI 53202-5729
Tel.: (414) 765-0333
Web Site: http://www.street-cance.com
Year Founded: 1981
Rev.: $15,000,000
Emp.: 10
Public Relations
N.A.I.C.S.: 541810
David J. Street (Pres)
John J. Cance (Copywriter)
Cassie Miletich (Dir-Media)
Amy Kluck (VP & Partner)

STREET MODA FOOTWEAR
104 Production Ct Ste 104, Louisville, KY 40299
Tel.: (712) 491-1889
Web Site: http://www.streetmoda.com
Sales Range: $1-9.9 Million
Emp.: 27
Fashion Apparel & Footwear Retailer
N.A.I.C.S.: 458110
Matt Kubancik (Founder, Pres & CEO)
Sarah Taylor (VP & Mgr-Ops)

STREET TOYOTA, INC.
4500 S Soncy Rd, Amarillo, TX 79119-6388
Tel.: (806) 355-9846
Web Site:
http://www.streettoyota.com
Year Founded: 1982
Sales Range: $10-24.9 Million
Emp.: 82
Car Whslr
N.A.I.C.S.: 441110
Joe Street (Pres)

STREETER ASSOCIATES INC.
101 E Woodlawn Ave, Elmira, NY 14901
Tel.: (607) 734-4151
Web Site:
http://www.streeterassociates.com
Rev.: $58,000,000
Emp.: 87
Nonresidential Construction
N.A.I.C.S.: 236220
Robert H. Lewis (VP-Project Mgmt)
Scott R. Proudfoot (Treas & Sec)
Donna Dartt (Asst Project Mgr)
Douglas J. Jones (Project Mgr)
Donald A. Rottmann (VP-Estimating)
James W. Penwell (Mgr-Store-Retail)
Mark A. Stirpe (Project Mgr)
Robert A. Stanton (Dir-Mktg)

STREETERVILLE CAPITAL LLC
303 E Wacker Drv Ste 1040, Chicago, IL 60601
Tel.: (312) 297-7000
Emp.: 100
Investment Services
N.A.I.C.S.: 523999
John M. Fife (Pres)

Subsidiaries:

Gibson Technical Services, Inc. (1)
230 Mountain Brook Ct, Canton, GA 30115
Tel.: (770) 345-1670
Web Site: http://www.gts-yes.com
Sales Range: $25-49.9 Million
Emp.: 65
Design & Consulting Services for Cable System Operators & Communication Signal Enhancement Network Services
N.A.I.C.S.: 541690
Michael McCracken (Pres & CTO)
Robert Moore (CFO)
Fred Christian (Dir-Broadband)
Ed Hickman (Dir-OSP Construction)
Don Landy (Dir-Building Technologies)
Blake Chapman (Dir-Wireless)

COMPANIES

STREETSENSE, INC.
3 Bethesda Metro Ste 140, Bethesda, MD 20814
Tel.: (301) 652-9020
Web Site:
http://www.streetsense.com
Year Founded: 2001
Sales Range: $10-24.9 Million
Emp.: 71
Real Estate Development Services
N.A.I.C.S.: 531390
Marc Ratner *(Chm)*
Guy Silverman *(Vice Chm)*
Brian Taff *(CEO)*
Bruce Leonard *(Mng Principal-Architecture & Plng)*
Jeff Pollak *(Mng Principal & VP)*
Angie Trosper *(Principal)*
Lee Engle *(Principal)*
Eric Burka *(Mng Principal)*
Gabby Rojchin *(Principal-Brand)*
Roberto Sablayrolles *(Principal & Dir-Creative)*
Ira Starr *(Chief Admin Officer)*
Heather Arnold *(Principal-Res & Analysis & Mng Dir-Pub Sector Work)*
Michael D. Smith *(Dir-Real Estate)*
Andrew Poncher *(Dir-Retail Strategy)*
Duk Kim *(Mng Principal-Place)*
Daniel Troconis *(Dir-Interactive)*
Eduardo Garcia-Lopez *(Dir-Art)*
Hugo Rodrigues *(Sr Project Mgr)*
Rich Amsellem *(Dir-Retail Strategy)*
Shawn Malhotra *(Project Dir)*
Joanne Williams *(Mng Dir-Brand Ops)*
Leo Zheng Sun *(CFO)*
Patty Delk *(Chief People Officer)*
Julie Chase *(Mng Dir-PR)*
Josh Collins *(Dir-Destination Activations & Mktg)*
Zachary Tindall *(Mng Dir-West Coast)*
John J. Huntz Jr. *(Sr Dir-Plng)*

STREETWISE REPORTS
101 2nd St Ste 110, Petaluma, CA 94952
Tel.: (707) 981-8999
Web Site:
http://www.theaureport.com
Year Founded: 2001
Sales Range: $1-9.9 Million
Emp.: 18
News Reporting Services
N.A.I.C.S.: 516210
Gordon Holmes *(Founder)*
Karen Roche *(Pres)*
Stephanie Seufert *(Dir-Mktg)*

STREMICKS HERITAGE FOODS LLC
4002 Westminster Ave, Santa Ana, CA 92703
Tel.: (714) 775-5000
Web Site:
http://www.stremicksheritagefoods.com
Rev.: $115,400,000
Emp.: 200
Fluid Milk
N.A.I.C.S.: 311511
Louis J. Stremick *(Chm & CEO)*
Jack Noenickx *(CFO)*

STRENGTH CAPITAL PARTNERS, LLC
350 N Old Woodward Ave Ste 100, Birmingham, MI 48009
Tel.: (248) 593-5800
Web Site:
http://www.strengthcapital.com
Year Founded: 2000
Aluminum Extruded Product Mfr & Distr
N.A.I.C.S.: 331318
Michael Bergeron *(Mng Partner)*
Steven C. LaBarre *(Partner)*
Robin Fenberg *(CFO)*
Mark McCammon *(Mng Partner)*
Adam Wise *(Partner)*

Subsidiaries:

Dascom Systems Group LLC (1)
2415 Ventura Dr, Woodbury, MN 55125
Tel.: (651) 578-1200
Web Site: http://www.dascom-systems.com
Audio, Video & Communication System Design Services
N.A.I.C.S.: 517810
Kris Apfelbacher *(Dir-IPTV Solutions)*

ESP Associates, Inc. (1)
3475 Lakemont Blvd, Fort Mill, SC 29708
Tel.: (803) 802-2440
Web Site: http://www.espassociates.com
Sales Range: $10-24.9 Million
Emp.: 147
Engineering Services
N.A.I.C.S.: 541330
Joe Hendrick *(Pres)*

Subsidiary (Domestic):

CivilCorp, LLC (2)
1501 E Mockingbird Ln Ste 406, Victoria, TX 77904-2157
Tel.: (361) 570-7500
Web Site: http://www.civilcorp.us
Engineering Services
N.A.I.C.S.: 541330

Postle Aluminum Co. LLC (1)
511 Pine Creek Ct, Elkhart, IN 46516-9090
Tel.: (574) 389-0800
Web Site: http://www.postledistributors.com
Distr of Aluminum & Related Metal Services
N.A.I.C.S.: 423510
Bill Kuehne *(VP-Sls)*
Kevin Robinson *(CEO)*
Jim Winters *(Mgr-Sls-Midwest Div)*

RW Specialties LLC (1)
9000 E 96th Ave, Henderson, CO 80640
Tel.: (303) 289-2226
Web Site: http://www.rwspecialties.com
Sales Range: $25-49.9 Million
Emp.: 45
Structural Assemblies, Prefabricated: Wood
N.A.I.C.S.: 423310
Wayne R. Pott *(Pres)*
Jon Krizman *(Mgr-Sls-Northern Colorado)*
Toni Mallory *(Coord-Front Desk)*

Subsidiary (Domestic):

All American Building Products (2)
11915 E 51st St Unit 25, Tulsa, OK 74146-4146
Tel.: (918) 249-0515
Web Site: http://www.aabpinc.com
Roofing, Siding & Insulation Material Merchant Whslr
N.A.I.C.S.: 423330
Dana McBride *(Mgr-Ops)*

Tiedemann-Bevs Industries, Inc. (1)
4225 W Industries Rd, Richmond, IN 47374
Tel.: (765) 962-4914
Web Site: http://www.tbevs.com
Miscellaneous Textile Product Mills
N.A.I.C.S.: 314999
Robert Galletly *(Pres)*
Peter Galletly *(Sec, Treas & Exec VP)*
Pam Soper *(Gen Mgr)*
Lisa Baker *(Controller)*
Jose Sierra *(Mgr-Ops)*
Pat Widau *(Mgr-Pur)*
Karen Crawford *(Mgr-Production)*
David Mopps *(Mgr-Shipping)*
Bill Jones *(Pres)*

Universal Aerospace Co., Inc. (1)
18640 59th Dr Ne, Arlington, WA 98223
Tel.: (360) 435-9577
Web Site: http://www.universalaero.com
Aircraft Parts & Auxiliary Equipment Mfr; Metal Fabrication & Metal Finishing
N.A.I.C.S.: 336413
Sean Myers *(Exec VP-Bus Dev)*

STRESS CON INDUSTRIES INC.
50500 Design Ln, Utica, MI 48315-3124
Tel.: (586) 731-1628
Web Site:
http://www.stressconindustries.com
Sales Range: $10-24.9 Million
Emp.: 3
Precast Terrazzo Or Concrete Products
N.A.I.C.S.: 327390
Jennifer Cooper *(Mgr-Fleet)*
Tom Grzeskowiak *(Mgr-Ops)*
Brian Curtis *(Mgr-Quality Control)*
Dave Thiel *(Project Mgr-Engrg)*

STRESSCON CORPORATION
3210 Astrozon Blvd, Colorado Springs, CO 80910-1032
Tel.: (719) 390-5041
Web Site: http://www.stresscon.com
Year Founded: 1967
Sales Range: $25-49.9 Million
Emp.: 150
Concrete Products
N.A.I.C.S.: 327390
Dave Bourgault *(Pres)*
Mark Brooks *(Project Mgr & Engr-Structural)*
Mike Norwood *(Exec VP)*
Christie White *(Controller)*

STRETCH ASSOCIATES, INC.
155 Verdin Rd, Greenville, SC 29607
Tel.: (864) 312-9200
Web Site:
http://stretchassociates.com
Year Founded: 1989
Sales Range: $10-24.9 Million
Emp.: 24
Plastics Material & Basic Form Whslr
N.A.I.C.S.: 424610
Jay Sullivan *(Pres)*
Patti Bridges *(CFO)*

STRETCH WRAP PACKAGING INDUSTRIES LLC
6520 Powerline Rd, Fort Lauderdale, FL 33309
Tel.: (954) 328-0933
Web Site:
http://www.thestretchwrap.com
Sales Range: $10-24.9 Million
Emp.: 20
Stretch Film & Bubble Rolls Mfr
N.A.I.C.S.: 326112
Preeti Singh *(CEO)*

STRETCH ZONE FRANCHISING, LLC
1702 Cordova Rd, Fort Lauderdale, FL 33316
Tel.: (954) 368-2117
Web Site:
http://www.stretchzone.com
Year Founded: 2005
Sales Range: $1-9.9 Million
Emp.: 50
Health Care Srvices
N.A.I.C.S.: 621610
Jorden Gold *(Founder)*

STRIA, INC.
4300 Resnik Ct Ste 102, Bakersfield, CA 93313
Tel.: (661) 617-6601
Web Site: http://www.stria.com
Sales Range: $1-9.9 Million
Emp.: 100
Record Management Services
N.A.I.C.S.: 541618
Jim Damian *(CEO)*
Rory Banks *(Partner & VP-PacWest)*
Shanna Wilson *(Dir-Admin & Fin)*
Robert Cleveland *(Mgr-Bus Sys)*

STRIBBONS INC.
2921 W Cypress Creek Rd Ste 101, Fort Lauderdale, FL 33309
Tel.: (305) 628-4000
Web Site: http://www.stribbons.com
Sales Range: $75-99.9 Million
Emp.: 134
Packaging, Branded Ribbon Treatments & Customized Embellishments
N.A.I.C.S.: 313210
Charles Vaughn *(Pres)*

STRIC-LAN COMPANIES CORP
104 Sable Dr, Duson, LA 70529
Tel.: (337) 984-7850
Web Site: http://www.stric-lan.com
Sales Range: $10-24.9 Million
Emp.: 40
Testing, Measuring, Surveying & Analysis Services
N.A.I.C.S.: 213112
Karen Oertling *(Treas)*

STRICK CORPORATION
225 Lincoln Hwy, Fairless Hills, PA 19030-1103
Tel.: (215) 949-3600
Rev.: $600,000,000
Emp.: 30
Mfr of Truck Trailers, Chassis & Parts
N.A.I.C.S.: 336212
JoAnn Marino *(Controller)*

Subsidiaries:

Strick Corporation (1)
301 N Polk St, Monroe, IN 46772-9703
Tel.: (260) 692-6121
Web Site: http://www.stricktrailer.com
Sales Range: $25-49.9 Million
Trailer Mfr
N.A.I.C.S.: 336212

STRICKLAND COMPANIES, INC.
481 Republic Cir, Birmingham, AL 35214-5967
Tel.: (205) 798-3000
Web Site:
http://www.stricklandpaper.com
Year Founded: 1928
Rev.: $30,000,000
Emp.: 100
Printing & Writing Paper
N.A.I.C.S.: 424110
Bayard S. Tynes Jr. *(Pres)*

STRICKLAND INSURANCE GROUP INC.
400 Commerce Ct, Goldsboro, NC 27534-7048
Tel.: (919) 759-3200
Web Site:
http://www.atlanticcasualty.net
Year Founded: 1951
Sales Range: $25-49.9 Million
Emp.: 100
Insurance Agent Broker & Service
N.A.I.C.S.: 524210
Bobby Strickland *(CEO)*
Robbie Strickland *(Pres)*

Subsidiaries:

Atlantic Security Insurance Company Inc. (1)
1107 Pkwy Dr, Goldsboro, NC 27534-3447
Tel.: (704) 522-2000
Web Site: http://www.royalsunalliance-usa.com
Sales Range: $25-49.9 Million
Emp.: 6
Insurance Agents, Brokers & Service
N.A.I.C.S.: 524210

Coastal Casualty Insurance Company (1)
PO Box 8010, Goldsboro, NC 27533-2027
Tel.: (919) 759-3200
Web Site: http://www.stricklandinsgroup.com
Casualty Insurance Services
N.A.I.C.S.: 524126
Robert Strickland *(CEO)*

Strickland Insurance Group Inc.—(Continued)

Strickland Insurance Brokers Inc. (1)
PO Box 8010, Goldsboro, NC 27533
Tel.: (919) 429-3028
Web Site: http://www.sibrokers.com
Sales Range: $1-9.9 Million
Insurance Agent Brokers & Service
N.A.I.C.S.: 524210

STRICKLAND RANCH AND EXPORTS, INC.
24615 Oak Knoll Rd, Myakka City, FL 34251
Tel.: (941) 776-0519
Web Site: http://www.stricklandranch.com
Sales Range: $1-9.9 Million
Livestock Rancher & Distr
N.A.I.C.S.: 112111
Renee Strickland (Owner)

STRIDE & ASSOCIATES INC.
206 Newbury St 3rd Fl, Boston, MA 02116
Tel.: (617) 585-6500   DE
Year Founded: 1994
Sales Range: $50-74.9 Million
Emp.: 200
Employment Agencies
N.A.I.C.S.: 561311
Bethann Gilfeather (Pres & CEO)
Crystal Mayo (Coord-Accts Payable)

STRIDE CONSULTING LLC
127 W 26th St, New York, NY 10001
Tel.: (212) 634-7240
Web Site: http://www.stridenyc.com
Year Founded: 2014
Sales Range: $10-24.9 Million
Emp.: 50
Software Development Services
N.A.I.C.S.: 541511
Debbie Madden (Founder & CEO)
Ken Judy (COO)
Chloe Summers (Dir-Strategic Accounts)

STRIDE, INC.
1021 Carlisle Blvd SE, Albuquerque, NM 87106
Tel.: (505) 232-3201   NM
Web Site: https://www.strideinc.com
Year Founded: 1988
Sales Range: $10-24.9 Million
Office Products Mfr & Distr
N.A.I.C.S.: 339940
Barbara Brennan (Founder & Owner)
Kerry Bertram (Pres & CEO)
Carl Kinkel (Exec Dir-Sales & Marketing)

STRIGLOS COMPANIES INC.
130-150 E William St, Decatur, IL 62523
Tel.: (217) 429-2500
Web Site: http://www.striglos.com
Sales Range: $10-24.9 Million
Emp.: 50
Computer & Software Stores
N.A.I.C.S.: 449210
Scott Striglos (Pres)

STRIKER OIL & GAS, INC.
3122 White Oak Dr, Houston, TX 77007
Tel.: (713) 869-6286
Crude Petroleum Extraction Services
N.A.I.C.S.: 211120
Kevan Casey (CEO)

STRINGERS INTERNATIONAL INC.
1000 Desoto Ave, Clarksdale, MS 38614
Tel.: (662) 624-4305

Web Site: http://www.stringersinc.com
Year Founded: 1983
Sales Range: $10-24.9 Million
Emp.: 100
Agricultural Machinery & Equipment
N.A.I.C.S.: 423820
Pat Dickerson (Controller)

STRINGFELLOW LUMBER COMPANY LLC
1900 Crestwood Blvd, Birmingham, AL 35210-2051
Tel.: (205) 271-2400   DE
Web Site: http://www.slco.com
Year Founded: 1913
Sales Range: $10-24.9 Million
Emp.: 10
Lumber, Plywood & Millwork
N.A.I.C.S.: 423310
Rob Steverson (CFO & Sr VP)
Bill Fisher (Pres & CEO)
Robert Stevenson (Controller)

STRINGFELLOW TECHNOLOGY GROUP INC.
2933 Armory Dr Ste 200, Nashville, TN 37204
Tel.: (615) 386-4920
Web Site: http://www.stringfellow.com
Year Founded: 2005
Sales Range: $1-9.9 Million
Emp.: 16
It Consulting
N.A.I.C.S.: 541690
Edward Stringfellow (CEO)
Timothy Herman (VP-Tech & Strategy)

STRIPE, INC.
3180 18th St Ste 100, San Francisco, CA 94110-2043   DE
Web Site: https://www.stripe.com
Year Founded: 2009
Emp.: 6,700
Software Publisher
N.A.I.C.S.: 513210
Patrick Collison (Co-Founder & CEO)
John Collison (Co-Founder & Pres)
David Singleton (Head-Engrg)
Dhivya Suryadevara (CFO)
Mike Clayville (Chief Revenue Officer)
Trish Walsh (Gen Counsel)
Karim Temsamani (Head-Global Partnerships)
Patricia Walsh (Chief Legal Officer)

STRIPING TECHNOLOGY L.P.
10112 Country Rd 489, Tyler, TX 75706
Tel.: (903) 595-6800
Web Site: http://www.st-lp.com
Sales Range: $10-24.9 Million
Emp.: 120
Pavement Marking Contractor
N.A.I.C.S.: 238320
Linda Rudd (Owner & Pres)
Destiny Seeton (Treas & Sec)

STRITT & PRIEBE, INC.
37 Clyde Ave, Buffalo, NY 14215
Tel.: (716) 834-1100   NY
Web Site: http://www.strittandpriebe.com
Year Founded: 1922
Emp.: 30
Pipe, Valve & Fitting Mfr
N.A.I.C.S.: 423720
Joel Scott (Co-Owner)
Bill Victor (Co-Owner)

Subsidiaries:

VJ Stanley, Inc.   (1)
595 Hague St, Rochester, NY 14606-1430
Tel.: (585) 546-4656

Web Site: http://www.vjstanley.com
Emp.: 24
Commercial & Industrial Hot Water Heating System Distr
N.A.I.C.S.: 423720
Mac Grantham (Mgr-Ops)

STROH DIE CASTING CO.
11123 W Burleigh St, Milwaukee, WI 53222
Tel.: (414) 476-2133
Web Site: http://strohdiecasting.com
Sales Range: $25-49.9 Million
Emp.: 225
Precision Die Casting Services
N.A.I.C.S.: 423830
Andy Stroh (Owner)

STROHMEYER & ARPE COMPANY
106 Allen Rd, Basking Ridge, NJ 07920
Tel.: (908) 580-9100
Web Site: http://www.strohmeyer.com
Year Founded: 1882
Sales Range: $75-99.9 Million
Emp.: 8
Distr & Importer of Canned Fruits
N.A.I.C.S.: 424490
Charles Kocot (Pres)
Pierre Crawley (VP-Mktg)

Subsidiaries:

C.M. Goettsche Company, Inc.   (1)
106 Allen Rd, Basking Ridge, NJ 07920
Tel.: (908) 580-9100
Web Site: http://www.strohmeyer.com
Canned Food Distr
N.A.I.C.S.: 424490
Charles Kocot (Pres)

STROHWIG INDUSTRIES, INC.
3285 Industrial Rd, Richfield, WI 53076
Tel.: (262) 628-4477
Web Site: http://www.strohwig.com
Rev.: $30,100,000
Emp.: 150
Nonferrous Die-Casting Foundries
N.A.I.C.S.: 331523
Larisa Ftankevics (Mgr-HR)

STROLID, INC.
7 Stiles Rd, Salem, NH 03079   NH
Web Site: http://www.strolid.com
Year Founded: 2014
Sales Range: $1-9.9 Million
Emp.: 116
Automotive Dealer Services
N.A.I.C.S.: 441120
Vincent Micciche (Founder & Pres)

STROLL
1600 JFK Blvd 3rd Fl, Philadelphia, PA 19103
Tel.: (215) 701-3300
Web Site: http://www.stroll.com
Year Founded: 2000
Sales Range: $10-24.9 Million
Emp.: 40
Self-Improvement Information Products
N.A.I.C.S.: 519290
Dan Roitman (Founder)
Joshua Smith (Supvr-Sls)
Jade Galos (Supvr-Customer Retention)
Tom Nalencz (Dir-Fulfillment)
Megan Starr (Dir-HR)
David O'Connell (Dir-Mktg)
Ajay Segal (COO)
Avik Roy (VP-Ops)

STROM PRODUCTS LTD.
1500 Lakeside Dr Ste 110, Bannockburn, IL 60015-1234
Tel.: (847) 236-9676   DE

Web Site: http://www.noyolks.com
Year Founded: 1999
Sales Range: $75-99.9 Million
Emp.: 10
Food Product Whslr
N.A.I.C.S.: 424490
Gary Henke (Pres)

STROMBERG METAL WORKS, INC.
6701 Distribution Dr, Beltsville, MD 20705
Tel.: (301) 931-1000 (N)
Web Site: http://www.strombergmetals.com
Year Founded: 1940
Sales Range: $25-49.9 Million
Emp.: 475
Fabrication Services
N.A.I.C.S.: 238390
Robert B. Gawne (CEO)
Jerry L. Robinson (Pres)
Richard B. Freeman (Exec VP)
Gary Valdisera (VP-Ops)
Patricia Suhr (VP-Fin)
R. C. Eliff (VP-Pur & IT)
William Mould (Dir-Safety)
Joseph Puckett (Mgr-Ops-Specialty Div)
Dennis Ridenour (Controller)
Billy Blank (Mgr-Ops-North Carolina Div)
Doug Williams (Mgr-Ops-Virginia Div)
Dave Weber (Sr Project Mgr)

STROMQUIST & COMPANY INC.
4620 Atlanta Rd S, Smyrna, GA 30339
Tel.: (404) 794-3440
Web Site: http://www.stromquist.com
Year Founded: 1951
Sales Range: $10-24.9 Million
Emp.: 75
Distr of Temperature Controls & Industrial Instrumentation Products
N.A.I.C.S.: 423830
Sam P. Lindley (Pres)

STRONG AUDI
979 S State St, Salt Lake City, UT 84111-4223
Tel.: (801) 433-2834
Web Site: http://www.strongaudi.com
Year Founded: 1969
Sales Range: $25-49.9 Million
Emp.: 53
Car Whslr
N.A.I.C.S.: 441110
Blake Strong (Principal)

STRONG VOLKSWAGON
1070 S Main St, Salt Lake City, UT 84101-3115
Tel.: (801) 596-2200
Web Site: http://www.strongvw.com
Year Founded: 1955
Sales Range: $25-49.9 Million
Emp.: 53
Car Whslr
N.A.I.C.S.: 441110
Bradford D. Strong (Owner & Pres)
Blake Strong (Owner & VP)
Justin Hunsaker (Coord-Customer Care)

STRONG-BRIDGE CONSULTING LLC.
545 Andover Park W Ste 215, Seattle, WA 98188
Tel.: (206) 905-4631
Web Site: http://www.strong-bridge.com
Year Founded: 2003
Sales Range: $10-24.9 Million
Emp.: 126

COMPANIES

Management Consulting Services
N.A.I.C.S.: 541611
Brian Hartnett *(Co-Founder & Co-CEO)*
Ken Simpson *(Co-Founder & Co-CEO)*
Tom Rayner *(Pres)*
Patricia Camden *(Mng Dir)*

STRONGBRIDGE CORPORATION
21355 Ridgetop Cir Ste 200, Sterling, VA 20166
Tel.: (571) 257-2370
Web Site:
http://www.strongbridgecorp.com
Year Founded: 2004
Sales Range: $10-24.9 Million
Emp.: 78
Information Technology Support Services
N.A.I.C.S.: 541512
Janaki Deshmukh *(Founder & CEO)*
Jeffrey Powell *(Pres)*
Doug Maurer *(CFO & Sr VP)*
Danny Taglienti *(Sr VP-Ops)*
Chery Waldrup *(Chief Growth Officer)*

STRONGHOLD ENGINEERING, INC.
2000 Market St, Riverside, CA 92501
Tel.: (951) 684-9303
Web Site:
http://www.strongholdengineering.com
Rev.: $76,800,000
Emp.: 170
Highway Street & Bridge Construction
N.A.I.C.S.: 237310
Beverly Bailey *(Pres)*
Patricia McNicholas *(Dir-Risk Mgmt)*
Kamel Khalil *(VP-Estimating)*
Michael Alvarez *(Mgr-Construction Quality Control)*

STRONGMAIL SYSTEMS, INC.
1300 Island Dr Ste 200, Redwood City, CA 94065
Tel.: (650) 421-4255
Web Site: http://www.selligent.com
Year Founded: 1990
Sales Range: $10-24.9 Million
Emp.: 130
Email & Social Media Marketing
N.A.I.C.S.: 541810
Tal Nathan *(Sr VP-Client Svcs)*
Katrina Conn *(VP-Mktg Svcs)*
John Hernandez *(CEO)*
Stanislas Van Oost *(Sr VP-Bus Ops)*
Nick Worth *(CMO)*
Nathalie Parent *(Chief Talent Officer)*
Roy Jugessur *(Sr VP-Sls-Global)*
Kevin Thompson *(CFO)*
Todd McCaslin *(Sr VP-Solutions Consulting-Global)*
Karthik Kripapuri *(Chief Customer Officer)*

Subsidiaries:

StrongMail Systems UK Ltd. (1)
Atlantic House Imperial Way, Reading, RG2 0TD, United Kingdom
Tel.: (44) 118 903 6068
Web Site: http://www.strongmail.com
Emp.: 3
Email & Social Media Marketing
N.A.I.C.S.: 541810

STRONGWELL CORPORATION
400 Commonwealth Ave, Bristol, VA 24201-3820
Tel.: (276) 645-8000 VA
Web Site: http://www.strongwell.com
Year Founded: 1993
Rev.: $106,000,000
Emp.: 900
Plastics Products
N.A.I.C.S.: 326199
David Gibbs *(VP-Sls & Engrg)*
Mike Jaszewski *(VP-Ops-Minnesota & Mexico Ops)*
Geoff Newman *(Mgr-Corp Contracts & Customer Rels)*
Angie Barr *(CFO)*

STRONGWOOD INSURANCE HOLDINGS CORP.
443 Crown Point Cir No A, Grass Valley, CA 95945
Tel.: (530) 274-3102
Web Site:
http://www.networkedins.com
Holding Company
Rick Quagliaroli *(Chm)*
George Biancardi *(Pres/CEO-Monterey)*
Larry Oslie *(Exec VP-Bus Dev & Mgr-Orange)*

STROOCK & STROOCK & LAVAN LLP
180 Maiden Ln, New York, NY 10038-4982
Tel.: (212) 806-5400
Web Site: http://www.stroock.com
Year Founded: 1876
Sales Range: $250-299.9 Million
Emp.: 501
Legal Advisory Services
N.A.I.C.S.: 541110
Conrad G. Bahlke *(Partner)*
Jacob Bart *(Partner)*
Robert Abrams *(Partner)*
James L. Bernard *(Partner)*
Sayan Bhattacharyya *(Partner)*
Micah W. Bloomfield *(Partner)*
Leonard Boxer *(Partner)*
Melvin A. Brosterman *(Partner)*
Diana M. Brummer *(Partner)*
William Campbell *(Partner)*
Charles E. Cantine *(Partner)*
Kevin J. Curnin *(Partner)*
Joseph Diamante *(Partner)*
Steven D. Atleex *(Partner-Fin Svcs & Class Action Practice Grp-Los Angeles)*
Loryn Dunn Arkow *(Partner)*
Kim Pagotto *(Partner)*
James G. Sammataro *(Partner)*
Lewis F. Murphy *(Partner)*
Jeffrey R. Keitelman *(Mng Partner)*
Seamus Curley *(Partner-Washington)*
Alan M. Klinger *(Mng Partner)*
Ellen Musante *(CMO)*
Kermit Wallace *(CIO)*
Evan Hudson *(Partner)*

STROTTMAN INTERNATIONAL INC.
36 Executive Park, Irvine, CA 92614
Tel.: (949) 852-1166 CA
Web Site: http://www.strottman.com
Year Founded: 1983
Sales Range: $10-24.9 Million
Emp.: 45
Provider of Promotion Marketing Services
N.A.I.C.S.: 541613
Stefan Schmitz *(Sr VP-Bus Dev)*
Amy Henry *(Sr VP-Strategic Insights)*

STROUD DESIGN, INC.
437 W Wilshire Ste C, Oklahoma City, OK 73116
Tel.: (405) 843-1462
Web Site:
http://www.strouddesign.com
Year Founded: 1982
Sales Range: $10-24.9 Million
Emp.: 2
Full Service
N.A.I.C.S.: 541810

Seth Schubert *(Graphic Designer)*

STROUHAL'S TIRE RECAPPING PLANT INC.
8206 Business Hwy 59, Hungerford, TX 77448
Tel.: (979) 532-1579
Web Site: http://www.strouhaltire.com
Year Founded: 1926
Sales Range: $50-74.9 Million
Emp.: 200
Recapping & Tire Retail Sales
N.A.I.C.S.: 423130
Gene Strouhal *(Dir-Central Pur)*

STROUM JEWISH COMMUNITY CENTER
3801 E Mercer Way, Mercer Island, WA 98040
Tel.: (206) 232-7115 WA
Web Site: http://www.sjcc.org
Year Founded: 1949
Sales Range: $1-9.9 Million
Emp.: 450
Jewish Community Support Services
N.A.I.C.S.: 813410
Renee Cohen Goodwin *(COO)*
Joel Mezistrano *(Treas)*
Kim Waldbaum *(Sec)*
Leigh Anne Kiviat *(Sec)*
Liz Friedman *(VP)*
Sharon Lott *(VP)*
Dalya Will *(Mgr-Membership)*
Dana Weiner *(Sr Dir-Community Connections)*
Dominick Szabo *(Mgr-Aquatics)*
Heidi Turner *(Dir-Mktg)*
Jennifer Magalnick *(Dir-Early Childhood School-Seattle)*
Zach Duitch *(Dir-Programs & Svcs)*
Amy Lavin *(CEO)*

STRUCTURA INC
9208 Waterford Centre Blvd Ste 100, Austin, TX 78758
Tel.: (512) 495-9702
Web Site:
http://www.structurainc.com
Year Founded: 2006
Sales Range: $10-24.9 Million
Emp.: 125
Commercial & Office Building Contractors
N.A.I.C.S.: 236115
Rusty Morgan *(Pres)*
James Cantwell *(Sr Superintendent)*

STRUCTURA, INC.
12358 Parklawn Dr Ste 140 N., Bethesda, MD 20852
Tel.: (301) 987-9234
Web Site: https://www.structura-inc.com
Year Founded: 1988
Engineeering Services
N.A.I.C.S.: 541330

Subsidiaries:

Fitzpatrick Engineering Group, PLLC (1)
19520 W Catawba Ave # 311, Cornelius, NC 28031
Tel.: (704) 987-9114
Web Site: http://www.fegstructural.com
Rev.: $1,035,000
Emp.: 5
Engineeering Services
N.A.I.C.S.: 541330
David Goodman *(Engr-Structural)*

STRUCTURAL COMPONENT SYSTEMS INC
1255 Front St, Fremont, NE 68025
Tel.: (402) 721-5622
Web Site: http://www.scstruss.com
Year Founded: 1991
Sales Range: $10-24.9 Million

Emp.: 100
Mfr of Trusses & Wooden Roofs
N.A.I.C.S.: 321215
Edwin K. Christoffersen *(Pres)*
Dave Christoffersen *(COO)*
Dan Christoffersen *(CFO)*

STRUCTURAL GRAPHICS, LLC
38 Plains Rd, Essex, CT 06426
Tel.: (860) 767-2661
Web Site:
http://www.structuralgraphics.com
Year Founded: 1985
Rev.: $12,000,000
Emp.: 80
Graphic Arts & Related Design Services
N.A.I.C.S.: 541430
Ethan Goller *(Pres)*
Gustavo Gutierrez *(VP-Ops)*
Julie A. Abraham *(CFO)*
Kevin Gilligan *(COO)*
Noel Boland *(VP-Creative Svcs)*
Ken Stokes *(VP-ECommerce)*

STRUCTURAL GROUP, INC.
101 50 Old Columbia Rd, Columbia, MD 21046
Tel.: (410) 850-7000
Web Site: http://www.structural.net
Sales Range: $200-249.9 Million
Emp.: 1,200
Concrete, Steel, Masonry, Wood & Soils Repair & Building Services
N.A.I.C.S.: 238110
Peter Emmons *(CEO)*
Scott Greenhaus *(Sr VP)*
Dan Fangio *(CFO)*
Jay Thomas *(VP-Structural Preservation Sys)*
Jim Kirkland *(VP-Comml Sls)*

Subsidiaries:

Pullman Power, LLC (1)
6501 E Commerce Ave Ste 200, Kansas City, MO 64120
Tel.: (816) 231-7400
Web Site: http://www.paulmann-services.com
Sales Range: $50-74.9 Million
Emp.: 400
Chimney, Silo & Stack Design, Construction, Maintenance & Repair Services
N.A.I.C.S.: 237990
David Bird *(Chief Engr)*

Pullman STT, Inc. (1)
10150 Old Columbia Rd, Columbia, MD 21046
Tel.: (410) 505-7042
Web Site: https://www.pullman-services.com
Product & Technical Support Services
N.A.I.C.S.: 541990
Bob Charles *(Pres)*

Subsidiary (Domestic):

Structural Maintenance Systems, Inc. (2)
179 Pennsylvania Ave, Malvern, PA 19355
Tel.: (610) 296-9252
Web Site:
http://www.structuralmaintenance.com
Rev.: $6,500,000
Emp.: 40
Masonry Contractors
N.A.I.C.S.: 238140
Joseph Russell *(Pres)*

Structural Preservation Systems, Inc. (1)
7455 New Rdg Rd Ste T, Hanover, MD 21076
Tel.: (410) 850-7000
Web Site: http://www.structural.net
Sales Range: $150-199.9 Million
Emp.: 1,000
Concrete, Masonry, Timber & Soil Repair Services
N.A.I.C.S.: 238110

VSL (1)
7455 New Ridge Rd Ste T, Hanover, MD 21076

STRUCTURAL GROUP, INC.   U.S. PRIVATE

Structural Group, Inc.—(Continued)
Tel.: (410) 850-7000
Web Site: http://www.vsl.net
Sales Range: $25-49.9 Million
Emp.: 175
Post-Tensioning & Specialty Reinforcement Systems Mfr
N.A.I.C.S.: 237990

STRUCTURAL INDUSTRIES, INC.
2950 Veterans Memorial Hwy, Bohemia, NY 11716
Tel.: (516) 822-5200   NY
Web Site:
   http://www.structuralindustries.com
Sales Range: $50-74.9 Million
Emp.: 55
Mfr of Picture Frames
N.A.I.C.S.: 339999
Stanley Hirsch (Chm)
Jamie Hirsch (Pres)
Judy Vietheer (CFO)

STRUCTURAL STEEL HOLDING INC.
6210 Saint Louis St, Meridian, MS 39307-7209
Tel.: (601) 483-5381   MS
Year Founded: 1988
Sales Range: $25-49.9 Million
Emp.: 270
Fabricated Structural Metal
N.A.I.C.S.: 332312
Tommy E. Dulaney (Pres)

Subsidiaries:

SSS Trucking Inc.   (1)
6215 Specktor St, Meridian, MS 39307-7209
Tel.: (601) 693-4711
Rev.: $1,343,027
Emp.: 15
Trucking Except Local
N.A.I.C.S.: 484121
Tommy E. Dulaney (Pres)

Structural Steel Services Inc.   (1)
6215 Saint Louis St, Meridian, MS 39307-9575
Tel.: (601) 483-5381
Rev.: $43,994,822
Emp.: 225
Fabricated Structural Metal
N.A.I.C.S.: 332312

STRUCTURE VENTURES LLC
215 W 95th St, New York, NY 10025
Tel.: (212) 874-9164
Web Site: http://www.structure-nyc.com
Year Founded: 2010
Sales Range: $1-9.9 Million
Emp.: 35
General Contractor Services
N.A.I.C.S.: 236210
Gino Capolino (Co-Founder)
Eric Capolino (Co-Founder)
Andrew Ferris (Project Mgr)
Tomek Chmielowiec (Dir-Field Ops)
Rodolfo Bonilla (Dir-Millwork Studio)

STRUCTURED COMMUNICATION SYSTEMS, INC.
12901 SE 97 Ave Ste 400, Clackamas, OR 97015
Tel.: (503) 513-9979
Web Site: http://www.structured.com
Year Founded: 1992
Sales Range: $25-49.9 Million
Emp.: 60
IT Services
N.A.I.C.S.: 541512
Ronald L. Fowler (Pres & CEO)
Mark Hickman (VP-Data Center Svcs)
Ty Trabosh (CTO)
Bill Tracy (VP-Tech Solutions)
Chris McDuffie (VP-Cloud Architecture)
Bill Coleman (CEO)

STRUCTURED EMPLOYMENT ECONOMIC DEVELOPMENT CORPORATION
22 Cortlandt St 33rd Fl, New York, NY 10007
Tel.: (212) 473-0255   NY
Web Site: http://www.seedco.org
Year Founded: 1976
Sales Range: $10-24.9 Million
Emp.: 135
Economic Development Services
N.A.I.C.S.: 541720
Ronald Kirk (VP-Budgets & Contracts)
Tara Colton (Sr VP-Programs)
Kristen Merkle Cutforth (Chief Compliance Officer & Gen Counsel)
Matthew LoCurto (CFO)
George A. Pruitt (Chm)
Sandra L. Phillips (Vice Chm)
Paul R. Franke III (Treas)

STRUCTUREDWEB, INC.
902 Broadway 20 W 20, New York, NY 10010
Tel.: (201) 325-3110
Web Site:
   http://www.structuredweb.com
Sales Range: $25-49.9 Million
Emp.: 30
Web-based Software Services & Marketing Solutions
N.A.I.C.S.: 541512
Daniel Nissan (Pres & CEO)
Yoram Ayalon (VP-R&D, SaaS Infrastructure & Ops)
Zeev Lotan (VP-Svcs & Customer Success)

STRUCTURES UNLIMITED, INC.
166 River Rd, Bow, NH 03304
Tel.: (603) 645-6539
Web Site:
   http://www.structuresunlimited.com
Year Founded: 1968
Sales Range: $10-24.9 Million
Emp.: 60
Structural Skylights, Skyroofs & Pool Enclosures Mfr
N.A.I.C.S.: 236220
Robert R. Keller (Chm)
Stacey Lambert (Mgr-Drafting)
Todd Riley (Mgr-Engrg)
Mark McNichol (Reg Mgr)

STRUEVER BROS. ECCLES & ROUSE INC.
1040 Hull St Ste 200, Baltimore, MD 21230-5349
Tel.: (443) 573-4000   MD
Year Founded: 1974
Sales Range: $25-49.9 Million
Emp.: 205
Residential Construction
N.A.I.C.S.: 236115
C. William Struever (Pres, CEO & Partner)
Fred Struever (VP)
Cobber Eccles (Partner-Construction Project Mgmt)

STRUKMYER, LLC
1801 Big Town Blvd Ste 100, Mesquite, TX 75149-1010
Tel.: (214) 275-9595   TX
Web Site: http://www.strukmyer.com
Sales Range: $10-24.9 Million
Emp.: 150
Medical Supplies Mfr & Distr
N.A.I.C.S.: 339112

Bob Delk (CEO)

STRUTHERS ELECTRONICS CORPORATION
15 Harold Ct, Bay Shore, NY 11706-2220
Tel.: (631) 434-7586   NY
Web Site: http://www.vdot.net
Year Founded: 1962
Sales Range: $10-24.9 Million
Emp.: 50
Mfr of Waveguide/Coaxial High Power Switches & Directional Couplers
N.A.I.C.S.: 334419
Robert Isaacson (Pres)
Dan Gibbons (Gen Mgr)

STRUXTURE ARCHITECTS, P.L.C.
314 E 4th St, Waterloo, IA 50703
Tel.: (319) 234-1515
Web Site: http://www.struxture.com
Year Founded: 1934
Emp.: 17
Architectural Services
N.A.I.C.S.: 541310
Craig Schwerdtfeger (Principal & Architect)
Mark Nickel (Mktg Dir)
Dan Channer (Principal & Architect)
Pam Johnson (Architect)

STRUXURE OUTDOOR, INC.
154 Ethan Allen Dr, Dahlonega, GA 30533
Web Site: http://www.struxure.com
Year Founded: 2011
Sales Range: $10-24.9 Million
Building Materials Mfr
N.A.I.C.S.: 327999
Scott Selzer (Founder & CEO)

STS AVIATION GROUP
2000 NE Jensen Beach Blvd, Jensen Beach, FL 34957
Tel.: (772) 232-0375
Web Site:
   http://www.stsaviationgroup.com
Year Founded: 1985
Sales Range: $25-49.9 Million
Emp.: 250
Holding Company; Aerospace Staffing, Engineering, Line Maintenance, Component Sales & Support Services
N.A.I.C.S.: 551112
Bob Greene (Chm)
Beth Oberacker (Dir-HR)
Camille Cannon (Mgr-Credit & Collections)
Richard Huff (Controller)
John Snyder (Acct Mgr)
Andrew C. Roberts (Chm)
Michael John Adams (Head-Europe)
Mark Smith (Pres)

Subsidiaries:

STS Component Solutions, LLC   (1)
52910 SW 42nd Ave, Palm City, FL 34990
Tel.: (561) 214-6508
Web Site: http://www.stsaviationgroup.com
Aircraft Component Distr
N.A.I.C.S.: 423860
Tom Covella (Pres)
Tim Russo (Dir-Customer Solutions)

STS Technical Services LLC   (1)
250 S Executive Dr Ste 101, Brookfield, WI 53005
Tel.: (262) 784-7410
Web Site: http://www.sts-ts.com
Sales Range: $50-74.9 Million
Employment Placement Services
N.A.I.C.S.: 561311
Rick Koenig (Pres)
Rich Ciampa (Dir-Engrg Svc)
Chuck Harrison (VP-Sls & Delivery)

Triumph Aviation Services - NAAS Division
11501 Jones Maltsberger Rd, San Antonio, TX 78216
Tel.: (210) 805-0049
Web Site: http://www.naasinc.com
Aviation Services
N.A.I.C.S.: 488119
Barry Larson (Exec VP)

STS ELECTRONICS RECYCLING, INC.
522 CR 1520, Jacksonville, TX 75766
Tel.: (903) 589-3705
Web Site:
   http://www.stselectronicrecyclinginc.com
Year Founded: 2010
Sales Range: $1-9.9 Million
Emp.: 46
Electronics Recycling Services
N.A.I.C.S.: 562920
Steven Norton (Pres & CEO)
Brad Guidry (COO)
Dannon Pate (CFO)
Brian Townsend (Mgr-Outside Sls)
Joshua Crow (Mktg Mgr)
Juan Rosales (Mgr-Wholesale)
Jose Trejo (Production Mgr)
Calvin Williams (Mgr-Customer Svc)
Jim Hanks (Mgr-Direct Sls)
Tyler Baker (Mgr-E-Commerce Sls)
Jerry-Michael Norton (Mgr-Online Sls)

STS HOLDINGS, INC.
2000 Northeast Jensen Beach Blvd, Jensen Beach, FL 34957-7238   DE
Web Site: http://www.stsholdings.com
Year Founded: 1997
Sales Range: $50-74.9 Million
Emp.: 20
Holding Company; Staffing Services for Aerospace Industry
N.A.I.C.S.: 541330
Mark Smith (Sr VP)

Subsidiaries:

Airplanes, Inc.   (1)
2000 NE Jensen Beach Blvd, Jensen Beach, FL 34957-7238
Tel.: (772) 232-2305
Web Site: http://www.airplanesinc.com
Aviation Maintenance Personnel
N.A.I.C.S.: 488190

STS Services, Inc.   (1)
2000 NE Jensen Beach Blvd, Jensen Beach, FL 34957-7238
Sales Range: $50-74.9 Million
Recruitment of Aerospace Technicians
N.A.I.C.S.: 561320

STS INTERNATIONAL, INC.
4695 Chabot Dr Ste 102, Pleasanton, CA 94588
Tel.: (925) 479-7800
Web Site: http://www.stsii.com
Year Founded: 1992
Sales Range: $25-49.9 Million
Emp.: 609
Information Technology Services
N.A.I.C.S.: 541512
Beri Kasper (CFO & VP)
John Leonhardt (CEO-Europe)
Kelley Stockton (Exec VP)
Kish Jha (Exec VP-Ops)
Phillippe Verhees (Dir-Sls)
Dave Morgan (Pres & CEO)
Robert Reeves (Dir-Growth & Strategy)

STS TRUCK EQUIPMENT
3496 Ct St, Syracuse, NY 13206
Tel.: (315) 437-5406
Web Site: http://www.ststrailer.com
Year Founded: 1949
Sales Range: $25-49.9 Million
Emp.: 43

Sales of Trailer Hitches & Automotive Products
N.A.I.C.S.: 493110
Pete Krais (Mgr-Sls-Trailer)
Steve Jacobs (Pres & CEO)

STS TURBO, INC.
165 N 1330 W Ste A-4, Orem, UT 84057
Tel.: (801) 224-3477 NV
Web Site: http://www.ststurbo.com
Sales Range: $1-9.9 Million
Emp.: 10
Automotive Rear-Mount Turbocharger Mfr
N.A.I.C.S.: 333611
Donna B. Squires (Sec)

STU EMMERT CHEVROLET-BUICK-CADILLAC, INC.
202 N Grant Ave, Liberal, KS 67901
Tel.: (620) 624-2584 DE
Web Site: http://www.autotraders.com
Year Founded: 1973
Sales Range: $10-24.9 Million
Emp.: 35
Automobiles, New & Used
N.A.I.C.S.: 441110
Fredrick Miller (Controller & Gen Mgr)
Duane Headrick (Mgr-Sls)
Stuart P. Emmert Jr. (Owner)

STU SEGALL PRODUCTIONS INC.
4705 Ruffin Rd, San Diego, CA 92123-1611
Tel.: (858) 974-8988 CA
Web Site: http://www.stusegall.com
Year Founded: 1991
Rev.: $49,850,000
Emp.: 30
Producer of Motion Pictures & Videos
N.A.I.C.S.: 512110
Stu Segall (Pres)
Joan Etchells (VP & Gen Mgr)
Eric Kiser (VP)

STUART & ASSOCIATES, INC.
15919 Industrial Pkwy, Cleveland, OH 44135
Tel.: (216) 267-0610 OH
Web Site: http://www.stuartassociates.com
Year Founded: 1978
Sales Range: $10-24.9 Million
Emp.: 26
Specialty Ad Sales & Printing Services
N.A.I.C.S.: 323111
Patricia J. McAllester (Owner & CEO)

STUART KING CAPITAL CORP.
1500 Cliff Branch Dr, Henderson, NV 89014
Tel.: (702) 539-3533 DE
Year Founded: 2011
Liabilities: $7,503
Net Worth: ($7,503)
Earnings: ($1,885)
Fiscal Year-end: 12/31/14
Investment Services
N.A.I.C.S.: 523999
David Koons (Pres, Treas & Sec)

STUART KITCHENS INC.
2221 Greenspring Dr, Lutherville Timonium, MD 21093
Tel.: (410) 252-6520 MD
Web Site: http://www.stuartkitchens.com
Year Founded: 1955
Sales Range: $10-24.9 Million
Emp.: 37
Kitchen Components Distr
N.A.I.C.S.: 449210

Joe Birner (Mgr)
Leonard Cosentini (Mgr-Warehouse)
William D. Gould Jr. (Pres)

STUART M. PERRY INC.
117 Limestone Ln, Winchester, VA 22602
Tel.: (540) 662-3431
Web Site: http://www.stuartmperry.com
Sales Range: $10-24.9 Million
Emp.: 150
Crushed & Broken Limestone
N.A.I.C.S.: 212312
Dennis W. Perry (Pres)

STUART POWELL FORD INC.
225 S Danville Bypass, Danville, KY 40422
Tel.: (859) 236-8917
Web Site: http://www.stuartpowellford.com
Sales Range: $25-49.9 Million
Emp.: 50
Automobiles, New & Used
N.A.I.C.S.: 441110
Stuart Powell (Owner & Pres)
Sharon Miller (Office Mgr)
Robbie Todd (Mgr-Sls)
Patti Powell (Gen Mgr)

STUART SPORTS SPECIALTIES, INC.
34 Front St, Indian Orchard, MA 01151
Tel.: (413) 543-1524
Web Site: http://www.alsgoldfish.com
Year Founded: 1954
Sales Range: Less than $1 Million
Emp.: 5
Mfr of Fishing Lures
N.A.I.C.S.: 339920
John Occhialini (Pres)

Subsidiaries:

Al's Goldfish Lure Co. (1)
40 Main St Ste 40 113, Biddeford, ME 04005
Tel.: (413) 543-1524
Web Site: http://www.alsgoldfish.com
Fishing & Hunting Gear Supplier
N.A.I.C.S.: 459110

STUART-BOWMAN AUTO CENTER
1709 E Dixie Dr, Asheboro, NC 27205
Tel.: (336) 625-6123
Sales Range: $75-99.9 Million
Emp.: 58
New & Used Car Dealers
N.A.I.C.S.: 441110
Dan Lackey (Pres)

STUART-DEAN CO. INC.
450 7th Ave Fl 38, New York, NY 10123
Tel.: (212) 273-6900 NY
Web Site: http://www.stuartdean.com
Year Founded: 1932
Sales Range: $50-74.9 Million
Emp.: 453
Specialty Trade Contractors
N.A.I.C.S.: 238990
Nick Pennings (Chm)
Michael Williams (Gen Mgr)
Chris Hughes (Pres & CEO)
Harold Pandian (Dir-Mktg)

STUARTS' PETROLEUM INC.
11 E 4th St, Bakersfield, CA 93307-1401
Tel.: (661) 325-6320
Web Site: http://www.stuartspetroleum.com
Year Founded: 1981

Sales Range: $10-24.9 Million
Emp.: 11
Provider of Petroleum Services
N.A.I.C.S.: 424720
John Stuart Sr. (Pres)

STUBBS OIL COMPANY INC.
10911 Hwy 301 S, Statesboro, GA 30458
Tel.: (912) 681-2261
Web Site: http://www.stubbsoilcompany.com
Rev.: $40,500,000
Emp.: 14
Petroleum Bulk Stations
N.A.I.C.S.: 424710
J. P. Stubbs (Pres)

STUDENT ACHIEVEMENT PARTNERS
58 E 11th St, New York, NY 10003
Tel.: (212) 510-8533 DE
Web Site: http://www.achievethecore.org
Year Founded: 2011
Sales Range: $10-24.9 Million
Emp.: 40
Student Achievement Services
N.A.I.C.S.: 611699
Beth Cocuzza (Dir-Mathematics Team)
Lisa Goldschmidt (Dir-Student-Digital Team)
Sabrina Chan (Fin Mgr)
Meredith Liben (Specialist-Literacy & English Language Arts Team)

STUDENT ALTERNATIVE PROGRAM, INC.
813 E Pike, Weslaco, TX 78596
Tel.: (956) 358-3856 TX
Year Founded: 1990
Sales Range: $10-24.9 Million
Emp.: 28
Educational Support Services
N.A.I.C.S.: 611710
San Juanita Villa (Chm)
David Ojeda (Vice Chm)

STUDENTCITY.COM INC.
8 Essex Ctr Dr, Peabody, MA 01960
Tel.: (978) 531-3301 MA
Web Site: http://www.studentcity.com
Year Founded: 1996
Sales Range: $10-24.9 Million
Emp.: 40
Internet Based Travel Agency Specializing in Student Travel
N.A.I.C.S.: 561510
Tony Mayers (Mgr-HR)

STUDENTPAINTERS.NET.
3600 15th Ave W Ste 200B, Seattle, WA 98119
Web Site: http://www.studentpainters.net
Year Founded: 1981
Sales Range: $1-9.9 Million
Emp.: 205
Wall Covering Contractors
N.A.I.C.S.: 238320
Dwayne Bishop (CFO)

STUDENTS BOOK CORPORATION
1500 NE Terrell Mall, Pullman, WA 99163
Tel.: (509) 332-2537
Web Site: http://www.wsubookie.bncollege.com
Sales Range: $10-24.9 Million
Emp.: 80
Book Stores
N.A.I.C.S.: 459210
Leslie Martin (Mgr-Stores)

STUDIO 921 SALON & DAY SPA
921 E Fort Ave Ste 108, Baltimore, MD 21230
Tel.: (410) 783-7727
Web Site: http://www.studio921spa.com
Year Founded: 2004
Rev.: $2,200,000
Emp.: 51
Beauty Salons
N.A.I.C.S.: 812112
A. M. Alonso (Principal)
Judy S. Kelly (Co-Owner)
Colleen Smith (Co-Owner)

STUDIO CALICO
420 Old Morgantown Rd, Bowling Green, KY 42101
Tel.: (646) 420-7618
Web Site: http://www.studiocalico.com
Year Founded: 2007
Sales Range: $1-9.9 Million
Emp.: 30
Membership-Based Scrapbooking Center Retailing Scrapbooking & Card Making Kits
N.A.I.C.S.: 513191
April Foster (CEO)
Kennon Ballou (CTO)
Samantha Shepard (Dir-Sls & Mktg)
Christine Jenkins (Mgr-HR & Pur)

STUDIO PLUS ARCHITECTURE CORP.
12730 New Brittany Blvd Ste 606, Fort Myers, FL 33907
Tel.: (239) 476-8888
Web Site: http://www.studioplusarch.com
Sales Range: $10-24.9 Million
Emp.: 15
Architectural & Interior Design Services
N.A.I.C.S.: 541310
Andrea Gil (Assoc Principal & Dir-Acctg)
Damon Romanello (CEO)
Jason Dontje (Mng Principal)
Mike Lendino (CFO)
Rachel Thomas (Assoc Principal & Project Mgr)
Valerie Marino (Assoc Principal & Designer-Interior)
Christopher Ressler (Sr Project Mgr)
Mark Shannon (Sr Project Mgr)
Sergio Lechuga (Sr Project Mgr)
Brianna Olsen (Coord-Bus Ops)
Daniel Roark (Project Mgr)
Gennifer Hunt (Coord-Interiors)
Jose Perez (Principal)
Nathalie White (Project Mgr)
Taylor Dupree Brewington (Mgr-Creative)

STUDIO RK SALON
6420 Plantation Park Ct Ste 102, Fort Myers, FL 33966
Tel.: (239) 489-4144
Web Site: http://www.studiorksalon.com
Year Founded: 1995
Sales Range: $1-9.9 Million
Emp.: 40
Hair Salon
N.A.I.C.S.: 812112
Renee Walker (Co-Owner)
Debby Marsh (Co-Owner)
Jennifer Pagnutti (Co-Owner)
Pamela DiRenzo-Knight (Co-Owner)

STUDIO RTA
7255 Rosemead Blvd, Pico Rivera, CA 90660-4047
Tel.: (562) 446-2255

STUDIO RTA

Web Site: http://www.studiorta.com
Rev.: $29,472,000
Emp.: 130
Furniture
N.A.I.C.S.: 423210
Paul Reitzin *(Pres)*
Scott Maynes *(CFO)*
Roger Abarientos *(Controller)*
John Yoder *(VP)*

STUDIO SBV, INC.
28 W 27th St 10F, New York, NY 10001
Tel.: (917) 382-2896
Web Site:
http://www.oysterbooks.com
Digital Book Subscription Services
N.A.I.C.S.: 459210
Eric Stromberg *(CEO)*
Andrew Brown *(Co-Founder & CTO)*
Willem Van Lancker *(Co-Founder & Chief Product Officer)*

STUDIO98, LLC
1300 N Fort Harrison Ave, Clearwater, FL 33755
Tel.: (727) 295-3441
Web Site: http://www.studio98.com
Year Founded: 2007
Sales Range: $10-24.9 Million
Emp.: 24
Digital Marketing Services
N.A.I.C.S.: 541810
Rafferty Pendery *(CEO)*

STUDIONOW, INC.
4017 Hillsboro Pike Ste 418, Nashville, TN 37215
Tel.: (615) 577-9400
Web Site:
http://www.corp.studionow.com
Year Founded: 2006
Video Production Platform Solutions
N.A.I.C.S.: 512110
Kelly Metz *(VP-Bus Dev)*
David Mason *(Founder, Chm & CEO)*
Nick Birren *(Dir-Bus Dev)*
David Corts *(Pres & COO)*
John Philpott *(CFO)*
Ben Tyson *(Sr VP)*
Ben Gortmaker *(Sr Acct Mgr)*
Brooks Hofstetter *(Sr Dir-Production Ops)*
Chris Jenkins *(Dir-Acctg)*
Eric Kridle *(Sr Editor)*
Erik Spangenberg *(Sr Mgr-Acct)*

STUDYPOINT, INC.
44 Court St Ste 340, Boston, MA 02180
Web Site: http://www.studypoint.com
Year Founded: 1999
Rev.: $4,300,000
Emp.: 26
Tutoring Services
N.A.I.C.S.: 611691
Greg Zumas *(Co-Founder & Pres)*

STULLER, INC.
302 Rue Louis XIV, Lafayette, LA 70508
Tel.: (337) 262-7700
Web Site: http://www.stuller.com
Year Founded: 1970
Sales Range: $50-74.9 Million
Emp.: 1,600
Mfr & Distr of Fine Jewelry & Jewelry-Related Products
N.A.I.C.S.: 339910
Matthew Stuller *(Founder & Chm)*
Coby Blanchard *(Chief Supply Chain Officer)*
Tammy Kidder *(VP-Tools & Supplies)*
Mike DeHart *(Chief Investment Officer)*

STULTZ, INC.
5276 Summerlin Commons Way Ste 701, Fort Myers, FL 33907
Tel.: (239) 590-3033
Web Site: http://www.stultzinc.com
Sales Range: $1-9.9 Million
Emp.: 6
General Contractors
N.A.I.C.S.: 236220
John M. Stultz *(Principal)*
Jeff Stultz *(VP & Project Mgr)*

STULZ-SICKLES STEEL CO., INC.
2 Campus Dr, Burlington, NJ 08016
Tel.: (609) 531-2172
Web Site:
http://www.stulzsicklessteel.com
Year Founded: 1916
Sales Range: $10-24.9 Million
Emp.: 25
Metal Whslr
N.A.I.C.S.: 423510
Kevin Kolacki *(Mgr-Ops)*

STUMBLEUPON, INC.
301 Brannan St, San Francisco, CA 94107
Tel.: (415) 979-0640
Web Site:
http://www.stumbleupon.com
Sales Range: $10-24.9 Million
Emp.: 75
Social Media Website
N.A.I.C.S.: 516210
Garrett Camp *(Co-Founder & Chm)*
Geoff Smith *(Co-Founder & Chief Scientific Officer)*
Mark Bartels *(CEO)*
Cody Simms *(VP-Product)*
Teal Newland *(VP-Sls)*

STUPP BROS., INC.
3800 Weber Rd, Saint Louis, MO 63125-1160
Tel.: (314) 638-5000
Web Site: http://www.stupp.com
Year Founded: 1856
Holding Company; Infrastructure Development & Construction Services; Steel Pipe Mfr & Coating Services; Commercial Banking
N.A.I.C.S.: 551112
Thomas L. Turner *(CFO)*
Robert P. Stupp Jr. *(VP)*

Subsidiaries:

Hammert's Iron Works, Inc. (1)
5319 Shreve Ave, Saint Louis, MO 63115-2229
Tel.: (314) 389-0666
Web Site: http://www.hammertsiron.com
Sales Range: $25-49.9 Million
Emp.: 80
Structural Steel Mfr
N.A.I.C.S.: 238120
R. Philip Stupp *(Pres)*
Kenneth J. Kubacki *(Vice Chm)*
Jim Schueler *(VP & Gen Mgr)*

Midwest BankCentre, Inc. (1)
2191 Lemay Ferry Rd, Saint Louis, MO 63125
Tel.: (314) 544-8599
Web Site:
http://www.midwestbankcentre.com
Rev.: $67,167,481
Assets: $1,842,919,366
Liabilities: $1,685,034,543
Net Worth: $157,884,823
Earnings: $12,322,841
Emp.: 289
Fiscal Year-end: 12/31/2016
Bank Holding Company
N.A.I.C.S.: 551111
Dale E. Oberkfell *(CFO & Exec VP)*
Orv Kimbrough *(Chm & CEO)*
Daniel T. Bloomfield *(Sr VP-Comml Lending-Chesterfield)*
Tim Walsh *(Pres-Jefferson County)*
Christina Dancy *(Asst VP)*

Subsidiary (Domestic):

Midwest BankCentre (2)
2191 Lemay Ferry Rd, Saint Louis, MO 63125
Tel.: (314) 631-5500
Web Site:
http://www.midwestbankcentre.com
Sales Range: $50-74.9 Million
Emp.: 289
Commericial Banking
N.A.I.C.S.: 522110
Mitch Bridges *(VP-Credit & Risk Mgmt)*
David Warning *(Chief Credit Officer & Exec VP)*
Kirby Morris *(VP-Comml Lending)*
Danny Pogue *(Exec VP-Comml Lending & Head-Comml Banking)*
Tony Edmonds *(Sr VP & Reg Mgr-Retail Banking)*
Marsha Benney *(COO)*
Dale E. Oberkfell *(Pres & CFO)*
Veta T. Jeffery *(Sr VP-Community & Economic Dev)*
Cari A. Noll *(Sr VP)*
Gregory Schaller *(Chief Risk Officer & Sr VP)*
Orv Kimbrough *(Chm & CEO)*

Stupp Bridge Company (1)
3800 Weber Rd, Saint Louis, MO 63125
Tel.: (314) 638-5000
Web Site: http://www.stuppbridge.com
Sales Range: $10-24.9 Million
Emp.: 45
Bridge & Other Architectural Girder Fabrication & Engineering Services
N.A.I.C.S.: 332312

Stupp Coatings, LLC (1)
12710 Leisure Rd, Baton Rouge, LA 70807
Tel.: (225) 775-3018
Web Site: http://www.stuppcoatings.com
Steel Pipe Coating Services
N.A.I.C.S.: 332812

Stupp Corporation (1)
12555 Ronaldson Rd, Baton Rouge, LA 70807-1503 (100%)
Tel.: (225) 775-8800
Web Site: http://www.stuppcorp.com
Sales Range: $25-49.9 Million
Emp.: 250
Mfr of Fabricated Sturctural Pipe
N.A.I.C.S.: 331210
John P. Stupp Jr. *(CEO)*
Lampros Kompotiatis *(VP-Tech)*
Aaron Litschewski *(Dir-Quality)*

STUPPY INCORPORATED
1212 Clay St, Kansas City, MO 64116
Tel.: (816) 842-3071
Web Site: http://www.stuppy.com
Rev.: $21,848,851
Emp.: 30
Flower Sales
N.A.I.C.S.: 424930
Matthew J. Stuppy *(Pres)*

STURDEVANTS INC.
2609 S Shirley Ave, Sioux Falls, SD 57106
Tel.: (605) 362-6970
Web Site:
http://www.sturdevants.com
Rev.: $20,000,000
Emp.: 66
Automotive Supplies & Parts
N.A.I.C.S.: 441330
Jack Sturdevant *(Pres)*
Ruth Ann Prostrollo *(Dir-HR)*

STURDY CORPORATION
1822 Carolina Beach Rd, Wilmington, NC 28401-6504
Tel.: (910) 763-2500
Web Site: http://www.sturdycorp.com
Year Founded: 1971
Sales Range: $1-9.9 Million
Emp.: 250
Provider of Motor Vehicle Services
N.A.I.C.S.: 336310

David R. Sturdy *(Pres)*
Tony Whitley *(VP)*
George Cafola *(Controller)*

STURDY MEMORIAL HOSPITAL
211 Park St, Attleboro, MA 02703-0963
Tel.: (508) 222-5200
Web Site:
http://www.sturdymemorial.org
Year Founded: 1913
Sales Range: $150-199.9 Million
Emp.: 1,639
Health Care Srvices
N.A.I.C.S.: 622110
Brian Kelly *(VP)*
Joseph Casey *(Interim Pres & Interim CEO)*
Marita Prater *(VP-Patient Svcs)*
Amy Pfeffer *(CFO & Treas)*

STURDY OIL COMPANY
1511 Abbott St, Salinas, CA 93901
Tel.: (831) 422-8801
Web Site: http://www.sturdyoil.com
Year Founded: 1933
Sales Range: $25-49.9 Million
Petroleum Products Mfr & Distr
N.A.I.C.S.: 424720
Jon Fanoe *(Pres)*
Keith Schwehr *(CFO)*
Neil Fanoe *(VP & Mgr-Retail)*
Berlette Stephens *(Mgr-Credit & HR)*
Don Smith *(Mgr-Fleet)*

STURDY SAVINGS BANK
506 Rte 9, Cape May Court House, NJ 08210
Tel.: (609) 463-5206
Web Site:
http://www.sturdyonline.com
Year Founded: 1922
Sales Range: $10-24.9 Million
Emp.: 100
Savings Bank
N.A.I.C.S.: 522180
Gerald L. Reeves *(Bd of Dirs, Executives)*
Kathryn M. Steiger *(VP & Mgr-Residential & Consumer Lending)*
Danette McDevitt *(Chief Risk Officer & Sr VP)*
James Fisher *(Chm)*
Gregory M. Matuson *(Pres & CEO)*

STURGEON & BECK INC.
350 S L St, Tulare, CA 93274
Tel.: (559) 686-2811
Web Site:
http://www.sturgeonandbeck.com
Sales Range: $10-24.9 Million
Emp.: 34
New & Used Car Dealers
N.A.I.C.S.: 441110
Don Beck *(VP)*

STURGEON & SON INCORPORATED
3511 Gilmore Ave, Bakersfield, CA 93308
Tel.: (661) 322-4408
Web Site:
http://www.sturgeonandson.com
Rev.: $17,000,000
Emp.: 70
Excavation Work
N.A.I.C.S.: 238910
Stella Hernandance *(Mgr-HR)*

STURGIS MOTORCYCLE INC.
2820 Harley Dr, Rapid City, SD 57702
Tel.: (605) 342-9362
Web Site:
http://www.blackhillshd.com

Sales Range: $10-24.9 Million
Emp.: 50
Motorcycle Dealers
N.A.I.C.S.: 441227
Aloysius Rieman *(Pres)*

STURMAN & LARKIN FORD INC.
900 Regis Ave, Pittsburgh, PA 15236
Tel.: (412) 653-5800
Web Site:
http://www.sturmanlarkin.com
Year Founded: 1978
Sales Range: $10-24.9 Million
Emp.: 65
Car Whslr
N.A.I.C.S.: 441110
Nancy Larkin *(Pres)*

STURTEVANT AUTO PARTS INC.
7622 Van Nuys Blvd, Van Nuys, CA 91405
Tel.: (818) 782-7811
Rev.: $13,400,000
Automotive Supplies & Parts
N.A.I.C.S.: 423120

STURTEVANT INC.
348 Circuit St, Hanover, MA 02339-2143
Tel.: (781) 829-6501
Web Site:
http://www.sturtevantinc.com
Year Founded: 1883
Sales Range: $50-74.9 Million
Emp.: 30
Materials Processing Equipment Mfr
N.A.I.C.S.: 333248
Kathleen Leary *(Mgr-Pur)*
Richard Robatzek *(Product Mgr)*
Chris Meadows *(VP-Sls & Mktg)*
William Sturtevant English Jr. *(Pres & CEO)*

STV GROUP, INC.
205 W Welsh Dr, Douglassville, PA 19518-8713
Tel.: (610) 385-8200   PA
Web Site: http://www.stvinc.com
Year Founded: 1912
Sales Range: $25-49.9 Million
Emp.: 1,000
Engineering, Architectural Consulting, Planning & Environmental & Construction Management
N.A.I.C.S.: 541330
Debra B. Trace *(Dir-Corp Comm)*
Dominick M. Servedio *(Chm)*
Steve Pressler *(COO & Exec VP-Construction Mgmt Div)*
Milo E. Riverso *(Pres & CEO)*
Thomas Butcher *(CFO)*
Gerald Donnelly *(Exec VP-STV Energy Svcs)*
William F. Matts *(COO-Transportation & Infrastructure & Exec VP)*
Tibor Menyhert *(CIO & VP)*
Thomas Prendergast *(Chief Strategic Officer & Exec VP)*
Randall Hallman *(VP)*
Jon Miller *(Exec VP-Buildings & Facilities Div)*
Vincent Zito *(VP)*
Ron Weathers *(Sr Project Mgr-Utilities Team-Charlotte)*
Chuck Kohler *(Co-COO)*
Edward Pogreba *(Exec VP-STV Construction Mgmt Div)*
John Pryor *(Chief HR Officer & VP)*
Judith E. Held *(Gen Counsel & Sr VP)*
David Miles Ziskind *(Sr VP-Buildings & Facilities Div)*

Subsidiaries:

Al Batin Business Centre L.L.C. (1)
C6 Tower First Floor Bainuna St 34, PO Box 113100, Abu Dhabi, United Arab Emirates   **(100%)**
Tel.: (971) 2 406 9444
Engineering, Architectural, Environmental & Construction Management Services
N.A.I.C.S.: 541330
Stephen E. Cheney *(Gen Mgr)*

Diversified Project Management, Inc. (1)
1 Gateway Ctr 300 Washington St Ste 951, Newton, MA 02458
Tel.: (617) 243-3888
Web Site: http://www.dpm-inc.com
Emp.: 65
Project Management Services
N.A.I.C.S.: 541618
Bob Keeley *(Sr VP)*
Bill Clegg *(VP-Ops)*
Phil Leonard *(VP-Ops)*
Carolyn Hickey *(Dir-Bus Dev)*
Bob Margolis *(Dir-Bus Dev)*
Joy Shapiro *(Dir-Bus Dev)*

STV Architects, Inc. (1)
205 W Welsh Dr, Douglassville, PA 19518-8713   **(100%)**
Tel.: (610) 385-8200
Web Site: http://www.stvinc.com
Sales Range: $25-49.9 Million
Emp.: 250
Architectural Services
N.A.I.C.S.: 541330
R.W. Darlington *(Sr VP)*
Gary Shane *(VP)*

STV Energy Services (1)
205 W Welsh Dr, Douglassville, PA 19518-8713   **(100%)**
Tel.: (610) 385-8200
Web Site: http://www.stvinc.com
Sales Range: $50-74.9 Million
Emp.: 325
Engineering, Architectural & Construction Management Services
N.A.I.C.S.: 541330
Gerald Donnelly *(Exec VP)*

STV Inc (1)
800 5th Ave Ste 4100, Seattle, WA 98104-3100
Tel.: (206) 447-1313
Web Site: http://www.stvinc.com
Construction Management & Architectural Services
N.A.I.C.S.: 541310
David L. Borger *(Sr VP)*
Randall S. Duncan *(VP-Construction Mgmt)*

STV Inc. (1)
1999 S Bascom Ave Suite 709, Campbell, CA 95008-2216
Tel.: (408) 879-2381
Web Site: http://www.stvinc.com
Architectural Design Services
N.A.I.C.S.: 541310
Rob Barthelman *(VP & Grp Leader-Education)*

STV Inc. (1)
114 Pacifica, Irvine, CA 92618-3608
Tel.: (949) 727-3238
Web Site: http://www.stvinc.com
Architectural Services
N.A.I.C.S.: 541310
Anthony Venturato *(VP)*

STV Inc. (1)
1055 W Seventh St Ste 3150, Los Angeles, CA 90017-2556
Tel.: (213) 482-9444
Web Site: http://www.stvinc.com
Emp.: 50
Architectural & Design Services
N.A.I.C.S.: 541310
Samuel Yu *(VP & Mgr-Western Territory)*
Tyler Bonstead *(VP)*

STV Inc. (1)
9130 Anaheim Pl Ste 210, Rancho Cucamonga, CA 91730-8540
Tel.: (909) 484-0660
Web Site: http://www.stvinc.com
Architectural & Design Services
N.A.I.C.S.: 541310
David L. Borger *(Sr VP)*

STV Inc. (1)
915 Highland Point Dr Ste 234, Roseville, CA 95678-5421
Tel.: (916) 724-5241
Web Site: http://www.stvinc.com
Architectural & Design Services
N.A.I.C.S.: 541310
Aaron Silver *(VP)*

STV Inc. (1)
1400 16th St Suite 400, Denver, CO 80202-5995
Tel.: (720) 932-8291
Web Site: http://www.stvinc.com
Architectural Services
N.A.I.C.S.: 541310
James E. Sampson *(VP)*

STV Inc. (1)
185 Plains Rd Ste 208E, Milford, CT 06461
Tel.: (203) 375-0521
Web Site: http://www.stvinc.com
Emp.: 33
Architectural & Design Services
N.A.I.C.S.: 541310
James E. Sherwonit *(VP)*

STV Inc. (1)
1400 I St NW Suite 1100, Washington, DC 20005-6529
Tel.: (202) 688-2190
Web Site: http://www.stvinc.com
Architectural Services
N.A.I.C.S.: 541310
Thomas S. Flournoy *(VP)*

STV Inc. (1)
200 W Monroe St Ste 1650, Chicago, IL 60606-5015
Tel.: (312) 553-0655
Web Site: http://www.stvinc.com
Architectural Services
N.A.I.C.S.: 541310
Jan Turner *(VP & Mgr-Midwest)*

STV Inc. (1)
1 Financial Ctr 3rd Fl, Boston, MA 02111-2621   **(100%)**
Tel.: (617) 482-7298
Web Site: http://www.stvinc.com
Emp.: 90
Architectural Services
N.A.I.C.S.: 541310
Mark W. Pelletier *(VP)*

STV Inc. (1)
320 Congress St 4th Fl, Boston, MA 02210-1250
Tel.: (617) 292-3363
Web Site: http://www.stvinc.com
Emp.: 85
Transportation & Infrastructure Engineering Services
N.A.I.C.S.: 237990
Scott A. Krieger *(VP)*

STV Inc. (1)
7125 Ambassador Rd Ste 200, Baltimore, MD 21244-2727
Tel.: (410) 944-9112
Web Site: http://www.stvinc.com
Architectural, Facility Management, Transportation & Infrastructure
N.A.I.C.S.: 541310
Timothy J. Mason *(VP)*
Joel Oppenheimer *(Sr VP)*
Charles B. Belser *(VP-Transportation Facilities)*
Donald Harris *(VP)*
Anthony J. Corteal Jr. *(Sr VP)*

STV Inc. (1)
1600 Perimeter Park Dr Ste 225, Morrisville, NC 27560-8414
Tel.: (919) 238-6672
Web Site: http://www.stvinc.com
Architectural Services
N.A.I.C.S.: 541310
Brian K. Lusk *(VP)*

STV Inc. (1)
1020 Atlantic Ave, Atlantic City, NJ 08401-7427
Tel.: (609) 344-1110
Web Site: http://www.stvinc.com
Transportation & Infrastructure Services
N.A.I.C.S.: 541310
Robert P. Gross *(VP)*

STV Inc. (1)
1037 Raymond Blvd Ste 200, Newark, NJ 07102-5425
Tel.: (973) 642-2201
Web Site: http://www.stvinc.com
Architectural Infrastructure & Engineering Services
N.A.I.C.S.: 237990

STV Inc. (1)
1009 Lenox Dr Ste 102A, Lawrenceville, NJ 08648
Tel.: (609) 530-0300
Web Site: http://www.stvinc.com
Transportation, Infrastructure, Construction Engineering & Management & Inspection Services
N.A.I.C.S.: 237990
Richard M. Amodei *(Sr VP)*

STV Inc. (1)
1920 Yonge St Suite 200 Office 220, Toronto, M4S 3E6, ON, Canada
Tel.: (416) 572-7687
Web Site: http://www.stvinc.com
Transportation & Engineering Services
N.A.I.C.S.: 541330

STV Inc. (1)
2000 Linglestown Rd Suite 201, Harrisburg, PA 17110-9347
Tel.: (717) 545-2103
Web Site: http://www.stvinc.com
Architectural & Structural Engineering Services
N.A.I.C.S.: 541310
Leonard R. Smith Jr. *(VP)*

STV Inc. (1)
1818 Market St Suite 1410, Philadelphia, PA 19103-3616
Tel.: (215) 832-3500
Web Site: http://www.stvinc.com
Construction Management, Transportation & Infrastructure Services
N.A.I.C.S.: 237310
Sunit V. Patel *(VP-Buildings & Facilities)*
Christopher J. Holliday *(Sr VP-Transportation & Infrastructure)*
Timothy J. Mason *(VP-Construction Mgmt)*

STV Inc. (1)
444 Liberty Ave Ste 800, Pittsburgh, PA 15222-1226
Tel.: (412) 392-3500
Web Site: http://www.stvinc.com
Architectural & Engineering Services
N.A.I.C.S.: 541310
Jeffrey A. Sestokas *(VP)*

STV Inc. (1)
2040 Linglestown Rd Ste 104, Harrisburg, PA 17110-9568
Tel.: (717) 409-7090
Web Site: http://www.stvinc.com
Energy & Business Development Services
N.A.I.C.S.: 561499

STV Inc. (1)
1320 Main St Suite 300, Columbia, SC 29201-3204
Tel.: (803) 724-1430
Web Site: http://www.stvinc.com
Architectural & Infrastructure Services
N.A.I.C.S.: 541310
Robert Dubnicka *(VP)*

STV Inc. (1)
10370 Richmond Ave Ste 850, Houston, TX 77042-4138
Tel.: (713) 651-0555
Web Site: http://www.stvinc.com
Emp.: 24
Energy & Business Development Services
N.A.I.C.S.: 561499

STV Inc. (1)
2722 Merrilee Dr Ste 350, Fairfax, VA 22031-4427
Tel.: (571) 633-2220
Web Site: http://www.stvinc.com
Buildings, Facilities, Transportation & Infrastructure
N.A.I.C.S.: 561210
Sandra A. Gitlin *(VP-Buildings & Facilities)*
Thomas S. Flournoy *(VP)*

STV Inc. (1)
448 Viking Dr Suite 200, Virginia Beach, VA 23452-7377
Tel.: (745) 790-5662
Web Site: http://www.stvinc.com

STV GROUP, INC.

STV Group, Inc.—(Continued)
Architectural, Energy & Construction Management Services
N.A.I.C.S.: 236210

STV Inc/Ralph Whitehead Associates (1)
6303 Blue Lagoon Dr Suite 400, Miami, FL 33126-6040
Tel.: (305) 537-4673
Web Site: http://www.stvinc.com
Architectural & Design Services
N.A.I.C.S.: 541310
Jorge Leon (Gen Mgr)

STV, Inc. (1)
225 Park Ave S, New York, NY 10003-1604 **(100%)**
Tel.: (212) 777-4400
Web Site: http://www.stvinc.com
Sales Range: $75-99.9 Million
Emp.: 500
Engineering Architectural Planning Environmental & Construction Management Services
N.A.I.C.S.: 541310
Dominick M. Servedio (Chm)
Linda Rosenberg (Sr VP-Mktg & Comm)
Milo E. Riverso (Pres & CEO)
Thomas W. Butcher (CFO)
Tibor D. Menyhert (CIO & VP)
Martin F. Boyle (Exec VP-Transportation & Infrastructure Div)
Sonja Glatzhofer (Chief HR Officer & VP)
David Kiwinski (Chief Health & Safety Officer & VP)
Frank J. Greene (VP)

Subsidiary (Domestic):

STV Construction Services, Inc. (2)
205 W Welsh Dr, Douglassville, PA 19518-8713 **(100%)**
Tel.: (610) 385-8200
Web Site: http://www.stvinc.com
Sales Range: $25-49.9 Million
Emp.: 250
Construction Management Services
N.A.I.C.S.: 541310
Brian J. Flaherty (Sr VP & Head-Transportation & Infrastructure)
Timothy Mason (VP)
James Vilbert (Gen Mgr)
Thomas Butcher (CFO)
Paul McIlree (VP-Transportation & Infrastructure-Florida)

STV Environmental, Inc. (2)
205 W Welsh Dr, Douglassville, PA 19518-8713 **(100%)**
Tel.: (610) 385-8200
Web Site: http://www.stvinc.com
Sales Range: $25-49.9 Million
Emp.: 28
Environmental Investigations & Engineering
N.A.I.C.S.: 541330

STV/GWD (1)
1421 S 12th St, Bismarck, ND 58504-6638
Tel.: (701) 258-6844
Web Site: http://www.stvinc.com
Design & Field Services
N.A.I.C.S.: 541490
Chris Anderson (Mgr-Field Svcs)

STV/GWD Inc (1)
621 17th St Ste 1200, Denver, CO 80293-2004
Tel.: (303) 951-9300
Web Site: http://www.stvinc.com
Emp.: 90
Architectural Services
N.A.I.C.S.: 541310
Gary W. Doven (Sr VP)

STV/Ralph Whitehead Associates (1)
5200 Belfort Rd Suite 400, Jacksonville, FL 32256-6054
Tel.: (904) 730-9777
Web Site: http://www.stvinc.com
Architectural & Design Services
N.A.I.C.S.: 541310
David C. Shearer (Grp Leader-Transportation)
John Erwin (Grp Leader-Rail)

STV/Ralph Whitehead Associates (1)
111 N Orange Ave Suite 710, Orlando, FL 32801-2323
Tel.: (321) 418-6604
Web Site: http://www.stvinc.com
Architectural & Design Services
N.A.I.C.S.: 541310
Tony L. Melton (VP)

STV/Ralph Whitehead Associates (1)
1201 Peachtree St NE Ste 1550, Atlanta, GA 30361
Tel.: (678) 735-7650
Web Site: http://www.stvinc.com
Emp.: 12
Architectural Design Services
N.A.I.C.S.: 541310
Doug Bess (VP)
Milo Riverso (Pres)

STV/Ralph Whitehead Associates (1)
6701 W 64th St Suite 320, Mission, KS 66202
Tel.: (913) 213-5110
Web Site: http://www.stvinc.com
Architectural, Transportation & Rail Design Services
N.A.I.C.S.: 541310
David A. Magistro (Grp Leader-Rail)

STV/Ralph Whitehead Associates (1)
2430 Mall Dr Ste 315 Bldg B, North Charleston, SC 29406-6552
Tel.: (843) 207-2020
Web Site: http://www.stvinc.com
Emp.: 10
Architectural, Energy & Infrastructure Services
N.A.I.C.S.: 541330
Dan P. Moses (Grp Leader-Transportation)

STV/Ralph Whitehead Associates (1)
454 S Anderson Rd Suite 3 BTC 517, Rock Hill, SC 29730-3392
Tel.: (803) 980-4970
Web Site: http://www.stvinc.com
Emp.: 10
Infrastructure, Transportation & Energy Services
N.A.I.C.S.: 541330
Richard Capps Jr. (VP)

STV/Ralph Whitehead Associates (1)
10800 Midlothian Turnpike Ste 302, Richmond, VA 23235-4700
Tel.: (804) 794-1185
Web Site: http://www.stvinc.com
Energy Services
N.A.I.C.S.: 541310
Ronald C. Briggs (Grp Leader-Transportation)

VBN Corp. (1)
560 14th St Ste 400, Oakland, CA 94612-1454
Tel.: (510) 763-1313
Web Site: http://www.vbnarch.com
Architectural Services
N.A.I.C.S.: 541310
Rob Barthelman (VP)

Subsidiary (Non-US):

VBN China - Beijing (2)
Jia 17 North Andeli Street Yiwanlida Building 3rd Floor, 100011, Beijing, Dongcheng, China **(100%)**
Tel.: (86) 1300 10 1610
Web Site: http://www.vbnarch.com
Architectural & Design Services
N.A.I.C.S.: 541310

STYKEMAIN BUICK GMC, LTD.
25124 Elliott Rd, Defiance, OH 43512-9003
Tel.: (419) 784-5252
Web Site: http://www.stykemain.com
Year Founded: 1998
Sales Range: $10-24.9 Million
Emp.: 100
Car Whslr
N.A.I.C.S.: 441110
Joe Stykemain (Pres)

STYLE CREST, INC.
2450 Enterprise St, Fremont, OH 43420
Tel.: (419) 332-7369
Web Site: http://www.stylecrestproducts.com
Sales Range: $25-49.9 Million
Emp.: 550
Mfr of Plastic Hardware & Building Products
N.A.I.C.S.: 326199
Tom Kern (CEO)
Michael Kern (VP-Opers)
Henry Valle (Exec VP)
Scott Miller (Mktg Mgr)

Subsidiaries:

Alumi - Cover Awning Co, Inc. (1)
604 W Mckellips Rd, Mesa, AZ 85201
Tel.: (480) 969-2286
Web Site: http://www.alumi-cover.com
Sales Range: $1-9.9 Million
Emp.: 33
Whol Roofing/Siding/Insulation Mfg Sheet Metalwork
N.A.I.C.S.: 423330
Annabel Griffin (Mgr)

Magic Mobile Homes, Inc. (1)
1915 Commercial St NE, Albuquerque, NM 87102
Tel.: (505) 831-1601
Web Site: http://www.magicmobilehomesupply.com
Motor Vehicle Supplies & New Parts Merchant Whslr
N.A.I.C.S.: 423120
Carl Ulibarri (Pres & GM)

STYLE-LINE FURNITURE INC.
116 Godfrey Rd, Verona, MS 38879
Tel.: (662) 566-1113
Web Site: http://www.styleline.us
Rev.: $22,906,049
Emp.: 206
Living Room Furniture Mfr
N.A.I.C.S.: 337121
Margie Anderson (Pres)
Harvey Bailey (VP-Sls & Mdse)

STYLESPOT, INC.
10951 W Pico Blvd Ste 404, Los Angeles, CA 90064
Tel.: (310) 441-5000
Web Site: http://www.stylespot.com
Year Founded: 2009
Online Fashion Publishing
N.A.I.C.S.: 513199
Alex Amin (Co-Founder)
Rafi Gordon (Co-Founder)

Subsidiaries:

Kaboodle, Inc. (1)
1700 S Amphlett Blvd Ste 221, San Mateo, CA 94402
Tel.: (650) 287-3700
Web Site: http://www.kaboodle.com
Shopping Forum Website Operator
N.A.I.C.S.: 513199
Keiron McCammon (Co-Founder & CTO)
Steven Chien (CMO)
Robert Carter (VP-Product)
Saro Hamamah (Dir-Data Analytics)
Jeff Brown (Pres)

STYLEWEST
561 Kinetic Dr Unit B, Oxnard, CA 93030
Tel.: (805) 485-5334
Web Site: http://www.stylewest.net
Year Founded: 2002
Rev.: $12,800,000
Emp.: 45
Consumer Products & Services
N.A.I.C.S.: 532289
David Sengstaken (Pres)
Robert Angstadt (Dir-Ops)
Vanessa Sandoval (Controller)

STYLINE INDUSTRIES INC.

U.S. PRIVATE

1204 E 6th St, Huntingburg, IN 47542
Tel.: (812) 683-4848   **IN**
Web Site: http://www.ofs.styline.com
Year Founded: 1954
Sales Range: $75-99.9 Million
Emp.: 1,400
Sales of Wood Office Furniture
N.A.I.C.S.: 337211
Robert Menke Jr. (Pres)

Subsidiaries:

Styline Brokerage Service Inc. (1)
1008 Styline Dr, Huntingburg, IN 47542
Tel.: (812) 683-4848
Web Site: http://www.ofs.com
Sales Range: $10-24.9 Million
Emp.: 3
Provider of Freight Transportation Arrangement Services
N.A.I.C.S.: 488510

Styline Diesel Service Center Inc. (1)
1008 Styline Dr, Huntingburg, IN 47542-0100
Tel.: (812) 683-7704
Web Site: http://www.ofs.styline.com
Sales Range: $10-24.9 Million
Emp.: 40
Provider of General Automotive Repair Shop Services
N.A.I.C.S.: 811111
Dan Knable (Gen Mgr)

Styline Transportation Inc. (1)
1008 Styline Dr, Huntingburg, IN 47542 **(100%)**
Tel.: (812) 683-4848
Web Site: http://www.styline.com
Sales Range: $25-49.9 Million
Emp.: 150
Provider of Trucking Services
N.A.I.C.S.: 484121

STYLMARK, INC.
6536 Main St NE, Fridley, MN 55432
Tel.: (800) 328-2495   **MN**
Web Site: http://www.stylmark.com
Year Founded: 1954
Designer & Mfr of Finished Fixtures & Interior Design Solutions, Including Aluminum & Steel Products, LED Lighting & Displays, Showcases, Shelving & Architectural Moldings
N.A.I.C.S.: 541410
Amber Kramer (Dir-HR)
Steve Goertz (Dir-Bus Dev)

SUAREZ CORPORATION INDUSTRIES
7800 Whipple Ave NW, Canton, OH 44720
Tel.: (330) 494-5504   **OH**
Web Site: http://www.suarez.com
Sales Range: $125-149.9 Million
Emp.: 300
Retailer of Sporting Goods, Jewelry & General Merchandise
N.A.I.C.S.: 458310
Benjamin D. Suarez (Founder & Pres)

Subsidiaries:

BioTech Medical, Inc. (1)
7800 Whipple Ave NW, Canton, OH 44767-0001
Tel.: (330) 494-5504
Web Site: http://www.biotechresearch.com
Mattress Mfr & Distr
N.A.I.C.S.: 337910

Chef Jon Molnar (1)
7800 Whipple Ave NW, Canton, OH 44767-0001
Tel.: (888) 755-4469
Web Site: http://www.chefjon.com
Restaurant Operators
N.A.I.C.S.: 722511

Endless Youth and Life LLC (1)
7800 Whipple Ave NW, North Canton, OH 44720
Tel.: (800) 870-5238

Web Site: http://www.biotechresearch.com
Emp.: 200
Beauty Supplies Retailer
N.A.I.C.S.: 456120

International Home Shopping (1)
7800 Whipple Ave NW, Canton, OH 44767-0001
Tel.: (330) 494-5504
Web Site: http://www.ihsmall.com
Emp.: 175
Home Furnishings Retailer
N.A.I.C.S.: 449129

Resource Partners Enterprises, LLC (1)
7800 Whipple Ave NW, North Canton, OH 44720
Tel.: (800) 839-0966
Web Site:
  http://www.edenpureopportunity.com
Household Appliance Whslr
N.A.I.C.S.: 423620

Suarez Manufacturing Industries (1)
334 Orchard Ave NE, North Canton, OH 44720
Tel.: (330) 526-8348
Web Site: http://www.scimanufacturing.com
Industrial Equipment Mfr
N.A.I.C.S.: 333248

SUB POP LTD.
2013 4th Ave 3rd Fl, Seattle, WA 98121
Tel.: (206) 441-8441 WA
Web Site: http://www.subpop.com
Year Founded: 1988
Sales Range: $10-24.9 Million
Emp.: 35
Independent Record Label
N.A.I.C.S.: 512250
Jonathan Poneman (Co-Founder)
Bruce Pavitt (Co-Founder)
Gareth Smith (Dir-A&R)

SUB ZERO ICE CREAM INC.
301 S 400 E, American Fork, UT 84003
Tel.: (801) 494-0960
Web Site:
  http://www.subzeroicecream.com
Year Founded: 2004
Sales Range: $1-9.9 Million
Emp.: 300
Ice Cream Store Owner & Franchisor
N.A.I.C.S.: 445298
Jerry Hancock (Co-Founder, Chm & CEO)
Naomi Hancock (Co-Founder & CFO)
Vern Hancock (Co-Founder)

SUB-ZERO FREEZER CO., INC.
4717 Hammersley Rd, Madison, WI 53711-2708
Tel.: (608) 271-2233 WI
Web Site: http://www.subzero.com
Year Founded: 1945
Sales Range: $350-399.9 Million
Emp.: 1,200
Residential Refrigeration & Wine Storage Units Mfr
N.A.I.C.S.: 335220
James Bakke (Pres & CEO)
Steve Dunlap (VP-Sls)
Ed Murphy (VP-Fin)
Michele Bedard (VP-Mktg)
Chuck Verri (VP-HR)

Subsidiaries:

Sub-Zero Wolf Southeast, Inc. (1)
9777 Satellite Blvd Ste 200, Orlando, FL 32837
Tel.: (407) 857-3777
Web Site: http://www.subzero-wolf.com
Sales Range: $10-24.9 Million
Emp.: 12
Kitchen Appliances Mfr
N.A.I.C.S.: 332215
Brendan Malloy (VP)

Wolf Appliance Co., LLC (1)
2866 Buds Dr, Fitchburg, WI 53719-5314
Tel.: (608) 271-2233
Web Site: http://www.wolfappliance.com
Sales Range: $75-99.9 Million
Mfr of Kitchen Appliances
N.A.I.C.S.: 332215

SUB-ZERO GROUP EAST LLC
2 Lambert St, Roslyn Heights, NY 11577-2074
Tel.: (516) 484-7800 NY
Web Site: http://www.subzero.com
Year Founded: 1952
Sales Range: $10-24.9 Million
Emp.: 150
Household Appliance Dealer
N.A.I.C.S.: 423620
Anthony Mazzeo (Mgr-Territory Sls)
Jeff Moore (Pres)
John Bacon (VP-Sls-New Jersey & New York)
Juan Rodriquez (Mgr-Warehouse)
Kimberly Little (Mgr-Showroom)

SUBCO FOODS, INC.
1150 Commerce Dr, West Chicago, IL 60185
Tel.: (708) 338-4488
Web Site:
  http://www.subcofoods.com
Year Founded: 1995
Sales Range: $25-49.9 Million
Emp.: 175
Food Preparations
N.A.I.C.S.: 311999
Mas Khan (Pres & CEO)

Subsidiaries:

Subco Foods of Wisconsin (1)
4350 S Taylor Dr, Sheboygan, WI 53081-8479
Tel.: (920) 457-7761
Web Site: http://www.subcofoods.com
Sales Range: $25-49.9 Million
Emp.: 39
Private Label & Contract Sugar Free Sweetner Dry Drink Mix Coffee Creamer Gelatin Pudding Mfr
N.A.I.C.S.: 311514

SUBCO INC.
653 W Fallbrook Ave Ste 101, Fresno, CA 93711-5503
Tel.: (800) 258-3350
Web Site: http://www.subco.com
Year Founded: 2004
Sales Range: $10-24.9 Million
Emp.: 40
Circulation Increase Consulting for Magazine Publishers
N.A.I.C.S.: 513120
Russell J. Rahm (Co-Founder & Principal)
Kelly Vucovich (Co-Founder & Principal)
Michael Mezzanotte (VP-Mktg)
Melanie Russell (VP-Ops)
Shirley Viel (Dir-PR)
Jonathan Eropkin (CTO)
Deborah Spaulding (VP-New Bus Dev)
Brian Knowles (Sr VP-PR)

Subsidiaries:

Periodical Publishers' Service Bureau, LLC (1)
653 W Fallbrook Ave Ste 101, Fresno, CA 93711
Tel.: (888) 206-0350
Web Site: http://www.ppsb.com
Magazine & Book Subscription, Circulation & Marketing Support Services
N.A.I.C.S.: 561499
Doug Brown (Gen Mgr-Paid During Svc Div)

SUBJEX CORPORATION
PO Box 475, Sanford, FL 32772
Tel.: (612) 382-5566 MN
Web Site: http://www.subjexcorp.com
Year Founded: 1999
Sales Range: Less than $1 Million
Software Publisher
N.A.I.C.S.: 513210
Paul W. Peterson (Dir-R&D)
Andrew Dean Hyder (Chm & CEO)
Sharon R. Hyder (CFO)

SUBLETTE COOPERATIVE INC.
500 W Lalande, Sublette, KS 67877
Tel.: (620) 675-2297
Web Site:
  http://www.sublettecoop.com
Sales Range: $10-24.9 Million
Emp.: 30
Grain Elevators
N.A.I.C.S.: 424510
Kendall Poland (CEO & Gen Mgr)

SUBLETTE ENTERPRISES INC.
1535 UU Rd, Sublette, KS 67877
Tel.: (620) 668-5501 KS
Year Founded: 1986
Sales Range: $10-24.9 Million
Emp.: 75
Cattle Supplies Distr
N.A.I.C.S.: 112112
Joe Scott (Mgr)

SUBMITTABLE HOLDINGS, INC.
Florence Bldg 111 N Higgins Ave Ste 300, Missoula, MT 59802
Tel.: (210) 513-9000
Web Site:
  http://www.submittable.com
Year Founded: 2010
Sales Range: $10-24.9 Million
Emp.: 68
Software Development Services
N.A.I.C.S.: 541511
Michael Fitzgerald (Co-Founder & CEO)
Bruce Tribbensee (Co-Founder & COO)

SUBSIDIUM HEALTHCARE, LLC
200 Corporate Blvd, Lafayette, LA 70508 GA
Web Site:
  http://www.schumacherclinical.com
Year Founded: 2015
Healthcare Professional Employment Organization
N.A.I.C.S.: 561330
William C. Schumacher (Founder & Chm)
Rich D'Amaro (CEO)
Lee White (COO)
Randy Pilgrim (Chief Medical Officer)
Thomas Dolan (CFO)
Keith Cantrell (Chief Revenue Officer)
Lissa Fry (Chief Bus Dev Officer)
Diane Broussard (Sr VP-HR)
Ryan Domengeaux (Gen Counsel)
Sarah Crass (Chief Compliance Officer)
Victoria Romero (CIO)

Subsidiaries:

The Schumacher Group of Louisiana, Inc. (1)
200 Corporate Blvd Ste 201, Lafayette, LA 70508
Tel.: (337) 237-1915
Web Site: http://www.schumachergroup.com
Sales Range: $50-74.9 Million
Emp.: 700
Holding Company; Health Care Employment Services
N.A.I.C.S.: 551112

Randy Pilgrim (Chief Medical Officer-Enterprise)
William C. Schumacher (Founder & Chm)
Douglas Menefee (CIO)
Jason Bradberry (Dir-Corp Residency Resources-Chattanooga)
Rich D'Amaro (CEO)
Lee White (COO)
Thomas Dolan (CFO)
Lisa Fry (Chief Bus Dev Officer)
Sarah Crass (Chief Compliance Officer)
Keith Cantrell (Chief Revenue Officer)
Chris Cotteleer (CTO)
Ryan Domengeaux (Gen Counsel)
Diane Broussard (Sr VP-HR)

Subsidiary (Domestic):

Medical Search Solutions, Inc. (2)
200 Corporate Blvd, Lafayette, LA 70508
Tel.: (337) 237-1915
Web Site: http://www.schumacher-group.com
Medical Help Service
N.A.I.C.S.: 561320

SUBSPLIT SERVICES GROUP, L.P.
6000 Briarcrest Ave., Memphis, TN 38120
Tel.: (901) 568-6098
Web Site: https://www.subsplitsg.com
Year Founded: 2003
Emp.: 100
Financial Services
N.A.I.C.S.: 532420
Matthew Brennan (Founder, CEO & Mng Partner)

Subsidiaries:

Miinc, LP (1)
1960 W NW Hwy, Dallas, TX 75220
Tel.: (214) 575-9600
Web Site: https://www.miinclp.com
Building Equipment Contractors
N.A.I.C.S.: 238290
William J. O'Dwyer (Pres)
Dennis Cowen (Exec VP-Ops)
Randy Bradshaw (Exec VP-Construction)
Marcia Rhoades (Office Mgr)

SUBSTANTIAL INC.
900 E Pine St Ste 202, Seattle, WA 98122
Tel.: (206) 838-0303
Web Site: http://www.substantial.com
Year Founded: 2006
Sales Range: $1-9.9 Million
Emp.: 26
Web & Mobile Applications
N.A.I.C.S.: 513210
Carey Jenkins (CEO)
Emily Griffin (Sr Mgr-Engagement)
Heather Griswold (Sr Mgr-Engagement)
Jeremy Borden (Founder)

SUBSYSTEM TECHNOLOGIES, INC.
2121 Crystal Dr Ste 680, Arlington, VA 22202
Tel.: (703) 841-0071
Web Site: http://www.subsystem.com
Engineering & Associated Technical Services
N.A.I.C.S.: 541330
Mary Ann Hoadley (VP-Bus Dev)

Subsidiaries:

KMS Solutions, LLC (1)
205 S Whiting St Ste 400, Alexandria, VA 22304-3632
Tel.: (321) 600-4905
Web Site: http://www.kmssol.com
Engineering & Associated Technical Services
N.A.I.C.S.: 541330
Bob Urso (Pres & COO)

SUBURBAN ADULT SERVICES INC.

SUBURBAN ADULT SERVICES INC.   U.S. PRIVATE

Suburban Adult Services Inc.—(Continued)
960 W Maple Ct, Elma, NY 14059
Tel.: (716) 805-1555   NY
Web Site: http://www.sasinc.org
Year Founded: 1975
Sales Range: $25-49.9 Million
Disability Assistance Services
N.A.I.C.S.: 624120
Anthony Annunziato *(Pres & CEO)*
Katie Siwek *(VP-Community Svcs)*
Camille Putnam *(VP-Program Svcs)*
Karen Vance *(Dir-Clinical Svcs)*
Patricia Watkins *(VP-HR, IT & Trng)*
Mark Balus *(Chm)*
Karen Gustina *(Exec VP-Ops & Day Svcs)*
Barbara Lamoreaux *(Exec VP-Quality & Community Svcs)*
Shawn Cunningham *(CFO & VP-Fin)*
Patrick Guerin *(VP-Claddagh Div)*
Steve Dietz *(Dir-IT)*
Sheila Dollas *(Dir-Moving Miracles)*
Lynn Kelly *(Dir-Dev)*
Dale Skoog *(Dir-Medical Svcs)*
John Bowles *(VP & Dir-Quality Assurance & Incidents)*

SUBURBAN CARTING CORPORATION
566 N State Rd, Briarcliff Manor, NY 10510
Tel.: (914) 698-4300   NY
Web Site: http://www.suburbancarting.com
Year Founded: 1950
Garbage Collection & Transportation Services
N.A.I.C.S.: 562111
Joseph Orlando *(VP)*

SUBURBAN LAWN & GARDEN INC.
13635 Wyandotte, Kansas City, MO 64145
Tel.: (816) 941-4700
Web Site: http://www.suburbanlg.com
Rev.: $14,500,000
Emp.: 325
Nursery & Tree Production
N.A.I.C.S.: 111421
William N. Stueck *(Pres)*
Martha L. Stueck *(Treas & Sec)*

SUBURBAN MORTGAGE INC.
7500 N Dreamydraw Dr Ste 110, Phoenix, AZ 85020
Tel.: (602) 942-7777
Web Site: http://www.submort.com
Rev.: $12,000,000
Emp.: 50
Mortgage Banker
N.A.I.C.S.: 522292
Tom Reid *(Owner)*
Heidi Ferraro *(VP & Branch Mgr)*
Matt Kelchner *(Mgr-Consumer Direct)*

SUBURBAN MOTORS COMPANY, LLC
1795 Maplelawn Dr, Troy, MI 48084
Tel.: (248) 458-2000   MI
Web Site: http://www.suburbancollection.com
Year Founded: 1950
Holding Company; New & Used Car Dealerships Owner & Operator
N.A.I.C.S.: 551112
David T. Fischer *(Chm & CEO)*
Dan Wiebelhaus *(Dir-eCommerce)*

Subsidiaries:

Farmington Hills Automotive, LLC   (1)
35200 Grand River Ave, Farmington Hills, MI 48335-3208
Tel.: (248) 699-7100

Web Site: http://www.suburbantoyotaoffarminghonhills.com
Sales Range: $10-24.9 Million
New & Used Car Dealer
N.A.I.C.S.: 441110
Jeff Kessler *(Gen Mgr)*

Suburban Ann Arbor, LLC   (1)
3515 Jackson Rd, Ann Arbor, MI 48103
Tel.: (734) 663-3321
Web Site: http://www.suburbanchevroletannarbor.com
Sales Range: $10-24.9 Million
New & Used Car Dealer
N.A.I.C.S.: 441110
David T. Fischer *(Chm & CEO)*

Suburban Chrysler Jeep Dodge, Inc.   (1)
38123 W Tenmile Rd, Farmington Hills, MI 48335
Tel.: (248) 476-7900
Web Site: http://www.suburban-mi.fivestardealers.com
Automobiles, New & Used
N.A.I.C.S.: 441110
David T. Fischer *(Owner)*

Suburban Ford of Ferndale, LLC   (1)
21600 Woodward Ave, Ferndale, MI 48220
Tel.: (248) 399-1000
Web Site: http://www.suburbanford.com
New & Used Car Dealer
N.A.I.C.S.: 441110
Michael Maceachern *(Sls Mgr-New Vehicle)*
Brad Rummer *(Sls Mgr-Pre-Owned)*

Suburban Haggerty Imported Cars, LLC   (1)
25100 Haggerty Rd, Farmington Hills, MI 48335
Tel.: (248) 471-9200
Web Site: http://www.suburbancollection.com
Sales Range: $10-24.9 Million
Emp.: 45
New & Used Car Dealer
N.A.I.C.S.: 441110

Suburban Imports of Troy, Inc.   (1)
1800 Maplelawn Dr, Troy, MI 48084
Tel.: (248) 649-2300
Web Site: http://www.suburbannissanoftroy.com
Sales Range: $10-24.9 Million
Non-Durable Goods Whslr
N.A.I.C.S.: 424990

Suburban of West Michigan, LLC   (1)
2700 29th St SE, Grand Rapids, MI 49512
Tel.: (616) 949-6555
Sales Range: $50-74.9 Million
New & Used Car Dealer
N.A.I.C.S.: 441110

SUBURBAN NATURAL GAS COMPANY
211 E Frnt St, Cygnet, OH 43413
Tel.: (419) 655-2345
Web Site: http://www.sngco.com
Sales Range: $25-49.9 Million
Emp.: 20
Natural Gas Distribution
N.A.I.C.S.: 221210
Andrew Solderman *(Pres)*

SUBURBAN PLASTICS CO
340 Renner Dr, Elgin, IL 60123
Tel.: (847) 741-4900
Web Site: http://www.suburbanplastics.com
Rev.: $37,400,000
Emp.: 325
Injection Molding Of Plastics
N.A.I.C.S.: 326199
W. Stuart Baxter *(Pres)*
Rick Baxter *(VP)*

SUBURBAN STEEL SUPPLY CO.
1900 Deffenbough Ct, Gahanna, OH 43230
Tel.: (614) 737-5501

Web Site: http://www.suburbansteelsupply.com
Sales Range: $10-24.9 Million
Emp.: 75
Steel Product Distr
N.A.I.C.S.: 331110
Chuck Obscur *(Mgr-Compliance & Facilities)*

SUBURBAN SURGICAL CO.
275 12th St, Wheeling, IL 60090
Tel.: (847) 537-9320
Web Site: http://www.suburbansurgical.com
Sales Range: $10-24.9 Million
Emp.: 100
Surgical Wire Cages Mfr & Distr
N.A.I.C.S.: 339112
James Pinkerman *(Pres)*

SUBURBAN TIRE COMPANY
755 North Ave, Glendale Heights, IL 60139
Tel.: (630) 790-1600
Web Site: http://www.suburbantire.com
Sales Range: $10-24.9 Million
Emp.: 25
Automotive Tires
N.A.I.C.S.: 441340
Steve Leffler *(Pres & Co-Owner)*
Gordon Leffler *(Gen Mgr & Co-Owner)*

SUBY, VON HADEN & ASSOCIATES, S.C.
1221 John Q Hammons Dr, Madison, WI 53717
Tel.: (608) 831-8181
Web Site: http://www.sva.com
Sales Range: $10-24.9 Million
Emp.: 400
Accounting, Business Consulting & Tax Planning & Preparation Services
N.A.I.C.S.: 541211
Karen M. Gallina *(Dir-Individual Taxation Svcs & Principal)*
John A. Baltes *(Dir-Info Svcs)*

SUBZERO CONSTRUCTORS, INC.
30055 Comercio, Rancho Santa Margarita, CA 92688
Tel.: (949) 216-9500
Web Site: http://www.szero.com
Year Founded: 1997
Emp.: 100
Designer & Mfr of Industrial Refrigeration Facilities
N.A.I.C.S.: 238220
Dean G. Soll *(Founder)*
Larry Gilliland *(Dir-Engrg-Industrial Refrigeration)*
Romil Angcaco *(Project Mgr-Industrial Refrigeration)*
James Y. Chao *(VP-Industrial Refrigeration)*

SUCCEED CORPORATION
908 W Chandler Blvd Ste D, Chandler, AZ 85225-2551
Tel.: (480) 899-8200
Year Founded: 2001
Sales Range: $100-124.9 Million
Emp.: 150
Web Site Building Tools for Online Small Businesses
N.A.I.C.S.: 513199
Omar Sayed *(Founder, Pres & CEO)*

SUCCESS 4 KIDS & FAMILIES, INC.
2902 N Armenia Ave Ste 200, Tampa, FL 33607
Tel.: (813) 490-5490
Web Site: http://www.s4kf.org

Sales Range: $1-9.9 Million
Emp.: 86
Family Services
N.A.I.C.S.: 624190
Clara Reynolds *(Exec Dir)*
John Mayo *(Deputy Exec Dir)*
Pam Jeffre *(Exec Dir)*
Michael Parks *(Dir-HR)*

SUCCESS ADVERTISING
26 Eastmans Rd, Parsippany, NJ 07054
Tel.: (973) 992-7800   NJ
Web Site: http://www.successcomgroup.com
Year Founded: 1961
Sales Range: $50-74.9 Million
Emp.: 50
Advertising Services
N.A.I.C.S.: 541810
Glenn Gershaw *(Pres & COO)*
Tom Marguccio *(VP & Dir-Creative)*
Dan Baczyk *(VP & Supvr-Mgmt)*
Michael Cherenson *(Exec VP)*
Kurt Praschak *(VP-PR)*
Elissa Jannicelli *(Dir-Client Svcs)*
Ian Hungate *(Dir-Art)*
Joanne Scala *(Dir-New Bus Dev)*
Jonathan Friedman *(VP)*
Keithan Jones *(Dir-Art)*
Lori Kantor *(Dir-New Bus Dev)*
Russ Zaborowski *(Assoc Dir-Creative)*
Vittoria Serino *(Mgr-Credit & Acct Coord)*

Subsidiaries:

Success Advertising   (1)
26 Eastmans Rd, Parsippany, NJ 07054-3703
Tel.: (212) 244-8811
Sales Range: $10-24.9 Million
Emp.: 7
Advertising Services
N.A.I.C.S.: 541810
Denise Davenport *(Office Mgr)*

Success Advertising   (1)
1661 Worcester Rd Ste 102, Framingham, MA 01701
Tel.: (508) 875-9767
Web Site: http://www.successcomgroup.com
Sales Range: $10-24.9 Million
Emp.: 7
Advertising Services
N.A.I.C.S.: 541810

Success Advertising   (1)
4000 N 3rd St Ste 430, Phoenix, AZ 85012
Tel.: (602) 264-7777
Advertising Services
N.A.I.C.S.: 541810

Success Advertising   (1)
1545 Hotel Circle S Ste 145, San Diego, CA 92108
Tel.: (619) 299-3858
Advertising Services
N.A.I.C.S.: 541810
Keithan Jones *(Dir-Art)*

Success Advertising   (1)
609 Deep Valley Dr Ste 200, Rolling Hills Estates, CA 90274
Tel.: (310) 265-9038
Advertising Services
N.A.I.C.S.: 541810

Success Communications Group   (1)
26 Eastmans Rd, Parsippany, NJ 07054
Tel.: (973) 535-9300
Web Site: http://www.successcomgroup.com
Rev.: $30,000,000
Emp.: 40
Advertising Services
N.A.I.C.S.: 541810
Kurt Schwartz *(Co-Pres)*
Kurt Praschak *(VP-PR)*
Glenn Gershaw *(Co-Pres)*
Michele Beere *(VP-Ops-West Coast)*
Tina Davis *(VP-Acct Svcs)*
Jonathan Friedman *(VP)*
Mike Gatta *(VP-Natl Dev)*
Tom Marguccio *(VP & Dir-Creative)*
Russ Zaborowski *(Assoc Dir-Creative)*
Donna Zolla *(Dir-Acct)*

COMPANIES

SUCCESS TRADE, INC.
1900 L St NW Ste 301, Washington, DC 20036-5019
Tel.: (202) 466-6890
Web Site: http://www.successtrade.com
Sales Range: $1-9.9 Million
Emp.: 9
Online Brokerage Services
N.A.I.C.S.: 551112
Fuad Ahmed *(Pres & CEO)*

Subsidiaries:

Success Trade Securities, Inc. (1)
1900 L St Nw Ste 301, Washington, DC 20036-5019
Tel.: (202) 466-6890
Provider of Online Securities Brokerage
N.A.I.C.S.: 551112

SUCCESSION CAPITAL PARTNERS
635 Maltby Ave, Norfolk, VA 23504
Tel.: (800) 910-1363
Web Site: http://www.successioncp.com
Year Founded: 2009
Privater Equity Firm
N.A.I.C.S.: 523999
Jack Anthony *(Partner)*
Steve Frey *(Partner)*
Jeannine Peregrine *(Dir-IR)*
Matt Malone *(Mng Partner)*

SUCCESSION RESOURCE GROUP, INC.
4800 Meadows Rd Ste 470, Lake Oswego, OR 97035
Tel.: (503) 427-9910
Web Site: http://www.successionresource.com
Year Founded: 2012
Sales Range: $1-9.9 Million
Emp.: 50
Financial Services
N.A.I.C.S.: 523999
Nicole Sinclair *(Mgr-Bus Dev)*
David Kuo-Hsuan Pan *(Mgr-Mktg & Brand)*
Christopher Choate *(Mgr-Multimedia)*
Anden Leesley *(Mgr-UX Product Design)*
David Grau Jr. *(Founder & CEO)*

SUDACO INC.
2837 Cattlemen Rd, Sarasota, FL 34232
Tel.: (941) 379-7872
Web Site: http://www.sudaco.com
Sales Range: $10-24.9 Million
Emp.: 30
Physician Billing & Electronic Health Records Services
N.A.I.C.S.: 541219
Susan Coles *(Founder & Pres)*

SUDDEN IMPACT MARKETING INC.
653 McCorkle Blvd Ste J, Westerville, OH 43082
Tel.: (614) 942-0906
Web Site: http://www.simarketing.net
Sales Range: $1-9.9 Million
Emp.: 21
Marketing Research
N.A.I.C.S.: 541910
Craig Conrad *(Pres)*
Jenny Poderys *(Acct Mgr)*

SUDDENLY SLENDER INTERNATIONAL, INC.
1620 N Hercules Ste G, Clearwater, FL 33765
Tel.: (727) 298-0808
Web Site: http://www.suddenlyslenderinc.com
Sales Range: $1-9.9 Million
Emp.: 20
Body-Wrap Salons
N.A.I.C.S.: 812112
Victoria Morton *(Pres)*

SUE & SAM CO. INC.
720 39th St, Brooklyn, NY 11223
Tel.: (718) 436-1672   NY
Year Founded: 1962
Sales Range: $1-9.9 Million
Emp.: 30
Girls', Children's & Infants' Shirts Mfr
N.A.I.C.S.: 315250
Louis Glueck *(Pres)*

SUES, YOUNG & BROWN INC.
5151 Commerce Dr, Baldwin Park, CA 91706-1451
Tel.: (626) 338-3800   CA
Web Site: http://www.sybinc.com
Year Founded: 1944
Sales Range: $10-24.9 Million
Emp.: 30
Retailer of Electrical Appliances
N.A.I.C.S.: 423620
Bob Woods *(Pres)*

SUFFIELD POULTRY INC.
90 Avocado St, Springfield, MA 01104
Tel.: (413) 737-8392
Web Site: http://www.royalharv.com
Processed Poultry & Meat Items
N.A.I.C.S.: 311615
James Vallides *(Pres)*

SUFFOLK CONSTRUCTION COMPANY, INC.
65 Allerton St, Boston, MA 02119-2901
Tel.: (617) 445-3500   MA
Web Site: http://www.suffolk.com
Year Founded: 1982
Sales Range: $1-4.9 Billion
Emp.: 401
General Contracting, Construction Management, Preconstruction & Design Services
N.A.I.C.S.: 236220
John F. Fish *(Founder, Chm & CEO)*
Angus Leary *(COO-Natl)*
Mark Dinapoli *(Gen Mgr-Northern California)*
John Planz *(VP-Ops)*
Jeff Gouveia *(Pres & Gen Mgr-Northeast)*
Jim Grossmann *(Dir-Construction Ops-Natl)*
Josh Christensen *(COO-Southeast Gulf Coast)*
Pete Tuffo *(Pres-Southeast)*
Rob Cruden *(VP-Ops)*
Linda Dorcena Forry *(VP-Diversity, Inclusion & Community Rels-Northeast)*
Puneet Mahajan *(CFO)*
Jay Tangney *(Gen Counsel & Exec VP)*
David Loomes *(Exec VP-Bus Dev)*
Tom Pernsteiner *(Exec VP)*
Alex Hall *(Exec VP-Bus Sys)*
Chris Mayer *(CIO & Exec VP)*
Dennis Berger *(Chief Culture Officer)*
Jit Kee Chin *(CTO & Exec VP)*
John Fall *(CFO-Southeast)*
Max Reed *(VP-Accelerated Talent Dev)*
Zach Hammond *(Gen Mgr-San Diego)*
Jennifer McCarthy *(Dir-Strategic Client Dev-San Diego)*
Mark Fulco *(VP-Bus Dev-Healthcare-Northeast)*
Ann Klee *(Exec VP)*
John B. Hood *(VP-Dallas)*
Mark Penny *(Gen Mgr-Dallas)*
Karri Novak *(VP-Project Dev-West)*
Tony Rango *(Pres-West)*
Ken Summers *(Gen Mgr-Los Angeles)*
Joshua Englander *(Sr Dir-External Affairs-West)*
Suzanne Roeder *(Chief Growth Officer)*

Subsidiaries:

Suffolk-Roel (1)
1615 Murray Canyon Rd Ste 1000, San Diego, CA 92108
Tel.: (619) 297-4156
Web Site: http://www.suffolkconstruction.com
Sales Range: $25-49.9 Million
Emp.: 260
Commercial Building Construction & General Contracting Services
N.A.I.C.S.: 236220
Wayne Hickey *(Gen Mgr)*
Matthew Gillespie *(Coord-Estimating)*
Steve Bastian *(Superintendent)*

SUFFOLK JEWELERS INC.
1888 Washington St, Boston, MA 02118-3211
Tel.: (617) 445-5087
Web Site: http://www.suffolkpawn.com
Year Founded: 1907
Used Merchandise Stores
N.A.I.C.S.: 459510
Edward D. Bean *(Pres)*

SUFFOLK REGIONAL OFF-TRACK BETTING
5 Davids Dr, Hauppauge, NY 11788
Tel.: (631) 853-1000
Web Site: http://www.suffolkotb.com
Year Founded: 1974
Sales Range: $10-24.9 Million
Emp.: 50
Off-Track Betting
N.A.I.C.S.: 713290
Herbert Hemendinger *(Vice Chm)*
Dominick P. Feeney *(Chm)*

SUGAR CANE GROWERS CO-OPERATIVE OF FLORIDA
1500 W Sugar House Rd, Belle Glade, FL 33430
Tel.: (561) 996-5556   FL
Web Site: http://www.scgc.org
Year Founded: 1960
Sales Range: $200-249.9 Million
Emp.: 900
Provider Of Agricultural Services
N.A.I.C.S.: 311314
George H. Wedgworth *(Founder & Chm)*
Jose F. Alvarez *(COO & Gen Mgr)*
Brent Woodham *(VP-HR)*
Matthew B. Hoffman *(VP-Mktg & Bus Dev)*
C. David Goodlett *(Sr VP-Govt & Grower Rels)*
James M. Shine Jr. *(VP-Agricultural Div)*

SUGAR CREEK FINANCIAL CORP.
28 W Broadway, Trenton, IL 62293
Tel.: (618) 224-9228   MD
Web Site: http://www.tempobank.com
SUGR—OTCBB
Bank Holding Company
N.A.I.C.S.: 551111

SUGAR CREEK FOODS INTERNATIONAL, INC.
301 N El Paso, Russellville, AR 72801-3721
Tel.: (479) 968-1005   NY
Web Site: http://www.getsugarcreek.com
Year Founded: 2007
Sales Range: $75-99.9 Million
Emp.: 50
Soft Serve Frozen Yogurt & Ice Cream Mfr
N.A.I.C.S.: 311919
Scott van Horn *(Pres-Ops)*
Bud Gunter *(VP-Sls & Mktg)*

SUGAR CREEK PACKING CO.
12021 Sheraton Ln, Cincinnati, OH 45246
Tel.: (513) 551-5280   OH
Web Site: http://www.sugarcreek.com
Year Founded: 1966
Sales Range: $200-249.9 Million
Emp.: 1,200
Bacon Processor Mfr
N.A.I.C.S.: 311612
John G. Richardson *(Founder & Chm)*
Thomas J. Bollinger *(CFO)*
Pete Tamborski *(Gen Counsel)*
Michael Richardson *(Pres)*
Jennifer Hutcheson *(Chief Relationship Officer)*
Curt Terry *(COO)*
Mike Rozzano *(Exec VP-Ops)*
Alan Riney *(Exec VP-Sls & Bus Dev Strategy)*

SUGAR LOAF FORD
1222 W Service Dr, Winona, MN 55987-5347
Tel.: (507) 454-5170
Web Site: http://www.sugarloaffordlm.com
Sales Range: $10-24.9 Million
Emp.: 50
Car Whslr
N.A.I.C.S.: 441110
Mike Puetz *(Owner)*
Ricky Torkelson *(Mgr-Sls-New & Used Vehicle)*
Rod Trachta *(Mgr-Collision Center)*
Jo An Moham *(Mgr-Fin)*
Lora Ehlenfeldt *(Controller)*
Mary Schneider *(Mgr-Parts)*
Harold Moham *(Mgr-Customer Rels)*

SUGAR RIVER SAVINGS BANK
10 N Main St, Newport, NH 03773
Tel.: (603) 863-3000
Web Site: http://www.sugarriverbank.com
Rev.: $10,419,871
Emp.: 43
Federal Savings & Loan Associations
N.A.I.C.S.: 522180
Mark Petkin *(Pres)*

SUGAR STORES INC.
470 Mundet Pl, Hillside, NJ 07205
Web Site: http://www.sugarstores.com
Year Founded: 2005
Sales Range: $10-24.9 Million
Emp.: 35
Home & Office Furniture
N.A.I.C.S.: 423210
Moshe Melamed *(CEO)*

SUHM SPRING WORKS INC.
2710 McKinney St, Houston, TX 77003
Tel.: (713) 224-9293
Web Site: http://www.suhm.net
Rev.: $10,965,303
Emp.: 100
Coiled Flat Springs
N.A.I.C.S.: 332613
Mark Scarborough *(Pres)*
Becky Espinoza *(Office Mgr)*
Oscar Acevedo *(Controller-Inventory)*
Richard Vargas *(VP)*

SUHM SPRING WORKS INC.

U.S. PRIVATE

Suhm Spring Works Inc.—(Continued)
Tim Higginbotham *(Plant Mgr-Dallas)*
Tye Womack *(Controller)*
Luis Espinoza *(Plant Mgr)*
Bob Flores *(Mgr-Shipping)*

SUHOR INDUSTRIES INC.
10965 Granada Ln Ste 300, Overland Park, KS 66211
Tel.: (913) 345-2120 MO
Web Site: http://www.suhor.com
Burial Vaults & Caskets Mfr
N.A.I.C.S.: 339995
Michael Forbes *(Mgr-Southeast Kansas)*
Dennis P. Welzenbach *(Pres)*
Jeanette Geiser *(Treas)*
Gary Mosier *(Sls Mgr-Wholesale Monument)*
Marvin G. Smith *(COO)*
Mike Long *(Mgr-Fleet)*
Michael Anderson *(Reg Mgr-Louisiana & East Texas)*
Dennis Brokaw *(Reg Mgr-Oregon)*
Greg Kelsey *(VP-New York & Pennsylvania)*
Kat Williams *(Creative Dir-Mktg)*
Donald R. Robinson *(Pres-Signet Supply)*
Greg Barrett *(Mgr-SI Precast Concrete Products)*
Lonnie Beeler *(Reg Mgr-Mktg-Oregon)*
Chris Carson *(VP-SI Construction Svcs)*
Debbie Fleming *(Reg Mgr-Mktg-Pennsylvania)*
Ted Hart *(VP-Fin)*
Nathan Hobson *(Reg Mgr-Mktg-Kansas)*
Steve Williams *(Dir-HR)*
Edgar Murphy *(Dir-Safety)*
Joseph U. Suhor III *(Chm)*

SUHRBIER COMPANY
2010 156th Ave NE Ste 100, Bellevue, WA 98007
Tel.: (425) 455-5055
Web Site: http://www.suhrcorp.com
Rev.: $11,000,000
Emp.: 7
Subdividers & Developers
N.A.I.C.S.: 531120
Edwin Craig Suhrbier *(Pres & CEO)*

SUISAN CO. LTD
1965 Kamehameha Ave, Hilo, HI 96720
Tel.: (808) 935-8511
Web Site: http://www.suisan.com
Sales Range: $25-49.9 Million
Emp.: 190
Packaged Frozen Goods
N.A.I.C.S.: 424420
Glenn Hashimoto *(Pres)*

SUIT-KOTE CORP.
1911 Lorings Crossing Rd, Cortland, NY 13045-9747
Tel.: (607) 753-1100 NY
Web Site: http://www.suit-kote.com
Year Founded: 1982
Sales Range: $25-49.9 Million
Emp.: 500
Asphalt Paving Mixture Mfr
N.A.I.C.S.: 324121
Frank Suits *(Pres)*
Brent Hall *(Mgr-Laboratory)*
Mike Guerin *(VP)*

SUITE EXPERIENCE GROUP LLC
1900 S Norfolk St Ste 205, San Mateo, CA 94403
Web Site: http://www.suiteexperience group.com
Year Founded: 2010
Sales Range: $10-24.9 Million
Emp.: 4
Online Marketing Services
N.A.I.C.S.: 541613
Scott Spencer *(Pres)*
Philip Wang *(CTO & Head-Customer Experience)*
Brian Jeffcoat *(VP-Client Svc)*
Brad Shaw *(VP-Engrg)*
Cameron Nickels *(Dir-Strategic Partnership)*

SUKLE ADVERTISING, INC.
2430 W 32nd Ave, Denver, CO 80211
Tel.: (303) 964-9100
Web Site: http://www.sukle.com
Year Founded: 1995
Sales Range: Less than $1 Million
Emp.: 10
Advetising Agency
N.A.I.C.S.: 541810
Mike Sukle *(Owner)*
Andy Dutlinger *(Sr Dir-Art)*
KC Koch *(Dir-Art)*
Jeff Euteneur *(Dir-Art)*
Zac Spector *(Copywriter)*
Steven Noble *(Illustrator)*

SUKUP MANUFACTURING CO
1555 255th St, Sheffield, IA 50475
Tel.: (641) 892-4222
Web Site: http://www.sukup.com
Rev.: $27,306,278
Emp.: 550
Farm Machinery & Equipment
N.A.I.C.S.: 333111
Hank Norem *(Chief Innovation Officer)*
Eugene G. Sukup *(Chm)*
Charles Sukup *(Pres)*
Doreen Dohlman *(Coord-Shipping)*
Teresa Bonnema *(Mgr-Accts Payable)*
James Shipley *(Coord-Metal Building Dev & Outside Sls)*

Subsidiaries:
Ramco Innovations, Inc. (1)
1207 Maple St, West Des Moines, IA 50265
Tel.: (515) 225-6933
Web Site: http://www.ramcoinnovations.com
Sales Range: $10-24.9 Million
Emp.: 50
Electrical Supplies Distr
N.A.I.C.S.: 423610
Hank Norem *(CEO)*
Mike Relitz *(VP)*
Brian Relitz *(Pres)*

SUKUT CONSTRUCTION INC.
4010 W Chandler Ave, Santa Ana, CA 92704
Tel.: (714) 540-5351
Web Site: http://www.sukut.com
Sales Range: $100-124.9 Million
Emp.: 200
Grading
N.A.I.C.S.: 237310
Eric Mauldin *(Pres-San Diego Div)*
Greg LeBlanc *(Project Mgr)*
Nick Osborne *(Project Mgr)*
Steve Moua *(Engr-Cost)*
Bryan Nesthus *(Project Mgr)*
Scott Emery *(Project Mgr)*
Michael Zanaboni *(VP)*

SULAAN SOLUTIONS INC.
410 N Roosevelt Ave Ste 106, Chandler, AZ 85226
Tel.: (480) 626-4041
Web Site: http://www.sulaan.com
Year Founded: 2006
Sales Range: $1-9.9 Million
Emp.: 10
Information Technology Consulting Services
N.A.I.C.S.: 541512
Gary Ciner *(Controller)*
Jude Williams *(Dir-HR)*
Steven Weiand *(Dir-SAP BI-BO Implementations)*
Surya Muvvala *(Founder & Pres)*

SULLIVAN & COGLIANO DESIGNERS INC.
230 2nd Ave, Waltham, MA 02451-1123
Tel.: (781) 890-7890 MA
Web Site: http://www.sulcog.com
Year Founded: 1966
Rev.: $31,000,000
Emp.: 170
Employment Agencies
N.A.I.C.S.: 561330

Subsidiaries:
S & C Permanent Placement Inc. (1)
230 2nd Ave, Waltham, MA 02451-1123
Tel.: (781) 890-7890
Web Site: http://www.sullivancogliano.com
Rev.: $2,100,000
Emp.: 40
Employment Services
N.A.I.C.S.: 561311
Herb Cogliano *(Gen Mgr)*

Sullivan & Cogliano (1)
230 2nd Ave, Waltham, MA 02451-1123
Tel.: (781) 890-7890
Web Site: http://www.sullivancogliano.com
Help Supply Services
N.A.I.C.S.: 561320
Herb Cogliano *(Gen Mgr)*

Sullivan & Cogliano Designers Inc., Rhode Island (1)
100 Jefferson Blvd Ste 114, Warwick, RI 02888-3849
Tel.: (401) 463-3811
Employment Agencies
N.A.I.C.S.: 531190

Sullivan & Cogliano Training Center Inc. (1)
7740 N Kendall Dr, Miami, FL 33156
Tel.: (305) 279-5877
Web Site: http://www.sctrain.com
Sales Range: $10-24.9 Million
Emp.: 15
Employment Agencies
N.A.I.C.S.: 561311

Sullivan & Cogliano Training Centers Inc. (1)
460 Belmont St, Brockton, MA 02301-1818
Tel.: (508) 584-9909
Web Site: http://www.sctrain.edu
Sales Range: $1-9.9 Million
Emp.: 90
Job Training
N.A.I.C.S.: 611420
Sheila Chapman *(VP)*

SULLIVAN & COMPANY
450 W 14th St 12th Fl, New York, NY 10014
Tel.: (212) 888-2881
Web Site: http://www.sullivannyc.com
Year Founded: 1990
Sales Range: $10-24.9 Million
Emp.: 54
Advetising Agency
N.A.I.C.S.: 541810
Barbara Sullivan *(Mng Partner)*

SULLIVAN & COZART INC.
822 W Kentucky St, Louisville, KY 40203-3316
Tel.: (502) 584-4213 KY
Web Site: http://www.sullivancozart.com
Year Founded: 1933
Sales Range: $125-149.9 Million
Emp.: 300
Construction & Contracting Services
N.A.I.C.S.: 236220
Michael A. Thorp *(Pres)*

SULLIVAN & CROMWELL LLP
125 Broad St, New York, NY 10004
Tel.: (212) 558-4000
Web Site: http://www.sullcrom.com
Year Founded: 1879
Sales Range: $1-4.9 Billion
Emp.: 750
Law Firm
N.A.I.C.S.: 541110
Francis J. Aquila *(Partner)*
Adam Sofen *(Atty-Comml Real Estate Grp)*
Naresh Rajpal *(Mgr-Database Svcs)*
Jenny Lewis *(Mgr-Electronic Discovery & Litigation Support)*
Jeffrey Scott *(Partner)*
Daisy Cartagena *(Sec-Legal)*
Keith A. Pagnani *(Partner-New York & Atty)*
David Tendler *(Asst Mgr-HRIS)*
Megan R. O'Flynn *(Atty)*
Julia Mirsky *(Coord-Legal Personnel)*
Brian Post *(Dir-Desktop Sys)*
Christopher Smith *(Dir-Knowledge Mgmt)*
Cait Wranovix Fergus *(Mgr-Comm)*
Carl Doebel *(Mgr-Quality Assurance)*
Ann Fisher *(Partner)*
Andrew Gerlach *(Partner)*
Alexandra D. Korry *(Partner-New York & Atty)*
Angelique Harris *(Project Coord-E-Discovery)*
Tim Wesely *(Project Mgr-Fin Syss)*
Chris Gambino *(Sec-Legal)*
Fiona Sullivan *(Asst Mgr)*
Sheree Feigelson *(Asst Mgr-Health & Welfare)*
Katherine A. Taylor *(Atty)*
Kate Sexton *(Bus Mgr-Fin)*
Roya Axtle *(Coord-Bus Dev)*
Patricia Langdale *(Dir-Conflicts Info Mgmt)*
Melanie Corpuz *(Dir-Global Benefits)*
Sue Vahrenkamp *(Dir-Secretarial Svcs & Document Processing)*
Tom Palumbo *(Dir-Software Dev)*
Lori-Ann Decio *(Mgr)*
Ralph Fernandez *(Mgr-Acctg)*
Jill Madeo *(Mgr-Bus Dev)*
Dominic Diangelo *(Mgr-Food & Conference)*
Wade Anderson *(Mgr-IT Ops)*
Rachel Marx Boufford *(Mgr-Legal Recruiting & Mktg)*
James Japal *(Mgr-Network)*
Sheila Lynch *(Mgr-RE Legal)*
Marilyn Mitchell *(Mgr-Tech Trng)*
Darrell S. Cafasso *(Partner-New York & Atty)*
Duncan C. McCurrach *(Atty)*
Frederick Wertheim *(Partner)*
Gandolfo V. Diblasi *(Atty)*
George J. Sampas *(Partner-New York & Atty)*
Joseph B. Frumkin *(Partner-New York & Atty)*
Krishna Veeraraghavan *(Partner)*
Marc De Leeuw *(Partner)*
Melissa Sawyer *(Partner)*
Michael Escue *(Partner)*
Richard Pepperman *(Partner)*
Theodore Rogers *(Partner)*
Anthony J. Colletta *(Partner-New York & Atty)*
Roman Peresiper *(Project Coord)*
Sherry Kilar *(Sr Mgr-Legal HR)*
Margaret Velasco *(Sr Mgr-Ops)*
Shauna Rush *(Sr Mgr-Word Processing)*
Arthur S. Adler *(Partner)*

COMPANIES

Werner F. Ahlers (Partner)
Izumi Akai (Partner)
Nikolaos G. Andronikos (Partner)
Richard Pollack (Mng Partner-London)
Robert J. Giuffra (Co-Chm)
Scott Miller (Co-Chm)
Robert W. Reeder III (Partner-New York & Atty)

SULLIVAN & MANN LUMBER CO., INC.
17671 Irvine Blvd Ste 105, Tustin, CA 92780
Tel.: (714) 665-2460
Web Site: http://www.sullivanmann.com
Sales Range: $10-24.9 Million
Emp.: 5
Whslr of Lumber & Plywood
N.A.I.C.S.: 423310
Gordon B. Mann (Pres)

SULLIVAN & MCLAUGHLIN COMPANIES, INC.
74 Lawley St, Boston, MA 02122
Tel.: (617) 474-0500
Web Site: http://www.sullymac.com
Sales Range: $25-49.9 Million
Emp.: 500
Electrical Contracting Services
N.A.I.C.S.: 238210
Dennis Miller (CEO)
John McLaughlin (Pres)
John Rudicus (Exec VP-Sls & Customer Rels)
Larry Richmond (VP)
Gary Hodlin (CFO)

SULLIVAN & WORCESTER LLP
One Post Office Sq, Boston, MA 02109
Tel.: (617) 338-2800   MA
Web Site: http://www.sandw.com
Year Founded: 1941
Sales Range: $100-124.9 Million
Emp.: 201
Legal Advisory Services
N.A.I.C.S.: 541110
Howard E. Berkenblit (Partner)
John G. Balboni (Partner)
Victor N. Baltera (Partner)
Susan M. Barnard (Partner)
Harvey E. Bines (Partner)
Aidan F. Browne (Partner)
Christopher Cabot (Partner)
Joel R. Carpenter (Mng Partner)
Kevin M. Colmey (Partner)
William J. Curry (Partner)
Christopher C. Curtis (Partner)
Jeanne P. Darcey (Partner)
Nicole M. Crum (Partner-Washington)
Amy A. Zuccarello (Partner)
Ashley Brooks (Partner)
Michael P. Kiskinis (COO)
Hayden S. Baker (Partner-Environment & Natural Resources Practice)
Jeffrey Gleit (Partner-Bankruptcy & Restructuring Practice)
John Hunt (Partner)
Maura C. Carney (Partner-Trusts & Estates Grp & Tax Dept)
Eric D. Simanek (Partner-Investment Mgmt Grp)
Henry W. Comstock Jr. (Partner)
Joseph B. Darby III (Partner)

SULLIVAN AND MERRITT INC.
91 Freedom Pk, Bangor, ME 04401
Tel.: (207) 848-5788
Web Site: http://www.sullivanandmerritt.com
Rev.: $18,700,000
Emp.: 30
Industrial Buildings, New Construction
N.A.I.C.S.: 236210
Jon E. Lee (CEO & Principal)
Rick Gnoks (Controller)

SULLIVAN BUICK GMC, INC.
777 W Dundee Rd, Arlington Heights, IL 60004
Tel.: (847) 666-5973   DE
Web Site: http://www.billsullivan.com
Sales Range: $10-24.9 Million
Emp.: 50
New & Used Car Dealer
N.A.I.C.S.: 441110
Ariel Szwec (Gen Mgr)
Dan Szwec (Mgr-New Car Sls)
Lou Mostaccio (Mgr-Used Cars)
Mike Baker (Mgr-Svc)
Maureen Vittas (Mgr-Internet Sls)
Neil Hulvey (Mgr-Parts)
Marcia Hulvey (Office Mgr)
Michael Bott (Mgr-Sls)
Mike O'Connell (Mgr-Bus)

SULLIVAN CADILLAC
4040 SW College Rd, Ocala, FL 34474
Tel.: (352) 732-4700
Web Site: http://www.sullivancadillac.com
Rev.: $56,511,366
Emp.: 80
New & Used Car Dealer
N.A.I.C.S.: 441110
Rich Gruber (Sls Mgr)

Subsidiaries:

Sullivan Buick GMC   (1)
4000 SW College Rd, Ocala, FL 34474
Tel.: (352) 620-0008
Web Site: http://www.ocalasullivangm.com
Sales Range: $25-49.9 Million
Emp.: 40
New & Used Car Dealer
N.A.I.C.S.: 441110
Tony Sullivan (Gen Mgr)

SULLIVAN CREATIVE SERVICES, LTD.
88 Black Falcon Ave Ste 237, Boston, MA 02210-2472
Tel.: (617) 597-0072
Web Site: http://www.sullivancreative.com
Year Founded: 1987
Sales Range: Less than $1 Million
Emp.: 5
Advertising Agencies
N.A.I.C.S.: 541810
Pamela E. Sullivan (Pres & Dir-Creative)
Carol Fusaro (VP & Acct Mgr)

Subsidiaries:

Sullivan Creative   (1)
6B Hills Ave, Concord, NH 03301
Tel.: (603) 228-0836
Web Site: http://www.sullivancreative.com
Sales Range: Less than $1 Million
Emp.: 4
Advertising Services
N.A.I.C.S.: 541810
Pam Sullivan (Pres & Dir-Creative)

SULLIVAN HIGDON & SINK INCORPORATED
255 N Mead St, Wichita, KS 67202-2707
Tel.: (316) 263-0124   KS
Web Site: http://www.wehatesheep.com
Year Founded: 1971
Sales Range: $25-49.9 Million
Emp.: 110
Advertising Services
N.A.I.C.S.: 541810
Lathi de Silva (Mng Dir-Wichita)
John January (Co-CEO)
P. Scott Flemming (Mng Dir-Wichita & Exec Dir-Creative)
Ali Mahaffy (Co-CEO)
Jim Vranicar (COO)
Alyssa Johnson (Dir-Art)
Amy Nichols (Mgr-Reputation)
Devin Brown (Dir-Art)
Staci Krause (Asst Mgr-Brand Contact)

Subsidiaries:

Sullivan Higdon & Sink Incorporated   (1)
2000 Central, Kansas City, MO 64108-2022
Tel.: (816) 474-1333
Web Site: http://www.wehatesheep.com
Sales Range: $10-24.9 Million
Emp.: 100
Advertising Services
N.A.I.C.S.: 541810
Lynell Stucky (Mng Partner)
Randall Mikulecky (Mng Partner)
John January (Sr VP & Exec Dir-Creative)
Tony Robinson (VP & Dir-Fin)
Ron Gunnarson (Dir-Practice-Aviation, Aerospace & Defense)
Tom Bertels (Mng Partner-Wichita)
Brock Campbell (VP & Dir-Brand Mgmt Grp)
Scott Flemming (VP & Exec Dir-Creative)
Ali Mahaffy (Co-CEO)
Jim Vranicar (VP-Connections Plng)
Samantha Yancey (Dir-Art)
Penny Hurd (Assoc Dir-Content)
Jessica Bukowski (Assoc Acct Dir)

Sullivan Higdon & Sink Incorporated   (1)
6801 Whittier Ave Ste 301, McLean, VA 22101-4549
Tel.: (703) 752-7845
Web Site: http://www.wehatesheep.com
Sales Range: $10-24.9 Million
Emp.: 15
Advertising Services
N.A.I.C.S.: 541810

SULLIVAN INTERNATIONAL GROUP, INC.
2750 Womble Rd Ste 100, San Diego, CA 92106
Tel.: (619) 260-1432
Web Site: http://www.onesullivan.com
Year Founded: 1998
Sales Range: $10-24.9 Million
Emp.: 100
Engineering, Technology & Logistics Services
N.A.I.C.S.: 541330
Steven E. Sullivan (CEO)
Neal Clements (COO & Mng Partner)
Stewart Bornhoft (Mgr-Client Svcs)
Kevin Hayford (VP-Mktg, PR & Community Outreach)
Scott Blount (COO-San Francisco)
Chad Dobrei (Mgr-Ops-Western Reg)

SULLIVAN INVESTMENT CORPORATION
550 S Country Club Dr, Mesa, AZ 85210
Tel.: (480) 844-7071   AZ
Web Site: http://www.trucksonlysales.com
Sales Range: $10-24.9 Million
Emp.: 50
New & Used Truck Dealer
N.A.I.C.S.: 441110
Robert M. Sullivan (Pres & CEO)
Bob Mulvania (Mgr-Sls)

SULLIVAN MOVING AND STORAGE CO
5704 Copley Dr, San Diego, CA 92111
Tel.: (858) 874-2600
Web Site: http://www.sullivunited.com
Sales Range: $50-74.9 Million
Emp.: 50

Long Haul Trucking
N.A.I.C.S.: 484110
Mark Fischer (Pres)
Mark Keiper (Gen Mgr)
Pat Reid (CFO)

SULLIVAN OIL COMPANY
11203 Proverbs Ave, Baton Rouge, LA 70816-4182
Tel.: (225) 952-7900   LA
Web Site: http://www.sullivanoil.com
Year Founded: 1966
Sales Range: $125-149.9 Million
Emp.: 30
Producer & Retailer of Petroleum; Operator of Retail Convenience Stores
N.A.I.C.S.: 445131
Anne G. Virgets (Controller)

SULLIVAN PAPER COMPANY
42 Progress Ave, West Springfield, MA 01089
Tel.: (413) 734-3107   DE
Web Site: http://www.sullivanpaper.com
Year Founded: 1941
Sales Range: $100-124.9 Million
Emp.: 230
Gift Wrap & Printing Paper Mfr
N.A.I.C.S.: 322299

Subsidiaries:

Sulpaco West   (1)
600 E Hancock St, Appleton, WI 54911-5024
Tel.: (920) 749-2140
Gravure Printing & Converting
N.A.I.C.S.: 322130

SULLIVAN PERKINS
2811 McKinney Ave Ste 320, Dallas, TX 75204-8566
Tel.: (214) 922-9080
Web Site: http://www.sullivanperkins.com
Year Founded: 1984
Sales Range: $25-49.9 Million
Emp.: 35
Advertising Agencies
N.A.I.C.S.: 541810
Mark Perkins (Principal)

SULLIVAN PETROLEUM COMPANY LLC
1000 Truxtun Ave, Bakersfield, CA 93301
Tel.: (661) 327-5008
Web Site: http://www.sullivanpetroleum.com
Rev.: $20,198,435
Emp.: 10
Petroleum Products
N.A.I.C.S.: 424720
Tim Sullivan (Pres)

SULLIVAN ROOFING, INC.
60 E State Pkwy, Schaumburg, IL 60173
Tel.: (847) 908-1000
Web Site: http://www.sullivanroofing.com
Sales Range: $25-49.9 Million
Emp.: 110
Roofing Contractors
N.A.I.C.S.: 238160
Timothy E. Sullivan (Pres)
Mary Barrett (VP-Fin)

SULLIVAN SOLAR POWER
8949 Kenamar Dr Ste 101, San Diego, CA 92121
Tel.: (858) 271-7758
Web Site: http://www.sullivansolarpower.com
Year Founded: 2004
Sales Range: $10-24.9 Million

SULLIVAN SOLAR POWER

Sullivan Solar Power—(Continued)
Emp.: 149
Solar Power Design & Installation Services
N.A.I.C.S.: 238210
Daniel Sullivan (Founder & CEO)
Bill Ness (VP-Sls & Mktg)

SULLIVAN TIRE CO. INC.
41 Accord Park Dr, Norwell, MA 02061-1614
Tel.: (781) 982-1550
Web Site: http://ww.sullivantire.com
Tires & Tubes Mfr
N.A.I.C.S.: 441340
Joseph M. Zaccheo (Pres & CEO)

Subsidiaries:

Sullivan Investment Co. Inc. (1)
41 Accord Pk Dr, Norwell, MA 02061-1614
Tel.: (781) 982-1550
Web Site: http://ww.sullivantire.com
Auto & Tire Distr
N.A.I.C.S.: 441340
Joseph Zaccheo (Pres & CEO)
Robert D. Sullivan (Dir)
Paul Sullivan (Treas)

SULLIVAN, INC.
1105 Nikki View Dr, Brandon, FL 33511
Tel.: (813) 314-2222
Web Site: http://www.sullivanbenefits.net
Sales Range: $1-9.9 Million
Emp.: 10
Benefits Consulting Services
N.A.I.C.S.: 541611
Joe Sullivan (Pres)
Lisa Juul (VP-Sls)
Nathan Skrove (Dir-Product Dev & Global Sourcing)
Tom Russo (CEO)

SULLIVANCURTISMONROE INSURANCE SERVICES, LLC
1920 Main St Ste 600, Irvine, CA 92614
Tel.: (949) 250-7172
Web Site: http://www.sullicurt.com
Sales Range: $10-24.9 Million
Emp.: 83
Insurance Broker Services
N.A.I.C.S.: 524210
Mark Eckenweiler (CFO)
John F. Monroe (Chm & CEO)
Jeannine Coronado (Exec VP & Gen Mgr)
Pam Braccini (Dir-HR)
David Kummer (Pres)
Hunt Turner (VP)
Blake Pierson (VP)
Shawn Kraatz (Exec VP)
Canaan Crouch (VP)
Gabriela Hernandez (Assoc VP-Benefits-Southern)
Thomas Petsche (VP-Los Angeles)
Dan Fein (VP)
Candice White (Dir-Mktg & Comm)
John Paganas (VP)
Greg Huston (VP-Employee Benefits)
Jaime Medrano (Assoc VP)
Rob Wallace (VP)

SULPHCO, INC.
4333 W Sam Houston Pkwy N Ste 190, Houston, TX 77043
Tel.: (713) 896-9100
Web Site: http://www.sulphco.com
Sales Range: Less than $1 Million
Emp.: 17
Crude Oil Processing & Technology
N.A.I.C.S.: 213112
M. Clay Chambers (COO)
Richard K. Sell (Dir-Bus Dev)

SULPHUR SPRINGS VALLEY ELECTRIC COOPERATIVE INC.
311 E Wilcox Dr, Sierra Vista, AZ 85635
Tel.: (520) 384-2221
Web Site: http://www.ssvec.org
Year Founded: 1938
Sales Range: $25-49.9 Million
Emp.: 200
Provider of Electric Services
N.A.I.C.S.: 221122
Creden W. Huber (CEO)
Jack Blair (CMO)
Dan Barrera (Pres)

SULPHURIC ACID TRADING CO.
3710 Corporex Park Dr Ste 205, Tampa, FL 33619-1160
Tel.: (813) 225-2000
Web Site: http://www.interacid-trading.com
Year Founded: 1989
Sales Range: $10-24.9 Million
Emp.: 13
Distr of Chemicals & Allied Products
N.A.I.C.S.: 424690
Brent Shonka (Gen Mgr)

SULTAN & SONS INC.
6601 Lyons Rd, Coconut Creek, FL 33073
Tel.: (954) 782-6600
Web Site: http://www.sultanandsons.com
Sales Range: $10-24.9 Million
Emp.: 40
Draperies, Plastics & Textiles Mfr & Distr
N.A.I.C.S.: 314120
Leon Sultan (Chm)
Ezra Sultan (Pres)

SULTANA DISTRIBUTION SERVICES INC.
600 Food Center Dr, Bronx, NY 10474-7037
Tel.: (718) 617-5500
Web Site: http://www.sultanadist.com
Year Founded: 1959
Sales Range: $10-24.9 Million
Emp.: 132
Confectionery Products Distr
N.A.I.C.S.: 424450
Christine Magnatta (CFO)

SUM EFFECT SOFTWARE, INC.
144 SE Pkwy Ste 260, Franklin, TN 37064
Tel.: (615) 790-0823
Web Site: http://www.corecommerce.com
Year Founded: 2001
Sales Range: $1-9.9 Million
Emp.: 25
Commerce Software Publisher
N.A.I.C.S.: 513210
Matt DeLong (Pres & CEO)
Kris Graffagnino (Dir-Sls & Design)
Terry Lawson (Dir-Customer Solutions)
Nikita Makeyev (Dir-Dev)

SUMAR REALTORS
3838 N Sam Houston Pkwy E, Houston, TX 77032
Tel.: (281) 449-0909
Sales Range: $10-24.9 Million
Emp.: 100
Nonresidential Building Operators
N.A.I.C.S.: 531110
Lawrence Hill (Pres)

SUMCO, LLC
1351 S Girls School Rd, Indianapolis, IN 46231-1352
Tel.: (317) 241-7600
Web Site: http://www.sumco.com
Year Founded: 1990
Electroplated Products Mfr
N.A.I.C.S.: 332813
Mark Brouillard (Owner)
Amy Schultz (Mgr-Quality)

SUMERU EQUITY PARTNERS LLC
950 Tower Ln Ste 1788, Foster City, CA 94404
Tel.: (650) 479-1080
Web Site: http://www.sumeruequity.com
Year Founded: 2014
Privater Equity Firm
N.A.I.C.S.: 523999
Paul Mercadante (Mng Dir)
Kyle Ryland (Mng Partner)
Randy Randleman (Mng Dir & COO)
Jason Babcoke (Mng Dir)
John D. Brennan (Mng Dir)
George Kadifa (Mng Dir)
Sanjeet Mitra (Mng Dir)
Mark Haller (VP)
Sean Kendra (VP)
Ajay B. Shah (Sr Operating Partner)
Michelle Ruggeri (Controller)

Subsidiaries:

3Gtms, Inc. (1)
8 Progress Dr, Shelton, CT 06484
Tel.: (203) 567-4610
Web Site: http://www.3gtms.com
Sales Range: $10-24.9 Million
Emp.: 25
Computer System Design Services
N.A.I.C.S.: 541512
Mitch Weseley (Co-Founder & CEO)
J. P. Wiggins (Co-Founder & VP-Logistics)
Jerry Rau (COO)
Chuck Fuerst (VP-Mktg)
Chris Haarmeyer (VP-Dev)
Chris Taurence (VP-Client Svcs)
David Sapienza (VP-Sls)
Michael Parmett (VP-Acct Mgmt)
Chris van der Harst (Mng Dir)
Terry Wray (VP-Implementation Svcs)
Jeff Ritter (CFO)
Stephanie Richelieu Stagger (Chief Revenue Officer)
Larry De Lutiis Jr. (CTO)

Division (Domestic):

Pacejet Logistics, Inc. (2)
8760 Onion Pl Ste 200, Columbus, OH 43240
Web Site: http://www.pacejet.com
Computer & Software Stores, Nsk
N.A.I.C.S.: 449210
Bill Knapp (CEO)
Larry DeLeon (Founder & Pres)

Q4 Inc. (1)
99 Spadina Ave Ste 500, Toronto, M5V 3P8, ON, Canada
Web Site: https://www.q4inc.com
Rev.: $56,075,053
Assets: $73,832,090
Liabilities: $29,458,554
Net Worth: $44,373,536
Earnings: ($36,369,152)
Emp.: 500
Fiscal Year-end: 12/31/2022
Software Development Services
N.A.I.C.S.: 541511
Darrell Heaps (CEO)
Kenneth Szeto (Gen Counsel)

SocialChorus, Inc. (1)
703 Market St Ste 470, San Francisco, CA 94103
Tel.: (415) 655-2700
Web Site: http://www.socialchorus.com
Online Marketing Platform Provider
N.A.I.C.S.: 541511
Gregory Shove (Co-Founder & Chm)
Nicole Alvino (Co-Founder)
Kane Baccigalupi (CTO)
Tim Christensen (VP-Engrg)

Adam Stiles (Dir-Engrg-Pasadena)
Blake Hayward (VP-Product)
Alan Tarkowski (VP-Sls)
Gary Nakamura (CEO)
Kristen Ribero (Dir-Product Mktg)
Alison Murdock (Chief Mktg Officer)
Dave Lutz (VP-Client Strategy & Success)
Cyrus Gilbert-Rolfe (Mng Dir-EMEA)

Telesoft Corp. (1)
1661 E Camelback Rd Ste 300, Phoenix, AZ 85016-3906
Tel.: (602) 308-2100
Web Site: http://www.telesoft.com
Sales Range: $10-24.9 Million
Emp.: 115
Communications Expense & Mobility Management Products & Services
N.A.I.C.S.: 513210
Thierry Zerbib (Founder & CTO)
Robert Sullivan (Exec VP)
James Jones (VP-R&D)
Kevin Donoghue (Pres)
Joan Lara (VP-Managed Svcs)
Daman Wood (COO)
Charles Layne (CEO)

SUMMA HOLDINGS, INC.
8223 Brecksville Rd Ste 100, Brecksville, OH 44141
Tel.: (440) 838-4700
Year Founded: 1983
Holding Company
N.A.I.C.S.: 551112
James Benenson III (Co-Pres)
John V. Curci (CFO, Treas & VP)
Clement C. Benenson (Co-Pres)
James Benenson Jr. (Chm & CEO)

Subsidiaries:

International Manufacturing Company LLC (1)
8223 Brecksville Rd Ste 100, Brecksville, OH 44141-1361
Tel.: (440) 838-4700
Web Site: http://www.mfgco.com
Sales Range: $100-124.9 Million
Emp.: 10
Holding Company; Metal Products Mfr
N.A.I.C.S.: 551112
James Benenson III (Co-Pres)
Clement C. Benenson (Co-Pres)
James Benenson Jr. (Chm & CEO)

Subsidiary (Domestic):

Bijur Lubricating Corporation (2)
2100 Gateway Ctr Blvd, Morrisville, NC 27560-6600
Tel.: (919) 465-4448
Web Site: http://www.bijurdelimon.com
Sales Range: $50-74.9 Million
Automatic Lubricating & Cooling Equipment Mfr & Whslr
N.A.I.C.S.: 333914
Roger M. Yamamoto (Pres)

Penco Products, Inc. (2)
2024 Cressman Rd, Skippack, PA 19474
Tel.: (610) 666-0500
Web Site: http://www.pencoproducts.com
Sales Range: $125-149.9 Million
Fabricated Metal Storage & Material Handling Products Mfr
N.A.I.C.S.: 337215
Alexandra Hook (Coord-Sls)
Angela Reid (Supvr-Customer Svc)
Bob Brett (Mgr-Northeast)
Jeff Haines (Dir-Mktg)
Jennifer Williamson (Mgr-Mktg)
Lamont Bland (Engr-Field Svc)
Mike Rochon (Mgr-Central)
Randy Polen (Mgr-Western)
Tony Taylor (Mgr-Southeast)
Yolanda Redden (Coord-Mktg)

Subsidiary (Domestic):

All Star Bleachers, Inc. (3)
6550 New Tampa Hwy, Lakeland, FL 33815-3148
Tel.: (863) 687-3141
Web Site: http://www.allstarbleachers.com
Sales Range: $25-49.9 Million
Emp.: 75
Metal Bleacher & Stadium Seating Mfr
N.A.I.C.S.: 332999

COMPANIES
SUMMIT BUSINESS MEDIA, LLC

Division (Domestic):

Schmidt Structural Products, Inc. (3)
2024 Cressman Rd, Skippack, PA 19474-0158 (100%)
Tel.: (610) 666-0500
Web Site: http://www.schmidtstructural.com
Sales Range: $50-74.9 Million
Emp.: 750
Fabricated Structural Steel Mezzanines Designer, Mfr & Installation Services
N.A.I.C.S.: 332312

SUMMA TRADING COMPANY INC.
1300 Clay St Ste 600, Oakland, CA 94523
Tel.: (510) 430-0121
Year Founded: 1988
Sales Range: $10-24.9 Million
Emp.: 20
Trader of Nondurable Goods
N.A.I.C.S.: 424990
Tim Toy (Pres)

SUMMER BAY RESORT
25 Town Center Blvd Ste C, Clermont, FL 34714
Tel.: (352) 242-1100
Web Site: http://www.summerbayresort.com
Sales Range: $10-24.9 Million
Emp.: 310
Resort & Hotel
N.A.I.C.S.: 721110
Paul Ojeda (Supvr-Customer Svc Center)
Vannessa Spitzer (Office Mgr)

SUMMER STREET CAPITAL PARTNERS LLC
70 W Chippewa St Ste 500, Buffalo, NY 14202
Tel.: (716) 566-2900 NY
Web Site: http://www.summerstreetcapital.com
Year Founded: 1999
Sales Range: $75-99.9 Million
Emp.: 25
Equity Investment Firm
N.A.I.C.S.: 523999
Michael P. McQueeney (Mng Partner)
Brian D'Amico (Mng Partner)
Jennifer Chalmers Balbach (Partner)
Douglas M. VanOort (Partner)
Garth T. Troxell (Partner)
Michael Petri (Partner)
Christian Gorino (Principal)
John Collins (Principal)
Mark Zogaria (CFO)

Subsidiaries:

Multisorb Technologies, Inc. (1)
325 Harlem Rd, Buffalo, NY 14224-1825
Tel.: (716) 824-8900
Web Site: http://www.multisorb.com
Desiccant Products, Contract Packaging & Sterilization Mfr & Packager
N.A.I.C.S.: 325998
Adrian Possumato (VP-Healthcare Pkg)
Laxmikant Khaitan (Dir-Comml-Healthcare Pkg-Asia Pacific)
Lex Wagteveld (Dir-Comml-Healthcare Pkg-Europe)
Chris Gilmor (Dir-Comml-Healthcare Pkg-Americas)
Mike Morelli (Sr Acct Exec-Logistics & Indus Pkg)

SUMMERS MANUFACTURING CO. INC.
338 Railway Ave, Maddock, ND 58348
Tel.: (701) 438-2855
Web Site: http://www.summersmfg.com
Rev.: $11,112,232
Emp.: 60
Farm Machinery & Equipment Suppliers
N.A.I.C.S.: 333111
Deb Anderson (Chm)
Brenda Howard (Mgr-Network Admin)
Ryan Gruhn (CEO)

SUMMERS-TAYLOR INC.
300 W Elk Ave, Elizabethton, TN 37643-2614
Tel.: (423) 543-3181 TN
Web Site: http://www.summerstaylor.com
Year Founded: 1948
Sales Range: $10-24.9 Million
Emp.: 400
Provider of Highway & Street Construction Services
N.A.I.C.S.: 237310
Robert T. Summers (Chm)
Ted Lane Bryant (Exec VP)
Danny Matthews (VP-Estimating)

SUMMERSET PROFESSIONAL GRILLS
17322 Gothard St, Huntington Beach, CA 92647
Tel.: (714) 966-9330
Web Site: http://www.summersetgrills.com
Year Founded: 1995
Sales Range: $1-9.9 Million
Emp.: 50
Outdoor Gas Grills
N.A.I.C.S.: 335220
Jeffrey Straubel (Pres)

SUMMERSVILLE REGIONAL MEDICAL CENTER
400 Fairview Heights Rd, Summersville, WV 26651
Tel.: (304) 872-2891 WV
Web Site: http://www.summersvilleregional.org
Year Founded: 1968
Sales Range: $25-49.9 Million
Emp.: 620
Community Health Care Services
N.A.I.C.S.: 621498
Deborah A. Hill (CEO)
Brian Kelbaugh (CFO)

SUMMERWINDS GARDEN CENTERS INC.
390 E Parkcenter Blvd, Boise, ID 83706
Tel.: (208) 345-2559 DE
Web Site: http://www.summerwindsnursery.com
Year Founded: 1998
Sales Range: $50-74.9 Million
Emp.: 350
Nursery & Garden Supply Services
N.A.I.C.S.: 444240
John Jozwik (CFO & VP-Fin)
Brian Hjelmstad (VP-Mdsg)
Frank Benzing (Pres & CEO)

Subsidiaries:

Summerwinds Garden Centers Inc. (1)
17826 N Tatum Blvd, Phoenix, AZ 85032
Tel.: (602) 867-1822
Web Site: http://www.summerwindsnursery.com
Sales Range: $10-24.9 Million
Emp.: 20
Provider of Nursery & Garden Supply Services
N.A.I.C.S.: 444240

Summerwinds Garden Centers of California Inc. (1)
2460 Winchester Blvd, Campbell, CA 95008-4802
Tel.: (408) 866-0171
Web Site: http://www.summerwindsgc.com
Sales Range: $10-24.9 Million
Emp.: 20
Provider of Nursery & Garden Supply Services
N.A.I.C.S.: 455219

SUMMIT 7 SYSTEMS, LLC
2 Parade St, Huntsville, AL 35806
Tel.: (256) 585-6868 DE
Web Site: https://www.summit7systems.com
Year Founded: 2008
Sales Range: $1-9.9 Million
Emp.: 24
Information Technology Consulting Services
N.A.I.C.S.: 541512
Scott Edwards (CEO)
Ben Curry (Mng Partner & Principal)
Jason Batchelor (VP-Bus Dev)
Brenda Perry (Project Mgr)
Esther Wangeci (Project Mgr)
Paul Smelser (Mgr-Bus Dev)
Vince Lombardo (CFO)

Subsidiaries:

CSW Superior IT Solutions, Inc. (1)
12849 Gentle Shade Dr, Bristow, VA 20136-2556
Tel.: (703) 574-6900
Web Site: http://www.cswas.com
Computer System Design Services
N.A.I.C.S.: 541512
John D. Carney (Pres)
Curtis Nare (CEO)

SUMMIT AGRICULTURAL GROUP, LLC
10640 Co Hwy D20, Alden, IA 50006
Tel.: (515) 854-9820
Web Site: http://www.summitag.com
Private Equity & Investment Management Services
N.A.I.C.S.: 523999
Bruce Rastetter (CEO)

Subsidiaries:

Summit Ag Investors, LLC (1)
10640 Co Hwy D20, Alden, IA 50006
Tel.: (515) 854-9820
Web Site: http://www.summitag.com
Investment Management & Advisory Services
N.A.I.C.S.: 541618

SUMMIT BANK
2969 Broadway, Oakland, CA 94611
Tel.: (510) 839-8800
Web Site: http://www.summitbanking.com
Year Founded: 1982
Sales Range: $25-49.9 Million
Emp.: 36
Provider of Banking Services
N.A.I.C.S.: 522110
Jenny Bennett (Pres-Eugene & Springfield)
George Yang (VP & Mgr-Relationship)
Jamie Henikoff Moffitt (Sr VP-Fin & Admin)
Kevin Holmquist (VP-Portland Metro & South West Washington)
Gabe Wells (VP-Portland Metro & South West Washington)
Brian Thomas (Sr VP-Portland & Southwest Washington)
Phil Czajka (Portfolio Mgr-Portland Metro & Southwest Washington Market)
Craig Wanichek (Pres & CEO)
Chris Hemmings (COO)
Gina Kaveny (VP)
Angela DeVita (VP & Mgr-Relationship Banking-Portland Metropolitan)
Jamie Shulman (Pres-Portland)
Maarty Leunen (Asst VP)
Gary O'Connell (Pres-Market)
Stacy Koos (Officer-Market Dev-Eugene & Springfield & Sr VP-Eugene & Springfield)
Matt Dynice (Sr VP-Credit Admin)
Aaron Walker (Chief Credit Officer)
Jackie Costello (VP-Portland & Southwest Washington)
Paul Weinhold (Chm)

SUMMIT BREWING CO.
910 Montreal Cir, Saint Paul, MN 55102
Tel.: (651) 265-7800
Web Site: http://www.summitbrewing.com
Sales Range: $10-24.9 Million
Emp.: 45
Brewery
N.A.I.C.S.: 312120
Mark O. Stutrud (Founder)
Mike Bamonti (Chief Sls Officer)

SUMMIT BUSINESS MEDIA, LLC
475 Park Ave S 6th Fl, New York, NY 10016-6908
Tel.: (212) 557-7480
Web Site: http://www.summitbusinessmedia.com
Year Founded: 2006
Sales Range: $25-49.9 Million
Emp.: 400
Business-to-Business Media & Information Services; Periodical Publisher
N.A.I.C.S.: 519290
F. Reilly Cobb (VP-Mktg Data Grp)
John Whelan (Exec VP-Media Div)
Chris Luke (Publr-Property & Casualty Grp)
Jonathan Moore (Mng Dir-Event Div & Sr VP)
Richard Kravitz (Mng Dir-Pro Publ Div & VP)
Steve Weitzner (Pres & CEO)
Adam Marder (CFO & Exec VP)
Jeff Patterson (Sr VP-Customer Solutions)
Brian Magnotta (CIO)
Peter Westerman (Chief Audience Officer)
Colleen Zelina (VP-HR)
Steve Grande (Sr VP-Ops & Mfg)
Josh Heitsenrether (Dir-Mktg-Customer Solutions Grp)
Tashawna Rodwell (Publr-Life & Health Grp)
Dave O'Neil (Dir-Sls)
Emily Holbrook (Exec Mng Editor-Natl Underwriter Life & Health)
Matthew Rothenberg (VP-Digital Products)
Charlie McCurdy (Chm)

Subsidiaries:

Futures Magazine Group (1)
107 W Van Buren Ste 203, Chicago, IL 60605
Tel.: (312) 846-4600
Web Site: http://www.futuresmag.com
Sales Range: $10-24.9 Million
Emp.: 5
Financial Forecasting Magazine Publisher
N.A.I.C.S.: 513120
Yesenia Duran (Mng Editor)
Jeff Joseph (CEO)

The National Underwriter Company (1)
4157 Olympic Blvd ste 225, Erlanger, KY 41018
Tel.: (859) 692-2100
Web Site: http://www.nationalunderwriter.com
Sales Range: $50-74.9 Million
Emp.: 135

SUMMIT BUSINESS MEDIA, LLC

Summit Business Media, LLC—(Continued)
Insurance & Financial Service Industries
Periodicals, e-Media & Software Publisher
N.A.I.C.S.: 513120
John Whelan (Exec VP-Media Div)

SUMMIT CONSTRUCTION CORP.
308 Cedar Lakes Dr, Chesapeake, VA 23322
Tel.: (757) 482-4424
Web Site:
http://www.summitconstructionvirginia.com
Sales Range: $10-24.9 Million
Emp.: 20
Provider of Construction Services
N.A.I.C.S.: 236115
Luke Kinser (VP)

SUMMIT CONTAINER CORPORATION
901 Synthes Ave, Monument, CO 80132
Tel.: (719) 481-8400
Web Site:
http://www.summitcontainer.com
Year Founded: 1984
Sales Range: $1-9.9 Million
Emp.: 29
Corrugated & Solid Fiber Box Mfr
N.A.I.C.S.: 322211
Dave Johnson (VP-Ops)
Stephen C. Turner (VP-Sls)
Adam C. Walker (CEO)
Joe Jaruszewski (Exec VP-Packing Solutions)
Jack R. McCurdy Jr. (CFO)

Subsidiaries:

Berkeley Contract Packaging LLC (1)
17 S Middlesex Ave, Monroe Township, NJ 08831
Tel.: (908) 810-4000
Web Site:
http://www.berkeleypackaging.com
Packaging & Labeling Services
N.A.I.C.S.: 561910
Don Serebrenik (Dir-Mktg)
Jack Concannon (Pres)

SUMMIT CORPORATION OF AMERICA
1430 Waterbury Rd, Thomaston, CT 06787-2029
Tel.: (860) 283-4391 CT
Web Site: http://www.scact.com
Sales Range: $75-99.9 Million
Emp.: 100
Electroplating
N.A.I.C.S.: 332813
Harry Skoble (Pres)
Dave Smith (Dir-Sls & Mktg)
Michael Montana (Mgr-Inside Sls & Estimating)

SUMMIT ELECTRIC SUPPLY COMPANY
2900 Stanford NE, Albuquerque, NM 87107-1814
Tel.: (505) 346-9000 NM
Year Founded: 1922
Sales Range: $150-199.9 Million
Emp.: 650
Electrical Distr
N.A.I.C.S.: 423610
Sheila Hernandez (Sr VP)
Dan Long (Gen Counsel & VP-Assoc Resources)
Brian Rindels (Dir-Credit)
Thomas Klemp (CFO)
Mike Richardson (VP-Supplier Collaboration-Houston)
Ralph Mouret (Dir-Sls-EP&C)
Ryan Oehring (VP-Desert Southwest District)
Todd Bockenfeld (VP-North Texas)
Randy Hudson (Mgr-Sls-Irving)
David Wascom (VP-IT)
Chad Eschete (VP-Louisiana)
Brian Chisholm (Dir-Ops-South Texas)
Loris Unruh (Dir-Ops-Desert Southwest)
Skeet Spangler (Dir-EP&C)
Dave Armstrong (VP-Strategic Sls)
Cedric Ravet (VP-Supply Chain)
Ed Gerber (Pres & CEO)
Victor R. Jury Jr. (Chm)

Subsidiaries:

Summit Electric Supply Company - Marine Division (1)
621 Time Saver Ave, Harahan, LA 70123
Tel.: (504) 535-2600
Electrical Products Mfr
N.A.I.C.S.: 335999

SUMMIT ENERGY LLC
1245 Brickyard Rd Ste 210, Salt Lake City, UT 84106-4094
Tel.: (435) 940-9001
Web Site: http://www.summitcorp.net
Sales Range: $200-249.9 Million
Emp.: 17
Energy Marketing & Production Solutions
N.A.I.C.S.: 221118
David Lillywhite (Pres & CEO)
Jeff Thatcher (Controller)

SUMMIT EQUITY GROUP, LLC
801 Grand Ave Ste 3560, Des Moines, IA 50309
Tel.: (515) 243-2329
Web Site:
http://www.summitequity.com
Year Founded: 2004
Private Investment Group
N.A.I.C.S.: 523940
Dennis Bailey (Mng Partner)

Subsidiaries:

Enviro-Log, Inc. (1)
200 Ocilla Hwy, Fitzgerald, GA 31750
Tel.: (229) 423-7233
Web Site: http://www.enviro-log.net
Wood Products Mfr
N.A.I.C.S.: 321999
Ross A. McRoy (Co-Founder & Pres)
Jenny Luke (Office Mgr)
Allen Conger Sr. (Co-Founder)

SUMMIT FUNDING GROUP INC.
11500 Northlake Dr Ste 300, Cincinnati, OH 45249-1662
Tel.: (513) 489-1222
Web Site: http://www.summit-funding.com
Sales Range: $10-24.9 Million
Emp.: 40
Equipment & Vehicle Finance Leasing Companies
N.A.I.C.S.: 522220
Richard L. Ross (Founder, Pres & CEO)
Philip Hold (VP)
Erik Niewald (Mgr-Mktg)
Carlton Zwilling (VP)
Brian Lowe (Gen Mgr-Equipment Fin)
Ron Kuhn (Branch Mgr)
Matthew Ross (VP-Sls-California)
Todd Maurer (Mgr-Sls-Natl)
Michael J. Fitzsimmons (Gen Mgr-Construction & Material Handling Div)
Dan Hathcoat (Sr VP-Sls & Mktg)
Ryan LeRoy (Sls Mgr-Construction & Matl Handling-Southeast)
T. Max Hall (Sr VP-Enterprise Sls)
Bob Stalfort (Reg Sls Mgr-West)
John Heist Jr. (VP-Syndications)
Robert Gordon Iler Jr. (Sls Mgr-Enterprise Fin-Natl)

SUMMIT GROUP INC.
2701 S Minnesota, Sioux Falls, SD 57105
Tel.: (605) 361-9566
Web Site: http://www.shpreit.com
Rev.: $53,000,000
Emp.: 55
Hotels & Motels
N.A.I.C.S.: 721110
Kerry W. Boekelheide (Chm)

SUMMIT GROUP SOFTWARE
1405 Prairie Pkwy Ste A W, Fargo, ND 58078
Tel.: (701) 478-1387
Web Site:
http://www.summitgroupsoftware.com
Year Founded: 2005
Rev.: $2,400,000
Emp.: 18
Computer Software Services
N.A.I.C.S.: 513210

SUMMIT HANDLING SYSTEMS INC.
11 Defco Park Rd, North Haven, CT 06473
Tel.: (203) 239-5351
Web Site:
http://www.summithandling.com
Sales Range: $10-24.9 Million
Emp.: 100
Materials Handling Machinery
N.A.I.C.S.: 423830
Paul Weynann (Gen Mgr)
Lawrence T. McKevitt Jr. (Pres)

SUMMIT HEALTHCARE REIT, INC.
2 S Pointe Dr Ste 100, Lake Forest, CA 92630 MD
Web Site:
http://www.summithealthcarereit.com
Year Founded: 2004
Rev.: $26,294,000
Assets: $213,303,000
Liabilities: $190,405,000
Net Worth: $22,898,000
Earnings: ($8,629,000)
Emp.: 10
Fiscal Year-end: 12/31/22
Real Estate Investment Services
N.A.I.C.S.: 531210
J. Steven Roush (Chm)
Elizabeth A. Pagliarini (CEO & Sec)
Brenda Daw (Mgr-Asset)
Chris Kavanagh (Sr VP)
Janet Bonetto (Mgr-Acctg)
Juli Davenport (Coord-Acquisitions)
Sharyn I. Grant (CFO & Treas)

Subsidiaries:

Cornerstone Healthcare Partners, LLC (1)
920 Justison St, Wilmington, DE 19801
Tel.: (302) 317-3040
Web Site: https://www.mychp.org
Healtcare Services
N.A.I.C.S.: 621999
Molly Hayes (Dir-Clinical)
Adrian McCullough (Founder)
Jessica Weaver (Dir-Finance & Communications)
Cindy Beach (Dir-Human Resources)
Ty Weaver (Dir-Transportation)
Samuel Weaver (Dir-Operations)

SUMMIT HOSTING LLC
6734 Jamestown Dr, Alpharetta, GA 30005

U.S. PRIVATE

Web Site:
http://www.summithosting.com
Cloud Hosting Services
N.A.I.C.S.: 519290
Stanley Kania (Chm)
Warrem Patterson (Founder & CEO)
Shannon Kaiser (CTO)
Kevin Armstrong (Chief Revenue Officer)
Jeff Ash (CFO)
Stephanie Pokowitz (Controller)

Subsidiaries:

Insynq Inc. (1)
3312 Rosedale St Ste 203, Gig Harbor, WA 98335
Tel.: (253) 857-9400
Web Site: http://www.insynq.com
Software Publisher
N.A.I.C.S.: 513210

SUMMIT IMAGING, LLC
15000 Woodinville-Redmond Rd Bldg B Ste 800, Woodinville, WA 98072
Tel.: (866) 586-3744
Web Site:
http://www.mysummitimaging.com
Year Founded: 2006
Sales Range: $1-9.9 Million
Emp.: 47
Ultrasound Medical Equipment Support Services
N.A.I.C.S.: 621511
Lawrence Nguyen (CEO & CTO)
Alan Dishlip (CFO)
Sonia Smith (Controller)

SUMMIT INDUSTRIES, INC.
839 Pickens Industrial Dr, Marietta, GA 30062-3100
Tel.: (770) 590-0600 DE
Web Site:
http://www.summitinds.com
Year Founded: 1920
Sales Range: $10-24.9 Million
Emp.: 30
Mfr & Distr of Pharmaceutical, Automotive Aftermarket & Equestrian Products
N.A.I.C.S.: 325412
Mark Jaggei (Pres & CEO)
Carolyn Gray (Mgr-Customer Svc)
Christy Roper (Mgr-HR)

Subsidiaries:

Summit Industries, Inc. - Lexol Division (1)
PO Box 7329, Marietta, GA 30065
Tel.: (770) 590-0600
Web Site: http://www.lexol.com
Leather Cleaning Product Mfr
N.A.I.C.S.: 316990

SUMMIT INDUSTRIES, INC.
475 Dodson Lake Dr, Arlington, TX 76012
Tel.: (817) 861-8144 TX
Web Site:
http://www.summitseal.com
Year Founded: 1992
Sales Range: $10-24.9 Million
Industrial Sealing Components Mfr & Distr
N.A.I.C.S.: 339991
Ryan W. Wells (Pres)
Charles W. Wells (Chm & CEO)
Roy L. Shockey (Mgr-Mktg & Engrg)
Chris Stahura (Mgr-Matls & Quality Control)
Billy Burden (Mgr-Warehouse & Production)

Subsidiaries:

Fast-Spec, Inc. (1)
475 Dodson Lk Dr, Arlington, TX 76012
Tel.: (817) 226-6444
Web Site: http://www.fastspecinc.com
Sales Range: $1-9.9 Million
Emp.: 50
Industrial Fastener & Hardware Distr

COMPANIES

N.A.I.C.S.: 423840
Sal Esquivel (Mgr-Warehouse)
June E. Kelley (Gen Mgr)
Patti Becker (Mgr-Acctg)
Sharon Snipes (Mgr-Matls)
Nicki Stahura (Mgr-Sls & Customer Svc)

SUMMIT INTERCONNECT, INC.
223 North Crescent Way, Anaheim, CA 92801
Tel.: (714) 239-2433
Web Site: https://www.summit-pcb.com
Year Founded: 2016
Emp.: 320
Circuit Board Mfr
N.A.I.C.S.: 334412
Shane Whiteside (CEO)
Sean Patterson (COO)

Subsidiaries:

Royal Circuit Solutions, Inc. (1)
21 Hamilton Ct, Hollister, CA 95023
Tel.: (831) 636-7789
Web Site: http://www.royalcircuits.com
Sales Range: $1-9.9 Million
Emp.: 100
Printed Circuit Boards
N.A.I.C.S.: 334412

Subsidiary (Domestic):

Advanced Assembly LLC (2)
20100 E 32nd Pkwy Ste 225, Aurora, CO 80011
Tel.: (303) 307-9900
Web Site: http://www.aapcb.com
Emp.: 105
Printed Circuit Boards Assembly Services
N.A.I.C.S.: 334418
Lawrence Davis (Founder & CEO)
Marty Rodin (Dir-Quality Operational Excellence)
Sandra Torres (Controller)
Sommer Carter (Dir-Client Svcs)
Tim Landavazo (Dir-Plng & Analysis)

South Coast Circuits, Inc. (2)
3506 W Lk Ctr Dr Ste A, Santa Ana, CA 92704-6985
Tel.: (714) 966-2108
Web Site: http://www.sccircuits.com
Bare Printed Circuit Board Mfr
N.A.I.C.S.: 334412
Victor Hemingway (Pres)

SUMMIT LABORATORIES INC.
17010 Halsted St, Harvey, IL 60426-1203
Tel.: (708) 333-2995   IL
Web Site: http://www.summitlabsinc.com
Year Founded: 1989
Sales Range: $10-24.9 Million
Emp.: 50
Toilet Preparation Mfr
N.A.I.C.S.: 325620
Clyde Hammond Sr. (Pres & Treas)

SUMMIT LEARNING SERVICES
6955 W Broward Blvd, Plantation, FL 33317
Tel.: (954) 583-9288
Web Site: http://www.summitlearning.net
Year Founded: 2007
Sales Range: $1-9.9 Million
Tutoring Services
N.A.I.C.S.: 611691
Ed Cwieka (Co-Founder)
Jeanee Thompson (Co-Founder)

SUMMIT MARKETING
425 N New Ballas Rd Ste 201, Saint Louis, MO 63141-7091
Tel.: (314) 569-3737   MO
Web Site: http://www.summitmarketing.com
Year Founded: 1996
Sales Range: $25-49.9 Million
Emp.: 390

N.A.I.C.S.: 541810
Julie Barnickol (Mgr-Production Svcs)
Michelle Noyes (Chief Dev Officer)
Dan Renz (CEO)
Susan Yockey (Dir-Strategic Fundraising Client Svcs)
Tammy Nigus (VP-Creative)
Lance Meerkatz (VP-IT)
Lisa Heinemann (Dir-Production)

Subsidiaries:

Summit Marketing (1)
2526-B E 71st St, Tulsa, OK 74136-5576
Tel.: (918) 492-6098
Web Site: http://www.summitmarketing.com
Sales Range: Less than $1 Million
Emp.: 6
N.A.I.C.S.: 541810
Billy Hughes (Exec VP & Branch Mgr)

Summit Marketing (1)
1100 Cir 75 Pkwy Ste 1200, Atlanta, GA 30339
Tel.: (770) 303-0400
Web Site: http://www.summitmg.com
Sales Range: $10-24.9 Million
Emp.: 60
Advertising Agencies
N.A.I.C.S.: 541810
Dan Weil (Pres-Atlanta Office)

Summit Marketing (1)
960 Maplewood Dr, Itasca, IL 60143
Tel.: (630) 775-2700
Web Site: http://www.summitmarketing.com
Emp.: 70
N.A.I.C.S.: 541810

Summit Marketing (1)
8515 Bluejacket St, Lenexa, KS 66214
Tel.: (913) 888-6222
Web Site: http://www.summitmarketing.com
Emp.: 80
N.A.I.C.S.: 541810
Michael Tritt (Pres)

Summit Marketing (1)
4930 Sabal Lk Cir, Sarasota, FL 34238
Tel.: (941) 927-8027
Web Site: http://www.summitmarketing.com
N.A.I.C.S.: 541810
Sue Jolly (Sr Acct Exec)

Summit Marketing Group (1)
11961 Tech Rd, Silver Spring, MD 20904
Tel.: (301) 625-0800
Web Site: http://www.summitmarketing.com
Emp.: 50
N.A.I.C.S.: 541810
Denis Harper (Exec VP & Gen Mgr)

SUMMIT MORTGAGE
399 Boylston St, Boston, MA 02116
Tel.: (617) 859-0900
Web Site: http://www.summitmortgage.com
Year Founded: 1996
Sales Range: $10-24.9 Million
Emp.: 158
Residential Mortgage Services
N.A.I.C.S.: 522310

SUMMIT MORTGAGE CORPORATION
13355 10th Ave N Ste 500, Plymouth, MN 55441
Tel.: (763) 390-7200
Web Site: http://www.summitmortgage.com
Sales Range: $10-24.9 Million
Emp.: 300
Mortgage Services
N.A.I.C.S.: 522310
Robert Carter (Pres)
Betsy Lowther (Mgr-Wayzata)
Diana Carter (Principal)

SUMMIT PACKAGING SYSTEMS INC.
400 Gay St, Manchester, NH 03103-6817
Tel.: (603) 669-5410   DE

Web Site: http://www.summitpackagingsystems.com
Year Founded: 1976
Sales Range: $25-49.9 Million
Emp.: 400
Plastics Products
N.A.I.C.S.: 326199
Gordon Gilroy (Founder)
John Lynch (VP-Mktg)
Michael Conway (CFO)

SUMMIT PARTNERS, L.P.
222 Berkeley St 18th Fl, Boston, MA 02116
Tel.: (617) 824-1000   DE
Web Site: http://www.summitpartners.com
Year Founded: 1984
Rev.: $37,000,000,000
Private Equity & Venture Capital Firm
N.A.I.C.S.: 523999
Peter L. Rottier (Mng Dir)
Christopher J. Dean (Mng Dir)
Matthew G. Hamilton (Mng Dir)
Christopher J. Dean (Mng Dir)
Mark A. deLaar (Mng Dir)
Thomas H. Jennings (Mng Dir)
Robin N. Devereux (Chief Admin Officer & Mng Dir)
Adam H. Hennessey (Mng Dir & CFO)
Scott Collins (Mng Dir & COO)
Alexander D. Whittemore (Mng Dir-Capital Markets)
John R. Carroll (Mng Dir)
Darren M. Black (Mng Dir)
Peter A. Francis (Mng Dir)
Colin T. Mistele (Mng Dir)
Matthias G. Allgaier (Mng Dir-London)
Meg Riley Devine (CMO)
Ross D. Stern (Mng Dir)
Scott R. Ferguson (Principal)
David H. Schiller (Mng Dir & Chief IR Officer)
Nancy Parrish (Officer-IR)
Paul G. Furer (VP)
Mark T. Nordstrom (Principal-Capital Mkts)
Mark F. Hexamer (VP-Talent & Recruiting)
Jay D. Pauley (Mng Dir)
Len Ferrington (Mng Partner)
Peter Y. Chung (CEO & Mng Dir)
Michael A. Medici (Mng Dir)

Subsidiaries:

AFCV Holdings, LLC (1)
6665 Delmar Blvd Ste 3000, Saint Louis, MO 63005
Tel.: (314) 664-2010
Web Site: http://www.afcv.com
Holding Company; Consumer Internet Technologies Developer & Operator
N.A.I.C.S.: 551112
David Karandish (Chm & CEO)

Animal Supply Company LLC (1)
600 E Las Colinas Blvd Ste 700, Irving, TX 75039
Tel.: (972) 616-9600
Web Site: http://www.animalsupply.com
Pet Food & Supplies Distr
N.A.I.C.S.: 424990
Randy Reber (Founder & Chm)
Andrey Legkiy (Sr VP-Ops)
Danny Selman (VP-Bus Dev)
Ken Fish (Exec VP-Corp Dev)
Tim Batterson (Pres & CEO)
Angela Spears (VP-Digital Strategy & Mktg)
Jerry Walker (Exec VP-Bus Transformation & Strategy)
Jill Shoush (Sr VP-Sls)
Jodi Sanchez (VP-Customer Svc)
Mike Neylon (Sr VP-Vendor Mgmt & Mktg)
Mike Springer (VP-Vendor Mgmt & Consumables)
Linda Keetch (VP-HR)
Michelle Waters (Chief Acctg Officer & Sr VP-Fin)

SUMMIT PARTNERS, L.P.

Division (Domestic):

Animal Supply Co. West (2)
32001 32nd Ave S Ste 420, Federal Way, WA 98001
Tel.: (253) 237-0400
Web Site: http://www.animalsupply.com
Emp.: 80
Pet Food & Supplies Distr
N.A.I.C.S.: 424990
Jeff Sutherland (Reg Pres)

Subsidiary (Domestic):

Holistic Pet Source (2)
1414 Fort Negley Blvd, Nashville, TN 37203-5036
Tel.: (615) 254-9721
Web Site: http://www.holisticpetsource.com
Pet & Pet Supplies Stores
N.A.I.C.S.: 459910
Gaia Melkumova (Sec)

Lad's Pet Supplies (2)
1701 Eden Evans Center Rd, Angola, NY 14006
Tel.: (716) 549-8800
Web Site: http://www.ladspet.com
Nondurable Goods Merchant Whslr
N.A.I.C.S.: 424990
James Corbett (Dir-Sls & Mktg)

Lone Star Pet Supply, Inc. (2)
17414 Triton Dr, Schertz, TX 78154
Tel.: (210) 651-4414
Web Site: http://www.lonestarpet.com
Pet Food & Supplies Distr
N.A.I.C.S.: 424990
Danny Selman (Pres)

TDC Pets, LLC (2)
1025 W Ironwood St, Olathe, KS 66061
Tel.: (913) 825-1760
Natural Pet Food Distr
N.A.I.C.S.: 424490

Central Security Group, Inc. (1)
2448 E 81st St Ste 4200, Tulsa, OK 74137
Tel.: (918) 836-3350
Web Site: http://www.centralsecuritygroup.com
Sales Range: $1-9.9 Million
Forestry Services
N.A.I.C.S.: 115310
Doug Hespe (Dir-HR)
Duane Dietrich (Dir-IT)
Denise Hill (Supvr-Acq)
Lora Tanner (Coord-Mktg)
Richard Ginsburg (CEO)
Brandon Hess (Mgr-Dealer Acq)

Subsidiary (Domestic):

Allied Protective Systems, Inc. (2)
6909 N Robinson Ave, Oklahoma City, OK 73116
Tel.: (405) 842-1314
Web Site: http://www.alliedokc.net
Emp.: 30
Alarm Systems Installation Services
N.A.I.C.S.: 561621
Johnny Fletcher (Pres)

Fineline Technologies, Inc. (1)
3145 Medlock Bridge Rd, Norcross, GA 30071
Tel.: (678) 969-0835
Web Site: http://www.finelinetech.com
Other Management Consulting Services
N.A.I.C.S.: 541618
David Antonini (CFO)
Kevin Garrison (Dir-Innovation)
George Hoffman (CEO)
Rebecca Zhang (Dir-Global Ops)
Kyle Sundaram (COO)
Brian Kohrman (CTO)

Harvey Tool Company, LLC (1)
428 Newburyport Tpke, Rowley, MA 01969-1729
Tel.: (978) 948-8555
Web Site: http://www.harveytool.com
Industrial Machine Tool Distr
N.A.I.C.S.: 423830
Bryce Watson (Mgr-Product Sourcing)

Paradigm Management Services, LLC (1)
1277 Treat Blvd Ste 800, Walnut Creek, CA 94597
Tel.: (925) 676-2300
Web Site: http://www.paradigmcorp.com

SUMMIT PARTNERS, L.P.

Summit Partners, L.P.—(Continued)
Sales Range: $25-49.9 Million
Complex & Catastrophic Medical Management Services
N.A.I.C.S.: 621999
Nathan Cope (Founder & Officer-Medical)
Tom Mastri (CFO & Chief Admin Officer)
Kevin Turner (Chief Sls Officer)
Jim Hudak (Chm & CEO)
David Chenok (VP-Pain Solutions)
Michael Choo (Chief Medical Officer)
Scott Goll (Sr VP-Ops)
Anthony Dolce (CIO)
Jennifer Hinshaw (VP-Product Dev)

Subsidiary (Domestic):

Alaris Group, Inc. (2)
4108 N 79th Ave W, Duluth, MN 55810
Tel.: (218) 730-9950
Web Site: http://www.alarisgroup.com
Administrative Management & General Management Consulting Service
N.A.I.C.S.: 541611
Marijo Storment (Co-Owner & CEO)
Nicolas Rizer (Acct Exec)
Randy Bradley (Acct Exec-Reg)
Regina Bartlett (Acct Exec)
Nancy J. Caven (Co-Owner & Chief Sls Officer)
Adam Drake (Acct Exec-Natl)
Christine Delich (Owner & COO)
Leigh Freskos (Acct Exec-Reg)
Mike McKenna (Acct Exec-Natl)
Nicole Hottmann (VP & Reg Acct Exec)
Robert Otos (Co-Owner & Chief HR Officer)
Tony Delich (Co-Owner & CFO)

Encore Unlimited LLC (2)
1265 Main St Ste 201, Stevens Point, WI 54481
Tel.: (715) 343-1500
Web Site: http://www.encoreunlimited.com
Family Medical & Social Services
N.A.I.C.S.: 561990
Liz Thompson (CEO)

Patriot Growth Partners, LLC (1)
501 Office Center Dr Ste 215, Washington, PA 19034
Tel.: (215) 600-1357
Web Site: https://patriotgis.com
Insurance Company
N.A.I.C.S.: 524210
Matt Gardener (CEO)

Subsidiary (Domestic):

Bagatta Associates, Inc. (2)
823 W Jericho Tpke Ste 1A, Smithtown, NY 11787
Tel.: (631) 864-1111
Web Site: http://www.bagatta.com
Insurance Agencies & Brokerages
N.A.I.C.S.: 524210
Frank Bagatta (Pres)

Benefits Alliance Insurance Services, LLC (2)
31248 Oak Crest Dr Ste 140, Westlake Village, CA 91361
Tel.: (800) 532-5941
Insurance Brokerage Services
N.A.I.C.S.: 524210
Aaryn Lamos (Sr Acct Mgr-Benefits)

Subsidiary (Domestic):

Bridgeport Benefits (3)
5210 Lewis Rd Ste 14, Agoura Hills, CA 91301-2662
Tel.: (818) 865-5800
Web Site: http://www.bridgeportbenefits.com
Insurance Agencies & Brokerages
N.A.I.C.S.: 524210
Kyle Blasman (Dir-Bus Dev)

Corporate Benefit Marketing (3)
18801 Ventura Blvd Ste 201, Tarzana, CA 91356-3343
Tel.: (818) 380-2500
Web Site:
    http://www.corporatebenefitmarketing.com
Insurance Agencies & Brokerages
N.A.I.C.S.: 524210
David Style (Pres)

Subsidiary (Domestic):

The Dougherty Company Inc. (2)
PO Box 7277, Long Beach, CA 90807
Tel.: (562) 424-1621
Web Site: http://www.daughertyinc.com
Insurance Agencies & Brokerages
N.A.I.C.S.: 524210
Lonna MacKay (Mgr-Mktg)

Sound Inpatient Physicians, Inc. (1)
1498 Pacific Ave Ste 400, Tacoma, WA 98402
Tel.: (855) 768-6363
Web Site: http://www.soundphysicians.com
Performance Management Services for Hospitals
N.A.I.C.S.: 541618
Robert Bessler (Founder & CEO)
Steven M. McCarty (Gen Counsel)
Lynn Purdy (VP-Comm & Mktg)
Jess Parks (Pres)
Julie Seitz (Chief Compliance Officer)
Brian Pope (Chief Dev Officer)
Mark Rudolph (VP-Physician Dev & Patient Experience)
Billy Watson (VP-Market Dev & Strategy)
Peter Brink (CFO)
Matt Knox (CIO)
John Birkmeyer (Chief Clinical Officer)
Greta Boynton (Assoc Chief Medical Officer-Northeast)
Kevin Letz (VP-Advanced Practice Providers)

Summit Partners Limited (1)
11-12 Hanover Square, London, W1S 1JJ, United Kingdom (100%)
Tel.: (44) 2076597500
Web Site: http://www.summitpartners.com
Sales Range: $25-49.9 Million
Emp.: 30
Investment Management Service
N.A.I.C.S.: 523940
Scott Collins (Mng Dir & COO)
Han Sikkens (Mng Dir)
Christian R. Strain (Mng Dir)
Thomas M. Tarnowski (Mng Dir)
Andrew J. Collins (Mng Dir)
Leonard C. Ferrington (Mng Dir)
C. J. Fitzgerald (Mng Dir)
Craig D. Frances (Mng Dir)
Greg S. Goldfarb (Mng Dir)
Steffan K. Peyer (Principal)

Summit Partners, L.P. - Palo Alto Office (1)
200 Middlefield Rd Ste 200, Menlo Park, CA 94025
Tel.: (650) 321-1166
Web Site: http://www.summitpartners.com
Sales Range: $50-74.9 Million
Privater Equity Firm
N.A.I.C.S.: 523999
Harrison B. Miller (Mng Dir)
Craig D. Frances (Mng Dir-Palo Alto)
Charles J. Fitzgerald Jr. (Mng Dir-Palo Alto)
Walter G. Kortschak (Mng Dir)
Walter G. Kortschak (Mng Dir)
Deborah T. Lower (VP-Admin)
Greg S. Goldfarb (Mng Dir)
Brandon J. Roach (VP)
Leonard Ferrington (Mng Dir-Menlo Park)
Andrew J. Collins (Mng Dir)
David W. Averett (Mng Dir)
Darren M. Black (Mng Dir)
Adam D. Britt (Mng Dir)
Robin W. Devereux (CFO & Mng Dir)
James M. Freeland (Mng Dir)
Gregg J. Nardone (Mng Dir)
Han Sikkens (Mng Dir)
Christian R. Strain (Mng Dir)

Syndigo LLC (1)
141 W Jackson Blvd Ste 1220, Chicago, IL 60604
Tel.: (312) 766-4801
Web Site: https://www.syndigo.com
Content Management, Syndication, Analytics & Verified Product Information Services
N.A.I.C.S.: 519290
Simon Angove (CEO)
Peter Rottier (Mng Dir)

Subsidiary (Domestic):

EdgeAQ, LLC (2)
2948 Sidco Dr, Nashville, TN 37204
Tel.: (615) 371-3848
Web Site: http://www.edgenet.com
Information Technology Consulting Services
N.A.I.C.S.: 541512

Brian Rudolph (CTO)
Kraig Haberer (Sr VP-Mktg)
Lisa East (Dir-Customer Support-Nashville)
Steve Proctor (CEO)
Deborah West (Program Mgr-Mooresville)
Andrea Jacobson (Engr-Product Knowledge)
Chris Roach (Sr VP-Growth-Nashville)
Scott Howat (Dir-Automotive Channel Strategy)
Joe Thomas (Mgr-Automotive Program)
Ben Sellers (Dir-Enterprise Accts)
Meredith Ziegler (Dir-Strategic Accts)
Philip Spelman (Dir-Strategic Accts)

Sell Points Inc. (2)
1198 65th St Ste 250, Emeryville, CA 94608
Tel.: (866) 343-4310
Web Site: http://www.sellpoints.com
Data Processing, Hosting & Related Services
N.A.I.C.S.: 518210
Alan Dyck (Product Mgr-Mktg)
Austen Middleton (VP-Customer Success)
Benny Blum (Sr VP-Product)
Carol Wong (Project Mgr)
Cheryl Sembrano (Dir-Customer Support)
David Franco (VP-Bus Info Sys)
Ivan Dejanovic (Sr VP-Technology)
Joe Mantor (Mgr-Customer Success)
John Kuo (Product Mgr)
Jon Gregg (Pres)

Southern Graphic Systems, LLC (2)
1720 W Detweiller Dr, Peoria, IL 61615
Tel.: (888) 594-5331
Web Site: http://www.kwikeesystems.com
Web Hosting Services
N.A.I.C.S.: 513199
Jeff Creek (Dir-Inside Sls)

Teaching Strategies, LLC (1)
7101 Wisconsin Ave Ste 700, Bethesda, MD 20814
Tel.: (301) 634-0818
Web Site:
    http://www.teachingstrategies.com
Education Services
N.A.I.C.S.: 611710
Andrea Valentine (COO)
Diane Trister Dodge (Founder)
Kai-lee Berke (CEO)
John Olsen (Pres)

Subsidiary (Domestic):

Quality Assist, Inc. (2)
17 Executive Park Dr NE, Atlanta, GA 30329
Tel.: (404) 325-2225
Web Site: http://www.qassist.com
Rev.: $3,500,000
Emp.: 30
Educational Support Services
N.A.I.C.S.: 611710
Annette Sibley (Pres)

Trintech Group Limited (1)
Suite 13B Classon House, Dundrum Business Park, Dublin, 14, Ireland
Tel.: (353) 12984472
Web Site: http://www.trintech.com
Holding Company; Transaction Reconciliation & Payment Infrastructure Software Publisher
N.A.I.C.S.: 551112
Teresa Mackintosh (CEO)
Omar Choucair (CFO)
Russ Hubbard (Chief Revenue Officer)
David King (CMO)
Robert Michlewicz (Chief Strategy Officer)
Michael Ross (Chief Product Officer)
Derick Schaefer (CTO)
Leo Yancey (Chief Customer Officer)
Felicia Taylor (Chief HR Officer)

Subsidiary (US):

Trintech Inc. (2)
15851 Dallas Pkwy Ste 900, Addison, TX 75001
Tel.: (972) 701-9802
Web Site: http://www.trintech.com
Transaction Reconciliation & Payment Infrastructure Software Distr
N.A.I.C.S.: 423430
Darren Heffernan (CFO)
Teresa Mackintosh (CEO)
Michael Ross (Chief Product Officer)
David King (CMO)

Leo Yancey (Chief Customer Officer)
Robert Michlewicz (Chief Strategy Officer)
Derick Schaefer (CTO)
Omar Choucair (CFO)
Russ Hubbard (Chief Revenue Officer)

Subsidiary (Domestic):

Trintech Technologies Limited (2)
Suite 13B Classon House Dundrum Business Park, Dublin, Ireland
Tel.: (353) 1 298 4472
Web Site: http://www.trintech.com
Transaction Reconciliation & Payment Infrastructure Software Publisher
N.A.I.C.S.: 513210
Teresa Mackintosh (CEO)

Subsidiary (Non-US):

Trintech UK Ltd. (2)
5th Floor 7 Princes Street, London, EC2R 8AQ, United Kingdom
Tel.: (44) 2076285235
Web Site: http://www.trintech.com
Transaction Reconciliation & Payment Infrastructure Software Distr
N.A.I.C.S.: 423430
Lars Owe Nyland (Mng Dir-Europe)

SUMMIT PET PRODUCTS DISTRIBUTORS, INC.
420 N Chimney Rock Rd, Greensboro, NC 27410
Tel.: (336) 294-3200
Web Site: http://www.summitpet.com
Rev.: $65,000,000
Emp.: 200
Veterinary Product Mfr
N.A.I.C.S.: 541940
James Stanley (VP-Pur)
Jeff Greene (Mgr-Customer Svc)

SUMMIT PLASTIC CO.
1169 Brittain Rd, Akron, OH 44305
Tel.: (330) 633-3668
Web Site:
    http://www.summitplastic.com
Sales Range: $1-9.9 Million
Emp.: 100
Plastics Product Mfr
N.A.I.C.S.: 326199
Norman Belliveau (Pres & CEO)
Chuck Snyder (VP)
Lou Mokodean (Plant Mgr)
Connie Carper (Mgr-Logistics)
Robert Gumpf (VP-Sls)
Bret Sulaver (Mgr-Bus Dev)
George Collins (VP)
Jim Pfeiffer (Gen Mgr)
Darden Jones (Mgr-Sls-SW Reg)
Mark Shimp (Mgr-Sls-West Reg)
Mike Gibbs (Mgr-Sls-SE Reg)
Wayne Thiel (Mgr-Sls-North Reg)
Robin Buckridge (Mgr-Customer Svc)

SUMMIT POLYMERS INC.
6715 S Sprinkle Rd, Portage, MI 49002
Tel.: (269) 324-9330   MI
Web Site:
    http://www.summitpolymers.com
Year Founded: 1972
Sales Range: $75-99.9 Million
Emp.: 1,616
Plastics Products
N.A.I.C.S.: 326199
Connie Jackson (Coord-Matls)
Mark Roodbeen (Mgr-European Bus Program)
Sharon Macpherson (Mgr-HR)
Jacob Friess (Mgr-Matls)
Cathy Yeager (Coord-Quality)
David Robinson (Mgr-Quality)
Chuck Devries (Gen Mgr-Vicksburg Plant)
Jorge Garza (Engr-Quality & Mfg)
Mary Anne Brightwell (Mgr-Acctg)

SUMMIT RESOURCES LLC
410 Peachtree Pkwy, Cumming, GA 30041-7066

Sales Range: $1-9.9 Million
Emp.: 13
Marketing Technology Services to Automotive Industry
N.A.I.C.S.: 541613
Jonathan H. Lucenay (Pres & CEO)
Charles H. Darwin (COO & Sr VP)
Christopher Martin (VP-Sls)
Gregory Geodakyan (VP-Tech)

SUMMIT RIDGE CORPORATION
250 W 39th St Rm 203, New York, NY 10018
Tel.: (212) 391-8222
Sales Range: $10-24.9 Million
Emp.: 15
Mfr & Sales of Women's Sportswear
N.A.I.C.S.: 424350
Joanne Wang (Controller)
Bernie Marks (Pres & CEO)

SUMMIT SECURITY SERVICES INC.
390 RXR Plz W Tower Lobby Level, Uniondale, NY 11556
Tel.: (516) 240-2400
Web Site: http://www.summitsecurity.com
Year Founded: 1976
Sales Range: $10-24.9 Million
Emp.: 27
Detective & Armored Car Services
N.A.I.C.S.: 561612
Catherine Walsh (Mgr-Billing & Payroll)
James Nicchio (Mgr-Client Svcs)
Nick M. Auletta (Co-Pres)
John Liberti (VP)
Scott Sturgess (VP-Sls & Mktg)
Kaitlin Burden (Mgr-Client Dev)

SUMMIT SPORTS, INC.
330 Enterprise Ct, Bloomfield Hills, MI 48302
Tel.: (248) 338-9980   MI
Web Site: http://www.summitonline.com
Year Founded: 1990
Sales Range: $1-9.9 Million
Emp.: 75
Sporting Goods Retailer
N.A.I.C.S.: 459110
Steve Kopitz (Pres)
Anna M. Steenland (Controller)
Trey Rouss (Gen Mgr-Retail Stores)

Subsidiaries:

Rocky Mountain Tours   (1)
82 Newark Pompton Tpke, Riverdale, NJ 07457
Tel.: (973) 831-7000
Web Site: http://www.rockymountaintours.com
Ski Resort Accommodations
N.A.I.C.S.: 561520

SUMMIT STRATEGIES INC.
8182 Maryland Ave 6th Fl, Saint Louis, MO 63105
Tel.: (314) 727-7211
Web Site: http://www.ssgstl.com
Year Founded: 1995
Sales Range: $50-74.9 Million
Emp.: 65
Investment Consulting Services
N.A.I.C.S.: 523940

SUMMIT TECH CONSULTING
2702 Mount Pleasant Trl, Duluth, GA 30097-7447
Tel.: (404) 731-9484
Web Site: http://www.summittechconsulting.com
Year Founded: 2003
Sales Range: $1-9.9 Million

Emp.: 43
Hospital Business Solutions & Consulting
N.A.I.C.S.: 561499
Sally Godzer (CEO)
Sherry Charters (VP-Sls & Ops)
Chuck Gozder (COO)

SUMMIT TECHNICAL SERVICES, INC.
300 Centerville Rd, Warwick, RI 02886-4320
Tel.: (401) 736-8323   RI
Web Site: http://www.summit-technical.com
Year Founded: 1988
Sales Range: $10-24.9 Million
Emp.: 550
Temporary IT & Engineering Placement Services
N.A.I.C.S.: 561320
Bruce Comolli (Engr-Mechanical)
Richard Jon Barry (Pres & Treas)

SUMMIT TECHNICAL SOLUTIONS, LLC
565 Space Centre Dr Ste 230, Colorado Springs, CO 80915
Tel.: (719) 520-9787   CO
Web Site: http://www.sts-llc.biz
Year Founded: 2001
Sales Range: $25-49.9 Million
Emp.: 350
It Consulting
N.A.I.C.S.: 541690
Kelly Terrien (Pres & CEO)
Rod McNeill (Dir-Bus Unit)

SUMMIT TECHNOLOGY, INC.
120 W Market St, Athens, AL 35611
Tel.: (256) 771-1656
Web Site: http://www.summitsti.com
Year Founded: 2001
Sales Range: $10-24.9 Million
Emp.: 14
Information Technology Consulting Services
N.A.I.C.S.: 541512
Gerald Newsom (Exec VP-Cloud Svcs)
Glenn Baker (COO)
Carl Hunt (CEO)
Kevin Chowning (Founder & VP-Consulting)
Bill Cade (Exec VP-Sls)

SUMMIT TOOL COMPANY
768 E North St, Akron, OH 44305
Tel.: (330) 535-7177   OH
Web Site: http://www.summittoolcompany.com
Year Founded: 1932
Sales Range: $25-49.9 Million
Emp.: 73
Tire Changing Tools Mfr
N.A.I.C.S.: 332216
Alexander Pendleton (Chm & CEO)
David Tallarico (Asst Treas)

Subsidiaries:

Ken-Tool   (1)
768 E N St, Akron, OH 44305-1164
Tel.: (330) 535-7177
Web Site: http://www.kentool.com
Sales Range: $10-24.9 Million
Emp.: 65
Mfr of Tire Changing Tools
N.A.I.C.S.: 332216
Rockford Tyson (VP-Sls & Mktg)
Leonard Broyles (Mgr-Customer Svc & Tech Support)
Susan Landis (Mgr-Matls)
Stephen Vyn (Dir-Sls & Mktg)
Douglas Ronstadt (Pres)
Eunice Boyes (Coord-Sls & Mktg)
Ben Graham (Mgr-Sls-Natl)

SUMMIT TRUCKING, INC.
1358 Medical District Dr, Dallas, TX 75207
Tel.: (214) 631-3080   TX
Web Site: https://www.summittransportation.com
Year Founded: 1997
Sales Range: $10-24.9 Million
General Freight Trucking, Long-Distance, Truckload
N.A.I.C.S.: 484121
Bart Plaskoff (Pres & CEO)
Randy Barnett (Dir-Safety)
Tim Roach (VP)

SUMMIT UTILITIES INC.
7810 Shaffer Pkwy Ste 120, Littleton, CO 80127
Tel.: (720) 981-2123
Web Site: http://www.summitutilitiesinc.com
Year Founded: 1996
Holding Company; Natural Gas Distr
N.A.I.C.S.: 551112
Bob Gunderman (CFO)
Roopesh Aggarwal (VP-Corp Strategy & Dev)
Kurt W. Adams (Pres & CEO)
Dave Moody (Sr VP-Ops)
Bryan L. Sutter (Chief Legal Officer, Sec & VP)
Jennifer Banks (VP-Engrg)
Amy Reininger (Chief HR Officer & VP)

Subsidiaries:

AOG Corporation   (1)
115 N 12th St, Fort Smith, AR 72902-2414
Tel.: (479) 783-3181
Web Site: http://www.aogc.com
Gas Transmission & Distribution Services
N.A.I.C.S.: 221210
Robert J. Mulson (Treas, Sr VP-Fin & Acctg)
Kim Linam (Pres)

Colorado Natural Gas, Inc.   (1)
7810 Shaffer Pkwy Ste 120, Littleton, CO 80127-3752
Tel.: (303) 979-7680
Web Site: http://www.coloradonaturalgas.com
Natural Gas Distr
N.A.I.C.S.: 221210
Aaron Williamson (Mgr)

Summit Natural Gas of Maine, Inc.   (1)
442 Civic Center Dr Ste 100, Augusta, ME 04330
Tel.: (800) 909-7642
Web Site: http://www.summitnaturalgasmaine.com
Natural Gas Distr
N.A.I.C.S.: 221210
Lizzy Reinholt (Dir-External Affairs)

Summit Natural Gas of Missouri, Inc.   (1)
7810 Shaffer Pkwy Ste 120, Littleton, CO 80127
Tel.: (800) 927-0787
Natural Gas Distr
N.A.I.C.S.: 221210
Dave Moody (Sr VP-Ops)

SUMMITT FORESTS INC.
2305 Ashland St Ste C PMB 432, Ashland, OR 97520
Tel.: (541) 535-8920
Web Site: http://www.summittforests.com
Year Founded: 1983
Sales Range: $25-49.9 Million
Emp.: 30
Forestry Services
N.A.I.C.S.: 115310
Scott Nelson (Co-Owner & Pres)

SUMMITVILLE TILES, INC.
PO Box 73, Summitville, OH 43962-0073
Tel.: (330) 223-1511
Web Site: http://www.summitville.com
Year Founded: 1911
Sales Range: $100-124.9 Million
Emp.: 200
Mfr of Glazed Wall, Decorative & Quarry Tile; Floor Brick; Glazed Porcelain Floor Tile
N.A.I.C.S.: 327120
Bruce Johnson (Owner)
David W. Johnson (CEO)
Brooke Carvalho (Dir-Human Rels)
Gregory Klocek (Mgr-IT)

SUMNER COMMUNICATIONS INC.
24 Stony Hill Rd, Bethel, CT 06801
Tel.: (203) 748-2050
Web Site: http://www.sumnercom.com
Sales Range: $10-24.9 Million
Emp.: 30
Publisher of Trade Magazine & Directories
N.A.I.C.S.: 513120
Ronald A. Fisher (Publr)
Amber Lautier (Dir-Adv)
Lisa Rioni (CTO)

SUMNER FINANCIAL CORPORATION
780 Browns Ln, Gallatin, TN 37066
Tel.: (615) 451-4151
Year Founded: 2021
Bank Holding Company
N.A.I.C.S.: 551111

SUMNER GROUP INC.
2121 Hampton Ave, Saint Louis, MO 63139-2904
Tel.: (314) 633-8000   MO
Web Site: http://www.sumner-group.com
Year Founded: 1972
Sales Range: $50-74.9 Million
Emp.: 500
Supplier of Office Equipment
N.A.I.C.S.: 423420
Steven P. Sumner (Pres)
Fred Weaver (CFO & VP)

SUMNER-COWLEY ELECTRIC COOPERATIVE, INC.
2223 N A St, Wellington, KS 67152
Tel.: (620) 326-3356   KS
Web Site: http://www.sucocoop.com
Year Founded: 1938
Sales Range: $10-24.9 Million
Emp.: 16
Electric Power Distribution Services
N.A.I.C.S.: 221122
Ed Amerein (Mgr-Warehouse)
Stacy White (Accountant)
Coni Adams (Mgr-Admin & HR)
Richard Mitchell (Mgr-Ops)
Clete Rains (CEO & Gen Mgr)

SUMTER ELECTRIC COOPERATIVE INC.
330 S US Hwy 301, Sumterville, FL 33585-4911
Tel.: (352) 793-3801   FL
Web Site: http://www.secoenergy.com
Year Founded: 1938
Sales Range: $350-399.9 Million
Electronic Services
N.A.I.C.S.: 221122
James P. Duncan (CEO)
Ben Brickhouse (VP-Engrg)
John LaSelva (VP-Ops)
Ray F. Vick (Pres)
Kathryn Gloria (VP-Corp Comm & Energy Svcs)

SUMTER ELECTRIC COOPERATIVE INC.

Sumter Electric Cooperative Inc.—(Continued)
Gene Kanikovsky (CFO)
Gregg Morrell (VP-Corp Svcs & HR)
Jerry T. Hatfield (VP)
Robin Henion (Treas & Sec)

SUMTER ELECTRIC MEMBERSHIP CORPORATION
1120 Felder St, Americus, GA 31709
Tel.: (229) 924-8041
Web Site: http://www.sumteremc.com
Rev.: $24,353,754
Emp.: 49
Transmission, Electric Power
N.A.I.C.S.: 221121
James Ted McMillan (Pres & CEO)
William E. Harris (Asst Sec)
Michael D. Webb (Sec)

SUN & SKIN CARE RESEARCH, LLC
851 Greensboro Rd, Cocoa, FL 32926-4516
Tel.: (321) 633-4644
Web Site: http://www.sscrllc.com
Year Founded: 1989
Sales Range: $25-49.9 Million
Emp.: 80
Toilet Product Mfr
N.A.I.C.S.: 325620
Stuart J. Straus (CEO)

SUN AVIATION, INC.
Sun Aviation Bldg 10010 E 87th St, Kansas City, MO 64138
Tel.: (816) 358-4925 MO
Web Site: http://www.sunav.com
Year Founded: 1987
Sales Range: $1-9.9 Million
Emp.: 10
Aviation Equipment Sales
N.A.I.C.S.: 423860
Jeff Gregg (Pres)

Subsidiaries:

Vero Beach Avionics, Inc. (1)
2620 Airport N Dr, Vero Beach, FL 32960-4506
Tel.: (772) 299-0770
Web Site:
http://www.verobeachavionics.com
Avionics Alteration & Installation Services
N.A.I.C.S.: 488999
Richard Peavley (Gen Mgr)
Albert Rice (Mgr)

SUN BELLE INC.
3810 Rose St, Schiller Park, IL 60176
Tel.: (708) 343-4545 DC
Web Site: http://www.sun-belle.com
Year Founded: 1986
Sales Range: $10-24.9 Million
Emp.: 70
Producers of Fresh Fruits & Vegetables
N.A.I.C.S.: 541430
John Hepgus (VP)

SUN BELT FOOD COMPANY, INC.
4755 Technology Way Ste 209, Boca Raton, FL 33431-3343
Tel.: (561) 995-9100
Web Site:
http://www.sunbeltfoods.com
Year Founded: 1990
Rev.: $70,000,000
Emp.: 6
Meat Packing Services
N.A.I.C.S.: 424470
Barry Dishman (Pres)

SUN BIOMASS, INC.
3700 Buffalo Speedway Ste 410, Houston, TX 77098
Tel.: (713) 907-1345 DE

Year Founded: 2009
Organic Fertilizer & Other Biomass Products from Biodegradable Wastes Developer & Mfr
N.A.I.C.S.: 325312
Alesia Bautina (Chm, Pres, CEO, CFO & Sec)

SUN BROTHERS LLC
754 W Pioneer Blvd Ste 101, Mesquite, NV 89027
Web Site: http://www.sunwarrior.com
Year Founded: 2008
Sales Range: $10-24.9 Million
Emp.: 28
Vegan Protein Powders
N.A.I.C.S.: 456191
Nick Stern (Co-Founder)
Denley Fowlke (Co-Founder)

SUN BULB COMPANY, INC.
1615 SW Hwy 17, Arcadia, FL 34266-7101
Tel.: (863) 494-4022 FL
Web Site: http://www.sunbulb.com
Year Founded: 1956
Sales Range: $125-149.9 Million
Emp.: 150
Flower Bulbs, Bromeliads, Orchids & Ferns Grower & Distr
N.A.I.C.S.: 424910
Rodney Hollingsworth (VP & Gen Mgr)
Tom Hollingsworth (Pres)

SUN CAPITAL PARTNERS, INC.
5200 Town Center 4th Fl, Boca Raton, FL 33486
Tel.: (561) 394-0550 FL
Web Site: http://www.suncappart.com
Year Founded: 1995
Privater Equity Firm
N.A.I.C.S.: 523999
Deryl C. Couch (Gen Counsel & Mng Dir)
M. Steven Liff (Sr Mng Dir & Head-Private Equity-North America)
Paul Daccus (Mng Dir)
Bruce E. Roberson (Head-North American Operations)
Daniel M. Florian (Mng Dir)
Raj Karanam (Mng Dir)
Sergei Spiridonov (Mng Dir)
Todd Plosker (Mng Dir & Head-Capital Markets)
Jeremy Stone (Mng Dir)
Jared Wien (Mng Dir)
Bruce Roberson (Partner & Head-North American Operations)
Tim Stubbs (Partner & Head-European Operations)
Elizabeth de Saint-Aignan (Mng Dir-Transactions)
Rodger R. Krouse (Co-Founder & Co-CEO)
Marc J. Leder (Co-CEO)

Subsidiaries:

AS America, Inc. (1)
1 Centennial Ave, Piscataway, NJ 08855-6820
Tel.: (732) 980-6000
Web Site: http://www.americanstandard-us.com
Bathroom & Kitchen Faucets, Fixtures, Furniture Mfr
N.A.I.C.S.: 327110
John Gillespie (VP-Mktg-Trade)
Chris Capone (VP-Trade Sls)
Michael Marchi (COO)
Steve Delarge (Acting CEO)

Subsidiary (Non-US):

American Standard B&K Mexico, S. de R.L. de C.V. (2)
Via Morelos No 330 Santa Clara Coatitla,
Ecatepec, 55540, Mexico
Web Site:
http://www.americanstandard.com.mx
Plumbing Fixture Mfr
N.A.I.C.S.: 327110

American Standard Canada, Inc. (2)
5900 Avebury Road, Mississauga, L5R 3M3, ON, Canada
Tel.: (905) 949-4800
Web Site: http://www.americanstandard.ca
Plumbing Fixtures & Supplies Whslr
N.A.I.C.S.: 423720

Subsidiary (Domestic):

Amstan Logistics Inc. (2)
101 Knightsbridge Dr, Hamilton, OH 45011
Tel.: (513) 863-4627
Web Site: http://www.amstan.com
Sales Range: $25-49.9 Million
Emp.: 123
Trucking Except Local
N.A.I.C.S.: 484121

Crane Plumbing, L.L.C. (2)
1235 Hartrey Ave, Evanston, IL 60202-1056
Tel.: (847) 864-7600
Web Site: http://www.craneplumbing.com
Sales Range: $250-299.9 Million
Plumbing Fixtures & Accessories Mfr
N.A.I.C.S.: 327110

Eljer, Inc. (2)
2105 Elm Hill Pike Ste 105, Nashville, TN 37210-3978
Tel.: (972) 560-2000
Web Site: http://www.eljer.com
Sales Range: $150-199.9 Million
Faucets, Kitchen & Bath Sinks, Toilets, Bidets, Tubs & Whirlpools Mfr & Whslr
N.A.I.C.S.: 332913

Porcher Luxury Designs (2)
6615 W Boston St, Chandler, AZ 85226-3314
Tel.: (480) 961-5353
Web Site: http://www.porcher-us.com
Sales Range: $10-24.9 Million
Emp.: 65
Plumbing Fixture Designing
N.A.I.C.S.: 332999

Subsidiary (Domestic):

Safety Tubs LLC (2)
902 W Carrier Pkwy, Grand Prairie, TX 75050
Tel.: (877) 304-2800
Web Site: http://www.safetytubs.com
Sales Range: $25-49.9 Million
Emp.: 100
Plastics Plumbing Fixture Mfr
N.A.I.C.S.: 326191
Rob Buete (Gen Mgr)

Sanitarios Dominicanos, S.A. (2)
EPS B105, Miami, FL 33102
Tel.: (809) 575-2657
Sales Range: $25-49.9 Million
Emp.: 40
Plumbing Fixtures & Vitreous Sanitary Wares Mfr
N.A.I.C.S.: 327110

Ames Taping Tool Systems Co. (1)
1327 Northbrook Pkwy Ste 400, Suwanee, GA 30024
Tel.: (800) 303-1827
Web Site: http://amestools.com
Mfr Sales & Leasing of Tools & Paper Tape For Finishing Gypsum Drywall Board Joints
N.A.I.C.S.: 532310
Amy Reinmeyer (Mgr-HR)

Andersen Commercial Plumbing, Inc. (1)
1608 Yeager Ave, La Verne, CA 91750
Tel.: (909) 599-5950
Web Site:
http://www.andersenplumbing.com
Plumbing, Heating & Air-Conditioning Contractors
N.A.I.C.S.: 238220
Christian Hand (CEO)
Duane Kerr (CFO)

BL Restaurant Operations, LLC (1)
4550 Beltway Dr, Addison, TX 75001

U.S. PRIVATE

Tel.: (214) 845-4800
Web Site: http://www.barlouie.com
Emp.: 40
Restaurant Operators
N.A.I.C.S.: 722511
Mike Mrlik (COO)
Brian Wright (CEO)

Bachrach Clothing, Inc. (1)
1430 Broadway Ste 308, New York, NY 10018
Tel.: (212) 354-4927
Web Site: http://www.bachrach.com
Sales Range: $100-124.9 Million
Men's & Boys' Clothing Retailer
N.A.I.C.S.: 458110

Coveris Holdings S.A. (1)
8600 W Bryn Mawr Ave Ste 800N, Chicago, IL 60631
Tel.: (773) 877-3300
Web Site: http://www.coveris.com
Rev.: $2,759,257,000
Assets: $2,456,557,000
Liabilities: $2,324,744,000
Net Worth: $131,813,000
Earnings: ($100,255,000)
Emp.: 9,825
Fiscal Year-end: 12/31/2014
Holding Company; Plastic Packaging, Container & Coating Products Mfr
N.A.I.C.S.: 551112
Duane A. Owens (Treas)
Michael E. Alger (CFO-Bus Unit-Americas)
Cynthia Bauman (VP-HR)
Anthony Fogel (Chief People & Culture Officer)
Dimitri Panayotopoulos (Chm)
Christopher Swalm (Mgr-Corp Mktg Comm)
Jakob A. Mosser (CEO)
Markus Petersen (Grp CFO)

Subsidiary (Domestic):

Coveris Holding Corp. (2)
3070 Southport Rd, Spartanburg, SC 29302
Tel.: (864) 596-7140
Web Site: http://www.coveris.com
Sales Range: $800-899.9 Million
Emp.: 2,265
Holding Company; Packaging Materials & Products Mfr
N.A.I.C.S.: 551112
Duane A. Owens (Treas)
Michael E. Alger (CFO)
Chris Swalm (Mgr-Mktg Comm)
Carla E. Stucky (Chief Acctg Officer)
Lee Marks (VP-Global Operational Excellence)
Kathleen McJohn (Gen Counsel)
Loic Sebileau (Dir-Global Bus Dev)

Subsidiary (Domestic):

Cello-Foil Products, Inc. (3)
155 Brook St, Battle Creek, MI 49017-3031
Tel.: (269) 964-7137
Sales Range: $25-49.9 Million
Packaging Products
N.A.I.C.S.: 322220

Subsidiary (Non-US):

Coveris Advanced Coatings Holdings (UK) Ltd. (3)
Ash Rd North, Wrexham Industrial Estate, Wrexham, LL13 9UF, United Kingdom (100%)
Tel.: (44) 1978660241
Web Site:
http://www.coverisadvancedcoatings.com
Sales Range: $50-74.9 Million
Emp.: 100
Holding Company; Coated Papers, Films & Special Substrates Mfr
N.A.I.C.S.: 551112
Joanne Parrett (Gen Mgr)

Subsidiary (Domestic):

Coveris Advanced Coatings (North Wales) Ltd. (4)
Ash Rd North Wrexham Industrial Estate, Wrexham, LL13 9UF, Cheshire, United Kingdom (100%)
Tel.: (44) 1978660241
Web Site:
http://www.coverisadvancedcoatings.com
Sales Range: $10-24.9 Million
Emp.: 100

COMPANIES SUN CAPITAL PARTNERS, INC.

Mfr of Coated Papers, Films & Specialty Substrates
N.A.I.C.S.: 322220
Joanne Parrott *(Sec)*

Subsidiary (Domestic):

Coveris Advanced Coatings US LLC (3)
700 Crestdale Rd, Matthews, NC 28105-4700 **(100%)**
Tel.: (704) 847-9171
Web Site: http://www.coverisadvancedcoatings.com
Sales Range: $25-49.9 Million
Emp.: 100
Mfr of High Technology Coatings & Laminates of Foils, Tissues & Films for Industrial Applications; Commercial Metal Analysis Plants
N.A.I.C.S.: 322220
Vic Hoffman *(Controller)*

Coveris Flexibles US LLC (3)
3070 Southport Rd, Spartanburg, SC 29302
Tel.: (864) 596-7140
Web Site: http://www.coveris.com
Plastic Film & Bag Mfr
N.A.I.C.S.: 326111
Pete Horgan *(Dir-Corp Fin)*

Subsidiary (Domestic):

Coveris Flexibles (Thomasville) US LLC (4)
1308 Blair St, Thomasville, NC 27360
Tel.: (336) 476-3131
Plastics Product Mfr
N.A.I.C.S.: 326199

Division (Domestic):

Coveris Flexibles US LLC - Consumer Food Division (4)
905 W Verdigris Pkwy, Catoosa, OK 74015
Tel.: (918) 739-4900
Packaging Services
N.A.I.C.S.: 561910

Coveris Flexibles US LLC - Performance Films Division (4)
1304 Arthur K Bolton Pkwy, Griffin, GA 30223
Tel.: (770) 227-4573
Web Site: http://www.coveris.com
Emp.: 50
Plastic Packaging Film Mfr
N.A.I.C.S.: 326112

Coveris Flexibles US LLC - Pet Food Division (4)
501 Williams St, Tomah, WI 54660
Tel.: (608) 372-2153
Pet Food Mfr
N.A.I.C.S.: 311119

Subsidiary (Domestic):

KubeTech Custom Molding Inc. (3)
400 Penn Center Blvd Ste 1000, Pittsburgh, PA 15235
Tel.: (412) 823-2100
Web Site: http://www.kubetechmolding.com
Plastics Product Mfr
N.A.I.C.S.: 326199

Delaware Valley Management Holdings, Inc. (1)
330 Middletown Blvd Ste 401, Langhorne, PA 19047-3204
Tel.: (215) 757-1574
Web Site: http://www.888smile10.com
Offices of Dentists
N.A.I.C.S.: 621210

DuraFiber Technologies (DFT), Inc. (1)
13620 Reese Blvd Ste 400, Huntersville, NC 28078
Tel.: (704) 912-3770
Web Site: http://www.durafibertech.com
Emp.: 1,500
Industrial Fibers & Fabrics Mfr
N.A.I.C.S.: 313230
Frank Papa *(CEO)*
Erwin Bette *(CFO)*
Rick Spurlock *(VP-HR)*
Richard Cutter *(Gen Counsel, Sec & VP)*
Kathy Marker *(Dir-Comml-Americas)*
Ralph Van Loo *(Dir-Comml-Europe)*

Plant (Domestic):

DuraFiber Technologies (DFT), Inc. - Salisbury Plant (2)
7401 Statesville Blvd Hwy 70 W, Salisbury, NC 28147
Tel.: (704) 636-6000
Web Site: http://www.durafibertech.com
Artificial & Synthetic Fiber Mfr
N.A.I.C.S.: 325220

DuraFiber Technologies (DFT), Inc. - Shelby Facility (2)
2525 Blacksburg Rd, Grover, NC 28073
Tel.: (704) 482-2411
Web Site: http://www.durafibertech.com
Polyester Thread Mfr
N.A.I.C.S.: 313110

DuraFiber Technologies (DFT), Inc. - Winnsboro Plant (2)
199 Maple St, Winnsboro, SC 29180
Tel.: (803) 635-4651
Web Site: http://www.durafibertech.com
Artificial & Synthetic Fiber Mfr
N.A.I.C.S.: 325220

EIS Holdings, LLC (1)
4028 Daley Ave, Fort Worth, TX 76180
Tel.: (800) 656-7071
Web Site: https://eisholdings.com
Emp.: 1,000
Environmental Infrastructure Services
N.A.I.C.S.: 518210

Subsidiary (Domestic):

Eagle Environmental Consulting, Inc (2)
8000 W 44th Ave, Wheat Ridge, CO 80033
Tel.: (850) 336-2385
Web Site: http://www.eagle-enviro.com
Process, Physical Distribution & Logistics Consulting Services
N.A.I.C.S.: 541614
Chris Posey *(Pres)*

Edwin Watts Golf Shops, LLC (1)
20 Hill Ave, Fort Walton Beach, FL 32548
Tel.: (850) 244-2066
Web Site: http://www.edwinwatts.com
Emp.: 3
Golf Equipment, Apparel & Accessories Retailer
N.A.I.C.S.: 459110
Bill Grigsby *(VP-Real Estate)*
Benn McCallisper *(VP-Mktg, Adv, Catalog & Online)*
John Kopacz *(VP-Retail Ops)*
Rick Powell *(VP-Pur & Inventory)*

Exadel, Inc. (1)
1340 Treat Blvd Ste 375, Walnut Creek, CA 94597
Tel.: (925) 363-9510
Web Site: http://www.exadel.com
Computer Related Services
N.A.I.C.S.: 541519
Alexander Sokolov *(Sr Engr-Software)*
Alex Kreymer *(COO)*
Jonathan Fries *(VP-Engrg & Digital Transformation)*
Oleg Boyko *(CTO)*
Marc Caponegro *(Chief Revenue Officer)*
Fima Katz *(Founder, Pres & CEO)*

Fresh Origins, LLC (1)
570 Quarry Rd, San Marcos, CA 92069
Tel.: (760) 736-4072
Web Site: http://www.freshorigins.com
Sales Range: $1-9.9 Million
Emp.: 45
Field Crops, Except Cash Grains, Nec, Nsk
N.A.I.C.S.: 111998
David Sasuga *(Principal)*
John Freitas *(Mgr-Natl Sls)*

Friendly Ice Cream Corporation (1)
1855 Boston Rd, Wilbraham, MA 01095-1002
Tel.: (413) 543-2400
Web Site: http://www.friendlys.com
Sales Range: $500-549.9 Million
Restaurant Chain Management & Ice Cream Mfr
N.A.I.C.S.: 722511
Maura Tobias *(Dir-Brand Engagement)*
John Maguire *(CEO)*
David Ulgenalp *(Chief Dev Officer & Sr VP)*
Randy Davis *(CMO & Exec VP)*

Connie Lennick *(Sr VP-HR)*
Bob Sawyer *(Gen Counsel, Sec & Sr VP)*
Todd Schwendenmann *(CFO & Exec VP)*
Steve Weigel *(COO & Exec VP)*

Gem Shopping Network, Inc. (1)
3259 Duluth Hwy 120, Duluth, GA 30096
Tel.: (770) 622-5505
Web Site: http://www.gemshopping.com
Emp.: 50
Jewelry Store Operator
N.A.I.C.S.: 458310
Colin Taylor *(CEO)*

Gordmans Stores Inc. (1)
1926 S 67th St, Omaha, NE 68106
Tel.: (402) 691-4000
Web Site: http://www.gordmans.com
Rev.: $648,967,000
Assets: $230,252,000
Liabilities: $195,358,000
Net Worth: $34,894,000
Earnings: ($4,338,000)
Emp.: 590
Fiscal Year-end: 01/30/2016
Discount Department Store Operator
N.A.I.C.S.: 455110
Arthur Gorling *(Chief Mdsg Officer & Sr VP)*
Richard H. Heyman *(CIO & Sr VP)*
Roger L. Glenn *(Sr VP-HR)*
Tracie L. Wickenhauser *(Sr VP-Stores)*
Amy Starr Myers *(Sr VP-Mktg)*
Michael F. Ricart *(Sr VP)*
Ramin Mozafari *(Sr VP-Plng & Allocation)*

Subsidiary (Domestic):

Gordmans, Inc. (2)
1926 S 67th St, Omaha, NE 68106
Tel.: (402) 691-4000
Web Site: http://www.gordmans.com
Fashion Apparels Retailer
N.A.I.C.S.: 458110
Michael Wirkkala *(VP-Ops)*
Larry Hudson *(Mgr-District Loss Prevention)*

Hickory Farms, LLC (1)
311 S Wacker Ste 2030, Chicago, IL 60606
Tel.: (419) 893-7611
Web Site: http://www.hickoryfarms.com
Sales Range: $150-199.9 Million
Emp.: 60
Specialty Food; Smoked Meats, Crackers & Snacks; Food Gift Packages
N.A.I.C.S.: 445298
Judy Ransford *(CMO)*
Matt James *(COO)*
Kevin Rule *(CFO-Chicago)*
Diana Davis *(Sr Dir-Integrated Mktg)*

Subsidiary (Domestic):

Wicked Good Cupcakes LLC (2)
342A Circuit St, Hanover, MA 02339
Tel.: (781) 923-1369
Web Site: http://www.wickedgoodcupcakes.com
Cupcake Mfr & Retailer
N.A.I.C.S.: 311813
Tracey Noonen *(Founder)*

InteliCoat Technologies, LLC (1)
28 Gaylord St, South Hadley, MA 01075
Tel.: (413) 536-7800
Web Site: http://www.intelicoat.com
Sales Range: $75-99.9 Million
Specialty Coated Papers & Labels Mfr
N.A.I.C.S.: 325992
Tom Moore *(CFO)*
Ed McCarron *(Dir-Mktg)*
John McCue *(Dir-Tech)*
Peggy Eichelberger *(Mgr-Customer Svc)*

Kellwood Company (1)
600 Kellwood Pkwy, Chesterfield, MO 63017-5800
Tel.: (314) 576-3100
Web Site: http://www.kellwood.com
Sales Range: $1-4.9 Billion
Emp.: 160
Branded Women's Apparel Designer & Marketer
N.A.I.C.S.: 424350
Christopher T. Metz *(Mng Partner)*
David Falwell *(CEO)*
Keith A. Grypp *(Gen Counsel & Sr VP)*
Janice Sullivan *(Pres-Rebecca Taylor Brand)*
Rebecca Taylor *(Dir-Creative-Rebecca Taylor Brand)*

Caren Belair *(Pres-Lifestyle & Juniors Grp)*
Linda Kinder *(CIO & VP)*
Brandi Wilson *(VP-Fin & Controller)*
Patricia Zabita *(VP-HR)*

Co-Headquarters (Domestic):

Kellwood Company - New York Office (2)
1441 Broadway 6th Fl, New York, NY 10018
Tel.: (212) 515-2600
Web Site: http://www.kellwood.com
Corporate Office; Branded Women's Apparel Designer & Marketer
N.A.I.C.S.: 551114

Unit (Domestic):

Briggs New York Corp. (3)
1441 Broadway Fl 7, New York, NY 10018
Tel.: (212) 515-2651
Web Site: http://www.kellwood.com
Emp.: 50
Branded Women's Sportswear Designer & Marketer
N.A.I.C.S.: 424350
Joe Lombardi *(CEO)*

David Meister (3)
550 7th Ave 19th Fl, New York, NY 10018
Tel.: (212) 730-8421
Web Site: http://www.davidmeister.com
Branded Women's Apparel Designer & Marketer
N.A.I.C.S.: 424350
David Meister *(Chm & Dir-Creative)*

Branch (Domestic):

Kellwood Company - Western Region (3)
13071 E Temple Ave, City of Industry, CA 91746
Tel.: (626) 934-4122
Web Site: http://www.kellwood.com
Branded Women's Apparel Designer & Marketer
N.A.I.C.S.: 424350
Marc Babins *(Pres)*

Unit (Domestic):

Democracy Clothing (4)
13071 E Temple Ave, City of Industry, CA 91746
Tel.: (626) 934-6463
Web Site: http://www.democracyclothing.com
Branded Women's Apparel Designer & Marketer
N.A.I.C.S.: 424350

My Michelle (4)
13071 E Temple Ave, City of Industry, CA 91746
Tel.: (626) 934-4122
Sales Range: $50-74.9 Million
Branded Girl's & Young Women's Sportswear Designer & Marketer
N.A.I.C.S.: 424350
Caren Belair *(Pres)*

Subsidiary (Domestic):

Phat Fashions, LLC (3)
512 7th Ave 29th Fl, New York, NY 10018
Tel.: (212) 798-3100
Web Site: http://www.babyphat.com
Sales Range: $50-74.9 Million
Emp.: 25
Clothing & Outerwear Designer & Retailer
N.A.I.C.S.: 458110

Unit (Domestic):

Sag Harbor (3)
1441 Broadway Fl 6, New York, NY 10018
Tel.: (212) 515-2651
Web Site: http://www.sag-harbor.com
Sales Range: $25-49.9 Million
Branded Women's Apparel Designer & Marketer
N.A.I.C.S.: 424350

Subsidiary (Domestic):

Vince Holding Corp. (3)
500 5th Ave 20th Fl, New York, NY 10110
Tel.: (323) 421-5980

SUN CAPITAL PARTNERS, INC.

U.S. PRIVATE

Sun Capital Partners, Inc.—(Continued)
Web Site: https://www.vince.com
Rev.: $357,442,000
Assets: $303,345,000
Liabilities: $283,088,000
Net Worth: $20,257,000
Earnings: ($38,346,000)
Emp.: 599
Fiscal Year-end: 01/28/2023
Holding Company; Women's Clothing Designer & Marketer
N.A.I.C.S.: 551112
David Stefko *(Interim CEO)*
Lee Meiner *(Chief HR Officer & Sr VP)*
John Szczepanski *(CFO & Exec VP)*

Subsidiary (Domestic):

Vince, LLC (4)
900 N Cahuenga Blvd, Los Angeles, CA 90038
Tel.: (323) 936-2939
Web Site: http://www.vince.com
Sales Range: $100-124.9 Million
Emp.: 60
Branded Women's & Men's Sportswear Designer, Marketer & Retailer
N.A.I.C.S.: 424350

Unit (Domestic):

XOXO (3)
1466 Broadway Rm 704, New York, NY 10036
Tel.: (212) 575-0273
Web Site: http://www.xoxo.com
Sales Range: $50-74.9 Million
Emp.: 10
Branded Young Women's Apparel Designer & Marketer
N.A.I.C.S.: 424350
Suzanne Desiderio *(Pres)*

Kraco Enterprises, LLC (1)
5900 Ami Dr, Richmond, IL 60071
Tel.: (815) 678-1600
Web Site: http://www.kraco.com
Sales Range: $25-49.9 Million
Emp.: 88
Automotive Floormat Mfr
N.A.I.C.S.: 326299
Bob Brocoff *(Pres)*
Kent Friend *(Sr VP-Sls & Mktg)*

Lemmen Oil Company (1)
13 E Randall St, Coopersville, MI 49404-1422
Tel.: (616) 837-6531
Sales Range: $10-24.9 Million
Emp.: 33
Supplier of Petroleum Bulk Stations & Terminals
N.A.I.C.S.: 424710

Marsh Supermarkets, Inc. (1)
9800 Crosspoint Blvd, Indianapolis, IN 46256
Tel.: (317) 594-2100
Web Site: http://www.marsh.net
Sales Range: $1-4.9 Billion
Emp.: 13,800
Supermarket & Convenience Store Operator; Catering Services
N.A.I.C.S.: 445110
Mary Snell *(Dir-Nutrition & Wellness)*

Subsidiary (Domestic):

Mar Properties Inc. (2)
333 S Franklin Rd, Indianapolis, IN 46219
Tel.: (317) 594-2100
Web Site: http://www.marsh.net
Sales Range: $75-99.9 Million
Grocery Stores
N.A.I.C.S.: 531120

O'Malia Food Markets Inc. (2)
9800 Crosspoint Blvd, Indianapolis, IN 46256-3300
Tel.: (317) 594-2100
Web Site: http://www.marsh.net
Sales Range: $75-99.9 Million
Grocery Stores
N.A.I.C.S.: 445110

Northern Wholesale Supply, LLC (1)
6800 Otter Lk Rd, Lino Lakes, MN 55038
Tel.: (651) 429-1515
Web Site: http://www.northernwholesale.com
Rev.: $5,000,000
Emp.: 23
Marine & RV Accessories Distr
N.A.I.C.S.: 423910
Lee N. Johnson *(Treas)*
Nick Gargaro *(CEO)*

PaperWorks Industries, Inc. (1)
5000 Flat Rock Rd, Philadelphia, PA 19127
Tel.: (215) 984-7000
Web Site: http://www.paperworksindustries.com
Sales Range: $300-349.9 Million
Emp.: 144
Clay-Coated Recycled Paperboard Mfr
N.A.I.C.S.: 322130
George Downey *(Dir-Sls-Folding Carton Bus)*
Brandon Clairmont *(Sr VP-Sls & Mktg)*
Brian Janki *(Pres & CEO)*

Unit (Domestic):

PaperWorks Industries, Inc. - Baldwinsville (2)
8800 Sixty Rd, Baldwinsville, NY 13027
Tel.: (315) 638-4355
Web Site: http://www.paperworksindustries.com
Sales Range: $25-49.9 Million
Gravure & Flexographic Printing Services
N.A.I.C.S.: 323111

Plant (Domestic):

PaperWorks Industries, Inc. - Dallas Plant (2)
4750 Simonton Rd, Dallas, TX 75244
Tel.: (972) 774-9161
Emp.: 32
Paperboard Distr
N.A.I.C.S.: 423840

PaperWorks Industries, Inc. - Hastings (2)
2000 Summit Ave, Hastings, NE 68901-6703
Tel.: (402) 463-1366
Sales Range: $25-49.9 Million
Packaging Products Designer, Mfr & Marketer
N.A.I.C.S.: 322212
James A. Downey *(VP & Gen Mgr-North Carolina Facility)*

Subsidiary (Domestic):

PaperWorks Industries, Inc. - Mount Gilead (3)
5465 NC Hwy 73, Mount Gilead, NC 27306
Tel.: (910) 439-6137
Sales Range: $50-74.9 Million
Emp.: 89
Packaging Products Designer, Mfr & Marketer
N.A.I.C.S.: 322212
Joanna Iwan *(Mgr-HR)*

Plant (Domestic):

PaperWorks Industries, Inc. - Mendon Plant (2)
26920 M-60, Mendon, MI 49072
Tel.: (269) 496-2715
Web Site: http://www.manind.com
Emp.: 43
Paperboard Distr
N.A.I.C.S.: 423840
Ranse McKinney *(Sr Mgr-Ops)*

PaperWorks Industries, Inc. - Philadelphia Mill (2)
5000 Flat Rock Rd, Philadelphia, PA 19127
Tel.: (215) 984-7000
Paperboard Mfr
N.A.I.C.S.: 322130
Randy Reidinger *(Dir-IT & Infrastructure)*

PaperWorks Industries, Inc. - Richmond Plant (2)
200 Orleans St, Richmond, VA 23231
Tel.: (804) 226-4250
Web Site: http://www.paperworksindustries.com
Sales Range: $10-24.9 Million
Emp.: 56
Custom Paperboard Products Mfr & Distr
N.A.I.C.S.: 322130
Debbie Brown *(Controller)*

PaperWorks Industries, Inc. - Wabash Mill (2)
455 W Factory St, Wabash, IN 46992
Tel.: (260) 563-3102
Paperboard Mfr
N.A.I.C.S.: 322130
Chris Wetherford *(Asst Gen Mgr)*
Scott Conner *(Engr-Process Control & Coord-LAN)*

PaperWorks Industries, Inc. - Wilkes-Barre Plant (2)
175 Stewart Rd, Wilkes Barre, PA 18706
Tel.: (570) 822-9308
Emp.: 30
Paperboard Distr
N.A.I.C.S.: 423840

Subsidiary (Domestic):

Standard Group LLC (2)
1010 Northern Blvd Ste 236, Great Neck, NY 11021
Tel.: (718) 335-5500
Web Site: http://www.thestandardgroup.com
Sales Range: $25-49.9 Million
Folding Paperboard Boxes
N.A.I.C.S.: 322212

Perfect Timing, Inc. (1)
N19 W23993 Ridgeview Pkwy W Ste 200, Waukesha, WI 53188
Tel.: (262) 523-9235
Web Site: http://www.perfecttimingbrands.com
Investment Management Service
N.A.I.C.S.: 523940
Bruce Hampton *(Mgr-Natl Sls)*
Lynn Bayer *(Supvr-Fin Svcs)*
John Corrigan *(CMO)*
Alan Patrick *(CFO)*
John Payne *(Sr VP-Sls)*
Julie Smith *(VP-Ops)*
Keith Strom *(Sr VP-Sls)*

Powertrain Products Corp. (1)
609 E Chaney St, Sullivan, IN 47882
Tel.: (812) 268-0322
Web Site: http://www.raybestospowertrain.com
Sales Range: $25-49.9 Million
Emp.: 110
Specialty Enginge Part Mfr
N.A.I.C.S.: 333618

Subsidiary (Domestic):

Allomatic Products Company (2)
102 Jericho Tpke, Floral Park, NY 11001
Tel.: (516) 775-0330
Web Site: http://www.allomatic.com
Friction & Reaction Plates Mfr, Transmission Filters & Automatic Transmission Parts
N.A.I.C.S.: 336390

Raybestos Powertrain, LLC (2)
711 Tech Dr, Crawfordsville, IN 47933-1400
Tel.: (765) 359-2559
Web Site: http://www.raybestospowertrain.com
Sales Range: $10-24.9 Million
Emp.: 10
Sales & Distribution of Aftermarket Products
N.A.I.C.S.: 336390
Al Avila *(VP-Sls & Mktg)*
Mike Zeller *(Plant Mgr)*

Protective Products Enterprises, Inc. (1)
1649 NW 136th Ave, Sunrise, FL 33323
Tel.: (954) 846-8222
Web Site: http://www.body-armor.com
Sales Range: $75-99.9 Million
Ceramic Ballistic Armor Systems Mfr
N.A.I.C.S.: 336992

Restaurants Unlimited, Inc. (1)
411 1st Ave S Ste 200, Seattle, WA 98104
Tel.: (206) 634-0550
Web Site: http://www.r-u-i.com
Sales Range: $125-149.9 Million
Owns & Operates Restaurant
N.A.I.C.S.: 722511
Jim Eschweiler *(Pres & CEO)*

Subsidiary (Domestic):

Pacific Coast Restaurants, Inc. (2)
1818 N Northlake Way, Seattle, WA 98103-9036
Tel.: (503) 684-2803
Sales Range: $100-124.9 Million
Owner & Operator of Seafood Restaurants
N.A.I.C.S.: 722511

Portland Seafood Company (2)
9722 SE Washington St, Portland, OR 97216
Tel.: (503) 255-2722
Web Site: http://www.portlandseafoodcompany.com
Restaurant Operators
N.A.I.C.S.: 722511
Karla Connelly *(Gen Mgr)*

Rita-Ann Distributors (1)
2051 McKenzie Dr, Carrollton, TX 75006-6846
Tel.: (410) 391-0677
Sales Range: $50-74.9 Million
Distribution of Cosmetics & Personal Care Products
N.A.I.C.S.: 424210

Rowe Furniture (1)
8484 W Park Dr Ste 710, McLean, VA 22102
Tel.: (703) 847-8670
Web Site: http://www.rowefurniture.com
Sales Range: $25-49.9 Million
Emp.: 15
Furniture Mfr
N.A.I.C.S.: 337121
Bobby Robinson *(VP-Sls)*

Subsidiary (Domestic):

Clayton-Marcus Company, Inc. (2)
2121 Gardner St, Elliston, VA 24087-3055
Tel.: (828) 495-2200
Web Site: http://www.claytonmarcus.com
Sales Range: $50-74.9 Million
Upholstered Furniture Mfr
N.A.I.C.S.: 337121

S&N Communications, Inc. (1)
636 Gralin St, Kernersville, NC 27284-3272
Tel.: (336) 992-5420
Web Site: http://www.sncomm.com
Sales Range: $150-199.9 Million
Telecommunications, Coaxial & Fiber Optic Cable Infrastructure Services
N.A.I.C.S.: 517810
George L. Baer *(COO)*
Dona Priebe *(VP)*
Marianna Frank *(Dir-HR)*
Debbie Scott *(CIO & VP-Fin)*
Ronald Smith *(CFO)*
Jerry Carmichael *(Sr Dir-HR & Benefits)*
Jannine Allen *(Dir-Safety & Risk Mgmt)*
James Gregory *(Dir-Application Dev & Support)*

Branch (Domestic):

S&N Communications (2)
3723 Three Notch Rd, Louisa, VA 23093-2719
Tel.: (434) 591-1080
Web Site: http://www.sncomm.com
Sales Range: $75-99.9 Million
Emp.: 50
Telecommunications, Coaxial & Fiber Optic Cable Infrastructure Services
N.A.I.C.S.: 238990
Darl Lofton *(Area Mgr)*
Bobby Poole *(Mgr-Fleet)*
Chris Kovachev *(Superintendent-Site)*
Lissa Gillispie *(Superintendent-Site)*
Chris Smith *(Mgr-Employee Dev)*

Subsidiary (Domestic):

Tower 16, Inc. (2)
415 Pulaski Hwy, Joppa, MD 21085
Tel.: (410) 679-9916
Web Site: http://www.tower16.com
Emp.: 50
Wood Container & Pallet Mfr
N.A.I.C.S.: 321920
Niaz Mian *(Pres)*

Scott Brass, Inc. (1)
1637 Elmwood Ave, Cranston, RI 02910-4937
Tel.: (401) 434-7640
Web Site: http://www.scottbrass.com
Sales Range: $25-49.9 Million
Electronic & Automotive Brass & Copper Components
N.A.I.C.S.: 331420

COMPANIES

SUN CAPITAL PARTNERS, INC.

Barry Golden *(Pres)*
David Martinelli *(VP-Sls & Mktg)*

Select Interior Concepts, Inc. (1)
400 Galleria Pkwy Ste 1760, Atlanta, GA 30339
Tel.: (714) 701-4200
Web Site:
  http://www.selectinteriorconcepts.com
Rev.: $554,025,000
Assets: $405,008,000
Liabilities: $250,817,000
Net Worth: $154,191,000
Earnings: ($9,853,000)
Emp.: 1,300
Fiscal Year-end: 12/31/2020
Building Product Distr
N.A.I.C.S.: 444180
Nadeem Moiz *(CFO & COO)*
Davis D'Andre *(Head-Strategy & M&A)*
Brett G. Wyard *(Chm)*
Shawn Baldwin *(Gen Counsel & Sec)*
Patrick Dussinger *(Pres-ASG)*

Subsidiary (Domestic):

Residential Design Services, LLC (2)
4675 E Cotton Center Blvd Ste 173, Phoenix, AZ 85040
Tel.: (480) 222-2958
Web Site: http://www.resdesign.com
Interior Design Services
N.A.I.C.S.: 541410
Kendall Hoyd *(Pres)*
John Hannum *(CFO)*
T. J. Wheeler *(Reg VP & Gen Mgr)*
Jennifer Kamenca *(VP-Design Studio Ops & Mktg)*
Tim Comstock *(VP-Accts-Natl)*

Somody Inc. (1)
Ste 900 913 N Market St, Wilmington, DE 19801-4926
Tel.: (320) 235-2454
Sales Range: $50-74.9 Million
Emp.: 140
Distr of Health & Beauty Aids, Housewares, School Supplies, Pet Supplies & Specialty Foods
N.A.I.C.S.: 424210

StonePoint Materials, LLC (1)
315 S 16th St, Philadelphia, PA 19102
Tel.: (215) 982-0405
Web Site: http://www.stonepointmaterials.com
Quarries Operations
N.A.I.C.S.: 212312
Colin Oerton *(CEO)*
Nick Coder *(VP-Bus Dev)*
Dennis Coker *(VP-Bus Dev-Dallas)*

Subsidiary (Domestic):

River Aggregates, LLC (2)
25963 Sorters Rd, Porter, TX 77365
Tel.: (281) 592-0503
Web Site: http://www.riveraggregates.com
Brick, Stone & Related Construction Material Merchant Whslr
N.A.I.C.S.: 423320
Rob Van Til *(Pres)*

Holding (Domestic):

Road Builders, LLC (2)
200 S Cherry St, Greenville, KY 42345
Tel.: (270) 338-2300
Web Site: http://www.roadbuildersllc.com
Sales Range: $10-24.9 Million
Emp.: 65
Asphalt Paving, Road Surfacing & Highway Construction
N.A.I.C.S.: 237310
John Stovall *(Pres & CEO)*
Larry Lile *(Controller)*

VantaCore Partners LP (2)
1600 Market St 38th Fl, Philadelphia, PA 19103
Tel.: (215) 751-1403
Web Site: http://www.vantacore.com
Quarries Operations
N.A.I.C.S.: 212312
Perry Donahoo *(CEO)*

Subsidiary (Domestic):

Laurel Aggregates LLC (3)
300 Dents Run Rd, Morgantown, WV 26501
Tel.: (304) 598-8204
Web Site: http://www.laurelaggregates.com
Sales Range: $25-49.9 Million
Emp.: 30
Limestone Aggregate Product Whslr
N.A.I.C.S.: 212312

Sun Capital Partners Japan K.K. (1)
5th Fl Toranomon 4 Chome MT Bldg, 4 1 8 Toranomon Minato ku, Tokyo, Japan
Tel.: (81) 364020900
Web Site: http://www.suncappart.com
Private Equity Investment Firm
N.A.I.C.S.: 523999

Sun Capital Partners Sourcing, LLC (1)
Room 2508 Nanzheng Bldg, 580 Nanjing W Rd, Shanghai, 200041, China
Tel.: (86) 2152285511
Private Investment Services
N.A.I.C.S.: 523999

Sun European Partners, LLP (1)
2 Park Street 1st Floor, London, W1K 2HX, United Kingdom
Tel.: (44) 2073181100
Web Site:
  http://www.suneuropeanpartners.com
Sales Range: $25-49.9 Million
Emp.: 20
Private Investment Services
N.A.I.C.S.: 523999
Paul Daccus *(Mng Dir)*
Lionel de Posson *(Mng Dir)*
Elena Filekova *(Principal)*

Holding (Domestic):

Adler & Allan Limited (2)
80 Station Parade, Harrogate, HG1 1HQ, North Yorkshire, United Kingdom
Tel.: (44) 14 2385 0360
Web Site: http://www.adlerandallan.co.uk
Emp.: 500
Oil & Environmental Support Services
N.A.I.C.S.: 213112
Ian Osborne *(Mng Dir)*

Subsidiary (Domestic):

A.J. Bayliss Petroleum Engineers Ltd (3)
Unit 9 Foley Business Park Stourport Road, Kidderminster, DY11 7QL, United Kingdom
Tel.: (44) 1562820038
Electrical Engineering Services
N.A.I.C.S.: 541330

E&S Environmental Services Ltd (3)
Unit 10 Viscount Court Ind Est, Norton, OX18 3QQ, Oxfordshire, United Kingdom
Tel.: (44) 1993852419
Web Site: http://www.eandsgroup.co.uk
Electrical Engineering Services
N.A.I.C.S.: 541330

Holding (Domestic):

American Golf Ltd. (2)
1030 Europa Boulevard, Warrington, WA5 7YW, Cheshire, United Kingdom
Tel.: (44) 8442258899
Web Site: http://www.americangolf.co.uk
Golf Clothing Store Operator
N.A.I.C.S.: 458110

Holding (Non-US):

BTX Group A/S (2)
Nordlundvej 1, 7330, Brande, Denmark
Tel.: (45) 96 42 40 00
Emp.: 150
Women's Clothing Whslr
N.A.I.C.S.: 424350
Jesper Roe *(CEO)*

Holding (Domestic):

Britton Group Holdings Ltd. (2)
Road One, Winsford Industrial Estate, Winsford, CW7 3RD, Cheshire, United Kingdom
Tel.: (44) 1606593434
Web Site: http://www.brittongroup.com
Sales Range: $250-299.9 Million
Plastic Packaging Sheet & Film Mfr
N.A.I.C.S.: 326112
Edwin Goffard *(CEO)*

Subsidiary (Domestic):

Britton Taco Ltd. (3)
20 Road One, Winsford Industrial Estate, Winsford, CW7 3RD, Cheshire, United Kingdom (100%)
Tel.: (44) 1606593434
Web Site: http://www.coveris.com
Sales Range: $50-74.9 Million
Emp.: 220
Plastic Sheet, Film & Packaging Mfr
N.A.I.C.S.: 326112
Darren Tean *(Mng Dir)*

Britton-Decfolex Ltd. (3)
Skerne Rd, Oakesway Business Park, Hartlepool, TS24 0RH, United Kingdom (100%)
Tel.: (44) 429272102
Web Site: http://www.decoflex-flexibles.com
Sales Range: $25-49.9 Million
Emp.: 100
Flexible Film Mfr
N.A.I.C.S.: 326112

Holding (Non-US):

Bundy Refrigeration S.r.l. (2)
Via G Ponassi 11 Localita La Palazzina, PO Box 9, 15060, Borghetto di Borbera, Italy
Tel.: (39) 01 43 63 86 11
Web Site: http://www.bundyrefrigeration.com
Emp.: 180
Air Conditioning Equipment Mfr
N.A.I.C.S.: 333415
Thomas Schabinger *(CEO)*

Subsidiary (Non-US):

Bundy Kft (3)
Ipari u 1, 5123, Jaszarokszallas, Hungary
Tel.: (36) 57531800
Web Site: http://www.bundyrefrigeration.com
Air Conditioning Equipment Mfr
N.A.I.C.S.: 333415
Zoltan Koskovics *(Gen Mgr)*

Bundy Refrigeracao Brasil Ind e Comercio (3)
Rua Rodolpho Hatschbach 1431, Curitiba, 81460-030, Parana, Brazil
Tel.: (55) 4131117250
Web Site: http://www.bundyoex.com
Air Conditioning Equipment Mfr
N.A.I.C.S.: 333415

Subsidiary (Domestic):

Bundy Refrigeration International Holding B.V. (3)
Strado Industriale ASI, 81032, Caserta, Italy
Tel.: (39) 081 89 11 708
Air Conditioning Equipment Mfr
N.A.I.C.S.: 333415

Subsidiary (Non-US):

Bundy Refrigeration Sp. zo.o. (3)
Wiosenna 14/2, 53017, Wroclaw, Poland
Tel.: (48) 62 76 49 820
Cooling System Mfr
N.A.I.C.S.: 333415

Holding (Non-US):

Init Polymers B.V. (2)
Mercurion 10-12, NL-6903 PZ, Zevenaar, Netherlands
Tel.: (31) 8847 4740
Polyethylene Terephthalate Resin Mfr
N.A.I.C.S.: 325211

Holding (Domestic):

Jacques Vert Group Ltd. (2)
32-38 Scrutton Street, London, EC2A 4RQ, United Kingdom
Tel.: (44) 2072887500
Web Site: http://www.jacquesvertgroup.com
Ladies Fashion Wear Mfr & Retailer
N.A.I.C.S.: 315250
Sarah Morris *(Dir-Trading)*
Julia Durbin *(Dir-HR)*
Shaun Wills *(CEO)*

Division (Domestic):

Irisa Group Limited (3)
Porter Tun House 500 Capability Green, Luton, LU1 3FX, United Kingdom
Tel.: (44) 1582723131
Web Site: http://www.alexon.co.uk
Sales Range: $1-4.9 Billion
Women's Clothing Retailer
N.A.I.C.S.: 458110

Subsidiary (Domestic):

Alex & Co. (4)
500 Capability Green, Luton, LU1 3FX, Bedfordshire, United Kingdom
Tel.: (44) 1582399813
Web Site: http://www.alex-and-co.co.uk
Ladies Clothing Retail Services
N.A.I.C.S.: 458110

Alexon International Limited (4)
500 Capability Green, Luton, LU1 3FX, Beds, United Kingdom
Tel.: (44) 1582723131
Sales Range: $100-124.9 Million
Ladies Clothing Retail Services
N.A.I.C.S.: 458110

Division (Domestic):

Ann Harvey Division (5)
Porter Tun House 500 Capability Green, Luton, LU1 3FX, United Kingdom
Tel.: (44) 1582399877
Web Site:
  http://www.annharveyfashion.co.uk
Ladies Clothing Retail Services
N.A.I.C.S.: 458110

Dash Division (5)
500 Capability Green, Luton, LU1 3FX, United Kingdom
Tel.: (44) 1582723131
Web Site: http://www.dashfashion.co.uk
Ladies Clothing Retail Services
N.A.I.C.S.: 458110

Subsidiary (Domestic):

Jacques Vert Group Limited (3)
Webber Pavilion Seaham Grange Industrial Estate, Durham, SR7 0PZ, United Kingdom
Tel.: (44) 2920101432
Web Site: http://www.jacques-vert.co.uk
Women's Clothing Store Operator
N.A.I.C.S.: 458110

Holding (Domestic):

K3 Capital Group Ltd (2)
KBS House 5 Springfield Court Summerfield Road, Bolton, BL3 2NT, United Kingdom
Tel.: (44) 1204555071
Web Site: https://www.k3capitalgroup.com
Rev.: $64,045,010
Assets: $96,119,787
Liabilities: $29,260,224
Net Worth: $66,859,564
Earnings: $7,013,982
Emp.: 410
Fiscal Year-end: 05/31/2021
Financial Brokerage Services
N.A.I.C.S.: 523160
John Rigby *(CEO)*
Andrew Melbourne *(CFO)*
Simon Daniels *(Sls Dir)*
Tony Ford *(Vice Chm)*
Carl Jackson *(Exec Dir)*
Ian Symes *(CEO & Mng Dir)*
Louise Roberts *(Chief People Officer)*
Lynsey Gregory *(Gen Counsel)*
Nicola Davies *(Dir-People)*

Subsidiary (Domestic):

KBS Corporate Sales Limited (3)
KBS House 5 Springfield Court Summerfield Road, Bolton, BL3 2NT, United Kingdom
Tel.: (44) 1612580118
Web Site: http://www.kbscorporate.com
Financial Services
N.A.I.C.S.: 523999
John Rigby *(CEO)*
Simon Daniels *(Sls Dir)*
Tony Ford *(Chm)*
Dave Gardner *(Fin Dir)*
Andrew Melbourne *(CFO)*

Knightsbridge Business Sales Limited (3)
KBS House 5 Springfield Court Summerfield Road, Bolton, BL3 2NT, United Kingdom
Tel.: (44) 1204227661
Web Site: https://www.knightsbridgeplc.com

SUN CAPITAL PARTNERS, INC.

Sun Capital Partners, Inc.—(Continued)
Real Estate Development Services
N.A.I.C.S.: 531390
Victoria Williams *(Mng Dir)*
Andrew Melbourne *(Fin Dir)*
Gary Edwards *(Head-Mktg)*
Sara Thomasson *(Dir-Ops)*
Joe Bull *(Comml Dir)*

Holding (Non-US):

Kobusch Sengewald GmbH (2)
Anton-Bohlen-Str 5, 34414, Warburg, Germany
Tel.: (49) 5641 96-0
Web Site: http://www.kobusch.com
Sales Range: $250-299.9 Million
Emp.: 1,100
Flexible Packaging Mfr
N.A.I.C.S.: 326112
Lee Mark *(CEO)*

Subsidiary (Non-US):

Kobusch UK Limited (3)
Tanfield Lea South Industrial Estate, Stanley Co, Durham, DH9 9XH, United Kingdom
Tel.: (44) 1207291800
Sales Range: $25-49.9 Million
Flexible Packaging Mfr
N.A.I.C.S.: 326112

Subsidiary (Domestic):

Kobusch-Sengewald GmbH - Halle (3)
16 Kreisstr, Halle, 33790, Germany
Tel.: (49) 5201708207
Web Site: http://www.kobusch.com
Sales Range: $50-74.9 Million
Plastic Packaging Solutions
N.A.I.C.S.: 326112

Holding (Non-US):

Neuheim Lux Group Holding V S.a.r.l. (2)
Aerogolf Center 1B rue Heienhaff, L-1736, Senningerberg, Luxembourg
Tel.: (352) 26340321
Private Investment Services
N.A.I.C.S.: 523999

Holding (Domestic):

NextPharma Technologies Holding Ltd. (2)
Connaught House Portsmouth Road, Send, GU23 7JY, Surrey, United Kingdom
Tel.: (44) 1 483 479 120
Web Site: http://www.nextpharma.com
Emp.: 7
Pharmaceutical Preparation Mfr
N.A.I.C.S.: 325412
Alan Dodsworth *(Exec VP-Corp Dev)*
Andrew Kelley *(COO)*
Benjamin Breitfeld *(Dir-Strategic Acct)*
John Porter *(Dir-Bus Dev-Pharmaceutical Dev)*
Karen Stoddart *(Exec VP-Quality)*
Pierre Delavaud *(Exec VP-Sls & Mktg)*
Sebastian Heckerodt *(Dir-Strategic Acct)*

Polestar UK Print Limited (2)
1 Apex Business Park, Boscombe Road, Dunstable, LU5 4SB, Bucks, United Kingdom
Tel.: (44) 1582678900
Web Site: http://www.polestar-group.com
Sales Range: $700-749.9 Million
Commercial Printing Services
N.A.I.C.S.: 323111
Barry Hibbert *(CEO)*
Peter Johnston *(Dir-Fin)*

Subsidiary (Domestic):

Polestar Applied Solutions Limited (3)
Byron House Willow Drive, Annesley, NG15 0DP, Notts, United Kingdom
Tel.: (44) 1623 727 500
Sales Range: $10-24.9 Million
Specialty Printing Services
N.A.I.C.S.: 323111

Plant (Domestic):

Polestar Applied Solutions Ltd. - Leeds (4)
501 Dewsbury Road, Leeds, LS11 5LL, W Yorkshire, United Kingdom
Tel.: (44) 1132016600
Web Site: http://www.polestar-group.com
Specialty Printing Services
N.A.I.C.S.: 323111

Subsidiary (Domestic):

Polestar Bicester Ltd (3)
Chaucer Business Park Launton Road, Bicester, OX26 4QZ, Oxon, United Kingdom
Tel.: (44) 1869 363333
Web Site: http://www.polestar-group.com
Commercial Printing Services
N.A.I.C.S.: 323113
David Gray *(Dir-Sls)*

Polestar Chantry Limited (3)
Cape House Brindley Way, Wakefield, WF2 0XQ, W Yorkshire, United Kingdom
Tel.: (44) 1924829811
Web Site: http://www.polestar-group.com
Sales Range: $10-24.9 Million
Emp.: 100
Digital Printing Services
N.A.I.C.S.: 323111

Polestar Chromoworks Limited (3)
Wigman Road, Aspley, Nottingham, NG8 3JA, United Kingdom
Tel.: (44) 1159008300
Web Site: http://www.polestar-group.com
Sales Range: $25-49.9 Million
Emp.: 100
Printing Services
N.A.I.C.S.: 323117

Polestar Colchester Limited (3)
2 Wyncolls Rd, Severalls Industrial Park, Colchester, CO 4 9PU, Essex, United Kingdom
Tel.: (44) 1206849500
Web Site: http://www.polestar-group.com
Sales Range: $25-49.9 Million
Commercial Lithographic Printing Services
N.A.I.C.S.: 323111

Polestar Petty Limited (3)
Petty House Whitehall Road, Leeds, LS12 1BD, United Kingdom
Tel.: (44) 1132432341
Sales Range: $50-74.9 Million
Commercial Lithographic Printing Services
N.A.I.C.S.: 323111

Polestar Purnell Limited (3)
Paulton, Bristol, BS39 7LQ, United Kingdom
Tel.: (44) 1761 404 142
Printing Services
N.A.I.C.S.: 323117

Polestar Sheffield Limited (3)
Shepcote Lane Tinsley, Sheffield, S9 1TR, York, United Kingdom
Tel.: (44) 1142841700
Web Site: http://www.polestar-group.com
Sales Range: $50-74.9 Million
Commercial Gravure Printing Services
N.A.I.C.S.: 323111
John Varley *(Dir-Fin)*
Mark Walkington *(Dir-Ops)*
Simon Robson *(Mgr-Projects & Engrg)*

Polestar Stones (3)
Unit 10 Wates Way, Banbury, OX16 3ES, Oxon, United Kingdom
Tel.: (44) 1295 819300
Emp.: 100
Commercial Printing Services
N.A.I.C.S.: 323111

Subsidiary (Non-US):

Revai Nyomeda (3)
Kunigunda Utca 68, 1037, Budapest, Hungary
Tel.: (36) 13879500
Web Site: http://www.revai-nyomba.hu
Printing Services
N.A.I.C.S.: 323117

Holding (Domestic):

Sharps Bedrooms Limited (2)
Springvale Park Industrial Park, Bilston, WV14 0QL, West Midlands, United Kingdom
Tel.: (44) 1902 483 000
Web Site: http://www.sharps.co.uk
Furniture Store Operator
N.A.I.C.S.: 449110
Kevin Smith *(CEO)*
Stephen Morley *(Mgr-Mktg)*

Subsidiary (Non-US):

Sun European Partners GmbH (2)
Mainzer Landstr 50, 60325, Frankfurt, Germany
Tel.: (49) 69274015575
Emp.: 10
Private Investment Services
N.A.I.C.S.: 523999
Markus Nagel *(CFO)*
Niclaus Haumann *(Gen Mgr)*

Holding (Domestic):

Reuther Verpackung GmbH & Co. KG (3)
Elisabethstrasse 6 D, 56564, Neuwied, Germany
Tel.: (49) 2631 875 0
Web Site: http://www.reuther.de
Packaging Materials Mfr
N.A.I.C.S.: 322220

Subsidiary (Non-US):

Sun European Partners, SAS (2)
29 Rue de Bassano, 75008, Paris, France
Tel.: (33) 172256578
Private Investment Services
N.A.I.C.S.: 523999
Fabrice I. Dumontheil *(CFO)*

Holding (Non-US):

V&D B.V. (2)
Laarderhoogtweg 25, Postbus 12640, 1100 AP, Amsterdam, Netherlands
Tel.: (31) 20 59 59 111
Web Site: http://www.vd.nl
Apparel Accessory Store Operator
N.A.I.C.S.: 458110

SUN CITY RV, INC.
9045 NW Grand Ave, Peoria, AZ 85345
Tel.: (623) 979-8585
Web Site: http://www.suncityrv.com
Year Founded: 1997
Sales Range: $10-24.9 Million
Emp.: 72
Recreational Vehicle Whslr
N.A.I.C.S.: 441210
Cindy Daly *(Sec)*
Charles R. Niday *(Pres)*

SUN COAST MEDIA GROUP, INC.
200 E Venice Ave, Venice, FL 34285
Tel.: (941) 207-1000   FL
Web Site:
   http://www.venicegondolier.com
Sales Range: $25-49.9 Million
Emp.: 500
Newspapers Publisher & Advertising Services
N.A.I.C.S.: 513110
Leslee Peth *(Dir-Adv-Charlotte Sun & Publr-Punta Gorda Herald)*
Robin Marotta *(Mgr-Customer Svc)*
Chris Porter *(Editor)*
Mark Yero *(Dir-Circulation)*

Subsidiaries:

Charlotte Sun (1)
23170 Harborview Rd, Charlotte Harbor, FL 33980
Tel.: (941) 206-1000
Web Site: http://www.charlotte-sun.com
Newspaper Publisher
N.A.I.C.S.: 513110
David Dunn-Rankin *(Pres & Publr)*
Leslee Peth *(Dir-Adv)*

DeSoto Sun (1)
108 S Polk Ave, Arcadia, FL 34266
Tel.: (863) 494-7600
Web Site: http://www.yoursun.com
Emp.: 5
Newspaper Publishers
N.A.I.C.S.: 513110
Craig Garret *(Editor)*

U.S. PRIVATE

The Highlands News-Sun (1)
207 Cir Park Dr, Sebring, FL 33870
Tel.: (863) 385-6155
Web Site: http://www.newssun.com
Daily Newspaper
N.A.I.C.S.: 513110
Cliff Yeazel *(Dir-Adv)*
Donna Scherlacher *(Dir-Multi Media)*
Glen Nickerson *(Publr)*
Romona Washington *(Exec Editor)*
Mike Henry *(Office Mgr)*
Tracey Weikel *(Classified Acct Mgr)*
Kevin Flores *(Dir-Circulation)*
Lyn Corcoran *(Asst District Mgr)*
Lewis Hall *(Asst District Mgr)*
Allen Moody *(Editor-Sports)*
Mat Delaney *(Editor-Highlands Sun)*
Karen Clogston *(Editor-Special Section)*
Pallavi Agarwal *(Editor)*
Ryan Danzey *(Dir-Adv)*
Kim Browning *(Acct Exec-Medical)*
Susan Jones *(Acct Exec)*
Ashlee Frymier *(Acct Exec)*
Alice Lyon *(Acct Exec)*
Robin Nichols *(Acct Exec)*
Amanda Young *(Acct Exec)*
Sue Walker *(Acct Exec-Real Estate)*
Vickie Watson *(Acct Exec)*

Venice Gondolier Sun (1)
200 E Venice Ave, Venice, FL 34285
Tel.: (941) 207-1000
Web Site:
   http://www.venicegondoliersun.com
Emp.: 75
Newspaper Publishers
N.A.I.C.S.: 513110
Tim Smolarick *(Publr)*
Kim Cool *(Editor)*
Mark Yero *(Dir-Circulation)*
Geri Kotz *(Mgr-Classified & Telemarketing)*

SUN COAST NURSING CENTERS INC
2 Bala Cynwyd Plz No 300, Bala Cynwyd, PA 19004
Tel.: (215) 346-6454   DE
Year Founded: 2003
Sales Range: $200-249.9 Million
Emp.: 3,990
Nursing Care Services
N.A.I.C.S.: 623110
Howard Jaffe *(Pres)*

SUN COAST PARTNERS, LLC
1430 Commonwealth Dr Ste 102, Wilmington, NC 28403
Tel.: (910) 350-1200   NC
Web Site:
   http://www.cbwilmington.com
Year Founded: 2005
Sales Range: $1-9.9 Million
Industrial & Commercial Real Estate Sales, Leasing & Property Management
N.A.I.C.S.: 531210
W. Grayson Powell *(Mng Partner)*
Tim Milam *(Partner)*
Chuck Lydon *(Sr VP)*

Subsidiaries:

Harley & Associates Commercial Real Estate, Inc. (1)
398 Carl St Ste 101, Wilmington, NC 28403-1864
Tel.: (910) 078-9800
Web Site: http://www.harleyassociates.com
Sales Range: $1-9.9 Million
Industrial & Commercial Real Estate Sales, Leasing & Property Management
N.A.I.C.S.: 531210
Donald L. Harley Jr. *(Pres)*

SUN COMPANY, INC.
4840 Van Gorden St Unit 1000, Wheat Ridge, CO 80033
Tel.: (303) 424-4651   CO
Web Site:
   http://www.suncompany.net
Year Founded: 1974
Outdoor Product Distr
N.A.I.C.S.: 459110

Alissa Neeley *(VP-Sls & Mktg)*

SUN COUNTRY RESTORATION, LLC
3121 E 33rd Pl, Yuma, AZ 85364
Tel.: (928) 783-0349
Web Site:
http://www.suncountryrestoration.com
Year Founded: 1998
Sales Range: $1-9.9 Million
Emp.: 49
Specialty Trade Contractors
N.A.I.C.S.: 238990
Chris Nossamun *(Gen Mgr)*

SUN DRAGON IMPORT, INC.
3742 E 26th St, Vernon, CA 90058
Tel.: (323) 362-5505
Web Site:
http://www.sundragonimport.com
Year Founded: 2005
Sales Range: $10-24.9 Million
Emp.: 9
Non-Durable Goods Whslr
N.A.I.C.S.: 424990
Qing Duncan *(Pres)*

SUN DRILLING PRODUCTS CORP
4400 Post Oak Pkwy Ste 2100, Houston, TX 77027-3428
Tel.: (713) 690-3939
Web Site: http://www.sundrilling.com
Sales Range: $10-24.9 Million
Emp.: 30
Drilling Products Mfr
N.A.I.C.S.: 333248
Michael Cook *(CFO & COO)*
Douglas P. Heller *(Pres)*
Richard J. Mapp *(Dir-Tech Svcs)*
Ron Coulter *(Mgr-Global Mktg)*

SUN ENERGY SOLUTIONS
2101 S Yale St, Huntington Beach, CA 92647
Tel.: (714) 210-5141
Web Site:
http://www.sunindustriesinc.com
Year Founded: 1991
Rev.: $12,000,000
Emp.: 75
Lighting Equipment Mfr
N.A.I.C.S.: 561499
Lynda Sun *(Owner & CEO)*
Scott Haerbig *(Program Mgr)*

SUN FINANCE COMPANY, LLC
3525 N Causeway Blvd Ste 900, Metairie, LA 70002
Tel.: (504) 837-9400
Web Site: http://www.sunfinance.com
Sales Range: $10-24.9 Million
Consumer & Mortgage Lending Services
N.A.I.C.S.: 522291
David Daube *(Co-Owner & Pres)*
Brian Daube *(Co-Owner & VP)*

SUN GRAPHIC TECHNOLOGIES, INC.
2310 Whitfield Park Ave, Sarasota, FL 34243
Tel.: (941) 753-7541
Web Site:
http://www.sungraphictechnologies.com
Year Founded: 1977
Sales Range: $1-9.9 Million
Emp.: 25
Commercial Art & Graphic Design
N.A.I.C.S.: 541430
Bill Blechta *(Founder & Pres)*
Karianne Haggard *(Controller)*
Bret Rohde *(Mgr-Production)*

SUN GRAPHICS INC.
1818 Broadway Ave, Parsons, KS 67357
Tel.: (620) 421-6200
Web Site: http://www.sun-graphics.com
Sales Range: $10-24.9 Million
Emp.: 72
Commercial Printing, Lithographic
N.A.I.C.S.: 323111
Blanch Weidert *(Controller)*

SUN GRAPHICS PRINTING, INC.
2125 S Arizona Ave, Yuma, AZ 85364
Tel.: (928) 783-8371
Web Site:
http://www.sungraphicsaz.com
Commercial Printing & Lithographic Services
N.A.I.C.S.: 323111
Glen Sparlin *(Pres & Gen Mgr)*

SUN HEALTH SERVICES
14719 W Grand Ave, Surprise, AZ 85374
Tel.: (623) 832-5350
Web Site: http://www.sunhealth.org
Year Founded: 2008
Sales Range: $10-24.9 Million
Emp.: 1
Health Care Srvices
N.A.I.C.S.: 622110
Ronald D. Guziak *(Pres)*
Herman L. Orcutt *(Chm)*
Michael Mandell *(Vice Chm)*
Dean L. Strycker *(Sec)*
Sharon Grambow *(COO-Sun Health Senior Living & Exec VP)*
Radha Ramamrutham *(Dir-Medical-Sun Health at Home)*
Joseph E. La Rue *(Exec VP)*
Lew Lancaster *(Treas)*
William T. Sellner *(CFO)*

SUN LAKES MARKETING LP
9532 E Riggs Rd, Sun Lakes, AZ 85248
Tel.: (480) 895-9200
Rev.: $11,300,000
Emp.: 7
Land Subdividers & Developers, Commercial
N.A.I.C.S.: 237210
Edward J. Robson *(Chm & CEO)*

SUN LEE INC.
12029 Telegraph Rd, Santa Fe Springs, CA 90670
Tel.: (562) 903-9883
Web Site: http://www.sunlee.com
Rev.: $20,833,242
Emp.: 29
Groceries, General Line
N.A.I.C.S.: 424410

SUN LIGHT & POWER
1035 Folger Ave, Berkeley, CA 94710
Tel.: (510) 845-2997
Web Site:
http://www.sunlightandpower.com
Year Founded: 1976
Sales Range: $10-24.9 Million
Emp.: 60
Plumbing, Heating & Air-Conditioning Contractors
N.A.I.C.S.: 238220
Gary T. Gerber *(Founder, Pres & CEO)*
Blake Gleason *(Dir-Engrg)*
Eric Nyman *(Mgr-Sls)*
Aurora Meerjans *(Dir-Ops)*
Kirsten Findlay *(Controller)*
Erinne Davis *(Project Mgr)*

SUN MECHANICAL CONTRACTING INC.
3951 E Columbia St, Tucson, AZ 85714
Tel.: (520) 790-3100
Web Site:
http://www.sunmechanical.net
Rev.: $26,600,000
Emp.: 100
General Contractors
N.A.I.C.S.: 238190
Karl Schlaefer *(Mgr-Smaller Projects Team)*
Todd Scholer *(Project Mgr)*
Diana J. McCurry *(Dir-Safety)*
Eric Buchholz *(Dir-PM)*
Ron Souther *(Project Mgr)*

SUN MEDICAL INC.
7112 Sandy Lake Rd, Quinlan, TX 75474-5275
Tel.: (817) 633-1373
Web Site:
http://www.sunmedicalinc.com
Sales Range: $10-24.9 Million
Emp.: 7
Medical Equipment & Supplies
N.A.I.C.S.: 423450
Steve Polk *(Pres)*
Ross Collins *(Mgr-Sls)*

SUN MOTORS BMW
6677 Carlisle Pike, Mechanicsburg, PA 17050
Tel.: (717) 697-2300
Sales Range: $10-24.9 Million
Emp.: 50
Car Whslr
N.A.I.C.S.: 441110
Daniel Sunderland *(VP)*

SUN MOUNTAIN LUMBER, INC.
181 Greenhouse Rd, Deer Lodge, MT 59722-2071
Tel.: (406) 846-1600
Web Site:
http://www.sunmtnlumber.com
Sales Range: $10-24.9 Million
Emp.: 175
Lumber Retailer
N.A.I.C.S.: 423310
Craig O'Rourke *(Mgr-Sls & Logistics)*
Sherm Anderson *(Owner, Chm & Pres)*
Tony Colter *(VP & Plant Mgr)*
April Kersch *(Mgr-Safety & Environmental)*
Nick Jose *(Mgr-Resource)*

SUN ORCHARD FRUIT COMPANY, INC.
2087 Transit Rd, Burt, NY 14028
Tel.: (716) 778-8544
Web Site:
http://www.sunorchardapples.com
Year Founded: 1952
Sales Range: $10-24.9 Million
Emp.: 60
Apple Storage, Packaging & Shipping Services
N.A.I.C.S.: 493120
Steve Riessen *(Pres)*
Pamela Laubacker *(Controller)*
Tony Ceasor *(Dir-HR)*
Kent Wakefield *(Mgr-Warehouse)*
Scott Penwright *(Gen Mgr-Production)*

SUN PACIFIC ENERGY
501 W Canal Dr, Kennewick, WA 99336
Tel.: (509) 586-1135
Web Site: http://www.sunpacific.net
Sales Range: $10-24.9 Million
Emp.: 100
Petroleum Products

N.A.I.C.S.: 424720
Ashley Lake *(Office Mgr)*
Craig D. Eerkes *(Pres & CEO)*

SUN PACIFIC FARMING CO., INC.
1300 E Myer Ave, Exeter, CA 93221-9302
Tel.: (559) 592-7121
Web Site: http://www.sunpacific.com
Year Founded: 1973
Sales Range: $25-49.9 Million
Emp.: 500
Farm Management Services
N.A.I.C.S.: 115116
Jeanne Wilkinson *(Controller)*

SUN PACKING, INC.
10077 Wallisville Rd, Houston, TX 77013
Tel.: (713) 673-4600
Web Site:
http://www.sunpacking.com
Year Founded: 1997
Sales Range: $1-9.9 Million
Emp.: 125
Export Packaging & Labeling
N.A.I.C.S.: 561910
John Grossman *(CFO)*
Rob Haupt *(Pres)*
Roberto Galan *(Supvr-Receiving & Checking)*

SUN PAINTS & COATINGS, INC.
4701 E 7th Ave, Tampa, FL 33605
Tel.: (813) 367-4444
Web Site:
http://www.sunpaintsandcoatings.com
Sales Range: $25-49.9 Million
Emp.: 30
Paints & Coatings Mfr
N.A.I.C.S.: 325510
Michael Hyer *(Pres)*

SUN PORTS INTERNATIONAL INC.
8319 Chancellor Row, Dallas, TX 75247
Tel.: (214) 905-9500
Web Site: http://www.sunports.com
Rev.: $18,000,000
Emp.: 300
Sheet Metalwork
N.A.I.C.S.: 332322

SUN POWERSPORTS INVESTMENTS, LLC
8877 N Washington St, Denver, CO 80229
Tel.: (303) 287-7566
Web Site: https://www.sunent.com
Year Founded: 2023
Powersports, Motorcycle, ATV & Side-by-Side Dealer
N.A.I.C.S.: 441227

Subsidiaries:

Sun Enterprises Incorporated (1)
8877 Washington St, Denver, CO 80229
Tel.: (303) 287-7566
Web Site: http://www.sunent.com
Sales Range: $1-9.9 Million
Emp.: 90
Motorcycle Dealers
N.A.I.C.S.: 441227

SUN PRINTING INC.
345 Dreher Rd, West Columbia, SC 29169
Tel.: (803) 791-1786
Web Site: http://www.sun-inc.com
Year Founded: 1983
Sales Range: $1-9.9 Million
Emp.: 70
Commercial Printing & Lithographic Services

SUN PRINTING INC.

Sun Printing Inc.—(Continued)
N.A.I.C.S.: 323111
Andrew Cook *(Pres)*
Philip Morris *(Owner)*
Tom Welsh *(Mgr-Ops)*

SUN PROCESS CONVERTING COMPANY, INC.
1660 W Kenneth Dr, Mount Prospect, IL 60056-5515
Tel.: (847) 593-0447
Web Site:
http://www.sunprocess.com
Year Founded: 1970
Sales Range: $75-99.9 Million
Emp.: 70
Mfr of Pressure Sensitive Decorative Appliques
N.A.I.C.S.: 326113
Michael Moore *(Pres & Dir-Sls)*

SUN REALTY & AUCTION SERVICE, LLC
109 SE Floresta Dr, Port Saint Lucie, FL 34983
Tel.: (772) 878-2600
Web Site: http://www.sunrlty.com
Year Founded: 2005
Sales Range: $1-9.9 Million
Emp.: 32
Real Estate Broker
N.A.I.C.S.: 531210
John Crawford *(Pres)*

SUN REALTY USA, INC.
3757 Tamiami Trl N, Naples, FL 34103
Tel.: (239) 649-1990
Web Site:
http://www.naplessunrealty.com
Year Founded: 2002
Sales Range: $500-549.9 Million
Emp.: 330
Real Estate Broker
N.A.I.C.S.: 531210
Gary L. Hicks *(Founder & Owner)*
Heather D. Markwardt *(Mgr-Acctg)*

SUN STATE COMPONENTS OF NEVADA
4915 Berg St, North Las Vegas, NV 89031
Tel.: (702) 657-1889
Web Site: http://www.sunstatenv.com
Sales Range: $10-24.9 Million
Emp.: 140
Wood & Floor Truss Components Mfr
N.A.I.C.S.: 321215
William Butler *(Pres)*
Glenn McClendon *(VP)*
Ron Barney *(Mgr-Production)*

SUN STATE FORD INC.
3535 W Colonial Dr, Orlando, FL 32808
Tel.: (407) 299-5900
Web Site:
http://www.sunstateford.com
Rev.: $102,218,814
Emp.: 180
Automobiles, New & Used
N.A.I.C.S.: 441110
Kuldeep S. Ohri *(Pres)*
Charles Kirkland *(Mgr-Fin)*
Brad Knight *(Mgr-Svcs)*
Linda Rakestraw *(Comptroller & Gen Mgr)*

SUN STATE INTERNATIONAL TRUCKS, LLC
6020 E Adamo Dr, Tampa, FL 33619
Tel.: (813) 621-1331
Web Site:
http://www.sunstateintl.com
Year Founded: 1982

Sales Range: $100-124.9 Million
Emp.: 170
Truck Dealership
N.A.I.C.S.: 441227
Oscar J. Horton *(CEO)*

SUN SUN TRADING CO. INC.
2817 Tyler Ave, El Monte, CA 91733
Tel.: (626) 575-1500
Rev.: $14,500,000
Emp.: 18
Restaurant Supplies
N.A.I.C.S.: 423850
Brandon Lam *(Pres)*

SUN SUPPLY INC.
2310 NW 24th Ave, Portland, OR 97210
Tel.: (503) 222-5080
Web Site: http://www.suncorp.com
Year Founded: 1972
Sales Range: $10-24.9 Million
Emp.: 18
Wholesale Of Transformers & Electric Equipment
N.A.I.C.S.: 423610
Chris Sullivan *(Pres)*

SUN TAN CITY
5226 Dixie Hwy, Louisville, KY 40216
Tel.: (502) 448-1337
Web Site: http://www.suntancity.com
Year Founded: 1999
Sales Range: $50-74.9 Million
Emp.: 322
Indoor Tanning Services
N.A.I.C.S.: 812112
Rick Kueber *(Co-Founder & CEO)*
David Kueber *(Co-Founder & Chm)*
Steve Greenlaw *(COO)*

SUN VALLEY GOLD LLC
620 Sun Valley Rd, Sun Valley, ID 83353
Tel.: (208) 726-2327
Investment Management Service
N.A.I.C.S.: 523940
Peter F. Palmedo *(Mng Partner)*
Linda J. Kish *(Chief Legal Officer)*

SUN VALLEY MASONRY INC.
10828 N Cave Creek Rd, Phoenix, AZ 85020
Tel.: (602) 943-6106
Web Site: http://www.svmasonry.com
Year Founded: 1979
Sales Range: $25-49.9 Million
Emp.: 420
Masonry Contractors
N.A.I.C.S.: 238140
David R. Beer *(CFO)*
Todd Baum *(Pres)*
Kenneth L. Nessler Jr. *(VP)*

SUN WEST COMMUNICATIONS, INC.
16212 Bothell Everett Hwy, Bothell, WA 98012-1603
Tel.: (214) 373-1601
Web Site: http://www.sunwestpr.com
Emp.: 100
Electrical Contractor
N.A.I.C.S.: 238210
Merrie Spaeth *(Founder-Spaeth Training)*

Subsidiaries:
Spaeth Communications, Inc. (1)
3405 Oak Grove Ave, Dallas, TX 75204-2332
Tel.: (214) 871-8888
Web Site: http://www.spaethcom.com
Emp.: 100
Scientific & Technical Consulting Services
N.A.I.C.S.: 541690

SUN WEST OIL COMPANY LLC
138 Broadway Ave, Alamosa, CO 81101
Tel.: (719) 589-6215
Sales Range: $10-24.9 Million
Emp.: 3
Petroleum Bulk Stations
N.A.I.C.S.: 424710
Rock Southway *(Pres)*
Mike Young *(VP)*

SUN WEST RESTAURANT CONCEPTS
6908 Hawaiian Sky Ct, Las Vegas, NV 89131
Tel.: (702) 368-6766
Sales Range: $10-24.9 Million
Emp.: 600
Eating Place
N.A.I.C.S.: 722511

SUN-AG INC.
7735 County Rd 512, Fellsmere, FL 32948-7802
Tel.: (772) 571-1205
Year Founded: 1988
Sales Range: $10-24.9 Million
Emp.: 260
Farm Management Services
N.A.I.C.S.: 111320
Michael Monroe *(Gen Mgr)*

SUN-MAID GROWERS OF CALIFORNIA
13525 S Bethel Ave, Kingsburg, CA 93631-9212
Tel.: (559) 896-8000
Web Site: http://www.sunmaid.com
Year Founded: 1912
Sales Range: $150-199.9 Million
Emp.: 500
Producer & Distr of Raisins, Dried Apricots, Peaches, Mixed Cut Fruit, Raisin Juice Concentrate, Dried Pears, Animal Feed & Gift Packs
N.A.I.C.S.: 424490
Pete J. Penner *(Vice Chm)*
Kayhan Hazrati *(Asst VP-Tech Svcs)*
Harry Overly *(Exec Chm)*
Steve Kister *(Chm)*
Braden Bender *(Interim Pres & CFO)*

SUNABON LIMITED PARTNERSHIP
23233 N Pima Rd Ste 113, Scottsdale, AZ 85255-8387
Tel.: (480) 502-3600
Sales Range: $10-24.9 Million
Emp.: 100
Commercial Bakery Services
N.A.I.C.S.: 311812
Nesbitt Plotke *(Gen Partner)*
Carol Plotke *(Partner)*
Don Kline *(Dir-Ops)*

SUNBEAM COUNTRY HEARTH THRIFT STORE
3355 W Memorial Blvd, Lakeland, FL 33815
Tel.: (863) 682-1155
Sales Range: $10-24.9 Million
Emp.: 400
Baked Goods Mfr
N.A.I.C.S.: 311811
Alan Christopherson *(Plant Mgr)*
Donna Johnson *(Dir-HR)*
Doug Wimberly *(Pres)*
John Lombardo *(Mgr-Maintenanace)*
Rick Leonard *(Mgr-Sls)*
Mike Ogrady *(Mgr-IT)*

SUNBEAM TELEVISION CORPORATION

U.S. PRIVATE

1401 79th St Causeway, Miami, FL 33141-4104
Tel.: (305) 751-6692
Year Founded: 1953
Sales Range: $25-49.9 Million
Emp.: 475
Television Broadcasting Stations Owner & Operator; Commercial Real Estate Investment & Property Management Services
N.A.I.C.S.: 516120
Edmund N. Ansin *(Pres & CEO)*
Roger G. Metcalf *(CFO & Sec)*
Robert W. Leider *(Exec VP & Gen Mgr-WSVN-TV)*

Subsidiaries:

Sunbeam Development Corporation (1)
9200 E 116th St, Fishers, IN 46037 (100%)
Tel.: (317) 842-1166
Web Site:
http://www.sunbeamdevelopment.com
Sales Range: $10-24.9 Million
Emp.: 5
Commercial Property Investment & Management Services
N.A.I.C.S.: 531390

WHDH TV Inc. (1)
7 Bulfinch Pl, Boston, MA 02114-2904 (100%)
Tel.: (617) 248-5413
Web Site: http://www.whdh.com
Sales Range: $25-49.9 Million
Emp.: 300
Television Broadcasting Services
N.A.I.C.S.: 516120
Joe Amorosino *(Dir-Sports)*

Unit (Domestic):

WLVI-TV (2)
7 Bullfinch Pl, Boston, MA 02114-2904
Tel.: (617) 725-0777
Web Site: http://www.whdh.com
Sales Range: $50-74.9 Million
Television Broadcasting Station
N.A.I.C.S.: 516120
Tom Agnus *(Gen Mgr)*

WSVN-TV (1)
1401 79th St Causeway, Miami, FL 33141
Tel.: (305) 751-6692
Web Site: http://www.wsvn.com
Television Broadcasting Station
N.A.I.C.S.: 516120
Cyndi Feinstein *(Gen Mgr-Sls)*
Lauren Levitus *(Mgr-Sls-Natl)*
Robert W. Leider *(VP)*

SUNBELT CONSTRUCTION INC.
1034 Searcy Way, Bowling Green, KY 42103
Tel.: (270) 781-2859
Web Site:
http://www.sunbeltconstruction inc.com
Sales Range: $1-9.9 Million
Emp.: 10
Commercial & Office Building Construction
N.A.I.C.S.: 236220
Quintin Littrell *(Pres)*

SUNBELT GOLF CORPORATION
167 Sunbelt Pkwy, Birmingham, AL 35211
Tel.: (205) 942-0444
Web Site:
http://www.sunbeltgolfcorp.com
Year Founded: 1990
Sales Range: $25-49.9 Million
Emp.: 700
Golf Course & Country Club Operating Services
N.A.I.C.S.: 713910
John Cannon *(Pres)*
Jonathon Romeo *(Dir-Bus Dev)*
Sharon Green *(VP)*

COMPANIES

SUNBELT HEALTH AND RE-HAB CENTER APOPKA
305 E Oak St, Apopka, FL 32703
Tel.: (407) 880-2266 FL
Web Site:
http://www.sunbeltapopka.com
Year Founded: 2006
Sales Range: $10-24.9 Million
Emp.: 200
Community Health Care Services
N.A.I.C.S.: 624190
Kent Johnson (CFO)

SUNBELT MARKETING INVESTMENT CORP.
3255 S Sweetwater Rd, Lithia Springs, GA 30122-2837
Tel.: (770) 739-3740
Web Site:
http://www.sunbeltmarketing.com
Year Founded: 1976
Sales Range: $25-49.9 Million
Emp.: 135
Provider of Plumbing Supply Services
N.A.I.C.S.: 423720
Tom Menefee (Pres)
Don Keller (Mgr-Acctg & Tech)
Chuck Huffmaster (Mgr-Ops)
Richard Goldsmith (Mgr-Sls)
Robb Horvat (Product Mgr)

Subsidiaries:

Sunbelt Marketing Inc. (1)
3255 S Sweetwater Rd, Lithia Springs, GA 30122
Tel.: (770) 739-3740
Web Site: http://www.sunbeltmarketing.com
Sales Range: $25-49.9 Million
Emp.: 80
Provider of Plumbing Supply Services
N.A.I.C.S.: 423720
Tom Menefee (Pres)
Richard Goldsmith (Mgr-Sls)
Chuck Huffmaster (Mgr-Ops)
Don Keller (Mgr-Acctg)

Sunbelt Marketing Investment Corp. - Deerfield Beach (1)
3901 NE 12th Ave, Pompano Beach, FL 33442
Tel.: (954) 571-3877
Plumbing & Heating Equipment Whsl
N.A.I.C.S.: 423720

SUNBELT MATERIAL HANDLING INC.
2255 Justin Trl, Alpharetta, GA 30004
Tel.: (770) 569-2244
Sales Range: $10-24.9 Million
Emp.: 22
Material Handling Equipment Mfr
N.A.I.C.S.: 423510
William Alan Darnell (Pres)
Mark McKinney (Controller)

SUNBELT TELECOMMUNICATIONS INC.
505 Century Pkwy Ste 100, Allen, TX 75013-8040
Tel.: (972) 235-0587
Web Site: http://www.sunbelt.com
Year Founded: 1983
Sales Range: $10-24.9 Million
Emp.: 68
Telecommunication Equipment & Services
N.A.I.C.S.: 423690

SUNBLOCK SYSTEMS, INC.
1900 Campus Commons Dr Ste 100, Reston, VA 20191
Tel.: (703) 485-4515
Web Site:
http://www.sunblocksystems.com
Computer & Network Security Services
N.A.I.C.S.: 541511

Andrew Levetown (Pres & Gen Counsel)

Subsidiaries:

Marquet International Ltd. (1)
462 Washington St 2nd FL, Wellesley, MA 02482
Tel.: (617) 733-3304
Web Site:
http://www.marquetinternational.com
Marketing Consulting Services
N.A.I.C.S.: 541613
Chris Marquet (Founder & CEO)

SUNBRITETV LLC
2001 Anchor Ct, Thousand Oaks, CA 91320
Tel.: (805) 214-7250
Web Site: http://www.sunbritetv.com
Year Founded: 2004
Sales Range: $1-9.9 Million
Emp.: 25
Outdoor Television Mfr
N.A.I.C.S.: 334220
Tom Dixon (VP-Mktg)
Larry Kaiser (Co-Founder)
Tom Weaver (Co-Founder)

SUNBURST CONTEMPORARY HOMES INC.
1441 Hwy 99 N, Eugene, OR 97402
Tel.: (541) 688-7523
Web Site:
http://www.sunbursthomes.com
Sales Range: $10-24.9 Million
Emp.: 10
Prefabricated Home Mfr & Sales
N.A.I.C.S.: 321992
Richard A. Jacobson (Pres)

SUNBURST FOODS INC.
1002 Sunburst Dr, Goldsboro, NC 27534
Tel.: (919) 778-2151
Web Site:
http://www.sunburstfood.net
Sales Range: $10-24.9 Million
Emp.: 170
Assembled & Packaged Sandwiches Distr
N.A.I.C.S.: 311991
Glenda Rogers (VP)
Terri Ingram (VP-Admin)

SUNBURST HOSPITALITY CORPORATION
10750 Columbia Pike Ste 300, Silver Spring, MD 20901-4448
Tel.: (301) 592-3800 DE
Web Site: http://www.snbhotels.com
Year Founded: 1997
Sales Range: $200-249.9 Million
Emp.: 2,500
Owner & Operator of Extended-Stay Hotels
N.A.I.C.S.: 721110
Leon Vainikos (Gen Counsel & VP)
Ned Heiss (VP-Ops)

Subsidiaries:

Boulevard Motel Corp. (1)
10770 Columbia Pike, Silver Spring, MD 20901-4438
Tel.: (301) 592-3800
Sales Range: $10-24.9 Million
Emp.: 5
Hotels & Motels
N.A.I.C.S.: 721110

Everglades Beverage Corp. (1)
10770 Clumbia Pike, Silver Spring, MD 20901-4427
Tel.: (301) 592-3800
Beer & Ale
N.A.I.C.S.: 424810

Fairways Beverage Corp. (1)
10770 Columbia Pike, Silver Spring, MD 20901-4448

Tel.: (301) 592-3800
Beer & Ale
N.A.I.C.S.: 424810

Fairways Inc. (1)
10770 Columbia Pike, Silver Spring, MD 20901-4438
Tel.: (301) 592-3800
Web Site: http://www.snbhotels.com
Sales Range: $10-24.9 Million
Emp.: 2
Hotels & Motels
N.A.I.C.S.: 721110

First Choice Properties Corp. (1)
10770 Columbia Pike, Silver Spring, MD 20901-4438 (100%)
Tel.: (301) 592-3800
Sales Range: $75-99.9 Million
Emp.: 1,500
Real Estate Agents & Managers
N.A.I.C.S.: 721110

MCH Management Inc. (1)
10770 Columbia Pike, Silver Spring, MD 20901-4448
Tel.: (301) 592-3800
Hotels & Motels
N.A.I.C.S.: 721110

MCHD Cypress Creek Corp. (1)
10770 Columbia Pike, Silver Spring, MD 20901-4448
Tel.: (301) 592-3800
Hotels & Motels
N.A.I.C.S.: 721110

MCHD Fort Lauderdale Corp. (1)
10770 Columbia Pike, Silver Spring, MD 20901-4448
Tel.: (301) 592-3800
Hotels & Motels
N.A.I.C.S.: 721110

West Montgomery Hotel Holdings Inc. (1)
3 Research Ct, Rockville, MD 20850-3211
Tel.: (301) 592-3800
Sales Range: $1-9.9 Million
Emp.: 1,400
Hotels & Motels
N.A.I.C.S.: 721191

SUNBURST SEED COMPANY
1815 N St, Muskogee, OK 74403
Tel.: (918) 687-0548
Web Site:
http://www.sunburstseed.com
Year Founded: 1983
Sales Range: $1-9.9 Million
Emp.: 1
Agricultural Product Whsl
N.A.I.C.S.: 424910
Wayne Herriman (Owner)

SUNBURY MOTOR COMPANY
943 N 4th St, Sunbury, PA 17801
Tel.: (570) 286-7746
Web Site:
http://www.sunburymotors.com
Sales Range: $50-74.9 Million
Emp.: 120
Sales of New & Used Automobiles
N.A.I.C.S.: 441110
Tom Mertz (Gen Mgr)
Robert W. Mertz Jr. (Pres)

SUNCHASE HOLDINGS, INC.
8601 N Scottsdale Rd, Scottsdale, AZ 85253
Tel.: (602) 852-5588
Web Site:
http://www.sunchaseholdings.com
Year Founded: 1983
Sales Range: $1-9.9 Million
Emp.: 60
Real Estate Investor & Developer & Computer Software Developer
N.A.I.C.S.: 551112
William A. Pope (CEO)
Stephen E. Renneckar (Pres)
Duane A. Grimsman (Sr VP)
Philip J. Handley (CFO)
Craig F. Pickett (Pres)

SUNCOAST FORMS & SYSTEMS, INC.

Subsidiaries:

INTRIX Technologies Inc. (1)
2260 Douglas Blvd Ste 240, Roseville, CA 95661-4208 (100%)
Tel.: (916) 577-1315
Web Site: http://www.intrix.com
Sales Range: $1-9.9 Million
Emp.: 25
System Software Development Services
N.A.I.C.S.: 541512
Jeff Connors (CEO)
Peter Matino (Chief Sls Officer)
Roger Arora (CFO, Sr VP & Head-Ops)
Suzanne Coleman (CTO & Sr VP)

SUNCHIP TECHNOLOGY, INC.
2501 E Aragon Blvd Unit 1, Sunrise, FL 33313
Tel.: (954) 366-9470 FL
Year Founded: 2013
Store Monitoring Software
N.A.I.C.S.: 513210
Ilyssa Suarez (Pres, CEO, CFO, Treas & Sec)

SUNCOAST BEVERAGE SALES, LLLP
2996 Hanson St, Fort Myers, FL 33916-7510
Tel.: (239) 334-3520
Web Site:
http://www.suncoastbeverage.com
Year Founded: 1993
Sales Range: $25-49.9 Million
Emp.: 160
Beer Distr
N.A.I.C.S.: 424810
Tim Mitchell (Pres)

SUNCOAST CENTER INC.
PO Box 10970, Saint Petersburg, FL 33733
Tel.: (727) 327-7656
Web Site:
http://www.suncoastcenter.org
Year Founded: 1944
Sales Range: $10-24.9 Million
Emp.: 325
Family Services
N.A.I.C.S.: 624190
Barbara Daire (Pres & CEO)
Linda Lefler (Dir-Medical)
Kevin Driscoll (CFO)
Angeline Howell (Dir-Clinical Svcs)
Kristin Mathre (COO)
Maria Ochoa (Dir-HR)
John Walsh (CIO)
Lynda Wagner (Dir-Clinical Svcs)

SUNCOAST CREDIT UNION
6801 E Hillsborough Ave, Tampa, FL 33680
Tel.: (813) 805-9922
Web Site: http://www.suncoastfcu.org
Credit Union
N.A.I.C.S.: 522130
Kevin Johnson (Pres & CEO)

SUNCOAST DIGITAL PRESS INC.
8047 Royal Birkdale Cir, Lakewood Ranch, FL 34202
Tel.: (888) 961-7011
Web Site:
http://www.suncoastdigitalpress.com
Sales Range: $1-9.9 Million
Emp.: 5
Book Publishers
N.A.I.C.S.: 513199
Veronica Belmont (CMO)

SUNCOAST FORMS & SYSTEMS, INC.
1045 N Lime Ave, Sarasota, FL 34237
Tel.: (941) 366-1123 FL

SUNCOAST FORMS & SYSTEMS, INC.

Suncoast Forms & Systems, Inc.—(Continued)
Web Site:
http://www.suncoastforms.com
Year Founded: 1979
Sales Range: $1-9.9 Million
Emp.: 28
Business Forms, Brochures, Letterhead, Booklets, Envelopes & Labels Printing Services; Stationery & Office Supplies Merchant Whslr
N.A.I.C.S.: 323111
Barbara D. Donnelly *(VP)*
David L. Donnelly *(Pres)*
Matt Clare *(Mgr-Print Shop)*
Patti Donnelly *(VP-Sls & Mktg)*

SUNCOAST OIL CO. OF FLORIDA INC.
3321 9th Ave N, Saint Petersburg, FL 33713-6511
Tel.: (727) 323-1511 FL
Year Founded: 1973
Sales Range: $10-24.9 Million
Emp.: 85
Petroleum Products Mfr & Distr
N.A.I.C.S.: 424720

SUNCOAST RHIO, INC.
2567 N Toledo Blade Blvd Ste 1, North Port, FL 34289
Tel.: (941) 426-6093
Web Site: http://www.sucoastrhio.org
Year Founded: 2008
Sales Range: $1-9.9 Million
Regional Health Information Services
N.A.I.C.S.: 519290
Lou Galterio *(Founder)*
Mark Klingel *(CFO)*
Stephen Weiss *(CTO)*
Christopher Sullivan *(VP-Mktg, Comm & Res)*
Kym Gerberich *(Treas)*

SUNCOAST SIGN SHOP, INC.
8466 N Lockwood Ridge Rd Ste 205, Sarasota, FL 34243
Tel.: (941) 866-7504
Web Site:
http://www.suncoastsignshop.com
Sales Range: $1-9.9 Million
Sign Mfr; Graphic Design Services
N.A.I.C.S.: 339950
Brian Gregg *(Owner & Pres)*

SUNCRAFT TECHNOLOGIES INC.
1301 Frontenac Rd, Naperville, IL 60563
Tel.: (630) 369-7900
Web Site: http://www.suncraft-tech.com
Sales Range: $25-49.9 Million
Emp.: 105
Commercial Printing Services
N.A.I.C.S.: 323111
Ronald Desanto *(Pres)*
Lisa DeSanto *(VP)*
Kent Hallgren *(VP-Sls)*
Maria Coles *(Coord-Production)*

SUNCREST FARMS COUNTRY HAMS, INC.
1148 Foster St, Wilkesboro, NC 28697
Tel.: (336) 667-4441
Web Site:
http://www.suncrestfarmscountryham.net
Year Founded: 1994
Sales Range: $10-24.9 Million
Emp.: 75
Meat Product Production Services
N.A.I.C.S.: 311612

Randall Gambill *(Pres & CEO)*
Annette Gambill *(Office Mgr)*
Russel Gambill *(Treas & Sec)*
John Jones *(Sec)*

SUNDANCE BEHAVIORAL HEALTHCARE SYSTEM
7000 US Highway 287 S, Arlington, TX 76001
Tel.: (817) 583-8080
Web Site:
http://www.sundancehealthcare.com
Year Founded: 2005
Sales Range: $10-24.9 Million
Emp.: 200
Behavioral & Mental Illness Services
N.A.I.C.S.: 622210
David Tucker *(Medical Dir)*

SUNDANCE CHEVROLET, INC.
5895 E Saginaw Hwy, Grand Ledge, MI 48837-9110
Tel.: (517) 627-4051 MI
Web Site: http://www.sundancechevyranch.com
Year Founded: 1981
Sales Range: $25-49.9 Million
Emp.: 61
New & Used Car Dealer
N.A.I.C.S.: 441110
Harold Terry Hanks *(Owner)*
John Viselli *(Gen Mgr)*

Subsidiaries:

Sundance Buick, GMC, Inc. (1)
1205 N US Hwy 27, Saint Johns, MI 48879
Tel.: (989) 224-3900
Web Site: http://www.1877sundance.com
Sales Range: $10-24.9 Million
Emp.: 20
New & Used Car Dealer
N.A.I.C.S.: 441110
Harold Terry Hanks *(Pres)*
Terrah Hanks *(Gen Mgr)*
Jennifer Catlin *(Mgr-Svc)*

SUNDANCE MARINE, INC.
2051 Griffin Rd, Fort Lauderdale, FL 33312
Tel.: (954) 621-1066 FL
Web Site:
http://www.sundancemarineusa.com
Year Founded: 1980
Sales Range: $25-49.9 Million
Emp.: 20
Boat Dealerships Operator
N.A.I.C.S.: 441222
Mitchell Milesi *(VP-Jensen Beach & Stuart)*

SUNDANCE VACATIONS
264 Highland Park Blvd, Wilkes Barre, PA 18702
Web Site:
http://www.sundancevacations.com
Year Founded: 1991
Sales Range: $25-49.9 Million
Emp.: 1,581
Travel Services
N.A.I.C.S.: 561599
Scott Brunnenmeyer *(Dir-Mktg)*
Marvin Metzger *(COO)*
Christina Allen *(Mgr-Quality Assurance)*
Tommy Shafer *(Mgr-HR)*
Joe Molitoris *(VP-Mktg)*
Tina Dowd *(Co-Founder & Co-Owner)*
John Dowd *(Co-Founder & Co-Owner)*
Denise Miller *(Gen Mgr)*
Ron Vaccaro *(Controller)*
Suann Ritter *(CTO)*
Valerie Burke *(Dir-Digital Media)*
Candy Bednar *(VP-Bus Dev)*

SUNDAY RIVER SKI RESORT

15 S Ridge Rd, Newry, ME 04261
Tel.: (207) 824-3000
Web Site:
http://www.sundayriver.com
Year Founded: 1958
Sales Range: $10-24.9 Million
Emp.: 1,500
Skiing Facility Operating Services
N.A.I.C.S.: 713920
Dana Bullen *(Gen Mgr)*

SUNDERLAND BROTHERS COMPANY
9700 J St, Omaha, NE 68127
Tel.: (402) 339-2220
Web Site:
http://www.sunderlands.com
Rev.: $19,494,000
Emp.: 45
Tile Cabinet Distributors
N.A.I.C.S.: 423310
Ron Bauer *(Pres)*
Kim Gawecki *(Exec VP-Sls & Mktg)*

SUNDIA CORPORATION
340 S Lemon Ave Ste 8093N, Walnut, CA 91789
Tel.: (415) 762-0600
Web Site: http://www.sundiafruit.com
Year Founded: 2004
Sales Range: $1-9.9 Million
Emp.: 30
Cut Fruit & Organic Products Producer & Distr
N.A.I.C.S.: 445230
Bradford S. Oberwager *(Co-Founder & Chm)*
Mark Sherburne *(VP-Sls)*
Daniel Hoskins *(Co-Founder & CEO)*

SUNDIN ASSOCIATES, INC.
34 Main St 3rd Fl, Natick, MA 01760
Tel.: (508) 650-3972
Web Site: http://www.sundininc.com
Year Founded: 1976
Rev.: $12,000,000
Emp.: 8
N.A.I.C.S.: 541810
Robert C. Donnelly *(Sr VP)*
Carol Suddath *(Dir-PR)*
Kristin Sundin Brandt *(VP)*
Edward J. O'Donnell *(Acct Exec)*
William R. Orsini *(Sr Dir-Art)*
David Bastille *(Dir-Art)*
Lisa Segarra *(Dir-Art)*
Andy Paul *(Copywriter)*
Roger W. Sundin Jr. *(Pres)*

SUNDOG
2000 44th St SW 6th Fl, Fargo, ND 58103
Tel.: (701) 235-5525 ND
Year Founded: 1977
Rev.: $18,000,000
Emp.: 60
Brand Development, Broadcast, Corporate Identity, Financial, Graphic Design, Health Care, Public Relations, Restaurant, Retail, Strategic Planning
N.A.I.C.S.: 541810
Greg Ness *(Chief Strategy Officer)*
Erick Kuntz *(Sr VP)*
Brent Teiken *(CEO)*
Johnathon Rademacher *(Exec VP-Tech)*
Eric Dukart *(COO, Exec VP-Insights & Plng)*
Jim Heilman *(Exec VP-Bus Dev)*
Ron Lee *(Exec VP-Client Svcs)*
Matt Gustafson *(Exec VP-Ops)*

SUNDOWN M RANCH
2280 State Route 821, Selah, WA 98901-8302
Tel.: (509) 457-0990 WA

U.S. PRIVATE

Web Site: http://www.sundown.org
Year Founded: 1968
Sales Range: $1-9.9 Million
Emp.: 211
Drug Treatment Services
N.A.I.C.S.: 621420
Neil Buren *(First VP)*
Pat Carey *(Sec)*
Felicia Holtzinger *(Treas)*
Maurice Peugh *(Pres)*

SUNDURANCE ENERGY, LLC
2045 Lincoln Hwy Edison Sq Ofc Park, Edison, NJ 08817
Tel.: (732) 520-5000
Web Site:
http://www.sunduranceenergy.com
Year Founded: 2007
Sales Range: $25-49.9 Million
Emp.: 33
Solar Power Systems Mfr
N.A.I.C.S.: 926130
Al Bucknam *(CEO)*
Todd Martin *(VP-Bus Dev)*
Andrew Nekus *(Dir-Bus Dev Utility-Scale Market)*
Karen Schneider *(Dir-Bus Dev-Federal Govt)*

SUNEDISON, INC.
13736 Riverport Dr, Maryland Heights, MO 63043
Tel.: (314) 770-7300 DE
Web Site: http://www.sunedison.com
Year Founded: 1984
Sales Range: $1-4.9 Billion
Holding Company; Solar Power & Renewable Energy Solutions Developer & Mfr
N.A.I.C.S.: 551112
John S. Dubel *(CEO & Chief Restructuring Officer)*
John S. Dubel *(CEO & Chief Restructuring Officer)*
Emmanuel T. Hernandez *(Chm)*
Martin H. Truong *(Gen Counsel, Sec & Sr VP)*
Paul J. Gaynor *(Exec VP-Utility-North America & Wind-Global)*
Stephen J. Cerrone *(Chief HR Officer & Exec VP)*
Jeremy Avenier *(VP-FP & A)*
Pashupathy Gopalan *(Pres-SunEdison Asia Pacific)*
Vikas Desai *(Sr VP & Gen Mgr-Residential & Small Comml Bus)*
Ben Harborne *(Sr Mgr-Mktg-Brand & Corp Comm)*
Philip J. Gund *(CFO)*
Salvatore LoBiondo Jr. *(Sr VP & Controller)*
Salvatore LoBiondo Jr. *(Sr VP & Controller)*

Subsidiaries:

Energy Matters Pty Ltd (1)
359-361 City Road, Southbank, 3006, VIC, Australia
Tel.: (61) 133786
Semiconductor Devices Mfr
N.A.I.C.S.: 334413
Han Wong *(Engr-Design)*

MEMC Kuching Sdn. Bhd. (1)
Lot 2118 Jalan Usaha Jaya, SamaJaya Free Industrial Zone, Kuching, 93450, Sarawak, Malaysia
Tel.: (60) 82530888
Emp.: 1,000
Solar Power Device & Component Mfr
N.A.I.C.S.: 334413
S. J. Ngieng *(Mgr)*

MEMC Pasadena, Inc. (1)
3000 N South St, Pasadena, TX 77503
Tel.: (713) 740-1420
Sales Range: $25-49.9 Million
Emp.: 200
Solar Device Granular Polysilicon Component Mfr

COMPANIES

N.A.I.C.S.: 334413

SunEdison Energy India Pvt. Ltd. (1)
Menon Eternity 10th Floor New 165 Old No 110 St Marys Road, Alwarpet, Chennai, 600018, Tamilnadu, India
Tel.: (91) 4442923818
Sales Range: $50-74.9 Million
Emp.: 100
Solar Electric Power Generation
N.A.I.C.S.: 221114

SunEdison Holdings Corporation (1)
501 Pearl Dr, Saint Peters, MO 63376
Tel.: (636) 474-5000
Holding Company
N.A.I.C.S.: 551112

SunEdison LLC (1)
12500 Baltimore Ave, Beltsville, MD 20705 (100%)
Tel.: (443) 909-7200
Web Site: http://www.sunedison.com
Sales Range: $10-24.9 Million
Emp.: 150
Solar Energy Technology Mfr
N.A.I.C.S.: 221118

SunEdison Semiconductor BV (1)
Naritaweg 165, 1043 BW, Amsterdam, Netherlands
Tel.: (31) 205722300
Semiconductor Devices Mfr
N.A.I.C.S.: 334413

SUNERA LLC
201 E Kennedy Blvd Ste 1750, Tampa, FL 33602
Tel.: (813) 402-1208
Web Site: http://www.sunera.com
Emp.: 300
IT & Internal Audit Consulting Services
N.A.I.C.S.: 541611
Christie Verscharen *(Partner)*
Joyce Block *(Partner)*
Andrew Cannata *(Partner)*
David Hollis *(Partner)*
Lee Cook *(VP-Bus Dev, Sls & Mktg)*
Michael Kano *(Sr Mgr)*

SUNERGY, INC.
14362 N Frank Lloyd Wright Blvd Ste 1000, Scottsdale, AZ 85260
Tel.: (480) 477-5810 NV
Web Site: http://www.sunergygold.com
Sales Range: Less than $1 Million
Mineral Exploration Services
N.A.I.C.S.: 212390
Larry Max Bigler *(CFO)*
Robert A. Levich *(Mgr-Ops-West Africa)*
Garrett Hale *(Pres & CEO)*

SUNESIS CONSTRUCTION COMPANY, INC.
2610 Crescentville Rd, West Chester, OH 45069
Tel.: (513) 326-6000
Web Site: http://www.sunesisconstruction.com
Sales Range: $10-24.9 Million
Emp.: 125
Highway & Street Construction Services
N.A.I.C.S.: 237310
Rick Jones *(Pres)*

SUNETRIC
905 Kalanianole Hwy, Kailua, HI 96734
Tel.: (808) 262-6600
Web Site: http://www.sunetric.com
Year Founded: 2004
Sales Range: $25-49.9 Million
Emp.: 130
Photovoltaic System Installation Services & Mfr
N.A.I.C.S.: 238210
Sean Mullen *(Founder & Co-Owner)*

SUNFLOWER ELECTRIC POWER CORPORATION
301 W 13th St, Hays, KS 67601
Tel.: (785) 628-2845 KS
Web Site: http://www.sunflower.net
Year Founded: 1957
Rev.: $218,019,926
Assets: $427,610,576
Liabilities: $99,935,695
Net Worth: $327,674,881
Earnings: $6,469,177
Emp.: 350
Fiscal Year-end: 12/31/18
Cooperative; Generation & Transmission of Electric Power
N.A.I.C.S.: 221118
Jana Horsfall *(VP-Corp Svcs)*
Stuart S. Lowry *(Pres & CEO)*
Davis Rooney *(CFO & VP)*
Kenny Wehkamp *(Vice Chm)*
Wes Campbell *(Chm)*

Subsidiaries:

Sunflower Electric Power Holcomb Station (1)
2440 Holcomb Ln, Holcomb, KS 67851-9600
Tel.: (620) 277-4513
Web Site: http://www.sunflower.net
Sales Range: $150-199.9 Million
Emp.: 210
Electric Generation & Transmission Utility
N.A.I.C.S.: 221122
Steve Ricard *(Plant Mgr)*

SUNFRESH PRODUCE, INC.
3037 S McCall Rd, Englewood, FL 34224
Tel.: (941) 475-7336 FL
Web Site: http://www.sunfreshfl.com
Year Founded: 1988
Sales Range: $10-24.9 Million
Emp.: 60
Fresh Fruit & Vegetable Merchant Whslr
N.A.I.C.S.: 424480
Steve Clark *(Owner)*

SUNGAME CORPORATION
3091 W Tompkins Ave, Las Vegas, NV 89103
Tel.: (702) 789-0848 DE
Web Site: http://www.sungame.com
Year Founded: 2006
Sales Range: Less than $1 Million
Emp.: 5
Online Games
N.A.I.C.S.: 541511
Nicholas Irwin *(CFO)*

SUNGARD AVAILABILITY SERVICES CAPITAL, INC.
680 E Swedesford Rd, Wayne, PA 19087
Tel.: (484) 582-2000 DE
Web Site: http://www.sungardas.com
Holding Company
N.A.I.C.S.: 551112
Andrew A. Stern *(CEO)*
Bill Price *(Chief Admin Officer & Gen Counsel)*
Alfred Binford *(Exec VP-Sls & Solutions-Worldwide)*
Andy Dzerovych *(Exec VP-Ops-Global)*
Haim Glickman *(Sr VP-Solutions & Engrg-Global)*
Josh Crowe *(CTO)*
Patricia Boujoukos *(Chief Compliance Officer)*
Scott Gibson *(Sr VP-HR-Global)*
Shawn Burke *(Chief Security Officer)*
Vincent Bugge *(Sr VP-Svc & Ops)*

Subsidiaries:

SunGard Availability Services LP (1)
680 E Swedesford Rd, Wayne, PA 19087
Tel.: (484) 582-2000
Web Site: http://www.sungardas.com
Sales Range: $1-4.9 Billion
Emp.: 2,000
IT Operations Support Services
N.A.I.C.S.: 561499
Josh Crowe *(CTO)*
Patricia Boujoukos *(Chief Compliance Officer)*
Vincent Bugge *(Sr VP-Svcs Ops)*
Shawn Burke *(Chief Security Officer-Global)*
Andy Dzerovych *(Exec VP-Global Ops)*
Carmel Owens *(Dir-Sls & Strategic Svcs & Mgr-Ireland)*
Alfred Binford *(Exec VP-Sls & Solutions-Worldwide)*
Haim Glickman *(Sr VP-Solutions Engrg-Global)*
Lisa Bakshi *(VP-Svc Transition-Global)*
Chris Huggett *(Sr VP-Sls-EMEA & India)*
Noel O'Grady *(Sr Dir-Sls-Ireland)*
Scott Gibson *(Sr VP-HR-Global)*

Subsidiary (Non-US):

SunGard Availability Services (France) SA (2)
93 cours des Petites Ecuries, 77185, Lognes, France
Tel.: (33) 164806161
Web Site: http://www.sungardas.fr
Sales Range: $25-49.9 Million
Emp.: 60
IT Support Services
N.A.I.C.S.: 541519
Keith Tilley *(Exec VP-Sls & Customer Svcs Mgmt-Global)*

SunGard Availability Services (UK) Limited (2)
Forum 1, Station Road, Theale, RG7 4RA, Berks, United Kingdom
Tel.: (44) 808 238 8080
Web Site: http://www.sungardas.com
IT Infrastructure & Organizational Services
N.A.I.C.S.: 513210
Keith Tilley *(Exec VP-Sls & Customer Svcs Mgmt-Global)*

Branch (Non-US):

SunGard Availability Services - Mississauga (2)
2330 Argentia Rd, Mississauga, L5N 5Z7, ON, Canada
Tel.: (484) 582-4926
Web Site: http://www.sungard.com
Sales Range: $10-24.9 Million
Emp.: 3,000
Recovery Services, Data Processing & Preparation Software
N.A.I.C.S.: 518210

Branch (Domestic):

SunGard Availability Services - San Ramon (2)
2481 Deerwood Dr, San Ramon, CA 94583-1540
Tel.: (925) 831-3700
Web Site: http://www.sungardas.com
Sales Range: $25-49.9 Million
Emp.: 5
IT Operations Support Services
N.A.I.C.S.: 513210
Frank Szalontay *(Sr Dir-Ops)*

SUNGDOENG USA
3775 Venture Dr Bldg D-400, Duluth, GA 30096
Tel.: (470) 885-5051
Electronic Product Retailer
N.A.I.C.S.: 449210

SUNGROW LANDSCAPE SERVICES
2007 Rutland Dr, Austin, TX 78758-5421
Tel.: (512) 331-1700
Web Site: http://www.sungrow.com
Rev.: $10,000,000
Emp.: 100
Landscape Contractors
N.A.I.C.S.: 561730
Pat Goulding *(Mng Partner)*
Mike Limberg *(Project Mgr)*

SUNHILLO CORPORATION
444 Kelly Dr, West Berlin, NJ 08091
Tel.: (856) 767-7676
Web Site: http://www.sunhillo.com
Year Founded: 1991
Sales Range: $10-24.9 Million
Custom Computer Programing Computer Systems Design
N.A.I.C.S.: 541511
Dave Whitman *(Pres & CEO)*

SUNKEN STONE INC.
2869 Historic Decatur Rd, San Diego, CA 92106
Tel.: (858) 212-0925 CA
Web Site: http://www.sunkenstone.com
Year Founded: 2009
Sales Range: $10-24.9 Million
Emp.: 22
Digital Marketing Services
N.A.I.C.S.: 541810
Adam Weiler *(Founder)*
Stacey Speck *(Gen Mgr)*
Emily Lindhal *(Acct Mgr)*
Chelsea Ruitenberg *(Acct Mgr)*
Eric Vjaters *(Mgr-Content)*

SUNKIST GROWERS, INC.
27770 Entertainment Dr, Valencia, CA 91355
Tel.: (661) 290-8900 CA
Web Site: http://www.sunkist.com
Year Founded: 1893
Sales Range: $1-4.9 Billion
Emp.: 4,500
Citrus Fruit Marketer
N.A.I.C.S.: 424480
Jeff Gaston *(Mng Dir-Sls-North America)*
Timothy Forseth *(Dir-Sls-West)*
Brian Slage *(Dir-Sls-Southeastern)*
Matt Shekoyan *(VP-Strategy)*

Subsidiaries:

SunMac Hawaii, Ltd. (1)
972 Queen St, Honolulu, HI 96803 (51%)
Tel.: (808) 593-2850
Web Site: http://www.sunkist.com
Rev.: $524,000
Emp.: 7
Warehousing & Distribution of Fruit
N.A.I.C.S.: 493120

Sunkist (Far East) Promotion, Ltd. (1)
1303 Bank Of America Tower 12 Harcourt Rd, Hong Kong, China (Hong Kong) (100%)
Tel.: (852) 25249219
Web Site: http://www.sunkist.com
Sales Range: $25-49.9 Million
Emp.: 10
Citrus Marketing Cooperative
N.A.I.C.S.: 541613
Maria Kwok *(Mng Dir)*

Sunkist Growers, Inc. - Processed Products (1)
616 E Sunkist, Ontario, CA 91761
Tel.: (909) 983-9811
Web Site: http://www.sunkist.com
Sales Range: $25-49.9 Million
Emp.: 304
Processed Fruit Products Mfr & Distr
N.A.I.C.S.: 311421

Sunkist Growers, Inc.-Central Division (1)
9600 Clerain Ave Ste 310, Cincinnati, OH 45251
Tel.: (513) 741-9845
Citrus Growers Cooperative
N.A.I.C.S.: 111336

Sunkist Growers, Inc.-Eastern Division (1)
1000 Gamma Dr Ste 605, Pittsburgh, PA 15238
Tel.: (412) 967-9801
Web Site: http://www.sunkistgrowers.com
Emp.: 8

SUNKIST GROWERS, INC.   U.S. PRIVATE

Sunkist Growers, Inc.—(Continued)
Regional Sales
N.A.I.C.S.: 445230
John Slagel (Reg Dir)

Sunkist Growers, Inc.-Southern Division (1)
Heritage Place Ste 360 4500 Hugh Howell Rd, Tucker, GA 30084
Tel.: (770) 938-9703
Citrus Growers Cooperative
N.A.I.C.S.: 445230

Sunkist Growers, Inc.-Western Division (1)
2929 W Main St Ste K, Visalia, CA 93291-5730
Tel.: (559) 739-7239
Web Site: http://www.sunkist.com
Citrus Growers Cooperative
N.A.I.C.S.: 445230

SUNLAND BUILDERS
4846a Highway 24, Newport, NC 28570
Tel.: (252) 393-2504
Web Site:
 http://www.sunlandbuilders.com
Year Founded: 1988
Rev.: $6,239,700
Emp.: 47
Grading & Utility Contractor Services
N.A.I.C.S.: 238990
Jack Thompson (Project Mgr)
Earl Boyd (VP-Ops)
Tom Elmore (VP-Estimator & Project Mgr)
Steven Byrum (Project Mgr)
David Kriegler (Mgr-Warehouse)
Jay Ahlquist (CFO)
Ray Langley (Sr Project Mgr)
Rick Williford (Pres)
Albert Taylor (VP-Utilities)

Subsidiaries:

Apple Tuck & Associates, Inc. (1)
200 US 221, Rutherfordton, NC 28139
Tel.: (828) 287-3767
Sales Range: $1-9.9 Million
Emp.: 20
Construction Services
N.A.I.C.S.: 237310
David C. Bare (Pres)

SUNLAND CONSTRUCTION INC.
2532 Aymond St, Eunice, LA 70535-6843
Tel.: (337) 546-0241   LA
Web Site:
 http://www.sunlandconstruction.com
Year Founded: 1974
Sales Range: $25-49.9 Million
Emp.: 565
Provider of Utility Construction Services
N.A.I.C.S.: 237120
James Daigle (Mgr-Directional Drilling Div)
Michael Oubre (Project Mgr)
Jason Leger (Project Mgr)

Subsidiaries:

Buffalo Gap Instrumentation & Electrical Co., Inc. (1)
325 N West St, Buffalo Gap, TX 79508
Tel.: (325) 572-3389
Web Site: http://www.bgie.net
Sales Range: $10-24.9 Million
Emp.: 300
General Electrical Contractor
N.A.I.C.S.: 238210
Leland Miller (Project Mgr)
Carlos Sanchez (Mgr-Div)

Foremost Pipeline Construction (1)
386 Frontage Rd, Gaston, SC 29053
Tel.: (803) 939-4832
Web Site:
 http://www.sunlandconstruction.com
Emp.: 25

Pipeline Construction Services
N.A.I.C.S.: 237120
Steve Locklear (Supvr)

SUNLAND OPTICAL COMPANY INC.
1156 Barranca Dr, El Paso, TX 79935
Tel.: (915) 591-9483
Web Site:
 http://www.sunlandoptical.com
Sales Range: $10-24.9 Million
Emp.: 250
Optical Goods Whslr
N.A.I.C.S.: 456130
Felix Castanon (Pres)

SUNLIGHTEN, INC.
7373 W 107th St, Overland Park, KS 66212
Tel.: (913) 754-0831
Web Site: http://www.sunlighten.com
Year Founded: 1999
Sales Range: $1-9.9 Million
Emp.: 46
Designs & Sells Infrared Saunas
N.A.I.C.S.: 456199
Aaron Zack (Co-Owner)
Connie Zack (Co-Owner)

SUNMAR SHIPPING, INC.
500 108th Ave NE S1710, Bellevue, WA 98121-1209
Tel.: (425) 577-1870   WA
Year Founded: 1979
Sales Range: $50-74.9 Million
Emp.: 7
Deep Sea & Coastal Freight Shipping Services
N.A.I.C.S.: 483111
Azim Qureshi (Pres)

SUNMERGE SYSTEMS INC.
15 Corporate Pl S Ste 430, Piscataway, NJ 08854
Tel.: (732) 981-0400
Web Site:
 http://www.sunmergesystems.com
Year Founded: 2002
Sales Range: $10-24.9 Million
Emp.: 82
Custom Computer Programming Services
N.A.I.C.S.: 541511
Harish Bathini (Owner)
Srujana Malligireddy (Mgr-HR)

SUNNEN PRODUCTS COMPANY
7910 Manchester Ave, Saint Louis, MO 63143-2712
Tel.: (314) 781-2100   DE
Web Site: http://www.sunnen.com
Year Founded: 1924
Sales Range: $150-199.9 Million
Emp.: 500
Industrial Honing Machines & Auto Engine Rebuilding Equipment; Precision Gages
N.A.I.C.S.: 333519
Tom Dustman (Dir-Intl Sls)
Matthew Sunnen Kreider (Chm)
Christopher Miltenberger (Pres, CEO & COO)

Subsidiaries:

OOO Sunnen RUS (1)
Korovinskoe highway 10 building 2 3rd entrance 4th floor office 21, 127486, Moscow, Russia
Tel.: (7) 4952589175
Web Site: http://www.sunnen.ru
Precision Tool Mfr
N.A.I.C.S.: 333515

Shanghai Sunnen Mechanical Company, Ltd. (1)

889 Kang Qiao East Road, Pu Dong, Shanghai, 201319, China
Tel.: (86) 21 5813 3322
Web Site: http://www.sunnensh.com
Sales Range: $10-24.9 Million
Emp.: 90
Oil & Gas Field Equipment Mfr
N.A.I.C.S.: 333132
Gary Mao (Dir-Sls)

Sunnen AG (1)
Fabrikstrasse 1 Ennetaach, 8586, Erlen, Switzerland
Tel.: (41) 71 649 33 33
Web Site: http://www.sunnen.eu
Sales Range: $10-24.9 Million
Emp.: 650
Automated Bore Sizing & Finishing System Mfr
N.A.I.C.S.: 333132
Georg Huber (CEO & Gen Mgr)

Sunnen Products Limited (1)
Unit 4B Finway Road, Hemel Hempstead, HP2 7PT, Hertfordshire, United Kingdom
Tel.: (44) 1442 393939
Web Site: http://www.sunnen.com
Emp.: 10
Automated Bore Sizing & Finishing System Sales
N.A.I.C.S.: 423830

Sunnen S.R.O. (1)
Nabrezi Otavy 73, 386 01, Strakonice, Czech Republic
Tel.: (420) 383 376 317
Web Site: http://www.sunnen.cz
Sales Range: $10-24.9 Million
Emp.: 3
Machine Tool Distr
N.A.I.C.S.: 423710

Sunnen SAS (1)
4 rue Rene Razel, 91892, Saclay, France
Tel.: (33) 1 69 30 00 00
Web Site: http://www.sunnen.fr
Sales Range: $10-24.9 Million
Emp.: 10
Precision Tools Distr
N.A.I.C.S.: 423830

SUNNILAND CORPORATION
PO Box 8001, Sanford, FL 32773
Tel.: (407) 322-2421   DE
Web Site:
 http://www.sunnilandcorp.com
Year Founded: 1884
Sales Range: $75-99.9 Million
Emp.: 210
Mfr & Retailer of Roofing Materials & Supplies; Provider of Fertilizer, Pesticides & Garden Supplies
N.A.I.C.S.: 423330
Thomas W. Moore (Pres & CEO)
John Cahill (CFO)
Billy Griffith (Mgr-Pro Turf Sls)

SUNNY CREEK FARM, LLC.
520 Pine Field Dr, Tryon, NC 28782
Tel.: (828) 863-2963
Web Site:
 http://www.sunnycreekfarm.com
Sales Range: $10-24.9 Million
Emp.: 30
Sprout Production Services
N.A.I.C.S.: 311213
Lee Ewing (Pres & Owner)
Ed Mills (CEO)
Kim Ewing (Office Mgr)

SUNNY DESIGN INC.
23751 Eichler St # E, Hayward, CA 94545-2744
Tel.: (510) 782-3500
Web Site:
 http://www.sunnydesigns.com
Sales Range: $10-24.9 Million
Emp.: 20
Whslr of Household Furniture
N.A.I.C.S.: 423210
Sunny Hwang (Pres)

SUNNY FARMS, INC.
261461 Highway 101 W, Sequim, WA 98382
Tel.: (360) 683-8003
Web Site:
 http://www.sunnyfarms.com
Sales Range: $10-24.9 Million
Emp.: 61
Fresh Fruit & Vegetable Whslr
N.A.I.C.S.: 424480
Scott Van Geystel (Mgr-Smokehouse)
Edwin Joseph Anderson III (Mgr)

SUNNY FLORIDA DAIRY INC.
2209 N 40th St, Tampa, FL 33605
Tel.: (813) 248-3151
Web Site:
 http://www.sunnyfloridadairy.com
Sales Range: $10-24.9 Million
Emp.: 60
Dairy Products Producer
N.A.I.C.S.: 424430
Joseph R. Guagliardo (Pres)
Dan Page (CFO)
A. Scionti (Branch Mgr)

SUNNY MORNING FOODS INC.
5330 NW 35th Ave, Fort Lauderdale, FL 33309-6314
Tel.: (954) 735-3447   FL
Web Site:
 http://www.sunnymorning.com
Year Founded: 1988
Sales Range: $10-24.9 Million
Emp.: 49
Dairy Products Producer
N.A.I.C.S.: 424430
Dale Volkert (Pres)
Ken Carlson (VP)

SUNNYHILL, INC.
11140 S Towne Sq Ste 101, Saint Louis, MO 63123
Tel.: (314) 845-3900   MO
Web Site: http://sunnyhillinc.org
Year Founded: 1978
Sales Range: $10-24.9 Million
Emp.: 623
Developmental Disability Assistance Services
N.A.I.C.S.: 624120
Donald Mitchell (VP-Client Svcs)
Kathleen Branson (Dir-Fin)
Victoria James (Pres & CEO)
Luke Mraz (Dir-Dev & Community Partnerships)
Bruce King (Dir-Jefferson County Svcs)
Linda Kresko (Dir-HR)
Mary Eichner (Dir-Nursing Svcs)
Rob Darroch (Dir-Sunnyhill Adventures)
Sean King (Chm)
Jennifer Seiler (Vice Chm-Client Svcs)
Jill Kesler (Vice Chm-Dev)
Russ Korte (Treas)
Mary Ann Rodenberg (Sec)
Calle Melkersman (Dir-Waiver)
Amy Wheeler (Dir-ISLA)
Tamico Love (Dir-Advocacy)
Katie James (Dir-HR)
Jim Schmitt (Dir-IT)

SUNNYSIDE AUTO PARTS
2424 W Montrose Ave, Chicago, IL 60618
Tel.: (773) 267-8200
Web Site:
 http://www.sunnysideco.com
Auto Parts & Accessories Whslr
N.A.I.C.S.: 423120
Dan DeMichele (Gen Mgr)

SUNNYSIDE AUTOMOTIVE INC.
7700 Pearl Rd, Cleveland, OH 44130

Tel.: (440) 243-5577
Web Site: http://www.sunnysideauto.com
Rev.: $59,200,000
Emp.: 50
Automobiles, New & Used
N.A.I.C.S.: 441110
Ron DiBiasio *(Mgr-Sys IT)*
Scott Klimack *(Mgr)*

SUNNYTECH INC.
80 Little Falls Rd, Fairfield, NJ 07004
Tel.: (201) 883-1130
Web Site: http://www.sunnytech.com
Year Founded: 1986
Sales Range: $25-49.9 Million
Emp.: 30
Computer Distr
N.A.I.C.S.: 423430
Jon Miller *(Dir-Sls)*

Subsidiaries:

Sunnytech Inc. (1)
6203 Johns Rd Ste 3, Tampa, FL 33634
Tel.: (813) 249-2100
Web Site: http://www.sunnyopen.com
Rev.: $15,128,991
Emp.: 10
Computer Peripheral Equipment
N.A.I.C.S.: 423430

SUNNYVALE LUMBER INC.
870 W Evelyn Ave, Sunnyvale, CA 94086
Tel.: (408) 736-5411
Web Site: http://www.sunnyvalelumber.com
Year Founded: 1945
Sales Range: $10-24.9 Million
Emp.: 30
Lumber & Other Building Materials
N.A.I.C.S.: 423310
James L. Roberts *(CFO)*
Rick Roberts *(CEO)*
John Brincko *(Chief Restructuring Officer)*
Jerry Martin *(Mgr)*

SUNNYWAY FOODS INC.
212 N Antrim Way, Greencastle, PA 17225-1406
Tel.: (717) 597-7121
Web Site: http://www.mysunnywayfoods.com
Sales Range: $10-24.9 Million
Emp.: 180
Independent Supermarket
N.A.I.C.S.: 445110
Ladean Martin *(Pres)*
Mike Martin *(Treas)*

SUNPLAY.COM
1278 S 1200 W, Ogden, UT 84404
Tel.: (877) 865-2493
Web Site: http://www.sunplay.com
Year Founded: 1967
Sales Range: $1-9.9 Million
Emp.: 10
Retails Pool & Spa Parts & Accessories
N.A.I.C.S.: 459999
Kasey LaRose *(Mktg Dir)*

SUNPORCH STRUCTURES INC.
495 Post Rd E, Westport, CT 06880-4400
Tel.: (203) 454-0040
Web Site: http://www.sunporch.com
Year Founded: 1974
Sales Range: $200-249.9 Million
Emp.: 50
Aluminum Greenhouses & Porches Mfr & Sales
N.A.I.C.S.: 332311
Dean Schwartz *(Pres)*
Suzanne Simmonds *(Bus Mgr)*

SUNRAY CO-OP. INC.
100 Main St, Sunray, TX 79086
Tel.: (806) 948-4121
Web Site: http://www.sunraycoop.com
Year Founded: 1939
Sales Range: $10-24.9 Million
Emp.: 70
Provider of Farm Supply Services
N.A.I.C.S.: 424510
Bret Brown *(CFO)*
Brian Martin *(Mgr-Mktg)*
Craig Lechner *(Branch Mgr)*
Pam Williams *(Controller)*
Dave Reinders *(Gen Mgr)*

SUNRAY ELECTRIC SUPPLY CO., INC.
711 Walnut St, McKeesport, PA 15132
Tel.: (412) 678-8826
Web Site: http://www.sunrayelectric.com
Rev.: $10,000,000
Emp.: 23
Electrical Supplies
N.A.I.C.S.: 493120
Irving J. Latterman *(Pres)*
Keith Latterman *(VP & Mgr)*
George Gadzich *(Mgr)*

SUNRAY ENTERPRISE INC.
3621 Vinings Slope SE Ste 4310, Atlanta, GA 30339
Tel.: (678) 584-1312
Web Site: http://www.sunraycorp.com
Year Founded: 2002
Rev.: $5,800,000
Emp.: 20
Computer System Design Services
N.A.I.C.S.: 541512
Ravi P. Srinivasan *(Pres & CEO)*
Sunita Shivaram *(VP-Sls & Mktg)*

SUNRIDGE PROPERTIES INC.
7255 E Hampton Ave Ste 122, Mesa, AZ 85209
Tel.: (480) 854-1414
Web Site: http://www.sunridgehotelgroup.com
Sales Range: $10-24.9 Million
Emp.: 15
Commercial & Office Building, New Construction
N.A.I.C.S.: 236220
Paul Welker *(CEO)*
Rhonda Ems *(Office Mgr)*
Brian D. Welker *(Pres)*
Chad Marsing *(Dir-Sls)*
Don Brooksby *(Dir-Tech)*
Margaret Radford *(Dir-Ops-South)*
Peggy Tedford *(Gen Mgr)*
Ron Mehringer *(Dir-Revenue Mgmt)*
Arthur Holman *(VP-Ops)*

SUNRISE ACQUISITION CORP.
801 S Figueroa St Ste 2500, Los Angeles, CA 90017
Tel.: (323) 780-8250 DE
Web Site: http://sunrisebrands.com
Year Founded: 2008
Sales Range: $50-74.9 Million
Emp.: 100
Holding Company; Private Label & Private Brand Casual Apparel Design & Sourcing Services
N.A.I.C.S.: 551112
Gerard Guez *(Chm & CEO)*
Todd Kay *(Vice Chm)*
Donald Waldman *(COO)*

Subsidiaries:

Sunrise Brands, LLC (1)
801 S Figueroa St Ste 2500, Los Angeles, CA 90017
Tel.: (323) 780-8250
Web Site: http://www.sunrisebrands.com
Sales Range: $150-199.9 Million
Private Label & Private Brand Casual Apparel Design & Sourcing Services
N.A.I.C.S.: 541490
Todd Kay *(Vice Chm)*
Rosa Castro *(Dir-HR)*
Jackie Swerz *(CMO-Sunrise Brands)*
Donald Waldman *(COO)*

Subsidiary (Non-US):

Tarrant Company Limited (2)
13/F & 14/F Lladro Centre 72 Hoi Yuen Road, Kwun Tong, Kowloon, China (Hong Kong)
Tel.: (852) 27978120
Web Site: http://www.tarrant.com.hk
Private Label & Private Brand Casual Apparel Sourcing Services
N.A.I.C.S.: 315250
Henry Chu *(Pres)*

SUNRISE ADVERTISING
700 Walnut St Ste 500, Cincinnati, OH 45202
Tel.: (513) 333-4100
Year Founded: 2003
Sales Range: $10-24.9 Million
Emp.: 35
Advetising Agency
N.A.I.C.S.: 541810
James Browning *(Agency Principal, Chief Strategist & Creative Officer)*
George Sabert *(Chief Media Officer & Agency Principal)*
John Young *(Exec Dir-Creative)*
Chris Fryburger *(Dir-Bus Dev)*
Todd Jessee *(Assoc Dir-Creative)*
Emily Sowders *(Acct Coord)*
Sarah Hartwig *(Acct Exec)*

SUNRISE AG COOPERATIVE
9361 Creamery Dr, Buckman, MN 56317
Tel.: (320) 468-6433
Web Site: http://www.sunriseagcooperative.com
Sales Range: $10-24.9 Million
Emp.: 36
Dairy Products Producer
N.A.I.C.S.: 424430
Jason Sadlovsky *(Mgr)*

SUNRISE BAKING CO. LLC.
4564 2nd Ave, Brooklyn, NY 11232-4215
Tel.: (718) 499-0800
Sales Range: $10-24.9 Million
Emp.: 115
Bakery Products Mfr
N.A.I.C.S.: 311812
Mary Lou *(Owner)*

SUNRISE BANCSHARES, INC.
5604 N Atlantic Ave, Cocoa Beach, FL 32931
Tel.: (321) 784-8333 FL
Web Site: http://www.sunrise.bank
Bank Holding Company
N.A.I.C.S.: 551111
Kevin M. Sacket *(Pres)*

Subsidiaries:

Sunrise Bank (1)
5604 N Atlantic Ave, Cocoa Beach, FL 32931
Tel.: (321) 784-8333
Web Site: http://www.sunrisebank.com
Commericial Banking
N.A.I.C.S.: 522110
Craig Crimmings *(Exec VP)*
Ward Kellogg *(Chm)*
Charle B. Lowe Jr. *(Exec VP, Mgr-Relationship & Officer-Bus Dev)*

SUNRISE BROADCASTING OF NEW YORK, INC.
661 Little Britain Rd, New Windsor, NY 12553-6150
Tel.: (845) 561-2131 NY
Web Site: http://www.wgny.us
Sales Range: $1-9.9 Million
Emp.: 25
Radio Broadcasting Services
N.A.I.C.S.: 516110
Robert DeFelice *(Mgr-Mktg)*

SUNRISE BUICK-PONTIAC-GMC-HUMMER WOLFCHASE
8500 US Hwy 64, Bartlett, TN 38133-4101
Tel.: (901) 333-8000
Year Founded: 1989
Sales Range: $25-49.9 Million
Emp.: 225
Car Whslr
N.A.I.C.S.: 441110
Robert G. Berkheimer *(Co-Owner)*
Ken Forbert *(Co-Owner)*

SUNRISE CAPITAL PARTNERS LP
444 Madison Ave 34th Fl, New York, NY 10022
Tel.: (212) 869-1732 DE
Web Site: http://www.sunriselp.com
Year Founded: 1998
Sales Range: $50-74.9 Million
Emp.: 185
Investment Services
N.A.I.C.S.: 523999
Stephanie Litfin *(Office Mgr)*

SUNRISE COMMUNITY, INC.
9040 Sunset Dr, Miami, FL 33173
Tel.: (305) 596-9040
Web Site: http://www.sunrisegroup.org
Sales Range: $125-149.9 Million
Emp.: 3,000
Residential Mental Health & Substance Abuse Facilities
N.A.I.C.S.: 623220
Zach Wray *(Pres & CEO)*

SUNRISE CONSTRUCTION INC.
905 Kalanianaole Hwy Bldg 23B, Kailua, HI 96734
Tel.: (808) 262-8626
Sales Range: $25-49.9 Million
Emp.: 100
New Single-Family Housing Construction
N.A.I.C.S.: 236115
Marcus Gillespie *(Owner & Pres)*

SUNRISE COOPERATIVE, INC.
2025 W State St, Fremont, OH 43420-1553
Tel.: (419) 332-6468
Web Site: http://www.sunriseco-op.com
Year Founded: 1996
Sales Range: $50-74.9 Million
Emp.: 150
Production of Grain & Field Beans
N.A.I.C.S.: 424510
George Secor *(Pres & CEO)*
Jack Ziegler *(Chm)*
Tammy Myers *(Office Mgr)*

SUNRISE DETOX
3185 Boutwell Rd, Lake Worth, FL 33461
Tel.: (561) 533-0074
Web Site: http://www.sunrisedetox.com
Year Founded: 2004
Sales Range: $10-24.9 Million
Emp.: 100
Detoxification & Substance Abuse Treatment Facility

SUNRISE DETOX

Sunrise Detox—(Continued)
N.A.I.C.S.: 623220
Morgan Poncy (Dir-Medical)
Jeffrey Gorin (Dir-Clinical)
David McCurley (Coord-Admissions)
Ira Levy (Dir-Mktg-Natl)
Nick Matteo (Dir-IT-Natl)
Susan Hugel (Dir-Nursing)
Linda Burns (Dir-Nursing)

SUNRISE DIGITAL
5915 N Northwest Hwy, Chicago, IL 60631
Tel.: (773) 792-8880
Web Site: http://www.sunrisedigital.us
Year Founded: 1988
Sales Range: $1-9.9 Million
Emp.: 20
Digital Printing
N.A.I.C.S.: 323111
Jimmy Sun (Owner)

SUNRISE FLOOR SYSTEMS LLC
4101 Cogswell Ave PO Box 192, Pell City, AL 35125
Tel.: (205) 338-1860
Sales Range: $10-24.9 Million
Emp.: 250
Floor Contracting Services
N.A.I.C.S.: 238330
John Na Castro (Pres)

SUNRISE HOMES
62250 West End Blvd, Slidell, LA 70461-5622
Tel.: (985) 649-9500
Web Site: http://www.sunrisehomes.net
Sales Range: $10-24.9 Million
Emp.: 100
Single-Family Home Construction & Mortgage Services
N.A.I.C.S.: 236115

SUNRISE IDENTITY
405 114th Ave SE Suite 200, Bellevue, WA 98004
Tel.: (425) 214-1700
Web Site: http://www.sunriseid.com
Year Founded: 1976
Sales Range: $10-24.9 Million
Emp.: 150
Full Service Marketing & Branding Agency
N.A.I.C.S.: 541613
Mitch Mounger (CEO)
Larry Mounger (Chm)
Bob Stahr (Dir-IT)
Mark Lynch (COO)
Michele Oldroyd (Dir-HR)
Tim Klabo (Controller)

Subsidiaries:

Seattle Coffee Gear (1)
6911 216th St SW Ste A, Lynnwood, WA 98036 (100%)
Tel.: (206) 774-3164
Web Site: http://www.seattlecoffeegear.com
Sales Range: $1-9.9 Million
Emp.: 20
Online Retailer of Home Espresso Machines, Coffee Makers, Related Accessories & Equipment Services
N.A.I.C.S.: 449210

SUNRISE LANDSCAPE, INC.
PO Box 16531, Tampa, FL 33687-6744
Tel.: (813) 985-9381
Web Site: http://www.sunriselandscape.com
Year Founded: 1978
Sales Range: $10-24.9 Million
Landscaping Services
N.A.I.C.S.: 561730
Shea Hughes (Pres)

SUNRISE NATIONAL DISTRIBUTORS
6004 Westside Saginaw Rd, Bay City, MI 48706
Tel.: (989) 684-1211
Web Site: http://www.75sunny.com
Year Founded: 1966
Rev.: $14,200,000
Emp.: 30
Automotive Supplies & Parts Mfr & Distr
N.A.I.C.S.: 423120

SUNRISE OF PHILADELPHIA
907 Cantrell St, Philadelphia, PA 19148
Tel.: (215) 952-2730 PA
Web Site: http://www.sunriseofphila.org
Year Founded: 1999
Sales Range: $1-9.9 Million
Emp.: 100
Educational & Family Support Services
N.A.I.C.S.: 611710
Loretta V. Crea (CFO)
Angela Jubinville (Program Mgr)
Anthony LaMorgia (Dir-Ops)
Vincent Litrenta (Exec Dir)
Alfonso A. Sorichetti (CEO)
Julie Laquer (Dir-Media & Site)
Anthony N. Di Pietro (Pres)
Michael Rosman (Treas)
Laura Johnson (Program Dir)

SUNRISE PACKAGING INC.
1214 98th Ave NE, Minneapolis, MN 55434
Tel.: (763) 785-2505
Web Site: http://www.sunpack.com
Year Founded: 1982
Sales Range: $10-24.9 Million
Emp.: 100
Plastic Container Mfr
N.A.I.C.S.: 326199
Mark Hector (Pres)
Chuck Rossetter (Controller)
Jay Schreyer (Sr Acct Exec)
Rod Herdina (VP)
Theodore Frank (Dir-Pur)

SUNRISE SHOP RITE INC.
540 Passaic Ave, West Caldwell, NJ 07006
Tel.: (973) 575-1770 NJ
Web Site: http://www.shoprite.com
Year Founded: 1956
Sales Range: $75-99.9 Million
Emp.: 168
Operator of Supermarkets
N.A.I.C.S.: 445110
Ned Gladstein (Pres & Owner)
Tom Harte (VP-Ops)
Scott Emerson (Mgr-Store)

SUNRISE SPORTS & ENTERTAINMENT LLLP
1 Panther Pkwy, Sunrise, FL 33323
Tel.: (954) 835-7000 DE
Web Site: http://www.sselive.com
Sales Range: $125-149.9 Million
Emp.: 2,500
Holding Company; Professional Hockey Team & Sports & Entertainment Arena Owner & Operator
N.A.I.C.S.: 551112
Matthew F. Sacco (Chief Comm Officer, Exec VP & Strategist-Govt Affairs)
Vincent J. Viola (Chm & Owner)
Douglas A. Cifu (Vice Chm & Partner)
Kevin Grove (VP-Event Programming)
John Peach (Mgr-Hockey Admin)
Richard Adler (Exec VP)
Charlie Turano (Exec VP)
Jim Willits (Exec VP-Sls)
Amy Perry (CFO)
Matthew Caldwell (Pres & CEO)

Subsidiaries:

Florida Panthers Hockey Club, Ltd. (1)
1 Panther Pkwy, Sunrise, FL 33323-5315
Tel.: (954) 835-7000
Web Site: http://www.floridapanthers.com
Sales Range: $10-24.9 Million
Emp.: 100
Professional Hockey Team
N.A.I.C.S.: 711211
Randy Moller (VP-Brdcst & Panthers Alumni)
Dale Tallon (Pres-Hockey Ops)
Scott Luce (Dir-Player Personnel)
Peggy Ziady (Mgr-Payroll & HR)
Tom Embrey (Dir-Event Ops & Guest Svcs)
Kevin Grove (VP-Event Programming)
Ed Wildermuth (Gen Counsel)
Peter Luukko (Chm)
Jim Willits (Exec VP-Sls)
Amy Perry (CFO)
Jason Bakula (Dir-Amateur Scouring)
Al Tauer (Head-Pro Scouting)
Toby O'Brien (Dir-Amateur Scouting)
Jerome Burke (Dir-Hockey Ops)
Stiles Burr (Mgr-Team Svcs)
Braden Birch (Asst Gen Mgr)
Richard Adler (Exec VP)
Christopher Liskiewicz (Dir-Creative Svcs)
Bryan McCabe (Dir-Player Dev)
Lane Miller (VP-HR & Payroll)
Greg Rieber (VP-Corp Partnerships)
Tom Rowe (Gen Mgr)
John Spade (VP-IT)
Charlie Turano (Exec VP)
Pamela Zager-Maya (VP-Mktg)
Matthew Caldwell (Pres & CEO)
Shawn Thornton (VP-Bus Ops)

SUNRIVER RESORT LIMITED PARTNERSHIP
17600 Center Dr, Sunriver, OR 97707
Tel.: (541) 593-1000
Web Site: http://www.destinationhotels.com
Year Founded: 1993
Sales Range: $25-49.9 Million
Emp.: 600
Provider of Real Estate Agency Services
N.A.I.C.S.: 237210
Thomas O'Shea (Mng Dir)
Libby Nations (Dir-Sls & Mktg)
Dan Rollins (Dir-Performance Optimization)

Subsidiaries:

Sunriver Utilities Company Inc. (1)
57850 W Cascade, Sunriver, OR 97707
Tel.: (541) 593-4197
Web Site: http://www.sunriver-resort.com
Sales Range: $25-49.9 Million
Emp.: 18
Water Supply Services
N.A.I.C.S.: 221310
Greg Mooney (Gen Mgr)

SUNROAD HOLDING CORPORATION
4445 Eastgate Mall Ste 400, San Diego, CA 92121
Tel.: (858) 362-8500 CA
Year Founded: 1977
Sales Range: $200-249.9 Million
Emp.: 700
Investment Holding Company
N.A.I.C.S.: 551112
Aaron Feldman (Pres)
Wayne Meyer (Exec VP)
Uri Feldman (Pres-Sunroad Holding Corp)
Mike Dow (Principal)
Rick Vann (Exec VP-Real Estate Div)
Jim McLennan (CFO & Exec VP)
Dan Feldman (Pres)

Subsidiaries:

Maderas Country Club LLC (1)
17750 Old Coach Rd, Poway, CA 92064
Tel.: (858) 451-8100
Web Site: http://www.maderasgolf.com
Rev.: $1,400,000
Emp.: 80
Country Club Membership
N.A.I.C.S.: 713910
Bill O'Brien (Gen Mgr)

SUNRX, INC.
815 E Gate Dr, Mount Laurel, NJ 08054
Tel.: (856) 910-7776
Web Site: http://www.sunrx.com
Year Founded: 2001
Sales Range: $25-49.9 Million
Emp.: 35
Prescription Benefit Administration Services
N.A.I.C.S.: 561110

SUNS LEGACY PARTNERS, LLC
201 E Jefferson St, Phoenix, AZ 85004-2412
Tel.: (602) 379-7900 DE
Web Site: http://www.nba.com
Year Founded: 2004
Holding Company; Professional Basketball Teams & Sports Arena Owner & Operator
N.A.I.C.S.: 551112
Robert Gary Sarver (Owner & Mng Partner)

Subsidiaries:

Phoenix Arena GP, LLC (1)
201 E Jefferson St, Phoenix, AZ 85004-2412
Tel.: (602) 379-2000
Web Site: http://www.usairwayscenter.com
Sports & Entertainment Arena Operator
N.A.I.C.S.: 711310
Ralph Marchetta (Gen Mgr)
Alvan Adams (VP-Facility Mgmt)
Nick Vaerewyck (Controller & Asst Mgr-Booking)
Jon Bloom (Dir-Security & Risk Mgmt)
Jim Bochenek (Dir-Event Svcs)
Woodie Browder (Dir-Traffic Support Svcs)

Phoenix Suns (1)
201 E Jefferson St, Phoenix, AZ 85004-2412
Tel.: (602) 379-7900
Web Site: http://www.nba.com
Sales Range: $10-24.9 Million
Emp.: 300
Professional Basketball Franchise
N.A.I.C.S.: 711211
Robert Gary Sarver (Mng Partner)
Ralph Marchetta (Sr VP-Ticket Ops & Gen Mgr-Sports & Entertainment Svcs)
Jim Pitman (Exec VP-Fin & Admin)
Harvey Shank (Sr Exec VP)
Jahm Najafi (Vice Chm)
Sam Garvin (Vice Chm)
Jason Rowley (Pres)
Mark West (VP-Player Rels)
Julie Fie (VP-Basketball Comm)
Matt Wright (Sr VP-Mktg Partnerships)
Jeramie McPeek (VP-Digital)
Todd Quinter (Dir-Player Personnel)
Kip Helt (VP-Game Entertainment)
Jon Phillips (VP-Fin)
Dan Siekmann (VP-Brdcst)
Jeff Ianello (VP-Sls)
Karen Rausch (VP-HR)
Tanya Wheeless (Sr VP-Comm & Pub Affairs)
Andy Kohlberg (Vice Chm)
Aaron Nelson (VP-Athlete Care & Head-Athletic Trainer)
Brad Casper (Co-Pres)
Jerry Colangelo (Chm)
Stefan Swiat (Coord-Digital Content)
James Jones (Interim Gen Mgr)
Trevor Bukstein (Asst Gen Mgr)
Jeff Bower (Sr VP-Basketball Ops)
Dean Stoyer (Chief Mktg & Comm Officer)

Unit (Domestic):

Phoenix Mercury (2)
201 E Jefferson St, Phoenix, AZ 85004-2412
Tel.: (602) 514-8333
Web Site: http://www.wnba.com
Professional Women's Basketball Franchise
N.A.I.C.S.: 711211
Amber Cox (COO)

SUNSET AIR INCORPORATED
5210 Lacey Blvd S E, Lacey, WA 98503
Tel.: (360) 456-4956
Web Site: http://www.sunsetair.com
Rev.: $14,299,623
Emp.: 120
Warm Air Heating & Air Conditioning Contractor
N.A.I.C.S.: 238220
Brian Fluetsch (Pres)
Jeff Garber (CFO)
Kim Dinsmore (Exec VP)
Ryan Pantier (Engr-Design)
Steve Westall (Project Mgr)
Terry Medlock (Coord-Comml Admin & Safety)

SUNSET AUTO COMPANY INC.
2020 Auburn Way N, Auburn, WA 98002
Tel.: (253) 735-2011
Web Site: http://www.sunsetcars.com
Year Founded: 1987
Sales Range: $25-49.9 Million
Emp.: 50
Automobile Sales
N.A.I.C.S.: 423110

SUNSET AUTOMOTIVE GROUP
1800 Bay Rd, Sarasota, FL 34239-6999
Tel.: (941) 366-7800
Web Site: http://www.sunsetautogroup.com
Sales Range: $100-124.9 Million
Emp.: 500
New & Used Car Dealership Owner & Operator
N.A.I.C.S.: 441110
Robert W. Geyer (Owner & Pres)

Subsidiaries:

Suncoast Porsche (1)
5005 S Tamiami Trl, Sarasota, FL 34231
Tel.: (941) 923-1700
Web Site: http://www.suncoastporsche.com
New & Used Car Dealer
N.A.I.C.S.: 441110
Gordon Hunter (Gen Mgr-Sls)
Mark Cobb (Gen Mgr)

Sunset Chevrolet, Inc. (1)
1800 Bay Rd, Sarasota, FL 34239
Tel.: (941) 312-2799
Web Site: http://www.sunsetchevroletsarasota.net
Sales Range: $10-24.9 Million
New & Used Car Dealer
N.A.I.C.S.: 441110
Robert W. Geyer (Pres)

SUNSET COMMUNITY HEALTH CENTER
2060 W 24th St, Yuma, AZ 85364
Tel.: (928) 819-8999 AZ
Web Site: http://www.sunsetcommunityhealthcenter.org
Year Founded: 1997
Sales Range: $10-24.9 Million
Emp.: 257
Community Health Care Services
N.A.I.C.S.: 621498
Zonia Pelroy (Dir-Patient Svcs)
Mary Castillo (Dir-Strategic Dev)

Lucy Murrieta (Mgr-Outreach & Community Rels)
David Rogers (CEO)
Whitney Sims (CFO)
Ching Wang (Chief Medical Officer)
Josefa Josie Uriarte (Chief Bus Dev Officer)
Manny Figueroa (Pres)
Josie Smith (Treas)
Maria Chavoya (VP)
Nohemi Valtierra (Sec)

SUNSET FOOD MART INC.
777 Central Ave Ste 12, Highland Park, IL 60035-3246
Tel.: (847) 432-0035 IL
Web Site: http://www.sunsetfoods.com
Year Founded: 1937
Sales Range: $50-74.9 Million
Emp.: 900
Supermarket
N.A.I.C.S.: 445110
Richard Cortesi (Pres & Mng Dir)
John E. Cortesi (Mng Dir)
Ron Cizzon (Mng Dir)

SUNSET HEALTHCARE SOLUTIONS
180 N Michigan Ave Ste 2000, Chicago, IL 60601
Tel.: (312) 533-2446
Web Site: http://www.sunsethcs.com
Year Founded: 2004
Sales Range: $10-24.9 Million
Emp.: 50
Mfr & Distr of CPAP & Oxygen Products
N.A.I.C.S.: 339112
Chris Slosar (Pres & CEO)

SUNSET MOULDING CO., INC.
2231 Paseo Rd, Live Oak, CA 95953-9721
Tel.: (530) 695-1000
Web Site: http://www.sunsetmoulding.com
Year Founded: 1946
Sales Range: $25-49.9 Million
Emp.: 340
Millwork
N.A.I.C.S.: 321912
Richard Morrison (Chm & VP-Production)
Wendy Forren (CFO)
John Morrison (Pres)
Mark Westlake (VP-Sls)

SUNSET RETIREMENT COMMUNITIES
4040 Indian Rd, Toledo, OH 43606
Tel.: (419) 724-1225 OH
Web Site: http://www.sunset-communities.org
Year Founded: 1871
Sales Range: $10-24.9 Million
Emp.: 389
Retirement Community Care Services
N.A.I.C.S.: 623311
Vicky Bartlett (Pres & CEO)
Judy Bishop-Pierce (VP-Ops)
Mark Minard (CFO & VP-Fin)
Victoria S. Bartlett (Pres & CEO)

SUNSHINE ACE HARDWARE INC.
9148 Bonita Beach Rd Ste 207, Bonita Springs, FL 34135
Tel.: (239) 992-0454
Web Site: http://www.sunshineace.com
Year Founded: 1958
Sales Range: $25-49.9 Million
Emp.: 300
Hardware Store Distr
N.A.I.C.S.: 444140

Michael Wynn (Pres)
Jim MacLean (Mgr-Sporting Goods)
Linda Collins (Coord-Inventory)
Mary Cunningham (Mgr-Lawn & Garden)
Jason Heimberger (Coord-Pur)

Subsidiaries:

Mortons Associates, Inc. (1)
3035 Tamiami Trl, Port Charlotte, FL 33952
Tel.: (941) 625-1454
Sales Range: $1-9.9 Million
Emp.: 25
Hardware Stores
N.A.I.C.S.: 444140

SUNSHINE BOTTLING, CO.
8447 NW 54th St, Doral, FL 33166-3320
Tel.: (305) 592-4366
Web Site: http://www.sunshinebottling.com
Year Founded: 1917
Sales Range: $10-24.9 Million
Emp.: 30
Brewery Mfr
N.A.I.C.S.: 312120
Carlos Blanco (Pres)

SUNSHINE BOUQUET COMPANY INC.
3 Chris Ct Ste 3, Dayton, NJ 08810
Tel.: (732) 274-2900
Web Site: http://www.sunshinebouquet.com
Year Founded: 1971
Rev.: $370,000,000
Emp.: 1,000
Sales & Delivery of Flowers
N.A.I.C.S.: 424930
John D. Simko (Pres)
Andrew Johnston (Controller)

SUNSHINE COMPUTERS & SOFTWARE
2244 NW 114th Ave Ste A, Miami, FL 33172
Tel.: (305) 715-7071
Web Site: http://www.innovationcomputer.com
Sales Range: $25-49.9 Million
Emp.: 8
Computer & Software Stores
N.A.I.C.S.: 449210
Ajay Khanna (Owner)

SUNSHINE DAIRY FOODS INC.
801 NE 21st Ave, Portland, OR 97232
Tel.: (503) 234-7526
Web Site: http://www.sunshinedairyfoods.com
Rev.: $48,000,000
Emp.: 35
Milk & Cream, Fluid
N.A.I.C.S.: 424430
James C. Noonan (Pres & CEO)

Subsidiaries:

Sunshine Dairy Inc. (1)
2023 W Maxwell Ave, Spokane, WA 99201-2834
Tel.: (509) 326-0963
Web Site: http://www.sunshinedairyfoods.com
Sales Range: $10-24.9 Million
Emp.: 25
Producer of Dairy Products
N.A.I.C.S.: 424430

SUNSHINE DRAPERY & INTERIOR FASHIONS
11800 Adie Rd, Maryland Heights, MO 63043-3304
Tel.: (314) 569-2980
Web Site: http://www.sunshinedrapery.com

Year Founded: 1969
Sales Range: $10-24.9 Million
Emp.: 45
Retailer of Draperies & Drapery Fabrics
N.A.I.C.S.: 449122
Bruce Bernstein (Owner)

SUNSHINE EQUIPMENT CO., INC.
2274 Hwy 70 Ste A, Donaldsonville, LA 70346
Tel.: (225) 473-9609
Web Site: http://www.sunequip.com
Rev.: $15,189,337
Emp.: 125
Agricultural Machinery & Equipment
N.A.I.C.S.: 423820
Ken Rodrigue (Pres & Gen Mgr)
Angela Robinson (Asst Mgr)
Nancy Thibodaux (Mgr-Aftermarket)

SUNSHINE HARDWARE INC.
141 9th St N, Naples, FL 34102
Tel.: (239) 262-2940
Web Site: http://www.sunshineace.com
Sales Range: $10-24.9 Million
Emp.: 200
Hardware Stores
N.A.I.C.S.: 444140
Jerry M. Wynn (Owner & CEO)

SUNSHINE HELICOPTERS, INC.
Kahului Heliport 107, Kahului, HI 96732
Tel.: (808) 871-5600 HI
Web Site: http://www.sunshinehelicopters.com
Year Founded: 1985
Sales Range: $25-49.9 Million
Emp.: 60
Helicopter Tour Services
N.A.I.C.S.: 561520
Ross Scott (Pres)
Anna Scott (Co-Owner)
Fred Adlard (Mgr-Safety)

SUNSHINE MILLS INC.
500 6th St SW, Red Bay, AL 35582
Tel.: (256) 356-9541 DE
Web Site: http://www.sunshinemills.com
Year Founded: 1945
Sales Range: $100-124.9 Million
Emp.: 1,155
Animal Feed Mfr
N.A.I.C.S.: 311111
Alan O. Bostick (Pres & CEO)
Philip Bates (Plant Mgr)
Dave Brown (Mgr-Logistics)
Daniel Jager (VP-R&D)
Alison McCrary (VP-Quality Assurance)
Thomas Murray (VP)
Michael Nichols (Coord-Safety)
Roy Turner (Office Mgr)
Bridget Holland (Superintendent-Production)
Janeice Gober (Mgr-HR)
Jose Makepeace (Superintendent-Ops)
Royal Witcher (COO)
Paul Sella (Dir-Procurement)

Subsidiaries:

Sunshine Homes Inc. (1)
100 Sunshine Ave, Red Bay, AL 35582
Tel.: (256) 356-4428
Web Site: http://www.sunshinehomes-inc.com
Sales Range: $25-49.9 Million
Emp.: 150
Modular Houses Mfr
N.A.I.C.S.: 321991

SUNSHINE MILLS INC.

Sunshine Mills Inc.—(Continued)
John Bopseck *(Pres)*
Mack Ballard *(Mgr-Svc)*
Carol Reynolds *(Office Mgr)*
Stan Posey *(Mgr-Sls)*

Sunshine Mills Inc. - Halifax Division (1)
100 Sunshine Dr, Halifax, VA 24558
Tel.: (434) 476-1451
Pet Food Mfr
N.A.I.C.S.: 311111

Sunshine Mills Inc. - Tupelo Division (1)
2103 S Gloster St, Tupelo, MS 38802
Tel.: (662) 842-6175
Pet Food Mfr
N.A.I.C.S.: 311111
Tim Browning *(Gen Mgr)*

Sunshine Mills of Virginia Inc. (1)
100 Sunshine Dr, Halifax, VA 24558
Tel.: (434) 476-1451
Web Site: http://www.sunshinemills.com
Sales Range: $25-49.9 Million
Emp.: 200
Provider of Animal Food
N.A.I.C.S.: 311111
Alan Bradrick *(Gen Mgr)*

Triumph Pet Industries, Inc. (1)
500 Sixth St SW, Red Bay, AL 35582
Tel.: (256) 356-9541
Web Site: http://www.triumphpet.com
Sales Range: $10-24.9 Million
Emp.: 26
Dog & Cat Food Distr
N.A.I.C.S.: 311111

World Pet Care (1)
506 6th St SW, Red Bay, AL 35582 (100%)
Tel.: (256) 356-9541
Web Site: http://www.sunshinepettreats.com
Sales Range: $10-24.9 Million
Emp.: 13
Provider of Dog & Cat Food
N.A.I.C.S.: 311111
Tory James *(Plant Mgr)*

World Pet Foods Inc. (1)
500 6th St SW, Red Bay, AL 35582
Tel.: (256) 356-9541
Web Site: http://www.worldpetfoods.com
Sales Range: $10-24.9 Million
Emp.: 5
Mfr Pet Treats
N.A.I.C.S.: 424910

SUNSHINE MINTING INC.
750 West Canfield Ave, Coeur D'Alene, ID 83815
Tel.: (208) 772-9592
Web Site:
 http://www.sunshinemint.com
Year Founded: 1979
Sales Range: $1-4.9 Billion
Emp.: 260
Precious Metal Supplier
N.A.I.C.S.: 423940
Tom Power *(Pres & CEO)*
Mike Needham *(Mgr-Customer Svc)*
Nancy Quinn *(Mgr-QS)*
Nino Randazzo *(Mgr-Ops)*
Ronn Bennett *(Mgr-Supply Chain)*

SUNSHINE PAPER LLC
12601 E 33rd Ave, Aurora, CO 80401
Web Site:
 http://www.sunshinepaper.com
Rev.: $18,172,263
Emp.: 5
Printing & Writing Paper
N.A.I.C.S.: 322130

SUNSHINE PHARMACY, INC.
6350 Davis Blvd, Naples, FL 34104
Tel.: (239) 775-6800
Year Founded: 1999
Sales Range: $25-49.9 Million
Emp.: 70
Pharmacies
N.A.I.C.S.: 456110

Del Parrish *(Pres)*

SUNSHINE PLUMBING HEATING AIR LLC
6810 E 53rd Pl Unit B, Commerce City, CO 80022
Tel.: (303) 622-5526   CO
Web Site:
 http://www.sunshineplumbingheating.com
Year Founded: 2008
Sales Range: $1-9.9 Million
Emp.: 15
Plumbing & Heating Contractor Services
N.A.I.C.S.: 238220
Susan Frew *(Owner, Pres & Mng Partner)*
William Frew *(Partner & VP-Ops)*

SUNSHINE RAISIN CORPORATION
626 S 5th St, Fowler, CA 93625-0219
Tel.: (559) 834-5981   CA
Web Site:
 http://www.nationalraisin.com
Year Founded: 1969
Dried Fruit & Nut Products Distr
N.A.I.C.S.: 424480
Jane Asmar *(Sr VP-Sls & Mktg)*
Davina Merkow *(Dir-HR)*
Linda Abdulian *(Pres & CEO)*
Kenny Bedrosian *(Founder)*
Carlotta Bedrosian *(Mgr-Accts Payable)*
Kimberly Bedrosian *(Dir-Accts Payable)*
Bryan Bedrosian *(VP)*
Michael Bedrosian *(VP-Grower Rels)*
Paul-David Bedrosian *(VP-Southern Properties)*

Subsidiaries:

Champion Raisin International (1)
PO Box 219, Fowler, CA 93625-9745
Tel.: (559) 834-5981
Web Site: http://www.nationalraisin.com
Sales Range: $25-49.9 Million
Emp.: 300
Supplier of Raisins
N.A.I.C.S.: 424490
Lindakay Abdulian *(Pres & CEO)*

Exeter Dehydrator Inc. (1)
26783 Rd 176, Exeter, CA 93221
Tel.: (559) 592-3221
Sales Range: $10-24.9 Million
Emp.: 21
Provider of Fruit Dehydration Services
N.A.I.C.S.: 311423

SUNSHINE RENTALS, INC.
985 Park Center Dr, Vista, CA 92081
Tel.: (760) 410-1525
Web Site:
 http://www.housewarerentals.com
Year Founded: 1980
Sales Range: $1-9.9 Million
Emp.: 25
Housewares & Furniture Rentals
N.A.I.C.S.: 532310
Mark Strumwasser *(Pres)*

SUNSHINE RESTAURANT PARTNERS, LLC
13650 NW 8th St Ste 103, Sunrise, FL 33325
Tel.: (954) 618-6300   FL
Web Site: http://www.ihopsrp.com
Year Founded: 1961
Sales Range: $200-249.9 Million
Emp.: 3,000
IHOP Restaurant Operator & Franchisor
N.A.I.C.S.: 722513
Jose Plasencia *(Controller)*
Daniel Enea *(CEO)*
John Salvaggio *(CFO)*

Raul Orellana *(Pres)*
Claudia Rodriguez *(VP-HR)*
Janet Alexander *(Dir-Mktg)*
Ian Allen *(VP-Real Estate)*
Christopher Howard *(Dir-Construction)*
Lisa Mendez *(Dir-Ops-South Florida)*
William Gowanloch *(Reg Dir)*

SUNSHINE ROOMS, INC.
3333 N Mead St, Wichita, KS 67219
Tel.: (316) 838-0033
Web Site:
 http://www.sunshinerooms.com
Year Founded: 1980
Sales Range: $10-24.9 Million
Emp.: 30
Greenhouse & Sunroom Structure Mfr
N.A.I.C.S.: 332311
Wade Griffith *(Mgr)*

SUNSHINE SILVER MINES CORPORATION
1660 Lincoln St Ste 2750, Denver, CO 80264
Tel.: (303) 784-5350   DE
Web Site:
 http://www.sunshinesilvermining.com
Sales Range: $25-49.9 Million
Emp.: 140
Silver Mining Services
N.A.I.C.S.: 212220
Stephen Orr *(Chm & Acting CEO)*
Roger Johnson *(CFO)*
Philip Pyle *(VP-Exploration-Mexico)*

Subsidiaries:

Formation Capital Corporation, U.S. (1)
812 Shoup St, Salmon, ID 83467-4305
Tel.: (208) 756-4578
Web Site: http://www.formationmetals.com
Mineral Exploration Services
N.A.I.C.S.: 213115

Subsidiary (Non-US):

Minera Terranova, S.A. de C.V. (2)
Independencia No 716-106B, C.P. 78000, San Luis Potosi, Mexico
Tel.: (52) 48 12 59 59
Mineral Exploration & Development
N.A.I.C.S.: 213115

SUNSHINE SUPPLY CO., INC.
4946 Naples St, San Diego, CA 92110-3820
Tel.: (619) 276-7442
Web Site:
 http://www.sunshinesupply.com
Year Founded: 1971
Sales Range: $10-24.9 Million
Emp.: 29
Construction Materials Whslr
N.A.I.C.S.: 423320
James Pyle *(Pres)*
Bryce Schafer *(Branch Mgr & Mgr-Pur)*
Brent Clute *(Product Mgr)*
Steve Robledo *(Dir-Ops)*

SUNSHINE TOYOTA INC.
1355 W Dickman Rd, Battle Creek, MI 49037
Tel.: (269) 965-1000
Web Site:
 http://www.sunshinetoyota.com
Year Founded: 1984
Sales Range: $10-24.9 Million
Emp.: 50
Dealer of Automobiles, New & Used
N.A.I.C.S.: 441110
Gary Minneman *(Pres)*
Dennis Walters *(Mgr-Fin)*
Josh Alger *(Mgr-New Car Sls)*

U.S. PRIVATE

SUNSOFT TECHNOLOGIES, INC.
21772 Manchester Ct, Farmington Hills, MI 48335
Tel.: (248) 426-9805
Web Site:
 http://www.sunsofttechnologies.com
Year Founded: 2000
Sales Range: $1-9.9 Million
Emp.: 40
Computer System Design Services
N.A.I.C.S.: 541512
Rashmi Upadhyaya *(Pres)*

SUNSOUTH BANCSHARES, INC.
108 Jamestown Blvd, Dothan, AL 36301
Tel.: (334) 677-4411   AL
Web Site:
 http://www.sunsouthbank.com
Year Founded: 2004
Bank Holding Company
N.A.I.C.S.: 551111
Roger Peterson *(Mng Dir)*
Travis Strickland *(VP)*
H. Monty Weigel *(Chm & CEO)*

Subsidiaries:

SunSouth Bank (1)
108 Jamestown Blvd, Dothan, AL 36301 (100%)
Tel.: (334) 677-4411
Web Site: http://www.sunsouthbank.com
Retail & Commercial Banking
N.A.I.C.S.: 522110
H. Monty Weigel *(Chm, Pres & CEO)*
Jeff Ratcliffe *(Chief Credit Admin & Sr VP)*
Misty Tyson *(CFO & Sr VP)*

SUNSOUTH LLC
168 Ross Clark Cir, Dothan, AL 36303
Tel.: (334) 794-0691   AL
Web Site: http://www.sunsouth.com
Sales Range: $75-99.9 Million
Emp.: 240
Holding Company; Tractor & Tractor Parts Dealership Owner & Operator
N.A.I.C.S.: 551112
John Blankenship *(Mgr-Store)*

Subsidiaries:

Columbus Tractor, LLC (1)
30 Parkman Ave, Columbus, GA 31901
Tel.: (706) 687-0752
Web Site: http://www.sunsouth.com
Tractor & Tractor Parts Dealer
N.A.I.C.S.: 441227
Ronnie Hayes *(Gen Mgr)*
Kevin McClellien *(Gen Mgr)*

Henry Farm Center, Inc. (1)
809 Columbia Rd, Abbeville, AL 36310
Tel.: (334) 585-5525
Web Site: http://www.sunsouth.com
Sales Range: $25-49.9 Million
Emp.: 50
Tractor & Tractor Parts Dealer
N.A.I.C.S.: 441227
John Blankenship *(Gen Mgr)*
Byron Snow *(Mgr-Svc)*
Ben Whitehead *(Mgr-Parts)*

Unit (Domestic):

SunSouth - Dothan (2)
168 Ross Clark Cir, Dothan, AL 36303
Tel.: (334) 794-0691
Web Site: http://www.sunsouth.com
Sales Range: $25-49.9 Million
Emp.: 20
Tractor & Tractor Parts Distr
N.A.I.C.S.: 441227
David Key *(Mgr-Parts)*
Kevin Harrell *(Mgr-Svc)*

SunSouth - Blakely (1)
6675 Chancey Mill Rd, Blakely, GA 39823
Tel.: (229) 723-3595
Web Site: http://www.sunsouth.com

COMPANIES

Sales Range: $10-24.9 Million
Emp.: 25
Tractor & Tractor Parts Dealer
N.A.I.C.S.: 441227
Doug Cunningham (Mgr-Store)
David Weaver (Mgr-Svc)
James Weaver (Mgr-Parts)

SunSouth - Samson (1)
3 W Main St, Samson, AL 36477
Tel.: (334) 898-7156
Web Site: http://www.sunsouth.com
Sales Range: $25-49.9 Million
Emp.: 25
Tractor & Tractor Parts Distr
N.A.I.C.S.: 441227
Allen Wise (Mgr-Store)
Allen Bock (Mgr-Parts)
Tim Martin (Mgr-Svc)

SunSouth - Tuscaloosa (1)
3610 Skyland Blvd E, Tuscaloosa, AL 35405
Tel.: (205) 556-7700
Web Site: http://www.sunsouth.com
Sales Range: $10-24.9 Million
Emp.: 15
Tractor & Tractor Parts Dealer
N.A.I.C.S.: 441227
Chris Barnette (Gen Mgr)

Wenco Group Incorporated (1)
1975 Forbes Dr, Montgomery, AL 36110
Tel.: (334) 834-6340
Web Site: http://www.sunsouth.com
Sales Range: $10-24.9 Million
Emp.: 25
Tractor & Tractor Parts Dealer
N.A.I.C.S.: 441227
Ronnie Hayes (Gen Mgr)

SUNSPORTS, INC.
7 Holland, Irvine, CA 92618
Tel.: (949) 609-1001 CA
Web Site:
    http://www.sunsportsapparel.com
Year Founded: 1991
Sales Range: $25-49.9 Million
Emp.: 200
Broadwoven Fabric Finishing Mills
N.A.I.C.S.: 313310
Carlos Ortiz (Dir-Screen Print Production)

SUNSTONE ASSURANCE, LLC
1007 Orange St Nemours Bldg Ste 1414, Wilmington, DE 19801
Tel.: (302) 472-7439
Year Founded: 2010
Sales Range: $10-24.9 Million
Insurance Services
N.A.I.C.S.: 525190
Andrew A. Lewis (Exec Dir)
Douglas F. Deitch (Exec Dir)
Jay S. Peichel (Exec Dir)
Joel B. Pina (Exec Dir)
John T. Naughton (Exec Dir)

SUNSTONE IMPORTS INC.
8350 Lehigh Ave, Morton Grove, IL 60053
Tel.: (847) 965-1700
Web Site: http://www.tsiholding.com
Rev.: $34,000,000
Emp.: 412
Jewelry, Precious Metal
N.A.I.C.S.: 339910
Michael C. Brown (Pres)

SUNSTONE PARTNERS MANAGEMENT LLC
400 S El Camino Real Ste 300, San Mateo, CA 94402
Tel.: (650) 289-4400
Web Site:
    http://www.sunstonepartners.com
Year Founded: 2015
Holding Company
N.A.I.C.S.: 523999
Gus Alberelli (Mng Dir)
Mike Biggee (Mng Dir)

Subsidiaries:

66degrees Inc. (1)
20 W Kinzie St Ste 1510, Chicago, IL 60654
Tel.: (312) 869-3128
Web Site: http://www.cloudbakers.com
Software & Technology Development Services
N.A.I.C.S.: 513210
Mitch Greenwald (Founder)

Subsidiary (Domestic):

Pandera Systems, LLC (2)
5325 Primrose Lk Cir, Tampa, FL 33647-3520
Web Site: http://www.panderasystems.com
Custom Computer Programming Services
N.A.I.C.S.: 541511
Ryan Schooler (Project Mgr)

Accuhealth Technologies LLC (1)
200 S 10th St Ste 103, McAllen, TX 78501
Tel.: (888) 407-4108
Web Site: https://www.accuhealth.tech
Hospitals & Health Care
N.A.I.C.S.: 621610
Stephen Samson (CEO)

Subsidiary (Domestic):

Signallamp Health Inc. (2)
321 Spruce St, Scranton, PA 18503
Tel.: (215) 315-3510
Web Site: http://www.signallamphealth.com
Sales Range: $1-9.9 Million
Emp.: 200
Health Care Srvices
N.A.I.C.S.: 621610
Drew Kearney (Co-Founder & CEO)
Andrew Goldberg (Co-Founder & CFO)
Jen Nicastro (Chief Nursing Officer)
Jeremy Floyd (VP-Sls)

Avertium, LLC (1)
20601 N 19th St Ste 150, Phoenix, AZ 85027
Web Site: http://www.avertium.com
Cybersecurity & Advisory Services
N.A.I.C.S.: 561621
Jeff Schmidt (CEO)
John McNeely (Sr VP-East)
Edward Vasko (Sr VP-West)
Paul Caiazzo (Sr VP-Virginia Office)
Mark Dallmeier (VP-Channels & Sls Ops)
R. Gregory Breetz Jr. (CFO)

Subsidiary (Domestic):

Avertium Tennessee, Inc. (2)
1431 Centerpoint Blvd Ste 150, Knoxville, TN 37932-1984
Tel.: (865) 244-3500
Network & IT Security & Compliance Services
N.A.I.C.S.: 541519
John McNeely (Grp Sr VP-East & Gen Mgr)

Cerna Solutions, LLC (1)
1850 Diamond St Ste 101, San Marcos, CA 92078
Tel.: (442) 222-0303
Web Site: http://www.cernasolutions.com
Computer System Design Services
N.A.I.C.S.: 541512
Matt Kite (CEO)

Evergreen Systems, Inc. (1)
215 Depot Ct SE 2nd Fl, Leesburg, VA 20175
Tel.: (571) 262-0977
Web Site: http://www.evergreensys.com
Computer System Design Services
N.A.I.C.S.: 541512
Donald D. Casson (Co-Founder & CEO)
Sean P. Dougherty (Co-Founder & Exec VP-Consulting)
Jason R. Whitesides (Exec VP-Bus Dev)

UserTesting, Inc. (1)
660 4th St Ste 246, San Francisco, CA 94107
Tel.: (650) 567-5616
Web Site: https://www.usertesting.com
Rev.: $147,398,000
Assets: $283,128,000
Liabilities: $133,449,000
Net Worth: $149,679,000
Earnings: ($50,721,000)
Emp.: 783

Fiscal Year-end: 12/31/2021
Software Development Services
N.A.I.C.S.: 541511
Andy MacMillan (Pres, CEO & Chm)
Jon Pexton (CFO)
Kaj Van de Loo (CTO)
Michelle Huff (CMO)
Matt Zelen (COO)

SUNSTREAM, INC.
6231 Estero Blvd, Fort Myers Beach, FL 33931
Tel.: (239) 765-4111 FL
Web Site: http://www.sunstream.com
Year Founded: 1986
Sales Range: $10-24.9 Million
Emp.: 250
Hotels & Condo Resorts Owner & Operator
N.A.I.C.S.: 721110
David A. Lawrence (Pres)
Jamie Gregor (Mgr-Guest Svs)
Barbara Fitz (Mgr-Reservations)
Kathy Gold (Mgr-Guest Svc)
Gary Lambert (Dir-HR)
Randy Kares (Dir-IT)
Sharie Mortenson (Dir-Fin)
Jennifer Ellis (Dir-Sls & Mktg)
Monica Flowers (Exec Dir)

Subsidiaries:

Bellasera (1)
221 9th St S, Naples, FL 34102
Tel.: (239) 649-7333
Web Site: http://www.bellaseranaples.com
Hotel
N.A.I.C.S.: 721110

DiamondHead Beach Resort (1)
2000 Estero Blvd, Fort Myers Beach, FL 33931
Tel.: (239) 765-7654
Web Site: http://www.diamondheadfl.com
Sales Range: $10-24.9 Million
Emp.: 100
Resort
N.A.I.C.S.: 721110
Neil Hopgood (Gen Mgr)

GullWing Beach Resort (1)
6620 Estero Blvd, Fort Myers Beach, FL 33931
Tel.: (239) 765-4300
Web Site: http://www.gullwingfl.com
Sales Range: $10-24.9 Million
Emp.: 25
Resort
N.A.I.C.S.: 721110
Dave Laurance (Pres)

Park Shore Resort (1)
600 Neapolitan Way, Naples, FL 34103
Tel.: (239) 263-2222
Web Site: http://www.parkshorefl.com
Sales Range: $10-24.9 Million
Emp.: 17
Resort
N.A.I.C.S.: 721110
Steve McIntire (Gen Mgr)

Pointe Estero Beach Resort (1)
6640 Estero Blvd, Fort Myers Beach, FL 33931
Tel.: (239) 765-1155
Web Site: http://www.pointeestero.com
Sales Range: $10-24.9 Million
Emp.: 20
Resort
N.A.I.C.S.: 721310
Cort Ternnar (Gen Mgr)

SUNSWEET GROWERS, INC.
901 N Walton Ave, Yuba City, CA 95993-8634
Tel.: (530) 674-5010 CA
Web Site: http://www.sunsweet.com
Year Founded: 1917
Sales Range: $200-249.9 Million
Emp.: 650
Dried Fruits Processor
N.A.I.C.S.: 311423
Harold Upton (Chief Information & Analytics Officer & VP)
Brendon S. Flynn (Chm)

SUNTRADE EXPORT SERVICES

Dane L. Lance (Pres & CEO)
Brad Schuler (VP-Global Sls & Mktg)
Bob Amarel (Vice Chm)
Jack Dixon (VP-HR)
Ana Klein (CFO & VP)

Subsidiaries:

MD Drinks, Inc. (1)
2639A Manhattan Bch Blvd, Redondo Beach, CA 90278
Tel.: (310) 725-9050
Web Site: http://www.functiondrinks.com
Beverages Mfr
N.A.I.C.S.: 312111

Sunsweet Dryers (1)
901 N Walton Ave, Yuba City, CA 95993
Tel.: (530) 674-5010
Web Site: http://www.sunsweetdryers.com
Dehydrated Fruits & Vegetables Mfr
N.A.I.C.S.: 311423
Mark Dalrymple (Pres)

SUNSYSTEM DEVELOPMENT CORPORATION
900 Hope Way, Altamonte Springs, FL 32714
Tel.: (407) 357-1000 FL
Year Founded: 1982
Sales Range: $25-49.9 Million
Health & Welfare Benefit Services
N.A.I.C.S.: 525120

SUNTEC INDUSTRIES INC.
60 Aberdeen Dr, Glasgow, KY 42141
Tel.: (270) 651-7116 DE
Web Site:
    http://www.suntecpumps.com
Year Founded: 1984
Sales Range: $10-24.9 Million
Emp.: 25
Fuel Oil Pumps Mfr
N.A.I.C.S.: 333914

SUNTECH BUILDING SYSTEMS INC.
11326 Perry Rd, Houston, TX 77064-4588
Tel.: (281) 897-8188
Web Site: http://www.suntech-inc.com
Year Founded: 1978
Sales Range: $10-24.9 Million
Emp.: 14
Commercial & Office Building, New Construction
N.A.I.C.S.: 236220
W. Douglass Larson (Pres)
Susan Martin (Sr VP & Sr Project Mgr)

SUNTIVA, LLC
7600 Leesburg Pike Ste 440E, Falls Church, VA 22043
Tel.: (703) 462-8470
Web Site: http://www.suntiva.com
Year Founded: 2002
Sales Range: $10-24.9 Million
Emp.: 100
Business Management Consulting Services
N.A.I.C.S.: 541611
Hany Malik (Pres & CEO)
Rodney Matsushima (Exec VP)
Sheryl Malik (Dir-Strategic Direction, Plng & Mgmt)
Kimberly Waldman (VP)
David Acton (CFO)
Aletha Walker (Sr Mgr-HR)
Gail Rissler (COO)
Scot Stitely (VP)
Sunny Yoo (Dir-Defense & Intelligence Bus Dev)

SUNTRADE EXPORT SERVICES

SUNTRADE EXPORT SERVICES

Suntrade Export Services—(Continued)
14542 Ventura Blvd Suite 203, Sherman Oaks, CA 91403
Tel.: (818) 789-5867
Web Site: http://www.suntradeexport.com
Year Founded: 2005
Sales Range: $10-24.9 Million
Emp.: 10
Supplies Quality Fruits & Vegetables for International Importers
N.A.I.C.S.: 445230
Derrick Stinnett *(Mgr-Export Sls)*
Scott Egan *(Owner & Pres)*

SUNTREAT PACKING & SHIPPING CO.
391 Oxford Ave, Lindsay, CA 93247
Tel.: (559) 562-4991 CA
Web Site: http://www.suntreat.com
Year Founded: 1965
Sales Range: $1-9.9 Million
Emp.: 200
Packing & Crating Services
N.A.I.C.S.: 488991
Franco Bernardi *(Gen Mgr)*
Daniel Thullen *(Mgr-Food Safety)*

SUNTURF INC.
5720 F St, Omaha, NE 68127
Tel.: (402) 331-0200
Web Site: http://www.sunturf.com
Sales Range: $10-24.9 Million
Emp.: 27
Mowers, Power
N.A.I.C.S.: 424910
Dave Wilson *(VP)*
Paul Davis *(Pres)*
David DePauw *(Controller)*

SUNTX CAPITAL PARTNERS, L.P.
2 Licoln Ctr 5420 LBJ Freeway Ste 1000, Dallas, TX 75240
Tel.: (972) 663-8900 TX
Web Site: http://www.suntx.com
Year Founded: 2000
Rev.: $1,000,000,000
Privater Equity Firm
N.A.I.C.S.: 523999
Michael D. Ilagan *(Principal)*
Mark R. Matteson *(Co-Founder & Partner)*
Craig Jennings *(Co-Founder, Partner & CFO)*
Ned N. Fleming III *(Co-Founder & Mng Partner)*

Subsidiaries:
CBI Laboratories, Inc. (1)
4201 Diplomacy Rd, Fort Worth, TX 76155
Tel.: (972) 241-7546
Web Site: http://www.cbiskincare.com
Sales Range: $10-24.9 Million
Emp.: 60
Skincare Products Developer, Mfr & Distr
N.A.I.C.S.: 325411
Harriet Robinette *(Mgr-Acct)*
Rosie Bryan *(Acct Mgr-Custom Sls)*
Jason Maxwell *(Mgr-Regulatory Affairs)*
Raeginia Shepherd *(Dir-Procurement, Logistics & HR)*

London Broadcasting Company, Inc. (1)
15455 Dallas parkway Ste100, Addison, TX 75001
Tel.: (214) 812-9500
Web Site: http://www.londonbroadcastingcompany.com
Emp.: 30
Holding Company; Television Broadcasting Stations
N.A.I.C.S.: 551112
Carl W. Kommeyer *(CFO, Chief Dev Officer & Exec VP)*

Subsidiary (Domestic):
KTXD Operating Company, LLC (2)
15455 Dallas Pkwy Ste 100, Addison, TX 75001
Tel.: (214) 628-9900
Web Site: http://www.ktxdtv.com
Television Broadcasting Station
N.A.I.C.S.: 516120
Kent Domingue *(Dir-Ops)*

Nouveau Eyewear, Inc. (1)
2853 Eisenhower St Ste 100, Carrollton, TX 75007
Tel.: (972) 242-3633
Web Site: http://www.nouveaueyewear.com
Sales Range: $25-49.9 Million
Emp.: 150
Opthalmic Frames Mfr
N.A.I.C.S.: 333310
Dominick Sblendorio *(Co-Pres & COO)*

SUNWEST BANCORP, INC.
2050 Main St Ste 100, Irvine, CA 92614
Tel.: (714) 730-4444 DE
Web Site: http://www.sunwestbank.com
Sales Range: $25-49.9 Million
Bank Holding Company
N.A.I.C.S.: 551111

Subsidiaries:
Sunwest Bank (1)
2050 Main St Ste 300, Irvine, CA 92614
Tel.: (714) 730-4444
Web Site: http://www.sunwestbank.com
Sales Range: $25-49.9 Million
Emp.: 142
Retail & Commercial Banking
N.A.I.C.S.: 522110
Eric Donald Hovde *(Chm & CEO)*
Kenneth Smith *(CFO & Exec VP)*
Kyle Legrand *(Asst VP & Mgr-Customer Rels)*
Carson Lappetito *(Pres)*
Shailesh Bhaid *(CIO)*
Thomas Chavez *(Sr VP & Sls Mgr-SBA)*
Alice Castrey *(Officer-Compliance & Sr VP)*
Ben Alvarado *(Exec VP & Head-Retail & Bus Banking)*
Chris Zimmerman *(Sr VP & Mgr-Loan Svcs)*
Jasmin Amaya *(Officer-BSA & Sr VP)*
Justin Archuleta *(Sr VP)*
Kara Trebs *(Sr VP & Dir-Human Capital)*
Sanya Allmaras *(Sr VP & Dir-Ops)*
Scott Peterson *(Chief Credit Officer & Exec VP)*
Chris Tillack *(Pres-Utah)*

SUNWEST ELECTRIC, INC.
135 N State College Blvd, Brea, CA 92823
Tel.: (714) 940-9995
Sales Range: $25-49.9 Million
Emp.: 175
Electrical Wiring Services
N.A.I.C.S.: 238210
Carlos Rodriguez *(Mgr-Prefab Detailer)*

SUNWEST FOODS INC.
No 150 1550 Drew Ave, Davis, CA 95616-6320
Tel.: (530) 758-8550
Web Site: http://www.sunwestfoods.com
Year Founded: 1986
Sales Range: $25-49.9 Million
Growers & Sales of Organic Rice
N.A.I.C.S.: 424510

SUNWEST MANAGEMENT, INC.
3723 Fairview Industrial Dr SE Ste 270, Salem, OR 97302
Tel.: (503) 375-9016 OR
Web Site: http://www.sunwestmanagement.com
Year Founded: 1991
Sales Range: $10-24.9 Million

Emp.: 158
Senior Citizen Assisted Living & Retirement Communities Management Services
N.A.I.C.S.: 623311
Larry Miller *(Mgr-Pur Project)*

SUNWEST MILLING COMPANY, INC.
PO Box 70, Biggs, CA 95917
Tel.: (530) 868-5421
Sales Range: $10-24.9 Million
Emp.: 53
Rice Milling Services
N.A.I.C.S.: 311212
Jim Errecarte *(Pres)*
Ken Calfee *(VP)*
Galo Williams *(Mgr)*

SUNZ INSURANCE COMPANY
7405 N Tamiami Trl, Sarasota, FL 34243
Tel.: (727) 497-1247
Web Site: http://www.sunzinsurance.com
Sales Range: $10-24.9 Million
Emp.: 20
Insurance Services
N.A.I.C.S.: 524298
Glen J. Distefano *(Chief Info Security Officer)*
Rick Leonard *(Pres)*
Steve Herrig *(CEO)*
Michael W. Grandstaff *(CFO)*
Karen Bolinder *(COO)*
Gene R. Levine *(Sr VP-Underwriting)*
Theodore G. Bryant *(Chief Legal Officer & Exec VP)*
Blake Souers *(Chief Underwriting Officer)*
Paul Marks *(Exec VP-Sls)*

SUPER 1 FOODS
240 W Hayden Ave, Hayden Lake, ID 83835-9629
Tel.: (208) 772-5722 WA
Web Site: http://www.super1foods.net
Year Founded: 1970
Sales Range: $10-24.9 Million
Emp.: 120
Grocery Stores
N.A.I.C.S.: 445110
Wayne Hudlemeyer *(Mgr-Store Ops)*
Brian Howell *(Dir-Store)*

SUPER A FOODS INCORPORATED
7200 Dominion Cir, Commerce, CA 90040
Tel.: (323) 869-0600
Web Site: http://www.superafoods.com
Rev.: $108,458,736
Emp.: 40
Grocery Stores, Independent
N.A.I.C.S.: 445110
Louis A. Amen *(Chm)*
Jim Amen *(Pres)*

SUPER AMERICA
17546 Kenrick Ave, Lakeville, MN 55044
Tel.: (952) 435-2622 MN
Web Site: http://www.superamerica.com
Year Founded: 1982
Sales Range: $10-24.9 Million
Emp.: 20
Convenience Stores & Gas Stations Operator & Franchiser
N.A.I.C.S.: 445131
Tony Kenney *(Pres)*
Heather Lewis *(Mgr)*
Natalie Simmons *(Mgr)*

SUPER C MART INC.

U.S. PRIVATE

PO Box 2117, Noble, OK 73068
Tel.: (405) 872-9220
Sales Range: $10-24.9 Million
Emp.: 51
Independent Supermarket
N.A.I.C.S.: 445110
Rod Carver *(Pres)*

SUPER CAMPARICO PITUSA
246 Calle Roberto Sanchez Ave, Carolina, PR 00982
Tel.: (787) 641-8200
Web Site: http://www.pitusa.com
Rev.: $137,683,397
Emp.: 20
Supermarkets, Chain
N.A.I.C.S.: 457110
Israel Kopell *(Pres)*

SUPER CARE INC.
16017 Vly Blvd, City of Industry, CA 91744
Tel.: (626) 854-2273
Web Site: http://www.supercaremad.com
Rev.: $19,110,903
Emp.: 150
Medical Apparatus & Supplies
N.A.I.C.S.: 456199
Gabriel Casser *(Pres)*
Camil Kassar *(Mgr-IT)*
Hayk Melkumyan *(Dir-Reimbursement)*

SUPER CENTER CONCEPTS INC.
15510 Carmenita Rd, Santa Fe Springs, CA 90670
Tel.: (562) 345-9000
Web Site: http://www.superiorgrocers.com
Sales Range: $300-349.9 Million
Emp.: 100
Grocery Stores
N.A.I.C.S.: 445110
Mimi R. Song *(Pres & CEO)*
Marie Song *(Exec VP)*
Glenda Apostol *(Supvr-Acctg)*

SUPER D, INC.
17822 Gillette Ste A, Irvine, CA 92614
Tel.: (949) 225-1170
Web Site: http://www.sdcd.com
Sales Range: $10-24.9 Million
Emp.: 161
Music & Video Whslr & Distr
N.A.I.C.S.: 512120
Bruce Ogilvie *(CEO)*
Bobby Miranda *(VP-Sls)*

SUPER GARDEN CENTERS, INC.
21812 Sherman Way, Canoga Park, CA 91305
Tel.: (818) 340-6400
Web Site: http://www.greenthumb.com
Rev.: $17,778,264
Emp.: 44
Nursery Stock
N.A.I.C.S.: 424930
Harold D. Bergquist *(Pres)*

SUPER PALLET RECYCLING CORP.
10144 Waterman Rd, Elk Grove, CA 95624
Tel.: (916) 686-1700
Sales Range: $10-24.9 Million
Emp.: 39
Pallets, Wood
N.A.I.C.S.: 423310
Bryan Wilson *(CEO)*

SUPER PLUS ACQUISITION CORPORATION

800 3rd Ave Ste 2800, New York, NY 10022
Tel.: (929) 299-9988   DE
Year Founded: 2021
Investment Services
N.A.I.C.S.: 523999
Long Yi *(Chm & CEO)*
Jing Lu *(CFO)*

SUPER QUIK INC.
2000 Ashland Dr Ste 105, Ashland, KY 41101
Tel.: (606) 836-9641   KY
Web Site: http://www.superquik.net
Year Founded: 1977
Sales Range: $25-49.9 Million
Emp.: 220
Convenience Store
N.A.I.C.S.: 457120
Lynn Rice *(Pres)*
Chip Lessner *(Coord-Tech)*
Tony Coriell *(CFO)*

SUPER RADIATOR COILS LTD.
104 Peavey Rd, Chaska, MN 55318-2324
Tel.: (952) 556-3330
Web Site: http://www.superradiatorcoils.com
Year Founded: 1985
Sales Range: $10-24.9 Million
Emp.: 250
Provider of Refrigeration & Heating Services
N.A.I.C.S.: 333415
Robert Holt *(Pres & CEO)*
Matt Holland *(VP-Ops-Richmond Div)*

SUPER STEEL LLC
7900 W Twr Ave, Milwaukee, WI 53223
Tel.: (414) 355-4800
Web Site: http://www.supersteel.com
Year Founded: 1966
Sales Range: $25-49.9 Million
Emp.: 350
Fabricated Plate Manufacturing
N.A.I.C.S.: 332313
Bruce Medd *(Mgr-Acctg)*
Richard Stewart *(Mgr-Quality)*
Ken Nash *(Mgr-IT)*
Jason Garre *(Pres)*

Subsidiaries:

Manitex Sabre, Inc.   (1)
5420 E State Rd 8, Knox, IN 46534
Tel.: (574) 772-5380
Web Site: http://www.manitexsabre.com
Storage Tank Mfr
N.A.I.C.S.: 336211

Subsidiary (Domestic):

Sabre Manufacturing LLC   (2)
5420 E State Rd 8, Knox, IN 46534
Tel.: (574) 772-5380
Web Site: http://www.sabremfgllc.com
Liquid Storage & Containment Tank Mfr
N.A.I.C.S.: 332420

SUPER STORE INDUSTRIES
2800 W March Ln Ste 210, Stockton, CA 95219-8200
Tel.: (209) 473-8100
Web Site: http://www.ssica.com
Year Founded: 1990
Sales Range: $25-49.9 Million
Emp.: 750
Fluid Milk
N.A.I.C.S.: 311511
Becky Keller *(Mgr-Warehouse & Web Based Sys)*
Bill Lawrence *(Mgr-Transportation)*
David Doneen *(CIO)*
Jenny Little *(Controller-Accts Payable)*
Kelly Martin *(Engr-Maintenance)*
Jon Skaggs *(Dir-IT)*
Janet Snowden *(Acct Coord)*
Karen Ferreira *(Mgr-Quality Assurance)*
Josh Devitt *(Bus Mgr-Sys)*
Kathy Stewart *(Dir-Mdse)*
Todd Hager *(Dir-Sls)*
Sheryl Bartholomew *(Mgr-Customer Svc)*
Don Warren *(Mgr-Production)*

Subsidiaries:

Super Store Industries - Fairfield Dairy Division   (1)
199 Red Top Rd, Fairfield, CA 94534
Tel.: (707) 864-0502
Dairy Products Mfr
N.A.I.C.S.: 311514

Super Store Industries - Turlock Dairy Division   (1)
2600 Spengler Rd, Turlock, CA 95380
Tel.: (209) 668-2100
Dairy Products Mfr
N.A.I.C.S.: 311514

SUPER TIENDAS LA TAPCHULTECA
6569 Van Nuys Blvd, Van Nuys, CA 91401
Tel.: (818) 787-9969   CA
Year Founded: 1996
Rev.: $10,000,000
Emp.: 60
Grocery Stores, Independent
N.A.I.C.S.: 445110
Irmi Torres *(Pres)*

SUPER WAREHOUSE
3944 Murphy Canyon Rd Ste C106, San Diego, CA 92123
Tel.: (858) 764-8900
Web Site: http://www.superwarehouse.com
Year Founded: 1998
Sales Range: $25-49.9 Million
Emp.: 10
Computer Peripheral Equipment & Software Merchant Whslr
N.A.I.C.S.: 423430
Dawn Hobbs *(Dir-Ops)*
Dennis Gowen *(Mgr-Sls & Acct)*

SUPER WASH INC.
707 W Lincolnway, Morrison, IL 61270-2004
Tel.: (815) 772-2111   IL
Web Site: http://www.superwash.com
Year Founded: 1982
Sales Range: $10-24.9 Million
Emp.: 85
Provider of Nonresidential Construction Services
N.A.I.C.S.: 236220
Robert Black *(Pres, CEO & Treas)*

SUPER-ELECTRIC CONSTRUCTION CO.
4300 W Chicago Ave, Chicago, IL 60651
Tel.: (773) 489-4400
Web Site: http://www.superelec.com
Sales Range: $10-24.9 Million
Emp.: 80
General Electrical Contractor
N.A.I.C.S.: 238210
William A. Schult *(Pres)*
J. C. Corte *(Controller)*
Gene Krupa *(Project Mgr)*
Greg Neuman *(Dir-Safety)*

SUPER-FLITE OIL CO. INC.
100 E Johnson St, Saginaw, MI 48604-1318
Tel.: (989) 752-8003   MI
Year Founded: 1963
Sales Range: $10-24.9 Million
Emp.: 70
Provider of Gasoline Services
N.A.I.C.S.: 457120
Stan Brown *(Pres)*

SUPER-SENSITIVE MUSICAL STRING CO.
1805 Apex Rd, Sarasota, FL 34240
Tel.: (941) 371-0016   IL
Web Site: http://www.supersensitive.com
Year Founded: 1930
Sales Range: $1-9.9 Million
Emp.: 43
Musical Instrument Mfr
N.A.I.C.S.: 339992
John V. Cavanaugh *(Chm)*
Ron Van Ostenbridge *(COO)*
Jim Cavanaugh *(Pres)*

SUPERB INDUSTRIES, INC.
330 3rd St NW, Sugarcreek, OH 44681
Tel.: (330) 852-0500   OH
Web Site: http://www.superbindustries.com
Year Founded: 1986
Sales Range: $1-9.9 Million
Emp.: 47
Precision Metal Stampings & Plastic Moldings Mfr
N.A.I.C.S.: 333517
John Miller *(Pres)*
Steve Blickensderfer *(Mgr-Plastics Ops)*

SUPERB SOUND INC.
6609 E 82nd St, Indianapolis, IN 46250-1504
Tel.: (317) 849-7729
Web Site: http://www.ovation-av.com
Year Founded: 1987
Sales Range: $25-49.9 Million
Emp.: 7
Retailer of High Fidelity Stereo Equipment
N.A.I.C.S.: 449210
Rob Lundstrom *(Owner)*

Subsidiaries:

Superb Sound Clarksville Inc.   (1)
1005 E Hwy 131, Clarksville, IN 47129
Tel.: (812) 284-4109
Web Site: http://www.ovation-av.com
Rev.: $540,000
Consumer Electronic Equipment
N.A.I.C.S.: 449210

SUPERFLOORS INC.
6911 S 196th St, Kent, WA 98032
Tel.: (253) 872-3555
Web Site: http://www.superfloors.com
Year Founded: 1982
Sales Range: $50-74.9 Million
Emp.: 200
Installer of Floor Products
N.A.I.C.S.: 236115
Michelle Conner *(Acct Mgr)*

SUPERFLOW TECHNOLOGIES GROUP
4060 Dixon St, Des Moines, IA 50313
Tel.: (515) 254-1654
Web Site: http://www.superflow.com
Rev.: $18,800,000
Emp.: 100
Measuring & Controlling Device Mfg
N.A.I.C.S.: 334519
Scott Giles *(Pres)*

SUPERFLY MANUFACTURING CO.,
34029 Schoolcraft Rd, Livonia, MI 48150
Tel.: (313) 454-1492
Web Site: http://www.superflykids.com
Year Founded: 2008
Sales Range: $1-9.9 Million
Emp.: 17
Mfr of Custom Superhero Capes & Costumes & Sells Directly to Consumers & Wholesale Customers
N.A.I.C.S.: 458110
Holly Bartman *(Founder)*

SUPERIOR AG RESOURCES CO-OP, INC.
901 N Main St, Huntingburg, IN 47542
Tel.: (812) 683-2809
Web Site: http://www.superiorag.com
Sales Range: $100-124.9 Million
Agricultural News, Market Information & Commodity Services
N.A.I.C.S.: 424910
Clarence Betz *(Pres)*

Subsidiaries:

Superior Ag Resources Co-op   (1)
520 S 4th St, Boonville, IN 47601 **(100%)**
Tel.: (812) 897-1100
Web Site: http://www.superiorag.com
Sales Range: $10-24.9 Million
Emp.: 24
Agricultural News, Market Information & Commodity Services
N.A.I.C.S.: 424910

Superior Ag Resources Co-op   (1)
511 N Main St, Chrisney, IN 47611 **(100%)**
Tel.: (812) 362-7701
Web Site: http://www.superiorag.com
Sales Range: $10-24.9 Million
Emp.: 10
Agricultural News, Market Information & Commodity Services
N.A.I.C.S.: 424910
Barry Day *(Pres & CEO)*
Jim Gauker *(CFO)*

Superior Ag Resources Co-op   (1)
Hwy 64 E, Princeton, IN 47670 **(100%)**
Tel.: (812) 385-4867
Web Site: http://www.superiorag.com
Sales Range: $10-24.9 Million
Emp.: 12
Agricultural News, Market Information & Commodity Services
N.A.I.C.S.: 424910

SUPERIOR AIR PARTS INC.
621 S Royal Ln Ste 100, Coppell, TX 75019-3805
Tel.: (972) 829-4600   TX
Web Site: http://www.superiorairparts.com
Year Founded: 1998
Sales Range: $10-24.9 Million
Emp.: 46
Supplier of Aircraft Engines & Engine Parts
N.A.I.C.S.: 336412
L. Scott Hayes *(VP-Sls & Mktg)*
Keith Chatten *(CEO)*
Wes Rayon *(Dir-Production & Inventory Control)*
Bill Ross *(VP-Product Support)*
Stephen J. Grimes *(Mgr-Quality Assurance)*

SUPERIOR AMBULANCE SERVICE, INC.
7600 La Morada Pl NW, Albuquerque, NM 87120
Tel.: (505) 247-8840   NM
Web Site: http://www.superior-nm.com
Year Founded: 1974
Sales Range: $1-9.9 Million
Emp.: 235
Contract Ambulance Service
N.A.I.C.S.: 621910
Chris L. Archuleta *(CEO & Exec Dir)*
Loretta Archuleta *(Dir-Admin)*
Manuel Archuleta *(Dir-Ops)*

SUPERIOR AMBULANCE SERVICE, INC.   U.S. PRIVATE

Superior Ambulance Service, Inc.—(Continued)
Joseph Chacon *(Coord-Special Projects)*
Matt Gowan *(Mgr-Dispatch)*
Gabriel Serna *(Reg Mgr)*
Scott Wilson *(Coord-Quality Assurance & Trng)*
Paul Vigil *(Mgr-SMT Ops)*
Jacquelyn Ryba *(Officer-Compliance)*

SUPERIOR AUTO GROUP
4264 N College, Fayetteville, AR 72703
Tel.: (479) 582-1002
Web Site:
    http://www.superiorsuperstores.com
New & Used Car Dealers
N.A.I.C.S.: 441110
Jim Teeter *(Gen Mgr)*
Subsidiaries:

Mercedes-Benz of Northwest Arkansas (1)
2400 SE Moberly Ln, Bentonville, AR 72712
Tel.: (479) 521-7281
Web Site: http://www.mbofnwa.com
Rev.: $20,677,703
Emp.: 38
New & Used Car Dealer
N.A.I.C.S.: 441110
Gerald Jones *(CEO)*
Jonathan McMichael *(Mgr-Sls)*

Superior Auto Mall (1)
504 Hwy 412 Bypass E, Siloam Springs, AR 72761
Tel.: (479) 524-4154
Web Site:
    http://www.superiorsuperstores.com
Sales Range: $1-9.9 Million
Emp.: 25
New & Used Car Dealer
N.A.I.C.S.: 441110
Dean Rollins *(Gen Mgr)*

SUPERIOR AUTOMATIC SPRINKLER CO.
4378 Enterprise Place, Fremont, CA 94538
Tel.: (408) 946-7272
Web Site:
    http://www.superiorfiresprinkler.com
Year Founded: 1973
Sales Range: $10-24.9 Million
Emp.: 92
Fire Sprinkler System Designer, Mfr, Installation & Maintenance Services
N.A.I.C.S.: 333998
Robert Lawson *(CEO)*
Marci Kearney *(Partner & CFO)*
Peter Hulin *(Pres)*

SUPERIOR AUTOMOTIVE
120 S Quintard Ave, Anniston, AL 36201
Tel.: (256) 237-1656
Web Site:
    http://www.superiorhyundaial.com
Rev.: $26,000,000
Emp.: 50
New Car Dealers
N.A.I.C.S.: 441110

SUPERIOR CAPITAL PARTNERS LLC
500 Griswold St Ste 2320, Detroit, MI 48226
Tel.: (313) 596-9600
Web Site:
    http://www.superiorfund.com
Year Founded: 2007
Sales Range: Less than $1 Million
Emp.: 10
Privater Equity Firm
N.A.I.C.S.: 523999
Mark H. Carroll *(Mng Partner)*
William Y. Campbell *(Chm)*

William F. McKinley *(Vice Chm)*
Scott A. Reilly *(Gen Partner)*
Scott J. Hauncher *(Partner)*
Subsidiaries:

Aftermarket Controls Holdings Corp. (1)
47119 Cartier Ct, Wixom, MI 48393
Tel.: (248) 960-8500
Sales Range: $50-74.9 Million
Emp.: 100
Holding Company; Aftermarket Auto Parts
N.A.I.C.S.: 551112

Holding (Domestic):

Aftermarket Controls Corporation (2)
47119 Cartier Ct, Wixom, MI 48393
Tel.: (248) 960-8500
Web Site: http://www.rostra.com
Sales Range: $25-49.9 Million
Aftermarket Automotive Parts Mfr & Distr
N.A.I.C.S.: 335999

Subsidiary (Domestic):

Rostra Precision Controls, Inc. (3)
2519 Dana Dr, Laurinburg, NC 28352
Tel.: (910) 276-4853
Web Site: http://www.rostra.com
Automotive Accessories, Cruise Control & Lumbar Support Mfr for the Automobile Industry
N.A.I.C.S.: 336390
Sibyl Ringsdorf *(Mgr-Mktg)*
Sibyl Ringfdorf *(Mgr-Customer Svc-Intl & West Coast)*
Peter Doddridge *(Dir-OE Sls)*
Bill Simmons *(Dir-Mktg)*
Thomas Callahan *(Mgr-Technical Support)*
Tom Eibel *(VP-Sls & Mktg)*
Jeff Gohrmann *(Mgr-Midwest)*
Chris Heimburg *(Mgr-West)*
Pete Kallgren *(VP-Sls & Mktg)*
Loren Mikesell *(Mgr-South)*
Charles Monroe *(Mgr-Applications Engrg)*

USA Switch Inc. (3)
47119 Cartier Ct, Wixom, MI 48393
Tel.: (248) 960-8500
Automotive Switch, Solenoid & Sensor Mfr & Distr
N.A.I.C.S.: 335999

SUPERIOR CHOICE CREDIT UNION
2817 Tower Ave, Superior, WI 54880
Tel.: (715) 392-5616
Web Site:
    http://www.superiorchoice.com
Year Founded: 1932
Sales Range: $10-24.9 Million
Emp.: 87
Credit Union
N.A.I.C.S.: 522130
Gary Elliott *(Pres & CEO)*
Peter Koskinen *(CFO & VP)*

SUPERIOR COMMUNICATIONS PRODUCTS
5027 Irwindale Ave Ste 900, Irwindale, CA 91706
Tel.: (626) 856-6020
Web Site:
    http://www.superiorcommunications.com
Sales Range: $25-49.9 Million
Emp.: 200
Telephone & Telegraphic Equipment
N.A.I.C.S.: 423690
Solomon Chen *(Founder & Chm)*
Mike Cavanah *(Exec VP)*
Jeff Banks *(Pres & CEO)*
Oscar Madrigal *(Mgr-Validation Grp)*
Sean Bailey *(Product Mgr-Southeast)*
Scott Shanks *(Chief Mktg Officer)*

SUPERIOR COMPANIES INC.
101 N Johnstone Ave, Bartlesville, OK 74003
Tel.: (918) 336-5075
Year Founded: 1929

Sales Range: $50-74.9 Million
Emp.: 60
Machine Shop, Jobbing & Repair
N.A.I.C.S.: 332710
J. Randall Judd *(Pres)*
Subsidiaries:

Superior Companies-Manufacturing Division (1)
101 N Johnstone, Bartlesville, OK 74003
Tel.: (918) 336-5075
Web Site:
    http://www.superiorcompanies.com
Sales Range: $10-24.9 Million
Machine Shop, Jobbing & Repair
N.A.I.C.S.: 336214

SUPERIOR CONCRETE FENCE OF TEXAS
1203 Raider Dr, Euless, TX 76040
Tel.: (817) 277-9255
Web Site:
    http://www.concretefence.com
Year Founded: 1986
Sales Range: $10-24.9 Million
Emp.: 45
Concrete Products Mfr
N.A.I.C.S.: 327390
Todd Sternfeld *(Owner & CEO)*
Kyle Wilson *(VP-Ops)*
Raul Rodriguez *(Gen Mgr-Mfg)*

SUPERIOR CONSTRUCTION CO., INC.
2045 E Dunes Hwy, Gary, IN 46402-1601
Tel.: (219) 886-3728
Web Site: http://www.superior-construction.com
Year Founded: 1959
Sales Range: $50-74.9 Million
Emp.: 500
Construction Services
N.A.I.C.S.: 237310
Raymond Nelson *(Controller)*
Rodney Vittetoe *(VP)*
Dick Ayers *(CFO)*
Tim Johnson *(COO)*
Pete Kelley *(Pres-Southeast)*
Nick Largura *(CEO)*
Dan Sopczak *(Pres-Midwest)*

SUPERIOR DAIRY, INC.
4719 Navarre Rd SW, Canton, OH 44706-2338
Tel.: (330) 477-4515
Web Site:
    http://www.superiordairy.com
Year Founded: 1922
Sales Range: $100-124.9 Million
Emp.: 260
Mfr & Distr of Fluid Milk, Ice Cream, Novelties, Cottage Cheese, Sour Cream & Dip
N.A.I.C.S.: 311511
Carolyn J. Schoeppner *(Coord-Customer Support)*
Barbara J. Green *(Dir-HR)*
Jill A. Frank *(Mgr-Benefits Admin)*
J. P. Soehnlen *(Mgr-Pur)*
Jim Innes *(VP-Ops)*
Greg Soehnlen *(VP)*
Al Soehnlen *(Mgr-Key Accts)*

SUPERIOR DENTAL CARE ALLIANCE, INC.
6683 Centerville Business Pkwy, Dayton, OH 45459
Tel.: (937) 438-0283
Web Site:
    http://www.superiordental.com
Year Founded: 1986
Sales Range: $25-49.9 Million
Emp.: 45
Direct Health & Medical Insurance Services

N.A.I.C.S.: 524114
Richard W. Portune *(Chm)*

SUPERIOR DESHLER INC.
PO Box 619, Deshler, NE 68340
Tel.: (402) 365-7216
Sales Range: $10-24.9 Million
Emp.: 15
Petroleum & Agricultural Products Distr
N.A.I.C.S.: 424720
Tom Dahl *(Mgr)*

SUPERIOR DESIGN INTERNATIONAL, INC.
1000 Corporate Dr Ste 3200, Fort Lauderdale, FL 33334
Tel.: (954) 938-5400
Web Site: http://www.sdintl.com
Year Founded: 1992
Sales Range: $100-124.9 Million
Emp.: 500
Provider of Employment Services
N.A.I.C.S.: 561311
Carmen M. Castillo *(Pres)*
Michael Clough *(VP)*
Brendan Curran *(Sr Dir-Programs-Natl)*
Cherie Mainville *(Acct Mgr-Natl)*

SUPERIOR DIE SET CORP.
900 W Drexel Ave, Oak Creek, WI 53154
Tel.: (414) 764-4900
Web Site: http://www.supdie.com
Sales Range: $10-24.9 Million
Emp.: 225
Special Dies, Tools, Jigs & Fixtures
N.A.I.C.S.: 333514
Casey Janiszewski *(CEO)*
Frank Janiszewski *(Pres & COO)*
Lynette Ellman *(CFO)*
Ed Wosilait *(Mgr-HR)*
Rodney Yeomans *(Mgr-Sls)*

SUPERIOR DISTRIBUTING CO., INC.
22116 Washington Township Rd 218, Fostoria, OH 44830
Tel.: (419) 435-1938
Sales Range: $10-24.9 Million
Emp.: 10
Provider of Beer & Other Fermented Malt Liquors
N.A.I.C.S.: 424810
Michael Klepper *(Chm)*
Kempt Brodeck *(Pres)*
Mindy Kidwell *(Mgr-Acctg)*

SUPERIOR DISTRIBUTION OF INDIANAPOLIS
2570 N Shadeland Ave, Indianapolis, IN 46219
Tel.: (317) 308-5525
Sales Range: $10-24.9 Million
Emp.: 13
Warm Air Heating & Air Conditioning
N.A.I.C.S.: 423730
Kevin Kelley *(Gen Mgr)*
Jeff Renn *(Mgr-Inside Sls)*
Subsidiaries:

Superior Distributors of Chicago (1)
155 International Blvd, Glendale Heights, IL 60139
Tel.: (847) 490-6812
Web Site: http://www.superior-hvac.com
Rev.: $1,500,000
Emp.: 4
Warm Air Heating & Air Conditioning
N.A.I.C.S.: 423730

SUPERIOR ECONOMIC MED PRODUCTS CO.
414 Culebra Rd, San Antonio, TX 78201
Tel.: (210) 734-7373

COMPANIES

Web Site: http://www.sempco.com
Sales Range: $10-24.9 Million
Emp.: 38
X-Ray Film & Supplies
N.A.I.C.S.: 423450
Jerry Hoyt (Owner & Pres)
Carolyn Hoyt (Mgr-Acctg)

SUPERIOR ENERGY SERVICES, INC.
1001 Louisiana St Ste 2900, Houston, TX 77002
Tel.: (713) 654-2200 DE
Web Site: https://www.superiorenergy.com
Year Founded: 1991
Rev.: $883,960,000
Assets: $1,191,012,000
Liabilities: $408,128,000
Net Worth: $782,884,000
Earnings: $286,465,000
Emp.: 2,200
Fiscal Year-end: 12/31/22
Oil Field Services & Equipment
N.A.I.C.S.: 213112
James W. Spexarth (CFO, Treas & Exec VP)
Michael Y. McGovern (Chm)
Mike Delahoussaye (Pres)
David J. Lesar (Vice Chm & CEO)
James S. Brown (COO)

Subsidiaries:

A&W Water Service, Inc. (1)
13025 WCR 16, Fort Lupton, CO 80621
Tel.: (303) 659-6523
Web Site: http://www.awwaterservice.com
Sales Range: $1-4.9 Billion
Emp.: 300
Oil & Gas Field Machinery Services
N.A.I.C.S.: 213112
Gary Wright (Pres)

CSI Technologies (1)
1930 W W Thorne Dr, Houston, TX 77073
Tel.: (281) 784-7990
Web Site: http://www.csi-tech.net
Sales Range: $50-74.9 Million
Emp.: 20
Engineering, Research Services & Oilfield Product Development for Energy Industry
N.A.I.C.S.: 541330
Fred Sabins (Founder & Pres)
David Brown (Mgr-Ops)

Complete Energy Services, Inc. (1)
407 S St E Unit A2, Raynham, MA 02767
Tel.: (405) 748-2200
Web Site: https://www.cescorp.com
Emp.: 1,500
Oil & Gas Well Drilling Services
N.A.I.C.S.: 213111

Complete Energy, LLC (1)
11000 Equity Dr, Houston, TX 77041
Tel.: (281) 999-0047
Oil Field Services
N.A.I.C.S.: 213112

Concentric Pipe & Tool, Inc. (1)
3529 Taxi Rd Airport Industrial Park, Houma, LA 70363
Tel.: (985) 851-0306
Web Site: http://www.concentricpipe.com
Sales Range: $250-299.9 Million
Emp.: 30
Well Control Equipment
N.A.I.C.S.: 237120
Ronnie Edge (VP)

Connection Technology Ltd. (1)
1215 Peters Rd, Harvey, LA 70058
Tel.: (504) 362-2628
Web Site: https://www.contechltd.com
Sales Range: $100-124.9 Million
Emp.: 11
Computerized Monitoring
N.A.I.C.S.: 541511

Fastorq, LLC (1)
1215 Peters Rd, Harvey, LA 70058
Tel.: (504) 392-2579
Web Site: http://www.fastorqllc.com
Sales Range: $100-124.9 Million
Emp.: 110
Specialized Technical Tools & Equipment
N.A.I.C.S.: 532490

H.B. Rentals, L.C. (1)
5813 Hwy 90 E, Broussard, LA 70518
Tel.: (337) 839-1641
Web Site: http://www.hbrentals.com
Oil & Gas Field Services
N.A.I.C.S.: 213111
Tasha Castille (VP-Fin)
John Nagel (VP-Ops-Global)

HB Rentals (1)
5813 Hwy 90 E, Broussard, LA 70518
Tel.: (713) 654-2200
Web Site: http://www.hbrental.com
Sales Range: $25-49.9 Million
Emp.: 100
Onshore & Offshore Lodging Solutions
N.A.I.C.S.: 532490
John Nagel (VP-Ops-Global)
Tasha Castille (VP-Fin)

HB Rentals Limited (1)
Kirkwood Business Park, Sauchen, AB51 7LE, Aberdeenshire, United Kingdom
Tel.: (44) 1224772304
Web Site: http://www.hbrentals.com
Emp.: 35
Oil & Gas Exploration Services
N.A.I.C.S.: 213112

Hallin Marine Pte. Ltd. (1)
25 Loyang Crescent Blk 106 Tops Street 12, PO Box 5083, Loyang Offshore Supply Base, Singapore, 508988, Singapore
Tel.: (65) 460341
Web Site: http://www.hallin.com.sg
Sales Range: $75-99.9 Million
Emp.: 100
Underwater Services
N.A.I.C.S.: 213112

Hallin Marine Singapore Pte Ltd. (1)
25 Loyang Crescent Blk 106 Tops Street 12, Singapore, 508988, Singapore
Tel.: (65) 65460341
Subsea Machinery Mfr
N.A.I.C.S.: 333131

High Plains Disposal, Inc. (1)
9117 County Rd Dd, Idalia, CO 80735-9611
Tel.: (970) 354-7380
Waste Collection & Disposal Services
N.A.I.C.S.: 562119

Integrated Production Services (1)
16800 Greenspoint Park Dri Ste 200 S, Houston, TX 77060 (100%)
Tel.: (281) 774-6700
Web Site: http://ipsadvantage.com
Sales Range: $150-199.9 Million
Production Enhancement Services & Products for Oil & Gas Industry
N.A.I.C.S.: 213112

International Snubbing Services (1)
190 Industries Ln, Arnaudville, LA 70512
Tel.: (337) 754-7233
Web Site: https://www.iss-snub.com
Sales Range: $25-49.9 Million
Emp.: 50
Custom Built Well Control Equipment
N.A.I.C.S.: 333132

LEED Tool Corporation (1)
1352 Factory Dr, Fort Lupton, CO 80621
Tel.: (303) 857-0876
Web Site: http://www.leedenergy.com
Sales Range: $75-99.9 Million
Emp.: 60
Oil & Gas Field Services
N.A.I.C.S.: 213112

Northern Plains Trucking, LLC (1)
18302 Hwy 392, Greeley, CO 80631
Tel.: (303) 654-9206
Web Site: http://www.northernplains.us
Emp.: 300
Trucking Service
N.A.I.C.S.: 484122

Production Management Industries, Inc. (1)
1200 Youngs Rd, Morgan City, LA 70380 (100%)
Tel.: (985) 631-3837
Web Site: https://www.pmi.net
Sales Range: $25-49.9 Million
Emp.: 15
Oil & Gas Property Management, Fabrication & Construction Of Production Facilities
N.A.I.C.S.: 211120

Pumpco Energy Services, Inc. (1)
117 Elm Grove Rd, Valley View, TX 76272
Tel.: (940) 726-1800
Web Site: http://www.pumpcoservices.com
Sales Range: $100-124.9 Million
Emp.: 180
Oil & Gas Support Services
N.A.I.C.S.: 213112

SPN Well Services, Inc. (1)
3333 IH-35 N Bldg F, Gainesville, TX 76240-1910
Tel.: (940) 668-5100
Web Site: http://www.spnws.com
Drilling & Oilfield Services
N.A.I.C.S.: 213111

Servicios Petrotec de S.A. de C.V. (1)
Boulevard Hidalgo 1545 Interior 20 Col Simon Rodriguez Cd, Reynosa, 88670, Mexico
Tel.: (52) 8999703000
Web Site: http://www.petrotec.net
Sales Range: $25-49.9 Million
Emp.: 69
Oil & Gas Field Construction Services
N.A.I.C.S.: 237120

Stabil Drill (1)
110 Consolidate Dr, Lafayette, LA 70508
Tel.: (337) 837-3001
Web Site: http://www.stabildrill.com
Sales Range: $75-99.9 Million
Emp.: 99
Well Drilling Tool Rentals
N.A.I.C.S.: 213112
Deidre Toups (Pres)
Todd Boudreaux (VP-Sls & Mktg)

Stabil Drill Specialties, L.L.C. (1)
110 Consolidated Dr, Lafayette, LA 70508
Tel.: (337) 837-3001
Web Site: http://www.stabildrill.com
Drilling Tools Mfr
N.A.I.C.S.: 333517

Stabil Drill Specialties, L.L.C. (1)
110 Consolidated Dr, Lafayette, LA 70508
Tel.: (337) 837-3001
Web Site: https://www.stabildrill.com
Drilling Tool Mfr & Distr
N.A.I.C.S.: 333517

Sub Surface Tools, LLC (1)
101 Myrtle St, Morgan City, LA 70380
Tel.: (985) 384-4425
Web Site: http://www.subsurface.com
Sales Range: $100-124.9 Million
Emp.: 50
Full Service Tool Rental
N.A.I.C.S.: 532490

Superior Energy Services (1)
1001 Louisiana St Ste 2900, Houston, TX 77002
Tel.: (713) 654-2200
Web Site: https://www.superiorenergy.com
Sales Range: $25-49.9 Million
Emp.: 75
Cementing & Pressure Pumping Services
N.A.I.C.S.: 213112
Terence E. Hall (Chm)

Superior Energy Services (Australia) Pty. Ltd. (1)
6-10 Hunt Place, Wurruk, Sale, 3850, VIC, Australia
Tel.: (61) 351432225
Web Site: https://www.superiorenergy.com.au
Emp.: 60
Oil & Gas Field Equipment Mfr
N.A.I.C.S.: 333132
Peter Jellis (Mgr-Engrg & Svcs)
Kranstan Bradley (Mgr-HSE)

Superior Energy Services (SPN) B.V. (1)
Karel Doormanstraat 4, Emmen, Netherlands
Tel.: (31) 591667687
Web Site: https://bpc.nl
Oil & Gas Field Services
N.A.I.C.S.: 213111

Superior Energy Services do Brasil (1)
Rua Joaquim Pinheiro 429, Macae, Rio de Janeiro, 22743-660, Brazil
Tel.: (55) 995849085
Oil & Gas Exploration Services
N.A.I.C.S.: 213111

Superior-Wild Well Energy Services Limited (1)
Unit 2 Dyce Avenue, Aberdeen, AB21 0LQ, United Kingdom
Tel.: (44) 1224215380
Emp.: 10
Oil & Gas Engineering Services
N.A.I.C.S.: 541330
Barry Moir (Mng Dir)

Warrior Energy Services Corporation (1)
100 Rosecrest Ln, Columbus, MS 39701
Tel.: (662) 329-1047
Web Site: http://www.warriorenergyservices.com
Sales Range: $50-74.9 Million
Emp.: 500
Oil & Gas Services
N.A.I.C.S.: 213112
Sam Hardy (Pres)

Wild Well Control, Inc. (1)
Drilling Tech Ctr 2202 Oil Ctr Ct, Houston, TX 77073
Tel.: (281) 784-4700
Web Site: https://www.wildwell.com
Sales Range: $150-199.9 Million
Emp.: 300
Firefighting, Well Control Engineering & Training Services
N.A.I.C.S.: 213112
Bryan Ellis (Pres)
Joe Dean Thompson (COO)
Larry Sims (Sr VP-Intl & Sls Ops)
David Moody (Sr VP-Well Control Ops)

Workstrings International Limited (1)
Kirkton Avenue, Dyce, Aberdeen, AB21 0BF, United Kingdom
Tel.: (44) 1224724900
Web Site: http://www.workstringsinternational.com
Sales Range: $25-49.9 Million
Emp.: 50
Oilfield Equipment Rental Providers
N.A.I.C.S.: 333131

Workstrings International, L.L.C. (1)
1150 Smede Hwy, Broussard, LA 70518
Tel.: (337) 989-9675
Web Site: http://www.workstringsinternational.com
Emp.: 50
Drill Pipe Rental Services
N.A.I.C.S.: 532490

Workstrings, LLC (1)
1150 Smede Hwy, Broussard, LA 70518
Tel.: (337) 989-9675
Web Site: http://www.workstrings.com
Sales Range: $10-24.9 Million
Emp.: 52
Drill Pipe Equipment Rental
N.A.I.C.S.: 532490

SUPERIOR EQUIPMENT SALES INC.
808 Live Oak Dr, Chesapeake, VA 23320
Tel.: (757) 420-4253
Web Site: http://www.seshvac.com
Sales Range: $10-24.9 Million
Emp.: 40
Air Conditioning & Heating & Ventilation & Duct Work Contractor
N.A.I.C.S.: 423730
Sherman Reece (Chm & CEO)
Anita Woods (Mgr-Pur)
Bill Arnold (Mgr-IS)
Mick Healey (CEO)

SUPERIOR EQUIPMENT SOLUTIONS

Superior Equipment Solutions—(Continued)

7039 E Slauson Blvd, Commerce, CA 90040
Tel.: (323) 722-7900
Sales Range: $50-74.9 Million
Emp.: 200
Holding Company; Automotion Equipment
N.A.I.C.S.: 551112
Stephen Bernstein (CEO)
Jeff Bernstein (CFO)

Subsidiaries:

Adamation (1)
7039 E Slauson Blvd, Commerce, CA 90040
Tel.: (888) 383-8800
Web Site: http://www.adamationinc.com
Sales Range: $10-24.9 Million
Emp.: 25
Food Conveyors, Commercial Dishwashers & Silver Burnishers Mfr
N.A.I.C.S.: 449210

SUPERIOR FABRICATION, INC.

1654 S County Rd 200 W, Rockport, IN 47635
Tel.: (812) 649-2630 KY
Web Site: http://www.sfabinc.com
Year Founded: 1997
Sales Range: $1-9.9 Million
Fabricated Structural Metal Mfr
N.A.I.C.S.: 332312
Curtis L. Drake (Owner & Ops Mgr)

SUPERIOR FABRICS, INC.

1571 N Powerline Rd, Pompano Beach, FL 33069-1698
Tel.: (954) 975-8122
Web Site: http://www.superiorfabrics.com
Sales Range: $10-24.9 Million
Emp.: 175
Broadwoven Fabric Mfr
N.A.I.C.S.: 313210
Robert Fryburg (Pres)

SUPERIOR FELT & FILTRATION LLC

1150 Ridgeview Dr, Mchenry, IL 60050
Tel.: (815) 759-1234
Web Site: http://www.superiorfelt.com
Year Founded: 1978
Sales Range: $10-24.9 Million
Emp.: 75
Mfr of Media for the Filtration, Glass Fibers & Nonwoven/Nonfiltration Industries
N.A.I.C.S.: 424990
Tom Leieberg (CFO)
Bill Walthall (Mgr-Customer Svc)
Ralph Klein (Mgr-Quality Assurance)
Matt Cox (Mgr-Sls-Spartanburg)
Frank Porto (Dir-Sls)
James Allan (Mgr-Sls)

SUPERIOR FOODS COMPANY INC.

4243 Broadmoor SE, Kentwood, MI 49512-3934
Tel.: (616) 698-7700 MI
Web Site: http://www.superior-foods.com
Year Founded: 1997
Sales Range: $10-24.9 Million
Emp.: 105
Supplier of Packaged Frozen Goods
N.A.I.C.S.: 424470
James Osterhaven (Pres & CFO)
Paul Osterhaven (VP)
John Barr (Controller)
Ken Kollar (Mgr-Ops)

SUPERIOR FORGE & STEEL CORPORATION

1820 McClain Rd, Lima, OH 45804
Tel.: (419) 222-4412
Web Site: http://www.sfsrolls.com
Year Founded: 1991
Forged Steel Mfr
N.A.I.C.S.: 332111

Subsidiaries:

Superior Forge & Steel Corporation - New Castle (1)
597 Commerce Ave, New Castle, PA 16101 (100%)
Tel.: (724) 658-6575
Sales Range: $50-74.9 Million
Emp.: 50
Mfr of Fabricated Pipe Fittings, Steel Rolls; Aluminum Rolling Mills
N.A.I.C.S.: 332111

SUPERIOR FREIGHT SERVICES INC.

1230 Trapp Rd, Saint Paul, MN 55121-1217
Tel.: (952) 854-5053
Web Site: http://www.supfrt.com
Year Founded: 1992
Foreign Freight Forwarding
N.A.I.C.S.: 488510
David Stark (CEO)
Brian O'Donnell (Exec VP)

SUPERIOR FUEL COMPANY

5102 S Cant Rd, Duluth, MN 55804
Tel.: (218) 722-2050 WI
Web Site: http://superiorfuelcompany.com
Year Founded: 2006
Propane & Heating Oil Dealer
N.A.I.C.S.: 457210
Ryan Scott Gunderson (Pres & CEO)
Joe Stariha (CFO)
Randy Kolanczyk (Controller)
Joe Benson (Mktg Mgr)
Cody Jones (Sls Mgr)
Taylor Vichorek (Ops Mgr)

SUPERIOR FUELS, INC.

208 E Washington, Newton, IL 62448
Tel.: (618) 783-8714 IL
Web Site: http://www.superiorlp.com
Year Founded: 1980
Sales Range: $25-49.9 Million
Fuel Distr & Sales
N.A.I.C.S.: 424710
Jerry L. McDaniel (Pres)

SUPERIOR GRAPHITE CO.

10 S Riverside Plz Ste 1470, Chicago, IL 60606-3830
Tel.: (312) 559-2999 IL
Web Site: http://www.superiorgraphite.com
Year Founded: 1917
Sales Range: $75-99.9 Million
Emp.: 280
Ground, Pulverized, Refined or Blended Natural Graphite, Advanced Ceramic Materials, Lubricants, Graphite Electrodes, Petroleum Coke
N.A.I.C.S.: 327992
Peter Roy Carney (Chm)
Edward O. Carney (Pres & CEO)
Carsten Wehling (Exec VP-Innovation & R&D)
Frank Rembs (Exec VP-Demand Chain)

Subsidiaries:

Superior Graphite Europe, Ltd. (1)
Stockviksverken 20, Sundsvall, 854 67, Sweden (100%)
Tel.: (46) 60134118
Web Site: http://www.superiorgraphite.com
Sales Range: $25-49.9 Million
Emp.: 40
Mfr & Retailer of Desulfurized Petroleum Coke
N.A.I.C.S.: 324110
Ronald G. Pawelko (Mgr-Fin)
Edward Carney (CEO)

SUPERIOR GROUP

740 Waterman Ave, Columbus, OH 43215
Tel.: (614) 488-8035
Web Site: http://www.superiorgroup.net
Sales Range: $10-24.9 Million
Emp.: 180
Electronic Services
N.A.I.C.S.: 238210
Greg Stewart (CEO)
Bryan Stewart (Pres)
Bob Shonkwiler (VP)
Rich Hartman (VP-Enterprise Svcs)

SUPERIOR GROUP, INC.

1 Tower Bridge 100 Front St Ste 525, West Conshohocken, PA 19428
Tel.: (610) 397-2040 PA
Web Site: http://www.superior-group.com
Year Founded: 1981
Sales Range: $75-99.9 Million
Emp.: 6
Mfr & Distributor of Fabricated Metal Products
N.A.I.C.S.: 423510
John Morrash (CFO)
Shion Hung (Global Dir-Customer Programs & Bus Intelligence-Superior Tube)
Kris Narasimhan (Mgr-Nuclear Product-Superior Tube)
William G. Warden IV (Vice Chm & CEO)

Subsidiaries:

Fine Tubes Limited (1)
Plymbridge Rd, Estover, Plymouth, PL6 7LG, Devon, United Kingdom
Tel.: (44) 1752735851
Web Site: https://www.finetubes.co.uk
Precision Tube Mfr
N.A.I.C.S.: 331210

SUPERIOR GUNITE INCORPORATED

12306 Van Nuys Blvd, Sylmar, CA 91342
Tel.: (818) 896-9199
Web Site: http://www.shotcrete.com
Rev: $20,000,000
Emp.: 150
Gunite Contractor
N.A.I.C.S.: 238990
Anthony M. Federico (Pres)
Dave Bowers (Controller)
Kalo Franklin (Project Coord)
Len Nicholls (Mgr)

SUPERIOR HOLDING CORP

2201 Pinnacle Pkwy, Twinsburg, OH 44087-2367
Tel.: (440) 248-8660
Rev: $13,500,000
Emp.: 2
Funeral Director's Equipment & Supplies
N.A.I.C.S.: 423850

SUPERIOR HONDA OF OMAHA

4111 S 144th St, Omaha, NE 68137
Tel.: (402) 408-1000
Web Site: http://www.hondaofomaha.com
Year Founded: 1983
Sales Range: $10-24.9 Million
Emp.: 70
Car Dealership
N.A.I.C.S.: 441110
Rodney D. Rhoden (Pres)
Kevin Woodard (Gen Mgr)
John Mendel (Exec VP)

SUPERIOR INDUSTRIES, INC.

315 E Hwy 28, Morris, MN 56267
Tel.: (320) 589-2406
Web Site: http://www.superior-ind.com
Industrial Machinery Mfr
N.A.I.C.S.: 333922
Bob Dominick (CEO)

SUPERIOR INTERNET SOLUTIONS

1754 Star Crest Pl, San Marcos, CA 92078-0910
Tel.: (619) 955-6799
Web Site: http://www.superiorroi.com
Sales Range: $10-24.9 Million
Emp.: 50
Internet Marketing Services
N.A.I.C.S.: 541613
Tom Otto (Mgr-Sls)

SUPERIOR IRON WORKS INC.

45034 Underwood Ln, Sterling, VA 20166
Tel.: (703) 471-5500
Web Site: http://www.superirironworks.com
Year Founded: 1968
Rev: $11,400,000
Emp.: 75
Fabricated Structural Metal
N.A.I.C.S.: 332312
Michael Kane (Pres)
Evan Bolthouse (Project Mgr)
Robert Bodmer (VP-Field Ops)
Teddy Long (VP-Production)

SUPERIOR LINEN SERVICE INC.

6959 E 12th St, Tulsa, OK 74112
Tel.: (918) 835-3777
Web Site: http://www.superlinen.com
Sales Range: $10-24.9 Million
Emp.: 350
Linen Supply
N.A.I.C.S.: 812331
Doug Waldman (Pres)
Brandon Scantlen (Mgr-Fort Smith)
Crystal Warner (Dir-Health Client Svcs)
Ronny Luthi (Mgr-Svcs)
Jarrad Shields (VP-Eastern Div)
Jeff Harrison (Dir-Client Svcs)
Sarah Canady (Mgr-Credit)
J. Little (COO)
Ashley Tosh (Dir-Mktg & Comm)
Bill Childs (Dir-Fleet & Logistics)
Kevin English (Dir-Bus Dev)
Russell Holt (Officer-Compliance)

SUPERIOR LOGISTICS SOLUTIONS LLC

1520 S Lapeer Rd Ste 220, Lake Orion, MI 48360
Tel.: (248) 690-7819 MI
Web Site: http://www.gosls.com
Year Founded: 2009
Sales Range: $10-24.9 Million
Emp.: 20
Freight Shipping Services
N.A.I.C.S.: 488510
Roger Gumz (Principal)

SUPERIOR LUBRICANTS COMPANY

32 Ward Rd, North Tonawanda, NY 14120
Tel.: (716) 693-6050
Web Site: http://www.superiorlubricants.com
Sales Range: $75-99.9 Million

Emp.: 75
Lubricating Oils & Greases
N.A.I.C.S.: 424720
Michael G. Anczok (Pres)
Brian Carney (VP-Ops)

SUPERIOR MATERIALS, INC.
585 Stewart Ave Ste 710, Garden City, NY 11530
Tel.: (516) 222-1010
Web Site: http://www.supmat.com
Year Founded: 1946
Rev.: $10,000,000
Emp.: 17
Distr of Industrial Chemicals
N.A.I.C.S.: 424690
Steven M. Kafka (Pres)
Theodore M. Budman (Exec VP)
David G. Kafka (Dir-Info Svcs & Mgr-Sls)

SUPERIOR MECHANICAL SYSTEMS, INC.
6482 Park Blvd, Pinellas Park, FL 33781
Tel.: (727) 548-1711 FL
Web Site: http://www.superiormechanical.net
Year Founded: 1994
Sales Range: $1-9.9 Million
Emp.: 40
Plumbing, Heating & Air-Conditioning Contractor
N.A.I.C.S.: 238220
Raul Perera (Pres)
Clinton Dulin (Treas & Project Mgr)
Thomas Stone (Sec & Project Mgr)
Gwen Hendry (Project Mgr)
Christine Perera (Exec VP)
Ray Mark (Project Mgr)

SUPERIOR MEDIA SOLUTIONS LLC
1 Ashford Ct, Lincolnshire, IL 60069
Tel.: (847) 793-0643
Web Site: http://www.superiormediasolutions.net
Sales Range: $1-9.9 Million
Computer Software
N.A.I.C.S.: 513210
Bill Walker (CEO)
Brian Tyler (CFO)
Robert Brai (COO)
Sina Adibi (CTO)
Kathy J. Kuehling (Dir-Production Tech)
Jamie Kleist (Mgr-Production Tech)
John Marshall (VP-Sls)

SUPERIOR METAL PRODUCTS CO.
116 Citation Ct, Birmingham, AL 35209
Tel.: (205) 945-1200
Web Site: http://www.superiormetalproducts.com
Year Founded: 1978
Sales Range: $10-24.9 Million
Emp.: 60
Aluminum Bars, Rods, Ingots, Sheets, Pipes & Plates Mfr
N.A.I.C.S.: 423510

SUPERIOR MIDSTREAM, LLC
8200 S Unit Dr, Tulsa, OK 74132
Tel.: (918) 382-7200 OK
Web Site: http://www.superiorpipeline.com
Year Founded: 1996
Sales Range: $150-199.9 Million
Emp.: 126
Natural Gas Gathering, Processing & Treatment
N.A.I.C.S.: 211130

Kevin Koerner (VP-Ops)
Ed Alexander (VP-Acctg & Admin)
Bill Ward (Pres & CEO)
Jim Leathers (VP-Comml Activity)
Jamey Langston (Mgr-Land-ROW)
David Hodges (Mgr-Gas Supply)
Tania Wilson (Mgr-Gas Acctg)
Patrick Ohlson (Dir-Fin Acctg)
Rob Koch (Mgr-Product Mktg)

SUPERIOR MOTORS INC.
835 5th Chop Rd, Orangeburg, SC 29115
Tel.: (803) 534-1123
Web Site: http://www.superiormotors.com
Sales Range: $25-49.9 Million
Emp.: 49
Automobiles, New & Used
N.A.I.C.S.: 441110
James M. Guthrie (Owner)
Kim Baker (Office Mgr)
Paul Magil (Controller)

SUPERIOR NATIONAL BANK & TRUST COMPANY
235 Quincy St, Hancock, MI 49930
Tel.: (906) 482-0404 MI
Web Site: http://www.snb-t.com
Year Founded: 1890
Sales Range: $10-24.9 Million
Emp.: 140
Banking Services
N.A.I.C.S.: 522110
Steven Palosaari (Exec VP)
J. David Vlahos (Pres & CEO)
Laurie Panian (VP-HR & Mktg)

SUPERIOR NATURAL GAS CORP.
1100 Louisiana St Ste 350, Houston, TX 77002
Tel.: (713) 759-6900
Web Site: http://www.superiornatgas.com
Year Founded: 1988
Sales Range: $10-24.9 Million
Emp.: 20
Natural Gas Transmission Services
N.A.I.C.S.: 486210
John W. Croft (Founder & Pres)
Mark C. Snapp (VP)

Subsidiaries:

Superior Processing Service Corporation (1)
1100 Louisiana St Ste 350, Houston, TX 77002-5258
Tel.: (713) 759-6900
Web Site: http://www.superiornatgas.com
Provider of Crude Petroleum & Natural Gas
N.A.I.C.S.: 211120
John W. Croft (Pres)

SUPERIOR NUT AND CANDY CO.
1111 W 40th St, Chicago, IL 60609
Tel.: (773) 254-7900
Web Site: http://www.superiornutandcandy.com
Sales Range: $10-24.9 Million
Emp.: 50
Nut & Candy Distr
N.A.I.C.S.: 424450
Anthony Mastrangelo (Pres)

SUPERIOR OIL CO., INC.
1402 N Capitol Ave Ste 100, Indianapolis, IN 46202
Tel.: (317) 781-4400 IN
Web Site: http://www.superioroil.com
Year Founded: 1932
Sales Range: $150-199.9 Million
Emp.: 240
Distr of Solvents & Chemicals

N.A.I.C.S.: 424690

Subsidiaries:

Superior Oil Co., Inc. - Cincinnati Plant (1)
320 Northpointe Dr, Fairfield, OH 45014
Tel.: (513) 870-9271
Chemical Products Mfr
N.A.I.C.S.: 325998
Ken Smith (Mgr-Sls)

Superior Oil Co., Inc. - Cowpens Plant (1)
5920 N Main St, Cowpens, SC 29330
Tel.: (864) 463-6441
Web Site: http://www.superioroilcompany.com
Emp.: 7
Chemical Products Mfr
N.A.I.C.S.: 325998
Jayson Blanton (Mgr-Sls)

Superior Oil Co., Inc. - Effingham Plant (1)
1901 W Evergreen Ste C, Effingham, IL 62401
Tel.: (217) 342-4390
Web Site: http://www.superioroil.com
Emp.: 5
Chemical Products Mfr
N.A.I.C.S.: 325998
Tom Edwards (Mgr-Sls)

Superior Oil Co., Inc. - Elkhart Plant (1)
1030 All Pro Dr, Elkhart, IN 46514
Tel.: (574) 264-0161
Web Site: http://www.superioroil.com
Emp.: 20
Chemical Products Mfr
N.A.I.C.S.: 325998
Steve McIlwain (Gen Mgr)

Superior Oil Co., Inc. - Indianapolis Plant (1)
400 W Regent St, Indianapolis, IN 46225
Tel.: (317) 781-4490
Web Site: http://www.superioroil.com
Emp.: 70
Chemical Products Mfr
N.A.I.C.S.: 325998
Michael Sullivan (Mgr-Sls)

Superior Oil Co., Inc. - Louisville Plant (1)
4211 Bramers Ln, Louisville, KY 40216
Tel.: (502) 449-1184
Emp.: 20
Chemical Products Mfr
N.A.I.C.S.: 325998
Wade Childress (Mgr-Sls)

Superior Oil Co., Inc. - Nashville Plant (1)
518 Swinging Bridge Rd, Old Hickory, TN 37138
Tel.: (615) 357-0336
Web Site: http://www.superioroil.com
Chemical Products Mfr
N.A.I.C.S.: 325998
Scott Bridges (Mgr-Sls)

Superior Oil Co., Inc. - Springfield Plant (1)
2055 E Blaine, Springfield, MO 65803
Tel.: (417) 862-6245
Web Site: http://www.superioroil.com
Emp.: 12
Chemical Products Mfr
N.A.I.C.S.: 325998
Dennis Parker (Gen Mgr)

Superior Oil Co., Inc. - St. Louis Plant (1)
3023 Arnold Tenbrook Rd, Arnold, MO 63010
Tel.: (636) 287-3600
Chemical Products Mfr
N.A.I.C.S.: 325998

SUPERIOR PACKAGING INC.
565 Broadhollow Rd Ste 5, Farmingdale, NY 11735-4826
Tel.: (631) 249-5500
Web Site: http://www.superiorpackaging.com
Rev.: $13,600,000

Emp.: 5
Plastics Bag Mfr
N.A.I.C.S.: 326111
Robert J. Lovett (Pres)

SUPERIOR PACKAGING INC.
355 E Campus View Blvd Ste 165, Columbus, OH 43235
Tel.: (614) 436-5630
Web Site: http://www.superiorpkg.com
Year Founded: 1975
Sales Range: $10-24.9 Million
Emp.: 10
Packing & Crating Products Sales
N.A.I.C.S.: 488991
Douglas Dye (Pres)

SUPERIOR PACKAGING SOLUTIONS
26858 Almond Ave, Redlands, CA 92374
Tel.: (951) 361-2838 CA
Web Site: http://www.sps4pkg.com
Year Founded: 2004
Sales Range: $10-24.9 Million
Emp.: 18
Paperboard Mills
N.A.I.C.S.: 322130
Richard Resendez (Owner)

SUPERIOR PETROLEUM COMPANY
865 N Superior Dr, Crown Point, IN 46307
Tel.: (800) 700-6457
Web Site: http://www.superiorpetroleum.com
Year Founded: 1994
Sales Range: $200-249.9 Million
Emp.: 402
Gasoline Distribution Services
N.A.I.C.S.: 424710
Milo C. Ritton (Owner & Pres)

SUPERIOR POOLS OF SOUTHWEST FLORIDA INC.
517 Tamiami Trl, Port Charlotte, FL 33953
Tel.: (941) 743-7171
Web Site: http://www.superiorpoolsswfl.net
Year Founded: 2001
Sales Range: $1-9.9 Million
Emp.: 15
Swimming Pools & Spas Contractor
N.A.I.C.S.: 238990
Bill Krawczyk (Pres)
Jon Krawczyk (Gen Mgr)
Josh Kline (Mgr-Field)

SUPERIOR PRESS, INC.
11930 Hamden Pl, Santa Fe Springs, CA 90670
Web Site: http://www.superior-press.com
Sales Range: $10-24.9 Million
Emp.: 94
Press Equipment Services
N.A.I.C.S.: 323120
Ryan Stidfole (Dir-Sls-Remote Cash Capture)
Steve Traut (Sr VP-Sls)
Kevin Traut (Pres & COO)
Brian Dinges (Mgr-Remote Cash Capture Implementation & Technical Support)
Colin Holden (Dir-Tech Solutions)

SUPERIOR PRINT & EXHIBIT, INC.
7636 Miramar Rd Ste 1400, San Diego, CA 92126-4247
Tel.: (858) 271-7446
Web Site: http://www.superiorprintandexhibit.com
Year Founded: 2012

SUPERIOR PRINT & EXHIBIT, INC.

U.S. PRIVATE

Superior Print & Exhibit, Inc.—(Continued)
Sales Range: $1-9.9 Million
Emp.: 5
Commercial Printing Services
N.A.I.C.S.: 323111
Robert Zievers *(Project Mgr & Project Coord)*

SUPERIOR PRINTING INK COMPANY INCORPORATED
100 N St, Teterboro, NJ 07608
Tel.: (201) 478-5600
Web Site: http://www.superiorink.com
Sales Range: $50-74.9 Million
Emp.: 350
Printing Ink
N.A.I.C.S.: 325910
Jeffrey Simons *(CEO & Owner)*
Peter Nunez *(VP-Fin & Admin)*

SUPERIOR PRODUCTION LLC
2301 Fairwood Ave, Columbus, OH 43207-2709
Tel.: (614) 444-2181 OH
Web Site: http://www.superior-dietool.com
Sales Range: $25-49.9 Million
Emp.: 250
Industrial Die, Tool & Metal Stamping Mfr
N.A.I.C.S.: 333514
Richard W. Holstein *(Owner & Pres)*
Jim Britt *(Mgr-Sls & Mktg)*
Michele Hager *(Mgr-HR)*
Paul Hook *(Gen Mgr)*
Jim Fisher *(Dir-Quality)*
Fred Hoyle *(Dir-Engrg)*
Jan Vanderlinden *(Mgr-Engrg Program)*
Jim Middleton *(Mgr-Engrg Program)*
Buddy Minnard *(Coord-Production)*

Subsidiaries:

Superior Production LLC - Stamping Division (1)
1405 Marion Rd, Columbus, OH 43207
Tel.: (614) 443-5244
Web Site: http://www.superior-dietool.com
Metal Stamping Services
N.A.I.C.S.: 332119
Tony Stockton *(Mgr-Mfg)*
Bill Middleton *(Coord-Production)*
Fred Hoyle *(Dir-Engrg)*
Jim Fisher *(Dir-Quality)*
Michele Hager *(Mgr-HR)*
Paul Hook *(Gen Mgr)*
Mike McKeivier *(CFO)*
Jim Middleton *(Mgr-Engrg Program)*
Buddy Minnard *(Coord-Production)*
Jan Vanderlinden *(Mgr-Engrg Program)*

SUPERIOR PRODUCTS DISTRIBUTORS INC.
1403 Meriden-Waterbury Rd, Milldale, CT 06467
Tel.: (860) 621-3621 CT
Web Site: http://www.spdionline.com
Year Founded: 1967
Sales Range: $125-149.9 Million
Emp.: 141
Distr of Plumbing Fixtures, Equipment & Supplies; Pipes & Fittings; Concrete Building Products
N.A.I.C.S.: 423720
Mike Picco *(CFO)*
Dennis Crispino *(Sec & VP)*
Ralph Crispino Jr. *(Pres & Treas)*

Subsidiaries:

Events By Superior (1)
20 Putnam Pl, Cheshire, CT 06410
Tel.: (203) 250-6600
Web Site: http://www.eventsbysuperior.com
Party Planning Services
N.A.I.C.S.: 812990
Kathleen Crispino *(Gen Mgr)*

Rex Precast Systems, Inc. (1)
210 Realty Dr, Cheshire, CT 06410
Tel.: (203) 250-6700
Web Site: http://www.rexprecast.com
Concrete Products Mfr
N.A.I.C.S.: 327390

Superior East, Inc. (1)
251 W Thames St Rte 32, Norwich, CT 06360
Tel.: (860) 886-9997
Web Site: http://www.superioreast.com
Emp.: 7
Industrial Supplies Whslr
N.A.I.C.S.: 423840
Brian Violette *(Mgr)*

SUPERIOR PRODUCTS, LLC.
3786 Rdg Rd, Cleveland, OH 44144
Tel.: (216) 651-9400
Web Site: http://www.superiorprod.com
Year Founded: 1946
Sales Range: $10-24.9 Million
Emp.: 80
Precision Turned Product Mfr
N.A.I.C.S.: 332721
Greg Gens *(Exec VP)*
Iain Hodgekins *(Gen Mgr)*

SUPERIOR READY MIX CONCRETE LP
1508 Mission Rd, Escondido, CA 92029-1105
Tel.: (760) 745-0556 CA
Web Site: http://www.superiorrm.com
Year Founded: 1946
Sales Range: $75-99.9 Million
Emp.: 1,200
Central-Mixed Concrete
N.A.I.C.S.: 327320
Jacob Brouwer *(Owner)*
Arnie Veldkamp *(Pres)*

Subsidiaries:

Superior Ready Mix Concrete LP - Aguanga Plant (1)
41690 Hwy 79, Aguanga, CA 92536
Tel.: (951) 277-3553
Readymix Concrete Mfr
N.A.I.C.S.: 327320

Superior Ready Mix Concrete LP - Carroll Canyon Plant (1)
9245 Camino Santa Fe, San Diego, CA 92121
Tel.: (858) 695-0666
Readymix Concrete Mfr
N.A.I.C.S.: 327320

Superior Ready Mix Concrete LP - Coachella Plant (1)
Tyler St 54th Ave, Coachella, CA 92274
Tel.: (760) 343-3418
Readymix Concrete Mfr
N.A.I.C.S.: 327320

Superior Ready Mix Concrete LP - El Centro Plant (1)
802 E Main St, El Centro, CA 92243
Tel.: (760) 352-4341
Readymix Concrete Mfr
N.A.I.C.S.: 327320

Superior Ready Mix Concrete LP - Fallbrook Plant (1)
1508 W Mission Rd, Escondido, CA 92029
Tel.: (760) 745-0556
Web Site: http://www.superiorrm.com
Emp.: 100
Readymix Concrete Mfr
N.A.I.C.S.: 327320
Chris Brouwer *(Mgr-Sls)*

Superior Ready Mix Concrete LP - Hemet (BCC) Plant (1)
1315 N State St, Hemet, CA 92546
Tel.: (951) 658-1562
Readymix Concrete Mfr
N.A.I.C.S.: 327320

Superior Ready Mix Concrete LP - Oceanside Plant (1)
3227 Oceanside Blvd, Oceanside, CA 91720

Tel.: (760) 745-0556
Web Site: http://www.superiorrm.com
Emp.: 100
Readymix Concrete Mfr
N.A.I.C.S.: 327320
Jack Brouwer *(Pres)*

Superior Ready Mix Concrete LP - Ramona Plant (1)
940 Olive St, Ramona, CA 92065
Tel.: (760) 789-1180
Readymix Concrete Mfr
N.A.I.C.S.: 327320

Superior Ready Mix Concrete LP - Southland Plant (1)
12117 Industry Rd, Lakeside, CA 92040
Tel.: (619) 443-7510
Readymix Concrete Mfr
N.A.I.C.S.: 327320

SUPERIOR ROLL FORMING CO., INC.
5535 Wegman Dr, Valley City, OH 44280
Tel.: (330) 225-2500
Web Site: http://www.gosrf.com
Sales Range: $10-24.9 Million
Emp.: 100
Miscellaneous Metalwork
N.A.I.C.S.: 332322
Timothy M. Synk *(Owner)*
Theresa Laheta *(Mgr-HR)*
Anthony Griggs *(Supvr-NTI Production)*

SUPERIOR SEWING MACHINE & SUPPLY LLC
48 W 25th St, New York, NY 10010
Tel.: (212) 691-3400
Web Site: http://www.supsew.com
Sales Range: $10-24.9 Million
Emp.: 60
Industrial Machinery & Equipment
N.A.I.C.S.: 423830
Lonny Schwartz *(Pres)*
Marcus Daniels *(Dir-IT)*
Jim Spaight *(Coord-Shipping)*
Puina Hon *(Controller)*

SUPERIOR STEEL INC.
10863 N Dual St, Baton Rouge, LA 70814
Tel.: (225) 275-7040
Web Site: http://www.superiorsteelinc.com
Sales Range: $25-49.9 Million
Emp.: 80
Fabricated Structural Metal
N.A.I.C.S.: 332312
Larry Questad *(Pres)*

SUPERIOR SUPPLY & STEEL
318 N Cities Svc Hwy, Sulphur, LA 70663
Tel.: (337) 625-2300
Web Site: http://www.supstl.com
Sales Range: $50-74.9 Million
Emp.: 200
Mfr of Industrial Supplies
N.A.I.C.S.: 423840
Steve Mitchell *(Pres)*
Joey Giametta *(Mgr-Acct)*
Zack Sprayberry *(Mgr-Acctg)*
Charlotte Labauve *(Mgr-Pur)*
Wayne Lebert *(Exec VP)*
Jada Cannon *(Mgr-Credit)*
Linda Shilling *(Mgr-Customer Svc)*
Bill Kotcher *(VP-Fittings Div)*
John Kernick *(Mgr-Mktg)*

SUPERIOR SUPPORT RESOURCES, INC.
405 N Calhoun Rd 3200, Brookfield, WI 53005
Tel.: (262) 784-9772 WI
Web Site: http://www.ssr-online.com
Year Founded: 1974

Sales Range: $10-24.9 Million
Emp.: 25
Information Technology Solutions & Consulting Services
N.A.I.C.S.: 541512
Sarit Singhal *(Pres)*
Scott Brys *(CTO & VP)*
Jordan Mendelblatt *(Engr-Sys)*
Rob Neijenhuis *(Engr-Sys)*
Rebecca Hitchcock *(Acct Exec)*

SUPERIOR TANK CO., INC.
9500 Lucas Ranch Rd, Rancho Cucamonga, CA 91730
Tel.: (909) 912-0580 CA
Web Site: http://www.superiortank.com
Rev.: $15,742,756
Emp.: 85
Fuel Tank Mfr
N.A.I.C.S.: 332420
James Marquez *(Pres)*

SUPERIOR TECHNOLOGY CORP
Lacey Pl, Southport, CT 06890-1241
Tel.: (203) 255-1501
Web Site: http://www.superiorplatingco.biz
Rev.: $11,010,340
Emp.: 30
Electroplating Services
N.A.I.C.S.: 332813
Jim Westwood *(CFO)*

SUPERIOR TIRE SERVICE INC.
4230 27th Ct SE, Salem, OR 97302
Tel.: (503) 585-1955
Web Site: http://www.ststires.com
Sales Range: $10-24.9 Million
Emp.: 95
Automobile Tires Sales & Services
N.A.I.C.S.: 423130
Greg Taylor *(Mgr-Store)*

SUPERIOR TOOL CORPORATION
2233 W 110th St, Cleveland, OH 44102
Tel.: (216) 398-8600 OH
Web Site: http://www.superiortool.com
Year Founded: 1946
Sales Range: $10-24.9 Million
Emp.: 100
Plumbing Hand Tools Mfr & Distr
N.A.I.C.S.: 332216
Jeff White *(Sec)*
Annette Dockus *(VP-Ops)*

SUPERIOR TRIM & DOOR, INC.
2840 W Orange Ave, Apopka, FL 32703
Tel.: (407) 598-1100
Rev.: $23,608,335
Emp.: 120
Doors & Architectural Building Trims & Moldings; Hardware Whslr
N.A.I.C.S.: 321911
David R. Buzzella *(VP & Gen Mgr)*
Linda Hoffan *(Controller & Dir-Acctg)*
Keith B. Lemieus *(Owner & Pres)*

SUPERIOR TRUSS SYSTEMS, LLC.
101 Industrial St, Belle Fourche, SD 57717-1026
Tel.: (605) 723-1300
Year Founded: 2002
Sales Range: $10-24.9 Million
Emp.: 5
Truss Mfr
N.A.I.C.S.: 321215

Merv Raisanen (Owner)

SUPERIOR VAN & MOBILITY, LLC.
1180 E New Cir Rd, Lexington, KY 40505
Tel.: (859) 253-1832
Web Site: http://www.superiorvan.com
Year Founded: 1976
Sales Range: $10-24.9 Million
Emp.: 40
Automotive Repair & Maintenance Services
N.A.I.C.S.: 811198
Charles Flickner (Gen Mgr)
Ed Carpenter (Dir-Corp HR)

SUPERIOR WASHER & GASKET CORP.
170 Adams Ave, Hauppauge, NY 11788
Tel.: (631) 273-8282
Web Site: http://www.superiorwasher.com
Sales Range: $10-24.9 Million
Emp.: 70
Washer & Gasket Mfr
N.A.I.C.S.: 332722
Richard Anderson (Dir-Quality Assurance)
Jack Cannizzaro (Mgr-Corp Sls)
Luann Racca (Asst Mgr-Sls)
Robert Bacharach (CTO)
Jason Garrick (Mgr-South Carolina)

SUPERIOR WASTE INDUSTRIES LLC
4650 N Harrison, Shawnee, OK 74804
Tel.: (405) 275-0900
Web Site: https://superiorusawaste.com
Emp.: 100
Holding Company
N.A.I.C.S.: 551112
Bill Dietrich (CEO)

Subsidiaries:

Central Disposal LLC (1)
700 E 45th St, Shawnee, OK 74804
Tel.: (405) 275-0900
Web Site: http://www.centraldisposalok.com
Emp.: 100
Waste Collection
N.A.I.C.S.: 562119
Mike Adcock (Chm & Partner)

Harley Hollan Companies, Inc. (1)
5677 S 107th E Ave, Tulsa, OK 74146
Tel.: (918) 317-7777
Web Site: http://www.317-7777.com
Nonhazardous Waste Treatment & Disposal
N.A.I.C.S.: 562219
Harley Hollan (Founder)

SUPERMARKET DISTRIBUTORS OF AMERICA
1626 Locust Ave Ste 6, Bohemia, NY 11716
Tel.: (631) 273-3900
Web Site: http://www.sdaccs.com
Sales Range: $10-24.9 Million
Emp.: 60
Drugs Whslr
N.A.I.C.S.: 424210
Terry Feinberg (VP)
Robert Nathanson (VP)

SUPERMARKET ENVIRONMENTAL SERVICES CO.
721A Park Center Dr, Kernersville, NC 27284
Tel.: (336) 996-2220
Web Site: http://www.trs-sesco.com
Rev.: $12,589,915
Emp.: 50

Warm Air Heating & Air Conditioning
N.A.I.C.S.: 423730
Patrick J. McNamara (Pres)
Phillip McNamara (VP & Gen Mgr)
Billy McCollough (Mgr-Svcs)
Jerry Watson (VP-Sls)

SUPERMARKET MANAGEMENT INC.
460 Niagara St Ste 1, Buffalo, NY 14201-1835
Tel.: (716) 853-5787
Year Founded: 1971
Sales Range: $100-124.9 Million
Emp.: 1,073
Provider of Grocery Store Services
N.A.I.C.S.: 445110
Phyllis Durkin (Office Mgr)

Subsidiaries:

Niagara-Lockport Enterprises Inc. (1)
460 Niagara St, Buffalo, NY 14201-1835
Tel.: (716) 853-5787
Sales Range: $25-49.9 Million
Emp.: 120
Provider of Grocery Store Services
N.A.I.C.S.: 445110

SUPERMARKET OPERATIONS INC.
116 Lowr Woodville Rd, Natchez, MS 39120-4472
Tel.: (601) 445-2095
Web Site: http://www.supermarketoperations.com
Year Founded: 1969
Sales Range: $25-49.9 Million
Emp.: 199
Provider of Grocery Services
N.A.I.C.S.: 445110
Mike Halley (Dir-Meat, Deli & Bakery)
Ricky Heffner (Mgr)
Ronnie Gamberi (Mgr)
Mark Nelson (Mgr)
David Taylor (Mgr)

SUPERMARKET SOURCE, INC.
2741 W 76th St, Hialeah, FL 33016
Tel.: (305) 827-4700
Web Site: http://www.supermarketsource.com
Year Founded: 2005
Sales Range: $1-9.9 Million
Emp.: 10
Store Shelving System Mfr & Distr
N.A.I.C.S.: 337215
Ray Pena (Pres)

SUPERMERCADO AGUEYBANA INC.
1 Calle EXT 25 De Julio, Guanica, PR 00653
Tel.: (787) 821-2552
Rev.: $11,576,592
Emp.: 41
Independent Supermarket
N.A.I.C.S.: 445110
Santos Ruiz Pietri (Pres)

SUPERMERCADO CONCHITA HATO REY
620 Ave Barbosa, San Juan, PR 00919
Tel.: (787) 751-7373
Rev.: $16,823,051
Emp.: 250
Supermarket
N.A.I.C.S.: 445110

SUPERMERCADO FACUNDO INC.
Ave Central Blvd 3rd Sta Villa Carolina, Carolina, PR 00985

Tel.: (787) 762-8605
Sales Range: $10-24.9 Million
Emp.: 230
Supermarket
N.A.I.C.S.: 445110
Facundo Colon (Pres)
Luis Martines (Controller)

SUPERMERCADO PLAZA GUAYAMA
Rd 3 Km 140 4, Guayama, PR 00784
Tel.: (787) 864-8252
Web Site: http://www.supermercadosplaza.com
Sales Range: $10-24.9 Million
Emp.: 190
Independent Supermarket
N.A.I.C.S.: 445110
Antonio Palau Martinez (Pres)
Antonio Palau (Gen Mgr)

SUPERMERCADOS DEL ESTE INC.
Ramal 9931 & RR 183, Las Piedras, PR 00754
Tel.: (787) 736-2929
Year Founded: 1987
Sales Range: $50-74.9 Million
Emp.: 240
Grocery Stores
N.A.I.C.S.: 457110
Rafael Soto (Pres)

SUPERMIX, INC.
4300 SW 74th Ave, Miami, FL 33155-7520
Tel.: (305) 262-3250
Web Site: http://www.supermix.com
Year Founded: 1976
Sales Range: $25-49.9 Million
Emp.: 230
Producer & Supplier of Ready-Mixed Concrete
N.A.I.C.S.: 327320
Tammy Suris (Controller)
Jose Cancio Sr. (Pres)

SUPERNOVA ENERGY, INC.
701 N Green Valley Pkwy Ste 200-258, Henderson, NV 89074
Tel.: (702) 335-0356
Year Founded: 2009
Sales Range: Less than $1 Million
Oil & Gas Exploration Services
N.A.I.C.S.: 211120
Kevin G. Malone (Pres, CEO, CFO & Sec)

SUPEROXYGEN, INC.
5037 Rosewood Ave Ste 207, Los Angeles, CA 90004
Tel.: (310) 948-1534
Web Site: http://www.superoxygen.com
Year Founded: 2002
Sales Range: $10-24.9 Million
Emp.: 10
Automotive, Brand Development, Broadcast, Consumer Marketing, Direct Marketing, Entertainment, Full Service, Print, Production, Radio
N.A.I.C.S.: 541810
Ray Campbell (Pres & Dir-Creative)

SUPERSONIC CAR WASH INC.
3851 Riverdale Rd, Ogden, UT 84405
Tel.: (801) 399-2434
Web Site: http://www.supersoniccarwash.com
Year Founded: 1959
Sales Range: $25-49.9 Million
Emp.: 375
Owner & Operator of Car Washes
N.A.I.C.S.: 811192

Dave Thornblad (Bus Mgr)
Shawn Ballard (Mgr-33rd South)
Jason Lewis (Mgr-Van Winkle)
Brandon Bishop (Mgr-Sandy)

Subsidiaries:

Supersonic Car Wash (1)
6500 S State St, Murray, UT 84107-7219
Tel.: (801) 268-9274
Web Site: http://www.supersonic1.com
Rev.: $1,300,000
Emp.: 47
Carwash
N.A.I.C.S.: 811192

SUPERSTITION CRUSHING LLC
3914 E Presidio St, Mesa, AZ 85215-1114
Tel.: (480) 962-5326
Year Founded: 1984
Sales Range: $25-49.9 Million
Emp.: 60
Construction Sand Mining
N.A.I.C.S.: 212321
Denny Dugger (Gen Mgr)

SUPERTEST OIL COMPANY INC.
205 S Hoover Blvd Ste 400, Tampa, FL 33609
Tel.: (813) 286-2323
Rev.: $32,300,000
Emp.: 11
Grocery Stores
N.A.I.C.S.: 445110
Shirley Carter (Pres)

Subsidiaries:

Imperial Oil Company Inc. (1)
205 S Hoover Blvd Ste 400, Tampa, FL 33609
Tel.: (813) 286-0032
Gases, Liquefied Petroleum (Propane)
N.A.I.C.S.: 424720
Shirley Carter (Pres)

Joy Food Stores Inc. (1)
205 S Hoover Blvd Ste 400, Tampa, FL 33609
Tel.: (813) 286-2323
Sales Range: $10-24.9 Million
Emp.: 12
Grocery Stores
N.A.I.C.S.: 445131
John Watson (Controller)

San Ann Oil Company (1)
205 S Hoover Blvd Ste 400, Tampa, FL 33609
Tel.: (813) 286-2323
Rev.: $1,300,000
Emp.: 5
Real Estate Managers
N.A.I.C.S.: 531210

SUPPES FORD
101 Main St, Johnstown, PA 15901
Tel.: (814) 535-5531
Web Site: http://www.suppesford.com
Sales Range: $10-24.9 Million
Emp.: 50
Car Whslr
N.A.I.C.S.: 441110
Courtney Droz (Gen Mgr)
Todd Euen (Controller)
Frank Arcurio (Gen Mgr-Sls)

SUPPLEMENTAL HEALTH CARE SERVICES, INC.
1640 Redstone Ctr Dr Ste 200, Park City, UT 84098
Tel.: (435) 645-0788
Web Site: http://www.supplementalhealthcare.com
Sales Range: $200-249.9 Million
Emp.: 3,000
Nurse Staffing Services
N.A.I.C.S.: 813212

SUPPLEMENTAL HEALTH CARE SERVICES, INC.

Supplemental Health Care Services, Inc.—(Continued)
Janet Elkin (Pres & CEO)
Travis Furlow (VP & Gen Mgr-Recruitment Process Outsourcing)
Steve Ure (CFO)

SUPPLIER.IO, INC.
4422 N Ravenswood Ave, Chicago, IL 60640
Web Site: http://supplier.io
Year Founded: 2011
Corporate Supplier & Solutions Provider
N.A.I.C.S.: 423490
Neeraj Shah (CEO)

Subsidiaries:

CVM Solutions, LLC (1)
1815 S Meyers Rd Fl 8 Ste 820, Oakbrook Terrace, IL 60181
Tel.: (630) 629-5800
Web Site: http://www.cvmsolutions.com
Sales Range: $10-24.9 Million
Emp.: 100
Supplier Management Solutions
N.A.I.C.S.: 513140
Brendan Taylor (Mng Dir)
Carol Attak (Sr Acct Exec)
Kenneth Apa (Dir-Data Content)
Fernando Cadena (Dir-Ops)
Lois Eichacker (Dir-Strategic Accts)
Suresh Kanna (Dir-Software Dev)
Mike McCarthy (Mgr-Mktg)
Todd Minden (VP-Sls & Mktg)
Nataliea Morris (Mgr-Managed Svcs)
Ashlee Nelson (VP-Sls & Innovation)

SUPPLY CHAIN SOLUTIONS LLC
2300 Sitler St Bldg 685, Memphis, TN 38114-4801
Tel.: (901) 774-6533   DE
Sales Range: $10-24.9 Million
Emp.: 200
Logistics Consulting Servies
N.A.I.C.S.: 541614
Robert Keskey (Co-Pres)
Bobby Thomas (Co-Pres)
James Rink (CEO)

SUPPLY CHAIN SOLUTIONS, INC.
4607 44th St SE, Grand Rapids, MI 49512
Tel.: (616) 554-8900   MI
Web Site: http://www.scsolutionsinc.com
Year Founded: 2002
Sales Range: $10-24.9 Million
Emp.: 125
Integrated Logistics Consulting & Supply Chain Management Services
N.A.I.C.S.: 541614
Jim Ward (Pres)
Leslie G. Brand III (CEO)

Subsidiaries:

Supply Chain Solutions, Inc. - Holland Office (1)
1451 M 40 Bldg 100 Ste A, Holland, MI 49423
Tel.: (616) 355-2563
Web Site: http://www.scsolutionsinc.com
Integrated Logistics Consulting & Supply Chain Management Services
N.A.I.C.S.: 541614

SUPPLY NEW ENGLAND INC.
123 East St, Attleboro, MA 02703
Tel.: (508) 222-5555
Web Site: http://www.supplynewengland.com
Rev.: $42,993,303
Emp.: 150
Plumbing & Hydronic Heating Supplies
N.A.I.C.S.: 423720

Joe Fouarty (Controller)
Jason Baldwin (Controller)
Jeff Tri (Mgr)
Sabrina DaLomba (Dir-Show Rooms)

SUPPLYCORE INC.
303 N Main St Ste 800, Rockford, IL 61101-1018
Tel.: (815) 964-7940
Web Site: http://www.supplycore.com
Sales Range: $25-49.9 Million
Emp.: 185
Hardware
N.A.I.C.S.: 423710
Peter Provenzano (CEO)
Steve Cotone (VP-Program Mgmt)
Mark Robinson (VP-Admin)
Patrick Patrick Voller (VP-Bus Dev)
Bryan Davis (VP-Govt Affairs & Community Engagement)
Richard Alpaugh (VP-Intl)

SUPPLYPRO INC.
8572 Spectrum Ln, San Diego, CA 92121
Tel.: (858) 587-6400
Web Site: http://www.supplypro.com
Sales Range: $10-24.9 Million
Emp.: 63
Office Equipment Whslr
N.A.I.C.S.: 423420
Michael Reynolds (CTO)
Floyd Miller (CEO)
Stan Sigman (Chief Revenue Officer)
Justin Dass (VP-Bus Dev-Domestic & Intl Div-Software Offerings)

SUPPLYSOURCE INC.
415 W 3rd St, Williamsport, PA 17701
Tel.: (570) 327-1500
Web Site: http://www.supplysourceinc.com
Sales Range: $10-24.9 Million
Emp.: 65
Office Furniture
N.A.I.C.S.: 423210
Ray A. Thompson (Founder, Pres & CEO)
Larry Basile (VP-Sls)
Yvonne Fogal (VP-Internal Ops)

SUPPORT OUR TROOPS, INC.
PO Box 70, Daytona Beach, FL 32115-0070
Tel.: (386) 767-8882   FL
Web Site: http://www.supportourtroops.org
Year Founded: 2005
Sales Range: $10-24.9 Million
Emp.: 1
Troops Support Services
N.A.I.C.S.: 813410
Martin C. Boire (Chm)
Bruce Jonas (Founder & VP)

SUPPORT SYSTEMS ASSOCIATES, INC.
Marina Twrs 709 S Harbor City Blvd Ste 350, Melbourne, FL 32901
Tel.: (321) 724-5566   NY
Web Site: http://www.ssai.org
Year Founded: 1969
Sales Range: $100-124.9 Million
Emp.: 250
Provider of Engineering Services
N.A.I.C.S.: 541330
Robert Zissel (Exec VP)
Cindy Cervantez (Dir-IT)
John Hamilton (VP-Contracts)

SUPPORT SYSTEMS INTERNATIONAL INC.
110 E Main St, Elkton, MD 21921-5907
Tel.: (410) 392-3927   FL
Web Site: http://www.ssicomp.com

Year Founded: 1993
Sales Range: $10-24.9 Million
Emp.: 45
Custom Computer Programming Services
N.A.I.C.S.: 541511

SUPPORTING FAMILIES TOGETHER ASSOCIATION
700 Rayovac Dr Ste 6, Madison, WI 53711
Tel.: (608) 443-2490   WI
Web Site: http://www.supportingfamiliestogether.org
Year Founded: 2007
Sales Range: $10-24.9 Million
Emp.: 25
Child Care & Development Services
N.A.I.C.S.: 624110
Abbe Braun (Mgr-Professional Dev)
Mary Beth Plane (Pres)
Kelly Jensen (Treas)
Penny Chase (Mgr-Quality Improvement)
Sarah Berry (Specialist-Micro-Grant Finance)
Gloria Campos (Specialist-Micro-Grant)
Melissa Chan (Specialist-Data)
Connie Dunlap (Specialist-Family Engagement)
Jenna Finley (Specialist-Professional Dev)
Pattie Godsell-Pierski (Specialist-Quality Assurance)
Jill Hoiting (Dir-Programs & External Rels)
Kathy Kadar (Specialist-Quality Assurance)
Erik Larson (Dir-Ops)
Kelly McClurg (Specialist-Comm)
Anna Ramirez (Mgr-Licensing Preparation)
Amanda Rose (Specialist-Micro-Grant)
Romilia Schlueter (Specialist-Bilingual Quality Improvement)
Sherri Underwood (Mgr-Micro-Grant)
Diana Zorn (Specialist-Quality Assurance)

SUPRE INC.
15770 N Dallas Pkwy Ste 700, Dallas, TX 75248
Tel.: (972) 788-5184
Web Site: http://www.supre.com
Rev.: $11,200,000
Emp.: 22
Cosmetics
N.A.I.C.S.: 424210
Bruce West Jr. (Pres)

SUPREME BEVERAGE CO. INC.
3217 Messer Airport Hwy, Birmingham, AL 35222-1259
Tel.: (205) 251-8010
Web Site: http://www.supremebeverage.com
Year Founded: 1945
Sales Range: $25-49.9 Million
Emp.: 175
Beer & Ale
N.A.I.C.S.: 424810
Diane Schilleci (Exec VP-HR)

SUPREME CHEVROLET, INC.
13354 Airline Hwy, Gonzales, LA 70737
Tel.: (225) 344-3726
Web Site: http://www.supremechevy.com
Sales Range: $10-24.9 Million
Emp.: 41
Car Whslr

N.A.I.C.S.: 441110
Chris Bradshaw (Mgr-Svc)

SUPREME COUNCIL OF THE ROYAL ARCANUM
61 Batterymarch St, Boston, MA 02110-3208
Tel.: (617) 426-4135   MA
Web Site: http://www.royalarcanum.com
Year Founded: 1877
Sales Range: $50-74.9 Million
Community Care Services
N.A.I.C.S.: 624190
Nicholas G. Benoit (Dir-Ops)
Nicholas F. Liadis (Dir-Sls)
Paul F. D'Emilio (Gen Counsel)
Matthew D'Emilio (Asst Gen Counsel)
Cynthia A. Macon (Dir-Fraternal)
Allan P. Ferone (Actuary)

SUPREME ELASTIC CORP
325 Spencer Rd, Conover, NC 28613
Tel.: (828) 322-6975
Web Site: http://www.supremecorporation.com
Sales Range: $10-24.9 Million
Emp.: 55
Elastic Products Mfr
N.A.I.C.S.: 313220
Nathaniel Kolmes (Pres)
Wesley Christopher (Controller)

SUPREME ENERGY, INC.
532 Freeman St, Orange, NJ 07050-1312
Tel.: (973) 678-1800   NJ
Web Site: http://www.supremeenergyinc.com
Year Founded: 1921
Sales Range: $25-49.9 Million
Emp.: 80
Fuel, Oil & Natural Gas Services
N.A.I.C.S.: 457210
Deborah Berna Fineman (Pres & Gen Counsel)
Manny Sevdalis (CFO)
Marian Tafuri (Mgr-Admin)
Robert Fentzlaff (Dir-Ops)
John Spillane (Mgr-IT)

SUPREME MACHINED PRODUCTS COMPANY, INC.
18686 172nd Ave, Spring Lake, MI 49456-9720
Tel.: (616) 842-6550   MI
Web Site: http://www.supreme1.com
Year Founded: 1949
Sales Range: $10-24.9 Million
Emp.: 100
Machined Cylinder, Shift Lever & Precision Turned Products Mfr
N.A.I.C.S.: 332710
Gregory Olson (Owner)
Bruce Rice (CFO)
Joshua Datte (Supvr-Quality)

SUPREME OIL COMPANY INC.
80 S Dean St, Englewood, NJ 07631-3514
Tel.: (201) 567-3177   DE
Web Site: http://www.admirationfoods.com
Year Founded: 1944
Sales Range: $25-49.9 Million
Emp.: 200
Pickles & Salad Dressings Mfr
N.A.I.C.S.: 311941
Seymour Unterman (Pres)
Nicole Acrish (Mgr-Sls)

SUPREME OIL COMPANY INC.
755 W A St 2nd Fl, San Diego, CA 92101-0700
Tel.: (619) 501-3300
Web Site: http://www.supremeoil.com

Year Founded: 1988
Sales Range: $10-24.9 Million
Emp.: 30
Fuel Oil Dealers
N.A.I.C.S.: 457210
Garth Davis (Pres)

SUPREME RESOURCES, INC.
5400 Laurel Springs Pkwy Ste 1103, Suwanee, GA 30024
Tel.: (770) 475-4638
Web Site:
 http://www.supremeresources.com
Year Founded: 1988
Sales Range: $25-49.9 Million
Emp.: 15
Other Chemical & Allied Products
N.A.I.C.S.: 424690
Geoffrey Kho (CEO)

SUPREME TELECOM SYSTEMS INC.
515 Houston St Ste 800, Fort Worth, TX 76102
Tel.: (817) 336-0000
Web Site:
 http://www.supremetelecom.com
Rev.: $14,000,000
Emp.: 3
Telecommunication Servicesb
N.A.I.C.S.: 517121
Farukh Aslam (Pres)

SUR GRO PLANT FOOD CO., INC.
1006 W North St, Plattsburg, MO 64477-1649
Tel.: (816) 539-2106
Year Founded: 1974
Sales Range: $50-74.9 Million
Emp.: 75
Agricultural Products Mfr & Sales
N.A.I.C.S.: 424910
Keith Clemens (VP-Sls)

SUR-FLO PLASTICS & ENGINEERING INC.
24358 Groesbeck Hwy, Warren, MI 48089-4718
Tel.: (586) 773-0400
Year Founded: 1977
Plastics & Related Products Mfr
N.A.I.C.S.: 326199
Don A. Wolfbauer (Owner)
Dave Kohler (Plant Mgr)
Mike Henning (Mgr-Matls)
Rick Wolber (Mgr-Pur)
Mary Graff (Pres & CEO)

SUR-SEAL LLC
6156 Wesselman Rd, Cincinnati, OH 45248
Tel.: (513) 574-8500
Web Site: http://www.sur-seal.com
Year Founded: 1965
Sales Range: $1-9.9 Million
Emp.: 150
Mfg Gasket/Packing/Seals Mfg Fabrcatd Rubber Prdt Mfg Plastic Products Mfg Industrial Machinery
N.A.I.C.S.: 339991

Subsidiaries:
Ameritape, Inc. (1)
11236-100 St Johns Industrial Pkwy South, Jacksonville, FL 32246
Tel.: (904) 565-9999
Web Site: http://www.ameritape.com
Rev.: $5,000,000
Emp.: 13
Coated & Laminated Paper Mfr
N.A.I.C.S.: 322220
Tom Whipple (Mgr-Quality Control)

SUR-SEAL, INC.
16 Edgeboro Rd Unit 4, East Brunswick, NJ 08816
Tel.: (732) 651-7070
Web Site: http://www.sur-sealinc.com
Year Founded: 1979
Sales Range: $1-9.9 Million
Emp.: 15
Industrial Supplies Merchant Whslr
N.A.I.C.S.: 423840
Gloria Solomon (Pres)

Subsidiaries:
Mueller Die Cut Solutions, Inc. (1)
9201 Stockport Pl, Charlotte, NC 28273
Tel.: (704) 588-3900
Web Site: http://www.muellerdcs.com
Rev.: $10,000,000
Emp.: 84
Gasket, Packing & Sealing Device Mfr
N.A.I.C.S.: 339991
Janelle Morgan (Dir-HR)
Ken Stober (Pres)
Chad Hall (Mgr-Sls)
John Chapman (Mgr-Sls & Mktg)

SURCO LOG, INC.
545 N 28th, Springfield, OR 97477-4499
Tel.: (541) 746-3213
Sales Range: $10-24.9 Million
Emp.: 80
Logging Services
N.A.I.C.S.: 113310
Rod Surcamp (Pres)
Aashild Surcamp (Sec)

SURCO PRODUCTS, INC.
292 Alpha Dr RIDC Indus Pk, Pittsburgh, PA 15238
Tel.: (412) 252-7000
Web Site: http://www.surco.com
Year Founded: 1946
Sales Range: $75-99.9 Million
Emp.: 75
Mfr of Air Fresheners, Deodorants, Odor Control Systems & Fan Deodorizers
N.A.I.C.S.: 333413
Arnold Zlotnik (Pres & CEO)

SURE PREP LEARNING LLC
44000 N Brown Ave, Scottsdale, AZ 85251
Tel.: (480) 946-7737
Web Site:
 http://www.surepreplearning.com
Year Founded: 2005
Sales Range: $1-9.9 Million
Emp.: 1
Academic Tutoring & Test Preparation
N.A.I.C.S.: 611691
David Dodge (CEO)

SURE TRACE SECURITY CORP.
1615 Walnut St 3rd Fl, Philadelphia, PA 19103
Tel.: (215) 972-6999
Year Founded: 1983
Software Development Services
N.A.I.C.S.: 541511
William Chan (CEO)

SURE WINNER FOODS INC.
2 Lehner Rd, Saco, ME 04072
Tel.: (207) 282-1258
Web Site: http://www.swfoods.com
Year Founded: 1979
Sales Range: $10-24.9 Million
Emp.: 85
Distr of Dairy Products
N.A.I.C.S.: 424430
Katrina Connolly (Mgr-HR)

SURECLICK PROMOTIONS, LLC
1211 Connecticut Ave NW Ste 608, Washington, DC 20036
Tel.: (202) 349-9620
Web Site: http://www.sureclick.com
Year Founded: 2000
Sales Range: $10-24.9 Million
Emp.: 10
Information Technology Solutions & Marketing Consulting Services
N.A.I.C.S.: 541690
Justin Abernathy (Co-Founder)
Jason Abernathy (Co-Founder)
Michael Popowski (Sr Acct Dir)

SUREFIL LLC
4560 Danvers Dr SE, Grand Rapids, MI 49512
Tel.: (616) 532-1700
Web Site: http://www.surefil.com
Year Founded: 2005
Sales Range: $10-24.9 Million
Emp.: 70
Toilet Preparation Mfr
N.A.I.C.S.: 325620
Mike Schmidt (Dir-Quality Ops)
Bill Currie (CEO)
William G. Currie (CEO)

SUREFIRE, LLC
18300 Mount Baldy Cir, Fountain Valley, CA 92708
Tel.: (714) 545-9444
Web Site: http://www.surefire.com
Sales Range: $75-99.9 Million
Emp.: 700
Mfr & Supplier of Flashlights & Weapon-Mounted Tactical Lights
N.A.I.C.S.: 335139
Ed Reynolds (VP)
Barry Dueck (Dir-SureFire Suppressors)
Sean Zo (CFO)
Derek McDonald (Sr VP-Sls & Mktg)
John S. Matthews (Founder & Pres)

SUREFOOT INC
1355 Lowell Ave Resort Center, Park City, UT 84060
Tel.: (435) 655-8110
Web Site: http://www.surefoot.com
Sales Range: $10-24.9 Million
Skiing Accessories Mfr
N.A.I.C.S.: 316210
Bob Shay (Co-Founder)
Russ Shay (Co-Founder)

Subsidiaries:
Super Runners Shop, Inc. (1)
355 New York Ave Ste 1, Huntington, NY 11743
Tel.: (631) 549-3006
Web Site: http://www.superrunnersshop.com
Sales Range: $1-9.9 Million
Emp.: 44
Shoe Stores
N.A.I.C.S.: 458210
Gary Muhrcke (Founder)

SURETEC
6975 SW Sandburg St Ste 250, Portland, OR 97223
Tel.: (555) 555-5555
Web Site: http://www.suretec.co
Custom Computer Programming Services
N.A.I.C.S.: 541511
Nicholas Hess (CEO)

Subsidiaries:
Linked Technologies, Inc. (1)
3183 C Beaver Vu Dr, Beavercreek, OH 45434
Tel.: (937) 427-9790
Web Site:
 http://www.linkedtechnologies.com
Sales Range: $25-49.9 Million
Emp.: 12
Customized Programming Support, Application Development, Web Applications, Turnkey e-Commerce Solutions, Distance Learning Projects & Software Outsourcing Services
N.A.I.C.S.: 541519
Nighat Chaudhry (Mgr-Mktg)

SURETY SYSTEMS, INC.
8081 Arco Corporate Dr Ste 200, Raleigh, NC 27617
Tel.: (919) 578-6485
Web Site:
 http://www.suretysystems.com
Year Founded: 2002
Sales Range: $1-9.9 Million
Emp.: 43
IT Consulting Services
N.A.I.C.S.: 541613
Roy Cook (VP)
JP Lexa (COO)
David Haney (CEO)

SURF ASSOCIATES, INC.
1701 N Federal Hwy, Fort Lauderdale, FL 33305
Tel.: (954) 563-1366
Web Site: http://www.bcsurf.com
Rev.: $18,700,000
Emp.: 200
Sporting Goods Retailer
N.A.I.C.S.: 459110
Joe Ferraro (Mgr-Fin)
Bruce Cromartie (Pres)

SURF CITY GARAGE, LLC
5872 Engineer Dr, Huntington Beach, CA 92649
Tel.: (714) 894-1707
Web Site:
 http://www.surfcitygarage.com
Year Founded: 1970
Motor Vehicle Detailing Products Mfr & Distr
N.A.I.C.S.: 325612
Timothy D. Miller (Founder)
Pattie Miller (Founder)
Matt Rigdon (VP-Bus Dev)
Carrie Piscotty (VP-Ops & Corp Branding)
Brandon Tell (Gen Mgr)

Subsidiaries:
Paradise Road LLC (1)
5872 Engineer Dr, Huntington Beach, CA 92649
Tel.: (714) 894-1779
Web Site:
 http://www.paradiseroadcarcare.com
Sales Range: $1-9.9 Million
Motor Vehicle Detailing Products Mfr & Distr
N.A.I.C.S.: 325612

SURFACE COMBUSTION, INC.
1700 Indian Wood Cir, Maumee, OH 43537-4005
Tel.: (419) 891-7150
Web Site:
 http://www.surfacecombustion.com
Year Founded: 1915
Sales Range: $75-99.9 Million
Emp.: 130
Thermal Processing Systems; Heat Treating Furnaces; Gas Generators for Metallurgical, Food & Chemical Industries Mfr
N.A.I.C.S.: 333994
W. J. Bernard (Pres & CEO)
M. Hoetzl (VP-Tech)
Daniel E. Goodman (VP-Production)
D. G. Elliot (VP-Contract Mgmt)
Lori Lingle (Mgr-Pur)
Stuart Fuller (VP-Fin & Admin)

SURFACE MATERIAL SALES INC.
6655 Parkland Blvd, Solon, OH 44139
Tel.: (440) 248-0000
Web Site:
 http://www.surfacematerials.com
Year Founded: 1976

SURFACE MATERIAL SALES INC.

U.S. PRIVATE

Surface Material Sales Inc.—(Continued)
Sales Range: $25-49.9 Million
Emp.: 30
Wallcoverings
N.A.I.C.S.: 424950
David M. Richards *(Pres)*
Laura O'Donnell *(VP-Ops)*

SURFACE MOUNT DISTRIBUTION
1 Oldfield, Irvine, CA 92618
Tel.: (949) 470-7700
Web Site: http://www.smdinc.com
Sales Range: $1-9.9 Million
Emp.: 27
Capacitors, Electronic
N.A.I.C.S.: 423690
Jerome Guiliano *(Owner)*
Rich Unruh *(Pres-SMD Inc)*

SURFACE MOUNT TECHNOLOGY CORPORATION
5660 Technology Cir, Appleton, WI 54914
Tel.: (920) 954-8324
Web Site: http://www.teamsmt.com
Rev.: $12,700,000
Emp.: 135
Semiconductor Machinery Mfr
N.A.I.C.S.: 333242
Christopher Sumnicht *(Founder)*
Paul Vander Maazen *(VP-Sls)*
Brian Lamers *(VP-Admin)*
Gregory Burneske *(Sr VP-Engrg)*

SURFACE TECHNOLOGIES CORP
2275 Atlantic Blvd, Neptune Beach, FL 32266
Tel.: (904) 241-1501
Web Site: http://www.surfacetechnologiescorp.com
Year Founded: 1985
Sales Range: $10-24.9 Million
Emp.: 250
Industrial Coatings & Sealants Mfr
N.A.I.C.S.: 325510
Trey Perry *(Acct Mgr-Payroll)*

SURFACECYCLE, INC.
9035 Wadsworth Pkwy, Ste 2275, Westminster, CO 80021
Web Site: https://www.surface-cycle.com
Highway Construction
N.A.I.C.S.: 237310
Joshua Chambers *(CEO)*

Subsidiaries:

Delta Contracting, Inc. (1)
580 Trollingwood Rd, Haw River, NC 27258-8751
Tel.: (336) 578-9006
Web Site: http://www.deltacontractinginc.com
Specialty Trade Contractors
N.A.I.C.S.: 238990
Kelly Wilson *(Office Mgr)*

Donegal Construction Corporation (1)
1235 Marguerite Lake Rd, Greensburg, PA 15601
Tel.: (724) 423-7500
Web Site: http://www.donegalconstruction.com
Rev.: $7,400,000
Emp.: 50
Highway, Street & Bridge Construction
N.A.I.C.S.: 237310
Robert Miner *(CEO)*
Michelle Gribble *(Controller)*

SURFECT HOLDINGS, INC.
180 W Broadway Rd Ste 1, Tempe, AZ 85282
Tel.: (480) 968-2897 **DE**
Web Site: http://www.surfect.com
Year Founded: 2001
Sales Range: Less than $1 Million
Emp.: 4
Electroplating Tool Developer
N.A.I.C.S.: 332813
Steven Anderson *(Pres, CEO, COO, Treas & Sec)*
Tom D. Benscoter *(CFO)*
Richard Tung *(VP-Ops)*
David Pham *(Product Mgr-Solar)*
Terry Gafron *(Product Mgr-Software)*

SURFRIDER FOUNDATION
942 Calle Negocio Ste 350, San Clemente, CA 92673
Tel.: (949) 492-8170 **CA**
Web Site: http://www.surfrider.org
Year Founded: 2004
Emp.: 300
Civic & Environmental Services
N.A.I.C.S.: 813410
Chad Nelsen *(CEO)*
Michelle Kremer *(COO)*
Angela Howe *(Dir-Legal)*

SURGCENTER DEVELOPMENT
722 Dulaney Valley Road #221, Towson, MD 21204-5109
Tel.: (800) 465-1725
Web Site: http://www.surgcenter.com
Electronics Stores
N.A.I.C.S.: 449210
Stephanie Leventis *(Exec VP-Dev)*

SURGE GLOBAL ENERGY, INC.
75-153 Merle Dr Ste B, Palm Desert, CA 92211
Tel.: (760) 610-6758 **DE**
Web Site: http://www.surgeglobalenergy.com
Year Founded: 1997
Sales Range: Less than $1 Million
Emp.: 4
Oil & Gas Exploration Services
N.A.I.C.S.: 211120
William E. Fitzgerald *(Pres)*
William A. Fitzgerald *(Sr VP)*
Clark Morton II *(Chm & CEO)*

SURGE LLC
11820 Northrup Way Ste E200, Bellevue, WA 98005
Web Site: http://www.surgeforward.com
Year Founded: 2007
Sales Range: $1-9.9 Million
Emp.: 35
Web & Mobile Applications
N.A.I.C.S.: 513210
Matt MacKay *(Founder & CEO)*
Alex Bean *(Dir-Sls)*
Eric Hufford *(Dir-Quality Assurance)*
Garrett Maudsley *(Dir-Design)*
Jim Hyde *(COO & Exec VP)*
Jonathan Martin *(Dir-IT)*
Joshua Philips *(Dir-Sls)*
Nately Desisto *(Dir-Project Mgmt)*
Paul Shiman *(CMO)*
Tyler Schroeder *(Dir-Dev)*

SURGE PRIVATE EQUITY LLC
2101 Cedar Springs Rd, Ste 1220, Dallas, TX 75201
Tel.: (214) 347-4273 **TX**
Web Site: http://www.surgepe.com
Year Founded: 2017
Privater Equity Firm
N.A.I.C.S.: 523999
Tom Beauchamp *(Partner)*

Subsidiaries:

Avalon Copy Centers of America, Inc. (1)
901 N State St., Syracuse, NY 13208
Tel.: (315) 471-3333
Web Site: https://teamavalon.com
Commercial Services
N.A.I.C.S.: 926150

Subsidiary (Domestic):

Tower Legal Staffing, Inc. (2)
65 Broadway 1703 Fl, New York, NY 10006
Tel.: (212) 430-6300
Web Site: http://www.towerls.com
Sales Range: $50-74.9 Million
Emp.: 50
Staffing Services
N.A.I.C.S.: 561330
Leslie Firtell *(Pres & CEO)*
Marcia Awobuluyi *(COO)*
Holly Meredith *(Mng Dir-Charlotte)*
Raoul Mills *(Mng Dir & Sr VP-Washington)*
Dwight Point *(Dir-Bus Dev-Natl)*
Laura Martino *(Gen Counsel & Dir-Compliance-Natl)*
Daniela Dakshaw *(Mng Dir-Los Angeles)*
Michael Higgins *(Mng Dir-New York)*
William A. Makin *(Mng Dir-Tower Consulting Svcs)*
Michael Blaes *(Mng Dir-Minneapolis)*

Global Bakeries, LLC (1)
13336 Paxton St, Pacoima, CA 91331-2339
Tel.: (818) 896-0525
Web Site: http://www.globalbakeriesinc.com
Sales Range: $10-24.9 Million
Emp.: 60
Bagel, Flatbread, Croissant, Pita Bread & Chip Whslr
N.A.I.C.S.: 424490

Subsidiary (Domestic):

Bubbles Baking Co. (2)
15215 Keswick St, Van Nuys, CA 91405-1050
Tel.: (818) 786-1700
Web Site: http://bubblesbakeryco.com
Retail Bakeries
N.A.I.C.S.: 311811

Norris Training Systems, Inc. (1)
9990 Richmond Ave Ste 102, Houston, TX 77042
Tel.: (713) 780-9387
Web Site: http://www.norriscenters.com
Sales Range: $1-9.9 Million
Emp.: 29
Management Consulting Services
N.A.I.C.S.: 541618
Aaron Rainone *(Gen Mgr)*
Brooke Cordova *(Mgr-Sls)*
Helen Guerrero *(Mgr-Sls)*
Javier Chavez *(Gen Mgr)*
Julia Keim *(Mgr-Sls)*
Priscilla Contreras *(Mgr-Sls)*
Scott Mundine *(Gen Mgr)*
Teresa Sim *(Gen Mgr)*
Thiago Farrias *(VP)*

SURGE VENTURES, LLC
1300 El Camino Real, Menlo Park, CA 94025
Tel.: (408) 320-0387
Web Site: https://www.surgeventures.com
Emp.: 100
Venture Capital Firm
N.A.I.C.S.: 523999
Sid Yenamandra *(Founder, CEO & Mng Partner)*

Subsidiaries:

Kovair Software, Inc. (1)
2410 Camino Ramon Ste 230, San Ramon, CA 94583
Tel.: (408) 262-0200
Web Site: http://www.kovair.com
Emp.: 1,500
Application Lifecycle Management Software Publisher
N.A.I.C.S.: 513210
Sid Yenamandra *(CEO)*
Rajshekar Bhattacharjee *(VP-Product Deliveries & Gen Mgr-Ops-Kolkata)*
Mukesh Ahuja *(VP-Bus Dev & Corp Dev)*
Akshay Sharma *(CTO)*

SURGICAL APPLIANCE INDUSTRIES, INC.
3960 Rosslyn Dr, Cincinnati, OH 45209-1195
Tel.: (513) 271-4594 **OH**
Web Site: http://www.saibrands.com
Year Founded: 1893
Sales Range: $75-99.9 Million
Emp.: 250
Mfr of Surgical Appliances & Supplies; Orthopedic Appliances; Braces; Elastic & Support Hosiery
N.A.I.C.S.: 339113
L. Thomas Applegate *(Pres & COO)*
Jack Crowley *(Controller)*
Pam Rogers *(Sec-Sls)*
Richard Stautberg *(Mgr-Quality Sys)*
Gary Parsons *(Product Mgr)*
Tim Donovan *(Mgr-Production)*

Subsidiaries:

Surgical Appliance Industries, Inc. - PCP-Champion Division (1)
3960 Rosslyn Dr, Cincinnati, OH 45209
Tel.: (800) 888-0867
Web Site: http://www.saibrands.com
Emp.: 200
Surgical Instrument Mfr
N.A.I.C.S.: 339112
Tom Applegate *(Pres)*

Truform Orthotics & Prosthetics (1)
3960 Rosslyn Dr, Cincinnati, OH 45209-1195
Tel.: (513) 271-4594
Web Site: http://www.saibrands.com
Sales Range: $25-49.9 Million
Mfr of Orthotic & Prosthetic Appliances & Support Hosiery
N.A.I.C.S.: 339113
Gary Parsons *(Product Mgr)*
David Perry *(Controller)*
Terri Mott *(Mgr-Customer Svcs)*
T. Applegate *(Pres)*

SURGICAL EYE EXPEDITIONS INTERNATIONAL
5638 Hollister Ave Ste 210, Santa Barbara, CA 93117-2807
Tel.: (805) 963-3303 **CA**
Web Site: http://www.seeintl.org
Year Founded: 1974
Sales Range: $10-24.9 Million
Emp.: 21
Eye Care Service
N.A.I.C.S.: 813311
Harry S. Brown *(Founder)*
Scott W. Groff *(Chm)*
Howard R. Hudson *(Treas & Sec)*
Randal Avolio *(Pres)*
Kate Bryant *(VP-Dev)*

SURGICAL PRINCIPALS, INC.
1625 S Tacoma Way, Tacoma, WA 98409
Tel.: (253) 441-6509
Web Site: http://www.surgicalprincipals.com
Year Founded: 2001
Sales Range: $10-24.9 Million
Emp.: 22
Hospital Equipment Whslr
N.A.I.C.S.: 423450
Timothy J. Wynne *(Pres)*

SURGICAL SOLUTIONS, LLC
136 2nd St Ste 600, Henderson, KY 42420
Tel.: (270) 827-7757 **KY**
Web Site: http://www.surgical-solutions.org
Sales Range: $10-24.9 Million
Emp.: 75
Endoscopic & Laparoscopic Surgical Procedure Support Services
N.A.I.C.S.: 621999
Alex Kellen *(Pres & COO)*
Kurt Kellen *(Dir-Ops)*

COMPANIES

Brian Marr *(Mgr-Ops)*
Eric L. Stinson *(CEO)*
Jason Bryant *(Dir-HR)*

SURGICAL STAFF, INC.
120 Saint Matthews Ave, San Mateo, CA 94401
Tel.: (650) 558-3999
Web Site:
  http://www.surgicalstaff.com
Year Founded: 1979
Sales Range: $10-24.9 Million
Emp.: 1,200
Provider of Surgical Staffing Services
N.A.I.C.S.: 561320
Beverly J. Foster *(Owner & Pres)*

SURLY BREWING CO.
4811 Dusharme Dr, Brooklyn Center, MN 55429-3940
Tel.: (763) 535-3330
Web Site:
  http://www.SurlyBrewing.com
Sales Range: $1-9.9 Million
Emp.: 20
Beer Brewers Mfr & Whslr
N.A.I.C.S.: 424490
Omar Ansari *(Pres)*
Gary Nicholas *(Coord-Special Projects)*

SURVEYING AND MAPPING, LLC
4801 Southwest Pkwy Building Two, Ste 100, Austin, TX 78735
Tel.: (800) 656-9525
Web Site: https://www.sam.biz
Year Founded: 1994
Emp.: 1,159
Business Consulting & Services
N.A.I.C.S.: 541618

Subsidiaries:

Precisionpoint Inc. (1)
301 E Carmel Dr, Carmel, IN 46032
Tel.: (317) 660-8620
Web Site: http://www.precisionpointinc.com
Surveying & Mapping Services
N.A.I.C.S.: 541370
Mark Hanna *(Pres & CEO)*

SURVEYMONKEY.COM LLC
1331 NW Lovejoy St Ste 720, Portland, OR 97209
Tel.: (503) 225-1202
Web Site:
  http://www.surveymonkey.com
Year Founded: 1999
Sales Range: $25-49.9 Million
Emp.: 50
Internet & Telephone Survey Solutions
N.A.I.C.S.: 513210
Zander Lurie *(CEO)*
Luis Franco *(VP-Intl Bus Ops)*
Rebecca Cantieri *(VP-HR)*
Jon Cohen *(VP-Survey Res)*
Ross Moser *(VP-Customer Ops)*
Bennett Porter *(VP-Mktg Comm)*
Will Wagner *(VP-Engrg)*
Tom Hale *(Pres)*
Teresa Brewer *(Head-Comm)*
Steve Norall *(Chief Product Officer)*
Elena Verna *(Sr VP-Growth)*
Brad O'Neill *(Sr VP-Sls-Global)*
Karim Damji *(VP-Fin)*
Ken Ricketts *(VP-Infrastructure Engrg)*
Stuart Kerst *(VP-Sls Strategy & Field Ops)*
David A. Ebersman *(Chm)*
Luke Siegfried *(VP-Enterprise Sls-Global)*
John Schoenstein *(Chief Sls Officer)*
Joe Cummiskey *(Sr Dir-Enterprise Sls-EMEA)*

DuVal Hicks *(VP-Sls Ops)*
Lara Sasken Lindenbaum *(VP-Comm)*
Denis Scott *(VP-Growth Mktg)*
Eric Johnson *(CIO)*
Karen Budell *(VP-Brand Mktg)*
Gary Fuges *(VP-IR)*
Amit Sethi *(VP-Data)*
Ken Ewell *(Chief Customer Officer)*
Alexander Lurie *(CEO)*

SURVEYVITALS, INC.
2723 County Rd 3672, Springtown, TX 76082-4287
Tel.: (972) 442-1484
Web Site:
  http://www.surveyvitals.com
Year Founded: 1992
Healthcare Analytics, Including Patient Surveys
N.A.I.C.S.: 541910
Robert Vosburgh *(CEO)*
Bill Jansen *(Dir-Tech)*
Blake Vosburgh *(COO)*
Geoff Thumma *(CFO)*
Grady Dougless *(Dir-Compliance)*
Heather Foxhill *(VP-Bus Dev)*
Sam Westbrook *(Dir-Education)*
Bud Dey *(VP-Market Strategy)*
Cindy Passhall *(Dir-Admin & Fin)*
Kyra Maples *(Mgr-Mktg)*
Robert Harrington *(Pres & Chief Medical Officer)*

Subsidiaries:

Novaetus Inc. (1)
43000 W 9 Mile Rd #202, Novi, MI 48377
Tel.: (248) 344-7572
Web Site: http://www.novaetus.com
Marketing Consulting Services
N.A.I.C.S.: 541613
Lori Moshier *(Pres)*

SURVIVAL MEDIA LLC
355 N Broadway, Burns, OR 97720
Tel.: (541) 573-2022
Web Site:
  http://www.btimesherald.com
Sales Range: $10-24.9 Million
Emp.: 6
Newspaper Publishers
N.A.I.C.S.: 513110
Randy Parks *(Editor)*

Subsidiaries:

Burns Times-Herald (1)
355 N Broadway, Burns, OR 97720-1704
Tel.: (541) 573-2022
Web Site: http://www.burnstimesherald.info
Sales Range: $10-24.9 Million
Newspaper Publishers
N.A.I.C.S.: 513110
Randy Parks *(Editor)*

SURYA INC.
140 Executive Dr SE, Calhoun, GA 30701
Tel.: (706) 625-4823
Web Site: http://www.surya.com
Year Founded: 1986
Sales Range: $50-74.9 Million
Emp.: 100
Homefurnishings
N.A.I.C.S.: 423220
Satya P. Tiwari *(Pres)*
Rob Rosenquist *(VP-Sls-Cartersville)*

SUSAN DAVIS INTERNATIONAL
1101 K St NW Ste 400, Washington, DC 20005
Tel.: (202) 408-0808
Web Site: http://www.susandavis.com
Sales Range: $10-24.9 Million
Advetising Agency
N.A.I.C.S.: 541810

Susan A. Davis *(Founder & Chm)*
Judith H. Whittlesey *(Exec VP)*
Tom E. Davis *(VP)*
Marcus Dunn *(Sr Acct Exec)*
Joe Hendrix *(Acct Exec)*
Lisa T. Miller *(VP)*
Victoria Shapiro *(Sr Acct Exec)*
Sara Neumann *(Sr Acct Exec)*
Michelle Reilly *(Dir-Mktg & Engagement)*
Frank Cilluffo *(Mng Dir)*
Daniel Gregory *(VP)*
Paulo Sibaja *(Sr Acct Exec)*
Abby Eastman *(Dir-Events & Comm)*

SUSAN SCHEIN AUTOMOTIVE
3171 Pelham Pkwy, Pelham, AL 35124
Tel.: (205) 664-1491
Web Site:
  http://www.susanschein.com
Sales Range: $25-49.9 Million
Emp.: 60
Automobiles, New & Used
N.A.I.C.S.: 441110
Susan Schein *(Pres)*

SUSPECT DETECTION SYSTEMS INC.
150 W 56th St Ste 4005, New York, NY 10019
Tel.: (973) 536-1016 DE
Year Founded: 2006
SDSS—(OTCBB)
Holding Company; Counter-Terrorism & Crime Prevention Technologies Mfr
N.A.I.C.S.: 551112

Subsidiaries:

Suspect Detection Systems Ltd. (1)
POB 121, Shoham, 69850, Israel
Tel.: (972) 544233181
Web Site: http://www.sds-cogito.com
Counter-Terrorism & Crime Prevention Technologies Developer
N.A.I.C.S.: 561621

SUSQUE-VIEW HOME, INC.
22 Cree Dr, Lock Haven, PA 17745
Tel.: (570) 748-9377 PA
Web Site:
  http://www.susqueviewhome.com
Year Founded: 1976
Sales Range: $10-24.9 Million
Emp.: 196
Nursing Care Services
N.A.I.C.S.: 623110
Rita Foley *(Dir-HR)*
Tina Yothers *(Dir-Nursing)*

SUSQUEHANNA INTERNATIONAL GROUP, LLP
401 E City Ave, Bala Cynwyd, PA 19004-1122
Tel.: (610) 617-2600 PA
Web Site: http://www.sig.com
Year Founded: 1987
Sales Range: $200-249.9 Million
Emp.: 900
Investment Research, Securities Brokerage, Investment Banking & Venture Capital Services
N.A.I.C.S.: 523150
Davita Brown *(Mgr-Accts Payable)*
Michelle Becht *(Mgr-IB Ops)*
Jeffery Shiflett *(Mgr-Global Support Svcs)*
Ron Dziuk *(Engr-Software)*
Mark Montemuro *(Engr-Sys Test)*
Jason Neer *(Assoc Dir)*
Igor Yudilevich *(Engr-Application Support)*
Brad Alles *(Mgr-Investment)*
Lloyd Smith *(Project Mgr-IT)*

SUSQUEHANNA INTERNATIONAL GROUP, LLP

Subsidiaries:

SIG Asia Investments, LLLP (1)
Suite 1705-09 Corporate Avenue 222 Hu Bin Road, Shanghai, 200021, China
Tel.: (86) 21 6122 2888
Web Site: http://www.sig-china.com
Investment Management Service
N.A.I.C.S.: 523940

Susquehanna Growth Equity, LLC (1)
401 City Ave Ste 220, Bala Cynwyd, PA 19004
Tel.: (610) 617-2600
Web Site: http://www.sgep.com
Emp.: 12
Investment Management Service
N.A.I.C.S.: 523940
Jonathan Klahr *(Mng Dir)*
Ben Weinberg *(Mng Dir)*
Scott J. Feldman *(Mng Dir)*
Amir Goldman *(Founder)*

Susquehanna International Securities, Ltd. (1)
International Centre Memorial Road IFSC, Dublin, Ireland
Tel.: (353) 1 802 8000
Securities Brokerage Services
N.A.I.C.S.: 523150

Susquehanna Private Capital, LLC (1)
401 E City Ave, Bala Cynwyd, PA 19004
Tel.: (610) 617-2600
Web Site: http://www.spcllc.com
Privater Equity Firm
N.A.I.C.S.: 523999
Amir Goldman *(Founder)*
Kyle Squillario *(Head)*
John McGinley *(VP)*

Holding (Domestic):

Premium Service Brands LLC (2)
126 Garrett St Ste J, Charlottesville, VA 22902
Tel.: (855) 908-3540
Home Furtinute & Fixture Services
N.A.I.C.S.: 337126
Paul Flick *(CEO)*

Subsidiary (Domestic):

The Grout Medic LLC (3)
2241 E Continental Blvd Ste 150, Southlake, TX 76092-6092
Tel.: (817) 416-7600
Web Site: http://www.thegroutmedic.com
Commercial & Institutional Building Construction
N.A.I.C.S.: 236220
Sue Johnston *(Dir-Franchise Admin & Customer Svc)*

Holding (Domestic):

Quality Collision Group, LLC (2)
211 E 7th St Ste 620, Austin, TX 78701
Tel.: (214) 221-6999
Web Site:
  https://www.qualitycollisiongroup.com
Emp.: 135
Motor Vehicles Mfr
N.A.I.C.S.: 336211
Mario Sano *(VP-Ops)*

Subsidiary (Domestic):

Brandywine Coach Works, Inc. (3)
891 S Matlock St, West Chester, PA 19382
Tel.: (610) 344-0800
Web Site:
  http://www.brandywinecoachworks.com
Automotive Body, Paint & Interior Repair & Maintenance
N.A.I.C.S.: 811121
Michelle Lewis *(Dir-Mktg)*

CCRO, LLC (3)
175 N 1200 E, Lehi, UT 84043-2224
Tel.: (801) 224-8020
Web Site: http://www.cascadecollision.com
Automotive Body, Paint & Interior Repair & Maintenance
N.A.I.C.S.: 811121
Terri Nichols *(Pres)*

Paramount Centre, Inc. (3)

SUSQUEHANNA INTERNATIONAL GROUP, LLP

Susquehanna International Group, LLP—(Continued)

6005 12th St E, Tacoma, WA 98424
Tel.: (253) 896-4400
Web Site: http://www.paramountcentre.com
Sales Range: $1-9.9 Million
Emp.: 25
Automotive Body, Paint & Interior Repair & Maintenance
N.A.I.C.S.: 811121

Schaefer Autobody Centers (3)
300 Biltmore Dr Ste 320, Fenton, MO 63026
Tel.: (636) 305-8288
Web Site: http://www.schaeferautobody.com
Sales Range: $1-9.9 Million
Emp.: 85
Top And Body Repair And Paint Shops
N.A.I.C.S.: 811121
Steve Schaefer (Pres)
Kevin Haller (Gen Mgr)
Jaime Matthews (VP)

Trew Auto Body, Inc. (3)
3700 W Loxie Eagans Blvd, Bremerton, WA 98312
Tel.: (360) 479-8739
Web Site: http://www.trewautobody.com
Sales Range: $1-9.9 Million
Emp.: 20
Automotive Repair & Maintenance Services
N.A.I.C.S.: 811121

U.S. Mills, LLC (1)
200 Reservoir St, Needham, MA 02494-3191
Tel.: (781) 444-0440
Sales Range: $10-24.9 Million
Emp.: 12
Breakfast Food & Cereal Mfr
N.A.I.C.S.: 311230

SUSSEX PUBLISHERS, LLC
115 E 23rd St 9th Fl, New York, NY 10010
Tel.: (212) 260-7210   DE
Web Site: http://www.psychologytoday.com
Year Founded: 1967
Sales Range: $10-24.9 Million
Emp.: 20
Publisher of Magazines
N.A.I.C.S.: 513120
Jo Colman (CEO)
Diana Sofko (Dir-Adv-West)
Ed Levine (Dir-Creative)
John Thomas (Publr & Exec VP)
Kaja Perina (Editor-in-Chief)
Robert Berner (Dir-Circulation)
Crispin Roven (VP-Product)

Subsidiaries:

Psychology Today (1)
115 E 23rd St 9th Fl, New York, NY 10010-6224
Tel.: (212) 260-7210
Web Site: http://www.psychologytoday.com
Sales Range: $10-24.9 Million
Magazine Publisher
N.A.I.C.S.: 513120
Jo Colman (CEO)
Ed Levine (Dir-Creative)
Charmine Bowden (Controller)
John Thomas (VP & Publr)
Kaja Perina (Editor-in-Chief)
Batya Lahav (VP-Bus Dev)
Robert Berner (Dir-Circulation)
Al Berman (Dir-Adv-Natl)
Diana Sofko (Dir-Adv-Northwest)
Mary Beth Lee (Dir-Adv-Southwest)
Matt Huston (Editor-News)
Crispin Roven (VP-Product)

SUSSEX RURAL ELECTRIC COOPERATIVE
64 Route 639, Sussex, NJ 07461
Tel.: (973) 875-5101
Web Site: http://www.sussexrec.com
Sales Range: $10-24.9 Million
Emp.: 47
Distribution, Electric Power
N.A.I.C.S.: 221122
Jack Haggerty (Chm)

SUSSMAN SALES COMPANY
250 East 54th St Ste 8A, New York, NY 10022
Tel.: (212) 371-9199
Web Site: http://www.sussmansales.com
Year Founded: 1971
Sales Range: $25-49.9 Million
Emp.: 21
Curriculum & Library Resources
N.A.I.C.S.: 611710
Ron Sussman (Pres-Sls Div)
Steve Sussman (Pres-Curriculum Div)

SUSTAINABLE COMFORT, INC.
146 Main St 3rd Fl, Worcester, MA 01608
Tel.: (508) 713-6680
Web Site: http://www.greenrater.com
Year Founded: 2014
Sales Range: $1-9.9 Million
Emp.: 31
Commercial Building Construction Services
N.A.I.C.S.: 236220
Albert LaValley (Co-Founder, Chm & Pres)
James Moriarty (Co-Founder & VP)
Andrea French (VP)
Chris Straile (Dir-Ops)
Elizabeth Brooks (Creative Dir)

SUSTAINABLE HARVEST COFFEE IMPORTERS
721 NW 9th Ave Ste 235, Portland, OR 97209
Tel.: (503) 235-1119
Web Site: http://www.sustainableharvest.com
Year Founded: 1997
Rev.: $20,200,000
Emp.: 22
Consumer Products & Services
N.A.I.C.S.: 311920
Oscar Canseco Magro (CTO)
Laura Parras (Dir-Fin)
Claudia Rocio Gomez (Mgr-Coffee Quality)
Dalila Portillo (Mgr-Customer Care)
Midori Hartford (Mgr-Import-North America)
Dane Loraas (Mgr-Relationship Coffee)
Wynne McAuley (Mgr-Relationship Coffee)

SUSTAINABLE INNOVATIONS, LLC
111 Roberts St, East Hartford, CT 06108
Tel.: (860) 652-9690
Web Site: http://www.sustainableinnov.com
Year Founded: 2007
Research & Development in the Physical, Engineering & Life Sciences
N.A.I.C.S.: 541715
Trent M. Molter (Founder)

SUSTAINSERV, INC.
31 State St 10th Fl, Boston, MA 02109
Tel.: (617) 330-5001   MA
Web Site: http://www.sustainserv.com
Year Founded: 2001
Management Consulting Services
N.A.I.C.S.: 541611
Matthew Gardner (Mng Partner)
Bernd Kasemir (Mng Partner)
Jeff Gowdy (Dir)

Subsidiaries:

J. Gowdy Consulting, LLC (1)
P.O. Box 128334, Nashville, TN 37215

Tel.: (615) 752-9329
Web Site: http://www.jgowdyconsulting.com
Management Consulting Services
N.A.I.C.S.: 541618
Jeff Gowdy (Founder)

SUSTINERE HOLDINGS, INC.
14201 N Hayden Rd Ste A-1, Scottsdale, AZ 85260
Tel.: (480) 659-6404   NV
Year Founded: 2017
Assets: $18,034
Liabilities: $25,833
Net Worth: ($7,799)
Earnings: ($47,194)
Fiscal Year-end: 12/31/18
Investment Services
N.A.I.C.S.: 523999
Neil Reithinger (Pres & Treas)
Christopher McCrory (Sec)

SUTHERLAND BUILDING MATERIAL COMPANY
302 E S St, Ozark, MO 65721
Tel.: (417) 581-7571
Web Site: http://www.sutherlands.com
Sales Range: $10-24.9 Million
Emp.: 25
Millwork & Lumber
N.A.I.C.S.: 444110
Thomas Sutherland (Partner)
Harlan Jones (Office Mgr)

SUTHERLAND GLOBAL SERVICES, INC.
1160 Pittsford Victor Rd, Pittsford, NY 14534-3825
Tel.: (585) 586-5757
Web Site: http://www.sutherlandglobal.com
Year Founded: 1986
Sales Range: $800-899.9 Million
Emp.: 30,000
Business Process Outsourcing Services
N.A.I.C.S.: 541519
Dilip R. Vellodi (Chm & CEO)
Ashok Jain (COO)
K. S. Kumar (Chief Comml Officer)
James S. Lusk (CFO)
Deepak Batheja (CTO)
Iris Goldfein (Chief People Officer)
H. Nancy Breed (VP-Indus Mktg)
Jan Uhrich (Chief Delivery Officer)
Darin C. Wright (Chief Client Engagement Officer)
Christopher Schyma (Head-Retail)
Sonia Sedler (Mng Dir)

Subsidiaries:

Apollo Health Street Ltd (1)
Apollo Health City, Jubilee Hills, Hyderabad, 500 096, Andhra Pradesh, India
Tel.: (91) 4023554000
Web Site: http://www.apollohealthstreet.com
Sales Range: $75-99.9 Million
Emp.: 3,000
Healthcare Business Process Outsourcing Services
N.A.I.C.S.: 561499

Subsidiary (US):

Apollo Health Street, Inc. (2)
225 Washington St Ste 250, Conshohocken, PA 19428
Tel.: (770) 280-2630
Web Site: http://www.apollohealthstreet.com
Sales Range: $125-149.9 Million
Emp.: 1,000
Healthcare Business Process Outsourcing & Enterprise Support Solutions Services
N.A.I.C.S.: 561499
Amy Grazer (Head-Strategic Initiatives & Brand)
Graham Hughes (Chief Medical Officer)
Thomas Laur (CEO)
Tom McCormick (Chief Comml Officer)

Ranjit Pisharoty (Chief Operating & Delivery Officer)
Karen Pugh (Head-Compliance)
Marie Sonde (CFO)

Sutherland (Suzhou) Information Consulting Co., Ltd. (1)
Unit 11-5A0 Creative Industrial Park 328 Xinghu Street, Suzhou Industrial Park, Suzhou, China
Tel.: (86) 18626240499
Business Process Outsourcing Services
N.A.I.C.S.: 561410

Sutherland Global Services Egypt, LLC (1)
7th Floor-1 Mahmoud Said St Shohada Square Main Post Office Building, Alexandria, Egypt
Tel.: (20) 3992000
Business Process Outsourcing Services
N.A.I.C.S.: 561410

Sutherland Global Services JLT (1)
JLT Clusrer T Fortune Executive Tower, PO Box 336954, Dubai, United Arab Emirates
Tel.: (971) 44320666
Web Site: http://www.sutherlandglobal.com
Business Process Outsourcing Services
N.A.I.C.S.: 561410

SUTHERLAND LUMBER & HOME CENTER INC.
3008 W Main St, Jenks, OK 74037
Tel.: (918) 296-4334   DE
Web Site: http://www.sutherlands.com
Year Founded: 1973
Sales Range: $25-49.9 Million
Emp.: 598
Lumber & Other Building Materials
N.A.I.C.S.: 459110
Peggy Folz (Sec)

SUTHERLAND LUMBER CO.
4000 Main St, Kansas City, MO 64117
Tel.: (816) 756-3000   MO
Web Site: http://www.sutherlandlumber.com
Year Founded: 1920
Sales Range: $100-124.9 Million
Emp.: 150
Home Improvement Products & Lumber Retail Stores
N.A.I.C.S.: 423310
Steven Scott (CFO & Controller)
Tina Keller (Mgr-Adv)

SUTHERLAND MANAGEMENT COMPANY
4394 Bonita Rd, Bonita, CA 91902
Tel.: (619) 482-2945
Sales Range: $10-24.9 Million
Emp.: 500
Franchise Owner of Fast-Food Restaurants
N.A.I.C.S.: 722513
Robert R. Sutherland (Owner)
Allan Kodicek (Controller)

SUTHERLAND'S FOODSERVICE, INC.
State Farmers Market 16 Forest Pkwy Bldg K, Forest Park, GA 30297
Tel.: (404) 366-8550
Web Site: http://www.suthfood.com
Sales Range: $125-149.9 Million
Emp.: 160
Producer & Retailer of Poultry, Eggs, Fruits, Vegetables, Meats, Dairy Products & Groceries
N.A.I.C.S.: 424440
Bonnie S. Wilson (Treas & VP)
James E. Sutherland Jr. (Pres)

SUTHERLIN AUTOMOTIVE GROUP, LLC
1855 Luke King Pkwy, Buford, GA 30519

Tel.: (678) 971-0334
Web Site:
https://www.sutherlinautomotive.com
Automobile Dealers
N.A.I.C.S.: 441110
Brett Sutherlin (CEO)

Subsidiaries:

Duff Auto Sales, Inc (1)
1028 S Roane St, Harriman, TN 37748-7418
Tel.: (865) 882-0113
Web Site: http://www.duffsubaru.com
New Car Dealers
N.A.I.C.S.: 441110
Tim Duff (Owner)

SUTLIFF AUTO GROUP
802 S 16th St, Harrisburg, PA 17105
Web Site: http://www.sutliffauto.com
Holding Company; Automotive Dealerships Owner & Operator
N.A.I.C.S.: 551112
Jonathan Casey (Pres)

Subsidiaries:

Sutliff Buick GMC Cadillac (1)
169 W Aaron Dr, State College, PA 16803
Tel.: (814) 308-0430
Web Site: http://www.sutliffbuick.com
Emp.: 30
New & Used Car Dealer
N.A.I.C.S.: 441110
Bill Kauffman (Dir-Ops)
Rob Gottshall (Sls Mgr)
Carrie Miller (Mgr-Fin)
John Lamotte (Mgr-Svc)

Sutliff Chevrolet Co. (1)
1251 Paxton St, Harrisburg, PA 17104
Tel.: (717) 234-4444
Web Site: http://www.sutliffchevrolet.com
Sales Range: $75-99.9 Million
Emp.: 550
New & Used Car Dealer
N.A.I.C.S.: 441110
Gregory L. Sutliff (Chm)
Perry Hurley (Mgr-Fin)
Robert Fannasy (VP & Mgr-Svc)
David Trone (Office Mgr)
Jonathan Casey (Gen Mgr)
Jeff Lang (Mgr-New Sls)
Jeffrey Millar (VP)

SUTTER HEALTH
2200 River Plaza Dr, Sacramento, CA 95833-4134
Tel.: (916) 733-8800   CA
Web Site: http://www.sutterhealth.org
Year Founded: 1981
Sales Range: $1-4.9 Billion
Emp.: 48,000
Health Care Services Administration Organization
N.A.I.C.S.: 813910
Dominic J. Nakis (Interim CFO & Sr VP)
Warner L. Thomas (Pres & CEO)
Grace Davis (Chief External Affairs Officer)

Subsidiaries:

Alta Bates Summit Medical Center (1)
350 Hawthorne Ave, Oakland, CA 94609-3108
Tel.: (510) 655-4000
Web Site: http://www.sutterhealth.org
Sales Range: $50-74.9 Million
Emp.: 5,000
Hospital Operator
N.A.I.C.S.: 622110
Chuck Prosper (CEO)

California Pacific Medical Center (1)
2333 Buchanan St, San Francisco, CA 94115-1925
Tel.: (415) 600-6000
Web Site: http://www.cpmc.org

Sales Range: $150-199.9 Million
Emp.: 1,000
Hospital Operator
N.A.I.C.S.: 622110
Hamila Kownacki (COO)
Nina Pacheco (Officer-Compliance)
Warren Browner (CEO)

Eden Medical Center (1)
20103 Lake Chabot Rd, Castro Valley, CA 94546
Tel.: (510) 537-1234
Web Site: http://www.sutterhealth.org
Sales Range: $50-74.9 Million
Emp.: 1,000
Hospital Operator
N.A.I.C.S.: 622110
Terry Glubka (CEO)
Bryan Daylor (COO)
Julie Peterson (CFO)
David Davini (Chm)
Kent Myers (Vice Chm)
Jeffrey Randall (Sec)

Mills-Peninsula Medical Center (1)
1501 Trousdale Dr, Burlingame, CA 94010
Tel.: (650) 696-5400
Web Site: http://www.mills-peninsula.org
Hospital Operator
N.A.I.C.S.: 622110
Yuk Wong (Mgr)

Sutter Amador Hospital (1)
200 Mission Blvd, Jackson, CA 95642
Tel.: (209) 223-7500
Web Site: http://www.sutterhealth.org
Hospital Operator
N.A.I.C.S.: 622110

Sutter Davis Hospital (1)
2000 Sutter Pl, Davis, CA 95616-6201
Tel.: (530) 756-6440
Web Site: http://www.sutterdavis.org
Hospital Operator
N.A.I.C.S.: 622110
Chris Dechoretz (Pres)
Rachael McKinney (CEO)

Sutter Delta Medical Center (1)
3901 Lone Tree Way, Antioch, CA 94509
Tel.: (925) 779-7200
Web Site: http://www.sutterhealth.org
Hospital Operator
N.A.I.C.S.: 622110

Sutter Lakeside Hospital (1)
5176 Hill Rd E, Lakeport, CA 95453-6357
Tel.: (707) 262-5000
Web Site:
http://www.sutterlakesidehospital.org
Hospital Operator
N.A.I.C.S.: 622110
Dan Peterson (Chief Admin Officer)

Sutter Medical Center Foundation (1)
1201 Alhmbra Blvd Ste 320, Sacramento, CA 95816
Web Site: http://www.sutterhealth.org
Health Care Services Organization
N.A.I.C.S.: 813920

Sutter Medical Center, Sacramento (1)
2825 Capitol Ave, Sacramento, CA 95816
Tel.: (916) 887-0000
Web Site:
http://www.suttermedicalcenter.org
Sales Range: $1-9.9 Million
Emp.: 60
Hospital Operator
N.A.I.C.S.: 622110

SUTTER INSURANCE COMPANY
1301 Redwood Way Ste 200, Petaluma, CA 94954
Tel.: (707) 793-0808
Web Site:
http://www.sutterinsurance.com
Sales Range: $10-24.9 Million
Emp.: 20
Automobile Insurance
N.A.I.C.S.: 524126
Angie Husk (Gen Mgr)
Bill Kleinecke (Pres)
George Lindh (VP-Claims)

SUTTER ROOFING COMPANY OF FLORIDA
8284 Vico Ct, Sarasota, FL 34240
Tel.: (941) 377-1000
Web Site:
http://www.sutterroofing.com
Year Founded: 1902
Sales Range: $10-24.9 Million
Emp.: 234
Roofing Contractors
N.A.I.C.S.: 238160
Stephen F. Sutter (Chm)
Douglas C. Sutter (Pres)
John Kenney (COO)

SUTTER'S PLACE INC.
1801 Bering Dr, San Jose, CA 95112
Tel.: (408) 451-8888
Web Site: http://www.bay101.com
Year Founded: 1994
Sales Range: $25-49.9 Million
Emp.: 600
Amusement & Recreation
N.A.I.C.S.: 713990
Timothy Bumb (Pres)

SUTTLE EQUIPMENT INC.
1390 Hwy 70 W 71 E, De Queen, AR 71832-2911
Tel.: (870) 584-4434   AR
Web Site:
http://www.suttleequipment.com
Year Founded: 1970
Sales Range: $10-24.9 Million
Emp.: 45
Logging Equipment Sales & Service
N.A.I.C.S.: 423810
Jim McLaughlin (CFO)
David Whisenhunt (Mgr-Sls)

SUTTLE MOTOR CORP.
12525 Jefferson Ave, Newport News, VA 23602-4313
Tel.: (757) 886-1700
Web Site: http://www.suttlemotors.net
Sales Range: $25-49.9 Million
Emp.: 150
Car Whslr
N.A.I.C.S.: 441110
Michael Suttle III (Pres)

SUTTON CORPORATION
611 E Stevenson Rd, Ottawa, IL 61350
Tel.: (815) 434-9707
Web Site: http://www.sshe.com
Sales Range: $25-49.9 Million
Emp.: 140
Diet Foods
N.A.I.C.S.: 424490
Seattle Sutton (Founder & Pres)

SUTTON FERNERIES, INC.
1950 NW 89th Pl, Doral, FL 33172
Tel.: (305) 477-4776   FL
Web Site: http://www.suttonfern.com
Year Founded: 1987
Sales Range: $1-9.9 Million
Emp.: 60
Ferns & Foliage Nursery
N.A.I.C.S.: 111422
Michele Sutton (Pres)

SUTTON'S WESTERN WHOLESALE FLOORING
823 S Main St, Salt Lake City, UT 84111
Tel.: (801) 363-4563
Web Site: http://www.carpet1.com
Rev.: $20,937,981
Emp.: 30
Carpets
N.A.I.C.S.: 449121
William Sutton (Pres)

SUVANZA

5401 Collins Ave Ste CU-9A, Miami Beach, FL 33140
Year Founded: 1998
Pharmaceuticals Product Mfr
N.A.I.C.S.: 325412
Luis Nunez (Pres)

SUWANNEE RIVER RENDEZVOUS RESORT & CAMPGROUND
828 NE Primrose Rd, Mayo, FL 32066
Tel.: (386) 294-2510
Web Site:
http://www.suwanneeriverrendezvous.com
Sales Range: $1-9.9 Million
Emp.: 9
RV Park & Campground
N.A.I.C.S.: 721211
Frank Page (Co-Owner)
Susie Page (Co-Owner)

SUWANNEE VALLEY ELECTRIC COOPERATIVE, INC.
11340 100th St, Live Oak, FL 32060
Tel.: (386) 362-2226   FL
Web Site: http://www.svec-coop.com
Year Founded: 1967
Sales Range: $50-74.9 Million
Emp.: 101
Electric Power Distr
N.A.I.C.S.: 221122
Andy Lawrence (Dir-Ops)
Vicky Talmadge (Dir-Admin Svcs)
Brenda Pryce (Mgr-Member Svcs)

SUZANNE EVANS COACHING LLC
PO Box 1089, Murrells Inlet, SC 29576
Web Site:
http://www.suzanneevans.org
Year Founded: 2007
Sales Range: $1-9.9 Million
Emp.: 6
Personalized Coaching for Women Business Owners
N.A.I.C.S.: 541618
Suzanne Evans (Founder & Owner)

SUZUKI OF LAKE WALES, INC.
20769 US Hwy 27, Lake Wales, FL 33853
Tel.: (863) 676-2245   FL
Web Site:
http://www.mckibbenpowersportslakewales.com
Year Founded: 1981
Sales Range: $10-24.9 Million
Motorcycle Water Craft ATV & Utility Vehicle Distr
N.A.I.C.S.: 441227
Roc Northey (Owner)

Subsidiaries:

Sky Powersports of Lakeland, Inc. (1)
1638 Kathleen Rd, Lakeland, FL 33805
Tel.: (863) 682-4607
Web Site:
http://www.skypowersportslakeland.com
Sales Range: $1-9.9 Million
Motorcycle Dealers
N.A.I.C.S.: 441227

SV HEALTH INVESTORS, LLP
1 Boston Pl 201 Washington St Ste 3900, Boston, MA 02108
Tel.: (617) 367-8100
Web Site:
http://svhealthinvestors.com
Life Sciences Venture Capital Firm
N.A.I.C.S.: 523999

SV HEALTH INVESTORS, LLP

SV Health Investors, LLP—(Continued)
Thomas M. Patton *(Operating Partner)*
Greg Madden *(Mng Partner)*
A.J. Rossi *(Principal)*
Bruce A. Peacock *(Partner-Venture)*
Eugene Hill *(Chm)*
Tom Flynn *(Mng Partner-Healthcare)*
Hamish Cameron *(Partner-Operating)*
Catherine Bingham *(Mng Partner-Biotechnology)*
Michael Balmuth *(Partner-Healthcare Svcs)*
Daniel D. Burgess *(Venture Partner)*
Denise Marks *(CFO)*
David Milne *(Mng Partner)*
Ravi Madduri Rao *(Venture Partner)*

Subsidiaries:

Robling Medical, Inc. (1)
90 Weathers St, Youngsville, NC 27596
Tel.: (919) 570-9605
Web Site: http://www.roblingmedical.com
Dental Equipment & Supplies Mfr
N.A.I.C.S.: 339114
Scott Culbreth *(Project Mgr-Engrg)*
Brent Robling *(Founder, Pres & CEO)*

Ximedica LLC (1)
55 Dupont Dr, Providence, RI 02907
Tel.: (401) 330-3163
Web Site: http://www.ximedica.com
Sales Range: $1-9.9 Million
Emp.: 125
Medical Technology Services
N.A.I.C.S.: 541715
Randall S. Barko *(Exec Dir)*
Aidan Petrie *(Founder)*
Robert Brown *(CEO)*
Tracy MacNeal *(Pres-Diagnostics & Digital Health)*
Michael Pereira *(Pres & COO-Medical Tech & Drug Delivery Sys)*

Subsidiary (Domestic):

Bridge Design, Inc. (2)
375 Alabama St Ste 410, San Francisco, CA 94110
Tel.: (415) 487-7100
Web Site: http://www.bridgedesign.com
Sales Range: $1-9.9 Million
Emp.: 25
Engineering Services
N.A.I.C.S.: 541330
Bill Evans *(Pres)*
Diana Greenberg *(Dir-User Experience Design)*
Solene Bourgeois *(Dir-Indus & Interaction Design)*
Stacy Evans *(Controller & Office Mgr)*

SV INVESTMENT PARTNERS

1700 E Putnam Ave, Greenwich, CT 06870
Tel.: (212) 735-0700
Web Site: http://www.svip.com
Year Founded: 1998
Privater Equity Firm
N.A.I.C.S.: 523999
Steven W. Korn *(Sr Operating Partner)*
Nicholas Somers *(Mng Partner)*
Philip Cole *(Principal)*

Subsidiaries:

Pennysaver Group Inc. (1)
1342 Charwood Rd, Hanover, MD 21076-3113
Tel.: (410) 865-4546
Web Site: http://www.mdpennysaver.com
Sales Range: $25-49.9 Million
Emp.: 100
Shopper & Community Newspaper Publisher
N.A.I.C.S.: 513199
Chris Shertzer *(VP-Sls)*

SVAM INTERNATIONAL, INC.

233 E Shore Rd Ste 201, Great Neck, NY 11023
Tel.: (516) 466-6655
Web Site: http://www.svam.com
Year Founded: 1994
Sales Range: $10-24.9 Million
Emp.: 65
IT Solutions & Staffing Services
N.A.I.C.S.: 541519
Anil Kapoor *(Pres & CEO)*
Vikas Dhablania *(COO)*
Manav Bhasin *(Mng Dir-Bus Dev)*
Michael Capilets *(Mng Dir-Sls)*
Allen Goldin *(Mng Dir-Pub Sector)*

Subsidiaries:

SVAM, India-North Shore Technologies (1)
Logix Techno Park 1st-Floor Tower B Plot No 5 Sector 127, Noida, 201301, India
Tel.: (91) 120 4043400
Web Site: http://www.svam.com
Technical Support Service Infrastructure & System Integration Services
N.A.I.C.S.: 541990

SVB FOOD & BEVERAGE CO.

717 Corning Way, Martinsburg, WV 25405
Tel.: (304) 267-8500
Web Site: https://www.svbfoods.com
Year Founded: 2012
Food Mfr
N.A.I.C.S.: 311999
Terry Hess *(CEO)*

Subsidiaries:

Vita Food Products, Inc. (1)
2222 W Lake St, Chicago, IL 60613
Tel.: (312) 738-4500
Web Site: http://www.vitafoodproducts.com
Sales Range: $50-74.9 Million
Emp.: 178
Herring & Smoked-Fish Products
N.A.I.C.S.: 311710
Clark L. Feldman *(Sec & Exec VP)*
Clifford K. Bolen *(Pres & CEO)*
Blanca Resendiz *(Mgr-Accts Payable)*
Angela Earll *(Mgr-Quality Assurance)*
Joan White *(Mgr-Customer Svc)*

Subsidiary (Domestic):

Vita Specialty Foods (2)
PO Box 1915, Inwood, WV 25428-1915
Tel.: (304) 263-0946
Honey & Molasses Packaging Facility
N.A.I.C.S.: 424490

SVB&T CORPORATION

505 S Maple St, French Lick, IN 47432
Tel.: (812) 936-9961
Web Site: http://www.svbt.com
Year Founded: 1903
Sales Range: $25-49.9 Million
Emp.: 75
Bank Holding Company
N.A.I.C.S.: 551111
Jamie Shinavarger *(Pres)*

Subsidiaries:

Springs Valley Bank & Trust Co. (1)
1500 Main St, Jasper, IN 47546
Tel.: (812) 634-1010
Web Site: http://www.svbt.bank
Rev: $7,053,000
Emp.: 42
Banking Services
N.A.I.C.S.: 522110
Carol Singelstad *(Branch Mgr)*
Nicole Ford *(Branch Mgr)*

SVENHARD'S SWEDISH BAKERY INC.

335 Adeline St, Oakland, CA 94607-2519
Tel.: (510) 834-5035 CA
Web Site: http://www.svenhards.com
Year Founded: 1963
Sales Range: $25-49.9 Million
Emp.: 300
Provider of Bakery Services
N.A.I.C.S.: 311812

Ronny D. Svenhard *(Pres)*
Michelle Barnette *(CEO)*
David Kunkle *(COO)*

SVERICA CAPITAL MANAGEMENT LP

1 Boston Pl Ste 3910, Boston, MA 02108
Tel.: (617) 695-0221 DE
Web Site: http://www.sverica.com
Year Founded: 2001
Privater Equity Firm
N.A.I.C.S.: 523999
David Finley *(Mng Partner)*
Jordan Richards *(Mng Partner)*
Frank M. Young *(Mng Partner)*
Ryan Harstad *(Partner)*
Gregg Osenkowski *(Partner)*
George Aggouras *(CFO & Chief Compliance Officer)*
Michael Dougherty *(Principal)*
Greg Hylant *(VP)*
Melanie Fiore *(Ops Mgr)*

Subsidiaries:

Career Quest Learning Centers, Inc. (1)
3215 S Pennsylvania Ave, Lansing, MI 48910
Tel.: (517) 318-3330
Web Site: http://www.cqlc.edu
Sales Range: $1-9.9 Million
Professional Education Centers Operator
N.A.I.C.S.: 611310
Kiyuana Coward *(Dir-Fin Aid)*
Sylvia Jackson *(Dir-Education)*
Robert McCart *(Pres & CEO)*

Center Rock, Inc. (1)
118 Schrock Dr, Berlin, PA 15530
Tel.: (814) 267-7100
Web Site: http://www.centerrock.com
Sales Range: $10-24.9 Million
Emp.: 80
Mining Pneumatic Drill Bits & Equipment Mfr & Distr
N.A.I.C.S.: 333131
Dan Stoner *(Mgr-Sls-Oil & Gas)*
Becky Dorcon *(Mgr-Inside Sls)*
Christen Fisher *(Sls Mgr-Construction-Global)*
Richard Soppe *(Sr Engr-Drilling Application)*

Gener8, LLC (1)
500 Mercury Dr, Sunnyvale, CA 94085
Tel.: (650) 940-9898
Web Site: http://www.gener8.net
Electronic & Mechanical Products Mfr
N.A.I.C.S.: 335999
David Klein *(Founder)*
James Quigley *(Engr-Software)*
Julie DuPre *(Office Mgr)*
Jerry Hurst *(Mgr-Engrg)*

Subsidiary (Domestic):

Symbient Product Development, LLC (2)
2077 Las Palmas Dr, Carlsbad, CA 92011
Tel.: (760) 687-4030
Web Site: http://www.symbientpd.com
Medical Product Development Services
N.A.I.C.S.: 339112
Scott Castanon *(Founder)*

Offsite Archive Storage & Integrated Services Limited (1)
Unit 15C Kinsealy Business Park, Kinsealy, Dublin, Ireland
Tel.: (353) 1 866 6317
Web Site: http://www.oasisgroup.eu
Emp.: 120
Holding Company; Records & Information Management Services
N.A.I.C.S.: 551112
Ronnie Carroll *(Exec VP-Ops & Sls)*
Brian Connolly *(CEO)*
Darren Walsh *(VP-Ops)*
Claire Gallagher *(Exec VP-Admin)*
Sarah Sweeney *(CFO)*

Subsidiary (Domestic):

Offsite Archive Storage & Integrated Services (Ireland) Limited (2)

U.S. PRIVATE

Unit 15C Kinsealy Business Park, Kinsealy, Dublin, Ireland
Tel.: (353) 1 866 6317
Web Site: http://www.oasisgroup.eu
Record & Information Management Services
N.A.I.C.S.: 561990
Darren Walsh *(VP-Ops)*

RestorixHealth LLC (1)
155 White Plains Rd, Tarrytown, NY 10591
Tel.: (914) 372-3150
Web Site: http://www.restorixhealth.com
Emp.: 50
Chronic Wound Healthcare Services
N.A.I.C.S.: 621399
Steve McLaughlin *(CEO)*
Leigh Boyd *(Sr VP-Bus Dev)*
Christopher A. Mitchell *(COO)*
Jeff Bowman *(Pres-Post-Acute Ops)*
Jill Garretson *(VP-Mktg)*

SG Homecare, Inc. (1)
15602 Mosher Ave, Tustin, CA 92780
Tel.: (949) 474-2050
Health & Personal Care Stores
N.A.I.C.S.: 456199
Candace Lee *(Pres)*
Randy Rowley *(Founder & CEO)*
Charles Lee *(Pres)*
Alexandra Hren *(Dir-Client Svcs)*

Sverica International (Boston) LLC (1)
Prudential Tower 800 Boylston St Ste 3325, Boston, MA 02199-8146
Tel.: (617) 695-0221
Web Site: http://www.sverica.com
Privater Equity Firm
N.A.I.C.S.: 523999
David Finley *(Mng Dir)*
Gregg Osenkowski *(VP)*
Melanie Fiore *(Mgr-Ops)*
Jordan Richards *(Mng Dir)*
Frank Young *(Mng Dir)*

Sverica International (San Francisco) LLC (1)
44 Montgomery St Ste 3000, San Francisco, CA 94104
Tel.: (415) 249-4906
Web Site: http://www.sverica.com
Investment Management Service
N.A.I.C.S.: 523940
Jordan Richards *(Mng Partner)*
Frank M. Young *(Mng Partner)*
Ryan Harstad *(Principal)*
David Finley *(Mng Partner)*
Melanie Fiore *(Mgr-Ops)*
George Aggouras *(CFO & Chief Compliance Officer)*
Gregg Osenkowski *(Principal)*

Synoptek, LLC (1)
19520 Jamboree Rd Ste 110, Irvine, CA 92612
Tel.: (949) 241-8600
Web Site: http://www.synoptek.com
Emp.: 800
IT Consulting & Services
N.A.I.C.S.: 541512
Timothy J. Britt *(CEO)*
Miguel Sanchez *(Sr VP-Professional Svcs)*
Mike Bank *(VP-Sls & Channel Alliances)*
John Frazier *(COO)*
Jeremy Daum *(CFO)*
Genya Akselrod *(Dir-Practice-Bus Applications-CRM)*
Bo Bray *(VP-ITSM & Ops)*
Brian Engel *(Sr Dir-Dynamics ERP Practice)*
Chris Gebhardt *(Chief Information Security Officer)*
Alexandra Gorrell *(Mktg Dir)*
Jeff Green *(Dir-Contracts)*
Jitendra Jani *(VP-Intl Sls)*
Joey Lei *(Dir-Svc Dev & Mgmt)*
Manoj Nair *(Dir-Practice-Bus Applications-ERP)*
Nandita Nityanandam *(Mktg Dir)*
Vanessa Novak *(Corp Counsel)*
Nisha Pillai *(Sr Dir-Delivery Excellence)*
Tiago Silverio Da Silva *(Dir-Practice-Bus Applications-ERP)*
Manan Thakkar *(Mgr-Practice-Consulting)*
Bridget Towt *(Dir-Practice-Infrastructure Performance)*
Lana Vernovsky *(VP-Bus Applications)*
Morgann Walker *(Controller)*
Darren White *(Dir-Practice-Cloud Advancement)*

Debbie Zelten (Dir-Practice-Custom Applications & Data Analytics)
Ian Au-Yeung (Chief Revenue Officer)

Subsidiary (Domestic):

Dynamics Resources Inc. (2)
935 Lakeview Pkwy Ste 105, Vernon Hills, IL 60061
Tel.: (847) 361-1978
Web Site: http://www.dynamics-resources.com
Information Technology Support Services
N.A.I.C.S.: 541512
Edward Tarnovsky (CEO)
Lana Vernovsky (COO)
Yury Zabella (CFO)

Rapid Technologies Inc. (2)
200 W Plaza Dr Ste 140, Highlands Ranch, CO 80129
Tel.: (303) 948-1014
Web Site: http://www.raptek.com
Rev.: $2,000,000
Emp.: 15
Computer System Design Services
N.A.I.C.S.: 541512
David Wilmot (Pres)

SVK SYSTEMS
11465 Johns Creek Pkwy Ste 180, Johns Creek, GA 30097
Tel.: (205) 267-5716
Web Site:
  http://www.svksystems.com
Year Founded: 2003
Sales Range: $10-24.9 Million
Emp.: 300
Systems Integration, Software Development & IT Staffing Services
N.A.I.C.S.: 513210
Hanuman Nandanampati (Pres)
Vijay Rao (Mgr)

SVOBODA CAPITAL PARTNERS LLC
1 N Franklin St Ste 1500, Chicago, IL 60606
Tel.: (312) 267-8750
Web Site: http://www.svoco.com
Year Founded: 1998
Sales Range: $10-24.9 Million
Emp.: 10
Privater Equity Firm
N.A.I.C.S.: 523999
John A. Svoboda (Founder & Mng Dir)
Andrew B. Albert (Operating Partner & Mng Dir)
Jeffrey S. Piper (Mng Dir)
Peter M. Gotsch (Mng Dir)
Thomas G. Brooker (Mng Dir & Operating Partner)
David B. Rubin (Principal)
Michelle L. Collins (Co-Founder)

SVRC INDUSTRIES, INC.
919 Veterans Memorial Pkwy, Saginaw, MI 48601
Tel.: (989) 752-6176   MI
Web Site:
  http://www.svrcindustries.com
Year Founded: 1962
Sales Range: $10-24.9 Million
Emp.: 248
Vocational Rehabilitation Services
N.A.I.C.S.: 624310
Charleen Boland (Chm)
Rose Jurek (Dir-Rehabilitation)
Pamela Johnson (Mgr-Marketplace)

SVS GROUP INC.
2336 Harrison St, Oakland, CA 94612
Tel.: (510) 923-9898
Web Site: http://www.svsjobs.com
Year Founded: 1996
Sales Range: $10-24.9 Million
Emp.: 29
Employment Placement
N.A.I.C.S.: 561311

Eugene Lupario (Pres)
Amy Farias (Asst Branch Mgr)

SWAG PROMO, INC.
8215 Roswell Rd Bldg 900, Atlanta, GA 30350
Tel.: (470) 769-1622
Web Site: http://www.orderswag.net
Year Founded: 2012
Sales Range: $1-9.9 Million
Emp.: 12
Advertising Agency Services
N.A.I.C.S.: 541810
Jim Owen (Pres)

SWAGELOK COMPANY
29500 Solon Rd, Solon, OH 44139
Tel.: (440) 248-4600   OH
Web Site: https://www.swagelok.com
Year Founded: 1947
Sales Range: Less than $1 Million
Emp.: 5,700
Other Metal Valve & Pipe Fitting Manufacturing
N.A.I.C.S.: 332919
David E. O'Connor (VP-Customer Svc)
Frank J. Roddy (Exec VP-Fin & Admin)
Matthew P. LoPiccolo (VP-Customer Svc & Supply Chain)
David Lucarelli (VP-HR-Global)
James Cavoli (CFO & VP)
Timothy G. Rosengarten (VP-Ops)
David H. Peace (VP-Engrg)
Theresa Polachek (VP-Corp Comm)
Robert G. Wilson (VP-Mktg)
Joey J. Arnold (VP-Continuous Improvement & Quality)
Brent A. Blouch (VP-Sourcing & Logistics-Global)
William A. Canady (Pres & COO)
Chris Nehez (CIO & VP-Info Svcs)
Katie Adelman (Sr Mgr-Global Comm)
Michael J. DiCesare (VP-IT)
Thomas F. Lozick (CEO)

Subsidiaries:

Nippon Swagelok FST Inc. (1)
1-1-1 Naruohama, Nishinomiya, 663-8142, Hyogo, Japan
Tel.: (81) 798 286300
Pipe Fitting Mfr
N.A.I.C.S.: 326122

Swagelok Baku (1)
31/33 Asef Zeynalli Street, Old Town, Baku, AZ1000, Azerbaijan
Tel.: (994) 12492 4617
Web Site: http://www.swagelok.com
Emp.: 2
Fluid System Component Distr
N.A.I.C.S.: 423830
Firuz Aliyev (Branch Mgr)

Swagelok Capital Projects Company (1)
31500 Aurora Rd, Solon, OH 44139
Tel.: (440) 349-5934
Web Site: http://www.swagelok.com
Fluid System Installation Services
N.A.I.C.S.: 237990
Jim Powers (Supvr-Production)

Swagelok Hy-Level (1)
15400 Foltz Pkwy, Strongsville, OH 44149-4737
Tel.: (440) 572-1540
Sales Range: $25-49.9 Million
Emp.: 275
Precision Machined Components & Assemblies
N.A.I.C.S.: 332721

Swagelok Kazakhstan (1)
Abai Str 2A Office 406, 060002, Atyrau, Kazakhstan
Tel.: (7) 7122586132
Web Site: http://www.swagelok.com

Sales Range: $10-24.9 Million
Emp.: 2
Fluid System Component Distr
N.A.I.C.S.: 423830
Askhat Gabdulov (Gen Dir)

SWAIM INC.
1801 S College Dr, High Point, NC 27260
Tel.: (336) 885-6131
Web Site: http://www.swaim-inc.com
Rev.: $25,000,000
Emp.: 180
Upholstered Furniture Mfr
N.A.I.C.S.: 337126
Glenn Swain Jr. (CFO)

SWAIM LOGISTICS LLC
30020 E 59th St, Broken Arrow, OK 74014
Tel.: (918) 379-0184
Web Site:
  http://www.swaimlogistics.com
Year Founded: 2007
Sales Range: $1-9.9 Million
Emp.: 5
Logistics & Transportation
N.A.I.C.S.: 488510
Shelley Gillion (Pres)

SWALLOW CONSTRUCTION CORPORATION
4250 Lacey Rd, Downers Grove, IL 60515
Tel.: (630) 512-9900
Rev.: $10,000,000
Emp.: 20
Water & Sewer Line & Related Structures Construction
N.A.I.C.S.: 237110
Antonio Rendina (Pres)
Rose Rendina (Sec)

SWALLOW OIL CO.
69 County Rd 264, Rifle, CO 81650
Tel.: (970) 625-1467
Web Site:
  http://www.swallowoilco.com
Rev.: $19,476,577
Emp.: 100
Petroleum Bulk Stations
N.A.I.C.S.: 424710
Kirk Swallow (Pres)

SWAN ELECTRIC COMPANY INC.
6133 Aurelius Rd, Lansing, MI 48911
Tel.: (517) 882-3904
Web Site:
  http://www.swanelectric.com
Sales Range: $10-24.9 Million
Emp.: 12
General Electrical Contracting Services
N.A.I.C.S.: 238210
Gil Mervis (Pres)
Jennifer Tascarella (Pres)

SWAN RETAIL INC.
950 N Michigan Ave Apt 4902, Chicago, IL 60611-7530
Tel.: (312) 787-1171   IL
Web Site: http://www.ultimo.com
Year Founded: 1969
Sales Range: $75-99.9 Million
Emp.: 10
Retailer of Women's Ready-to-Wear Apparel
N.A.I.C.S.: 458110
Freddy Vos (Mgr-Sls)
Jeroen ter Bruggen (Sr Acct Mgr)

SWAN STONE CORPORATION
515 Olive St, Saint Louis, MO 63101-1874
Tel.: (314) 231-8148   MO
Web Site: http://www.swanstone.com

Year Founded: 1964
Sales Range: $25-49.9 Million
Emp.: 210
Kitchen Product Mfr
N.A.I.C.S.: 326191
Wesley Moore (Pres)

SWAN SUPER CLEANERS INC.
1535 Bethel Rd, Columbus, OH 43220
Tel.: (614) 442-5000
Web Site:
  http://www.swancleaners.com
Rev.: $10,000,000
Emp.: 150
Dry Cleaning Services
N.A.I.C.S.: 812320
Paul A. Gelpi (Pres)

SWANBERG CONSTRUCTION, INC.
250 Central Ave S, Valley City, ND 58072
Tel.: (701) 845-6946   ND
Web Site:
  http://www.swanbergconstruction.com
Year Founded: 1996
Sales Range: $10-24.9 Million
Emp.: 20
Underground Utilities Contractor
N.A.I.C.S.: 237110
Mark Swanberg (Pres)

SWANDER PACE CAPITAL, LLC
101 Mission St Ste 1900, San Francisco, CA 94105
Tel.: (415) 477-8500   DE
Web Site: http://www.spcap.com
Year Founded: 1996
Privater Equity Firm
N.A.I.C.S.: 523999
Mark Poff (Mng Dir)
Dan Swander (Operating Partner)
Tyler Matlock (Sr VP & Mng Dir)
Mo Stout (Mng Dir)
Robert DesMarais (Mng Dir)
Andrew Richards (Founder, CEO & Mng Dir)
Corby Reese (Mng Dir)
Heather Fraser (CFO & Chief Compliance Officer)
Robert Vassel (Principal)
Valerie Scott (Principal)
Heather Smith Thorne (Mng Dir)
Alex Litt (VP)
Tara Hyland (VP)
Michael Macias (Controller)
Donna Valcarcel (Office Mgr & Coord-IT)
Amparo Calderon (Mgr-Mktg & Office)

Subsidiaries:

Backerhaus Veit Ltd. (1)
6745 Invader Crescent, Mississauga, L5T 2B6, ON, Canada
Tel.: (905) 850-9229
Web Site: http://www.backerhausveit.com
Bakery Products Mfr & Distr
N.A.I.C.S.: 311813
Sabine Veit (Pres & CEO)

Bragg Live Food Products, LLC (1)
111 W Michieltorena St, Santa Barbara, CA 93101
Tel.: (800) 446-1990
Web Site: http://www.bragg.com
Grocery & Related Products Merchant Whslr
N.A.I.C.S.: 424490
Rhonda McGaughey (Office Mgr)

Cafe Valley Inc. (1)
7000 W Buckeye Rd, Phoenix, AZ 85043
Tel.: (602) 278-2909
Web Site: http://www.cafevalley.com
Emp.: 133
Bakery Products Mfr

SWANDER PACE CAPITAL, LLC

Swander Pace Capital, LLC—(Continued)
N.A.I.C.S.: 311813
Tyler Matlock (Chm)
Brian Owens (CEO)

Subsidiary (Domestic):

Freed's Bakery LLC (2)
299 Pepsi Rd, Manchester, NH 03109
Tel.: (603) 627-7746
Web Site: http://www.freedsbakery.org
Bakery Product Distr
N.A.I.C.S.: 311812

Captek Softgel International, Inc. (1)
16218 Arthur St, Cerritos, CA 90703
Tel.: (562) 921-9511
Web Site: http://www.capteksoftgel.com
Rev.: $9,333,333
Emp.: 40
Medicinal & Botanical Mfr
N.A.I.C.S.: 325411
Theresa Johnson (Dir-HR)

Frozen Specialties Inc. (1)
720 W Barre Rd, Archbold, OH 43502-9304
Tel.: (419) 445-9015
Sales Range: $100-124.9 Million
Mfr of Frozen Pizza & Sandwiches
N.A.I.C.S.: 311412

Subsidiary (Domestic):

FSI/MFP Incorporated (2)
1465 Timber Wolf Dr, Holland, OH 43528-8302
Tel.: (203) 934-5233
Sales Range: $25-49.9 Million
Mfr of Frozen Pizza & Sandwiches
N.A.I.C.S.: 311412

Passport Food Group, LLC (1)
2539 E Philadelphia St, Ontario, CA 91761
Tel.: (855) 734-2742
Web Site: http://www.passportfood.com
Food Products Mfr & Distr
N.A.I.C.S.: 311999
Bill Yattaw (Dir-Tech)
Terra Jacobs (CFO & VP)
Mark Thompson (COO)
Peggy Moll (Dir-HR)

Subsidiary (Domestic):

Golden Pheasant Foods LLC (2)
6931 S 234th St, Kent, WA 98032-2920
Tel.: (253) 520-9299
Web Site:
    http://www.goldenpheasantfoods.com
Food Product Mfr & Distr
N.A.I.C.S.: 311999

Patriot Pickle Co. (1)
30 Edison Dr, Wayne, NJ 07470
Tel.: (973) 709-9487
Web Site: https://patriotpickle.com
Pickles Mfr & Distr
N.A.I.C.S.: 311421
Bill McEntee (CEO)

Subsidiary (Domestic):

First Place Foods, LLC. (2)
515 Mills Rd, Garland, TX 75040
Tel.: (972) 272-1111
Web Site: http://www.firstplacefoods.com
Sales Range: $1-9.9 Million
Emp.: 20
Frozen Specialty Food Mfr
N.A.I.C.S.: 311412
Pat Hunn (Pres)
Cyndy Hunn (Mgr-Office)

Pineridge Foods Inc. (1)
91 Delta Park Blvd Unit 2, Brampton, L6T 5E7, ON, Canada
Tel.: (905) 458-8696
Web Site: http://www.pineridgefoods.com
Prepared Frozen Dessert Mfr
N.A.I.C.S.: 311412

Subsidiary (Domestic):

Gourmet Baker, Inc. (2)
502 4190 Lougheed Hwy, Burnaby, V5C 6A8, BC, Canada
Tel.: (604) 298-2652
Web Site: https://www.aspirebakeries.ca
Sales Range: $10-24.9 Million
Frozen Bakery Products
N.A.I.C.S.: 311813

RAJ Manufacturing LLC (1)
2692 Dow Ave, Tustin, CA 92780
Tel.: (714) 838-3110
Web Site: http://www.rajman.com
Sales Range: $25-49.9 Million
Bathing Suits: Women's, Misses' & Juniors'
N.A.I.C.S.: 315990
Alex Bhathal (Founder & Mng Partner)
Lisa Bhathal-Vogel (Co-Pres)

SPC Management Co., Inc. (1)
100 Spear St Ste 1900, San Francisco, CA 94105
Tel.: (415) 477-8500
Web Site: http://www.spcap.com
Private Equity Portfolio Management
N.A.I.C.S.: 523940
Mark Poff (Mng Dir)
C. Morris Stout (Mng Dir)
Corby Reese (Mng Dir)
Park Rone (VP)
Nathan Ngai (VP)
Amparo Calderon (Office Mgr & Coord-Mktg)
Robert DesMarais (Mng Dir)
Heather Fraser (CFO & Chief Compliance Officer)
Andrew Richards (Mng Dir)
Donna Valcarcel (Office Mgr)

Branch (Domestic):

SPC Management Co., Inc. - Bedminster Office (2)
550 Hills Dr Ste 106, Bedminster, NJ 07921
Tel.: (908) 719-2322
Web Site: http://www.spcap.com
Sales Range: $75-99.9 Million
Private Equity Portfolio Management
N.A.I.C.S.: 523940
Andrew Richards (Mng Dir)
Robert DesMarais (Mng Dir)
Donna Valcarcel (Officer Mgr & Mgr-HR)

Swanson Health Products (1)
4075 40th Ave SW, Fargo, ND 58104-3912
Tel.: (701) 356-2700
Web Site: http://www.swansonvitamins.com
Catalog & Mail-Order Houses
N.A.I.C.S.: 456191
Tom Audette (Dir-Product Dev)
Mike Harlan (Project Mgr-Digital)
Terry Kraft (Dir-Ops)
Karen Sather (Supvr-Pur)
Scott Trana (Mgr-Facility)
Rex Dahl (Sr Ops Mgr-Customer Svc)
Kelly Haman (Mgr-Web Mdsg)
Andrea Sinclair (Mgr-Quality Assurance)
Maggie McCalip (Dir-Market Res)
Teresa Johnson (Dir-HR & Customer Svc)
Jeremy Skogen (Mgr-Mgmt Info Sys Programming)
LaShalle Leingang (Mgr-Quality Control)
John Kulink (Project Coord)
Troy Ruscheinsky (Sr Mgr-Process Engrg)
Cathleen Wendel (Mgr-Web Content)
Katie Doyle (CEO)

SWANER HARDWOOD COMPANY, INC.

5 W Magnolia Blvd, Burbank, CA 91502-1719
Tel.: (818) 953-5350   CA
Web Site:
    http://www.swanerhardwood.com
Year Founded: 1967
Sales Range: $100-124.9 Million
Emp.: 300
Sales of Lumber
N.A.I.C.S.: 321212
Gary Swaner (Pres)

Subsidiaries:

Mt. Baker Products, Inc. (1)
2929 Roeder Ave, Bellingham, WA 98225
Tel.: (360) 733-3960
Web Site: http://www.mtbakerproducts.com
Sales Range: $10-24.9 Million
Emp.: 130
Producer of Plywood
N.A.I.C.S.: 321211
Patricia Proctor (Controller)

SWANILLON, INC.

455 N Twin Oaks Vly Rd, San Marcos, CA 92069
Tel.: (760) 759-2366
Web Site: http://www.sderosion.com
Rev.: $22,632,504
Emp.: 38
Environmental Engineering Services
N.A.I.C.S.: 541330
Greg Sickels (Mgr-IT)

SWANK ASSOCIATED COMPANIES INC.

632 Hunt Valley Cir, New Kensington, PA 15068-7067
Tel.: (724) 335-6000
Web Site: http://www.swankco.com
Sales Range: $25-49.9 Million
Emp.: 400
General Contractor, Highway & Street Construction
N.A.I.C.S.: 237310
Chad Fuhrman (Controller)
Russell C. Swank III (Pres)

SWANK CAPITAL, LLC

8117 Preston Rd Ste 440, Dallas, TX 75225
Tel.: (214) 692-6334   TX
Web Site:
    http://www.cushineasset.com
Year Founded: 2000
Emp.: 40
Holding Company; Investment Advisory & Portfolio Management Services
N.A.I.C.S.: 551112
Jerry V. Swank (Mng Partner & Chief Investment Officer)
John Alban (CFO & COO)
Barry Y. Greenberg (Chief Compliance Officer & Gen Counsel)

Subsidiaries:

Cushing Asset Management, LP (1)
8117 Preston Rd Ste 440, Dallas, TX 75225   (100%)
Tel.: (214) 692-6334
Web Site: http://www.cushingasset.com
Rev.: $3,400,000,000
Emp.: 38
N.A.I.C.S.: 523940
Jerry V. Swank (Mng Partner & Chief Investment Officer)
John Alban (CFO & COO)
Barry Y. Greenberg (Chief Compliance Officer & Gen Counsel)
Matt Wenk (Treas)
Guillermo Femat (VP-Ops)
Geoffrey G. Crumrine (Head-Bus Dev-Institutional & Intl)
Parker Roy (Head-Bus Dev-Retail)
Chelsey Meyer (Mktg Mgr)
R. Gavin Worthy (Dir-Investment & Portfolio Mgr-Client)
Nick Brown (Dir-Bus Dev & Portfolio Mgr-Client)
Todd Sunderland (Head-Risk Mgmt & Quant-Strategies)
Judd Cryer (Portfolio Mgr)
Paul Euseppi (Portfolio Mgr)
Kevin Gallagher (Portfolio Mgr)
Saket Kumar (Portfolio Mgr)
Matthew Lemme (Portfolio Mgr)
John Musgrave (Portfolio Mgr)
Libby F. Toudouze (Portfolio Mgr)

Affiliate (Domestic):

NXG NextGen Infrastructure Income Fund (2)
300 Crescent Ct Ste 1700, Dallas, TX 75201
Tel.: (214) 692-6334
Web Site: http://www.cushingcef.com
Rev.: $6,611,416
Assets: $151,957,589
Liabilities: $318,601
Net Worth: $151,638,988
Earnings: $3,214,936
Fiscal Year-end: 11/30/2019
Closed-End Investment Fund
N.A.I.C.S.: 525990

The Cushing Energy Income Fund (2)
8117 Preston Rd Ste 440, Dallas, TX 75225
Tel.: (214) 692-6334
Web Site: http://www.cushingcef.com
Rev.: $654,202
Assets: $20,198,319
Liabilities: $3,360,447
Net Worth: $16,837,872
Earnings: ($95,771)
Fiscal Year-end: 11/30/2019
Closed-End Investment Fund
N.A.I.C.S.: 525990

SWANK ENTERPRISES INC.

615 Pondera Ave, Valier, MT 59486
Tel.: (406) 279-3241   MT
Web Site:
    http://www.swankenterprises.com
Year Founded: 1946
Sales Range: $10-24.9 Million
Emp.: 100
Nonresidential Construction
N.A.I.C.S.: 236220
Dean Swank (Founder, Pres & CEO)
Rene Swank (Exec VP-Fin)
Derek Swank (Exec VP & Project Mgr)
Scott Wright (Project Mgr)

SWANKE HAYDEN CONNELL LTD

295 Lafayette St, New York, NY 10012
Tel.: (212) 226-9696
Web Site: http://www.shca.com
Sales Range: $25-49.9 Million
Emp.: 150
Interior Designer
N.A.I.C.S.: 541410
Richard Seth Hayden (Chm)
Robert Strasser (CFO)

SWANKTEK, INC.

510 Franklin Ave Ste 6 7 & 8, Nutley, NJ 07110
Tel.: (973) 542-8326
Web Site: http://www.swanktek.com
Year Founded: 2006
Sales Range: $10-24.9 Million
Emp.: 185
Information Technology Management Services
N.A.I.C.S.: 541513
K. Rahul (Founder & CEO)
Bala Chitteti (VP-Talent on Demand)
Ranjan Roy Chowdhury (Head-Sls & Mktg)

SWANSON & YOUNGDALE INC.

6565 W 23rd St, Minneapolis, MN 55426-2853
Tel.: (952) 545-2541   MN
Web Site:
    http://www.swansonyoungdale.com
Year Founded: 1946
Provider of Paper Hanging Services
N.A.I.C.S.: 238320
Clark Anderson (Treas & Sec)
Doug Rynda (VP)
Greg Guimont (Pres)
Mike Athman (Superintendent-Field Ops-Drywall)
Kevin Halvorson (VP-Drywall)
Joel Swanson (VP)

Subsidiaries:

Davis Drywall, Inc. (1)
24186 Co Rd 9, Bemidji, MN 56601-6198
Tel.: (218) 444-2532
Drywall & Insulation Contractors
N.A.I.C.S.: 238310

SWANSON BUILDING MATERIALS

525 W 2890 S, Salt Lake City, UT 84115
Tel.: (801) 973-2736
Web Site: http://www.swanbuild.com
Sales Range: $10-24.9 Million
Emp.: 20
Drywall Materials
N.A.I.C.S.: 423320
Kevin Kennington *(Pres)*
Anthony Child *(Controller)*
Megan Ashcroft *(Mgr-Credit)*

SWANSON GROUP INC.
2695 Glendale Valley Rd, Glendale, OR 97442
Tel.: (541) 832-1121 OR
Web Site:
http://www.swansongroup.biz
Year Founded: 1951
Sawmills, Planning Mills & Home Construction Services
N.A.I.C.S.: 321113
Steve Swanson *(Pres & CEO)*
Chris Swanson *(Exec VP)*
Jim Dudley *(VP-Timber Resources)*
Rick Bernheisel *(CFO)*
Tim Hennessey *(VP-HR)*
Jeff Remington *(VP-Engrg)*
Jeff Thompson *(VP-Springfield Mfr)*
Greg Johnson *(VP-Sls & Mktg)*

SWANSON RUSSELL ASSOCIATES
1222 P St, Lincoln, NE 68508-1425
Tel.: (402) 437-6400 NE
Web Site:
http://www.swansonrussell.com
Year Founded: 1962
Sales Range: $10-24.9 Million
Emp.: 150
Advertising Agencies
N.A.I.C.S.: 541810
Brian Boesche *(Chief Creative Officer & Partner)*
Dave Hansen *(CEO)*
Dave Wegener *(VP & Acct Supvr)*
Ed Salem *(Mng Dir & Exec Dir-Creative)*
Tracy Stanko *(Exec VP & Mng Dir-Omaha)*
Brittany Lentz *(Acct Mgr)*
Neale Stadler *(Acct Mgr)*
Subsidiaries:

Swanson Russell Associates (1)
14301 FNB Pkwy Ste 312, Omaha, NE 68154-5299
Tel.: (402) 818-1100
Web Site: http://www.swansonrussell.com
Sales Range: $10-24.9 Million
Emp.: 30
Agriculture Business-To-Business Health Care Outdoor Recruitment Services
N.A.I.C.S.: 541810
Steve Johnson *(VP & Dir-Acct)*
Ed Salem *(Exec Creative Dir-Omaha)*
Dave Hansen *(Partner & CEO-Lincoln)*
Brent Schott *(Mng Dir & Exec VP)*

SWANSON SYSTEMS, INC.
814 E Eight St, Erie, PA 16503-1406
Tel.: (814) 453-5841
Web Site:
http://www.swansonsystems.com
Year Founded: 1981
Sales Range: $10-24.9 Million
Emp.: 150
Mfr of General Industrial Machinery
N.A.I.C.S.: 333998
Douglas L. Swanson *(Pres & Treas)*
Subsidiaries:

Swanson-Anaheim Corp (1)
9825 Magnolia Ave Ste B319, Riverside, CA 92503
Tel.: (714) 685-1532
Web Site: http://www.swanson-anaheim.com

Industrial Machinery Mfr & Whslr
N.A.I.C.S.: 333248

Swanson-Erie Corporation (1)
810 E 8th St Ste 14, Erie, PA 16503-1406
Tel.: (814) 453-5841
Web Site: http://www.swanson-erie.com
Sales Range: $10-24.9 Million
Emp.: 50
Mfr of General Industrial Machinery
N.A.I.C.S.: 333998
Douglas L. Swanson *(Pres & Treas)*
Charles Trudnowski *(Controller)*

Swanson-Japan Ltd (1)
7-10 Honmoku Makado Naku-Ku, Yokohama, 231-0825, Japan
Tel.: (81) 45 662 3665
Industrial Machinery Mfr & Whslr
N.A.I.C.S.: 423830

SWANSON-FAHRNEY FORD SALES
3105 Highland Ave, Selma, CA 93662
Tel.: (559) 896-4121
Web Site:
http://www.swansonfahrneyford.com
Rev: $25,000,000
Emp.: 60
Automobiles; New & Used
N.A.I.C.S.: 441110
Gerald Fahrney *(Pres)*
Mike Fahrney *(Mgr-Sls)*

SWANSON-FLOSYSTEMS CO.
151 Cheshire Ln N Ste 700, Plymouth, MN 55441
Tel.: (763) 383-4700
Web Site: http://www.swanflo.com
Sales Range: $10-24.9 Million
Emp.: 35
Industrial Supplies
N.A.I.C.S.: 423840
Tom Howe *(Pres & CEO)*
Bill Hansen *(Asst Controller)*
John Schempp *(Mgr-Warehouse)*
Robbin Jensen *(Mgr-Inside Sls)*
Tamma Whealy *(Coord-Event)*

SWANSONS FOOD OF ABERDEEN
1401 Simpson Ave, Aberdeen, WA 98520
Tel.: (360) 532-2495
Web Site:
http://www.swansonsfoods.com
Rev: $20,100,000
Emp.: 150
Grocery Stores, Independent
N.A.I.C.S.: 445110

SWANTON WELDING & MACHINING CO, INC.
407 Broadway St, Swanton, OH 43558
Tel.: (419) 826-4816
Web Site:
http://www.swantonweld.com
Year Founded: 1956
Sales Range: $10-24.9 Million
Emp.: 190
Ornamental & Architectural Metal Work Mfr
N.A.I.C.S.: 332323
Norm D. Zeiter *(Owner & CEO)*
Jan Sulewski *(Controller)*
Norm E. Zeiter *(Pres)*
Nick Nijakowski *(Mgr-CWI, Welding & Quality)*
Bret Silveus *(Engr-Estimating)*
Ron Fischer *(Mgr-Quality-Georgia)*
Chuck Morgan *(VP-Ops)*
Tim Hamlet *(Mgr-Fabrication-Swanton)*
Kody Kessler *(Project Mgr & Engr)*
Chad Perry *(Project Mgr & Engr)*
Bill Zeiter *(Plant Mgr-Heavy Fab Facility)*

SWAT ENVIRONMENTAL INC.
2607 Eaton Rapids Rd, Lansing, MI 48911
Tel.: (517) 322-2999
Web Site:
http://www.radonsystem.com
Year Founded: 2002
Sales Range: $1-9.9 Million
Emp.: 100
Radon Gas Mitigation
N.A.I.C.S.: 213112
Jamey Gelina *(Pres)*
Bill Sublette *(CEO)*
Kyle Larkin *(COO)*

SWAT FAME INC.
16425 Gale Ave, City of Industry, CA 91745-1711
Tel.: (626) 961-7928
Web Site: http://www.swatfame.com
Year Founded: 1978
Sales Range: $25-49.9 Million
Emp.: 330
Mfr of Girls Clothing
N.A.I.C.S.: 315250
Bruce Stern *(Chm & Co-CEO)*
Joseph Walk *(Exec VP-Fin)*
Mitchell Quaranta *(Pres & CEO)*
Brenda Casimire *(Mgr-Customer Svc)*
John McIntyre *(Coord-Production)*

SWATI ENTERPRISES INC.
8146 9th Ave, Port Arthur, TX 77642
Tel.: (409) 727-6700
Rev: $45,086,370
Emp.: 13
Fuel Product Distr
N.A.I.C.S.: 424710
Mohammad A. Swati *(Owner & Pres)*
Syed Bilgrami *(Controller-Accts & Fin)*
Osman Swati *(Mng Dir)*

SWAVELLE/MILL CREEK FABRICS, INC.
15 E 26th St Fl 2, New York, NY 10010
Tel.: (212) 532-8670
Web Site:
http://www.swavellehospitality.com
Sales Range: $125-149.9 Million
Emp.: 180
Textiles Mfr & Whslr
N.A.I.C.S.: 313210
Jeffrey Thomases *(CEO)*
Richard Hanfling *(Pres)*
Kenneth Lazar *(Treas)*
Alan Halpern *(VP-Fin)*

SWD CORPORATION
435 N Main St, Lima, OH 45801-4314
Tel.: (419) 227-2436 OH
Year Founded: 1968
Sales Range: $10-24.9 Million
Emp.: 50
Provider of Tobacco Products
N.A.I.C.S.: 424940
Carl Berger *(Pres)*
Dave Cockerelle *(Exec VP)*
Cheryl Wehner *(Product Mgr)*

SWEDA CORPORATION
3030 Lyndon B Johnson Fwy Ste 905, Dallas, TX 75234-7704
Tel.: (972) 887-8000 DE
Web Site: http://www.sweda.com
Year Founded: 1992
Retail Point-of-Sale Technologies Developer & Mfr
N.A.I.C.S.: 333310
James Chao *(Vice Chm)*
Norman Tsui *(Chm & CEO)*
Subsidiaries:

Sweda Canada Inc. (1)

4101 Yonge Street Suite 500, Toronto, M2P 1N6, ON, Canada
Tel.: (416) 614-0199
Web Site: http://www.sweda.com
Sales Range: $10-24.9 Million
Emp.: 23
Retail Point-of-Sale Technologies Developer & Mfr
N.A.I.C.S.: 333310

Sweda International Ltd. (1)
10/F Chinaweal Centre 414-424 Jaffe Road, Wanchai, China (Hong Kong)
Tel.: (852) 25712381
Web Site: http://www.sweda.com
Retail Point-of-Sale Technologies Developer & Mfr
N.A.I.C.S.: 541511

SWEDISHAMERICAN HEALTH SYSTEM
1401 E State St, Rockford, IL 61104
Tel.: (779) 696-4400
Web Site:
http://www.swedishamerican.org
Year Founded: 2006
Hospital & Health Care Services
N.A.I.C.S.: 622110
Tom OConnor *(Pres & CEO)*

SWEENEY
20325 Center Rdg Rd Ph Ste, Cleveland, OH 44116
Tel.: (440) 333-0001
Web Site: http://www.sweeneypr.com
Year Founded: 1986
Sales Range: Less than $1 Million
Emp.: 4
Advertising, Brand Development & Integration, Collateral, Corporate Identity, Exhibit/Trade Shows, Experiential, Graphic Design, Internet/Web Design, Public Relations, Strategic Planning/Research
N.A.I.C.S.: 541810
James B. Sweeney *(Founder & CEO)*
Jennifer Manocchio *(Pres)*
Kelly Erickson *(Office Mgr)*
Kayleigh Fitch *(Acct Exec)*
Subsidiaries:

SWEENEY, INC. (1)
201 N Front St Ste 904, Wilmington, NC 28401
Tel.: (910) 772-1688
N.A.I.C.S.: 541810
Jennifer Manocchio *(Pres)*

SWEENEY BROTHERS TRACTOR CO.
4001 38th St SW, Fargo, ND 58104
Tel.: (701) 492-7300
Sales Range: $10-24.9 Million
Emp.: 50
Road Construction & Maintenance Machinery
N.A.I.C.S.: 423810
Mike Sweeney *(Pres)*
Kevin Sweeney *(Mgr)*

SWEENEY STEEL SERVICE CORP
91 Sawyer Ave, Tonawanda, NY 14150
Tel.: (716) 821-9201
Web Site: http://www.sweeneysteel.com
Rev: $10,700,000
Emp.: 38
Steel
N.A.I.C.S.: 423510
Joe Pardee *(CFO)*
Michael Sweeney Sr. *(Pres)*

SWEEPSTER ATTACHMENTS LLC
2800 N Zeeb Rd, Dexter, MI 48130-9499
Tel.: (734) 996-9116 MI

SWEEPSTER ATTACHMENTS LLC

U.S. PRIVATE

Sweepster Attachments LLC—(Continued)
Web Site: http://www.sweepster.com
Year Founded: 1945
Sales Range: $10-24.9 Million
Emp.: 160
Service Industry Machines
N.A.I.C.S.: 333310
Kristen Schroder *(Dir-HR)*

SWEET CANDY COMPANY
3780 W Directors Row 1100 S, Salt Lake City, UT 84104-5502
Tel.: (801) 886-1444
Web Site:
  http://www.sweetcandy.com
Year Founded: 1892
Sales Range: $100-124.9 Million
Emp.: 150
Mfr of Candy
N.A.I.C.S.: 311340
Curtis Anderson *(Treas & Sec)*
Bruce Thompson *(Mgr-Natl Sls)*
Richard Kay *(Pres & COO)*
Greg Cater *(VP-Bus Dev)*

SWEET FLAVOR OF FLORIDA LLC
14501 NW 57 Ave Ste 104, Miami, FL 33054
Tel.: (305) 532-3731
Web Site:
  http://www.sweetflavorfl.com
Year Founded: 2004
Sales Range: $25-49.9 Million
Emp.: 3
Culinary Disposable Tableware Mfr
N.A.I.C.S.: 327110
Arnaud Lefebvre *(Owner & CEO)*

SWEET PRODUCTIONS LTD.
5100 New Horizons Blvd, Amityville, NY 11701
Tel.: (631) 842-0548
Sales Range: $25-49.9 Million
Emp.: 300
Candy & Other Confectionery Products
N.A.I.C.S.: 311340

SWEET SISTERS, INC.
755 Monroe, Eugene, OR 97402
Tel.: (541) 683-5676
Web Site:
  http://www.sweetlifedesserts.com
Year Founded: 1993
Sales Range: $10-24.9 Million
Emp.: 50
Commercial Bakery Services
N.A.I.C.S.: 311812
Catherine Reinhart *(Co-Owner)*
Sheryl Reinhart *(Co-Owner)*

SWEET SPARKMAN ARCHITECTS, INC.
2186 Main St, Sarasota, FL 34237
Tel.: (941) 952-0084
Web Site:
  http://www.sweetsparkman.com
Sales Range: $10-24.9 Million
Emp.: 12
Architectural Services
N.A.I.C.S.: 541310
Todd M. Sweet *(Founder)*

SWEET STREET DESSERTS INC.
722 Hiesters Ln, Reading, PA 19605-3039
Tel.: (610) 921-8113 PA
Web Site:
  http://www.sweetstreet.com
Year Founded: 1982
Sales Range: $25-49.9 Million
Emp.: 450
Mfr Frozen Bakery Products
N.A.I.C.S.: 311813

Sandy Solmon *(CEO)*

SWEETEN TRUCK CENTER
10111 East Freeway, Houston, TX 77029
Tel.: (713) 675-1515
Web Site:
  http://www.sweetentruckcenter.com
Sales Range: $10-24.9 Million
Emp.: 65
Car Whslr
N.A.I.C.S.: 441110
Christy Val *(Gen Mgr)*

SWEETVIEW PARTNERS, INC.
9102 Rappahanook Ln, Rosenberg, TX 77469
Tel.: (816) 372-4954
Web Site:
  http://www.sweetviewpartners.com
Privater Equity Firm
N.A.I.C.S.: 523999
Jeremy Davis *(Partner)*
Daniel Sweet *(Partner)*

Subsidiaries:
Mlink Technologies Inc. (1)
550 S Edmonds Ln Ste 204, Lewisville, TX 75067-3577
Tel.: (972) 436-0778
Web Site: http://www.mlinktech.com
Educational Support Services
N.A.I.C.S.: 611710
Curt Swayne *(Pres & CEO)*

SWEETWATER BREWING COMPANY, LLC
195 Ottley Dr, Atlanta, GA 30324
Tel.: (404) 691-2537 GA
Web Site:
  http://www.sweetwaterbrew.com
Year Founded: 1996
Sales Range: $25-49.9 Million
Emp.: 50
Beer Mfr & Distr
N.A.I.C.S.: 312120
Kevin McNerney *(Co-Founder)*
Frederick Bensch *(Co-Founder & CEO)*
Steve Farace *(Dir-Mktg)*
Dave Guender *(VP-Sls)*
Bill Burge *(Dir-Compliance)*
Brian Diggelmann *(Dir-Digital Dank)*
Chance Edwards *(Mgr-POS)*
Jeff Chassner *(Dir-New Mktg Dev)*
Diana Setser *(Mgr-Distributor Accounts)*
Kevin Duffy *(Sls Mgr)*
Molly Duncan *(Mgr-Retail Store & E-commerce)*
Phil Gramaglia *(Dir-Northern Sls)*
Chris Thoren *(Dir-Art)*

SWEETWATER HOSPITAL ASSOCIATION
304 Wright St, Sweetwater, TN 37874
Tel.: (865) 213-8200 TN
Web Site:
  http://www.sweetwaterhospital.org
Year Founded: 1934
Sales Range: $50-74.9 Million
Emp.: 544
Health Care Srvices
N.A.I.C.S.: 622110
Debbie J. Thompson *(CFO)*
Andrea B. Henry *(Dir-Nursing)*

SWEETWATER LLC
Copper Rim Trail, Durango, CO 81301
Tel.: (970) 259-2171
Web Site:
  http://www.cleanairpurewater.com
Year Founded: 2002
Water Filter Equipment Distr
N.A.I.C.S.: 423720

Terry L. Dunlap *(Principal)*
James P. McMahon *(Founder)*

SWEETWATER ORGANIC COMMUNITY FARM, INC.
6942 W Comanche Ave, Tampa, FL 33634
Tel.: (813) 887-4066
Web Site: http://www.sweetwater-organic.org
Year Founded: 1995
Sales Range: $10-24.9 Million
Emp.: 5
Urban Organic Farm & Environmental Education Center
N.A.I.C.S.: 111998
Rick Martinez *(Founder)*

SWEETWATER SECURITY SYSTEMS LLC
4800 Sugar Grove Blvd Ste 615, Stafford, TX 77477
Tel.: (281) 340-9700
Web Site:
  http://www.sweetwatersecurity.com
Sales Range: $1-9.9 Million
Electronic Security & Video Surveillance Services
N.A.I.C.S.: 561621

SWEETWATER SOUND INC.
5501 US Hwy 30 W, Fort Wayne, IN 46818
Tel.: (260) 432-8176
Web Site: http://www.sweetwater.com
Sales Range: $25-49.9 Million
Emp.: 360
Musical Instrument Stores
N.A.I.C.S.: 459140
Charles Surack *(Founder & Pres)*
Mike Ross *(Sr VP-Mktg)*
Phil Rich *(Sr VP-Mdsg)*
Adam Chesi *(Engr-Sls)*
Josh Dillon *(Engr-Sls)*
Nate Edwards *(Engr-Sls)*
Dontae Harris *(Engr-Sls)*
Troy Hartman *(Sr VP-Sls)*
John Hopkins *(COO & Exec VP)*
Carson McClain *(Engr-Sls)*
Brian Randol *(VP-Distr)*
David Klausner *(VP-Sls)*
Jeff Radke *(Chief Sls Officer & Exec VP-Sls)*
David Stewart *(CMO & Exec VP)*

SWEETWATER STEEL CO., INC.
10416 N Interstate 20, Sweetwater, TX 79556
Tel.: (325) 235-3644
Web Site: http://sweetwatersteel.net
Rev.: $13,000,000
Emp.: 30
Iron & Steel Products Mfr
N.A.I.C.S.: 423510

SWEETWATER VALLEY OIL CO.
1236 Hwy 68, Sweetwater, TN 37874
Tel.: (423) 337-6671
Web Site:
  http://www.sweetwatervalleyoil.com
Rev.: $26,181,060
Emp.: 11
Petroleum Bulk Stations
N.A.I.C.S.: 424710
Scott Shankle *(Pres)*
Shirley Woodcock *(VP)*

SWEETWORKS, INC.
3500 Genesee St, Buffalo, NY 14225
Tel.: (716) 634-0880
Web Site: http://www.sweetworks.net
Year Founded: 2002
Sales Range: $10-24.9 Million
Emp.: 400

Candy Mfr
N.A.I.C.S.: 311340
Lori Molitor *(Controller)*
Todd Fisher *(Mgr-IT)*

SWELL ENERGY INC
1014 Broadway Ste 949, Santa Monica, CA 90401
Tel.: (941) 265-8956
Web Site:
  https://www.swellenergy.com
Emp.: 100
Energy Storage System Services
N.A.I.C.S.: 237130
Suleman Khan *(CEO)*

Subsidiaries:
Renu Energy Solutions LLC (1)
801 Pressley Rd Ste 100, Charlotte, NC 28217
Tel.: (704) 525-6767
Web Site:
  http://www.renuenergysolutions.com
Sales Range: $1-9.9 Million
Emp.: 50
Energy Storage System Services
N.A.I.C.S.: 237130
Jay Radcliffe *(Pres)*
Hannah Elliott *(Ops Mgr)*
Martin Blacker *(Dir-Ops)*
Sha Stollar *(Mktg Dir)*
Holly Bearden *(Mgr-Customer Success)*

SWELL INTERNATIONAL INC
1441 Kapiolani Blvd, Ste 1915, Honolulu, HI 96814
Tel.: (808) 951-4177
Year Founded: 2010
Real Estate
N.A.I.C.S.: 531390

Subsidiaries:
Hawaiiana Group, Inc. (1)
711 Kapiolani Blvd # 700, Honolulu, HI 96813 (50%)
Tel.: (808) 593-9100
Web Site: http://www.hawaiipottersguild.org
Sales Range: $1-9.9 Million
Emp.: 87
Offices of Real Estate Agents & Brokers
N.A.I.C.S.: 531210
Eiichi Matsumoto *(CEO)*

SWENSON GROUP INC.
207 Boeing Ct, Livermore, CA 94551
Tel.: (925) 960-8910
Web Site:
  http://www.theswensongroup.com
Sales Range: $25-49.9 Million
Emp.: 20
Office Equipment
N.A.I.C.S.: 423420
Carl Swenson *(CEO)*
Dean Swenson *(Pres)*

SWEPCO TUBE CORPORATION
1 Clifton Blvd, Clifton, NJ 07015
Tel.: (973) 778-3000 DE
Web Site:
  http://www.swepcotube.com
Year Founded: 1949
Sales Range: $75-99.9 Million
Emp.: 100
Stainless Steel Pipe & Tubing Mfr
N.A.I.C.S.: 331491
Kenneth Shultz *(Pres & COO)*
Steve Oberhelman *(CFO)*
Bob Catanzariti *(VP-Sls)*
Victor Battistuz *(VP-Ops)*
Holly Keller Koeppel *(CFO & VP)*
Steve Overhelmann *(Treas & VP)*

SWERDLOW GROUP
2901 Florida Ave Ste 806, Miami, FL 33133
Tel.: (305) 476-0100
Web Site: http://www.swerdlow.com
Year Founded: 1987

Sales Range: $25-49.9 Million
Emp.: 10
Real Estate Development, Management, Leasing & Ownership
N.A.I.C.S.: 237210
Michael J. Swerdlow (Chm, CEO & Mng Partner)
Brett M. Dill (Pres)
Sean Posner (Exec VP-Acq)
Kenneth J. Scott (CFO)
Randy Foltz (Exec VP-Projects)
Maria Compain (Controller)

SWETZ OIL CO. INC.
3912 Hwy 10, Blenker, WI 54415
Tel.: (715) 652-2380
Sales Range: $10-24.9 Million
Emp.: 10
Petroleum Bulk Stations
N.A.I.C.S.: 424710
George C. Swetz (Pres)
Helen Swetz (Sec)

SWIDERSKI EQUIPMENT, INC.
820 Old Hwy 51 N, Mosinee, WI 54455
Tel.: (715) 693-3015
Web Site:
   http://www.swiderskiequipment.com
Rev.: $11,000,000
Emp.: 110
Farm & Garden Machinery & Equipment Merchant Whslr
N.A.I.C.S.: 423820
Alex Swiderski (Owner)
Sylvester Krautkramer (Gen Mgr)
Linda Fletcher (Sec)

SWIFT COMMUNICATIONS, INC.
580 Mallory Way, Carson City, NV 89701
Tel.: (775) 283-5500
Web Site: http://www.swiftcom.com
Sales Range: $25-49.9 Million
Emp.: 500
Newspaper Publisher; Information Services
N.A.I.C.S.: 513110
Bill Waters (Chm)
Betty Harwood (Dir-Comm & Pro Excellence)
Diane Parkinson (CFO)
Dick Larson (CEO)

Subsidiaries:

Post Independent   (1)
824 Grand Ave, Glenwood Springs, CO 81601-4116   (100%)
Tel.: (970) 945-8515
Web Site: http://www.postindependent.com
Sales Range: $10-24.9 Million
Emp.: 15
Newspaper Publishing
N.A.I.C.S.: 513120

Snowmass Village Sun   (1)
16 Kearns Rd Unit 211, Snowmass Village, CO 81615
Tel.: (970) 923-5829
Web Site: http://www.snowmasssun.com
Sales Range: $10-24.9 Million
Emp.: 4
Newspapers
N.A.I.C.S.: 513110
Louise Walker (Mgr-Acct-Adv)
Rick Carroll (Mng Editor)
Evan Gibbard (Mgr-Production)
Samantha Johnston (Gen Mgr)
Tim Kurnos (Mgr-Adv Acct)
David Laughren (Mgr-Bus Dev)
Andrew Travers (Mgr-Production)
Max Vadnais (Mgr-Adv Acct)
Maria Wimmer (Mgr-Distr)
Dottie Wolcott (Office Mgr)

SWIFT ELECTRICAL SUPPLY CO.
709 Exec Blvd, Valley Cottage, NY 10989
Tel.: (845) 623-3425
Web Site:
   http://www.swiftelectrical.com
Sales Range: $10-24.9 Million
Emp.: 100
Electrical Apparatus & Equipment
N.A.I.C.S.: 423610
Chris Sodora (VP)
August A. Sodora Jr. (Chm & Pres)

SWIFT INDUSTRIAL POWER INC.
10917 Mcbride Ln, Knoxville, TN 37932
Tel.: (865) 966-9758
Web Site: http://www.swiftpower.com
Sales Range: $10-24.9 Million
Emp.: 50
Industrial Machinery & Equipment
N.A.I.C.S.: 423830
Mike Swirt (Pres)
Torston Ericson (Mgr-Ops-Alabama)

SWIFT OPTICAL INSTRUMENTS, INC.
6508 tri-County Pkwy, Schertz, TX 78154
Tel.: (210) 967-9438   MA
Web Site: http://www.swiftoptical.com
Year Founded: 1926
Sales Range: $50-74.9 Million
Emp.: 20
Whslr & Distr of Binoculars, Field Glasses, Astronomical Telescopes, Barometers, Thermometers, Hydrometers Specialty Magnifiers, Spotting Scopes, Microscopes & Related Accessories
N.A.I.C.S.: 333310
Cynthia Syverson-Mercer (Dir-Mktg & Catalog Sls)
Michael Hart (Gen Mgr)

Subsidiaries:

Swift Instruments, Inc.-Technical Instruments Div.   (1)
2055 Gateway Pl Ste 500, San Jose, CA 95110
Tel.: (408) 293-2380
Web Site: http://www.swiftmicroscope.com
Sales Range: $1-9.9 Million
Mfr & Sales Of Microscopes
N.A.I.C.S.: 333310

SWIFT SUPPLY, INC.
1450 Swift Mill Rd, Atmore, AL 36502
Tel.: (251) 368-8800   AL
Web Site: http://www.swiftsupply.com
Year Founded: 1957
Sales Range: $10-24.9 Million
Emp.: 143
Lumber & Other Building Materials
N.A.I.C.S.: 423310
David Swift (Pres)
Carolyn Fragale (Coord-Construction Sls)
Jeff Silvers (Mgr-Sls)
Idaross Hicks (Pres)

SWIFTEL COMMUNICATIONS INC.
415 4th St Downtown, Brookings, SD 57006
Tel.: (605) 692-6211
Web Site: http://www.swiftel.net
Sales Range: $25-49.9 Million
Emp.: 200
Data Processing & Preparation
N.A.I.C.S.: 518210
Jim Adkins (Mgr-Network Ops)
Mark Thompson (Gen Mgr)
Brooke Barhite (Mgr-Mktg & PR)

SWIFTS SUPERSTORE
4318 Chiles Rd, Davis, CA 95618
Tel.: (530) 757-3770   CA
Web Site:
   http://www.swiftsuperstore.com
Year Founded: 1997
Sales Range: $75-99.9 Million
Emp.: 55
Automobile Sales
N.A.I.C.S.: 441110
Dan Kokotas (VP-Ops)
Lorrie Heil (Bus Mgr)
Alice Swift (Chm & Pres)

SWIFTSURE CAPITAL LLC
1325 4th Avenue Ste 1500, Seattle, WA 98101
Tel.: (206) 903-1001
Web Site:
   http://www.swiftsurecapital.com
Investment Services
N.A.I.C.S.: 523940
Gordon Gardine (Mng Partner)
Bill Douglass (Mng Partner)

Subsidiaries:

Quantum Windows & Doors, Inc.   (1)
2720 34th St, Everett, WA 98201
Tel.: (425) 259-6650
Web Site: http://www.quantumwindows.com
Sales Range: $1-9.9 Million
Emp.: 75
Wood Window & Door Mfr
N.A.I.C.S.: 321911
Melissa Benton (Pres)
Stephanie Carr (Coord-Mktg)
Tim Kummer (Mgr-Production)
Jeff Klein (CEO)

SWIFTY OIL, LLC
1515 W Tipton St, Seymour, IN 47274
Tel.: (812) 522-1640   IN
Web Site: http://www.swiftyoil.com
Fuel Product Distr
N.A.I.C.S.: 457120
William Klinger (Chm & Pres)
James Moore (Mgr)

SWIM ACROSS AMERICA INC.
1 International Pl Ste 4600, Boston, MA 02110
Tel.: (617) 330-5274   CT
Web Site:
   http://www.swimacrossamerica.org
Year Founded: 1992
Sales Range: $1-9.9 Million
Emp.: 4
Cancer Awareness Services
N.A.I.C.S.: 813212
Craig Beardsley (Dir-Pool)
Blake Chanowski (VP-Ops)
Janel Jorgensen (Pres & CEO)
Matt Vossler (Founder)

SWIMKIDS SWIM SCHOOLS
Potomac Festival 14531 Potomac Mills Rd, Woodbridge, VA 22192
Tel.: (703) 396-7946
Web Site: http://www.swimkids.us
Year Founded: 1996
Sales Range: $1-9.9 Million
Emp.: 143
Swim Schools
N.A.I.C.S.: 611699
Cindy Tonnesen (Co-Founder & CEO)
Dave Tonnesen (Co-Founder)

SWIMWEAR ANYWHERE, INC.
85 Sherwood Ave, Farmingdale, NY 11735
Tel.: (212) 221-1014
Web Site:
   http://www.swimwearanywhere.com
Year Founded: 1998
Sales Range: $25-49.9 Million
Emp.: 150
Men's & Women's Swimwear Mfr & Whslr
N.A.I.C.S.: 339920
Joe Roehrig (CFO)
Rosemarie DiLorenzo (Co-Owner & CEO)
Joseph DiLorenzo (Co-Owner & COO)

Subsidiaries:

The Finals   (1)
1790 Apollo Ct, Seal Beach, CA 90740
Tel.: (631) 420-1400
Web Site: http://www.thefinals.com
Sales Range: $25-49.9 Million
Emp.: 40
Competitive Swimwear & Accessories Mfr & Whslr
N.A.I.C.S.: 423910
Joe Roehrig (CFO)
Rosemarie DiLorenzo (Pres)

SWINDELL DRESSLER INTERNATIONAL CO.
5100 Casteel Dr, Coraopolis, PA 15108
Tel.: (412) 788-7100
Web Site:
   http://www.swindelldressler.com
Year Founded: 1915
Sales Range: $10-24.9 Million
Emp.: 100
Industrial Buildings Construction Services
N.A.I.C.S.: 236210
David F. Gaylord (Chm)
Carl E. Sutherland (Mgr-Sls)
Richard W. Perryman (Gen Mgr-Pittek Div)
Ken Hopkins (Pres)

SWINDOLL, JANZEN, HAWK & LLOYD, LLC
123 S Main, McPherson, KS 67460-1337
Tel.: (620) 241-1826
Web Site: http://www.sjhl.com
Year Founded: 1936
Accounting, Tax & Advisory Services
N.A.I.C.S.: 541211
D. Scott Loyd (Partner)
Chet Buchman (Mng Partner)
Keith S. Janzen (Partner)
Kyle J. Hawk (Partner)
Jesse Glazier (Partner)
Stephanie Thurman (Controller)
Anne Downing (Partner)
Jaymie Rothrock (Partner)
Stacie Wilson (Partner)
Jo Alexander (Acct)
Darren Anderson (Acct)
Jody Bohnenblust (Acct)
Debbie Coan (Partner)
Michael Costello (Digital Mktg Strategist)
Kelly Garcia (Office Mng Partner)
Jenny Lang (Tax Mgr)
Adam Grilliot (Sr Tax Mgr)
Kandy Graber (Acct)

SWINE GRAPHICS ENTERPRISES LP
1620 Superior St, Webster City, IA 50595-2925
Tel.: (515) 832-5481
Web Site: http://www.sgepork.com
Year Founded: 1982
Sales Range: $10-24.9 Million
Emp.: 200
Pork Products Mfr
N.A.I.C.S.: 112210
Eugene R. Barrick (CEO)
Craig Loffredo (Mgr-Production)
Chad Vogelbacher (Controller)
Rod Leman (Mgr-Ops)
Gene Gourley (Mgr-Nutrition & Res)

SWINERTON INCORPORATED

SWINERTON INCORPORATED — U.S. PRIVATE

Swinerton Incorporated—(Continued)
260 Townsend St, San Francisco, CA 94107-1719
Tel.: (415) 421-2980 CA
Web Site: https://www.swinerton.com
Year Founded: 1888
Sales Range: $1-4.9 Billion
Emp.: 4,000
Commercial & Institutional Building Construction
N.A.I.C.S.: 236220
Simon Pollard (Mgr-Design Build-San Diego)
B. Moon Hajjar (Mgr-Preconstruction Svcs)
Don Adair (Chief Rels Officer & Exec VP)
Liz Hawkins (Mgr-Ops-San Diego)
Mark Payne (VP/Mgr-San Diego)
Dave Callis (Pres)
Jason Chupp (VP & Mgr-Northwest)
Bobby Jennings (Mgr-Portland)
Ciaran Creighton (Mgr-Self-Perform Grp-Northern California)
Rebecca Anicich (Mgr-Bus Dev)
Lauren Nunnally (Chief Talent Officer & Sr VP)
SheriAnn Murphy (Gen Counsel & Sr VP)
Alison Satt (VP & Mgr-Austin)
Nick Vovakes (VP/Mgr-Seattle)
Kevin Smith (Mgr-Carolinas)
Ray Haj (Sr VP & Reg Mgr)
Subsidiaries:

Keller Builders, Inc. (1)
9350 Flair Dr Ste 102, El Monte, CA 91731
Tel.: (714) 424-5113
Web Site: http://www.swinerton.com
Sales Range: $10-24.9 Million
Emp.: 45
Provider of General Contracting Services
N.A.I.C.S.: 236220

Swinerton Builders (1)
260 Townsend St, San Francisco, CA 94107
Tel.: (415) 421-2980
Web Site: http://www.swinerton.com
Construction Services
N.A.I.C.S.: 237990

SWING MEDIA
7421 Beverly Blvd Ste 13, Los Angeles, CA 90036
Tel.: (323) 936-3000
Web Site: http://www.swingmediaoutdoor.com
Year Founded: 1998
Sales Range: $10-24.9 Million
Emp.: 11
Media Buying Services
N.A.I.C.S.: 541810
Jason Swing (Founder & CEO)
Majd Elias (Pres)

SWING TRANSPORT INC.
1405 N Salisbury Ave, Salisbury, NC 28144
Tel.: (704) 633-3567
Web Site: http://www.swingtransport.com
Rev.: $15,144,266
Emp.: 200
Contract Haulers
N.A.I.C.S.: 484121
James B. Swing (Chm)
Dan Summitt (Pres)
Donnie Parsons (Office Mgr)
Wayne Whitley (Dir-Safety)

SWISH WHITE RIVER LTD.
1118 Rte 14, Hartford, VT 05047
Tel.: (802) 295-3188 VT
Web Site: http://sfwhiteriverpaper.ubsynergy.net

Sanitation & Maintenance Company; Industrial & Personal Service Paper
N.A.I.C.S.: 424130
Bill Ladd (Controller)

SWISHER ELECTRIC COOPERATIVE, INC.
401 SW 2nd St, Tulia, TX 79088
Tel.: (806) 995-3567 TX
Web Site: http://www.swisherelectric.org
Year Founded: 1939
Sales Range: $25-49.9 Million
Emp.: 40
Electric Power Distr
N.A.I.C.S.: 221122
Mary Matsler (Mgr-HR)
Dwain Tipton (Mgr-Fin & Admin)
Andy Stewart (Coord-Safety & Loss Control & Training)

SWISHER HYGIENE INC.
201 E Las Olas Blvd Ste 1800, Fort Lauderdale, FL 33301
Tel.: (203) 682-8331 DE
Web Site: http://www.swshinvestors.com
Year Founded: 2016
Assets: $29,405,000
Liabilities: $5,047,000
Net Worth: $24,358,000
Earnings: ($57,590,000)
Fiscal Year-end: 12/31/15
Holding Company
N.A.I.C.S.: 551112
William T. Nanovsky (CFO, Chief Acctg Officer, Sec & Sr VP)
William M. Pierce (CTO)
Albert J. Detz (CFO, Chief Acctg Officer & Sr VP)
Richard L. Handley (Chm, Pres, CEO & Sec)
Subsidiaries:

1283465 Ontario Inc. (1)
570 Alden Rd Unit 5, Markham, L3R 8N5, ON, Canada
Tel.: (416) 650-5536
Emp.: 6
Chemical & Allied Products Merchant Whslr
N.A.I.C.S.: 424690

7324375 Canada Inc. (1)
Wb82-14630 128 Ave NW, Edmonton, T5L 3H7, AB, Canada
Tel.: (780) 448-0977
Chemical & Allied Products Merchant Whslr
N.A.I.C.S.: 424690

Eskimo Pie Corporation (1)
901 Moorefield Park Dr, Richmond, VA 23236
Tel.: (804) 560-8400
Emp.: 105
Food Store Operator
N.A.I.C.S.: 445298

Swisher Hygiene USA Operations, Inc. (1)
2425 O'Connor Rd, Green Bay, WI 54313
Tel.: (920) 434-2333
Chemical & Allied Products Merchant Whslr
N.A.I.C.S.: 424690

Swisher Maids, Inc. (1)
4725 Piedmont Row Dr, Charlotte, NC 28210-4270
Tel.: (980) 819-4210
Chemical & Allied Products Merchant Whslr
N.A.I.C.S.: 424690

SWISS AMERICAN CDMO, LLC
2055 Luna Rd Ste 126, Carrollton, TX 75006
Web Site: http://www.swissamericancdmo.com
Year Founded: 1988
Sales Range: $75-99.9 Million
Emp.: 360
Skin Care Product Mfr & Distr
N.A.I.C.S.: 325620

Phil O'Neill (CEO)
Komel V. Grover (Pres)
Ede Payne (COO)
Cory Johnson (CFO)

SWISS CHALET FINE FOODS INC.
9455 NW 40th St Rd, Miami, FL 33178
Tel.: (305) 592-0008
Web Site: http://www.scff.com
Rev.: $17,209,254
Emp.: 60
Groceries & Related Products
N.A.I.C.S.: 424490
Hans Baumann (Founder & CEO)
Osmel Hernandez (Dir-Ops)
Tim Polster (Mgr-Logistics)
Naz Balsara (COO)

SWISS COLONY DATA CENTER INC.
1112 7th Ave, Monroe, WI 53566
Tel.: (608) 328-8600
Web Site: http://www.theswisscolony.com
Rev.: $76,200,000
Emp.: 1,000
Data Processing Services
N.A.I.C.S.: 424430
John Baumann (Pres)

SWISS TEKNIK LLC
205 S Clark Dr, Tempe, AZ 85281
Tel.: (602) 288-9080
Web Site: http://www.swissteknik.com
Year Founded: 2006
Sales Range: $1-9.9 Million
Emp.: 7
Aircraft Parts
N.A.I.C.S.: 336413
Vince Switzer (Pres)

SWISS WATCH INTERNATIONAL INC.
101 S State Rd 7 St 201, Hollywood, FL 33023
Tel.: (954) 985-3827
Web Site: http://www.swisswatchintl.com
Year Founded: 1995
Sales Range: $100-124.9 Million
Emp.: 180
Watch Distr
N.A.I.C.S.: 334519
E. Benshmuel (Pres)
Shlomie Benshmuel (VP)
Russell Ackner (CMO)
Keith Bradley (CEO)

SWISS-AMERICAN PRODUCTS, INC.
2055 Luna Rd Ste 126, Carrollton, TX 75006
Tel.: (972) 385-2900 TX
Web Site: http://www.elta.net
Year Founded: 1988
Sales Range: $25-49.9 Million
Emp.: 80
Skin & Wound Care Products Mfr
N.A.I.C.S.: 325412
Ede Payne (COO)

SWISSINSO HOLDING INC.
845 3rd Ave 6th Fl, New York, NY 10022
Tel.: (646) 290-5000 DE
Web Site: http://www.swissinso.com
Sales Range: Less than $1 Million
Emp.: 3
Self-Contained Solar Powered Water Purification & Bottling System Mfr & Sales
N.A.I.C.S.: 221310
Rafic Hanbali (Chm, Pres & CEO)

SWISSTEX COMPANY
220 61st St, West New York, NJ 07093-2931
Tel.: (201) 861-8000 NJ
Year Founded: 1934
Sales Range: $75-99.9 Million
Emp.: 20
Foundation Garments, Bathing Suits, Sportswear, Underwear & Control Top Pantyhose Mfr
N.A.I.C.S.: 315250
Robert Wolfe (Owner & Chm)

SWITCHFAST TECHNOLOGIES LLC
4043 N Ravenswood Ste 203, Chicago, IL 60613
Tel.: (773) 241-3007
Web Site: http://www.switchfast.com
Year Founded: 2001
Rev.: $3,500,000
Emp.: 50
Computer Related Services
N.A.I.C.S.: 541512
Jim Anderson (CEO)
Victor Kelly (Acct Mgr)
Craig Hasselberger (Dir-Fin)
David Beiler (Engr-Software)
Rick Vines (CIO)
Subsidiaries:

Axcell Technologies, Inc. (1)
1901 N Roselle Rd #800, Schaumburg, IL 60195
Tel.: (866) 429-2355
Web Site: http://www.axcelltech.com
Computer Related Services
N.A.I.C.S.: 541519
Harry Reczek (VP)

SWITCHPLACE
7557 Rambler Rd Ste 1080, Dallas, TX 75231
Tel.: (972) 692-0983
Web Site: http://www.switchplace.com
Year Founded: 1998
Sales Range: $10-24.9 Million
Emp.: 18
Temporary Housing Services
N.A.I.C.S.: 721310
Cindy Kerr (COO & Exec VP)
Tammy Gillespie (Pres)
Jose Vargas (Coord-Acctg)
Ben Lugiai (VP-Sls)

SWITLIK PARACHUTE COMPANY INC.
1325 E State St, Trenton, NJ 08609
Tel.: (609) 587-3300
Web Site: http://www.switlik.com
Rev.: $14,352,929
Emp.: 120
Safety & Survival Products Mfr
N.A.I.C.S.: 326299
Stanley Switlik II (Pres)

SWIVELIER CO., INC.
600 Bradley Hill Rd, Blauvelt, NY 10913-1187
Tel.: (845) 353-1455 NY
Web Site: http://www.swivelier.com
Year Founded: 1947
Sales Range: $50-74.9 Million
Emp.: 150
Mfr of Adjustable Lighting Fixtures, Track Lighting & Recessed Lighting Fixtures for Commercial, Institutional & Residential Use
N.A.I.C.S.: 335132
Michael I. Schwartz (Pres)
Subsidiaries:

Point Electric (1)
600 Bradley Hill Rd, Blauvelt, NY 10913-1187
Tel.: (845) 353-1455

COMPANIES

Web Site: http://www.swivelier.com
Mfr of Adjustable Lighting Products for Do-It-Yourself Installation
N.A.I.C.S.: 335132
M.I. Schwartz *(Pres)*

SWLA CENTER FOR HEALTH SERVICES, INC.
2000 Opelousas St, Lake Charles, LA 70616-9010
Tel.: (337) 439-9983 LA
Web Site: http://www.swlahealth.org
Year Founded: 1978
Sales Range: $10-24.9 Million
Emp.: 150
Community Care Services
N.A.I.C.S.: 624190
Barbara Hardy *(Pres)*
Bernita Brown *(Sec)*

SWOPE HEALTH SERVICES
3801 Blue Pkwy, Kansas City, MO 64130
Tel.: (816) 923-5800 MO
Web Site:
 http://www.swopehealth.org
Year Founded: 1969
Sales Range: $25-49.9 Million
Physical & Behavioral Health Care Services
N.A.I.C.S.: 621420
Dave Barber *(Pres & CEO)*
LeAna Champion *(Dir-Nursing)*
Michelle Keller *(VP-Community Engagement, Dev & Outreach)*
Mark Miller *(VP-Behavioral Health Svcs)*
Naimish Patel *(CFO)*
Brian Thomas *(CIO & VP-Support Svcs)*
Robin Wheeler *(VP-HR)*
Harry E. Wilkins III *(Chm)*

SWOPE VENTURES, INC.
253 S Dixie Blvd, Radcliff, KY 40160
Tel.: (270) 351-2181
Web Site:
 http://www.swopehyundai.com
Sales Range: $10-24.9 Million
Emp.: 28
Car Whslr
N.A.I.C.S.: 441110
Carl Swope *(Pres)*

SWORDFISH COMMUNICATIONS
5 Stoneleigh Dr, Laurel Springs, NJ 08021
Tel.: (856) 767-7772
Web Site:
 http://www.swordfishcomm.com
Sales Range: Less than $1 Million
Emp.: 1
Advertising, Crisis Communications, Exhibit/Trade Shows, Media Relations, Media Training, Radio, Travel & Tourism
N.A.I.C.S.: 541820
Gary Frisch *(Founder & Pres)*

SWS ENVIRONMENTAL SERVICES
1619 Moylan Rd, Panama City, FL 32407
Tel.: (850) 234-8428
Web Site:
 http://www.swsenvironmental.com
Year Founded: 2008
Sales Range: $75-99.9 Million
Emp.: 450
Environmental Remediation Services Contractor
N.A.I.C.S.: 562910

Jesse Hixson *(Mgr-Svcs Center)*
Billy Flagel *(Dir-Emergency Response)*
James J. Weber Jr. *(Chm & CEO)*

SWS RE-DISTRIBUTION COMPANY, INC.
1440 LeMay Ste 104, Carrollton, TX 75007
Tel.: (972) 466-9720
Web Site: http://www.swsco.net
Year Founded: 1952
Sales Range: $250-299.9 Million
Emp.: 41
Janitorial Services
N.A.I.C.S.: 561720
Camille Fournier *(Owner & CEO)*
Bobby Cheney *(Pres)*
Lynn Robertson *(Controller)*
Dave Fournier *(Gen Mgr)*

SWYFT, INC.
140 Geary St Fl 7, San Francisco, CA 94108
Tel.: (844) 447-9938
Web Site: http://www.swyftstore.com
Year Founded: 2013
Automated Retail Solutions
N.A.I.C.S.: 445132
Gower Smith *(Co-Founder, Chm & CEO)*
Lincoln Smith *(Co-Founder & Pres)*
Brian Levin *(Co-Founder & VP-Sls)*
Jordan Smith *(Co-Founder & Dir-Ops)*
Richard Hashim *(COO)*
Julia Angelen Joy *(Acct Dir)*
Brent Beeman *(CFO)*
Geoff Williamson *(CMO & Pres-Health Care)*
Vikranth Katpally *(CTO)*
Marianne Hindsgaul *(Sr VP-Sls)*
Subsidiaries:

NewZoom, Inc. (1)
245 S Spruce Ave, South San Francisco, CA 94080-4581
Tel.: (917) 428-1061
Web Site: http://www.newzoom.com
Automated Retail Solutions
N.A.I.C.S.: 445132
Gower Smith *(Pres)*

SYAPPS LLC
13873 Park Ctr Rd Ste 104, Herndon, VA 20171
Tel.: (571) 421-1000
Web Site: http://www.syapps.com
Sales Range: $10-24.9 Million
Emp.: 175
Technology & Management Consulting Services
N.A.I.C.S.: 541690
Bala Sundar *(Co-Founder, Pres & CEO)*
Shankar Iyer *(Co-Founder & Chm)*
Jeremy T. Slater *(VP-Tech)*

SYAR INDUSTRIES, INC.
2301 Napa Vallejo Hwy, Napa, CA 94558-6242
Tel.: (707) 252-8711 CA
Web Site: http://www.syar.com
Year Founded: 1933
Sales Range: $25-49.9 Million
Emp.: 350
Retailer of Construction & Building Materials
N.A.I.C.S.: 423320
James M. Syar *(Pres)*
Denton Syar *(VP)*
Subsidiaries:

Syar Concrete LLC (1)
39820 Kentucky Ave, Woodland, CA 95695
Web Site: http://www.syarconcrete.com
Ready Mix Concrete Distr
N.A.I.C.S.: 423320
Molly Randall *(Mgr-Credit & Collections)*
Plant (Domestic):

Syar Concrete LLC - Fairfield Ready-mix Plant (2)
4969 Vanden Rd, Fairfield, CA 94533
Web Site: http://www.syarconcrete.com
Concrete Product Supplier Distr
N.A.I.C.S.: 423320

Syar Industries, Inc. - Healdsburg Plant (1)
13666 Healdsburg Ave, Healdsburg, CA 95448
Tel.: (707) 433-3366
Asphalt Product Mfr
N.A.I.C.S.: 324121

Syar Industries, Inc. - Todd Road Plant (1)
260 Ghilotti Ave, Santa Rosa, CA 95407
Tel.: (707) 584-0262
Asphalt Product Mfr
N.A.I.C.S.: 324121

SYBARIS CLUBS INTERNATIONAL INC.
2430 E Rand Rd, Arlington Heights, IL 60004
Tel.: (847) 637-3000
Web Site: http://www.sybaris.com
Rev.: $11,000,000
Emp.: 12
Hotel
N.A.I.C.S.: 721110
Kenneth Knudson *(Founder & Pres)*
Charlene Farrell *(Dir-Ops)*
Randy Repke *(Mgr)*

SYCAMORE ENGINEERING
1010 Chestnut St, Terre Haute, IN 47807
Tel.: (812) 232-0968
Web Site:
 http://www.sycamoreengineeringinc.com
Sales Range: $25-49.9 Million
Emp.: 200
Plumbing Services
N.A.I.C.S.: 238220
Randy Reinoehl *(Mgr-Sheet Metal)*
Sara Smith *(VP-Engrg)*
Wade Hood *(Project Mgr)*

SYCAMORE PARTNERS MANAGEMENT, LP
9 W 57th St 31st Fl, New York, NY 10019
Tel.: (212) 796-8500 DE
Web Site:
 http://www.sycamorepartners.com
Year Founded: 2011
Privater Equity Firm
N.A.I.C.S.: 523999
Stefan L. Kaluzny *(Founder & Mng Dir)*
Rob Sweeney *(Pres)*
Subsidiaries:

ANN Inc. (1)
7 Times Sq, New York, NY 10036
Tel.: (212) 541-3300
Web Site: http://www.anninc.com
Sales Range: $1-4.9 Billion
Holding Company; Women's Apparel, Shoes & Accessories Stores Operator
N.A.I.C.S.: 551112
Lisa Axelson *(Head Designer)*
Subsidiary (Domestic):

AnnTaylor Retail, Inc. (2)
7 Times Sq, New York, NY 10036
Tel.: (212) 541-3300
Women's Apparel, Shoes & Accessories
N.A.I.C.S.: 458110
Gary P. Muto *(CEO)*

AnnTaylor, Inc. (2)
7 Times Sq, New York, NY 10036
Tel.: (212) 541-3300

SYCAMORE PARTNERS MANAGEMENT, LP

Web Site: http://www.anntaylor.com
Women's Apparel, Shoes & Accessories Retailer
N.A.I.C.S.: 458110

Belk, Inc. (1)
2801 W Tyvola Rd, Charlotte, NC 28217-4500
Tel.: (704) 357-1000
Web Site: https://www.belk.com
Sales Range: $1-4.9 Billion
Emp.: 17,000
Department Stores
N.A.I.C.S.: 455110
Lisa M. Harper *(Chm)*
Ralph A. Pitts *(Gen Counsel, Sec & Exec VP)*
Don Hendricks *(CEO)*
Chris Kolbe *(Chief Mdsg Officer & Exec VP)*

Chico's FAS, Inc. (1)
11215 Metro Pkwy, Fort Myers, FL 33966
Tel.: (239) 277-6200
Web Site: https://www.chicosfas.com
Rev.: $2,142,020,000
Assets: $1,187,841,000
Liabilities: $852,208,000
Net Worth: $335,633,000
Earnings: $108,999,000
Emp.: 14,238
Fiscal Year-end: 01/28/2023
Holding Company; Women's Apparel Whslr & Retailer
N.A.I.C.S.: 551112
David M. Oliver *(CFO, Chief Acctg Officer & Exec VP)*
Kristin M. Gwinner *(Chief HR Officer & Exec VP)*
Nancy Johnson *(Sr VP)*
Kirsten Bowen *(Sr VP)*
Lizanne Kindler *(Exec Chm & Co-CEO)*

Subsidiary (Domestic):

Chico's Distribution Services, LLC (2)
11215 Metro Pkwy, Fort Myers, FL 33966-1206
Tel.: (239) 277-6200
Web Site: http://www.chicos.com
Sales Range: $150-199.9 Million
Emp.: 800
Ladies Apparel Chain of Exclusively Designed Casual Clothing
N.A.I.C.S.: 458110

Chico's Retail Services, Inc. (2)
11215 Metro Pkwy, Fort Myers, FL 33966
Tel.: (239) 277-6200
Web Site: http://www.chicos.com
Sales Range: $100-124.9 Million
Emp.: 600
Business Services
N.A.I.C.S.: 458110

Soma Intimates, LLC (2)
11215 Metro Pkwy, Fort Myers, FL 33966
Tel.: (954) 563-6360
Web Site: https://www.soma.com
Women's Clothing Retailer
N.A.I.C.S.: 458110

White House Black Market, Inc. (2)
3040 NW Federal Hwy, Jensen Beach, FL 34957-4446
Tel.: (772) 232-9220
Women's Clothing Retailer
N.A.I.C.S.: 458110

Digital Room, LLC (1)
14931 Califa St 301, Sherman Oaks, CA 91411
Tel.: (310) 575-4440
Web Site: http://www.digitalroominc.com
Sales Range: $50-74.9 Million
Emp.: 504
Commercial Printing Services
N.A.I.C.S.: 323113
Michael Turner *(CEO)*

Hot Topic, Inc. (1)
18305 E San Jose Ave, City of Industry, CA 91748
Tel.: (626) 839-4681
Web Site: http://www.hottopic.com
Rev.: $741,745,000
Assets: $274,945,000
Liabilities: $102,191,000

3895

SYCAMORE PARTNERS MANAGEMENT, LP

U.S. PRIVATE

Sycamore Partners Management, LP—(Continued)
Net Worth: $172,754,000
Earnings: $19,470,000
Emp.: 2,100
Fiscal Year-end: 02/02/2013
Music & Popular Culture-Inspired Clothing & Accessories Retailer
N.A.I.C.S.: 458110
Mike Barton (Dir-Loss Prevention)

Subsidiary (Domestic):

hottopic.com, Inc. (2)
18305 E San Jose Ave, City of Industry, CA 91748
Tel.: (626) 839-4681
Web Site: http://www.hottopic.com
Sales Range: $75-99.9 Million
Emp.: 400
Internet Clothing Sales
N.A.I.C.S.: 458110
Lisa Harbor (CEO)

Lane Bryant, Inc. (1)
3344 Morse Crossing, Columbus, OH 43219 (100%)
Tel.: (215) 633-2497
Web Site: http://www.lanebryant.com
Sales Range: $200-249.9 Million
Emp.: 250
Women's Special-Size Apparel Mfr & Retailer
N.A.I.C.S.: 458110

Subsidiary (Domestic):

Lane Bryant Charities, Inc. (2)
3750 State Rd, Bensalem, PA 19020-5903
Tel.: (215) 245-9100
Fundraising Services
N.A.I.C.S.: 561499

Nielsen & Bainbridge, LLC (1)
12303 Technology Blvd Ste 950, Austin, TX 78727
Tel.: (512) 506-8844
Web Site: http://www.nielsenbainbridgegroup.com
Picture Framing Products Mfr & Distr
N.A.I.C.S.: 339999
Hope Margala (CEO)

Plant (Domestic):

Nielsen & Bainbridge, LLC - Nielsen Manufacturing (2)
1267 N Grundy Quarles Hwy, Gainesboro, TN 38562
Tel.: (931) 268-0241
Web Site: http://www.nielsen-bainbridge.com
Picture Framing Products Mfr & Distr
N.A.I.C.S.: 339999

Subsidiary (Non-US):

Nielsen Design GmbH (2)
Rontgenstrasse 10, Rheda-Wiedenbruck, 33378, Germany
Tel.: (49) 524241050
Web Site: http://www.nielsen-design.de
Frama Mouldings Mfr
N.A.I.C.S.: 321999
Andreas Montag (Mng Dir)

Subsidiary (Domestic):

Plantation Patterns, LLC (2)
400 Chase Park S Ste 212, Hoover, AL 35244
Tel.: (205) 554-9369
Web Site: http://www.plantationpatterns.com
Home & Personal Fabric Product Producers
N.A.I.C.S.: 313240
Scott Crumrine (COO)
Patrick Moyer (VP-Sls)
Randy Mooreland (Dir-Domestic Ops)
Jeannie COst (Dir-IT, Planning & Analytics)
Jessica Wilson (Mgr-Intl Procurement)

Quoizel Inc. (2)
6 Corporate Pkwy, Goose Creek, SC 29445
Tel.: (843) 553-6700
Web Site: http://www.quoizel.com
Lamps & Lighting Fixtures Mfr
N.A.I.C.S.: 335131
Brittany Withers (Sr Mgr-Logistics)

Pure Fishing, Inc. (1)
7 Science Ct, Columbia, SC 29203

Web Site: http://www.purefishing.com
Sales Range: $500-549.9 Million
Emp.: 500
Sporting & Athletic Goods Mfr
N.A.I.C.S.: 339920
Jon Schlosser (VP-Mktg)
Harlan M. Kent (CEO)

Subsidiary (Domestic):

Penn Fishing Tackle Manufacturing Company (2)
3028 W Hunting Park Ave, Philadelphia, PA 19132-1121
Tel.: (215) 229-9415
Web Site: http://www.pennreels.com
Sales Range: $50-74.9 Million
Emp.: 50
Fishing Reels Mfr
N.A.I.C.S.: 339920
Peter Yaskowski (Dir-Product Dev)

Subsidiary (Non-US):

Pure Fishing Asia Co., Ltd. (2)
13F 366 Beituan Rd, Beitun, Taichung, 40654, Taiwan
Tel.: (886) 422463949
Web Site: http://www.purefishing.com.tw
Sales Range: $25-49.9 Million
Emp.: 20
Fish Catching Services
N.A.I.C.S.: 114119
John Dorell (CEO)

Subsidiary (Non-US):

Pure Fishing (Guangzhou) Trading Co., Ltd. (3)
Unit B 16th Fl SanXin Plaza No 33 Huangpu W Ave Tianhe District, Guangzhou, 510620, China
Tel.: (86) 2028815029
Fishing Tackle Products Mfr
N.A.I.C.S.: 424990

Pure Fishing (Thailand) Co., Ltd. (3)
54 Soi Ari 5 Nuea Phahon Yothin 7, Phaya Thai, Bangkok, 10400, Thailand
Tel.: (66) 865364727
Non-Durable Goods Whslr
N.A.I.C.S.: 424990

Pure Fishing Malaysia Sdn. Bhd. (3)
No 36 Kartunis U1/47 Seksyen U1 Kawasan Perindustrian Temasya, Shah Alam, 40150, Selangor, Malaysia
Tel.: (60) 350329288
Web Site: http://www.purefishingasia.com
Marine Fishing Services
N.A.I.C.S.: 114119
Quek Jin King (Gen Mgr)

Subsidiary (Non-US):

Pure Fishing Europe S.A.S. (2)
396 Rue de la Precision, 74970, Marignier, France
Tel.: (33) 450967700
Fishing Equipment Whslr
N.A.I.C.S.: 114119

Subsidiary (Non-US):

Abu AB (3)
Hollandarev 35, Svangsta, 376 81, Sweden
Tel.: (46) 8002284472
Web Site: http://www.abugarcia.se
Fishing Reels & Equipment Mfr
N.A.I.C.S.: 339920
Jan Sjoblom (Gen Mgr)

Pure Fishing (UK) Ltd. (3)
1 Brooklands Moons Mt Dr, Redditch, B98 9DW, Worcestershire, United Kingdom
Tel.: (44) 1527405410
Sales Range: $25-49.9 Million
Emp.: 2
Fishing Equipment Whslr
N.A.I.C.S.: 114119

Pure Fishing Deutschland GmbH (3)
Uferweg 40-42, 63571, Gelnhausen, Germany
Tel.: (49) 605182870
Web Site: http://www.de.purefishing.com
Sales Range: $25-49.9 Million
Emp.: 1
Fish Catching Services
N.A.I.C.S.: 112511

Pure Fishing Netherlands B.V. (3)
Ecustraat 13, Etten-Leur, 4879 NP, Netherlands
Tel.: (31) 365474000
Web Site: http://www.eu.purefishing.com
Marine Fishing Services
N.A.I.C.S.: 114119

Staples, Inc. (1)
500 Staples Dr, Framingham, MA 01702
Tel.: (508) 253-5000
Web Site: https://www.staples.com
Sales Range: $15-24.9 Billion
Emp.: 34,000
Offices of Other Holding Companies
N.A.I.C.S.: 551112
Steve Matyas (Pres-Retail-North America)
Michael T. Williams (Chief Legal Officer, Gen Counsel & Sec)
Faisal Masud (CTO)
John B. Wilson (Pres-Intl)
John A. Lederer (Chm & CEO)
Jeffrey L. Hall (CFO)
Mark Conte (Sr VP & Controller)
Neil Ringel (Pres-Delivery-North America)
Brett Wahlin (Chief Info Security Officer)
Michelle Bottomley (CMO)
Pragati Mathur (CIO)
Amy Steel Vanden-Eykel (CMO)

Subsidiary (Non-US):

Auxilia Graphica S.r.L. (2)
40 Via Ivrea, 10098, Rivoli, Italy
Tel.: (39) 0119572566
Sales Range: $10-24.9 Million
Emp.: 5
Printing Machinery & Equipment Mfr
N.A.I.C.S.: 333248

Subsidiary (Domestic):

DEX Imaging, Inc. (2)
5109 W Lemon St, Tampa, FL 33609
Tel.: (813) 288-8080
Web Site: http://www.deximaging.com
Document Imaging & Other Office Equipment Distr
N.A.I.C.S.: 423420
Scott Casey (Controller)
Crystal Mallard (Dir-Sls)
Daniel M. Doyle Jr. (Pres & CEO)
Daniel M. Doyle Sr. (Chm)

Subsidiary (Domestic):

Modular Document Solutions, LLC (2)
12320 Crystal Commerce Loop, Fort Myers, FL 33966-1082
Tel.: (239) 481-9200
Web Site: http://www.modulardocument.com
Office Machinery & Equipment Rental & Leasing
N.A.I.C.S.: 532420
Liz Shaver (Mgr-HR)

Subsidiary (Non-US):

EMO AS (2)
Solheimvn. 6-8, 146, Lorenskog, Norway
Tel.: (47) 63 84 92 50
Web Site: http://www.emo.no
Sales Range: $25-49.9 Million
Office Supplies & Services
N.A.I.C.S.: 459410
Henning Rolfson (Dir)

Subsidiary (Domestic):

Essendant Inc. (2)
1 Parkway N Blvd Ste 100, Deerfield, IL 60015-2559
Tel.: (847) 627-7000
Web Site: http://www.essendant.com
Sales Range: $5-14.9 Billion
Emp.: 6,400
Holding Company; Business Products Distr
N.A.I.C.S.: 424120
Harry A. Dochelli (Pres-Office & Facilities)

Subsidiary (Non-US):

Essendant Canada, Inc. (3)
6400 Ordan Dr, Mississauga, L5T 2H6, ON, Canada
Tel.: (905) 670-1223
Web Site: http://www.adoxoki.com
Industrial Equipment Distr
N.A.I.C.S.: 423830

Jilles Paquette (Mgr-Sls-Ontario)
Mike Besner (Mgr-Sls-Western Canada & Alberta)

Subsidiary (Domestic):

Label Industries, Inc. (3)
221 W 4th St Ste 4, Carthage, MO 64836
Tel.: (417) 358-1919
Web Site: http://www.nationaltoolwarehouse.com
Emp.: 10
Automotive Parts Merchant Whslr
N.A.I.C.S.: 423120

Liberty Bell Equipment Corp. (3)
3201 S 76th St, Philadelphia, PA 19153
Tel.: (215) 492-6700
Web Site: http://www.medcocorp.com
Sales Range: $10-24.9 Million
Emp.: 88
Automobile Service Station Equipment Whslr
N.A.I.C.S.: 423120
Mike Muenzer (VP-Sls)

Medco Tool of Ohio, Inc (3)
21548 Alexander Rd, Bedford, OH 44146
Tel.: (215) 492-6700
Automotive Part Whslr
N.A.I.C.S.: 423120

Medco Tool of St. Louis, Inc. (3)
810 N Jefferson Ave, Saint Louis, MO 63106
Tel.: (314) 588-1111
Industrial Machinery Distr
N.A.I.C.S.: 423830
D. Josh (Gen Mgr)

Nestor Sales LLC (3)
7337 Bryan Dairy Rd, Largo, FL 33777
Tel.: (727) 544-6114
Web Site: http://www.nestorsales.com
Emp.: 70
Motor Vehicle Supplies & Parts Distr
N.A.I.C.S.: 423120
Barry Katz (Dir-Fin)

Subsidiary (Domestic):

ACE Tool Co. (3)
14200 E 35th Pl 103, Aurora, CO 80011
Tel.: (303) 371-4500
Web Site: http://www.acetoolco.com
Emp.: 4
Industrial Supplies Whslr
N.A.I.C.S.: 423840
Nick Brown (Branch Mgr)

Subsidiary (Non-US):

OKI Bearing Canada Inc. (3)
6400 Ordan Dr, Mississauga, L5T 2H6, ON, Canada
Tel.: (905) 670-1223
Web Site: https://orscanada.com
Industrial Equipment Distr
N.A.I.C.S.: 423830

OKI Bering Middle East, FZE (3)
RA07 AC03 Jafza Liu 15near R/A Jabel Ali Free Zone, PO Box 17589, Dubai, United Arab Emirates
Tel.: (971) 48860679
Web Site: http://www.oki-me.com
Financial Transaction Services
N.A.I.C.S.: 522320

Subsidiary (Domestic):

United Stationers Supply Co. (3)
1 Pkwy N Blvd Ste 100, Deerfield, IL 60015 (100%)
Tel.: (847) 627-7000
Web Site: http://www.ussco.com
Sales Range: $5-14.9 Billion
Business Products Distr
N.A.I.C.S.: 424120

Subsidiary (Domestic):

CPO Commerce, Inc. (4)
120 West Bellevue Dr Ste 300, Pasadena, CA 91105
Tel.: (626) 585-3600
Web Site: http://www.cpooutlets.com
Sales Range: $75-99.9 Million
Emp.: 75
Refurbished Products
N.A.I.C.S.: 813910

SYCAMORE PARTNERS MANAGEMENT, LP

Rob Tolleson *(Founder, Chm, Pres & CEO)*
Jeff Emmons *(VP-E-Commerce)*

Subsidiary (Non-US):

Essendant Hong Kong Limited (4)
3 Lockhart Rd, Wanchai, China (Hong Kong)
Tel.: (852) 28652020
Stationery & Office Product Whslr
N.A.I.C.S.: 424120

Subsidiary (Domestic):

Essendant Management Services LLC (4)
1 Parkway N Ste 100, Deerfield, IL 60015-2559
Tel.: (847) 627-7000
Emp.: 270
Stationery Store Operator
N.A.I.C.S.: 459410
Jim Klocek *(Mgr-Mainframe Sys)*

Lagasse, Inc. (4)
One Parkway N Blvd Ste 100, Deerfield, IL 60015
Tel.: (847) 627-2400
Web Site: http://www.essendent.com
Sales Range: $250-299.9 Million
Emp.: 600
Janitorial & Sanitation Products Distr
N.A.I.C.S.: 423850
Paul J. Barrett *(Pres)*

ORS Nasco, Inc. (4)
907 S Detroit Ste 400, Tulsa, OK 74120
Tel.: (918) 687-5441
Web Site: http://www.orsnasco.com
Sales Range: $250-299.9 Million
Emp.: 150
Industrial Equipment & Supplies Whslr
N.A.I.C.S.: 423840
Mark Prox *(VP-Ops)*
Dave McCann *(VP-Assoc Rels)*
Diane Locandro *(VP-Trade Compliance & Assoc Gen Counsel)*
Chris Kempa *(Pres)*
Ben Brumfield *(VP-Sls)*

Subsidiary (Non-US):

United Stationers Hong Kong Limited (4)
28 Fl 3 Lockhart Rd, Wanchai, China (Hong Kong)
Tel.: (852) 28652020
Web Site: http://www.ussco.com
Sales Range: $50-74.9 Million
Emp.: 15
Stationery Whslr
N.A.I.C.S.: 424130

Subsidiary (Domestic):

United Stationers Technology Services LLC (4)
1 Parkway N Ste 100, Deerfield, IL 60015-2559
Tel.: (847) 627-7000
Web Site: http://www.essendant.com
Stationery & Office Products Whslr
N.A.I.C.S.: 424120

Subsidiary (Domestic):

Faison Office Products, Inc. (2)
12508 E Briarwood Ave 1A, Centennial, CO 80112
Tel.: (303) 340-3672
Web Site: https://www.faisonopc.com
Office Products Whslr
N.A.I.C.S.: 459410

Subsidiary (Non-US):

Grieg Kalenderforlag AS (2)
Hvamsvingen 4, PO Box 90, Skjetten, 2026, Norway
Tel.: (47) 63849160
Web Site: http://www.griegkalender.no
Emp.: 170
Office Supply & Stationery Store Operator
N.A.I.C.S.: 459410
Lisa Lundberg *(Sec-Sls)*

Macchingraf Srl (2)
Via Trento 61, Ospiate di Bollate, 20021, Italy
Tel.: (39) 02350031
Web Site: http://www.macchingraf.it

Maquinaria Artes Graficas Hartmann SA (2)
Ctra de L'Hospitalet 98, 08940, Cornella, Spain
Tel.: (34) 934758000
Web Site: http://www.hartmann.es
Sales Range: $100-124.9 Million
Emp.: 70
Graphic Design Systems
N.A.I.C.S.: 541430
Vicente Tur *(Dir-Fin)*

Marke Creative Merchandise Ltd. (2)
Units 6-8 Liongate Enterprise Park Morden Road, Mitcham, CR4 4NY, United Kingdom
Tel.: (44) 2086402999
Web Site: https://markecreativemerchandise.com
Emp.: 79
Office Supplies & Services
N.A.I.C.S.: 459410
Lisa Munro *(Mng Dir)*

Milbro, Inc. (2)
9200 Av Du Parc, Montreal, H2N 1Z4, QC, Canada
Tel.: (514) 387-9282
Administrative Management Consulting Services
N.A.I.C.S.: 541618

Neat Ideas Ltd (2)
Unit 5 Belton Lane Industrial Estate, Grantham, NG31 9HN, Lincolnshire, United Kingdom
Tel.: (44) 1476576289
Web Site: http://www.neatideasdirect.co.uk
Sales Range: $100-124.9 Million
Emp.: 180
Kitchen & Home Product Distr
N.A.I.C.S.: 449129

Subsidiary (Domestic):

Office Superstore West LLC (2)
500 Staples Dri Fl 3, Framingham, MA 01702-4478
Tel.: (508) 253-5000
Office Equipments Supplies
N.A.I.C.S.: 459410
Steven D. Bussberg *(Mgr)*

Subsidiary (Domestic):

Staples the Office Superstore, LLC. (3)
500 Staples Dr, Framingham, MA 01702
Tel.: (508) 253-5000
Sales Range: $450-499.9 Million
Office Supplies
N.A.I.C.S.: 424120

Subsidiary (Non-US):

OfficeCentre Equipamentos de Escritorio Lda (2)
Rua Quinta Do Pinheiro Edificio Tejo 5 Pisao, 2794-079, Carnaxide, Portugal
Tel.: (351) 214255800
Web Site: http://www.staples.pt
Sales Range: $250-299.9 Million
Emp.: 100
Office Supplies
N.A.I.C.S.: 459410
Joe Andrave *(Mgr-Ops)*

PNI Digital Media ULC (2)
#100 425 Carrall Street, Vancouver, V6B 6E3, BC, Canada
Tel.: (604) 893-8955
Web Site: http://www.pnimedia.com
Sales Range: $10-24.9 Million
Emp.: 185
Custom Digital Media Platform Solutions
N.A.I.C.S.: 541511
Roger Canann *(VP-Dev-US & Gen Mgr)*

Pressel Post b.v.b.a. (2)
Rueherbesthal 325, 4700, Eupen, Belgium
Tel.: (32) 92451144
Sales Range: $25-49.9 Million
Emp.: 3
Office Supplies & Services
N.A.I.C.S.: 459410

Pressel Sp.z.o.o. (2)
Wybrzeze Slowackiego 12-14, 50-411, Wroclaw, Poland
Tel.: (48) 713410360
Office Supplies & Services
N.A.I.C.S.: 459410

Pressel Versand GmbH (2)
Gropiusplatz 10, 70563, Stuttgart, Germany
Tel.: (49) 57737 70
Web Site: http://www.pressel.com
Electronics & Office Furniture Product Mfr
N.A.I.C.S.: 337214
Nathalie Gaspard *(Mng Dir)*

Pressel Versand International GmbH (2)
Industriestrasse 8, Bad Voslau, 2540, Vienna, Austria
Tel.: (43) 225270444
Web Site: http://www.pressel.at
Emp.: 8
Office Supplies & Services
N.A.I.C.S.: 459410

Subsidiary (Domestic):

QS Quarterhouse Software, Inc. (2)
3445 Executive Ctr Dr Ste 150, Austin, TX 78731
Tel.: (512) 351-8783
Web Site: http://www.quarterhouse.net
Software Development Services
N.A.I.C.S.: 541511

Quill LLC (2)
100 Schelter Rd, Lincolnshire, IL 60069
Tel.: (847) 634-6690
Web Site: https://www.quill.com
Emp.: 576
Online Office Supplies, Furniture, Equipment & Cleaning Products Retailer
N.A.I.C.S.: 459410

Quill LLC (2)
100 Schelter Rd, Lincolnshire, IL 60069
Tel.: (847) 634-6690
Web Site: https://www.quill.com
Emp.: 576
Online Office Supplies, Furniture, Equipment & Cleaning Products Retailer
N.A.I.C.S.: 459410

Subsidiary (Domestic):

Quill Lincolnshire, Inc. (3)
100 Schelter Rd, Lincolnshire, IL 60069
Tel.: (847) 634-6690
Web Site: http://www.quill.com
Sales Range: $75-99.9 Million
Emp.: 150
Office Supplies
N.A.I.C.S.: 459410

Subsidiary (Domestic):

Quill LLC (2)
100 Schelter Rd, Lincolnshire, IL 60069
Tel.: (847) 634-6690
Web Site: https://www.quill.com
Emp.: 576
Online Office Supplies, Furniture, Equipment & Cleaning Products Retailer
N.A.I.C.S.: 459410

Quill LLC (2)
100 Schelter Rd, Lincolnshire, IL 60069
Tel.: (847) 634-6690
Web Site: https://www.quill.com
Emp.: 576
Online Office Supplies, Furniture, Equipment & Cleaning Products Retailer
N.A.I.C.S.: 459410

Subsidiary (Domestic):

Quill Lincolnshire, Inc. (3)
100 Schelter Rd, Lincolnshire, IL 60069
Tel.: (847) 634-6690
Web Site: http://www.quill.com
Sales Range: $75-99.9 Million
Emp.: 150
Office Supplies
N.A.I.C.S.: 459410

Subsidiary (Non-US):

Rich Andvord Grafisk AS (2)
Lunden 25/243 Pb Alnabru, Oslo, 0614, Norway
Tel.: (47) 22726600
Web Site: http://andvordgrafisk.no

Office Supply & Stationery Store Operator
N.A.I.C.S.: 459410

Staples Advantage Ireland Ltd. (2)
Block B The Crescent Building Northwood Santry, Dublin, Ireland
Tel.: (353) 15530078
Web Site: http://www.staplesadvantage.ie
Stationery Store Operator
N.A.I.C.S.: 459410
Eddie Doyle *(Mgr-Pur)*

Staples Canada, ULC (2)
6 Staples Ave, Richmond Hill, L4B 4W3, ON, Canada
Tel.: (905) 737-1147
Web Site: http://www.staples.ca
Emp.: 10,000
Office Products Whslr
N.A.I.C.S.: 459410
Paul Trickett *(Dir-Asset Protection-Natl)*

Division *(Domestic)*:

Staples Business Depot (3)
45 Red Maple Rd, Richmond Hill, L4B 4M6, ON, Canada (100%)
Tel.: (905) 882-6995
Web Site: http://www.staples.ca
Sales Range: $150-199.9 Million
Office Supplies
N.A.I.C.S.: 459410
Alessandra Saccal *(Mgr-PR)*

Subsidiary (Domestic):

Staples Contract & Commercial, Inc. (2)
500 Staples Dr, Framingham, MA 01702
Tel.: (508) 253-5000
Web Site: http://www.staples.com
Office Equipment Distr
N.A.I.C.S.: 424120

Subsidiary (Non-US):

Staples International B.V. (2)
Hoogoorddreef 62, 1101 BE, Amsterdam, Netherlands
Tel.: (31) 206511111
Holding Company; Regional Managing Office
N.A.I.C.S.: 551112
Gordon Glover *(Mgr-Fin & Admin)*

Subsidiary (Domestic):

Staples Europe B.V. (3)
Hoogoorddreef 62, PO Box 23456, Amsterdam, 1101 BE, Netherlands
Tel.: (31) 206511111
Web Site: http://www.staplesadvantage.eu
Office Products Whslr
N.A.I.C.S.: 459410
Thomas Nowak *(Sr VP-Mdsg)*
John Wilson *(Pres)*

Subsidiary (Non-US):

Staples Austria GmbH (4)
Boschstrasse 31, Wels, 4600, Austria
Tel.: (43) 16029121
Electronics & Office Furniture Product Mfr
N.A.I.C.S.: 337214

Staples Belgium BVBA (4)
Ringlaan 39, 1853, Strombeek-Bever, Belgium
Tel.: (32) 26619611
Web Site: http://www.staplesadvantage.be
Sales Range: $50-74.9 Million
Emp.: 60
Office Supplies Retail & Renting
N.A.I.C.S.: 459410
Sandra Kohna *(Mgr-HR)*

Subsidiary (Domestic):

Staples Shared Service Center (Europe) II, BVBA (5)
Ilgatlaan 9, Hasselt, 3500, Limburg, Belgium
Tel.: (32) 11370511
Office Supply & Stationery Store Operator
N.A.I.C.S.: 459410
Michael Henckaers *(Office Mgr)*

Subsidiary (Non-US):

Staples Denmark ApS (4)
Lhegnet 71-75, Albertslund, 2620, Denmark

SYCAMORE PARTNERS MANAGEMENT, LP

Sycamore Partners Management, LP—(Continued)
Tel.: (45) 43667777
Office Supply & Stationery Store Operator
N.A.I.C.S.: 459410

Staples Deutschland GmbH & Co. KG (4)
Barmbeker Strasse 10, 22303, Hamburg, Germany (100%)
Tel.: (49) 40767410
Web Site: http://www.staples.de
Sales Range: $50-74.9 Million
Emp.: 80
Office Supplies
N.A.I.C.S.: 459410
Jochen Bohl (Mng Dir-Retail)

Subsidiary (Domestic):

Staples Verwaltungs GmbH (5)
Gropiusplatz 10, 70563, Stuttgart, Germany
Tel.: (49) 711906760
Web Site: http://www.staples.eu
Office Supply & Stationery Store Operator
N.A.I.C.S.: 459410

Subsidiary (Non-US):

Staples Finland Oy (4)
Heikkilantie 7, PO Box 109, FIN-00101, Helsinki, Finland
Tel.: (358) 10681681
Web Site: http://www.staples.fi
Emp.: 7
Office Supply & Stationery Store Operator
N.A.I.C.S.: 459410
Poul Lindqvist (Country Mgr)

Staples France Holding SAS (4)
63 Rue Grande, 95470, Survilliers, France
Tel.: (33) 134683940
Holding Company
N.A.I.C.S.: 551112

Staples Nordic AS (4)
Per Krogh vei 1, 1065, Oslo, Norway
Tel.: (47) 22329500
Web Site: http://www.staples.com
Emp.: 200
Electronics & Office Furniture Product Mfr
N.A.I.C.S.: 337214
Mats Karlsson (Gen Mgr)

Staples Norway AS (4)
Per Krohgs vei 1, 1065, Oslo, Norway
Tel.: (47) 22329500
Web Site: http://www.staplesnetshop.no
Emp.: 214
Office Supplie Products Mfr
N.A.I.C.S.: 459210
Madskalsson Kalsson (Gen Mgr)

Subsidiary (Domestic):

Staples Retail Norway AS (5)
karihaugen, Per Krohgs Vei 1, PO Box 5, Oslo, 1065, Norway
Tel.: (47) 81000700
Office Supplies & Services
N.A.I.C.S.: 459410

Subsidiary (Non-US):

Staples Polska Sp.z o.o. (4)
ul Bysewska 18, 80-298, Gdansk, Poland
Tel.: (48) 587815200
Web Site: http://www.staplesadvantage.pl
Emp.: 20
Office Supplies & Services
N.A.I.C.S.: 459410

Staples Portugal Equipamento de Escritoria, SA (4)
Rua Quinta do Pinheiro Tagus Building 5th Floor, Carnaxide, 2794079, Portugal
Tel.: (351) 214255800
Web Site: http://www.staples.pt
Sales Range: $25-49.9 Million
Emp.: 80
Office Supplies & Services
N.A.I.C.S.: 459410

Staples Sweden AB (4)
Humlegatan 15, 504 51, Boras, Sweden
Tel.: (46) 33206550
Web Site: http://www.staplesnetshop.se
Emp.: 300
Office Supplies & Services
N.A.I.C.S.: 459410
Per Carlsson (Mgr)

Subsidiary (Domestic):

Staples International Group Services B.V. (3)
Hoogoorddreef 62, 1101 BE, Amsterdam, Zuidoost, Netherlands
Tel.: (31) 206511111
Electronics & Office Furniture Products Whslr
N.A.I.C.S.: 459410

Staples Nederland Holding B.V. (3)
Rondebeltweg 102, 1329 BH, Almere, Netherlands
Tel.: (31) 884545700
Web Site: http://www.staplesadvantage.nl
Holding Company
N.A.I.C.S.: 551112

Subsidiary (Domestic):

Staples Nederland BV (4)
Rondebeltweg 102, Almere, 1329 BH, Netherlands
Tel.: (31) 884545250
Web Site: https://staples.nl
Office Supplies & Services
N.A.I.C.S.: 459410

Subsidiary (Domestic):

Staples Promotional Products (2)
7500 W 110th St, Overland Park, KS 66210
Tel.: (913) 319-3100
Web Site: https://staplespromo.com
Sales Range: $600-649.9 Million
Product Advertising & Promotion Services
N.A.I.C.S.: 541890

Branch (Domestic):

Staples Promotional Products (3)
1520 Albany Pl SE, Orange City, IA 51041
Tel.: (712) 737-4925
Web Site: http://www.staplespromotionalproducts.com
Sales Range: $10-24.9 Million
Advertising, Product Development, Sales & Marketing Services
N.A.I.C.S.: 541890

Subsidiary (Non-US):

Staples Promotional Products Canada Ltd. (2)
55 Interchange Way Unit 4, Concord, L4K 5W3, ON, Canada
Tel.: (800) 369-5343
Advertising Services
N.A.I.C.S.: 541890

Unit (Domestic):

Staples Technology Solutions (2)
1096 E Newport Center Dr Ste 300, Deerfield Beach, FL 33442-7747
Tel.: (954) 379-5500
Sales Range: $50-74.9 Million
Technology Supplies & Services Distr
N.A.I.C.S.: 423430

Subsidiary (Non-US):

Staples UK Limited (2)
Newland House Tuscany Park Express Way, Normanton, WF6 2TZ, United Kingdom
Tel.: (44) 3339993393
Web Site: http://www.staples.co.uk
Office Supplies & Services
N.A.I.C.S.: 459410

The Limited Stores, Inc. (1)
7775 Walton Pkwy, New Albany, OH 43054
Tel.: (844) 737-7544
Sales Range: $500-549.9 Million
Women's Clothing Retailer
N.A.I.C.S.: 458110

The Talbots, Inc. (1)
1 Talbots Dr, Hingham, MA 02043
Tel.: (781) 749-7600
Sales Range: $650-699.9 Million
Women's Classic Clothing Mail Order & Store Retailer
N.A.I.C.S.: 458110
Deirdre Fitzgerald (Pres)

Unit (Domestic):

Talbots Product Development Center (2)
2 Park Ave Fl 2, New York, NY 10016
Tel.: (212) 841-1900
Web Site: http://www.talbots.com
Sales Range: $25-49.9 Million
Clothing Retailer
N.A.I.C.S.: 458110
Christa Carone (CMO & VP)

SYDENSTRICKERS FARM & LAWN
1810 N Missouri St, Macon, MO 63552
Tel.: (660) 385-2177
Web Site: http://www.sydenstrickers.com
Year Founded: 1994
Sales Range: $1-9.9 Million
Emp.: 50
Agricultural Machinery
N.A.I.C.S.: 423820
Greg Gabriel (Pres)

SYDNOR HYDRO INC.
2111 Magnolia St, Richmond, VA 23223
Tel.: (804) 643-2725
Web Site: http://www.sydnorhydro.com
Sales Range: $25-49.9 Million
Emp.: 100
Industrial Machinery & Equipment
N.A.I.C.S.: 423830
Charles S. Verdery (Chm)

SYDYS CORPORATION
7 Orchard Ln, Lebanon, NJ 08833
Tel.: (908) 236-9885
Year Founded: 2004
Advertising & Marketing Services
N.A.I.C.S.: 541810

SYFAN MANUFACTURING CORP.
1522 Twin Bridges Rd, Everetts, NC 27825
Tel.: (252) 792-2083
Web Site: http://www.syfanmfg.com
Year Founded: 1985
Sales Range: $10-24.9 Million
Emp.: 50
Plastic Packaging Film & Sheet Mfr
N.A.I.C.S.: 326112
Ramy Diga (Exec VP-Sls)
Frank Markowitz (Pres)

SYGNETICS INCORPORATED
691 N Squirrel Rd, Auburn Hills, MI 48361
Tel.: (248) 844-1900   MI
Web Site: http://www.sygnetics.com
Year Founded: 1986
Sales Range: $10-24.9 Million
Emp.: 30
Information Technology & Human Resources Staffing
N.A.I.C.S.: 561320
Chad Tarkowski (Mgr-IT)

SYKEL ENTERPRISES INC.
Fl 4 48 W 38th St, New York, NY 10018-0047
Tel.: (212) 244-0099
Web Site: http://www.sykelenterprises.com
Year Founded: 1984
Rev.: $44,889,042
Emp.: 26
Piece Goods & Notions
N.A.I.C.S.: 424310

SYLHAN LLC
210 Rodeo Dr, Brentwood, NY 11717
Tel.: (631) 243-6600
Web Site: http://www.sylhan.com
Year Founded: 1977
Sales Range: $10-24.9 Million
Emp.: 20

Provider of Industrial Services
N.A.I.C.S.: 332710
Steve Paskoff (Office Mgr)
Bob Luisi (VP-Mfg)
Victor Fomchenko (VP-Sls)

SYLINT GROUP INC.
240 N Washington Blvd Ste 600, Sarasota, FL 34236
Tel.: (941) 951-6015
Web Site: http://www.sylint.com
Year Founded: 1998
Sales Range: $1-9.9 Million
Emp.: 15
Information Security & Data Forensics
N.A.I.C.S.: 518210
John Jorgensen (Pres & CEO)
Serge Jorgensen (CTO & VP)
Steve Teppler (Gen Counsel)
Elli Streit (Mgr-Rels-Intl)
Jeff Birnbach (Mng Dir)

SYLVIA MARKETING & PUBLIC RELATIONS, LLC
1200 E High St Suite 201, Pottstown, PA 19464
Tel.: (610) 323-3500
Web Site: http://www.sylviamarketing.com
Year Founded: 2004
Sales Range: $1-9.9 Million
Emp.: 7
Marketing & Public Relations
N.A.I.C.S.: 541820
Ken Kilpatrick (Pres)
Jody Nester (Bus Mgr)
Jan Griesemer (Mgr-Media Rels)

SYLVIA WOODS, INC.
328 Malcolm X Blvd Frnt, New York, NY 10027
Tel.: (212) 996-0660
Web Site: http://www.sylviassoulfood.com
Year Founded: 1962
Sales Range: $10-24.9 Million
Emp.: 100
Frozen Specialty Food Mfr
N.A.I.C.S.: 311412
Sylvia Woods (Founder & Owner)
Bedelia Woods (Dir-Catering)

SYLVITE SALES (USA)
6395 State Rte 103 N, Lewistown, PA 17044
Tel.: (717) 242-2644
Web Site: http://www.sylvite.com
Fertilizers & Agricultural Chemicals
N.A.I.C.S.: 424910
Suzanne Byler (Office Mgr & Mgr-Credit)

SYMBIA LOGISTICS
216 Main St, Ste C100, Edwards, CO 81632
Tel.: (970) 337-7070
Web Site: http://www.symbia.com
Year Founded: 2007
Sales Range: $25-49.9 Million
Emp.: 250
Logistics & Transportation Services
N.A.I.C.S.: 541614
Megan Smith (CEO)
Jim Smith (Founder)

SYMBIO, LLC
5300 Stevens Creek Blvd Ste 110, San Jose, CA 95129
Tel.: (408) 996-9700   DE
Web Site: http://www.symbio.com
Year Founded: 1994
Emp.: 18,000
Information Technology Application Software Engineering, Research & Development

Anders Carlsarv *(Mng Dir)*
Baoguo Zhou *(COO)*
Jari Mylly *(Mng Dir)*
Jeff Wu *(CEO)*
Ben Wang *(Pres/Gen Mgr-Greater China)*

Subsidiaries:

Freeborders, Inc. (1)
150 Spear St Ste 850, San Francisco, CA 94105-5173
Tel.: (415) 433-4700
Sales Range: $10-24.9 Million
Emp.: 25
Computer Software Application Developer
N.A.I.C.S.: 541511
Bob Harned *(VP-Engrg)*
Jean Cholka *(CEO)*

Symbio (APAC) Co., Ltd. (1)
1F GaoLi 2000 Building No 5, 5th Street
ShangDi, Beijing, 100085, China
Tel.: (86) 1082784012
Web Site: http://www.symbio.com
Sales Range: $125-149.9 Million
Emp.: 1,000
Information Technology Application Software Engineering, Research & Development
N.A.I.C.S.: 541511
Henry Tang *(Mng Dir-Asia Pacific Reg)*
Baoguo Zhou *(Country Mgr-China)*

SYMBIONT SERVICE CORP.
4372 N Access Rd, Englewood, FL 34224
Tel.: (941) 474-9306 FL
Web Site:
http://www.symbiontservice.com
Year Founded: 1991
Sales Range: $1-9.9 Million
Emp.: 40
Geothermal Heating & Cooling
N.A.I.C.S.: 238220
Sandy L. King *(Owner & Pres)*
Rick Krieger *(Dir-Fin)*
Jim Howarth *(Dir-Customer Fulfillment)*
Bruce Carr *(Mgr-Warehouse)*
Michael King *(Mgr-Sls)*
Tom Hilton *(Mgr-Svc)*

SYMBIONT, INC.
8730 Georgia Ave Ste 306, Silver Spring, MD 20910
Tel.: (202) 887-6800
Web Site: http://www.symbiont.com
Year Founded: 1985
Sales Range: $1-9.9 Million
Emp.: 35
Information Technology Services
N.A.I.C.S.: 541512
Mark Smith *(CEO)*
Lisa Yin *(Chief Security Officer)*
Adam Krellenstein *(Founder & CTO)*

SYMBIOSYS, INC.
931 Farm Haven Dr, Rockville, MD 20852-4215
Tel.: (301) 340-3988 MD
Web Site: http://www.symbio-group.com
Year Founded: 1994
Sales Range: $1-9.9 Million
Emp.: 600
Software Development, Testing & Outsourcing Services
N.A.I.C.S.: 513210
Jacob Hsu *(CEO)*

SYMBOLARTS, LLC
6083 S 1550 E, Ogden, UT 84405
Tel.: (801) 475-6000
Web Site: http://www.symbolarts.com
Year Founded: 1986
Rev.: $10,300,000
Emp.: 41
Miscellaneous Fabricated Metal Product Mfr
N.A.I.C.S.: 332999
Elton Yost *(Mgr-Ops)*
Mike Leatham *(Owner)*
John Child *(Mgr-Mktg)*

SYMDON CHEVROLET
369 Union St, Evansville, WI 53536
Tel.: (608) 882-4803
Web Site: http://www.symdon.com
Sales Range: $10-24.9 Million
Emp.: 25
New Car Dealers
N.A.I.C.S.: 441110
Rick Symdon *(Pres)*
Ryan Symdon *(Gen Mgr-Sls)*
Beth Zee *(Office Mgr)*
Kelli Schneider *(Office Mgr)*
John Henning *(Mgr-Sls)*
Kevin Geiwitz *(Mgr-Sls)*
Dennis Koepp *(Mgr-Svc)*
Tim Meredith *(Mgr-Budget Lot)*
Brent Meyer *(Mgr-Internet)*
Eric Oldenburg *(Bus Mgr)*
Paul Prater *(Mgr-Detail)*
Eric Skau *(Mgr-Parts)*
Jeff Furseth *(Mgr-Collision Center)*

SYMES CADILLAC, INC.
3475 E Colorado Blvd, Pasadena, CA 91107-3879
Tel.: (626) 795-3381
Web Site:
http://www.symespasadena.com
Sales Range: $10-24.9 Million
Emp.: 64
Car Whslr
N.A.I.C.S.: 441110
Darryl Glasco *(Mgr-Sls)*

SYMMCO GROUP INC.
40 S Park St, Sykesville, PA 15865
Tel.: (814) 894-2461
Web Site: http://www.symmco.com
Sales Range: $10-24.9 Million
Emp.: 100
Mfr of Metal Powders, Pastes & Flakes
N.A.I.C.S.: 331221
Greg Torretti *(Dir-Mktg)*
Kathy Wise *(Mgr-Sls)*
Beth Krise *(Dir-Sls & Mktg)*

Subsidiaries:

HD Symmco Inc. (1)
300 Delaware Ave Ste 302, Wilmington, DE 19801
Tel.: (302) 427-7602
Sales Range: Less than $1 Million
Emp.: 3
Nonresidential Building Operators
N.A.I.C.S.: 531120

South Park Street Inc. (1)
300 Delaware Ave Ste 302, Wilmington, DE 19801
Tel.: (302) 427-7602
Rev.: $300,000
Emp.: 5
Nonresidential Building Operators
N.A.I.C.S.: 531120

Stump Creek Inc (1)
500 Delaware Ave Ste 1500, Wilmington, DE 19801-1494
Tel.: (302) 427-7602
Rev.: $160,000
Emp.: 5
Nonresidential Building Operators
N.A.I.C.S.: 531120

Symmco Realty Inc (1)
500 Delaware Ave Ste 1500, Wilmington, DE 19801-1494
Tel.: (302) 427-7602
Sales Range: $10-24.9 Million
Emp.: 2
Nonresidential Building Operators
N.A.I.C.S.: 531120

SYMMES LIFE CARE INC.
1010 Waltham St Ste 600, Lexington, MA 02421-8052
Tel.: (781) 863-9660 MA
Web Site:
http://www.brookhavenatlexington.org
Year Founded: 1984
Sales Range: $25-49.9 Million
Emp.: 258
Elder Care Services
N.A.I.C.S.: 623312
Linda Robillard *(Dir-Resident Health)*
Susanna Kirkpatrick *(COO & Exec VP)*
Kenneth Deroeck *(Dir-Food Svcs)*
Diana Zampell *(Dir-Nursing)*
Lorraine Kelley *(Dir-Mktg)*

SYMMES MAINI & MCKEE ASSOCIATES, INC.
1000 Massachusetts Ave, Cambridge, MA 02138
Tel.: (617) 547-5400
Web Site: http://www.smma.com
Year Founded: 1955
Sales Range: $25-49.9 Million
Emp.: 180
Architectural Services
N.A.I.C.S.: 541310
Marie E. Fitzgerald *(Principal, Sr VP & Dir-Interior Design)*
Alex C. Pitkin *(Principal, Sr VP & Dir-Institutional Practice Studios)*
Ara Krafian *(Chm, Pres & CEO)*
Brian W. Lawlor *(Principal & Exec VP)*
Joel G. Seeley *(COO, Principal & Exec VP)*
Mark A. Spaulding *(Principal, Sr VP & Dir-Design)*
H. Geoffrey Neale *(CFO)*
Ryan Farias *(Principal & Dir-Mktg)*
Carlos Charry *(Principal & Dir-IT)*

SYMMETRI MARKETING GROUP, LLC
500 N Michigan Ave Ste 1600, Chicago, IL 60611
Tel.: (312) 222-2500
Web Site:
http://www.symmetrimarketing.com
Year Founded: 2003
Sales Range: $1-9.9 Million
Emp.: 26
Business-to-Business Communications & Marketing Services
N.A.I.C.S.: 541613
Carl Triemstra *(Pres)*
Julie Schenck *(Acct Exec)*

SYMMETRY CREATIVE PRODUCTION
1300 S Grove Ave Ste 103, Barrington, IL 60010
Tel.: (847) 382-8750
Web Site:
http://www.symmetrycp.com
Year Founded: 2002
Sales Range: $1-9.9 Million
Emp.: 20
Editorial, Design & Production Services to Textbook Publishers
N.A.I.C.S.: 541490
Christine Birkett *(Mgr-Design)*
Katie Horn *(Coord-Art & Design)*
John Deady *(Partner)*

SYMMETRY GLOBAL, LLC
1250 E 200 S Ste 2C, Lehi, UT 84043 UT
Web Site:
http://www.symmetrydirect.com
Year Founded: 1995
Sales Range: $25-49.9 Million
Emp.: 100
Nutritional Supplements Developer, Mfr & Online Retailer
N.A.I.C.S.: 325412
Mark Crapo *(Sr VP-Product Tech & Trng)*
Kevin Gull *(Pres)*
Varlin Law *(Exec VP-Sls-Global)*
Suzie Read *(VP-Field Svcs & Trng)*

SYMMONS INDUSTRIES, INC.
31 Brooks Dr, Braintree, MA 02184
Tel.: (781) 848-2250 MA
Web Site: http://www.symmons.com
Year Founded: 1939
Sales Range: $100-124.9 Million
Emp.: 300
Commercial & Residential Plumbing Products Mfr
N.A.I.C.S.: 332913
Robert Rosenquist *(VP-Sls)*
Steven Kinney *(Dir-Mfg Engrg)*

SYMONS AMBULANCE
18592 Cajon Blvd, San Bernardino, CA 92407
Tel.: (909) 880-2979
Web Site:
http://www.symonsambulance.com
Year Founded: 1989
Sales Range: $1-9.9 Million
Emp.: 200
Event & Air Ambulance Services
N.A.I.C.S.: 621910
Jeff T. Grange *(Pres & CEO)*
Dawn Downs *(Chief Nursing Officer)*
Erika Cypert *(Office Mgr)*
Wendy Summers *(Supvr-Field)*
Gilbert Lopez *(Supvr-Dispatch)*

SYMPHONY CORP.
22 E Mifflin St Ste 400, Madison, WI 53703
Tel.: (608) 294-4090 WI
Web Site:
http://www.symphonycorp.com
Year Founded: 1997
Custom Computer Programming Services
N.A.I.C.S.: 541511
Ravi K. Kalla *(Founder & CEO)*
Raghu Gandra *(CTO)*
Gary Smith *(VP-ERP Solutions)*

SYMPHONY FABRICS CORP.
263 W 38th St Fl 3, New York, NY 10018-7529
Tel.: (212) 244-6700
Web Site:
http://www.symphonyfabrics.com
Year Founded: 1966
Sales Range: $10-24.9 Million
Emp.: 85
Supplier Piece Goods & Notions
N.A.I.C.S.: 424310

SYMPHONY INNOVATION, LLC
4 Main St Ste 100, Los Altos, CA 94022
Web Site:
http://www.symphonyai.com
Privater Equity Firm
N.A.I.C.S.: 523999
Romesh Wadhwani *(Founder, Chm & CEO)*

Subsidiaries:

1010data, Inc. (1)
750 3rd Ave 4th Fl, New York, NY 10017
Tel.: (212) 405-1010
Web Site: http://www.1010data.com
Software Publisher
N.A.I.C.S.: 513210
Sandy Steier *(Co-Founder)*
Joel Kaplan *(Co-Founder & CTO)*
Jed Alpert *(Sr VP-Mktg)*

SYMPHONY INNOVATION, LLC

Symphony Innovation, LLC—(Continued)
T. C. Fleming (CFO)
John Seaner (CMO)
Jeri Allan (Chief Revenue Officer)

TeraRecon, Inc. (1)
4000 E 3rd Ave Ste 200, Foster City, CA 94404-4805
Tel.: (650) 372-1100
Web Site: http://www.terarecon.com
Electromedical & Electrotherapeutic Apparatus Mfr
N.A.I.C.S.: 334510
Randolph Sternberg (Dir-Sls)
Stefan Phillips (Dir-Ops)
Martina Zimmermann (Controller-Fin & Bus Mgr)
Fumio Urano (Chm)
Dave MacCutcheon (VP-Product Mgmt)
Pratik Nanavati (VP-Software Dev)
Walter Muller (Gen Mgr-EMEA)
Dan McSweeney (Pres)

SYMPHONY TECHNOLOGY GROUP, LLC

428 University Ave, Palo Alto, CA 94301
Tel.: (650) 935-9500
Web Site: http://www.stgpartners.com
Year Founded: 2002
Private Equity Firm
N.A.I.C.S.: 523999
William Chisholm (Founder & Mng Partner)
Marc Bala (Mng Dir)
Chris Langone (Mng Dir & Head-Bus Dev)
Marshall Haines (Mng Dir)
Stephen Henkenmeier (Mng Dir & CFO)
Adam Hendricks (Principal)
Sunit Mukherjee (Mng Dir)
Gee Rittenhouse (CEO)

Subsidiaries:

Bond International Software, Inc. (1)
1805 Old Alabama Rd Ste 340, Roswell, GA 30076
Tel.: (804) 266-3300
Web Site: http://www.bond-us.com
Staffing Software Solutions
N.A.I.C.S.: 513210
Kendall Johnson (Coord-HR)

Subsidiary (Non-US):

Bond International Japan K.K. (2)
First Square East 4F Otemachi 1-5-1, Chiyoda-Ku, Tokyo, 100 0004, Japan
Tel.: (81) 352191232
Web Site: http://www.bond-jp.com
Staffing & Recruitment Software Solutions
N.A.I.C.S.: 541511

Bond International Software (UK) Limited (2)
Courtlands Parklands Avenue, Goring by Sea, Worthing, BN12 4NG, W Sussex, United Kingdom
Tel.: (44) 1903707070
Web Site: http://www.bondadapt.com
Emp.: 150
Staffing & Recruitment Software Solutions
N.A.I.C.S.: 541511
Tim Richards (Mng Dir)
Zoe Rachel Cadiz (Sec)

Bond International Software China Limited (2)
1104 Crawford House 70 Queen's Road, Central, China (Hong Kong)
Tel.: (852) 28927605
Web Site: http://www.bondadapt.com.hk
Staffing & Recruitment Software Solutions
N.A.I.C.S.: 541511
Cody Wong (Gen Mgr)

Branch (Domestic):

Bond International Software, Inc. - Minneapolis Office (2)
2051 Killebrew Dr Ste 520, Bloomington, MN 55425
Tel.: (952) 854-3050
Web Site: http://www.bond-us.com

Staffing Software Solutions
N.A.I.C.S.: 541511

Connexity, Inc. (1)
2120 Colorado Ave Ste 400, Los Angeles, CA 90404
Tel.: (310) 571-1235
Web Site: http://www.connexity.com
Online Shopping Marketing Software Publisher
N.A.I.C.S.: 513210
Bill Glass (CEO)
Blythe Holden (Chief Legal Officer & Exec VP)
Bob Michaelian (Pres-Connexity Commerce)
Bob Caputo (Sr VP-Sls & Acct Mgmt-Connexity Commerce)
Tara Fraser (Sr VP-Program Mgmt)

Subsidiary (Domestic):

Become, Inc. (2)
1300 Crittenden Ln, Mountain View, CA 94043
Tel.: (650) 694-7900
Web Site: http://connexity.com
Sales Range: $1-9.9 Million
Emp.: 42
Online Shopping Sites Operations
N.A.I.C.S.: 513210

PriceGrabber.com Inc. (2)
4859 W Slauson Ave #259, Los Angeles, CA 90056
Tel.: (323) 601-1200
Web Site: http://www.pricegrabber.com
Online Comparison Shopping Services
N.A.I.C.S.: 518210

Subsidiary (Non-US):

Skimbit Ltd. (2)
2nd Floor 52 Bevenden Street, London, N1 6BL, United Kingdom
Tel.: (44) 20 3397 1240
Web Site: http://www.skimlinks.com
Marketing Software Publisher
N.A.I.C.S.: 513210
Alicia Navarro (Co-Founder & CEO)
Shaun Barron (CFO-Skimlinks)

Subsidiary (US):

Skimlinks Inc. (3)
235 Pine St Ste 1050, San Francisco, CA 94104
Tel.: (415) 598-8696
Web Site: http://www.skimlinks.com
Software Publisher
N.A.I.C.S.: 513210

Dodge Data & Analytics LLC (1)
830 3rd Ave 6th Fl, New York, NY 10022
Tel.: (877) 784-9556
Web Site: http://www.construction.com
Construction Information Publications
N.A.I.C.S.: 513130
Burleigh Morton (VP)
David Cohen (COO)
Daniel McCarthy (Pres & CEO)

Subsidiary (Domestic):

Contractors Register Inc. (2)
800 E Main St, Jefferson Valley, NY 10535
Tel.: (914) 245-0200
Web Site: http://www.thebluebook.com
Publisher of Books
N.A.I.C.S.: 513130
Mark Griswold (CIO)

Integrated Marketing Systems, Inc. (2)
945 Hornblend St Ste G, San Diego, CA 92109
Tel.: (858) 490-8800
Web Site: http://www.imsinfo.com
Agency-verified Notification Research Firm
N.A.I.C.S.: 541910

Escalent, Inc. (1)
17430 College Pkwy, Livonia, MI 48152
Tel.: (734) 542-7600
Web Site: http://www.escalent.co
Market Research & Consulting Services
N.A.I.C.S.: 541910
Rob Stone (Chief Strategy Officer)
Arundhati Mehrotra (Sr VP-International Research Operations)
Jill Colley (VP)

Andrew J. Morrison (Founder, Chm & CEO)
Christopher Montaglione (Mng Dir-Energy)
Raymond Reno (Sr VP-Mktg & Data Sciences)
Jack Fyock (Sr VP-Healthcare)
Bob Rayner (Sr VP-Mktg & Data Sciences)
Phil Giroux (CFO)
Paul Donagher (Mng Dir-Consumer & Retail)
Randy Hanson (VP-Mktg & Data Sciences)
Randall Hula (VP-Consumer & Retail)
Erin Leedy (Sr VP-Tech)
Pamela S. McGill (Sr VP-Telecom)
Janice Anderson (VP-Tech)
Lindsey Dickman (VP-Fin Svcs)
Jeff Dietrich (VP-Mktg & Data Sciences)
Paul Hartley (Sr VP & Mng Dir-Tech, Telecom, Consumer & Retail)
Gwen Ishmael (Sr VP-Qualitative)
Mary Beth Marino (VP-Fin Ops)
Gregory Mishkin (VP-Telecom)
Chris Oberle (Sr VP-Energy & Syndicated)
Dawn Palace (Sr VP-Life Sciences)
Kendra Schuchard (Sr VP-Healthcare)
Lisa Viselli (VP-Corp Mktg)
Linda York (Sr VP-Syndicated)
Jeremy Bowler (Sr VP-Fin Svcs)
Melissa Sauter (Pres)
Todd Mundorf (COO)
Christopher Barnes (Mng Dir-Fin Svcs)
Leigh Admirand (Sr VP-Tech)
Jason Stephens (VP-Energy)
Loribeth McCann (VP-Fin Svcs)
Mike Berinato (VP-Fin Svcs)
Caroline Brennan (VP-Life Sciences)
Lorraine DerMoushegian (VP-Mktg & Data Sciences)
George Dichiaro (VP-Qualitative)
Nicky Kearney (VP-Qualitative)

Subsidiary (Non-US):

Grail Insights (2)
2 Norwich Cl, Sandown, Sandton, 2196, South Africa
Tel.: (27) 10 591 2272
Web Site: http://www.grailinsights.com
Research & Data Analytics Consulting Services
N.A.I.C.S.: 541690
Arundhati Mehrotra (Head-Global Res)

Experian Simmons (1)
600 3rd Ave, New York, NY 10016
Tel.: (212) 883-0407
Web Site: http://www.experian.com
Market Research Services
N.A.I.C.S.: 541910

Findly, LLC (1)
720 Market St Ste 300, San Francisco, CA 94108
Tel.: (650) 403-4819
Web Site: http://www.findly.com
Recruiting Software-as-a-Service Firm
N.A.I.C.S.: 561499
Jason Kerr (Founder & CTO)
John R. Kelly (Chief Revenue Officer & Head-Field Ops-Global)
Gayleen Robinson (Sr VP-Ops & Svc-Global)
Vangie Sison (Sr VP-Acct Mgmt)
Lisa Bordinat (Sr VP & Gen Mgr-Assessment Div)
James Killian (VP-Assessment Sls)
Paul Slakey (Exec VP-Acct Svcs)
Samantha Loveland (Sr VP-Customer Success)
Sal Apuzzio (Sr VP-New Bus Sls-Eastern Reg)
Anthony Kong (VP-Pro Svcs)

Subsidiary (Domestic):

Findly Talent, LLC (2)
630 5th Ave Ste 659 6th Fl, New York, NY 10111
Tel.: (212) 999-9000
Web Site: http://www.findly.com
Advetising Agency
N.A.I.C.S.: 541810
Lynn Greenbaum (Sr VP)
Andrew Katz (Sr VP-Bus Dev)
Roopesh Nair (Pres & CEO)

Branch (Domestic):

Findly Talent - Atlanta (3)
1230 Peachtree St NE Ste 2200, Atlanta, GA 30309

Tel.: (404) 602-1050
Sales Range: $25-49.9 Million
Emp.: 25
Advetising Agency
N.A.I.C.S.: 541810

Findly Talent - Houston (3)
7676 Hillmont St Ste 290, Houston, TX 77040-6423
Tel.: (713) 690-0272
Web Site: http://www.findly.com
Sales Range: $25-49.9 Million
Emp.: 95
Advetising Agency
N.A.I.C.S.: 541810
Jill Hawkins (Sr VP)

Findly Talent - New Jersey (3)
100 Paragon Dr Ste 125, Montvale, NJ 07654
Tel.: (201) 474-9820
Sales Range: $25-49.9 Million
Emp.: 15
Advetising Agency
N.A.I.C.S.: 541810
Fran Levendusky (VP & Branch Mgr)

Findly Talent - Orlando (3)
1101 N Lake Destiny Rd, Maitland, FL 32751
Tel.: (407) 740-5002
Sales Range: $25-49.9 Million
Emp.: 19
Advetising Agency
N.A.I.C.S.: 541810

Findly Talent - Washington, DC (3)
8229 Boone Blvd Ste 450, Vienna, VA 22182
Tel.: (703) 848-0810
Sales Range: $25-49.9 Million
Emp.: 16
Advetising Agency
N.A.I.C.S.: 541810
David Willard (VP)
Gregg Petermann (VP & Creative Dir)
Sandi Freer (VP & Branch Mgr)

Gresham Technologies plc (1)
Aldermary House 10-15 Queen Street, London, EC4N 1TX, United Kingdom
Tel.: (44) 2076530222
Web Site: https://www.greshamtech.com
Rev.: $61,498,359
Assets: $101,782,378
Liabilities: $39,921,737
Net Worth: $61,860,641
Earnings: $3,637,970
Emp.: 215
Fiscal Year-end: 12/31/2022
Mfr & Reproducing Magnetic & Optical Media
N.A.I.C.S.: 334610
Neil Vernon (CTO)
Jonathan Cathie (Sec)
David Eagan (Dir-Global-Customer Success & Svc Delivery)
Mark Bolton (Head-Intl Sls)
Joel Jerome (Dir-Sls-Asia Pacific)

Subsidiary (Domestic):

Gresham Computer Services Limited (2)
Sopwith House Brook Ave, Southampton, SO31 9ZA, Hampshire, United Kingdom
Tel.: (44) 1489555500
Sales Range: $25-49.9 Million
Emp.: 20
Computer Database Management Services
N.A.I.C.S.: 518210

Subsidiary (US):

Gresham Enterprise Storage Inc (2)
505 E Huntland Dr Ste 450, Austin, TX 78752
Tel.: (512) 450-0900
Sales Range: $25-49.9 Million
Emp.: 17
Computer Storage Devices
N.A.I.C.S.: 541512

Subsidiary (Domestic):

Electra Information Systems, Inc. (3)
381 Park Ave S Rm 1413, New York, NY 10016
Tel.: (212) 696-1595
Web Site: http://www.electrainfo.com

U.S. PRIVATE

COMPANIES
SYMPHONY TECHNOLOGY GROUP, LLC

Sales Range: $1-9.9 Million
Emp.: 16
Custom Computer Programming Services
N.A.I.C.S.: 541511
John Landry (Pres)
Scott Rhodes (COO)
Paul Chung (VP-Client Svcs)

Subsidiary (Domestic):

Gresham Financial Systems Limited (2)
28 Queen St, London, EC4R 1BB, United Kingdom
Tel.: (44) 2076530200
Sales Range: $25-49.9 Million
Emp.: 10
Software Development Services
N.A.I.C.S.: 541511

Subsidiary (US):

Gresham Technologies (US) Inc. (2)
381 Park Ave S Ste 1413, New York, NY 10016
Tel.: (212) 696-1595
Software Development Services
N.A.I.C.S.: 541511

Medisked LLC (1)
860 University Ave, Rochester, NY 14607-1236
Web Site: http://www.medisked.com
Business Support Services
N.A.I.C.S.: 561499
Lauren Schieck (Supvr-Implementation)

Momentive Global Inc. (1)
1 Curiosity Way, San Mateo, CA 94403
Tel.: (650) 543-8400
Web Site: https://www.momentive.ai
Rev.: $375,610,000
Assets: $877,817,000
Liabilities: $531,461,000
Net Worth: $346,356,000
Earnings: ($91,581,000)
Emp.: 1,367
Fiscal Year-end: 12/31/2020
Software Development Services
N.A.I.C.S.: 541511
Richard Sullivan (CFO)
Lora Blum (Chief Legal Officer & Sec)
Rebecca Cantieri (Chief People Officer)
Robin Ducot (CTO)
Eric Johnson (CIO)
Antoine Andrews (Chief Diversity & Social Impact Officer)
Ken Ewell (Chief Customer Officer)
Cherie Buntyn (Chief Acctg Officer & VP)
Eric Johnson (CEO)
Katie Miserany (VP)
Leela Srinivasan (CMO)

Subsidiary (Domestic):

GetFeedback, Inc. (2)
123 Mission St 26th Fl, San Francisco, CA 94105
Tel.: (415) 987-9326
Web Site: http://www.getfeedback.com
Online Survey Software Developer
N.A.I.C.S.: 513210
Craig Shull (CEO)

Nomis Solutions, Inc. (1)
8000 Marina Blvd Ste 700, Brisbane, CA 94005
Tel.: (650) 588-9800
Web Site: http://www.nomissolutions.com
Custom Computer Programming Services
N.A.I.C.S.: 541511
Brian Buckingham (VP-Deposits)
Frank Rohde (CEO)
Robert Philips (Chief Science Officer)
David Hornik (Gen Partner)
Hollis Fishelson (VP)
Karen Beale (Sr VP-Sls)
Prashant Balepur (VP-Product Mgmt)
Richard Whittow (VP & CFO)
Scott Friend (Mng Dir)
Sriram Kumar (VP-Product Dev)
Frank Bria (VP)
Albert Van Wyk (Dir-Client-Asia Pacific)
Damian Young (Mng Dir-Asia Pacific & Europe)

RSA Security LLC (1)
174 Middlesex Tpke, Bedford, MA 01730
Tel.: (781) 515-5000
Web Site: http://www.rsa.com

Security Management Services
N.A.I.C.S.: 561621
Zulfikar Ramzan (CTO)
Holly Rollo (CMO & Sr VP)
Doug Howard (VP-Global Svcs)
Rohit Ghai (CEO)
William Chrisholm (Chm)
Bill Diaz (CEO-RSA Archer)

Subsidiary (Non-US):

RSA Security GmbH (2)
Osterfeldstrasse 84, 85737, Ismaning, Germany
Tel.: (49) 89930910
Web Site: http://www.rsa.com
Network Security Systems & Risk Solutions
N.A.I.C.S.: 541512

RSA Security UK Limited (2)
Rsa House Western Road, Bracknell, RG12 1RT, Berkshire, United Kingdom
Tel.: (44) 1344781000
Web Site: http://www.rsa.com
Network Security Systems
N.A.I.C.S.: 541512

SIGMA3 Integrated Reservoir Solutions (1)
17171 Park Row Ste 247, Houston, TX 77084
Tel.: (281) 363-8500
Web Site: http://www.sigmacubed.com
Support Activities for Oil & Gas Operations
N.A.I.C.S.: 213112
Alan R. Huffman (CTO)
Charlotte Kula (CFO)
Kevin S. Boyle Sr. (Executives)

Subsidiary (Domestic):

Fusion Geophysical LLC (2)
25231 Grogans Mill Rd, Spring, TX 77380
Tel.: (281) 363-4903
Sales Range: $25-49.9 Million
Emp.: 13
Commercial & Institutional Building Construction
N.A.I.C.S.: 236220

Prism Seismic, Inc. (2)
13275 E Frmont Pl Ste 209, Parker, CO 80134
Tel.: (720) 488-0006
Web Site: http://www.prismseismic.com
Sales Range: $25-49.9 Million
Emp.: 25
Support Activities for Oil & Gas Operations
N.A.I.C.S.: 213112

STG Partners, LLC (1)
1300 El Camino Real Ste 300, Menlo Park, CA 94025
Tel.: (650) 935-9500
Investment Services
N.A.I.C.S.: 525990
Patrick Fouhy (Principal)
William Chisholm (Mng Partner)

Subsidiary (Domestic):

Avid Technology, Inc. (2)
75 Blue Sky Dr, Burlington, MA 01803
Tel.: (978) 640-6789
Web Site: https://www.avid.com
Rev.: $417,413,000
Assets: $287,453,000
Liabilities: $406,235,000
Net Worth: ($118,782,000)
Earnings: $55,241,000
Emp.: 1,485
Fiscal Year-end: 12/31/2022
Nonlinear Film, Video, Audio & 3D Solutions Developer
N.A.I.C.S.: 333310
Tom Cordiner (Sr VP)
Kevin Riley (CTO & Sr VP)
Deb Sanders (Chief Customer Officer)
Wellford Dillard (CEO)
Paul Burgdorf (CFO)
Angela Stelle (CMO)

Subsidiary (Non-US):

AVID DEVELOPMENT GmbH (3)
Paul-Heyse-Strasse 29, Munich, 80336, Germany
Tel.: (49) 89502060
Computer Programming Services
N.A.I.C.S.: 541511

AVID GENERAL PARTNER B.V. (3)
Kabelweg 37, 1014 BA, Amsterdam, Netherlands
Tel.: (31) 206441805
Computer Programming Services
N.A.I.C.S.: 541511

Subsidiary (Domestic):

AVID SYSTEMS, INC. (3)
2904 Back Acre Cir Ste 101, Mount Airy, MD 21771
Tel.: (301) 703-8195
Web Site: https://www.avid-systems.com
Electric Equipment Mfr
N.A.I.C.S.: 334416

Subsidiary (Non-US):

AVID TECHNOLOGY (S.E. ASIA) PTE LTD (3)
315 Alexandra Road No 03-01 Sime Darby Business Centre, Singapore, 159944, Singapore
Tel.: (65) 64767666
Web Site: http://www.avid.com
Emp.: 20
Computer Peripheral Equipment Distr
N.A.I.C.S.: 423430

AVID TECHNOLOGY CANADA CORP. (3)
3510 St Laurent Blvd Suite 300, Montreal, H2X 2V2, QC, Canada
Tel.: (514) 845-1636
Emp.: 100
Computer Programming Services
N.A.I.C.S.: 541511

AVID TECHNOLOGY HOLDING GmbH (3)
Paul-Heyse-Str 29, 80336, Munich, 80336, Germany
Tel.: (49) 8950206404
Emp.: 50
Holding Company
N.A.I.C.S.: 551112
Jochen Pielage (Gen Mgr)

AVID TECHNOLOGY INTERNATIONAL B.V. (3)
4051 Kingswood Drive Citywest Business Campus, Sandyford, D24 T021, Dublin, 24, Ireland
Tel.: (353) 12950066
Web Site: http://www.avid.com
Emp.: 40
Computer Programming Services
N.A.I.C.S.: 541511

AVID TECHNOLOGY S.L. (3)
Centro Empresarial VK Locales A & B 3a Plata, Camino de la Zarzuela 21, 28023, Madrid, 28023, Spain
Tel.: (34) 917628600
Computer Peripheral Equipment Distr
N.A.I.C.S.: 423430

Avid North Asia Limited (3)
Unit E&F 11th Floor Neich Tower, No 128 Gloucester, Wanchai, China (Hong Kong) (100%)
Tel.: (852) 31651841
Web Site: http://cn.avid.com
Sales Range: $1-9.9 Million
Emp.: 6
Nonlinear Film, Video, Audio & 3D Solutions Developer
N.A.I.C.S.: 333310

Avid Technology Europe Ltd. (3)
Pinewood Studios West Side Complex Pinewood Road, Iver, SL0 0NH, Bucks, United Kingdom (100%)
Tel.: (44) 1753655999
Web Site: http://www.avid.com
Sales Range: $125-149.9 Million
Emp.: 100
Developer of Nonlinear Film, Video, Audio & 3D Solutions
N.A.I.C.S.: 333310

Avid Technology GmbH (3)
Paul-Heyse Str 29 2nd Floor, 80336, Munich, Germany
Tel.: (49) 89502060
Web Site: http://www.avid.com
Nonlinear Film, Video, Audio & 3D Solutions Developer
N.A.I.C.S.: 333310

Avid Technology K.K. (3)
ATT Building 4F 2-11-7 Akasaka, Minato-Ku, Tokyo, 107-0052, Japan
Tel.: (81) 335057937
Web Site: http://www.avid.com
Nonlinear Film, Video, Audio & 3D Solutions Developer
N.A.I.C.S.: 333310

Avid Technology S.A.R.L (3)
Immeuble Place de Seine 157 rue Anatole France 8ieme etage, 92300, Levallois-Perret, France
Tel.: (33) 141494000
Web Site: http://www.avid.com
Sales Range: $10-24.9 Million
Emp.: 35
Nonlinear Film, Video, Audio & 3D Solutions Developer
N.A.I.C.S.: 333310

Avid Technology Sales Limited (3)
Unit 38 Carmanhall Rd, Sandyford Industrial Estate, Dublin, Ireland
Tel.: (353) 12078200
Sales Range: $10-24.9 Million
Emp.: 40
Nonlinear Film, Video, Audio & 3D Solutions Developer
N.A.I.C.S.: 333310
Patrick Oberne (Mng Dir)

Avid Technology, Inc. (S.E. Asia) Pte. Ltd. (3)
80 Raffles Place 32-01 UOB PLAZA, 03 01 Sime Deby Bus Center, Singapore, 048624, Singapore (100%)
Tel.: (65) 64767666
Web Site: http://www.avid.com
Sales Range: $10-24.9 Million
Emp.: 45
Developer of Nonlinear Film, Video, Audio & 3D Solutions
N.A.I.C.S.: 333310

Branch (Domestic):

Avid Technology, Inc. - Madison (3)
6400 Enterprise Ln, Madison, WI 53719
Tel.: (608) 274-8686
Web Site: http://www.avid.com
Sales Range: $10-24.9 Million
Emp.: 40
Mfr of Newsroom Automation Systems
N.A.I.C.S.: 541511

Subsidiary (Non-US):

D-Design Nordic AB (3)
Linnegatan 87 B, 115 23, Stockholm, Sweden
Tel.: (46) 84425570
Web Site: http://www.avid.com
Sales Range: $1-9.9 Million
Emp.: 7
Nonlinear Film, Video, Audio & 3D Solutions Developer
N.A.I.C.S.: 333310

Degidesign Italy s.r.l (3)
Palazzo T2 Strada 7, Rozzano, 20089, Milan, Italy
Tel.: (39) 025778971
Web Site: http://www.avid.com
Sales Range: $1-9.9 Million
Emp.: 1
Nonlinear Film, Video, Audio & 3D Solutions Developer
N.A.I.C.S.: 333310

INTEGRATED BROADCAST SERVICES LIMITED (IBIS) (3)
32 The Maltings Lower Charlton Trading Estate Charlton Road, Shepton Mallet, Somerset, BA4 5QE, United Kingdom
Tel.: (44) 1483280208
Web Site: http://www.ibistv.com
Broadcast Services
N.A.I.C.S.: 541512

Orad Hi-tec Systems Poland sp. Z.o.o. (3)
Bulwar M Beniowskiego 5a, 70-642, Szczecin, Poland
Tel.: (48) 914648619
Web Site: http://www.orad.pl
Software Publisher
N.A.I.C.S.: 513210

Subsidiary (Domestic):

Pinnacle Systems, Inc. (3)

SYMPHONY TECHNOLOGY GROUP, LLC

Symphony Technology Group, LLC—(Continued)

1510 Hubbard Ave, Batavia, IL 60510
Tel.: (630) 443-8542
Web Site: https://pinnaclesystems.com
Sales Range: $300-349.9 Million
Emp.: 888
Designer, Mfr & Marketer of Digital Video Post Production Tools
N.A.I.C.S.: 334220

Subsidiary (Non-US):

Pinnacle Systems Ltd. (4)
Pinewood Studios Pinewood Rd, Iver Heath, SL0 0NH, United Kingdom **(100%)**
Tel.: (44) 1753655999
Web Site: http://www.pinnaclesys.com
Designer, Mfr & Marketer of Digital Video Post Production Tools
N.A.I.C.S.: 334111

Holding (Domestic):

CAI Software, LLC (2)
24 Albion Rd, Ste 230,, Lincoln, RI 02865
Tel.: (800) 422-4782
Web Site: https://caisoft.com
Software Devolopment
N.A.I.C.S.: 513210
Brian Sweat (VP & Gen Mgr)

Subsidiary (Domestic):

Alterity Inc. (3)
600 6 Flags Dr Ste 642, Arlington, TX 76011-6332
Tel.: (817) 870-1311
Web Site: http://www.acctivate.com
Sporting Goods Retailer
N.A.I.C.S.: 459110
Ron Souder (Pres)

Subsidiary (Non-US):

Maritech AS (3)
Karvagvegen 126, 6532, Averoy, Norway
Tel.: (47) 71517300
Web Site: https://maritech.com
Software Development Services
N.A.I.C.S.: 513210

Subsidiary (Non-US):

Maritech Dynamics Limited (4)
5475 Spring Garden Road Suite 602 Cornwallis House, Halifax, B3J 3T2, NS, Canada
Tel.: (902) 482-2663
Application Software Development Services
N.A.I.C.S.: 541511

Subsidiary (Non-US):

MediaValet Inc. (2)
990 Homer St 5th Fl, Vancouver, V6B 2W7, BC, Canada
Tel.: (604) 688-2321
Web Site: https://www.mediavalet.com
Rev.: $3,949,931
Assets: $4,949,931
Liabilities: $8,209,912
Net Worth: ($3,259,981)
Earnings: ($2,748,992)
Emp.: 60
Fiscal Year-end: 12/31/2019
Software Publisher
N.A.I.C.S.: 513210
Jean Lozano (CTO)
Eric Simmons (VP-Sls)
Dave Miller (CFO)
Sarah Laughlin (VP)
James Armstrong (VP)
Brona O'Connor (VP)

Subsidiary (Domestic):

VRX Studios Inc. (3)
Ste 250 970 Homer St, Vancouver, V6B 2W7, BC, Canada **(100%)**
Tel.: (604) 605-0050
Web Site: http://www.vrxstudios.com
Online Travel Related Content Services
N.A.I.C.S.: 561599
Tinu Mathur (Pres)

Division (Domestic):

Xplore Travel Group (4)
375 Water St Suite 415, Vancouver, V6B 5C6, BC, Canada
Tel.: (604) 629-0595
Web Site: http://www.xploretravelgroup.com

Online Travel Services
N.A.I.C.S.: 561599

SymphonyEYC (1)
1040 Crown Pointe Pkwy Ste 905, Atlanta, GA 30327 **(100%)**
Tel.: (404) 355-3220
Web Site: http://www.eyc.com
Emp.: 600
Customer Insight Software Developer
N.A.I.C.S.: 513210
Romesh Wadhwani (Founder)
Pallab Chatterjee (CEO)
Bill Chisholm (Mng Dir)
Patrick Buellet (CTO)
Stephanie Kelly (VP-HR)
Matt Kistler (Exec VP)

Subsidiary (Non-US):

SymphonyEYC (2)
Svardvagen 23, SE 18233, Danderyd, Sweden **(100%)**
Tel.: (46) 850300700
Web Site: http://www.eyc.com
Sales Range: $25-49.9 Million
Emp.: 30
Business Support Software
N.A.I.C.S.: 513210
Henrik Lindstrom (Mng Dir)

SymphonyEYC France S.A.S. (2)
37 rue du Colonel Pierre Avia, 75015, Paris, France **(100%)**
Tel.: (33) 146482800
Sales Range: $25-49.9 Million
Emp.: 100
Business Support Software
N.A.I.C.S.: 513210
Nicolas Cron (VP-Sls)

SymphonyEYC GmbH (2)
Ruppmannstrasse 33a, 70565, Stuttgart, Germany **(100%)**
Tel.: (49) 711780720
Emp.: 10
Business Support Software
N.A.I.C.S.: 513210
Markus Timmermann (Dir-Pro Svcs)

SymphonyEYC Solution UK Ltd. (2)
5 Kew Road, Richmond, TW9 2PR, Surrey, United Kingdom
Tel.: (44) 208 255 2205
Sales Range: $25-49.9 Million
Emp.: 35
Business Support Software
N.A.I.C.S.: 513210
Mark Croxton (Mng Dir)
Sarah Jandu (Dir-Mktg)

SymphonyEYC d.o.o. (2)
Trzaska cesta 515, SL 1351, Brezovica, Slovenia **(81.2%)**
Tel.: (386) 8 2000 700
Sales Range: $25-49.9 Million
Emp.: 25
Business Support Software
N.A.I.C.S.: 513210
Ivan Guzelj (Mng Dir)

System C Healthcare Ltd. (1)
The Maidstone Studios Vinters Business Park, New Cut Road, Maidstone, ME14 5NZ, Kent, United Kingdom
Tel.: (44) 1622691616
Web Site: http://www.systemc.com
Sales Range: $50-74.9 Million
Emp.: 50
IT Solutions for Health & Social Care
N.A.I.C.S.: 541512
Jane Conner (Sec & Dir-HR & Admin)
Judi Holly (Dir-Comml)
Markus Bolton (Co-CEO)
Ian Denley (Co-CEO)
Antony Smith (Fin Dir)
Beverley Bryant (COO)
Chris Keightley (Dir-Solutions)
Hayley Neal (Dir-Clinical Solutions)
Jon Shaw (Dir-Clinical Strategy & Design)
Kenny Maxwell (Dir-Customer)
Sarah Peart Bentham (Dir-Customer)
Simon Cavell (CTO)
Lawrence Brooks (Gen Counsel)

Trace One SAS (1)
Spaces Le Belvedere 1-7 Cours Valmy, Puteaux, 92800, France
Tel.: (33) 18716903
Web Site: https://www.traceone.com

Software Development Services
N.A.I.C.S.: 513210
Christophe Vanackere (CEO)

Subsidiary (Non-US):

Selerant Srl (2)
Via Leonardo da Vinci n 19, 20060, Milan, Cassina de Pecchi, Italy
Tel.: (39) 02 786 203
Web Site: http://www.selerant.com
Emp.: 500
Product Lifecycle Management Software Developer
N.A.I.C.S.: 513210
Carlo Colombo (CEO)
Jacopo Colombo (CTO)

Ventiv Technology (1)
3350 Riverwood Prkwy, Atlanta, GA 30339
Tel.: (866) 452-2787
Web Site: http://www.ventivtech.com
Risk Managemeng Srvices
N.A.I.C.S.: 524210
Steve Cloutman (Mng Dir-Intl)
Nick Pessimisis (CFO)
Bill Diaz (CEO)
Brijesh Kumar (Exec VP-Strategic Svcs)
Peter Yang (CIO)
Kristi McFarlin (VP-Analytics)
Bret Kirkland (Sr VP-Pro Svcs)
Scott Wilson (Chief Info Security Officer)
Peter Govek (Sr VP-Comml Sls)
David Greiff (Sr VP-Corp Sls)
James Dickinson (VP-Global Mktg)
Bobby Hunter (VP- Product Mgmt)
Angus Rhodes (VP-Product Mgmt)
Stephen Thomas (VP-Prod Mgmt)
Michael Hamann (VP-Dev)

Winshuttle LLC (1)
19820 N Creek Pkwy Ste 200, Bothell, WA 98011
Tel.: (425) 368-2708
Web Site: http://www.winshuttle.com
Data Quality, Data Synchronization & Data Incorporation Software Products for SAP Business Suite Applications
N.A.I.C.S.: 513210
Rajat Oberoi (Co-Founder)
Vikram Chalana (Co-Founder & Chm)
Mark Hallam (VP-EMEA & APAC)
John Pierson (CEO)
Brian Berg (VP-Customer Success)
Mary Lee (VP-Mktg)
Jeff Bergstrom (CFO)
Vishal Chalana (Co-Founder & Chief Software Architect)

Subsidiary (Domestic):

Enterworks, Inc. (2)
46040 Center Oak Plz Ste 115, Sterling, VA 20166
Tel.: (888) 242-8356
Web Site: http://www.enterworks.com
Software Developer
N.A.I.C.S.: 513210
Kerry Young (VP& Gen Mgr)

SYMPLIFIED INC.

1600 Pearl St Ste 200, Boulder, CO 80302
Tel.: (303) 318-4188
Web Site: http://www.symplified.com
Sales Range: $1-9.9 Million
Emp.: 60
Software Developer
N.A.I.C.S.: 513210
Shayne Higdon (Pres & CEO)
Darren Platt (Co-Founder & CTO)
Andrew Evans (CFO)
Brian Doheny (Sr VP-Worldwide Field Ops)
Vasanthan Dasan (VP-Engrg)
Randy Streu (VP-Bus Dev)
Eric Olden (Co-Founder & Chm)

SYMPOINT COMMUNICATIONS

21 N Oak Forest Dr, Asheville, NC 28803
Tel.: (503) 567-9677
Web Site: http://www.sympoint.com
Year Founded: 2004
Sales Range: Less than $1 Million

U.S. PRIVATE

Emp.: 2
Communications Specialists & Public Relations
N.A.I.C.S.: 541820
Peter terHorst (Pres)
Alexandra Terhorst (VP)

SYMVIONICS, INC.

488 E Santa Clara St Ste 201, Arcadia, CA 91006-7230
Tel.: (626) 305-1400
Web Site: http://www.symvionics.com
Year Founded: 1988
Sales Range: $10-24.9 Million
Emp.: 203
Engineeering Services
N.A.I.C.S.: 541330
Lawrence B. Barraza (Pres & CEO)
Walt Kelly (COO)
Harold Gault (Dir-Contracts)

SYNAGEX, INC

103 Hawthorne Ave, Pittsfield, MA 01201
Tel.: (413) 650-5230
Web Site: https://www.synagex.com
Year Founded: 2017
Cybersecurity Firm
N.A.I.C.S.: 513210
John Sinopoli (Pres & CEO)

Subsidiaries:

Ascentek, Inc. (1)
7 Westview Rd, Pittsfield, MA 01201
Tel.: (413) 496-9900
Web Site: http://www.ascentek.com
Rev.: $1,100,000
Emp.: 10
Data Processing, Hosting & Related Services
N.A.I.C.S.: 518210
Edward Frederick (Pres)
David Siegel (Dir-Acctg)

SYNAPSE STUDIOS, LLC

520 S Mill Ave Ste 202, Tempe, AZ 85281
Web Site:
http://www.synapsestudios.com
Year Founded: 2003
Sales Range: $1-9.9 Million
Software Services
N.A.I.C.S.: 541511
Chris Cardinal (Principal)

SYNAPTICORE

1822 Snake River Rd Ste E, Katy, TX 77449
Tel.: (281) 833-1000
Web Site:
http://www.SynaptiCore.com
Sales Range: $1-9.9 Million
Emp.: 21
Business Consulting Services
N.A.I.C.S.: 541618
Mustafa Raja (Co-Founder & Pres)

SYNCFUSION, INC

2501 Aerial Ctr Pkwy Ste 200, Morrisville, NC 27560
Tel.: (919) 481-1974
Web Site: http://www.syncfusion.com
Sales Range: $1-9.9 Million
Emp.: 25
Custom Computer Programming Services
N.A.I.C.S.: 541511
Stefan Hoenig (Pres & CEO)
Daniel Jebaraj (VP)
Clay Burch (Dir-Technical Support)

SYNCH-SOLUTIONS

211 W Wacker Dr Ste 300, Chicago, IL 60606
Tel.: (312) 252-3700
Web Site: http://www.synch-solutions.com

Sales Range: $1-4.9 Billion
Emp.: 20
Personal Services
N.A.I.C.S.: 812990
John Sterling (CEO)

SYNCREON INTERNATIONAL GROUP
2851 High Meadow Cir Ste 250, Auburn Hills, MI 48326
Tel.: (248) 377-4700
Web Site: http://www.syncreon.com
Sales Range: $500-549.9 Million
Emp.: 9,000
Integrated Logistics for Global Industries
N.A.I.C.S.: 541614
Brian Enright (CEO)
Julian Mordaunt (CIO)
Michael Neumann (Pres & Exec VP)
Michael Enright (Chm)
Kenneth Pocius (Gen Counsel)
Jim Barnett (Pres-Automotive-Americas)
Carine Van Landschoot (CFO)

Subsidiaries:

syncreon Dublin (1)
1A Airport Business Park, Dublin Airport, Cloghran, Ireland
Tel.: (353) 18067150
Web Site: http://www.syncreon.com
Emp.: 170
Integrated Logistics for Global Industries
N.A.I.C.S.: 541614
Eamon Murphy (Gen Mgr)

SYNCRONESS, INC.
10875 Dover St, Westminster, CO 80021
Tel.: (303) 429-5005
Web Site: http://www.syncroness.com
Year Founded: 1998
Sales Range: $25-49.9 Million
Emp.: 50
Product Development & Engineering Services
N.A.I.C.S.: 541330
Mark Henault (Founder & CTO)
Raymond W. Cohen (Chm)

Subsidiaries:

Magpie Software Services Corp. (1)
12050 Pecos St Ste 210, Westminster, CO 80234 **(100%)**
Tel.: (303) 453-8300
Web Site: http://www.magpiesw.com
Sales Range: $1-9.9 Million
Custom Computer Programming Services, Enterprise Software, Data Analytics & Firmware
N.A.I.C.S.: 541511
Margaret Burd (Chm)
Barry Ostroff (CTO)
Janice Jones (Dir-Engrg)
Todd Towles (Dir-Sls)
Judson A. Smith Jr. (CEO)

SYNDAVER LABS INC.
8506 Benjamin Rd, Tampa, FL 33634
Tel.: (813) 600-5530
Web Site: http://www.syndaver.com
Year Founded: 2004
Sales Range: $1-9.9 Million
Emp.: 100
Synthetic Human Tissues & Body Parts Mfr
N.A.I.C.S.: 339113
Christopher Sakezles (Founder)
William Wright (Dir-Ops)
Terence Terenzi (CFO)

SYNDERO, INC.
2629 Manhattan Ave 283, Hermosa Beach, CA 90254
Tel.: (213) 342-3700 DE
Year Founded: 2006

Sales Range: $25-49.9 Million
Emp.: 80
Miscellaneous Product Whslr
N.A.I.C.S.: 456120

SYNDICATE SALES INC.
2025 N Wabash Ave, Kokomo, IN 46901
Tel.: (765) 457-7277
Web Site: http://www.syndicatesales.com
Sales Range: $25-49.9 Million
Emp.: 300
Injection Molding Of Plastics
N.A.I.C.S.: 326199
Laura D. Shinall (Pres)

SYNDICATED RESORTS ASSOCIATION, INC.
5530 S Valley View Blvd Ste 105, Las Vegas, NV 89118
Tel.: (480) 666-4116 DE
Year Founded: 2016
Assets: $1,669
Liabilities: $4,989
Net Worth: ($3,320)
Earnings: ($42,407)
Emp.: 2
Fiscal Year-end: 12/31/19
Online Travel Management Services
N.A.I.C.S.: 561599
William Barber (Pres, CEO, CFO, Treas & Sec)

SYNDICATION, INC.
Box 503, Damascus, MD 20872
Tel.: (888) 422-5515
Web Site: http://www.syndicationinc.net
Year Founded: 1999
Consulting Services
N.A.I.C.S.: 541611

SYNECHRON INC.
15 Maiden Ln Ste 1100, New York, NY 10038
Tel.: (212) 619-5200 DE
Web Site: http://www.synechron.com
Year Founded: 2001
Sales Range: $350-399.9 Million
Emp.: 5,000
Information Technology Services & Offshore Back-Office Support to Firms in Mortgage Banking, Financial Services & Insurance
N.A.I.C.S.: 541519
Faisal Husain (Founder & CEO)
David Horton (Head-Innovation)
Tanveer Saulat (Co-Founder & Gen Mgr)
Bas Heijnen (Mng Dir-Bus & Mgmt Consultancy)
Pascal Rellier (Mng Dir)
Laurent Salvinien (Mng Dir & Head-Paris)
John Gaunt (Chief HR Officer)
Peter Memon (Head-Emerging Tech)
Charles Bokman (Head-Asia Pacific)
Sebastien Glineur (Head-Digital Practice-Paris)

Subsidiaries:

Hatstand Ltd. (1)
Level 7 95 Gresham Street, London, EC2V 7NA, United Kingdom
Tel.: (44) 207 423 5 660
Web Site: http://www.hatstand.com
Emp.: 500
Financial Consulting Services
N.A.I.C.S.: 541611
Adam Bennett (Chm & Pres)
Brad O'Brien (CEO)
Roger Bishton (COO)
Silvano Stagni (Grp Head-Mktg & Res)
Chris Willard (Head & Dir-Plng & Resourcing)
Robyn O'Kane (Dir)

Synechron (1)
212 S Tryon St Ste 980, Charlotte, NC 28281 **(100%)**
Tel.: (704) 323-7133
Web Site: http://www.synechron.com
Sales Range: $10-24.9 Million
Emp.: 250
Information Technology & Off-Shore Support Services
N.A.I.C.S.: 519290
Faisal Husain (CEO)

Synechron IT Towers (1)
MIDC Knowledge Park, Pune, 411 014, Kharadi, India **(100%)**
Tel.: (91) 2030513400
Web Site: http://www.synechron.com
IT Solutions Development Center
N.A.I.C.S.: 519290

Synechron Limited (1)
Level 7 95 Gresham Street, London, EC2V 7NA, United Kingdom
Tel.: (44) 2038663888
Web Site: http://www.synechron.com
Emp.: 8,000
IT Solutions Services
N.A.I.C.S.: 519290
Pankaj Gupta (Mng Dir-Bus Consulting Team)
Tony Clark (Mng Dir)
Samantha Screene (Assoc Dir-HR)

SYNERFAC TECHNICAL STAFFING
100 West Commons Blvd, New Castle, DE 19720
Tel.: (302) 324-9400
Web Site: http://www.synerfac.com
Emp.: 200
Technical Staffing Solutions
N.A.I.C.S.: 561311
Dave Cooper (Controller)
Michael Schlenner (Coord-Staffing)
Lauren Hesketh (Sr Mgr-Sls)
Ashley Warner (Branch Mgr)

SYNERGETIC INFORMATION SYSTEMS INC.
1200 G St NW Ste 800, Washington, DC 20005
Tel.: (202) 434-8680
Web Site: http://www.gosynergetic.com
Year Founded: 2008
Sales Range: $1-9.9 Million
Emp.: 36
Custom Computer Programming Services
N.A.I.C.S.: 541511
Achuta K. Rayaprolu (Pres)

SYNERGETIC, INC.
10 Woodcross Dr, Columbia, SC 29212
Tel.: (803) 750-7041
Web Site: http://www.synergetic-peo.com
Year Founded: 2004
Sales Range: $50-74.9 Million
Emp.: 1,300
Outsourced Human Resources Services
N.A.I.C.S.: 561499
Yvonne Yarborough (Controller)
Diane Hagen (Mgr-Benefits)

SYNERGETICS DCS INC.
501 Hwy 12 W, Starkville, MS 39759
Tel.: (662) 323-9484
Web Site: http://www.synergeticsdcs.com
Year Founded: 1992
Sales Range: $10-24.9 Million
Emp.: 58
It Consulting
N.A.I.C.S.: 541690
David Palmer (CEO)
Jim Pryor (Mgr-Pur)
Sandra Simpson (Mgr-HR)

SYNERGIC SOLUTIONS, INC.
6 Courthouse Ln, Chelmsford, MA 01824
Tel.: (978) 935-4096
Web Site: http://www.synergicsolutionsinc.com
Year Founded: 1998
Sales Range: $1-9.9 Million
Emp.: 50
Business Consulting Services
N.A.I.C.S.: 541690
Vidhyadhar Mitta (Pres)
Vaishali Raghoji (VP)

SYNERGIS
1145 Sanctuary Pkwy Ste 150, Alpharetta, GA 30009
Tel.: (770) 346-7200
Web Site: http://www.synergishr.com
Year Founded: 1997
Rev.: $13,900,000
Emp.: 150
Computer Related Services
N.A.I.C.S.: 541519
Douglas L. Ross (Pres)
Kathleen Carey (Mgr-Acctg)
Cindy E. Ross (CEO)

SYNERGIS TECHNOLOGIES GROUP
3755 36th St, Kentwood, MI 49512
Tel.: (616) 245-4400 MI
Year Founded: 1957
Sales Range: $50-74.9 Million
Emp.: 250
Mfr & Designer of Chassis & Body Stamping Dies for Car Manufacturers
N.A.I.C.S.: 811121
Larry Dirkse (Treas)

Subsidiaries:

Development Corp. (1)
4327 Airlane Dr Southeast, Kentwood, MI 49512-3954
Tel.: (616) 245-4400
Designs & Manufacturers Chassis & Body Stamping Dies for Car Manufacturers
N.A.I.C.S.: 624310

Dieline Corp. (1)
3755 36th St Southeast, Kentwood, MI 49512-2913
Tel.: (616) 245-4400
Designs & Manufacturers Chassis & Body Stamping Dies for Car Manufacturers
N.A.I.C.S.: 333514

Dielink (1)
2066 Bristol Ave Nw, Grand Rapids, MI 49504-1402 **(100%)**
Tel.: (616) 245-4400
Sales Range: $10-24.9 Million
Emp.: 110
Large Sheetmetal Stamping Dies
N.A.I.C.S.: 333514

Q-Check Systems (1)
3755 36th St, Kentwood, MI 49512
Tel.: (616) 245-4400
Check Fixtures Models, Aids Styros
N.A.I.C.S.: 561110

SYNERGISTICS, INC.
2300 Windy Ridge Pkwy SE Ste 450n, Atlanta, GA 30339-8426
Tel.: (508) 655-1340
Web Site: http://www.synergisticsinc.com
Year Founded: 1960
Sales Range: $10-24.9 Million
Emp.: 20
Access Control Systems Mfr
N.A.I.C.S.: 561621
Greg Goldman (Pres & CEO)
Pam Weber (CFO)

SYNERGISTIX, INC.
480 Sawgrass Corp Pkwy Ste 200, Sunrise, FL 33325
Tel.: (954) 707-4200

SYNERGISTIX, INC.

Synergistix, Inc.—(Continued)
Web Site:
http://www.synergistixdata.com
Year Founded: 1997
Sales Range: $1-9.9 Million
Emp.: 90
Custom Computer Programing
N.A.I.C.S.: 541511
Don Schenker *(Pres & CEO)*
Jay Lambert *(Dir-Client Sys)*
Darren Coleman *(COO)*

SYNERGY ASSOCIATES LLC
550 Clydesdale Trl, Medina, MN 55340
Tel.: (763) 383-9920
Web Site: http://www.synllc.com
Year Founded: 1998
Sales Range: $10-24.9 Million
Emp.: 18
Computer System Design Services
N.A.I.C.S.: 541512
Gary Dean *(Owner)*

SYNERGY BANCSHARES INC.
210 Synergy Ctr Blvd, Houma, LA 70360
Tel.: (985) 851-3341
Web Site:
https://www.synergybank.com
Emp.: 100
Bank Holding Company
N.A.I.C.S.: 551111
Morris P. Hebert *(Chm)*

Subsidiaries:

Peoples Bancshares-Pointe Coupee, Inc. (1)
805 Hospital Rd, New Roads, LA 70760
Tel.: (225) 638-3713
Web Site: http://www.thefriendlybank.com
Offices of Bank Holding Companies
N.A.I.C.S.: 551111

Synergy Bank (1)
210 Synergy Ctr Blvd, Houma, LA 70360
Tel.: (985) 851-3341
Web Site: https://www.synergybank.com
Banking Services
N.A.I.C.S.: 522110
Stephen P. David *(Pres-Market)*

SYNERGY COMMUNICATIONS MANAGEMENT
400 Imperial Blvd, Cape Canaveral, FL 32920
Tel.: (321) 783-2400
Holding Company; Desktop Telephony Products Marketer
N.A.I.C.S.: 551112
Berchet E. O'Daniel *(Owner, Pres & CEO)*
William R. Mays *(VP)*

Subsidiaries:

Call One, Inc. (1)
400 Imperial Blvd, Cape Canaveral, FL 32920
Tel.: (321) 783-2400
Web Site: http://www.calloneonline.com
Sales Range: $10-24.9 Million
Emp.: 100
Online Telephony Equipment Marketer
N.A.I.C.S.: 459999

Hello Direct, Inc. (1)
77 Northeastern Blvd, Nashua, NH 03062
Tel.: (603) 598-1100
Web Site: http://www.hellodirect.com
Sales Range: $25-49.9 Million
Emp.: 75
Desktop Telephony Products Developer & Marketer
N.A.I.C.S.: 334290
Berchet E. O'Daniel *(Pres & CEO)*

SYNERGY CONSORTIUM SERVICES, LLC
350 Junction Rd, Madison, WI 53717
Tel.: (608) 203-6200
Web Site:
http://www.SynergyConsortium.com
Sales Range: $1-9.9 Million
Emp.: 3
Information Technology Services
N.A.I.C.S.: 449210
Tony Supanich *(Pres)*
Bob Lucas *(Dir-Bus Dev)*

SYNERGY CORE LLC
7123 Ramsgate Rd, Charlotte, NC 28270
Tel.: (704) 336-9700
Web Site: http://www.synergy-core.com
Emp.: 25
IT & Telecommunications Services
N.A.I.C.S.: 541519
Larry W. Jones *(Founder & CEO)*
James P. Burke *(Owner)*

Subsidiaries:

SDN Global, Inc. (1)
11101 Nations Ford Rd, Pineville, NC 28134
Tel.: (704) 588-2233
Web Site: http://www.sdnglobal.com
Sales Range: $25-49.9 Million
Emp.: 20
Satellite Broadband Services
N.A.I.C.S.: 517410
Larry Jones *(CEO)*
Timothy R. McKee *(VP-Network Svcs)*
Dennis Ewald *(Dir-Bus Dev)*
Joy Head *(Dir-Network Admin)*
Les Dickert *(Dir-Engrg)*

SYNERGY DIRECT MORTGAGE, INC.
9 Peddlers Vlg, Newark, DE 19702
Tel.: (302) 283-0833 DE
Year Founded: 2000
Sales Range: $10-24.9 Million
Emp.: 30
Residential Mortgage Brokers
N.A.I.C.S.: 522310
Don Scioli *(CEO)*

SYNERGY GLOBAL SOLUTIONS
1100 Pittsford Victor Rd, Pittsford, NY 14534-3801
Tel.: (585) 381-4120
Web Site: http://www.synergy.gs
Year Founded: 1971
Sales Range: $25-49.9 Million
Emp.: 230
Information Technology Solutions
N.A.I.C.S.: 423430
Lynne Caputi *(Engr-Sys)*
Barbara Duffy *(Mgr-HR)*
Robert Phillips *(CFO)*
Kathleen Sweda *(Mgr-Ops-Solution Center)*
Jeremy McLaughlin *(Mgr-Virtualization Practice)*
Alan Knapton *(VP-Sls)*
Chris Trageser *(Mgr-Acct)*
Jennifer Weinschreider *(Mgr-HR)*
MaryLynn DeSimone *(Sr Acct Exec)*
Wendy Nagy *(Project Mgr)*
Jim Stefano *(Pres)*

SYNERGY HOMECARE FRANCHISING LLC
1757 E Baseline Rd Ste 124, Gilbert, AZ 85233
Web Site:
http://www.synergyhomecare.com
Year Founded: 2001
Sales Range: $50-74.9 Million
Emp.: 26
Home Care Services
N.A.I.C.S.: 621610

Peter Tourian *(Founder & Chm)*
Charlie Young *(CEO)*
Jennifer Chasteen *(CMO)*

SYNERGY PETROLEUM LLC
622 S 56th Ave, Phoenix, AZ 85043-4622
Tel.: (602) 272-6795 AZ
Web Site: http://www.gosenergy.com
Year Founded: 1941
Petroleum & Petroleum Products Mfr
N.A.I.C.S.: 424720
Tim Sweeney *(Mgr-Ops-Cardlock)*

SYNERGY RELOCATIONS INC.
12657 Alcosta Blvd Ste 550, San Ramon, CA 94583
Tel.: (925) 807-1155
Web Site:
http://www.synergyrehousing.com
Sales Range: $10-24.9 Million
Emp.: 50
Real Estate Leasing & Rentals
N.A.I.C.S.: 531210
Henry Luebbert *(Co-Founder & Partner)*
Jack Jensky *(Co-Founder & Partner)*
Ana Tacorda *(Mgr-IT)*
Leslie Batsford *(Mgr-Sls)*
Lance Bradwell *(Head-IT)*

SYNERGY TECHNOLOGIES, INC.
5338 Old Mooringsport Rd, Shreveport, LA 71107
Tel.: (866) 743-8573
Web Site: http://www.syntrx.net
Specialty Chemicals Mfr & Marketer Focused on Food Protection Products
N.A.I.C.S.: 325998
Randy Allen *(Pres)*
John Dankert *(Chief Scientific Officer)*

Subsidiaries:

SteriFx, Inc. (1)
BioSpace 1 2031 Kings Hwy Ste 218, Shreveport, LA 71103
Tel.: (318) 425-2515
Web Site: http://www.sterifx.com
Rev.: $2,500,000
Emp.: 14
Supplier of Anti-Microbial Protection Products to Poultry Processing Industry
N.A.I.C.S.: 424690

SYNERGYST RESEARCH GROUP
4242 Medical Dr Bldg 5, San Antonio, TX 78229
Tel.: (210) 447-2345
Web Site:
http://www.synergystresearch.net
Sales Range: $1-9.9 Million
Emp.: 33
Clinical Research Services
N.A.I.C.S.: 541720
Trudy Madan *(CEO)*

SYNERZIP
14228 Midway Rd Ste 130, Dallas, TX 75244
Tel.: (469) 322-0349
Web Site: http://www.synerzip.com
Sales Range: $1-9.9 Million
Emp.: 146
Software Development & Testing Services
N.A.I.C.S.: 513210
Hemant Elhence *(Co-Founder & CEO)*
Vinayak Joglekar *(Co-Founder & CTO)*
Ashish Shanker *(VP-Software Svcs)*
Rohit Sinha *(Project Mgr)*
Florence Lowe *(COO)*

SYNOVA, INC.
1000 Town Ctr Ste 700, Southfield, MI 48075
Tel.: (248) 281-2500
Web Site: http://www.synovainc.com
Year Founded: 1998
Sales Range: $50-74.9 Million
Emp.: 1,100
IT Staffing Services
N.A.I.C.S.: 561311
Gopal Chakravarthy *(Exec VP)*

SYNQOR INC.
155 Swanson Rd, Boxborough, MA 01719
Tel.: (978) 849-0600 MA
Web Site: http://www.synqor.com
Year Founded: 1997
Sales Range: $10-24.9 Million
Emp.: 162
Power Supplies & Related Services
N.A.I.C.S.: 334419
Martin F. Schlecht *(Chm, Pres & CEO)*
Buzz Hofmann *(Exec VP)*
Rene W. Hemond Jr. *(Exec VP)*

SYNSOR CORPORATION
1920 Merrill Creek Pkwy, Everett, WA 98203
Tel.: (425) 551-1300
Web Site: http://www.synsor.com
Year Founded: 1971
Sales Range: $10-24.9 Million
Emp.: 110
School Furniture
N.A.I.C.S.: 337127
Edward J. Kramer *(Chm)*
Gary Bullock *(Pres)*
Wade Anderson *(Controller)*

SYNTEC INDUSTRIES INC.
438 Lavender Dr, Rome, GA 30165-2172
Tel.: (706) 235-1158
Web Site: http://www.syntecind.com
Year Founded: 1986
Sales Range: $10-24.9 Million
Emp.: 25
Carpets & Rugs
N.A.I.C.S.: 314110
William N. Watters *(Pres)*

SYNTECH DEVELOPMENT & MANUFACTURING, INC.
13948 Mountain Ave, Chino, CA 91710
Tel.: (909) 465-5554 CA
Web Site:
http://www.sdmplastics.com
Year Founded: 1998
Sales Range: $1-9.9 Million
Emp.: 25
Plastics Products Mfr
N.A.I.C.S.: 326199
Bob Hobbs *(Pres)*

Subsidiaries:

Accent Plastics, Inc. (1)
1925 Elise Cir, Corona, CA 92879
Tel.: (951) 273-7777
Web Site: http://www.accentplastics.com
Rev.: $12,000,000
Emp.: 60
Injection Molding Of Plastics
N.A.I.C.S.: 326199
Tom Pridonoff *(CEO)*

SYNTECH RESEARCH, INC.
1617 Arena Dr, Davis, CA 95618
Tel.: (530) 753-8880 CA
Web Site:
http://www.syntechresearch.com
Year Founded: 1999
Biological & Ecological Research & Development Services
N.A.I.C.S.: 541715

COMPANIES

Khosro Khodayari (Pres, CEO & Dir-Mktg & Sls)
Colin Ruscoe (Dir-Comm)

SYNTER RESOURCE GROUP, LLC
5935 Rivers Ave Ste 102, North Charleston, SC 29406
Tel.: (843) 746-2200
Web Site:
 http://www.synterresource.com
Year Founded: 2005
Sales Range: $1-9.9 Million
Emp.: 125
Financial Management & Collection Agency Services
N.A.I.C.S.: 522320
John Church (VP-Ops)
Jennifer Murphy (Mgr-Client Svcs)
Reggie McCaskill (Pres)
Mike Daugherty (VP-Partnership Dev)

SYNTERACTIVE
1100 H St NW Ste 900, Washington, DC 20005
Tel.: (202) 904-2165
Web Site:
 http://www.synteractive.com
Year Founded: 2003
Sales Range: $1-9.9 Million
Emp.: 36
Information Technology Consulting Services & Products
N.A.I.C.S.: 519290
Diane Johnson (Dir-Tech)

SYNTERRA CORP.
148 River St Ste 220, Greenville, SC 29601
Tel.: (864) 421-9999
Web Site: http://synterracorp.com
Scientific & Engineering Consulting Services
N.A.I.C.S.: 541690
Mark Taylor (Pres)
Kathy Webb (VP-Sciences)
Ruth Albright (VP-Engrg)
Vick Crowley (CFO)
Linda Erwin (Dir-HR)
Judd Mahan (Dir-Science Ops)
Josh Fowler (Dir-Cleint Rels)
Bill Husk (Sr Project Mgr)

Subsidiaries:

ECSI, LLC (1)
340 S Broadway Ste 200, Lexington, KY 40508
Tel.: (859) 233-2103
Web Site: http://www.engrservices.com
Sales Range: $25-49.9 Million
Emp.: 30
Consulting Services
N.A.I.C.S.: 541690
J. Steven Gardner (Pres & CEO)
Seth Mittle (Project Mgr)
Karen Rose (Sr Project Mgr)
Andy Willis (Sr VP & Dir-Appalachian)
Douglas Mynear (COO)
Fred Eastridge (VP-Civil Engrg)
Charles Reeves Jr. (VP)

SYNTHETIC GENOMICS, INC.
11149 N Torrey Pines Rd, La Jolla, CA 92037
Tel.: (858) 754-2900
Web Site:
 http://www.syntheticgenomics.com
Year Founded: 2005
Sales Range: $10-24.9 Million
Emp.: 130
Biotechnology Researcher, Developer & Mfr
N.A.I.C.S.: 541714
Joseph Mahler (CFO & COO)
Hamilton O. Smith (Founder & Chief Scientific Officer)
Toby Richardson (VP-Bioinformatics)
David Kiernan (Founder & Partner)
Nathan Wood (Pres-SGI-DNA & Sr VP)
Laurence Warden (VP-Engrg & Instrumentation)
Natasha O. Bowman (VP-HR)
Teresa Spehar (VP-Intellectual Property)
Anthony Artuso (Chief Bus Officer)
Rob Cutler (Sec)
Ben Chiarelli (VP-Corp Dev & Strategy)
Todd C. Peterson (CTO)
Oliver Steffen Fetzer (CEO)

SYNTHETIC ORGANIC CHEMICAL MANUFACTURERS ASSOCIATION
1850 M St NW Ste 700, Washington, DC 20036-5810
Tel.: (202) 721-4100
Web Site: http://www.socma.com
Year Founded: 1921
Sales Range: $10-24.9 Million
Emp.: 30
Trade Association for the Chemicals Industry
N.A.I.C.S.: 813910
Dolores Alonso (Sr Dir)
Lawrence D. Sloan (Pres & CEO)

SYNUTRA INTERNATIONAL, INC.
2275 Research Blvd Ste 500, Rockville, MD 20850
Tel.: (301) 840-3888   DE
Web Site: http://www.synutra.com
Rev.: $365,039,000
Assets: $817,097,000
Liabilities: $680,297,000
Net Worth: $136,800,000
Earnings: $20,961,000
Emp.: 2,600
Fiscal Year-end: 03/31/16
Infant Formula Product Mfr
N.A.I.C.S.: 311514
Liang Zhang (Chm & CEO)
Weiguo Zhang (Pres)
Xisen Mu (VP-Production)
Feng Zha (VP-HR & Admin)
Ning Cai (CFO)

Subsidiaries:

Meitek Technology (Qingdao) Co., Ltd. (1)
North to 204 Country Rd Eastern of Langyatai Rd, Qingdao, 266400, Shandong, China
Tel.: (86) 53288136005
Dairy Products Mfr
N.A.I.C.S.: 311514

Shengyuan Nutritional Food Co., Ltd. (1)
Jiaonan Seashore Industry Zone, Qingdao, 266400, Shandong, China
Tel.: (86) 53288138318
Sales Range: $150-199.9 Million
Emp.: 700
Dairy Products Mfr
N.A.I.C.S.: 311514
Ke Li (Gen Mgr)

Synutra, Inc. (1)
2275 Research Blvd Ste 500, Rockville, MD 20850-6203
Tel.: (301) 840-3888
Dairy Products Mfr
N.A.I.C.S.: 311514

SYNXIS CORPORATION
3150 Sabre Dr, Southlake, TX 76092
Tel.: (817) 567-9792
Web Site: http://www.synxis.com
Year Founded: 1996
Sales Range: $10-24.9 Million
Emp.: 80
Distribution Systems & Reservation Management Services for Hotels, Resorts & Casinos
N.A.I.C.S.: 541511
Alex Alt (Pres & Gen Mgr)
David Meltzer (Chief Comml Officer)

SYNYGY, INC.
2501 Seaport Dr Ste 100, Chester, PA 19013-2249
Tel.: (610) 494-3300   PA
Web Site: http://www.synygy.com
Year Founded: 1991
Sales Range: $25-49.9 Million
Emp.: 450
Enterprise Incentive Management, Software & Services
N.A.I.C.S.: 541611
Mark A. Stiffler (Founder, Pres & CEO)
Walt E. Montague (Gen Counsel & VP)
Scott Cawood (Exec VP-Global Ops)
Karen Tulis (Mng Dir)
Kenneth Bjorkelo (Reg VP)
Amit Gupta (Reg VP)

SYRACUSE BRICK HOUSE, INC.
329 N Salina St Ste 200, Syracuse, NY 13203
Tel.: (315) 474-5506   NY
Web Site: http://www.sbh.org
Year Founded: 1920
Sales Range: $10-24.9 Million
Emp.: 303
Behavioral Healthcare Services
N.A.I.C.S.: 621420
Kathleen Gaffney-Babb (VP)
Jeremy Klemanski (Pres & CEO)
Bill Ruckyj (Dir-Facilities Mgmt)
Nathan Rauscher (Dir-Continuous Quality Improvement & Compliance)
Lisa Nurnberger (Dir-Fin)
James Antonacci (Chm)

SYRACUSE COMMUNITY HEALTH CENTER, INC.
819 S Salina St, Syracuse, NY 13202
Tel.: (315) 476-7921   NY
Web Site: http://www.schcny.com
Year Founded: 1978
Sales Range: $10-24.9 Million
Community Health Care Services
N.A.I.C.S.: 621498
Ruben P. Cowart (Pres & CEO)
Michael J. Sullivan (CFO)

SYRACUSE OFFICE EQUIPMENT
375 Erie Blvd W, Syracuse, NY 13202
Tel.: (315) 476-9091   NY
Web Site: http://www.soesyr.com
Year Founded: 1958
Sales Range: $10-24.9 Million
Emp.: 35
Distr Of Furniture
N.A.I.C.S.: 423210
Vincent Sweeney (Pres)
David Sweeney (Exec VP)
Kevin Sweeney (VP)

SYRACUSE SYMPHONY ORCHESTRA
411 Montgomery St Ste 40, Syracuse, NY 13202
Tel.: (315) 424-8222
Sales Range: $10-24.9 Million
Emp.: 100
Symphony Orchestra
N.A.I.C.S.: 711130
David A.A. Ridings (Vice Chm)
Daniel Hege (Dir-Music)
Edward Kochian (Interim Dir)
Rocco Mangano (Chm)
Peter H. Soderberg (Vice Chm)

SYRACUSE TRAILER SALES
3496 Court St, Syracuse, NY 13206
Tel.: (315) 437-5406
Web Site: http://www.ststrailer.com
Sales Range: $10-24.9 Million
Emp.: 43
Automotive Parts & Accessories Whslr
N.A.I.C.S.: 441330
Steve Jacobs (Co-Pres & Co-CEO)
Shawn Jacobs (Co-Pres & Co-CEO)
Sue Copps (Office Mgr)
Pete Krais (Mgr-Trailer Sls)
Sheryl Fromwiller (Coord-Svc & Parts)
Barb Mudge (Dir-Parts & Svc)
Joe Post (Mgr-Parts-Columbus)
Jim Brown (Mgr-Svc-Columbus)
Kim Lindh (Mgr-Svc-Columbus)
Mike Moran (Mgr-Svc-Columbus)

SYRACUSE UNIVERSITY PRESS
621 Skytop Rd Ste 110, Syracuse, NY 13244-5290
Tel.: (315) 443-5535
Web Site:
 http://www.syracuseuniversitypress.syr.edu
Year Founded: 1943
Sales Range: Less than $1 Million
Emp.: 16
Scholarly & Regional Books Retailer
N.A.I.C.S.: 513130
Deanna McCay (Editor-Acq)
Suzanne Guiod (Editor-in-Chief-Acq)
Kay Steinmetz (Mgr-Editorial & Production)
Deborah Mannion (Editor-Acq)

SYRAINFOTEK LLC
6110 McFarland Station Dr Ste 201, Alpharetta, GA 30004
Tel.: (404) 410-1441
Web Site: http://www.cloudq.net
Year Founded: 2013
Sales Range: $10-24.9 Million
Emp.: 200
Software Development Services
N.A.I.C.S.: 541511
Yaser Hameed (CEO)
Maiko Mills (Dir-Bus Dev)
Sanjai Meesala (Dir-HR Ops)
Ben Weaver (Dir-Ops)

SYS-CON MEDIA, INC.
577 Chestnut Ridge Rd, Woodcliff Lake, NJ 07677
Tel.: (201) 802-3000
Web Site: http://www.sys-con.com
Year Founded: 1994
Sales Range: $10-24.9 Million
Emp.: 10
IT Magazines Publisher; Trade Shows Producer
N.A.I.C.S.: 513120
Carmen Gonzalez (Sr VP-Sls & Mktg)

SYSCOM (USA) INC.
1 Exchange Plz 55 Broadway 11th Fl, New York, NY 10006
Tel.: (212) 797-9131   NY
Web Site: http://www.syscomusa.com
Year Founded: 1990
Sales Range: $10-24.9 Million
Information Technology Product Sales & Support Services
N.A.I.C.S.: 541519
Seishi Sato (Pres & CEO)
Norifumi Watarai (Sr Engr)
Frank Cheng (Mgr-ESI Ops)
Yukihiko Ito (Dir-SE)
Chikara Isetani (CTO & Exec Officer)
Evita Ynacay (Treas & Sec)
Hiroshi Kubota (Gen Mgr-Eastern)
Mitsuhiro Nagata (Gen Mgr-Western Reg-IT Solution Dept)

SYSCOM (USA) INC.

Syscom (USA) Inc.—(Continued)
Yutaka Mori (Dir-ERP-Bus Solution Dept)
Hiromasa Takeda (Dir-SI Operation)
Masaya Kanno (Dir-SF & Bay Area Operation-IT Solution Dept)
Tokusuke Akashi (Dir-Sls & Mktg)
Umi Yokota (Dir-ERP Sls & Mktg)

SYSCOM INC.
400 E Pratt St Ste 502, Baltimore, MD 21202
Tel.: (410) 539-3737
Web Site: http://www.syscom.com
Year Founded: 1982
Sales Range: $10-24.9 Million
Emp.: 75
System Software Development Services
N.A.I.C.S.: 541512
Theodore E. Bayer (Founder, Pres & CEO)
Mark Anzmann (VP-Professional Svcs)
Michael Voytilla (VP-Sls & Mktg-Solution Svcs Div)
Neil Peckman (VP-Product Strategy)

SYSCOM TECHNOLOGIES
2160 Kingston Ct Ste D, Marietta, GA 30067
Tel.: (770) 952-5537
Web Site:
http://www.syscomtechnologies.com
Year Founded: 1980
Sales Range: $25-49.9 Million
Emp.: 48
Computer & Software Stores
N.A.I.C.S.: 449210
Bernard Westwood (CFO)
Don Schrenk (VP-Sls)
Randy Delp (Engr-Software)
Tim Cutlip (Engr-Sys)
Blake Smith (Mgr-Mktg)

SYSKA HENNESSY GROUP INC.
1515 Broadway, New York, NY 10036
Tel.: (212) 921-2300 NY
Web Site: http://www.syska.com
Year Founded: 1928
Provider of Consulting, Engineering, Technology & Construction Services
N.A.I.C.S.: 541330
Cyrus Izzo (Co-Pres)
James Coe (Sr Principal & Sr Dir-Practice Area-Critical Facilities)
John Passanante (Sr Mng Dir-Western & Sr Principal)
James Regan (Sr Mng Dir-Western & Sr Principal)
Gary Brennen (Co-Pres)
G. Venkata Ramu (Exec VP & Chief Engr)
Robert Ioanna (Sr Mng Dir-NY & Sr Principal)
Joseph O'Sullivan (Sr Mng Dir-Chicago & MENA & Sr Principal)
Ing Lim (Sr Mng Dir-Shanghai & Sr Principal)
Louis Curatolo (Dir-Fin Ops)
Michelle Galindez (Dir-Mktg & Comm)
Guy Pascarello (Dir-IT)
Vicki A. Hobson (Dir-HR)
Anjanette Bobrow (Gen Counsel)
Larry Ollice (Assoc Partner-Chicago)
Will B. Hodges (Mng Dir-Dallas)

SYSMIND LLC
38 Washington Rd, Princeton Junction, NJ 08550
Tel.: (609) 897-9670
Web Site: http://www.sysmind.com
Year Founded: 1999
Sales Range: $10-24.9 Million

Emp.: 125
Software & Consulting Services for Financial Industry
N.A.I.C.S.: 513210
Venkata Gorty (Co-Founder & VP-Ops & Tech)
Sharon Wen (Mgr)
Vikram Mahajan (Mgr-Resource)

SYSOP TOOLS, INC.
1880 Century Park E Ste 1402, Los Angeles, CA 90067-1630
Tel.: (213) 995-5060
Web Site: http://www.sysoptools.com
Software Publisher
N.A.I.C.S.: 513210
Kurt Lewis (CEO)

SYSPRO IMPACT SOFTWARE INC.
959 S Coast Dr Ste 100, Costa Mesa, CA 92626-1786
Tel.: (714) 437-1000
Web Site: http://www.syspro.com
Year Founded: 1987
Sales Range: $25-49.9 Million
Emp.: 200
Computers, Peripherals & Software
N.A.I.C.S.: 423430
Stanley Goodrich (Mgr-PR)
Doug Garnhart (CFO)
Joey Benadretti (Pres)
Dawna Olsen (CMO)
David Doyle (Dir-Customer Success-Canada)
James Moffatt (Pres-Canada)
James Weir (VP-Sls-Mississauga)
Gavin Verreyne (Chief Svcs Officer)
Piero Broccardo (CFO-North America)
Geoff Garrett (CEO)
Erin Schlee (Mgr-Mktg Comm)

SYSTECH CORPORATION
10908 Technology Pl, San Diego, CA 92127
Tel.: (858) 674-6500 CA
Web Site: http://www.systech.com
Year Founded: 1981
Sales Range: $50-74.9 Million
Emp.: 35
Computer Interface Equipment Mfr
N.A.I.C.S.: 334290
Mark Fowler (Pres)
Don Armerding (VP-Software Dev)

SYSTEL BUSINESS EQUIPMENT CO. INC.
2604 Ft Bragg Rd, Fayetteville, NC 28303-4719
Tel.: (910) 483-7114 NC
Web Site: http://www.systeloa.com
Year Founded: 1981
Sales Range: $25-49.9 Million
Emp.: 200
Office Equipment
N.A.I.C.S.: 423420
D Keith Allison (Owner, Pres & CEO)
Warren Jackson (Mgr-Div Sls)

SYSTEM DESIGN ADVANTAGE LLC
3711 Kennebec Dr, Eagan, MN 55122
Tel.: (952) 703-3500 MN
Web Site: http://www.sdallc.com
Year Founded: 1992
Sales Range: $10-24.9 Million
Emp.: 75
Provider of Computer Hardware & Peripherals
N.A.I.C.S.: 423430
Shane Anderson (Sr Acct Exec)

SYSTEM DEVELOPMENT.INTEGRATION LLC

33 W Monroe St, Chicago, IL 60603
Tel.: (312) 580-7500
Web Site:
http://www.sdienterprises.com
Sales Range: $75-99.9 Million
Emp.: 220
Computer Software & Technology Systems Mfr
N.A.I.C.S.: 513210
Dawn Nash Pfeiffer (Chief Mktg Officer)
Linda Petty (Gen Counsel & Exec VP)

Subsidiaries:

i-sys Corporation (1)
2460 Remount Rd Ste 106, Charleston, SC 29406
Tel.: (843) 554-7622
Web Site: http://www.i-syscorp.com
Sales Range: $1-9.9 Million
Emp.: 27
Security System Services
N.A.I.C.S.: 561621
Alfredo Moussset (Mgr)

Subsidiary (Domestic):

i-sys Corporation - El Dorado Hills (2)
5030 Hillsdale Circle Ste 102, El Dorado Hills, CA 95762
Tel.: (916) 933-7750
Web Site: http://www.yamas.com
Warm Air Heating & Air Conditioning Contractor
N.A.I.C.S.: 238220

SYSTEM DYNAMICS INTERNATIONAL INC.
560 Discovery Dr NW, Huntsville, AL 35806-2810
Tel.: (256) 689-9000
Web Site: http://www.sdi-inc.com
Sales Range: $10-24.9 Million
Engineeering Services
N.A.I.C.S.: 541330
Pamela Barrett White (CEO)
Michael B. Spiegel (Pres)
Stephen C. Smith (VP)
Kimberly D. Rose (VP-Bus Ops)

SYSTEM ELECTRIC CO.
1278 Montalvo Way, Palm Springs, CA 92262
Tel.: (760) 327-7847 CA
Web Site:
http://www.systemelectric.com
Year Founded: 1961
Sales Range: $25-49.9 Million
Emp.: 300
Electrical Contracting Services
N.A.I.C.S.: 238210
Bob Stephens (VP)

SYSTEM FREIGHT INC.
7 Ctr Dr Ste 4, Jamesburg, NJ 08831
Tel.: (609) 395-8600
Web Site:
http://www.systemfreight.net
Rev.: $32,864,335
Emp.: 200
Trucking Except Local
N.A.I.C.S.: 484121
Rich Garcia (Dir-Fleet Maintenance)
Anthony Siragusa (VP-Ops)
Michael Pagliuca (Pres & CEO)
James LaMarca Jr. (Dir-Ops)

SYSTEM INTEGRATORS, L.L.C.
23630 N 35th Dr, Glendale, AZ 85310-4503
Tel.: (623) 434-3136
Web Site:
http://www.syintegrators.com
Die Cut Parts Mfr & Distr
N.A.I.C.S.: 339991

U.S. PRIVATE

Sam Gaston (Owner & Pres)
Jeff Paulson (VP-Ops)
Ann Gaston (Owner & VP-Sls)
Bob Okuda (Controller)

Subsidiaries:

CGS Technologies, Inc. (1)
23630 N 35th Dr Ste 1, Glendale, AZ 85310
Tel.: (623) 434-3136
Web Site: http://cgstech.com
Die Cut Parts Mfr & Distr
N.A.I.C.S.: 339991
Diana Kincart (Sec & Office Mgr)

SYSTEM ONE HOLDINGS, LLC
210 Sixth Ave Ste 3100, Pittsburgh, PA 15222
Tel.: (412) 995-1900
Web Site:
http://www.systemoneservices.com
Year Founded: 2008
Emp.: 100
Engineering & Technical Outsourcing Solutions
N.A.I.C.S.: 541690
Troy Gregory (Chm & CEO)
Daniel J. Moran (CFO)
Greg Lignelli (Pres & COO)
Mark A. Fenske (Exec VP)
Lisa Biondi (CIO)
Susan Burgess Tencza (Chief HR Officer)
Richard H. Weede (Dir-Mktg)
Cami Davis (Gen Counsel)
Richard Weede (Dir-Mktg)

Subsidiaries:

ALTA IT Services LLC (1)
9210 Corporate Blvd Ste 200, Rockville, MD 20850
Tel.: (301) 948-8700
Web Site: http://www.altaits.com
Sales Range: $1-9.9 Million
Emp.: 40
Information Technology Services
N.A.I.C.S.: 541519
Rich Paolicelli (Exec VP)

Subsidiary (Domestic):

Cohesion Corporation (2)
5151 Pfeiffer Rd Ste 105, Cincinnati, OH 45242
Tel.: (513) 587-7700
Web Site: http://www.cohesion.com
Sales Range: $10-24.9 Million
Emp.: 190
IT & Business Strategy Consulting
N.A.I.C.S.: 541618
John Owens (Pres & CEO)
Dawn Simons (Mng Dir)
Joanna Hunter (Mgr-Salesforce Dev)

GAP Solutions, Inc. (1)
205 Van Buren St Ste 205, Herndon, VA 20170
Tel.: (703) 707-2090
Web Site: http://www.gapsi.com
Government Support & Consulting Services
N.A.I.C.S.: 561499
Diane Pairel (Pres)

Subsidiary (Domestic):

Quadel Consulting Corp. (2)
10 W Market St Ste 750, Indianapolis, IN 46204
Tel.: (317) 656-8808
Web Site: http://www.quadel.com
Other Management Consulting Services
N.A.I.C.S.: 541618
Allan Hardy (VP-Bus Dev)
Katie Goar (Pres)

Joule Inc. (1)
1245 Rte 1 S, Edison, NJ 08837
Tel.: (732) 548-5444
Web Site: http://www.jouleinc.com
Sales Range: $50-74.9 Million
Staffing Solutions
N.A.I.C.S.: 561311
Stephen Demanovich (VP)
John Logothetis (VP)
John Porch (VP)

COMPANIES

Subsidiary (Domestic):

Joule Staffing Services, Inc. (2)
295 Pierson Ave, Edison, NJ 08837
Tel.: (732) 906-0906
Web Site:
http://www.joulestaffingsolutions.com
Sales Range: $25-49.9 Million
Emp.: 16
Staffing Services
N.A.I.C.S.: 561320
Wendy Tordilio *(Dir-Joule Staffing Solutions)*

KeyLogic Associates, Inc. (1)
104 Union Vly Rd, Oak Ridge, TN 37830-8044
Tel.: (703) 203-8065
Web Site: http://www.iiaweb.com
Computer Facilities Management Services
N.A.I.C.S.: 541513
Martha Wallus *(VP-HR & Admin)*

Subsidiary (Domestic):

KeyLogic Systems, LLC (2)
3168 Collins Ferry Rd, Morgantown, WV 26505-3352
Tel.: (304) 296-9100
Web Site: http://www.keylogic.com
Sales Range: $10-24.9 Million
Emp.: 100
Knowledge Management, Program Management & Portfolio & Performance Management Solutions
N.A.I.C.S.: 541512
Jon Hammock *(Pres & CEO)*
Frank J. Vitale *(Chief HR Officer)*
Kevin Reid *(CIO & VP-Natl Security)*

Subsidiary (Domestic):

OnLocation, Inc. (3)
501 Church St NE, Vienna, VA 22180
Tel.: (703) 938-5151
Web Site: http://www.onlocationinc.com
Other Scientific & Technical Consulting Services
N.A.I.C.S.: 541690
Lessly A. Goudarzi *(Founder & CEO)*
Stephan E. Bonnaire *(Mng Dir & COO)*

P2P Holdings LLC (1)
5810 Coral Rdg Dr Ste 250, Coral Springs, FL 33076-3381
Tel.: (954) 656-8600
Web Site: http://www.tpgsfed.com
Wired Telecommunications Carriers
N.A.I.C.S.: 517111
Alfred Mazzo *(CEO)*

SYSTEM PAVERS INC.
3750 S Susan St Ste 200, Santa Ana, CA 92704-6964
Tel.: (949) 263-8300
Web Site:
http://www.systemspavers.com
Sales Range: $10-24.9 Million
Emp.: 150
Masonry & Other Stonework
N.A.I.C.S.: 238140
Larry Green *(Co-Founder & CEO)*
Doug Luezk *(Co-Founder & Pres)*
Marc Bernstein *(Controller-Fin)*
Randy Mansfield *(Mgr-Sls)*
Syed Zaidi *(COO)*

SYSTEM PLANNING CORPORATION
3601 Wilson Blvd, Arlington, VA 22201
Tel.: (703) 351-8200   DE
Web Site: http://www.sysplan.com
Year Founded: 1970
Sales Range: $150-199.9 Million
Emp.: 100
Provider of Scientific Research & Engineering Design Services; Manufacturer of Instrumentation Radars & Electronic Equipment
N.A.I.C.S.: 541720
Mike Bergquist *(VP)*

Subsidiaries:

TriData Inc. (1)
3601 Wilson Blvd, Arlington, VA 22201   (100%)
Tel.: (703) 351-8300
Web Site: http://www.sysplan.com
Sales Range: $10-24.9 Million
Emp.: 16
Fire Prevention Studies; Local Government Analyses
N.A.I.C.S.: 541618

SYSTEM PROPERTY DEVELOPMENT COMPANY, INC.
975 E Green St, Pasadena, CA 91106-2410
Tel.: (213) 687-7275   CA
Year Founded: 1956
Sales Range: $75-99.9 Million
Emp.: 3
Real Estate Development Services
N.A.I.C.S.: 531210
Duane H. Cameron *(Pres)*

SYSTEM SCALE CORPORATION
4393 W 96th St, Indianapolis, IN 46268
Tel.: (317) 876-9335   IN
Web Site: http://www.system-scale.com
Year Founded: 1979
Industrial Scales Whslr, Precision Calibration & Technical Support Services
N.A.I.C.S.: 423830
Harry Owens *(Gen Mgr)*
Michael Sale *(CFO)*
Patsy Stambaugh *(Coord-Svcs)*
Joe Culp *(COO)*
Curtis Justen *(Ops Mgr)*

SYSTEMATIC POWER SOLUTIONS, LLC
2847 John Deere Sr Ste 102, Knoxville, TN 37917
Tel.: (865) 688-5953
Web Site: http://www.4xspower.com
Year Founded: 2005
Batteries, Chargers, Cables & Accessories Mfr & Distr
N.A.I.C.S.: 335910
Scottie Johnson *(Founder & CEO)*

Subsidiaries:

Systematic Power Manufacturing, LLC (1)
2847 John Deere Ste 102, Knoxville, TN 37917
Tel.: (865) 688-5953
Batteries, Chargers, Capacitors & Accessories Mfr & Distr
N.A.I.C.S.: 334416

Subsidiary (Domestic):

Ioxus, Inc. (2)
18 Stadium Circle, Oneonta, NY 13820
Tel.: (607) 441-3500
Web Site: http://www.ioxus.com
Sales Range: $10-24.9 Million
Emp.: 150
Designs & Manufactures Ultracapacitors & Other Products Used in Wind Turbines, Hybrid Vehicles & Renewable Energy
N.A.I.C.S.: 334416
Chad Hall *(Co-Founder & Sr VP-Sls & Mktg)*
Henry Barber *(CFO)*
Ken Rudisuela *(CTO)*
Nick Cataldo *(Sr VP-Global Sls & Mktg)*
Philip Meek *(COO)*

SYSTEMONE TECHNOLOGIES INC.
8305 NW 27th St Ste 107, Miami, FL 33122
Tel.: (305) 593-8015   FL
Web Site:
http://www.systemonetechnologies.com
Sales Range: $10-24.9 Million
Emp.: 12
Self-Contained, Recycling Industrial Parts Washers Designer, Mfr & Sales
N.A.I.C.S.: 333248
Paul I. Mansur *(Pres & CEO)*
Oscar Sanchez *(Controller & Finl Officer)*

SYSTEMS ALLIANCE, INC.
11350 McCormick Rd Ste 1203 Executive Plz III, Hunt Valley, MD 21031
Tel.: (410) 584-0595
Web Site:
http://www.systemsalliance.com
Year Founded: 1993
Sales Range: $25-49.9 Million
Emp.: 50
E-solutions, Consulting & Integration Services
N.A.I.C.S.: 541511
Richard Hughes *(Pres & CEO)*
Janet Pilarski *(Sr Dir-Integrated Mktg)*
Matt Weigl *(Sr Dir-Bus Dev)*
Joshua Crone *(CTO & VP-Software Products)*

SYSTEMS AND METHODS INC.
106 Wedgewood Dr, Carrollton, GA 30117
Tel.: (770) 834-0831
Web Site: http://www.smi-inc.com
Year Founded: 1971
Sales Range: $50-74.9 Million
Emp.: 500
Data Processing Services
N.A.I.C.S.: 518210
Joe Stone *(CEO)*
Bart Stone *(CTO)*
Janet Statts *(VP-Govt Svcs)*
Lou Hall *(COO)*
Mark Carlson *(VP-Information Svcs)*
Karen Middlebrooks *(Chief Mktg Officer)*

SYSTEMS CONNECTION OF MARYLAND
8839 Greenwood Pl, Savage, MD 20763
Tel.: (301) 725-6680
Sales Range: $10-24.9 Million
Emp.: 150
Office Furniture Installation
N.A.I.C.S.: 238990
Dan Maskell *(Pres)*
Campbell Brooks *(Partner)*

SYSTEMS CONTRACTING CORP
214 N Washington Ave Ste 700, El Dorado, AR 71730
Tel.: (870) 862-1315
Web Site:
http://www.thesystemsgroup.biz
Rev.: $13,613,187
Emp.: 100
Industrial Plant Construction
N.A.I.C.S.: 237990
Charles A. Hays *(Chm)*
Jonathan Taylor *(Asst Dir-Safety)*

SYSTEMS DEPOT
1510 Tate Blvd SE, Hickory, NC 28602
Tel.: (828) 397-2172
Web Site: http://www.sdepot.com
Sales Range: $10-24.9 Million
Emp.: 60
Security Control Equipment & Systems
N.A.I.C.S.: 423690
Brent Weldy *(CFO)*

SYSTEMS DESIGN ENGINEERING, INC. (SDE)

SYSTEMS MACHINE AUTOMATION COMPONENTS

1032 James Dr, Leesport, PA 19533
Tel.: (610) 916-8500
Web Site: http://www.sdei.net
Year Founded: 1988
Sales Range: $1-9.9 Million
Emp.: 43
Engineering, Surveying & Land Planning Services
N.A.I.C.S.: 541330
Thomas S. Unger *(Principal)*
Keith R. Showalter *(Project Mgr & Asst VP)*
Kevin M. Mohn *(Sr Project Mgr)*
Gregory T. Unger *(Principal)*
Michael G. Pohronezny Jr. *(Pres)*

SYSTEMS ENGINEERING SERVICES
11921 Freedom Dr Ste 550, Reston, VA 20190
Tel.: (703) 716-0200
Web Site: http://www.sesc.com
Sales Range: $10-24.9 Million
Emp.: 70
Computer Related Consulting Services
N.A.I.C.S.: 541512
Jeffrey H. Lutman *(Pres)*
Daniel Rodenas *(CFO)*

SYSTEMS FINANCE GROUP INC.
2655 S Le Jeune Rd No 527, Coral Gables, FL 33134
Tel.: (305) 461-1952
Sales Range: $10-24.9 Million
Emp.: 2
Financial Services
N.A.I.C.S.: 561499
James C. Hutson-Wiley *(Pres)*

SYSTEMS HARDWARE INC.
17011 Green Dr Ste A, City of Industry, CA 91745
Tel.: (626) 935-0050
Web Site: http://www.maxgroup.com
Year Founded: 1994
Rev.: $43,909,883
Emp.: 17
Computers, Peripherals & Software
N.A.I.C.S.: 423430
Sue Tsai *(Pres)*

SYSTEMS INTEGRATION AND DEVELOPMENT, INC.
9900 Belward Campus Dr Ste 200, Rockville, MD 20850
Tel.: (301) 840-2120
Web Site: http://www.sidonline.com
Year Founded: 1991
Rev.: $11,300,000
Emp.: 140
Computer Programming Services
N.A.I.C.S.: 541511
Ajay K. Agrawal *(Pres)*
Susan Phillips *(Gen Mgr-HR)*
Ezinne Amaonwu *(Editor-Production Support)*

SYSTEMS INTEGRATION SOLUTIONS INC.
1255 Treat Blvd Ste 100, Walnut Creek, CA 94597
Tel.: (925) 465-7400
Web Site: http://www.sisinc.com
Year Founded: 1990
Sales Range: $10-24.9 Million
Emp.: 35
Computer Related Services
N.A.I.C.S.: 541512
Jerry Heath *(Pres)*
Peter Ling *(CEO)*

SYSTEMS MACHINE AUTOMATION COMPONENTS

SYSTEMS MACHINE AUTOMATION COMPONENTS

Systems Machine Automation Components—(Continued)
5807 Van Allen Way, Carlsbad, CA 92008
Tel.: (760) 929-7575
Web Site: http://www.smac-mca.com
Sales Range: $10-24.9 Million
Emp.: 100
Synthetic Rubber
N.A.I.C.S.: 335314
Edward A. Neff (CEO)

SYSTEMS MANAGEMENT PLANNING, INC. (SMP)
1020 John St, Rochester, NY 14623
Tel.: (585) 475-0670
Web Site: http://www.smp-corp.com
Year Founded: 1997
Sales Range: $25-49.9 Million
Emp.: 40
Computer Hardware & Software Reseller
N.A.I.C.S.: 423430
Kristin Rorapaugh (CEO)
Brian Lawrence (Acct Mgr-Natl)
Peter Allen (COO)
Mike Keller (District Mgr)

SYSTEMS PRODUCTS AND SOLUTIONS, INC.
307 Wynn Dr, Huntsville, AL 35805
Tel.: (256) 319-2135
Web Site: http://www.services-sps.com
Sales Range: $10-24.9 Million
Emp.: 97
Mission Support Services
N.A.I.C.S.: 524114
Nilmini Thompson (CEO)

SYSTEMS SOURCE, INC.
3161 Michelson Dr Ste 110, Irvine, CA 92612
Tel.: (949) 852-0920
Web Site: http://www.systemsource.com
Year Founded: 1982
Sales Range: $50-74.9 Million
Emp.: 80
Retailer of Office Furniture
N.A.I.C.S.: 423210
Mimi Anderson (Mgr-Acct)
Betsy Brown (Mgr-Mktg)
Margaret Hall (Mgr-Acct)
Yvette Peschelt (Acct Mgr)
Sherri Manjou (Mgr-Acct)
Rosemarie Smith (Pres & CEO)
Laura Reyes (Controller)
Liz Hatch (Supvr-Acct)

SYSTEMS SPECIALTIES COMPANY
390 Enterprise Ct, Bloomfield Hills, MI 48302
Tel.: (248) 332-0099
Web Site: http://www.sysspec.com
Sales Range: $10-24.9 Million
Emp.: 10
Provider of Industrial Machinery & Equipment
N.A.I.C.S.: 423830
Gary Cirillo (Mgr-Pur)

SYSTEMS TECHNOLOGY ASSOCIATES INC.
3002 Dow Ave Ste 126, Tustin, CA 92780
Tel.: (714) 734-1340
Web Site: http://www.staweb.com
Sales Range: $10-24.9 Million
Emp.: 40
IT Consulting Services
N.A.I.C.S.: 541512
Simon Palmer (Pres)

SYSTEMS TECHNOLOGY GROUP, INC.
3155 W Big Beaver Rd Ste 220, Troy, MI 48084
Tel.: (248) 643-9010
Web Site: http://www.stgit.com
Year Founded: 1985
Sales Range: $25-49.9 Million
Emp.: 395
IT Consulting Services
N.A.I.C.S.: 541519
Anup Popat (CEO)
Brenda Gorney (Mgr-HR)

SYSTEMS TECHNOLOGY, INC.
1350 E Riverview Dr, San Bernardino, CA 92408-2945
Tel.: (909) 799-9950 DE
Web Site: http://www.systems-technology-inc.com
Year Founded: 2000
Sales Range: $10-24.9 Million
Emp.: 25
Packaging Machinery Mfr
N.A.I.C.S.: 333993
John St. John (Pres)

SYSTEMWARE, INC.
15301 Dallas Pkwy Ste 1100, Addison, TX 75001
Tel.: (972) 239-0200 TX
Web Site: http://www.systemware.com
Year Founded: 1981
Sales Range: $10-24.9 Million
Emp.: 85
Provider of Computer Software Development Services
N.A.I.C.S.: 541511
David J. Basso (VP-Sls & Mktg)
Michael R. Vander Linden (Co-Founder & CTO)
Frankie A. Basso (Pres & COO)
Ronald D. Denheyer (CFO & VP-Fin & Admin)
Steven A. Carrillo (VP-Support)
Patrick M. Sheehan (VP-Dev)
Dan Basso (Co-Founder & CEO)

SYSTEST LABORATORIES INC.
216 16th St Ste 700, Denver, CO 80202
Tel.: (303) 575-6881 CO
Web Site: http://www.sliglobalsolutions.com
Year Founded: 1996
Sales Range: $10-24.9 Million
Emp.: 85
Consulting, Testing & Quality Assurance Services
N.A.I.C.S.: 541380
Mark Phillips (VP-Compliance Svcs)

SYSTM BRANDS, LLC
3419 Via Lido Syuite 365, Newport Beach, CA 92663
Tel.: (415) 235-2335
Web Site: https://www.systm.com
Investment Services
N.A.I.C.S.: 523999
Andy Fathollahi (CEO)

Subsidiaries:

SYSTM Foods Inc. (1)
3419 Via Lido Syuite 365, Newport Beach, CA 92663
Tel.: (415) 235-2335
Web Site: https://www.systmfoods.com
Food & Beverage Services
N.A.I.C.S.: 722310

Subsidiary (Domestic):

Humm Kombucha, LLC (2)
1125 NE 2nd St, Bend, OR 97701
Tel.: (541) 306-6329
Web Site: http://www.hummkombucha.com

Sales Range: $1-9.9 Million
Green Tea Distr
N.A.I.C.S.: 424490

SYSTRONICS INC.
Calle Federico Costas 40 Urb Tres Monjitas, Hato Rey, PR 00918
Tel.: (787) 758-6800
Web Site: http://www.systronics-pr.com
Year Founded: 1978
Rev.: $17,000,000
Emp.: 90
Computer & Software Stores
N.A.I.C.S.: 449210
Eulogio Villena (Pres)

Subsidiaries:

Systronics Depot (1)
Urbanisacion Tres Monjitas No 40, Hato Rey, PR 00918 (100%)
Tel.: (787) 754-2888
Sales Range: $25-49.9 Million
Supplier of Electronics
N.A.I.C.S.: 449210
Eulogio Villena (Owner)

SYVANTIS TECHNOLOGIES, INC.
13822 Bluestem Ct, Baxter, MN 56425
Tel.: (218) 828-9550 MN
Web Site: http://www.syvantis.com
Year Founded: 2000
Computer Integrated Systems Design Services
N.A.I.C.S.: 541512
Janelle Riley (Co-Owner & CEO)

SYVERSON TILE INC.
4015 SW Ave, Sioux Falls, SD 57105
Tel.: (605) 336-1175
Web Site: http://www.syversontile.com
Sales Range: $10-24.9 Million
Emp.: 80
Ceramic Tile Mfr
N.A.I.C.S.: 423320
Maureen Flynn (Office Mgr)
Steve Syverson (Pres & Gen Mgr)
Dave Syverson (VP)

SZANCA SOLUTIONS, INC.
100 E Pitt St Ste 300, Bedford, PA 15532
Tel.: (814) 624-0123
Web Site: http://www.szanca.com
Year Founded: 2002
Sales Range: $1-9.9 Million
Emp.: 50
Professional Services & Solutions to Government & Commercial Sectors
N.A.I.C.S.: 561311
Mark Szanca (Pres & CEO)
Lorri Black (Mgr-HR)

SZOTT M-59 CHRYSLER JEEP
6700 Highland Rd, White Lake, MI 48383
Tel.: (248) 889-8989
Web Site: http://www.szottm59chryslerjeep.com
Year Founded: 1955
Sales Range: $10-24.9 Million
Emp.: 55
New Car Dealers
N.A.I.C.S.: 441110
Eric Mann (Mgr-Sls-New Vehicle)
Andy Haller (Mgr-Fin)
Larry Flowers (Mgr-Leasing & Internet Sls)
Tom Quinn (Mgr-Lease Retention)
Jeff Schneider (Mgr-Gen Sls)
Terry Kaufman (Mgr-Sls-New Vehicle)

T & B TUBE COMPANY
15525 S LaSalle St, South Holland, IL 60473
Tel.: (708) 333-1282
Web Site: http://www.tbtube.com
Year Founded: 1982
Sales Range: $10-24.9 Million
Emp.: 65
Iron Steel Pipe & Tube Mfr
N.A.I.C.S.: 331211
Jack Jones (Pres)
Kevin Barker (Mgr-Ops)

T & C CONTRACTING INC.
6301 Pendleton Rd, Valley Station, KY 40272
Tel.: (502) 937-3433
Sales Range: $10-24.9 Million
Emp.: 150
Water & Sewer Line & Related Structures Construction Services
N.A.I.C.S.: 237110
Scott Hayes (Principal)
Scott Thornberry (Gen Mgr)

T & D CONCRETE INC.
1969 County Rd 228, Wildwood, FL 34785
Tel.: (352) 748-2111
Year Founded: 1981
Sales Range: $10-24.9 Million
Emp.: 440
Fence Installation Services
N.A.I.C.S.: 238990
Terry Yoder (Pres)
Glendora Yoder (VP)

T & E CATTLE COMPANY
4444 W 13th St, Grand Island, NE 68803-2815
Tel.: (308) 384-1981
Web Site: http://www.tecattle.com
Year Founded: 1935
Sales Range: $10-24.9 Million
Emp.: 22
Cattle Feedlot Services
N.A.I.C.S.: 112112
Greg Baxter (Owner & Mgr)

T & M ASPHALT PAVING
4755 Old Plank Rd, Milford, MI 48381
Tel.: (248) 684-2300
Web Site: http://www.tmasphalt.com
Year Founded: 1971
Sales Range: $10-24.9 Million
Emp.: 200
Land Subdividing Services
N.A.I.C.S.: 237210
Darryl Fegan (Pres)

T & N, INC.
815 Hwy T, Foristell, MO 63348
Tel.: (636) 673-2505
Web Site: http://www.tandninc.com
Year Founded: 1988
Sales Range: $10-24.9 Million
Emp.: 18
Chemical Products Mfr
N.A.I.C.S.: 325998
Mark Stephens (CEO)
Kurt Ehlert (Mgr-Feed Mill)
Sarah Huck (Mgr-Credit & Adv)
Mike Tribley (Mgr-Production)
Lenny Brown (VP-Sls & Mktg)
Erin Stephens (Acct Exec)
Kris Floth (Acct Exec)
Kevin Stephens (Acct Exec)

T DISTRIBUTION
1880 Oakcrest Ave, Saint Paul, MN 55113
Tel.: (651) 636-6367 MN
Web Site: http://www.artresourcesgallery.com
Year Founded: 2004
Sales Range: $10-24.9 Million
Emp.: 60

COMPANIES

Frames & Framing, Picture & Mirror
N.A.I.C.S.: 423220
Richard Thompson (CEO)
Richard Thompson (Pres & CEO)

T ENTERPRISES, INC.
5105 E 41st Ave, Denver, CO 80216
Tel.: (888) 403-5980
Web Site: https://1-vision.com
Emp.: 100
Printing & marketing Solutions
N.A.I.C.S.: 323113
Allen Taheri (Pres & CEO)

Subsidiaries:

Preferred Marketing Solutions, Inc. (1)
2002 Papa Johns Blvd, Louisville, KY 40299-3393
Tel.: (502) 261-2766
Web Site: http://www.preferredms.com
Food Service Contractors
N.A.I.C.S.: 722310

T H AGRI-CHEMICALS, INC.
617 E North St, Plainfield, WI 54966
Tel.: (715) 335-6343   WI
Web Site:
https://www.thagrichemicals.com
Year Founded: 1982
Sales Range: $10-24.9 Million
Emp.: 30
Farming Supplies Whslr
N.A.I.C.S.: 424910
Robert L. Zimpel (Pres)

T R FOODS, INC.
1290 Arrowhead Ct Ste B, Crown Point, IN 46307
Tel.: (219) 769-6850
Year Founded: 1979
Sales Range: $10-24.9 Million
Emp.: 317
Restaurant Operating Services
N.A.I.C.S.: 722511
Brenda Bane (Gen Mgr)

T STATS SUPPLY INC.
3931 Penn Belt Pl, Forestville, MD 20747
Tel.: (301) 420-7300
Web Site:
http://www.tstatssupply.com
Sales Range: $10-24.9 Million
Emp.: 12
Electrical Apparatus & Equipment
N.A.I.C.S.: 423610
Bob Ryerson (Gen Mgr)

T T BARGE SERVICES MILE 237, LLC.
7324 LA-405, Donaldsonville, LA 70346
Tel.: (225) 473-8222
Other Support Activities for Water Transportation
N.A.I.C.S.: 488390
Mark Toepfer (Pres)

T&A INDUSTRIAL LTD
12550 Robin Ln, Brookfield, WI 53005
Tel.: (262) 783-4900
Web Site: http://www.tainindustrial.com
Sales Range: $10-24.9 Million
Emp.: 50
Industrial Supplies
N.A.I.C.S.: 423840
James Ketter (Pres)
Tim Turay (Mgr-Receivable)

T&A SUPPLY CO. INC.
7113 216th St, Kent, WA 98032
Tel.: (206) 282-3770
Web Site: http://www.tasupply.com
Rev.: $60,000,000
Emp.: 84

Floor Coverings
N.A.I.C.S.: 423220
Owen Strecker (Owner)

T&C HOLDING LTD
99-1295 Waiua Pl Ste 2A, Aiea, HI 96701
Tel.: (808) 483-8383
Web Site: http://www.tt.com
Rev.: $20,600,000
Emp.: 5
Clothing, Sportswear, Men's & Boys'
N.A.I.C.S.: 458110
Craig H. Sugihara (Pres)

Subsidiaries:

T&C Surf Designs (1)
99-1295 Waiua Pl Unit 2A, Aiea, HI 96701
Tel.: (808) 483-8383
Web Site: http://www.tcsurf.com
Sales Range: $10-24.9 Million
Surfboard Mfr
N.A.I.C.S.: 339920
Craig H. Sugihara (Founder)
Ryan Sugihara (Pres)

Town & Country Surf Shop Inc. (1)
99-1295 Waiua Pl Unit 2a, Aiea, HI 96701
Tel.: (808) 483-8383
Web Site: http://www.tcsurf.com
Sales Range: $25-49.9 Million
Sportswear, Men's & Boys'
N.A.I.C.S.: 458110
Craig H. Sugihara (Pres)

T&C MARKETS IRON MOUNTAIN INC.
1600 S Stephenson, Iron Mountain, MI 49801
Tel.: (906) 774-1911
Web Site:
http://www.tadychseconofoods.com
Year Founded: 1968
Grocery Stores
N.A.I.C.S.: 445110
James Tadych (Founder & Owner)

T&C STAMPING INC.
1403 Freeman Dr, Athens, AL 35613
Tel.: (256) 233-7383
Web Site:
http://www.tandcstamping.com
Year Founded: 1985
Sales Range: $10-24.9 Million
Emp.: 65
Stampings & Related Assemblies
N.A.I.C.S.: 332119
David Hanserd (Dir-Mktg & Sls)
Bill Beam (Engr-Tooling Design)
Will Speed (Plant Mgr)
Leah Stephens (VP & Mgr-HR)

T&D METAL PRODUCTS LLC
602 E Walnut St, Watseka, IL 60970-1459
Tel.: (815) 432-4938
Web Site: http://www.tdmetal.com
Year Founded: 1996
Sales Range: $10-24.9 Million
Emp.: 109
Partitions & Fixtures Mfr
N.A.I.C.S.: 337126
Shane Dittrich (Owner)
Gerald Adams (Plant Mgr)

T&E OIL COMPANY INC.
911 N Halstead St, Hutchinson, KS 67501-2008
Tel.: (620) 663-3777   KS
Year Founded: 1979
Sales Range: $10-24.9 Million
Emp.: 57
Gasoline Service Stations
N.A.I.C.S.: 457120

T&G CORPORATION
8623 Commodity Cir, Orlando, FL 32819

Tel.: (407) 352-4443
Web Site: http://www.t-and-g.com
Year Founded: 1987
Sales Range: $10-24.9 Million
Emp.: 60
Commercial & Office Building, New Construction & Renovation
N.A.I.C.S.: 236220
Mike Wright (CFO)

T&G INDUSTRIES INC.
120 3rd St, Brooklyn, NY 11231
Tel.: (718) 237-0060
Web Site: http://www.tgioa.com
Year Founded: 1964
Sales Range: $10-24.9 Million
Emp.: 120
Business Machines & Equipment
N.A.I.C.S.: 459999
Steve Adler (Pres)

T&J RESTAURANTS LLC
940 Hemsath Rd, Saint Charles, MO 63303
Tel.: (636) 946-6000
Web Site: http://www.chevys.com
Rev.: $15,800,000
Emp.: 8
Eating Place
N.A.I.C.S.: 722511
John Whicker (Pres)

T&K FOODS INC.
13735 Round Lk Blvd, Andover, MN 55304-2083
Tel.: (763) 422-1768   MN
Web Site:
http://www.kingscountymarket.com
Year Founded: 1972
Sales Range: $25-49.9 Million
Emp.: 300
Grocery Stores
N.A.I.C.S.: 445110
Robert King (Pres & CEO)
John Thomas (Mgr-Store Ops)

T&K MECHANICAL INC.
25500 Hawthorne Blvd No 1000, Torrance, CA 90505
Tel.: (310) 373-3320
Web Site: http://www.secmet.com
Rev.: $33,800,000
Emp.: 200
Heavy Construction
N.A.I.C.S.: 236220
Kalayil M. Chacko (Pres)

T&L DISTRIBUTING COMPANY INC.
7350 Langfield Rd, Houston, TX 77092
Tel.: (713) 461-7802   TX
Web Site:
http://www.tldistributing.com
Year Founded: 1964
Sales Range: $25-49.9 Million
Emp.: 100
Homefurnishings
N.A.I.C.S.: 423220
Bob Eady (Pres)

T&M ASSOCIATES
Eleven Tindall Rd, Middletown, NJ 07748
Tel.: (732) 671-6400
Web Site:
http://www.tandmassociates.com
Year Founded: 2010
Sales Range: $1-9.9 Million
Emp.: 59
Transportation, Civil, Environmental, Energy & Structural Engineering
N.A.I.C.S.: 237990
Gary C. Dahms (Pres & CEO)
Michael Roeder (COO & Exec VP)

T&M ASSOCIATES

James Valenti (Sr VP & Chief Legal Officer)
Michael Dentici (CFO & Sr VP)
Ihsan Al-Fayyomi (Sr VP, Reg Mgr-Ops & Asst Sec)

Subsidiaries:

T&M Associates (1)
1144 Hooper Ave Ste 202, Toms River, NJ 08753   (100%)
Tel.: (732) 473-3400
Web Site: http://www.tandmassociates.com
Transportation & Structural Engineering Services
N.A.I.C.S.: 237990
Donato DiZuzio (Sr VP-Transportation Bus Unit)
Violet Koehler (CFO & Sr VP)
Keith Lieberman (Sr VP & Reg Mgr-Ops)
Francis Mullan (Sr VP & Mgr-Ops)
Michael Regan (Sec, Sr VP & Mgr-Ops)
John Walsh (Sr VP)

T&M Associates (1)
1455 Broad St Ste 250, Bloomfield, NJ 07003   (100%)
Tel.: (973) 614-0005
Web Site: http://www.tandmassociates.com
Emp.: 12
Structural, Civil & Structural Engineering Services
N.A.I.C.S.: 237990
Lynn Spence (Sr VP, Dir-HR & Asst Treas)

T&M Associates (1)
525 Plymouth Rd Suite 315, Plymouth Meeting, PA 19462   (100%)
Tel.: (484) 530-1270
Web Site: http://www.tandmassociates.com
Environmental, Energy & Civil Engineering Services
N.A.I.C.S.: 237990
Michael Mandzik (Dir-Energy Procurement)

T&M Associates (1)
188 Lincoln Hwy Ste 206, Fairless Hills, PA 19030   (100%)
Tel.: (215) 486-5770
Web Site: http://www.tandmassociates.com
Emp.: 10
Civil, Transportation & Structural Engineering Services
N.A.I.C.S.: 237990
Lynn Spence (Dir-HR)
Evan J. Stone (Grp Mgr)

T&M Associates (1)
74 W Broad St Ste 230, Bethlehem, PA 18018   (100%)
Tel.: (610) 625-2999
Web Site: http://www.tandmassociates.com
Civil, Structural, Energy & Environmental Engineering Services
N.A.I.C.S.: 237990
Daniel Swayze (Sr VP-Energy & Utilities)

T&M Associates (1)
1853 William Penn Way, Lancaster, PA 17601   (100%)
Tel.: (717) 735-3979
Web Site: http://www.tandmassociates.com
Transportation, Civil & Structural Engineering Services
N.A.I.C.S.: 237990
Gary Dahms (Pres & CEO)
Ihsan Al-Fayyomi (Treas, Sr VP & Mgr-Reg Ops)
Violet Koehler (CFO & Sr VP)
Keith Lieberman (Sr VP, Mgr-Reg Ops & Asst Sec)
Francis Mullan (Sr VP, Mgr-Ops & Asst Sec)
Michael Regan (Sec, Sr VP & Mgr-Ops)
Lynn Spence (Sr VP, Dir-HR & Asst Treas)

T&M Associates (1)
2523 Pennsylvania Ave Ste 102, Sayre, PA 18840   (100%)
Tel.: (570) 886-2213
Web Site: http://www.tandmassociates.com
Civil Structural Energy & Environmental Engineering Services
N.A.I.C.S.: 541330
Violet Koehler (CFO & Sr VP)

T&M Associates (1)
300 E Business Way Ste 200, Cincinnati, OH 45241   (100%)

T&M ASSOCIATES

T&M Associates—(Continued)
Tel.: (513) 247-6120
Web Site: http://www.tandmassociates.com
Structural, Civil & Energy Engineering Services
N.A.I.C.S.: 237990
Violet Koehler (CFO & Sr VP)
Keith Lieberman (Sr VP, Reg Mgr-Ops & Asst Sec)
Francis Mullan (Sr VP, Mgr-Ops & Asst Sec)
Michael Regan (Sec, Sr VP & Mgr-Ops)
John Walsh (Sr VP)

T&M Associates (1)
1000 N W St Suite 1203, Wilmington, DE 19801 (100%)
Tel.: (302) 295-4925
Web Site: http://www.tandmassociates.com
Civil, Structural & Energy Services
N.A.I.C.S.: 237990
Doug Barry (Group Mgr)

T&M Associates (1)
10200 Forest Green Blvd Ste 112, Louisville, KY 40223
Tel.: (502) 214-6243
Web Site: http://www.tandmassociates.com
Civil, Transportation & Structural Engineering Services
N.A.I.C.S.: 237990
Thomas Tri (Principal Engr)
Chris Jaquet (Mgr-Grp)

T&M Associates - Columbus (1)
4675 Lakehurst Ct Ste 250, Columbus, OH 43016
Tel.: (614) 339-3380
Web Site: http://www.tandmassociates.com
Civil & Structural Engineering Services
N.A.I.C.S.: 237990

T&M Associates - Moorestown (1)
1256 N Church St, Moorestown, NJ 08057
Tel.: (856) 722-6700
Web Site: http://www.tandmassociates.com
Civil & Structural Engineering Services
N.A.I.C.S.: 237990
Richard Moralle (Sr VP)

T&N ASPHALT SERVICES, INC.
3643 S 700 W Ste C, Salt Lake City, UT 84119-4181
Tel.: (801) 266-1626
Web Site: http://www.tnasphaltservices.com
Sales Range: $100-124.9 Million
Emp.: 5
Highway & Street Construction Services
N.A.I.C.S.: 237310
Nick Howell (Owner)

T&R ELECTRIC SUPPLY COMPANY, INC.
308 SW 3rd St, Colman, SD 57017
Tel.: (605) 534-3555
Web Site: http://www.t-r.com
Sales Range: $125-149.9 Million
Emp.: 140
Whslr of New & Used Electrical Equipment & Line Materials
N.A.I.C.S.: 423610
James R. Thompson (Pres)
Janice Ross (Treas)

T&R MARKET INC.
N US 491, Gallup, NM 87301
Tel.: (505) 722-4366
Web Site: http://www.t-rmarket.com
Sales Range: $10-24.9 Million
Emp.: 100
Grocery Stores
N.A.I.C.S.: 445110
Colin Tanner (Pres)
Racheal Bowling (Dir-Ops)
Oliver Barlow (Controller)
Shannon Tanner (Owner)

T&S BRASS & BRONZE WORKS, INC.
2 Saddleback Cove, Travelers Rest, SC 29690-2232
Tel.: (864) 834-4102
Web Site: http://www.tsbrass.com
Year Founded: 1947
Sales Range: $75-99.9 Million
Emp.: 250
Plumbing Products; Faucets, Valves & Fittings for Commercial, Industrial & Institutional Projects
N.A.I.C.S.: 332913
Bill Stella (Dir-Sls-Intl)
Julia Xu (Mgr-Sls & Mktg-Greater China)

Subsidiaries:

EnviroPure Systems, Inc. (1)
50 Saddleback Cove, Travelers Rest, SC 29690
Web Site: http://www.enviropuresystems.com
Environmental Consulting Services
N.A.I.C.S.: 541620

T&S PERFECTION CHAIN PRODUCTS, INC.
301 Goodwin Rd, Cullman, AL 35058
Tel.: (256) 734-6538
Web Site: http://www.tsperfection.com
Year Founded: 1848
Weldless & Welded Chain Mfr
N.A.I.C.S.: 332618
Don Zimomra (Pres)
Lee Holder (Controller)

T&S PRODUCTS INC.
525 Duncan Perry Rd, Arlington, TX 76011
Tel.: (817) 633-4600
Web Site: http://www.tandsproducts.com
Year Founded: 1986
Sales Range: $10-24.9 Million
Emp.: 50
Mfr of Paper Tubes & Cores
N.A.I.C.S.: 322219
Tom Stewart (Pres)
Jody Collier (VP)

T&S TRUCKING COMPANY
333 N James St, Kansas City, KS 66118
Tel.: (913) 371-6500
Sales Range: $10-24.9 Million
General Freight Trucking
N.A.I.C.S.: 484110
Howard Henselle (VP-Sls)
Brenda Miller (CTO)

T&T COMPUTERS, INC.
11254 W Hillsborough Ave, Tampa, FL 33635
Tel.: (813) 855-9501
Web Site: http://www.t-t-computers.com
Year Founded: 1994
Sales Range: $1-9.9 Million
Emp.: 25
Software Publisher & Computer Equipment Distr
N.A.I.C.S.: 513210
Hiep Tang (Pres)

T&T FOODS INC.
1060 North Rose Hill Rd, Rose Hill, KS 67133
Tel.: (316) 776-2014
Sales Range: $10-24.9 Million
Emp.: 300
Grocery Stores, Independent
N.A.I.C.S.: 445110
Tim Voegeli (Pres)

T&T MOTORS INC.
4195 S Hwy 27, Somerset, KY 42503
Tel.: (606) 679-1601
Web Site: http://www.toyotaofsomerset.com
Sales Range: $10-24.9 Million
Emp.: 35
New & Used Car Dealers
N.A.I.C.S.: 441110
Larry Turpen (Pres)
Lorrie Walllace (Office Mgr)

T&T SOLUTIONS, INC.
7018 Owensmouth Ave Ste 201, Canoga Park, CA 91303-4240
Tel.: (818) 676-1786
Year Founded: 2001
Sales Range: $1-9.9 Million
Emp.: 65
Technical Management & Staffing Support
N.A.I.C.S.: 541990
Sarvath Gowhar (CEO)

T&T TRUCKING INCORPORATED
11396 N Hwy 99, Lodi, CA 95240
Tel.: (209) 931-6000
Web Site: http://www.tttrucking.com
Year Founded: 1956
Sales Range: $10-24.9 Million
Emp.: 200
Provider of Transportation Services
N.A.I.C.S.: 484121
Terry Tarditi (Owner & Pres)
George Watson (Dir-Maintenance)
Christy Tarditi (CFO & Controller)

T&W OF KNOXVILLE INC.
10415 Parkside Dr, Knoxville, TN 37922
Tel.: (865) 218-3300
Web Site: http://www.toyotaknoxville.com
Sales Range: $25-49.9 Million
Emp.: 285
Automobiles; New & Used
N.A.I.C.S.: 441110
Doug White (VP)
Lila Downs (Controller)

T&W SALES INC.
13592 Stemmons Fwy, Dallas, TX 75244
Tel.: (972) 243-3265
Web Site: http://www.tandwsales.com
Sales Range: $10-24.9 Million
Emp.: 28
Motor Vehicle Audio Visual Equipment
N.A.I.C.S.: 423620
Brian Barcherding (Mgr-Sls)

T&W TIRE COMPANY
25 N Council Rd, Oklahoma City, OK 73127
Tel.: (405) 787-6711
Web Site: http://www.tandwtire.com
Rev: $41,000,000
Emp.: 60
Automotive Tires
N.A.I.C.S.: 441340
Ryan Woodard (Mgr)
Blair Homer (Mgr-Outside Sls)
Darrin Newfield (Mgr)
Jeff Jones (Mgr-Inventory)

T-C DISTRIBUTION COMPANY
849 Honeyspot Rd, Stratford, CT 06615
Tel.: (203) 377-8955
Sales Range: $10-24.9 Million
Emp.: 14
Groceries, General Line
N.A.I.C.S.: 424410
Ernest C. Trefz (Pres)
Bob Kowelski (Mgr-Ops)

T-C OIL COMPANY INC.
1 O'Connor Plz Ste 1100, Victoria, TX 77901-6549
Tel.: (361) 526-4693
Web Site: http://www.tcoil.net
Year Founded: 1971
Sales Range: $10-24.9 Million
Emp.: 16
Producer of Oil & Gas
N.A.I.C.S.: 561110
Robert Hewitt (Owner)

T-CELLULAR, INC.
407 N Howard Ave, Tampa, FL 33606
Year Founded: 2001
Sales Range: $25-49.9 Million
Emp.: 230
Cellular Phone Retailer
N.A.I.C.S.: 517112

T-FORCE GROUP
8831 Research Dr Ste 200, Irvine, CA 92618
Web Site: http://www.t-force.com
Year Founded: 2004
Sales Range: $25-49.9 Million
Emp.: 314
Telecommunications Strategy & Consulting
N.A.I.C.S.: 541618
Raid Khawaldeh (Pres)

T-H MARINE SUPPLIES INC.
200 Finney Dr, Huntsville, AL 35824
Tel.: (256) 772-0164
Web Site: http://www.thmarinesupplies.com
Year Founded: 1975
Sales Range: $10-24.9 Million
Emp.: 50
Boat Accessories Mfr & Whslr
N.A.I.C.S.: 332510
Derek Trovillion (Dir-Digital Mktg)
Gene Eisenmann (Dir-Mktg)
Jeff Huntley Sr. (CEO)

Subsidiaries:

CMC Marine, Inc. (1)
3920 S 13th St, Duncan, OK 73533-9069
Tel.: (580) 252-1699
Web Site: http://www.cmcmarineproducts.com
Marine Hydraulic Actuators & Other Related Products Mfr
N.A.I.C.S.: 333995
Greg Cook (COO)
Rick Presley (Exec VP-Sls & Mktg)
Debbie Cook (Controller)
Jeff Huntley (Pres & CEO)
Eric Cook (VP-Gen Ops)
Del Harvey (Plant Mgr)
Malea Miller (Asst VP)
Federico Fiocchini (Mgr-Sls & Mktg)
Travis Christian (Supvr-Machine Shop)
Tyler Whetstone (Supvr-Machine Shop)

YakGear, Inc. (1)
4000 Airline Dr Ste C, Houston, TX 77022
Tel.: (866) 610-7931
Web Site: http://www.yak-gear.com
Sales Range: $1-9.9 Million
Sports Equipment Whslr
N.A.I.C.S.: 423910
Myles Bragman (Mgr-Pur & Fin)

T-L IRRIGATION CO.
151 East Hwy 6 & AB Rd, Hastings, NE 68901
Tel.: (402) 462-4128
Web Site: http://www.tlirr.com
Sales Range: $50-74.9 Million
Emp.: 225
Fertilizing, Spraying, Dusting & Irrigation Equipment
N.A.I.C.S.: 333111
Le Roy W. Thom (Pres)
Dave Thom (VP-Sls)
Jim Thom (VP-Fin)

T-REX SOLUTIONS, LLC

7501 Greenway Ctr Dr, Greenbelt, MD 20770
Tel.: (703) 742-0566
Web Site: http://www.trexsolutionsllc.com
Computer System Design Services
N.A.I.C.S.: 541512
Trevor Wilby (Pres)
Amy Miller Feehery (Dir-Bus Dev)
Cathy Lerche (Chief People Officer)
Leslie Hubbard-Darr (Exec VP-Natl Security)
Dab Kern (Exec VP-Natl Security)
Subsidiaries:
Cyber Cloud Technologies, LLC (1)
6605 Meadowfield Ct, Elkridge, MD 21075-6880
Tel.: (410) 480-7196
Web Site: http://www.cyber-cloud.com
Engineeering Services
N.A.I.C.S.: 541330
Frank Kippenbrock (Pres & CEO)

ZOT, Inc. (1)
6731 Columbia Gateway Dr Ste 110, Columbia, MD 21046-2263
Tel.: (410) 953-6336
Web Site: http://www.zot.com
Computer System Design Services
N.A.I.C.S.: 541512
Michael McNeil (Owner)

T-SHIRT INTERNATIONAL INC.
2101 Grace St, Culloden, WV 25510
Tel.: (304) 743-7905
Web Site: http://www.tsisportswear.com
Rev.: $11,700,000
Emp.: 140
Screen Printing & Embroidery on Cotton Broadwoven Fabrics
N.A.I.C.S.: 313310
Dennis Thornburg (CEO)
Bob Slaw (VP-Sourcing)

T-STAFF, INC.
4343 Shallowford Rd C3B, Marietta, GA 30062
Tel.: (770) 552-7767
Web Site: http://www.t-staff.com
Sales Range: $10-24.9 Million
Emp.: 200
Provider of Temporary Help Services
N.A.I.C.S.: 561320
Bruce Astrom (Treas & VP)
Tammy Martin (CEO)
Jared Huller (Mgr-Ops)

T. ANTHONY LTD.
445 Park Ave, New York, NY 10022
Tel.: (212) 750-9797
Web Site: http://www.tanthony.com
Sales Range: $10-24.9 Million
Emp.: 35
Mfr & Retailer of Luggage & Leather Goods
N.A.I.C.S.: 458320
Karen Fee (Mgr-Corp Accts)
Michael Root (Pres)

T. BAIRD MCILVAIN CO.
100 Filbert St, Hanover, PA 17331
Tel.: (717) 630-0025
Web Site: http://www.tbmhardwoods.com
Rev.: $22,912,615
Emp.: 60
Lumber: Rough, Dressed & Finished
N.A.I.C.S.: 423310
Thomas B. McIlvain Jr. (Chm & Pres)

T. BROWN CONSTRUCTORS INC.
515 Rankin Rd NE PO Box 26508, Albuquerque, NM 87107
Tel.: (505) 345-9051
Web Site: http://www.tedbrown.net

Sales Range: $10-24.9 Million
Emp.: 44
Asphalt Mixture
N.A.I.C.S.: 423320
Ted F. Brown (Pres)
Tracy Madrid (Superintendent)

T. BRUCE SALES, INC.
9 Carbough St, West Middlesex, PA 16159
Tel.: (724) 528-9961   PA
Web Site: http://www.tbrucesales.com
Year Founded: 1964
Sales Range: $75-99.9 Million
Emp.: 80
Custom Steel Fabrication
N.A.I.C.S.: 332312
T. Scott Campbell (Pres)
Robert E. Campbell (Exec VP)
Bob Jackson (Office Mgr)

T. E. C. WELL SERVICE, INC.
851 W Harrison Rd, Longview, TX 75604-5208
Tel.: (903) 759-0082
Web Site: http://www.tecwell.com
Sales Range: $10-24.9 Million
Emp.: 140
Oil & Gas Operating Services
N.A.I.C.S.: 213112
Bill Beadles (Acct Mgr)
Stephen Shore (Pres & COO)
Kenneth Shore (VP)
David Etchelecu (Mgr-HSE & HR)
Terry Baker (Mgr-High Pressure Pump Truck Div)
Doug Swaim (Mgr-Personnel & Trucking)
Shawn Davenport (Mgr-Swab & Braided Line)
Ronald Shore (CEO)

T. GERDING CONSTRUCTION CO. (TGCC)
200 SW Airport Ave, Corvallis, OR 97333
Tel.: (541) 753-2012
Web Site: http://www.tgerding.com
Year Founded: 1968
Sales Range: $50-74.9 Million
Emp.: 70
Nonresidential Construction Services
N.A.I.C.S.: 236220
Nate Gerding (Pres)

T. JERULLE CONSTRUCTION, LLC
2640 Golden Gate Pkwy Ste 111, Naples, FL 34105
Tel.: (239) 213-1143
Web Site: http://www.tjflorida.com
Sales Range: $1-9.9 Million
Single & Multifamily Homes & Commercial Buildings Construction & Development
N.A.I.C.S.: 236115
Terrance Jerulle (Pres)
William Saccone (VP)
Michael Demerly (VP)
Rhonda Matury (Controller)

T. L. MONTGOMERY & ASSOCIATES
5100 Boyle Ave, Los Angeles, CA 90058
Tel.: (323) 583-1645
Rev.: $13,200,000
Emp.: 19
Pet Foods & Pharmaceutical Products Mfr
N.A.I.C.S.: 311111
Dana Montgomery (Pres)

T. M. COBB COMPANY

500 Palmyrita Ave, Riverside, CA 92507
Tel.: (951) 248-2440
Web Site: http://www.tmcobbco.com
Rev.: $23,800,000
Emp.: 23
Door Frames, Wood
N.A.I.C.S.: 321911
Marty Gibbons (Mgr-Sls)

T. M. INC.
200 Quality Way, Holly, MI 48442
Tel.: (810) 694-5763
Web Site: http://www.tmicustomair.com
Year Founded: 1982
Sales Range: $10-24.9 Million
Emp.: 130
Mfr of Air Handling Systems, Dust & Oil Mist Collectors & Target-Air Humidification Systems
N.A.I.C.S.: 484121

T.A. LOVING COMPANY
PO Drawer 919, Goldsboro, NC 27533-0919
Tel.: (919) 734-8400   NC
Web Site: http://www.taloving.com
Year Founded: 1926
Sales Range: $200-249.9 Million
Emp.: 360
Provider of Highway, Bridge & Utility Construction Services
N.A.I.C.S.: 237310
Samuel P. Hunter (Chm & CEO)
Al Grisette (CFO)
Michael Richter (Pres)
Steve Bryan (Vice Chm)
Ken Gerrard (VP-Bus Dev & Coord-Mktg)
Kelsey Hales (Coord-Mktg-Triangle)

T.A. PELSUE COMPANY
2500 S Tejon St, Englewood, CO 80110
Tel.: (303) 936-7432
Web Site: http://www.pelsue.com
Sales Range: $10-24.9 Million
Emp.: 60
Power Transformers, Electric
N.A.I.C.S.: 335311
Brad A. Pelsue (Owner & CEO)

T.A. SHEETS GENERAL CONTRACTORS, INC.
1128 Cooke Ave, Norfolk, VA 23504
Tel.: (757) 627-3000
Web Site: http://www.tasheetsinc.com
Year Founded: 1966
Sales Range: $25-49.9 Million
Emp.: 70
Plumbing, Heating & Air-Conditioning Contracting Services
N.A.I.C.S.: 238220
Frankie L. Bridgeman (Pres & CEO)
Hans De Jong (CFO & Sec)
Roland Liverman (Project Mgr)

T.A. SOLBERG CO., INC.
420 Oneida St, Minocqua, WI 54548
Tel.: (715) 356-7711   WI
Web Site: http://www.trigs.com
Year Founded: 1974
Sales Range: $100-124.9 Million
Emp.: 1,200
Grocery Stores
N.A.I.C.S.: 445110
Julie Enerson (Dir-Food Svc Ops)
Sandy Buss (Dir-Floral Ops)

T.C. JACOBY & COMPANY, INC.
1716 Hidden Creek Ct, Saint Louis, MO 63131
Tel.: (314) 821-4456   MO

Web Site: http://www.jacoby.com
Year Founded: 1948
Sales Range: $10-24.9 Million
Emp.: 30
Producer of Milk & Cheese Products
N.A.I.C.S.: 424430
Bob Fassbender (VP-Indus & Technical Affairs)
Keith Kirchoff (CFO)
Diane Floyd (Mgr-Acct-Cooperative)
Brianne Breed (Mgr-Cheese Sls)
Yara Morales (Mgr-Logistics-Intl)
Jeff Johnson (Mgr-Powder Sls)
Mayra Jara (Mgr-Sls & Traffic)
Ted J. Jacoby Jr. (Pres & CEO)
Ted Jacoby III (VP-Cheese Sls & Risk Mgmt)

T.D. WILLIAMSON, INC.
6120 S Yale Ave Ste 1700, Tulsa, OK 74136-4235
Tel.: (918) 447-5001   OK
Web Site: http://www.tdwilliamson.com
Year Founded: 1920
Sales Range: $150-199.9 Million
Emp.: 730
Engineered Pipeline Equipment & Plant Piping System Mfr
N.A.I.C.S.: 333132
Robert D. McGrew (CEO)
Subsidiaries:
T.D. Williamson Asia Pacific Pty Ltd. (1)
3 International Business Park Nordic European Centre, Singapore, 609927, Singapore
Tel.: (65) 63648520
Sales Range: $10-24.9 Million
Emp.: 40
Pipeline Equipment Distr
N.A.I.C.S.: 423830
Chee Wong (Gen Mgr)
Rolf Gunnar Lie (Reg Mgr-Bus Dev)

TDW Offshore Services (1)
Fabrikkveien 15, PO Box 8011, 4068, Stavanger, Norway
Tel.: (47) 51443240
Web Site: http://www.tdwilliamson.com
Sales Range: $10-24.9 Million
Emp.: 100
Pipeline Maintenance & Equipment Mfr
N.A.I.C.S.: 332996
Lawrence Ryan (Gen Mgr)

TDW Pigging Products (1)
10727 E 55th Pl, Tulsa, OK 74146-6702   (100%)
Tel.: (918) 447-5400
Web Site: http://www.tdwilliamson.com
Sales Range: $25-49.9 Million
Emp.: 50
Mfr of Urethane Products
N.A.I.C.S.: 333132

TDW Services, Inc. (1)
6801 S 65th W Ave, Tulsa, OK 74131-2424   (100%)
Tel.: (918) 446-1941
Web Site: http://www.tdwilliamson.com
Sales Range: $25-49.9 Million
Emp.: 75
Maintenance & Inspection of Pipeline & Plant Piping Systems; Corporate Management Office
N.A.I.C.S.: 213112

TDW, Inc. (1)
261 Quigley Blvd Ste 18, New Castle, DE 19720-4187
Tel.: (302) 594-9880
Web Site: http://www.tdwilliams.com
Sales Range: Less than $1 Million
Emp.: 13
Business Services
N.A.I.C.S.: 333132

Tulsa Manufacturing Plant (1)
6801 S 65th W Ave, Tulsa, OK 74131-2424   (100%)
Tel.: (918) 446-1941

T.D. WILLIAMSON, INC.

T.D. Williamson, Inc.—(Continued)
Sales Range: $50-74.9 Million
Emp.: 400
Mfr & Maintenance of Engineered Pipeline Equipment & Plant Piping Systems
N.A.I.C.S.: 333132

Williamson International Corp. (1)
5727 S Lewis Ste 300, Tulsa, OK 74105
Tel.: (918) 447-5000
Web Site: http://www.tdwilliamson.com
Sales Range: Less than $1 Million
Coordinator of International Activities
N.A.I.C.S.: 541611

T.F. COLLETTE COMPANIES, INC.
2445 Grand Ave, Vista, CA 92081
Tel.: (760) 407-6000   CA
Web Site: http://www.mpgproductions.com
Year Founded: 1989
Sales Range: $1-9.9 Million
Emp.: 18
Trade Show Production & Management Services
N.A.I.C.S.: 561920
Kathy Collette (VP)
Francis Collette (CEO)
David Eppolito (Mgr-Ops)

T.F. KURK INC.
78 Sawyer Ave, Tonawanda, NY 14150
Tel.: (716) 824-1298
Sales Range: $10-24.9 Million
Emp.: 10
Fuel Oil
N.A.I.C.S.: 424720
John Deleo (Controller)

T.H. MARSH CONSTRUCTION COMPANY
100 W Long Lake Rd, Royal Oak, MI 48073
Tel.: (248) 586-4130
Web Site: http://www.thmarsh.com
Year Founded: 1954
Sales Range: $25-49.9 Million
Emp.: 45
Construction & Remodeling Services
N.A.I.C.S.: 236116
Ryan S. Marsh (Pres)
Tom Plagens (CFO)

T.H. ROGERS LUMBER CO.
1717 S State St, Edmond, OK 73013-3633
Tel.: (405) 330-2181   MO
Web Site: http://www.throgers.com
Year Founded: 1901
Sales Range: $25-49.9 Million
Emp.: 210
Mfr of Building Materials
N.A.I.C.S.: 423310
Jonathan Kennedy (Pres)
William G. Lindley (Treas & Sec)
Steve Howe (Dir-HR & Mgr-Risk)

T.J. CAMPBELL CONSTRUCTION CO.
6900 S Sunnylane Rd, Oklahoma City, OK 73135
Tel.: (405) 672-6768
Web Site: http://www.tjcampbell.com
Sales Range: $25-49.9 Million
Emp.: 150
Highway & Street Paving Contractor
N.A.I.C.S.: 237310
Mike Thompson (Pres)

T.J. HAGGERTY, INC.
9320 Michigan Ave, Sturtevant, WI 53177-2435
Tel.: (262) 884-4278   WI
Web Site: http://www.tjhaggerty.com
Holding Company
N.A.I.C.S.: 551112
Thomas J. Haggerty (Owner)

Subsidiaries:

A.R.T. Studio Clay Company, Inc. (1)
9320 Michigan Ave, Sturtevant, WI 53177-2425 (100%)
Tel.: (262) 884-4278
Web Site: http://www.artclay.com
Sales Range: Less than $1 Million
Emp.: 4
Clays & Pottery Tools Mfr & Distr
N.A.I.C.S.: 327110

Glassen Consulting & Automation, LLC (1)
9320 Michigan Ave, Sturtevant, WI 53177-2425 (50%)
Tel.: (262) 806-7286
Web Site: http://www.glassen.net
Sales Range: $25-49.9 Million
Emp.: 4
Commercial & Residential Information Technology Consulting & Maintenance Services
N.A.I.C.S.: 541513

T.J. HALE COMPANY INC.
W139 N 9499 Hwy 145, Menomonee Falls, WI 53051
Tel.: (262) 255-5555
Web Site: http://www.tjhale.com
Rev.: $24,489,000
Emp.: 120
Store Fixtures, Wood
N.A.I.C.S.: 337212
Bob Rosean (CEO)
Gena Felder (Mgr-Acctg)

T.J. LAMBRECHT CONSTRUCTION
10 Gougar Rd, Joliet, IL 60432
Tel.: (815) 726-7722
Web Site: http://www.tjlambrecht.com
Sales Range: $150-199.9 Million
Emp.: 100
Excavation Services
N.A.I.C.S.: 238910

T.J. MCGEEHAN'S SALES & SERVICE LTD.
5215 N Lehigh Gorge Rd, White Haven, PA 18661
Tel.: (570) 443-8224
Web Site: http://www.tjmcgeehan.com
Rev.: $11,000,000
Emp.: 34
Provider of Transport & Delivery of Automobiles
N.A.I.C.S.: 484122
Thomas J. McGeehan Sr. (Pres)

T.K. CONSTRUCTORS INC.
2401 N Executive Park Dr, Muncie, IN 47396-9806
Tel.: (765) 282-5500   IN
Web Site: http://www.tk-constructors.com
Year Founded: 1990
Sales Range: $25-49.9 Million
Emp.: 140
Single Family Housing Contractor
N.A.I.C.S.: 236115
Mark E. Thurston (Pres)
Nathan Vannatter (Dir-HR)

T.K. STANLEY, INC.
6739 Hwy 184 W, Waynesboro, MS 39367
Tel.: (601) 735-2855   MS
Web Site: http://www.tkstanley.com
Year Founded: 1979
Sales Range: $25-49.9 Million
Emp.: 400
Oil Filed Construction Services
N.A.I.C.S.: 237120
Dennis Singletary (Controller)

T.L. EDWARDS INC.
100 Wales Ave, Avon, MA 02322
Tel.: (508) 583-2029
Web Site: http://tledwards.net
Sales Range: $10-24.9 Million
Emp.: 70
Provider of Highway & Street Paving Contracting Services
N.A.I.C.S.: 237310
Terry Edwards (Pres)

T.N. WARD COMPANY
129 Coulter Ave, Ardmore, PA 19003
Tel.: (610) 649-0400
Web Site: http://www.tnward.com
Rev.: $18,900,000
Emp.: 2
General Contractor & Construction Management Services
N.A.I.C.S.: 236220
David Panichi (Chm & CEO)
Thomas Falvey (Pres)
John Marks (VP-Indus & Energy Grp)
Gary Pergolini (VP-Ops-Pennsylvania & Delaware)
Mark Smith (VP-Fin)

T.N.T. EQUIPMENT INC.
800 W Sanilac Rd, Sandusky, MI 48471
Tel.: (810) 648-4050
Web Site: http://www.tnteq.com
Year Founded: 2000
Sales Range: $10-24.9 Million
Emp.: 25
Farm & Garden Machinery Equipment Whslr
N.A.I.C.S.: 423820
David Page (Pres)

T.O.P. MARKETING GROUP INC.
4141 Crescent St Ste 5B, Long Island City, NY 11101
Tel.: (718) 361-5880
Web Site: http://www.topmarketinginc.com
Year Founded: 1998
Sales Range: $1-9.9 Million
Emp.: 15
Outsourced, Face-to-Face Marketing Services for Clients in Energy, Telecoms & Financial Services
N.A.I.C.S.: 541613
Michael D'Adamo (Founder & CEO)
Kevin D'Adamo (Pres)

T.P.S. AVIATION INC.
1515 Crocker Ave, Hayward, CA 94544-7038
Tel.: (510) 475-1010   CA
Web Site: http://www.tpsaviation.com
Year Founded: 1963
Sales Range: $10-24.9 Million
Emp.: 112
Transportation Equipment & Supplies
N.A.I.C.S.: 423860
Grace Kitagawa (Mgr-Sls)
David Lim (Mgr-Pur)
Steve Kajikawa (Mgr-Facilities)
George S. Kujiraoka Sr. (Pres & Treas)

T.R. DILLON LOGGING INC.
144 Main St, Madison, ME 04950
Tel.: (207) 696-8137
Sales Range: Less than $1 Million
Emp.: 15
Logging Camps & Contractors
N.A.I.C.S.: 113310
Thomas R. Dillon (Pres)
June Wyman (Gen Mgr)

T.R. WINSTON & COMPANY, LLC
376 Main St, Bedminster, NJ 07921

Tel.: (908) 234-0300   DE
Web Site: http://www.trwinston.com
Year Founded: 2003
Securities Broker & Dealer
N.A.I.C.S.: 523150
John W. Galuchie Jr. (Pres & COO)
G. Tyler Runnels (Chm & CEO)
Russell J. Steward (Mng Dir)
Karen Kang (VP)
Michael Evan Meyers (Mng Dir & Head-Investment Banking)

T.W. LEWIS COMPANY INC.
850 W Elliott Rd Ste 101, Tempe, AZ 85284
Tel.: (480) 820-0807   AZ
Web Site: http://www.twlewis.com
Year Founded: 1991
Sales Range: $10-24.9 Million
Emp.: 30
Residential Construction Services
N.A.I.C.S.: 236115
Tom Lewis (Founder, Owner & CEO)

T.W.E. WHOLESALE, INC. OF SAN DIEGO
3910 Cherry Ave Ste 1, Long Beach, CA 90807
Tel.: (562) 981-2686   CA
Web Site: http://www.performanceplustire.com
Year Founded: 1976
Sales Range: $10-24.9 Million
Emp.: 75
Automotive Supplies & Parts
N.A.I.C.S.: 423120
Hank Feldman (Pres)

T.W.L CORP
3025 West 17th St, Erie, PA 16505
Tel.: (814) 825-1881   PA
Web Site: http://www.lel-erie.com
Year Founded: 1936
Sales Range: $10-24.9 Million
Emp.: 85
Renter & Leaser of Trucks
N.A.I.C.S.: 532120
Joseph A. Benacci (CEO)
Ray Benacci (Pres)

T.Y. LIN INTERNATIONAL GROUP LTD.
345 California St Ste 2300, San Francisco, CA 94104
Tel.: (415) 291-3700   CA
Web Site: http://www.tylin.com
Year Founded: 1954
Sales Range: $150-199.9 Million
Emp.: 1,650
Transportation Infrastructure Engineering Services
N.A.I.C.S.: 541330
Michael J. Hope (Sr VP)
Maribel Castillo (VP & Dir-Corp Comm)
Man-Chung Tang (Chm)
John M. Young (CIO-Intl & VP)
Tony Peterson (Exec VP)
Veronica Fennie (Chief Acctg Officer & VP)
Joseph Giulietti (VP & Dir-Rail Transit Svcs)
Robert Radley (Sr VP & Dir-East)
William K. Harnagel (CFO-Intl & VP)
Teh Hee Seang (Chm-Singapore)
Sajid Abbas (Sr VP & Dir-Special Projects-Americas)
Mark Ashley (Sr VP & Dir-West)
John Flint (Mng Dir-Lines of Bus & Sr VP)
Richard R. Garcia (Exec VP-Lindbergh & Sr VP)
David Goodyear (Sr VP)

Marwan Nader (Sr VP & Dir-Technical-Bridge Line of Bus)
Paula C. Pienton (Sr VP & Dir-Central)
Mariano Valle (Sr VP, Dir-South & Caribbean Latin America)
Richard A. Waters (Sr VP & Dir-Aviation Line of Bus)
Joseph M. Yesbeck (Sr VP & Dir-Rail & Transit Line of Bus)
Sheila Jordan (CMO)
Matthew G. Cummings (Pres & CEO)
Ian MacLeod (Chief HR Officer & Sr VP)
Michael Luhning (Officer-Global Brand & Comm)

Subsidiaries:

Greeley & Hansen LLC (1)
100 S Wacker Dr Ste 1400, Chicago, IL 60606-4084
Tel.: (312) 558-9000
Web Site: http://www.greeley-hansen.com
Environmental Engineering
N.A.I.C.S.: 541330
Michael J. Hope (Pres)
Paul Haglund (CFO & Partner)
Paul Vogel (Exec VP)
Tom Sullivan (Mng Principal)
John C. Robak (CEO)
Andrew Richardson (Chm)
Kim A. Tanner (Mng Dir-Southwest Operating Grp)
Sundaram Solai (Principal & Mng Dir-Operating Grp-Northeast)
Reed Meriwether (Mng Dir-Southeast)
Val S. Frenkel (VP-Process Engrg)
Andrew Martin (Mng Dir/Principal-Midwest Operating Grp)
Glenn R. DiGiovanni (Mng Dir-Northeast Operating Grp)
Dan Coleman (Mng Dir-South Atlantic)
Kenneth Kamper (Mng Dir-Construction Engrg & Mgmt Operating Grp)
Eyad Mizian (Mng Dir-Operating Grp-Mid-Atlantic)

Branch (Domestic):

Greeley & Hansen LLC, Ft. Myers (2)
5252 Summerlin Commons Way Ste 104, Fort Myers, FL 33907-2109 (100%)
Tel.: (239) 226-9660
Web Site: http://www.greeley-hansen.com
Sales Range: $10-24.9 Million
Emp.: 6
N.A.I.C.S.: 541330
Kevin Higginson (Project Mgr & Engr)

Greeley & Hansen LLC, Gary (2)
650 S Lake St Ste D, Gary, IN 46403-2928
Tel.: (219) 938-8354
Web Site: http://www.greeley-hansen.com
Sales Range: $10-24.9 Million
Emp.: 2
Environmental Engineering Services
N.A.I.C.S.: 541330

Greeley & Hansen LLC, Indianapolis (2)
7820 Innovation Blvd Ste 150, Indianapolis, IN 46278
Tel.: (317) 924-3380
Web Site: http://www.greeley-hansen.com
Sales Range: $10-24.9 Million
Emp.: 15
N.A.I.C.S.: 541330

Greeley & Hansen LLC, Las Vegas (2)
6236 W Desert End Rd Ste 100, Las Vegas, NV 89146
Tel.: (702) 736-7062
Web Site: http://www.greeley-hansen.com
Sales Range: $10-24.9 Million
Emp.: 3
Consulting Engineer
N.A.I.C.S.: 541330

Greeley & Hansen LLC, New York (2)
111 Broadway Fl 21 Ste 2101, New York, NY 10006-1900
Tel.: (212) 227-1250
Web Site: http://www.greeley-hansen.com

Sales Range: $10-24.9 Million
Emp.: 40
Environmental Engineering
N.A.I.C.S.: 541330
Clifford Pomerantz (Principal)

Greeley & Hansen LLC, Philadelphia (2)
1818 Market St Ste 3400, Philadelphia, PA 19103-3656
Tel.: (215) 563-3460
Web Site: http://www.greeley-hansen.com
Sales Range: $10-24.9 Million
Emp.: 30
Consulting Engineer
N.A.I.C.S.: 541330

Greeley & Hansen LLC, Phoenix (2)
2800 N 44th St Ste 650, Phoenix, AZ 85008-7696
Tel.: (602) 275-5595
Web Site: http://www.greeley-hansen.com
Sales Range: $10-24.9 Million
Emp.: 12
Civil Engineering Services
N.A.I.C.S.: 541330
Joe Gorgan (Principal)

Greeley & Hansen LLC, Richmond (2)
9020 Stony Point Pkwy Ste 475, Richmond, VA 23235-1946
Tel.: (800) 837-9779
Web Site: http://www.greeley-hansen.com
Sales Range: $10-24.9 Million
Emp.: 25
Civil & Environmental Engineering
N.A.I.C.S.: 541330
Federico Maisch (Gen Mgr)

Greeley & Hansen LLC, Sarasota (2)
2601 Cattleman Rd Ste 100, Sarasota, FL 34232-6254
Tel.: (941) 378-3579
Web Site: http://www.greeley-hansen.com
Sales Range: $10-24.9 Million
Emp.: 3
Engineeering Services
N.A.I.C.S.: 541330
Mike Knowles (Gen Mgr)

Greeley & Hansen LLC, Tampa (2)
1715 NW Shore Blvd Ste 464, Tampa, FL 33607
Tel.: (813) 873-3666
Web Site: http://www.greeley-hansen.com
Sales Range: $25-49.9 Million
Emp.: 19
Civil Engineering Services
N.A.I.C.S.: 541310

Lindbergh & Associates, LLC (1)
2170 Ashley Phosphate Rd Ste 504, Charleston, SC 29406
Tel.: (843) 553-6670
Emp.: 40
Construction Engineering Services
N.A.I.C.S.: 541330
Richard R. Garcia (Sr VP)

T.Y. Lin International - Medina (1)
1 Edgeview Dr, Hackettstown, NJ 07840
Tel.: (908) 850-3366
Web Site: http://www.tylin.com
Sales Range: $10-24.9 Million
Emp.: 125
Engineering & Land Surveying Services
N.A.I.C.S.: 541330
Lynne M. Schmoyer (Mgr-Admin Tech)
Wassim Y. Nader (Principal)
Chandu J. Bhoraniya (Principal)
Brian K. Strout (Dir-Ops)
James F. Steere III (Principal)

T2 INTERNATIONAL LLC
144 Talbert Pointe Dr Ste 103, Mooresville, NC 28117
Tel.: (704) 663-1899
Web Site: http://www.t2products.com
Year Founded: 2000
Sales Range: $1-9.9 Million
Emp.: 24
Product Development
N.A.I.C.S.: 339999
Todd Youngblood (Co-Founder)
Tara Youngblood (Co-Founder)

T2 PARTNERS GROUP, LLC
152 W 57th St 46th Fl, New York, NY 10019
Tel.: (212) 277-5606   DE
Web Site: http://www.t2partnersllc.com
Year Founded: 1998
Holding Company; Investment Advisory & Asset Management Services
N.A.I.C.S.: 551112
Whitney R. Tilson (Founder, Mng Partner & Chief Compliance Officer)

Subsidiaries:

T2 Partners Management, LP (1)
152 W 57th St 46th Fl, New York, NY 10019
Tel.: (212) 277-5606
Web Site: http://www.t2partnersllc.com
Investment Management Service
N.A.I.C.S.: 523940
Whitney R. Tilson (Founder, Mng Partner, Chief Compliance Officer & Mgr)

T3 CORPORATION
309 Cleveland Ave Ste 501, Fairmont, WV 26554
Tel.: (304) 368-9147   WV
Web Site: http://www.t3corp.com
Year Founded: 1985
Sales Range: $10-24.9 Million
Emp.: 30
On-Site Information Technology Services; Computer Software & Hardware Reseller
N.A.I.C.S.: 541511
David Pujals (Pres & CEO)
Anita Martindel (CFO)

T3 LIVE LLC
1 State St 10th Fl Ste 1003, New York, NY 10004
Tel.: (646) 214-7240
Web Site: http://www.t3live.com
Stock Trading & Investment Advice
N.A.I.C.S.: 523940
Scott Redler (Chief Strategic Officer)
Sean Hendelman (CEO)

Subsidiaries:

Pristine Capital Holdings, Inc. (1)
130 Shore Rd Ste 110, Port Washington, NY 11050
Tel.: (914) 682-7613
Web Site: http://www.pristine.com
Sales Range: $1-9.9 Million
Emp.: 27
Mgmt Consulting Svcs Security Broker/Dealer
N.A.I.C.S.: 541611

T3 MOTION, INC.
2990 Airway Ave Bldg A, Costa Mesa, CA 92626
Tel.: (714) 619-3600   DE
Web Site: http://www.t3motion.com
Year Founded: 2006
Sales Range: $1-9.9 Million
Emp.: 37
Personal Mobility Vehicles Mfr, Designer & Marketer
N.A.I.C.S.: 336991
Jeff Simpson (Mgr-Mktg)
Noel Cherowbrier (CEO)
Jay Whitt (Dir-Bus Dev)

T3MEDIA, INC.
1530 16th St 6th Fl, Denver, CO 80202
Tel.: (720) 382-2869
Web Site: http://www.t3media.com
Sales Range: $10-24.9 Million
Emp.: 165
Marketing Consulting Services
N.A.I.C.S.: 541613
Mark Lemmons (CTO)
Josh Wiggins (Sr VP-Sls & Bus Dev)

Tori Donovan (Gen Counsel, Sr VP & Sec)
Harris Morris (CEO)
Frank Cardello (Pres)
Danielle Wilkie (Sr VP-Mktg)
Matt Weiser (Sr VP & Gen Mgr-Stock Licensing)
Mark Pougnet (CFO & COO)

T5 CORP.
3 Monroe Pkwy Ste P #223, Lake Oswego, OR 97035
Tel.: (503) 789-0316
Web Site: http://www.t5corp.com
Year Founded: 2007
Emp.: 1
Management Consulting Services
N.A.I.C.S.: 541618
R. Patrick Garrett (CEO)
Roger T. Richter (Pres & COO)
Allen H. Adams (CFO)
Jesus Solis (VP-Bus Dev)
Christopher Aaron Wilson (Sec)

TA ASSOCIATES, INC.
200 Clarendon St 56th Floor, Boston, MA 02116
Tel.: (617) 574-6700   DE
Web Site: http://www.ta.com
Year Founded: 1968
Privater Equity Firm
N.A.I.C.S.: 523999
Brian J. Conway (Chm & Mng Partner)
Roger B. Kafker (Officer-Senior Adviser)
Kenneth T. Schiciano (Mng Dir)
Michael S. Berk (Mng Dir)
Marcia Z. O'Carroll (Dir-Mktg)
Jeffrey S. Barber (Mng Dir)
Mark H. Carter (Mng Dir)
Harry D. Taylor (Mng Dir)
Dave R. Wilson (Mng Dir)
Jennifer M. Mulloy (Mng Dir & Head-Menlo Park)
M. Roy Burns (Mng Dir)
Hythem T. El-Nazer (Mng Dir)
Christopher Parkin (Mng Dir)
Pamela Harris (Dir-IR)
Emily C. McGinty (Mng Dir)
Jeffrey C. Hadden (Mng Dir, COO & Gen Counsel)
Ashutosh Agrawal (Mng Dir)
Jason P. Werlin (Mng Dir)
Clara M. Jackson (Dir)
Amara Suebsaeng (Sr VP)
William D. Christ (Mng Dir)
Diana Martz (VP-Human Capital & Strategic Resource Grp)
Michael Libert (Dir)
Lee Mooney (VP)
Sarah Wang (VP)
Birker B. Bahnsen (Mng Dir)
Danoiel Brujis (VP)
Max Cancre (Dir)
Stefan A. Dandl (VP)
Jeremy Drean (VP)
Jessica Gilligan (VP)
Darlene M. Karis (Dir-HR)
Damon M. Khouri (Dir-IT)
Philp P. Yotov (VP-Strategic Resource Grp)
Naveen Wadhera (Mng Dir-London & Mumbai)
Akshay Srimal (Sr VP-Strategic Resource Grp)
J. Morgan Seigler (Mng Dir)
Edward F. Sippel (Mng Dir-Hong Kong)
Nicholas D. Leppla (VP)
Charles Ha (VP)
Todd R. Crockett (Mng Dir)

TA ASSOCIATES, INC.

U.S. PRIVATE

TA Associates, Inc.—(Continued)

Subsidiaries:

AFCV Holdings, LLC (1)
6665 Delmar Blvd Ste 3000, Saint Louis, MO 63005
Tel.: (314) 664-2010
Web Site: http://www.afcv.com
Holding Company; Consumer Internet Technologies Developer & Operator
N.A.I.C.S.: 551112
David Karandish (Chm & CEO)

Accion Labs US, Inc. (1)
1225 Washington Pike Ste 401, Pittsburgh, PA 15017
Tel.: (724) 260-5139
Web Site: http://www.accionlabs.com
Sales Range: $10-24.9 Million
Information Technology Support Services
N.A.I.C.S.: 541512
Kinesh Doshi (Co-Founder & CEO)
Ashutosh Bijoor (CTO)
Tony Kernan (Co-Founder & Sr VP-Sls)
Anand Raja (Co-Pres)
Sandesh Sukumaran (Co-Founder & VP-Talent Acq)
Suresh Akunuri (CEO-Singapore)
Howard Goodkind (Co-Pres & CEO-UK & Europe)
Ramesh Narasimhan (Mng Dir)
Shyam Upadhyay (Sr VP-Bus Dev)
Amy Halter (VP-Ops & HR)
Gopal Tiple (VP-Delivery)
Jane Poojari (Mgr-Delivery)
Arvind Itagi (Dir-Delivery)
Mahesh Bandaru (Mgr-Bus & HR)
Naveen Chandra Sagar (Mgr-Delivery)
Relton Alexander (Mgr-Delivery)
Saurabh Periwal (Mgr-Delivery)
Venugopal Reddy (Mgr-Delivery)
Priscilla Angeline Pereira (Sr Mgr-HR)
Jennifer Wells (Mgr-Ops)
Nadim Khalid (Dir-Sls Dev)
Amit Gulati (Dir-Bus Dev-India Accts)
Michael DuPlessis (Sr Mgr-Engagement)
Poornima Prasad (Chief People Officer-Global Ops)

Aptean, Inc. (1)
4325 Alexander Dr Ste 100, Alpharetta, GA 30022-3740
Tel.: (770) 351-9600
Web Site: http://www.aptean.com
Software Developer
N.A.I.C.S.: 513210
Kim Eaton (CEO)
Jack Blaha (COO & Exec VP)
Kyle L. Bowker (Exec VP-Acct Mgmt & Mktg-Global)
Bhaskar Appacudal (CTO & Sr VP)
Todd Schulte (Sr VP-Customer Solutions)
Brad Steger (Sr VP-Supply Chain & Vertical Solutions Product Grp)
Matt Keenan (Sr VP-CRM Product Grp)
Joanna Luth (VP-HR)
TVN Reddy (CEO)

Subsidiary (Domestic):

Advanced Public Safety, Inc. (2)
400 Fairway Dr Ste 101, Deerfield Beach, FL 33441
Tel.: (954) 354-3000
Web Site: http://ww2.aps.us
Computer Software Development Services
N.A.I.C.S.: 541511
Jacqueline Bartlett (VP-Solution Delivery)

Apparel Business Systems, LLC (2)
2 W Lafayette St, Norristown, PA 19401
Tel.: (610) 592-0880
Web Site: http://www.apparelbusiness.com
Rev.: $3,400,000
Emp.: 29
Computer & Computer Peripheral Equipment & Software Merchant Whslr
N.A.I.C.S.: 423430

Apprise Software, Inc. (2)
3101 Emrick Blvd, Bethlehem, PA 18020
Tel.: (610) 991-3900
Web Site: http://www.apprise.com
Rev.: $5,300,000
Emp.: 60
Custom Computer Programming Services
N.A.I.C.S.: 541511
Jeff Broadhurst (CEO)

Unit (Domestic):

Aptean - GoMembers AMS (2)
1 E Wacker Dr Ste 3550, Chicago, IL 60601-1802
Tel.: (571) 262-5171
Web Site: http://www.aptean.com
Sales Range: $10-24.9 Million
Computer Software Development
N.A.I.C.S.: 541511

Aptean - Made2Manage ERP (2)
450 E 96th St Ste 300, Indianapolis, IN 46240
Tel.: (317) 249-1700
Web Site: http://www.aptean.com
Enterprise Software for Small & Midsize Manufacturers
N.A.I.C.S.: 513210

Aptean - TradeBeam SCM (2)
2 Waters Park Dr Ste 100, San Mateo, CA 94403-1148
Tel.: (650) 653-4800
Web Site: http://www.aptean.com
Global Trade/Supply Chain Management Software & Services Solutions
N.A.I.C.S.: 513210

Subsidiary (Domestic):

Beck Consulting (2)
4309 Hacienda Dr Ste 465, Pleasanton, CA 94588-2883
Tel.: (510) 747-1970
Web Site: http://www.beckconsulting.com
Business to Business Electronic Markets
N.A.I.C.S.: 425120
Allen Beck (Owner)

Subsidiary (Non-US):

CDC Software OY (2)
Ayritie 12A, FI-01510, Vantaa, Finland
Tel.: (358) 9 873 3522
Web Site: http://www.aptean.com
Supply Chain Management Software Solutions
N.A.I.C.S.: 541512

CDC Software Singapore Pte. Ltd. (2)
20 Kramat Ln United House Unit 05-03, Singapore, 228773, Singapore
Tel.: (65) 6333 8205
Web Site: http://www.aptean.com
Software Solutions
N.A.I.C.S.: 541512
Christopher Lenig (VP-Global Pro Svcs)

Subsidiary (Domestic):

CoreTrac, Inc. (2)
8200 N Mopac Park N Bldg 1 Ste 280, Austin, TX 78759
Tel.: (512) 236-9120
Web Site: http://www.coretrac.com
Software Publisher
N.A.I.C.S.: 513210
Dan Martin (CEO)
Bill Gibson (VP-Sls & Mktg)

Subsidiary (Non-US):

FDM Software Ltd. (2)
113-949 W 3rd Street, North Vancouver, V7P 3P7, BC, Canada
Tel.: (604) 986-9941
Web Site: http://www.fdmsoft.com
Mapping & Analysis, Records Management & Computer-Aided Dispatch Software Solutions
N.A.I.C.S.: 513210

Industri-Matematik Nederland B.V. (2)
Sparrenheuvel 32, 3708 JE, Zeist, Netherlands
Tel.: (31) 306985550
Web Site: http://www.aptean.com
Sales Range: $10-24.9 Million
Emp.: 4
N.A.I.C.S.: 541512

Industri-Matematik, Limited (2)
7 Rushmills Northampton, Northampton, NN4 7YB., Bucks, United Kingdom
Tel.: (44) 1604 614 100
Sales Range: $10-24.9 Million
N.A.I.C.S.: 541512

Subsidiary (Domestic):

Innovative Systems, LLC (2)
22921 Triton Way Ste 228, Laguna Hills, CA 92653
Tel.: (949) 707-1560
Web Site: http://www.isllc.com
Management Consulting Services
N.A.I.C.S.: 541611
Kent Johnson (Project Mgr)

Subsidiary (Non-US):

Kauri Business Systems Limited (2)
570 Whitford Rd, Whitford, Auckland, 2571, New Zealand
Tel.: (64) 95309245
Sales Range: $25-49.9 Million
Computer & Business Data Systems
N.A.I.C.S.: 541519

Merlin Business Software Limited (2)
Chatsworth House Millennium Way, Chesterfield, S41 8ND, Derbyshire, United Kingdom
Tel.: (44) 1246457150
Web Site: https://www.merlinbusinesssoftware.com
Emp.: 50
Software Publishing Services
N.A.I.C.S.: 513210
Clive Mallender (Mng Dir)

Paragon Software Systems plc (2)
Parsonage House Parsonage Square, Dorking, RH4 1UP, Surrey, United Kingdom
Tel.: (44) 1306732600
Web Site: http://www.paragonrouting.com
Sales Range: $10-24.9 Million
Emp.: 55
Transport Management Software Services
N.A.I.C.S.: 488999
William Salter (Mng Dir)

Subsidiary (US):

Paragon Software Systems inc (3)
2591 Dallas Pkwy Ste 300, Frisco, TX 75034
Tel.: (972) 731-4308
Software Development Services
N.A.I.C.S.: 541511
Jim Endres (Mgr-Sls)

Subsidiary (Non-US):

Pivotal Corporation (2)
1066 West Hastings St 23rd Floor, Vancouver, V6E 3X2, BC, Canada
Tel.: (604) 699-8000
Web Site: http://www.aptean.com
Sales Range: $25-49.9 Million
Provider of Customer Relationship Management Software
N.A.I.C.S.: 541512

Ross Systems (UK) Limited (2)
Pioneer House 7 Rushmills, Northampton, NN4 7YB, Northants, United Kingdom
Tel.: (44) 1604 630 050
Web Site: http://www.aptean.com
Sales Range: $25-49.9 Million
Financial, Accounting & Manufacturing Software
N.A.I.C.S.: 513210

Ross Systems Iberica S.L. (2)
c/ Frederic Mompou 5 - 5a pl, Sant Just Desvern, 08960, Barcelona, Spain
Tel.: (34) 934802850
Web Site: http://www.aptean.com
Sales Range: $25-49.9 Million
Emp.: 20
Software Services
N.A.I.C.S.: 541511
Aroon Almansa (Gen Mgr)

Sanderson Group plc (2)
Sanderson House Manor Road, Coventry, CV1 2GF, W Midlands, United Kingdom
Tel.: (44) 3331231400
Web Site: http://www.sanderson.com
Rev.: $43,244,692
Assets: $82,806,287
Liabilities: $36,430,287
Net Worth: $46,376,000
Earnings: $4,082,437
Emp.: 318
Fiscal Year-end: 09/30/2018
Holding Company; Retail & Manufacturing Software & Information Technology Solutions

N.A.I.C.S.: 513210
Ian Newcombe (CEO)

Subsidiary (Domestic):

Sanderson Limited (3)
Sanderson House, Manor Road, Coventry, CV1 2GF, West Midlands, United Kingdom
Tel.: (44) 3331231400
Web Site: http://www.sanderson.co.uk
Sales Range: $75-99.9 Million
Manufacturing, Food & Print Industry Software & Information Technology Solutions
N.A.I.C.S.: 513210

Subsidiary (Domestic):

Sanderson NI Limited (4)
Ocean House Edgewater Business Park, 13 Edgewater Road, Belfast, BT3 9JQ, Northern Ireland, United Kingdom
Tel.: (44) 2890373500
Web Site: http://www.sanderson.com
Sales Range: $25-49.9 Million
Emp.: 55
Sales & Service of Computer Systems
N.A.I.C.S.: 449210

Subsidiary (Domestic):

Sanderson Multi-Channel Solutions Limited (3)
Sanderson House Manor Road, Coventry, CV1 2GF, W Midlands, United Kingdom
Tel.: (44) 2476555466
Sales Range: $10-24.9 Million
Emp.: 45
Multi-Channel Retail Information Technology Products & Services
N.A.I.C.S.: 513210
Ian Newcombe (CEO)

AutoQuotes LLC (1)
8800 W Baymeadows Way Ste500, Jacksonville, FL 32256
Tel.: (904) 384-1923
Web Site: http://www.aq-fes.com
Sales Range: $1-9.9 Million
Emp.: 12
Custom Computer Programming Services
N.A.I.C.S.: 541511
Kent Motes (Pres)
Jim Contardi (CEO)

Subsidiary (Domestic):

Axonom, Inc. (2)
11010 Prairie Lakes Dr Ste 375, Eden Prairie, MN 55344
Tel.: (952) 653-0400
Web Site: http://www.axonom.com
Sales Range: $1-9.9 Million
Emp.: 26
Custom Computer Programming Services
N.A.I.C.S.: 541511
Mike Belongie (CEO)

Biocomposites Ltd. (1)
700 Military Cutoff Rd Ste 320, Wilmington, NC 28405-4774
Tel.: (910) 350-8015
Web Site: http://www.biocomposites.com
Surgical & Medical Instrument Mfr
N.A.I.C.S.: 339112
Hamish White (CMO)
Michael Harris (CEO)
Davina Lawrence (Natl Dir-Sls-UK)

CTM Software Corp. (1)
6275 Simms St Ste 300, Arvada, CO 80004-4485
Tel.: (303) 399-3579
Web Site: http://www.ctmsoftware.com
Electronics Stores
N.A.I.C.S.: 449210
Claudio Riello (CEO)

Confluence Technologies, Inc. (1)
600 River Ave, Pittsburgh, PA 15212
Tel.: (412) 802-8632
Web Site: http://www.confluence.com
Software Publisher
N.A.I.C.S.: 511210
Mark S. Evans (Founder & CEO)
Gary Casagrande (VP-Global Market Strategy)
Christopher S. Evans (Gen Counsel, Sec & Sr VP)
Frederick Winston (CFO)
Todd L. Moyer (Pres & COO)

COMPANIES

TA ASSOCIATES, INC.

Jory Wheeler *(Sr VP-Engrg)*
Dario Cintioli *(Mng Dir-Delta Div)*
Clinton Moseley *(Dir-Client Experience Strategy)*
Katie Kiss *(VP-M&A Integration)*
Sunil Rajan *(Global Head-Sls)*
Tom Pfister *(VP-Global Product Strategy)*

Subsidiary (Non-US):

StatPro Group Limited (2)
Mansel Court Mansel Road, Wimbledon, London, SW19 4AA, United Kingdom
Tel.: (44) 2084109876
Web Site: http://www.confluence.com
Performance Measurement Software for Asset Management Industry
N.A.I.C.S.: 513210

Subsidiary (Non-US):

StatPro (Deutschland) GmbH (3)
KirchnerstraSSe 6-8, 60311, Frankfurt am Main, Germany
Tel.: (49) 69244322000
Web Site: http://www.confluence.com
Performance Measurement Software for Asset Management Industry
N.A.I.C.S.: 513210

StatPro Asia Ltd. (3)
The Center 99 Queen's Road Central, Central, China (Hong Kong)
Tel.: (852) 3796 7085
Web Site: http://www.confluence.com
Software Publisher
N.A.I.C.S.: 513210

StatPro Australia Pty Ltd. (3)
Suite 202 Level 2 67 Albert Avenue, Chatswood, Sydney, 2067, NSW, Australia
Tel.: (61) 2 9884 9045
Web Site: http://www.confluence.com
Software Development Services
N.A.I.C.S.: 541511
Greg Howell *(Mng Dir)*

StatPro France SARL (3)
33 Rue la Fayette, 75009, Paris, France
Tel.: (33) 1 40 20 1200
Web Site: http://www.confluence.com
Software Publisher
N.A.I.C.S.: 513210

Subsidiary (US):

StatPro Inc. (3)
100 High St 1550, Boston, MA 02110
Tel.: (617) 692-1150
Web Site: http://www.confluence.com
Performance Measurement Software for Asset Management Industry
N.A.I.C.S.: 513210

Subsidiary (Non-US):

StatPro Italia Srl (3)
Via Edmondo De Amicis 53, 20123, Milan, Italy
Tel.: (39) 02 00 693 1
Web Site: http://www.confluence.com
Performance Measurement Software for Asset Management Industry
N.A.I.C.S.: 513210

StatPro S.A. (3)
c/o Silversquare 21 Rue Glesener L-16-31, 2330, Luxembourg, Luxembourg
Tel.: (352) 30 74 24 1
Web Site: http://www.confluence.com
Software Publisher
N.A.I.C.S.: 513210

StatPro South Africa Pty Ltd. (3)
2nd Floor Liesbeek House River Park Gloucester Road Mowbray, Cape Town, 7700, South Africa
Tel.: (27) 21 443 2140
Web Site: http://www.confluence.com
Software Publisher
N.A.I.C.S.: 513210

DigiCert, Inc. (1)
2801 N Thanksgiving Way Ste 500, Lehi, UT 84043
Tel.: (801) 701-9600
Web Site: http://www.digicert.com
Software Publisher
N.A.I.C.S.: 513210
Flavio Martins *(COO)*
Chris Call *(Engr-Support)*
Jeremy Rowley *(Exec VP-Emerging Markets)*
John Merrill *(CEO)*
Sue Allen *(Office Mgr)*
Eric Porter *(VP-Fin & Admin)*
Mike Nelson *(VP-Healthcare Solutions)*
Michael Olson *(CFO)*
Jeff Chandler *(Dir-PR)*
Alan Raymond *(VP-Sls)*
Jason Sabin *(CTO)*
Benjamin T. Wilson *(VP-Compliance & Indus Rels)*
Mark Packham *(VP-Mktg)*
Mike Johnson *(Gen Counsel)*
Amit Sinha *(Pres & CEO)*

Subsidiary (Domestic):

Mocana Corporation (2)
1735 N 1st St Ste 306, San Jose, CA 94104
Tel.: (415) 617-0055
Web Site: http://www.mocana.com
Software Publisher
N.A.I.C.S.: 513210
Brian Nugent *(Chm)*
Dave Smith *(Chief Revenue Officer)*
Hope Frank *(CMO & Chief Digital Officer)*
Jeanne Pardo *(CFO)*
W. William Diotte *(CEO)*
Srinivas Kumar *(CTO)*

Subsidiary (Non-US):

Mocana Solutions Private Limited (3)
10 Shreeniwas Classic 273/1/1+2/1 Baner, Pune, 411 045, Maharashtra, India
Tel.: (91) 20 27291608
Software Publisher
N.A.I.C.S.: 513210

DiscoverOrg, LLC (1)
805 Broadway St Ste 900, Vancouver, WA 98660
Tel.: (800) 914-1220
Web Site: http://www.discoverorg.com
Marketing Consultancy Services
N.A.I.C.S.: 541613
Katie Bullard *(Pres)*
Patrick Purvis *(Chief Revenue Officer)*
Roger Cracel *(CEO)*
Derek Smith *(Sr VP-Data & Res)*
Chris Hays *(COO)*
Nir Keren *(CTO)*
Hila Nir *(CMO)*
Seth Low *(Chief Information Officer)*
Justin Withers *(Sr VP-Product)*

Subsidiary (Domestic):

Rain King Software, Inc. (2)
6430 Rockledge Dr, Bethesda, MD 20817
Tel.: (240) 482-4570
Sales & Marketing Intelligence Solutions
N.A.I.C.S.: 541512

Zoom Information Inc. (2)
307 Waverley Oaks Rd Ste 405, Waltham, MA 02452
Tel.: (781) 693-7500
Web Site: http://www.zoominfo.com
Business Information Services
N.A.I.C.S.: 513140
Henry Schuck *(Executives)*
Hila Nir *(CMO)*
Leo Laferriere *(CTO)*
Nir Keren *(VP-R&D)*
Philip Garlick *(VP-Corp Dev)*
John Rogers *(CFO)*

iProfile, LLC. (2)
611 S Congress Ave Ste 420, Austin, TX 78704
Tel.: (512) 263-9246
Web Site: http://www.iprofile.net
Software & Technology Development Services
N.A.I.C.S.: 513210
Gautham Viswanathan *(CEO)*
Arun Prakash *(VP-Mktg)*

Flexera Software LLC (1)
300 Park Blvd Ste 500, Itasca, IL 60143
Tel.: (847) 466-4000
Web Site: http://www.flexerasoftware.com
Sales Range: $50-74.9 Million
Emp.: 250
Software Developer
N.A.I.C.S.: 513210
Jim Ryan *(Pres & CEO)*
Richard Northing *(Sr VP-Products & Svcs)*
Vincent Smyth *(Sr VP-Worldwide Sls)*
Kraig Washburn *(Gen Counsel)*
Dana Sacks *(VP-HR)*
John Shackleton *(Chm)*
Steve Beards *(VP- Asia Pacific & Japan)*
Hugh Darvall *(Dir-Australia & New Zealand)*
David Zwick *(CFO)*
Mike Gibson *(Chief Info Security Officer)*
Conal Gallagher *(CIO)*

Subsidiary (Non-US):

Flexera Software Ltd. (2)
Vision House Wellfield Road, Preston Brook, Runcorn, WA7 3FR, Cheshire, United Kingdom
Tel.: (44) 8708736300
Sales Range: $25-49.9 Million
Software Developer
N.A.I.C.S.: 513210

Subsidiary (Domestic):

Palamida, Inc. (2)
215 2nd St 2nd Floor, San Francisco, CA 94105
Tel.: (415) 777-9400
Web Site: http://www.palamida.com
Sales Range: $1-9.9 Million
Emp.: 200
Application Software Security Solutions
N.A.I.C.S.: 423430
Jeffrey Luszcz *(VP-Svcs & Support)*
Alex Rybak *(Dir-Product Mgmt)*
Ethan Le *(Dir-Pro Svcs)*
Mark Tolliver *(CEO)*
Stacey Potter *(Mktg Mgr)*

RightScale, Inc. (2)
402 E Gutierrez St, Santa Barbara, CA 93101
Tel.: (805) 500-4164
Web Site: http://www.rightscale.com
Sales Range: $10-24.9 Million
Emp.: 110
Software Applications
N.A.I.C.S.: 513210
Michael Crandell *(Co-Founder & CEO)*
Thorsten von Eicken *(Co-Founder & CTO)*
Josh Fraser *(Sr VP-Sls & Bus Dev)*
Rafael H. Saavedra *(Co-Founder & VP-Engrg)*
Bailey Caldwell *(VP-Customer Success)*
Kim Weins *(VP-Mktg)*
Tim Miller *(Pres)*
Stephen Morrison *(CFO)*

Subsidiary (Non-US):

RightScale Asia Pacific (3)
9 Battery Road 11-00, The Straits Trading Building, Singapore, 49910, Singapore
Tel.: (65) 3158 2491
Software Applications
N.A.I.C.S.: 513210

RightScale Australia (3)
100 Walker Street, North Sydney, 2060, NSW, Australia
Tel.: (61) 2 8607 8266
Software Applications
N.A.I.C.S.: 513210

RightScale UK Ltd (3)
1 Lyric Square, Hammersmith, London, W6 0NB, United Kingdom
Tel.: (44) 203 3184425
Software Applications
N.A.I.C.S.: 513210

Global Software, LLC (1)
8529 Six Forks Rd #400, Raleigh, NC 27615
Tel.: (919) 872-7800
Web Site: http://www.insightsoftware.com
Financial Software Applications
N.A.I.C.S.: 513210
Spencer Kupferman *(Pres & CEO)*
Becky Kaufman *(VP-Client Svcs)*
David Oakes *(VP-Application Dev & IT)*
Harry Powell *(VP-R&D)*
Sherry Puckett *(VP-Solutions Enablement)*
Steve Carnevale *(CFO)*
Phil Sandy *(COO)*
Mark Osborne *(CTO)*
Lori Needham *(VP-Customer Engagement)*
Paul Zunker *(VP-West Coast Ops)*
Jim Triandiflou *(CEO)*

Subsidiary (Non-US):

Dundas Data Visualization, Inc. (2)
500 250 Ferrand Drive, Toronto, M3C 3G8, ON, Canada
Tel.: (416) 467-5100
Data Visualization & Dashboarding Solutions
N.A.I.C.S.: 513210

Subsidiary (Domestic):

Izenda, Inc. (2)
5775 Peachtree Dunwoody Rd Bldg C Ste 300, Atlanta, GA 30342
Tel.: (678) 619-5889
Web Site: http://www.izenda.com
Information Technology & Services
N.A.I.C.S.: 519290
Bill Curran *(Pres & CEO)*
Lee Nagel *(VP-Mktg)*
Dawn Russell *(VP-Dev & Customer Success)*
David Yasson *(VP-Sls)*
Christopher Carter *(CEO)*

Logi Analytics, Inc. (2)
7900 Westpark Dr Ste A500, McLean, VA 22102
Tel.: (703) 752-9700
Emp.: 200
Commercial & Enterprise Applications Solutions Developer
N.A.I.C.S.: 513210

Subsidiary (Domestic):

Zoomdata, Inc. (3)
11921 Freedom Dr Ste 800, Reston, VA 20190
Tel.: (888) 600-6996
Web Site: http://www.zoomdata.com
Emp.: 20
Big Data Analytics Software
N.A.I.C.S.: 513210
Justin Langseth *(Founder)*
Russ Cosentino *(VP-Channel Sls)*
Igor Semenko *(Dir-Engrg)*
Jonathan Avila *(Mgr-Consulting)*
Yusuf Abediyeh *(Engr-Sls)*
Nick Halsey *(Pres & CEO)*
Michael Proia *(VP-Sls)*

Subsidiary (Non-US):

Longview Europe GmbH (2)
Elisabeth-Selbert-Str 5, 40764, Langenfeld, Dusseldorf, Germany
Tel.: (49) 217316760
Business Intelligence & Corporate Performance Management Software Publr
N.A.I.C.S.: 513210

Subsidiary (Domestic):

Magnitude Software, Inc. (2)
8529 Six Forks Rd, Raleigh, NC 27615
Web Site: https://www.magnitude.com
Holding Company; Enterprise Information Management Software Publisher
N.A.I.C.S.: 551112
Jeffrey Shoreman *(CEO)*

Subsidiary (Non-US):

Agility Multichannel Ltd. (3)
Unit 4 Triune Court Monks Cross Dr, York, YO32 9GZ, United Kingdom
Tel.: (44) 1904717800
Web Site: http://www.agilitymultichannel.com
Software Publisher
N.A.I.C.S.: 513210
Richard Hunt *(VP)*
Graham Cook *(VP-Engrg)*
Jason Simpson *(Dir-European)*

Subsidiary (Domestic):

Kalido Inc. (3)
1 Wall St, Burlington, MA 01803
Tel.: (781) 202-3200
Web Site: http://www.kalido.com
Information Management Software Development Services
N.A.I.C.S.: 541511
Chris Ney *(Chm & CEO)*
Coman Wakefield *(VP-Engrg)*
Darren Peirce *(CTO & VP-Products)*
Olaf Thiemann *(Mgr-Plng, Data Mgmt & Integration Imperial Brands)*

TA ASSOCIATES, INC.

TA Associates, Inc.—(Continued)

Noetix Corporation (3)
5010 148th Ave NE Ste 100, Redmond, WA 98052-5119
Tel.: (425) 372-2699
Web Site: http://www.noetix.com
Business Intelligence & Data Analytics Software
N.A.I.C.S.: 513210
Doug Moore *(Grp CFO & Exec VP)*
Chris Ney *(Chm & CEO)*
Pat Roche *(VP-Engrg)*
Joe Pesce *(Gen Mgr-Sls-East & EMEA)*
Michael Huffines *(Gen Sls Mgr-Central & West)*

ITRS Group Ltd. (1)
6th Floor The Bonhill Building 15 Bonhill Street, London, EC2A 4DN, United Kingdom
Tel.: (44) 20 7638 6700
Web Site: http://www.itrsgroup.com
Software Development Services
N.A.I.C.S.: 513210
Guy Warren *(CEO)*
Iveta Cabajova *(CFO)*
Steve Christinson *(CTO)*
Steve Turner *(COO)*

International Decision Systems, Inc. (1)
220 S 6th St Ste 700, Minneapolis, MN 55402
Tel.: (612) 851-3200
Web Site: http://www.idsgrp.com
Sales Range: $25-49.9 Million
Emp.: 385
Business Oriented Computer Software & Services
N.A.I.C.S.: 513210
Katie Emmel *(COO)*
Deborah Schmidt *(Sr VP-Sls & Mktg)*
David Hamilton *(CEO)*
Patricia Elias *(Gen Counsel)*
Duncan Smith *(Mng Dir-APAC)*
Debbie Whitehurst *(Sr VP-Client Success)*
Eldon Richards *(CTO)*
Bill Noel *(Chief Product Officer)*
Brendan Gleeson *(Chief Strategy Officer)*
Mithu Bhargava *(Pres)*

Kofax Inc. (1)
15211 Laguna Canyon Rd, Irvine, CA 92618-3146
Tel.: (949) 783-1000
Web Site: http://www.kofax.com
Emp.: 1,900
Software Development Services
N.A.I.C.S.: 513210
Reynolds C. Bish *(CEO)*
Jim Nicol *(Exec VP-Products)*
Lynne Scheid *(Sr VP-HR)*
Karl Doyle *(Sr VP-Corp Dev)*
Peter Hantman *(Pres & COO)*
Cort Townsend *(CFO)*
Greg Mermis *(Gen Counsel & Sr VP-Legal Affairs)*
Kevin McKay *(Exec VP-Customer Success)*
Tim Battis *(Exec VP-Global Sls)*
Kathleen Delaney *(CMO)*
Chris Huff *(Chief Strategy Officer)*
Nicolas Rochard *(Sr VP-Growth Mktg)*

Subsidiary (Domestic):

Atalasoft, Inc. (2)
15211 Laguna Canyon Rd, Irvine, CA 92618
Tel.: (781) 743-2119
Web Site: http://www.atalasoft.com
Software Developer
N.A.I.C.S.: 513210
Mark Goldblatt *(Acct Exec)*

Ephesoft Inc. (2)
8707 Research Dr, Irvine, CA 92618
Tel.: (949) 331-7500
Web Site: http://www.ephesoft.com
Electronics Stores
N.A.I.C.S.: 449210
Ike Kavas *(Founder & CEO)*
Naren Goel *(CFO)*
Stephen Boals *(Sr VP-Strategy & Evangelism)*
Lynn Tanatannawin *(Head-Strategy)*
Heather Dilley *(Sr VP-Culture & People)*

Subsidiary (Non-US):

Kofax Australia Pty. Ltd. (2)
6-10 O'Connell Street Suite 701, Sydney, 2000, NSW, Australia
Tel.: (61) 289160200
Software Publisher

Kofax Austria GmbH (2)
Talpagasse 1, 1230, Vienna, Austria
Tel.: (43) 18664555000
Electronic Mass Data Capture & Retrieval Product Mfr
N.A.I.C.S.: 334112

Kofax Benelux NV (2)
Schalienhoevedreef 20 E, 2800, Mechelen, Belgium
Tel.: (32) 15444900
Software Development Services
N.A.I.C.S.: 513210

Kofax Danmark A/S (2)
Lottenborgvej 26 Blok B 2 sal, Lyngby, Copenhagen, Denmark
Tel.: (45) 4324 1650
Applications Software Developer
N.A.I.C.S.: 513210

Kofax Deutschland AG (2)
Wentzinger Strasse 19, 79106, Freiburg, Germany
Tel.: (49) 761 452 690
Applications Software Developer
N.A.I.C.S.: 513210
Frank Carl *(Dir-Technical Support Svcs)*
Christian Hefner *(Gen Counsel & VP)*

Kofax Holding AG (2)
Grundstrasse 14, 6343, Rotkreuz, Switzerland
Tel.: (41) 41 799 82 82
Holding Company
N.A.I.C.S.: 551112

Subsidiary (Domestic):

Kofax Schweiz AG (3)
Grundstrasse 14, 6343, Rotkreuz, Switzerland
Tel.: (41) 41 799 82 82
Applications Software Developer
N.A.I.C.S.: 513210

Subsidiary (Non-US):

Kofax Italia S.r.l. (2)
Viale Monza 20, 20128, Milan, Italy
Tel.: (39) 02 252051
Applications Software Developer
N.A.I.C.S.: 513210

Kofax Japan Co. Ltd. (2)
9F SOC Takanawa Building 3-19-26 Takanawa, Minato-ku, Tokyo, 108-0074, Japan
Tel.: (81) 3 6853 0001
Applications Software Developer
N.A.I.C.S.: 513210

Kofax Malaysia Sdn. Bhd. (2)
Suite 13 06 Level 13 The Gardens South Tower Mid Valley City, Lingkaran Syed Putra, Kuala Lumpur, 59200, Malaysia
Tel.: (60) 3 2092 0202
Applications Software Developer
N.A.I.C.S.: 513210

Kofax Netherlands BV (2)
Papendorpseweg 99 5th Floor, 3528 BJ, Utrecht, Netherlands
Tel.: (31) 30 264 3030
Applications Software Developer
N.A.I.C.S.: 513210
Martin van Ginkel *(VP-Sls-Benelux)*

Kofax Portugal, S.A. (2)
Av Clotilde Edificio Centro Congressos do Estoril 4A, 2765-211, Estoril, Portugal
Tel.: (351) 21 464 6190
Applications Software Developer
N.A.I.C.S.: 513210

Kofax Produtos de Imagem Do Brasil Ltda (2)
R Gomes de Carvalho 1069 CJ 102, Itaim Bibi, 04547-004, Sao Paulo, Brazil
Tel.: (55) 11 3047 4000
Applications Software Developer
N.A.I.C.S.: 513210

Kofax Singapore Pte. Ltd. (2)
9 Raffles Place Suite 53-01 Republic Plaza, Singapore, 048619, Singapore
Tel.: (65) 62787662

Applications Software Developer
N.A.I.C.S.: 513210
Jesslyn Lee *(Dir-HR-Asia Pacific)*

Kofax Software Iberica S.A.U. (2)
Torre Mapfre C/ de la Marina 16-18 11-B, 08005, Barcelona, Spain
Tel.: (34) 934 090 459
Applications Software Developer
N.A.I.C.S.: 513210

Kofax Sverige AB (2)
Energigatan 11 Rm 308, 434 37, Kungsbacka, Sweden
Tel.: (46) 8 566 110 00
Applications Software Developer
N.A.I.C.S.: 513210

Kofax UK Ltd. (2)
7 Elmwood Chineham Business Park, Chineham, Basingstoke, RG24 8WG, United Kingdom
Tel.: (44) 1256 89 1000
Applications Software Developer
N.A.I.C.S.: 513210
Darryl Heffernan *(VP-Global Sls Ops)*

Kofax Vietnam Co., Ltd. (2)
521 Kim Ma Street 11 Fl A Tower RESCO Building, Ba Dinh District, Hanoi, 100000, Vietnam
Tel.: (84) 4 3771 2546 7
Applications Software Developer
N.A.I.C.S.: 513210

Subsidiary (Domestic):

PSIGEN Software, Inc. (2)
7027 Old Madison Pike NW Ste 108, Huntsville, AL 35806
Tel.: (949) 916-7700
Web Site: http://www.psigen.com
Sales Range: $1-9.9 Million
Emp.: 16
Custom Computer Programming Services
N.A.I.C.S.: 541511
Bruce Hensley *(CEO)*
Victoria Hensley *(COO)*
Joe Do *(Dir-Global Products & Svcs)*
Glenn Johnson *(Pres)*
Robert Esquivel *(Dir-Channel Enablement-West)*

Subsidiary (Non-US):

Tungsten Corporation PLC (2)
Leaf A Level 1 Tower 42 25 Old Broad Street, London, EC2N 1HQ, United Kingdom
Tel.: (44) 2072807807
Web Site: http://www.tungsten-network.com
Rev.: $49,035,416
Assets: $109,042,566
Liabilities: $32,684,394
Net Worth: $76,358,173
Earnings: $47,093,876
Emp.: 260
Fiscal Year-end: 04/30/2021
Invoicing Software
N.A.I.C.S.: 513210
Cort Steven Townsend *(Sec)*

Subsidiary (US):

Tungsten Network Inc (3)
1040 Crown Pointe Pkwy Ste 350, Atlanta, GA 30338
Tel.: (770) 698-1420
Electronic Invoicing Services
N.A.I.C.S.: 561499
Prabhat Vira *(Pres-Fin)*
Rick Hurwitz Rick Hurwitz *(CEO-Americas)*

Subsidiary (Domestic):

Image Intergration Systems, Inc. (4)
885 Commerce Dr, Perrysburg, OH 43551
Tel.: (419) 872-1930
Web Site: http://www.docusphere.com
Emp.: 25
Data Processing, Hosting & Related Services
N.A.I.C.S.: 518210
Bradley White *(Pres & CEO)*
Tina Dominique *(VP-Professional Svcs)*
Dave Litzenberg *(VP-Sls & Mktg)*
Kathleen Faltys *(Controller)*

NetWrix Corporation (1)
300 Spectrum Ctr Dr Ste 200, Irvine, CA 92618

U.S. PRIVATE

Tel.: (949) 407-5125
Web Site: http://www.netwrix.com
Software Development Services
N.A.I.C.S.: 541511
Steve Dickson *(CEO)*
Scott Parnell *(CFO)*
Bill Evans *(CMO)*
Mike Tierney *(VP-Customer Success)*
Jen Ilsley *(Dir-Global HR)*
John Newsom *(VP-Bus Dev)*
Anthony Chin *(VP-Sls Ops)*
Jim Smith *(VP-North America Sls)*
Vadim Balandin *(VP-Mktg)*
Ilia Sotnikov *(VP-Product Mgmt)*

Subsidiary (Domestic):

Stealthbits Technologies, Inc. (2)
200 Central Ave, Hawthorne, NJ 07506
Tel.: (201) 447-9300
Web Site: http://www.stealthbits.com
Sales Range: $1-9.9 Million
Emp.: 20
Computer & Software Stores
N.A.I.C.S.: 449210
Jill Twomey *(VP-Fin)*
Steve Cochran *(Founder & CEO)*
Adam Laub *(Sr VP-Product Mktg)*
Carol Volk *(Sr VP-Mktg & Product Mgmt)*
Jeff Warren *(VP-Technical Product Mgmt)*
John Albanese *(VP-Sls & Channel Ops)*
Mark Pilgrim *(VP-EMEA)*

Netrisk.hu (1)
Madarasz Viktor u 47-49 1 epulet 4 emelet, Budapest, 1138, Hungary (75%)
Tel.: (36) 6 1 413 3480
Web Site: http://www.netrisk.hu
Insurance Brokerage Services
N.A.I.C.S.: 524210
Tamas Scheidler *(CFO)*

Netsmart Technologies, Inc. (1)
11100 Nall Ave, Overland Park, KS 66211
Web Site: http://www.ntst.com
Emp.: 2,100
Health & Human Services Software Developer, Marketer & Technical Support Services
N.A.I.C.S.: 513210
Kevin Scalia *(Exec VP-Corp Dev)*
Paul Anderson *(Exec VP-Client Org)*
Michael Brand *(Exec VP-Engrg)*
Tom Herzog *(COO)*
Dawn Iddings *(Mng Dir & Sr VP)*
Scott Green *(Mng Dir & Sr VP-Careguidance)*
Mike Valentine *(CEO)*

Subsidiary (Domestic):

DeVero, Inc. (2)
300 Park Ave 2nd Fl, San Jose, CA 95110
Web Site: http://www.devero.com
Sales Range: $10-24.9 Million
Healthcare Software Development Services
N.A.I.C.S.: 541511

McBee Associates Inc. (2)
565 East Swedesford Rd, Suite 100, Wayne, PA 19087
Tel.: (610) 964-9680
Web Site: http://www.mcbeeassociates.com
Health Care Services & Consulting Firm
N.A.I.C.S.: 621491
Mike Dordick *(Pres)*
Keith Boroch *(VP-Advisory Consulting)*
Bob Braun *(Sr VP-Sls)*

Subsidiary (Domestic):

Quality In Real Time (3)
15 Verbena Ave, Floral Park, NY 11001
Tel.: (855) 485-7478
Web Site: http://www.qualityinrealtime.com
Electronic Medical Record Audits
N.A.I.C.S.: 541614
Laura Page-Greifinger *(Pres & CEO)*
Thomas Cannon *(COO)*
Philip Keating *(Chief Clinical Officer)*

Subsidiary (Domestic):

Netsmart Technologies, Inc. - Missouri (2)
5100 N Town Centre Dr, Ozark, MO 65721
Tel.: (417) 799-6600
Web Site: http://www.ntst.com
Software Publisher
N.A.I.C.S.: 513210

COMPANIES

TA ASSOCIATES, INC.

Carol Reynolds *(Exec VP-Client Experience)*

Tellus, LLC (2)
800 Fairway Dr Ste, Deerfield Beach, FL 33441
Tel.: (954) 719-0004
Web Site: http://4tellus.com
Rev.: $2,295,000
Emp.: 15
Data Processing, Hosting & Related Services
N.A.I.C.S.: 518210
Brad Levine *(CEO)*

NorthStar Financial Services Group LLC (1)
17605 Wright St, Omaha, NE 68130
Tel.: (402) 895-1600
Web Site: http://www.nstar-financial.com
Emp.: 990
Third Party Money Management Services
N.A.I.C.S.: 523940
Michael Miola *(Founder)*

Paula's Choice LLC (1)
1030 SW 34th St Ste A, Renton, WA 98057-4810
Tel.: (425) 988-6068
Web Site: http://www.paulaschoice.com
Cosmetics Developer, Distr & Online Retailer
N.A.I.C.S.: 325620
Paula Begoun *(Founder)*
Kate Mee *(Dir-Product Dev)*
Cynthia Short *(Sr Dir-Mktg & ECommerce)*
Tara Poseley *(CEO)*

Planview, Inc. (1)
12301 Research Blvd Research Park Plz V Ste 101, Austin, TX 78759-8770
Tel.: (512) 346-8600
Web Site: http://www.planview.com
Portfolio Management Solutions
N.A.I.C.S.: 523940
Scott Hardey *(Exec VP-Customer Svc)*
Jeff Durbin *(Gen Mgr-Ops-Global)*
Patrick A. Tickle *(Chief Product Officer)*
Eric S. Hurley *(VP-Legal Affairs)*
Linda Roach *(VP-Mktg)*
Vic Chynoweth *(Exec VP)*
Louise K. Allen *(Sr VP-Product Mgmt & Solutions Mktg)*
Rob Reesor *(Sr VP-Product Dev)*
Bryan Urioste *(Exec VP-Worldwide Mktg)*
Brian Prokaski *(Exec VP-Comml Sls)*
Razat Gaurav *(CEO)*
Gregory Gilmore *(Bd of Dirs, Executives)*

Subsidiary (Domestic):

Enrich Consulting, Inc. (2)
3031 Tisch Way Ste 711, San Jose, CA 95128
Tel.: (408) 871-9000
Web Site: http://www.enrichconsulting.com
Software Development Services
N.A.I.C.S.: 541511
Richard Sonnenblick *(Founder & CEO)*
Daniel Smith *(VP)*
Amisha Boucher *(Sr Mgr)*
Ohad Berman *(Sr Mgr)*
Assaf Shomer *(Mgr)*
Alison Pool *(Mgr)*

Innotas, Inc. (2)
111 Sutter St Ste 300, San Francisco, CA 94104
Tel.: (415) 263-9800
Web Site: http://www.innotas.com
Cloud-Based Portfolio Management Services
N.A.I.C.S.: 541511

Plutora, Inc. (2)
2445 Augustine Dr Ste 150, Santa Clara, CA 95054
Tel.: (628) 899-2084
Web Site: http://www.plutora.com
Sales Range: $1-9.9 Million
Emp.: 100
Software Development Services
N.A.I.C.S.: 541511
Bob Davies *(CMO)*
Mukund Singh *(Chief Customer Officer)*
Simon Farrell *(CTO)*
Alex Webb *(Fin Dir)*

Power Line Systems, Inc. (1)
610 N Whitney Way Ste 160, Madison, WI 53705-2157

Tel.: (608) 238-2171
Web Site: http://www.powline.com
Custom Computer Programming Services
N.A.I.C.S.: 541511
Maurizio Leva *(Mgr-Engrg)*

PowerGEM, LLC (1)
632 Plank Rd Ste 101, Clifton Park, NY 12065
Tel.: (518) 393-8100
Web Site: https://www.power-gem.com
Emp.: 100
Transmission Reliability Modeling, Market Analysis Software & Technical Services
N.A.I.C.S.: 541690
Joe DeMatteo *(CEO)*

Subsidiary (Domestic):

Astrape Consulting LLC (2)
5330 Stadium Trace Pkwy Ste 208, Birmingham, AL 35244-4526
Tel.: (205) 988-4404
Web Site: http://www.astrape.com
General Management Consulting Services
N.A.I.C.S.: 541611
Nick Wintermantel *(Principal)*

Precisely, Inc. (1)
1700 District Ave #300, Burlington, MA 01803
Tel.: (877) 700-0970
Web Site: http://www.precisely.com
Data Integration Software Developer & Publisher
N.A.I.C.S.: 513210
Josh Rogers *(CEO)*
Tendu Yogurtcu *(CTO)*
Jay Johnson *(Sr VP-Sls-Americas)*
Jason Smith *(Sr VP-Sls-APAC)*
Bryan Ashley *(Sr VP-Sls-APAC)*
Mads Toubro *(VP-Sls-EMEA)*
Kevin Ruane *(CMO)*
Lisa Crawford *(Chief HR Officer)*
Amy O'Connor *(CIO & Chief Data Officer)*

Subsidiary (Domestic):

Infogix, Inc. (2)
1240 E Diehl Rd Ste 400, Naperville, IL 60563
Tel.: (630) 505-1800
Data Controls & Analytics Software Services
N.A.I.C.S.: 513210

PlaceIQ, Inc. (2)
1732 1st Ave Ste 20951, New York, NY 10128
Tel.: (646) 963-5062
Web Site: http://www.placeiq.com
Media Representatives
N.A.I.C.S.: 541840
Anna Nguyen *(COO)*
Nadya Kohl *(Sr VP-Bus Dev)*
John Sedlak *(Chief Revenue Officer)*
Mandeep Mason *(Gen Mgr-EMEA)*
Duncan McCall *(Founder & CEO)*

Vision Solutions, Inc. (2)
15300 Barranca Pkwy Ste 250, Irvine, CA 92618
Tel.: (949) 253-6500
Web Site: http://www.visionsolutions.com
Information Technology Solutions
N.A.I.C.S.: 513210
Edward Vesely *(CMO & Exec VP)*
Mike Khattab *(VP-Sls-Growth Markets)*
Robert Johnson *(Exec VP-Sls)*
Rob Humbach *(VP-Sls-Americas)*
Chuck Davis *(VP-Fin)*
Kristin Brooks *(Gen Counsel)*

Professional Datasolutions, Inc. (1)
11675 Rainwater Dr Ste 350, Alpharetta, GA 30009
Tel.: (254) 410-7600
Web Site: http://www.pdisoftware.com
Enterprise Management Software
N.A.I.C.S.: 513210
Jimmy Frangis *(CEO)*
Nadine Routhier *(CMO)*
Douglas Henderson *(Chief Sales Officer)*
Christopher Berry *(CTO)*
Linnea Geiss *(COO)*
Stacey Smotherman *(Chief Legal Officer)*
Beth Strickland *(Chief HR Officer)*
Nicole Wu *(CFO)*
Adam Berger *(Chm)*
Brad McGuinness *(Sr VP-Point of Sale Solutions)*

Subsidiary (Domestic):

Cybera, Inc. (2)
9009 Carothers Pkwy Ste C5, Franklin, TN 37067
Tel.: (615) 301-2040
Web Site: http://www.cybera.net
Sales Range: $10-24.9 Million
Emp.: 80
Computer Services
N.A.I.C.S.: 517111
Cliff Duffey *(Founder & Pres)*
Paul Melton *(Sr VP-Strategic Sls)*
Kristen Hudson *(VP-Customer Ops)*
Ron Robinson *(Sr VP-Sls)*
Ken Norman *(CTO & Sr VP)*
Ken Kaley *(VP-Product Mktg)*
Andrew Lev *(CEO)*
Jon Howard *(Co-CFO)*
Jeff Manning *(Exec VP-Sls & Channels-Worldwide)*
Shaf Begen *(VP-Channel Sls)*
Hubert Da Costa *(Sr VP & Gen Mgr-EMEA)*

Excentus Corp. (2)
14241 Dallas Pkwy Ste 1200, Dallas, TX 75254
Tel.: (972) 793-6000
Computer Systems Design Services; Marketing Programs & Services
N.A.I.C.S.: 541512

GreenPrint Holdings, Inc. (2)
3405 Piedmont Rd NE Ste 220, Atlanta, GA 30305
Tel.: (404) 207-1947
Web Site: http://www.greenprint.eco
Sales Range: $1-9.9 Million
Emp.: 13
Biomass Energy Services
N.A.I.C.S.: 221117
Pete Davis *(Co-Founder & CEO)*
Trenton Spindler *(Co-Founder & Pres)*
Scot Crawford *(CFO)*
Michele Koch *(CMO)*
Maryann Michela *(VP-Ops & Acct)*

Subsidiary (Non-US):

Inform Information Systems Limited (2)
Maidenhead Court Boathouse Court Road, Maidenhead, SL6 8LQ, United Kingdom
Tel.: (44) 1628768200
Information Technology & Services
N.A.I.C.S.: 519290
Brandon Logsdon *(Pres/Gen Mgr-Mktg Cloud & Fuel Pricing Solutions)*

Subsidiary (Domestic):

Universe Group Plc (3)
George Curl Way, Southampton, SO18 2RX, United Kingdom
Tel.: (44) 238 068 9200
Web Site: http://www.universe-group.co.uk
Rev.: $26,814,970
Assets: $51,663,961
Liabilities: $19,693,729
Net Worth: $31,970,233
Earnings: ($834,998)
Emp.: 213
Fiscal Year-end: 12/31/2020
Retail, Point-of-sale & Inventory Management Software
N.A.I.C.S.: 513210
Jeremy Lewis *(CEO)*
Daryl Paton *(CFO & Sec)*

Subsidiary (Domestic):

HTEC Ltd (4)
Southampton Intl Park, George Curl Way, Southampton, SO18 2RX, United Kingdom
Tel.: (44) 2380689200
Web Site: http://www.htec.co.uk
Sales Range: $25-49.9 Million
Emp.: 150
Payment & Information System Services
N.A.I.C.S.: 541512

Subsidiary (Domestic):

Intellifuel Systems Inc. (2)
1650 Chaffee Dr, Titusville, FL 32780
Tel.: (321) 264-8707
Web Site: http://www.intellifuel.com
Sales Range: $1-9.9 Million
Emp.: 5
Fuel Management & Logistics Services

N.A.I.C.S.: 541519
Patrick Durland *(Project Mgr)*
Rick Evans *(Pres)*

National Payment Card Association (2)
72 Commercial St, Portland, ME 04101
Tel.: (954) 449-9541
Web Site: http://www.zipline.biz
Mobile Payment, Reward Programs & Technologies Services
N.A.I.C.S.: 541519

Subsidiary (Domestic):

Smartclixx, LLC (3)
6501 Congress Ave Ste 300, Boca Raton, FL 33487
Tel.: (561) 998-8515
Web Site: http://www.smartclixx.com
Custom Computer Programming Services
N.A.I.C.S.: 541511

RLDatix Limited (1)
10 York Road, London, SE1 7ND, United Kingdom
Tel.: (44) 2089711971
Web Site: http://www.rldatix.com
Healthcare Services
N.A.I.C.S.: 621610
Vincent E. Estrada *(Sr Exec VP-Corp Dev)*
Terence Clifton *(CTO)*
Peter Holbrook *(CFO)*
Barbara Staruk *(Chief Product Officer)*
Jeff Surges *(CEO)*
Tim McDonald *(Officer-Patient Safety & Risk)*

Subsidiary (Domestic):

Allocate Software plc (2)
1 Church Road, Richmond, TW9 2QE, United Kingdom
Tel.: (44) 207 355 5555
Web Site: https://www.allocatesoftware.com
Workforce Optimization Software Developer
N.A.I.C.S.: 513210
Terence Clifton *(CTO)*
Erik Stone *(Mng Dir-Europe)*
Mil Milojevic *(Chief Product Officer)*
Hugh Ashley *(Mng Dir-Uk & Ireland)*
Nick Wilson *(CEO)*
Jon Harston *(CFO)*
Claire John *(Dir-HR)*
Maddy Phipps-Taylor *(Dir-Corp Dev)*
Liz Jones *(CMO)*
Paul Scandrett *(Dir-Intl Health)*
Matt Durtson *(Mng Dir-Australia, New Zealand & Asia Pacific)*

Subsidiary (Non-US):

Allocate Software Pty. Ltd. (3)
Suite 4 Level 4 441 St Kilda Road, Melbourne, 3004, VIC, Australia
Tel.: (61) 39 534 4477
Web Site: https://www.allocatesoftware.com
Workforce Optimization Software Developer
N.A.I.C.S.: 513210
Matt Durston *(Mng Dir)*

Time Care AB (3)
Tel.: (46) 85 055 1800
Web Site: https://www.allocatesoftware.se
Workforce Management Software Mfr
N.A.I.C.S.: 541511
Marie Munkhammar *(Mgr-Mgmt Svcs)*
Gunilla Norling *(Mgr-Support)*
Jessica Widerberg *(Mgr-Implementation)*
Petteri Vuokko *(Mgr-Sls)*
Rickard Lindstrom *(Mgr-Dev)*
Andreas Nou *(Dir-Product)*

Subsidiary (US):

Ecteon, Inc. (2)
5214 Maryland Way Ste 110, Brentwood, TN 37027
Tel.: (212) 268-9800
Web Site: https://www.ecteon.com
Rev.: $2,100,000
Emp.: 20
Contract Management Solutions Services
N.A.I.C.S.: 561499
Amy G. Harkins *(Dir & Sr VP)*
Lonnie Blackwood *(CTO)*
Richard Eckerstrom *(CEO)*
Eran Baram *(Controller)*
Marlene Bauer *(VP)*
Ralph Mayes *(COO)*

TA ASSOCIATES, INC.

TA Associates, Inc.—(Continued)

Galen Healthcare Solutions (2)
PO Box 36715, Grosse Pointe, MI 48236
Tel.: (888) 425-3644
Web Site: http://www.galenhealthcare.com
Sales Range: $1-9.9 Million
Emp.: 29
Electronic Health Records
N.A.I.C.S.: 541519
Stephen McQueen *(Chm)*
Matthew Nice *(Pres)*
Cary Bresloff *(VP-Sls)*
Mike Dow *(CIO)*
Erin Sain *(COO)*
Justin Campbell *(VP-Mktg)*
Steve Brewer *(CEO)*
John Moore *(Founder & Mng Partner)*

Verge Solutions, LLC (2)
11 eWall St, Mount Pleasant, SC 29464
Tel.: (843) 628-4168
Web Site: http://www.vergehealth.com
Software Publisher
N.A.I.C.S.: 513210
Jon Piebenga *(Partner)*
Connie Moser *(CEO)*

iContracts, Inc. (2)
1011 US Route 22 W Ste 104, Bridgewater, NJ 08807
Tel.: (908) 393-9550
Web Site: http://www.icontracts.com
Contract, Policy & Revenue Management Services
N.A.I.C.S.: 541611
Todd Venetianer *(COO)*
Leigh Powell *(CEO)*
Erik Sieverding *(CIO)*

Subsidiary (Domestic):

PolicyStat, LLC (3)
550 Congressional Blvd Ste 100, Carmel, IN 46032-9439
Tel.: (317) 644-1296
Web Site: http://www.policystat.com
Policy Management Software Publisher
N.A.I.C.S.: 513210
Jill Sawyer *(Mgr-Product Mktg)*

Revalize, Inc. (1)
8800 W Baymeadows Way 500, Jacksonville, FL 32256
Web Site: http://www.revalizesoftware.com
Software Publisher
N.A.I.C.S.: 519290
Michael Sabin *(CEO)*
David Kuhl *(Chief People Officer)*
Kevin McAdams *(CFO)*
Don Stockslager *(VP-Bus Sys)*
Mark Friedman *(Chm)*

Subsidiary (Domestic):

Attainia, Inc. (2)
650 Castro St, Mountain View, CA 94041
Tel.: (650) 691-4555
Web Site: http://www.attainia.com
Rev.: $1,800,000
Emp.: 18
Data Processing, Hosting & Related Services
N.A.I.C.S.: 518210
Jeff Kleck *(Founder & Chief Strategy Officer)*
Jerry Kizziar *(CTO)*
D. J. Chhabra *(Chm & CEO)*
Ron Villarreal *(CFO)*
Kevin Keller *(VP-Sls)*

BCA Technologies Inc. (2)
1059 Maitland Ctr Commons Blvd, Maitland, FL 32751-7453
Tel.: (407) 659-0653
Web Site: http://www.bcatech.com
Custom Computer Programming Services
N.A.I.C.S.: 541511
Brian Cumming *(Owner)*

Kochman Consultants Ltd. (2)
5545 Lincoln Ave, Morton Grove, IL 60053-3430
Tel.: (847) 223-0777
Web Site: http://www.kclcad.com
Management Consulting Services
N.A.I.C.S.: 541618
Ronald Kochman *(Pres)*

Riskonnect, Inc. (1)
1701 Barrett Lakes Blvd Ste 500, Kennesaw, GA 30144-4517
Tel.: (770) 790-4700
Web Site: http://www.riskonnect.com
Emp.: 200
Risk Management Website & Platform Host
N.A.I.C.S.: 518210
Teri McEvily *(CFO)*
Jim Wetekamp *(CEO)*
Andrea Brody *(Chief Mktg Officer)*
Kevin Crow *(Chief HR Officer)*

Subsidiary (Domestic):

Riskonnect ClearSight LLC (2)
200 W. Monroe S Ste 1100, Chicago, IL 60606
Tel.: (770) 790-4700
Web Site: http://www.riskonnect.com
Software Development Services
N.A.I.C.S.: 541512

Subsidiary (Non-US):

Sword GRC Ltd. (2)
1 Grenfell Road, Maidenhead, SL6 1HN, Berkshire, United Kingdom
Tel.: (44) 1628582500
Information Technology Services
N.A.I.C.S.: 541511

Subsidiary (Domestic):

Ventiv Technology Inc. (2)
3350 Riverwood Pkwy 20th Fl, Atlanta, GA 30339
Tel.: (866) 452-2787
Web Site: http://www.ventivtech.com
Cloud-Base Company
N.A.I.C.S.: 513210
Peter Yang *(Chief Information Officer)*

Subsidiary (Domestic):

DAVID Corporation (3)
200 Pine St 2nd Fl, San Francisco, CA 94104
Tel.: (415) 362-4555
Web Site: http://www.davidcorp.com
Mfr, Developer & Marketer of Risk Management Software for Workers Compensation & Liability Claims Management
N.A.I.C.S.: 513210
Lissette Hetterly *(VP-Client Svcs)*
Mary-Margaret Dale *(Dir-Mktg)*
Mark E. Dorn *(Pres & CEO)*
Joseph Bako *(VP-Software Dev)*
Michael Hamann *(VP-Software Dev)*

Russell Investments Group, LLC. (1)
1301 2nd Ave 18th Fl, Seattle, WA 98101
Tel.: (206) 505-7877
Web Site: http://www.russell.com
Alternative Investment Management Services
N.A.I.C.S.: 523940
Jeff Hussey *(Chief Investment Officer-Global)*
Brian Meath *(Mng Dir & Sr Portfolio Mgr)*
Mark Spina *(Head-US Private Client Svcs)*
Toby Hoden *(CMO)*
Michelle Seitz *(Chm & CEO)*
Michael Hall *(Mng Dir-Institutional-Americas)*
Gene Raffone *(Chief HR Officer-Global)*
Kate El-Hillow *(Co-Pres & Chief Investment Officer-Global)*
Kevin Klingert *(Co-Pres)*

Stadion Money Management, LLC (1)
1061 Cliff Dawson Rd, Watkinsville, GA 30677
Tel.: (706) 353-8737
Web Site: http://www.stadionmoney.com
Investment Management Service
N.A.I.C.S.: 523940
Tim Chapman *(Chm)*
Jud Doherty *(CEO)*
Michael Chlan *(COO & CTO)*
Brad Thompson *(Chief Investment Officer)*
Steve Beard *(Sr VP-Mktg)*
Michael Isaac *(Chief Compliance Officer)*
Clay Alliston *(Sr VP)*
Duane Bernt *(CFO)*
David Lacusky *(Chief Distribution Officer)*
Chris Barrett *(Reg VP)*
Will McGough *(Sr VP & Portfolio Mgr)*
Todd Lacey *(Chief Bus Dev Officer-Retirement Bus)*
Kerr McGowan *(Sr VP-Retirement Solutions)*
Holly MacMillan *(Chief Mktg Officer)*
Brandon Lowe *(VP-Bus Dev-Retirement Bus Dev Team)*
Lucy Pelsma *(VP-Mktg)*

Stonewall Kitchen LLC (1)
2 Stonewall Ln, York, ME 03909
Tel.: (207) 351-2713
Web Site: http://www.stonewallkitchen.com
Jams, Sauces, Crackers & Other Foods Mfr
N.A.I.C.S.: 311421
Jonathan King *(Co-Founder & VP)*
Janine Somers *(CMO)*
Natalie King *(Chief Sls & Mktg Officer)*
Jim Stott *(Co-Founder & Partner)*
Sheri Tripp *(Mgr-Mktg)*
Carrie S. McDermott *(CEO)*
Rick Lees *(CFO)*
Kathy Gilbert *(Chief Sls Officer)*
Corey Fogarty *(Chief Mdsg Officer)*
Steve Barone *(COO)*

Synokem Pharmaceuticals Ltd. (1)
A1-14, Paschim Vihar Near Paschim Vihar West Metro Opposite Metro Pillar No - 261A, Delhi, 110 063, India
Tel.: (91) 1142428600
Web Site: https://www.synokempharma.com
Pharmaceuticals Product Mfr
N.A.I.C.S.: 325412
Yash Baheti *(VP)*

Subsidiary (Domestic):

Nitin Lifesciences Ltd. (2)
92-93 Sector-3 H S I D C G T Road, Industrial Area, Karnal, 132 001, Haryana, India (74%)
Tel.: (91) 1842221590
Web Site: http://www.nitinlifesciences.com
Pharmaceuticals Product Mfr
N.A.I.C.S.: 325412

TA Associates (UK), LLP (1)
3rd Floor Devonshire House, 1 Mayfair Place, London, W1J 8AJ, United Kingdom
Tel.: (44) 20 7823 0200
Web Site: http://www.ta.com
Emp.: 17
Investment Management Service
N.A.I.C.S.: 523940
Dietrich Hauptmeier *(Principal)*
Ajit Nedungadi *(Mng Dir)*
Birker B. Bahnsen *(Principal)*
Patrick Sader *(Dir-Europe)*
J. Morgan Seigler *(Mng Dir)*
Christopher Parkin *(Mng Dir)*
Naveen Wadhera *(Mng Dir)*

TA Associates Advisory Pvt. Ltd. (1)
13th Floor Birla Aurora Tower, Dr Annie Besant Road Worli, Mumbai, 400 030, India
Tel.: (91) 22 6144 3100
Web Site: http://www.ta.com
Emp.: 12
Private Equity
N.A.I.C.S.: 523999
Naveen Wadhera *(Country Head)*
Aditya Sharma *(Sr VP)*
Vivek Mohan *(VP)*

TA Associates Asia Pacific Ltd. (1)
One Exchange Square 16th Floor 8 Connaught Place, Central, China (Hong Kong)
Tel.: (852) 3656 6300
Web Site: http://www.ta.com
Emp.: 10
Private Equity
N.A.I.C.S.: 523999
Edward F. Sippel *(Mng Dir & Head-Asia)*
Naveen Wadhera *(Head-European)*
Daniel Brujis *(Sr VP)*
Andrew Z. Tay *(Sr VP)*

TA Associates Ltd. (1)
3rd FL Devonshire House 1 Mayfair Pl, London, W1J8AJ, United Kingdom
Tel.: (44) 20 7823 0200
Web Site: http://www.ta.com
Emp.: 20
Private Equity
N.A.I.C.S.: 523999
Ajit Nedungadi *(Mng Dir)*
Birker Bahnsen *(Mng Dir)*

TA Associates Management, L.P. (1)
56th Fl 200 Clarendon St, Boston, MA 02116

U.S. PRIVATE

Tel.: (617) 574-6700
Web Site: http://www.ta.com
Investment Management Service
N.A.I.C.S.: 523940
Jason S. Mironov *(Dir-Menlo Park)*
Jeffrey S. Barber *(Mng Dir)*
Michael S. Berk *(Mng Dir)*
Jonathan M. Goldstein *(Mng Dir)*
A. Bruce Johnston *(Mng Dir)*
Dhiraj Poddar *(Mng Dir)*
Clara Jackson *(Principal)*
Emily McGinty *(Principal-Menlo Park)*
Michael Libert *(Sr VP)*
Tony Marsh *(Chief Capital Markets Officer)*
Melanie Toomey *(CFO)*
Gregory Wallace *(CFO-Funds)*

Holding (Non-US):

Elos Medtech AB (2)
Torsgatan 5B, 411 04, Gothenburg, Sweden
Tel.: (46) 101712000
Web Site: https://www.elosmedtech.com
Rev.: $70,806,400
Assets: $122,328,433
Liabilities: $56,368,853
Net Worth: $65,959,580
Earnings: $4,398,787
Emp.: 522
Fiscal Year-end: 12/31/2020
Medical & Precision Technology Products
N.A.I.C.S.: 339112
Yvonne Martensson *(Chm)*
Ewa Linsater *(CFO)*
Andreas Glanfalt *(CIO)*
Monica Tapper *(Chief People Officer)*

Subsidiary (Non-US):

Elos Medtech Pinol A/S (3)
Engvej 33, 3330, Gorlose, Denmark (100%)
Tel.: (45) 48216400
Web Site: http://www.elos-pinol.dk
Sales Range: $50-74.9 Million
Emp.: 150
Surgical & Medical Instrument Mfr
N.A.I.C.S.: 339112
Soren Oleson *(Mng Dir)*

Elos Medtech Tianjin Co. Ltd. (3)
D5-3 Rong Cheng San Zhi Lu Xeda International Industrial City, 300385, Tianjin, China
Tel.: (86) 22 23 82 86 60
Web Site: http://www.elos.se
Medical Instrument Mfr
N.A.I.C.S.: 339112

Subsidiary (Domestic):

Elos Medtech Timmersdala AB (3)
Backedalsvagen 5, Box 45, 54016, Timmersdala, Sweden
Tel.: (46) 511440600
Web Site: http://www.elosmedtech.com
Sales Range: $50-74.9 Million
Emp.: 11
Surgical & Medical Instrument Mfr
N.A.I.C.S.: 339112

Subsidiary (US):

Onyx Medical LLC (3)
1800 N Shelby Oaks Dr, Memphis, TN 38134
Tel.: (800) 238-6981
Web Site: http://www.onyxmedical.net
Emp.: 100
Surgical & Medical Instrument Mfr
N.A.I.C.S.: 339112
Jason Mitchell *(Engr-Mfg)*
Jodie Gilmore *(CEO & Mng Dir)*

Triple Point Technology, Inc. (1)
57 Greens Farms Rd, Westport, CT 06880
Tel.: (203) 429-3000
Web Site: http://www.tpt.com
Sales Range: $200-249.9 Million
Software Solutions to Manage Commodities & Enterprise Risk
N.A.I.C.S.: 513210
Howard Adams *(Mgr-Security)*
Wah Chu *(Chief Customer Officer)*
Megan Lamp *(Dir-HR-Global)*
Simon Woods *(Head-Sls & Mktg-Global)*
Igor Starovoitov *(VP-Architecture & Tech)*
Gary Bernhardt *(Dir-IT-Global)*
Carlos Lebrija *(VP & Dir-Solutions)*

COMPANIES

TABER CRANE CONSTRUCTION SERVICES CORP.

Branch (Non-US):

Triple Point Technology Pty Ltd. (2)
Ste D level 4, 251 Wharf Rd, Newcastle, 2300, NSW, Australia
Tel.: (61) 249082222
Sales Range: $50-74.9 Million
Emp.: 20
Software Solutions to Manage Commodities & Enterprise Risk
N.A.I.C.S.: 513210
Steve Maxwell (CEO)
Hayden Shilling (Mgr-Software Dev)
Frederic Flament (Gen Mgr-Algosys Div)
Brett Thomas (Mgr-Client Svcs)

Subsidiary (Domestic):

WAM Systems, Inc. (2)
100 Tournament Dr Ste 300, Horsham, PA 19044
Tel.: (484) 530-4380
Web Site: http://www.tpt.com
Emp.: 25
Supply Chain Management Solutions
N.A.I.C.S.: 513210
Jack Weiss (VP-Supply Chain Mgmt)
Mark Zod (VP & Dir-Solutions-Supply Chain Mgmt)
Doug Ditillo (Dir-Software Dev-Supply Chain Mgmt)

Truck Hero, Inc. (1)
5400 Data Ct, Ann Arbor, MI 48108
Tel.: (734) 677-0444
Web Site: http://www.truck-hero.com
Automotive Accessories Mfr
N.A.I.C.S.: 336390
William J. Reminder (CEO)
Marla Zwas (Gen Counsel)
Kelly Kneifl (COO)
Ryan Herman (Exec VP-Sls)
Mark Hickey (Exec VP-Ops)
Christina Baldwin (Chief HR Officer)

Subsidiary (Domestic):

Lund International Holding Company (2)
4325 Hamilton Mill Rd Ste 400, Buford, GA 30518
Tel.: (770) 339-5800
Web Site: http://www.lundinternational.com
Sales Range: $75-99.9 Million
Automotive Aftermarket Accessory Designer, Mfr & Distr
N.A.I.C.S.: 336390
Mitch Fogle (Pres & CEO)
Tammy Gracek (COO & Gen Mgr-OE)
Lee McGuire (Sr Dir-Mktg-Jeep & Off Road)

Subsidiary (Domestic):

Roadworks Manufacturing, Inc. (3)
3565 E 300 N, Lafayette, IN 47905
Tel.: (765) 742-7200
Web Site: http://www.roadworksmfg.com
Motor Vehicle Body Mfr
N.A.I.C.S.: 336211

Roll-N-Lock Corp. (3)
2033 W McNab Rd Ste 2, Pompano Beach, FL 33069
Web Site: http://www.rollnlock.com
Sales Range: $1-9.9 Million
Emp.: 80
Manufactures Tonneau Covers & Other Cargo Management Product Mfr
N.A.I.C.S.: 336120

Subsidiary (Domestic):

Omix-ADA, Inc. (2)
460 Horizon Dr, Suwanee, GA 30024
Tel.: (770) 614-6101
Web Site: http://www.omix-ada.com
Automotive Accessories Mfr
N.A.I.C.S.: 336390

Twin Med LLC (1)
11333 Greenstone Ave, Santa Fe Springs, CA 90670
Tel.: (323) 582-9900
Web Site: http://www.twinmed.com
Sales Range: $75-99.9 Million
Medical & Hospital Equipment
N.A.I.C.S.: 423450
Steve Rechnitz (Co-Founder)
Shlomo Rechnitz (Co-Founder)

WU Holdco, Inc. (1)
705 Tri State Pkwy, Gurnee, IL 60031
Tel.: (847) 263-3500
Web Site: http://www.weiman.com
Surface Care Mfr
N.A.I.C.S.: 325612
Carl DeMasi (Chm)
John Brennan (Sr VP-Sls)
Brandon Alvarez (Coord-Shipping)
Greg Weeg (Dir-Facilities)
James Sommerfield (Coord-Warehouse)
Melanie Loomis (Dir-Sls Dev)
Minerva Alday (Dir-Acctg)
Rhonda Fonk (Dir-Art)
Tania Camacho (Acct Coord)
Wendy Burr (Acct Mgr)
Edward Duffy (VP-Weiman Healthcare)
Billy Vanderploeg (Mgr-Supply Chain)
Coleen Smith (Mgr-Logistics)
Sylwia Aldrin (Dir-R&D)
Chris Bauder (CEO)
Dexter Reid Jr. (Coord-Medical Accts)

Division (Domestic):

Burnishine Products (2)
755 Tri State Pkwy, Gurnee, IL 60031
Tel.: (847) 263-3500
Web Site: http://www.weiman.com
Sales Range: $10-24.9 Million
Chemical Products Mfr
N.A.I.C.S.: 325998
Patty Vick (Mgr-Natl Sls)
Carl DeMasi (Pres & CEO)

J.A. Wright & Co. (2)
755 Tri State Pkwy, Gurnee, IL 60031
Tel.: (847) 263-3500
Web Site: http://www.jawright.com
Metal Care Products Mfr
N.A.I.C.S.: 325612

Wealth Enhancement Group, LLC (1)
505 N Highway 169 Ste 900, Plymouth, MN 55441
Tel.: (763) 417-1700
Web Site: http://www.wealthenhancement.com
Investment Advisory Services
N.A.I.C.S.: 523940
Jeff Dekko (CEO)
Jim Cahn (Chief Investment & Bus Officer)
Terri Kallsen (COO)
Kelly Windorski (CFO)
Eric Weiss (Officer-Chief Growth)
Brian Vnak (Sr VP-Advisor Services)

Subsidiary (Domestic):

10-15 Associates, Inc. (2)
168 Main St, Goshen, NY 10924
Tel.: (845) 294-2080
Rev: $2,254,000
Emp.: 7
Portfolio Management
N.A.I.C.S.: 523940
Michael Matteo (Founder, CFO & Mng Dir)
Deborah DeMatteo (Founder, Pres & CEO)

BTR Capital Management Inc. (2)
1999 Harrison St, Oakland, CA 94612
Tel.: (415) 989-0100
Web Site: http://www.btrcap.com
Rev: $3,320,000
Emp.: 8
Portfolio Management
N.A.I.C.S.: 523940
Lewis H. Katcher (Co-Founder & Principal)
John A. Stratton (Pres, Principal & Portfolio Mgr)
Stephen P. Yeatman (Co-Founder & Principal)
Jonathan W. Bulter (Principal, Dir-Res & Portfolio Mgr)
Mark A. Keeling (Chief Investment Officer, Principal & Portfolio Mgr)
Ward P. Lindenmayer (Sr VP & Portfolio Mgr)
Anna Formicola (Principal & Head-Admin)
Elizabeth Kurniawan Ormeno (Principal & Mgr-Ops)
Gregory A. Welch (Sr VP & Portfolio Mgr)
Robert C. Welch (VP & Portfolio Mgr)
Robert C. Maples (VP & Portfolio Mgr)
John O. Jenkins (Sr VP & Portfolio Mgr)

Cetera Advisors LLC (2)
1990 N California Blvd 8th Fl, Walnut Creek, CA 94596
Tel.: (510) 834-3917
Web Site: http://www.prozanfinancial.com
Investment Advice
N.A.I.C.S.: 523940

Equius Partners Inc. (2)
3 Hamilton Landing Ste 130, Novato, CA 94949
Tel.: (415) 382-2500
Web Site: http://www.equiuspartners.com
Investment Advisory Services
N.A.I.C.S.: 523940
Phil Jonckheer (Mng Dir & CFO)
Jeff Troutner (Mng Dir, CEO & CIO)
Katie Calagui (CEO)
Jason Zahorenko (Mgr-Relationship)
David Wootton (Mgr-Client Svc)
Max Rudsten (Mgr-Relationship)

GDM Advisory Group Ltd. (2)
501 W Office Center Dr, Fort Washington, PA 19034
Tel.: (215) 886-5800
Investment Advice
N.A.I.C.S.: 523940

Landmark Financial Advisors, LLC (2)
911 College St Ste 301, Bowling Green, KY 42101-2183
Tel.: (270) 782-5196
Web Site: http://www.landmarkfa.com
Consumer Lending
N.A.I.C.S.: 522291
Brent Mason (Pres)

Legacy Financial Planning LLC (2)
1507 Monroe Ave, Rochester, NY 14618
Tel.: (585) 241-5250
Portfolio Management
N.A.I.C.S.: 523940

Napa Valley Wealth Management (2)
2255 Contra Costa Blvd, Pleasant Hill, CA 94523-3772
Tel.: (925) 827-4393
Web Site: http://www.napavalleywealthmanagement.com
Specialty Trade Contractors
N.A.I.C.S.: 238990
Kelly Crane (Owner)

New Era Financial Advisors, Inc. (2)
801 2 Oaks Center Dr, Wayzata, MN 55391
Tel.: (952) 473-1116
Web Site: http://www.newerafinancial.com
Sales Range: $1-9.9 Million
Emp.: 15
Insurance Agencies & Brokerages
N.A.I.C.S.: 524210

Piermont Wealth Management, Inc. (2)
135 Crossways Park Dr Ste 102, Woodbury, NY 11797
Tel.: (516) 697-8200
Web Site: http://www.piermontwealth.com
Financial Investment Activities
N.A.I.C.S.: 523999
Jaclyn Pagano (Dir-Admin)
Philip j. Capell (CEO)

Retirement Advisory Group (2)
6200 Baker Rd Ste 100, Eden Prairie, MN 55346
Tel.: (952) 975-9770
Web Site: http://www.retirementadvisorygroup.com
Investment Advice
N.A.I.C.S.: 523940
Terry Kerber (Owner)

Retirement Strategies, Inc. (2)
10751 Deerwood Park Blvd Ste 302, Jacksonville, FL 32256-4850
Tel.: (904) 600-5920
Web Site: http://www.wealthenhancement.com
Financial Planning
N.A.I.C.S.: 524210

Sadoff Investment Management (2)
250 W Coventry Ct, Milwaukee, WI 53217
Tel.: (414) 352-8460
Web Site: http://www.sadoffinvestments.com
Rev: $2,075,000
Emp.: 5
Portfolio Management
N.A.I.C.S.: 523940

Ronald Sadoff (Founder)

Serafini Financial Service Inc. (2)
1110 Opal Ct, Hagerstown, MD 21740
Tel.: (301) 739-1500
Web Site: http://www.serafinifinancial.com
Rev.: $2,010,000
Emp.: 5
Investment Banking & Securities Dealing
N.A.I.C.S.: 523150
Andrew Serafini (Founder)

Titus Wealth Management, Inc. (2)
700 Larkspur Landing Circle Suite 109, Larkspur, CA 94939
Tel.: (415) 461-4800
Web Site: http://www.tituswealth.com
Financial Investment Activities
N.A.I.C.S.: 523999
Clark L. Miller (Mng Dir)
Scot Lance (Mng Dir)
Eric Aanes (Founder & Pres)

Wealth Enhancement Brokerage Services, LLC (2)
505 N Highway 169 Ste 900, Plymouth, MN 55441
Tel.: (763) 417-1444
Web Site: http://www.we-brokerageservices.com
Investment Management Service
N.A.I.C.S.: 523940

TA CHEN INTERNATIONAL INC
11101 South Tacoma Way, Lakewood, WA 98499
Tel.: (253) 584-2161
Web Site: http://www.tachen.com
Rev.: $1,200,000
Emp.: 13
Sheet Metal Work Mfg
N.A.I.C.S.: 332322

Subsidiaries:

Peachtree Metals Co. (1)
2963 Pleasant Hill Rd, Duluth, GA 30096
Tel.: (770) 232-8667
Web Site: http://www.peachtreemetals.com
Rolled Steel Shape Mfr
N.A.I.C.S.: 331221
Tim Dove (Mgr-Prodduction Plng)
Frank Everett (Plant Supvr)

TABATCHNICK FINE FOODS, INC.
1230 Hamilton St, Somerset, NJ 08873-3343
Tel.: (732) 247-6668
Web Site: http://www.tabatchnick.com
Year Founded: 1905
Frozen Soups Mfr & Distr
N.A.I.C.S.: 311412
Barry Ansel (Sr VP-Sls & Mktg)

TABCOM, LLC
1 Maplewood Dr, Hazleton, PA 18202-9798
Tel.: (570) 384-5555 PA
Web Site: http://www.petsupplies.com
Year Founded: 1969
Web Site Owner & Operator; Pet-Related Products & Accessories Online Sales
N.A.I.C.S.: 459910
Alexander Tabibi (Co-Founder)
Carlo Tabibi (Co-Founder)
Jaime Nuckles (Sls Mgr-Territory Sls)

TABER CRANE CONSTRUCTION SERVICES CORP.
1617 W Old US Hwy 50, Washington, IN 47501
Tel.: (812) 254-1610
Web Site: http://www.tabercrane.com
Sales Range: $10-24.9 Million
Emp.: 10
Commercial & Office Building, New Construction
N.A.I.C.S.: 236220

TABER CRANE CONSTRUCTION SERVICES CORP. U.S. PRIVATE

Taber Crane Construction Services Corp.—(Continued)
David F. Crane (Treas & Sec)
Coy J. Taber (Pres)
Roxanne Kitzman (Office Mgr)
Mike Clark (Project Mgr)

TABLE TO TABLE
PO Box 1051, Englewood Cliffs, NJ 07632
Tel.: (201) 444-5500 NJ
Web Site: http://www.tabletotable.org
Year Founded: 1999
Sales Range: $10-24.9 Million
Emp.: 12
Hunger Relief Services
N.A.I.C.S.: 624210
Michelle Weinraub (Dir-Dev)
Anthony Math (Dir-Food Sourcing & Donor Rels)
Julie Sciaino (Dir-Recipient Rels & Community Affairs)
Ilene Isaacs (Exec Dir)

TABLECRAFT PRODUCTS CO., INC.
801 Lakeside Dr, Gurnee, IL 60031
Tel.: (847) 855-9000
Web Site: http://www.tablecraft.com
Tableware Mfr & Distr
N.A.I.C.S.: 332215
Carlos Bendfeldt (Dir-Intl Sls)
Michael Jay (Owner)

Subsidiaries:

Professional Bakeware Co., Inc. (1)
11739 N Highway 75, Willis, TX 77378
Tel.: (936) 890-8470
Sales Range: $1-9.9 Million
Emp.: 20
Cooking Equipment Mfr
N.A.I.C.S.: 332215

TABOR CITY LUMBER COMPANY INCORPORATED
510 N Main St, Tabor City, NC 28463
Tel.: (910) 653-3162
Web Site: http://taborcitylumber.com
Sales Range: $10-24.9 Million
Emp.: 6
Lumber: Rough, Dressed & Finished
N.A.I.C.S.: 423310
Rod Sanders (Pres)

TABOR COMMUNICATIONS, INC.
8445 Camino Santa Fe Ste 101, San Diego, CA 92121
Tel.: (858) 625-0070 CA
Web Site: http://www.taborcommunications.com
Year Founded: 2002
Sales Range: $1-9.9 Million
Emp.: 15
Internet Publishing, Broadcasting & Advertising
N.A.I.C.S.: 541890
Tom Tabor (Founder & CEO)
Jeff Hyman (Publr)
Alan El Faye (Pres)
Matt Walters (Assoc VP-Digital Strategy)
Tiffany Trader (Mng Editor-HPCwire)
Isaac Lopez (Dir-Editorial Ops)
Mitch Becker (Dir-Sls)
Chelsea Lang (Mgr-Mkt Insights)
Lynn Bergin (Mgr-Mktg Programs)
Ana Vasquez (Sr Mgr-Sls & Media Ops)
Anna Suarez (VP-Workforce)

TABULA, INC.
3250 Olcott St Ste 300, Santa Clara, CA 95054-3026
Tel.: (408) 986-9140

Web Site: http://www.tabula.com
Year Founded: 2003
Sales Range: $10-24.9 Million
Emp.: 100
3D Programmable Logic Device Distr
N.A.I.C.S.: 423690
Alain Bismuth (VP-Mktg & Bus Dev)
Rajeev Jayaraman (VP-Svcs)
Steve Teig (Founder)
Matt Crowly (Sr VP-Product Dev)
Daniel Gitlin (VP-Mfg Tech)
Steve Haynes (VP-Sls)
Steffen Rochel (VP-Software Dev)
Chris Taylor (VP-HR)

TAC PARTNERS, INC.
53 State St Ste 2602, Boston, MA 02109
Tel.: (617) 345-7200 MA
Web Site: http://www.mcpartners.com
Year Founded: 1986
Privater Equity Firm
N.A.I.C.S.: 523999
Gillis S. Cashman (Mng Partner)
Brian M. Clark (Mng Partner)
James F. Wade (Chm)
Edward J. Keefe (CFO & Chief Compliance Officer)
Travis A. Keller (Mng Partner)
Arvind Viswanathan (VP)
Samuel P. Rector (VP-Fin)
Carolyn Burke (Controller)

Subsidiaries:

Ascend Technologies, LLC (1)
200 W Adams St Ste 1600, Chicago, IL 60606
Tel.: (312) 386-6100
Web Site: http://www.teamascend.com
Information Technology Services
N.A.I.C.S.: 519290
Wayne Kiphart (CEO)

Subsidiary (Domestic):

Doextra CRM Solutions, LLC (2)
309 Ct Ave Ste 550, Des Moines, IA 50309-2222
Tel.: (515) 875-4970
Web Site: http://www.doextra.com
Information Technology Services
N.A.I.C.S.: 519290
Brad Williams (CEO)

Bel Air Internet, LLC (1)
15301 Ventura Blvd Ste 250, Sherman Oaks, CA 91403
Tel.: (818) 449-2626
Web Site: http://www.belairinternet.com
Telecommunication Servicesb
N.A.I.C.S.: 517111
Terry Koosed (Pres)

Connectivity Wireless, Inc. (1)
2707 Main St Ste 1, Duluth, GA 30096
Tel.: (678) 584-5799
Web Site: http://www.connectivitywireless.com
Sales Range: $25-49.9 Million
Emp.: 111
Wireless Telecommunication Services
N.A.I.C.S.: 517112
Clayt Mason (COO)
Bryce Bregen (Dir-Sls & Mktg)
Eric Ellis (COO-Connectivity Wireless Solutions)
Paul McGinn (CEO)

Denovo Ventures LLC (1)
6328 Monarch Park Pl Ste 200, Niwot, CO 80503
Tel.: (877) 433-6686
Web Site: http://www.denovo-us.com
Enterprise Software & Hosting & Cloud Computing Services
N.A.I.C.S.: 541519
David Shimoni (CEO)
Paul Cioni (CTO & Exec VP-Ops)
Chris Gartner (Chief Revenue Officer & Exec VP)

Subsidiary (Domestic):

CD Group, Inc. (2)

2 Sun Ct Ste 220, Peachtree Corners, GA 30092
Tel.: (678) 268-2000
Web Site: http://www.cdgroup.com
Software Solutions
N.A.I.C.S.: 513210
Larry Campbell (Founder & Pres)

M/C Venture Partners, LLC (1)
75 State St Ste 2500, Boston, MA 02109
Tel.: (617) 345-7200
Web Site: http://www.mcventurepartners.com
Sales Range: $25-49.9 Million
Emp.: 20
Venture Capital Investment Firm
N.A.I.C.S.: 523999
Gillis Cashman (Gen Partner)
James F. Wade (Mng Gen Partner)
Brian M. Clark (Gen Partner)
David D. Croll (Mng Gen Partner)
John W. Watkins (Mng Gen Partner)
Salvatore Tirabassi (Partner)
Robert Savignol (Partner)
Edward J. Keefe (CFO)
David Ingraham (VP)

TACALA, LLC
3750 Corporate Woods Dr, Birmingham, AL 35242
Tel.: (205) 443-9600
Web Site: http://www.tacala.com
Sales Range: $10-24.9 Million
Fast Food Restaurants
N.A.I.C.S.: 722513
Don Ghareeb (Founder)
Tim Morrison (Pres & COO)
Joey Pierson (CFO & Exec VP)
Michael Border (VP-Dev & Facilities)
Mazen Albatarseh (VP-Ops)
Javier Maravi (VP-Training & Staffing)
Ragan Cain (Treas & VP)
Angelique DeFranco (VP-HR)

TACO DEL MAR FRANCHISING CORP.
400 Boren Ave North, Seattle, WA 98109
Tel.: (206) 624-7060
Web Site: http://www.tacodelmar.com
Year Founded: 1992
Rev: $5,000,000
Emp.: 20
Fiscal Year-end: 06/30/06
Eating Place
N.A.I.C.S.: 722513
Larry Destro (Pres & CEO)

TACO INCORPORATED
1160 Cranston St, Cranston, RI 02920-7335
Tel.: (401) 942-8000 RI
Web Site: http://www.taco-hvac.com
Year Founded: 1920
Sales Range: $150-199.9 Million
Emp.: 500
Pumping, Heat Transfer, Hydronic Control & Solar Equipment Mfr
N.A.I.C.S.: 333414
Glenn Graham (Treas & Exec VP-Fin)
Kyle Adamonis (Sr VP-HR)
Tim Smith (Dir-Brand Mgmt & Mktg Programs)
Tom Lawrence (Sr VP-Sls & Mktg)
Chris Integlia (Exec VP-Residential Div)
Candy Castaldi (Sr VP-Circulator Div)
Robert Lee (Exec VP-Ops)
Rae Aldrich (Coord-Mktg)
Nelson Redo (VP)
Todd Facey (Sr VP-Residential Sls)
Mark Chaffee (VP-Govt Affairs & Sustainability)
Nelson Rego (VP-Quality Svcs)
Bryan Payne (Sr VP-Engineered Products & Sys)
Gene Fina (VP-Mktg)

Greg Case (Exec VP-Res & New Product Dev)
Steve Thompson (Sr VP-Product Mgmt)
Vicki Fry (VP-HR)

Subsidiaries:

Taco (Canada) Ltd. (1)
8450 Lawson Road Unit 3, Milton, L9T0J8, ON, Canada
Tel.: (905) 564-9422
Pumping Equipment Mfr
N.A.I.C.S.: 333914

Taco Electronic Solutions, Inc. (1)
1160 Cranston St, Cranston, RI 02920
Tel.: (401) 942-8000
Web Site: http://www.taco-hvac.com
Pumping Equipment Mfr
N.A.I.C.S.: 333914
Ric Turmell (VP)

TACO JOHN'S INTERNATIONAL, INC.
808 W 20th St, Cheyenne, WY 82001-3404
Tel.: (307) 635-0101 WY
Web Site: http://www.tacojohns.com
Year Founded: 1969
Sales Range: $75-99.9 Million
Emp.: 60
Fast Food Franchised Restaurants
N.A.I.C.S.: 533110
Harold Holmes (Founder)
Renee Swisher (Controller)
Jim Creel (Pres & CEO)
Shawn Eby (VP-Ops-México)
Tom Meyer (VP-Mktg)
Barry Westrum (CMO)
Gerard Lewis (Chm)
Richard Bundy (CFO)
Mark Kocer (COO)

TACO MAYO FRANCHISE SYSTEMS, INC.
10405 Greenbriar Pl, Oklahoma City, OK 73159
Tel.: (405) 691-8226 OK
Web Site: http://www.tacomayo.com
Sales Range: $1-4.9 Billion
Emp.: 1,400
Fast-Food Restaurant, Chain
N.A.I.C.S.: 722513
Randy K. Earhart (Chm)
Gary Kurzer (VP-Ops)

TACO METALS INC.
50 NE 179th St, Miami, FL 33162
Tel.: (305) 652-8566
Web Site: http://www.tacometals.com
Sales Range: $10-24.9 Million
Emp.: 100
Aluminum Bars, Rods, Ingots, Sheets, Pipes & Plates Distr
N.A.I.C.S.: 423510
Mike Kushner (VP-Sls)
Jesus Gancedo (Controller)
Elana M. Murray (Mgr-Mktg)
Betsy Torres (Controller)
Liliana Lorenzo (Dir-Creative)

TACO TRUCK CREATIVE, LLC
3172 Lionshead Ave, Carlsbad, CA 92010
Tel.: (760) 517-8800
Web Site: http://www.tacotruckcreative.com
Year Founded: 2013
Sales Range: $1-9.9 Million
Emp.: 14
Digital Advertising Services
N.A.I.C.S.: 541850
Travis Graham (Partner & Creative Dir)
Dave Huerta (Partner & Creative Dir)

TACOMA ELECTRIC SUPPLY, INC.
1311 S Tacoma Way, Tacoma, WA 98409
Tel.: (253) 475-0540 WA
Web Site: http://www.tacomaelectric.com
Sales Range: $10-24.9 Million
Emp.: 100
Electrical Construction Materials Mfr & Distr
N.A.I.C.S.: 335999
Karen Eversol (Mgr-HR)

TACOMA INC.
328 E Church St, Martinsville, VA 24112
Tel.: (276) 666-9417
Web Site: http://www.gototaco.com
Rev.: $13,209,964
Emp.: 300
Franchise Owner of Fast-Food Restaurants
N.A.I.C.S.: 722513
Amy Lance (CEO)

TACOMA LUTHERAN RETIREMENT COMMUNITY
1301 N Highlands Pkwy, Tacoma, WA 98406
Tel.: (253) 752-7112 WA
Web Site: http://www.tacomalutheran.org
Year Founded: 1938
Sales Range: $10-24.9 Million
Emp.: 393
Senior Living Services
N.A.I.C.S.: 623311
Lynette L. Ladenburg (COO)
David Hoffman (CFO)
Kristine Grant (Dir-Community Rels)
Paul M. Opgrande (Pres & CEO)

TACOMA PUBLIC UTILITIES
3628 S 35th St, Tacoma, WA 98409-3115
Tel.: (253) 502-8000
Web Site: http://www.tacomapublicutilities.org
Year Founded: 1880
Sales Range: $25-49.9 Million
Emp.: 1,162
Electronic Services
N.A.I.C.S.: 221118
William A. Gaines (Dir-Utilities)
Christine Gleason (Mgr-Community & Media Svcs)
Steven Hatcher (Mgr-Customer Svc)
Robert Mack (Deputy Dir-Pub Affairs)
Alan Matheson (Chief Mechanical Officer)
Janene Franklin (Mgr-Customer Accts)
Jim Clark (Mgr-Customer Svc & Mktg)
Josh Banks (Mgr-Operating Practices)
Lori Luscher (Project Mgr)
Kari Halliday (Supvr-Mechanical)
Lena Bentley (Supvr-Office)

TACOMA SCREW PRODUCTS, INC.
2001 Center St, Tacoma, WA 98409
Tel.: (253) 572-3444
Web Site: http://www.tacomascrew.com
Year Founded: 1946
Sales Range: $25-49.9 Million
Hardware Tools Mfr & Whslr
N.A.I.C.S.: 423710
Gary Myers (Mgr-IT)
Tim Staffanson (Mgr-Distr Center)

TACONIC FARMS, INC.
1 Hudson City Centre, Hudson, NY 12534
Tel.: (518) 697-3900
Web Site: http://www.taconic.com
Year Founded: 1952
Sales Range: $75-99.9 Million
Emp.: 1,000
Laboratory Rodent Breeding & Supply Services
N.A.I.C.S.: 112990
Todd F. Little (Pres-Corp Dev)
Kathrin Phelan Midgley (Chm)
Donna Gulezian (VP-Portfolio Innovation & Dev)
Michael Mullen (CFO & Sr VP-Strategic Projects)
Nancy Sandy (COO & Exec VP)
Robert J. Rosenthal (Chm)

Subsidiaries:

Taconic Europe A/S (1)
Tornbjergvej 40 Ejby, 4623, Lille Skensved, Denmark
Tel.: (45) 70230405
Sales Range: $25-49.9 Million
Emp.: 150
Laboratory Rodent Breeding & Supply Services
N.A.I.C.S.: 112990

TaconicArtemis GmbH (1)
Neurather Ring 1, Cologne, 51063, Germany (80.1%)
Tel.: (49) 221964530
Sales Range: $10-24.9 Million
Emp.: 100
Transgenic Mouse Generation Services
N.A.I.C.S.: 541715
Peter Stadler (Mng Dir)
Oliver Radtke (Dir-Fin)
Branko Zevnik (Head-Applied Genetics Dept & Assoc Dir)
Jost Seibler (Head-Tech Dept & RNAi Res)
Chris Schleiermacher (Head-Computational Biology & IT)

TACONY CORPORATION
1760 Gilsinn Ln, Fenton, MO 63026-2004
Tel.: (636) 349-3000 MO
Web Site: http://www.tacony.com
Year Founded: 1946
Sales Range: $125-149.9 Million
Emp.: 640
Importer & Electric & Household Fans; Electric Household Sewing Machines; Vacuum Cleaners; Household Appliance Parts Distr
N.A.I.C.S.: 423620
Kenneth J. Tacony (Chm)
Kristi Tacony Humes (CEO)
Pam Jordan (Sr VP-ECommerce-Direct to Consumer Channel)
Nick Tacony (Founder)
Shannon Wilson (CFO)

Subsidiaries:

Koala Studios (1)
333 Charles Ct, West Chicago, IL 60185
Tel.: (630) 818-1289
Furniture Mfr
N.A.I.C.S.: 337211

Mac Molding Company, Inc. (1)
12814 Gravois Rd, Saint Louis, MO 63127
Tel.: (314) 849-0646
Web Site: http://www.macmolding.com
Sales Range: $10-24.9 Million
Emp.: 10
Plastics Product Mfr
N.A.I.C.S.: 326199
Lance Loeffelman (Mgr)

Nancy's Notions (1)
333 Beichl Ave, Beaver Dam, WI 53916
Tel.: (800) 833-0690
Web Site: http://www.nancysnotions.com
Sewing Supplies Retailer
N.A.I.C.S.: 459130

Powr-Flite (1)
3101 Wichita Ct, Fort Worth, TX 76140
Tel.: (800) 880-2913
Web Site: http://www.powr-flite.com
Emp.: 80
Vaccum Cleaner Whslr
N.A.I.C.S.: 423620
Louis Rios (Gen Mgr)

Riccar America, Inc. (1)
1800 E Walnut Ave, Fullerton, CA 92831-4844
Tel.: (714) 525-4400
Web Site: http://www.riccar.com
Vacuum Cleaner Mfr & Distr
N.A.I.C.S.: 333310

Tacony Manufacturing (1)
3 Industrial Dr, Saint James, MO 65559-0219 (50%)
Tel.: (573) 265-0500
Web Site: http://www.tacony.com
Sales Range: $10-24.9 Million
Emp.: 130
Assembling Of Vaccum Cleaners
N.A.I.C.S.: 335210
Ken Tacony (Chm)
Andy Touchette (Sr VP-Sls)
Brad Overby (CFO)
Brian Kearins (COO)
Craig Meyer (Sr VP-Mktg)
Nick Tacony (Founder)

Tornado Industries, Inc. (1)
333 Charles Ct Ste 109, West Chicago, IL 60185-2604
Tel.: (630) 818-1300
Web Site: http://www.tornadovac.com
Sales Range: $10-24.9 Million
Emp.: 120
Carpet Care Machine & Industrial Vacuum Cleaner Portable Blower Floor Machine & Combination Scrub-Vacuum-Dry Machine Mfr
N.A.I.C.S.: 333310
Larry Kays (Dir-Ops)

Truvox International Limited (1)
Unit C (East) Hamilton Business Park Hedge End, Southampton, SO30 2JR, Hampshire, United Kingdom
Tel.: (44) 23 8070 2200
Web Site: http://www.truvox.com
Sales Range: $10-24.9 Million
Emp.: 25
Floor Care Equipment Mfr
N.A.I.C.S.: 333310
David Overell (Mng Dir)

TACORI ENTERPRISES
1736 Gardena Ave, Glendale, CA 91204
Tel.: (818) 863-1536
Web Site: http://www.tacori.com
Sales Range: $10-24.9 Million
Emp.: 20
Fine Jewelry Mfr
N.A.I.C.S.: 423940
Haig Tacorian (Pres)
Paul Tacorian (Pres-Sls & Mktg)
Ofer Saha (Mgr-Texas)
Michael Lalonde (Mgr-South)
Charlene Chiu (Mgr-Retail & Brand Partnership)

TACTICAL PRODUCTS GROUP, INC.
601 N Congress Ave Ste 305, Delray Beach, FL 33445
Tel.: (561) 265-4066 FL
Web Site: http://www.tacprogroup.com
Year Founded: 2005
Sales Range: $1-9.9 Million
Emp.: 8
Procurement & Logistics Services
N.A.I.C.S.: 541614
Dan T. Lounsbury (Pres)

TACTICAL SUPPORT EQUIPMENT INC.
4039 Barefoot Rd, Fayetteville, NC 28306
Tel.: (910) 425-3360
Web Site: http://www.tserecon.com
Year Founded: 2002
Rev.: $97,600,000
Emp.: 16
Electron Tube Mfr
N.A.I.C.S.: 334419
Ed Connor (Dir-Sls)
Mark Conway (Dir-Trng)

TADLOCK PIPE & EQUIPMENT INC.
6844 Hwy 90 E, Lake Charles, LA 70615
Tel.: (337) 436-0426
Web Site: http://www.tadlockpipe.com
Sales Range: $10-24.9 Million
Emp.: 38
Pipe & Tubing, Steel
N.A.I.C.S.: 423510
Robert Tadlock (Pres)

TAFEL MOTORS INCORPORATED
4156 Shelbyville Rd, Louisville, KY 40207
Tel.: (502) 896-4411
Web Site: http://www.tafelmotors.com
Rev.: $70,000,000
Emp.: 91
Automobiles, New & Used
N.A.I.C.S.: 441110
David Peterson (Owner)

TAFT STETTINIUS & HOLLISTER LLP
425 Walnut St Ste 1800, Cincinnati, OH 45202-3957
Tel.: (513) 381-2838 OH
Web Site: http://www.taftlaw.com
Year Founded: 1885
Emp.: 500
Law firm
N.A.I.C.S.: 541110
Arthur A. Weiss (Partner)
Thomas T. Terp (Partner-Environmental Grp)
Beth Silvers (Chief Personnel Officer)
Mark S. Feuer (Partner)
Janica P. Tucker (Partner)
Lynn M. Schulte (Partner)
Jonathan Sams (Partner)
David H. Thomas (Partner-Columbus)
Meredith K. Sugar (Partner)
Adrian D. Thompson (Partner & Chief Diversity Officer)
Kelly M. Sharpe (Dir-Bus Dev-Indianapolis)
Dawn L. Sizemore (Dir-IT Solutions & Support-Cincinnati)
Enzo Spinelli (Dir-Litigation Tech Sys-Chicago)
Lisa M. Watson (Dir-Recruiting, Dev & Admin-Indianapolis)
Thomas A. Barnard (Partner)
Philip R. Bautista (Partner)
Marci A. Reddick (Partner)
Kevin M. Kinross (Partner-Columbus)
Lacy M. Johnson (Partner)
Nadia Klarr (Atty)
Christopher Hartman (Atty)
Elizabeth Shuster (Partner-Intellectual Property Grp)
Michael Restle (CFO)
Andrew M. Alul (Partner)
Andrew J. Art (Partner)
Beth A. Bryan (Partner)
Donald C. Biggs (Partner)
Doreen Canton (Partner)
Ian D. Arnold (Partner)
Irv Berliner (Partner)
James D. Abrams (Partner)
Jayna M. Cacioppo (Partner)
Jeffrey A. Abrams (Partner)
Jillian S. Cole (Partner)
John Allie (Partner)
Jonathan B. Amarilio (Partner)

TAFT STETTINIUS & HOLLISTER LLP

Taft Stettinius & Hollister LLP—(Continued)
Kevin D. Barnes *(Partner)*
Kimberly M. Copp *(Partner)*
Marcia Voorhis Andrew *(Partner)*
Richard E. Aderman *(Partner)*
Robert A. Bilott *(Partner)*
Sara M. Cooperrider *(Partner)*
Scott Alexander *(Partner)*
Stacia A. Buechler *(Partner)*
Stephen R. Auten *(Partner)*
Tom R. Biehl *(Partner)*
Tracy N. Betz *(Partner)*
Kyle Hupfer *(Partner)*
Douglas C. Anspach Jr. *(Partner)*

Subsidiaries:

Taft Stettinius & Hollister LLP - Chicago (1)
111 E Wacker Ste 2800, Chicago, IL 60601
Tel.: (312) 527-4000
Web Site: http://www.taftlaw.com
Emp.: 79
Law firm
N.A.I.C.S.: 541110
Anthony R. Licata *(Partner)*
Michael A. Cramarosso *(Partner)*
Kimberly M. Copp *(Partner)*
Kathryn Kovitz Arnold *(Partner)*
Richard E. Aderman *(Partner)*
James D. Wilson *(Partner)*
Jeffry A. Mullins *(Partner)*
Lawrence C. Rubin *(Partner)*
Paul L. Kelley *(Partner)*
Michael P. Sheehan *(Partner)*
Pablo L. Petrozzi *(Partner-Real Estate Grp)*
Andrew M. Alul *(Partner)*
Cary E. Donham *(Partner)*
Cezar M. Froelich *(Chm)*
Joseph M. Bennett-Paris *(Partner)*
Jillian S. Cole *(Partner)*
Maura L. Downs *(Coord-Govt Svcs)*
Stephen R. Auten *(Partner)*
J. Timothy Eaton *(Partner)*
Howard Zweig *(Chm-Higher Education Practice)*
Barton J. O'Brien *(Partner)*
Carrie A. Hall *(Partner)*
Daniel D. Lindgren *(Partner)*
Daniel R. Saeedi *(Partner)*
Elijah J. Hammans *(Partner)*
Elizabeth E. Babbitt *(Partner)*
Erin Lynch Cordier *(Partner)*
Graham C. Grady *(Partner)*
Jeffrey M. Schieber *(Partner)*
John F. Kennedy *(Partner)*
John M. Riccione *(Partner)*
Jonathan B. Amarilio *(Partner)*
Joseph P. Gattuso *(Partner)*
Kenneth Klassman *(Partner)*
Kostas A. Poulakidas *(Partner)*
Kristine M. Kolky *(Partner)*
Marcus S. Harris *(Partner)*
Matthew R. Godfrey *(Partner)*
Michael C. Jurasek *(Partner)*
Michael J. Schaller *(Partner)*
Mitchell D. Goldsmith *(Partner)*
Payal Keshvani *(Partner)*
Philip Y. Kouyoumdjian *(Partner)*
Richard T. Ruzich *(Partner)*
William B. Gont *(Partner)*

TAG CONSULTING
3541 Chain Bridge Rd Ste 6, Fairfax, VA 22030
Tel.: (703) 352-0660
Web Site: http://www.tagconsulting.org
Year Founded: 1998
Sales Range: $1-9.9 Million
Emp.: 16
Business Management Consulting Services
N.A.I.C.S.: 541618
Joe Jurkowski *(CEO & Principal)*
Kevin G. Ford *(Chief Visionary Officer & Principal)*
Mike Marino *(Pres & Partner)*
Kurt Andre *(Sr Partner)*
James P. Osterhaus *(Sr Partner)*
Anne Berry *(Mgr-HR & Client Relationship)*
Kelly Ann Jasen *(Project Mgr)*
LuAnn Orie *(Coord-Client Svcs)*
Mike Sweetland *(Mgr-Acct)*
Shane Roberson *(VP-Client Svcs)*

TAG ELECTRIC COMPANY
16422 Huffsmith Kohrville Rd, Houston, TX 77070
Tel.: (281) 376-6700
Web Site:
http://www.tagcompanies.com
Sales Range: $10-24.9 Million
Emp.: 100
Provider of General Electrical Contracting Services
N.A.I.C.S.: 238210
Thomas A. Gonzales *(Pres)*
Nita Gonzales *(VP)*

TAG EMPLOYER SERVICES, LLC
20815 N Cave Creek Rd, Phoenix, AZ 85024
Tel.: (623) 580-4900
Web Site: http://www.tagpay.com
Year Founded: 2003
Sales Range: $25-49.9 Million
Emp.: 45
Payroll & Benefits Management Solutions
N.A.I.C.S.: 513210
Ron Bleich *(Co-Founder & Partner)*
Jack Biltis *(Co-Founder, Partner & Pres)*
Heather Smith *(VP-Mktg & Co-Founder)*
Danny Goldberg *(VP-Natl Sls)*

TAG HOLDINGS, LLC
30260 Oak Creek Dr, Wixom, MI 48393
Tel.: (248) 822-8056
Web Site: http://www.taghold.com
Year Founded: 2001
Sales Range: $50-74.9 Million
Emp.: 350
Holding Company; Manufacturing & Service Solutions
N.A.I.C.S.: 551112
Joseph B. Anderson Jr. *(Founder, Chm & CEO)*
Anthony Jackson *(Pres)*
Pancho D. Hall *(COO)*

Subsidiaries:

Great Lakes Assemblies, LLC (1)
11590 Township Rd 298, East Liberty, OH 43319
Tel.: (937) 645-3900
Web Site: http://www.modularai.com
Mfr of Automotive Tire & Wheel Assemblies
N.A.I.C.S.: 336390

North American Assemblies, LLC (1)
1322 Young Rd, Timmonsville, SC 29161-7772
Tel.: (843) 420-5354
Web Site: http://www.naa-llc.com
Sales Range: $10-24.9 Million
Emp.: 4
All-Terrain Vehicle Tire & Wheel Assemblies Mfr
N.A.I.C.S.: 336390
James R. Tolston III *(Pres & CEO)*

TAG MANUFACTURING, INC.
6989 Discovery Dr, Chattanooga, TN 37416
Tel.: (423) 893-3345
Web Site: http://www.tagmfg.us
Sales Range: $10-24.9 Million
Emp.: 200
Fabricated Structural Metal Mfr
N.A.I.C.S.: 332312
Gary Wilt *(Co-Founder & Pres)*
Paul Davidson *(Supvr-Oxy Fuel)*
Terry Wilt *(Co-Founder)*
Dean O'Donald *(COO)*

TAG TRUCK CENTER
4450 American Way, Memphis, TN 38118
Tel.: (901) 345-5633
Web Site:
http://www.tagtruckcenter.com
Year Founded: 1986
Sales Range: $50-74.9 Million
Emp.: 250
Car Whslr
N.A.I.C.S.: 441110
Gary Dodson *(Co-Owner, CFO & VP)*
Tommy Earl *(Co-Owner & Pres)*

TAGAWA GREENHOUSES, INC.
17999 Weld Cnty Rd 4, Brighton, CO 80603-9731
Tel.: (303) 659-1260
Sales Range: $10-24.9 Million
Emp.: 500
Malt Mfr
N.A.I.C.S.: 311213
Gary Schoneman *(CFO)*
Kenneth Tagawa *(Pres)*
Bill Kluth *(Bus Mgr)*
Yoshi Tagawa *(Mgr-IT)*

TAGGED, INC.
110 Pacific Ave Mall Box #117, San Francisco, CA 94111
Tel.: (415) 946-1953
Web Site: http://www.about-tagged.com
Year Founded: 2004
Sales Range: $10-24.9 Million
Emp.: 57
Social Network
N.A.I.C.S.: 517810
Greg Tseng *(Co-Founder)*
Louis Willacy *(Sr VP-Legal & Head-Corp Dev)*
Johann Schleier-Smith *(Co-Founder)*
Dash Gopinath *(COO)*
Gene Sokolov *(Co-CTO)*
Geoffrey Cook *(CEO)*
David Clark *(CFO)*
William Alena *(Chief Revenue Officer)*
Niklas Lindstrom *(Co-CTO)*
Frederic Beckley *(Gen Counsel & Exec VP-Bus Affairs)*
Jim Bugden *(Sr VP-Corp Dev & Gen Mgr-West Coast)*
Richard Friedman *(Sr VP-Engrg)*
Jeremy Zorn *(VP-Product Dev)*

TAGLICH BROTHERS, INC.
790 New York Ave Ste 209, Huntington, NY 11743
Tel.: (631) 757-1500
Web Site: http://www.taglich.com
Year Founded: 1991
Sales Range: $75-99.9 Million
Emp.: 40
Investment Banking, Private Equity & Securities Brokerage Services
N.A.I.C.S.: 523150
William M. Cooke *(Chm)*
Richard C. Oh *(Mng Dir & Dir-Res)*
Michael R. Brunone *(Exec VP)*
Michael N. Taglich *(Co-Founder, Chm, Pres & Principal)*
Robert F. Taglich *(Mng Dir)*

Subsidiaries:

Taglich Brothers, Inc. (1)
790 New York Ave Ste 209, Huntington, NY 11743
Tel.: (631) 757-1500
Web Site: http://www.taglichbrothers.com
Sales Range: $100-124.9 Million
Emp.: 20
Investment Banking, Private Equity & Securities Brokerage Services
N.A.I.C.S.: 523150

Douglas E. Hailey *(Mng Dir & VP-Investment Banking)*
Denis McEvoy *(VP)*

TAGLICH PRIVATE EQUITY LLC
275 Madison Ave Ste 1618, New York, NY 10016
Tel.: (212) 661-0936
Web Site: http://www.taglichpe.com
Year Founded: 2001
Emp.: 25
Privater Equity Firm
N.A.I.C.S.: 523999
Douglas E. Hailey *(Mng Dir-Investment Banking)*

Subsidiaries:

Unique Fabricating, Inc. (1)
800 Standard Pkwy, Auburn Hills, MI 48326
Tel.: (248) 853-2333
Web Site: http://www.uniquefab.com
Rev.: $125,669,000
Assets: $103,677,000
Liabilities: $72,550,000
Net Worth: $31,127,000
Earnings: ($6,963,000)
Emp.: 915
Fiscal Year-end: 12/31/2021
Gaskets, Packing & Sealing Devices Mfr
N.A.I.C.S.: 339991
Richard L. Baum Jr. *(Chm)*
Brian P. Loftus *(CFO)*
Brad Hazen *(VP-Engrg & Product Dev)*
Ron Jones *(Dir-Ops-Canada)*
Mike Carson *(VP-Market Dev Medical/Consumer)*
Bryant Click *(Dir-Appliance Market)*
Tim Packer *(Dir-Product Dev & Engrg)*
Thomas Charnley *(Dir-Pur)*
Lisa Yaldo *(Dir-HR)*
Juan Lozano *(Dir-Ops-Mexico)*
Byrd Douglas Cain III *(Pres & CEO)*

Subsidiary (Domestic):

Great Lakes Foam Technologies, Inc. (2)
13221 Allman Rd, Concord, MI 49237
Tel.: (517) 524-9010
Web Site: http://www.greatlakesfoam.com
Sales Range: $1-9.9 Million
Fabric Coating Mills
N.A.I.C.S.: 313320

Unique-Intasco USA, Inc. (2)
125 Runnels St, Port Huron, MI 48060
Tel.: (810) 982-3360
Web Site: http://www.intasco.com
Rev.: $5,700,000
Emp.: 10
Industrial Supplies Merchant Whslr
N.A.I.C.S.: 423840

Unique-Prescotech, Inc. (2)
1001 W Oak St, Louisville, KY 40210-1528
Tel.: (502) 585-5866
Web Site: http://www.uniqueprescotech.com
Sales Range: $25-49.9 Million
Die Cut Paper & Board Mfr
N.A.I.C.S.: 322130
Denny Amshoff *(Mgr-Louisville Div)*

TAGUE LUMBER INC.
560 E High St, Philadelphia, PA 19144
Tel.: (215) 848-2500
Web Site:
http://www.taguelumber.com
Year Founded: 1908
Sales Range: $10-24.9 Million
Emp.: 75
Provider of Services for Professional Builders, Remodelers & Industrial Customers
N.A.I.C.S.: 423310
Thomas J. Vanleer *(VP-Sls)*
Vincent Tague Sr. *(CEO)*
Vincent J. Tague Jr. *(Pres)*

TAHER INC
5570 Smetana Dr, Minnetonka, MN 55343

Tel.: (952) 945-0505
Web Site: http://www.taher.com
Sales Range: $10-24.9 Million
Emp.: 1,500
Provider of Restaurant Services
N.A.I.C.S.: 722514
Bruce Taher *(Pres & CEO)*
Shawn Taher *(VP-Bus Dining & Vending)*
Barb Koehn *(Dir-Food Svc)*
Sandy Barrett *(Dir-Food Svc)*

TAHLEQUAH PUBLIC WORKS AUTHORITY
101 N College A, Tahlequah, OK 74464
Tel.: (918) 456-2564
Web Site: http://www.tpwa.cityoftahlequah.com
Sales Range: $10-24.9 Million
Emp.: 72
Electronic Services
N.A.I.C.S.: 221118
Mike Doublehead *(Gen Mgr)*

TAHOE DONNER ASSOCIATION
11509 Northwoods Blvd, Truckee, CA 96161
Tel.: (530) 587-9400   CA
Web Site: http://www.tahoedonner.com
Year Founded: 1971
Sales Range: $1-9.9 Million
Homeowner Association
N.A.I.C.S.: 813990
Steve Miller *(Treas)*
Jeff Bonzon *(Pres)*
Jeff Schwerdtfeger *(Sec)*
Brinn Talbot *(Dir-Mktg & Membership Svcs)*
Ashley Quadros *(Coord-Mktg Content)*

TAHOE PARTNERS, LLC
770 N Halsted Ste 502, Chicago, IL 60642
Tel.: (312) 491-3000
Web Site: http://www.tahoe-partners.com
Year Founded: 2002
Sales Range: $10-24.9 Million
Emp.: 100
Management Consulting Services
N.A.I.C.S.: 541618
Bob Carpenter *(CFO)*
Mike Crisanti *(Mng Dir)*

TAHOKA FIRST BANCORP INC.
1601 S 1st St, Tahoka, TX 79343
Tel.: (806) 561-4511
Web Site: http://www.fnbtahoka.com
Bank Holding Company
N.A.I.C.S.: 551111

Subsidiaries:

The First National Bank of Tahoka   (1)
1601 S 1st St, Tahoka, TX 79373
Tel.: (806) 561-4511
Web Site: http://www.fnbtahoka.com
Sales Range: $1-9.9 Million
Emp.: 15
Commericial Banking
N.A.I.C.S.: 522110
Dawn Little *(VP)*
Frederick B. Hegi Jr. *(Chm)*

TAHZOO LLC
1005 7th St NW, Washington, DC 20001
Tel.: (202) 621-7160
Web Site: http://www.tahzoo.com
Digital Customer Experience Services
N.A.I.C.S.: 513210

Brad Heidemann *(Founder & CEO)*
John P. Kottcamp *(CMO)*
Gabrielle Macy *(VP-Ops)*
David Sterenberg *(Pres)*
Don Low *(Mng Dir-Studios)*

Subsidiaries:

HintTech BV   (1)
Delftechpark 37-i, Delft, 2628, Netherlands
Tel.: (31) 88 268 2500
Web Site: http://www.hinttech.com
IT Services
N.A.I.C.S.: 541512
Egbert Hendriks *(CEO)*
Patrick Dekker *(COO)*

TAI CORPORATION
2615 River Rd, Cinnaminson, NJ 08077
Tel.: (856) 778-5353
Web Site: http://www.taicorp.com
Year Founded: 1991
Sales Range: $10-24.9 Million
Emp.: 25
Mfr of Electronic Parts & Equipment
N.A.I.C.S.: 423690
Steve Buroojy *(Mgr-Sls)*
Scott Bibus *(Acct Mgr)*

TAIGMARKS INC.
223 S Main St Ste 100, Elkhart, IN 46516
Tel.: (574) 294-8844   IN
Web Site: http://www.taigmarks.com
Year Founded: 1967
Sales Range: $10-24.9 Million
Emp.: 15
Advertising Agencies, Health Care, Industrial, Leisure, Magazines, Medical, Point of Sale, Print, Production, Public Relations, Sales Promotion, Sweepstakes, Trade & Consumer Magazines, Transportation
N.A.I.C.S.: 541810
Sue Truckowski *(Art Dir)*
Debbie Smith *(Production Mgr)*
Stephen Taig *(Pres)*
Craig Hosterman *(Acct Mgr)*
Mike Knaack *(Mgr-PR)*
Jennifer Lantz *(Office Mgr)*
Rob Hartzler *(Partner & VP)*
Jeff Prugh *(Art Dir)*
Daniel Carter *(Acct Mgr)*
Robert Williams *(Acct Mgr)*

TAIL INC.
2105 Nw 86th Ave, Doral, FL 33122-1527
Tel.: (305) 638-2650   FL
Web Site: http://www.tailactivewear.com
Year Founded: 1974
Sales Range: $25-49.9 Million
Emp.: 180
Women's & Misses' Outerwear
N.A.I.C.S.: 315250
Jerry Edwards *(CEO)*
Donald Fleming *(Mgr-Mgmt Info Sys)*

TAILOR MADE COMPOUNDING, LLC
200 Moore Dr, Nicholasville, KY 40356
Tel.: (859) 887-0013
Web Site: http://www.tailormadecompounding.com
Year Founded: 2015
Sales Range: $10-24.9 Million
Emp.: 45
Pharmaceutical Product Mfr & Distr
N.A.I.C.S.: 325412
Tory Newton *(Dir-Sls Ops)*

TAILORED LABEL PRODUCTS, INC.

W165 N5731 Ridgewood Dr, Menomonee Falls, WI 53051
Tel.: (262) 703-5000   WI
Web Site: http://www.tailoredlabel.com
Year Founded: 1984
Emp.: 100
Custom Labels & Identification Products for Electronics Mfr
N.A.I.C.S.: 561910
Igor B. Zelenovskiy *(Pres & CEO)*

TAILORED MANAGEMENT, INC.
1165 Dublin Rd Ste-400, Columbus, OH 43215-5424
Tel.: (614) 859-1500   OH
Web Site: http://www.tailoredmanagement.com
Year Founded: 1988
Sales Range: $10-24.9 Million
Emp.: 100
Temporary Staffing Services
N.A.I.C.S.: 561320
Chris McCoy *(Office Mgr)*

TAILWATER CAPITAL LLC
2021 Mckinney Ave Unit 1250, Dallas, TX 75201
Tel.: (214) 269-1183
Web Site: http://www.tailwatercapital.com
Year Founded: 2013
Private Equity Firm for Energy Industry
N.A.I.C.S.: 523999
Jason Downie *(Co-Founder & Mng Partner)*
Edward Herring *(Co-Founder & Mng Partner)*
David Cecere *(Principal)*
William DeArman *(Principal)*
Joel Fry *(Principal)*
Brian Blakeman *(CFO)*
Stephen Lipscomb *(VP)*
Scott Peters *(VP)*
Lindsay Grider *(Head-IR)*

Subsidiaries:

Southcross Holdings LP   (1)
1717 Main St Ste 5200, Dallas, TX 75201   (33.3%)
Tel.: (214) 979-3700
Web Site: http://www.southcrossholdings.com
Holding Company
N.A.I.C.S.: 551112
John Bonn *(Pres)*

Holding (Domestic):

Southcross Energy Partners,LLC   (2)
1717 Main St Ste 5200, Dallas, TX 75201
Tel.: (214) 979-3720
Web Site: http://www.southcrossenergy.com
Sales Range: $400-449.9 Million
Oil & Gas Exploration
N.A.I.C.S.: 211120
Patrick Geroir *(CEO)*
James Lee *(CFO & Sr VP)*
William C. Boyer *(COO & Sr VP)*
John Happ *(Chief Comml Officer & Sr VP)*
Nicole Devore *(Dir-HR)*
William Waldheim *(Chm)*

Subsidiary (Domestic):

Southcross Energy GP LLC   (3)
1700 Pacific Ave Ste 2900, Dallas, TX 75201
Tel.: (214) 979-3700
Web Site: http://www.southxenergy.com
Gathering, Processing & Pipeline Transportation of Natural Gas
N.A.I.C.S.: 486210

Southcross Mississippi Industrial Gas Sales, L.P.   (3)
1717 Main St Ste 5200, Dallas, TX 75201-4617
Tel.: (214) 979-3700
Oil & Gas Operation Supporting Services

N.A.I.C.S.: 213112

Southcross Mississippi Pipeline, L.P.   (3)
1700 Pacific Ave Ste 2900, Dallas, TX 75201-4666
Tel.: (214) 979-3760
Sales Range: $10-24.9 Million
Emp.: 12
Natural Gas Pipeline Transportation Services
N.A.I.C.S.: 486210

Southcross NGL Pipeline Ltd.   (3)
1717 Main St Ste 5200, Dallas, TX 75201
Tel.: (214) 979-3767
Web Site: http://www.southcrossenergy.com
Natural Gas Pipeline Transportation Services
N.A.I.C.S.: 486210

TAILWIND CAPITAL GROUP, LLC
485 Lexington Ave, New York, NY 10017
Tel.: (212) 271-3800   DE
Web Site: http://www.tailwind.com
Privater Equity Firm
N.A.I.C.S.: 523999
Lawrence B. Sorrel *(Partner)*
Frank Vincent Sica *(Partner)*
Jeffrey M. Calhoun *(Mng Partner)*
James S. Hoch *(Partner)*
Geoffrey S. Raker *(Partner)*
Will Fleder *(Partner)*
Andrew Mayer *(Partner)*
Syed O. Mohsin *(Mng Dir & CFO)*
Caitlin B. Guinee *(Partner)*
Brian Berkin *(Partner)*
Michael Bertisch *(Chief Compliance Officer, Gen Counsel & Mng Dir)*
Sanjay Swani *(Mng Partner)*

Subsidiaries:

ASC Engineered Solutions, LLC   (1)
2867 Vail Ave, Commerce, CA 90040
Tel.: (800) 766-0076
Web Site: http://www.smithcooper.com
Fitting & Valve Product Mfr & Distr
N.A.I.C.S.: 332919
Bob Cooper *(Co-Founder & Pres)*

Subsidiary (Domestic):

Anvil International, LLC   (2)
2 Holland Way, Exeter, NH 03833
Tel.: (800) 301-2701
Web Site: http://www.anvilintl.com
Pipe Fittings & Pipe Hangers Mfr
N.A.I.C.S.: 332996

Subsidiary (Domestic):

Flexhead Industries, Inc.   (3)
56 Lowland St, Holliston, MA 01746
Tel.: (508) 893-9596
Adjustable Sprinkler Piping Drops & Sprinkler Applications Mfr
N.A.I.C.S.: 327332

Subsidiary (Domestic):

Trenton Pipe Nipple Company LLC   (2)
PO Box 40, Federalsburg, MD 21632-1632
Web Site: http://www.trentonpipe.com
Plumbing Fixture Fitting & Trim Mfr
N.A.I.C.S.: 332913
Larry Yeatman *(Plant Mgr)*

Ward Manufacturing, Inc.   (2)
117 Gulick St, Blossburg, PA 16912
Tel.: (570) 638-2131
Web Site: http://www.wardmfg.com
Sales Range: $50-74.9 Million
Emp.: 450
Mfr of Malleable & Gray Iron Ductile Castings, Pipe Fittings & Connectors
N.A.I.C.S.: 331511
John Benglar *(CFO)*

Plant (Domestic):

Ward Manufacturing LLC - Wisconsin Nipple Facility   (3)
1900 S 89th St, Milwaukee, WI 53227

TAILWIND CAPITAL GROUP, LLC

Tailwind Capital Group, LLC—(Continued)
Web Site: http://www.wardmfg.com
Metal Valve & Pipe Fitting Mfr
N.A.I.C.S.: 332919

Core BTS, Inc. (1)
5875 Castle Creek Pkwy N Dr Ste 320, Indianapolis, IN 46250
Tel.: (608) 661-7700
Web Site: http://www.corebts.com
Sales Range: $25-49.9 Million
Emp.: 140
Computer Systems Design Services; Computer Consulting & Training
N.A.I.C.S.: 541512
Paul F. Lidsky (CEO)
Bill Wilshire (COO & Gen Mgr-Svcs)
Jason Eickmann (Gen Counsel & Sr VP)
Jaime L. McGowin (Gen Counsel & Sr VP)
Robert J. Sensenig (Sr VP-Bus Dev & Security)
Mark Zerbe (Sr VP-Sls & Mktg)
Gal Greenberg (Dir-Mktg)
Jeff Crow (CMO)

Division (Domestic):

Core BTS Inc. (2)
720 Cool Springs Blvd Ste 150, Franklin, TN 37067
Tel.: (615) 277-3000
Web Site: http://www.corebts.com
Sales Range: $1-9.9 Million
Emp.: 20
Computer System Design Services
N.A.I.C.S.: 541512

Diamondback Drugs, LLC (1)
7631 E Indian School Rd, Scottsdale, AZ 85251
Tel.: (480) 946-2223
Web Site: http://www.diamondbackdrugs.com
Sales Range: $1-9.9 Million
Emp.: 25
Veterinary Medicinal Preparation Mfr & Distr
N.A.I.C.S.: 325412
Michael Blaire (VP-Govt & Regulatory Affairs)
Stephen De La Cruz (Mgr-Territory)
Fabian McCarthy (Pres)
A. J. DeLorenzi (Mgr-Florida)
Anne Borelli (Mgr-Northern California)
Brandon Fields (Mgr-Field Sls)
David Perkins (Dir-Pharmacy Ops)
Kristi Maier (Mgr-Arizona)
Melissa Hofberger (Mgr-Mktg)
Paul McMakin (Mgr-Washington)
Giano Panzarella (VP & Gen Mgr)

Long's Drugs, Inc. (1)
111 Executive Center Dr Ste 202, Columbia, SC 29210
Tel.: (803) 217-1088
Web Site: http://www.longsrx.com
Emp.: 200
Pharmacies & Drug Stores
N.A.I.C.S.: 456110
Kenneth Long (Pres)

Subsidiary (Domestic):

Avita Drugs LLC (2)
5551 Corporate Blvd Ste 102, Baton Rouge, LA 70808
Tel.: (888) 284-8279
Web Site: http://www.avitapharmacy.com
Pharmacies
N.A.I.C.S.: 456110
Jerry Purcell (Founder & CEO)
Dawn DePorter (VP-Pharmacy Ops)
Reem Mughrabi (Mgr-Audit)

Material Holdings, LLC (1)
1900 Ave of the Stars 16th Fl, Los Angeles, CA 90067
Tel.: (310) 553-0550
Web Site: https://www.materialplus.io
Marketing Research Service
N.A.I.C.S.: 541910
David Sackman (Chm & CEO)
Jeremy Sack (Pres & Pres-Insights, Data & Science)
Bill Kanarick (Pres)

Subsidiary (Domestic):

Kelton Research, LLC (2)
1900 Avenue of the Stars, Los Angeles, CA 90067
Tel.: (310) 479-4040
Web Site: http://www.keltonglobal.com
Market Research
N.A.I.C.S.: 541613
Gareth Schweitzer (Founder)
Courtney Clark (VP-Insights & Strategy-New York)
Alexandria Price (Founder)
Brenna Malta (Assoc Dir-Quantitative Res)
Erin Casement (Sr Dir-Mktg)
Jaclyn Jakucki (Sr VP-Insights & Strategy)
Jaime McMahon (Sr Dir-Ops)
Mary Wang-Boucher (Field Mgr)
Susan Braun (COO-Material Action Division)

Material US, Inc. (2)
1250 53rd St Ste 5, Emeryville, CA 94608
Tel.: (510) 446-8200
Web Site: http://www.greenberginc.com
Marketing Research & Public Opinion Polling
N.A.I.C.S.: 541910
Andrew Lum (Creative Dir)
Allison Wilt (Gen Mgr)
Alysha Primmer (Dir-Ops)
Gareth Walters (VP-Creative)

Salt Branding, LLC (2)
1620 Montgomery St Ste 120, San Francisco, CA 94111
Tel.: (415) 616-1500
Web Site: http://www.saltbranding.com
Full-service Branding Agency
N.A.I.C.S.: 541430
Paul Parkin (Co-Founder)
David Neugebauer (Co-Founder)
Rick Herrick (Co-Founder)

Strativity Group, LLC (2)
401 Hackensack Ave 8th Fl, Hackensack, NJ 07601
Tel.: (201) 808-8500
Web Site: http://www.strativity.com
Strategic Planning & Research Consulting Services
N.A.I.C.S.: 541690
Ed Murphy (COO)
Steve Cohn (Sr Mgr-Learning)
Lacey Zuretti (Sr Mgr-Consulting)
Tim Douek (Principal-Consulting)
Elizabeth Real (Pres)

Onix Networking, Corp. (1)
18519 Detroit Ave, Lakewood, OH 44107
Tel.: (440) 871-0295
Web Site: http://www.onixnet.com
Sales Range: $1-9.9 Million
Emp.: 15
Computer & Computer Peripheral Equipment & Software Whslr
N.A.I.C.S.: 423430
Tim Needles (CEO)

Tailwind Management LP (1)
485 Lexington Ave, New York, NY 10017
Tel.: (212) 271-3800
Web Site: http://www.tailwind.com
Privater Equity Firm
N.A.I.C.S.: 523940
Lawrence B. Sorrel (Mng Partner)

Holding (Domestic):

Acertus (2)
110 Rock Cliff Ct, Saint Louis, MO 63123
Tel.: (855) 223-7887
Web Site: http://acertusdelivers.com
Automotive Logistics Provider
N.A.I.C.S.: 488999
William Billiter (Co-Founder)
Scott Naz (Co-Founder)
Michael Malakhov (Exec VP-Sls & Mktg)
Eric Kaseff (Exec VP-Title & Registration & Bus Dev)
Trent J. Broberg (CEO)
Paul Malone (Chief Revenue Officer)
Ross Rachey (COO)

Subsidiary (Domestic):

Rcg Logistics LLC (3)
9300 Tech Ctr Dr. Ste 190, Sacramento, CA 95826
Tel.: (916) 290-7232
Web Site: http://www.rcgauto.com
Automotive Repair & Maintenance
N.A.I.C.S.: 811198

Subsidiary (Domestic):

HMT, LLC (2)
2002 Timberloch Pl Ste 550, The Woodlands, TX 77380
Tel.: (281) 681-7000
Web Site: http://www.hmttank.com
Sales Range: $50-74.9 Million
Maintenace of Oil Storage Tanks
N.A.I.C.S.: 332322
Wendy Knight (Asst Gen Counsel)

Subsidiary (Domestic):

Dunham Engineering (3)
12815 FM 2154 Rd, College Station, TX 77845-3981
Tel.: (979) 690-6555
Web Site: http://www.dunhamengineering.com
Engineeering Services
N.A.I.C.S.: 541330
Jimmy D. Dunham (Owner)

Subsidiary (Non-US):

HMT Australia Pty Ltd (3)
Unit 3 66 Whiting Street, Artarmon, 2064, NSW, Australia
Tel.: (61) 2 8437 2100
Metal Storage Tank Mfr
N.A.I.C.S.: 332420

HMT Pte Ltd. (3)
23 Tuas Avenue 6, Singapore, 639310, Singapore
Tel.: (65) 6481 3150
Emp.: 20
Metal Tank Mfr
N.A.I.C.S.: 332420
Steve Byrnes (Gen Mgr)

HMT Rubbaglas, Ltd. (3)
Unit 3 Fitsroy Business Park Sandylane, Sidcup, DA145NL, Kent, United Kingdom
Tel.: (44) 208 464 7888
Web Site: http://www.hmttank.com
Storage Tank Mfr
N.A.I.C.S.: 332420

Nayler Petroseals Ltd (3)
Logans Road, PO Box 4, Motherwell, ML1 3NP, United Kingdom
Tel.: (44) 20 8290 8548
Emp.: 7
Storage Tank Whslr
N.A.I.C.S.: 423510
Andrew Duncan (Gen Mgr)

Subsidiary (Domestic):

Paramount Painting & Industrial Services, Inc. (3)
5702 John Martin Rd, Baytown, TX 77521
Tel.: (281) 839-1660
Paint Contracting Services
N.A.I.C.S.: 238320

Subsidiary (Non-US):

Petroleum Seals & Systems Ltd. (3)
Hmt Block C Brunswick, Oldham, OL1 1DE, Manchester, United Kingdom
Tel.: (44) 161 633 4199
Web Site: http://www.pss-seals.co.uk
Emp.: 3
Storage Tank Mfr
N.A.I.C.S.: 332420
Craig Turner (Mgr-Sls)

Tank Systems BV (3)
Scheepmakersstraat 5, PO Box 95, Zwijndrecht, 3334 KG, Netherlands
Tel.: (31) 78 6990194
Web Site: http://www.tanksystems.nl
Emp.: 23
Metal Tank Mfr
N.A.I.C.S.: 332420
Paul Van Da (Gen Mgr)

Subsidiary (Domestic):

Techcote Industrial Coating, Ltd. (3)
15917 Jacintoport Blvd, Houston, TX 77015-6536
Tel.: (281) 862-9937
Sales Range: $1-9.9 Million
Coating Mfr
N.A.I.C.S.: 325510

United Tank Technology Inc. (3)
50 Maltese Dr, Totowa, NJ 07512
Tel.: (973) 256-1753
Emp.: 60
Metal Tank Mfr
N.A.I.C.S.: 332420
John Walsh (Plant Mgr)

Weld Spec, Inc. (3)
3314 Hwy 69 S, Lumberton, TX 77657
Tel.: (409) 751-6700
Web Site: http://www.weldspecinc.com
Other Health & Personal Care Stores
N.A.I.C.S.: 456199
Mark Hardy (VP-Ops)

TAILWIND INTERNATIONAL ACQUISITION CORP.
150 Greenwich St 29th Fl, New York, NY 10006
Tel.: (212) 266-0085   Ky
Web Site: http://www.twni.tailwindacquisition.com
Year Founded: 2020
Rev.: $14,770,094
Assets: $349,930,273
Liabilities: $364,421,622
Net Worth: ($14,491,349)
Earnings: $11,699,648
Fiscal Year-end: 12/31/22
Investment Services
N.A.I.C.S.: 523999
Philip Krim (CEO & CFO)

TAILWIND TECHNOLOGIES INC.
1 Propeller Pl, Piqua, OH 45356
Tel.: (937) 778-4200   OH
Web Site: http://www.tailwindtechnologiesinc.com
Year Founded: 1987
Sales Range: $100-124.9 Million
Emp.: 450
Holding Company; Aerospace Products Mfr & Whslr
N.A.I.C.S.: 551112
Joseph W. Brown (CEO)
Matthew L. Jesch (CFO)
James W. Brown III (Pres)

Subsidiaries:

Hartzell Propeller Inc. (1)
1 Propeller Pl, Piqua, OH 45356-2655
Tel.: (937) 778-4200
Web Site: http://www.hartzellprop.com
Sales Range: $10-24.9 Million
Emp.: 270
Aircraft Parts & Equipment
N.A.I.C.S.: 336413
Joseph W. Brown (Pres)
Bruce C. Hanke (VP-Engrg)
Burt Mattice (VP-Regulatory Sys & Strategic Sourcing)
Dean Ward (Dir-Aftermarket Parts & Svc)
Gary Chafin (VP-OEM Sls & Product Support)
Heidi Hennessy (Dir-HR)
J. J. Frigge (Exec VP)

TAILWINDS DEVELOPMENT, LLC
100 Colonial Center Pkwy Ste 230, Lake Mary, FL 32756
Tel.: (321) 363-4955
Web Site: http://www.tailwindsdevelopment.com
Sales Range: $1-9.9 Million
Real Estate Development, Management & Brokerage Services
N.A.I.C.S.: 237210
James T. Gendreau (Pres)
Stephen T. Infantino (Dir-Leasing & Acq)

TAIMEN TRANSPORT, LLC
1209 Pointe Center Dr Ste 205, Chattanooga, TN 37421
Tel.: (423) 693-0280
Web Site: http://www.taimentransport.com

Year Founded: 2012
Sales Range: $25-49.9 Million
Emp.: 17
Freight Transportation Services
N.A.I.C.S.: 488510
Christopher Wang (Founder, Owner & CEO)

TAIT TOWERS INC.
9 Wynfield Dr, Lititz, PA 17543-8001
Tel.: (702) 798-3838
Web Site: http://www.taittowers.com
Sound Recording Industries
N.A.I.C.S.: 512290
Michael Tait (Owner)

Subsidiaries:

Thinkwell Group, Inc. (1)
2710 Media Ctr Dr, Los Angeles, CA 90065
Tel.: (818) 333-3444
Web Site: https://thinkwellgroup.com
Concept Development, Design & Production Services
N.A.I.C.S.: 541490
Craig Hanna (Chief Creative Officer)
Joe Zenas (CEO)
Kelly Ryner (Pres-Thinkwell Asia)
Amin Rashmani (Dir-Bus Dev-Middle East)
Tyler Thornberg (Dir-Asset Dev)
Francois Girard (Sr VP-Bus Dev-Global)
Dave Cobb (Principal-Creative Dev)
Evi Sari (Mng Dir-Art-Asia)
Francois Bergeron (COO)
Paul Redding (VP-Thinkwell Asia)
Randy Ewing (VP-Design)
Regina Eise (VP-Fin & Acctg Ops)
Alexandra Dunn (Dir-Art)
Brad Kissling (Principal-Plng & Architecture)
Chris Durmick (Principal-Attractions & Museums)
Chuck Roberts (Sr Dir-Art)
Cynthia Sharpe (Principal-Cultural Attractions & Res)
Laurie E. Knight (VP-People)
Steve Johnson (VP-Bus Dev)
Diane Michioka (VP-Production)

TAJ TECHNOLOGIES INC.
1168 Northland Dr, Saint Paul, MN 55120
Tel.: (651) 688-2801
Web Site: http://www.tajtech.com
Sales Range: $25-49.9 Million
Emp.: 200
System Software Development Services
N.A.I.C.S.: 541512
K. C. Sukumar (Pres)
Jeff Monsas (COO)
Henri Mabilais (Project Mgr)
Shailesh Koppikar (Mgr-Talent Acq & Delivery)
Tom Morley (Mgr-HR)
Varma Jampana (Mgr-IT Project)

TAK CONSTRUCTION, INC.
60 Walnut Ave Ste 400, Clark, NJ 07066
Tel.: (732) 340-0700
Web Site: http://www.takgroupinc.com
Year Founded: 1987
Sales Range: $25-49.9 Million
Construction Management Services
N.A.I.C.S.: 532412
Kenny Desai (Pres)
Randy Whitt (Exec VP)

TAKATA GLOBAL GROUP
2500 Takata Dr, Auburn Hills, MI 48326-2634
Tel.: (248) 373-8040   DE
Web Site: http://www.takata.com
Year Founded: 1984
Sales Range: $600-649.9 Million
Emp.: 1,275
Mfr of Automobile Seatbelts
N.A.I.C.S.: 336360
Tim Healy (Pres)

Subsidiaries:

Highland Industries Inc. (1)
629 Green Valley Rd Ste 210, Greensboro, NC 27408-7726
Tel.: (336) 547-1600
Web Site: http://www.highlandindustries.com
Sales Range: $10-24.9 Million
Emp.: 25
Industrial Textile Administration & Sales
N.A.I.C.S.: 314999
Bill Fields (Product Mgr)
Justin Barnett (Product Mgr-Military Segment)

TAKE CARE PRIVATE DUTY HOME HEALTH CARE
3982 Bee Ridge Rd Bldg H Ste A, Sarasota, FL 34233
Tel.: (941) 927-2292
Web Site: http://www.takecarehomehealth.com
Year Founded: 1995
Sales Range: $10-24.9 Million
Emp.: 500
Home Health & Personal Care Services
N.A.I.C.S.: 621610
Susanne S. Wise (Owner & CEO)
Matthew Borland (Project Mgr)
Jennifer J. Halloran (Sr Mgr-Acctg)
Mary Pedersen (Dir-HR)
Erika Wise Borland (Mgr-Mktg Comm)
Barbara Renzi (Dir-Clinical Projects)
Teresa Kaufman (Dir-Clinical)
Sharon M. Bateman (Mgr-Geriatric Care)
Connie Wolken (Mgr-Accts Receivable)
Jan English (Mgr-Payroll)
Abby L. Gerrity (Asst Dir-Client Svcs)
Alicia Uelmen (Dir-Clinical)
DaVonne Miller (Mgr-Geriatric Care)
Ginny Hilton (Mgr-Geriatric Care)
Leah Aiken (Dir-Clinical)
Sharon McQuillen (Mgr-HR)
Tammie Karlafa (Dir-Clinical)

TAKE2 CONSULTING, LLC
1593 Spring Hill Rd Ste 710, Vienna, VA 22182
Tel.: (703) 752-6500
Web Site: http://www.take2it.com
Year Founded: 2014
Sales Range: $10-24.9 Million
Emp.: 200
Technical Consulting Services
N.A.I.C.S.: 541690
Serge Khoury (Founder & Chief Growth Officer)
Lisa Kurz (Pres & COO)
Nick Defelice (Partner)
Mark Dever (Partner)

TAKECARE INSURANCE COMPANY INC.
415 Chalan San Antonio St Baltej Pavilion Ste 108, Tamuning, GU 96913
Tel.: (671) 646-6956
Web Site: http://www.takecareasia.com
Year Founded: 1973
Health Care Insurance Services
N.A.I.C.S.: 524114
Jeff Larsen (Pres)

TAL CONSOLIDATED INC.
377B Pearsall Ave, Cedarhurst, NY 11516
Tel.: (516) 415-7850   NY
Year Founded: 2017
Emp.: 65
Online Shopping Services
N.A.I.C.S.: 312111

Jeremy J. Reichmann (Chm, Pres & CEO)
Daniel Braun (Interim CFO)

TAL HOLDINGS LLC
201 NE Park Plz Dr Ste 240, Vancouver, WA 98684
Tel.: (514) 382-0957
Web Site: http://www.talholdingsllc.com
Holding Company; Lumber & Building Material Dealer
N.A.I.C.S.: 551112
Dave Dittmer (CEO)
Jeremy Swanson (CFO)
Erin Doehring (Dir-HR)
Renee Coffman (Dir-Purchasing)
Natalia Dittmer (Mktg Dir)

Subsidiaries:

Gerretsen Building Supply, Co. (1)
1900 NE Airport Rd, Roseburg, OR 97470-1421
Tel.: (541) 672-2636
Web Site: http://www.gerretsen.com
Sales Range: $10-24.9 Million
Emp.: 60
Lumber, Plywood, Millwork & Wood Panel Whslr
N.A.I.C.S.: 423310
Donda Gerretsen-King (Pres)

Tum-A-Lum Lumber, Inc. (1)
408 Hwy 35, Hood River, OR 97031
Tel.: (541) 386-1001
Building Materials & Solutions Mfr
N.A.I.C.S.: 238290
Tina Kipper (Branch Mgr)

Subsidiary (Domestic):

Marson & Marson Lumber, Inc. (2)
105 S Bradley, Chelan, WA 98816
Tel.: (509) 682-1617
Web Site: http://www.marsonandmarson.com
Home Center Operator
N.A.I.C.S.: 444110
Jerry Larson (Mgr)
Sue Baker (Asst Mgr)

TALAN PRODUCTS, INC.
18800 Cochran Ave, Cleveland, OH 44110
Tel.: (216) 458-0170   OH
Web Site: http://www.talanproducts.com
Year Founded: 1986
Sales Range: $25-49.9 Million
Emp.: 60
Metal Stamping, Aluminum Extrusion Fabrication & Supply
N.A.I.C.S.: 332119
Steve Peplin (Pres & CEO)
John Hisel (Controller)
Fran Adler (Mgr-Sls)

TALASCEND, LLC
5700 Crooks Rd Ste 320, Troy, MI 48098
Tel.: (248) 537-1300   DE
Web Site: http://www.talascend.com
Year Founded: 1946
Recruitment Firm;Technical & Engineering Employment Sourcing & Placement Services
N.A.I.C.S.: 561311
Ron Wood (CEO)

TALBERT HOUSE
2600 Victory Pkwy, Cincinnati, OH 45206
Tel.: (513) 751-7747
Web Site: http://www.talberthouse.org
Year Founded: 1965
Rev.: $38,300,000
Emp.: 900
Community & Individual Social Services

N.A.I.C.S.: 624190
Amelia Orr (VP-Community Care)
Josh Arnold (VP-Court & Corrections)
Neil F. Tilow (Pres & CEO)
Juwana Hall (Dir-Housing)
Brad Gray (Dir-IT)
Harold Howard (Dir-Community Care)
Tom Bach (Dir-Court & Corrections)
Carla Brooks (CFO & VP)
Erin Mitchell (Dir-Behavioral Health)
Jeffrey Wyder (Dir-Food Svcs)

TALBERT MANUFACTURING INC.
1628 W State Rd 114, Rensselaer, IN 47978-7266
Tel.: (219) 866-7141   IN
Web Site: http://www.talbertmfg.com
Year Founded: 1938
Sales Range: $10-24.9 Million
Emp.: 100
Mfr Of Motor Truck Trailers
N.A.I.C.S.: 336212
Andrew Tanner (Pres)
Troy Geisler (VP-Sls & Mktg)
Brian Sharp (Mgr-Engrg)
Connie Chapman (Coord-Parts & Warranty)
Gary Braasch (Coord-Sls)
James Hall (VP-Ops)
Jamie Myers (VP-Pur)
Steve Kingman (Coord-Parts & Warranty)
David Henderson (Mgr-Dealer Dev)

TALBOT HOLDINGS INC.
200 Frnt St, Millersburg, PA 17061
Tel.: (717) 692-2113
Web Site: http://www.talbotholdings.com
Sales Range: $25-49.9 Million
Emp.: 210
Holding Company
N.A.I.C.S.: 551112
William F. Coyle (Pres)

Subsidiaries:

Brubaker Tool Corporation (1)
200 Frnt St, Millersburg, PA 17061-1324
Tel.: (717) 692-2113
Web Site: http://www.brubakertool.com
Sales Range: $25-49.9 Million
Emp.: 195
Taps, Reamers, Milling Cutters, End Mills, Dies, Standard & Specialty Jig & Fixture Components Mfr
N.A.I.C.S.: 333517
Kim Headdings (Mgr-Acctg)

Dauphin Precision Tool, LLC (1)
200 Front St, Millersburg, PA 17061
Tel.: (717) 692-2113
Web Site: http://www.heritagecutter.com
Sales Range: $25-49.9 Million
Precision Machinery Parts Mfr
N.A.I.C.S.: 332216
Linda Butler (Mgr-HR)

Fastcut Tool Corporation (1)
200 Frnt St, Millersburg, PA 17061
Tel.: (717) 692-2113
Web Site: http://www.fastcut.com
Sales Range: $10-24.9 Million
Emp.: 6
Marketing Office for End Mills, Milling Cutters, Taps & Reamers, Jig & Fixture Components
N.A.I.C.S.: 423830

TALCO PLASTICS INC.
1000 W Rincon St, Corona, CA 92880
Tel.: (951) 531-2000
Web Site: http://www.talcoplastics.com
Sales Range: $10-24.9 Million
Emp.: 150
Waste Material Recycling Services
N.A.I.C.S.: 562920

TALCO PLASTICS INC.

Talco Plastics Inc.—(Continued)
Pamela Karmann (Mgr-Admin)
Robert Petty (Mgr-Sls)
John L. Shedd Jr. (Pres)

TALENS MARINE & FUEL INC.
225 Pleasant St, Lake Arthur, LA 70549
Tel.: (337) 774-5480
Web Site: http://www.talensmarine.com
Sales Range: $50-74.9 Million
Emp.: 100
Petroleum Products
N.A.I.C.S.: 424720
Billy Bird (Reg Mgr)
Chris Booth (Gen Counsel, Sec & VP)
Larry Williams (Reg Mgr)
Phil Creel (Reg Mgr)
Steve Nattin (Reg Mgr)
Steve Smith (Reg Mgr)
Terry D. King (Sr VP)
Ruben S. Martin III (Pres & CEO)

TALENT BRIDGE, LLC
6100 Fairview Rd Ste 500, Charlotte, NC 28210
Tel.: (704) 644-7000
Web Site: http://www.talentbridge.com
Year Founded: 1985
Sales Range: $1-9.9 Million
Emp.: 5,000
Staffing & Recruitment Services
N.A.I.C.S.: 561311
Thomas C. Ioele (CEO)
Michael Collins (CFO)
Paul Meyer (COO)
Lori Crimmins (VP-HR)
Mark Salisbury (Dir-Tech)

TALENT CONNECTIONS, LLC
4805 W Village Way Se Apt 2401, Smyrna, GA 30080-9230
Tel.: (770) 552-1550
Web Site: http://www.talentconnections.net
Year Founded: 1999
Sales Range: $10-24.9 Million
Emp.: 11
Professionals Recruitment Services
N.A.I.C.S.: 541612
Tom Darrow (Founder, CEO & Principal)
Susan Kent (Dir-Bus Dev)
Mary Reany (Dir-Mktg)

TALENT CURVE SOLUTIONS LLC
1016 Thompson St, Pittsboro, NC 27312
Tel.: (919) 542-3723
Web Site: http://www.talentcurve.com
Year Founded: 2007
Sales Range: $1-9.9 Million
Emp.: 58
Career Counseling
N.A.I.C.S.: 541611
Anne Brister (Pres & CEO)

TALENT PARTNERS
541 N Fairbanks Ct, Chicago, IL 60611-3373
Tel.: (312) 923-7900
Web Site: http://www.talentpartners.com
Year Founded: 1989
Sales Range: $10-24.9 Million
Emp.: 90
Employee-of-Record Payroll Service Company
N.A.I.C.S.: 541214
Paul Muratore (Pres & CEO)
Jessica Figlio (Supvr-Client Svc & Bus Affairs)

Subsidiaries:
Talent Partners (1)
115 W 118th St, New York, NY 10011 (100%)
Tel.: (212) 727-1800
Web Site: http://www.talentpartners.com
Provider of Support Services to Advertising Industry
N.A.I.C.S.: 541214
Susan Renaldo (Dir-Ops)
Dustin Guzowski (Mgr-Global Bus Dev)

TALENT PLUS INC.
One Talent Plus Way, Lincoln, NE 68506-5987
Tel.: (314) 421-9400 MO
Web Site: https://talentplus.com
Year Founded: 1989
Independent Artists, Writers & Performers
N.A.I.C.S.: 711510
Sharon Lee Tucci (Pres)
Makenzie Rath (Pres)
Karl Giuseffi (Exec VP-Res & Dev)
John Henley (Chief Growth Officer)
Doug Rath (Co-Founder & Co-Chm)
Kimberly Rath (Co-Founder & Co-Chm)

TALENT, INC.
420 Lexington Ave Suite 1402-1063, New York, NY 10170 NY
Web Site: http://www.talentinc.com
Year Founded: 2014
Emp.: 100
Employment Services
N.A.I.C.S.: 541618
Byron Matthews (CEO)
Armando Roman (COO)
Christian Dwyer (Chief Product Officer)
Lauren Lippello (VP-HR)
Todd Goldstein (Exec VP-Bus Dev)
Joe Bussichella (CFO)

Subsidiaries:
Career Services Group, Inc. (1)
4120 Meridian St Ste 280, Bellingham, WA 98226
Tel.: (360) 527-1171
Web Site: http://www.careerperfect.com
Sales Range: $1-9.9 Million
Emp.: 75
Vocational Rehabilitation Services
N.A.I.C.S.: 624310
Bruce Wayne (CEO)

TALENTBURST, INC.
679 Worcester St, Natick, MA 01760
Tel.: (508) 628-7500
Web Site: http://www.talentburst.com
Year Founded: 2002
Rev.: $15,000,000
Emp.: 300
Human Resouce Services
N.A.I.C.S.: 541612
Bharat Singh Talwar (Co-Founder & CEO)
Baljit Gill (Co-Founder & COO)
Deep Deshpande (Co-Founder & CFO)
Jay Westbrook (Sr VP)
Namrata Anand (VP-Client Acq & Bus Dev)
Kevin Callanan (VP)

Subsidiaries:
TalentBurst (1)
71 Stevenson Rd Ste 424, San Francisco, CA 94105 (100%)
Tel.: (415) 655-6843
Web Site: http://www.talentburst.com
Contract Information Technology & Staffing Solutions
N.A.I.C.S.: 561311

Dave Singh (Dir-Ops)

TALENTED IT INC.
800 W 5th Ave Ste 208A, Naperville, IL 60563
Tel.: (630) 364-4112
Web Site: http://www.talentedit.com
Year Founded: 2004
Sales Range: $10-24.9 Million
Emp.: 26
Consulting, Staffing & Software Integration
N.A.I.C.S.: 541519
Sudheera Tripuraneni (Pres)

TALENTFIRST LLC
1011 Route 22 W Ste 201, Bridgewater, NJ 08807
Tel.: (908) 725-2500
Web Site: http://www.talentfirst.com
Sales Range: $10-24.9 Million
Emp.: 50
Talent Management Services
N.A.I.C.S.: 611430
Ted Power (Partner)
Julie Zadow (CMO)
Rishav Gupta (CEO)

TALENTQUEST INC.
1275 Peachtree St Ne Ste 400, Atlanta, GA 30309-3576
Tel.: (404) 266-9368
Web Site: http://www.talentquest.com
Year Founded: 1972
Sales Range: $10-24.9 Million
Emp.: 36
Human Resource Consulting Services
N.A.I.C.S.: 541612
Kevin Sessions (Pres)
Frank Merritt (CEO)
Rick Brandt (Pres-Consulting Svcs)
Jim Basile (Mng Dir-NW Reg)
Niranjan Nimkar (CTO)
Russ Settles (Mng Dir-Carolinas)
Rachel Finglass (COO)

TALISMAN CAPITAL PARTNERS LLC
330 W Spring St Ste 400, Columbus, OH 43215
Tel.: (614) 857-5000
Web Site: http://www.talismancp.com
Privater Equity Firm
N.A.I.C.S.: 523999
Robert D. Walter (Founder)

TALISMARK
1000 Primera Blvd, Lake Mary, FL 32746
Tel.: (407) 478-8800
Web Site: http://www.talismark.com
Year Founded: 1999
Sales Range: $10-24.9 Million
Emp.: 21
Waste Management Services
N.A.I.C.S.: 562998
Charles Muszynski (Co-Founder & CEO)
Marshall Staiman (Co-Founder & Pres)
Thomas Eppich (CFO)
David J. Reimel (Dir-IT & Process Mgmt)

TALK RADIO NETWORK
PO Box 3755, Central Point, OR 97502
Tel.: (541) 474-2297
Web Site: http://www.talkradionetwork.com
Year Founded: 1992
Sales Range: $25-49.9 Million
Emp.: 20
Nationally Syndicated Talk Radio Network

U.S. PRIVATE

N.A.I.C.S.: 516110
Mark Masters (CEO)
Brad Silvers (Dir-Network Ops)

TALK, INC.
215 Racine Dr Ste 201, Wilmington, NC 28403
Tel.: (910) 395-5051
Web Site: http://www.talkinc.com
Year Founded: 1990
Sales Range: $10-24.9 Million
Emp.: 6
Advertising, Advertising Specialties, Event Planning & Marketing, Graphic Design, Health Care, Public Relations, Publicity/Promotions, Real Estate
N.A.I.C.S.: 541810
Debbie Elliott (Pres & Dir-Creative)

TALK-A-PHONE CO.
7530 N Natchez Ave, Niles, IL 60714
Tel.: (773) 539-1100 IL
Web Site: http://www.talkaphone.com
Year Founded: 1937
Sales Range: $50-74.9 Million
Emp.: 50
Communication Equipment Mfr
N.A.I.C.S.: 334290
Zvie Liberman (Pres)
Samuel Shanes (Chm & CEO)
Robert Shanes (VP-Sls)

TALK2REP, INC.
3363 W Commercial Blvd Ste A220, Fort Lauderdale, FL 33309
Tel.: (954) 933-0660 FL
Web Site: http://www.talk2rep.com
Year Founded: 2000
Sales Range: $10-24.9 Million
Emp.: 110
Telemarketing & Business Consulting Services
N.A.I.C.S.: 561422
Jim Ryan (CEO)
Ike Ahmed (VP-Client Care & Strategy)
Dana Goldsholle (Dir-Client Care & Bus Dev)

TALLADEGA MACHINERY & SUPPLY CO., INC.
301 Johnson Ave N 6, Talladega, AL 35161
Tel.: (256) 362-4124
Web Site: http://www.tmsco.com
Rev.: $18,652,250
Emp.: 115
Mill Supplies
N.A.I.C.S.: 423840
Gary Heacock (Pres)
Sam Yates (VP-Mktg)
James W. Heacock Sr. (Chm)

TALLAHASSEE AUTOMOTIVE, LLC
3400 Western Branch Blvd, Chesapeake, VA 23321 VA
Web Site: http://www.firstteamauto.com
Emp.: 200
New & Used Car Dealerships Operator
N.A.I.C.S.: 441110
David Dillon (Pres)
George Pelton (Founder & CEO)

Subsidiaries:
First Team Honda (1)
3444 Western Branch Blvd, Chesapeake, VA 23321-5108
Tel.: (757) 686-1000
Web Site: http://www.firstteamhonda.com
New & Used Car Dealer
N.A.I.C.S.: 441110
George Pelton (CEO)

First Team Nissan of Christianburg (1)
2130 N Franklin St, Christianburg, VA 24073-1110
Tel.: (540) 382-2903
Web Site: http://www.firstteamnissannrv.com
Emp.: 32
New & Used Car Dealer
N.A.I.C.S.: 441110
James Nardo (Gen Mgr)

First Team Toyota (1)
3400 Western Branch Blvd, Chesapeake, VA 23321
Tel.: (757) 673-2345
Web Site: http://www.firstteamtoyota.com
New & Used Car Dealer
N.A.I.C.S.: 441110
George Pelton (CEO)

TALLAHASSEE LAND COMPANY, INC.
3520 Thomas St 200 2309, Tallahassee, FL 32303
Tel.: (850) 385-6363
Web Site: http://www.tallahasseeland.com
Year Founded: 1993
Sales Range: $1-9.9 Million
Emp.: 13
Real Estate Brokerage Services
N.A.I.C.S.: 531210
R. Bradford Parker (Co-Owner)
Kayla Holloway (Office Mgr)
A.L. Buford Jr. (Co-Owner)
Ben H. Wilkinson Jr. (Co-Owner)
A. Lewis Buford III (Co-Owner)

TALLAHASSEE MEMORIAL HEALTHCARE
1300 Miccosukee Rd, Tallahassee, FL 32308
Tel.: (850) 431-1155
Web Site: http://www.tmh.org
Emp.: 4,457
Hospital Owner & Operator
N.A.I.C.S.: 622110
Cynthia Blair (Chief Improvement & Plng Officer & VP)
Don Lindsey (CIO & VP)
William Giudice (CFO & VP)
Barbara Alford (Chief Clinical Officer, Chief Nursing Officer & VP)
Dean Watson (Chief Health Ops Officer & VP)
John Mahoney (Chief Integration Officer & VP)
Stephanie Derzypolski (Chief Comm Officer & VP)
Martha Barnett (Treas)
Andrea Friall (Chief Medical Officer & VP)
Alma Littles (Chm)
Christopher Rumana (Sec)
Steven Haynes (Chief HR Officer & VP)
Mickey S. Moore (Pres & Chief Advancement Officer)
Yashica Wilson-Hearns (VP-Support Svcs)

TALLAHATCHIE VALLEY ELECTRIC POWER ASSOCIATION
250 Power Dr, Batesville, MS 38606
Tel.: (662) 563-4742
Web Site: http://www.tvepa.com
Rev.: $47,189,161
Emp.: 106
Electric Power Distribution
N.A.I.C.S.: 221122
Brad Robinson (Gen Mgr)
Daniel Pittman (Office Mgr)
Earl Gibson (Dir-Member Svcs & Controller)

TALLAN INC.
45 Glastonbury Blvd, Glastonbury, CT 06033
Tel.: (860) 633-3693
Web Site: http://www.tallan.com
Year Founded: 1985
Sales Range: $50-74.9 Million
Emp.: 140
Computer Software Development
N.A.I.C.S.: 541511
Craig Branning (CEO)

TALLAPOOSA RIVER ELECTRIC CO-OP
15163 US Hwy 431 S, Lafayette, AL 36862
Tel.: (334) 864-9331 AL
Web Site: http://www.trec.coop
Year Founded: 1939
Sales Range: $150-199.9 Million
Emp.: 60
Distribution of Electric Power
N.A.I.C.S.: 221122
Louie Ward (Gen Mgr)
Rhonda Phillips (Mgr-Fin)
C. B. Parker Jr. (Pres)

TALLEY INC.
12976 Sandoval St, Santa Fe Springs, CA 90670
Tel.: (562) 906-8000 CA
Web Site: http://www.talleycom.com
Year Founded: 1983
Wireless Communications Infrastructure & Mobile Products Distr
N.A.I.C.S.: 423690
John R. Talley (Co-Founder)
Elizabeth Talley (Co-Founder)
Jeffrey R. Talley (Exec VP)
Mark Talley (CEO)
Rick Talley (Exec VP)
Scott Wenk (VP-Infrastructure Sls)
Pat Flynn (VP-Mktg Dev)

TALOMA FARMERS GRAIN COMPANY
308 E 6th St, Delavan, IL 61734
Tel.: (309) 244-7541
Web Site: http://www.talomagrain.com
Rev.: $28,824,503
Emp.: 6
Grain Elevators
N.A.I.C.S.: 424510
Andi Wolls (Asst Controller)
Jeff Duckworth (Gen Mgr)

TALON AIR, INC.
7110 Republic Airport Rte 109, Farmingdale, NY 11735
Tel.: (631) 753-8881
Web Site: http://www.talonairjets.com
Sales Range: $10-24.9 Million
Emp.: 120
Private Jet Charter Services
N.A.I.C.S.: 481211
Jason Sanders (VP)

TALON GROUP LLC
400 Talon Ctr Dr, Detroit, MI 48207
Tel.: (313) 392-1000
Web Site: http://www.talon.us
Holding Company
N.A.I.C.S.: 551112
Jim Agley (Pres)

Subsidiaries:

Thomas Industrial Rolls, Inc. (1)
8526 Brandt St, Dearborn, MI 48126
Tel.: (313) 584-9696
Metal Stamping
N.A.I.C.S.: 332119

TALON LLC
96 Kercheval Ave # 200, Grosse Pointe Farms, MI 48236-3619
Tel.: (313) 396-4300
Web Site: http://www.talonllc.com
Privater Equity Firm
N.A.I.C.S.: 523999
Randolph J. Agley (Chm)
Michael T. Timmis (Vice Chm)

Subsidiaries:

ACT Test Panels, Inc. (1)
273 Industrial Dr, Hillsdale, MI 49242
Tel.: (517) 439-1485
Web Site: http://www.acttestpanels.com
Sales Range: $10-24.9 Million
Emp.: 120
Industrial Process Measurement Equipment Testing
N.A.I.C.S.: 334513

R & B Plastics Machinery, LLC (1)
1605 E Woodland Dr, Saline, MI 48176-0100
Tel.: (734) 429-9421
Web Site: http://www.rbplasticsmachinery.com
Sales Range: $10-24.9 Million
Emp.: 32
Machine Mold, Tooling & Trimming Systems
N.A.I.C.S.: 333511
Fred Piercy (Pres & Gen Mgr)

Subsidiary (Domestic):

Monroe Mold, LLC (2)
1402 W 7th St, Monroe, MI 48161
Tel.: (734) 241-6898
Web Site: http://www.monroemold.com
Plastic Molds & Cold End Tooling
N.A.I.C.S.: 333511
Jim Ghesquire (Pres)
Eric Colley (Mgr-Sls)
Mark Gardner (VP)
Mary Wickenheiser (Office Mgr)
Perry Schwemmin (Mgr-Engrg)

TALON PROFESSIONAL SERVICES, LLC
50 Millstone Rd Bldg 200 Ste 180, East Windsor, NJ 08520
Tel.: (609) 924-8900 NJ
Web Site: http://www.talonpro.com
Year Founded: 2001
Technology Staffing Services
N.A.I.C.S.: 561320
Dan Reynolds (Founder & CEO)
Joe Kelly (COO)
Steven Mantila (Controller)
Sharon Simon (Sls Mgr)
Jennifer Venturo (Sls Mgr)
Cynthia Antonacci (Sls Mgr)
Lori Magee (Mgr-Recruiting & Acct)
Gillian Rummler (Mgr-Recruiting)
Frank Paparelli (Mgr-Recruiting)
Thomas Stephan (Mgr-Trng)

TALON/LPE
921 N Bivins, Amarillo, TX 79107
Tel.: (806) 467-0607
Web Site: http://www.talonlpe.com
Rev.: $22,800,000
Emp.: 130
Environmental Services
N.A.I.C.S.: 213111
Larry Brown (CFO & Partner)
W. D. Prescott II (CEO & Partner)
Shane Currie (COO & Partner)

TALQUIN ELECTRIC COOPERATIVE, INC.
1640 W Jefferson St, Quincy, FL 32351-2134
Tel.: (850) 627-7651 FL
Web Site: http://www.talquinelectric.com
Year Founded: 1940
Sales Range: $25-49.9 Million
Emp.: 170
Electric & Other Services Combined
N.A.I.C.S.: 221118
Tracy Allen Bensley (Gen Mgr)
Jeremy Nelms (Dir-Engrg & Ops)
Bobby Kimbro (Mgr)
Ken Cowen (Dir-Admin Svcs)
Susan Vickers (Dir-Member Svcs)
Dane Clemons (Dir-Tech & Comm Svcs)
Tim Waddle (Dir-Water Svcs)

TALYST, INC.
11100 NE 8th St 6 Fl, Bellevue, WA 98004
Tel.: (425) 289-5400
Web Site: http://www.talyst.com
Year Founded: 2002
Sales Range: $10-24.9 Million
Emp.: 140
Medication Management Solutions
N.A.I.C.S.: 513210
Carla Corkern (Chm & CEO)
Alesia Pinney (Gen Counsel & VP-Legal Affairs)
Huan Nguyen (VP-Automation Ops-Long Term Care)
George Kondrach (Gen Mgr-Long Term Care)
Michael Blondin (Dir-Mktg & Sls Ops)

TAM BUSINESS SYSTEMS INC.
150 Fulton Ave, New Hyde Park, NY 11040
Tel.: (516) 739-0200
Web Site: http://www.nybs.com
Rev.: $11,273,070
Emp.: 45
Copying Equipment
N.A.I.C.S.: 423420
Myung Nam Kim (Pres)
Tai Kim (Sr VP)

TAM CERAMICS GROUP OF NY, LLC
4511 Hyde Park Blvd, Niagara Falls, NY 14305
Tel.: (716) 278-9403 NY
Web Site: http://www.tamceramics.com
Year Founded: 2010
Sales Range: $10-24.9 Million
Emp.: 60
Holding Company; Dielectric Materials Mfr
N.A.I.C.S.: 551112
George Bilkey (Pres)

Subsidiaries:

TAM Ceramics LLC (1)
4511 Hyde Park Blvd, Niagara Falls, NY 14305
Tel.: (716) 278-9400
Web Site: http://www.tamceramics.com
Sales Range: $10-24.9 Million
Dielectric Materials Mfr
N.A.I.C.S.: 327110
George Bilkey (Pres)

TAM INTERNATIONAL INC.
4620 Southerland Rd, Houston, TX 77092-3020
Tel.: (713) 462-7617 TX
Web Site: http://www.tamintl.com
Year Founded: 1973
Sales Range: $10-24.9 Million
Emp.: 85
Supplier of Oil & Gas Field Machinery
N.A.I.C.S.: 333132
Lawrence Sanford (Chm)
Michael Machowski (Pres)
Barton Sponchia (VP-Western Hemisphere)

TAMA TRADING COMPANY
1920 E 20th St, Los Angeles, CA 90058
Tel.: (213) 748-8262
Web Site: http://www.tamatrading.com
Year Founded: 1920
Sales Range: $10-24.9 Million
Emp.: 61

Tama Trading Company—(Continued)
Grocery & Related Product Whslr
N.A.I.C.S.: 424490
Phil Balistreri *(Acct Exec)*

TAMA-BENTON COOPERATIVE CO.
504 Estelle St, Dysart, IA 52224
Tel.: (319) 476-3666
Web Site: http://www.tamabentoncoop.com
Year Founded: 1947
Sales Range: $10-24.9 Million
Emp.: 15
Agricultural Services
N.A.I.C.S.: 424510
Alan Bredehoeft *(Mgr-Ops-Dysart)*
Brian Kreutner *(Chm)*
Ross Monroe *(Sec)*
Doug Elliott *(Controller)*
Charles Gabehart *(Gen Mgr)*
John Hayek *(Sec)*
Clayton Wieben *(Sr Project Mgr)*

TAMALPAIS GROUP INC.
1210 5th Ave Ste 100, San Rafael, CA 94901
Tel.: (415) 455-5770
Web Site: http://www.tamgroup.com
Sales Range: $10-24.9 Million
Emp.: 12
System Integration Services
N.A.I.C.S.: 541512
Rick Lowrey *(Chm)*

TAMANDA HOLDINGS USA INC.
288 Mazeppa Rd, Mooresville, NC 28115
Tel.: (704) 664-4300
Sales Range: $25-49.9 Million
Emp.: 4
Candy & Other Confectionery Products
N.A.I.C.S.: 311340
Richard Zulman *(CEO)*

Subsidiaries:

BestCo, Inc. (1)
288 Mazeppa Rd, Mooresville, NC 28115
Tel.: (704) 664-4300
Web Site: http://www.bestco.com
Healthcare Products Mfr & Marketer
N.A.I.C.S.: 325412
Richard Zulman *(CEO)*
Victor Clark *(Treas)*
Steve Berkowitz *(Exec VP)*
Paul Hervey *(VP-Bus Dev-Private Label)*
Mark Knight *(Exec VP)*
Tim Condron *(Pres)*
Scott Wattenberg *(CFO)*
Kathy Powell *(VP-Quality Ops & Compliance)*
Debbie Brower *(VP-HR)*

TAMAROFF MOTORS, INC.
28585 Telegraph Rd, Southfield, MI 48034-7507
Tel.: (248) 353-1300   DE
Web Site: http://www.tamaroff.com
Year Founded: 1969
Sales Range: $125-149.9 Million
Emp.: 300
New & Used Automobiles Dealer
N.A.I.C.S.: 441110
Marvin Tamaroff *(Owner)*
Susan Haas *(Treas)*

Subsidiaries:

Tamaroff Leasing Co. (1)
28585 Telegraph Rd, Southfield, MI 48034-7507   (100%)
Tel.: (248) 353-1564
Web Site: http://www.tamaroff.com
Sales Range: $10-24.9 Million
Emp.: 5
Automotive Rental & Leasing
N.A.I.C.S.: 532111

TAMCO HOLDINGS, LLC
777 E Wisconsin Ave Ste 2350, Milwaukee, WI 53202-5306
Tel.: (414) 765-1980   DE
Web Site: http://www.ti-am.com
Year Founded: 2012
Holding Company
N.A.I.C.S.: 551112
Robert Brooks *(CEO)*

Subsidiaries:

Boyd Watterson Asset Management, LLC (1)
1801 E 9th St Ste 1400, Cleveland, OH 44114   (100%)
Tel.: (216) 771-3450
Web Site: http://www.boydwatterson.com
Sales Range: $50-74.9 Million
Emp.: 30
Investment Advisory & Asset Management Services
N.A.I.C.S.: 523940
James R. Shirak *(Mng Partner & Deputy Chief Investment Officer)*
David M. Dirk *(Exec VP & Dir-Portfolio Mgmt & Trading)*
Deborah S. Kidd *(Sr VP & Portfolio Mgr)*
Theodore N. Hellmuth *(Sr VP-Platform Sls)*
Deborah J. Leet *(VP)*
Timothy M. Hyland *(Mng Partner & Dir-Sls & Mktg-Natl)*
Michael E. Bee *(Mng Partner & Dir-Client Svc)*
Kenneth R. Coffman *(Sr VP-Platform Sls)*
Brian C. Larson *(Sr VP-Platform Sls)*
G. David Hollins *(Sr VP & Dir-Credit Res)*
Justin C. Waggoner *(Sr VP & Portfolio Mgr)*
Brian A. Convery *(Sr VP & Portfolio Mgr-Credit Res)*
James A. Waler *(CTO & Exec VP)*
Teresa J. Burchfield *(Sr VP & Dir-Ops)*
Susan J. Simi *(VP & Controller)*
Robert J. Strnad *(VP & Portfolio Mgr-Credit Res)*
Christie Espin *(Asst VP & Portfolio Mgr)*
Robert Fernald *(VP & Portfolio Mgr)*
J. Deeds Kienker *(Asst VP-Credit Res)*
Mike Vandenbossche *(VP & Portfolio Mgr)*
Tracy Taylor *(Asst VP)*
Dixon Morgan Jr. *(Sr VP & Portfolio Mgr-Intl Equities)*

TAMER MEDIA, LLC
13 Broadcast Plz SW, Albuquerque, NM 87104
Tel.: (505) 797-1919
Year Founded: 2012
Holding Company; Radio Broadcasting Stations Owner & Operator
N.A.I.C.S.: 516120
John S. Viall Jr. *(Founder & Pres)*

Subsidiaries:

KASY-TV (1)
13 Broadcast Pl SW, Albuquerque, NM 87104
Tel.: (505) 243-2285
Web Site: http://www.krqe.com
Television Broadcasting Station Services
N.A.I.C.S.: 516120
John S. Viall Jr. *(Pres & Gen Mgr)*

KWBQ-TV (1)
13 Broadcast Plz SW, Albuquerque, NM 87104
Tel.: (505) 797-1919
Web Site: http://www.kwbq.com
Emp.: 20
Television Broadcasting Station
N.A.I.C.S.: 516120
John S. Viall Jr. *(Pres & Gen Mgr)*
Bill Case *(Dir-Creative Svcs)*
Taunya Tourville *(Mgr-Sls)*

TAMIMI PHARMACY LLC
12643 N 56th St, Temple Terrace, FL 33617
Tel.: (813) 515-7918
Web Site: http://www.stores.healthmart.com
Year Founded: 2013
Sales Range: $10-24.9 Million
Emp.: 40

Pharmacy Product Retailer
N.A.I.C.S.: 456110
Rachel Miller *(Reg Sls Mgr-Dermatology)*

TAMKO ROOFING PRODUCTS INC.
220 W 4th St, Joplin, MO 64801-2504
Tel.: (417) 624-6644   MO
Web Site: http://www.tamko.com
Year Founded: 1941
Sales Range: $350-399.9 Million
Emp.: 5,000
Asphalt Felts & Coatings Mfr
N.A.I.C.S.: 324122
David Humphreys *(Pres & CEO)*

TAMPA ARMATURE WORKS INC.
6312 78th St, Riverview, FL 33578
Tel.: (813) 621-5661   FL
Web Site: http://www.tawinc.com
Year Founded: 1921
Sales Range: $125-149.9 Million
Emp.: 630
Armature Rewinding Shops
N.A.I.C.S.: 811310
Byrd Scott *(Supvr-Shop)*
John Carlson *(Mgr-Quality-BSME)*
Kevin Pope *(Mgr)*

Subsidiaries:

TAW (1)
9930 NW 89th Ave, Miami, FL 33178-1425
Tel.: (305) 884-1717
Web Site: http://www.tawinc.com
Rev.: $12,000,000
Emp.: 80
Electrical Molars
N.A.I.C.S.: 811310

TAW Inc. (1)
3400 Bartlett Blvd, Orlando, FL 32811-6404   (100%)
Tel.: (407) 423-1886
Web Site: http://www.taw.com
Rev.: $4,000,000
Emp.: 35
Armature Rewinding Shops
N.A.I.C.S.: 811310
J. Arthur Turner Jr. *(Pres)*

TAW Macon Service Ctr (1)
1950 Canton St, Macon, GA 31204-5588
Tel.: (478) 743-5827
Web Site: http://www.tawinc.com
Rev.: $7,600,000
Emp.: 65
Armature Rewinding Shops
N.A.I.C.S.: 423610
Keith Amerson *(Mgr)*

TAMPA BANKING CO.
601 Bayshore Blvd, Tampa, FL 33606
Tel.: (813) 872-1222
Web Site: http://www.bankoftampa.com
Bank Holding Company
N.A.I.C.S.: 551111
William O. West *(Pres)*

Subsidiaries:

The Bank of Tampa (1)
601 Bayshore Blvd, Tampa, FL 33606
Tel.: (813) 872-1222
Web Site: http://www.bankoftampa.com
Rev.: $45,767,000
Assets: $1,259,572,000
Liabilities: $1,160,498,000
Net Worth: $99,074,000
Earnings: $8,486,000
Emp.: 214
Fiscal Year-end: 12/31/2013
Commercial Banking
N.A.I.C.S.: 522110
Stephen P. Fluharty *(Mng Dir & Sr VP-Sunset Park)*
David W. Feeman *(Sr VP)*
William O. West *(Pres)*
Laurence Whiting *(Asst VP-Comml Banking)*

Andre Kirwan *(Mgr-Comml Relationship)*
Owen LaFave *(Sr VP-Comml Real Estate)*
Lauren Fernandez *(Sr VP & Dir-Middle Market Banking)*
Scott Gault *(Pres-Hillsborough)*
Ramsey Chabbar *(Asst VP & Mgr-Comml Relationship)*
Jennifer Noel *(VP & Mgr-Private Relationship)*
Sarah Schelling Peet *(VP)*
Katrina Trump *(Sr VP & Dir-Cleanwater Market-Pinellas County)*
Chuck Catanese *(Dir-Market-Bryan Dairy)*
Doug Smith *(VP & Mgr-Comml Relationship)*
Becky Cagno *(Mgr-Personal Relationship)*
Donna Walsh *(Mgr-Comml Relationship)*
Kathryn Dinsmore *(Chief Credit Policy Officer)*
Joel Smith *(CMO)*
John M. Unger *(Mng Dir & Sr VP-Armenia)*
J. Kevin Riffey *(Sr VP & Dir-Small Bus Admin-Bayshore)*
David E. Brown *(Mng Dir & Sr VP-Brandon)*
Oliviana Catrone *(VP & Mgr-Private Relationship-Brandon)*
Darrell R. Turner *(VP & Mgr-Comml Relationship-Carrollwood)*
Craig L. West *(Mgr-Private Relationship)*
Kaley Infield *(Mgr-Mktg)*
Robert Smedley *(Sr Mgr-Cmml Relationship)*
Mike Krieg *(CIO & Sr VP)*
Patrick Ryan *(Portfolio Mgr)*
Michelle Caicedo *(Mgr-Personal Relationship)*
Anthony Perez *(VP & Mgr-Comml Relationship)*
Frank Vitarelli *(Sr VP & Dir-Largo)*
Kyle Keith *(Sr VP & Dir-Westshore)*
Jordan Young *(Sr VP/Mgr-Comml Relationship-Hillsborough)*
Katya Perez *(VP & Dir-Acctg)*
Dotti Overton *(VP & Mgr-Comml Relationship-Clearwater)*
Katrina Walters *(VP)*
Chad Wammock *(VP/Mgr-Comml Relationship-Central Pinellas)*
Eric Walley *(VP & Mgr-Comml Relationship)*
Corey Neil *(Chief Banking Officer)*
Angie Gardner *(VP & Mgr-Comml Relationship-New Port Richey)*
Sharon DeLong *(Sr VP)*
Courtney Lewis *(VP)*
Kenneth Braga *(Sr VP & Dir-Treasury Svcs)*
Drew Aldridge *(VP & Mgr-Relationship-Middle Market)*

TAMPA BAY & CO.
401 E Jackson St Ste 2100, Tampa, FL 33602
Tel.: (813) 223-1111
Web Site: http://www.visittampabay.com
Rev.: $10,731,439
Emp.: 60
Convention & Visitors Bureau
N.A.I.C.S.: 561591
Jennifer Friday *(Mgr-Natl Sls-Northeast, Southeast & Canada)*
Lisa Chamberlain *(Mgr-Natl Sls-Florida & Georgia)*
Susan Williams *(Dir-Svcs & Special Events)*
Holly Coger *(Mgr-Sls-Natl)*
Joyce Fisk *(VP-Partnership)*
Gregory Orchard *(CFO)*
JoLynn Lokey *(VP-Admin)*
Alex Kaptzan *(VP-Convention Sls)*
Brittany Callahan *(Mgr-Natl Sls)*
Sherri Brown *(Mgr-Natl Sls)*
Marisol Berrios *(Mgr-Leisure Sls)*
Jane Hahn Godfrey *(Sr Mgr-Svcs)*
Janette Carter *(Mgr-Mktg)*

TAMPA BAY INNOVATION CENTER
244 2nd Ave N, Saint Petersburg, FL 33701
Tel.: (727) 547-7340

COMPANIES

Web Site:
http://www.tbinnovates.com
Sales Range: $1-9.9 Million
Emp.: 6
Management & Business Innovation Services
N.A.I.C.S.: 541611
Tonya Elmore *(Pres & CEO)*
J. J. Roberts *(Mgr-Client Svcs)*
Mary Gort *(Office Mgr)*
Ken Evans *(Mng Dir)*
Chris Paradies *(Chm)*

TAMPA BAY ORTHOPAEDIC SPECIALISTS, PA
6500 66th St, Pinellas Park, FL 33781
Tel.: (727) 347-1286   FL
Web Site:
http://www.tampabayortho.com
Year Founded: 1968
Sales Range: $1-9.9 Million
Emp.: 50
Orthopedic Specialists
N.A.I.C.S.: 621111
Michael D. Slomka *(Partner)*
Steven B. Warren *(Partner)*
Howard W. Sharf *(Partner)*
Glenn S. Fuoco *(Partner)*
Richard T. Herrick *(Partner)*
Michael J. Smith *(Partner)*
John B. Pope *(Partner)*
Douglas B. Moss *(Partner)*

TAMPA BAY PARTNERSHIP FOR REGIONAL ECONOMIC DEVELOPMENT, INC.
4300 W Cypress St Ste 250, Tampa, FL 33607
Tel.: (813) 878-2208   FL
Web Site: http://www.tampabay.org
Year Founded: 1994
Sales Range: $1-9.9 Million
Emp.: 12
Economic Development & Marketing
N.A.I.C.S.: 926110
Kelly Kavanaugh *(CFO)*
Dave Sobush *(Dir-Res)*
Zachary Thorn *(Dir-Advocacy)*

TAMPA BAY PUBLICATIONS, INC.
2531 Landmark Dr Ste 101, Clearwater, FL 33761
Tel.: (727) 791-4800   FL
Web Site:
http://www.tampabaymagazine.com
Year Founded: 1986
Sales Range: $1-9.9 Million
Emp.: 18
Magazine Publisher
N.A.I.C.S.: 513120

Subsidiaries:

Tampa Bay Magazine   (1)
2531 Landmark Dr Ste 101, Clearwater, FL 33761
Tel.: (727) 791-4800
Web Site:
http://www.tampabaymagazine.com
Magazine Publisher
N.A.I.C.S.: 513120

TAMPA BAY RAYS BASEBALL, LTD.
Tropicana Field 1 Tropicana Dr, Saint Petersburg, FL 33705
Tel.: (727) 825-3137   FL
Web Site:
http://tampabay.rays.mlb.com
Year Founded: 1995
Sales Range: $10-24.9 Million
Emp.: 300
Professional Baseball Club
N.A.I.C.S.: 711211

John P. Higgins *(Gen Counsel & Sr VP-Admin)*
Rick Nafe *(VP-Stadium Ops & Facilities)*
Patrick Smith *(Controller)*
Matthew P. Silverman *(Pres)*
Robert Bennett *(Dir-Ticket Ops)*
Debbie Brooks *(Mgr-Mdse)*
Larry McCabe *(Sr Dir-Brdcst)*
Brian Richeson *(VP-Ticket Sls & Mktg)*
Stuart Sternberg *(Owner)*
Brian Auld *(Sr VP-Bus Ops)*
Melanie Lenz *(VP-Dev)*
Cass Halpin *(Sr Dir-Guest Rels)*
Juan Ramirez *(VP-IT)*
William Walsh *(VP-Strategy & Dev)*
Jennifer Lyn Tran *(Dir-HR)*
Mitch Lukevics *(Dir-Minor League Ops)*
Chris Westmoreland *(Dir-Travel & Clubhouse Ops)*
Eric Weisberg *(Dir-Customer Svc & Stadium Experience)*
Scott Kelyman *(Sr Dir-Stadium Ops)*
Michael Griffith *(Mgr-Security)*
Jeff Tanzer *(Sr Dir-Ticket Dev & Svcs)*
Suzanne Luecke *(Sr Dir-Community Rels)*
Stephen Thomas *(Dir-Strategy & Dev)*
Chad Collard *(Dir-Sls & Svc)*
Devin O'Connell *(Mgr-Corp Partnership Svcs)*
Sean Liston *(Dir-Corp Partnership Svcs)*
Jake Hornstein *(Mgr-Corp Partnership Svcs)*
Eric Kampfmann *(Mgr-Sys)*
Erik Neander *(VP-Baseball Ops)*
Dave Haller *(Dir-Comm)*

TAMPA BAY SPORTS & ENTERTAINMENT LLC
401 Channelside Dr, Tampa, FL 33602
Tel.: (813) 301-6500   DE
Web Site:
http://www.tampabaylighting.com
Year Founded: 2010
Sales Range: $1-9.9 Million
Emp.: 200
Holding Company; Professional Hockey Club & Sports Arena Owner & Operator
N.A.I.C.S.: 551112
Jeff Vinik *(Founder, Owner & Chm)*
Todd Leiweke *(CEO)*
Jarrod Dillon *(Exec VP-Sls & Mktg)*

Subsidiaries:

Lightning Hockey LP   (1)
401 Channelside Dr, Tampa, FL 33602-5400
Tel.: (813) 301-6600
Web Site: http://www.lightning.nhl.com
Professional Hockey Club
N.A.I.C.S.: 711211
Jeff Vinik *(Owner, Chm & Governor)*
William Wickett *(Exec VP-Comm)*
Ray Thill *(Mgr-Equipment)*
Keith Harris *(VP-HR)*
James Mannino *(VP-Ticket Ops)*
Steve Griggs *(CEO)*
Jamie Spencer *(Exec VP-Sls)*
Phil Esposito *(VP-Corp Rels)*
Adam Lawson *(Mgr-Inside Sls)*
Colin Cook *(Mgr-Corp Sls)*
Julien BriseBois *(Gen Mgr)*

Unit (Domestic):

Amalie Arena   (2)
401 Channelside Dr, Tampa, FL 33602
Tel.: (813) 301-6500
Web Site: http://www.amaliearena.com
Sports & Entertainment Arena Operator
N.A.I.C.S.: 711310

TAMPA BAY SYSTEMS SALES INC.
902 N Himes Ave, Tampa, FL 33609
Tel.: (813) 877-8251
Web Site:
http://www.tampabaytrane.com
Year Founded: 1969
Sales Range: $10-24.9 Million
Emp.: 200
Air Conditioning Room Units Sales
N.A.I.C.S.: 423620
Robert Garcia *(VP)*
Doug Cohn *(CEO)*
Jay Allison *(Pres & COO)*

TAMPA BAY WATER-REGIONAL WATER SUPPLY AUTHORITY
2575 Enterprise Rd, Clearwater, FL 33763-1102
Tel.: (727) 796-2355
Web Site:
http://www.tampabaywater.org
Year Founded: 1998
Sales Range: $25-49.9 Million
Emp.: 120
Water Utility Services
N.A.I.C.S.: 221310
Whitney Kiehn *(Coord-Environmental Permit)*
Mandi Rice *(Sr Mgr-Construction)*
Matt Jordan *(Gen Mgr)*

TAMPA BAY WORKFORCE ALLIANCE
4902 Eisenhower Blvd, Tampa, FL 33634
Tel.: (813) 397-2021   FL
Web Site:
http://www.workforcetampa.com
Year Founded: 2000
Sales Range: $10-24.9 Million
Emp.: 300
Employment Placement Services
N.A.I.C.S.: 561311
Sue Pagan *(CFO)*
Mark Douglass *(COO)*

TAMPA BRASS & ALUMINUM CORP.
8511 Florida Mining Blvd, Tampa, FL 33634-1221
Tel.: (813) 885-6064
Web Site:
http://www.tampabrass.com
Year Founded: 1957
Sales Range: $10-24.9 Million
Emp.: 105
Nonferrous Foundry Services
N.A.I.C.S.: 331529
Chris Leto *(Pres-Bus Dev)*
Sam Leto *(Chm)*
Tim Leto *(CFO)*
Jason Leto *(COO)*
Nilla Leto *(Mgr-Supply Chain)*
Paul Rehsi *(VP-Sls & Engrg)*
Bill Martin *(Mgr-Foundry)*
Kyle Warren *(Mgr-Program)*
Doug Murphy *(Mgr-Program)*
Tim Hemphill *(Mgr-Machine Shop)*
Troy Morris *(Mgr-Quality)*

TAMPA DIGITAL STUDIOS, INC.
1600 E 8th Ave Ste A117, Tampa, FL 33605
Tel.: (813) 241-2012   FL
Web Site:
http://www.tampadigital.com
Year Founded: 1995
Sales Range: $1-9.9 Million
Emp.: 28
Digital Production Services
N.A.I.C.S.: 512199
George Cornelius *(Pres)*

TAMPA DOWNTOWN PARTNERSHIP, INC.
400 N Ashley Dr Ste 2125, Tampa, FL 33602
Tel.: (813) 221-3686
Web Site:
http://www.tampasdowntown.com
Sales Range: $1-9.9 Million
Emp.: 10
Economic Development
N.A.I.C.S.: 926110
Shaun M. Drinkard *(Dir-Placemaking)*
Karen Kress *(Dir-Transportation & Plng)*
Lynda S. Remund *(COO)*
Angela Ruth *(Dir-Market Dev)*
Kelsy Van Camp *(Dir-Mktg & Comm)*
Mickey Jacob *(Chm)*

TAMPA FORK LIFT INC.
3221 N 40th St, Tampa, FL 33605
Tel.: (813) 623-5251
Web Site:
http://www.tampaforklift.com
Sales Range: $10-24.9 Million
Emp.: 50
Industrial Machinery & Equipment
N.A.I.C.S.: 423830
Dan Von Holt *(Gen Mgr-Sls)*

TAMPA HOUSING AUTHORITY
5301 W Cypress St, Tampa, FL 33607
Tel.: (813) 253-0551
Web Site: http://www.thafl.com
Year Founded: 1986
Sales Range: $1-9.9 Million
Emp.: 227
Housing Programs Administration
N.A.I.C.S.: 925110
Jerome D. Ryans *(Pres & CEO)*
Leroy Moore *(COO & Sr VP)*
Lillian Stringer *(Dir-PR)*
Martin Williams *(Dir-HR)*
Susi Begazo-McGourty *(CFO & Sr VP)*

TAMPA PALMS TRAVELWORLD
16051 W Tampa Palms Blvd, Tampa, FL 33647
Tel.: (813) 978-0877
Web Site:
http://www.travelworld1.com
Sales Range: $10-24.9 Million
Emp.: 14
Travel Agency
N.A.I.C.S.: 561510
Donald E. O'Neal Jr. *(Pres)*

TAMPA PORT AUTHORITY INC.
1101 Channelside Dr, Tampa, FL 33602
Tel.: (813) 905-7678
Web Site: http://www.tampaport.com
Sales Range: $25-49.9 Million
Emp.: 145
Port Authority
N.A.I.C.S.: 488310
Mike Macaluso *(CFO)*
Ken Washington *(CIO & VP)*
Wade Elliott *(VP-Mktg & Bus Dev)*
Greg Lovelace *(Dir-Mktg & Bus Dev-Cargo & Cruise)*
Ram Kancharla *(Sr Dir-Plng & Economic)*
Andy W. Fobes *(Dir-Special Events)*
Wade Elliot *(Dir-Project Mktg)*
Patrick H. Allman *(Treas & Sec)*
Paul Anderson *(CEO)*
Bob Callahan *(Sr Dir-Ops)*
Bruce A. Laurion *(VP-Engrg)*
Raul Alfonso *(Chief Comml Officer & Exec VP)*
Sandra L. Murman *(Mgr-HR)*

TAMPA PORT AUTHORITY INC.

U.S. PRIVATE

Tampa Port Authority Inc.—(Continued)
Rick Sharp *(COO & VP)*
John T. Thorington Jr. *(VP-Govt Affairs & Bd Coordination)*

TAMPA SPORTS AUTHORITY
4201 N Dale Mabry Hwy, Tampa, FL 33607
Tel.: (813) 350-6500
Web Site: http://www.tampasportsauthority.com
Year Founded: 1965
Sales Range: $10-24.9 Million
Emp.: 30
Sporting Events Promoter; Stadium Owner & Operator
N.A.I.C.S.: 711211
Mickey Farrell *(Dir-Stadium Ops)*
Jeanette Baker *(Dir-Fin & Admin)*
Mike Davis *(Asst Dir-Ops)*
Tony Munoz *(Vice Chm)*
Sue Maciejewski *(Mgr-HR)*
Bobby Silvest *(Dir-Comm & Mktg)*

TAMPA STEEL ERECTING COMPANY
5127 Bloomingdale Ave, Tampa, FL 33619
Tel.: (813) 677-7184
Web Site: http://www.tampasteelerecting.com
Year Founded: 1945
Sales Range: $10-24.9 Million
Emp.: 100
Steel Erector
N.A.I.C.S.: 237310
Robert Clark Jr. *(Pres)*

TAMPA THEATRE, INC.
711 N Franklin St, Tampa, FL 33602
Tel.: (813) 274-8286
Web Site: http://www.tampatheatre.org
Year Founded: 1926
Sales Range: $1-9.9 Million
Emp.: 25
Theater Operations
N.A.I.C.S.: 711310
John Bell *(Pres & CEO)*
Jill Witecki *(Dir-Mktg & Community Rels)*
Cathy Prance *(Bus Mgr & Dir-Ops)*
J. L. Wagner *(Dir-Dev)*
Maggie Ciadella *(Dir-Annual Giving)*
Lloyd Pearson *(Dir-Technical)*
Maggie Webber *(Dir-Dev)*

TAMRAC INC.
9240 Jordan Ave, Chatsworth, CA 91311
Tel.: (818) 407-9500
Web Site: http://www.tamrac.com
Sales Range: $10-24.9 Million
Emp.: 146
Camera Carrying Bags
N.A.I.C.S.: 316990
Cathy Blin *(Mgr-Admin)*
Rose Ramos *(Mgr-Credit)*
Jessie Cyr *(VP-Mfg)*
Linda Solano *(Supvr-Customer Svc)*
Castine Rees *(Coord-Mktg)*

TAMURA SUPERETTE INC.
86 032 Farrington Hwy, Waianae, HI 96792
Tel.: (808) 696-3321
Web Site: http://www.tamurasupermarket.com
Sales Range: $1-9.9 Million
Emp.: 166
Supermarkets & Other Grocery Stores
N.A.I.C.S.: 445110
Clifford Tamura *(Pres)*
Jill Tamura *(Treas)*

TANADGUSIX CORP.
615 E 82nd Ste 200, Anchorage, AK 99518
Tel.: (907) 278-2312
Web Site: http://www.beringsea.net
Sales Range: $10-24.9 Million
Emp.: 12
Hotel
N.A.I.C.S.: 721110
Ron Philemonoff *(CEO)*
Bob Odenheimer *(Dir-HR)*
Subsidiaries:
Bering Sea Eccotech Inc. (1)
3601 C St Ste 100030, Anchorage, AK 99503
Tel.: (907) 762-8520
Web Site: http://www.bse.com
Emp.: 97
Construction Project Management Consultant
N.A.I.C.S.: 541618
Barbara Mandregan *(Mgr-Contracts)*
Dean Hughes *(COO)*
Dan Skrobialowski *(Dir-Munitions Response Svcs Div)*
Mike Taylor *(Dir-Contracting)*
Coast International Inn (1)
3450 Aviation Ave, Anchorage, AK 99502
Tel.: (907) 243-2233
Web Site: http://www.coasthotels.com
Emp.: 100
Hotel
N.A.I.C.S.: 721110
Sandy Perkins *(Controller)*

TANAGER, INC.
10010 Jct Dr Ste 120 N, Annapolis Junction, MD 20701
Tel.: (240) 547-3150
Web Site: http://www.tanagerinc.com
Sales Range: $10-24.9 Million
Emp.: 75
Data Management Services
N.A.I.C.S.: 541511
Deborah Fedore *(CEO)*

TANAKA OF TOKYO RESTAURANTS
150 Kaiulani Ave Ste 3, Honolulu, HI 96815
Tel.: (808) 922-4233
Web Site: http://www.tanakaoftokyo.com
Sales Range: $10-24.9 Million
Emp.: 70
Japanese Restaurant
N.A.I.C.S.: 722511
Richard E. Tanaka *(Chm & CEO)*
Chester Kaneshiro *(Pres & COO)*
Hiroshi Lamansky *(VP)*

TANASEYBERT
525 W 52nd St, New York, NY 10019-5074
Tel.: (212) 206-0100
Sales Range: $25-49.9 Million
Emp.: 206
Commercial Printing & Lithographs
N.A.I.C.S.: 323111
David Jurist *(Chm)*

TANDEM
2400 Wolf Rd Ste 100, Westchester, IL 60154
Tel.: (630) 928-0510
Web Site: http://www.tandemhr.com
Year Founded: 1998
Sales Range: $125-149.9 Million
Emp.: 2,307
Human Resouce Services
N.A.I.C.S.: 541612
Bruce Leon *(Pres)*
Maureen Bostick *(Mgr-Risk)*

TANDEM HR, INC.
2400 Wolf Rd Ste 100, Westchester, IL 60154
Tel.: (630) 928-0510
Web Site: http://www.tandemhr.com
Year Founded: 1998
Sales Range: $350-399.9 Million
Emp.: 7,612
Human Resource Management Services
N.A.I.C.S.: 541612
Bruce Leon *(Founder)*
Debra Cleaveland *(Dir-Fin)*
Salo Doko *(Pres)*

TANDEM INC.
202 W Main St, Elizabeth City, NC 27909
Tel.: (252) 338-1793
Web Site: http://www.billmtaylor.com
Year Founded: 1971
Sales Range: $25-49.9 Million
Emp.: 700
Franchise Owner of Fast-Food Restaurants
N.A.I.C.S.: 722513
Bill M. Taylor *(CEO)*

TANDEM PUBLISHING GROUP, INC.
3131 Fleur Dr Unit 508, Des Moines, IA 50321-1741
Tel.: (515) 246-0402
Web Site: http://www.proimagecards.com
Commercial Lithographic Printing
N.A.I.C.S.: 323111

TANDEM TIRE & AUTO SERVICE
400 Harrison St, Dubuque, IA 52003
Tel.: (563) 557-8300
Web Site: http://www.tandemtire.com
Sales Range: $10-24.9 Million
Emp.: 50
Automotive Tires
N.A.I.C.S.: 441340
Don Hirsch *(Mgr)*

TANG INDUSTRIES INC.
8960 Spanish Ridge Ave, Las Vegas, NV 89148
Tel.: (702) 734-3700
Year Founded: 1961
Sales Range: $1-4.9 Billion
Emp.: 3,200
Diversified Holding Company
N.A.I.C.S.: 423510
Cyrus Tang *(Chm, Pres & CEO)*
Kurt R. Swanson *(CFO)*
Vytas Ambutas *(VP-Legal & Admin)*
Subsidiaries:
Curatek Pharmaceuticals Ltd. (1)
1965 Pratt Blvd, Elk Grove Village, IL 60007-5905
Tel.: (847) 806-7674
Sales Range: $10-24.9 Million
Emp.: 4
Pharmaceuticals Mfr
N.A.I.C.S.: 325412
National Material Limited Partnership (1)
1965 Pratt Blvd, Elk Grove Village, IL 60007 (100%)
Tel.: (847) 806-7200
Web Site: http://www.nmlp.com
Sales Range: $25-49.9 Million
Emp.: 90
Steel Service Center
N.A.I.C.S.: 423510
Michael Tang *(CEO)*
James Barry *(Pres & COO)*
Subsidiary (Domestic):
Interstate Steel Co. Inc. (2)
401 E Touhy Ave, Des Plaines, IL 60018-2607
Tel.: (847) 827-5151
Web Site: http://www.interstatesteelco.com
Sales Range: $25-49.9 Million
Primary Metal Industries; Slitting, Leveling, Blanking & Shearing of Flat Rolled Steel
N.A.I.C.S.: 423510
Taber Extrusions LP (1)
915 S Elmira, Russellville, AR 72802-1418
Tel.: (479) 968-1021
Web Site: http://www.taberextrusions.com
Sales Range: $10-24.9 Million
Emp.: 100
Custom Aluminum Extrusions
N.A.I.C.S.: 331318
Eric Angermeier *(Pres)*

TANGENT COMPUTER INC.
197 Airport Blvd, Burlingame, CA 94010-2006
Tel.: (650) 342-9388
Web Site: http://www.tangent.com
Year Founded: 1989
Sales Range: $10-24.9 Million
Emp.: 90
Computer Mfr
N.A.I.C.S.: 334111
Kevin Bradley *(Dir-Medical Solutions)*
Alex Kucich *(Mgr-IT)*
Ron Skinner *(Sr Acct Mgr)*

TANGENT FUND MANAGEMENT LLC
One Union Sq 180 Geary St Ste 500, San Francisco, CA 94108
Tel.: (415) 392-9228
Year Founded: 1995
Privater Equity Firm
N.A.I.C.S.: 523999
Mark Gilles *(Principal)*
Bob Andrew Sick *(Principal)*
Subsidiaries:
Borets International Ltd. (1)
Moldavskaya St, 121467, Moscow, Russia
Tel.: (7) 495 660 21 90
Sales Range: $1-4.9 Billion
Emp.: 9,000
Mfr & Distr of Electric Submersible Pump Equipment for Oil & Gas Industry
N.A.I.C.S.: 333132
Lev Stulberg *(CEO)*
Cheri Vetter *(Mgr-Bus Dev-Houston)*
Stan Herl *(Mgr-Sls-Oklahoma City)*
Chad Hamilton *(Mgr-Kilgore)*
Phyllis Mitchell *(VP-HR-Houston)*
Kent C. Crago *(VP-Fin-Houston)*
Subsidiary (Non-US):
Borets-Weatherford do Brasil Ltda. (2)
Av Americas 3434 Bloco 5 sala 306, Barra da Tijuca, Rio de Janeiro, 22640-102, Brazil
Tel.: (55) 21 3388 5531
Pumping Equipment Sales & Service
N.A.I.C.S.: 423830

TANGENT TECHNOLOGIES, LLC
1001 Sullivan Rd, Aurora, IL 60506-1065
Tel.: (630) 264-1110
Web Site: http://www.tangentusa.com
Recycled Plastic Products Mfr
N.A.I.C.S.: 326199
Guy Feo *(Owner)*
Andrew Stephens *(Owner)*

TANGERINE HOLDINGS, INC.
5541 Prospero Ln, Herriman, UT 84096
Tel.: (801) 599-8499
Year Founded: 2010
Metal Mining Services
N.A.I.C.S.: 212290
Randall Farr *(Pres, CEO, Treas & Sec)*

TANGIBLE MEDIA, INC.
12 W 37th St Fl 2, New York, NY 10018-7391

Tel.: (212) 359-1440
Web Site:
http://www.tangiblemedia.com
Year Founded: 1972
Sales Range: $100-124.9 Million
Emp.: 27
Media Buying Services
N.A.I.C.S.: 541830
Mitchell Boden *(Pres & Owner)*
Phyllis Starsia *(Exec VP)*

TANGLEWOOD INVESTMENTS INC.
5051 Westheimer Rd Ste 300, Houston, TX 77056-5604
Tel.: (713) 629-5525   TX
Web Site:
http://www.tanglewoodinv.com
Equity Investment Firm
N.A.I.C.S.: 523999
Sam Grover *(VP)*
Michael E. Humphrey *(Mng Dir)*
James J. Nelson *(Mng Dir)*
Michael L. Tiner *(Mng Dir)*

Subsidiaries:

Verantis Corporation   (1)
7251 Engle Rd Ste 300, Middleburg Heights, OH 44130
Tel.: (440) 243-0700
Web Site: http://www.verantis.com
Sales Range: $25-49.9 Million
Emp.: 30
Designs, Fabricates, Installs & Services Pollution Control Equipment
N.A.I.C.S.: 334512
Lars Buttkus *(Pres & CEO)*

TANGO INDUSTRIES LTD.
8839 H Kelso Dr, Baltimore, MD 21221
Tel.: (410) 780-4594
Web Site:
http://www.plantabbsproducts.com
Year Founded: 1921
Sales Range: Less than $1 Million
Emp.: 6
Fertilizers & Pesticides Mfr
N.A.I.C.S.: 325312
Wayne Davis *(Pres)*

Subsidiaries:

Plantabbs Products Company   (1)
8839 H Kelso Dr, Baltimore, MD 21221
Tel.: (410) 780-5495
Web Site:
http://www.plantabbsproducts.com
Small Package Garden & Plant Chemicals, Animal Repellents
N.A.I.C.S.: 325312

TANGO MANAGEMENT CONSULTING, LLC
5525 MacArthur Blvd Ste 450, Irving, TX 75038
Tel.: (817) 291-8987
Web Site: http://www.tangomc.com
Sales Range: $1-9.9 Million
Emp.: 60
Software Consulting Services
N.A.I.C.S.: 541512
Brad Biagini *(COO & Sr VP-Client Svcs)*
Bart Waldeck *(CMO & Sr VP-Product Strategy)*
Mark Wise *(CFO)*
Mark Zygmontowicz *(Sr VP-Sls & Client Mgmt)*
Pranav Tyagi *(Pres & CEO)*
Devon Wolfe *(Sr VP-Analytical Svcs)*
Paul Thompson *(VP-Client Mgmt)*
Amandeep Gill *(VP-Mgmt Consulting)*
Naresh Nalam *(VP-Product Dev)*
Rick Zelinsky *(VP-Product Strategy)*
Chris Smith *(VP-Sls)*
Don Wood *(VP-Support Svcs)*
Amit Sharma *(VP-Svcs)*
Bill Thornton *(VP-Tango Edge Platform & Quality Assurance)*

TANGO SUPPLIES, INC.
1890 S 3850 W Ste C, Salt Lake City, UT 84104   NV
Year Founded: 2010
Liquid Oxygen Drink
N.A.I.C.S.: 311411
Gerald Ricks *(Pres, CEO, CFO, Chief Acctg Officer & Sec)*

TANGOME, INC.
605 Fairchild Dr, Mountain View, CA 94043
Tel.: (650) 375-2620
Web Site: http://www.tango.me
Year Founded: 2009
Emp.: 160
Mobile Messaging Application Developer
N.A.I.C.S.: 513210
Uri Raz *(Co-Founder & CEO)*
Eric Setton *(Co-Founder & CTO)*
Gary Chevsky *(VP-Engrg)*
Brian Hansen *(VP-Technical Ops)*
Mark Stockford *(Sr VP-Ops)*
Cynthia Dinh *(VP-Global Bus Dev)*

TANIMURA & ANTLE INC.
1 Harris Rd, Salinas, CA 93908-8608
Tel.: (831) 455-2950   CA
Web Site: http://www.taproduce.com
Year Founded: 1982
Sales Range: $75-99.9 Million
Emp.: 2,200
Vegetable & Melon Farming & Distr
N.A.I.C.S.: 111219
Chris Glynn *(Dir-Organics)*
John McKeon *(Sr Mgr-Organic Compliance & Sustainability)*
Helena Beckett *(Sr Dir-Retail, VMI & Delivered Sls)*
Sarah Burns *(Sr Mgr-Organic Sls)*
Tom Casas *(VP-IT)*
Tim Escamilla *(CFO & Exec VP-Fin)*
Scott Grabau *(Pres & CEO)*
Gurmail Mudahar *(VP-R&D & Food Safety)*
Eric Wexler *(VP-Supply Chain Mgmt)*
Kyla Oberman *(Dir-Mktg)*
Ashley Pipkin *(Sr Mgr-Mktg)*
Nick Sgheiza *(VP-Harvest)*
Don Klusendorf *(Exec VP-Sls & Mktg)*
Steve Bassi *(Chief Agriculture Officer)*
Kerry Varney *(Chief Admin Officer)*

TANKNOLOGY INC
11000 N MoPac Ste 500, Austin, TX 78759-5338
Tel.: (512) 451-6334   DE
Web Site: http://www.tanknology.com
Year Founded: 1988
Sales Range: $10-24.9 Million
Emp.: 230
Environmental Compliance Services
N.A.I.C.S.: 541330
Pete DeWeese *(CFO & Exec VP)*
Allen Porter *(Pres & CEO)*
Brad Hoffman *(VP-R&D)*
Ignacio Allende *(VP-Intl Div & Intellectual Property)*
Kevin Callaway *(VP-Gulf Coast)*
Mark Lindsey *(VP-Southern California Reg)*

Subsidiaries:

Tanknology Ohio Valley Region   (1)
470 Schrock Rd Ste L, Columbus, OH 43229
Tel.: (800) 964-0010
Web Site: http://www.tanknology.com
Sales Range: $10-24.9 Million
Emp.: 3
Environmental Compliance Services
N.A.I.C.S.: 541330
Jason Bloch *(Mgr-Ops)*

Tanknology/NDE Corporation   (1)
11000 N Mopac Expy Ste 500, Austin, TX 78759   (100%)
Tel.: (512) 451-6334
Web Site: http://www.tanknology.com
Sales Range: $10-24.9 Million
Emp.: 25
Provider of Environmental Consulting Services
N.A.I.C.S.: 541330
Allen Porter *(Pres & CEO)*
Lauren Arons *(Mgr-Ops)*
Deanna Davenport *(Mgr-Ops)*
Todd Ferguson *(VP-Central Div)*
Jon Smith *(Mgr-Ops)*

TANKSTAR USA, INC.
611 S 28th St, Milwaukee, WI 53215-1201
Tel.: (414) 671-3039   WI
Web Site:
http://www.tankeryankers.com
Year Founded: 1987
Sales Range: $100-124.9 Million
Emp.: 1,100
Holding Company; Trucking Services
N.A.I.C.S.: 484121
Tom Budnik *(Controller)*
Jack Schwerman *(Pres & CFO)*
Allison Garcia *(Mgr-HR)*
Elliot Alderman *(VP-Sls)*
Craig Casey *(Dir-Maintenance)*

Subsidiaries:

Bulk Logistics Inc.   (1)
611 S 28th St, Milwaukee, WI 53215-1201
Tel.: (414) 671-3039
Web Site: http://www.tankstar.com
Sales Range: $10-24.9 Million
Emp.: 50
Third Party Logistics
N.A.I.C.S.: 532120

North American Bulk Transport Inc.   (1)
3190 Daniels Rd, Nazareth, PA 18064-9054
Tel.: (610) 759-9783
Web Site: http://www.tankstar.com
Sales Range: $10-24.9 Million
Emp.: 55
Trucking
N.A.I.C.S.: 484121

Schwerman Real Estate & Development Corp.   (1)
611 S 28th St, Milwaukee, WI 53215-1201
Tel.: (414) 671-1600
Web Site: http://www.tankstar.com
Sales Range: $10-24.9 Million
Emp.: 5
Nonresidential Building Operators
N.A.I.C.S.: 531120
Geoffery Redman *(VP)*

Schwerman Trucking Co. Inc.   (1)
611 S 28th St, Milwaukee, WI 53215-1201
Tel.: (414) 671-1600
Sales Range: $10-24.9 Million
Emp.: 15
Trucking
N.A.I.C.S.: 484121

TANNAHILL ADVERTISING
4025 Tannahill Dr, Gurnee, IL 60031
Tel.: (847) 336-6280   IL
Web Site:
http://www.paysoncasters.com
Year Founded: 1873
Sales Range: $10-24.9 Million
Emp.: 6
Advertising Agencies
N.A.I.C.S.: 541810
Travis Temple *(Dir-Adv)*

TANNEHILL INTERNATIONAL INDUSTRIES
10 Arthur Dr, Lynn Haven, FL 32444
Tel.: (850) 265-3611   FL
Web Site: http://www.merrick-inc.com
Rev.: $25,000,000
Emp.: 180
Weighing Machines & Apparatus
N.A.I.C.S.: 333998
Charlie Woods *(Mgr-Sls)*
Jay K. Tannehill Sr. *(Chm)*

Subsidiaries:

Merrick Environmental Technologies   (1)
10 Arthur Dr, Lynn Haven, FL 32444
Tel.: (850) 265-3611
Web Site: http://www.merrick-inc.com
Emp.: 200
Air Pollution Control & Dust Collection Equipment Supplier
N.A.I.C.S.: 334512

Merrick Industries Inc   (1)
10 Arthur Dr, Lynn Haven, FL 32444
Tel.: (850) 265-3611
Web Site: http://www.merrick-inc.com
Rev.: $10,100,000
Emp.: 115
Weighing Machines & Apparatus
N.A.I.C.S.: 333998
J. K. Tannehill Jr. *(Pres)*

Subsidiary (Non-US):

MERRICK Industries Pvt. Ltd.   (2)
103 113 & 114 7th Main 3rd Cross Peenya Industrial Area 3rd Phase, Bengaluru, 560 058, Karnataka, India
Tel.: (91) 80 28394500
Web Site: http://www.merrick-inc.com
Emp.: 40
Industrial Scale Mfr
N.A.I.C.S.: 333998
Yeshwant Ghorpade *(Mng Dir)*
A. Giridhar *(Dir-Ops)*

Weighing & Control, Inc.   (1)
10 Arthur Dr, Lynn Haven, FL 32444
Tel.: (850) 265-3611
Web Site: http://www.wcsrvs.com
Rev.: $900,000
Emp.: 6
Scale Repair Service
N.A.I.C.S.: 811490

TANNER COMPANIES, LP
537 Rock Rd, Rutherfordton, NC 28139-8125
Tel.: (828) 287-4205   NC
Web Site: http://www.doncaster.com
Year Founded: 1931
Sales Range: $75-99.9 Million
Emp.: 350
Women's Apparel
N.A.I.C.S.: 315250
Rich Hendricks *(Mgr-Tech Svcs)*

Subsidiaries:

Doncaster   (1)
537 Rock Rd, Rutherfordton, NC 28139-8125
Tel.: (828) 287-4205
Web Site: http://www.doncaster.com
Sales Range: $25-49.9 Million
Emp.: 80
Women's Apparel
N.A.I.C.S.: 315250
Stacy Guarriello *(Mgr-Adv & Mdsg)*
Twyla Pruett *(Mgr-Sls Network Mktg Admin)*

TANNER HOME & ENERGY
1120 Mt Rock Rd, Shippensburg, PA 17257
Tel.: (717) 477-9700
Web Site:
http://www.thebestheat.com
Sales Range: $10-24.9 Million
Emp.: 10
Petroleum Bulk Stations & Propane
N.A.I.C.S.: 424710
Robert Rohr *(Pres)*

TANNER INDUSTRIES INC.
735 Davisville Rd, Southampton, PA 18966-3276
Tel.: (215) 322-1238   PA
Web Site: http://www.tannerind.com
Year Founded: 1977

TANNER INDUSTRIES INC.

Tanner Industries Inc.—(Continued)
Sales Range: $10-24.9 Million
Emp.: 98
Wholesale Distributors of Ammonia Products
N.A.I.C.S.: 424690
Stephen B. Tanner *(Pres, CEO & COO)*
Greg W. Tanner *(VP)*
Eric Hindawi *(Treas & Sec)*
Tom Hearn *(Dir-Sls)*
Mark R. Tanner *(VP)*
Frank Bramble *(Dir-Transportation)*
John Long *(Dir-Ops)*
David B. Binder *(Dir-Quality, Safety & Regulatory Affairs)*

TANNER MATERIALS COMPANY LLC
10201 N 19th Ave, Phoenix, AZ 85021
Tel.: (602) 943-9868
Web Site: http://www.tannertile.com
Rev.: $10,000,000
Emp.: 15
Ceramic Wall & Floor Tile
N.A.I.C.S.: 327120
James Tanner *(Pres & CEO)*
Mike Tanner *(VP)*

TANNER SERVICES, LLC
302 Unatex Rd, Eunice, LA 70535
Tel.: (337) 432-5417
Web Site: http://www.tannerservices.net
Sales Range: $75-99.9 Million
Inland Marine & Oilfield Construction
N.A.I.C.S.: 237990
Brian J. Tanner *(Pres)*

Subsidiaries:
Tanner Services - Timber Division (1)
4527 Hwy 327, Kountze, TX 77625
Tel.: (409) 246-3573
Web Site: http://www.tannerservices.net
Sales Range: $10-24.9 Million
Emp.: 42
Timber Products
N.A.I.C.S.: 321999
Mike Griffin *(Gen Mgr-Ops)*

TANNIN CORPORATION
65 Walnut St, Peabody, MA 01960
Tel.: (978) 532-4010
Web Site: http://www.tannincorporation.com
Rev.: $10,700,000
Emp.: 17
Chemicals & Allied Products Sales
N.A.I.C.S.: 424690
Thomas W. Thompson *(Pres)*

TANSKY'S SALES INC.
6300 Sawmill Rd, Dublin, OH 43017
Tel.: (614) 766-4800
Web Site: http://www.tansky.com
Year Founded: 1967
Sales Range: $75-99.9 Million
Emp.: 90
Owner & Operator of Car Dealerships
N.A.I.C.S.: 441110
Thomas Tansky *(Pres)*
Nathaniel Tansky *(VP)*
Judy Tansky *(Treas)*

TANSKY'S SAWMILL TOYOTA INC.
6300 Sawmill Rd, Dublin, OH 43017
Tel.: (614) 766-4800
Web Site: http://www.tanskysawmilltoyota.com
Sales Range: $25-49.9 Million
Emp.: 90
Car Whslr
N.A.I.C.S.: 441110

Thomas J. Tansky *(Pres)*
Johanna Williams *(Dir-Ops)*

TANTARA TRANSPORTATION GROUP
46051 Michigan Ave, Canton, MI 48188
Tel.: (734) 879-4400
Web Site: http://www.tantara.com
Rev.: $20,197,220
Emp.: 25
Trucking Except Local
N.A.I.C.S.: 484121
Alan R. Fisher *(Pres)*
Bob Fisher *(Controller)*

Subsidiaries:
Tantara Services Inc. (1)
46051 Michigan Ave, Canton, MI 48188
Tel.: (734) 879-4400
Web Site: http://www.tantara.com
Sales Range: $10-24.9 Million
Transportation Agents & Brokers
N.A.I.C.S.: 488510
Alan R. Fisher *(Pres)*

TANTUS TECHNOLOGIES, INC.
501 School St SW Ste 800, Washington, DC 20024-2754
Tel.: (202) 567-2738
Web Site: http://www.tantustech.com
Year Founded: 2002
Rev.: $8,100,000
Emp.: 35
Computer System Design Services
N.A.I.C.S.: 541512
Buck Keswani *(Pres & CEO)*
Rhian Thompson *(COO)*
Greg Cioffi *(VP-Bus Dev)*

TANZARA INTERNATIONAL INC.
1407 Broadway Rm 1616, New York, NY 10018-2885
Tel.: (212) 354-9276
Rev.: $15,000,000
Emp.: 15
Womens Sportswear Manufacturer
N.A.I.C.S.: 424350
Gul Samtani *(Chm)*

TAOS SKI VALLEY, INC.
116 Sutton Pl, Taos Ski Valley, NM 87525-0090
Tel.: (575) 776-2291 **NM**
Web Site: http://www.skitaos.org
Year Founded: 1954
Sales Range: $150-199.9 Million
Emp.: 600
Ski Area Operations; Ski Shop; Ski School; Ski-Rental; Restaurants; Bar; Package Liquor Sales; Resort-Related Activities & Services
N.A.I.C.S.: 487990
Chris Stagg *(VP)*
David Norden *(CEO)*

Subsidiaries:
Taos Ski & Boot Company (1)
116 Fronte Pl, Taos Ski Valley, NM 87525
Tel.: (866) 769-7386
Web Site: http://www.skitaos.org
Recreational Goods Rental Services
N.A.I.C.S.: 532284
Daniel Aguilar *(Supvr)*

TAP ENTERPRISES INC.
650 N Lincoln St, Spring Hill, KS 66083
Tel.: (913) 592-2120
Web Site: http://www.toolsnow.com
Tools
N.A.I.C.S.: 444140
Tina D. Cone *(Office Mgr & Mgr-Accts Payable)*

Subsidiaries:
Cummings Tool (1)
650 N Lincoln, Spring Hill, KS 66083
Tel.: (913) 592-2120
Web Site: http://www.toolsnow.com
Sales Range: $10-24.9 Million
Emp.: 6
Tools, Hand
N.A.I.C.S.: 444140

TAP PLASTICS INC.
3011 Alvarado St Ste A, San Leandro, CA 94577
Tel.: (510) 895-8249
Web Site: http://www.tapplastics.net
Sales Range: $10-24.9 Million
Emp.: 160
Lumber & Other Building Materials
N.A.I.C.S.: 493190
Sam Sauber *(Mgr)*

TAPCO CREDIT UNION
6312 19th St W, Tacoma, WA 98466
Tel.: (360) 425-2130 **WA**
Web Site: http://www.redcanoecu.com
Year Founded: 1934
Sales Range: $10-24.9 Million
Emp.: 68
Financial Services
N.A.I.C.S.: 523999
Carlyn Roy *(CEO)*
Scott Drabb *(VP)*

TAPE
6363 Walker Ln Ste 300, Alexandria, VA 22310
Tel.: (703) 924-5020
Web Site: http://www.tape-llc.com
Year Founded: 1992
Sales Range: $25-49.9 Million
Emp.: 170
Program Management Services
N.A.I.C.S.: 926110
Louisa L. Jaffe *(Pres & CEO)*
William W. Jaffe *(Exec VP & Gen Mgr)*
Jill McFarlane *(CFO & Sr VP-Admin)*
Christine Workman *(VP-Admin)*
Mike Kelliher *(VP-DoD Enterprise Solutions)*
Daria Gray *(VP-Mktg & Program Ops)*
Matthew T. Clarke *(VP-Modeling, Simulation & Trng)*
Jeff Fleck *(VP-Defense Programs)*
William G. Lese Jr. *(Sr VP-Strategic Solutions)*

TAPE PRODUCTS COMPANY INC.
11630 Deerfield Rd, Cincinnati, OH 45242-1422
Tel.: (513) 489-8840 **OH**
Web Site: http://www.tapeproducts.com
Year Founded: 1967
Sales Range: $10-24.9 Million
Emp.: 50
Provider of Packaging Materials & Packaging Equipment
N.A.I.C.S.: 424130
John Fette *(CEO)*
Lawrence McHaffie *(Project Mgr)*

TAPHANDLES INC.
1424 4th Ave Ste 201, Seattle, WA 98101
Tel.: (206) 462-6800 **WA**
Web Site: http://www.taphandles.com
Year Founded: 1999
Sales Range: $1-9.9 Million
Emp.: 330
Mfr & Seller of Custom Beer Tap Handles, Tap Markers & Tap Knobs for Breweries

N.A.I.C.S.: 541430
Colin Gold *(CEO)*
Paul Fichter *(Founder & Pres)*
Paul Fichter *(Pres)*
Evan Lin *(Project Mgr)*
Becca Traub *(Acct Mgr)*
Bror Lawrence *(Mgr-Production)*
Karen Cheung *(Mgr-Acctg)*
Dave Kaplan *(Dir-Ops)*
Matt Rouleau *(Project Mgr)*

TAPIA BROS. CO.
6067 District Blvd, Maywood, CA 90270
Tel.: (323) 560-7415
Web Site: http://www.tapiabrothers.com
Year Founded: 1985
Sales Range: $50-74.9 Million
Emp.: 95
Grocery Distr
N.A.I.C.S.: 424410
Raul Tapia *(Pres & CEO)*

TAPJOY, INC.
111 Sutter St 12th Fl, San Francisco, CA 94104
Tel.: (415) 766-6900
Web Site: http://www.tapjoy.com
Year Founded: 2007
Emp.: 201
Mobile Advertising Services
N.A.I.C.S.: 541890
Steve Wadsworth *(Chm)*
Jeff Drobick *(Pres & CEO)*
Matthew Service *(CFO & COO)*
Shannon Jessup *(Chief Revenue Officer-Global)*
Benjamin Chen *(Sr VP & Gen Mgr-Global Developer Rels)*
Sarah Chafer *(Sr VP-Global Performance)*
Emily McInerney *(VP-Mktg-Global)*
Surendra Pathak *(Sr VP-Platform Enrg)*
Moonsik Kang *(Sr VP-Engrg)*
Lauren Baca *(Dir-Mktg)*

TAPP'S SUPERMARKETS INC.
575 Grand St, Brooklyn, NY 11211
Tel.: (718) 782-1222
Year Founded: 1987
Sales Range: $25-49.9 Million
Emp.: 650
Grocery Stores
N.A.I.C.S.: 445110
Paul Conte *(Pres)*

TAPPER'S
6337 Orchard Lake Rd, West Bloomfield, MI 48322
Tel.: (248) 932-7700
Web Site: http://www.tappers.com
Year Founded: 1976
Sales Range: $25-49.9 Million
Emp.: 100
Jewelry Whslr
N.A.I.C.S.: 458310
Mike Salzenstein *(Controller)*
Mark Tapper *(Pres)*

TAPSTONE ENERGY INC.
100 E Main St, Oklahoma City, OK 73104
Tel.: (405) 702-1600 **DE**
Web Site: http://www.tapstoneenergy.com
Year Founded: 2016
Emp.: 140
Oil & Natural Gas Exploration Services
N.A.I.C.S.: 211120
Steven C. Dixon *(Chm, Pres & CEO)*
David M. Edwards *(CFO & Sr VP)*
Stephen W. Miller *(Sr VP-Drilling)*
Robert P. Costello *(Gen Counsel & VP-Land)*

COMPANIES

TARGUS GROUP INTERNATIONAL, INC.

TAR HEEL CAPITAL CORPORATION NO. 2
166 Southgate Dr 10, Boone, NC 28607-4906
Tel.: (828) 262-1811 TN
Web Site:
http://www.tarheelcapital.com
Year Founded: 1977
Sales Range: $150-199.9 Million
Emp.: 3,000
Restaurant
N.A.I.C.S.: 722513
Susan Burnett *(Controller)*

TAR HEEL HOUSING CENTER INC.
4046 US Hwy 70 E, Goldsboro, NC 27534
Tel.: (919) 751-1706
Web Site:
http://www.modernhousing.net
Sales Range: $10-24.9 Million
Emp.: 6
Mobile Home Dealers
N.A.I.C.S.: 459930
Joseph C. Daughtery *(Pres)*

TARA GOLF & COUNTRY CLUB
6602 Drewrys Bluff, Bradenton, FL 34203
Tel.: (941) 756-7775 FL
Web Site: http://www.taragcc.com
Year Founded: 1988
Sales Range: $1-9.9 Million
Golf & Country Club Operator
N.A.I.C.S.: 713910
Larry Perkins *(Controller & Asst Mgr)*
Linda Calderone *(Office Mgr)*
Warren Lee *(Mgr-Clubhouse)*
Melissa Williams *(Head-Golf Pro)*

TARA MATERIALS INC.
322 Industrial Park Dr, Lawrenceville, GA 30046
Tel.: (770) 963-5256 GA
Web Site:
http://www.fredrixartistcanvas.com
Year Founded: 1966
Sales Range: $25-49.9 Million
Emp.: 200
Provider of Lead Pencils & Art Goods
N.A.I.C.S.: 339940
Yolanda Smith *(Coord-Intl Sls)*
Pat Allen *(Mgr-Customer Svc)*

Subsidiaries:

Tara Picture Frames (1)
7615 Siempre Viva Rd, San Diego, CA 92154 **(100%)**
Tel.: (619) 671-1018
Sales Range: $10-24.9 Million
Emp.: 22
Homefurnishings
N.A.I.C.S.: 423220

TARADEL, LLC
4805 Lk Brook Dr Ste 140, Glen Allen, VA 23060
Tel.: (804) 364-8444
Web Site: http://www.taradel.com
Year Founded: 2003
Emp.: 30
Print & Digital Marketing Services
N.A.I.C.S.: 323111
Jim Fitzgerald *(Founder & CEO)*
Wendy J. Urquhart *(VP-Bus Dev)*
Chris Barr *(Dir-Mktg)*
Tom McNally *(CFO)*
Dani Wolf *(Mgr-Creative Svcs)*
Michael Chambers *(Sr VP-Sls & Bus Dev)*
Michael Krentz *(Dir-Sls)*
Russell Smith *(Dir-Tech)*

TARAH ASPHALT PRODUCTS
1778 Zinetta Rd, Calexico, CA 92231
Tel.: (760) 357-4821
Web Site: http://www.tarah.com
Sales Range: $10-24.9 Million
Emp.: 10
Roofing Sales
N.A.I.C.S.: 423330
Meyte Durazo *(Sec)*
Mayra Montero *(Gen Mgr)*

TARAY INTERNATIONAL CORPORATION
1112 N Collier Blvd, Marco Island, FL 34145
Tel.: (239) 394-6099 FL
Web Site: http://www.taray.com
Year Founded: 1979
Sales Range: $10-24.9 Million
Emp.: 15
Tire & Tube Merchant Whslr; Various Other Equipment Whslr
N.A.I.C.S.: 423130
Janice Ayasun *(CFO)*
Tarik Ayasun *(Pres)*
Jerol Ayasun *(Gen Mgr)*
Tim Loden *(Mgr-Sls-US & Canada)*

TARBELL FINANCIAL CORPORATION
1403 N Tustin Ave Ste 380, Santa Ana, CA 92705
Tel.: (714) 972-0988
Web Site: http://www.tarbell.com
Sales Range: $250-299.9 Million
Emp.: 1,300
Holding Company
N.A.I.C.S.: 522310
Michael Montgomery *(VP-Fin)*

Subsidiaries:

Tarbell Realtors (1)
1403 N Tustin Ave Ste 380, Santa Ana, CA 92705
Tel.: (714) 972-0988
Web Site: http://www.tarbell.com
Sales Range: $100-124.9 Million
Emp.: 1,159
Loan Broker
N.A.I.C.S.: 531210

Subsidiary (Domestic):

F.M. Tarbell Co. Inc. (2)
1403 N Tustin Ave Ste 380, Santa Ana, CA 92705-8620
Tel.: (714) 972-0988
Web Site: http://www.tarbell.com
Sales Range: $25-49.9 Million
Emp.: 40
Real Estate Agents & Managers
N.A.I.C.S.: 531210
Donald M. Tarbell *(Pres)*
Tina Jimov *(Pres)*

Hartford Escrow Inc. (2)
1403 N Tustin Ave Ste 130, Santa Ana, CA 92705-8620
Tel.: (714) 972-1344
Web Site: http://www.hartford-escrow.com
Sales Range: $25-49.9 Million
Emp.: 6
Real Estate Agents & Managers
N.A.I.C.S.: 531210

Landwood Title Co. Inc. (2)
1403 N Tustin Ave Ste 380, Santa Ana, CA 92705-8620
Tel.: (714) 835-4070
Web Site: http://www.landwood.com
Sales Range: $50-74.9 Million
Emp.: 15
Title Insurance Services
N.A.I.C.S.: 524127

Tarbell Realtors (2)
1403 N Tustin Ave Ste 320, Santa Ana, CA 92705-8620
Tel.: (714) 972-1331
Web Site: http://www.tarbell.com
Sales Range: $50-74.9 Million
Emp.: 30
Insurance Agents, Brokers & Service
N.A.I.C.S.: 524210

TARCO INC.
9515 Hwy 165 S, North Little Rock, AR 72117
Tel.: (501) 945-4506 AR
Web Site:
http://www.tarcoroofing.com
Year Founded: 1977
Sales Range: $75-99.9 Million
Emp.: 110
Mfr of Roofing Materials
N.A.I.C.S.: 324122
David Snowden Jr. *(VP)*

Subsidiaries:

Tarco of Texas, Inc. (1)
2403 Taylors Vly Rd, Belton, TX 76513-9602 **(100%)**
Tel.: (800) 365-4506
Web Site: http://www.tarcoroofing.com
Sales Range: $10-24.9 Million
Emp.: 60
Roled Roofing
N.A.I.C.S.: 324122

TARGET + RESPONSE INC.
420 N Wabash Ave Ste 201, Chicago, IL 60611-3569
Tel.: (312) 321-0500
Web Site: http://www.target-response.com
Year Founded: 1987
Rev.: $15,000,000
Emp.: 14
Direct Response Marketing, Internet/Web Design, Radio
N.A.I.C.S.: 541810
Gary Kretchmer *(Mng Dir)*
Larry Levis *(Founder & Chm)*
Mike Collins *(Dir-Client Svcs)*
Mike Battisto *(Pres)*

TARGET ENTERPRISES LTD.
15260 Ventura Blvd Ste 1240, Sherman Oaks, CA 91403
Tel.: (818) 905-0005 CA
Web Site: http://www.targetla.com
Year Founded: 1979
Sales Range: $10-24.9 Million
Emp.: 20
Cable T.V.,
Government/Political/Public Affairs, Media Buying Services, Outdoor, Planning & Consultation, Print, Media Buying Services
N.A.I.C.S.: 541830
David L. Bienstock *(CEO & Founder)*
Julie Iadanza *(Dir-Media)*
Adam D. Stoll *(Pres)*
Nick Ayers *(Partner)*

TARGET FREIGHT MANAGEMENT
5905 Brownsville Rd, Pittsburgh, PA 15236
Tel.: (888) 653-1323
Web Site: http://www.targetfmi.com
Year Founded: 2008
Sales Range: $10-24.9 Million
Emp.: 25
LTL (Less-than-Truckload) Freight Management Services
N.A.I.C.S.: 488510
Michael Wagner *(Founder & Pres)*

TARGET INTERSTATE SYSTEMS INC.
33A New York City Terminal Market, Bronx, NY 10474
Tel.: (718) 842-4291
Web Site:
http://www.targetinterstate.com
Sales Range: $10-24.9 Million
Emp.: 25
Truck Transportation Services
N.A.I.C.S.: 488510
Paul Kazan *(Pres)*

TARGET MARKETING MAINE
120 Tillson Ave Ste 205, Rockland, ME 04841
Tel.: (207) 596-6203
Web Site:
http://www.targetmaine.com
Year Founded: 1991
Sales Range: $1-9.9 Million
Emp.: 60
Advetising Agency
N.A.I.C.S.: 541810
Keith Klein *(Gen Mgr)*
Sherry Stone *(Mgr-Mktg)*
Amanda Booker *(Mgr-Ops)*
Denis Walsh *(Mgr-Sls)*
Jen Langley *(Mgr-Production Control)*

TARGET OMAHA MARKETING, INC.
4145 S 87th St, Omaha, NE 68127
Web Site: http://www.firesprint.com
Year Founded: 2007
Sales Range: $1-9.9 Million
Emp.: 19
Graphic Design Advertising & Printing Services
N.A.I.C.S.: 541430
Gene Hamzhie *(Pres)*

TARGET PRINT & MAIL
2843 Industrial Plaza Dr., Tallahassee, FL 32301
Tel.: (850) 671-6600
Web Site: https://targetprintmail.com
Year Founded: 1982
Printing Services
N.A.I.C.S.: 323111
Tracey Cohen *(Pres)*

Subsidiaries:

Bowman Promotional Specialties Inc. (1)
3465 Hyde Park Way, Tallahassee, FL 32309
Tel.: (850) 906-0811
Web Site: http://www.bowmanpromo.com
Direct Selling Establishments
N.A.I.C.S.: 455219
Kristine K. Bowman *(Pres)*

TARGETABLE MARKETING SERVICES LLC
235 Park Ave S 8th Fl, New York, NY 10003
Web Site: http://www.targetable.com
Year Founded: 2019
Advertsing & Marketing Services
N.A.I.C.S.: 541810
Andrew J. Nash *(CEO)*

Subsidiaries:

ShopAdvisor, Inc. (1)
9 Damon Mill Sq Ste 3C, Concord, MA 01742
Tel.: (617) 818-6574
Web Site: http://www.shopadvisor.com
Custom Computer Programming Services
N.A.I.C.S.: 541511
Karen Macumber *(CMO)*

TARGETED CELL THERAPIES, LLC
Gateway Park/MBI 60 Prescott St, Worcester, MA 01605
Tel.: (508) 363-0001 MA
Web Site:
http://www.targetedcelltherapies.us
Pharmaceutical Developer & Mfr
N.A.I.C.S.: 325412
Edward Ginns *(Chief Scientific Officer)*

TARGUS GROUP INTERNATIONAL, INC.
1211 N Miller St, Anaheim, CA 92806-1933
Tel.: (714) 765-5555 DE

TARGUS GROUP INTERNATIONAL, INC.

Targus Group International, Inc.—(Continued)
Web Site: http://www.targus.com
Year Founded: 1983
Sales Range: $400-449.9 Million
Emp.: 250
Notebook Computer Carrying Cases & Accessories Designer, Mfr & Marketer
N.A.I.C.S.: 423990
Carolyn Perrier (VP-Mktg)

Subsidiaries:

Port Inc. (1)
1211 N Miller St, Anaheim, CA 92806-1933
Tel.: (714) 765-5555
Web Site: http://www.port.com
Sales Range: $10-24.9 Million
Emp.: 25
Briefcases & Backpacks
N.A.I.C.S.: 541990

Sanho Corporation (1)
1292 Kifer Rd Ste 808, Sunnyvale, CA 94086-5311
Tel.: (408) 737-7878
Web Site: http://www.hypershop.com
Advertising Material Distribution Services
N.A.I.C.S.: 541870
Daniel Chin (Pres)

Targus Asia Pacific Limited (1)
Unit 1202-1207 Miramar Tower 13 Unit 1202-1204 Miramar Tower 132, Kowloon, China (Hong Kong)
Tel.: (852) 25893200
Web Site: http://www.targus.com
Sales Range: $1-9.9 Million
Emp.: 20
Briefcases & Backpacks
N.A.I.C.S.: 316990

Targus Asia Pacific Pte. Ltd. (1)
10 Genting Rd 02 00 The Blue Bldg, Singapore, 349473, Singapore
Tel.: (65) 63831330
Web Site: http://www.targus.com
Sales Range: $10-24.9 Million
Emp.: 15
Briefcases & Backpacks
N.A.I.C.S.: 316990

Targus Australia Pty. Ltd. (1)
117-119 Bowden St, Meadowbank, 2114, NSW, Australia
Tel.: (61) 298071222
Web Site: http://www.targus.com.au
Sales Range: $10-24.9 Million
Emp.: 30
Briefcases & Backpacks
N.A.I.C.S.: 316990
Alenka Tindale (Mng Dir)

Targus Canada Ltd. (1)
420 Britannia Road East Suite 201, Mississauga, L4Z 3L5, ON, Canada
Tel.: (905) 564-9300
Web Site: http://www.targus.ca
Sales Range: $10-24.9 Million
Emp.: 35
Briefcases & Backpacks
N.A.I.C.S.: 316990

Targus India Pvt. Ltd. (1)
30 SF-1 2nd Floor Sapthagiri 10th Cross 15th Main Road, RMV Extension Sadashivnagar, Bengaluru, 560080, India
Tel.: (91) 80 41137568
Web Site: http://www.targus.com
Emp.: 6
Mobile Phone Accessory Distr
N.A.I.C.S.: 423690
Sukumaran Pallikari (Gen Mgr)

Targus Japan Ltd. (1)
Daini Sankei Building 1-16-5 Ueno, Taito-ku, Tokyo, 110 0005, Japan
Tel.: (81) 356881874
Web Site: http://www.targus.com
Sales Range: $10-24.9 Million
Emp.: 10
Briefcases & Backpacks
N.A.I.C.S.: 316990

Targus Korea Co., Ltd. (1)
Anam Tower Ste 1508, 702 10 Yuksam Dong Kangnam Gu, Seoul, 135 080, Korea (South)
Tel.: (82) 25662888
Web Site: http://www.targus.com
Sales Range: $10-24.9 Million
Emp.: 8
Briefcases & Backpacks
N.A.I.C.S.: 316990

TARHEEL BILLBOARD, INC.
933 Poindexter Dr, Charlotte, NC 28209
Tel.: (907) 953-2000 NV
Web Site: http://tarheelbillboard.com
Year Founded: 2012
Outdoor Advertising
N.A.I.C.S.: 541850
David Temple (Co-CEO)
Lau Hau Hung (Pres, CEO, CFO & Sec)

TARHEEL PAPER & SUPPLY CO.
3200 Centre Park Blvd, Winston Salem, NC 27107
Tel.: (336) 714-4747
Web Site: http://www.tarheelpaper.com
Sales Range: $50-74.9 Million
Emp.: 30
Industrial & Personal Service Paper
N.A.I.C.S.: 424130
Ted Shelton (Gen Mgr)

TARLTON CORPORATION
5500 W Park Ave, Saint Louis, MO 63110-1853
Tel.: (314) 633-3300 MO
Web Site: http://www.tarltoncorp.com
Year Founded: 1945
Sales Range: $100-124.9 Million
Emp.: 250
Contracting & Construction Services
N.A.I.C.S.: 236210
Matthew Pfund (Sr VP)
Jason Bretz (VP)
Joe Scarfino (VP)
John T. Doerr (Exec VP)
Anthony J. Eftimoff (VP-Fin)
Dirk G. Elsperman (COO & Exec VP)
Tracy Elsperman Hart (Pres & CEO)
Sondra Rotty (VP)
John P. Smith (Mgr-Estimates)

TARP WORLDWIDE
1100 Wilson Blvd Ste 950, Arlington, VA 22209
Tel.: (703) 524-1456
Web Site: http://www.tarp.com
Year Founded: 1971
Sales Range: Less than $1 Million
Emp.: 100
Customer Experience Research Consultancy
N.A.I.C.S.: 541910
Dennis Gonier (CEO)
Crystal D. Collier (COO & Sr VP-Practices)

Subsidiaries:

TARP Worldwide Europe (1)
Ingram House 13-15 John Adam St, London, WC2N 6LU, United Kingdom
Tel.: (44) 845 130 4690
Web Site: http://www.tarp.co.uk
Customer Experience Research Consultancy
N.A.I.C.S.: 541910

TARR LLC
2946 NE Columbia Blvd, Portland, OR 97211
Tel.: (503) 288-5294
Web Site: http://www.tarrllc.com
Sales Range: $10-24.9 Million
Emp.: 50
Petroleum Bulk Stations
N.A.I.C.S.: 424710

Skip Tarr (Pres & CEO)
Butch Roberts (Gen Mgr & Mgr-Sls)
Phyllis Giggers (Mgr-Pur)

TARRANT COUNTY INDIGENT CARE CORPORATION
612 E Lamar Blvd, Arlington, TX 76011
Tel.: (682) 236-7900 TX
Year Founded: 2007
Sales Range: $75-99.9 Million
Indigent Health Care Services
N.A.I.C.S.: 622110
Tom Corley (Sec)
Jack Roper (Chm)

TARRANT SERVICE, INC.
9901 Taylorsville Rd, Louisville, KY 40299-0586
Tel.: (502) 491-2511 KY
Web Site: http://www.tarrantparts.com
Year Founded: 1932
Sales Range: $1-9.9 Million
Emp.: 6
Distr of HVAC Replacement Parts
N.A.I.C.S.: 423730
R. Lane Tarrant (Chm, Pres & CEO)
Donnie Buchheit (Mgr-Ops)

TARSADIA INVESTMENTS, LLC
520 Newport Ctr Dr 21st Fl, Newport Beach, CA 92660
Tel.: (714) 929-9060
Web Site: http://www.tarsadia.com
Privater Equity Firm
N.A.I.C.S.: 523940
Gautam Patel (Mng Dir)
Mitchell Caplan (Pres)
Tushar Patel (Founder & Chm)

TARTAN MARKETING
10467 93rd Ave N, Maple Grove, MN 55369
Tel.: (763) 391-7575 MN
Year Founded: 1989
Sales Range: $25-49.9 Million
Emp.: 13
N.A.I.C.S.: 541810
James J. Maclachlan (Owner & Pres)
Margie Maclachlan (CEO)
Angie Zebell (Dir-Art)
Kris Pierro (Acct Supvr)
Lynn Lewis (Acct Supvr)
John Andreini (Sr Copywriter)
Kim Welter (Dir-Art)

TARTARIC CHEMICALS CORPORATION
24951 Rushmore Ter, Little Neck, NY 11362-1325
Tel.: (212) 752-0727
Web Site: http://www.tartarics.com
Rev: $15,000,000
Emp.: 40
Whslr & Importer of Industrial Chemicals
N.A.I.C.S.: 424690

TARUS PRODUCTS INC.
38100 Commerce Dr, Sterling Heights, MI 48312
Tel.: (586) 977-1400
Web Site: http://www.tarus.com
Sales Range: $10-24.9 Million
Emp.: 100
Mfr of Industrial Machines
N.A.I.C.S.: 333517
Dreux Strauch (Engr-Applications)
Rob Valente (Mgr-Trng & Quality)

TAS ENVIRONMENTAL SERVICES, L.P.
3929 California Pkwy E, Fort Worth, TX 76119-7340

Tel.: (817) 535-7222
Web Site: http://www.taslp.com
Year Founded: 2004
Waste Collection
N.A.I.C.S.: 562998
Ed Genovese (CEO)
Steve Black (COO)
Tim Grout (CFO)
Gordon Roberts (Dir-Bus Dev)

Subsidiaries:

Delmar Disposal (1)
8508 C F Hawn Fwy, Dallas, TX 75217
Tel.: (214) 391-1109
Web Site: http://www.taslp.com
Industrial Waste Services
N.A.I.C.S.: 562219

TASC TECHNICAL SERVICES LLC
73 Newton Rd, Plaistow, NH 03865
Tel.: (603) 382-1114
Web Site: http://www.tasctechnh.com
Year Founded: 1988
Sales Range: $10-24.9 Million
Emp.: 12
Computer-Aided Design Systems Service
N.A.I.C.S.: 541512
Patricia McDonough (Owner & Mgr-Ops)
Mark McDonough (Mgr-Global Mktg)

TASCA LINCOLN MERCURY, INC.
200 Fall River Ave, Seekonk, MA 02771
Tel.: (508) 336-7200
Web Site: http://www.tasca.com
Year Founded: 1972
Sales Range: $10-24.9 Million
Emp.: 100
New Car Dealers
N.A.I.C.S.: 441110
Alex Castergini (Gen Mgr)

TASCON, INC.
7607 Fairview St, Houston, TX 77041
Tel.: (713) 937-0900
Web Site: http://www.tasconindustries.com
Year Founded: 1976
Sales Range: $75-99.9 Million
Emp.: 60
Cellulose Insulation Mfr
N.A.I.C.S.: 238310
Vic Bosnich (Mgr-Sls-Insulation Products)

TASCOSA OFFICE MACHINES, INC.
1005 SW 8th Ave, Amarillo, TX 79116
Tel.: (806) 373-6268
Web Site: http://www.tascosaofficemachines.com
Sales Range: $10-24.9 Million
Emp.: 85
Office Equipment Whslr
N.A.I.C.S.: 423420
John King (Pres)
Kelly King (VP)
Lynn Pipkin (Sec)

TASK FORCE FOR GLOBAL HEALTH, INC.
330 W Ponce de Leon Ave, Decatur, GA 30030
Tel.: (404) 371-0466 GA
Web Site: http://www.taskforce.org
Year Founded: 1986
Rev: $1,042,661,147
Assets: $76,441,049
Liabilities: $16,766,123
Net Worth: $59,674,926
Earnings: $7,078,246
Fiscal Year-end: 08/31/21

COMPANIES

Public Health Care Services
N.A.I.C.S.: 622110
Vivian Singletary *(Dir-Pub Health Informatics Institute)*
Ellen Wild *(Dir-Bus Strategy)*
David A. Ross *(Pres & CEO)*
William P. Nichols *(COO & Exec VP)*
Lynn Heinisch *(Chief Comm Officer)*
Mark McKinlay *(Dir-Center-Vaccine Equity)*
Patrick O'Carroll *(Head-Health Sys Strengthening Sector)*
Joseph Bresee *(Dir-Partnerships-Influenza Vaccine Introduction)*
Robert Chen *(Dir-Brighton Collaboration)*
Paul Emerson *(Dir-Intl Trachoma Initiative)*
Katie Gass *(Dir-Res-Neglected Tropical Diseases Support Center)*
Rubina Imtiaz *(Dir-Children Without Worms)*
Carla Johnson *(Mgr-Supply Chain-Intl Trachoma Initiative)*
Patrick Lammie *(Dir-Neglected Tropical Diseases Support Center)*
Carla Reddy *(Dir-Trng Programs-Epidemiology & Pub Health Interventions Network)*
Yao Sodahlon *(Dir-Mectizan-Donation Program)*
John Ward *(Dir-Coalition-Global Hepatitis Elimination)*
Lori Warrens *(Dir-Medsurplus Alliance)*
David Addiss *(Officer-Global Health & Dir-Focus Area-Compassion & Ethics)*
Courtenay Dusenbury *(Dir-Global & Federal Affairs)*
Bill Gallo *(Dir-Global Partnership-Zero Leprosy)*
Martha Rogers *(Dir-African Health Workforce Project)*
Kristin Saarlas *(Dir-Health Campaign Effectiveness Coalition)*

TASK SOURCE INC.
3830 Turman Loop Ste 101, Wesley Chapel, FL 33544
Tel.: (813) 406-4890
Web Site:
http://www.tasksourceinc.com
Emp.: 11
Promotional Products, Industrial Safety, Protective & Operational Equipment
N.A.I.C.S.: 424990
Robert Shannon *(CEO)*
Jerry Smith *(Pres)*
Lindsay M. Shannon *(Dir-Ops)*

TASK TECHNOLOGIES, INC.
1971 E Beltline Ave NE Ste 217, Grand Rapids, MI 49525 NV
Web Site: http://www.task-technologies.net
Year Founded: 2006
Sales Range: Less than $1 Million
Emp.: 7
Healthcare Related IT Consulting, Database Programming & Placement Services
N.A.I.C.S.: 541519
Mark Ismond *(VP-IR)*
Guy D. Roberts *(CEO)*
Steven R. Visser *(Pres, CFO, VP-Fin & Admin, Treas & Sec)*
Allan Vander Hart *(VP-Sls & Mktg)*

TASKUS
3221 Donald Douglas Loop S Ste C, Santa Monica, CA 90405
Web Site: http://www.taskus.com
Year Founded: 2008
Sales Range: $1-9.9 Million
Emp.: 424

Business Services Outsourcer for Internet Companies
N.A.I.C.S.: 561311
Jaspar Weir *(Pres)*
Bryce Maddock *(CEO)*
Matthew Mink *(Sr Dir-Consulting)*
Emma Guevarra *(Dir-Corp Social Responsibility)*
Ryan Bobos *(Dir-Workforce Mgmt)*
Balaji Sekar *(CFO)*
Christopher McLaughline-Brooks *(CIO)*
Jarrod Johnson *(Chief Customer Officer)*
Mason Jones *(VP-Bus Dev)*
Nikkole Sgamsuddin *(VP-Consulting & Tech)*
Isabel Bernal *(VP-Culture Philippines)*
Dan Nacarato *(Sr VP-Ops)*
Joe Buggy *(COO)*
Kerry Carstairs *(Sr VP-Client Svcs)*
Porfirio Diaz *(VP-Ops)*
Robert Hayes *(Chief Delivery Officer)*

Subsidiaries:

TaskUS (1)
ARC Center Real 1 Aguinaldo Hwy, 4102, Cavite, Bacoor, Philippines **(100%)**
Tel.: (63) 908 337 0127
Web Site: http://www.taskus.com
Emp.: 500
Business Services Outsourcer for Internet Companies
N.A.I.C.S.: 561499
Carlo Victorino Mendoza *(Sr Mgr-Ops)*
Jimi Malipot *(Supvr-Trng Dev)*
Mel Guerzon *(Mgr-Ops)*
Louie Gauzon *(Mgr-Ops)*
Ryan Bobo *(Mgr-Ops)*
Sonny Narcelles *(Mgr-IT)*
Marissa Javier *(Mgr-Budget)*
Nia Mangulabnan *(Mgr-Recruitment)*
Elaine Darvin *(Mgr-Ops)*
Charles Gavino *(Mng Dir)*
Jasper Darvin *(Mgr-Ops)*
Frisco Octavo *(Mgr-Ops)*
Janice Biscocho *(Mgr-Administration)*
Frank Malabanan *(Dir-IT)*
Johnny Catabay *(Dir-Fin)*

TASLER INC.
1804 Tasler Dr PO Box 726, Webster City, IA 50595-7625
Tel.: (515) 832-5200 IA
Web Site: http://www.tasler.com
Year Founded: 1972
Sales Range: $25-49.9 Million
Emp.: 200
Lumber & Pallet Sales; Pallet Recycling & Repair Services
N.A.I.C.S.: 326150
Greg Tasler *(Pres & CEO)*
Brent Johnson *(Mgr-Credit)*

TASMAN INDUSTRIES INC.
930 Geiger St, Louisville, KY 40206
Tel.: (502) 587-0701
Web Site: http://www.tasmanusa.com
Year Founded: 1947
Sales Range: $10-24.9 Million
Emp.: 30
Cattle Hides & Finished Leather Product Sales
N.A.I.C.S.: 424590

TASTE BUDS, INC.
8301 Oak St, New Orleans, LA 70118-2043
Tel.: (504) 486-4570
Web Site: http://tastebudsmgmt.com
Restaurants Owner & Management Consulting
N.A.I.C.S.: 722511
Greg Reggio *(Co-Owner)*
Hans Limburg *(Co-Owner)*
Gary Darling *(Co-Owner)*

Subsidiaries:

Semolina Inc. (1)

8301 Oak St, New Orleans, LA 70118
Tel.: (504) 486-4570
Web Site: http://www.semolina.com
Rev.: $22,013,678
Emp.: 15
Italian Restaurant
N.A.I.C.S.: 722511
Gary Darling *(Co-Founder)*
Hans Limburg *(Co-Founder)*
Greg Reggio *(Co-Founder)*

TASTEFULLY SIMPLE INC.
1920 Turning Leaf Ln SW, Alexandria, MN 56308
Tel.: (320) 763-0695
Web Site:
http://www.tastefullysimple.com
Year Founded: 1995
Sales Range: $10-24.9 Million
Emp.: 180
Direct Sales of Gourmet Foods
N.A.I.C.S.: 722511
Bob Seward *(VP-Strategic Initiatives)*
Jill Blashack Strahan *(Founder & CEO)*
Nancy Dahl *(Pres & COO)*
Bill Bill Finley *(CFO)*
Travis Bautz *(VP-Mktg)*
Chet Seely *(VP-Sls)*
Jan Finazzo *(VP-Tech Svcs)*

TASTY BLEND FOODS, INC.
Ste 1 Tasty Blend Way, Fraziers Bottom, WV 25082
Tel.: (304) 757-6686
Web Site: http://www.tastyblend.com
Year Founded: 1980
Sales Range: $10-24.9 Million
Emp.: 40
Bakery Products Mfr
N.A.I.C.S.: 311812
Roy Elswick *(Pres & CEO)*
Jim Adkins *(Plant Mgr)*
Dennis Chaney *(Engr-Project)*

TASTY CATERING, INC.
1900 Touhy Ave, Elk Grove Village, IL 60007
Tel.: (847) 593-2000
Web Site:
http://www.tastycatering.com
Year Founded: 1984
Rev.: $5,300,000
Emp.: 156
Catering
N.A.I.C.S.: 722320
Ellen Harte *(Dir-Key Accts)*
Kristen Banks *(Dir-Corp Sls)*
Eugene Rios *(Dir-Ops)*
Larry Walter *(Founder & Partner)*
Tekla Wendoll *(Comptroller)*
Erin Walter *(Dir-Mktg)*
Kornel Grygo *(CEO)*
Tommy Menzer *(Dir-Project)*
Tony Sansone *(Dir-Sls)*

TASTY PURE FOOD CO. INC.
841 S Broadway St, Akron, OH 44310
Tel.: (330) 434-8141
Web Site: http://www.tastypure.com
Sales Range: $10-24.9 Million
Emp.: 42
Provider of Dairy Foods
N.A.I.C.S.: 424430
Jim Heilmeier *(Pres)*
Bill Heilmeier *(CFO)*
Heil Meier *(CEO)*

TASTY SEAFOOD CO. INC.
13 Marconi Ln, Marion, MA 02738
Tel.: (508) 748-3784
Web Site:
http://www.tastyseafood.com
Rev.: $16,000,000
Emp.: 8
Seafoods
N.A.I.C.S.: 424460

Peter Levine *(Pres)*

TASTY-TOPPINGS, INC.
2804 13th St, Columbus, NE 68602-0728
Tel.: (402) 564-1347 NE
Web Site:
http://www.dorothylynch.com
Year Founded: 1964
Sales Range: $1-9.9 Million
Emp.: 25
Home Style Dressing
N.A.I.C.S.: 311941
Mac Hull *(Pres)*

TASZ, INC.
240 Polychem Ct, Lenoir, NC 28645
Tel.: (828) 754-7570
Web Site: http://www.neocork.com
Cork Mfr
N.A.I.C.S.: 339999
Chakra K. Gupta *(Owner & Pres)*

Subsidiaries:

TASZ, Inc. (1)
537 Stone Rd, Benicia, CA 94510
Tel.: (707) 642-6800
Sales Range: $1-9.9 Million
Emp.: 31
Cork Mfr
N.A.I.C.S.: 339999

TATANGO, INC.
2211 Elliott Ave Ste 200, Seattle, WA 98121
Tel.: (206) 274-6599
Web Site: http://www.tatango.com
Year Founded: 2007
Mobile Marketing Services
N.A.I.C.S.: 541810
Derek Johnson *(CEO)*

TATE AUTOMOTIVE GROUP
7535 Ritchie Hwy, Glen Burnie, MD 21061
Tel.: (410) 766-2560
Web Site:
http://www.tateautomotive.com
Emp.: 200
Onwer & Operator of Car Dealerships
N.A.I.C.S.: 441110
Glenn Jackson *(Gen Mgr)*

Subsidiaries:

Chrysler Jeep-Glen Burnie (1)
7429 Ritchie Hwy, Glen Burnie, MD 21061
Tel.: (410) 994-2737
Web Site:
http://www.tatedodgechryslerjeep.net
Sales Range: $10-24.9 Million
Emp.: 100
Automobiles, New & Used
N.A.I.C.S.: 441110
Glen Jackson *(Gen Mgr)*

Tate Chevrolet (1)
1833 West St, Annapolis, MD 21401 **(100%)**
Tel.: (410) 757-6300
Rev.: $49,000,000
Emp.: 30
Automobiles, New & Used
N.A.I.C.S.: 441110

TATE CAPITAL REAL ESTATE SOLUTIONS, LLC
1175 NE 125th St, Miami, FL 33161
Tel.: (305) 891-1107
Web Site: http://www.tatecapital.com
Sales Range: $150-199.9 Million
Emp.: 50
Real Estate Investment Services
N.A.I.C.S.: 531390
Stanley Tate *(Chm)*
James D. Tate *(Pres)*

TATE DODGE CHRYSLER JEEP, INC.

TATE DODGE CHRYSLER JEEP, INC.

Tate Dodge Chrysler Jeep, Inc.—(Continued)
7429 Ritchie Hwy, Glen Burnie, MD 21061-3101
Tel.: (410) 766-2560
Web Site:
http://www.tatedodgechrysler jeep.net
Year Founded: 1952
Sales Range: $50-74.9 Million
Emp.: 300
Car Whslr
N.A.I.C.S.: 441110
Michael Johnson (Dir-Svc)
Ron Ward (Gen Mgr-Sls)

TATE ENGINEERING SYSTEMS INC.
3921 Vero Rd, Arbutus, MD 21227
Tel.: (410) 242-8800
Web Site: http://www.tate.com
Year Founded: 1998
Sales Range: $100-124.9 Million
Emp.: 135
Distribution of Industrial Machinery & Equipment
N.A.I.C.S.: 423830
Daniel R. Baker (Owner)
Sue Lannon (Gen Mgr-PA)

Subsidiaries:

Site Support Services, Inc. (1)
8511 Loch Raven Blvd, Towson, MD 21286
Tel.: (410) 771-0911
Web Site:
http://www.sitesupportservices.com
Precision Cooling & Power Solutions Services
N.A.I.C.S.: 333415
Don Mellinger (CEO)

TATE'S AUTO CENTER
1001 Navajo Blvd, Holbrook, AZ 86025
Tel.: (928) 524-6268
Web Site:
http://www.tatesautocenter.com
Sales Range: $25-49.9 Million
Emp.: 70
New & Used Car Dealers
N.A.I.C.S.: 441110
Linda Tate (Pres)
Dan Bradley (Controller)

TATEAUSTINHAHN
1105 N Lamar Blvd Ste 100, Austin, TX 78703-4941
Tel.: (512) 476-7696
Year Founded: 1991
Sales Range: $1-9.9 Million
Emp.: 16
Public Relations Agency
N.A.I.C.S.: 541820
Kerry Tate (Principal-Civic Interest & Sr Counsel)
Steve Lanier (Controller)
Brian Dolezal (VP-Client Svcs)
Russ Rhea (VP & Dir-Media Svcs)
Jeff Hahn (Principal)

TATNUCK BOOKSELLERS INC.
18 Lyman St, Westborough, MA 01581
Tel.: (508) 366-4292
Web Site: http://www.tatnuck.com
Sales Range: $10-24.9 Million
Emp.: 115
Book Stores
N.A.I.C.S.: 459210

Subsidiaries:

Chandler House Press (1)
West Side Sta PO Box 2010, Worcester, MA 01602
Tel.: (508) 753-7419
Web Site:
http://www.chandlerhousebooks.com

Publishers of Personalized Books for Individual Authors, Businesses, Groups & Organizations
N.A.I.C.S.: 459210

TATRO & WHEELER CORP.
48571 Milmont Dr, Fremont, CA 94538
Tel.: (408) 734-3600
Web Site: http://www.proexhibits.com
Sales Range: $1-9.9 Million
Emp.: 40
Trade Show Booths
N.A.I.C.S.: 561920
Jody Tatro (Founder, CEO & Principal)
Dick Wheeler (Pres)
Tom Hopkins (CFO)
Matt Rulis (VP-Sls)
Paul Miller (VP-Mktg)
Tom Foley (VP-Ops)

TATTERSALL COMPANIES, LLC
1620 Central Ave NE Ste 150, Minneapolis, MN 55413
Tel.: (612) 584-4152
Web Site:
http://www.tattersalldistilling.com
Year Founded: 2014
Sales Range: $1-9.9 Million
Emp.: 45
Alcoholic Beverages Mfr
N.A.I.C.S.: 312130
Dan Oskey (Co-Founder)
Jon Kreidler (Co-Founder)
Bentley Gillman (Mgr-Delivery)

TATUM DEVELOPMENT CORP.
11 Pkwy Blvd, Hattiesburg, MS 39401-8893
Tel.: (601) 544-6043
Year Founded: 1981
Sales Range: $150-199.9 Million
Emp.: 700
Holding Company
N.A.I.C.S.: 551112
Robert O. Tatum (Pres & CEO)
Joseph F. Tatum Jr. (Treas & Sec)

Subsidiaries:

Industrial Welding Supplies of Hattiesburg, Inc. (1)
5051 Hwy 42, Hattiesburg, MS 39401-2814
Tel.: (601) 545-1800
Sales Range: $25-49.9 Million
Emp.: 143
Welding Equipment & Industrial Supplies Retailer
N.A.I.C.S.: 423840

The Merchants Company Inc. (1)
1100 Edward St, Hattiesburg, MS 39401 (100%)
Tel.: (601) 583-4351
Web Site:
http://www.themerchantscompany.com
Sales Range: $50-74.9 Million
Emp.: 585
Grocery Whslr & Distr
N.A.I.C.S.: 424410
Andrew B. Mercier (Pres & CEO)

Division (Domestic):

Merchants Foodservice (2)
1100 Edward St, Hattiesburg, MS 39401
Tel.: (601) 583-4351
Web Site:
http://www.merchantsfoodservice.com
Sales Range: $25-49.9 Million
Emp.: 60
Food Whslr
N.A.I.C.S.: 424410
Andrew B. Mercier (Pres & CEO)
Jimmy Triggs (Dir-Maintenance)
Doyle Gentry (Pres-Jackson Div)
Ricky Reed (VP-Sls & Mktg)
Jim Strzelecki (Pres-Newberry Div)

Branch (Domestic):

Merchants Foodservice (3)
11531 South Carolina Hwy 34, Newberry, SC 29108-0038
Tel.: (803) 276-0510
Web Site:
http://www.merchantsfoodservices.com
Sales Range: $25-49.9 Million
Emp.: 60
Wholesale Food Distribution
N.A.I.C.S.: 424410

TAUBENPOST, INC.
9272 Jeronimo Rd Ste 107A, Irvine, CA 92618
Tel.: (949) 770-3233
Web Site: http://www.taubenpost.com
Year Founded: 1981
Holding Company; Direct Mail Advertising Services
N.A.I.C.S.: 551112
Carroll L. Goldsworth (Owner & Pres)
James Goldsworth (VP)

Subsidiaries:

Taubenpost Mailing, Inc. (1)
9272 Jeronimo Rd Ste 107A, Irvine, CA 92618
Tel.: (949) 770-3233
Web Site: http://www.taubenpost.com
Direct Mail Advertising Services
N.A.I.C.S.: 541860
Carroll L. Goldsworth (Pres)
James Goldsworth (VP)

TAUBENSEE STEEL & WIRE COMPANY INC.
600 Diens Dr, Wheeling, IL 60090-2645
Tel.: (847) 459-5100
Web Site: http://www.taubensee.com
Year Founded: 1946
Sales Range: $10-24.9 Million
Emp.: 100
Supplier of Steel Wire & Related Products
N.A.I.C.S.: 331222
Dale Taubensee (Pres)
Kent Taubensee (Exec VP)

TAUBER OIL COMPANY
55 Waugh Dr Ste 700, Houston, TX 77007
Tel.: (713) 869-8700
Web Site: https://www.tauberoil.com
Year Founded: 1953
Sales Range: $75-99.9 Million
Emp.: 170
Petroleum & Petroleum Products Merchant Wholesalers (except Bulk Stations & Terminals)
N.A.I.C.S.: 424720
Richard E. Tauber (Co-Owner & Principal)
Stephen E. Hamlin (VP)
Joseph E. Sassin (Controller)
Connie M. Kubiak (VP)
Lisa K. Simon (Mgr-Credit)
Jan M. Hicks (VP-Trasportation & Mktg)
Kevin A. Wilson (VP)
Steven M. Elliott (VP)
David W. Tauber (Co-Owner & Principal)
Clayton Tauber (VP)
Jonathan C. Tauber (VP)
Lory T. Whitley (VP)

TAUNTON MUNICIPAL LIGHTING PLANT INC.
55 Weir St, Taunton, MA 02780-3915
Tel.: (508) 824-5844
Web Site: http://www.tmlp.com
Year Founded: 1882
Sales Range: $25-49.9 Million
Emp.: 170
Provider of Electric Services

U.S. PRIVATE

N.A.I.C.S.: 221118
Kenneth Goulart (Gen Mgr)

TAUNTON TRUSS, INC.
5441 S Hwy 71, Wewahitchka, FL 32465
Tel.: (850) 639-2337
Web Site:
http://www.tauntontruss.com
Sales Range: $10-24.9 Million
Emp.: 25
Corrugated & Solid Fiber Box Mfr
N.A.I.C.S.: 322211
Adam Taunton (Owner)

TAUNTON, INC.
63 S Main St, Newtown, CT 06470-2355
Tel.: (203) 426-8171
Web Site: http://www.taunton.com
Year Founded: 1995
Sales Range: $25-49.9 Million
Emp.: 265
Publisher of Periodicals
N.A.I.C.S.: 513120
Dan McCarthy (Interim CEO)

TAVA ORGANICS, LTD.
230 W Ave 26, Los Angeles, CA 90031
Tel.: (323) 686-2868
Web Site:
http://www.fourthandheart.com
Year Founded: 2014
Sales Range: $10-24.9 Million
Emp.: 10
Food & Beverage Retailer
N.A.I.C.S.: 445298
Raquel Tavares Gunsagar (Co-Founder & CEO)
Lilly Wunsch (Founder & COO)

TAVANT TECHNOLOGIES, INC.
396 Freedom Cir Ste 750, Santa Clara, CA 95054
Tel.: (408) 519-5400
Web Site: http://www.tavant.com
Rev.: $52,400,000
Emp.: 1,000
IT Solutions & Services
N.A.I.C.S.: 541511
Sarvesh Mahesh (CEO)
Manish Arya (Founder & CTO)
Hassan Rashid (Chief Revenue Officer)
Srini Vudumula (VP-HR)
Raj Nair (VP-Sls)
Chitbhanu Nagri (Head-HR-Global)
Rohit Jain (CIO)
Sesha Devana (CFO)
Dain Ehring (Sr VP-Market Dev)
Vikas Khosla (VP-Sls)
Atul Varshneya (Head-Artificial Intelligence Practice)
Raj Menon (CMO)

TAVENS CONTAINER INCORPORATED
22475 Aurora Rd, Bedford, OH 44146-1270
Tel.: (216) 883-3333
Web Site: http://www.tavens.com
Year Founded: 1997
Rev.: $10,100,000
Emp.: 77
Container Mfr
N.A.I.C.S.: 322211
Graham Klintworth (VP-Fin)
Jan Piko (VP-Ops)
Steve Sutker (VP-Sls)

TAVERN ON THE GREEN LP
Central Pk at W 67. St, New York, NY 10023
Tel.: (212) 873-3200

Web Site:
http://www.tavernonthegreen.com
Year Founded: 1973
Sales Range: $25-49.9 Million
Emp.: 500
Eating Place
N.A.I.C.S.: 722511
Bryan Kalman *(Exec Dir-Private Dining)*

TAVISTOCK GROUP, INC.
9350 Conroy Windermere Rd, Windermere, FL 34786
Tel.: (407) 909-9000   FL
Web Site: http://www.tavistock.com
Emp.: 50
Equity Investment Firm
N.A.I.C.S.: 523999
Andy Odenbach *(VP-Sports Ventures)*
Rasesh Thakkar *(Sr Mng Dir)*

Subsidiaries:

BayCorp Holdings, Ltd. (1)
1 New Hampshire Ave Ste 207, Portsmouth, NH 03801
Tel.: (603) 294-4850
Energy Asset Holding Company
N.A.I.C.S.: 551112
Frank W. Getman Jr. *(Chm, Pres & CEO)*
Patrycia T. Barnard *(Treas & VP-Fin)*
Anthony M. Callendrello *(COO & Sec)*

Great Bay Power Marketing, Inc. (1)
1 New Hampshire Ave Ste 125, Portsmouth, NH 03801 **(100%)**
Tel.: (603) 766-4990
Power Supply Whslr
N.A.I.C.S.: 221122

Lake Nona Golf & Country Club, LLC (1)
9100 Chiltern Dr, Orlando, FL 32827
Tel.: (407) 859-3402
Web Site: http://www.lakenona.com
Golf Course & Country Club
N.A.I.C.S.: 713910
Andy Odenback *(Pres)*
Belinda Carll *(Mgr-Lodge & Comm)*
Mark Bayer *(Controller-Club)*

Tavistock Restaurants, LLC (1)
6475 Christie Ave Ste 300, Emeryville, CA 94608-2263 **(100%)**
Tel.: (510) 594-4262
Web Site:
http://www.tavistockrestaurants.com
Investment Holding Company
N.A.I.C.S.: 551112
John T. Bettin *(CEO)*
Steve Byrne *(VP-Food & Beverage)*
John Fisher *(Dir-Sls)*
Lisa Helmke *(VP-Construction & Design)*
Marc Hinson *(VP-HR)*

TAWA SUPERMARKET INC.
6281 Regio Ave, Buena Park, CA 90620-1023
Tel.: (714) 521-8899   CA
Web Site: http://www.99ranch.com
Year Founded: 1984
Grocery Stores
N.A.I.C.S.: 445110
Roger Chen *(Founder)*
Danny Au *(Sr VP-Facility)*
Ming Sun *(VP-Food Processing Center)*
Shuchen Chu *(Mgr-Insurance)*

TAWIL ASSOCIATES INC.
Empire State Building, New York, NY 10118
Tel.: (212) 279-3211   NJ
Web Site: http://www.tawil.com
Sales Range: $100-124.9 Million
Emp.: 180
Mfr of Infant's & Children's Clothing
N.A.I.C.S.: 424350
Edward T. Tawil *(Pres & CEO)*
Mitchell Tawil *(Treas & Exec VP)*
Mark Conway *(Sr VP)*
Amy Pang *(VP-Design)*

TAX AIRFREIGHT INC.
5975 S Howell Ave, Milwaukee, WI 53207
Tel.: (414) 769-6565
Web Site: http://www.taxair.com
Year Founded: 1977
Sales Range: $25-49.9 Million
Emp.: 430
Vehicle Delivery Services
N.A.I.C.S.: 484110
Gregory H. Groth *(Founder & Chm)*
Rick Sabbatini *(Founder & VP)*
Larry Haase *(VP-Svcs)*

TAX ANALYSTS
400 S Maple Ave, Falls Church, VA 22046-3537
Tel.: (703) 533-4400
Web Site: http://www.taxnotes.com
Year Founded: 1971
Sales Range: $10-24.9 Million
Emp.: 200
Periodical Publishers
N.A.I.C.S.: 513120
Forest Marodelli *(CFO)*
Cara Griffith *(Pres & CEO)*
Martin Lobel *(Chm)*

TAX TRILOGY, LLC
4 Parkland Blvd Ste 160, Dearborn, MI 48126
Tel.: (313) 827-4100
Web Site: http://www.taxtrilogy.com
Year Founded: 2007
Sales Range: $1-9.9 Million
Emp.: 8
Tax Compliance & Consulting Services
N.A.I.C.S.: 541219
Nancy E. Hazely *(Founder, Pres & CEO)*
Rachel A. Lawson *(Mgr-Property Tax)*
Linda L. Freitag *(Coord-HR & Compliance Production)*
Keith D. Hazely II *(COO)*

TAXBREAK LLC
2010 Club Dr Ste 100, Gadsden, AL 35901
Tel.: (256) 549-4829   AL
Web Site: http://www.taxbreakllc.com
Year Founded: 1998
Sales Range: $1-9.9 Million
Emp.: 22
Corporate Tax Consulting Services
N.A.I.C.S.: 541213
Shannon Scott *(Pres & CEO)*

TAXOPS LLC
215 Union Blvd Ste 325, Lakewood, CO 80228
Tel.: (720) 227-0070
Web Site: http://www.taxops.com
Year Founded: 2003
Sales Range: $1-9.9 Million
Emp.: 17
Tax Consulting Services
N.A.I.C.S.: 541213
Brian Amann *(Founder & Partner)*
Chris Becze *(Partner)*
Mark Dunning *(Partner)*
John Monahan *(Partner)*
Andrea Collins *(Dir-Ops)*
Alex Leugers *(Mgr-Tax)*
Sherri Overdorf *(Mgr-Tax)*
Carolyn Neyer *(Sr Mgr-Tax)*
Lisa Clark *(Mgr-Tax)*
Judy Vorndran *(Partner)*
Cara Marczewski *(Mgr-Tax)*
James S. Miele *(CFO)*
Kristine Newkirk *(Dir-Comm)*
Peter Murphy *(Sr Mgr-Tax)*
Rachel Sawyer *(Partner)*

TAXUS PHARMACEUTICALS HOLDINGS, INC.
245-16 Horace Harding Expy, Little Neck, NY 11362
Tel.: (718) 631-1522   NY
Year Founded: 2002
TXSP—(OTCBB)
Pharmaceuticals & Dietary Supplements Retailer
N.A.I.C.S.: 456110
Jiayue Zhang *(Pres, CEO & CFO)*

TAYCOR LLC
222 N 675, Los Angeles, CA 90056
Tel.: (310) 568-9900
Web Site: http://www.taycor.com
Sales Range: $10-24.9 Million
Emp.: 50
Equipment Rental & Leasing
N.A.I.C.S.: 532490
Bob Skibinski *(Founder)*
Michael Hong *(CEO)*
Suzanne Costa *(VP-Biotechnology & Medical Device)*
Robert Butler *(CTO)*
Pallavi Kharbanda *(Head-Data Science)*
Justin Wheeler *(Head-Product & Bus Dev)*

TAYLOR & ASSOCIATES LAW GROUP, PLLC
5100 Poplar Ave, Memphis, TN 38137
Tel.: (901) 244-3922   TN
Web Site:
http://www.taylorinjurylaw.com
Year Founded: 1991
Law firm
N.A.I.C.S.: 541110
Donald W. Fisher *(Partner)*

TAYLOR & HILL, INC.
9941 Rowlett Rd, Houston, TX 77075
Tel.: (713) 941-2671   TX
Web Site:
http://www.taylorandhill.com
Year Founded: 1974
Sales Range: $10-24.9 Million
Emp.: 150
Contract Personnel & Engineering Services
N.A.I.C.S.: 561311
Ray Nunez *(Pres)*

TAYLOR & MARTIN ENTERPRISES INC.
1865 N Airport Rd, Fremont, NE 68025
Tel.: (402) 721-4500
Web Site:
http://www.taylorandmartin.com
Year Founded: 1935
Sales Range: $10-24.9 Million
Emp.: 50
Auctioneer Fee Basis Distr
N.A.I.C.S.: 541990
J. Jessup Wilson *(CEO & CFO)*
Stacy Tracy *(Pres)*

Subsidiaries:

Preferred Leasing Inc. (1)
1865 N Airport Rd, Fremont, NE 68025
Tel.: (402) 721-8288
Rev.: $140,000
Truck Leasing, Without Drivers
N.A.I.C.S.: 532120
Paul C. Wachter *(Pres)*

Taylor & Martin Inc. (1)
1865 N Airport Rd, Fremont, NE 68025
Tel.: (402) 721-4500
Web Site: http://www.taylorandmartin.com
Rev.: $11,009,000
Auctioneers, Fee Basis
N.A.I.C.S.: 455219
Paul C. Wachter *(Pres)*
Stacy Tracy *(Dir-Sls-Natl)*

TAYLOR & MATHIS, INC.
600 Townpark Ln Ste 550, Kennesaw, GA 30144
Tel.: (770) 795-1330   GA
Web Site:
http://www.taylormathis.com
Sales Range: $10-24.9 Million
Emp.: 40
Commercial & Industrial Building Operation
N.A.I.C.S.: 531120
Carroll M. Battey *(Sr VP-Ops)*
Kerry O'Brien *(Sr VP-Mktg)*
Annette Arnold *(CFO & Sr VP)*
Mike Irby *(Sr VP-Dev)*

TAYLOR & MURPHY CONSTRUCTION CO.
1121 Brevard Rd, Asheville, NC 28806
Tel.: (828) 667-4526
Sales Range: $25-49.9 Million
Emp.: 300
Highway & Street Paving Contractor
N.A.I.C.S.: 237310
Kenneth D. Murphy *(CEO)*
Michael F. Long *(Pres)*
William Newman *(VP)*
Daryl L. Crouse *(CFO)*

TAYLOR ASSOCIATES
13191 Starkey Rd # 7, Largo, FL 33773
Tel.: (727) 443-4430
Web Site:
http://www.taylorinsurancerecruiters.com
Sales Range: $1-9.9 Million
Insurance Recruiting Services
N.A.I.C.S.: 561311
Helen D. Dalzell *(Principal)*

TAYLOR BUILDING CORPORATION OF AMERICA
6100 Hitt Ln, Louisville, KY 40241-1342
Tel.: (502) 582-1800   KY
Web Site:
http://www.taylorhomes.com
Year Founded: 1993
Sales Range: $10-24.9 Million
Emp.: 20
Single-Family Housing Construction
N.A.I.C.S.: 524298
Eric Taylor *(CEO)*
Chris Taylor *(Pres & CEO)*

TAYLOR CHEVROLET COMPANY, INC.
819 S Yellowstone Hwy, Rexburg, ID 83440
Tel.: (208) 356-6600
Web Site: http://www.taylorchev.com
Rev.: $11,000,000
Emp.: 45
New Car Dealers
N.A.I.C.S.: 441110
David Taylor *(Gen Mgr)*

TAYLOR COMMERCIAL, INC.
3955 Marconi Dr, Alpharetta, GA 30005
Tel.: (770) 587-0157
Web Site:
http://www.taylorcommercial.com
Year Founded: 1969
Sales Range: $10-24.9 Million
Emp.: 10
Multi-Family Construction Services
N.A.I.C.S.: 236116
Perry Greene *(Pres)*

TAYLOR CORPORATION
1725 Roe Crest Dr, North Mankato, MN 56003
Tel.: (507) 625-2828   MN
Web Site: https://www.taylor.com
Year Founded: 1948

TAYLOR CORPORATION

Taylor Corporation—(Continued)
Sales Range: Less than $1 Million
Emp.: 12,000
Commercial Printing Services
N.A.I.C.S.: 323111
Glen A. Taylor *(Founder, Owner & Chm)*
Charlie Whitaker *(CEO)*

Subsidiaries:

123Print, Inc. (1)
7430 New Technology Way, Frederick, MD 21703
Tel.: (301) 631-2153
Web Site: http://www.123print.com
Business Card Publisher
N.A.I.C.S.: 326199
Mindy Carbaugh Nunemaker *(Mgr-Customer Rels)*

Acrylic Design Associates (1)
6050 Nathan Ln, Minneapolis, MN 55442-5442
Tel.: (763) 559-8395
Web Site: http://www.acrylicdesign.com
Synthetic Rubber Mfr
N.A.I.C.S.: 325212
Bruce Iverson *(Sr Acct Mgr)*

AdGraphics (US), Inc. (1)
1520 Contour Dr, San Antonio, TX 78212-1237
Tel.: (210) 826-0229
Graphical Design & Printing Services
N.A.I.C.S.: 541430

Amsterdam Printing & Litho (1)
166 Wallins Corners Rd, Amsterdam, NY 12010
Tel.: (518) 842-6000
Web Site: http://www.amsterdamprinting.com
Sales Range: $25-49.9 Million
Emp.: 300
Promotional Product Mfr
N.A.I.C.S.: 322230
Tim Broadhead *(Pres)*

Artco (US), Inc. (1)
1 Stationery Pl, Rexburg, ID 83441
Tel.: (208) 359-1000
Web Site: http://www.artcoprinting.com
Emp.: 30
Commercial Printing Services
N.A.I.C.S.: 323113

CCA Occasions Ltd (1)
91 Clydesdale Place Moss Side Industrial Estate, Leyland, PR26 7QS, United Kingdom
Tel.: (44) 8442 57 04 04
Web Site: http://www.ccaoccasions.co.uk
Sales Range: $10-24.9 Million
Emp.: 50
Commercial Printing Services
N.A.I.C.S.: 323113
Mark Seekins *(Mng Dir)*

Card Fulfillment Services Inc (1)
1730 James Dr, North Mankato, MN 56003
Tel.: (507) 388-2610
Web Site: http://www.cardfulfillmentservices.com
Sales Range: $10-24.9 Million
Emp.: 60
Commercial Printing Services
N.A.I.C.S.: 323113
Sue Hanson *(Office Mgr)*

Carlson Craft (1)
1750 Tower Blvd, North Mankato, MN 56003
Tel.: (507) 625-5011
Web Site: http://www.carlsoncraft.com
Sales Range: $25-49.9 Million
Emp.: 900
Social Printing Services
N.A.I.C.S.: 323111
Brenda Crosby *(Project Mgr)*
Kevin Svenson *(Gen Mgr)*

Carlson Craft Catalog (1)
1750 Tower Blvd, North Mankato, MN 56003-1708
Tel.: (507) 625-0542
Web Site: http://www.carlsoncraft.com
Commercial Printing Services
N.A.I.C.S.: 323111

Barb Kaus *(Pres)*

Corporate Graphics Commercial (1)
1750 Northway Dr, North Mankato, MN 56003
Tel.: (507) 388-3300
Web Site: http://www.corpgraph.com
Emp.: 400
Commercial Printing Services
N.A.I.C.S.: 323113
Dan Kvasnicka *(Pres)*
Grant Davis *(Mgr-Production)*
Justin Nordby *(Mgr-Finishing)*
Shanon Schauer *(Dir-Admin Svcs)*
Eric Lee *(Mgr-HR)*
Larry Iverson *(Supvr-Safety)*
Rick Makela *(Supvr-Press)*
Diane Murray *(Supvr-Art & Imposition)*
Justin Geerdes *(Supvr-Fulfillment)*
John Zellmer *(VP-Fin)*

Corporate Graphics International (1)
1885 Northway Dr, North Mankato, MN 56003
Tel.: (507) 625-4400
Web Site: http://www.cgintl.com
Sales Range: $10-24.9 Million
Emp.: 100
Offset & Photolithographic Printing
N.A.I.C.S.: 323111
Dave Gahn *(Pres)*

Subsidiary (Domestic):

Corporate Graphics International (2)
5160 Rivergrade Rd, Baldwin Park, CA 91706-1436
Tel.: (626) 814-8181
Web Site: http://www.cgintl.com
Business Cards & Quality Stationery
N.A.I.C.S.: 323111

Thayer Publishing (2)
150 Kingswood Rd, Mankato, MN 56001
Tel.: (507) 388-8647
Web Site: http://www.cordialgreetings.com
Rev.: $3,500,000
Emp.: 100
Greeting Card & Calendar Publishers
N.A.I.C.S.: 323111
Tom Stierlen *(Supvr-Production)*
Terry Krueger *(Gen Mgr)*

Cosco Industries, Inc. (1)
7220 W Wilson Ave, Harwood Heights, IL 60706
Tel.: (708) 457-2410
Web Site: http://www.coscoindustries.com
Office Stamp Mfr
N.A.I.C.S.: 339940
Rich Williams *(Pres)*

Curtis 1000, Inc. (1)
1725 Breckinridge Pkwy Ste 500, Duluth, GA 30096
Tel.: (678) 380-9095
Web Site: http://www.curtis1000.com
Sales Range: $100-124.9 Million
Emp.: 1,800
Envelopes & Business Forms
N.A.I.C.S.: 323111
Tanja Popovich *(Project Coord)*

Division (Domestic):

Curtis 1000, Inc. (2)
5150 Blaylock Rd, Houston, TX 77041
Tel.: (713) 462-8981
Web Site: http://www.curtis1000.com
Sales Range: $25-49.9 Million
Emp.: 10
Commercial Printing
N.A.I.C.S.: 323111

Curtis 1000, Inc. (2)
36 Holly Dr, Newington, CT 06111-2243
Tel.: (860) 666-1974
Web Site: http://www.curtis1000.com
Sales Range: $25-49.9 Million
Emp.: 100
Forms & Envelopes
N.A.I.C.S.: 323111

Curtis 1000, Inc. (2)
1725 Breckinridge Pkwy Ste 500, Duluth, GA 30096
Tel.: (678) 380-9095
Web Site: http://www.curtis1000.com
Sales Range: $25-49.9 Million
Emp.: 7
Printing & Envelope Distr

N.A.I.C.S.: 424120
Holly Quartaro *(Mgr-Ops)*

Curtis 1000, Inc. (2)
2300 Main St, Hugo, MN 55038-9761
Tel.: (651) 483-6651
Web Site: http://www.curtis1000.com
Sales Range: $25-49.9 Million
Emp.: 100
Commercial Printer Mfr
N.A.I.C.S.: 323111
Dave Hromyak *(Mgr-Production)*

Drawing Board (1)
101 E 9th St, Waynesboro, PA 17268
Tel.: (800) 527-9530
Web Site: http://www.drawingboard.com
Sales Range: $10-24.9 Million
Emp.: 80
Imprinted Products, Including Labels, Envelopes, Stationery, Forms, Checks & Promotional Products
N.A.I.C.S.: 424120
Glen A. Taylor *(CEO)*

Everglades Direct Inc (1)
720 International Pkwy, Sunrise, FL 33325
Tel.: (954) 846-8899
Web Site: http://www.evergladesdirect.com
Sales Range: $25-49.9 Million
Emp.: 300
Business Management Consulting Services
N.A.I.C.S.: 541612
Lillian Mojica *(Atty)*
Denise Gians *(Dir-Compliance & Brand Product)*
Gail Mitchell Bourbeau *(Dir-Customer Svc)*
Adrienne Bryan *(Mgr-Email Mktg Program)*
Liz Laureano *(Mgr-Adv Production)*
Helene Kopel *(Brand Mgr)*

Fine Impressions, Inc. (1)
1680 Roe Crest Dr, North Mankato, MN 56003
Tel.: (507) 625-4355
Web Site: http://www.fineimpressions.com
Emp.: 100
Stationery Paper Product Mfr
N.A.I.C.S.: 322230
Kevin Sevenson *(Gen Mgr)*

Flexo Impressions (1)
8647 Eagle Creek Pkwy, Savage, MN 55378
Tel.: (952) 884-9442
Web Site: http://www.flexoimpressions.com
Label & Tag Mfr
N.A.I.C.S.: 323111
Mark Kapsner *(Gen Mgr)*

Garvey Products Inc. (1)
5428 Duff Dr, West Chester, OH 45246
Tel.: (513) 771-8710
Web Site: http://www.garveyproducts.com
Sales Range: $10-24.9 Million
Emp.: 15
Labeling Equipment & Product Supplier
N.A.I.C.S.: 561910
Douglas Kelley *(Mgr-Customer Svc)*

Heinrich Envelope Corporation (1)
925 Zane Ave N, Minneapolis, MN 55422
Tel.: (763) 544-3571
Web Site: http://www.heinrichenvelope.com
Envelope Mfr
N.A.I.C.S.: 322230

International Graphics ULC (1)
505 Douro Street, Stratford, N5A 3S9, ON, Canada
Tel.: (519) 271-3010
Web Site: https://internationalgraphics.ca
Emp.: 60
Wholesale & Direct Mail Wedding Stationery & Wholesale Commercial Printing Services
N.A.I.C.S.: 323113
Warren Dinsmore *(Gen Mgr)*

Label Works (1)
2025 Lookout Dr, North Mankato, MN 56003
Tel.: (507) 304-6300
Web Site: http://www.labelworks.com
Label Mfr
N.A.I.C.S.: 323111
Angie Nessler *(Mgr)*

Litho Tech, Inc. (1)
1600 W 92nd St, Bloomington, MN 55431
Tel.: (952) 888-7945

Web Site: http://www.lithotechusa.com
Sales Range: $10-24.9 Million
Emp.: 80
Commercial Printing Services
N.A.I.C.S.: 323113
Floyd Stanley *(Pres)*

Marketing General Inc. (1)
625 N Washington St Ste 450, Alexandria, VA 22314-1930
Tel.: (703) 739-1000
Web Site: http://www.marketinggeneral.com
Marketing Consulting Services
N.A.I.C.S.: 541613
Rick Whelan *(Pres)*
Harold L. Maurer *(Mng Dir-Acct Svcs)*
Tony Rossell *(Sr VP)*
Erik Schonher *(VP)*
Thomas Beauchamp *(VP-Ops)*
Adina W. Wasserman *(Dir-Market Res)*
Jason Gudenius *(Sr Dir-Acct)*
Raylene Kershaw *(COO & Sr VP)*
Aleda Ahmed *(Dir-Studio)*
Kimberly Humphries *(Sr Dir-Production)*

Masterpiece Studios, Inc. (1)
2080 Lookout Dr, North Mankato, MN 56003-1713
Tel.: (507) 388-8788
Web Site: http://www.masterpiecestudios.com
Sales Range: $10-24.9 Million
Emp.: 120
Boxed Holiday Cards, Boxed Social Stationery, Imprintable Invitations, Scrapbooking & Paper Crafts & Preprinted Decorated Paper Mfr, Marketer & Distr
N.A.I.C.S.: 513191

National Recognition Products, Inc. (1)
150 Kingswood Dr, Mankato, MN 56001
Tel.: (507) 386-7700
Web Site: http://www.nrponline.com
Collectible, Giftware & Commemorative Product Mfr
N.A.I.C.S.: 323111

Navitor East (1)
725 Clayton Ave, Waynesboro, PA 17268-2060
Tel.: (717) 762-7161
Web Site: http://www.navitor.com
Sales Range: $25-49.9 Million
Emp.: 150
Engraving
N.A.I.C.S.: 323111
Kendra Braithwaite *(Gen Mgr)*
Michelle Moats *(Coord-Safety)*

NowDocs International, Inc. (1)
1985 Lookout Dr, North Mankato, MN 56003
Tel.: (954) 317-6211
Web Site: http://www.nowdocs.com
Document Management Services
N.A.I.C.S.: 541511

Optima Graphics, Inc. (1)
1540 Fencorp Dr, Fenton, MO 63026
Tel.: (636) 349-3396
Web Site: http://www.optimagfx.com
Graphic Design Services
N.A.I.C.S.: 541430
Robin Talbott *(Dir-Customer Support)*
Sidney Clark *(Acct Exec)*
Matt Jennings *(Dir-Sls)*

Original Smith Printing (1)
2 Hardman Dr, Bloomington, IL 61701
Tel.: (309) 663-0325
Web Site: http://www.originalsmith.com
Sales Range: $25-49.9 Million
Emp.: 150
Commercial Printing Services
N.A.I.C.S.: 323113
Mitch Bankord *(VP-Sls)*
Kim Breckler *(VP-Sls Consulting)*
Steve Dylo *(Dir-Bus Dev)*
Amy Fuller *(Mgr-Ops)*
Kirsten Smith *(Gen Mgr)*

Photocraft, Inc. (1)
13555 SW Millikan Way, Beaverton, OR 97005
Tel.: (503) 924-8500
Web Site: http://www.photocraft.com
Sales Range: $10-24.9 Million
Emp.: 80
Graphic Design Services

COMPANIES

TAYLOR FORGE ENGINEERED SYSTEMS INC.

N.A.I.C.S.: 323111
Darcy O. Connor (Project Mgr)

Precision Press, Inc. (1)
2020 Lookout Dr, North Mankato, MN 56003
Tel.: (507) 625-7155
Web Site: http://www.precisionpressinc.com
Commercial Printing Services
N.A.I.C.S.: 323111
Brenda Lundberg (Engr-Quality)
Lane Gravley (Gen Mgr)
Todd Schlager (Mgr-Production Comml Div)
Kurt Kroening (Project Mgr-Production & Tech-Pkg)
Karen Yess (Supvr-Customer Svc)
Pat Conley (Supvr-IT)
Jay Utter (Office Mgr)

Print Craft, Inc. (1)
315 5th Ave NW, Saint Paul, MN 55112
Tel.: (651) 633-8122
Web Site: http://www.printcraft.com
Emp.: 150
Printing & Packaging Services
N.A.I.C.S.: 561910
Nancy Ronning (Gen Mgr)

Progressive Communications International (1)
1001 Sand Pond Rd, Lake Mary, FL 32746
Tel.: (407) 333-9500
Web Site: http://www.progressivecommunications.com
Commercial Printing Services
N.A.I.C.S.: 323113
Gabe Hernandez (Pres)

Progressive Impressions International (1)
1 Hardman Dr, Bloomington, IL 61701
Tel.: (309) 664-0444
Web Site: http://www.whateverittakes.com
Sales Range: $25-49.9 Million
Emp.: 200
Marketing Consulting Services
N.A.I.C.S.: 541910
Jamie Huff (Pres)
Ron Drenning (VP)
Tim Henning (VP-Ops)
Richard Eames (VP-Quality)
Briana Henning (VP-Client Svcs)
Ken Orr (Gen Mgr)
Dana Reischauer (VP-Ops)
Jim Vasilou (VP-Tech)
Jon Young (VP-Admin)

Quadris Medical (1)
2030 Lookout Dr, North Mankato, MN 56003
Tel.: (507) 385-2709
Web Site: http://www.quadrismedical.com
Business Management Consulting Services
N.A.I.C.S.: 541613

Regency Thermographers (1)
1625 Roe Crest Dr, North Mankato, MN 56003
Tel.: (866) 628-6868
Web Site: http://www.regencythermo.com
Custom Printed Products
N.A.I.C.S.: 323111

Schmidt Printing (1)
1101 Frontage Rd NW, Byron, MN 55920-1386
Tel.: (507) 775-6400
Web Site: http://www.schmidt.com
Sales Range: $50-74.9 Million
Emp.: 350
Commercial Printing
N.A.I.C.S.: 323111
Chris R. Moran (Mgr-Production)
Jacob Staloch (Mgr-Finishing & Bindery)
Roger Sinneg (Mgr-IT)

TFP Data Systems (1)
3451 Jupiter Ct, Oxnard, CA 93030-8957
Tel.: (805) 981-0992
Web Site: http://www.tfpdata.com
Sales Range: $25-49.9 Million
Emp.: 60
Business Form Mfr
N.A.I.C.S.: 323111
Rick Rodiff (Pres & COO)

Tatex Inc. (1)
2800 Gholson Rd, Waco, TX 76704
Tel.: (254) 799-4911
Web Site: http://www.tatex.com
Screen Printing Services
N.A.I.C.S.: 323113
Mike Scherr (Gen Mgr)
Don Oliver (Plant Mgr)
Brad Gyorko (Supvr-Production)

Taylor Communications, Inc. (1)
1725 Roe Crest Dr, North Mankato, MN 56003
Tel.: (507) 625-2828
Web Site: http://www.standardregister.com
Holding Company; Healthcare, Financial Services, Commercial & Industrial Markets Information & Communications Services
N.A.I.C.S.: 551112
Mark O'Leary (Pres-Taylor Healthcare)

Subsidiary (Domestic):

Standard Register, Inc. (2)
1725 Roe Crest Dr, North Mankato, MN 56003
Tel.: (507) 625-2828
Web Site: http://www.standardregister.com
Healthcare, Financial Services, Commercial & Industrial Markets Information & Communications Services
N.A.I.C.S.: 323111
Mark O'Leary (Pres-Taylor Healthcare)

Taymark, Inc. (1)
4875 White Bear Pkwy, White Bear Lake, MN 55110
Tel.: (651) 426-1667
Web Site: http://www.taymarkinc.com
Sales Range: $25-49.9 Million
Emp.: 150
Commercial Printing Services
N.A.I.C.S.: 323111
Pat Deck (Pres)

The Ligature (1)
4909 Alcoa Ave, Los Angeles, CA 90058-3022
Tel.: (323) 585-6000
Web Site: http://www.theligature.com
Commercial Printing Services
N.A.I.C.S.: 323111
Miguel Gonzalez (Mgr-Production)
Angela Grieser (Mgr-Acctg)

The Occasions Group, Inc. (1)
1750 Tower Blvd, North Mankato, MN 56003
Tel.: (800) 296-9029
Web Site: https://www.theoccasionsgroup.com
Printing Services
N.A.I.C.S.: 323113
Cory Hanna (Pres)

Subsidiary (Domestic):

Accu Copy of Greenville, Inc. (2)
1055 Greenville Blvd SW, Greenville, NC 27834-7021
Tel.: (252) 321-5805
Web Site: http://www.acculink.com
Printing
N.A.I.C.S.: 323111
Roger Buck (Dir-Mktg)

Travel Tags, Inc. (1)
5842 Carmen Ave, Inver Grove Heights, MN 55076
Tel.: (651) 450-1201
Web Site: http://www.traveltags.com
Emp.: 300
Gift Card Mfr
N.A.I.C.S.: 323111
Al Rausch (Pres)
Timothy Lebens (VP-Sls & Mktg)

Division (Non-US):

Narboni Holdings, SARL (2)
3 Avenue d Amazonie ZA de Courtaboeuf, 91952, Les Ulis, Cedex, France
Tel.: (33) 1 60 92 23 23
Web Site: http://www.narboni.com
Sales Range: $25-49.9 Million
Emp.: 80
Greeting Card Mfr
N.A.I.C.S.: 513191
Marc Fisher (Gen Mgr)

Vectra, Inc. (1)
3950 Business Park Dr, Columbus, OH 43204
Tel.: (614) 351-6868
Web Site: http://www.vectrainc.com
Sales Range: $25-49.9 Million
Emp.: 200
Marketing Consulting Services
N.A.I.C.S.: 541613
Craig Taylor (Founder & Pres)

Venture Solutions Inc. (1)
1170 Grey Fox Rd, Arden Hills, MN 55112-6908
Tel.: (651) 494-1740
Web Site: http://www.venturesolutions.com
Emp.: 300
Business Management Consulting Services
N.A.I.C.S.: 541613
Tommie Braddock (Pres)
Wendy Jenkins (VP-Tech Solutions-Dallas & Fort Worth)
Jennifer Spear (Dir-Client Svcs-North)
Sharon Brock (Dir-Client Svcs-South)
Sherryl Smith (Acct Dir-Strategic)

Virtual Images (1)
425 S Rockefeller Ave, Ontario, CA 91761
Web Site: http://www.virtual-images.com
Emp.: 4
Printing & Packaging Services
N.A.I.C.S.: 561910
Jordan Salk (Mgr-Ops)

Web Graphics, Inc. (1)
428 Corinth Rd, Queensbury, NY 12804
Tel.: (518) 792-6501
Web Site: http://www.printatweb.com
Sales Range: $50-74.9 Million
Emp.: 150
Commercial Printing Services
N.A.I.C.S.: 323111
Ron Bakers (Mgr-Production)

Western Graphics & Data (1)
11603 SE Foster Rd, Portland, OR 97266
Tel.: (503) 222-1731
Sales Range: $25-49.9 Million
Emp.: 300
Commercial Printing Services
N.A.I.C.S.: 323113

TAYLOR COTTON & RIDLEY INC.
4410 SW 35th Ter, Gainesville, FL 32608
Tel.: (352) 378-1608
Web Site: http://www.taylorcottonridley.com
Year Founded: 1973
Sales Range: $10-24.9 Million
Emp.: 50
Builders' Hardware
N.A.I.C.S.: 423710
Brian Ridley (VP)
Armin Goldberg (Project Mgr)
Robert Byrd (Mgr-Shop)

TAYLOR CUTLERY CO. LLC
1043 Fordtown Rd, Kingsport, TN 37663-3211
Tel.: (423) 247-2406
Web Site: http://www.taylorbrandsllc.com
Year Founded: 1975
Rev.: $11,379,669
Emp.: 40
Knives Mfr
N.A.I.C.S.: 332215
Stewart Alan Taylor (Pres)

TAYLOR DYNAMOMETER, INC.
3602 W Wheelhouse Rd, Milwaukee, WI 53208
Tel.: (414) 755-0040   WI
Web Site: http://www.taylordyno.com
Year Founded: 1999
Sales Range: $1-9.9 Million
Emp.: 25
Measuring & Controlling Device Mfr
N.A.I.C.S.: 334519
Arthur Downey (Pres)

Subsidiaries:

Dyne Systems, Inc. (1)
3602 W Wheelhouse Rd, Milwaukee, WI 53208
Tel.: (414) 755-0040
Web Site: http://www.dynesystems.com
Sales Range: $1-9.9 Million
Emp.: 23
Measuring And Controlling Devices, Nec, N
N.A.I.C.S.: 334519
Mark Melchiori (Reg Mgr-Sls)
Jeff Gilmore (Reg Mgr-Sls)
Joel Lueneburg (Reg Mgr-Sls)

TAYLOR ELECTRIC CO-OPERATIVE
226 Country Rd Ste 287, Merkel, TX 79536
Tel.: (325) 793-8500
Web Site: http://www.taylorelectric.com
Rev.: $20,835,367
Emp.: 76
Electric Power Distribution
N.A.I.C.S.: 221122
Darryl Schriver (Pres & CEO)
Park Thomas (Treas & Sec)
Brad Robinson (Supvr-AMI)

TAYLOR ENERGY COMPANY
1 Lee Cir, New Orleans, LA 70130
Tel.: (504) 581-5491
Web Site: http://www.taylorenergy.com
Sales Range: $25-49.9 Million
Emp.: 50
Crude Petroleum & Natural Gas
N.A.I.C.S.: 211120

TAYLOR ENERGY, LLC
152 Broad Brook Rd. E, Windsor, CT 06016
Tel.: (860) 623-3308
Web Site: https://www.taylorenergyct.com
Year Founded: 2018
Professional, Scientific & Technical Services
N.A.I.C.S.: 541990
Catherine Erasmus (Pres)

Subsidiaries:

Somers Oil Service, Inc. (1)
11 S Rd, Somers, CT 06071-2109
Tel.: (860) 749-4490
Web Site: http://www.somersoil.com
Petroleum & Petroleum Products Merchant Whslr
N.A.I.C.S.: 424720
Dennis Hutton (Owner)

TAYLOR FARMS
890 N Newport Rd, Colorado Springs, CO 80916-2741
Tel.: (719) 473-8251   CO
Web Site: http://www.taylorfarmsfoodservice.com
Year Founded: 1976
Sales Range: $25-49.9 Million
Emp.: 120
Provider of Fresh Fruits & Vegetables
N.A.I.C.S.: 424480
William T. Stevenson (Pres)
Russ Crossen (Controller)

TAYLOR FORGE ENGINEERED SYSTEMS INC.
208 N Iron St, Paola, KS 66071-1207
Tel.: (913) 294-5331   KS
Web Site: http://www.tfes.com
Year Founded: 1984
Sales Range: $10-24.9 Million
Emp.: 300
Fabricated Plate Work
N.A.I.C.S.: 332313
R. Gary Kilkenny (Chm)
Michael Kilkenny (Pres & CEO)
David McCarthy (Mgr-Engrg)
Deborah Sommer (Coord-HR)
Brenda Wright (Coord-Traffic)
Tony Osborn (VP & Gen Mgr)
John Kennedy (Project Mgr)
Tom Balas (CFO)

TAYLOR FORGE ENGINEERED SYSTEMS INC.

U.S. PRIVATE

Taylor Forge Engineered Systems Inc.—(Continued)
Rick Pysher *(COO)*
Aaron Poe *(Engr-Dev)*
Mario Douglas *(Engr-Sls)*
Jeff Lipko *(Engr-Welding)*

TAYLOR FREEZER OF MICHIGAN
13341 Stark Rd, Livonia, MI 48150
Tel.: (734) 525-2535   MI
Web Site: http://www.taylor-michigan.com
Year Founded: 1946
Sales Range: $10-24.9 Million
Emp.: 35
Provider of Commercial Cooking & Food Service Equipment
N.A.I.C.S.: 423440
Robert D. Willard *(Pres)*
Tim Lennon *(CFO)*

TAYLOR FREEZERS SALES CO., INC.
6825 E Washington Blvd, Los Angeles, CA 90040
Tel.: (323) 889-8700
Web Site:
   http://www.taylorfreezers.com
Sales Range: $10-24.9 Million
Emp.: 85
Commercial Refrigeration Equipment
N.A.I.C.S.: 423740
Lawrence J. Capalbo *(CEO)*
John Capalbo *(VP)*
Tom Capalbo *(VP)*

TAYLOR FRESH FOODS INC.
150 Main St, Salinas, CA 93901-4449
Tel.: (831) 754-1715   CA
Web Site: http://www.taylorfarms.com
Year Founded: 1995
Sales Range: $75-99.9 Million
Emp.: 1,850
Provider of Fresh Vegetable Processing
N.A.I.C.S.: 115114
Drew Burnham *(Dir-Info Sys)*
Ron Guzman *(VP-Logistics & Transportation)*
Bruce C. Taylor *(Founder & CEO)*

Subsidiaries:

Club Chef LLC   (1)
3776 Lake Park Dr, Covington, KY 41017-9826
Tel.: (859) 578-3100
Web Site: http://www.clubchef.com
Rev: $50,000,000
Emp.: 250
Distr & Wholesaler of Fresh Fruits & Vegetables
N.A.I.C.S.: 424480
Ted Rebholz V *(VP-Ops)*

Taylor Farms California Inc.   (1)
1207 Abbott St, Salinas, CA 93902-4504
Tel.: (831) 751-3081
Web Site: http://www.taylorfarms.com
Sales Range: $25-49.9 Million
Emp.: 850
Provider of Crop Preparation Services
N.A.I.C.S.: 115114

Taylor Farms Florida Inc.   (1)
7492 Chancellor Dr, Orlando, FL 32809-6242
Tel.: (407) 859-3373
Sales Range: $25-49.9 Million
Emp.: 210
Provider of Farm Machinery & Equipment
N.A.I.C.S.: 333111

TAYLOR GLOBAL INC.
640 5th Ave 8th Fl, New York, NY 10019
Tel.: (212) 714-1280
Web Site:
   http://www.taylorstrategy.com
Year Founded: 1984
Sales Range: $10-24.9 Million
Emp.: 85
Public Relations Agency
N.A.I.C.S.: 541820
Bryan Harris *(Mng Partner & COO)*
Tony Signore *(CEO & Mng Partner)*
Jessie Snider Mann *(VP)*
Taryn Parker *(Acct Supvr)*
Brianna Kauffman Matz *(Dir-Digital Strategy)*
Brianna Kauffman *(VP-Digital Strategy)*
Benjamin E. Robinson III *(Chief Admin Officer)*

Subsidiaries:

Taylor Global Inc.   (1)
10150 Mallard Creek Rd Ste 300, Charlotte, NC 28262
Tel.: (704) 548-8556
Web Site: http://www.taylorstrategy.com
Emp.: 35
Public Relations Agency
N.A.I.C.S.: 541820
Bates Grainger *(VP)*
Ted Fragulis *(Mng Partner)*
John Liporace *(Mng Partner)*
Mark Beal *(Mng Partner)*
Bryan Harris *(COO & Mng Partner)*
Helen Galindo *(Dir-HR)*
Kruti Joshi *(Dir-Art)*
Brianna Kauffman Matz *(Dir-Digital Strategy)*
Taryn Parker *(Acct Exec)*
Jenna Rathke *(Supvr-Acct)*
Katina Scott *(Sr VP-Brand Plng)*
Jessie Snider *(Dir-Acct)*

TAYLOR INTERNATIONAL CO. INC.
1128 16th St NW 1667 KSt, Washington, DC 20006
Tel.: (202) 955-1330
Web Site: http://www.tay.com
Sales Range: $10-24.9 Million
Emp.: 50
Brokers, Business: Buying & Selling Business Enterprises
N.A.I.C.S.: 541990
Rosario Boxx *(Mgr-Bus Dev-Intl)*
Hal Nowell *(Dir-Sls)*
Ralph C. Taylor Jr. *(Chm)*

TAYLOR MADE GOLF COMPANY, INC.
5545 Fermi Ct, Carlsbad, CA 92008-7324
Tel.: (760) 918-6000   DE
Web Site:
   http://www.taylormadegolf.com
Year Founded: 1998
Golf Equipment Designer, Mfr & Whslr
N.A.I.C.S.: 339920
Pete Sanchez *(Sr VP-HR-Global)*
Klauf Flock *(CFO)*
David Abeles *(Pres & CEO)*
Laura Garrett *(Sr VP-HR-Global)*
Bill Reimus *(Gen Counsel & Sr VP)*
Brian Coffman *(VP & Gen Mgr)*
Bob Maggiore *(Chief Mktg Officer)*
David Bradley *(Mng Dir-Canada & Latin America & VP)*
David Silvers *(Mng Dir-Europe & VP)*
David Brownie *(Sr VP-Ops & Svc-Global)*
Mark Sheldon-Allen *(Mng Dir-Asia & VP)*
Todd Beach *(Sr VP-Res Design & Engrg)*
Brian Bazzel *(VP-Product Creation)*

Subsidiaries:

Adams Golf, Inc.   (1)
2801 E Plano Pkwy, Plano, TX 75074-7418
Tel.: (972) 673-9000
Web Site: http://www.adamsgolf.com
Holding Company; Golf Clubs & Accessories Designer, Mfr & Distr
N.A.I.C.S.: 423910

Taylor Made Golf Limited   (1)
TaylorMade Court Viables Business Park Jays Close, Basingstoke, RG22 4BS, United Kingdom
Tel.: (44) 1256479797
Web Site: http://www.taylormadegolf.eu
Sport Equipment Distr
N.A.I.C.S.: 423910
David Abeles *(Pres & CEO)*
Chuck Presto *(Sr VP-Global Sports Mktg)*
David Brownie *(Sr VP-Global Ops & Svc)*
Laura Garrett *(Sr VP-Global HR)*
David Silvers *(Mng Dir-Europe & VP)*
Bill Reimus *(Gen Counsel & Sr VP)*
Jeff Barker *(CFO)*
Robert Johnson *(Exec VP-TaylorMade Product Creation)*
David Chin *(Mng Dir-Asia & VP)*
Mark Sheldon-Allen *(Mng Dir-Asia & VP)*
Bob Maggiore *(Chief Mktg Officer)*
David Bradley *(Mng Dir-Canada & Latin America & VP)*

TAYLOR OIL CO. OF WASHINGTON NC
708 River Rd, Washington, NC 27889
Tel.: (252) 946-0066
Sales Range: $10-24.9 Million
Emp.: 10
Petroleum Bulk Stations
N.A.I.C.S.: 424710
John Allen Moore *(Pres)*
Tillie Moore *(Treas & Sec)*

TAYLOR OIL CO., INC.
77 2nd St, Somerville, NJ 08876
Tel.: (908) 725-9200   NJ
Web Site: http://www.tayloroilco.com
Year Founded: 1939
Sales Range: $100-124.9 Million
Emp.: 40
Provider of On-Site Fueling Services to Construction Crews, Contractors, Trucking Fleets, Boats & Marinas
N.A.I.C.S.: 424720
Rick Workman *(Pres)*
Frank Bloom *(Mgr-Sls-NY & NJ)*
Bob Phillips *(Gen Mgr)*
Matt Reynolds *(Mgr-Connecticut)*

TAYLOR OIL COMPANY INCORPORATED
1904 S St, Blair, NE 68008
Tel.: (402) 426-9505
Sales Range: $10-24.9 Million
Emp.: 90
Owner & Operator of Convenience Stores
N.A.I.C.S.: 445131
Bradley E. Taylor *(Pres)*
Roger Schultz *(Office Mgr)*

TAYLOR OIL INC.
504 Main St, Wellsville, KS 66092
Tel.: (785) 883-2072
Web Site: http://tayloroilinc.com
Sales Range: $10-24.9 Million
Emp.: 8
Petroleum Bulk Stations
N.A.I.C.S.: 424710
Harold D. Taylor *(Pres)*
Karen Wright *(Sec)*

TAYLOR POWER SYSTEMS, INC.
415 Hwy 49 S, Richland, MS 39218
Tel.: (601) 922-4444
Web Site:
   http://www.taylorpower.com
Rev.: $3,922,000
Emp.: 25
Motor & Generator Mfr
N.A.I.C.S.: 335312
Lex Taylor *(Pres)*

Subsidiaries:

TCF, Inc.   (1)
6005 N McRaven Rd, Jackson, MS 39209
Tel.: (601) 922-4444
Web Site: http://www.taylorpower.com
Sales Range: $25-49.9 Million
Generators
N.A.I.C.S.: 423610
Steve Duke *(Mgr-Gen Svc)*
Reed Nicholas *(Gen Mgr-Corp Accts)*
John Scarborough *(Gen Mgr)*

TAYLOR PRODUCTS
2205 Jothi Ave, Parsons, KS 67357-8460
Tel.: (620) 421-5550
Web Site:
   http://www.taylorproducts.com
Year Founded: 1969
Rev.: $11,400,000
Emp.: 40
Packaging Machinery
N.A.I.C.S.: 333993
Gary Saunders *(CEO)*

TAYLOR RAFFERTY ASSOCIATES, INC.
111 Broadway, New York, NY 10006
Tel.: (212) 889-4350   NY
Web Site: http://www.taylor-rafferty.com
Year Founded: 1982
Sales Range: $10-24.9 Million
Emp.: 15
Investment Advisory Services
N.A.I.C.S.: 523940
Brian Rafferty *(Founder, Pres & CEO)*

TAYLOR STUDIOS, INC.
1320 Harmon Dr, Rantoul, IL 61866
Tel.: (217) 893-4874
Web Site:
   http://www.taylorstudios.com
Year Founded: 1991
Sales Range: $25-49.9 Million
Emp.: 38
Professional, Scientific & Technical Services
N.A.I.C.S.: 541990

TAYLOR UNITED INC.
130 SE Lynch Rd, Shelton, WA 98584
Tel.: (360) 432-3300   WA
Web Site:
   http://www.taylorshellfishfarms.com
Year Founded: 1969
Sales Range: $10-24.9 Million
Emp.: 400
Holding Company
N.A.I.C.S.: 551112
William Taylor *(Pres)*

Subsidiaries:

Taylor Shellfish Farms   (1)
130 SE Lynch Rd, Shelton, WA 98584
Tel.: (360) 432-3300
Web Site:
   http://www.taylorshellfishfarms.com
Fish & Seafood Whlsr
N.A.I.C.S.: 424460
Bill Taylor *(CEO)*

Subsidiary (Domestic):

Ekone Oyster Co.   (2)
378 Bay Ctr Rd, Bay Center, WA 98586
Tel.: (888) 875-5494
Web Site: http://www.ekoneoyster.com
Emp.: 50
Fish & Seafood Merchant Whlsr
N.A.I.C.S.: 424460
Nick Jambor *(Co-Founder)*
Joanne Jambor *(Co-Founder)*
Kevin Funkhouser *(Gen Mgr)*

TAYLOR WHITE SPECIALIZED STAFFING SERVICES, INC.

5426 Bay Center Dr Ste 110, Tampa, FL 33609
Tel.: (813) 223-2230 FL
Web Site: http://www.taylorwhite.com
Sales Range: $10-24.9 Million
Employment Placement, Consulting & Recruiting Services
N.A.I.C.S.: 561311
Heather Ceresoli (*COO & Principal*)
Katie Halkett (*Sr Mgr-Area Dev*)
Tracy T. Tringali (*Principal*)
Kim O'Brien (*Principal*)
John Sarmanian (*Sr Mgr-Recruiting*)
Karin Klare (*Mgr-Recruiting*)
Jim Roberts (*Dir-Sarbanes-Oxley & Control Assurance Svcs*)
Jeni Donaldson (*Controller*)

TAYLOR'S AUTO MAX
4100 10th Ave S, Great Falls, MT 59405
Tel.: (406) 727-0380
Web Site: http://www.taylorsautomax.com
Sales Range: $10-24.9 Million
Emp.: 60
Used Car Retailer
N.A.I.C.S.: 441120
Mike Taylor (*Co-Founder & Co-Owner*)
John Zuris (*Bus Mgr*)
Bamma Taylor (*Co-Founder & Co-Owner*)
Steve Taylor (*Partner*)
Jim Taylor Sr. (*Co-Founder & Co-Owner*)

TAYLOR'S INDUSTRIAL SERVICES, L.L.C.
151 Wardell Rd, Neptune, NJ 07753-7623
Tel.: (732) 922-4422
Sales Range: $10-24.9 Million
Emp.: 20
Industrial Services
N.A.I.C.S.: 423830
Christopher Filos (*Pres & CEO*)
Rick Eichler (*Opers Dir*)

Subsidiaries:

HPM America Division (1)
820 W Marion Rd, Mount Gilead, OH 43338-1087
Tel.: (419) 946-0222
Plastics Molding Machinery, Die Casting Machines & Extrusion Systems Mfr
N.A.I.C.S.: 333517

TAYLOR-LISTUG INC.
1980 Gillespie Way, El Cajon, CA 92020
Tel.: (619) 258-1207
Web Site: http://www.taylorguitars.com
Year Founded: 1968
Sales Range: $25-49.9 Million
Emp.: 370
Guitar & Guitar Parts Mfr
N.A.I.C.S.: 339992
Kurt Listug (*Co-Founder & CEO*)
Robert Taylor (*Pres*)

TAYLOR-MADE TRANSPORTATION INC.
740 Hwy 139, Maplesville, AL 36750
Tel.: (334) 366-4041
Web Site: http://www.taylormadeinc.com
Rev.: $12,000,000
Emp.: 100
Trucking Service
N.A.I.C.S.: 484121
Allen Taylor (*Pres & CEO*)
Philip Kelley (*Mgr-Millworks Ops*)

TAYLOR-PANSING INC.
3351 Marinatown Ln, Fort Myers, FL 33903
Tel.: (239) 995-6669
Sales Range: $1-9.9 Million
Emp.: 16
Commercial & Institutional Building Construction
N.A.I.C.S.: 236220
Steve Pansing (*Project Mgr*)

TAYSE INTERNATIONAL TRADING, INC.
501 Richardson Rd, Calhoun, GA 30701 GA
Web Site: http://www.tayse.com
Year Founded: 2005
Sales Range: $10-24.9 Million
Emp.: 65
Rug Product Distr
N.A.I.C.S.: 423220
Sadi Sevimli (*Owner*)

TBA GLOBAL, LLC
220 W 42nd St 10th Fl, New York, NY 10036
Tel.: (646) 445-7000 DE
Web Site: http://www.tbaglobal.com
Year Founded: 1993
Sales Range: $25-49.9 Million
Emp.: 50
Live Event Planning & Marketing Agency
N.A.I.C.S.: 541810
Paula Balzer (*CEO*)
Nicholas Mirabile (*Sr VP-Bus Dev*)
Daniel Hilbert (*Sr VP-Client Engagement & Strategy*)
Kevin Rupnik (*Sr VP-Creative*)
Rob Casinover (*CFO*)

Subsidiaries:

TBA Global, LLC - Chicago (1)
200 S Wacker Dr Ste 3100, Chicago, IL 60606
Tel.: (312) 335-9595
Web Site: http://www.tbaglobal.com
Live Event Planning & Marketing Agency
N.A.I.C.S.: 541810

TBA Global, LLC - Nashville (1)
113 Seaboard Ln Ste A105, Franklin, TN 37067
Tel.: (615) 986-7100
Web Site: http://www.tbaglobal.com
Live Event Planning & Marketing Agency
N.A.I.C.S.: 541810
Stacey Caravetta (*Coord-Production*)

TBA INSURANCE INC.
1900 L Down Dollson Dr, Bedford, TX 76021
Tel.: (817) 265-2000
Web Site: http://www.statenational.com
Sales Range: $50-74.9 Million
Emp.: 300
Fire, Marine & Casualty Insurance
N.A.I.C.S.: 524126
David Cleff (*Gen Counsel, Sec & Exec VP-Bus Affairs*)
David Hale (*CFO*)

TBA STUDIO ARCHITECTURE, A PROFESSIONAL CORPORATION
103 Cypress St. W, Monroe, LA 71291
Tel.: (318) 340-1550
Web Site: https://tbastudio.com
Year Founded: 2004
Architecture & Planning
N.A.I.C.S.: 541310

Subsidiaries:

Douglas Architects, Inc (1)
118 Broadway St Ste 606, San Antonio, TX 78205-1997
Tel.: (210) 226-5500
Web Site: http://www.douglasarchitects.net
Architectural Services
N.A.I.C.S.: 541310
Andrew Douglas (*Pres*)

TBB GLOBAL LOGISTICS INC.
802 Far Hills Dr, New Freedom, PA 17349
Tel.: (717) 227-5000
Web Site: http://www.tbbgl.com
Year Founded: 1947
Rev.: $44,303,902
Emp.: 115
Providers of Logistics & Economic Resources to the Shipping & Receiving Industry
N.A.I.C.S.: 488510
Samuel R. Polakoff (*CEO*)
Phil Polakoff (*Mng Partner*)
Ryan Polakoff (*Pres*)

Subsidiaries:

TBB Global Logistics Inc., Truckload Division (1)
802 Far Hills Dr, New Freedom, PA 17349
Tel.: (717) 227-5000
Web Site: http://www.tbbgl.com
Sales Range: $25-49.9 Million
Emp.: 100
Brokers, Shipping
N.A.I.C.S.: 488510
Sean Sabre (*VP-Sls*)

TBC INC.
900 S Wolfe St, Baltimore, MD 21231
Tel.: (410) 347-7500 MD
Web Site: http://www.tbc.us
Year Founded: 1974
Sales Range: $75-99.9 Million
Emp.: 115
Advertising & Public Relation Agency Services
N.A.I.C.S.: 541810
Allan Charles (*Co-Founder, Chm & Chief Creative Officer*)
Erin Borkowski (*VP & Dir-Media*)
Howe Burch (*Co-Pres*)
Jason Middleton (*Sr VP & Dir-Creative*)
Jen Beck (*Sr VP-Strategy & Acct Mgmt*)

Subsidiaries:

TBC Direct, Inc. (1)
900 S Wolfe St, Baltimore, MD 21231
Tel.: (410) 347-7500
Web Site: http://www.tbc.us
Emp.: 80
Direct Marketing
N.A.I.C.S.: 541810
Erin Borkowski (*VP & Dir-Media*)

TBC Inc. (1)
575 8th Ave Ste 1704, New York, NY 10018-3011
Tel.: (646) 366-1470
Emp.: 5
Business-To-Business, Government/Political/Public Affairs, Health Care, Sports Marketing, Travel & Tourism
N.A.I.C.S.: 541820

TBC Public Relations (1)
900 S Wolfe St, Baltimore, MD 21231
Tel.: (410) 347-7500
Web Site: http://www.tbc.us
Rev.: $2,500,000
Emp.: 100
Business-To-Business, Event Marketing, Government/Political/Public Affairs, Health Care, Publicity/Promotions, Retail, Sports Marketing, Travel & Tourism
N.A.I.C.S.: 541820
Brent Burkhardt (*Mng Dir-PR & Exec VP*)

TBC NET INC.
444 E Hillcrest Dr Ste 350, Dekalb, IL 60115
Tel.: (815) 899-4600
Web Site: http://www.tbc.net
Year Founded: 1989
Sales Range: $1-9.9 Million
Emp.: 17
Computer Cables & Installation Services
N.A.I.C.S.: 541513
Cohen Barnes (*Pres & CEO*)
Josh Halpern-Givens (*Mgr-In-House Svc*)
Dale Boughton (*Mgr-Svc*)

TBG HOLDINGS CORP.
2929 E Commercial Blvd PH-D, Fort Lauderdale, FL 33308
Tel.: (954) 440-4678
Web Site: http://www.tbgholdings.us
Emp.: 40
Holding Company
N.A.I.C.S.: 551112
Neil Swartz (*CEO*)
Tim Hart (*CFO*)
Sharon R. Ford (*COO*)

Subsidiaries:

MediXall Group, Inc. (1)
2929 E Commercial Blvd Ste Ph D, Fort Lauderdale, FL 33308
Tel.: (954) 440-4678
Rev.: $59,268
Assets: $862,013
Liabilities: $4,531,378
Net Worth: ($3,669,365)
Earnings: ($7,143,820)
Emp.: 7
Fiscal Year-end: 12/31/2022
Healthcare Technology Products & Services
N.A.I.C.S.: 923120
Travis Jackson (*CEO & CEO-Health Karma*)
Timothy S. Hart (*Chm & CFO*)

TBI INC.
2386 N Batavia St, Orange, CA 92862
Tel.: (714) 449-7750
Web Site: http://www.royalroof.com
Rev.: $15,353,707
Emp.: 33
Roofing Contractors
N.A.I.C.S.: 238160
Thomas Beattie (*Pres*)
Michael Johannes (*VP-Systems*)
Mike Barnes (*VP*)
Doug Berger (*VP*)
Dave Harrison (*VP-Corp Mktg*)
Larry Cimarusti (*VP*)
Phil Hacche (*VP*)
Ron Ossenberg (*VP*)
Steve Pinkus (*VP*)
Rodney Sizemore (*Mgr-Channel Program*)
Mike Onystok (*VP*)

TBL GROUP, INC.
15734 Aldine Westfield Rd, Houston, TX 77032
Tel.: (713) 988-5466
Emp.: 100
Transportation Services
N.A.I.C.S.: 485113

Subsidiaries:

Gbj, Inc. (1)
15734 Aldine Westfield Rd, Houston, TX 77032
Tel.: (713) 988-5466
Web Site: http://www.afchouston.com
Sales Range: $10-24.9 Million
Limousine Service
N.A.I.C.S.: 485320

TBL NETWORKS, INC.
1801 Bayberry Ct Ste 202, Richmond, VA 23226
Tel.: (804) 822-3640
Web Site: http://www.theblinkylight.com
Sales Range: $1-9.9 Million
Emp.: 20
Advanced Technology & Support Services

TBL NETWORKS, INC.

TBL Networks, Inc.—(Continued)
N.A.I.C.S.: 541512
Alan Sears *(Pres & CEO)*
Gary Woods *(Mgr-Acct)*
Cameron Corbin *(VP-Sls)*
Steve Glissman *(Project Mgr)*
Erin Jett *(Coord-Process)*
Hal Jordan *(Mgr-Bus Dev)*
Nicole Beasley *(Mgr-Fin)*
Toni Harrison *(Mgr-Inside Sls Acct)*
George Fitzgerald *(Supvr-Acct)*

TC GLOBAL, INC.
2003 Western Ave Ste 660, Seattle, WA 98121
Tel.: (206) 233-2070   WA
Web Site: http://www.tullycoffeeshop.com
Year Founded: 1992
Sales Range: $25-49.9 Million
Emp.: 500
Coffee Stores
N.A.I.C.S.: 445298
Catherine Campbell *(CFO & Controller)*
Scott M. Pearson *(Pres & CEO)*
Diane Geurts *(Dir-Mktg)*
Mark Dringenberg *(Dir-Corp Ops)*
Jeff Schneider *(Mgr-HR)*

TC HEARTLAND LLC
14300 Clay Ter Blvd Ste 249, Carmel, IN 46032
Tel.: (317) 566-9750   IN
Web Site: http://www.heartlandfpg.com
Artificial Sweetener & Water Enhancer Products Mfr & Whslr
N.A.I.C.S.: 325199
Ted Gelov *(Chm & CEO)*

TC MANUFACTURING CO., INC.
2500 N Longview St, Kilgore, TX 75662
Tel.: (903) 984-8596
Web Site: http://www.paksher.com
Sales Range: $10-24.9 Million
Emp.: 161
Unlaminated Plastics Film & Sheet Mfr
N.A.I.C.S.: 326113
Terry Gebhardt *(VP)*
Tommy Vaughan *(Mgr-Plant)*
Troy Fischer *(Pres & CEO)*

TC NU-STAR, INC.
1425 Stagecoach Rd, Shakopee, MN 55379
Tel.: (952) 445-8295   MN
Web Site: http://www.nustarinc.com
Year Founded: 1964
Sales Range: $1-9.9 Million
Emp.: 27
Miscellaneous General Purpose Machinery Mfr
N.A.I.C.S.: 333998

TC STUDIOS, LLC
1260 Corporate Blvd, Lancaster, PA 17601
Tel.: (717) 898-7999
Web Site: http://tcstudios.net
Commercial Photography & Video Services
N.A.I.C.S.: 541922
Ted Clements *(CEO)*

Subsidiaries:
The Shadowlight Group, Ltd   (1)
34 Zimmerman Rd, Leola, PA 17540
Tel.: (717) 656-5500
Web Site: http://www.shadowlightgroup.com
Services Related to Advertising
N.A.I.C.S.: 541890
Philip Hiestand *(Pres)*

TC3 TELECOM INC.
247 S Main St, Adrian, MI 49221
Tel.: (517) 265-7872   MI
Web Site: http://www.tc3net.com
Year Founded: 1991
Sales Range: $1-9.9 Million
Emp.: 25
Telecommunications Resellers
N.A.I.C.S.: 517121
Joseph P. Mattausch *(Pres)*
Ashley Hutchison *(VP)*
Christina Strachn *(Accountant)*

TCA FINANCIAL, LLC
51 Plum St Ste 260, Beavercreek, OH 45440
Tel.: (937) 425-6900
Web Site: http://www.instanttaxservice.com
Year Founded: 2000
Sales Range: $25-49.9 Million
Emp.: 20
Tax Preparation Services
N.A.I.C.S.: 541213
Fesum B. Ogbazion *(Founder & CEO)*

TCA HOLDINGS, LLC
3611 N Kedzie Ave, Chicago, IL 60618-4513
Tel.: (773) 463-1234
Web Site: http://www.tcaholdings.com
Sales Range: $25-49.9 Million
Emp.: 2,500
Athletic Court Construction & Operation Services
N.A.I.C.S.: 238990
Alan G. Schwartz *(Chm)*
Steven L. Schwartz *(Pres & CEO)*
Debra Siena *(Pres-Proactive Partners)*
Frank Nusko *(CFO & Sr VP)*

TCAA
4555 Lk Forest Dr Ste 550, Cincinnati, OH 45242-3792
Tel.: (513) 956-5550   OH
Web Site: http://www.tcaausa.com
Year Founded: 1996
Rev: $60,397,000
Emp.: 15
Advetising Agency
N.A.I.C.S.: 541810
Mike Schrader *(VP & Dir-Creative)*
Tony Ciafardini *(Founder)*

TCC PROPERTIES INC.
1224 Cottonwood St, Woodland, CA 95695
Tel.: (530) 666-5799
Rev: $12,000,000
Apartment Building Operator
N.A.I.C.S.: 531110
Lee Sayers *(Controller)*

TCE, INCORPORATED
5801 Allentown Rd Ste 305, Camp Springs, MD 20746-4553
Tel.: (301) 316-0501
Web Site: http://www.tceincorp.com
Year Founded: 1994
Sales Range: $1-9.9 Million
Emp.: 120
Management Consulting Services
N.A.I.C.S.: 541618
C. Gail Bassette *(Pres)*
Diane Peters *(VP)*
Quinten Washington *(VP-Construction Mgmt)*

TCG
306 Florida Ave NW, Washington, DC 20001
Tel.: (202) 986-5533
Web Site: http://www.tcg.com

Sales Range: $10-24.9 Million
Emp.: 110
Information Technology Consulting Services
N.A.I.C.S.: 541512
Peter F. Chernin *(Partner)*
Daniel A. Turner *(Pres)*
Robert Buccigrossi *(CTO)*
David G. Cassidy *(VP)*
Maureen Sullivan *(VP)*
Judith Axler Turner *(VP)*
Jesse Jacobs *(Founder & Mng Partner)*

TCH INDUSTRIES INC.
7441 Division Ave S Ste A1, Grand Rapids, MI 49548-7137
Tel.: (616) 942-0505   MI
Year Founded: 1982
Sales Range: $50-74.9 Million
Emp.: 1
Mfr of Custom Zinc & Aluminum Die Castings
N.A.I.C.S.: 331523
Theodore Hohman *(Pres)*
Patrick Greene *(Sec)*

TCH RESTAURANT GROUP INC.
5909 Breckenridge Pkwy Ste E, Tampa, FL 33610
Tel.: (813) 664-1500
Year Founded: 2005
Sales Range: $25-49.9 Million
Emp.: 775
Fast Food Restaurant Owner & Operator
N.A.I.C.S.: 722513
Robert M. Dorfman *(Pres & CEO)*

TCI ARCHITECTS ENGINEERS CONTRACTORS INC.
1718 State Rd 16, La Crosse, WI 54601-3011
Tel.: (608) 781-5700
Web Site: http://www.tciaec.com
Year Founded: 1977
Sales Range: $10-24.9 Million
Emp.: 100
Provider of Nonresidential Construction Services
N.A.I.C.S.: 236220
Tod Poss *(CFO)*

TCI HOLDING COMPANY
7996 N Point Blvd, Winston Salem, NC 27106
Tel.: (336) 759-7335   NC
Web Site: http://www.technologycrops.com
Sales Range: $10-24.9 Million
Specialty Crop Management Services
N.A.I.C.S.: 115116
Andrew Hebard *(Pres & CEO)*
Andrew Kampen *(Mgr-Fin)*

TCI PRECISION METALS, INC.
240 E Rosecrans Ave, Gardena, CA 90248
Tel.: (310) 323-5613   CA
Web Site: http://www.tciprecision.com
Year Founded: 1956
Sales Range: $75-99.9 Million
Emp.: 80
Metal Distr with Job Shop Services
N.A.I.C.S.: 423510
John D. Belzer *(Pres)*
John Martinez *(Mgr-Sls)*

Subsidiaries:
E-Z Lok   (1)
240 E Rosecrans Ave, Gardena, CA 90248-1942   (100%)
Tel.: (310) 323-5613
Web Site: http://www.ezlok.com

U.S. PRIVATE

Sales Range: $25-49.9 Million
Threaded Insert Mfr
N.A.I.C.S.: 423510
Burton E. Belzer *(Chm & CEO)*
Steven A. Schaeper *(Reg Mgr)*
Kevin Saito *(Div Mgr)*

TCIM SERVICES INC.
1013 Centre Rd, Wilmington, DE 19805-1281
Tel.: (302) 633-3000   DE
Web Site: http://www.tcim.com
Year Founded: 1987
Sales Range: $450-499.9 Million
Emp.: 2,000
Call Center Operations
N.A.I.C.S.: 561422
Patrick Ward *(CEO)*
Richard Sauter *(CFO)*

TCM COMPANY
2929 Pine Lk Rd, Lincoln, NE 68516
Tel.: (402) 420-2002   NE
Web Site: http://www.citybankandtrust.com
Sales Range: $1-9.9 Million
Emp.: 27
Bank Holding Company
N.A.I.C.S.: 551111
Susan Chrastil *(Pres & CEO)*
Paul Schelstraete *(Pres-City Bank & Trust)*

Subsidiaries:
City Bank & Trust Co.   (1)
2929 Pine Lk Rd, Lincoln, NE 68516
Tel.: (402) 420-2002
Web Site: http://www.citybankandtrust.com
Sales Range: $1-9.9 Million
Commericial Banking
N.A.I.C.S.: 522110
Chris Linhart *(VP-Crete Branch)*
David Kilgore *(VP)*
Patty Bauer *(VP-Crete Branch)*
Susan Chrastil *(CEO)*
Paul Schelstraete *(Pres)*
Dennis Bornschlegl *(VP-Mortgage Lending)*
Terry Kurtenbach *(VP)*

TCMI, INC.
250 Middlefield Rd, Menlo Park, CA 94025
Tel.: (650) 614-8200   DE
Web Site: http://www.tcv.com
Year Founded: 1995
Sales Range: $25-49.9 Million
Emp.: 45
Venture Capital Firm
N.A.I.C.S.: 523999
John Drew *(Gen Partner)*
Woody Marshall *(Gen Partner)*
Rick Kimball *(Gen Partner)*
John C. Rosenberg *(Gen Partner)*
David L. Yuan *(Gen Partner)*
Douglas L. Gilstrap *(Venture Partner)*
Nari Ansari *(Principal)*
Nathan Sanders *(Gen Partner & Head-IR)*
Sean Giese *(Principal)*
Ted Coons *(Gen Partner)*
Doug Gilstrap *(Venture Partner)*
Jay C. Hoag *(Gen Partner)*
Kapil Venkatachalam *(Gen Partner)*
Bob Burke *(Venture Partner)*
Eric Blachford *(Partner-Venture-Palo alto)*
Muz Ashraf *(VP)*
Nicholas Crowne *(VP)*
John Delfino *(VP)*
Aaron Ford *(VP)*
Amol Helekar *(VP)*
Scott Kirk *(VP)*
Maya Noeth *(VP)*
Ramzi Ramsey *(VP)*
Patrick Reilly *(CFO & Principal)*
Matt Robinson *(VP)*
Allison Walker *(Principal & Head-Human Capital)*

COMPANIES

Adam Silverschotz *(Principal)*
John Doran *(Gen Partner)*
Katja Gagen *(Principal & Head-Mktg)*
Robert Trudeau *(Gen Partner)*
Tim McAdam *(Gen Partner)*

Subsidiaries:

GoDaddy, Inc. (1)
100 S Mill Ave Ste 1600, Tempe, AZ 85281
Tel.: (406) 760-7600
Web Site: https://www.godaddy.com
Rev.: $4,254,100,000
Assets: $7,564,900,000
Liabilities: $7,502,700,000
Net Worth: $62,200,000
Earnings: $1,374,800,000
Emp.: 6,159
Fiscal Year-end: 12/31/2023
Holding Company; Domain Name Registration Services
N.A.I.C.S.: 551112
Amanpal S. Bhutani *(CEO)*
Auguste Goldman *(Pres-Care & Svcs)*
Jared Sine *(Chief Strategy Officer & Chief Legal Officer)*
Charles Beadnall *(CTO)*
Monica Bailey *(Chief People Officer)*
Fara Howard *(CMO)*
Roger Chen *(COO)*
Nick Daddario *(Chief Acctg Officer)*
Osama Bedier *(Pres-Commerce)*
Mark D. McCaffrey *(CFO)*
Paul Nicks *(Pres-Domain Registrars & Investors)*
Laura Messerschmitt *(Pres-Intl Independents)*
Gourav Pani *(Pres-US Independents)*
Paul Bindel *(Pres-Partners)*

Subsidiary (Domestic):

GoDaddy.com, LLC (2)
14455 N Hayden Rd, Scottsdale, AZ 85260
Tel.: (480) 505-8800
Web Site: http://www.godaddy.com
Domain Name Registration Services
N.A.I.C.S.: 518210
Amanpal S. Bhutani *(CEO)*

Subsidiary (Non-US):

Host Europe Group Limited (2)
The Shipping Building Old Vinyl Factory
252-254 Blyth Road, Hayes, London, UB3 1HA, Mddx, United Kingdom
Tel.: (44) 345 450 2310
Web Site: http://www.heg.com
Domain Registrar Services
N.A.I.C.S.: 517810
Richard Winslow *(Brand Dir-123 Reg)*

Subsidiary (Domestic):

123-Reg Limited (3)
The Shipping Building Old Vinyl Factory
252-254 Blyth Road, Hayes, London, UB3 1HA, Mddx, United Kingdom
Tel.: (44) 3454502310
Web Site: https://www.123-reg.co.uk
Custom Web Hosting Services
N.A.I.C.S.: 517810
Richard Winslow *(Brand Dir)*

Subsidiary (Non-US):

Host Europe GmbH (3)
c/o WeWork Friesenplatz 4, 50672, Cologne, Germany
Tel.: (49) 22199999301
Web Site: https://www.hosteurope.de
Internet Hosting Services
N.A.I.C.S.: 518210
Claus Boyens *(Mng Dir)*
Tobias Mohr *(Mng Dir)*

Subsidiary (Domestic):

Main Street Hub Inc. (2)
600 Congress Ave Ste 1200, Austin, TX 78701
Tel.: (888) 900-0920
Online Reputation Management Services
N.A.I.C.S.: 561499

Media Temple, Inc. (2)
12655 W Jefferson Blvd Ste 400, Los Angeles, CA 90066
Tel.: (310) 841-5500
Web Site: https://www.mediatemple.net

Sales Range: $1-9.9 Million
Emp.: 225
Hosts Websites for Motion Graphic Artists, Art Directors & Broadcast & Web Design Firms
N.A.I.C.S.: 518210
Lou Kikos *(VP-Mktg)*

Outright, Inc. (2)
100 Mathilda Pl, Sunnyvale, CA 94086
Tel.: (650) 440-6352
Web Site: http://www.outright.com
Sales Range: $1-9.9 Million
Billing & Accounting Software Mfr
N.A.I.C.S.: 513210

Subsidiary (Non-US):

Special Domains Services, Inc. (2)
Tel.: (480) 505-8800
Domain Name Registration Services
N.A.I.C.S.: 541519

Subsidiary (Non-US):

Domains by Proxy, LLC (3)
Tel.: (480) 505-8800
Web Site: http://www.domainsbyproxy.com
Domain Name Registration Services
N.A.I.C.S.: 541519

Subsidiary (Domestic):

Starfield Technologies, Inc. (2)
14455 N Hayden Rd, Scottsdale, AZ 85260
Tel.: (480) 505-8825
Web Site: http://www.starfieldtech.com
Technology-Based Business Solutions Developer
N.A.I.C.S.: 541512

Wild West Domains, Inc. (2)
2150 E Warner Rd, Tempe, AZ 85284
Tel.: (480) 624-2500
Web Site: https://www.wildwestdomains.com
Domain-Related Products & Services Reseller
N.A.I.C.S.: 541519
Blake J. Irving *(CEO)*

Oversight Systems, Inc. (1)
1090 Northchase Pkwy SE Ste 350, Marietta, GA 30067
Tel.: (770) 984-4654
Web Site: http://www.oversightsystems.com
Software Development Services
N.A.I.C.S.: 541511
Dan Kuokka *(CTO)*
Chris Rossie *(Exec VP-Bus & Corp Dev)*
H. Keith Cooley *(Exec VP-Engrg)*
Patrick Taylor *(Founder)*
Manish Singh *(Exec VP-Sls Solutions & Client Svcs)*
Geoff Brannon *(CFO)*
Scott Kingsfield *(Chm)*
Terrence McCrossan *(CEO)*
Chris Juneau *(CMO)*

Technology Crossover Ventures L.P. - Millburn (1)
56 Main St Ste 210, Millburn, NJ 07041
Tel.: (973) 467-5320
Web Site: http://www.tcv.com
Sales Range: $50-74.9 Million
Emp.: 40
Venture Capital Firm
N.A.I.C.S.: 523999

TCN, INC.
560 S Vly View Dr, Saint George, UT 84770
Tel.: (435) 627-2107
Web Site: http://www.tcnp3.com
Software Mfr
N.A.I.C.S.: 513210
Dave Bethers *(VP-Enterprise Sls)*

Subsidiaries:

Global Connect, LLC (1)
5218 Atlantic Ave Ste 300, Mays Landing, NJ 08330-2003
Tel.: (609) 837-8200
Web Site: http://www.gc1.com
Sales Range: $1-9.9 Million
Emp.: 50
Web-Based Voice Messaging
N.A.I.C.S.: 517810
Darrin Bird *(COO & Exec VP)*

TCOM, L.P.
7125 Thomas Edison Dr, Columbia, MD 21046-2209
Tel.: (410) 312-2300
Web Site: http://www.tcomlp.com
Emp.: 100
Motorcycle, ATV & All Other Motor Vehicle Dealers
N.A.I.C.S.: 441227
Ron Bendlin *(Pres & CEO)*

Subsidiaries:

Aerostar International, Inc. (1)
205 E 6th St, Sioux Falls, SD 57104
Tel.: (605) 331-3500
Web Site: http://www.ravenaerostar.com
Hot Air Balloons, Large Advertising Inflatables, Remote Control Blimps & Specialty Apparel
N.A.I.C.S.: 336411
Evan Hegge *(Dir-Fin)*
Jim Nelson *(Pres)*

TCOOMBS & ASSOCIATES LLC
21268 Mirror Rdg Pl, Sterling, VA 20164
Tel.: (703) 798-6944   VA
Web Site:
http://www.tcassociates.com
Year Founded: 1998
Sales Range: $10-24.9 Million
Emp.: 65
Software-based Solutions for the Healthcare Industry
N.A.I.C.S.: 518210
Tony Coombs *(Pres & CEO)*
Courtney Coombs *(COO & VP-HR)*

TCR CORPORATION
1600 67th Ave N, Minneapolis, MN 55430-1742
Tel.: (763) 560-2200
Web Site: http://www.tcr-corp.com
Year Founded: 1953
Specialty Threaded Fasteners
N.A.I.C.S.: 531120
Tim Dooher *(Pres & CEO)*
Tom Mikulay *(CFO)*

TCR INDUSTRIES, INC.
3703 S Route 31, Crystal Lake, IL 60012
Tel.: (815) 459-2400
Web Site:
http://www.tcindustries.com
Rev.: $75,936,073
Emp.: 500
Commercial Heat Treating of Carbon & Alloy Steel Bars
N.A.I.C.S.: 332999
John Nelson *(CFO)*
Pat Pipitone *(Mgr-Sls)*
Mark Walter *(Mgr-Quality Assurance)*
Bill Weber *(Mgr-Div)*
Thomas Z. Hayward Jr. *(Chm)*

TCS CONTRACTING CORPORATION
16649 NE 19th Ave, Miami, FL 33162
Tel.: (305) 756-8700
Web Site: http://www.tcsccorp.com
Rev.: $22,456,780
Emp.: 30
Single Family Home Construction Services
N.A.I.C.S.: 236115
Timothy Smith *(Pres)*

TCS MEDIA, INC.
2688 Queen Mary Pl, Maitland, FL 32751
Tel.: (407) 252-1026
Web Site: http://www.tcsmedia.com
Year Founded: 2003
Sales Range: Less than $1 Million
Emp.: 1

Advetising Agency
N.A.I.C.S.: 541810
Tom Vittetow *(Owner)*

TCSI/TRANSLAND INC.
1601 W Old Rte 66, Strafford, MO 65757
Tel.: (417) 864-5710
Web Site: http://www.transland.biz
Sales Range: $10-24.9 Million
Emp.: 40
General Freight Trucking Services
N.A.I.C.S.: 484121
Mark Walker *(CEO)*

TCT MINISTRIES, INC.
11717 Rt 37, Marion, IL 62959
Tel.: (618) 997-4700
Web Site: http://www.tct.tv
Year Founded: 1977
Religious Organizations
N.A.I.C.S.: 813110
Garth W. Coonce *(Pres)*

Subsidiaries:

Tri State Christian Television (1)
11717 Rt 37, Marion, IL 62959
Tel.: (618) 997-4700
Web Site: http://www.tct-net.org
Sales Range: $10-24.9 Million
Emp.: 30
Christian Television Broadcasting Stations
N.A.I.C.S.: 516120
Tina Coonce *(Co-Founder & VP)*

TCW DIRECT LENDING LLC
200 Clarendon St, Boston, MA 02116
Tel.: (617) 936-2275   DE
Year Founded: 2014
Rev.: $43,224,000
Assets: $1,022,589,000
Liabilities: $629,374,000
Net Worth: $393,215,000
Earnings: $30,156,000
Fiscal Year-end: 12/31/22
Investment Advisory & Management Services
N.A.I.C.S.: 523940
Richard T. Miller *(Chm & Pres)*
James G. Krause *(CFO)*

TD INDUSTRIES, INC.
13850 Diplomat Dr, Dallas, TX 75234-8812
Tel.: (972) 888-9500   TX
Web Site:
http://www.tdindustries.com
Year Founded: 1946
Sales Range: $400-449.9 Million
Emp.: 1,800
Air Conditioning, Heating, Plumbing & Refrigeration Supplies Whslr
N.A.I.C.S.: 238220
Harold F. MacDowell *(CEO)*
Steve Canter *(CTO)*
Maureen Underwood *(Exec VP-People Dept)*
Mike Kotubey *(Pres-North Texas)*
Graham Moore *(Pres-Houston)*
Bob Richards *(Pres-Central Texas)*
Ed R. White *(Exec VP-Arizona)*
Dave Youden *(Sr VP-Major Projects-Dallas)*
Nikki Morgan *(Sr VP-Houston)*
Robert G. Wilken *(Exec VP)*
Ronell Peters *(Sr VP-Houston Special Projects)*
Scott Burrows *(Sr VP-Dallas Svc Grp)*
Chuck Swallow *(Sr VP-Austin)*
Randee Herrin *(Sr VP-New Construction-Houston)*
Matt Terry *(Sr VP)*
Nicolas Sfeir *(VP-Austin)*
David Fultz *(Sr VP-Special Projects)*

TD INDUSTRIES, INC.

TD Industries, Inc.—(Continued)
Gary Roden (VP-Bus Dev-North Texas)
Sheri Tillman (Gen Counsel)
Chris Brown (Sr VP-Special Projects)
Jay Layton (Sr VP-Construction & Svc-Arizona)

TDA ADVERTISING & DESIGN
1500 Pearl St Ste 300, Boulder, CO 80302
Tel.: (303) 247-1180   CO
Web Site: http://www.tdaadvertising.com
Year Founded: 1989
Sales Range: $25-49.9 Million
Emp.: 15
Full Service
N.A.I.C.S.: 541810
Thomas Dooley (Co-Founder & Co-Dir-Creative)
Jonathan Schoenberg (Co-Founder & Co-Dir-Creative)
Jim Moscou (Mng Dir & Dir-Strategy)
Neal Desai (Dir-Art)
Jeremy Seibold (Assoc Dir-Creative)
Sarah Tefs (Supvr-Media)
Ryan Dean Waite (Sr Copywriter)

TDA INDUSTRIES, INC.
122 E 42nd St Ste 1618, New York, NY 10168-1199
Tel.: (212) 972-1510   NY
Sales Range: $50-74.9 Million
Emp.: 1
Roofing Supplies & Related Products Distr
N.A.I.C.S.: 423330

TDC SYSTEMS INTEGRATION
2875 Springhill Pky, Smyrna, GA 30080
Tel.: (770) 805-9300
Web Site: http://www.tdcsi.com
Year Founded: 1995
Rev.: $7,200,000
Emp.: 35
Prepackaged Software Services
N.A.I.C.S.: 513210
Tony Dozier (Pres)

TDG INC.
11463 S Foothills Blvd, Yuma, AZ 85367
Tel.: (928) 342-5253
Rev.: $10,000,000
Emp.: 125
New Construction, Single-Family Houses
N.A.I.C.S.: 236115
Subsidiaries:
Foothills Self Storage (1)
13245 E 44th St, Yuma, AZ 85367
Tel.: (928) 342-9000
Rev.: $100,000
Emp.: 2
Warehousing, Self Storage
N.A.I.C.S.: 531130

TDI POWER SYSTEMS
36 Newburgh Rd, Hackettstown, NJ 07840
Tel.: (908) 850-5088
Web Site: http://www.tdipower.com
Sales Range: $150-199.9 Million
Emp.: 300
Transistor Devices Mfr
N.A.I.C.S.: 334413
Kelly Atkinson (Dir-Sls)
Sam Wolfe (Dir-Sls-East PA, DE & South NJ)
Declan Walsh (Dir-Sls-Intl)
Neil Barron (Dir-Sls-EMEA & Asia)
Bill Gray (VP-Sls-Global)

Subsidiaries:
TDI Advanced Conversion Products (1)
85 Horsehill Rd, Cedar Knolls, NJ 07927-2003
Tel.: (973) 267-1900
Web Site: http://www.tdipower.com
Sales Range: $10-24.9 Million
Emp.: 100
Mfr of Solid State DC-AC Sine Wave Inverters
N.A.I.C.S.: 335314

TDI Power Systems - COMMERCIAL PRODUCTS DIVISION (1)
36 Newburgh Rd, Hackettstown, NJ 07840
Tel.: (908) 850-5088
Sales Range: $50-74.9 Million
Electric Power Equipment Distr
N.A.I.C.S.: 423610

TDI Power Systems - Dynaload Division (1)
36A Newburgh Rd, Hackettstown, NJ 07840-3904
Tel.: (908) 850-5088
Electric Power Equipment Distr
N.A.I.C.S.: 423610

TDI-Circuitek (1)
36 Newburgh Rd, Hackettstown, NJ 07840-3904
Tel.: (908) 475-8694
Web Site: http://www.circuitek.com
Sales Range: $10-24.9 Million
Emp.: 40
Mfr Of Circuit Boards
N.A.I.C.S.: 334416

TDI-Enterprise Power Systems (1)
36 Newburgh Rd, Hackettstown, NJ 07840
Tel.: (908) 850-5088
Web Site: http://www.tdipower.com
Sales Range: $25-49.9 Million
Mfr of Transistor Devices
N.A.I.C.S.: 334413

Transistor Devices Europe Ltd. (1)
Carrigtwohill Industrial Estate, Carrigtwohill, Cork, Ireland (100%)
Tel.: (353) 214853020
Sales Range: $10-24.9 Million
Emp.: 40
Mfr of Electronic Power Supplies & Related Products
N.A.I.C.S.: 332410

TDI TERRAPLAN DEVELOPMENT
8698 E San Alberto Dr, Scottsdale, AZ 85258
Tel.: (480) 951-2262
Web Site: http://www.regalautowash.com
Sales Range: $25-49.9 Million
Emp.: 4
Commercial & Industrial Building Operation
N.A.I.C.S.: 531120
Volker Rossnagel (Pres)

TDK CONSTRUCTION CO. INC.
7203 Hwy 416 W, Robards, KY 42452
Tel.: (270) 521-7825
Web Site: http://www.tdkconstruction.com
Sales Range: $10-24.9 Million
Emp.: 8
Commercial & Office Building, New Construction
N.A.I.C.S.: 236220
Tim Keach (Pres)

TDK TECHNOLOGIES, LLC
12977 N Forty Dr Ste 108, Saint Louis, MO 63141
Tel.: (314) 878-1005   MO
Web Site: http://www.tdktech.com
Year Founded: 2001
Sales Range: $1-9.9 Million

Emp.: 175
Computer Software Systems Analysis & Design
N.A.I.C.S.: 541511
David W. Kocs (Principal)
Kristin Tucker (Mgr-Technical & Solutions Practice)

TDS CONSTRUCTION INC.
4239 63rd St W, Bradenton, FL 34209
Tel.: (941) 795-6100
Web Site: http://www.tdsconstruction.com
Year Founded: 1987
Sales Range: $25-49.9 Million
Emp.: 75
Retail Construction
N.A.I.C.S.: 236220
David K. Scherer (Founder & Pres)
Robert D. Baker (VP-Construction & Project Mgr)
Ron E. Strange (Sr Project Mgr)
Chris S. Paynter (Project Mgr)
William E. Leeka (Project Mgr)
William Gentry (Project Mgr)

TDW INC.
5501 Nob Hill Rd, Sunrise, FL 33351
Tel.: (954) 746-8000
Web Site: http://www.tdwcloseouts.com
Year Founded: 1996
Sales Range: $1-9.9 Million
Emp.: 8
Exports & Distributes Surplus, Salvage & Closed Out General Merchandise
N.A.I.C.S.: 455219
Raphael Shabtai (Owner & Pres)

TEA COLLECTION
1 Arkansas St Ste B, San Francisco, CA 94107
Tel.: (415) 621-9400
Web Site: http://www.teacollection.com
Year Founded: 2002
Sales Range: $10-24.9 Million
Emp.: 100
Children's Clothing Mfr & Retailer
N.A.I.C.S.: 458110
Emily Meyer (Co-Founder & Chief Creative Officer)
Leigh Rawdon (Co-Founder & CEO)

TEA PARTY PATRIOTS, INC.
1025 Rose Creek Dr Ste 620-322, Woodstock, GA 30189
Tel.: (404) 593-0877   GA
Web Site: http://www.teapartypatriots.org
Year Founded: 2009
Sales Range: $10-24.9 Million
Emp.: 30
Political Organizations
N.A.I.C.S.: 813940
Tim Murphy (CFO)
Scot Crocket (Exec Dir)
Jenny Beth Martin (Founder & Pres)
Bill Walton (Chm)

TEACH FOR AMERICA
315 W 36th St 8th Fl, New York, NY 10018
Tel.: (212) 279-2080
Web Site: http://www.teachforamerica.org
Sales Range: $10-24.9 Million
Emp.: 2,027
Teacher Recruiting Services
N.A.I.C.S.: 561311
Wendy Kopp (Founder & CEO)
Paula A. Sneed (Vice Chm)
Susan Asiyanbi (Exec VP-Continuum Program)

Josh Griggs (CFO & Exec VP-Talent Ops)
Tracy-Elizabeth Clay (Gen Counsel & Sr VP-Legal Affairs)
Eric C. Scroggins (Exec Dir)
Raychel Robbins (Dir-Dev-Metro Atlanta)
Ben Schumacher (Exec Dir-Greater Nashville)
Amar Patel (Exec Dir-Indianapolis)
Walter Bond (Exec Dir-Milwaukee)
Lereca Monik (Mng Dir-Corp & Foundation Rels)
Ronald Augustin (Mng Dir-Alumni & Community Affairs)
Molly Friedland (Sr Mng Dir-Corp Partnerships)
Claiborne Taylor (Mng Dir-Alumni Affairs)
Armen Hratchian (Exec Dir-Detroit)
Damon Bailey (Exec Dir-Alabama)

TEACHER RETIREMENT SYSTEM OF TEXAS
1000 Red River St, Austin, TX 78701
Tel.: (512) 542-6400
Web Site: http://www.trs.state.tx.us
Year Founded: 1937
Education Pension Fund Administrator
N.A.I.C.S.: 524292
Brian Guthrie (Exec Dir)
Jarvis V. Hollingsworth (Chm)

Subsidiaries:
Bremer Kreditbank AG (1)
Wachtstrasse 16, 28195, Bremen, Germany
Tel.: (49) 42136840
Web Site: http://www.bkb-bank.com
Commercial Banking Asset Management & Investment Banking Services
N.A.I.C.S.: 522110
Jutta Nikolic (Sr VP)

Subsidiary (Domestic):
Oldenburgische Landesbank AG (2)
Stau 15/17, 26122, Oldenburg, Germany
Tel.: (49) 4412210
Web Site: https://www.olb.de
Sales Range: $400-449.9 Million
International Banking
N.A.I.C.S.: 522299

Subsidiary (Domestic):
Degussa Bank AG (3)
Theodor Heuss Allee 74, 60486, Frankfurt am Main, Germany
Tel.: (49) 6936005555
Web Site: http://www.degussa-bank.de
Sales Range: $50-74.9 Million
Emp.: 400
Banking Services
N.A.I.C.S.: 522299

TEACHERS CREDIT UNION
110 S Main St, South Bend, IN 46601
Tel.: (574) 232-8011
Web Site: http://www.tcunet.com
Credit Union
N.A.I.C.S.: 522130
Dave Chapman (CIO)
Chad Douglass (Chief Lending Officer & Sr VP)
Gene Novello (COO)
Jon Glesing (Dir-PR)
Dominic Zultanski (Sr Dir-Security & Loss Prevention)
Nicole Alcorn (Chief Member Experience Officer & Sr VP)
Angie Dvorak (VP-Mktg)
DeAnna Moyers (VP-Mortgage Svcs)
Paul Marsh (Pres & CEO)
Jeff Benefiel (VP-Digital Delivery & Payments)
Joshua Neff (VP-Comml Lending)
Sandy H. Burd (Asst VP-Payments & Digital Fraud)

COMPANIES

TEACHERS INSURANCE ASSOCIATION - COLLEGE RETIREMENT FUND

Sharri Tafelski *(Asst VP-Branch Ops & Project Mgmt)*
Kara Kelly *(Mgr-PR)*
Jacquelyn Burns Rucker *(Dir-Diversity, Equity & Inclusion)*
Catrina Tate *(VP-Retail)*

TEACHERS INSURANCE ASSOCIATION - COLLEGE RETIREMENT FUND
730 3rd Ave, New York, NY 10017-3206
Tel.: (212) 490-9000
Web Site: http://www.tiaa-cref.org
Sales Range: Less than $1 Million
Holding Company; Pensions & Retirement Annuities, Insurance, Investment & Other Financial Services
N.A.I.C.S.: 551112
Ronald L. Thompson *(Chm)*
Doug Chittenden *(Vice Chm-Institutional Relationships)*
Vijay Advani *(CEO-Nuveen)*
Sean N. Woodroffe *(Chief HR Officer & Sr Exec VP)*
John Douglas *(Sr VP & Chief Oversight & Advocacy Officer)*
Kourtney Gibson *(Chief Institutional Client Officer)*
Thasunda Brown Duckett *(Pres & CEO)*
Rahul N. Merchant *(Sr Exec VP & Head-Client Svcs & Tech)*
Kourtney Gibson *(CEO & Chief Institutional Client Officer)*

Subsidiaries:

College Retirement Equities Fund (1)
730 3rd Ave, New York, NY 10017-3206
Tel.: (212) 916-4905
Sales Range: $1-4.9 Billion
Pension & Annuity Products & Services
N.A.I.C.S.: 525110
Edward D. Van Dolsen *(COO & Exec VP)*
Howell E. Jackson *(Chm)*

Subsidiary (Domestic):

Green Seal Environmental, Inc. (2)
114 State Rd Ste B1, Sagamore Beach, MA 02562
Tel.: (508) 888-6034
Web Site: http://www.gseenv.com
Solid Waste Collection
N.A.I.C.S.: 562111
Christie Lee Wirsen *(Pres & Treas)*

Self Storage Group ASA (1)
Karenslyst Alle 2, 0278, Oslo, Norway (99.12%)
Tel.: (47) 92429438
Web Site: https://www.selfstoragegroup.no
Rev.: $30,255,738
Assets: $227,622,671
Liabilities: $113,498,903
Net Worth: $114,123,768
Earnings: $7,009,782
Emp.: 94
Fiscal Year-end: 12/31/2019
Self Storage Facility Services
N.A.I.C.S.: 624190
Fabian Emil Sobak *(CEO)*
Cecilie M. Braend Hekneby *(CFO)*
Steven Skaar *(Chm)*

Subsidiary (Non-US):

City Self-Storage A/S (2)
Roskildevej 5, 2620, Albertslund, Denmark
Tel.: (45) 70151111
Web Site: http://www.cityselfstorage.dk
Logistic Services
N.A.I.C.S.: 488510

Subsidiary (Domestic):

City Self-Storage Norge AS (2)
Karenslyst alle 2, 0278, Oslo, Norway
Tel.: (47) 81012345
Web Site: http://www.cityselfstorage.no
Logistic Services
N.A.I.C.S.: 488510

OK Minilager AS (2)
Karenslyst alle 2, 0278, Oslo, Norway
Tel.: (47) 22654000
Web Site: http://www.ok-minilager.no
Real Estate Services
N.A.I.C.S.: 531390

TIAA Henderson Real Estate Ltd. (1)
TIAA Henderson Real Estate 201 Bishopsgate, London, EC2M 3BN, United Kingdom (100%)
Tel.: (44) 20 3727 8000
Web Site: http://www.threalestate.com
Emp.: 400
Real Estate Investment Management Services
N.A.I.C.S.: 531390
Gemma Bradley *(Head-Mktg & Comm)*
Ray Adderley *(Chief Investment Officer)*
Tom Garbutt *(Chm)*
Peter Winstanley *(Pres)*
Mark Wood *(COO)*

Joint Venture (Non-US):

Warburg - Henderson Kapitalanlagegesellschaft fur Immobilien mbH (2)
Gertrudenstrasse 9, 20095, Hamburg, Germany (50%)
Tel.: (49) 40 32 82 36 00
Web Site: http://www.warburg-hih.com
Sales Range: $50-74.9 Million
Emp.: 15
Investment Services
N.A.I.C.S.: 525910
Andreas Beckers *(Chief Scientific Officer)*

Teachers Insurance & Annuity Association of America (1)
730 3rd Ave, New York, NY 10017-3206
Tel.: (212) 490-9000
Web Site: http://www.tiaa.org
Sales Range: Less than $1 Million
Life, Property & Casualty Insurance Products & Services
N.A.I.C.S.: 524298
Ronald R. Pressman *(COO & Exec VP)*
Sanjay Gupta *(Chief Customer Officer-TIAA Fin Solutions)*
Reginald Chambers *(Chief Transformation Officer & Exec VP)*
Marilyn S. Adler *(Executives)*

Subsidiary (Domestic):

Myvest Corporation (2)
500 Howard St Ste 425, San Francisco, CA 94105
Tel.: (415) 369-9511
Web Site: http://www.myvest.com
Rev.: $1,600,000
Emp.: 20
Custom Computer Programming Services
N.A.I.C.S.: 541511
William Harris *(Chm)*
Anton Honikman *(CEO)*
Brian Marchiel *(VP)*
John Fennelly *(Mng Dir)*
Mike Marcus *(Mng Partner)*
Paul Bergholm *(CFO)*
Mark Worsey *(COO)*
Arlene Pons *(CTO)*
Josh Moats *(CIO)*

Nuveen LLC (2)
333 W Wacker Dr, Chicago, IL 60606
Tel.: (312) 917-7700
Management Investment Services
N.A.I.C.S.: 525910
Tara Giuliano *(Head-Mktg)*
Michael Perry *(Exec VP & Head-Global Client Grp)*
Seun Salami *(CFO & Exec VP)*

Subsidiary (Domestic):

Nuveen Asset Management, LLC (3)
333 W Wacker Dr Fl 30, Chicago, IL 60606
Tel.: (800) 558-4487
Web Site: http://www.nuveen.com
Investment Management Service
N.A.I.C.S.: 523940
Stephen P. Ban *(Mng Dir-Bus Dev & Portfolio Advisory)*
William Huffman *(Pres)*
David Chalupnik *(Mng Dir & Head-Equities)*

Keith B. Hembre *(Mng Dir & Head-Quantitative Strategies)*
James A. Diedrich *(Sr VP & Portfolio Mgr)*
Derek M. Sadowsky *(VP & Portfolio Mgr)*
Scott M. Tonneson *(VP & Portfolio Mgr)*
Karen L. Bowie *(Sr VP & Portfolio Mgr)*
Jon A. Loth *(VP & Portfolio Mgr)*
Gregory J. Ryan *(VP & Portfolio Mgr)*
Mark A. Traster *(Sr VP & Portfolio Mgr)*
Tony R. Burger *(Sr VP, Portfolio Mgr & Dir-Quantitative Equity Res)*
Derek B. Bloom *(Sr VP & Portfolio Mgr)*
David A. Friar *(SR VP & Portfolio Mgr)*
Michael N. Lindh *(VP, Head-Options Trading & Portfolio Mgr)*
John M. Stevens *(Mng Dir & Dir-Res)*
Stephanie C. Weiss *(Sr VP & Head-Equity Trading)*
Derek S. Wolff *(Sr VP & Head-Strategic Product Dev)*
Fernando Cristiano *(Sr VP-Client Svcs & Mgr-Relationship)*
Gordon Telfer *(Sr VP & Portfolio Mgr-Client)*
Maria M. Peterson *(VP-Equity Trading)*
Ruth E. Wilkens *(VP-Equity Trading)*
Kristen A. Goodman *(VP-Strategic Product Mgmt)*
Eric Kurzweg *(VP & Portfolio Mgr-Client)*
Justin F. Amand *(VP-Res)*
Thomas W. Conklin *(VP-Res)*
Tony R. Boase *(VP-Res)*
Mark A. Hesse-Withbroe *(VP-Res)*
Bihag Patel *(VP-Res)*
Jane A. Snorek *(VP-Res)*
Evan F. Staples *(VP-Res)*
Laura E. Starr *(VP-Res)*
David F. Johnson *(VP-Res)*
Andrew O. Rem *(VP-Res)*
John Beam *(VP-Res)*
Tracy P. Stouffer *(Sr VP & Portfolio Mgr)*
Vijay Advani *(CEO)*
Jose Minaya *(Pres-Global)*
John Nersesian *(Sr Mng Dir)*
Phyllis G. Thomas *(Sr Mng Dir)*

Holding (Domestic):

Nuveen AMT-Free Municipal Credit Income Fund (4)
333 W Wacker Dr, Chicago, IL 60606
Tel.: (312) 917-7810
Rev.: $243,105,524
Assets: $5,514,238,998
Liabilities: $2,037,276,720
Net Worth: $3,476,962,278
Earnings: $160,212,808
Fiscal Year-end: 10/31/2019
Investment Management Service
N.A.I.C.S.: 525990
Gifford R. Zimmerman *(Sec)*

Nuveen AMT-Free Municipal Value Fund (4)
333 W Wacker Dr, Chicago, IL 60606
Tel.: (312) 917-7700
Rev.: $11,019,581
Assets: $265,356,671
Liabilities: $3,166,924
Net Worth: $262,189,747
Earnings: $9,172,492
Fiscal Year-end: 10/31/2019
Investment Management Service
N.A.I.C.S.: 525990
Terence John Toth *(Chm)*
Daniel J. Close *(Portfolio Mgr & Mgr-Fund)*

Nuveen AMT-Free Quality Municipal Income Fund (4)
333 W Wacker Dr, Chicago, IL 60606
Tel.: (312) 917-7700
Rev.: $268,307,419
Assets: $6,515,941,902
Liabilities: $2,422,553,354
Net Worth: $4,093,388,548
Earnings: $173,706,452
Fiscal Year-end: 10/31/2019
Investment Management Service
N.A.I.C.S.: 525990
Christopher L. Drahn *(Mgr-Fund)*

Nuveen Arizona Quality Municipal Income Fund (4)
333 W Wacker Dr, Chicago, IL 60606
Tel.: (312) 917-7700
Rev.: $10,461,643
Assets: $279,606,830
Liabilities: $99,582,903
Net Worth: $180,023,927
Earnings: $6,464,341

Fiscal Year-end: 02/29/2020
Investment Management Service
N.A.I.C.S.: 525990
Terence John Toth *(Chm)*
Michael S. Hamilton *(Mgr-Fund)*

Nuveen California AMT-Free Quality Municipal Income Fund (4)
333 W Wacker Dr, Chicago, IL 60606
Tel.: (312) 917-8146
Rev.: $47,641,276
Assets: $1,276,443,139
Liabilities: $455,781,409
Net Worth: $820,661,730
Earnings: $30,142,314
Fiscal Year-end: 02/29/2020
Investment Management Service
N.A.I.C.S.: 525990
Terence John Toth *(Chm)*
Scott R. Romans *(Mgr-Fund)*

Nuveen California Municipal Value Fund, Inc. (4)
333 W Wacker Dr, Chicago, IL 60606
Tel.: (312) 917-7810
Rev.: $11,149,627
Assets: $312,010,797
Liabilities: $1,732,774
Net Worth: $310,278,023
Earnings: $9,607,706
Fiscal Year-end: 02/29/2020
Investment Management Service
N.A.I.C.S.: 525990
Scott R. Romans *(Mgr-Fund)*

Subsidiary (Domestic):

Nuveen California Municipal Value Fund 2 (5)
333 W Wacker Dr, Chicago, IL 60606
Tel.: (312) 917-7700
Rev.: $2,138,287
Assets: $55,989,353
Liabilities: $192,844
Net Worth: $55,796,509
Earnings: $1,757,745
Fiscal Year-end: 02/29/2020
Investment Management Service
N.A.I.C.S.: 525990
Scott R. Romans *(Mgr-Fund)*

Holding (Domestic):

Nuveen California Quality Municipal Income Fund (4)
333 W Wacker Dr, Chicago, IL 60606
Tel.: (312) 917-7783
Rev.: $146,312,254
Assets: $3,746,451,874
Liabilities: $1,328,029,327
Net Worth: $2,418,422,547
Earnings: $94,354,321
Fiscal Year-end: 02/29/2020
Investment Management Service
N.A.I.C.S.: 525990
Terence John Toth *(Chm)*
Scott R. Romans *(Mgr-Fund)*

Nuveen Churchill Direct Lending Corp. (4)
430 Park Ave 14th Fl, New York, NY 10022
Tel.: (212) 478-9200
Rev.: $82,453,000
Assets: $1,253,959,000
Liabilities: $729,002,000
Net Worth: $524,957,000
Earnings: $45,460,000
Fiscal Year-end: 12/31/2022
Investment Services
N.A.I.C.S.: 523940
Kenneth J. Kencel *(Chm, Pres & CEO)*

Nuveen Core Equity Alpha Fund (4)
333 W Wacker Dr, Chicago, IL 60606
Tel.: (312) 259-6694
Rev.: $3,791,390
Assets: $242,582,503
Liabilities: $1,558,417
Net Worth: $241,024,086
Earnings: $1,479,283
Fiscal Year-end: 12/31/2019
Investment Management Service
N.A.I.C.S.: 525990

TEACHERS INSURANCE ASSOCIATION - COLLEGE RETIREMENT FUND

U.S. PRIVATE

Teachers Insurance Association - College Retirement Fund—(Continued)
Adrian Banner *(Mgr-Fund)*

Nuveen Credit Strategies Income Fund (4)
333 W Wacker Dr, Chicago, IL 60606
Tel.: (312) 917-7700
Rev.: $103,389,958
Assets: $1,923,548,232
Liabilities: $771,770,826
Net Worth: $1,151,777,406
Earnings: $62,624,489
Fiscal Year-end: 07/31/2019
Investment Management Service
N.A.I.C.S.: 525990
Scott Caraher *(Mgr-Fund)*

Nuveen Diversified Commodity Fund (4)
333 W Wacker Dr, Chicago, IL 60606
Tel.: (877) 827-5920
Web Site: http://www.nuveen.com
Rev.: $160,723
Assets: $88,901,061
Liabilities: $3,269,520
Net Worth: $85,631,541
Earnings: $(27,858,989)
Fiscal Year-end: 12/31/2015
Investment Fund Services
N.A.I.C.S.: 523999
Douglas Baker *(Portfolio Mgr)*
Randy Migdal *(Portfolio Mgr)*
Susan Wager *(Portfolio Mgr)*

Nuveen Diversified Dividend & Income Fund (4)
333 W Wacker Dr, Chicago, IL 60606
Tel.: (312) 917-7700
Investment Services
N.A.I.C.S.: 525910
Kevin F. Murphy *(Mgr-Fund)*

Nuveen Dow 30sm Dynamic Overwrite Fund (4)
333 W Wacker Dr, Chicago, IL 60606
Tel.: (312) 917-7700
Rev.: $15,874,695
Assets: $666,135,141
Liabilities: $4,880,229
Net Worth: $661,254,912
Earnings: $9,685,597
Fiscal Year-end: 12/31/2019
Investment Management Service
N.A.I.C.S.: 525990
David A. Friar *(Mgr-Fund)*

Nuveen Emerging Markets Debt 2022 Target Term Fund (4)
333 W Wacker Dr 32Nd Fl, Chicago, IL 60606
Tel.: (312) 917-8146
Fund Operate Services
N.A.I.C.S.: 523940
Katherine Renfrew *(Mgr-Fund)*

Nuveen Enhanced Municipal Value Fund (4)
333 W Wacker Dr, Chicago, IL 60606-1218
Tel.: (312) 917-7810
Rev.: $24,201,645
Assets: $503,870,707
Liabilities: $123,910,005
Net Worth: $379,960,702
Earnings: $18,229,243
Fiscal Year-end: 10/31/2019
Investment Management Service
N.A.I.C.S.: 525990

Nuveen Floating Rate Income Fund (4)
333 W Wacker Dr, Chicago, IL 60606
Tel.: (312) 917-7700
Rev.: $61,349,162
Assets: $1,046,058,404
Liabilities: $417,839,958
Net Worth: $628,218,446
Earnings: $39,606,948
Fiscal Year-end: 07/31/2019
Investment Management Service
N.A.I.C.S.: 525990
Jenny Rhee *(Mgr-Fund)*

Nuveen Global High Income Fund (4)
333 W Wacker Dr, Chicago, IL 60606
Tel.: (312) 917-7700
Rev.: $38,359,760
Assets: $599,068,389
Liabilities: $178,588,562
Net Worth: $420,479,827
Earnings: $27,681,653
Fiscal Year-end: 12/31/2019
Investment Management Service
N.A.I.C.S.: 525990
Margaret L. Wolff *(Trustee)*

Nuveen Long/Short Commodity Total Return Fund (4)
333 W Wacker Dr, Chicago, IL 60606
Web Site: http://www.nuveen.com
Sales Range: Less than $1 Million
Investment Services
N.A.I.C.S.: 523999
John Amboian *(Chm & CEO)*
Bill Adams *(Sr Exec VP-Global Structured Products)*
Carl Katerndahl *(Exec VP & Head-Private Client & Retail Distr)*
John MacCarthy *(Gen Counsel, Sec & Exec VP)*

Nuveen Massachusetts Quality Municipal Income Fund (4)
333 W Wacker Dr, Chicago, IL 60606
Tel.: (312) 917-7700
Rev.: $8,106,114
Assets: $212,133,059
Liabilities: $74,851,671
Net Worth: $137,281,388
Earnings: $4,875,152
Fiscal Year-end: 05/31/2019
Investment Management Service
N.A.I.C.S.: 525990
Joanne T. Medero *(Trustee)*
Margaret L. Wolff *(Trustee)*

Nuveen Michigan Quality Municipal Income Fund (4)
333 W Wacker Dr, Chicago, IL 60606
Tel.: (312) 917-8146
Rev.: $18,577,757
Assets: $517,463,349
Liabilities: $186,459,648
Net Worth: $331,003,701
Earnings: $11,360,653
Fiscal Year-end: 02/29/2020
Investment Management Service
N.A.I.C.S.: 525990

Nuveen Minnesota Quality Municipal Income Fund (4)
333 W Wacker, Chicago, IL 60606-1286
Tel.: (312) 917-7700
Rev.: $5,880,105
Assets: $141,073,938
Liabilities: $53,262,275
Net Worth: $87,811,663
Earnings: $3,569,638
Fiscal Year-end: 05/31/2019
Investment Management Service
N.A.I.C.S.: 525990
Stephen J. Candido *(Mgr-Portfolio)*

Nuveen Missouri Quality Municipal Income Fund (4)
333 W Wacker Dr, Chicago, IL 60606
Tel.: (312) 917-7700
Rev.: $2,076,475
Assets: $52,637,819
Liabilities: $20,194,237
Net Worth: $32,443,582
Earnings: $1,223,981
Fiscal Year-end: 05/31/2019
Investment Management Service
N.A.I.C.S.: 525990
Joanne T. Medero *(Trustee)*
Margaret L. Wolff *(Trustee)*
Albin F. Moschner *(Trustee)*
Joseph A. Boateng *(Trustee)*

Nuveen Mortgage Opportunity Term Fund 2 (4)
333 W Wacker Dr, Chicago, IL 60606
Tel.: (312) 917-8146
Investment Management Service
N.A.I.C.S.: 525990
John V. Miller *(Mgr-Fund)*

Nuveen Multi-Market Income Fund (4)
Riverfront Plz 901 E Byrd St, Richmond, VA 23219
Tel.: (804) 782-3294
Rev.: $4,696,134
Assets: $108,242,333
Liabilities: $32,402,916
Net Worth: $75,839,417
Earnings: $3,057,077
Fiscal Year-end: 06/30/2019
Investment Management Service
N.A.I.C.S.: 525990
Jason O'brien *(Mgr-Fund)*

Nuveen Municipal 2021 Target Term Fund (4)
333 W Wacker Dr, Chicago, IL 60606
Tel.: (312) 917-7700
Rev.: $2,568,968
Assets: $85,435,053
Liabilities: $227,235
Net Worth: $85,207,818
Earnings: $1,973,753
Fiscal Year-end: 05/31/2019
Investment Management Service
N.A.I.C.S.: 525990
Gifford Ross Zimmerman *(Mgr-Fund)*

Nuveen Municipal Credit Income Fund (4)
333 W Wacker Dr, Chicago, IL 60606
Tel.: (312) 917-8146
Rev.: $166,159,469
Assets: $3,765,258,373
Liabilities: $1,401,236,870
Net Worth: $2,364,021,503
Earnings: $106,791,813
Fiscal Year-end: 10/31/2019
Investment Management Service
N.A.I.C.S.: 525990

Nuveen Municipal High Income Opp Fund (4)
333 W Wacker Dr, Chicago, IL 60606
Tel.: (312) 917-7700
Rev.: $69,075,321
Assets: $1,447,541,581
Liabilities: $478,473,154
Net Worth: $969,068,427
Earnings: $49,736,206
Fiscal Year-end: 10/31/2019
Investment Management Service
N.A.I.C.S.: 525990
John V. Miller *(Mgr-Fund)*

Nuveen Municipal Income Fund, Inc. (4)
333 W Wacker Dr, Chicago, IL 60606
Tel.: (312) 917-7700
Rev.: $4,508,659
Assets: $100,216,164
Liabilities: $393,829
Net Worth: $99,822,335
Earnings: $3,736,918
Fiscal Year-end: 10/31/2019
Investment Management Service
N.A.I.C.S.: 525990
Terence John Toth *(Chm)*
Mark L. Winget *(Sec & VP)*

Nuveen Municipal Value Fund, Inc. (4)
333 W Wacker Dr, Chicago, IL 60606
Tel.: (312) 917-8200
Rev.: $88,844,695
Assets: $2,236,501,253
Liabilities: $49,578,350
Net Worth: $2,186,922,903
Earnings: $77,305,974
Fiscal Year-end: 10/31/2019
Investment Management Service
N.A.I.C.S.: 525990
Daniel J. Close *(Mgr-Fund)*

Nuveen NASDAQ 100 Dynamic Overwrite Fund (4)
333 W Wacker, Chicago, IL 60606-1286
Tel.: (312) 259-6694
Rev.: $10,210,136
Assets: $962,366,470
Liabilities: $10,421,315
Net Worth: $951,945,155
Earnings: $2,189,322
Fiscal Year-end: 12/31/2019
Investment Management Service
N.A.I.C.S.: 525990
David A. Friar *(Mgr-Fund)*

Nuveen NJ Municipal Value Fund (4)
333 W Wacker Dr, Chicago, IL 60606-1286
Tel.: (312) 917-8146
Rev.: $932,804
Assets: $25,420,180
Liabilities: $1,047,862
Net Worth: $24,372,318
Earnings: $699,471
Fiscal Year-end: 02/29/2020
Investment Management Service
N.A.I.C.S.: 525990
Paul L. Brennan *(Mgr-Fund)*

Nuveen NY Municipal Value Fund 2 (4)
333 W Wacker Dr, Chicago, IL 60606
Tel.: (312) 917-7700
Rev.: $1,294,228
Assets: $38,460,837
Liabilities: $131,768
Net Worth: $38,329,069
Earnings: $1,015,341
Fiscal Year-end: 02/29/2020
Investment Management Service
N.A.I.C.S.: 525990

Nuveen New Jersey Quality Municipal Income Fund (4)
333 W Wacker Dr, Chicago, IL 60606
Tel.: (312) 917-8146
Rev.: $40,703,196
Assets: $1,063,393,630
Liabilities: $352,957,060
Net Worth: $710,436,570
Earnings: $26,706,428
Fiscal Year-end: 02/29/2020
Investment Management Service
N.A.I.C.S.: 525990
Terence John Toth *(Chm)*
Paul L. Brennan *(Mgr-Fund)*

Nuveen New York AMT-Free Quality Municipal Income Fund (4)
333 W Wacker Dr, Chicago, IL 60606
Tel.: (312) 917-7700
Rev.: $80,093,994
Assets: $2,154,674,359
Liabilities: $806,703,145
Net Worth: $1,347,971,214
Earnings: $50,069,479
Fiscal Year-end: 02/29/2020
Investment Management Service
N.A.I.C.S.: 525990
Scott R. Romans *(Mgr-Fund)*
Terence John Toth *(Chm)*

Nuveen New York Municipal Value Fund, Inc. (4)
333 W Wacker Dr, Chicago, IL 60606
Tel.: (312) 917-7700
Rev.: $6,243,010
Assets: $161,616,123
Liabilities: $2,364,151
Net Worth: $159,251,972
Earnings: $5,332,574
Fiscal Year-end: 02/29/2020
Investment Management Service
N.A.I.C.S.: 525990
Terence John Toth *(Chm)*
Mark L. Winget *(Sec & VP)*

Nuveen New York Quality Municipal Income Fund (4)
333 W Wacker Dr, Chicago, IL 60606
Tel.: (312) 917-7700
Rev.: $29,545,826
Assets: $767,376,267
Liabilities: $272,493,359
Net Worth: $494,882,908
Earnings: $18,468,038
Fiscal Year-end: 02/29/2020
Investment Management Service
N.A.I.C.S.: 525990

Nuveen New York Select Tax-Free Income Portfolio (4)
430 W 7th St Ste 219140, Kansas City, MO 64105-1407
Web Site: http://www.nuveen.com
Bond Investment Services
N.A.I.C.S.: 523999
Terence John Toth *(Chm)*
Scott R. Romans *(Portfolio Mgr)*

Nuveen Ohio Quality Municipal Income Fund (4)
333 W Wacker Dr, Chicago, IL 60606
Tel.: (312) 917-8146
Rev.: $15,727,495
Assets: $502,279,228
Liabilities: $175,993,386
Net Worth: $326,285,842
Earnings: $8,418,469
Fiscal Year-end: 02/29/2020
Investment Management Service
N.A.I.C.S.: 525990
Terence John Toth *(Chm)*

Nuveen Pennsylvania Municipal Value Fund (4)

COMPANIES TEACHERS INSURANCE ASSOCIATION - COLLEGE RETIREMENT FUND

333 W Wacker Dr, Chicago, IL 60606-1286
Tel.: (312) 917-8146
Rev.: $742,737
Assets: $19,670,285
Liabilities: $600,885
Net Worth: $19,069,400
Earnings: $551,303
Fiscal Year-end: 02/29/2020
Investment Management Service
N.A.I.C.S.: 525990
Paul L. Brennan (Mgr-Fund)

Nuveen Pennsylvania Quality Municipal Income Fund (4)
333 W Wacker Dr, Chicago, IL 60606
Tel.: (312) 917-7700
Rev.: $36,341,132
Assets: $973,370,466
Liabilities: $361,350,526
Net Worth: $612,019,940
Earnings: $23,186,876
Fiscal Year-end: 02/29/2020
Investment Management Service
N.A.I.C.S.: 525990
Terence John Toth (Chm)
Paul L. Brennan (Mgr-Portfolio)
Steven M. Hlavin (Mgr-Portfolio)

Nuveen Preferred & Income 2022 Term (4)
333 W Wacker Dr, Chicago, IL 60606
Tel.: (312) 917-8146
Rev.: $12,506,271
Assets: $209,881,799
Liabilities: $44,259,105
Net Worth: $165,622,694
Earnings: $9,307,947
Fiscal Year-end: 07/31/2019
Investment Management Service
N.A.I.C.S.: 525990
Brenda Langenfeld (Mgr-Fund)

Nuveen Preferred & Income Opportunities Fund (4)
333 W Wacker Dr, Chicago, IL 60606
Tel.: (312) 917-7700
Rev.: $103,143,001
Assets: $1,661,097,115
Liabilities: $613,171,806
Net Worth: $1,047,925,309
Earnings: $72,203,943
Fiscal Year-end: 07/31/2019
Investment Management Service
N.A.I.C.S.: 525990

Nuveen Preferred & Income Term Fund (4)
333 W Wacker Dr, Chicago, IL 60606
Sales Range: $50-74.9 Million
Closed-End Investment Fund
N.A.I.C.S.: 525990
Margaret L. Wolff (Trustee)

Nuveen Preferred Securities Income Fund (4)
333 W Wacker Dr, Chicago, IL 60606
Rev.: $225,301,753
Assets: $3,879,752,735
Liabilities: $18,952,439
Net Worth: $3,860,800,296
Earnings: $194,861,417
Fiscal Year-end: 09/30/2019
Investment Management Service
N.A.I.C.S.: 525990

Nuveen Quality Municipal Income Fund (4)
333 W Wacker Dr, Chicago, IL 60606
Tel.: (312) 917-8146
Rev.: $210,092,484
Assets: $5,097,460,375
Liabilities: $1,886,187,521
Net Worth: $3,211,272,854
Earnings: $134,446,471
Fiscal Year-end: 10/31/2019
Investment Management Service
N.A.I.C.S.: 525990
Terence John Toth (Chm)
Christopher L. Drahn (Mgr-Fund)
Terence John Toth (Chm)

Nuveen Real Asset Income and Growth Fund (4)
333 W Wacker Dr, Chicago, IL 60606
Tel.: (312) 917-7700
Rev.: $39,404,344
Assets: $845,484,348
Liabilities: $295,020,091
Net Worth: $550,464,257
Earnings: $24,980,534

Fiscal Year-end: 12/31/2019
Closed-End Investment Fund
N.A.I.C.S.: 525990
Terence John Toth (Chm)

Nuveen Real Estate Income Fund (4)
333 W Wacker, Chicago, IL 60606
Tel.: (312) 917-7700
Rev.: $15,527,473
Assets: $462,297,156
Liabilities: $134,509,370
Net Worth: $327,787,786
Earnings: $7,689,496
Fiscal Year-end: 12/31/2019
Investment Management Service
N.A.I.C.S.: 525990
Kevin Wendell Bedell (Mgr-Fund)
Terence John Toth (Chm)

Nuveen S&P 500 Buy-Write Income Fund (4)
333 W Wacker Dr, Chicago, IL 60606
Tel.: (312) 917-7700
Rev.: $28,876,573
Assets: $1,467,777,087
Liabilities: $45,105,193
Net Worth: $1,422,671,894
Earnings: $16,266,625
Fiscal Year-end: 12/31/2019
Investment Management Service
N.A.I.C.S.: 525990
Daniel Ashcraft (Mgr-Fund)

Nuveen S&P 500 Dynamic Overwrite Fund (4)
333 W Wacker, Chicago, IL 60606
Tel.: (312) 259-6694
Rev.: $5,468,944
Assets: $277,713,293
Liabilities: $2,433,321
Net Worth: $275,279,972
Earnings: $2,890,348
Fiscal Year-end: 12/31/2019
Investment Management Service
N.A.I.C.S.: 525990
David A. Friar (Mgr-Portfolio)
Jim Campagna (Head-Equity Index Strategies)
Darren Tran (Mgr-Portfolio)

Nuveen Select Maturities Municipal Fund (4)
333 W Wacker Dr, Chicago, IL 60606
Tel.: (312) 917-7200
Rev.: $4,603,122
Assets: $130,337,223
Liabilities: $458,469
Net Worth: $129,878,754
Earnings: $3,849,169
Fiscal Year-end: 03/31/2020
Investment Management Service
N.A.I.C.S.: 525990
Paul L. Brennan (Mgr-Fund)

Nuveen Select Tax Free Income Port 2 (4)
333 W Wacker Dr, Chicago, IL 60606
Tel.: (312) 917-8200
Bond Investment Services
N.A.I.C.S.: 523999
Michael S. Hamilton (Mgr-Fund)

Nuveen Select Tax-Free Income Portfolio (4)
333 W Wacker Dr, Chicago, IL 60606
Tel.: (312) 917-8200
Investment Services
N.A.I.C.S.: 523150
Michael S. Hamilton (Mgr-Fund)

Nuveen Tax-Advantaged Dividend Growth Fund (4)
333 W Wacker Dr, Chicago, IL 60606
Tel.: (312) 917-7700
Rev.: $12,635,777
Assets: $376,118,383
Liabilities: $113,987,796
Net Worth: $262,130,587
Earnings: $6,031,120
Fiscal Year-end: 12/31/2019
Investment Management Service
N.A.I.C.S.: 525990
Terence John Toth (Chm)
David A. Chalupnik (Mgr-Fund)

Subsidiary (Domestic):

Nuveen Tax-Advantaged Total Return Strategy Fund (5)

333 W Wacker Dr, Chicago, IL 60606
Tel.: (312) 917-7700
Rev.: $10,203,899
Assets: $253,818,172
Liabilities: $78,917,984
Net Worth: $174,900,188
Earnings: $5,813,730
Fiscal Year-end: 12/31/2019
Investment Management Service
N.A.I.C.S.: 525990
Terence John Toth (Chm)
Scott Caraher (Mgr-Fund)

Holding (Domestic):

Nuveen Taxable Municipal Income Fund (4)
333 W Wacker Dr, Chicago, IL 60606
Tel.: (312) 917-8146
Rev.: $41,464,929
Assets: $786,736,704
Liabilities: $242,563,283
Net Worth: $544,173,421
Earnings: $30,428,404
Fiscal Year-end: 03/31/2019
Investment Management Service
N.A.I.C.S.: 525990
John V. Miller (Mgr-Fund)
Terence John Toth (Chm)

Holding (Non-US):

Nuveen Virginia Quality Municipal Income Fund (4)
Tel.: (312) 259-6694
Rev.: $15,803,477
Assets: $417,848,480
Liabilities: $155,646,573
Net Worth: $262,201,907
Earnings: $9,564,575
Fiscal Year-end: 05/31/2019
Investment Management Service
N.A.I.C.S.: 525990
Stephen Candido (Mgr-Fund)

Subsidiary (Domestic):

Nuveen Investments, Inc. (3)
333 W Wacker Dr, Chicago, IL 60606
Tel.: (800) 257-8787
Web Site: http://www.nuveen.com
Investment Services
N.A.I.C.S.: 523999
Kathleen H. Cardoza (VP-Corp Comm)
Sherri A. Hlavacek (Controller)
Maureen Beshar (Exec VP & Head-Global Institutional Distr)
Timothy J. Stegner (Mng Dir-Sub Advisory Distr)
Carl M. Katerndahl (Sr Exec VP & Head-Global Retail Distr)
Derek Sasveld (Mng Dir & Head-Multi Asset Class Solution)
Martin Kremenstein (Mng Dir & Head-Exchange Traded Funds)
Bill Adam (Sr Exec VP-Global Structured Products)
Anthony Ciccarone (Exec VP & Head-Strategic Partner Dev & Advisory Products)
Bob Luse (Exec VP-HR)
Diane Whelan (Exec VP-Ops & Tech)
Mike Perry (Mng Dir & Head-Alternative Investments)
Bill Stout (Mng Dir & Head-Alternative Investments Bus Dev-New York)
Glenn R. Richter (COO & Chief Admin Officer)

Subsidiary (Domestic):

Gresham Investment Management LLC (4)
257 Park Ave S Ste 700, New York, NY 10010
Tel.: (212) 984-1430
Web Site: http://www.greshamllc.com
Investment Management Service
N.A.I.C.S.: 523940
Henry G. Jarecki (Founder & Chm)
Jonathan S. Spencer (Pres & CIO)
Douglas J. Hepworth (Exec VP)
Robert Reeves (CFO)

NWQ Investment Management Company, LLC (4)
2029 Century Park E Ste 1600, Los Angeles, CA 90067-3101
Tel.: (310) 712-4000
Web Site: http://www.nwq.com
Emp.: 100

Value Investment Services
N.A.I.C.S.: 523940
Jon D. Bosse (Chief Investment Officer & Co-Head)
James H. Galbreath (Mng Dir & Portfolio Mgr-Client)
Kirk Allen (Mng Dir-Trading)
Andrew C. Hwang (Mng Dir-Investment & Res & Portfolio Mgr)
Susi Budiman (Mng Dir-Investment & Res, Co-Head-Fixed Income & Portfolio Mgr)
Thomas Lavia (Co-Head, Dir-Res & Portfolio Mgr)
Cynthia Henn Olsen (Sr VP-Investment & Res)
Thomas J. Ray (Mng Dir-Investment & Res, Co-Head-Fixed Income & Portfolio Mgr)
Jujhar Sohi (Mng Dir-Investment & Res)
James T. Stephenson (Mng Dir-Investment & Res & Portfolio Mgr)
Sean M. Renkly (Mng Dir-Trading)
Gregory P. Robitshek (VP-Trading)
Avi M. Mizrachi (Mng Dir & Gen Counsel)
Mary Ann Iudice (Chief Compliance Officer)
Michael Mullane (Mng Dir & Portfolio Mgr-Client)
Peter Boardman (Mng Dir-Investment & Res & Portfolio Mgr)
Raymond O. Wicklander (Mng Dir-Investment & Res & Portfolio Mgr)
Craig O. Bailey Jr. (Exec VP & Head-Client Portfolio Mgmt & Strategic Partner Rels)

Nuveen Global Cities REIT, Inc. (4)
730 3rd Ave, New York, NY 10017
Tel.: (212) 490-9000
Web Site: https://www.nuveen.com
Rev.: $130,683,000
Assets: $2,670,861,000
Liabilities: $829,420,000
Net Worth: $1,841,441,000
Earnings: ($54,052,000)
Fiscal Year-end: 12/31/2022
Real Estate Investment Services
N.A.I.C.S.: 531210
Michael J. L. Sales (Chm & CEO)
Bill Huffman (CEO-Nuveen)
Tara Giuliano (CMO)
Vijay Kasarabada (CIO)
Amy O'Brien (Head-Responsible Investing)
Seun Salami (CFO)
Josh Shamansky (Chief HR Officer)
Kevin Mccarthy (Chief Legal Officer)

Nuveen Securities, LLC (4)
333 W Wacker Dr, Chicago, IL 60606
Tel.: (800) 257-8787
Investment Management Service
N.A.I.C.S.: 523940
Jose M. Minaya (CEO)

Santa Barbara Asset Management, LLC (4)
2049 Century Pk E 17th Fl, Los Angeles, CA 90067
Tel.: (310) 552-5100
Web Site: http://www.sbasset.com
Investment Management Service
N.A.I.C.S.: 523999
James R. Boothe (Chief Investment Officer & Portfolio Mgr)
Hai H. Vu (Sr VP & Dir-Res)
David S. Park (Sr VP)
Aaron J. Brunette (VP)
Predrag S. Jovanovic (VP)
John A. Gomez (Pres)
Avi M. Mizrachi (Chief Compliance Officer, Mng Dir & Head-Nuveen L.A. Legal)
Emily M. Fox (VP)
Chris L. Perry (VP)
Raymond E. Camacho (Sr VP & Head-Trading)
Matthew W. Amundson (VP-Trading)

Symphony Asset Management, LLC (4)
555 California St Ste 3100, San Francisco, CA 94104-1503
Tel.: (415) 676-4000
Web Site: http://www.symphonyasset.com
Emp.: 75
Investment Management Service
N.A.I.C.S.: 523940
Gunther M. Stein (Chm)
Anne B. Popkin (Pres)

TEACHERS INSURANCE ASSOCIATION - COLLEGE RETIREMENT FUND

U.S. PRIVATE

Teachers Insurance Association.- College Retirement Fund—(Continued)

Tradewinds Global Investors, LLC (4)
2049 Century Park E 20th Fl, Los Angeles, CA 90067
Tel.: (310) 552-8900
Web Site: http://www.nuveen.com
Emp.: 70
Investment Management Service
N.A.I.C.S.: 523999
Peter Boardman (Mng Dir & Portfolio Mgr)
Jeff Cusack (Pres & Exec Mng Dir)
Emily Alejos (Exec Mng Dir, Chief Investment Officer & Portfolio Mgr)
Andrew Thelen (Exec Mng Dir, Chief Investment Officer & Portfolio Mgr)
F. Rowe Michels (Mng Dir, Portfolio Mgr & Dir-Res)
Joann M. Barry (Mng Dir & Portfolio Mgr)
Ben Brodkowitz (Mng Dir)
Jae H. Chung (Mng Dir)
Michael A. Mullane (Mng Dir & Portfolio Mgr-Client)
Rod Parsley (Mng Dir & Portfolio Mgr)
Prasant Sahoo (Mng Dir)
Harisch K. Sood (Mng Dir)
Raymond O. Wicklander (Mng Dir & Deputy Dir-Res)
Sally A. Yanchus (Mng Dir)
Reed D. Walters (Mng Dir & Portfolio Mgr)
William L. Gurner (Sr VP & Portfolio Mgr)
Kenneth L. Riffle (VP & Portfolio Mgr-Client)
Stephen A. Smith (Mng Dir & Head-Trading)
Sandra E. Alvarenga (Sr VP)
Olivia Song (Sr VP)
Lafayette A. George (Mng Dir & Head-Ops)
Nga L. Nguyen (Sr VP)
Patrick Lam (VP)
Nancy Wamai (VP)
Mary Ann Iudice (Chief Compliance Officer)
Daniel Carey (Gen Counsel)
Mary Catherine Mortell (VP-Private Client Investor Rels)
Dan Driscoll (VP-Distr)

Winslow Capital Management, LLC (4)
4720 IDS Twr 80 S 8th St, Minneapolis, MN 55402
Tel.: (612) 376-9100
Web Site: http://www.nuveen.com
Investment Management Service
N.A.I.C.S.: 523940
Clark J. Winslow (CEO)
Roger Mendel (Mng Dir)
Mitchell A. Kaiser (Mng Dir)
Michael S. Palmer (Pres)
Laura J. Hawkins (Chief Compliance Officer, Chief Risk Officer & Mng Dir)
Patrick M. Burton (Mng Dir & Portfolio Mgr)
Kelly A. Flynn (Mng Dir & Portfolio Mgr)
Stephan C. Petersen (Mng Dir & Portfolio Mgr)
Stephen E. Clear (Mng Dir-Mktg & Client Svcs)
John A. Maschoff (Mng Dir-Mktg & Client Svcs)
Barry F. Peters (Mng Dir-Mktg & Client Svcs)
Jeff D. Wieneke (Mng Dir-Mktg & Client Svcs)
Christine M. Tomlinson (Dir-Mktg & Client Svcs)
Joshua J. Fuller (Dir-IT)

Subsidiary (Domestic):

TIAA FSB Holdings, Inc. (2)
501 Riverside Ave, Jacksonville, FL 32202
Tel.: (904) 281-6000
Web Site: http://www.tiaabank.com
Sales Range: $1-4.9 Billion
Bank Holding Company
N.A.I.C.S.: 551111
Robert M. Clements (Chm & CEO)
Seth Waller (Exec VP & Chief Credit Officer)
Lisa S. Johnston (CMO & Exec VP)
Joseph B. Long (Exec VP & Head-Strategic Bus Dev & Investments)
Karen Perkner (Exec VP & Chief Admin Officer)
Michael C. Koster (Exec VP-Mortgage Ops)
Blake Wilson (Pres & CEO)
Steven J. Fischer (CFO & Sr VP)
James R. Hubbard (Exec VP, Gen Counsel & Corp Sec)
Stephanie Adams (Exec VP & Head-Trust Svcs)
Rick Blasi (Exec VP & Head-Banking & Comml Ops)
Frank Ervin (Exec VP & Chief Risk Officer)
Janine Pappas (Exec VP & Chief Auditor)
John Pataky (Exec VP)

Subsidiary (Domestic):

TIAA, FSB (3)
501 Riverside Ave, Jacksonville, FL 32202
Tel.: (888) 882-3837
Web Site: http://www.everbank.com
Federal Savings Bank
N.A.I.C.S.: 522180
Seth Waller (Chief Credit Officer & Exec VP)
William Blake Wilson (CEO-Retail Financial Svcs)
Lisa S. Johnston (CMO & Exec VP)
Joseph B. Long (Exec VP & Head-Strategic Bus Dev & Investments)
Karen Perkner (Chief Admin Officer & Exec VP)
Michael C. Koster (Exec VP-Mortgage Ops)
Steve Fisher (Pres & COO)
Rick Blasi (Exec VP & Head-Banking & Comml Ops)
Frank Ervin (Chief Risk Officer & Exec VP)
Jim Hubbard (Gen Counsel, Sec & Exec VP)
Janine Pappas (Chief Auditor & Exec VP)
John Pataky (Exec VP)
Jill Streit (CFO, Treas & Exec VP)

Subsidiary (Domestic):

EverBank Wealth Management, Inc. (4)
501 Riverside Ave, Jacksonville, FL 32202
Tel.: (904) 281-6000
Wealth Management Services
N.A.I.C.S.: 523940

EverInsurance, Inc. (4)
8100 Nations Way, Jacksonville, FL 32256
Tel.: (904) 281-6393
Insurance Brokerage Services
N.A.I.C.S.: 524210

Tygris Asset Finance, Inc (4)
500 W Monroe St 28th Fl, Chicago, IL 60661-3773
Tel.: (312) 880-4147
Financial Management Services
N.A.I.C.S.: 523999

Affiliate (Domestic):

TIAA Real Estate Account (2)
730 3rd Ave, New York, NY 10017-3206
Tel.: (212) 490-9000
Web Site: http://www.tiaa.org
Rev.: $1,194,800,000
Assets: $31,276,400,000
Liabilities: $3,204,400,000
Net Worth: $28,072,000,000
Earnings: $707,700,000
Fiscal Year-end: 12/31/2021
Real Estate Investment Trust
N.A.I.C.S.: 525990
Ronald L. Thompson (Chm)

Subsidiary (Domestic):

TIAA-CREF Life Insurance Company (2)
730 3rd Ave, New York, NY 10017-3206
Tel.: (212) 490-9000
Web Site: http://www.tiaa.org
Sales Range: $350-399.9 Million
Fire Insurance Services
N.A.I.C.S.: 524113
Ronald R. Pressman (COO & Exec VP)

TEACHFORALL, INC.
315 W 36th St 8th Fl, New York, NY 10018
Tel.: (646) 898-4900 NY
Web Site: http://www.teachforall.org
Year Founded: 2007
Sales Range: $25-49.9 Million
Emp.: 101
Educational Support Services
N.A.I.C.S.: 611710
Brett Wigdortz (Co-Founder)
Wendy Kopp (Co-Founder & CEO)
Paul Fletcher (Chm)

TEACHING RESOURCE CENTER AB
2566 Cypress Ave, Lemon Grove, CA 91945-2908
Tel.: (619) 482-2298
Web Site: http://www.trcabc.com
Year Founded: 1983
Sales Range: $10-24.9 Million
Emp.: 31
Education Aids, Devices & Supplies
N.A.I.C.S.: 459999

TEAGUE ELECTRIC CONSTRUCTION
12425 W 92nd St, Lenexa, KS 66215
Tel.: (913) 529-4600
Web Site: http://www.teagueelectric.com
Rev.: $14,000,000
Emp.: 150
General Electrical Contractor
N.A.I.C.S.: 238210
David Saunder (Pres)
Arlin Saville (VP)
Brian Graves (Project Mgr)
Israel Abundis (Controller & Mgr-Benefits)
Ray Russell (Mgr-Comml Svcs)

TEAGUE LUMBER COMPANY INC.
300 Duck Rd, Grandview, MO 64030
Tel.: (816) 767-1500
Rev.: $25,000,000
Emp.: 100
Lumber, Plywood & Millwork
N.A.I.C.S.: 423310
Don Margritier (Pres)
Bill Wilson (Owner)

TEAKWOOD CAPITAL, L.P.
8226 Douglas Ave Douglas Plz Ste 355, Dallas, TX 75225
Tel.: (214) 750-1590
Web Site: http://www.teakwoodcapital.com
Financial Investment Activities
N.A.I.C.S.: 523999
Laura Kusching (Mgr-Ops)
Stu Bell (Mng Dir-Bus Dev)
David Sikora (Exec Partner)
Dave Ellett (Exec Partner)
Edward E. Olkkola (Executives)
Ed H. Bowman Jr. (Exec Partner)

TEAL
1520 Belle View Blvd Ste 250, Alexandria, VA 22307
Tel.: (833) 367-8325
Web Site: https://tealtech.com
Year Founded: 2023
IT Consulting & Services
N.A.I.C.S.: 541512
Don Sauer (Co-Founder & CEO)
Gar Whaley (Co-Founder & Chief Revenue Officer)
Reid Johnston (Co-Founder & CIO)

Subsidiaries:

Aligned Technology Solutions, LLC (1)
1602 Belle View Blvd Ste 250, Alexandria, VA 22307
Tel.: (703) 740-8797
Web Site: http://www.myalignedit.com
Sales Range: $1-9.9 Million
Emp.: 18
Information Technology Management Services
N.A.I.C.S.: 541513
Don Sauer (Co-Founder & Partner)
Gar Whaley (Co-Founder)
Jeremiah Best (VP-Svc Delivery)

Justin Weeks (VP-Cybersecurity & Compliance)
Stephen Polidore (Dir-Helpdesk Ops)

TechGen Consulting, Inc. (1)
2300 Kennedy St NE#195, Minneapolis, MN 55413
Tel.: (612) 279-2400
Web Site: https://techgen.com
IT Services
N.A.I.C.S.: 541519

TEAL CONSTRUCTION COMPANY
1335 Brittmoore Rd, Houston, TX 77043
Tel.: (713) 465-8306
Web Site: http://www.tealcon.com
Sales Range: $50-74.9 Million
Emp.: 40
Commercial & Office Building, New Construction
N.A.I.C.S.: 236220
Mike McGlynn (Superintendent)
Robert Fram (Superintendent)
Michael Losoya (Project Mgr)
John A. Murray Jr. (Chm & Pres)

TEALIUM INC.
445 Marine View Ave Ste 320, Del Mar, CA 92014
Tel.: (858) 779-1344
Web Site: http://www.tealium.com
Year Founded: 2008
Sales Range: $1-9.9 Million
Computer Related Services; Software Publisher
N.A.I.C.S.: 541519
Mike Anderson (Co-Founder)
Ali Behnam (Co-Founder)
Charles Glommen (VP-Engrg)
Doug Lindroth (CFO)
Jeff Lunsford (CEO)
Javier Lopez (Mgr-Bus Dev-Spain, Portugal & Italy)
Andy Clark (Gen Mgr-Asia Pacific)
Phil Maynard (Chief Legal Officer)
Lindsay McEwan (Mng Dir-EMEA & VP)
Ray Rauch (VP-Client Success)
Adam Corey (VP-Mktg & Bus Dev)
Oliver Silvestre (Co-Founder)
Ted Purcell (Chief Revenue Officer)
Heidi Bullock (CMO)
Brent Reed (Sr VP-Enterprise-Americas)
Adrianne Court (Chief HR Officer)
Tony Nadalin (Chief Customer Officer)
Rob Coyne (Sr VP-Europe, Middle East & Africa & Mng Dir-Europe, Middle East & Africa)

TEALL CAPITAL PARTNERS, LLC
1001 W 4th St, Winston Salem, NC 27101 NC
Web Site: http://www.teallcapital.com
Year Founded: 2016
Privater Equity Firm
N.A.I.C.S.: 523999
Kelli Hilliard (Partner & Chief People Officer)
Lou Doherty (Partner & COO)
Wes Day (Partner-Deal Mgmt & Chief Strategy Officer)
Mark McKeen (CTO)
Rex Hough (Partner & Exec VP-Bus Dev)
Amanda Elder (Dir-Fin)
Kristine Horne (Mgr-Office)
Mary McElwee (Dir-Employee Relations)
Benjamin C. Sutton Jr. (Founder & Mng Partner)

Subsidiaries:

Dyehard Fan Supply, LLC (1)

500 W 5th St Ste 1200, Winston Salem, NC 27101
Tel.: (336) 283-3867
Web Site: http://www.dyehardfansupply.com
Holding Company; Event Commemorative Merchandise Concession Services
N.A.I.C.S.: 551112
Scott Killian *(CEO)*
Ryan OCallaghan *(COO)*
Shannon Dennison *(Dir-Fin)*

Subsidiary (Domestic):

Team Retail Solutions LLC (2)
533 Summit St, Winston Salem, NC 27101
Tel.: (917) 770-7122
Web Site: http://www.teamretailsolutions.com
Sales Range: $1-9.9 Million
Event Commemorative Merchandise Concession Services
N.A.I.C.S.: 459999
Rex Hough *(CEO)*

TEALS EXPRESS INC.
22411 Teal Dr, Watertown, NY 13601
Tel.: (315) 788-6437 NY
Web Site: http://www.teals.com
Year Founded: 1926
Sales Range: $10-24.9 Million
Emp.: 100
Provider of Transportation Services
N.A.I.C.S.: 531120
Michael Teal *(Pres)*
Joseph Teal *(CEO)*
John Teal Jr. *(Chm)*

TEAM ACQUISITION CORPORATION
901 W Alameda Ave Ste 100, Burbank, CA 91506-2801
Tel.: (818) 558-3261
Web Site: http://www.teamservices.net
Rev.: $349,165,721
Emp.: 60
Accounting, Auditing & Bookkeeping
N.A.I.C.S.: 541219
Gerald K. Schwartz *(Pres)*

TEAM BUILDERS PLUS
112 Centre Blvd Ste A, Marlton, NJ 08053-4134
Tel.: (856) 596-4196
Web Site: http://www.teambuildersplus.com
Year Founded: 1991
Rev.: $2,100,000
Emp.: 15
Human Resource Consulting Services
N.A.I.C.S.: 541612
Stew Bolno *(Mgr)*
Jeff Backal *(Pres)*
Dolores Woodington *(Controller)*
Lesley Cruz *(Dir-Admin)*

TEAM CHEVROLET BUICK GMC CADILLAC
404 Jake Alexander Blvd S, Salisbury, NC 28144
Tel.: (704) 754-8360
Web Site: http://www.teamchevync.com
Sales Range: $50-74.9 Million
Emp.: 50
Automobiles, New & Used
N.A.I.C.S.: 441110
Thom Dillard *(Pres)*
Jamie Fritt *(Sls Mgr)*
Cindy Landry *(Dir-Bus Dev)*
David Coltrane *(Gen Mgr)*

TEAM COMPANIES
4250 Glass Rd NE, Cedar Rapids, IA 52402
Tel.: (319) 294-8300 DE
Web Site: http://www.oneneck.com
Year Founded: 2003
Sales Range: $1-9.9 Million
Emp.: 550
Data Storage & Security Services
N.A.I.C.S.: 518210
Karla Myers *(Dir-Bus Dev)*

TEAM EXPRESS DISTRIBUTING, LLC
1003 E Nakoma St Ste 104, San Antonio, TX 78216
Tel.: (210) 525-9161
Web Site: http://www.baseballexpress.com
Sales Range: $25-49.9 Million
Emp.: 80
Distr of Baseball Equipment & Accessories
N.A.I.C.S.: 459110
Howard Duckworth *(Founder)*

TEAM FITZ GRAPHICS, LLC
11320 Mosteller Rd, Cincinnati, OH 45241
Web Site: http://www.teamfitzgraphics.com
Year Founded: 2008
Sales Range: $1-9.9 Million
Emp.: 22
Graphic Design Services
N.A.I.C.S.: 541430
Shaun Fitzgibbons *(Owner & Dir-Ops)*
Seth Thitoff *(Sls Dir)*
Ryan Willi *(Dir-Air)*
Jon Hoelle *(Project Mgr)*
Adam Wood *(Project Mgr)*

TEAM FORD LINCOLN
5445 Drexel Rd, Las Vegas, NV 89130-1605
Tel.: (702) 395-5100
Web Site: http://www.teamfordlasvegas.com
Sales Range: $75-99.9 Million
Emp.: 150
Car Whslr
N.A.I.C.S.: 441110
Steven Olliges *(Principal)*
Russ Barrie *(Asst Mgr-Parts)*
Leanna Cowan *(Dir-Fin)*
Neal Westfall *(Mgr-Svc)*

TEAM INDUSTRIES, INC.
105 Park Ave NW, Bagley, MN 56621-0639
Tel.: (218) 694-3550 MN
Web Site: http://www.team-ind.com
Year Founded: 1967
Sales Range: $75-99.9 Million
Emp.: 1,300
Holding Company; Motor Vehicle Drive Train Technologies & Components Engineering & Manufacturing Services
N.A.I.C.S.: 551112
David Ricke *(Pres & CEO)*
Krysten Westrum *(Mgr-IT)*
Robert Nordstrom *(Coord-Safety)*
Tricia Young *(Mgr-Sls)*
Brandon Bonham *(Engr-Design)*
Susan Pederson *(Mgr-HR)*
Tom Riewer *(Controller & Mgr-Fin)*
Ron Wendt *(Engr-Design)*
Carri Pickett *(Mgr-HR)*
Pam Brouwer *(Coord-Safety)*
Joshua Vorderbruggen *(Engr-Design)*
Dave McBride *(Supvr-Production)*

Subsidiaries:

Motek-TEAM Industries, Inc. (1)
625 Second Ave SE, Cambridge, MN 55008-0273
Tel.: (763) 689-1333
Web Site: http://www.motekeng.com
Sales Range: $25-49.9 Million
Emp.: 186
Provider of Industrial Machinery Services
N.A.I.C.S.: 332322
Steve Kast *(Controller)*

TEAM Industries - Detroit Lakes (1)
1551 Ridgwood Rd, Detroit Lakes, MN 56501
Tel.: (218) 846-9111
Web Site: http://www.team-ind.com
Sales Range: $10-24.9 Million
Emp.: 75
Aluminum Die-Castings Mfr
N.A.I.C.S.: 331523
David Ricke *(Gen Mgr)*

TEAM Industries - Park Rapids (1)
501 Industrial Park Rd, Park Rapids, MN 56470
Tel.: (218) 732-4666
Web Site: http://www.team-ind.com
Sales Range: $10-24.9 Million
Emp.: 54
Provider of Industrial Machinery Services
N.A.I.C.S.: 332710

TEAM Industries Andrews, Inc. (1)
3750 Airport Rd, Andrews, NC 28901
Tel.: (828) 837-5311
Web Site: http://www.team-ind.com
Emp.: 90
Precision Machining Services
N.A.I.C.S.: 332710
Greg Boehm *(Plant Mgr)*

TEAM Industries Bagley-Audubon, Inc. (1)
105 Park Ave, Bagley, MN 56621
Tel.: (218) 694-3550
Web Site: http://www.team-ind.com
Sales Range: $25-49.9 Million
Emp.: 278
Motor Vehicle Drive Train Technologies & Components Engineering & Manufacturing Services
N.A.I.C.S.: 336350

Plant (Domestic):

TEAM Industries - Audubon (2)
4th & Robin, Audubon, MN 56511
Tel.: (218) 439-6186
Web Site: http://www.team-ind.com
Sales Range: $10-24.9 Million
Emp.: 230
Gear Mfr
N.A.I.C.S.: 333612

TEAM INDUSTRIES, INC.
1200 Maloney Rd, Kaukauna, WI 54130
Tel.: (920) 766-7977 WI
Web Site: http://www.teamind.com
Year Founded: 1987
Sales Range: $25-49.9 Million
Emp.: 150
Fabricated Pipe, Pipe Fitting & Vessel Mfr
N.A.I.C.S.: 332996
Michael Mincks *(VP-Sls, Proposals & Supply Chain)*

TEAM INFORMATION SERVICES
1485 International Pkwy Ste 1071, Lake Mary, FL 32746
Tel.: (407) 548-6300
Web Site: http://www.truefitnow.com
Sales Range: $10-24.9 Million
Emp.: 25
Custom Computer Programming Services
N.A.I.C.S.: 541511
Teresa Veltri *(CEO)*
Rakesh Bhandari *(Sr Mgr-Recruiting)*

TEAM INTEGRATED ENGINEERING, INC.
8918 Tesoro Dr Ste 401, San Antonio, TX 78217
Tel.: (210) 341-4316
Web Site: http://www.team-ie.com
Year Founded: 2001
Sales Range: $25-49.9 Million
Emp.: 80
Advises & Assists Government Agencies Worldwide in Environmental, Engineering, Architectural & Logistics Projects
N.A.I.C.S.: 541620
Lisa Morgan *(CEO)*
James Morgan *(Pres)*
Maria Jaramillo *(Dir-Support Svcs)*
Charles Attebery *(Exec VP)*
Heather Lisenbee *(Dir-Medical Logistics)*
Nancy Miller *(VP)*
Greg Klemm *(VP)*
Brett Matlick *(CFO)*
Beth Gentry *(Dir-Bus Dev)*
Rick Mays *(Dir-IT)*

TEAM IP.COM
850 NW Federal Hwy Ste 229, Stuart, FL 34994
Tel.: (772) 398-4664
Web Site: http://www.teamip.com
Year Founded: 1992
Sales Range: $1-9.9 Million
Emp.: 30
Screen Printed Apparel & Customized Promotional Merchandise
N.A.I.C.S.: 323113
Randy Sparks *(Pres & CEO)*
Krystin Nobles *(Dir-Event Mktg)*
Andy Sparks *(VP)*

TEAM LENDING CONCEPTS LLC
4590 S Yosemite St Ste F2-335, Greenwood Village, CO 80111
Tel.: (720) 489-5871
Web Site: http://www.teamlending.com
Sales Range: $10-24.9 Million
Emp.: 5
Mortgage Lending Services
N.A.I.C.S.: 522310
Jeff Lowrey *(Owner)*

TEAM MOTOR SPORTS INC.
6520 Peters Creek Rd, Roanoke, VA 24019
Tel.: (540) 366-4830
Web Site: http://www.firstteamautomall.com
Sales Range: $25-49.9 Million
Emp.: 54
Automobiles, New & Used
N.A.I.C.S.: 441110
David Dillon *(Pres)*
Marsha Wirt *(Controller)*
Gary Baber *(VP-Ops)*

TEAM NATIONAL
8210 W State Rd 84, Davie, FL 33324
Tel.: (954) 584-2151
Web Site: http://www.bign.com
Sales Range: $25-49.9 Million
Emp.: 30
Membership Savings Program for Various Products & Services
N.A.I.C.S.: 541990
Andres Forero *(VP-IT)*
Angela Loehr Chrysler *(Pres & CEO)*

TEAM NISSAN INC.
70 Keller St, Manchester, NH 03103
Tel.: (603) 644-8326
Web Site: http://www.teamnissannh.com
Rev.: $30,000,000
Emp.: 38
Automobiles, New & Used
N.A.I.C.S.: 441110
Jacob Clark *(Mgr-Fin)*
Vicki Marcinkevich *(Pres)*
Frank Leone *(Controller)*

TEAM OIL TOOLS, LLC

U.S. PRIVATE

Team Oil Tools, LLC—(Continued)

TEAM OIL TOOLS, LLC
1400 Woodloch Forest Dr Ste 400, The Woodlands, TX 77380
Tel.: (281) 602-7815
Web Site: http://www.teamoiltools.com
Year Founded: 1997
Sales Range: $1-9.9 Million
Emp.: 20
Oil & Gas Field Machinery & Equipment Mfr
N.A.I.C.S.: 333132
Byron Cowart *(Chm)*
David Fleming *(Co-CFO)*
Stev Chauffe *(VP-Tech & Bus Dev)*
Wes Pixley *(Mgr-Eastern Div)*
Adam Anderson *(CEO)*
Justin Kellner *(VP-Engrg)*
Mark Reddout *(VP-Ops-Western US)*
Chris Ruffner *(Co-CFO)*

Subsidiaries:

Chancellor Oil Tools, Inc. (1)
3521 Gulf St, Bakersfield, CA 93308
Tel.: (661) 324-2213
Web Site: http://www.chancelloroiltool.com
Liner Hangers, Packers, Adapters & Circulating Equipment Mfr
N.A.I.C.S.: 333132
Tom Townsend *(Pres & Gen Mgr)*
Billy McIntosh *(Supvr-Svc)*

TEAM ONE GM AUTO MALL
12899 Garrett Hwy, Oakland, MD 21550-1162
Tel.: (301) 334-9494
Web Site: http://www.team1auto.com
Year Founded: 1980
Sales Range: $10-24.9 Million
Emp.: 35
New Car Whslr
N.A.I.C.S.: 441110
Greg Shockey *(Owner)*

TEAM ONE PLASTICS INC.
927 Elliott St, Albion, MI 49224
Tel.: (517) 629-2178
Web Site: http://www.team1michigan.com
Year Founded: 1987
Sales Range: $10-24.9 Million
Emp.: 20
Injection Molding of Plastics
N.A.I.C.S.: 326199
Craig Carrel *(Pres & Dir-Sls & Mktg)*
Gary Grigowski *(VP)*
Susie Muma *(Controller)*

TEAM RAHAL OF MECHANICSBURG, INC.
6715 Carlisle Pike, Mechanicsburg, PA 17050
Tel.: (717) 691-0500
Year Founded: 1991
Sales Range: $10-24.9 Million
Emp.: 75
Car Whslr
N.A.I.C.S.: 441110
Rolen E. Ferris *(VP)*

TEAM SCHIERL COMPANIES
2201 Madison St, Stevens Point, WI 54481-0308
Tel.: (715) 345-5060
Web Site: http://www.tsctoday.com
Year Founded: 1936
Sales Range: $50-74.9 Million
Emp.: 350
Provider of Petroleum & Automotive Services
N.A.I.C.S.: 424710
Timothy Schierl *(Co-CEO)*
Fritz Schierl *(Co-CEO)*
Bill Fritz *(Co-CEO)*

Subsidiaries:

Schierl Sales Corp. (1)
2201 Madison St, Stevens Point, WI 54481
Tel.: (715) 345-5060
Web Site: http://www.tsctoday.com
Rev.: $26,900,000
Emp.: 52
Convenience Stores, Independent
N.A.I.C.S.: 445131
Tim Schierl *(Pres)*

TEAM SERVICES, INC.
45 Sammis Rd, Sussex, NJ 07461
Tel.: (973) 764-6240 NJ
Web Site: http://www.teamservicesinc.com
Year Founded: 1996
Sales Range: $1-9.9 Million
Emp.: 63
Maintenance of Bank Vaults & Security Alarms
N.A.I.C.S.: 561621
Dena Mastrogiovanni *(Owner & Pres)*

TEAM SOLUTIONS GROUP, INC.
16525 Sherman Way, Suite C-3, Van Nuys, CA 91406
Tel.: (818) 728-1444
Web Site: https://www.tsg-la.com
Year Founded: 2006
It Consulting
N.A.I.C.S.: 513210
Gregory Chun *(CEO)*

Subsidiaries:

Latitude 34 Technologies, LLC (1)
5880 Hollister Ave, Goleta, CA 93117-3612
Tel.: (805) 275-2386
Web Site: http://www.l34tech.com
Computer System Design Services
N.A.I.C.S.: 541512
Paul Avolio *(Owner & Pres)*

TEAM SOLUTIONS PROJECT GROUP, INC.
12640 Delta St, Taylor, MI 48180-6833
Tel.: (734) 946-5900
Web Site: https://www.team-group.com
Facilities Management Services
N.A.I.C.S.: 561210

Subsidiaries:

Tri-Dim Filter Corporation (1)
93 Indus Dr, Louisa, VA 23093-4126
Tel.: (540) 967-2600
Web Site: http://www.tridim.com
Sales Range: $25-49.9 Million
Emp.: 325
Mfr of Blowers & Fans
N.A.I.C.S.: 333413
Mark King *(COO & Exec VP)*
Aleks Kupcis *(VP-Fin)*
Erik Savalox *(VP)*
Ron Moyer *(Mng Dir)*

Subsidiary (Domestic):

Indoor Environmental Technology Inc. (2)
600 Ryerson Rd, Lincoln Park, NJ 07035
Tel.: (973) 709-1122
Web Site: http://www.tridim.com
Sales Range: $25-49.9 Million
Emp.: 150
Provider of Research Services
N.A.I.C.S.: 561720

TEAM SUPERSTORES OF VALLEJO
301 Auto Mall Pkwy, Vallejo, CA 94591-3870
Tel.: (707) 643-9000
Web Site: http://www.teamsuperstores.com
Year Founded: 1994
Sales Range: $10-24.9 Million
Emp.: 60

New Car Whslr
N.A.I.C.S.: 441110
Trish Gress *(Controller)*

TEAM TANKERS INTERNATIONAL LTD.
1 Gorham Island, Westport, CT 06880
Tel.: (203) 341-3600 BM
Web Site: http://www.teamtankers.com
Year Founded: 2014
Rev.: $312,738,000
Assets: $634,037,000
Liabilities: $248,949,000
Net Worth: $385,088,000
Earnings: ($53,839,000)
Emp.: 89
Fiscal Year-end: 12/31/18
Holding Company; Chemical Shipping Services
N.A.I.C.S.: 551112
Morten Arntzen *(Chm)*
Hans Feringa *(Pres & CEO)*
Jens Gisle Schnelle *(CFO)*
Michael Vilson *(COO)*

Subsidiaries:

Team Tankers Management AS (1)
Ruselokkveien 6, 0251, Oslo, Norway
Tel.: (47) 2311 4320
Web Site: http://www.teamtankers.com
Sales Range: $350-399.9 Million
Emp.: 1,378
Chemical Shipping Services
N.A.I.C.S.: 483111

Subsidiary (US):

Team Tankers (USA) LLC (2)
One Gorham Island, Westport, CT 06880
Tel.: (203) 341-3620
Sales Range: $25-49.9 Million
Emp.: 13
Marine Chemical Transportation Services
N.A.I.C.S.: 483111

Subsidiary (Non-US):

Team Tankers Management A/S (2)
Camillo Eitzen House Amerika Plads 38, 2100, Copenhagen, Denmark
Tel.: (45) 39970300
Sales Range: $25-49.9 Million
Chemical Shipping Services
N.A.I.C.S.: 483111

Subsidiary (US):

Team Tankers Management LLC (2)
1 Gorham Is, Westport, CT 06880
Tel.: (203) 341-3600
Sales Range: $25-49.9 Million
Emp.: 19
Marine Chemical Transportation Services
N.A.I.C.S.: 483111
Jan Hansen *(Gen Mgr)*

Subsidiary (Non-US):

Team Tankers Management Pte. Ltd. (2)
One Temasek Avenue 35-05 Millenia Tower, Singapore, 039192, Singapore
Tel.: (65) 6557 7600
Sales Range: $25-49.9 Million
Emp.: 15
Chemical Shipping Services
N.A.I.C.S.: 483111
Michael Olbing *(Pres)*

Team Tankers Management S.A. (2)
Avda Severo Ochoa 28-5D, 29603, Marbella, Spain
Tel.: (34) 95 276 5177
Sales Range: $25-49.9 Million
Emp.: 8
Chemical Shipping Services
N.A.I.C.S.: 483111

TEAM TRIDENT LLC
16300 Katy Fwy Ste 180, Houston, TX 77094
Tel.: (281) 600-1412
Web Site: http://www.teamtrident.com

Year Founded: 2006
Sales Range: $1-9.9 Million
Emp.: 8
Technicians for the Oil & Gas Industry
N.A.I.C.S.: 213112
Rod Long *(Pres)*

TEAM VELOCITY MARKETING LLC
13825 Sunrise Vly Dr Ste 150, Herndon, VA 20171
Tel.: (703) 661-3350
Web Site: http://www.teamvelocitymarketing.com
Year Founded: 2005
Sales Range: $25-49.9 Million
Emp.: 200
Advetising Agency
N.A.I.C.S.: 541810
David Boice *(Co-Founder)*
Budd Blackburn *(Co-Founder)*
Sean Wolfington *(Co-Founder)*

TEAM VOLKSWAGEN OF HAYWARD
25115 Mission Blvd, Hayward, CA 94544-2516
Tel.: (510) 885-1000
Web Site: http://www.vwhayward.com
Year Founded: 1982
Sales Range: $10-24.9 Million
Emp.: 28
New Car Whslr
N.A.I.C.S.: 441110
Sami Mujadadi *(Gen Mgr)*
Abby Mujadadi *(Mgr-Sls)*

TEAM WASHINGTON, INC.
8381 Old Courthouse Rd Ste 100, Vienna, VA 22182
Tel.: (703) 734-7080 DE
Web Site: http://www.dominos.com
Year Founded: 1983
Sales Range: $25-49.9 Million
Emp.: 2,000
Take-out Pizzeria Franchise Restaurant Owner & Operator
N.A.I.C.S.: 722513
Mary Lynne Carraway *(Owner & Pres)*

TEAM WORLDWIDE
639 West Broadway St, Winnsboro, TX 75494
Tel.: (903) 342-3516
Web Site: http://www.teamair.com
Sales Range: $10-24.9 Million
Emp.: 88
Freight Forwarding
N.A.I.C.S.: 488510
LaWanda Ray Smelley *(VP)*

TEAM-CRUCIBLE, LLC
60 Jack Ellington Rd, Fredericksburg, VA 22406
Tel.: (540) 752-2800
Web Site: http://www.team-crucible.com
Year Founded: 1993
Security Management & Training Services
N.A.I.C.S.: 611430

TEAM-ONE STAFFING SERVICES
Ste 116 2999 Overland Ave, Los Angeles, CA 90064-4256
Tel.: (310) 815-3530
Web Site: http://www.teamone.la
Sales Range: $10-24.9 Million
Emp.: 25
Placement Agencies
N.A.I.C.S.: 561311
Frank Moran *(Founder, Pres & CEO)*

COMPANIES

TEAMBONDING
298 Tosca Dr, Stoughton, MA 02072
Tel.: (781) 793-9700
Web Site:
http://www.teambonding.com
Year Founded: 1998
Sales Range: $1-9.9 Million
Emp.: 15
Team Building Activities & Events
N.A.I.C.S.: 561499
David Goldstein *(COO)*

TEAMMATES COMMERCIAL INTERIORS
320 S Teller St Ste 250, Lakewood, CO 80226
Tel.: (303) 639-5885
Web Site: http://www.team-mates.com
Year Founded: 1995
Sales Range: $10-24.9 Million
Emp.: 12
Full Service Office Furniture Dealership
N.A.I.C.S.: 423210
Michael Berkery *(Co-Founder & Pres)*
Dawnyele Horton *(Project Mgr)*
Debbie Diver *(Project Mgr)*
Jeff Singer *(Sr Acct Mgr)*
Kimberly Dawes *(Dir-Design)*
Kristen Smith *(Dir-Sls)*
Lauren Montealegre *(Mgr-Acct)*
Whitney Chomko *(Mgr-Acct)*

TEAMSHARES INC.
214 Sullivan St Ste 6B, New York, NY 10012
Tel.: (332) 333-4123   DE
Web Site:
https://www.teamshares.com
Year Founded: 2019
Financial Services
N.A.I.C.S.: 523999

Subsidiaries:

Mow Power, Inc.   (1)
250 N Gilbert Rd, Mesa, AZ 85203-8219
Tel.: (480) 854-7233
Web Site: http://www.mowpoweraz.com
Home & Garden Equipment Repair & Maintenance Services
N.A.I.C.S.: 811411

TEAMSON DESIGN CORP.
668 Pine Aire Dr, Bay Shore, NY 11706
Web Site: http://www.teamson.com
Year Founded: 1997
Sales Range: $10-24.9 Million
Emp.: 60
Online Shopping Services
N.A.I.C.S.: 423210
Jerry Su *(Pres)*

TEAMSOURCE INC.
2300 N Austin Ave, Georgetown, TX 78626-4515
Tel.: (512) 275-0941
Rev.: $13,720,130
Emp.: 5
Employment Agencies
N.A.I.C.S.: 561311

Subsidiaries:

Champion Temporaries Inc   (1)
2300 N Austin Ave, Georgetown, TX 78626-7846
Tel.: (512) 931-2787
Help Supply Services
N.A.I.C.S.: 561320

TEAMTEK WHOLESALE
7616 South Land, Orlando, FL 32809-6768
Tel.: (407) 857-1714   FL
Web Site: http://www.vbpnet.com
Year Founded: 1981
Sales Range: $10-24.9 Million
Emp.: 20
Stationery & Office Supplies Distr
N.A.I.C.S.: 424120
James H. Rogers *(Chm & CEO)*
Mary Bunch *(VP-Mktg)*
Mac Rogers *(Pres & COO)*
Karen Esposita *(Controller & Mgr-Ops)*
Wes Pollock *(VP-Sls)*

TEAMWORKNET INC.
6550 New Tampa Hwy Ste B, Lakeland, FL 33815
Tel.: (863) 327-1080
Web Site:
http://www.teamworknet.com
Rev.: $16,800,000
Emp.: 22
Educational Support Services
N.A.I.C.S.: 611710
Tommy Ashline *(VP)*
Rue Hestand *(VP)*
Christopher W. Seelig *(Pres)*
Harry J. Tittel *(VP)*
Paul Wood *(VP)*

TEAMWORLD INC.
498 Conklin Ave, Binghamton, NY 13903
Tel.: (607) 770-1005
Web Site: http://www.teamworld.com
Sales Range: $10-24.9 Million
Emp.: 80
Corporate Apparel & Promotional Items Mfr & Sales
N.A.I.C.S.: 315990
Stephen G. Wozniak *(Pres)*
Henry Cook *(VP)*
Mark LaTourette *(Mgr-Production)*

TEC CORP
721 14th St, Sioux City, IA 51105
Tel.: (712) 252-4275
Web Site: http://www.tec-corp.com
Rev.: $25,000,000
Emp.: 250
General Electrical Contractor
N.A.I.C.S.: 238210
Skip Perley *(Pres & CEO)*
Craig Thompson *(COO & VP)*
Renee Beaulieu *(CFO & Treas)*

TEC DIRECT MEDIA, INC.
134 N LaSalle St Ste 840, Chicago, IL 60602
Tel.: (312) 551-0832
Web Site: http://www.tec-direct.com
Year Founded: 2001
Sales Range: $10-24.9 Million
Emp.: 10
Media Buying Services
N.A.I.C.S.: 541830
Charles Fetterly *(Pres)*
Larisa Fetterly *(Sr VP)*

TEC EQUIPMENT, INC.
750 NE Columbia Blvd, Portland, OR 97211
Tel.: (503) 285-7667
Web Site: http://www.tectrucks.com
Sales Range: $600-649.9 Million
Emp.: 80
Trucks, Commercial
N.A.I.C.S.: 423110
Kathy Mahaffy *(COO)*
Dave Schwanke *(Mgr-Mktg)*
Resa Kee *(CFO)*
Steve Andros *(Gen Mgr-Seattle & Tacoma)*

TEC UTILITIES SUPPLY INC.
1005B Frontage Rd, Greenville, SC 29615
Tel.: (864) 288-6755
Web Site: http://tecusa.us
Rev.: $15,000,000
Emp.: 20
Plumbing & Hydronic Heating Supplies
N.A.I.C.S.: 423720
Joye R. Schmidt *(Pres)*

TEC, INC.
33851 Curtis Blvd Ste 216, Eastlake, OH 44095
Tel.: (440) 953-8760   OH
Web Site: http://www.tecinc1.com
Year Founded: 1983
Sales Range: $10-24.9 Million
Emp.: 23
Mechanical, Electrical, Lighting Design & Technology Design Engineering Firm
N.A.I.C.S.: 541330
Terrance Kilbourne *(Pres)*
Adam B. Kilbourne *(Mgr-Info Svcs)*
Jon Alexander *(Principal)*

Subsidiaries:

W.E. Monks & Co.   (1)
3073 N High St, Columbus, OH 43202
Tel.: (614) 218-7328
Web Site: http://www.tecinc1.com
Engineering Services
N.A.I.C.S.: 541330
Jon Alexander *(VP)*
Russell T. Edwards *(Mng Principal)*

TEC-AIR INC.
1 Tec Air Ave, Willow Springs, IL 60480
Tel.: (708) 839-1400
Web Site: http://www.tecairinc.com
Rev.: $11,500,000
Emp.: 125
Injection Molded Finished Plastics Product Mfr
N.A.I.C.S.: 326199
Robert J. McMurtry *(Pres)*
Nancy Pearson *(Mgr-Acctg)*

TEC-MASTERS INC.
1500 Perimeter Pkwy NW, Huntsville, AL 35806-3562
Tel.: (256) 830-4000   AL
Web Site: http://www.tecmasters.com
Year Founded: 1988
Sales Range: $25-49.9 Million
Emp.: 312
Provider of Engineering Services
N.A.I.C.S.: 541330
Marvin P. Carroll *(Pres & CEO)*
Christie Sanford *(Mgr-Contracts)*
Joanne Lucid *(Mgr-HR)*
Paul Secrest *(Chief Strategy Officer)*
John Broyles *(VP-Ops)*
Carol Frazier *(COO)*

TECH ADVANCED COMPUTERS INC.
1508 Creighton Rd, Pensacola, FL 32504
Tel.: (850) 479-9227
Web Site:
http://www.techadvanced.com
Year Founded: 1991
Sales Range: $10-24.9 Million
Emp.: 30
Modems, Monitors, Terminals & Disk Drives: Computers
N.A.I.C.S.: 449210
Patrick Tan *(Pres)*

TECH AGRICULTURAL, INC.
125 Front St, Buttonwillow, CA 93206
Tel.: (661) 323-1001
Web Site: http://www.techag.com
Year Founded: 1963
Sales Range: $10-24.9 Million
Emp.: 75
Farm Supplies Whslr
N.A.I.C.S.: 424910
Donald Houchin *(Pres)*

Subsidiaries:

Buttonwillow Warehouse Co., Inc.   (1)
125 W Front St, Buttonwillow, CA 93206
Tel.: (661) 764-5234
Web Site: http://www.techag.com
Farm Supplies; Distr Farm Chemicals-Herbicides, Pesticides & Fertilizer
N.A.I.C.S.: 424910
Donald Houchin *(Pres)*

Pintail Corporation   (1)
125 W Frnt St, Buttonwillow, CA 93206
Tel.: (661) 764-5234
Sales Range: $10-24.9 Million
Emp.: 1
Fine Chemicals
N.A.I.C.S.: 484110

TECH AMERICAS USA, INC.
22503 Katy Fwy, Katy, TX 77450   TX
Web Site: http://www.tech-americas.com
Year Founded: 2012
Sales Range: $1-9.9 Million
Emp.: 100
Information Technology Services
N.A.I.C.S.: 541512
Tom Voss *(Pres)*

TECH CREDIT UNION CORPORATION
10951 Broadway, Crown Point, IN 46307
Tel.: (219) 663-5120   IN
Web Site: http://www.techcu.org
Year Founded: 1936
Sales Range: $10-24.9 Million
Emp.: 110
Financial Services
N.A.I.C.S.: 523999
Michael Casey *(VP-Fin)*
Michael M. Hussey *(Pres & CEO)*
Mary Jo Duncan *(VP-Lending)*
Richard D. Lundstrom *(Exec VP)*
Edward Petyo *(Sec)*
Richard Young *(Chm)*
Joseph Machara *(Vice Chm)*
Patricia Cordray *(Vice Chm)*
James Mack *(Treas)*
Larry Schaffer *(VP-Mktg)*
Lora Sturtridge *(Dir-IT)*

TECH ENTERPRISES, INC.
1009 Jonathon Dr, Madison, WI 53713
Tel.: (608) 274-3838   WI
Web Site:
http://www.techstainremover.com
Year Founded: 1975
Sales Range: $1-9.9 Million
Emp.: 26
Mfg Household Cleaners & Does Custom Packaging & Labeling
N.A.I.C.S.: 325612
Kenneth Grant *(Pres)*

TECH IMPACT
417 N 8th St Ste 203, Philadelphia, PA 19123
Tel.: (215) 557-1559   PA
Web Site: http://www.techimpact.org
Year Founded: 2002
Sales Range: $1-9.9 Million
Information Technology Services
N.A.I.C.S.: 541519
John Baker *(Acct Mgr)*
Lauren Cannon *(Mgr-HR)*
Linda Widdop *(Dir-Client Solutions & Education)*
Mark Mason *(Sr Acct Mgr)*
Sam Chenkin *(Dir-Consulting Svcs)*
Patrick Callihan *(Exec Dir)*
Elizabeth Levy *(Acct Mgr)*

TECH IMPACT

Tech Impact—(Continued)
Sara Thompson (Mgr-Mktg & Community)
Grace Harpole (Program Dir)
Ebony Taylor (Project Mgr)
Barry Hartzberg (Dir-Fin & Admin)

TECH MOLD, INC.
1735 W 10th St, Tempe, AZ 85281-5207
Tel.: (480) 968-8691
Web Site: http://www.techmold.com
Sales Range: $50-74.9 Million
Emp.: 80
Plastic Injection Molds Mfr
N.A.I.C.S.: 333511

TECH NH INC.
8 Continental Blvd, Merrimack, NH 03054
Tel.: (603) 424-4404
Web Site: http://www.technh.com
Rev.: $10,000,000
Emp.: 80
Injection Molded Finished Plastics Products
N.A.I.C.S.: 326199
Richard C. Grosky (Pres)
Pamela Young (CFO)
Greg Gardener (Gen Mgr)

TECH RESOURCES, INC.
2025 Riverside Dr, Columbus, OH 43221
Tel.: (614) 255-3166
Web Site: http://www.questline.com
Year Founded: 1991
Sales Range: $1-9.9 Million
Emp.: 20
Management Consulting Services
N.A.I.C.S.: 541613
David Reim (VP)

TECH SYN CORPORATION
455 Brighton Dr, Bloomingdale, IL 60108
Tel.: (630) 351-9500
Web Site: http://www.tech-syn.com
Sales Range: $50-74.9 Million
Emp.: 30
Rubber Goods Sales
N.A.I.C.S.: 423840
Gary Nanning (Pres)
Joe Murawski (Sr Acct Mgr-Sls)

TECH USA INC.
8334 Veterans Hwy, Millersville, MD 21108
Tel.: (410) 729-4328
Web Site: http://www.techusa.net
Sales Range: $25-49.9 Million
Emp.: 150
Help Supply Services
N.A.I.C.S.: 561320
Thomas B. Howell (Pres)
Chris Frew (VP-Scientific)
Rachel Rachfal (Mgr-Mktg)

TECH-ETCH INC.
45 Aldrin Rd, Plymouth, MA 02360-4803
Tel.: (508) 747-0300
Web Site: http://www.tech-etch.com
Year Founded: 1964
Sales Range: $10-24.9 Million
Emp.: 500
Metal Stamping Services
N.A.I.C.S.: 332119
Richard Cammarano (Pres & CEO)

TECH-PRO INC.
3000 Center Point Dr, Roseville, MN 55113-1122
Tel.: (651) 634-1400
Web Site: http://www.tech-pro.com
Year Founded: 1989

Sales Range: $25-49.9 Million
Emp.: 250
Provider of Computers & Consulting Services
N.A.I.C.S.: 541512
David Vadis (Founder, CEO & Pres)
Dustin Schwichtenberg (Acct Exec)
Cara Dunn (Dir-First Impressions)

TECH-R2
6606 Tussing Rd Ste B, Reynoldsburg, OH 43068-4174
Tel.: (614) 755-5100
Web Site: http://www.techr2.com
Sales Range: $1-9.9 Million
Emp.: 35
Technology Data, Hardware & Software Retirement & Disposal Services
N.A.I.C.S.: 423930
Sepp Rajaie (Founder & Pres)
Keith Kinnison (Mgr-Logistics)
A. S. Duque (Dir-Mgmt)
Charles Robbins (Dir-R&D)
David K. Kunchal (Exec VP)
Devin Peach (Mgr-Bus Dev)
Matt Burdick (Dir-Tech Svcs)
Mandy Prifogle Conklin (Dir-Client Rels)

TECH-STEEL INC.
Freeport Ctr Bldg D2, Clearfield, UT 84016
Tel.: (801) 825-9769
Web Site: http://www.tech-steel.com
Rev.: $13,365,188
Emp.: 14
Stadium Construction
N.A.I.C.S.: 236220
Steve Rowley (Mgr-Joist & Deck Div)

TECHAPP SOLUTIONS, INC.
115 W California Blvd #553, Pasadena, CA 91105
Tel.: (206) 339-7617
Year Founded: 2010
Sales Range: $10-24.9 Million
Emp.: 1
Computer & Mobile Device Software Programs
N.A.I.C.S.: 513210
Karim Rawji (Chm, Pres, CFO & Sec)

TECHAU'S INC.
310 S Church St, Cynthiana, KY 41031-1512
Tel.: (859) 234-3408
Web Site: http://www.techaus.com
Year Founded: 1979
Sales Range: $25-49.9 Million
Emp.: 300
Grocery Stores
N.A.I.C.S.: 459310
Kenneth Techau (Owner)

TECHBARN.COM, INC.
5850 Osgood Ave N, Stillwater, MN 55082
Tel.: (651) 275-8300
Web Site: http://www.techbarn.com
Year Founded: 2000
Sales Range: $1-9.9 Million
Emp.: 35
Technology Services
N.A.I.C.S.: 517810
John Uppgren (VP)

TECHCXO
75 5th St Suite 405B, Atlanta, GA 30308
Tel.: (678) 636-0004
Web Site: http://www.techcxo.com
Year Founded: 2003
Sales Range: $1-9.9 Million
Emp.: 40
Strategic & Functional Consulting Services for Technology Companies

N.A.I.C.S.: 541690
Kent Elmer (Mng Partner)
Sherwin Krug (Partner)
Brad Milner (Mng Partner)
David Kelley (CFO/Partner-Charleston)
Neal Miller (Partner)
Michael J. Casey (Partner)
William J. Keneally (Partner-CXO Partners)
Wes Pollard (Mng Partner-Carolinas)
Wesley T. Pollard (Mng Partner-Carolinas)

TECHDEMOCRACY LLC
499 Thornall St Ste 301, Edison, NJ 08837
Tel.: (732) 404-8350
Web Site: http://www.techdemocracy.com
Year Founded: 2000
Sales Range: $1-9.9 Million
Emp.: 100
IT Solutions & Professional Services
N.A.I.C.S.: 541511
Kiran Patibandla (CEO)
Krishnan Balasubramanian (CFO)
Harish Jangada (Dir-Enterprise Security Practice)
Anant Kadiyala (Dir-Oracle ACE & VP-SOA)

TECHDIGITAL CORP.
764 Southcross Dr W Ste 202, Burnsville, MN 55306
Tel.: (952) 956-2043
Web Site: http://www.techdigitalcorp.com
Information Technology Consulting & Software Development Services
N.A.I.C.S.: 541690
Balaji Thiagarajan (Pres & CEO)
Frank Gordon (Chief Bus Officer)

TECHE ACTION BOARD INC
1115 Weber St, Franklin, LA 70538
Tel.: (337) 828-2550
Web Site: http://www.tabhealth.org
Year Founded: 1974
Sales Range: $10-24.9 Million
Emp.: 180
Healthcare Services
N.A.I.C.S.: 622110
Paulette Lofton (COO)
Jennifer Fabre (Chief Nursing Officer)
Gary M. Wiltz (CEO & Chief Health Officer-Clinical)
Leroy Willis (Pres)
Barbara Hills (Sec)
Rose Susan Dorsey (Treas)
Cleveland Farlough (VP)
William Brent III (CFO)

TECHEAD
111 N 17th St, Richmond, VA 23219
Tel.: (804) 782-6971
Web Site: http://www.techead.com
Year Founded: 1988
Rev.: $6,600,000
Emp.: 125
Staffing, Training & Marketing Services
N.A.I.C.S.: 561499
Phil Conein (Pres)

TECHFINO LLC
1900 Market St 8th Fl, Philadelphia, PA 19103
Tel.: http://www.techfino.com
Year Founded: 2014
Sales Range: $1-9.9 Million
Emp.: 16
Information Technology Services
N.A.I.C.S.: 541512

Wiktor Borowiec (Mng Partner)
Bryan Willman (Mng Partner)
Joe Giegerich (Sls Dir)

TECHHOUSE INTEGRATED INFORMATION SYSTEM SOLUTIONS, INC.
6910 Professional Pkwy E, Lakewood Ranch, FL 34240
Tel.: (941) 756-2602
Web Site: http://www.tech-house.com
Year Founded: 1995
Sales Range: $1-9.9 Million
Emp.: 13
IT Consulting Services
N.A.I.C.S.: 541690
Kathy Durfee (CEO)
Karen Reynolds (Dir-HR)

TECHLAW HOLDINGS, INC.
14500 Avion Pkwy Ste 300, Chantilly, VA 20151
Tel.: (703) 818-1000
Web Site: http://www.techlawholdings.com
Holding Company
N.A.I.C.S.: 551112
Brian Shutler (Chm & Pres)
Patricia Derocher (COO)
Stephen Smithson (Gen Counsel & VP)

Subsidiaries:
TechLaw Inc. (1)
14500 Avion Pkwy Ste 300, Chantilly, VA 20151
Tel.: (703) 818-1000
Web Site: http://www.techlawinc.com
Sales Range: $25-49.9 Million
Emp.: 300
Provider of Business Consulting Services
N.A.I.C.S.: 541618
Brian Shutler (Pres)
Patricia Brown-Derocher (Pres-Tech)

TECHLINE INC.
9609 Beck Cir, Austin, TX 78758-5401
Tel.: (512) 833-5401
Web Site: http://www.techline-inc.com
Year Founded: 1987
Sales Range: $10-24.9 Million
Emp.: 80
Electronic Parts & Equipment Sales
N.A.I.C.S.: 423690
Robert A. Brode (Pres)
Brad Slaughter (COO)
Louis Rhoden (CFO)

TECHLINK SYSTEMS, INC.
51 E 42nd St, New York, NY 10017
Tel.: (212) 661-2707
Web Site: http://www.techlinksystems.com
Year Founded: 1998
Sales Range: $10-24.9 Million
Emp.: 400
Employment Services
N.A.I.C.S.: 561311
Jane Kim (Pres)

TECHMER PM, LLC
18420 Laurel Park Rd, Rancho Dominguez, CA 90220-6015
Tel.: (310) 632-9211
Web Site: http://www.techmerpm.com
Year Founded: 1997
Sales Range: $10-24.9 Million
Emp.: 540
Plastic Materials Mfr
N.A.I.C.S.: 325211
John Manuck (Chm & CEO)
Vicki Morey (Controller)
Joe Gonzalez (Supvr-Shipping)
Mark Jones (Mgr-Global Nonwovens Bus)

COMPANIES

Ryan Howley *(Pres)*
Michael McHenry *(COO)*
Erika Mitchell *(VP-Supply Chain)*
Dwayne Miller *(CFO)*
Subsidiaries:

Opticolor, Inc. (1)
15501 Computer Ln, Huntington Beach, CA 92649
Tel.: (714) 893-8839
Web Site: http://www.opticolorinc.com
Sales Range: $1-9.9 Million
Emp.: 11
Plastics Product Mfr
N.A.I.C.S.: 326199
Daniel Neufeld *(Founder)*

TECHMETALS, INC.
345 Springfield St, Dayton, OH 45403
Tel.: (937) 253-5311
Web Site: http://www.techmetals.com
Rev.: $10,000,000
Emp.: 135
Provider of Metal Finishing Engineering Services
N.A.I.C.S.: 332813
Dan Brockman *(Owner)*
Tony George *(Plant Mgr)*
Sherry Evans *(CFO)*

TECHNA GLASS, INC.
460 W 9000 S, Sandy, UT 84070 UT
Web Site:
   http://www.technaglass.com
Year Founded: 1991
Automotive Glass Repair & Replacement Shops Operator
N.A.I.C.S.: 811122
Troy Mason *(Founder & CEO)*

TECHNATOMY CORPORATION
3877 Fairfax Ridge Rd, Fairfax, VA 22030
Tel.: (703) 268-5525
Web Site:
   http://www.technatomy.com
Sales Range: $10-24.9 Million
Emp.: 45
Data Processing, Hosting & Related Services
N.A.I.C.S.: 518210
Nadeem Butler *(Pres & CEO)*
Bill Burns *(COO)*
Sean Cate *(Dir-Quality Programs)*
Todd Reynolds *(Dir-Dept-Homel & Security Programs)*
Cliff Freeman *(Chief Health Interoperability Officer)*
Bruno Pesanti *(CTO)*
Karie Newmyer *(Dir-Contract Admin)*
Wei Li *(Dir-Fin & Acctg)*

TECHNET RESOURCES, INC.
4080 Mcginnis Ferry Rd Ste 604, Alpharetta, GA 30005-1739
Tel.: (678) 527-1440
Web Site: http://www.tnri.net
Year Founded: 1998
Sales Range: $10-24.9 Million
Emp.: 211
IT Staffing & Consulting Services
N.A.I.C.S.: 541690
Richard Knox *(Pres)*

TECHNI-CAR INC.
450 Commerce Blvd, Oldsmar, FL 34677
Tel.: (813) 855-0022
Web Site: http://www.techni-car.com
Rev.: $12,740,011
Emp.: 200
Automotive Repair Shops
N.A.I.C.S.: 811114
Paul Martanovic *(Gen Mgr)*
Mary Rankin *(Asst Controller)*
Victoria Borges *(Supvr-Customer Support)*

TECHNIC INCORPORATED
1 Spectacle St, Cranston, RI 02910-1032
Tel.: (401) 781-6100 RI
Web Site: http://www.technic.com
Year Founded: 1945
Sales Range: $150-199.9 Million
Emp.: 500
Chemical & Metallurgical Product Mfr
N.A.I.C.S.: 325998
James Frick *(Mgr-Global Sls & Mktg)*
Subsidiaries:

Dongguan City Precimet Trading Co Ltd (1)
Office no 13 Floor Block A Plainvim Third Industrial Area, Xiaobian ChangAn Town, Dongguan, 523851, Guangdong, China
Tel.: (86) 769 81885111
Metal Products Mfr
N.A.I.C.S.: 332999

Italgalvano (Technic Group) Slovakia (1)
Stefanikova 30 059 1, Svit, Slovakia
Tel.: (421) 52 77 56 318
Analytical Control System Mfr
N.A.I.C.S.: 334513

Korea Technic Co. Ltd. (1)
4th Fl Seohung Bldg 8 Nonhyeon-ro, Gangnam-ku, Seoul, 06313, Korea (South)
Tel.: (82) 2 576 3830
Web Site: http://www.technic-kr.com
Emp.: 9
Metal Products Mfr
N.A.I.C.S.: 332999

Technic (China-HK) Ltd. (1)
Rm 04 10/F Block A HK Worsted Mills Ind'l Bldg, 31-39 Wo Tong Tsui Street, Kwai Chung, New Territories, China (Hong Kong)
Tel.: (852) 3590 8989
Electronic Component & Specialty Chemical Mfr
N.A.I.C.S.: 334419

Technic (Suzhou) Semiconductor Engineering Co., Ltd (1)
97 Su Tong Road Suzhou Industrial Park, Suzhou, 215021, Jiangsu, China
Tel.: (86) 512 6761 0097
Web Site: http://www.technic-suzhou.com
Sales Range: $25-49.9 Million
Emp.: 250
Semiconductor Equipment Mfr
N.A.I.C.S.: 334413

Technic Asia-Pacific Pte Ltd. (1)
25 Gul Avenue, Singapore, 629665, Singapore
Tel.: (65) 6793 8000
Web Site: http://www.technic.com.sg
Specialty Chemical Mfr & Distr
N.A.I.C.S.: 424690

Technic Asia-Pacific Sdn. Bhd. (1)
1-2-3A Plaza Ivory Halaman Bukit Gambir-Gambir, Penang, 11700, Malaysia
Tel.: (60) 4 656 9300
Web Site: http://www.tecnic.com
Sales Range: $10-24.9 Million
Emp.: 3
Electronic Component & Specialty Chemical Mfr
N.A.I.C.S.: 334419
Kok Guan Ng *(Mng Dir)*

Technic Canada (1)
195 Riviera Drive, Markham, L3R 5J6, ON, Canada (100%)
Tel.: (905) 940-4020
Web Site: http://www.technic.com
Sales Range: $10-24.9 Million
Emp.: 12
Mfr of Engineered Materials; Chemicals & Catalysts
N.A.I.C.S.: 325998

Technic France (1)
15 Rue de la Montjoie, BP 79, 93212, Saint Denis, Cedex, La Plaine, France
Tel.: (33) 149 465 100
Web Site: http://www.technic.com
Electronic Components Mfr, Sales & Distr & Customer Service Lab
N.A.I.C.S.: 541380

Plant (Domestic):

TECHNIC Innovative Surface Technologies Facility (2)
Parc d'Activite du Ruisset, BP 10, 38360, Noyarey, France
Tel.: (33) 476 859 185
Web Site: http://www.technic.fr
Electronic Equipment Distr, Mfr & Technical Laboratory Facilities
N.A.I.C.S.: 423690

Technic Incorporated - Chalon Plant (2)
1 rue Georges Claude, 71100, Chalon-sur-Saone, Cedex, France
Tel.: (33) 149 465 100
Web Site: http://www.technic.fr
Metal Products Mfr
N.A.I.C.S.: 332999

Technic Incorporated - Technic Advanced Technology Division (1)
111 E Ames Ct, Plainview, NY 11803
Tel.: (516) 349-0700
Web Site: http://www.technic.com
Emp.: 12
Laboratory Research & Development Services
N.A.I.C.S.: 541715
Rob Schetty *(VP-Global Sls & Mktg)*

Technic Incorporated - Technic Engineered Powders Division (1)
300 Park E Dr, Woonsocket, RI 02895
Tel.: (401) 769-7000
Web Site: http://www.technic-epd.com
Emp.: 80
Engineered Powder & Flake Distr
N.A.I.C.S.: 423310
Gary Hemphill *(Gen Mgr)*
James Rocha *(Dir-Quality)*

Technic Incorporated-Equipment Div. (1)
55 Maryland Ave, Pawtucket, RI 02860 (100%)
Tel.: (401) 728-7081
Web Site: http://www.technic.com
Sales Range: $10-24.9 Million
Emp.: 50
Mfr of Precious Metal Chemicals & Equipment for Electroplating
N.A.I.C.S.: 333248

Technic Japan, Inc. (1)
Nakajima No2 Bldg 2-5 Nishinakajima 5-Chome, Yodogawa-ku, Osaka, 532-0011, Japan
Tel.: (81) 6 6301 7520
Industrial Chemical Mfr & Distr
N.A.I.C.S.: 325998

Technic Taiwan Co., Ltd. (1)
No 335 Dafu Road Lu-chu Hsiang, Taoyuan, 33862, Taiwan
Tel.: (886) 3 3230933
Web Site: http://www.technic.com
Emp.: 100
Specialty Chemicals Distr
N.A.I.C.S.: 424690
Arthur Chang *(Gen Mgr)*

Technic UK (1)
Unit 9 Liberty Way Attleborough Fields Industrial Estate, Nuneaton, CV11 6RZ, Warwickshire, United Kingdom
Tel.: (44) 2476 374999
Web Site: http://www.technic.com
Emp.: 4
Chemical Products Mfr
N.A.I.C.S.: 325998
Robert Townsin *(Gen Mgr)*

TECHNICA CORPORATION
22970 Indian Creek Dr Ste 500, Dulles, VA 20166
Tel.: (703) 662-2000
Web Site:
   http://www.technicacorp.com
Sales Range: $25-49.9 Million
Emp.: 150
Computer Integrated Systems Design
N.A.I.C.S.: 541512
Miguel Collado *(CEO & CTO)*
Daniel Doherty *(Dir-Bus Program & Alliances)*

TECHNICAL COMMUNITIES, INC.

Jeffrey Hallett *(Dir-Bus Ops)*
Michelle Veghte *(Dir-Proposal Svcs)*
Paul Gentry *(Gen Counsel & Mgr-Contracts)*
Rhonda Eldridge *(Dir-Engrg)*
Riaz Siddiqui *(Dir-Fin & Acctg)*
Lisa Trombley *(COO)*
Brian Fogg *(Chief Innovation Officer)*
Mark Cabrey *(CFO)*

TECHNICAL AND PROJECT ENGINEERING, LLC
6363 Walker Ln Ste 300, Alexandria, VA 22310
Tel.: (703) 924-5020
Web Site: http://www.tape-llc.com
Year Founded: 2000
Sales Range: $10-24.9 Million
Emp.: 110
Federal Agency Management Consulting
N.A.I.C.S.: 541611
Louisa Long Jaffe *(Pres & CEO)*
Ted Harrison *(Exec VP & Gen Mgr)*
John Moore *(Chief Growth Officer)*
Debbie Gallop *(CFO)*

TECHNICAL APPLICATIONS ASSOCIATES, INC.
188 Central St, Hudson, MA 01749
Tel.: (978) 567-9771
Web Site: http://www.ta-squared.com
Sales Range: $10-24.9 Million
Emp.: 8
Computers, Peripherals & Software
N.A.I.C.S.: 423430
Robert Blanding *(Pres)*

TECHNICAL ASSOCIATES OF GEORGIA INC.
2423 Westgate Dr, Albany, GA 31707-2225
Tel.: (229) 888-6632 GA
Web Site:
   http://www.technicalassociates.com
Year Founded: 1980
Sales Range: $25-49.9 Million
Emp.: 350
Employment Agencies
N.A.I.C.S.: 561311
John Howard *(Program Dir)*
Matthew Scolforo *(Project Mgr-Engrg)*
Graham Thompson *(Pres)*

TECHNICAL CHEMICAL COMPANY INC.
3327 Pipeline Rd, Cleburne, TX 76033-7749
Tel.: (817) 645-6088 TX
Web Site:
   http://www.technicalchemical.com
Year Founded: 1961
Sales Range: $10-24.9 Million
Emp.: 120
Provider of Automotive Services
N.A.I.C.S.: 423120
Howard Dudley *(Pres)*
Scott Dudley *(VP)*

TECHNICAL COMMUNITIES, INC.
1000 Cherry Ave Ste 100, San Bruno, CA 94066-3022
Tel.: (650) 624-0525 CA
Web Site:
   http://www.technicalcommunities.com
Year Founded: 1998
Sales Range: $10-24.9 Million
Emp.: 20
Test & Measurement Equipment Products, Information & Services
N.A.I.C.S.: 517810
Peter Ostrow *(Pres & CEO)*
Jeffrey Wheeler *(CFO)*

TECHNICAL COMMUNITIES, INC.

Technical Communities, Inc.—(Continued)
Sudip Barman *(VP-Engrg)*
Matthew McMahon *(VP)*
Johnhenry Giddings *(VP-Mktg Svcs)*

TECHNICAL DEVICES CO.
560 Alaska Ave, Torrance, CA 90503
Tel.: (310) 618-8437
Web Site: http://www.technicaldev.com
Year Founded: 1952
Rev.: $10,000,000
Emp.: 46
Soldering Cleaning Equipment Mfr
N.A.I.C.S.: 333992
Douglas Winther *(Pres)*
Ronn Berri *(VP)*
Isaias Ramirez *(Mgr-Production Control)*

TECHNICAL EDUCATION RESEARCH CENTERS, INC.
2067 Massachusetts Ave, Cambridge, MA 02140
Tel.: (617) 873-9600 MA
Web Site: http://www.terc.edu
Year Founded: 1965
Sales Range: $10-24.9 Million
Emp.: 121
Educational Research Services
N.A.I.C.S.: 611710
Barbara MacEachern *(Dir-Outreach)*
Carol I. Lumm *(Dir-HR)*
David Libby *(Dir-Tech)*
Ken Mayer *(Dir-Comm)*
Glen M. Secor *(Mgr-Products & Publications)*

TECHNICAL FOUNDATIONS INC.
100 Dry Bridge Ct, Sandston, VA 23150
Tel.: (804) 328-4500
Web Site: http://www.technicalfoundation.com
Sales Range: $25-49.9 Million
Emp.: 15
Commercial Construction
N.A.I.C.S.: 238110
Butch Stoneman *(Principal)*
Steve King *(Principal)*

TECHNICAL GAS PRODUCTS, INC.
66 Leonardo Dr, North Haven, CT 06473
Tel.: (203) 239-1002
Web Site: http://www.tgpoxygen.com
Year Founded: 1994
Sales Range: $10-24.9 Million
Emp.: 55
Medical Oxygen Equipment Mfr
N.A.I.C.S.: 334510

TECHNICAL IMAGE PRODUCTS, INC.
1250 Pratt Blvd, Elk Grove Village, IL 60007-5709
Tel.: (847) 593-0500 IL
Web Site: http://www.technicalimage.com
Year Founded: 1978
Sales Range: $50-74.9 Million
Emp.: 30
Provider of Printers for Engineering & Drafting Companies
N.A.I.C.S.: 323111

TECHNICAL INSTRUMENTS SAN FRANCISCO
1826 Rollins Rd, Burlingame, CA 94010-2200
Tel.: (650) 651-3000 CA
Web Site: http://www.techinst.com
Year Founded: 1950

Microscopy Products & Services Whslr
N.A.I.C.S.: 423490
Dane Maxfield *(Mgr-Product)*
Raymond Williams *(Asst Mgr-Sls)*
Brian Lundy *(Pres)*

TECHNICAL MARKETING ASSOCIATES
223 W 138th St, Los Angeles, CA 90061-1006
Tel.: (310) 323-1981
Rev.: $15,000,000
Emp.: 25
Sewing Supplies
N.A.I.C.S.: 424990
Hiroshi Niwa *(Pres)*

TECHNICAL RESOURCES INTERNATIONAL, INC.
6500 Rock Spring Dr Ste 650, Bethesda, MD 20817
Tel.: (301) 564-6400
Web Site: http://www.tech-res.com
Year Founded: 1979
Sales Range: $25-49.9 Million
Emp.: 250
Information Technology Consulting Services
N.A.I.C.S.: 541512
Nora Lee *(Pres & CEO)*
Margarite Lin *(CFO & Treas)*

TECHNICAL RUBBER COMPANY, INC.
9711 Sportsman Club Road, Johnstown, OH 43031-0486
Tel.: (740) 967-9015 OH
Web Site: http://trc4r.com
Year Founded: 1939
Rubber Tire Mfr & Distr; Tire & Tube Repair Services
N.A.I.C.S.: 326211
Dan Layne *(Chm, Pres & CEO)*
Mitch Langford *(Mktg Mgr-TECH-North America)*

TECHNICAL SALES INTERNATIONAL, LLC (TSI)
8310 N Capital Of Texas Hwy Bldg 2-200, Austin, TX 78731-1005
Web Site: http://www.technicalsalesinternational.com
Year Founded: 2002
Sales Range: $10-24.9 Million
Emp.: 29
Software Design for Construction
N.A.I.C.S.: 541990
Bernie Tamasy *(Principal)*

TECHNICAL SOLUTIONS, LLC.
300 Route 17 S Ste E, Mahwah, NJ 07430
Tel.: (201) 579-6200 NY
Web Site: http://www.tsllc.net
Year Founded: 1998
Sales Range: $10-24.9 Million
Emp.: 213
Telecommunication Servicesb
N.A.I.C.S.: 517810
Dominick Terrone *(Chief Bus Dev Officer)*

TECHNICAL TRANSPORTATION INC.
2850 Market Loop, Southlake, TX 76092
Tel.: (817) 421-0470
Web Site: http://www.techtrans.com
Sales Range: $25-49.9 Million
Emp.: 100
Freight Forwarding
N.A.I.C.S.: 488510

Len Batcha *(Pres)*
Becky Parks *(Mgr-Accts)*
Bill Putnam *(CFO)*

TECHNICAL YOUTH LLC.
8395 Keystone Crossing, Indianapolis, IN 46240
Tel.: (317) 475-0079
Web Site: http://www.technicalyouth.com
Rev.: $12,000,000
Emp.: 200
Computer System Design Services
N.A.I.C.S.: 541512
Brian Hasbrouck *(Pres)*

TECHNICORP INTERNATIONAL II
512 N Main St, Orange, CA 92868
Tel.: (714) 639-7810
Web Site: http://www.statek.com
Rev.: $12,500,000
Emp.: 1
Electronic Circuits
N.A.I.C.S.: 334419
Brian T. McCarthy *(CFO)*

Subsidiaries:

Greenray Industries (1)
840 W Church Rd, Mechanicsburg, PA 17055-3103 (100%)
Tel.: (717) 766-0223
Web Site: http://www.greenrayindustries.com
Sales Range: $1-9.9 Million
Emp.: 20
N.A.I.C.S.: 334418
Bonnie Crawford *(Controller)*

TECHNICOTE INC.
222 Mound Ave, Miamisburg, OH 45342
Tel.: (937) 859-4448
Web Site: http://www.technicote.com
Year Founded: 1980
Rev.: $22,000,000
Emp.: 200
Supplier of Pressure Sensitive Adhesive Products
N.A.I.C.S.: 322220
Jim Boyer *(Mgr-Acctg)*

TECHNIFAX CORPORATION
3220 Keller Springs Rd, Carrollton, TX 75006-5049
Tel.: (972) 478-2800
Web Site: http://www.technifaxdfw.com
Year Founded: 1987
Sales Range: $10-24.9 Million
Emp.: 77
Document Imaging And Information Technology Services
N.A.I.C.S.: 423420
Michael Moon *(Pres & CEO)*

TECHNIFORM METAL CURVING INC.
375 S Cactus Ave, Rialto, CA 92376
Tel.: (909) 877-6886
Web Site: http://www.techniform.com
Rev.: $10,500,000
Emp.: 100
Machine Shop, Jobbing & Repair
N.A.I.C.S.: 332710
Jon Harrison *(VP-Ops)*
Jim Lowther *(VP-Aerospace Div)*
Rob Sammons *(Dir-Ops)*

Subsidiaries:

Techniform Metal Curving of Texas (1)
723 E Mason St, Mabank, TX 75147
Tel.: (903) 887-2363
Web Site: http://www.techniform.com
Rev.: $3,100,000
Emp.: 34
Metal Reshaping & Replating Services

U.S. PRIVATE

N.A.I.C.S.: 332323
Rick Jones *(Pres)*

TECHNIPAK
149 Old Gray Station Rd, Gray, TN 37615
Tel.: (423) 477-6066
Web Site: http://www.technipak.com
Year Founded: 1999
Rev.: $5,800,000
Emp.: 63
Management Consulting Services
N.A.I.C.S.: 541614
George Creasy *(Supvr-Logistics)*

TECHNIPAQ, INC.
975 Lutter Dr, Crystal Lake, IL 60014
Tel.: (815) 477-1800
Web Site: http://www.technipaq.com
Year Founded: 1984
Sales Range: $10-24.9 Million
Emp.: 180
Plastics Pipe & Pipe Fitting Mfr
N.A.I.C.S.: 326122
Phil Rosenburg *(Founder & Pres)*

TECHNIPLAS, LLC
N44 W33341 Watertown Plank Rd, Nashotah, WI 53058-9707
Tel.: (262) 369-5555 DE
Web Site: http://www.techniplas.com
Year Founded: 1941
Custom Molded Plastic Products Mfr
N.A.I.C.S.: 326199
George Votis *(Founder & Chm)*
David Knill *(CFO & Chief Admin Officer)*
Avi Reichental *(Vice Chm)*
Bob Brzozowski *(Pres)*
Daniel Spirig *(Pres-Techniplas Prime)*
Frederic Desmarchelier *(Chief Transformation Officer)*
Manfred Kwade *(COO)*
Ali El-Haj *(CEO)*

Subsidiaries:

Dickten Masch Plastics (1)
N44 W33341 Watertown Plank Rd, Nashotah, WI 53058
Tel.: (262) 369-5555
Web Site: http://www.dicktenplastics.com
Custom Molded Plastic Products Mfr
N.A.I.C.S.: 326199
Scott McDonald *(Mgr-Facilities-Nashotah)*
Bob Brzozowski *(Pres)*

TECHNIS, INC.
140 Broadway 46th Fl, New York, NY 10005
Tel.: (202) 858-7583 NV
Year Founded: 2010
Intellectual Property Assets Acquisition of Software & Other Technology
N.A.I.C.S.: 533110
Jack Kaye *(Pres, CEO, CFO & Treas)*
Steven Smith *(Sec)*

TECHNISCAN, INC.
3216 S Highland Dr Ste 200, Salt Lake City, UT 84106
Tel.: (801) 521-0444 DE
Web Site: http://www.techniscanmedicalsystems.com
Year Founded: 2007
Sales Range: Less than $1 Million
Emp.: 5
Ultrasound Imaging System Mfr
N.A.I.C.S.: 339112
David C. Robinson *(Pres & CEO)*

TECHNO COATINGS INC.
1391 Allec St, Anaheim, CA 92805
Tel.: (714) 635-1130
Web Site: http://www.technocoatings.com

Sales Range: $25-49.9 Million
Emp.: 180
Commercial & Office Buildings, Renovation & Repair
N.A.I.C.S.: 236220
Kathleen Smith *(Mgr-Accts Receivable)*
Nick Cichirillo *(Mgr-Sls)*
Thomas Vega *(CFO)*
Dan Heemstra *(Project Mgr)*
Chris Radovich *(Plant Mgr)*
Randy Gordon *(Plant Mgr)*

TECHNO-GRAPHICS & TRANSLATIONS, INC.
1451 E 168th St, South Holland, IL 60473-2641
Tel.: (708) 331-3333   IL
Web Site: http://www.wetrans4u.com
Year Founded: 1983
Sales Range: $10-24.9 Million
Emp.: 10
Publishing Services
N.A.I.C.S.: 513199
David L. Bond *(Pres)*

TECHNOLOGY & BUSINESS INTEGRATORS INC.
136 Summit Ave Se 205, Montvale, NJ 07645
Tel.: (201) 573-0400
Web Site: http://www.tbicentral.com
Year Founded: 1985
Sales Range: $25-49.9 Million
Emp.: 52
IT & Business Operations Consulting Services
N.A.I.C.S.: 541611
Stanley J. Goldman *(Pres)*
Greg Merideth *(CTO)*

TECHNOLOGY ASSOCIATES EC INC.
3115 Melrose Dr Ste 110, Carlsbad, CA 92010
Tel.: (760) 765-5275
Web Site: http://www.taec.net
Year Founded: 2000
Sales Range: $50-74.9 Million
Emp.: 325
Telecommunication Servicesb
N.A.I.C.S.: 517810
Jeff Doggendorf *(Dir-Ops)*
Louis Topacio *(VP-Tech Svcs)*
Stephen P. Meyer *(Exec VP & COO)*

TECHNOLOGY CONCEPTS & DESIGN, INC.
4510 Weybridge Ln, Greensboro, NC 27407
Web Site: http://www.tcdi.com
Computer Softwares Mfr
N.A.I.C.S.: 513210
Bill Johnson *(Pres & CEO)*
Ginny Gonzalez *(Chief Mktg & Bus Dev Officer)*
Lisa Cain *(CFO)*
Geoff McPherson *(COO)*
Tim Opsitnick *(Gen Counsel & Exec VP)*

Subsidiaries:
Jurinnov Ltd.   (1)
1375 Euclid Ave, Cleveland, OH 44115
Tel.: (216) 664-1100
Web Site: http://www.jurinnov.com
Rev.: $1,400,000
Emp.: 15
Administrative Management & General Management Consulting Service
N.A.I.C.S.: 541611

TECHNOLOGY DYNAMICS, INC.
100 School St, Bergenfield, NJ 07621-2915
Tel.: (201) 385-0500   NJ
Web Site: http://www.technologydynamicsinc.com
Year Founded: 1976
Sales Range: $10-24.9 Million
Emp.: 100
Inverters, Uninterruptible Power Systems & Frequency Converter Mfr
N.A.I.C.S.: 334419
Aron Levy *(Pres)*
Carol Dawkins *(Mgr-Sls)*

Subsidiaries:
Electronics Integration Technology, Inc.   (1)
10 Industrial Way E, Eatontown, NJ 07724
Tel.: (732) 542-2292
Web Site: http://www.eit-inc.com
Electric Equipment Mfr
N.A.I.C.S.: 335999

Subsidiary (Domestic):
NOVA Integration Solutions, Inc.   (2)
19 E 17th St, Saint Cloud, FL 34769
Tel.: (407) 556-3934
Web Site: http://www.novaintegration.com
Emp.: 15
Electric Equipment Mfr
N.A.I.C.S.: 335999
Dean Markley *(VP-Ops & Gen Mgr)*
Michael Martyniak *(VP-Mktg)*

Mid-Eastern Industries, Inc.   (1)
100 School St, Bergenfield, NJ 07621
Tel.: (201) 385-0500
Web Site: http://www.mideastind.com
Electric Equipment Mfr
N.A.I.C.S.: 335999

Nova Electric   (1)
100 School St, Bergenfield, NJ 07621-2915   (100%)
Tel.: (201) 385-0500
Web Site: http://www.novaelectric.com
Inverters, Uninterruptible Power System Mfr
N.A.I.C.S.: 334419

TECHNOLOGY FINANCE PARTNERS INC.
1250 Bayhill Dr Ste 380, San Bruno, CA 94066
Tel.: (650) 353-4231
Web Site: http://www.tfpllc.com
Year Founded: 2000
Sales Range: $1-9.9 Million
Emp.: 13
Financial Management Consulting Services
N.A.I.C.S.: 541611
Ann Flynn *(Co-Founder)*
Drew Wright *(Co-Founder)*
Greg Turtletaub *(Sec)*
Denise Garcia *(Engr-Creative Fin)*
Jack Shea *(VP-IT Equipment Financing)*

TECHNOLOGY FOR ENERGY CORPORATION
10737 Lexington Dr, Knoxville, TN 37932-3294
Tel.: (865) 966-5856
Web Site: http://www.tec-usa.com
Year Founded: 1975
Sales Range: $10-24.9 Million
Diagnostic Instrument Mfr
N.A.I.C.S.: 334519
William Simpkins *(CEO)*

Subsidiaries:
Dynamic Instruments Inc.   (1)
4393 Viewridge Ave Ste C, San Diego, CA 92123
Tel.: (858) 810-7900
Web Site: http://www.dynamicinst.com
Emp.: 10
Monitoring System Mfr
N.A.I.C.S.: 333515
Paul F. Whitten Sr. *(VP-Sls & Mktg)*

Subsidiary (Domestic):
Hardy Process Solutions, Inc.   (2)
9440 Carroll Park Dr Ste 150, San Diego, CA 92121-5201
Tel.: (858) 278-2900
Web Site: http://www.hardysolutions.com
Process Control Instruments Mfr & Design
N.A.I.C.S.: 334513
Carlos Moya *(Reg Mgr-Latin America)*

TECHNOLOGY INSURANCE ASSOCIATES, LLC
225 Gordons Corner Rd Ste 1H, Manalapan, NJ 07726
Tel.: (732) 832-7997
Web Site: http://www.insureyourcompany.com
Year Founded: 2001
Sales Range: $1-9.9 Million
Emp.: 24
Insurance Brokerage Services
N.A.I.C.S.: 524210
Alan Levenson *(Founder)*
Benjamin Levenson *(VP-Ops)*
Gauri Gupta *(Dir-Employee Benefits)*
Daniel Levenson *(Mktg Dir)*
David Mallow *(Sr Mgr-Sls)*

TECHNOLOGY ONE
1740 Westwood Blvd, Los Angeles, CA 90024-5608
Tel.: (310) 470-8282   CA
Year Founded: 1982
Sales Range: $25-49.9 Million
Retailer & Wholesaler of Computers & Accessories
N.A.I.C.S.: 541512
Roger Manu *(Gen Mgr-Enterprise Content Mgmt-DataWorks)*

TECHNOLOGY PARTNERS INC.
707 Spirit No 40 Park Dr Ste 120, Chesterfield, MO 63005
Tel.: (636) 519-1221
Web Site: http://www.technologypartners.net
Year Founded: 1994
Rev.: $22,647,831
Emp.: 205
Computer Software Systems Analysis & Design
N.A.I.C.S.: 541511
Greg Nichols *(Pres)*
Matt Nicolls *(CTO)*
Tyler Dougherty *(Mgr-Acct)*
Lisa Nichols *(Co-Founder & CEO)*

TECHNOLOGY PARTNERS, INC.
8757 Red Oak Blvd, Charlotte, NC 28217
Tel.: (704) 553-1004
Web Site: http://www.imagineteam.com
Year Founded: 2000
Sales Range: $1-9.9 Million
Emp.: 125
Software Development Services
N.A.I.C.S.: 541511
Michael J. Hershman *(Chm)*
Sam Khashman *(Founder, Pres & CEO)*
Daniel Beckmann *(COO)*
Tyler Baker *(Officer-Client Success)*
Dan Gotte *(CFO)*
Elizabeth Suppa *(Chief Mktg Officer)*
Emiliya Cvetanova *(Chief Results Officer)*

TECHNOLOGY PLUS INC.
3430 McKelvey Rd Ste i, Bridgeton, MO 63044
Tel.: (816) 795-7720
Web Site: http://www.tplusinc.com
Sales Range: $10-24.9 Million

Emp.: 10
Engineering Help Service
N.A.I.C.S.: 561320
Bobby Watson *(Exec VP)*
Jim Boudreau *(Mgr-St Louis-Missouri)*
Mark Hinton *(Mgr-Bus Dev)*
Eric Guess *(Engr-Sys)*
Chuck Carpenter *(Dir-Telecom)*
John Mills *(Mgr-Safety)*
Richard D. Bronson *(Pres)*

TECHNOLOGY RECOVERY GROUP LTD.
31390 Viking Pkwy, Westlake, OH 44145-4145
Tel.: (440) 250-9970
Web Site: http://www.trgrepair.com
Year Founded: 2002
Mobile Computers, Barcode Scanners, Printer, Pos & Payments & Software Accessories Mfr
N.A.I.C.S.: 334111
Sean Kennedy *(Pres)*
Christopher Free *(CFO)*
Tim Steiner *(Dir-IT)*

Subsidiaries:
Dowling Consulting Group, Inc.   (1)
4833 Darrow Rd Ste 100, Stow, OH 44224
Tel.: (330) 656-1136
Web Site: http://questintegratedsolutions.com
Software Services
N.A.I.C.S.: 513210

TECHNOLOGY RESOURCE CENTER OF AMERICA, LLC (TRCA)
2600 Virginia Cir, Denton, TX 76209
Tel.: (940) 565-5000
Web Site: http://www.trca.com
Sales Range: $10-24.9 Million
Emp.: 47
Telephone Equipment & Support Services
N.A.I.C.S.: 517112
Michael J. Harding *(Sr Acct Exec)*
John Hunnicutt *(VP-Govt Sys)*

TECHNOLOGY SERVICE CORPORATION
251 18th St S Ste 705, Arlington, VA 22202
Tel.: (703) 251-4600
Web Site: http://www.tsc.com
Year Founded: 1966
Software Engineering & Intelligence Support Services
N.A.I.C.S.: 541330
Michael Lee *(Sr Program Mgr)*

TECHNOLOGY SERVICES CORP.
2000 Town Ctr Ste 1900, Southfield, MI 48075-1152
Tel.: (313) 581-0960
Sales Range: $10-24.9 Million
Emp.: 50
Computer Integrated Systems Design
N.A.I.C.S.: 541512
Leon Brudek *(Pres)*

TECHNOLOGY STAFFING ON CALL
103 Fifth Ave # 24, Pelham, NY 10803-1503
Tel.: (212) 986-7100   NY
Web Site: http://www.tsoc.net
Year Founded: 1995
Sales Range: $1-9.9 Million
Emp.: 6
Employment Agencies
N.A.I.C.S.: 561311
Lou Mastropasqua *(Principal)*

TECHNOLOGY SUPPORT, INC.

Technology Support, Inc.—(Continued)
7021 Alder Dr, Houston, TX 77081
Tel.: (713) 626-8324   TX
Web Site:
http://www.technologysupport.com
Year Founded: 1994
Sales Range: $10-24.9 Million
Emp.: 17
Computer & Software Stores
N.A.I.C.S.: 449210
Jack Brandt (CEO)

TECHNOLOGY TRANSFER INSTITUTE/VANGUARD
741 10th St, Santa Monica, CA 90402-2821
Tel.: (310) 394-8305   CA
Web Site: http://www.ttivanguard.com
Year Founded: 1976
Sales Range: $50-74.9 Million
Emp.: 15
Provider of Educational Seminars & Conferences; Consulting in Computer Technology
N.A.I.C.S.: 519290
Robin Lockett (Program Mgr)
Claudia Miklas (Mgr-Client Svcs)
Lisa Yao (CEO)

TECHNOLOGY UNLIMITED INC.
6802 S 220th St, Kent, WA 98032
Tel.: (206) 575-8644
Web Site: http://www.tuiusa.com
Sales Range: $10-24.9 Million
Emp.: 35
Store Machines
N.A.I.C.S.: 811210
Robert Sproul (Chm & CEO)
Bill Vannet (CFO)
Erik Fitterer (VP)

TECHNOLOGY VENTURES, INC
25200 Malvina, Warren, MI 48089
Tel.: (586) 573-6000
Web Site: http://www.tvihq.com
Year Founded: 1992
Sales Range: $10-24.9 Million
Emp.: 10
Logistics, IT, Engineering & Technical Support
N.A.I.C.S.: 541614
Constance Blair (Pres & CEO)

TECHNOMARINE YACHTS, INC.
1208 US Hwy 1 Ste C, North Palm Beach, FL 33408
Tel.: (561) 420-7299   FL
Web Site:
http://www.technomarineyachts.com
Yacht Sales, Customization & Management Services; Marina Construction & Management Services
N.A.I.C.S.: 441222
Dennis A. Close (Pres & Mng Partner)

TECHNOMAX LLC
196 Princeton-Hightstown Rd Bldg 1A Ste 12, Princeton Junction, NJ 08550
Tel.: (609) 456-0186
Web Site:
http://www.technomaxllc.com
Year Founded: 2006
Sales Range: $1-9.9 Million
Emp.: 10
IT Consulting, Staff Augmentation & Implementation Services
N.A.I.C.S.: 541618
Sai Varanasi (Pres & CEO)
Padma Varanasi (CFO)
Swati Patki (Mgr-HR)
Tina Anand (Mgr-Bus Dev)

TECHNOMILE LLC
1861 International Dr Ste 270, McLean, VA 22102
Tel.: (703) 340-1308
Web Site: http://www.technomile.com
Custom Computer Programming Services
N.A.I.C.S.: 541511
Sean Reid (VP-Wholesale)
Daniel Osborne (Mng Dir)
Ashish Khot (CEO)
Subsidiaries:
Carrollpub, Inc.   (1)
4701 Sangamore Rd Ste S-155, Bethesda, MD 20816
Tel.: (301) 263-9800
Web Site: http://www.carrollpub.com
Data Processing, Hosting & Related Services
N.A.I.C.S.: 518210

TECHNOSYSTEMS CONSOLIDATED CORPORATION
217 9th St, Pittsburgh, PA 15222-3506
Tel.: (412) 288-1300   DE
Year Founded: 1988
Sales Range: $10-24.9 Million
Holding Company; Invention Submission, Licensing, Marketing & Other Support Services
N.A.I.C.S.: 551112
Bob Hohn (Dir-Creative)
Gary Jones (Dir-Sls)
Kirsten Piatt (Dir-HR)
Alexis Fisher (Coord-HR)
Robert Susa (Pres)
Subsidiaries:
Intromark, Inc.   (1)
217 9th St, Pittsburgh, PA 15222
Tel.: (412) 288-1368
Web Site: http://www.intromark.com
Emp.: 200
Invention Licensing & Marketing Services
N.A.I.C.S.: 533110
Chris Rosleck (Dir-Licensing)
Invention Submission Corporation   (1)
217 9th St, Pittsburgh, PA 15222-3506   (100%)
Tel.: (412) 288-1300
Web Site: http://www.inventhelp.com
Invention Submission Services
N.A.I.C.S.: 561990
Liv Dobo (Mgr-Interactive Adv)
Robert Susa (Pres)
Kirsten Piatt (Dir-HR)
Bob Hohn (Dir-Creative)
Matthew Tagliavia (Dir-Mktg)
Nicole Lininger (Dir-Corp Comm)
Kendal Hilko (Mgr-Mktg)

TECHPOWER SOLUTIONS INC.
14656 NE 95th St, Redmond, WA 98052
Tel.: (425) 883-9112
Web Site:
http://www.techpowerusa.com
Rev.: $21,660,376
Emp.: 20
Computer Integrated Systems Design
N.A.I.C.S.: 541512
Glen Jones (Pres)
Chip Cantrell (CTO)
Pauline Gallardo (Mgr-Acctg)
Sean Donlin (Acct Mgr-Comml-Pub Sector)

TECHPRO POWER GROUP, INC.
15825 Trinity Blvd, Forth Worth, TX 76115
Tel.: (817) 465-9494
Web Site:
https://www.techpropowergroup.com
Year Founded: 2007
Emp.: 100
Electrical, Instrumentation & Control Testing & Start-Up & Commissioning Services
N.A.I.C.S.: 238210
Michael Kilpatrick (CEO)
Subsidiaries:
Sentinel Power Services, Inc.   (1)
2720 N Hwy 167, Catoosa, OK 74015
Tel.: (918) 266-0067
Web Site:
http://www.sentinelpowerservices.com
Sales Range: $1-9.9 Million
Emp.: 20
Electronic & Precision Equipment Repair & Maintenance
N.A.I.C.S.: 811210
Finley Ledbetter (VP)
Greg Ellis (CEO)

TECHRADIUM, INC.
One Sugar Creek Center Blvd Ste 1100, Sugar Land, TX 77478
Tel.: (281) 207-4893
Web Site: http://www.techradium.com
Year Founded: 2000
Sales Range: $1-9.9 Million
Emp.: 31
Mass Notification & Emergency Alerting Software to Government, Educational, Commercial & Non-Profit Organizations
N.A.I.C.S.: 334610
Ryan Rodkey (CEO)

TECHSKILLS, LLC
110 Wild Basin Rd Ste 310, Austin, TX 78746
Tel.: (512) 328-4235   WI
Web Site: http://www.techskills.com
Year Founded: 1996
Sales Range: $25-49.9 Million
Emp.: 430
Computer Classes & Educational Services
N.A.I.C.S.: 611420
Tom Bezek (Dir-Campus-Las Vegas)

TECHSMITH CORPORATION
2405 Woodlake Dr, Okemos, MI 48864
Tel.: (517) 381-2300
Web Site: http://www.techsmith.com
Year Founded: 1987
Rev.: $22,300,000
Emp.: 212
Computer Software Services
N.A.I.C.S.: 513210
Tony Dunckel (VP-Market Solutions)
Dewey Hou (VP-Product Dev)
William Hamilton (Founder & Chm)
Dean Craven (CTO)
Wendy Hamilton (CEO)

TECHSOL4U, INC.
94 W 11th St Ste 206, Tracy, CA 95376
Tel.: (888) 803-1603
Web Site: http://www.techsol4u.com
Year Founded: 2007
Sales Range: $1-9.9 Million
Emp.: 18
Technology Services
N.A.I.C.S.: 513210
Suneel Ravi (COO)

TECHSOUP GLOBAL
435 Brannan St Ste 100, San Francisco, CA 94107
Tel.: (415) 512-7784   CA
Web Site:
http://www.techsoupglobal.org
Year Founded: 1987
Sales Range: $25-49.9 Million
Emp.: 221

Technology Support Services
John McDermott (Controller)
Dara Westling (VP-Dev)
Geri Jin Doran (COO)
Richard Collins (Sr Dir-Infrastructure)

TECHSOURCE, INC.
1475 Central Ave Ste 250, Los Alamos, NM 87544
Tel.: (505) 988-1726   NM
Web Site: http://www.techsource-inc.com
Year Founded: 1997
Sales Range: $1-9.9 Million
Emp.: 75
Technical & Management Services
N.A.I.C.S.: 541690
Victor Brian D'Andrea (Pres & CEO)
Don Trost (Exec VP & Dir-Ops-Washington)
K. Ammons (Mgr-Fin)
Will Sanchez (Mgr-Contracts)
Thomas Ward (Chm & VP)
James Rhone (VP & Sr Program Mgr)
Robert Hollen (Head-Staff)

TECHSTACKERY, INC.
501 Brickell Key Dr Ste 300, Miami, FL 33135-3250   DE
Year Founded: 2021
Investment Services
N.A.I.C.S.: 523999
Scott W. Absher (Chm & CEO)
Domonic J. Carney (CFO & Treas)
Robert S. Gans (Gen Counsel & Sec)

TECHSTAR GROUP, INC.
222 W Las Colinas Blvd Ste 540 E Tower, Irving, TX 75039
Tel.: (972) 756-1300
Web Site:
http://www.techstargroup.com
Year Founded: 2002
Sales Range: $10-24.9 Million
Emp.: 230
Information Technology Development Services
N.A.I.C.S.: 541512
Raghu Chittimalla (CEO & Mng Partner)
Ashok K. Chitiprolu (CTO & Mng Partner)
Nimish Mishra (Partner-Emerging Technologies)
Michael O'Neill (Dir-Sls & Mktg)
Mark Castaneda (Dir-Staffing Sls)

TECHWAVE CONSULTING INC.
1 E Uwchlan Ave Ste 101, Exton, PA 19341
Tel.: (484) 872-8707
Web Site:
http://www.techwavenet.com
Year Founded: 2004
Sales Range: $1-9.9 Million
Emp.: 73
It Consulting
N.A.I.C.S.: 541690
Vanaja Gummadapu (Pres)
Tribhuvan Kongonda (Mgr-Fin)
Tony Dastra (Sr Acct Exec)

TECMA GROUP, LLC
2000 Wyoming Ave, El Paso, TX 79903-3501
Tel.: (915) 534-4252   TX
Web Site: http://www.tecma.com
Year Founded: 1985
Emp.: 7,000
Industrial Support Services
N.A.I.C.S.: 541611
K. Alan Russell (Founder, Chm & CEO)

Toby Spoon *(Exec VP)*
Mark Earley *(Pres)*
Jose Grajeda *(VP-Ops)*
Manuel Ochoa *(VP-Bus Dev)*
Ernesto Bravo *(Pres-Tecma West)*

TECNIQ, INC.
9100 E Michigan Ave, Galesburg, MI 49053
Tel.: (269) 629-4440
Web Site: http://www.tecniqinc.com
Year Founded: 2004
Sales Range: $1-9.9 Million
Emp.: 80
Designs & Manufactures Interior & Exterior LED Lighting Products for Heavy-Duty Vehicles, Boats & Boat Trailers
N.A.I.C.S.: 336320
Jeff Condon *(Pres)*

TECOLOTE RESEARCH INC.
420 Fairview Av Ste 201, Goleta, CA 93117-3626
Tel.: (805) 571-6366   CA
Web Site: http://www.tecolote.com
Year Founded: 1973
Sales Range: $25-49.9 Million
Emp.: 323
Financial Management & Cost Analysis Services
N.A.I.C.S.: 541715
Michael Underwood *(Dir-Contracts)*
Ronald S. Bowen *(Gen Mgr-Programs)*
Kevin Jackameit *(Program Mgr)*
James Y. Takayesu *(Pres)*

TECON CORPORATION
4144 N Central Expy Ste 900, Dallas, TX 75204
Tel.: (214) 647-2200
Web Site: http://www.holidayvillages.com
Rev.: $22,200,000
Emp.: 30
Subdividers & Developers
N.A.I.C.S.: 237210
Mitzi Pool *(Office Mgr)*
Angel Smith *(Controller)*
Bob Hardwick *(Pres)*
Deborah Roberts *(Mgr-Payroll)*
Clint W. Murchison III *(Chm)*

TECON SERVICES INC.
515 Garden Oaks Blvd, Houston, TX 77018
Tel.: (713) 691-2700
Web Site: http://www.teconservices.com
Sales Range: $10-24.9 Million
Emp.: 95
Engineering Construction Contractor
N.A.I.C.S.: 237990
Curtis Ward *(VP)*
Jimmy Robertson *(Dir-Safety)*
Curtis Ford *(Owner)*
Jose Silva *(Project Mgr)*

TECTONIC ENGINEERING AND SURVEYING CONSULTANTS P.C.
70 Pleasant Hill Rd, Mountainville, NY 10953
Tel.: (845) 534-5959
Web Site: http://www.tectonicengineering.com
Sales Range: $10-24.9 Million
Emp.: 200
Provider of Engineering Services
N.A.I.C.S.: 541330
Ed Frawley *(VP)*
Jeffrey Scala *(VP & Reg Dir)*

TECTONIC LLC
1644 Platte St, Denver, CO 80202
Tel.: (303) 549-9034
Web Site: http://www.gettectonic.com
N.A.I.C.S.:
Blair Linville *(Chm & CEO)*
Terry Wisner *(Exec VP)*

Subsidiaries:

Stryve Advisors (1)
10333 Richmond A, Houston, TX 77042-4483
Tel.: (713) 600-5696
Web Site: http://www.istryve.com
Consulting & Advisory Services for IT Sector
N.A.I.C.S.: 541690
Ron Christman *(Partner)*

TECTURA CORPORATION
4309 Hacienda Dr Ste 550, Pleasanton, CA 94588   DE
Web Site: http://www.tectura.com
Year Founded: 2001
Information Technology Consulting Services
N.A.I.C.S.: 541690
Vincent Castiglione *(VP-Corp Dev)*

TECUM CAPITAL PARTNERS, LLC
8000 Brooktree Rd Ste 310, Wexford, PA 15090
Tel.: (724) 602-4399   DE
Web Site: http://www.tecum.com
Year Founded: 2005
Mezzanine Debt & Equity Investment Firm
N.A.I.C.S.: 523999
Matthew L. T. Harnett *(Partner)*
Tyson Smith *(Partner)*
Stephen J. Gurgovits Jr. *(Mng Partner)*

Subsidiaries:

Gibraltar Cable Barrier Systems, LP (1)
1208 Houston Clinton Dr, Burnet, TX 78611
Tel.: (833) 715-0810
Web Site: http://www.gibraltarglobal.com
Fabricated Metal Cable Barrier Product Mfr
N.A.I.C.S.: 332999
Bryan Hoefling *(Reg Sls Mgr-US)*
Jay Winn *(Reg Sls Mgr-US)*
Ron Faulkenberry *(Pres)*
Clay Amuny *(Controller)*
Julie Ray *(Dir-Ops)*

Powertrack International, LLC (1)
4625 Campbells Run Rd, Pittsburgh, PA 15205
Tel.: (412) 787-4444
Web Site: http://www.powertrackhose.com
Sales Range: $10-24.9 Million
Industrial & Hydraulic Hose & Fittings Distr
N.A.I.C.S.: 423840
Andrew Kuron *(Pres)*

TED BARKUS COMPANY, INC.
8017 Anderson St, Philadelphia, PA 19118
Tel.: (215) 545-0616   PA
Year Founded: 1958
Sales Range: $125-149.9 Million
Emp.: 150
Public Relations
N.A.I.C.S.: 541810
Harriet A. Barkus *(Exec VP-Media)*
Rhoda Sachs *(VP-HR)*
Allen E. Barkus *(Pres & Creative Dir)*
B. Solomon *(VP-New Media)*

Subsidiaries:

TBC Public Relations (1)
8017 Anderson St, Philadelphia, PA 19118
Tel.: (215) 545-0616
Sales Range: $10-24.9 Million
Emp.: 18
Public Relations Agency
N.A.I.C.S.: 541820

TBC Sales Promotion (1)
8017 Anderson St, Philadelphia, PA 19118
Tel.: (215) 545-0616
Sales Range: $1-9.9 Million
Emp.: 8
Advetising Agency
N.A.I.C.S.: 541810

TED BRITT FORD SALES INC.
11165 Fairfax Blvd, Fairfax, VA 22030
Tel.: (703) 591-8484
Web Site: http://www.tedbrittford.com
Sales Range: $125-149.9 Million
Emp.: 230
New & Used Car Dealers
N.A.I.C.S.: 441110
Mike Andress *(CFO)*
Janet Omohundro *(Mgr-Accts Payable)*
Evelyn Akers *(Gen Mgr)*
M. Gardner Britt Jr. *(Owner)*

TED BROWN MUSIC COMPANY, INC.
6228 Tacoma Mall Blvd, Tacoma, WA 98409-6827
Tel.: (253) 272-3211
Web Site: http://www.tedbrownmusic.com
Sales Range: $10-24.9 Million
Emp.: 100
Musical Instrument Whslr
N.A.I.C.S.: 459140
Whitney Grisaffi *(Pres)*

TED RUSSELL ENTERPRISES INC.
8551 Kingston Pike, Knoxville, TN 37919
Tel.: (865) 693-7611
Web Site: http://www.tedrussellford.net
Sales Range: $25-49.9 Million
Emp.: 150
New & Used Car Dealers
N.A.I.C.S.: 441110
Ted Russell *(Owner & Pres)*

TED TODD INSURANCE, INC.
10020 Coconut Rd Ste 144, Bonita Springs, FL 34135
Tel.: (239) 561-1100
Web Site: http://www.tedtoddinsurance.com
Year Founded: 1986
Sales Range: $1-9.9 Million
Emp.: 40
Insurance Agencies
N.A.I.C.S.: 524210
Tedd A. Todd *(CEO & Principal)*
Al Hernandez *(Comptroller)*
Jeff East *(Mgr-Sls)*
Jennifer Todd *(Mgr-Ops)*
Jodi Marturano *(Mgr-HR)*

TED WIENS TIRE & AUTO CENTERS
1701 Las Vegas Blvd S, Las Vegas, NV 89104
Tel.: (702) 732-2382
Web Site: http://www.tedwiens.com
Year Founded: 1948
Sales Range: $25-49.9 Million
Emp.: 225
General Automotive Repair Shops
N.A.I.C.S.: 811111
Ted Wiens Jr. *(Pres)*

TED'S & FRED'S INC.
115 2nd St, Reedsburg, WI 53959
Tel.: (608) 524-4533
Sales Range: $10-24.9 Million
Emp.: 75
Independent Supermarket
N.A.I.C.S.: 445110
David Sorenson *(Pres)*

TEDDY'S TRANSPORT
4201 Lincoln Rd, Holland, MI 49423
Tel.: (269) 751-8050
Web Site: http://www.teddystransport.com
Year Founded: 1982
Sales Range: $1-9.9 Million
Emp.: 75
Truck Load Services
N.A.I.C.S.: 484121
Mary Gibbs *(Founder)*

TEDDY'S TRANSPORTATION SYSTEM, INC.
18 Rowan St, Norwalk, CT 06855
Tel.: (203) 866-2231
Web Site: http://www.teddyslimousine.com
Year Founded: 1932
Rev.: $4,100,000
Emp.: 50
Limousine Service
N.A.I.C.S.: 485320
Charles Wisniewski *(Pres)*

TEDESCHI FOOD SHOPS, INC.
14 Howard St, Rockland, MA 02370-1998
Tel.: (781) 878-8210   MA
Web Site: http://www.tedeschifoodshops.com
Year Founded: 1972
Sales Range: $250-299.9 Million
Emp.: 600
Provider of Grocery Services
N.A.I.C.S.: 445131
Peter Tedeschi *(Pres & CEO)*

TEDESCHI VINEYARDS, LTD.
Hwy 31 Ulpalakua Ranch, Kula, HI 96790
Tel.: (808) 878-6058
Web Site: http://www.mauiwine.com
Year Founded: 1974
Sales Range: $10-24.9 Million
Emp.: 28
Wine Mfr
N.A.I.C.S.: 312130
Paula Hegele *(Pres)*

TEE GROUP FILMS
605 N Main St, Ladd, IL 61329-0425
Tel.: (815) 894-2331   DE
Web Site: http://www.tee-group.com
Sales Range: $75-99.9 Million
Emp.: 60
Unsupported Plastics & Film Mfr
N.A.I.C.S.: 326113
Thomas H. Malpass *(Co-Pres)*
Paula Fues *(Office Mgr)*
Kelley Fisher *(Mgr-Sls, Customer Svc & Traffic)*
Dave Bejster *(Mgr-Ops)*
Bob Lund *(Mgr-Maintenance)*
John Buckner *(Co-Pres)*

TEE PEE CONTRACTORS INC.
3095 N Lear Ave, Casa Grande, AZ 85222
Tel.: (520) 836-8513
Web Site: http://www.teepeecontractors.com
Rev.: $10,000,000
Emp.: 60
Water, Sewer & Utility Lines
N.A.I.C.S.: 237110
Terry D. Tate *(Pres & CEO)*
Kermit Schafersman *(VP-Construction)*

TEE PEE OLIVES, INC./ITALICA IMPORTS
411 Theodore Fremd Ave Ste 120, Rye, NY 10580-1411
Web Site: http://www.teepeeolives.com
Sales Range: $10-24.9 Million

TEE PEE OLIVES, INC./ITALICA IMPORTS

U.S. PRIVATE

Tee Pee Olives, Inc./Italica Imports—(Continued)
Emp.: 50
Olive Oil Importer & Distr
N.A.I.C.S.: 424490
Lucy Landesman (Pres)

TEECO PRODUCTS INC.
16881 Armstrong Ave, Irvine, CA 92606
Tel.: (949) 261-6295
Web Site: http://www.teecoproducts.com
Sales Range: $10-24.9 Million
Emp.: 50
Petroleum Industry Machinery
N.A.I.C.S.: 423830
Bob Bailey (COO)
Gary Childress (CFO)

TEEL CONSTRUCTION INC.
768 Walker Rd Fl 2, Great Falls, VA 22066
Tel.: (703) 759-4754
Web Site: http://www.teelconstruction.com
Year Founded: 1987
Rev.: $17,464,916
Emp.: 10
Commercial & Office Building Contracting Services
N.A.I.C.S.: 236220
Parker Teel (Pres)
Kevin Nielsen (Controller)
John Mimnaugh (Sr Project Mgr)
Brian Weathers (Project Mgr)

TEEMA SOLUTIONS GROUP INC.
8001 Irvine Ctr Dr 4th Fl, Irvine, CA 92618
Tel.: (949) 681-8179
Web Site: http://www.teemagroup.com
Year Founded: 2008
Sales Range: $25-49.9 Million
Emp.: 90
Executive Search Service
N.A.I.C.S.: 561312
Brian Antenbring (Pres)

TEETER IRRIGATION INC.
201 E Oklahoma Ave, Ulysses, KS 67880
Tel.: (620) 353-1111
Web Site: http://www.teeterirrigation.com
Sales Range: $10-24.9 Million
Emp.: 40
Irrigation Equipment
N.A.I.C.S.: 423820
Monty Teeter (Owner & Pres)

TEEWINOT LIFE SCIENCES CORPORATION
13033 W Linebaugh Ave, Tampa, FL 33626
Tel.: (813) 803-6300
Web Site: http://www.tlscorp.com
Biotechnology Research & Development Services
N.A.I.C.S.: 541714
Michael A. Luther (Pres & CEO)
Steve Orndorff (COO)
Charles Brink (Chm)

TEGRA CORPORATION
2651 Murray St, Sioux City, IA 51111
Tel.: (712) 258-6596
Web Site: http://www.tegracorp.com
Year Founded: 1918
Sales Range: Less than $1 Million
Emp.: 20
Holding Company; Provider of Agricultural Services
N.A.I.C.S.: 493110
Douglas E. Palmer (Pres & CFO)

TEICHERT, INC.
3500 American River Dr, Sacramento, CA 95864-5802
Tel.: (916) 484-3011 CA
Web Site: http://www.teichert.com
Year Founded: 1887
Sales Range: $1-4.9 Billion
Emp.: 2,500
Heavy Engineering Contractors & Building Materials Producers
N.A.I.C.S.: 237310
Frederick Teichert (Exec Dir)
Judson T. Riggs (Chm & CEO)

Subsidiaries:

Mathews Readymix LLC (1)
4711 Hammonton Rd, Marysville, CA 95901
Tel.: (530) 749-6525
Web Site: https://www.mathewsreadymixllc.com
Readymix Concrete Mfr
N.A.I.C.S.: 327320

Teichert Land Co. (1)
3500 American River Dr, Sacramento, CA 95864-5802 (100%)
Tel.: (916) 484-3011
Web Site: http://www.teichert.com
Sales Range: $25-49.9 Million
Emp.: 130
Ground & Surface Construction Services
N.A.I.C.S.: 531210

Western Aggregates LLC (1)
4711 Hammonton Rd, Marysville, CA 95901
Tel.: (530) 749-8670
Concrete & Aggregate Products Mfr & Distr
N.A.I.C.S.: 327320

TEIKAMETRICS LLC
280 Summer St 9th Fl, Boston, MA 02210
Tel.: (855) 846-2677
Web Site: http://www.teikametrics.com
Year Founded: 2012
Commerce Software Publisher
N.A.I.C.S.: 513210
Alasdair McLean-Foreman (CEO)
Joseph Gaetano (CTO)
Andy Coughlin (Chief Revenue Officer)
Srini Guddanti (Chief Product Officer)

Subsidiaries:

Lab Escape, Inc. (1)
33 Coxe Ave 7556, Asheville, NC 28802
Tel.: (646) 964-6463
Web Site: http://www.labescape.com
Visual Data Discovery Software Publishers
N.A.I.C.S.: 513210
Baron Davis (Co-Founder & COO)
Trevor Lohrbee (Co-Founder & CEO)

TEIKURO CORPORATION
135 Main St Fl 9, San Francisco, CA 94105-1815
Tel.: (415) 273-2650
Web Site: http://www.teikuro.com
Year Founded: 1985
Sales Range: $10-24.9 Million
Emp.: 80
Provider of Electroplating Services
N.A.I.C.S.: 332813
Toyohiko Ichikawa (Chm)

TEIXEIRA FARMS INC.
2600 Bonita Lateral Rd, Santa Maria, CA 93458-9703
Tel.: (805) 928-3801 CA
Web Site: http://www.teixeirafarms.com
Year Founded: 1950
Sales Range: $10-24.9 Million
Emp.: 188
Vegetables & Melons
N.A.I.C.S.: 111219
Pam Lind (Mgr-Cooler)
Mark Teixeira (Gen Mgr)

TEJAS INDUSTRIES
FM 2943 Hwy 60, Hereford, TX 79045
Tel.: (806) 322-2800
Web Site: http://www.tejasindustries.com
Sales Range: $50-74.9 Million
Emp.: 500
Mfr of Dog Food
N.A.I.C.S.: 311111
Cory Schumacher (Controller)

TEJAS TOYOTA INC.
19011 Hwy 59 N, Humble, TX 77338
Tel.: (281) 446-0271
Web Site: http://www.tejastoyota.com
Rev.: $26,400,000
Emp.: 120
Automobiles, New & Used
N.A.I.C.S.: 441110
Benard J. Toomey (Pres)
Mike Davidson (Mgr-Svc)

TEK INDUSTRIES INC.
8843 S 137th Cir, Omaha, NE 68138
Tel.: (402) 721-5777
Web Site: http://www.tekindustries.com
Rev.: $17,400,000
Emp.: 140
Holding Company
N.A.I.C.S.: 334220
Stephen W. Nabity (CEO)

TEKCOM RESOURCES, INC.
1150 First Ave Ste 905, King of Prussia, PA 19406
Tel.: (610) 491-9144
Web Site: http://www.tekcomresources.com
Year Founded: 2005
Sales Range: $1-9.9 Million
Emp.: 13
Telecommunication Servicesb
N.A.I.C.S.: 517810
Kary Raddant (Owner & CEO)
Ian Raddant (Pres-Sls & Mgmt)
Cindy Vilkauskas (Mgr-Resource)
Steve Hillman (Dir-Sls Acct)
Kara Reiter (VP-Sls, Telco & Consulting Svcs)

TEKEYAN CULTURAL ASSOCIATION INC.
755 Mount Auburn St, Watertown, MA 02472
Tel.: (617) 924-4420 MA
Web Site: http://www.tekeyan.net
Year Founded: 1969
Sales Range: $1-9.9 Million
Emp.: 30
Cultural Event Organizer
N.A.I.C.S.: 711310
Maro Bedrosian (Treas)

TEKNETEX INC.
209 10th Ave S Ste 320, Nashville, TN 37203
Tel.: (615) 750-3425
Web Site: http://www.teknetex.com
Year Founded: 2007
Sales Range: $1-9.9 Million
Emp.: 18
It Consulting
N.A.I.C.S.: 541690
John Kepley (Owner & CEO)

TEKNETIX INC.
2501 Garfield Ave, Parkersburg, WV 26101
Tel.: (304) 424-9400
Web Site: http://www.teknetix.com
Rev.: $12,200,000
Emp.: 200
Bare Printed Circuit Board Mfr
N.A.I.C.S.: 334412

John W. Florence (Co-Founder, Sec & Exec VP-Sls & Mktg)
Kathi Ross (Mgr-Mfg)

TEKNICKS LLC
416 Lake Ave, Bay Head, NJ 08742
Tel.: (732) 714-6683
Web Site: http://www.teknicks.com
Sales Range: $1-9.9 Million
Emp.: 52
Internet Marketing Services
N.A.I.C.S.: 541810
Nick Chasinov (Founder & CEO)

TEKNOL INC.
5751 Webster St, Dayton, OH 45414
Tel.: (937) 890-6547
Web Site: http://teknolr.openfos.com
Sales Range: $10-24.9 Million
Emp.: 42
Manufacturers of Sealants
N.A.I.C.S.: 325520
Elizabeth Back (Mgr-Quality Control)

TEKNOR APEX COMPANY
505 Central Ave, Pawtucket, RI 02861-1945
Tel.: (401) 725-8000 DE
Web Site: http://www.teknorapex.com
Year Founded: 1924
Sales Range: $1-4.9 Billion
Emp.: 2,400
Mfr of PVC & TPE Compounds, Chemicals, Rubber, Color Concentrates for Plastics, Garden Hoses, Anti-Fatigue Mats & Cutting Boards; Custom Processing Systems
N.A.I.C.S.: 325991
William J. Murray (Pres)
Suresh Swaminathan (Exec VP)

Subsidiaries:

Teknor Apex (Suzhou) Advanced Polymer Compounds Co. Pte Ltd. (1)
No 78 Ping Sheng Road, Suzhou Industrial Park, Suzhou, 215126, Jiangsu, China
Tel.: (86) 512 6287 1550
Sales Range: $10-24.9 Million
Emp.: 50
Vinyl Compound Mfr
N.A.I.C.S.: 325211

Teknor Apex Asia Pacific Pte. Ltd. (1)
41 Shipyard Road, Singapore, 628134, Singapore (100%)
Tel.: (65) 62652544
Web Site: http://www.teknorapex.com
Sales Range: $25-49.9 Million
Emp.: 195
Polymer Compound Mfr
N.A.I.C.S.: 325211
Kelleen Chin (CFO)
Lian Koon Tan (Mng Dir)
William J. Murray (Pres-Asia Pacific)

Teknor Apex B.V. (1)
Mijnweg 1, 6167 AC, Geleen, Netherlands (100%)
Tel.: (31) 46 7020966
Web Site: http://www.teknorapex.com
Sales Range: $25-49.9 Million
Emp.: 30
Mfr of Elastomers
N.A.I.C.S.: 326199
Gert Joly (Mgr-R&D-TPE Div)

Teknor Apex Company - Thermoplastic Elastomer Division (1)
3070 Ohio Dr, Henderson, KY 42420
Tel.: (270) 827-8890
Web Site: http://www.teknorapex.com
Thermoplastic & Elastomer Mfr
N.A.I.C.S.: 325211
Sachin Sakhalkar (VP-Global)

Teknor Apex Elastomers, Inc. (1)
31 Fuller St, Leominster, MA 01453
Tel.: (978) 534-1010
Web Site: http://www.teknorapex.com
Elastomer Mfr
N.A.I.C.S.: 325211

COMPANIES

Elizabeth Ponte *(Mgr-Mktg)*

Teknor Apex Vermont Company (1)
300 Industrial Park Rd, Saint Albans, VT 05478
Tel.: (802) 524-7704
Web Site: http://www.texnorapex.com
Thermoplastic & Elastomer Mfr
N.A.I.C.S.: 325211
Paul Burke *(Gen Mgr)*

Teknor Color Co. (1)
505 Central Ave, Pawtucket, RI 02861-1945
Tel.: (401) 725-8000
Web Site: http://www.texnorapex.com
Sales Range: $100-124.9 Million
Emp.: 450
Color Concentrate Compounds
N.A.I.C.S.: 325211
Jonathan D. Fain *(Pres)*
Dina Munroe *(Sec)*

Viking Polymers, LLC (1)
109 Ragsdale Rd, Jamestown, NC 27282
Tel.: (336) 454-1174
Web Site: http://www.vikingpolymers.com
Emp.: 35
Custom Compounding of Purchased Resins
N.A.I.C.S.: 325991
Louis R. Cappucci *(VP)*

TEKONTROL INC.
711 W Amelia St, Orlando, FL 32805
Tel.: (407) 398-6575
Web Site: http://www.tekontrol.com
Rev.: $12,200,000
Emp.: 60
Computer System Design Services
N.A.I.C.S.: 541512
Morris G. Middleton *(Sr VP-Engrg & Intl Svcs)*
Thomas S. Kornegay *(Founder, Chm & CEO)*
David O. Kornegay *(Dir-Sls Support)*
Glen A. Ballenger *(VP-Contracts)*
Jim Ricks *(Pres)*

TEKPROS INC.
5068 W Plano Pkwy Ste 255, Plano, TX 75093
Tel.: (972) 267-8357
Web Site: http://www.tekpros.com
Year Founded: 2005
Sales Range: $1-9.9 Million
Emp.: 55
It Consulting
N.A.I.C.S.: 541690
Rozmin Aamir *(Mgr-HR)*
Sree Nandi *(Mgr-Accts & HR)*

TEKSAVERS, INC.
2120 Grand Ave Pkwy Ste 150, Austin, TX 78728
Tel.: (512) 491-5304
Web Site: http://www.teksavers.com
Year Founded: 2002
Sales Range: $10-24.9 Million
Emp.: 40
Computer Equipment Reseller
N.A.I.C.S.: 423430
Rick Louden *(CEO & VP)*
Ruben Staalenburg *(CFO & VP)*
Troy Hall *(Mgr-Pur & Reseller Sls)*

TEKSCAPE
247 W 30th St, New York, NY 10001
Tel.: (800) 955-9078
Web Site: http://www.tekscapeit.com
Year Founded: 2007
Sales Range: $1-9.9 Million
Emp.: 18
Remote Workforces, Mobile Devices Integration & Data Security Management Solutions
N.A.I.C.S.: 541618
David Smith *(Founder & CEO)*

TEKSELL, INC.
3121 Bartlett Corp Dr Ste 104, Memphis, TN 38133-8936
Tel.: (901) 758-8179   NC
Web Site: http://www.teksell.com
Year Founded: 1999
Sales Range: $10-24.9 Million
Emp.: 25
Online Marketplace for IT Professionals to Buy & Sell New, Remanufactured & Previously Owned Data, Video & Voice Equipment
N.A.I.C.S.: 517810
Tara Williams *(Dir-Mktg)*

TELAID INDUSTRIES, INC.
13 W Main St, Niantic, CT 06357
Tel.: (860) 739-4461
Web Site: http://www.telaid.com
Year Founded: 1981
Sales Range: $10-24.9 Million
Information Technology & Communication Line Services
N.A.I.C.S.: 519290
Bill Patsiga *(CEO)*
Charles Demarino *(CFO)*
Chris Patsiga *(COO)*
Scott Patsiga *(Pres)*
Keith Aubele *(Chief Security Officer)*
Roger Gatto *(Sr VP-Bus Ops)*
Tim Harper *(Sr VP-Client Svcs)*
Justin Mason *(Sr VP)*
Mike Reedy *(Sr VP-Ops Strategic Acct)*

TELALASKA INC.
201 E 56th Ave, Anchorage, AK 99518
Tel.: (907) 563-2003
Web Site: http://www.telalaska.com
Year Founded: 1968
Sales Range: $10-24.9 Million
Emp.: 90
Telecommunication Servicesb
N.A.I.C.S.: 517810
David J. Goggins *(VP-Ops)*
Celine M. Kaplan *(Sr Mgr-Mktg & PR)*

Subsidiaries:

Eyecom Inc. (1)
201 E 56th Ave Ste 100, Anchorage, AK 99518
Tel.: (907) 563-2003
Web Site: http://www.telalaska.com
Cable Television Services
N.A.I.C.S.: 516210
Brenda Shepard *(Pres)*

Interior Telephone Company (1)
201 E 56th Ave, Anchorage, AK 99518
Tel.: (907) 563-2003
Web Site: http://www.telalaska.com
Rev.: $8,293,320
Emp.: 10
Telecommunication Servicesb
N.A.I.C.S.: 517810

Mukluk Telephone Company Inc (1)
201 E 56th Ave, Anchorage, AK 99518
Tel.: (907) 563-2003
Web Site: http://www.telalaska.com
Telecommunication Servicesb
N.A.I.C.S.: 517810
Dave Goggins *(Pres)*

Telco Properties (1)
201 E 56th Ave, Anchorage, AK 99518
Tel.: (907) 563-2016
Rev.: $150,000
Emp.: 2
Telephone Equipment & Systems
N.A.I.C.S.: 449210
Brenda Shepherd *(Pres)*

TELAMON CORPORATION
1000 E 116th St, Carmel, IN 46032
Tel.: (317) 818-6888
Web Site: http://www.telamon.com
Year Founded: 1985
Sales Range: $450-499.9 Million
Emp.: 400
Provider of Communication Services
N.A.I.C.S.: 423690
Albert Chen *(Founder & Chm)*
Stanley Chen *(CEO)*
Reggie Henderson *(Gen Mgr-Energy Solutions)*
Stephanie Fuhrmann *(Chief Admin Officer)*
Robert Ashburner *(CFO)*
Ralf Lorenzen *(Pres-Bus Process Solutions)*

Subsidiaries:

Telamon International Corp. (1)
1000 E 116th St, Carmel, IN 46032
Tel.: (317) 818-6888
Web Site: http://www.telamon.com
Rev.: $350,000
Emp.: 310
Communications Equipment
N.A.I.C.S.: 423690
Albert Chen *(Pres)*

Telamon Technologies Corp (1)
1000 E 116th St, Carmel, IN 46032
Tel.: (317) 818-6888
Web Site: http://www.telamon-corp.com
Sales Range: $75-99.9 Million
Emp.: 275
Wireline & Wireless Infrastructure
N.A.I.C.S.: 334210
Albert Chen *(Pres)*

TELAPEX INC.
1018 Highland Colony Pkwy Ste 700, Ridgeland, MS 39157
Tel.: (601) 355-1522   MS
Web Site: http://www.telapex.com
Year Founded: 1987
Telephone Communications
N.A.I.C.S.: 517121
Larry Morrison *(CFO)*
Carson Hughes *(CEO)*
Helen Simmons *(Dir-Acctg)*
Wesley Goings *(Pres)*

Subsidiaries:

Cellular South (1)
9471 3 Rivers Rd, Gulfport, MS 39503-4230
Tel.: (228) 865-0500
Web Site: http://www.cellularsouth.com
Sales Range: $10-24.9 Million
Emp.: 20
Cellular Telephone Communication
N.A.I.C.S.: 517112

Cellular South Inc. (1)
1018 Highland Colony Pkwy Ste 300, Ridgeland, MS 39157-3301
Tel.: (601) 355-1522
Web Site: http://www.cspire.com
Sales Range: $25-49.9 Million
Emp.: 300
Radiotelephone Communication Services
N.A.I.C.S.: 517112
Wade Creekmore *(Pres)*
Suzy Hays *(Sr VP-Mktg)*
Hu Meena *(CEO)*

Subsidiary (Domestic):

Harbor Communications, LLC (2)
1509 Government St Ste 300, Mobile, AL 36604
Tel.: (251) 662-1532
Web Site: http://www.harborcom.com
Rev.: $4,800,000
Emp.: 31
Fiber Optic Network Switching Technology & Communication Mfr
N.A.I.C.S.: 334290
Chuck Nylander *(VP-Mktg)*

Subsidiary (Domestic):

Convenience Store Decisions (3)
19111 Detroit Rd Ste 201, Rocky River, OH 44116
Tel.: (440) 250-1583
Web Site: http://www.csdecisions.com
Sales Range: $10-24.9 Million
Emp.: 5
Commercial Printing Services
N.A.I.C.S.: 323111
Bill Donohue *(Founder)*

Delta Telephone Co. Inc. (1)
1314 Main St, Louise, MS 39097
Tel.: (662) 836-5111
Web Site: http://www.deltaphone.net
Sales Range: $10-24.9 Million
Emp.: 13
Telephone Communications
N.A.I.C.S.: 517121
Brooks Derryberry *(VP)*

Franklin Telephone Company Inc. (1)
154 Main St E, Meadville, MS 39653
Tel.: (601) 384-5851
Sales Range: $10-24.9 Million
Emp.: 45
Providing Telephone Communication Services
N.A.I.C.S.: 517121
Wade Creekmore *(Pres)*
James Creekmore *(VP)*

Telepak Networks, Inc. (1)
1018 Highland Colony Pkwy Ste 400, Ridgeland, MS 39157
Tel.: (888) 806-4357
Web Site: http://www.telepaknetworks.com
Internet Service Provider
N.A.I.C.S.: 517810

TELCOIQ, INC.
4300 Forbes Blvd Ste 210, Lanham, MD 20706-4360
Tel.: (202) 595-1500
Web Site: http://www.telcoiq.com
Sales Range: $25-49.9 Million
Emp.: 20
Telecom Resellers
N.A.I.C.S.: 517121
Kmele Foster *(Co-Founder)*

TELDATA
11491 Woodside Ave, Santee, CA 92071
Tel.: (858) 874-2151
Web Site: http://www.teldata.com
Sales Range: $10-24.9 Million
Emp.: 50
Telephone & Telephone Equipment Installation
N.A.I.C.S.: 517112
Bruce Madden *(CEO)*
Roger Ramsey *(VP)*
Nancy Lemus *(Controller)*

TELE RESOURCES, INC.
1203 London Rd, Duluth, MN 55802
Tel.: (218) 724-2026   WI
Web Site: http://www.teleresources.net
Year Founded: 1996
Sales Range: $1-9.9 Million
Emp.: 200
Telemarketing Services
N.A.I.C.S.: 561422
Jeremy Locke *(Supvr-Program)*
Mary Bradley *(Supvr-Info Svcs)*
Wendie Johnson *(Dir-HR)*

TELE-CONSULTANTS, INC.
4080 McGinnis Ferry Rd 902, Alpharetta, GA 30005
Tel.: (678) 893-7900
Web Site: http://www.teleinc.com
Year Founded: 1985
Sales Range: $10-24.9 Million
Emp.: 153
Software Engineering Services
N.A.I.C.S.: 541330
Martha Renshaw *(CEO)*
Curt Renshaw *(Founder, Pres & COO)*

TELE-MEDIA CORPORATION
804 Jacksonville Rd, Bellefonte, PA 16823
Tel.: (814) 353-2025
Web Site: http://www.tele-media.com
Year Founded: 1970
Sales Range: $10-24.9 Million
Emp.: 50

TELE-MEDIA CORPORATION

Tele-Media Corporation—(Continued)
Radio Broadcasting & Cable Television
N.A.I.C.S.: 516210
Lesley Strouse *(Gen Mgr)*

TELE-OPTICS INC.
1041 Tidewater Ct, Kingsport, TN 37660
Tel.: (423) 246-5704
Web Site: http://www.tele-optics.com
Year Founded: 1984
Rev.: $15,279,987
Emp.: 150
Fiber Optic Cable Installation
N.A.I.C.S.: 238210
Jeff Carr *(Pres & VP)*
Jeff Hostetler *(Dir-Sls & Mktg)*
Kurt Grishaber *(Mgr)*
Dave Waldo *(Owner & CEO)*
Allen Spivey *(Project Mgr)*

TELEBYTE, INC.
355 Marcus Blvd, Hauppauge, NY 11788
Tel.: (631) 423-3232   DE
Web Site: http://www.telebyteusa.com
Year Founded: 1983
Sales Range: $1-9.9 Million
Emp.: 40
Fiber & Copper Connectivity Products Mfr
N.A.I.C.S.: 334290
Kenneth Schneider *(CEO)*
Michael Breneisen *(Pres)*
Reinhold Neufeld *(Controller)*

TELECLOUD, LLC
1 Cattano Ave., Morristown, NJ 07960
Tel.: (908) 851-0444
Web Site: https://www.telecloud.net
Rev.: $2,300,000
Emp.: 21
Electrical Contractor
N.A.I.C.S.: 238210
Vince Finaldi *(VP-Tele Data Solutions)*

Subsidiaries:

Dirad Technologies, Inc.   (1)
9 Corporate Dr, Clifton Park, NY 12065
Tel.: (518) 438-6000
Web Site: http://www.dirad.com
Sales Range: $1-9.9 Million
Emp.: 20
Telecommunications Resellers
N.A.I.C.S.: 517121
Lisa Wissert *(Controller)*

TELECO INC.
430 Woodruff Rd Ste 300, Greenville, SC 29607
Tel.: (864) 297-4400   SC
Web Site: http://www.teleco.com
Year Founded: 1981
Sales Range: $10-24.9 Million
Emp.: 90
Wireless Communications & Telephone Systems Services
N.A.I.C.S.: 517112
William M. Rogers *(Owner)*
Billy Rogers *(Co-Owner & VP)*
Gary Sarmento *(Exec VP)*

TELECOM DECISION MAKERS, INC
7608 W Hwy 146 300, Pewee Valley, KY 40056
Tel.: (502) 244-1668
Web Site: https://tdm.cc
Rev.: $3,663,000
Emp.: 11
Wired Telecommunications Carriers
N.A.I.C.S.: 517111
Ron Shields *(Owner)*

TELECOM ENTERPRISES INC.
5304 Derry Ave Ste IJ, Agoura Hills, CA 91301
Tel.: (818) 865-8861
Web Site: http://www.telecomintl.com
Sales Range: $10-24.9 Million
Emp.: 12
Electronic Parts & Equipment
N.A.I.C.S.: 423690

TELECOMMUNICATIONS DEVELOPMENT CORPORATION
1919 13th St NW, Washington, DC 20009
Tel.: (202) 234-9400
Web Site: http://www.telcomdc.com
Year Founded: 1995
Sales Range: $10-24.9 Million
Emp.: 46
Scientific & Technical Consulting Services
N.A.I.C.S.: 541690
James Woodyard *(Pres & CEO)*

TELECOMMUNICATIONS INDUSTRY ASSOCIATION
1320 N Courthouse Rd Ste 200, Arlington, VA 22201
Tel.: (703) 907-7700   VA
Web Site: http://www.tiaonline.org
Year Founded: 1988
Sales Range: $10-24.9 Million
Emp.: 35
Trade Assocation
N.A.I.C.S.: 813910
Mary Piper Waters *(Sr Dir-Ops)*
Taly Walsh *(VP-Mktg, Networking & Intelligence)*
Limor Schafman *(Dir-Content Dev)*
Jennifer Pentecost Sims *(Treas)*
Betty Manetta *(Sec)*
Brenda Boehm *(Chief Strategy Officer & Exec VP-Tech & Products)*
Susan Medick *(CFO)*
Susan Schramm *(CMO & Sr VP-Membership)*
Cinnamon Rogers *(Sr VP-Govt Affairs)*
David W. Heard *(Chm)*
Melissa Newman *(VP-Govt Affairs)*
David Stehlin *(CEO)*

TELECOMMUNICATIONS ON DEMAND, INC.
1 S 2nd St, Pottsville, PA 17901
Tel.: (570) 581-8300
Web Site: http://www.tcdemand.com
Year Founded: 1994
Sales Range: $10-24.9 Million
Emp.: 60
Marketing Consulting
N.A.I.C.S.: 541613
Diane Bornstein *(CFO)*
Craig Buffington *(CIO)*
Marcy Santoyo *(Sr Project Mgr)*
Justin Olds *(Pres)*
Jeff Bornstein *(Founder & Chm)*
Dave Hartranft *(Dir-Mktg & Adv)*
Greg Verchick *(Controller)*
Christian Zimmerman *(Dir-Bus Dev-Natl)*
Amy Roman *(Project Mgr)*
Amanda Mummert *(Project Mgr-Internal & Coord-Sls)*
Kirk Greenhalgh *(VP-Call Center Sls)*
Susan Koziel *(VP-Sls Ops)*
Dori Bornstein *(Exec VP-Ops & Community Dev)*

TELEDESIC LLC
3740 Carillon Pt, Kirkland, WA 98033
Tel.: (425) 602-0000
Rev.: $12,300,000
Emp.: 58
Data Communication Services
N.A.I.C.S.: 517810

Craig McCaw *(Chm)*

TELEDEX CORPORATION
5025 Galley Rd, Colorado Springs, CO 80915-2374
Tel.: (408) 363-3100   CA
Web Site: http://www.teledex.com
Year Founded: 1985
Sales Range: $10-24.9 Million
Emp.: 90
Telephone & Telegraph Apparatus
N.A.I.C.S.: 334210
Ronald S. Lesniak *(CEO)*
Rick Jones *(CFO & VP-Admin)*
Mitch Heinlein *(Regl Sls Mgr)*
Nick Steigelman *(Reg Mgr-Sls-North American)*
Dean Compoginis *(VP-Mktg)*
Nina Pacione *(Mgr-Sls)*
Joe Shek *(Gen Mgr-Sls)*
Kathy Katusha *(VP-HR)*

TELEGAMES INC.
2415 Hwy 334, Gun Barrel City, TX 75156
Tel.: (903) 887-4100
Web Site: http://www.telegames.com
Sales Range: $10-24.9 Million
Emp.: 100
Video Game Developer & Publisher
N.A.I.C.S.: 339930
Terry L. Grantham *(Pres)*

TELEGRAPH HILL PARTNERS MANAGEMENT COMPANY, LLC
360 Post St Ste 601, San Francisco, CA 94108
Tel.: (415) 765-6980   DE
Web Site: http://www.thpartners.net
Year Founded: 2001
Private Equity Firm
N.A.I.C.S.: 523999
J. Matthew Mackowski *(Chm & Mng Dir)*
Deval A. Lashkari *(Sr Partner)*
Jeanette M. Welsh *(COO & Partner)*
Rob C. Hart *(Partner)*
Paul D. Grossman *(Partner)*
Alexander C. Herzick *(Partner)*
Gary D. Curtis *(Partner)*
Thomas A. Raffin *(Founder & Sr Partner)*

Subsidiaries:

Dynex Technologies, Inc.   (1)
14340 Sullyfield Cir, Chantilly, VA 20151-1621
Tel.: (703) 631-7800
Web Site: http://www.dynextechnologies.com
Emp.: 150
Clinical Laboratory Instrument Automated Workstation & Associated Consumable Developer Mfr
N.A.I.C.S.: 334516
Doug Kaspar *(CFO)*
Michael Nyalka *(Dir-Field Svc)*
Duane Steele *(VP-Sls & Mktg)*
Robert Wolfert *(VP-Res & Dev)*
Candy Prowse *(Dir-Quality Assurance & Regulatory Affairs)*
Miguel Lopez *(Sr Dir-Customer Support)*
Sarah Vannozzi *(Dir-Project Mgmt)*
Deepak Valaparla *(Dir-Ops)*
Karen Freeman *(Dir-HR)*

Magstim, Inc.   (1)
9855 W 78th St Ste 12, Eden Prairie, MN 55344
Web Site: http://www.magstim.com
Magnetic Stimulation & Medical Device Mfr
N.A.I.C.S.: 339112
Lothar Krinke *(CEO)*

Subsidiary (Domestic):

Electrical Geodesics, Inc.   (2)
500 E 4th Ave Suite 200, Eugene, OR 97401

U.S. PRIVATE

Tel.: (541) 687-7962
Web Site: http://www.egi.com
Medical Device Mfr
N.A.I.C.S.: 339112

TELEION CONSULTING LLC
1100 Dexter Ave N Ste 503, Seattle, WA 98109
Tel.: (206) 282-0884
Web Site: http://www.teleionconsulting.com
Year Founded: 2008
Sales Range: $1-9.9 Million
Emp.: 51
Information Technology Consulting Services
N.A.I.C.S.: 541512
Derek Wang *(Mng Partner)*
Craig Watson *(Mng Partner)*
Melynda Kite *(Mgr-HR)*

TELEMESSAGING SERVICES INC.
6600 York Rd Ste 203, Baltimore, MD 21212
Tel.: (410) 377-3000
Sales Range: $10-24.9 Million
Emp.: 40
Telephone Answering Services
N.A.I.C.S.: 561421
John Sophocles *(Pres)*
Joseph Turszkowski *(VP)*

TELENAV, INC.
4655 Great America Pkwy Ste 300, Santa Clara, CA 95054
Tel.: (408) 245-3800   DE
Web Site: http://www.telenav.com
Rev.: $240,351,000
Assets: $293,751,000
Liabilities: $196,781,000
Net Worth: $96,970,000
Earnings: ($930,000)
Emp.: 696
Fiscal Year-end: 06/30/20
Location-Based Services Including Voice Guided Navigation on Mobile Phones
N.A.I.C.S.: 334290
H. P. Jin *(Co-Founder, Chm, Pres & CEO)*
Yi Chung Chao *(Co-Founder & Chief Technical Officer)*
Salman Dhanani *(Co-Founder & COO)*
Hassan Wahla *(Chief Customer Officer)*
Adeel Manzoor *(CFO & Treas)*

Subsidiaries:

Local Merchat Services, Inc.   (1)
10549 Jefferson Blvd, Culver City, CA 90232
Tel.: (917) 282-8573
Web Site: http://www.thinknear.com
Digital Advertising Services
N.A.I.C.S.: 541810
Brent Fraser *(Co-Pres & Co-Gen Mgr)*
Brett Kohn *(Co-Pres & Co-Gen Mgr)*
Gabriel Huerta *(VP-Product)*
Elmar Mamedov *(VP-Engrg)*
Mandana Mellano *(VP-Mktg)*
Peter Olsen *(VP-Bus Dev)*

TeleNav do Brasil Servicos de Localizacao Ltda.   (1)
Av Paulista 2300 Andar Pilotis, Sao Paulo, 01310-300, Brazil
Tel.: (55) 1128474725
Web Site: http://www.telenav.com
Detection & Navigation Equipment Mfr
N.A.I.C.S.: 334511

Telenav GmbH   (1)
Fasanenstr 81, 10623, Berlin, Germany
Tel.: (49) 1724597015
Web Site: http://www.skobbler.com
Mobile Application Development Services
N.A.I.C.S.: 541511

Philipp Kandal *(Mng Dir)*
Franz Morawetz *(Mng Dir)*

Telenav Korea, Limited (1)
Woorim Lions Valley B-905 425
ChungChun2-Dong, Bupyung-Gu, Incheon,
Korea (South)
Tel.: (82) 7040326687
Advertisement Services
N.A.I.C.S.: 541890

TELEO CAPITAL MANAGEMENT, LLC
2121 Rosecrans Ste 3320, El Segundo, CA 90245
Tel.: (424) 323-3995   DE
Web Site: http://teleocapital.com
Privater Equity Firm
N.A.I.C.S.: 523999
George Kase *(Partner)*
Max Vaughan *(VP)*

Subsidiaries:

Industrial Defender, Inc. (1)
225 Foxborough Blvd Ste 202, Foxboro, MA 02035
Tel.: (617) 675-4206
Web Site: http://www.industrialdefender.com
Computer Related Services
N.A.I.C.S.: 541519
Brian M. Ahern *(Pres & CEO)*

Sharpen Technologies Inc. (1)
101 W Washington St Ste 600E, Indianapolis, IN 46204
Web Site: http://www.sharpencx.com
Sales Range: $1-9.9 Million
Emp.: 200
Software Development Services
N.A.I.C.S.: 541511
Bill Gildea *(CEO)*
Pamela Hynes *(COO)*
Kevin Schatz *(CTO)*
Ty Baldwin *(Chief Revenue Officer)*
Murph Krajewski *(CMO)*

Subsidiary (Domestic):

The Plum Group, Inc. (2)
131 Varick St Fl 9, New York, NY 10013
Tel.: (212) 941-5015
Web Site: http://www.plumvoice.com
Sales Range: $1-9.9 Million
Emp.: 25
Personal Services
N.A.I.C.S.: 812990
Matthew Ervin *(Founder & Pres)*
Matt Jones *(CTO)*
Scott Wilson *(CMO & VP-Bus Dev)*

TELEPHONE ELECTRONICS CORPORATION
236 E Capitol St Ste 500, Jackson, MS 39225
Tel.: (601) 354-9066   DE
Web Site: http://www.tec.com
Year Founded: 1972
Sales Range: $10-24.9 Million
Emp.: 300
Telecommunication Servicesb
N.A.I.C.S.: 517121
Wayne Skelton *(Sec)*
Joey Garner *(VP-Ops)*
Larry Howle *(Mgr-Regulatory Reporting)*
Tim Loecher *(Mgr-Network Ops & Sr Engr-Sys)*
Bryce Hopkins *(Dir-Sls)*

Subsidiaries:

Air Laurel, Inc. (1)
131 Hngr Ln, Laurel, MS 39440
Tel.: (601) 649-2198
Sales Range: $10-24.9 Million
Emp.: 2
Air Transportation, Nonscheduled
N.A.I.C.S.: 481211

Bay Springs Telephone Company, Inc. (1)
2988 Hwy 15, Bay Springs, MS 39422
Tel.: (601) 764-2121
Web Site: http://www.bayspringstel.com
Sales Range: $10-24.9 Million
Emp.: 20
Local Telephone Communication Services
N.A.I.C.S.: 517121

CommuniGroup of K.C. Inc. (1)
9260 Glenwood St, Overland Park, KS 66212-1365
Tel.: (913) 722-6005
Sales Range: $10-24.9 Million
Emp.: 28
Telephone Communications
N.A.I.C.S.: 517121

Crockett Telephone Company, Inc. (1)
563 Main St, Friendship, TN 38034
Tel.: (731) 677-8181
Rev.: $2,812,874
Emp.: 30
Local Telecommunication Services
N.A.I.C.S.: 517121

National Telephone of Alabama, Inc. (1)
955 2nd St, Cherokee, AL 35616 **(100%)**
Tel.: (256) 359-4321
Web Site: http://www.tec.com
Rev.: $1,800,000
Emp.: 8
Local Telephone Communication Services
N.A.I.C.S.: 517121
Troy Rutland *(Gen Mgr)*

Peoples Telephone Co., Inc. (1)
4587 E Main St, Erin, TN 37061
Tel.: (931) 289-4221
Web Site: http://www.peoplestel.net
Rev.: $3,737,684
Emp.: 20
Telecommunication Servicesb
N.A.I.C.S.: 517121
Doug Schroeder *(Pres & CEO)*

Roanoke Telephone Company, Inc. (1)
950 Main St, Roanoke, AL 36274
Tel.: (334) 863-2111
Web Site: http://www.tec.com
Sales Range: $10-24.9 Million
Emp.: 15
Local Telecommunication Services
N.A.I.C.S.: 517121

TEC Services, Inc. (1)
1100 N 18 2nd Fl, Monroe, LA 71201
Tel.: (318) 322-0015
Web Site: http://www.tec.com
Sales Range: $10-24.9 Million
Emp.: 10
Local Telecommunication Services
N.A.I.C.S.: 517121
Lera Roark *(VP)*

TEC of Jackson Inc. (1)
700 SW St, Jackson, MS 39201-5507
Tel.: (601) 353-9118
Telecommunication Servicesb
N.A.I.C.S.: 517121
Joseph Austin *(Acct Exec-Contract Sls)*

Video, Inc. (1)
2988 Hwy 15, Bay Springs, MS 39422
Tel.: (601) 764-2121
Sales Range: $10-24.9 Million
Emp.: 30
Local Telephone Communication Services
N.A.I.C.S.: 516210

West Tennessee Telephone Co., Inc. (1)
224 E Main St, Bradford, TN 38316 **(100%)**
Tel.: (731) 742-2211
Sales Range: $1-9.9 Million
Emp.: 14
Local Telecommunication Services
N.A.I.C.S.: 517121

TELEPHONE SERVICE CO.
2 Willipie St, Wapakoneta, OH 45895
Tel.: (419) 739-2200
Web Site: http://www.telserco.com
Sales Range: $10-24.9 Million
Emp.: 57
Local Telephone Communications
N.A.I.C.S.: 517121
Randy Heinl Heinl *(Mgr-Facilities)*

TELEPHONE SERVICES INC.
1501 Eagle Ct Ste 1101, Lewisville, TX 75057
Tel.: (972) 436-4285
Web Site:
  http://www.telephoneservices.net
Year Founded: 1971
Sales Range: $10-24.9 Million
Emp.: 55
Communications Specialization
N.A.I.C.S.: 811210

TELEPHONY PARTNERS LLC
442 W Kennedy Blvd Ste 200, Tampa, FL 33606
Tel.: (813) 769-4690
Web Site: http://www.thinkacuity.com
Year Founded: 2002
Sales Range: $1-9.9 Million
Emp.: 6
Telecommunications Consultant
N.A.I.C.S.: 541618
Josh Anderson *(Founder & CEO)*

TELEPROVIDERS INC.
23461 Southpointe Dr Ste 185, Laguna Hills, CA 92653
Tel.: (949) 215-8600
Web Site:
  http://www.teleproviders.com
Year Founded: 2004
Sales Range: $1-9.9 Million
Emp.: 15
Scientific Technical Consulting Services
N.A.I.C.S.: 541690
Jason Sharek *(Founder & CEO)*
Kelly Ratcliff *(Pres)*
Cindy Frerking *(Partner & Mgr-Dev)*

TELEQUERY.NET, INC.
3409 Paint Dr, Denton, TX 76210
Tel.: (214) 526-9692
Web Site: http://www.telequery.net
Sales Range: $1-9.9 Million
Emp.: 40
Telecommunication Servicesb
N.A.I.C.S.: 517810
Jerome Gilels *(CEO)*

TELES PROPERTIES
9470 Wilshire Blvd Ste 120, Beverly Hills, CA 90212
Tel.: (424) 202-3200
Web Site:
  http://www.telesproperties.com
Year Founded: 2007
Sales Range: $25-49.9 Million
Emp.: 40
Real Estate Agency Offering Luxury Residential Properties
N.A.I.C.S.: 531210
Sharran Srivatsaa *(Co-Pres & COO)*
Peter Hernandez *(Co-Pres)*
Bill Grasska *(Pres-Affiliates)*

TELESCOPE CASUAL FURNITURE INC.
82 Church St, Granville, NY 12832-1621
Tel.: (518) 642-1100   NY
Web Site:
  http://www.telescopecasual.com
Year Founded: 1903
Sales Range: $100-124.9 Million
Emp.: 300
Mfr of Aluminum, Wood & Casual Furniture
N.A.I.C.S.: 337126
William Vanderminden *(Exec VP)*
Kathy Juckett *(CEO)*
Robert Vanderminden Jr. *(Sr VP)*
Henry Vanderminden IV *(Pres)*

Subsidiaries:

Mettowee Lumber & Plastic Co., Inc. (1)
82 Church St, Granville, NY 12832 **(100%)**
Tel.: (518) 642-1100
Web Site: http://www.telescopecasual.com
Sales Range: $10-24.9 Million
Emp.: 15
Plastic Extrusions & Lumber
N.A.I.C.S.: 321113
Kathy Juckett *(CEO)*

TELESEARCH INC.
251 US Hwy 206, Flanders, NJ 07836
Tel.: (973) 927-7870
Web Site: http://www.telesearch.com
Sales Range: $10-24.9 Million
Emp.: 25
Employment Agencies
N.A.I.C.S.: 561311
Polly McDonald *(Founder & Pres)*
Kim Carsillo *(Mgr-Flanders)*
Beth Farrell *(Branch Mgr)*
Bob McDonald *(VP & Mgr-Tech)*
Karrie McNulty *(Mgr-Acctg)*
Andrea Powell *(Mgr-Newton)*
Cristina Stuto *(Mgr-Lakewood District)*

TELESIS CORPORATION
4700 Corridor Pl Ste D, Beltsville, MD 20705-1163
Tel.: (240) 241-5600
Web Site: http://www.telesishq.com
Year Founded: 1998
Sales Range: $25-49.9 Million
Emp.: 30
Information Technology Services
N.A.I.C.S.: 541511
Payal Tak *(Pres & CEO)*
Bill Rubin *(Mgr-Community Investment)*
David Godschalk *(Gen Counsel)*
Georgia Abraham *(Dir-New Bus Dev)*
Alex Vanjani *(Dir-Contracts)*
Bruce Thoms *(Dir-DoD Programs)*
Dustin Goetz *(Dir-Homeland Security Programs)*
Jill Waltersdorff-Rich *(Dir-HR)*
Sonia Dua *(Dir-Managed Svcs Programs)*
Jorge Arias *(Dir-Programs)*
Dave Jefferson *(VP)*
Rick Simis *(VP)*
Cheryl Brummell *(VP-Programs)*

TELESOURCE, INC.
9606 Caldwell Commons Cir Ste A, Cornelius, NC 28031
Tel.: (704) 990-7600
Web Site:
  http://www.telesourceinc.net
Year Founded: 1997
Sales Range: $1-9.9 Million
Emp.: 13
Telecommunications Expense Management Solutions
N.A.I.C.S.: 517810
Ronnie J. Bice *(Pres & CEO)*

TELESPHERE
9237 E Via de Ventura Ste 250, Scottsdale, AZ 85258
Tel.: (480) 385-7000
Web Site: http://www.telesphere.com
Year Founded: 2000
Sales Range: $10-24.9 Million
Emp.: 105
Mfr Cloud-Based Communications System
N.A.I.C.S.: 513210
Clark Peterson *(CEO)*
Sanjay Srinivasan *(CTO)*
Tamara Saunders *(Controller)*
Jeff Savage *(VP-Indirect Sls)*

TELESPHERE

Telesphere—(Continued)
Kristi Brown (VP-Mktg)
Karen Smith (VP-People Dev)
Todd Miszner (VP-Fin)
Mark Bland (VP-Direct Sls)
Aqeel Shahid (Gen Mgr)
Derek Sandhoff (Gen Mgr-Denver)
Rob McCarthy (Mgr-Indirect Channel-California)
Josh Redick (Mgr-Indirect Channel-Eastern Reg)
Tom Rancel (Reg Mgr-Indirect Channel)
Jordan Meyerowitz (Dir-Product Innovation)

Subsidiaries:

Telesphere (1)
9100 E Panorama Dr Ste 175, Englewood, CO 80112 (100%)
Tel.: (720) 227-0200
Web Site: http://www.telesphere.com
Cloud Communication Services
N.A.I.C.S.: 517121
Derek Sandhoff (Gen Mgr)

TELESTO GROUP LLC
1060 State Rd Ste 102, Princeton, NJ 08540
Tel.: (609) 503-4201
Web Site: http://www.telestogroup.com
Year Founded: 2001
Sales Range: $10-24.9 Million
Emp.: 50
Data Processing, Hosting & Related Services
N.A.I.C.S.: 518210
Soren Hastrup (CEO)
Debra Patrick (Co-Partner)
Toralf Peters (Co-Partner)

TELETRACKING TECHNOLOGIES, INC.
336 Fourth Ave The Times Bldg, Pittsburgh, PA 15222-2004
Tel.: (412) 391-7862
Web Site: http://www.teletracking.com
Year Founded: 1991
Sales Range: $100-124.9 Million
Emp.: 264
Software Publisher
N.A.I.C.S.: 513210
Kimberly Roberts (Gen Counsel & Sr VP)
Kirk Stephen (Co-CFO & Exec VP)
Michael Zamagias (Chm & CEO)
Nanne Finis (VP-TeleTracking Consulting Svcs)
Diane Watson (COO)
Joseph Tetzlaff (CTO)
Keith Young (Sr VP-HR)
Mike Caffrey (Co-CFO & Exec VP)
Christopher Johnson (Pres)
Matthew Rudolph (Exec VP-Comml & Bus Dev)

TELETRONIC SERVICES INC.
22600 Ascoa Ct, Strongsville, OH 44149
Tel.: (216) 778-6500
Web Site: http://www.teletronics-inc.com
Sales Range: $10-24.9 Million
Emp.: 30
Telephone Equipment
N.A.I.C.S.: 423690
Gale Kenney (CEO)
Tom Ursem (Pres)
Gary Reffert (VP-Ops)

TELFER OIL COMPANIES
211 Foster St, Martinez, CA 94553
Tel.: (925) 228-1515

Web Site: http://www.telfercompanies.com
Sales Range: $25-49.9 Million
Emp.: 55
Highway & Street Paving Contractor
N.A.I.C.S.: 237310
Michael Telfer (Pres)
Bob Putz (Mgr-Sls)
Dan Frankel (VP-Ops)
Hans Ho (Dir-Tech & Environment)
John A. Telfer (Founder & Exec VP)

TELGIAN INC.
2615 S Industrial Park Ave, Tempe, AZ 85282
Tel.: (858) 795-1000
Web Site: http://www.telgian.com
Sales Range: $10-24.9 Million
Emp.: 60
Fire Protection Services
N.A.I.C.S.: 561990
Tracey Bellamy (Chief Engrg Officer)
James W. Tomes (CEO)
Stephen Goyette (VP-Bus Dev)
Russell B. Leavitt (Chm)
Steven R. Smith (Exec VP-HR)
Jason Hand (Exec VP-Compliance Solutions)
Bob Caputo (Exec VP-Sls & Mktg)
Brian Ballard (CFO & COO)
Leonard Ramo (Exec VP-Engred Solutions)
Randy Walti (Gen Counsel & Sec)
Tom Parrish (VP-Integrated Sys)
William S. Holden (Exec VP-Installation Svcs)
Al Gargano (Pres)
Dave M. Gomez (Gen Counsel & Sec)
Craig Saloman (Dir-Ops)
Vincent Joven (VP-Fin & Controller)
Ralph E. Bless Jr. (VP-Acct Mgmt)
John C. Fannin III (Exec VP-Risk Solutions)
William E. Reiter II (VP-Security Ops)

TELHIO CREDIT UNION
96 N 4th St, Columbus, OH 43215
Tel.: (614) 221-3233 OH
Web Site: http://www.telhio.org
Year Founded: 1934
Rev.: $49,258,226
Assets: $835,311,840
Liabilities: $756,924,498
Net Worth: $78,387,342
Earnings: $9,104,314
Fiscal Year-end: 12/31/18
Financial Services
N.A.I.C.S.: 523999
Kathy Foor (Vice Chm)

TELISIMO INTERNATIONAL CORPORATION
2488 Historic Decatur Rd Ste 210, San Diego, CA 92106-6134
Tel.: (858) 654-9000
Web Site: http://www.telisimo.com
Rev.: $26,411,000
Emp.: 10
Call Center Services
N.A.I.C.S.: 561422
Linda Hobbs (Pres & CEO)

TELLA TOOL & MANUFACTURING COMPANY
1015 N Rdg Ave, Lombard, IL 60148
Tel.: (630) 495-0545
Web Site: http://www.tellatool.com
Sales Range: $25-49.9 Million
Emp.: 100
Mfr of Special Dies, Tools, Jigs & Fixtures
N.A.I.C.S.: 333514
Daniel M. Provenzano (Pres)
Jorge Gomez (Engr-Mfg)

Robert McLaughlin (Engr-Tool)
Paul Mikl (Engr-Sls)
Meissner Kurt (Sr Acct Mgr)

TELLAGO INC.
Gateway Executive Park Ctr 1821 Walden Office Sq Ste 400, Schaumburg, IL 60173
Web Site: http://www.tellago.com
Year Founded: 2008
Sales Range: $1-9.9 Million
Emp.: 40
Software Developer
N.A.I.C.S.: 513210
Jesus Rodriguez (Co-Founder & CEO)
Elizabeth Redding (Co-Founder & Pres)

TELLENNIUM, INC.
PO Box 724 13025 Hwy 44 E, Mount Washington, KY 40047
Web Site: http://www.tellennium.com
Year Founded: 1999
Sales Range: $10-24.9 Million
Emp.: 16
Business Consulting Services
N.A.I.C.S.: 541690
Greg McIntyre (Pres)

TELLEPSEN BUILDERS LP
777 Benmar Dr Ste 400, Houston, TX 77060
Tel.: (281) 447-8100
Web Site: http://www.tellepsen.com
Year Founded: 1909
Sales Range: $25-49.9 Million
Emp.: 100
Oil & Gas Pipeline Construction
N.A.I.C.S.: 237990
Howard Tellepsen (Chm & CEO)
Francois Harvey (Project Mgr)
William L. Peel Jr. (Chief Dev Officer & Exec VP)

TELLURIDE SKI & GOLF COMPANY LLP
565 Mtn Vlg Blvd, Telluride, CO 81435-9521
Tel.: (970) 728-6900 CO
Web Site: http://www.tellurideskiresort.com
Year Founded: 1972
Sales Range: $25-49.9 Million
Emp.: 371
Recreational Services
N.A.I.C.S.: 487990
Patrick Rothe (Dir-Sls)
Chuck Horning (Owner)

TELLUS INSTITUTE INC.
2 Garden St, Cambridge, MA 02138
Tel.: (617) 266-5400 MA
Web Site: http://www.tellus.org
Year Founded: 1976
Sales Range: $1-9.9 Million
Emp.: 6
Environmental Research Services
N.A.I.C.S.: 541715
Paul D. Raskin (Pres)
David R. McAnulty (Dir-Admin)

TELPRO INC.
200 Public Sq Ste 2300, Cleveland, OH 44114-2309
Tel.: (419) 729-4800
Sales Range: $10-24.9 Million
Emp.: 35
Mfr of Communication Equipment
N.A.I.C.S.: 423690
Denny McBroom (Pres)
Ken Magy (Controller)
Jim Baringer (Dir & Mgr-HR)

TELREPCO INC.

101 N Plains Industrial Rd Bldg 2, Wallingford, CT 06492
Tel.: (203) 284-0566
Web Site: http://www.telrepcopcstore.com
Sales Range: $1-9.9 Million
Emp.: 20
Computer & Computer Peripheral Equipment & Software Merchant Whslr
N.A.I.C.S.: 423430
Ron Brodeur (Sr Mgr-Sls)
John A. Krawski (Pres)
Lynn Krawski (CEO)
Cheryl Harlow (Coord-Accts Receivable Sls & Mktg)
Justin Ruotolo (Acct Mgr-Sls)

TELRITE HOLDINGS, INC.
4113 Monticello St, Covington, GA 30014
Tel.: (866) 890-4135 GA
Web Site: http://www.telrite.com
Holding Company
N.A.I.C.S.: 551112
William Curry (Chief Strategy Officer)

Subsidiaries:

Locus Telecommunications, Inc. (1)
2200 Fletcher Ave 6th Fl, Fort Lee, NJ 07024
Tel.: (201) 585-3600
Web Site: http://www.locus.net
Sales Range: $50-74.9 Million
Emp.: 200
Wireless, Point-of-Sale & Carrier Telecommunications Services
N.A.I.C.S.: 517112
Koji Shikano (CEO)
Andrew J. Miesiak (CFO)

Telrite Corporation (1)
4113 Monticello St, Covington, GA 30014-4953
Tel.: (866) 890-4135
Web Site: http://www.telrite.com
Custom Computer Programming Services
N.A.I.C.S.: 541511
Reggie McFarland (CEO)

TELSCO INDUSTRIES, INC.
3301 W Kingsley Rd, Garland, TX 75041-2207
Tel.: (972) 278-6131 TX
Web Site: http://www.weathermatic.com
Year Founded: 1945
Sales Range: $50-74.9 Million
Emp.: 53
Underground Sprinkler Mfr
N.A.I.C.S.: 332913
L. Mike Mason (Pres & CEO)
Brodie Bruner (Exec VP-Mktg)
Darryl Halbert (CFO & COO)
Bill Savelle (Exec VP-Products)

TELSEON INCORPORATED
Ste 350 6300 S Syracuse Way, Centennial, CO 80111-6791
Tel.: (720) 554-7000
Rev.: $33,900,000
Emp.: 5
Local & Long Distance Telephone Communications
N.A.I.C.S.: 517121

TELTECH COMMUNICATIONS, LLC
1099 Capitol St Ste 200, Eagle, CO 81631
Tel.: (970) 328-7040
Web Site: http://www.teltechcomm.com
Sales Range: $10-24.9 Million
Emp.: 180
Wireless Communication Infrastructure Equipment Asset Recovery, Inventory Management, Sales, Installation & Liquidation Services

N.A.I.C.S.: 334220
Lisa Hanlon *(Co-Founder & Mng Partner)*
Deb Tasset *(Dir-Admin)*
John McIlveen *(Sr VP)*
Randy Wilkens *(VP-Process Controls)*

TELTRONIC INC.
7051 Muirkirk Meadows Dr Ste E, Beltsville, MD 20705-6342
Tel.: (301) 468-6500
Web Site: http://www.teltronic.com
Year Founded: 1961
Sales Range: $10-24.9 Million
Emp.: 80
Retailer of Communication Equipment
N.A.I.C.S.: 459999
Paul Manders *(Pres)*
Jim Murphy *(Co-Owner)*
Ted Weitzel *(Project Mgr)*
Scott Cameron *(Engr-Sys)*
Gerry Boyd *(Co-Owner & VP-Engrg)*
Austin Miles *(Mgr-Beltsville Svc)*
Justin Dysart *(Mgr-Salisbury Svc)*
Chris DePalma *(Mgr-Winchester Svc)*

TELVISTA COMPANY
200 1605 Lyndon B Johnson Fwy, Dallas, TX 75234-6034
Tel.: (972) 312-6000
Web Site: http://www.telvista.com
Sales Range: $250-299.9 Million
Emp.: 600
Telephone & Video Communications
N.A.I.C.S.: 517111
Hector Gonzalez *(Mktg Dir)*

TELVUE CORPORATION
16000 Horizon Way Ste 500, Mount Laurel, NJ 08054
Tel.: (856) 273-8888   DE
Web Site: http://www.telvue.com
Year Founded: 1986
Sales Range: $1-9.9 Million
Emp.: 26
Broadcasting Communications Equipment
N.A.I.C.S.: 334220
H. F. Lenfest *(Chm)*
Jesse Lerman *(Pres & CEO)*
Paul Andrews *(Sr VP-Sls & Mktg)*
Donna Liu *(Dir-New Media Svcs)*
Denise Rolfe *(Dir-Community Brdcst Sls)*
Mark Steele *(CIO)*
Dan Joworisak *(Treas, Sec & Controller)*
Chris Perry *(Dir-Brdcst Product Mgmt)*
Matt Christy *(Mgr-Product-Pro Brdcst)*
Ben Liu *(Dir-Cloud Dev)*
Matt Smith *(Dir-Brdcst Dev)*
Lauren Caputo *(Coord-Sls)*
Jerry Budge *(Dir-Technical Sls)*
Charley Paige *(Mgr-Sls-Northeast Reg)*

TEM ENTERPRISES
800 W Idaho St, Boise, ID 83702
Tel.: (775) 738-6040
Web Site: http://www.xtraairways.com
Rev.: $12,000,000
Emp.: 125
Passenger Transportation Services
N.A.I.C.S.: 481111
Dan Fortnam *(Dir-Sls)*
T'resa Alzugaray *(CFO)*
Joshua Weinshank *(Dir-Ops)*
Lisa Dunn *(Pres)*

TEM SYSTEMS, INC.
4747 N Nob Hill Rd Ste 5, Sunrise, FL 33351-4742
Tel.: (954) 577-6044
Web Site: http://www.temsystems.com
Rev.: $12,000,000
Emp.: 60
Whslr of Recording Instruments & Accessories
N.A.I.C.S.: 423830
Renee McIntosh *(Pres)*

TEMKIN & TEMKIN
156 Barberry Rd, Highland Park, IL 60035-4420
Tel.: (847) 831-0237   IL
Web Site: http://www.temkin.com
Year Founded: 1945
Sales Range: $100-124.9 Million
Emp.: 4
N.A.I.C.S.: 541810
Laura W. Temkin *(Co-Owner)*

TEMO INC.
20400 Hall Rd, Clinton Township, MI 48038
Tel.: (586) 286-0410
Web Site: http://www.temosunrooms.com
Sales Range: $25-49.9 Million
Emp.: 195
Mfr of Sunrooms & Patio Enclosures
N.A.I.C.S.: 332311
Giovanni Vitale *(Pres)*
Jim Hall *(VP)*

TEMP-AIR, INC.
3700 W Preserve Blvd, Burnsville, MN 55337-7746
Tel.: (952) 894-3000   MN
Web Site: http://www.temp-air.com
Year Founded: 1965
Sales Range: $25-49.9 Million
Emp.: 150
Refrigeration & Heating Equipment Rental Services
N.A.I.C.S.: 532490
Dan Grinols *(VP-Engrg)*
Scott Brainard *(VP-Product Dev)*
James A. Korn *(CEO)*
Amanda Rahn *(Mgr-Mktg)*

TEMP-CONTROL MECHANICAL CORP.
4800 N Channel Ave, Portland, OR 97217
Tel.: (503) 285-9851   OR
Web Site: http://www.tcmcorp.com
Year Founded: 1953
Sales Range: $10-24.9 Million
Emp.: 200
Provider of Mechanical Contracting Services
N.A.I.C.S.: 238220
Chris Hutchings *(Dir-Ops-Industrial)*
Dan Sneeringer *(Dir-Ops-Comml)*
Joe Baguio *(Dir-Post Project Svcs)*
Tony Barsotti *(Dir-Safety & Quality Assurance)*
Jay Culbertson Jr. *(CEO)*

TEMPCO ELECTRIC HEATER CORP
607 N Central Ave, Wood Dale, IL 60191
Tel.: (630) 350-2252
Web Site: http://www.tempco.com
Year Founded: 1972
Sales Range: $25-49.9 Million
Emp.: 360
Industrial Electric Heating Units Mfr
N.A.I.C.S.: 333994
Fermin Adames *(Pres)*

TEMPE LIFE CARE VILLAGE INC
2645 E Southern Ave, Tempe, AZ 85282
Tel.: (480) 831-5000   AZ
Web Site: http://www.friendshipvillageaz.com
Year Founded: 1976
Sales Range: $25-49.9 Million
Emp.: 599
Continuing Care Retirement Community Operator
N.A.I.C.S.: 623311
Terry Belles *(CFO)*
Cole Marvin *(Exec Dir)*

TEMPERATURE SERVICE COMPANY, INC.
350 Bonnie Ln, Elk Grove Village, IL 60007
Tel.: (847) 640-0505   IL
Web Site: http://www.temperatureservicecompany.com
Year Founded: 1982
Sales Range: $1-9.9 Million
Heating, Ventilation, Air Conditioning & Refrigeration Contractor
N.A.I.C.S.: 238220
Scott K. Templin *(Owner, Pres & CEO)*

TEMPERATURE SYSTEMS, INC.
PO Box 8030, Madison, WI 53708-8030
Tel.: (608) 271-7500   WI
Web Site: http://www.tsihvac.com
Year Founded: 1947
Sales Range: $10-24.9 Million
Emp.: 96
Warm Air Heating & Air Conditioning Services
N.A.I.C.S.: 423730
Mark Krueger *(Controller)*
Grant Gelhar *(Mgr-Credit)*
Steve Blankenheim *(Mgr-Supplies Sls)*

TEMPERPACK TECHNOLOGIES, INC.
4447 Carolina Ave, Richmond, VA 23222
Tel.: (888) 647-3630
Web Site: https://www.temperpack.com
Year Founded: 2015
Sustainable Thermal Packaging Materials Mfr
N.A.I.C.S.: 561910
Walker Dales *(CFO)*

Subsidiaries:

KTM Industries Inc.   (1)
2325 Jarco Dr, Holt, MI 48842
Tel.: (517) 703-9140
Web Site: http://www.ktmindustries.com
Sales Range: $1-9.9 Million
Biodegradable Foam Packaging Material Developer & Mfr
N.A.I.C.S.: 339999
Kathy Easterling *(VP)*

TEMPEST TELECOM SOLUTIONS, LLC
136 W Cañon Perdido Ste 100, Santa Barbara, CA 93101
Tel.: (805) 879-4800   CA
Web Site: http://www.tempesttelecom.com
Year Founded: 2005
Sales Range: $50-74.9 Million
Emp.: 164
Telecommunication Equipment Sales & Repair Services
N.A.I.C.S.: 423690
Jessica Firestone *(CEO)*
Julie Lubin *(CFO)*
Dan Firestone *(Founder & COO)*
Richard Smith *(VP-Supply & Vendor Rel)*
Christopher Roten *(Dir-Sls & PLM Wireline)*
Dave Smargon *(VP & Gen Mgr)*
Elda Rudd *(VP-Sls & Strategic Accounts)*

TEMPLE & TEMPLE EXCAVATING & PAVING, INC.
1367 S State Rd 60, Salem, IN 47167
Tel.: (812) 883-6644
Web Site: http://templeandtemple.com
Year Founded: 1957
Sales Range: $10-24.9 Million
Emp.: 100
Highway, Street & Bridge Construction Services
N.A.I.C.S.: 237310
Walter Temple *(Pres)*
Ken Temple *(Treas & Sec)*

TEMPLE BOTTLING COMPANY LTD
3510 Pkwy Dr, Temple, TX 76504
Tel.: (254) 773-3376
Web Site: http://www.templebot.com
Rev.: $12,300,000
Emp.: 90
Soft Drink Bottling Services
N.A.I.C.S.: 312111
T.F. Floca *(Pres)*

TEMPLETON COAL COMPANY, INC.
701 Wabash Ave Ste 501, Terre Haute, IN 47807-3219
Tel.: (812) 232-7037   IN
Web Site: http://www.templetoncoal.com
Year Founded: 1920
Rev.: $154,500,000
Emp.: 400
Plumbing Fixtures, Equipment & Supplies
N.A.I.C.S.: 423720
Tom Thomas *(Treas & Sec)*

Subsidiaries:

Dickson's, Inc.   (1)
709 B Ave E, Seymour, IN 47274-3244   (100%)
Tel.: (812) 522-1308
Web Site: http://www.dicksonsgifts.com
Rev.: $30,325,992
Emp.: 200
Costume Jewelry
N.A.I.C.S.: 339910
Steve Vandivier *(Pres)*

Plumb Supply Company, Inc.   (1)
1622 NE 51st Ave, Des Moines, IA 50313-2125
Tel.: (515) 262-9511
Web Site: http://www.plumbsupply.com
Rev.: $41,200,000
Emp.: 60
Plumbing Fixtures, Equipment & Supplies
N.A.I.C.S.: 423720
Scott Anshutz *(Pres)*
Alan Darnielle *(Treas)*
Jason Metcalf *(COO)*

Sherwood-Templeton Coal Company, Inc.   (1)
701 Wabash Ave Ste 501, Terre Haute, IN 47807   (100%)
Tel.: (812) 232-7037
Sales Range: $10-24.9 Million
Emp.: 8
Industrial Furnaces & Ovens
N.A.I.C.S.: 333994
Curtis Brighton *(Pres)*

TEMPLETON CONSTRUCTION CO.
521 W Beauregard Ave, San Angelo, TX 76903-6330
Tel.: (325) 653-6904

TEMPLETON CONSTRUCTION CO.

Templeton Construction Co.—(Continued)
Web Site:
http://www.templetonconstruction.com
Year Founded: 1927
Rev.: $34,000,000
Emp.: 150
Provider of Commercial & Office Building Construction Services
N.A.I.C.S.: 236220
Gary McClure *(Pres)*
Rebecca McClure *(VP)*
Shirley Hamlin *(Controller)*

TEMPO INDUSTRIES INC.

2137 E 55th St, Los Angeles, CA 90058
Tel.: (323) 583-2423
Web Site:
http://www.tempofurniture.com
Rev.: $10,000,000
Emp.: 133
Sleep Furniture
N.A.I.C.S.: 337910
Dennis Pearson *(CEO)*
John Thomas *(VP-Ops)*
Robbie Das *(COO)*
Ian Shaw *(VP-Architectural Sls)*
Eric Pantano *(Mgr-Architectural Sls-East)*

TEMPO SOFTWARE, INC.

67 S Bedford St, Ste 400 W, Burlington, MA 01803
Web Site: https://www.tempo.io
Year Founded: 2015
Emp.: 100
Software Devolepment
N.A.I.C.S.: 513210

Subsidiaries:

LiquidPlanner, Inc. (1)
300 Lenora St Ste 1831, Seattle, WA 98121
Tel.: (800) 971-1601
Web Site: http://www.liquidplanner.com
Sales Range: $1-9.9 Million
Application Software Development Services
N.A.I.C.S.: 541511
Tom Murphy *(VP-Customer Success)*
Brett Bender *(VP-Engrg)*
Aashish Dhamdhere *(VP-Customer Acq)*
Charles Seybold *(Co-Founder)*
Jason Carlson *(Co-Founder)*

TEMPOGRAPHICS INC.

455 E N Ave, Carol Stream, IL 60188
Tel.: (630) 462-8200
Web Site:
http://www.tempographics.com
Year Founded: 1973
Sales Range: $10-24.9 Million
Emp.: 115
Offset Printing
N.A.I.C.S.: 323111
Peter Vouros *(Pres)*
Richard Walsh *(Mgr-Sls)*

TEMPORARY HOUSING DIRECTORY, INC.

3308 Preston Rd Ste 350-341, Plano, TX 75093
Tel.: (720) 524-3809
Web Site:
http://www.temporaryhousingdirectory.com
Sales Range: $25-49.9 Million
Emp.: 33
Temporary Housing Services
N.A.I.C.S.: 624221
Teresa Vidger *(Founder & Pres)*
Tony LaRocca *(Dir-Natl Sls)*

TEMPUS INC.

7519 Pennsylvania Ave Ste 101, Sarasota, FL 34243
Tel.: (941) 316-8800

Web Site:
http://tempusproservices.com
Sales Range: $10-24.9 Million
Emp.: 50
Home Automation Systems
N.A.I.C.S.: 541512
Brett Price *(Pres)*

TEMPUS IT STAFFING

Ste W115 1117 Perimeter Ctr W, Atlanta, GA 30338-5417
Tel.: (404) 832-2200
Rev.: $13,130,352
Emp.: 12
Employment Agencies
N.A.I.C.S.: 561311
Jennifer Humphries *(Mgr-Bus Dev)*

TEN D. ENTERPRISES, INC.

6520 Sunplex Dr, Ocean Springs, MS 39564
Tel.: (228) 875-0232
Sales Range: $10-24.9 Million
Emp.: 800
Limited Restaurant Services
N.A.I.C.S.: 722513
William H. Descher *(Pres)*
Jeffery H. Descher *(Sec)*
Patricia L. Descher *(VP)*
Gregory S. Descher *(Treas)*

TEN OAKS GROUP

1133 Metropolitan Ave, Charlotte, NC 28204
Web Site:
http://www.tenoaksgroup.com
Private Equity Investor
N.A.I.C.S.: 523999
Michael Hahn *(Partner)*
Matt Magan *(Partner)*

Subsidiaries:

Master-Bilt Products (1)
908 Hwy 15 N, New Albany, MS 38652 (100%)
Tel.: (662) 534-9061
Web Site: http://www.master-bilt.com
Sales Range: $100-124.9 Million
Mfr of Refrigerator Warehouses, Walk-in & Reach-in Coolers & Freezers, Ice Cream Cabinets, Egg Coolers & Insulated Shipping Containers for Dairy, Grocery, Restaurant & Food Chain Stores
N.A.I.C.S.: 333415
James Watkins *(Reg Sls Mgr)*
Steve Gill *(VP-Sls)*

Nor-Lake Inc. (1)
727 2nd St, Hudson, WI 54016-1515
Tel.: (715) 386-2323
Web Site: http://www.norlake.com
Sales Range: $100-124.9 Million
Mfr & Wholesale of Refrigeration Units & Equipments
N.A.I.C.S.: 333415
Merilly Hessburg *(Dir-Customer Care)*

Westerman, Inc. (1)
245 N Broad St, Bremen, OH 43107-9903
Tel.: (740) 569-4143
Metal Products Mfr
N.A.I.C.S.: 331110

TEN THOUSAND VILLAGES

704 Main St, Akron, PA 17501
Tel.: (717) 859-8100
Web Site:
http://www.tenthousandvillages.com
Sales Range: $10-24.9 Million
Emp.: 200
Arts & Crafts Equipment & Supplies
N.A.I.C.S.: 423920
Darlene DeLaPaz *(Mgr-Fair Trade Store)*
Marilyn Bender *(Asst Mgr)*
Thomas Wenger *(Dir-Sls)*
Carl Lundblad *(CEO)*
Ed Diller *(Chm)*

TEN-8 FIRE EQUIPMENT INC.

2904 59th Ave Dr E, Bradenton, FL 34203
Tel.: (941) 756-7779
Web Site: http://www.ten8fire.com
Sales Range: $10-24.9 Million
Emp.: 32
Fire Trucks
N.A.I.C.S.: 423110
Dan Dower *(Pres)*
Ron Ribbons *(Mgr-Svcs)*
Mark Jones *(VP)*
Ted Adent *(Mgr-Equipment Svc-MSA Div)*

TEN: THE ENTHUSIAST NETWORK, INC.

831 S Douglas St, El Segundo, CA 90245
Tel.: (310) 531-9900 DE
Web Site:
http://www.enthusiastnetwork.com
Year Founded: 1995
Sales Range: $1-4.9 Billion
Emp.: 2,200
Holding Company; Magazine Publication & Entertainment Distribution
N.A.I.C.S.: 551112
Scott Dickey *(Pres & CEO)*
Bill Sutman *(CFO & Exec VP)*
Eric Schwab *(Chief Comml Officer & Exec VP)*
Jonathan Anastas *(CMO)*
Angus Mackenzie *(Chief Content Officer & Exec VP)*
Scott Bailey *(Pres-Automotive)*
Norb Garrett *(Exec VP-Sports & Entertainment)*
Kevin Mullan *(Exec VP-Ops)*
Bobby Akin *(Sr VP-Branded Content & Motorsport Ops)*
Geoff DeFrance *(Sr VP-Automotive Digital)*
Matt Boice *(Sr VP-Sls Ops)*
Mike Cummings *(Sr VP-Fin Plng)*
Ryan Payne *(Sr VP-Mktg)*
Dan Bednar *(Sr VP-Digitial Ops)*
Tom Slater *(Sr VP-Circulation)*
Shilpa Joshi *(VP & Controller)*
David Hope *(VP-HR)*

Subsidiaries:

TEN: The Enthusiast Network, LLC (1)
831 S Douglas St, El Segundo, CA 90245
Tel.: (310) 531-9900
Web Site: http://www.enthusiastnetwork.com
Print & Digital Media Publisher
N.A.I.C.S.: 513120
Alan Alpanian *(Chief Creative Officer)*
Doug Evans *(Sr VP)*
David G. Algire *(Pres-The Media Source & Exec VP)*
Scott P. Dickey *(Pres & CEO)*
Bill Sutman *(CFO & Exec VP)*

Unit (Domestic):

Automobile Magazine
120 E Liberty St, Ann Arbor, MI 48104-2156
Tel.: (734) 994-3500
Web Site: http://www.automobilemag.com
Sales Range: $10-24.9 Million
Emp.: 14
Periodicals
N.A.I.C.S.: 513120
Jackie Guenther *(Office Mgr)*
Robert Cumberford *(Editor-Automotive Design)*
Conner Golden *(Editor-Daily News)*
Jake Holmes *(Editor-Daily News)*
Rory Jurnecka *(Editor-Features)*

Subsidiary (Domestic):

GrindMedia, LLC (2)
236 Avenida Fabricante Ste 201, San Clemente, CA 92672
Tel.: (949) 325-6200
Web Site: http://www.grindmedia.com
Magazine Publisher
N.A.I.C.S.: 513120

U.S. PRIVATE

Norb Garrett *(Grp Publr & Sr VP)*
Greg Morrow *(VP-Digital)*
Chris Engelsman *(VP-Print Sls Strategy)*
Elisabeth Murray *(Dir-Digital Sls Strategy)*
Sean Nielsen *(Dir-Event Ops)*
Jamey Stone *(Dir-Mktg)*

Motor Trend (2)
831 S Douglas St, El Segundo, CA 90245
Web Site: http://www.motortrend.com
Emp.: 2,500
Automobile Magazine
N.A.I.C.S.: 513120

Subsidiary (Domestic):

IntelliChoice Source Interlink Media, Inc. (3)
901 Campisi Way Ste 120, Campbell, CA 95008
Tel.: (408) 377-4300
Web Site: http://www.intellichoice.com
New & Used Car Dealer
N.A.I.C.S.: 441120

Unit (Domestic):

Power & Motoryacht (2)
261 Madison Ave 6th Fl, New York, NY 10016-2401
Tel.: (212) 915-4000
Web Site:
http://www.powerandmotoryacht.com
Sales Range: $10-24.9 Million
Emp.: 10
Magazine Publisher
N.A.I.C.S.: 513120
Bob Bauer *(Grp Publr)*
Wade Luce *(Mgr-Sls-West Coast)*

Sail Magazine (2)
23a Glendale St, Salem, MA 01970
Tel.: (860) 767-3200
Web Site: http://www.sailmagazine.com
Sales Range: $10-24.9 Million
Emp.: 25
Periodical Publisher Services
N.A.I.C.S.: 513120
Chris Allen *(Publr)*

Soap Opera Weekly (2)
261 Madison Ave 6th Fl, New York, NY 10016-2303
Tel.: (212) 915-4248
Web Site: http://www.soapoperadigest.com
Sales Range: $10-24.9 Million
Emp.: 22
Periodicals
N.A.I.C.S.: 513120

Surfer Magazine (2)
950 Calle Amanecer Ste C, San Clemente, CA 92673-4203
Tel.: (949) 492-7873
Web Site: http://www.surfer.com
Sales Range: $25-49.9 Million
Periodical Publishers
N.A.I.C.S.: 513120

TENABLE NETWORK SECURITY, INC.

7021 Columbia Gateway Dr Ste 500, Columbia, MD 21046
Tel.: (410) 872-0555
Web Site: http://www.tenable.com
Sales Range: $25-49.9 Million
Emp.: 500
Network Security Software Development Services
N.A.I.C.S.: 541511
Ron Gula *(Co-Founder)*
Renaud Deraison *(Co-Founder & CTO)*
Steve Vintz *(CFO)*
Dave Cole *(Chief Product Officer)*
John Negron *(Chief Revenue Officer)*
Jennifer Johnson *(CMO)*
Gordon Gakovic *(Mgr-Australia & New Zealand)*
Jill Shapiro *(Sr Dir-Govt Affairs)*
John C. Huffard Jr. *(Co-Founder)*

TENASKA, INC.

14302 FNB Pkwy, Omaha, NE 68154-5212
Tel.: (402) 691-9500
Web Site: https://www.tenaska.com
Year Founded: 1987

Sales Range: $5-14.9 Billion
Emp.: 751
Natural Gas Distribution
N.A.I.C.S.: 221210
Timothy G. Kudron (Sr VP-Fin & Admin)
Gregory A. Van Dyke (Co-CFO & Treas)
Thomas E. Hendricks (Exec VP)
Howard L. Hawks (Chm)
David W. Kirkwood (Sr VP-Fin)
Ronald N. Quinn (Sec & Exec VP)
Nicholas N. Borman (Sr VP-Engrg & Construction)
Drew J. Fossum (Gen Counsel & Sr VP)
Todd S. Jonas (Sr VP-Ops)
Bradley K. Heisey (Sr VP)
Jay M. Frisbie (Mng Dir)
John G. Obermiller (Co-CFO & Exec VP)
Timberly Ross (Dir-Comm & PR)

Subsidiaries:

Tenaska BioFuels, LLC (1)
1045 N 115th St Ste 200, Omaha, NE 68154-4422
Tel.: (402) 938-6905
Web Site: http://www.tenaska.com
Sales Range: $10-24.9 Million
Emp.: 100
Biofuels Marketing
N.A.I.C.S.: 457210

Tenaska Capital Management, LLC (1)
14302 FNB Pkwy, Omaha, NE 68154-5212
Tel.: (402) 691-9700
Web Site: http://www.tenaskacapital.com
Emp.: 300
Portfolio Management Services
N.A.I.C.S.: 523940
Thomas E. Hendricks (Exec VP)
Paul S. Smith (Sr Mng Dir)
Jay M. Frisbie (Mng Dir)
Daniel E. Lonergan (CEO & Sr Mng Dir)
Howard L. Hawks (Chm)
Bradley K. Heisey (Sr VP)
Chris A. Leitner (Mng Dir)
Ryan T. Schroer (Mng Dir & CFO)

Subsidiary (Domestic):

US Power Generating Company (2)
300 Atlantic St Ste 500, Stamford, CT 06901-3524
Tel.: (212) 792-0800
Web Site: http://www.uspowergen.com
Sales Range: $100-124.9 Million
Electric Power Generation Producer & Whslr
N.A.I.C.S.: 221122
Mark R. Sudbey (CEO)
Theodore A. Babcock (CFO)
John P. Reese (Sr VP-Regulatory & Govt Affairs)
Richard Branson (VP & Controller)
Katherine Chang (VP & Treas)
Glenn E. Camus (VP, Gen Counsel & Sec)
Jeff D. Hunter (Co-Founder)

Tenaska Marketing Canada (1)
300-5th Avenue Southwest 2500, Stock Exchange Tower, Calgary, T2P 3C4, AB, Canada
Tel.: (403) 716-1387
Web Site: http://www.tenaska.com
Sales Range: $25-49.9 Million
Emp.: 8
Natural Gas Marketing
N.A.I.C.S.: 221210

Tenaska Marketing Ventures (1)
14302 FNB Pkwy, Omaha, NE 68154
Tel.: (402) 758-6100
Web Site: http://www.tenaska.com
Sales Range: $25-49.9 Million
Emp.: 20
Natural Gas Marketing
N.A.I.C.S.: 221210

Tenaska Power Services Co. (1)
1701 E Lamar Blvd Ste 100, Arlington, TX 76006-7320
Tel.: (817) 462-1521
Web Site: http://www.tenaska.com

Sales Range: $25-49.9 Million
Emp.: 120
Electric Power Management & Marketing Services
N.A.I.C.S.: 221122
Kevin R. Smith (Pres)
Keith E. Emery (VP-Mktg)
Mark G. Foreman (VP-Trading)
William W. Horton (VP-Risk Mgmt)
Curry D. Aldridge (VP-Origination & Comml Ops)

TENAX USA
7606 Whitehall Executive Centre Dr Ste 400, Charlotte, NC 28273
Tel.: (704) 583-1173
Web Site: http://www.tenax4you.com
Year Founded: 2000
Sales Range: $10-24.9 Million
Emp.: 50
Wholesale Seller of Stone Related Products, Glues, Polishing Tools & Diamond Tools
N.A.I.C.S.: 327991
James Herrick (Mgr-Natl Sls)
John Thomas (Reg Mgr-Southern Territory)
Rich Cleveland (Reg Mgr-Western Territory)
James Oglesby (Mgr-Tech)

TENAYA ACQUISITIONS COMPANY
1930 Village Ctr Cir #3-201, Las Vegas, NV 89134
Tel.: (702) 982-2463   NV
Year Founded: 2013
Investment Services
N.A.I.C.S.: 523999
Brian Blaszczak (Pres, CEO, CFO, Chief Acctg Officer, Treas & Sec)

TENAYA CAPITAL, LLC
3280 Alpine Rd, Portola Valley, CA 94028
Tel.: (650) 687-6500   DE
Web Site: http://www.tenayacapital.com
Emp.: 10
Private Investment Firm
N.A.I.C.S.: 523999
Tom Banahan (Mng Dir)
Ben Boyer (Mng Dir)
Stewart Gollmer (Mng Dir)
Brian Melton (Mng Dir)
Brian Paul (Mng Dir)
Dave Markland (CFO & Partner-Admin)
Paul Drews (Principal)

TENCARVA MACHINERY COMPANY, LLC
1115 Pleasant Ridge Rd, Greensboro, NC 27409-9529
Tel.: (336) 665-0250   NC
Web Site: http://www.tencarva.com
Year Founded: 1978
Sales Range: $100-124.9 Million
Emp.: 370
Industrial Pumps Distr, Repair & Maintenance Services
N.A.I.C.S.: 423830
Walter Hieber (Dir-Mktg)
Edwin W. Pearce III (Pres)

Subsidiaries:

Electric Service & Sales, Inc. (1)
1800 Sullivan St, Greensboro, NC 27405
Tel.: (336) 275-5321
Web Site: http://www.esscoinc.com
Sales Range: $10-24.9 Million
Emp.: 15
Industrial Equipment Servicing & Whslr
N.A.I.C.S.: 811310

Fischer Pump & Valve Company (1)
155 Commerce Dr, Loveland, OH 45140
Tel.: (513) 583-4800
Web Site: https://www.fischerprocess.com

Sales Range: $10-24.9 Million
Emp.: 380
Pumps & Pumping Equipment
N.A.I.C.S.: 423830
Kenneth A. Fischer (Pres)
Steve Melchers (Mgr-Svcs)

Tencarva Machinery Company, LLC - Alcoa (1)
3057 Regal Dr, Alcoa, TN 37701
Tel.: (865) 588-7674
Web Site: http://www.tencarva.com
Industrial Pumps Distr, Repair & Maintenance Services
N.A.I.C.S.: 423830

Tencarva Machinery Company, LLC - Brookhaven (1)
984 Hwy 84 E, Brookhaven, MS 39601-8779
Tel.: (601) 823-0510
Web Site: http://www.tencarva.com
Industrial Pumps Distr, Repair & Maintenance Services
N.A.I.C.S.: 423830
Collins K. Allen (Branch Mgr)

Tencarva Machinery Company, LLC - Charlotte (1)
417 B Minuet Ln, Charlotte, NC 28217
Tel.: (704) 521-9400
Web Site: http://www.tencarva.com
Industrial Pumps Distr, Repair & Maintenance Services
N.A.I.C.S.: 423830
J. Jones (Branch Mgr)

Tencarva Machinery Company, LLC - Chattanooga (1)
4101 Crowell Rd, Chattanooga, TN 37421-2172
Tel.: (423) 892-8928
Web Site: http://www.tencarva.com
Industrial Pumps Distr, Repair & Maintenance Services
N.A.I.C.S.: 423830

Tencarva Machinery Company, LLC - Chesapeake (1)
933 Corporate Ln, Chesapeake, VA 23320-3651
Tel.: (757) 548-0400
Web Site: http://www.tencarva.com
Industrial Pumps Distr, Repair & Maintenance Services
N.A.I.C.S.: 423830
Ed Pears (Pres)

Tencarva Machinery Company, LLC - Columbia (1)
1405 Old Dairy Rd, Columbia, SC 29201-4839
Tel.: (803) 256-8100
Web Site: http://www.tencarva.com
Industrial Pumps Distr, Repair & Maintenance Services
N.A.I.C.S.: 423830

Tencarva Machinery Company, LLC - Greenville (1)
14 Park Pl Ct, Greenville, SC 29607
Tel.: (864) 277-6860
Web Site: http://www.tencarva.com
Industrial Pumps Distr, Repair & Maintenance Services
N.A.I.C.S.: 423830

Tencarva Machinery Company, LLC - Jackson (1)
326 Elton Rd, Jackson, MS 39212
Tel.: (601) 502-2400
Web Site: http://www.tencarva.com
Emp.: 3
Industrial Pumps Distr, Repair & Maintenance Services
N.A.I.C.S.: 423830
B. S. Jones (Branch Mgr-Sls)

Tencarva Machinery Company, LLC - Johnson City (1)
5 Worth Cir Ste 3, Johnson City, TN 37601-4338
Tel.: (423) 282-5455
Web Site: http://www.tencarva.com
Industrial Pumps Distr, Repair & Maintenance Services
N.A.I.C.S.: 423830

Tencarva Machinery Company, LLC - Little Rock (1)

9720A Interstate 30, Little Rock, AR 72209-3304
Tel.: (501) 565-0105
Web Site: http://www.tencarva.com
Emp.: 3
Industrial Pumps Distr, Repair & Maintenance Services
N.A.I.C.S.: 423830
J.S. Watson Sr. (Office Mgr)

Tencarva Machinery Company, LLC - Memphis (1)
3616 Cherry Rd, Memphis, TN 38118-6355
Tel.: (901) 794-7570
Web Site: http://www.tencarva.com
Industrial Pump Repair & Maintenance Distr
N.A.I.C.S.: 423830
Don Wirth (VP)
Don Wirth (VP)

Tencarva Machinery Company, LLC - Nashville (1)
839 Fesslers Pkwy, Nashville, TN 37210-2902
Tel.: (615) 742-3101
Web Site: http://www.tencarva.com
Industrial Pumps Distr, Repair & Maintenance Services
N.A.I.C.S.: 423830

Tencarva Machinery Company, LLC - North Charleston (1)
2460 Remount Rd Ste 101, Charleston, SC 29406-6172
Tel.: (843) 747-1173
Web Site: http://www.tencarva.com
Industrial Pumps Distr, Repair & Maintenance Services
N.A.I.C.S.: 423830
David Lee (Branch Mgr)

Tencarva Machinery Company, LLC - Richmond (1)
12200 Wilfong Ct, Midlothian, VA 23112-3976
Tel.: (804) 639-4646
Web Site: http://www.tencarva.com
Industrial Pumps Distr, Repair & Maintenance Services
N.A.I.C.S.: 423830

Tencarva Machinery Company, LLC - Salem (1)
1410 Mill Race Dr, Salem, VA 24153-3113
Tel.: (540) 375-7240
Web Site: http://www.tencarva.com
Industrial Pumps Distr, Repair & Maintenance Services
N.A.I.C.S.: 423830

Tencarva Machinery Company, LLC - Wilmington (1)
1200 N 23rd St Ste 111, Wilmington, NC 28405-7485
Tel.: (910) 799-8800
Web Site: http://www.tencarva.com
Sales Range: $25-49.9 Million
Emp.: 5
Industrial Pumps Distr, Repair & Maintenance Services
N.A.I.C.S.: 423830
Rod Lee (Pres)

TENCO SERVICES, INC.
783 Old Hickory Blvd, Ste 263, Brentwood, TN 37027
Tel.: (615) 292-0088
Web Site: http://www.tenco.com
Year Founded: 1947
Emp.: 100
Claim Adjusting Services
N.A.I.C.S.: 524291
Tom Moss (Pres)
Deanna Scales (Dir-Fin & HR)
Brian Duncan (VP-Special Ops)
David Whitaker (Asst VP & Mgr)
Rebe Trickey (Exec VP)
Belinda Richardson (VP & Mgr)
Bill Sharpe (Sr VP)
Tim Feldman (VP & Mgr)

Subsidiaries:

James C. Greene Company (1)
7500 Six Forks Rd Ste 100, Raleigh, NC 27615
Tel.: (919) 832-6614

TENCO SERVICES, INC.

U.S. PRIVATE

Tenco Services, Inc.—(Continued)
Web Site: http://www.jcgreeneco.com
Leather Goods Mfr
N.A.I.C.S.: 315210
James Peck (VP)

TENDER CORPORATION
106 Burndy Rd, Littleton, NH 03561
Tel.: (603) 444-5464   NH
Web Site: http://www.tendercorp.com
Year Founded: 1975
Sales Range: $75-99.9 Million
Emp.: 40
First Aid Kits, Insect Repellants & After Bite Treatments Mfr
N.A.I.C.S.: 325412
Jason Cartwright (CEO)
Leslie Lindberg (CFO)
John Gaulin (COO)
Susan Scheibenpflug (Mgr-Sls-Ready 4 Kits)

TENDER LOVING THINGS INC.
26203 Production Ave Ste 4, Hayward, CA 94545
Tel.: (510) 300-1260
Rev.: $7,000,000
Emp.: 12
Stress Release Health Therapy Products Distr
N.A.I.C.S.: 325620
Mark Juarez (Pres)
Cindy Souza (Dir)

Subsidiaries:

The Happy Company   (1)
26203 Production Ave Ste 4, Hayward, CA 94545-3800
Tel.: (510) 300-1260
Web Site: http://www.thehappycompany.com
Sales Range: $10-24.9 Million
Emp.: 5
Children's Products Mfr & Sales
N.A.I.C.S.: 325620
Mark Juarez (Founder & CEO)

TENDO SYSTEMS INC.
1851 Horseshoe Trl Annex, Chester Springs, PA 19425
Tel.: (844) 412-2800   DE
Web Site: https://tendo.com
Year Founded: 2020
Software Development Services
N.A.I.C.S.: 513210
Dan Goldsmith (CEO)

Subsidiaries:

MDSave, Inc.   (1)
100 Winners Cir Ste 202, Brentwood, TN 37027
Web Site: https://www.mdsave.com
Online Medical Service Platform Provider
N.A.I.C.S.: 513210
Paul Ketchel (CEO & Founder)
Ryan Aipperspach (CTO)
Kitty Cawiezell (Exec VP-Sales)
Greg Born (Pres & COO)
Toryn Slater (Exec VP-Operations)
Mark Kaufman (VP-Product)
Shelby Schott (VP-Sales)
Blake Stevenson (VP-Sales)
Lydia Griffy (VP-Finance)
Robert Atnip (VP-Implementation)
Kate Rogow (Sr VP-Acct Mgmt & Strategic Growth)
Kar Martirosyan (VP-Engineering)
Anne Glatts (Dir)
Courtney McNamee (Mktg Dir)
Charlie Byrge (Chief Comml Officer)
Michael O'Brien (VP-Sales)
Branson Lankster (VP-Ops & Strategy)
Christy Friedman (Mktg Dir)
Charlie Byrge (Chief Revenue Officer)
Michael O'Brien (VP-Sales)

TENERITY, INC.
6 High Ridge Park, Stamford, CT 06905
Tel.: (203) 956-1000   DE
Web Site: https://www.tenerity.com
Year Founded: 2005
AFGR—(OTCQX)
Emp.: 1,400
Holding Company; Technological & Analytical Solution Services
N.A.I.C.S.: 551112
Michael L. Iaccarino (Chm & CEO)
Gilbert S. Palter (Vice Chm)
Michele Conforti (Pres, Exec VP & Mng Dir-Intl)
Loic Blondel (CTO & Exec VP)
Iphigenie Fossati-Kotz (Gen Counsel & Exec VP)
Lynn Doonan (Chief People Officer & Exec VP)
David Treybig (CIO & Exec VP)

Subsidiaries:

Webloyalty.com   (1)
6 High Ridge Park, Stamford, CT 06905
Tel.: (203) 846-3300
Web Site: http://www.webloyalty.com
Loyalty Programs for Internet Sales
N.A.I.C.S.: 541519

TENEX CAPITAL MANAGEMENT, L.P.
60 E 42nd St Ste 4510, New York, NY 10165-0015
Tel.: (212) 457-1138   DE
Web Site: http://www.tenexcm.com
Sales Range: $10-24.9 Million
Emp.: 52
Privater Equity Firm
N.A.I.C.S.: 523150
Michael Green (CEO & Mng Dir-Ops)
Varun Bedi (Mng Dir-Investments)
J. P. Bretl (Mng Dir-Ops)
Joe Cottone (Mng Dir-Ops)
Chad Spooner (Mng Dir-Ops)
Perrin Monroe (VP-Investments)
Scott Galletti (Mng Dir-Capital Markets & Bus Dev)
Ben Kramer (CFO & Sr VP)
Ron Lejman (Mng Dir-Ops)
Gabriel Wood (VP-Investments)
Stephens Johnson (Dir-IR)
Priyanka Sharma (Controller)
Alessandra Catalano (Office Mgr)
Ryan MacIntyre (VP-Investments)
Kevin Doyle (Dir-Bus Dev)

Subsidiaries:

Brown Machine Group   (1)
330 N Ross St, Beaverton, MI 48612
Web Site: http://brownmachinegroup.com
Holding Company; Thermoforming Equipment Mfr
N.A.I.C.S.: 333248
Bob Gordert (VP-Sls)
John Block (VP-Customer Svc & Pur)
Brian Keeley (COO)
Tom Blonde (Mgr-Engrg)
Michael Johnson (CFO)
Kevin Daley (Dir-Sls-Intl)
Jason Newman (Natl Sls Mgr-US & Canada)
Dan Bartholomew (Mgr-Natl Sls-Kits)
Mike Witer (Mgr-Product-Sls-Tooling)
Flent Brubaker (Specialist-Parts)
Greg Wolf (CEO)

Subsidiary (Domestic):

Brown Machine, LLC   (2)
330 N Ross St, Beaverton, MI 48612   (100%)
Tel.: (989) 435-7741
Web Site: http://www.brown-machine.com
Plastic Thermoforming & Packaging Machinery Mfr
N.A.I.C.S.: 333248
Bob Gordert (VP-Sls)
Mike Witer (Product Mgr-Sls-Tooling)
Jason Newman (Natl Sls Mgr-US & Canada)
Brian Keeley (COO)
Kevin Daley (Dir-Intl-Sls)
Flent Brubaker (Specialist-Parts)
John Block (VP-Customer Svc & Pur)

Tom Blonde (Mgr-Engrg)
Michael Johnson (CFO)
Dan Bartholomew (Mgr-Natl Sls-Kits)

Compass Health Brands Corp.   (1)
6753 Engle Rd, Middleburg Heights, OH 44130
Web Site: http://www.compasshealthbrands.com
Holding Company; Medical & Personal Care Products Distr
N.A.I.C.S.: 551112
Stuart J. Strauss (Pres & CEO)
Jim Hileman (CFO)
Henry Lin (COO)
Laura Casto (VP-Mktg-Pro Div)
Ryan Moore (VP-Sls-Pro)
Jeff Swain (VP-Mktg & Product Dev-Retail Channel)
Tony West (VP-Sls-Retail)

Subsidiary (Domestic):

Apex Medical Corporation   (2)
921 E Amidon St, Sioux Falls, SD 57104-0909
Tel.: (605) 332-6689
Web Site: http://www.carex.com
Medical & Hospital Equipment
N.A.I.C.S.: 423450
Daniel Lee (Chm)
Charles Liu (Pres)

Co-Headquarters (Domestic):

Apex Medical Corporation - Norwell Executive Office   (3)
600 Cordwainer Dr, Norwell, MA 02061
Tel.: (781) 871-2710
Web Site: http://www.carex.com
Executive Office
N.A.I.C.S.: 921110
Matt McElduff (Pres)
Jeff Swain (Dir-Mktg & Comm)

Subsidiary (Domestic):

Roscoe Medical, Inc.   (2)
21973 Commerce Pkwy, Strongsville, OH 44149
Tel.: (440) 572-1962
Web Site: http://www.roscoemedical.com
Sales Range: $1-9.9 Million
Medical Appliance & Supplies Mfr & Whslr
N.A.I.C.S.: 339113
Paul Guth (Pres & CEO)
Henry Lin (Sr VP-Global Sourcing & OEM Sls)
Laura Castro (VP-Mktg & Comm)
Paul Lin (VP-Quality)
John Medina (VP-Sls-Home Medical Equipment)

Custom Molded Products, Inc.   (1)
36 Herring Rd, Newnan, GA 30265
Tel.: (770) 632-7115
Web Site: http://www.c-m-p.com
Roofing, Siding & Insulation Material Merchant Whslr
N.A.I.C.S.: 423330

JPW Industries Inc.   (1)
427 New Sanford Rd, La Vergne, TN 37086-4184
Tel.: (615) 793-8900
Web Site: http://www.jettools.com
Sales Range: $550-599.9 Million
Emp.: 1,700
Industrial Tool & Machining Systems Mfr & Distr
N.A.I.C.S.: 333517
Robert Romano (Pres)
Robert Varzino (Sr VP-Natl Sls Accts Mktg & Internet)
Anthony Stratton (CFO & VP-Fin & Controlling)
Virginia Schmidt (VP-HR)
William Ward (VP-Sls)

Subsidiary (Domestic):

Edward's Manufacturing Co, Inc.   (2)
1107 Sykes St, Albert Lea, MN 56007   (100%)
Tel.: (507) 373-8206
Web Site: http://www.edwardsironworkers.com
Sales Range: $1-9.9 Million
Emp.: 100

Designs & Manufactures Ironworkers Products & Heavy-Duty Rain Gauges
N.A.I.C.S.: 333248
Alex Friend (Pres)
Doug Friend (COO)

Subsidiary (Non-US):

JPW (Tool) AG   (2)
Tamperlistrasse 5, 8117, Fallanden, Switzerland
Tel.: (41) 44 806 4748
Industrial Tools Distr
N.A.I.C.S.: 423840

Tool France S.a.r.l.   (2)
57 Rue Du Bois Chaland Zl du Bois Chaland, 91029, Evry, Cedex, France
Tel.: (33) 1 6911 3737
Web Site: http://www.promac.fr
Industrial Tools Distr
N.A.I.C.S.: 423990
Christophe Saint Sulpice (Gen Mgr)

JTM Foods, LLC   (1)
2126 E 33rd St, Erie, PA 16510
Tel.: (814) 899-0886
Web Site: http://www.jjsbakery.net
Bakery Product Mfr & Distr
N.A.I.C.S.: 311813
Byard Ebling (VP-Sls & Mktg)
Monty Pooley (Pres & CEO)

Subsidiary (Domestic):

Cookies-N-Milk, Inc.   (2)
10983 Guilford Rd Ste A, Annapolis Junction, MD 20701-1191
Tel.: (301) 953-7426
Sales Range: $1-9.9 Million
Emp.: 10
Perishable Prepared Food Mfr
N.A.I.C.S.: 311991
Mike Blasko (Pres)

Rush Sales Company   (1)
2700 E Interstate 20, Odessa, TX 79766
Tel.: (432) 337-2397
Web Site: http://www.rushoverland.com
Sales Range: $10-24.9 Million
Industrial Truck, Trailer & Other Related Machinery Mfr
N.A.I.C.S.: 333924
Jerry Rush (Pres)

Subsidiary (Domestic):

Overland Tank, Inc.   (2)
4725 FM 18, Abilene, TX 79602
Tel.: (325) 673-7132
Web Site: http://www.rushoverland.com
Sales Range: $1-9.9 Million
Emp.: 20
Industrial Truck, Trailer & Other Related Machinery Mfr
N.A.I.C.S.: 333924
Betty Atkins (Office Mgr)

Unirac, Inc.   (1)
1411 Broadway Blvd NE, Albuquerque, NM 87102-1545
Tel.: (505) 242-6411
Web Site: http://www.unirac.com
Sales Range: $1-9.9 Million
Emp.: 65
Solar Panel Racking Mfr
N.A.I.C.S.: 332999
Peter Lorenz (CEO)
Charles Lubecke (Sr Project Mgr-Mktg)
Mark Zwolak (CFO)

Subsidiary (Domestic):

Ecolibrium Solar, Inc.   (2)
507 Richland Ave, Athens, OH 45701
Tel.: (740) 249-1877
Web Site: http://www.ecolibriumsolar.com
Sales Range: $25-49.9 Million
Emp.: 10
Solar Panel Mfr
N.A.I.C.S.: 333414
Jan Willem Van Der Werff (CEO)
Chad Parsons (Dir-Ops)
Devin MacRostie (Dir-Engrg & Tech)
Liz Hammer (Controller)

TENEX CORPORATION
1001 Green Bay Rd, Winnetka, IL 60093
Tel.: (847) 504-0400   IL

COMPANIES

Year Founded: 1964
Sales Range: $25-49.9 Million
Emp.: 400
Plastics Products
N.A.I.C.S.: 326199
Albert B. Cheris *(Pres)*
Paul Moniuszko *(VP-Fin)*

TENGCO INC.
14030 Bolsa Ln, Cerritos, CA 90703
Tel.: (714) 676-8200
Web Site: http://www.tengco.com
Sales Range: $10-24.9 Million
Emp.: 30
Provider of Industrial Fasteners
N.A.I.C.S.: 423840
Thomas J. English *(Pres)*

TENGOINTERNET
106 E Sixth St Ste 900, Austin, TX 78701
Tel.: (512) 322-3959
Web Site: http://www.tengointernet.com
Year Founded: 2002
Rev.: $2,600,000
Emp.: 13
Wired Telecommunications Carriers
N.A.I.C.S.: 517111
Eric B. Stumberg *(Founder & CEO)*
Alex Dehoyos *(Dir-Network Ops)*
Elisa Harvey *(Acct Mgr)*
Kevin Lloyd *(Dir-Sls & Mktg)*
Tami Tock *(Acct Mgr)*

TENGRAM CAPITAL PARTNERS, LIMITED PARTNERSHIP
15 Riverside Ave, Westport, CT 06880
Tel.: (203) 454-6999   DE
Web Site: http://www.tengramcapital.com
Private Equity Firm
N.A.I.C.S.: 523999
William Sweedler *(Co-Founder & Mng Partner)*
Matthew D. Eby *(Co-Founder & Mng Partner)*
Brenda De Luca *(Office Mgr)*
Brian Cooper *(Principal)*
Robin Lamb *(Principal)*
Kelly Mansdorf-Dentz *(CFO & Chief Compliance Officer)*
Kris Parks *(Principal)*
Subsidiaries:

Fashionology Group LLC   (1)
575 7th Ave, New York, NY 10018
Tel.: (212) 515-5301
Sales Range: $100-124.9 Million
Men's, Women's & Children's Apparel Mfr;
Owned by Windsong Allegiance Apparel Group, LLC, Hilco Trading, LLC & Radius Partners, LLC
N.A.I.C.S.: 424350
William Sweedler *(Co-Chm)*

Lime Crime Inc.   (1)
20501 Ventura Blvd, Woodland Hills, CA 91364
Web Site: http://www.limecrime.com
Electronic Shopping
N.A.I.C.S.: 456120
Mark Dumbelton *(CO-Founder & Pres)*
Kim Walls *(Gen Mgr-Global)*
Doe Deere *(Co-Founder)*
Andrea Blieden *(CEO)*

Robert Graham Designs LLC   (1)
264 W 40th St 10th Fl, New York, NY 10018
Tel.: (212) 869-8001
Web Site: http://www.robertgraham.us
Sales Range: $100-124.9 Million
Emp.: 60
Clothing Mfr
N.A.I.C.S.: 315250
Michael Buckley *(CEO)*
Robert Stock *(Co-Chm & Chief Creative Officer)*
Andrew Berg *(CEO)*

TENIBAC-GRAPHION INC.
35155 Automation Dr, Clinton Township, MI 48035
Tel.: (586) 792-0150
Web Site: http://www.tenibac.com
Rev.: $13,094,016
Emp.: 75
Texturing & Embossing Services
N.A.I.C.S.: 332119
Bill Arms *(Controller)*
John Kayi *(Mgr-Intl Bus & Sls)*
Jim Deliz *(Partner & Dir-Global Ops)*

TENIR INVESTMENTS INC.
2704 Lipscomb St, Fort Worth, TX 76110
Tel.: (817) 926-0231
Web Site: http://www.edawilson.com
Sales Range: $10-24.9 Million
Emp.: 16
Holding Company; Commercial & Office Building & New Construction Services
N.A.I.C.S.: 551112
Jerrell B. Wilson *(Pres)*
Mark Ramsey *(Controller)*
Subsidiaries:

Ed A. Wilson Inc.   (1)
2704 Lipscomb St, Fort Worth, TX 76110
Tel.: (817) 926-0231
Web Site: http://www.edawilson.com
Concrete Sitework Contractor
N.A.I.C.S.: 236220
Edward A. Wilson Jr. *(Pres)*

TENMAST SOFTWARE CO.
132 Venture Ct Ste 1, Lexington, KY 40511
Tel.: (859) 455-8061
Web Site: http://www.tenmast.com
Year Founded: 1984
Sales Range: $1-9.9 Million
Emp.: 65
Housing Software Services
N.A.I.C.S.: 541511
Darren Lorusso *(Deputy Dir-Community Dev)*
David Stromquist *(Controller)*
Earlene Wardlaw *(Dir-Maintenance)*
James C. Mauch *(CEO)*
Adam Block *(Mgr-Bus Dev)*
Lance Nodine *(Dir-Construction Mgmt)*
Mark Lewis *(Pres)*
Julie Bell *(Dir-Implementation)*
Nita Winford *(Controller)*
Roslyn Lukasiewicz *(Dir-Community Dev)*
Zelma Frei *(Dir-Housing Dev)*
Darryl Bazile *(Dir-Pub Housing)*
Erik Castonguay *(Exec Dir)*
Clinton Blahnik *(Mgr-Housing Dev)*
Nelson Stiefel *(Mgr-Maintenance)*

TENNESSEE ALUMINUM PROCESSORS
7207 Hoover Mason Rd, Mount Pleasant, TN 38474
Tel.: (931) 379-5836
Web Site: http://www.tap-rsi.com
Rev.: $15,000,000
Emp.: 150
Primary Aluminum
N.A.I.C.S.: 331313
Kathy Tucker *(Sr VP)*
Jay Green *(Mgr-Rolling Stock)*
Kim Sproul *(VP-Admin)*
Jared Sweeney *(VP)*

TENNESSEE APPAREL CORP.
1809 Old Estill Springs Rd, Tullahoma, TN 37388-5510
Tel.: (931) 455-3491   TN
Year Founded: 1975
Sales Range: $25-49.9 Million
Emp.: 100
Military Apparel Sales
N.A.I.C.S.: 315250
Rick Francis *(Co-Pres)*
David Robbins *(Co-Pres)*
JoAnn Stowers *(Mgr-Info Sys)*

TENNESSEE BUN COMPANY, LLC
197 Printwood Dr, Dickson, TN 37055
Tel.: (615) 441-4600   TN
Web Site: http://www.bakerycos.com
Year Founded: 1996
Fresh & Frozen Baked Goods Mfr & Whslr
N.A.I.C.S.: 311812
Todd Bruinsma *(VP-Quality Assurance)*
Neil Bailey *(VP-Tech Svcs)*
Cordia W. Harrington *(CEO & Co-Founder)*
Tom Harrington *(Co-Founder & CFO)*
Joe Waters *(Chief Bus Dev Officer)*
Gary Hanson *(VP-Supply Chain)*
Koby Stein *(VP-Bus Dev)*
Bill Serie *(Plant Mgr-Nashville Bun, Cornerstone & Cold Storage)*
Beth Westjohn *(Co-CFO)*
Yianny Caparos *(Pres)*
Subsidiaries:

Masada Bakery, LLC   (1)
1500 Oakbrook Dr, Norcross, GA 30093-2245
Tel.: (404) 377-4555
Web Site: http://www.masadabakery.com
Commercial Bakery
N.A.I.C.S.: 311812
Jackie Bouysou *(Mgr-HR)*
Michael Scalera *(Controller)*
Thomas Maruhn *(Mgr-Distr)*
Koby Stein *(Pres)*
Alan Fishman *(Bus Mgr)*
Ken Ellis *(Reg Sls Mgr-FL)*
Scott Belcher *(Reg Sls Mgr-NC, SC & VA)*
Hezi Stein *(Founder)*
Brandon Waters *(Reg Sls Mgr-AL & GA)*
Jason Peacock *(Reg Sls Mgr-AL & GA)*
Larry Murray *(Plant Mgr)*

Steck Wholesale Foods, Inc.   (1)
1001 River Dr, North Sioux City, SD 57049
Tel.: (605) 242-5006
Web Site: http://www.steckfoods.com
Sales Range: $1-9.9 Million
Emp.: 16
Bakery Products Whslr
N.A.I.C.S.: 311812
Craig Stanley *(Pres)*
Doug Heck *(VP-Mfg)*
Jim Calvert *(VP-Sls)*

Tennessee Bun Company, LLC - Dickson Plant   (1)
197 Printwood Dr, Dickson, TN 37055
Tel.: (615) 441-4600
Web Site: http://www.bakerycos.com
Commercial Bakery
N.A.I.C.S.: 311812
Trey Fowler *(Plant Mgr)*

TENNESSEE COMMERCIAL WAREHOUSE INC.
22 Stanley St, Nashville, TN 37210-2133
Tel.: (615) 255-1122   TN
Web Site: http://www.tcwonline.com
Year Founded: 1948
Sales Range: $25-49.9 Million
Emp.: 300
Provider of Freight Transportation Services
N.A.I.C.S.: 488510
Dave Manning *(Pres)*
Scott George *(CEO)*
Alan D. Witt *(VP-Fin)*

TENNESSEE FARMERS CO-OPERATIVE

TENNESSEE FOOTBALL, INC.

180 Old Nashville Hwy, La Vergne, TN 37086-3221
Tel.: (615) 793-8011   TN
Web Site: http://www.ourcoop.com
Year Founded: 1945
Sales Range: $700-749.9 Million
Emp.: 700
Animal Feeds & Other Farm Supply Mfr & Distr
N.A.I.C.S.: 459999
David Moss *(Chief Risk Officer)*
Kenneth Nixon *(Chm)*
Mark Thompson *(Vice Chm)*
Subsidiaries:

Ag Distributors, Inc.   (1)
6615 Robertson Ave, Nashville, TN 37209-1631
Tel.: (615) 356-9113
Sales Range: $10-24.9 Million
Emp.: 10
Fertilizer Distr
N.A.I.C.S.: 424910

Gibson Farmers Cooperative   (1)
PO Box 550, Dyersburg, TN 38025-0550   (100%)
Tel.: (731) 285-7161
Sales Range: $25-49.9 Million
Emp.: 4
Retail Farm Supplies
N.A.I.C.S.: 424910
Jim Brown *(Pres)*

GreenPoint AG, LLC   (1)
3350 Players Club Pkwy, Memphis, TN 38125
Tel.: (901) 758-1341
Web Site: http://www.greenpointag.com
Retail Farm Supply Stores
N.A.I.C.S.: 424910
Tim Witcher *(Pres & CEO)*

Subsidiary (Domestic):

Tipton Farmers Cooperative   (2)
2060 Hwy 51 S, Covington, TN 38019
Tel.: (901) 476-8692
Farm Supplies
N.A.I.C.S.: 424910
Joey Caldwell *(Treas)*

Stockdale   (1)
14840 Highway 18 S, Bolivar, TN 38008-0447
Tel.: (731) 658-3931
Web Site: http://www.stockdales.com
Emp.: 5
Lifestyle Product Retailer
N.A.I.C.S.: 459120
J. D. Sims *(Gen Mgr)*

TENNESSEE FOOTBALL, INC.
Saint Thomas Sports Park 460 Great Circle Rd, Nashville, TN 37228
Tel.: (615) 565-4000   TN
Web Site: http://www.titansonline.com
Year Founded: 1959
Sales Range: $50-74.9 Million
Emp.: 80
Professional Football Franchise
N.A.I.C.S.: 711211
Jenneen Kaufman *(CFO & Sr VP)*
Ralph Ockenfels *(VP-Mktg, Brdcst & Digital Rights)*
Mike Keith *(Dir-Brdcst)*
Russ Hudson *(Dir-Info Sys)*
Gary Glenn *(Sr Dir-Digital Media)*
Bill Wainwright *(Dir-Suite Sales & Svcs)*
Anthony Pastrana *(Dir-Video)*
Brad McClanahan *(Dir-Mktg)*
Brent Akers *(Dir-Team Ops)*
Paul Noska *(Mgr-Equipment)*
Vin Marino *(VP-Football Admin)*
Jim Arts *(Dir-Security)*
Brian Gardner *(Coord-Pro Scouting)*
Gil Beverly *(Chief Mktg & Revenue Officer & Sr VP)*
Burke Nihill *(Pres & CEO)*

TENNESSEE FOOTBALL, INC.

Tennessee Football, Inc.—(Continued)
Gary Treangen (VP-Corp Partnerships & Activation)
Shannon Myers (VP-Fin)

TENNESSEE HOSPITAL ASSOCIATION
5201 Virginia Way, Brentwood, TN 37027
Tel.: (615) 256-8240   TN
Web Site: http://www.tha.com
Year Founded: 1938
Sales Range: $10-24.9 Million
Health Care Association
N.A.I.C.S.: 813910
Craig Becker (Pres & CEO)
Beth Atwood (Sr Dir-Comm & Mktg)
Suzette Crutchfield (Asst VP-HR)
Mary Layne Van Cleave (COO & Exec VP)
Michael Dietrich (VP-Member Svcs)
Bryan Metzger (Sr VP-Info Svcs)
Carol Darnell (Mgr-Building)
David Neiger (CFO & VP)
Darlene Swart (VP-Clinical & Regulatory Res & Consulting)
Gwyn Walters (VP-Res & Reimbursement)
Alan Watson (Chm)
Joe Burchfield (Sr VP-Govt Affairs & Comm)
Larissa Lee (Dir-Health Info Network)
Robert Penick (Mgr-Acctg-Payroll & Accts Payable)
Emily Schott (Dir-Digital Media & Design)
Patrick Turri (Asst VP-Data Analysis)
Mary Ann Watson (Dir-Workforce Network & Dev)
Karen Wood (Mgr-Acctg-Accts Receivable)
Jerrod Daniels (Gen Counsel)

TENNESSEE PRESS SERVICE, INC
625 Market St Ste 1100, Knoxville, TN 37902
Tel.: (865) 584-5761
Web Site: http://www.tnpress.com
Year Founded: 1947
Sales Range: $1-9.9 Million
Emp.: 8
Media Buying Services
N.A.I.C.S.: 541810
Laurie Alford (Controller)
Kevin Slimp (Dir-Tech)
David Wells (Dir-Adv)
Earl Goodman (Sr Media Buyer)

TENNESSEE STATE BANK
2210 Parkway, Pigeon Forge, TN 37863
Tel.: (865) 429-7825
Web Site: http://www.tnstatebank.com
Sales Range: $10-24.9 Million
Emp.: 500
Banking Services
N.A.I.C.S.: 522110
Todd Profitt (Pres & CEO)
Kristin Lewis (VP-Lending)
Rachel Campbell (Mgr-Operational-Seymour)

TENNESSEE VALLEY ELECTRIC COOPERATIVE
590 Florence Rd, Savannah, TN 38372
Tel.: (731) 925-4916
Web Site: http://www.tennesseevalleyec.com
Sales Range: $10-24.9 Million
Emp.: 150
Electric Power Distr
N.A.I.C.S.: 221122

Bob Laden (Dir-Fin)
Gerald Taylor (Gen Mgr & Dir-Engrg)
Don Doran (Dir-Member Svcs & Safety)

TENNESSEE VALLEY HAM CO., INC.
PO Box 1146, Paris, TN 38242
Tel.: (731) 642-9740   TN
Web Site: http://www.cliftyfarm.com
Year Founded: 1954
Meat Product Distr
N.A.I.C.S.: 424470
Michael Murphey (Pres)

TENNESSEE VALLEY PRINTING CO.
201 1st Ave SE, Decatur, AL 35609
Tel.: (256) 340-2433
Web Site: http://www.decaturdaily.com
Year Founded: 1911
Sales Range: $10-24.9 Million
Emp.: 100
Newspaper Publishing Services
N.A.I.C.S.: 513110
Barrett C. Shelton (Gen Mgr)
Leta Milstead (Mgr-Circulation Office)

Subsidiaries:

TimesDaily   (1)
219 W Tennessee St, Florence, AL 35630-5440   (100%)
Tel.: (256) 766-3434
Web Site: http://www.timesdaily.com
Newspaper Publishing Services
N.A.I.C.S.: 513110
Mike Goens (Mng Editor)
Renita Jimmar (Mgr-Display Adv)
Leta Milstead (Office Mgr)
Lin Reynolds (Mgr-Prepress)
Darrell Sandlin (Publr)
Anita Sykes (Accountant)
Cherri Sutherland (Acct Exec)

TENNESSEE VALLEY RECYCLING LLC
1300 Hwy 20, Decatur, AL 35601
Tel.: (256) 353-6351
Web Site: http://www.tvrllc.com
Sales Range: $10-24.9 Million
Emp.: 100
Nonferrous Metals Scrap
N.A.I.C.S.: 423930
Morley Denbo (Co-Chm)
Joel Denbo (Mgr)
Solomon I. Miller (Mgr-Admin)
Manuel Carrizo (Mgr-Huntsville Div)
Terry C. Rice (Dir-Fin)
Jeff Dumes (Dir-Nonferrous Metals)
Alan Springer (Mgr-Recovery Div)
Barry Parks (Mgr-Transportation)

TENNESSEE VALLEY SIGN & PRINTING, INC.
301 Thomas French Dr, Scottsboro, AL 35769
Tel.: (256) 574-2515
Web Site: http://www.tennesseevalleysigns.com
Rev: $1,500,000
Emp.: 20
Commercial Screen Printing
N.A.I.C.S.: 323113
Debbie Johnson (Dir-Art)

TENNIER INDUSTRIES INC.
N Side Plz RR 45, Pomona, NY 10970
Tel.: (845) 362-0800
Sales Range: $10-24.9 Million
Emp.: 5
Military Uniforms, Men's & Youths'
N.A.I.C.S.: 315250

TENNSCO CORPORATION
201 Tennsco Dr, Dickson, TN 37055

Tel.: (615) 446-8000   FL
Web Site: http://www.tennsco.com
Year Founded: 1962
Sales Range: $150-199.9 Million
Emp.: 600
Mfr of Office Furniture & Storage Cabinets
N.A.I.C.S.: 337214
Mike Easley (VP-Fin)
Roy L. Stinson (VP-Mfg)
Stuart Speyer (Pres)
Johnny Morris (VP-Mfg)

Subsidiaries:

Tennsco Corporation - Plant 2   (1)
1101 W 1st St, Dickson, TN 37055
Tel.: (615) 446-8000
Storage Cabinet Mfr
N.A.I.C.S.: 337110

TENNYSON CHEVROLET
32570 Plymouth Rd, Livonia, MI 48150
Tel.: (734) 425-6500
Web Site: http://www.tennysonchevy.com
Year Founded: 1955
Sales Range: $10-24.9 Million
Emp.: 50
Car Dealer
N.A.I.C.S.: 441110
Matthew Grimes (Dir-Svc)
Jason Curie (Gen Mgr)
Jay Seldman (CEO)

TENON TOURS
319 Main St, Stoneham, MA 02180
Tel.: (781) 435-0425
Web Site: http://www.tenontours.com
Year Founded: 2007
Sales Range: $1-9.9 Million
Emp.: 12
Travel & Tour Operator
N.A.I.C.S.: 561520
Bryan Lewis (Owner & Pres)
Gerardo Barrera (Co-Founder & Dir-Fin)
Erika Gustafson (Dir-Ops)
Taryn Harrison (Co-Founder & Acct Mgr)
Barbara Brown (Acct Mgr)
Janet Dudley (Sr Acct Mgr)
Karen DiGangi (Acct Mgr)
Manisha Nainani (Acct Mgr)
Matthew Minieri (Accountant)
Liz Aungier (Dir-Product & Vendor Rels)
Art Cox (Mng Dir)

TENSION ENVELOPE CORPORATION
819 E 19th St, Kansas City, MO 64108-1781
Tel.: (816) 471-3800   DE
Web Site: https://tensionenvelope.com
Year Founded: 1886
Rev: $200,000,000
Emp.: 1,000
Custom Envelopes Mfr
N.A.I.C.S.: 322230
E. Bertram Berkley (Chm)
Bill Berkley (Pres & CEO)

TENTH AVENUE HOLDINGS LLC
950 Clifton Ave, Clifton, NJ 07013-2708
Tel.: (212) 273-4920
Web Site: http://www.tenave.com
Professional, Scientific & Technical Services
N.A.I.C.S.: 541990
Constance D'Aurizio (CFO)

Subsidiaries:

From You Flowers LLC   (1)
PO Box 805, Old Saybrook, CT 06475-1516
Web Site: http://www.fromyouflowers.com
Flower, Nursery Stock & Florists' Supplies Merchant Whslr
N.A.I.C.S.: 424930
Nicole Adams (Dir-Creative)

Subsidiary (Domestic):

FTD, Inc.   (2)
3113 Woodcreek Dr, Downers Grove, IL 60515
Tel.: (630) 719-7800
Web Site: http://www.ftd.com
Sales Range: $600-649.9 Million
Emp.: 984
Holding Company; Flowers & Specialty Gifts Marketer & Floral Network Operator
N.A.I.C.S.: 459420

Subsidiary (Domestic):

Florists' Transworld Delivery, Inc.   (3)
3113 Woodcreek Dr, Downers Grove, IL 60515-5412
Tel.: (630) 719-7800
Web Site: http://www.ftdi.com
Sales Range: $250-299.9 Million
Emp.: 500
Flower & Specialty Gift Marketer & Floral Network Operator
N.A.I.C.S.: 425120

Subsidiary (Domestic):

FTD.com Inc.   (4)
3113 Woodcreek Dr, Downers Grove, IL 60515
Tel.: (630) 719-7756
Web Site: http://www.ftd.com
Sales Range: $75-99.9 Million
Emp.: 300
Flowers & Specialty Gifts Marketing Website Publisher & Operator
N.A.I.C.S.: 518210
Lawrence B. Plawsky (Sr VP-Consumer Div)

Proflowers.com   (4)
1650 S Dixie Hwy 4th Fl, Boca Raton, FL 33432-7462
Tel.: (561) 417-0776
Web Site: http://www.proflowers.com
Emp.: 119
Online Florist Services
N.A.I.C.S.: 459310

Subsidiary (Domestic):

Provide Commerce, Inc.   (3)
4840 Eastgate Mall, San Diego, CA 92121-1977
Tel.: (858) 729-2800
Emp.: 175
Online Flower Distr
N.A.I.C.S.: 424930

TENTH STREET CAPITAL, LLC
901 Tallan Bldg Two Union Square, Chattanooga, TN 37402
Tel.: (423) 266-7196
Web Site: http://www.tenthstreet.com
Year Founded: 2005
Privater Equity Firm
N.A.I.C.S.: 523999
Al Duke (Co-Founder & Partner)
Meredith Duke (Partner)
Joe Decosimo (Co-Founder)

TEO TECHNOLOGIES
11609 49th Pl W, Mukilteo, WA 98275-4255
Tel.: (425) 349-1000   WA
Web Site: http://www.teotech.com
Year Founded: 1972
Sales Range: $10-24.9 Million
Emp.: 200
Mfr of Telephone Systems
N.A.I.C.S.: 334210
Stephen R. Hill (Chm & Pres)

TEOCO CORPORATION

COMPANIES

12150 Monument Dr Ste 400, Fairfax, VA 22033
Tel.: (703) 322-9200
Web Site: http://www.teoco.com
Year Founded: 1995
Sales Range: $10-24.9 Million
Emp.: 1,500
Software Related Services to Telecom & Financial Service Industries
N.A.I.C.S.: 541512
Atul Jain *(Chm & CEO)*
Philip M. Giuntini *(Vice Chm & Pres)*
Avi Goldstein *(CFO)*
Rob Roy *(Exec VP)*
Andrew Miceli *(VP-Sls-MENA)*
Shachar Ebel *(CTO)*
Hemant Minocha *(Exec VP)*
Warren Dumanski *(VP-Americas Sls)*
Thomas Neubauer *(VP-Bus Dev & Innovations)*
Charles Privitera *(VP-Global Engrg)*
Roman Cybyk *(VP-Global Ops)*
Alexis Kaltreider *(VP-Global Resource Mgmt)*
Inbar Charash *(Gen Counsel & VP-Legal Affairs)*
Carlos Varela *(VP-CALA Sls)*
Aloke Paskar *(Exec VP)*
Michael Bercovich *(VP-Fin)*

Subsidiaries:

AIRCOM International Ltd. (1)
Cassini Court Randalls Research Park Randalls Way, Leatherhead, KT22 7TW, Surrey, United Kingdom
Tel.: (44) 1932 442 000
Web Site:
   http://www.aircominternational.com
Emp.: 150
Network Planning & Telecommunication Services
N.A.I.C.S.: 517810
Alwyn Welch *(CEO)*
Parminder Dost *(CFO)*
Calum Byers *(COO)*
Steve Bowker *(CTO)*
Thomas Neubauer *(Mng Dir-Symena)*
Suzanna Barrett *(Head-Legal)*
Susan Brady *(Head-Mktg & Comm)*

Subsidiary (Non-US):

Apolo Tool & Die Manufacturing Inc. (2)
75 Haist Avenue, Woodbridge, L4L 5V5, ON, Canada
Tel.: (905) 856-4443
Web Site:
   http://www.apolomanufacturing.com
N.A.I.C.S.: 331318
Larry Sullivan *(Mgr-Ops)*

Respond.com (1)
12150 Monument Dr Ste 400, Fairfax, VA 22033
Tel.: (703) 651-2060
Web Site: http://www.respond.com
Affiliate Marketing & Local Business Advertising
N.A.I.C.S.: 519290
Murtaza Amil *(CEO)*

TTI TEAM TELECOM INTERNATIONAL LTD. (1)
12 Amal Street Afek Park, Rosh Ha'Ayin, 48092, Israel
Tel.: (972) 39269700
Web Site: http://www.teoco.com
Sales Range: $25-49.9 Million
Emp.: 345
Software Products & Services for Telecommunications Industry
N.A.I.C.S.: 513210

Division (US):

TTI Telecom (2)
2 Hudson Pl, Hoboken, NJ 07030-5618
Tel.: (201) 795-3883
Web Site: http://www.tti-telecom.com
Software Products & Services for Telecommunications Industry
N.A.I.C.S.: 513210

TEPHA, INC.
99 Hayden Ave E Wing Ste 360, Lexington, MA 02421
Tel.: (781) 357-1700
Web Site: http://www.tepha.com
Chemicals Mfr
N.A.I.C.S.: 325412
Said Rizk *(Sr VP-Mfg & Process Tech)*

TERA TECHNOLOGIES, INC.
3859 SW Hall Blvd, Beaverton, OR 97005
Tel.: (503) 643-4835
Web Site: http://www.terainc.com
Sales Range: $10-24.9 Million
Emp.: 25
Software Developer
N.A.I.C.S.: 513210
Nirmal Agarwal *(CEO)*

TERACORE, INC.
3300 Holcomb Bridge Rd, Norcross, GA 30092
Tel.: (770) 454-9119
Web Site: http://www.teracore.com
Year Founded: 2002
Sales Range: $1-9.9 Million
Emp.: 80
Management & Information Technology Consulting Services
N.A.I.C.S.: 541618
Luis Perez *(Founder & Mng Partner)*

Subsidiaries:

Teracore, Inc. (Mid-Atlantic Region) (1)
2201 Cooperative Way, Herndon, VA 20171 (100%)
Tel.: (703) 788-6661
Emp.: 8
Management Consulting & IT Services to Government Agencies
N.A.I.C.S.: 541618
Kim Irving *(VP)*

TERAGREN
12715 Miller Rd NE Ste 301, Bainbridge Island, WA 98110
Tel.: (206) 842-9477
Web Site: http://www.teragren.com
Year Founded: 1994
Sales Range: $10-24.9 Million
Emp.: 24
Homefurnishings
N.A.I.C.S.: 423220
David M. Knight *(Principal & CEO)*
Drew Diehl *(Mgr-Ops)*
Mark Jordan *(VP-Sls)*

TERAKEET, LLC
318 S Clinton St Ste 500, Syracuse, NY 13202
Tel.: (800) 655-2724
Web Site: http://www.terakeet.com
Sales Range: $1-9.9 Million
Search Engine Optimization & Internet Marketing
N.A.I.C.S.: 541519
MacLaren Cummings *(Co-Founder & CEO)*
Patrick Danial *(Co-Founder & CTO)*
Ralph Torrillo *(COO)*
Ryan Garver *(Sr VP-Engrg)*
Chris Loman *(VP-Ops)*
Shannon Welch *(Dir-Client Engagement)*
Angela Trapasso *(VP-Brand Strategy)*
Joseph Torrillo *(Dir-Reputation Mgmt)*
Rich Ezzo *(Sr VP-Sls & Mktg)*
Caryn Quinn *(Acct Exec)*
Adam Marinelli *(Coord-Pro Dev)*
Brent Scott *(Dir-Brand Strategy)*
Brian Quoss *(Dir-Design)*
Jennifer Thornton *(Dir-HR)*
Michael Tianello *(Mgr-IT & Facilities)*
Andres Echenique *(Sr VP-Brand Experience)*

TERATHINK CORPORATION
11955 Freedom Dr Ste 7800, Reston, VA 20190
Tel.: (703) 773-6232
Web Site: http://www.terathink.com
Year Founded: 2002
Sales Range: $10-24.9 Million
Emp.: 120
IT & Management Consulting Solutions for Federal Government Agencies
N.A.I.C.S.: 541611
Paul Lombardi *(Chm)*
Rick E. Dansey *(Sr VP)*
Dan Maguire *(CEO)*

TERICO
1723 Junction Ave, San Jose, CA 95112
Tel.: (408) 441-8868
Web Site: http://www.terico.biz
Sales Range: $10-24.9 Million
Emp.: 13
Whslr of Imported Marble, Granite, Slate, Limestone, Ceramic Tile, Tile Setting Tools & Adhesives
N.A.I.C.S.: 423320
Douglas Gunn *(Owner)*

TERLYN INDUSTRIES, INC.
11256 47th St N, Clearwater, FL 33762
Tel.: (727) 592-0772
Web Site: http://www.terlyn.com
Year Founded: 1996
Sales Range: $1-9.9 Million
Water Conservation Cooling Towers Mfr
N.A.I.C.S.: 333248
Terence M. Rushmore *(Pres & CEO)*

TERMINAL CONSOLIDATION CO. INC.
3600 NE Great Midwest Dr, Kansas City, MO 64161
Tel.: (816) 453-5101
Web Site: http://www.kcpiggy.com
Sales Range: $10-24.9 Million
Emp.: 50
Freight Consolidation
N.A.I.C.S.: 488510
David R. Nickell *(Pres)*

TERMINAL CONSTRUCTION CORPORATION
215 State Highway 17 S, Wood Ridge, NJ 07075
Tel.: (201) 939-9150
Web Site:
   http://www.terminalconstruction.com
Year Founded: 1945
Sales Range: $200-249.9 Million
Emp.: 2,250
General Contractors, Construction Managers, Design/Builders & Developers
N.A.I.C.S.: 238990
Donald N. Dinallo *(Pres)*
Bennett S. Lazare *(Exec VP-Admin)*
Frederick R. Bormann *(VP-Pur)*

TERMINAL CORPORATION
1657A S Highland Ave, Baltimore, MD 21224
Tel.: (410) 246-0500
Web Site: http://www.termcorp.com
Sales Range: $10-24.9 Million
Emp.: 200
General Warehousing & Transportation
N.A.I.C.S.: 493110
Scott Menzies *(Pres)*
Bill Cavanaugh *(VP-Warehouse Ops)*
Leon F. Smith *(Dir-Tech)*

TERMINUS CAPITAL PARTNERS, LLC

Thomas Huesman *(Pres-Terminal Transportation Svcs)*
John T. Menzies III *(Chm)*

TERMINAL RAILROAD ASSOCIATION
1000 Union Sta, Saint Louis, MO 63102
Tel.: (314) 231-5196
Web Site:
   http://www.terminalrailroad.com
Rev.: $37,601,097
Emp.: 25
Railroad Switching
N.A.I.C.S.: 488210
Matt Whitney *(Sr Dir-Ops-Train)*
Adam Mahlandt *(Superintendent)*
Mike McCarthy *(Pres)*
Brent Wood *(Co-CFO)*

TERMINAL SUPPLY INC.
1800 Thunderbird Dr, Troy, MI 48084
Tel.: (248) 362-0790
Web Site:
   http://www.terminalsupplyco.com
Sales Range: $10-24.9 Million
Emp.: 100
Distr of Electrical Products
N.A.I.C.S.: 423690

TERMINAL TRANSPORT INC.
2982 Cleveland Ave N, Saint Paul, MN 55113-1101
Tel.: (800) 432-4340
Web Site: http://www.trmnl.com
Year Founded: 1964
Trucking Except Local
N.A.I.C.S.: 484121
Brent Coatney *(Pres)*

TERMINIX SERVICE, INC.
3618 Fernandina Rd, Columbia, SC 29210-5221
Tel.: (803) 772-1783
Web Site:
   http://www.trustterminix.com
Year Founded: 1947
Sales Range: $100-124.9 Million
Emp.: 1,147
Pest Control Services
N.A.I.C.S.: 561710
Trevor Knox *(VP-Sls & Mktg)*

Subsidiaries:

Antimite Associates Inc. (1)
142 N 6th Ave #1101, Upland, CA 91786
Tel.: (909) 946-4616
Web Site:
   http://www.antimitepestcontrol.com
Sales Range: $10-24.9 Million
Disinfecting & Pest Control Services
N.A.I.C.S.: 561710

TERMINUS CAPITAL PARTNERS, LLC
3424 Peachtree Rd NE Ste 2200, Atlanta, GA 30326
Web Site:
   https://www.terminuscp.com
Year Founded: 2017
Private Equity
N.A.I.C.S.: 523940

Subsidiaries:

Delta Data Software, Inc. (1)
700 Brokstone Centre Pkwy, Columbus, GA 31904
Tel.: (706) 321-5551
Web Site: https://deltadata.com
Rev.: $2,500,000
Emp.: 30
Custom Computer Programming Services
N.A.I.C.S.: 541511
John N. Blalock *(Sr VP)*
Bret Bange *(Sr VP & Head-Sls & Mktg)*
Eric Litz *(CTO)*
Joy Ingham *(Dir-Risk Mgmt)*
Kem Hutchinson *(Dir-Ops)*

TERMINUS CAPITAL PARTNERS, LLC

Terminus Capital Partners, LLC—(Continued)
Tyson M. Begly (CFO)
W. Whitfield Athey (CEO)
W. Colt Younger (VP-Client Svcs)

Subsidiary (Domestic):

National Quality Review, LLC (2)
101 Arch St Ste 50, Boston, MA 02110
Tel.: (617) 426-0616
Web Site: http://www.nqrinc.com
Sales Range: $10-24.9 Million
Other Management Consulting Services
N.A.I.C.S.: 541618
Douglas Fortin (Partner)

TERPIN COMMUNICATIONS GROUP
2550 E Desert Inn Road #600, Las Vegas, NV 89169
Tel.: (702) 410-7818
Web Site: http://www.terpin.com
Year Founded: 1990
Public Relations Services
N.A.I.C.S.: 541820
Michael Terpin (CEO)

TERRA GROUP
2665 S Bayshore Dr Ste 1020, Coconut Grove, FL 33133
Tel.: (305) 416-4556
Web Site: http://www.terragroup.com
Year Founded: 2001
Real Estate Developers
N.A.I.C.S.: 237210
Pedro Martin (Co-Founder, Chm & CEO)
David Martin (Co-Founder & Pres)

Subsidiaries:

Terra Real Estate Advisors (1)
990 Biscayne Blvd Ste 1501, Miami, FL 33132
Tel.: (305) 416-4556
Web Site: http://www.treaglobal.com
Real Estate Services
N.A.I.C.S.: 531390
Pedro Martin (Chm & CEO)
David Martin (COO)

TERRA INVENTIONS CORP.
4894 Lone Mountain 168, Las Vegas, NV 89130
Tel.: (702) 425-4289 NV
Web Site: http://www.terrainventions.com
Year Founded: 2000
Sales Range: Less than $1 Million
Emp.: 1
Lithium Ion Battery Powered Motor Vehicle Mfr
N.A.I.C.S.: 336110
Stacey Fling (Pres & CEO)

TERRA MILLENIUM CORPORATION
1060 Hensley St, Richmond, CA 94801
Tel.: (510) 233-2500
Web Site: http://www.tmcorp.us
Holding Company
N.A.I.C.S.: 551112
Mark C. Stutzman (CEO)

Subsidiaries:

Brahma Group, Inc. (1)
1132 S 500 W, Salt Lake City, UT 84101
Tel.: (801) 521-5200
Web Site: http://www.brahmagroupinc.com
Industrial Construction Services
N.A.I.C.S.: 236210
Sean Davis (Pres & COO)
David Zimmerman (Gen Counsel & VP)

J.T. Thorpe & Son, Inc. (1)
1060 Hensley St, Richmond, CA 94801
Tel.: (510) 233-2500
Web Site: http://www.jtthorpe.com
Emp.: 690
Refractory & Acid Brick Masonry Services

N.A.I.C.S.: 238140
Mark C. Stutzman (CEO)

Liberty Industrial Group, Inc. (1)
3749 E Atlanta Ave, Phoenix, AZ 85040
Tel.: (480) 568-7007
Web Site: http://www.libertyindustrialgroup.com
Scaffolding & Insulation Services
N.A.I.C.S.: 238310
Gregg S. Dyakon Sr. (Pres)

Quantum International Group, Inc. (1)
1060 Hensley St Ste A, Richmond, CA 94801
Tel.: (510) 235-3242
Web Site: http://www.quantumig.com
Refractory Engineering & Construction Services
N.A.I.C.S.: 237990
Gary Stewart (Pres & CEO)
Kelvin McAlister (VP-Projects & Bus Dev)
Jim Detwiler (Project Engr)

Subsidiary (Non-US):

Thorpe Canada Corporation (2)
6-34346 Manufacturers Way, Abbotsford, V2S 7M1, BC, Canada
Tel.: (604) 855-4004
Web Site: http://www.thorpecanada.ca
Refractory Engineering & Construction Services
N.A.I.C.S.: 541330
Gregg Dyakon (Pres & CEO)
Neil Lawson (VP)
Derek Drekic (Mgr-Corp Safety)
Len Demos (Project Mgr)
Brad Price (Mgr-Bus Dev)
Mike Doucette (Project Engr)
Thomas Cousineau (Project Mgr)
Olek Kubicki (Project Engr)
Steve Dorbolo (Mgr-Construction)

TERRA SECURED INCOME TRUST, INC.
805 Third Ave 8th Fl, New York, NY 10022 MD
Year Founded: 2011
Real Estate Investment Services
N.A.I.C.S.: 525990
Bruce D. Batkin (CEO)
Simon J. Milde (Chm)
James J. Flood (CFO & COO)

TERRA UNIVERSAL INC.
800 S Raymond Ave, Fullerton, CA 92831-5234
Tel.: (714) 526-0100
Web Site: http://www.terrauniversal.com
Rev.: $20,500,000
Emp.: 150
Purification & Dust Collection Equipment
N.A.I.C.S.: 333413
Rod Behnia (Mgr-Intl Sls)

TERRA VERDE GROUP, LLC
6200 Wildings Blvd, College Grove, TN 37046
Tel.: (615) 368-3044 DE
Web Site: http://www.tvgllc.com
Real Estate Investment & Development
N.A.I.C.S.: 531390
Craig Martin (Founder & Partner)
Mark Enderle (Partner)
Mike Aiken (Partner)
Andre Jaeckle (Partner)
Lisa Reynolds (COO)
John Ohanian (Dir-Dev)

Subsidiaries:

Boot Ranch Circle LLC (1)
1447 Boot Ranch Cir, Fredericksburg, TX 78624
Tel.: (830) 997-6200
Web Site: http://www.bootranch.com
Sales Range: $1-9.9 Million
Performing Arts Companies
N.A.I.C.S.: 711190

Hal Sutton (Owner)
Leigh Lacy (Dir-Member Svcs)
Sean Gioffre (Dir-Real Estate Sls & Mktg)

TERRABANK NA
3191 Coral Way, Miami, FL 33145
Tel.: (305) 448-4898
Web Site: http://www.terrabank.com
Year Founded: 1985
Sales Range: $10-24.9 Million
Emp.: 100
National Commercial Banks
N.A.I.C.S.: 522110
JeanCarlo Pallais (VP-Intl Banking)
Rita Mongelli (VP-Consumer Compliance)
Thaymell Martin (Sr VP & Mgr-Bus Dev-Domestic)
Yisel Bello-Rodriguez (Portfolio Mgr-Lending Div Dept)

TERRACON CONSULTANTS, INC
10841 S Ridgeview Rd, Olathe, KS 66061
Tel.: (417) 659-6083
Web Site: http://www.terracon.com
Rev.: $5,900,000
Emp.: 99
Engineeering Services
N.A.I.C.S.: 541330
Jeff Roberts (Mgr-Texas)

Subsidiaries:

Texplor of Dallas, Inc. (1)
PO Box 793928, Dallas, TX 75379
Tel.: (214) 274-4320
Web Site: http://www.texplordrilling.com
Geotechnical & Environmental Drilling Services
N.A.I.C.S.: 541330
Dianna Thomason (Pres)

TERRACON CONSULTANTS, INC.
10841 S Ridgeview Rd, Olathe, KS 66061
Tel.: (913) 599-6886 DE
Web Site: http://www.terracon.com
Year Founded: 1965
Engineering Consulting Services
N.A.I.C.S.: 541690
Kevin F. Langwell (Sr VP-Client Dev)
Todd E. Swoboda (VP & Reg Mgr)
Cale Wilson (Sr Principal)
Tim W. Anderson (Exec VP-West)
Steve Mary (Program Mgr)
Ozzie Quezada (Mgr-CMT Dept)
Matthew Sloan (Mgr-Winter Park Office)
Eric A. McAra (Mgr-Geotechnical Dept)
Richard G. Acree (Mgr-Florida)
Dan Mahrt (Mgr-Geotechnical Dept)
Keith Connor (Mgr-Environmental Dept-Lenexa)
Mohamad Ibrawish (Mgr-Geotechnical Dept-Lenexa)
Adrian Keller (Mgr-Transportation & Info Sector-Natl)
M. Gayle Packer (Pres & CEO)
Don Malone (Sr Engr-Environmental-Raleigh)
Greg J. Taddicken (Principal)
Lori Cathcart (Dir-Corp Sustainability)
Fred Buhamdan (Reg Mgr-Los Angeles, Orange County, Colton & Las Vegas)

Subsidiaries:

Aquaterra, LLC (1)
2822 O'Neal Ln Bldg B, Baton Rouge, LA 70816
Tel.: (225) 344-6052
Web Site: http://www.terracon.com
Sales Range: $10-24.9 Million
Emp.: 45
Engineering Consulting Services

U.S. PRIVATE

N.A.I.C.S.: 541690
Victor R. Donald (Pres)
Jeffrey J. Breedlove (VP-IT & Corp Dev)
Stephen Greaber (Project Engr)

Argus Pacific, Inc. (1)
1900 W Nickerson St Ste 315, Seattle, WA 98119
Tel.: (206) 285-3373
Web Site: http://www.arguspacific.com
Sales Range: $1-9.9 Million
Emp.: 8
Health & Safety Training & Consulting Services
N.A.I.C.S.: 541690
Scott Parker (Principal)
Sue Maas (Mgr-Trng Div)

Building Exterior Solutions (1)
6975 Portwest Dr Ste 100, Houston, TX 77024-8015
Tel.: (713) 467-9840
Web Site: http://www.besgrp.com
Emp.: 20
Building Engineering & Architectural Services
N.A.I.C.S.: 541310
Jerry L. Abendroth (Pres & Principal)
Amy M. Peevey (Partner & Principal)
Dale Clark (Sr Assoc & Partner)

Burleson Consulting, Inc. (1)
1625 Creekside Dr Ste 202, Folsom, CA 95630
Tel.: (916) 984-4651
Web Site: http://www.burlesonconsulting.com
Sales Range: $1-9.9 Million
Emp.: 15
Business Consulting, Nec, Nsk
N.A.I.C.S.: 541690
Nadia Burleson (Pres & CEO)

Drilling Engineers Inc. (1)
1309 Duff Dr, Fort Collins, CO 80524-2787
Tel.: (970) 484-5183
Web Site: http://www.drillingengineers.com
Specialty Trade Contractors
N.A.I.C.S.: 238990
Doug Leafgren (Pres)

Dunkelberger Engineering & Testing, Inc. (1)
1225 Omar Rd, West Palm Beach, FL 33405
Tel.: (561) 689-4299
Web Site: http://www.terracon.com
Sales Range: $25-49.9 Million
Emp.: 60
Geotechnical Engineering, Construction Materials Testing, Building Inspection & Environmental Services
N.A.I.C.S.: 541330

Branch (Domestic):

Dunkelberger Engineering & Testing, Inc. - Sarasota Office (2)
8260 Vico Ct Ste B, Sarasota, FL 34240
Tel.: (941) 379-0621
Web Site: http://www.dunkelberger-engineering.com
Emp.: 12
Geotechnical Engineering, Construction Materials Testing, Building Inspection & Environmental Services
N.A.I.C.S.: 541330
Douglas S. Dunkelberger (Pres & CEO)
Scott Parrish (Branch Mgr)

Earth Exploration, Inc. (1)
2204 Yankee St, Niles, MI 49120-9120
Tel.: (574) 233-6820
Web Site: http://www.earthengr.com
Engineeering Services
N.A.I.C.S.: 541330
Rick Olson (Pres)

Engineered Concepts Consulting Services Inc. (1)
PO Box 35286, Greensboro, NC 27425-5286
Tel.: (336) 605-8020
Web Site: http://www.engconcepts.com
Engineeering Services
N.A.I.C.S.: 541330
Robert G. Kennerly (Pres)
Niels Andresen (Project Mgr)
Laura Kennerly (Mgr-Admin)
David Cochran (Mgr-Drafting/BIM)

COMPANIES

Environmental Planning Group, LLC (1)
4141 N 32nd St Ste 102, Phoenix, AZ 85018
Tel.: (602) 956-4370
Web Site: http://www.epgaz.com
Sales Range: $1-9.9 Million
Emp.: 50
Scientific & Technical Consulting Services
N.A.I.C.S.: 541690
Michael Doyle (Co-COO)
Mickey Siegel (Sr Project Mgr)
Paul Trenter (CEO)
Newton Debardeleben (Dir-Phoenix Office & Sr Project Mgr)
Scott Peters (Dir-Salt Lake City Office & Sr Project Mgr)
Marc Schwartz (Sr Project Mgr)
Cindy Smith (Sr Project Mgr)
Dave Wilson (Dir-Landscape Architecture)

Environmental Services, Inc. (1)
40 Zorn Blvd, Yaphank, NY 11980
Tel.: (631) 395-9888
Web Site: http://www.environmentalsvc.com
Plumbing, Heating & Air-Conditioning Contractors
N.A.I.C.S.: 238220

GeoCapitol Engineering LLC (1)
4545 42nd St NW Ste 307, Washington, DC 20016-4368
Tel.: (202) 375-7900
Web Site: http://www.geocapeng.com
Engineeering Services
N.A.I.C.S.: 541330
Daniel Gradishar (Principal)

High Plains Drilling, Inc. (1)
883 S 12th W, Rexburg, ID 83440
Tel.: (208) 356-5582
Web Site: http://www.highplainsdrilling.com
Drilling Services
N.A.I.C.S.: 213111

IHI Environmental Inc (1)
640 E Wilmington Ave, Salt Lake City, UT 84106
Tel.: (801) 466-2223
Web Site: http://www.ihi-env.com
Environmental Consulting Services
N.A.I.C.S.: 541620
Donald E. Marano (Pres)
Ken White (VP-Indus Hygiene Svcs)

Liesch Associates, Inc. (1)
13400 15th Ave N, Minneapolis, MN 55441
Tel.: (763) 489-3100
Web Site: http://www.liesch.com
Sales Range: $1-9.9 Million
Environmental Consulting Services
N.A.I.C.S.: 541620
Mike Willey (Project Mgr)

Mayes Testing Engineers, Inc. (1)
20225 Cedar Vly Rd Ste 110, Lynnwood, WA 98036
Tel.: (425) 742-9360
Web Site: http://www.mayestesting.com
Rev.: $1,100,000
Emp.: 75
Engineeering Services
N.A.I.C.S.: 541330
Michael Mayes (Pres)
Skip Szurek (Sr Project Mgr)

New England EnviroStrategies, Inc. (1)
1 Tremont St 2nd Fl, Concord, NH 03301
Tel.: (603) 856-8815
Web Site: http://www.neenvirostrategies.com
Environmental Consulting Services
N.A.I.C.S.: 541620

Pollution Management, Inc. (1)
3512 S Shackleford Rd, Little Rock, AR 72205-6933
Tel.: (501) 221-7122
Web Site: http://www.pmico.com
Engineeering Services
N.A.I.C.S.: 541330
Daniel Clark (Project Mgr)
Richard Davis (Pres)
Richard Davis (Pres)

Stafford Consulting Engineers, Inc. (1)
2020-E Starita Rd, Charlotte, NC 28206
Tel.: (704) 597-9000
Web Site: http://www.stafford-usa.com
Engineering Consulting Services
N.A.I.C.S.: 541690
Alex T. Sutton (Project Mgr-Field)
Brett M. Eichler (Project Mgr)
Brian D. Lang (Project Mgr)
Charles R. Rehm (Project Mgr-Field)
Dennis W. Mashburn (Project Mgr-Field)
James B. Wiggins (Project Mgr-Field)
Stephen B. Brown (Project Mgr)
Joseph J. Anetrella (Sr Project Mgr)
Keith R. Cappelluti (Project Mgr)
Louis T. Hall (Sr Engr-Project)
Vu T. Nguyen (Sr Project Mgr)
Christine Quigley (Principal)
Stuart Sutton (Reg Mgr)

TAM Consultants, Inc. (1)
4350 New Town Ave Ste 203, Williamsburg, VA 23188-2810
Tel.: (757) 564-4434
Web Site: http://www.tamconsultants.com
Engineeering Services
N.A.I.C.S.: 541330
Christopher J. Mills (Partner)

Terracon Consultants, Inc. - Ames (1)
1523 S Bell Ave Ste 104, Ames, IA 50010-7718
Tel.: (515) 232-0950
Web Site: http://www.terracon.com
Emp.: 4
Engineering Consulting Services
N.A.I.C.S.: 541690
Mike Sampson (Mgr-Dept)

Terracon Consultants, Inc. - Birmingham (1)
110 12th St N, Birmingham, AL 35203
Tel.: (205) 942-1289
Web Site: http://www.terracon.com
Sales Range: $10-24.9 Million
Emp.: 60
Engineering Consulting Services
N.A.I.C.S.: 541690
Frank Nowicki (Dir-Environ Svcs)
Terry Rippstein (Office Mgr)

Terracon Consultants, Inc. - Cincinnati (1)
611 Lunken Park Dr, Cincinnati, OH 45226
Tel.: (513) 321-5816
Web Site: http://www.terracon.com
Sales Range: $10-24.9 Million
Emp.: 80
Engineering Consulting Services
N.A.I.C.S.: 541690
Jason Sander (Dir-Matls Svcs-Natl)

Terracon Consultants, Inc. - Dallas (1)
10841 S Ridgeview Rd, Olathe, KS 66061
Tel.: (214) 630-1010
Web Site: http://www.terracon.com
Rev.: $79,070,585
Emp.: 100
Engineering Consulting Services
N.A.I.C.S.: 541690
Jack Spriggs (VP)
Pete Keener (Sr Mgr-Facilities Project)
Art Laikram (Sr Engr-Geotechnical)

Terracon Consultants, Inc. - Sioux City (1)
3301 Northbrook Dr Ste1, Sioux City, IA 51105-2211
Tel.: (712) 233-5492
Web Site: http://www.terracon.com
Engineering Consulting Services
N.A.I.C.S.: 541690
Rowdy Miller (Office Mgr)

Terracon Consultants, Inc. - Tampa (1)
5463 W Waters Ave Ste 830, Tampa, FL 33634
Tel.: (813) 221-0050
Web Site: http://www.terracon.com
Sales Range: $1-9.9 Million
Emp.: 30
Environmental Consulting Services
N.A.I.C.S.: 541620
Craig Anstett (Office Mgr)
Jim Wright (Dir-Safety & Health)
Nicholas Mata (Project Engr-Geotechnical)

Terracon Consultants, Inc. - West Fargo (1)
860 9th St NE Unit K, West Fargo, ND 58078
Tel.: (701) 282-9633
Web Site: http://www.terracon.com
Emp.: 30
Engineering Consulting Services
N.A.I.C.S.: 541690
Jonathan Ellingson (Office Mgr)

WPC, Inc. (1)
1450 Fifth St W, North Charleston, SC 29405
Tel.: (843) 884-1234
Web Site: http://www.wpceng.com
Sales Range: $10-24.9 Million
Emp.: 40
Engineering Consulting Services
N.A.I.C.S.: 541690

Wang Engineering, Inc. (1)
1145 N Main St, Lombard, IL 60148-1360
Tel.: (630) 953-9928
Web Site: http://www.wangeng.com
Testing Laboratories
N.A.I.C.S.: 541380

TERRACYCLE INC.
121 New York Ave, Trenton, NJ 08638
Tel.: (609) 393-4252
Web Site: http://www.terracycle.com
Year Founded: 2001
Sales Range: $10-24.9 Million
Emp.: 120
Hazardous Waste Treatment & Disposal
N.A.I.C.S.: 562211
Robin Tator (Co-Founder & Pres)
Tom Szaky (Co-Founder & CEO)
Chris Baker (Pres-Europe)
Damian Finio (CFO)

Subsidiaries:

Complete Recycling Solutions LLC (1)
1075 Airport Rd, Fall River, MA 02720
Tel.: (508) 402-7700
Web Site: http://www.crsrecycle.com
Rev.: $3,000,000
Emp.: 20
Business to Business Electronic Markets
N.A.I.C.S.: 425120
Stephen C. Hopkins (Treas)

TERRADYNE ENGINEERING, INC.
3033 Clairemont Ln, Euless, TX 76039
Tel.: (817) 952-7217 TX
Web Site: http://www.terradyne.com
Year Founded: 1995
Sales Range: $1-9.9 Million
Emp.: 61
Engineeering Services
N.A.I.C.S.: 541330
A. Kumar Palaniappan (Pres)

TERRAHEALTH INC.
9830 Colonnade Blvd Ste 300, San Antonio, TX 78230
Tel.: (210) 475-9881
Web Site: http://www.thi-terra.com
Year Founded: 2001
Sales Range: $25-49.9 Million
Emp.: 411
Medical Operations Support, Consulting Services & IT & Engineering Solutions
N.A.I.C.S.: 541611
Ted Terrazas (Pres)
Marty Bartlett (VP-Bus Dev)

TERRAL RIVERSERVICE, INC.
10100 Hwy 65 S, Lake Providence, LA 71254
Tel.: (318) 559-1500 LA
Web Site:
  http://www.terralriverservice.com
Year Founded: 1946
Sales Range: $25-49.9 Million
Emp.: 70
Inland Water Freight Transportation, Bulk Material Storage & Handling Services
N.A.I.C.S.: 483211
Danny Terral (CFO)
Kim King (Coord-Logistics)
Thomas M. Gattle Jr. (Chm, Pres & CEO)

TERRAMAR CAPITAL LLC
11812 San Vicente Blvd Ste 503, Los Angeles, CA 90049
Tel.: (310) 806-9070 CA
Web Site:
  https://www.terramarcapital.com
Privater Equity Firm
N.A.I.C.S.: 523999

Subsidiaries:

Francesca's Holdings Corporation (1)
8760 Clay Rd, Houston, TX 77080
Tel.: (713) 864-1358
Web Site: http://www.francescas.com
Rev.: $407,536,000
Assets: $328,608,000
Liabilities: $282,082,000
Net Worth: $46,526,000
Earnings: ($25,020,000)
Emp.: 1,159
Fiscal Year-end: 02/01/2020
Holding Company; Women's Clothing Retailer
N.A.I.C.S.: 551112
Cynthia Thomassee (CFO, Chief Acctg Officer & Exec VP)
Andrew Clarke (Pres & CEO)

Subsidiary (Domestic):

Francesca's Collections, Inc. (2)
8760 Clay Rd, Houston, TX 77080
Tel.: (713) 864-1358
Sales Range: $25-49.9 Million
Emp.: 350
Women's Clothing & Accessories Retailer
N.A.I.C.S.: 458110
Neill P. Davis (Pres & CEO)

Richer Poorer, Inc. (2)
31531 Rancho Viejo Rd Ste 101, San Juan Capistrano, CA 92675
Tel.: (949) 388-9994
Web Site: http://www.richer-poorer.com
Socks Mfr & Distr
N.A.I.C.S.: 315120
Vincent Marjes (Brand Mgr)
Iva Pawling (Founder, Pres & CEO)
Sean Fleuriau (Dir-Sls)

TERRAMAR RETAIL CENTERS, LLC
5973 Avenida Encinas Ste 300, Carlsbad, CA 92008
Tel.: (760) 804-8600
Web Site: http://www.trcretail.com
Sales Range: $50-74.9 Million
Emp.: 50
Real Estate Investment Trust
N.A.I.C.S.: 531120
Stephen Bowers (Pres & CEO)
Pamela Aguirre (Sr VP-Asset Mgmt)
Alexander Liftis (Sr VP-Dev & Acq)
David Ristau (Sr VP-Construction)
Glenn S. Rosen (Sr VP-Leasing)

TERRANEXT L.L.C.
1660 S Albion St Ste 900, Denver, CO 80222
Tel.: (303) 399-6145 CO
Web Site: http://www.terranext.net
Year Founded: 1997
Sales Range: $10-24.9 Million
Emp.: 15
Environmental Remediation Services
N.A.I.C.S.: 541690
Kim Martin (Owner, Pres & CEO)
Richard Seay (Mgr-Ops-Birmingham)
Christopher Kinn (Dir-Ops-Midwest)
Richard Rao (Dir-Ops-Northeast)

Terranext L.L.C.—(Continued)

TERRAPHASE ENGINEERING INC.
1404 Franklin St Ste 600, Oakland, CA 94612
Tel.: (510) 645-1850
Web Site: http://www.terraphase.com
Year Founded: 2010
Environmental Consulting Services
N.A.I.C.S.: 541620
Tomer Sehetrit *(Sr Project Engr)*
Collin Briese *(Mgr-Field Ops)*
Jen Otto *(Mgr-Bus)*

TERRAPIN 3 ACQUISITION CORPORATION
1700 Broadway, New York, NY 10019
Tel.: (212) 710-4100   DE
Year Founded: 2013
Sales Range: Less than $1 Million
Emp.: 2
Investment Services
N.A.I.C.S.: 523999
Nathan David Leight *(Chm)*
Sanjay Arora *(CEO)*

TERRAPIN 4 ACQUISITION CORPORATION
2655 S Le Jeune Rd Ste 550, Coral Gables, FL 33134
Tel.: (212) 710-4100   DE
Year Founded: 2017
Emp.: 2
Investment Services
N.A.I.C.S.: 523999
Nathan David Leight *(Chm & CEO)*
Guy Barudin *(CFO & COO)*

TERRAPIN PARTNERS LLC
1700 Broadway 18th Fl, New York, NY 10019
Tel.: (212) 710-4100
Web Site: http://www.terrapinpartners.com
Emp.: 20
Asset Management Services
N.A.I.C.S.: 523999
Nathan David Leight *(Partner)*
Stephen Schifrin *(Chief Compliance Officer)*
Stephen Spence *(Dir-Quanitative Analysis)*

Subsidiaries:

Terrapin Asset Management, LLC   (1)
1700 Broad Way 18th Fl, New York, NY 10019
Tel.: (212) 710-4100
Asset Management Services
N.A.I.C.S.: 523999
Nathan David Leight *(Chm & Chief Investment Officer)*

Subsidiary (Domestic):

Hennessee Group LLC   (2)
500 5th Ave, New York, NY 10110
Tel.: (212) 857-4400
Web Site: http://www.hennesseegroup.com
Sales Range: $1-9.9 Million
Emp.: 15
Management Consulting Services
N.A.I.C.S.: 541611
Charles Gradante *(Principal)*
E. Lee Hennessee *(Principal)*

TERRAPIN RIDGE FARMS, LLC
1212 S Myrtle Ave, Clearwater, FL 33756
Tel.: (727) 442-3663
Web Site: http://www.terrapinridge.com
Sales Range: $1-9.9 Million
Emp.: 10

Condiment & Gourmet Product Mfr & Sales
N.A.I.C.S.: 311941
Brian Coughlin *(Co-Owner)*
Mary O'Donnell *(Co-Owner & CEO)*

TERRASSA CONCRETE INDUSTRIES
Urb Santa Rosa 35 17 Rd 24 St, Bayamon, PR 00959
Tel.: (787) 785-7820
Sales Range: $10-24.9 Million
Emp.: 70
Concrete Block & Brick
N.A.I.C.S.: 327331
Luis Terrassa *(Pres)*

TERRE HILL CONCRETE PRODUCTS, INC.
485 Weaverland Vly Rd, Terre Hill, PA 17581
Tel.: (717) 445-3100   PA
Web Site: http://www.terrehill.com
Year Founded: 1919
Sales Range: $25-49.9 Million
Emp.: 225
Mfr of Concrete Blocks & Precast Concrete Products
N.A.I.C.S.: 327390
E.G. Smith *(Chm)*
Dale Wiest *(Controller)*
Gene Martin *(Pres)*
Nelson Martin *(VP)*

Subsidiaries:

Terre Hill Composites, Inc.   (1)
400 W Main St Ste 105, Ephrata, PA 17522
Tel.: (717) 738-9164
Web Site: http://www.thcomposites.com
Manhole Rehabilitation Services
N.A.I.C.S.: 238190

Terre Hill Concrete Products, Inc. - Terre Hill Stormwater Systems Division   (1)
485 Weaverland Valley Rd, Terre Hill, PA 17581
Tel.: (717) 445-3100
Web Site: http://www.terrestorm.com
Stormwater Treatment System Sales & Installation Services
N.A.I.C.S.: 423830
Gene LaManna *(Mgr-Mktg)*

TERRESTAR CORPORATION
One Discovery Sq 12010 Sunset Hills Rd 6Fl, Reston, VA 20190
Tel.: (703) 483-7800   DE
Web Site: http://www.terrestarcorp.com
Year Founded: 1988
Sales Range: $1-9.9 Million
Emp.: 104
Satellite Wireless Communication Services
N.A.I.C.S.: 517410
Dennis W. Matheson *(CTO)*
Douglas Brandon *(Gen Counsel, Sec & Sr VP)*
Nadia Sa'd Mulaire *(VP-Mktg)*

TERRI'S CONSIGN & DESIGN HOLDING
4747 E Elliot Rd #29-700, Phoenix, AZ 85044
Tel.: (480) 969-1121
Web Site: http://www.shopterris.com
Sales Range: $25-49.9 Million
Emp.: 105
Secondhand Home Furnishings, Jewelry, Electronics & Household Items
N.A.I.C.S.: 459510
Terri Bowersock *(Founder)*

TERRIO THERAPY-FITNESS, INC.
2838 Oswell St, Bakersfield, CA 93306
Tel.: (661) 873-7100
Web Site: http://www.terriotherapy.com
Year Founded: 1998
Sales Range: $1-9.9 Million
Emp.: 145
Physical, Occupational, Speech, Pediatric & Aquatic Therapy; Athletic Training & Weight-Loss Programs
N.A.I.C.S.: 621340
Maria Terndrup *(Controller)*
Alisa Suburu *(Dir-Outpatient Svcs)*

TERROS INC.
3003 N Central Ave Ste 200, Phoenix, AZ 85012
Tel.: (602) 685-6000
Web Site: http://www.terros.org
Rev: $18,915,420
Emp.: 450
Behavioral Health Services
N.A.I.C.S.: 621420
Tiara Crouse *(VP-Health Initiatives)*
Saffron Wanger *(Chief Innovation Officer)*
Amal Mullin *(Dir-Co-Occurring Svcs)*
Adnan Alasadi *(Dir-Deval Disability Crisis Svcs)*
Cynthia Pio-Padilla *(Supvr-Clinical Site)*
Steve Haynes *(Chm)*
Nancy McKenna *(Treas)*
Ken Lafleur *(Vice Chm)*
Liz Ketter *(CFO)*
Karen Hoffman Tepper *(Chief Admin & Compliance Officer)*
Andrea Smiley *(Chief Mktg & Bus Dev Officer)*
Karen Chaney *(CMO)*
Yvonne Fortier *(VP-Diversity)*
Sherry Henson *(VP-Recovery Svcs)*
Randy Brazie *(Chief Medical Officer)*
Jennifer Siozos *(Chief Transformation Officer)*

TERRY ENVIRONMENTAL SERVICES, INC.
1753 N Main St, Summerville, SC 29483
Tel.: (843) 873-8200
Web Site: http://www.terryenvironmental.com
Year Founded: 1999
Rev: $3,000,000
Emp.: 12
Business Consulting Services
N.A.I.C.S.: 541618
Annette Balsitis *(Mgr)*
Jason A. Terry *(Pres)*

TERRY HUNT CONSTRUCTION
3737 Madison Hwy, Valdosta, GA 31601
Tel.: (229) 244-6707
Sales Range: $10-24.9 Million
Emp.: 300
Civil Engineering Services
N.A.I.C.S.: 237310
Mike Novack *(Mgr-Bus Dev)*

TERRY SLIGH AUTOMOTIVE, INC.
1630 2nd Ave E, Oneonta, AL 35121
Tel.: (205) 625-3741
Year Founded: 2000
Sales Range: $25-49.9 Million
Emp.: 30
Car Whslr
N.A.I.C.S.: 441110
Terry Sligh *(Pres)*

TERRY WYNTER AUTO SERVICE CENTER, INC.
3811 Fowler St, Fort Myers, FL 33901
Tel.: (239) 939-2500
Web Site: http://www.terrywynterauto.com
Year Founded: 1996
Sales Range: $1-9.9 Million
Emp.: 15
General Automotive Repair
N.A.I.C.S.: 811111
Terry Wynter *(Co-Owner & Pres)*
Kay Wynter *(Co-Owner & VP)*

TERRY'S ELECTRIC INC.
600 N Thacker Ave Ste A, Kissimmee, FL 34741
Tel.: (407) 572-2100
Web Site: http://www.terryselectric.com
Sales Range: $25-49.9 Million
Emp.: 160
Electrical Work
N.A.I.C.S.: 238210
Karrie Jones *(Mgr-Accts Payable)*
Buddy Padgett *(VP-Residential & Svc)*
Earl Lomas *(Project Mgr)*

TERRY'S LINCOLN MERCURY
9401 W 143rd St, Orland Park, IL 60462
Tel.: (708) 349-3400
Web Site: http://terrys.com
Year Founded: 1963
Sales Range: $10-24.9 Million
Emp.: 80
Automobile Dealers
N.A.I.C.S.: 441120
Paul Decker *(Mgr-Fin)*
Mike Ciemny *(Mgr-Sls)*

TERRYBERRY COMPANY LLC
2033 Oak Industrial Dr NE, Grand Rapids, MI 49505
Tel.: (616) 458-1391
Web Site: http://www.terryberry.com
Emp.: 200
Employee Recognition Program Management Services; Corporate Award & Jewelry Designer & Mfr
N.A.I.C.S.: 561499
Mike Byam *(Mng Partner)*

Subsidiaries:

Talisman Company   (1)
2033 Oak Industrial Dr NE, Grand Rapids, MI 49505
Tel.: (616) 458-1391
Web Site: http://www.talisman-corp-jewelry.com
Sales Range: $10-24.9 Million
Emp.: 114
Corporate Jewelry Retailer
N.A.I.C.S.: 339910
David Beemer *(COO)*

TERUYA BROS., LTD.
1276 Young St, Honolulu, HI 96814-1817
Tel.: (808) 591-8946   HI
Year Founded: 1948
Sales Range: $100-124.9 Million
Emp.: 80
Investments, Retail Food Convenience Stores, Petroleum Marketing & Hotels
N.A.I.C.S.: 445110
Raymond Teruya *(Chm, Pres & CEO)*

TERVIS TUMBLER COMPANY
201 Triple Diamond Blvd N, Venice, FL 34275
Tel.: (941) 966-2114   FL
Web Site: http://www.tervis.com
Year Founded: 1946
Sales Range: $125-149.9 Million
Emp.: 800

Insulated Cups Mfr
N.A.I.C.S.: 326160
Patrick Redmond (CEO)
Todd Lohrenz (Dir-Creative)
Gary King (Chief Sls & Bus Dev Officer)
Jim Athey (Chief Comml Officer)

TES ENGINEERING
25760 1st St, Cleveland, OH 44145
Tel.: (440) 871-2410
Web Site:
http://www.tesengineering.com
Sales Range: $1-9.9 Million
Emp.: 32
Engineeering Services
N.A.I.C.S.: 541330
Larry Thomas (Pres)
Steve Chase (Exec VP)
Daniel Jackson (Dir-Project Mgmt)
Joseph Zaworski (Engr-Energy)
Robert Schneider (Project Mgr)
Bob Catino (Mgr-Acct)
Corey Hicar (Engr-Mechanical)
Deb Lape (Controller)
Mike Ruff (Dir-Electrical Engrg)
Dieter Hausmann (Dir-Mechanical Engrg)
John Edwards (Mgr-Engrg)
Hugh Fisher (Mgr-HR)
Nick Gingerich (Project Mgr)
Erica Verheyen (Project Mgr)
Rob Green (Sr Project Mgr)

TESCHGLOBAL LLC
1350 14th Ave Ste 1, Grafton, WI 53024
Web Site:
http://www.teschglobal.com
Year Founded: 2005
Sales Range: $1-9.9 Million
Emp.: 49
Software Development Services
N.A.I.C.S.: 541511
Will Tesch (Founder & CEO)
Joel Walker (COO)
Kelly Ross (CTO)
Aaron Konkol (Dir-Software Dev)
Dan Mcfalls (Dir-Resources & Engagement)

TESCOR, INC.
341 Ivyland Rd, Warminster, PA 18974
Tel.: (215) 957-9112
Web Site: http://www.tescor-inc.com
Year Founded: 1991
Rev.: $5,600,000
Emp.: 34
Analytical Instrument Mfr
N.A.I.C.S.: 334516
Margaret Boudin (Sec & Treas)
Xiaoliang Sun (Sr Engr-Software Sys)
Steve Krick (Engr-Design)
Charles Beaver (VP)
John Wurtz (Mgr-Production)
Bruce Knapp (Asst Mgr-Svcs)

TESEI PETROLEUM INC.
1300 S Gateway Dr, Madera, CA 93637
Tel.: (559) 673-3597
Web Site: http://www.teseipetro.com
Sales Range: $25-49.9 Million
Emp.: 33
Petroleum Bulk Stations & Terminals
N.A.I.C.S.: 424710
Kim Thomas (Dir-Fin)
Fred Gaumnitz (Mgr-Retail)
Dave Souza (Dir-Ops)
Sandra Ortega (Mgr-Credit)
Robert Hernandez (Mgr-Sls)
Pat Cox (Mgr-Store)
Lenor Salinas (Mgr-Store)

TESIS BIOSCIENCES, INC.
8125 N 86th Pl, Scottsdale, AZ
Tel.: (855) 668-3747
Web Site:
https://tesisbiosciences.com
Emp.: 100
Medical Testing Services
N.A.I.C.S.: 541380

TESSA CONSTRUCTION & TECH COMPANY LLC.
43149 John Mosby Hwy Ste 101, Chantilly, VA 20152
Tel.: (703) 327-4481
Web Site:
http://tessaconstruction.com
Sales Range: $10-24.9 Million
Emp.: 110
Highway & Street Construction Services
N.A.I.C.S.: 237310
Fardiss Ettehar (Gen Partner)

TESSY PLASTICS CORP
700 Visions Dr, 13152, Skaneateles, NY
Tel.: (315) 689-3924
Web Site: http://www.tessy.com
Year Founded: 1973
Sales Range: $50-74.9 Million
Emp.: 620
Injection Molding Of Plastics
N.A.I.C.S.: 326199
Henry Beck (Founder)
Gary Miller (Mgr)
Stuart Smurthwaite (VP-Ops)
Corina Toothaker (Engr-Quality)
Joe Raffa (VP & Gen Mgr)
Willie Werner (Dir-R&D)
Jason Jewsbury (Engr-Quality)
Camille Loperfido (Engr-Quality)
Kathryn Neal (Mgr-Bus Dev)
Mark Halstead (Dir-Consumer Products)
Nils Hammerich (Gen Mgr-China)
Linda Bowes (Mgr-Matls)
Larry Vatter (Mgr-Pur)

Subsidiaries:
Tessy Automation, LLC (1)
18114 Research Dr, Meadville, PA 16335
Tel.: (814) 724-6336
Web Site: https://tessyautomation.com
Special Die & Tool, Die Set, Jig & Fixture Mfr
N.A.I.C.S.: 333514

TESTING MACHINES INC.
40 McCullough Dr, New Castle, DE 19720
Tel.: (302) 613-5600
Web Site:
http://www.testingmachines.com
Rev.: $13,626,642
Emp.: 150
Measuring & Testing Equipment, Electrical
N.A.I.C.S.: 334519
John Sullivan (Pres)

TESTMASTERS EDUCATIONAL SERVICES, INC.
13100 Southwest Fwy, Sugar Land, TX 77478
Tel.: (281) 276-7777
Web Site:
http://www.testmasters.com
Year Founded: 1991
Sales Range: $10-24.9 Million
Emp.: 100
Offers Classroom, One-on-One & Online Courses in Professional Engineering Exams
N.A.I.C.S.: 923110
Roger Israni (Founder & Pres)

TETCO, INC.
1100 NE Loop 410 Ste 900, San Antonio, TX 78209-5234
Tel.: (210) 821-5900
Web Site: http://www.tetco.com
Year Founded: 1982
Emp.: 120
Holding Company Services
N.A.I.C.S.: 551112
Javier Trevino (Pres)

Subsidiaries:
Armortex, Inc. (1)
5926 Corridor Pkwy, Schertz, TX 78154
Tel.: (210) 661-8306
Web Site: http://www.armortex.com
Sales Range: $1-9.9 Million
Bullet, Blast & Forced Entry Resistant Products Mfr
N.A.I.C.S.: 339999

Mission Petroleum Carriers, Inc. (1)
8450 Mosley Rd, Houston, TX 77075 (100%)
Tel.: (713) 943-8250
Web Site: http://www.mipe.com
Sales Range: $25-49.9 Million
Petroleum Trucking Services
N.A.I.C.S.: 484230
Tom Loop (VP-Admin)
David Fontenot (Pres)

V.K. Knowlton Construction & Utilities, Inc. (1)
18225 FM 2252, San Antonio, TX 78266-2717
Tel.: (210) 651-6860
Sales Range: $10-24.9 Million
Paving, Excavating, Street Construction & Other Concrete Work Services
N.A.I.C.S.: 237310
Virgil K. Knowlton (Pres)
Monica Garcia (Mgr-Accts Payable)
Scott Knowlton (Exec VP)

TETERS FLORAL PRODUCTS, INC.
1425 S Lillian Ave, Bolivar, MO 65613-2316
Tel.: (417) 326-7654
Web Site: http://www.teters.com
Year Founded: 1957
Artificial Flowers Importer, Assembler & Distr
N.A.I.C.S.: 424930
Rick Looker (COO)
Corey Harbour (VP-Product Dev & Design)
Mike Johnson (CFO)

TETHYS BIOSCIENCE, INC.
5858 Horton St Ste 280, Emeryville, CA 94608
Tel.: (510) 420-6700
Web Site: http://www.tethysbio.com
Year Founded: 2005
Sales Range: $10-24.9 Million
Emp.: 103
Pharmaceutical Preparation Mfr
N.A.I.C.S.: 325412
Michael S. Urdea (Founder & Chief Scientific Officer)
Juan P. Frias (Chief Medical Officer)
Randall K. Strahan (Pres & CEO)
William J. Christy (VP-Sls)

TETON AUTO GROUP
2252 W Sunnyside Rd, Idaho Falls, ID 83402
Tel.: (208) 522-2911
Web Site:
https://www.tetontoyota.com
Emp.: 100
Car Dealership
N.A.I.C.S.: 441110
Cody Scott (Gen Sls Mgr)

Subsidiaries:
Coos Bay Toyota Inc. (1)
2001 North Bayshore Dr, Coos Bay, OR 97420
Tel.: (541) 267-3121
Web Site: http://www.coosbaytoyota.com
Rev.: $9,000,000
Emp.: 100
New Car Dealers
N.A.I.C.S.: 441110
Lee Hawthorne (Chm)
Amanda Fitzlaff (Mgr-Bus)
Glen Arnsperger (Gen Mgr-Sls)
Mary Rose (Office Mgr)
Rick Brown (Mgr-Used Car)
Ted Noble (Mgr-Svc)
Tim Murray (Mgr-Parts)

TETON BUILDINGS LLC
2701 Magnet St, Houston, TX 77054
Tel.: (713) 351-6300
Web Site:
http://www.tetonbuildings.com
Sales Range: $25-49.9 Million
Emp.: 210
Industrial Construction
N.A.I.C.S.: 236210
Brandon Gray (Mgr-Sls)
James Case (VP)

TETON HERITAGE BUILDERS INC.
160 W Deloney Ave, Jackson, WY 83001
Tel.: (307) 733-8771
Web Site:
http://www.tetonheritagebuilder.com
Year Founded: 1996
New Single Family Housing Construction Services
N.A.I.C.S.: 236115
Gregory A. O'Gwin (Co-Owner, VP, Head-Office & Superintendent)
Mark S. Dalby (Co-Owner & Project Mgr)
Dan J. Clancy (Co-Owner)
Russell E. Weaver (Co-Owner)
Peter C. Lee (Co-Owner, Pres, Head-Office & Project Mgr)
John A. Venner (Co-Owner & Project Mgr)
Scott E. Walden (Co-Owner)
Matthew C. Niska (Superintendent)
Andrew Holland (Project Mgr)
Jessi Ellis (Co-Owner)
Trent Dayton (Superintendent)
Mike Sullivan (Superintendent)
Tim Weaver (Superintendent)
Matt Lennon (Superintendent)
Jackie Kline (Asst Superintendent)
Mauricio Alvarado (Asst Superintendent)
Simone Bayens (Asst Project Mgr)
Larry C. Dressell (Asst Project Mgr)
Colin Prato (Asst Superintendent)
Katie Brooks (Office Mgr & Mgr-Mktg)

TETON VALLEY HEALTH CARE, INC.
120 E Howard Ave, Driggs, ID 83422
Tel.: (208) 354-2383
Web Site: http://www.tvhcare.org
Year Founded: 2012
Sales Range: $10-24.9 Million
Health Care Srvices
N.A.I.C.S.: 622110
Laurel Ricks (Mgr-Clinic)
Ann Loyola (Dir-Mktg & PR)
Dory Harris (Dir-HR)
Laura Piquet (Dir-Quality Svcs)
Angela Booker (Chief Nursing Officer)

TETRAD ELECTRONICS INC.
2048 Joseph Lloyd Pkwy, Willoughby, OH 44094
Tel.: (440) 946-6443
Web Site:
http://www.tetradelectronics.com
Sales Range: $10-24.9 Million
Emp.: 40
Assembled Printed Circuit Boards

TETRAD ELECTRONICS INC. U.S. PRIVATE

Tetrad Electronics Inc.—(Continued)
N.A.I.C.S.: 334412
Jeff Waterman (VP-Sls)

TEUCRIUM NATURAL GAS FUND
232 Hidden Lake Rd, Brattleboro, VT 05301
Tel.: (802) 257-1617   DE
Web Site:
  http://www.teucriumnags.com
Year Founded: 2009
Emp.: 9
Investment Services
N.A.I.C.S.: 523999
Sal Gilbertie (Pres & Chief Investment Officer)
Dale Riker (CEO)
Steve Kahler (COO)
Barbara Riker (CFO & Chief Acctg Officer)
Carleton M. Miller (Co-Founder)

TEUFEL LANDSCAPE, INC.
7431 NW Evergreen Pkwy Ste 200, Hillsboro, OR 97124
Tel.: (503) 646-1111
Web Site: http://www.teufel.com
Year Founded: 1890
Sales Range: $25-49.9 Million
Emp.: 335
Landscaping Services, Nursery & Florists Supplies
N.A.I.C.S.: 561730
Larry Teufel (Pres)
Mike Kolodziejczak (Reg Mgr)
Greg Swartz (CFO)

Subsidiaries:

Teufel Holly Farms, Inc.   (1)
160 SW Miller Rd, Portland, OR 97225   (100%)
Tel.: (503) 292-9181
Web Site: http://www.teufelhollyfarms.com
Emp.: 25
Seasonal Holly & Evergreens
N.A.I.C.S.: 111422
Larry Teufel (Pres)

Teufel Nursery Inc.   (1)
6833 S 220th St, Kent, WA 98032 (100%)
Tel.: (253) 373-0344
Web Site: http://www.teufellandscape.com
Sales Range: $10-24.9 Million
Emp.: 65
Flowers & Florists Supplies
N.A.I.C.S.: 561730
Larry Teufel (Pres)

TEUTEBERG INCORPORATED
12200 W Wirth St, Wauwatosa, WI 53222
Tel.: (414) 257-4110
Web Site: http://www.teuteberg.com
Sales Range: $10-24.9 Million
Emp.: 49
Business Forms
N.A.I.C.S.: 323111
Matt Teuteberg (Pres)
Chad Carpenter (VP-Sls)
Jenny Bergmann (Acct Mgr)
Midge Langer (Supvr-Fulfillment)

TEVET, LLC
85 Spring St S, Mosheim, TN 37818
Tel.: (678) 905-1300
Web Site: http://www.tevetllc.com
Year Founded: 2004
Sales Range: $50-74.9 Million
Emp.: 12
Test & Measurement, Life Science & Chemical analysis Products
N.A.I.C.S.: 541380
Paul Daniel (Dir-Ops)
Tracy Solomon (Founder, Pres & CEO)
Makinne Lane (Dir-Mktg)

TEX ISLE SUPPLY INC.
10000 Meml Dr Ste 600, Houston, TX 77024
Tel.: (713) 461-1012
Web Site: http://www.texisle.com
Sales Range: $50-74.9 Million
Emp.: 120
Pipe & Tubing; Steel
N.A.I.C.S.: 423510
Gail Donahue (Dir-HR)

TEX-BEST TRAVEL CENTERS INC.
317 N 12th St, McAllen, TX 78501
Tel.: (956) 686-0505
Franchise Owner of Fast-Food Restaurants; Operator of Travel Centers
N.A.I.C.S.: 722513
Joseph F. Phillips (Pres)

TEX-LA ELECTRIC COOPERATIVE OF TEXAS INC
PO Box 631623, Nacogdoches, TX 75963-1623
Tel.: (936) 560-9532   TX
Year Founded: 1979
Sales Range: $100-124.9 Million
Emp.: 6
Electric Power Distr
N.A.I.C.S.: 221121
Ryan Thomas (CFO)
Floyd Watson (Dir-Advisory)
Debra Robinson (Treas & Sec)
Greg Jones (VP)

TEX-TRUDE LP
2001 Sheldon Rd, Channelview, TX 77530
Tel.: (281) 452-5961
Web Site: http://www.tex-trude.com
Sales Range: $25-49.9 Million
Emp.: 190
Plastics Film & Sheet
N.A.I.C.S.: 326113
Wayne Brune (Plant Mgr)

TEXADIA SYSTEMS LLC
4355 Excel Pkwy Ste 600, Addison, TX 75001
Tel.: (214) 956-5820
Web Site:
  http://www.texadiasystems.com
Year Founded: 2013
Sales Range: $10-24.9 Million
Emp.: 39
Audio Consulting Services
N.A.I.C.S.: 532490
Steve Burke (Founder & Pres)
Dawna Payne (Exec VP)
Scott Birdsong (VP-Engrg)
Trent Godby (VP-Comml Bus Dev)
Scott Heaney (Mgr-Customer Support)

TEXAN MARKETS INC.
1100 Gattis School Rd Ste 300c, Round Rock, TX 78664
Tel.: (512) 218-0881
Sales Range: $1-9.9 Million
Emp.: 45
Owner & Operator of Convenience Stores
N.A.I.C.S.: 445131
Bonnie Russell (VP)
William L. Longshore Jr. (Pres)

TEXANS CREDIT UNION
777 E Campbell Rd, Richardson, TX 75081
Tel.: (972) 348-2001   TX
Web Site: http://www.texanscu.org
Year Founded: 1953
Sales Range: $150-199.9 Million
Emp.: 450
Credit Union
N.A.I.C.S.: 522130

Kevin Durance (Pres & CEO)
Tiffany Chisnall (COO)

Subsidiaries:

Texans CUSO Services   (1)
777 E Campbell Rd, Richardson, TX 75081
Tel.: (972) 348-2000
Web Site: http://www.texanscu.org
Holding Company; Financial & Insurance Services
N.A.I.C.S.: 551112

Subsidiary (Domestic):

The Woodlands Financial Group   (2)
1201 Lake Woodlands Dr Ste 4020, Woodlands, TX 77380-7056
Tel.: (972) 991-6677
Web Site: http://www.twfg.com
Sales Range: $25-49.9 Million
Emp.: 75
Retail Insurance Services
N.A.I.C.S.: 524126
Richard Bunch (Founder, Pres & CEO)
Katherine Nolan (COO)
Judy Rush (Dir-Natl Agency Relationship)
John Scully (VP-IT)
Alex Bunch (CMO & Chief Creative Officer)
Jerry Mackey (Chief Underwriting Officer)

Division (Domestic):

Heartland Specialty Insurance   (3)
1201 Lake Woodland Dr Ste 4020, Woodlands, TX 77380
Tel.: (972) 991-6677
Sales Range: $50-74.9 Million
Emp.: 50
Property & Casualty Insurance Broker
N.A.I.C.S.: 524210
Jess Ellis (Pres)

TEXARKANA WATER UTILITIES
801 Wood St, Texarkana, TX 75501
Tel.: (903) 798-3800
Web Site: http://www.txkusa.org
Sales Range: $25-49.9 Million
Emp.: 178
Water Supply
N.A.I.C.S.: 221310
Richard Hutchinson (Supvr-Maintenance)
John Murphy (Mgr-Ops)

TEXAS ALLIED HOLDINGS INC.
7124 Richter Rd, Elmendorf, TX 78112
Tel.: (210) 635-7744
Web Site:
  http://www.vpracingfuels.com
Sales Range: $10-24.9 Million
Emp.: 17
Gasoline Blending Plants
N.A.I.C.S.: 324110
Bruce Hendel (VP & Mgr-Sls)
David Millice (Controller)
Marc Wesler (VP & Reg Mgr)

Subsidiaries:

Texas Allied Chemicals Inc.   (1)
7124 Richter Rd, Elmendorf, TX 78112
Tel.: (210) 635-7755
Industrial Chemicals
N.A.I.C.S.: 424690
David Millice (Controller)

VP Racing Fuels Inc.   (1)
204 E Rhapsody Dr, San Antonio, TX 78216
Tel.: (210) 635-7744
Web Site: http://www.vpracingfuels.com
Emp.: 160
Gasoline Blending Plants
N.A.I.C.S.: 324110
Chris Wall (Sr Dir-Natl Sponsorships & OEM Relationships-East Coast)
Richard Glady (Mgr-Lubricants)
Bruce Hendel (Sr VP-Global Sls)
Alan Cerwick (Pres & CEO)
Bob Merz (Sr Mgr-Corp Comm)
Ben Dolan (VP-Mktg)

Karen Madden (COO)
Ben Dolan (VP-Product Mgmt)
Kevin Temple (VP-Branded Retail)

VP Transportation Co. Inc.   (1)
4100 E Steelton Ave, Terre Haute, IN 47805
Tel.: (812) 466-1175
Rev.: $350,000
Emp.: 10
Petroleum Haulage, Local
N.A.I.C.S.: 424720

TEXAS BANKERS ASSOCIATION
203 W 10th St, Austin, TX 78701
Tel.: (512) 472-8388   TX
Web Site:
  http://www.texasbankers.com
Year Founded: 1885
Emp.: 40
Banking Association
N.A.I.C.S.: 813910
James Eric T. Sandberg Jr. (Pres & CEO)
John M. Heasley (Gen Counsel, Treas, Sec & Exec VP-Legal)
Celeste M. Embrey (Asst Gen Counsel)
Olivia Carmichael Solis (VP-Mktg & Comm)
John R. Brigance (Chief Admin Officer)
Donny R. Palmer (Exec VP-Member Rels)
Kathy E. Box (Exec VP-Pro Dev)
Gary Claxton (Chm)
Robert W. Hoxworth (Vice Chm)
William R. Jenkins III (Treas)

Subsidiaries:

Texas Bankers Insurance Agency, Inc.   (1)
203 W 10th St, Austin, TX 78701-2321
Tel.: (512) 472-8388
Web Site: http://www.texasbankers.com
Emp.: 5
Insurance Agents
N.A.I.C.S.: 524210
Brien G. O'Connor (VP)
Latresa M. Powell (VP)

TEXAS BARCODE SYSTEMS INC.
4217 Charles St, Carrollton, TX 75010
Tel.: (972) 267-7900
Web Site:
  http://www.texasbarcode.com
Sales Range: $10-24.9 Million
Emp.: 10
Computer Peripheral Equipment
N.A.I.C.S.: 423430
David W. Edwards (Pres)

TEXAS BAY AREA CREDIT UNION
12611 Fuqua St, Houston, TX 77034
Tel.: (713) 852-6700   TX
Web Site: http://www.tbacu.org
Year Founded: 1936
Sales Range: $10-24.9 Million
Emp.: 127
Credit Union
N.A.I.C.S.: 522130
Syed Dinar (CFO & VP)
Lance Wortham (VP-Lending)
Dennis Y'Barbo (CTO & VP)
Rachel Hunt (VP-Lending & Trng)
Jesse Gutierrez (Pres & CEO)
Raymond Andrews (Sec)
Deena Knox (Exec VP)
John Swanson (Treas)
Tom Merchant (Vice Chm)
Rudy Wright (Chm)

TEXAS BEEF LTD.
800 S Monroe St, Amarillo, TX 79101-3324

COMPANIES

Tel.: (806) 372-3877
Web Site: http://www.tbp.com
Year Founded: 1965
Sales Range: $50-74.9 Million
Emp.: 120
Ranching, Farming & Cattle Feeding Services
N.A.I.C.S.: 112112
W. H. O'Brien (Partner)

TEXAS BIOMEDICAL RESEARCH INSTITUTE
7620 NW Loop 410, San Antonio, TX 78227-5301
Tel.: (210) 258-9400 TX
Web Site: http://www.txbiomed.org
Year Founded: 1941
Sales Range: $50-74.9 Million
Emp.: 405
Biomedical Research Services
N.A.I.C.S.: 541715
Keith A. Davis (CFO & VP-Fin & Admin)
John E. Newman (Vice Chm)
Emmy Ballantyne (VP-Social Media)
Brian Bounds (CIO)
Justin Cole (VP-Membership)
Trey Dawson (VP-Corp Membership)
James Griffin (VP-Corp Membership)
Kourtney Little (Treas)
David Mauze (VP-Hospitality)
Johnny Moorman (VP-Sponsorship)
Chris Petty (Co-Pres)
Paul Rohlfs (VP-Membership)
Larry S. Schlesinger (Co-Pres & CEO)
Akudo Anyanwu (VP-Dev)
James B. Smith Jr. (Sec)

TEXAS COMMUNITY MEDIA LLC
320 E Methvin St, Longview, TX 75601
Tel.: (903) 757-3311
Web Site: http://www.texascommunitymedia.com
Sales Range: $25-49.9 Million
Newspaper Publishers
N.A.I.C.S.: 513110
Stephen McHaney (Pres)
Denise Lytle (CFO)
Josh Hart (Dir-Circulation)
Janet Owen (Dir-Ops)

Subsidiaries:

Longview News-Journal (1)
320 E Methvin St, Longview, TX 75601
Tel.: (903) 757-3311
Web Site: http://www.news-journal.com
Newspaper Publishers
N.A.I.C.S.: 513110
Stephen N. McHaney (Publr)

The Marshall News Messenger (1)
309 E Austin St, Marshall, TX 75670
Tel.: (903) 935-7914
Web Site: http://www.marshallnewsmessenger.com
Sales Range: $1-9.9 Million
Emp.: 40
Newspaper Publishers
N.A.I.C.S.: 513110
Dana Morton (Bus Mgr)
Jerry Pye (Publr)

The Panola Watchman (1)
109 W Panola St, Carthage, TX 75633
Tel.: (903) 693-7888
Web Site: http://www.panolawatchman.com
Sales Range: $25-49.9 Million
Emp.: 200
Newspaper Publishers
N.A.I.C.S.: 513110
Jerry Pye (Publr)

TEXAS CRUSHED STONE CO.
5300 South IH 35, Georgetown, TX 78626

Tel.: (512) 863-5511
Web Site: http://www.texascrushedstoneco.com
Rev.: $44,000,000
Emp.: 130
Crushed & Broken Limestone
N.A.I.C.S.: 212312
W. B. Snead (Pres)

TEXAS CUSTOM POOLS INC.
4016 W Plano Pkwy Ste 100, Plano, TX 75093
Tel.: (972) 596-7393
Web Site: http://www.riverbendsandlerpools.com
Year Founded: 1975
Sales Range: $10-24.9 Million
Emp.: 45
Swimming Pool Construction
N.A.I.C.S.: 238990
Charles Barnes (Chm)

TEXAS DISPOSAL SYSTEMS INC.
12200 Carl Rd, Austin, TX 78747
Tel.: (512) 421-1300
Web Site: http://www.texasdisposal.com
Sales Range: $25-49.9 Million
Emp.: 500
Garbage Collection & Processing Services
N.A.I.C.S.: 562111
Bob Gregory (Chm & CEO)
Jim Gregory (VP & Mgr)
Gary T. Newton (Gen Counsel)

TEXAS DODGE
7800 I-40 W, Amarillo, TX 79106-1819
Tel.: (806) 353-6343
Web Site: http://www.texasdodge.com
Sales Range: $10-24.9 Million
Emp.: 60
Car Whslr
N.A.I.C.S.: 441110
Daren Marcum (Mgr-Svc)

TEXAS DOW EMPLOYEES CREDIT UNION
1001 FM 2004, Lake Jackson, TX 77566
Tel.: (979) 297-1154 TX
Web Site: http://www.tdecu.org
Year Founded: 1955
Sales Range: $150-199.9 Million
Emp.: 891
Credit Union
N.A.I.C.S.: 522130
Richard Smith (Chm)
George Hornback (Sec)
Daniel L. Buche (Vice Chm)
Roland Hendricks (Treas)
Stephanie Sherrodd (Pres & CEO)
Michael Hubbell (Chief Risk Officer)

TEXAS ELECTRIC COOPERATIVES, INC.
1122 Colorado St, Austin, TX 78701
Tel.: (512) 454-0311 TX
Web Site: http://www.texas-ec.org
Year Founded: 1940
Sales Range: $75-99.9 Million
Emp.: 180
Power Line Poles & Electrical Transformer Mfr
N.A.I.C.S.: 321114
Mike Williams (Pres & CEO)

Subsidiaries:

Texas Electric Cooperatives, Inc. -
TEC Pole Manufacturing Plant (1)
2240 Bevil Loop Rd, Jasper, TX 75951

Tel.: (409) 384-4633
Emp.: 70
Steel & Concrete Pole Distr
N.A.I.C.S.: 423390

TEXAS ENERGY HOLDINGS INC.
3320 Oak Grove Ave, Dallas, TX 75204
Tel.: (214) 231-4000
Web Site: http://www.tx-energy.com
Year Founded: 2003
Sales Range: $25-49.9 Million
Emp.: 107
Asset Management Firm
N.A.I.C.S.: 523999
Phillip Willis (Co-Founder, Pres & CEO)
Casey Ladymon (Co-Founder & Exec VP)
Louis Litwin (Dir-HR)

TEXAS ENGINEERING EXT SERVICE
200 Technology Way, College Station, TX 77845
Tel.: (979) 458-6902
Web Site: http://www.teex.org
Sales Range: $75-99.9 Million
Emp.: 700
Engineering Help Service
N.A.I.C.S.: 541612
Gary Sera (Dir-Agency)

TEXAS ENTERPRISES INC.
5005 E 7th St, Austin, TX 78702-5022
Tel.: (800) 545-4412
Web Site: http://www.alliedsalesco.com
Year Founded: 1975
Sales Range: $125-149.9 Million
Emp.: 160
Provider of Petroleum Products
N.A.I.C.S.: 424720
Cody Douglas (Controller)
Ed Looney (VP)
Ford Smith Jr. (Pres)

TEXAS EXCAVATION SAFETY
11880 Greenville Ave Ste 120, Dallas, TX 75243-3568
Tel.: (972) 231-5497
Sales Range: $10-24.9 Million
Emp.: 130
Construction Engineering Services
N.A.I.C.S.: 237310
Lee Marrs (Principal)

TEXAS FARM BUREAU MUTUAL INSURANCE
7420 Fish Pond Rd, Waco, TX 76710
Tel.: (254) 772-3030
Web Site: http://www.txfb-ins.com
Sales Range: $75-99.9 Million
Emp.: 425
Insurance Agents, Brokers & Service
N.A.I.C.S.: 524210
Gene Hall (Dir-PR)
Billy Howe (Assoc Dir-Legislative)

TEXAS FARM PRODUCTS COMPANY
915 S Fredonia St, Nacogdoches, TX 75964
Tel.: (936) 564-3711
Web Site: http://www.texasfarm.com
Year Founded: 1930
Sales Range: $25-49.9 Million
Emp.: 188
Provider of Agricultural Products
N.A.I.C.S.: 424490
M. S. Wright (Pres & CEO)
Raymond Batten (VP-Sls)
Richard Green (Mgr-Info Sys)

TEXAS INTERNATIONAL GAS & OIL CO., INC.

Subsidiaries:

ANF Specialties Inc. (1)
915 S Fredonia St, Nacogdoches, TX 75964-5913 (100%)
Tel.: (936) 564-3711
Web Site: http://www.anf.com
Sales Range: $25-49.9 Million
Emp.: 60
Mfr of Pet Food & Animal Feed
N.A.I.C.S.: 424490

Precision Pet Products, Inc. (1)
PO Box 630009, Nacogdoches, TX 75963-0009
Tel.: (888) 477-3247
Web Site: http://www.precisepet.com
Pet Food Mfr
N.A.I.C.S.: 311119
Kirk Young (Exec VP-Sls & Mktg)
Stuart Chiu (Mgr-Sls-Western Canada)
Alyssa Crosby (Mgr-Sls-New England)
Megan Jacober (Mgr-Sls-North West)
Scott Johnson (Mgr-Sls-Territory)
Donavan Meyer (Mgr-Sls-Territory)
Pete Pennell (Dir-Sls-Western Reg)
Ben Pennell (Mgr-Sls-Territory)
Scott Steed (Dir-Sls-Eastern Reg)
Marnee White (Mgr-Customer Care & Logistics)

TEXAS FIRST NATIONAL BANK
9315 Bellaire Blvd, Houston, TX 77036
Tel.: (713) 777-3838
Web Site: http://www.goldenbank-na.com
Year Founded: 1985
Rev.: $27,387,000
Emp.: 92
National Commercial Banks
N.A.I.C.S.: 522110

TEXAS FRENCH BREAD INC.
2900 Rio Grande, Austin, TX 78705
Tel.: (512) 499-0544
Web Site: http://www.texasfrenchbread.com
Year Founded: 1981
Sales Range: $10-24.9 Million
Bakery & Restaurant Operator
N.A.I.C.S.: 311812
Murph Wilcott (Owner)

TEXAS HEALTH RESOURCES
612 E Lamar Blvd, Arlington, TX 76011
Tel.: (682) 236-7900
Web Site: http://www.texashealth.org
Year Founded: 1997
Emp.: 23,000
Hospital Operations & Related Services
N.A.I.C.S.: 622110
Harold Berenzweig (Exec VP)
Aaron M. Bujnowski (Chief Strategy Officer & Sr VP)
Jeffrey L. Canose (COO & Sr Exec VP)
Kirk King (Exec VP)
Michelle Kirby (Sr VP)
Ronald R. Long (CFO & Exec VP)
Joey Sudomir (CIO & Sr VP)
Barclay E. Berdan (CEO)
Joan Clark (Exec VP)
Brett S. McClung (Exec VP)
Winjie Tang Miao (Exec VP)
Jim Parobek (Exec VP)
Elizabeth Ransom (Exec VP)
David J. Tesmer (Sr VP)
Daniel Varga (Sr Exec VP)

TEXAS INTERNATIONAL GAS & OIL CO., INC.
9681 Joe Rodriguez, El Paso, TX 79927-2121
Tel.: (915) 860-8803 TX
Web Site: http://www.tbp.com
Year Founded: 1985
Sales Range: $25-49.9 Million
Emp.: 27

TEXAS INTERNATIONAL GAS & OIL CO., INC. — U.S. PRIVATE

Texas International Gas & Oil Co., Inc.—(Continued)
Wholesale Propane & Petroleum
N.A.I.C.S.: 213112
Eduardo V. Fuentes *(Pres, Treas & Sec)*
Sergio Correa *(Controller)*

TEXAS JASMINE
7051 SW Fwy, Houston, TX 77074
Tel.: (713) 784-4335
Web Site: http://www.texasjasmine.com
Year Founded: 1992
Sales Range: $75-99.9 Million
Emp.: 80
Grocery Wholesaler
N.A.I.C.S.: 424410
Zulfiqar Momin *(Pres)*

TEXAS KEYSTONE INC.
560 Epsilon Dr Ste 1, Pittsburgh, PA 15238-2837
Tel.: (412) 434-5616
Web Site: http://www.texaskeystone.com
Sales Range: $10-24.9 Million
Emp.: 20
Oil & Gas Well Drilling
N.A.I.C.S.: 213111
Rob Kozel *(Pres)*

TEXAS LAND & CATTLE
1101 S Mo Pac, Austin, TX 78746
Tel.: (512) 330-0030
Web Site: http://www.texaslandandcattle.com
Year Founded: 1993
Rev.: $32,500,000
Emp.: 30
Restaurant Owner & Operator
N.A.I.C.S.: 722511
John Drake *(Mgr-Kitchen)*

TEXAS LIGHTING SALES INCORPORATED
831 W Euless Blvd Ste 15, Euless, TX 76040
Tel.: (915) 771-7772
Web Site: http://www.texaslighting.com
Rev.: $60,000,000
Emp.: 50
Lighting Fixtures
N.A.I.C.S.: 423610
Jim Weathers *(Pres)*
Cathi Cox *(Engr-Applications)*
Ron Shields *(VP)*

TEXAS LINEN COMPANY
1307 Smith Rd, Austin, TX 78721
Tel.: (512) 389-0220
Sales Range: $10-24.9 Million
Emp.: 200
Linen Supply Services
N.A.I.C.S.: 812331
Karl Schulte *(Principal)*

TEXAS LOTTERY COMMISSION
611 E 6th St, Austin, TX 78701
Tel.: (512) 344-5000 TX
Web Site: http://www.txlottery.org
Year Founded: 1992
Sales Range: $25-49.9 Million
Emp.: 335
Lottery Gaming & Charitable Bingo Licensing in the State of Texas
N.A.I.C.S.: 921130
Robert Tirloni *(Product Mgr-Mktg)*
Ray Page *(Mgr-Adv & Promos)*
Mary Ann Williamson *(Chm)*

TEXAS LPG STORAGE CO. INC.
11390 Gtwy Blvd E, El Paso, TX 79927-7701
Tel.: (915) 872-1100 TX
Year Founded: 1988
Sales Range: $25-49.9 Million
Emp.: 15
Provide Storage & Distribution Services of Liquified Petroleum Gas
N.A.I.C.S.: 221210
Ermesto Carrillo *(Pres)*

TEXAS MARKET RESEARCH GROUP LLC
10333 Richmond Ave Ste 275, Houston, TX 77042
Tel.: (713) 782-8788
Polling & Research Services
N.A.I.C.S.: 541910
Sanjay Vrudhula *(CMO)*

Subsidiaries:

Voter Consumer Research, Inc. (1)
325 Sawdust Rd, Spring, TX 77380
Tel.: (281) 893-1010
Web Site: http://www.vcrhouston.com
Sales Range: $1-9.9 Million
Emp.: 300
Marketing Research & Public Opinion Polling
N.A.I.C.S.: 541910
Daniel Kessler *(Pres)*
Barbara Maddin *(Dir-Ops)*
Phyllis Maier *(Controller)*
Mike Reed *(Dir-IT)*
Jan Van Lohuizen *(Chm)*

TEXAS MEDICAL CENTER CORP.
2450 Holcombe Blvd Ste 1, Houston, TX 77021
Tel.: (713) 791-8800
Web Site: http://www.texasmedicalcenter.edu
Year Founded: 1945
Emp.: 106,000
Medical Facilities Operator
N.A.I.C.S.: 622110
Bill McKeon *(CEO)*
Shawn W. Cloonan *(COO & Exec VP)*

TEXAS MOLECULAR, LLC
2525 Independence Pkwy S Battleground Rd, Deer Park, TX 77536
Tel.: (281) 930-2525
Web Site: http://www.texasmolecular.com
Environmental Services/Hazardous Waste Management & Custom Chemical Mfr
N.A.I.C.S.: 562211

TEXAS MONTHLY, INC.
PO Box 1569, Austin, TX 78767-1569
Tel.: (512) 320-6900 TX
Web Site: http://www.texasmonthly.com
Year Founded: 1973
Magazine Publisher
N.A.I.C.S.: 513120
Lorelei Calvert *(Gen Mgr)*
David Barr Dunham *(VP-Dev)*
Skip Hollandsworth *(Exec Editor)*
Patricia Sharpe *(Exec Editor)*
Julie Lee *(VP-Natl Sls)*
Tim Taliaferro *(CIO)*
Scott Brown *(Pres & Chief Creative Officer)*
Carolyn Davis Chavana *(COO)*
Brett Bowlin *(Dir-Digital Strategy)*
Robert Henry Vela Davila *(VP-Audience & Res)*
Jackie Buchan *(Mgr-Special Events)*
Erin Beil *(Controller)*
Emily Kimbro *(Dir-Design)*
Dan Goodgame *(Editor)*
Regina Mack *(Editor-Social Media)*

TEXAS MUNICIPAL POWER AGENCY
12824 FM 244, Anderson, TX 77830
Tel.: (936) 873-2013
Web Site: http://www.texasmpa.org
Year Founded: 1975
Sales Range: $200-249.9 Million
Emp.: 160
Generation, Electric Power
N.A.I.C.S.: 221118
Craig York *(Gen Mgr)*
Pat Potter *(Supvr-Maintenance)*
Philip T. Flowers *(Project Mgr)*
Russell Huff *(CFO)*

TEXAS MUTUAL INSURANCE COMPANY
6210 E Hwy 290, Austin, TX 78723-1098
Tel.: (512) 224-3800
Web Site: http://www.texasmutual.com
Sales Range: $700-749.9 Million
Emp.: 677
Workers' Compensation Insurance Services
N.A.I.C.S.: 524126
Terry Frakes *(Sr VP-Pub Affairs)*
Bernie Francis *(Sec)*
Bob Barnes *(Chm)*
Linda Foster-Smith *(Vice Chm)*
Leonard Randy Johnson *(Sr VP-Investments)*
Steve Math *(Sr VP-Underwriting)*
Bill McLellan *(Sr VP-IT)*
Mary Nichols *(Gen Counsel & Sr VP)*
Jeanette Ward *(COO)*
Richard Gergasko *(Pres & CEO)*
Jeremiah Bentley *(VP-Mktg & Customer Engagement)*
Amy Green-Hinojosa *(VP-Project Mgmt Office)*
Nathan Scott *(VP-Investments)*
Benjamin A. Siddons *(VP-Bus Dev)*
Kim Haugaard *(Sr VP-Policyholder Svcs)*
Richard Dabney *(VP-Corp Underwriting)*
Larry Martin *(Sr VP-HR)*
Bill Potter *(CFO)*

TEXAS ONCOLOGY, PA
12221 Merit Dr Ste 500, Dallas, TX 75251
Web Site: http://www.texasoncology.com
Cancer Treatment Centers
N.A.I.C.S.: 622310
R. Steven Paulson *(Chm & Pres)*
J. Ernest Sims *(Exec Dir-Fin & Ops)*
Charles S. White III *(VP)*

Subsidiaries:

Texas Oncology - San Antonio Northeast (1)
2130 NE Loop 410 Ste 100, San Antonio, TX 78217
Tel.: (210) 614-0880
Web Site: http://www.texasoncology.com
Cancer Treatment Center
N.A.I.C.S.: 621498

TEXAS ORGAN SHARING ALLIANCE
8122 Datapoint Ste 200, San Antonio, TX 78229
Tel.: (210) 614-7030 TX
Web Site: http://www.txorgansharing.org
Year Founded: 1975
Sales Range: $25-49.9 Million
Emp.: 62
Human Organ Transplantation Services
N.A.I.C.S.: 813212

TEXAS PEOPLES NATIONAL BANCSHARES, INC.
35 S Plaza, Paris, TX 75460
Tel.: (903) 783-3800
Web Site: http://www.pbparis.com
Sales Range: $10-24.9 Million
Emp.: 10
Bank Holding Company
N.A.I.C.S.: 551111
Ronald E. Abbott *(CEO)*
Terry Christian *(Pres)*

Subsidiaries:

Peoples Bank (1)
35 S Plaza, Paris, TX 75460
Tel.: (903) 783-3800
Web Site: http://www.pbparis.com
Sales Range: $1-9.9 Million
Banking Services
N.A.I.C.S.: 522110
Ronald E. Abbott *(Chm & CEO)*
John C. Blackwell *(Sr VP)*
T. Bradley Perry *(Pres)*

TEXAS PETROLEUM INVESTMENT CO.
5850 San Felipe St No 250, Houston, TX 77057
Tel.: (713) 789-9225
Rev.: $10,689,901
Emp.: 80
Petroleum Exploration & Production Services
N.A.I.C.S.: 213112
Bruce Sallee *(Pres)*

TEXAS PHYSICAL THERAPY SPECIALISTS
8335 Agora Pkwy Ste 100, Selma, TX 78154
Tel.: (210) 658-8483
Web Site: http://www.texpts.com
Year Founded: 2004
Sales Range: $1-9.9 Million
Emp.: 140
Physical & Occupational Therapy
N.A.I.C.S.: 621340
Jeanne Smith *(COO)*
Cindy Pixley *(Office Mgr)*
Mike McTague *(Dir-Physical Therapy)*
Pamela Davis *(Chief Billing Officer)*
Steve Clark *(Dir-Clinic)*

TEXAS PIPE & SUPPLY COMPANY LTD.
2330 Holmes Rd, Houston, TX 77051-1014
Tel.: (713) 799-9235
Web Site: http://www.texaspipe.com
Year Founded: 1918
Sales Range: $125-149.9 Million
Emp.: 140
Carbon & Stainless Steel Pipes Distr
N.A.I.C.S.: 423510
Jerry R. Rubenstein *(Chm)*
Maury Rubenstein *(CEO)*
Carl Lenz *(Controller)*

TEXAS PIPE WORKS INC.
9444 Industrial Dr, Navasota, TX 77868
Tel.: (936) 825-6571
Web Site: http://www.texaspipeworks.com
Year Founded: 1985
Sales Range: $100-124.9 Million
Emp.: 160
Fabricated Pipe & Pipe Fitting Mfr
N.A.I.C.S.: 327910

Texas International Gas & Oil Co., Inc. not found in the index? See "How To Use Directories" in Volume 1.

Marilou A. Donley *(CFO & Sr Dir-Admin)*
Joseph Nespral *(CEO)*
Vince Speeg *(Chm)*

COMPANIES

Clarence Thomas *(Mgr-Finishing & Shipping)*
Ken Oberholz *(Pres)*

TEXAS PRESS ASSOCIATION
8800 Business Park Dr Ste100, Austin, TX 78759
Tel.: (512) 477-6755   TX
Web Site: http://www.texaspress.com
Year Founded: 1880
Sales Range: $1-9.9 Million
Emp.: 13
Media Buying Services
N.A.I.C.S.: 541810
Michael Hodges *(Exec Dir)*
Stephanie Hearne *(Controller & Office Mgr)*
Diane Byram *(Dir-Adv)*

TEXAS PROCESS EQUIPMENT CO.
5215 Ted St, Houston, TX 77040-6209
Tel.: (713) 460-5555
Web Site: http://www.texasprocess.com
Sales Range: $10-24.9 Million
Emp.: 40
Pumps & Pumping Equipment
N.A.I.C.S.: 423830
Donald L. Grogg *(Mgr-Accts)*
Kyle Drennan *(Controller)*

TEXAS PROPERTY & CASUALTY INSURANCE GUARANTY ASSOCIATION
9120 Burnet Rd, Austin, TX 78758-5204
Tel.: (512) 345-9335   TX
Web Site: http://www.tpciga.org
Year Founded: 1971
Sales Range: $25-49.9 Million
Emp.: 55
Insurance Guaranty Association
N.A.I.C.S.: 524126
Marvin Kelly *(Exec Dir)*
David P. Fleming *(Treas & Sec)*

TEXAS RECREATION CORPORATION
PO Box 539, Wichita Falls, TX 76307-0539
Tel.: (940) 322-4463
Web Site: http://www.texasrec.com
Sales Range: $10-24.9 Million
Emp.: 120
Plastics Foam Products
N.A.I.C.S.: 326150
Pat Rominger *(Pres)*

TEXAS REFINERY CORP.
1 Refinery Pl 840 N Main St, Fort Worth, TX 76106
Tel.: (817) 332-1161   TX
Web Site: http://www.texasrefinery.com
Year Founded: 1922
Sales Range: $10-24.9 Million
Emp.: 120
Protective Roof Coating & Lubricant Mfr
N.A.I.C.S.: 324191
Johnny McGee *(VP & Mgr-Protective Coatings Sls)*
Patrick M. Walsh *(Pres)*
Chris Pate *(Chm & CEO)*
J. R. Hannan *(COO & Sr VP)*

Subsidiaries:

Texas Refinery Corp of Canada Limited   (1)
25 Industrial St, Toronto, M4G 1Z2, ON, Canada
Tel.: (306) 692-9241
Web Site: http://www.texasrefinery.ca
Emp.: 4

Petroleum Product Mfr
N.A.I.C.S.: 324191
Patrick M. Walsh *(Pres)*
Cassandra Warner *(Mgr-Credit)*

Texas Refinery Corp. - Lubricants Division   (1)
840 N Main St, Fort Worth, TX 76164
Tel.: (817) 332-1161
Petroleum Lubricating Oil Mfr
N.A.I.C.S.: 324191
Dennis Parks *(VP & Mgr-Sls)*
Patty Collins *(Asst VP & Mgr-Sls)*
John Spoonts *(Mgr-Sls)*
David Eder *(Mgr-Sls)*

Texas Refinery Corp. - Protective Coatings Division   (1)
840 N Main St, Fort Worth, TX 76164
Tel.: (817) 332-1161
Web Site: http://www.texasrefinery.com
Emp.: 80
Petroleum Lubricating Oil Mfr
N.A.I.C.S.: 324191
Carrol Aycock *(Mgr-Sls)*

TEXAS REPUBLIC CAPITAL CORPORATION
13215 Bee Cave Pkwy Ste A120, Austin, TX 78738
Tel.: (512) 330-0099   TX
Web Site: http://www.texasrepubliccapital.com
Year Founded: 2012
Rev.: $4,227,163
Assets: $40,255,138
Liabilities: $31,739,632
Net Worth: $8,515,506
Earnings: ($1,149,984)
Emp.: 15
Fiscal Year-end: 12/31/22
Insurance Holding Company
N.A.I.C.S.: 551112
William Sherman Lay *(Asst Sec & Asst Treas)*
Timothy R. Miller *(Founder, Pres & CEO)*
Shane S. Mitchell *(CFO & Principal Acctg Officer)*
Jared Moore *(Dir-Agency)*
Jeff Wingfield *(Dir-Trng)*
Ben Schleppenbach *(Dir-Agency Dev)*

Subsidiaries:

Texas Republic Life Insurance Company   (1)
13215 Bee Cave Pkwy Ste A120, Austin, TX 78738-0056
Tel.: (512) 330-0099
Web Site: https://www.texasrepubliclife.com
Insurance Providing Services
N.A.I.C.S.: 524210
Tim Miller *(Pres & CEO)*
William Sherman Lay *(Treas & Sec)*

Texas Republic Life Solutions   (1)
13215 Bee Cave Pkwy Ste A120, Austin, TX 78738-0056
Tel.: (512) 333-0073
Web Site: https://www.texasrepubliclifesolutions.com
Insurance Management Services
N.A.I.C.S.: 524210

TEXAS SCENIC COMPANY INC.
8053 Potranco Rd, San Antonio, TX 78251
Tel.: (210) 684-0091
Web Site: http://www.texasscenic.com
Sales Range: $50-74.9 Million
Emp.: 100
Theatrical Scenery
N.A.I.C.S.: 423490
Stephen G. Surratt *(COO & Gen Mgr)*
Richard Mecke *(Pres)*
Ron Fairchild *(CFO)*
John Owens *(VP-Sls)*
Michael Freeman *(Project Mgr)*

Tim Rufenacht *(Coord-Safety)*
Joel Guerra *(Dir-Engrg & Svcs)*
Cristina Rodriguez *(Mgr-Front Sls)*

TEXAS SCOTTISH RITE HOSPITAL FOR CHILDREN
2222 Welborn St, Dallas, TX 75219
Tel.: (214) 559-5000   TX
Web Site: http://www.tsrhc.org
Year Founded: 1921
Sales Range: $200-249.9 Million
Child Health Care Services
N.A.I.C.S.: 622110
Graham H. Childress *(VP)*
Ellen Haynes *(VP-Major Gifts & Corp Giving)*
Daniel H. Chapman *(VP)*
Harold D. Carter *(Vice Chm)*
Lee Drain *(Vice Chm)*
Ronald L. Skaggs *(Sec & VP)*
Connie Wright *(VP-HR)*
Matt Chance *(Sr VP-Ops)*
Jeremy Howell *(VP)*
William R. Huston *(CFO & Sr VP)*
Lyndon L. Olson Jr. *(Chm)*

TEXAS SOUTH ENERGY, INC.
4550 Post Oak Place Dr Ste 300, Houston, TX 77027
Tel.: (713) 820-6300   NV
Web Site: http://www.texasouth.com
Year Founded: 2010
Rev.: $11,818
Assets: $16,932,634
Liabilities: $9,027,901
Net Worth: $7,904,733
Earnings: ($3,110,744)
Emp.: 6
Fiscal Year-end: 12/31/18
Investment Management Service
N.A.I.C.S.: 523999
Michael J. Mayell *(Pres & CEO)*
Lecia Alexander *(Controller)*
James L. Gunderson *(Mgr-Land)*
Brenda Mabry *(Office Mgr)*
Michael W. Mayell *(Mgr-Ops)*
John B. Connally III *(Chm)*

TEXAS STAR BANK
177 E Jefferson St, Van Alstyne, TX 75495
Tel.: (903) 482-5234
Web Site: http://www.texasstarbank.com
Year Founded: 1890
Sales Range: $1-9.9 Million
Emp.: 75
Provider of Banking Services
N.A.I.C.S.: 522110
Randle W. Jones *(Pres)*
Robert Jaska *(Exec VP-Ops)*
Robert H. Hynds *(Chm)*
Michael R. Hynds *(Vice Chm)*

TEXAS STATE BANKSHARES, INC.
2019 S 77 Sunshine Strip, Harlingen, TX 78550
Tel.: (956) 428-7400   TX
Web Site: http://www.texasregionalbank.com
Sales Range: $10-24.9 Million
Bank Holding Company
N.A.I.C.S.: 551111
Michael Scaief *(Chm)*
Paul S. Moxley *(Pres & CEO)*
Michael K. Lamon *(Chief Credit Officer)*
Brent M. Baldree *(Chief Lending Officer)*
Robert R. Farris *(Vice Chm)*
Lincoln Talbert *(CFO)*

Subsidiaries:

Estrada Hinojosa & Co., Inc.   (1)

TEXAS TRANSEASTERN INC.

1717 Main St Ste 4700, Dallas, TX 75201-7361
Tel.: (214) 658-1670
Web Site: http://www.estradahinojosa.com
Rev.: $543,000,000
Emp.: 70
Investment Banking Services
N.A.I.C.S.: 523150
Noe Hinojosa Jr. *(Chm, Pres & CEO)*
Robert A. Estrada *(Chm)*

Texas Regional Bank   (1)
2019 S 77 Sunshine Strip, Harlingen, TX 78550
Tel.: (956) 428-7400
Web Site: http://www.texasregionalbank.com
Sales Range: $10-24.9 Million
Commericial Banking
N.A.I.C.S.: 522110
Rolando Carrasco *(Chief Compliance Officer & Exec VP)*
Michael Scaief *(Chm & CEO)*
Michael K. Lamon *(Chief Credit Officer)*
Brent M. Baldree *(Chief Lending Officer & Reg Pres-South Texas Market)*
Ronda Johnson *(CIO & Exec VP)*
Lincoln Talbert *(CFO & Exec VP)*

TEXAS STEEL CONVERSION, INC.
3101 Holmes Rd, Houston, TX 77051
Tel.: (713) 733-6013
Web Site: http://texassteelconversion.com
Year Founded: 1976
Drill Pipe Mfr
N.A.I.C.S.: 331210
Raul Herrera *(Mgr-Safety)*

Subsidiaries:

Superior Drillpipe Manufacturing   (1)
7203 Miller Rd, Houston, TX 77049-4821
Tel.: (281) 452-2260
Web Site: http://www.tsc-hdd.com
Diameter Friction Welded Horizontal Directional Drilling Drill Pipe Mfr
N.A.I.C.S.: 332996
Warren Hoover *(Owner)*

TEXAS SUBS
1711 Central Texas Expy, Killeen, TX 76541
Tel.: (254) 634-2882
Web Site: http://www.texassubs.com
Year Founded: 1997
Sales Range: $25-49.9 Million
Emp.: 500
Sandwich Restaurants
N.A.I.C.S.: 722513
Robert Stephens *(Principal)*
Michael Ebers *(COO)*

TEXAS TOOL DISTRIBUTORS INC.
13317 Seydler Rd, Weimar, TX 78962
Tel.: (979) 263-5015
Web Site: http://www.texastooltraders.com
Year Founded: 1973
Sales Range: $25-49.9 Million
Emp.: 65
Tools & Harware Distr
N.A.I.C.S.: 423710
Garrett Anders *(Pres)*

TEXAS TRANSEASTERN INC.
3438 Pasadena Blvd, Pasadena, TX 77505
Tel.: (281) 604-3100
Web Site: http://www.texastranseastern.com
Year Founded: 1984
Sales Range: $10-24.9 Million
Emp.: 100
Liquid Petroleum Transport Services
N.A.I.C.S.: 484230

TEXAS TRANSEASTERN INC.

Texas Transeastern Inc.—(Continued)
Randy W. Googins (VP)
Jeff Bolner (Mgr-Ops)
Tammy Boyd (Supvr-Payroll Benefits)
J. J. Isbell Jr. (Pres)

TEXAS TRIBUNE INC.
823 Congress Ave Ste 1400, Austin, TX 78701
Tel.: (512) 716-8600   TX
Web Site: http://www.texastribune.org
Year Founded: 2009
Sales Range: $1-9.9 Million
Emp.: 48
Public Media Services
N.A.I.C.S.: 541910
Natalie Choate (Dir-Media Rels & Partnerships)
Rodney Gibbs (Chief Product Officer)
Amanda Zamora (Chief Audience Officer)
Evan Smith (Co-Founder & CEO)
John Thornton (Co-Founder)
April Hinkle (Chief Revenue Officer)
Terry Quinn (Chief Dev Officer)

TEXAS TRUST CREDIT UNION
1900 Country Club Dr, Mansfield, TX 76063
Tel.: (972) 263-5171
Web Site: http://www.texastrustcu.org
Year Founded: 1936
Rev.: $59,721,626
Assets: $1,240,896,515
Liabilities: $1,117,855,563
Net Worth: $123,040,952
Earnings: $7,436,568
Emp.: 300
Fiscal Year-end: 12/31/18
Credit Union
N.A.I.C.S.: 522130
James Minge (Pres & CEO)
David Pickney (CFO)
William Kelsey (Chief Retail Officer & Exec VP)
Pamela Stephens (COO & Exec VP)
Alvin Meaux (Sr VP-Lending & Collections)
David Turner (CIO)
Rebecca White (VP-HR)
Leann Santiago (Sr VP-Talent)

TEXAS VISITING NURSE LTD.
814 E Tyler Ave, Harlingen, TX 78550-7132
Tel.: (956) 412-1401
Web Site: http://www.tvnsltd.com
Year Founded: 1981
Sales Range: $10-24.9 Million
Emp.: 145
Provider of Home Health Care Services
N.A.I.C.S.: 621610

TEXAS WILSON OFFICE FURNITURE & SERVICES
6812 Fairgrounds Pkwy, San Antonio, TX 78238-4536
Tel.: (210) 647-8800   TX
Web Site: http://www.texaswilson.com
Year Founded: 1985
Sales Range: $10-24.9 Million
Emp.: 70
Office Furniture; Upholstery & Furniture Distr
N.A.I.C.S.: 423210
Tammy Poe (VP-Sls, Mktg & Design)
Mike Luna (Pres & CEO)
John Walvoord (Controller)

TEXASWEET CITRUS MARKETING INC.
901 Business Park Dr Ste 100, Mission, TX 78572-6048
Tel.: (956) 580-8004
Web Site: http://www.texasweet.com
Year Founded: 1966
Sales Range: $10-24.9 Million
Emp.: 3
Citrus Fruit Whslr
N.A.I.C.S.: 445230
Paul Heller (VP)
Dennis Holbrook (Pres)
Fred Karle (Treas & Sec)
Linda Lopez (Office Mgr)
Lou Chow (Mgr)
Eleisha Ensign (Exec Dir)
Kymberly Penn (Coord-Mktg)

TEXATRONICS INC.
1501 N Plano Rd Ste 300, Richardson, TX 75081
Tel.: (214) 379-8550
Web Site: http://www.texatronics.com
Sales Range: $10-24.9 Million
Emp.: 100
Electronics Contract Manufacturing
N.A.I.C.S.: 334412
Lou Tran (Dir-Mfg)

TEXELL CREDIT UNION
PO Box 983, Temple, TX 76503-0983
Tel.: (254) 773-1604   TX
Web Site: http://www.texell.org
Year Founded: 1948
Sales Range: $10-24.9 Million
Emp.: 159
Credit Union
N.A.I.C.S.: 522130
Amy Merriman (COO)
Ferretti George (CFO)
John A. Hale (CEO)

TEXHOMA ENERGY, INC.
100 Highland Pk Vlg, Dallas, TX 75205
Tel.: (214) 295-3380
Year Founded: 1998
Oil & Natural Gas Exploration Services
N.A.I.C.S.: 213112
Nicolo Golia Bedendo (Pres, CEO, Treas, Sec & Dir)

TEXHOMA WHEAT GROWERS INC.
Hwy 54 W, Texhoma, OK 73949
Tel.: (806) 827-7261
Web Site: http://www.wheatgrowersinc.com
Rev.: $15,817,161
Emp.: 18
Grains Elevators
N.A.I.C.S.: 424510

TEXOMA PEANUT COMPANY
433 E Main St, Madill, OK 73446
Tel.: (580) 795-5555   OK
Web Site: http://www.texomapeanut.com
Year Founded: 1961
Sales Range: $25-49.9 Million
Emp.: 200
Whslr of Peanuts
N.A.I.C.S.: 424590
Tim Jones (Controller)

Subsidiaries:

Texoma Peanut Inn   (1)
912 S 1st St, Madill, OK 73446
Tel.: (580) 795-7693
Web Site: http://www.peanutinn.com
Grocery Store Operator
N.A.I.C.S.: 445110
Linda Jones (Mgr)

The Clint Williams Company   (1)
PO Box 310, Madill, OK 73446
Tel.: (580) 795-5555
Web Site: http://www.texomapeanut.com
Sales Range: $25-49.9 Million
Emp.: 150
Processor of Peanuts
N.A.I.C.S.: 424590
David Kerry (Office Mgr)

TEXON LP
11757 Katy Fwy Ste 1400, Houston, TX 77079-1725
Tel.: (281) 531-8400
Web Site: http://www.texonlp.com
Year Founded: 1997
Sales Range: $10-24.9 Million
Emp.: 120
Provider of Petroleum Products
N.A.I.C.S.: 424720
Terry L. Looper (Pres & CEO)
Wade Jones (Sr VP-Crude Oil Supply)
Reid Smith (Sr VP-Natural Gas Liquids)

TEXPAR ENERGY INC.
920 10th Ave N, Onalaska, WI 54650
Tel.: (608) 779-6601
Web Site: http://www.texpar.com
Rev.: $19,900,000
Emp.: 35
Market Terminal & Fuel Distributor
N.A.I.C.S.: 424710
Lori Wisch (Mgr-Dispatch)

TEXSUN SWIMMING POOLS & SPAS, INC.
7622 Louetta Rd Ste B, Spring, TX 77379
Tel.: (281) 320-8242   TX
Web Site: http://www.texsunpools.com
Year Founded: 1982
Sales Range: $1-9.9 Million
Emp.: 80
Services, Repairs & Renovates Swimming Pools & Spas & Related Equipment
N.A.I.C.S.: 811310
Tom Steinbacher (Pres)

TEXTAPE, INC.
915 Pendale Rd, El Paso, TX 79937
Tel.: (915) 595-1525
Web Site: http://www.textape.net
Year Founded: 1987
Sales Range: $10-24.9 Million
Emp.: 30
Industrial & Personal Service Paper Whslr
N.A.I.C.S.: 424130
Van Scott (Owner)

TEXTILE CARE SERVICES, INC.
225 Wood Lake Dr SE, Rochester, MN 55904-5530
Tel.: (507) 252-7500   MN
Web Site: http://www.textilecs.com
Year Founded: 1915
Commercial Laundry & Dry Cleaning Services
N.A.I.C.S.: 812332
Paul Jewison (Pres & CEO)
Vicky Vessey (Mgr-Sls)
Roger Derby (Mgr-Inventory & Quality Control)
Anne Wilson (Mgr-Customer Svc)
Mandy Elias (Mgr-HR)

TEXTILE CARE SERVICES, INC.
2295 W Custer Rd, Salt Lake City, UT 84104
Tel.: (801) 994-1220   UT
Web Site: http://www.tcsutah.com
Sales Range: $10-24.9 Million
Emp.: 100
Commercial Laundry & Dry Cleaning Services
N.A.I.C.S.: 812332

TEXTILE IMPORT LLC
1410 Broadway, New York, NY 10018
Tel.: (212) 354-2200
Rev.: $61,500,000
Emp.: 29
Textile Import Services
N.A.I.C.S.: 424310
Stuart Tell (CEO)
Paul Sheiness (VP-Sls)
John Turner (VP)
David Tell (Pres)

TEXTILE RUBBER & CHEMICAL CO., INC.
1300 Tiarco Dr SW, Dalton, GA 30721-1907
Tel.: (706) 277-1300   GA
Web Site: http://www.trcc.com
Year Founded: 1953
Sales Range: $350-399.9 Million
Emp.: 400
Chemical & Machinery Mfr
N.A.I.C.S.: 325520
Chip Howalt (Pres)

Subsidiaries:

Perpetual Machine Company   (1)
1810 Lessco Dr, Dalton, GA 30722   (100%)
Tel.: (706) 226-1534
Web Site: http://www.perpetualmachine.com
Sales Range: $10-24.9 Million
Emp.: 50
Mfr of Roll-Up, Cutting & Packaging Machinery
N.A.I.C.S.: 333248
Danny Morgan (Pres)

Textile Rubber & Chemical Co., Inc. - Coatings & Adhesives Division   (1)
63 Water St, Fall River, MA 02722
Tel.: (508) 675-0181
Web Site: http://www.coatingsadhesivesdiv.com
Sales Range: $10-24.9 Million
Emp.: 25
Latex & Polymer Mfr
N.A.I.C.S.: 326299
Ray Minardi (Dir-Tech)
William Tripp (Gen Mgr)

TEXTILES FROM EUROPE INC.
2170 Rte 27, Edison, NJ 08817
Tel.: (212) 213-1828
Web Site: http://www.victoriaclassic.com
Year Founded: 1987
Sales Range: $25-49.9 Million
Emp.: 200
Piece Goods & Notions Distr
N.A.I.C.S.: 424310
Joe Cohen (Pres)

TFC ASSOCIATES, LLC
800 Main St, Hackensack, NJ 07601
Tel.: (201) 678-1144   NJ
Web Site: http://www.tfc-associates.com
Year Founded: 1995
Sales Range: $125-149.9 Million
Emp.: 33
Collection Agencies
N.A.I.C.S.: 561440
Howard Seares (Pres)

TFI INC.
24355 Capitol Ave, Redford, MI 48239
Tel.: (313) 531-6600
Sales Range: $10-24.9 Million
Emp.: 40
Holding Company
N.A.I.C.S.: 551112
Ed Hirschberg (Co-Owner)

COMPANIES

THALHIMER COMMERCIAL REAL ESTATE

Subsidiaries:

Alpine Power Systems Inc. (1)
4355 Capitol Ave, Redford, MI 48239-2426
Tel.: (313) 531-6600
Web Site:
http://www.alpinepowersystems.com
Power System & Battery Equipment Installation Services
N.A.I.C.S.: 238210
Jon Centella (Dir-Sls-Critical Power)
Sean Davis (VP-Sls)

TFI/EPI LLC
1065 Marauder St, Chico, CA 95973
Tel.: (530) 891-6390
Rev.: $31,639,624
Emp.: 60
Provider of General Warehousing & Storage Services
N.A.I.C.S.: 423710
Chris Peters (Pres & CEO)

TFP CORPORATION
460 Lake Rd, Medina, OH 44256-2457
Tel.: (330) 725-7741 OH
Web Site: http://www.tfpcorp.com
Year Founded: 1928
Sales Range: $100-124.9 Million
Emp.: 200
Special Cold Headed Fasteners & Bolts Mfr
N.A.I.C.S.: 332722
R. E. Workman (Pres)

TFSUPPLEMENTS
600 Hwy 3N, League City, TX 77573
Tel.: (281) 678-8710
Web Site:
http://www.tfsupplements.com
Year Founded: 2007
Sales Range: $10-24.9 Million
Emp.: 15
Online Distr of Vitamins & Supplements
N.A.I.C.S.: 456191

TFW INC.
1045 Kessler Dr, El Paso, TX 79907
Tel.: (915) 595-3933
Year Founded: 2003
Sales Range: $10-24.9 Million
Emp.: 80
Civil Engineering Services
N.A.I.C.S.: 237310
Oscar A. Contreras (Pres)
David Meza (Principal)

TG CONSTRUCTION INC.
139 Nevada St, El Segundo, CA 90245-4209
Tel.: (310) 640-0220
Web Site: http://www.tgconst.com
Year Founded: 1980
Sales Range: $10-24.9 Million
Emp.: 15
Nonresidential Construction
N.A.I.C.S.: 236220
Tom Georgouses (CEO)
Mike Rotolo (Pres)

TG MADISON
3340 Peachtree Rd NE Ste 2850, Atlanta, GA 30326-1027
Tel.: (404) 262-2623 GA
Web Site: http://www.tgmadison.com
Year Founded: 1986
Sales Range: $25-49.9 Million
Emp.: 36
Advertising Agencies
N.A.I.C.S.: 541810
Ned Show (CEO)
Rob Pizzica (VP-Acct Svcs)
Taylor Guglielmo (Exec VP-Bus Dev)

TG VALENTINE, LLC
2601 Sequoia Dr, South Gate, CA 90280
Tel.: (310) 660-0110 DE
Year Founded: 2014
Holding Company; Infant Bedding & Nursery Accessories Mfr & Whslr
N.A.I.C.S.: 551112
Brad Sell (Owner)

Subsidiaries:

CoCaLo, Inc. (1)
2121 Alton Pkwy Ste 150, Irvine, CA 92606-4954
Tel.: (714) 434-7200
Web Site: http://www.cocalo.com
Emp.: 40
Nursery Furniture & Decor Products Designer, Mfr & Whslr
N.A.I.C.S.: 337122
Betty Gonzalez (Office Mgr)

TGG ACCOUNTING
10188 Telesis Ct Ste 130, San Diego, CA 92121
Tel.: (760) 697-1033
Web Site: http://www.tgg-accounting.com
Year Founded: 2006
Sales Range: $1-9.9 Million
Emp.: 45
Outsourced Bookkeeping & Accounting Services
N.A.I.C.S.: 541219
Matt Garrett (Founder & CEO)
Jessica McCarthy (VP-Sls & Mktg)
Greg Wilson (Mng Partner)
Nadia Tafreshi (VP-Ops)
Greg Sonzogni (COO)
J. Andrew Ruff (Pres & CFO)

TGP INVESTMENTS, LLC
4900 Main St Ste 900, Kansas City, MO 64112
Tel.: (816) 994-8600
Web Site: http://www.tgpinvestments.com
Investment Services
N.A.I.C.S.: 523940
Eric V. Graham (Mng Dir)
Shan C. Parr (Mng Dir)

Subsidiaries:

Drive Source International, Inc. (1)
7900 Durand Ave, Sturtevant, WI 53177
Tel.: (262) 554-7977
Web Site: http://www.drivesourceusa.com
Mechanical Power Transmission Equipment Mfr
N.A.I.C.S.: 333613

MAPP Technologies, LLC (1)
1927 W 4th St, Joplin, MO 64801
Tel.: (417) 623-2285
Web Site: http://www.mapp-technologies.com
Sheet Metal Work Mfg
N.A.I.C.S.: 332322
Darin Eubanks (Mgr-Sls & Customer Svc)
Luis Coreano (CEO)
Kaycee Wirsig (CFO)
Todd Barnes (Exec VP-Sls & Mktg)
Matt Osborne (Dir-HR)
Maurice Condon (Dir-Ops)
Michelle Owen (Mgr-Engrg)
Linda Bullette (Acting Mgr-Quality)
Travis Sills (Dir-Sls & Bus Dev)

TGR FINANCIAL INC.
3560 Kraft Rd, Naples, FL 34105
Tel.: (239) 348-8000 FL
Web Site:
http://www.firstfloridaintegritybank.com
Year Founded: 2012
Sales Range: $25-49.9 Million
Emp.: 154
Bank Holding Company
N.A.I.C.S.: 551111
Garrett S. Richter (Pres)
Gary L. Tice (Chm & CEO)
Robert T. Reichert (CFO)

Subsidiaries:

First National Bank of the Gulf Coast (1)
3560 Kraft Rd, Naples, FL 34105
Tel.: (239) 348-8000
Web Site: http://www.fnbofgc.com
Rev.: $20,110,000
Assets: $613,046,000
Liabilities: $546,363,000
Net Worth: $66,683,000
Earnings: $1,100,000
Emp.: 96
Fiscal Year-end: 12/31/2012
Federal Savings Bank
N.A.I.C.S.: 522180
Garrett S. Richter (Pres)
Gary L. Tice (Chm & CEO)
Robert T. Reichert (Chief Admin Officer & Sr Exec VP)
C.C. Coghill (Chief Credit Officer & Sr Exec VP)
Peter Setaro (CIO & Exec VP)
Terry Read Walston (Exec VP)
Brian Keenan (Pres-West & Central Florida)
Ronald L. Rucker (Chief Lending Officer & Exec VP)
Nancye Hire (Exec VP & Dir-Loan Ops)

TGRP SOLUTIONS LLC
3279 S Santa Fe Dr, Englewood, CO 80110
Tel.: (303) 789-1500
Web Site:
http://www.tgrpsolutions.com
Year Founded: 2010
Sales Range: $1-9.9 Million
Emp.: 31
Recruitment Consulting Services
N.A.I.C.S.: 541612
Mark Reister (Pres)
Trish Herl (Dir-Consulting)
Jim Lockhart (Mng Dir-Consulting)
W. Kelly Rice (Dir-Consulting)
Susan Sowl (Dir-Consulting)

TH LEE PUTNAM VENTURES
1120 Avenue of the Americas Ste 1807, New York, NY 10036
Tel.: (212) 951-8600
Web Site: http://www.thlpv.com
Sales Range: $25-49.9 Million
Emp.: 110
Privater Equity Firm
N.A.I.C.S.: 523999
Jim Brown (Mng Dir & Partner)
Sharon Pipe (Mng Dir & Partner)
Ramanan Raghavendran (Mng Dir & Partner)

TH PLASTICS INC.
106 E Main St, Mendon, MI 49072
Tel.: (269) 496-8495
Web Site: http://www.thplastics.com
Year Founded: 1974
Rev.: $18,200,000
Emp.: 150
Injection Molded Plastic Products Mfr
N.A.I.C.S.: 326199
Patrick Haas (CEO)
Chris Haas (Pres)
Mike McCaw (VP-Ops)

TH PROPERTIES
345 Main St Suite 112, Harleysville, PA 19438
Tel.: (215) 513-4270
Web Site:
http://www.thproperties.com
Year Founded: 1992
Rev.: $52,333,323
Emp.: 25
Residential Land Subdividers & Developers
N.A.I.C.S.: 237210
W. Todd Hendricks (Pres & Owner)
David Monaco (Project Mgr)
Tobias Norris (Mgr-Tech)

THAD ZIEGLER GLASS LTD.
3055 N Panam Expy, San Antonio, TX 78208
Tel.: (210) 224-2061
Web Site:
http://www.zieglerglass.com
Rev.: $11,000,000
Emp.: 80
Glass & Glazing Work
N.A.I.C.S.: 238150
Thad M. Ziegler (Chm)
Arthur Longoria (Superintendent-Glazing)

THALER MACHINE COMPANY INC.
216 Tahlequah Trl, Springboro, OH 45066
Tel.: (937) 550-2400
Web Site:
http://www.thalermachine.com
Rev.: $11,300,000
Emp.: 75
Machine Shop, Jobbing & Repair
N.A.I.C.S.: 332710
William L. Thaler (Pres)

THALER OIL COMPANY, INC.
310 S Main St, Chippewa Falls, WI 54729
Tel.: (715) 723-2822 WI
Web Site: http://www.thaleroil.com
Year Founded: 1955
Sales Range: $10-24.9 Million
Emp.: 15
Heating Oil, Propane & Lubricant Dealer
N.A.I.C.S.: 457210
Steve Thaler (Co-Pres)
Ferne Thaler (Co-Pres)

THALHEIMER'S JEWELERS, INC.
3200 Tamiami Trl N, Naples, FL 34103
Tel.: (239) 261-8422
Web Site:
http://www.thalheimers.com
Sales Range: $1-9.9 Million
Jewelry Stores
N.A.I.C.S.: 458310
Sanford Thalheimer (Pres)
Nancy Thalheimer (VP)

THALHIMER COMMERCIAL REAL ESTATE
11100 W Broad St, Glen Allen, VA 23060
Tel.: (804) 648-5881
Web Site: http://www.thalhimer.com
Rev.: $24,800,000
Emp.: 100
Commercial & Office Building Contractors
N.A.I.C.S.: 236220
Paul Silver (Chm)
Dawn Calabrese (VP)
Jeff Cooke (Sr VP)
Mark Douglas (Sr VP)
Scott Douglas (Sr VP)
Connie Jordan Nielsen (Sr VP)
Dean Meyer (Sr VP)
Evan Magrill (Exec VP)
George Stuckey (Sr VP)
Richard Thalhimer (Sr VP)
Birck Turnbull (Sr VP)
David Smith (Sr VP)
Pam Strieffler (VP)
Pete Waldbauer (First VP)
Mac Wilson (First VP)
Ann Albrecht (VP-HR)
Chip Dustin (CFO)
Paula English (Dir-Comm)
John Nielsen (Sr VP)
Jerad Nielsen (Sr Portfolio Mgr)
Wilson Greenlaw (VP)
Kyle Kneeland (Dir-Property Svcs)

THALHIMER COMMERCIAL REAL ESTATE

Thalhimer Commercial Real Estate—(Continued)
Brendan Gower (Dir-Property Svcs)
Curtis Mummau (Sr VP)
Alan Mudd (Sr Portfolio Mgr)
Andy Dallas (First VP)
Berkley Mitchell (VP)
Philip Owens (VP)
Rob Wright (Sr VP)
Dave Butchello (VP-Hospitality)
Nick Schimick (VP-Mktg)
Karen M. Stiansen (VP-Property Svcs)
Bruce Bigger (Sr VP)
John Tison (Sr VP)
Nicki Jassy (Sr VP)
Virgil Nelson (Sr VP)
Clay Culbreth (Sr VP-Industrial Properties)
Boyd Johnson (VP)
Christine Kaempfe (VP)
David Crawford (VP)
David Tunnicliffe (VP)
Geoff Poston (VP)
Gregg Beck (VP)
Kacie Jackson (VP)
Kevin South (VP)
Mark Erickson (VP)
James Ashby IV (Sr VP)
John Duffy Jr. (VP)
John Pritzlaff IV (VP)
Kenneth Penrose Jr. (VP)

THALLE CONSTRUCTION CO., INC.
900 NC Hwy 86 N, Hillsborough, NC 27278
Tel.: (919) 245-1490
Web Site: http://www.thalle.com
Year Founded: 1947
Sales Range: $10-24.9 Million
Emp.: 80
Highway & Street Construction
N.A.I.C.S.: 237310
Bill May (CFO & Treas)

THANKSGIVING COFFEE COMPANY, INC.
19100 S Harbor Dr, Fort Bragg, CA 95437
Tel.: (707) 964-0118   CA
Web Site:
   http://www.thanksgivingcoffee.com
Year Founded: 1972
Rev: $4,165,917
Assets: $1,719,231
Liabilities: $802,249
Net Worth: $916,982
Earnings: $268,800
Emp.: 25
Fiscal Year-end: 12/31/19
Grocery Product Mfr & Distr
N.A.I.C.S.: 311920
Paul Katzeff (Co-Founder, Chm & CEO)
Jonah Katzeff (Gen Mgr)
Joan Katzeff (Co-Founder, COO, Treas & Sec)

THANKSGIVING POINT
3003 N Thanksgiving Way, Lehi, UT 84043
Tel.: (801) 768-2300
Web Site:
   http://www.thanksgivingpoint.org
Sales Range: $10-24.9 Million
Emp.: 100
Entertainment Services; Museum, Golf, Botanical Garden, Shopping, Dining & Children's Zoo
N.A.I.C.S.: 713990
Mike Washburn (CEO)
Tracy Erdmann (Dir-Facilities)
Allen Ash (CFO)
Molina Welcker (Dir-Events & Catering)
Kendall Wimmer (VP-Ops)
Wendy Herzog (Mgr-HR)
Varden Hadfield (Dir-Dev)
Ruth White (Dir-Membership)
Lacy Johnston (Mgr-Event)
Emily Landon (Mgr-Event)
Brad Burr (Mgr-Protective Svcs)
Lorraine Gaufin (Mgr-Sls)
Chandler Flitton (Mgr-Wedding Event)
Heather Zierenberg (Mgr-Wedding Event)
Blake Wigdahl (VP-Design & Programming)
Erica Brown (VP-Mktg)

THARALDSON DEVELOPMENT CO.
1201 Page Dr Ste 200, Fargo, ND 58103
Tel.: (701) 271-2700   ND
Year Founded: 1987
Sales Range: $10-24.9 Million
Emp.: 100
Commercial & Office Building, New Construction
N.A.I.C.S.: 236220
Gary D. Tharaldson (Pres)

THAT'S GOOD HR
8440 Woodfield Crossing Blvd Ste 370, Indianapolis, IN 46240
Tel.: (317) 469-4141
Web Site:
   http://www.thatsgoodhr.com
Sales Range: $1-9.9 Million
Emp.: 15
Permanent & Temporary Staffing Services
N.A.I.C.S.: 561311
Greta Cline (CFO)
Mary Springer (Partner)
Jaime Flannagan (Mgr-Staffing Ops)

THAXTON BARCLAY GROUP
100 N Tampa St Ste 3530, Tampa, FL 33602
Tel.: (813) 251-2580
Web Site:
   http://www.thaxtonbarclay.com
Sales Range: $1-9.9 Million
Emp.: 15
Insurance Brokers
N.A.I.C.S.: 524210
Michael Shea (Pres & CEO)
Talyn Guercio (CFO)

THAYER MEDIA, INC.
9000 E Nichols Ave Ste 202, Centennial, CO 80112
Tel.: (303) 221-2221
Web Site:
   http://www.thayermedia.com
Year Founded: 1993
Sales Range: $10-24.9 Million
Emp.: 10
Media Buying Services
N.A.I.C.S.: 541810
April Thayer (Founder & Pres)
Chessie Little (Assoc Dir-Media)
Michelle Watson (Sr Media Planner & Media Buyer)
Nicole Martinez (Media Buyer & Media Planner)

THAYERMAHAN, INC.
120B Leonard Dr, Groton, CT 06340
Tel.: (860) 785-9994   DE
Web Site:
   http://www.thayermahan.com
Year Founded: 2016
Maritime Technology Services
N.A.I.C.S.: 561621
Mike Connor (CEO)
Richard Jude Hine (COO)

Subsidiaries:

Ocean Acoustical Services and Instrumentation Systems, Inc.   (1)
5 Militia Dr, Lexington, MA 02421
Tel.: (781) 862-8339
Web Site: http://www.oasislex.com
Underwater & Airborne Acoustics Consulting Services
N.A.I.C.S.: 541690
Philip Abbot (Founder & CEO)

THB INC.
95 N 400 W, North Salt Lake, UT 84054
Tel.: (801) 298-1923
Web Site: http://www.thb-inc.net
Sales Range: $10-24.9 Million
Emp.: 75
Industrial Fasteners Distr
N.A.I.C.S.: 423840
Robert B. Harbertson (Pres)
Chris Diaz (Mgr)

THE 20 MSP GROUP LLC
6600 Chase Oaks Blvd Ste 100, Plano, TX 75023
Tel.: (972) 461-0880   DE
Web Site: https://www.the20.com
Year Founded: 2022
Emp.: 100
IT Services
N.A.I.C.S.: 518210
Tim Conkle (Founder & CEO)

Subsidiaries:

Accurate Computer Solutions, LLC   (1)
234 W Bandera Rd, Boerne, TX 78006-2805
Tel.: (210) 343-0427
Custom Computer Programming Services
N.A.I.C.S.: 541511
Rodney Sees (CEO)

Integrated Business Technologies, LLC   (1)
1914 W Reno St Ste A, Broken Arrow, OK 74012
Tel.: (918) 770-8738
Web Site: http://www.ibtsupport.co
Sales Range: $1-9.9 Million
Emp.: 20
Business Technology Support to Law Firms, Banking, Health Care, Finance & Accounting Businesses
N.A.I.C.S.: 561499
David Doyle (Mgr-Svc)

JS Computek LLC   (1)
1005 Cherry St Ste 107, Columbia, MO 65201-7918
Tel.: (573) 234-6214
Web Site: http://www.jscomputek.com
Data Processing, Hosting & Related Services
N.A.I.C.S.: 518210
Jacob Sarnecki (Gen Mgr)

Manus Dei, Inc.   (1)
35 S 4th St, Warrenton, VA 20186-3307
Web Site: http://www.manusdei.net
Computer Facilities Management Services
N.A.I.C.S.: 541513
Frederick Duca (CEO)

THE 410 BRIDGE
35 Old Canton St, Alpharetta, GA 30009
Tel.: (770) 664-4949   GA
Web Site: http://www.410bridge.org
Year Founded: 2006
Sales Range: $1-9.9 Million
Emp.: 17
Religious Organizations
N.A.I.C.S.: 813110
James Ward (Dir-Intl Programs)
Steve Smith (COO)
Kurt Kandler (Exec Dir)
Anne Marie Carlisi (Vice Chm)

U.S. PRIVATE

Wendell Robinson (Dir-US Program-Haiti)
David Muchai (Officer-Projects)
Geoffrey Mucheke (Officer-Comm)

THE 501 ALLIANCE
20300 Superior Rd Ste 190, Taylor, MI 48180
Tel.: (800) 968-9675
Web Site: http://www.501alliance.org
Year Founded: 1972
Sales Range: $1-9.9 Million
Unemployment Compensation Services
N.A.I.C.S.: 561990
Michael Blau (Treas)
Remi Montigny (Sec)
Jan Mack (Pres)
Laurie Zarzecki Emelander (Dir-Fin)

THE A TEAM, LLC
232 Madison Ave, New York, NY 10018
Tel.: (212) 239-0499   NY
Web Site:
   http://www.theateamagency.com
Year Founded: 1999
Sales Range: $1-9.9 Million
Emp.: 15
Sales Promotion
N.A.I.C.S.: 541810
Andrew Cohen (Pres & CEO)

Subsidiaries:

The A Team Promotional   (1)
8001 Irvine Ctr Dr 4th Fl, Irvine, CA 92618
Tel.: (949) 754-3022
Web Site: http://www.theateamagency.com
Emp.: 3
Sales Promotion
N.A.I.C.S.: 541810
Bernard Lee (Gen Mgr)

THE A.H. EMERY COMPANY
73 Cogwheel Ln, Seymour, CT 06483
Tel.: (203) 881-9333
Web Site:
   http://www.emerywinslow.com
Sales Range: $25-49.9 Million
Emp.: 100
Scales Mfr & Distr
N.A.I.C.S.: 333998
William Fischer (Pres)

Subsidiaries:

Emery Winslow Scale Company   (1)
73 Cogwheel Ln, Seymour, CT 06483
Tel.: (203) 881-9333
Web Site: http://www.emerywinslow.com
Sales Range: $10-24.9 Million
Emp.: 60
Mfr & Distr of Scales
N.A.I.C.S.: 333998
Rudi Baisch (VP-Sls)

Pennsylvania Scale Company   (1)
665 N Reservoir St, Lancaster, PA 17602
Tel.: (717) 295-6935
Web Site: http://www.pascale.com
Rev.: $6,000,000
Emp.: 12
Mfr of Scales
N.A.I.C.S.: 333998
Rob Woodward (VP & Gen Mgr)

THE AAGARD GROUP, LLC
3711 Iowa St, Alexandria, MN 56308
Tel.: (320) 763-6043
Web Site: http://www.aagard.com
Sales Range: $1-9.9 Million
Emp.: 100
Automated Packaging Machinery
N.A.I.C.S.: 333993
Bruce Harvey (Controller)

THE ACADEMY OF RADIO BROADCASTING, INC.
16052 Beach Blvd Ste 263, Huntington Beach, CA 92647-3819

COMPANIES   **THE ADEC GROUP**

Tel.: (714) 842-0100
Web Site: http://www.arbradio.com
Year Founded: 1983
Sales Range: $50-74.9 Million
Emp.: 25
Vocational Training School for Radio & Television Broadcasting
N.A.I.C.S.: 611519
Tom King (Co-Owner)

Subsidiaries:

The Academy of Radio & TV   (1)
4914 E Mcdowell Rd, Phoenix, AZ 85008-4202
Tel.: (602) 267-8001
Web Site: http://www.arbradio.com
Sales Range: $10-24.9 Million
Emp.: 20
Vocational Training School For Radio Broadcasting & Television & Video Production
N.A.I.C.S.: 611519

THE ACCEL GROUP LLC
315 Lemay Ferry Rd Ste 128, Saint Louis, MO 63125-1550
Tel.: (314) 631-5000
Web Site:
   http://www.theaccelgroup.com
Emp.: 70
Insurance Agents
N.A.I.C.S.: 524210
Tim Gassman (CEO)

THE ACCURO GROUP, INC.
2301 Sugar Bush Rd Ste 425, Raleigh, NC 27612
Tel.: (919) 851-9880
Web Site:
   http://www.accurogroup.com
Year Founded: 2003
Sales Range: $1-9.9 Million
Emp.: 500
Staffing & Recruitment Services
N.A.I.C.S.: 561311
Jennifer Dunleavy (Founder & CEO)

THE ACTORS FUND
729 7th Ave 10th Fl, New York, NY 10019
Tel.: (212) 221-7300   NY
Web Site: http://www.actorsfund.org
Year Founded: 1882
Sales Range: $25-49.9 Million
Emp.: 326
Performing Art & Entertainment Professional Welfare Services
N.A.I.C.S.: 711130
Marc Grodman (Sec)
Abby Schroeder (Vice Chm)
Philip S. Birsh (Vice Chm)
Joseph P. Benincasa (Pres & CEO)
Barbara Davis (Asst Sec)
Thomas M. Exton (Chief Advancement Officer)
Brian Stokes Mitchell (Chm)
Connie Yoo (CFO)

THE AD ART COMPANY
3260 E 26th St, Los Angeles, CA 90023
Tel.: (323) 981-8941
Web Site: http://www.adartco.com
Rev.: $13,500,000
Emp.: 1,200
Displays & Cutouts Window & Lobby
N.A.I.C.S.: 339950
Joseph DeMarco (Pres)
Andrew Gorman (Dir-Ops)
Roger Keech (CEO)

THE AD PROS GROUP
1810 NE 153 St, North Miami Beach, FL 33162
Tel.: (305) 956-9906   FL
Web Site:
   http://www.adprosgroup.com
Year Founded: 1996
Sales Range: $10-24.9 Million
Emp.: 10
N.A.I.C.S.: 541810
Jose Escardo (Pres)
Barry Yoskowitz (Dir-Creative)

THE AD STORE, INC.
638 W 28th St # 1, New York, NY 10001-1108
Tel.: (212) 685-8899   NY
Web Site: http://www.theadstore.com
Year Founded: 1993
Sales Range: $10-24.9 Million
Emp.: 20
Advetising Agency
N.A.I.C.S.: 541810
Paul Cappelli (Chm)
Julie Browning (Bus Mgr)
Tim Shaw (Dir-Creative)
Marc Pascucci (Acct Exec)
Aaron Brown (Copy Writer)
Gunnar Wilmot (CEO)
Kevin Moehlenkamp (Chief Creative Officer)

Subsidiaries:

The Ad Store Brussels   (1)
450 Chaussee De Waterioo, 1050, Brussels, Belgium
Tel.: (32) 2 648 56 13
Web Site: http://www.the-adstore.be
Sales Range: Less than $1 Million
Emp.: 10
Full Service
N.A.I.C.S.: 541810
Anne Van de Velde (Co-Pres & Dir-Creative)
Eric Kawan (Co-Pres & Dir-Creative)

The Ad Store GmbH   (1)
Alter Wandrahm 8/9, 20457, Hamburg, Germany
Tel.: (49) 40 4109810
Web Site: http://www.the-adstore.de
Sales Range: Less than $1 Million
Emp.: 10
Full Service
N.A.I.C.S.: 541810
Matthias Kroeger (Mng Dir)

The Ad Store Italia   (1)
Viale Fratti 20/D, 43100, Parma, Italy
Tel.: (39) 05 21 504 345
Web Site: http://www.adstore.it
N.A.I.C.S.: 541810
Natalia Borri (Mng Dir)
Delia Zana (Acct Mgr)

The Ad Store Pacifique   (1)
PO Box 20596, Papeete, Tahiti, French Polynesia
Tel.: (689) 50 34 50
Web Site: http://www.theadstore.com
Emp.: 3
N.A.I.C.S.: 541810
Christiane Restelli (Pres)

The Ad Store Romania   (1)
Anina Street No 3, Bucharest, Romania
Tel.: (40) 31 425 15 65
Web Site: http://www.the-adstore.ro
N.A.I.C.S.: 541810
Remus Frunza (Mng Dir)

The Ad Store Washington   (1)
3325 M St NW, Washington, DC 20007
Tel.: (202) 342-0222
Web Site: http://www.theadstoredc.com
Sales Range: $10-24.9 Million
Emp.: 13
Full Service
N.A.I.C.S.: 541810
Tina Bagapor O'Harrow (Pres)
Kevin C. O'Harrow (COO)

THE ADAM CORPORATION/GROUP
1 Momentum Blvd Ste 1000, College Station, TX 77845-6335
Tel.: (979) 776-1111   TX
Year Founded: 1977
Investment Holding Companies
N.A.I.C.S.: 551112
Donald A. Adam (Chm & CEO)
James L. Wolfe (Pres)
Shannaz Ali (VP & Controller)

Subsidiaries:

Adam Bank Group, Inc.   (1)
1 Momentum Blvd, College Station, TX 77845
Tel.: (979) 774-1111
Web Site:
   http://www.americanmomentum.bank
Sales Range: $75-99.9 Million
Emp.: 272
Bank Holding Company
N.A.I.C.S.: 551111
Donald A. Adam (Chm & CEO)
James L. Wolfe (Pres)

Subsidiary (Domestic):

American Momentum Bank   (2)
1 Momentum Blvd, College Station, TX 77845
Tel.: (979) 774-1111
Web Site:
   http://www.americanmomentum.bank
Sales Range: $75-99.9 Million
Emp.: 272
Commericial Banking
N.A.I.C.S.: 522110
Donald A. Adam (Chm & CEO)
Clay Riebe (Chief Lending Officer & Exec VP)
George Lea (Exec VP & Dir-Mktg)
William R. Falzone (CFO & Exec VP)
Maureen Gallagher (Chief Admin Officer & Exec VP)
Julius Dunlap (Sr VP & Sr Mgr-Credit Admin)
Douglas A. Tuttle (Pres-Tampa Bay Market)
Lou Garcia (Sr VP & Sr Mgr-Commi Relationship)
Michael Dittmer (Sr VP & Mgr-IT)
Joe Moss (Officer-Bus Dev-SBA & Sr VP)
Patrick Fenech (Sr VP & Mng Dir-SBA Lending)

Adam Development Properties, L.P.   (1)
1111 Briarcrest Dr Ste 300, Bryan, TX 77802-2530
Tel.: (979) 776-1111
Sales Range: $10-24.9 Million
Emp.: 2
Provider of Real Estate Services
N.A.I.C.S.: 531210
Donald A. Adam (Chm & CEO)

THE ADAM GROUP
5764 Crossings Blvd, Antioch, TN 37013
Tel.: (615) 794-1436
Web Site:
   http://www.tagwebstore.com
Year Founded: 1999
Rev.: $8,100,000
Emp.: 48
Commercial Lithographic Printing
N.A.I.C.S.: 323111
Beth Hall (Controller)
Scott Snoyer (Owner)

THE ADAMS GROUP
925 Gervais St, Columbia, SC 29201
Tel.: (803) 765-1223
Web Site:
   http://www.adamsgroup.com
Year Founded: 1983
Rev.: $13,200,000
Emp.: 16
Brand Development, Financial, Full Service, Health Care, High Technology, Internet/Web Design
N.A.I.C.S.: 541810
Wayne Adams (CEO)
Karis Hallman (VP & Mgr-Production)
Amy Carter (Acct Mgr)
Liz Nettles (Dir-Art)
Melissa Speir (Dir-PR)
Andrew Evans (Copywriter)
Julie Turner (Copywriter)
Sue Watson (Mgr-Production)
Dean Bryant (Dir-Creative)
Paula Hensley-Mallory (Mgr-Acctg)
Debra Branson (Acct Mgr)

THE ADAMS GROUP INC.
7301 John Galt Way, Arbuckle, CA 95912
Tel.: (530) 668-2000
Web Site: http://www.adamsgrp.com
Animal Feed
N.A.I.C.S.: 424910
William O. Adams (Pres)

Subsidiaries:

Adams Vegetable Oils, Inc.   (1)
7301 John Galt Way, Arbuckle, CA 95912
Tel.: (530) 668-2000
Web Site:
   http://www.adamsvegetableoils.com
Fats & Oils Refining & Blending
N.A.I.C.S.: 311225

THE ADCOM GROUP, INC.
1370 W 6th St Ste 300, Cleveland, OH 44113-1222
Tel.: (216) 574-9100   OH
Web Site:
   http://www.theadcomgroup.com
Year Founded: 1990
Advertising Services
N.A.I.C.S.: 541810
Joe Kubic (Founder & CEO)

Subsidiaries:

Arras Keathley Advertising   (1)
1151 N Marginal Rd, Cleveland, OH 44114
Tel.: (216) 621-1601
Web Site: http://www.arraskesphley.com
Rev.: $65,000,000
Emp.: 15
Advertising Agencies
N.A.I.C.S.: 541810
James T. Hickey (Pres)
Tom Keathley (Exec Dir-Creative)

Branch (Domestic):

The Arras Group   (2)
1901 Newport Blvd Ste 350, Costa Mesa, CA 92627
Tel.: (949) 999-2033
Web Site: http://www.arrasgroup.com
N.A.I.C.S.: 541810

THE ADEC GROUP
10 Monument St, Deposit, NY 13754
Tel.: (607) 467-4600
Web Site: http://www.adec-group.com
Year Founded: 1998
Sales Range: $1-4.9 Billion
Emp.: 5,000
Holding Company; Technical Consulting & Business Support Services
N.A.I.C.S.: 551112
James M. Donovan (Pres & CEO)
Carol S. Esguerra (CFO)
Michele B. Hincks (CMO)
Robert Francisco (Pres-North America)

Subsidiaries:

ADEC Solutions USA, Inc.   (1)
10 Monument St, Deposit, NY 13754
Tel.: (607) 467-4600
Web Site: http://www.adecsolutionsusa.com
Sales Range: $1-9.9 Million
Emp.: 80
Document Management & Business Process Outsourcing Services
N.A.I.C.S.: 561499
Robert Francisco (Pres-North America)
George Vastardis (Dir-Mktg & Sls)

FirstCarbon Solutions Corporation   (1)
250 Commerce Ste 250, Irvine, CA 92602
Tel.: (714) 508-4100
Web Site:
   http://www.firstcarbonsolutions.com

THE ADEC GROUP
U.S. PRIVATE

The ADEC Group—(Continued)
Environmental & Sustainability Consulting Services
N.A.I.C.S.: 541990
Robert Francisco (Pres-North America)
Mary Bean (Dir-Environmental Plng Project-North California)
Jason Brandman (Dir-Environmental Plng Sls)
Justin Holt (Gen Mgr-Australia)
Michele Carchman (VP-Mktg & Comm)
Frank Coyle (Dir-Environmental Plng Project-Southern California)
Jennifer M. Guenther (Gen Counsel)
Greg Scandrett (Dir-Product Dev)
Patrick Schultz (COO)

THE ADLER PLANETARIUM & ASTRONOMY MUSEUM
1300 S Lakeshore Dr, Chicago, IL 60605-2403
Tel.: (312) 922-7827
Web Site: http://www.adlerplanetarium.org
Year Founded: 1930
Sales Range: $75-99.9 Million
Emp.: 200
Planetarium, History & Science Museum
N.A.I.C.S.: 712110
Ginevra Ranney (VP-Institutional Advancement)
Michelle Larson (Pres)
William J. Lutz (Treas)
John W. Estey (Chm)

THE ADMARK GROUP
96 N Sunny Slope Ave, Pasadena, CA 91106
Tel.: (626) 583-1610
Web Site: http://www.admarkgroup.com
Sales Range: Less than $1 Million
Emp.: 6
Full Service, Hispanic Marketing, Outdoor
N.A.I.C.S.: 541810
Adriana Blanco (CEO)
Charlene Barone (Dir-IT)
Denise Bautista (Supvr-Media)
Michele Cordoba (Dir-Res)
Eddy Blanco (COO)
Gabriela Cabrera (Dir-Art)

THE ADRIENNE ARSHT CENTER FOR THE PERFORMING ARTS OF MIAMI-DADE COUNTY, INC.
1300 Biscayne Blvd, Miami, FL 33132
Tel.: (786) 468-2000
Web Site: http://www.arshtcenter.org
Sales Range: $10-24.9 Million
Emp.: 250
Performing Arts Facilities
N.A.I.C.S.: 711310
Scott Shiller (Exec VP)
Valerie Riles (VP-Govt Rels)
Chantal Honore (Mgr-Board Rels)
Trish Brennan (VP-HR)
Kimba King (Mgr-HR)
Teresa Randolph (Controller & Sr Dir-Fin)
Suzette Espinosa (Asst VP-PR)
John Copeland (Dir-Mktg)
Fernando Olalla (Mgr-e-Marketing)
Ken Harris (VP-Ops)
Daniel Alzuri (Sr Dir-Ops)
Nicole Keating (Sr Dir-Ticket Svcs)
Alice Fifelski (Mgr-Theater)
James J. Thompson (Asst VP-IT)
Michael Sampson (Dir-Applications)
Elizabeth Wallace (VP-Programming)
David Green (Asst VP-Advancement)
Suzette Espinosa Fuentes (VP-Comm)
Ira D. Hall (Co-Chm)
Matilde Aguirre (Treas)
Richard C. Milstein (Sec)
Adrienne Arsht (Founder & Co-Chm)
Dale Edwards (VP-Mktg)

THE ADTRACK CORPORATION
6060 Huntington Ct NE, Cedar Rapids, IA 52402
Tel.: (319) 395-9777
Web Site: http://www.smartlead.com
Sales Range: $10-24.9 Million
Emp.: 75
Marketing Solutions Software
N.A.I.C.S.: 513210
Dan Rogers (Chm & CEO)

THE ADVANCE GROUP
185 Price Pkwy, Farmingdale, NY 11735
Tel.: (877) 273-6480
Web Site: https://www.theadvancegrp.com
Emp.: 100
Moving, Logistics & Warehousing Services
N.A.I.C.S.: 541614
Anthony Parziale (CEO)

Subsidiaries:

Sorensen Moving & Storage Company, Inc. (1)
950 W Eau Gallie Blvd, Melbourne, FL 32935
Tel.: (321) 254-2770
Web Site: http://www.sorensen-allied.com
Sales Range: $1-9.9 Million
Emp.: 64
Used Household & Office Goods Moving
N.A.I.C.S.: 484210
Scott Sorensen (CEO)

THE ADVANCED GROUP OF COMPANIES
200 W Jackson, Chicago, IL 60606
Tel.: (847) 418-3700
Web Site: http://www.advancedresources.com
Year Founded: 1994
Sales Range: $25-49.9 Million
Emp.: 70
Management Services; Holding Company
N.A.I.C.S.: 551112
Leo Sheridan (Founder & CEO)
Denise Kurowski (Sr VP-FSP)
Julie Ross (Pres)
Jessica Miller-Merrell (VP-Talent Strategies)
Sara Drake (Mgr-Mktg)
Cheryle Evans (Sr VP-Clinical & Medical Ops)
Sheri Madrid (Exec Dir-Clinical Ops)
Julie Bell (Chief HR Officer)
Kristin Kelley (Assoc HR Mktg)
Caroline Redeker (Sr VP-Corp Dev)
Akin Tosyali (VP-Mktg)
Jeffrey Wolniakowski (CIO)
Joseph Scott (CFO)

Subsidiaries:

Advanced Clinical Services LLC (1)
3010 Highland Pkwy Ste 440, Downers Grove, IL 60515
Tel.: (630) 493-9111
Web Site: http://www.advancedclinical.com
Sales Range: $10-24.9 Million
Provides National Staffing Services
N.A.I.C.S.: 423430
Kimberly Wanick (Exec Dir-Compliance & Quality)
Bill McGuckin (Sr VP-Consulting Svcs)
Stacey Arrambide (VP-Biometrics)
Julie Ross (Pres)
Kristin Kelley (Assoc Dir-Mktg)
Daniel Rhodes (Exec Dir-Consulting Svcs)

Subsidiary (Domestic):

Advanced Clinical Services (2)
570 Pacific Ave, San Francisco, CA 94133-4608
Tel.: (415) 358-2400
Web Site: http://www.advancedclinical.com
Emp.: 6
Staffing Services
N.A.I.C.S.: 541512
Leo Sheridan (Co-Founder, Pres & CEO)

Advanced Resources Inc. (1)
111 W Jackson Blvd Ste 750, Chicago, IL 60604
Tel.: (312) 422-9333
Web Site: http://www.advancedresources.com
Office Support Staffing Firm
N.A.I.C.S.: 561499
Rich Diaz (Pres)
Mike Lonnay (Dir-Fin Div)
Jim Dimitriou (Mng Dir-Fin Consulting Svcs Practice)
Amy Brandenburg (Dir-Fin-Milwaukee)
Ericka Ehman (Dir-Tech-Milwaukee)

Subsidiary (Domestic):

Advanced Financial Inc. (2)
111 W Jackson Ste 750, Chicago, IL 60604
Tel.: (312) 422-9333
Web Site: http://www.advfinancial.com
Staffing Firm For Medical Financial Professionals
N.A.I.C.S.: 523999
Rich Diaz (Gen Mgr)

Advanced Resources Inc. (1)
1300 E Woodfield Rd Ste 312, Schaumburg, IL 60173-4984
Tel.: (847) 995-9111
Web Site: http://www.advancedresources.com
Sales Range: $10-24.9 Million
Emp.: 20
Staffing Firm For Hardware & Systems Software Professionals
N.A.I.C.S.: 561320
Paul Shanahan (Mng Dir-Healthcare)
Steve Mogle (Mng Dir-Tech-New York)
Patty Bogosh (Dir-Corp Dev)

Advanced Resources Inc. (1)
570 Pacific Ave, San Francisco, CA 94133
Tel.: (415) 358-2400
Web Site: http://www.advancedclinical.com
Sales Range: $10-24.9 Million
Emp.: 6
Staffing Firm For Hardware & Systems Software Professionals
N.A.I.C.S.: 541512
Shan Gerstenlauer (VP)

Advanced Resources LLC (1)
1033 Skokie Blvd, Northbrook, IL 60062
Tel.: (847) 418-3700
Web Site: http://www.advancedresources.com
Sales Range: $10-24.9 Million
Emp.: 25
Staffing Services
N.A.I.C.S.: 561320
Leo Sheridan (CEO)

MedAscend LLC (1)
1011 Warrenville Rd Ste 260, Lisle, IL 60532
Tel.: (855) 633-2723
Web Site: http://www.medascend.net
Health Care Srvices
N.A.I.C.S.: 621999
Jan Casford (Pres)
Jeff Jacobsen (Dir-Allied Health Div)

Tri-Worth Solutions, LLC (1)
44 Cook St Ste 510, Denver, CO 80206
Tel.: (720) 409-4307
Web Site: http://www.triworth.com
Executive Search Service
N.A.I.C.S.: 561312
Kevin Armstrong (Acct Mgr)
John Hess (Exec VP-Ops)

THE ADVANTAGE COMPANY
1955 Wehrle Dr, Williamsville, NY 14221
Tel.: (716) 204-2344
Web Site: http://www.theadvantage.com
Rev.: $72,632,129
Emp.: 100
Consumer Electronic Equipment, Nec
N.A.I.C.S.: 449210
Butch Kreuz (CEO)

THE ADVERTISING SPECIALTY INSTITUTE
4800 E St Rd, Trevose, PA 19053
Tel.: (215) 953-4000
Web Site: http://www.asicentral.com
Rev.: $101,700,000
Emp.: 400
Publisher of Computer Software
N.A.I.C.S.: 513210
Norman Unger Cohn (Chm)
Richard Fairfield (Publr & Sr VP)
Vince Bucolo (COO)
Larry Basinait (Exec Dir-Market Res Svcs)
Steve Bright (Gen Counsel & Exec VP)
Timothy M. Andrews (Pres & CEO)
Mark Quinn (CFO)
Carol Albright (Sr VP-HR)
Victoria Hain (VP-Member Svcs & Support)
Melinda Ligos (Editor-in-Chief-ASI Magazines & VP-Dev)
Matthew N. Cohn (Vice Chm)
Armughan Rafat (CTO & Exec VP)
Dawn Marie (Mgr-PR)
Nancy Carmona (VP-Fin)
Rob Watson (Sr VP-Mktg)

THE AEGIS MOBILE, LLC
6518 Meadowridge Rd Ste 124, Columbia, MD 21075
Tel.: (443) 459-9233
Web Site: http://www.aegismobile.com
Year Founded: 2006
Sales Range: $1-9.9 Million
Emp.: 36
Cellular Telephones Mfr
N.A.I.C.S.: 334220
John Bruner (COO)

THE AEP GROUP
2495 Main St Ste 230, Buffalo, NY 14214
Tel.: (716) 446-0739
Web Site: http://www.theaepgroup.com
Year Founded: 1992
Sales Range: $10-24.9 Million
Emp.: 49
Book Publishers
N.A.I.C.S.: 513130
Kenneth Pronti (CEO)
Adam Sestokas (Mgr-IT)

THE AEROSPACE CORPORATION
2310 E El Segundo Blvd, El Segundo, CA 90245-4609
Tel.: (310) 336-5000 CA
Web Site: http://www.aero.org
Year Founded: 1960
Sales Range: $650-699.9 Million
Emp.: 4,000
Engineering & Integration Research
N.A.I.C.S.: 541715
Ray F. Johnson (VP-Space Launch Ops)
Mark Brosmer (Gen Mgr-Launch & Satellite Control Div)
Sabrina Steele (Exec Dir-Corp Comm & Pub Affairs)
Chuck Gustafson (Sr VP-Engrg & Tech Grp)
Ed Swallow (CFO)
Heather Laychak (Chief HR Officer & VP)

Wayne Goodman (Exec VP)
Steve Isakowitz (Pres & CEO)
Malina M. Hills (Sr VP-Space Sys Grp)
Catherine J. Steele (Sr VP-Sys-Natl)
Jamie Morin (VP-Defense Sys Ops)
Kevin Bell (VP-Space Program Ops)
Susan Herbulock (Gen Mgr-Enterprise Ground & Launch Div)
Paul J. Selva (Vice Chm)
Debra Emmons (VP-Special Studies)
Dave Miller (CTO)
Glenn McKeown (Gen Counsel, Sec & Sr VP)
Edward L. Bolton Jr. (Sr VP-Defense Sys Grp)

THE AFFINIS GROUP
1050 Indianapolis Rd, Mooresville, IN 46158
Tel.: (317) 831-3830
Web Site: http://www.affinis.biz
Sales Range: $10-24.9 Million
Emp.: 55
Holding Company
N.A.I.C.S.: 326199
Stephen Dowling (VP-Sls & Mktg)

Subsidiaries:

SaniServ (1)
451 E County Line Rd, Mooresville, IN 46158
Tel.: (317) 831-7030
Web Site: http://www.saniserv.com
Sales Range: $10-24.9 Million
Foodservice Equipment Mfr
N.A.I.C.S.: 333241
Steve Dowling (VP)

THE AGENCY
331 Foothill Rd Ste 100, Beverly Hills, CA 90210
Tel.: (424) 230-3700
Web Site: http://www.theagencyre.com
Year Founded: 2011
Sales Range: $25-49.9 Million
Real Estate Brokerage Services
N.A.I.C.S.: 531210
Mauricio Umansky (Founder & CEO)
Farrah Aldjufrie (Dir-Client Rels)
Alejandro Aldrete (VP-Estates Div)
Ben Belack (Dir-Residential Estates)
Blair Chang (Founder & Partner)
Aileen Comora (Founder & Partner)
Christopher Dyson (Dir-Estates Div)
David Findley (Partner)
Edward Fitz (Partner)
Brendan Fitzpatrick (Dir-Estates Div)
Sharyn Gertz (Dir-Residential Estates Div)
Stacy Gottula (Dir-Estates Div)
Jon Grauman (Dir-Estates Div)
Jay Harris (Dir-Estates Div)
Jonas Heller (Dir-Estates Div)
Deedee Howard (Founder & Partner)
Craig Knizek (Dir-Estates Div)
Jeff Kohl (Founder)
Meir Kroll (Dir-Residential Estates Div)
Daniel Lam (Dir-Residential Div)
Eric Lavey (Mng Dir & Partner)
Paul Lester (Partner)
Gina Martino (Dir-Estates Div)
John McCann (Dir-Residential Div)
Laura Corrigan (VP-PR & Comm)
Rainy Hake Austin (Pres)
Jeff Barnett (Mng Dir)

Subsidiaries:

Suitey, Inc. (1)
220 W 42nd St 22nd Fl, New York, NY 10036
Tel.: (866) 371-6468
Web Site: http://www.triplemint.com
Sales Range: $1-9.9 Million
Emp.: 85
Real Estate Services

N.A.I.C.S.: 531210
David Walker (Founder & CEO)

THE AGRICULTURAL & LABOR PROGRAM INC.
300 Lynchburg Rd, Winter Haven, FL 33885
Tel.: (863) 956-3491
Web Site: http://www.alpi.org
Rev.: $10,200,000
Emp.: 280
Family & Child Support Services
N.A.I.C.S.: 624190
Deloris Johnson (CEO)
William Holt (Chm)
David Walker (Vice Chm)
Christine Samuel (Dir-HR)
Marjorie Gaskin (Treas)
Elizabeth Young (Deputy Dir-Child Dev & Family Svcs)
Cheryl Burnham (Dir-Community Svcs)

THE AIR FORCE ASSOCIATION
1501 Lee Hwy, Arlington, VA 22209-1198
Tel.: (703) 247-5800 VA
Web Site: http://www.afa.org
Year Founded: 1956
Sales Range: $10-24.9 Million
Emp.: 81
Air Force Assistance Services
N.A.I.C.S.: 813219
Nora Ruebrook (Treas)
Tim Brock (Sec)
Mark A. Barrett (Exec VP)
David Dietsch (Vice Chm)
Bruce Wright (Pres)
F. Whitten Peters (Chm)

THE AIROLITE COMPANY
525 Western Rd, Schofield, WI 44476
Tel.: (740) 373-7676 OH
Web Site: http://www.airolite.com
Year Founded: 1919
Sales Range: $50-74.9 Million
Emp.: 20
Ventilating Louvers, Grills & Sun Controls
N.A.I.C.S.: 332323
N. Light Murray (Mgr-Sls & Mktg)

THE ALAMEDA COUNTY FAIR ASSOCIATION
4501 Pleasanton Ave, Pleasanton, CA 94566
Tel.: (925) 426-7600 CA
Web Site: http://www.alamedacountyfair.com
Year Founded: 1939
Sales Range: $10-24.9 Million
Emp.: 744
Agricultural Fair Association
N.A.I.C.S.: 813910
Randy Magee (CFO)
Jerome Hoban (CEO)
Gordon Galvan (VP)

THE ALAMO TRAVEL GROUP, INC.
8930 Wurzbach Rd, San Antonio, TX 78240
Tel.: (210) 593-0084
Web Site: http://www.alamotravel.com
Year Founded: 1982
Sales Range: $10-24.9 Million
Emp.: 230
Travel Services
N.A.I.C.S.: 561510
Suzan Carrillo (Gen Mgr)
Monica Sanford (Mgr-Bus Dev)

THE ALAN WHITE COMPANY INC.
506 Thomas St, Stamps, AR 71860
Tel.: (870) 533-4471 AR
Web Site: http://www.alanwhiteco.com
Year Founded: 1961
Sales Range: $25-49.9 Million
Emp.: 140
Upholstered Household Furniture
N.A.I.C.S.: 337121
Bill Malisch (Owner)

THE ALBRECHT COMPANIES, INC.
24600 Northwestern Hwy, Southfield, MI 48076
Tel.: (248) 356-8870 MI
Web Site: http://www.actionbenefits.com
Year Founded: 1962
Sales Range: $1-9.9 Million
Insurance Agents, Brokers & Services
N.A.I.C.S.: 524210
Gary Albrecht (CEO)

Subsidiaries:

Professional Life Underwriters Services, LLC (1)
2155 Butterfield Dr Ste 102, Troy, MI 48084
Tel.: (248) 356-7587
Web Site: http://www.plusonweb.com
Insurance Services
N.A.I.C.S.: 524113
Marshall Annette (Dir-Ops)

THE ALDEN SHOE COMPANY
1 Taunton St, Middleboro, MA 02346-1426
Tel.: (508) 947-3926 MA
Web Site: http://www.aldenshoe.com
Year Founded: 1884
Sales Range: $100-124.9 Million
Emp.: 150
Shoe Mfr
N.A.I.C.S.: 316210
Robert J. Clark (VP)
Richard Hajjar (VP)
Arthur S. Tarlow Sr. (Chm)
Arthur S. Tarlow Jr. (Pres)

THE ALDERMAN COMPANY
325 Model Farm Rd, High Point, NC 27263-1825
Tel.: (336) 889-6121 NC
Web Site: http://www.aldermancompany.com
Year Founded: 1898
Sales Range: $150-199.9 Million
Emp.: 100
Photography, Design, Photo Labwork, Advertising, Public Relations & Publicity for Manufacturers, Retailers & Advertising Agencies
N.A.I.C.S.: 541922
Eugene Johnston (Chm)
Jeffrey B. Williams (Pres)
Sharon K. Allen (Gen Counsel)
Ed Charles (VP)

THE ALDRIDGE COMPANY
4543 Post Oak Place Dr Ste 200, Houston, TX 77027
Tel.: (713) 403-9150
Web Site: http://www.aldridge.com
Year Founded: 1984
Sales Range: $10-24.9 Million
Emp.: 90
Information Technology Services
N.A.I.C.S.: 541519
David L. Aldridge (Founder & Chm)
Patrick R. Wiley (CEO)
Valerie Burson (Gen Counsel & VP)
Bryan P. Gregory (Pres)
Luke Blankenship (Dir-HR)
Brittany L. Aldridge (VP-Fin)
Chad Hiatt (VP-Tech)

Subsidiaries:

Arterian, Inc. (1)
100 West Harrison Street Suite N-330, Seattle, WA 98119
Tel.: (888) 287-1176
Web Site: http://www.arterian.com
Information Technology Support Services
N.A.I.C.S.: 541512
Jamison West (Pres)

Entrust Technology Consulting Services (1)
901 Console Dr Ste 100, San Antonio, TX 78229-2000
Tel.: (210) 424-3827
Web Site: http://www.ntrusts.com
Computer & Office Machine Repair & Maintenance
N.A.I.C.S.: 811210
Mitchell Sowards (Founder & Pres)

The Aldridge Company - Dallas Office (1)
201 E Carpenter Fwy Ste 600, Irving, TX 75062
Tel.: (817) 461-3393
Web Site: http://www.aldridge.com
Sales Range: $1-9.9 Million
Emp.: 40
Information Technology Services
N.A.I.C.S.: 541519
Gabe Austein (Mgr-Bus Growth)

Twist Solutions, LP (1)
12001 N Central Expy Ste 225, Dallas, TX 75243
Tel.: (214) 341-2300
Web Site: http://www.twistsolutions.com
Sales Range: $1-9.9 Million
Emp.: 30
Computer & Software Stores
N.A.I.C.S.: 449210
Alex H. Famili (CTO)
Gretchen Waide (COO)
Patrick Chen (Mng Dir)
Belinda Rupp (Dir-Ops)
Kevin Trottier (CEO)

THE ALESCO GROUP, LLC
5276 Summerlin Commons Way Ste 703, Fort Myers, FL 33907
Tel.: (239) 275-5006 FL
Web Site: http://www.alescodata.com
Year Founded: 2003
Sales Range: $10-24.9 Million
Emp.: 60
Data & Related Services for Direct Mail, E-Mail, Telemarketing & Digital Advertising Campaigns
N.A.I.C.S.: 518210
Michael Sklorenko (CEO)
Paul Theriot (Pres)

Subsidiaries:

Stat Resource Group, Inc. (1)
69 Kenosia Ave, Danbury, CT 06810
Tel.: (203) 778-8700
Web Site: http://www.statlistics.com
Sales Range: $1-9.9 Million
Emp.: 35
List Management & List Brokerage Services
N.A.I.C.S.: 513140
John Papalia (Pres & CEO)
Isabel Arvoy (Sr Mgr-Accts)
Stacie Nester (Dir-Databases)
Barbara Salles (Mgr-Mktg Svcs)

THE ALEUT CORPORATION
4000 Old Seward Hwy Ste 300, Anchorage, AK 99503-6090
Tel.: (907) 561-4300 AK
Web Site: http://www.aleutcorp.com
Year Founded: 1972
Sales Range: $100-124.9 Million
Emp.: 1,300
Economic & Social Development of the Aleut Unanagan People
N.A.I.C.S.: 523999
David Nevzuroff (Controller)
Melvin Smith (Mgr-Facilities & Resource)
Thomas Mack (Pres)
Matt Fagnani (CEO)

THE ALEUT CORPORATION   U.S. PRIVATE

The Aleut Corporation—(Continued)

Subsidiaries:

ARS International LLC (1)
2609 N River Rd, Port Allen, LA 70767
Tel.: (225) 381-2991
Web Site: http://www.amrad.com
Emp.: 70
Environmental Consulting Services
N.A.I.C.S.: 541620
Danny Coleman (Pres)

Alaska Instrument Company, LLC. (1)
907 E Dowling Rd Ste 5, Anchorage, AK 99518
Tel.: (907) 561-7511
Web Site: http://www.alaskainstrument.com
Emp.: 5
Electric Equipment Mfr
N.A.I.C.S.: 335999
Shaun Stark (Mgr-Warehouse & Coord-Svcs)
Crystal Baloran (Office Mgr)
R. C. Cromwell (Gen Mgr)

Aleut Global Solutions (1)
5520 Tech Center Dr, Colorado Springs, CO 80919-2331
Tel.: (719) 264-0620
Sales Range: $10-24.9 Million
Emp.: 115
Computer Related Services
N.A.I.C.S.: 541519

Aleut Management Services (1)
5520 Tech Ctr Dr, Colorado Springs, CO 80919-2308
Tel.: (719) 531-9090
Web Site: http://www.aleutmgt.com
Sales Range: $10-24.9 Million
Emp.: 60
Management Consulting Services
N.A.I.C.S.: 541618
Damian J. Guerin (VP-HR)
Breke Harnagel (VP-Legal & Contracts)
Brenda J. Gallegos (VP-Bus Dev)

Subsidiary (Domestic):

Aleut Communications Services, LLC (2)
1422 Sultan Dr, Fort Detrick, MD 21702
Tel.: (301) 619-7743
Fiscal Year-end: 12/31/2006
Information Technology Consulting Services
N.A.I.C.S.: 541512
Krista Ochlech (Gen Mgr)

Analytica Inc. (1)
12189 Pennsylvania St, Thornton, CO 80241
Tel.: (303) 469-8868
Web Site: http://www.analyticagroup.com
Laboratory Testing Services
N.A.I.C.S.: 541380

C&H Testing Service, LLC (1)
6224 Price Way, Bakersfield, CA 93308
Tel.: (661) 589-4030
Web Site: http://www.candhtesting.com
Sales Range: $1-9.9 Million
Emp.: 15
Hydro Static Testing Services
N.A.I.C.S.: 561499
Ken Dickinson (Gen Mgr)

Patrick Mechanical LLC (1)
3307 International St, Fairbanks, AK 99701-7383
Tel.: (907) 452-3334
Web Site: http://www.patrickmechanical.com
Sales Range: $1-9.9 Million
Emp.: 50
Mechanical Contracting Service
N.A.I.C.S.: 238220
Keith Anders (Mgr-Logistics)

THE ALISON GROUP
2090 NE 163rd St, North Miami Beach, FL 33162
Tel.: (305) 893-6255   FL
Web Site:
  http://www.alisongroup.com
Year Founded: 1959
Sales Range: $10-24.9 Million
Emp.: 25

Sales Promotion
N.A.I.C.S.: 541810
Larry J. Schweiger (Pres)
Jeff Schweiger (VP)
Kimberly Lipscomb (CFO)
Charles Cerami (Acct Exec)

THE ALLEN COMPANY INC.
3009 Atkinson Ave, Lexington, KY 40509
Tel.: (859) 543-3361   DE
Web Site: http://www.theallen.com
Year Founded: 1939
Sales Range: $75-99.9 Million
Emp.: 105
Highway & Street Construction Services
N.A.I.C.S.: 237310
Joseph Robert Kerrey (Executives)
Jason Gabbard (VP-Ops)
Kim French (Sls Mgr-Natl)
Doug Jenner (VP-Sls & Mktg)

THE ALLIANCE, INC.
400 Clifton Ave, Minneapolis, MN 55403-3212
Tel.: (612) 874-4100   MN
Web Site: http://www.alliiance.us
Year Founded: 1970
Architectural & Interior Design Services
N.A.I.C.S.: 541310
Thomas DeAngelo (Principal)
Carey Brendalen (Principal)
Eric Peterson (Principal)
Tom Hysell (Principal)
Bruce Albinson (Principal)
Paul Anderson (Principal)
Cliff Dunham (Principal)
Cindy Ellsworth (Principal)
Mamie Harvey (Principal)
Ashley Ilvonen (Principal)

THE ALMORE DYE HOUSE, INC.
6850 Tujunga Ave, North Hollywood, CA 91605
Tel.: (818) 506-5444   IL
Web Site:
  http://www.almoredyehouse.com
Rev.: $10,000,000
Emp.: 40
Dyeing: Raw Stock, Yarn & Narrow Fabrics
N.A.I.C.S.: 313310
Jeffery Teichner (Pres)
Don Teichner (VP)

THE ALPHA CORPORATION OF TENNESSEE
955 Hwy 57E, Collierville, TN 38017-9016
Tel.: (901) 854-2800   TN
Web Site: http://www.aoc-resins.com
Year Founded: 1960
Sales Range: $150-199.9 Million
Emp.: 700
Holding Company Manufacturer of Unsaturated Polyester Resin & Circuit Board Laminate Mfr
N.A.I.C.S.: 326199
John W. Griggs (Treas & VP)
Ed Norman (CEO)

Subsidiaries:

AOC, LLC (1)
950 Hwy 57 E, Collierville, TN 38017-5204   (100%)
Tel.: (901) 854-2800
Web Site: http://www.aoc-resins.com
Sales Range: $25-49.9 Million
Emp.: 300
Mfr of Polyester Resins
N.A.I.C.S.: 313320
Frederick S. Norman (Pres & COO)
James A. Griffith (Sr VP)

Subsidiary (Non-US):

A.O.C. Canada, Inc. (2)
Royal Road 38, Guelph, N1H 1G3, ON, Canada   (100%)
Tel.: (519) 821-5180
Web Site: http://www.aoc-resins.com
Rev.: $48,275,381
Emp.: 80
Plastics Materials or Resins
N.A.I.C.S.: 325211
Paul Chang (Plant Mgr)

AOC (UK) Ltd. (2)
Factory Lane, Brantham, Manningtree, CO11 1NH, Essex, United Kingdom
Tel.: (44) 1206 390400
Web Site: http://www.aoc-resinsuk.co.uk
Sales Range: $25-49.9 Million
Emp.: 20
Composite Materials Distr
N.A.I.C.S.: 424690
Peter Cheshire (Mng Dir)

AOC India Pvt. Ltd. (2)
Apt No 2 Pooja Enclave S No 11/2, Karvenagar, Pune, 411 052, India
Tel.: (91) 20 2547 2011
Web Site: http://www.aoc-resins.com
Resin Mfr
N.A.I.C.S.: 325211
Jitendra Bavale (Sr Mgr-Fin)

Plant (Domestic):

AOC, LLC - AOC California Plant (2)
19991 Seaton Ave, Perris, CA 92570-8724
Tel.: (951) 943-9700
Resin Mfr
N.A.I.C.S.: 325211
Jim Earl (Plant Mgr)

AOC, LLC - AOC Florida Plant (2)
4620 N Galloway, Lakeland, FL 33810
Tel.: (863) 815-5000
Resin Mfr
N.A.I.C.S.: 325211

AOC, LLC - AOC Indiana Plant (2)
955 Hwy 57 E, Collierville, TN 38017
Tel.: (219) 465-1611
Resin Mfr
N.A.I.C.S.: 325211

Plant (Non-US):

AOC, LLC - AOC Mexico Plant (2)
Potrerillos Lote No 12 Manz 2 Col Esperanza CD Parque Industrial, Nezahualcoyotl, Mexico, 057819, Mexico
Tel.: (52) 55 5716 7000
Resin Mfr
N.A.I.C.S.: 325211

AOC, LLC - AOC Ontario Plant (2)
38 Royal RdRd, Guelph, N1H 1G3, ON, Canada
Tel.: (519) 821-5180
Web Site: http://www.aoc.com
Emp.: 80
Resin Mfr
N.A.I.C.S.: 325211
Paul Chang (Plant Mgr)

Plant (Domestic):

AOC, LLC - AOC Tennessee Plant (2)
860 Hwy 57 E, Collierville, TN 38017
Tel.: (901) 854-2890
Resin Mfr
N.A.I.C.S.: 325211

THE ALPHA GROUP
32711 Glendale St, Livonia, MI 48150-1611
Tel.: (734) 523-9000   MI
Web Site: http://www.alphausa.com
Sales Range: $10-24.9 Million
Emp.: 20
Holding Company
N.A.I.C.S.: 332812
Nick Strumbos (Pres)
Chuck Dardis (COO)

Subsidiaries:

Alpha Stamping Company (1)
33375 Glendale Ave, Livonia, MI 48150-1615
Tel.: (734) 523-1000
Web Site: http://www.alphausa.com
Mfr of Metal Washers & Bolts
N.A.I.C.S.: 332722
Chuck Dardas (COO)

THE ALPINE GROUP, INC.
1 Meadowlands Plz Ste 801, East Rutherford, NJ 07073
Tel.: (201) 549-4400   DE
Web Site: http://www.alpine-group.net
Year Founded: 1957
Sales Range: $75-99.9 Million
Emp.: 410
Holding Company; Industrial Mfr
N.A.I.C.S.: 551112
Steven S. Elbaum (Chm & CEO)

Subsidiaries:

Synergy Cables Ltd. (1)
PO Box 102, Sderot, 80100, Israel   (52%)
Tel.: (972) 8 6809 444
Web Site: http://www.synergy-cables.com
Sales Range: $100-124.9 Million
Emp.: 430
Copper, Aluminum, Fiber Optic & Electrical Cables Mfr & Distr
N.A.I.C.S.: 331420

Subsidiary (US):

Superior Cables USA Ltd. (2)
5802 Riverstone Cir, Atlanta, GA 30339
Tel.: (770) 226-9898
Web Site: http://www.superior-us.com
Mfr of Copper, Aluminum & Fiber Optic Cables
N.A.I.C.S.: 331420

Subsidiary (Non-US):

Synergy Cables GmbH (2)
Am Weidenbach 6, 82362, Weilheim, Germany
Tel.: (49) 881 927 9320
Web Site: http://www.synergy-cables.de
Cable Mfr
N.A.I.C.S.: 335921
Frank Moeller (Gen Mgr)

THE ALTA GROUP, LLC
45 Sharps Cir, Reno, NV 89519
Tel.: (775) 787-8640   NV
Web Site:
  http://www.thealtagroup.com
Year Founded: 1992
Equipment Leasing, Financing & Management Consulting Services
N.A.I.C.S.: 541618
Paul W. Frechette (Dir-Client Rels & Consulting)
John C. Deane (Founder)
Paul Bent (Sr Mng Dir-Legal Svcs)
Bruce Kropschot (Sr Mng Dir-Mergers)
Hugh Swandel (Sr Mng Dir-Canada)
Thomas C. Wajnert (Chm & Sr Mng Dir-Client Dev)
Carl C. Chrappa (Sr Mng Dir-Asset Mgmt)
Valerie L. Gerard (Co-CEO)
John A. Hurt (Dir-Digital Bus Advisory Practice)
John D. Rizzi (Mng Dir & Head-Practice)
Damian Broadbent (Mng Dir-Advisory Svcs-Asia-Pacific)
Rick Remiker (Co-Vice Chm)
Paul Menzel (Co-Vice Chm)
Francis Maier (CFO)
James R. Jackson Jr. (Co-CEO)

Subsidiaries:

Invigors EMEA LLP (1)
Antrobus House 18 College Street, Petersfield, GU31 4AD, Hants, United Kingdom
Tel.: (44) 845 003 1000
Web Site: http://www.invigors.com

COMPANIES

Emp: 20
Equipment Leasing, Financing & Management Consulting Services
N.A.I.C.S.: 541618
Chris Boobyer (Partner)
Richard Guilbert (Partner)
Malcolm Ogle (Partner)
Mike Roberts (Partner)

The Alta Group, LLC - Asset Management Practice (1)
2471 N McMullen Booth Rd Ste 309, Clearwater, FL 33759
Tel.: (727) 796-7733
Web Site: http://www.thealtagroup.com
Sales Range: $1-9.9 Million
Emp.: 6
Equipment Remarketing Contractor
N.A.I.C.S.: 561499
Carl Chrappa (Sr Mng Dir)

THE ALTER GROUP LTD.
5500 W Howard St, Skokie, IL 60077
Tel.: (847) 676-4300   IL
Web Site: http://www.altergroup.com
Year Founded: 1955
Sales Range: $10-24.9 Million
Emp.: 120
Provider of Land Development Services
N.A.I.C.S.: 237210
Michael J. Alter (Pres)
Ronald F. Siegel (CFO)
Richard Gatto (Exec VP)
Randolph F. Thomas (Exec VP)
Matt Ward (Sr VP)
Scott Latter (Sr VP-Capital Markets & Asset Mgmt)

Subsidiaries:

Alter Asset Management, Inc (1)
1980 Springer Dr, Lombard, IL 60148
Tel.: (630) 620-3600
Web Site:
  http://www.alterassetmanagement.com
Emp.: 15
Real Estate Manangement Services
N.A.I.C.S.: 531390
Samuel Gould (Pres)
Joanne Cusack (Mgr-Property)
Carolyn Jacob (Mng Dir-Chicago Cosmetic Surgery & Dermatology)

Alter Design Builders LLC (1)
5500 W Howard St, Skokie, IL 60077
Tel.: (847) 676-4300
Sales Range: $10-24.9 Million
Emp.: 40
General Contractors
N.A.I.C.S.: 236210

Alter+Care (1)
5500 W Howard St, Skokie, IL 60077
Tel.: (800) 637-4842
Web Site: http://www.altercare.net
Emp.: 15
Real Estate Manangement Services
N.A.I.C.S.: 531390
Donna F. Jarmusz (Sr VP)
John Driscoll (Pres)

THE ALTMAN GROUP
240 New York Dr Ste 1, Fort Washington, PA 19034
Tel.: (215) 884-0500
Web Site: http://www.altmanco.com
Rev.: $10,365,532
Emp.: 47
Remodeling, Multi-Family Dwellings
N.A.I.C.S.: 531210
Brett Altman (Pres)
Aaron Altman (Owner)
Irene Ingram (Supvr-Call Center)
Joe Contorno (Mng Dir)
Mark Binder (Mng Dir)
Nick Bell (Sr Mng Dir)
Robert Bluth (Principal)

THE AMERICAN ACADEMY OF PEDIATRICS
141 Northwest Point Blvd, Elk Grove Village, IL 60007-1098
Tel.: (847) 434-4000   IL
Web Site: http://www.aap.org
Year Founded: 1930
Sales Range: $100-124.9 Million
Emp.: 512
Child Health Care Services
N.A.I.C.S.: 622310
Karen Remley (CEO & Exec Dir)
Benard P. Dreyer (Chm)

THE AMERICAN AUTOMOBILE ASSOCIATION, INC.
1000 AAA Dr, Heathrow, FL 32746-5062
Tel.: (407) 444-4240   CT
Web Site: http://www.aaa.com
Year Founded: 1902
Sales Range: $1-4.9 Billion
Emp.: 45,000
Travel, Insurance, Financial & Auto Related Services Organization
N.A.I.C.S.: 813990
Mark H. Brown (Exec VP-Association & Club Svcs)
Marshall L. Doney (Pres & CEO)
Satish Mahajan (CIO & VP)
Richard D. Rinner (Exec VP-Admin & Publ)
Kathleen F. Marvaso (VP-Pub Affairs)
Paula Twidale (VP)
Jason Hosaflook (CFO)

Subsidiaries:

AAA Auto Club South (1)
1515 N Westshore Blvd, Tampa, FL 33607
Tel.: (813) 289-5000
Web Site: http://www.aaasouth.com
Sales Range: $50-74.9 Million
Emp.: 300
Insurance & Travel Services
N.A.I.C.S.: 561599
Sandy Klim (Editor-in-Chief-GoingPlaces)
Mike Kiral (Mgr-Safety)

AAA Club Alliance Inc. (1)
1 River Pl, Wilmington, DE 19801
Web Site: http://cluballiance.aaa.com
Automobile Support & Services Association
N.A.I.C.S.: 813990

Affiliate (Domestic):

AAA Allied Group, Inc (2)
15 W Central Pkwy, Cincinnati, OH 45202
Tel.: (513) 762-3100
Web Site: http://ohiovalley.aaa.com
Emp.: 1,650
Driver Membership Services Organization
N.A.I.C.S.: 813410
Sheryl Parker (Mgr-Pub Affairs)
Dan Scroggins (Dir-Insurance Sls)
Tony Newman (Exec VP)
Tom Wiedemann (Pres & COO)
Nancy Petrosky (Mgr-HR)
James L. Pease III (Chm & CEO)

Subsidiary (Domestic):

AAA Allied Insurance Services, Inc. (3)
15 W Central Pkwy, Cincinnati, OH 45202
Tel.: (513) 345-5600
Web Site: http://ohiovalley.aaa.com
Insurance Products & Services
N.A.I.C.S.: 524298
Anna Fightmaster (Sr Acct Mgr & Mgr-Corp Risk)
Dan Scroggins (Dir-Insurance Sls)

Subsidiary (Domestic):

Energy Insurance Agency, Inc. (4)
3008 Atkinson Ave, Lexington, KY 40509
Tel.: (859) 273-1549
Web Site:
  http://www.energyinsuranceagency.com
Sales Range: $10-24.9 Million
Insurance Agents
N.A.I.C.S.: 524210
Mark T. Kelder (Pres)
Tim Fryman (CFO)
Lea Ann Coleman (Mgr-Acct-Comml Insurance)
Leslie Cain (Mgr-Acct-Comml Insurance)

Erna Everman (Mgr-Acct-Comml Insurance)
Jeni Jackson (Mgr-Acct-Comml Insurance)
Melissa Clark (Mgr-Personal Lines Acct)
Mary Elliott (Mgr-Acct-Comml Insurance)
Katy Hibbard (Coord-Claims)
Diana Meadows (Mgr-Comml Acct)
Maggie Metcalf (Mgr-Acct-Personal Insurance)
Belinda Moore (Mgr-Acct-Comml Insurance)
Kelli Neal (Mgr-Acct)

Affiliate (Domestic):

AAA Mid-Atlantic Inc. (2)
1 River Pl, Wilmington, DE 19801-5125
Web Site: http://www.aaamidatlantic.com
Travel Arrangement & Reservation Services
N.A.I.C.S.: 561599
John Townsend (Mgr)
Thomas Calcagni (Dir-Public & Govt Affairs)

AAA Northwest Ohio (2)
1007 N Clinton St Ste 2, Defiance, OH 43512
Tel.: (419) 782-3876
Web Site: http://www.nwohio.aaa.com
Sales Range: $10-24.9 Million
Emp.: 139
Travel Arrangement & Reservation Services
N.A.I.C.S.: 561599
A. Karl Halbedl (Pres)
Phyllis Johnson (Mgr-Acctg)

AAA Investment Co. (1)
1403 Foulk Rd Ste 200, Wilmington, DE 19803-2788   (100%)
Tel.: (302) 656-5580
Maintenance & Management of Intangible Investments
N.A.I.C.S.: 523999

AAA Northern California, Nevada & Utah (1)
3055 Oak Rd, Walnut Creek, CA 94597
Tel.: (925) 279-2300
Web Site: http://www.csaa.com
Sales Range: $1-4.9 Billion
Emp.: 6,000
Automobile Insurance & Travel Arrangement
N.A.I.C.S.: 561599
Paula F. Downey (Pres & CEO)

Auto Club Insurance Association (1)
1 Auto Club Dr, Dearborn, MI 48126-4213
Tel.: (313) 336-1234
Sales Range: $1-4.9 Billion
Emp.: 3,800
Insurance Services
N.A.I.C.S.: 524298
Charles Podowski (Pres)

Subsidiary (Domestic):

AAA Life Insurance Company (2)
17900 N Laurel Park Dr, Livonia, MI 48152-3985
Web Site: http://www.aaalife.com
Life Insurance Products & Services
N.A.I.C.S.: 524113
John W. DuBoseIII (Pres & CEO)

MEEMIC Insurance Company (2)
1685 N Opdyke Rd, Auburn Hills, MI 48326-2656
Tel.: (248) 373-0200
Web Site: http://www.meemic.com
Sales Range: $75-99.9 Million
Emp.: 300
Insurance Company
N.A.I.C.S.: 524126

THE AMERICAN BANKERS ASSOCIATION
1120 Connecticut Ave NW, Washington, DC 20036-3902
Tel.: (202) 663-5000   DC
Web Site: http://www.aba.com
Year Founded: 1875
Sales Range: $50-74.9 Million
Banking Trade Association
N.A.I.C.S.: 813910
Virginia Dean (Exec Dir-Commun)
Michael L. Scudder (Chm-CEO Council)
Bob Edy (CFO)
Barry Epstein (Sr VP & Controller)

Maggie Kelly (VP-Mktg)
Stephen G. Crowe (Treas)
Corey Carlisle (Sr VP-Bank Community Engagement)

THE AMERICAN BAR ASSOCIATION MEMBERS/NORTHERN TRUST COLLECTIVE TRUST
50 S LaSalle St, Chicago, IL 60603
Tel.: (312) 630-6000   IL
Web Site:
  http://www.northerntrust.com
Year Founded: 1991
Sales Range: $50-74.9 Million
Emp.: 10,000
Investment Services
N.A.I.C.S.: 523999
Stephen N. Potter (Pres-Asst Mgmt)
Shundrawn A. Thomas (Exec VP & Head-Funds & Managed Accts Grp)
Robert P. Browne (Chief Investment Officer & Exec VP)
Frederick Waddell (Chm & CEO)
R. Hugh Magill (Chief Fiduciary Officer)
Deborah Liverett (Dir-Community Affairs)
Art Fogel (Exec VP)
Aaron Overy (Sr VP)
David Lester (Sr VP)
Descia Milinkovich (Sr VP)
Jeff Feeney (Sr VP)
Michael Slater (Sr VP)
William Huber (Sr VP)
Gwyn Koepke (VP)
Bradley J. Blackwell (Sr VP & Mgr-Customer Rels)
Dino DeVita (Pres)
Steve MacLellan (Pres-Central Reg)
Jan B. Smedley (Officer-Investment)
Clint Zweifel (Pres-Northern Trust Missouri)
Lloyd A. Wennlund (Pres-Northern Funds & Northern Institutional Funds & Exec VP)

THE AMERICAN BICYCLE GROUP LLC
PO Box 22666, Chattanooga, TN 37422
Tel.: (800) 229-0198
Web Site:
  http://www.quintanarootri.com
Bicycles, Tours, News & Related Parts
N.A.I.C.S.: 336991
Peter Hurley (CEO)

Subsidiaries:

American Bicycle Group (1)
9308 Ooltewah Industrial Dr, Ooltewah, TN 37363
Tel.: (800) 229-0198
Web Site: http://www.litespeed.com
Sales Range: $10-24.9 Million
Emp.: 45
Mfr of Bicycles & Bicycle Related Materials
N.A.I.C.S.: 331529
Peter Harley (Pres)

Hotlines Europe Ltd. (1)
Unit 17 The Loan Viewforthbank, Indus Estate, South Queensferry, EH30 9SD, United Kingdom
Tel.: (44) 1313191444
Web Site: http://www.hotlines-uk.com
Bicycles & Bicycle Related Materials Mfr
N.A.I.C.S.: 336991
David Flynn (Mgr-Sls)
Declan Deehan (Head-Mktg)

Quintana Roo Bicycles Inc. (1)
PO Box 22666, Chattanooga, TN 37422
Tel.: (423) 238-5530
Web Site: http://www.rooworld.com
Sales Range: $10-24.9 Million
Mfr of Bicycles & Bicycle Related Materials
N.A.I.C.S.: 336991

THE AMERICAN BICYCLE GROUP LLC

The American Bicycle Group LLC—(Continued)

Quintana Roo Wetsuits Inc. (1)
9308 Ooltewah Industrial Dr, Ooltewah, TN 37363
Tel.: (423) 591-8830
Web Site: http://www.rooworld.com
Sales Range: $10-24.9 Million
Emp.: 40
Wetsuits & Watersport Materials Mfr
N.A.I.C.S.: 326299
Peter Hurley (CEO)

THE AMERICAN BOARD OF ANESTHESIOLOGY, INC.
4208 6 Forks Rd Ste 1500, Raleigh, NC 27609-5765
Tel.: (866) 999-7501   CT
Web Site: http://www.theaba.org
Year Founded: 1938
Sales Range: $10-24.9 Million
Emp.: 52
Anesthesiologist Association
N.A.I.C.S.: 813920
Mary Post (Exec Dir)
Michele Pore (Dir-Mktg & Comm Svcs)
James Crawford (Controller)
Ann Harman (Chief Assessment Officer)
John Markey (CFO)
James P. Rathmell (Sec)
Brenda G. Fahy (VP)
Cynthia A. Lien (Pres)
Daniel J. Cole (Treas)

THE AMERICAN BOARD OF PEDIATRICS
111 Silver Cedar Ct, Chapel Hill, NC 27514
Tel.: (919) 929-0461   NC
Web Site: http://www.abp.org
Year Founded: 1933
Sales Range: $25-49.9 Million
Emp.: 103
Pediatric Health Care Services
N.A.I.C.S.: 621111
Virginia A. Moyer (VP-Maintenance of Certification & Quality)
Linda A. Althouse (VP-Psychometrics & Assessment Svcs)
Dongming Zhang (VP-IT)
Carol L. Carraccio (VP-Competency-Based Assessment)
David G. Nichols (Pres & CEO)
Gail A. McGuinness (Exec VP)
Michele J. Wall (COO & VP)
Ann E. Hazinski (CFO & VP-Fin)

THE AMERICAN JUNIOR GOLF ASSOCIATION
1980 Sports Club Dr, Braselton, GA 30517
Tel.: (770) 868-4200   GA
Web Site: http://www.ajga.org
Year Founded: 1980
Sales Range: $10-24.9 Million
Emp.: 142
Golf Association
N.A.I.C.S.: 711211
Jason Etzen (Chief Bus Officer)
Jason Miller (CFO)
Mark Oskarson (COO)
Scott Carlson (VP-Fin)
Stephen A. Hamblin (Exec Dir)
Kevin Rinker (VP-Dev)

THE AMERICAN LEGION MAGAZINE
700 N Pennsylvania St, Indianapolis, IN 46204-1129
Tel.: (317) 630-1200
Web Site: http://www.legion.org
Year Founded: 1919
Sales Range: $100-124.9 Million
Emp.: 281
Magazine Publisher
N.A.I.C.S.: 513120
Diane Andretti (Mgr-Adv)

THE AMERICAN REGISTRY OF PATHOLOGY, INC.
9210 Corporate Blvd Ste 120, Rockville, MD 20850
Tel.: (240) 654-1685   DC
Web Site: http://www.arpsciences.com
Year Founded: 1921
Sales Range: $10-24.9 Million
Emp.: 158
Research & Development Services
N.A.I.C.S.: 541720
Fred Gorstein (Chm)
Maximilian Buja (Vice Chm)
Gresford Gray (Pres)
George Frederick Worsham Jr. (Sec)

THE AMGRAPH GROUP
2091 Del Rio Way, Ontario, CA 91761
Tel.: (909) 937-7570
Web Site: http://www.theamgraphgroup.com
Year Founded: 2006
Sales Range: $1-9.9 Million
Emp.: 30
Advertising & Graphic Design
N.A.I.C.S.: 541430
Brian Stewart (Pres)
Tricia Mayer (Mgr-Bus Dev)

THE ANDERSON GROUP
879 Fritztown Rd, Sinking Spring, PA 19608
Tel.: (610) 678-1506
Web Site: http://www.theandersongrp.com
Year Founded: 1987
Sales Range: $1-9.9 Million
Emp.: 17
Advertising Specialties, Corporate Identity, Interactive Agencies, Public Relations, Strategic Planning
N.A.I.C.S.: 541810
Linda Anderson (CEO)
Christina L. Faller (Dir-PR & Social Media)
Derek M. Hollister (Dir-Digital Strategies)
Missy Orlando (Pres & COO)

THE ANDERSON GROUP, LLC
111 2nd Ave NE Ste 1250, Saint Petersburg, FL 33701
Tel.: (727) 897-5630   MI
Web Site: http://www.andersongroup.com
Year Founded: 1985
Privater Equity Firm
N.A.I.C.S.: 523999
Barry Shapiro (Co-Founder & Partner)
Thomas Gaffney (Co-Founder & Partner)
Cory Gaffney (Partner)
Joe Maddox (Partner)
Robin Harris (Partner)
Michael Serwer (Partner)
Scott Hukari (Partner)
Harvey Zorn (Partner)
Bernadette Dennehy (Gen Counsel)

Subsidiaries:

After Six, LLC (1)
420 Thornton Rd Ste 109, Lithia Springs, GA 30122-1582
Tel.: (706) 543-5286
Web Site: http://www.aftersix.com
Sales Range: $10-24.9 Million
Emp.: 60
Formal Wear Designer & Mfr
N.A.I.C.S.: 315250

Alliance Food Equipment Processing, LLC (1)
267 Livingston St, Northvale, NJ 07647
Tel.: (201) 784-1101
Web Site: http://www.wcbicecream.com
Sales Range: $1-9.9 Million
Emp.: 100
Ice Cream Production & Packaging Equipment Mfr
N.A.I.C.S.: 333241

LaBella Sausage, LLC (1)
16170 Aviation Loop Dr, Brooksville, FL 34604
Tel.: (352) 799-6301
Web Site: http://www.labellasausage.net
Sales Range: $1-9.9 Million
Emp.: 30
Sausages & Other Prepared Meats Mfr
N.A.I.C.S.: 311612

Michigan Wheel Operations, LLC (1)
1501 Buchanan Ave SW, Grand Rapids, MI 49507-1697
Tel.: (616) 452-6941
Web Site: http://www.miwheel.com
Sales Range: $1-9.9 Million
Emp.: 85
Inboard & Outboard Boat Propeller Mfr & Distr
N.A.I.C.S.: 336390
Kevin Mitchell (VP-Mktg & Sls)

Perfect Fit Industries, LLC (1)
8501 Tower Point Dr, Charlotte, NC 28227-7730
Tel.: (704) 815-2200
Web Site: http://www.perfectfitindustries.com
Sales Range: $100-124.9 Million
Bedspreads, Comforters, Mattress Pads, Draperies & Bed Pillows Mfr & Distr
N.A.I.C.S.: 314999
Carmen Waite (VP-Mktg & Product Dev)
Ken Hedrick (CEO)
Jay Schroeder (CFO & Sr VP-Fin)
Geri Wetmore (Chief Sls Officer & Sr VP-Sls)
Lucia Fitzgerald (Sr VP-Mdsg, Product Dev & Mktg)

Thayer Power & Communication Line Contruction Co., LLC (1)
7400 Market Rd, Fairview, PA 16415
Tel.: (814) 474-1174
Web Site: http://www.thayerpc.com
Sales Range: $1-9.9 Million
Power & Communication Line Construction Services
N.A.I.C.S.: 237130

THE ANDOVER COMPANIES
95 Old River Rd, Andover, MA 01810
Tel.: (978) 475-3300   MA
Web Site: http://www.andovercos.com
Sales Range: $400-449.9 Million
Emp.: 250
Holding Company; Homeowners Insurance Services
N.A.I.C.S.: 551112
Paul Nadeau (Reg VP)
John Cole (Asst Sec)

Subsidiaries:

Bay State Insurance Company (1)
95 Old River Rd, Andover, MA 01810
Tel.: (978) 475-3300
Web Site: http://www.andovercos.com
Sales Range: $50-74.9 Million
Emp.: 200
Homeowners Insurance Services
N.A.I.C.S.: 524126
Malcolm Brawn (Pres)
Janet Wallace (VP)

Merrimack Mutual Fire Insurance Co. (1)
95 Old River Rd, Andover, MA 01810
Tel.: (978) 475-3300
Web Site: http://www.andovercos.com
Sales Range: $50-74.9 Million
Emp.: 200
Homeowners Insurance Services
N.A.I.C.S.: 524126
Janet Wallace (VP)

THE ANDREWS MOVING & STORAGE COMPANY INC.
10235 Philipp Pkwy, Streetsboro, OH 44241
Tel.: (330) 656-8700
Web Site: http://www.andrewsmoving.com
Year Founded: 1908
Sales Range: $25-49.9 Million
Emp.: 50
Trucking Service
N.A.I.C.S.: 484210
Thomas T. Marshall (CEO)

THE ANGELO IAFRATE COMPANIES
26300 Sherwood Ave, Warren, MI 48091-4168
Tel.: (586) 756-1070   MI
Web Site: http://www.iafrate.com
Year Founded: 1960
Sales Range: $1-9.9 Million
Emp.: 500
Construction Materials Mfr
N.A.I.C.S.: 324121
Duane Laurila (Sr VP)
Bob Adcock (Pres)
Hal Howlett (VP-Estimating)

Subsidiaries:

Angelo Iafrate Construction Company (1)
26300 Sherwood Ave, Warren, MI 48091-4168
Tel.: (586) 756-1070
Web Site: http://www.iafrate.com
Excavation & Paving Services
N.A.I.C.S.: 237310
Mike DeFinis (VP-Mgmt)
Hal Howlett (VP-Estimating)
Duane Laurila (VP-Contract Svcs)
Bruce Young (VP-Ops)

THE ANSCHUTZ CORPORATION
555 17th St Ste 2400, Denver, CO 80202
Tel.: (303) 298-1000   KS
Year Founded: 1958
Holding Company; Oil & Gas Extraction; General Building Contractors; Real Estate; Entertainment & Media
N.A.I.C.S.: 551112
Steven Cohen (Exec VP)

Subsidiaries:

Anschutz Entertainment Group (1)
800 W Olympic Blvd Ste 305, Los Angeles, CA 90015
Tel.: (213) 763-7700
Web Site: http://www.aegworldwide.com
Sports & Entertainment Venue Operator
N.A.I.C.S.: 711310
Dan Beckerman (Pres & CEO)
Steven Cohen (Chief Strategic Officer)
John Langford (COO-Europe)
Paul Reeve (CFO-Europe)
Emma Bownes (VP-Programming)
Alex Hill (Pres-Europe)
David Jones (CIO)

Subsidiary (Domestic):

AEG Presents LLC (2)
800 West Olympic Blvd Ste 305, Los Angeles, CA 90015
Tel.: (323) 930-5700
Music Company
N.A.I.C.S.: 711130

Subsidiary (Domestic):

Promowest Productions, Inc. (3)
405 Neil Ave, Columbus, OH 43215
Tel.: (614) 461-5483
Web Site: http://www.promowestlive.com
Promoters of Performing Arts, Sports & Similar Events without Facilities
N.A.I.C.S.: 711320
Amy Cooper-Salvatore (Dir-Mktg)
Kathleen Cleary (Dir-Special Events)

Jeremy Olson (Asst Gen Mgr & Mgr-Box Office)
Justin Lucotch (Mgr-Production)
Mike Cash (Mgr-Sls-Sponsorship)
Marissa McClellan (Mktg Dir)
Jeff Railsback (Dir-Social Media)
BJ Rayburn (Dir-Ticketing)
Tim Burris (Gen Mgr)

Subsidiary (Domestic):

Los Angeles Kings Hockey Club L.P. (2)
1111 S Figueroa St, Los Angeles, CA 90015
Tel.: (213) 742-7100
Web Site: http://www.lakings.com
Sales Range: $75-99.9 Million
Professional Hockey Team Owner & Operator
N.A.I.C.S.: 711211
Michael Altieri (Sr VP-Mktg, Comm & Content)
Jeff Moeller (Sr Dir-Comm & Heritage)
Chris Crotty (Sr VP-Hockey Dev)
Nelson Emerson (Dir-Player Personnel)
Dieter Ruehle (Dir-Music)
Josh Veilleux (Sr VP-Partnership Sls)
Aaron LeValley (Sr VP-Bus Ops & Strategy)
Darren Abbott (Pres-Affiliates & Sr VP-Revenue)
Jeff Solomon (Exec VP-Hockey Ops & Legal Affairs)
Jonathan Lowe (Sr VP-Bus Dev & Brand Strategies)
Kelly Cheeseman (Co-COO)
Luc Robitaille (Co-Pres)
Nam McGrail (Sr VP-Partnership Activation)
Nick Baker (Co-COO)
Russell Silvers (Co-COO)

The Bowery Presents, LLC (2)
156 Ludlow St 5th Fl, New York, NY 10002-2385
Tel.: (212) 260-4700
Web Site: http://www.bowerypresents.com
Live Music & Other Event Management Services
N.A.I.C.S.: 711310
Tony Melchior (Dir-Production)
Jim Glancy (Partner)
John Moore (Partner)
Don Simpson (COO)

Anschutz Film Group, LLC (1)
1888 Century Park E 14th Fl, Los Angeles, CA 90067 (100%)
Tel.: (781) 418-5300
Web Site: http://www.walden.com
Sales Range: $50-74.9 Million
Emp.: 74
Holding Company; Motion Picture & Video Production & Book Publisher
N.A.I.C.S.: 551112

Subsidiary (Domestic):

Bristol Bay Productions, LLC (2)
1888 Century Park E 14th Fl, Los Angeles, CA 90067
Tel.: (310) 887-1000
Web Site: http://www.walden.com
Sales Range: $25-49.9 Million
Movie Production
N.A.I.C.S.: 512110
Frank Smith (CEO)

Walden Media, LLC (2)
1888 Century Park E 14th Fl, Los Angeles, CA 90067
Tel.: (310) 887-1000
Web Site: http://www.walden.com
Sales Range: $25-49.9 Million
Emp.: 60
Motion Picture & Video Production; Book Publisher
N.A.I.C.S.: 512110
Debbie Kovacs (Sr VP-Publ)
Frank Smith (CEO)
Naia Cucukov (VP-Dev & Production)

Clarity Media Group, Inc. (1)
555 17th St Ste 425, Denver, CO 80202
Tel.: (303) 299-1504
Web Site: http://www.claritymg.com
Sales Range: $50-74.9 Million
Emp.: 16
Holding Company; Newspaper Publisher
N.A.I.C.S.: 551112
Ryan McKibben (Pres & CEO)
Philip F. Anschutz (Chm)
Frederick Anderson (CFO & COO)

Subsidiary (Domestic):

SF Newspaper Company, LLC (2)
835 Market St Ste 550, San Francisco, CA 94103
Tel.: (415) 359-2600
Web Site: http://www.sfexaminer.com
Newspaper Publishers
N.A.I.C.S.: 513110
Aaron Barbero (VP-Ops)
Jay Curran (Publr)

Unit (Domestic):

The Gazette (2)
30 E Pikes Peak Ave Ste 100, Colorado Springs, CO 80903 (100%)
Tel.: (719) 632-5511
Web Site: http://www.gazette.com
Sales Range: $50-74.9 Million
Newspaper Publishers
N.A.I.C.S.: 513110
Ryan McKibben (Chm)
Vicki Cederholm (Dir-Ops)
Stephanie Weber (VP-Mktg & Tech)
Christian Anschutz (Vice Chm)
Vince Bzdek (Editor)
Sabrina Brown (Mgr-Digital Adv)
Mark Vujcevic (Mgr-Automotive & Real Estate)

Subsidiary (Domestic):

The Oklahoma Publishing Company (2)
100 W Main St Ste 100, Oklahoma City, OK 73102
Tel.: (405) 475-3311
Web Site: http://www.theomc.com
Sales Range: $25-49.9 Million
Publisher
N.A.I.C.S.: 513110
Michelle Geries (Office Mgr)

Unit (Domestic):

The Oklahoman (3)
100 W Main Suite 100, Oklahoma City, OK 73102
Tel.: (405) 475-3000
Sales Range: $100-124.9 Million
Publishers of Newspaper
N.A.I.C.S.: 513110
Mike Shannon (Mng Editor)

Subsidiary (Domestic):

The Washington Newspaper Publishing Company, LLC (2)
1015 15th St NW Ste 500, Washington, DC 20005
Tel.: (202) 903-2000
Web Site: http://www.washingtonexaminer.com
Newspaper Publishers
N.A.I.C.S.: 513110
Hugo Gurdon (Dir-Editorial)
Philip Klein (Mng Editor)
Chris Irvine (Editor-News)

Xanterra Leisure Holding, LLC (1)
6312 S Fiddlers Green Cir Ste 600 N, Greenwood Village, CO 80111
Tel.: (303) 600-3400
Web Site: http://www.xanterra.com
Holding Company; Park Concessions, Resort, Cruise & Tour Operator
N.A.I.C.S.: 551112
Andrew N. Todd (Pres & CEO)
Kirk H. Anderson (Chief Legal Officer & Gen Counsel)
Betsy O'Rourke (CMO)
Gordon R. Taylor (Chief Parks Officer)
Hans Desai (Sr VP-Leisure Travel)
Jim Forester (CIO)
Lonnie S. Clark (CFO)
Shannon Dierenbach (Chief HR Officer)
Tim Schoonover (Chief Mdsg & Supply Chain Officer)

Subsidiary (Domestic):

Xanterra Parks & Resorts, Inc. (2)
6312 S Fiddlers Green Cir Ste 600N, Greenwood Village, CO 80011
Tel.: (303) 600-3400
Web Site: http://www.xanterra.com
Sales Range: $50-74.9 Million
Emp.: 200

Park Concessions, Resorts, Cruise & Tour Operator
N.A.I.C.S.: 721110
Andrew N. Todd (Pres & CEO)
Michael F. Welch (CFO & VP-Fin)
Kirk H. Anderson (Gen Counsel & VP)
Chris R. Lane (VP-Environmental Affairs)
Hans Desai (VP)
James W. McCaleb (VP-Parks North)
Gordon R. Taylor (VP-Parks South)
John W. Wimmer (CIO)
Betsy O'Rourke (VP-Sls & Mktg)
Shannon Dierenbach (VP-HR)
Catherine Greener (VP-Sustainability)
Tim Schoonover (VP-Retail)

Subsidiary (Domestic):

Broadmoor Hotel, Inc. (3)
1 Lake Ave, Colorado Springs, CO 80906-4254
Tel.: (719) 634-7711
Web Site: http://www.broadmoor.com
Sales Range: $50-74.9 Million
Resort Hotel & Spa
N.A.I.C.S.: 721110
Russell D. Miller (Dir-Golf)
Joshua Garcia (Dir-Natl Sls-Northeast & Intl Reg)
Jeremy Wilson (Dir-Natl Sls-Rocky Mountain)
Laurie Meacham (Dir-Natl Sls-Mid-Atlantic)
Maureen Carter (Dir-Natl Sls-West)
Tammy Page (Dir-Natl Sls-Mid-West)

Holiday Vacations, LLC (3)
2727 Henry Ave, Eau Claire, WI 54701
Tel.: (715) 834-5555
Web Site: http://www.holidayvacations.net
Health & Beauty Care Products & Baby Products Mfr
N.A.I.C.S.: 325620
Becky Zimmerman (Brand Dir)
Michelle Underwood (Dir-Media Sls)
Jace Vogler (Dir-Hotel, Rail & Cruise Lines)
Jerre Fuqua (Pres)
Andrew Todd (CEO)

Windstar Cruises, LLC (3)
2101 4th Ave Ste 210, Seattle, WA 98121
Tel.: (206) 733-2703
Web Site: http://www.windstarcruises.com
Cruise Line Services
N.A.I.C.S.: 483114
Joe Duckett (VP-Sls & Mktg)
Peter Beck (VP-Acctg)
Alan McGrory (VP-Ops)
Steven Simao (VP-Travel Agency Sls)
Doug Santoni (VP-Deployment & Revenue Ops)
Gina Smith (Controller)
Brian Kimmons (Dir-IT)
Mary Schimmelman (Dir-PR & Social Media)
Jay Juang (Mgr-Risk)
Christopher Prelog (Pres)
Paul Barrett (VP-Technical Ops)
Natalie Drain (Sr Mgr-Pur-Marine Fleet Ops)
George Howell (Sr Dir-Guest Svcs)
Jess Peterson (Dir-Revenue & Itinerary Plng)
Sarah Scoltock (Dir-PR)
Andrew N. Todd (CEO)
Lyall Duncan (VP-Legal & Asst Gen Counsel)
Kirk H. Anderson (Chief Legal Officer)
Dianna Rom (Sr Dir-Sls)
Betsy O'Rourke (Chief Comml Officer)

Xanterra South Rim, LLC (3)
1 Main St, Grand Canyon, AZ 86023 (100%)
Tel.: (928) 638-2631
Web Site: http://www.grandcanyonlodges.com
Local Passenger Transportation
N.A.I.C.S.: 485999
Jon Streit (Gen Mgr)

THE APPAREL GROUP, LTD.
883 Trinity Dr, Lewisville, TX 75056
Tel.: (214) 469-3300 NY
Web Site: http://www.theapparelgroup.com
Men's Suits, Sportswear & Sweaters; Ladies' Wear Mfr
N.A.I.C.S.: 315250

John Liu (CEO)
Winifred Liao (Dir-Design)

THE ARC MERCER, INC.
180 Ewingville Rd, Ewing, NJ 08638
Tel.: (609) 406-0181 NJ
Web Site: http://www.arcmercer.org
Year Founded: 1958
Sales Range: $10-24.9 Million
Emp.: 851
Developmental Disability Assistance Services
N.A.I.C.S.: 624120
Patti Szenczi (Dir-Program Dev & Comm)
Steven Cook (Exec Dir)

THE ARCHER GROUP
233 N King St, Wilmington, DE 19801
Tel.: (302) 429-9120
Web Site: http://www.archer-group.com
Sales Range: $10-24.9 Million
Emp.: 65
Advertising Agencies
N.A.I.C.S.: 541810
Michael Derins (Mng Partner)

THE ARCHWAY PROGRAMS, INC.
280 Jackson Rd, Atco, NJ 08004
Tel.: (856) 767-5757 NJ
Web Site: http://www.archwayprograms.org
Year Founded: 1983
Sales Range: $10-24.9 Million
Emp.: 555
Assisted Living Services
N.A.I.C.S.: 623312
Terriann Procida (Chm)
Margaret Haldeman (Sec)
Gail M. Smith (Vice Chm)

THE ARCTICOM GROUP, LLC
1676 N California Blvd Ste 550, Walnut Creek, CA 94596
Tel.: (925) 334-7222 DE
Web Site: http://www.thearcticomgroup.com
Heating, Ventilation & Air Conditioning Services
N.A.I.C.S.: 333415
Jim Pape (CEO)

Subsidiaries:

Chiller Systems Service, Inc. (1)
1510 Swadley St, Lakewood, CO 80215
Tel.: (303) 275-6250
Web Site: http://www.chillersystemsservice.com
Sales Range: $1-9.9 Million
Emp.: 17
Appliance Repair & Maintenance Services
N.A.I.C.S.: 811412
R. Scott Tracy (Pres)

THE ARDELL GROUP
495 NW Flagline Dr, Bend, OR 97701
Tel.: (619) 925-8191 CA
Web Site: http://www.ardellgroup.com
Year Founded: 1985
Sales Range: $1-9.9 Million
Emp.: 15
Public Relations Firm
N.A.I.C.S.: 541820
David Stowe (Pres & CEO)

THE ARGENTUM GROUP
60 Madison Ave Ste 701, New York, NY 10010
Tel.: (212) 949-6262
Web Site: http://www.argentumgroup.com
Year Founded: 1988
Rev.: $400,000,000
Emp.: 7

THE ARGENTUM GROUP

The Argentum Group—(Continued)
Privater Equity Firm
N.A.I.C.S.: 523999
Daniel Raynor *(Mng Partner)*
Steve Berman *(CFO & VP)*
Walter H. Barandiaran *(Mng Partner)*

Subsidiaries:

LAUNCH Technical Workforce Solutions, LLC (1)
700 Commerce Dr Ste 140, Oak Brook, IL 60523
Web Site: http://www.launchtws.com
Sales Range: $1-9.9 Million
Emp.: 5,000
Staffing Services
N.A.I.C.S.: 561311
Michael Lorenzini *(Chief Strategic Officer & Pres-Svcs)*
Mike Reporto *(Pres-Staffing)*
Jason Adams *(Sr VP-Strategic Sls)*
Marie-Claude Payant *(VP-Fin)*
James J. Janicki *(VP-Quality)*

Subsidiary (Domestic):

PlaneTechs, LLC (2)
1520 Kensington Rd Ste 311, Oak Brook, IL 60523
Tel.: (630) 990-8804
Contract Aircraft Maintenance Personnel
N.A.I.C.S.: 561311

THE ARGUS RESEARCH GROUP, INC.
61 Broadway Ste 1910, New York, NY 10006
Tel.: (212) 425-7500   DE
Web Site:
 http://www.argusresearch.com
Rev.: $15,600,000
Emp.: 48
Holding Company; Investment Research, Stock Tracking & Money Management Services
N.A.I.C.S.: 551112
Fern Dorsey *(Treas)*
John Eade *(Pres)*

Subsidiaries:

Argus Investors' Counsel, Inc. (1)
Soundview Plz 1266 E Main St, Stamford, CT 06902
Tel.: (203) 316-9000
Web Site: http://www.argusinvest.com
Rev.: $860,000
Emp.: 12
Investment Advisory & Management Services
N.A.I.C.S.: 523940
Sharon D. Wagoner *(Chm & Pres)*

Argus Research Company (1)
61 Broadway Fl 19, New York, NY 10006
Tel.: (212) 425-7500
Web Site: http://www.argusresearch.com
Rev.: $5,300,000
Emp.: 40
Investment Research & Corporate Rating Information Services
N.A.I.C.S.: 561450
John Eade *(Pres & Dir-Portfolio Strategies)*
Richard Cuneo *(Sr VP-Ops)*

Argus Vickers American Equity Research Ltd. (1)
1st Floor 64 London Wall, London, EC2M 5TP, United Kingdom
Tel.: (44) 207 256 8383
Web Site: http://www.argus-vickers.co.uk
Emp.: 20
Share Register Analysis Services
N.A.I.C.S.: 541990
Christopher Mangen *(Mgr-Sls)*
Susan Baldry *(Mng Dir)*
Peter Dewey *(Head-Analyst Team)*
Peter Jones *(Mgr-IT)*

Vickers Stock Research Corporation (1)
61 Bdwy Ste 1910, New York, NY 10006
Tel.: (516) 945-0030
Web Site: http://www.vickers-stock.com

Sales Range: $1-9.9 Million
Emp.: 20
Stock Research & Tracking Data Publisher
N.A.I.C.S.: 513140

THE ARIEL GROUP LLC
1050 Waltham St, Lexington, MA 02421
Tel.: (781) 761-9000
Web Site: http://www.arielgroup.com
Year Founded: 1993
Emp.: 77
Adult Training & Coaching Services
N.A.I.C.S.: 611699
Elizabeth Martin *(Sr VP-Ops)*
Leah Shabouk *(Sr VP-Fin)*
Scott Simmons *(CEO)*
Ellen Wilsker *(Sr VP-Global Clients)*

Subsidiaries:

Better Communications, Inc. (1)
200 5th Ave, Waltham, MA 02451
Tel.: (781) 862-3800
Web Site: http://www.bettercom.com
Sales Range: $1-9.9 Million
Emp.: 25
Professional Training Services
N.A.I.C.S.: 611699
Deborah Dumaine *(Founder)*

THE ARISTOS GROUP
750 E Lake St, Wayzata, MN 55391
Tel.: (952) 449-4100
Web Site:
 http://www.thearistosgroup.com
Year Founded: 1998
Rev.: $10,000,000
Emp.: 25
Advetising Agency
N.A.I.C.S.: 541810
Jay Wissink *(Pres & CEO)*
Alan R. Dakay *(Partner)*

THE ARLINGTON RESORT HOTEL & SPA
239 Central Ave, Hot Springs, AR 71901
Tel.: (501) 623-7771
Web Site:
 http://www.arlingtonhotel.com
Sales Range: $10-24.9 Million
Emp.: 300
Hotels & Motels
N.A.I.C.S.: 721110
Bob Martorana *(Gen Mgr)*
Stephen Zelnick *(Dir-Security)*
Dee Ann Soderstrom *(Mgr-Sls)*

THE ARMCO GROUP INC.
219 E Garfield St Ste 600, Seattle, WA 98102-3776
Tel.: (206) 505-6800
Rev.: $14,000,000
Emp.: 1
Apartment Building Operator
N.A.I.C.S.: 531110
John W. Stephanus *(Pres)*

Subsidiaries:

US Suites of San Diego Inc. (1)
10439 Roselle St, San Diego, CA 92121
Tel.: (858) 554-0300
Sales Range: Less than $1 Million
Corporate Housing Operators
N.A.I.C.S.: 531110

US Suites of Seattle Inc. (1)
219 E Garfield St, Seattle, WA 98102
Tel.: (206) 505-6800
Apartment Hotel Operation
N.A.I.C.S.: 531110

THE ARMOR GROUP, INC.
4600 N Mason-Montgomery Rd, Mason, OH 45040
Tel.: (513) 923-5260
Web Site:
 http://www.thearmorgroup.com
Year Founded: 1927

Sales Range: $25-49.9 Million
Emp.: 400
Mfr Services
N.A.I.C.S.: 332999
David K. Schmitt *(CEO)*
Frank Ahaus *(Pres)*
Brett Fortener *(Supvr-Shipping)*
Jeff Strasser *(Pres)*
Krista Stacey *(Coord-Mktg)*

Subsidiaries:

Cincinnati Industrial Machinery (1)
4600 N Mason Montgomery Rd, Mason, OH 45040
Tel.: (513) 923-5600
Web Site: http://www.cinind.com
Sales Range: $25-49.9 Million
Emp.: 270
Specialty Machinery Mfr
N.A.I.C.S.: 333248
Joe Bohlen *(Mgr-Sls)*
Tony Wolke *(Mgr-Parts)*

Witt Industries, Inc. (1)
4600 N Mason-Montgomery Rd, Mason, OH 45040
Tel.: (513) 923-5631
Web Site: http://www.witt.com
Sales Range: $25-49.9 Million
Emp.: 165
Waste Receptacle Mfr
N.A.I.C.S.: 332999

THE AROUNDCAMPUS GROUP
88 VilCom Center Dr Ste 160, Chapel Hill, NC 27514
Tel.: (919) 968-4811
Web Site:
 http://www.aroundcampusgroup.com
Year Founded: 1953
Sales Range: $10-24.9 Million
Emp.: 90
College Media & Marketing Services & Publisher of Campus Directories
N.A.I.C.S.: 541840
Claudia Quiros *(Mgr-Customer Rels)*
Alex Gates *(VP-Inside Sls)*
Chip Crawford *(CFO)*
Anna Bowland *(Mng Dir-Publ)*
Mary Yow *(Exec VP)*
Melissa Sturtzel *(VP-Ops)*
Jeff Stencel *(VP-Sls)*
John O'Brien *(Pres)*
Keri Efird *(Dir-Publ Plng)*
Josh Jones *(Mgr-Bus Dev-Campus Mktg)*
Abby Anderson *(Sr Mgr-Customer Rels)*
Jacqueline Dunn *(Mgr-Customer Rels)*
Chelsea Payne *(Mgr-Customer Rels)*
Neely Droessler *(Mgr-Inside Sls Dept)*
Kelsey diGirolamo *(Project Mgr)*
Kathryn Olivieri *(Project Mgr)*
Rob Moody *(VP-Fin & Admin)*

Subsidiaries:

University Directories (1)
88 VilCom Cir, Chapel Hill, NC 27514
Tel.: (919) 968-0225
Web Site:
 http://www.universitydirectories.com
Sales Range: $10-24.9 Million
Publisher of University Directories & Planners
N.A.I.C.S.: 513140
Jeff Stencel *(VP-Planner Div)*
Sandy Greene *(Mgr-Project Design & Customer Rels)*
Keri Hall Efird *(Dir-Creative Planner)*
Meredith Rutala *(Mng Dir-Publications)*
Libby Welch *(Dir-Customer Comm)*

THE ARTCRAFT COMPANY
200 John L Dietsch Blvd, North Attleboro, MA 02763
Tel.: (508) 695-4042
Web Site: http://www.artcraft.com

Year Founded: 1939
Rev.: $7,600,000
Emp.: 69
Printing Services
N.A.I.C.S.: 323111
Danny Sutherland *(Mgr-CIS)*
Michelle Wagner *(Mgr-Social Stationery)*
John Dumouchel *(Pres)*
Brian Rotchford *(VP-Sls)*
Eleni Mastin *(Mgr-Mktg)*
Scott Shreve *(VP-Mktg & Bus Dev)*
Mark Resnick *(VP-Sls & Promotional Branding)*

THE ARTERY GROUP, LLC
5550 Friendship Blvd, Chevy Chase, MD 20815
Tel.: (301) 961-8000
Year Founded: 1959
Sales Range: $10-24.9 Million
Emp.: 15
Developer of Real Estate
N.A.I.C.S.: 531210
Henry H. Goldberg *(Chm & CEO)*
Richard M. Aronoff *(Pres)*
Bruce Schulman *(CFO)*

THE ARTIME GROUP
65 N Raymond Ave Ste 205, Pasadena, CA 91103-3947
Tel.: (626) 583-1855
Web Site:
 http://www.artimegroup.com
Year Founded: 1991
Sales Range: $10-24.9 Million
Emp.: 10
Advetising Agency
N.A.I.C.S.: 541810
Henry Artime *(Pres-Brand Strategist)*
Bill Myers *(Dir-New Bus Dev)*
Christopher John Ramirez *(VP, Acct Dir & Dir-Creative)*
Tracy Nightingale *(Acct Dir)*
Van Nguyen *(Dir-Media)*

THE ASCENT GROUP LLC
28 W Adams Ave Ste 800, Detroit, MI 48226
Tel.: (313) 908-0476
Web Site: http://ascentgroupmi.com
Investment Services
N.A.I.C.S.: 523999
Larry D. Leinweber *(Co-Founder & Pres)*
David Leinweber *(Co-Founder & Partner)*

Subsidiaries:

Ascent Cloud LLC (1)
28 W Adams Ste 800, Detroit, MI 48226
Tel.: (313) 251-1716
Web Site: http://www.ascentcloud.io
Geolocation & Performance Management Services
N.A.I.C.S.: 541511
Mike Aloe *(VP-Sls)*

Subsidiary (Domestic):

Arrowpointe Corp. (2)
16795 Von Karman Ave Ste 250, Irvine, CA 92606
Tel.: (714) 475-3837
Web Site: http://www.geopointe.com
Geo-location Application Solutions Developer
N.A.I.C.S.: 513210
Scott Hemmeter *(Founder & CEO)*

Level Eleven, LLC (2)
28 W Adams Ste 800, Detroit, MI 48226
Tel.: (313) 373-5542
Web Site: http://www.leveleleven.com
Sales Performance Optimization Platform Developer
N.A.I.C.S.: 541511
Kyle Gostinger *(Product Mgr)*
David Leinweber *(CEO)*

COMPANIES

THE ASCENT SERVICES GROUP
3000 Oak Rd Ste 200, Walnut Creek, CA 94597
Tel.: (925) 627-4900
Web Site: http://www.ascentsg.com
Year Founded: 2000
Rev.: $51,800,000
Emp.: 426
Computer System Design Services
N.A.I.C.S.: 541512
Joseph Nordlinger *(Pres & CEO)*
Michelle Miller *(VP-Sls)*

THE ASCII GROUP, INC.
7101 Wisconsin Ave Ste 1000, Bethesda, MD 20814
Tel.: (301) 718-2600   DE
Web Site: http://www.ascii.com
Year Founded: 1984
Sales Range: $75-99.9 Million
Emp.: 30
Computer Resale Services
N.A.I.C.S.: 423430
Alan D. Weinberger *(Founder & CEO)*
Jerry Koutavas *(Pres)*
Shannon Mayer *(VP-Channel Dev)*

THE ASH GROUP, INC.
5802 Benjamin Ctr Dr Ste 101, Tampa, FL 33634
Tel.: (813) 290-8899   FL
Web Site: http://www.ash-grp.com
Year Founded: 1993
Sales Range: $10-24.9 Million
Emp.: 14
Civil Engineering & Environmental Services
N.A.I.C.S.: 541330
Janice Ash *(Pres)*
Richard I. Piccininni *(Mgr-Civil Engrg Grp)*
Sandi Simmons *(Controller-Fin)*

THE ASHTON COMPANY
1510 Prime W Pkwy, Houston, TX 77003
Tel.: (281) 578-0165
Web Site: http://www.ashtoncompany.com
Rev.: $13,400,000
Emp.: 77
Frames & Framing, Picture & Mirror
N.A.I.C.S.: 423220
John Kemper *(Pres)*
James Krimel *(CEO)*

THE ASIA FOUNDATION
465 California St 9th Fl, San Francisco, CA 94104
Tel.: (415) 982-4640   CA
Web Site: http://www.asiafoundation.org
Year Founded: 1952
Sales Range: $125-149.9 Million
Emp.: 203
Community Development Services
N.A.I.C.S.: 624190
David A. Arnold *(Pres & CEO)*
Gordon Hein *(Sr VP-Programs)*
Nancy Yuan *(VP & Dir-Washington)*
Ken Krug *(CFO & VP-Fin)*
Julian Rhoads *(Asst Sec)*
Jane Sloane *(Dir-Women's Empowerment Programs)*
Kim McQuay *(Mng Dir-Program Specialists Grp)*
Adam Burke *(Dir-Conflict & Fragility Program)*
Reuben Jeffery III *(Treas)*

THE ASIA PACIFIC FUND, INC.
Gateway Center 3 100 Mulberry St, Newark, NJ 07102-4077
Tel.: (973) 802-6000   MD
Web Site: http://www.asiapacificfund.com
Year Founded: 1987
Rev.: $4,812,547
Assets: $135,175,768
Liabilities: $1,071,593
Net Worth: $134,104,175
Earnings: $2,266,747
Fiscal Year-end: 03/31/17
Investment Services
N.A.I.C.S.: 523999
M. Sadiq Peshimam *(Treas)*
Deborah A. Docs *(Chief Legal Officer & Sec)*
Andrew R. French *(Asst Sec)*
Theresa C. Thompson *(Deputy Chief Compliance Officer)*
Ann Marie Swanson *(Chief Compliance Officer)*
King Lun Au *(Pres)*

THE ASNY CORPORATION
801 S Rampart Blvd Ste 200, Las Vegas, NV 89145-4898
Tel.: (702) 967-5000   NV
Year Founded: 1993
Sales Range: $150-199.9 Million
Emp.: 80
Real Estate Agents & Managers
N.A.I.C.S.: 531210
Arthur Spector *(Pres)*

Subsidiaries:

Soleil Management, LLC (1)
7200 Las Vegas Blvd S Ste A, Las Vegas, NV 89119
Tel.: (702) 367-4010
Web Site: http://www.crmlv.com
Resort Management Services
N.A.I.C.S.: 531312
Dan Haynes *(Dir-HR)*

THE ASPEN BRANDS
2400 Chattahoochee Dr, Duluth, GA 30097
Tel.: (678) 282-0053
Web Site: http://www.theaspenbrands.com
Year Founded: 2004
Sales Range: $10-24.9 Million
Emp.: 55
Wedding Supplies & Services
N.A.I.C.S.: 541921
Jennifer Nichols *(Pres)*

THE ASPEN GROUP, INC.
1100 Wayne Ave Ste 1200, Silver Spring, MD 20910-5644
Tel.: (301) 650-6200
Web Site: http://www.theaspengroupinc.com
Sales Range: $25-49.9 Million
Emp.: 392
Temporary Help Service
N.A.I.C.S.: 561320
Armentha B. Cruise *(Pres & CEO)*
Christina Fitts *(Dir-Corp Rels)*

THE ASSOCIATED GENERAL CONTRACTORS OF AMERICA
2300 Wilson Blvd Ste 300, Arlington, VA 22201
Tel.: (703) 548-3118   DC
Web Site: http://www.agc.org
Year Founded: 1918
Sales Range: $10-24.9 Million
Emp.: 73
Contractor Association
N.A.I.C.S.: 813910
Stephen E. Sandherr *(CEO)*
David R. Lukens *(COO)*
Carolyn McFadden *(Exec Dir)*

THE ASSOCIATED PRESS
200 Liberty St, New York, NY 10281
Tel.: (212) 621-1500   NY
Web Site: https://www.ap.org
Year Founded: 1846
Sales Range: $550-599.9 Million
Newspaper & Broadcast Stations; News Gathering, Reporting & Distribution Services
N.A.I.C.S.: 516210
Gracia C. Martore *(Chm)*
Daisy Veerasingham *(Pres, CEO, COO & Exec VP)*
Karen Kaiser *(Gen Counsel, Sec & Sr VP)*
Ron Nixon *(VP-News, Head-Investigations, Enterprise, Partnerships, and Grants & Editor-Investigations-Intl)*
Howie Rumberg *(Deputy Dir-Digital News, Special Events, and Story Initiatives & Deputy Editor-Sports-Newsgathering,Storytelling)*
Jaime Holguin *(Dir-Original Programming)*
Drew Stoneman *(VP-Consumer Revenue)*
Ted Anthony *(Dir-News Storytelling & Newsroom Innovation)*
Ken Dale *(CFO & Sr VP)*
Kristin Heitmann *(Chief Revenue Officer & Sr VP)*
Julie Pace *(Sr VP & Exec Editor)*

Subsidiaries:

AP Images (1)
200 Liberty St, New York, NY 10281 (100%)
Tel.: (212) 621-1930
Web Site: http://www.apimages.com
Sales Range: $25-49.9 Million
Emp.: 30
Photo Syndication Services
N.A.I.C.S.: 541922
Ken Dale *(VP-Bus-Global)*

The Associated Press (1)
Holbergate 1, N 0166, Oslo, Norway (100%)
Tel.: (47) 22201030
Sales Range: $10-24.9 Million
Emp.: 1
News Syndicates
N.A.I.C.S.: 516210

The Associated Press (Belgium) S.A. (1)
Blvd Charlemagne No 1 Box 49, 1040, Brussels, Belgium
Tel.: (32) 22850110
Web Site: http://www.ap.com
Sales Range: $10-24.9 Million
Emp.: 20
News Syndicates
N.A.I.C.S.: 516210

The Associated Press A/S (1)
Studiutrapee 45, Copenhagen, 1455, Denmark (100%)
Tel.: (45) 33111504
Sales Range: $10-24.9 Million
Emp.: 1
News Syndicates
N.A.I.C.S.: 516210

The Associated Press AB (1)
Skeppsbron 34, Stockholm, 11130, Sweden
Tel.: (46) 854513080
Web Site: http://www.ap.org
Sales Range: $10-24.9 Million
Emp.: 3
News Syndicates
N.A.I.C.S.: 711510
Karl Ritter *(Mgr-Editorial)*

The Associated Press de Venezuela, S.A. (1)
Ave Urdaneta Esquina Animas Edificio El Universal, Office 2D, Caracas, 1010, Venezuela (100%)
Tel.: (58) 2125641834
Web Site: http://www.ap.org
Sales Range: $10-24.9 Million
Emp.: 14
Independent Non-Profit News Cooperative
N.A.I.C.S.: 516210
Joshua Goodman *(Gen Mgr)*

The Associated Press, Inc. (1)
36 King St East Ste 301, Toronto, M5C 2L9, ON, Canada (100%)
Tel.: (416) 368-1388
Web Site: http://www.ap.org
Sales Range: $10-24.9 Million
Emp.: 2
International News Agency
N.A.I.C.S.: 541810
Robert Gillies *(Gen Mgr)*

The Associated Press, Ltd. (1)
3201 Oval Road Camden Lock, London, NW1 7DZ, United Kingdom
Tel.: (44) 2074827400
Web Site: http://www.aptn.com
Sales Range: $25-49.9 Million
Emp.: 250
News Syndicates
N.A.I.C.S.: 516210
Jane Seagrade *(Chief Revenue Officer)*
Darren Long *(Mgr-Video Integration)*
Derl McCrudden *(Deputy Mng Editor-Digital & Visual Journalism)*
James Jordan *(Deputy Dir-News)*

Division (Domestic):

Associated Press Television News (2)
The Interchange Oval Rd Camden Lock, London, NW1 7DZ, United Kingdom
Tel.: (44) 2074827400
Web Site: http://www.aptn.com
Sales Range: $25-49.9 Million
Emp.: 200
News Distribution Services
N.A.I.C.S.: 519290

THE ASSOCIATION OF PLASTIC RECYCLERS
1776 K St NW, Washington, DC 20006
Tel.: (202) 316-3046
Web Site: http://plasticsrecycling.org
Plastics Recycling
N.A.I.C.S.: 423930
Steve Alexander *(Pres)*

Subsidiaries:

Resource Recycling, Inc. (1)
PO Box 42270, Portland, OR 97242-0270
Tel.: (503) 233-1305
Web Site: http://www.resource-recycling.com
Periodical Publishers
N.A.I.C.S.: 513120
Rick Downing *(Dir-Adv)*
Dan Leif *(Mng Editor)*
Jef Drawbaugh *(Dir-Business Operations & Publ)*
Scott Beck *(Mgr-Web Content)*

THE ASSURED GROUP
5613 Blue Bird Ave, Dallas, TX 75237
Tel.: (972) 230-2626
Web Site: http://www.theassuredgroup.com
Sales Range: $10-24.9 Million
Emp.: 6
Warehousing, Self Storage
N.A.I.C.S.: 531130
Donald Valk *(Pres)*

THE ASTOR CROWNE PLAZA NEW ORLEANS
739 Canal St at Bourbon, New Orleans, LA 70130
Tel.: (504) 962-0500
Web Site: http://www.astorneworleans.com
Sales Range: $10-24.9 Million
Emp.: 100
Hotel Services
N.A.I.C.S.: 721110
Melinda Oates *(Dir-HR)*

THE ASYLUM
72 E Palm Ave, Burbank, CA 91502
Tel.: (323) 850-1214
Web Site: http://www.theasylum.cc
Sales Range: $10-24.9 Million

The Asylum—(Continued)
Emp.: 40
Video Production Services
N.A.I.C.S.: 512110
David Michael Latt *(Partner-Production)*
David Rimawi *(Partner-Sls & Distr)*
Paul Bales *(Partner-Admin & Ops)*
Micho Rutare *(Dir-Dev)*

THE ATLANTA BREAD COMPANY
1200 Wilson Way Ste 100, Smyrna, GA 30082-7212
Tel.: (770) 432-0933
Web Site: http://www.atlantabread.com
Year Founded: 1993
Sales Range: $1-9.9 Million
Emp.: 130
Bakery & Sandwich Cafe
N.A.I.C.S.: 722513
Jerry Couvaras *(Pres & CEO)*
Basil Couvaras *(COO & VP)*
Robert Cross *(VP-Dev)*
David Robins *(Sr Dir-R&D)*

THE ATLAS GROUP
4425 W May St Building A, Wichita, KS 67209-2841
Tel.: (316) 942-7931
Web Site: http://www.atlasgroupaero.com
Aerospace Products & Services
N.A.I.C.S.: 336412
Jim McMullen *(CEO)*

Subsidiaries:

WASI, Inc. (1)
4425 W May St, Wichita, KS 67209
Tel.: (316) 219-5862
Web Site: http://www.atlasgroupaero.com
Aircraft Parts & Auxiliary Equipment Mfr
N.A.I.C.S.: 336413

THE AUBURN MANUFACTURING COMPANY
29 Stack St, Middletown, CT 06457-2265
Tel.: (860) 346-6677 CT
Web Site: http://www.auburn-mfg.com
Year Founded: 1925
Sales Range: $10-24.9 Million
Emp.: 27
Sealing Components, Bushings, Gaskets, Packings, O-Rings, Rod Wipers, Shims & Spacers
N.A.I.C.S.: 339991
Gary Mittelman *(VP-Adv)*

THE AURORA FUNDS INC.
2525 Meridian Pkwy, Durham, NC 27713
Tel.: (919) 484-0400
Web Site: http://www.aurorafunds.com
Rev.: $1,100,000
Emp.: 12
Commodity Contracts Dealing
N.A.I.C.S.: 523160
Bill Willis *(CIO)*
Jeff Clark *(Mng Gen Partner)*
Scott Albert *(Partner)*
Jan Bouten *(Partner)*
Chris Kroeger *(Partner)*

THE AUTISM PROGRAM OF VIRGINIA, INC.
2201 W Broad St Ste 107, Richmond, VA 23220
Tel.: (804) 355-0300 VA
Web Site: http://www.autismva.org
Year Founded: 1995
Sales Range: $1-9.9 Million
Emp.: 35

Developmental Disability Assistance Services
N.A.I.C.S.: 623210
Donald Oswald *(Dir-Diagnostics & Res)*
Jessica G. Philips *(COO & VP)*
John Toscano *(Pres)*
Doug Garrou *(Chm)*
Kerry Blumberg *(Chm-Dev)*
Nan Pemberton *(Treas)*
Patrick Wood *(Sec)*
Tyler Hart *(CEO)*

Subsidiaries:

Good Foods Grocery, Inc. (1)
3062 Stony Point Rd, Richmond, VA 23235
Tel.: (804) 320-6767
Web Site: http://www.goodfoodsgrocery.com
Rev.: $2,900,000
Emp.: 45
Local Specialty Grocery Store
N.A.I.C.S.: 445110
Angela Wiggins *(VP)*
Susan Daniel *(Gen Mgr)*

THE AUTO CLUB GROUP
1 Auto Club Dr, Dearborn, MI 48126
Tel.: (313) 336-1234 MI
Web Site: http://www.aaa.com
Automobile Passenger Advocacy & Services Organization
N.A.I.C.S.: 813410
Joseph Richardson *(Pres & CEO)*
Tony Alberton *(VP-Tennessee)*
Siewhiang McCreight *(Chief Risk Officer & VP)*

Subsidiaries:

ACG Insurance Agency, LLC (1)
1 Auto Club Dr, Dearborn, MI 48126
Tel.: (313) 336-1234
Web Site: http://michigan.aaa.com
Insurance Agents
N.A.I.C.S.: 524210

Auto Club Trust, FSB (1)
1 Auto Club Dr, Dearborn, MI 48126
Tel.: (313) 336-8400
Web Site: http://aaabanking.mi.aaa.com
Emp.: 52
Federal Savings Bank
N.A.I.C.S.: 522180
Diane Mallette *(COO)*
Suzanne Mendlik *(Chief Risk Officer)*
Greg Barta *(Chief Credit Officer)*
Bart Qualsett *(Pres & CEO)*

Co-Headquarters (Domestic):

Auto Club Trust, FSB - Omaha (132nd St.) Branch (2)
2606 S 132nd St, Omaha, NE 68144
Tel.: (402) 861-3100
Web Site: http://aaabanking.mi.aaa.com
Emp.: 3
Executive Office; Savings, Lending & Investment Bank
N.A.I.C.S.: 921110
Bart Qualsett *(Pres & CEO)*
Suzanne Mendlik *(Chief Risk Officer)*

THE AVEON GROUP L.P.
30 Doaks Ln, Marblehead, MA 01945
Tel.: (781) 639-3000 DE
Sales Range: $50-74.9 Million
Investment Management Service
N.A.I.C.S.: 523150
John J. Hassett *(Chm, Pres & CEO)*
Jeffrey C. Landle *(Chief Investment Officer)*

THE AVI GROUP
985 Old Eagle School Rd Ste 509, Wayne, PA 19087
Tel.: (610) 687-4076
Web Site: http://www.avigrp.net
Insurance Brokerage, Risk Management & Consulting Services
N.A.I.C.S.: 524210
Andre Duggin *(Chm & CEO)*

THE AYRES GROUP, LLC
123 W Hatch St, Sturgis, MI 49091
Tel.: (269) 651-1761 MI
Web Site: http://www.theayres-group.com
Year Founded: 2012
Holding Company; Insurance Agencies
N.A.I.C.S.: 551112
Jeffrey M. Mohney *(Owner)*
Thomas N. Olvitt *(Partner)*

Subsidiaries:

A.W. Ayres Agency, Inc. (1)
123 W Hatch St, Sturgis, MI 49091
Tel.: (269) 651-1761
Web Site: http://www.theayres-group.com
Sales Range: $1-9.9 Million
Emp.: 14
Insurance Agents
N.A.I.C.S.: 524210
Jeffrey M. Mohney *(Pres)*
Patricia L. Barnard *(Principal)*
Jeff Brazo *(Principal)*

Ayres-Rice Insurance Agency, Inc. (1)
452 N Grand St, Schoolcraft, MI 49087
Tel.: (269) 679-4918
Web Site: http://www.theayres-group.com
Emp.: 23
Insurance Agents
N.A.I.C.S.: 524210
Thomas N. Olvitt *(Principal)*
Timothy Ashcraft *(Mgr-Ops)*
Diana Mezo *(Office Mgr)*

Noecker Agency LLC (1)
67125 US Hwy 131, Constantine, MI 49042
Tel.: (269) 435-3455
Web Site: http://www.theayres-group.com
Emp.: 7
Insurance Agents
N.A.I.C.S.: 524210
Jeffrey Mohney *(Principal)*
Thomas N. Olvitt *(Principal)*
Crystal Scott *(Mgr-Life & Health Risk)*
Deana Bowman *(Mgr-Comml Lines Risk)*
Jane Dimmick *(Mgr-Comml Lines Risk)*
Jo Van Horn *(Mgr-Personal Lines Risk)*
Kim Tackett *(Mgr-Personal Lines Risk)*
Rose Brenner *(Mgr-Personal Lines Risk)*
Tracy Larsen *(Mgr-Comml Lines Risk)*

South County Insurance Agency, LLC (1)
220 W Prairie Rd, Vicksburg, MI 49097
Tel.: (269) 649-1914
Web Site: http://www.theayres-group.com
Emp.: 6
Insurance Agents
N.A.I.C.S.: 524210
Thomas N. Olvitt *(Principal)*
Steven Brundige *(Principal)*
Shelly Hochstedler *(Office Mgr)*

THE AZTECA-OMEGA GROUP
2518 Chalk Hill Rd, Dallas, TX 75212
Tel.: (214) 689-3815
Web Site: http://www.azteca-omega.com
Sales Range: $100-124.9 Million
Emp.: 450
Engineeering Services
N.A.I.C.S.: 236220
Luis Spinola *(Pres & CEO)*
Kurt Diedrich *(Mgr-Program & Project Mgr)*

THE B. F. SHAW PRINTING COMPANY
7717 South Illinois Route 3, Crystal Lake, IL 60014
Tel.: (815) 459-4040
Web Site: http://www.shawmedia.com
Year Founded: 1851
Newspaper Publishers
N.A.I.C.S.: 513110
J. Tom Shaw *(VP & Publisher-Illinois Grp)*
John Rung *(Pres & CEO)*

Don Bricker *(VP-Ops)*
Jason Hegna *(Dir-IL Revenue)*
Bob Edwards *(Dir-Grp Circulation)*
Laura Shaw *(Dir-Mktg & Specialty Printing)*
Jim Ringness *(Gen Mgr-Northwest Herald)*
Ryan Wells *(Gen Mgr-Suburban Grp Weeklies)*
Steve Vanisko *(Gen Mgr-Joliet Herald-News)*
Rich Paulsen *(Publisher-Creston News Advertiser)*

Subsidiaries:

Daily News Tribune Inc. (1)
426 2nd St, La Salle, IL 61301
Tel.: (815) 223-3200
Web Site: http://www.newstrib.com
Rev.: $10,200,000
Emp.: 142
Fiscal Year-end: 12/31/2015
Newspapers, Publishing & Printing
N.A.I.C.S.: 513110
Joyce McCullough *(Publr)*
Scott Stavrakas *(VP-Sls & Mktg)*

Kendall County Record, Inc. (1)
109 W Veterans Pkwy, Yorkville, IL 60560
Tel.: (630) 553-7034
Web Site: http://www.kendallcountynow.com
Emp.: 8
Newspaper Publishers
N.A.I.C.S.: 513110
John Etheredge *(Editor)*
Ryan Wells *(Gen Mgr)*

THE BABY FOLD
108 E Willow St, Normal, IL 61761
Tel.: (309) 454-1770 IL
Web Site: http://www.thebabyfold.org
Year Founded: 1902
Sales Range: $10-24.9 Million
Emp.: 250
Child Development Services
N.A.I.C.S.: 624110
Dianne Schultz *(Pres & CEO)*
Margaret Gould *(Dir-Residential Svcs)*
Jennifer Keen *(VP-Fin & Facilities)*
Robert Lusk *(Dir-Clinical)*
Karen Rousey *(VP-Programs)*
Deb Armstrong *(VP-Quality Info Sys)*
Karen Major *(Dir-Family & Community Svcs)*
Veronica Manzella *(VP-HR)*
Patricia Grogg *(Interim VP-Dev & PR)*
Aimee Beam *(Dir-Major Gifts)*

THE BACON VENEER COMPANY
6951 High Grove Blvd, Burr Ridge, IL 60527
Tel.: (630) 323-1414
Web Site: http://www.baconveneer.com
Year Founded: 1898
Sales Range: $10-24.9 Million
Emp.: 125
Wood Products Mfr
N.A.I.C.S.: 321999
Jim McCracken *(Pres)*
David McCracken *(VP)*

THE BAILEY COMPANY INC.
501 Cowan St, Nashville, TN 37207-5617
Tel.: (615) 238-2601 TN
Web Site: http://www.baileycompany.com
Year Founded: 1979
Sales Range: $75-99.9 Million
Emp.: 300
Distr of Material Handling Equipment
N.A.I.C.S.: 423830
Bert Bailey *(CEO)*

THE BAILIWICK COMPANY

4 Sanford Rd, Stockton, NJ 08559
Tel.: (609) 397-4880
Web Site: http://www.bailiwickpr.com
Year Founded: 1992
Sales Range: Less than $1 Million
Emp.: 7
Public Relations Agency
N.A.I.C.S.: 541820
Janis Burenga *(Founder & CEO)*
Meridith Scott *(Sr VP)*

THE BAINBRIDGE COMPANIES LLC
12765 W Forest Hill Blvd Ste 1307, Wellington, FL 33414
Tel.: (561) 333-3669
Web Site:
  http://www.bainbridgecompanies.com
Year Founded: 1993
Sales Range: $100-124.9 Million
Emp.: 275
Luxury Multifamily Apartment Communities Owner, Developer & Manager
N.A.I.C.S.: 531311
Gail A. Ruggles *(Exec VP-Ops)*
Richard Schechter *(Chm, CEO & Mng Principal)*
Thomas J. Keady *(Pres)*
Robert W. Gaherty *(Principal)*
Paul DeCain *(Chief Investment Officer & Principal)*
Burk Hedrick *(Mgr-Dev)*
Alex Eyssen *(VP-Student Housing)*
Shannon Lee *(Dir-Dev)*
Kevin Keane *(COO & Exec VP)*
Tony Lopez *(CIO)*
Shae Shults *(Chief Strategy Officer)*

THE BAIRD MACHINERY CORPORATION
171 River St, Thomaston, CT 06787
Tel.: (860) 283-1000
Web Site: http://www.us-baird.com
Production Machine Tools Mfr
N.A.I.C.S.: 333517

THE BAKER COMPANIES
1 W Red Oak Ln, White Plains, NY 10604
Tel.: (914) 461-9000
Web Site:
  http://www.thebakercompanies.com
Sales Range: $10-24.9 Million
Emp.: 250
Residential Construction Services
N.A.I.C.S.: 236118
William Baker *(Owner)*

THE BAKERSFIELD CALIFORNIAN
1707 Eye St, Bakersfield, CA 93301-5208
Tel.: (661) 395-7500 CA
Web Site: http://www.bakersfield.com
Year Founded: 1866
Sales Range: $75-99.9 Million
Emp.: 100
Newspaper Publishing & Commercial Printing Services
N.A.I.C.S.: 513110
Logan Molen *(COO & Sr VP)*
Andrea Johnston *(Acct Exec)*
Michelle L. Chantry *(Pres & CEO)*
Aileen Tejero *(Coord-Sls)*
Christine Benavente *(Dir-Interactive Ops & Product Dev)*
Chris Ladd *(Mgr-Online Dev)*
Charmaine Lyons *(Mgr-Ops)*
Mike Skrocki *(VP-Ops)*
Jim Lawitz *(VP & Exec Editor)*
John Cox *(Editor-Bus)*

THE BAKERY, CONFECTIONERY, TOBACCO WORKERS AND GRAIN MILLERS INTERNATIONAL UNION
10401 Connecticut Ave 4th Fl, Kensington, MD 20895
Tel.: (301) 933-8600 MD
Web Site: http://www.bctgm.org
Year Founded: 1886
Sales Range: $10-24.9 Million
Emp.: 41
Labor Union
N.A.I.C.S.: 813930
David B. Durkee *(Pres)*
Steve Bertelli *(Treas & Sec)*
Ron Baker *(Coord-Strategic Campaign)*

THE BALCOM AGENCY
1500 Ballinger, Fort Worth, TX 76102
Tel.: (817) 877-9933
Web Site:
  http://www.balcomagency.com
Year Founded: 1993
Sales Range: $10-24.9 Million
Emp.: 39
Advertising Agencies
N.A.I.C.S.: 541810
Stuart Balcom *(Pres & CEO)*
Carol Glover *(Dir-Creative)*
David Sims *(Sr Dir-Art)*
Toni Stuard *(Acct Mgr)*
Richie Escovedo *(Acct Dir)*
Christina McKinney *(Acct Dir)*
Taylor Potts *(Dir-Creative-Multimedia)*
Lesley Dupre *(Dir-Acct)*
Norma Ramos *(Coord-Accts Payable)*
Audrey Stewart *(Acct Dir)*
Lynne Swihart *(Dir-Production Svcs)*
Trey Sprinkle *(Dir-Creative-Brand)*
Jessica Murdock *(Mgr-Front Desk & Office)*
Christine Cantrell *(Acct Mgr)*

THE BALTIMORE MUSEUM OF ART
10 Art Museum Dr, Baltimore, MD 21218-3898
Tel.: (443) 573-1700 MD
Web Site: http://www.artbma.org
Year Founded: 1914
Sales Range: $10-24.9 Million
Emp.: 237
Art Museum Operator
N.A.I.C.S.: 712110
Christine Dietze Bonanno *(CFO)*
Virginia Anderson *(Head-American Art)*

THE BALTUS COMPANY
407 S Chestnut Ave, Marshfield, WI 54449
Tel.: (715) 384-3178
Web Site: http://www.baltusoil.com
Rev.: $12,400,000
Emp.: 95
Gasoline Stations
N.A.I.C.S.: 457120
Frank Baltus *(VP)*
John Baltus *(Pres)*

THE BANC FUNDS COMPANY LLC
20 N Waker Dr, Chicago, IL 60606
Tel.: (312) 855-6202 IL
Year Founded: 1986
Sales Range: $10-24.9 Million
Emp.: 10
Investors in Bank Stocks
N.A.I.C.S.: 523999
Charles Joseph Moore *(Pres)*
Susan Hill *(Sec)*

THE BANK OF CANTON
557 Washington St, Canton, MA 02021
Tel.: (781) 828-1690
Web Site:
  http://www.ibankcanton.com
Sales Range: $25-49.9 Million
Emp.: 400
Mutual Benefit Associations
N.A.I.C.S.: 522291
Peter M. Shea *(Sr VP-Ops)*
Stephen P. Costello *(Pres & CEO)*
Brian J. Allsop *(VP-Fin Svcs)*
Rhonda L. Kale *(Sr VP-Compliance & CRA)*
John G. McCarthy *(VP-Comml Lending)*
Michelle Higgins *(Sr VP-HR)*
Paula M. Burke *(VP-Bus Dev & Govt Banking)*
George M. DeMello *(Sr VP-Residential Lending)*
John M. Sweeney *(CFO & Sr VP)*
Michael F. Lindberg *(Sr VP)*
Anthony F. Caruso *(Sr VP-Branch Admin)*
Lori J. Webber *(Chief Credit Officer & Sr VP)*
Peter Fredericksen *(Dir-Life Solutions)*
Juan Barrera *(Asst VP & Branch Mgr)*
Elaine Joseph *(Asst VP & Branch Mgr)*
John Sharry *(Sr VP-Comml Lending)*
Deborah Bearde *(Asst Mgr-Randolph)*
Lisa Goble *(VP-Residential Lending)*
Mary Rezendes *(VP)*
Dana MacKinnon *(Mgr-Loan Ops & Client Support)*

THE BANK OF EDWARDSVILLE INC.
330 W Vandalia St, Edwardsville, IL 62025-1911
Tel.: (618) 656-0057 IL
Web Site: http://www.4thebank.com
Year Founded: 1868
Sales Range: $350-399.9 Million
Emp.: 400
Commercial Banking Services
N.A.I.C.S.: 522110
Joann Barton *(Sr VP)*
Rick R. Parks *(Sr VP-Comml Banking Grp)*
Kevin Powers *(Pres & CEO)*

THE BANK OF ELK RIVER
630 Main St, Elk River, MN 55330
Tel.: (763) 441-1000
Web Site:
  http://www.thebankofelkriver.com
Year Founded: 1885
Sales Range: $10-24.9 Million
Emp.: 122
Commerical Banking
N.A.I.C.S.: 522110
Tom Lund *(VP)*

THE BANK OF MAUSTON
503 Gtwy Ave 82 E, Mauston, WI 53948
Tel.: (608) 847-6200
Web Site:
  http://www.bankofmauston.com
Rev.: $12,900,000
Emp.: 108
Commerical Banking
N.A.I.C.S.: 522110
William H. Bosshard *(Chm)*
Kari L. Schmidt *(Sec)*
Robert L. Fait *(Pres)*
Michael Lindert *(Exec VP)*

THE BANK OF MISSOURI
916 N Kings Hwy, Perryville, MO 63775
Tel.: (573) 547-6541 MO
Web Site:
  http://www.bankofmissouri.com
Year Founded: 1891
State Commercial Banks
N.A.I.C.S.: 522110
R. David Crader *(Exec Chm)*
Martha J. Rollet *(Exec VP-Ops Officer)*
Adrian Breen *(Pres & CEO)*
Dawn Dauer *(Chief Banking Officer)*
Stanley Naeger *(CFO)*
Wendell Mueller *(Chief Credit Officer)*

THE BANK OF ROMNEY
95 E Main St, Romney, WV 26757
Tel.: (304) 822-3541
Web Site:
  http://www.bankofromney.net
Sales Range: $10-24.9 Million
Emp.: 90
Commericial Banking
N.A.I.C.S.: 522110
Dean Young *(CFO & VP)*
Lawrence E. Foley *(Pres)*
Marlin C. Biggs *(Chm)*

THE BANK STREET GROUP LLC
Four Landmark Sq 3rd Fl, Stamford, CT 06901
Tel.: (203) 252-2800
Web Site:
  http://www.bankstreetgroup.com
Investment Banking Services
N.A.I.C.S.: 523150
Richard S. Lukaj *(Sr Mng Dir)*
James H. Henry *(Sr Mng Dir)*
Amy Seach Johnson *(Mng Dir)*
Gardner L. Grant *(Mng Dir)*
Jon Vanden Heuvel *(Mng Dir)*

THE BAPTIST HOME OF PHILADELPHIA
8301 Roosevelt Blvd, Philadelphia, PA 19152
Tel.: (215) 624-7575 PA
Web Site: http://www.deer-meadows.org
Year Founded: 1869
Sales Range: $25-49.9 Million
Emp.: 534
Lifecare Retirement Community Operator
N.A.I.C.S.: 623311
Lisa Sofia *(Pres & CEO)*
Margi Johnston *(Dir-Community Education)*
Eric Gales *(Dir-Maintenance)*

THE BAPTIST HOME, INC.
101 Riggs-Scott Ln, Ironton, MO 63650
Tel.: (573) 546-2709
Web Site:
  http://www.thebaptisthome.org
Sales Range: $10-24.9 Million
Emp.: 212
Senior Living Services
N.A.I.C.S.: 623312
Karl Snider *(CFO)*
Frank E. Fain *(Dir-Educational Svcs)*
Steven R. Jones *(Pres & CEO)*

THE BARBOUR GROUP, LLC
20 Liberty St Ste 2D, Westminster, MD 21157
Tel.: (410) 876-9610
Web Site:
  http://www.thebarbourgroup.com
Year Founded: 2002
Rev.: $3,600,000
Emp.: 9
Business Support Services
N.A.I.C.S.: 561499
Karen Barbour *(Founder & Pres)*
Christopher R. Smith *(VP-Sls & Mktg)*
Debby Nash *(VP-Ops)*
Vanessa Lopez *(Dir-Underwriter)*

The Barbour Group, LLC—(Continued)

THE BARDEN & ROBESON CORPORATION
103 Kelly Ave, Middleport, NY 14105-1242
Tel.: (716) 735-3732
Web Site: http://www.bardenhomes.com
Year Founded: 1909
Sales Range: $75-99.9 Million
Emp.: 50
Mfr of Prefabricated Homes
N.A.I.C.S.: 321992
Tim Gelder (VP)

THE BARKING DOG, LTD.
7 Beech Hill Rd, Exeter, NH 03833
Tel.: (603) 773-2275
Web Site: http://www.thebarkingdog.com
Year Founded: 1998
Sales Range: $1-9.9 Million
Emp.: 52
Animal Care Services, Including Boarding & Grooming & Pet Products
N.A.I.C.S.: 812910
Jody Rodgers (Owner & Pres)
Stephanie Workinger (Dir-Ops)

THE BARTHOLOMEW COMPANY, INC.
370 Main St Ste 1000, Worcester, MA 01608
Tel.: (508) 753-8807
Web Site: http://www.bartandco.com
Investment Services
N.A.I.C.S.: 523999
Thomas Bartholomew (Pres & CEO)

THE BASEBALL CLUB OF SEATTLE, L.P.
1250 1st Ave S, Seattle, WA 98134-1216
Tel.: (206) 346-4001
Web Site: http://www.mariners.com
Year Founded: 1977
Sales Range: $150-199.9 Million
Emp.: 200
Professional Baseball Club
N.A.I.C.S.: 711211
Randy Adamack (Sr VP)
Bob Aylward (Exec VP-Bus Ops)
Kevin Martinez (Sr VP-Mktg & Comm)
Kevin Mather (CEO)
Joe Chard (VP-Community Rels & Corp Bus)
Tim Kornegay (CFO & Exec VP)
Greg Massey (Controller)
Dave Curry (VP-Info Svcs)
Frances Traisman (Sr VP-Sls)
Chris Gwynn (Dir-Player Dev)
Alisia Anderson (Dir-Ballpark Sls & Mktg-Safeco Field)
John Stanton (Chm & Mng Partner)
Jerry Dipoto (Exec VP & Gen Mgr-Baseball Ops)
Fred Rivera (Exec VP & Gen Counsel-Legal & Govt Affairs)
Trevor Gooby (Sr VP-Ballpark Ops)

THE BATEMAN GROUP
1550 Bryant St Ste 450, San Francisco, CA 94103-4832
Tel.: (415) 503-1818
Web Site: http://www.bateman-group.com
Year Founded: 2004
Sales Range: $1-9.9 Million
Emp.: 500
Digital Communications, Content Marketing, Social Media, Analytics & Public Relations
N.A.I.C.S.: 541820

Frederick Bateman (Founder & CEO)
Bill Bourdon (Co-Pres & Partner)
Tyler L. Perry (Co-Pres & Partner)
Paula Cavagnaro (Exec VP)
Elinor Mills (Sr VP-Content Studio)
Shannon Hutto (Exec VP & Gen Mgr-SF)
Jennifer Steinle (VP-Ops)
Shannon Osthimer (Mgr-Ops)
James Niccolai (Dir-Content & Media Strategy)

Subsidiaries:

The Bateman Group (1)
20 Jay St Suite 1005, Brooklyn, NY 11201 (100%)
Tel.: (718) 576-2463
Web Site: http://www.bateman-group.com
New Business Development, Communications & Public Relations
N.A.I.C.S.: 541820
Chris Heine (Dir-Content & Media Strategy)

THE BAUPOST GROUP LLC
10 Saint James Ave Ste 1700, Boston, MA 02116
Tel.: (617) 210-8300
Web Site: http://www.baupost.com
Investment Management Service
N.A.I.C.S.: 523999
Seth Klarman (CEO & Portfolio Mgr)
Tom Blumenthal (Partner & Head-Private Corp Investments)

THE BAWMANN GROUP
3511 Ringsby Ct No 101, Denver, CO 80216
Tel.: (303) 320-7790
Web Site: http://www.morethanpr.com
Year Founded: 1995
Sales Range: $10-24.9 Million
Emp.: 7
Consulting, Corporate Identity, Public Relations
N.A.I.C.S.: 541820
Brad Bawmann (Owner)
Tammy Stratton (VP-Client Svcs)
Jennifer Nuhfer (VP-Comm)

THE BCB GROUP, INC.
10 Alexander Dr, Wallingford, CT 06492
Tel.: (203) 630-7800
Web Site: http://www.bcbgroup.com
Year Founded: 1985
Sales Range: $25-49.9 Million
Emp.: 12
Advertising Agencies, Automotive, Aviation, Brand Development, Communications, E-Commerce, Internet/Web Design, Public Relations
N.A.I.C.S.: 541810
Dick Belmont (VP-Creative Svcs)
John Cordone (VP)
Tracy Bugryn (Mgr-Media AE)
Joseph Bunovsky Jr. (Sr Acct Exec)

Subsidiaries:

ByDesign, Inc. (1)
10 Alexander Dr, Wallingford, CT 06492-8400
Tel.: (203) 630-7810
Web Site: http://www.bydesigninc.com
Rev.: $10,000,000
Advetising Agency
N.A.I.C.S.: 541810

THE BEACH HOUSE SWIMWEAR, INC.
15870 Pine Ridge Rd Ste 2, Fort Myers, FL 33908
Tel.: (239) 466-3414
Web Site: http://www.aquabeachwear.com
Year Founded: 1987
Sales Range: $1-9.9 Million

Emp.: 60
Clothing Stores
N.A.I.C.S.: 458110
Donald Bauer (Pres & CEO)

THE BEAIRD GROUP
236 S Washington St Ste 208, Naperville, IL 60540
Tel.: (630) 637-0430
Web Site: http://www.beairdgroup.com
Year Founded: 1981
Sales Range: $1-9.9 Million
Emp.: 56
Management Consulting Services
N.A.I.C.S.: 541611
Deborah Wiley Beaird (Owner & Co-Pres)
Laura Coulter (Mng Dir)

THE BEAVER EXCAVATING COMPANY, INC.
2000 Beaver Pl Ave SW, Canton, OH 44706-1935
Tel.: (330) 478-2151
Web Site: http://www.beaverexcavating.com
Year Founded: 1953
Sales Range: $25-49.9 Million
Emp.: 300
Provider of Excavation Work
N.A.I.C.S.: 238910
Mark Sterling (Pres & CEO)
Jack Ford (VP)
Samantha Bour (Project Mgr)
Randy Martin (Dir-Safety)

Subsidiaries:

Stone Products Inc. (1)
3105 Varley Ave, Canton, OH 44706-1935
Tel.: (330) 484-6088
Web Site: http://www.stonepro.com
Sales Range: $10-24.9 Million
Emp.: 23
Mfr of Construction & Mining Machinery
N.A.I.C.S.: 423810
Tom Kovesci (VP & Gen Mgr)

THE BECK GROUP
1807 Ross Ave Ste 500, Dallas, TX 75201-4691
Tel.: (214) 303-6200
Web Site: http://www.beckgroup.com
Year Founded: 1912
Sales Range: $500-549.9 Million
Emp.: 600
Building Design & Contracting Services
N.A.I.C.S.: 236220
Brad Phillips (CEO-Intl)
Kip E. Daniel (Mng Dir)
Rick del Monte (Chief Design Officer)
Mark Collins (CFO)
Mark House (Mng Dir)
Paul Higgins (COO)
Ben Bard (Dir-Atlanta)
Matt Williamson (Gen Counsel)
Joe Flores (Chief Admin Officer)
Scot Bennett (Dir-Fort Worth)
David Morris (Principal-Design-Denver)
David Hutchison (Dir-Client Svcs-Atlanta)
Matt Pickens (Mgr-Ops-Austin)
Bob Proske (Sr Project Mgr)
Bryce Morrow (CIO)
Holly Crowder (Chief HR Officer)
Jeff Forbes (Reg Dir)
Norma Lehman (Dir-Sustainability)
Frederick P. Perpall (CEO)
Caroline Vostrejs (Dir-Bus Dev-Tampa)
Bryan Wilson (Mgr-Ops-Tampa)
Humberto Trevino (Dir Gen)
Drew Thigpen (Mng Dir-Fort Worth)
Chad Prochaska (Dir-Preconstruction)

Chad Schieber (Chief Mktg Officer)
Olu Beck (Founder & CEO)
Henry C. Beck III (Chm)

THE BEDROOM STORE
2440 Adie Rd, Maryland Heights, MO 63043-3504
Tel.: (314) 997-5222
Web Site: http://www.thebedroomstore.com
Year Founded: 1977
Sales Range: $100-124.9 Million
Emp.: 100
Retail of Bedroom Furnishings; Fluid Suspension Beds, Air Beds & Related Furniture
N.A.I.C.S.: 449110
Brian Davis (Gen Mgr)
Brenden Weco (Mgr)
Jason Hessell (Mgr)

Subsidiaries:

Accent Furniture, Inc. (1)
2440 Adie Rd, Maryland Heights, MO 63043-3504
Tel.: (314) 569-0259
Web Site: http://www.accentbedroomfurniture.com
Sales Range: $25-49.9 Million
Emp.: 30
Mfr & Wholesale Distribution of Oak & Pine Bedroom Furniture
N.A.I.C.S.: 337122

Boyd Flotation, Inc (1)
2440 Adie Rd, Maryland Heights, MO 63043-3504 (100%)
Tel.: (314) 569-0259
Web Site: http://www.boydflotation.com
Sales Range: $25-49.9 Million
Emp.: 80
Mfr And Distributer Of Vinyl Waterbeds, Softside & Fluid Suspension Beds, Latex & Airbeds & All Related Accessories
N.A.I.C.S.: 337910

THE BEEKMAN GROUP, LLC
530 5th Ave 23rd Fl, New York, NY 10036
Tel.: (646) 502-3300
Web Site: http://www.thebeekmangroup.com
Year Founded: 2004
Privater Equity Firm
N.A.I.C.S.: 523999
John G. Troiano (Co-Founder, CEO & Mng Partner)
Vincent Aiello (CFO)
Alex Grzymala (VP)
Crystal Smith (Principal-IR)
Jonathan Kelemen (Principal)

Subsidiaries:

Another Broken Egg of America LLC (1)
5955 T G Lee Blvd Ste 100, Orlando, FL 32822
Tel.: (407) 440-0450
Web Site: http://www.anotherbrokenegg.com
Breakfast & Brunch Restaurants
N.A.I.C.S.: 722513
Ronald Stuart (Dir-Design & Construction)

Convenient Payments, LLC (1)
12884 Frontrunner Blvd Ste 220, Draper, UT 84020
Tel.: (855) 872-6632
Web Site: http://www.convenientpayments.com
Online Payment Services
N.A.I.C.S.: 425120
Casey Leloux (CEO)

Subsidiary (Domestic):

Mainstreet Computers, Inc. (2)
330 Charles St Ste 101, Belleville, MI 48111
Tel.: (734) 699-0025
Web Site: http://mainstreetcomp.com
Computer Integrated Systems Design, Nsk
N.A.I.C.S.: 541512
David Carnahan (CEO)

COMPANIES

Division (Domestic):

DialMark, LLC (3)
7390 S Creek Rd Ste 203, Sandy, UT 84093
Tel.: (801) 413-1831
Web Site: http://www.dbcontrols.com
Rev.: $1,105,000
Emp.: 5
Computer System Design Services
N.A.I.C.S.: 541512
John Whornton (Founder)

GED Integrated Solutions, Inc. (1)
9280 Dutton Dr, Twinsburg, OH 44087-1967
Tel.: (330) 963-5401
Web Site: http://www.gedusa.com
Insulating Glass, Vinyl Window & Door Fabrication Systems Mfr
N.A.I.C.S.: 327212
Bill Weaver (Pres & CEO)
Chris Wale (Sls Mgr-Europe)
Ken Farrell (Project Mgr)
Randy Moss (Mgr-Vinyl Design & Dev)

P&R Dental Strategies, LLC (1)
300 American Metro Blvd Ste 190, Hamilton, NJ 08619
Tel.: (609) 783-9004
Web Site: https://www.pandrdental.com
Dental Informatics Company
N.A.I.C.S.: 561990

Subsidiary (Domestic):

Dentistat, Inc. (2)
455 Los Gatos Blvd, Ste 206, Los Gatos, CA 95032
Tel.: (800) 336-8250
Web Site: https://www.dentistat.com
Business Consulting Services
N.A.I.C.S.: 541618
Richard H. Guenther (Chm)

THE BEHLER-YOUNG CO., INC.
4900 Clyde Park Ave SW, Grand Rapids, MI 49509-5118
Tel.: (616) 531-3400   MI
Web Site: http://www.behler-young.com
Year Founded: 1926
Sales Range: $25-49.9 Million
Emp.: 200
Provider of Warm Air Heating & Air Conditioning Services
N.A.I.C.S.: 423730
Doug Young (Pres)
Bob Compton (Mgr-Northeast Reg-Warren)
Jim Kemper (Mgr-Grand Rapids)
Mark Newald (Mgr-Muskegon)
John Santiago (Mgr-Ann Arbor)
Dave DeJonge (CFO)

THE BEISTLE COMPANY, INC.
1 Beistle Plz, Shippensburg, PA 17257-9746
Tel.: (717) 532-2131   PA
Web Site: http://www.beistle.com
Year Founded: 1900
Rev.: $12,071,314
Emp.: 300
Mfr of Converted Paper Products
N.A.I.C.S.: 322299
Christopher Keegan (VP-Fin)
Tricia Lacy (Pres)

THE BELDEN BRICK COMPANY INC.
PO Box 20910, Canton, OH 44701-0910
Tel.: (330) 451-2031   DE
Web Site: http://www.beldenbrick.com
Year Founded: 1885
Sales Range: $50-74.9 Million
Emp.: 500
Brick, Stone & Concrete Block Mfr & Distr
N.A.I.C.S.: 327120

Robert F. Belden (Chm, Pres & CEO)
Brian Belden (VP-Sls & Mktg)
Robert T. Belden (VP-Ops)
Bradley H. Belden (Dir-Support Svcs)

Subsidiaries:

Belden Tri-State Building Materials (1)
333 7th Ave 5th Fl, New York, NY 10001-5004
Tel.: (212) 686-3939
Web Site: http://www.btsbm.com
Sales Range: $10-24.9 Million
Emp.: 9
Brick, Stone & Concrete Block Distr
N.A.I.C.S.: 423320
Joseph W. Ricevito (Pres)

Redland Brick Inc. (1)
15718 Clear Spring Rd, Williamsport, MD 21795-1009
Tel.: (301) 223-7700
Web Site: http://www.redlandbrick.com
Sales Range: $10-24.9 Million
Emp.: 132
Mfr Brick & Structural Clay
N.A.I.C.S.: 327120
Sherry Harper (Controller)

The Belden Brick Sales Company Inc. (1)
31470 Utica Rd, Fraser, MI 48026-3926
Tel.: (586) 294-5400
Web Site: http://www.beldenbricksales.com
Sales Range: $10-24.9 Million
Emp.: 14
Retail of Brick Stone & Related Material Distr
N.A.I.C.S.: 423320

THE BELET GROUP, INC.
117 W Jefferson St, Bolivar, TN 38008
Tel.: (731) 659-2215
Web Site: http://www.belet.com
Year Founded: 1983
Sales Range: $10-24.9 Million
Emp.: 100
Holding Company
N.A.I.C.S.: 551112

Subsidiaries:

Belet Acquisitions, Inc. (1)
117 W Jefferson St, Bolivar, TN 38008   (100%)
Tel.: (731) 659-2215
Web Site: http://www.belet.com
Sales Range: $25-49.9 Million
Emp.: 6
Privater Equity Firm
N.A.I.C.S.: 523999
Jacques H. Belet III (Chm, Pres & CEO)
Joe Ross (COO)

THE BELKNAP WHITE GROUP, LLC.
111 Plymouth St, Mansfield, MA 02048-2073
Tel.: (508) 337-2700
Web Site: https://www.belknapwhite.com
Year Founded: 1986
Sales Range: $25-49.9 Million
Emp.: 200
Retailer of Home Furnishings
N.A.I.C.S.: 423220
Paul Castagliuolo (Pres)
Stephen Mancini (COO-North)

Subsidiaries:

Alcco Corp. (1)
12 Commercial Rd, Albany, NY 12205-5704
Tel.: (518) 489-2512
Web Site: http://www.alcco.com
Sales Range: $10-24.9 Million
Emp.: 53
Retailer of Home Furnishings
N.A.I.C.S.: 423220

Patriot Flooring Supply, Inc. (1)
250 Ballardvale St, Wilmington, MA 01887
Tel.: (978) 988-2490

Web Site: http://www.patriothardwoodfloors.com
Flooring Contractors
N.A.I.C.S.: 238330

Swiff-Train Company Inc. (1)
10850 Train Ct, Houston, TX 77041
Tel.: (361) 883-1706
Web Site: https://stcfloors.com
Sales Range: $10-24.9 Million
Emp.: 40
Distr of Home Furnishings
N.A.I.C.S.: 423220
Joe Reddington (COO)
Cole Hood (Dir-Sls-Distr)
Shane Calloway (Pres & CEO)

THE BELLWETHER GROUP
510 College Ave, Racine, WI 53403
Tel.: (262) 639-9093   WI
Web Site: http://www.thebellwethergroup.com
Year Founded: 1986
Rev.: $15,000,000
Emp.: 20
N.A.I.C.S.: 541810
Michael P. Sucharda (Pres)
M.J. Sucharda (Dir-Media)
Andrea Nordquist (Art Dir)

THE BEN SILVER CORPORATION
149 King St, Charleston, SC 29401
Tel.: (843) 577-4556   SC
Web Site: http://www.bensilver.com
Year Founded: 1983
Sales Range: $10-24.9 Million
Emp.: 40
Mfr & Sales of Men's Clothing & Accessories
N.A.I.C.S.: 327999
Sue Prenner (Pres)
James Prenner (VP)
Robert Prenner (Chm)

THE BENCHMARK FINANCIAL GROUP
4053 Maple Rd Ste 200, Amherst, NY 14226
Tel.: (716) 833-4986
Web Site: http://www.benchmarkgrp.com
Year Founded: 1983
Sales Range: $200-249.9 Million
Emp.: 300
Building Operating Services
N.A.I.C.S.: 531120
Steve Longo (COO)
George I. Gellman (Partner)
Arthur M. Gellman (Partner)
Clarke H. Narins (Pres & Partner)
Martin J. DelleBovi (Exec VP & Dir-Real Estate)
Mark T. DelleBovi (VP-Construction)
George O. Bergantz (VP)
Jeff Withee (CFO)
Lorraine O'Connor (VP & Dir-Affordable Housing)
Margaret E. Shotwell (Pres)
John F. Rehak Jr. (Dir-Acq & Fin)

THE BENECON GROUP
3175 Oregon Pike, Leola, PA 17540
Tel.: (717) 656-9404
Web Site: http://www.benecon.com
Year Founded: 1942
Rev.: $17,100,000
Emp.: 54
Management Consulting Services
N.A.I.C.S.: 541612
Samuel N. Lombardo (Chm & CEO)
Joel E. Callihan (CFO & Exec VP)
Brad Kopcha (Exec VP-Actuarial Svcs & Bus Dev)
Matthew Kirk (Pres)
Donald Palmer Jr. (Sr VP-Sls & Producer Svcs)

THE BENEFIT SERVICES GROUP, INC.
N25 W23050 Paul Rd, Pewaukee, WI 53072
Tel.: (262) 521-5700   WI
Web Site: http://www.bsg.com
Year Founded: 1987
Emp.: 50
Employee Benefits & Wellness Consulting Services
N.A.I.C.S.: 541618
Phil Krajnek (VP-Benefits Consulting)
Gerald Frye (CEO)
Lenny Spingola (VP-Security & Tech Svcs)

Subsidiaries:

Hausmann Johnson Insurance, Inc. (1)
700 Regent St, Madison, WI 53715
Tel.: (608) 257-3795
Web Site: http://www.hausmann-johnson.com
Insurance Agencies & Brokerages
N.A.I.C.S.: 524210
Craig Butler (Principal & VP-Ops)
Caroline Cole (Principal & Mgr-Acct Benefits)
Jeff Frey (Principal)
Pat Kelly (Dir-Healthcare Reform Compliance)
Doug Lefeber (Mgr-Personal Lines)
Barry Richter (Pres)
Tim Hausmann (Chm & Principal)
John Erikson (Principal)
Susan Dorsch (Mgr-Claims & Loss Control)
Marc Flood (Principal)
Sandy Hasz (Principal & VP-Fin)
Erik Hausmann (Principal)
Phil Hausmann (Principal)
Scott Hausmann (Principal)
Dan Martin (Principal)
Pat McKenna (Principal & Asst VP-Surety)

THE BENNINGTON STATE BANK
2130 S Ohio St, Salina, KS 67401
Tel.: (785) 827-5522
Web Site: http://www.bsbks.com
Year Founded: 1884
Commericial Banking
N.A.I.C.S.: 522110
Larry Britegam (Chief Strategy Officer)
Burke Matthews (Pres)
Brandy Felzien (Trust Officer & VP)

THE BERGE GROUP
1720 S Mesa Dr, Mesa, AZ 85210
Tel.: (480) 813-4900
Web Site: http://www.bergegroup.com
Rev.: $115,600,000
Emp.: 335
Automobiles, New & Used
N.A.I.C.S.: 441110
Jim Krbec (Dir-HR)

Subsidiaries:

Bell Ford Inc. (1)
2401 W Bell Rd, Phoenix, AZ 85023
Tel.: (602) 866-1776
Web Site: http://www.bellford.com
Rev.: $85,000,000
Emp.: 175
Automobiles, New & Used
N.A.I.C.S.: 441110
Lee Spencer (Gen Mgr)
Duane Wilkes (Controller)
Ed Robbins (Mgr-Collision Center)
Ken Martin (Mgr-Collision Center)

THE BERLIN STEEL CONSTRUCTION COMPANY
76 Depot Rd, Berlin, CT 06037-1439
Tel.: (860) 828-3531   CT
Web Site: http://www.berlinsteel.com
Year Founded: 1900
Sales Range: $10-24.9 Million
Emp.: 135

THE BERLIN STEEL CONSTRUCTION COMPANY U.S. PRIVATE

The Berlin Steel Construction Company—(Continued)
Structural & Miscellaneous Fabricators & Erectors
N.A.I.C.S.: 332312
David E. Hunt *(Pres)*
Michael O'Sullivan *(Exec VP-Fin & Admin)*

Subsidiaries:

Curtain Walls And Windows Inc. (1)
41 Sequin Dr, Glastonbury, CT 06033-2481 (100%)
Tel.: (860) 659-1426
Rev.: $7,032,689
Emp.: 8
Specialty Trade Contractors
N.A.I.C.S.: 238990

Division (Domestic):

Curtainwalls & Windows, Inc. - CW Fabrication Systems Division (2)
76 Depot Rd Bldg 2, Kensington, CT 06037
Tel.: (860) 828-6400
Fabricated Aluminum Product Mfr
N.A.I.C.S.: 332999

Pillar Enterprise Ltd. (1)
204 Lenoir Dr, Winchester, VA 22603-4607 (100%)
Tel.: (540) 678-0150
Sales Range: $10-24.9 Million
Emp.: 12
Fabricated Structural Metal
N.A.I.C.S.: 332312

The Berlin Steel Construction Company - Berlin Steel Baltimore/Washington Division (1)
796 Cromwell Park Dr Ste T, Glen Burnie, MD 21061
Tel.: (443) 749-5500
Web Site: http://www.berlinsteel.com
Emp.: 75
Fabricated Steel Product Mfr
N.A.I.C.S.: 332312
Rick Bailey *(Mgr)*

The Berlin Steel Construction Company - Berlin Steel Mid-Atlantic Division (1)
200 Lindenwood Dr Valleybrooke Corporate Ctr, Malvern, PA 19355
Tel.: (610) 240-8953
Fabricated Steel Product Mfr
N.A.I.C.S.: 332312

The Berlin Steel Construction Company - MA Division (1)
5 Industrial Park Rd W, Oxford, MA 01540
Tel.: (508) 987-7924
Web Site: http://www.berlinsteel.com
Fabricated Steel Product Mfr
N.A.I.C.S.: 332312

THE BERNSTEIN COMPANIES
3299 K St NW Ste 700, Washington, DC 20007
Tel.: (202) 333-9000
Web Site:
http://www.thebernsteincompanies.com
Sales Range: $10-24.9 Million
Emp.: 45
Real Estate Agents & Managers
N.A.I.C.S.: 531210
Adam K. Bernstein *(Pres)*
Marc N. Duber *(COO & Exec VP)*
Joseph S. Galli *(Exec VP)*

THE BERRY COMPANY LLC
3100 Research Blvd, Dayton, OH 45420
Tel.: (937) 610-4100 DE
Web Site:
http://www.theberrycompany.com
Year Founded: 1960
Sales Range: $150-199.9 Million
Emp.: 300
Marketing Services
N.A.I.C.S.: 541613

Richard G. Halle *(CFO)*
James V. Continenza *(Chm)*
Jim Moran *(COO)*
W. Aaron Bowlds *(Gen Counsel)*
Mark J. Lane *(Sr VP-Sls)*
Joe Pellitteri *(Sr VP)*
Bartolome Soriano *(Sr VP-Production)*
Tony Bulugaris *(VP-Ops)*
Laura Cole *(VP-Mktg)*

Subsidiaries:

The Berry Company LLC - Cincinnati (1)
312 Plum St Ste 600, Cincinnati, OH 45202-4122
Tel.: (513) 768-7700
Sales Range: $75-99.9 Million
Emp.: 11
Marketing Services
N.A.I.C.S.: 541613
Mike Webster *(Dir-Client Svcs)*

The Berry Company LLC - Inglewood (1)
188 Inverness Dr W Ste 800, Englewood, CO 80112
Tel.: (303) 867-1600
Web Site: http://www.theberrycompany.com
Sales Range: $25-49.9 Million
Emp.: 100
Marketing Services
N.A.I.C.S.: 541613

THE BERYL COMPANIES
3600 Harwood Rd Ste A, Bedford, TX 76021
Tel.: (817) 785-5000
Web Site: http://www.beryl.net
Year Founded: 1985
Sales Range: $25-49.9 Million
Emp.: 360
Outsourcing of Call Center Services for the Health Care Industry
N.A.I.C.S.: 561330
Paul Spiegelman *(Founder & CEO)*
Lance Shipp *(COO)*
Kim Thomas *(Dir-Client Svcs)*

THE BESSEMER GROUP, INCORPORATED
100 Woodbridge Center Dr, Woodbridge, NJ 07095
Tel.: (732) 855-0800 DE
Web Site:
http://www.bessemertrust.com
Financial Holding Company; Investment Banking & Trust Services
N.A.I.C.S.: 551111

Subsidiaries:

The Bessemer Group, Incorporated - New York Office (1)
630 5th Ave, New York, NY 10111-0333
Tel.: (212) 708-9100
Web Site: http://www.bessemertrust.com
Financial Holding Company; Corporate Office
N.A.I.C.S.: 551114

Subsidiary (Domestic):

Bessemer Group Trust Company of Florida (2)
222 Royal Palm Way, Palm Beach, FL 33480-4303
Tel.: (561) 655-4030
Web Site:
http://www.bessemerholdings.com
Sales Range: $50-74.9 Million
Emp.: 43
Wealth Management Services
N.A.I.C.S.: 523940
Barton C. Francis *(Sr Mgr-Client Acct)*
George Wilcox *(Mng Dir)*
Marc Stern *(Pres)*

Branch (Domestic):

Bessemer Group Trust Company of Florida - Miami (3)

801 Brickell Ave Ste 2250, Miami, FL 33131-2951
Tel.: (305) 372-5005
Web Site: http://www.bessemer.com
Sales Range: $50-74.9 Million
Emp.: 17
Wealth Management Services
N.A.I.C.S.: 523991
Marianela Collado *(Principal)*

Bessemer Group Trust Company of Florida - Naples (3)
3777 Tamiami Trl N Ste 200, Naples, FL 34103-3587
Tel.: (239) 435-0034
Web Site: http://www.bessemer.com
Sales Range: $50-74.9 Million
Emp.: 5
Trust Services
N.A.I.C.S.: 523991
W. David Bunce *(Mng Dir & Head-Northeast)*
Michael A. Marquez *(COO)*

Subsidiary (Non-US):

Bessemer Group UK Ltd. (2)
9 S St, London, W1K 2XA, United Kingdom
Tel.: (44) 2072909300
Web Site: http://www.bessemer.com
Sales Range: $50-74.9 Million
Emp.: 10
N.A.I.C.S.: 522210
Christopher Judge *(Office Mgr)*
William Tyna *(Mng Dir)*

Subsidiary (Domestic):

Bessemer Trust Company (2)
100 Woodbridge Ctr Dr, Woodbridge, NJ 07095-1191
Tel.: (732) 694-5500
Web Site: http://www.bessemertrust.com
Rev.: $3,400,000
Emp.: 20
Trust Services
N.A.I.C.S.: 523991
Ilka Gregory *(Principal)*

Subsidiary (Non-US):

Bessemer Trust Company (Cayman) Limited (2)
Dr Roy's Dr, Box 694, Georgetown, KY1-1107, Grand Cayman, Cayman Islands
Tel.: (345) 9496674
Web Site: http://www.bessemer.com
Emp.: 3
N.A.I.C.S.: 522210

Subsidiary (Domestic):

Bessemer Trust Company of California, N.A. (2)
101 California St Ste 2500, San Francisco, CA 94111-6139
Tel.: (415) 291-1810
Web Site: http://www.bessemertrust.com
Sales Range: $50-74.9 Million
Emp.: 11
Real Estate Investment Trust Services
N.A.I.C.S.: 531110

Branch (Domestic):

Bessemer Trust Company of California - Los Angeles (3)
10250 Constellation Blvd Ste 2600, Los Angeles, CA 90067-6240
Tel.: (213) 892-0900
Web Site: http://www.bessemer.com
Sales Range: $50-74.9 Million
Emp.: 15
Investment Management Service
N.A.I.C.S.: 523940
Jeffrey J. Glowacki *(Head-Western)*

Subsidiary (Domestic):

Bessemer Trust Company, N.A. (2)
630 5th Ave, New York, NY 10111
Tel.: (212) 708-9364
Web Site: http://www.bessemertrust.com
Sales Range: $50-74.9 Million
Emp.: 300
Trust Services
N.A.I.C.S.: 523991
George Wilcox *(Pres)*
Rebecca H. Patterson *(Chief Investment Officer)*

Chuck Bryceland *(Mng Dir & Head-Alternative Investments)*
Kenneth C. Handy *(VP-New York)*
Michael A. Gragnani *(Principal-Atlanta)*
Michael A. Marquez *(Mng Dir & Head-Southeast Reg)*
Ilka Gregory *(Principal-New York)*
Murray C. Stoltz *(Principal-New York)*
Teresa Principe *(Sr VP-New York)*
Marc D. Stern *(CEO)*
Donovan B. Moore Jr. *(Mng Dir-New York)*

Branch (Domestic):

Bessemer Trust Co. - Atlanta (3)
3455 Peachtree Rd NE Ste 850, Atlanta, GA 30326-3257
Tel.: (404) 965-9300
Web Site: http://www.bessemer.com
Sales Range: $50-74.9 Million
Emp.: 10
Management Services
N.A.I.C.S.: 522110
Stuart S. Janney III *(Chm)*

Bessemer Trust Co. - Chicago (3)
70 W Madison St, Chicago, IL 60602-4213
Tel.: (312) 220-9898
Web Site: http://www.bessemertrust.com
Sales Range: $50-74.9 Million
Emp.: 30
Asset Management
N.A.I.C.S.: 522110
S. Alexander Haverstick *(Principal)*

Bessemer Trust Co. - Washington, DC (3)
900 17th St NW Ste 1000, Washington, DC 20006-5371
Tel.: (202) 659-3330
Web Site: http://www.bessemer.com
Rev.: $12,000,000
Emp.: 12
Trust Company
N.A.I.C.S.: 541191

THE BETESH GROUP, INC.
250 Passaic St, Newark, NJ 07104
Tel.: (212) 686-4666 NY
Web Site:
http://www.beteshgroup.com
Year Founded: 1974
Mfr, Designer & Distributor of Accessories, Handbags & Small Leather Goods
N.A.I.C.S.: 551112
Sol Betesh *(Dir-Production)*
Len Carpentiri *(CFO)*
Ron Shandorf *(Dir-IT)*

THE BETHLEHEM CORPORATION
25th & Lennox Sts, Easton, PA 18045
Tel.: (610) 258-7111 PA
Web Site: http://www.bethcorp.com
Year Founded: 1856
Sales Range: $1-9.9 Million
Emp.: 15
Materials Processing Equipment Mfr
N.A.I.C.S.: 333310

Subsidiaries:

Bethlehem Intl. Sales Corp. (1)
25th & Lennox St, Easton, PA 18045 (100%)
Tel.: (610) 258-7111
Web Site: http://www.bethcorp.com
Exports Products of Parent Company-Inactive
N.A.I.C.S.: 333310

THE BETTY MILLS COMPANY, INC.
161 W 25th Ave Ste 203, San Mateo, CA 94403
Tel.: (650) 344-8228 CA
Web Site: http://www.bettymills.com
Year Founded: 2002
Sales Range: $10-24.9 Million
Emp.: 20
Janitorial, Break Room Food & Vending Supplies Online Retailer
N.A.I.C.S.: 459999

THE BETZ COMPANIES

10940 W Sam Houston Pkwy N Ste 300, Houston, TX 77064
Tel.: (281) 873-4444
Web Site:
    http://www.betzcompanies.com
Sales Range: $10-24.9 Million
Emp.: 10
Real Estate Brokers & Agents
N.A.I.C.S.: 531210
Raymond R. Betz *(CEO)*
Ron Dagley *(Pres)*
Joanna Gober *(VP-Fin)*

THE BIG VIEW
121 Chanlon Rd, New Providence, NJ 07974
Tel.: (908) 555-1212 CT
Sales Range: $750-799.9 Million
Emp.: 22,000
Big Picture
N.A.I.C.S.: 532289
Tonja View *(Dir_Content Oper)*

THE BILTRITE CORPORATION
51 Sawyer Rd, Waltham, MA 02453
Tel.: (781) 647-1700 DE
Web Site: http://www.biltrite.com
Year Founded: 1908
Sales Range: $200-249.9 Million
Emp.: 525
Mfr of Rubber Materials
N.A.I.C.S.: 316210
Stanley J. Bernstein *(Chm)*
David Amidon *(Gen Counsel & VP-Legal)*
Stephen A. Fine *(Pres & COO)*

THE BIOENGINEERING GROUP, INC.
18 Commercial St, Salem, MA 01970
Tel.: (978) 740-0096
Web Site:
    http://www.bioengineering.com
Year Founded: 1992
Rev.: $9,200,000
Emp.: 62
Environmental Consulting Services
N.A.I.C.S.: 541620
Wendi Goldsmith *(Founder & CEO)*
Duke Bitsko *(Dir-Interdisciplinary Design)*

THE BIONETICS CORPORATION
101 Production Dr Ste 100, Yorktown, VA 23693
Tel.: (757) 873-0900 VA
Web Site: http://www.bionetics.com
Year Founded: 1969
Sales Range: $75-99.9 Million
Emp.: 60
Government Services Contractor
N.A.I.C.S.: 561210
Charles J. Stern *(CEO)*
John Smartt *(VP)*

THE BIRCHWOOD
340 Beach Dr NE St, Saint Petersburg, FL 33701
Tel.: (727) 896-1080
Web Site:
    http://www.thebirchwood.com
Emp.: 130
Hotel, Restaurant & Bar
N.A.I.C.S.: 721110
Chuck Prather *(Owner)*
Angela Meeker *(Gen Mgr)*

THE BIRKETT MILLS
PO Box 440, Penn Yan, NY 14527
Tel.: (315) 536-3311 NY
Web Site:
    http://www.thebirkettmills.com
Year Founded: 1797
Rev.: $6,500,000
Emp.: 40
Flour & Grain Products Mfr
N.A.I.C.S.: 311211
Clifford S. Orr *(VP)*
Wayne Wagner *(Chm)*
Jeffrey S. Gifford *(Chm & CEO)*

THE BLACK PHOENIX GROUP
5420 W. Roosevelt Rd, Ste 314, Chicago, IL 60644
Tel.: (312) 493-3000
Web Site:
    https://www.blackphoenixgroup.com
Private Equity
N.A.I.C.S.: 523940
Mark Pickett *(Partner)*

Subsidiaries:

PACCAR Winch Inc.   (1)
777 106th Ave NE, Bellevue, WA 98004
Tel.: (425) 468-7400
Web Site: https://www.paccar.com
Motor Vehicle Parts Mfr
N.A.I.C.S.: 336390

THE BLAINE GROUP
8665 Wilshire Blvd Ste 301, Beverly Hills, CA 90211-2932
Tel.: (310) 360-1499 CA
Web Site:
    http://www.blainegroupinc.com
Year Founded: 1975
Sales Range: $1-9.9 Million
Emp.: 10
Advertising & Public Relations Agency
N.A.I.C.S.: 541820
Devon Blaine *(Pres & CEO)*
Gene Siciliano *(CFO)*

THE BLOCK AGENCY, INC.
1720 W End Ave Ste 330, Nashville, TN 37203-3203
Tel.: (615) 259-7812
Web Site:
    http://www.theblockagency.com
Professional Employer Organizations
N.A.I.C.S.: 561330
Mark Block *(Owner)*

Subsidiaries:

Maximum Talent Agency   (1)
621 Kalamath St Ste 150, Denver, CO 80204
Tel.: (303) 691-2344
Web Site: http://www.maxtalent.com
Employment Placement Agencies
N.A.I.C.S.: 561311

THE BLOOD & TISSUE CENTER OF CENTRAL TEXAS
4300 N Lamar Blvd, Austin, TX 78756
Tel.: (512) 206-1266 TX
Web Site: http://www.inyourhands.org
Year Founded: 1951
Sales Range: $25-49.9 Million
Emp.: 203
Blood & Tissue Bank
N.A.I.C.S.: 621991
Marshall G. Cothran *(Pres & CEO)*
Marian Garrard *(COO)*
Arlin Hall *(CFO)*
Denise Ballinger *(Chief HR Officer)*
Cari Unger *(Chief Quality Officer)*
Cindy Rowe *(Mgr-PR)*

THE BLOOMFIELD MANUFACTURING CO., INC.
46 W Spring St, Bloomfield, IN 47424-1473
Tel.: (812) 384-4441 IN
Web Site: http://www.hi-list.com
Year Founded: 1895
Jacks & Fence Products, Door Products & Cargo Tie Down Products Mfr
N.A.I.C.S.: 332216

Subsidiaries:

Harrah Mfg. Co.   (1)
46 W Spring, Bloomfield, IN 47424
Tel.: (812) 384-4441
Web Site: http://www.hi-list.com
Sales Range: $10-24.9 Million
Emp.: 45
Mfr of Various Jacks & Hi-Lift Tools
N.A.I.C.S.: 332216
Steve Dowden *(VP-Sls)*

HiLift Jack Co.   (1)
46 W Spring St, Bloomfield, IN 47424
Tel.: (812) 384-4441
Web Site: http://www.hilift.com
Sales Range: $10-24.9 Million
Emp.: 40
Mfr of Gate & Door Self-Closer Installations
N.A.I.C.S.: 333517
Steve Dowden *(VP-Sls)*

Kant-Slam Door Check Co.   (1)
46 W Spring St, Bloomfield, IN 47424
Tel.: (812) 384-4441
Web Site: http://www.hi-lift.com
Sales Range: $10-24.9 Million
Emp.: 50
Mfr of Gate & Door Self-Closer Installations
N.A.I.C.S.: 333517
Steve Dowden *(Sr VP-Sls)*

THE BLOSSMAN COMPANIES INC.
809 Washington Ave, Ocean Springs, MS 39564-4637
Tel.: (228) 875-2261 MS
Web Site:
    http://www.blossmangas.com
Year Founded: 1951
Sales Range: $25-49.9 Million
Emp.: 600
Liquefied Petroleum Gas Dealers
N.A.I.C.S.: 457210
David Reynolds *(COO)*
Stuart E. Weidie *(Pres & CEO)*
Jessie W. Johnson *(VP-R&D)*
Randall R. Doyle *(CFO)*
Todd M. Reinke *(VP-Admin)*

Subsidiaries:

Blossman Gas Inc.   (1)
809 Washington Ave, Ocean Springs, MS 39564-4637
Tel.: (228) 875-2261
Web Site: http://www.blossmangas.com
Sales Range: $10-24.9 Million
Emp.: 25
Liquefied Petroleum Gas Dealers
N.A.I.C.S.: 457210

THE BLUE VENTURE FUND
225 N Michigan Ave, Chicago, IL 60601
Tel.: (312) 297-6560
Web Site:
    http://www.blueventurefund.com
Corporate Venture Fund
N.A.I.C.S.: 523999
John Banta *(Exec Dir)*

THE BOARDWALK COMPANY
31640 US Hwy 19 N Ste 1, Palm Harbor, FL 34684
Tel.: (727) 784-1007
Web Site:
    http://www.boardwalkcompany.com
Sales Range: $1-9.9 Million
Emp.: 6
Commercial Brokerage, Management, Development & Consulting
N.A.I.C.S.: 531210
John Quattrocki *(Pres)*

THE BOELTER COMPANIES INC.
N22W23685 Ridgeview Pkwy W, Waukesha, WI 53188
Tel.: (262) 523-6200 WI
Web Site: http://www.boelter.com
Year Founded: 1929
Sales Range: $1-9.9 Million
Emp.: 200
Food Service Industry Products Mfr & Distr
N.A.I.C.S.: 424130
Eric Boelter *(Pres)*
Karen Loritz *(CFO)*
Jason Prondzinski *(VP-Sls)*
Rick Boelter *(CEO)*

Subsidiaries:

Custom Deco, LLC   (1)
1343 Miami St, Toledo, OH 43605
Tel.: (419) 698-2900
Web Site: http://www.customdeco.com
Sales Range: $10-24.9 Million
Glass Products Mfr
N.A.I.C.S.: 327212
Clif Perryman *(Pres)*
Ivy Russell *(Acct Mgr-Food Svc)*

The Boelter Companies Inc.   (1)
945 N Edgewood Ave Ste G, Wood Dale, IL 60191-1252   (100%)
Tel.: (847) 675-0505
Web Site: http://www.boelter.com
Restaurant Equipment & Supplies; Industrial & Personal Service Paper
N.A.I.C.S.: 424130
Ann McCabe *(Mgr-Sls)*
Tim Scott *(Gen Mgr)*

THE BOHLE COMPANY
1625 Stanford St, Los Angeles, CA 90077
Tel.: (310) 785-0515 CA
Web Site: http://www.bohle.com
Year Founded: 1987
Sales Range: $1-9.9 Million
Emp.: 18
Public Relations Agency
N.A.I.C.S.: 541820
Sue Bohle *(Pres)*

THE BOHN ZONE
3737 Lapalco Blvd, Harvey, LA 70058-2331
Tel.: (504) 347-7000
Web Site: http://www.bohnzone.com
Sales Range: $125-149.9 Million
Emp.: 300
Auto Dealership
N.A.I.C.S.: 441110
Donald B. Bohn Jr. *(Pres)*

THE BOLDT GROUP INC.
2525 N Roemer Rd, Appleton, WI 54911
Tel.: (920) 739-6321 WI
Web Site:
    http://www.theboldtcompany.com
Year Founded: 1984
Sales Range: $350-399.9 Million
Emp.: 2,200
Holding Company; General Construction Services; Golf Course Operator
N.A.I.C.S.: 551112
James M. Rossmeissl *(CMO & Sr Exec VP)*
Robert J. DeKoch *(Pres & COO)*
Oscar C. Boldt *(Chm)*
Jeff H. Johnson *(Pres-Central & Svcs Div)*
Linda Nila *(CFO & Exec VP)*
Shelly Peterson *(Exec VP & Gen Mgr)*
Paul Reiser *(Exec VP-Performance & Innovation Resources)*
Jim Lee *(Pres-Greater Northern)*
Dave Kievet *(Pres-Western & Southern Div)*
Steve Ford *(Pres-Southern Ops)*

Subsidiaries:

Boldt Consulting Services   (1)
1110 N Old World 3rd St Ste 610, Milwaukee, WI 53203
Tel.: (414) 276-4666
Web Site: http://www.theboldtcompany.com

THE BOLDT GROUP INC.

The Boldt Group Inc.—(Continued)
Sales Range: $25-49.9 Million
Emp.: 12
Planning & Program Implementation Services for Building Expansions & Renovations
N.A.I.C.S.: 236220

Boldt Technical Services (1)
2525 N Roemer Rd, Appleton, WI 54911
Tel.: (920) 739-6321
Web Site: http://www.theboldtcompany.com
Project Development, Design Management & Engineering Services
N.A.I.C.S.: 541330

Oscar J. Boldt Construction Co. Inc. (1)
2525 N Roemer Rd, Appleton, WI 54911
Tel.: (920) 739-6321
Web Site: http://www.boldt.com
Sales Range: $125-149.9 Million
Emp.: 2,000
Planning, Design Management & Industrial, Institutional & Commercial Construction Services
N.A.I.C.S.: 236220
Thomas J. Boldt (Co-CEO)
Bob Dekoch (Pres & COO)
Jim Kleinfeldt (Pres-Real Estate Div)
Jim Lee (Pres-Greater Northern Div)
Jeff Niesen (Chief Admin Officer & Sr Exec VP)
Linda Nila (CFO & Sr Exec VP)
Shelly Peterson (Exec VP & Gen Mgr)
Paul Reiser (Sr Exec VP-Performance & Innovation Resources)
Jim Rossmeissl (CMO & Sr Exec VP)

Paper Valley Corporation (1)
2525 N Roemer Rd, Appleton, WI 54911-8623
Tel.: (920) 739-3080
Rev.: $750,000
Emp.: 2
Operates Golf Course
N.A.I.C.S.: 713910

The Boldt Company (1)
2525 N Roemer Rd, Appleton, WI 54912-0419
Tel.: (920) 246-4195
Emp.: 2,000
Industrial Building Construction Services
N.A.I.C.S.: 236210
Jim Rossmeissl (CMO & Sr Exec VP)
Oscar Boldt (Chm)
Tom Boldt (CEO)
Bob DeKoch (Pres & Co-COO)
Linda Nila (Sr Exec VP)
Jim Kleinfeldt (Pres-Real Estate)
Will Lichtig (Exec VP-Performance & Innovation Resources)
John Heck (Exec VP & Gen Mgr-Power & Industrial-Natl)
Jeff Shipley (Exec VP & Gen Mgr-Southern Ops)
Jeff Niesen (Pres-Central Ops)
Jake Garro (Exec VP-Real Estate)
David Larson (Dir-Estimating & Preconstruction)

Subsidiary (Domestic):

Bold Thinking, LLC (2)
2692 Madison Rd, Cincinnati, OH 45208
Tel.: (513) 310-0601
Construction Engineering Services
N.A.I.C.S.: 541330

THE BOLER COMPANY
2021 Parkside Dr, Schaumburg, IL 60173
Tel.: (630) 773-9111 DE
Year Founded: 1977
Emp.: 100
Holding Company
N.A.I.C.S.: 551112
Matthew J. Boler (Pres & CEO)

Subsidiaries:

Hendrickson International Corporation (1)
500 Park Blvd Ste 450, Itasca, IL 60143-1285 (100%)
Tel.: (630) 874-9700
Web Site: http://www.hendrickson-intl.com
Sales Range: $10-24.9 Million
Emp.: 100
Truck Suspensions Mfr
N.A.I.C.S.: 336390
Gary Gerstenslager (Pres & CEO)
Perry Bahr (VP & Gen Mgr-Trailer Comml Vehicle Sys)
Matt Joy (VP & Gen Mgr-Truck Comml Vehicle Sys)
Rence Oliphant (VP-Sls-Global)
Andrew Martin (VP-Ops-Intl)
Rick Johnson (VP-IT)
David Templeton (VP-HR)
Kevin Mullinax (VP-Pur)
John Boler (Founder)
Arthur Mitsel (Gen Mgr-Asia Pacific)
Richard Mudd (VP & Gen Mgr-Specialty Products Grp)
Mark Page (Mng Dir-Hendrickson)
Zhonghou Zhao (Mng Dir-China)
Mohit Khosla (Mng Dir-India)

Subsidiary (Non-US):

Hendrickson Asia Pacific Pty. Ltd. (2)
32-44 Letcon Drive, PO Box 1063, Dandenong, 3175, VIC, Australia
Tel.: (61) 3 8792 3600
Web Site: http://www.aus.hendrickson-intl.com
Emp.: 65
Truck, Trailer & Motor Vehicle Parts Mfr
N.A.I.C.S.: 336212
Arthur Mitsel (Gen Mgr)

Hendrickson Austria GmbH (2)
Gussstahlwerkstrasse 21, 8750, Judenburg, Austria
Tel.: (43) 3572 44011 0
Emp.: 130
Motor Vehicle Leaf Spring Component Mfr & Distr
N.A.I.C.S.: 336390
Armin Goessler (Mng Dir)
Tadej Strahovnik (Sr Acct Mgr)

Unit (Domestic):

Hendrickson Auxiliary Axle Systems (2)
277 N High St, Hebron, OH 43025-9669
Tel.: (740) 929-5600
Web Site: http://www.hendrickson-intl.com
Emp.: 50
Mfr of Axles
N.A.I.C.S.: 336390
Dave Armold (Plant Mgr)

Hendrickson Bumper & Trim (2)
501 Caton Farm Rd, Crest Hill, IL 60441
Tel.: (815) 727-4031
Web Site: http://www.hendrickson-intl.com
Mfr of Metal Stamping
N.A.I.C.S.: 336390

Subsidiary (Non-US):

Hendrickson Canada (2)
250 Chrysler Drive Unit 3, Brampton, L6S 6B6, ON, Canada
Tel.: (905) 789-1030
Web Site: http://www.hendrickson-intl.com
Sales Range: $10-24.9 Million
Emp.: 15
Truck, Trailer & Motor Vehicle Parts Mfr
N.A.I.C.S.: 336390

Hendrickson China (2)
Suite 1007 YOUYOU International Plaza No 76 Pujian Road, Pudong Xin District, Shanghai, 200127, China
Tel.: (86) 21 5876 5710
Web Site: http://china.hendrickson-intl.com
Truck, Trailer & Motor Vehicle Parts Mfr
N.A.I.C.S.: 336212
Zhonghou Zhao (Mng Dir)

Plant (Domestic):

Hendrickson China - Jinan Plant (3)
1 Workshop in Huayi Group No 8 Xinggang Road, Lixia District, Jinan, 250100, Shandong, China
Tel.: (86) 531 8880 9055
Web Site: http://china.hendrickson-intl.com
Truck, Trailer & Motor Vehicle Parts Mfr
N.A.I.C.S.: 336212

Subsidiary (Non-US):

Hendrickson Commercial Vehicle Systems UK (2)
1-9 Booth Drive Park Farm Industrial Estate, Wellingborough, NN8 6GR, United Kingdom
Tel.: (44) 1604 493161
Web Site: http://uk.hendrickson-intl.com
Truck, Trailer & Motor Vehicle Parts Mfr
N.A.I.C.S.: 336390

Joint Venture (Non-US):

Muelles y Ballestas Hispani-Alemanas S.A. (3)
Camino Viejo de Castellon a Onda s/n, Villarreal, 12520, Spain
Tel.: (34) 964 521 050
Sales Range: $25-49.9 Million
Motor Vehicle Component Mfr
N.A.I.C.S.: 336390
Miguel Ruiz (Gen Mgr)

Subsidiary (Non-US):

Hendrickson France S.A.S. (2)
Avenue des Forges, Chatenois-les-Forges, 90700, Chatenois, France
Tel.: (33) 384582500
Motor Vehicle Leaf Spring & Stabilizer Component Mfr & Distr
N.A.I.C.S.: 336390
Jean-Francois Kristof (Dir-Tech)
Betrand Boivert (Mgr-Mktg & Bus Dev)

Hendrickson India (2)
Plot No 4 & 5 Gat 679/2 Behind Hotel Gandharva Alandi Kuruli Road, Kuruli Taluka Khed, Pune, 410501, India
Tel.: (91) 98 90194444
Truck, Trailer & Motor Vehicle Parts Mfr
N.A.I.C.S.: 336212
Mohit Khosla (Mng Dir)

Hendrickson Japan GK (2)
Level 10 TOC Minato Mirai 1-1-7 Sakuragicho, Naka-ku, Yokohama, 220-0012, Kanagawa, Japan
Tel.: (81) 45 228 5160
Web Site: http://www.hendrickson.com
Truck, Trailer & Motor Vehicle Parts Mfr
N.A.I.C.S.: 336212
Olivier Aparicio (Mng Dir)

Hendrickson Mexicana (2)
Avenida Rassini 801 Col Bravo, Piedras Negras, 26030, Coahuila, Mexico
Tel.: (52) 8787826251
Web Site: http://www.hendrickson-intl.com
N.A.I.C.S.: 336211

Hendrickson Romania (2)
Forjorilor Str 22, 550233, Sibiu, Romania
Tel.: (40) 269207347
Motor Vehicle Leaf Spring Component Mfr & Distr
N.A.I.C.S.: 336390
Daniel Preda (Mng Dir)
Farcas Flaviu (Head-Warehouses & Transports)

Unit (Domestic):

Hendrickson Trailer Commercial Vehicle Systems (2)
2070 Industrial Pl SE, Canton, OH 44707-2641
Tel.: (330) 456-7288
Web Site: http://www.hendrickson-intl.com
Mfr of Suspensions For Tractor Trailers
N.A.I.C.S.: 541715
Perry Bahr (VP & Gen Mgr)

Hendrickson Truck Commercial Vehicle Systems (2)
800 S Frontage Rd, Woodridge, IL 60517-4900
Tel.: (630) 910-2800
Web Site: http://www.hendrickson-intl.com
Mfr of Truck Suspension Systems
N.A.I.C.S.: 336390
John Jeffrey (Dir-Mktg-Trailer Suspension)
Matt Joy (VP & Gen Mgr)

Subsidiary (Domestic):

Hendrickson USA LLC (2)
800 S Frontage Rd, Woodridge, IL 60517-4904

U.S. PRIVATE

Tel.: (630) 910-2844
Motor Vehicle Parts & Accessories Mfr
N.A.I.C.S.: 423110

Subsidiary (Domestic):

Liteflex, LLC (3)
100 Holiday Dr Ste 2707, Englewood, OH 45322
Tel.: (937) 836-7025
Emp.: 100
Spring Mfr
N.A.I.C.S.: 332613

THE BONER GROUP, INC.
440 Columbia Dr Ste 105, West Palm Beach, FL 33409-1801
Tel.: (561) 688-2880 FL
Web Site: http://www.bonergroup.com
Year Founded: 1990
Rev.: $10,000,000
Emp.: 12
Fiscal Year-end: 12/31/03
N.A.I.C.S.: 541810
Kim Donovan (Client Svcs Dir)
John Holloway (Fin Mgr)
Geri Camarda (Production Mgr)
Kim French (VP-Client Svcs)
Mark Minter (VP & Creative Dir)
Aimee Shaughnessy (Sr Acct Mgr)

Subsidiaries:

The Boner Group, Inc./Ann K. Savage (1)
611 Talmadge Ct SE, Leesburg, VA 20175-8991
Tel.: (703) 589-1445
Emp.: 11
N.A.I.C.S.: 541810
Ann K. Savage (Pres)

THE BORDEN AGENCY
1975 Pioneer Rd, Huntingdon Valley, PA 19006
Tel.: (215) 442-0590
Web Site: http://www.thebordenagency.com
Year Founded: 2004
Sales Range: $10-24.9 Million
Emp.: 20
Advertising Services
N.A.I.C.S.: 541810
Larry Borden (CEO)

THE BORDEN-PERLMAN INSURANCE AGENCY, INC.
250 Phillips Blvd Ste 280, Ewing, NJ 08618
Tel.: (609) 896-3434 NJ
Web Site: http://www.bordenperlman.com
Year Founded: 1995
Insurance Agents
N.A.I.C.S.: 524210
Jeff Perlman (Co-Founder & Mng Dir)
Richard Perlman (Founder-Perlman Insurance Agency)
Douglas C. Borden (Founder & Mng Dir)
Chris Borden (Acct Exec)
Jeremy Perlman (Acct Exec)
Douglas Coleman (Exec VP)
Jonathan Hitzges (Acct Exec)
Kelly Myers (VP & Risk Advisor)
Megan Sweigart (Acct Exec)
Sharon Cappella (Acct Exec)
Shelleen Piselli (Acct Exec)
Linda Peruto (Fin Mgr)
Katie Jones (Acctg Supvr)
Karen Chingery (Mgr-Personal Lines)

THE BORENSTEIN GROUP, INC.
11240 Waples Mill Rd Ste 420, Fairfax, VA 22030
Tel.: (703) 385-8178

COMPANIES

Web Site:
http://www.borensteingroup.com
Year Founded: 1995
Sales Range: $1-9.9 Million
Emp.: 10
Advertising Services
N.A.I.C.S.: 541810
Gal S. Borenstein *(Founder & CEO)*
Kim Plyler *(VP-Govt Comm)*
Dominick Terry *(Dir-Digital Creative)*

THE BOSMA GROUP, PC
401 Ryland St Ste 300, Reno, NV 89502
Tel.: (775) 786-4900
Web Site:
http://www.thebosmagroup.com
Year Founded: 2007
Sales Range: $1-9.9 Million
Emp.: 15
Accounting Services
N.A.I.C.S.: 541219
Kelsey K. Hernandez *(Mgr-Tax)*
Jack Buice *(Mgr)*
Aurora Tracy *(Sec)*

THE BOSTON CONSULTING GROUP, INC.
200 Pier 4 Blvd, Boston, MA 02210
Tel.: (617) 973-1200   MA
Web Site: https://www.bcg.com
Year Founded: 1963
Emp.: 30,000
Other Management Consulting Services
N.A.I.C.S.: 541618
Hans-Paul Burkner *(Mng Dir)*
Miki U. Tsusaka *(Sr Partner, CMO & Mng Dir-Japan)*
Janmejaya Sinha *(Chm-India)*
Richard Lesser *(Chm-Global)*
Debbie Simpson *(Head-Functions-Global)*
Lars Faeste *(Sr Partner & Mng Dir-China)*
Matthew Krentz *(Sr Partner & Mng Dir-Chicago)*
Sharon Marcil *(Sr Partner & Mng Dir-Washington)*
Thomas Reichert *(Sr Partner, Mng Dir & Chm-Practice Areas-New York)*
Christoph Schweizer *(CEO)*
Wendy Woods *(Sr Partner & Mng Dir-Boston)*
Jean Le Corre *(Sr Partner & Mng Dir-Sao Paulo)*
Ulrike Schwarz-Runer *(Partner, Mng Dir & Gen Counsel-London)*
David Bronstein *(Sr Partner & Mng Dir)*
Alpesh Shah *(Sr Partner & Mng Dir-Mumbai)*
Joe Davis *(Sr Partner, Mng Dir & Chm-North America)*
Tawfik Hammoud *(Sr Partner & Mng Dir-Toronto)*
Neeraj Aggarwal *(Chm-Asia Pacific)*
Nidhi Sinha *(Dir-Media Rels-New York)*
Paul Tranter *(CFO)*
Amanda Luther *(Partner & Mng Dir)*
Megan DeFauw *(Partner & Mng Dir)*
Brian Anderson *(Partner & Mng Dir)*
Carolyn Ford *(Partner & Mng Dir)*
Tomer J. Tzur *(Partner & Sr Mng Dir)*
Neveen F. Awad *(Partner & Mng Dir)*

Subsidiaries:

Maya Design, Inc.   (1)
444 Liberty Ave Ste 1600, Pittsburgh, PA 15222
Tel.: (412) 488-2900
Web Site: http://www.maya.com
Technology Research & Product Development Services
N.A.I.C.S.: 541715

Jeff Senn *(CTO)*
Mike Boselowitz *(Engr)*
Stuart Roth *(Sr Engr)*
Jon Larkin *(Sr Engr)*
Derek Lasher *(Sr Mgr-Product)*
Dutch MacDonald *(Dir-Digital)*
Adam Paulisick *(Chief Product Officer)*
Kent Vasko II *(Engr)*

The Boston Consulting Group - Abu Dhabi   (1)
Al Niyadi Building 1st Floor Airport Rd, PO Box 109619, Abu Dhabi, United Arab Emirates
Tel.: (971) 2 6529 600
Web Site: http://www.bcgmiddleeast.com
Multibusiness Management Services
N.A.I.C.S.: 541618
Joerg Hildebrandt *(Partner & Mng Dir)*

The Boston Consulting Group - Athens   (1)
18 Vassilissis Sophias Ave, 10674, Athens, Greece
Tel.: (30) 210 7260200
Web Site: http://www.bcg.com
Emp.: 6
Financial & Industrial Business Services
N.A.I.C.S.: 541613
Vassilis Antoniades *(Sr Partner & Mng Dir)*

The Boston Consulting Group - Bangkok   (1)
37th Fl U Chu Liang Building Rama IV Rd, Silom Bangrak, 10500, Bangkok, Thailand
Tel.: (66) 2 667 3000
Web Site: http://www.bcg.com
Sales Range: $25-49.9 Million
Emp.: 5
Management Consulting Services
N.A.I.C.S.: 541618
Vincent Chin *(Sr Partner & Mng Dir)*

The Boston Consulting Group - Barcelona   (1)
Avda Diagonal 640-4A, 8017, Barcelona, Spain
Tel.: (34) 93 363 4700
Web Site:
http://www.thebostonconsultinggroup.es
Management Consulting Services
N.A.I.C.S.: 541618
Ramon Baeza *(Sr Partner & Mng Dir)*

The Boston Consulting Group - Beijing   (1)
15F East Tower Twin Towers B-12 Jian Guo Men Wai Ave, 100022, Beijing, Chaoyang, China
Tel.: (86) 10 8527 9000
Web Site: http://www.bcg.com.cn
Sales Range: $10-24.9 Million
Emp.: 45
Financial & Management Consulting Services
N.A.I.C.S.: 541618
Christoph Nettesheim *(Sr Partner & Mng Dir)*

The Boston Consulting Group - Brussels   (1)
Keizerinlaan 13 Boulevard de l'Imperatrice, 1000, Brussels, Belgium
Tel.: (32) 22890202
Web Site: http://www.bcg.be
Financial Management Consulting Services
N.A.I.C.S.: 541618
Christophe Brognaux *(Partner & Mng Dir)*

The Boston Consulting Group - Budapest   (1)
Piarista Koz 2, 1052, Budapest, Hungary
Tel.: (36) 1 888 0200
Web Site: http://www.bcg.com
Emp.: 5
Financial & Management Consulting Services
N.A.I.C.S.: 541618
Laszlo Juhasz *(Partner & Mng Dir)*

The Boston Consulting Group - Buenos Aires   (1)
Bouchard 547-10, C1106ABG, Buenos Aires, Argentina
Tel.: (54) 11 4317 5900
Web Site: http://www.bcg.com.ar
Management Consulting
N.A.I.C.S.: 541618
Rodrigo Rivera *(Partner & Mng Dir)*

The Boston Consulting Group - Casablanca   (1)
104 Boulevard Abdellatif Ben Kaddour, 20050, Casablanca, Morocco
Tel.: (212) 529 023 049
Web Site: http://www.bcg.ma
Financial & Management Consulting Services
N.A.I.C.S.: 541618
Patrick Dupoux *(Sr Partner & Mng Dir)*
Lisa Ivers *(Partner & Mng Dir)*
Jorge Tomaz *(Partner & Mng Dir)*
Nicolas Kachaner *(Sr Partner & Mng Dir)*

The Boston Consulting Group - Dubai   (1)
Office Park at Dubai Internet City Block D 4th Fl, PO Box 32257, Dubai, 32257, United Arab Emirates
Tel.: (971) 4 4480 300
Web Site: http://www.bcgmiddleeast.com
Business Management Consulting Services
N.A.I.C.S.: 541618
Joerg Hildebrandt *(Sr Partner & Mng Dir)*

The Boston Consulting Group - Hong Kong   (1)
34th Floor Tower Two Times Square, Causeway Bay, Hong Kong, China (Hong Kong)
Tel.: (852) 2506 2111
Web Site: http://www.bcg.com.cn
Sales Range: $25-49.9 Million
Emp.: 6
Financial, Technology & Telecommunications Consultations
N.A.I.C.S.: 541618
Christoph Nettesheim *(Sr Partner & Mng Dir)*

The Boston Consulting Group - Jakarta   (1)
Jalan Jenderal Sudirman Kav 45-46, Jenderal Sudirman Kav 45-46, 12930, Jakarta, Indonesia
Tel.: (62) 21 3006 2888
Web Site: http://www.bcg.com
Emp.: 7
Business & Management Consulting Services
N.A.I.C.S.: 541618
Vincent Chin *(Sr Partner & Mng Dir)*

The Boston Consulting Group - Kuala Lumpur   (1)
Level 28 Menara IMC No 8 Jalan Sultan Ismail, 50250, Kuala Lumpur, Malaysia
Tel.: (60) 3 2688 5000
Web Site: http://www.bcg.com
Business Management Consulting Services
N.A.I.C.S.: 541618
Vincent Chin *(Sr Partner & Mng Dir)*

The Boston Consulting Group - Madrid   (1)
Alcala 95-2nd Floor, Madrid, 28009, Spain
Tel.: (34) 91 520 6100
Web Site:
http://www.thebostonconsultinggroup.es
Emp.: 20
Management Consulting Services
N.A.I.C.S.: 541618
Ramon Baeza *(Sr Partner & Mng Dir)*

The Boston Consulting Group - Shanghai   (1)
21F Central Plaza 227 Huangpi Bei Lu, 200003, Shanghai, China
Tel.: (86) 21 2306 4000
Web Site: http://www.bcg.com.cn
Sales Range: $25-49.9 Million
Emp.: 80
Financial & Management Consulting Services
N.A.I.C.S.: 541618
Christoph Nettesheim *(Sr Partner & Mng Dir)*

The Boston Consulting Group - Taipei   (1)
Taipei 101 Tower 61st Fl Unit F No 7 Xin Yi Rd Sec 5, Taipei, 11049, Taiwan
Tel.: (886) 2 8722 2000
Web Site: http://www.bcg.com.cn
Sales Range: $10-24.9 Million
Emp.: 30
Financial & Management Consulting Services

THE BOSTON CONSULTING GROUP, INC.

N.A.I.C.S.: 541618
Carol Liao *(Mng Dir & Sr Partner)*

The Boston Consulting Group - Tokyo   (1)
The New Otani Garden Court 4-1 Kioi-cho, Chiyoda-ku, Tokyo, 102-0094, Japan
Tel.: (81) 3 5211 0300
Web Site: http://www.bcg.co.jp
Financial Management Consulting Services
N.A.I.C.S.: 541618
Hiroaki Sugita *(Sr Partner & Mng Dir)*

The Boston Consulting Group AB   (1)
Gustav Adolfs Torg 18, SE-111 30, Stockholm, Sweden
Tel.: (46) 84024400
Web Site: http://www.bcg.dk
Sales Range: $25-49.9 Million
Emp.: 25
Various Business Management Services
N.A.I.C.S.: 541618
Ulrik Sanders *(Sr Partner & Mng Dir)*
Johan Oberg *(Mng Dir & Partner)*

Branch (Non-US):

The Boston Consulting Group Nordic AB - Copenhagen   (2)
Kalvebod Brygge 24 8th Floor, 1560, Copenhagen, Denmark
Tel.: (45) 77 32 3400
Web Site: http://www.bcg.dk
Global Management Consulting
N.A.I.C.S.: 541618
Ulrik Sanders *(Sr Partner & Mng Dir)*

The Boston Consulting Group Nordic AB - Helsinki   (2)
Kluuvikatu 3A 4th Floor, 100, Helsinki, Finland
Tel.: (358) 985686000
Web Site: http://www.bcg.dk
Business Management Consulting Services in Various Industries
N.A.I.C.S.: 541618
Ulrik Sanders *(Sr Partner & Mng Dir)*

The Boston Consulting Group Nordic AB - Oslo   (2)
Parkveien 53A, Oslo, 0256, Norway
Tel.: (47) 21 04 6800
Web Site: http://www.bcg.com
Emp.: 10
Business Management Services
N.A.I.C.S.: 541618
Ulrik Sanders *(Sr Partner & Mng Dir)*

The Boston Consulting Group B.V.   (1)
Gustaav Mahlerlaan 40, 1082 MC, Amsterdam, Netherlands
Tel.: (31) 20 548 4000
Web Site: http://www.bcg.nl
Emp.: 200
Business Management Consultant
N.A.I.C.S.: 541618
Huib Kurstjens *(Sr Partner & Mng Dir)*

The Boston Consulting Group GmbH   (1)
Ludwigstrasse 21, 80539, Munich, Germany
Tel.: (49) 89 231 740
Web Site: http://www.bcg.com
Emp.: 880
Business Management Consultant
N.A.I.C.S.: 541611

Branch (Domestic):

The Boston Consulting Group GmbH - Berlin   (2)
Dircksenstrasse 41, 10178, Berlin, Germany
Tel.: (49) 30 28 87 10
Web Site: http://www.bcg.de
Sales Range: $50-74.9 Million
Emp.: 15
Management Consulting Services
N.A.I.C.S.: 541618
Reinhard Messenbock *(Partner & Mng Dir)*

The Boston Consulting Group GmbH - Cologne   (2)
Koln Turm Im Mediapark 8, 50670, Cologne, Germany
Tel.: (49) 221 55 00 50
Web Site: http://www.bcg.de

THE BOSTON CONSULTING GROUP, INC.   U.S. PRIVATE

The Boston Consulting Group, Inc.—(Continued)
Sales Range: $25-49.9 Million
Emp.: 100
Business Consulting Services
N.A.I.C.S.: 541618
Rainer Minz (Sr Partner & Mng Dir)

The Boston Consulting Group Pty. Ltd. (1)
101 Collins Street Level 52, Melbourne, 3000, VIC, Australia
Tel.: (61) 3 9656 2100
Web Site: http://www.bcg.com
Emp.: 120
Business Management Consulting Services
N.A.I.C.S.: 541618
Nicholas Glenning (Sr Partner & Mng Dir)

Branch (Domestic):

The Boston Consulting Group Pty. Ltd. - Canberra (2)
Level 5 16 Marcus Clarke Street, Canberra, 2601, ACT, Australia
Tel.: (61) 2 6243 2800
Web Site: http://www.bostonconsulting.com.au
Emp.: 2
Governmental & Business Management Services
N.A.I.C.S.: 921190
Miguel Carrasco (Partner & Mng Dir)

Branch (Non-US):

The Boston Consulting Group Pty. Ltd. - New Zealand (2)
23-29 Albert St Level 30, 1010, Auckland, New Zealand
Tel.: (64) 9 377 2297
Web Site: http://www.bostonconsulting.co.nz
Management Consulting
N.A.I.C.S.: 541618
Andrew Clark (Sr Partner & Mng Dir)

Branch (Domestic):

The Boston Consulting Group Pty. Ltd. - Sydney (2)
Level 28 Chifley Tower 2 Chifley Square, Sydney, 2000, NSW, Australia
Tel.: (61) 2 9323 5600
Web Site: http://www.bostonconsulting.com.au
Management & Consulting Services
N.A.I.C.S.: 541618

The Boston Consulting Group RSA Pty. Ltd.
West Tower 2nd Fl Nelson Mandela Square Maude Street, 2146, Sandton, Johannesburg, South Africa
Tel.: (27) 11 881 55 11
Web Site: http://www.bcg.com
Financial & Business Management Services
N.A.I.C.S.: 541618

The Boston Consulting Group Singapore Pte. Ltd. (1)
50 Raffles Place 44-02/03 Singapore Land Tower, Singapore, 048623, Singapore
Tel.: (65) 64292500
Web Site: http://www.bcg.com.sg
Emp.: 140
Business Management Consulting Services
N.A.I.C.S.: 541618
Vincent Chin (Sr Partner & Mng Dir)

The Boston Consulting Group, Inc. - Atlanta (1)
1075 Peachtree St NE Ste 3800, Atlanta, GA 30309
Tel.: (404) 877-5200
Web Site: http://www.bcg.com
Financial & Business Management Consulting Services
N.A.I.C.S.: 541618
Alan Wise (Sr Partner & Mng Dir)

The Boston Consulting Group, Inc. - Chicago (1)
300 N LaSalle, Chicago, IL 60654
Tel.: (312) 993-3300
Web Site: http://www.chicago.bcg.com
Emp.: 500
Management Consulting, Corporate Development & Strategy Services
N.A.I.C.S.: 541618
Marin Gjaja (Sr Partner & Mng Dir)

The Boston Consulting Group, Inc. - Dallas (1)
2501 N Harwood Ste 2200, Dallas, TX 75201
Tel.: (214) 849-1500
Web Site: https://www.bcg.com
Business Management Services in Technology/Telecommunications, Consumer Goods, Healthcare & Energy/Utilities Industries
N.A.I.C.S.: 541618
Tom Lutz (Sr Partner, Mng Dir & Vice Chm-Consumer & Retail-Dallas)
Stephen Edison (Partner & Mng Dir)
Yogesh Mishra (Partner & Mng Dir)
Suketu Shah (Partner & Mng Dir)

The Boston Consulting Group, Inc. - Houston (1)
LyondellBasell Twr 1221 McKinney Ste 3050, Houston, TX 77010
Tel.: (713) 286-7000
Web Site: http://www.texas.bcg.com
Sales Range: $10-24.9 Million
Emp.: 40
Business Management Consultant
N.A.I.C.S.: 541618
Tom Lutz (Sr Partner & Mng Dir)
Andrea Ostby (Partner)
Jeffrey Shaddix (Mng Dir & Partner)
Laura Juliano (Mng Dir & Partner)
Marie-Helene Ben Samoun (Mng Dir & Partner)
Matthew Abel (Mng Dir & Partner)
Mike Lyons (Mng Dir & Partner)
Alan Thomson (Sr Partner & Head-Energy Practice Globally)
Parsons Parsons (Partner & Mng Dir)
Kenny Kurtzman (Partner & Mng Dir)
Ilshat Kharisov (Partner & Mng Dir)

The Boston Consulting Group, Inc. - Washington, D.C. (1)
4800 Hampden Ln Ste 400, Bethesda, MD 20814
Tel.: (301) 664-7400
Web Site: http://www.bcg.com
Administrative Management & General Management Consulting Service
N.A.I.C.S.: 541611
Ken Keen (Sr Partner & Mng Dir)
Mike Marquis (Principal)

THE BOSTON HOME, INC.
2049 Dorchester Ave, Boston, MA 02124-4799
Tel.: (617) 825-3905   MA
Web Site: http://www.thebostonhome.org
Year Founded: 1884
Sales Range: $10-24.9 Million
Emp.: 254
Voluntary Health Organizations
N.A.I.C.S.: 813212
Mark Williamson (Dir-HR)
Florence Rawls (Dir-Dev)
Fran Murphy (CFO)
Cindy Walsh (Dir-Clinical Svcs)
Steven E. Carr (Dir-Medical)
Lucille Haratsis (Dir-Wellness, Spirituality Program & Admissions)
John Hannon (Treas)
Josefina Martinez Stamatos (Dir-Food Svc)
Christine Reilly (Pres & CEO)

THE BOUCHER GROUP, INC.
4141 S 108th St, Greenfield, WI 53228
Tel.: (414) 427-4141   WI
Web Site: http://www.boucher.com
Year Founded: 1977
Sales Range: $300-349.9 Million
Emp.: 1,000
Holding Company; New & Used Car Dealerships Owner & Operator
N.A.I.C.S.: 551112
Gordon F. Boucher (Pres)
Tony Karabon (VP & Gen Counsel)
Fred Czuta (VP-Fleet Grp)

Subsidiaries:

Gordie Boucher Ford of Kenosha, Inc. (1)
8301 75th St, Kenosha, WI 53142
Tel.: (262) 697-0700
Web Site: http://www.boucherfordkenosha.com
Sales Range: $10-24.9 Million
Emp.: 60
New & Used Car Dealer
N.A.I.C.S.: 441110
Dan Schlitt (Gen Mgr)
Joe Kobriger (Branch Mgr)
Tom Sparks (Mgr-Sls-Used Cars)
Scott Verhagen (Mgr-Sls-New Cars)

Gordie Boucher Ford of Menomonee Falls, Inc. (1)
N88 W14300 Main St, Menomonee Falls, WI 53051
Tel.: (262) 255-9010
Web Site: http://www.boucherfordmenomoneefalls.com
Sales Range: $10-24.9 Million
Emp.: 45
New & Used Car Dealer
N.A.I.C.S.: 441110
Jeffery Samp (Gen Mgr)

THE BOUNCE AGENCY
201 Riverplace Ste 400, Greenville, SC 29601
Tel.: (864) 271-8340
Web Site: http://www.thebounceagency.com
Year Founded: 1959
Sales Range: $10-24.9 Million
Emp.: 30
Full Service, Health Care, Print, Public Relations, Real Estate
N.A.I.C.S.: 541810
Carlos Jimenez (CEO)
John McDermott (Pres & Dir-Creative)
Jennifer Famiglietti (VP & Grp Dir)
Gary Cherrett (VP & Grp Dir)
Brent Campbell (Dir-Bus Dev)
Jennifer Aughtry (Acct Supvr)
Jason Manges (Dir-Partnership Mktg)
Megan DeMoise (Acct Coord)
Brandi Browning (Acct Coord)
Scott Ziegler (Gen Mgr)
Brendan Center (Mgr-Digital Ops)
Brook Guinn (Mgr-Acctg)
Aarika Woods (Assoc Acct Mgr)

THE BOWDOIN GROUP, INC.
40 William St, Wellesley, MA 02481
Tel.: (781) 263-5200   MA
Web Site: http://www.bowdoingroup.com
Year Founded: 1994
Sales Range: $10-24.9 Million
Emp.: 40
Executive Search & Consulting Services
N.A.I.C.S.: 561312
David Melville (Founder & CEO)
Karen Walker Beecher (COO)
Jordan Goldberg (Partner & VP)
Bev Lania (Principal)
Paul Manning (Principal-Software & Tech)
Thomas Stevens (Dir-Fin Svcs)
Lindsey Muldoon (Dir-Ops & Client Engagement)
Jim Urquhart (Mgr-Acct-Fin Info Svcs & Tech-Natl)
Josh Gottlieb (Mgr-Acct-Healthcare Info Svcs & Tech-Natl)
Scott Aldsworth (Pres)
Scott Vierra (VP)
Emily Leinbach (Head-Mktg)
Kara Barr (VP-Delivery)
Terri Ryan (VP-Fin)

THE BOWEN CONSULTING GROUP, INC.
10 Center St Ste 103, Stafford, VA 22556
Tel.: (540) 658-0490   VA
Web Site: http://www.bowenconsulting.com
Year Founded: 2005
Sales Range: $1-9.9 Million
Emp.: 50
Business Research & Development Services
N.A.I.C.S.: 541720
Deborah Mayberry (Pres)
Tom Mayberry (CFO)
Anna Jones (VP-HR & Admin)
Tom Baker (VP-Ops)
Ray Babbie (Dir-Bus Dev)
Cate Florenz Michaud (Dir-Comm)
Lawrence Gaines (Dir-Bus Mgmt)
Mary Craig (Program Dir)
Sarah Coon (Dir-Creative Svcs)

THE BOWERSTON SHALE COMPANY
515 Main St, Bowerston, OH 44695
Tel.: (740) 269-2921
Web Site: http://www.bowerstonshale.com
Year Founded: 1929
Sales Range: $10-24.9 Million
Emp.: 200
Clay Refractory Mfr
N.A.I.C.S.: 327120
Mark R. Willard (Pres & CEO)
Edward C. Milliken (VP)
Beth K. Hillyer (VP)

THE BOWLIN GROUP LLC
12200 Chandler Dr, Walton, KY 41094
Tel.: (859) 485-6922
Web Site: http://www.bowlingroup.com
Year Founded: 1978
Sales Range: $10-24.9 Million
Emp.: 100
Providers of Telephone & Communication Line Construction
N.A.I.C.S.: 238210
Kerry Bowlin (Pres)
Bill Stephens (Coord-Fleet)
Rick Ryan (Mgr-HR)

THE BOXMAKER INC.
6412 S 190th St, Kent, WA 98032-2148
Tel.: (425) 251-5428   WA
Web Site: http://www.boxmaker.com
Year Founded: 1981
Sales Range: $100-124.9 Million
Emp.: 150
Corrugated & Solid Fiber Boxes
N.A.I.C.S.: 322211
Dwight Sawtell (VP-Fin & Admin)
Richard Brown (Pres)

Subsidiaries:

The Boxmaker Inc. (1)
2524 NE Riverside Way, Portland, OR 97211
Tel.: (503) 445-1983
Web Site: http://www.boxmaker.com
Sales Range: $10-24.9 Million
Emp.: 12
Corrugated & Solid Fiber Boxes
N.A.I.C.S.: 424130
Dave Bouta (Plant Mgr)

The Boxmaker Inc. (1)
3285A W 1st Ave, Eugene, OR 97402-5419
Tel.: (541) 484-7233
Web Site: http://www.boxmaker.com
Sales Range: $10-24.9 Million
Emp.: 10
Corrugated & Solid Fiber Boxes
N.A.I.C.S.: 424130
Dave Hill (Owner)
Dave Taylor (Owner)
Daniel Dixon (Dir-Operational Excellence)
Ann Graham (Mgr-HR)
Toni Lyerla (VP-Sls)
Jennifer Main (Dir-Corrugated)
Tonia Olson (Dir-Mktg)

COMPANIES

Tina Rospond *(Mgr-Portland)*
Dwight Sawtell *(VP-Fin & Admin)*
Justin Stacey *(Dir-Innovation & Emerging Bus)*

THE BOYER COMPANY, LLC
101 S 200 E Ste 200, Salt Lake City, UT 84111-1975
Tel.: (801) 521-4781 — UT
Web Site: http://www.boyercompany.com
Year Founded: 1972
Sales Range: $10-24.9 Million
Emp.: 100
Developer of Commercial Real Estate
N.A.I.C.S.: 531120
H. Roger Boyer *(Founder & Chm)*
Paul D. Kelley *(CFO)*
Jake Boyer *(Pres & CEO)*

THE BOZZUTO GROUP
6406 Ivy Lane Ste 700, Greenbelt, MD 20770
Tel.: (301) 220-0100
Web Site: http://www.bozzuto.com
Year Founded: 1988
Sales Range: $50-74.9 Million
Emp.: 5,000
Real Estate Development & Construction
N.A.I.C.S.: 236115
Thomas S. Bozzuto *(Chm & Co-Founder)*
Daniel C. Murphy *(CFO & Partner)*
Richard L. Mostyn *(Founder, Co-Owner, Vice Chm & COO)*
Mike Schlegel *(Pres-Bozzuto Construction Company & Partner)*
Julie A. Smith *(Chief Admin Officer)*
John Slidell *(Co-Founder)*
Toby Bozzuto *(Co-Owner & Chm)*
Thomas A. Baum *(Pres-Bozzuto Homes, Inc.)*
Steve Strazzella *(Pres-Bozzuto Dev Co)*
Jamie S. Gorski *(CMO)*
Tom Geyer *(Dir-Brand Mgmt)*
Daniel High *(Sr VP-HR)*
Kristen Reese *(VP-Talent Mgmt)*
Steven Fretwell *(VP-Learning & Dev)*
Brian Valle *(VP-Fin)*
Jeff Cellio *(Dir-Warranty Svcs)*
Mark Franceski *(VP-Res)*
Betty O'Brien *(Dir-Network Infrastructure)*
Jessica Itzel *(Sr Dir-Mktg, Brand Dev)*
Mark Digby *(Mgr-Retail Asset)*
Glen Seidlitz *(Sr VP-Debt & Equity)*
Stephanie L. Williams *(Pres)*
Pei Pei Mirabella *(VP-Downtown Chicago Portfolio)*
Ben Burns *(VP-Lead Generation & Digital Strategy)*
Brad Coker *(Sr VP & Dir-Asset Mgmt)*

Subsidiaries:

Bozzuto Construction Company (1)
6406 Ivy Lane Suite 700, Greenbelt, MD 20770
Tel.: (301) 220-0100
Web Site: http://www.bozzuto.com
Sales Range: $25-49.9 Million
Emp.: 200
General Contractors & Residential Construction Services
N.A.I.C.S.: 236116
Michael Schlegel *(Pres)*
Kelly Cantley *(VP-Bus Dev)*
Rob Rodgers *(Sr Mgr-Projects)*
David Schorr *(Chief Acctg Officer)*
Josh Peters *(VP-Field Ops)*
Nathan Slavin *(Dir-Safety)*
Zach Anduiza *(VP & Controller)*

Bozzuto Development Co. Inc (1)
6406 Ivy Ln Ste 700, Greenbelt, MD 20770
Tel.: (301) 220-0100
Web Site: http://www.bazzuto.com
Rev.: $65.930
Emp.: 200
Multifamily Developers, Construction of High-End, Mixed-Income & Affordable Housing & Senior Living Communities
N.A.I.C.S.: 237201
Steve Strazzella *(Pres)*
Mike Henehan *(Co-Mng Dir & Sr VP)*
Jeff Kayce *(Co-Mng Dir & Sr VP)*
Hilary Goldfarb *(Sr VP)*
Lauren Jezienicki *(Sr VP)*
Alisa Rosenberg *(VP)*

Bozzuto Homes (1)
6406 Ivy Lane Suite 700, Greenbelt, MD 20770
Tel.: (866) 698-7513
Web Site: http://www.bozzuto.com
Homebuilding Services
N.A.I.C.S.: 236115
Chris Block *(Sr VP-Ops)*
Kerri Paulino *(VP)*

Bozzuto Land Services (1)
6406 Ivy Lane Suite 700, Greenbelt, MD 20770
Tel.: (301) 446-2264
Site Development, Zoning, Lot Sales & Entitlements
N.A.I.C.S.: 237210
John B. Slidell *(Vice Chm & Pres)*

Bozzuto Management Company (1)
6406 Ivy Lane Ste 700, Greenbelt, MD 20770
Tel.: (301) 220-0100
Web Site: http://www.bozzuto.com
Sales Range: $600-649.9 Million
Emp.: 200
Cooperative Apartment Manager
N.A.I.C.S.: 531110
Stephanie L. Williams *(Pres)*
John M. Pezzulla *(Dir-Retail Assets)*
Keri Walker *(Reg VP)*
David Curcio *(Sr VP-Ops)*
Patrick Butler *(VP)*
Richard Brigstocke *(Dir-Tenant Coordination)*
Michael Barry *(VP)*
Lauren Athas *(VP)*
Mark Digby *(Mgr-Retail Asset)*
Paul Gantos *(VP-Maintenance, Design & Programs)*
Andrew DiSchino *(VP)*
Juliana Thomas *(Reg Portfolio Mgr)*
Clark Pritchett *(Reg Portfolio Mgr)*
Jenn Popoola *(Reg Portfolio Mgr)*
Dan Lienert *(VP-Property Ops)*
Monica LaVorgna *(Dir-Retail Assets-Mid-Atlantic)*
Stephanie Griffin *(Dir-Fin Analysis & Advisory Svcs)*
Jon Lane *(VP-Maintenance & Engrg Svcs)*
Stephanie Rath *(Sr VP-Ops)*

THE BRADEN SUTPHIN INK COMPANY
3650 E 93rd St, Cleveland, OH 44105-1620
Tel.: (216) 271-2300 — OH
Web Site: http://www.bsink.com
Year Founded: 1913
Rev.: $38,700,000
Emp.: 265
Printing Ink Products
N.A.I.C.S.: 325910
Bob Nowak *(Gen Mgr-Flexo Mfg & Ops)*
Andrea Boufford *(Coord-Sls & Mktg)*
Scott Dodson *(Reg Mgr-Sls)*
Ray Stoney Jr. *(VP)*

THE BRADFORD GROUP
9333 N Milwaukee Ave, Niles, IL 60714-1381
Tel.: (847) 966-2770 — DE
Web Site: http://www.bradfordexchange.com
Year Founded: 1973
Sales Range: $100-124.9 Million
Emp.: 600
Direct Mail Retail Marketing of Collectors Items
N.A.I.C.S.: 424990

Brooke Berger *(Acct Exec)*
Erica Freckelton *(Acct Coord)*
Damon Maida *(Acct Dir)*
Melinda Dale *(Sr Acct Exec)*
Spencer Turney *(Acct Exec)*
Lauren Hamilton *(Acct Exec)*

Subsidiaries:

Ashton-Drake Galleries, Ltd. (1)
9200 N Maryland Ave, Niles, IL 60714
Tel.: (847) 966-2770
Web Site: http://www.ashtondrake.com
N.A.I.C.S.: 541860

The Hamilton Collection, Inc. (1)
7018 A C Skinner Pkwy Ste 300, Jacksonville, FL 32256-6069 (100%)
Tel.: (904) 279-1300
Sales Range: $10-24.9 Million
Emp.: 55
Direct Mail & Distributor for Collectibles
N.A.I.C.S.: 459420

THE BRADLEY MARKETING GROUP
170 Wilbur Pl Ste 700, Bohemia, NY 11716
Tel.: (631) 231-9200
Web Site: http://www.bmgpromos.com
Rev.: $16,028,616
Emp.: 3
Business Forms, Printing, Inventory Management, Web Site Services & Promotional Products
N.A.I.C.S.: 424120
John Deangelis *(Co-Owner & Pres)*
Joe DeMeo *(Co-Owner)*

THE BRADY COMPANIES
8104 Comml St, La Mesa, CA 91942-2926
Tel.: (619) 589-7575
Web Site: http://www.brady.com
Year Founded: 1946
Sales Range: $50-74.9 Million
Emp.: 700
Holding Company; Steel Framing, Plastering, Drywall & Insulation Contractor
N.A.I.C.S.: 551112
Scott Brady *(Pres-San Diego)*

Subsidiaries:

Brady Company/Central California, Inc. (1)
13540 Blackie Rd, Castroville, CA 95012
Tel.: (831) 633-3315
Web Site: http://www.brady.com
Steel Framing, Plastering, Drywall & Insulation Contractor
N.A.I.C.S.: 238990
Gregg W. Brady *(Pres)*

Brady Company/Los Angeles, Inc. (1)
1010 N Olive, Anaheim, CA 92801
Tel.: (714) 533-9850
Web Site: http://www.brady.com
Emp.: 10
Steel Framing, Plastering, Drywall & Insulation Contractor
N.A.I.C.S.: 238990
William Saddler *(Pres)*

Brady Company/San Diego, Inc. (1)
8100 Ctr St, La Mesa, CA 91942
Tel.: (619) 589-7575
Web Site: http://www.brady.com
Sales Range: $75-99.9 Million
Emp.: 50
Steel Framing, Plastering, Drywall & Insulation Contractor
N.A.I.C.S.: 238990
Scott Brady *(Pres)*
Rasmus Honeywell *(Controller)*

THE BRANCH GROUP, INC.
442 Rutherford Ave NE, Roanoke, VA 24016-2116
Tel.: (540) 982-1678 — VA
Web Site: http://www.branchgroup.com
Year Founded: 1986
Emp.: 800
Holding Company
N.A.I.C.S.: 236220
Robert Wills *(CFO)*
Julie Beth *(CMO & Chief HR Officer)*
Ron Oakley *(Interim CEO)*

Subsidiaries:

Branch & Associates, Inc. (1)
5732 Airport Rd, Roanoke, VA 24012-3048
Tel.: (540) 989-5215
Web Site: http://www.branch-associates.com
Sales Range: $25-49.9 Million
Emp.: 60
General Contractors & Construction
N.A.I.C.S.: 236220
Craig Floyd *(Pres)*

Division (Domestic):

Branch & Associates, Inc. - Richmond Division (2)
13B S 15th St, Richmond, VA 23219
Tel.: (804) 525-5458
Construction Management Services
N.A.I.C.S.: 541611
Michael Vos *(VP)*

Branch Highways, Inc. (1)
442 Rutherford Ave NE, Roanoke, VA 24016-2116 (100%)
Tel.: (540) 982-1678
Web Site: http://www.branchgroup.com
Rev.: $95,000,000
Emp.: 400
Builder of Roads & Highways
N.A.I.C.S.: 237310
Michael Tomlinson *(VP)*
Mike Higgins *(VP-Ops & Design-Build Svcs)*
David Mitchell *(Project Mgr)*
Randall Clark *(Mgr-Ops Construction)*

E.V. Williams, Inc. (1)
925 S Military Hwy, Virginia Beach, VA 23464 (100%)
Tel.: (757) 420-1140
Web Site: http://www.evwilliams.com
Sales Range: $25-49.9 Million
Emp.: 310
Concrete Paving Construction Services
N.A.I.C.S.: 237310
Jay Openshaw *(Pres)*
Jim Akers *(Controller)*
Brian Evans *(VP-Ops)*
Carie Carley *(Coord-Trng)*
Dave LePage *(Mgr-Construction)*
Dennis Miller *(VP)*
Jeff Floyd *(Treas, VP & Controller)*
Walter Wallace Jr. *(Mgr-Equipment Ops)*

G.J. Hopkins, Inc. (1)
714 5th St NE, Roanoke, VA 24016-2124 (100%)
Tel.: (540) 982-1873
Web Site: http://www.gjhopkins.com
Sales Range: $10-24.9 Million
Emp.: 50
Full-Service Mechanical & Electrical Contractor
N.A.I.C.S.: 238220
E. M. Clifton *(Pres)*
Mark Maloney II *(Coord-Building Info Modeling)*

L.A. Lacy, Inc. (1)
1809 Broadway St, Charlottesville, VA 22902-5880
Tel.: (434) 296-7542
Web Site: http://www.lalacy.com
Electrical Contractor
N.A.I.C.S.: 238210
Jeff Lewis *(Pres)*
James Harrison *(Sr Project Mgr)*

R.E. Daffan, Inc. (1)
8428 Quarry Rd Ste 101, Manassas, VA 20110
Tel.: (703) 368-3500
Web Site: http://www.redaffan.com
Commercial Building Construction Services
N.A.I.C.S.: 236220

THE BRANDING AGENCY, LLC

THE BRANDING AGENCY, LLC

The Branding Agency, LLC—(Continued)

2281 Dabney Rd Ste E, Richmond, VA 23230
Tel.: (804) 278-9004
Web Site: http://www.branding-proforma.com
Year Founded: 2014
Sales Range: $1-9.9 Million
Emp.: 17
Custom Printing Services
N.A.I.C.S.: 323113
Ryan Andrews *(Pres)*
Andy Harmatz *(Partner)*
Robyn Patterson *(Office Mgr & Mgr-Inside Sls)*
Bob Smith *(Sls Mgr)*
Phillip Simson *(Sr Dir-Sls)*

THE BRANDT CO.

3020 Hickory Grove Rd, Davenport, IA 52806
Tel.: (563) 386-9740
Web Site: http://www.brandtco.com
Rev.: $8,360,000
Emp.: 55
Commercial Lithographic Printing
N.A.I.C.S.: 323111
Dave Huber *(VP & Gen Mgr)*
Marc Brandt *(Owner)*
Rich Farrar *(Mgr)*

THE BRANDYWINE COMPANIES, LLC

2 Ponds Edge Dr PO Box 500, Chadds Ford, PA 19317
Tel.: (610) 388-9600   PA
Web Site: http://www.brandywine-financial.com
Emp.: 50
Holding Company; Residential & Commercial Real Estate Owner & Property Manager; Accounting & Tax Services
N.A.I.C.S.: 551112
Bruce E. Moore *(CEO)*
Michael A. Lynam *(CFO)*

Subsidiaries:

Brandywine Financial Services Corporation   (1)
2 Ponds Edge Dr PO Box 500, Chadds Ford, PA 19317
Tel.: (610) 388-9600
Web Site: http://www.brandywine-financial.com
Sales Range: $25-49.9 Million
Emp.: 30
Accounting & Tax Preparation Services
N.A.I.C.S.: 541219

Brandywine Real Estate Management Services Corporation   (1)
2 Ponds Edge Dr PO Box 500, Chadds Ford, PA 19317
Tel.: (610) 388-9600
Web Site: http://www.brandywine-financial.com
Residential & Commercial Real Estate Acquisition, Development & Property Management Services
N.A.I.C.S.: 237210

THE BRAUN AGENCY, INC.

4664 S Blvd, Virginia Beach, VA 23452
Web Site: http://www.braunagency.com
Year Founded: 1998
Sales Range: $1-9.9 Million
Commercial Insurance Services
N.A.I.C.S.: 524210
Richard Braun *(Pres)*
Kelley Carter *(Mktg Dir)*
Denese Balino *(Office Mgr-Accts)*

THE BREAST CANCER CHARITIES OF AMERICA

8505 Technology Forest Pl Ste 604, The Woodlands, TX 77381
Tel.: (936) 231-8460
Web Site: http://www.thebreastcancercharities.org
Sales Range: $10-24.9 Million
Emp.: 6
Breast Cancer Treatment Services
N.A.I.C.S.: 622310
Erica A. Johnson *(Exec Dir)*
Stephanie Flores *(Mgr-Fin & Missions)*
Alix Angelelli *(Mgr-Program Outreach)*

THE BREAST CANCER SOCIETY, INC.

6859 E Rembrandt Ave Ste 128, Mesa, AZ 85212
Tel.: (480) 284-4014   AZ
Web Site: http://www.breastcancersociety.org
Year Founded: 2007
Sales Range: $25-49.9 Million
Emp.: 15
Breast Cancer Treatment Services
N.A.I.C.S.: 622310
Andrina Shields *(Pres)*
Brad Cates *(Treas)*
Sarah Allen *(Sec)*
James T. Reynolds II *(Exec Dir)*

THE BRENLIN GROUP, LLC

121 S Main St Ste 500, Akron, OH 44308-1325
Tel.: (330) 996-0202   OH
Sales Range: $25-49.9 Million
Emp.: 70
Holding Company
N.A.I.C.S.: 551112
David L. Brennan *(Chm & Pres)*
Joseph Weber *(CFO)*

Subsidiaries:

Prior Remanufacturing, Inc.   (1)
4874 Olson Dr, Dallas, TX 75227-2103   (100%)
Tel.: (972) 494-4254
Sales Range: $10-24.9 Million
Emp.: 25
Remanufactured Brake Systems for Passenger Cars & Heavy Duty Trucks
N.A.I.C.S.: 336340

THE BRETHREN HOME COMMUNITY

2990 Carlisle Pike, New Oxford, PA 17350
Tel.: (717) 624-2161   PA
Web Site: http://www.crosskeysvillage.org
Year Founded: 1908
Sales Range: $25-49.9 Million
Emp.: 858
Elder Care Services
N.A.I.C.S.: 624120
Linda Titzell *(Dir-Pastoral Care)*
Cindy Boyer *(Mgr-Volunteer Svcs)*
Holly Shearer *(Mgr-Wellness)*
Mary Van Buren *(Dir-Community Life)*
Ed Sharrah *(Dir-Safety & Transportation)*
Oliver Hazan *(VP-Sls & Mktg)*
Kelley Mitchell *(VP-HR)*
Vanessa Berger *(VP-Advancement)*
Jeffrey M. Evans *(Pres & CEO)*
Kathy Staub *(Coord-Residential Support)*
Jennifer Holcomb *(Dir-Memory Support)*
Joy Bodnar *(COO)*
Brett A. Hoffacker *(Treas)*
Rosemary L. Stoner *(Sec)*
James W. Balthaser *(Chm)*
Scott Sowers *(VP-Fin)*
Traci Rabenstein *(Vice Chm)*
John D. Miller Jr. *(Asst Sec & Asst Treas)*

THE BREWER COMPANY

1354 US Hwy 50, Milford, OH 45150-9205
Tel.: (513) 576-6300   OH
Web Site: http://www.thebrewerco.com
Year Founded: 1933
Sales Range: $50-74.9 Million
Emp.: 15
Asphalt Products
N.A.I.C.S.: 324122
Pinckney W. Brewer *(Founder & Pres)*
Mike Dooley *(VP-Fin)*

THE BREWER COMPANY

N 88 W 13901 Main St Ste 100, Menomonee Falls, WI 53051
Tel.: (262) 251-9530
Web Site: http://www.brewercompany.com
Year Founded: 1947
Rev.: $13,300,000
Emp.: 120
Surgical & Medical Instrument Mfr
N.A.I.C.S.: 339112
Paul Siepmann *(Pres)*

THE BRIAD GROUP

78 Okner Pkwy, Livingston, NJ 07039
Tel.: (973) 597-6433
Web Site: http://www.briad.com
Year Founded: 1987
Restaurant Operators
N.A.I.C.S.: 722511
Bradford Honigfeld *(Founder & Co-CEO)*
Dave Cahill *(Exec VP & CFO)*
Rick Barbrick *(Pres, COO & Co-CEO)*

THE BRIDGE INC.

248 W 108th St, New York, NY 10025
Tel.: (212) 663-3000   NY
Web Site: http://www.thebridgeny.org
Year Founded: 1954
Sales Range: $25-49.9 Million
Emp.: 362
Community Care Services
N.A.I.C.S.: 621498
Anthea Sutherland *(Sr VP-HR)*
Michael Blady *(COO)*
Donald Gorsica *(Co-CFO)*
Lisa Green *(Sr VP-Residential Svcs)*
Stephen Jorgensen *(Co-CFO)*
Nora Kershaw *(VP-IT)*
Christina Mansfield *(Sr VP-Outpatient Svcs)*
Lynda Selde *(Sr VP-Dev & External Rels)*
Cynthia C. Wainwright *(Pres)*
Howard Rothschild *(Sec)*
Mel P. Barkan *(Treas)*

THE BRIDGE OF CENTRAL MASSACHUSETTS, INC.

4 Mann St, Worcester, MA 01602
Tel.: (508) 755-0333   MA
Web Site: http://www.thebridgecm.org
Year Founded: 1980
Sales Range: $25-49.9 Million
Emp.: 701
Developmental Disability Assistance Services
N.A.I.C.S.: 624120
Erica Robert *(VP-Community Svc)*
Frederick Battersby *(Exec VP-Admin & Fin)*
Kennet Bates *(Pres & CEO)*
Rebecca Lynch *(VP-Advancement)*
Lorie C. Martiska *(VP-Advancement)*

THE BRIEN CENTER

359 Fenn St, Pittsfield, MA 01201
Tel.: (413) 499-0412   MA
Web Site: http://www.briencenter.org
Year Founded: 1997
Sales Range: $10-24.9 Million
Emp.: 566
Mental Health Care Services
N.A.I.C.S.: 621420
M. Christine MacBeth *(CEO)*
Lois Hobbs *(Dir-HR)*
Richard Lombardi *(Treas)*
Thomas Stokes *(Pres)*
Kenin Strout *(CFO)*

THE BRIGANTINE RESTAURANT CORP.

7889 Ostrow St, San Diego, CA 92111
Tel.: (858) 268-1030
Web Site: http://www.brigantine.com
Year Founded: 1969
Sales Range: $25-49.9 Million
Emp.: 700
Owner & Operator of Seafood Restaurants
N.A.I.C.S.: 722511
Michael A. Morton *(Co-Founder)*

THE BRIX GROUP INC.

541 Division St, Campbell, CA 95008-6905
Tel.: (408) 374-7900   CA
Web Site: http://www.brixcom.com
Year Founded: 1971
Sales Range: $125-149.9 Million
Emp.: 180
Electronic Parts & Equipment
N.A.I.C.S.: 423690
Harrison Brix *(CEO)*

THE BROADLEAF GROUP, LLC

13100 Wortham Ctr Dr Ste 150, Houston, TX 77065
Tel.: (305) 975-4964
Web Site: http://www.broadleafgroup.com
Year Founded: 2005
Data Processing & Hosting Services
N.A.I.C.S.: 518210

THE BROADSTONE GROUP, INC.

Ste 1604 156 W 56th St, New York, NY 10019-3878
Tel.: (212) 333-2100
Year Founded: 1975
Sales Range: $10-24.9 Million
Emp.: 4
Subdividers & Developers
N.A.I.C.S.: 237210

THE BROE COMPANIES, INC.

252 Clayton St Ste 400, Denver, CO 80206-4814
Tel.: (303) 393-0033   CO
Web Site: http://www.broe.com
Year Founded: 1972
Sales Range: $75-99.9 Million
Emp.: 100
Investment Holding Company
N.A.I.C.S.: 531120
Patrick D. Broe *(Founder & CEO)*
Alex Yeros *(Mng Dir)*
Claude Pumilia *(CFO & COO)*
Greg Gallagher *(Chief Investment Officer)*
Charmaine Cook *(Sr VP-HR)*
Doug Van Wyk *(Chief Compliance Officer & Gen Counsel)*

Subsidiaries:

Great Western Development Company   (1)
252 Clayton St, Denver, CO 80206
Tel.: (970) 686-8831
Web Site: http://www.greatwesternindustrialpark.com

COMPANIES

Railroad Construction Services
N.A.I.C.S.: 237990
Clay Drake (Dir-Bus Dev)

Great Western Oil and Gas Company (1)
1700 Broadway Ste 650, Denver, CO 80290
Tel.: (303) 398-0302
Web Site: http://www.gwogco.com
Emp.: 50
Oil & Gas Exploration Services
N.A.I.C.S.: 213112
Rich Frommer (Pres & CEO)
Jay Smith (Sr VP-Engrg)
Steve R. Stacy (Sr VP-Land)
Ty Watson (Sr VP-Ops)
Michael Walker (VP-Plng & Analysis)
Carl Thorngren (Controller)
Jeremy Conger (Sr VP-Ops)
Brady Parish (CFO)

OmniTRAX, Inc. (1)
252 Clayton St Ste 400, Denver, CO 80206-4814
Tel.: (303) 398-4500
Web Site: http://www.omnitrax.com
Rev.: $13,600,000
Emp.: 80
Short-Line Railroad Services
N.A.I.C.S.: 482112
Justin Moon (Dir-Mechanical)
Peter Touesnard (Chief Comml Officer)
Andy C. Engeman (Gen Counsel)
Pierre-Luc Mathieu (Chief Strategy Officer)
Sergio A. Sabatini (Pres & COO)
Justin Strickland (Dir-Economic Dev)
Ean Johnson (VP-Economic Dev)
Robert Walker (CFO)
Cameron A. Scott (Chm)
Dean Piacente (CEO)
John Bradley (Sr VP)

Subsidiary (Domestic):

ALABAMA & TENNESSEE RIVER RAILWAY, LLC (2)
3425 Forrest Ave, Gadsden, AL 35904
Tel.: (256) 547-9079
Rail Transportation Services
N.A.I.C.S.: 488210

Subsidiary (Non-US):

CARLTON TRAIL RAILWAY COMPANY (2)
1545-5th Ave, Prince Albert, S6V7Z5, SK, Canada
Tel.: (306) 763-9474
Sales Range: $25-49.9 Million
Emp.: 12
Rail Transportation Services
N.A.I.C.S.: 488210
Matt Jurgens (Gen Mgr)

Subsidiary (Domestic):

Chicago Rail Link (2)
2728 E 104th St, Chicago, IL 60617-5766
Tel.: (773) 721-4000
Web Site: http://www.omnitrax.com
Sales Range: $25-49.9 Million
Emp.: 50
Railroad Switching & Terminal Services
N.A.I.C.S.: 482111

FULTON COUNTY RAILWAY, LLC (2)
600 Wilson Mill R SW, Atlanta, GA 30331
Tel.: (404) 505-7785
Railroad Transportation Services
N.A.I.C.S.: 488210

GEORGIA & FLORIDA RAILWAY, LLC (2)
1019 Coastline Ave, Albany, GA 31705
Tel.: (229) 435-6629
Railroad Transportation Services
N.A.I.C.S.: 482112

GREAT WESTERN RAILWAY OF COLORADO, LLC (2)
950 Taylor Ave, Loveland, CO 80539
Tel.: (970) 667-6883
Web Site: http://www.omnitrax.com
Railroad Transportation Services
N.A.I.C.S.: 488210
Chris Barrett (Gen Mgr)

Georgia Woodlands Railroad (2)

210 Depot St, Washington, GA 30673-1616
Tel.: (706) 678-3000
Web Site: http://www.omnitrax.com
Sales Range: $25-49.9 Million
Emp.: 40
Short Line Railroad
N.A.I.C.S.: 488210

Subsidiary (Non-US):

Hudson Bay Railway Company (2)
728 Bignell Ave, PO Box 2129, The Pas, R9A 1L8, MB, Canada
Tel.: (204) 627-2007
Rail Transportation Services
N.A.I.C.S.: 488210
Andrew Glastetter (Gen Mgr)

Subsidiary (Domestic):

Illinois Railway, LLC (2)
430 W Madison St, Ottawa, IL 61350
Tel.: (815) 431-0940
Web Site: http://omnitrax.com
Railroad Transportation Services
N.A.I.C.S.: 488999
Thomas Murphy (Gen Mgr)

KETTLE FALLS INTERNATIONAL RAILWAY, LLC (2)
125 E Meyers St, Kettle Falls, WA 99141
Tel.: (509) 738-2965
Railroad Transportation Services
N.A.I.C.S.: 482111

Manufacturers' Junction Railway, LLC (2)
2335 S Cicero Ave, Cicero, IL 60804-2451
Tel.: (773) 721-4000
Web Site: http://www.omnitrax.com
Sales Range: $25-49.9 Million
Emp.: 6
Short-Line Railroad, Switching & Storage Services
N.A.I.C.S.: 488210

NEBRASKA, KANSAS & COLORADO RAILWAY, LLC (2)
128 1st St, Grant, NE 69140
Tel.: (800) 331-3115
Railroad Transportation Services
N.A.I.C.S.: 482112

NORTHERN OHIO & WESTERN RAILWAY, LLC (2)
525 Wall St, Tiffin, OH 44883
Tel.: (419) 448-8896
Web Site: http://www.omnitrax.com
Emp.: 3
Railroad Transportation Services
N.A.I.C.S.: 482111
Billie Johnson (Gen Mgr)

Newburgh & South Shore Railroad Company (2)
4200 E 71st St Marcelline Yard, Cleveland, OH 44105-5726
Tel.: (216) 658-1383
Web Site: http://www.omnitrax.com
Sales Range: $25-49.9 Million
Emp.: 3
Short-Line Railroad & Storage Services
N.A.I.C.S.: 482112

Subsidiary (Non-US):

Omnitrax Canada, Inc. (2)
155 Carlton Street Suite 300, Winnipeg, R3C 3H8, MB, Canada
Tel.: (204) 947-0033
Web Site: http://www.omnitrax.com
Emp.: 5
Marine Transportation Services
N.A.I.C.S.: 488510
Joe Shedden (Dir-Logistics)
Mervin C. Tweed (Pres)
Trent Weber (Dir-Bus Dev)
Lenny Berz (VP-Indus Dev)

Subsidiary (Domestic):

Hudson Bay Port Company (3)
1 Axworthy Way, PO Box 217, Churchill, R0B0E0, MB, Canada
Tel.: (204) 675-8823
Deep Sea Freight Transportation Services
N.A.I.C.S.: 483111

Subsidiary (Domestic):

Panhandle Northern Railroad (2)

100 E Grand St, Borger, TX 79007
Tel.: (806) 273-3513
Rev.: $2,200,000
Emp.: 25
Line-Haul Operations
N.A.I.C.S.: 482111

Quality Terminal Services, L.L.C. (2)
5500 Wallisville Rd, Houston, TX 77020
Tel.: (303) 398-4560
Rail Transportation Services
N.A.I.C.S.: 488210

Sand Springs Railway, Co. (2)
1650 S 81 St W Ave, Tulsa, OK 74127
Tel.: (918) 245-8625
Emp.: 15
Line-Haul Railroads
N.A.I.C.S.: 482111
James Nolan (CEO)

Winchester & Western Railroad Company (2)
5550 Winchester Ave Ste 3, Martinsburg, WV 25405
Tel.: (304) 596-2680
Railroad Transportation
N.A.I.C.S.: 488210
Mariane Ceballo (Mgr-North America Comms)

THE BROOKDALE GROUP LLC
3455 Peachtree Rd NE Ste 700, Atlanta, GA 30326
Tel.: (404) 364-8080
Web Site: http://www.brookdalegroup.com
Year Founded: 1994
Sales Range: $25-49.9 Million
Emp.: 14
Real Estate Investment
N.A.I.C.S.: 523999
Fred H. Henritze (Co-Founder, Pres & COO)
David Hendrickson (Sr VP & Controller)
Patrick D. Walsh (Partner & Sr VP-Ops)
Dan Ethridge (Partner & Exec VP)
Robert Turner (Partner & Exec VP)
Charles L. Davidson III (Co-Founder, Chm & CEO)
Seabie W. Hickson III (Exec VP)

Subsidiaries:

Brookdale Realty Service, LLC (1)
3455 Peachtree Rd NE Ste 650, Atlanta, GA 30326
Tel.: (404) 364-8080
Web Site: http://www.brookdalegroup.com
Emp.: 17
Portfolio Management
N.A.I.C.S.: 523940
David Hendrickson (Sr VP & Controller)
Patrick D. Walsh (Partner & Sr VP-Ops)
Fred H. Henritze (Pres & COO)
Dan Ethridge (Partner & Exec VP)
Robert Turner (Partner & Exec VP)
Charles L. Davidson III (Chm & CEO)
Seabie W. Hickson III (Partner & Exec VP)

THE BROOKESIDE GROUP, INC.
524 Main St, Acton, MA 01720
Tel.: (978) 266-9876
Web Site: http://www.brookeside.com
Sales Range: $1-9.9 Million
Emp.: 17
Consulting Services
N.A.I.C.S.: 541690
Thomas Cates (Pres)
Karen Priscella (Controller)
Bill Glencross (Dir-Sls)

THE BROOKINGS INSTITUTION
1775 Massachusetts Ave NW, Washington, DC 20036
Tel.: (202) 797-6000
Web Site: http://www.brookings.edu

THE BRYNAVON GROUP, INC.

Year Founded: 1916
Sales Range: $25-49.9 Million
Emp.: 400
Researching & Publishing Services
N.A.I.C.S.: 541720
Jonathan D. Schwartz (Interim Gen Counsel)
Strobe Talbott (Pres)
William Antholis (Mng Dir)
Steven Bennett (COO & VP)
Kimberly Churches (VP-Institutional Advancement & External Rels)
Kemal Dervis (VP & Dir-Global Economy & Dev)
Ona Alston Dosunmu (Gen Counsel)
Bruce Katz (VP & Dir-Metropolitan Policy Program)
David Nassar (VP-Comm)
Stewart Uretsky (CFO, Treas & VP)
Darrell West (VP & Dir-Govt Studies)
Ted Gayer (VP & Dir-Economic Studies)
Mireya Solis (Dir-Center for East Asia Policy Studies)
Bruce Jones (VP-Foreign Policy)
Martin Indyk (Exec VP)

THE BROWNSTONE SCHOOL
128 W 80th St, New York, NY 10024
Tel.: (212) 874-1341   NY
Web Site:
  http://www.brownstoneschool.org
Year Founded: 1963
Sales Range: $1-9.9 Million
Emp.: 100
Early Childhood Educational Center
N.A.I.C.S.: 611699
Barbara LaVallee (Bus Dir)
Loren DeNicola (Dir)
Brooke Emmerich (Asst Dir)

THE BRULIN CORPORATION
2920 Dr Andrew J Brown Ave, Indianapolis, IN 46205-4066
Tel.: (317) 923-3211   IN
Web Site: http://www.brulin.com
Year Founded: 1935
Sales Range: $100-124.9 Million
Emp.: 150
Mfr of Specialty Chemicals
N.A.I.C.S.: 325612
Chris Jones (Dir-Ops-Intl)

THE BRYDON GROUP LLC
71 Arch St, 3rd Fl, Greenwich, CT 06830
Tel.: (202) 990-7605
Web Site: https://www.brydon.com
Investment Firm
N.A.I.C.S.: 523999
Alex Mears (Co-Founder & Mng Partner)

Subsidiaries:

Focus Learning Corporation (1)
1880 Santa Barbara St Ste 120, San Luis Obispo, CA 93401-7597
Tel.: (805) 543-4895
Web Site: http://www.focuslearning.com
Software Publisher
N.A.I.C.S.: 513210
Garrett Sprague (Founder)
Jay Steele (CEO)

Manufacturing Automation & Software System, Inc. (1)
21601 Devonshire St, Chatsworth, CA 91311
Tel.: (818) 709-1255
Web Site: http://www.massgroup.com
Sales Range: $1-9.9 Million
Emp.: 18
Computer Software Development Computer Consulting And Training
N.A.I.C.S.: 541511

THE BRYNAVON GROUP, INC.
PO Box 160, Villanova, PA 19085

THE BRYNAVON GROUP, INC.

U.S. PRIVATE

The Brynavon Group, Inc.—(Continued)
Tel.: (610) 525-2102
Web Site: http://www.brynavon.com
Year Founded: 1973
Sales Range: $10-24.9 Million
Financial Investment Services
N.A.I.C.S.: 523999
George B. Lemmon Jr. (Mng Dir)

THE BUCCINI/POLLIN GROUP, INC.
5425 Wisconsin Ave Ste 700, Chevy Chase, MD 20815
Tel.: (302) 691-2100   DE
Web Site: http://www.bpgroup.net
Year Founded: 1993
Holding Company; Real Estate Investment, Development & Management Services
N.A.I.C.S.: 551112
Christopher F. Buccini (Co-Pres)
Robert E. Buccini (Co-Founder & Co-Pres)
David B. Pollin (Co-Founder & Co-Pres)
James Rowe (VP-Portfolio Mgmt)
Barbara Neuse (CFO)
Jim O'Hara (CFO-PMHS)
Darren Anzelone (Co-Chief Investment Officer)
Karl Wagner (Co-Chief Investment Officer)
Ralph Rossi (Sr VP-Comml Ops)
Sarah Lamb (VP-Design & Mktg)
John Snyder (Dir-Security)
Michael Mazzagatti (Dir-Residential Facilities)
Joseph G. Lisicky (Gen Counsel)
Dan McCarthy (COO)
Michael J. Hare (Exec VP-Dev)
Steve Schroeder (Sr VP-Legal Affairs & Dev)
Jeff Sareyka (Controller)
Anita Neubauer (Officer-Treasury Mgmt)
Ruby Ann Velez (Controller-Property)
Peter Murphy (Mgr-Dev Asset)
Randall Thayer (VP-Asset Mgmt)
Michael Turick (VP-Asset Mgmt)
Miranda J. Sorrels (Mgr-Asset)
Jeffrey Gannett (VP-Transactions)
Marco DiPrinzio (Mgr-Transactions)
Paul Watts (Dir-Comml Ops)

Subsidiaries:
BPG Real Estate Services LLC (1)
322 A St Ste 300, Wilmington, DE 19801
Tel.: (302) 691-2100
Web Site: http://www.bpgroup.net
Commercial Property Management & Leasing Services
N.A.I.C.S.: 531312
Christopher F. Buccini (Founder & Pres)
Ralph Rossi (Sr VP-Ops)

BPG Residential Services, LLC (1)
322 A St Ste 300, Wilmington, DE 19801
Tel.: (302) 691-2128
Web Site: http://www.residebpg.com
Residential Property Management & Leasing Services
N.A.I.C.S.: 531311
Melinda B. Sosco (Sr VP-Multifamily Ops)
Michael Mazzagatti (Dir-Residential Facilities)

BPGS Construction LLC (1)
322 A St Ste 300, Wilmington, DE 19801
Tel.: (302) 691-2111
Web Site: http://www.bpgsconstruction.com
Construction Management & General Contracting Services
N.A.I.C.S.: 541330
H. Wesley Schwandt (Pres)
John Groth (Exec VP)
K. Cole Flickinger (Sr VP)
W. Wayne Dunlop (VP-Ops)
Donna Owens (VP & Controller)
Brian DeLawder (VP-Hospitality Construction & Dev)

Hotel du Pont Company (1)
42 W 11th St, Wilmington, DE 19801
Tel.: (302) 594-3100
Web Site: http://www.hoteldupont.com
Hotel
N.A.I.C.S.: 721110

PM Hospitality Strategies, Inc. (1)
2020 K St NW Ste 600, Washington, DC 20006
Tel.: (202) 835-1000
Web Site: http://www.pmhotelgroup.com
Home Management Services
N.A.I.C.S.: 561110
Joseph Bojanowski (Pres & CEO)
James O'Hara (CFO)
Woody Montgomery (Exec VP-HR)
Leticia Proctor (Sr VP-Sls, Revenue Mgmt & Digital Strategies)
Greg J. Miller (Co-Founder & Mng Dir)
Amish Naik (VP-Bus Dev & Owner Rels)
Libbi Carlson (Dir-Revenue Mgmt)
Raina Taillon (Mgr-Dev)
Fran Owen (Dir-Sls & Mktg)
Lovell Casiero (Sr VP-Sls & Mktg-Chevy Chase)
Sage Patel (Dir-Strategic Initiatives)

THE BUCKLIN TRACTOR & IMPLEMENT CO
115 W Railroad, Bucklin, KS 67834
Tel.: (620) 826-3271
Web Site: http://www.btiequip.com
Rev.: $12,600,000
Emp.: 35
Tractors, Agricultural
N.A.I.C.S.: 423820

THE BUDD GROUP INC.
2325 S Stratford Rd, Winston Salem, NC 27103-6223
Tel.: (336) 765-7690   NC
Web Site: http://www.buddgroup.com
Year Founded: 1963
Sales Range: $25-49.9 Million
Emp.: 3,100
Janitorial, Landscaping & Other Integrated Facility Support Services
N.A.I.C.S.: 561210
Joseph R. Budd (CEO)
Yasser Youssef (Pres)
Gerald L. Chrisco (Treas)
Keith Bagby (CFO)
Hal Rollins (VP-HR & Shared Svcs)
Jon Larsen (COO)
Charles Keenum (VP-Janitorial Ops)
Nancy Criscoe (VP-Org Dev)
Katherine Martin (Dir-Strategic Accts)

Subsidiaries:
Cross Gate Services, Inc. (1)
1730 Gen George Patton Dr, Brentwood, TN 37027   (100%)
Tel.: (615) 373-4712
Web Site: http://www.crossgateservices.com
Rev.: $5,000,000
Emp.: 218
Janitorial & Custodial Services
N.A.I.C.S.: 561720
Marge Barraclough (Treas & Sec)
Roy Finch (Mgr-Payroll & Pur)
Steve Southard (Pres)
Carolyn Clay (Sr VP)
Wynedka Palmer (Dir-Acctg)

The Budd Group Inc. - Charlotte Office (1)
1000 Amble Dr, Charlotte, NC 28206-1302
Tel.: (704) 334-1494
Web Site: http://www.buddgroup.com
Sales Range: $25-49.9 Million
Emp.: 22
Janitorial, Landscaping & Other Integrated Facility Support Services
N.A.I.C.S.: 561210

The Budd Group Inc. - Durham Office (1)
4601 Creekstone Dr Ste 124, Durham, NC 27703-5238
Tel.: (919) 544-9793
Web Site: http://www.buddgroup.com
Sales Range: $50-74.9 Million
Emp.: 300

Janitorial, Landscaping & Other Integrated Facility Support Services
N.A.I.C.S.: 561210
Joe Budd (Gen Mgr)

The Budd Group Inc. - Greensboro Office (1)
218 Industrial Ave, Greensboro, NC 27406-4507
Tel.: (336) 272-4300
Sales Range: $50-74.9 Million
Emp.: 4,000
Janitorial, Landscaping & Other Integrated Facility Support Services
N.A.I.C.S.: 561210
Brian Wheler (Mgr)

The Budd Group Inc. - Greenville/Spartanburg, SC Office (1)
528 Howell Rd Ste 22, Greenville, SC 29615-2050
Tel.: (864) 288-4046
Web Site: http://www.buddgroup.com
Sales Range: $50-74.9 Million
Emp.: 160
Janitorial, Landscaping & Other Integrated Facility Support Services
N.A.I.C.S.: 561210

The Budd Group Inc. - Orlando Office (1)
1820 N Goldenrod Rd Ste 102, Orlando, FL 32807-8419
Tel.: (407) 823-8188
Web Site: http://www.buddgroup.com
Sales Range: $25-49.9 Million
Emp.: 40
Janitorial, Landscaping & Other Integrated Facility Support Services
N.A.I.C.S.: 561210
Susan Barnes (Office Mgr)

The Budd Group Inc. - Tampa Office (1)
2202 N Howard Ave, Tampa, FL 33607
Tel.: (813) 635-9770
Web Site: http://www.buddgroup.com
Sales Range: $25-49.9 Million
Emp.: 100
Janitorial, Landscaping & Other Integrated Facility Support Services
N.A.I.C.S.: 561210

THE BUFFALO FINE ARTS ACADEMY
1285 Elmwood Ave, Buffalo, NY 14222
Tel.: (716) 882-8700   NY
Web Site: http://www.albrightknox.org
Year Founded: 1862
Sales Range: $10-24.9 Million
Art Event Organizer
N.A.I.C.S.: 711310
John R. Sanderson (Treas)
Thomas R. Hyde (Pres)
Catherine B. Foley (VP)
Frederick G. Pierce II (Sec)

THE BUILDING CENTER, INC.
1012 Industrial Park Dr, Pineville, NC 28134
Tel.: (704) 889-8182
Web Site: http://www.thebuildingcenterinc.com
Year Founded: 1977
Sales Range: $10-24.9 Million
Emp.: 125
Lumber, Plywood & Millwork Distr
N.A.I.C.S.: 423310
Skip Norris (Pres)
Buddy Ashley (Mgr)
Deborah Donahue (Coord-Sls)

Subsidiaries:
Contractors Building Supply, Inc. (1)
1900 Skwy Dr, Monroe, NC 28110-2717
Tel.: (704) 283-1152
Home Center Operator
N.A.I.C.S.: 444110

Mountain Lumber Company, Inc. (1)
9877 NC Hwy 105 S, Banner Elk, NC 28604

Tel.: (828) 898-5272
Web Site: http://www.mountainlumbercompany.com
Rev.: $1,900,000
Emp.: 19
Building Materials Mfr
N.A.I.C.S.: 444180

THE BUNCHER COMPANY
1300 Penn Ave Ste 300, Pittsburgh, PA 15222
Tel.: (412) 422-9900
Web Site: http://www.buncher.com
Year Founded: 1954
Sales Range: $50-74.9 Million
Emp.: 600
Real Estate Investment & Development; New & Reconditioned Rail Car Components Whslr
N.A.I.C.S.: 531390
Thomas J. Balestrieri (Pres & CEO)
Mike Kutzer (VP-Real Estate)
Dino DePaulo (VP-Real Estate)

Subsidiaries:
Multi-Service Supply (1)
Bldg #5 Ferry St & Ave C, Leetsdale, PA 15056-1384
Tel.: (412) 741-1500
Web Site: http://www.multiservicesupply.com
Emp.: 30
Rail Car Component Refurbishment & Repair Services
N.A.I.C.S.: 811310
Paul J. Bittner (VP)
Mark Jackovic (Gen Sls Mgr)

THE BUNTIN GROUP
716 Division St, Nashville, TN 37203-4758
Tel.: (615) 244-5720
Web Site: http://www.buntingroup.com
Year Founded: 1972
Sales Range: $25-49.9 Million
Emp.: 120
Advetising Agency
N.A.I.C.S.: 541810
Brian Harkness (Exec VP-Ops)
Kathy Canady (Exec VP & Chief Insights Officer)
Tom Gibney (Sr VP & Dir-Content Production)
Jeff Parson (VP & Dir-Grp Digital Creative)
Ray Reed (Sr VP & Deputy Dir-Creative)
Geoff Lysaught (Exec VP-Strategy & Brand Mgmt)
Ben Thomas (Exec VP-Channel & Innovation)
Mark Young (Mng Dir & Exec VP)
Ronnie Ferrell (Sr VP-Tech & Facilities)
Jeffrey Buntin Jr. (Pres & CEO)

Subsidiaries:
Buntin Out-of-Home Media (1)
230 Willow St, Nashville, TN 37210
Tel.: (615) 244-5720
Web Site: http://www.buntinoutofhome.com
Sales Range: $25-49.9 Million
Emp.: 20
Out-of-Home Media Services
N.A.I.C.S.: 541810
Mark Young (Mng Dir & Exec VP)

THE BUREAU OF ENGRAVING, INC.
2354 English St, Maplewood, MN 55109
Tel.: (612) 788-1000   MN
Web Site: http://www.thebureau.com
Year Founded: 1898
Sales Range: $25-49.9 Million
Emp.: 100
Printing Services
N.A.I.C.S.: 323111

COMPANIES

Arnold Stull (CFO)
Judy Turner (Sec)
Mark Schoeben (Pres-Graphics Div)
Patrick Stuart (VP-Mktg)
Lynne Alexander (Chm & CEO)
Jeffry Love (Mgr-Mktg Ops-Premedia Svcs)
Kim Lueck (Controller)

THE BURGER IRON COMPANY
3100 Gilchrist Rd, Mogadore, OH 44260-1624
Tel.: (330) 794-1716 OH
Web Site: http://www.burgeriron.com
Year Founded: 1896
Sales Range: $25-49.9 Million
Emp.: 200
Metals Service Centers & Offices
N.A.I.C.S.: 423510
Carl Burger (Founder & Gen Mgr-Opers)

Subsidiaries:

Bico Akron Inc. (1)
3100 Gilchrist Rd, Mogadore, OH 44260-1246 (100%)
Tel.: (330) 794-1716
Web Site: http://www.bicoakron.com
Sales Range: $25-49.9 Million
Emp.: 75
Metals Service Center
N.A.I.C.S.: 423510

Bico Michigan Inc. (1)
O-99 Steele St, Grand Rapids, MI 49534
Tel.: (616) 453-2400
Web Site: http://www.bicosteel.com
Rev.: $80,300,000
Emp.: 25
Steel Service Centers & Offices
N.A.I.C.S.: 423510
Michael A. Ensminger (Pres & CEO)

Bico South Inc. (1)
4231 Orchard Park Blvd, Spartanburg, SC 29303-4400
Tel.: (864) 595-1025
Web Site: http://www.bicosouth.com
Rev.: $1,300,000
Emp.: 15
Fabrication of Structural Metal
N.A.I.C.S.: 423510

THE BURGGRAF CORPORATION
329 Main St Ste 334, Quapaw, OK 74363
Tel.: (918) 674-2281 OK
Web Site: http://www.burggraftire.com
Year Founded: 1940
Sales Range: $10-24.9 Million
Emp.: 30
Automobile Tires & Tubes
N.A.I.C.S.: 423130
Terry Joe Karnes (Chm)

THE BURKE GROUP, INC.
80 Linden Oaks Ste 210, Rochester, NY 14625
Tel.: (585) 624-5500
Web Site: http://burkegroup.com
Year Founded: 1985
Geophysical Surveying & Mapping Services
N.A.I.C.S.: 541360
David Sporina (Pres)

THE BURKE PORTER GROUP
4670 Fulton St E Ste 201, Ada, MI 49301
Tel.: (616) 855-1480
Web Site: http://www.burkeportergroup.com
Year Founded: 1953
Intelligent Machine Mfr
N.A.I.C.S.: 339999
David DeBoer (CEO)

Subsidiaries:

D&K Engineering, Inc. (1)
15890 Bernardo Center Dr, San Diego, CA 92127
Tel.: (858) 376-2500
Web Site: https://www.dkengineering.com
Sales Range: $25-49.9 Million
Emp.: 300
Electro Mechanical Product Mfr
N.A.I.C.S.: 334514
Scott Dennis (CEO)
Alex Y. Kunczynski (Pres)
Bruce Pinkston (Chief Admin Officer)
Jody Zevenbergen (CFO)
Bill Suttner (VP-Bus Dev)
Brad Cooley (CTO)
Dan O'Leary (VP-Mfg)
Sam Smookler (Co-Founder & Pres)
Teoh Hoo Seong (Dir-Ops-Singapore)
Koh Joo Beng (Dir-R&D-Singapore)
Patrick Choy Kim Hoe (Dir-Supply Chain-Singapore)
Lin Chee Seng (Gen Mgr-Singapore)
Mike Stanicek (VP-Mktg)
Erol Erturk (VP-Research & Dev)
Nate Doemling (VP-Ops-San Diego)

Titan, Inc. (1)
1340 Grandview pkwy Ste 200, Sturtevant, WI 53177
Tel.: (262) 884-2890
Web Site: http://www.titansystems.com
Special Die & Tool, Die Set, Jig & Fixture Mfr
N.A.I.C.S.: 333514

THE BURNETT COMPANIES CONSOLIDATED INC.
9800 Richmond Ave Ste 800, Houston, TX 77042-4548
Tel.: (713) 977-2590 TX
Web Site: http://www.burnettspecialist.com
Year Founded: 1974
Sales Range: $25-49.9 Million
Emp.: 100
Employment Agencies
N.A.I.C.S.: 561311
Rick Burnett (VP & Reg Mgr)
Sue Burnett (Pres)
Jane Coronado (Controller)

THE BURTON FOUNDATION
81 S McLean Blvd Ste C, South Elgin, IL 60177
Tel.: (630) 938-7625 IL
Year Founded: 1992
Sales Range: $10-24.9 Million
Community Housing & Health Care Assistance Services
N.A.I.C.S.: 624229
Heather Sotelo (Chm)
Tracey Manning (Pres)
DesMarie Tanner (Treas)

THE BUSEY GROUP
4747 Gaillardia Pkwy Ste 200, Oklahoma City, OK 73142-1856
Tel.: (405) 721-7776
Web Site: http://www.buseygroup.com
Year Founded: 2000
Sales Range: $10-24.9 Million
Emp.: 13
Business Development & Consulting Services
N.A.I.C.S.: 561499
Phil G. Busey (Founder, Chm & CEO)
Laila Dabbakeh (Coord-Resource)

THE BUSH COMPANY
4029 Ironbound Rd Ste 200, Williamsburg, VA 23188-2549
Tel.: (757) 220-2874 VA
Year Founded: 1981
Sales Range: $25-49.9 Million
Emp.: 200
Construction Developer

N.A.I.C.S.: 236117
Marc Sharp (VP)
Michele Ball (VP)

Subsidiaries:

WHH Trice & Co., Inc. (1)
4029 Ironbound Rd Ste 100, Williamsburg, VA 23188-2549 (100%)
Tel.: (757) 220-2874
Sales Range: $10-24.9 Million
Emp.: 10
Construction Real Estate Management & Developers
N.A.I.C.S.: 531210

THE C. M. PAULA COMPANY
6049 Hi Tek Ct, Mason, OH 45040
Tel.: (513) 336-3100 OH
Web Site: http://www.cmpaula.com
Year Founded: 1958
Sales Range: $1-9.9 Million
Emp.: 50
Holding Company
N.A.I.C.S.: 551112
Charles McCullough (Founder & Chm)
Gregory Ionna (Pres & CEO)
Bill Creager (Exec VP)
Bill Ash (CFO)

Subsidiaries:

ART Technologies, Inc. (1)
3795 Symmes Rd, Hamilton, OH 45015
Tel.: (513) 942-8800
Web Site: http://www.art-technologies.com
Emp.: 32
Thrust Bearings & Precision Metal Stamping Components Supplier
N.A.I.C.S.: 336370
Paul Alati (Mgr-Sls & Mktg-Natl)
Marlon Bailey (Pres & CEO)

Remtec Automation LLC (1)
10148 Commerce Park Dr, Cincinnati, OH 45246
Tel.: (513) 860-4299
Web Site: http://www.remtecautomation.com
Sales Range: $1-9.9 Million
Emp.: 45
Robotic Packaging & Material Handling Systems Mfr
N.A.I.C.S.: 333248
Keith Rosnell (Pres & CEO)

THE C.A. LAWTON COMPANY
1950 Enterprise Dr, De Pere, WI 54115
Tel.: (920) 337-2470
Web Site: http://www.calawton.com
Sales Range: $10-24.9 Million
Emp.: 96
Power Transmission Speed Changer Mfr
N.A.I.C.S.: 333612
Patrick Kotowski (Dir-Bus Dev)
Alex Lawton (Pres)

THE C.I. THORNBURG CO., INC.
4034 Altizer Ave, Huntington, WV 25705
Tel.: (304) 523-3484
Web Site: https://citcowater.com
Rev.: $44,000,000
Emp.: 92
Industrial Machinery & Equipment Merchant Whslr
N.A.I.C.S.: 423830
Allen Gibbs (VP-Ops)
Marc Templeton (VP-Pur)
Mary Beth Anderson (VP-Mktg)
Bill Spino (Mgr-Bridgeport)
Weston Clary (Mgr-Panel Shop Ops)
Todd Bennett (VP-Engineered Solutions Grp)
Randall W. Clark (VP-Engineered Products)
Jeremy McComas (VP-Municipal Sls)
Alan Morrison (VP)
Edward Morrison (Pres)

Subsidiaries:

National Road Utility Supply, Inc. (1)
RR 40, Valley Grove, WV 26060
Tel.: (304) 547-0101
Web Site: http://www.nrusi.com
Sales Range: $1-9.9 Million
Emp.: 15
Wholesale Water And Sewer Supplies
N.A.I.C.S.: 423720

THE CABANA GROUP, LLC
220 S School Ave, Fayetteville, AR 72701
Tel.: (479) 442-6464
Web Site: http://www.thecabanagroup.com
Year Founded: 2008
Sales Range: $1-9.9 Million
Emp.: 21
Financial Investment Services
N.A.I.C.S.: 523940
Chadd Mason (Co-Founder & CEO)
Louis Shaff (Co-Founder & CFO)
Neal Prevost (Mng Partner)
Daniel Ippolito (Chief Compliance Officer)
Chris Carns (COO)

THE CABLE CENTER
2000 Buchtel Blvd, Denver, CO 80210
Tel.: (303) 871-4885
Web Site: http://www.cablecenter.org
Sales Range: $1-9.9 Million
Emp.: 25
Education & Information Services about the Cable Television Industry
N.A.I.C.S.: 516210
Jana Henthorn (Pres & CEO)
Karen Chipley (CFO & Sr VP)

THE CADLE COMPANY INC.
100 N Ctr St, Newton Falls, OH 44444
Tel.: (330) 872-0918
Web Site: http://www.cadleco.com
Rev.: $11,400,000
Emp.: 120
Investment Bankers
N.A.I.C.S.: 523910
Richard Pursinger (Pres)

THE CAFARO CO.
2445 Belmont Ave, Youngstown, OH 44505-2418
Tel.: (330) 747-2661 OH
Web Site: http://www.cafarocompany.com
Year Founded: 1945
Sales Range: $10-24.9 Million
Emp.: 200
Real Estate Development Services
N.A.I.C.S.: 531120
Dan Mancuso (Dir-Specialty Leasing)
William A. Cafaro (Co-Pres)
Anthony Cafaro Jr. (Co-Pres)

THE CALVERT COUNTY NURSING CENTER, INC.
85 Hospital Rd, Prince Frederick, MD 20678
Tel.: (410) 535-2300 MD
Web Site: http://www.calvertcountynursingcenter.org
Year Founded: 1966
Sales Range: $10-24.9 Million
Emp.: 271
Nursing Care Services
N.A.I.C.S.: 623110
Robyn Simpkins (Dir-Admissions)

THE CAMERA COMPANY
6742 Odana Rd, Madison, WI 53719
Tel.: (478) 922-2930
Web Site: http://www.cameraco.com
Electronics Stores

THE CAMERA COMPANY

The Camera Company—(Continued)
N.A.I.C.S.: 449210
David Katz (Owner)

THE CANEEL GROUP, LLC
59 N Lakeview Dr Bldg #2 Top Floor, Gibbsboro, NJ 08026
Tel.: (856) 504-6953
Web Site:
 http://www.caneelgroup.com
Year Founded: 2008
Sales Range: $1-9.9 Million
Emp.: 20
Real Estate Brokers & Agents Specializing in Liquidation & Pres/Post Foreclosures
N.A.I.C.S.: 531390
Jason Osborne (Partner)

THE CANNABIS DEPOT HOLDING CORP.
500 S Australian Ave Ste 630, West Palm Beach, FL 33401
Tel.: (561) 651-4160
Web Site:
 http://www.thecannabisreit.com
Cannabis Company
N.A.I.C.S.: 325411
Jennifer Woodend (Member-Exec Bd)

Subsidiaries:

Credex Corporation (1)
1881 General George Patton Dr Ste 107, Franklin, TN 37067 **(99.2%)**
Tel.: (386) 218-6823
Web Site:
 https://www.credexcorporation.com
Liabilities: $81,187
Net Worth: ($81,187)
Earnings: ($8,150)
Emp.: 1
Fiscal Year-end: 12/31/2020
Credit & Other Financial Services
N.A.I.C.S.: 522390

THE CANNON GROUP INC.
5037 Pine Creek Dr, Westerville, OH 43081-4849
Tel.: (614) 890-0343 OH
Year Founded: 1987
Sales Range: $25-49.9 Million
Emp.: 22
Mfr of Polyethylene Bags
N.A.I.C.S.: 424130
Frank T. Cannon (Pres & CEO)

THE CANTWELL MACHINERY COMPANY INC.
3180 Valleyview Dr, Columbus, OH 43204-2073
Tel.: (614) 276-5171 OH
Year Founded: 1946
Sales Range: $25-49.9 Million
Emp.: 68
Industrial Machinery & Equipment
N.A.I.C.S.: 423830
Mark Cantwell (Pres)
Tom Reynolds (Controller)

THE CAPFINANCIAL GROUP, LLC
4208 Six Forks Rd Ste 1700, Raleigh, NC 27609
Tel.: (919) 870-6822 NC
Web Site: http://www.captrust.com
Year Founded: 2015
Holding Company; Investment Advisory Services
N.A.I.C.S.: 551112
J. Fielding Miller (Co-Founder & CEO)
Ben Goldstein (COO & Head-Bus Ops)
Eric Freedman (Chief Investment Officer & Head-Consulting Res)
John Appleby (Mng Dir-Project Mgmt & Acq)
Wilson S. Hoyle III (Mng Dir & Head-Advisor Support Grp)

Subsidiaries:

CapFinancial Partners, LLC (1)
4208 Six Forks Rd Ste 1700, Raleigh, NC 27609
Tel.: (919) 870-6822
Web Site: http://www.captrustadvisors.com
Rev.: $176,000,000,000
Emp.: 340
Investment Advisory & Portfolio Management Services
N.A.I.C.S.: 523940
J. Fielding Miller (Founder & CEO)
Michael D. Strother (Sr Dir-Advisor Support Grp)
John Appleby (Mng Dir-Project Mgmt & Acq)
Ben Goldstein (Pres)
Rick Shoff (Mng Dir-Advisor Support Grp)
Phyllis Klein (Sr Dir-Consulting Res Grp)
Scott T. Matheson (Sr Dir-Consulting Res Grp)
Jason Stephens (Dir-Consulting Res Grp)
Grant Verhaeghe (Sr Dir-Consulting Res Grp)
Denise Buchanan (Chief Compliance Officer)
John Curry (Sr Dir-Mktg)
Kathy Del Corso-Chase (Sr Dir-HR)
Bonnie McCullough (CFO)
Doreen O'Dowd (Sr Dir-Client Svcs)
James Stafford (Dir-IT)
Michael E. Hudson (Sr Dir-Institutional Consulting)
John Leissner (Dir-Defined Contribution Svcs)
Mark Paccione (Dir-Investment Res)
Rush Benton (Sr Dir-Strategic Wealth)
Abigail J. C. Russell (Dir-Advisor Support Grp)
Greg Middleton (Dir-Advisor Support Grp)
David Will (VP)
Jennifer Kelly (Mgr-Client Relationship)
Kim Huppertz (Mgr-Client Relationship)
Kyle L. Tucker (VP)
Lori Dillingham (Dir-Client Svcs)
Lourens Prinsloo (Dir-Application Dev)
Mike Woods (Sr VP)
Roberta Angelo (Dir-Client Svcs)
Steve Wilt (Sr VP)
Travis Whitten (VP)
Brian Pollard (VP)
Eddie Welch (Mng Principal-Wealth Mgmt Grp)
Wilson S. Hoyle III (Mng Dir & Head-Advisor Support Grp)

Subsidiary (Domestic):

Frontier Wealth Management, LLC (2)
4435 Main St Ste 650, Kansas City, MO 64111
Tel.: (816) 753-5100
Web Site: http://www.frontierwealth.com
Investment Management Service
N.A.I.C.S.: 523940
Nick Blasi (CEO & Partner)
Brandon Sifers (CFO & Partner)
Aaron Anson (Partner & Dir-Ops)

Holding (Domestic):

Karstens Investment Counsel, Inc. (3)
10250 Regency Cir, Omaha, NE 68114
Tel.: (402) 492-2727
Web Site:
 http://www.karstensinvestments.com
Rev.: $200,000,000
Financial Investment Activities
N.A.I.C.S.: 523999
Bailey Buller (Office Mgr)

Subsidiary (Domestic):

Southern Wealth Management LLP (2)
19206 Huebner Rd Ste 101, San Antonio, TX 78258
Tel.: (972) 661-4607
Web Site: http://www.southernwealth.com
Investment Services
N.A.I.C.S.: 523940

THE CAPITAL GROUP COMPANIES, INC.
333 S Hope ST 55TH FL, Los Angeles, CA 90071-1447
Tel.: (213) 486-9277 DE
Year Founded: 1931
Sales Range: $15-24.9 Billion
Emp.: 7,500
Portfolio Management & Investment Advice
N.A.I.C.S.: 523940

Subsidiaries:

American Funds Distributors, Inc. (1)
333 S Hope St, Los Angeles, CA 90071 **(100%)**
Tel.: (213) 486-9988
Web Site: http://www.americanfunds.com
Mutual Funds; Assets Management
N.A.I.C.S.: 523940

Capital Group International, Inc. (1)
333 S Hope St, Los Angeles, CA 90071-1406
Tel.: (213) 486-9200
Sales Range: $125-149.9 Million
Emp.: 800
Investment Advisory & Asset Management Services
N.A.I.C.S.: 523940

Capital Guardian Trust Company (1)
333 S Hope St, Los Angeles, CA 90071 **(100%)**
Tel.: (213) 486-9200
Web Site: http://www.capgroup.com
Investment Management Service
N.A.I.C.S.: 523940
Michael A. Burik (Sr VP)

Capital International Asset Management (Canada), Inc. (1)
Brookfield Place Bay Wellington Tower 181 Bay Street Suite 3730, Toronto, M5J 2T3, ON, Canada
Web Site: http://www.capitalgroup.com
Asset Management Services
N.A.I.C.S.: 523940
Mark Tiffin (Pres)

Capital International Private Equity Funds (1)
40 Grosvenor Place, London, SW1X 7GG, United Kingdom
Tel.: (44) 20 7864 5000
Privater Equity Firm
N.A.I.C.S.: 523999
Koenraad Foulon (Sr Mng Partner)
Lam Nguyen-Phuong (Sr Mng Partner)

The Capital Research & Management Co. (1)
333 S Hope St, Los Angeles, CA 90071-1406
Tel.: (213) 486-9200
Web Site: http://www.americanfunds.com
Manager of Mutual Funds
N.A.I.C.S.: 523940
Paul G. Haaga Jr. (Vice Chm)

THE CAPITAL TIMES COMPANY
1901 Fish Hatchery Rd, Madison, WI 53713
Tel.: (608) 252-6400
Web Site:
 http://www.capitalnewspapers.com
Sales Range: $25-49.9 Million
Emp.: 950
Newspaper Publishers
N.A.I.C.S.: 513110
Judy Ettenhofer (Editor-News)
Clayton Frink (Publr)
Paul Fanlund (Editor)
Chris Murphy (Mng Editor)

Subsidiaries:

Madison Newspapers, Inc. (1)
1901 Fish Hatchery Rd, Madison, WI 53713-1248 **(50%)**
Tel.: (608) 252-6200
Web Site: http://www.madison.com
Sales Range: $50-74.9 Million
Emp.: 500
Newspaper Publishers
N.A.I.C.S.: 513110

Unit (Domestic):

The Capital Times (2)
1901 Fish Hatchery Rd, Madison, WI 53713-1297
Tel.: (608) 252-6400
Web Site: https://captimes.com
Sales Range: $100-124.9 Million
Emp.: 300
Online Newspaper Publisher
N.A.I.C.S.: 513110

Wisconsin State Journal (2)
1901 Fish Hatchery Rd, Madison, WI 53713-1248
Tel.: (608) 252-6200
Web Site: https://www.madison.com
Sales Range: $75-99.9 Million
Emp.: 400
Newspaper Publishers
N.A.I.C.S.: 513110

THE CAPSTREET GROUP LLC
1001 Louisiana St Ste 3200, Houston, TX 77002
Tel.: (713) 332-2700 DE
Web Site: http://www.capstreet.com
Year Founded: 1990
Privater Equity Firm
N.A.I.C.S.: 523999
George B. Kelly (Mng Partner)
M. Neil Kallmeyer (Mng Partner)
Katherine L. Kohlmeyer (Partner)
Brooke Meinkowsky (Controller)
Adrian Guerra (Partner)
Kevin Johnson (Principal)
Michelle A. Lewis (Principal)
Mary Anne Capo (CFO)
Walker Kahle (VP)
Charlotte Bentlif (VP-Admin)
Wayne Washburn (VP-Tech)
Chas Richard (VP)
Paul M. De Lisi Jr. (Partner)

Subsidiaries:

APG L.P. (1)
6039 Armour Dr, Houston, TX 77020
Tel.: (713) 675-5271
Web Site: http://www.callapg.com
Fluid Sealing Product Distr
N.A.I.C.S.: 423840

Unit (Domestic):

APG L.P. - Knoxville (2)
5324 S National Dr, Knoxville, TN 37914-6521
Tel.: (865) 540-8199
Fluid Sealing Product Distr
N.A.I.C.S.: 423840

Analytic Stress Relieving, Inc. (1)
3118 W Pinhook Rd Ste 202, Lafayette, LA 70508
Tel.: (337) 237-8790
Web Site: https://www.analyticstress.com
Sales Range: $10-24.9 Million
Emp.: 320
Metal Heat Treating Services
N.A.I.C.S.: 332811
Dalton Meaux (CFO)
Cindy Prejean (Dir-Safety)
David Herzog (Pres & COO)

General LED, Inc. (1)
1074 Arion Cir Ste 116, San Antonio, TX 78216
Tel.: (210) 360-1444
Web Site: http://www.agilight.com
LED Lighting Fixture Mfr
N.A.I.C.S.: 335132
Steven Moya (Pres & CEO)
Katherine Yu (Mgr-Ops)

HungerRush (1)
1315 W Sam Houston Pkwy N Ste 100, Houston, TX 77043
Tel.: (713) 785-4646
Web Site: http://www.hungerrush.com
Miscellaneous Retail Stores, Nec, Nsk
N.A.I.C.S.: 459999

COMPANIES — THE CASSIDY ORGANIZATION, INC.

Perry Turbes *(CEO)*

Planetbids Inc (1)
20929 Ventura Blvd, Woodland Hills, CA 91364
Tel.: (818) 992-1771
Rev.: $1,200,000
Emp.: 8
Computer & Office Machine Repair & Maintenance
N.A.I.C.S.: 811210
Alan Zavian *(Pres)*

Thorpe Specialty Services Corporation (1)
6833 Kirbyville St, Houston, TX 77033
Tel.: (713) 644-1247
Web Site: http://www.thorpessc.com
Sales Range: $10-24.9 Million
Holding Company; Contract Masonry Engineering & Construction Services
N.A.I.C.S.: 551112
Keith West *(VP)*
Michael Bilski *(Controller)*
Sean Rizzo *(Engr-Tech Svcs)*
Andy Piper *(VP-Sls & Mktg)*

Subsidiary (Domestic):

Energy Specialty Contracting, Inc. (2)
7838 S Elm Pl, Broken Arrow, OK 74011
Tel.: (918) 455-8928
Web Site: http://www.energyspecialty.com
Power & Petrochemical Services
N.A.I.C.S.: 236220
Ed Mendoza *(Mgr-Western Construction)*

Thorpe-Sunbelt, Inc. (2)
4718 Ranger St, Houston, TX 77028
Tel.: (713) 671-2458
Web Site: http://www.thorpessc.com
Sales Range: $1-9.9 Million
Emp.: 6
Masonry Contracting Services
N.A.I.C.S.: 238140
Tommy Knight *(VP & Branch Mgr)*

Trinity Steel Fabricators, Inc. (1)
205 E Pine Vly Dr, Trinity, TX 75862
Tel.: (936) 594-3513
Web Site: http://www.trinitysteel.com
Sales Range: $10-24.9 Million
Fabricated Structural Metal
N.A.I.C.S.: 332312

THE CARA GROUP, INC.
Drake Oak Brook Plz 2215 York Rd Ste 300, Oak Brook, IL 60523
Tel.: (630) 574-2272
Web Site: http://www.caracorp.com
Year Founded: 2002
Sales Range: $10-24.9 Million
Emp.: 90
Computer Related Services
N.A.I.C.S.: 541512
Tina Jandris *(COO)*
Jim Bush *(VP & Controller)*
Bush Jim *(Controller)*
Jim McQuaid *(Pres & CEO)*

THE CARIOCA COMPANY INC.
2601 W Dunlap Ave Ste 10, Phoenix, AZ 85021-2711
Tel.: (602) 395-2600   AZ
Year Founded: 1972
Sales Range: $25-49.9 Million
Emp.: 100
Service Station & Convenience Store Operator
N.A.I.C.S.: 457120
Marvin L. Rose *(Pres)*
Eric Young *(CEO)*
Howard Magee *(Gen Mgr)*

THE CARLYLE GROUP, INC.
9073 Nemo St, West Hollywood, CA 90069
Tel.: (310) 550-8656   CA
Year Founded: 1975
Real Estate Buying Agent
N.A.I.C.S.: 531210

Ronald H. Singer *(Pres)*
Howard Fuhrman *(Dir-Real Estate)*
Joseph Weber *(COO)*

THE CARLYLE JOHNSON MACHINE COMPANY, LLC
291 Boston Tpke, Bolton, CT 06043-7252
Tel.: (860) 643-1531
Web Site: http://www.cjmco.com
Year Founded: 1903
Sales Range: $10-24.9 Million
Emp.: 50
Industrial Clutches Mfr
N.A.I.C.S.: 333613
Ron Gamache *(Mgr-Sls-US Comml)*

Subsidiaries:

Metronics, Inc. (1)
291 Boston Tpke, Bolton, CT 06043-7252
Tel.: (860) 643-1531
Web Site: http://www.cjmco.com
Emp.: 40
Power Transmission Product Mfr
N.A.I.C.S.: 333613
Jeff Myshrall *(CFO)*

THE CARNEGIE ENDOWMENT FOR INTERNATIONAL PEACE
1779 Massachusetts Ave NW, Washington, DC 20036-2103
Tel.: (202) 483-7600   NY
Web Site: http://carnegieendowment.org
Year Founded: 1929
Sales Range: $25-49.9 Million
Emp.: 189
Peace Advocacy Services
N.A.I.C.S.: 813319
Richard Giordano *(Chm)*
Paul Balaran *(Exec VP-Carnegie Endowment for Intl Peace)*
William W. George *(Chm)*
Higgs Kathleen *(Dir-Library)*
George Perkovich *(VP-Studies)*
Thomas Carothers *(VP-Studies)*
Douglas H. Paal *(VP-Studies)*
Marwan Muasher *(VP-Studies)*
Thomas Carver *(VP-Comm & Strategy)*
Charles Gauvin *(Chief Dev Officer)*
Veronika Arrington *(Office Mgr)*
Melissa Sanoff *(CFO)*
Marina Barnett *(Program Mgr-Russia & Eurasia Program)*
Kristine Bergstrom-Stahl *(Coord-Comm)*
Eli Keene *(Coord-Program)*
Jessica Katz *(Mgr-Web)*
Viktoria Shapovalova *(Coord-Program-Moscow Center)*
Lea Kenig *(Deputy Chief Dev Officer)*
Yelena Sheetova *(Coord-Program-Moscow Center)*
Aiysha Kirmani *(Controller)*
Eric Simpson *(Mgr-IT Help Desk)*
Jocelyn Anderson Soly *(Sr Mgr-Design & Mktg)*
Lynne Sport *(Sr Dir-HR & Admin)*
Kristina Kudlaenko *(Coord-Program-Moscow Center)*
Sylvie Burns *(Mgr-HR)*
Fatima Kukeyeva *(Co-Dir-Al-Farabi Carnegie Program-Central Asia)*
David Burwell *(Dir-Energy & Climate Program)*
Charita Law *(Mgr-Media)*
Patricia Stottlemyer *(Coord-Comm)*
Izabella Tabarovsky *(Mgr-Program-Russia & Eurasia)*
Vincent Taylor *(Dir-IT)*
James F. Collins *(Dir-Program-Russia & Eurasia)*
Alexander Taylor *(Coord-Program)*
Jan Techau *(Dir-Carnegie Europe)*
Tim Martin *(Dir-Digital)*

Leila Delovarova *(Coord-Program-AL-Farabi Carnegie Program)*
Dmitri Trenin *(Dir-Moscow Center)*
Rebecca White *(Mgr-Editorial)*
Jin Wang *(Sr Mgr-Acctg)*
Ilonka Oszvald *(Mgr-Content)*
Yaping Wang *(Sr Editor)*
Sri Partowardojo *(Mgr-Conference Center)*
Brian Radzinsky *(Project Coord)*
Paul Haenle *(Dir-Global Policy-Carnegie-Tsinghua Center)*
Mary Ellen Fraser *(Chief Dev Officer)*
James M. Acton *(Dir-Nuclear Policy Program)*
Toby Dalton *(Dir-Nuclear Policy Program)*
Randi Kimble *(Mgr-Acct)*
Hilary McGraw *(Mgr-Grants)*
Clara Hogan *(Mgr-Media Rels)*
Andrew S. Weiss *(VP-Studies)*
Nick Parrott *(Dir-Comm)*
Lauren Dueck *(Mgr-Event)*
Christopher Dockrey *(Mgr-Govt Affairs)*
Stephen R. Lewis Jr. *(Vice Chm)*

THE CARNEY GROUP
1777 Sentry Pkwy W Veva 14 Ste 301, Blue Bell, PA 19422
Tel.: (215) 646-6200
Web Site: http://www.carneyjobs.com
Year Founded: 1992
Sales Range: $1-9.9 Million
Emp.: 15
Professional Staffing Services
N.A.I.C.S.: 561311
Nanette Sciolla Carney *(CEO)*
Michael T. Carney *(Sr Acct Mgr)*
Lori Finn *(Sr Mgr-Recruitment)*
Barbara Trotter *(Sr Mgr-Recruitment)*
Aimee Senour *(Sr Acct Mgr)*
Suzanne Carney *(Mgr-Mktg & Ops)*

THE CARPENTER GROUP
222 Napoleon St, San Francisco, CA 94124-1017
Tel.: (415) 285-1954
Web Site: http://www.carpenterrigging.com
Sales Range: $50-74.9 Million
Emp.: 50
Industrial Packing
N.A.I.C.S.: 332618
Bruce Yoder *(Pres)*

Subsidiaries:

American Rigging & Supply (1)
2380 Main St, San Diego, CA 92113-3643   (100%)
Tel.: (619) 233-5625
Web Site: http://www.carpentergroup.com
Sales Range: $10-24.9 Million
Emp.: 30
Rigging Supplies
N.A.I.C.S.: 423840
Bruce Yoder *(Gen Mgr)*

Cable/Cisco (1)
771 Northport Dr B, West Sacramento, CA 95691-2146
Tel.: (916) 371-6781
Sales Range: $25-49.9 Million
Emp.: 8
N.A.I.C.S.: 425120
Joe Licastro *(Gen Mgr)*

Cableco (1)
9816 Arlee Ave, Santa Fe Springs, CA 90670
Tel.: (562) 942-8076
Web Site: http://www.cablecorigging.com
Sales Range: $10-24.9 Million
Emp.: 15
Rigging Supplies Mfr & Distr
N.A.I.C.S.: 314994
Greg Bailey *(VP)*

Carpenter Rigging (1)

222 Napoleon St, San Francisco, CA 94124-1017
Tel.: (415) 285-1954
Web Site: http://www.carpenterrigging.com
Sales Range: $10-24.9 Million
Emp.: 25
Industrial Rigging Wire Rope Mfr & Distr
N.A.I.C.S.: 332618
Bruce Yoder *(Pres)*

Hood Industries (1)
1836 Norris Rd, Bakersfield, CA 93308-5919
Tel.: (661) 633-3620
Web Site: http://www.thecarpentergroup.com
Sales Range: $25-49.9 Million
Emp.: 9
Broker Service
N.A.I.C.S.: 425120
Harvey Booth *(Gen Mgr)*

THE CARROLL ELECTRIC MEMBERSHIP CORPORATION
155 N Hwy 113, Carrollton, GA 30117
Tel.: (770) 832-3552   GA
Web Site: http://www.cemc.com
Year Founded: 1936
Sales Range: $25-49.9 Million
Emp.: 120
Electronic Services
N.A.I.C.S.: 221118
Alvin Ginn *(Treas & Sec)*
Don DeFoor *(Chm)*
Ronnie Jordan *(Vice Chm)*

THE CARSON GROUP
1708 Hwy 6 S, Houston, TX 77077
Tel.: (281) 496-2600   TX
Web Site: http://www.thecarsongroup.net
Year Founded: 1974
Sales Range: Less than $1 Million
Emp.: 6
Advetising Agency
N.A.I.C.S.: 541810
John M. Carson *(Principal)*
Kris Reeves *(Dir-Art)*
Joy Wallace *(Media Planner)*
Lauren McClendon *(Project Mgr)*

THE CARTEL GROUP
5835 Callaghan Rd Ste 600, San Antonio, TX 78228
Tel.: (210) 696-1099
Year Founded: 1994
Rev.: $90,000,000
Emp.: 52
N.A.I.C.S.: 541810
Marissa Ybarbo *(Controller)*
Cory Matthews *(Dir-Creative)*

THE CARY COMPANY
1195 W Fullerton Ave, Addison, IL 60101
Tel.: (630) 629-6600
Web Site: http://www.thecarycompany.com
Year Founded: 1895
Chemical Raw Material Distr
N.A.I.C.S.: 424690
Kenneth E. Tyrrell *(Pres & CEO)*
Brian Ehlert *(VP-Sls)*

Subsidiaries:

Three Rivers Packaging, Inc. (1)
20 39th St., Pittsburgh, PA 15201
Tel.: (412) 778-3900
Web Site: https://www.thecarycompany.com
All Other Personal Services
N.A.I.C.S.: 812990

THE CASSIDY ORGANIZATION, INC.
346 East Central Ave, Winter Haven, FL 33880
Tel.: (863) 324-3698   FL
Web Site: http://www.cassidyhomes.com

THE CASSIDY ORGANIZATION, INC.

U.S. PRIVATE

The Cassidy Organization, Inc.—(Continued)
Year Founded: 1981
Sales Range: $1-9.9 Million
Emp.: 54
Residential Construction
N.A.I.C.S.: 236115
Albert Cassidy (Pres)

THE CASTLE GROUP
38 3rd Ave Charlestown Navy Yard, Boston, MA 02129
Tel.: (617) 337-9500
Web Site: http://www.thecastlegrp.com
Sales Range: $10-24.9 Million
Emp.: 30
Advertising Services
N.A.I.C.S.: 541810
Sandy Lish (Co-Founder & Principal)
Wendy Spivak (Co-Founder & Principal)
Keri McIntosh (Sr VP)
Hilary Allard (Exec VP)

THE CATHOLIC FOUNDATION FOR THE ROMAN CATHOLIC CHURCH IN NORTHERN COLORADO
3801 E Florida Ave Ste 909, Denver, CO 80210
Tel.: (303) 468-9885   CO
Web Site: http://www.thecatholicfoundation.com
Year Founded: 1998
Sales Range: $25-49.9 Million
Emp.: 40
Christian Ministry Services
N.A.I.C.S.: 813110
Michelle Fehn (Controller)
Denise McCarthy (Office Mgr)
Hal Goldwire (Mgr-Campaign)
Jean R. Finegan (Dir-Dev)
Tony W. Church (Sec)
Dave Fantz (Officer-Admin)

THE CATHOLIC SCHOOLS FOUNDATION INC
260 Franklin St Ste 630, Boston, MA 02110
Tel.: (617) 778-5981   MA
Web Site: http://www.csfboston.org
Year Founded: 1983
Sales Range: $10-24.9 Million
Emp.: 10
Financial Support Services
N.A.I.C.S.: 523910
Michael B. Reardon (Exec Dir)
Susan Gartside (Office Mgr)
Naila Asif (Mgr-Data)
Christine T. Komola (Treas)
William S. Mosakowski (Pres)
James F. Mooney III (VP)

THE CATSKILL REGIONAL OFF-TRACK BETTING CORPORATION
PO Box 3000, Pomona, NY 10970
Tel.: (845) 362-0400
Web Site: http://www.interbets.com
Year Founded: 1975
Sales Range: $25-49.9 Million
Emp.: 200
Amusement & Recreation Services
N.A.I.C.S.: 713290
Donald Groth (Pres)

THE CAVALRY COMPANY
15504 Adagio Ct, Los Angeles, CA 90077
Tel.: (310) 266-3530
Year Founded: 2002
Sales Range: $10-24.9 Million
Emp.: 10
N.A.I.C.S.: 541810
Kenneth Gal (Pres & CEO)

THE CAXTON PRINTERS LTD.
312 Main St, Caldwell, ID 83605-3235
Tel.: (208) 459-7421   ID
Web Site: http://www.caxtonprinters.com
Year Founded: 1907
Sales Range: $75-99.9 Million
Emp.: 40
Distr of Commercial Printers, Textbook & School Supplies
N.A.I.C.S.: 424920
Dave Gipson (Pres)
Ron Gipson (VP & Mgr-Printing)
Scott Gipson (Pres)
Steve Cornell (Mgr-Shipping)

THE CEDARS RETIREMENT COMMUNITY
1021 Cedars Dr, McPherson, KS 67460
Tel.: (620) 241-0919   KS
Web Site: http://www.thecedars.org
Year Founded: 1891
Sales Range: $10-24.9 Million
Emp.: 361
Retirement Community Operator
N.A.I.C.S.: 623311
Michelle D'Amico (Coord-Care-Cedar Houses)
Carma Wall (CEO)
Randy Keasling (Dir-HR & Mktg)
Mike Harold (VP-Plant Ops)
Margaret Henningsen (Mgr-Billing)
Bob Baldwin (VP-Living & Wellness)
Gustafson Steven (VP-Advancement)

THE CEDARWOOD COMPANIES
1765 Merriman Rd, Akron, OH 44313-5251
Tel.: (330) 836-9971   OH
Web Site: http://www.cedarwooddevelopment.com
Year Founded: 1972
Sales Range: $100-124.9 Million
Emp.: 215
Provider of Real Estate Development & Contracting Services
N.A.I.C.S.: 531210
Anthony A. Petrarca (COO & Exec VP)
Philip Migas (Project Mgr)
Tony Petrarca (Founder)

Subsidiaries:

Cedarwood Architectural, Inc. (1)
1745 Merriman Rd Ste 200, Akron, OH 44313
Tel.: (330) 836-9971
Web Site: http://www.cedarwoodcompanies.com
Sales Range: $10-24.9 Million
Emp.: 6
Building Architectural Services
N.A.I.C.S.: 541310
Robert Marshall (Pres)

Cedarwood Development, Inc. (1)
1765 Merriman Rd, Akron, OH 44313
Tel.: (330) 836-9971
Web Site: http://www.cedarwodd.com
Real Estate Development Services
N.A.I.C.S.: 531210

THE CELLER ORGANIZATION
4611 Johnson Rd Ste 6 & 8, Coconut Creek, FL 33073
Tel.: (561) 869-8989
Web Site: http://www.thecellerorganization.com
Holding Company
N.A.I.C.S.: 551112
Bobbie Celler (Founder & CEO)

Subsidiaries:

Celler Law, P.A. (1)
3600 FAU Blvd Ste 101, Boca Raton, FL 33431
Tel.: (855) 235-5375
Web Site: http://www.cellerlaw.com
Emp.: 50
Law firm
N.A.I.C.S.: 541110
Bobbie Celler (CEO)

Electronic Payment Systems Global (1)
3600 FAU Blvd Ste 101, Boca Raton, FL 33431
Tel.: (855) 377-4562
Web Site: http://www.eps-global.com
Payment Processing Systems
N.A.I.C.S.: 522320
Bobbie Celler (CEO)

THE CEMENTWORKS, LLC
32 Old Slip, New York, NY 10005
Tel.: (212) 524-6200   NY
Web Site: http://www.thecementbloc.com
Year Founded: 2000
Sales Range: $50-74.9 Million
Emp.: 140
Advertising Services
N.A.I.C.S.: 541810
Susan Miller (Partner-The Cementbloc)
Rico Viray (Partner-The Cementbloc)
Elizabeth Elfenbein (Partner-The Cementbloc)
Jennifer Matthews (Partner-The Cementbond)
Jose Arturo Chavez (Partner-The Stoneworks)

THE CENTENNIAL GROUP LLC
511 S Washington Ave, Lansing, MI 48933
Tel.: (517) 485-9350
Web Site: http://wwwcentennialgroup.com
Year Founded: 1967
Financial Consulting Services & Investment Advice
N.A.I.C.S.: 523940
Marcie Durso (VP-Mktg)

THE CENTER FOR COMPREHENSIVE CARE & DIAGNOSIS OF INHERITED BLOOD DISORDERS
2670 N Main St Ste 150, Santa Ana, CA 92705
Tel.: (714) 600-4712   CA
Web Site: http://www.cibd-ca.org
Year Founded: 2009
Sales Range: $10-24.9 Million
Emp.: 4
Healtcare Services
N.A.I.C.S.: 622110
Marianne McDaniel (Coord-Nurse)
Diane Nugent (Founder & Pres)
Kathie Birschbach (Sec)
Barry Staton (Treas)
Amit Soni (VP)
Lori Gillespie (Coord-Pharmacy Program)
Matthew Cianciulli (Dir-Ops & Admin)
Michele Khatami (Mgr-Acctg)

THE CENTER FOR FAMILY SUPPORT
333 7th Ave 9th Fl, New York, NY 10001
Tel.: (212) 629-7939   NY
Web Site: http://www.cfsny.org
Year Founded: 1953
Sales Range: $25-49.9 Million
Emp.: 993
Developmental Disability Assistance Services
N.A.I.C.S.: 624120
Virgil Seepersad (Dir-Fin)
Sharon Lax (Dir-HR)
Eileen Berg (Dir-Quality Assurance)

THE CENTER FOR INNOVATION, EXCELLENCE & LEADERSHIP
110 Cambridge St, Cambridge, MA 02141
Tel.: (617) 500-7150
Web Site: http://www.ixl-center.com
Year Founded: 2008
Sales Range: $1-9.9 Million
Emp.: 12
Management Consulting & Training Services
N.A.I.C.S.: 541618
Hitendra Patel (Mng Dir)
Ronald Jonash (Partner)
Pamela McNamara (Principal)
Tyler McNally (Partner)
Massimo Andriolo (Principal-XL Center-Italy)
Marc Chason (Dir-Tech & Innovation)
Youngsang Kwon (Principal-IXL Korea)
Milagros Masini (Principal)
Choong-Il Nam (Assoc Dir-Korea)
Bert Fickel (Principal)
Carolina Chitiva (Dir-Bus Dev)
Julius Bautista (Sr Mgr)
Karla Gomes (Sr Mgr)

THE CENTER FOR REPRODUCTIVE RIGHTS, INC.
199 Water St, New York, NY 10038
Tel.: (917) 637-3600   DE
Web Site: https://www.reproductiverights.org
Year Founded: 1992
Rev.: $8,100,000
Emp.: 55
Fiscal Year-end: 12/31/06
Legal/Litigation Services And Public Education In The Area Of Reproductive Laws And Policies
N.A.I.C.S.: 541110
Nancy Northup (Pres & CEO)
Gabriella Morris (Chief Dev Officer)
Michelle Dees (Chief Strategy Officer & Chief Operations Officer)
Joung-ah Ghedini-Williams (CMO & Chief Comm Officer)
Rachana Desai Martin (Chief Government Officer & Chief External Relations Officer)
Enid Muthoni Ndiga (Chief Program Officer)
Travis J. Tu (Gen Counsel)

THE CENTER: RESOURCES FOR TEACHING AND LEARNING
2626 S Clearbrook Dr, Arlington Heights, IL 60005-4626
Tel.: (224) 366-8500   IL
Web Site: http://www.thecenterweb.org
Year Founded: 1998
Sales Range: $10-24.9 Million
Emp.: 162
Educational Support Services
N.A.I.C.S.: 611710
Jim Zabel (Project Dir)
Lisa Groff (CFO)
Rodrigo Garreton (Dir-Tech)
Brian Michalski (Dir-Early Childhood Pro Dev)
Michael Mangan (Dir-Service-Learning Project)

THE CENTERS FOR FAMILIES

COMPANIES

AND CHILDREN
4500 Euclid Ave, Cleveland, OH 44103
Tel.: (216) 432-7200 OH
Web Site:
http://www.thecentersohio.org
Year Founded: 1970
Sales Range: $10-24.9 Million
Emp.: 395
Child & Family Support Services
N.A.I.C.S.: 624190
Elizabeth Newman (Pres & CEO)
James Penman (Chief Program Officer)
Ann Holt-Wiolland (CFO)
Judith Z. Peters (Exec VP)
Diana Rosa (COO)
Kerry Bohac (VP-HR)
Lynnette Forde (VP-Govt Rels & Dev)
Elizabeth Hijar (Gen Counsel)
Nicole Martin (Dir-Svcs Integration)
Alexa New (Sr VP-Strategic Initiatives & External Affairs)

THE CESAR CHAVEZ FOUNDATION
29700 Woodford-Tehachapi Rd, Keene, CA 93531
Tel.: (661) 823-6134 CA
Web Site:
http://www.chavezfoundation.org
Sales Range: $10-24.9 Million
Emp.: 346
Farmer Welfare Services
N.A.I.C.S.: 624229
Michael Nowakowski (Exec VP-Comm Fund)
Maria Barquin (Program Dir-Network)
Richard M. Torres (Dir-HR)
Paul F. Chavez (Chm & Pres)
Alfredo Izmajtovich (Exec VP-Housing & Economic Dev Fund)
Cliff Timmermans (CFO)
Monica Parra (Dir-Ops)
Bill Barquin (COO)

THE CHADMAR GROUP
2716 Ocean Park Blvd Ste 1064, Santa Monica, CA 90405-5263
Tel.: (310) 314-2590
Web Site: http://chadmar.com
Year Founded: 1990
Sales Range: $10-24.9 Million
Emp.: 8
Land Subdividing Services
N.A.I.C.S.: 237210
Charles Lande (CEO)

THE CHAIR KING, INC.
5405 W Sam Houston Pkwy N, Houston, TX 77041
Tel.: (713) 690-1919
Web Site: http://www.chairking.com
Rev.: $18,593,290
Emp.: 14
Furniture Retailer
N.A.I.C.S.: 449110
Marvin G. Barish (Pres)
Jerry Bradley (Dir-Art)
Joe Weisman (VP)

THE CHALLENGE MACHINERY COMPANY
6125 Norton Center Dr, Norton Shores, MI 49441
Tel.: (231) 799-8484
Web Site:
http://www.challengemachinery.com
Year Founded: 1870
Sales Range: $50-74.9 Million
Emp.: 50
Mfr of Graphic Arts Bindery Equipment
N.A.I.C.S.: 333243
Larry Ritsema (Pres & CEO)
Britt Cary (Dir-Sls & Mktg)

THE CHALLENGE PRINTING COMPANY
2 Bridewell Pl, Clifton, NJ 07014
Tel.: (973) 471-4700
Web Site: http://www.challprint.com
Sales Range: $10-24.9 Million
Emp.: 106
Offset Printing
N.A.I.C.S.: 323111
Peter Laurie (Mgr)

THE CHAMPAIGN TELEPHONE COMPANY
126 Scioto St, Urbana, OH 43078
Tel.: (937) 653-4000
Web Site: http://www.ctcn.net
Rev.: $11,692,403
Emp.: 55
Local Telephone Communications
N.A.I.C.S.: 517121
Tim Bolander (Pres & Gen Mgr)

THE CHAMPION COMPANY INC.
400 Harrison St, Springfield, OH 45505
Tel.: (937) 324-5681 OH
Web Site: http://www.champion-newera.com
Year Founded: 1988
Sales Range: $10-24.9 Million
Emp.: 68
Provider of Metal Barrels, Drums & Pails
N.A.I.C.S.: 325199
Art Gianakopoulos (Pres)

THE CHAN SOON-SHIONG FAMILY FOUNDATION
9922 Jefferson Blvd, Culver City, CA 90232
Tel.: (213) 683-8790 DE
Non Profit Healcare & Research Foundation
N.A.I.C.S.: 923120
Michele B. Chan (Co-Owner)
Patrick Soon-Shiong (Co-Owner)
Subsidiaries:

St. Vincent Medical Center (1)
2131 W 3rd St, Los Angeles, CA 90057-1901
Tel.: (213) 484-7111
Web Site:
http://www.stvincentmedicalcenter.org
Sales Range: $75-99.9 Million
Emp.: 1,500
Medical Center
N.A.I.C.S.: 622110
Catherine Fickes (CFO)
Jan Stein (VP & Exec Dir-Foundation)
Robert Amaro (Dir-Matl Mgmt)
Alan Jasper (Dir-Medical-Intensive Care Unit)
Pedro Ramirez (Dir-Multicultural Health Awareness & Prevention Center)
Heddy Hoopfer (Mgr-Quality)
Frank J. Cracolici (Pres & CEO)

THE CHAR GRILL INC.
16840 W Cleveland Ave, New Berlin, WI 53151
Tel.: (262) 432-1120
Web Site:
http://www.charcoalgrill.com
Rev.: $15,800,000
Emp.: 470
Full-Service Restaurants
N.A.I.C.S.: 722511
Randy Ortloff (Mgr)
Jeff Marsh (Pres)
Steve Meyer (VP-Ops)

THE CHARLES STARK DRAPER LABORATORY, INC.
555 Technology Sq, Cambridge, MA 02139-3539
Tel.: (617) 258-1000 MA
Web Site: http://www.draper.com
Year Founded: 1972
Sales Range: $500-549.9 Million
Emp.: 1,407
Noncommercial Research Services
N.A.I.C.S.: 541715
Darryl G. Sargent (VP-Space Sys & Security-Natl)
John R. Dowdle (VP-Engrg)
Kathleen Granchelli (Dir-Community Rels)
Jeremy Singer (Mgr-Media Rels)
William LaPlante (Pres & CEO)

THE CHARTWELL LAW OFFICES, LLP
970 Rittenhouse Rd Ste 300, Valley Forge, PA 19403
Tel.: (610) 666-7700 PA
Web Site:
http://www.chartwelllaw.com
Year Founded: 2002
Law firm
N.A.I.C.S.: 541110
Clifford Goldstein (CEO)
John J. Winter (Partner & Chm-Creditors' Rights Dept)
Charles J. Barreras (Partner)
Subsidiaries:

The Chartwell Law Offices, LLP - Harrisburg (1)
150 Corporate Cntr Dr Ste 103, Harrisburg, PA 17011
Tel.: (717) 909-5170
Web Site: http://www.chartwelllaw.com
Law firm
N.A.I.C.S.: 541110
Joshua A. Gray (Partner)
Robert J. Baker (Partner)

The Chartwell Law Offices, LLP - New York (1)
1 Battery Park Plz 35th Fl, New York, NY 10004
Tel.: (212) 968-2300
Web Site: http://www.chartwelllaw.com
Emp.: 15
Law firm
N.A.I.C.S.: 541110
Kenneth D. Goldberg (Mng Partner)
William H. Grae (Partner)
Jack Gross (Partner)
Alan S. Katkin (Partner)

THE CHAS. C. HART SEED CO.
304 Main St, Wethersfield, CT 06109-1826
Tel.: (860) 529-2537 CT
Web Site: http://www.hartseed.com
Year Founded: 1892
Sales Range: $1-9.9 Million
Emp.: 30
Producer & Distr of Packet Seeds, Bulk Vegetable & Flower Seeds, Lawn Seeds, Fertilizers & Other Landscape Products
N.A.I.C.S.: 424910
James C. Harris (Pres)
William Hart (Sec & Mgr-Wholesale)
Robert Hart (VP & Asst Treas)

THE CHATFIELD GROUP, INC.
1955 S Val Vista Dr Ste 118, Mesa, AZ 85204
Tel.: (480) 776-6390
Web Site:
http://www.thechatfieldgroup.com
Year Founded: 2001
Sales Range: $1-9.9 Million
Emp.: 10
Software Publisher
N.A.I.C.S.: 513210
Simon Chatfield (CEO)

THE CHATTERJEE GROUP
888 Seventh Ave 37th Fl, New York, NY 10106-3099
Tel.: (212) 271-1947
Web Site:
https://www.thechatterjeegroup.com
Year Founded: 1989
Private Investment Firm Services
N.A.I.C.S.: 523999
Purnendu Chatterjee (Founder & Chm)
Subsidiaries:

Haldia Petrochemicals Limited (1)
1 Auckand Place, Kolkata, 700 017, India (79%)
Tel.: (91) 33 2283 1640
Web Site:
http://www.haldiapetrochemicals.com
Petrochemical Mfr
N.A.I.C.S.: 325110
Rabin Mukhopadhyay (Exec VP-Strategic Initiatives & Projects)
Ashok Kumar Ghosh (Exec VP & Head-Plant)
Surinder Singh (Sr VP & Head-Engrg)
Purnendu Chatterjee (Chm)
Neel Patnaik (CFO & Exec VP)
Sajal Ghosh (Exec VP-CS & Legal)
Chandan Sengupta (Sr VP-CBT & Mktg)

MCPI Private Limited (1)
Bengal Eco Intelligent Park Tower 1 3rd Floor Block EM Plot No3, Kolkata, 700 091, India
Tel.: (91) 33 71122334
Web Site: http://www.mcpi.co.in
Terephthalic Acid Mfr
N.A.I.C.S.: 325199
Debi Prasad Patra (Chm)

Subsidiary (Domestic):

Garden Silk Mills Private Limited (2)
Solarium Business Centre 7th Floor VIP Main Road Vesu, Dumbhal, Surat, 395007, India
Tel.: (91) 2614105222
Web Site: https://www.gardenvareli.com
Rev.: $393,207,360
Assets: $223,995,135
Liabilities: $294,478,275
Net Worth: ($70,483,140)
Earnings: ($28,337,400)
Emp.: 4,351
Fiscal Year-end: 03/31/2020
Polyester Yarn Mfr
N.A.I.C.S.: 313110
Amitava Banerjee (COO)
Shashi B. Sharma (Head-Jolwa Project)
Ranjini Roy (Head-Bus Vareli Division)

THE CHECK CASHING PLACE, INC.
945 5th Ave Ste D, San Diego, CA 92101
Tel.: (619) 235-9700
Web Site:
http://www.thecheckcashingplaceinc.com
Rev.: $10,200,000
Emp.: 9
Check Cashing Agencies
N.A.I.C.S.: 522390
Richard Barr (Pres)

THE CHEMICAL COMPANY
44 SW Ave, Jamestown, RI 02835
Tel.: (401) 423-3100
Web Site: http://www.thechemco.com
Sales Range: $10-24.9 Million
Emp.: 15
Chemicals & Allied Products Mfr & Distr
N.A.I.C.S.: 424690
Robert N. Roach (Pres)
Forest Goodman (Exec VP)

THE CHERTOFF GROUP, LLC
1399 New York Ave NW Ste 1100, Washington, DC 20005-4728
Tel.: (202) 552-5280
Web Site:
http://www.chertoffgroup.com

THE CHERTOFF GROUP, LLC

U.S. PRIVATE

The Chertoff Group, LLC—(Continued)
Management Consulting Services
N.A.I.C.S.: 541618
Michael Chertoff (Co-Founder & Chm)
Chad Sweet (Co-Founder & CEO)
Jason Kaufman (Pres)
Jayson Ahern (Principal & Head-Strategic Advisory Svcs)
Kanad Virk (Principal & Head-Private Equity)
Charles Allen (Principal)
Jay Cohen (Principal)
Michael Hayden (Principal)
Adam Isles (Principal)
Emily Siciliano (Dir-Ops)
Mira Ricardel (Principal)
Ellen Murray (Dir-Comm)

Subsidiaries:

Trustwave Holdings, Inc. (1)
70 W Madison St Ste 600, Chicago, IL 60602
Tel.: (312) 873-7500
Web Site: http://www.trustwave.com
Emp.: 1,400
Holding Company; On-Demand Data Security & Payment Card Industry Compliance Management Products & Services
N.A.I.C.S.: 551112
James Kunkel (Exec VP-Corp Dev)
Michael Petitti (Sr VP-Global Alliances)
Robert J. McCullen (Founder & CEO)
J. Lawrence Podmolik (CTO)
Cas Purdy (VP-Corp Mktg & Comm)
Steve Kelley (CMO)
Tom Wallace (Sr VP-Delivery & Ops)
Chris Schueler (Sr VP-Managed Security Svcs)
Anandh Maistry (Mng Dir & VP-ANZ)
Robert Pizzari (Sr VP-Sls-Asia Pacific)
Dave Feringa (Exec VP-Global Sls)
Kevin Kilraine (CFO)
Charles Spallitta (Sr VP-Product Mgmt)
Jim Ritchings (Sr VP-Worldwide Channel Sls)
Karen Lindgren (Sr VP-Strategy & Plng)
Rick Miller (COO)
Julie Nagle (Sr VP-HR)

THE CHICAGO COUNCIL ON GLOBAL AFFAIRS
332 S Michigan Ave Ste 1100, Chicago, IL 60604-4416
Tel.: (312) 726-3860   IL
Web Site:
  http://www.thechicagocouncil.org
Year Founded: 1922
Sales Range: $10-24.9 Million
Emp.: 52
Civic & Social Organization
N.A.I.C.S.: 813410
Glenn F. Tilton (Vice Chm)
Ivo H. Daalder (Pres)
Niamh King (VP-Programs)
Douglas A. Doetsch (Sec)
John F. Manley (Vice Chm)
Leah Joy Zell (Vice Chm & Treas)
Louis B. Susman (Vice Chm)
Shirley Welsh Ryan (Vice Chm)
Matthew Abbott (Dir-Govt & Diplomatic Programs)
Audra Berger (Dir-HR)
Jenny Cizner (COO)
Robert G. Cordes (VP-Fin & Admin)
Anna Edwards (Dir-Rels)
Josephine E. Heindel (VP-External Rels)
Laura Lucas Magnuson (Dir-Media Rels)
Elizabeth Marquardt (Dir-Foundation Rels & Grants)
Tony Mitchell (VP-Comm)
Christy Thomas (Dir-Digital Strategy)
Sebastian Burca (Dir-Corp Programs)

THE CHICAGO LIGHTHOUSE FOR PEOPLE WHO ARE BLIND OR VISUALLY IMPAIRED
1850 W Roosevelt Rd, Chicago, IL 60608-1298
Tel.: (312) 666-1331   IL
Web Site:
  http://www.chicagolighthouse.org
Year Founded: 1906
Sales Range: $10-24.9 Million
Emp.: 308
Visually Impaired People Assistance Services
N.A.I.C.S.: 623990
Pamela Tully (COO & Exec VP)
Mary Lynne Januszewski (CFO & Exec VP)
Thoams Perski (Sr VP-Rehabilitation Svcs)
Gary Rich (Vice Chm)
Janet P. Szlyk (Pres)
John Coleman (Sec)
Richard H. Schnadig (Chm)
Robert Clarke (Treas)
Jennifer Miller (Chief Dev Officer-Fin Dev)
Sheila Perkins (Sr VP-Employment Svcs)
Jeanette Bonzani (Sr VP-HR)
Dominic Calabrese (Sr VP-PR)
Greg Polman (Sr VP-Pub Policy)
Ricardo Vilchez (VP-IT)
Kara Crumbliss (VP-Low Vision Svcs)

THE CHICANO FEDERATION, INC.
3180 University Ave Ste 317, San Diego, CA 92104-2074
Tel.: (619) 285-5600   CA
Web Site:
  http://www.chicanofederation.org
Year Founded: 1969
Sales Range: $10-24.9 Million
Emp.: 202
Community Action Services
N.A.I.C.S.: 624190
Raymond Uzeta (Pres & CEO)

THE CHICKASAW NATION
520 E Arlington, Ada, OK 74820
Tel.: (580) 436-2603
Web Site: http://www.chickasaw.net
Native American Tribal Government Organization
N.A.I.C.S.: 921150
Bill G. Lance Jr. (Sec)
Bill Anoatubby (Governor)

Subsidiaries:

Chickasaw Foundation (1)
PO Box 1726, Ada, OK 74821-1726
Tel.: (580) 421-9030
Web Site:
  http://www.chickasawfoundation.org
Rev: $2,228,476
Fiscal Year-end: 12/31/2012
Grantmaking Foundations
N.A.I.C.S.: 813211
Johnna R. Walker (CEO)
Matthew Chesnut (Asst Treas)
Jalinda Kelley (Vice Chm)
Jerry Jones (Treas)
Robyn Elliott (Chm)

Chickasaw Nation Industries, Inc. (1)
2600 John Saxon Blvd, Norman, OK 73069
Tel.: (405) 253-8200
Web Site: http://www.chickasaw.com
Emp.: 1,600
Holding Company
N.A.I.C.S.: 551112
David Nimmo (Pres & CEO)
Bob Engle (Treas & Sec)
Neal McCaleb (Chm)
Steve Woods (Vice Chm)
Carl Cooper (CFO)
Kirk Johnson (Gen Counsel)
Tom Leydorf (Exec VP)

Subsidiary (Domestic):

CNI Global Solutions, LLC (2)
2600 John Saxon Blvd, Norman, OK 73071
Tel.: (405) 253-8200
Web Site: http://www.chickasaw.com
Information Security & Information Technology Support Services
N.A.I.C.S.: 541519
Aaron Link (Mgr)

Filtra-Systems Company (2)
23900 Haggerty Rd, Farmington Hills, MI 48335
Tel.: (248) 427-9090
Web Site: http://www.filtrasystems.com
Filters Mfr & Distr
N.A.I.C.S.: 333998
Scott Bratten (CEO)

IPKeys Technologies LLC (2)
44 Gilbert St W, Tinton Falls, NJ 07701
Tel.: (732) 389-8112
Web Site: http://www.ipkeys.com
Emp.: 100
Information Security & System Engineering Services
N.A.I.C.S.: 921190
Robert M. Nawy (CEO & Member-Mgmt Bd)
Lanfen C. Nawy (Member-Mgmt Bd)
Jeff Bochonok (COO-Federal Svcs)
Art Clomera (CTO-Federal Svcs)
Shawn Elliott (VP-Federal Solutions)
Duane Farmer (VP-Fin)

Subsidiary (Domestic):

Excentul Technology Services, Inc. (3)
4300 Youree Dr Bldg 1, Shreveport, LA 71105
Tel.: (318) 221-2055
Information Technology & Services
N.A.I.C.S.: 518210

Subsidiary (Domestic):

InnovationOne, LLC (2)
601 NE 2nd Ave, Marietta, OK 73448
Tel.: (580) 276-3306
Web Site: http://www.chickasaw.com
Sales Range: $1-9.9 Million
Emp.: 48
Engineering, Construction, Logistics & Supply Chain Management Services
N.A.I.C.S.: 561499
Kent Foster (Mgr)

THE CHILDREN'S CENTER OF HAMDEN, INC.
1400 Whitney Ave, Hamden, CT 06517
Tel.: (203) 248-2116   CT
Web Site:
  http://www.childrenscenterhamden.org
Year Founded: 1833
Sales Range: $10-24.9 Million
Emp.: 288
Behavioral Healthcare Services
N.A.I.C.S.: 623220
Bill Everett (Dir-Maintenance)
Elizabeth Bacon (VP)
Krista Hart (Treas & Treas)
Tina Garrity (Pres)
Claudia Grantham (Pres)
Tina Garrity (Pres & Sec)
Selma N. Ward (CEO)
Jennifer W. Jencks (COO)
Anthony Zeolla (CFO)
Sarah Lockery (Chief Dev & Engagement Officer)
Pieter Joost Van Wattum (Chief Medical Officer)
John M. Cuozzo Jr. (Sec)

THE CHILDREN'S CLINIC, "SERVING CHILDREN AND THEIR FAMILIES"
2790 Atlantic Ave, Long Beach, CA 90806
Tel.: (562) 933-0432   CA
Web Site:
  http://www.thechildrensclinic.org
Year Founded: 1939
Sales Range: $10-24.9 Million
Emp.: 313
Community Care Services
N.A.I.C.S.: 624190
Albert Ocampo (CFO)
Elisa Nicholas (CEO)
Maria Chandler (Chief Medical Officer)
Jina Lee Lawler (COO)
Andrew Horvath (CIO)
Martha Herrera (VP-Consumer)
Mel Marks (Chief Admin Officer)

THE CHILDREN'S GUILD INC.
6802 McClean Blvd, Baltimore, MD 21234-7260
Tel.: (410) 444-3800   MD
Web Site:
  http://www.childrensguild.org
Year Founded: 1953
Sales Range: $10-24.9 Million
Emp.: 404
Disabled Child Assistance Services
N.A.I.C.S.: 624120
Stephen M. Baldwin (CFO & Exec VP-Support Svcs)
A. Duane Arbogast (COO & VP-Educational Svcs)
Terry W. Manning (VP-Human Capital Mgmt & Regulatory Compliance)
Steve Howe (VP-Children, Families & Communities Svcs)
Andrew L. Ross (Pres & CEO)
Claire L. Turberville (VP-Special Projects)
LaRon Martin (Principal-Special Education School)
Alex Morris (Exec Dir-HR)
Gary Kellner (Chief Dev Officer)

THE CHILDREN'S HOME OF PITTSBURGH & LEMIEUX FAMILY CENTER
5324 Penn Ave, Pittsburgh, PA 15224
Tel.: (412) 441-4884   PA
Web Site:
  http://www.childrenshomepgh.org
Year Founded: 1893
Sales Range: $10-24.9 Million
Emp.: 160
Child Adoption Services
N.A.I.C.S.: 624110
Kimberly Phillips (CFO)
Pamela Schanwald (CEO)

THE CHILDREN'S HOME SOCIETY OF NEW JERSEY
635 S Clinton Ave, Trenton, NJ 08611
Tel.: (609) 695-6274   NJ
Web Site: http://www.chsofnj.org
Year Founded: 1894
Sales Range: $10-24.9 Million
Emp.: 277
Child & Family Care Services
N.A.I.C.S.: 624190
Joseph Rizziello (Chief Program Officer)
Denise Wentzler (Dir-Mktg, Comm & Funds Dev)
Florence Paric (Dir-Admin)
Robert Notta (CFO)
Mary Graycar (Dir-HR)
Timothy P. Ryan (VP)
Miranda Alfonso-Williams (Treas)
James Graham (Sec)
Donna C. Pressma (Pres & CEO)
Kati Chupa (Chm)
Angela Garcia (Dir-IT)
Maureen Lawrence (Dir-Ocean County Child Care Resource & Referral)
Sheryl Roach (Dir-Quality Assurance & Prof Dev)

Pamela Cipriano *(Dir-Corp Dev & Volunteerism)*
Dolores Ijames-Bryant *(Dir-Kinship, Clinical & School-Based Svcs)*
Karen Courtney *(VP)*
Alan Zulick *(VP-Policy)*

THE CHILDREN'S HOSPITAL OF PHILADELPHIA
34th St & Civic Center Blvd, Philadelphia, PA 19104
Tel.: (215) 590-1000
Web Site: http://www.chop.edu
Year Founded: 1855
Sales Range: $1-4.9 Billion
Emp.: 10,500
Children's Hospital
N.A.I.C.S.: 622310
Jeffrey D. Kahn *(Gen Counsel & Exec VP)*
Paula M. Agosto *(Chief Nursing Officer & Sr VP)*
Deanne Taylor *(Dir-Bioinformatics)*
Patrick K. FitzGerald *(VP-Entrepreneurship & Innovation)*
Douglas G. Hock *(COO & Exec VP)*
Madeline S. Bell *(Pres & CEO)*
Peter Grollman *(Sr VP-Pub Affairs)*
Jan P. Boswinkel *(Chief Safety Officer & VP-Medical Ops)*
Kisha Hortman Hawthorne *(CIO & Sr VP)*
Janet Holcombe *(Chief Compliance Officer, Chief Privacy Officer & VP)*
Ron Keren *(Chief Quality Officer & VP)*
Spencer Kowal *(VP-Fin Strategy)*
Monica Taylor Lotty *(Co-Chief Dev Officer & Exec VP)*
Joni Rittler *(VP-Supply Chain)*
Jenny Chan *(Chief Investment Officer)*
Sophia G. Holder *(CFO & Exec VP)*
Susan L. Furth *(Chief Scientific Officer)*

THE CHILDREN'S HOSPITAL OF PHILADELPHIA FOUNDATION
3401 Civic Center Blvd, Philadelphia, PA 19104
Tel.: (267) 426-5332
Web Site: https://www.chop.edu
Year Founded: 1855
Educational Support Services
N.A.I.C.S.: 611710

THE CHILDREN'S INSTITUTE
1405 Shady Ave, Pittsburgh, PA 15217-1350
Tel.: (412) 420-2400 PA
Web Site: http://www.amazingkids.org
Year Founded: 1998
Sales Range: $25-49.9 Million
Emp.: 670
Child & Youth Care Services
N.A.I.C.S.: 624110
Tim Bittner *(VP-Ops)*
Linda Allen *(VP-HR)*
Stacey Vaccaro *(COO)*
Wendy Ann Pardee *(Pres & CEO)*

THE CHILDREN'S MUSEUM OF INDIANAPOLIS
3000 N Meridian St, Indianapolis, IN 46208
Tel.: (317) 334-4000 IN
Web Site: http://www.childrensmuseum.org
Year Founded: 1925
Sales Range: $25-49.9 Million
Emp.: 418
Child Museum
N.A.I.C.S.: 712110

David W. Gray *(Chm)*
James D. Bremner *(Vice Chm)*
Jeffrey H. Patchen *(Pres)*
Elizabeth Cooke *(Sec)*
Katy Allen *(VP-HR & Org Dev)*
Andy Bawel *(CFO)*
Heather Bice *(VP)*
David Donaldson *(CTO)*
Amy Kwas *(VP-Dev)*
Jennifer Pace Robinson *(VP-Experience Dev & Family Learning Exhibits)*
Brian Statz *(VP-Ops)*
Allison Stitle *(Pres)*
Lisa Townsend *(VP-Mktg & External Rels)*
Katherine Mathena *(CIO)*

THE CHILDRENS MERCY HOSPITAL
2401 Gillham Rd, Kansas City, MO 64108
Tel.: (816) 234-3000 MO
Web Site: http://www.childrensmercy.org
Year Founded: 1901
Sales Range: $800-899.9 Million
Emp.: 6,721
Child Health Care Services
N.A.I.C.S.: 622110
Cheri Hunt *(Chief Nursing Officer & Sr VP)*
Jo Stueve *(Co-COO & Exec VP)*
Karen Cox *(Co-COO & Exec VP)*
Mark Hoffman *(Chief Res Information Officer)*
Paul Kempinski *(Pres & CEO)*

THE CHOICE GROUP, LLC
2265 Livernois Rd Ste 500, Troy, MI 48083
Tel.: (248) 362-4150 MI
Web Site: http://www.choiceproperties.com
Rev: $14,000,000
Emp.: 80
Real Estate Investment Trust
N.A.I.C.S.: 525990
Kamal H. Shouhayib *(Founder & CEO)*

THE CHOSEN, INC.
4 S 2600 W Ste 5, Hurricane, UT 84737
Tel.: (435) 767-1338 DE
Web Site: https://www.thechosen.tv
Year Founded: 2017
Rev: $80,929,000
Assets: $198,205,000
Liabilities: $163,785,000
Net Worth: $34,420,000
Earnings: ($3,569,000)
Emp.: 61
Fiscal Year-end: 12/31/23
Media Streaming Distribution Services
N.A.I.C.S.: 516210

THE CHRISKEN RESIDENTIAL TRUST
345 N Canal St Ste 201, Chicago, IL 60606
Tel.: (312) 454-1626
Web Site: http://www.chrisken.com
Year Founded: 1997
Sales Range: $50-74.9 Million
Emp.: 225
Real Estate Investment Trust
N.A.I.C.S.: 525990
John F. Kennedy *(Pres & CEO)*
Robert Mayer *(CFO & Exec VP-Fin)*
David R. Heitzman *(Dir-Property Mgmt)*

THE CHRIST HOSPITAL

2139 Auburn Ave, Cincinnati, OH 45219
Tel.: (513) 585-2000 OH
Web Site: http://www.thechristhospital.com
Year Founded: 1891
Sales Range: $750-799.9 Million
Emp.: 5,715
Community Health Care Services
N.A.I.C.S.: 621498
Peter Greis *(CIO & VP)*
Heather Adkins *(Chief External Officer & VP)*
Berc Gawne *(Chief Medical Officer & VP)*
Elizabeth Johnson *(Chief Compliance Officer & VP)*
Justin Gamble *(Dir-Pharmacy Ops-Health Network)*
Robert Summe *(Dir-Medical-Radiation Oncology)*
Chris Bergman *(CFO & VP)*
Paul Gelter *(Chief Admin Officer & VP)*
Victor DiPilla *(Chief Bus Dev Officer & VP)*
Michael Jennings *(Chief Clinical Officer & VP)*
Julie Holt *(Chief Nursing Officer & VP)*
Deborah Hayes *(COO & VP)*
Mike Keating *(Pres & CEO)*
Scott Hamlin *(Sr VP-Fin & Physician Ops)*
Casey Liddy *(VP-Physician Svcs)*
John Campbell *(CIO & VP)*

THE CHRISTIAN BROADCASTING NETWORK INC.
977 Centerville Tpke, Virginia Beach, VA 23463-7701
Tel.: (757) 226-7000
Web Site: http://www1.cbn.com
Year Founded: 1960
Television Broadcasting Station
N.A.I.C.S.: 813110
Pat Robertson *(Founder & Chm)*
Gordon Robertson *(CEO)*

THE CHRISTMAN COMPANY INC.
208 N Capitol Ave, Lansing, MI 48933-1901
Tel.: (517) 482-1488 MI
Web Site: http://www.christmanco.com
Year Founded: 1915
Sales Range: $25-49.9 Million
Emp.: 150
Management Services
N.A.I.C.S.: 541618
Steven F. Roznowski *(Pres & CEO)*
Angela E. Bailey *(VP-Brand Strategy & Comm)*
Jay H. Smith *(Exec VP-Construction Ops)*
Ronald D. Staley *(Sr VP-Ops-Southeast)*
John A. Holmstrom *(Sr VP-Industrial & Power)*
Matthew T. Chappelle *(CFO & Sr VP-Fin)*
Daniel C. LaMore *(Sr VP-Ops-West)*

Subsidiaries:

Christman Constructors Inc. (1)
324 E S St, Lansing, MI 48910-1627 (100%)
Tel.: (517) 482-0554
Web Site: http://www.christmanconstructors.com
Sales Range: $25-49.9 Million
Emp.: 100
Carpentry Work
N.A.I.C.S.: 238130
Doug Peters *(Pres)*

Medco Construction, LLC (1)
8757 Autobahn Dr Ste 100, Dallas, TX 75237
Tel.: (214) 820-9449
Web Site: http://www.medcoconstruction.com
Sales Range: $1-9.9 Million
Emp.: 59
Construction Services
N.A.I.C.S.: 236210
Andy Kelly *(Project Mgr)*
Bill Sullivan *(Project Mgr)*
Gary Holmes *(Mgr-Dept)*
Kent Metzger *(Project Mgr)*
Louis Schindler *(VP)*
Spencer Leigh *(Project Mgr)*

Rentenbach Engineering Company (1)
2400 Sutherland Ave, Knoxville, TN 37919-2354
Tel.: (865) 546-2440
Web Site: http://www.rentenbach.com
Sales Range: $125-149.9 Million
General Contractor Construction Management & Design
N.A.I.C.S.: 236210
Donald W. Freeman *(Pres & CEO)*

Subsidiary (Domestic):

Rentenbach Constructors Incorporated (2)
2400 Sutherland Ave, Knoxville, TN 37919-2354
Tel.: (865) 546-2440
Web Site: http://www.rentenbach.com
Sales Range: $25-49.9 Million
Emp.: 125
General Contractors
N.A.I.C.S.: 236210

Unit (Domestic):

Rentenbach Constructors Inc. (3)
1102 Grecade St, Greensboro, NC 27408
Tel.: (336) 333-2872
Web Site: http://www.rentenbach.com
Emp.: 20
Construction Services
N.A.I.C.S.: 236115
Donald Freeman *(Pres & CEO)*
Greg A. Ratcliff *(Treas & Sec)*
Ken D. Norton *(Exec VP)*
Michael Rentenbach *(Chm)*
Tim Gray *(Sr VP)*

THE CHRISTMAS LIGHT CO.
4645 E Cotton Ctr Blvd, Phoenix, AZ 85040
Tel.: (480) 966-0625
Web Site: http://www.ezupchristmaslights.com
Sales Range: $1-9.9 Million
Emp.: 6
Tools for Decorating
N.A.I.C.S.: 335139
Jamie Limber *(CEO)*

THE CHURCH AID OF THE PROTESTANT EPISCOPAL CHURCH
390 Church St, Saratoga Springs, NY 12866
Tel.: (518) 584-3317 NY
Web Site: http://www.homeofthegoodshepherd.com
Year Founded: 1870
Sales Range: $10-24.9 Million
Emp.: 556
Assisted Living Facility Services
N.A.I.C.S.: 623312
Michael Penfold *(Treas)*
Diane Robinson *(Sec)*
John Van Der Veer *(VP)*
Mary Withington *(Pres)*

THE CHURCH STREET CORPORATION
25 Hancock St, Keansburg, NJ 07734
Tel.: (732) 787-6161 NJ
Year Founded: 1978
Sales Range: $10-24.9 Million

THE CHURCH STREET CORPORATION

U.S. PRIVATE

THE CHURCH STREET CORPORATION—(Continued)
Emp.: 7
Elderly & Disabled People Assisted Services
N.A.I.C.S.: 624120
Robert Graham (Pres)
Patrick Antonacci (Chm)

THE CIGARETTE STORE CORP.
6790 Winchester Cir, Boulder, CO 80301
Tel.: (303) 442-2520   CO
Web Site: http://smokerfriendly.com
Year Founded: 1991
Rev.: $85,000,000
Emp.: 500
Holding Company; Tobacco Stores & Stands Operator
N.A.I.C.S.: 551112
Ben Chaney (CFO)
Ken Kramer (Gen Counsel & VP-Admin)
Terry Gallagher Jr. (Pres)

Subsidiaries:

Smoker Friendly International LLC   (1)
6790 Winchester Cir, Boulder, CO 80301
Web Site: http://smokerfriendly.com
Tobacco Stores
N.A.I.C.S.: 459991
Terry Gallagher Jr. (Pres)

Subsidiary (Domestic):

Cigars on 6th   (2)
707 E 6th Ave, Denver, CO 80203-3818
Tel.: (303) 830-8100
Web Site: http://www.cigarson6th.com
Tobacco Stores
N.A.I.C.S.: 459991
Dan Dunne (Pres)

THE CINCINNATI GILBERT MACHINE TOOL COMPANY, LLC
3366 Beekman St, Cincinnati, OH 45223-2424
Tel.: (513) 541-4815
Web Site: http://www.cincinnatigilbert.com
Year Founded: 1893
Horizontal Drilling, Boring & Milling Machines & Rotary Tables Mfr; Horizontals, Machining Centers
N.A.I.C.S.: 333517
Reinhold Petry (Principal)

THE CIRCUS ARTS CONSERVATORY, INC.
2075 Bahia Vista St, Sarasota, FL 34239
Tel.: (941) 355-9335   FL
Web Site: http://www.circusarts.org
Year Founded: 1997
Circus Operations
N.A.I.C.S.: 713990
Pedro Reis (Founder & CEO)
Dolly Jacobs-Reis (Co-Founder & Assoc Dir)
Jennifer Mitchell (Mng Dir)
Henry Barragan (Dir-Ops & Logistics)
Patrick Smith (Mgr-Acctg & Admin)
Michelle Brault (Mgr-Dev & Fundraising)
Beth Graves (Mktg Mgr)
Mary Jo Heider (Partner-Community & Mgr-Dev)
Mateo Cristiani (Mgr-Box Office CRM)
Courtney Wyatt (Mgr-Circus Arts)
Chuck Sidlow (Mgr-Outreach)
Karen Bell (Mgr-Outreach, Education & Program)
Jack Brown (Chm)
Jack Dean (Vice Chm)
Deborah Walk (Sec)
Bruce Mantia (Treas)

THE CIRLOT AGENCY, INC.
1505 Airport Rd, Flowood, MS 39232
Tel.: (601) 664-2010   MS
Web Site: http://www.cirlot.com
Year Founded: 1984
Rev.: $21,000,000
Emp.: 36
Advetising Agency
N.A.I.C.S.: 541810
David Hobart (Sr Art Dir)
Lynda Lesley (VP & Dir-Creative)
Greg Gilliland (VP-Multimedia)
Lisa Comer (Dir-Mktg Svcs)
Liza C. Looser (CEO)
Sharon Grubbs (Gen Mgr & Bus Mgr)
Steve Erickson (Exec Art Dir)
Ashley Strange (Acct Exec-Pub Rel)
Richard W. Looser Jr. (COO)

THE CLEAN BEDROOM
Dan's Crossing Ste 108 5 Shapleigh Rd, Kittery, ME 03904
Tel.: (207) 438-9778
Web Site: http://www.thecleanbedroom.com
Year Founded: 2004
Sales Range: $1-9.9 Million
Emp.: 17
Mattresses & Bed Retailer
N.A.I.C.S.: 449110
Christine Chamberlin (Founder)

THE CLEARING, INC.
1250 Connecticut Ave NW Ste 625, Washington, DC 20036
Tel.: (202) 558-6499
Web Site: http://www.theclearing.com
Year Founded: 2007
Sales Range: $1-9.9 Million
Emp.: 50
Business Management Consulting Services
N.A.I.C.S.: 541618
Chris J. McGoff (Founder)
Jonathan Spector (Sr Principal)
Tom Wade (CFO)
Tara McKee Carcillo (Pres & CEO)

THE CLEVELAND CLINIC FOUNDATION
8615 Euclid Ave, Cleveland, OH 44195
Tel.: (216) 445-8904
Web Site: http://my.clevelandclinic.org
Non-Profit Services
N.A.I.C.S.: 813410
Tomislav Mihaljevic (Pres & CEO)
Brian Donley (CEO-Cleveland Clinic London)
Robert E. Rich Jr. (Chm)

THE CLIFFS COMMUNITIES, INC.
3598 Hwy 11, Travelers Rest, SC 29690
Tel.: (864) 371-1000
Web Site: http://www.cliffscommunities.com
Year Founded: 1991
Sales Range: $100-124.9 Million
Emp.: 50
Hotel, Golf Course & Spa Owner & Operator
N.A.I.C.S.: 721110

THE CLIMATIC CORPORATION
1001 Pinnacle Pt Dr, Columbia, SC 29223-5712
Tel.: (803) 765-2595   SC
Web Site: http://www.climaticcorp.com
Year Founded: 1959
Sales Range: $75-99.9 Million
Emp.: 80
Whslr of Microwave Oven Television Air Conditioner & Heater Distr
N.A.I.C.S.: 423620
Cindee Bailey (Co-Pres)
Gilly Bailey (Co-Pres & COO)
Dennie Wetherley (CFO)

Subsidiaries:

Climatic Comfort Products, LLC   (1)
1074 Pinnacle Point Dr Ste 110, Columbia, SC 29223
Web Site: http://www.climaticcomfortproducts.com
Air Conditioning Equipment Whslr
N.A.I.C.S.: 423730

Climatic Home Products   (1)
1074 Pinnacle Point Dr Ste 102, Columbia, SC 29223
Tel.: (800) 845-4994
Web Site: http://www.climatichomeproducts.com
Sales Range: $10-24.9 Million
Emp.: 15
Consumer Electronics Whslr
N.A.I.C.S.: 423620
Doug Allen (Pres)
Fredricka Jones (Mgr-Call Center)
Sean Bowie (Mgr-Ops & Logistics)
Roger Longenecker (Dir-Ops)

Matrix Consulting, LLC   (1)
1074 Pinnacle Point Dr Ste 100, Columbia, SC 29223
Tel.: (803) 254-4221
Web Site: http://www.matrixconsulting.net
Sales Range: $10-24.9 Million
Emp.: 25
Information Technology Consulting Services
N.A.I.C.S.: 541512
Neely Loring (Pres & COO)
Tom Colton (VP-Bus Dev)
Lindsey Segars (Office Mgr)
Rich Erickson (Dir-Sls & Engrg)
Scott Lee (Exec VP-Sls)
Sharon Neuman (Dir-Project Mgmt)
Frank Richardson (Dir-Customer Experience)
Chip Schutte (Dir-Platform Svcs & Implementation)

Southeastern Appliances and More, LLC   (1)
1186 Clark St, Covington, GA 30014
Tel.: (770) 786-2330
Web Site: http://www.seappliances.com
Home Appliance Distr
N.A.I.C.S.: 423620

The Climatic Development Corporation.   (1)
1074 Pinnacle Point Dr, Columbia, SC 29223
Tel.: (803) 765-2595
Web Site: http://www.climaticdevelopment.com
Commercial & Real Estate Development Services
N.A.I.C.S.: 531210

THE CLINTON NATIONAL BANK
235 6th Ave S, Clinton, IA 52732
Tel.: (563) 243-1243
Web Site: http://www.clintonnational.com
Year Founded: 1865
Sales Range: $10-24.9 Million
Emp.: 108
Federal Savings Bank
N.A.I.C.S.: 522180
Robert P. Holleran (Vice Chm & CEO)
Alvin J. Goerdt (Chm)
Steven E. Thacker (Pres)
Jennifer L. Boysen (Exec VP & Mgr-Ops)
Norlan L. Hinke (Sr VP & Sr Lender)
Carol A. Peterson (Sr VP & Mgr-Trust)
Helenea M. Graves (Asst VP)
Dianne L. Papke (Office Mgr-Miles)
Verna R. Mitchell (Officer-Bus Dev)
Jason S. Wheat (Officer-Comml Loan & VP)
Deborah A. Farrell (VP & Office Mgr-Camanche)
Sara Misiewicz (Asst VP)
Amy L. Horst (VP & Mgr-Lyons)
Christine C. Smith (Officer-Ops & VP)
David J. Helscher (Officer-Trust & Sr VP)
Joel E. Kaczinski (VP & Mgr-Andover)
Kathy J. Hand (Officer-Loan Ops & VP)
Mark W. Milder (VP)
Ricci S. Aquilani (Officer-Compliance & VP-Ops)
Ritch J. Skrivseth (Officer-Loan & VP)
Ted W. Shemwell (Officer-Trust & VP)
Toni J. Milnes (VP)
Mindy Burggraaf (VP & Mgr-Real Estate Dept)

THE CLUB AT BOCA POINTE
7144 Boca Pointe Dr, Boca Raton, FL 33433-5908
Tel.: (561) 864-8500   FL
Web Site: http://www.bocapointecc.com
Year Founded: 1988
Sales Range: $10-24.9 Million
Emp.: 253
Country Club Operator
N.A.I.C.S.: 713910
Helen Karpel (CFO & Gen Mgr)
William Buck Deibel (Dir-Golf)
Angel Rodriguez (Dir-Tennis)

THE CLUB AT EAGLEBROOKE
1300 Eaglebrooke Blvd, Lakeland, FL 33813
Tel.: (863) 701-0101
Web Site: http://www.eaglebrooke.com
Sales Range: $1-9.9 Million
Emp.: 120
Member-Only Country Club & Golf Course
N.A.I.C.S.: 713910
John Seitz (Gen Mgr)

THE CLUB AT LAS CAMPANAS, INC.
132 Clubhouse Dr, Santa Fe, NM 87506
Tel.: (505) 995-3500   NM
Web Site: http://www.theclubatlascampanas.com
Year Founded: 1997
Sales Range: $10-24.9 Million
Emp.: 257
Country Club
N.A.I.C.S.: 713910
Colleen Edwards (Dir-Dev & Membership)
Kay Lee (Dir-IT Svcs & Comm)
Bob Berger (CFO)
Kelly Stoochnoff (Dir-Equestrian)
Ruth Hamilton (Mgr-Catering Sls)
Tom Egelhoff (Dir-Agronomy)
Todd Shaw (Dir-Fitness & Tennis Center)
Tony Dawson (Gen Mgr & COO)
Brad Lardon (Dir-Golf)

THE CLUB AT MEDITERRA INC.
15755 Corso Mediterra Cir, Naples, FL 34110
Tel.: (239) 254-3000   FL
Web Site: http://www.mediterraliving.com
Year Founded: 2009
Sales Range: $10-24.9 Million

COMPANIES   THE COMMERCIAL GROUP LIFTING PRODUCTS

Emp.: 292
Social Club Operator
N.A.I.C.S.: 813410
Keith Hughes (CFO)
Manon Passino (Dir-Membership & Mktg)
Robert Anderson (Dir-Golf)
Tim Hiers (Dir-Agronomy)

THE CLY-DEL MANUFACTURING COMPANY
151 Sharon Rd, Waterbury, CT 06705
Tel.: (203) 574-2100
Web Site: https://cly-del.com
Year Founded: 1939
Rev.: $7,500,000
Emp.: 76
Precision Metal Stamping Services
N.A.I.C.S.: 332119
Robert Garthwait III (Exec VP)

Subsidiaries:

Semco Tool & Manufacturing Co., Inc.   (1)
30 Naugatuck Dr, Naugatuck, CT 06770-2024
Tel.: (203) 723-7411
Web Site: http://semcoeyelets.com
Rev.: $1,500,000
Emp.: 5
Fastener, Button, Needle & Pin Mfr
N.A.I.C.S.: 339993
Rose Semeraro (VP)

THE CM GROUP, LLC
25 Recreation Park Dr Ste 200, Hingham, MA 02043
Tel.: (781) 556-5738   MA
Web Site:
  http://www.thecmgroup.com
Year Founded: 2005
Meeting, Event Planning & Management Consulting Services
N.A.I.C.S.: 561920
Cherie Myatt (Co-Founder)
Maggie Butler (Co-Founder)

Subsidiaries:

Scientific Commercialization, LLC   (1)
6515 Grand Teton Plz Ste 241, Madison, WI 53719
Tel.: (610) 983-4668
Web Site: http://www.scientificcommercialization.com
Rev.: $2,300,000
Emp.: 12
Management Consulting Services
N.A.I.C.S.: 541618
Bill W. Massey (Principal)

THE COFFEE BEANERY LTD.
3429 Pierson Pl, Flushing, MI 48433-2413
Tel.: (810) 733-1020   MI
Web Site:
  http://www.coffeebeanery.com
Year Founded: 1976
Sales Range: $125-149.9 Million
Emp.: 200
Retail Gourmet Coffee Specialty Store
N.A.I.C.S.: 445298
JoAnne M. Shaw (Pres)
Kirk Shaw (VP-Franchise Sls)

THE COFFEE WORKS INC.
3418 Folsom Blvd, Sacramento, CA 95816
Tel.: (916) 452-1086
Web Site:
  http://www.coffeeworks.com
Year Founded: 1982
Sales Range: $10-24.9 Million
Emp.: 25
Roasted Coffee Mfr
N.A.I.C.S.: 311920

John Shahabian (Pres)
Alexandria Shahabian (Dir-Mktg)
Edwin Alagozian (Gen Mgr)

THE COLLECTION, INC.
200 Bird Rd, Coral Gables, FL 33146
Tel.: (305) 444-5555
Web Site:
  http://www.thecollection.com
Sales Range: $25-49.9 Million
Emp.: 180
Car Dealership Owner & Operator
N.A.I.C.S.: 441110
Ken Gorin (Pres)
Mike George (Mgr-Wholesale)
Alex Polo (Mgr-Audi Sls)
Giuseppe Todisco (Mgr-Audi Sls)
Lisa Chmela (Mgr-Audi Bus)
Michael Slyman (Mgr-Audi Svc)
Timothy Beno (CFO)

THE COLLECTIVE GROUP, LLC
9433 Bee Caves Rd Bldg III Ste 200, Austin, TX 78733-6135
Tel.: (512) 263-5500   DE
Web Site: http://www.colltech.com
Year Founded: 1994
Computer Related Services; IT Service Delivery, Backup & Recovery
N.A.I.C.S.: 541512
Jason Thomas (Pres)
Phil Hornsey (VP-Fin & Admin)

THE COLLEGE OF HEALTH CARE PROFESSIONS
6330 E Hwy 290 Ste 180, Austin, TX 78723
Tel.: (800) 487-6728
Web Site: https://www.chcp.edu
Medical Education Services
N.A.I.C.S.: 611710

Subsidiaries:

Medical Technology Management Institute, LLC   (1)
10361 Innovation Dr Ste 400, Milwaukee, WI 53226
Tel.: (800) 765-6864
Web Site: https://www.mtmi.net
Education Administration Programs
N.A.I.C.S.: 923110
Jay Mazurowski (Pres)
Jill Munce (Exec Dir-Mktg)
Steve Cushman (Sr Dir-Mktg)
Jim Flaherty (Dir-Bus Dev)

THE COLLIER COMPANIES, INC.
220 N Main St, Gainesville, FL 32601
Tel.: (352) 375-2152   FL
Web Site:
  http://www.colliercompanies.com
Year Founded: 1972
Sales Range: $100-124.9 Million
Emp.: 450
Apartment Building Operator & Manager
N.A.I.C.S.: 531110
Jennifer Clince (CEO)
Nathan Collier (Founder, Chm & Principal)
Dianna Miner (Pres-Asset Mgmt)
Eric Heninger (Dir-Fin)
Mark Wilkie (VP-Asset Mgmt)
Diana Brockington (VP-Ops)
Betsy Guynn (Dir-HR)

THE COLLINS COMPANIES, INC.
1618 SW 1st Ave Ste 500, Portland, OR 97201-5708
Tel.: (503) 227-1219   OR
Web Site: http://www.collinsco.com
Year Founded: 1996
Sales Range: $10-24.9 Million
Emp.: 546

Softwood Veneer Mfr
N.A.I.C.S.: 321912
Lee Jimerson (Mgr-Pacific Albus Product)
Laurie Moore (Coord-Hardwood Lumber Logistics)
Aly Kingsley (Mgr-Sls Ops)
Dean Johnson (Mgr-Sls-Softwood Lumber)
Larry Broadfoot (VP-Sls & Mktg)

THE COLONIAL ELECTRIC SUPPLY COMPANY
201 W Church Rd, King of Prussia, PA 19406-3231
Tel.: (610) 312-8100   PA
Web Site:
  http://www.colonialelectricsupply.com
Year Founded: 1972
Sales Range: $25-49.9 Million
Emp.: 500
Electrical Equipment Distr
N.A.I.C.S.: 423610
Steve Bellwoar (Pres)
Peter Bellwoar (Exec VP-Sls)
Sean Healy (VP-Supply Chain)
George Millison (VP-Logistics)

THE COLORADO EDUCATION INITIATIVE
1660 Lincoln St Ste 2000, Denver, CO 80264
Tel.: (303) 736-6477   CO
Web Site:
  http://www.coloradoedinitiative.org
Year Founded: 2007
Sales Range: $1-9.9 Million
Educational Support Services
N.A.I.C.S.: 611710
Rebecca Holmes (Pres & CEO)
Gail Bantugan (Office Mgr)
Paul Beck (Mgr-Initiatives & Next Generation Learning)
John Blumenfield (Coord-Next Generation Learning & Spacelab)
Rachel Bock (Accountant-Payroll & Benefit)
Jackie Brauhn (Coord-Res & Impact)
Jason Burke (Coord-Accelerator Project)
Leslie Burkholder (Dir-Special Projects)
Heather Chikoore (Dir-Policy)
Amy Dyett (Dir-Health & Wellness)
Finessa Ferrell (Dir-Health & Wellness)
Sarah Forbes (Mgr-Res & Impact)
Mike Gradoz (Sr Dir-Pro Learning)
Karen Herbert (Dir-Pro Learning)
Greg Hessee (Dir-Colorado Legacy Schools)
Tara Jahn (Sr Mgr-Spacelab)
Caroline Jackson (Dir-Acctg)
Christina Jean (Dir-Next Gen Learning)
Elizabeth Kuehl (Mgr-STEM)
Emily Love (Dir-Res & Impact)
Danielle Otsuka (Dir-Dev)
Samantha Olson (VP-Strategic Learning & Org Dev)
Susan Paulsen (Designer-Graphic & Design)
Lisa Powers (Coord-Colorado Legacy Schools)
Andrea Pulskamp (Sr Mgr-Initiatives, Health & Wellness)
Sandy Sales (CFO)
Lisa Smith (Sr Dir-HR & Talent Dev)
Amy Spicer (Dir-Pro Learning)
Leroy J. Williams (Vice Chm)
Monika Skok (Vice Chm)
Elaine Gantz Berman (Sec)
Scott Zirbel (Treas)

THE COLUMBIA GROUP, INC.

100 M St SE Ste 900, Washington, DC 20003
Tel.: (202) 546-1435   DC
Web Site:
  http://www.columbiagroup.com
Year Founded: 1967
Sales Range: $10-24.9 Million
Emp.: 100
Defence Contractors
N.A.I.C.S.: 541715
Martin Arase (Pres)
Rick Perkins (COO)
Jim Ferguson (Sr VP-Corp Dev & Strategy)
Harold Hanson (VP-Quality Assurance)
Ray King (Sr VP-Army Programs Div)
Bob May (VP-Health Svcs Div)
Kevin Meek (VP-Fin Mgmt & IT Svcs Div)

THE COLUMBUS DISTRIBUTING COMPANY INC.
4949 Fwy Dr E, Columbus, OH 43229-5401
Tel.: (614) 846-1000   OH
Web Site:
  http://www.columbusdistributing.com
Year Founded: 1935
Sales Range: $25-49.9 Million
Emp.: 250
Beer & Ale Distr
N.A.I.C.S.: 424810
Eric McFarland (Mgr-Key Acct Sls)
Paul Jenkins Jr. (Pres)

THE COLUMBUS EQUIPMENT COMPANY INC.
65 Kingston Ave, Columbus, OH 43207-2400
Tel.: (614) 443-6541   OH
Web Site:
  http://www.columbusequipment.com
Year Founded: 1951
Sales Range: $50-74.9 Million
Emp.: 200
Construction & Mining Machinery
N.A.I.C.S.: 423810
Ernie Potter (VP-Rental)
Josh Stivison (Pres)
Bob Weber (VP-Product Support)
Tim Albright (VP-Sls & Mktg)
Jeff Reichert (Mgr-Fin)
Jon St. Julian (Mgr-Used Equipment)
Jason Crain (Gen Mgr-Sls)
Ray Frase (Gen Mgr-Svc)
Mark Klatt (Gen Mgr-Parts)
Rick Ferri (Mgr-Parts-Cadiz)
Patty Davidson (Mgr-Parts-Dayton)
Al Shepherd (Mgr-Parts-Cincinnati)
Jason Deeds (Mgr-Parts-Columbus)
Neil Ehrhardt (Mgr-Parts-Toldeo)
Gene Wyer (Mgr-Svc-Columbus)
Joe Dragan (Mgr-Svc-Massillon)

THE COMMERCIAL GROUP LIFTING PRODUCTS
12801 Universal Dr, Taylor, MI 48180-2003
Tel.: (313) 931-6100   MI
Web Site: http://www.cglift.com
Year Founded: 1953
Sales Range: $25-49.9 Million
Emp.: 135
Industrial Supplies Mfr
N.A.I.C.S.: 423840
Garland Knight Sr. (Chm)
Garland Knight Jr. (Pres)

Subsidiaries:

Detroit Chain Products Inc.   (1)
8881 Central St, Detroit, MI 48204-2832
Tel.: (313) 931-1611
Web Site: http://www.commercial-group.com

4011

THE COMMERCIAL GROUP LIFTING PRODUCTS — U.S. PRIVATE

The Commercial Group Lifting Products—(Continued)
Sales Range: $10-24.9 Million
Emp.: 15
Mfr of Cordage & Twine
N.A.I.C.S.: 314994

The Commercial Group Lifting Products (1)
2427 E Judd Rd, Burton, MI 48529-2456 (100%)
Tel.: (810) 744-4540
Web Site: http://www.cglift.com
Sales Range: $10-24.9 Million
Emp.: 25
Providers of Industrial Services
N.A.I.C.S.: 423510

THE COMMON SOURCE
14500 N Freeway, Houston, TX 77090
Tel.: (281) 260-9220
Web Site:
 http://www.commonsource.com
Year Founded: 1997
Sales Range: $10-24.9 Million
Emp.: 15
Document Management & Litigation Support Services
N.A.I.C.S.: 541110
Angel Ruiz (Mgr-IT)
L. Ann Zdansky (Pres & CEO)
Shannon Reed (COO)

THE COMMUNICATIONS GROUP
400 W Capitol Ste 1391, Little Rock, AR 72201
Tel.: (501) 376-8722
Web Site: http://www.comgroup.com
Year Founded: 1987
Sales Range: $25-49.9 Million
Emp.: 20
Advertising Services
N.A.I.C.S.: 541810
Dana Rogers (VP & Sr Dir-Art)
Johnice L. Hopson (VP & Mgr-Acctg)
Claude Locke (Exec Dir-Creative)
Jennifer Pearson (Office Mgr)
Jason Brown (Dir-PR)
Casey Baker (Mktg Dir-Digital)
Lisa Van Hook (Principal & Dir-Client Svcs)

THE COMMUNIQUE GROUP, INC.
10559 E Democrat Rd, Parker, CO 80134
Tel.: (303) 220-5080
Year Founded: 1988
Rev.: $10,000,000
Emp.: 25
Advertising Agencies, High Technology, Real Estate
N.A.I.C.S.: 541810
Thomas V. Clark (Owner)
Micki G. Clark (CEO)

THE COMMUNITY BLOOD CENTER, INC.
4406 W Spencer St, Appleton, WI 54914
Tel.: (920) 738-3131 WI
Web Site:
 http://www.communityblood.org
Year Founded: 1955
Sales Range: $10-24.9 Million
Emp.: 180
Blood Collection & Distribution Services
N.A.I.C.S.: 621991
Lori Glynn (Dir-Fin)
Andrea Michaud (VP-Collections)
Matt McCarter (VP-Customer Rels & Lab Ops)
Rick Hart (Pres)

THE COMMUNITY FOUNDATION FOR GREATER NEW HAVEN
70 Audubon St, New Haven, CT 06510-9755
Tel.: (203) 777-2386 CT
Web Site: http://www.cfgnh.org
Year Founded: 1928
Assets: $570,985,410
Liabilities: $221,136,481
Net Worth: $349,848,929
Earnings: ($39,655,238)
Emp.: 45
Fiscal Year-end: 12/31/18
Community Foundation
N.A.I.C.S.: 813211
Angela G. Powers (Sr VP-Plng & Ops)
Jolyn Washington Walker (Officer-Admin)
Leigh Curtis Higgins (Sr Dir-Professional Dev-Exec Office)
Margo Bloom (VP-Dev)
Andrew Blossom (Dir-Digital Strategy)
Hector Echevarria (Sr Mgr-Facilities)
Khalilah L. Brown-Dean (Chm)
Flemming Norcott (Vice Chm)
William Ginsberg (Pres & CEO)
Dotty Weston-Murphy (Sr VP-Dev & Donor Svcs)
Sharon Cappetta (Dir-Dev)
Carmen Burgos (Officer-Dev)
Magaly Cajigas (Mgr-Dev)
Linda Estacion (Dir-Donor Svcs & Dev Ops)
Liana Garcia (Dir-Gift Plng)
Wendy Gamba (VP-Fin & Ops)
Jennifer Glover-Keller (Chief Compliance Officer & Dir-Investments)
Brandi L. Kryvonis (Mgr-Disbursements)
Marcie Monaco (Dir-Fin & Acctg)
Jose R. Ruiz (Officer-Endowment)
Vilandria Turner (Dir-Information Mgmt & Analysis)
Christina Ciociola (Sr VP-Grantmaking & Strategy)
Sarah Fabish (VP-Grantmaking & Scholarships)
Jackie Downing (Dir-Grantmaking & Nonprofit Effectiveness)
Denise Canning (Dir-Grant Ops)
Matthew Higbee (Mgr-Content & Engagement)
Stephanie Chung (Mgr-Nonprofit Rels)
Eliezer Lee Cruz (Dir-Community Outreach)
Monica Anderson-Snow (Project Mgr-Fin)
Nikhil Aziz (Dir-Land, Water & Climate Justice)
Leon Bailey Jr. (Sr VP-HR & Organizational Culture)

THE COMMUNITY FOUNDATION FOR NORTHEAST FLORIDA
245 Riverside Ave Ste 310, Jacksonville, FL 32202
Tel.: (904) 356-4483 FL
Web Site: http://www.jaxcf.org
Year Founded: 1988
Sales Range: $50-74.9 Million
Emp.: 16
Charity Services
N.A.I.C.S.: 813219
John Zell (VP-Dev)
Kathleen Shaw (VP-Programs)
Grace Sacerdote (CFO & Exec VP)
Joanne E. Cohen (VP-Philanthropic Svcs)
Deborah Pass-Durham (Chm)
Nina Waters (Pres)
Carol Nieves (Mgr-Grants & Database)

Amy Crane (Program Dir)
Emmanuel Fortune (Program Dir)
Susan Datz Edelman (VP-Strategic Comm)

THE COMMUNITY FOUNDATION OF FREDERICK COUNTY, MD, INC
312 E Church St, Frederick, MD 21701
Tel.: (301) 695-7660 MD
Web Site: http://www.cffredco.org
Year Founded: 1986
Sales Range: $25-49.9 Million
Emp.: 10
Community Action Services
N.A.I.C.S.: 624190
Gail Fitzgerald (CFO)
Joyce Summers (Dir-Mktg & Comm)
Joanne R. McCoy (Sec)
Dale T. Summers (Treas)

THE COMMUNITY FOUNDATION SERVING BOULDER COUNTY
1123 Spruce St, Boulder, CO 80302
Tel.: (303) 442-0436 CO
Web Site: http://www.commfound.org
Year Founded: 1991
Sales Range: $10-24.9 Million
Emp.: 15
Community Development Services
N.A.I.C.S.: 624190
Gretchen Minekime (VP-Comm)
Elvira Ramos (Dir-Programs)
Margaret Katz (Dir-Philanthropic Svcs)
Chris Barge (Dir-School Readiness)
Jennifer Kilpatrick (CFO)
James Graham (Treas)

THE COMMUNITY FOUNDATION SERVING RICHMOND & CENTRAL VIRGINIA
7501 Boulders View Dr 110, Richmond, VA 23225-4047
Tel.: (804) 330-7400 VA
Web Site: http://www.tcfrichmond.org
Year Founded: 1968
Sales Range: $1-9.9 Million
Emp.: 28
Community Foundation
N.A.I.C.S.: 813211
Thomas Sinnickson Gayner (Chm)
Amy Singleton (VP-Philanthropic Svcs)
Elaine Summerfield (VP-Programs)
Lisa Pratt OMara (VP-Philanthropic Svcs)
Molly Dean Bittner (Sr VP-Philanthropic Svcs)
Dee Ann Remo (Sec)
Robert C. Sledd (Treas)
Michelle Nelson (CFO)
Scott Blackwell (Chief Community Engagement Officer)
Kimberly Russell (Sr VP-Mktg & Comm)
Karen Hand (Sr VP-Ops)
Kathleen Radford Demro (VP-Capacity Building)
Annette Cousins (VP-Community Engagement)

THE COMMUNITY GROUP
190 Hampshire St 2nd Fl, Lawrence, MA 01840
Tel.: (978) 682-6628 MA
Web Site:
 http://www.thecommunitygroup.org
Year Founded: 1970
Sales Range: $75-99.9 Million
Emp.: 267
Education & Social Services
N.A.I.C.S.: 813410

Bruce Bean (Mgr-Data)
Matt Einson (Mgr-IT)
Meera Krishnan (Dir-Strategic Plng)

THE COMMUNITY HOSPICE, INC.
295 Vly View Blvd, Rensselaer, NY 12144
Tel.: (518) 285-8150 NY
Web Site:
 http://www.communityhospice.org
Year Founded: 1997
Sales Range: $10-24.9 Million
Hospice Care Services
N.A.I.C.S.: 621610
Steve Manny (Dir-Dev)
Paul Heasley (Chief Medical Officer)
James O'Connor (Chm)
James Lebrou (Sec)
Maureen Buckley (Treas)
David Parente (Vice Chm)

THE COMMUNITY PRESERVATION CORPORATION
28 E 28th St 9th Fl, New York, NY 10016-7943
Tel.: (212) 869-5300 NY
Web Site:
 http://www.communityp.com
Year Founded: 1974
Sales Range: $300-349.9 Million
Emp.: 150
Mortgage & Construction Loans
N.A.I.C.S.: 522292
Richard A. Kumro (Gen Counsel, Sec & Exec VP)
Sadie McKeown (COO & Exec VP)
Carolyn Au (Sr VP & Dir-Portfolio Svcs)
Rafael E. Cestero (Pres & CEO)
Wanda Chin (Chief Credit Officer & Sr VP)
Tom McGrath (Dir-Upstate Revitalization)
Elizabeth Propp (Sr VP-Investments & Acq)
Richard Conley (Sr VP & Dir-Originations)
Doug Olcott (Sr VP & Reg Dir-Hudson Valley)
Jeff Ely (Sr VP-Admin)
David Rothberg (CFO & Exec VP)
Michael Skrebutenas (Sr VP & Dir-The Capital Reg)
Arthur Phidd (CIO & VP)
Jaime Sharrock (VP-Strategic Initiatives & External Affairs)
Michael Staton (VP)
Michael Dewitt (Sr VP & Dir-Western New York)
Robert Riggs (Sr VP & Dir-New York City & Long Island)
Louis Tiberio (VP-Mid Atlantic)
Nicholas V. Petragnani Jr. (Sr VP & Dir-Central New York)

Subsidiaries:

CPC Resources Inc. (1)
28 E 28th St, New York, NY 10016 (100%)
Tel.: (212) 869-5300
Web Site: http://www.communityp.com
Sales Range: $50-74.9 Million
Mortgage Bankers & Correspondents
N.A.I.C.S.: 522310

THE COMPANY OF OTHERS
1800 W Loop S Ste 2100, Houston, TX 77027
Tel.: (713) 862-5100 TX
Web Site:
 http://www.thecompany.com
Year Founded: 1980
Sales Range: $200-249.9 Million
Emp.: 200
Advetising Agency
N.A.I.C.S.: 541810

COMPANIES
THE CONFERENCE BOARD, INC.

Kyle Allen *(Partner & Dir-Media)*
Jose Lozano *(CEO)*
Scott Brown *(Pres & Chief Creative Officer)*
Suzie Jennings *(Sr VP & Creative Dir)*

Subsidiaries:

Connect FKM (1)
6500 River Place Blvd Bldg 2 Ste 102, Austin, TX 78730-1116
Tel.: (512) 261-6816
Emp.: 15
Yellow Pages Advertising
N.A.I.C.S.: 541810

FKM (1)
4040 N Central Expy Ste 700, Dallas, TX 75204-3179
Tel.: (214) 824-7774
Emp.: 15
Full Service
N.A.I.C.S.: 541810

MITTONMedia (1)
12946 Dairy Ashford Ste 250, Sugar Land, TX 77478
Tel.: (281) 242-4473
Web Site: http://www.mittonmedia.com
N.A.I.C.S.: 541810

Stevens FKM Public Relations (1)
1800 W, Houston, TX 77027-2130
Tel.: (713) 867-3200
Communications, Event Marketing, Government/Political/Public Affairs, Planning & Consultation, Public Relations
N.A.I.C.S.: 541820

Targeting Group (1)
7155 Old Katy Rd Ste 100 N, Houston, TX 77024
Tel.: (713) 867-3242
Web Site: http://www.targetinggroup.com
Rev.: $200,000,000
Emp.: 35
Media Buying Agency
N.A.I.C.S.: 541830

THE COMPASS MANAGEMENT GROUP, LLC
4851 Tamiami Trl N Ste 400, Naples, FL 34103
Tel.: (239) 593-1233 FL
Web Site: http://www.mycompassgroup.com
Sales Range: $1-9.9 Million
Property Management
N.A.I.C.S.: 531390
Jeff Mitchell *(Pres & CEO)*

THE COMPLIANCE DOCTOR, LLC
2643 S Halm Ave, Los Angeles, CA 90034
Tel.: (424) 235-0114
Web Site: http://www.thecompliancedoctor.com
Year Founded: 2005
Sales Range: $1-9.9 Million
Emp.: 10
Consulting & Accreditation Services to Health Care Professionals
N.A.I.C.S.: 541618
Troy Lair *(Founder & Principal)*

THE COMPOUNDING SHOP INC.
4000 Park St N, Saint Petersburg, FL 33709-4034
Tel.: (727) 381-9799
Web Site: http://www.gotocompoundingshop.com
Sales Range: $10-24.9 Million
Emp.: 25
Pharmaceutical Compounding Services
N.A.I.C.S.: 456110
Mike Haulsee *(Office Mgr)*

THE COMPUTER COMPANY, INC.
15 Commerce Dr, Cromwell, CT 06416
Tel.: (860) 635-0500
Web Site: http://www.computercompany.net
Year Founded: 1959
Sales Range: $1-9.9 Million
Emp.: 22
Information Technology Solutions
N.A.I.C.S.: 519290

THE COMPUTER MERCHANT LTD.
95 Longwater Cir, Norwell, MA 02061-1616
Tel.: (781) 878-1070 MA
Web Site: http://www.tcml.com
Year Founded: 1979
Sales Range: $25-49.9 Million
Emp.: 972
Computer Related Services
N.A.I.C.S.: 541512
Kevin Carroll *(Acct Exec)*
William Allen *(Asst Controller)*

THE COMPUTER PLACE, INC.
50 Bureau Dr, Gaithersburg, MD 20878
Tel.: (301) 330-6016
Web Site: http://www.tcponline.com
Rev.: $4,200,000
Emp.: 5
Computer & Software Stores
N.A.I.C.S.: 449210
Dehwei Tu *(Pres)*

THE COMTRAN GROUP INC
5036 B U Bowman Dr, Buford, GA 30518
Tel.: (770) 904-4444
Web Site: http://www.comtrangroup.com
Year Founded: 2005
Sales Range: $10-24.9 Million
Emp.: 130
Electrical Contractor
N.A.I.C.S.: 238210
Bryan Epperson *(VP)*
Gregory L. Bostwick *(Owner)*

THE CONAIR GROUP, INC.
200 W Kensinger Dr, Cranberry Township, PA 16066
Tel.: (724) 584-5500 DE
Web Site: http://www.conairgroup.com
Year Founded: 1956
Sales Range: $150-199.9 Million
Emp.: 500
Mfr of Auxiliary Plastic Machinery & Equipment; Installer of Plastic Powder & Particles Handling Systems
N.A.I.C.S.: 333248
Raymond Kelly *(VP-Engrg)*
Brian Dowler *(VP-Alternative Svcs)*
Chris Weinrich *(Gen Mgr-Downstream Extrusion)*
Bill Hricsina *(Bus Mgr-Intl)*
Sam Rajkovich *(VP-Sls & Mktg)*
Larry Doyle *(Pres)*

Subsidiaries:

Conair Brazil (1)
Rua Santa Eudoxia, Sao Paulo, 94 02533 010, SP, Brazil
Tel.: (55) 1182241432
Web Site: http://www.conairnet.com
Sales Range: $10-24.9 Million
Emp.: 3
Mfr of Machinery for Plastics
N.A.I.C.S.: 333310
William Hricsina *(Gen Mgr)*

Conair East Asia (1)
10Th Fl 202 Ta Tung Rd, Sec 3 Hsi Chih, Taipei, ROC, Hsien, Taiwan (100%)
Tel.: (886) 286472088
Web Site: http://www.conairnet.com
Sales Range: $10-24.9 Million
Emp.: 12
Mfr of Machinery for Plastics
N.A.I.C.S.: 333310
Hiroyuki Nakanishi *(Gen Mgr)*

Conair Europe Ltd. (1)
350 Edinburgh, Slough, SL14TU, Berkshire, United Kingdom (100%)
Tel.: (44) 753215100
Web Site: http://www.conaireurope.co.uk
Sales Range: $10-24.9 Million
Emp.: 16
Mfr of Machinery for Plastics
N.A.I.C.S.: 333310

Conair Mexicana S.A. de C.V. (1)
Calle De Parque N 632, Urb Ind San Rafael, 67110, Guadalupe, Mexico (51%)
Tel.: (52) 8183271238
Web Site: http://www.conairnet.com
Sales Range: Less than $1 Million
Emp.: 17
Mfr of Machinery for Plastics
N.A.I.C.S.: 333310
William Hridsina *(Gen Mgr)*

Conair Pacific Equipment Pte. Ltd. (1)
65 Kaki Bukit Ave 1, Shun Li Industrial Park, Singapore, 417945, Singapore (100%)
Tel.: (65) 62720707
Web Site: http://www.conairnet.com
Sales Range: $10-24.9 Million
Emp.: 5
Mfr of Machinery for Plastics
N.A.I.C.S.: 333310
Joachim Lim *(Gen Mgr)*

Branch (Non-US):

Conair Pacific Equipment Pte. Ltd. - Philippines (2)
Unit 2C 45 Visayas Ave, Quezon City, Philippines
Tel.: (63) 24566808
Web Site: http://www.cornairnet.com
Mfr of Machinery for Plastics
N.A.I.C.S.: 333310

THE CONAM GROUP OF COMPANIES
3990 Ruffin Rd Ste 100, San Diego, CA 92123
Tel.: (858) 614-7200
Web Site: http://www.conam.com
Year Founded: 1975
Sales Range: $75-99.9 Million
Emp.: 50
Real Estate Management & Investing
N.A.I.C.S.: 531210
Daniel J. Epstein *(Founder & Chm)*
E. Scott Dupree *(Gen Counsel & Sr VP)*
Robert J. Svatos *(Co-Pres & COO)*
Rob Singh *(Co-Pres & Chief Investment Officer)*
George Lloyd *(Exec VP & Head-Acq)*
Julie Brawn-Whitesides *(Exec VP-Property Mgmt)*
LaDon Beck *(VP-Pacific Northwest)*
James R. Kent *(Sr VP)*
Noel Webb *(Sr VP-Investment Mgmt & IR)*

Subsidiaries:

ConAm Investment Group (1)
3990 Ruffin Rd, San Diego, CA 92123
Tel.: (858) 614-7200
Web Site: http://www.conam.com
Sales Range: $50-74.9 Million
Real Estate Investment
N.A.I.C.S.: 525990
Michael Mahoney *(VP-Dev)*

ConAm Management Corporation (1)
3990 Ruffin Rd, San Diego, CA 92123
Tel.: (858) 614-7200
Web Site: http://www.conam.com
Emp.: 1,600
Real Estate Management

N.A.I.C.S.: 531210
Holly Granger Buss *(VP & Natl Dir-Mktg & Education)*
Caleb McKinley *(Dir-Ops Review)*

Subsidiary (Domestic):

ConAm Management (2)
3333 E Camelback Rd Ste 252, Phoenix, AZ 85018-2390
Tel.: (602) 957-8410
Web Site: http://www.conam.com
Sales Range: $25-49.9 Million
Real Estate Agency & Management Services
N.A.I.C.S.: 531210
Allen Glidewell *(Reg VP)*

THE CONANT AUTO RETAIL GROUP
18500 Studebaker Rd, Cerritos, CA 90703
Tel.: (562) 345-9700
Web Site: http://www.thecargroup.com
Emp.: 900
Car Dealership
N.A.I.C.S.: 441110

Subsidiaries:

Cerritos Ford, Inc. (1)
18900 Studebaker Rd, Cerritos, CA 90703-5309
Tel.: (562) 991-6696
Web Site: http://www.normreevesford.com
Sales Range: $25-49.9 Million
Emp.: 170
New & Used Automobile Distr
N.A.I.C.S.: 441110
Mike Gilligan *(Gen Mgr)*
Ron Gissinger *(Dir-Parts)*

Norm Reeves Honda Superstore (1)
18500 Studebaker Rd, Cerritos, CA 90703
Tel.: (562) 402-3844
Web Site: http://www.normreeves.com
Rev.: $244,000,000
Emp.: 300
Automobiles, New & Used
N.A.I.C.S.: 441110

THE CONCESSION GOLF CLUB LLC
7700 Lindrick Ln, Bradenton, FL 34202
Tel.: (941) 322-1922
Web Site: http://www.theconcession.com
Sales Range: $1-9.9 Million
Emp.: 72
Golf Course & Country Club
N.A.I.C.S.: 713910
Lorraine DiOrio *(Controller)*
Zac Mendiola *(Dir-Food & Beverage)*
Alan Pope *(Dir-Membership)*
Bruce A. Cassidy Sr. *(Owner & Pres)*
Jeffrey Parsons *(Gen Mgr)*

THE CONCORDE GROUP, INC.
400 Park Ave, New York, NY 10022
Tel.: (917) 338-7710
Web Site: http://www.concorde-us.com
Sales Range: $25-49.9 Million
Emp.: 7
Investment Holding Company
N.A.I.C.S.: 551112
Craig A. Zabala *(Founder)*

THE CONFERENCE BOARD, INC.
845 Third Ave, New York, NY 10022
Tel.: (212) 759-0900
Web Site: http://www.conference-board.org
Emp.: 250
Consulting Services
N.A.I.C.S.: 541611
Ilene S. Gordon *(Vice Chm)*
Steve Odland *(CEO)*

THE CONFERENCE BOARD, INC.

U.S. PRIVATE

The Conference Board, Inc.—(Continued)

Harry M. Jansen Kraemer Jr. (Vice Chm)
Edward Barry Rust Jr. (Vice Chm)
Susan C. Schwab (Vice Chm)
George S. Barrett (Vice Chm)
Robert E. Moritz (Vice Chm)
Susan C. Schwab (Vice Chm)
Chiqui Cartagena (CMO)
Ivan Pollard (Head-Mktg & Comm Center)
Ronald A. Williams (Vice Chm)

Subsidiaries:

Committee For Economic
Development (1)
2000 L St Nw Lbby, Washington, DC 20036
Tel.: (202) 296-5860
Web Site: http://www.ced.org
Emp.: 20
Fiber Optic Cable Mfr
N.A.I.C.S.: 335921
Elliot Schwartz (VP & Dir-Economic Studies)
Michael Petro (Exec VP)
Joseph Minarik (Sr VP & Dir-Res)
Mindy Berry (VP-External Rels)
Cindy Cisneros (VP-Education Programs)
Joseph Diblasi (Assoc Dir-Corp Comm)
Steve Forrey (CFO)
Monica Herk (VP-Education Res)
Diane Lim (Principal)
Anthony Pigninelli (Mgr-Outreach)

THE CONGREGATIONAL HOME

1205 SW 29th St, Topeka, KS 66611
Tel.: (785) 267-1666 KS
Web Site:
http://www.brewsterplace.org
Year Founded: 1958
Sales Range: $10-24.9 Million
Emp.: 331
Lifecare Retirement Community Operator
N.A.I.C.S.: 623311
Larry Riggins (CFO & VP)
David Beck (Pres & CEO)

THE CONLAN COMPANY

1800 Pkwy Pl SE Ste 1010, Marietta, GA 30067-8200
Tel.: (770) 423-8000 GA
Web Site:
http://www.conlancompany.com
Year Founded: 1987
Sales Range: $50-74.9 Million
Emp.: 80
Non-Residential Building Construction Contractor
N.A.I.C.S.: 236220
Gary Condron (CEO)
Bill Hayne (CFO)

THE CONNECTION

11351 Rupp Dr, Burnsville, MN 55337
Tel.: (952) 948-5488
Web Site:
http://www.theconnection.com
Year Founded: 1981
Sales Range: $25-49.9 Million
Emp.: 1,600
Outsourced Contact Center Services including Sales Support, Customer Support & Technical Support
N.A.I.C.S.: 561499
Fredrick Weiner (Pres)
Ken Unruh (CTO & VP)
Paul Howe (VP-Bus Dev)
Karen Danielson (Dir-Mktg)
Michele Tupper (Dir-Trng)

THE CONNECTION, INC.

100 Roscommon Dr Ste 203, Middletown, CT 06457
Tel.: (860) 343-5500 CT
Web Site:
http://www.theconnectioninc.org
Year Founded: 1972
Sales Range: $25-49.9 Million
Emp.: 513
Community Action Services
N.A.I.C.S.: 624190
Lynn Spencer (VP-HR)
Alex Tarnoski (Dir-Behavioral Health)
Thomas Forschner (CFO)
Lisa DeMatteis-Lepore (CEO)

THE CONNELL COMPANY

200 Connell Dr, Berkeley Heights, NJ 07922-2732
Tel.: (908) 673-3700 NJ
Web Site: http://www.connellco.com
Year Founded: 1926
Sales Range: $1-4.9 Billion
Emp.: 245
Importer & Distr of Food Products; Food Processing; Heavy Equipment Leasing
N.A.I.C.S.: 424510
Grover Connell (Pres)

Subsidiaries:

Connell Finance Company, Inc. (1)
200 Connell Dr, Berkeley Heights, NJ 07922-2732
Tel.: (908) 673-3700
Sales Range: $10-24.9 Million
Emp.: 120
Provides Equipment, Project & Real Estate Financing
N.A.I.C.S.: 423810
Grover Connell (Pres)
Nina Psihoules (VP & Office Mgr)

Division (Domestic):

Connell Equipment Leasing (2)
200 Connell Dr, Berkeley Heights, NJ 07922-2732 (100%)
Tel.: (908) 673-3700
Web Site: http://www.connellco.com
Emp.: 150
Providing Financing & Leasing
N.A.I.C.S.: 424510
Grover Connell (Pres)
Nina Psihoules (VP)

Connell Mining Products, LLC. (1)
200 Connell Dr, Berkeley Heights, NJ 07922
Tel.: (908) 673-3700
Web Site: http://www.connellrealty.com
Sales Range: $1-9.9 Million
Emp.: 100
Metal Mining Services
N.A.I.C.S.: 213114
Larry Johnston (Sr VP)

Connell Realty & Development Co. (1)
200 Connell Dr, Berkeley Heights, NJ 07922-2732 (100%)
Tel.: (908) 673-3700
Web Site: http://www.connellco.com
Sales Range: $25-49.9 Million
Emp.: 150
Provides Realty, Land Development & Financing Services
N.A.I.C.S.: 424510
Grover Connell (Pres)

Connell Rice & Sugar Div. (1)
100 Sunrise Blvd Ste A, Colusa, CA 95932
Tel.: (530) 458-8554
Sales Range: $25-49.9 Million
Emp.: 125
Importer & Distributor of Rice & Sugar
N.A.I.C.S.: 423810

THE CONTEMPORARY ART MUSEUM

3809 W 35th St, Austin, TX 78703
Tel.: (512) 323-6380 TX
Web Site:
http://www.thecontemporaryaustin.org
Year Founded: 1961
Sales Range: $10-24.9 Million

Emp.: 77
Contemporary Art Promotion Services
N.A.I.C.S.: 711310
Milam Newby (Sec)
Mark Hanna (Treas)
Richard Marcus (Chm)
Jeanne Klein (Pres)

THE CONTI GROUP

2045 Lincoln Hwy, Edison, NJ 08817
Tel.: (732) 520-5000 NJ
Web Site: http://www.conticorp.com
Year Founded: 1906
Sales Range: $300-349.9 Million
Emp.: 830
Energy, Environment, Infrastructure & Industrial Services
N.A.I.C.S.: 237310
Kurt Conti (Pres & CEO)
Jay Price (VP-Bus Dev)
Patrick Hogan (COO-Civil Svcs)
William Picken (COO-Federal & Natl Accts)
Dominic Mustillo (CFO)
Robert Scerbo (VP-Estimating)
Anthony Blommel (Chief Admin Officer)
Cullin Wible (CIO & Chief Investment Officer)
Jeanine Wright (VP-Sls & Mktg)
Paul Force (VP-Pur & Contracts)
Matthew Skidmore (VP-Ops Solar)

THE CONTRIBUTIONSHIP COMPANIES

212 S 4th St, Philadelphia, PA 19106
Tel.: (215) 627-1752
Web Site:
http://www.contributionship.com
Year Founded: 1752
Sales Range: $100-124.9 Million
Emp.: 60
Fire, Marine & Casualty Insurance
N.A.I.C.S.: 524126
Shaun F. O'Malley (Chm)

THE CONVENIENT WHOLESALERS OF AMERICA, INC.

4750 NW 15th Ave Ste D, Fort Lauderdale, FL 33309-7211
Tel.: (954) 351-0080 FL
Web Site: http://www.cwasales.com
Year Founded: 1996
Consumer Merchandise Whslr
N.A.I.C.S.: 424490
Adam Hasan (Pres & CEO)

THE CONVERSE PROFESSIONAL GROUP, INC.

222 E Huntington Dr Ste 211, Monrovia, CA 91016-3500
Tel.: (626) 930-1200 CA
Web Site:
http://www.converseconsultants.com
Year Founded: 1946
Sales Range: $100-124.9 Million
Emp.: 244
Provider of Engineering Services
N.A.I.C.S.: 541330
Pamela J. Keith (VP-HR)
Hashme Quazi (Chm)
Beth George (Mgr-Mktg)
Ruben Romero (CFO & Controller)

THE CONVEX GROUP, INC.

1 Capital City Plz 3350 Peachtree Rd Ste 1500, Atlanta, GA 30326
Tel.: (404) 760-4729
Sales Range: $10-24.9 Million
Emp.: 160
Media & Entertainment Technology & Services
N.A.I.C.S.: 523910

THE COOKSON COMPANY

1901 South Litchfield Rd, Phoenix, AZ 85338
Tel.: (602) 272-4244
Web Site:
http://www.cooksondoor.com
Rev.: $19,300,000
Emp.: 150
Rolling Doors For Industrial Buildings or Warehouses, Metal
N.A.I.C.S.: 332321
Andrew Cornell (CEO)

THE COPPER CELLAR CORPORATION

3001 Industrial Pkwy E, Knoxville, TN 37921
Tel.: (865) 522-3500
Web Site:
http://www.coppercellar.com
Year Founded: 1975
Sales Range: $50-74.9 Million
Emp.: 1,000
American Restaurant
N.A.I.C.S.: 722511
Mike Chase (Pres)
Bill Smith (Mgr-Spectacular Bars)
Kimberly Sterchi (Dir-Catering & Wedding)
Nathan Wade (Mgr-Svc)
Snow Bobby (Mgr-Host)

Subsidiaries:

Cappuccino's (1)
7316 Kingston Pike, Knoxville, TN 37919
Tel.: (865) 673-3422
Web Site: http://www.cappuccinos-italian.com
Sales Range: $10-24.9 Million
Emp.: 50
Full-Service Restaurants
N.A.I.C.S.: 722511
Bart Farkas (CFO)

Cherokee Grill (1)
1002 Pkwy, Gatlinburg, TN 37916
Tel.: (865) 436-4287
Sales Range: $10-24.9 Million
Emp.: 60
Full-Service Restaurants
N.A.I.C.S.: 722511
Christy Sheffield (Gen Mgr)

Chesapeake's (1)
600 Union Ave, Knoxville, TN 37902
Tel.: (865) 673-3433
Web Site: http://www.chesapeakes.com
Full-Service Restaurants
N.A.I.C.S.: 722511
Ken Scoonver (Gen Mgr)

Smoky Mountain Brewery (1)
1004 Pkwy, Gatlinburg, TN 37738
Tel.: (865) 436-4200
Web Site: http://www.smoky-mtn-brewery.com
Sales Range: $10-24.9 Million
Emp.: 35
Full-Service Restaurants
N.A.I.C.S.: 722511
Tammy Perkins (Gen Mgr)

The Cumberland Grill (1)
1807 Cumberland Ave, Knoxville, TN 37916
Tel.: (865) 673-3411
Web Site: http://www.coppercellar.com
Sales Range: $10-24.9 Million
Emp.: 80
Full-Service Restaurants
N.A.I.C.S.: 722511

THE CORAL GABLES TRUST COMPANY

255 Alhambra Cir Ste 333, Coral Gables, FL 33134
Tel.: (786) 497-1212
Web Site: http://www.cgtrust.com
Sales Range: $75-99.9 Million
Emp.: 12
Wealth Management & Trust Services
N.A.I.C.S.: 523991
Linda M. Haskins (COO & Mng Dir)
John W. Harris (Mng Dir & Chief Wealth Officer)

Richard B. Conger *(Chief Trust Officer & Sr VP)*
Eileen Santana *(VP & Sr Mgr-Relationship)*
James W. Davidson *(Founder & Chm)*
Allan J. Pekor *(Vice Chm)*
Donald A. Kress *(Sr VP)*
Diana Batchelor *(VP)*
Isabela Sanchez *(Officer-Trust)*
Michelle Viteri *(Officer-Trust)*
Denise M. Nunez Casale *(VP)*
Dominique Alexander *(VP, Controller & Mgr-HR)*
Gerardo Rodriguez *(Officer-Investment & VP)*

THE CORDISH COMPANIES
601 E Pratt St Ste 600, Baltimore, MD 21202-3118
Tel.: (410) 752-5444
Web Site: http://www.cordish.com
Year Founded: 1988
Sales Range: $1-9.9 Million
Emp.: 25
Land Subdividing Services
N.A.I.C.S.: 237210
Blake Cordish *(Principal)*
David Cordish *(Chm & CEO)*
Jonathan A. Cordish *(Principal, VP & Dir-Fin)*
Charles Jacobs *(Principal, Gen Counsel & Sr VP)*
Melissa Frank *(VP-Fin)*
Taylor Gray *(VP-Dev)*
Luwanda W. Jenkins *(VP-Community Rels & Diversity)*
Jack Rose *(VP-Construction)*
Abraham Rosenthal *(VP-Dev & Design)*
Zed Smith *(COO)*
Kim Townsend *(Exec VP-Design, Dev & Ops)*
Ryan Bordner *(CFO-Real Estate Div)*
Cathy Beeding *(Gen Counsel/Exec VP-Cordish Gaming Grp)*
Suzanne Trout *(CMO/Exec VP-Cordish Gaming Grp)*
Rob Norton *(Pres-Cordish Gaming Grp)*

Subsidiaries:

Diamond Jacks Casino & Hotel (1)
711 Diamondjacks Blvd, Bossier City, LA 71111
Tel.: (318) 678-7777
Web Site: http://www.diamondjacks.com
Casino Hotels
N.A.I.C.S.: 721120
Candace Bennett *(Coord-Mktg)*

THE CORKY MCMILLIN COMPANIES
2750 Womble Rd Ste 200, San Diego, CA 92106
Tel.: (619) 477-4117 DE
Web Site: http://www.mcmillin.com
Year Founded: 1960
Real Estate Investments, Land Development & Home-Building Services
N.A.I.C.S.: 531190
Mark McMillin *(Pres & CEO)*
Mark Doyle *(Exec VP)*
Mark Tate *(Project Coordinator)*

THE CORNWELL QUALITY TOOLS CO., INC.
667 Seville Rd, Wadsworth, OH 44281-1077
Tel.: (330) 336-3506 OH
Web Site: http://www.cornwelltools.com
Year Founded: 1961
Sales Range: $25-49.9 Million
Emp.: 165
Mfr & Sales of Industrial Supplies
N.A.I.C.S.: 423840
Bob Studenic *(Pres)*

THE CORPORATE COMMISSION OF MILLE LACS BAND OJIBWE INDIANS
717 Grand Ave, Onamia, MN 56359
Tel.: (320) 532-7777
Web Site: http://millelacsband.com
Sales Range: $100-124.9 Million
Emp.: 4,000
Gambling Establishment
N.A.I.C.S.: 713290
Robert Johnson *(Gen Mgr)*

THE CORPORATE COMMUNICATIONS GROUP
14 Henderson Dr, West Caldwell, NJ 07006-6608
Tel.: (973) 808-0009 NJ
Web Site: http://www.home.corpcomm.com
Year Founded: 1964
Sales Range: $75-99.9 Million
Emp.: 150
Advertising Agencies
N.A.I.C.S.: 541860
Barbara Grasso *(Dir-Art)*

THE CORPORATE ENVIRONMENTS GROUP
605 E Broad St, Bethlehem, PA 18018
Tel.: (610) 974-7990
Web Site: http://www.ceg-pa.com
Sales Range: $10-24.9 Million
Emp.: 40
Mfr of Office Furniture
N.A.I.C.S.: 423210
Lori Nardon *(Controller)*
Patrick McMahon *(Chm & Pres)*

THE CORPORATE PROMOTIONS GROUP
30 W 61st St Ste 30A, New York, NY 10023
Tel.: (212) 692-0749
Web Site: http://www.cpgroup.net
Year Founded: 1984
Sales Range: $1-9.9 Million
Emp.: 6
Sales Promotion
N.A.I.C.S.: 541810
David Mihalik *(VP)*

THE CORY GROUP, INC.
151 East 22nd St E Wing, Lombard, IL 60148
Tel.: (630) 629-2229
Web Site: http://www.corygroup.com
Rev.: $18,000,000
Emp.: 10
Provider of Loss Control Services
N.A.I.C.S.: 524210
Andrew C. Cory *(Pres)*

THE COUNSELING SERVICE OF ADDISON COUNTY, INC.
89 Main St, Middlebury, VT 05753
Tel.: (802) 388-6751 VT
Web Site: http://www.csac-vt.org
Year Founded: 1959
Sales Range: $10-24.9 Million
Emp.: 412
Behavioral Healthcare Services
N.A.I.C.S.: 623220
Robert S. Thorn *(Exec Dir)*
Greg Mairs *(Dir-Ops-Community Associates, Adult Outpatient & Emergency Svcs)*
Alexander Smith *(Dir-Community Rehabilitation & Treatment Svcs)*
Bill Claessens *(CFO)*
Alexa Euler *(Dir-HR)*
Barbara Doyle-Wilch *(VP)*
Joanne Scott *(Treas)*
Kitty Oxholm *(Pres)*
Cheryl Huntley *(Dir-Youth & Family Svcs & Substance Abuse Svcs)*

THE COUNTRY CLUB
2825 Lander Rd, Pepper Pike, OH 44124
Tel.: (216) 831-9200 OH
Web Site: http://www.thecountryclub.com
Year Founded: 1940
Sales Range: Less than $1 Million
Emp.: 269
Golf Club
N.A.I.C.S.: 713910

THE COUNTRY CLUB OF WINTER HAVEN
4200 Country Club Rd S, Winter Haven, FL 33881
Tel.: (863) 324-6666 FL
Web Site: http://www.ccofwinterhaven.com
Year Founded: 1923
Sales Range: $1-9.9 Million
Emp.: 100
Golf Courses & Country Clubs
N.A.I.C.S.: 713910
Tom Kratovil *(Dir-Food & Beverage)*
Randy Houseman *(Gen Mgr)*
Donna Snow *(Dir-Membership)*
Josh Anderson *(Head-Golf Pro)*
Brandy Booth *(Mgr-Food & Beverage)*
John Haggar *(Dir-Tennis)*

THE COUNTY LINE ENTERPRISES, INC.
512 E Riverside Dr Ste 200, Austin, TX 78704
Tel.: (512) 327-1959
Web Site: http://www.countyline.com
Rev.: $21,500,000
Emp.: 500
Lessors Nonresidential Buildings
N.A.I.C.S.: 531120
Don Miller *(Pres)*
Edwin K. Norton III *(VP)*

THE COURT COMPANY
3059 Forest Hill Irene Rd, Germantown, TN 38138-3868
Tel.: (901) 682-2600 TN
Web Site: http://www.squashcourt.com
Year Founded: 1978
Sales Range: $75-99.9 Million
Emp.: 15
Builder of Racquetball Courts
N.A.I.C.S.: 238990
Mike Mattingly *(Pres)*

THE COURTNEY GROUP, INCORPORATED
610 Newport Ctr Dr Ste 330, Newport Beach, CA 92660
Tel.: (949) 706-3600 NY
Web Site: http://www.thecourtneygroup.com
Year Founded: 1999
Privater Equity Firm
N.A.I.C.S.: 523999
Tom Courtney *(Pres & Mng Dir)*

Subsidiaries:

Peninsulators, Inc. (1)
360 Piercy Rd, San Jose, CA 95138-1401
Tel.: (408) 229-8100
Web Site: http://www.peninsulators.com
Specialty Trade Contractors
N.A.I.C.S.: 238990
Ross Haisley *(Co-Founder & CEO)*
John Thomas *(Co-Founder & COO)*

THE COWLES CENTER
528 Hennepin Ave, Minneapolis, MN 55403
Tel.: (612) 206-3636 MN
Web Site: http://www.thecowlescenter.org
Year Founded: 2009
Sales Range: $1-9.9 Million
Emp.: 158
Dance & Performing Art Promotion Services
N.A.I.C.S.: 711310
Mary Ellen Childs *(Program Dir)*
Lynn A. Von Eschen *(Exec Dir)*
Randy Ingram-Lile *(Gen Mgr)*
Jessi Fett *(Dir-Education)*
L. Kelley Lindquist *(Pres)*
Will Law *(Treas)*
Colin Hamilton *(Sec)*
Elyse Chambers *(Mgr-Education)*
Robert Droddy *(Dir-Dev)*

THE CPI GROUP, INC.
112 5th St N, Columbus, MS 39703
Tel.: (662) 328-1042
Web Site: http://www.cpi-group.com
Year Founded: 1983
Sales Range: $25-49.9 Million
Emp.: 14
Staffing & Human Resource Management Services
N.A.I.C.S.: 561311
Mark Smith *(CEO)*

THE CRAIG BUSINESS GROUP
895 Winton Rd S, Rochester, NY 14618
Tel.: (585) 244-4940
Web Site: http://www.thecraiggroup.com
Year Founded: 2004
Sales Range: Less than $1 Million
Emp.: 5
Advertising Agencies, Direct Marketing, Interactive Agencies, Retail, Travel & Tourism, Yellow Pages Advertising
N.A.I.C.S.: 541810
Bob Craig *(CEO)*
Robert Craig *(Owner)*

THE CRAMER-KRASSELT CO.
225 N Michigan Ave, Chicago, IL 60601-7601
Tel.: (312) 616-9600 DE
Web Site: http://www.c-k.com
Year Founded: 1898
Rev.: $990,500,000
Emp.: 500
Advetising Agency
N.A.I.C.S.: 541810
Peter G. Krivkovich *(Chm & CEO)*
Karen L. Seamen *(Pres & COO)*
Alexa Bazanos *(Sr VP & Dir-HR)*

Subsidiaries:

The Cramer-Krasselt Co. - Milwaukee (1)
246 E Chicago St, Milwaukee, WI 53202
Tel.: (414) 227-3500
Web Site: http://www.c-k.com
Emp.: 100
Advetising Agency
N.A.I.C.S.: 541810
Betsy Brown *(Exec VP & Gen Mgr)*
Lisa Rios *(Sr VP & Dir-Brand Plng)*
Alexa Bazanos *(Sr VP & Dir-HR)*
Karen Seamen *(Pres & COO)*
Nancy Aresu *(Exec VP & Gen Mgr)*
Peter Krivkovich *(Chm & CEO)*
Wanda McDonald *(CFO & Exec VP)*

The Cramer-Krasselt Co. - New York (1)
902 Broadway Fl 5, New York, NY 10010-6026
Tel.: (212) 889-6450
Web Site: http://www.ck.com
Emp.: 25

THE CRAMER-KRASSELT CO.

The Cramer-Krasselt Co.—(Continued)
Advetising Agency
N.A.I.C.S.: 541810
Larry Hampel (Co-Exec Dir-Creative)

The Cramer-Krasselt Co. - Phoenix (1)
1850 N Central Ave Ste 1800, Phoenix, AZ 85004-4561
Tel.: (602) 417-0600
Web Site: http://www.c-k.com
Advetising Agency
N.A.I.C.S.: 541810
Lisa Noble (Sr VP & Dir-PR)
Ian Barry (Sr VP & Exec Dir-Creative)
Kristin Bloomquist (Exec VP & Gen Mgr)
Alexa Bazanos (Sr VP & Dir-HR)
Betsy Brown (Exec VP & Gen Mgr)
Janice Hamblin (Gen Counsel & Sr VP)
Jasmine Dadlani (Sr VP & Dir-Brand Plng)
Mary Gura (Sr VP & Dir-PR & Social)
Chris Jacobs (Sr VP & Exec Dir-Creative)
Peter Krivkovich (Chm & CEO)
Wanda McDonald (CFO & Exec VP)
John Mose (Sr VP & Dir-PR)
Karen Seamen (Pres & COO)

THE CRANDALL-HICKS COMPANY, INC.
233 Tpke Rd, Westborough, MA 01581-2845
Tel.: (508) 898-3500   MA
Web Site: http://www.crandall-hicks.com
Year Founded: 1985
Sales Range: $10-24.9 Million
Emp.: 50
Supplier of Farm & Garden Machinery
N.A.I.C.S.: 444230
Peter Panagian (Controller-AP, AR & Payroll)
Chris Leysath (Mgr-Central & Western New York District)
Ray Fredericksen (Mgr-Connecticut & Long Island East Lower Hudson Valley)
Kevin Stafford (Mgr-Eastern MA, SE New Hampshire & Rhode Island)
Charlie Jillson (Mgr-Maine, North Eastern & New Hampshire District)
Lee Ann Bartolini (Mgr-Ops)
Joe Ronca (District Mgr)
Shaun Pangman (Mgr-Eastern New York & Northern New Jersey)
Gabe Baker (Mgr-Maine)
Jon Gamelin (Mgr-Sls)

Subsidiaries:

Boston Lawnmower Company (1)
233 Turnpike Rd, Westborough, MA 01581-2050
Tel.: (508) 898-3500
Web Site: http://www.bostonlawnmower.com
Garden Equipment
N.A.I.C.S.: 423820
David Kennedy (Gen Mgr)

THE CRAWFORD GROUP INC.
3190 S Bascom Ave Ste 230, San Jose, CA 95124
Tel.: (408) 343-0200
Web Site: http://www.crawfordgroup.com
Sales Range: $50-74.9 Million
Emp.: 18
Management Consulting Services
N.A.I.C.S.: 541611
Edward F. Crawford (Chm & CEO)
Judy Crawford (Founder & Chief Strategy Officer)
Laurie Stein (Pres)
Robert White (Co-CEO)

Subsidiaries:

Federal Hose Manufacturing Inc. (1)
25 Florence Ave, Painesville, OH 44077-1103   (100%)
Tel.: (440) 352-8927
Web Site: http://www.federalhose.com
Sales Range: $10-24.9 Million
Mfr of Flexible Metal Hose & Distributor of Silicone Hose
N.A.I.C.S.: 332999
John Lally (Controller)
Dave Lally (VP-Sls)
Jon Stencil (Mgr-Plant & Quality)

THE CRAWFORD GROUP, L.L.C.
999 Vanderbuilt Beach Rd Ste 610, Naples, FL 34110-1444
Tel.: (239) 593-6160   MI
Web Site: http://www.crawfordgrp.com
Sales Range: $10-24.9 Million
Emp.: 10
Holding Company
N.A.I.C.S.: 531210
Richard Crawford (Chm & CEO)
Ira Jaffe (Pres)

THE CREATIVE DEPARTMENT
1132 Main St, Cincinnati, OH 45202
Tel.: (513) 651-2901
Web Site: http://www.creativedepartment.com
Year Founded: 1992
Sales Range: $1-9.9 Million
Emp.: 25
Advetising Agency
N.A.I.C.S.: 541810
Lauren Anderson (Partner & Dir-Creative)

THE CREATIVE UNDERGROUND
33 E Camino Real Apt 603, Boca Raton, FL 33432-6154
Tel.: (561) 862-6004
Web Site: http://www.thecreativeunderground.com
Year Founded: 2005
Sales Range: Less than $1 Million
Emp.: 5
N.A.I.C.S.: 541810
Dan Gershenson (Chief Strategic Officer)
Tom Olivieri (Dir-Creative & Mng Partner)

THE CREDIT BUREAU OF BATON ROUGE, INC.
9489 Interline Ave, Baton Rouge, LA 70809
Tel.: (225) 926-6161
Year Founded: 1923
Sales Range: $10-24.9 Million
Emp.: 63
Consumer Credit Reporting Bureau
N.A.I.C.S.: 561450

THE CRETEX COMPANIES, INC.
311 Lowell Ave, Elk River, MN 55330-2508
Tel.: (763) 441-2121   MN
Web Site: http://www.cretexinc.com
Year Founded: 1917
Sales Range: $350-399.9 Million
Emp.: 1,000
Concrete Products Mfr & Retailer
N.A.I.C.S.: 327390
Dennis Wold (Controller)
Jeffrey S. Wollerman (COO & VP)
Steven J. Ragaller (CFO & VP)

Subsidiaries:

Cretex Concrete Products Midwest, Inc. (1)
6655 Wedgwood Rd Ste 130, Maple Grove, MN 55311
Tel.: (515) 223-8761
Web Site: http://www.cretexmidwest.com
Sales Range: $10-24.9 Million
Emp.: 50
Concrete Products Mfr
N.A.I.C.S.: 327332

Cretex Concrete Products North, Inc. (1)
6550 Wedgwood Rd, Maple Grove, MN 55311   (100%)
Tel.: (763) 545-7473
Web Site: http://www.cretexnorth.com
Sales Range: $10-24.9 Million
Emp.: 35
Concrete Products Mfr
N.A.I.C.S.: 327390

Plant (Domestic):

Cretex Concrete Products North, Inc. (2)
1340 6th St, Elk River, MN 55330-2436   (100%)
Tel.: (763) 441-2123
Web Site: http://www.ercp.com
Mfr And Distribution Of Concrete Products
N.A.I.C.S.: 327390

Elk River Machine Co. (1)
828 4th St, Elk River, MN 55330-1394
Tel.: (763) 441-1581
Web Site: http://www.ermc.com
Industrial Equipment & Machinery Mfr
N.A.I.C.S.: 332999

JunoPacific, Inc. (1)
1040 Lund Blvd, Anoka, MN 55303
Tel.: (763) 703-5000
Web Site: http://www.junopacific.com
Custom Molded Injection & Compression Plastic Components Mfr
N.A.I.C.S.: 326199
Nick Morrison (Dir-Site)

Pacific Plastics & Engineering Inc. (1)
2840 Research Park Dr, Soquel, CA 95073
Tel.: (831) 462-1141
Web Site: http://www.pacificplastics.com
Sales Range: $10-24.9 Million
Emp.: 26
Mfr of Molded Plastics & Injection Molds
N.A.I.C.S.: 333248
Yolanda O'Grady (Dir-Regulatory Affairs & Quality)

Spectralytics, Inc. (1)
145 S 3rd St, Dassel, MN 55325
Tel.: (320) 275-2118
Web Site: http://www.spectralytics.com
Sales Range: $1-9.9 Million
Emp.: 30
Machine Shops
N.A.I.C.S.: 332710
Gary Oberg (Founder & CEO)

THE CRIMINAL JUSTICE INSTITUTE, INC.
1110 Opal Ct Ste 5, Hagerstown, MD 21740-5942
Tel.: (301) 393-4500   MD
Web Site: http://www.cji-inc.com
Year Founded: 1978
Sales Range: $1-9.9 Million
Emp.: 8
Legal Aid Services
N.A.I.C.S.: 541199
Camille G. Camp (Co-Pres)
George M. Camp (Co-Pres)

THE CRISPIN COMPANY
Steel House 2009 Lubbock St, Houston, TX 77007-7621
Tel.: (713) 224-8000   TX
Web Site: http://www.crispinco.com
Year Founded: 1949
Sales Range: $75-99.9 Million
Emp.: 10
Whslr of Iron & Steel Products; International Trader & Marketer of Steel Products & Other Metals
N.A.I.C.S.: 423510
Jacques Bouchez (Pres & COO)
Patrick Gregoire (Sr Exec VP)

THE CROM CORPORATION
250 SW 36th Ter, Gainesville, FL 32607-2863
Tel.: (352) 372-3436   FL
Web Site: http://www.cromcorp.com
Year Founded: 1953
Sales Range: $50-74.9 Million
Emp.: 500
Specialty Construction; Pre-stressed Concrete Tanks
N.A.I.C.S.: 237990
Christopher T. Mincey (VP)
Talmadge B. Mincey (Co-Pres)
Robert G. Oyenarte (Co-Pres)
Jeffrey A. Pomeroy (CFO)

Subsidiaries:

CECS Inc. (1)
2000 Park St Ste 201, Columbia, SC 29201
Tel.: (803) 779-0311
Web Site: http://www.cecsinc.com
Construction Engineering Services
N.A.I.C.S.: 541330

Crom Equipment Rentals Inc. (1)
6801 SW Archer Rd, Gainesville, FL 32608-4720
Tel.: (352) 378-6966
Web Site: http://www.cromequipment.com
Sales Range: $10-24.9 Million
Emp.: 30
Provider of Equipment Rental & Leasing Services
N.A.I.C.S.: 532490

THE CROSLAND GROUP INC.
227 W Trade St Ste 800, Charlotte, NC 28202-1675
Tel.: (704) 529-1166   NC
Web Site: http://www.crosland.com
Year Founded: 1937
Sales Range: $50-74.9 Million
Emp.: 350
Real Estate Sales & Management
N.A.I.C.S.: 531210
Stephanie Repak (VP-Fin)
Katie Hardman (VP & Dir-Taxation)
Myra Zweier (VP-Acctg & Fin Reporting)
Adam J. Ford (Pres, CFO & Gen Mgr)

Subsidiaries:

Crosland Retail (1)
227 W Trade St Ste 800, Charlotte, NC 28202
Tel.: (704) 523-0272
Web Site: http://www.crosland.com
Sales Range: $10-24.9 Million
Emp.: 50
Real Estate Sales & Management
N.A.I.C.S.: 531210
David Arnold (Mgr-Forecasting & Analysis)
Katie Hardman (VP & Dir-Taxation)
Myra Zweier (VP-Acctg & Fin Reporting)

THE CROSS AGENCY
701 San Marco Blvd Ste 1603, Jacksonville, FL 32207
Tel.: (904) 642-8902
Web Site: http://thecrossagency.com
Marketing & Advertising Agency
N.A.I.C.S.: 541810
Todd Taylor (Pres)
Jon Nicolosi (Exec VP & Exec Creative Dir)
Natalie Wollet (VP-Media)
Colin Williams (Dir-Digital Media)

THE CROSS COUNTRY GROUP, LLC
1 Cabot Rd, Medford, MA 02155
Tel.: (781) 396-3700
Web Site: http://www.ccgroup.com
Year Founded: 1972
Sales Range: $700-749.9 Million
Emp.: 1,500
Holding Company; Personal Assistance Services
N.A.I.C.S.: 551112

Sidney Wolk (Founder)
Linda Soucy (Mgr-Tax & Treasury)
Howard L. Wolk (Co-Pres)
Jeffrey C. Wolk (Co-Pres)
Peggy Glander Ward (CFO)

Subsidiaries:

Agero, Inc. (1)
1 Cabot Rd, Medford, MA 02155
Tel.: (781) 393-9300
Web Site: http://www.agero.com
Sales Range: $25-49.9 Million
Emp.: 500
Vehicle Roadside Assistance Services
N.A.I.C.S.: 812990
Sidney Wolk (Founder)
Dave Ferrick (Pres & CEO)
Peter Necheles (Chief Legal Officer, Sr VP-Corp Dev & Sec)
Craig Schmeizer (Sr VP-Mktg)
Jeffrey Blecher (Sr VP-Strategy)
Bryan Sander (Sr VP-Ops)
Cathy Orrico (Sr VP-Sls & Acct Mgmt)
George Horvat (COO)
Bill Gerraughty (CFO)

Cross Country Home Services (1)
1625 NW 136th Ave Ste 200, Fort Lauderdale, FL 33323-2842
Tel.: (954) 845-9100
Web Site: http://www.cchs.com
Rev.: $58,928,000
Emp.: 400
Home Warranty & Homeowner Assistance Services
N.A.I.C.S.: 812990
Shausta Merrill (VP)
Sandy Sinn (Pres)
Joel Steigelfest (CIO)
Steven Upshaw (CEO)
Douglas Stein (Exec VP)
David Tripp (VP-HR)
Chris Askew (COO)
Chris White (Sr VP-Mktg)
Patrick Young (Sr VP-Bus Dev & Acct Mgmt)

Financial Recovery Technologies LLC (1)
200 Rivers Edge Dr Ste 300, Medford, MA 02155
Tel.: (339) 674-1000
Web Site: http://www.frtservices.com
Investment Management Service
N.A.I.C.S.: 523940
Rob Adler (Pres)
Jeffrey B. Kirstein (COO)
Howard L. Wolk (Chm)
Mark O'Brien (Sr VP-Sls & Mktg)
Kathy Mumma (VP-HR)
Michael Cotter (Chief Revenue Officer)
Brian Moran (Sr VP-Fin & Compliance)
Charlie Pendleton (Sr VP-Product Mktg)
Alan Cooke (CFO)

THE CROWLEY GROUP INC.
2000 Webber St, Sarasota, FL 34239-5236
Tel.: (941) 954-5454   FL
Web Site: https://www.alliancegroupfl.com
Year Founded: 1989
Sales Range: $25-49.9 Million
Emp.: 7,300
Offices of Real Estate Agents & Brokers
N.A.I.C.S.: 531210
Peter Crowley (Pres)

THE CROWNE PLAZA TIMES SQUARE MANHATTAN
1605 Broadway, New York, NY 10019-7406
Tel.: (212) 977-4000
Web Site: http://www.cpmanhattantimessquare.com
Year Founded: 1987
Sales Range: $25-49.9 Million
Emp.: 500
Provider of Hotel & Motel Services
N.A.I.C.S.: 721110

Fanny de la Rosa (Asst Mgr-Credit)
Gregory Colon (Dir-Banquets)

THE CSI GROUP, INC.
11 Fairview Terr, Paramus, NJ 07652
Tel.: (201) 587-1400   NJ
Web Site: http://www.thecsigroup.com
Year Founded: 1988
Rev.: $12,000,000
Emp.: 25
Advetising Agency
N.A.I.C.S.: 541810
Kurt Von Seekamm (Founder & Chm)
Jim Wurster (Exec VP)
Alan Tardieu (Dir-Art)
Chris Connolly (Editor)
Christine DiSebastian (Coord-Video & Motion Design)
Erin English (Designer-Graphic)
Frankie Pergola (Dir-Client Dev)
Kathy Marrazzo (Dir-Acct Svcs)
Kat McBride (Dir-Art)
Rich Cannava (Pres & Partner)

THE CUMMINGS GROUP
1105 NW 44th St, Oklahoma City, OK 73118
Tel.: (405) 524-9441   OK
Web Site: http://www.cummingsgrp.com
Year Founded: 1960
Sales Range: Less than $1 Million
Emp.: 2
N.A.I.C.S.: 541810
Ross W. Cummings (Owner)

THE CURTIS PUBLISHING COMPANY
1100 Waterway Blvd, Indianapolis, IN 46202-2155
Tel.: (317) 634-1100   PA
Web Site: http://www.curtispublishing.com
Publisher & Licensor of Illustrations
N.A.I.C.S.: 711510

THE CUSTOM COMPANY, INC.
3165 N Nimitz Hwy, Honolulu, HI 96819
Tel.: (808) 845-8511
Web Site: http://www.thecustomcompanyhawaii.com
Year Founded: 1993
Sales Range: $1-9.9 Million
Emp.: 22
Personalized Apparel Mfr
N.A.I.C.S.: 314999
Milton Ebesu (Owner)
Cookie Segi (Mgr-Sls)

THE CUTLER CORPORATION
4640 SW Macadam Ave, Portland, OR 97201
Tel.: (503) 223-9700
Year Founded: 1980
Sales Range: $25-49.9 Million
Emp.: 300
Mfr of Adhesives & Sealants
N.A.I.C.S.: 325520

Subsidiaries:

Rol-Away Truck Manufacturing Co. Inc. (1)
6143 SE Foster Rd, Portland, OR 97206-3738
Tel.: (503) 777-3388
Web Site: http://www.rol-away.com
Sales Range: $10-24.9 Million
Emp.: 25
Mfr Of Material Handling Equipment
N.A.I.C.S.: 337127

THE CYBRIX GROUP, INC.
4508 Oak Fair Blvd Ste 240, Tampa, FL 33610

Tel.: (813) 630-2744
Web Site: http://www.cybrixgroup.com
Year Founded: 2002
Sales Range: $10-24.9 Million
Emp.: 30
Computer System Design Services
N.A.I.C.S.: 541512
Keith Vassalotti (CFO & COO)
Timothy H. Jones (Pres & CEO)
Skip Durbin (VP-Govt Projects & Contract Admin)

THE CYNTHIA WOODS MITCHELL PAVILION
2005 Lake Robbins Dr, The Woodlands, TX 77380
Tel.: (281) 363-3300   TX
Web Site: http://www.woodlandscenter.org
Year Founded: 1989
Sales Range: $25-49.9 Million
Emp.: 548
Performing Art Promotion Services
N.A.I.C.S.: 711310
J. D. Villasenor (Dir-Premium Seat Sls)
Carol P. Garner (Chm)
Jeff Young (VP)
Jerry MacDonald (Pres & CEO)
Jonathan Homeyer (Vice Chm)
Steven W. Nance (Sec)
Cameron Klepac (Dir-Mktg & Education-Entertainment Venue)
Craig Bourgeois (CFO)

THE CYPRESS GROUP LLC
437 Madison Ave 33rd Fl, New York, NY 10022-3219
Tel.: (212) 705-0150   DE
Web Site: http://www.cypressgp.com
Year Founded: 1994
Rev.: $22,000,000,000
Emp.: 4
Privater Equity Firm
N.A.I.C.S.: 523999
Lynn Horn (Chief Acctg & Admin Officer)
James A. Stern (Co-Founder, Chm & CEO)
John Nicholson (Co-Founder)

Subsidiaries:

Pellegrino Distribuidora Autopecas Ltda. (1)
Rua Imperatriz Leopoldina 86, Sao Paulo, 05405-000, SP, Brazil
Tel.: (55) 1138 742 204
Web Site: http://www.pellegrino.com.br
Sales Range: $50-74.9 Million
Automobile Parts Mfr
N.A.I.C.S.: 336390

Republic National Cabinet Corporation (1)
1400 Warren Dr, Marshall, TX 75672
Tel.: (903) 935-3680
Kitchen & Bathroom Cabinet Mfr
N.A.I.C.S.: 337110
Jeff Kroyer (Dir-Ops)

THE D.A. COLLINS CONSTRUCTION CO., INC.
269 Ballard Rd, Wilton, NY 12831
Tel.: (518) 664-9855
Web Site: http://www.dacollins.com
Year Founded: 1948
Sales Range: $10-24.9 Million
Emp.: 125
Provider of Construction Services
N.A.I.C.S.: 237310
John Sheeran (CFO)

Subsidiaries:

Jointa Galusha LLC (1)
269 Ballard Rd, Gansevoort, NY 12831-1357
Tel.: (518) 792-5029

Sales Range: $10-24.9 Million
Emp.: 25
Provider of Construction Services
N.A.I.C.S.: 423320

Kubricky Construction Corp. (1)
238 Bay Rd Queensberry, Glens Falls, NY 12804-2006   (100%)
Tel.: (518) 792-5864
Web Site: http://www.dacollins.com
Provider of Construction Services
N.A.I.C.S.: 237310
Robert Hughes (Pres)

Pallette Stone Corporation (1)
373 Washington St, Saratoga Springs, NY 12866-5909
Tel.: (518) 584-2421
Web Site: http://www.dacollins.com
Sales Range: $10-24.9 Million
Emp.: 120
Construction Materials Mfr
N.A.I.C.S.: 327991
Dan Collins (VP-Sls)

THE DAILY ITEM
110 Munroe St, Lynn, MA 01903
Tel.: (781) 593-7700
Web Site: http://www.itemlive.com
Year Founded: 1877
News Media Publisher
N.A.I.C.S.: 513110

THE DALLAS COUNTY LOCAL WORKFORCE DEVELOPMENT BOARD, INC.
Ross Twr 500 N Akard St Ste 3030, Dallas, TX 75201
Tel.: (214) 290-1000   TX
Web Site: http://www.wfsdallas.com
Year Founded: 1983
Sales Range: $75-99.9 Million
Emp.: 28
Workforce Development Services
N.A.I.C.S.: 611430
Laurie Bouillion Larrea (Pres)
Rebecca Monnette (Mgr-Quality Systems)
Richard Perez (Mgr-Resource Dev & Deployment)
J. Michael Purcell (CFO)
Demetria Robinson (VP)

THE DALLAS FOUNDATION
3963 Maple Ave Ste 390, Dallas, TX 75219
Tel.: (214) 741-9898   TX
Web Site: http://www.dallasfoundation.org
Year Founded: 1929
Sales Range: $50-74.9 Million
Emp.: 16
Grantmaking Services
N.A.I.C.S.: 813211
Mary M. Jalonick (Pres & CEO)
Lesley H. Martinelli (Sr Dir-Donor Svcs)
Gary W. Garcia (Sr Dir-Dev)
Dawn Townsend (Dir-Mktg & Comm)
Torrey Littleton (Controller)
Timothy J. Nealon (CFO)
Helen Holman (Chief Philanthropy Officer)

THE DALLAS GROUP OF AMERICA, INC.
374 Rte 22, Whitehouse, NJ 08888
Tel.: (908) 534-7800   NJ
Web Site: http://www.dallasgrp.com
Year Founded: 1989
Sales Range: $10-24.9 Million
Emp.: 25
Industrial Inorganic Chemicals Services
N.A.I.C.S.: 325180
David D. Dallas (CEO)
Jay Munson (Mgr-Mktg)
Robert H. Dallas II (Pres)

THE DALTON AGENCY, INC.

The Dallas Group of America, Inc.—(Continued)

THE DALTON AGENCY, INC.
140 W Monroe St Ste 200, Jacksonville, FL 32202
Tel.: (904) 398-5222 FL
Web Site:
http://www.daltonagency.com
Year Founded: 1989
Sales Range: $10-24.9 Million
Emp.: 88
Advetising Agency
N.A.I.C.S.: 541810
Jim Dalton *(Pres & CEO)*
Patrick McKinney *(Chief Creative Officer)*
Dave Josserand *(Chief Strategic Officer & Exec VP)*
Michael Munz *(Pres-PR)*
Kevyn Faulkenberry *(VP & Exec Dir-Creative)*
Jo Ann Stephens *(VP & Bus Mgr)*
Heather Smith *(Mgr-Community-Social Media)*
Bill Coontz *(Pres-Atlanta)*
Brendan Cumiskey *(VP-Strategy & Plng)*
Brian Kinkade *(VP-Acct Svc)*
Devon Suter *(VP & Dir-Creative)*
Ellen Repasky *(VP & Acct Dir)*
Samantha Lueder *(VP & Dir-PR)*
Kristen Curtiss *(Mgr-Social Media)*
Kassi Belz *(VP-PR)*

Subsidiaries:

Dalton+Anode (1)
105 Broadway Fl 2, Nashville, TN 37201 **(100%)**
Tel.: (615) 742-1490
Web Site: http://www.anode.com
Visual Information Design & Interactive Media
N.A.I.C.S.: 541511
Chant Soundara *(Dir-Art)*
Erik Edmondson *(Dir-Animation)*
Mark N. Magnuson *(Pres)*

THE DANELLA COMPANIES INC.
2290 Butler Pike, Plymouth Meeting, PA 19462-1436
Tel.: (610) 828-6200 PA
Web Site: http://www.danella.com
Year Founded: 1972
Sales Range: $100-124.9 Million
Emp.: 1,400
Water, Sewer & Utility Line Services
N.A.I.C.S.: 237130
James D. Danella *(Chm & CEO)*
Dennis Daly *(Pres & CFO)*

Subsidiaries:

Danella Associates (1)
2450 Eastgate Pl Ste E, Snellville, GA 30078
Tel.: (770) 972-0050
Construction Engineering Services
N.A.I.C.S.: 541330

Danella Atlantic Corporation (1)
3351 Fort Meade Rd, Laurel, MD 20724
Tel.: (301) 483-0324
Construction Engineering Services
N.A.I.C.S.: 541330
Mike Straney *(Mgr-Div)*

Danella Construction Corp. of New York (1)
80 Business Park Dr Ste 200, Armonk, NY 10504
Tel.: (914) 273-7979
Web Site: http://www.danella.com
Sales Range: $100-124.9 Million
Water Sewer & Utility Line Services
N.A.I.C.S.: 237110

Danella Construction Corporation of Florida Inc. (1)
581 Washburn Rd, Melbourne, FL 32934-7316
Tel.: (321) 259-6124

Web Site: http://www.danella.com
Sales Range: $10-24.9 Million
Emp.: 55
Provider of Water, Sewer & Utility Line Services
N.A.I.C.S.: 237130
Tom Schinske *(VP)*

Danella Construction Corporation of New Jersey, Inc. (1)
2290 Butler Pike, Plymouth Meeting, PA 19462
Tel.: (610) 828-6200
Construction Engineering Services
N.A.I.C.S.: 541330
Bob Brust *(Mgr-Div)*

Danella Engineering and Construction Corporation (1)
2290 Butler Pike, Plymouth Meeting, PA 19462
Tel.: (610) 397-0919
Construction Engineering Services
N.A.I.C.S.: 541330

Danella Rental Systems Inc. (1)
2290 Butler Pike, Plymouth Meeting, PA 19462-1436 **(100%)**
Tel.: (610) 828-6200
Web Site: http://www.danella.com
Sales Range: $25-49.9 Million
Emp.: 100
Provider of Heavy Construction Equipment Rental Services
N.A.I.C.S.: 532412

Danella Rental Systems, Inc. (1)
14101 E Moncrieff Pl, Aurora, CO 80011-1621 **(100%)**
Tel.: (303) 371-7799
Web Site: http://www.danella.com
Sales Range: $10-24.9 Million
Emp.: 25
Water, Sewer & Utility Line Services
N.A.I.C.S.: 237110
Tim Schilling *(Mgr-Div)*

Danella Utility Construction, Inc. (1)
170 Commerce Rd Unit Ste 5, Boynton Beach, FL 33426
Tel.: (561) 327-5320
Construction Engineering Services
N.A.I.C.S.: 541330
Fredie Brady *(Mgr-Div)*

J. Daniel & Company, Inc. (1)
1975 Phoenix Dr, Loveland, OH 45140
Tel.: (513) 575-3100
Web Site: http://www.jdanielco.com
Construction Engineering Services
N.A.I.C.S.: 541330
Daniel Derenski *(VP)*
Doug Boden *(Mgr-Fleet)*
Vicki Iler *(Controller)*
Jeff Sturgill *(Mgr-Matl & Field)*

THE DANIEL GROUP, LTD.
400 Clarice Ave Ste 200, Charlotte, NC 28204
Tel.: (704) 367-4242 NC
Web Site:
http://www.thedanielgroup.com
Year Founded: 1989
Sales Range: $1-9.9 Million
Emp.: 45
Management Consulting Services
N.A.I.C.S.: 541611
Lynn Daniel *(Pres)*
Doug Fowler *(COO)*

THE DATA ENTRY COMPANY
8120 Woodmont Ave Ste 550, Bethesda, MD 20814
Tel.: (301) 718-0703
Web Site: http://www.tdec.com
Year Founded: 1958
Business Process Outsourcing Services
N.A.I.C.S.: 518210
Dennis DuFour *(Pres)*
John DuFour *(Exec VP)*
Mike Sperry *(Dir-Bus Dev)*
Laura Teter *(Dir-Ops, ODC & WDC)*
Denis Lyatkin *(Mgr-Application Delivery)*

Amy Fortney *(Dir-Ops, OHDC & CODC)*
Lorraine McBride *(Dir-Ops)*
Lisa Flynn *(Dir-Proposal)*

THE DAVEY TREE EXPERT COMPANY
1500 N Mantua St, Kent, OH 44240
Tel.: (330) 673-9511 OH
Web Site: https://www.davey.com
Year Founded: 1880
Rev: $1,511,081,000
Assets: $956,221,000
Liabilities: $826,421,000
Net Worth: $129,800,000
Earnings: $61,290,000
Emp.: 10,400
Fiscal Year-end: 12/31/22
Tree Maintenance & Horticultural Services
N.A.I.C.S.: 541320
Patrick M. Covey *(Chm, Pres & CEO)*
Joseph R. Paul *(CFO, Exec VP & Asst Sec)*
Brent R. Repenning *(Exec VP-Utility & Davey Resource Grp)*
Thea R. Sears *(VP & Controller)*
Dan Herms *(VP-R&D)*
Joseph E. Day *(Exec VP-U.S. Residential Ops)*
Michael Mittiga *(VP)*
Larry Evans *(Pres)*

Subsidiaries:

Arbor Tree Service Inc. (1)
1209 N Lk George Rd, Attica, MI 48412-8412
Tel.: (810) 724-3800
Web Site: http://www.arbortreesvc.com
Emp.: 27
Landscaping Services
N.A.I.C.S.: 561730

Arborguard, Inc. (1)
111 N Clarendon Ave, Avondale Estates, GA 30002
Tel.: (866) 228-0624
Web Site: https://www.arborguard.com
Landscaping Services
N.A.I.C.S.: 561730

B. Haney & Sons, Inc. (1)
1200 N Lombard Rd, Lombard, IL 60148
Tel.: (630) 495-1831
Personal & Household Goods Repair & Maintenance
N.A.I.C.S.: 811490

Chippers, Inc. (1)
1241 Pomfret Rd, Woodstock, VT 05091
Tel.: (802) 457-5100
Web Site: http://www.chippersinc.com
Landscape Architectural Services
N.A.I.C.S.: 541320
Mundy Wilson *(Pres & CEO)*

Davey Resource Group, Inc. (1)
4 Walter E Foran Blvd Ste 209, Flemington, NJ 08822
Tel.: (908) 948-6337
Environmental Consulting & Natural Resource Research
N.A.I.C.S.: 541690
Lauren Curtis *(Mgr-Project)*

Davey Tree Expert Company of Canada, Ltd. (1)
500-611 Tradewind Dr, Ancaster, L9G 4V5, ON, Canada **(100%)**
Tel.: (905) 304-7359
Web Site: https://www.daveytree.ca
Tree Service & Utility Service
N.A.I.C.S.: 561730
James Doyle *(Exec VP & Gen Mgr)*
Mike Nash *(VP-Ops)*
Blair Veitch *(VP-Ops)*

Subsidiary (US):

Land Management Group, Inc. (2)
3805 Wrightsville Ave Ste 15, Wilmington, NC 28403
Tel.: (910) 452-0001
Web Site: https://www.davey.com

Environmental Consulting Firms
N.A.I.C.S.: 541620
Kim Williams *(Mgr-Ecological Restoration Svcs Section)*
Christian Preziosi *(Pres & Mgr-Area)*
Randy Brant *(Mgr-Geology Section)*
Greg Finch *(Mgr-CAMA Section)*
Wes Fryar *(Mgr-Wetlands Section)*
Christopher Smith *(Sr Project Mgr-Raleigh Stream Design Branch)*

Davey Tree Surgery Company (1)
500 C Deerwood Rd, San Ramon, CA 94583
Tel.: (925) 272-7721
Web Site: http://www.daveytree.com
Sales Range: Less than $1 Million
Emp.: 20
Complete Tree & Lawn Service
N.A.I.C.S.: 561730

Rockland Tree Expert Co, Inc. (1)
11 McNamara Pl, Spring Valley, NY 10977
Tel.: (845) 354-3400
Web Site: http://www.rocklandtree.com
Sales Range: $1-9.9 Million
Emp.: 22
Lawn & Garden Services
N.A.I.C.S.: 561730
James B. Wickes *(District Mgr)*
John Wickes *(Asst District Mgr)*

Wolf Tree, Inc. (1)
3310 Greenway Dr, Knoxville, TN 37918
Tel.: (865) 687-3400
Web Site: https://www.wolftreeinc.com
Tree Care Services
N.A.I.C.S.: 561730

THE DAVIS COMPANIES INC.
201 Boston Post Rd W, Marlborough, MA 01752-1867
Tel.: (508) 481-9500 MA
Web Site: http://www.daviscos.com
Year Founded: 1985
Sales Range: $25-49.9 Million
Emp.: 50
Staffing Services
N.A.I.C.S.: 561320
Robert M. Davis *(CEO)*
Jill Cosgrove-Danksewicz *(CFO)*
Richard McCready *(Pres)*
Steve Coyle *(Mng Dir-IR & Mktg)*
Patrick Davis *(VP-Bus Ops)*
Ryan Clutterbuck *(COO)*
Ravi Ragnauth *(Mng Dir, CFO & Chief Compliance Officer)*

Subsidiaries:

Davis Companies (1)
415 Horizon Dr Bldg 200 Ste 250, Suwanee, GA 30043-5763
Tel.: (770) 962-5800
Web Site: http://www.daviscos.com
Sales Range: $10-24.9 Million
Emp.: 30
Provider of Help Supply Services
N.A.I.C.S.: 561311
Brendon Davis *(Pres)*

Davis Companies (1)
1415 Marlton Pike E Ste Ll1, Cherry Hill, NJ 08034-2210
Tel.: (800) 482-9494
Web Site: http://www.daviscos.com
Sales Range: $10-24.9 Million
Emp.: 3
Employment Agencies
N.A.I.C.S.: 561311

The Davis Companies Inc. (1)
1415 Marlton Pike E Rte 70 Ste Ll1, Cherry Hill, NJ 08034-2210 **(100%)**
Tel.: (856) 616-8430
Sales Range: $10-24.9 Million
Emp.: 7
Provider of Help Supply Services
N.A.I.C.S.: 561320
Dick C. E. Davis *(CEO)*

THE DAVIS GROUP INC.
209 San Carlos Ave, Sanford, FL 32771
Tel.: (407) 688-0261

Web Site: http://www.davisgroup-inc.com
Sales Range: $10-24.9 Million
Emp.: 10
Commercial & Institutional Building Construction
N.A.I.C.S.: 236220
James F. Davis (Pres)
David Oppenheimer (Partner)

THE DAY & ZIMMERMANN GROUP, INC.
1500 Spring Garden St, Philadelphia, PA 19130-3638
Tel.: (215) 299-8000   DE
Web Site: https://www.dayzim.com
Year Founded: 1901
Sales Range: Less than $1 Million
Emp.: 43,000
Offices of Other Holding Companies
N.A.I.C.S.: 551112
Michael P. McMahon (Pres-Engrg, Construction & Maintenance)
Michael H. Yoh (Pres-Munitions & Govt)
James S. Merante (Sr VP-Fin, Strategy & Corp Dev)
Fran Coady (Sr VP-HR)
Sankara Viswanathan (CIO & Sr VP)
Jeff Miller (VP/Grp Controller-Govt Svcs)
Mike McGovern (VP-Bus Dev)
Doug Magee (Pres-Govt Svcs)
Kathleen King (CFO & Sr VP-Fin)
Harold L. Yoh III (Chm & CEO)

Subsidiaries:

Day & Zimmermann - Munitions & Government   (1)
1500 Spring Garden St, Philadelphia, PA 19130   (100%)
Tel.: (215) 299-8000
Web Site: http://www.dayzim.com
Munitions Production & Related Government Support Services
N.A.I.C.S.: 332993
Michael H. Yoh (Pres)
Frances Coady (Sr VP-HR)

Subsidiary (Domestic):

American Ordinance LLC   (2)
207 E 29th St, Pittsburg, KS 66762   (100%)
Tel.: (620) 232-9238
Sales Range: $25-49.9 Million
Emp.: 150
Ammunition Mfr
N.A.I.C.S.: 332993

Day & Zimmermann International, Inc.   (1)
1500 Spring Garden St, Philadelphia, PA 19130   (100%)
Tel.: (215) 299-8000
Web Site: http://www.dayzim.com
Sales Range: $75-99.9 Million
Emp.: 250
Professional Engineering, Architectural, Construction Management & Facilities Support Services
N.A.I.C.S.: 541330

Day & Zimmermann NPS, Inc.   (1)
1809 Olde Homestead Ln Ste 104, Lancaster, PA 17601   (100%)
Tel.: (717) 481-5600
Web Site: http://www.dayzim.com
Sales Range: $25-49.9 Million
Emp.: 30
Power Plant Maintenance, Modification & Specialty Services
N.A.I.C.S.: 561210
Tony Downey (Dir-Safety)
Pete Grandi (Dir-Tooling & Warehousing)
Ilya Tlumach (Mgr-Bus Improvement Svcs)
Darren Gale (VP-Nuclear Ops)
Fran Coady (Sr VP-HR)
Rick Domyslawski (Exec VP-Engrg)
Sankara Viswanathan (CIO & Sr VP)
Michael Yoh (Pres-Munitions & Govt)
Walter M. Sanders IV (Pres)

Day & Zimmermann Security Services   (1)
1500 Spring Garden St, Philadelphia, PA 19130   (100%)
Tel.: (215) 656-2612
Web Site: http://www.dayzim.com
Sales Range: $350-399.9 Million
Emp.: 3,100
Security Services
N.A.I.C.S.: 561612

Day & Zimmermann Validation Services   (1)
1500 Spring Garden St, Philadelphia, PA 19130   (100%)
Tel.: (215) 299-8288
Web Site: http://www.dayzim.com
Medical, Pharmaceutical & Biotechnology Industry Systems Validation & Facility Regulatory Compliance Services
N.A.I.C.S.: 561499

Sunrise Beach Corporation   (1)
5900 S Lk Forrest Dr Ste 240, McKinney, TX 75070-2203
Tel.: (512) 826-5149
Prime Defense Contractor; Heavy Duty Truck Mfr
N.A.I.C.S.: 336120

The Mason & Hanger Group Inc.   (1)
300 W Vine St Ste 1300, Lexington, KY 40507-1814   (100%)
Tel.: (859) 252-9980
Web Site: http://www.masonandhanger.com
Sales Range: $50-74.9 Million
Emp.: 200
Architectural, Engineering & Construction Services
N.A.I.C.S.: 541310
Benjamin A. Lilly (Pres)

Yoh Services, LLC   (1)
1500 Spring Garden St, Philadelphia, PA 19130   (100%)
Tel.: (215) 656-2650
Web Site: http://www.yoh.com
Human Resource Contract Consulting & Outsourcing Services
N.A.I.C.S.: 541612
Lisa Ann Cooney (Gen Counsel)
Jonathan Grosso (Sr VP-Specialty Practices)
Matt Rivera (VP-Mktg & Comm)
William Yoh (Chm)
Emmett McGrath (Pres)
Tracey Griffin (VP-HR)
Kathleen King (SR VP-Enterprise Solutions)
John Comito (VP-Fin & Ops)

THE DAY PUBLISHER COMPANY
47 Eugene ONeill Dr, New London, CT 06320-6306
Tel.: (860) 442-2200
Web Site: http://www.theday.com
Year Founded: 1939
Sales Range: $25-49.9 Million
Emp.: 356
Publisher of Newspapers
N.A.I.C.S.: 513110

Subsidiaries:

The Day Publishing Company Inc.   (1)
47 Eugene Oneill Dr, New London, CT 06320-6306
Tel.: (860) 442-2200
Web Site: http://www.theday.com
Sales Range: $25-49.9 Million
Emp.: 352
Publisher of Newspapers
N.A.I.C.S.: 513110

THE DDC GROUP
2000 Riveredge Pkwy Ste GL 150, Sandy Springs, GA 30328
Tel.: (770) 644-7230
Web Site:
    http://www.theddcgroup.com
Emp.: 3,500
Holding Company; Business Process Outsourcing
N.A.I.C.S.: 551112

Jan Trevalyan (Co-Founder & CEO)
Jericho Petilla (Co-Founder)
Brett Trevalyan (CFO)
Marissa Crotty (Pres-Ops-North America)
Art Zipkin (Pres-Sls-North America)

Subsidiaries:

CGF Marketing Services Ltd.   (1)
Manton Wood Enterprise Park, Worksop, S80 2RT, Notts, United Kingdom
Tel.: (44) 1909 488600
Web Site: http://www.ddcos.com
Business Process Outsourcing
N.A.I.C.S.: 561499
Colin Gray (Mng Dir)

DDC Freight Process Outsourcing LLC   (1)
4611 Plettner Ln Ste 130, Evergreen, CO 80439
Tel.: (303) 674-0681
Web Site: http://www.theddcgroup.com
Freight Process Outsourcing Services
N.A.I.C.S.: 518210
Marissa Crotty (Pres)
Chad Crotty (VP-Sls)
Teresa Peyton (VP-Project Dev)
Quetura Hudson (VP-Project Mgmt)
Dan Kaiser (VP-IT)

THE DE LONG CO. INC.
214 Allen St, Clinton, WI 53525
Tel.: (608) 676-2255   WI
Web Site:
    http://www.delongcompany.com
Year Founded: 1952
Sales Range: $75-99.9 Million
Emp.: 145
Provider of Products & Information to the Farming Industry
N.A.I.C.S.: 424910

Subsidiaries:

The De Long Company, Inc.   (1)
513 Front St, Clinton, WI 53525   (100%)
Tel.: (608) 676-2255
Web Site: http://www.delongcompany.com
Sales Range: $10-24.9 Million
Emp.: 4
Provider of Farm Supplies
N.A.I.C.S.: 424910
David DeLong (Pres)

THE DECKER COMPANIES INC.
4000 5th Ave S, Fort Dodge, IA 50501-6426
Tel.: (515) 576-4141   IA
Web Site:
    http://www.deckertruckline.com
Year Founded: 1931
Sales Range: $25-49.9 Million
Emp.: 750
Provider of Transport Services
N.A.I.C.S.: 484230
Donald L. Decker (Chm & Pres)
Timothy J. Burns (CFO & Treas)
Bradley Baade (CFO-Transportation)
Dale Decker (Exec VP)

Subsidiaries:

B-T Brokerage Inc.   (1)
1443 Industrial Rd SW, Le Mars, IA 51031-3004
Tel.: (712) 546-8168
Web Site: http://www.deckercompanies.com
Sales Range: $10-24.9 Million
Emp.: 8
Provider of Transport Arrangement Services
N.A.I.C.S.: 488510
Donald L. Decker (Pres)

B-T Inc.   (1)
1443 Industrial Rd SW, Le Mars, IA 51031-3004   (100%)
Tel.: (712) 546-8168
Web Site: http://www.deckercompanies.com
Sales Range: $10-24.9 Million
Emp.: 100
Provider of Transport Services
N.A.I.C.S.: 484121

Donald L. Decker (Pres)

Decker Truck Line Inc.   (1)
4000 5th Ave S, Fort Dodge, IA 50501-6426   (100%)
Tel.: (515) 576-4141
Web Site: http://www.deckertruckline.com
Sales Range: $25-49.9 Million
Emp.: 400
Provider of Transport Services
N.A.I.C.S.: 484230
Donald L. Decker (Pres)
Anthony Russell (VP)
Tim J. Burns (Chief Investment Officer)

THE DECORATORS UNLIMITED INC.
4700 Riverside Dr, Palm Beach Gardens, FL 33410
Tel.: (561) 625-3000
Web Site:
    http://www.decoratorsunlimited.com
Rev.: $27,600,000
Emp.: 62
Interior Design Services
N.A.I.C.S.: 541410
Robert B. Martin (Pres)

THE DEGOL ORGANIZATION
3229 Pleasant Vly Blvd, Altoona, PA 16602-4435
Tel.: (814) 941-7777
Web Site: http://www.degol.com
Year Founded: 1958
Sales Range: $50-74.9 Million
Emp.: 325
Provider of Lumber, Plywood & Millwork
N.A.I.C.S.: 423310
Bruno DeGol (CEO)

Subsidiaries:

DeGol Aviation, Inc.   (1)
3229 Pleasant Valley Blvd, Altoona, PA 16602
Tel.: (814) 937-0030
Web Site: http://www.degoljet.com
Passenger Air Transportation Services
N.A.I.C.S.: 481211

DeGol Brothers Carpet   (1)
851 Plank Rd, Duncansville, PA 16635
Tel.: (814) 695-1111
Web Site: http://www.degolcarpet.com
Carpet Distr
N.A.I.C.S.: 423220

Seven D Industries, L.P.   (1)
977 DeGol Industrial Dr, Hollidaysburg, PA 16648
Tel.: (814) 317-4077
Web Site: http://www.7dindustries.com
Metal Window & Door Distr
N.A.I.C.S.: 423310

Seven D Wholesale L.L.P.   (1)
700 W Hillsboro Blvd Ste 2-207, Deerfield Beach, FL 33441-1616   (100%)
Tel.: (864) 284-6550
Web Site: http://www.degol.com
Sales Range: $10-24.9 Million
Emp.: 4
Provider of Lumber, Plywood & Millwork
N.A.I.C.S.: 424990

THE DELTA COMPANIES
Four Hickory Ctr 1755 Whittington Pl Ste 175, Dallas, TX 75234
Tel.: (214) 442-4000
Web Site: http://www.tdcpeople.com
Year Founded: 2004
Sales Range: $50-74.9 Million
Emp.: 200
Direct-Hire & Temporary Staffing Services
N.A.I.C.S.: 561311
Jaeson Babb (VP-Permanent Recruiting-Delta Flex Partners)
Ryan Anholt (Exec VP-Delta Healthcare Providers)
Eric Sasser (VP-Advertising)
Bill Tracewell (CEO)

THE DELTA COMPANIES

The Delta Companies—(Continued)

Paul Estrada (Sr VP-Delta Physician Placement)
DeLibra Wesley (Exec VP-Ops)

THE DELTONA CORPORATION
8014 SW 135th St Rd, Ocala, FL 34473-6807
Tel.: (352) 347-2322 DE
Web Site: http://www.deltona.com
Year Founded: 1962
Sales Range: $10-24.9 Million
Emp.: 42
Community Developer, Commercial Operations
N.A.I.C.S.: 237210
Antony Gram (Owner)
Sharon J. Hummerhielm (Exec VP)
Beth Fisher (Mgr-Marion Oaks)

Subsidiaries:

Deltona Corp. Realty Co. (1)
100 Marion Oaks Blvd, Miami, FL 34473 (100%)
Tel.: (352) 347-2322
Web Site: http://www.marionoaksrealty.com
Realty Brokerage
N.A.I.C.S.: 237210

Deltona Land & Investment Corp. (1)
8014 SW 135th St Rd, Ocala, FL 34473 (100%)
Tel.: (352) 347-2322
Wholesale Realty Sales
N.A.I.C.S.: 523999

Deltona Marketing Corp. (1)
3250 S.W. Third Ave., Miami, FL 33129 (100%)
Tel.: (305) 854-1111
Retail Sale of Property
N.A.I.C.S.: 236117

Five Points Title Co, (1)
8014 SW 135th St Rd, Ocala, FL 34473 (100%)
Tel.: (352) 307-0796
Sales Range: $10-24.9 Million
Emp.: 4
Title Insurance Company
N.A.I.C.S.: 445320

THE DEMOSS COMPANY
4205 Stadium Dr Ste 100, Fort Worth, TX 76133
Tel.: (817) 920-9990
Web Site: http://www.demossco.com
Year Founded: 1979
Sales Range: $10-24.9 Million
Emp.: 20
Provider of General Contracting, Consulting, Pre-Construction Assistance & Full-Project Construction Management Services
N.A.I.C.S.: 236220
James B. Demoss III (Pres)

THE DENTAL CARE PLUS GROUP
100 Crowne Point Pl, Cincinnati, OH 45241
Tel.: (513) 554-1100
Web Site:
  http://www.dentalcareplus.com
Year Founded: 1986
Sales Range: $75-99.9 Million
Emp.: 50
Dental Insurance Services
N.A.I.C.S.: 524114
Jodi Fronczek (COO)
Stephen T. Schuler (Chm)
Natalie Mason (Dir-Regulatory Compliance)
Sam Guffey (Mgr-Technical Svcs)
Daniel Burghy (Mgr-Reg Sls)
Jim Hamrick (Reg Mgr-Sls)
Jill Schulten (Acct Mgr-Louisville)
Robert Hodgkins Jr. (CFO & VP)

THE DENTALEZ GROUP
2 W Liberty Blvd Ste 160, Malvern, PA 19355-1742
Tel.: (610) 725-8004 PA
Web Site: http://www.dentalez.com
Year Founded: 1958
Sales Range: $10-24.9 Million
Emp.: 20
Mfr of Dental Education & Practice Equipment
N.A.I.C.S.: 339114
Francisco Rodriguez (Mgr-Sls-Intl)
Mark Frankenfield (Key Accts Mgr)

Subsidiaries:

Columbia Dentoform Corporation (1)
3110 37th Ave Ste 307, Long Island City, NY 11101-2531 (100%)
Tel.: (718) 482-1569
Web Site:
  http://www.columbiadentoform.com
Sales Range: $10-24.9 Million
Dental Education & Practice Equipment Mfr
N.A.I.C.S.: 339114
Penelope Pichardo (VP & Gen Mgr)

THE DENVER HOSPICE AND OPTIO HEALTH SERVICES
501 S Cherry St Ste 700, Denver, CO 80246-1328
Tel.: (303) 321-2828 CO
Web Site:
  http://www.thedenverhospice.org
Year Founded: 1977
Sales Range: $25-49.9 Million
Emp.: 533
Hospice Care Services
N.A.I.C.S.: 621610
Julie Gustafson (CFO)
David Koets (Chief Medical Officer)
Dale Anders (CIO)
Janelle McCallum (Pres)
Alicia Prescott (Officer-Dev)
Kristen Tucker (Mgr-Events)
Ron Mirenda (VP-Philanthropy)
John Blaschke (CIO)

THE DEPOSITORY TRUST & CLEARING CORPORATION
55 Water St Fl 3, New York, NY 10041-0099
Tel.: (212) 855-1000
Web Site: http://www.dtcc.com
Year Founded: 1999
Sales Range: $900-999.9 Million
Emp.: 2,000
Securities Trading Services
N.A.I.C.S.: 523150
Francis La Salla (Pres & CEO)
Lynn Bishop (CIO)
Timothy Keady (Mng Dir/Head-Solutions)
Derek West (Chief Compliance Officer-Global Trade Repository Bus-Europe)
Andrew Douglas (CEO-Global Trade Repository-Europe)
Michael McClain (Mng Dir/Gen Mgr-Equity Clearing)
Matthew Stauffer (Mng Dir & Head-Institutional Trade Processing)
Timothy Lind (Mng Dir-Data Svcs)
Tim Cuddihy (Grp Chief Risk Officer)
Nashira Spencer (Chief Security Officer)

Subsidiaries:

National Securities Clearing Corporation (1)
55 Water St, New York, NY 10041
Tel.: (212) 855-1000
Web Site: http://www.nscc.com
Securities Trading Clearinghouse
N.A.I.C.S.: 522320
Francis La Salla (Pres & CEO)

The Depository Trust Company (1)
55 Water St, New York, NY 10041
Tel.: (212) 855-1000
Web Site: http://www.dtcc.com
Security & Commodity Services
N.A.I.C.S.: 523210
Francis La Salla (Pres & CEO)
Mieko Shibata (Mng Dir)
James Lee (Mng Dir & Head-Enterprise Computing)
Amy Bladen-Shatto (Pres-Talent Mgmt & Leadership Dev)

THE DESIGN AGENCY INC.
1380 Industrial Dr, Itasca, IL 60143
Tel.: (847) 463-8000
Web Site:
  http://www.designagency.com
Sales Range: $10-24.9 Million
Emp.: 20
Exhibit Construction By Industrial Contractors
N.A.I.C.S.: 561990
Monika Jordan (Coord-Exhibit)
Alex Rychtytzkyj (Mgr-IT)

THE DESIGN PEOPLE, INC.
1700 E Walnut Ave Ste 240, El Segundo, CA 90245-2609
Tel.: (310) 577-9111
Web Site:
  http://www.thedesignpeople.com
Year Founded: 1998
Sales Range: $1-9.9 Million
Emp.: 160
Website Design & Hosting
N.A.I.C.S.: 518210
Tiger Bitanga (CEO)
Jon Krabbe (CFO)

THE DETROIT LIONS, INC.
222 Republic Dr, Allen Park, MI 48101
Tel.: (313) 216-4000 MI
Web Site: http://www.detroitlions.com
Year Founded: 1934
Sales Range: $75-99.9 Million
Emp.: 200
Professional Football Franchise
N.A.I.C.S.: 711211
Bill Keenist (Sr VP-Comm)
Matt Barnhart (Dir-Football Comm)
Bryan Bender (Dir-Event Presentation)
Mark Glenn (Mgr-Facilities)
Michael Richardson (Asst Dir-Video)
Mark Graham (Dir-Ticket Ops)
Bill McCall (Asst Dir-Ticket Ops)
Chris Fritzsching (Dir-Football Education)
Tim O'Neill (Mgr-Equipment)
Robert Yanagi (Dir-Video Ops)
Allison Maki (CFO & Sr VP-Admin)
Ben Manges (Sr Dir-Corp Comm)
Deanna Caldwell (Mgr-Football Media Svcs)
Anne Campbell (Mgr-Premium Svcs)
Dan Jaroshewich (Sr Dir-Sports Events & Bus Dev)
Joel Scott (Sr Dir-Mktg)
Elton Moore (Dir-Security)
Kyle O'Brien (Dir-Player Personnel)
Kelly Kozole (Sr VP-Bus Dev)
Emily Griffin (VP-Mktg)
Jay Colvin (Sr VP-Legal Affairs)
Rod Wood (Pres-Team)
Brian Haberkorn (Mgr-Production)
Colleen Gallo (Mgr-Payroll)
Jon Dykema (Mgr-Football Admin)
Kristen Dale (Dir-Ops)
Robbie Biederman (Creative Dir)
Veronica Bonner (Sr Mgr-HR)
Elizabeth Ford Kontulis (Vice Chm)
Martha Ford Morse (Vice Chm)
Sheila Ford Hamp (Vice Chm)
Bob Quinn (Exec VP & Gen Mgr)
Elliott Kessler (VP-Fin)
Todd Argust (VP-Ops)
Todd Lambert (VP-Ticketing & Premium Seating)
Eamonn Reynolds (Dir-Football Ops)
Mike Disner (VP-Football Admin)

THE DEVEREUX FOUNDATION, INC.
444 Devereux Dr, Villanova, PA 19085
Tel.: (610) 520-3000
Web Site: http://www.devereux.org
Year Founded: 1912
Emp.: 6,000
Behavioral Healthcare Services Organization
N.A.I.C.S.: 813212
Lawrence W. Williams (VP-Audit & Compliance)
Martha Lindsay (VP-Product Dev)
Sarah Ellen Lenahan (VP-Ops & Org Dev)
Robert C. Dunne (CFO, Treas & Sr VP)
Timothy Dillon (VP-HR)
L. Gail Atkinson (VP-Ops)
Margaret McGill (COO & Sr VP)
Robert Q. Kreider (Pres & CEO)
Carol Oliver (VP-Ops)
David Griffith (Controller)
Leah S. Yaw (Sr VP & External Affairs)
Lorraine Barrett (Asst Sec)
Marilyn Benoit (Chief Clinical Officer & Sr VP-Pro Affairs)
Tom Shurer (VP-Info Resources)
Francis Genuardi (Vice Chm)

Subsidiaries:

Devereux Florida (1)
5850 TG Lee Blvd Ste 400, Orlando, FL 32822
Tel.: (407) 362-9210
Web Site: http://www.devereuxfl.org
Behavioral Healthcare Services
N.A.I.C.S.: 623210
Steven J. Murphy (Exec Dir)
Eva Horner (Asst Exec Dir)
Carlos F. Pozzi-Montero (Dir-Clinical)
Lindsey Phillips (Dir-External Affairs)
Dan Samuels (Dir-Dev)
Philip Putnam (Dir-Legal, Risk & Quality Mgmt)
Kelly Messer (Dir-Fin)
Mary Margaret Hansell (Dir-HR)

THE DEVINE GROUP, INC.
4455 Montgomery Rd Ste 100, Cincinnati, OH 45241
Tel.: (513) 792-7500
Web Site:
  http://www.devinegroup.com
Year Founded: 1970
Sales Range: $1-9.9 Million
Emp.: 20
Human Resouce Services
N.A.I.C.S.: 541612
David Devine (Chm & CEO)
Erik Lutz (COO)
Pamela Walters (Exec VP)
Joe Koczwara (VP-Analytics)

THE DEWBERRY COMPANIES INC.
8401 Arlington Blvd, Fairfax, VA 22031-4619
Tel.: (703) 849-0100
Web Site: http://www.dewberry.com
Professional Services
N.A.I.C.S.: 541990
Sean Reney (CIO)
Don Stone (CEO)
Dan Pleasant (COO)

Subsidiaries:

Edmonds Engineering, Inc. (1)
2 Riverchase Office Plaza, Hoover, AL 35244-2018
Tel.: (205) 988-2069

COMPANIES

Web Site:
http://www.edmondsengineering.com
Rev.: $1,100,000
Emp.: 7
Scientific & Technical Consulting Services
N.A.I.C.S.: 541690
Dan Blackman (Pres)
Chris Robinson (CTO)
Adam Cone (Project Mgr)
Phillip Graydon (Project Mgr)
Tracy Worley (Reg Mgr-Nashville)
Joey Roach (Grp Mgr-Property Mgmt Svcs)
David Garrett (Project Mgr-Arc Flash)

Hydro Solutions Consulting LLC (1)
3616 Harden Blvd Ste 110, Lakeland, FL 33803
Tel.: (863) 559-2472
Web Site: http://www.hydrosc.com
Engineeering Services
N.A.I.C.S.: 541330
Scott Ethier (Sr Engr)

THE DEWITT COMPANY, INC.
905 S Kings Hwy St, Sikeston, MO 63801-4415
Tel.: (573) 472-0048
Web Site:
http://www.dewittcompany.com
Year Founded: 1977
Sales Range: $10-24.9 Million
Emp.: 68
Landscaping Product & Plant Fabric Mfr
N.A.I.C.S.: 313210
Larry Dewitt (Founder & CEO)
Meredith Dewitt (VP)

THE DIAMOND DISTRICT LLC
7995 Plaza Del Lago Dr, Estero, FL 33928
Tel.: (239) 947-3434
Web Site:
http://www.diamonddistrictusa.com
Sales Range: $1-9.9 Million
Emp.: 15
Jewelry Retailer
N.A.I.C.S.: 458310
Todd Schusterman (Co-Owner)
Jason Sherman (Co-Owner)
Stacy Sherman (Office Mgr)

THE DIAMOND GROUP INC.
17103 Preston Rd Ste 170, Dallas, TX 75248
Tel.: (972) 788-1111
Web Site:
http://www.thediamondgroup.com
Year Founded: 1994
Sales Range: $10-24.9 Million
Emp.: 472
Provider of Private Investigative & Security Services
N.A.I.C.S.: 561611
Jeanette S. Diamond (Pres & CEO)
Thil Border (Dir-Ops)

THE DICKERSON GROUP, INC.
1501 N Charlotte Ave, Monroe, NC 28110-2525
Tel.: (704) 289-3111   FL
Sales Range: $25-49.9 Million
Emp.: 150
Holding Company; Real Estate Management & Construction Services
N.A.I.C.S.: 551112
John F. Joyner (Pres)

Subsidiaries:

Dickerson Florida, Inc. (1)
3122 N 25th St, Fort Pierce, FL 34946   (96%)
Tel.: (772) 429-4444
Web Site: http://www.dickersonflorida.com
Rev.: $360,000
Emp.: 35
Highway & Site Construction Services
N.A.I.C.S.: 237310
Larry T. Dale (Pres)
Dale Mctaggart (Office Mgr)

Dickerson Realty Corporation (1)
1501 Charlotte Ave, Monroe, NC 28110   (100%)
Tel.: (704) 289-3111
Sales Range: $10-24.9 Million
Emp.: 5
Real Estate Management, Development & Sales
N.A.I.C.S.: 531210
John F. Joyner (Pres)

South Atlantic Equipment Company, Inc. (1)
1501 N Charlotte Ave, Monroe, NC 28110   (100%)
Tel.: (704) 289-3111
Sales Range: $25-49.9 Million
Emp.: 4
Equipment Rental & Repair
N.A.I.C.S.: 237310

THE DICKLER CORP.
18430 Pacific St, Fountain Valley, CA 92708
Tel.: (714) 435-9222   CA
Web Site: http://www.chefstoys.com
Year Founded: 1986
Sales Range: $50-74.9 Million
Emp.: 26
Restaurant Equipment & Supplies
N.A.I.C.S.: 423440
Steve Dickler (Founder)

Subsidiaries:

Michael Blackman & Associates, Inc. (1)
2306 Cotner Ave, Los Angeles, CA 90064   (100%)
Tel.: (310) 656-1010
Web Site:
http://www.michaelblackmanandassociates.com
Sales Range: $10-24.9 Million
Emp.: 18
Restaurant Kitchen Designer & Supplier
N.A.I.C.S.: 423440
Michael Blackman (Pres)

THE DIETRICH FOUNDATION
US Steel Tower 600 Grant St Rm 5360, Pittsburgh, PA 15219
Tel.: (412) 261-2766   PA
Web Site:
http://www.dietrichfoundation.net
Year Founded: 2011
Sales Range: $700-749.9 Million
Emp.: 6
Fundraising Organization
N.A.I.C.S.: 813211
Matthew W. Rozyczka (Mgr-Investment)
Ryan L. Vaccaro (Mgr-Investment)
Edward J. Grefenstette (Pres, CEO & CIO)

THE DIGITAL RING, LLC
8401 Excelsior Dr Ste 104, Madison, WI 53717
Tel.: (608) 836-7464
Web Site:
http://www.thedigitalring.com
Year Founded: 2015
Sales Range: $1-9.9 Million
Emp.: 22
Digital Marketing Services
N.A.I.C.S.: 541810
Nick Ring (Co-Founder & Partner)
Mason Kemp (Co-Founder & Partner)
Matt Kemp (Partner)
Nate Finch (VP-Dev)
Josh Jurrens (VP-Paid Digital)

THE DIRECT RESPONSE GROUP, LLC
445 Broadhollow Rd Ste CL 42, Melville, NY 11747
Tel.: (631) 752-3590   NY
Web Site:
http://www.directresponsegroup.com
Year Founded: 2002
Sales Range: $1-9.9 Million
Emp.: 10
Marketing Consulting Services
N.A.I.C.S.: 541613
Christopher Ulrich (Owner)

THE DISPATCH PRINTING COMPANY
770 Twin Rivers Dr, Columbus, OH 43215
Tel.: (614) 460-3700   OH
Year Founded: 1871
Sales Range: $400-449.9 Million
Emp.: 2,300
Media Holding Company
N.A.I.C.S.: 551112
Abby Clark (VP-Sls)
Poe A. Timmons (CFO & Exec VP)
Joseph Y. Gallo (Pres & COO)
Bradley Campbell (CFO, Treas & VP)

Subsidiaries:

Dispatch Broadcast Group (1)
770 Twin Rivers Dr, Columbus, OH 43215
Tel.: (614) 460-3700
Web Site:
http://www.dispatchbroadcast.com
Holding Company
N.A.I.C.S.: 551112
Michael J. Fiorile (Vice Chm-)
John Cardenas (VP-News)
Tani Mann (VP & Dir-HR)
Larry Delia (Pres)

THE DISTILLATA COMPANY
1608 E 24th St, Cleveland, OH 44114
Tel.: (216) 771-2900
Web Site: http://www.distillata.com
Year Founded: 1897
Sales Range: $10-24.9 Million
Emp.: 90
Chemical Product & Preparation Mfr
N.A.I.C.S.: 325998
William F. Schroeder (Pres)
Keith Schroeder (VP)
Herbert Buckman (Treas)

THE DISTINGUISHED PROGRAM GROUP
1180 Ave of the Americas 16th Fl, New York, NY 10036
Tel.: (212) 297-3100
Web Site:
http://www.distinguished.com
Year Founded: 1995
Sales Range: $25-49.9 Million
Emp.: 1,125
Competitive Property & Liability Programs Services
N.A.I.C.S.: 524126
Jeremy Hitzig (CEO)
David Watkins (CFO)
Andrew Potash (Founder & CEO)
Helen English (COO)
Carla Vel (Pres)
Mark Kissick (Chief Sls Officer)
Kurt Meister (Sr VP & Mgr-Bus Dev)

THE DIVE SHOP, INC.
999 S Yates Rd, Memphis, TN 38119
Tel.: (901) 763-3483
Web Site: http://www.diveshop1.com
Sales Range: $10-24.9 Million
Emp.: 30
Sporting Goods Whslr
N.A.I.C.S.: 459110
Randy Wright (Principal)

THE DOCTORS COMPANY
185 Greenwood Rd, Napa, CA 94558
Tel.: (707) 226-0100   CA
Web Site: http://www.thedoctors.com
Year Founded: 1976
Sales Range: $550-599.9 Million
Emp.: 500
Medical Malpractice & Liability Insurance Carrier & Services
N.A.I.C.S.: 524128
Richard E. Anderson (Chm & CEO)
Bill Fleming (COO)
Tammy Clark (Sr VP)
Crystal R. Brown (Sr VP-Underwriting)
Kerin Torpey Bashaw (Sr VP-Patient Safety & Risk Mgmt)
Marco Spadacenta (Sr VP-Claims)
Robert White (Exec VP-Medical Pro Liability)

Subsidiaries:

Alpha Advisors, Inc. (1)
70 W Madison Ste 5300, Chicago, IL 60602   (100%)
Tel.: (312) 263-7673
Sales Range: $50-74.9 Million
Emp.: 2
Financial Assets Management Services
N.A.I.C.S.: 523940

American Physicians Assurance Corporation (1)
1301 N Hagadorn Rd, East Lansing, MI 48823   (100%)
Tel.: (517) 351-1150
Web Site: http://www.thedoctors.com
Sales Range: $50-74.9 Million
Emp.: 130
Healthcare Liability Insurance
N.A.I.C.S.: 524126
Richard Anderson (Pres & CEO)

FPIC Insurance Group, Inc. (1)
1000 Riverside Ave Ste 800, Jacksonville, FL 32204
Tel.: (904) 354-2482
Web Site: http://www.thedoctors.com
Sales Range: $150-199.9 Million
Emp.: 151
Holding Company; Medical Professional Liability Insurance Products & Services
N.A.I.C.S.: 551112
Richard E. Anderson (Pres & CEO)
David G. Preimesberger (CFO & Treas)
Robert D. Francis (COO)
David McHale (Sec)

OHIC Insurance Company (1)
155 E Broad St, Columbus, OH 43215-3614
Tel.: (614) 221-7777
Medical Insurance Services
N.A.I.C.S.: 524114

Professional Underwriters Liability Insurance Company (1)
1888 Century Park E Ste 850, Los Angeles, CA 90067   (100%)
Tel.: (707) 226-0100
Web Site: http://www.pulic.com
Sales Range: $50-74.9 Million
Emp.: 300
Insurance Services for Doctors
N.A.I.C.S.: 524126

Subsidiary (Domestic):

PULIC Insurance Services, Inc. (2)
1888 Century Park E Ste 850, Los Angeles, CA 90067
Tel.: (310) 571-0730
Web Site: http://www.pulic.com
Rev.: $3,300,000
Emp.: 20
Insurance Services
N.A.I.C.S.: 524126

The Doctors Company (1)
1301 N Hagadorn Rd, East Lansing, MI 48823-2320
Tel.: (517) 351-1150
Web Site: http://www.thedoctors.com
Sales Range: $125-149.9 Million
Emp.: 145
Personal & Commercial Lines of Medical-Liability & Workers Compensation
N.A.I.C.S.: 524114
Richard E. Anderson (Chm, Pres & CEO)
Catherine Shutack (VP-Claims)
Bryan Lawton (Sec)

The Doctors Company Insurance Services (1)
185 Greenwood Rd, Napa, CA 94558-6270   (100%)
Tel.: (707) 226-0100

THE DOCTORS COMPANY

The Doctors Company—(Continued)
Web Site: http://www.doctorscompany.com
Sales Range: $50-74.9 Million
Emp.: 300
Insurance Services for Doctors
N.A.I.C.S.: 524126
Jack Meyer (Sr VP)
Richard E. Anderson (Chm)

The Doctors Company/Northwest
Physicians (1)
2965 Ryan Dr SE, Salem, OR
97301 (100%)
Tel.: (503) 371-8228
Web Site: http://www.thedoctors.com
Sales Range: $10-24.9 Million
Emp.: 20
Insurance Services
N.A.I.C.S.: 524126
William J. Gallagher (Sr VP & Reg Dir-Medical)

Subsidiary (Domestic):

NPMIC Insurance Agency, Inc. (2)
2965 Ryan Dr SE, Salem, OR 97301
Tel.: (503) 371-8228
Insurance Agents
N.A.I.C.S.: 524210
Christopher Clark (VP)
James T. Dorigan Jr. (Pres)

The Doctors' Life Insurance Company
Inc. (1)
185 Greenwood Rd, Napa, CA
94558-6270 (100%)
Tel.: (707) 226-0100
Web Site: http://www.doctors.com
Sales Range: $50-74.9 Million
Emp.: 180
Life Insurance Services for Doctors
N.A.I.C.S.: 524113
Richard E. Anderson (Chm)

The Doctors' Management
Company (1)
185 Greenwood Rd, Napa, CA
94558-6270 (100%)
Tel.: (707) 226-0100
Web Site: http://www.thedoctors.com
Sales Range: $25-49.9 Million
Emp.: 183
Management & Administrative Services
N.A.I.C.S.: 561499
Richard E. Anderson (Chm)
William J. Gallagher (Sr VP & Dir-Medical-Northwest Reg)
Valora S. Gurganious (Partner)

Underwriter for the Professions Insurance Company (1)
185 Greenwood Rd, Napa, CA
94558-6270 (100%)
Tel.: (707) 226-0100
Web Site: http://www.doctorscompany.com
Sales Range: $100-124.9 Million
Emp.: 350
Insurance Services for Doctors
N.A.I.C.S.: 524126
Bruce Crile (COO)

THE DODSON GROUP, INC.
201 N Illinois St Ste 1701, Indianapolis, IN 46204
Tel.: (800) 908-2111
Web Site:
http://www.dodsongroup.net
Year Founded: 1986
Sales Range: $10-24.9 Million
Emp.: 68
Computer Software Services
N.A.I.C.S.: 541519
James Dodson (CEO)

THE DOHRING GROUP, INC.
518 N Tampa St Ste 300, Tampa, FL 33602
Tel.: (813) 223-9111
Web Site:
http://www.dohringgroup.com
Sales Range: $1-9.9 Million
Emp.: 11
Real Estate Brokerage & Other Related Services
N.A.I.C.S.: 531210

Brenda Dohring Hicks (CEO)
Jeff Hicks (Pres)
Abbey Dohring (VP-Brokerage)
Ryan M. Hill (VP-Appraisal)

THE DOLAN COMPANY
222 S 9th St Ste 2300, Minneapolis, MN 55402
Tel.: (612) 317-9420 DE
Year Founded: 1992
Sales Range: $250-299.9 Million
Emp.: 1,708
Holding Company; Business & Professional Publisher
N.A.I.C.S.: 551112
Vicki J. Duncomb (CFO & VP-Fin)
Mark A. McEachen (Pres & CEO)
Kevin J. Nystrom (Chief Restructuring Officer)

Subsidiaries:

Arizona News Service, LLC (1)
1835 W Adams St, Phoenix, AZ 85007
Tel.: (602) 258-7026
Web Site: https://www.aznewsservice.com
Sales Range: $10-24.9 Million
Emp.: 20
Business Information Services
N.A.I.C.S.: 516210
Luige del Puerto (Assoc Publr & Editor)

Daily Journal of Commerce, Inc. (1)
1618 SW 1st Ave Ste 400, Portland, OR 97201
Tel.: (503) 226-1311
Web Site: https://www.djcoregon.com
Sales Range: $10-24.9 Million
Emp.: 25
Business Information Services
N.A.I.C.S.: 513199

Daily Reporter Publishing
Company (1)
225 E Michigan St Ste 300, Milwaukee, WI 53202
Tel.: (414) 225-1801
Web Site: https://www.dailyreporter.com
Sales Range: $10-24.9 Million
Emp.: 13
Internet News Publisher
N.A.I.C.S.: 513110

DataStream Content Solutions,
LLC (1)
5000 College Ave, College Park, MD 20742
Tel.: (301) 405-5423
Web Site: http://www.dscs.com
Information Management Services
N.A.I.C.S.: 518210
Jason Myers (Pres)

Finance and Commerce, Inc. (1)
Ste 900 Campbell Mithun Tower 222 S 9th St, Minneapolis, MN 55402
Tel.: (612) 333-4244
Web Site: https://www.finance-commerce.com
Sales Range: $10-24.9 Million
Emp.: 25
Internet News Publisher
N.A.I.C.S.: 513110
Bill Gaier (Pres & Publr)

Idaho Business Review, LLC (1)
4696 W Overland Rd Ste 180, Boise, ID 83707
Tel.: (208) 336-3768
Web Site:
https://www.idahobusinessreview.com
Sales Range: $10-24.9 Million
Emp.: 15
Business Journal Publisher Services
N.A.I.C.S.: 513110

Legislative Information Services of America, LLC (1)
1835 W Adams St, Phoenix, AZ 85007
Tel.: (877) 792-9991
Web Site: http://www.lisausa.net
Business Information Services
N.A.I.C.S.: 519290

Long Island Business News, LLC (1)
2150 Smithtown Ave Ste 7, Ronkonkoma, NY 11779
Tel.: (631) 737-1700

Web Site: https://www.libn.com
Sales Range: $10-24.9 Million
Emp.: 20
Business Journal Publisher
N.A.I.C.S.: 513110

Massachusetts Lawyers Weekly,
Inc. (1)
10 Milk St Ste 1000, Boston, MA 02108
Tel.: (617) 451-7300
Web Site:
http://www.masslawyersweekly.com
Sales Range: $10-24.9 Million
Emp.: 50
Legal Newspapers Publisher
N.A.I.C.S.: 513110
Henriette Campagne (VP-Editorial)
Thomas E. Egan (Editor-Opinion)
Matt Yas (Assoc Editor)
Scott Ziegler (VP-Sls)

Missouri Lawyers Media, Inc. (1)
319 N 4th St 5th Fl, Saint Louis, MO 63102 (100%)
Tel.: (314) 421-1880
Web Site: http://www.molawyersmedia.com
Sales Range: $10-24.9 Million
Emp.: 40
Newspaper Publishing
N.A.I.C.S.: 513110
Amanda Passmore (Gen Mgr)
Cindi Lash (Editor)

Division (Domestic):

St. Louis Countian (2)
319 N 4th St 5th Fl, Saint Louis, MO 63102
Tel.: (314) 421-1880
Web Site:
http://www.missourilawyersmedia.com
Sales Range: $10-24.9 Million
Emp.: 30
Weekly Legal Newspapers
N.A.I.C.S.: 513110
Amanda Passmore (Bus Mgr)

New Orleans Publishing Group,
L.L.C. (1)
3445 N Causeway Blvd Ste 901, Metairie, LA 70002
Tel.: (504) 834-9292
Web Site:
https://www.neworleanscitybusiness.com
Sales Range: $10-24.9 Million
Emp.: 22
Business Journal Publisher
N.A.I.C.S.: 513110

The Daily Record Company, LLC (1)
200 St Paul Pl Ste 2480, Baltimore, MD 21202
Tel.: (443) 524-8100
Web Site: https://www.thedailyrecord.com
Emp.: 35
Business Information Services
N.A.I.C.S.: 513199
Suzanne E. Fischer-Huettner (Grp Publr)
Thomas Baden Jr. (Editor)

The Journal Record Publishing Co.,
LLC (1)
211 N Robinson Ave Ste 201 S, Oklahoma City, OK 73102
Tel.: (405) 235-3100
Web Site: https://www.journalrecord.com
Sales Range: $25-49.9 Million
Emp.: 50
Business Information Journal Publisher
N.A.I.C.S.: 513110
Vicki Madden (Sr Acct Exec-Multimedia)
Shelly Sanderson (Acct Exec-Multimedia)
Lisa Blossman (Mng Dir)

THE DOLSEN COMPANIES, INC.
301 N 3rd St, Yakima, WA 98901-2340
Tel.: (509) 248-2831 WA
Year Founded: 1958
Sales Range: $100-124.9 Million
Emp.: 200
Provider of Dairy Farm Services
N.A.I.C.S.: 112120
Ken William (Gen Mgr)
Margaret Smart (Dir-HR)

THE DON CHAPIN CO. INC.

560 Crazy Horse Canyon Rd, Salinas, CA 93907
Tel.: (831) 449-4273
Web Site: http://www.donchapin.com
Rev.: $33,981,849
Emp.: 185
Surfacing & Paving
N.A.I.C.S.: 237310
Terry Nelson (Controller)
John LaCaze (Owner & Mgr)
Caroline D. Chapin (Exec VP)
Donald Chapin Jr. (Pres)

THE DONERAIL GROUP LP
240 26th Stt Ste 3, Santa Monica, CA 90402
Tel.: (310) 564-9990
Web Site: http://www.donerail.com
Investment Management Service
N.A.I.C.S.: 523940
Wes Calvert (Partner)

THE DONOHOE COMPANIES, INC.
7101 Wisconsin Ave Ste 700, Bethesda, MD 20814
Tel.: (202) 333-0880 DE
Web Site: http://www.donohoe.com
Year Founded: 1884
Sales Range: $200-249.9 Million
Emp.: 400
Provider of Real Estate Development & Management Services
N.A.I.C.S.: 236220
Timothy Gallagher (Pres-Real Estate Svcs)
Peter G. Gartlan (Pres-Dev)
Steven J. Dohohoe (Vice Chm & Pres-Construction)
David E. Barry (Pres-Facilities & VP-Ops)
Christopher Bruch (Pres & Co-CEO)
Nicholas M. Krieger (Controller & Asst Treas)
Eric Maggio (Co-CEO & Sr VP)
Laurie G. Ballenger (Gen Counsel & Sec)
Philip A. Carrescia (VP & Dir-Tax)
Deirdre K. Robinson (VP-HR)
Mohamed Allibhai (VP-IT)
Brian Gianfelice (VP-Risk Mgmt)
Tim Loftus (VP-Ops)
Tracy Caswell (Treas & VP)
Robert B. Donohoe Jr. (Chief Investment Officer, Sr VP & Asst Sec)
Thomas Penny III (Pres-Hospitality)

Subsidiaries:

Donohoe Construction Company (1)
2101 Wisconsin Ave NW, Washington, DC 20007
Tel.: (202) 333-0880
Web Site:
http://www.donohoeconstruction.com
Building Maintenance Services
N.A.I.C.S.: 561790
Steven J. Donohoe (Pres)
John G. Fenton (VP-Ops-Specialty Construction Div)
George B. Heacox (VP-Fin)
Robert McNeil (VP-Ops)
Larry Miller (Sr VP-Estimating & Preconstruction Svcs)
Neil Stablow (Sr VP)
Robert G. Wilson (Sr VP-Ops)
Lance M. Wolin (VP)
Steve Crowder (VP & Gen Mgr-Specialty Construction Div)

Donohoe Development Company (1)
7101 Wisconsin Ave Ste 700, Bethesda, MD 20814
Tel.: (202) 333-0880
Web Site: http://donohoe.com
Building Maintenance Services
N.A.I.C.S.: 561790
Evan J. Weisman (Sr VP)

Donohoe Hospitality Services,
LLC (1)

2101 Wisconsin Ave NW, Washington, DC 20007
Tel.: (202) 625-8400
Web Site:
 http://www.donohoehospitality.com
Home Management Services
N.A.I.C.S.: 561790
Drew McCafferty (Exec VP)
Jack D. Fritsche (CFO & Sr VP)
Deirdre Robinson (VP-HR)
Fekade Stephanos (Mgr-Info & Tech Corp)
Cheryl S. Haughton (Mgr-Market)
Leticia Proctor (Sr VP-Sls, Mktg & Revenue Mgmt)

Donohoe Real Estate Services (1)
2101 Wisconsin Ave NW, Washington, DC 20007
Tel.: (202) 333-0880
Web Site: http://www.donohoe.com
Emp.: 200
Real Estate Manangement Services
N.A.I.C.S.: 561790
Brian K. Coakley (Sr VP-Bus Dev)
Dean R. Drewyer (VP)
Timothy K. Gallagher (Pres)
Bryan S. Gray (Assoc VP)
George Labarraque (VP)
Thomas J. Long (Sr VP)
Charles M. Matincheck (Sr VP)
Don Konz (Assoc VP)
Stephen D. Colangelo (Asst VP-Facilities Mgmt)
James M. Falcone (VP)
William W. Moyer (VP-Hotel Brokerage)
Allen Owens (Asst VP)

THE DORRIS LUMBER & MOULDING CO.
2601 Redding Ave, Sacramento, CA 95820-2155
Tel.: (916) 452-7531 CA
Web Site:
 http://www.dorrismoulding.com
Year Founded: 1924
Sales Range: $100-124.9 Million
Emp.: 200
Provider of Millwork & Moulding
N.A.I.C.S.: 321918
Robert Reynolds (Mgr-Sls)
Joshua Tyler (Pres)
Dennis Murcko (CFO)
Kathy Saito (Mgr-Mktg-Sls)

THE DOT NET FACTORY LLC
4393-A & 4353-D Tuller Rd, Dublin, OH 43017-5106
Tel.: (614) 652-6825
Web Site: http://www.empowerid.com
Year Founded: 2005
Sales Range: $1-9.9 Million
Identity Management, Cloud Security & Workflow Automation Solutions
N.A.I.C.S.: 513210
Patrick Parker (Co-Founder & CEO)
Bradford Mandell (Co-Founder & Gen Partner)
Carles Dalmau (VP-Product Architecture)

THE DOUGLAS COMPANY, INC.
1716 Perrysburg Holland Rd, Holland, OH 43528-9581
Tel.: (419) 865-8600 OH
Web Site:
 http://www.douglascompany.com
Year Founded: 1976
Sales Range: $100-124.9 Million
Emp.: 50
Multifamily, Retail & Commercial Building Construction
N.A.I.C.S.: 236220
Peter Douglas (Pres)
Brian McCarthy (VP-Construction)
David L. Bockbrader (Exec VP)
Ronald E. Siebenaler (VP-Construction)
Dave Kelbley (CFO & VP)
Bob Ritter (Dir-Bus Dev)
Paul Rooney (Exec VP)
Bruce Douglas (Dir-Preconstruction Svcs)

THE DOUGLAS STEWART COMPANY INC.
2402 Advance Rd, Madison, WI 53718-6737
Tel.: (608) 221-1155 WI
Web Site: http://www.dstewart.com
Year Founded: 1945
Sales Range: $75-99.9 Million
Emp.: 150
Computers, Peripherals & Software
N.A.I.C.S.: 423430
Chuck Hulan (Pres & CEO)
Angela Bluhm (Mgr-Mktg)
Robert Bernier (COO)
Peter W. Collins (CFO)

THE DOW HOTEL COMPANY LLC
16400 Southcenter Pkwy Ste 405, Seattle, WA 98188
Tel.: (206) 575-3600
Web Site:
 http://www.dowhotelco.com
Year Founded: 1997
Sales Range: $500-549.9 Million
Emp.: 1,484
Owns & Manages Hotels
N.A.I.C.S.: 721110
Robert Levy (Sr VP-Asset Dev)
David Fincannon (Reg VP)
Randall King (COO & Exec VP)
Stephen Griffin (CFO & Exec VP)
A. J. Kamra (VP-HR)
Tracey Vargas (Asst Dir-Corp & HR)
Greg Denton (Sr VP-Hotel Investments)
Lisa Martin (Controller)
Murray L. Dow II (Founder & Pres)

Subsidiaries:

Embassy Suites Chicago O'Hare-Rosemont (1)
5500 River Rd N, Des Plaines, IL 60018
Tel.: (847) 678-4000
Web Site: http://www.embassyohare.com
Sales Range: $10-24.9 Million
Emp.: 150
Hotel Services
N.A.I.C.S.: 721110
Bill Mcguigan (Dir-Sls)

THE DOZIER COMPANY
2547 Farrington St, Dallas, TX 75207-6607
Tel.: (214) 744-2800
Web Site:
 http://www.thedoziercompany.com
Year Founded: 1987
Sales Range: $10-24.9 Million
Emp.: 10
Advertising Services
N.A.I.C.S.: 541810
David C. Dozier (Principal)
Connie Dozier (Principal)
Michael Dozier (Pres)

THE DREES COMPANY, INC.
211 Grandview Dr, Fort Mitchell, KY 41017-2097
Tel.: (859) 578-4200 KY
Web Site:
 http://www.dreeshomes.com
Year Founded: 1928
Sales Range: $800-899.9 Million
Emp.: 700
Single Family Attached & Detached Home Apartment Community & Commercial Office & Retail Land Development Contractor Services
N.A.I.C.S.: 236115
David Drees (Pres & CEO)

Subsidiaries:

Drees Homes (1)
7210 Corporate Ct, Frederick, MD 21703
Tel.: (301) 663-6104
Web Site: http://www.dreeshomes.com
Sales Range: $25-49.9 Million
Emp.: 50
Single Family Homes & Townhouses Construction Services
N.A.I.C.S.: 236115
Deveraux Hamilton (Gen Mgr-Offsite Div)
David Hausfeld (Pres-Southeast)
Jennifer Zabkar (Pres-Cleveland)
Andy Seitz (VP-Land)

Drees Preferred Collection, Inc. (1)
211 Grandview Dr Ste 100, Fort Mitchell, KY 41017-2726 (100%)
Tel.: (859) 578-4200
Web Site: http://www.dreeshomes.com
Sales Range: $50-74.9 Million
Emp.: 400
Custom Site-Built Home Building Services
N.A.I.C.S.: 236115
David Drees (CEO)
Ralph Drees (Chm)
Mark Williams (CFO)
Jack Schroeder (Controller)
Larry Herbst (Treas & Sr VP)

THE DRUKER COMPANY, LTD.
50 Federal St, Boston, MA 02110
Tel.: (617) 357-5700
Year Founded: 1901
Sales Range: $10-24.9 Million
Emp.: 326
Hotel & Motel Operating Services
N.A.I.C.S.: 721110
Ronald M. Druker (Pres)

THE DUCHOSSOIS GROUP, INC.
444 W Lake St Ste 2000, Chicago, IL 60606
Tel.: (312) 586-2110 DE
Web Site: http://www.duch.com
Year Founded: 1916
Sales Range: $1-4.9 Billion
Emp.: 300
Holding Company
N.A.I.C.S.: 551112
Craig J. Duchossois (Chm)

Subsidiaries:

Controlled Products Systems Group, Inc. (1)
5000 Osage St Ste 500, Denver, CO 80221
Tel.: (303) 333-1141
Web Site:
 http://www.controlledproducts.com
Perimeter Access Control Equipment Whslr
N.A.I.C.S.: 423990
Lilia Diaz (Branch Mgr-Miami)
Andy Smith (Branch Mgr-Albuquerque)
Brian Pruitt (Branch Mgr-Atlanta)
Adam Witczak (Branch Mgr-Cleveland)
Alan Crenshaw (Branch Mgr-Columbus)
Daron Jaco (Branch Mgr-Corona)
Henry Hinojoza (Branch Mgr-Dallas & Plano-CPSG)
Teresa Moya (Branch Mgr-Escondido)
Dean Brown (Branch Mgr-Ft Lauderdale)
Stephen Epperson (Branch Mgr-Houston)
Jimmy Lee (Branch Mgr-Long Island)
Darren Avant (Branch Mgr-Los Angeles)
John Insani (Branch Mgr-Nashville)
Esmeralda Lozano (Branch Mgr-North Hollywood)
Robert Hobbick (Branch Mgr-Orlando)
Chris Garcia (Branch Mgr-Orange)
Jason Krenke (Branch Mgr-Phoenix)
Chris Peterson (Branch Mgr-Plano-RFID)
Brian Powell (Branch Mgr-Salt Lake City)
Kurt Starry (Branch Mgr-Denver)

Branch (Domestic):

Controlled Products Systems Group, Inc. - Los Angeles (2)
15541 Broadway Ctr St, Gardena, CA 90248-2137
Tel.: (310) 217-0675
Web Site:
 http://www.controlledproducts.com
Perimeter Access Control Equipment Whslr
N.A.I.C.S.: 423990
Darren Avant (Branch Mgr)

Duchossois Capital Management LLC (1)
444 W Lake St Ste 2000, Chicago, IL 60606
Tel.: (312) 586-2080
Web Site: http://www.dcmllc.com
Privater Equity Firm
N.A.I.C.S.: 523999
Michael E. Flannery (CEO)
Eric A. Reeves (Mng Dir & Chief Admin Officer)
Craig J. Duchossois (Chm)
Michael E. Flannery (CEO)
David J. Jallits (Chief Invesgtment Officer)
William J. Connell (CFO)
Jason B. Moskowitz (Partner)
Lauren K. Bugay (Principal)
Thomas E. Costello (Mng Dir)
Michelle A. Waldusky (Mgr-Investment Ops)

The Chamberlain Group, LLC (1)
300 Windsor Dr, Oak Brook, IL 60523 (100%)
Tel.: (630) 279-3600
Web Site: http://www.chamberlaingroup.com
Garage Door Openers, Remote Access Control Systems & Communication Systems Mfr, Sales & Installation Services
N.A.I.C.S.: 335999
JoAnna L. Sohovich (Chm)

Subsidiary (Domestic):

Chamberlain Manufacturing Corp. (2)
845 N Larch Ave, Elmhurst, IL 60126-1114
Tel.: (630) 279-3600
Web Site: http://www.chamberlin.com
Sales Range: $250-299.9 Million
Emp.: 200
Ordnance Products, Research & Development
N.A.I.C.S.: 333992

Subsidiary (Domestic):

Guardian Gate Hardware, LLC (3)
4261 S Country Club Rd, Tucson, AZ 85714-2009
Tel.: (520) 881-3380
Web Site:
 http://www.guardiangatehardware.com
Sales Range: $1-9.9 Million
Emp.: 35
Gate Hardware Mfr
N.A.I.C.S.: 332510

Guardian Traffic Systems, LLC (3)
4261 S Country Club Rd, Tucson, AZ 85714-2009
Tel.: (520) 881-3380
Web Site: http://www.guardiantraffic.com
Sales Range: $1-9.9 Million
Traffic Road Spikes & Barrier Systems Mfr
N.A.I.C.S.: 339999

THE DUGGAN RHODES GROUP
310 Grant St Ste 2300, Pittsburgh, PA 15219
Tel.: (412) 227-3670
Web Site: http://www.rhodes-group.com
Year Founded: 1999
Sales Range: $1-9.9 Million
Emp.: 21
Boutique Construction Consulting
N.A.I.C.S.: 236115
Andrew Rhodes (Pres)
Shawn Modar (VP)
Michael Birmingham (Exec Dir)
Leroy Trimbath (Exec Dir)
Carren Gallick (Project Mgr)
Jeffrey Hogan (Project Mgr)
Donald Kaplan (Project Mgr)
Nathan McNeil (Project Mgr)

THE DUNE COMPANY OF IMPERIAL VALLEY INC.

THE DUNE COMPANY OF IMPERIAL VALLEY INC.   U.S. PRIVATE

The Dune Company of Imperial Valley Inc.—(Continued)
521 E 2nd St, Imperial, CA 92251-1714
Tel.: (760) 352-0134
Web Site: http://www.gowan.net
Year Founded: 1975
Sales Range: $10-24.9 Million
Emp.: 60
Retail Services
N.A.I.C.S.: 459999
John Jessen *(Pres)*

THE DUPPS COMPANY
548 N Cherry St, Germantown, OH 45327-0189
Tel.: (937) 855-6555   OH
Web Site: http://www.dupps.com
Year Founded: 1935
Sales Range: $75-99.9 Million
Emp.: 150
Recycling & Food Product Machinery Mfr
N.A.I.C.S.: 333241
John A. Dupps Jr. *(Chm)*

Subsidiaries:

The Dupps Company Thermal Technology Div.   (1)
548 N Cherry St, Germantown, OH 45327-0189
Tel.: (937) 855-6555
Web Site: http://www.dupps.com
Sales Range: $25-49.9 Million
Emp.: 146
Food Processing Machinery Mfr
N.A.I.C.S.: 333241
Jim Vose *(Mgr-HR)*

THE DUTRA GROUP INC.
1000 Point San Pedro Rd, San Rafael, CA 94901-8312
Tel.: (415) 258-6876
Web Site: http://www.dutragroup.com
Year Founded: 1973
Sales Range: $25-49.9 Million
Emp.: 280
Heavy Construction Services
N.A.I.C.S.: 236210
Bill Dutra *(Exec Chm)*
Aimi Dutra *(Dir-PR)*
Chris Peterson *(Mgr-Alameda Marine Facility & Heavy)*
Aaron Johnson *(Mgr-Materials Div)*
Chuck Walker *(Mgr-Delta Div)*
James Hagood *(CFO)*
Molly F. Jacobson *(Chief Admin Officer & Gen Counsel)*
Harry K. Stewart *(CEO)*

Subsidiaries:

San Rafael Rock Quarry Inc.   (1)
1000 Point San Pedro Rd, San Rafael, CA 94901-8312
Tel.: (415) 459-7740
Web Site: http://www.dutragroup.com
Sales Range: $25-49.9 Million
Emp.: 100
Sale of Crushed & Broken Stone
N.A.I.C.S.: 212319
Bill Dutra *(CEO)*

THE DYSON-KISSNER-MORAN CORPORATION
2515 South Rd 5th Fl, Poughkeepsie, NY 12601-9971
Tel.: (212) 661-4600   DE
Web Site: http://www.dkmcorp.com
Year Founded: 1954
Sales Range: $800-899.9 Million
Emp.: 4,600
Holding Company
N.A.I.C.S.: 551112
Robert R. Dyson *(Chm & CEO)*
Mark Chamberlin *(CFO & Sr VP)*
Pamela M. Lunny *(Controller)*
John H. FitzSimmons *(Gen Counsel, Sec & Sr VP)*
Lynn A. McCluskey *(Treas & VP)*
Michael J. Harris *(Pres & COO)*

Subsidiaries:

Coto Technology, Inc.   (1)
66 Whitecap Dr, North Kingstown, RI 02852
Tel.: (401) 943-2686
Web Site: http://www.cotorelay.com
Sales Range: $200-249.9 Million
Emp.: 20
Coil Winding Reed Relay & Switche & NENS-based Sensor Mfr
N.A.I.C.S.: 335314
Bob Gentry *(Mgr-Product Mktg)*

Subsidiary (Non-US):

Coto Technology, Inc.   (2)
7F No 33 Sec 1 Jongsiao W Road, Taipei, Taiwan
Tel.: (886) 2 24220368
Coil Winding & Reed Relay Mfr & Distr
N.A.I.C.S.: 334416

HAPCO   (1)
26252 Hillman Hwy, Abingdon, VA 24210
Tel.: (276) 628-7171
Web Site: http://www.hapco.com
Sales Range: $25-49.9 Million
Emp.: 145
Aluminum Lighting & Traffic Signal Support Structures
N.A.I.C.S.: 332323
Bob Bell *(Mgr-Sls)*
John Costello *(Mgr-Sls)*
Ann Ferguson *(Mgr-Customer Svc)*
Britty Hunt *(Mgr-Sls)*
Ray Reuning *(Mgr-Natl Sls)*
Eddie Roberts *(Mgr-Sls)*
Chad Thompson *(Mgr-Inside Sls)*

Plaid Enterprises, Inc.   (1)
3225 Westech Dr, Norcross, GA 30092-3500
Tel.: (678) 291-8100
Web Site: http://www.plaidonline.com
Sales Range: $25-49.9 Million
Emp.: 200
Broad Line Craft Product Mfr
N.A.I.C.S.: 339940
Mike Mccooey *(Pres, CEO & COO)*
Marilyn Jones *(Deputy Pres)*
Erica Stephens *(Mgr-Commodity)*
Katrien Van Minsel *(Mgr-Sls-Intl)*

Thetford Corporation   (1)
7101 Jackson Rd, Ann Arbor, MI 48103
Tel.: (734) 769-6000
Web Site: http://www.thetford.com
Sales Range: $75-99.9 Million
Emp.: 300
Sanitation Products & Systems For Recreation Vehicles Mfr & Whslr
N.A.I.C.S.: 335220
William Croonenberg *(Sr VP-European Opers)*
Brett Motheral *(Dir-Aftermarket Sls)*
Stephane Cordeille *(CEO)*
Barry Eckel *(Exec VP-Americas)*
Pete Salmon *(VP-Ops)*
Mary Pouliot *(VP-Sls & Mktg)*
Alissa Reyes *(VP-HR)*

Division (Domestic):

Norcold   (2)
600 S Kuther Rd, Sidney, OH 45365-8840   (100%)
Tel.: (937) 497-3080
Web Site: http://www.norcold.com
Sales Range: $25-49.9 Million
Emp.: 300
Household Appliances Mfr
N.A.I.C.S.: 335220
Mike Mesharer *(Dir-RV Sls-Thetford)*
John Johnson *(Gen Mgr)*
Kevin Phillips *(VP-Sls & Mktg)*

Subsidiary (Non-US):

Thetford B.V.   (2)
29 Nijverheidsweg, PO Box 169, Etten-Leur, 4879 AP, Netherlands   (100%)
Tel.: (31) 765042200
Web Site: http://www.thetford-europe.com
Emp.: 350
Distribution of Sanitary Ware
N.A.I.C.S.: 423720
Bartho Anderson *(Mgr-HR)*
Peter Struijs *(Dir-Fin)*
Martin Roos *(Dir-Mktg)*
Martin Deroos *(Dir-Mktg)*

Division (Domestic):

Thetford Corp. - Warehousing Div   (2)
800 Baker Rd, Dexter, MI 48130-1517   (100%)
Tel.: (734) 769-6000
Web Site: http://www.thetford.com
Sales Range: $25-49.9 Million
Emp.: 200
Warehousing Services
N.A.I.C.S.: 493110

Thetford Corp. Manufacturing Facility   (2)
800 Baker Rd, Dexter, MI 48130-1517   (100%)
Tel.: (734) 769-6000
Web Site: http://www.thetford.com
Sales Range: $25-49.9 Million
Emp.: 150
Mfr of Plastic Plumbing Fixtures
N.A.I.C.S.: 332999

Tri-City Extrusion, Inc.   (1)
1610 Arkansas Ave, Bristol, TN 37620
Tel.: (423) 764-8931
Web Site: http://www.tricityextrusion.com
Aluminum Extrusion Product Mfr
N.A.I.C.S.: 331313
Terry Mullins *(Mgr-Sls)*
Robert Buckles *(Dir-HR)*
Wendy Rumley *(Mgr-Sls)*

THE E.B. BRADLEY CO., INC.
5080 S Alameda St, Los Angeles, CA 90058-2810
Tel.: (323) 585-9917   CA
Web Site: http://www.ebbradley.com
Year Founded: 1929
Rev.: $57,000,000
Emp.: 225
Wholesale Distributor of Cabinet Hardware, Surfacing Products, Woodworking & Flooring Supplies
N.A.I.C.S.: 423710
Robert E. Bradley Jr. *(CEO)*
Don Lorey *(Pres)*

Subsidiaries:

West Coast Laminating LLC   (1)
13833 Borate St, Santa Fe Springs, CA 90670
Tel.: (562) 906-2489
Web Site: http://www.ebbradley.com
Sales Range: $10-24.9 Million
Emp.: 15
Prefabricated Wood Buildings
N.A.I.C.S.: 321992

THE EADS COMPANY
13843 N Promenade Blvd Ste 100, Stafford, TX 77477
Tel.: (281) 243-2900
Web Site: http://www.eadsdistribution.com
Year Founded: 1953
Rev.: $12,400,000
Emp.: 60
Industrial Supply Whslr
N.A.I.C.S.: 423840

Subsidiaries:

Control Equipment Company   (1)
605 Commerce Park Dr, Marietta, GA 30060-2742
Tel.: (770) 427-8776
Web Site: http://www.cecsales.com
Emp.: 31
Business to Business Electronic Markets
N.A.I.C.S.: 425120
Silvia Little *(Controller)*
Janice Balko *(Mgr-Ops)*

Jatasco, Inc.   (1)
3702 S Elwood Ave, Tulsa, OK 74107
Tel.: (918) 627-4381
Web Site: http://www.jatasco.com
Sales Range: $1-9.9 Million
Emp.: 14
Industrial Machinery & Equipment Merchant Whslr
N.A.I.C.S.: 423830
John Strauss *(Branch Mgr)*

THE EAGLE GROUP
100 Industial Blvd, Clayton, DE 19938
Tel.: (302) 653-3000   MD
Web Site: http://www.eaglegrp.com
Sales Range: $150-199.9 Million
Emp.: 360
Commercial Food Equipment Mfr
N.A.I.C.S.: 333310
Larry N. McAllister *(Pres)*
Mark Brenner *(VP-Sls-FoodService Div)*

THE EARLY LEARNING COALITION OF FLAGLER AND VOLUSIA COUNTIES, INC.
135 Executive Cir Ste 100, Daytona Beach, FL 32114
Tel.: (386) 323-2400   FL
Web Site: http://www.elcfv.org
Year Founded: 2005
Sales Range: $10-24.9 Million
Emp.: 51
Child Care Services
N.A.I.C.S.: 624110
D. J. Lebo *(Exec Dir)*

THE EASTON GROUP
10165 NW 19th St, Miami, FL 33172
Tel.: (305) 593-2222
Web Site: http://www.theeastongroup.com
Year Founded: 1974
Sales Range: $1-9.9 Million
Emp.: 20
Real Estate Brokerage Services
N.A.I.C.S.: 531210
Edward W. Easton *(Chm)*
Edward J. Easton *(VP-Sls & Investments)*
Jose A. Hernandez-Solaun *(Pres)*
Elliot LaBreche *(VP)*

THE EASTRIDGE GROUP, INC.
2355 Northside Dr Ste 100, San Diego, CA 92108
Tel.: (619) 260-2000
Web Site: http://www.eastridge.com
Year Founded: 1971
Rev.: $86,000,000
Emp.: 220
Provider of Employment Services
N.A.I.C.S.: 561311
Robert Svet *(Founder & Pres)*
Debra Thompson *(Controller)*

Subsidiaries:

Abbott Staffing Group   (1)
1201 Dove St Ste 600, Newport Beach, CA 92660
Tel.: (949) 756-8000
Web Site: http://www.abbottstaffinggroup.com
Sales Range: $25-49.9 Million
Emp.: 25
Employment Agencies
N.A.I.C.S.: 561311
Seth Stein *(Pres)*
Lina Savage *(Area Mgr-Direct Hire Staffing)*
Jairo Carrion *(Exec VP)*
Judith L. Enns *(Exec VP)*
Brandon Stanford *(CFO)*
Robert Svet *(Founder & CEO)*
Brad Taylor *(CIO)*

Eastridge Personnel of Las Vegas   (1)
650 White Dr, Las Vegas, NV 89119
Tel.: (702) 854-1760
Rev.: $30,553,139
Employment Mangement Services
N.A.I.C.S.: 561311

COMPANIES

THE EBELING GROUP, INC.
628 California Ave, Venice, CA 90291
Tel.: (310) 577-9963   CA
Web Site:
  http://www.theebelinggroup.com
Advetising Agency
N.A.I.C.S.: 541810
Leslie G. Ebeling (Founder & CEO)
Terrence Bergeron (Head-Brdcst)

THE ECHO DESIGN GROUP, INC.
10 E 40th St 16th Fl, New York, NY 10016
Tel.: (212) 686-8771   NY
Web Site:
  http://www.echodesign.com
Year Founded: 1923
Sales Range: $50-74.9 Million
Emp.: 200
Scarfs, Fashion Accessories, Handbags & Home Products Designer & Distr
N.A.I.C.S.: 424350
Dorothy H. Roberts (Chm)
Steven D. Roberts (Pres & CEO)
Geri Riordan (Mng Dir)
Susan Farrell (CFO)
Jacki Wilson (VP-Bus Dev-Phoenix)

THE ECONOMIC DEVELOPMENT CORPORATION OF KANSAS CITY, MISSOURI
300 Wyandotte Ste 400, Kansas City, MO 64105
Tel.: (816) 221-0636   MO
Web Site: http://www.edckc.com
Year Founded: 1978
Sales Range: $1-9.9 Million
Emp.: 34
Economic Development Services
N.A.I.C.S.: 541720
Rick DeSimone (Accountant)
T'Risa McCord (Chief Admin Officer & Sr VP)
Sandra Rayford (Mgr-Contract Compliance)
Greg Flisram (Sr VP-Bus & Real Estate Dev)
Alan Ballew (Mgr-IT)
Lee Brown (Controller)

THE ECONOMY ADVERTISING COMPANY INC.
2800 Hwy 6 E, Iowa City, IA 52240-2614
Tel.: (319) 337-9623   IA
Web Site: http://www.truart.com
Year Founded: 1896
Sales Range: $10-24.9 Million
Emp.: 110
Provider of Commercial Printing Services
N.A.I.C.S.: 323111
Cory Cremers (CFO)
Steve Horner (Dir-Bus Dev)
Erica Kelley Gogel (VP-Sls)
Bob Kral (Sr VP-Mktg)
Keisha Tompkin (Dir-Ops)

THE EDUCATION TRUST
1250 H St NW Ste 700, Washington, DC 20005
Tel.: (202) 293-1217   DC
Web Site: http://www.edtrust.org
Year Founded: 1996
Sales Range: $10-24.9 Million
Emp.: 83
Educational Support Services
N.A.I.C.S.: 611710
Christina Theokas (Dir-Res)
Robin Harris Smiles (Mng Editor)
Nicolle Grayson (Dir-Comm)
Jose Luis Santos (VP-Higher Education Policy & Practice)
Sonja Santelises (VP-K-12 Policy & Practice)
Andrew Nichols (Dir-Higher Education Res & Data Analytics)
David Britt (Chm)
Deborah Veney (VP-Govt Affairs & Comm)
Ericka Miller (VP-Ops & Strategic Leadership)
John King (Pres & CEO)

THE EDWARD S. QUIRK CO., INC.
12 Lexington St, Lewiston, ME 04240
Tel.: (207) 784-5423
Sales Range: $10-24.9 Million
Automobile Tires & Tubes Whslr
N.A.I.C.S.: 423130
John Quirk (Owner & Pres)

Subsidiaries:

VIP Inc.   (1)
12 Lexington St, Lewiston, ME 04240-3509
Tel.: (207) 784-5423
Web Site: http://www.vipauto.com
Sales Range: $50-74.9 Million
Provider of Auto Supplies
N.A.I.C.S.: 441330
John Quirk (Pres & CEO)
Allan Kirkland (VP-Fin)

THE EGAN COMPANIES
7625 Boone Ave N, Brooklyn Park, MN 55428
Tel.: (763) 544-4131   MN
Web Site: http://www.eganco.com
Year Founded: 1950
Sales Range: $125-149.9 Million
Emp.: 900
Mechanical & Electrical Contractors, Curtainwall, Insulation
N.A.I.C.S.: 238220
Duane Hendricks (Pres & CEO)
Tim Woolworth (Sr VP)
Jim Nonn (CIO)
James Ford (CFO)

Subsidiaries:

Egan Automation, Inc.   (1)
7625 Boon Ave N, Brooklyn Park, MN 55428-3502
Tel.: (763) 544-4131
Web Site: http://www.egan.com
Rev.: $17,000,000
Emp.: 100
Building Automation; Control-Systems; Fire Alarms; Building Monitoring Systems
N.A.I.C.S.: 238210
Duane Hendricks (COO)

Egan Electrical Contractors   (1)
7625 Boone Ave N, Brooklyn Park, MN 55428-1011   (100%)
Tel.: (763) 544-4131
Web Site: http://www.eganco.com
Sales Range: $100-124.9 Million
Emp.: 100
Electrical Contractor
N.A.I.C.S.: 238210
Duane Hendricks (Exec VP)

Egan Mechanical Contractors Inc.   (1)
7625 Boone Ave N, Brooklyn Park, MN 55428   (100%)
Tel.: (763) 544-4131
Web Site: http://www.eganco.com
Sales Range: $50-74.9 Million
Warm Air Heating & Air Conditioning Contractor
N.A.I.C.S.: 238220

Industrial Electric Company   (1)
7625 Boone Ave N, Brooklyn Park, MN 55428
Tel.: (763) 544-4131
Sales Range: $10-24.9 Million
Emp.: 65
Electrical Contractor
N.A.I.C.S.: 238210

Interclad   (1)
11611 Business Park Blvd, Champlin, MN 55316   (100%)
Tel.: (763) 544-4131
Web Site: http://www.eganco.com
Rev.: $18,000,000
Emp.: 100
Mfr & Installer of External Clad Metal & Glass
N.A.I.C.S.: 332812
Tim Woolworth (Exec VP)

Nietz Electric, Inc.   (1)
4475 Highway 14 W, Rochester, MN 55901
Tel.: (507) 289-4522
Electrical Contractor
N.A.I.C.S.: 238210
Rachel Welt (Controller)

THE EGC GROUP
1175 Walt Whitman Rd Ste 200, Melville, NY 11747-3030
Tel.: (516) 935-4944
Web Site: http://www.egcgroup.com
Year Founded: 1985
Sales Range: $25-49.9 Million
Emp.: 35
N.A.I.C.S.: 541810
Ernest G. Canadeo (Founder & CEO)
Angela Raduazzo Mertz (Dir-Media)
Nicole Bardsley (Dir-Client Svcs)
Tony Pasquariello (Acct Supvr)
Len Rothberg (Sr Acct Mgr)
Fred Appel (Sr Dir-Art)
Steve Commando (Sr Dir-Art-Print & Interactive)
Nicole Larrauri (Pres)
Christine Carroll (Acct Supvr)
Tony Volado (VP)
Rich DeSimone (Assoc Dir-Creative)
Kim Sivillo (Acct Supvr)
Meg Parente (Acct Supvr)
Shawn Haarstick (Dir-Art)
Amanda Mauceri (Coord-Acct & Social Media)
Stephanie Robedee (Acct Exec)
Stephanie Weingart (Mgr-Community & Coord-Social Media)

THE EISEN AGENCY
515 Monmouth St Ste 302, Newport, KY 41071
Tel.: (859) 291-4302
Web Site:
  http://www.theeisenagency.com
Year Founded: 2005
Sales Range: $1-9.9 Million
Emp.: 16
Marketing Consulting Services
N.A.I.C.S.: 541613
Rodger Roeser (Owner & CEO)
Elizabeth Schuler (Acct Mgr)
Cresta Lewis (VP-Client Svcs)
Christine Cornelius (Acct Coord)

THE ELECTRIC CAR COMPANY
1903 N Barnes Ave, Springfield, MO 65803
Tel.: (417) 866-6565
Electric Vehicle Mfr
N.A.I.C.S.: 336110
Gary Spaniak (Pres)

THE ELECTRONIC EXPRESS INC.
418 Harding Industrial Dr, Nashville, TN 37211
Tel.: (615) 259-2031   TN
Web Site:
  http://www.electronicexpress.com
Year Founded: 1983
Sales Range: $25-49.9 Million
Emp.: 100
Radio, Television & Electronics Sales
N.A.I.C.S.: 449210
Sam Yazdian (Pres)
Abe Yazdian (Treas & Sec)
Fred Yazdian (VP)

THE ELKHART COOPERATIVE EQUITY EXCHANGE
840 Border Ave, Elkhart, KS 67950
Tel.: (620) 697-2135   KS
Web Site: http://www.elkhart.coop
Year Founded: 1917
Sales Range: $10-24.9 Million
Emp.: 40
Grain Storage, Crop & Livestock Supplies
N.A.I.C.S.: 493130
Morgan Walls (Gen Mgr)

THE ELLIOT GROUP LLC
505 White Plains Rd Ste 228, New York, NY 10591
Tel.: (914) 631-4904
Web Site:
  http://www.theelliotgroup.com
Executive Search Service
N.A.I.C.S.: 561312
Alice Elliot (Founder & CEO)
Catalina Ganis (Exec VP)
Bernadette Kane (Exec VP)
Gerri Kies (Exec VP)
Joan Ray (Exec VP)
Jeff Gillett (Exec VP)
Rodney Morris (Sr VP)
Connie Paris (Sr VP)
Paula Renick (Sr VP)
Dan Searby (Sr VP)
John Pothin (Sr VP)
Carol Cozzi (Office Mgr)
Laura Scott (Dir-Ops Support)

THE ELLISON CO. INC.
706 Green Vly Rd Ste 504, Greensboro, NC 27408
Tel.: (336) 275-8565
Sales Range: $100-124.9 Million
Emp.: 150
Radiographic X-Ray Apparatus & Tubes
N.A.I.C.S.: 334517
John B. Ellison Jr. (Pres)

THE ELOCEN GROUP LLC
1341 H St NE Ste 301, Washington, DC 20002
Tel.: (202) 644-8500
Web Site:
  http://www.elocengroup.com
Year Founded: 2007
Sales Range: $1-9.9 Million
Emp.: 64
Consulting Services
N.A.I.C.S.: 541611
Necole Parker (CEO)
Taryn Butler Lewis (Dir-Ops)

THE ELTRON COMPANY
3611 Cahuenga Blvd W, Hollywood, CA 90068
Tel.: (323) 876-5454   CA
Web Site:
  http://www.eltronshavers.com
Year Founded: 1957
Sales Range: $50-74.9 Million
Emp.: 25
Electric Shavers & Shaving Accessories Mfr
N.A.I.C.S.: 541810
John R. Parks (Pres)

Subsidiaries:

The Eltron Co.   (1)
3611 Cahuenga Blvd W, Hollywood, CA 90068-1205   (100%)
Tel.: (323) 876-5454
Web Site: http://www.eltronshavers.com
Sales Range: $10-24.9 Million
Emp.: 20
Electric Shavers & Shaving Accessories Mfr
N.A.I.C.S.: 335210

THE EMBARRAS RIVER BA-

THE EMBARRAS RIVER BA—(CONTINUED)

SIN AGENCY, INC.
400 W Pleasant St, Greenup, IL 62428
Tel.: (217) 923-3113
Web Site: http://www.erbainc.org
Year Founded: 1965
Sales Range: $10-24.9 Million
Emp.: 234
Individual & Family Support Services
N.A.I.C.S.: 624190
Marsha Roll (Exec Dir)

THE EMPIRE
1520 Sawgrass Village Dr Ste351, Ponte Vedra Beach, FL 32082
Tel.: (904) 708-9434
Year Founded: 1995
Rev.: $15,000,000
Emp.: 20
Advertising Agencies, Brand Development, Full Service, Graphic Design, Internet/Web Design, Strategic Planning
N.A.I.C.S.: 541810
William Robinson (CEO & Exec Dir-Creative)

THE ENERGY & MINERALS GROUP LP
2229 San Felipe St Ste 1300, Houston, TX 77019
Tel.: (713) 579-5000
Web Site: http://www.emgtx.com
Privater Equity Firm
N.A.I.C.S.: 523999
John T. Raymond (CEO & Mng Partner)

Subsidiaries:

The Energy & Minerals Group LP - Dallas Office (1)
2000 McKinney Ave Ste 1250, Dallas, TX 75201-1985
Tel.: (972) 432-1800
Web Site: http://www.emgtx.com
Privater Equity Firm
N.A.I.C.S.: 523999
John T. Raymond (CEO & Mng Partner)

THE ENERGY COOPERATIVE, INC.
1500 Granville Rd, Newark, OH 43055-1536
Tel.: (740) 344-2102
Web Site: http://www.theenergycoop.com
Year Founded: 1981
Sales Range: $10-24.9 Million
Emp.: 168
Electric, Gas & Oil Cooperative
N.A.I.C.S.: 813990
Todd P. Ware (Pres/CEO-Licking Rural Electrification)
Pat McGonagle (CFO & VP)
Gary Glover (COO & VP)
Connie Hogue (Dir-HR)
Lija Kaleps-Clark (Dir-Land & Legal Svcs Office)

Subsidiaries:

National Gas & Oil Cooperative (1)
1500 Granville Rd, Newark, OH 43055-1536 (100%)
Tel.: (740) 344-2102
Natural Gas Cooperative
N.A.I.C.S.: 813990
Todd P. Ware (Pres/CEO-Licking Rural Electrification)
Andy Nader (Coord-Safety & Trng)

Subsidiary (Domestic):

NGO Development Corporation (2)
1500 Granville Rd, Newark, OH 43055 (100%)
Tel.: (740) 344-2102

Exploration, Development & Production of Oil & Gas
N.A.I.C.S.: 486210

National Gas & Oil Company (2)
1500 Granville Rd, Newark, OH 43058-4970 (100%)
Tel.: (740) 344-2102
Rev.: $22,000,000
Emp.: 90
Natural Gas Public Utility
N.A.I.C.S.: 486210

Subsidiary (Domestic):

NGO Propane Cooperative (3)
2820 S River Rd, Wayne, OH 43466
Tel.: (740) 455-9200
Propane Fuel Distr
N.A.I.C.S.: 424720

NGO Transmission, Inc. (3)
1500 Granville Rd, Newark, OH 43058-4970
Tel.: (800) 255-6815
Web Site: http://www.ngotransmission.com
Natural Gas Transportation Services
N.A.I.C.S.: 486210
Todd Ware (Pres)
Pat McGonagle (CFO)
Dan McVey (COO)
Donald C. Wheeler (Mgr-Ops)

Subsidiary (Domestic):

Producers Gas Sales, Inc. (2)
1500 Granville Rd, Newark, OH 43055 (100%)
Tel.: (740) 344-2102
Rev.: $5,000,000
Emp.: 60
Marketing of Natural Gas for Producers to End User
N.A.I.C.S.: 221210
Todd P. Ware (CFO)

THE ENERGY FOUNDATION
301 Battery St 5th Fl, San Francisco, CA 94111
Tel.: (415) 561-6700
Web Site: http://www.ef.org
Year Founded: 1991
Sales Range: $125-149.9 Million
Emp.: 55
Energy Conservation Services
N.A.I.C.S.: 813312
Jenny Coyle (Mgr-Comm-Strategic Partnerships)
Carrie Doyle (VP-Pub Engagement)
Jason Mark (Sr VP-Programs)
Barbara Wagner (COO & Sr VP)

THE ENGINE ROOM
109 Night Heron Ln, Aliso Viejo, CA 92656
Tel.: (949) 683-3227
Web Site: http://www.the-engine-room.net
Sales Range: Less than $1 Million
Emp.: 2
Advertising & Design Company
N.A.I.C.S.: 541810
Steve Lauri (Pres & Dir-Creative)
Jim Bazis (Dir-Tech)

THE ENGLE GROUP
1420 Springhill Rd Ste 400, McLean, VA 22102
Tel.: (703) 247-1400
Web Site: http://www.theenglegroup.com
Year Founded: 1984
Rev.: $6,800,000
Emp.: 50
Information Technology Services
N.A.I.C.S.: 541519
Marty Engle (Founder & CEO)
Jennifer Luce (VP-Ops)

THE ENJOIYA GROUP, LLC
1740 Massachusetts Ave, Boxborough, MA 01719

Web Site: http://www.enjoiyagroup.com
Women's Shoe Designer, Mfr & Distr
N.A.I.C.S.: 316210
Frank Cammarata (CEO & Principal)

THE ENKEBOLL COMPANY
16506 Avalon Blvd, Carson, CA 90746-1096
Tel.: (310) 532-1400
Web Site: http://www.enkeboll.com
Year Founded: 1956
Sales Range: $25-49.9 Million
Emp.: 107
Architectural Accents Mfr
N.A.I.C.S.: 337212
Xavier Durcholz (Owner)

THE ENTRUST GROUP, INC.
555 12th St Ste 1250, Oakland, CA 94607
Tel.: (510) 587-0950
Web Site: http://www.theentrustgroup.com
Sales Range: $25-49.9 Million
Emp.: 65
Account Administration Services
N.A.I.C.S.: 523940
Hubert Bromma (Founder & CEO)
Gary Kowalski (CFO)
John Paul Ruiz (Dir-Pro Dev)

THE ENTWISTLE CO.
Bigelow St, Hudson, MA 01749-2697
Tel.: (508) 481-4000
Web Site: http://www.entwistleco.com
Year Founded: 1918
Sales Range: $25-49.9 Million
Emp.: 200
Electro-Mechanical Equipment for the Government; Machinery for Insulated Wire & Cable & Engineered Mobile Equipment
N.A.I.C.S.: 332994
C. Corkin (Pres)
George Kaplan (VP)

Subsidiaries:

The Entwistle Co. (1)
1940 Halifax Rd, Danville, VA 24540 (100%)
Tel.: (434) 799-6186
Web Site: http://www.entwistleco.com
Sales Range: $10-24.9 Million
Emp.: 65
Mfr Of Defence Products
N.A.I.C.S.: 332313

THE EPICUREAN GROUP
1380 E Jefferson, Detroit, MI 48207
Tel.: (248) 646-0370
Web Site: http://www.theepicureangroup.com
Sales Range: $10-24.9 Million
Emp.: 1,200
Restaurant Owner & Operator
N.A.I.C.S.: 722511
Eric Djordjevic (Pres)
Rebecca Pino (Mgr-Mktg)

THE EPSTEN GROUP, INC.
399 Edgewood Ave, Atlanta, GA 30312
Tel.: (404) 577-0370
Web Site: http://www.epstengroup.com
Year Founded: 1991
Sales Range: $1-9.9 Million
Emp.: 42
Residential Construction Services
N.A.I.C.S.: 236116
Bill D'Onofrio (Dir-Pro Svcs)
Michael O'Brien (Sr Project Mgr-Commissioning)
Mickey Leso (Mgr-Building Enclosure Dept)

THE EQUITABLE BANK SSB
2290 N Mayfair Rd, Wauwatosa, WI 53226-2208
Tel.: (414) 476-6434
Web Site: http://www.theequitablebank.com
Year Founded: 1927
Sales Range: $250-299.9 Million
Emp.: 160
Savings Banking Services; Mortgages & Consumer Loans
N.A.I.C.S.: 522180
Mike Block (Officer-IT & VP)
Timothy Lausier (Coord-Facilities)
Lisa Kopplin (Coord-HR & Benefits)
Heidi Gumz (Project Mgr-Trng & Ops)
Bruce Andrich (Sr VP)
Irina Dianov (Branch Mgr)
Jane Scalf (Branch Mgr)
John Udvare (CFO)
Lauren Poppen (Treas, Controller & Asst VP)
John Udvare (CFO)
Lauren Poppen (Treas, Controller & Asst VP)

Subsidiaries:

The Equitable Bank (1)
5225 S 108th St, Hales Corners, WI 53130-1330 (100%)
Tel.: (414) 425-4321
Web Site: http://www.theequitablebank.com
Sales Range: $50-74.9 Million
Emp.: 7
Financial Center-Mortgage & Consumer Loans
N.A.I.C.S.: 522180
Jay Sciachitano (VP)
John P. Matter (Pres)

THE EQUITIUM GROUP, LLC
1001 Brickell Bay Dr Ste 2414, Miami, FL 33131
Tel.: (305) 455-5900
Web Site: http://www.equitiumgroup.com
Management Consulting & Active Ownership Investing Services
N.A.I.C.S.: 523999
Amir R. Amir (Mng Partner)

Subsidiaries:

Caswell-Massey Co. Ltd. (1)
29 Northfield Ave, Edison, NJ 08837
Tel.: (732) 225-2181
Web Site: http://www.caswell-massey.com
Sales Range: $25-49.9 Million
Emp.: 80
Fragrance Stores & Catalog
N.A.I.C.S.: 456120

THE ERIN COMPANY
50 Monument Sq 2nd Fl, Portland, ME 04101
Tel.: (207) 874-9990
Year Founded: 1969
Sales Range: $125-149.9 Million
Emp.: 565
Owner & Operator of Hotels
N.A.I.C.S.: 721110
Kevin P. Mahaney (Pres & CEO)

THE EROSION COMPANY
3213 S Cherokee Ln Ste 1720, Woodstock, GA 30188
Tel.: (678) 990-0207
Web Site: http://www.tecompanies.com
Sales Range: $10-24.9 Million
Emp.: 100
Erosion Control Contracting Services
N.A.I.C.S.: 541620
Wilson Borden (Founder, Pres & CEO)
Craig S. Richards (CFO)
Darrell Sheets (VP-Sls)

COMPANIES

THE ESSENTIAL BAKING COMPANY
1604 N 34th St, Seattle, WA 98103
Tel.: (206) 545-3804
Web Site:
http://www.essentialbaking.com
Rev.: $38,500,000
Emp.: 180
Bakery & Food Items Merchant Whslr
N.A.I.C.S.: 424490
Mike Sincawitc (*Dir-Quality Control*)

THE ESTATES AT CARPENTERS
1001 Carpenter's Way, Lakeland, FL 33809
Tel.: (863) 858-3847   FL
Web Site:
http://www.estatesatcarpenters.com
Year Founded: 1984
Sales Range: $10-24.9 Million
Emp.: 405
Continuing Care Retirement Community Services
N.A.I.C.S.: 623311
Lilybeth Lucas (*Dir-Therapy*)
Brian Robare (*Exec Dir*)
John Thompson (*CFO*)
Leo Gillman (*Pres*)
Lou McCraney (*VP*)
Sammy Taylor (*Treas & Sec*)

THE ESTRIDGE GROUP INC.
14300 Clay Terrace Blvd Ste 244, Carmel, IN 46032-3636
Tel.: (317) 846-7311
Web Site: http://www.estridge.com
Year Founded: 1983
Sales Range: $75-99.9 Million
Emp.: 125
Residential Construction
N.A.I.C.S.: 236115
Paul Estridge (*Pres*)
Brad Love (*Exec VP*)
Mike Keller (*CFO, Controller & Gen Mng Partner*)
Tom Korecki (*Dir-Mktg*)
Randy McNutt (*Exec VP-Sls & Mktg*)

THE ETICA GROUP INC.
7172 N Keystone Ave Ste G, Indianapolis, IN 46240
Tel.: (317) 466-9520   IN
Web Site: http://www.eticagroup.com
Year Founded: 2005
Architectural, Engineering & Construction Inspection Services
N.A.I.C.S.: 541618
Jessica A. Nickloy (*Pres & CEO*)
Sheena Lee (*VP-Ops*)
Mark Westphal (*Pres-Engrg*)
Natalie K. Stephen (*Mgr-Engrg*)
Kate Zale (*Mgr-Client Rels*)
Kevin Miller (*Mgr-Transportation Engrg*)
Nicole Kalck (*Project Mgr*)
E. Frank Gidden (*Mgr-Inspection*)
Rodney Kelly (*Mgr-Land Survey Dept*)
Brian Stanoch (*Project Mgr-Survey*)
Toby J. Winiger (*Mgr-Architecture Dept*)
Chris Baker (*Mgr-Building Envelope*)

THE EVANGELINE BANK & TRUST CO.
PO Box 346, Ville Platte, LA 70586
Tel.: (337) 363-5541
Web Site:
http://www.therealbank.com
Year Founded: 1907
Sales Range: $900-999.9 Million
Emp.: 150
State Commercial Banks
N.A.I.C.S.: 522110
Randel Chapman (*Pres & CEO*)

THE EVANS-SHERRATT CO.
13050 Northend Ave, Oak Park, MI 48237-3405
Tel.: (248) 584-5500
Web Site: http://www.evans-sherratt.com
Year Founded: 1965
Sales Range: $10-24.9 Million
Emp.: 55
Medical & Hospital Equipment Distr
N.A.I.C.S.: 423450
John H. Lyngklip (*Pres*)

THE EVENT AGENCY
120 S El Camino Real Ste A, San Clemente, CA 92672
Tel.: (949) 218-9037
Web Site: http://www.eventagent.us
Year Founded: 2003
Sales Range: $10-24.9 Million
Emp.: 10
N.A.I.C.S.: 541810
Brian Bouquet (*Pres*)
Brad Hazelton (*Dir-Creative*)

THE EVERGREEN GROUP VENTURES, LLC
Media Ctr 4th Fl 1600 Rosecrans Ave, Manhattan Beach, CA 90266   DE
Web Site: http://www.the-evergreen-group.com
Investment Holding Company
N.A.I.C.S.: 551112
Jim L. Wagner (*Mng Dir*)

THE EXPERTS, INC.
2400 E Commercial Blvd Ste 614, Fort Lauderdale, FL 33308
Tel.: (954) 493-8040
Web Site: http://www.expertsit.com
Year Founded: 1998
Sales Range: $10-24.9 Million
Emp.: 175
IT & Engineering Consulting Services
N.A.I.C.S.: 541690
Thomas E. Hoshko (*Pres & CEO*)
Timothy McLean (*Exec VP-Comml Svcs*)
Mark Zanki (*Chief Strategy Officer*)
Brian King (*Exec VP-Govt Solutions*)
Thomas Paul Hoshko (*COO*)
Kellie Kilgore (*VP-Federal Contracts*)
Oliver Barrera (*Sr Mgr-Dev & Application Consulting*)
George Schimenti (*VP-Client Delivery*)
Alex Zaldivar (*CFO*)

THE F.A. BARTLETT TREE EXPERT COMPANY
1290 E Main St, Stamford, CT 06902-3555
Tel.: (203) 323-1131   CT
Web Site: http://www.bartlett.com
Year Founded: 1907
Sales Range: $400-449.9 Million
Emp.: 1,700
Tree & Shrub Maintenance Service
N.A.I.C.S.: 561730
John E. Signorini (*Treas & Exec VP*)
Nicholas J. Cirillo (*VP & Controller*)
Gregory S. Daniels (*Pres & COO*)
Frederick M. Tobin (*Gen Counsel*)
Robert A. Bartlett (*Chm & CEO*)

Subsidiaries:

Bartlett Tree Service   (1)
PO Box 212, Bracebridge, P1L 1T6, ON, Canada   (100%)
Tel.: (705) 646-8733
Web Site: http://www.bartlett.com
Sales Range: $25-49.9 Million
Emp.: 6
Tree Cutting Services
N.A.I.C.S.: 561730
Philip Adams (*Gen Mgr*)

Collier Arbor Care Inc.   (1)
11814 SE Jennifer St, Clackamas, OR 97015
Tel.: (503) 722-7267
Web Site: http://www.bartlett.com
Sales Range: $10-24.9 Million
Emp.: 30
Soil Preparation, Planting & Cultivating
N.A.I.C.S.: 115112
Kevin Carr (*Gen Mgr*)

Tree Medics, Inc.   (1)
614 Central Ave, Jefferson, LA 70121
Tel.: (504) 488-9115
Web Site: http://www.tree-medics.com
Tree Trimming Services
N.A.I.C.S.: 561730

THE F.D. LAWRENCE ELECTRIC COMPANY
3450 Beekman St, Cincinnati, OH 45223-2425
Tel.: (513) 542-1100   OH
Web Site:
http://www.fdlawrenceelectric.com
Year Founded: 1904
Sales Range: $75-99.9 Million
Emp.: 125
Wholesale Distributor of Electrical Supplies & Equipment
N.A.I.C.S.: 423610
John Voellnecke (*Exec VP*)
Mark Thiel (*Mgr-Acctg*)

THE F.X. MATT BREWING CO.
811 Edward St, Utica, NY 13502-4001
Tel.: (315) 624-2400   NY
Web Site: http://www.saranac.com
Year Founded: 1888
Sales Range: $25-49.9 Million
Emp.: 140
Brewer of Malt Beverages
N.A.I.C.S.: 312120
Alfred D. Matt (*Pres*)
Robert Cooley (*Controller*)

THE FALL RIVER GROUP, INC.
670 S Main St, Fall River, WI 53932
Tel.: (920) 484-2230
Web Site:
http://www.fallrivergroup.com
Sales Range: $50-74.9 Million
Emp.: 195
Die-Casting Services
N.A.I.C.S.: 331529
Raymond J. Weigel (*Chm*)
Scott Sitkin (*Mgr-Sls*)

THE FALLS AGENCY
2550 Blaisdell Ave S, Minneapolis, MN 55404
Tel.: (612) 872-6372   MN
Web Site: http://www.fallsagency.com
Year Founded: 1982
Sales Range: $25-49.9 Million
Emp.: 25
Full Service
N.A.I.C.S.: 541810
Sharon Lund (*Partner*)
Robert Falls (*Partner*)
Deanna Davis (*Controller*)

THE FAMILY CONSERVANCY
444 Minnesota Ave Ste 200, Kansas City, KS 66101
Tel.: (913) 342-1110   MO
Web Site:
http://www.thefamilyconservancy.org
Year Founded: 1880
Sales Range: $10-24.9 Million
Emp.: 111
Child & Family Support Services
N.A.I.C.S.: 624190
Jocelyn Mourning (*VP-Dev & Comm*)
Matt Webb (*Vice Chm-Resource Dev*)
Tracy Benteen (*Sec*)

THE FARMERS' MUSEUM, INC.

Joe Harmon (*Vice Chm-Plng & Assessment*)
Nick Nash (*Vice Chm-Head Start Oversight*)
Amanda Keller (*Vice Chm-Bd Dev*)
Paula Neth (*VP-Programs*)
Stephen Nixon (*Vice Chm-Fin*)
Dean Olson (*Pres & CEO*)
Christopher Potthast (*VP-Admin & Fin*)
Neila Whitt (*Chm*)

THE FARASH CORPORATION
130 Linden Oaks Dr Ste B, Rochester, NY 14625-1633
Tel.: (585) 244-1886
Web Site: http://www.farash.com
Year Founded: 1944
Sales Range: $25-49.9 Million
Emp.: 150
Provider of Subdivider & Developer Services
N.A.I.C.S.: 531110
Stede Leonhard (*Controller*)

THE FARMERS & MERCHANTS BANKSHARES, INC.
708 S Main St, Stuttgart, AR 72160
Tel.: (870) 673-6911   AR
Web Site: http://www.mebanking.com
Year Founded: 1983
Sales Range: $50-74.9 Million
Bank Holding Company
N.A.I.C.S.: 551111
Gary Hudson (*Pres & CEO*)

Subsidiaries:

The Farmers & Merchants Bank   (1)
708 S Main St, Stuttgart, AR 72160
Tel.: (870) 673-6911
Web Site: http://www.mebanking.com
Sales Range: $50-74.9 Million
Emp.: 375
Federal Savings Bank
N.A.I.C.S.: 522180
Gary Hudson (*Pres & CEO*)
Barry Barnett (*Pres-Eastern Div Market*)
Kirk Vansandt (*Chief Lending Officer*)

THE FARMERS COOP GRAIN ASSOCIATION
524 E Parallel St, Conway Springs, KS 67031
Tel.: (620) 456-2222
Web Site: http://www.cscoop.net
Agricultural Services
N.A.I.C.S.: 424510
Pat J. Lies (*Mgr*)
Pete Nulik (*Ops Mgr-Belle Plaine*)
Kevin Zoglmann (*Ops Mgr-Conway Springs*)
Cary Morrison (*Office Mgr*)
Gary Wolke (*Vice Chm*)
Joe Allen (*Treas & Sec*)
Kevin Friess (*Chm*)
Jared Allen (*Assoc Dir*)

THE FARMERS' MUSEUM, INC.
5775 State Hwy 80, Cooperstown, NY 13326
Tel.: (607) 547-1450   NY
Web Site:
http://www.farmersmuseum.org
Year Founded: 1941
Sales Range: $10-24.9 Million
Emp.: 181
Museums
N.A.I.C.S.: 712110
Barbara Fischer (*Sr Dir-HR*)
Danielle Henrici (*Dir-Education*)
Todd A. Kenyon (*Dir-Mktg & Comm*)
Michelle Murdock (*Dir-Exhibitions*)
Jane Forbes Clark (*Chm*)
J. Michael Moffat (*Vice Chm*)
Paul S. D'Ambrosio (*Pres & CEO*)
Joseph Siracusa (*VP-Ops*)

THE FARMERS' MUSEUM, INC.

The Farmers' Museum, Inc.—(Continued)
Alexander Charlton *(Sec)*
Richard C. Vanison *(Treas)*
Douglas E. Evelyn *(Chm)*
Glenn A. Perrone *(Sec)*
Thomas O. Putnam *(Vice Chm)*
Garet D. Livermore *(VP-Education)*

THE FATHER'S TABLE, LLC.
2100 Country Club Rd, Sanford, FL 32771
Tel.: (407) 324-1200
Web Site: http://www.thefatherstable.com
Year Founded: 1998
Sales Range: $25-49.9 Million
Emp.: 225
Dessert Food Mfr
N.A.I.C.S.: 311813
Dan Gilardi *(Dir-HR)*
Denise Clark *(Acct Mgr)*

THE FCM GROUP, INC.
76 Progress Dr, Stamford, CT 06902
Tel.: (203) 961-1210
Web Site: https://www.thefcmgroup.com
Year Founded: 1927
General Construction Contractor
N.A.I.C.S.: 236220
Frank C. Mercede III *(Pres)*

THE FEDELI GROUP, INC.
5005 Rockside Rd Ste 500, Independence, OH 44131
Tel.: (216) 328-8080
Web Site: http://www.thefedeligroup.com
Year Founded: 1980
Sales Range: $10-24.9 Million
Emp.: 90
Insurance Brokerage Services
N.A.I.C.S.: 524210
Umberto Fedeli *(Pres & CEO)*
Danny Fedeli *(Exec VP)*
Nick Fedeli *(VP)*
Ed Kraine *(Chief Insurance Officer)*
Ryan Milligan *(Dir-IT)*
Andre Lukez Sr. *(Chief Consulting Officer)*
Thomas A. Visconsi Jr. *(Gen Counsel & Sr VP)*

THE FEDERALIST SOCIETY FOR LAW & PUBLIC POLICY STUDIES
1776 I Ste 300, Washington, DC 20006
Tel.: (202) 822-8138
Web Site: http://www.federalistsociety.org
Year Founded: 1982
Sales Range: $10-24.9 Million
Emp.: 33
Legal Aid Services
N.A.I.C.S.: 541199
Katelynd Mahoney *(Asst Dir-Dev)*
Cynthia Searcy *(Dir-Dev)*
Peter Bisbee *(Dir-Membership)*
Brent O. Hatch *(Treas)*
David M. McIntosh *(Vice Chm)*
Eugene B. Meyer *(Pres)*
Gary Lawson *(Sec)*
Lee Liberman Otis *(Sr VP & Dir-Faculty Div)*
Leonard A. Leo *(Exec VP)*
Steven G. Calabresi *(Chm)*
Joanne T. Medero *(Chm-Corporations, Antitrust & Securities Practice Grp)*

THE FEDERATED GROUP, INC.
3025 W Salt Creek Ln, Arlington Heights, IL 60005-1083
Tel.: (847) 577-1200   IL

Web Site: http://www.fedgroup.com
Year Founded: 1900
Grocery & Foodservice Sales, Sourcing, Quality Assurance, Supply Chain, Private Branding & Marketing Operations
N.A.I.C.S.: 424410
Mark Smith *(COO & VP-Fin)*
Bill Bradshaw *(VP-Sls)*

THE FELTERS GROUP
5965 Hwy 221, Roebuck, SC 29376-0228
Tel.: (864) 576-7900   DE
Web Site: http://www.felters.com
Year Founded: 1898
Sales Range: $100-124.9 Million
Emp.: 200
Needle Mechanical Roll Felt & Fabricated Nonmetallic Material Mfr
N.A.I.C.S.: 313230
Gern Lowe *(Pres)*

Subsidiaries:

Felters of SC, LLC   (1)
5965 Highway 221, Roebuck, SC 29376
Tel.: (864) 576-7900
Web Site: http://www.felters.com
Apparels Mfr
N.A.I.C.S.: 314999
Vernon Lowe *(Pres)*

THE FENCE STORE
5009 W Lake St, Melrose Park, IL 60160-2754
Tel.: (708) 410-1400
Web Site: http://www.thefencestore.com
Year Founded: 1989
Rev.: $4,000,000
Emp.: 8
Fence Products & Installation Services
N.A.I.C.S.: 444180
Mary Kowalski *(VP-Ops)*

THE FENTON ART GLASS COMPANY
700 Elizabeth St, Williamstown, WV 26187-1028
Tel.: (304) 375-6122   WV
Web Site: http://www.fentonartglass.com
Year Founded: 1905
Sales Range: $75-99.9 Million
Emp.: 130
Mfr of Handmade Glassware
N.A.I.C.S.: 327212
George W. Fenton *(Pres)*

THE FENTON GROUP
44 Weybosset St, Providence, RI 02903
Tel.: (401) 490-4888
Web Site: http://www.thefentongroup.net
Sales Range: Less than $1 Million
Emp.: 4
N.A.I.C.S.: 541613
Joshua Fenton *(Founder & CEO)*

THE FESSLER AGENCY INC.
3165 N McMullen Booth Rd Bldg G2, Clearwater, FL 33761
Tel.: (727) 726-3377
Web Site: http://www.fessleragency.com
Year Founded: 1984
Sales Range: $25-49.9 Million
Emp.: 15
Insurance, Employee Benefits & Risk Management
N.A.I.C.S.: 524210
Jack L. Fessler *(Pres)*
Campbell Small *(VP)*

THE FIBERSMITH COMPANY
10283 685th St, Blooming Prairie, MN 55917
Tel.: (507) 200-0526
Web Site: http://www.fibersmith.co
Year Founded: 2013
Sales Range: $1-9.9 Million
Emp.: 50
Telecommunication Servicesb
N.A.I.C.S.: 517810
Donny Smith *(CEO)*

Subsidiaries:

Ahneman Kirby LLC
1171 E Putnam Ave, Riverside, CT 06878
Tel.: (203) 869-7707
Web Site: http://www.ahnemankirby.com
Surveying & Mapping Services
N.A.I.C.S.: 541370
Bryan Smith *(Project Engr)*

THE FIDELITY BANK INC.
100 S Main St, Fuquay Varina, NC 27526-2221
Tel.: (919) 552-2242   NC
Web Site: http://www.fidelitybanknc.com
Year Founded: 1909
Sales Range: $50-74.9 Million
Emp.: 280
State Commercial Banks
N.A.I.C.S.: 522110
Mary W. Willis *(Pres & CEO)*
Lynn Fowler *(VP)*
Kim Fox *(VP-Roxboro)*
Seth Moore *(VP)*
Leslie A. Brun *(Co-Founder-Investment Banking Grp)*

THE FIELD MUSEUM
1400 S Lake Shore Dr, Chicago, IL 60605-2496
Tel.: (312) 922-9410
Web Site: http://www.fieldmuseum.org
Year Founded: 1893
Sales Range: $125-149.9 Million
Emp.: 490
Natural History Museum
N.A.I.C.S.: 712110
Thomas Gnoske *(Asst Mgr-Collections)*
Jochen Gerber *(Mgr-Collections)*
John Phelps *(Asst Mgr-Collections)*
Alan Resetar *(Mgr-Collections)*
Madeleine Tudorrr *(Mgr-Applied Cultural Res)*
Neil S. Novich *(Bd of Trustees, Executives)*

THE FILM DEPARTMENT HOLDINGS, INC.
232 N Canon Dr, Beverly Hills, CA 90210-5302
Tel.: (323) 785-3700   DE
Year Founded: 2007
Sales Range: $25-49.9 Million
Emp.: 21
Motion Picture Production & Finance Services
N.A.I.C.S.: 512110
Mark Gill *(Chm & CEO)*
Neil Sacker *(Vice Chm & COO)*
Gerry Rich *(Vice Chm)*
Robert Katz *(Pres-Production)*
Bernd Stephan *(CFO)*
Daniel Stutz *(Exec VP-Bus & Legal Affairs)*

THE FINANCE STORE
200 Sandpointe Ave #750, Santa Ana, CA 92707
Tel.: (949) 777-5959
Web Site: http://www.financestore.com
Year Founded: 2000
Sales Range: $1-9.9 Million

Emp.: 40
Financing For Start-Ups & Small Businesses
N.A.I.C.S.: 525990
Grey Nguyen *(Fin Dir)*
Tim McCormack *(Pres)*
Jason Edwards *(Dir-Mktg)*
Trey Sublette *(Dir-Sls)*

Subsidiaries:

The Business Finance Store   (1)
600 Fairmount Ave #206, Towson, MD 21286
Tel.: (888) 840-0302
Web Site: http://www.financestore.com
Financing for Start-Ups & Small Businesses
N.A.I.C.S.: 525990
Matt Sochurek *(Mng Dir)*

THE FINIT GROUP LLC
103 Chesley Dr Ste 207, Media, PA 19063-1757
Tel.: (610) 565-5412
Web Site: http://www.finitsolutions.com
Year Founded: 2002
Sales Range: $1-9.9 Million
Emp.: 51
Finance Information Technology Consulting Services
N.A.I.C.S.: 541511
Robert Cybulski *(Pres)*
Angie Apple *(Pres)*
Jay Hampton *(Pres)*
Cathy Lawton *(Dir-Bus Dev)*
Greg Barrett *(Mng Dir)*
Joe Mizerk *(Dir-Bus Dev)*

THE FIORE COMPANIES
150 E Gilman St, Madison, WI 53703
Tel.: (608) 255-5060
Web Site: http://www.fiorecompanies.com
Year Founded: 1921
Sales Range: $10-24.9 Million
Emp.: 14
Real Estate Development & Management Services
N.A.I.C.S.: 531390
David W. Kruger *(Chm & Pres)*
William J. Kunkler *(Exec VP)*
Stacy M. Nemeth *(COO)*
Lee Ferderer *(CEO)*
Jackie Saint Onge *(Dir-Corp Admin)*
Deanna Shank *(CFO)*
Phillip Maier *(VP-Facilities)*
Rosemary Temby *(Coord-Admin Svcs)*

Subsidiaries:

Twentieth Century Markets, Inc.   (1)
150 E Gilman St Ste 1600, Madison, WI 53703
Tel.: (608) 255-5060
Web Site: http://fiorecompanies.com
Commercial & Industrial Building Operation
N.A.I.C.S.: 531120
David W. Kruger *(Pres)*
Diana Shank *(Controller)*
Lee Ferderer *(CEO)*
Lindsay Kruger *(VP-Investments)*
Phillip Maier *(VP-Facilities)*
Stacy Nemeth *(COO)*
Jackie St. Onge *(Dir-Corp Admin)*
Rosemary Temby *(Coord-Admin Svcs)*

THE FIP CORPORATION
308 Farmington Ave, Farmington, CT 06032-1913
Tel.: (203) 699-2300   CT
Web Site: http://www.fipconstruction.co
Year Founded: 1985
Rev.: $60,000,000
Emp.: 65
Subdividers & Developer
N.A.I.C.S.: 237210

COMPANIES

David T. Shopis *(Pres & CEO)*
William G. Hardy *(Exec VP)*
Philip E. Anderson *(CFO & VP)*
Daniel T. Burns *(VP)*

Subsidiaries:

FIP Construction Inc. (1)
1536 New Britain Ave, Farmington, CT 06032-1913 **(100%)**
Tel.: (860) 470-1800
Web Site: http://www.fipconstruction.com
Construction Design & Engineering Services
N.A.I.C.S.: 236220
Bill Hardy *(Pres)*
Allan Cox Jr. *(Project Mgr)*

THE FIRM ADVISORS, LLC

210 N 78th St 2nd Fl, Omaha, NE 68114
Tel.: (402) 998-5288
Web Site: http://www.thefirmadv.com
Year Founded: 2010
Sales Range: $1-9.9 Million
Emp.: 10
Business Management Services
N.A.I.C.S.: 541611
Cortney Sells *(Pres)*
Cassandra Powers *(COO)*
Makayla Holliday *(Principal)*
Mckenna Thorngren *(Portfolio Mgr)*
Lori Hulshof *(Coord-Client)*

THE FIRST CATHOLIC SLOVAK LADIES ASSOCIATION

24950 Chagrin Blvd, Beachwood, OH 44122-5634
Tel.: (216) 464-8015   OH
Web Site: http://www.fcsla.org
Year Founded: 1892
Rev.: $85,047,138
Assets: $990,832,264
Liabilities: $886,273,584
Net Worth: $104,558,680
Earnings: $2,109,788
Fiscal Year-end: 12/31/18
Direct Life Insurance Carriers
N.A.I.C.S.: 524113
Cynthia M. Maleski *(Pres)*
Barbara A. Sekerak *(Auditor)*
Dennis L. Povondra *(Auditor)*
Dorothy Urbanowicz *(Auditor)*

THE FIRST CITIZENS NATIONAL BANK

100 N Sandusky Ave, Upper Sandusky, OH 43351
Tel.: (419) 294-2351
Web Site:
   http://www.firstcitizensnational.com
Rev.: $12,753,000
Emp.: 34
National Commercial Banks
N.A.I.C.S.: 522110
Mark G. Johnson *(Pres & CEO)*
Robert E. McClure *(COO & Exec VP)*
Nancy Johnson *(Chm)*
Larry Carmen *(Mgr)*
Kevin C. Smith *(Pres-Marion & North Delaware County)*

THE FIRST NATIONAL BANK IN TREMONT

134 S Sampson St, Tremont, IL 61568
Tel.: (309) 925-2121
Web Site:
   http://www.tremontbank.com
Year Founded: 1931
Sales Range: $25-49.9 Million
Emp.: 20
Commericial Banking
N.A.I.C.S.: 522110
W. Coleman Bitting *(VP-HR & IT)*

THE FIRST NATIONAL BANK OF CENTRAL TEXAS

1835 N Valley Mills Dr, Waco, TX 76710
Tel.: (254) 772-9330
Web Site: http://www.fnbct.com
Year Founded: 1901
Sales Range: $10-24.9 Million
Emp.: 64
National Commercial Banks
N.A.I.C.S.: 522110
Randall W. Crawford *(Pres & CEO)*
Monte Hulse *(Chm)*
Sloan Kuehl *(Exec VP)*
Joe Barrow *(Exec VP)*
Steve Mullens *(Exec VP)*

THE FISHEL COMPANY INC.

1366 Dublin Rd, Columbus, OH 43215
Tel.: (614) 274-8100   OH
Web Site: http://www.teamfishel.com
Year Founded: 1936
Sales Range: $100-124.9 Million
Emp.: 2,200
Provider of Utility Engineering Services
N.A.I.C.S.: 237130
John E. Phillips *(Pres & CEO)*
Ken Hensel *(Asst Controller)*
Diane Fishel Keeler *(Chm)*
William E. Pauley *(VP-Western Reg)*

THE FLATLEY COMPANY

Bldg 45 Braintree Hill Office Park, Braintree, MA 02184
Tel.: (781) 848-2000   MA
Web Site: http://www.flatleycove.com
Sales Range: $1-9.9 Million
Emp.: 40
Cooperative Industrial Buildings, Shopping Centers & Commercial Property Developers
N.A.I.C.S.: 531210
Bill Bush *(VP)*

THE FLEA MARKET, INC.

1590 Berryessa Rd, San Jose, CA 95133
Tel.: (408) 453-1110
Web Site: http://www.sjfm.com
Year Founded: 1960
Sales Range: $10-24.9 Million
Emp.: 185
Fruit & Vegetable Canning Services
N.A.I.C.S.: 311421
Mike Williams *(Mgr-Food Svc)*
Bob Bumb *(Dir-IT Mgmt)*

THE FLORIDA AQUARIUM, INC.

701 Channelside Dr, Tampa, FL 33602
Tel.: (813) 273-4000
Web Site: http://www.flaquarium.org
Sales Range: $10-24.9 Million
Emp.: 163
Aquarium
N.A.I.C.S.: 712130
Kimberly Casey *(CFO & Exec VP)*
Bill Eggert *(VP-HR)*
Mark Haney *(VP-Advancement)*
Allan Marshall *(VP-Biological Resources)*
Debbi Stone *(VP-Education)*
John Muller *(Sr VP-Ops & Engrg)*
Mark Watson *(Chm)*
Roger Germann *(Pres & CEO)*
Margo Wolanin *(Chief Dev Officer)*

THE FLORIDA BAR FOUNDATION, INC.

875 Concourse Pkwy S Ste 195, Maitland, FL 32751
Tel.: (407) 960-7000   FL
Web Site:
   http://www.floridabarfoundation.org
Year Founded: 1956

Sales Range: $1-9.9 Million
Emp.: 130
Legal Aid Services for Low-Income Individuals & Families
N.A.I.C.S.: 541199
Bruce B. Blackwell *(Exec Dir)*
Chuck Hays *(Dir-IT)*
Donna C. Marino *(Dir-Dev)*
Dominic C. MacKenzie *(Pres)*
Jasmine Lee-Gaumier *(Controller)*
Jennifer Wimberly *(Dir-Grants)*

THE FLORIDA VALUE FUND LLLP

2999 NE 191st St Ste 906, Aventura, FL 33180
Tel.: (305) 933-5800
Web Site: http://www.floridavalue.net
Sales Range: $1-9.9 Million
Real Estate Investment
N.A.I.C.S.: 523999
Gil Hermon *(Mng Partner)*
Michael Landa *(Venture Partner)*

THE FMG GROUP

618 Conroy St Apt 1, Cincinnati, OH 45214-3922
Tel.: (513) 314-0826
Year Founded: 2008
Sales Range: $10-24.9 Million
Emp.: 20
Advetising Agency
N.A.I.C.S.: 541810
Frank J. Meyer *(Mng Partner)*

THE FOOD BANK OF NORTHEAST GEORGIA

861 Newton Bridge Rd, Athens, GA 30607
Tel.: (706) 354-8191   GA
Web Site:
   http://www.foodbanknega.org
Year Founded: 1992
Sales Range: $10-24.9 Million
Emp.: 29
Hunger Relief Services
N.A.I.C.S.: 624210
Jim Heider *(Mgr-Ops)*
David Williams *(Mgr-Food Procurement)*
Tonya Bolton *(Mgr-Programs)*
Shannon Arnold *(Mgr-Facilities)*
Susan Dodson *(Dir-External Rels)*
John Graham *(Treas)*
Kevin Lang *(Sec)*
John Becker *(Pres & CEO)*
Edd Lowe *(Chm)*
Brock Toole *(Co-Chm)*

THE FOOD BANK OF WESTERN MASSACHUSETTS

97 N Hatfield Rd, Hatfield, MA 01038
Tel.: (413) 247-9738   MA
Web Site:
   http://www.foodbankwma.org
Year Founded: 1981
Sales Range: $10-24.9 Million
Emp.: 55
Food Bank Operator
N.A.I.C.S.: 624210
Alan Peterfreund *(Second VP)*
Christel Harju *(Treas)*
Christina Maxwell *(Dir-Programs)*

THE FOOTBRIDGE COMPANIES

40 Shattuck Rd Ste 100, Andover, MA 01810
Tel.: (978) 474-4455
Web Site:
   http://www.footbridgestaffing.com
Year Founded: 2000
Sales Range: $10-24.9 Million
Emp.: 24
Staffing Services
N.A.I.C.S.: 541612

Richard W. O'Donnell *(Co-Founder & Pres)*

THE FORD METER BOX COMPANY, INC.

775 Manchester Ave, Wabash, IN 46992
Tel.: (260) 563-3171   IN
Web Site:
   http://www.fordmeterbox.com
Year Founded: 1898
Rev.: $15,000,000
Emp.: 600
Mfr of Water Meter Setting & Testing Equipment, Valves & Fittings for Water Utility Industry
N.A.I.C.S.: 332913
Charles Chapman *(Mgr-Adv)*
Steve Ford *(Pres)*
Gary Larson *(CFO & Corp Sec)*

THE FOREIGN CANDY COMPANY, INC.

1 Foreign Candy Dr, Hull, IA 51239-7499
Tel.: (712) 439-1496   IA
Web Site: http://www.foreign-candy.com
Year Founded: 1978
Sales Range: $25-49.9 Million
Emp.: 35
Retailer of Imported Candy
N.A.I.C.S.: 424450
Peter W. De Yager *(Owner, Pres & CEO)*

THE FOREST AT DUKE, INC.

2701 Pickett Rd, Durham, NC 27705
Tel.: (919) 490-8000   NC
Web Site: http://www.forestduke.org
Year Founded: 1988
Sales Range: $25-49.9 Million
Emp.: 367
Retirement Community Operator
N.A.I.C.S.: 623311
Gwendolen Buhr *(Dir-Medical)*
Karen Henry *(Treas & Dir-Fin)*
Leslie Jarema *(Dir-Health Svcs)*
Alice Sharpe *(Dir-Dev-Durham County Library)*
Jim Normandin *(Dir-Facility Svcs)*
Ibby Wooten *(Dir-Activities & Community Rels)*
Tony Ellis *(Dir-Dining Svcs)*
Anita L. Holt *(Pres & CEO)*
Beth Maxwell *(Vice Chm)*
Andrea McDade *(Dir-HR)*

THE FORT MILLER GROUP INC.

PO Box 98, Schuylerville, NY 12871
Tel.: (518) 695-5000
Web Site: http://www.fmgroup.com
Year Founded: 1991
Sales Range: $25-49.9 Million
Emp.: 500
Concrete Products Mfr
N.A.I.C.S.: 327390
John Hedbring *(CEO)*
Rick Schumaker *(CFO)*
Mary Ann Spiezio *(VP-HR)*

Subsidiaries:

Anvil Fence & Supply Co. Inc. (1)
1009 General Fellows Rd, Greenwich, NY 12834 **(100%)**
Tel.: (518) 383-0500
Web Site: http://www.anvilaccess.com
Sales Range: $10-24.9 Million
Emp.: 6
Provider of Special Trade Contractor Services
N.A.I.C.S.: 238990
Ken Fischer *(VP-Sls)*

Duke Concrete Products Inc. (1)
50 Duke Industrial Pk, Queensbury, NY 12804 **(100%)**

THE FORT MILLER GROUP INC.

U.S. PRIVATE

The Fort Miller Group Inc.—(Continued)
Tel.: (518) 793-7743
Web Site: http://www.dukeconcrete.com
Sales Range: $10-24.9 Million
Emp.: 25
Concrete Block & Brick Product Mfr
N.A.I.C.S.: 327331
Gary Hukey (VP)

Loughberry Mfg. Corp. (1)
249 Excelsior Ave, Saratoga Springs, NY 12866
Tel.: (518) 584-4400
Web Site: http://www.loughberry.com
Road Maintenance Equipment Mfr
N.A.I.C.S.: 333120
Jeff Burt (Pres)
Zach Novick (Mgr-Engrg & Drafting Dept)

The Fort Miller Company Inc. (1)
688 Wilbur Ave, Greenwich, NY 12834-4413 (100%)
Tel.: (518) 695-5000
Web Site: http://www.fortmiller.com
Sales Range: $25-49.9 Million
Emp.: 400
Mfr of Concrete Products
N.A.I.C.S.: 327390
Mark Bold (Branch Mgr)

The Fort Miller Service Corp. (1)
PO Box 98, Schuylerville, NY 12871
Tel.: (518) 695-5000
Web Site: http://www.fortmillerservice.com
Burial Casket Mfr
N.A.I.C.S.: 339995
Bill Wirene (Pres)
Peter McBride (Dir-Funeral Svc & Safety)

The Tymetal Corp. (1)
678 Wilbur Ave, Greenwich, NY 12834
Tel.: (518) 692-9930
Web Site: http://www.tymetal.com
Sales Range: $10-24.9 Million
Emp.: 50
Mfr & Distribution of Security Gates
N.A.I.C.S.: 332323
Bob Doughlas (Pres)

THE FORTRESS CORPORATION
1 Design Ctr Pl Ste 715, Boston, MA 02210-2313
Tel.: (617) 790-3070
Web Site: http://www.thefortress.com
Rev.: $15,900,000
Emp.: 70
Trucking Service
N.A.I.C.S.: 493190
Ladd Thorne (VP)
Kim Jones (VP & Gen Mgr)

THE FORTUNE SOCIETY
29-76 Northern Blvd, Long Island City, NY 11101
Tel.: (212) 691-7554 NY
Web Site: http://www.fortunesociety.org
Year Founded: 1967
Sales Range: $10-24.9 Million
Emp.: 310
Community Support Services
N.A.I.C.S.: 624190
JoAnne Page (Pres & CEO)
Peggy Arroyo (VP-Programs)
Stanley Richards (Sr VP)
Simon Jaffe (Chief Program Officer)

THE FOUNTAIN GROUP, LLC
4505 Woodland Corporate Blvd Ste 200, Tampa, FL 33614
Tel.: (813) 356-0033
Web Site: http://www.thefountaingroup.com
Year Founded: 2001
Sales Range: $50-74.9 Million
Emp.: 100
Employment Placement Agency
N.A.I.C.S.: 561311
Hunter Cone (Pres)

THE FOUNTAINHEAD GROUP, INC.
23 Garden St, New York Mills, NY 13417
Tel.: (315) 736-0037
Web Site: http://www.thefountainheadgroup.com
Year Founded: 1888
Sales Range: $10-24.9 Million
Emp.: 260
Paint & Chemical Spraying Equipment Mfr
N.A.I.C.S.: 333912
F. Eugene Romano (Chm)
Jackie Romano (VP)
Dawn Gubbins (Mgr-Production & Inventory Control)
Chris Cady (Dir-Sls)

THE FOUNTAINS, INC.
2001 W Rudasill Rd, Tucson, AZ 85704
Tel.: (520) 797-2001
Web Site: http://www.watermarkcommunities.com
Sales Range: $150-199.9 Million
Emp.: 200
Senior Living Community Services
N.A.I.C.S.: 623311
Fran Donnellan (Exec Dir)

Subsidiaries:

The Fountains at Franklin (1)
28301 Franklin Rd, Southfield, MI 48034 (100%)
Tel.: (248) 353-2810
Web Site: http://www.thefountains.com
Sales Range: $1-9.9 Million
Emp.: 80
Senior Living Community Services
N.A.I.C.S.: 623311
Cathy Loubanski (Gen Mgr)

The Freshwater Group, Inc. (1)
2020 W Rudasill, Tucson, AZ 85704
Tel.: (520) 297-9800
Web Site: http://www.thefreshwatergroup.com
Senior Living Community Services
N.A.I.C.S.: 623312
Carl Mittendorff (Chief Investment Officer)
David Freshwater (Pres)
Frederick P. Zarrilli (Vice Chm)
James Goebel (Sr VP-Design & Dev)
Jeff Kelly (Dir-Bus Dev)
Rachel Rangelov (VP-Design & Dev)
Scott J. Salkill (Dir-Renovation & Design)
Denise Barnes (Coord-Image)

THE FRAN HAASCH LAW GROUP
1275 Nebraska Ave, Palm Harbor, FL 34683
Tel.: (727) 784-8191
Web Site: http://www.lawfran.com
Emp.: 25
Law Firm
N.A.I.C.S.: 541110
Francoise M. Haasch (Atty)
Joshua R. Lipton (Atty)
Laura K. Smith (Atty)
David Fuller (Atty)
Rhett Jones (Dir-Mktg & Adv)

THE FRANGOS GROUP, LLC
1325 Carnegie Ave, Cleveland, OH 44115
Tel.: (216) 621-9255 OH
Web Site: http://www.thefrangosgroup.com
Year Founded: 1991
Holding Company; Office Buildings & Apartment Buildings Owner, Manager & Lessor
N.A.I.C.S.: 551112
Louis A. Frangos (Pres & CEO)
Jennifer Meyer (Dir-HR)

Subsidiaries:

USA Parking Systems, Inc. (1)
1325 Carnegie Ave, Cleveland, OH 44115
Tel.: (216) 621-9255
Web Site: http://www.usaparking.com
Parking Facility Operator
N.A.I.C.S.: 812930

THE FRANK AGENCY, INC.
10561 Barkley Ste 200, Overland Park, KS 66212
Tel.: (913) 648-8333 KS
Web Site: http://www.thefrankagency.com
Year Founded: 1981
Emp.: 40
Advertising & Marketing Services
N.A.I.C.S.: 541810
Susan Reiter (COO)
Tony Ali (Pres & CEO)
Tom Stofac (Exec VP & Exe Creative Dir)
Kelly Bohlken (VP)
Andrew Booth (Sr VP-Media Svcs)
Sarah Cline (VP-Bus Dev)
Nick Barkman (VP-Bus Dev)
Brett Suddreth (VP-Interactive Mktg)

THE FRANKLIN GROUP, INC.
8701 Belleville Rd, Belleville, MI 48111
Tel.: (734) 699-7700 MI
Web Site: http://www.franklinhomesales.com
Year Founded: 1982
Rev.: $10,000,000
Emp.: 40
Subdividers & Developers
N.A.I.C.S.: 237210
Ronald A. Blank (Pres)

THE FRANKLIN MUTUAL INSURANCE COMPANY
5 Broad St, Branchville, NJ 07826
Tel.: (973) 948-3120
Web Site: http://www.fmiweb.com
Year Founded: 1879
Sales Range: $100-124.9 Million
Emp.: 100
Commercial & Residential Insurance Products & Services
N.A.I.C.S.: 524126
Vicent Noggle (Controller)
George H. Guptill Jr. (Chm)
Sarah Shave (Mgr-HR)
Brian Lytwynec (Pres)

THE FRED JONES COMPANIES INC.
9225 Lake Hefner Pkwy Ste 200, Oklahoma City, OK 73120-2061
Tel.: (405) 231-2400 OK
Web Site: http://www.hall-capital.com
Year Founded: 1922
Sales Range: $25-49.9 Million
Emp.: 20
Investment Banking Services
N.A.I.C.S.: 523999
Fred Hall (Chm & CEO)
Vicki Schilling (Chief Compliance Officer)
Brooks Hall Jr. (Vice Chm)

THE FRED W. ALBRECHT GROCERY CO.
2700 Gilchrist Rd, Akron, OH 44305-4433
Tel.: (330) 733-2263
Web Site: http://www.acmestores.com
Year Founded: 1891
Sales Range: $250-299.9 Million
Emp.: 2,000
Grocery Store Operator
N.A.I.C.S.: 445110

Steven Albrecht (Pres & CEO)
James Trout (Pres)
Marilyn Guthier (Dir-Consumer Mktg)
David Nestor (Dir-Adv)

THE FREE LANCE-STAR PUBLISHING CO.
616 Amelia St, Fredericksburg, VA 22401
Tel.: (540) 374-5000 VA
Web Site: http://www.fredericksburg.com
Year Founded: 1885
Sales Range: $150-199.9 Million
Emp.: 435
Newspaper Publishers; Radio Broadcasting; Internet Service
N.A.I.C.S.: 513110
Mildred C. Cavin (CFO)
Bill Smith (Dir-Adv)
Josiah P. Rowe III (Publr)

Subsidiaries:

The Freelance-Star Radio Groups (1)
616 Amelia St, Fredericksburg, VA 22401-3887 (100%)
Tel.: (540) 373-1500
Web Site: http://www.starradiogroup.com
Sales Range: $10-24.9 Million
Emp.: 44
Radio Broadcasting
N.A.I.C.S.: 513110
Frank Hammon (Dir-News)
Shelly Bynum (Dir-Production)
Paul Johnson (Mgr-Ops)

THE FREEDOM FORUM INC.
555 Pennsylvania Ave NW, Washington, DC 20001-2114
Tel.: (202) 292-6100 VA
Web Site: http://www.museum.org
Year Founded: 1935
Sales Range: $10-24.9 Million
Emp.: 300
First Amendment Promoter
N.A.I.C.S.: 813410
Scott Williams (VP)
Jan Neuharth (Chm & CEO)
Pamela Galloway-Tabb (Sr VP-Conferences & Special Svcs)
Nicole F. Mandeville (CFO, Treas & Sr VP)
Cathy Trost (VP-Exhibits & Programs)
Michael Coleman (Sec)

THE FREMONT COMPANY
802 N Front St, Fremont, OH 43420-1917
Tel.: (419) 334-8995 OH
Web Site: http://www.fremontcompany.com
Year Founded: 1905
Sales Range: $100-124.9 Million
Emp.: 200
Mfr of Canned Foods: Sauerkraut, Barbecue Sauce & Ketchup
N.A.I.C.S.: 311421
Dave Stark (VP-HR)
Eric Kadrovach (VP-Ops)
Mary Bellerose (Dir-Quality Assurance)

Subsidiaries:

Paisley Farm, Inc. (1)
38180 Airport Pkwy, Willoughby, OH 44094
Tel.: (440) 269-3920
Web Site: http://www.paisleyfarminc.com
Sales Range: $1-9.9 Million
Emp.: 20
Fruit & Vegetable Canning Services
N.A.I.C.S.: 311421
Donald Anderson (VP)
Ken Anderson (Owner)

The Fremont Co. (1)
150 Hickory St, Rockford, OH 45882-0326 (100%)
Tel.: (419) 363-2924

Web Site: http://www.fremont.com
Sales Range: $10-24.9 Million
Emp.: 60
Mfr & Exporter of Ketchup & Barbecue Sauces
N.A.I.C.S.: 311421
Richard Smith (Pres)

THE FRESH DIET INC.
9429 Harding Ave #34, Surfside, FL 33154
Web Site:
  http://www.thefreshdiet.com
Year Founded: 2006
Sales Range: $10-24.9 Million
Emp.: 200
Freshly Prepared Gourmet Meals
N.A.I.C.S.: 722310
Yosef Schwartz (Founder)
Silvia De Antonio (Chief Culinary Officer)
Tom Bollich (CIO)
Asif Syed (COO)
Bryan Janeczko (CEO)
Linda Mignone (CMO)
Vojkan Dimitrijevic (CFO)
Zalmi Duchman (Founder)

THE FRETZ CORPORATION INC.
4050 S 26th St, Philadelphia, PA 19112
Tel.: (215) 671-8300
Web Site: http://www.fretz.com
Rev.: $20,000,000
Emp.: 30
Electrical Appliances, Television & Radio
N.A.I.C.S.: 423620
Jim Dunleavy (CFO)
Jennifer Care (Dir-Corp Mktg)
McNeil Scott (Mgr-Warehouse)
Mike Andrews (Dir-Ops)
Jarrrod Sward (Mgr-IT)
Bill Schnepp (Mgr-Credit)
Thomas J. Dolan (Pres)

THE FRICK COLLECTION
1 E 70th St, New York, NY 10021
Tel.: (212) 288-0700
Web Site: http://www.frick.org
Year Founded: 1920
Sales Range: $10-24.9 Million
Emp.: 240
Museum Operator
N.A.I.C.S.: 712110
Alison Lonshein (Gen Counsel & Asst Sec)
Michael Paccione (CFO & Asst Treas)
Joseph Shatoff (COO)

THE FRIEDKIN GROUP, INC.
1375 Enclave Pkwy, Houston, TX 77077
Tel.: (713) 580-3300
Web Site: https://www.friedkin.com
Year Founded: 1969
Sales Range: $1-4.9 Billion
Emp.: 9,280
Investment Banking & Securities Intermediation
N.A.I.C.S.: 523150
Marcus A. Watts (Pres)
Michelle Phelps (Portfolio Mgr)
Dale Rasco (Sr Mgr-IT Ops & Infrastructure)
Mary Jane Rivera (VP)
Ana Dunkel (Treas & VP)
Ed Dickinson (CFO)
Subsidiaries:
A.S. ROMA S.p.A. (1)
Piazzale Dino Viola 1, 00128, Rome, Italy (86.6%)
Tel.: (39) 06501911
Web Site: http://www.asroma.it

Soccer Team
N.A.I.C.S.: 711211
Giorgio Francia (CFO)

Gulf States Toyota, Inc. (1)
1375 Enclave Pkwy, Houston, TX 77077-2168
Tel.: (713) 580-3300
Sales Range: $1-4.9 Billion
Emp.: 1,200
New Automobile & Motor Vehicle Parts Distr
N.A.I.C.S.: 423110
Thomas Friedkin (Chm)
Tom Bittenbender (VP-Sls Ops)
David Copeland (Dir-Admin)

THE FRIST CENTER FOR THE VISUAL ARTS, INC.
919 Broadway, Nashville, TN 37203-3822
Tel.: (615) 244-3340
Web Site: http://www.fristcenter.org
Year Founded: 1998
Sales Range: $10-24.9 Million
Emp.: 99
Arts Promotion Services
N.A.I.C.S.: 711310
Anne Henderson (Dir-Education & Outreach)
Sheri Horn (Mgr-HR)
Susan H. Edwards (CEO)

THE FROG, SWITCH & MANUFACTURING COMPANY
600 E High St, Carlisle, PA 17013-2651
Tel.: (717) 243-2454
Web Site: http://www.frogswitch.com
Year Founded: 1881
Sales Range: $25-49.9 Million
Emp.: 170
Mfr of Manganese Steel Castings; High Chrome Iron Castings; Pulvomatic Impact Crushers
N.A.I.C.S.: 331513
Bill Walters (VP & Gen Mgr)
Alf Basson (VP-Sls & Mktg)
Tony Baldwin (Mgr-Sls & Engrg)
Kim Hurley (Mgr-Inside Sls)
Warren Bieger (Pres & CEO)
Dan Gibbs (Dir-Environmental Health & Safety)

THE FRUITGUYS
490 Eccles Ave, South San Francisco, CA 94080
Tel.: (650) 246-1200
Web Site: http://www.fruitguys.com
Year Founded: 1998
Food & Beverage Services
N.A.I.C.S.: 722310
Chris Mittelstaedt (Founder & CEO)
Erik D. Muller (Pres)
Erin Mittelstaedt (COO)
Pia Hinckle (Publr)

THE FUSCO CORPORATION
555 Long Wharf Dr Ste 14, New Haven, CT 06511
Tel.: (203) 777-7451
Web Site: http://www.fusco.com
Year Founded: 1924
Sales Range: $75-99.9 Million
Emp.: 70
Provider of Contracting & Construction Services
N.A.I.C.S.: 236220
Will Lorenz (Dir-Leasing)
Laura Carpenter (VP-Property Mgmt)

THE FUTON SHOP
2150 Cesar Chavez St, San Francisco, CA 94124
Tel.: (415) 920-6800
Web Site:
  http://www.thefutonshop.com
Rev.: $13,761,531
Emp.: 55

Futon Mfr
N.A.I.C.S.: 449110
Suzanne Diamond (Founder)

THE G.A. AVRIL CO.
4445 Kings Run Dr, Cincinnati, OH 45232
Tel.: (513) 641-0566
Web Site: http://www.gaavril.com
Rev.: $10,000,000
Emp.: 16
Brass Smelting & Refining Services
N.A.I.C.S.: 331492
Thomas B. Avril (Pres)

THE G.W. VAN KEPPEL COMPANY
1801 N 9th St, Kansas City, KS 66110-2023
Tel.: (913) 281-4800
Web Site: http://www.vankeppel.com
Year Founded: 1926
Sales Range: $100-124.9 Million
Emp.: 250
Construction & Mining Machinery
N.A.I.C.S.: 423810
Kevin Kientz (Exec VP)
Rick Krause (CFO)
Subsidiaries:
Peerless Conveyor & Manufacturing Co. (1)
201 E Quindaro Blvd, Kansas City, KS 66115-1424 (100%)
Tel.: (913) 342-2240
Web Site: http://www.peerlessconveyor.com
Sales Range: $10-24.9 Million
Emp.: 20
Construction Machinery
N.A.I.C.S.: 333120

The G.W. Van Keppel Co. - Kansas City, Missouri (1)
1449 Genessee St, Kansas City, MO 64102-1031
Tel.: (816) 921-4040
Web Site: http://www.vankeppel.com
Sales Range: $1-9.9 Million
Emp.: 7
Construction & Mining Machinery Distr
N.A.I.C.S.: 423810
Bill Walker (Pres)
Kevin Kientz (Exec VP)
Dave Hruska (Gen Mgr-Svc)
Rick Krause (CFO)
Brian Loderhose (VP-Product Support)
Kelly Russell (Sls Mgr-Construction)
Jared Ward (Gen Mgr-Matl Handling)

The G.W. Van Keppel Co. - Oklahoma City (1)
8233 W Reno Ave, Oklahoma City, OK 73127
Tel.: (405) 495-0606
Web Site: http://www.vankeppel.com
Rev.: $2,000,000
Emp.: 25
Construction, Mining & Forestry Machinery & Equipment Rental & Leasing
N.A.I.C.S.: 532412
Brian Loderhose (VP-Product Support)
Krissy Lund (Gen Mgr-Used Parts)
Michael Murray (Gen Mgr-Supply Div)
Kelly Russell (Mgr-Construction Sls)
Jared Ward (Gen Mgr-Matl Handling)

THE G3 GROUP
832 Oregon Ave Ste L, Linthicum, MD 21090
Tel.: (410) 789-7007
Web Site: http://www.g3group.com
Year Founded: 1984
Sales Range: $10-24.9 Million
Emp.: 17
N.A.I.C.S.: 541810
Mary Berman (CFO)
Anita Schott (CEO)
Dan Appleget (Dir-Sls-Mktg)
Andy Goolsby (Mgr-Admin)

THE GABBER
1419 49th St S, Gulfport, FL 33707
Tel.: (727) 321-6965
Web Site: http://www.thegabber.com
Year Founded: 1968
Sales Range: Less than $1 Million
Emp.: 10
Newspaper Publishers
N.A.I.C.S.: 513110
Ken Reichart (Publr & Editor)
Debbie Reichert (Publr & Editor)

THE GAGE COMPANY
172 St John St, Portland, ME 04104
Tel.: (207) 773-4755
Web Site: http://www.redlon-johnson.com
Year Founded: 1892
Sales Range: $125-149.9 Million
Emp.: 250
Pipes, Valves, Fittings, Plumbing, Heating & Industrial Supplies Whslr & Distr
N.A.I.C.S.: 423510
Robert A. Chute (Chm & CEO)
Tom Mullen (Pres & COO)

THE GALLUP ORGANIZATION
The Gallup Bldg 901 F St NW, Washington, DC 20004
Tel.: (202) 715-3030
Web Site: http://www.gallup.com
Year Founded: 1935
Sales Range: $450-499.9 Million
Emp.: 2,500
Marketing Research, Public Opinion Polling & Management Consulting Services
N.A.I.C.S.: 541910
James K. Clifton (Chm & CEO)
Jane E. Miller (COO)
Subsidiaries:
Gallup Consulting (1)
901 F St NW, Washington, DC 20004
Tel.: (202) 715-3030
Sales Range: $10-24.9 Million
Emp.: 100
Business Consulting Services
N.A.I.C.S.: 541611
Jim Cliston (CEO)

The Gallup Organization-Princeton (1)
502 Carnegie Ctr Ste 300, Princeton, NJ 08540
Tel.: (609) 924-9600
Web Site: http://www.gallup.com
Sales Range: $1-9.9 Million
Emp.: 30
Management Consulting, Public Opinion Services & Periodical Publisher
N.A.I.C.S.: 541910
James K. Clifton (CEO)

THE GAMBONE GROUP
1030 W Germantown Pike, East Norriton, PA 19403-3929
Tel.: (610) 539-4700
Web Site: http://www.gambone.com
Year Founded: 1958
Sales Range: $10-24.9 Million
Emp.: 120
Land Development, Housing & Commercial Construction & Rental Services
N.A.I.C.S.: 237210
Brian Miles (Dir-HR)
Jennifer Matthews (Mgr-AP & AR)
Melissa Carbone (Coord-Accts Payable)
Stephen Cicala Jr. (Mgr-Property)
Joe Gambone Jr. (Pres)

THE GAMBRINUS COMPANY
14800 San Pedro Ave Fl 3, San Antonio, TX 78232-3733
Tel.: (210) 490-9128

THE GAMBRINUS COMPANY

The Gambrinus Company—(Continued)
Web Site:
http://www.gambrinusco.com
Year Founded: 1986
Sales Range: $10-24.9 Million
Emp.: 190
Beer Brewer & Distr
N.A.I.C.S.: 312120
Carlos E. Alvarez *(Founder & Chm)*

Subsidiaries:

Spoetzl Brewery (1)
603 E Brewery St, Shiner, TX 77984
Tel.: (361) 594-3852
Web Site: http://www.shiner.com
Brewery
N.A.I.C.S.: 327910

THE GAMS GROUP, INC.
308 W Erie St Ste 400, Chicago, IL 60654-3624
Tel.: (312) 280-2740
Web Site: http://www.gamscom.com
Year Founded: 1974
Rev.: $38,000,000
Emp.: 20
Advertising Services
N.A.I.C.S.: 541810
Dale Mitchell *(VP-Bus Dev)*

Subsidiaries:

CoteTonic (1)
912 Grande Allee Ouest, Quebec, G1S 1C5, QC, Canada
Tel.: (418) 525-5165
Web Site: http://www.cotetonic.com
Emp.: 16
Advertising Services
N.A.I.C.S.: 541810
Jean Cote *(Pres)*

THE GARDEN CITY CO-OP INC.
106 N 6th St, Garden City, KS 67846-5545
Tel.: (620) 275-6161 KS
Web Site: http://www.gccoop.com
Year Founded: 1919
Sales Range: $10-24.9 Million
Emp.: 100
Grain & Field Beans Distr
N.A.I.C.S.: 424510
John McClelland *(Gen Mgr)*
Lakin Dreiling *(VP-Petroleum)*
Tim Giesick *(VP-Crop Production)*
Toby Wilson *(COO)*
Tom Mulville *(Chm)*
Tyler Hands *(Vice Chm)*
Bruce Howard *(Treas & Sec)*

Subsidiaries:

Country Corner Inc. (1)
106 N 6th St, Garden City, KS 67846-5545 (100%)
Tel.: (620) 275-6161
Web Site: http://www.gccoop.com
Sales Range: $10-24.9 Million
Emp.: 24
Grocery Stores
N.A.I.C.S.: 445131
John McClellend *(Gen Mgr)*

The Garden City Co-Op Inc - Dighton (1)
245 W George St, Dighton, KS 67839
Tel.: (620) 397-5343
Web Site: http://www.gccoop.com
Grain Production
N.A.I.C.S.: 424510

THE GARDEN WHOLESALE, INC.
5400 Longleaf St, Jacksonville, FL 32209
Tel.: (904) 768-6888 FL
Web Site:
http://www.thegardenproduce.com
Year Founded: 1976
Sales Range: $10-24.9 Million

Fresh Fruit & Vegetable Distr
N.A.I.C.S.: 424480
Jonathan Wasson *(Co-Owner & Pres)*
Steve Wasson *(Mgr-Fleet)*
Matthew Wasson *(Co-Owner & VP)*
Gary Ireland *(Dir-Sls)*
Lori Rasor *(Controller)*
Rick Jeffries *(Mgr-Receiving & Quality Control)*
Randy Murdock *(Mgr-Ops)*
Mary Demchak *(Mgr-Shipping)*
Mike Anthony *(VP-Ops)*

THE GARDNER ZEMKE COMPANY
6821 Academy Pkwy NE, Albuquerque, NM 87109
Tel.: (505) 881-0555 NM
Web Site:
http://www.gardnerzemke.com
Year Founded: 1965
Sales Range: $25-49.9 Million
Emp.: 120
Commercial Electrical & Mechanical Construction
N.A.I.C.S.: 238210
Richard Zemke *(Co-Founder)*
George Gardner *(Co-Founder)*

Subsidiaries:

The Gardner Zemke Company - Mechanical Division (1)
5750 Pino Rd NE, Albuquerque, NM 87109
Tel.: (505) 822-8858
Construction Engineering Services
N.A.I.C.S.: 541330

THE GART COMPANIES, INC.
299 Milwaukee St, Denver, CO 80206
Tel.: (303) 333-1933
Web Site:
http://www.gartcompanies.com
Year Founded: 1986
Holding Company; Real estate Investments & Private Equity firm
N.A.I.C.S.: 551112
Ken Gart *(Principal)*
Tom Gart *(Principal)*
John Gart *(Principal)*

Subsidiaries:

Work World America Inc. (1)
2030 Peabody Rd Ste 300, Vacaville, CA 95687
Tel.: (707) 453-7800
Web Site: http://www.workworldamerica.com
Clothing Stores
N.A.I.C.S.: 458110
Dan Meyer *(Co-Owner)*

THE GARY GROUP
2040 Broadway, Santa Monica, CA 90404-2910
Tel.: (310) 264-1700 CA
Year Founded: 1976
Sales Range: $25-49.9 Million
Emp.: 30
N.A.I.C.S.: 541810
Richard M. Gary *(Chm & Principal)*
Elsa H. Gary *(Chm)*
Dana Chung *(Media Buyer)*
Rick Rogers *(Pres)*

THE GAZETTE COMPANY
500 3rd Ave SE, Cedar Rapids, IA 52401-1608
Tel.: (319) 398-8333 IA
Web Site:
http://www.thegazettecompany.com
Year Founded: 1883
Emp.: 500
Holding Company; Newspaper & Internet Publishing, Television Broadcasting & Commercial Printing Services
N.A.I.C.S.: 551112

Charles M. Peters *(Pres & CEO)*

Subsidiaries:

Fusionfarm (1)
501 2nd Ave SE Ste 300, Cedar Rapids, IA 52401
Tel.: (319) 398-8201
Web Site: http://www.fusionfarm.com
Creative Marketing Agency
N.A.I.C.S.: 541810
Chris Edwards *(Pres-Agency, Digital & Res Svcs)*
Seth Smith *(Dir-Art)*
Neil Brewster *(Dir-Art)*
Jake Vardaman *(Dir-Art)*
Michael Zydzik *(Dir-Creative)*
Alicia Anderson *(Mgr-Social Media)*
Aaron Frerichs *(Mgr-Web Applications)*
Joe Matar *(Mgr-Product-Web Dev)*
Jessica Flatgard *(Mgr-Product)*
Tracy Pratt *(Mgr-Product-SEO & SEM)*
Keaton Reeder *(Asst Dir-Art)*
Shawn Reineke *(Mgr-Sls)*

Gazette Communications, Inc. (1)
500 3rd Ave SE, Cedar Rapids, IA 52401-1608
Tel.: (319) 398-8333
Web Site: http://www.thegazette.com
Sales Range: $200-249.9 Million
Newspaper Publishers
N.A.I.C.S.: 513110
Charles M. Peters *(Pres & CEO)*
Jeff Tecklenburg *(Editor-Opinion Page)*

THE GEARY COMPANY
3136 E Russell Rd, Las Vegas, NV 89120-3463
Tel.: (702) 382-9610 NV
Web Site:
http://www.gearycompany.com
Year Founded: 1969
Rev.: $10,000,000
Emp.: 18
Advetising Agency
N.A.I.C.S.: 541810
James D. McKusick *(Chm & CEO)*
Alice Anderson *(Dir-Media)*
Grant R. Garrison *(Dir-Art)*
Glenn Larsen *(Dir-Creative)*
Lance Knadle *(Graphic Designer)*

THE GEHR GROUP
7400 E Slauson Ave, Los Angeles, CA 90040-3300
Tel.: (323) 728-5558
Web Site: http://www.gehr.com
Sales Range: $10-24.9 Million
Emp.: 100
Holding Company; Wire Mfr, Commercial & Multi-Family Real Estate Services, Industrial Supplies Distr
N.A.I.C.S.: 551112
David Lifschitz *(Pres & CEO)*
Mark Goldman *(COO)*
Eric Kang *(VP-IT)*
Dennis Nishida *(VP-Admin)*
Thuong Luong *(Chief Investment Officer-Gehr Hospitality)*
Max Paetzold *(VP-Fin)*
Ed Duess *(VP-Asset Mgmt)*
Molly Caccamo *(COO & Exec VP)*

Subsidiaries:

Gehr Development (1)
7400 E Slauson Ave, Los Angeles, CA 90040-0330
Tel.: (323) 728-5558
Web Site: http://www.gehrdevelopment.com
Real Estate-Focused Investment Firm
N.A.I.C.S.: 531210
David Lifschitz *(CEO)*
Mark Goldman *(COO & Chief Counsel)*
Alfred somekh *(Pres)*
Max Paetzold *(VP-Fin)*

Gehr Industries Inc. (1)
7400 E Slauson Ave, Los Angeles, CA 90040-3308
Tel.: (323) 728-5558
Web Site: http://www.gehr.com

U.S. PRIVATE

Mfr of Electrical Cables; Supplier of Electric Wire & Related Products
N.A.I.C.S.: 331222
Carl Rosenthal *(Exec VP-Admin)*
Eric Kang *(VP-IT)*
Dennis Nishida *(VP-Admin)*
Rowdy Oxford *(VP-Sls & Mktg)*

THE GEL GROUP, INC.
2040 Savage Rd, Charleston, SC 29407
Tel.: (843) 556-8171
Web Site: http://www.gel.com
Year Founded: 1981
Rev.: $17,100,000
Emp.: 330
Technical & Professional Services
N.A.I.C.S.: 541330
Russ Moser *(Dir-IT)*
George R. McAbee *(Mgr-Facilities)*
John I. Crawford *(Dir-HR & Safety)*
Douglas E. Earnst *(Co-CFO)*
James M. Stelling *(Pres & CEO)*
Laurie S. Herrington *(Co-CFO)*
Joseph M. Hodgson Jr. *(Pres)*

THE GENESIS GROUP
541 Avellino Isles Cir 30101, Naples, FL 34119
Tel.: (239) 989-3062
Web Site:
http://www.thegenesisgroup.us
Year Founded: 1975
Sales Range: $10-24.9 Million
Emp.: 6
Advetising Agency
N.A.I.C.S.: 541810
Donna C. Heiser APR *(Mng Dir)*
Elizabeth McBride *(Controller & Traffic Mgr)*
Gene A. Heiser *(Mng Partner)*

THE GENEVA FOUNDATION
917 Pacific Ave Ste 600, Tacoma, WA 98402
Tel.: (253) 383-1398 WA
Web Site: http://www.genevausa.org
Year Founded: 1993
Sales Range: $50-74.9 Million
Emp.: 568
Medical Research Services
N.A.I.C.S.: 541715
Kelli Blaize-Wise *(Mgr-Client Relationship)*
Kathy Carey *(Mgr-Client Relationship)*
Randal LeBlanc *(Mgr-Reg Program)*
David Blanford *(Treas)*
Elise W. Huszar *(Pres & Sec)*
Jane S. Taylor *(Founder & Chief Strategy Officer)*
Michael W. Hansch *(Chm)*

THE GEORGETOWN COMPANY, LLC
667 Madison Ave Fl 23, New York, NY 10021
Tel.: (212) 755-2323
Web Site:
http://www.georgetownco.com
Year Founded: 1979
Sales Range: $1-9.9 Million
Emp.: 16
Management Consulting Services
N.A.I.C.S.: 541618
Adam R. Flatto *(Pres & CEO)*

THE GERONTOLOGICAL SOCIETY OF AMERICA
1220 L St NW Ste 901, Washington, DC 20005
Tel.: (202) 842-1275 DC
Web Site: http://www.geron.org
Year Founded: 1945
Sales Range: $10-24.9 Million
Emp.: 30
Social Advocacy Organization
N.A.I.C.S.: 813319

Judie Lieu (Sr Dir-Innovation)
James Appleby (CEO & Exec Dir)
Amy Conradt (Mgr-Education & Publ)
Karen Tracy (Sr Dir-Strategic Alliances & Bus Dev)
Jim Woolwine (Sr Dir-Fin & Admin)
Angela Baker (Dir-Association for Gerontology in Higher Education)
Jason Petty (Mgr-Exhibits & Advertising)
Megan McCutcheon (Mgr-Publ)
Rachel Whidden (Dir-Meetings)
Tamara Baker (Sec)
Anthony Rogers (Dir-IT)
Kimberly Muse (Office Mgr)
Suzanne Kunkel (Treas)
Todd Kluss (Sr Mgr-Comm)

THE GERSON COMPANY INC.
1450 S Lone Elm Rd, Olathe, KS 66061
Tel.: (913) 262-7400   MO
Web Site:
http://www.gersoncompany.com
Year Founded: 1942
Sales Range: $25-49.9 Million
Emp.: 265
Provider of Personal & Household Products
N.A.I.C.S.: 424990
John Jalmarson (COO)
Jim Gerson (Pres)

THE GETTYSBURG FOUNDATION
1195 Baltimore Pike, Gettysburg, PA 17325
Tel.: (717) 338-1243   PA
Web Site:
http://www.gettysburgfoundation.org
Year Founded: 1998
Sales Range: $25-49.9 Million
Emp.: 131
Historical Resource Preservation Services
N.A.I.C.S.: 712110
Robert A. Kinsley (Chm)
Barbara J. Finfrock (Vice Chm)
Barbara Sardella (Sec)
Matthew C. Moen (Pres)
Shanon Toal Jr. (Treas)

THE GIBSON GROUP INC.
2985 Madison Rd, Cincinnati, OH 45209-2027
Tel.: (513) 351-9966   OH
Web Site: http://www.gibson.co.nz
Year Founded: 1981
Sales Range: $25-49.9 Million
Emp.: 100
Wholesale Paper & Paper Products
N.A.I.C.S.: 424130
Rex Potier (Mgr-Facilities)
David Crossan (Dir-Tech)
Liqin Mi (Sr Mgr-Projects Dev)
Victoria Spackman (CEO)

Subsidiaries:

HPE Inc,   (1)
2985 Madison Rd, Cincinnati, OH 45209-2027   (100%)
Tel.: (513) 351-9966
Web Site: http://www.hpepaper.com
Sales Range: $10-24.9 Million
Emp.: 30
Paper Broker
N.A.I.C.S.: 424130

THE GILDER LEHRMAN INSTITUTE OF AMERICAN HISTORY
49 W 45th St 6th Fl, New York, NY 10036
Tel.: (646) 366-9666   NY
Web Site:
http://www.gilderlehrman.org
Year Founded: 1994

Sales Range: $1-9.9 Million
Emp.: 143
Historical Educational Support Services
N.A.I.C.S.: 611710
Lesley S. Herrmann (Exec Dir)
James G. Basker (Pres)

THE GINN GROUP, INC.
200 Westpark Dr Ste 100, Peachtree City, GA 30269
Tel.: (404) 669-9214
Web Site:
http://www.theginngroup.com
Year Founded: 2016
Sales Range: $1-9.9 Million
Emp.: 200
Logistics Consulting Servies
N.A.I.C.S.: 541614
Billy Gragg (Sr VP-Ops)
James Ginn (Owner)

THE GLADSTONE COMPANIES, INC.
1521 Westbranch Dr Ste 100, McLean, VA 22102
Tel.: (703) 287-5800   DE
Web Site:
https://www.gladstonecompanies.com
Year Founded: 2009
Rev.: $61,817,970
Assets: $67,696,006
Liabilities: $33,513,679
Net Worth: $34,182,327
Earnings: $6,763,517
Emp.: 29
Fiscal Year-end: 06/30/21
Investment Services
N.A.I.C.S.: 523150
Terry Lee Brubaker (Co-Founder, COO & Vice Chm)
David Gladstone (CEO, Co-Founder & Chm)
Michael Malesardi (CFO & Treas)
Terry Lee Brubaker (Co-Founder, COO & Vice Chm)
Jack Dellafiora (Chief Compliance Officer)
Susan Garza (Compliance Officer)

THE GLASS BARON INC.
1601 Diamond Springs Rd, Virginia Beach, VA 23455
Tel.: (757) 464-1131
Web Site: http://www.glassbaron.com
Rev.: $18,667,432
Emp.: 30
Provider of Decorative Glasswear
N.A.I.C.S.: 327212
Ivan Morris (Founder & Pres)
Jennifer R. Alvarez (Dir-Art)

THE GLENMEDE TRUST COMPANY
1650 Market St Ste 1200, Philadelphia, PA 19103
Tel.: (215) 419-6000
Web Site: http://www.glenmede.com
Year Founded: 1956
Sales Range: $75-99.9 Million
Emp.: 200
Investment Trust Services
N.A.I.C.S.: 523940
Laura A. Williamson (Mng Dir & COO)
Chip Wilson (Exec Dir-Relationship Mgmt)
Stephen Mahoney (Mgr-Taxable Fixed Income)
Paul T. Sullivan (Portfolio Mgr-Glenmede Investment Mgmt LP)
Peter J. Zuleba (Dir-Investment Mgmt)
Vladimir de Vassal (Dir-Quantitative Res)

Rhonda R. Cohen (Chm)
Laura LaRosa (Dir-Business Development & Mng Dir)
Jason Pride (Chief Investment Officer-Private Client Bus)
Kent E. Weaver (Dir-Client Svc-Glenmede Investment Management LP)
Lee P. Miller (Mng Dir & Dir-New York)
Lea Emery (Dir-Bus Dev-New York)
Brian K. Green (Dir-Family Wealth)
Susan Mucciarone (Dir-Private Client Relationship Mgmt)
Eric Grasinger (Mgr-Relationship & Portfolio-New York)
Jordan Savitch (Mng Dir, Gen Counsel & Dir-Bus Assurance)
Stephen C. Lehman (Chief Investment Officer-Endowments & Foundations)
Michael Dellapa (Portfolio Mgr/Mgr-Customer Rels-Washington)
Thomas P. Melcher (Mng Dir & Assoc Dir-Investment Mgmt-Glenmede Investment)
Mark Hays (Dir-Impact & Sustainable Investing)
John Church (Dir-Endowment & Foundation Impact Portfolio Mgmt)
Elizabeth Eldridge (Dir-Mgr Res)

THE GLENN GROUP
50 Washington St Ste 200, Reno, NV 89503-5603
Tel.: (775) 686-7777   NV
Web Site:
http://www.theglenngroup.com
Year Founded: 1969
Rev.: $65,000,000
Emp.: 30
Advertising Agencies
N.A.I.C.S.: 541810
Flip Wright (Chief Brand Officer & Exec VP)
Kelly Glenn (Exec VP)

THE GLIK COMPANY
3248 Nameoki Rd, Granite City, IL 62040-5014
Tel.: (618) 876-6717   DE
Web Site: http://www.gliks.com
Year Founded: 1897
Sales Range: $200-249.9 Million
Emp.: 400
Men's & Ladies' Apparel Stores
N.A.I.C.S.: 458110
Jeff Glik (Pres & CEO)
Darryl Gerstenecker (CFO & CIO)
Kristi Ham (Dir-Mktg)

THE GLOBAL FUND FOR WOMEN, INC.
800 Market St 7th Fl, San Francisco, CA 94102
Tel.: (415) 248-4800   CA
Web Site:
http://www.globalfundforwomen.org
Year Founded: 1987
Rev.: $18,926,631
Earnings: $42,924
Emp.: 40
Fiscal Year-end: 06/30/19
Woman Welfare Services
N.A.I.C.S.: 813410
Leila Hessini (VP-Programs)
Sharon Bhagwan Rolls (Co-Chm)
Blythe S. Masters (Co-Chm)
Sangeeta Chowdhry (Sr Dir-Program-Economic Justice)
Peiyao Chen (VP-Impact & Effectiveness)
Valeria Brabata (Dir-Program-Latin America & The Caribbean)
Camille Matson (Officer-Annual Giving)

Maria Nunez (Sec)
Latanya Mapp Frett (Pres & CEO)
Anil Awasti (Chief HR Officer)
Jen Quinn (CFO)
Lori Adelman (VP-Influence & Engagement)
Janelle Cavanagh (VP-Strategic Partnerships)
Aida Akim-Escriva (Officer-Program-Adolescent Girls Rights)
Lisa Block (Officer-Program)
Nicole Crossley (Mgr-Web & Creative)
Cinthia Carvajal (Officer-Program-Grantmaking & Movement Building)
Zarina Dyussen (Coord-Grants)
Kelly Gannon (Dir-Learning & Evaluation)
Mira Khawam (Dir-Grants Ops)
Laura Lopez-Blazquez (Officer-Dev-East)
Ammarah Maqsood (Officer-Dev-West)
Narjes Mathlouthi (Coord-Grants)
Chelsea Meacham (Officer-Grantwriting & Comm)
Daniela Miramontes (Coord-Grants)
Sangeeta Nandi (Officer-Dev-Grants Mgmt)
Renee Saedi (Mgr-Champions-Equality Program)
Allison Sambo (Officer-Learning, Evaluation & Impact)
Siri Svanoe-Loggins (Mgr-Programs Ops)
Anja Tranovich (Sr Mgr-PR & Comm)
Randy Trigg (Dir-Information Mgmt)
Zahra Vieneuve (Program Dir)
Rashida Petersen (Reg Dir-East)

THE GODWIN GROUP
200 Champion Dr, Dunn, NC 28334
Tel.: (910) 897-4995
Web Site:
http://www.godwingrouponline.com
Truck Equipment Mfr
N.A.I.C.S.: 333924
Patrick Godwin (Dir-Art & Mktg)

Subsidiaries:

Godwin Manufacturing Company Inc.   (1)
17665 US-421, Dunn, NC 28334-6485
Tel.: (910) 892-0141
Web Site: http://www.godwinmfg.com
Motor Vehicle Body Mfr
N.A.I.C.S.: 336211
Pamela G. Faircloth (Treas & Sec)

Subsidiary (Domestic):

Willamsen-Godwin Truck Body Company   (2)
1925 W Indiana Ave, Salt Lake City, UT 84101-3610
Tel.: (801) 973-9400
Web Site: http://www.williamsen-godwin.com
Sales Range: $1-9.9 Million
Trailers & Dump Bodies Design & Mfr
N.A.I.C.S.: 333924

THE GOG FOUNDATION, INC.
4 Penn Ctr 1600 JFK Blvd Ste 1020, Philadelphia, PA 19103
Tel.: (215) 854-0770   DC
Web Site: http://www.gog.org
Year Founded: 2002
Sales Range: $25-49.9 Million
Emp.: 28
Healtcare Services
N.A.I.C.S.: 622110
Denise Mackey (Dir-Admin)
Laura Reese (Exec Dir)
Mary C. Sharp (CFO)
Kathy Shumaker (Dir-Dev)

THE GOLD CORPORATION

THE GOLD CORPORATION   U.S. PRIVATE

The Gold Corporation—(Continued)
96-1173 Waihona St Ste B3, Pearl City, HI 96782
Tel.: (808) 456-8577
Web Site: http://www.skcookies.com
Year Founded: 1998
Sales Range: $10-24.9 Million
Emp.: 35
Cookies & Cracker Mfr
N.A.I.C.S.: 311821
Steven Gold (Pres)
Sheila Gold (VP)

THE GOLDBERGER COMPANY, LLC
36 W 25th St 14th Fl, New York, NY 10010
Tel.: (212) 924-1194   NY
Web Site:
 http://www.babysfirstdoll.com
Year Founded: 1916
Sales Range: $75-99.9 Million
Emp.: 50
Dolls Mfr
N.A.I.C.S.: 339930
Jeff Holtzman (Pres & CEO)

THE GOOD SAMARITAN HOME OF QUINCY
2130 Harrison St, Quincy, IL 62301
Tel.: (217) 223-8717   IL
Web Site: http://www.gshq.org
Year Founded: 1953
Sales Range: $10-24.9 Million
Emp.: 440
Elder Care Services
N.A.I.C.S.: 624120
Sarah Dolbeare (Sec & Dir-Cottage Admissions)
Missy Loos (Dir-HR)
Lanse Tomlinson (Dir-Dev & PR)
Sarah Riggs (Dir-Food Svcs)
Tina Kroeger (Dir-Nursing Svcs)
Sally Hodgson (Dir-Activity & Volunteer Coord)
Stacy Arrowsmith (Dir-Environ Svcs)
James Riley (Dir-Pastoral Svcs)
Tiffany Nowacki (Dir-Social Svcs & Beauty Shop)
Cindy Gilbert (Dir-Admissions)
Jerry Manton (Dir-Maintenance)
Barb Lowary (Dir-Payroll & Benefits)

THE GOODMAN GROUP, INC.
1107 Hazeltine Blvd Ste 200, Chaska, MN 55318
Tel.: (952) 361-8000
Web Site:
 http://www.thegoodmangroup.com
Year Founded: 1965
Rev.: $1,000,000,000
Emp.: 4,000
Real Estate Development, Construction & Management
N.A.I.C.S.: 237210
Kathy Nelson (Mgr-Community)
Wayne Kinneman (Dir-IT)
Phyllis Gaspar (Natl Dir-R&D)
Peg Macaluso (Dir-Mktg-Cypress Palms)
Brad Marburger (Natl Dir-Platinum Career Solutions)
Craig Edinger (CEO)
Dee Leman (Dir-Physical & Occupational Therapy)
Mark Holmes (Natl Dir-Culinary Ops)
Tim Getty (Natl Dir-Sls)
Jennifer Ballantine (Exec Dir-Able Palms Home Health)
Matthew Kern (Natl Dir-Ops)
Kim Te Brugge (VP-Ops-Senior Living & Health Care)
Ian Douglas Ferrier (Chm)
Nick Vrondas (Grp CFO)
Scott Farquhar (Grp CTO)

Subsidiaries:
Millennium Ventures Limited Partnership, L.L.P.   (1)
3140 Forest Rd, Spring Hill, FL 34606-3379
Tel.: (352) 683-9009
Web Site:
 http://www.residenceattimberpines.com
Nursing Care Services
N.A.I.C.S.: 623311

The Goodman Group UK   (1)
1 Saint Peter's Road, Maidenhead, SL6 7QU, Berkshire, United Kingdom
Tel.: (44) 1628 876830
Web Site:
 http://www.thegoodmangroupuk.com
Real Estate Development, Construction & Management
N.A.I.C.S.: 237210
Simon Webster (Mng Dir)

THE GOODMAN THEATRE
170 N Dearborn St, Chicago, IL 60601
Tel.: (312) 443-3811
Web Site:
 http://www.goodmantheatre.org
Year Founded: 1925
Sales Range: $10-24.9 Million
Emp.: 100
Theatrical Producers & Services
N.A.I.C.S.: 711110
Robert A. Falls (Dir-Artistic)
Lori Kleinerman (Dir-Mktg & Sls Revenue)
Jay Corsi (Dir-Adv, Sls & Mktg)
Jodi J. Brown (Mgr-Bus & Admin)
Scott Conn (Mgr-Production)
Dorlisa Martin (Dir-Dev)
Jeff M. Ciaramita (Sr Dir-Special Events & Stewardship-Dev)
Bridget Melton (Mgr-Ticket Svcs)
Carolyn Walsh (Dir-HR)
Chuck Smith (Dir-Resident)
Erik Schnitger (Dir-Ticket Svcs)
John Collins (Gen Mgr)
Mary Zimmerman (Dir-Manilow Resident)
Summer Snow (Assoc Dir-Ticket Svcs)
Adnaan Hamid (Pres)
Susan J. Wislow (Sec)
Alice Young Sabl (Vice Chm)
Patrick Wood-Prince (Vice Chm)
Roger Baskes (Vice Chm)
David W. Fox Jr. (Treas)

THE GORDON LUMBER COMPANY
1515 Croghan St, Fremont, OH 43420
Tel.: (419) 333-5444   OH
Web Site:
 http://www.gordonlumber.com
Year Founded: 1868
Sales Range: $50-74.9 Million
Emp.: 150
Home Centers Owner & Operator; Lumber, Paint & Hardware Whslr
N.A.I.C.S.: 444110
Erin Leonard (Pres)

THE GORES GROUP, LLC
10877 Wilshire Blvd 18th Fl, Los Angeles, CA 90024
Tel.: (310) 209-3010   DE
Web Site:
 http://www.thegoresgroup.com
Year Founded: 1987
Rev.: $3,300,000,000
Privater Equity Firm
N.A.I.C.S.: 523999
Steven C. Yager (Sr Mng Dir)
Andrew Freedman (Mng Dir)
Eric Hattler (Mng Dir & Gen Counsel)
Mark R. Stone (Sr Mng Dir)
Chris Sznewajs (Principal)
Anthony Guagliano (Mng Dir-M&A)
Jennifer Kwon (Mng Dir)
Robbie Reynders (Mng Dir-Ops)
Igor Chacartegui (Mng Dir-M&A)
John P. Danner (Mng Dir)
Thomas Waldman (Mng Dir-Legal)
Wesley J. Johnston (Mng Dir-Ops)
Edward Johnson (Mng Dir-Merger & Acquisition)
Catherine Pollard (Mng Dir)
Alec E. Gores (Chm & CEO)
Victor C. Otley III (Mng Dir-M&A)

Subsidiaries:
Aprisma Management Technologies   (1)
273 Corporate Dr, Portsmouth, NH 03801-4716
Tel.: (603) 334-2100
Web Site: http://www.ca.com
Sales Range: $25-49.9 Million
Emp.: 200
Mfr of Software for Network Infrastructure & Management
N.A.I.C.S.: 541511
Peter Clairmont (VP)
John A. C. Swainson (CEO)

Astadia Inc.   (1)
3010 Gaylor Pkwy Ste 260, Frisco, TX 75034
Tel.: (469) 828-0990
Web Site: http://www.astadia.com
Sales Range: $25-49.9 Million
Emp.: 35
Business Consulting & IT Services
N.A.I.C.S.: 561499
Blake Wolff (Exec VP-Bus Dev)

Branch (Non-US):
Astadia Consulting - India   (2)
B 807 08 8th Floor BPTP Park Centra, Sector 30, Gurgaon, 12201, Haryana, India
Tel.: (91) 1244102872
Web Site: http://www.astadia.com
Sales Range: $25-49.9 Million
Sales, Marketing & Customer Relations Consulting Services
N.A.I.C.S.: 561499

Astadia Consulting UK Limited   (2)
19 Bolsover Street, London, W1W 5NA, United Kingdom
Tel.: (44) 8450559758
Sales, Marketing & Customer Relations Consulting Services
N.A.I.C.S.: 561499
David Woodhead (Sr VP-Intl Ops)

Branch (Domestic):
Astadia, Inc.-Atlanta   (2)
2839 Paces Ferry Rd Ste 350, Atlanta, GA 30339
Tel.: (678) 589-7670
Web Site: http://www.astadia.com
Sales Range: $10-24.9 Million
Sales, Marketing & Customer Relations Consulting Services
N.A.I.C.S.: 541618

Cosmo Specialty Fibers, Inc.   (1)
1701 1st St, Cosmopolis, WA 98537
Tel.: (360) 500-4600
Web Site:
 http://www.cosmospecialtyfibers.com
Wood Pulp Mfr
N.A.I.C.S.: 322110
Andrew Freedman (Chm)
Regina G. Wyse (CFO)
Robert Buchan (VP-Govt Rels, Mktg & Comm)
James E. Smith (Mgr-Mill)
Larry Davis (Dir-Fiber Resources)
Shayne Bird (Mgr-Safety & Health)
Sandy L. Corrion (Mgr-Contracting & Procurement)
Katie Heikkila (Coord-HR)
Nicholas B. Dottino (CEO)

DMN Ltd.   (1)
Unit B1 Elgin Drive Estate Kembrey Street, Swindon, SN2 8UY, Wilts, United Kingdom
Tel.: (44) 1793 430 430
Web Site: http://www.dmn.co.uk

Sales Range: $10-24.9 Million
Emp.: 64
Communications Network Engineering & Support Services
N.A.I.C.S.: 517810
Toby Richards (Dir-Support Svcs)
Edd Aston (Mng Dir)

GatesAir, Inc.   (1)
5300 Kings Island Dr Ste 101, Mason, OH 45040-2353
Tel.: (513) 459-3400
Web Site: http://www.gatesair.com
Sales Range: $75-99.9 Million
Emp.: 70
Broadcast Communications Equipment & Software Mfr & Distr
N.A.I.C.S.: 334220
Rich Redmond (Pres/Mng Dir-Intl)
Joseph Mack (VP-Sls-Americas)
Bryant Burke (VP-Ops)
John Howell (Dir-Global Svcs)
Jeffrey Hills (Controller & Dir-Fin)
Bruce D. Swail (CEO)
John Danner (Chm)
Avery Schultz (Mgr-Sls- New Mexico, Oklahoma & Texas)
Mark Goins (Dir-Transmission Sls-North America)
Andy McClelland (Mng Dir-EMEA)

Unit (Domestic):
GatesAir, Inc. - Quincy   (2)
3200 Wisman Ln, Quincy, IL 62301
Tel.: (217) 222-8200
Electronic Equipment for Broadcasting
N.A.I.C.S.: 334220
Bryan Burke (VP-Ops & Svcs-Global)

Glotel Inc.   (1)
8700 W Bryn Mawr Ave Ste 400N, Chicago, IL 60631
Tel.: (312) 612-7480
Web Site: http://www.glotel.com
Staffing Services
N.A.I.C.S.: 561320
Michele Casey (CEO)
Greg Lynch (Pres)
Shawn Feeney (VP-Recruitment-Boston)
Michelle Lanza (Dir-Project Controls)
Anthony Castillo (Mgr-Program)
Daniel Arasin (VP-Northeast)
Gary Barnett (Mgr-Recruiting)
Julian Minnard (Mgr-Recruiting)

Hovis Ltd.   (1)
The Lord Rank Centre, Lincoln Road, High Wycombe, AL1 2RE, United Kingdom
Tel.: (44) 870 728 1111
Web Site: http://www.hovisbakery.co.uk
Sales Range: $1-4.9 Billion
Emp.: 200
Wrapped Bread, Morning Goods & Bulk & Bagged Flour Mfr
N.A.I.C.S.: 311211
Nish Kankiwala (CEO)

Idea Integration Corp.   (1)
10151 Deerwood Park Blvd Bldg 200 Ste 400, Jacksonville, FL 32256   (100%)
Tel.: (904) 360-2700
Web Site: http://www.idea.com
Sales Range: $50-74.9 Million
Emp.: 200
e-Business Solutions; IT Consulting Services
N.A.I.C.S.: 541690
Ed Cox (VP-Infrastructure Svcs)

Imagine Communications Corp.   (1)
7950 Legacy Dr Ste 400-485, Plano, TX 75024
Tel.: (469) 803-4900
Web Site:
 http://www.imaginecommunications.com
Emp.: 100
Media Software & Networking Solutions
N.A.I.C.S.: 513210
Steve Reynolds (CTO)
Ramnik Kamo (CMO)
Glodina Connan-Lostanlen (Sr VP & Gen Mgr-Playout & Networking Solutions)
John Higgins (Chief People Officer)
Anas Hantash (Dir-Sls-MENA)
Tom Cotney (CEO)
Donald Rowley (CIO)
Eric Toler (CFO)
Mathias Eckert (Sr VP & Gen Mgr-Playout & Networking Solutions-EMEA & APAC)

COMPANIES

Subsidiary (Non-US):

Imagine Communications - Argentina (2)
Lola Mora 421, Torre 1, Oficina 1601 Madero Harbour, Puerto Madero, Buenos Aires, Argentina
Tel.: (54) 911 4048 5511
Broadcast Communications Equipment Mfr & Distr
N.A.I.C.S.: 334220

Imagine Communications - Australia (2)
Suite 2 Level 1 13b Narabang Way, Belrose, 2085, NSW, Australia
Tel.: (61) 2 9479 4900
Web Site: http://www.imaginecommunications.com
Broadcast Communications Software Publisher & Distr
N.A.I.C.S.: 513210

Imagine Communications - Austria (2)
Schweizer Strasse 96, 6830, Rankweil, Austria
Tel.: (43) 552290112285
Sales Range: $1-9.9 Million
Emp.: 5
Radio & TV Communications Equipment Mfr
N.A.I.C.S.: 334220

Imagine Communications - Brazil (2)
Av Eng Luiz Carlos Berrini 1511 8 andar Conj 82, Brooklin, Sao Paulo, CP 04571-011, SP, Brazil
Tel.: (55) 1135384150
Sales Range: $10-24.9 Million
Emp.: 20
Broadcast Communications Equipment Mfr & Distr
N.A.I.C.S.: 334220
Nahuel Villegas (VP)

Imagine Communications - China (2)
Room 801 Tower B, China Electronics Plaza 3 Dan Ling Street, Haidian, Beijing, 100080, China
Tel.: (86) 10 5795 1300
Broadcast Communications Equipment Mfr & Distr
N.A.I.C.S.: 334220

Imagine Communications - France (2)
Immeuble le Signac 5 allee des Bas Tilliers, 92230, Gennevilliers, France
Tel.: (33) 147924400
Broadcast Communications Equipment Mfr & Distr
N.A.I.C.S.: 334220

Imagine Communications - Germany (2)
Carl-Zeiss-Ring 19a, Ismaning, 85737, Germany
Tel.: (49) 8914 9049 0
Sales Range: $10-24.9 Million
Emp.: 21
Broadcast Communications Equipment Mfr & Distr
N.A.I.C.S.: 334220
Mathias Eckert (Mng Dir)

Imagine Communications - Hong Kong (2)
Room 1015-1018 10F Tower 1 Grand Century Place, 193 Prince Edward Road West, Kowloon, China (Hong Kong)
Tel.: (852) 27760628
Sales Range: $10-24.9 Million
Emp.: 30
Broadcast Communications Equipment Mfr & Distr
N.A.I.C.S.: 334220
Dario Choi (VP-Sls & Svcs-Brdcst Comm Bus-Asia Pacific)

Imagine Communications - Hungary (2)
Mazsa ter 2-6, HU-1107, Budapest, Hungary
Tel.: (36) 18142540
Broadcast Communications Equipment Mfr & Distr
N.A.I.C.S.: 334220

Imagine Communications - India (2)
Lobe-02 7th Floor Tower A The Corenthum Office Complex, Sector 62, Noida, 201301, India
Tel.: (91) 1204775400
Sales Range: $10-24.9 Million
Emp.: 11
Broadcast Communications Equipment Mfr & Distr
N.A.I.C.S.: 334220

Imagine Communications - Japan (2)
5F Urban Shimbashi Bldg 4-5-1 Shimbashi, Minato-ku, Tokyo, 101 0063, Japan
Tel.: (81) 3 6721 5720
Sales Range: $100-124.9 Million
Broadcast Equipment Manufacturing & Sales
N.A.I.C.S.: 334220
Olaf Brunswicker (Reg Mgr-Sls-Eastern Europe)

Imagine Communications - Mexico (2)
Ave Insurgentes Sur 688 Piso 8, Colonia Del Valle, Mexico, 03100, DF, Mexico (100%)
Tel.: (52) 55 3640 2730
Sales Range: $25-49.9 Million
Emp.: 32
Electronic Communication Equipment Provider
N.A.I.C.S.: 423690

Imagine Communications - Singapore (2)
300 Tampines Avenue 5 06-04 Tampines Junction, Singapore, 529653, Singapore
Tel.: (65) 6595 4600
Broadcast Communications Software Publisher & Distr
N.A.I.C.S.: 513210

Imagine Communications Canada Ltd. (2)
25 Dyas Road, Toronto, M3B 1V7, ON, Canada
Tel.: (416) 445-9640
Sales Range: $250-299.9 Million
Broadcast Interface Equipment Mfr
N.A.I.C.S.: 334220

Unit (Domestic):

Imagine Communications Corp. - Chesapeake (2)
Volvo Office Park 1228 Progressive Dr Ste 101, Chesapeake, VA 23320-3641
Tel.: (757) 548-2300
Sales Range: $10-24.9 Million
Broadcast Routing & Distribution Equipment Mfr
N.A.I.C.S.: 334220

Imagine Communications Corp. - Northridge (2)
9451 Corbin Ave Ste 150, Northridge, CA 91324
Tel.: (818) 717-6800
Emp.: 60
Electronic Equipment for Broadcasting
N.A.I.C.S.: 334220

Intelliverse (1)
5900 Windward Pkwy Ste 500, Atlanta, GA 30005
Tel.: (770) 325-8000
Web Site: http://www.voicecom.com
Sales Range: $25-49.9 Million
Emp.: 170
Telecommunication Servicesb
N.A.I.C.S.: 561421
Sean H. Gordon (CEO)

Meridian Medical Management (1)
75 Post Office Park, Wilbraham, MA 01095
Tel.: (617) 519-2422
Web Site: http://www.meridianmanage.com
Computer System Design Services
N.A.I.C.S.: 541512
Rob Gontarek (Pres & CEO)
Karen Simonenko (VP-Ops)
Jeanine Joncas-Lenczuk (VP-IT)
Ed Medina (CFO)
Stuart Schmidt (VP-Client Dev)
Judi Rooney (Chief Compliance Officer)
Jaime Ojeda (Exec VP-Healthcare Bus & Clinical Intelligence Div & Gen Mgr)

Scovill Fasteners Inc. (1)
1802 Scovill Dr, Clarkesville, GA 30523
Tel.: (706) 754-1000
Web Site: http://www.scovill.com
Sales Range: $25-49.9 Million
Emp.: 200
Apparel Fastener & Specialty Industrial Fastener Designer Mfr
N.A.I.C.S.: 339993
Richard Sanderson (Dir-Sls & Mktg-Apparel Americas)
Dave Butts (Mgr-Market-Military & Tactical)
Mark Brucchieri (Mgr-Market-Medical)
Scott Seitz (Mgr-Market-Distr)
Tim Crocker (Mgr-Market-Indus Products)

Subsidiary (Non-US):

GSG Scovill Fasteners Asia Limited (2)
3rd F China Aerospace Center No 143 Hoitonroad, Kwun Tong, Kowloon, China (Hong Kong)
Tel.: (852) 3658 7700
Apparels Mfr
N.A.I.C.S.: 315250

Scovill Fasteners India Private Limited (2)
Door No 47 4th Street Swarnapuri Avenue, 15 Velampalayam, Tirupur, 641652, India
Tel.: (91) 421 6457 910
Web Site: http://www.scovill.com
Emp.: 6
Apparels Mfr
N.A.I.C.S.: 315990
Rajiv Joy (Mng Dir)

The Gores Group, LLC - Boulder Branch (1)
6260 Lookout Rd, Boulder, CO 80301
Tel.: (303) 531-3100
Web Site: http://www.gores.com
Emp.: 10
Privater Equity Firm
N.A.I.C.S.: 523999
Steven C. Yager (Sr Mng Dir)
Michael Nutting (Mng Dir & Head-Corp Fin)
Thomas T. Stone (Sr Mng Dir)
Chris Crowell (Mng Dir-Ops)
John P. Danner (Mng Dir-Ops)
Andrew Freedman (Mng Dir-Ops)
Anthony Guagliano (Mng Dir-M&A)
Eric Hattler (Mng Dir & Gen Counsel)
Cathy Pollard (CFO & Mng Dir)
Robbie Reynders (Mng Dir-Ops)
Thomas Waldman (Mng Dir-Legal)
Lindsay Wynter (Mng Dir-Fin)

U.S. Farathane Holdings Corp. (1)
2700 High Meadow Cir, Auburn Hills, MI 48326
Tel.: (248) 754-7000
Web Site: http://www.usfarathane.com
Sales Range: $450-499.9 Million
Emp.: 2,500
Holding Company; Engineered Plastic Injection-Molded Components Mfr & Whslr
N.A.I.C.S.: 551112
Andrew J. Greenlee (Pres & CEO)
Bart Bernocco (Fin Mgr)
Jason Brake (Sr Acct Mgr)
Rodney Turton (Dir-Pur & Supply Chain)
Amy Wood (Sr Mgr-HR)
Jeff DeVries (Mgr-Mfg)
Stephanie La Fond (Mgr-Corp HR)

Subsidiary (Domestic):

U.S. Farathane, LLC (2)
2700 High Meadow Cir, Auburn Hills, MI 48326
Tel.: (248) 754-7000
Web Site: http://www.usfarathane.com
Sales Range: $450-499.9 Million
Emp.: 4,200
Engineered Plastic Injection-Molded Components Mfr & Whslr
N.A.I.C.S.: 326199
Andrew Greenlee (Pres & CEO)
Rodney Turton (Dir-Pur & Supply Chain)
Amy Wood (Sr Mgr-HR)
Jeff DeVries (Mgr-Mfg)
Stephanie La Fond (Mgr-Corp HR)

Zmags Corp. (1)
332 Congress St 2nd Fl, Boston, MA 02210
Tel.: (617) 963-8000
Web Site: http://www.zmags.com

THE GRAHAM GROUP

Sales Range: $10-24.9 Million
Emp.: 100
Marketing Software
N.A.I.C.S.: 513210
David Powell (Chief Fin & Admin Officer)
Grant Coleman (VP-Sls)
Jens Lauritsen (VP-Product Mgmt)
Stanley Bowers (Mgr-Sls & Mktg)
Joseph Caparrotta (Mgr-Bus Dev)
Alex Evans (Acct Mgr)
Molly O'Leary (Acct Mgr)
Jacob Midtgaard-Olesen (VP-Engrg)
Zack Torman (VP-Sls-North America)
Derek Yimoyines (CTO)
Jeffrey Lortz (CEO)

THE GORES GROUP, LLC
9800 Wilshire Blvd, Beverly Hills, CA 90212
Tel.: (310) 209-3010   DE
Web Site: http://www.gores.com
Holding Company
N.A.I.C.S.: 551112
Alec E. Gores (Chm & CEO)

Subsidiaries:

UWM Holdings Corporation (1)
585 S Blvd E, Pontiac, MI 48341
Web Site: https://www.uwm.com
Rev.: $1,311,327,000
Assets: $11,871,854,000
Liabilities: $9,397,183,000
Net Worth: $2,474,671,000
Earnings: ($13,230,000)
Emp.: 6,700
Fiscal Year-end: 12/31/2023
Holding Company
N.A.I.C.S.: 551112
Mat Ishbia (Chm & CEO)
Andrew Hubacker (CFO, Chief Acctg Officer & Exec VP)
Jeffrey A. Ishbia (Founder)

Subsidiary (Domestic):

United Wholesale Mortgage, LLC (2)
585 South Blvd E, Pontiac, MI 48341
Tel.: (248) 433-3300
Web Site: http://www.unitedshore.com
Scientific & Technical Consulting Services
N.A.I.C.S.: 541690
Mat Ishbia (Pres & CEO)
David Hall (Pres-Retail Mortgage Div)
Melinda Wilner (COO)
Sarah DeCiantis (CMO)
Andrew Hubacker (CFO)

THE GRAHAM COMPANIES INC.
6843 Main St, Hialeah, FL 33014-2048
Tel.: (305) 820-8039
Web Site: http://www.miamilakes.com
Year Founded: 1932
Sales Range: $75-99.9 Million
Emp.: 410
Residential & Commercial Development
N.A.I.C.S.: 236117
Andre L. Teixeira (CFO)
Elizabeth Graham Martinez (VP-Residential)
Ellen Selmer (VP-HR)
Stuart S. Wyllie (Pres & CEO)
Carol Graham Wyllie (Pres-Comml)
Luis O. Martinez (Pres-Residential)
Babb Toms (Pres-Farms)
David Healy (VP & Gen Mgr-Hospitality)
Steven L. Style (VP-Mktg)

THE GRAHAM GROUP
2014 W Pinhook Rd Ste 210, Lafayette, LA 70508-3297
Tel.: (337) 232-8214   LA
Web Site: http://www.graham-group.com
Year Founded: 1979
Rev.: $23,700,000
Emp.: 30

THE GRAHAM GROUP — U.S. PRIVATE

The Graham Group—(Continued)

Financial, Health Care, Travel & Tourism
N.A.I.C.S.: 541810
George Graham (CEO)
Michelle Constantin (COO)
Kerry Palmer (Mng Dir-Art)
Anne Taber (Production Supvr)
Kathy Andersen (VP & Acct Supvr)
Natalie Lemoine (VP & Dir-Media)

Subsidiaries:

The Graham Group (1)
11505 Perkins Rd Bldg 3 Ste 3, Baton Rouge, LA 70810
Tel.: (225) 767-8520
Web Site: http://www.graham-group.com
Emp.: 20
N.A.I.C.S.: 541810

THE GRAHAM GROUP, INC.
505 5th Ave Ste 200, Des Moines, IA 50309-2449
Tel.: (515) 244-0387 IA
Web Site:
    http://www.thegrahamgroupinc.com
Year Founded: 1946
Sales Range: $10-24.9 Million
Emp.: 55
Real Estate Development Company
Property Management & Construction
N.A.I.C.S.: 531120
George D. Milligan (Pres & CEO)

Subsidiaries:

Graham Construction Corp. (1)
421 Grand Ave, Des Moines, IA 50309-4104 (100%)
Tel.: (515) 244-0387
Web Site:
    http://www.thegrahamgroupinc.com
Sales Range: $10-24.9 Million
Emp.: 25
N.A.I.C.S.: 237210
Evan Stark (Engr-Field)
Derek Dunn (Coord-Acct)
Casey Fluegge (Sr Dir-Copy)

THE GRAHAM GROUP, INC.
1420 6th Ave, York, PA 17405
Tel.: (717) 849-4053 PA
Web Site:
    http://www.thegrahamgroup.com
Year Founded: 1960
Sales Range: $1-4.9 Billion
Holding Company; Private Equity & Investment Management
N.A.I.C.S.: 551112
Donald Graham (Co-Chm)
Paul Rudy (Co-Chm & CEO)
Bill Scott (Chief HR Officer & VP-HR)
Chuck Silverman (VP & Controller-Admin)
Mike Granbois (VP-Legal & Tax)

Subsidiaries:

Graham Architectural Products Corporation (1)
1551 Mount Rose Ave, York, PA 17403-2909
Tel.: (717) 849-8100
Web Site: http://www.grahamwindows.com
Sales Range: $50-74.9 Million
Emp.: 250
Windows, Doors & Curtain Walls Mfr
N.A.I.C.S.: 332321
Bruce Croak (Mgr-Mktg)
Mark Hiscock (Sls Mgr-Natl)
Tim Cooper (Mgr-Southeast)

Subsidiary (Domestic):

Continental Glass Systems LLC (2)
325 W 74th Pl, Hialeah, FL 33014
Tel.: (305) 231-1101
Web Site: http://www.cgsfl.com
Sales Range: $1-9.9 Million
Emp.: 150
Glass & Glazing Contractors
N.A.I.C.S.: 238150

Shlomo Epstein (Co-Owner)
Samir Moussa (Co-Owner)

Graham Engineering Corporation (1)
1203 Eden Rd, York, PA 17402-1965
Tel.: (717) 848-3755
Web Site:
    http://www.grahamengineering.com
Sales Range: $10-24.9 Million
Emp.: 65
Mfr of Blow Molding Equipment
N.A.I.C.S.: 333248
Robert Deitrick (VP-Global Sls)

Subsidiary (Domestic):

American Kuhne, Inc. (2)
1203 Eden Rd, York, PA 17402
Tel.: (717) 848-3755
Web Site: http://www.americankuhne.com
Industrial Machinery Mfr
N.A.I.C.S.: 333248

Graham Partners, Inc. (1)
3811 W Chester Pike Bldg 2 Ste 200, Newtown Square, PA 19073
Tel.: (610) 408-0500
Web Site: http://www.grahampartners.net
Sales Range: $25-49.9 Million
Emp.: 50
Privater Equity Firm
N.A.I.C.S.: 523999
Steven C. Graham (CEO)
Christopher A. Lawler (Mng Principal)
Joseph G. May (Mng Principal)
Christina W. Morin (Mng Principal)
Robert A. Newbold (Mng Principal)
Dalibor Pivcevic (Principal)
Joshua M. Wilson (Principal)
Sandra Williamson (Controller)
Adam B. Piatkowski (Principal)
Andrew R. Snyder (Mng Principal)
Elizabeth Haering (Controller)
Dennis Dunegan (VP-Investment)
Eric Ciarlante (VP-Investment)
Jason Crowl (VP-Investment)
Joseph Heinmiller (Principal-Investment)
Sara Boyd Iannaccone (VP-Investment)
Lizzie Grobbel (Dir-Sustainability)
Anthony J. Folino III (CFO)
William P. McKee Jr. (Mng Principal)
William Timmerman III (Principal-Investment)

Holding (Domestic):

Abrisa Technologies (2)
200 S Hallock Dr, Santa Paula, CA 93060 (100%)
Tel.: (805) 525-4902
Web Site:
    http://www.abrisatechnologies.com
Sales Range: $50-74.9 Million
Mfr of Custom Glass & Coatings
N.A.I.C.S.: 327211
Susan Hirst (Mgr-Product Dev)
Lance Kling (Sls Mgr-Specialty Glass Products & Custom Glass Fabrication Svcs)

Subsidiary (Domestic):

ZC&R Coatings for Optics, Inc. (3)
1401 Abalone Ave, Torrance, CA 90501 (100%)
Tel.: (310) 381-3060
Web Site: http://www.zcrcoatings.com
Sales Range: $10-24.9 Million
Emp.: 38
Optical Coatings Mfr
N.A.I.C.S.: 325510

Holding (Domestic):

Advanced Barrier Extrusions, LLC (2)
4390 Anderle Dr, Rhinelander, WI 54501
Tel.: (715) 365-2020
Web Site: http://www.abx-films.com
Sales Range: $1-9.9 Million
Emp.: 12
Unsupported Plastics Film & Sheet (except Packaging) Mfr
N.A.I.C.S.: 326113
Tony Haug (Pres)

Subsidiary (Domestic):

Flexographic Packaging Co. (3)
4 Taylor St, Waupun, WI 53963
Tel.: (920) 324-4462

Web Site: http://www.fpcwaupun.com
Commercial Flexographic Printing
N.A.I.C.S.: 323111

Holding (Domestic):

Barcoding, Inc. (2)
3840 Bank St, Baltimore, MD 21224
Tel.: (410) 385-8532
Web Site: http://www.barcoding.com
Sales Range: $10-24.9 Million
Emp.: 55
Barcoding Services
N.A.I.C.S.: 518210
Jay Steinmetz (Founder & CEO)

Subsidiary (Domestic):

Danforth Systems LLC (3)
2500 Wilcrest Dr, Houston, TX 77042
Tel.: (713) 782-6000
Web Site: http://www.danforthsystems.com
Computer & Computer Peripheral Equipment & Software Merchant Whslr
N.A.I.C.S.: 423430
Victoria Tarpey (Pres & CEO)

DecisionPoint Systems, Inc. (3)
1615 S Congress Ave Ste 103, Delray Beach, FL 33445
Tel.: (561) 900-3723
Web Site: https://www.decisionpt.com
Rev: $97,415,000
Assets: $55,557,000
Liabilities: $38,975,000
Net Worth: $16,582,000
Earnings: $3,111,000
Emp.: 116
Fiscal Year-end: 12/31/2022
Computer System Design Services
N.A.I.C.S.: 541512
Melinda Wohl (CFO & Principal Acctg Officer)
Stanley P. Jaworski Jr. (Chm)
Steven Smith (CEO)
Eric O. Baez (VP-Software Dev & Svcs)
Asya Smith (COO)

Subsidiary (Domestic):

DecisionPoint Systems CA, Inc. (4)
23456 S Pointe Dr, Laguna Hills, CA 92653
Tel.: (949) 465-0065
Sales Range: $25-49.9 Million
Emp.: 30
Mobility & Supply Chain Technology, Hardware, Software & Support Services
N.A.I.C.S.: 541512

DecisionPoint Systems CT, Inc. (4)
4 Armstrong Rd, Shelton, CT 06484
Tel.: (203) 929-5101
Mobility & Supply Chain Technology, Hardware, Software & Support Services
N.A.I.C.S.: 541512

Macro Integration Services Inc. (4)
420-A N Chimney Rock Rd, Greensboro, NC 27410
Tel.: (336) 931-0674
Web Site:
    https://www.macrointegrations.com
Rev: $5,000,000
Emp.: 25
Electrical Contractor
N.A.I.C.S.: 238210
D. W. Williams (Pres)

Subsidiary (Non-US):

Commercial Bakeries Corp. (2)
45 Torbarrie Rd, Toronto, M3L 1G5, ON, Canada
Tel.: (416) 247-5478
Web Site:
    http://www.commercialbakeries.com
Rev: $22,000,000
Emp.: 200
Cookies & Biscuits Mfr
N.A.I.C.S.: 311821
Phillip Fusco (VP)
Joseph Fusco (VP)
Steve Brain (Plant Mgr)
Ijeoma Ojibe (Mgr-Quality Assurance)
Anthony Fusco Jr. (VP)

Subsidiary (Domestic):

E-Technologies Group, LLC (2)
6230 Mulhauser Rd, West Chester, OH 45069

Tel.: (513) 771-7271
Web Site: http://www.etech-group.com
Sales Range: $10-24.9 Million
Emp.: 100
Computer Software Development
N.A.I.C.S.: 513210
Steve Veldhuis (Co-Founder & Co-Owner)
Doug Fagaly (Co-Founder & Co-Owner)
Amy Clyde (Office Mgr)
Rick Pierro (Pres-Life Sciences Solutions)
Matthew Wise (CEO)

Subsidiary (Domestic):

E-Volve Systems LLC (3)
4600 McAuley Pl Ste 120, Cincinnati, OH 45242
Tel.: (877) 302-1788
Web Site: http://www.e-volvesystems.com
Sales Range: $1-9.9 Million
Engineering & Manufacturing Services
N.A.I.C.S.: 541330
Kevin Stout (Pres)
Jason Antolovich (Principal)
Vivek Puthezath (Principal)

Glenmount Global Solutions, Inc. (3)
805 Las Cimas Pkwy Ste 440, Austin, TX 78746
Tel.: (512) 821-3798
Web Site: http://www.glenmountglobal.com
Steel Production; Water & Waste Water Management; Technology Services Firms
N.A.I.C.S.: 541330
Ralph Carter (CEO)
Jason Rich (CFO)
Tom Johnson (Exec VP-West Ops)
Tom Nelson (VP-Water Indus)
Fred Fontaine (Exec VP-East Southwest Ops)
Troy Miller (Exec VP-Mktg & Corp Strategy)
Brad Hendrickson (Exec VP-Midwest Ops)

Superior Controls, Inc. (3)
135 Folly Mill Rd, Seabrook, NH 03874
Tel.: (603) 468-3000
Web Site: http://www.superiorcontrols.com
Automation & Control Systems Integration Services
N.A.I.C.S.: 238210
Rick Pierro (Founder & Pres)
Mark LaRoche (COO)
Robert Patrick (VP-Engrg)
Kenneth Hackett (Mgr-Bus Dev)
Allen Schweitzer (CFO)
Damon Robbins (VP-Ops)
Matt Lyles (Sr Engr-Bus Dev)
Ray Boudreau (VP-Bus Dev)

Subsidiary (Domestic):

Banks Integration Group, Inc. (4)
600 E Main St Ste 100, Vacaville, CA 95688
Tel.: (707) 451-1100
Web Site: http://www.banksintegration.com
Whol Drugs/Sundries
N.A.I.C.S.: 424210
Gary Powell (VP)
Stan Reyna (Dir-Ops-Vacaville CA)
John Simpson (Dir-Ops-South San Francisco CA)
Christina Lamparski (Mgr-Bus Dev)
Brittany Peterson (Head-HR)
Danni Bynum (Head-Admin)

Holding (Domestic):

Gatekeeper Systems, Inc. (2)
90 Icon, Foothill Ranch, CA 92610
Tel.: (949) 453-1940
Web Site:
    http://www.gatekeepersystems.com
Shopping Cart Containment System Mfr
N.A.I.C.S.: 339999
Brett Osterfeld (Pres)
Erik Paulson (CEO)
Evan Lawson (Officer-Bus Dev)

Subsidiary (Non-US):

Gatekeeper Systems (HK), Ltd. (3)
Unit 2305 Level 23 Tower 2 Metroplaza No 223 Hing Fong Road, Kwai Fong, NT, China (Hong Kong)
Tel.: (852) 2413 3050
Web Site:
    http://www.gatekeepersystems.com
Shopping Cart Containment Systems Sales

N.A.I.C.S.: 423440

Gatekeeper Systems Canada, Ltd. (3)
272 Galaxy Boulevard, Etobicoke, M9W 5R8, ON, Canada
Tel.: (416) 798-8719
Web Site: http://www.gatekeepersystems.com
Shopping Cart Containment Systems Sales
N.A.I.C.S.: 423440

Gatekeeper Systems UK, Ltd. (3)
2 Roseberry Court Great Ayton, Middlesbrough, TS9 5QT, United Kingdom
Tel.: (44) 1908 827333
Web Site: http://www.gatekeepersystems.com
Shopping Cart Containment Systems Sales
N.A.I.C.S.: 423440

Holding (Domestic):

Infiltrator Systems Inc. (2)
6 Business Park Rd, Old Saybrook, CT 06475
Tel.: (860) 388-6639
Web Site: http://www.infiltratorsystems.com
Sales Range: $100-124.9 Million
Plastic Drainage Chambers for OA-Site Septic & Storm Water Management Mfr
N.A.I.C.S.: 326199
Steve Engels (Controller)
Robert F. McHugh (CFO)
Bryan A. Coppes (VP-Engrg & R&D)
Ronald Brochu (VP-Mfg)
Carl Thompson (VP-Sls & Mktg)
Roy E. Moore Jr. (Pres & CEO)

Mercer Foods LLC (2)
1836 Lapham Dr, Modesto, CA 95354
Tel.: (209) 529-0150
Web Site: http://www.mercerfoods.com
Emp.: 500
Dried & Dehydrated Food Mfr
N.A.I.C.S.: 311423

Rhythmlink International, LLC (2)
1140 1st S, Columbia, SC 29209
Tel.: (803) 252-1222
Web Site: http://www.rhythmlink.com
Sales Range: $1-9.9 Million
Emp.: 30
Mfr of Surgical/Medical Instruments
N.A.I.C.S.: 339112
Shawn Regan (CEO)
Chris Dearing (Mgr-Logistics)
Joe Straczek (CFO & COO)

Subsidiary (Domestic):

Chalgren Enterprises (3)
380 Tomkins Ct, Gilroy, CA 95020
Tel.: (408) 847-3994
Sales Range: $1-9.9 Million
Emp.: 15
Electromedical & Electrotherapeutic Apparatus Mfr
N.A.I.C.S.: 334510
Richard Kaiser (Pres)

Holding (Non-US):

Taoglas Ltd. (2)
Unit 5 Kilcannon Business Park, Old Dublin Road, Enniscorthy, Wexford, Ireland
Tel.: (353) 539169500
Web Site: http://www.taoglas.com
Antennas, Filters, Cables & Connectors Mfr & Distr
N.A.I.C.S.: 335999
Dermot O'Shea (CEO)
Tim Dolan (VP-North America Sls)
Joanna Liao (VP-Taiwan Ops)
Peter Knaz (VP-Technical Sls-Taiwan)

Inverness Graham Investments, Inc. (1)
3811 W Chester Pke Bldg 2 Ste 100, Newtown Square, PA 19073
Tel.: (610) 722-0300
Web Site: http://www.invernessgraham.com
Rev.: $200,000,000
Emp.: 22
Private Equity Firm
N.A.I.C.S.: 523999
Kenneth A. Graham (Co-Founder & Chm)
Scott A. Kehoe (Co-Founder & Mng Principal)
Courtney Comer (Dir-IR)

Trey Sykes (Mng Principal)
Michael B. Morrissey (Mng Principal)
Matt Moran (Principal & Head-Bus Dev)
Sean Dougherty (VP-Direct Sourcing & Exec Partnerships)
Chris Frystock (VP)
Aliya Khaydarova (Principal)
Paul Nolen (Principal)
Steven Wood (Co-Founder & Vice Chm)
John Reilly Jr. (CFO)

Holding (Domestic):

DSI/DataSource, Inc. (2)
1400 Universal Ave, Kansas City, MO 64120
Tel.: (816) 483-3282
Web Site: http://www.data-source.com
Sales Range: $25-49.9 Million
Emp.: 200
Print Supply Chain Management Services
N.A.I.C.S.: 541614
Eugene Arokiasamy (CTO)
Walt Smith (Pres-Texas Grp)
Donna Heberer (VP-Sls)
Charlie Jenkins (Dir-Digital Production)
Vince Lee (Dir-Ops)
Phil Schoonmaker (CEO)
Kendra Wright (COO)
Christopher Lamb (Chief Strategy Officer)
Yesenia Medina (VP-Client Engagement)
Peter Heil (Sr VP-Bus Dev)

Electron Microscopy Sciences, Inc. (2)
1560 Industry Rd, Hatfield, PA 19440
Tel.: (215) 412-8400
Web Site: http://www.emsdiasum.com
Sales Range: $25-49.9 Million
Emp.: 135
Laboratory Product Mfr & Distr
N.A.I.C.S.: 334516
Stacie Kirsch (Pres)
Carole McNamara (Office Mgr)

Subsidiary (Domestic):

Negafile Systems (3)
3069 Edison Furlong Rd, Furlong, PA 18925-1235
Tel.: (215) 348-2356
Web Site: http://www.negafile.com
Sales Range: $10-24.9 Million
Emp.: 10
Files & Preservers Mfr for Negatives, Slides & Prints
N.A.I.C.S.: 333310

Holding (Domestic):

Innovia Medical, Inc. (2)
815 Vikings Pkwy Ste 100, Saint Paul, MN 55121
Tel.: (888) 229-2875
Web Site: http://www.innoviamedical.com
Holding Company
N.A.I.C.S.: 551112
Terry Meredith (CEO)

Subsidiary (Domestic):

Summit Medical, Inc. (3)
815 NW Pkwy Ste 100, Saint Paul, MN 55121-1658
Tel.: (651) 789-3939
Web Site: http://www.summitmedicalusa.com
Sales Range: $1-9.9 Million
Surgical & Medical Instrument Developer, Mfr & Whslr
N.A.I.C.S.: 339112
Lorraine Duchene (CFO)

Holding (Domestic):

MC2 Consulting Services, Inc. (2)
10813 S Riverfront Pkwy 500, South Jordan, UT 84095
Tel.: (888) 223-3450
Web Site: http://www3.swipeclock.com
Business Products & Services
N.A.I.C.S.: 541219

Nobles Manufacturing, Inc. (2)
1105 E Pine St, Saint Croix Falls, WI 54024
Tel.: (715) 483-3079
Web Site: http://www.noblesmfg.com
Sales Range: $50-74.9 Million
Emp.: 45

Ammunition Feeding Systems & Gun Mounts Mfr
N.A.I.C.S.: 336413

RACO Holdings, LLC (2)
5480 Creek Rd, Cincinnati, OH 45242
Tel.: (513) 792-4272
Web Site: http://www.racowireless.com
Holding Company; Wireless Telecommunications Support Services
N.A.I.C.S.: 551112
Rob Adams (CEO)
John Horn (Pres)

Subsidiary (Domestic):

RACO Wireless LLC (3)
5480 Creek Rd, Cincinnati, OH 45242
Tel.: (513) 792-4272
Web Site: http://www.racowireless.com
Wireless Telecommunications Support Services
N.A.I.C.S.: 561990

Subsidiary (Domestic):

Position Logic, LLC (4)
4522 Executive Dr 2nd Fl, Naples, FL 34119
Tel.: (239) 465-0587
Web Site: http://www.positionlogic.com
GPS Software
N.A.I.C.S.: 513210
Hong Long (Co-Founder & CTO)

Tulkoff Food Products, Inc. (1)
2301 Chesapeake Ave, Baltimore, MD 21222
Tel.: (410) 327-6585
Web Site: http://www.tulkoff.com
Sales Range: $10-24.9 Million
Emp.: 95
Mayonnaise Dressing & Sauce Mfr
N.A.I.C.S.: 311941
Karen Suter (Dir-Food Svc Sls)
Phil Tulkoff (Pres)
Mark Natale (Exec VP-Sls & Mktg)

THE GRAND HEALTHCARE SYSTEM
1720 Whitestone Expy Ste 500, Whitestone, NY 11357
Tel.: (718) 215-6000
Web Site: http://www.thegrandhealthcare.com
Year Founded: 2014
Rehabilitation & Nursing Services
N.A.I.C.S.: 623110
Jeremy B. Strauss (CEO)
Jonathan J. Strauss (Exec VP)
Joe Yurowitz (Sr VP)
Avi Kahn (Dir-Facilities Mgmt)
Jake Walden (VP-Bus Dev)

Subsidiaries:

The Grand Rehabilitation and Nursing at River Valley (1)
140 Main St, Poughkeepsie, NY 12601
Tel.: (845) 454-7600
Web Site: http://www.thegrandhealthcare.com
Sales Range: $1-9.9 Million
Emp.: 100
Rehabilitation & Nursing Care Facilities
N.A.I.C.S.: 623110
Israel Wulliger (Gen Mgr)
Roseann Sellers (Dir-Admissions)
Michael Hurtes (Asst Gen Mgr)
Valerie Tucci (Dir-Rehabilitation)
Tish Mosiello (Dir-Social Work)
Jeff Pryluck (Dir-Recreation)
Ari Zadeh (Dir-Adult Day Healthcare)

THE GRAND LODGE OF MARYLAND
304 International Cir, Cockeysville, MD 21030
Tel.: (410) 527-0600   MD
Web Site: http://www.mdmasons.org
Year Founded: 1934
Sales Range: $10-24.9 Million
Emp.: 342
Social Support Services
N.A.I.C.S.: 813410

Charlie Fraim (Dir-Plant Ops)

THE GRANDOE CORPORATION
74 Bleecker St, Gloversville, NY 12078-2919
Tel.: (518) 725-8641   NY
Web Site: http://www.grandoe.com
Year Founded: 1898
Sales Range: $450-499.9 Million
Emp.: 2,000
Men's & Ladies' Dress, Ski, Bicycle & Snowboarding Gloves Retailer
N.A.I.C.S.: 315990
Eric Friedman (Pres & CEO)
Karen Ferjanec (Mgr-Accts Receivable)
Mike D'Arcy (Mgr-Natl Sls)

THE GRAPHIC EDGE, INC.
743 E US Hwy 30, Carroll, IA 51401
Tel.: (712) 792-7777
Web Site: http://www.thegraphicedge.com
Rev.: $19,000,000
Emp.: 150
Miscellaneous Textile Product Mills
N.A.I.C.S.: 314999
Donna Reglein (Pres)
Mike Riddle (VP-Fin)
John Reglein (Owner)
Jeff Puffett (Mgr-Production)

THE GREAT AMERICAN HANGER COMPANY INC.
8250 NW 27th St Ste 304, Miami, FL 33122
Tel.: (305) 477-4250
Web Site: http://www.hangers.com
Sales Range: $1-9.9 Million
Emp.: 40
Clothes Hanger Mfr & Whslr
N.A.I.C.S.: 332618
Devon Rifkin (Pres)

THE GREAT AMERICAN OUTDOORS GROUP LLC
2500 E Kearney, Springfield, MO 65898
Tel.: (800) 227-7776
Holding Company
N.A.I.C.S.: 551112
Johnny Morris (CEO)

Subsidiaries:

Bass Pro Group, LLC (1)
2500 E Kearney St, Springfield, MO 65898
Tel.: (800) 227-7776
Web Site: http://www.basspro.com
Emp.: 10,000
Holding Company; Sporting Goods Mfr, Whslr & Retailer
N.A.I.C.S.: 551112
Johnny Morris (Founder & CEO)
Stan Lippelman (VP-Mktg)

Subsidiary (Domestic):

Bass Pro Shops, Inc. (2)
2500 E Kearney, Springfield, MO 65898-0001
Tel.: (417) 873-5000
Web Site: http://www.basspro.com
Mail Order Retail Sales of Fishing, Hunting & Camping Equipment & Supplies; Wholesale Distribution of Sporting Goods
N.A.I.C.S.: 339920
Johnny Morris (Founder & CEO)

Subsidiary (Domestic):

Bass Pro Outdoors Online, LLC (3)
2500 E Kearney, Springfield, MO 65898-0001
Tel.: (417) 873-5000
Web Site: http://www.basspro.com
Online Sporting Goods Retailer
N.A.I.C.S.: 459110
Mikey Black (Gen Mgr)

THE GREAT AMERICAN OUTDOORS GROUP LLC

The Great American Outdoors Group LLC—(Continued)

Subsidiary (Domestic):

Cabela's LLC (2)
1 Cabela Dr, Sidney, NE 69160
Tel.: (308) 254-5505
Web Site: http://www.cabelas.com
Sales Range: $1-4.9 Billion
Catalog & In-Store Sales of Sporting Goods
N.A.I.C.S.: 459110

Subsidiary (Non-US):

Cabela's Retail Canada, Inc. (3)
25 De Baets Street, Winnipeg, R2J 4G5, MB, Canada
Web Site: http://www.cabelas.ca
Sporting Goods Mfr
N.A.I.C.S.: 459110
Will Yakielashek (Gen Mgr-Visual Merchandising)

Subsidiary (Domestic):

Cabela's Retail IL, Inc. (3)
5225 Prairie Stone Pkwy, Hoffman Estates, IL 60192
Tel.: (847) 645-0400
Web Site: http://www.cabelas.com
Sporting Goods Mfr
N.A.I.C.S.: 459110

Cabela's Retail MO, LLC (3)
5555 St Louis Mills Blvd Ste #167, Hazelwood, MO 63042
Tel.: (314) 225-0100
Web Site: http://www.cabelas.com
Sporting Goods Mfr
N.A.I.C.S.: 459110

Subsidiary (Domestic):

Tracker Marine Group LLC (2)
2500 E Kearny St, Springfield, MO 65898
Tel.: (417) 873-5900
Web Site: http://www.trackermarine.com
Sales Range: $25-49.9 Million
Emp.: 300
Ski & Fishing Boats
N.A.I.C.S.: 336612
Les Crawford (Pres)

Subsidiary (Domestic):

The Fishing Holdings, LLC (3)
PO Box 179, Flippin, AR 72634
Tel.: (870) 453-2222
Web Site: http://www.stratosboats.com
Fishing Boat Mfr
N.A.I.C.S.: 336612

Unit (Domestic):

Tracker Boat Centers Corbin (3)
831 W Cumberland Gap Pkwy, Corbin, KY 40701
Tel.: (606) 528-2628
Web Site: http://www.uk.boats.com
Sales Range: $25-49.9 Million
Emp.: 9
Dealer of Motor Boats
N.A.I.C.S.: 441222

Tracker Boating Center - Snowden (3)
2501 Bass Pro Dr, Grapevine, TX 76051
Tel.: (972) 436-2628
Web Site: http://www.trackermarine.com
Sales Range: $25-49.9 Million
Emp.: 6
Boat Dealers
N.A.I.C.S.: 441222

Tracker Marine - Arlington (3)
1900 E Division St, Arlington, TX 76011-7814
Tel.: (817) 265-3232
Web Site: http://www.travisboatingcenter.com
Sales Range: $25-49.9 Million
Emp.: 15
Boat Dealers
N.A.I.C.S.: 441222

Tracker Marine - Beaumont (3)
7660 College St, Beaumont, TX 77707-3146
Tel.: (409) 860-9444
Web Site: http://www.trackerboatcenter.com

Sales Range: $25-49.9 Million
Emp.: 11
Boat Dealers
N.A.I.C.S.: 441222
Jimmy Clark (Bus Mgr)

Subsidiary (Domestic):

Travis Boats & Motors Baton Rouge Inc. (3)
175 Bass Pro Blvd, Denham Springs, LA 70726
Tel.: (225) 271-3100
Web Site: http://www.travisboats.com
Sales Range: $1-9.9 Million
Emp.: 10
Boat Dealers
N.A.I.C.S.: 441222
Johnny Morris (Owner)

THE GREAT AMERICAN SMOKED FISH CO.

1400 SW 1st Ct, Pompano Beach, FL 33069   FL
Tel.: (954) 942-5598
Year Founded: 1989
Sales Range: $10-24.9 Million
Emp.: 60
Supermarket
N.A.I.C.S.: 424460
Stanley Markman (Pres)

THE GREAT ATLANTIC & PACIFIC TEA COMPANY, INC.

2 Paragon Dr, Montvale, NJ 07645-1718   MD
Tel.: (201) 573-9700
Web Site: http://www.aptea.com
Year Founded: 1859
Emp.: 34,000
Supermarket Owner & Operator
N.A.I.C.S.: 445110
Paul Hertz (Pres & CEO)

Subsidiaries:

BEST CELLARS, INC. (1)
1291 Lexington Ave 87th St, New York, NY 10128
Tel.: (212) 426-4200
Wine & Spirit Merchant Whslr
N.A.I.C.S.: 424820

Pathmark Stores, Inc. (1)
2 Paragon Dr, Montvale, NJ 07645
Tel.: (201) 573-9700
Web Site: http://www.pathmark.com
Sales Range: $1-4.9 Billion
Emp.: 7,400
Retail Chain Supermarkets
N.A.I.C.S.: 445110

Subsidiary (Domestic):

AAL Realty Corp. (2)
2 Paragon Dr, Montvale, NJ 07645
Tel.: (201) 573-9700
Sales Range: $25-49.9 Million
Emp.: 2
Real Estate Agents & Managers
N.A.I.C.S.: 531210

East Brunswick Stuart LLC (2)
200 Milk St, Carteret, NJ 07008
Tel.: (732) 499-3000
Sales Range: $75-99.9 Million
Emp.: 600
Operator of Grocery Stores
N.A.I.C.S.: 531210

Plainbridge LLC (2)
200 Milik St, Carteret, NJ 07008-1102
Tel.: (732) 499-3000
Sales Range: $25-49.9 Million
Emp.: 3
Operator of Grocery Stores
N.A.I.C.S.: 445110

Super Fresh Company (1)
2 Paragon Dr, Montvale, NJ 07645   (100%)
Tel.: (410) 594-7500
Web Site: http://www.superfreshfood.com
Sales Range: $350-399.9 Million
Emp.: 3,500
Supermarket
N.A.I.C.S.: 445110

THE SOUTH DAKOTA GREAT ATLANTIC & PACIFIC TEA CO., INC. (1)
2 Paragon Dr, Montvale, NJ 07645
Tel.: (201) 573-9700
Food Store Services
N.A.I.C.S.: 445298

Waldbaum's Supermarkets, Inc. (1)
PO Box 3068, Paterson, NJ 07509
Tel.: (631) 582-9300
Web Site: http://www.waldbaums.com
Sales Range: $1-4.9 Billion
Emp.: 6,500
Supermarkets, Chain
N.A.I.C.S.: 457110

THE GREAT ATLANTIC PROPERTY MANAGEMENT COMPANY

293 Independence Blvd Ste 400, Virginia Beach, VA 23462-4054   VA
Tel.: (757) 217-3400
Year Founded: 1964
Sales Range: $10-24.9 Million
Emp.: 510
Provider of Real Estate Investment, Development & Management Services
N.A.I.C.S.: 531210
Aubrey Layne (Pres)
Michael Heath (Dir-Admin)
Joseph Byrne (Dir-Acctg)

THE GREAT GOURMET, INC.

5115 Clark Canning House Rd, Federalsburg, MD 21632
Tel.: (410) 754-8800
Web Site: http://www.thegreatgourmet.com
Year Founded: 2003
Rev.: $3,600,000
Emp.: 30
Fresh & Frozen Seafood Processing
N.A.I.C.S.: 311710
Kimberly J. Scott (Founder & CEO)

THE GREAT LAKES CHEESE CO., INC.

17955 Great Lakes Pkwy, Hiram, OH 44234-1806   OH
Tel.: (440) 834-2500
Web Site: https://www.greatlakescheese.com
Year Founded: 1958
Sales Range: $450-499.9 Million
Emp.: 4,000
Cheese Manufacturing
N.A.I.C.S.: 311513
Heidi Eller (Chm)

Subsidiaries:

Empire Cheese, Inc. (1)
4520 Haskell Rd, Cuba, NY 14727   (100%)
Tel.: (585) 968-1552
Web Site: http://www.greatlakescheese.com
Sales Range: $10-24.9 Million
Emp.: 130
Mfr & Packager of Natural Cheese & Whey
N.A.I.C.S.: 311513
Don Butler (Plant Mgr)

Great Lakes Cheese of La Crosse Wisconsin, Inc. (1)
2200 Enterprise Ave, La Crosse, WI 54603-1712
Tel.: (608) 781-2800
Web Site: http://www.greatlakescheese.com
Sales Range: $25-49.9 Million
Emp.: 250
Processed & Natural Cheese Mfr
N.A.I.C.S.: 311513
Gary Vanic (CEO)

Great Lakes Cheese of New York, Inc. (1)
23 Phelps St, Adams, NY 13605-1022   (100%)
Tel.: (315) 232-4511
Web Site: http://www.greatlakescheese.com

U.S. PRIVATE

Sales Range: $10-24.9 Million
Emp.: 73
Cheddar Cheese & Dried Whey Mfr
N.A.I.C.S.: 311513

Great Lakes Cheese of Wisconsin (1)
2602 County Rd PP, Plymouth, WI 53073-4242   (100%)
Tel.: (920) 893-1121
Web Site: http://www.greatlakescheese.com
Processed & Natural Cheese Mfr
N.A.I.C.S.: 311999
Michael Schroeder (Gen Mgr)

THE GREAT LAKES CONSTRUCTION CO.

2608 Great Lks Way, Hinckley, OH 44233-9590
Tel.: (330) 220-3900
Web Site: http://www.tglcc.com
Year Founded: 1948
Sales Range: $200-249.9 Million
Emp.: 500
Provider of Heavy & Highway Construction Contracting Services
N.A.I.C.S.: 237310
George Palko (Pres)
Mark E. Bacon (VP-Project Mgmt)
John Habanek (VP-Fin)
Jim Fox (VP-Ops)

THE GREATER CINCINNATI FOUNDATION

200 W 4th St, Cincinnati, OH 45202-2775   OH
Tel.: (513) 241-2880
Web Site: http://www.gcfdn.org
Year Founded: 1963
Sales Range: $75-99.9 Million
Emp.: 39
Philanthropic Services
N.A.I.C.S.: 813211
Karen L. Bond (Mgr-Grants)
Lori A. Beiler (Sr Mgr-Grants)
Shiloh Turner (VP-Community Investment)
Scott McReynolds (VP-Fin & Admin)
Christopher L. Fister (Vice Chm)
Dianne M. Rosenberg (Chm)
Ellen Katz (Pres & CEO)
Shelly Espich (Mgr-Sys)
Cara Jacob (Coord-Res)
Will Woodward (CFO)
Phillip Lanham (VP-Donor Rels)
Jenny Powell (VP-Mktg)
Harold Brown (VP-Community Strategies)
Jaclyn Sablosky (Mktg Dir)
Rickell Howard Smith (Dir-Community Strategies)
Robert Killins Jr. (Dir-Giving Strategies)

THE GREATER FAIRBANKS COMMUNITY HOSPITAL FOUNDATION, INCORPORATED

1650 Cowles St 5th Fl Rm 542ST, Fairbanks, AK 99707-1390   AK
Tel.: (907) 458-5550
Web Site: http://www.fairbankshospitalfoundation.com
Year Founded: 1968
Sales Range: $25-49.9 Million
Community Health Care Services
N.A.I.C.S.: 621498
Shelley D. Ebenal (Exec Dir)
Gary Roderick (First VP)
Roger Floerchinger (Treas)
Jeff Cook (Pres)
Joe Faulhaber (Sec)
Ruth Wendler (CFO)

THE GREATER WASHINGTON EDUCATIONAL TELECOMMU-

COMPANIES

NICATIONS ASSOCIATION, INC.
3939 Campbell Ave, Arlington, VA 22206
Tel.: (703) 998-2600 — DC
Web Site: http://www.weta.org
Year Founded: 1953
Sales Range: $50-74.9 Million
Emp.: 214
Television & Radio Broadcasting Services
N.A.I.C.S.: 334220
Karen Fritz *(VP-Program Dev, Syndication & Outreach)*
Rick Schneider *(COO & Exec VP)*
Dalton Delan *(Chief Programming Officer & Exec VP)*
Jeff Bieber *(VP-Content Dev & Production)*
Jim Corbley *(VP-Production Mgmt)*
Kari Waldack *(Asst Sec)*
Sharon Percy Rockefeller *(Pres & CEO)*
Timothy C. Coughlin *(Chm)*
Ann Dibble Jordan *(Vice Chm & Sec)*
James C. Bond *(CFO & Sr VP)*
Lisa Lindstrom Delaney *(Gen Counsel & Sr VP)*
Adam Gronski *(VP-Corp Mktg)*
Jeff Regen *(VP-Dev)*
Vibha Jain Miller *(VP-HR)*
Noel Gunther *(VP-Learning Media)*
Kathy Connolly *(VP-Major & Planned Giving)*
Chris Lane *(VP-Ops & Engrg)*
Kevin Harris *(VP & Mgr-Television Station)*
Mary Stewart *(VP-External Affairs)*

THE GREEN MOUNTAIN CORPORATION
2901 W Oakland Park Blvd, Fort Lauderdale, FL 33311
Tel.: (954) 484-7800 — FL
Web Site: http://www.peterglenn.com
Year Founded: 1958
Sales Range: $25-49.9 Million
Emp.: 200
Sell Skiing Equipment
N.A.I.C.S.: 459110
Edward J. Hamilton *(Chm)*
Tina Reed *(Controller)*

THE GREENE COMPANY OF VIRGINIA INC.
2075 Stultz Rd PO Box 711, Martinsville, VA 24112-7411
Tel.: (276) 638-7101
Web Site: http://www.thegreenecompany.com
Sales Range: $10-24.9 Million
Emp.: 12
Knit & Fleece Apparel Mfr
N.A.I.C.S.: 315250
Edith K. Greene *(Pres)*

Subsidiaries:

Dodger Industries Inc. (1)
2075 Stultz Rd PO Box 711, Martinsville, VA 24112-0711
Tel.: (276) 638-7101
Web Site: http://www.dodgerindustries.com
Sales Range: $10-24.9 Million
Athletic Apparel Mfr
N.A.I.C.S.: 315250
Eydie Greene *(Pres)*
Barry Greene *(Sec & Treas)*

THE GREENLEAF COMPANY INC.
245 Birchwood Ave, Cranford, NJ 07016
Tel.: (908) 272-0100 — NJ
Web Site: http://www.dgdco.com
Year Founded: 1931
Sales Range: $25-49.9 Million
Emp.: 200
Construction & Maintenance Services
N.A.I.C.S.: 236220
Ricardo Pradilla *(VP)*
Ray Koning *(Mgr-Bus Dev)*
Samuel N. Prisco *(Pres & CEO)*

Subsidiaries:

Damon G. Douglas Company Inc. (1)
245 Birchwood Ave, Cranford, NJ 07016-2510
Tel.: (908) 272-0100
Web Site: http://www.dgdco.com
Rev.: $800,000
Emp.: 30
Construction & Maintenance Services
N.A.I.C.S.: 236220

THE GREENSPAN COMPANY
400 Oyster Point Blvd Ste 519, South San Francisco, CA 94080
Tel.: (650) 583-4300 — CA
Web Site: https://www.greenspanai.com
Year Founded: 1960
Sales Range: $1-9.9 Million
Emp.: 100
Claims Adjusting
N.A.I.C.S.: 524291
Gary Johnson *(Principal)*
Mark Fratkin *(Dir-Sls)*
Matthew Blumkin *(Principal)*
Cindy Fortune *(Chief Admin Officer)*
Matthew Goldstein *(Reg Mgr-Claims)*
Susy Kim *(Chief Sls Officer & Exec VP)*
Samuel Shakib *(CFO)*
Kevin Stanger *(Reg Mgr-Claims)*
Tonia Tanguay *(COO & Gen Counsel)*
Megan Withnell *(Mgr-Contents Division)*
Linda Barba *(Project Mgr-Technical)*
Sydney Greenspan *(Dir-Business Development)*
Sandra Jackson *(Mktg Dir)*
Julie Larios *(Coord-Accounting)*
Isabel Lopez *(Mgr-Facilities)*

THE GREENSPUN CORPORATION
2360 Corporate Cir 3rd Fl, Henderson, NV 89074
Tel.: (702) 990-2550 — NV
Web Site: http://www.thegreenspuncorp.com
Media & Real Estate Holding Company
N.A.I.C.S.: 551112
Daniel Greenspun *(Vice Chm)*
Paul Hamilton *(Pres & CEO)*

Subsidiaries:

American Nevada Company (1)
2360 Corporate Cir Ste 330, Henderson, NV 89074
Tel.: (702) 458-8855
Web Site: http://www.americannevada.com
Emp.: 40
Real Estate Investment Development Brokerage Property Management & Leasing Services
N.A.I.C.S.: 531390
Darbie Adams *(VP-Property Mgmt)*
Phillip N. Ralston *(Pres)*

Greenspun Media Group, LLC (1)
2275 Corporate Cir 3rd Fl, Henderson, NV 89074
Tel.: (702) 990-2550
Web Site: http://www.gmgvegas.com
Magazine, Weekly Newspaper & Pamphlet Publisher
N.A.I.C.S.: 513120
Brian L. Greenspun *(Publr & Editor)*
Paul Hamilton *(Pres & CEO)*
Robert Cauthorn *(COO)*
Steve Gray *(CFO)*
Travis Keys *(VP-Bus Dev)*
Maria Blondeaux *(VP-Mfg)*
Jamey Lien *(Sr VP-HR)*
Sean Rademacher *(Art Dir-Adv & Mktg Svcs)*

Unit (Domestic):

Las Vegas Magazine (2)
2275 Corporate Cir Fl 3, Henderson, NV 89074-7723
Tel.: (702) 383-7185
Web Site: http://www.lasvegasmagazine.com
Magazine Publisher
N.A.I.C.S.: 513120
Ken Miller *(Editor)*
Nina King *(Mng Editor)*
Erik Stein *(Dir-Creative)*
Wesley Gatbonton *(Dir-Art)*

Las Vegas Weekly (2)
2275 Corporate Cir 3rd Fl, Henderson, NV 89074
Tel.: (702) 990-2400
Web Site: http://www.lasvegasweekly.com
Weekly Local Newspaper Publisher
N.A.I.C.S.: 513110
Ric Anderson *(Mng Editor)*

VEGAS INC (2)
2275 Corporate Cir 3rd Fl, Henderson, NV 89074
Tel.: (702) 990-2550
Web Site: http://www.vegasinc.com
Local Business Trade Journal Publisher
N.A.I.C.S.: 513120
Donn Jersey *(Publr)*
Delen Goldberg *(Editor)*
Dave mondt *(Mng Editor)*
John Fritz *(Deputy Mng Editor-Digital)*

Las Vegas Sun, Inc. (1)
2275 Corporate Cir Ste 300, Henderson, NV 89074
Tel.: (702) 385-3111
Web Site: http://www.lasvegassun.com
Sales Range: $75-99.9 Million
Emp.: 130
Newspaper Publishers
N.A.I.C.S.: 513110
Brian L. Greenspun *(CEO, Publr & Editor)*
Robert Cauthorn *(COO)*
Ric Anderson *(Mng Editor)*

THE GREENWICH GROUP INTERNATIONAL LLC
805 3rd Ave 8th Fl, New York, NY 10022
Tel.: (212) 754-0100 — NY
Web Site: http://www.greenwichgrp.com
Rev.: $10,000,000
Emp.: 15
Real Estate Investment Banking
N.A.I.C.S.: 523150
Simon J. Milde *(Founder, Chm & CEO)*
James Flood *(COO-New York)*
Larry Baucom *(Pres-Washington)*
Peter Witham *(Mng Dir & Head-Capital Markets-Washington)*
Robert Beeney *(Mng Dir-Los Angeles)*
Don Atchison *(Mng Partner-Washington)*
Gregg Delany *(Mng Dir)*
Steve Lorenz *(Mng Partner)*
Boaz Shattan Jr. *(Sr Dir-Investments)*

Subsidiaries:

The Greenwich Group International LLC - California (1)
235 Montgomery St Ste 900, San Francisco, CA 94104
Tel.: (415) 268-2408
Web Site: http://www.greenwichgrp.com
Real Estate Investment Banking
N.A.I.C.S.: 525990

The Greenwich Group International LLC - Virginia (1)
1700 N Moore St Ste 1805, Arlington, VA 22209
Tel.: (703) 525-8300
Web Site: http://www.greenwichgrp.com

THE GROUP INC.

Real Estate Investment Banking
N.A.I.C.S.: 525990
Larry Baucom *(Pres & Mng Dir-Washington)*
Peter Witham *(Mng Dir-Washington)*
Gary Barth *(Mng Dir)*
Robert Beeney *(Mng Dir)*
Simon Milde *(Chm & CEO)*
James Flood *(COO)*

THE GRIEVE CORPORATION
500 Hart Rd, Round Lake, IL 60073-2835
Tel.: (847) 546-8225 — IL
Web Site: http://www.grievecorp.com
Year Founded: 1949
Sales Range: $75-99.9 Million
Emp.: 100
Mfr of Industrial & Laboratory Ovens & Furnaces
N.A.I.C.S.: 333994
D. V. Grieve *(Pres)*

THE GRIFFIN GROUP, LLC
4 Rebelo Ln Ste D, Novato, CA 94947
Tel.: (415) 892-4569 — CA
Web Site: http://www.tgg.us.com
Alcohol Beverage Investment Firm
N.A.I.C.S.: 523999
Keith C. Greggor *(CEO)*
Chad Farmer *(Chief Creative Officer)*
Crystal Marty *(CFO)*
Lynn Lackey *(VP-Mktg)*
Tony Foglio *(Chm)*

Subsidiaries:

Anchor Brewers & Distillers, LLC (1)
1705 Mariposa St, San Francisco, CA 94107
Tel.: (415) 863-8350
Web Site: http://www.anchorbrewing.com
Sales Range: $25-49.9 Million
Emp.: 50
Brewery Mfr
N.A.I.C.S.: 312120
Keith Greggor *(Owner)*

THE GROCERS SUPPLY CO., INC.
3131 E Holcombe Blvd, Houston, TX 77021-2199
Tel.: (713) 747-5000 — TX
Web Site: http://www.grocerssupply.com
Year Founded: 1923
Sales Range: $1-4.9 Billion
Emp.: 8,900
Holding Company; Wholesale Grocery Distr; Supermarkets Operator
N.A.I.C.S.: 551112
Max Levit *(Pres)*
James Nelson II *(VP-Credit)*

THE GROUP INC.
2803 E Harmony Rd, Fort Collins, CO 80528
Tel.: (970) 229-0700
Web Site: http://www.thegroupinc.com
Sales Range: $25-49.9 Million
Emp.: 300
Real Estate Brokers & Agents
N.A.I.C.S.: 531210
Larry Kendall *(Founder)*
Kim Allen *(CFO)*
Brenda Nickel *(Bus Mgr)*
Helen Gray *(Dir-Mktg)*
Nick Hansen *(Partner)*
Mitch Benner *(Partner)*
Mark Shea *(Partner)*
Ryan DeHaan *(Partner)*
Troy Onda *(Partner)*
Mike O'Keefe *(Partner)*
John Hanrahan *(Partner)*
Brandon Wells *(CTO)*
Kathleen Hollerbach *(Dir-Relocation)*
Ceri Anderson *(Mng Partner)*
Susan Orth *(Mng Partner)*

THE GROUP INC.

The Group Inc.—(Continued)

Arthur R. Collins (Founder, Chm & Mng Partner)
Doug Miller (Chm)
Susie Ewing (Pres)

THE GROWTH FOR GOOD ACQUISITION CORPORATION
12 E 49th St 11th Fl, New York, NY 10017
Tel.: (973) 762-7645 Ky
GFGD—(NASDAQ)
Assets: $258,040,715
Liabilities: $9,341,632
Net Worth: $248,699,083
Earnings: ($2,319,152)
Fiscal Year-end: 12/31/22
Investment Services
N.A.I.C.S.: 523999
David Birnbaum (Pres, CEO & Chief Comml Officer)

THE GUARDIAN LIFE INSURANCE COMPANY OF AMERICA
10 Hudson Yards, New York, NY 10001
Tel.: (212) 598-8000
Web Site: http://www.guardianlife.com
Emp.: 100
Mutual Life Insurance Company
N.A.I.C.S.: 524298
Dean Del Vecchio (Chief Info & Ops Officer)
Andrew J. McMahon (Pres & CEO)
Michael Ferik (Head-Individual Markets)
Kevin Molloy (CFO)
Kermitt Brooks (Chief Legal Officer)
Wendy Wahl (Chief Mktg & Comm Officer)
Phil Pescatore (Chief Ethics & Compliance Officer)
Jonathan Mayhew (Head-Grp Benefits)
Stacey Hoin (Chief HR Officer)
Nick Liolis (Chief Investment Officer)
Erin Culek (Head-Strategy & Corp Dev)

Subsidiaries:

Avesis, Inc. (1)
10400 N 25th Ave Ste 200, Phoenix, AZ 85021
Tel.: (602) 241-3400
Web Site: http://www.avesis.com
Sales Range: $1-9.9 Million
Emp.: 440
Vision, Dental & Hearing Services
N.A.I.C.S.: 524114
Christopher Swanker (CEO)

Baillie Gifford Ltd. (1)
Calton Square 1 Greenside Row, Edinburgh, EH1 3AN, Scotland, United Kingdom
Tel.: (44) 1312752000
Web Site: http://www.bailliegifford.com
Sales Range: $300-349.9 Million
Emp.: 650
Insurance & Annuities; Joint Venture of The Guardian Life Insurance Company of America & Baillie Gifford & Co.
N.A.I.C.S.: 524128
Richard Barry (Dir-HR)
Piers Lowson (Dir)
Kath Murphy (Mgr-Interactive Sls-Australia & New Zealand)

Berkshire Life Insurance Company of America (1)
700 S St, Pittsfield, MA 01201-8212 (100%)
Tel.: (413) 499-4321
Web Site: http://www.theberkshire.com
Sales Range: $100-124.9 Million
Emp.: 460
Life Insurance, Disability Income Insurance, Pensions, Annuities & Mutual Fund Services
N.A.I.C.S.: 524113

Gordon Dinsmore (VP)

Broadshore Capital Partners LLC (1)
11777 San Vicente Blvd Ste 900, Los Angeles, CA 90049
Tel.: (310) 820-6661
Web Site: http://www.leinvestors.com
Real Estate Investment Activities
N.A.I.C.S.: 531390
Bradford W. Howe (Co-CEO)
Bleecker P. Seaman III (Co-CEO)
Alon I. Kraft (Sr VP)
John Gaghan (Sr VP)
Jeff Allen (Exec VP)
Julian Auzenne (VP-Payroll)
Jeremy Iaccino (CFO)
Andrew I. Sands (Mng Dir)
Russell D. Munn (Mng Dir)
Peter J. Finley (Sr VP)
Peter Houghton (Sr VP)
Peter Morgan (Sr VP)
Alicia Fernandes (Sr VP)
Christopher W. Bollinger (VP)
Benjamin Suit (VP)
Michael Kane (VP-Acq-West Coast)

Subsidiary (Domestic):

Lowe Enterprises Investment Management Inc. (2)
11777 San Vicente Blvd Ste 900, Los Angeles, CA 90049-5011
Tel.: (310) 820-6661
Web Site: http://www.loweenterprises.com
Investment Office
N.A.I.C.S.: 237210
Bradford W. Howe (Mng Dir)
Bleecker P. Seaman III (Mng Dir)
Robert J. Lowe Jr. (Chm & CEO)

Innovative Underwriters Inc. (1)
1800 JSK Blvd Ste 700, Philadelphia, PA 19103
Tel.: (215) 875-8650
Web Site: http://www.innovativeunderwriters.com
Sales Range: $25-49.9 Million
Emp.: 32
Fire Insurance Services
N.A.I.C.S.: 524113
Barry I. Belfer (Treas)
Leyla Lesina (Pres)
Karen Black (Dir-Ops & Fin)
Susan Clark (VP-Millennium Settlements)
Angie Defazio (Mgr-New Bus Case)
Yara Komorowsky (Mgr-New Bus Case)
Linda Lalande (Mgr-New Bus Case)
Antoinette Lowery (Mgr-New Bus Case)
Richard Machado (VP-Sls)
Martin Micklin (Controller)
Maureen Mitchell (VP-Strategic Relationships)
Franci Neill (Mgr-New Bus)

Park Avenue Life Insurance Company (1)
7 Hanover Sq, New York, NY 10004 (100%)
Tel.: (610) 861-0733
Web Site: http://www.guardianlife.com
Fire Insurance Services
N.A.I.C.S.: 524113
Armand M. De Palo (Pres & Exec VP)
Joseph A. Caruso (Sec & Sr VP)

The Guardian Insurance & Annuity Company, Inc. (1)
7 Hanover Sq, New York, NY 10004-2616 (100%)
Tel.: (212) 598-8000
Web Site: http://www.guardianlife.com
Sales Range: $250-299.9 Million
Emp.: 2,000
Stock Life Insurance & Equity Products
N.A.I.C.S.: 524128
Emily Viner (VP-Agency Mgmt & Dev)
Jeff Purbish (Reg VP-Retirement Plan Sls)

Subsidiary (Domestic):

Guardian Investor Services LLC (2)
7 Hanover Sq, New York, NY 10004 (100%)
Tel.: (212) 598-8000
Web Site: http://www.glic.com
Sales Range: $150-199.9 Million
Emp.: 500
Broker-Dealer
N.A.I.C.S.: 523999

THE GUIDA-SEIBERT DAIRY COMPANY INC.
433 Park St, New Britain, CT 06051-2730
Tel.: (860) 224-2404 CT
Web Site: http://www.supercow.com
Year Founded: 1932
Sales Range: $125-149.9 Million
Emp.: 400
Wholesale of Dairy Products
N.A.I.C.S.: 311511
Michael P. Guida (Pres)

THE GUILD FOR EXCEPTIONAL CHILDREN, INC.
260 68th St, Brooklyn, NY 11220
Tel.: (718) 833-6633 NY
Web Site: http://www.gecbklyn.org
Year Founded: 1958
Sales Range: $25-49.9 Million
Emp.: 615
Disability Assistance Services
N.A.I.C.S.: 624120
Judith Kraut (Dir-HR)
Paul Cassone (CEO & Exec Dir)
Annette Schoen (CFO)
Anthony Cetta (First VP)
Arlene Rutuelo (Pres)
Frank Sena (Second VP)
Mary Dory (Sec)
Stanley Ramsdal (Treas)
Elaine DeBerardine (Chief Compliance Officer)

THE GUILD FOR HUMAN SERVICES, INC.
521 Virginia Rd, Concord, MA 01742
Tel.: (781) 893-6000 MA
Web Site: http://www.theguildhumanservices.org
Year Founded: 1952
Sales Range: $10-24.9 Million
Emp.: 300
Disability Assistance Services
N.A.I.C.S.: 624120
Maureen Costello-Shea (Chief Residential Officer)
Julia Fomicheva (Chief Clinical Officer)

THE GUILD INC.
3118 International Lane, Madison, WI 53704
Tel.: (608) 257-2590
Web Site: http://www.artfulhome.com
Year Founded: 1985
Sales Range: $10-24.9 Million
Emp.: 35
Direct Retailer of Hand-Crafted Art & Home Furnishings
N.A.I.C.S.: 449129
Lisa Bayne (CEO)

THE GUITAMMER COMPANY
6117 Maxtown Rd, Westerville, OH 43082
Tel.: (614) 898-9370
Web Site: http://www.guitammer.com
Year Founded: 2011
Telecommunication Servicesb
N.A.I.C.S.: 517810
Mark A. Luden (Pres & CEO)

THE GURWIN JEWISH GERIATRIC CENTER
68 Hauppauge Rd, Commack, NY 11725
Tel.: (631) 715-2000
Web Site: http://www.gurwin.org
Year Founded: 1988
Sales Range: $75-99.9 Million
Emp.: 1,000
Health Care Srvices
N.A.I.C.S.: 621610

Lawrence Simon (Chm)
Dennine Cook (Dir-Community & Media Rels)
Berk Brotesky (Pres)

THE GUTHRIE CLINIC
Guthrie Sq, Sayre, PA 18840
Tel.: (570) 888-5858 PA
Web Site: http://www.guthrie.org
Year Founded: 1987
Sales Range: $200-249.9 Million
Emp.: 1,825
Health Care Srvices
N.A.I.C.S.: 622110

THE GUTIERREZ COMPANY
1 Wall St, Burlington, MA 01803
Tel.: (781) 272-7000 DE
Web Site: http://www.gutierrezco.com
Rev.: $67,933,582
Emp.: 30
Commercial Real Estate Development & Construction Services
N.A.I.C.S.: 237210
Doug Fainelli (VP-Ops)
Arthur Gutierrez Jr. (Pres)

THE H GROUP
902 W Main St, West Frankfort, IL 62896
Tel.: (618) 937-6483 IL
Web Site: http://www.buildingbettertomorrows.org
Year Founded: 1969
Sales Range: $10-24.9 Million
Emp.: 703
Individual & Family Support Services
N.A.I.C.S.: 624190
Chris Julian-Fralish (Pres)

THE H. LEFF ELECTRIC COMPANY
4700 Spring Rd, Independence, OH 44131-1027
Tel.: (330) 379-9800 OH
Web Site: http://www.leffelectric.com
Year Founded: 1921
Sales Range: $25-49.9 Million
Emp.: 100
Electrical Component Distr
N.A.I.C.S.: 423610
Larry Goldstein (Controller)
Bruce Leff (Vice Chm)
Jim Bracken (CEO)
Dan Nitowsky (Pres)
Sanford Leff Jr. (VP)

Subsidiaries:

Leff Electric - Bedford Heights (1)
23209 Miles Rd Ste C, Cleveland, OH 44128
Tel.: (216) 432-3000
Web Site: http://www.leffelectric.com
Sales Range: $25-49.9 Million
Emp.: 3
Electrical Component Distr
N.A.I.C.S.: 423610

Leff Electric - Elyria (1)
42307 N Ridge Rd, Elyria, OH 44035-1130
Tel.: (440) 324-5483
Sales Range: $25-49.9 Million
Emp.: 5
Electrical Component Distr
N.A.I.C.S.: 423610
John Volarcik (Office Mgr)
Sanford Leff Jr (VP)

Leff Electric - Mentor (1)
7520 Clover Ave Ste 7, Mentor, OH 44060-5231
Tel.: (440) 946-5448
Web Site: http://www.leffelectric.com
Sales Range: $25-49.9 Million
Emp.: 3
Electrical Component Distr
N.A.I.C.S.: 423610

Leff Electric - Strongsville (1)

12925 Pearl Rd, Strongsville, OH 44136-3425
Tel.: (440) 572-8188
Web Site: http://www.leffelectric.com
Sales Range: $25-49.9 Million
Emp.: 2
Electrical Component Distr
N.A.I.C.S.: 423610
Adam Prather (Gen Mgr)

Leff Electric - Warren (1)
1230 N River Rd, Warren, OH 44483
Tel.: (330) 372-3344
Web Site: http://www.leffelectric.com
Sales Range: $25-49.9 Million
Emp.: 3
Electrical Component Distr
N.A.I.C.S.: 423610
Mike Rushin (Office Mgr)

Leff Electric - Youngstown (1)
1230 N River Rd, Warren, OH 44483-2353
Tel.: (330) 372-3344
Web Site: http://www.leffelectric.com
Sales Range: $25-49.9 Million
Emp.: 5
Electrical Component Distr
N.A.I.C.S.: 423610

THE H.T. HACKNEY COMPANY
502 S Gay St, Knoxville, TN 37902-1503
Tel.: (865) 717-6800 TN
Web Site: https://www.hthackney.com
Year Founded: 1891
Sales Range: $1-4.9 Billion
Emp.: 4,000
General Line Grocery Merchant Wholesalers
N.A.I.C.S.: 424410
Mike Morton (CFO & VP)
Leonard Robinette (CIO)
Tommy R. Thomas (Dir-Sls & Bus Dev)
Dean Ballinger (COO & VP)
Heather Butler (Mgr-Events)
Mike Anderson (Dir-Pur)

Subsidiaries:

Great American Deli, Inc. (1)
5828 Ooltewah Ringgold Rd, Ooltewah, TN 37363-0027
Tel.: (423) 648-6510
Web Site: http://www.greatamericandeli.com
Sandwich Mfr
N.A.I.C.S.: 722513
Keith J. Sullivan (Pres)

Hackney Home Furnishings (1)
3036 S Congress Pkwy, Athens, TN 37303
Tel.: (423) 745-9127
Web Site:
  http://www.hackneyhomefurnishings.com
Home Furnishing Whslr
N.A.I.C.S.: 423220

Subsidiary (Domestic):

Hackney Contract Furniture (2)
3036 Congress Pkwy, Athens, TN 37303
Tel.: (423) 745-9127
Emp.: 100
Furniture Whslr
N.A.I.C.S.: 423210
Patrick Priest (Product Mgr-Contract)

Hackney Petroleum, Inc. (1)
1209 Hilton Rd, Knoxville, TN 37921-0238 (100%)
Tel.: (865) 584-9600
Sales Range: $10-24.9 Million
Emp.: 40
Petroleum Jobber & Operation of Chain of Convenience Stores
N.A.I.C.S.: 424720
Larry Henriott (Gen Mgr)

Holland House Furniture (1)
9420 E 33rd St, Indianapolis, IN 46235
Tel.: (317) 895-4300
Web Site:
  http://www.hollandhousefurniture.com
Emp.: 80
Home Furnishing Whslr
N.A.I.C.S.: 423210

Judy Hotka (Coord-Import Logistic)
David Blake (VP-Mdsg)

Natural Springs Water Group, LLC (1)
128 LP Auer Road, Johnson City, TN 37604
Tel.: (423) 926-7905
Sales Range: $10-24.9 Million
Emp.: 12
Bottled Water Mfr
N.A.I.C.S.: 312112

The H.T. Hackney Co. (1)
1180 58th St SW, Wyoming, MI 49509-9536
Tel.: (616) 530-6600
Web Site: http://www.hthackney.com
Sales Range: $1-9.9 Million
Emp.: 180
Distr of Tobacco
N.A.I.C.S.: 424940
Ann Chappell (Mgr-Food Svc)

The H.T. Hackney Co. (1)
1586 Berea Rd, Richmond, KY 40475-9580 (100%)
Tel.: (859) 623-2416
Web Site: http://www.hthackney.com
Sales Range: $25-49.9 Million
Emp.: 50
Wholesale Distributor of General Line of Groceries
N.A.I.C.S.: 424410

The H.T. Hackney Co. (1)
PO Box 249, Harold, KY 41635-0249
Tel.: (606) 478-9591
Sales Range: $25-49.9 Million
Emp.: 65
Provider of Wholesale Grocery
N.A.I.C.S.: 424410
Bill Simms (Pres)

The H.T. Hackney Co. (1)
118 Enterprise Dr, Madison Heights, VA 24572
Tel.: (434) 929-6515
Web Site: http://www.hthackney.com
Sales Range: $25-49.9 Million
Emp.: 100
Grocery Supply Wholesale Distr
N.A.I.C.S.: 424410
Dale Geary (Mgr-Sls)
Dale Smith (Gen Mgr)

Uncle Ray's, LLC (1)
14245 Birwood St, Detroit, MI 48238
Tel.: (313) 834-0800
Web Site: http://www.unclerays.com
Rev: $14,869,486
Emp.: 100
Potato Chips & Other Potato-Based Snacks
N.A.I.C.S.: 311919

THE HAARTZ CORPORATION
87 Hayward Rd, Acton, MA 01720-3005
Tel.: (978) 264-2600 MA
Web Site: http://www.haartz.com
Year Founded: 1922
Sales Range: $75-99.9 Million
Emp.: 320
Coated Fabrics for the Automotive Industry
N.A.I.C.S.: 313320
John Fox (Pres)
Charles Quimby (CFO & VP)
Timothy E. Jackson (VP-Sls & Mktg)
Doug Sieber (VP-Ops)
Doug Haartz (Mgr-Sls-Intl)
Matthew Williams (Dir-Bus Dev)
Andy Nicoletti (Dir-Pur & Matls)

Subsidiaries:

Haartz GmbH (1)
Kafertaler Strasse 318, 68167, Mannheim, Germany
Tel.: (49) 621 338 15 0
Web Site: http://www.haartz.com
Emp.: 50
Coated Fabrics for the Automotive Industry
N.A.I.C.S.: 336390
Rudiger Ernst (Mng Dir)

The Haartz Corporation - Bloomfield Hills (1)

40950 Woodward Ave Ste 150, Bloomfield Hills, MI 48304
Tel.: (248) 646-8200
Web Site: http://www.haartz.com
Emp.: 7
Interior Automotive Materials Mfr
N.A.I.C.S.: 313320
Timothy E. Jackson (VP-Sls)

THE HABEGGER CORPORATION
4995 Winton Rd, Cincinnati, OH 45232-1504
Tel.: (513) 681-6313 OH
Web Site:
  http://www.habeggercorp.com
Year Founded: 1952
Sales Range: $100-124.9 Million
Emp.: 300
Wholesale Distributor of Heating & Air Conditioning Equipment
N.A.I.C.S.: 423730
Fred Habegger (Chm)

THE HABITAT COMPANY INC.
350 W Hubbard St Ste 500, Chicago, IL 60654
Tel.: (312) 527-5400 IL
Web Site: http://www.habitat.com
Year Founded: 1971
Sales Range: $50-74.9 Million
Emp.: 700
Provider of Real Estate Services
N.A.I.C.S.: 531210
Matt Fiascone (Pres)
Bryan Sullivan (VP-Acquisition & Investment)
Jack Devedjian (VP-Ops)
Lori Chacos (VP & Asst Gen Counsel)
Patrick Ryan (Sr VP)
Sheila Byrne (Exec VP-Property Mgmt)

THE HAGADONE CORPORATION
111 S 1st St, Coeur D'Alene, ID 83814
Tel.: (208) 667-3431 ID
Web Site: http://www.hagadone.com
Year Founded: 1966
Sales Range: $300-349.9 Million
Emp.: 2,000
Holding Company; Publisher & Hospitality Operations
N.A.I.C.S.: 551112
Duane Hagadone (Founder & CEO)

Subsidiaries:

Columbia Basin Publishing Co., Inc. (1)
813 W 3rd Ave, Moses Lake, WA 98837-2008 (100%)
Tel.: (509) 765-4561
Web Site:
  http://www.columbiabasinherald.com
Sales Range: $10-24.9 Million
Emp.: 40
Provider of Newspaper Services
N.A.I.C.S.: 513110
Eric Lafontain (Publr)

Greater Beloit Publishing Co., Inc. (1)
111 S1st St PO Box 6200 83816, Coeur D'Alene, ID 83814-2794
Tel.: (208) 667-3431
Sales Range: $10-24.9 Million
Emp.: 120
Provider of Newspaper Services
N.A.I.C.S.: 721110

H&J Inc. (1)
111 S 1st, Coeur D'Alene, ID 83814
Tel.: (208) 667-3431
Web Site: http://www.hagadone.com
Sales Range: $25-49.9 Million
Emp.: 30
Provider of Nonresidential Building Operator Services
N.A.I.C.S.: 531120

Hagadone Directories Inc. (1)
102 E Wallace Ave, Coeur D'Alene, ID 83814-2948
Tel.: (208) 667-8744
Web Site: http://www.blackphonebook.com
Sales Range: $10-24.9 Million
Emp.: 25
Provider of Newspaper Services
N.A.I.C.S.: 513140
James Hail (Co-owner, Founder & Pres)

Hagadone Hospitality Inc. (1)
111 S First St, Coeur D'Alene, ID 83814-2794
Tel.: (208) 667-3431
Web Site: http://www.hagadone.com
Sales Range: $10-24.9 Million
Emp.: 100
Provider of Hotels & Motels Services
N.A.I.C.S.: 721110

Subsidiary (Domestic):

The Coeur d'Alene Resort (2)
115 S 2nd St, Coeur D'Alene, ID 83814
Tel.: (208) 765-4000
Web Site: http://www.cdaresort.com
Resort, Golf Course & Spa Operations
N.A.I.C.S.: 721110
Jerry Jaeger (Pres & Co-Owner)
William T. Reagan (Gen Mgr)

Hagadone Photography Inc. (1)
319 E Front Ave, Coeur D'Alene, ID 83815
Tel.: (208) 765-4099
Web Site:
  http://www.quicksilverphotography.com
Sales Range: $10-24.9 Million
Emp.: 12
Provider of Photographic Services
N.A.I.C.S.: 541921

Hagadone Printing Company Inc. (1)
274 Puuhale Rd, Honolulu, HI 96819-2234 (100%)
Tel.: (808) 847-5310
Web Site: http://www.hagadoneprinting.com
Sales Range: $25-49.9 Million
Emp.: 150
Commercial & Publication Printing & Mailing
N.A.I.C.S.: 323120
Plint Schroeder (Pres)

Lake Coeur D'Alene Cruises Inc. (1)
115 S Second St, Coeur D'Alene, ID 83814-2794
Tel.: (208) 765-4000
Web Site: http://www.cdaresort.com
Sales Range: $75-99.9 Million
Emp.: 900
Water Passenger Transportation
N.A.I.C.S.: 487210
Bill Reagan (Gen Mgr)

Pend Oreille Printers Inc. (1)
310 Church St, Sandpoint, ID 83864
Tel.: (208) 263-9534
Web Site:
  http://www.bonnercountydailybee.com
Sales Range: $10-24.9 Million
Emp.: 25
Provider of Newspaper Services
N.A.I.C.S.: 323111
Carolyn Lobsinger (Editor-in-Chief)

THE HALIFAX GROUP LLC
1133 Connecticut Ave NW Ste 700, Washington, DC 20036
Tel.: (202) 530-8300
Web Site:
  http://www.thehalifaxgroup.com
Year Founded: 1999
Privater Equity Firm
N.A.I.C.S.: 523999
Kenneth M. Doyle (Sr Partner)
Michael T. Marshall (CFO, Chief Compliance Officer & Sr Partner)
Scott S. Plumridge (Mng Partner)
Chris Cathcart (Mng Partner)
David Calder (Principal)
Davis Hostetter (VP-Dallas)
David Bard (Mng Dir)
Thomas High (Controller)
Doug Hill (Partner)
Jamie Cavanaugh (VP)
Amit Swaroop (VP)

THE HALIFAX GROUP LLC

The Halifax Group LLC—(Continued)

Alessandra Christiani (VP-Bus Dev)
Jerry Lavell Johnson (Partner)
David W. Dupree (Sr Partner)

Subsidiaries:

BCI Burke Company Co (1)
727 NW Way, Fond Du Lac, WI 54937
Tel.: (920) 921-9220
Web Site: http://www.bciburke.com
Sporting & Athletic Goods Mfr
N.A.I.C.S.: 339920
Mark Sondergard (COO & CFO)
Tim Ahern (Owner & CEO)

Interim HealthCare Inc. (1)
1601 Sawgrass Corporate Pkwy Ste 220, Sunrise, FL 33323
Tel.: (954) 858-6000
Web Site: http://www.interimhealthcare.com
Sales Range: $750-799.9 Million
Emp.: 60
Home Health Care, Personal Care & Support Services & Healthcare Staffing Services Franchisor
N.A.I.C.S.: 561320
Linda Shaub (Sr VP-Mktg & Brand)
Barbara A. McCann (Chief Indus Officer)
Jane Hinton (Sr VP-Clinical Practice & Sys)
Michael Moran (VP-Sls Dev-Natl)
Bob Diaz (CTO)
Sonya Hinds (Sr VP-HR, Trng & IT)
Steve Turner (Sr VP-New Franchise Support)
Jennifer Ballard (Chief Clinical Officer)

K2 Industrial Inc. (1)
5233 Hohman, Hammond, IN 46320
Tel.: (219) 933-5300
Web Site: http://www.k2industrial.com
Sales Range: $10-24.9 Million
Emp.: 75
Industrial & Commercial Specialty Services
N.A.I.C.S.: 561210

Subsidiary (Domestic):

Cannon Sline Inc. (2)
2 Lukens Dr Ste 600, New Castle, DE 19720-2796
Tel.: (302) 658-1420
Web Site: http://www.cannonsline.com
Sales Range: $10-24.9 Million
Emp.: 3
Industrial Painting, Structure Coating & Lighting Systems
N.A.I.C.S.: 541410

Division (Domestic):

Cannon Sline Industrial, Inc. - Hopewell Division (3)
300 E Poythress St, Hopewell, VA 23860
Tel.: (804) 541-0285
Industrial Cleaning Services
N.A.I.C.S.: 562998

Cannon Sline Industrial, Inc. - Mid Atlantic Division (3)
2584 Aviator Dr Ste 101, Virginia Beach, VA 23453
Tel.: (757) 427-0878
Industrial Cleaning Services
N.A.I.C.S.: 562998
Tony Bochniak (Pres)

Cannon Sline Industrial, Inc. - Wilmington Division (3)
2 Lukens Dr Ste 600, New Castle, DE 19720
Tel.: (302) 658-1420
Web Site: http://www.cannonsline.com
Emp.: 2
Coating Mfr
N.A.I.C.S.: 325510
Tony Bochniak (Pres)

Subsidiary (Domestic):

KA Industrial Services, LLC (2)
26 Colonial Ave Ste 4, Woodbury, NJ 08096
Tel.: (856) 686-4772
Industrial Cleaning Services
N.A.I.C.S.: 562998
Steve Hart (Controller)

KM Industrial, Inc. (2)
1411 W Gaylord St1411, Long Beach, CA 90813
Tel.: (562) 786-6200
Web Site: http://www.kmindustrial.net
Industrial Cleaning Services
N.A.I.C.S.: 562998

Division (Domestic):

KM Industrial, Inc. - Benicia Division (3)
3867 Teal Ct, Benicia, CA 94510
Tel.: (219) 937-8240
Industrial Cleaning Services
N.A.I.C.S.: 562998

KM Industrial, Inc. - Las Vegas Division (3)
3139 W Post Rd, Las Vegas, NV 89118
Tel.: (702) 616-9799
Industrial Cleaning Services
N.A.I.C.S.: 562998

Subsidiary (Domestic):

KM Plant Services, Inc. (2)
2552 Industrial Dr, Highland, IN 46322
Tel.: (219) 937-8240
Web Site: http://www.k2industrial.com
Industrial Cleaning Services
N.A.I.C.S.: 562998

Division (Domestic):

KM Plant Services, Inc. - Pekin Division (3)
1314 Koch St, Pekin, IL 61554
Tel.: (309) 353-9033
Emp.: 35
Industrial Cleaning Services
N.A.I.C.S.: 562998
Randy Julius (Project Mgr)

North American Video, Inc. (1)
301 Drum Point Rd, Brick, NJ 08723
Tel.: (732) 477-0686
Web Site: http://www.navcctv.com
Sales Range: $25-49.9 Million
Emp.: 50
Video Surveillance, Digital Video Management, Remote Video Monitoring, Remote Systems Management & Access Control Systems
N.A.I.C.S.: 561621
Jason Oakley (Pres & CEO)
Jason Woodward (Dir-Ops)

Branch (Domestic):

North American Video - North East Regional Headquarters (2)
1 Blue Hill Plz, Pearl River, NY 10965
Tel.: (845) 620-0240
Web Site: http://www.navcctv.com
Security Systems Integration Technology & Services
N.A.I.C.S.: 561621

The PromptCare Companies, Inc. (1)
41 Spring St, New Providence, NJ 07974
Web Site: http://www.promptcare.net
Specialty Respiratory & Infusion Healthcare Services
N.A.I.C.S.: 621498
Tom Voorhees (Pres & CEO)

Subsidiary (Domestic):

HomeTown Oxygen, Charlotte, LLC (2)
2626 Glenwood Ave Ste 550, Charlotte, NC 27608
Tel.: (704) 347-2233
Clinical Home Respiratory Therapy & Equipment
N.A.I.C.S.: 532283
Moises Zayas (Mgr-Pur & Logistics)

United States Environmental Services, LLC (1)
15109 Heathrow Forest Pkwy 150, Houston, TX 77032
Tel.: (281) 606-4960
Web Site: http://www.usesgroup.com
Emp.: 20
Environmental Consulting Services
N.A.I.C.S.: 541620
Rod Powell (Exec VP)

THE HALL CHINA COMPANY
1 Anna St, East Liverpool, OH 43920-3675
Tel.: (330) 385-2900   OH
Web Site: http://www.hallchina.com
Year Founded: 1903
Sales Range: $75-99.9 Million
Emp.: 60
Mfr of Ceramic Products for the Food Service Industry; Fireproof Cooking China
N.A.I.C.S.: 327110
James Clark (Controller)

THE HALLSTAR COMPANY
120 S Riverside Plz Ste 1620, Chicago, IL 60606
Tel.: (312) 385-4494
Web Site: http://www.hallstar.com
Year Founded: 1986
Sales Range: $25-49.9 Million
Emp.: 140
Specialty Industrial Organic Chemicals
N.A.I.C.S.: 325199
John Joseph Paro (Chm, Pres & CEO)
Carmen B. Masciantonio (Pres-Indus Solutions)
Germano S. Coelho (VP-Global Commercial Ops-Beauty)
Robert Hu (Pres-Beauty)
Ashley Gertz (Chief HR Officer)

THE HAMBLETONIAN SOCIETY, INC.
109 S Main St Ste 18, Cranbury, NJ 08512
Tel.: (609) 371-2211   NY
Web Site: http://www.hambletonian.org
Year Founded: 1949
Sales Range: $10-24.9 Million
Emp.: 7
Horse Breeding Support Services
N.A.I.C.S.: 115210
Mary Lou Dondarski (Office Mgr)
Moira Fanning (COO)
John Campbell (Pres & CEO)
David Janes (Mgr-Stakes)
Ed O'Connor (Founder)

THE HAMISTER GROUP, INC.
10 Lafayette Sq Ste 1900, Buffalo, NY 14203
Tel.: (716) 839-4000
Web Site: http://www.hamistergroup.com
Year Founded: 1977
Sales Range: $50-74.9 Million
Emp.: 4,000
Adult Homes & Home Health Care Operators
N.A.I.C.S.: 621610
Mark Hamister (Chm & CEO)
Jack Turesky (Pres & COO)
Denise Peacock (Corp Dir-Sls)
David Paul (Chief Capital Officer & Exec VP)
Daniel Hamister (Chief Investment Officer & Exec VP)
Lindsey Kovel (Mgr-Payroll & Benefits)
Mark Miller (VP-Hotel Ops)
Ryan Landry (Treas & VP)
Amy Baumcratz (Dir-Revenue Mgmt)
Marguerite McAfee (Dir-Acq)
Emily Bolles (Coord-Construction)
Jason Senske (Coord-Construction)
Josh Klotzbach (VP-Construction)
Earl W. McCartney (CFO & Exec VP)
Laura Kurtz (Dir-Mktg)
Janene DiBerardino (Dir-Clinical Svcs)
Kyle Metcalfe (Dir-IR)

Subsidiaries:

Brompton Heights, Inc. (1)
275 Brompton Rd, Williamsville, NY 14221
Tel.: (716) 634-5734
Web Site: http://www.bromptonheights.com
Assisted Living Facility Operator
N.A.I.C.S.: 623312
Helen Kurzdorfer (Dir-Recreation)
Peter Riester (Dir-Maintenance)
Denis Berg (Dir-Personal Care)
Tom Porto (Dir-Culinary)
Sharon Wisniewski (Mgr-Case)

Health Services of Northern New York, Inc. (1)
56 Market St, Potsdam, NY 13676
Tel.: (315) 265-4065
Web Site: http://www.hsnny.com
Women Healthcare Services
N.A.I.C.S.: 621610

Heather Heights of Pittsford, Inc. (1)
160 W Jefferson Rd, Pittsford, NY 14534
Tel.: (585) 264-1600
Web Site: http://www.heatherheights.com
Assisted Living Facility Operator
N.A.I.C.S.: 623312
Evelyn Suarez (Dir-Personal Care & Mgr-Case)
Tiffany Arnold (Office Mgr-Bus)
Andy Armstrong (Dir-Culinary)
Tony Rivera (Dir-Maintenance & Environmental Svcs)

Orchard Heights, Inc. (1)
5200 Chestnut Ridge Rd, Orchard Park, NY 14127
Tel.: (716) 662-0651
Web Site: http://www.orchardheights.com
Sales Range: $25-49.9 Million
Emp.: 105
Assisted Living Facility Operator
N.A.I.C.S.: 623312
Colleen Roy (Dir-Admissions)
Laura Weston (Mgr-RN Case)
Lee Watson (Dir-Recreation)
Paula McGrath (Office Mgr)
Brian Castiglia (Dir-Maintenance)
Patricia Suranyi (Dir-Personal Care)
Amy Ladowski (Dir-Admissions)
Denise Siuda (Dir-Culinary)
Rosalie DeLio (Dir-Sls & Mktg)

THE HAMNER INSTITUTES FOR HEALTH SCIENCES
6 Davis Dr, Research Triangle Park, NC 27709-2137
Tel.: (919) 558-1200   NC
Web Site: http://www.thehamner.org
Year Founded: 1974
Sales Range: $10-24.9 Million
Research Services
N.A.I.C.S.: 541715
Geoffrey R. Bock (Dir-Mktg & Bus Dev)
M. Bud Nelson (Gen Counsel & Exec Dir-Tech Dev)
Richard Cravener (Dir-Facilities Ops & Plng)
Andrew M. Howard (Mgr-Facilities & Maintenance)
Kristin O. Overman (Mgr-HR)
Mary Ellen Budzyna (Sr Mgr-Sponsored Research)
William F. Greenlee (Pres & CEO)
Jamie H. Wilkerson (Exec Dir-Fin & Admin)

THE HANDY/KENLIN GROUP
29 E Hintz Rd, Wheeling, IL 60090
Tel.: (847) 459-0900
Web Site: http://www.handykenlin.com
Year Founded: 1898
Sales Range: $10-24.9 Million
Emp.: 30
Mfr of Button Covering Machines, Metal Stamps & Furniture Hardware
N.A.I.C.S.: 339993
Michael Baritz (CEO)
Ken Shonfeld (Pres)
Dawn Graese (Controller)

COMPANIES

THE HEALTH MANAGEMENT GROUP, INC.

Subsidiaries:

Handy Button Machine Company (1)
22 Brandywine Rd, Stamford, CT 06905
Tel.: (203) 322-1675
Sales Range: $10-24.9 Million
Small Metal Stamping
N.A.I.C.S.: 339993

Subsidiary (Domestic):

Liberty Metal Products Co. (2)
22 Brandywine Rd, Stamford, CT 06905
Tel.: (203) 322-1675
Small Metal Stampings for Apparel
N.A.I.C.S.: 423830

THE HANOR COMPANY, INC.
E4614 US Hwy 14 60, Spring Green, WI 53588
Tel.: (608) 588-9170
Web Site: http://www.hanorcompany.com
Rev.: $32,200,000
Emp.: 525
Animal Production
N.A.I.C.S.: 112990
Baxter Gutknecht (Sr VP)
Myrl Mortenson (Sr VP)

THE HANOVER CONSUMER COOPERATIVE SOCIETY, INC.
45 S Park St, Hanover, NH 03755-2157
Tel.: (603) 643-2667 NH
Web Site: http://www.coopfoodstore.com
Year Founded: 1936
Sales Range: $25-49.9 Million
Emp.: 270
Grocery Stores
N.A.I.C.S.: 445110
Bruce Follett (Dir-Mdsg)
Mark Langlois (Dir-Fin)
Steve Miller (Mgr-Hanover Store)
Harrison Drinkwater (Sec)
Michael Bettmann (VP)
Tony Roisman (Pres)

THE HARDY CORPORATION
350 Industrial Dr, Birmingham, AL 35211
Tel.: (205) 252-7191 AL
Web Site: http://www.hardycorp.com
Year Founded: 1943
Sales Range: $10-24.9 Million
Emp.: 80
Plumbing, Heating & Air Conditioning Services
N.A.I.C.S.: 238220
Thomas N. Cordell (Pres)

THE HARFORD MUTUAL INSURANCE COMPANY INC.
200 N Main St, Bel Air, MD 21014-3544
Tel.: (410) 838-4000 MD
Web Site: http://www.harfordmutual.com
Year Founded: 1842
Sales Range: $25-49.9 Million
Emp.: 122
Property & Casualty Insurance Products & Services
N.A.I.C.S.: 524126
Steven D. Linkous (Pres & CEO)
June A. Poole (Treas & VP)
Kenneth G. Thompson (Controller & Asst VP-Fin)
Stephen T. Scott (Chm)
Karen Mashinski (CFO & VP)
Timothy F. Baum (CIO)
Jeffrey S. Rink (Exec VP)
Jeffrey Bischoff (Asst VP-IT)
Matt Summerell (Dir-Bus Dev)
Pauline Bao (Sr Dir-Actuarial)
Timothy Fitzpatrick (Dir-Loss Control & Premium Audit)
Brigette Reed (Dir-Acctg)
Bryan Yekstat (Dir-Claims-Workers Compensation)
Frank P. Kellner III (Sec & VP-Claims)

Subsidiaries:

Firstline National Insurance Company (1)
200 N Main St, Bel Air, MD 21014-3554 (100%)
Tel.: (410) 879-2360
Web Site: http://www.harfordmutual.com
Sales Range: $50-74.9 Million
Property & Casualty Insurance Products & Services
N.A.I.C.S.: 524126
Steven D. Linkous (Pres & CEO)

THE HARPER COMPANY
1648 Petersburg Rd, Hebron, KY 41048
Tel.: (859) 586-8890
Web Site: http://harperco.com
Year Founded: 1935
Sales Range: $25-49.9 Million
Emp.: 150
Highway & Street Construction Services
N.A.I.C.S.: 237310
Bruce M. Huff (VP)

THE HARPER CORPORATION
35 W Ct St Ste 400, Greenville, SC 29601-2875
Tel.: (864) 527-2500 SC
Web Site: http://www.harpergc.com
Year Founded: 1950
Nonresidential Construction Services
N.A.I.C.S.: 236220
Douglass Harper (Chm)
David Wise (Pres)
Kyle Snipes (Dir-Bus Dev)
Bryan Royal (VP-Environmental Sys Div)
Matt Johnson (VP-Ops)
Andy Hall (Dir-Preconstruction)
Rob Major (Dir-Estimating)
Peyton Howell (Dir-Indus Markets)
Tim Lewis (Sr Project Mgr & Dir-Ashville Office)
Kate Dotten-Holder (Project Mgr & Dir-Charlotte)

THE HARTFORD DISPENSARY
335 Broad St, Manchester, CT 06040-4036
Tel.: (860) 643-3200 CT
Year Founded: 1871
Sales Range: $10-24.9 Million
Emp.: 228
Health Care Srvices
N.A.I.C.S.: 622110
Darcie Boiano (Sec)
Paul McLaughlin (Exec Dir)

THE HARTY PRESS INC.
25 James St, New Haven, CT 06513
Tel.: (203) 562-5112 CT
Web Site: http://www.hartynet.com
Year Founded: 1900
Sales Range: $10-24.9 Million
Emp.: 200
Provider of Full Range of Desktop, Prepress, Printing, Mailing & Data Processing Services
N.A.I.C.S.: 323111
George R. Platt (Pres & CEO)
Mike Platt (COO & VP)
Robert J. Graham (Controller)

THE HARTZ GROUP, INC.
667 Madison Ave, New York, NY 10021
Tel.: (212) 308-3336
Web Site: http://www.hartzmountain.com
Holding Company
N.A.I.C.S.: 551112
Leonard Stern (Chm & CEO)

Subsidiaries:

Hartz Mountain Industries, Inc. (1)
400 Plaza Dr, Secaucus, NJ 07096-1515
Tel.: (201) 348-1200
Web Site: http://www.hartzmountain.com
Sales Range: $50-74.9 Million
Emp.: 100
Commercial Real Estate Development & Management
N.A.I.C.S.: 531390
Ernest A. Christoph (Sr VP-Sls & Leasing)
Charles Reese (VP-Sls & Leasing)
Gus Milano (Pres & COO)
Richard Vanderbeck (VP-Sls & Leasing)

THE HASKELL COMPANY
111 Riverside Ave, Jacksonville, FL 32202-4921
Tel.: (904) 791-4500 DE
Web Site: http://www.haskell.com
Year Founded: 1965
Sales Range: $550-599.9 Million
Emp.: 790
Civil Infrastructure, Commercial & Industrial Construction Services
N.A.I.C.S.: 236220
James L. O'Leary (Pres)
Paul Raudenbush (Sr VP-Plng, Dev, Infrastructure & Transportation Grp)
Paul Tyler (Pres-Comml Grp)
Brad A. Slappey (CFO & Exec VP)
David A. Thaeler (Chief HR Officer & Exec VP)
John Paul Saenz (COO & Exec VP)
Peter Kinsley (Pres-Govt & Pub Svcs Grp)
Mike Woods (Grp Pres-Consumer & Packaged Goods)
Don Baldwin (CMO, Chief Strategy Officer & Sr VP)

Subsidiaries:

Haskell de Mexico, S.A. de C.V. (1)
Avenida Prolongacion Paseo de la Reforma 1015 Torre A-403, Colonia Santa Fe, 1376, Mexico, Mexico
Tel.: (52) 5552926580
Nonresidential Construction Services
N.A.I.C.S.: 236210
Luis Jimenez (VP)

Seiberling Associates, Inc. (1)
655 3rd St Ste 203, Beloit, WI 53511
Tel.: (608) 313-1235
Web Site: http://www.seiberling.com
Sales Range: $10-24.9 Million
Emp.: 40
Engineering & Technical Consulting Services
N.A.I.C.S.: 541330
John Miller (Pres)
Brian Weathers (Project Mgr)

THE HAT CLUB, LLC
1834 W 3rd St, Tempe, AZ 85281
Tel.: (480) 829-0545 AZ
Web Site: http://www.hatclub.com
Year Founded: 1992
Sales Range: $10-24.9 Million
Emp.: 120
Miscellaneous Apparel & Accessory Store
N.A.I.C.S.: 458110
Paul Stachel (Owner & Principal)
Stephen Stachel (Owner & Principal)

THE HATCHER GROUP
4340 E W Hwy Ste 912, Bethesda, MD 20814-4447
Tel.: (301) 656-0348
Web Site: http://www.thehatchergroup.com
Public Relations Agencies
N.A.I.C.S.: 541820
Ed Hatcher (Pres)
Amy Buckley (Partner)
Amy Fahnestock (Partner)

Subsidiaries:

Horne Creative Group, Inc. (1)
2000 Duke St Ste 300, Alexandria, VA 22314
Tel.: (703) 966-6227
Web Site: http://www.hornecreativegroup.com
News Syndicates
N.A.I.C.S.: 516210
Yanely Allen (Sr Acct Mgr)

THE HAWAII FOODBANK
2611 Kilihau St, Honolulu, HI 96819-2021
Tel.: (808) 836-3600 HI
Web Site: http://www.hawaiifoodbank.org
Year Founded: 1982
Sales Range: $25-49.9 Million
Emp.: 47
Community Food Services
N.A.I.C.S.: 624210
Connie Bennett (Dir-Fin)
Roxanne Stark (Dir-Agency Affiliations)
Ken Ito (Dir-Warehouse Ops)
Wes Perreira (Mgr-Kauai)
Beverly Santos (Mgr-Special Events)
Laura Kay Rand (Sr Mgr-Grant & Comm)
Malcolm Inamine (Chief Admin Officer)
Gerald Shintaku (Pres & CEO)

THE HEALTH CARE AUTHORITY OF THE CITY OF ANNISTON
400 E 10th St, Anniston, AL 36207
Tel.: (256) 235-5121 AL
Web Site: http://www.rmccares.org
Year Founded: 1974
Health Care Services Organization
N.A.I.C.S.: 813910
Doug Scott (VP-HR)

Subsidiaries:

Anniston HMA, LLC (1)
301 E 18th St, Anniston, AL 36207
Tel.: (256) 235-8900
Web Site: https://www.stringfellowhealth.com
Hospital Services
N.A.I.C.S.: 622110
Joseph Weaver (CEO)

THE HEALTH MANAGEMENT GROUP, INC.
395 Springside Dr, Akron, OH 44333-2434
Tel.: (330) 666-7952
Web Site: http://www.healthmanagementgroup.com
Sales Range: $25-49.9 Million
Emp.: 25
Holding Company
N.A.I.C.S.: 551112
Charles E. Sekeres (Pres & CEO)

Subsidiaries:

Diet Center Worldwide, Inc. (1)
395 Springside Dr, Akron, OH 44333
Tel.: (330) 665-5861
Web Site: http://www.dietcenter.com
Franchised Weight Loss Centers
N.A.I.C.S.: 812191
Charles E. Sekeres (Pres & CEO)
Mike Zsely (Dir-Admin)

Physicians Weight Loss Centers, Inc. (1)
395 Springside Dr, Akron, OH 44333
Tel.: (330) 666-7952
Web Site: http://www.pwlc.com

THE HEALTH MANAGEMENT GROUP, INC.   U.S. PRIVATE

The Health Management Group, Inc.—(Continued)
Sales Range: $25-49.9 Million
Franchised Weight Loss Centers
N.A.I.C.S.: 812191
Charles E. Sekeres (Founder, Pres & CEO)
Mike Zsely (Dir-Admin)
Kristyn Austriaco (Dir-Nutritional Svcs)
Linda Maksim (Mgr-Internet Website)
Scott Orlando (Sr Dir-Franchise Area)
Tony Pittman (VP-Ops)

THE HEALTH TRUST
3180 Newberry Dr Ste 200, San Jose, CA 95118
Tel.: (408) 513-8700   CA
Web Site: http://www.healthtrust.org
Year Founded: 1996
Sales Range: $10-24.9 Million
Emp.: 199
Healtcare Services
N.A.I.C.S.: 622110
Todd Hansen (COO)
Ira Holtzman (CFO)
Paul Hepfer (VP-Programs)
Roberta L. Robins (Vice Chm)
Charles Bullock (Chm)
Irene Segura (Dir-HR)
Rachel Poplack (Dir-Strategy)
Cindy Ruby (Sec)
Carla Freeman (Officer-Program)
Jennifer Loving (Exec Dir-Destination)
Mary Patterson (Dir-Strategic Partnerships)

THE HEALTHY BACK INSTITUTE
141 E Mercer St Ste E, Dripping Springs, TX 78620
Tel.: (240) 780-5977
Web Site:
   http://www.losethebackpain.com
Year Founded: 2001
Sales Range: $1-9.9 Million
Emp.: 30
Products That Promote Relief of Neck & Back Pain
N.A.I.C.S.: 325411
Jesse Cannone (Co-Founder)
Steve Hefferon (Co-Founder)

THE HEARN COMPANY
55 W Monroe St, Chicago, IL 60603
Tel.: (312) 408-3000
Web Site:
   http://www.hearncompany.com
Sales Range: $10-24.9 Million
Emp.: 40
Land Subdividers & Developers, Commercial
N.A.I.C.S.: 237210
Stephen G. Hearn (Pres & CEO)

THE HEARST CORPORATION
300 W 57th St, New York, NY 10019
Tel.: (212) 649-2000   DE
Web Site: https://www.hearst.com
Year Founded: 1887
Sales Range: $1-4.9 Billion
Emp.: 20,000
Offices of Other Holding Companies
N.A.I.C.S.: 551112
Frank A. Bennack Jr. (Vice Chm)
James M. Asher (Chief Legal & Dev Officer & Sr VP)
Richard P. Malloch (Exec VP-Bus Media)
Steven R. Swartz (Pres & CEO)
Mitchell Scherzer (CFO & Exec VP)
Carlton J. Charles (Sr VP-Treasury & Risk Mgmt)
Eve Burton (Chief Legal Officer & Exec VP)
Elisa Benson (Dir-Digital Special Projects-Young Women's Network)
Peter Ricker (Dir-Accts-Natl)
John McKeon (Pres-Texas Newspapers)
Kate Kelly Smith (Dir-Publ-Design Grp)
Gregory Dorn (Sr VP)
Jordan Wertlieb (Sr VP)
Paul Taylor (Sr VP)
Ollie Lloyd (Head-Client Solutions-UK)
Jane Wolfson (Chief Comml Officer-UK)
Jeffrey M. Johnson (Sr VP)
William Randolph Hearst III (Chm)

Subsidiaries:

CAMP Systems International, Inc.   (1)
11 Continental Blvd Ste C, Merrimack, NH 03054
Tel.: (603) 595-0030
Web Site: http://www.campsystems.com
Aircraft Health Management & Enterprise Information Systems Solutions
N.A.I.C.S.: 488190
Marc Gould (VP-Ops)
Tom Benson (Chief Strategy Officer)
Kevin Ryan (VP-Market Dev)
Raju Mudunuri (Gen Mgr-CAMP India)
John Nelson (Sr VP-Maintenance Mgmt)
Tom Grace (Sr VP-Product Dev)
Ahmed Hafeez (CTO)
Scott Pokrywa (VP-Sls & Customer Success)
Dan Brooks (Product Mgr-Inventory Mgmt Sys)
Lynn Sosnowski (Sls Mgr-Fin Programs)
Sean Barry (Mgr-Large Aircraft Svcs)
Edward Murphy (Product Mgr-Flight Scheduling)
Dennis Foote (Sr Mgr-Reg Field Svc)
Simon Leonard (Gen Mgr-Montreal & EHM)
Christophe Coiffet (Mng Dir-Europe)
Robert Sotack (Sr VP-Aircraft Health Mgmt Svcs)
Sean Lanagan (Pres & CEO)

Subsidiary (Domestic):

AMSTAT Corp.   (2)
44 Apple St Ste 5, Tinton Falls, NJ 07724
Tel.: (732) 530-6400
Web Site: http://www.amstatcorp.com
Aviation Marketing Research Services
N.A.I.C.S.: 541910
Chris Skurat (Dir-Sls)
Judy Nerwinski (Dir-Res)
Jim Morford (Mgr-Customer Svc)
Peter Koeppel (Dir-Ops)
Andrew Young (Gen Mgr)

Subsidiary (Non-US):

Avinode Group AB   (2)
Gamlestads torg 7, SE-415 12, Gothenburg, Sweden
Tel.: (46) 317510000
Web Site: https://www.avinodegroup.com
Aviation Services
N.A.I.C.S.: 488119
Oliver King (CEO)
Charlotta Kajanus (CFO)
Alexandra MacRae (CMO)
Noel Trout (CTO)
Per Marthinsson (Co Founder)

CAMP Europe SAS   (2)
15 rue de la Montjoie, BP 58, Saint Denis, 93210, France
Tel.: (33) 1 55 93 45 80
Web Site: http://www.campsystems.com
Emp.: 20
Aircraft Maintenance Tracking Solutions
N.A.I.C.S.: 488190
Marc Digoix (Mng Dir)

Branch (Domestic):

CAMP Systems International, Inc. - Wichita   (2)
8201 E 34th St N Bldg 1100 Ste 1101, Wichita, KS 67226
Tel.: (316) 462-2267
Web Site: http://www.campsystems.com
Emp.: 100
Aircraft Maintenance Tracking Solutions
N.A.I.C.S.: 488190
Ken Grey (Pres)
Shawn Crandall (Gen Mgr)

Subsidiary (Domestic):

Continuum Applied Technology, Inc.   (2)
9601 Amberglen Blvd Ste 109, Austin, TX 78729
Tel.: (512) 918-8900
Web Site:
   http://www.continuumapptech.com
Aviation Software Solution
N.A.I.C.S.: 541511

Cosmopolitan TV Iberia S.L.   (1)
Avenida de Manoteras 46 2 Floor Bavenida, 28050, Madrid, Spain
Tel.: (34) 91 426 06 10
Web Site: http://www.cosmopolitantv.es
Emp.: 28
Television Broadcasting Services
N.A.I.C.S.: 516120
Almudena Ledo (Gen Mgr)

Fitch Group, Inc.   (1)
300 W 57th St 38th fl, New York, NY 10019
Tel.: (212) 908-0800
Web Site: https://www.fitch.group
Emp.: 4,000
Financial Information Services
N.A.I.C.S.: 522390
Paul Taylor (CEO)
Bruce Legorburu (Gen Counsel)

Division (Domestic):

Fitch Ratings, Inc.   (2)
33 Whitehall St, New York, NY 10004
Tel.: (212) 908-0500
Web Site: http://www.fitchratings.com
Sales Range: $75-99.9 Million
Emp.: 750
Credit Ratings, Opinions, Research & Financial Data Reporting Services
N.A.I.C.S.: 561450
Ian Linnell (Pres)
Peter Shaw (Head-Latin America)
Daniel Noonan (Mng Dir & Head-Corp Comm-Global)
Robert Harpel (CTO)
Brett Hemsley (Head-Global Analytical)
Mark Oline (Mng Dir-Bus & Rels Mgmt-Global)
Paul Taylor (Pres/CEO-Fitch Grp)
Theodore E. Niedermayer (CFO & Exec VP)
Jeff Horvath (Chief Compliance Officer)
Clemens Frech (Head-Germany)
Gautam Mitra (Head-Internal Audit)
Jill Zelter (Head-Global)
Andrew Jackson (Mng Dir & Head-HR-Global)
David Samuel (Chief Acctg Officer)
Jon Ewing (CMO)
Kevin Duignan (Head-Fin Institutions Grp-Global)
Marjan van der Weijden (Head-Structured Fin & Covered Bonds)
Nathan Flander (Head-Non Bank Fin Institutions-Global)
Mark Young (Head-Non Bank Fin Institutions-EMEA & Asia Pacific)
Rui Pereira (Head-Structured Fin-North America)
Susanne Matern (Head-Structured Fin-EMEA)
Eileen A. Fahey (Chief Risk Officer)
Jeremy Carter (Chief Credit Officer)
Karen Skinner (COO)
Peter Patrino (Chief Criteria Officer)
Andrew Collyer (CTO-Fitch Grp)
Heather Merrigan (Chief Compliance Officer)

Subsidiary (Non-US):

Business Monitor International Ltd.   (3)
2 Broadgate Circle, London, EC2M 2QS, United Kingdom
Tel.: (44) 2072480468
Web Site: http://www.businessmonitor.com
Sales Range: $50-74.9 Million
Emp.: 300
Business Data, Analysis, Ratings & Rankings Publisher
N.A.I.C.S.: 513140
Simmon Longfield (Dir-Fin)

Branch (Domestic):

Fitch Ratings, Inc. - Chicago   (3)
70 W Madison St Ste 1300, Chicago, IL 60602
Tel.: (312) 368-3100
Web Site: http://www.fitchratings.com
Sales Range: $50-74.9 Million
Emp.: 250
Credit Ratings, Opinions, Research & Financial Data Reporting Services
N.A.I.C.S.: 561450
Emily Wadhwani (Assoc Dir)
Bain K. Rumohr (Assoc Dir-Fin Institutions)
Doug Meyer (Mng Dir)
Tom Stone (Sr Dir)
Paul Taylor (CEO)

Fitch Ratings, Inc. - San Francisco   (3)
650 California St, San Francisco, CA 94108
Tel.: (415) 732-5770
Web Site: http://www.fitchratings.com
Emp.: 20
Credit Ratings, Opinions, Research & Financial Data Reporting Services
N.A.I.C.S.: 561450
Charles D. Brown (Gen Counsel & Sec)
Brett Hemsley (Head-Asia Pacific)
Andy Jackson (Head-HR)
Daniel Noonan (Head-Comm)
John Olert (Chief Risk Officer)
Mark Oline (Head-Bus & Relationship Mgmt)
Karen Ribble (Sr Dir-Acctg)

Subsidiary (Domestic):

Fitch Solutions, Inc.   (2)
300 W 57th St 38th fl, New York, NY 10019
Tel.: (212) 908-0800
Web Site: https://www.fitchsolutions.com
Financial Information Services
N.A.I.C.S.: 541690
Ted Niedermayer (Pres)

Francis Emory Fitch, Incorporated   (1)
229 W 28th St, New York, NY 10001
Tel.: (212) 619-3800
Web Site: http://www.fitchgroup.com
Sales Range: $1-9.9 Million
Emp.: 60
Commercial Printing Services
N.A.I.C.S.: 323111
William Contessa (Owner)
Paul Taylor (CEO)

Subsidiary (Domestic):

CreditSights, Inc.   (2)
2 Park Ave 24th Fl, New York, NY 10016
Tel.: (212) 340-3840
Web Site: http://www.creditsights.com
Marketing Research & Public Opinion Polling
N.A.I.C.S.: 541910
David Good (CFO)
Peter Petas (CEO)

Hearst Brand Development   (1)
320 W 57th St 5th Fl, New York, NY 10019
Tel.: (212) 492-1301
Web Site: http://www.hearstcorporation.com
Magazine Publisher
N.A.I.C.S.: 424920
Glen Ellen Brown (VP)

Hearst Business Media   (1)
50 Charles Lindbergh Blvd Ste 100, Uniondale, NY 11553
Tel.: (516) 227-1300
Web Site: http://www.hearst.com
Sales Range: $10-24.9 Million
Emp.: 55
Catalog of Electronic Products, Equipment & Services
N.A.I.C.S.: 513120
Richard P. Malloch (Pres)
Steven A. Hobbs (Chief Dev Officer & Exec VP)
James M. Asher (Chief Legal & Dev Officer & Sr VP)
Gregory Dorn (Exec VP)
Justin Graham (Chief Innovation Officer-Healthcare)
Denielle deWynter (VP-Fin)

Subsidiary (Domestic):

First DataBank, Inc.   (2)

COMPANIES THE HEARST CORPORATION

701 Gateway Blvd Ste 600, San Francisco, CA 94080 **(100%)**
Tel.: (650) 588-5454
Web Site: http://www.firstdatabank.com
Pharmaceutical, Medical & Nutritional Information Database Publisher
N.A.I.C.S.: 513140
David Manin *(Sr Dir-Mktg)*
Bob Katter *(Chief Revenue Officer & Exec VP)*
Tracy Lofland *(VP-Quality Mgmt)*
Patrick Lupinetti *(Sr VP & Dir-Editorial)*
Karl Matuszewski *(VP-Clinical & Editorial Knowledge Base Svcs)*
Charles Tuchinda *(Pres)*
Tom Bizzaro *(VP-Health Policy & Indus Rels)*
Dewey Howell *(VP-Clinical Applications)*
John Doulis *(Sr VP-Clinical Solutions)*

Branch (Domestic):

First DataBank **(3)**
500 E 96th St Ste 500, Indianapolis, IN 46240-4338
Tel.: (317) 571-7200
Web Site: http://www.fdbhealth.com
Sales Range: $25-49.9 Million
Pharmaceutical Medical & Nutritional Information Database Publisher
N.A.I.C.S.: 513140
Thomas R. Bizzaro *(VP-Health Policy & Indus Rels)*
Bob Katter *(Chief Comml Officer & Exec VP)*
Tracy Lofland *(VP-Quality Mgmt)*
Patrick Lupinetti *(Sr VP-Legal Affairs & Medical Device)*
David Manin *(Sr Dir-Mktg)*
Charles Tuchinda *(Pres & Exec VP-Hearst Health)*

Subsidiary (Non-US):

First DataBank Europe Ltd. **(3)**
Swallowtail House Grenadier Road, Exeter Business Park, Exeter, EX1 3LH, United Kingdom
Tel.: (44) 1392440100
Web Site: http://www.firstdatabank.co.uk
Sales Range: $25-49.9 Million
Emp.: 65
Pharmaceutical, Medical & Nutritional Information Database Publisher
N.A.I.C.S.: 513140
Darren Nichols *(Mng Dir)*

Subsidiary (Domestic):

Hearst Business Publishing, Inc. **(2)**
300 W 57th St, New York, NY 10019
Tel.: (212) 969-7500
Trade Magazine Publishing
N.A.I.C.S.: 513120

Group (Domestic):

Hearst Electronics Group **(2)**
50 Charles Lindbergh Blvd Ste 100, Uniondale, NY 11553
Tel.: (516) 227-1300
Web Site: http://www.hearstadvantage.com
Electronics Industry Product Information Publisher
N.A.I.C.S.: 513120

Unit (Domestic):

Electronic Products Magazine **(3)**
50 Charles Lindbergh Blvd Ste 100, Uniondale, NY 11553
Tel.: (516) 227-1300
Web Site: http://www2.electronicproducts.com
Sales Range: $10-24.9 Million
Monthly Magazine Providing Electronic Engineers with Information on New Products & Heir Application
N.A.I.C.S.: 541810

Stocknet **(3)**
720 Ave F, Plano, TX 75074
Tel.: (972) 943-1305
Sales Range: $10-24.9 Million
Emp.: 25
Electronic Components Services
N.A.I.C.S.: 334419

Subsidiary (Domestic):

Homecare Homebase, LLC **(2)**
6688 N Central Expy Ste 800, Dallas, TX 75206 **(85%)**
Tel.: (214) 239-6700
Web Site: http://www.hchb.com
Healthcare Software Developer & Publisher
N.A.I.C.S.: 513210
April K. Anthony *(Founder & Exec Chm)*
Sam High *(CTO)*
Scott D. Decker *(Pres)*
Luke Rutledge *(Sr VP-Ops)*
Neal Reizer *(Sr VP-Product Mgmt)*
Martha Stuart Williams *(Sr VP-Professional Svcs Optimization)*

MCG Health, LLC **(2)**
901 5th Ave Ste 2000, Seattle, WA 98164
Tel.: (206) 389-5300
Web Site: http://www.careguidelines.com
Software Development Services
N.A.I.C.S.: 541511
Jon Shreve *(Pres & CEO)*
Nick Beard *(Sr VP-Product Mgmt)*
Rajesh Godavarthi *(CIO)*
Peter Kern *(CFO)*
Lynn Nemiccolo *(Sr VP-Customer Satisfaction)*
Conor Bagnell *(VP-Product Mgmt)*
Jennifer Freeman *(VP-Fin)*
Jeff Hermosillo *(Sr VP-Sls & Mktg)*
William Rifkin *(Mng Editor)*
Chris Van Waters *(CIO)*

Subsidiary (Domestic):

Work-Loss Data Institute, LLC **(3)**
3006 Bee Caves Rd Ste A200, Austin, TX 78746
Tel.: (760) 753-9992
Web Site: http://www.mcg.com
Healthcare Data & Guidelines Services
N.A.I.C.S.: 621999
Kenneth Eichler *(VP)*

Subsidiary (Domestic):

MOTOR Information Systems **(2)**
1301 W Long Lake Rd Ste 300, Troy, MI 48098
Tel.: (248) 828-0000
Web Site: http://www.motor.com
Multimedia Automotive Data Publisher
N.A.I.C.S.: 513120
Marian Maasshoff *(Dir-Product Dev)*
Chris Edd *(Dir-Production & Sls)*
Jesse Brown *(Mgr-Natl Sls)*
Justin Dwyer *(Mgr-Natl Sls)*
Paul Moszak *(VP & Gen Mgr)*
Steven D. Birdsall *(COO & Exec VP)*
Jeff Nosek *(Pres)*

Subsidiary (Domestic):

FleetCross Holdings, Inc. **(3)**
1465 Jefferson Rd, Rochester, NY 14623
Tel.: (585) 256-0375
Web Site: http://www.fleetcross.com
Transportation & Equipment Industry Custom Database, Software & Network Solutions
N.A.I.C.S.: 541519

Unit (Domestic):

MOTOR Magazine **(3)**
1301 W Long Lake Rd Ste 300, Troy, MI 48098
Tel.: (248) 828-0000
Web Site: http://www.motor.com
Emp.: 100
Automotive Magazine Publisher
N.A.I.C.S.: 513120
John Lypen *(Publr & Editor)*
Karl Seyfert *(Exec Editor)*
Paul M. Eckstein *(Mng Editor)*

Technologue **(3)**
1301 W Long Lake Rd Ste 300, Troy, MI 48098
Tel.: (248) 828-0000
Automotive OEM Parts Research & Database Management Publishing & Services
N.A.I.C.S.: 518210
Nick Porrini *(Founder & Pres)*
Keith Wurzer *(Dir-Sls & Mktg)*
Nicholas Porrini Jr. *(Coord-Sls & Mktg)*

Subsidiary (Domestic):

National Auto Research **(2)**
2620 Barrett Rd, Gainesville, GA 30507
Tel.: (770) 532-4111
Web Site: http://www.blackbook.com
Periodicals
N.A.I.C.S.: 513120
Tom Cross *(Pres-Black Book & Exec VP)*
Rene Abdalah *(Sr VP-Bus Dev)*
Jared Kalfus *(Exec VP-Revenue)*

Subsidiary (Domestic):

Veretech Holdings, Inc. **(3)**
150 E Palmetto Park Rd Ste 600, Boca Raton, FL 33432
Tel.: (561) 544-1400
Web Site: http://www.blackbookactivator.com
Sales Range: $10-24.9 Million
Emp.: 50
Automobile Trade-in Value Online Information Services
N.A.I.C.S.: 551112
J. Michael McFall *(Pres)*
Art DeLaurier *(COO)*

Subsidiary (Domestic):

Zynx Health Incorporated **(2)**
10880 Wilshire Blvd Tower Ste 300, Los Angeles, CA 90024
Tel.: (310) 954-1950
Web Site: http://www.zynx.com
Healthcare Consulting Services & Developer of Related Technology Products
N.A.I.C.S.: 541511
Guillermo Ramas *(Exec VP)*
Bertina Yen *(Exec VP-Product)*
Kevin Daly *(Pres)*
Jim Connolly *(Sr VP-Product Dev)*
Victor Lee *(VP-Clinical Informatics)*
Siva Subramanian *(Sr VP-Mobile Products)*

Hearst Communications, inc. **(1)**
300 W 57th St, New York, NY 10019
Tel.: (212) 586-5404
Media Production & Information Services
N.A.I.C.S.: 513120

Subsidiary (Domestic):

SAN Antonio Magazine **(2)**
1042 Central Pkwy, San Antonio, TX 78232-5021
Tel.: (210) 201-3786
Web Site: http://www.sanantoniomag.com
Periodical Publishers
N.A.I.C.S.: 513120
Ceslie Armstrong *(Editor & Publr)*

Hearst Entertainment & Syndication **(1)**
300 W 57th St, New York, NY 10019-5238
Tel.: (212) 969-7553
Web Site: http://www.hearstcorp.com
Sales Range: $250-299.9 Million
Emp.: 2,000
Television Programming, Cable Networks, Newspaper Syndication & Merchandise Licensing Services
N.A.I.C.S.: 516210

Joint Venture (Domestic):

A&E Television Networks, LLC **(2)**
235 E 45th St, New York, NY 10017 **(50%)**
Tel.: (212) 210-1400
Web Site: http://www.aenetworks.com
Holding Company; Cable Television Networks Operator
N.A.I.C.S.: 551112
Michael Feeney *(Exec VP-Corp Comm)*
Peter Olsen *(Pres-Ad Sls)*
David Zagin *(Pres-Distr)*
Henry Hoberman *(Chief Legal Officer)*
Paul Buccieri *(Pres)*
David Granville-Smith *(CFO & COO)*
Robert Sharenow *(Pres-Programming)*
Karen Gray *(Exec VP-HR)*
Gena McCarthy *(Exec VP & Head-Programming-Lifetime, Unscripted & FYI)*
Elaine Frontain Bryant *(Exec VP & Head-Programming)*
Tanya Lopez *(Exec VP-Movies, Limited Series-Lifetime Movies)*
Eli Lehrer *(Exec VP & Gen Mgr-History)*
David Bank *(Exec VP-Corp Dev & Strategy)*
Amy Winter *(Exec VP & Head-Programming & Lifetime)*
Steve MacDonald *(Pres-Global Content Licensing & Intl)*
Juliana Stock *(Exec VP-Corp Brand Strategy)*

Unit (Domestic):

A&E Network **(3)**
235 E 45th St, New York, NY 10019
Tel.: (212) 210-1400
Web Site: http://www.aetv.com
Cable Television Network
N.A.I.C.S.: 516210
Elaine Frontain Bryant *(Exec VP & Head-Programming)*

Branch (Domestic):

A&E Television Networks, LLC - Detroit Office **(3)**
201 W Big Beaver Rd Ste 1010, Troy, MI 48084-4154
Tel.: (248) 740-1300
Web Site: http://www.aenetworks.com
Emp.: 8
Advertising Sales
N.A.I.C.S.: 541890

Subsidiary (Domestic):

Lifetime Entertainment Services, LLC **(3)**
235 E 45th St, New York, NY 10017
Tel.: (212) 210-1400
Web Site: http://www.mylifetime.com
Sales Range: $750-799.9 Million
Emp.: 300
Operator of Cable Television Network with Informational Programming About Lifestyles, Relationships, Personal Development & Health
N.A.I.C.S.: 516210

Unit (Domestic):

Lifetime Television **(4)**
2049 Century Park E Ste 840, Los Angeles, CA 90067-3110
Tel.: (310) 556-7500
Web Site: http://www.mylifetime.com
Sales Range: $10-24.9 Million
Emp.: 80
Motion Picture & Video Production
N.A.I.C.S.: 512110

Unit (Domestic):

The Biography Channel **(3)**
235 E 45th St Ste 1104, New York, NY 10017-3303
Tel.: (212) 649-4099
Web Site: http://www.biography.com
Biographical Programming Cable Network
N.A.I.C.S.: 516210

The History Channel **(3)**
235 E 45th St, New York, NY 10017
Tel.: (212) 210-1400
Web Site: http://www.history.com
History Programming Cable Network
N.A.I.C.S.: 516210

Subsidiary (Domestic):

Hearst Entertainment, Inc. **(2)**
300 W 57th St, New York, NY 10019
Tel.: (212) 969-7553
Web Site: http://www.hearstent.com
Sales Range: $50-74.9 Million
Emp.: 3
Motion Picture & Television Program Production & Distribution
N.A.I.C.S.: 512110
Stacey Valenza *(Sr VP-Sls & Mktg)*

King Features Syndicate, Inc. **(2)**
300 W 57th St 15th Fl, New York, NY 10019-5238
Tel.: (212) 969-7550
Web Site: http://www.kingfeatures.com
Sales Range: $25-49.9 Million
Emp.: 100
Comics, Columns, Editorial Cartoons, Puzzles & Games Distr to Newspapers
N.A.I.C.S.: 516210
Keith McCloat *(VP & Gen Mgr)*
Brendan Burford *(Editor-Comics)*
Claudia Smith *(Dir-PR)*
Cathleen Titus *(VP-Intl Sls-North America)*
Frank Caruso *(VP-Creative Svcs)*
Glenn Mott *(Mng Editor)*

THE HEARST CORPORATION

U.S. PRIVATE

The Hearst Corporation—(Continued)

Michael G. Chan *(Dir-Digital & Tech)*
Carin Bacchiocchi *(Coord-Domestic Sls-North America)*
Dennis Danko *(Mgr-Inside Sls-North America)*
John Killian *(VP-Sls-North America)*
Jim Nolan *(Mgr-Sunday Comics-North America)*
C. J. Kettler *(Pres)*
Rebecca Kaplan Haase *(VP-Sls & Distr)*

Reed Brennan Media Associates, Inc. (2)
628 Virginia Dr, Orlando, FL 32803
Tel.: (407) 894-7300
Web Site: http://www.rbma.com
Emp.: 45
Custom Newspaper Electronic Pagination & Editing Services
N.A.I.C.S.: 561499
Timothy Brennan *(Pres)*
Jeff Talbert *(VP)*
Wayne Kester *(Mgr-Production)*
Diana Smith *(Exec Editor)*
Tony DeCarlo *(Mgr-Distr)*

Hearst Interactive Media (1)
300 W 57th St, New York, NY 10019
Tel.: (212) 649-2000
Sales Range: $50-74.9 Million
Emp.: 600
N.A.I.C.S.: 513120

Hearst Magazines (1)
300 W 57th St, New York, NY 10019
Tel.: (212) 649-2000
Sales Range: $1-4.9 Billion
Emp.: 18,300
Magazine, Book & Internet Publisher
N.A.I.C.S.: 513120
Michael A. Clinton *(Dir-Mktg & Publ)*
Donna Kalajian Lagani *(Chief Revenue Officer, Sr VP & Dir-Publishing)*
Debi Chirichella *(Pres)*
Sarah Bailey *(Grp Dir-Editorial-Good Housekeeping, Red & Prima-UK)*
Liberta Abbondante *(Sr VP-Consumer Mktg)*
Anna Jones *(CEO)*
Thomas Ghareeb *(VP & Controller)*
Brooke Siegel *(Dir-Editorial Ops)*
Kate Lewis *(Chief Content Officer)*
Judith Secombe *(Grp Dir-Publ-Hearst Made)*
Michelle Spinale *(VP-Consumer Engagement)*
Giacomo Moletto *(CEO-Italy)*
Duncan Chater *(Chief Brand Officer-UK)*
Claire Sanderson *(Editor-Women's Health)*
James Wildman *(Pres-Europe/CEO-UK)*
Steve Ross *(VP)*
Susy Smith *(Grp Dir-Editorial-Country Living, House Beautiful)*
Sharon Douglas *(Chief Brand Officer-Lifestyle & Homes-UK)*
Robert Ffitch *(Chief Strategy Officer-UK)*
Jon Gluck *(Exec Dir-Editorial Talent, Dev & Special Projects)*
Keesha Jean-Baptiste *(Sr VP-HR)*
Mike Smith *(Chief Data Officer)*
Matt Sanchez *(Pres-Hearst Autos)*
Rajiv Pant *(Chief Tech & Product Officer & Gen Mgr-Tech Platforms)*

Subsidiary (Domestic):

CDS Global, Inc. (2)
1901 Bell Ave, Des Moines, IA 50315-1099 (100%)
Tel.: (515) 247-7500
Web Site: http://www.cds-global.com
Sales Range: $800-899.9 Million
Emp.: 3,000
Magazine & Media Subscription Data Management & Fulfillment Services
N.A.I.C.S.: 518210
Christine Simpson *(VP & Gen Mgr-Canada)*
Mike Luksan *(VP-Sls-Magazines & Media)*
Mark Judd *(Mng Dir-UK & Australia)*
Paul Polus *(CFO)*
Michelle McDonald *(VP-Client Svcs)*
Lisa Mentzer *(VP-Ops & Support Svcs)*
Barbara Nelson *(Chief Client Officer)*
John Noll *(Chief Workforce Officer)*
Matt Sanchez *(Pres)*

Unit (Domestic):

Car and Driver (2)
1585 Eisenhower Pl, Ann Arbor, MI 48108
Tel.: (734) 352-8000
Web Site: http://www.caranddriver.com
Magazine Publisher
N.A.I.C.S.: 513120

Cosmopolitan (2)
300 W 57th St 38 Fl, New York, NY 10019-3212
Tel.: (212) 649-3570
Web Site: http://www.cosmopolitan.com
Sales Range: $10-24.9 Million
Emp.: 100
Publisher of Women's Magazine
N.A.I.C.S.: 513111
Jessica Goodman *(Sr Editor)*
Meredith Bryan *(Sr Deputy Editor)*
Holly Meadows *(Editor-South Africa)*
Jessica Pels *(Editor)*
Nancy Berger *(Publr)*
Eddie Alterman *(Chief Brand Officer)*

Country Living (2)
300 W 57th St, New York, NY 10019-3212
Tel.: (212) 649-3500
Web Site: http://www.countryliving.com
Sales Range: $50-74.9 Million
Emp.: 400
Periodical with American Traditional Emphasis
N.A.I.C.S.: 323111
Rachel Hardage Barrett *(Editor-in-Chief)*
Charlyne Mattox *(Dir-Food & Crafts)*
Amy Lowe Mitchell *(Mng Editor)*
Eva Spring *(Dir-Design Art)*

ELLE (2)
300 W 57th St 24th Fl, New York, NY 10019
Tel.: (212) 903-5000
Web Site: http://www.elle.com
Magazine Publisher
N.A.I.C.S.: 513120
Leah Chernikoff *(Editor)*
Morgan Sheff *(Sr Dir-Mktg)*
Anne-Marie Curtis *(Editor-in-Chief-UK)*
Jacqui Cave *(Grp Dir-Publ-UK)*
Tom Meredith *(Dir-Creative-UK)*
Gilles Bensimon *(Founder)*
Nina Garcia *(Editor-in-Chief)*
Rose Minutaglio *(Sr Editor)*

ELLE DECOR (2)
300 W 57th St, New York, NY 10019
Tel.: (212) 649-2000
Web Site: http://www.elledecor.com
Magazine Publisher
N.A.I.C.S.: 513120
William Pittel *(Assoc Publr)*
Stellene Volandes *(Dir-Editorial-Brand)*
Asad Syrkett *(Editor-in-Chief)*

Esquire (2)
300 W 57th St, New York, NY 10019-5201
Tel.: (212) 649-4020
Web Site: http://www.esquire.com
Sales Range: $10-24.9 Million
Emp.: 70
Magazine Publishing Services
N.A.I.C.S.: 513120
Jay Fielden *(Editor-in-Chief)*
Michael Hainey *(Exec Dir-Editorial)*
Miles Dunbar *(Assoc Publr)*
Jacqui Cave *(Grp Dir-Publ)*
Bob Mankoff *(Editor-Cartoon & Humor)*

Food Network Magazine (2)
1700 Broadway 30th Fl, New York, NY 10019
Tel.: (212) 484-1445
Web Site: http://www.foodnetwork.com
Magazine Publisher
N.A.I.C.S.: 513120
Vicki Wellington *(Chief Revenue Officer, VP & Publr)*
Pam Thompson *(Exec Acct Dir-Chicago)*

Good Housekeeping (2)
300 W 57th St, New York, NY 10019
Tel.: (212) 649-2551
Web Site: http://www.goodhousekeeping.com
Sales Range: $10-24.9 Million
Emp.: 100
Publisher of Women's Magazine
N.A.I.C.S.: 513120
Patricia Haegele *(Publr & Sr VP)*
Sara Rad *(Dir-Brand Dev)*
Jane Francisco *(Editor-in-Chief)*
Rachel Rothman *(Dir-Technical)*

Kristen Saladino *(Dir-Fashion)*
Julia Edelstein *(Editor-Health)*
Kristine Brabson *(Dir-Site)*
Charlotte Hollands *(Assoc Publr)*

HGTV Magazine (2)
300 W 57th St, New York, NY 10019
Tel.: (212) 649-2989
Web Site: http://www.hgtv.com
Magazine Publisher
N.A.I.C.S.: 513120
Sara Peterson *(Editor-in-Chief)*
Carrie Cullen *(Assoc Publr-Adv)*
Kate English *(Assoc Publr-Mktg)*
Kathleen Donohue *(Acct Dir)*
Sara Burns *(Sr VP-Scheduling & Program Strategy)*
Julie Taylor *(Sr VP-US Scheduling & Program Strategy)*
Liz Brach *(Sr Dir-Programming)*
Betsy Ayala *(Sr VP-Programming & Dev)*

Harper's Bazaar (2)
300 W 57th St, New York, NY 10019
Tel.: (212) 903-5000
Web Site: http://www.harpersbazaar.com
Sales Range: $10-24.9 Million
Emp.: 50
Publishing Company
N.A.I.C.S.: 513120
Olivier Berton *(Dir-Digital Sls)*
Christine Najjar *(Mgr-Digital Sls)*
John Weisgerber *(Exec Dir-Digital Adv)*
Christopher Tennant *(Exec Editor)*
Amy Synnott *(Exec Editor-Magazine)*
Jessica Matlin *(Dir-Beauty-Luxury Editorial Beauty Div)*
Eugenie Kelly *(Acting Editor)*
Samira Nasr *(Editor-in-Chief)*

Division (Domestic):

Hearst Books (2)
300 W 57th St, New York, NY 10019-3741 (100%)
Tel.: (212) 649-4115
Web Site: http://www.hearst.com
Sales Range: $25-49.9 Million
Emp.: 40
Trade Books Publisher
N.A.I.C.S.: 513130
Jacqueline Deval *(Publr & VP)*

Hearst Integrated Media (2)
300 W 57th St 12th Fl, New York, NY 10019
Tel.: (212) 649-2000
Web Site: http://www.hearstintegratedmedia.com
Commercial Advertising Sales & Marketing Services
N.A.I.C.S.: 541890
Jeffrey W. Hamill *(Exec VP-Sls & Mktg)*
Amy Lane *(Assoc Dir-Integrated Mktg)*

Hearst Magazines Digital Media (2)
300 W 57th St, New York, NY 10019-3791
Tel.: (212) 649-4468
Web Site: http://www.hearst.com
Online Magazine Publisher
N.A.I.C.S.: 513120
Chris Wilkes *(VP-Digital)*
Tom Kirwan *(VP-Natl Sls & Key Accts)*
Kate Lewis *(Sr VP & Dir-Editorial)*
Michael Sebastian *(Sr Editor-News)*
Jason Kleinman *(VP-Brand Solutions)*
Adam Harris *(VP-Data Products)*
Roselle Schjong *(Sr Dir-Res & Insights)*
Michael Dugan *(CTO)*

Subsidiary (Domestic):

eCrush.com, Inc. (3)
2035 W Wabansia Fl 2, Chicago, IL 60647
Tel.: (773) 384-5131
Web Site: http://www.ecrush.com
Sales Range: $10-24.9 Million
Emp.: 8
Teen Social Networking Website Operator
N.A.I.C.S.: 516210

Division (Domestic):

Hearst Magazines International (2)
300 W 57th St, New York, NY 10019-3791
Tel.: (212) 649-2275
Web Site: http://www.hearstmagazinesinternational.com
International Edition Magazine Publisher

N.A.I.C.S.: 513120
Kim St. Clair Bodden *(VP & Exec Dir)*
Jeannette Chang *(Sr VP & Dir-Intl Publ)*
Simon Horne *(CFO, Sr VP & Gen Mgr)*
Gautam Ranji *(Sr VP-Licensing & Bus Dev)*
Bernardo Chevez *(VP-Tech)*
Gary Ellis *(Chief Digital Officer)*
Rudy Konyushkov *(CTO)*
Richard Bean *(Dir-Intl Licensing & Bus Dev)*

Subsidiary (Non-US):

The National Magazine Company Ltd. (3)
72 Broadwick St, London, W1F 9EP, United Kingdom (100%)
Tel.: (44) 2074395000
Web Site: http://www.hearst.co.uk
Sales Range: $100-124.9 Million
Emp.: 1,000
Magazine Publisher
N.A.I.C.S.: 513120
Sharon Douglas *(Dir-New Bus)*
Greg Withem *(Dir-Trading Partnership)*
Anna Jones *(CEO)*

Unit (Domestic):

House Beautiful (2)
300 W 57th St 24th Fl, New York, NY 10019
Tel.: (212) 903-5103
Web Site: http://www.housebeautiful.com
Sales Range: $10-24.9 Million
Emp.: 45
Magazine
N.A.I.C.S.: 513120
Sabine Rothman *(Dir-Market)*
Gretchen Smelter *(Dir-Design)*
Brenda Saget *(Assoc Publr)*
Joanna Saltz *(Dir-Editorial)*
Hadley Keller *(Sr Editor)*

O, The Oprah Magazine (2)
300 W 57th St, New York, NY 10019
Tel.: (212) 903-5366
Sales Range: $10-24.9 Million
Emp.: 60
Magazine For Women
N.A.I.C.S.: 513120
Oprah Winfrey *(Founder)*
Lucy Kaylin *(Editor-in-Chief)*
Megan Deem *(Exec Editor-Beauty)*
Jayne Jamison *(Chief Revenue Officer)*
Julia Fry *(Assoc Publr-Adv)*
Maureen Mooney *(Natl Dir-Sls & Bus Dev)*
Adam Bell *(Mng Editor & Dir-Editorial Partnerships)*

Popular Mechanics (2)
300 W 57th St, New York, NY 10019
Tel.: (212) 649-2000
Web Site: http://www.popularmechanics.com
Sales Range: $10-24.9 Million
Emp.: 75
Publisher of Automotive Magazine
N.A.I.C.S.: 323111
Roy Berendsohn *(Assoc Editor-Home)*
Allyson Torrisi *(Dir-Photography)*
David Cohen *(Dir-Res)*
Aimee E. Bartol *(Deputy Mng Editor)*
Zachary Gilyard *(Assoc Dir-Art)*
Michael Wilson *(Dir-Design)*
Alexander George *(Editor-in-Chief)*

Redbook (2)
224 W 57th St, New York, NY 10019-3212
Tel.: (212) 649-3450
Sales Range: $25-49.9 Million
Emp.: 250
Women's Magazine
N.A.I.C.S.: 323111
Meredith Rollins *(Editor-in-Chief)*
Marianne Civiletto *(Assoc Publr-Mktg)*
Sue Katzen *(Publr)*

Road & Track
1350 Eisenhower Pl, Ann Arbor, MI 48108
Tel.: (734) 352-8000
Web Site: http://www.roadandtrack.com
Magazine Publisher
N.A.I.C.S.: 513120
Travis Okulski *(Editor-in-Chief)*

Seventeen Magazine (2)
300 W 57th St 17Fl, New York, NY 10019 (100%)
Tel.: (212) 649-3100
Web Site: http://www.seventeen.com

COMPANIES — THE HEARST CORPORATION

Sales Range: $10-24.9 Million
Emp.: 115
Periodical Publishers
N.A.I.C.S.: 513120
Miranda Sheppard *(Deputy Dir-Art)*
Wendy Robison *(Dir-Design)*
Michelle Tan *(Editor-in-Chief)*
Laura Brounstein *(Dir-Special Projects)*
Steven Brown *(Dir-Bookings)*
Alix Campbell *(Exec Dir-Photography)*
Aya Kanai *(Exec Dir-Fashion)*
Fabienne Le Roux *(Dir-Photography)*
Nicole Mazur *(Dir-Creative)*
Dana Stern Schwartz *(Exec Dir-Entertainment)*
Leah Wyar *(Exec Dir-Beauty)*

Town & Country (2)
300 W 57th St, New York, NY 10019-3794
Tel.: (212) 903-5000
Web Site: http://www.townandcountrymag.com
Sales Range: $10-24.9 Million
Emp.: 50
Luxury Lifestyle Magazine Publisher
N.A.I.C.S.: 513120
Stellene Volandes *(Editor-in-Chief)*

Veranda (2)
300 W 57th St, New York, NY 10019
Tel.: (212) 649-3236
Web Site: http://www.veranda.com
Magazine Publisher
N.A.I.C.S.: 513120
Lisa Newsom *(Co-Founder)*
Sabine Rothman *(Dir-Market)*
Carolyn Englefield *(Editor-Interiors)*
Vicki Lowry *(Dir-Features)*
Lillian Dondero *(Mgr-Digital Production)*
Jee E. Lee *(Assoc Dir-Art)*
Suzanne Noli *(Dir-Design)*
Newell Turner *(Co-Founder)*
David Hamilton *(Assoc Publr)*
Steele Marcoux *(Editor-in-Chief)*

Womans Day (2)
300 W 57th St, New York, NY 10019
Tel.: (212) 649-2000
Web Site: http://www.womansday.com
Sales Range: $25-49.9 Million
Emp.: 40
Magazine Publisher
N.A.I.C.S.: 513120
Patricia Haegele *(Dir-Publ)*
Sara Williams *(Dir-Creative)*
Sue Katzen *(Mng Editor)*
Isabel Abdai *(Dir-Art)*
Stephanie Kim *(Dir-Photo)*
Stephanie Dolgoff *(Dir-Features)*
Kate Merker *(Dir-Food & Nutrition)*
David Carey *(Pres)*
Michael Clinton *(Pres-Mktg & Dir-Publ)*
Peter Hemmel *(Dir-Design)*
Ellen Levine *(Dir-Editorial)*
John P. Loughlin *(Exec VP & Gen Mgr)*
Melanie Ryan *(Asst Dir-Art)*
Steven R. Swartz *(Pres & CEO)*
Frank A. Bennack Jr. *(Vice Chm)*
William R. Hearst III *(Chm)*

Hearst News Service (1)
700 12th St NW Ste 1000, Washington, DC 20005
Tel.: (202) 263-6400
Emp.: 5
Newspaper Publishers
N.A.I.C.S.: 513110
Stephan Swartz *(CEO)*

Hearst Newspapers (1)
300 W 57 St, New York, NY 10019
Tel.: (212) 649-2000
Sales Range: $125-149.9 Million
Emp.: 1,500
Newspaper Publishing
N.A.I.C.S.: 513110
Mark E. Aldam *(Pres)*
Mike DeLuca *(Exec VP-Adv Sls)*
Renee Peterson *(VP-HR)*
Rob Angel *(Sr VP-Bus Dev)*
Robertson Barrett *(Pres-Digital Media)*
Michael Sacks *(Sr VP-Ops)*
David Ho *(VP & Exec Editor-Digital Audience & News Innovation)*
Barnabas Kui *(Sr VP-Fin)*
Bridget Williams *(Sr VP-Strategy & Ops-Digital Media)*
John McKeon *(Exec VP)*

Unit (Domestic):

Albany Times Union (2)
645 Albany Shaker Rd, Albany, NY 12211
Tel.: (518) 454-5694
Web Site: http://www.timesunion.com
Sales Range: $50-74.9 Million
Emp.: 450
Newspaper Publishers
N.A.I.C.S.: 513120
Rex Smith *(VP & Editor)*
Kathleen Hallion *(VP-Adv)*
Brad Calhoun *(Dir-Technical Svcs)*
Dan Couto *(VP-Ops & Integrated Svcs)*
Patti Hart *(Dir-Cross-Media Bus Dev)*
Ruth Fantasia *(Dir-HR)*
Todd Peterson *(VP-Circulation)*

Subsidiary (Domestic):

Associated Publishing Company (2)
303 S Pioneer Dr, Abilene, TX 79605 (100%)
Tel.: (325) 676-4032
Web Site: http://www.area-wide.com
Sales Range: $25-49.9 Million
Emp.: 45
Telephone Directories Publisher
N.A.I.C.S.: 513140

Unit (Domestic):

Beaumont Enterprise (2)
380 Main St, Beaumont, TX 77701-2331
Tel.: (409) 833-3311
Web Site: http://www.beaumontenterprise.com
Sales Range: $25-49.9 Million
Emp.: 260
Newspaper Publishers
N.A.I.C.S.: 513110
Danielle Matthews *(Mgr-Circulation)*
Vyki Derrick *(Mgr-Integrated Mktg)*
Craig Hatcher *(Chief Revenue Officer)*
Edna McZeal *(Acct Exec-Natl)*
Ronnie Crocker *(Editor)*

Joint Venture (Non-US):

Conde Nast & National Magazine Distributors Limited (2)
Tavistock Road, West Drayton, UB7 7QE, Middlesex, United Kingdom
Tel.: (44) 1895 433600
Web Site: http://www.comag.co.uk
Sales Range: $10-24.9 Million
Emp.: 170
Magazine Publisher
N.A.I.C.S.: 424920
Charlotee Macleod *(Mng Dir)*

Subsidiary (Domestic):

COMAG Forward (3)
Forward House Toledo Close Coventry Business Park, Coventry, CV5 6UN, United Kingdom
Tel.: (44) 2476 854 750
Web Site: http://www.comagforward.co.uk
Magazine Publisher
N.A.I.C.S.: 424920
Rob Everett *(Head-Client Svcs)*
Dominic Byrne *(Mng Dir)*
Shaun Callaghan *(Dir-Ops)*

COMAG Specialist (3)
Tavistock Works Tavistock Road, West Drayton, UB7 7QX, Middlesex, United Kingdom
Tel.: (44) 1895 433800
Web Site: http://www.comagspecialist.co.uk
Magazine Publisher
N.A.I.C.S.: 424920
Pete Lewis *(Gen Mgr)*
Neil Selby *(Acct Mgr)*
Jenna Spearing *(Acct Mgr)*
Santosh Jairajh *(Acct Mgr)*
Pippa Boothroyd *(Acct Mgr)*
Mark Foker *(Acct Mgr)*

Gold Key Media (3)
3rd Floor Josaron House 5-7 John Princes Street Oxford Circus, Mayfair, London, W1G 0JN, United Kingdom
Tel.: (44) 20 7491 4065
Web Site: http://www.gkml.co.uk
Magazine Publishing Services
N.A.I.C.S.: 513120
Chris Horn *(Mng Dir)*
Duncan MacGillivray *(Deputy Mng Dir)*
Oliver Morgan *(Dir-Bus Dev)*
Ruth Atkinson *(Publr & Acct Mgr)*
Duncan McIntosh *(Head-Publr Svcs)*
Sally Ingram *(Dir-Sls-Venue)*
Natalie Gibson *(Mgr-Bus Dev)*
Clare Scott *(Head-New Bus)*
Katie Stevens *(Publr & Acct Mgr)*
Alex Nicholls *(Publr & Acct Mgr)*
Charlotte Turton *(Publr & Acct Mgr)*

Unit (Domestic):

Connecticut Post (2)
410 State St, Bridgeport, CT 06604
Tel.: (203) 333-0161
Web Site: http://www.connpost.com
Sales Range: $50-74.9 Million
Emp.: 350
Newspaper Publishers
N.A.I.C.S.: 513110
Ron Darr *(Dir-Ops)*
Kelly Edwards *(VP-Fin)*
Karen Geffert *(Dir-HR)*
Eugene Jackson *(Dir-Adv)*
Doreen Madden *(Mgr-Community Rels)*
Bill Mason *(Dir-Circulation Ops)*
Rich Medeiros *(Sr VP-Sls & Mktg)*
Chuck Northrup *(Mgr-IT Ops)*
Patty Passarelli *(Mgr-New Bus Dev)*
Dennis Tidrick *(Mgr-IT Ops)*
Alaine Griffin *(Mng Editor)*

Edwardsville Publishing Company, LLC (2)
117 N 2nd St, Edwardsville, IL 62025-1938 (100%)
Tel.: (618) 656-4700
Web Site: http://www.goedwardsville.com
Sales Range: $10-24.9 Million
Emp.: 55
Newspaper Publishing
N.A.I.C.S.: 513110
Bill Tucker *(Mng Editor)*

Greenwich Time (2)
1455 E Putnam Ave, Old Greenwich, CT 06830-6529
Tel.: (203) 625-4400
Web Site: http://www.greenwichtime.com
Sales Range: $10-24.9 Million
Emp.: 20
Newspaper Publishers
N.A.I.C.S.: 513110
David McCumber *(Editor)*
Paul Barbetta *(Pres & Publr-Grp)*
Ron Darr *(Dir-Ops)*
Mike Demis *(Dir-Real Estate Sls)*
Kelly Edwards *(VP-Fin)*
Tony Fasanella *(VP-Digital Media Svcs)*
Karen Geffert *(Dir-HR)*
Bill Mason *(Dir-Subscription Svcs)*
Rich Medeiros *(Sr VP-Sls & Mktg)*
Carrie Sandor *(Dir-Adv)*
Kerry Turner *(Dir-Audience Dev)*

Houston Chronicle (2)
801 Texas Ave, Houston, TX 77210
Tel.: (713) 362-7211
Web Site: http://www.chron.com
Sales Range: $125-149.9 Million
Emp.:
Newspaper Publishing Services
N.A.I.C.S.: 513110
Jeff Cohen *(Exec Editor-Opinions & Editorials)*
Nancy C. Barnes *(Exec VP-News & Editor)*
Nancy Meyer *(Publr)*
Jordan Ray-Hart *(Editor-Project & Innovation)*

Subsidiary (Domestic):

Houston Community Newspapers (2)
100 Ave A, Conroe, TX 77301
Tel.: (936) 521-3300
Web Site: http://www.chron.com
Newspaper Publishing
N.A.I.C.S.: 513110
Jason Joseph *(Gen Mgr)*

Unit (Domestic):

Huron Daily Tribune (2)
211 N Heisterman St, Bad Axe, MI 48413-1239 (100%)
Tel.: (989) 269-6461
Web Site: http://www.michigansthumb.com
Sales Range: $10-24.9 Million
Emp.: 20
Publishing
N.A.I.C.S.: 513110
Gary Wamsley *(Dir-Circulation)*

Jasper News-Boy (2)
702 S Wheeler, Jasper, TX 75951-1419
Tel.: (409) 384-3441
Sales Range: $10-24.9 Million
Emp.: 12
Printing of Periodicals
N.A.I.C.S.: 513110

Laredo Morning Times (2)
111 Esperanza Dr, Laredo, TX 78041-2607
Tel.: (956) 728-2500
Web Site: http://www.lmtonline.com
Sales Range: $10-24.9 Million
Emp.: 120
Newspaper Publishers
N.A.I.C.S.: 513110

Subsidiary (Domestic):

LocalEdge (2)
1945 Sheridan Dr, Buffalo, NY 14223-1203
Tel.: (716) 875-9100
Web Site: http://www.localedge.com
Advertising & Digital Products Mfr
N.A.I.C.S.: 541870
Mike DeLuca *(CEO)*

Division (Domestic):

LocalEdge Media, Inc. (3)
1945 Sheridan Dr, Buffalo, NY 14223-1203 (100%)
Tel.: (716) 875-9100
Web Site: http://www.localedge.com
Commercial Internet Search Engine Marketing & Website Development Services
N.A.I.C.S.: 541613
Kevin Payne *(VP)*
Erick Backus *(Mgr-Distr)*
Stephen Felman *(Mgr-Digital Mktg)*
Dan Conway *(Mgr-Digital Mktg)*
Lauren Dunn *(Mgr-Social & Content)*
Rick Mariano Jr. *(Dir-Internet Mktg Svcs)*

Subsidiary (Domestic):

Metrix4Media, LLC (2)
1701 Legacy Dr Ste 2000, Frisco, TX 75034
Tel.: (469) 287-7326
Web Site: http://www.metrix4media.com
Online Advertising Services
N.A.I.C.S.: 541810
James Walsh *(VP-Media Mgmt)*

Unit (Domestic):

Midland Daily News (2)
124 S McDonald St, Midland, MI 48640-5161
Tel.: (989) 835-7171
Web Site: http://www.ourmidland.com
Sales Range: $10-24.9 Million
Emp.: 100
Publishing
N.A.I.C.S.: 513110
Kevin Remer *(Mgr-IT)*
Tony Lascari *(Editor-News)*
AnnMarie Schneider *(Controller)*
Cathy Bott *(Dir-Retail Adv)*
Carol VanSluyters *(Mgr-Acctg & Distr)*
Gary Wamsley *(Dir-Circulation)*
John Eddy *(Mgr-Ad Production)*
Marc Morris *(Dir-Digital Sls)*
Rita Watkins *(Mgr-Acct)*
Rebecca Watson *(Gen Mgr)*

Midland Reporter-Telegram (2)
201 E Illinois Ave, Midland, TX 79701-4852
Tel.: (432) 682-5311
Web Site: http://www.mywesttexas.com
Sales Range: $25-49.9 Million
Emp.: 150
Newspaper Publishers
N.A.I.C.S.: 513110
Stewart Doreen *(Editor)*
Mary Dearen *(Mng Editor)*
Jeffrey P. Shabram *(Publr)*

Plainview Daily Herald (2)
820 Broadway St, Plainview, TX 79072
Tel.: (806) 296-1300
Web Site: http://www.myplainview.com
Sales Range: $10-24.9 Million
Emp.: 8
Newspaper Publishing
N.A.I.C.S.: 513110
Carmen Ortega *(Mgr-Retail Adv)*

San Antonio Express News (2)

THE HEARST CORPORATION

U.S. PRIVATE

The Hearst Corporation—(Continued)
Ave E & 3rd St, San Antonio, TX 78205
Tel.: (210) 250-3000
Web Site: http://www.mysanantonio.com
Sales Range: $125-149.9 Million
Emp.: 1,500
Newspaper Publishing
N.A.I.C.S.: 513110
Joseph A. Braunschweig (VP-Circulation)
Jamie Stockwell (Mng Editor)

San Francisco Chronicle (2)
901 Mission St, San Francisco, CA 94103-2905
Tel.: (415) 777-1111
Web Site: http://www.sfgate.com
Newspaper Publishers
N.A.I.C.S.: 513110
Stephane Saux (Dir-Software Dev)
Bill Disbrow (Dir-Content)
Ginger Neal (Sr VP-Sls)
Demian Bulwa (Mng Editor)

Seattle Post-Intelligencer (2)
101 Elliott Ave W, Seattle, WA 98119-4236
Tel.: (206) 448-8000
Web Site: http://www.seattlepi.com
Sales Range: $10-24.9 Million
Emp.: 20
Newspaper Publishing
N.A.I.C.S.: 513110
David McCumber (Mng Editor)
Karl Johnson (VP-Sls)

Subsidiary (Domestic):

Seattlepi.com (2)
101 Elliott Ave W, Seattle, WA 98119-4220
Tel.: (206) 448-8000
Web Site: http://www.seattlepi.com
Newspaper Publishers
N.A.I.C.S.: 513110
Karl Johnson (Gen Mgr)

Unit (Domestic):

The Advocate (2)
9A Riverbend Dr S, Stamford, CT 06907
Tel.: (203) 964-2200
Web Site: http://www.stamfordadvocate.com
Sales Range: $25-49.9 Million
Emp.: 150
Newspaper Publishing
N.A.I.C.S.: 513110
Craig L. Allen (VP-Ops & Dir-Circulation)
Carrie Sandor (Dir-Adv)
Karen Geffert (Dir-HR)
Ron Darr (Dir-Ops)
Tony Fasanella (VP-Digital Media Svcs)
Paul Barbetta (Pres & Publr-Grp)
Stephanie Borise (Mng Editor)
Kelly Edwards (VP-Fin)
Doreen Madden (Mgr-Community Rels)
Rich Medeiros (Sr VP-Sls & Mktg)

The News-Times (2)
333 Main St, Danbury, CT 06810-5818
Tel.: (203) 744-5100
Web Site: http://www.newstimes.com
Sales Range: $10-24.9 Million
Emp.: 70
Newspaper Publishers
N.A.I.C.S.: 513110
Linda Tuccio-Koonz (Editor-Features)
Jacqueline Smith (Editor)
Tony Fasanella (VP-Digital Media Svcs)

Hearst Ranch (1)
5 3rd St Ste 200, San Francisco, CA 94103
Tel.: (866) 547-2624
Web Site: http://www.hearstranch.com
Beef Cattle Ranching & Farming Services
N.A.I.C.S.: 112111

Hearst Television, Inc. (1)
300 W 57th St, New York, NY 10019
Tel.: (212) 887-6800 (96%)
Web Site: http://www.hearsttelevision.com
Sales Range: $700-749.9 Million
Emp.: 300
Holding Company; Television Broadcasting Stations Owner & Operator
N.A.I.C.S.: 551112
Jonathan C. Mintzer (Gen Counsel, Sec & VP)
Philip M. Stolz (Sr VP)
Alvin Lustgarten (VP-Admin & IT)
Candy Altman (VP-News)
Emerson Coleman (Sr VP-Programming)
Roger Keating (Chief Strategy & Bus Dev Officer)
David J. Barrett (Chm & CEO)
Michael J. Hayes (Pres)
Michael Rosellini (VP-Digital Ops)
Jonathan D. Sumber (VP-Digital Sls)
Barbara Maushard (Sr VP-News)
Andrew Vrees (VP-News-Boston)
Andrew Fitzgerald (Chief Digital Content Officer)
Gerry McGavick (VP-Sls)
Kevin Johnson (Dir-Veteran Recruiting)
Bryan Curb (Exec VP & Gen Mgr-Educational Info Programming)
Angelica Rosas McDaniel (Exec VP & Gen Mgr-Entertainment)
Chris Matthews (CFO)
Kenneth Murphy (VP-IT)
Stefan Hadl (Sr VP-Brdcst Engrg & Tech)

Subsidiary (Domestic):

Arkansas Hearst Argyle Television, Inc. (2)
2415 N Albert Pike Ave, Fort Smith, AR 72904
Tel.: (479) 783-4040
Web Site: http://www.4029tv.com
Sales Range: $25-49.9 Million
Emp.: 130
Television Broadcasting Station
N.A.I.C.S.: 516120
Sarah Landau (Mgr-Digital Sls)
Chad Happersett (Gen Mgr-Sls)
Shawn Oswald (Pres & Gen Mgr)

Unit (Domestic):

Floor Covering Weekly (2)
300 W 57th St 15th Fl, New York, NY 10019
Tel.: (212) 649-7981
Web Site: http://www.floorcoveringweekly.com
Sales Range: $10-24.9 Million
Emp.: 15
Business Newspaper for Floor Covering Industry Services
N.A.I.C.S.: 513110
Tim Koorbusch (Chief Revenue & Bus Dev Officer)

Subsidiary (Domestic):

KCCI-TV (2)
888 9th St, Des Moines, IA 50309 (100%)
Tel.: (515) 247-8888
Web Site: http://www.kcci.com
Sales Range: $25-49.9 Million
Emp.: 110
Television Broadcasting Station
N.A.I.C.S.: 516120
Amanda Brink Hull (Gen Mgr-Sls)
Patti Snyder (Mgr-Bus)
Jerry Hoehle (Mgr-Sls-Digital)
Steve Parrot (Mgr-Bus)
Scott Reister (Dir-Sports)

Unit (Domestic):

KCRA-TV (2)
3 Television Cir, Sacramento, CA 95814-0794
Tel.: (916) 446-3333
Web Site: http://www.kcra.com
Sales Range: $25-49.9 Million
Emp.: 150
Television Broadcasting Station
N.A.I.C.S.: 516120
Elliott Troshinsky (Pres & Gen Mgr)
Steve Lombard (Dir-Creative)
Larry Eastteam (Chief Engr)
Del Rodgers (Dir-Sports)
Derek Schnell (Dir-News)

Subsidiary (Domestic):

KETV Hearst-Argyle Television, Inc. (2)
2665 Douglas St, Omaha, NE 68108 (100%)
Tel.: (402) 345-7777
Web Site: http://www.ketv.com
Sales Range: $25-49.9 Million
Emp.: 115
Television Broadcasting Station
N.A.I.C.S.: 516120

Sarah Smith (Pres & Gen Mgr)
Ariel Roblin (Pres & Gen Mgr)
Eric Hanneman (Gen Mgr-Sls)

Unit (Domestic):

KITV-TV (2)
801 S King St, Honolulu, HI 96813
Tel.: (808) 536-9979
Web Site: http://www.kitv.com
Sales Range: $25-49.9 Million
Emp.: 200
Television Broadcasting Station
N.A.I.C.S.: 516120
Russell Elwell (Gen Mgr-Sls)
Cathy Im (Mgr-Digital Sls)

Subsidiary (Domestic):

KMBC Hearst-Argyle Television, Inc. (2)
6455 Winchester Ave, Kansas City, MO 64133
Tel.: (816) 221-9999
Web Site: http://www.kmbc.com
Sales Range: $25-49.9 Million
Emp.: 150
Television Broadcasting Station
N.A.I.C.S.: 516120

KOAT Hearst-Argyle Television, Inc. (2)
3801 Carlisle Blvd NE, Albuquerque, NM 87107-4501 (100%)
Tel.: (505) 884-7777
Web Site: http://www.koat.com
Sales Range: $25-49.9 Million
Emp.: 130
Television Broadcasting Station
N.A.I.C.S.: 516120
Lori Waldon (Pres & Gen Mgr)

KOCO-TV (2)
1300 E Britton Rd, Oklahoma City, OK 73131-2007
Tel.: (405) 478-3000
Web Site: http://www.koco.com
Sales Range: $10-24.9 Million
Emp.: 100
Television Broadcasting Station
N.A.I.C.S.: 516120
Brent Hensley (Pres & Gen Mgr)
Shayne Vigil (Gen Mgr-Sls)
Rebecca Gaylord (Dir-News)

Unit (Domestic):

KSBW-TV (2)
238 John St, Salinas, CA 93901-3339 (100%)
Tel.: (831) 758-8888
Web Site: http://www.ksbw.com
Sales Range: $10-24.9 Million
Emp.: 100
Television Broadcasting Station
N.A.I.C.S.: 516120
Wendy Hillan (Gen Sls Mgr)
Robert Dickenson (Mgr-Natl Sls)

Subsidiary (Non-US):

Map of Medicine Ltd. (2)
Fox Court 14 Gray's Inn Road, London, WC1X 8HN, United Kingdom
Tel.: (44) 3301000037
Web Site: http://www.mapofmedicine.com
Online Clinical Information Services
N.A.I.C.S.: 513199

Subsidiary (Domestic):

New Orleans Hearst-Argyle Television, Inc. (2)
846 Howard Ave, New Orleans, LA 70113-1134
Tel.: (504) 679-0600
Web Site: http://www.wdsu.com
Sales Range: $25-49.9 Million
Emp.: 135
Television Broadcasting Station
N.A.I.C.S.: 516120
Frank Ratermann (Gen Mgr-Sls)
Luke Commare (Dir-Sls)

Ohio/Oklahoma Hearst-Argyle Television, Inc. (2)
300 W 57th St, New York, NY 10019 (100%)
Tel.: (212) 887-6800

Sales Range: $25-49.9 Million
Emp.: 20
Holding Company; Television Broadcasting Stations
N.A.I.C.S.: 551112
David J. Barrett (Pres & CEO)
Richard Dyer (Pres/Gen Mgr-WLWT-Ohio)
Brent Hensley (Pres/Gen Mgr-KOCO-Oklahoma)

Orlando Hearst Television Inc. (2)
1021 N Wymore Rd, Winter Park, FL 32789-1717
Tel.: (407) 645-2222
Web Site: http://www.wesh.com
Sales Range: $50-74.9 Million
Emp.: 200
Television Broadcasting Station
N.A.I.C.S.: 516120
Jim Carter (Pres & Gen Mgr)
Lenora Boutte (Dir-Programming & Pub Affairs)
Juston Jones (Mgr-Natl Sls)

WAPT Hearst-Argyle Television, Inc. (2)
7616 Channel 16 Way, Jackson, MS 39209-9634 (100%)
Tel.: (601) 922-1607
Web Site: http://www.wapt.com
Sales Range: $25-49.9 Million
Emp.: 85
Television Broadcasting Station
N.A.I.C.S.: 516120
Joe Cook (Dir-Sports)

WBAL Hearst-Argyle Television, Inc. (2)
3800 Hooper Ave, Baltimore, MD 21211-1313
Tel.: (410) 467-3000
Web Site: http://www.wbaltv.com
Sales Range: $25-49.9 Million
Emp.: 150
Television Broadcasting Station
N.A.I.C.S.: 516120
Jeff Halapin (Dir-Engrg)
Wanda Draper (Dir-Programming & Pub Affairs)
Barbara Anderson (Gen Mgr-Sls)

Unit (Domestic):

Hearst Baltimore Radio Management (3)
3800 Hooper Ave, Baltimore, MD 21211-1313
Tel.: (410) 467-3000
Web Site: http://www.wbal.com
Emp.: 82
Radio Broadcasting Station Management Services
N.A.I.C.S.: 541611
Cary Pahigian (Pres & Gen Mgr)

Unit (Domestic):

WBAL-AM (4)
3800 Hooper Ave, Baltimore, MD 21211-1313
Tel.: (410) 467-3000
Web Site: http://www.wbal.com
Sales Range: $50-74.9 Million
Emp.: 150
Radio Broadcasting Stations
N.A.I.C.S.: 516110
Cary L. Pahigian (Gen Mgr)
Clinton Box (Gen Mgr-Sls)
Scott Mastellar (Dir-Program)
Lori Smyth (Dir-Promotions)

WIYY-FM (4)
3800 Hooper Ave, Baltimore, MD 21211-1313
Tel.: (410) 889-0098
Web Site: http://www.98online.com
Sales Range: $50-74.9 Million
Emp.: 200
Radio Broadcasting Stations
N.A.I.C.S.: 516110
Cary L. Pahigian (Pres & Gen Mgr-WBAL Radio & 98 Rock)

Subsidiary (Domestic):

WCVB Hearst-Argyle Television, Inc. (2)
5 Television Pl, Needham, MA 02494
Tel.: (781) 449-0400
Web Site: http://www.wcvbnews.com

COMPANIES

THE HEART GROUP OF LANCASTER GENERAL HEALTH

Sales Range: $25-49.9 Million
Emp.: 200
Television Broadcasting Station
N.A.I.C.S.: 516120
Andy Hoffman *(Mgr-Sls)*
Leona McCarthy *(Dir-Fin)*

WGAL Hearst-Argyle Television, Inc. (2)
1300 Columbia Ave, Lancaster, PA 17603-4765
Tel.: (717) 393-5851
Web Site: http://www.wgal.com
Sales Range: $25-49.9 Million
Emp.: 137
Television Broadcasting Station
N.A.I.C.S.: 516120
Kyle Grimes *(Pres & Gen Mgr)*

WISN Hearst-Argyle Television, Inc. (2)
759 N 19th St, Milwaukee, WI 53233-2126
Tel.: (414) 342-8812
Web Site: http://www.wisn.com
Emp.: 150
Television Broadcasting Station
N.A.I.C.S.: 516120
Dan Needles *(Dir-Sports)*
Jan Wade *(Pres & Gen Mgr)*
Joe Viglietta *(Mgr-Local Sls)*

Unit (Domestic):

WJCL-TV (2)
1375 Chatham Pkwy 3rd Fl, Savannah, GA 31405
Tel.: (912) 925-0022
Web Site: http://www.wjcl.com
Emp.: 100
Television Broadcasting Station
N.A.I.C.S.: 516120
Jason Usry *(Dir-Mktg)*
Timothy J. Morrissey *(Pres & Gen Mgr)*
Sinan Sadar *(Dir-News)*
Cher Stewart *(Bus Mgr)*

Subsidiary (Domestic):

WLKY Hearst-Argyle Television, Inc. (2)
1918 Mellwood Ave, Louisville, KY 40206-1035 (100%)
Tel.: (502) 893-3671
Web Site: http://www.wlky.com
Sales Range: $25-49.9 Million
Emp.: 100
Television Broadcasting Station
N.A.I.C.S.: 516120
Greg Baird *(Gen Mgr-Sls)*
Glenn Haygood *(Pres & Gen Mgr)*
Andrea Stahlman *(Dir-News)*

Unit (Domestic):

WLWT-TV (2)
1700 Young St, Cincinnati, OH 45202
Tel.: (513) 412-5000
Web Site: http://www.wlwt.com
Sales Range: $25-49.9 Million
Emp.: 140
Television Broadcasting Station
N.A.I.C.S.: 516120
Mark DiAngelo *(Gen Mgr-Sls)*
Brent Dierson *(Mgr-Digital Projects)*

WMTW-TV (2)
99 Danville Corner Rd, Auburn, ME 04210-8607
Tel.: (207) 782-1800
Web Site: http://www.wmtw.com
Sales Range: $10-24.9 Million
Emp.: 100
Television Broadcasting Station
N.A.I.C.S.: 516120
Dave Abel *(Pres & Gen Mgr)*
Amy Beveridge *(Dir-News)*

WMUR-TV (2)
100 S Commercial St, Manchester, NH 03101
Tel.: (603) 669-9999
Web Site: http://www.wmur.com
Sales Range: $25-49.9 Million
Emp.: 110
Television Broadcasting Station
N.A.I.C.S.: 516120
Michael Taffaro *(Gen Mgr-Sls)*

WPTZ-TV (2)
5 Television Dr, Plattsburgh, NY 12901
Tel.: (518) 561-5555
Web Site: http://www.wptz.com
Television Broadcasting Station
N.A.I.C.S.: 516120
Justin Antoniotti *(Pres & Gen Mgr)*

Division (Domestic):

WNNE-TV (3)
203 Dewitt Dr, White River Junction, VT 05001
Tel.: (802) 295-3100
Web Site: http://www.wptz.com
Sales Range: $25-49.9 Million
Emp.: 100
Television Broadcasting Station
N.A.I.C.S.: 516120
Justin Antoniotti *(Pres & Gen Mgr)*

Subsidiary (Domestic):

WTAE Hearst-Argyle Television, Inc. (2)
400 Ardmore Blvd, Pittsburgh, PA 15221-3019 (100%)
Tel.: (412) 242-4300
Web Site: http://www.thepittsburghchannel.com
Sales Range: $25-49.9 Million
Emp.: 200
Television Broadcasting Station
N.A.I.C.S.: 516120
Jim Parsons *(Dir-News)*
Tracy Oliver *(Dir-Creative Svcs)*
Mike Pascarella *(Mgr-Bus)*
Lauren Sablowsky *(Mgr-Sls-Natl)*
Laurie Thompson *(Mgr-Digital Sls)*
Charles W. Wolfertz III *(Pres & Gen Mgr)*

Unit (Domestic):

WVTM-TV (2)
1732 Valley View Dr, Birmingham, AL 35209
Tel.: (205) 933-1313
Web Site: http://www.nbc13.com
Sales Range: $25-49.9 Million
Emp.: 120
Television Broadcasting
N.A.I.C.S.: 516120
Thomas Allen *(Asst Dir-News)*
Henry Price *(Gen Mgr)*
Brent Lane *(Gen Sls Mgr)*
Sue Stephens *(Dir-News)*
Elizabeth Frazier *(Dir-Mktg)*
Cynthia Isom *(Coord-Programming)*

Subsidiary (Domestic):

WXII Hearst-Argyle Television, Inc. (2)
700 Coliseum Dr, Winston Salem, NC 27106-5313
Tel.: (336) 721-9944
Web Site: http://www.wxii12.com
Sales Range: $25-49.9 Million
Emp.: 130
Television Broadcasting Station
N.A.I.C.S.: 516120
Connie Sullivan *(Gen Mgr-Sls)*
Lisa Eldridge *(Dir-Res & Programming)*
Michelle Butt *(Mgr-Station)*

WYFF Hearst-Argyle Television, Inc. (2)
505 Rutherford St, Greenville, SC 29609-5313 (100%)
Tel.: (864) 242-4404
Web Site: http://www.wyff4.com
Sales Range: $25-49.9 Million
Emp.: 130
Television Broadcasting Station
N.A.I.C.S.: 516120

Ifactor Consulting, Inc. (1)
60E Rio Salado Parkway Ste 715, Tempe, AZ 85281
Tel.: (480) 584-3041
Web Site: http://www.ifactorinc.com
Rev.: $1,312,000
Emp.: 200
Data Processing, Hosting & Software Developer
N.A.I.C.S.: 518210
Shazir Khan *(Pres & CEO)*
Chad Swenka *(CTO)*
Brad Sileo *(VP-Bus Dev)*

Jumpstart Automotive Media (1)
747 Front St Ste 400, San Francisco, CA 94111
Tel.: (415) 844-6300
Web Site: http://www.jumpstartautomotivemedia.com
Business Support Services
N.A.I.C.S.: 561499
Nick Matarazzo *(CEO)*
Jason Koenigsknecht *(VP-Sls-Natl)*
Choon Choi *(Sr VP-Strategy & Bus Dev)*
Francois Thery *(VP-Fin)*
Brian Ledoux *(Sr VP-Revenue Ops)*
Aaron Serrao *(VP-Audience Dev)*

NorthSouth Productions (1)
1140 Broadway Ste 1201, New York, NY 10001
Tel.: (212) 414-8670
Web Site: http://www.northsouth.tv
Emp.: 100
Television Broadcasting Services
N.A.I.C.S.: 516120
Charlie DeBevoise *(Partner)*
Mark Hickman *(Partner)*
Blaine Hopkins *(Partner & Exec VP)*
James Murray *(Sr VP-Dev)*
Jennifer Holbach *(VP)*
Celia Winchester *(CFO)*
Marsha Ballard *(VP-Production Resources)*
Margot Gattuso *(VP-Post Production)*
Daniel Callis *(Dir-Technical)*
Sarah Glaser *(Mgr-Dev)*
Lee Jacobs *(VP-Dev)*
Lisa Kleinman *(Sr Dir-Dev Comedy Div)*
Nick Kneece *(Chief Technical Officer)*
Dane Reiley *(VP-Comedy Dev & Production)*

The Hearst Service Center, in Charlotte, N.C. (1)
214 N Tryon St, Charlotte, NC 28202
Tel.: (704) 348-8000
Sales Range: $25-49.9 Million
Emp.: 400
Business Support Services
N.A.I.C.S.: 561499
Alfredo Gatto *(VP & Gen Mgr)*

iCrossing, Inc. (1)
300 W 57th St, New York, NY 10019
Tel.: (212) 649-3900
Web Site: http://www.icrossing.com
Sales Range: $25-49.9 Million
Emp.: 750
Advertising Agencies
N.A.I.C.S.: 541810
Mike Parker *(Pres-Global)*
David Santos *(Chief Talent Officer)*
Mark Mulhern *(Pres-East)*
Anne Bologna *(Chief Engagement Officer)*
Lori B. Wilson *(Sr VP & Exec Dir-Creative-Central Reg)*
Frederic Bonn *(Exec Dir-Creative-New York & East)*
Kayvan Salmanpour *(Chief Content Officer)*
Emma Armstrong *(Mng Dir)*
Joe Grigsby *(Mng Dir-Chicago)*
Dirk Thum *(Mng Dir)*
Celia Herrera *(Mng Dir-Mexico)*
Clifford Lopez *(Mng Dir-Dallas)*
Chris Apostle *(Chief Media Officer)*

Division (Non-US):

iCrossing Brighton (2)
Moore House 13 Black Lion St, Brighton, BN1 1ND, United Kingdom
Tel.: (44) 1 273 827 700
Emp.: 100
Advetising Agency
N.A.I.C.S.: 541810
Paul Doleman *(CEO)*

Division (Domestic):

iCrossing Chicago (2)
333 W Wacker Dr Ste 950, Chicago, IL 60606
Tel.: (312) 277-4700
Web Site: http://www.icrossing.com
Sales Range: $25-49.9 Million
Emp.: 105
Advetising Agency
N.A.I.C.S.: 541810
Steve Shay *(VP & Grp Dir-Creative)*
Stephen Thompson *(Exec VP & Exec Dir-Creative)*

iCrossing Dallas (2)
2828 Routh St Ste 777, Dallas, TX 75201
Tel.: (214) 210-6800
Web Site: http://www.icrossing.com
Sales Range: $25-49.9 Million
Emp.: 20
Advetising Agency
N.A.I.C.S.: 541810
Lori Wilson *(VP & Grp Dir-Creative)*

iCrossing Irvine (2)
15420 Laguna Canyon Rd Ste 210, Irvine, CA 92618
Tel.: (949) 242-1900
Advetising Agency
N.A.I.C.S.: 541810

Division (Non-US):

iCrossing London (2)
22 Chapter St 2nd Fl, London, SW1P 4NP, United Kingdom
Tel.: (44) 20 7821 2300
Web Site: http://www.icrossing.co.uk
Emp.: 45
Advetising Agency
N.A.I.C.S.: 541810
Bridgetta Worsley *(Dir-Fin)*
Esther Schneider *(Dir-Creative)*
June Robinson *(Dir-Bus Dev)*
Ben Myall *(Dir-Bus Dev)*
Mark Iremonger *(CEO)*
Paula Jago *(Head-Ops)*
Mark Williams *(Head-Search)*
Alistair Dent *(Chief Media Officer)*

Division (Domestic):

iCrossing Los Angeles (2)
12910 Culver Blvd Ste B, Los Angeles, CA 90066
Tel.: (480) 282-6058
Advetising Agency
N.A.I.C.S.: 541810

iCrossing Reston (2)
1902 Campus Commons Ste 600, Reston, VA 20191
Tel.: (703) 262-3200
Web Site: http://www.icrossing.com
N.A.I.C.S.: 541890

iCrossing Salt Lake City (2)
231 E 400 S Ste 300, Salt Lake City, UT 84111
Tel.: (801) 456-1560
Advetising Agency
N.A.I.C.S.: 541810

iCrossing San Francisco (2)
550 Kearny St Ste 400, San Francisco, CA 94108
Tel.: (415) 869-1120
Web Site: http://www.icrossing.com
Sales Range: $25-49.9 Million
Emp.: 90
Marketing Services
N.A.I.C.S.: 541613
Gary Stein *(Sr VP-Strategy & Plng)*

iCrossing Scottsdale (2)
15169 N Scottsdale Rd Ste C400, Scottsdale, AZ 85254
Tel.: (480) 505-5800
Advetising Agency
N.A.I.C.S.: 541810
Dave Corchado *(CIO)*

THE HEART GROUP OF LANCASTER GENERAL HEALTH
217 Harrisburg Ave, Lancaster, PA 17603
Tel.: (717) 544-4926   PA
Web Site: http://www.lancastergeneralhealth.org
Year Founded: 2010
Sales Range: $10-24.9 Million
Emp.: 198
Health Care Srvices
N.A.I.C.S.: 621498
Geoffrey Eddowes *(Sr VP-Post-Acute Care)*
Jan L. Bergen *(Pres & CEO)*
Gary Davidson *(CIO & Sr VP)*
Norma J. Ferdinand *(Chief Quality Officer & Sr VP-Quality & Performance Improvement)*
C. Clair McCormick *(Chm)*

THE HEART GROUP OF LANCASTER GENERAL HEALTH   U.S. PRIVATE

The Heart Group of Lancaster General Health—(Continued)

Robert P. Macina *(Chief Admin Officer, Chief Legal Officer, Sec & Exec VP)*
Dennis R. Roemer *(Co-CFO & Exec VP)*
F. Joseph Byorick *(Co-CFO & Sr VP)*
Susan Wynne *(Sr VP-Bus Dev)*
Stacey Youcis *(Sr VP-Svc Lines & Population Health)*
Lee M. Duke II *(Chief Medical Officer & Sr VP)*

THE HEAT AND WARMTH FUND
607 Shelby St Ste 400, Detroit, MI 48226
Tel.: (313) 226-9465 MI
Web Site: http://www.thawfund.org
Year Founded: 1985
Sales Range: $10-24.9 Million
Emp.: 19
Energy Assistance Services
N.A.I.C.S.: 624229
Lisa Jones *(Dir-Customer Advocacy)*
Sheri McAboy *(Dir-Programs)*
Ganelle Lesnew *(Dir-Strategic Initiatives)*
Saunteel Jenkins *(CEO)*

THE HEBREW HOME AT RIVERDALE
5901 Palisade Ave, Bronx, NY 10471
Tel.: (718) 581-1000 NY
Web Site:
 http://www.hebrewhome.org
Year Founded: 1917
Sales Range: $75-99.9 Million
Emp.: 909
Elder Care Services
N.A.I.C.S.: 624120
Luz Liebeskind *(CFO & Asst Treas)*
David Pomeranz *(COO)*
Daniel A. Reingold *(Pres & CEO)*
Jennifer Cabal *(Office Mgr-Volunteer Svcs)*
Josephine Catalano *(Dir-Volunteer Svcs Dept)*

THE HEICO COMPANIES, L.L.C.
70 W Madison St Ste 5600, Chicago, IL 60602
Tel.: (312) 419-8220 DE
Web Site:
 https://www.heicocompanies.com
Year Founded: 1979
Sales Range: Less than $1 Million
Emp.: 9,400
Offices of Other Holding Companies
N.A.I.C.S.: 551112
Emily Heisley Stoeckel *(Chm)*
Steve Frediani *(Pres & CEO)*
Eric Gunia *(Sr VP)*

Subsidiaries:

Ancra International LLC **(1)**
875w 8th St, Azusa, CA 90250-6614 **(100%)**
Tel.: (310) 973-5000
Web Site: http://www.ancra-llc.com
Sales Range: $10-24.9 Million
Emp.: 120
Mfr of Winches, Fasteners & Cargo Nets
N.A.I.C.S.: 333923
George Bates *(Mgr-Sls-Atlantic & Central Canada)*
Mark Daugherty *(Pres & Gen Mgr-Cargo Sys)*
Neil McCall *(Mgr-Sls-Cargo Sys Div Products-Central Canada)*
Brian Larocque *(Mng Dir-Canada)*

Division (Domestic):

Aircraft Systems Division, Los Angeles **(2)**
875 W 8th St, Azusa, CA 91702
Tel.: (310) 973-5000
Web Site: http://www.ancra.com
Aircraft Systems Designer
N.A.I.C.S.: 541512
Tammy Carson *(Exec VP-HR Admin)*
Steve Frediani *(Pres)*

Holding (Non-US):

Ancra ABT AB **(2)**
Verkstadsgatan 2, PO Box 100, Vargarda, 44737, Sweden
Tel.: (46) 322667800
Web Site: http://www.forankra.se
Mfr of Winches, Fasteners & Cargo Nets
N.A.I.C.S.: 333923
Ter Englund *(Mng Dir)*

Ancra Australia Pty. Ltd. **(2)**
250 Governor Road, Braeside, 3195, VIC, Australia
Tel.: (61) 395876700
Mfr of Winches, Fasteners & Cargo Nets
N.A.I.C.S.: 333923

Ancra Espana **(2)**
Ave Universidad Autonoma 15 Parque Tecnologico Del Valles, Cerdanyola Del Valles, Barcelona, 8920, Spain **(100%)**
Tel.: (34) 935800660
Web Site: http://www.ancra.es
Mfr of Winches, Fasteners & Cargo Nets
N.A.I.C.S.: 333923
Han Voskuilen *(Mng Dir)*

Division (Domestic):

Ancra International LLC **(2)**
2685 Circleport Dr, Erlanger, KY 41018-1486
Tel.: (859) 371-7272
Web Site: http://www.ancracargo.com
Winche Fastener & Cargo Net Mfr
N.A.I.C.S.: 314994

Ancra International LLC - Cargo Division **(2)**
2685 Circleport Dr, Erlanger, KY 41018
Tel.: (800) 929-2627
Emp.: 65
Airport Cargo Handling Services
N.A.I.C.S.: 488119
Larry Bethel *(Pres & Gen Mgr)*

Holding (Non-US):

Ancra International Sarl **(2)**
Rue Vaucanson ZAC de la Pesseliere, 69780, Mions, France **(100%)**
Tel.: (33) 474944777
Web Site: http://www.ackforankra.fr
Mfr of Winches, Fasteners & Cargo Nets
N.A.I.C.S.: 333923

Ancra New Zealand Limited **(2)**
5A Hunters Park Drive Three Kings, Auckland, 1024, New Zealand
Tel.: (64) 9 633 4015
Web Site: http://www.ancra.com
Emp.: 10
Winches, Fasteners & Cargo Nets
N.A.I.C.S.: 423830
Carl Twiws *(Mng Dir)*

Subsidiary (Domestic):

S-LINE, LLC **(2)**
301 VZ County Rd 1117, Grand Saline, TX 75140
Tel.: (800) 687-7900
Web Site: http://www.sline.com
Emp.: 60
Industrial Equipment Whsr
N.A.I.C.S.: 423830
David Douthit *(CFO)*

Ancra Systems BV **(1)**
Staarten 14, 5281 PL, Boxtel, Netherlands
Tel.: (31) 880247111
Web Site: http://www.ancra.nl
Cargo Handling System Mfr
N.A.I.C.S.: 333922
Marc Hezemans *(Mng Dir)*
Jos den Teuling *(Mgr-Technical)*
Marcel Berkers *(Sls Dir)*

Subsidiary (Non-US):

Ancra Espana S.L. **(2)**
Avda Universidad Autonoma 15 Parque tecnologico del Valles, Cerdanyola del Valles, 8290, Barcelona, Spain
Tel.: (34) 935800660
Web Site: http://www.ancra.es
Logistics Consulting Servies
N.A.I.C.S.: 541614
Tatyana Popenko *(Mgr-Acctg)*

Subsidiary (US):

Ancra International LLC **(2)**
2685 Cirport Dr, Erlanger, KY 41018
Tel.: (859) 371-7272
Web Site: http://www.ancra.com
Cargo Transportation Services
N.A.I.C.S.: 488490
Larry Bethel *(Pres)*
Andrey Molodykh *(CFO)*

Ifastgroupe and Company, Limited Partnership **(1)**
700 Rue Ouellette, Marieville, J3M 1P6, QC, Canada **(100%)**
Tel.: (450) 658-8741
Web Site: http://www.infasco.com
Sales Range: $25-49.9 Million
Emp.: 250
Bolts & Rivets Mfr
N.A.I.C.S.: 332722

Division (Domestic):

Galvano Division **(2)**
2620 Rue Bernard Pilon, Beloeil, J3G4F5, QC, Canada **(100%)**
Tel.: (450) 464-0547
Web Site: http://www.ivaco.com
Sales Range: $25-49.9 Million
Emp.: 50
Electro-Galvanizing & Hot Dip Galvanizing of Fasteners & Nails
N.A.I.C.S.: 332812

Infasco Division **(2)**
700 Rue Ouellette, Marieville, J3M 1P6, QC, Canada
Tel.: (450) 658-8741
Web Site: http://www.infasco.com
Sales Range: $50-74.9 Million
Bolts, Nuts & Fastener Products
N.A.I.C.S.: 332722

Ivaco Rolling Mills, LP **(1)**
1040 Hwy 17, PO Box 322, L'Orignal, K0B 1K0, ON, Canada
Tel.: (800) 463-7637
Web Site: http://www.ivacorm.com
Rolled Wire Mfr
N.A.I.C.S.: 331221

National-Standard Co. **(1)**
1631 Lake St, Niles, MI 49120
Tel.: (269) 683-8100
Web Site: http://www.nationalstandard.com
Rev.: $200,000,000
Emp.: 1,000
Tire Bead Wire, Fine & Specialty Wire, Welding Wire, Wire Cloth
N.A.I.C.S.: 423610
G.R. Northcutt *(Controller & Asst Sec)*

Division (Domestic):

National Standard **(2)**
1631 Lake St, Niles, MI 49120-1243
Tel.: (269) 683-8100
Web Site: http://www.nationalstandard.com
Sales Range: $50-74.9 Million
Emp.: 180
Mfr of Stainless, Carbon & Stainless Steel Weld Wire
N.A.I.C.S.: 423610
Terry O'Brien *(Mgr-Shipping)*

Neo Industries, Inc. **(1)**
1775 Willowcreek Rd, Portage, IN 46368
Tel.: (219) 762-6075
Web Site: http://www.neodelivers.com
Logistics Consulting Servies
N.A.I.C.S.: 541614

Subsidiary (Non-US):

NEO Slovakia, s.r.o. **(2)**
Vstupny Areal U S Steel, 04454, Kosice, Slovakia
Tel.: (421) 55 673 8473
Logistics Consulting Servies
N.A.I.C.S.: 541614
Michal Fedor *(Gen Mgr)*

Neo Hungary Kft. **(2)**
Vasmu ter 1-3, 2400, Dunaujvaros, Hungary
Tel.: (36) 25 582 8390
Logistics Consulting Servies
N.A.I.C.S.: 541614

Pettibone, LLC **(1)**
2626 Warrenville Rd, Downers Grove, IL 60515-1775
Tel.: (630) 353-5000
Web Site: http://www.pettibone.com
Sales Range: $750-799.9 Million
Emp.: 2,000
Construction Equipment Mfr
N.A.I.C.S.: 333120
Scot Jenkins *(Pres)*

Division (Domestic):

ARDCO/Traverse Lift **(2)**
2202 SW Evangeline Trwy, Lafayette, LA 70508
Tel.: (337) 233-4330
Web Site: http://www.ardco.net
Sales Range: $1-9.9 Million
Emp.: 8
Mfr of Geophysical Machinery & All Terrain Forklifts
N.A.I.C.S.: 336999
David Wall *(Gen Mgr)*

Barko Hydraulics LLC **(2)**
1 Banks Ave, Superior, WI 54880-1319
Tel.: (715) 392-5641
Web Site: http://www.barko.com
Sales Range: $1-9.9 Million
Emp.: 60
Mfr of Heavy-Duty Forestry Industry Equipment
N.A.I.C.S.: 333120
Scot Jenkins *(Pres)*

Davies Molding LLC **(2)**
350 Kehoe Blvd, Carol Stream, IL 60188-1818
Tel.: (630) 510-8188
Web Site: http://www.daviesmolding.com
Sales Range: $1-9.9 Million
Emp.: 125
Injection Molding
N.A.I.C.S.: 326199
Rick Friel *(VP-Ops)*
Derran Smith *(Pres)*

Field Controls LLC **(2)**
2630 Airport Rd, Kinston, NC 28504-7319
Tel.: (252) 522-3031
Web Site: http://www.fieldcontrols.com
Sales Range: $25-49.9 Million
Emp.: 100
HVAC Products Mfr
N.A.I.C.S.: 334519
Patrick Holleran *(Pres)*
Tony Schrank *(VP-Ops)*
Carl Moody *(Mgr-Sls-Western)*
Ed Reynolds *(Mgr-Sls-Northeast)*
Kyle Glover *(Project Mgr)*
Mark Lundberg *(Mgr-Engrg)*
Michael Afarian *(VP-Fin)*
Ozden Karakut *(Mgr-Sls-Southeast)*
Tim Begoske *(Mgr-Sls-Midwest)*
Timothy Barton *(Dir-Wholesale Sls & Mktg)*
Tommy Askew *(Mgr-Mfg)*

Pettibone Traverse List LLC **(2)**
1100 Superior Ave, Baraga, MI 49908-0368
Tel.: (906) 353-6611
Web Site: http://www.gopettibone.com
Sales Range: $1-9.9 Million
Emp.: 100
Construction Machinery Mfr
N.A.I.C.S.: 333924
Scott Raffaelli *(VP & Gen Mgr)*

Subsidiary (Domestic):

RMS Equipment LLC **(2)**
1 Vision Ln, Cuyahoga Falls, OH 44223
Tel.: (330) 564-1360
Web Site: http://www.rms-ca.com
Emp.: 100
Industrial Machinery Mfr
N.A.I.C.S.: 333248
Chris Wenhold *(VP-Sls)*

Division (Domestic):

Spartan Tool **(2)**
1506 W Division St, Mendota, IL 61342-2426
Tel.: (815) 539-7411

Web Site: http://www.spartantool.com
Sales Range: $10-24.9 Million
Emp.: 300
Commercial & Industrial Sewer Cleaner & Barometric Draft Controls Mfr; Material Handling Equipment
N.A.I.C.S.: 333310
Tom Pranka (Pres)

Subsidiary (Domestic):

Steelastic Company, LLC (2)
One Vision Ln, Cuyahoga Falls, OH 44223
Tel.: (330) 633-0505
Web Site: http://www.steelastic.com
Sales Range: $10-24.9 Million
Emp.: 33
Mfr of Steel Products
N.A.I.C.S.: 331210
Ian Dennis (Pres)

Stenograph LLC (2)
596 W Lamont Rd, Elmhurst, IL 60126-1022
Tel.: (847) 803-1400
Web Site: http://www.stenograph.com
Sales Range: $10-24.9 Million
Emp.: 162
Mfr of Court Reporting Equipment, Shorthand Machines & Computer Aided Transcription Systems
N.A.I.C.S.: 333310
John P. Wenclawski (Pres)
Robert J. Panfil (Sr VP-Fin)
Judy Wolf (Mgr-Product)
David W. Wynne (VP-Sls)
William Plasschaert (VP-Mfg & Svc)

Division (Domestic):

Tiffin Parts LLC (2)
235 Miami St 450 Market, Tiffin, OH 44883-2111
Tel.: (419) 447-6545
Web Site: http://www.tiffinparts.com
Sales Range: $1-9.9 Million
Emp.: 5
Mfr Of Hydraulic Crane Parts
N.A.I.C.S.: 423810
Ryan Rostetter (Mgr-Parts)

Subsidiary (Domestic):

Zalk Josephs Fabricators, LLC (2)
400 Industrial Cir, Stoughton, WI 53589-1308
Tel.: (608) 873-6646
Web Site: http://www.zalkjosephs.com
Sales Range: $25-49.9 Million
Emp.: 80
Structural Steel Fabricators
N.A.I.C.S.: 332312
Bryan Frazier (VP-Pur)
Joseph Lammers (Pres)

Precision Engineering, Inc (1)
29 Industrial Dr, Uxbridge, MA 01569
Tel.: (508) 278-5700
Web Site: http://www.precisionengineering.com
Rev: $2,952,000
Emp.: 35
Metal Stamping
N.A.I.C.S.: 332119
John Martinelli (Plant Mgr)

Sarclad Ltd. (1)
Advanced Manufacturing Park Whittle Way, Rotherham, S60 5BL, United Kingdom
Tel.: (44) 114 293 9300
Web Site: http://www.sarclad.com
Industrial Machinery Mfr
N.A.I.C.S.: 333248
Richard Cowlishaw (Mng Dir)

Subsidiary (US):

Sarclad North America LP (2)
RIDC Riverplace 30 S Linden St, Duquesne, PA 15110
Tel.: (412) 466-2000
Web Site: http://www.sarcladna.com
Emp.: 11
Surface Monitoring Equipment Mfr
N.A.I.C.S.: 334519
Ian Denis (Gen Mgr)

Shred-Tech Inc. (1)
295 Pinebush Rd, Cambridge, N1T 1B2, ON, Canada
Tel.: (519) 621-3560

Web Site: http://www.shred-tech.com
Sales Range: $50-74.9 Million
Shredding Equipment & Reduction Systems
N.A.I.C.S.: 333310
Rob Glass (Pres & CEO)

Sivaco Ontario Processing Division (1)
330 Thomas St, PO Box 220, Ingersoll, N5C 3K5, ON, Canada
Tel.: (519) 485-4150
Web Site: http://www.sivaco.com
Sales Range: $10-24.9 Million
Emp.: 75
Processing of Wire Rods
N.A.I.C.S.: 333992
Lynn Matthews (Mgr-HR)

Sivaco Quebec Division (1)
800 Rue Ouellette St, Marieville, J3M 1P5, QC, Canada (100%)
Tel.: (450) 658-8741
Web Site: http://www.sivaco.com
Sales Range: $25-49.9 Million
Emp.: 300
Galvanized Wire & Nail Mfr
N.A.I.C.S.: 332618

Sivaco Wire Group L.P. (1)
800 Rue Ouellette, Marieville, J3M 1P5, QC, Canada
Tel.: (450) 658-8741
Web Site: http://www.sivaco.heicowiregroup.com
Wire Mfr & Distr
N.A.I.C.S.: 331221

Plant (Domestic):

Sivaco Wire Group L.P. - Ontario Plant (2)
330 Thomas St, PO Box 220, Ingersoll, N5C 3K5, ON, Canada
Tel.: (800) 265-0418
Emp.: 80
Wire Mfr & Distr
N.A.I.C.S.: 331221
Lawrence Pye (Mgr-Ops)

Wakefield Thermal Solutions (1)
33 Bridge St, Pelham, NH 03076-3475
Tel.: (603) 635-2800
Web Site: http://www.wakefield.com
Sales Range: $1-9.9 Million
Emp.: 273
Heat Sinks Mfr
N.A.I.C.S.: 332410
Kevin Kreger (Pres)

Wakefield-Vette, Inc. (1)
33 Bridge St, Pelham, NH 03076
Tel.: (603) 635-2800
Web Site: http://www.wakefield-vette.com
Emp.: 200
Heat Exchanger Mfr
N.A.I.C.S.: 332410
Mark Daugherty (Pres)

Division (Domestic):

Wakefield-Vette, Inc. - Coolcentric Division (2)
33 Bridge St, Pelham, NH 03076
Tel.: (603) 635-5199
Web Site: http://www.coolcentric.com
Heat Exchanger Mfr
N.A.I.C.S.: 332410

THE HELLENIC WOMEN'S BENEVOLENT ASSOCIATION, INC.
601 Sherman St, Canton, MA 02021
Tel.: (781) 828-7450 MA
Year Founded: 1954
Sales Range: $10-24.9 Million
Emp.: 271
Nursing & Rehabilitation Services
N.A.I.C.S.: 623110
Jacqueline Beverly (Dir-Rehabilitation)
Elizabeth Zubrycki (Dir-Nursing)

THE HELM GROUP
2283 US Route 20 E, Freeport, IL 61032
Tel.: (815) 235-0990

Web Site: http://www.helmgroup.com
Year Founded: 1946
Sales Range: $100-124.9 Million
Emp.: 200
Holding Company; Construction Services
N.A.I.C.S.: 551112
Craig Buikema (Treas)
Art Snyder (CEO)
Greg Peet (Pres)
Rich Lower (VP)

Subsidiaries:

Civil Constructors, Inc. (1)
2283 US Rte 20, Freeport, IL 61032
Tel.: (815) 235-2200
Web Site: http://www.helmgroup.com
Sales Range: $10-24.9 Million
Emp.: 50
Commercial & Industrial Construction & Civil Engineering
N.A.I.C.S.: 237990
Art Sneider (Pres)

Conmat (1)
1307 W Longhollow Rd, Elizabeth, IL 61028
Tel.: (815) 858-2691
Web Site: http://www.helmgroup.com
Sales Range: $25-49.9 Million
Emp.: 15
Limestone Aggregates Supplier
N.A.I.C.S.: 212312

Heavy Equipment Services, Inc. (1)
2290 Business Rt 20 E, Freeport, IL 61032
Tel.: (815) 235-7131
Web Site: http://www.helmgroup.com
Sales Range: $10-24.9 Million
Emp.: 20
Construction Equipment Sales, Supplies & Repairs
N.A.I.C.S.: 423810
Rich Lower (VP & Gen Mgr)

Industrial Solutions, Inc. (1)
2283 Yellow Creek Rd, Freeport, IL 61032
Tel.: (815) 235-2202
Web Site: http://www.helmgroup.com
Sales Range: $10-24.9 Million
Emp.: 55
Engineeering Services
N.A.I.C.S.: 541330

Mechanical, Inc. (1)
2279 Yellow Creek Rd, Freeport, IL 61032
Tel.: (815) 235-1955
Web Site: http://www.mechinc.com
Mechanical Contractor
N.A.I.C.S.: 238220
Brian Helm (Pres)

THE HELP GROUP
13130 Burbank Blvd, Sherman Oaks, CA 91401
Tel.: (818) 781-0360 CA
Web Site: http://www.thehelpgroup.org
Year Founded: 1953
Sales Range: $10-24.9 Million
Emp.: 485
Disability Assistance Services
N.A.I.C.S.: 624120
Michael Love (Sr VP)
Elena Brewer (VP-Ops)
Susan Berman (COO)
Tom Komp (Sr VP)
Edna Ramos (Controller)
Jason Bolton (VP-Programs)

THE HENDERSON CORPORATION
575 State Route 28, Raritan, NJ 08869-1354
Tel.: (908) 685-1300 NJ
Web Site: http://www.henco.com
Year Founded: 1953
Sales Range: $75-99.9 Million
Emp.: 100
Industrial Buildings & Warehouses
N.A.I.C.S.: 236220
Edward F. Mcmahon (Pres & CEO)
Mark C. Walton (VP)
George W. Alston (Sr VP)

THE HENDRICK COMPANIES, LLC
6000 Monroe Rd Ste 100, Charlotte, NC 28212-6175
Tel.: (704) 568-5550 NC
Holding Company; Car Dealerships & Professional Motorsports Organization Owner & Operator
N.A.I.C.S.: 551112
Joseph Riddick Hendrick III (Chm & CEO)
Charles Ricks (Vice Chm)

Subsidiaries:

Hendrick Corporation, LLC (1)
6000 Monroe Rd Ste 100, Charlotte, NC 28212-6175
Tel.: (704) 568-5550
Web Site: http://www.hendrickauto.com
Sales Range: $5-14.9 Billion
Emp.: 8,200
Franchised Automobile Dealerships & Collision Repair Shops
N.A.I.C.S.: 441110
Joseph Riddick Hendrick III (Chm)

Unit (Domestic):

Gwinnett Place Honda (2)
3325 Satellite Blvd, Duluth, GA 30096
Tel.: (678) 534-2208
Web Site: http://www.gphonda.com
New & Used Car Dealer
N.A.I.C.S.: 441110
Kam Cheung (Mgr-Svc)
Jae Kim (Asst Mgr-Svc)

Hendrick BMW (2)
6950 E Independence Blvd, Charlotte, NC 28227-9417
Tel.: (704) 535-0885
Web Site: http://www.hendrickbmw.com
Sales Range: $10-24.9 Million
Emp.: 200
New & Used Automobile Dealer
N.A.I.C.S.: 441110
John Desmond (Gen Mgr)

Hendrick Motors of Charlotte (2)
5201 E Independence Blvd, Charlotte, NC 28212
Tel.: (704) 535-6400
Web Site: http://www.hendrickmotorsofcharlotte.com
Sales Range: $25-49.9 Million
Emp.: 90
New & Used Car Dealer
N.A.I.C.S.: 441110
Tim Calo (Mgr-Svc)
Joey Seay (Mgr-Parts)

Hendrick Motorsports, LLC (1)
4400 Papa Joe Hendrick Blvd, Charlotte, NC 28262
Tel.: (704) 455-3400
Web Site: http://www.hendrickmotorsports.com
Sales Range: $25-49.9 Million
Emp.: 500
Professional Motorsports Organization
N.A.I.C.S.: 711211
Joseph Riddick Hendrick III (Owner)
Scott Lampe (CFO & Exec VP)
Marshall Carlson (Pres)
Ken Howes (VP)
Patrick Perkins (VP-Mktg)
Jeff Andrews (VP-Competition)
Brian Whitesell (VP-Ops)
Jim Wall (Dir-Powertrain)
Darian Grubb (Dir-Competition Sys)
Diane Holl (Dir-Vehicle Engrg)
Michael Landis (Dir-Operational Support)

THE HERALD, INC.
625 S Kibler St, New Washington, OH 44854
Tel.: (419) 492-2133
Web Site: http://www.heraldinc.com
Sales Range: $10-24.9 Million
Emp.: 40
Offset Printing
N.A.I.C.S.: 323111
David A. Stump (Pres & CEO)

THE HERITAGE BANK

THE HERITAGE BANK

The Heritage Bank—(Continued)
300 S Main St, Hinesville, GA 31313
Tel.: (912) 368-3332 GA
Web Site: http://www.the-heritage-bank.com
Year Founded: 1911
Sales Range: $10-24.9 Million
Emp.: 193
Banking Services
N.A.I.C.S.: 522110
Brian J. Smith (Exec VP)
Stephen Parker (Chief Credit Officer)
Melissa Deal (COO)
Corey Jones (VP)

THE HERITAGE CO.
2402 Wildwood Ave, Sherwood, AR 72120
Tel.: (501) 835-9111
Rev.: $45,162,304
Emp.: 1,000
Fundraising, Marketing & Consulting Services
N.A.I.C.S.: 541613
John Braune (Pres & CEO)

THE HERRICK CORPORATION
3003 E Hammer Ln, Stockton, CA 95212
Tel.: (209) 956-4751
Web Site: http://www.herricksteel.com
Year Founded: 1988
Sales Range: $25-49.9 Million
Emp.: 900
Structural Steel Fabricator & Erector
N.A.I.C.S.: 332312
Doug Griffin (Pres)

Subsidiaries:

Central Texas Iron Works Inc. (1)
1100 Winchell Dr, Waco, TX 76712 (100%)
Tel.: (254) 776-8000
Web Site: http://www.ctiw.com
Sales Range: $25-49.9 Million
Emp.: 208
Mfr of Fabricated Structural Metal
N.A.I.C.S.: 332312
Richard Wood (Project Mgr)
David Dornsife (Chm)
Curtis Cleveland (VP-Mktg)
Don Gooch (VP-Sls)
David Harwell (Pres)
Roy Eaton (VP-Ops)

Monotech of Mississippi Inc. (1)
27 County Rd, Iuka, MS 38852
Tel.: (662) 423-2033
Sales Range: $10-24.9 Million
Emp.: 110
Mfr of Industrial Machinery
N.A.I.C.S.: 333998
Steve Hudson (Plant Mgr)

PSP Industries Inc. (1)
300 Montague Expy Ste 200, Milpitas, CA 95035-6830 (100%)
Tel.: (408) 942-1155
Web Site: http://www.pspindustries.com
Sales Range: $25-49.9 Million
Emp.: 450
Mfr of Blowers & Fans
N.A.I.C.S.: 333413

Thai Herrick Co., Ltd. (1)
1 MD Tower 10/F Soi Bangna-Trad 25, Bangna, Bangkok, 10260, Thailand
Tel.: (66) 2 361 8231
Web Site: http://www.thaiherrick.com
Fabricated Structural Metal Mfr
N.A.I.C.S.: 332312
Wittawat Smuthranond (Deputy Mng Dir)

Plant (Domestic):

Thai Herrick Co., Ltd. - Thai Herrick Prachinburi Plant (2)
1/6 M 5 Chachoengsao-Kabinburi Road Kokthai, Srimahosod, Prachin Buri, 25190, Thailand
Tel.: (66) 38 854 313
Fabricated Structural Metal Mfr
N.A.I.C.S.: 332312

Thai Herrick Co., Ltd. - Thai Herrick Rayong Plant (2)
131/1 M 3 Bankhai-Nonglalok Road, Bankhai, Rayong, 21120, Thailand
Tel.: (66) 38 026 684
Fabricated Structural Metal Mfr
N.A.I.C.S.: 332312

THE HESSE COMPANIES
25 1st Ave, Atlantic Highlands, NJ 07716
Tel.: (732) 291-8100
Web Site: http://www.thehessecompanies.com
Year Founded: 1908
Construction & Real Estate Industries
N.A.I.C.S.: 236210
Martin Ryan (VP-Engrg)

Subsidiaries:

C.J. Hesse, Inc. (1)
25 1st Ave, Atlantic Highlands, NJ 07716
Tel.: (732) 787-0226
Web Site: http://www.thehessecompanies.com
Highway, Street & Bridge Construction
N.A.I.C.S.: 237310

THE HF GROUP LLC
8834 Mayfield Rd, Chesterland, OH 44026
Tel.: (440) 729-2445
Web Site: http://www.thehfgroup.com
Year Founded: 1982
Rev.: $20,700,000
Emp.: 21
Bookbinding & Related Work
N.A.I.C.S.: 323120
Jay Fairfield (Chm & CEO)
Paul Parisi (COO)

Subsidiaries:

Assurevault LLC (1)
8844 Mayfield Rd, Chesterland, OH 44026
Tel.: (440) 729-3911
Web Site: http://www.assurevault.com
Emp.: 10
Data Processing Services
N.A.I.C.S.: 518210
Barb Voyer (Mgr-HR)

General Bookbinding Company (1)
8844 Mayfield Rd, Chesterland, OH 44026
Tel.: (440) 729-9411
Web Site: http://www.hfgroup.com
Bookbinding & Repairing: Trade, Edition, Library, Etc.
N.A.I.C.S.: 323120
Jay Fairfield (CEO)
Jim Bratton (VP-Ops)
Paul Parisi (COO)

Hawaii Library Bindery Inc. (1)
94-287 Aaahi St, Mililani, HI 96789-1814
Tel.: (808) 566-9447
Web Site: http://www.thehfgroup.com
Rev.: $950,000
Emp.: 1
Binding Only: Books, Pamphlets, Magazines, Etc.
N.A.I.C.S.: 323120

Hoag & Sons Book Bindery Inc. (1)
145 N Main St, Eaton Rapids, MI 48827
Tel.: (517) 857-3466
Rev.: $400,000
Emp.: 16
Bookbinding & Related Work
N.A.I.C.S.: 323120

Hoster Bindery, Inc. (1)
Jacksonville Rd Industrial Park 17 Vincent Cir, Ivyland, PA 18974
Tel.: (215) 443-7250
Web Site: http://www.hosterbindery.com
Book Binding Services
N.A.I.C.S.: 323117

Mid Atlantic Book Bindery Inc. (1)
1440 Hickory Hill Rd, Petersburg, VA 23803
Tel.: (804) 732-8970
Web Site: http://www.thehfgroup.com
Bookbinding & Related Work

N.A.I.C.S.: 323120
Southeast Library Bindery Inc. (1)
6204 Corporate Park Dr, Browns Summit, NC 27214
Tel.: (336) 931-0800
Web Site: http://www.acmebinding.com
Binding Only: Books, Pamphlets, Magazines, Etc.
N.A.I.C.S.: 323120
Scott May (VP & Gen Mgr)

The HF Group LLC - Book Partner Division (1)
1010 N Sycamore St, North Manchester, IN 46962
Tel.: (800) 334-3628
Web Site: http://www.bookpartners.com
Book Binding Services
N.A.I.C.S.: 323117
Jim Heckman (VP & Gen Mgr)

THE HIBBERT GROUP
400 Pennington Ave, Trenton, NJ 08650
Tel.: (609) 394-7500 NJ
Web Site: http://www.hibbert.com
Year Founded: 1881
Marketing Support Services
N.A.I.C.S.: 541860
Timothy J. Moonan (Co-Chm & CEO)
Thomas J. Moonan (Co-Chm)
Rosemary Mengel Hober (Sr VP-Ops)
Kenneth J. Swiatkowski (Sr VP-IT)
Michelle Spedding (Sr VP)

THE HIDE & LEATHER HOUSE
595 Monroe St, Napa, CA 94559
Tel.: (707) 255-6160
Web Site: http://www.hidehouse.com
Sales Range: $10-24.9 Million
Emp.: 18
Leather Distr
N.A.I.C.S.: 458320
Earle E. Deits (Sec)
Rob Deits (Pres & CEO)

THE HIEBING GROUP, INC.
315 Wisconsin Ave, Madison, WI 53703-2107
Tel.: (608) 256-6357 WI
Web Site: http://www.hiebing.com
Year Founded: 1981
Sales Range: $25-49.9 Million
Emp.: 80
Advetising Agency
N.A.I.C.S.: 541810
Dave Florin (Pres & Partner)
Sean Mullen (Partner, VP & Dir-Creative)
Jeane Kropp (Partner & Dir-Brand Strategy)
Barry Edison (Partner & Dir-Touchpoint)
Ann Dencker (Partner & Dir-Insight & Strategic Res)
Amanda Fier (Acct Mgr-Austin)
Ted Jun (Dir-Bus Dev)
Eena Taylor (Dir-Digital)
Angie James (Dir-Fin & Admin)
Dana Arnold (Partner & Dir-PR & Social Media)
Christina Brown (Acct Exec)

THE HIGGINS GROUP, INC.
1499 Post Rd Ste 1, Fairfield, CT 06824-5940
Tel.: (203) 254-9000 CT
Web Site: http://www.higginsgroup.com
Year Founded: 1977
Emp.: 400
Real Estate Agency
N.A.I.C.S.: 531210
Rick Higgins (Chm & CEO)

THE HIGHLANDS AT WYOMISSING

U.S. PRIVATE

2000 Cambridge Ave, Wyomissing, PA 19610-2714
Tel.: (610) 775-2300 PA
Web Site: http://www.thehighlands.org
Year Founded: 1989
Sales Range: $25-49.9 Million
Emp.: 523
Lifecare Retirement Community Operator
N.A.I.C.S.: 623311
Elton P. Richards (Sec)
Gerald P. Malick (Vice Chm)
Michael A. Hajost (Treas)
David L. Thun (Chm)

THE HIGNELL COMPANIES
1750 Humboldt Road, Chico, CA 95928
Tel.: (530) 576-5376
Web Site: http://www.hignell.com
Real Estate Broker
N.A.I.C.S.: 531210
Douglas Hignell (Co-Founder)
Philip Larios (Pres & CEO)
Matthew Dietz (VP)
Katharine Dietz (Dir-HR)

THE HIGRO GROUP LLC
433 Broadway 5th Fl, New York, NY 10013
Tel.: (800) 535-4302 DE
Web Site: http://www.higrogroup.com
Year Founded: 2016
Privater Equity Firm
N.A.I.C.S.: 523999
Nick Jean-Baptiste (Principal)
Ernest Lyles (Principal)

Subsidiaries:

DRS Imaging Services, LLC (1)
299 Broadway, New York, NY 10007
Tel.: (877) 924-8680
Web Site: http://www.drsimaging.com
Document Conversion & Technology Services
N.A.I.C.S.: 561410
Clifford Newman (CEO)
Doug Phelan (Pres)
Jim Sheridan (Exec VP)
Jeff Russo (Exec VP-Sls & Mktg)
Paul Solomon (COO)

Subsidiary (Domestic):

DocuLynx, Inc. (2)
6916 N 97th Cir, Omaha, NE 68122
Tel.: (402) 339-9972
Document Management Software & Solutions
N.A.I.C.S.: 513210

THE HILL GROUP
11045 Gage Ave, Franklin Park, IL 60131-1437
Tel.: (847) 451-5000 IL
Web Site: http://www.hillgrp.com
Year Founded: 1936
Sales Range: $250-299.9 Million
Emp.: 1,000
Plumbing, Heating & Air-Conditioning Services
N.A.I.C.S.: 238220
Warren Hill (Chm)
Marc Pittas (VP-Svcs)
Jim Hill (Pres)
Steve Schumm (CFO)
Jim Billard (VP-Risk Mgmt)
Bryan Teyema (VP-Construction Ops)
Jim Kamilis (VP-Engrg)
Don J. Flight (VP-Construction)
Jason Rahn (VP-Construction)
Scott Tranter (VP-Construction)
David Pikey (VP-Corp Tech)
Shannon Coomes (Pres-Fire Protection)

THE HILLMAN COMPANY

COMPANIES — THE HOH GROUP

330 Grant St Ste 1900, Pittsburgh, PA 15219-2203
Tel.: (412) 281-2620 — PA
Year Founded: 1951
Sales Range: $75-99.9 Million
Emp.: 60
Holding Company; Diversified Investment Operations & Real Estate
N.A.I.C.S.: 551112
John W. Hall *(VP-Acctg & Info Svcs)*
Eric C. Johnson *(Chm & CFO)*
Joseph C. Manzinger *(Pres & CEO)*
Vicky J. Brilmyer *(VP-HR & Admin)*
Timothy O. Fisher *(Sr VP)*
Russell Ayres *(Assoc Gen Counsel & VP)*
Marian Dietrich *(VP-Legal & Risk Mgmt)*

Subsidiaries:

Hyattsville Land Co., Inc. (1)
824 Market St Ste 900, Wilmington, DE 19801-4902
Tel.: (302) 655-4294
Nonresidential Building Operators
N.A.I.C.S.: 531120

The Hillman Fluid Power Group (1)
330 Grant St Ste 1212, Pittsburgh, PA 15219-2304
Tel.: (412) 281-2620
Holding Company
N.A.I.C.S.: 551112

Wilmington Investments Inc. (1)
824 N Market St Ste 900, Wilmington, DE 19801-4902
Tel.: (302) 655-4294
Sales Range: $25-49.9 Million
Emp.: 4
Holding Companies
N.A.I.C.S.: 551112

Wilmington Securities Inc. (1)
824 Mkt St Ste 900, Wilmington, DE 19801-4902
Tel.: (302) 655-4294
Sales Range: $25-49.9 Million
Emp.: 5
Investment Services
N.A.I.C.S.: 523999

THE HINES GROUP, INC.
5680 Old Hwy 54, Philpot, KY 42366
Tel.: (270) 729-4242
Web Site: http://www.thehinesgroup.com
Year Founded: 1999
Sales Range: $25-49.9 Million
Emp.: 600
Holding Company; Metal Stamping; Aviation
N.A.I.C.S.: 335312
Allen Mills *(Mgr-Mktg)*
Steve Shultz *(VP-Intl Mktg)*
Bill Young *(VP-Acctg)*
Perry G. Hines *(Owner & Principal)*

Subsidiaries:

MidAmerica Jet, Inc. (1)
1 Bullfrog Blvd, Owensboro, KY 42301-9400 (100%)
Tel.: (270) 926-6700
Web Site: http://www.midamericajet.com
Sales Range: $10-24.9 Million
Emp.: 41
Oil Transportation Services
N.A.I.C.S.: 481219
Tim Miller *(Dir-Ops)*

Owensboro Manufacturing Llc (1)
3001 Tamarack Rd, Owensboro, KY 42301
Tel.: (270) 689-1818
Web Site: http://www.owensboromanufacturing.com
Rev.: $1,900,000
Emp.: 30
Electric Motor & Generator Part Mfr
N.A.I.C.S.: 335312

Premium Allied Tool Inc. (1)
5680 Old Hwy 54, Philpot, KY 42366-9645
Tel.: (270) 729-4242
Web Site: http://www.premiumalliedtool.com
Sales Range: $25-49.9 Million
Emp.: 200
Mfr of Metal Stampings
N.A.I.C.S.: 332119

Subsidiary (Non-US):

Electro Partes de Matamoros, S.A. de C.V. (2)
Carretera Lauro Villar Km 4 700, 87470, Matamoros, Tamaulipas, Mexico
Tel.: (52) 8688140025
Sales Range: $25-49.9 Million
Emp.: 150
Electronic Television Components Mfr
N.A.I.C.S.: 334220

THE HITE COMPANY
Beale Ave & 31st St, Altoona, PA 16603-1754
Tel.: (814) 944-6121 — PA
Web Site: http://www.hiteco.com
Year Founded: 1949
Sales Range: $100-124.9 Million
Emp.: 240
Electrical Distr
N.A.I.C.S.: 423610
Ron Eberhart *(Exec VP)*
Nicole Duffy *(Project Mgr)*

THE HOFFMAN AGENCY
325 South 1st St 3rd Fl, San Jose, CA 95113-1204
Tel.: (408) 286-2611
Web Site: http://www.hoffman.com
Year Founded: 1987
Sales Range: $1-9.9 Million
Emp.: 200
Public Relations Agency
N.A.I.C.S.: 541820
Lou Hoffman *(CEO)*
Caroline Hsu *(Mng Dir-Asia Pacific)*
Mark Pinsent *(Mng Dir-Europe)*
Syreeta Mussante *(Mng Dir-North America)*
Thomas Franky *(Gen Mgr-Indonesia)*
Gerard LaFond *(Chief Digital Officer-North America)*
Natalie Kessler *(Exec VP-Global Talent Mktg Practice)*

Subsidiaries:

The Hoffman Agency (1)
6215 S Macon Way, Englewood, CO 80111-5819
Tel.: (720) 932-8515
Web Site: http://www.hoffman.com
Public Relations Agency
N.A.I.C.S.: 541820

The Hoffman Agency (1)
2420 Regent Centre 88 Queens Road, Central, China (Hong Kong)
Tel.: (852) 2581 9380
Web Site: http://www.hoffman.com
Emp.: 20
Public Relations Agency
N.A.I.C.S.: 541820
Lydia Lau *(VP-Global Ops)*
Dong Chen *(Gen Mgr)*
Jenny Chan *(VP-Bus Dev & Mktg-APAC)*
Kevin Chen *(Gen Mgr)*
Jenny Yip *(Gen Mgr-Ops)*
Jason Cao *(Gen Mgr-Beijing & Shanghai)*
Marc Sparrow *(Gen Mgr)*

The Hoffman Agency (1)
CITIC Bldg 19 Jianguomenwai St Ste 2104, Beijing, 100004, China
Tel.: (86) 10 6507 0985
Web Site: http://www.hoffman.com
Emp.: 9
Public Relations Agency
N.A.I.C.S.: 541820
Sandra Cheong *(Gen Mgr)*
Jason Cao *(Gen Mgr)*

The Hoffman Agency (1)
Burex Kyobashi Suite 515 2-7-14 Kyobashi, Chuo-ku, Tokyo, 104-0031, Japan
Tel.: (81) 3 5159 2145
Web Site: http://www.hoffmanasia.com
Public Relations Agency
N.A.I.C.S.: 541820

Shingo Nomura *(Gen Mgr)*

The Hoffman Agency (1)
301 Korean Re Bldg 80 Susong-dong, Jongro-gu, Seoul, 110-733, Korea (South)
Tel.: (82) 2 737 2942
Web Site: http://www.hoffmanasia.com
Emp.: 5
Public Relations Agency
N.A.I.C.S.: 541820
Ruger Iglesias *(CEO)*
Miranda Lee *(Gen Mgr)*

The Hoffman Agency (1)
175A Bencoolen St, 08-01/02 Burlington Sq, Singapore, 189650, Singapore
Tel.: (65) 6252 2866
Web Site: http://www.hoffmanasia.com
Public Relations Agency
N.A.I.C.S.: 541820

The Hoffman Agency (1)
Garden Studios 11-15 Betterton Street, London, WC2H 9BP, United Kingdom
Tel.: (44) 20 7470 8762
Web Site: http://www.hoffman.com
Public Relations Agency
N.A.I.C.S.: 541820

The Hoffman Agency (1)
Untere Bahnhofstr 38 A, 82110, Germering, Germany
Tel.: (49) 89 8940 63800
Web Site: http://www.hoffman.com
Public Relations Agency
N.A.I.C.S.: 541820

THE HOFFMANN FAMILY OF COMPANIES
405 5th Ave S, Naples, FL 34102
Web Site: https://hoffmannfamilyofcompanies.com
Emp.: 100
Investment Services & Portfolio Management
N.A.I.C.S.: 523940
Geoff Hoffmann *(CEO)*

Subsidiaries:

Besse Forest Products Group, Co. (1)
933 N 8th St, Gladstone, MI 49837
Tel.: (906) 428-3113
Web Site: https://www.bessegroup.com
Sales Range: $100-124.9 Million
Emp.: 1,100
Hardwood Products Mfr & Distr
N.A.I.C.S.: 423310
Greg Besse *(CEO)*

Division (Domestic):

Besse Forest Products Group - The Baraga Lumber Division (2)
16522 Westland Dr, Baraga, MI 49908
Tel.: (906) 353-7193
Web Site: http://www.bessegroup.com
Emp.: 25
Lumber Mfr
N.A.I.C.S.: 321113
Frank Bakewell *(Plant Mgr)*

Subsidiary (Domestic):

Besse Lumber Company (2)
401 Gustafson Rd, Ladysmith, WI 54848
Tel.: (715) 532-6026
Sales Range: $1-9.9 Million
Lumber Mfr
N.A.I.C.S.: 321113
Greg Hussy *(Pres)*

Birchwood Manufacturing Company (2)
38 East Messenger St, Rice Lake, WI 54868
Tel.: (715) 234-8181
Emp.: 106
Lumber Mfr
N.A.I.C.S.: 321113
David Lohman *(Plant Mgr)*

Goodman Veneer & Lumber Company (2)
200 C Ave, Goodman, WI 54125
Tel.: (715) 336-2311
Hardwood Veneer & Lumber Mfr
N.A.I.C.S.: 321211

Northern Michigan Veneers, Inc. (2)
710 Rains Dr, Gladstone, MI 49837-1129
Tel.: (906) 428-1082
Web Site: http://www.bessegroup.com
Sales Range: $10-24.9 Million
Emp.: 60
Veneer Stock Hardwood Mfr
N.A.I.C.S.: 321211
Greg Besse *(Owner, Pres & CEO)*

Wisconsin Veneer & Plywood, Inc. (2)
610 Railroad St, Mattoon, WI 54450
Tel.: (715) 489-3611
Emp.: 125
Hardwood Veneer & Plywood Mfr
N.A.I.C.S.: 321211
John Sampson *(CEO)*

Linstol LLC (1)
3845 Beck Blvd Ste 821, Naples, FL 34114-1216
Tel.: (239) 530-7865
Web Site: http://www.linstol.com
Airport Operations
N.A.I.C.S.: 488119

Viking Plastics Inc. (1)
1 Viking St, Corry, PA 16407
Tel.: (814) 664-8671
Web Site: http://www.vikingplastics.com
Sales Range: $10-24.9 Million
Emp.: 86
Mfr of Custom Injection-Molded Plastic Products
N.A.I.C.S.: 326199
Kelly Goodsel *(Pres & CEO)*
Cathy Pitts *(Controller)*
Bob Senz *(Dir-Quality)*
Michelle McCray *(Mgr-Customer Svc)*

THE HOGAN COMPANY
107 W 5th Ave, Knoxville, TN 37917
Tel.: (865) 951-1517 — TN
Web Site: http://www.thehoganco.net
Year Founded: 1954
Rev.: $10,000,000
Emp.: 9
Business-to-Business & High Technology Services
N.A.I.C.S.: 541810
Douglas W. Hogan *(Pres & CEO)*
Marcia Griswold *(Coord-PR)*

THE HOH GROUP
55 E Jackson, Chicago, IL 60604
Tel.: (312) 346-8131 — IL
Web Site: http://www.hohgroup.com
Year Founded: 1959
Sales Range: $75-99.9 Million
Emp.: 125
Holding Company; Consulting Engineering & Architectural Services
N.A.I.C.S.: 541330
Harry O. Hefter *(Chm, Pres & CEO)*
Tom Kutas *(COO)*

Subsidiaries:

HOH Architects, Inc. (1)
1 N LaSalle St 7th Fl, Chicago, IL 60602
Tel.: (312) 346-8131
Web Site: http://www.hohgroup.com
Sales Range: $10-24.9 Million
Emp.: 70
Architectural Design of Plants, Office Buildings, Warehouses & Educational, Health & Computer Facilities
N.A.I.C.S.: 541310
Mark Miller *(Mgr-Architecture)*

HOH Engineers, Inc. (1)
55 E Jackson Ste 600, Chicago, IL 60604-3608
Tel.: (312) 346-8131
Web Site: http://www.hohgroup.com
Sales Range: $10-24.9 Million
Emp.: 55
Engineering Services for Metal, Manufacturing, Food, Chemical & Pharmaceutical Industries & Environmental & Hazardous Wastes
N.A.I.C.S.: 541330
Harry O. Hefter *(Chm & Pres)*

THE HOH GROUP

The HOH Group—(Continued)

Harry O. Hefter Associates, Inc. (1)
55 E Jackson Blvd Ste 600, Chicago, IL 60604   (100%)
Tel.: (312) 346-8131
Web Site: http://www.hohgroup.com
Sales Range: $10-24.9 Million
Emp.: 52
Engineering Services for Government Specializing in Transportation, Municipal Structures & Waterworks
N.A.I.C.S.: 541330
David Torelli (CFO)

THE HOLLAND COMPANY, INC.
121 Thomas Mill Rd, Holly Springs, NC 27540-9320
Tel.: (919) 557-2001
Web Site: http://www.hollandgrill.com
Sales Range: $10-24.9 Million
Emp.: 27
Mfr & Sales of Barbecues & Grills
N.A.I.C.S.: 335220
Barry Byars (VP)
Mike O'Grady (COO)

THE HOLLAND, INC.
109 W 17th St, Vancouver, WA 98660-2932
Tel.: (360) 694-1521
Web Site: http://www.burgerville.com
Year Founded: 1992
Sales Range: $50-74.9 Million
Emp.: 1,500
Fast Food Restaurant Operator
N.A.I.C.S.: 722513
Tom Mears (Chm)
Jack Graves (Chief Cultural Officer)
Janice Williams (COO)
Subsidiaries:

Burgerville USA (1)
109 W 17th St, Vancouver, WA 98660
Tel.: (866) 264-2313
Web Site: http://www.burgerville.com
Sales Range: $75-99.9 Million
Emp.: 1,200
Fast Food Restaurants
N.A.I.C.S.: 722513
Jeff Harvey (Pres & CEO)

THE HOLLAR COMPANY INC.
2012 Rainbow Dr, Gadsden, AL 35901-5550
Tel.: (256) 547-1644
Year Founded: 1976
Sales Range: $10-24.9 Million
Emp.: 14
Convenience Store
N.A.I.C.S.: 445131
Wayne Hollar (Pres)
Orva McDonald (Controller)

THE HOME AGENCY
210 Smith St, Elwood, NE 68937
Tel.: (308) 785-2803
Web Site: http://www.thehomeagency.com
Year Founded: 1986
Sales Range: $1-9.9 Million
Emp.: 35
Issuer of Crop Insurance, Personal, Business & Financial Services
N.A.I.C.S.: 524126
James Baldonado (Owner)
Deb Arends (Mgr-Property & Casualty)
Dan Tinlin (Mgr)

THE HOME SALES COMPANY
216 Schilling Cir Ste 300, Hunt Valley, MD 21031
Tel.: (410) 628-6000
Rev.: $23,100,000
Emp.: 150
Real Estate Agency
N.A.I.C.S.: 531210

Carl T. Julio (Pres)
Subsidiaries:

Hill Management Services Inc. (1)
964 Deereco Rd, Timonium, MD 21093
Tel.: (410) 666-1000
Web Site: http://www.hsales.com
Rev.: $4,100,000
Real Estate Managers
N.A.I.C.S.: 621210
Tracee M. Cutair (Mgr-Property)
Danielle Beyrodt (VP)
Lynn White-Huggins (Mgr-Property)

THE HOMER GROUP
2605 Egypt Rd, Trooper, PA 19403
Tel.: (610) 539-8400
Web Site: http://www.homergroup.com
Year Founded: 1958
Sales Range: $1-9.9 Million
Emp.: 8
Digital Media, Marketing, Creative Design & Commercial Printing Services
N.A.I.C.S.: 541840
Guy Homer (Pres & CEO)
Bernie Homer (Founder)
Michael Smith (Mgr-Customer Svc)

THE HOMER LAUGHLIN CHINA COMPANY
672 Fiesta Dr, Newell, WV 26050-1067
Tel.: (304) 387-1300
Web Site: http://www.hlchina.com
Year Founded: 1871
Sales Range: $400-449.9 Million
Emp.: 1,100
Mfr of Lead Free Vitreous China Dinnerware for Hotel, Restaurant, Health Care & Retail Markets
N.A.I.C.S.: 327110
Judi Noble (Dir-Art)
Subsidiaries:

Newell Bridge & Railway Company (1)
672 Fiesta Dr, Newell, WV 26050-0593   (100%)
Tel.: (304) 387-1300
Sales Range: $10-24.9 Million
Emp.: 12
Interstate Toll Bridge
N.A.I.C.S.: 488490
Pete Wicks (VP)
J.M. Wells III (Pres)

The Newell Company (1)
672 Fiesta Dr, Newell, WV 26050-1067   (100%)
Tel.: (304) 387-1300
Sales Range: $25-49.9 Million
Emp.: 30
Water & Sewer Public Utility
N.A.I.C.S.: 221310

THE HONEST KITCHEN, INC.
111 14th St, San Diego, CA 92101
Tel.: (619) 544-0018
Web Site: http://www.thehonestkitchen.com
Year Founded: 2002
Sales Range: $10-24.9 Million
Emp.: 40
Pet Food Product Mfr & Distr
N.A.I.C.S.: 311111
Lucy Postins (Co-Founder & Chief Integrity Officer)
Charlie Postins (Co-Founder)
Laurette Sipe (Dir-Procurement)
Carmen Velasquez (Dir-Mktg)
Jerry Scheffers (Dir-Production)

THE HORST GROUP INC.
320 Granite Run Dr, Lancaster, PA 17601
Tel.: (717) 581-9800
Web Site: http://www.horstgroup.com

Year Founded: 1979
Sales Range: $50-74.9 Million
Emp.: 625
Provider of Construction & Property Management Insurance Services
N.A.I.C.S.: 236220
David Charles King (Mgr-Corp Risk)
Randall L. Horst (Pres & CEO)
Harry F. Scheid (CEO-Horst Construction & Excavating)
Michael Giordano (CFO)
Subsidiaries:

Horst Construction Company Inc. (1)
320 Granite Run Dr PO Box 3310, Lancaster, PA 17601-6806   (100%)
Tel.: (717) 581-9910
Web Site: http://www.horstgroup.com
Sales Range: $25-49.9 Million
Emp.: 200
Provider of Construction Services
N.A.I.C.S.: 236220
Ken Fetterolf (VP)
Ryan Null (Dir-Special Construction Svcs)
Harry F. Scheid II (Pres & CEO)

Horst Insurance Agency (1)
320 Granite Run Dr, Lancaster, PA 17601
Tel.: (610) 459-8285
Web Site: http://www.horstgroup.com
Sales Range: $50-74.9 Million
Emp.: 120
Provider of Insurance Construction & Property Management Services
N.A.I.C.S.: 524210
David Charles King (Pres & CEO)

Horst Property Management (1)
320 Granite Run Dr, Lancaster, PA 17601-6806   (100%)
Tel.: (717) 581-9850
Web Site: http://www.horstgroup.com
Sales Range: $50-74.9 Million
Emp.: 400
Provider of Building Operation Services
N.A.I.C.S.: 531110

THE HORTON FRUIT COMPANY, INC.
4701 Jennings Ln, Louisville, KY 40218-2925
Tel.: (502) 969-1371
Web Site: http://www.hortonfruit.com
Year Founded: 1940
Sales Range: $25-49.9 Million
Emp.: 150
Fresh Fruits & Vegetables
N.A.I.C.S.: 424480
Albert C. Horton (Chm & CEO)
Steve Edelen (Treas)
Jackson Woodward (Pres & COO)

THE HOTH CORP.
111 2nd Ave NE Ste 1500, Saint Petersburg, FL 33701
Web Site: http://www.thehoth.com
Year Founded: 2010
Sales Range: $1-9.9 Million
Information Technology Consulting Services
N.A.I.C.S.: 541512
Marc Hardgrove (Partner)
David Martin (Partner)
Clayton Johnson (CMO)
George Papadeas (COO)
Jason Gill (CTO)

THE HOUSING PARTNERSHIP NETWORK
1 Washington Mall 12th Fl, Boston, MA 02108
Tel.: (617) 720-1999
Web Site: http://www.housingpartnership.net
Year Founded: 1992
Sales Range: $10-24.9 Million
Emp.: 45
Community Housing Services
N.A.I.C.S.: 624229

U.S. PRIVATE

Sherree Capello (VP-Fin & Acct)
Kathleen M. Farrell (Asst Treas)
Rebecca Regan (Exec VP)
Randy J. Parker (CFO & Mng Dir-Poah)
Shannon Ross (Dir-Govt Rels)
Liza Dube (VP-Comm)
Mike Hynes (Pres)

THE HUMANE SOCIETY OF THE UNITED STATES
1255 23rd St NW Ste 450, Washington, DC 20037
Tel.: (202) 452-1100
Web Site: https://www.humanesociety.org
Year Founded: 1954
Rev.: $85,857,349
Emp.: 300
Fiscal Year-end: 12/31/09
Humane Treatment of Animals Promoter
N.A.I.C.S.: 813312
Kelly O'Meara (Dir-Program)
Eugene W. Lorenz (Treas)
Roger A. Kindler (Chief Legal Officer & Gen Counsel)
Sarah Mesa (Mgr-Web Content)
Thomas Wait (CFO)
Wayne Tacelle (Reg Dir)
Kitty Block (Acting Pres & Acting CEO)
Rick Bernthal (Chm)

THE HUNGARY INITIATIVES FOUNDATION
1100 H St NW Ste 915, Washington, DC 20005
Tel.: (202) 733-2263
Web Site: http://www.hungaryfoundation.org
Year Founded: 2012
Sales Range: $10-24.9 Million
Emp.: 1
American Civic Association
N.A.I.C.S.: 813920
Elizabeth Perch (CFO)
Tamas Fellegi (Pres & CEO)

THE HUNT CORPORATION
7720 N 16th St Ste 100, Phoenix, AZ 85020
Tel.: (480) 368-4700
Web Site: http://www.huntconstructiongroup.com
Year Founded: 1944
Sales Range: $1-4.9 Billion
Emp.: 1,000
Holding Company; Contract Commercial Construction Services
N.A.I.C.S.: 551112
Jose Pienknagura (Gen Counsel)
Stephen E. Atkins (CFO & Exec VP)
Michael Fratianni (COO)
Paul Wylie (CIO)

THE HUNTE CORPORATION
121 Roy Hill Blvd, Goodman, MO 64843
Tel.: (417) 364-8597
Web Site: http://www.thehuntecorporation.com
Sales Range: $25-49.9 Million
Emp.: 170
Puppies
N.A.I.C.S.: 424990
Darrell Offutt (CIO & VP)
Bill Oxford (Dir-Veterinary Svcs)
Jackie Smith (Dir-Safety Regulatory Compliance)
Michael Stolkey (Dir-Sls)

THE HUNTINGTON LIBRARY, ART COLLECTIONS, AND BOTANICAL GARDENS

COMPANIES THE INLAND REAL ESTATE GROUP OF COMPANIES, INC.

1151 Oxford Rd, San Marino, CA 91108
Tel.: (626) 405-2100 CA
Web Site: http://www.huntington.org
Year Founded: 1919
Sales Range: $75-99.9 Million
Emp.: 522
Library, Museum & Botanical Garden Operator
N.A.I.C.S.: 519210
Randy Shulman *(VP-Advancement)*
Russel T. Kully *(Dir-Art Collections)*
Susan Turner-Lowe *(VP-Comm)*
Anne F. Rothenberg *(Chm)*
Catherine Allgor *(Dir-Education)*
Coreen A. Rodgers *(VP-Fin Affairs)*
Kevin Salatino *(Dir-Art Collections)*
Mitchell Morris *(CIO)*
Steve Hindle *(Pres-Interim)*
Larry J. Burik *(VP-Facilities)*
Karen R. Lawrence *(Pres)*

THE HUNTON GROUP
10555 Westpark Dr, Houston, TX 77042-5232
Tel.: (713) 266-3551 TX
Web Site: http://www.huntongroup.com
Year Founded: 1981
Sales Range: $200-249.9 Million
Emp.: 350
Heating & Air Conditioning Services
N.A.I.C.S.: 423730
Richard O. Hunton *(Chm & CEO)*
Albert Mireles *(VP-HR)*
Bruce Seher *(CFO)*
Chris Stanziale *(Mgr-Ops-Hunton Distr-Houston)*
Klint S. Nunn *(VP & Gen Mgr)*
Robert Tyler *(VP-Equipment Sls & Hunton Distr)*
John Dearman *(VP-Parts-Hunton Distr)*
Richard Hunton Jr. *(Pres & COO)*

THE HYLAND COMPANY
PO Box 5129, Ashland, KY 41105
Tel.: (606) 928-4011
Web Site: http://www.thepridedogfood.com
Sales Range: $10-24.9 Million
Emp.: 20
Dog & Cat Food Mfr
N.A.I.C.S.: 311111
Barbara Hinton *(Pres)*
Laura Warnick *(Office Mgr)*
Gary Cook *(Mgr-Safety)*

THE I SUPPLY COMPANY
1255 Spangler Rd, Fairborn, OH 45324
Tel.: (937) 878-5240
Web Site: http://www.isupplyco.com
Year Founded: 1944
Sales Range: $25-49.9 Million
Emp.: 75
Custom Food, Paper Products & Janitorial Supplies Distr
N.A.I.C.S.: 424130
Gerald L. Parisi *(Chm & CEO)*
Mario Parisi *(Co-Pres)*
Tim Detrick *(VP-Food Sys Div)*
Dan Strawn *(CFO & VP-Corp Svcs)*
Gene F. Shepard *(VP-Broad line Paper Sls & Procurement)*
Ted Chambers *(VP-Ops)*
Joe Parisi II *(Co-Pres)*

THE ICEBOX, LLC
700 Lake Ave, Atlanta, GA 30307
Tel.: (404) 460-1275
Web Site: http://www.iceboxonline.com
Year Founded: 1992
Sales Range: $10-24.9 Million
Emp.: 50
Mfr & Designer of Custom Branded Apparel & Corporate Branded Merchandise
N.A.I.C.S.: 315250
Scott Alterman *(Owner)*
Donnie Browne *(COO)*
Jordy Gamson *(Pres & CEO)*
Chuck Norton *(Dir-Ops)*
Janice McNamara *(Controller)*

THE ICLA DA SILVA FOUNDATION
311 W 43rd St 12 Fl, New York, NY 10036
Tel.: (212) 593-1807 NJ
Web Site: http://www.icla.org
Year Founded: 1992
Sales Range: $1-9.9 Million
Emp.: 36
Child Care Support Services
N.A.I.C.S.: 624110
Airam Da Silva *(Pres)*
Shawn V. Austin *(Chm)*
Andrew M. Wuertele *(Vice Chm)*
Kala Maxym *(Sec)*
Lawrence M. Itskowitch *(Treas)*

THE IDEAL COMPANY INC.
8313 Kimmel Rd, Clayton, OH 45315
Tel.: (937) 836-8683
Web Site: http://www.idealco.net
Emp.: 30
General Contractor & Commercial Construction Services
N.A.I.C.S.: 236220
Kent Filbrun *(Co-Owner & Officer)*
Doug Shearer *(CFO)*
Fred Sink *(Co-Owner & Officer)*

THE IDEAL GROUP, INC.
2525 Clark St, Detroit, MI 48209
Tel.: (313) 849-0000 MI
Web Site: https://www.weareideal.com
Year Founded: 2000
Sales Range: $25-49.9 Million
Holding Company
N.A.I.C.S.: 551112
Jesse Venegas *(Pres-Ideal Setech & VP)*
Loren Venegas *(CEO)*
Frank Venegas Jr. *(Chm)*
Linzie Venegas *(Pres)*
Matthew Hickey *(CFO)*

Subsidiaries:

Ideal Contracting L.L.C. (1)
2525 Clark St, Detroit, MI 48209
Tel.: (313) 843-8000
Web Site: https://www.idealcontracting.com
Sales Range: $50-74.9 Million
Emp.: 400
Commercial & Industrial Construction Contractor
N.A.I.C.S.: 236220
Loren Venegas *(CEO)*
Richard Brown *(Pres)*

Ideal Setech HoldCo, Inc. (1)
2525 Clark Ave, Detroit, MI 48209
Tel.: (313) 359-8004
Web Site: https://idealsetech.com
Holding Company
N.A.I.C.S.: 551112
Jesse Venegas *(Pres)*

Subsidiary (Domestic):

Ideal Setech Share-The-Spare LLC (2)
1415 Durant Dr, Howell, MI 48843
Tel.: (517) 292-7100
Automotive Industry Procurement & Support Services
N.A.I.C.S.: 541614

Ideal Setech, L.L.C. (2)
3104 S Creyts Rd, Lansing, MI 48917
Tel.: (517) 580-0789
Web Site: https://idealsetech.com
Business Optimization, Procurement & Consulting Services
N.A.I.C.S.: 561499

Ideal Shield, L.L.C. (1)
2525 Clark St, Detroit, MI 48209
Tel.: (313) 842-7290
Web Site: http://www.idealshield.com
Sales Range: $1-9.9 Million
Commercial & Industrial Steel Protection Products Mfr
N.A.I.C.S.: 332999
Dennis Knittel *(Dir-Natl Distr)*

Ideal Steel & Builders' Supplies, LLC (1)
2525 Clark Ave, Detroit, MI 48209
Tel.: (313) 849-0000
Construction Materials Whslr
N.A.I.C.S.: 423510

THE IDI GROUP COMPANIES
1700 N Moore St Ste 2020, Arlington, VA 22209-1921
Tel.: (703) 558-7300 VA
Web Site: http://www.idigroup.com
Year Founded: 1975
Sales Range: $75-99.9 Million
Emp.: 63
Provider of Real Estate Development Services
N.A.I.C.S.: 531120
Giuseppe Cecchi *(Pres & CEO)*
Norman Dreyfuss *(COO & Exec VP)*
Carlo Baietti *(Dir-Sls)*
Enrico Cecchi *(Gen Counsel & VP)*

THE IMAGE GROUP
31 E 8th St Ste 200, Holland, MI 49423
Tel.: (616) 393-9588
Web Site: http://www.imagegroup.com
Sales Range: Less than $1 Million
Emp.: 20
N.A.I.C.S.: 541810
Ade Snyder *(Mgr-Production)*
Scott Kramer *(Sr Dir-Art)*
Ed Van Poolen *(Dir-Creative)*
Julie Berghoef *(Sr Acct Exec)*
Mark Tanis *(Pres)*
Rich Evenhouse *(Sr Dir-Art)*
Andrea Beckman *(Dir-Art)*
Layne Fuller *(Acct Mgr)*
Pete Lounsbury *(Dir-Art)*

THE IMAGINATION FACTORY
648 Monroe NW Ste 118, Grand Rapids, MI 49503
Tel.: (616) 356-2545 MI
Web Site: http://www.what-if.com
Year Founded: 1985
Sales Range: $10-24.9 Million
Emp.: 6
Advertising Agencies
N.A.I.C.S.: 541810
Kate McCrindle *(Partner & Project Mgr)*

THE IMPEX GROUP OF COMPANIES
12 Roszel Rd, Princeton, NJ 08540-7063
Tel.: (609) 720-0300
Web Site: http://www.send.com
Sales Range: $10-24.9 Million
Emp.: 20
E-Commerce Network Services
N.A.I.C.S.: 541611
Ranjan Wijesinghe *(Founder, Chm, Pres & CEO)*

Subsidiaries:

SendOnline.com, Inc. (1)
12 Roszel Rd Ste A-204, Princeton, NJ 08540-7063
Tel.: (609) 720-0300
Web Site: http://www.send.com

Sales Range: $10-24.9 Million
Emp.: 5
E-Commerce Network Operator
N.A.I.C.S.: 459420
Ranjan Wijesinghe *(Founder & CEO)*

THE IN-HOUSE AGENCY, INC.
55 Madison Ave Ste 400, Morristown, NJ 07960
Tel.: (973) 285-3259
Web Site: http://www.theinhouseagency.com
Year Founded: 1996
Rev.: $10,000,000
Emp.: 10
N.A.I.C.S.: 541810
Doug MacGibbon *(Pres & Exec Dir-Creative)*

THE INCREDIBLE CHRISTMAS PLACE
2470 Pkwy, Pigeon Forge, TN 37863
Tel.: (865) 453-0415
Web Site: http://www.christmasplace.com
Year Founded: 1986
Sales Range: $10-24.9 Million
Emp.: 250
Christmas Items, Gifts & Collectibles Retailer
N.A.I.C.S.: 459999
Marion Biggs *(Founder)*
Caroline Fairbank *(Pres & COO)*

THE INDIANA HEMOPHILIA & THROMBOSIS CENTER, INC.
8326 Naab Rd, Indianapolis, IN 46260
Tel.: (317) 871-0000 IN
Web Site: http://www.ihtc.org
Year Founded: 1998
Sales Range: $25-49.9 Million
Emp.: 112
Health Care Srvices
N.A.I.C.S.: 622110
Phillip E. Himelstein *(Chm)*

THE INDIGO ROAD HOSPITALITY GROUP, LLC
90 Alexander St, Charleston, SC 29403
Tel.: (843) 297-8385
Web Site: http://www.theindigoroad.com
Year Founded: 2009
Sales Range: $25-49.9 Million
Emp.: 960
Restaurant Operators
N.A.I.C.S.: 722511
Steve Palmer *(Mng Partner)*

THE INLAND REAL ESTATE GROUP OF COMPANIES, INC.
2901 Butterfield Rd, Oak Brook, IL 60523
Tel.: (630) 218-8000
Web Site: http://www.inlandgroup.com
Rev.: $20,200,000,000
Emp.: 1,000
Holding Company; Real Estate Investment
N.A.I.C.S.: 551112
Mitchell A. Sabshon *(CEO)*
Robert Douglas Parks *(Mgr)*
Daniel L. Goodwin *(Chm)*
Chong P. Huan *(CIO)*
Timothy Hutchison *(COO)*
Prashant Bodhanwala *(Chief Acctg Officer)*
Ernest Fiorante *(CFO)*
Anthony Casaccio *(Pres)*
G. Joseph Cosenza *(Vice Chm)*
Richard Jurek *(CMO)*

THE INLAND REAL ESTATE GROUP OF COMPANIES, INC.   U.S. PRIVATE

The Inland Real Estate Group of Companies, Inc.—(Continued)

Robert H. Baum (Vice Chm, Exec VP & Gen Counsel)
Les Sweetow (Head-Client Strategy & Res)
Michael Ezzell II (CEO)

Subsidiaries:

InPoint Commercial Real Estate Income, Inc. (1)
2901 Butterfield Rd, Oak Brook, IL 60523
Web Site: https://www.inland-investments.com
Rev.: $38,044,000
Assets: $914,495,000
Liabilities: $635,938,000
Net Worth: $278,557,000
Earnings: $4,430,000
Emp.: 1,001
Fiscal Year-end: 12/31/2022
Real Estate Investment Services
N.A.I.C.S.: 531210
Mitchell A. Sabshon (Chm & CEO)
Donald MacKinnon (Pres)
Catherine L. Lynch (CFO & Treas)
Matthew Donnelly (Chief Investment Officer)
Cathleen M. Hrtanek (Sec)

Inland Mortgage Capital, LLC (1)
2901 Butterfield Rd, Oak Brook, IL 60523-1159
Tel.: (630) 218-8000
Web Site: http://inlandmtg.com
Mortgage Bankers & Correspondents
N.A.I.C.S.: 522292
Art Rendak (Pres)
Scott Filippelli (Portfolio Mgr)
Eileen McDonald (Sr VP & Dir-Credit)
Dan Schmitz (VP-Loan Origination)
Kevin Baradziej (VP-Underwriter)
Kristen Santiago (Officer Mgr & Coord-Loan)
Anna Kuta (Coord-Mktg)

Inland Real Estate Investment Corporation (1)
2901 Butterfield Rd, Oak Brook, IL 60523
Web Site: http://www.inland-investments.com
Real Estate Investment Fund Management Services
N.A.I.C.S.: 523940
Catherine L. Lynch (CFO, Treas & Sec)
Colin G. Cosgrove (Exec VP & Natl Sls Mgr)
Roderick S. Curtis (Sr VP-Res & Product Dev)
Sandra L. Perion (Sr VP-Ops)
Daniel W. Zatloukal (Exec VP & Head-Asset Mgmt)
Robert Braun (VP-Self-Storage Asset Mgmt)

Affiliate (Domestic):

Inland Residential Properties Trust, Inc. (2)
2901 Butterfield Rd, Oak Brook, IL 60523
Tel.: (630) 218-8000
Web Site: http://www.inland-investments.com
Real Estate Investment Trust
N.A.I.C.S.: 525990
Catherine L. Lynch (CFO, Chief Acctg Officer & Treas)
Roderick S. Curtis (VP)
Cathleen M. Hrtanek (Sec)

Subsidiary (Domestic):

Inland Securities Corporation (2)
2901 Butterfield Rd, Oak Brook, IL 60523-1159
Tel.: (630) 218-8000
Web Site: http://www.inland-investments.com
Sales Range: $1-4.9 Billion
Security Brokerage Services
N.A.I.C.S.: 523150
Michael T. Ezzell (Pres & CEO)
Colin Cosgrove (Exec VP & Mgr-Sls-Natl)
Carlos Hammer (VP)
Jonathan Freeman (VP)
Jeff Noblin (VP)
Charles Jensen (Sr VP)
Jeni Middaugh (VP)

Miguel Aguilar (VP)
Peter Fisher (Sr VP-Building Networks-North California)
Sarita Vishakanta (VP-Broker Dealer Rels)
Phil Graham (Exec VP-Strategic Rels)
J. Rick Martens (Sr VP-External Wholesaler)
Midquel McClendon (Sr VP-External Wholesaler)
Stephen Blazick (Sr VP-External Wholesaler)

The Inland Real Estate Group, LLC (1)
2901 Butterfield Rd, Oak Brook, IL 60523
Tel.: (630) 218-8000
Web Site: http://www.inlandgroup.com
Real Estate Investment
N.A.I.C.S.: 531390
Daniel L. Goodman (Chm, CEO & Principal)
Anthony Chereso (CFO)

THE INNOVATION INSTITUTE
1 Centerpointe Dr Ste 200, La Palma, CA 90623
Tel.: (714) 735-3750
Web Site: http://www.ii4change.com
Year Founded: 2013
Emp.: 650
Healtcare Services
N.A.I.C.S.: 621610
Joe Randolph (Pres & CEO)
Steve Gilbert (COO & Exec VP)
Edward Wong (CFO & Exec VP)
Larry Stofko (Exec VP-Innovation Lab)
Diane Hejna (VP-Mission Integration)

Subsidiaries:

HB Network Solutions, Inc. (1)
9036 Pulsar Ct Ste B, Corona, CA 92883
Tel.: (888) 602-5882
Web Site: http://www.hbns.net
Emp.: 50
IT Managed Services; Low Voltage Infrastructure & Technology Solutions
N.A.I.C.S.: 541330

THE INSPIRATION NETWORKS
7910 Crescent Executive Dr, Charlotte, NC 28217
Tel.: (803) 578-1000
Web Site: http://www.insp.com
Sales Range: $10-24.9 Million
Emp.: 200
Cable Television Services
N.A.I.C.S.: 516210
Mark Kang (Sr VP-Worldwide Distr)
Bill McCall (VP-Worldwide Distr)
Christine Rodocker (VP-Affiliate Mktg)
Debbie Stallings (Mgr-Database)
Kimberli O'Meara (Mgr-Affiliate Mktg)
Tammy Burklin (VP-Worldwide Distr)

Subsidiaries:

The Inspiration Networks (1)
PO Box 7750, Charlotte, NC 28241
Tel.: (803) 578-1000
Web Site: http://www.insp.com
Cable Television Services
N.A.I.C.S.: 516210
David Cerullo (CEO)
Matthew Saxon (VP-Fin Reporting & Sys)

THE INSTANT WEB COMPANIES
7951 Powers Blvd, Chanhassen, MN 55317-9502
Tel.: (952) 474-0961   MN
Web Site: http://www.iwco.com
Year Founded: 1968
Sales Range: $75-99.9 Million
Emp.: 2,500
Plastic Cards & Envelope Mfr & Direct Mail Advertising Services
N.A.I.C.S.: 323111
James N. Andersen (CEO)
Mary Hyland (VP-Bus Svcs)
Beverly Lohs (VP-HR)

Kurt Ruppel (Dir-Postal Policy & Mktg Comm)
Debora Haskel (VP-Mktg & Corp Comm)
Mike Dietz (Dir-Creative Svcs)
James S. Leone (VP-Sls)
Steven W. Myrvold (Exec VP-Ops & Customer Experience)
Joseph F. Morrison (Pres & CEO)
Mike Ertel (Exec VP-Sls & Mktg)
James Gartrell (VP-Content Dev)
Michael Henry (VP-Mail-Gard)
Jake Hertel (VP-Fin)
Tom Hexamer (VP-Sls)
Wes Sparling (VP-Mktg Strategy)
Chris Van Houtte (VP-IT)
Alan Sherman (VP-Mktg Strategy)

Subsidiaries:

The Instant Web Companies - Mail-Gard Division (1)
65 Steamboat Dr, Warminster, PA 18974
Tel.: (800) 220-2066
Computer Disaster Recovery Services
N.A.I.C.S.: 541519

THE INSTITUTE FOR FAMILY HEALTH
16 E 16th St, New York, NY 10003
Tel.: (212) 633-0800   NY
Web Site: http://www.institute.org
Year Founded: 1985
Sales Range: $100-124.9 Million
Emp.: 1,076
Health Care Srvices
N.A.I.C.S.: 622110
Edward Fried (Sr VP-Admin)
Virna Little (Sr VP-Psychosocial Svcs & Community Affairs)
Nicole Nurse (Sr VP-HR & Regulatory Affairs)
Maxine Golub (Sr VP-Plng & Dev)
Robert Schiller (Chief Medical Officer & Sr VP-Clinical Affairs)
Kathleen Cresswell (CIO-Practice Ops)
Alan Woghin (CFO & VP-Fin)

THE INSTITUTE FOR HEALTHCARE IMPROVEMENT
53 State St 19th Fl, Boston, MA 02109
Tel.: (617) 301-4800   MA
Web Site: http://www.ihi.org
Year Founded: 1992
Rev.: $46,657,261
Assets: $121,328,029
Liabilities: $21,551,141
Net Worth: $99,776,888
Emp.: 177
Fiscal Year-end: 04/30/18
Health Care Srvices
N.A.I.C.S.: 622110
Pedro Delgado (Head-Europe & Latin America)
Carol Beasley (Sr VP)
Pierre M. Barker (Chief Global Partnerships & Programs Officer)
Don Goldmann (Chief Medical & Scientific Officer)
Donald M. Berwick (Bd of Dirs, Executives)
Karen Baldoza (Exec Dir)
Joanne Healy (Sr VP)
Andrea Kabcenell (VP)
Kenneth Tebbetts (VP-HR)
Cathleen Duffy (Exec Dir-Fin)
Kedar Mate (Pres & CEO)
Carol Haraden (VP)
Patricia Rutherford (VP)
Frank Federico (VP)
Robert Lloyd (VP)

THE INSTITUTE OF CLASSICAL ARCHITECTURE
20 W 44th St, New York, NY 10036

Tel.: (212) 730-9646   NY
Web Site: http://www.classicist.org
Year Founded: 1996
Sales Range: $1-9.9 Million
Emp.: 44
Art School
N.A.I.C.S.: 611519
Peter Lyden (Pres)
Mark Ferguson (Chm)
Suzanne R. Santry (Sec)
Russell Windham (Treas)

THE INSTITUTE OF FINANCIAL OPERATIONS
3319 Maguire Blvd Ste 125, Orlando, FL 32803
Tel.: (407) 351-3322
Web Site: http://www.financialops.org
Emp.: 15
Financial Services Organization
N.A.I.C.S.: 813910
Ken Brown (VP-Event Svcs)
Bally Jennings (Exec Dir-UK)
Joe Flynn (Chm)
Kathy Shannon (Asst VP-Acctg Sys Design & Dev)
William Lowman (Vice Chm & Treas)
Tina Kidd (Dir-Partnerships & Exhibitor Svcs)

Subsidiaries:

International Accounts Payable Professionals (1)
T Wing Crowthorne Business Estate, Old Wokingham Road, Crowthorne, RG45 6AW, United Kingdom
Tel.: (44) 845.680 9871
Web Site: http://www.theiapp.co.uk
Financial Services Organization
N.A.I.C.S.: 813910

THE INSTITUTE OF PROFESSIONAL PRACTICE, INC.
PO Box 1249, Montpelier, VT 05601
Tel.: (802) 229-9515   VT
Web Site: http://www.ippi.org
Year Founded: 1981
Sales Range: $50-74.9 Million
Emp.: 1,428
Developmental Disability Assistance Services
N.A.I.C.S.: 623210
Steven W. Harris (CIO)
Kim M. Kelly (VP-Clinical Svcs)
George M. Durham (VP-Program Svcs)
Elaine J. Lussier (Exec VP)
Michael Chater (Chm)
Lois MacGill Nial (CFO)
Susan Frederickson (Mgr-Mktg & Admin-Clinical Svcs)
Louis Giramma (CEO)
Steve Schultz (Chief HR Officer)

THE INTEC GROUP INC.
666 S Vermont St, Palatine, IL 60067
Tel.: (847) 358-0088
Web Site: http://www.intecgrp.com
Sales Range: $25-49.9 Million
Emp.: 125
Molding Primary Plastics
N.A.I.C.S.: 326199
Char Kovac (Office Mgr-Admin)
Yvonne Kowall (Coord-Bus Dev)
Gary Santos (Mgr-QA)
Lorena Drewes (Asst Mgr-Quality)
Tricia Nash (Sr Project Mgr)

THE INTEGRAL GROUP LLC
191 Peachtree St, Atlanta, GA 30303
Tel.: (404) 224-1860
Web Site: http://www.integral-online.com
Rev.: $20,327,155
Emp.: 150
Commercial Real Estate; Subdividers & Developers

COMPANIES

THE IVY GROUP, LTD.

N.A.I.C.S.: 237210
Egbert L. J. Perry *(Founder, Chm & CEO)*
A. Rian Smith *(Chief Legal Officer & VP)*
Arthur Lomenick *(Principal-Comml Real Estate Div)*
Dalila Sotelo *(Mng Dir-Western Reg Community Dev Div)*
Denise C. Koehl *(Pres-Property Mgmt Div)*
Hope Boldon *(Sr VP)*
Valerie Edwards *(Chief Admin Officer)*
Denise Cleveland-Leggett *(Sr VP-Bus Dev)*
Vicki Lundy Wilbon *(Pres-Real Estate Dev & Mgmt, Principal & Exec VP)*

Subsidiaries:

Integral Properties LLC (1)
191 Peachtree St Ste 4100, Atlanta, GA 30303
Tel.: (404) 224-1860
Web Site: http://www.integral-online.com
Rev.: $2,799,334
Emp.: 4
Real Estate Agents & Managers
N.A.I.C.S.: 531210
Egbert L. J. Perry *(Founder, Chm & CEO)*
Vicky Lundy Wilbon *(Exec VP)*

The Integral Building Group LLC (1)
60 Piedmont Ave NE, Atlanta, GA 30303
Tel.: (404) 224-1860
Web Site: http://www.integral-online.com
Construction Management
N.A.I.C.S.: 541618
Egbert L. J. Perry *(Chm & CEO)*

THE INTERCHURCH CENTER
475 Riverside Dr, New York, NY 10115
Tel.: (212) 870-2200 NY
Web Site: http://www.interchurch-center.org
Year Founded: 1948
Sales Range: $10-24.9 Million
Emp.: 16
Religious Organizations
N.A.I.C.S.: 813110
Michele Fox *(Dir-Capital Projects & Plng)*
Paula M. Mayo *(Pres & Exec Dir)*
Christopher Johnson *(Dir-Music)*
Alex Casasola *(Mgr-Telecom)*
Rachel Rivera *(Mgr-Tenanat Rels)*
Christine Kaminski *(Dir-HR)*
Timothy Hogan *(Mgr-Sr Property)*

THE INTERCONNECT GROUP
4470 Chamblee Dunwoody Rd Ste 324, Atlanta, GA 30338
Tel.: (678) 990-0919
Web Site: http://www.addate.com
Year Founded: 2001
Sales Range: $25-49.9 Million
Emp.: 8
Media Buying Agency
N.A.I.C.S.: 541830
Narayan Swamy *(Co-Founder & Pres)*
Joe Dey *(Mktg Mgr)*

THE INTERNATIONAL ASSOCIATION OF FIRE CHIEFS
4025 Fair Ridge Dr Ste 300, Fairfax, VA 22033
Tel.: (703) 273-0911 NY
Web Site: http://www.iafc.org
Year Founded: 1873
Sales Range: $10-24.9 Million
Emp.: 71
Fire Chief Association
N.A.I.C.S.: 813920
Lisa Yonkers *(Dir-Conferences & Education)*
Ken LaSala *(Dir-Govt Rels & Policy)*
Dan Eggleston *(Second VP)*
Mark W. Light *(CEO & Exec Dir)*
Richard R. Carrizzo *(Treas)*
Thomas Jenkins *(Chm & Pres)*
Gary Curmode *(First VP)*
E. Thomas Hicks IV *(CTO, Chief Programs Officer & Asst Exec Dir)*

THE INTERNATIONAL SPY MUSEUM
700 L'Enfant Plz SW, Washington, DC 20024
Tel.: (202) 393-7798
Web Site: https://www.spymuseum.org
Year Founded: 2002
Museum Exhibition Services
N.A.I.C.S.: 711510

THE INTERNET LANGUAGE COMPANY
5519 University Way NE, Seattle, WA 98105
Tel.: (206) 384-3728
Web Site: http://www.multilingualbooks.com
Year Founded: 1995
Language & Translation Products Whslr
N.A.I.C.S.: 424920
Kenneth Tomkins *(Founder & Dir-Bus Dev)*

THE INTERTECH GROUP, INC.
4838 Jenkins Ave, North Charleston, SC 29405-4816
Tel.: (843) 744-5174 SC
Web Site: https://www.theintertechgroup.com
Year Founded: 1978
Sales Range: $1-4.9 Billion
Emp.: 15,000
Offices of Other Holding Companies
N.A.I.C.S.: 551112
Joseph L. Myers *(Dir-Fin)*
J. Tiedemann *(COO & Exec VP)*
Grant Reeves *(VP)*
Robert B. Johnston *(Chief Strategy Officer & Exec VP)*

Subsidiaries:

The Rug Barn Inc. (1)
Hwy 28 Bypass Industrial Park Rd, Abbeville, SC 29620-1187
Tel.: (864) 446-2123
Sales Range: $10-24.9 Million
Emp.: 100
Mfr of Throws, Pillows & Tapestries
N.A.I.C.S.: 313210

THE INTRUST GROUP, INC.
4675 Cornell Rd Ste 162, Cincinnati, OH 45241
Tel.: (513) 469-6500
Web Site: http://www.intrust-it.com
Year Founded: 1992
Sales Range: $1-9.9 Million
Emp.: 22
Computer Management Services
N.A.I.C.S.: 518210
Tim Rettig *(Pres)*

THE INVUS GROUP, LLC
750 Lexington Ave 30th Fl, New York, NY 10022
Tel.: (212) 371-1717 DE
Web Site: http://www.invus.com
Year Founded: 1985
Equity Investment Firm
N.A.I.C.S.: 523999
Raymond Debbane *(Chm, Pres & CEO)*
Christopher J. Sobecki *(Mng Dir)*
Jonas M. Fajgenbaum *(Mng Dir-Private Equity-New York)*
Philippe J. Amouyal *(Mng Dir)*
Aflalo Guimaraes *(Mng Dir-Private Equity-New York)*
Evren Bilimer *(Mng Dir-Private Equity-New York)*
Benedetto Staccia *(Mng Dir-Private Equity-Europe)*
Benjamin Felt *(Mng Dir-Private Equity-New York)*
Francis Cukierman *(Mng Dir-Private Equity-Asian Emerging Markets)*
Luc Ta-Ngoc *(Mng Dir-Private Equity-Europe)*
Mario Kaloustian *(Mng Dir-Private Equity-Europe)*
Sheryl Zhou *(Principal-Public Equity-New York)*
Wassim Sacre *(Mng Dir-Private Equity-Europe)*
Khalil Barrage *(Mng Dir-Pub Equity-New York)*

Subsidiaries:

Ashley Stewart, Inc. (1)
150 Meadowlands Pkwy Ste 403, Secaucus, NJ 07094
Tel.: (605) 271-6130
Web Site: http://www.ashleystewart.com
Retailer of Women's Clothing
N.A.I.C.S.: 458110

Invus Financial Advisors, LLC (1)
126 E 56th St 20th Fl, New York, NY 10022-2050
Tel.: (212) 616-2555
Investment Advisory Services
N.A.I.C.S.: 523940
Sacha Lainovic *(Partner)*
Leslie Lake *(Partner)*

THE IOWA CLINIC PC
5950 University Ave Ste 321, West Des Moines, IA 50266
Tel.: (515) 875-9100 IA
Web Site: http://www.iowaclinic.com
Year Founded: 1993
Sales Range: $25-49.9 Million
Emp.: 600
Medical Clinic Operator
N.A.I.C.S.: 621111
Amy Hilmes *(CMO)*
David Zielke *(CFO)*
Christina Taylor *(Chief Quality Officer)*
Jamie Carlson *(Chief HR Officer)*
Jennifer Tinnermeier *(Chief Legal Officer)*
Rob Heen *(COO)*
Beth McGinnis *(CIO & Chief Revenue Cycle Officer)*
Ben Vallier *(CEO)*

THE IRON DOOR COMPANY LLC
220 Scotland Dr, Alabaster, AL 35007
Web Site: http://www.castleentries.com
Year Founded: 2007
Sales Range: $1-9.9 Million
Emp.: 2
Iron Door Design & Mfr
N.A.I.C.S.: 332321
Glen Blickenstaff *(CEO)*

THE IRONEES COMPANY
207 Barclay Cir, Cheltenham, PA 19012-1001
Tel.: (215) 782-1516 PA
Year Founded: 1962
Rev.: $4,000,000
Emp.: 140
Mfr of Housewares & Domestics
N.A.I.C.S.: 314120

THE IRONSIDE GROUP, INC.
10 Maguire Rd, Lexington, MA 02421
Tel.: (781) 860-8840
Web Site: http://www.ironsidegroup.com
Year Founded: 1999
Sales Range: $10-24.9 Million
Emp.: 70
Data Processing & Hosting Services
N.A.I.C.S.: 518210
Timothy Kreytak *(Founder & CEO)*
Steve Kaplan *(VP-Consulting Svcs)*
Gregory Bonnette *(VP-Solution Dev)*
David Michelson *(COO)*

THE IRVINE COMPANY INC.
550 Newport Ctr Dr, Newport Beach, CA 92660-7011
Tel.: (949) 720-2000 DE
Web Site: http://www.irvinecompany.com
Year Founded: 1894
Sales Range: $1-4.9 Billion
Emp.: 3,200
Real Estate Investment Services
N.A.I.C.S.: 237210
Donald Bren *(Chm)*
Marc Ley *(Chief Investment Officer & Exec VP)*
Frank Abeling *(Exec VP-Real Estate Ops)*
Scott Hermes *(Pres-Resort Properties)*
Butch Knerr *(Pres-Retail Properties)*
Paul Hernandez *(Sr VP-Corp Affairs)*
Gino J. Blanchini *(Sr VP-Tax)*
Julie Sokol *(Sr VP-Info & Mktg Tech)*
Darren Thomas *(Sr VP-HR)*
Jim Krohn *(Pres-Apartment Ops)*
Chris Marsh *(Pres-Apartment Dev)*
Clay Halvorsen *(Gen Counsel, Sec & Sr VP)*
Bryan Stevens *(Treas & Sr VP-Fin)*
Charles Fedalen Jr. *(CFO & Exec VP)*

Subsidiaries:

Irvine Apartment Communities Incorporated (1)
110 Innovation Dr, Irvine, CA 92617 (100%)
Tel.: (949) 720-2000
Web Site: http://www.rentiac.com
Sales Range: $50-74.9 Million
Emp.: 500
Multi-Family Properties Developers & Operators
N.A.I.C.S.: 531110

Irvine Community Development Company (1)
550 Newport Center Dr, Newport Beach, CA 92660-7011 (100%)
Tel.: (949) 720-2000
Web Site: http://www.irvinecompany.com
Sales Range: $50-74.9 Million
Emp.: 500
Community Development
N.A.I.C.S.: 237210
Donald Bren *(Chm)*

THE IT PROS
409 Camino Del Rio S Ste 203, San Diego, CA 92108
Tel.: (619) 749-7831
Web Site: http://www.theitpros.com
Year Founded: 2002
Rev.: $4,900,000
Emp.: 23
Administrative & General Management Consulting Services
N.A.I.C.S.: 541611
George C. Vahle III *(VP)*
Ed Sternagle *(Exec VP)*
Scott Kaufmann *(Dir-Managed Svcs)*

THE IVY GROUP, LTD.
123 E Main St 2nd Fl, Charlottesville, VA 22902
Tel.: (434) 979-2678
Web Site: http://www.ivygroup.com
Year Founded: 1989
Sales Range: Less than $1 Million
Emp.: 11
N.A.I.C.S.: 541810

THE IVY GROUP, LTD.

The Ivy Group, Ltd.—(Continued)
Pamela Fitzgerald (Mng Partner)
Jan Garrison (Office Admin)

Subsidiaries:

The Ivy Group, Ltd. (1)
1100 N Providence Rd, Media, PA 19063
Tel.: (610) 566-5680
Web Site: http://www.ivylibrary.com
N.A.I.C.S.: 541810
Nancy Harvey Davis (Owner)

THE J. PAUL GETTY TRUST

1200 Getty Center Dr, Los Angeles, CA 90049-1687
Tel.: (310) 440-7330
Web Site: https://www.getty.edu
Year Founded: 1953
Museum Exhibition Services
N.A.I.C.S.: 711510

THE J.C. ROBINSON SEED COMPANY

100 JC Robinson Blvd, Waterloo, NE 68069
Tel.: (402) 779-2531
Year Founded: 1888
Sales Range: $10-24.9 Million
Emp.: 275
Whslr of Hybrid Seed, Corn, Sorghum, Soybeans & Alfalfa
N.A.I.C.S.: 424910
Edward T. Robinson Jr. (Chm & Pres)

THE J.N. PHILLIPS GLASS CO. INC.

11 Wheeling Ave, Woburn, MA 01801-2008
Tel.: (781) 939-3400
Web Site: http://www.jnphillips.com
Year Founded: 1951
Sales Range: $25-49.9 Million
Emp.: 250
Automotive Glass Replacement Shops
N.A.I.C.S.: 811122
Robert Rosenfield (Pres)
Maureen Confalone (Controller)

THE JACK OLSTA COMPANY

810 IH 45 N, Huntsville, TX 77320
Tel.: (936) 291-7940
Web Site: http://www.olstaco.com
Rev.: $24,000,000
Emp.: 25
Supplier of Tank Trailers
N.A.I.C.S.: 441227
John Olsta (VP)
Christopher Kern (Mgr-Lease Fleet)

THE JACK PARKER CORPORATION

9001 Daniels Pkwy Ste 200, Fort Myers, FL 33912
Tel.: (239) 481-5040
Web Site:
http://www.thejackparkercorporation.com
Year Founded: 1955
Sales Range: $1-9.9 Million
Emp.: 6
Multi-Family Dwelling Construction
N.A.I.C.S.: 236116
John Reisman (Pres)
Terry Trowbridge (Sr VP)

THE JACKSON LABORATORY

600 Main St, Bar Harbor, ME 04609
Tel.: (207) 288-6000
Web Site: https://www.jax.org
Year Founded: 1929
Sales Range: $250-299.9 Million
Emp.: 3,000
Genetic Research Services
N.A.I.C.S.: 541715

S. Catherine Longley (COO & Exec VP)
Michael E. Hyde (VP-External Affairs & Strategic Partnerships)
Thomas S. Litwin (VP-Education)
Nadia Rosenthal (Dir-Scientific)
Auro Nair (Gen Mgr)
Kenneth Fasman (VP-Strategic Initiatives)
Charles E. Hewett (COO & Exec VP)
Charles Lee (Dir-Scientific)
Kristen Rozansky (VP-Dev & Comm)
Douglas Abbott (CFO)
Lon Cardon (Pres & CEO)
Timothy Dattels (Vice Chm)
Meghan Finn (Chief Comm Officer & VP)
Lon Cardon (Pres & CEO)

THE JACKSONVILLE PORT AUTHORITY

2831 Talleyrand Ave PO Box 3005, Jacksonville, FL 32206
Tel.: (904) 357-3000
Web Site: http://www.jaxport.com
Year Founded: 1963
Sales Range: $50-74.9 Million
Port Operations
N.A.I.C.S.: 488310
John Daniel Baker II (Sec)
Eric Green (CEO)
Chris Kauffmann (COO)
Roy Schleicher (Chief Comml Officer & Exec VP)
Victoria Robas (Dir-Terminal-Blount Island, Dames Point & Cruise Ops)
Doug Menefee (Dir-Terminal-Talleyrand)
Alberto Cabrera (Dir-Cruise & Cargo Dev)
Deborah Lofberg (Mgr-Foreign Trade Zone-Comml Team)
Robert Peek (Dir & Gen Mgr-Bus Dev)
Linda Williams (Dir-Corp Performance & Contracting)
Michael Poole (CFO)
Nancy Rubin (Sr Dir-Comm)
David Stubbs (Dir-Properties & Environmental Compliance)
Marvin Grieve (Dir-Project Mgmt)
Mike McClung (Controller)
Aaron Kendrick (Sr Dir-Fin)
Louis Naranjo (Dir-Procurement Svcs)
Lisa Wheldon (Dir-Natl Accts & Containerized Cargo Sls)
John J. Falconetti (Treas)
Chris Crouch (Mgr-Risk Mgmt)
Lisa Diaz (Mgr-Foreign Trade Zone & Florida Sls)
Steve Kapustka (Mgr-Blount Island Ops)
Ricardo Schiappacassee (Dir-Sls-Latin America)
Frank Camp (Dir-Non-Containerized Sls)
Paul Soares (Sr Dir-Facilities Dev)
David Kaufman (Sr Dir-Plng & Comml Dev)
Daniel Bean (Vice Chm)
Bradley S. Talbert (Treas)
Justin Damiano (Dir-Govt Affairs)
Dwight Collins (Dir-Pub Safety & Security)
Wendy Hamilton (Sec)

THE JAMES MADISON INSTITUTE

100 N Duval St, Tallahassee, FL 32301
Tel.: (850) 386-3131
Web Site:
http://www.jamesmadison.org
Year Founded: 1987

Sales Range: $10-24.9 Million
Emp.: 20
Market Policy Research
N.A.I.C.S.: 541910
Robert H. Gidel (Vice Chm)
Rebecca Liner (Exec VP)
Sal Nuzzo (VP-Policy & Dir-Center For Economic Prosperity)
Glen T. Blauch (Treas)
John Hrabusa (Sr VP-HR & Pub Affairs)
Jeffrey V. Swain (Sec)
Daniel Peterson (Dir-Property Rights Center)
William Mattox (Dir-Marshall Center-Educational Options)
Jill Mattox (Mgr-Foundation Grants)
Don Orrico (Dir-Dev-Southwest Florida)
J. Robert McClure III (Pres & CEO)

THE JAN COMPANIES

35 Sockanosset Cross Rd, Cranston, RI 02920-5535
Tel.: (401) 946-4000
Web Site:
http://www.jancompanies.com
Year Founded: 1969
Sales Range: $800-899.9 Million
Emp.: 2,500
Fast Food Restaurants Owner & Operator
N.A.I.C.S.: 722513
Nicholas W. Janikies (Pres)
William N. Janikies (COO)
Janice Mathews (VP-Admin Ops)
Brian Colton (Mgr-Mktg)

Subsidiaries:

Newport Creamery LLC (1)
35 Sockanosset Cross Rd, Cranston, RI 02920
Tel.: (401) 946-4000
Web Site: http://www.newportcreamery.com
Sales Range: $25-49.9 Million
Emp.: 50
Ice Cream & Sandwich Restaurants Operator
N.A.I.C.S.: 722513
William N. Janikies (COO)

THE JANSEN GROUP INC.

330 E Kilbourn Ave Ste 1085, Milwaukee, WI 53202-3146
Tel.: (414) 357-8800
Web Site:
http://www.jansengroup.com
Rev.: $67,127,379
Emp.: 100
Construction Services
N.A.I.C.S.: 236220
John Schultz (VP)

Subsidiaries:

Jansen Recycling Group (1)
Van Leeuwenhoekweg 21, PO Box 3118, 3316 AV, Dordrecht, Netherlands
Tel.: (31) 786522633
Ferrous & Non Ferrous Material Recycling Services
N.A.I.C.S.: 331492

Signature Group Inc (1)
330 E Kilbourn Ave Ste 1085, Milwaukee, WI 53202-3146
Tel.: (414) 357-8845
Web Site: http://www.jansengroup.com
Sales Range: $10-24.9 Million
Masonry & Other Stonework
N.A.I.C.S.: 238140
Rich Dobry (CEO)

THE JAY GROUP

700 Indian Springs Dr, Lancaster, PA 17601
Tel.: (717) 285-6200
Web Site: http://www.jaygroup.com
Rev.: $51,100,000
Emp.: 474

Logistics & Supply Chain Management
N.A.I.C.S.: 541614
J. Freeland Chryst (Pres)
Dana A. Chryst (CEO)
Rick Miller (VP-Bus Dev)
Tarrah Berrier (Gen Mgr-Acctg)
Blake Dudek (VP)
Brad Weise (VP-Ops)

THE JED FOUNDATION

Tel.: (212) 647-7544
Web Site:
https://www.jedfoundation.org
Year Founded: 2000
Sales Range: $1-9.9 Million
Emp.: 9
Behavioral Healthcare Services
N.A.I.C.S.: 623220
John A. MacPhee (CEO & Exec Dir)
Lynn Toth (Mgr-Ops)
Augusta Foshay-Rothfeld (Mgr-Comm)
Alexa White (Sr Program Mgr)
Donna Satow (Co-Founder)
Courtney Knowles (Dir-Love is Louder)
Jillian Niesley (Program Dir)
Phillip M. Satow (Co-Founder)
Victor Schwartz (Dir-Medical)
Annie Cofone McLaughlin (Mgr-Engagement-Grants & Dev)
Omar Tungekar (CEO)
Rita Weinberger (Dir-Fin & Admin)

THE JEL SERT COMPANY

Rte 59 & Conde St, West Chicago, IL 60185-0261
Tel.: (630) 231-7590
Web Site: http://www.jelsert.com
Year Founded: 1926
Sales Range: $200-249.9 Million
Emp.: 420
Gelatin, Puddings & Ice Pops Mfr & Distr
N.A.I.C.S.: 311930
Charles T. Wegner (Chm & CEO)
Tony Damma (CFO)
Bob Clements (VP-Sls & Mktg)
Kenneth Wegner (Pres)
Susie Frausto (Sr Dir-Mktg)
Mike Gomolski (Mgr-Mktg)
Joseph Bouma (Exec VP-Sls)
Kate Howard (VP-Accts-Natl)

THE JELLYVISION LAB, INC.

848 W Eastman Ste 104, Chicago, IL 60642-2635
Tel.: (312) 667-0252
Web Site: http://www.jellyvision.com
Professional, Scientific & Technical Services
N.A.I.C.S.: 541990
Harry Gottlieb (Founder)
Jessica Watts (VP-Sls)
Kelly Dean (VP-People)
Greg Healy (Chief Product Officer)

Subsidiaries:

Flexminder, Inc. (1)
216 1st Ave S Ste 435, Seattle, WA 98104
Tel.: (206) 363-1492
Web Site: http://www.flexminder.com
Ambulatory Health Care Services
N.A.I.C.S.: 621999
Will Miceli (Chief Product Officer)

THE JERALD DEVELOPMENT GROUP INC.

2101 Hwy 34 S Ste A, Wall, NJ 07719
Tel.: (732) 974-3330
Web Site:
http://www.jeralddevelopment.com
Sales Range: $10-24.9 Million
Emp.: 15
Land Subdividing Services
N.A.I.C.S.: 237210
Connie Pallante (Pres)

COMPANIES

THE JERRY BROWN CO, INC.
2690 Prairie Rd, Eugene, OR 97404
Tel.: (541) 688-8211
Web Site: http://www.jbco.com
Year Founded: 1947
Sales Range: $100-124.9 Million
Petroleum Products Mfr & Distr
N.A.I.C.S.: 424720
Terry Likens *(Pres & CEO)*

THE JERUSALEM FOUNDATION, INC.
420 Lexington Ave Ste 1645, New York, NY 10170
Tel.: (212) 697-4188 NY
Web Site:
  http://www.jerusalemfoundation.org
Year Founded: 1966
Sales Range: $10-24.9 Million
Emp.: 4
Grantmaking Services
N.A.I.C.S.: 813211
Moshe Fogel *(Exec Dir)*

THE JEWELERS
2400 Western Ave, Las Vegas, NV 89102
Tel.: (702) 382-1234
Web Site:
  http://www.thejewelers.com
Year Founded: 1976
Sales Range: $10-24.9 Million
Emp.: 60
Jewelry & Related Product Distr
N.A.I.C.S.: 458310
Joanie Schultz *(Mgr-Store)*

THE JEWISH FEDERATIONS OF NORTH AMERICA, INC.
25 Broadway Ste 1700, New York, NY 10004-1010
Tel.: (212) 284-6500 NY
Web Site:
  http://www.jewishfederations.org
Year Founded: 1935
Sales Range: $25-49.9 Million
Emp.: 187
Educational Support Services
N.A.I.C.S.: 541820
Pamela Zaltsman *(CFO)*
Renee Rothstein *(CMO)*

THE JEWISH HOME OF EASTERN PENNSYLVANIA
1101 Vine St, Scranton, PA 18510-2126
Tel.: (570) 344-6177 PA
Web Site: http://www.jhep.org
Year Founded: 1916
Sales Range: $10-24.9 Million
Elder Care Services
N.A.I.C.S.: 623312
Nicole Lipinski *(Dir-Activities)*
Mae Murawski *(Dir-Nursing)*
Beth Rielly *(Dir-Food Svc)*
Kevin Tetreault *(Dir-Environmental & IT Svcs)*
Todd Kelleher *(Dir-Admissions)*
Rabbi Samuel K. Sandhaus *(Exec Dir)*
Brittany Elko *(Dir-Social Svcs)*
Mary Rose Applegate *(COO)*
Joyce Petrovsky *(Coord-Resident Billing)*
Mike Marion *(Dir-Maintenance)*

THE JIM HENSON COMPANY
1416 N La Brea Ave, Hollywood, CA 90028
Tel.: (323) 802-1500
Web Site: http://www.henson.com
Year Founded: 1958
Sales Range: $25-49.9 Million
Emp.: 300
Children & Family Entertainment Television Programming & Movie Production
N.A.I.C.S.: 512110
Brian Henson *(Chm)*
Joe Henderson *(Exec VP-Worldwide Admin)*
Lisa Henson *(CEO)*
Laurie Don *(CFO & Exec VP)*
Lisa O'Brien *(VP-Sprout)*
Blanca Lista *(VP-Feature Film Production)*
Halle Stanford *(Pres-Television & Production)*
Karen Lee Arbeeny *(VP-Bus Ops-Global Distr)*
Anna Moorefield *(VP-Distr-Global)*
Tara Billik *(VP-Feature Films)*
Chris Lytton *(Pres & COO)*
Sarah Maizes *(VP-Children's Entertainment)*
Shane Mang *(Exec Dir-Consumer Products-Global)*
Claudia Balzer Scott-Hansen *(Sr VP-Distr-Global)*
Sidney Clifton *(Sr VP-Animation & Mixed Media)*

THE JOCKEY CLUB
40 East 52nd St 15 Fl, New York, NY 10022
Tel.: (212) 371-5970 NY
Web Site: http://www.jockeyclub.com
Year Founded: 1894
Sales Range: $25-49.9 Million
Emp.: 110
Equine Breeders Organization; Horse Breed Registry Information Services & Publisher
N.A.I.C.S.: 813920
Laura Barillaro *(CFO & Exec VP)*
Bob Curran *(VP-Corp Comm)*
Ian D. Highet *(Treas & Sec)*
Matt Iuliano *(Exec VP)*
Alexa Ravit *(Coord-Comm-Comm Dept)*
Stuart S. Janney III *(Chm)*
William M. Lear Jr. *(Vice Chm)*

THE JOEY CO.
45 Main St Ste 632, Brooklyn, NY 11201
Tel.: (718) 852-7730
Year Founded: 1993
Rev.: $28,000,000
Emp.: 15
N.A.I.C.S.: 541810
Joey Cummings *(Founder, CEO & Chief Creative Officer)*
Jim Trowell *(Dir-Creative)*
Thomas Upshur *(Exec Art Dir)*
Michael Petrucelly *(Dir-Production)*

THE JOHN A. BECKER COMPANY
1341 E 4th St, Dayton, OH 45402-2235
Tel.: (937) 226-1341 OH
Web Site:
  http://www.beckerelectric.com
Year Founded: 1920
Sales Range: $75-99.9 Million
Emp.: 150
Mfr of Electrical Apparatus & Equipment
N.A.I.C.S.: 423610
Dave K. Adkinson *(Pres)*
Thomas J. Becker *(CEO)*

THE JOHN JOHNSON CO.
1481 14th St, Detroit, MI 48216-1806
Tel.: (313) 496-0600 MI
Web Site:
  http://www.johnjohnsonco.com
Year Founded: 1886
Sales Range: $75-99.9 Million
Emp.: 100
Mfr of Awnings, Tarpaulins, Cargo Covers, Drop Cloths & Canvas Specialties
N.A.I.C.S.: 314910

THE JOHN P. BROOKS FAMILY CORPORATION
2710 Vly View Ln, Farmers Branch, TX 75234
Tel.: (800) 300-1655
Web Site:
  http://www.johnpbrooks.com
Funeral Homes & Services
N.A.I.C.S.: 812210
John P. Brooks *(Pres & CEO)*

Subsidiaries:

Aria Cremation Services, LLC (1)
19310 Preston Rd, Dallas, TX 75252
Tel.: (214) 306-6700
Web Site: http://www.ariacremation.com
Sales Range: $10-24.9 Million
Emp.: 14
Cremation Services
N.A.I.C.S.: 812220
John P. Brooks *(Owner & Dir-Funeral)*

Avalon Mortuary Service Corp. (1)
2710 Valley View Ln, Dallas, TX 75234
Tel.: (972) 241-9100
Web Site:
  http://www.northdallasfuneralhome.com
Sales Range: $1-9.9 Million
Emp.: 17
Funeral Homes & Funeral Services
N.A.I.C.S.: 812210

THE JOHNSON GROUP
436 Market St, Chattanooga, TN 37402-1203
Tel.: (423) 756-2608 TN
Web Site: http://www.johngroup.com
Year Founded: 1996
Sales Range: $10-24.9 Million
Emp.: 65
Full Service
N.A.I.C.S.: 541810
Joe Johnson *(Pres)*
Joyce Debter *(Comptroller)*
Pat Buckley *(Mng Dir-Creative)*
Rachel Daigh *(Dir-Media)*
Sandy Buquo *(Partner)*
Roger Vaughn *(Partner & Dir-Creative)*
Mike Polcari *(Partner & Dir-Creative)*
Chris Jones *(Dir-Creative)*
Joe Johnson *(Pres)*

THE JOHNSON GROUP, INC.
15720 NE 14th CT, Miami, FL 33162
Tel.: (386) 767-8000
Sales Range: $25-49.9 Million
Operative Builders
N.A.I.C.S.: 237210
Larry J. Dale *(CEO)*
Jill Johnson Beatty *(VP)*
Jerry S. Johnson Sr. *(Pres)*

THE JORDAN AUTOMOTIVE GROUP
609 E Jefferson Blvd, Mishawaka, IN 46545
Tel.: (574) 259-1981
Web Site: http://www.jordanauto.com
Rev.: $19,900,000
Emp.: 200
New & Used Car Dealers
N.A.I.C.S.: 441110
Craig A. Kapson *(Pres)*

THE JORDAN COMPANY
6001 River Rd Ste 100, Columbus, GA 31904
Tel.: (706) 649-3000 GA
Web Site:
  http://www.thejordanco.com
Year Founded: 1904
Emp.: 40
Real Estate Investment, Development, Property Management & Brokerage Services; Private Equity & Investment Management Services
N.A.I.C.S.: 531390
Kimberly Wise *(CFO, Treas & Sec)*
Stella Shuman *(VP-Sls)*

Subsidiaries:

Jordan Capital AM, LLC (1)
6001 River Rd Ste 100, Columbus, GA 31904
Tel.: (706) 649-3000
Web Site: http://www.jordancapitalam.com
Investment Management Service
N.A.I.C.S.: 523940
Gunby J. Garrard *(Mng Dir)*
Vad Yazvinski *(Portfolio Mgr)*

Jordan-Blanchard Capital, LLC (1)
6001 River Rd Ste 100, Columbus, GA 31904
Tel.: (706) 649-3000
Web Site: http://www.jordanblanchard.com
Emp.: 4
Private Equity Firm
N.A.I.C.S.: 523999
Gardiner W. Garrard Jr. *(Principal)*
James H. Blanchard *(Founder & Chm)*
Gunby J. Garrard *(Mng Dir)*
Greg Chesnutt *(Principal)*
Jeff Thomas *(Principal)*
Robbie Raybon *(VP-Bus Dev)*

THE JORDAN COMPANY, L.P.
399 Park Ave 30th Fl, New York, NY 10022
Tel.: (212) 572-0800 NY
Web Site:
  http://www.thejordancompany.com
Year Founded: 1982
Rev.: $2,000,000,000
Privater Equity Firm
N.A.I.C.S.: 523999
Michael R. Denvir *(Partner)*
Eion Hu *(Partner)*
Jeb Boucher *(Partner-Advisory)*
Adam Max *(Partner)*
Dave Butler *(Partner)*
Joseph C. Linnen *(Partner)*
Doug Zych *(Partner)*
Brian J. Higgins *(Partner)*
Ian F. Arons *(Partner)*
Jeffrey B. Miller *(Partner)*
Brad Wilford *(Partner)*
Kristin A. Custar *(Partner & Head-Investor Capital Group-Global)*
Peter Carbonara *(Partner & CFO)*
Erik J. Fagan *(Partner)*
Daniel D. Pezley *(Partner)*
John C. Straus *(Partner)*
Peter D. Suffredini *(Partner)*
Daniel S. Williams *(Partner-New York)*
Bruce H. Hittleman *(Office Mgr-New York)*
Michael Epstein *(VP & Controller)*
Jay Jordan *(Founder)*
Eric O'Brien *(Partner)*
A. Richard Caputo Jr. *(CEO)*
Barry Gallup Jr. *(Partner)*

Subsidiaries:

ACR Electronics, Inc. (1)
5757 Ravenswood Rd, Fort Lauderdale, FL 33312-6603
Tel.: (954) 981-3333
Web Site: http://www.acrartex.com
Sales Range: $25-49.9 Million
Emp.: 180
Electronic Rescue Beacon & Survival Equipment Mfr
N.A.I.C.S.: 335139
Mikele D'Arcangelo *(VP-Mktg & Product Mgmt-Global)*

Subsidiary (Domestic):

Freeflight Systems, Ltd. (2)
3700 Interstate 35 S, Waco, TX 76706

THE JORDAN COMPANY, L.P.

U.S. PRIVATE

The Jordan Company, L.P.—(Continued)
Tel.: (254) 662-0000
Web Site: http://www.freeflightsystems.com
Search, Detection, Navigation, Guidance, Aeronautical & Nautical System & Instrument Mfr
N.A.I.C.S.: 334511
John DeBusk *(CTO & VP-Engrg)*
Pete Ring *(VP-Sls & Mktg)*
Tim Taylor *(CEO)*

ARCH Global Precision LLC (1)
2600 South Telegraph Ste 180, Bloomfield Hills, MI 48302
Tel.: (734) 266-6900
Web Site:
http://www.archglobalprecision.com
Precision Cutting Tools Mfr
N.A.I.C.S.: 333515
Eli Crotzer *(Pres & CEO)*
Don Piper *(CFO, Treas & Exec VP-Fin)*
Paul Barck *(Pres-ARCH Medical Solutions)*

Subsidiary (Domestic):

ARCH Medical Solutions Corp (2)
2600 S Telegraph Rd Ste 180, Bloomfield Hills, MI 48302
Tel.: (603) 474-1919
Web Site: https://arch-medical.com
Emp.: 100
Medical Equipment Mfr
N.A.I.C.S.: 339112
John Ruggieri *(Sr VP-Bus Dev)*

Subsidiary (Domestic):

American Prosthetic Components, LLC (3)
900 Ontario Rd, Green Bay, WI 54311
Tel.: (920) 406-9550
Web Site: http://www.apcomponents.com
Sales Range: $1-9.9 Million
Emp.: 19
Medical And Hospital Equipment, Nsk
N.A.I.C.S.: 423450
Jeff Braun *(Pres)*

gSource, LLC (3)
19 Bland St, Emerson, NJ 07630
Tel.: (201) 599-2277
Web Site: http://www.gsource.us
Sales Range: $1-9.9 Million
Emp.: 10
Medical, Dental & Hospital Equipment & Supplies Merchant Whslr
N.A.I.C.S.: 423450
Gerd Billmann *(Pres)*

Subsidiary (Domestic):

Advanced Precision Inc. (2)
15 Wilson Dr, Sparta, NJ 07871
Web Site:
http://www.advancedprecision.com
Machine Shops
N.A.I.C.S.: 332710
Vincent Fay *(Founder)*

Arch Cutting Tools Corp. (2)
2600 S Telegraph Rd, Bloomfield Hills, MI 48302
Web Site: https://www.archcuttingtools.com
Precision Machined Parts, Products & Tools Mfr
N.A.I.C.S.: 332721

Subsidiary (Domestic):

AGI-VR/Wesson Inc (3)
2673 NE 9th Ave, Cape Coral, FL 33909
Tel.: (239) 573-5132
Sales Range: $1-9.9 Million
Emp.: 30
Carbide Cutting Tool Products Mfr
N.A.I.C.S.: 333515
Tom Fliss *(Pres & CEO)*
Tod Grabo *(VP)*
Steve Scott *(VP-Sls)*

Division (Domestic):

Arch Cutting Tools - Flushing, LLC (3)
7162 Sheridan Rd, Flushing, MI 48433
Tel.: (810) 638-5388
Web Site:
https://www.beamerlasermarking.com

Sales Range: $1-9.9 Million
Emp.: 47
Machine Tools Mfr
N.A.I.C.S.: 333517
Mark Birchmeier *(Pres)*
Nicholas Kaczmarski *(Natl Sls Mgr)*

Subsidiary (Domestic):

DPSS Lasers, Inc. (4)
2525 Walsh Ave, Santa Clara, CA 95051
Tel.: (408) 988-4300
Web Site: http://www.dpss-lasers.com
Sales Range: $1-9.9 Million
Emp.: 30
Miscellaneous Electrical Equipment & Component Mfr
N.A.I.C.S.: 335999
Alex Laymon *(Pres)*

Subsidiary (Domestic):

Greene Tool Systems, Inc. (3)
19 Krug St, Dayton, OH 45408
Tel.: (937) 223-8665
Web Site: http://www.greenetool.com
Sales Range: $1-9.9 Million
Emp.: 18
Industrial Supplies Merchant Whslr
N.A.I.C.S.: 423840
Beverly Greene *(VP)*

Subsidiary (Domestic):

Arundel Machine Tool Co. (2)
20 Technology Dr, Arundel, ME 04046
Tel.: (207) 985-8555
Web Site: http://www.arundelmachine.com
Sales Range: $1-9.9 Million
Emp.: 53
Metal Stamping Services
N.A.I.C.S.: 332119
Marcel Bertrand *(Pres)*
Patrick Shrader *(VP-Sls)*
Chris Amoling *(Mgr-Quality Assurance)*
Joe Fournier *(Mgr-Acct)*
John Hebert *(Mgr-Engrg)*
Shane McAlevey *(Mgr-Acct)*

H. & S. Swansons' Tool Company (2)
9000 68th St, Pinellas Park, FL 33782
Tel.: (727) 541-3575
Web Site: http://www.hsswansons.com
Sales Range: $1-9.9 Million
Emp.: 100
Industrial Machinery, Nec, Nsk
N.A.I.C.S.: 332710
Alan Burgess *(Pres)*

Jade Equipment Corp. (2)
3063A Philmont Ave, Huntingdon Valley, PA 19006-4243
Tel.: (215) 947-3333
Web Site: http://www.jadecorp.com
Custom Equipment, Precision Stamping, Precision Tooling & Contract Mfr
N.A.I.C.S.: 333515
Brian T. Manley *(Pres & CEO)*
John Delp *(Pres)*

Seabrook International, LLC (2)
15 Woodworkers Way, Seabrook, NH 03874
Tel.: (603) 474-1919
Web Site:
http://www.seabrookinternational.com
Precision Instruments, Orthopaedic Implants & Other Devices Mfr & Supplier
N.A.I.C.S.: 339113

Smiths Machine, LLC (2)
14120 Hwy 11 N, Cottondale, AL 35453
Tel.: (205) 553-7623
Web Site: http://www.smithsmachine.com
Emp.: 80
Precision Machined Components Mfr & Services
N.A.I.C.S.: 332710
Robert Smith *(Dir-Mfg)*
Tim Smith *(VP-Sls & Ops)*

Tier One, LLC (2)
31 Pecks Ln, Newtown, CT 06470
Tel.: (203) 426-3030
Web Site: http://www.tieronemachining.com
Sales Range: $10-24.9 Million
Emp.: 60
Machining & Assembly Solutions
N.A.I.C.S.: 333248

R. Joe Young *(Dir-Sls)*
Rick Hall *(Mgr-Tech Support)*
Mike Iassogna *(Dir-Ops & HR)*
Linda Iassogna *(Dir-Acctg)*

Wilsey Tool Co., Inc. (2)
140 Penn Am Dr, Quakertown, PA 18951
Tel.: (215) 538-0800
Web Site: http://www.wilseytool.com
Rev: $4,500,000
Emp.: 65
All Other Miscellaneous General Purpose Machinery Mfr
N.A.I.C.S.: 333998
Timothy W. Wilsey *(Pres)*

American Fast Freight, Inc. (2)
7400 45th St Ct E, Fife, WA 98424
Tel.: (206) 382-0750
Web Site: http://www.americanfast.com
Sales Range: $25-49.9 Million
Freight Shipping, Transportation & Logistics Services
N.A.I.C.S.: 488510
Ron Moore *(Mgr-Sls-Alaska)*
Kevin Kelly *(Pres & CEO)*

Subsidiary (Domestic):

Caribbean Shipping Services, Inc. (2)
2550 Carbettt Commerce Dr, Jacksonville, FL 32226
Tel.: (904) 247-0031
Web Site:
http://www.caribbeanshipping.com
Sales Range: $25-49.9 Million
Freight Shipping Arrangement & Warehousing Services
N.A.I.C.S.: 488510
Paul Robbins *(Co-Founder & Pres)*

Global Transportation Services, Inc. (2)
18209 80th Ave S Ste A, Kent, WA 98032
Tel.: (425) 207-1500
Web Site: http://www.shipglobal.com
Emp.: 140
Integrated Logistics Solutions & Services
N.A.I.C.S.: 488510
Jason F. Totah *(Pres & CEO)*
Richard Jellison *(Sr VP-IT Solutions)*
Sarah B. Dorscht *(Sr VP-Ops)*
Debbie Brule *(VP-Customs Brokerage Sys)*
Ben L. Paz *(VP-Fin & Admin)*
Saori Takayoshi *(VP-Bus Dev)*
Jeanni Sargent *(VP-Trng & Compliance)*
Chad D. Laden *(Reg VP-Ops-Midwest & Eastern Reg)*

Grand Worldwide Logistics Corp. (2)
4350 W Ohio St, Chicago, IL 60624
Tel.: (773) 265-0403
Web Site: http://www.grandwarehouse.com
General Warehousing & Storage
N.A.I.C.S.: 493110
David Schulman *(Pres & CEO)*

Hawaiian Ocean Transport, Inc. (2)
1400 Talbot Rd S Ste 460, Renton, WA 98055-4282
Tel.: (206) 382-0750
Freight Transportation Services
N.A.I.C.S.: 488510

Bojangles', Inc. (1)
9432 Southern Pine Blvd, Charlotte, NC 28273
Tel.: (704) 527-2675
Web Site: http://www.bojangles.com
Sales Range: $550-599.9 Million
Emp.: 9,900
Fast Food Restaurant Operator
N.A.I.C.S.: 722513
Laura Roberts *(Officer-Compliance, Gen Counsel, Sec & VP)*
Kenneth M. Koziol *(Chief Restaurant Support Officer)*
Brian Unger *(COO)*
Keith Vigness *(VP-Fin)*
Reese Stewart *(CFO)*
Jackie Woodward *(CMO)*
Jose R. Costa *(Chief Growth Officer)*
Marshall Scarborough *(VP-Menu & Culinary Innovation)*
Byron Chandler *(Chief Dev Officer)*
Jose Armario *(Pres & CEO)*

Subsidiary (Domestic):

Bojangles' Restaurants, Inc. (2)
9432 Southern Pine Blvd, Charlotte, NC 28273
Tel.: (704) 527-2675
Web Site: http://www.bojangles.com
Franchised Fast Food Restaurants
N.A.I.C.S.: 722513

Borchers SAS (1)
1 Rue Albert Calmette, 81100, Castres, France
Tel.: (33) 563726570
Coating Additive Product Mfr & Distr
N.A.I.C.S.: 325998

CAP-CON Automotive Technologies, Inc. (1)
855 Main St 10th Fl, Bridgeport, CT 06604
Tel.: (203) 922-3200
Web Site: http://www.cap-conauto.com
Emp.: 2,900
Holding Company; Motor Vehicle Airbag & Power Connectivity Device Mfr & Distr
N.A.I.C.S.: 551112

Subsidiary (Domestic):

Casco Products Corporation (2)
855 Main St 10th Fl, Bridgeport, CT 06604
Tel.: (203) 922-3200
Web Site: http://www.casco-cpcn.com
Sales Range: $200-249.9 Million
Motor Vehicle Power Outlet & Connectivity Component Mfr & Distr
N.A.I.C.S.: 336320

CFS Brands LLC (1)
4711 E Hefner Rd, Oklahoma City, OK 73131
Tel.: (405) 475-5600
Web Site: http://www.cfsbrands.com
Holding Company
N.A.I.C.S.: 551112
Trent Feriberg *(Pres & CEO)*

Subsidiary (Domestic):

Carlisle FoodService Products Incorporated (2)
4711 E Hefner Rd, Oklahoma City, OK 73131
Tel.: (405) 475-5600
Web Site: http://www.carlislefsp.com
Injection Molding, Food Service Equipment & Supply Items, Packaging Containers Mfr
N.A.I.C.S.: 326199
Trent Freiberg *(Pres)*

Subsidiary (Domestic):

The Colman Group Inc. (3)
555 Koopman Ln, Elkhorn, WI 53121
Tel.: (262) 723-6133
Web Site: http://www.sanjamar.com
Foodservice Apparel, Food Safety Tools, Disposable & Hand Safety Products Supplier & Whslr
N.A.I.C.S.: 423830

Subsidiary (Domestic):

Piper Products, Inc. (3)
300 S 84th Ave, Wausau, WI 54401
Tel.: (715) 842-2724
Web Site: http://www.piperonline.net
Sales Range: $1-9.9 Million
Food Product Machinery Mfr
N.A.I.C.S.: 333241
Tony Sweeney *(Pres)*

Echo Global Logistics, Inc. (1)
600 W Chicago Ave Ste 200, Chicago, IL 60654
Web Site: https://www.echo.com
Rev.: $2,511,515,000
Assets: $963,944,000
Liabilities: $564,575,000
Net Worth: $399,369,000
Earnings: $15,832,000
Emp.: 2,593
Fiscal Year-end: 12/31/2020
Process, Physical Distribution & Logistics Consulting Services
N.A.I.C.S.: 541614
David B. Menzel *(Pres & COO)*
Sean Burke *(Chief Comml Officer)*
Paula Frey *(Chief HR Officer)*
Peter M. Rogers *(CFO)*
Zach Jecklin *(Sr VP-Strategy)*
Christopher Clemmensen *(Sr VP-Mktg)*

COMPANIES

THE JORDAN COMPANY, L.P.

Brian Parchem (CIO)
Bradley A. Keywell (Co-Founder)
Douglas R. Waggoner (CEO)

Subsidiary (Domestic):

Advantage Transport, Inc. (2)
2224 W Northern Ave Ste D 100, Phoenix, AZ 85021
Tel.: (602) 331-0808
Sales Range: $25-49.9 Million
Emp.: 16
Transportation Services
N.A.I.C.S.: 488510

Freight Management Plus (2)
4074 Mount Royal Blvd Ste 102, Allison Park, PA 15101-2995
Tel.: (412) 486-3170
Web Site: http://freightmanagementplus.com
Real Estate Credit
N.A.I.C.S.: 522292

HGIM Holdings, LLC (1)
701 Poydras St Ste 3700, New Orleans, LA 70139
Tel.: (504) 348-2466
Marine Transportation Services
N.A.I.C.S.: 488390

PEP Industries LLC (1)
110 Frank Mossberg Dr, Attleboro, MA 02703
Tel.: (508) 226-5600
Web Site: http://www.pep-corp.com
Holding Company; Precision Engineered Products Mfr
N.A.I.C.S.: 551112
John Manzi (Pres & COO)

PRG Holdings, LLC (1)
200 Business Park Dr Ste 109, Armonk, NY 10504
Tel.: (212) 589-5400
Web Site: http://www.prg.com
Emp.: 25
Corporate Event Organizer
N.A.I.C.S.: 711310
Jeremiah Harris (Chm & CEO)
Scott Hansen (CFO)
Nicole Scano-Schwiebert (Chief Admin Officer & Exec VP)
Robert Manners (Gen Counsel & Exec VP)
Darren DeVerna (CEO-Theatre)

Subsidiary (Non-US):

MHG Media Holdings AG (2)
Breite Strasse 27, 40213, Dusseldorf, Germany
Tel.: (49) 211 30143 211
Holding Company
N.A.I.C.S.: 551112

PRG EML Productions (2)
Ontariodreef 10, Utrecht, 3565 AN, Holland, Netherlands
Tel.: (31) 30 26 32 040
Web Site: http://www.prg.com
Entertainment Equipment & Lighting Supplier
N.A.I.C.S.: 423610
Scott Hansen (Mng Dir)

PRG K.K. (2)
DS Kaigan Bldg 6F 2-2-6 Kaigan, Minato-ku, Tokyo, 105-0022, Japan
Tel.: (81) 364148600
Web Site: http://www.prg.com
Emp.: 63
Event Organizing Services
N.A.I.C.S.: 711310
Tsuneo Imai (Pres)

Production Resource Group (Australia) Pty Ltd. (2)
88 Nathan Road, Dandenong South, 3175, VIC, Australia
Tel.: (61) 3 8710 2555
Web Site: http://www.prg.com
Entertainment Equipment & Lighting Supplier
N.A.I.C.S.: 444230

Production Resource Group AG (2)
Am Coloneum 1 Building D3, 50829, Cologne, Germany
Tel.: (49) 221870740
Web Site: http://www.prg.com
Sales Range: $150-199.9 Million
Technical Services for Film & Television Production Services
N.A.I.C.S.: 512110
Jorn Kubiak (CEO)
Udo Willburger (Dir-Sls & Acct Mgmt)

Subsidiary (Domestic):

Production Resource Group LLC (2)
539 Temple Hill Rd, New Windsor, NY 12553-5533
Tel.: (845) 567-5700
Web Site: http://www.prg.com
Emp.: 100
Entertainment Technology Solution & Services
N.A.I.C.S.: 532490
James Lehner (Sr VP-Design & Construction)
Darren DeVerna (CEO-Theatre-Global)
Rusty Brutsche (Vice Chm & CTO)
Tony Ward (Acct Mgr)
Matthew Carson (CEO-Corp & Events Grp)
Joseph T. Cirillo (CFO)
Nicole Scano-Schwiebert (Chief Admin Officer & Exec VP)
Manus McHugh (Sr VP-Corp Events, Staging & Hotels)
Danton Hardman (Dir-Bus Dev-Corp Events Grp-Washington)
Murray Ryan (Dir-Bus Dev-Corp Events Grp-Chicago)

Subsidiary (Domestic):

Chaos Visual Productions LLC (3)
2333 N Vly St, Burbank, CA 91505-1114
Tel.: (818) 748-2200
Web Site: http://www.chaosvisual.com
Motion Picture & Video Production
N.A.I.C.S.: 512110
Chris Wickman (Owner)

Unit (Domestic):

PRG Dallas (3)
8617 Ambassador Row Ste 120, Dallas, TX 75247-4639
Tel.: (214) 819-3100
Web Site: http://www.prg.com
Automated Lighting Systems & Related Services to the Entertainment Industry
N.A.I.C.S.: 532289
Charles Reese (Mgr-Engrg)
Andrew Spilberg (Dir-Technical)
Clay Powers (Gen Mgr)
Greg Bright (Mgr-Mfr)
Sherron Toney (Controller)
Ted Samuelson (Mgr-Engrg)
Anthony Fisher (Mgr-Asset)
Chris Conti (Mgr-Production)
Michael Maloughney (Mgr-Inventory)
Matt Corke (Mgr-Production)
Tim Wiley (VP-Tech)
Mike Snyder (Product Mgr)

PRG Nocturne (3)
300 Harvestore Dr, Dekalb, IL 60115
Tel.: (815) 756-9600
Web Site: http://www.nocturneproductions.com
Emp.: 25
Entertainment Equipment & Lighting Supplier
N.A.I.C.S.: 423610
Bob Brigham (Co-Pres)
Ron Proesel (Co-Pres)
Paul Becher (Exec VP)
Damian Walsh (Mgr-Ops)
John Schaeffer (Mgr-Asset)
Abe Main (Mgr-LED Prep)
Leon Roll (Mgr-LED Project)
Stefaan Michels (Acct Dir)
Mark O'Herlihy (Supvr-LED Engr)
David Lemmink (Gen Mgr)

Subsidiary (Domestic):

PRG Paskal Lighting (3)
1245 Aviation Place, Los Angeles, CA 91340
Tel.: (818) 252-2600
Web Site: http://www.prg.com
Emp.: 50
Entertainment & Event Technologies & Production Services
N.A.I.C.S.: 541820
Evan Green (Pres)
David Miranda (Ops Mgr)
Brian Edwards (CEO & Gen Mgr)
Steven Greenberg (Exec VP-North American Ops)

Paskal Lighting, Inc. (3)
12685 Van Nuys Blvd, Pacoima, CA 91331
Tel.: (818) 896-5233
Web Site: http://www.paskal.com
Lighting Equipment Rental Services
N.A.I.C.S.: 532490
Evan Green (Pres)
David Miranda (Mgr-Ops)
John Smith (Mgr-Svc)
Christopher Nadal (Mgr-Rental)
Richard Pilla (Mgr-Sls)
Ramon Manzo (Mgr-Warehouse)

Unit (Domestic):

Production Resource Group (3)
6050 S Valley View Blvd, Las Vegas, NV 89118-3151
Tel.: (702) 942-4774
Web Site: http://www.prg.com
Sales Range: $25-49.9 Million
Theatrical Production Services
N.A.I.C.S.: 339999
Jeremiah Harris (Chm & CEO)
Joseph Cirillo (CFO)
Darren DeVerna (CEO-Theatre-Global)

PSC Group LLC. (1)
4949 Fairmont Pkwy Ste 203, Pasadena, TX 77504
Tel.: (281) 991-3500
Web Site: http://www.petroleumservice.com
Product Handling Services & Logistics Solutions
N.A.I.C.S.: 541614
Joel Dickerson (Pres & CEO)
Brian Camp (VP-Ops)

Subsidiary (Domestic):

Delta Petroleum Company Inc. (2)
10352 River Rd, Saint Rose, LA 70087
Tel.: (504) 467-1399
Web Site: http://www.deltacompanies.net
Sales Range: $75-99.9 Million
Emp.: 60
Oils & Greases, Blending & Compounding
N.A.I.C.S.: 324191

Subsidiary (Domestic):

Olympic Oil, Ltd. (3)
5000 W 41st St, Cicero, IL 60804
Tel.: (708) 876-7900
Web Site: http://www.deltacogroup.com
Lubricating Oils & Greases
N.A.I.C.S.: 324191

Subsidiary (Domestic):

Prokar, Inc. (2)
300 E Mcneese St, Lake Charles, LA 70605
Tel.: (337) 475-9955
Web Site: http://www.prokar.com
Rev.: $1,900,000
Emp.: 28
Railcar Repair Services
N.A.I.C.S.: 488210
Lee Schreve (Pres)
Tom White (Bus Mgr)

Polymer Solutions Group LLC (1)
12819 Coit Rd, Cleveland, OH 44108
Tel.: (216) 249-4900
Web Site: http://polymersolutionsgroup.com
Specialty Polymers & Additives Mfr
N.A.I.C.S.: 325199
Michael Ivany (CEO)

Subsidiary (Domestic):

Flow Polymers LLC (2)
12819 Coit Rd, Cleveland, OH 44108
Tel.: (216) 249-4900
Web Site: http://www.flowpolymers.com
Emp.: 125
Rubber & Plastic Additives & Dispersions Mfr
N.A.I.C.S.: 325199
Jamie Justice (Supvr-Production)
Lynda Hicks (Mgr-Tech Svc)
Bob Dragolic (Plant Mgr)
Monica Balyer (Mgr-Product & Inside Sls)
John Zeleznik (VP-Sls & Mktg)
Mike Ivany (Pres & CEO)

Potters Industries, LLC (1)
1200 W Swedesford Rd, Berwyn, PA 19312
Tel.: (610) 651-4700
Web Site: http://www.pottersbeads.com
Sales Range: $200-249.9 Million
Emp.: 650
Engineered Glass Materials Mfr
N.A.I.C.S.: 327215

Sabre Industries, Inc. (1)
8653 E Hwy 67, Alvarado, TX 76009
Tel.: (817) 852-1700
Web Site: http://www.sabreindustriesinc.com
Wireless Communications Infrastructure Products & Ancillary Equipment
N.A.I.C.S.: 237130
Timothy Rossetti (CFO & COO)
Brian Newberg (Pres-Telecom Div)
James Ruddy (CEO)
Bill Sales (Pres-Utility Div)

Division (Domestic):

CellXion LLC (2)
5031 Hazel Jones Rd, Bossier City, LA 71111
Tel.: (318) 213-2900
Web Site: http://www.cellxion.com
Sales Range: $75-99.9 Million
Telecommunications Towers Construction
N.A.I.C.S.: 237130
Morgan Wicker (Engr-Civil)
Lukasz Drozdz (Mgr-CAD Dev)
Don Martin (Mgr-Night Shift)
Ted Bogues (Mgr-Pur)
Scott C. Leggett Sr. (Project Mgr)

Division (Domestic):

Cellxion Lightweight Division LLC (3)
5031 Hazel Jones Rd, Bossier City, LA 71111
Tel.: (318) 213-2900
Web Site: http://www.cellxion.com
Rev.: $15,164,384
Portable Buildings, Prefabricated Metal Mfr
N.A.I.C.S.: 332313

Subsidiary (Domestic):

Sabre Communications Corp. (2)
2101 Murray St, Sioux City, IA 51102
Tel.: (712) 258-6690
Sales Range: $25-49.9 Million
Communications Towers Mfr
N.A.I.C.S.: 334220

Division (Domestic):

Sabre Site Solutions (2)
2101 Murray St, Sioux City, IA 51102-0658
Tel.: (712) 293-1961
Web Site: http://www.sabresitesolutions.com
Communication Equipment Distr
N.A.I.C.S.: 423690
Michael Burnett (Mgr-Natl Sls)

Sabre Telecom Services (2)
2626 Midwest Ct, Champaign, IL 61822
Tel.: (217) 819-3040
Emp.: 5
Tower Construction Services
N.A.I.C.S.: 237130
Brian Newberg (Pres-Telecom Products & Svcs)

Sabre Towers and Poles (2)
7101 Southbridge Dr, Sioux City, IA 51111
Tel.: (712) 258-6690
Web Site: http://www.sabre-stp.com
Fabricated Structural Metal Mfr
N.A.I.C.S.: 332312
Tim Hornbeck (Mgr-Sls)

Sabre Tubular Structures (2)
8653 E Highway 67, Alvarado, TX 76009
Tel.: (817) 852-1700
Web Site: http://www.sabretubularstructures.com
Fabricated Structural Metal Mfr332312
N.A.I.C.S.: 332312
April Carson (Coord-Shipping Logistics)
Robert L. Schultz (Pres)

Plant (Domestic):

Sabre Tubular Structures - Ellwood City Facility (3)
700 2nd St, Ellwood City, PA 16117
Tel.: (724) 201-9968
Fabricated Structural Metal Mfr
N.A.I.C.S.: 332312

THE JORDAN COMPANY, L.P.

The Jordan Company, L.P.—(Continued)

Sabre Tubular Structures - Sioux City Facility (3)
7101 Southbridge Dr, Sioux City, IA 51102
Tel.: (712) 258-6690
Web Site: http://www.sabreindustries.com
Emp.: 500
Fabricated Structural Metal Mfr
N.A.I.C.S.: 332312
Brian Newberg *(Pres-Telecom Products & Svcs)*

Sechrist Industries, Inc. (1)
4225 E La Palma Ave, Anaheim, CA 92807
Tel.: (714) 579-8400
Web Site: http://www.sechristusa.com
Sales Range: $75-99.9 Million
Mfr of Medical Products & Industrial Measuring Instruments
N.A.I.C.S.: 339112
Deepak Talati *(Gen Mgr)*

Spartech LLC (1)
11650 Lakeside Crossing Ct, Maryland Heights, MO 63146
Tel.: (314) 569-7400
Web Site: http://www.spartech.com
Packaging, Plastic Sheet & Rollstock Material Mfr
N.A.I.C.S.: 326130
Dave Gorenc *(VP-Mfg)*
George A. Abd *(Exec VP & VP)*
Suzanne Fenton *(Sr Mgr-Mktg Comm)*
JuliAnn Bock *(Dir-HR)*
John Manzi *(Chm)*
Jaclyn Snyder *(Mgr-Bus Dev-Specialty Packaging)*
Matt Gisoni *(VP-Supply Chain & Sourcing)*
John Inks *(CEO)*
Joe Herres *(VP-Sls & Mktg)*
Michael Reed *(VP-Bus Mgmt, M&A & Sustainability)*
John Alfano *(Gen Mgr-Thin Gauge Sheet)*
Jessica Sekely *(Dir-Environmental Health & Safety)*
Mario Columbia *(Gen Mgr-Polycast Acrylic Sheet Div)*
Larry Baer *(Plant Mgr-Paulding)*

Subsidiary (Domestic):

Crawford Industries, LLC (2)
1414 Crawford Dr, Crawfordsville, IN 47933
Tel.: (765) 362-6733
Web Site: http://www.crawford-industries.com
Sales Range: $10-24.9 Million
Plastic Book Binders Mfr
N.A.I.C.S.: 326199
Earl Guinter *(VP-Mktg)*
Kendall Faulstich *(Pres & CEO)*

Plant (Domestic):

Spartech - Cape Girardeau (2)
2500 Spartech Dr, Cape Girardeau, MO 63702
Tel.: (573) 339-8400
Web Site: http://www.spartech.com
Packaging, Plastic Sheet & Rollstock Materials Mfr
N.A.I.C.S.: 325211
Matthew Werden *(Sr Mgr)*

Spartech - Goodyear (2)
Bldg 2 W Vly Tech Ctr 1300 S Litchfield Rd, Goodyear, AZ 85338
Tel.: (623) 882-2771
Web Site: http://www.spartech.com
Plastic Sheet & Rollstock Material Mfr
N.A.I.C.S.: 325211

Spartech - La Mirada (2)
14263 Gannet St, La Mirada, CA 90638-5220
Tel.: (800) 557-4338
Web Site: http://www.spartech.com
Plastic Sheet & Rollstock Material Mfr
N.A.I.C.S.: 326112

Spartech - McMinnville (2)
4150 Riverside Dr, McMinnville, OR 97128
Tel.: (503) 472-6191
Web Site: http://www.spartech.com
Rigid Plastic Sheet & Rollstock Mfr
N.A.I.C.S.: 326113

Spartech - Paulding (2)
925 W Gasser Rd, Paulding, OH 45879
Tel.: (419) 399-4050
Web Site: http://www.spartech.com
Rigid Plastic Sheet & Rollstock Mfr
N.A.I.C.S.: 326199

Spartech - Salisbury (2)
601 Marvel Rd, Salisbury, MD 21801
Tel.: (410) 548-7759
Web Site: http://www.spartech.com
Engineered Thermoplastic Material Mfr
N.A.I.C.S.: 325211

Spartech - Stamford (2)
70 Carlisle Pl, Stamford, CT 06902
Tel.: (203) 327-6010
Web Site: http://www.spartech.com
Plastic Sheet & Rollstock Material Mfr
N.A.I.C.S.: 326113

Spartech - Townsend (2)
4400 Vandalia Rd, Pleasant Hill, IA 50327
Tel.: (515) 265-4157
Web Site: http://www.spartech.com
Plastic Material & Resin Mfr
N.A.I.C.S.: 325211

Subsidiary (Domestic):

Tufpak, Inc. (2)
698 Browns Ridge Rd, Ossipee, NH 03864
Tel.: (603) 539-4126
Web Site: http://www.tufpak.com
Sales Range: $1-9.9 Million
Emp.: 25
Bags: Plastic, Laminated, And Coated, Nsk
N.A.I.C.S.: 326111
Annette Fox *(Controller)*

Spectrio, LLC (1)
7624 Bald Cypress Place, Tampa, FL 33614
Tel.: (727) 787-2440
Web Site: http://www.spectrio.com
Audio & Video Marketing Solutions
N.A.I.C.S.: 541890
Jeff Juszczak *(CTO)*
Tamara Bebb *(CEO)*

Subsidiary (Domestic):

Codigo LLC (2)
1201 Story Ave Ste 400, Louisville, KY 40206-1763
Tel.: (502) 779-8981
Web Site: http://www.gocodigo.com
Marketing Consulting Services
N.A.I.C.S.: 541613

InReality, LLC (2)
120 Interstate N Pkwy E Ste 226, Atlanta, GA 30339
Tel.: (770) 953-1500
Web Site: http://www.inreality.com
Sales Range: $1-9.9 Million
Emp.: 33
Graphic Design Services
N.A.I.C.S.: 541430
Brooks Ballard *(Sr Mgr-Mktg & Revenue Analytics)*
Lisa Cramer *(VP-Mktg & Sls)*
Carl Davis *(VP-Digital)*
Kevin Greer *(Dir-Solutions Design)*
Kristin Harripaul *(Mgr-Content Mktg)*
Ron Levac *(CEO)*
Ryan Cahoy *(Chief Revenue Officer)*

Industry Weapon, Inc. (2)
900 Parish St, Pittsburgh, PA 15220
Tel.: (724) 941-5298
Web Site: http://www.industryweapon.com
Emp.: 210
Software Publisher
N.A.I.C.S.: 513210
Craig Hanna *(CEO)*
David Wible *(Founder)*
Wil Chufo *(CTO & Chief Info Security Officer)*

Lifeshare Technologies LLC (2)
4202 N EMS Blvd Ste 180, Greenfield, IN 46140
Tel.: (317) 825-0320
Custom Computer Programming Services
N.A.I.C.S.: 541511
Steve Payne *(Mgr-Customer Success)*

Ping HD LLC (2)
2114 Market St, Denver, CO 80205
Tel.: (303) 593-1252
Web Site: http://www.pinghd.com
Computer System Design Services

N.A.I.C.S.: 541512

Sound Marketing Concepts of CT LLC (2)
1800 Silas Deane Hwy Ste 7N, Rocky Hill, CT 06067
Tel.: (860) 257-9367
Web Site: http://www.4smc.com
On-Hold Telephonic Marketing Services
N.A.I.C.S.: 541890
Steve Avroch *(Pres)*

Sunny Sky Products, LLC (1)
11747 Windfern Rd Ste 100, Houston, TX 77064
Tel.: (713) 683-9399
Web Site: http://www.sunnyskyproducts.com
Dispensed Beverage Mfr
N.A.I.C.S.: 312111
W. Ashley Edens *(Pres & CEO)*

Subsidiary (Domestic):

Americas Food Technologies, Inc. (2)
7700 West 185th St, Tinley Park, IL 60477
Tel.: (708) 532-1222
Web Site: http://www.amfotek.com
Sales Range: $1-9.9 Million
Emp.: 58
Dehydrated Food Mfr
N.A.I.C.S.: 311423

Goodwest Industries, Inc. (2)
48 Quarry Rd, Douglassville, PA 19518
Web Site: http://goodwest.com
Beverage Product Mfr
N.A.I.C.S.: 311920
Bill Goodwin *(Founder)*

Syndigo LLC (1)
141 W Jackson Blvd Ste 1220, Chicago, IL 60604
Tel.: (312) 766-4801
Web Site: https://www.syndigo.com
Content Management, Syndication, Analytics & Verified Product Information Services
N.A.I.C.S.: 519290
Simon Angove *(CEO)*
Peter Rottier *(Mng Dir)*

Subsidiary (Domestic):

EdgeAQ, LLC (2)
2948 Sidco Dr, Nashville, TN 37204
Tel.: (615) 371-3848
Web Site: http://www.edgenet.com
Information Technology Consulting Services
N.A.I.C.S.: 541512
Brian Rudolph *(CTO)*
Kraig Haberer *(Sr VP-Mktg)*
Lisa East *(Dir-Customer Support-Nashville)*
Steve Proctor *(CEO)*
Deborah West *(Program Mgr-Mooresville)*
Andrea Jacobson *(Engr-Product Knowledge)*
Chris Roach *(Sr VP-Growth-Nashville)*
Scott Howat *(Dir-Automotive Channel Strategy)*
Joe Thomas *(Mgr-Automotive Program)*
Ben Sellers *(Dir-Enterprise Accts)*
Meredith Ziegler *(Dir-Strategic Accts)*
Philip Spelman *(Dir-Strategic Accts)*

Riversand Technologies, Inc. (2)
9800 Richmond Ave Ste 140, Houston, TX 77042
Tel.: (713) 934-8899
Web Site: http://www.riversand.com
Software Publisher
N.A.I.C.S.: 513210
Upen Varanasi *(Co-Founder & CEO)*
Anil Kini *(Co-Founder & CTO)*
Omer Farooque *(VP-Product Strategy)*
Raman Parthasarathy *(VP-Strategy, Products & Bus Dev)*
York Richards *(CFO)*
Andrew Simpson *(VP-Bus Dev)*
Raul Rom *(VP-Customer Rels)*
Rob MacEwan *(VP-Oil & Gas)*
Tom Hathaway *(VP-Global Sls)*
Vishy Vallamkonda *(VP-Engrg)*
Charlie Lawhorn *(Chief Customer Officer)*
Shamanth Shankar *(VP-Cloud Solutions)*
Ben Rund *(VP-Bus Dev-Europe & Gen Mgr-Germany, Austria & Switzerland)*
Mikkel Jensen *(Exec VP-Europe & Middle East)*
Michael Robinson *(VP-Mktg)*
Ilana Friedman *(Dir-Comm & Events)*

U.S. PRIVATE

Sell Points Inc. (2)
1198 65th St Ste 250, Emeryville, CA 94608
Tel.: (866) 343-4310
Web Site: http://www.sellpoints.com
Data Processing, Hosting & Related Services
N.A.I.C.S.: 518210
Alan Dyck *(Product Mgr-Mktg)*
Austen Middleton *(Mgr-Customer Success)*
Benny Blum *(Sr VP-Product)*
Carol Wong *(Project Mgr)*
Cheryl Sembrano *(Dir-Customer Support)*
David Franco *(VP-Bus Info Sys)*
Ivan Dejanovic *(Sr VP-Technology)*
Joe Mantor *(Mgr-Customer Success)*
John Kuo *(Product Mgr)*
Jon Gregg *(Pres)*

Southern Graphic Systems, LLC (2)
1720 W Detweiller Dr, Peoria, IL 61615
Tel.: (888) 594-5331
Web Site: http://www.kwikeesystems.com
Web Hosting Services
N.A.I.C.S.: 513199
Jeff Creek *(Dir-Inside Sls)*

TIDI Products LLC (1)
570 Enterprise Dr, Neenah, WI 54956
Tel.: (920) 751-4300
Web Site: http://www.tidiproducts.com
Single-Use Infection Prevention Product Mfr
N.A.I.C.S.: 339114
Kevin McNamara *(Pres & CEO)*
Brian Wilt *(VP-Innovation & Product Dev)*
Jeff Hebbard *(COO & VP)*
Jennifer Jones *(VP-Mktg)*
Evelina Leece *(Dir-Mktg)*

The Jordan Company China (1)
CITIC Sq 1168 Nanjing Xi Lu Fl 23 Ste 2308, Shanghai, 200041, China
Tel.: (86) 2152925566
Web Site: http://www.thejordancompany.com
Sales Range: $25-49.9 Million
Emp.: 13
Investment Activities
N.A.I.C.S.: 523999
Andrew W. Rice *(Sr VP)*
Youming Ye *(Mng Dir)*

Tolin Mechanical Systems Co. (1)
12005 E 45th Ave, Denver, CO 80239
Tel.: (303) 455-2825
Web Site: http://www.tolin.com
Emp.: 300
Warm Air Heating & Air Conditioning Contractor
N.A.I.C.S.: 238220
Tom Trefz *(Pres)*
Bryant Kuvakos *(VP)*
Dave Joslyn *(VP-Sls & Engrg)*
Nancy Locklin *(CFO & Sr VP)*
Thomas Padilla *(Pres)*

Top Knobs USA, Inc. (1)
170 Township Line Rd Bldg D1, Hillsborough, NJ 08844-3867
Tel.: (908) 359-6174
Web Site: http://www.topknobs.com
Rev.: $3,333,333
Emp.: 20
Decorative Knobs & Drawer Pulls
N.A.I.C.S.: 332510
Christine Zimmer *(Product Mgr)*
Michael DeLucia *(Mgr-Warehouse Ops)*
Matt Vecchiolla *(Sls Mgr-Natl)*
Warren Ramsland *(Pres)*
Mike Perez *(Mgr-Pur)*

Subsidiary (Domestic):

Atlas Homewares, Inc. (2)
1310 Cypress Ave, Los Angeles, CA 90065
Tel.: (818) 240-3500
Web Site: http://www.atlashomewares.com
Emp.: 25
Vitreous China, Fine Earthenware & Other Pottery Product Mfr
N.A.I.C.S.: 327110
Adrian Morea *(CEO & Creative Dir)*

Transportation Impact LLC (1)
PO Box 4758, Emerald Isle, NC 28594
Tel.: (252) 764-2885
Web Site: http://www.ransportationimpact.com
Sales Range: $1-9.9 Million
Emp.: 12
Parcel Management Services

COMPANIES

N.A.I.C.S.: 541614
Keith Byrd *(Co-Founder & Co-Partner)*
Travis Burt *(Co-Founder & Co-Partner)*
John Howard *(VP-Ops)*
Berkley Stafford *(VP-Sls)*

Worldwide Clinical Trials, Inc. (1)
3800 Paramount Pkwy Ste 400, Morrisville, NC 27560
Tel.: (610) 632-8150
Web Site: http://www.worldwide.com
Sales Range: $25-49.9 Million
Emp.: 35
Drug Mfr
N.A.I.C.S.: 325412
Neal R. Cutler *(Co-CEO)*
Angelico Carta *(Founder)*
Fabio Dorigotti *(Pres-Global Clinical)*
Michael F. Murphy *(Chief Medical Officer & Chief Scientific Officer)*
Barry Lederman *(CFO)*
Henry J. Riordan *(Exec VP-Medical & Scientific Affairs)*
Margo Holland *(VP-Global Quality Assurance)*
Peter Benton *(Pres & Co-CEO)*
William Hirschman *(Exec VP & Head-Global Bus Dev)*
Karen Nowatkoski *(VP-Clinical Ops & Site Mgmt)*
Jeffrey Zucker *(Sr VP-Clinical Ops Site Mgmt & Trial Optimization)*
Sarah Davis *(Chief Comml Officer)*
Chris Hill *(Sr VP-Bus Dev-Intl)*
Nikola Strumberger *(VP-Therapeutic Area Strategy Leads-Germany)*
Dave Bowser *(COO)*
Tamara Ast *(Sr VP-Project Delivery Svcs Neuroscience)*
Val Aldcroft *(Sr VP-Biometrics, Tech & Pharmacovigilance)*
Ian Braithwaite *(Sr VP-Project Mgmt-Global)*
Ted Finlan *(Sr VP-Project Plng & Admin)*
Karen Hill *(Sr VP-Project Mgmt-Global)*
Jeff Trotter *(Sr VP-Evidence-Worldwide)*
Joy Clark *(Chief HR Officer)*
Hiromi Wakita *(VP-Clinical Ops-Japan)*
Aman Khera *(Head-Regulatory Strategy-Global)*
Gerardo Pascuali *(Exec Dir-Clinical Ops-Latin America)*
Clare Wallis *(Sr VP-Oncology)*
Sherri Stuart *(VP-Global Mktg & Comm)*
Emile Youssef *(Sr VP-Oncology Scientific Solutions)*
Gary Fishbein *(Exec Dir-Medical)*
Jose L. Martinez *(Sr Dir-Medical-Oncology)*
Mike Mencer *(Exec VP & Gen Mgr-Early Phase)*
Sherilyn Adcock *(Chief Scientific Officer-Early Phase Dev)*
Rosemarie Corrigan *(Exec VP-Global Quality)*
Karen Hagens *(VP-Global Corp Comm)*
Jill Mastrangelo *(Dir-Global Corp Comm)*
Pete Duprat *(Sr VP-Comml-Early Phase)*

Division (Domestic):

Worldwide Clinical Trials Early Phase Services & Bioanalytical Sciences (2)
8605 Cross Park, Austin, TX 78754
Tel.: (512) 834-7766
Web Site: http://www.wwctrials.com
Sales Range: $10-24.9 Million
Emp.: 150
Biotechnical Research, Commercial
N.A.I.C.S.: 541720
Steve E. Unger *(VP & Dir-Laboratory)*
Thomas L. Lloyd *(Dir-Automation-Bioanalytical Grp)*
Cathy Brown *(Mgr-Accts)*
Keith Fern *(CEO)*

Young Innovations, Inc. (1)
2260 Wendt St, Algonquin, IL 60102
Tel.: (847) 458-5400
Web Site: http://www.ydnt.com
Holding Company; Dental Products Designer, Mfr & Marketer
N.A.I.C.S.: 551112
Dave Sproat *(CEO)*
Mark Peluse *(VP-HR & Corporate Legal Affairs)*
Dave Misiak *(Chief Comml Officer)*
John Frymark *(VP-Product Dev & Product Strategy)*

Scott Leece *(VP-Business Process Optimization)*
Jose A. Espino *(VP-Quality & Regulatory Affairs)*
Brian Werner *(COO & Chief Quality Officer)*

Subsidiary (Non-US):

Astek Innovations Ltd. (2)
Astek House Atlantic St, Altrincham, WA14 5DH, Cheshire, United Kingdom
Tel.: (44) 1619423900
Web Site: http://www.astekinnovations.co.uk
Dental Products Mfr & Whslr
N.A.I.C.S.: 339114

Subsidiary (Domestic):

Biotrol International (2)
13705 Shoreline Ct E, Earth City, MO 63045
Tel.: (800) 822-8550
Web Site: http://www.biotrol.com
Dental Disinfecting & Sterilizing Products Mfr
N.A.I.C.S.: 339114

Mydent International, Inc. (2)
2260 Wendt St, Algonquin, IL 60102
Tel.: (631) 434-3190
Web Site: http://www.defend.com
Infection Control Products (for the Dental, Medical & Healthcare Industry)
N.A.I.C.S.: 423450

Panoramic Rental Corp. (2)
4321 Goshen Rd, Fort Wayne, IN 46818
Tel.: (800) 654-2027
Web Site: http://www.pancorp.com
Medical Equipment & Supplies Whslr
N.A.I.C.S.: 423450
Andrew Jones *(VP)*

Preat Corp. (2)
100 S 4th St, Grover Beach, CA 93433-1910
Tel.: (805) 202-3070
Web Site: http://www.preat.com
Dental Equipment & Supplies Mfr
N.A.I.C.S.: 339114
Chris Bormes *(CEO)*

Puragraft, LLC (2)
22001 Northpark Dr Ste 700, Kingwood, TX 77339
Web Site: http://www.puragraft.com
Biomaterial Solutions Mfr
N.A.I.C.S.: 339112
Lee Majerus *(Mng Partner)*

Salvin Dental Specialties, Inc. (2)
3450 Latrobe Dr, Charlotte, NC 28211
Tel.: (704) 442-5400
Web Site: http://www.salvin.com
Dental Surgical Instrument Mfr & Distr
N.A.I.C.S.: 339112
William Simmons *(CEO)*
Greg Slayton *(Pres)*

The Orthodontic Store, Inc. (2)
2260 Wendt St, Algonquin, IL 60102
Tel.: (800) 558-6684
Web Site: http://www.plaksmacker.com
Supplies Orthodontic Appliances & Instruments
N.A.I.C.S.: 339112

Young Dental Manufacturing I, LLC (2)
13705 Shoreline Ct E, Earth City, MO 63045-1202
Tel.: (352) 323-3500
Web Site: http://www.youngdental.com
Dental Equipment & Supplies Mfr
N.A.I.C.S.: 339114
Daniel Garrick *(VP)*
Brett Gordon *(Dir-Ops)*
Michael Turner *(Mgr-Chemical Mfg)*

Young Microbrush International, LLC (2)
1376 Cheyenne Ave, Grafton, WI 53024
Tel.: (262) 375-4011
Web Site: http://www.microbrush.com
Surgical & Medical Instrument Mfr
N.A.I.C.S.: 339112

Subsidiary (Non-US):

Young Microbrush Ireland, Ltd. (2)

Clogherane, Dungarvan, Waterford Co, Ireland
Tel.: (353) 58 45966
Web Site: http://www.microbrush.com
Irradiation Apparatus Mfr
N.A.I.C.S.: 334517
Mary O'keeffe *(Gen Mgr)*

iNRCORE, LLC (1)
311 Sinclair Rd, Bristol, PA 19007
Tel.: (215) 781-6400
Web Site: http://inrcore.com
Magnetic Components Mfr
N.A.I.C.S.: 336992
Sarah Harris *(CEO)*

Subsidiary (Domestic):

Gowanda Components Group (2)
1 Magnetics Pkwy, Gowanda, NY 14070
Tel.: (716) 532-2234
Web Site: http://www.gowandacomponentsgroup.com
Holding Company
N.A.I.C.S.: 551112
Don McElheny *(CEO)*

Subsidiary (Domestic):

Gowanda - GEC LLC (3)
1 Magnetics Pkwy, Gowanda, NY 14070
Tel.: (716) 532-2234
Web Site: http://www.gowanda.com
Sales Range: $1-9.9 Million
Emp.: 80
Electronic Components Mfr
N.A.I.C.S.: 334419
Claude Badawy *(COO)*
Don McElheny *(CEO)*
Denis Kohlhagen *(VP-Sls)*
Thomas Norsen *(CFO)*

RCD Components Inc. (3)
520 E Industrial Park Dr, Manchester, NH 03109
Tel.: (603) 669-0054
Web Site: http://www.rcdcomponents.com
Sales Range: $25-49.9 Million
Emp.: 200
Resistor Networks
N.A.I.C.S.: 334416
Paul Sorenson *(Controller)*
Daniel Roy *(Mgr-Quality)*
Mike Arcidy *(VP)*

TTE Filters, LLC (3)
7426A Tanner Pkwy, Arcade, NY 14009
Tel.: (716) 532-2234
Web Site: http://www.tte.com
Radio Frequency & Microwave Filters Mfr
N.A.I.C.S.: 334419
David Zavac *(Mgr-Sls)*

Wist Enterprises, Inc. (3)
7426A Tanner Pkwy, Arcade, NY 14009
Tel.: (716) 532-2234
Web Site: http://www.butlerwinding.com
Electronic Transformers & Inductors Mfr
N.A.I.C.S.: 335311
Joyce Weston *(Office Mgr)*
Jay Smith *(VP-Ops)*
Denny Wist *(CEO)*

THE JORDAN, EDMISTON GROUP, INC.
150 E 52nd St 18th Fl, New York, NY 10022
Tel.: (212) 754-0710
Web Site: http://www.jegi.com
Year Founded: 1987
Sales Range: $1-9.9 Million
Emp.: 40
Investment Banking
N.A.I.C.S.: 523150
Tolman Geffs *(Pres)*
Wilma Jordan *(Founder & CEO)*
Richard Mead *(Mng Dir)*
David Clark *(Chief Mktg Officer)*
William Hitzig *(COO)*
Adam Gross *(Mng Dir)*
Thomas Creaser *(Exec VP-Pro Svcs Grp)*
Daniel Avrutsky *(Mng Dir)*
Chris Calton *(Mng Dir)*

THE JUDAICA PRESS, INC.

THE JUDGE GROUP, INC.

123 Ditmas Ave, Brooklyn, NY 11218
Tel.: (718) 972-6200
Web Site: http://www.judaicapress.com
Year Founded: 1963
Rev.: $24,400,000
Emp.: 7
Book Publishers
N.A.I.C.S.: 513130
Chaim Schneider *(Mgr-Sls)*
Gloria Goldman *(Pres)*

THE JUDGE GROUP, INC.
4 Falls Corp Ctr 300 Conshohocken State Rd, West Conshohocken, PA 19428-2949
Tel.: (610) 667-7700   PA
Web Site: http://www.judge.com
Year Founded: 1970
Sales Range: $75-99.9 Million
Emp.: 677
Employment & Staffing Services
N.A.I.C.S.: 541612
Martin E. Judge Jr. *(Founder & Chm)*
Robert G. Alessandrini *(CFO)*
Kenneth F. Krieger *(CIO)*
Dennis Judge *(Pres-Internet Division)*
Katharine A. Wiercinski *(COO)*
Amy E. Feldman *(Gen Counsel)*
Stephen D. Green *(Pres-Direct Placement)*
Brian Anderson *(Pres)*
Abhishek Agarwal *(Pres-India Bus & Global Delivery)*
Ryan Miller *(Mktg Dir)*
Michael R. Tedesco *(Exec VP-Sls)*
Peter Pedone *(Pres-Learning Solutions)*
James D. Miner *(Pres-Tech Solutions & Unified Comm)*
Michael A. Glinter *(Sr VP-Direct Placement)*
Mick J. Angelichio *(Pres-Healthcare)*
Patrick E. Ronen *(Sr VP-IT & Life Sciences)*
Janet L. Harbour *(Sr VP-MSP Programs)*
Shane Connor *(Mng Dir)*
Justin Sellers *(Dir-Dallas)*
Nancy Burr *(VP-Enterprise Accts)*
Martin Judge III *(CEO)*

Subsidiaries:

Judge Technical Services Inc. (1)
300 Conshohocken State Rd Ste 300, West Conshohocken, PA 19428
Tel.: (610) 667-7700
Web Site: http://www.judge.com
Sales Range: $10-24.9 Million
Emp.: 110
Staffing of IT Professionals on a Contract Basis
N.A.I.C.S.: 541612
Martin E. Judge Jr. *(Founder & CEO)*
Robert G. Alessandrini *(CFO)*
Katy A. Wiercinski *(COO)*
Brian T. Anderson *(Pres-North America)*
Amy E. Feldman *(Gen Counsel)*
Peter L. Fong *(CMO & Exec VP)*
Michael A. Glinter *(Sr VP-Direct Placement)*
Patrick E. Ronen *(Sr VP-IT & Life Sciences)*
Michael R. Tedesco *(Exec VP-Sls)*

Judge.com, Inc. (1)
300 W Cornshohocken Rd Ste 300, Conshohocken, PA 19428
Tel.: (610) 667-7700
Web Site: http://www.judge.com
Sales Range: $10-24.9 Million
Emp.: 75
Provider of Employment & Staffing Services; Technical Recruiting
N.A.I.C.S.: 541612
Katy Wiercinski *(COO)*

On-Site-Solutions, Inc (1)
Two Bala Plz, Bala Cynwyd, PA 19004
Tel.: (610) 667-1199
Provider of Employment Staffing Services
N.A.I.C.S.: 621399

THE JUDGE GROUP, INC.

The Judge Group, Inc.—(Continued)

The Berkeley Associates
Corporation (1)
4 Falls Corporate Ctr 300 Conshohocken
State Rd, West Conshohocken, PA 19004-
1501
Tel.: (610) 667-7700
Web Site: http://www.berkeleytraining.com
Sales Range: $10-24.9 Million
Emp.: 10
Employment Agencies
N.A.I.C.S.: 541612
Martin E. Judge Jr. *(Founder & CEO)*
Peter Pedone *(Pres)*

THE KANE COMPANY

6500 Kane Way, Elkridge, MD
21075-6291
Tel.: (410) 799-3200   MD
Web Site:
   http://www.kanecompany.com
Year Founded: 1969
Sales Range: $75-99.9 Million
Emp.: 1,500
Provider of Trucking Services
N.A.I.C.S.: 484110
John M. Kane *(CEO)*
Richard Snyder *(Dir-Resource Plng)*
Jack Kane *(VP-Info & Hospitality Svcs)*
David Purk *(VP-Staffing Svcs)*

Subsidiaries:

KANE 3PL, LLC (1)
3636 Pennsy Dr D-1, Landover, MD 20785
Tel.: (866) 375-5263
Web Site: http://www.kane3pl.com
Logistics Consulting Servies
N.A.I.C.S.: 541614
Tony Little *(Mgr)*

Kane Staffing Services, LLC (1)
6402 Coventry Way Unit 11B, Clinton, MD
20735
Tel.: (800) 331-3045
Web Site: http://www.kaneofficestaffing.com
Staff Recruiting Services
N.A.I.C.S.: 561320

Office Installers Inc. (1)
3636 Pennsy Dr Unit D1, Landover, MD
20785
Tel.: (410) 799-3200
Web Site: http://www.officeinstallers.com
Sales Range: $10-24.9 Million
Emp.: 25
Provider of Office Services
N.A.I.C.S.: 238990
Dawn Harrison *(Mgr-Mktg)*
David Korottin *(CFO)*

Office Movers Inc. (1)
6500 Kane Way, Elkridge, MD
21075 **(100%)**
Tel.: (410) 799-3200
Web Site: http://www.officemovers.com
Sales Range: $10-24.9 Million
Emp.: 30
Provider of Trucking Services
N.A.I.C.S.: 484110
Dawn Harrison *(Mgr-Mktg)*
John M. Kane *(Pres & CEO)*
Tina Chism *(Office Mgr)*

eCyclers, LLC (1)
6500 Kane Way Ste A, Elkridge, MD 21075
Tel.: (800) 331-4025
Web Site: http://www.ecyclers.com
Office Goods Moving Services
N.A.I.C.S.: 484210

THE KANZA CO-OPERATIVE EXCHANGE, INC.

102 Main St, Iuka, KS 67066
Tel.: (620) 546-2231   KS
Web Site: http://www.kanzacoop.com
Year Founded: 1915
Sales Range: $10-24.9 Million
Emp.: 57
Agricultural Services
N.A.I.C.S.: 424510
Bruce W. Krehbiel *(Pres & Mgr)*

THE KARGES FURNITURE COMPANY, INC.

1501 W Maryland St, Evansville, IN
47719-1831
Tel.: (812) 425-2291   IN
Web Site: http://www.karges.com
Year Founded: 1886
Sales Range: $75-99.9 Million
Emp.: 95
Furniture Mfr
N.A.I.C.S.: 337122
Gretchen Keith *(VP)*

THE KASPAR COMPANIES

959 Hwy 95 N, Shiner, TX 77984
Tel.: (361) 594-3327
Web Site:
   http://www.kasparcompanies.com
Sales Range: $50-74.9 Million
Emp.: 700
Holding Company; Design & Manu-
facturing Operations for Sheetmetal,
Wire & Plastics
N.A.I.C.S.: 551112
David Kaspar *(Chm)*
Jason Kaspar *(CEO)*

Subsidiaries:

Kaspar Electroplating
Corporation (1)
959 Hwy 95 N, Shiner, TX 77984
Tel.: (361) 594-3327
Web Site:
   http://www.kasparelectroplating.com
Electroplating & Polishing Services
N.A.I.C.S.: 332813
Mike Zella *(Gen Mgr)*

Kaspar Wire Works, Inc. (1)
959 State Hwy 95 N, Shiner, TX 77984
Tel.: (361) 594-3327
Web Site: http://www.kasparmfg.com
Custom Sheet Metal, Wire & Tube Products
Mfr
N.A.I.C.S.: 332618
Lori Malina *(Controller)*

Subsidiary (Domestic):

Kaspar Die & Tool, Inc. (2)
959 Hwy 95 N, Shiner, TX 77984
Tel.: (361) 594-3321
Web Site: http://www.kasparmfg.com
Sheet Metal Stamping Mfr
N.A.I.C.S.: 332119

Ranch Hand, Inc. (1)
32954 IH 10 W, Boerne, TX 78006
Tel.: (830) 249-5600
Web Site: http://www.ranchhand.com
Emp.: 4
Automotive Part Whslr
N.A.I.C.S.: 423120
Scott McClaugherty *(Mgr-Natl Sls)*
Mavis Arambula-Medellin *(Mgr-Mktg)*

THE KAY COMPANY, INC.

509 W Barner St, Frankfort, IN
46041-1606
Tel.: (765) 659-3388   IN
Web Site: http://www.kay.com
Year Founded: 1961
Sales Range: $75-99.9 Million
Emp.: 150
Mfr of Hardboard & Particle Board
Parts for Television, Audio, Appli-
ances, Sporting Goods, Furniture,
Displays, Store Fixtures & Signs
N.A.I.C.S.: 339950
John W. Kay *(Chm)*
Michael S. Kay *(Pres)*
Dawn Golden *(Controller)*
Norma Melson *(Pur Mgr)*

THE KEELEY COMPANIES

500 S Ewing Ave Ste G, Saint Louis,
MO 63103
Tel.: (314) 426-5200   MO
Web Site:
   https://www.keeleycompanies.com
Holding Company; Construction &
Engineering Services
N.A.I.C.S.: 551112
David Fischer *(CFO)*
Rusty Keeley *(CEO)*
Lawrence P. Keeley Jr. *(Chm)*

Subsidiaries:

Keeley Development Group, Inc. (1)
500 S Ewing Ave Ste G, Saint Louis, MO
63103
Tel.: (314) 993-5800
Web Site:
   http://www.keeleydevelopmentgroup.com
Real Estate Development Services
N.A.I.C.S.: 531390
Rusty Keeley *(CEO)*

Subsidiary (Domestic):

The Koman Group, LLC (2)
8025 Bonhomme Ave Ste 200, Saint Louis,
MO 63105
Tel.: (314) 993-5800
Web Site: http://www.komangroup.com
Real Estate Services
N.A.I.C.S.: 531390
Garrick Hamilton *(Gen Counsel & Exec VP)*
Jason Braidwood *(Pres)*
Bill Koman *(Chm & CEO)*

L. Keeley Construction Co. (1)
500 S Ewing Ave Ste G, Saint Louis, MO
63103
Tel.: (618) 337-9494
Web Site: http://www.lkeeley.com
Paving, Civil Engineering & Commercial
Construction Services
N.A.I.C.S.: 541330
Raymond J. Boehm *(Sr VP-Risk Mgmt)*
Curt Peitzman *(Exec VP)*
Ted Mettler *(VP-Indus)*
Al Dreste *(Sr VP-Bus Dev)*
Rusty Keeley *(CEO)*
Tom Birkemeier *(Pres)*
David Fischer *(CFO)*
Ryan Perryman *(VP-Building)*
Ron Roellig *(VP-Infrastructure)*
Matt Taylor *(VP-Paving)*
Mark Wojtal *(VP-Energy)*
Daniel Bradley *(Controller)*
April Lopinot *(Dir-HR)*
Lawrence P. Keeley Jr. *(Chm)*

THE KEHILLAH JEWISH EDUCATION FUND

8180 Mccormick Blvd, Skokie, IL
60076
Tel.: (224) 470-2926   IL
Web Site: http://www.kehillahfund.org
Year Founded: 2009
Sales Range: $1-9.9 Million
Educational Support Services
N.A.I.C.S.: 611710
Nesanel Siegal *(COO)*
Mark Campbell *(Sec)*
Avrohom M. Siegal *(Co-Chm)*
Yosef Walder *(Founder & Co-Chm)*

THE KELLEHER CORPORATION

1543 5th Ave, San Rafael, CA 94901-
1806
Tel.: (415) 454-8861   CA
Web Site: http://www.kelleher.com
Year Founded: 1970
Sales Range: $100-124.9 Million
Emp.: 125
Distr of Lumber Plywood & Millwork
N.A.I.C.S.: 423310
Donald Kelleher *(Pres)*
Matt Caramagno *(CFO)*

THE KELLOGG COLLECTION INC.

3424 Wisconsin Ave NW, Washing-
ton, DC 20016
Tel.: (202) 363-6878
Web Site:
   http://www.kelloggcollection.com
Sales Range: $50-74.9 Million

U.S. PRIVATE

Emp.: 15
Sales of Furniture & Floor Coverings
N.A.I.C.S.: 449121
Ernesto Salgado *(Mgr-Acctg)*

THE KELLY COMPANIES

1701 Cabin Branch Dr, Cheverly, MD
20785-3820
Tel.: (301) 386-2800   MD
Web Site: http://www.kellypress.com
Sales Range: $100-124.9 Million
Emp.: 50
Lithographic Commercial Printing
N.A.I.C.S.: 323111
Daniel Kelly *(Pres)*

THE KEN BLANCHARD COMPANIES

125 State Pl, Escondido, CA 92029
Tel.: (760) 489-5005
Web Site:
   http://www.kenblanchard.com
Rev.: $55,399,998
Emp.: 265
Management Consulting Services
N.A.I.C.S.: 561110
Howard Farfel *(Pres)*
Debbie Blanchard *(Exec VP-North America)*
Shirley Y. Bullard *(Chief Admin Officer)*
Scott Blanchard *(Principal & Exec VP-Client Solutions)*
Thomas McKee *(CEO)*
R. Craig Spitz *(CFO)*
Cathy Huett *(VP-Professional Svcs)*
Jay Campbell *(Sr VP-Products & Contents)*
Joni Wickline *(VP-Intl Growth)*
Ken Blanchard *(Co-Founder)*
Margie Blanchard *(Co-Founder)*
Mark Manning *(Sr VP-Sls-North America)*
Mark Forsyth *(Sr VP-Bus Dev-Global)*
Randy Conley *(VP-Client Svcs)*

THE KENDALL GROUP, INC.

5101 S Sprinkle Rd, Portage, MI
49002
Tel.: (269) 345-0101   MI
Web Site: http://kendallgroup.com
Year Founded: 1973
PVF, Electrical & Pipes Whlsr
N.A.I.C.S.: 423610

Subsidiaries:

Kendall Electric Inc. (1)
5101 S Sprinkle Rd, Portage, MI 49002-
2225
Tel.: (269) 345-0101
Web Site: http://www.kendallelectric.com
Electrical Apparatus & Equipment Distr
N.A.I.C.S.: 423610

Subsidiary (Domestic):

J.O. Galloup Company (2)
130 N Helmer Rd, Battle Creek, MI 49037
Tel.: (269) 965-4005
Web Site: http://www.galloup.com
Sales Range: $50-74.9 Million
Emp.: 30
Metals Service Centers & Offices
N.A.I.C.S.: 423510
Martin Reinly *(Pres)*

Subsidiary (Domestic):

Smith Instrument (3)
1987 Concept Dr, Warren, MI 48091
Tel.: (586) 755-3110
Web Site: http://www.smithinstrument.com
Sales Range: $10-24.9 Million
Emp.: 25
Distr of Industrial Machinery & Equipment
N.A.I.C.S.: 423830
Dean Maxwell *(Mgr-Ops & Quality)*

Subsidiary (Domestic):

Kendall Electric (2)

170 Mabry Hood Rd, Knoxville, TN 37922
Tel.: (865) 546-8755
Web Site: http://www.kendallelectric.com
Sales Range: $75-99.9 Million
Emp.: 50
Electrical Supplies & Equipment
N.A.I.C.S.: 423610
John Higdon (Mgr-Jackson)
Bob Thomas (Engr-Automation)

THE KENJYA GROUP, INC.
8894 Stanford Blvd Ste 400, Columbia, MD 21045
Tel.: (410) 740-4045
Web Site: http://www.kenjya.com
Sales Range: $25-49.9 Million
Emp.: 50
Business Management Consulting Services
N.A.I.C.S.: 541618
Larry Medler (CEO)
Bruce Gwilliam (CFO & CTO)

THE KENT COMPANIES
3510 N. A St., Midland, TX 79705
Tel.: (432) 520-4000
Web Site:
  https://thekentcompanies.com
Year Founded: 1957
Retail Food Stores
N.A.I.C.S.: 445110
Bill Kent (Owner)

Subsidiaries:

DC Oil Co Inc. (1)
2522 Valleydale Rd Ste 300, Hoover, AL 35244-2703
Tel.: (205) 333-1008
Web Site: http://www.qshop.us
Petroleum & Petroleum Products Merchant Whslr
N.A.I.C.S.: 424720

THE KESSLER ENTERPRISE INC.
4901 Vineland Rd Ste 650, Orlando, FL 32811
Tel.: (407) 996-9999
Web Site:
  http://www.kesslercollection.com
Sales Range: $75-99.9 Million
Emp.: 1,200
Hotel Owner & Operator
N.A.I.C.S.: 721110
Richard C. Kessler (Pres & CEO)
Brian Py (Sr VP-Investments & Fin)
John Luckett (COO)

Subsidiaries:

Casa Monica Hotel (1)
95 Cordova St, Saint Augustine, FL 32084
Tel.: (904) 827-1888
Web Site: http://www.casamonica.com
Emp.: 200
Hotel
N.A.I.C.S.: 721110
Richard C. Kessler (Pres & CEO)

THE KEYES COMPANY
2121 SW 3rd Ave, Miami, FL 33129
Tel.: (305) 371-3592   FL
Web Site: http://www.keyes.com
Year Founded: 1926
Sales Range: $1-4.9 Billion
Emp.: 2,000
Real Estate Services
N.A.I.C.S.: 531210
Michael I. Pappas (Pres & CEO)
Timothy D. Pappas (VP)
Chris Ferguson (Dir-HR)
Kevin Leonard (VP-Luxury)
Jennifer Mendoza (VP-Bus Dev)
Dana McAlister (Mgr-Relocation)
Marco Zarfati (Mgr-Aventura)
Bonnie Josefski (Mgr-Pembroke Pines & Miramar)

Subsidiaries:

Illustrated Properties Real Estate, Inc. (1)
1810 S Dixie, Palm Beach, FL 33401
Tel.: (561) 588-2002
Web Site: http://www.ipre.com
Real Estate Broker
N.A.I.C.S.: 531210
F. F. Adams (Founder)
Virginia Spencer (Gen Mgr)
Amanda Fell (VP)
Dina Shiber (VP-Global Relocation & Corp Svcs)
Diane Edgley (Dir-Education & Trng)
Daniel Dennis (Pres)
Mike Pappas (CEO)

Keyes Asset Management (1)
2121 SW 3rd Ave, Miami, FL 33129   (100%)
Tel.: (305) 371-3592
Web Site: http://www.keyes.com
Sales Range: $10-24.9 Million
Emp.: 60
Investment
N.A.I.C.S.: 531210

Keyes National Referral (1)
2121 SW 3rd Ave, Miami, FL 33129-1714   (100%)
Tel.: (305) 371-3592
Web Site: http://www.keyes.com
Sales Range: $25-49.9 Million
Emp.: 110
Investment
N.A.I.C.S.: 531210

THE KIA STORE
5325 Preston Hwy, Louisville, KY 40213
Tel.: (502) 968-6111
Web Site: http://www.kiastore.com
Year Founded: 1921
Sales Range: $25-49.9 Million
Emp.: 110
Car Whslr
N.A.I.C.S.: 441110
Don Hobden (Gen Mgr)
Raymond Montgomery (Pres)
Greg Meiners (CFO)

THE KING ARTHUR FLOUR COMPANY, INC.
135 Route 5 S, Norwich, VT 05055
Tel.: (802) 649-3881   VT
Web Site:
  http://www.kingarthurflour.com
Year Founded: 1896
Sales Range: $50-74.9 Million
Emp.: 160
Retailer of Flour Products & Baking Utensils
N.A.I.C.S.: 311211
Steve Voigt (CEO)

THE KING GROUP
1801 Northhampton Ste 410, Desoto, TX 75115
Tel.: (214) 720-9046   TX
Year Founded: 1987
Rev.: $12,000,000
Emp.: 8
Fiscal Year-end: 12/31/04
N.A.I.C.S.: 541810
Delva King (VP)
Johnnie King (CEO)

THE KINTOCK GROUP
20142 Valley Forge Cir, King of Prussia, PA 19406
Tel.: (610) 687-1336   PA
Web Site: http://www.kintock.org
Year Founded: 1987
Sales Range: $10-24.9 Million
Emp.: 172
Community Correction Services
N.A.I.C.S.: 624190
Gretchen Wiseman (Chief Admin Officer)
Debora Oree (Dir-Trng & Diversity)
Priya Raja (CFO)
Diane DeBarri (Chm & CEO)
Kathy Mulqueen (Dir-HR Mgmt)
Kristal Miller (Dir-Program Ops)
Mike Kuhn (Dir-IT)
Paul Taggines (Dir-Facility Ops)
Walter Simpkins (COO)

THE KITCHEN GUILD
3739 Pickett Rd, Fairfax, VA 22031
Tel.: (703) 323-1660
Web Site:
  http://www.kitchenguild.com
Year Founded: 2001
Sales Range: $1-9.9 Million
Emp.: 35
Kitchens & Baths Designer & Builder
N.A.I.C.S.: 236118
Jim McCoy (Pres & CEO)
Mary Jo Jackson (Mgr-Showroom-Reg)

THE KMW GROUP INC.
5085 Corporate Exchange Blvd, Grand Rapids, MI 49512
Tel.: (616) 656-0755   MI
Web Site: http://www.skytron.us
Year Founded: 1972
Sales Range: $10-24.9 Million
Emp.: 100
Medical Equipment & Supplies Distr
N.A.I.C.S.: 423450
David P. Mehney (Pres)

THE KNAPHEIDE MANUFACTURING COMPANY
1848 Westphalia Strasse, Quincy, IL 62305
Tel.: (217) 222-7131   IL
Web Site: http://www.knapheide.com
Year Founded: 1848
Sales Range: $150-199.9 Million
Emp.: 600
Mfr of Truck Bodies
N.A.I.C.S.: 336120
Jim Bockenfeld (VP-Sls)
Mike Francis (Mgr-Transportation)
H. W. Knapheide IV (Pres & CEO)

THE KNOWLEDGE TREE INC.
5000 Summer Ave, Memphis, TN 38122-7315
Tel.: (901) 324-9251   TN
Web Site:
  http://www.theknowledgetree.com
Year Founded: 1957
Sales Range: $75-99.9 Million
Emp.: 50
School Supply Stores, Games & Learning Resources for Teachers & Students
N.A.I.C.S.: 459410
Andy Gattas (Pres)
Fred Ernest (VP-Sls)

THE KOLTER GROUP LLC
701 S Olive Ave Ste 104, West Palm Beach, FL 33401
Tel.: (561) 682-9500
Web Site:
  http://www.thekoltergroup.com
Year Founded: 1993
Real Estate Development, Investment & Construction
N.A.I.C.S.: 237210
Robert L. Julien (CEO)

Subsidiaries:

Kolter Commercial LLC (1)
701 S Olive Ave Ste 104, West Palm Beach, FL 33401
Tel.: (561) 682-9500
Commercial Real Estate Investor, Developer & Manager
N.A.I.C.S.: 237210

Kolter Homes, LLC (1)
701 S Olive Ave Ste 104, West Palm Beach, FL 33401
Tel.: (561) 682-9500
Web Site: http://www.kolterhomes.com
Sales Range: $1-9.9 Million
Emp.: 17
Residential Construction
N.A.I.C.S.: 236115

Kolter Land Partners LLC (1)
Riveredge Dr Ste 175, Tampa, FL 33637
Tel.: (813) 615-1244
Web Site: http://www.kolterlandpartners.com
Emp.: 7
Land Acquisition & Development
N.A.I.C.S.: 237210
Jim Harvey (Pres)
Troy Simpson (Mgr-Land Acq)
David Langhout (VP-Land Acq)

THE KRAFT GROUP LLC
1 Patriot Pl, Foxboro, MA 02035
Tel.: (508) 384-4230   DE
Web Site:
  https://www.thekraftgroup.com
Year Founded: 1965
Sales Range: Less than $1 Million
Emp.: 9,500
Offices of Other Holding Companies
N.A.I.C.S.: 551112
Robert K. Kraft (Chm & CEO)
Jonathan A. Kraft (Pres-Kraft Grp)
Daniel A. Kraft (Pres-Intl Kraft Grp)
Josh Kraft (Pres-New England Patriots Foundation)

Subsidiaries:

International Forest Products Corporation (1)
1 Patriot Pl, Foxboro, MA 02035
Tel.: (508) 698-4600
Web Site: http://www.ifpcorp.com
Emp.: 100
Pulp, Paper, Solid Wood & Other Forestry Products Distr
N.A.I.C.S.: 424130
Robert K. Kraft (Chm & CEO)
Daniel A. Kraft (Pres & CEO)
Bradley J. Ayers (VP-Containerboard Sls & Trading)
Daniel Moore (COO)
Jim Cobery (VP-Legal & Bus Affairs)
Henry Linares (Dir-Latin American Sls)
Karen Ziemba (Mgr-Sls)

Subsidiary (Non-US):

IFP Canada Corporation (2)
300-541 Howe Street, Vancouver, V6C 2C2, BC, Canada
Tel.: (604) 677-9930
Web Site: http://www.ifpcorp.com
Sales Range: $25-49.9 Million
Emp.: 10
Industrial & Personal Service Paper
N.A.I.C.S.: 424130

IFP Corporate Services Sdn. Bhd. (2)
No 1 Jln Damai Perdana 8/1D, Damai Gayana, 56000, Kuala Lumpur, Malaysia
Tel.: (60) 193318883
Web Site: http://www.ifpcorp.com
Sales Range: $25-49.9 Million
Emp.: 25
Industrial & Personal Service Paper
N.A.I.C.S.: 424130
Stanley Ng (Mng Dir)

International Forest Products (H.K.) Ltd. (2)
Boss Commercial Rm 305, 28 Ferry St Yau Ma Tei, Kowloon, China (Hong Kong)
Tel.: (852) 27108805
Web Site: http://www.iftcorp.com
Sales Range: $25-49.9 Million
Emp.: 10
Industrial & Personal Service Paper
N.A.I.C.S.: 424130

International Forest Products (Shanghai) (2)
Ste 1503 Blk C New Century Plz, 48 Xing Yi Rd, Shanghai, 200336, China
Tel.: (86) 2162954411

THE KRAFT GROUP LLC — U.S. PRIVATE

The Kraft Group LLC—(Continued)
Web Site: http://www.ifpcorp.com
Sales Range: $25-49.9 Million
Emp.: 10
Industrial & Personal Service Paper
N.A.I.C.S.: 424130

International Forest Products (UK) (2)
St Anne's Oxford Square, Oxford Street, Newbury, RG14 1JQ, Berks, United Kingdom
Tel.: (44) 1635581732
Web Site: http://www.ifpcorp.com
Sales Range: $25-49.9 Million
Emp.: 6
Industrial & Personal Service Paper
N.A.I.C.S.: 424130
Jonathan Heywood *(Mng Dir)*

International Forest Products Svenska KB (2)
Teatergatan 24, Gothenburg, 411 15, Sweden
Tel.: (46) 317743690
Web Site: http://www.iftcorp.com
Sales Range: $25-49.9 Million
Emp.: 10
Industrial & Personal Service Paper
N.A.I.C.S.: 424130
Ter Malgerud *(Gen Mgr)*

New England Patriots Football Club, Inc. (1)
1 Patriot Pl, Foxboro, MA 02035
Tel.: (508) 543-8200
Web Site: http://www.patriots.com
Sales Range: $10-24.9 Million
Emp.: 150
Professional Football Franchise
N.A.I.C.S.: 711211
Robert K. Kraft *(Chm & CEO)*
Jonathan A. Kraft *(Pres)*

New-Indy Containerboard LLC (1)
5936 Perkins Rd, Oxnard, CA 93033-9044
Tel.: (805) 986-3881
Web Site: http://www.new-indy.com
Containerboard Mfr
N.A.I.C.S.: 322130
Christine Lacey *(Dir-HR)*
Richard Hartman *(COO)*

Subsidiary (Domestic):

Carolina Container Company (2)
909 Prospect St, High Point, NC 27260
Tel.: (336) 883-7146
Web Site: http://www.carolinacontainer.com
Corrugated & Solid Fiber Boxes
N.A.I.C.S.: 322211
Ron Sessions *(Pres)*
Rodney McSwain *(Dir-HR)*
Deon Griffith *(Mgr-ISO)*
Frank Nolley *(Mgr-Customer Svc)*
James Karriker *(Mgr-Credit)*
Randy Russell *(Sls Mgr)*
Susan Rogers *(Coord-POP Special Project)*
John Stamper *(Acct Mgr)*
Julie Zornes *(Mgr-Design)*
Brad Bible *(Ops Mgr)*
Brian Healy *(Gen Mgr-Hickory)*
Christopher Lyon *(Mgr-Sustainability)*
Gene Terrill *(Mgr-Process Improvement)*
Tony Trent *(Plant Mgr)*

Proactive Packaging and Display, Inc. (2)
602 S Rockefeller Ave, Ontario, CA 91761-8190
Tel.: (909) 390-5624
Web Site: http://www.proactivepkg.com
Retails Graphics Mfr
N.A.I.C.S.: 322211
Memo Gonzalez *(VP-Ops)*
Gary Hartog *(CEO)*

Shoreline Container Inc. (2)
4450 136th Ave, Holland, MI 49424
Tel.: (616) 399-2088
Web Site: http://www.shorelinecontainer.com
Sales Range: $50-74.9 Million
Emp.: 250
Containers & Corrugated Boxes
N.A.I.C.S.: 322220
Jeff Mooney *(Mgr-Production)*
Tom Timmer *(Mgr-Fin Div)*
Kevin Houle *(Plant Mgr)*

Thomas Deater *(CFO)*
Scott Bush *(Mgr-Logistics)*
Pat Clifford *(Sr Acct Mgr)*
Bob Zuker *(COO)*

Rand-Whitney Group, LLC (1)
1 Agrand St, Worcester, MA 01607
Tel.: (508) 791-2301
Web Site: http://www.randwhitney.com
Sales Range: $50-74.9 Million
Emp.: 685
Corrugated & Solid Fiber Containers Mfr
N.A.I.C.S.: 322211
Robert K. Kraft *(Chm & CEO)*
Chris Harrigan *(CFO)*

THE KRETSINGER GROUP, INC.
1700 E Old State Rt 210, Liberty, MO 64068
Tel.: (816) 781-9600
Year Founded: 1997
Sales Range: $25-49.9 Million
Emp.: 135
Holding Company; Freight Trucking & Truck Rental Services
N.A.I.C.S.: 551112
Carolyn Kretsinger *(Chm)*
Robert C. Kretsinger *(CIO & Sr VP)*
William T. Kretsinger Sr. *(CMO & Sr VP-Sls)*
Tom B. Kretzinger Jr. *(Pres & COO)*

Subsidiaries:

American Central Transport, Inc. (1)
1700 E Old Hwy 210, Liberty, MO 64068
Tel.: (816) 781-9600
Web Site: http://www.americancentral.com
Sales Range: $25-49.9 Million
N.A.I.C.S.: 484121
Robert C. Kretsinger *(CIO & Sr VP)*
Tim F. Zeyer *(CFO & Sr VP-Fin)*
Phillip L. Wilt *(Pres & COO)*
David A. Warner *(VP-Asset Mgmt)*
Anita Simpson *(Controller)*
Matthew Armstrong *(Mgr-IT)*
Richie Runions *(Dir-Maintenance)*
Brook Utesch *(Mgr-Customer Svc)*
William T. Kretsinger Sr. *(Chm & Chief Customer Officer)*

Subsidiary (Domestic):

Excel Leasing & Sales Company (2)
3359 Brinkerhoff Rd, Kansas City, KS 66115-1112
Tel.: (913) 321-1182
Truck Rental & Leasing Services
N.A.I.C.S.: 532120

THE KRIETE GROUP
614 N Bdwy, Milwaukee, WI 53202
Tel.: (414) 224-9300
Web Site: http://www.krietegroup.com
Year Founded: 1951
Truck & Automobile Sales & Services
N.A.I.C.S.: 441227
David Kriete *(Owner)*
Otto Mattke *(Gen Mgr-Leasing & Rental)*
Marty Dudenhoeffer *(Exec VP-Dealer Ops)*
Tom Vetta *(CFO)*
David Barletta *(Exec VP & Dir-Mack Truck Sls)*
Jeff Martell *(Dir-Volvo Truck Sls)*
Andy Holverson *(Dir-Hino & Fuso Truck Sls)*
Dan Brown *(Dir-Used Truck Sls)*
Adam Kriete *(Mgr-Leasing & Rental)*
Tim Smith *(Dir-Fixed Ops)*
Mike Mauermann *(Dir-Parts Ops)*
Brian Wood *(Mgr-Mktg & Comms)*
Taylor Pfeuti *(Mgr-Fin & Insurance)*
Tami Halverson *(Controller)*
Wendy Halverson *(Coord-Truck Sls)*
Steve Adams *(Coord-Truck Sls)*
Cheryl Mauermann *(Mgr-Corp Acct Receivable)*
Kurt Yust *(Mgr-Accts Payable)*

THE KUIKEN BROTHERS COMPANY, INC.
PO Box 1040, Fair Lawn, NJ 07410-8040
Tel.: (201) 796-2082
Web Site: http://www.kuikenbrothers.com
Year Founded: 1912
Sales Range: $10-24.9 Million
Emp.: 110
Retailer of Building Materials
N.A.I.C.S.: 423310
Douglas Kuiken *(Pres)*
Tom Gubridy *(Controller)*

THE KULJIAN CORPORATION
3700 Market St No 2, Philadelphia, PA 19104-3169
Tel.: (215) 243-1900
Web Site: http://www.kuljian.com
Year Founded: 1941
Sales Range: $1-9.9 Million
Emp.: 200
Engineering Consulting Services
N.A.I.C.S.: 541330
Mike Shome *(VP-Mktg)*
Ronald Szostak *(Exec VP)*
Mary Hart *(VP-Sls)*

THE KUNKEL SERVICE COMPANY INC.
331 Baltimore Pike, Bel Air, MD 21014
Tel.: (410) 838-3344
Year Founded: 1921
Sales Range: $25-49.9 Million
Emp.: 315
Paint, Autobody & Auto-Detailing Services
N.A.I.C.S.: 423120
John N. Kunkel *(VP)*
Richard Row *(VP)*

THE L&L COMPANY
10689 Gateway Blvd, Manassas, VA 20110
Tel.: (703) 881-7100
Web Site: http://www.thelandlcompany.com
Year Founded: 1964
Rev.: $55,000,000
Emp.: 70
Quality Floor Coverings, Blinds & Custom Services to Homebuilders & Homeowners
N.A.I.C.S.: 326199
Michael Geisler *(Pres)*
Jeff Sproles *(Dir-Sls & Mktg)*
Skip Davis *(Dir-Accts Mgmt)*
Brian Ransom *(Controller)*

Subsidiaries:

The L&L Company - Pittsburgh Division (1)
321 Commerce Park Dr, Cranberry, PA 16006
Tel.: (717) 265-0355
Floor Covering Mfr
N.A.I.C.S.: 326199

The L&L Company - Timonium Division (1)
2241 Greenspring Dr, Lutherville, MD 21093
Tel.: (410) 558-6942
Floor Covering Mfr
N.A.I.C.S.: 326199

The L&L Company-Baltimore/Delaware Division (1)
509 Mccormick Dr Ste F, Glen Burnie, MD 21061-8201 (100%)
Tel.: (302) 292-3712
Web Site: http://www.thelandlcompany.com
Floor Covering Designer & Mfr
N.A.I.C.S.: 326199
Scott Outten *(Reg Mgr)*

The L&L Company-Central Virginia (1)
7459 Mason King Ct, Manassas, VA 20109 (100%)
Tel.: (703) 331-1230
Web Site: http://www.thelandlcompany.com
Sales Range: $10-24.9 Million
Emp.: 35
Floor Coverings
N.A.I.C.S.: 326199
Glenn Brixius *(Reg Mgr)*

The L&L Company-Ceramic Division (1)
509 McCormick Dr Ste F, Glen Burnie, MD 21061 (100%)
Tel.: (410) 553-0250
Web Site: http://www.thelandlcompany.com
Floor & Ceramic Tile Designer & Mfr
N.A.I.C.S.: 326199
Don Recine *(Dir-Ceramics)*
Eddy Ross *(Mgr-Mktg)*

The L&L Company-Charlotte Division (1)
7463 Mason King Ct, Manassas, VA 20109-5220 (100%)
Tel.: (704) 599-6050
Web Site: http://www.thelandlcompany.com
Floor Covering Designer & Mfr
N.A.I.C.S.: 326199

The L&L Company-Franklin Division (1)
800 Airpark Commerce Dr, Nashville, TN 37219 (100%)
Tel.: (615) 771-1243
Web Site: http://www.thelandlcompany.com
Floor Covering Designer & Mfr
N.A.I.C.S.: 326199

The L&L Company-Frederick (1)
5123 Pegasus Ct Ste M, Frederick, MD 21704 (100%)
Tel.: (301) 696-9340
Web Site: http://www.thelandlcompany.com
Floor Covering Mfr & Designer
N.A.I.C.S.: 326199
Tim Kelley *(Mgr-Production)*

The L&L Company-Greenville Division (1)
24 Concourse Way, Greer, SC 29650 (100%)
Tel.: (868) 848-0600
Web Site: http://www.thelandlcompany.com
Floor Covering Designer & Mfr
N.A.I.C.S.: 326199

The L&L Company-Owings Mills (1)
509 Mccormick Dr Ste F, Glen Burnie, MD 21061-8201 (100%)
Tel.: (410) 902-4651
Web Site: http://www.thelandlcompany.com
Floor Coverings Mfr & Designer
N.A.I.C.S.: 326199

The L&L Company-Pointer Ridge & Blinds Divisions (1)
17201 Medford Blvd Ste L-Q, Bowie, MD 20715 (100%)
Tel.: (301) 249-9171
Web Site: http://www.thelandlcompany.com
Floor Coverings & Blinds Mfr
N.A.I.C.S.: 326199
Donna Scallion *(Mgr-Window Coverings)*
Skip Davis *(Dir-Accts Mgmt)*
Mike Geisler *(Pres)*
Dan Lane *(CEO)*
Jeff Sproles *(Dir-Sls & Mktg)*

The L&L Company-Richmond (1)
12830 W Creek Pkwy Ste E, Richmond, VA 23238 (100%)
Tel.: (804) 784-5030
Web Site: http://www.thelandlcompany.com
Sales Range: $10-24.9 Million
Emp.: 4
Floor Covering Designer & Mfr
N.A.I.C.S.: 326199

The L&L Company-Salisbury Division (1)
101 Park Ave No 4, Seaford, DE 19973 (100%)
Tel.: (410) 677-0420
Web Site: http://www.thelandlcompany.com
Sales Range: $10-24.9 Million
Emp.: 5
Floor Covering Designer & Mfr

COMPANIES

THE L.C. DOANE COMPANY
110 Pond Meadow Rd, Ivoryton, CT 06442
Tel.: (860) 767-8295
Web Site: http://www.lcdoane.com
Sales Range: $1-9.9 Million
Emp.: 70
Commercial Industrial & Institutional Electric Lighting Fixture Mfr
N.A.I.C.S.: 335132
William Psillos (VP)
Margaret P. Eagan (Pres)
Steve Shapiro (Mgr)
Brian Schoch (Dir-Engrg Staff)

THE L.H. THOMSON COMPANY, INC.
7800 NE Industrial Blvd, Macon, GA 31216
Tel.: (478) 788-5052
Web Site: http://www.lhthomson.com
Year Founded: 1981
Sales Range: $10-24.9 Million
Emp.: 92
Machine Shops
N.A.I.C.S.: 332710
Brian Thomson (Pres)
Margaret C. Thomson (CEO)

THE LABORERS PACIFIC SOUTHWEST REGIONAL ORGANIZING COALITION
4399 Santa Anita Ave Ste 204, El Monte, CA 91731
Tel.: (626) 350-9403   CA
Web Site: http://www.lpswroc.com
Year Founded: 1999
Sales Range: $10-24.9 Million
Employee Welfare Services
N.A.I.C.S.: 813930
Mando Esparza (Co-Chm)
Ralph Velador (Coord)

THE LACKEY GROUP
420 3rd Ave NW, Hickory, NC 28601
Tel.: (828) 328-1142   NC
Web Site:
http://www.protectclose.com
Year Founded: 2001
Holding Company
N.A.I.C.S.: 551112
Robert Lackey Sr. (Pres)

Subsidiaries:

Web Products Inc. (1)
3155 Terrance St, Kansas City, MO 64111
Tel.: (816) 777-3735
Web Site: http://www.webproducts.com
Sales Range: $10-24.9 Million
Emp.: 40
Filter Mfr
N.A.I.C.S.: 333413

THE LAITRAM LLC
220 Laitram Ln, Harahan, LA 70123
Tel.: (504) 733-6000   LA
Web Site: http://www.laitram.com
Year Founded: 1949
Sales Range: $350-399.9 Million
Emp.: 1,100
Shrimp Processing Machinery, Plastic Modular Conveyor Belting, Alternating Metal Stairtreads
N.A.I.C.S.: 333922
James M. Lapeyre Jr. (Pres)
Lawrence P. Oertling (CFO)
Robert Munch (Treas)
Frank Profumo (Dir-Creative)

Subsidiaries:

Intralox LLC (1)
301 Plantation Rd, New Orleans, LA 70123 (100%)
Tel.: (504) 733-0463
Web Site: http://www.intralox.com
Sales Range: $25-49.9 Million
Emp.: 500
Conveyor Belting & Accessories Mfr
N.A.I.C.S.: 333922
James M. Lapeyre Jr. (Chm & Pres)

Subsidiary (Non-US):

Intralox (India) Private Ltd. (2)
No 18/23 Peenya 1st Stage Peenya Industrial Area, Yeshwanthpur Hobli, Bengaluru, 560058, Karnataka, India
Tel.: (91) 8001001029
Conveyor Belts Mfr
N.A.I.C.S.: 333922

Intralox LLC (1)
Lemelerweg 31, Post box 23280, 1101 AJ, Amsterdam, Netherlands (100%)
Tel.: (31) 205403600
Web Site: http://www.intralox.com
Sales Range: $25-49.9 Million
Emp.: 170
Mfr of Conveyor Belting
N.A.I.C.S.: 326220
Thomas Jaarsma (Mgr-Fin)

Intralox Ltd. (1)
Bldg 90 3rd Avenue Pensnett Trading Estate, Kingswinford, DY6 7FW, West Midlands, United Kingdom (100%)
Tel.: (44) 1384355600
Web Site: http://www.intralox.com
Sales Range: $10-24.9 Million
Emp.: 90
Mfr of Conveyor Belting
N.A.I.C.S.: 326220

Intralox Shanghai Ltd. (1)
7/F Tower A Central Tower No 555 Lan Gao Road, 200333, Shanghai, China
Tel.: (86) 2151118400
Web Site: http://www.intralox.com
Conveying Equipment Mfr
N.A.I.C.S.: 333922

Laitram Machinery ApS (1)
Laesovej 2, Hjorring, 9800, Denmark
Tel.: (45) 98900780
Web Site: http://www.laitram.com
Emp.: 7
Seafood Processing Equipment Mfr
N.A.I.C.S.: 333241
Lars Vedsed (CEO)

Laitram Machinery Inc. (1)
220 Laitram Ln, Harahan, LA 70123-5308 (100%)
Tel.: (504) 733-6000
Web Site: http://www.laitrammachinery.com
Sales Range: $10-24.9 Million
Emp.: 85
Mfr of Shrimp Processing Equipment
N.A.I.C.S.: 333241

Lapeyre Stair, Inc. (1)
5117 Toler St, Harahan, LA 70123-5308 (100%)
Tel.: (504) 733-6009
Web Site: http://www.lapeyrestair.com
Sales Range: $10-24.9 Million
Emp.: 25
Alternating Tread Stair
N.A.I.C.S.: 333921
J. M. Lapeyre (Pres)

THE LAMARJEAN GROUP, INC.
12399 Stowe Dr Ste 123, Poway, CA 92064-0000
Tel.: (858) 663-5858
Web Site: http://www.ljtech-displays.com
Leather Goods Mfr
N.A.I.C.S.: 315210

Subsidiaries:

Stratasys Direct, Inc. (1)
28309 Ave Crocker, Valencia, CA 91355
Tel.: (661) 295-4400
Web Site: http://www.stratasysdirect.com
Custom Manufacturing & Prototyping Services
N.A.I.C.S.: 339999

Plant (Domestic):

Stratasys Direct, Inc. - Belton Plant (2)
815 Kirkley Dr, Belton, TX 76513
Tel.: (254) 933-1000
Web Site: http://www.stratasysdirect.com
Custom Additive Manufacturing & Prototyping Services
N.A.I.C.S.: 339999

Stratasys Direct, Inc. - Detroit Plant (2)
2701 Industrial Row Dr, Troy, MI 48084
Tel.: (248) 280-5905
Web Site: http://www.stratasysdirect.com
Custom Manufacturing & Prototyping Services
N.A.I.C.S.: 339999

THE LANG COMPANY, INC.
540 S 13th St, Louisville, KY 40203
Tel.: (502) 584-2383
Web Site:
http://www.langcompany.com
Year Founded: 1945
Sales Range: $10-24.9 Million
Emp.: 76
Office Equipment Whslr
N.A.I.C.S.: 423420
Tom Welter (Pres)

THE LANGDALE COMPANY
1202 Madison Hwy, Valdosta, GA 31603-1088
Tel.: (229) 242-7450
Web Site:
http://www.thelangdalecompany.com
Year Founded: 1894
Sales Range: $10-24.9 Million
Emp.: 425
Sawmill Services
N.A.I.C.S.: 321113
Larry K. Fudge (VP)
Gregory J. Miller (CFO)
Donald K. Warren (VP)
Jackson R. Langdale (Gen Counsel)
James H. Langdale (Exec VP-Ops)
John W. Langdale III (Pres & CEO)

THE LANMARK GROUP INC.
804 Broadway Ste 4, West Long Branch, NJ 07764-2203
Tel.: (732) 389-4500   NJ
Year Founded: 1977
Sales Range: $10-24.9 Million
Emp.: 40
Advetising Agency
N.A.I.C.S.: 541810
Judy Adelman (Mgr-Media)
Howard Klein (Owner & Pres)
Ed Yasser (Dir-Interactive)
Michael McCarthy (Mng Partner & Chief Strategy Officer)
Kurt Algayer (VP-Production Svcs)
Michael Ventriello (Mgr-PR)
Derek VanVolkom (VP & Acct Supvr)
Tracey Clayton (Dir-Opers)
Michael A. Caiafa (VP-Mktg & Regulatory Affairs)
Andrew Saklas (Dir-Creative)
Sheri Doniger (Dir-Clinical)
Edwin Decena (Multimedia Developer)

THE LANTIS EYEWEAR CORPORATION
489 5th Ave, New York, NY 10017
Tel.: (212) 561-7500
Year Founded: 1978
Sales Range: $100-124.9 Million
Emp.: 1,600
Mfr of Eyeglasses & Sunglasses
N.A.I.C.S.: 423990
Bill Deyo (Pres)

THE LARAMAR GROUP, LLC
7900 E Union Ave Ste 500, Denver, CO 80237
Tel.: (303) 991-0094

Web Site:
http://www.laramargroup.com
Year Founded: 2001
Rev.: $1,000,000,000
Emp.: 1,000
Real Estate Investment & Management Services
N.A.I.C.S.: 523999
Jeff Elowe (Pres & CEO)
Keith Harris (Chief Investment Officer)
Tom Klaess (COO)
Steve Boyack (COO)
Bennett Neuman (Sr VP-Acq)
Scott McMillan (CFO)
Benjamin Slad (VP-Investments)
Matthew P. Levy (VP-Acq)
Shannon Baker (VP-Ops)
Shannon Kay (VP-Acq)
Michael Burnaz (VP-Construction)
Yolanda Meberg (VP-HR Ops)
David Egeland (VP-Mktg)
Stacey Valentine (Sr VP-Ops)

THE LARSON GROUP
3026 N Mulroy, Strafford, MO 65757
Tel.: (417) 865-5355
Web Site: http://www.tlgtrucks.com
Sales Range: $50-74.9 Million
Emp.: 1,000
Truck Tractor Dealership
N.A.I.C.S.: 441227
Glenn Larson (Pres)
Mike Headley (CFO)

Subsidiaries:

Peterbilt Springfield Inc. (1)
3026 N Mulroy Rd, Strafford, MO 65757
Tel.: (417) 865-5355
Web Site: http://www.tlgtrucks.com
Truck Distr
N.A.I.C.S.: 441110
Glenn Larson (Pres)
Connie Huff (Dir-Fin)

THE LARSON GROUP, INC.
720 N Tejon St Ste 201, Colorado Springs, CO 80903
Tel.: (719) 471-7676
Web Site: http://www.tlgtrucks.com
Year Founded: 1986
Sales Range: $1-9.9 Million
Emp.: 12
Architectural Services
N.A.I.C.S.: 541310
Gary Larson (Pres)

Subsidiaries:

Piedmont Peterbilt, LLC (1)
7061 Albert Pick Rd, Greensboro, NC 27409-9654
Tel.: (336) 665-0221
Web Site: http://www.piedmontpeterbilt.com
New Car Dealers
N.A.I.C.S.: 441110
Jerry Stafford (Pres)

THE LASALLE NETWORK
200 N LaSalle St Ste 2500, Chicago, IL 60601
Tel.: (312) 419-1700
Web Site:
http://www.thelasallenetwork.com
Year Founded: 1998
Sales Range: $1-9.9 Million
Emp.: 70
Technology Services
N.A.I.C.S.: 927110
Tom Gimbel (Founder & CEO)
Krisi Rossi O'Donnell (Chief Recruiting Officer)
Lawrence Casas (CFO)
Maureen Hoersten (Chief Revenue Officer)

THE LASIK VISION INSTITUTE, LLC

THE LASIK VISION INSTITUTE, LLC

The LASIK Vision Institute, LLC—(Continued)
1555 Palm Beach Lakes Blvd #200,
West Palm Beach, FL 33401
Tel.: (561) 686-0843 — FL
Web Site: http://www.lasikvisioninstitute.com
Year Founded: 1998
Sales Range: $25-49.9 Million
Emp.: 360
Laser Surgery & Optical Products & Services
N.A.I.C.S.: 456130
Ben Cook *(CEO)*
Michael Insler *(Medical Officer & Surgeon)*
G. Stanley Okoye *(Medical Officer & Ophthalmologist)*

THE LASTER GROUP
5407 N Mesa St 2nd Fl, El Paso, TX 79912
Tel.: (915) 581-7900
Web Site: http://www.lastergroup.com
Sales Range: $10-24.9 Million
Emp.: 20
N.A.I.C.S.: 541810
Nancy Laster *(Pres)*
Kurt Gross *(Partner & VP)*
Gabriela Camacho *(Assoc Dir-Media)*

THE LAUERER MARKIN GROUP, INC.
1700 Woodlands Dr, Maumee, OH 43537-4043
Tel.: (419) 893-2500 — OH
Web Site: http://www.lmgnet.com
Year Founded: 1968
Rev.: $24,000,000
Emp.: 23
Advetising Agency
N.A.I.C.S.: 541810
William R. Markin *(Chm & CEO)*
Kenneth G. Lauerer *(Owner)*
Jill A. Barry *(Specialist-HR)*
John Tarpy *(Controller)*
Mike Driehorst *(Mgr-Media Rels)*

THE LAVIDGE COMPANY
2777 E Camelback Rd Ste 300, Phoenix, AZ 85016
Tel.: (480) 998-2600
Web Site: http://www.lavidge.com
Year Founded: 1982
Rev.: $35,000,000
Emp.: 60
Brand Development, Full Service, Internet/Web Design, Media Buying Services, Public Relations, Sports Marketing, Strategic Planning, Yellow Pages Advertising
N.A.I.C.S.: 541810
William R. Lavidge *(Pres & CEO)*
Bob Case *(Chief Creative Officer & Dir-Creative)*
Anne Robertson *(Dir-PR)*
Alicia Wadas *(COO)*
Ben Smith *(Dir-Interactive Mktg)*
Tim Trull *(Dir-Acct Strategy)*
Kathy Knudson *(Office Mgr)*
Betsey Griffin *(Dir-Media)*
Kyra Harmanos *(Assoc Dir-Adv)*
Caitlin Wendt *(Acct Coord-PR)*
Jennifer Disbrow *(Acct Coord-PR)*
Teri Morris *(Acct Supvr-PR)*
Carissa Vivirito *(Dir-Interactive Svcs)*
Juliana Gonzales Scott *(Dir-Interactive Art)*
Clint Bosman *(Jr Dir-Art-Creative)*
Brittany Williams *(Acct Exec-Acct Svcs)*
Coco Sollomi *(Sr Acct Exec-Acct Svcs)*
Ronda Parker *(Dir-Production)*
Greg Sexton *(Assoc Dir-PR)*

Keller Perry *(Acct Dir-PR)*
Amy Singer *(Sr Acct Exec)*
Beth Logan *(Acct Coord-PR)*

THE LAW COMPANY, INC.
345 Riverview St, Wichita, KS 67203-4200
Tel.: (316) 268-0200 — KS
Web Site: http://www.law-co.com
Year Founded: 1959
Sales Range: $50-74.9 Million
Emp.: 50
Provider of Contracting Services
N.A.I.C.S.: 236220
Richard Kerschen *(CEO)*
Marc A. Porter *(CFO & Exec VP)*
Josh Gordon *(Treas)*
Doug Kimple *(Exec VP)*
Dennis Kerschen *(Pres)*

THE LAW FIRM OF ANIDJAR & LEVINE, P.A.
300 SE 17th St, Fort Lauderdale, FL 33316
Tel.: (954) 525-0050
Web Site: http://www.anidjarlevine.com
Year Founded: 2005
Sales Range: $10-24.9 Million
Law firm
N.A.I.C.S.: 541110
Marc Anidjar *(Sr Partner)*
Glen B. Levine *(Sr Partner)*

THE LAWSON COMPANIES, INC.
373 Edwin Dr, Virginia Beach, VA 23462
Tel.: (757) 499-6161
Web Site: http://www.lawsoncompanies.com
Year Founded: 1946
Provider of Real Estate Services
N.A.I.C.S.: 531210
Amy Harris *(Dir-Mktg & Trng)*
Sue Glancy *(Pres-Realty Corp)*
David Carneal *(Dir-Property Mgmt)*

THE LEADERS GROUP, INC.
2001 York Rd Ste 150, Oak Brook, IL 60523
Tel.: (630) 572-5323 — IL
Web Site: http://www.leadersbank.com
Sales Range: $10-24.9 Million
Emp.: 44
Bank Holding Company
N.A.I.C.S.: 551111
Patrick J. Kelly *(Chm)*
Stephen M. Schuster *(Sec & VP)*
William P. Gleason *(Pres & COO)*
Nancy Lindamood *(Gen Mgr)*
John J. Gleason Jr. *(Vice Chm & CEO)*

THE LEADERSHIP INSTITUTE
1101 N Highland St, Arlington, VA 22201
Tel.: (703) 247-2000 — VA
Web Site: http://www.leadershipinstitute.org
Year Founded: 1979
Rev.: $15,031,246
Assets: $23,694,474
Liabilities: $4,057,393
Net Worth: $19,637,081
Earnings: ($4,266,879)
Emp.: 135
Fiscal Year-end: 12/31/18
Educational Support Services
N.A.I.C.S.: 611710
David Fenner *(VP-Programs)*
Steven Sutton *(VP-Dev)*
Mark Centofante *(VP-Tech & Ops)*
Daniel Klenck *(Dir-Building Mgmt)*

Bryan Bernys *(VP-Campus Leadership Program)*
Morton Blackwell *(Pres)*
Patricia Rausch *(Dir-Career Programs)*
Ben Woodward *(Coord-Programs Coalitions)*
Stephen Rowe *(Dir-Digital Trng)*
Deirdre Hackleman *(Dir-Events)*
Kelsey Mix *(Mgr-Professional Dev)*
Jared Cummings *(Coord-Studio Trng & Video Production)*
Emma Siu *(Coord-Digital Trng)*
Tiffany Roberts *(Coord-Comm & Trng Studios)*
Carol Cocks *(Dir-External Affairs)*
Robert Arnakis *(Sr Dir-Domestic & Intl Programs)*
Ron Nehring *(Dir-Intl Trng)*
Kirsten Holmberg *(Coord-Programs)*
Sarah Morrison *(Coord-Comm)*
Dena Espenscheid *(Dir-Grassroots Coalitions)*
Autumn Campbell *(Coord-Intl Programs)*
Matt Pearson *(Coord-Digital Content)*
Scot Crockett *(Dir-Grassroots Engagement)*
Cabot Phillips *(Dir-Campus Outreach)*
Kristin Dobson *(Natl Dir-Field)*
Carly Tomaine *(Coord-YLS)*
Jackson Lee *(Dir-YLS)*
Jon Street *(Mng Editor)*
Trevor Benson *(Coord-Reg Field)*
Bailey Zimmitti *(Officer-Donor Svcs)*
John Davis *(Dir-Donor Comm)*

THE LEADING HOTELS OF THE WORLD, LTD.
99 Park Ave, New York, NY 10016-1601
Tel.: (212) 515-5600
Web Site: http://www.lhw.com
Sales Range: $10-24.9 Million
Emp.: 120
Hotel Operator
N.A.I.C.S.: 721110
Daniel Neumann *(CFO & Sr VP)*
Phil Koserowski *(VP-Interactive Mktg)*
Andrea Kracht *(Chm)*
Shannon Knapp *(Pres & CEO)*
Susan Ziluca *(Gen Counsel & VP)*
Wilke See-Tho *(Sr VP-Corp Dev)*
Jon Londeen *(Sr VP-Distr & Reservations Mgmt)*
Philip Ho *(Sr VP-Europe, Middle East, Africa & Asia Pacific)*
Patricia Smith *(Sr VP-HR & Org Dev)*
Chris Walker *(Sr VP-Sls-Americas)*
Deniz Omurgonulsen *(VP-Membership)*

THE LEADS NETWORK, LLC
70439 Courtano Dr, Covington, LA 70433
Tel.: (800) 300-2780
Web Site: http://www.theleadsnetwork.com
Year Founded: 2002
Rev.: $5,500,000
Emp.: 11
Advertising & Marketing
N.A.I.C.S.: 541810

THE LEASING EXPERTS INC.
9710 E Indigo St Ste 203, Miami, FL 33157
Tel.: (305) 235-1222
Web Site: http://www.leasingexperts.com
Sales Range: $150-199.9 Million
Emp.: 46
Equipment Leasing & Loans
N.A.I.C.S.: 532490
Arjun Saluja *(Founder & CEO)*
Ginny Saluja *(Dir-Ops)*

THE LEAVITT CORPORATION
100 Santilli Hwy, Everett, MA 02149-1938
Tel.: (617) 389-2600
Web Site: http://www.teddie.com
Year Founded: 1924
Sales Range: $50-74.9 Million
Emp.: 100
Peanut Butter & Nut Product Mfr
N.A.I.C.S.: 311911
Mark Hintlian *(Pres & CEO)*

Subsidiaries:

Leavitt International (FSC Corp.) (1)
100 Santilli Hwy, Everett, MA 02149
Tel.: (617) 389-2600
Web Site: http://www.teddie.com
Sales Range: $10-24.9 Million
Emp.: 55
Mfr of All Natural Teddie Peanut Butter
N.A.I.C.S.: 311911

THE LEDLIE GROUP
2970 Peachtree Rd Ste 805, Atlanta, GA 30305
Tel.: (404) 266-8833
Web Site: http://www.theledliegroup.com
Year Founded: 1998
Sales Range: $10-24.9 Million
Emp.: 11
Public Relations Agency
N.A.I.C.S.: 541820
Joseph M.A. Ledlie *(Pres)*
Allison Johnson *(Mng Dir)*

THE LEE COMPANY
2 Pettipaug Rd, Westbrook, CT 06498
Tel.: (860) 399-6281 — CT
Web Site: http://www.theleeco.com
Year Founded: 1949
Sales Range: $150-199.9 Million
Emp.: 860
Miniature Hydraulic Inserts & Electro-Fluidic Systems Mfr
N.A.I.C.S.: 334513
J. A. Stamos *(VP-Sls)*
John Kingsbury *(Mgr-Adv)*
William Lee *(Pres)*
Brad Gipson *(VP-Ops)*
Lee Leighton III *(Chm)*

Subsidiaries:

Lee Company S.A. (1)
44 Rue Jean Bart, 78960, Voisins-le-Bretonneux, Voisins Le Bretonneu, France **(100%)**
Tel.: (33) 130649944
Web Site: http://www.leecompany.fr
Sales Range: $50-74.9 Million
Emp.: 6
N.A.I.C.S.: 336413

Lee Hydraulische Miniaturkomponenten (1)
Am Limespark 2, Sulzbach, 65843, Germany **(100%)**
Tel.: (49) 699050660
Web Site: http://www.lee.de
Sales Range: $25-49.9 Million
Emp.: 8
Mfr of Airplane Parts
N.A.I.C.S.: 336413
Gurgen Prochno *(Mng Dir)*

Lee Products Ltd. (1)
3 High Street Chalfont St Peter, Gerrards Cross, SL9 9QE, Bucks, United Kingdom **(100%)**
Tel.: (44) 1753886664
Web Site: http://www.leeproducts.co.uk
Sales Range: $25-49.9 Million
Emp.: 5
Electro-Fluidic Systems & Microhydraulic Products Distr
N.A.I.C.S.: 423830
Mike Spott *(Gen Mgr)*

Lee Srl (1)
Via Dei Gracchi 30, 20146, Milan, Italy **(100%)**

U.S. PRIVATE

Tel.: (39) 0243981750
Web Site: http://www.leesrl.it
Sales Range: $50-74.9 Million
Emp.: 5
N.A.I.C.S.: 336413

The Lee Company Scandinavia AB (1)
Pajalagatan 56, 162 65, Vallingby, Sweden
Tel.: (46) 8 579 701 70
Miniature & Precision Fluid Control Product Supplier
N.A.I.C.S.: 423830

THE LEGACY COMPANIES
3355 Enterprise Ave Ste 160, Weston, FL 33331
Tel.: (954) 202-7419
Web Site:
https://www.thelegacycompanies.com
Year Founded: 1998
Restaurant Product Providers
N.A.I.C.S.: 561499
Neal Asbury *(CEO)*

Subsidiaries:

Avanti Products, LLC (1)
3265 Meridian Pkwy Ste 114, Weston, FL 33331
Tel.: (305) 592-7830
Web Site: http://www.avantiproducts.com
Electrical Apparatus & Related Equipment Merchant Whslr
N.A.I.C.S.: 423610

Edgecraft Corporation (1)
825 Southwood Rd, Avondale, PA 19311-9727
Tel.: (610) 268-0500
Web Site: http://www.chefschoice.com
Hand Tool Manufacturer
N.A.I.C.S.: 333515
Stephen Lasker *(Mgr-Operational)*
Sam Weiner *(Pres)*

Legion Industries, Inc. (1)
370 Mills Rd, Waynesboro, GA 30830 (100%)
Tel.: (706) 554-4411
Web Site: http://www.legionindustries.com
Rev.: $6,400,000
Emp.: 95
Kitchen & Food Industry Cookware Mfr
N.A.I.C.S.: 332215
Charles Brown *(Pres & CEO)*

THE LEMNA CORPORATION
2445 Park Ave, Minneapolis, MN 55404-1937
Tel.: (612) 253-2000 MN
Web Site: http://www.lemna.com
Year Founded: 1983
Sales Range: $25-49.9 Million
Emp.: 40
Mfr of Plumbing Fixtures
N.A.I.C.S.: 423720
Viet Ngo *(Pres & CEO)*

Subsidiaries:

Lemna International Inc. (1)
2445 Park Ave, Minneapolis, MN 55404 (100%)
Tel.: (612) 253-2000
Web Site: http://www.lemna.com
Sales Range: $10-24.9 Million
Emp.: 15
Mfr of Plumbing Fixtures
N.A.I.C.S.: 423720

Lemna Technologies, Inc. (1)
2445 Park Ave, Minneapolis, MN 55404
Tel.: (612) 253-2000
Web Site:
http://www.lemnatechnologies.com
Waste Water Treatment Services
N.A.I.C.S.: 237110
Dave Appel *(Sr Project Mgr)*

Lemna USA Inc. (1)
2445 Park Ave, Minneapolis, MN 55404
Tel.: (612) 253-2002
Web Site: http://www.lemna.com

Sales Range: $10-24.9 Million
Emp.: 15
Mfr of Plumbing Fixtures
N.A.I.C.S.: 423720

THE LEMOINE COMPANY INCORPORATED
214 Jefferson St Ste 200, Lafayette, LA 70501
Tel.: (337) 896-7720 LA
Web Site:
http://www.lemoinecompany.com
Year Founded: 1979
Sales Range: $25-49.9 Million
Emp.: 150
Nonresidential Construction
N.A.I.C.S.: 236220
Mark Broussard *(Controller)*
Leonard K. Lemoine *(Pres)*

THE LEONARD COMPANY
566 Holly Springs Rd, Mount Airy, NC 27030
Tel.: (336) 789-5018
Web Site: http://www.leonardusa.com
Rev.: $13,000,000
Emp.: 300
Supplier of Truck Equipment & Parts
N.A.I.C.S.: 333120
Sandra P. Leonard *(Pres)*
David O'Neal *(CEO)*

THE LESLIE CORPORATION
15110 Mintz Ln, Houston, TX 77014
Tel.: (281) 591-0915
Web Site: http://www.lesliecorp.com
Year Founded: 1993
Sales Range: $1-9.9 Million
Emp.: 40
Brand Marketing & Promotions
N.A.I.C.S.: 541810
Miguel Colon *(Owner)*

THE LESTER GROUP INC.
101 E Commonwealth Blvd, Martinsville, VA 24112-1828
Tel.: (276) 632-2195 VA
Web Site: http://www.lestergroup.com
Year Founded: 1896
Rev.: $39,100,000
Emp.: 200
Lumber & Other Building Materials
N.A.I.C.S.: 444110
George W. Lester II *(Chm)*
Tim Joyce *(Treas & VP-Admin)*
Jay Dickens *(Pres)*
Jim O'Brien *(CEO)*

Subsidiaries:

Carpenter Company of Spotsylvania Inc. (1)
1 Joseph Mills Dr, Fredericksburg, VA 22408-7304
Tel.: (540) 899-0031
Web Site: http://www.jimcarpenter.com
Sales Range: $10-24.9 Million
Emp.: 50
Lumber, Plywood & Millwork Distr
N.A.I.C.S.: 423310

Fortress Wood Products Inc. (1)
1 Metals Dr, Greensboro, NC 27407-7042
Tel.: (336) 854-5121
Web Site: http://www.fortresswood.com
Sales Range: $10-24.9 Million
Emp.: 12
Wood Preserving
N.A.I.C.S.: 321114
Brandt Mitchell *(Pres)*
Jeff Kern *(Dir-Sls & Pur)*
Timothy D. Parker *(VP)*

Jim Carpenter Company (1)
1 Joseph Mills Dr, Fredericksburg, VA 22408-7304
Tel.: (540) 899-0031
Web Site: http://www.jimcarpenter.com
Emp.: 40
Wood Products Mfr
N.A.I.C.S.: 321999

Jeff Faircloth *(Mgr-Store)*
Clayton Mullins *(Mgr-Installed Sls)*
Tina Garrett *(Coord-Sls)*

Lester Building Supply Co. (1)
14 E Liberty St, Martinsville, VA 24112-1828
Tel.: (276) 638-8834
Web Site:
http://www.lesterbuildingsupply.com
Sales Range: $25-49.9 Million
Emp.: 20
Nonresidential Building Operators
N.A.I.C.S.: 444110
Brian Whitlow *(Gen Mgr)*
Gene Clark *(Mgr-Store)*

Lester Development Corporation (1)
101 Commonwealth Blvd E, Martinsville, VA 24112
Tel.: (276) 632-2195
Real Estate Development Services
N.A.I.C.S.: 531390

Taylor Brothers Lumber Company (1)
905 Graves Mill Rd, Lynchburg, VA 24502
Tel.: (434) 237-8100
Web Site: http://www.taylorbrothers.com
Wood Products Mfr
N.A.I.C.S.: 321999

THE LEUKEMIA & LYMPHOMA SOCIETY, INC.
Tel.: (914) 949-5213 NY
Web Site: https://www.lls.org
Year Founded: 1949
Rev.: $310,095,987
Assets: $242,581,527
Liabilities: $145,444,419
Net Worth: $97,137,108
Earnings: ($7,102,295)
Emp.: 1,439
Fiscal Year-end: 06/30/14
Blood Cancer Research Funding Services
N.A.I.C.S.: 813212
Lisa Stockmon *(CMO & Exec VP)*
James H. Davis *(Chm)*
Kenneth M. Schwartz *(Treas & Sec)*
Mark Roithmayr *(Chief Dev Officer)*
Louis J. DeGennaro *(Pres & CEO)*
Jeff Como *(CIO)*
James T. Nangle *(CFO & Sr VP)*
George Omiros *(Chief Campaign & Field Dev Officer & Exec VP)*
Philip Kozlowski *(Sr VP-HR)*
Richard Winneker *(Sr VP-Res)*
David Timko *(Sr VP-Volunteer)*
Rosemarie Loffredo *(CFO & Chief Admin Officer)*
Bruce Watson *(Mgr-Campaign-Student Series)*

THE LEWIS BEAR COMPANY
6120 Enterprise Dr, Pensacola, FL 32505
Tel.: (850) 432-9368 FL
Web Site:
http://www.lewisbearcompany.com
Year Founded: 1876
Sales Range: $100-124.9 Million
Emp.: 155
Whslr of Beer
N.A.I.C.S.: 424810
Ed Koontz *(VP-Beer)*
Steve Cox *(Treas & Controller)*
Lewis Bear Jr. *(Pres)*

THE LIBERTY BLUE GROUP LLC
1270 Broadway Ste 1003, New York, NY 10001
Tel.: (212) 494-0003 NY
Web Site:
http://www.libertybluegroup.com
Year Founded: 2011
Sales Range: $25-49.9 Million
Emp.: 80

Construction Services Including Construction Management, General Contracting & Consulting.
N.A.I.C.S.: 236210
Florim Lajqi *(Founder, CEO & Principal)*
Michael Hyman *(COO & Principal)*
Christopher Godfrey *(Project Mgr)*

THE LIBERTY COMPANY INSURANCE BROKERS, INC.
5955 De Sotto Ave Ste 250, Woodland Hills, CA 91367 CA
Web Site:
http://www.libertycompany.com
Year Founded: 1987
Sales Range: $1-9.9 Million
Emp.: 40
Insurance Agencies & Brokerages
N.A.I.C.S.: 524210
Jerry Pickett *(CEO)*
Sherri Ben-Nun *(Mgr-Comml Lines)*
Alon Ben-Nun *(Sr VP & Dir-Carrier Mgmt)*
Rick Butts *(Pres-Liberty-Orange County)*
Tammy Gray *(Dir-Acctg & Fin)*
Bill Johnson *(Chm)*
Arpy Mardirosian *(Dir-Mktg)*
Matt Muirhead *(Pres-Liberty-New Gate)*
Kathy Quick *(Mgr-Personal Lines)*
Ian Rice *(Pres-Liberty-Filice)*
Megvarran Lalsa *(CFO)*
Carter Herrin *(VP)*
Keith Binkley *(Exec VP)*
Marshall Heron *(Sr VP)*
Adam Baillie *(COO)*

Subsidiaries:

Gray-Stone & Company (1)
275 E Hillcrest Dr # 250, Thousand Oaks, CA 91360
Tel.: (805) 494-4440
Web Site: http://www.gray-stone.com
Sales Range: $1-9.9 Million
Emp.: 19
Insurance Agencies & Brokerages
N.A.I.C.S.: 524210
Howard Stone *(Pres & CEO)*

THE LIBMAN COMPANY
220 N Sheldon St, Arcola, IL 61910
Tel.: (217) 268-4200
Web Site: http://www.libman.com
Year Founded: 1896
Sales Range: $10-24.9 Million
Emp.: 500
Brooms, Brushes & Mops Mfr
N.A.I.C.S.: 339994
Robert Libman *(Pres)*
Andrew Libman *(VP-Mktg)*
William Libman *(CFO)*
Donna Hobbs *(Controller)*

THE LIBRARY CORPORATION
Research Park, Inwood, WV 25428
Tel.: (304) 229-0100
Web Site: http://www.tlcdelivers.com
Sales Range: $10-24.9 Million
Emp.: 110
Computer Software Development & Applications
N.A.I.C.S.: 541511
Annette Harwood Murphy *(Pres & CEO)*
Calvin Whittington *(Dir-Fin & Admin)*
Gary Kirk *(Exec VP)*
Gar Sydnor *(Sr VP)*

THE LIFETIME HEALTHCARE COMPANIES
165 Court St, Rochester, NY 14647
Tel.: (585) 454-1700
Web Site: http://www.lifethc.com
Sales Range: $900-999.9 Million
Emp.: 7,000
Holding Company
N.A.I.C.S.: 551112

THE LIFETIME HEALTHCARE COMPANIES

U.S. PRIVATE

The Lifetime Healthcare Companies—Continued

David H. Klein *(Pres)*
Christopher C. Booth *(CEO)*
Randall L. Clark *(Chm)*

Subsidiaries:

EBS-RMSCO, Inc. (1)
115 Continuum Dr, Liverpool, NY 13088-
Tel.: (315) 448-9000
Web Site: http://www.ebsrmsco.com
Sales Range: $10-24.9 Million
Emp.: 435
Health, Property & Casualty Insurance Services
N.A.I.C.S.: 524210
Michelle Meyer *(Coord-Billing & Fin)*
Diane Fowler *(Coord-Defined Benefits)*
Debra Markel *(Coord-Flexible Spending Team)*
Jeannette Flowers *(Dir-Client Svcs & Sls Support)*
Beth Gleason *(Mgr-Provider Svcs)*
Paula Stuck *(Project Mgr-Ops)*
Jean Hopkins *(Supvr-Benefit Plan Admin)*
Eileen Perry *(Supvr-Compliance Svcs)*
Amy Spotts *(Supvr-Customer Svc-Call Center)*
Dara Williams *(Supvr-Defined Contribution Plan Svcs)*
Elizabeth Tabacco *(Supvr-FSA Dept)*
Todd Kittell *(Mgr-Defined Contribution Plan Svcs)*
Robyn Rusyn *(Dir-Javelina Program & Ops)*

Excellus Health Plan, Inc. (1)
165 Court St, Rochester, NY 14647
Tel.: (585) 232-2632
Web Site: http://www.excellusbcbs.com
Sales Range: $750-799.9 Million
Emp.: 3,000
Health Insurance Services
N.A.I.C.S.: 524114
David H. Klein *(CEO)*
Paul M. von Ebers *(COO)*
Willie Simmons *(Sr VP-Fin)*
James D. Spencer *(Sr VP-Fin Transition Mgmt)*
Barry J. Thornton *(Sr VP-Transformation Mgmt)*
Dorothy A. Coleman *(CFO & Exec VP)*
Stan Proffitt *(Dir-Org Dev, Diversity & Inclusion)*

Sibley Nursing Personnel Service, Inc. (1)
1655 Elmwood Ave, Rochester, NY 14620
Tel.: (585) 325-3220
Web Site: http://www.sibleynursing.com
Sales Range: $1-9.9 Million
Emp.: 700
Home Nursing Services
N.A.I.C.S.: 621610

THE LIGHTNING GROUP, INC.
722 N Market St, Duncannon, PA 17020-1716
Tel.: (717) 834-3031
Year Founded: 1904
Sales Range: $1-9.9 Million
Emp.: 51
Antique & Craft Market
N.A.I.C.S.: 459510
Norman Rosen *(Owner)*

Subsidiaries:

Carrom Co. (1)
218 E Dowland St, Ludington, MI 49431-2309 (100%)
Tel.: (231) 845-1263
Web Site: http://www.carrom.com
Wooden Games & Juvenile Furniture Mfr
N.A.I.C.S.: 339930

Rochelle Furniture (1)
218 E Dowland St, Ludington, MI 49431 (100%)
Tel.: (231) 845-1263
Web Site: http://www.carrom.com
Juvenile Furniture Mfr
N.A.I.C.S.: 337122

THE LIGHTSTONE GROUP, LLC
299 Park Ave, New York, NY 10171
Tel.: (212) 616-9969 NJ
Web Site: http://www.lightstonegroup.com
Year Founded: 1986
Sales Range: $200-249.9 Million
Emp.: 1,200
Holding Company; Real Estate Investment, Property Management & Brokerage Services
N.A.I.C.S.: 551112
David W. Lichtenstein *(Founder, Chm & CEO)*
Akiva Elazary *(First VP-Investment & Asset Mgmt)*
Joseph E. Teichman *(Gen Counsel & Exec VP)*
Mitchell C. Hochberg *(Pres)*
Mark C. Green *(Sr VP-Construction)*
Ariel Feldhamer *(Sr VP-Asset Mgmt & Investments)*
Meghan Bobertz *(Dir-Hotel Mgmt)*
Meir Milgraum *(Dir-Acq & Dev)*
Seth Molod *(CFO & Exec VP)*
Kara Morett *(Exec VP-HR)*
Scott J. Avram *(Sr VP-Dev)*
Christopher Baxter *(Sr VP-Hospitality)*
Jonathan Rabinow *(Sr VP-Investments & Capital Markets)*
Lauren Levin *(Sr VP-Moxy Hotels Mktg & PR)*

Subsidiaries:

Lightstone Value Plus REIT LLC (1)
460 Park Ave 13th Fl Ste B, New York, NY 10022
Web Site: http://lightstonecapitalmarkets.com
Real Estate Investment Trust Management Services
N.A.I.C.S.: 523940
David W. Lichtenstein *(Chm, Pres & CEO)*

Holding (Domestic):

Lightstone Value Plus REIT I, Inc. (2)
1985 Cedar Bridge Ave Ste 1, Lakewood, NJ 08701
Tel.: (732) 367-0129
Rev.: $14,999,000
Assets: $509,894,000
Liabilities: $283,120,000
Net Worth: $226,774,000
Earnings: ($27,714,000)
Fiscal Year-end: 12/31/2022
Real Estate Investment Trust
N.A.I.C.S.: 525990
David W. Lichtenstein *(Chm & CEO)*

Lightstone Value Plus REIT II, Inc. (2)
1985 Cedar Bridge Ave Ste 1, Lakewood, NJ 08701
Tel.: (732) 367-0129
Rev.: $75,265,000
Assets: $293,355,000
Liabilities: $152,733,000
Net Worth: $140,622,000
Earnings: $5,716,000
Fiscal Year-end: 12/31/2019
Real Estate Investment Trust
N.A.I.C.S.: 525990
David W. Lichtenstein *(Chm & CEO)*
Mitchell C. Hochberg *(Pres & COO)*
Joseph Teichman *(Gen Counsel)*
Seth Molod *(CFO & Treas)*

Lightstone Value Plus REIT III, Inc. (2)
1985 Cedar Bridge Ave Ste 1, Lakewood, NJ 08701
Tel.: (732) 367-0129
Rev.: $28,311,000
Assets: $142,815,000
Liabilities: $64,076,000
Net Worth: $78,739,000
Earnings: ($215,000)
Fiscal Year-end: 12/31/2022
Real Estate Investment Trust
N.A.I.C.S.: 525990
David W. Lichtenstein *(Chm & CEO)*

Lightstone Value Plus REIT IV, Inc. (2)
1985 Cedar Bridge Ave Ste 1, Lakewood, NJ 08701
Tel.: (732) 367-0129
Rev.: $90,900
Assets: $138,272,543
Liabilities: $83,583,012
Net Worth: $54,689,531
Earnings: ($2,229,936)
Emp.: 1
Fiscal Year-end: 12/31/2022
Real Estate Investment Trust
N.A.I.C.S.: 525990
David W. Lichtenstein *(Chm & CEO)*

Lightstone Value Plus REIT V, Inc. (2)
1985 Cedar Bridge Ave Ste 1, Lakewood, NJ 08701
Rev.: $46,970,000
Assets: $434,708,000
Liabilities: $298,804,000
Net Worth: $135,904,000
Earnings: ($8,650,000)
Fiscal Year-end: 12/31/2022
Real Estate Investment Trust
N.A.I.C.S.: 525990
David W. Lichtenstein *(CEO-LSG Development LLC & LSG-BH II Property Manager LLC)*
Mitchell C. Hochberg *(Pres)*
Seth D. Molod *(CFO, Treas & Exec VP)*

Park Avenue Funding, LLC (1)
460 Park Ave 11th Fl, New York, NY 10022
Tel.: (212) 324-0200
Financial Management Services
N.A.I.C.S.: 523999

THE LILIAN RAJI AGENCY
55 Pharr Rd Ste A304, Atlanta, GA 30305
Tel.: (646) 789-4427
Web Site: http://www.lmrpr.com
Year Founded: 2003
Sales Range: Less than $1 Million
Emp.: 6
Brand Identity, Media Relations & Special Events
N.A.I.C.S.: 541820
Lilian M. Raji *(Pres)*

THE LILLY COMPANY INC.
3613 Knight Arnold Rd, Memphis, TN 38118-2729
Tel.: (901) 363-6000 DE
Web Site: http://www.lillytoyota.com
Year Founded: 1919
Sales Range: $100-124.9 Million
Emp.: 190
Industrial Machinery & Equipment
N.A.I.C.S.: 423830
Eric Wisher *(COO)*

THE LINICK GROUP, INC.
Linick Bldg Seven Putter Ln, Middle Island, NY 11953-1920
Tel.: (631) 924-3888 NY
Year Founded: 1972
Sales Range: $50-74.9 Million
Emp.: 70
Advertising Agencies
N.A.I.C.S.: 541860
Andrew S. Linick *(Chm & CEO)*
Roger Dextor *(Dir-Creative)*

Subsidiaries:

Blitz Media-Direct (1)
Linick Bldg 7 Putter Ln, Middle Island, NY 11953-0102
Tel.: (631) 924-8555
Web Site: http://www.linick.net
Sales Range: $25-49.9 Million
Emp.: 36
Public Relations
N.A.I.C.S.: 541820
Barbara J. Deal *(Dir-PR)*
Shane Clarke *(Editor-Bus)*
Peter Schwartz *(Dir-Creative)*
Chet Soloman *(Dir-Media)*
Marsha Ray *(Dir-Art)*
Tom Vignola *(Dir-Mktg)*
Gene Brookman *(Media Buyer)*
Glen Hart *(Acct Supvr)*
Ben Kravitz *(Acct Supvr)*
Marvine Ladmer *(Acct Supvr)*
Sue Ross *(Acct Supvr)*
Andy Schwartz *(Acct Supvr)*
Jill Thompson *(Acct Supvr)*

L.K. Advertising Agency (1)
Linick Bldg 7 Putter Ln Dept RB08, Middle Island, NY 11953-0102
Tel.: (631) 924-3888
Emp.: 27
Advertising Agencies
N.A.I.C.S.: 541810

THE LINN CONTRACTING COMPANIES INC.
309 S Green St, Chicago, IL 60607-3501
Tel.: (312) 454-0200 IL
Web Site: http://www.linn-mathes.com
Year Founded: 1919
Sales Range: $25-49.9 Million
Emp.: 25
Holding Company; Residential Construction
N.A.I.C.S.: 551112

Subsidiaries:

Linn-Mathes Inc. (1)
309 S Green St, Chicago, IL 60607-3501 (100%)
Tel.: (312) 454-0200
Web Site: http://www.linnmathes.com
Rev.: $60,000,000
Emp.: 20
Residential Construction
N.A.I.C.S.: 236118
Brad Mathes *(Pres)*

THE LIPPIN GROUP
6100 Wilshire Blvd Ste 400, Los Angeles, CA 90048-5109
Tel.: (323) 965-1990 CA
Web Site: http://www.lippingroup.com
Year Founded: 1986
Sales Range: $1-9.9 Million
Emp.: 50
Public Relations Agency
N.A.I.C.S.: 541820
Pamela Golum *(Pres-Entertainment-West Coast)*
Alexandra Lippin *(Sr VP)*
Dick Lippin *(CEO)*

Subsidiaries:

The Lippin Group (1)
31 Southampton Row, London, WC1B 5HJ, United Kingdom
Tel.: (44) 203 008 5406
Web Site: http://www.lippingroup.com
Emp.: 5
Public Relations Agency
N.A.I.C.S.: 541820

The Lippin Group, Inc. - New York (1)
300 Park Ave 12th Fl, New York, NY 10022
Tel.: (212) 986-7080
Web Site: http://www.lippingroup.com
Emp.: 8
Public Relations Agency
N.A.I.C.S.: 541820

THE LIRO GROUP
3 Aerial Way, Syosset, NY 11791
Tel.: (516) 938-5476 NY
Web Site: http://www.liro.com
Sales Range: $200-249.9 Million
Emp.: 700
Construction Services
N.A.I.C.S.: 541310
Rocco Trotta *(Chm)*
Luis M. Tormenta *(Vice Chm & CEO)*
Lawrence S. Roberts *(CFO & Sr VP)*
Michael Bailey *(Sr VP-Resident Engrg & Inspection)*
Alfred C. Bereche *(Gen Counsel & Sec)*
Lawrence H. Blond *(Sr VP & Gen Mgr-Program & Construction Mgmt)*

Michael Burton *(Sr VP & Mgr-Ops-Natl)*
Peter J. Gerbasi *(VP)*
Murray L. Levi *(VP-Architecture & Sustainability)*
Michael P. Rennard *(VP)*
Joseph Grant *(VP & Architect)*
John B. McCaffrey *(CIO)*

THE LITCHFIELD COMPANY
14240 Ocean Hwy 17, Pawleys Island, SC 29585-0097
Tel.: (843) 237-4000
Web Site: http://www.thelitchfieldcompany.com
Year Founded: 1956
Sales Range: $10-24.9 Million
Emp.: 100
Real Estate Services
N.A.I.C.S.: 531390
Royce King *(Pres)*

THE LITTLE GYM INTERNATIONAL, INC.
7001 N Scottsdale Rd Ste 1050, Paradise Valley, AZ 85253
Tel.: (480) 948-2878
Web Site: http://www.thelittlegym.com
Year Founded: 1992
Sales Range: $100-124.9 Million
Emp.: 40
Child Development Recreational Facilities & Learning Programs
N.A.I.C.S.: 611699
Robin Wes *(Founder)*
Gerald Moore *(VP-Real Estate Dev)*
Martha Moore *(VP-Western Reg)*
Randy McCoy *(Dir-Curriculum)*
Heather Anderson *(VP-Ops)*
Jessica Papa *(Creative Dir)*
Samantha Ward *(Dir-Consulting)*
Nancy Bigley *(Pres & CEO)*

THE LITTLE OIL COMPANY, INC.
PO Box 6863, Richmond, VA 23230-7501
Tel.: (804) 358-8877   VA
Web Site: http://www.littleoilco.com
Year Founded: 1921
Sales Range: $10-24.9 Million
Emp.: 20
Petroleum Bulk Station & Terminal Services
N.A.I.C.S.: 424710
Stratford Ward *(Pres)*

THE LITTLE TRAVELER INC.
404 S 3rd St, Geneva, IL 60134
Tel.: (630) 232-4200
Web Site: http://www.littletraveler.com
Rev.: $10,700,000
Emp.: 175
All Other General Merchandise Stores
N.A.I.C.S.: 455219
Michael H. Simon *(Pres)*
Alvin L. Rosenthal *(VP)*

THE LIVEKINDLY COMPANY, INC.
6 St Johns Ln, New York, NY 10013
Tel.: (917) 371-8690
Web Site: https://thelivekindlyco.com
Specialty Foods Mfr
N.A.I.C.S.: 311999
David Knopf *(CEO)*

Subsidiaries:

Alpha Foods Inc.   (1)
2130 Beaver Rd, Landover, MD 20785
Tel.: (301) 322-2222
Rev.: $6,822,000
Emp.: 100
Supermarkets & Other Grocery, except Convenience, Stores
N.A.I.C.S.: 445110
Angelo Magafan *(Pres)*
Eugenia Stubos *(VP)*
Loren Wallis *(Co-Founder & Chief Innovation Officer)*
Cole Orobetz *(Co-Founder & CEO)*

THE LLOYD GROUP, INC.
263 W 38th St 7th Fl, New York, NY 10018
Tel.: (212) 221-3320
Web Site: http://www.lloydgroup.com
Year Founded: 1995
Sales Range: $1-9.9 Million
Emp.: 48
Information Technology Management & Support Services for Small & Medium Businesses
N.A.I.C.S.: 541690
Brian M. David *(COO)*

THE LOCKTON COMPANIES, LLC
444 W 47th St Ste 900, Kansas City, MO 64112-1957
Tel.: (816) 960-9000   MO
Web Site: http://www.lockton.com
Year Founded: 1966
Sales Range: $300-349.9 Million
Emp.: 1,600
Insurance & Risk Management
N.A.I.C.S.: 524210
Claudia Mandato *(Exec VP-Ops)*
Edward J. Schloesslin *(Sr VP-HR)*
Tim Ryan *(COO-Northeast)*
Pamela Popp *(Chief Inclusion Officer)*
Bob Reiff *(Pres-Benefit Grp)*
Chuck McDaniel *(Exec VP)*
Eric Collison *(Mgr/VP-Memphis)*
Brandon Luckett *(VP-Washington)*
Caitlin Shea McGrath *(VP-Natl Product Recall & Accidental Contamination Risk Consulting)*
Paul Primavera *(Exec VP-Natl Risk Control Svcs)*
Alex Petrovich *(VP-Omaha)*
Jack Struyk *(Pres-Omaha)*
Angelo Galioto *(Sr VP)*
Brett Moulton *(Sr VP)*
Kevin Loppnow *(Mgr-Property & Casualty-Milwaukee)*
Christina Zapantoulis *(Head-Marine-Northeast)*
Chris DiLullo *(Exec VP-Northeast)*
Peter Clune *(CEO)*
Neil Nimmo *(CEO-Intl)*
Henry Bond *(CFO)*
Paul Marsden *(CEO-Australia)*
Timothy Folk *(Exec VP-Property & Casualty-Philadelphia)*
Steve Bonnington *(Sr VP)*
Suzette Clark *(Sr VP)*
Leyla Coker *(Sr VP)*
Arturo Fisher *(VP)*
Fred Flemig *(Sr VP-Risk Mgmt)*
Leigh Harris *(VP)*
Sarah Martin *(VP)*
Mary Mosqueda *(VP)*
Brian Neary *(Sr VP)*
Tammy Quinn *(Sr VP)*
Mark Seely *(Sr VP)*
Matt Tritz *(VP)*
Rob Warrington *(VP)*
Michael Garner *(VP-Employee Benefit)*
Bill Husic *(Exec VP-Hartford)*
Nate Mundy *(COO/Sr VP-Pacific)*
Tim Noonan *(CEO-Pacific)*
Debbie Goldstine *(Exec VP)*
Chris Panettiere *(Sr VP-Employee Benefits-Atlanta)*
Nathan Hudson *(Sr VP-Lockton Power Team)*
Alexander Post *(Sr VP-Lockton Power Team & Acct Exec)*
Peter McGoldrick *(Sr VP-Lockton Power Team & Acct Exec)*
Jonathan Keller *(Sr VP-Lockton Power Team & Acct Exec)*
Jim Skeen *(Founder)*
Sallie Giblin *(Pres-San Diego)*
Tate McCoy *(CEO-Mountain West)*
Kevin Cummings *(Pres-Arizona)*
Leo Tokar *(Pres-Employee Benefits Ops-Mountain West)*
Said Taiym *(Chief Digital Officer & COO-United States)*
Julie Gibson *(Sr VP & Dir-Mktg, Comm & External Affairs)*
Byron Clymer *(CIO)*
Robert Hausler *(Sr VP)*
Anthony Dagostino *(Exec VP-Global Cyber)*
Tom Schaffler *(CEO-Midwest Series)*
Nicholas Dobelbower *(Sr VP & Dir-Global Benefits Practice)*
Hiram Marrero *(Pres-Global Growth Officer & Exec VP)*
Brian Roberts *(Chief Diversity Officer)*
Kelly Conway *(Chief People Officer)*
Judy Worrall *(Sr VP)*
Neil Metzheiser *(Pres-Atlanta)*
Paul Bruno *(Pres-Carolinas)*
Kyle Anthony *(Pres-Ohio)*
Matthew Clodwick *(VP-Cleveland)*

Subsidiaries:

Lockton Companies LLP   (1)
The Saint Botolph Building 138 Houndsditch, London, EC3 7AG, United Kingdom   (100%)
Tel.: (44) 2079330000
Sales Range: $150-199.9 Million
Emp.: 600
Holding Company; Regional Managing Office
N.A.I.C.S.: 551112
Mike Goudime *(Dir-Lockton Global)*
Matthew Gooda *(Sr VP)*
Tim Law *(Chm-Global Energy)*

Subsidiary (Domestic):

Lockton Companies International Limited   (2)
The St Botolph Building 138 Houndsditch, London, EC3A 7AG, United Kingdom   (100%)
Tel.: (44) 2079330000
Web Site: http://www.locktoninternational.com
Sales Range: $150-199.9 Million
Insurance Services
N.A.I.C.S.: 524298

Branch (Domestic):

Lockton Companies LLP - Belfast   (2)
40 Linenhall Street, Belfast, BT2 8BA, United Kingdom
Tel.: (44) 2890248989
Sales Range: $75-99.9 Million
Emp.: 50
Direct Insurance Brokerage
N.A.I.C.S.: 524210
Gary Ennis *(Mng Partner)*

Lockton Companies LLP - Birmingham   (2)
12th Floor Bank House Cherry Street, Birmingham, B2 5AL, United Kingdom
Tel.: (44) 1216163150
Web Site: http://www.lockton.com
Sales Range: $150-199.9 Million
Emp.: 50
N.A.I.C.S.: 524128
Garry Moseley *(Partner)*
Debbie Day *(Mng Partner)*

Lockton Companies LLP - Manchester   (2)
19 Spring Gardens, Manchester, M2 1FB, United Kingdom
Tel.: (44) 1618283300
Sales Range: $150-199.9 Million
Emp.: 34
N.A.I.C.S.: 524128
Ian Cooper *(Gen Mgr)*

Lockton Companies of Colorado, Inc.   (1)
8110 E Union Ste 700, Denver, CO 80237   (100%)
Tel.: (303) 414-6000
Web Site: http://www.lockton.com
Sales Range: $50-74.9 Million
Emp.: 300
Brokerage Firm Dealing in Commercial Insurance
N.A.I.C.S.: 524210

Lockton Dunning Benefit Company   (1)
2100 Ross Ave Ste 1200, Dallas, TX 75201
Tel.: (214) 969-6100
Web Site: http://www.lockton.com
Sales Range: $50-74.9 Million
Emp.: 65
Risk Management, Insurance & Employee Benefits Services
N.A.I.C.S.: 524210
Steve Idoux *(Sr VP)*
David Stewart *(VP)*

Subsidiary (Domestic):

Excelsior Solutions, LLC   (2)
7401 Metro Blvd Ste 210, Edina, MN 55439
Tel.: (952) 657-5457
Web Site: http://www.excelsiorsolutions.com
Pharmaceutical Consulting Services
N.A.I.C.S.: 541690
Kenneth Dowell *(Sr VP)*
Robert Kordella *(Chief Clinical Officer & Sr VP)*
Sharon Reed *(Sr VP)*
DeeDee Tillitt *(VP)*
Greg Bigwood *(VP)*
Heather Hambrick *(VP)*
Kim Foerster *(VP)*

Lockton Insurance Brokers LLC   (1)
725 S Figueroa St Fl 35, Los Angeles, CA 90017-5524   (100%)
Tel.: (213) 689-0500
Web Site: http://www.lockton.com
Rev.: $6,300,000
Emp.: 300
Insurance Agents Brokers & Services
N.A.I.C.S.: 524210
Lenny Fodemski *(CFO)*
Paul Albarian *(Project Mgr)*
Paul Boucher *(VP)*
Ian Walton *(CEO-UAE)*
Jeff Schermerhorn *(VP-Cyber Tech Practice)*
Andrew Szot *(VP-Client Svcs Consultant)*

Lockton Overseas Ltd.   (1)
The St Botolph Building 138 Houndsditch, London, EC3A 7AG, United Kingdom
Tel.: (44) 2079330000
Web Site: https://global.lockton.com
Holding Company
N.A.I.C.S.: 551112

The Lockton Insurance Agency Inc.   (1)
5847 San Felipe Ste 320, Houston, TX 77057   (100%)
Tel.: (713) 458-5200
Web Site: http://www.lockton.com
Rev.: $34,400,000
Emp.: 300
Insurance Agents, Brokers & Services
N.A.I.C.S.: 524210
Tim Kelly *(Pres)*
Doug Burnham *(CEO)*

THE LOEB ELECTRIC COMPANY, INC.
1800 E 5th Ave, Columbus, OH 43219
Tel.: (614) 294-6351   OH
Web Site: http://www.loebelectric.com
Year Founded: 1911
Sales Range: $10-24.9 Million
Emp.: 110
Mfr of Electrical Apparatus & Equipment
N.A.I.C.S.: 423610
Charles A. Loeb *(Pres)*

THE LOJETA GROUP

THE LOJETA GROUP

The Lojeta Group—(Continued)
3501 N Ocean Dr, Hollywood, FL 33109
Tel.: (954) 922-6491   NJ
Web Site: http://www.lojeta.com
Year Founded: 1985
Sales Range: $1-9.9 Million
Emp.: 10
Real Estate Development & Construction
N.A.I.C.S.: 237210
Lon Tabatchnick *(Pres)*
Ricki Tabatchnick Auerbach *(VP-Comm & Mktg)*
Robert Tabatchnick *(VP-Construction)*

THE LOMBARD INVESTMENT CO.
4245 W 123rd St, Alsip, IL 60803-1805
Tel.: (708) 389-1060   IL
Web Site:
  http://www.lombardcompany.com
Year Founded: 1980
Sales Range: $10-24.9 Million
Emp.: 30
Nonresidential Construction
N.A.I.C.S.: 236220
George Lombard *(Chm & CEO)*
Michael G. Lombard *(Pres)*
John G. Lombard *(CFO & Exec VP)*

Subsidiaries:

Lombard Architectural Precast Products Co., Inc.   (1)
4245 W 123rd St, Alsip, IL 60803   (100%)
Tel.: (708) 389-1060
Sales Range: $10-24.9 Million
Concrete Products
N.A.I.C.S.: 327390

The Lombard Co., Inc.   (1)
4245 W 123rd St, Alsip, IL 60803-1805
Tel.: (708) 389-1060
Web Site: http://www.lombardcompany.com
Nonresidential Construction
N.A.I.C.S.: 236220
George Lombard *(Founder)*

THE LONG & FOSTER COMPANIES, INC.
14501 George Carter Way, Chantilly, VA 20151
Tel.: (703) 653-8500   VA
Web Site:
  http://www.longandfoster.com
Year Founded: 1968
Sales Range: $1-4.9 Billion
Emp.: 2,500
Holding Company; Real Estate, Mortgage & Title Insurance Brokerage Services
N.A.I.C.S.: 551112
Bruce Enger *(CFO & Sr VP)*
Barry S. Redler *(CMO)*
Jeffrey S. Detwiler *(Pres & COO)*
Terrence P. Dwyer *(CIO & Sr VP)*
Bob Albanese *(Sr VP & Mgr-New Jersey)*
Cindy Ariosa *(Sr VP & Mgr-Lutherville)*
Ron Clarke *(Sr VP & Mgr-Doylestown)*
Brian J. Evans *(Chief Legal Officer & Sr VP)*
Brian Haug *(Sr VP & Reg Mgr)*
Lonnie Plaster *(Sr VP & Reg Mgr)*
Fatima Pereira-Shepherd *(Mgr-Training)*
Yanira Rodriguez *(Mgr-Capitol Hill)*
Gregory Hangemanole *(Mgr-Woodley Park)*
P. Wesley Foster Jr. *(Chm & CEO)*
George T. Eastment III *(Vice Chm)*

Subsidiaries:

Fonville Morisey Realty   (1)
1000 Saint Albans Dr, Raleigh, NC 27609
Tel.: (919) 785-4363
Web Site: http://www.fmrealty.com
Real Estate Consulting Service
N.A.I.C.S.: 531390
Mary Kay Pendergraph *(Gen Mgr)*
Eddie Brown *(VP & Mgr-Sls)*
Kim Saylor *(Mgr-Trng)*
Jim Dinkel *(Pres-FM Lending)*
John Morisey *(Founder)*
Vickie Cardin *(VP-Mktg)*
John Schweighardt *(CIO)*
Camille Mims *(VP-Relocation & Corp Svcs)*
Sharon Pelt *(VP-Career Dev)*
Amy Aldridge *(VP & Mgr-Sls)*
Amy Butler *(VP & Mgr-Sls)*
Diane Donnelly *(VP & Mgr-Sls)*
Greg Stevenson *(Mgr-Web-IT Dept)*
Heather Gool *(Asst Mgr)*
Jennifer K. Stenner *(VP & Mgr-Sls)*
Jenny Lynch *(Coord-Mktg)*
Lauren Richardson *(Dir-Mktg-Digital Media)*
Leah Cooke *(VP & Mgr-Sls)*
Lindsey Foster *(Coord-Transaction)*
Lori Ransom *(Mgr-Trng)*
Louise Guemple *(Mgr-Trng)*
Mark Parker *(VP & Mgr-Sls)*
Renee Smith *(VP & Mgr-Sls)*
Sam Pyrtle *(VP & Mgr-Sls)*
Vicki Ferneyhough *(VP-Assoc Education)*
Rod Eller *(Sr VP)*
Olivia Bennett *(Dir-Digital Media Mktg)*
Jennifer Cook *(Sec)*
Gina Crouse *(VP & Mgr-Sls-Durham)*

Long & Foster Real Estate, Inc.   (1)
11351 Random Hills Rd, Fairfax, VA 22030-6081   (100%)
Tel.: (703) 359-1500
Web Site: http://www.longandfoster.com
Sales Range: $350-399.9 Million
Emp.: 300
Residential & Commercial Real Estate Brokers & Property Managers
N.A.I.C.S.: 531210
Bruce Enger *(CFO & Sr VP)*
Gary Scott *(Pres)*
Lydia Martinez *(Chief HR Officer & Sr VP)*
Arnie Kernus *(VP-Bus Dev)*
Larry Foster *(Co-Pres-Gen Brokerage)*
Danai Mattison Sky *(Mgr-Sls)*
Michael McGreevy *(Mgr-Woodley Park)*
Stacey Cousineau *(Mgr-Waldorf & Lexington Park)*
Jeremiah Ganeto *(Mgr-Silver Spring)*
Kara Chaffin-Donofrio *(Mgr)*
Christine Schuster *(Mgr-Bus Dev)*
Cindy Ariosa *(Sr VP & Mgr-Baltimore, West Maryland & East Shore)*
Bob Albanese *(Sr VP & Reg Mgr)*
Jeffrey S. Detwiler *(Pres & COO)*
Terry Dwyer *(CIO & Sr VP)*
Brian J. Evans *(Chief Legal Officer & Sr VP)*
Barry S. Redler *(CMO & Sr VP)*
Wes Foster *(Founder, Chm & CEO)*
Pauline Dent *(Dir-Corp Real Estate Svcs)*
Ross Mackesey *(Mgr-Lake Roland)*
Vicki Hamp *(Sr VP-Corp Real Estate Svcs)*
Paul Muessig *(VP-Comml Property Div-Tysons)*
George T. Eastment III *(Vice Chm)*

Subsidiary (Domestic):

Evers & Co. Real Estate, Inc.   (2)
4400 Jenifer St NW, Washington, DC 20015
Tel.: (202) 364-1700
Web Site: http://www.everssco.com
Sales Range: $1-9.9 Million
Emp.: 35
Real Estate Services
N.A.I.C.S.: 531210
Donna Evers *(Pres)*
Pierson Lamb *(Dir-Art)*
Ju Yon Yu *(Office Mgr)*
Billy Alder *(Mgr-Ops & Tech)*
Andrea Herrera *(Designer-Graphic)*

The Corus Group of Long & Foster   (2)
8227 Old Courthouse Rd, Vienna, VA 22182
Tel.: (703) 827-0075
Web Site: http://www.corushome.com
Emp.: 13
Residential Real Estate
N.A.I.C.S.: 531210

Michael T. Gorman *(Founder & CEO)*

The Long & Foster Companies, Inc. - Harrison St   (1)
17 N Harrison St, Easton, MD 21601
Tel.: (410) 820-7707
Web Site:
  http://longandfostereasternshore.com
Real Estate Mangement Services
N.A.I.C.S.: 531390
Martha Witte Suss *(Branch Mgr)*

The Virginia Properties   (1)
412 Libbie Ave, Richmond, VA 23226-2658
Tel.: (804) 282-7300
Web Site: http://www.longandfoster.com
Emp.: 75
Real Estate Consulting Service
N.A.I.C.S.: 531390

THE LONG COMPANY
909 S Rte 83 Ste 105, Elmhurst, IL 60126
Tel.: (312) 726-4606   IL
Web Site: http://www.thelongco.com
Year Founded: 1900
Sales Range: $75-99.9 Million
Emp.: 35
Provider of Services to Bakers
N.A.I.C.S.: 424490
Albert Bachman *(Dir-Quality & R&D)*
Joan Ginda *(Mgr-Pur)*
Eddie Davis *(Dir-HR & Fin Svc)*
Michael Hull *(Dir-Food Safety & Sanitation Svcs)*

THE LONG NOW FOUNDATION
2 Marina Blvd Fort Mason Ctr Bldg A, San Francisco, CA 94123
Tel.: (415) 561-6582   CA
Web Site: http://www.longnow.org
Year Founded: 1996
Sales Range: $1-9.9 Million
Emp.: 16
Cultural Promotion Services
N.A.I.C.S.: 711310
Kurt Bollacker *(Dir-Digital Res)*
Catherine Borgeson *(Office Mgr)*
Laura Welcher *(Dir-Ops & The Long Now Library)*
Alexander Rose *(Exec Dir & Mgr-Clock Project)*
Charlotte Hajer *(Mgr-Outreach & Dev)*
Kevin Kelly *(Sec)*
Danielle Engelman *(Dir-Programs)*
Danny Hillis *(Co-Chm)*
Stewart Brand *(Co-Chm & Pres)*
David Rumsey *(Treas)*

THE LONGFORD GROUP, INC.
3077 East Warm Springs Rd, Las Vegas, NV 89120
Tel.: (702) 454-5300
Rev.: $46,051,361
Emp.: 80
Residential Construction
N.A.I.C.S.: 236115
John Murtagh *(Pres)*

Subsidiaries:

Wexford Homes Inc.   (1)
3067 E Warm Springs Rd, Las Vegas, NV 89120   (100%)
Tel.: (702) 433-2770
Rev.: $15,000,000
Single-Family Housing Construction
N.A.I.C.S.: 236115

THE LONGHORN COUNCIL, BOY SCOUTS OF AMERICA
850 Cannon Dr, Hurst, TX 76054
Tel.: (817) 231-8500
Web Site:
  https://www.longhorncouncil.org
Year Founded: 1908
Youth Organization Services
N.A.I.C.S.: 813410

THE LOOMIS AGENCY
17120 Dallas Pkwy Ste 200, Dallas, TX 75248-1189
Tel.: (972) 331-7000   TX
Web Site:
  http://www.theloomisagency.com
Year Founded: 1984
Rev.: $52,000,000
Emp.: 25
Advetising Agency
N.A.I.C.S.: 541810
Paul Loomis *(CEO)*
J. Michael Sullivan *(Pres)*
Tina Tackett *(Exec Dir-Creative)*
Aimee Herron *(Dir-Media)*
Jenn Nelson *(Dir-Art)*
Chelsea Ratliff *(Dir-Brand)*
Tim Childress *(Dir-Creative)*
Jim Green *(Dir-Creative)*
Cecily Worthy *(Dir-Creative)*
Jacy Cochran *(Dir-PR)*
Carl Thompson *(Dir-Strategy)*
Vikki Phy *(Mgr-Traffic)*
Mark Platt *(Partner)*

THE LOS ANGELES DEPARTMENT OF WATER & POWER
111 N Hope St 15th Fl, Los Angeles, CA 90012-2607
Tel.: (213) 481-5411   CA
Web Site: http://www.ladwp.com
Year Founded: 1936
Sales Range: $1-4.9 Billion
Emp.: 8,450
Public Water & Power Services
N.A.I.C.S.: 221118
Nicole Neeman Brady *(Commissioner)*
Ron Nichols *(Gen Mgr)*
Mel Levine *(CEO)*
William W. Funderburk *(VP)*
Thomas S. Sayles *(Pres)*

THE LOS ANGELES LAKERS, INC.
2275 E Mariposa Ave, El Segundo, CA 90245
Tel.: (310) 426-6000   CA
Web Site: http://www.nba.com
Year Founded: 1975
Sales Range: $125-149.9 Million
Emp.: 60
Professional Basketball Franchise
N.A.I.C.S.: 711211
Carlos Maples *(Mgr-Equipment)*
Rob Pelinka *(Gen Mgr)*
Gunnar Peterson *(Dir-Strength & Endurance Training)*

THE LOS ANGELES RAMS, LLC
29899 Agoura Rd Ste 210, Agoura Hills, CA 91301   DE
Web Site: http://www.therams.com
Year Founded: 2010
Holding Company; Professional Football Team & Stadium Operator
N.A.I.C.S.: 551112
E. Stanley Kroenke *(Owner & Chm)*
Kevin Demoff *(COO)*
Jennifer Prince *(Chief Comml Officer)*

Subsidiaries:

The Rams Football Company, LLC   (1)
29899 Agoura Rd, Agoura Hills, CA 91301
Tel.: (855) 438-8121
Web Site: http://www.therams.com
Professional Football Franchise
N.A.I.C.S.: 711211
E. Stanley Kroenke *(Chm)*
Kevin Demoff *(COO & Exec VP-Football Ops)*
Mike O'Keefe *(VP-Sls)*
Keely Fimbres *(Dir-Special Events)*

COMPANIES

Molly Higgins *(VP-Corp Comm & Civic Affairs)*
Artis Twyman *(Sr Dir-Comm)*
Les Snead *(Gen Mgr)*
Taylor Morton *(Dir-Player Personnel)*
Jim Lake *(Head-Equipment)*
Todd Davis *(VP-Legal Affairs)*
Bruce Warwick *(Dir-Ops)*
Brad Holmes *(Dir-College Scouting)*
Ted Monago *(Asst Dir-College Scouting)*
Ray Agnew *(Dir-Pro Personnel)*
JW Jordan *(Dir-Draft Mgmt)*
Skarpi Hedinnson *(CTO)*

THE LOUIS BERGER GROUP, INC.
412 Mount Kemble Ave, Morristown, NJ 07962
Tel.: (973) 407-1000   NJ
Web Site: http://www.louisberger.com
Year Founded: 1953
Sales Range: $1-4.9 Billion
Emp.: 6,000
Engineering, Environmental Consulting & Architectural Design Services
N.A.I.C.S.: 541330
Charles Bell *(Grp VP)*
John Hotopp *(Sr VP-Cultural Resource Grp)*
D. James Stamatis *(Pres & CEO)*
Meg Lassarat *(CFO)*
James G. Bach *(Pres-Intl)*
Susan Knauf *(Chief Learning Officer & VP)*
Ernest Portfors *(Chm)*
Adelle Elia *(Chief Integrity Officer)*
Andrew V. Bailey II *(Pres-Svcs)*

Subsidiaries:

BergerABAM Inc.   (1)
33301 9th Ave S Ste 300, Federal Way, WA 98003-2600   **(100%)**
Tel.: (206) 431-2300
Web Site: http://www.abam.com
Sales Range: $25-49.9 Million
Emp.: 120
Engineering, Environmental Consulting & Underwater Inspection & Design Services
N.A.I.C.S.: 541330
Ann B. Kennedy *(Sec & Mgr-HR)*
Michael W. LaNier *(Chm)*
Thomas Wilcox *(VP)*
Mark Lee Marsh *(Pres & CEO)*
Robert F. Mast *(Sr Principal)*

Branch (Domestic):

BergerABAM   (2)
210 E 13th St Ste 300, Vancouver, WA 98660-2958
Tel.: (360) 823-6100
Web Site: http://www.abam.com
Sales Range: $25-49.9 Million
Emp.: 30
Land Use Planning & Natural Resources Consulting Services
N.A.I.C.S.: 541620
John White *(VP)*

The Louis Berger Group, Inc. - Providence   (1)
166 Valley St Bldg 5, Providence, RI 02909
Tel.: (401) 521-5980
Web Site: http://www.louisberger.com
Engineeering Services
N.A.I.C.S.: 541330

THE LOXCREEN COMPANY, INC.
1630 Old Dunbar Rd, West Columbia, SC 29172-1936
Tel.: (803) 822-8200   GA
Web Site: http://www.loxcreen.com
Year Founded: 1946
Sales Range: $75-99.9 Million
Emp.: 120
Aluminum & Vinyl Products Mfr
N.A.I.C.S.: 331318
Rick Wheeler *(VP)*

THE LUNADA BAY CORPORATION
2000 E Winston Rd, Anaheim, CA 92806-5546
Tel.: (714) 490-1313   CA
Web Site: http://www.beccaswim.com
Year Founded: 1980
Sales Range: $10-24.9 Million
Emp.: 80
Womens & Misses Outerwear
N.A.I.C.S.: 315250
Adeline Bernardo *(CFO)*
Susan Crank *(Pres & CEO)*
Patricia Osmanson *(VP-Mktg)*

THE LURIE COMPANIES
5656 W Clinton Ave, Milwaukee, WI 53223
Tel.: (414) 536-8000
Sales Range: $10-24.9 Million
Emp.: 100
Mfr of Glass Products for Commercial, Industrial, Residential & Automotive Use
N.A.I.C.S.: 238150
Marc S. Lurie *(Pres)*

Subsidiaries:

Lurie Glass Company   (1)
12000 W Wirth St, Milwaukee, WI 53222
Tel.: (414) 536-8000
Web Site: http://www.lurieglass.com
Rev.: $7,000,000
Emp.: 95
Mfr of Glass Products For Commercial, Industrial, Residential & Automotive Use
N.A.I.C.S.: 238150

THE LUTHERAN HOME, INC.
7500 W North Ave, Wauwatosa, WI 53213
Tel.: (414) 258-6170   WI
Web Site: http://www.thelutheranhome.org
Year Founded: 1906
Sales Range: $10-24.9 Million
Emp.: 553
Elder Care Services
N.A.I.C.S.: 623312
Scott McFadden *(Pres & CEO)*
Mary Swoboda *(VP-Support Svcs)*

THE LUZERNE FOUNDATION
140 Main St 2nd Fl, Luzerne, PA 18709
Tel.: (570) 714-1570   PA
Web Site: http://www.luzfdn.org
Year Founded: 1994
Sales Range: $10-24.9 Million
Emp.: 4
Grantmaking Services
N.A.I.C.S.: 813211
Charles Barber *(Pres & CEO)*
Diane M. Dutko *(Dir-Ops)*

THE LYDON COMPANY, LLC.
284 Bodwell St, Avon, MA 02322
Tel.: (508) 897-1700
Web Site: http://www.lydonco.com
Year Founded: 2003
Sales Range: $10-24.9 Million
Emp.: 180
Building Equipment Contracting Services
N.A.I.C.S.: 238290
Michael Lewis *(Dir-Assets, Safety & Mgmt)*
Quan C. Pham *(CIO)*
Aron Danielson *(Project Mgr)*
Robert C. Corey *(CFO)*
James E. Lydon Jr. *(Pres)*
John T. Dunn Jr. *(Project Mgr)*

THE LYND COMPANY
8000 IH 10 W Ste 1200, San Antonio, TX 78230
Tel.: (210) 733-6125
Web Site: http://www.lyndliving.com
Sales Range: $10-24.9 Million

Real Estate Development & Investment
N.A.I.C.S.: 237210
Samuel J. Kasparek *(CFO)*
Connie Arambula *(Gen Counsel)*
Ken Miller *(Sr VP-Strategic Initiatives)*
Kevin L. Wilfley *(Exec VP)*
Paul Valdez *(VP-Property Performance & Analytics)*
Randy Brown *(VP-HR & Employee Dev)*
Michael Lynd Jr. *(CEO & Chief Investment Officer)*

THE LYON & BILLARD CO., INC.
38 Gypsy Ln, Meriden, CT 06451-7910
Tel.: (203) 235-4487   CT
Web Site: http://www.lyon-billard.com
Year Founded: 1847
Sales Range: $25-49.9 Million
Emp.: 124
Lumber & Other Building Materials
N.A.I.C.S.: 423310
Edd Goralnik *(Owner & Pres)*
Al Goralnik *(Exec VP)*

Subsidiaries:

Cheshire Lumber Co. Inc.   (1)
504 W Main St, Cheshire, CT 06410-2420   **(100%)**
Tel.: (203) 272-5351
Sales Range: $10-24.9 Million
Emp.: 14
Retail of Lumber & Other Building Materials
N.A.I.C.S.: 444110
Edd Goralnik *(Pres)*
Al Goralnik *(Exec VP)*

THE LYONS COMPANIES
501 Carr Rd Ste 301 Rpckwood Office Park, Wilmington, DE 19809
Tel.: (302) 658-5508
Web Site: http://www.lyonsinsurance.com
Year Founded: 1984
Rev.: $10,900,000
Emp.: 48
Providing Risk Management Solutions
N.A.I.C.S.: 524298
David F. Lyons Sr. *(Founder, Pres & CEO)*

THE M. CONLEY COMPANY
1312 4th St SE, Canton, OH 44707-3243
Tel.: (330) 456-8243
Web Site: http://www.mconley.com
Year Founded: 1901
Sales Range: $10-24.9 Million
Emp.: 110
Provider of Industrial & Personal Services
N.A.I.C.S.: 424130
Dertha Stromsky *(Office Mgr)*

THE M.E. WILSON COMPANY, INC.
300 W Platt St, Tampa, FL 33606
Tel.: (813) 229-8021   FL
Web Site: http://www.mewilson.com
Year Founded: 1920
Insurance, Risk Management & Employee Benefits Services
N.A.I.C.S.: 524210
Douglas W. King *(CEO)*
Robin Moch *(Partner)*
Dwight Wilson *(Partner)*
Janet Dayton *(Partner)*
Rob Nation *(Partner)*
Billy West *(Chief Revenue Officer)*
Jim Rogan *(Sr VP)*
Jeff Lenderman *(VP)*

Cindy Buttrill *(VP)*
Wendy Solei *(Mgr-Private Client)*
John Weatherford *(Sr VP)*
Guy King III *(Pres)*

THE MACALUSO GROUP
271 Route 46 W Ste D103, Fairfield, NJ 07004
Tel.: (973) 244-9110
Year Founded: 2001
Sales Range: $10-24.9 Million
Emp.: 10
Technology Solutions for Healthcare Marketing
N.A.I.C.S.: 541512
Joe Macaluso *(Founder)*
Jo Joann *(COO)*

THE MACDONALD BROADCASTING COMPANY
2000 Whittier St, Saginaw, MI 48601
Tel.: (989) 752-8161   MI
Year Founded: 1972
Sales Range: $1-9.9 Million
Emp.: 60
Radio Broadcasting Stations
N.A.I.C.S.: 516110
Ken McDonald *(Owner)*
Jason Addams *(Project Dir-WKCQ, WMJO, WSAM & WSAG & Mgr-Ops-WKCQ, WMJO, WSAM)*

Subsidiaries:

Wqhh 96 5 Fm   (1)
1011 Northcrest Rd Ste 4, Lansing, MI 48906
Tel.: (517) 393-1320
Web Site: http://power965fm.com
Radio Stations
N.A.I.C.S.: 516110

THE MACHINE
445 Venetia Way, Oceanside, CA 92057
Tel.: (760) 433-7749
Web Site: http://www.themachinedesign.com
Year Founded: 2003
Sales Range: Less than $1 Million
Emp.: 20
Advetising Agency
N.A.I.C.S.: 541810

THE MACOMB GROUP, INC.
6600 15 Mile Rd, Sterling Heights, MI 48312
Tel.: (586) 274-4100   MI
Web Site: http://www.macombgroup.com
Year Founded: 1977
Sales Range: $75-99.9 Million
Emp.: 235
Pipes, Valves & Fittings Distr
N.A.I.C.S.: 423720
Bill McGivern *(Co-Owner, Pres & CEO)*
Keith Schatko *(Co-Owner & VP)*
David Margolis *(CFO)*
Dick Dixon *(Treas)*
Bill Vail *(Exec VP)*

Subsidiaries:

Deacon Industrial Supply Company Inc.   (1)
1510 Gehman Rd, Harleysville, PA 19438
Tel.: (610) 265-5322
Web Site: http://www.deaconind.com
Sales Range: $25-49.9 Million
Emp.: 100
Plumbing Fixtures, Equipment & Supplies
N.A.I.C.S.: 423720

Woodhill Supply Inc.   (1)
4665 Beidler Rd, Willoughby, OH 44094
Tel.: (440) 269-1100
Web Site: http://www.woodhillsupply.com
Rev.: $14,157,295
Emp.: 80
Plumbing & Hydronic Heating Supplies
N.A.I.C.S.: 423720

THE MACOMB GROUP, INC.

The Macomb Group, Inc.—(Continued)
Edward Carpenter (Mgr-Sls)
Ann Norris (Mgr-Credit)

THE MADDEN CORPORATION
94-411 Koaki St, Waipahu, HI 96797
Tel.: (808) 564-8800
Web Site: http://www.welcometotheis
lands.com
Emp.: 100
Hawaiian Gifts & Novelties Mfr & Distr
N.A.I.C.S.: 459420
Dale Madden (Dir)

THE MAHONEY COMPANY
2342 Walsh Ave, Santa Clara, CA 95051-1301
Tel.: (408) 970-9211
Web Site:
http://www.themahoneycompany.com
Year Founded: 1986
Sales Range: $1-9.9 Million
Emp.: 15
Marketing & Public Relations Solutions
N.A.I.C.S.: 541820
Patrick Mahoney (Dir-Ops)

THE MAJOR AUTOMOTIVE COMPANIES, INC.
43-40 Northern Blvd, Long Island City, NY 11101
Tel.: (718) 937-3700
Web Site: http://www.majorworld.com
Sales Range: $350-399.9 Million
Emp.: 520
Car Dealership Owner & Operator
N.A.I.C.S.: 441120
Andrew Jasyk (Mgr-Mktg)

THE MALISH CORP.
7333 Corporate Blvd, Mentor, OH 44060
Tel.: (440) 951-5356
Web Site: http://www.malish.com
Year Founded: 1945
Commercial & Industrial Brushes Design & Mfr
N.A.I.C.S.: 339994
Jeffery Malish (Pres & CEO)
Kevin Young (VP-Sls & Mktg)
Gordon Overs (VP-Ops)
Ken Shary (VP-Asian Ops & Global New Product Dev)

Subsidiaries:

Abtex LLC (1)
89 Main St, Dresden, NY 14441
Tel.: (315) 536-7403
Web Site: http://www.abtex.com
Abrasive Nylon Deburring Brushes Mfr
N.A.I.C.S.: 339994
Jason Saner (Pres)

THE MANAGEMENT EDGE, INC.
12360 66th St Ste S, Largo, FL 33773
Tel.: (727) 588-9481
Web Site:
http://www.themanagementedge.com
Year Founded: 1986
Sales Range: $1-9.9 Million
Emp.: 12
Organizational Development, Training & Consulting
N.A.I.C.S.: 611430
Gayle Waldron (Founder & Pres)
Patricia L. Dunn (Dir-Ops & Fin)

THE MANHATTAN INSURANCE GROUP
10777 NW Fwy, Houston, TX 77092
Tel.: (713) 529-0045
Web Site:
http://www.manhattanlife.com
Year Founded: 1962
Sales Range: $450-499.9 Million
Emp.: 200
Holding Company; Life & Health Insurance Products & Services
N.A.I.C.S.: 551112
David W. Harris (Chm & CEO)
Lee Ann Blakey (COO & Sr VP)
David Parsons (Sr VP-IT)
Daniel J. George (Pres & Treas)
Kent W. Lamb (CFO & Sr VP)
John E. McGettigan (Gen Counsel, Sec & Exec VP)
Todd Z. Hayden (CMO & Sr VP)
William Bay Jr. (Sr VP-IT Web & Mobile)

Subsidiaries:

Family Life Insurance Co (1)
PO Box 149138, Austin, TX 78714
Tel.: (512) 404-5000
Web Site: http://www.familylifeins.com
Life Insurance
N.A.I.C.S.: 524113

Investors Consolidated Insurance Company (1)
10700 NW Freeway, Houston, TX 77092
Tel.: (713) 529-0045
Web Site: http://www.manhattanlife.com
Sales Range: $50-74.9 Million
Emp.: 175
Provider of Insurance Services
N.A.I.C.S.: 524113
David W. Harris (CEO)
Daniel J. George (Pres)

Manhattan Life Insurance Company (1)
10777 NW Fwy, Houston, TX 77092 (79%)
Tel.: (713) 529-0045
Web Site: http://www.centralunited.com
Sales Range: $50-74.9 Million
Emp.: 150
Fire Insurance Services
N.A.I.C.S.: 524210
Teresa Moro (Sr VP-Investments)
Daniel J. George (Pres & Treas)
Bill Bay (VP-IT Web)
Lee Ann Blakey (COO & Sr VP)
David Harris (Chm & CEO)
Geneva Harris (Portfolio Mgr)
Todd Hayden (Sr VP-Mktg)
Kent Lamb (CFO & Sr VP)
Carolyn Pratt (VP & Controller)
Bicky Tran (VP-Internal Audit)
Alan Vala (VP-Mktg)

THE MAPLE CITY ICE COMPANY
371 Cleveland Rd, Norwalk, OH 44857-8859
Tel.: (419) 668-2531
Web Site: http://www.maplecityice.net
Year Founded: 1917
Sales Range: $10-24.9 Million
Emp.: 82
Beer Distr
N.A.I.C.S.: 424810
Patricia Hipp (Pres)
Sara Bodell (Mgr-HR)

THE MAPLE-VAIL BOOK MANUFACTURING GROUP
480 Willow Springs Ln, York, PA 17402
Tel.: (717) 764-5911
Web Site:
http://www.maplepress.com
Year Founded: 1983
Rev.: $75,700,000
Emp.: 1,050
Publishing Services
N.A.I.C.S.: 323117
James U. Wisotzkey (Chm & CEO)
Bill Long (VP-Sls & Mktg)

Subsidiaries:

Lebanon Distribution Center (1)
704 Legionaire Dr, Fredricksburg, PA 17026 (100%)
Tel.: (717) 865-7600
Web Site: http://www.maple-vail.com
Sales Range: $10-24.9 Million
Emp.: 50
Distribution of Books
N.A.I.C.S.: 459210

Maple Logistics Solutions (1)
60 Grumbacher Rd, York, PA 17406
Tel.: (717) 764-4596
Web Site:
http://www.maplelogisticssolutions.com
Sales Range: $10-24.9 Million
Emp.: 100
Distribution Services for Books
N.A.I.C.S.: 424920
Chris Benyovszky (VP-Distr Svcs)

The Maple Press Company (1)
480 Willow Springs Ln, York, PA 17405-2695
Tel.: (717) 764-5911
Web Site: http://www.maple-vail.com
Sales Range: $25-49.9 Million
Emp.: 400
Publishing Services
N.A.I.C.S.: 323117
Bill Long (VP-Sls)
Jim Wisotzkey (Pres)

THE MARAMONT CORPORATION
5600 1st Ave Bldg C, Brooklyn, NY 11220-2558
Tel.: (718) 439-8900
Year Founded: 1981
Sales Range: $25-49.9 Million
Emp.: 450
Food Service
N.A.I.C.S.: 311991
Harry Reichman (Pres)

THE MARFO COMPANY INC.
799 N Hague Ave, Columbus, OH 43204-1424
Tel.: (614) 276-3352
Web Site: http://www.marsala.com
Year Founded: 1977
Sales Range: $10-24.9 Million
Emp.: 120
Jewelry & Precious Metal
N.A.I.C.S.: 339910
William Giovanello (Pres & CEO)

THE MARINA LIMITED PARTNERSHIP
11691 Fall Creek Rd, Indianapolis, IN 46256
Tel.: (317) 845-0270
Web Site:
http://www.marinalimitedpartnership.com
Sales Range: $10-24.9 Million
Emp.: 34
Land Subdividers & Developers, Residential
N.A.I.C.S.: 713930
Allen E. Rosenberg Sr. (Founder & Pres)

THE MARINO ORGANIZATION, INC.
171 Madison Ave 12th Fl, New York, NY 10016
Tel.: (212) 889-0808
Web Site: http://www.themarino.org
Year Founded: 1993
Rev.: $2,100,000
Emp.: 20
Fiscal Year-end: 12/31/06
Advetising Agency
N.A.I.C.S.: 541810
Francis C. Marino (Pres & CEO)
Lee A. Silberstein (Exec VP)
Richard D. Mulieri (Sr VP)

Steve Vitoff (Sr VP)
Robert J. Barletta (Exec VP)
Alyson Leiter (Sr Acct Suprvr)
Cara Marino Gentile (Sr VP)
Ross Wallenstein (VP)
Danielle Friedman (Dir-Digital & Brand Strategy)

THE MARITIME AQUARIUM AT NORWALK
10 N Water St, Norwalk, CT 06854
Tel.: (203) 852-0700
Web Site:
https://www.maritimeaquarium.org
Year Founded: 1985
Sales Range: $10-24.9 Million
Emp.: 173
Aquarium Operator
N.A.I.C.S.: 712130
Tom Naiman (Dir-Education & Volunteers)
Sanders Davies (Vice Chm)
Richard Hokin (Treas)
Michael L. Widland (Chm)
Alicia Wettenstein (Dir-Dev)
Dave Truedson (COO)
Maureen Hanley (Pres & CEO)
John F. Erdmann III (Vice Chm-Philanthropy)

THE MARKET CONNECTION
20051 SW Birch St Ste 310, Newport Beach, CA 92660
Tel.: (949) 851-6313
Web Site: http://www.tmcauto.com
Year Founded: 1986
Sales Range: Less than $1 Million
Emp.: 3
Public Relations Agency
N.A.I.C.S.: 541820
Jay Jones (Pres & CEO)
Paul Puleo (Dir-Creative)

THE MARKET CREATION GROUP, LLC
1801 California St Ste 2400, Denver, CO 80204
Tel.: (303) 325-7423
Web Site: http://www.marketcreationgroup.com
Year Founded: 2006
Management Consulting Services
N.A.I.C.S.: 541618
Brett Schklar (Founder & CEO)

THE MARKETING AGENCY LLC
2881 E Oakland Park Blvd Ste 425, Fort Lauderdale, FL 33306
Tel.: (954) 771-1177
Web Site:
http://www.themarketingagency.com
Year Founded: 1982
Sales Range: $1-9.9 Million
Media Buying Services
N.A.I.C.S.: 541830
David A. Kramer (Pres)
Rikke Wichmann-Bruun (Mng Dir)

THE MARKETING CENTER FOR SOCIAL SECURITY LAW PRACTICES
1539 Jackson Ave 5th Fl, New Orleans, LA 70130
Tel.: (504) 525-0932
Web Site:
http://www.themarketingcenter.com
Year Founded: 1991
Sales Range: $1-9.9 Million
Emp.: 25
N.A.I.C.S.: 541810
Nathan Chapman (Pres & Founder)
Katie Hiatt (Mgr-Acct)
Karen Boudreaux (Officer-Employee Dev)
Ellen Kramer (Chief of Staff)
Alex Lidwig (Sr Acct Exec)

COMPANIES

THE MARKETING STORE
55 W Monroe Ste 1400, Chicago, IL 60603
Tel.: (312) 614-4600
Web Site: http://www.tmsw.com
Year Founded: 1987
Emp.: 100
Brand Development, Consumer Marketing, Corporate Identity, Electronic Media, Event Marketing, Retail, Sales Promotion
N.A.I.C.S.: 541810
Mark Landolt *(Pres)*
Brian Barthelt *(Mng Dir-Retail)*
Vanessa Smith *(Mng Dir)*
Michael Rivera *(Chief Creative Officer)*

Subsidiaries:

Boxer Creative (1)
Boxer Fort Dunlop, Fort Parkway, Birmingham, B24 9FD, United Kingdom
Tel.: (44) 121 384 9000
Web Site: http://www.boxerbranddesign.com
Emp.: 50
Brand Marketing & Promotional Services
N.A.I.C.S.: 541820
Sonia Richardson *(Acct Mgr)*
Paul Castledine *(Chm & Chief Creative Officer)*

The Marketing Store (1)
39 Rue Anatole France, 92300, Levallois-Perret, France
Tel.: (33) 1 46 17 02 21
Web Site: http://paris.tms.agency
Emp.: 13
Brand Marketing & Promotional Services
N.A.I.C.S.: 541820
Caroline Radat *(Reg Dir)*
Emmanuelle Blanc-Brun *(Dir-Client Svcs)*

The Marketing Store (1)
1 Concorde Gate Suite 703, Toronto, M3C 3N6, ON, Canada
Tel.: (416) 583-3905
Web Site: http://www.themarketingstore.com
Brand Marketing & Promotional Services
N.A.I.C.S.: 541820
Carlos Garavito *(VP & Dir-Creative)*
Stephanie Berrie *(Acct Dir)*
Louie Gonzalez *(Dir-Fin & Acctg)*
Micheal Oliver *(Partner & Mgr)*

The Marketing Store (1)
17F One Island East 18 Westlands Road, Quarry Bay, China (Hong Kong)
Tel.: (852) 2880 8100
Web Site: http://www.tmsw.com
Emp.: 9
Brand Marketing & Promotional Services
N.A.I.C.S.: 541820

The Marketing Store (1)
Rua do Rocio 430, 04552-000, Sao Paulo, SP, Brazil
Tel.: (55) 11 3848 1733
Web Site: http://www.tmsw.com
Brand Marketing & Promotional Services
N.A.I.C.S.: 541820

The Marketing Store Worldwide (Europe) Limited (1)
16 Hatfields, Southwark, London, SE1 8DJ, United Kingdom
Tel.: (44) 20 7981 9300
Web Site:
  http://www.themarketingstore.co.uk
Sales Range: $50-74.9 Million
Brand Marketing & Promotional Services
N.A.I.C.S.: 541820
Neil Arnott *(Acct Dir)*
Jane Creaner-Glen *(Mgr-Recruitment)*
Lisa Bonney *(Mng Dir)*

THE MARLIN NETWORK, INC.
1200 E Woodhurst Dr, Springfield, MO 65804-4240
Tel.: (417) 885-4500   MO
Web Site: http://www.marlinco.com
Year Founded: 1985
Sales Range: $10-24.9 Million
Emp.: 70
N.A.I.C.S.: 541810
Michael M. Stelzer *(Pres-Marlin)*
Todd Carroll *(Controller)*
Matt Rose *(Dir-Creative)*

Subsidiaries:

Deep (1)
4350 S National B 110, Springfield, MO 65810
Tel.: (417) 887-7446
Sales Range: $10-24.9 Million
Emp.: 35
N.A.I.C.S.: 541810
Phil Daniels *(Pres)*
Patrick McWhirt *(Dir-Creative)*
Dennis Marlin *(Pres-Network)*

Marlin (1)
1200 E Woodhurst Dr Bldg V, Springfield, MO 65804
Tel.: (417) 887-7446
Web Site: http://www.marlinco.com
Sales Range: $10-24.9 Million
Emp.: 40
N.A.I.C.S.: 541810
Michael Seltzer *(Pres)*
Matt Rose *(Creative Dir)*
Tom Kujawa *(Dir-Acct Svcs)*

iMarlin (1)
1200 E Woodhurst Bldg V, Springfield, MO 65804
Tel.: (417) 885-4500
Rev.: $1,000,000
Emp.: 9
N.A.I.C.S.: 541810
Jason Stanley *(Project Mgr)*
Jeff Kern *(Sr Dir-Art)*
Tom Rankin *(Dir-Tech)*
Tim Bade *(Partner-Creative Svcs)*
Stacey Peek *(Acct Supvr)*

THE MARTIN GROUP LLC
477 Main St, Buffalo, NY 14203
Tel.: (716) 853-2757
Web Site:
  http://www.martingroupmarketing.com
Year Founded: 2001
Emp.: 50
Advertising Agencies
N.A.I.C.S.: 541810
Tod Martin *(Founder, Pres & Chief Creative Officer)*
Lisa Strock *(Sr VP & Mng Dir-Buffalo)*
Chase Martin *(Coord-Traffic)*
Tim Coppola *(CFO & COO)*
John Jiloty *(VP-Social Media & Content Mktg)*
Rosemary Witschard *(Mgr-Traffic)*
Andrew Henesey *(Dir-Art)*
Victoria Kopra *(Coord-Ops)*
Meg Hunter *(Mgr-Bus Dev)*
Michael Tsanis *(VP & Dir-Creative)*
Dion Pender *(Sr VP, Mng Dir-Rochester & Exec Dir-Creative)*
Duane Bombard *(VP & Creative Dir)*
Jim Lynch *(VP & Dir-Media)*
Karen Higman *(VP-Strategic Initiatives)*
Kelli Putney *(Sr VP)*
Levi Neuland *(VP-Digital Strategy)*
Michael Prezioso *(VP-Ops)*

THE MARVEL GROUP, INC.
3843 W 43rd St, Chicago, IL 60632
Tel.: (773) 523-4804   IL
Web Site:
  http://www.marvelgroup.com
Year Founded: 1946
Sales Range: $10-24.9 Million
Emp.: 235
Office Furniture
N.A.I.C.S.: 337214
Mike Brock *(Mgr-Engrg)*

THE MARYJANE GROUP, INC.
910 16th St Ste 412, Denver, CO 80202
Tel.: (303) 835-8603   NV
Web Site:
  http://www.themaryjanegrp.com
Year Founded: 2012
Rev.: $609,113
Assets: $117,666
Liabilities: $863,655
Net Worth: ($745,989)
Earnings: ($2,680,584)
Emp.: 18
Fiscal Year-end: 04/30/15
Investment Services for Marijuana Development
N.A.I.C.S.: 523999
Joel Schneider *(Pres, CEO, CFO, Treas & Sec)*

THE MARYLAND & DELAWARE GROUP OF LONG & FOSTER
107 Williamsport Cir, Salisbury, MD 21804
Tel.: (443) 339-9200
Web Site:
  http://www.easternshorehomesolutions.com
Year Founded: 2014
Sales Range: $100-124.9 Million
Emp.: 18
Real Estate Investment Services
N.A.I.C.S.: 531390
Brandon Brittingham *(CEO)*

THE MASA CORPORATION
5445 Henneman Dr 2nd Fl, Norfolk, VA 23513
Tel.: (757) 855-3013
Web Site: http://www.masacorp.com
Year Founded: 1961
Sales Range: $10-24.9 Million
Emp.: 140
Paper Mill Services
N.A.I.C.S.: 322120
Tommy Frame *(Principal)*
Sam Adsit *(VP)*

THE MASSACHUSETTS LEGAL ASSISTANCE CORPORATION
7 Winthrop Sq Fl 2, Boston, MA 02110-1245
Tel.: (617) 391-5633   MA
Web Site: http://www.mlac.org
Year Founded: 1983
Sales Range: $10-24.9 Million
Emp.: 20
Law firm
N.A.I.C.S.: 541199
Danielle Hines-Graham *(Mgr-Ops)*
Donna Southwell *(Dir-Policy Analysis)*
Patricia Swansey *(Program Dir)*
Tobey Johnson *(Dir-IT)*
Lonnie A. Powers *(Exec Dir)*

THE MASTERLINK GROUP, INC.
601 Silveron Blvd Ste 200, Flower Mound, TX 75028
Tel.: (214) 323-2100   TX
Web Site: http://www.masterlink.com
Year Founded: 1995
Sales Range: $1-9.9 Million
Emp.: 15
Internet Marketing & Related Services
N.A.I.C.S.: 541613
Brenda Molloy *(VP)*
Donnie Clary *(Treas)*
Kady Bentley *(Project Mgr)*
Edward Frazier *(Pres)*

THE MASTERSON COMPANY, INC.
4023 W National Ave, Milwaukee, WI 53215
Tel.: (414) 647-1132

THE MATHWORKS, INC.

Web Site:
  http://www.mastersoncompany.com
Year Founded: 1848
Sales Range: $100-124.9 Million
Emp.: 150
Dessert Toppings Mfr
N.A.I.C.S.: 311999
Joe A. Masterson *(Chm & CEO)*
Irene Groh *(Dir-Customer Svcs)*

THE MATCO GROUP, INC.
320 N Jensen Rd, Vestal, NY 13850
Tel.: (607) 729-8973   NY
Year Founded: 1965
Emp.: 100
Holding Company
N.A.I.C.S.: 551112
Lawrence Davis *(CFO)*
James F. Matthews *(Pres & CEO)*

Subsidiaries:

American Board Companies, Inc. (1)
200 Stage Rd, Vestal, NY 13850-1609
Tel.: (607) 754-4054
Rev.: $13,500,000
Emp.: 4
Printed Circuit Boards
N.A.I.C.S.: 334412
James F. Matthews *(Chm, Pres & CEO)*

THE MATHER GROUP, LLC
353 N Clark St Ste 2775, Chicago, IL 60654
Tel.: (888) 537-1080
Web Site:
  http://www.themathergroup.com
Year Founded: 2011
Investment Management & Financial Planning
N.A.I.C.S.: 523999
Andy Byron *(Mng Dir-Wealth Mgmt)*
Dawn Cornwall *(Sr Dir-Client Svcs)*
Chris Behrens *(CEO)*
Joan Rockey *(CFO)*
Kate Demet *(CMO)*
Stephen Biggs *(Mng Dir & Head-Alternative Investments)*
Karla McAvoy *(Mng Dir-Wealth Mgmt)*
Stuart Evans *(Chief Compliance Officer)*

Subsidiaries:

HC Financial Advisors Inc. (1)
3685 Mt Diablo Blvd Ste 200, 94549, Lafayette, CA
Tel.: (925) 254-1023
Web Site: http://www.hcfinancial.com
Portfolio Management
N.A.I.C.S.: 523940
Peggy S. Cabaniss *(Pres)*

RPH Financial Services Inc. (1)
5109 Neola Rd, Stroudsburg, PA 18360
Tel.: (570) 992-1675
Investment Advice
N.A.I.C.S.: 523940

Resource Advisory Services Inc. (1)
2035 Lakeside Centre Way Ste 110, Knoxville, TN 37922-6593
Tel.: (865) 560-0140
Web Site: http://www.resourceadv.com
Investment Advice
N.A.I.C.S.: 523940
David Lewis *(Pres)*

THE MATHWORKS, INC.
3 Apple Hill Dr, Natick, MA 01760-2096
Tel.: (508) 647-7000   CA
Web Site: http://www.mathworks.com
Year Founded: 1984
Sales Range: $1-4.9 Billion
Emp.: 4,500
Develops & Supplies Technical Computing Software for Math
N.A.I.C.S.: 513210
Jack Little *(Co-Founder & Pres)*
Cleve Moler *(Co-Founder & Chm)*

Subsidiaries:

The MathWorks Australia Pty Ltd (1)
Level 6 Tower 2 475 Victoria Avenue,

THE MATHWORKS, INC.

U.S. PRIVATE

The Mathworks, Inc.—(Continued)

Chatswood, 2067, NSW, Australia
Tel.: (61) 286694700
Web Site: http://www.mathworks.com.au
Emp.: 20
Computer Programming Services
N.A.I.C.S.: 541511

The MathWorks Korea, LLC (1)
13F DukMyung Building 625 Teheran-ro, Gangnam-gu, Seoul, 135-741, Korea (South)
Tel.: (82) 260065100
Web Site: http://www.mathworks.co.kr
Software Development Services
N.A.I.C.S.: 541511

The MathWorks S.A.S. (1)
20 Rue Troyon, Sevres, 92316, France
Tel.: (33) 141146714
Web Site: http://www.mathworks.fr
Computer Programming Services
N.A.I.C.S.: 541511

THE MATRIX COMPANIES
644 Linn St Ste 900, Cincinnati, OH 45203
Tel.: (513) 351-1222 OH
Web Site: http://www.matrixtpa.com
Year Founded: 2000
Sales Range: $1-9.9 Million
Emp.: 50
Management Consulting Services
N.A.I.C.S.: 541611
Brent Messmer (Pres & CEO)
Jessica Esterkamp (VP-Corp Dev)
Laurie Ritter (Mgr-Client Relations)
Courtney Miller (Mgr-Bus Dev)
Staci Farmer (Dir-Mktg)
Alicia Bishop (Mgr-Bus Dev)

THE MATTHEWS GROUP INC.
2900 State Rte 9, Ballston Spa, NY 12020-3904
Tel.: (518) 584-2400 NY
Web Site:
  http://www.matthewsbuses.com
Year Founded: 1985
Rev.: $34,549,543
Emp.: 169
Provider of Investment Services
N.A.I.C.S.: 423110
Guy R. Matthews (Dir-Sls)

Subsidiaries:

Matthews Buses Inc. (1)
2900 Rte 9, Ballston Spa, NY 12020-3904 (100%)
Tel.: (518) 584-2400
Web Site: http://www.matthewsbuses.com
Sales Range: $10-24.9 Million
Emp.: 35
Provider of Automobile Services
N.A.I.C.S.: 423110
Glenn Matthews (Pres)

Rifled Air Conditioning (1)
2810 Earham Pl, High Point, NC 27263
Tel.: (336) 434-1000
Web Site: http://www.rifledair.com
Sales Range: $10-24.9 Million
Emp.: 35
Provider of Automobile Services
N.A.I.C.S.: 811121
Bradley J. Matthews (Pres)
Cheyne Rauber (Gen Mgr)
Dicky Campbell (Dir-Ops)
Carl Johnson (Mgr-Production)
Harry Rushbrook (Mgr-Ops)

THE MAYOR'S FUND TO ADVANCE NEW YORK CITY
253 Broadway 6th Fl, New York, NY 10007
Tel.: (212) 788-7794 NY
Year Founded: 1994
Sales Range: $50-74.9 Million
Emp.: 20
Financial Management Services
N.A.I.C.S.: 813920
Darren Bloch (Exec Dir)

THE MAZER CORPORATION
6680 Poe Ave, Dayton, OH 45414-2528
Tel.: (937) 264-2600 OH
Web Site: http://www.mazer.com
Year Founded: 1964
Sales Range: $10-24.9 Million
Emp.: 125
Educational Publishing Services
N.A.I.C.S.: 513199
Jack Neal (Mgr-Natl Sls)
David Mazer (CEO)

THE MAZEROV GROUP
5675 DTC Blvd Ste 260, Greenwood Village, CO 80111
Tel.: (303) 741-2369
Sales Range: Less than $1 Million
Emp.: 15
Advertising, Digital/Interactive, Public Relations
N.A.I.C.S.: 541810
Bob Mazerov (Pres)

THE MCBURNEY CORPORATION
1650 Intl Ct, Norcross, GA 30093
Tel.: (770) 925-7100 GA
Web Site: http://www.mcburney.com
Year Founded: 1911
Sales Range: $25-49.9 Million
Emp.: 150
Supplier of Industrial Engineering Construction & Steam Boilers
N.A.I.C.S.: 238220
Blake McBurney (Pres)
Willard B. McBurney Jr. (Chm)

THE MCC GROUP, LLC
3001 17th St, Metairie, LA 70002-3805
Tel.: (504) 833-8291 LA
Web Site: http://www.mccgroup.com
Year Founded: 1958
Sales Range: $50-74.9 Million
Emp.: 350
Mechanical, Electrical & Plumbing Construction Services
N.A.I.C.S.: 238220
Carol T. Lagasse (Exec VP)
Joseph A. Jaeger Jr. (Chm, Pres & CEO)
Glenn Perilloux (VP-Preconstruction)
Randy Simon (VP-Estimating)
Thomas W. Boudreaux (VP-Engrg)

Subsidiaries:

MCC Electric, L.L.C. (1)
3001 17th St, Metairie, LA 70002
Tel.: (504) 833-8291
Electrical Contractor
N.A.I.C.S.: 238210

MCC Mechanical LLC (1)
3001 17th St, Metairie, LA 70002
Tel.: (504) 833-8291
Web Site: http://www.mccgroup.com
Sales Range: $75-99.9 Million
Mechanical, Electrical & Plumbing Services
N.A.I.C.S.: 238220
Thomas W. Boudreaux (VP-Engrg)
Glenn Perilloux (VP-Construction)

MCC Mechanical of the Carolinas, L.L.C. (1)
9233 Forsyth Park Dr, Charlotte, NC 28273
Tel.: (704) 817-1800
Sales Range: $10-24.9 Million
Emp.: 100
Mechanical Engineering Services
N.A.I.C.S.: 541330

Division (Domestic):

MCC Mechanical of the Carolinas, L.L.C. - Benner & Fields Division (2)
813 Winston St, High Point, NC 27405
Tel.: (336) 373-1654
Mechanical Engineering Services
N.A.I.C.S.: 541330

MCC Services, L.L.C. (1)
3001 17th St, Metairie, LA 70002
Tel.: (504) 833-5901
Web Site: http://www.mccservices.com
Mechanical Engineering Services
N.A.I.C.S.: 541330
Cindy Mauterer (Mgr-Bus Unit)
Cyrus Barnhill (Mgr-Bus Unit)

THE MCCARRON GROUP
120 NW 9th Ave Ste 206, Portland, OR 97209
Tel.: (503) 432-4621
Web Site:
  http://www.mccarrongroup.com
Year Founded: 1998
Sales Range: $1-9.9 Million
Emp.: 3
Health & Medical Consulting Services
N.A.I.C.S.: 541618
Kathleen A. McCarron (Founder & CEO)

THE MCFARLAND GROUP, INC.
39 Point Elkhart Dr, Elkhart Lake, WI 53020-1836
Tel.: (262) 786-5891
Year Founded: 1978
Sales Range: $25-49.9 Million
Emp.: 8
Agriculture, Business-To-Business, Retail, Sports Marketing
N.A.I.C.S.: 541613
Harold Strohmeier (Mgr-Bus Dev)
Mike McFarland (Pres)
Andy Mansfield (Dir-Creative)
Annie McFadzen (Dir-Media)

THE MCGILL CORPORATION
1 Mission Pk, Groveport, OH 43125-1149
Tel.: (614) 829-1200
Web Site:
  http://www.unitedmcgill.com
Year Founded: 1986
Sales Range: $25-49.9 Million
Emp.: 500
Provider of Sheet Metalwork Services
N.A.I.C.S.: 332322
James D. McGill (Chm & Pres)

Subsidiaries:

McGill Airclean Corp. (1)
1779 Refugee Rd, Columbus, OH 43207-2119
Tel.: (614) 829-1200
Web Site: http://www.mcgillairclean.com
Sales Range: $10-24.9 Million
Emp.: 85
Provider of Air Purification Services
N.A.I.C.S.: 333413
James D. McGill (Pres)

McGill Airflow Corp. (1)
1 Mission Park, Groveport, OH 43125-1149
Tel.: (614) 829-1200
Web Site: http://www.mcgillairflow.com
Sales Range: $10-24.9 Million
Emp.: 2
Provider of Sheet Metalwork Services
N.A.I.C.S.: 332322

McGill Airpressure Corp. (1)
One Mission Pk, Groveport, OH 43125
Tel.: (614) 829-1200
Web Site: http://www.mcgillairpressure.com
Sales Range: $10-24.9 Million
Emp.: 35
Provider of Boiler Shop Services
N.A.I.C.S.: 541330
Jim McGill (Pres)

McGill Airseal LLC (1)
2400 Fairwood Ave, Columbus, OH 43207-2708
Tel.: (614) 829-1200
Web Site: http://www.mcgillairseal.com
Sales Range: $10-24.9 Million
Emp.: 10
Provider of Chemicals & Allied Products services

N.A.I.C.S.: 424690
Brad McGill (Gen Mgr)

United McGill Corporation (1)
1 Mission Park, Groveport, OH 43125-1100
Tel.: (614) 829-1200
Web Site: http://www.themcgillcorp.com
Sales Range: $10-24.9 Million
Emp.: 75
Provider of Sheet Metalwork Services
N.A.I.C.S.: 332322
James D. McGill (Pres)
Kathy Cauley (Dir-Personnel Svcs)

Subsidiary (Domestic):

McGill AirSilence LLC (2)
2400 Fairwood Ave, Columbus, OH 43207
Tel.: (614) 829-1200
Web Site: http://www.mcgillairsilence.com
Acoustical Engineering Services
N.A.I.C.S.: 541330

Plant (Domestic):

United McGill Corporation - Bennington Plant (2)
452 Harwood Hill Rd, Bennington, VT 05201
Tel.: (802) 442-1900
Sheet Metal Work Mfg
N.A.I.C.S.: 332322

United McGill Corporation - Fountain Inn Plant (2)
300 Dale Dr, Fountain Inn, SC 29644
Tel.: (864) 241-1535
Sheet Metal Work Mfg
N.A.I.C.S.: 332322

United McGill Corporation - Grand Prairie Plant (2)
2100 N Highway 360 No 709B, Grand Prairie, TX 75050
Tel.: (972) 606-8553
Sheet Metal Work Mfg
N.A.I.C.S.: 332322

United McGill Corporation - Grinnell Plant (2)
900 Pinder Ave, Grinnell, IA 50112
Tel.: (641) 236-1580
Sheet Metal Work Mfg
N.A.I.C.S.: 332322

United McGill Corporation - Hillsboro Plant (2)
206 Pecos St, Hillsboro, TX 76645
Tel.: (254) 580-1680
Sheet Metal Work Mfg
N.A.I.C.S.: 332322

United McGill Corporation - San Antonio Plant (2)
10615 Perrin Beitel Rd No 702A, San Antonio, TX 78217
Tel.: (210) 599-1957
Sheet Metal Work Mfg
N.A.I.C.S.: 332322

United McGill Corporation - Stockton Plant (2)
1747 E Dr Martin Luther King Jr Blvd, Stockton, CA 95205
Tel.: (209) 466-2351
Sheet Metal Work Mfg
N.A.I.C.S.: 332322

THE MCGRAW GROUP
3601 Haven Ave, Menlo Park, CA 94025
Tel.: (650) 780-4800 CA
Web Site:
  http://www.mcgrawgroup.com
Sales Range: $50-74.9 Million
Emp.: 200
Insurance Services
N.A.I.C.S.: 524210
Michael J. McGraw (CEO)
Tim Summers (VP)
Brian McSweeney (Pres)
Ted Longworth (Mgr-Product Dev)

Subsidiaries:

Western Service Contract Corp. (1)
3601 Haven Ave, Menlo Park, CA 94025 (100%)

Tel.: (650) 780-4800
Web Site: http://www.psic-onespot.com
Sales Range: $50-74.9 Million
Emp.: 125
Warranty Insurance, Product; Except Automobile
N.A.I.C.S.: 524128

Affiliate (Domestic):

McGraw Insurance, Inc. (2)
2200 Geng Rd Ste 200, Palo Alto, CA 94303
Tel.: (800) 303-5000
Web Site: http://www.mcgrawgroup.com
Sales Range: $1-9.9 Million
Emp.: 100
Insurance Agencies & Brokerages
N.A.I.C.S.: 524210
Michael J. McGraw (CEO)

Subsidiary (Domestic):

Pacific Speciality Insurance Company (2)
3601 Haven Ave, Menlo Park, CA 94025
Tel.: (650) 780-4800
Web Site: http://www.psic-onespot.com
Sales Range: $50-74.9 Million
Emp.: 100
Insurance Agents & Brokers
N.A.I.C.S.: 524210
Michael J. McGraw (CEO)

THE MCGUIRE GROUP, INC.
560 Delaware Ave Ste 400, Buffalo, NY 14202
Tel.: (716) 826-2010   NY
Web Site: http://www.mcguiregroup.com
Year Founded: 1998
Sales Range: $10-24.9 Million
Emp.: 170
Nursing Care Facilities Operator
N.A.I.C.S.: 623110
Michael Cronmiller (Treas & VP)
Melissa Graziano (Dir-Rehabilitative Svcs)
Susan Grigg (VP-Health Care Svcs)
F. James McGuire (Pres & CEO)
Anne Marie Smith (Dir-HR)

THE MCINTYRE COMPANY
872 Towne Center Dr, Pomona, CA 91767-5902
Tel.: (909) 598-9744
Web Site: http://www.themcintyrecompany.com
Rev.: $15,000,000
Emp.: 57
Structural Steel Erection
N.A.I.C.S.: 238120
E. Roger McIntyre (Mng Partner)

THE MCKENZIE RIVER CORPORATION
2 Central Ave Ste 1, Whitefish, MT 59937
Tel.: (415) 362-7822   CA
Year Founded: 1987
Holding Company; Breweries Owner, Operator & Beer Whslr
N.A.I.C.S.: 551112
J. Minott Wessinger (Mng Partner)

Subsidiaries:

Great Northern Brewing Company (1)
2 Central Ave Ste 1, Whitefish, MT 59937
Tel.: (406) 863-1000
Web Site: http://www.greatnorthernbrewing.com
Sales Range: $1-9.9 Million
Emp.: 35
Brewery, Beer Whslr & Pub
N.A.I.C.S.: 312120
Marcus Duffey (Partner & Gen Mgr)
Anthony Lansing (Mgr-Sls-Montana)
Uwe Schaefer (Controller)
Thomas Sierra (Head-Ops)

THE MCLAUGHLIN COMPANY
9210 Corporate Blvd Ste 250, Rockville, MD 20850
Tel.: (202) 293-5566
Web Site: http://www.mclaughlin-online.com
Year Founded: 1929
Rev.: $21,000,000
Emp.: 20
Provider of Insurance Services
N.A.I.C.S.: 524210
Brenda Mantz (Pres-Risk Mgmt & Exec VP)
John T. Pappas (Chm)

THE MCRAE AGENCY
5150 E Orchid Ln, Paradise Valley, AZ 85253
Tel.: (480) 990-0282   AZ
Web Site: http://www.mcraeagency.com
Year Founded: 1995
Full-Service Marketing Communications
N.A.I.C.S.: 541820
Beth McRae (Pres)

THE MEADOWS STANDARDBRED OWNERS ASSOCIATION
200 Racetrack Rd, Meadow Lands, PA 15347
Tel.: (724) 228-3644   PA
Web Site: http://www.themsoa.com
Year Founded: 1977
Sales Range: $1-9.9 Million
Emp.: 2
Harness Racing Promotion Services
N.A.I.C.S.: 711310
Kim Hankins (Exec Dir)
Lori Romanetti (Sec)
Tim Twaddle (Treas)
Richard Gillock (Pres)
Jack B. Piatt II (VP)

THE MEAT MARKET INC.
454 W Alluvial Ave, Fresno, CA 93650-1160
Tel.: (559) 436-6688   CA
Web Site: http://www.themeatmarket.com
Year Founded: 1976
Sales Range: $10-24.9 Million
Emp.: 40
Retail of Meats & Meat Products
N.A.I.C.S.: 424470
Jeff Aivazian (Owner)
Vince Barger (Gen Mgr)

THE MEDIA CREW
12597 Walsingham Rd Ste 2, Largo, FL 33774
Tel.: (727) 517-3839
Web Site: http://www.themediacrew.com
Year Founded: 1999
Sales Range: $1-9.9 Million
Emp.: 4
Online Marketing & Advertising Services
N.A.I.C.S.: 541810
Nick Foley (CEO)

THE MEDICAL CENTER COMPANY
2250 Circle Dr, Cleveland, OH 44106
Tel.: (216) 368-4256   OH
Web Site: http://www.mcco.org
Year Founded: 1932
Sales Range: $25-49.9 Million
Emp.: 41
Electric Power Distr
N.A.I.C.S.: 221122
Todd Gadawski (VP-Ops & Construction)
Bradley Bond (Chm)

Robert C. Brown (Vice Chm)
Frank DiTomaso (Supvr-Distr)
John Bradley (Pres)

THE MEDICAL SUPPLY DEPOT, INC.
1702 47th St, Brooklyn, NY 11204
Tel.: (718) 785-5791
Web Site: http://www.medicalsupplydepot.com
Year Founded: 2005
Sales Range: $1-9.9 Million
Emp.: 3
Medical Equipment Distr
N.A.I.C.S.: 423450
Meir Tsinman (Owner)

THE MEG & BENNETT GOODMAN FAMILY FOUNDATION
165 Township Line Rd Ste 150, Jenkintown, PA 19046
Tel.: (215) 277-3010   PA
Year Founded: 2002
Sales Range: $10-24.9 Million
Charitable Services
N.A.I.C.S.: 813211
Bennett Goodman (Pres)
Andrea Rush (Sec)
Margaret A. Bandera (Treas)

THE MENDED HEARTS, INC.
8150 N Central Expy Ste M2248, Dallas, TX 75206
Tel.: (214) 206-9259   TX
Web Site: http://www.mendedhearts.org
Year Founded: 1951
Sales Range: $1-9.9 Million
Emp.: 12
Heart Patient Wellness Services
N.A.I.C.S.: 813212
Donnette Smith (Pres)
Millie Henn (Exec VP)
Randy Gay (Treas)
Patrick Farrant (VP)

THE MENKITI GROUP
3401 8th St NE, Washington, DC 20017
Tel.: (202) 243-7777
Web Site: http://www.menkitigroup.com
Year Founded: 2004
Sales Range: $1-9.9 Million
Emp.: 35
Real Estate Business Services
N.A.I.C.S.: 531120
Bo Menkiti (Founder & CEO)
Kymber Lovett-Menkiti (Dir-Sls)
Mary Hodges (Dir-Mktg)
Yohance Fuller (VP-Dev & Asset Mgmt)
Jennifer Motruk (Dir-Corp Mktg & Comm)
Feras Qumseya (Exec VP-Dev)
Michael McElaney (VP-Comml Real Estate)

THE MENNEL MILLING COMPANY
319 S Vine St, Fostoria, OH 44830-2315
Tel.: (419) 435-8151
Web Site: http://www.mennel.com
Year Founded: 1958
Sales Range: $75-99.9 Million
Emp.: 600
Provider of Farm Supply Services
N.A.I.C.S.: 311211
Donald L. Mennel (Chm)
D. Ford Mennel (Pres)
Scott Osborne (VP-Innovation)

Subsidiaries:

Class Eight Truck Repair Inc. (1)
22250 State Rte 12, Fostoria, OH 44830-9680
Tel.: (419) 435-8725
Web Site: http://www.mennelmilling.com
Sales Range: $10-24.9 Million
Emp.: 9
Provider of Repair Services
N.A.I.C.S.: 811111
Bud Wely (Mgr-Svc)

Foraker Elevator (1)
9603 County Rd Ste 89, Alger, OH 45812-9608
Tel.: (419) 675-2655
Web Site: http://www.forakerelevator.com
Emp.: 3
Wheat Farming Services
N.A.I.C.S.: 111140
Keith Van Hoose (Mgr)
Mitch Marshall (Office Mgr)

MMC Transport of Virginia, Inc. (1)
5185 Benois Rd, Roanoke, VA 24018
Tel.: (540) 776-6201
Emp.: 45
General Freight Trucking Services
N.A.I.C.S.: 484121
James Elkins (Gen Mgr)

MMC Transport, Inc. (1)
550 W 4th St, Fostoria, OH 44830
Tel.: (419) 436-1274
General Freight Trucking Services
N.A.I.C.S.: 484121

The Mennel Milling Company - Bucyrus Flour Mill (1)
970 Nevada Rd, Bucyrus, OH 44820
Tel.: (419) 562-7565
Emp.: 10
Flour Mfr
N.A.I.C.S.: 311211
Kevin G. Mohr (Plant Mgr)

The Mennel Milling Company - Valley Grain Division (1)
4 Railroad St, Kingston, OH 45644
Tel.: (740) 642-2041
Web Site: http://www.valleygrain.net
Wheat Farming Services
N.A.I.C.S.: 111140
Josh Gatewood (Mgr)

The Mennel Milling Company of Illinois Inc. (1)
415 E Main St, Mount Olive, IL 62069-1709
Tel.: (217) 999-2161
Web Site: http://www.mennelmilling.com
Sales Range: $10-24.9 Million
Emp.: 10
Flour Mfr
N.A.I.C.S.: 311211

The Mennel Milling Company of Indiana Inc. (1)
2602 W Third St, Mexico, IN 46958 (100%)
Tel.: (765) 985-3530
Web Site: http://www.mennelmilling.com
Sales Range: $10-24.9 Million
Emp.: 7
Provider of Farm Supply Services
N.A.I.C.S.: 493130
Robert Cain (Gen Mgr)

The Mennel Milling Company of Michigan Inc. (1)
301 S Mill St, Dowagiac, MI 49047-1445 (100%)
Tel.: (269) 782-5175
Web Site: http://www.mannel.com
Sales Range: $10-24.9 Million
Emp.: 20
Provider of Farm Supply Services
N.A.I.C.S.: 311211
Ted Tyrakowski (Plant Mgr)

The Mennel Milling Company of Virginia, Inc. (1)
5185 Benois Rd, Roanoke, VA 24018-4910
Tel.: (540) 776-6201
Web Site: http://www.mennel.com
Sales Range: $10-24.9 Million
Emp.: 50
Farm Supply Services; Grain
N.A.I.C.S.: 311211
D. Ford Mennel (Pres)

Division (Domestic):

Old Dominion Grain Corporation (2)

THE MENNEL MILLING COMPANY

The Mennel Milling Company—(Continued)
3100 Southern Ave, West Point, VA 23181
Tel.: (804) 843-2922
Web Site: http://www.mennel.com
Grain Distr
N.A.I.C.S.: 424510

Troy Elevator, Inc. (1)
2600 N Dixie Hwy, Troy, OH 45373
Tel.: (937) 335-8334
Web Site: http://www.troyelevator.com
Emp.: 8
Wheat Farming Services
N.A.I.C.S.: 111140
Dianna Medley (Office Mgr)

THE MENTAL HEALTH CENTER OF GREATER MANCHESTER
2 Wall St 4th Fl, Manchester, NH 03103
Tel.: (603) 668-4111
Web Site: http://www.mhcgm.org
Sales Range: $10-24.9 Million
Emp.: 370
Behavioral Healthcare Services
N.A.I.C.S.: 621420
Quentin Turnbull (Chief Medical Officer & VP)
Paul Michaud (CFO & VP)
William Rider (Pres & CEO)

THE MENTOR LUMBER & SUPPLY CO., INC.
7180 N Ctr St, Mentor, OH 44060-4940
Tel.: (440) 255-8814 OH
Web Site:
  http://www.mentorlumber.com
Year Founded: 1922
Sales Range: $25-49.9 Million
Emp.: 150
Lumber & Building Supplier
N.A.I.C.S.: 423310
Reed Martin (Pres)

THE MENTOR NETWORK
313 Congress St 5th Fl, Boston, MA 02210-1218
Tel.: (617) 790-4800 IL
Web Site:
  http://www.thementornetwork.com
Year Founded: 1980
Sales Range: $25-49.9 Million
Emp.: 150
Health Services
N.A.I.C.S.: 624190
Dwight D. Robson (Chief Pub Strategy & Mktg Officer)
Denis Holler (CFO)
Edward M. Murphy (Chm)
Bruce F. Nardella (Pres & CEO)
Linda DeRenzo (Chief Legal Officer)
Gerry Morrissey (Chief Quality Officer)
Jeffrey Cohen (CIO)
Jim Ashby (Pres & CEO-Care Meridian)
William Duffy (Pres-Neuro Restorative)
Jen Bligh (VP-Fin Plng & Analysis)
Joy Kruppa (VP-Org Dev & Talent Mgmt)
Jon Fisher (VP-Ops & Community Support Svcs)

THE MERCHANTS NATIONAL BANK
100 North High St, Hillsboro, OH 45133
Tel.: (937) 393-1993 OH
Web Site:
  http://www.merchantsnat.com
Year Founded: 1879
Sales Range: $25-49.9 Million
Emp.: 136
Commericial Banking

N.A.I.C.S.: 522110
James Evans (Pres)
Subsidiaries:
Citizens Independent Bancorp, Inc. (1)
188 W Main St, Logan, OH 43138
Tel.: (740) 385-8561
Web Site: http://www.tcbol.com
Rev.: $9,448,000
Assets: $191,196,000
Liabilities: $172,291,000
Net Worth: $18,905,000
Earnings: ($194,000)
Emp.: 55
Fiscal Year-end: 12/31/2017
Bank Holding Company
N.A.I.C.S.: 551111
James V. Livesay (CFO & Exec VP)

Subsidiary (Domestic):
Citizens Bank of Logan (2)
188 W Main St, Logan, OH 43138
Tel.: (740) 385-8561
Web Site: http://www.tcbol.com
Emp.: 40
Banking Services
N.A.I.C.S.: 522110
Donald P. Wood (Chm)
James V. Livesay (CFO & Exec VP)
Daniel C. Fischer (Pres & CEO)
Brian Ogle (Sr VP)
Carol Goss (VP)
Darren Blake (CTO & Sr VP)
Greg Vermillion (Sr VP)
Kelly Lemon (VP)
Kory Horton (VP)
Mark Fuller (VP)
Mary Wilson (VP-Private Banking & Customer Svc)
Paula Baker (Sr VP-Retail Ops & Dir-HR)

THE MERCO GROUP INC.
7711 N 81st St, Milwaukee, WI 53223-3847
Tel.: (414) 365-2600
Web Site: http://www.generalpet.com
Year Founded: 1989
Sales Range: $10-24.9 Million
Emp.: 250
Provider of Medical & Dental Services
N.A.I.C.S.: 424990
Erwin Merar (Chm & CEO)
David Merar (Pres)
Bob Merar (VP)

THE MERIDIAN GROUP
575 Lynnhaven Pkwy 3rd Fl, Virginia Beach, VA 23452-7350
Tel.: (757) 340-7425 VA
Web Site:
  http://www.themeridiangroup.com
Year Founded: 1980
Rev.: $33,000,000
Emp.: 50
Fiscal Year-end: 12/30/04
N.A.I.C.S.: 541810
Joseph Takach (Founder & CEO)
Rick Mytych (Dir-Creative Consumer)
David Stearns (VP & Leader-Consumer Team)
Becky Naujoks (Dir-Media)
Elizabeth Lester (Pres-Launch Interactive Team Lead)
Shane Webb (Art Dir)
Terry Kelley (VP)
Erin Hagee (Acct Coord)
Ayla Terzel (PR Counselor)
David Watson (Assoc Art Dir & Production Mgr)
Barbara Windham (Acct Exec)
Jasmine Stark (Acct Coord)

THE METAL WARE CORP.
1700 Monroe St, Two Rivers, WI 54241-2928
Web Site: http://www.nesco.com
Electric Housewares & Appliances Mfr & Marketer

N.A.I.C.S.: 335210
Don Kozlowski (COO & Exec VP)
Tina Brouchoud (Coord-Shipping)
Tim Umphlett (Mgr-Pur)
Darlene Schmitz (VP-Sls & Mktg)
Mike Berger (VP-Sls & Mktg)
Subsidiaries:
Metal Ware (1)
1700 Monroe St, Two Rivers, WI 54241-2928
Tel.: (920) 793-1000
Web Site: http://www.nesco.com
Sales Range: $10-24.9 Million
Emp.: 90
Injection & Compression Molding of Thermoplastic
N.A.I.C.S.: 335210

Nesco American Harvest Inc. (1)
1700 Monroe St, Two Rivers, WI 54241-2928
Tel.: (920) 793-1368
Web Site: http://www.nesco.com
Sales Range: $10-24.9 Million
Household Cooking Appliances Mfr & Marketer
N.A.I.C.S.: 335210

THE METHODIST HOSPITALS, INC.
600 Grant St, Gary, IN 46402
Tel.: (219) 886-4000 IN
Web Site:
  http://www.methodisthospitals.org
Year Founded: 1941
Sales Range: $350-399.9 Million
Emp.: 2,755
Health Care Srvices
N.A.I.C.S.: 622110
Wright Alcorn (VP-Ops)
Alex Horvath (VP-Mktg & HR)
Matthew Doyle (Pres & CEO)
James M. Kirchner (VP-Physician Integration)
Allen Harrison (CEO-San Antonio)
Jim Renneker (Chief Nursing Officer & VP)
Sheila Cook (Asst VP)
Trischa Turner (Asst VP)
Raquel Prendkowski (Asst VP-Patient Care Svcs-Northlake Campus)
Stephany Husemann (Dir-Rehabilitation Svcs)
Lauren Trumbo (CFO & VP-Fin)

THE METROHEALTH FOUNDATION, INC.
2500 Metrohealth Dr, Cleveland, OH 44109
Tel.: (216) 778-5665
Web Site:
  https://www.metrohealth.org
Year Founded: 1954
Health Care Srvices
N.A.I.C.S.: 621610

THE METROPOLITAN DISTRICT
555 Main St, Hartford, CT 06103
Tel.: (860) 278-7850
Web Site: http://www.themdc.com
Year Founded: 1929
Sales Range: $25-49.9 Million
Emp.: 526
Water Utility
N.A.I.C.S.: 221310
John M. Zinzarella (CFO)
Scott W. Jellison (CEO)
Maureen Magnan (Vice Chm)

THE METROPOLITAN MUSEUM OF ART
1000 5th Ave, New York, NY 10028-0198
Tel.: (212) 535-7710 NY
Web Site:
  https://www.metmuseum.org

Year Founded: 1870
Sales Range: $350-399.9 Million
Art Museum
N.A.I.C.S.: 712110
Harold Holzer (Sr VP-Public Affairs)
Sharon Cott (Gen Counsel, Sec & Sr VP)
Daniel H. Weiss (Pres & CEO)
Ken Weine (Chief Comm Officer)
Daniel Brodsky (Chm)
Nancy Chilton (Chief Comm Officer-Costume Institute)
Lavita McMath Turner (Chief Diversity Officer)
Clyde B. Jones III (Sr VP-Institutional Advancement)

THE METROPOLITAN WATER DISTRICT OF SOUTHERN CALIFORNIA INC.
700 N Alameda St, Los Angeles, CA 90012-2944
Tel.: (213) 217-6000
Web Site: http://www.mwdh2o.com
Year Founded: 1928
Sales Range: $150-199.9 Million
Emp.: 2,000
Provider of Water Utility Services
N.A.I.C.S.: 221310
Fidencio M. Mares (Chief Admin Officer & Asst Gen Mgr-Interim)
Gary Breaux (CFO & Asst Gen Mgr)
Randy A. Record (Chm)
Gerald C. Riss (Officer-Acting-Ethics)
Marcia Scully (Gen Counsel)

THE MEYOCKS GROUP
6800 Lake Dr Ste 150, West Des Moines, IA 50266-2544
Tel.: (515) 225-1200 IA
Web Site:
  http://www.areyoubrave.com
Year Founded: 1989
Sales Range: $50-74.9 Million
Emp.: 30
Advetising Agency
N.A.I.C.S.: 541810
Doug Jeske (Pres-Agency)
Katie Schetzsle (Acct Coord)
Chad Baker (VP)
Deb Mitchell (Mgr-Acct Svc & Print Production)
Karlyn Nosbush (Mgr)
Rachel Allinson (Sr VP-Creative & Art)
Jennifer Drucker (Acct Exec)

THE MGS GROUP
3639 N Harding Ave, Chicago, IL 60618-4024
Tel.: (773) 583-5383
Year Founded: 1993
Sales Range: Less than $1 Million
Emp.: 3
N.A.I.C.S.: 541810
Maureen Gorman (Pres)

THE MICHAEL'S DEVELOPMENT COMPANY INC.
3 E Stow Rd, Marlton, NJ 08053-3118
Tel.: (856) 596-3008 NJ
Web Site:
  http://www.michaelsdevelopmentcompany.com
Sales Range: $75-99.9 Million
Emp.: 100
Real Estate Developers
N.A.I.C.S.: 237210
Joel B. Silver (Sr VP)
Whitney Weller (Sr VP)
Gary Buechler (Pres)
Kenneth Crawford (COO)
Ann O'Shea (Sr VP-Fin)
Joseph Weatherly (Reg VP-Acq & Emerging Markets)

COMPANIES

Greg Olson (VP-Design Dev & Construction Mgmt)
David LukensVP (VP-Underwriting)
Karen Seddon (Reg VP-Hawaii)
Michael Boettger (Reg VP-Northern California)

Subsidiaries:

Michaels Military Housing, LLC (1)
3 E Stow Rd, Marlton, NJ 08053-3108
Tel.: (856) 596-3008
Web Site: http://www.mmhusa.com
Residential Housing Rental & Leasing Services
N.A.I.C.S.: 531110
Ronald J. Hansen (Pres)

Prestige Building Company (1)
89 Redwing Road, Chatham, ME5 7TH, United Kingdom
Tel.: (44) 1634 318 781
Web Site: http://www.prestigebuildingcompanyltd.co.uk
Construction Management Services
N.A.I.C.S.: 236220
Russell Maynard (Sr VP)
Richard Armstrong (VP)

THE MICHAEL-ANN RUSSELL JEWISH COMMUNITY CENTER

Sanford L Ziff Campus 18900 NE 25th Ave, North Miami Beach, FL 33180
Tel.: (305) 932-4200 FL
Web Site: http://www.marjcc.org
Year Founded: 1987
Sales Range: $10-24.9 Million
Emp.: 590
Community Welfare Services
N.A.I.C.S.: 624190
Phil Solomon (Vice Chm-Fin)
Sami Shiro (Vice Chm-Long Range Plng)
Rick Mars (Vice Chm-Dev)
Paul Kruss (Chm)
Denise Tamir (Vice Chm-Program Svcs)
Derek Hodes (Vice Chm-Membership Mktg)
Mike Segal (Sec)
Ariel Bentata (Vice Chm-Dev)
Norman Leopold (Asst Sec)
Bill Ogene (Head-Tennis Pro)
Dany Weil (Dir-Health & Wellness)
Donna Tollefsen (Dir-Tennis)
Dror Gershoni (Dir-Children & Family Svcs)
Enid Cohn (Dir-Fin)
Francis Farberoff (Dir-JCC Soccer)
Galit Shemesh (Sr Dir-Programs)
Gena Bresler (Supvr-Maintenance)
Gloria Castano (Asst Dir-Aquatics)
Hellen Jena (Dir-Swim Gym Program)
Jenny Moscatel (Asst Dir-Camp & Coord-Maccabi Tzair)
Jenny Tettner-Gugig (Dir-Early Childhood Dept)
Jordan Bradley (Coord-Gymnastics)
Lillian Andron (Dir-J-CAT Educational)
Marci Kaplan (Dir-Gymnastics)
Marleny Rosemberg (Dir-Hebraica's Youth Movement)
Michael Andron (Dir-J-CAT Artistic)
Mijal Abramovich (Dir-Grp Exercise)
Neal Buchholz (Dir-Camp & Elementary Svcs)
Roger Weiger (Dir-Bamachol Academy)
Shai Habosha (Dir-Campus & Facilities Ops)
Simon Erdfrocht (Coord-Party Central)
Tammy Slimak (Asst Dir-Bamachol)
Tanya Copernik (Dir-Membership)
Michael Bauer (VP-Fin)
Alan Bittman (Pres)
Alan Sataloff (CEO)

THE MIDDLESEX CORPORATION

1 Spectacle Pond Rd, Littleton, MA 01460-1128
Tel.: (978) 742-4400
Web Site: http://www.middlesexco.com
Year Founded: 1972
Sales Range: $50-74.9 Million
Emp.: 350
Provider of Highway & Street Construction Services
N.A.I.C.S.: 237310
Robert W. Pereira (Chm)
Carl Gustenhoven (Mgr-Cost)
Darren Hohn (Dir-Corp Safety)
Dave Skerrett (Sr VP)
John Reddy (Mgr-Pur)
Tim Toth (Mgr-Risk)

THE MILES GROUP, LLC

630 5th Ave Ste 3210, New York, NY 10111
Tel.: (212) 899-6928
Web Site: http://www.miles-group.com
Sales Range: $1-9.9 Million
Executive Coaching & Advisory Services
N.A.I.C.S.: 611430
Nathan Bennett (Dir-Executive Education & Learning)
Taylor M. Griffin (COO & Partner)
Stephen A. Miles (CEO)
Endre Holen (Mng Dir)

THE MILFORD AGENCY

335 Madison Ave 14th Fl, New York, NY 10017
Tel.: (212) 350-2373
Year Founded: 1976
Rev.: $13,400,000
Emp.: 7
N.A.I.C.S.: 541810
Rick Silberman (Exec Dir)

THE MILL STEEL CO., INC.

5116 36th St SE, Grand Rapids, MI 49512-2010
Tel.: (616) 949-6700 MI
Web Site: http://www.millsteel.com
Year Founded: 1959
Sales Range: $25-49.9 Million
Emp.: 155
Metals Service Centers & Offices
N.A.I.C.S.: 423510
Carl Quenneville (Chief Comml Officer & Sr VP)
Pam Heglund (Chm & Pres)
Rob Vella (Partner)
Joe Poot (Sr VP)
Marc Rabitoy (CFO)

Subsidiaries:

Cleveland Metal Exchange Inc. (1)
3550 Lander Rd Ste 200, Pepper Pike, OH 44124
Tel.: (216) 464-4480
Web Site: https://www.clevelandmetal.com
Metal Service Centers & Other Metal Merchant Whslr
N.A.I.C.S.: 423510
Randy Horvat (CEO)
Ron Glazer (CFO)
Jeff Haas (Pres)

Prassas Metal Products, Inc. (1)
1411 W 190th St, Gardena, CA 90248
Tel.: (310) 217-4530
Web Site: http://www.pmpsteel.com
Coal, Mineral & Ore Merchant Whslr
N.A.I.C.S.: 423520
Jason Kim (VP-Pur)
Jim Prassas (CEO)

S & S Steel Services (1)
213 E 10th Dr Ste 4, Mesa, AZ 85210
Tel.: (480) 461-8730
Web Site: http://www.sssteelservice.com
Carbon Steel Products to Metal Stamping & Roll Forming Industries
N.A.I.C.S.: 332114

THE MILLARD GROUP

7301 N Cicero Ave, Lincolnwood, IL 60712
Tel.: (847) 674-4100 IL
Web Site: http://www.millardgroup.com
Year Founded: 1958
Sales Range: $700-749.9 Million
Emp.: 3,700
Office Buildings & Institutional Janitorial Services & Personnel Supply Services
N.A.I.C.S.: 561720
Lawrence B. Kugler (Pres & CEO)
Paul Millard (Co-Founder & Mng Partner)
Lamar Carter (Sr VP-Ops-Natl)
Rich Magid (CFO)
Craig Millard (Co-Founder)

Subsidiaries:

Millard Maintenance Service Company Inc. (1)
7301 N Cicero Ave, Lincolnwood, IL 60712-1613
Tel.: (847) 674-4100
Web Site: http://www.millardgroup.com
Building Maintenance Services
N.A.I.C.S.: 561720
Lawrence B. Kugler (Pres)

THE MILLCRAFT PAPER COMPANY INC.

6800 Grant Ave, Cleveland, OH 44105-5628
Tel.: (216) 441-5500 OH
Web Site: http://www.millcraft.com
Year Founded: 1920
Sales Range: $125-149.9 Million
Emp.: 65
Envelope & Writing Paper Converting & Commercial Printing
N.A.I.C.S.: 424110
Charles Mlakar (CEO)
Travis Mlakar (Pres)

Subsidiaries:

Deltacraft Paper & Converting Company (1)
99 Bud Mil Dr, Buffalo, NY 14206-1801
Tel.: (716) 856-1102
Web Site: http://www.deltacraft.com
Sales Range: $1-9.9 Million
Emp.: 30
Paper Products Converting
N.A.I.C.S.: 322299

Millcraft Paper - Cincinnati Sales & Distribution Center (1)
1900 River Rd, Cincinnati, OH 45204-1396
Tel.: (513) 244-2300
Web Site: http://www.millcraft.com
Printing & Writing Paper Merchant Whlsr
N.A.I.C.S.: 424110
Mike Davoran (VP & Reg Mgr)

TNT Papercraft, Inc. (1)
1200 Knowlton St, Cincinnati, OH 45223-1845
Tel.: (513) 681-2244
Web Site: http://www.tntpapercraft.com
Electronics Stores
N.A.I.C.S.: 449210
Donald S. Trautmann (Founder)

THE MILLENNIUM ALLIANCE LLC

475 Park Ave S 31st Fl, New York, NY 10016
Tel.: (212) 256-9890 NY
Web Site: http://www.mill-all.com
Year Founded: 2014
Sales Range: $10-24.9 Million
Emp.: 66
Education Management Services
N.A.I.C.S.: 611710

Alex Sobol (Founder & CEO)

THE MILLENNIUM GROUP

106 Apple St Ste 101 D, Tinton Falls, NJ 07724
Web Site: http://www.tmgofficeservices.com
Year Founded: 1984
Sales Range: $50-74.9 Million
Emp.: 1,475
Management Support Solutions
N.A.I.C.S.: 541618
Frank W. Farnacci (Exec VP)
Merrick Colson (Mng Dir-Strategic Accts)
Peggy Pojawa (Mgr-HR)
Brian Guerriere (Dir-Eastern Reg Ops)
Timothy P. Kerner (Pres)
Debra Alessi (Dir-HR)
Dermot Murphy Jr. (Dir-Quality)

THE MILLER GROUP

1516 S Bundy Dr Ste 200, Los Angeles, CA 90025
Tel.: (310) 442-0101 CA
Year Founded: 1990
Rev.: $10,000,000
Emp.: 20
Fiscal Year-end: 12/31/04
Advetising Agency
N.A.I.C.S.: 541810
Renee Miller (Pres & Dir-Creative)
Gary Bettman (VP)
Tina Montri (Acct Coord)
Renee Smith (Art Dir)
Duncan McLeod (Acct Exec)
Jeff Camp (Sr Acct Exec)

THE MILLER GROUP

101 Schilling Rd Ste 30, Hunt Valley, MD 21031-1104
Tel.: (410) 823-5020 MD
Year Founded: 1975
Sales Range: $50-74.9 Million
Emp.: 10
N.A.I.C.S.: 541810
Jack S. Miller (Pres)
Diane Miller (CFO)
John Eckard (Sr VP-Graphic Svcs)
Meghan Brody (CMO)
John McHue (Art Dir)
Alaina Wagner (Dir-Fin Analytics)

THE MILLWORK, CO.

607 Brazos St Ste C, Ramona, CA 92065-1884
Tel.: (760) 788-1533
Sales Range: $10-24.9 Million
Emp.: 16
Wood Products Mfr.
N.A.I.C.S.: 321999
Gregory J. Lucas (Pres)
Tammy Palmer (Office Mgr)

THE MINCO GROUP

1 Summit Sq 1st Fl Ste 100, Langhorne, PA 19047
Tel.: (262) 367-4421
Rev.: $20,000,000
Emp.: 160
Metal Stamping
N.A.I.C.S.: 332119
Joel Falk (Pres)

THE MINER-DEDERICK COMPANIES INC.

1532 Peden St, Houston, TX 77006-1030
Tel.: (713) 529-3001 TX

THE MINER-DEDERICK COMPANIES INC. U.S. PRIVATE

The Miner-Dederick Companies Inc.—(Continued)
Year Founded: 1947
Sales Range: $25-49.9 Million
Emp.: 125
Nonresidential Construction
N.A.I.C.S.: 236220
Dale Hoover (Treas & Sec)
Thad S. Miner (CEO)
Julia Odell (VP-Project Mgmt & Sr Project Mgr)
Arthur Miller (Dir-Safety & Mgr-Control Mgr)
Stephen Horvath (Dir-Field Ops)

THE MINNESOTA CHEMICAL COMPANY
2285 Hampden Ave, Saint Paul, MN 55114
Tel.: (651) 646-7521
Web Site:
http://www.minnesotachemical.com
Sales Range: $1-9.9 Million
Emp.: 27
Dry Cleaning Plant Equipment & Supplies
N.A.I.C.S.: 423850
Michael F. Baker (Owner)
Stephen Baker (Owner)
Dan Baker (Owner)

THE MITCHELL COMPANY, INC.
41 W Interstate 65 Svc Rd N, Mobile, AL 36608-1201
Tel.: (251) 380-2929   AL
Web Site:
http://www.mitchellcompany.com
Year Founded: 1967
Sales Range: $25-49.9 Million
Emp.: 200
Building Services
N.A.I.C.S.: 236117
John B. Saint (Pres & CEO)
Chester J. Stefan (Sr Exec VP)
Marvin Anderson (CFO)
Paul C. Wesch (Gen Counsel & Exec VP)
Ronnie Johnson (Sr VP-Comml Div)

THE MITRE CORPORATION
202 Burlington Rd, Bedford, MA 01730-1420
Tel.: (781) 271-2000   MA
Web Site: http://www.mitre.org
Year Founded: 1958
Sales Range: $1-4.9 Billion
Emp.: 7,887
Systems Engineering Research & Development
N.A.I.C.S.: 541715
Mark W. Kontos (Treas & Sr VP)
Richard J. Byrne (Sr VP-Programs & Tech-Center for Connected Govt)
Gary Gagnon (Chief Security Officer & VP-Cyber Strategy)
Jason F. Providakes (Pres & CEO)
Peter Sherlock (COO)
Julie Bowen (Sr VP)
John Wilson (VP-Program & Tech)
Julie Gravallese (VP-Programs & Tech Integration)
John Kreger (VP & Dir-Homeland Security Sys Engrg & Dev Institute)
Jay Schnitzer (CTO, Chief Medical Officer & Sr VP)
Lauren Libitz (Head-Pub Affairs)
Kerry Buckley (VP-Center for Advanced Aviation Sys Dev)
Eileen Boettcher (VP-Joint & Svcs Programs-Programs & Tech)
Douglas Robbins (VP-Air Force Programs)
Katharyn White (Sr VP/Gen Mgr-MITRE Public Sector)

Kathleen Federico (Chief HR & Strategic Comm Officer & Sr VP)
Wilson Wang (CFO & Sr VP)
Usha Chaudhary (Chief Transformation Officer & Sr VP-Corp Ops)
Laurie Giandomenico (Chief Acceleration Officer & Sr VP)
Charles Clancy (Sr VP/Gen Mgr-Mitre Labs)
Gus Bentivegna (VP-HR & Talent Enablement-McLean)
Gus Bentivenga (VP-HR & Talent Enablement)
Craig Ackerman (VP-Ops & Transformation)
Eliahu H. Niewood (VP-Air & Space Forces-MITRE Natl Security Sector)
Stephanie Turner (VP-Inclusion, Diversity & Social Innovation-McLean)
Wen Masters (VP-Cyber Technologies)
Keoki Jackson (Sr VP-MITRE Natl Security Sector & Gen Mgr-MITRE Natl Security Sector)
Cedric Sims (Sr VP-Enterprise Innovation & Integration)
Austin Wang (VP-Intelligence Center-Natl Security)
Deborah Youmans (CIO)

THE MITRE CORPORATION
7515 Colshire Dr, McLean, VA 22102
Tel.: (703) 269-8515
Web Site: https://www.mitre.org
Year Founded: 1958
Federal Fund Research & Development Services
N.A.I.C.S.: 541715

THE MODEL GROUP INC.
2170 Gilbert Ave Ste 300, Cincinnati, OH 45206
Tel.: (513) 559-0048
Web Site: http://www.modelgroup.net
Year Founded: 1978
Sales Range: $1-9.9 Million
Emp.: 50
Real Estate Brokerage Services
N.A.I.C.S.: 531210
Arthur J. Reckman (CEO)

THE MOM CORPS, INC.
#507 1205 Johnson Ferry Rd Ste 136, Marietta, GA 30068
Tel.: (678) 277-2789
Web Site: http://www.corpsteam.com
Year Founded: 2005
Talent Advisory, Search & Staffing Firm
N.A.I.C.S.: 561311
Allison O'Kelly (CEO)
Maria Goldsholl (COO)
Joanna Genser (CFO)

THE MONAHAN COMPANY
21321 Kelly Rd, Eastpointe, MI 48021
Tel.: (586) 774-3800   MI
Web Site:
http://www.themonahanco.com
Year Founded: 1922
Sales Range: $25-49.9 Million
Emp.: 15
Provider of Contracting Services
N.A.I.C.S.: 236220
Michael J. Monahan (Pres)
Michael P. Monahan (Controller)
W. Daniel Monahan (VP)

THE MONARCH BEVERAGE COMPANY, INC.
1123 Zonolite Rd Ste 10, Atlanta, GA 30306
Tel.: (404) 262-4040   MA
Web Site:
http://www.monarchbeverages.com

Year Founded: 1965
Sales Range: $75-99.9 Million
Emp.: 25
Mfr & Distr of Branded & Custom Beverage Products
N.A.I.C.S.: 312111
Jacques Bombal (Pres & CEO)

THE MONARCH HOTEL & CONFERENCE CENTER
12566 SE 93rd Ave, Clackamas, OR 97015-9760
Tel.: (503) 652-1515
Web Site:
http://www.monarchhotel.cc
Year Founded: 1985
Sales Range: $10-24.9 Million
Emp.: 150
Hotel & Motel Operating Services
N.A.I.C.S.: 721110
Paul Euler (Mgr)
Samuel Allen (Pres)

THE MONEY TREE INC.
114 S Broad St, Bainbridge, GA 39817
Tel.: (229) 246-6536   GA
Web Site:
http://www.themoneytreeinc.com
Sales Range: $10-24.9 Million
Emp.: 296
Debenture Investment Services
N.A.I.C.S.: 523999
Steven P. Morrison (CFO)
Jennifer L. Ard (Sec)

THE MONTICELLO COMPANIES, INC.
1604 Stockton St, Jacksonville, FL 32204-4524
Tel.: (904) 384-3666   FL
Web Site: http://monticellodrug.com
Year Founded: 1909
Sales Range: $50-74.9 Million
Emp.: 10
Holding Company; Over-the-Counter Drug Companies; Banking
N.A.I.C.S.: 325412
Thomas S. Dean (Exec VP)
Susan Crouse (VP)

Subsidiaries:

Monticello Drug Co.   (1)
1604 Stockton St, Jacksonville, FL 32204-4524
Tel.: (904) 384-3666
Web Site:
http://www.monticellocompanies.com
Cold Preparations, Liquid & Tablets Mfr
N.A.I.C.S.: 325412

THE MOODY ENDOWMENT
1528 Post Office St, Galveston, TX 77550
Tel.: (409) 762-6661   TX
Year Founded: 1985
Sales Range: $25-49.9 Million
Grantmaking Services
N.A.I.C.S.: 813211
Brent Masel (Pres)
Shelley Kessler (Treas)
Ross Rankin Moody (Chm)

THE MOORINGS, INC.
120 Moorings Park Dr, Naples, FL 34105
Tel.: (239) 643-9111   FL
Web Site:
http://www.mooringspark.org
Year Founded: 1975
Sales Range: $50-74.9 Million
Emp.: 512
Lifecare Retirement Community Operator
N.A.I.C.S.: 623311
Steve Brinkert (VP-Resident Svcs)
Tim Buist (CFO)

THE MORANDE AUTOMOTIVE GROUP
8300 Radio Rd, Naples, FL 34104
Tel.: (239) 732-8909
Web Site: http://www.morande.com
Rev.: $24,000,000
Emp.: 33
Used Car Dealers
N.A.I.C.S.: 441120
James A. Morande Jr. (Pres)

THE MOREY CORPORATION
100 Morey Dr, Woodridge, IL 60517-8135
Tel.: (630) 754-2300   IL
Web Site: http://www.moreycorp.com
Year Founded: 1934
Sales Range: $25-49.9 Million
Emp.: 300
Printed Circuit Board Mfr
N.A.I.C.S.: 334412
Nicholas Carter (Head-Software Engrg)
Mauro Hernandez (Head-Sys & ITV)
Alan Mindlin (Mgr-Technical)
Justin Smith (Head-Electrical Design Engrg)
Scott Lima (Mgr-Engrg Technical-Electronic Sys & Product Dev)

THE MORRISON AGENCY
3365 Piedmont Rd Ste 1400, Atlanta, GA 30305
Tel.: (404) 233-3405
Web Site:
http://www.morrisonagency.com
Year Founded: 1986
Sales Range: $25-49.9 Million
Emp.: 30
Advertising Agencies
N.A.I.C.S.: 541810
Bob Morrison (CEO)
Jeff Silverman (Chief Strategy Officer)
Amanda Forgione (Partner)
Jeff Bell (Dir-Art & Designer)
Jeremy Heilpern (Chief Digital Officer & Partner)
Kyle Lewis (Chief Creative Officer)
Jason Hatfield (Chief Client Officer)

THE MORRISSEY GROUP LLC
720 Center St, Oregon City, OR 97045
Tel.: (503) 657-3305
Web Site:
http://www.morrisseyfp.com
Emp.: 3
Accounting Services
N.A.I.C.S.: 541211
Marilyn Morrissey (Founder & Principal)

Subsidiaries:

Bandages Plus, Inc.   (1)
1701 NW 82nd Ave, Miami, FL 33126
Tel.: (305) 477-0062
Web Site: http://www.bandagesplus.com
Sales Range: $1-9.9 Million
Miscellaneous Retail Stores
N.A.I.C.S.: 456199

THE MORTON ARBORETUM
4100 Illinois Route 53, Lisle, IL 60532
Tel.: (630) 968-0074   IL
Web Site: http://www.mortonarb.org
Year Founded: 1922
Sales Range: $25-49.9 Million
Emp.: 413
Environmental Conservation Services
N.A.I.C.S.: 813312
Susan Wagner (VP-Info & Education)
Kris Bachtell (VP-Collections & Facilities)
Jill Koski (VP-Dev)
Gerard T. Donnelly (Pres & CEO)
Charles H. Cannon (Dir-Center for Tree Science)

Greg Mueller *(VP-Science & Academic Programs)*
Matt Kramer *(Dir-Res)*
Catherine Bechtoldt *(Coord-Science & Conservation Project)*
Gary Watson *(Head-Res)*
James Fawley *(CFO & VP-Fin)*
Kurt Dreisilker *(Head-Natural Resources)*
Nicole Cavender *(VP-Science & Conservation Programs)*
Kathleen Spiess *(VP-Dev)*
Alicia LaVire *(VP-Mktg & Comm)*
Julie Janoski *(Plant Mgr-Clinic)*

THE MOSAIC COMPANY
555 S Renton Vlg Pl Ste 280, Renton, WA 98057
Tel.: (425) 254-1724
Web Site: http://www.themosaiccompany.com
Rev.: $15,300,000
Emp.: 116
Professional & Management Development Training
N.A.I.C.S.: 611430
Ross Hight *(CTO & VP-Tech Svcs)*
Alvin Reyes *(Exec VP)*
Eileen Stuart *(VP-Pub Affairs-Phosphates)*

THE MOSAICA GROUP LLC
N53 W24615 S Corporate Cir, Sussex, WI 53089
Tel.: (262) 820-9025
Web Site: http://www.printmosaica.com
Sales Range: $25-49.9 Million
Emp.: 45
Printing & Writing Paper Merchant Whslr
N.A.I.C.S.: 424110
Randall M. Peters *(Pres & CEO)*
Melanie S. Bond *(CFO & Gen Mgr)*
Matt Fehn *(Dir-Tech)*
Karen Seidl *(Mgr-Ops)*
Tina Kellicut *(Controller)*
Art Debnam *(Mgr-Pur)*
Ray Neumann *(Mgr-Warehouse)*
Jay Zawerschnik *(Dir-Client Svcs)*
Jodi Rossin *(Mgr-Product Art)*
Brandon Dart *(Acct Mgr & Coord-Sls)*
Kathy Murtell *(Coord-Mktg)*

THE MOTLEY FOOL, INC.
2000 Duke St 4th FL, Alexandria, VA 22314
Tel.: (703) 838-3665 VA
Web Site: http://www.fool.com
Year Founded: 1993
Sales Range: $25-49.9 Million
Emp.: 200
Investment Information Publisher
N.A.I.C.S.: 513199
Tom Gardner *(Founder & CEO)*
Scott Shedler *(Pres)*
Kerra McDonough *(CFO)*

THE MOTORLEASE CORPORATION
1506 New Britain Ave, Farmington, CT 06032-3126
Tel.: (860) 677-9711 CT
Web Site: http://www.motorleasecorp.com
Year Founded: 1946
Sales Range: $10-24.9 Million
Emp.: 30
Passenger Automobile Leasing
N.A.I.C.S.: 532112
Jack Leary *(Pres)*
Beth Kandrysawtz *(CEO)*
Dave Deslauriers *(Mgr-Bus Dev)*
Jeffrey Perkins *(VP-Ops)*

THE MOUNT VERNON COMPANY, INC.
29 Commonwealth Ave 6th Fl, Boston, MA 02116
Tel.: (617) 267-0006
Web Site: http://www.mvernon.com
Year Founded: 1985
Sales Range: $10-24.9 Million
Emp.: 25
Apartment Home & Commercial Property Rental Services
N.A.I.C.S.: 531190
Bruce A. Percelay *(Chm)*

THE MOUNT VERNON LADIES' ASSOCIATION OF THE UNION
PO Box 110, Mount Vernon, VA 22121-0110
Tel.: (703) 799-8699 VA
Year Founded: 1853
Sales Range: $50-74.9 Million
Emp.: 698
Historical Site Preservation Services
N.A.I.C.S.: 712120
Curtis C. Viebranz *(Pres & CEO)*
Philip Manno *(CFO)*
Barton Groh *(COO)*
Carol Cadou *(Sr VP-Historic Preservation & Collections)*
Susan Magill *(VP-Advancement)*
Doug Bradburn *(Pres/CEO-George Washington)*

THE MSR GROUP
1121 N 102nd Ct Ste 100, Omaha, NE 68114
Tel.: (402) 392-0755 NE
Web Site: http://www.themsrgroup.com
Year Founded: 1952
Sales Range: $1-9.9 Million
Emp.: 160
Market Research
N.A.I.C.S.: 541910
Dick Worick *(Founder & Chm)*
Rob Noha *(Sr VP)*
Julian Vermaas *(VP-Acct Svcs)*
Terry Scholten *(Office Mgr)*
Cherie Carlson *(VP-Res-Energy Div)*
Thomas Hatton *(Pres & CEO)*

THE MUNDY COMPANIES
11150 S Wilcrest Dr Ste 300, Houston, TX 77099-4343
Tel.: (281) 530-8711
Web Site: http://www.mundycos.com
Year Founded: 1955
Sales Range: $300-349.9 Million
Emp.: 25
Machinery & Equipment Repair Services
N.A.I.C.S.: 811210
David Mundy *(Pres)*

Subsidiaries:

Mundy Contract Maintenance (1)
11150 S Wilcrest Dr Ste 300, Houston, TX 77099 (100%)
Tel.: (281) 530-8711
Building Maintenance Services
N.A.I.C.S.: 561720

Mundy Industrial Contractors (1)
11150 S Wilcrest Dr Ste 300, Houston, TX 77099
Tel.: (281) 530-8711
Web Site: http://www.mundycos.com
Nonresidential Construction, Nec
N.A.I.C.S.: 236220
David Mundy *(Pres & CEO)*

THE MUSEUM OF CONTEMPORARY ART, LOS ANGELES
250 S Grand Ave, Los Angeles, CA 90012
Tel.: (213) 621-2766 CA
Web Site: http://www.moca.org
Year Founded: 1979
Sales Range: $10-24.9 Million
Emp.: 218
Contemporary Art Museum Operator
N.A.I.C.S.: 712110
Catherine Arias *(Dir-Visitor Engagement)*
Maurice Marciano *(Co-Chm)*
Lilly Tartikoff Karatz *(Co-Chm)*
Eugenio Lopez *(Co-Vice Chm)*
Lillian Lovelace *(Co-Vice Chm)*

THE MUSEUM OF MODERN ART
11 W 53rd St, New York, NY 10019
Tel.: (212) 708-9400
Web Site: http://www.moma.org
Year Founded: 1929
Sales Range: $25-49.9 Million
Emp.: 700
Museum of Twentieth Century & Contemporary Art & Design
N.A.I.C.S.: 712110
James Gara *(Asst Treas)*
Patty Lipshutz *(Sec)*
Jerry I. Speyer *(Chm)*
Ines Katzenstein *(Dir-The Patricia Phelps De Cisneros Research Institute For The)*

THE MUSTANG GROUP, LLC
339 Auburn St, Newton, MA 02466
Tel.: (617) 467-6800
Web Site: http://www.mustanggroup.com
Year Founded: 2003
Privater Equity Firm
N.A.I.C.S.: 523999
Bob Crowley *(Mng Partner)*
Carson Biederman *(Mng Partner)*
Ben Coes *(Mng Partner)*
Stephen Owen *(Principal)*

Subsidiaries:

The Vermont Teddy Bear Company (1)
6655 Shelburne Rd, Shelburne, VT 05482-6500
Tel.: (802) 985-3001
Web Site: http://www.vermontteddybear.com
Sales Range: $50-74.9 Million
Emp.: 352
Customized Teddy Bear Mfr & Distr
N.A.I.C.S.: 339930
Bob Crowley *(Chm)*
Cathy Carlisle *(Dir-Mfg)*
Mark J. Sleeper *(Asst Controller)*
Mark Ranalletti *(VP-Ops)*
William C. Shouldice IV *(Pres & CEO)*

Subsidiary (Domestic):

Calyx & Corolla, Inc. (2)
6655 Shelburne Rd, Shelburne, VT 05482
Tel.: (802) 985-3001
Sales Range: $25-49.9 Million
Emp.: 30
Direct Response, Online & Catalog Florists
N.A.I.C.S.: 459310
Bill Shouldice *(Office Mgr)*

THE MX GROUP
7020 High Grove Blvd, Burr Ridge, IL 60527-7599
Tel.: (630) 654-0170 IL
Web Site: http://www.themxgroup.com
Year Founded: 1988
Sales Range: $10-24.9 Million
Emp.: 89
Advertising Agencies
N.A.I.C.S.: 541810
Andrew S. Mahler *(Co-Founder & CEO)*
Peter Wroblewski *(Co-Founder & Principal)*
Tom Barg *(Partner & Exec Creative Dir)*
Tim Cook *(Partner & VP-Client Svcs)*
Kevin Coe *(Partner & VP-Digital Dev)*
Tony Riley *(Pres)*

THE MYLER COMPANY INC.
970 N Englewood Dr, Crawfordsville, IN 47933-9725
Tel.: (765) 362-3353
Web Site: http://www.myler.com
Year Founded: 1973
Sales Range: $10-24.9 Million
Emp.: 30
Provider of Nonresidential Construction Services
N.A.I.C.S.: 236220
Earl O. Myler *(Chm)*
Jim Gillikin *(Pres & COO)*
Nancy Weliver *(Controller)*

Subsidiaries:

Myler Church Building Systems, Inc. (1)
970 N Englewood Dr, Crawfordsville, IN 47933
Tel.: (765) 362-3353
Web Site: http://www.myler.com
Sales Range: $10-24.9 Million
Emp.: 7
Nonresidential Construction Services
N.A.I.C.S.: 236220
Earl Myler *(CEO)*

THE NAJAFI COMPANIES
2525 E Camelback Rd Ste 850, Phoenix, AZ 85016
Tel.: (602) 476-0600
Web Site: http://najafi.com
Year Founded: 2002
Privater Equity Firm
N.A.I.C.S.: 523999
Jam Najafi *(Founder)*

THE NANNY TAX COMPANY
104 Main St Ste 2F, Park Ridge, IL 60068
Tel.: (847) 696-7260
Web Site: http://www.nannytaxprep.com
Year Founded: 1995
Tax Preparation Services
N.A.I.C.S.: 541213
Laura Weiland *(Owner & Pres)*
Judy Connolly *(Dir-Ops)*
Sharon Connolly *(Dir-Data & Analytics)*
Sheila Connolly *(Dir-Client Svcs)*
Arthur Ellis *(Founder)*

THE NATHAN ADELSON HOSPICE
4141 University Ctr Dr, Las Vegas, NV 89119
Tel.: (702) 733-0320 NV
Web Site: http://www.nah.org
Year Founded: 1978
Nursing & Personal Care
N.A.I.C.S.: 623311
April Stewart *(Chief Nursing Officer-Nonprofit Hospice)*
Betty Dobbs-Funk *(Dir-Palliative Care Ops)*
Karen Rubel *(Pres & CEO)*

Subsidiaries:

Southern Nevada Home Health Care, Inc. (1)
9121 W Russell Rd Ste 118, Las Vegas, NV 89148
Tel.: (702) 228-0282
Health Care Srvices
N.A.I.C.S.: 621610

THE NATIONAL ASSOCIATION FOR GUN RIGHTS, INC.

THE NATIONAL ASSOCIATION FOR GUN RIGHTS, INC.

U.S. PRIVATE

The National Association for Gun Rights, Inc.—(Continued)
PO Box 7002, Fredericksburg, VA 22404
Tel.: (877) 405-4570 — VA
Web Site: http://www.nationalgunrights.org
Year Founded: 2001
Sales Range: $10-24.9 Million
Emp.: 55
Social Advocacy Organization
N.A.I.C.S.: 813319
Jacob Leis *(VP-Mktg & Dev)*
Zach Lautenschlager *(VP-Political Affairs)*
Dudley Brown *(Pres)*

THE NATIONAL ASSOCIATION FOR HISPANIC ELDERLY
234 E Colorado Blvd Ste 300, Pasadena, CA 91101
Tel.: (626) 564-1988 — CA
Web Site: http://www.anppm.org
Year Founded: 1975
Sales Range: $10-24.9 Million
Elder Care Services
N.A.I.C.S.: 624120
Carmela G. Lacayo *(Pres & CEO)*
Helen Hernandez *(Chm)*

THE NATIONAL BANK OF INDIANAPOLIS CORPORATION
107 N Pennsylvania Ste 700, Indianapolis, IN 46204
Tel.: (317) 261-9000 — IN
Web Site: http://www.nbofi.com
Year Founded: 1993
Sales Range: $50-74.9 Million
Emp.: 274
Bank Holding Company
N.A.I.C.S.: 551111
Debra L. Ross *(CFO & Exec VP)*
Michael S. Maurer *(Chm)*
Mark E. Bruin *(Pres & CEO)*

Subsidiaries:

The National Bank of Indianapolis (1)
107 N Pennsylvania St, Indianapolis, IN 46204
Tel.: (317) 261-9000
Web Site: http://www.nbofi.com
Commericial Banking
N.A.I.C.S.: 522110
Mark E. Bruin *(Pres & CEO)*
Debra L. Ross *(CFO & Exec VP)*
Douglas C. Talley *(Chief Banking Officer, Chief Lending Officer & Exec VP)*
Terry K. Scott *(Chief Credit Officer & Sr VP)*
Ann M. Merkel *(Chief Dev Officer & Sr VP)*
Thomas A. Urick *(Chief Client Officer & Sr VP)*
Evan L. Thomas *(CTO & First VP)*
Pamela J. Fogle *(Chief HR Officer & First VP)*

THE NATIONAL CANCER COALITION, INC.
333 Fayetteville St Ste 1500, Raleigh, NC 27601
Tel.: (919) 821-2182 — DE
Web Site: http://www.nationalcancercoalition.org
Year Founded: 1993
Sales Range: $10-24.9 Million
Emp.: 5
Health Care Srvices
N.A.I.C.S.: 622110
Hall C. Overall *(CFO)*
Robert Landry *(Pres & CEO)*

THE NATIONAL CORVETTE MUSEUM
350 Corvette Dr, Bowling Green, KY 42101
Tel.: (270) 781-7973 — NM
Web Site: http://www.corvettemuseum.org
Year Founded: 1988
Sales Range: $10-24.9 Million
Emp.: 113
Historical Museum
N.A.I.C.S.: 712110
Stephanie Morrill *(Mgr-Guest Svcs & Membership)*
Karen Renfrow *(Mgr-Events)*
Shane Webb *(Mgr-Delivery Dept)*
Debbie Willis Eaton *(Coord-Grp Sls)*
Katie Ellison *(Mgr-Mktg & Comm)*
Sharon Brawner *(Pres & CEO)*
Glenn Johnson *(Chm)*

THE NATIONAL GUARD ASSOCIATION OF THE UNITED STATES
1 Massachusetts Ave NW, Washington, DC 20001
Tel.: (202) 789-0031 — DC
Web Site: http://www.ngaus.org
Year Founded: 1878
Sales Range: $10-24.9 Million
Emp.: 29
Security Guard Association
N.A.I.C.S.: 813920
Gus Hargett *(Pres)*
Jose Palacios *(Mgr-Support Svcs)*
Patricia R. O'Connell *(Dir-Contracts, Fin & HR)*
Luke Guthrie *(Dir-Industry Rels & Dev)*
Roy Robinson *(Co-Pres)*
James Hoyer *(Chm)*
Joanne Sheridan *(Sec)*

THE NATIONAL INSTITUTE FOR HOMETOWN SECURITY
368 N Hwy 27 Ste 1, Somerset, KY 42503
Tel.: (606) 451-3440 — KY
Web Site: http://www.thenihs.org
Year Founded: 2004
Sales Range: $10-24.9 Million
Emp.: 6
Community Protection Services
N.A.I.C.S.: 561612
John D. Taylor *(Dir-Tech)*
Wayne Harris *(VP-Fin & Compliance)*
Holly Hurd *(Dir-Comm & Outreach)*
Amanda White *(Mgr-Program)*
Ewell H. Balltrip *(Pres & CEO)*
Bob Wilson *(Dir-Board)*
Donna Gregg *(Dir-Board)*
John Knox Mills *(Dir-Board)*

THE NATIONAL THEATRE CORPORATION
1321 Pennsylvania Ave, Washington, DC 20004
Tel.: (202) 783-6854
Web Site: http://www.nationaltheatre.org
Year Founded: 1835
Sales Range: $10-24.9 Million
Emp.: 50
Theatrical Producer
N.A.I.C.S.: 711110
Victor S. Kamber *(Treas & Acting Sec)*
Schehera Stolarik *(Treas-Box Office)*
Tom Lee *(Exec Dir)*
Sarah Bartell *(Exec Dir)*
Don Borud *(Treas & Acting Sec)*
Alastair Coomer *(Head-Casting)*

THE NATIONAL UNDERGROUND RAILROAD FREEDOM CENTER
50 E Freedom Way, Cincinnati, OH 45202-2739
Tel.: (513) 333-7500
Web Site: http://www.freedomcenter.org
Year Founded: 2004
Sales Range: $1-9.9 Million
Emp.: 29
Underground Railroad & the Abolitionist Movement Information
N.A.I.C.S.: 712120
Susan Redman-Rengstorf *(VP-Institutional Advancement)*
Sherri Fillingham *(Dir-Dev Ops)*
Yolanda Sherrer *(Dir-Institutional Effectiveness)*
Jamie Glavic *(Dir-Mktg & Comm)*
Elizabeth Pierce *(CEO)*
Dan Hurley *(Interim Pres)*
Steve Hightower *(Pres & CEO)*

THE NATURAL BABY COMPANY, LLC
1203 N Rouse Ave Ste 3E, Bozeman, MT 59715
Tel.: (406) 522-0800
Web Site: http://www.naturalbabyco.com
Sales Range: $1-9.9 Million
Emp.: 17
Baby Clothing & Accessory Mfr & Retailer
N.A.I.C.S.: 315250
Hiller Higman *(Dir-Design)*
Troy Paulson *(Controller)*

THE NATURE CONSERVANCY
4245 N Fairfax Dr Ste 100, Arlington, VA 22203-1606
Tel.: (703) 841-5300
Web Site: http://www.nature.org
Year Founded: 1951
Sales Range: $500-549.9 Million
Conservation Services
N.A.I.C.S.: 813410
Robert Bendick *(Dir-Gulf of Mexico Program)*
Jessie Israel *(Dir-Puget Sound Conservation)*
Kelly Hall *(Dir-Philanthropy)*
Craig O. McCaw *(Co-Chm)*
Frances A. Ulmer *(Co-Chm)*
James E. Rogers *(Vice Chm)*
Joseph H. Gleberman *(Treas)*
Collin Haffey *(Mgr-Forest & Watershed Health)*
Kari Kostka *(Dir-External Affairs)*
Jennifer Morris *(CEO)*
Nathalie Augustin *(Gen Counsel)*
David Banks *(Chief Conservation Officer)*
Meg Goldthwaite *(Chief Mktg & Comm Officer)*
Bola Olusanya *(Chief Investment Officer)*
Tom Neises *(Chief Dev Officer)*
Lynn Scarlett *(Chief External Affairs Officer)*
Theresa Shaw *(CIO)*
Mike Tetreault *(Chief People Officer)*
Leonard Williams *(Chief Fin & Admin Officer)*
Senator Bill *(Co-Chm)*
Monica Thornton *(Exec Dir-Georgia)*
Nancy-Clair McInaney *(Chm-Georgia)*
James E. Page Jr. *(Chief Global Diversity, Equity & Inclusion Officer)*
Shona L. Brown *(Sec)*

THE NEAT COMPANY
3401 Market St Ste 100, Philadelphia, PA 19104
Web Site: http://www.neatco.com
Year Founded: 2002
Sales Range: $10-24.9 Million
Document Scanning Equipment & Software Solutions
N.A.I.C.S.: 334118

Andrew Schaps *(VP-Dev)*
Jeff Gove *(VP-Sys & Support Svcs)*
Jim Conroy *(VP-Fin)*
Kevin Miller *(Chief Mktg Officer)*
Michael Crincoli *(Pres)*

THE NEMOURS FOUNDATION
10140 Centurion Pkwy, Jacksonville, FL 32256
Tel.: (904) 697-4100 — FL
Web Site: http://www.nemours.org
Sales Range: $800-899.9 Million
Pediatric Health Care Services Organization
N.A.I.C.S.: 813920
Gina Altieri *(Sr VP)*
Debbie I. Chang *(Sr VP-Policy & Prevention)*
Stephen T. Lawless *(Chief Clinical Officer & Sr VP)*
Rodney A. McKendree *(CFO & Sr VP)*
Theresa Mullins Young *(Sr VP-HR)*
Mariane Stefano *(Chief Experience Officer & Sr VP)*
Richard T. Christopher *(Vice Chm)*
Bernie Rice *(CIO & VP-Enterprise)*
Dana Nicholoson Bledsoe *(Sr VP-Enterprise)*
Martha McGill *(VP-Enterprise)*
Tony Sudler *(Chief Dev Officer-Orlando)*
Nancy E. Stephenson *(Chief Compliance Officer & VP-Enterprise)*
R. Lawrence Moss *(Pres & CEO)*
Sarah C. Sanders *(Chief Mktg Officer & Sr VP)*
Kara Odom Walker *(Chief Population Health Officer & Sr VP)*
Rachel Salis-Silverman *(Dir-PR-Enterprise)*
William Higginbotham II *(VP-Fin & Cost Containment)*

THE NERDERY
9555 James Ave S Ste 245, Bloomington, MN 55431
Tel.: (877) 664-6373
Web Site: http://www.nerdery.com
Year Founded: 2003
Sales Range: $10-24.9 Million
Emp.: 392
Developer of Websites, Social Media & Mobile Applications
N.A.I.C.S.: 541810
Michael Derheim *(Co-Founder & Chm)*
Michael Schmidt *(Co-Founder & CEO)*
John Mathiasen *(VP-Ops)*
Steve Arndt *(CFO)*
Fred Beecher *(Dir-User Experience Design)*
Amanda Anderson *(VP-Sls)*
Danny Estavillo *(Dir-Bus Dev)*
Douglas Linsmeyer *(Dir-Digital Tech-Phoenix)*
Chris Locher *(VP-Software Dev)*
Laura Etches *(VP-Mktg)*
Chris Cobb *(VP-Design)*
Nick Katzenbach *(Chief Growth Officer)*
Hallie Steele *(Mktg Dir)*

THE NEW 42ND STREET, INC
229 W 42nd St, New York, NY 10036
Tel.: (646) 223-3000 — NY
Web Site: http://www.new42.org
Year Founded: 1988
Sales Range: $10-24.9 Million
Emp.: 368
Studio & Theatre Operator
N.A.I.C.S.: 711110
Lauren P. Fitzgerald *(Dir-Mktg & Comm)*
Lisa Lawer Post *(Exec VP)*

COMPANIES

Kim Dobbie Neuer *(VP-Fin)*
Jessica Baker *(VP-Ops)*
Deborah Ann Trimble *(VP-Dev)*
Alma Malabanan-McGrath *(Dir-Ops)*
Chris Tusciuk *(Dir-IT)*
Courtney J. Boddie *(Dir-Education & School Engagement)*
Dave Upton *(Dir-Technical)*
Julia Putnam *(Mgr-Ops)*
Katherine Freedman *(Dir-Institutional Giving)*
Lilaia Kairis *(Dir-Digital Svcs)*
Theodore Matthew *(Supvr-Maintenance)*
Travis Bell *(Mgr-Technical)*

THE NEW CHILDRENS MUSEUM
200 W Island Ave, San Diego, CA 92101
Tel.: (619) 233-8792   CA
Web Site:
   http://www.thinkplaycreate.org
Year Founded: 1981
Sales Range: $1-9.9 Million
Emp.: 97
Child Museum
N.A.I.C.S.: 712110
Gerson Martinez *(Mgr-Acctg)*
Tomoko Kuta *(Deputy Dir-Museum)*
Tammy Gamboa *(Sr Mgr-Event Svcs)*
Kerri Fox *(Dir-Mktg & Comm)*
Megan Dickerson *(Mgr-Exhibition Dev)*
Lani Bautista Cabanilla *(Mgr-Visitor Programs)*
Judy Forrester *(CEO)*

THE NEW LEADER
535 W 114 St, New York, NY 10027-6708
Tel.: (212) 854-1640
Web Site:
   http://www.thenewleader.com
Year Founded: 1924
Sales Range: Less than $1 Million
Emp.: 2
Magazine Publisher
N.A.I.C.S.: 513120
Mitchel Levitas *(Chm)*

THE NEW REPUBLIC INC.
1620 L St NW Ste 300C, Washington, DC 20036
Tel.: (646) 779-8000   DE
Web Site:
   http://www.newrepublic.com
Year Founded: 1914
Sales Range: $10-24.9 Million
Emp.: 65
Weekly Magazine Publisher
N.A.I.C.S.: 513120
Jamil Smith *(Editor)*
Win McCormack *(Owner)*
Eric Bates *(Editor)*
Mindy Kay Bricker *(Dir-Digital)*
Moira Donegan *(Asst Editor-Cultural Coverage)*
Michael Tomasky *(Editor-Top)*

THE NEW YORK BLOWER COMPANY, INC.
7660 S Quincy St, Willowbrook, IL 60527-5530
Tel.: (630) 794-5700   IN
Web Site: http://www.nyb.com
Year Founded: 1889
Sales Range: $25-49.9 Million
Emp.: 450
Blowers & Fan Mfr
N.A.I.C.S.: 333413
Joseph Centers *(Pres)*
Subsidiaries:

MAS Air Systems, LLC   (1)
2008 County Line Rd, New Castle, PA 16101
Tel.: (724) 652-1367
Web Site: http://www.mas-fan.com
Industrial Fans Mfr
N.A.I.C.S.: 333413
Micheal Schlemmer *(Mgr-Application)*

Mechanovent Corporation   (1)
171 Factory St, La Porte, IN 46350-2582
Tel.: (219) 326-1767
Web Site: http://www.mechanovent.com
Sales Range: $10-24.9 Million
Emp.: 7
Mfr of Blowers & Fans
N.A.I.C.S.: 333413

TLT-Babcock, Inc.   (1)
260 Springside Dr, Akron, OH 44333-2433
Tel.: (330) 867-8540
Web Site: http://www.tltbabcock.com
Sales Range: $10-24.9 Million
Emp.: 85
Mfr of Industrial Fans & Dampers
N.A.I.C.S.: 333413
Mark Sanders *(Pres)*

THE NEW YORK BOTANICAL GARDEN
2900 Southern Blvd, Bronx, NY 10458-5126
Tel.: (718) 817-8700
Web Site: https://www.nybg.org
Year Founded: 1891
Botanical Garden Operator
N.A.I.C.S.: 712130

THE NEW YORK GENOME CENTER
101 Avenue of The Americas, New York, NY 10013
Tel.: (646) 977-7000   DE
Web Site: http://www.nygenome.org
Year Founded: 2010
Sales Range: $10-24.9 Million
Emp.: 68
Biomedical Research Services
N.A.I.C.S.: 541715
Andrea Armstrong *(VP-HR & Admin)*
Carol Ashe *(Chief Bus Officer)*
Sarah Lesser-Avins *(Chief Dev Officer & VP-External Affairs)*
Christopher C. Duignan *(VP-Fin & Controller)*
Matthew J. Pelo *(VP-Fin & Ops Strategy)*
Robert B. Darnell *(Pres, CEO & Dir-Scientific)*
Kathleen McGovern *(VP-Dev & Comm)*

THE NEW YORK INSTITUTE FOR SPECIAL EDUCATION
999 Pelham Pkwy, Bronx, NY 10469
Tel.: (718) 519-7000   NY
Web Site: http://www.nyise.org
Year Founded: 1831
Sales Range: $25-49.9 Million
Emp.: 378
Educational Support Services
N.A.I.C.S.: 611710
Kim M. Benisatto *(Mgr-Ops)*
Lisa Blasone *(Mgr-HR)*
Maria Grullon *(Dir-Fiscal Affairs)*
Bernadette M. Kappen *(Exec Dir)*
John B. Rhodes *(Pres)*
Phillip G. Foote *(VP)*
Rosanne K. Silberman *(Sec)*
William L. Musser *(Treas)*

THE NEW YORK LOOK INC.
570 7th Ave, New York, NY 10018
Tel.: (212) 382-2760
Web Site:
   http://www.newyorklook.com
Sales Range: $10-24.9 Million
Emp.: 40
Provider of Modeling Related Services
N.A.I.C.S.: 458110
Joseph Arabian *(Pres)*
Subsidiaries:

7th Avenue Showcase Ltd   (1)
570 7th Ave, New York, NY 10018
Tel.: (212) 382-2760
Rev.: $240,000
Emp.: 4
Provider of Ready-to-Wear Women's Apparel
N.A.I.C.S.: 458110

Dinuccio Ltd.   (1)
30 Lincoln Plz, New York, NY 10023
Tel.: (212) 765-4758
Rev.: $600,000
Emp.: 4
Provider of Women's Shoes
N.A.I.C.S.: 458210

New York Look at Fifth Ave Inc.   (1)
570 7 Ave 44 St, New York, NY 10018
Tel.: (212) 382-2760
Web Site: http://www.newyorklook.com
Rev.: $370,000
Emp.: 7
Provider of Ready-to-Wear Women's Apparel
N.A.I.C.S.: 458110
Masoud Arabian *(VP & Gen Mgr)*
Joseph Arabian *(CEO)*

The New York Look Inc.   (1)
30 Lincoln Plz, New York, NY 10023
Tel.: (212) 245-6511
Rev.: $180,000
Emp.: 30
Provider of Ready-To-Wear Women's Apparel
N.A.I.C.S.: 458110
Joseph Arabian *(Mgr)*

THE NEW YORK PUBLIC LIBRARY
476 5th Ave, New York, NY 10018
Tel.: (212) 930-0800
Web Site: http://www.nypl.org
Sales Range: $300-349.9 Million
Emp.: 3,124
Library Services
N.A.I.C.S.: 519210
Anthony W. Marx *(Pres & CEO)*
Abby S. Milstein *(Vice Chm)*
Fay Rosenfeld *(VP-Pub Programs)*
Iris Weinshall *(CFO, COO & Treas)*
Evan R. Chesler *(Chm)*
Risa Honig *(VP-Capital Plng & Construction)*
George Mihaltses *(VP-Govt & Community Affairs)*
Louise Shea *(VP-HR)*
Geetanjali Gupta *(Chief Investment Officer)*
Michele Coleman Mayes *(Gen Counsel, Sec & VP)*

THE NEWBERRY
60 W Walton St, Chicago, IL 60610
Tel.: (312) 943-9090   IL
Web Site: http://www.newberry.org
Year Founded: 1982
Sales Range: $10-24.9 Million
Emp.: 142
Library Operator
N.A.I.C.S.: 519210
Will Hansen *(Dir-Reader Svcs)*
Meredith Petrov *(Mgr-Governance & External Rels)*
Lesa Dowd *(Dir-Conservation Svcs Dept)*
David Spadafora *(Pres)*
Alex Teller *(Dir-Comm & Editorial Svcs)*
David C. Hilliard *(Vice Chm)*
David E. McNeel *(Treas)*
Mark Hausberg *(Sec)*
Victoria J. Herget *(Chm)*
Michael Mitchell *(Chief Security Officer & Mgr-Facilities)*
Sarah Alger *(Dir-Dev)*

Judy Rayborn *(Dir-HR)*
Drin Gyuk *(Dir-IT)*
Ron Kniss *(Controller)*
Alan Leopold *(Dir-Collection Svcs Dept)*
Diane Dillon *(Dir-Exhibitions & Major Projects)*
Katy Hall *(VP-Dev)*
James P. Burke Jr. *(VP-Fin & Admin)*

THE NEWBERRY GROUP, INC.
2510 Old Hwy 94 S Ste 200, Saint Charles, MO 63303
Tel.: (636) 928-9944
Web Site:
   http://www.thenewberrygroup.com
Sales Range: $25-49.9 Million
Emp.: 140
Information Technology & Systems Consulting Services
N.A.I.C.S.: 541519
Brenda D. Newberry *(Co-Founder)*
Christopher J. Steinbach *(Chm & CEO)*
Christopher J. Pugh *(CFO & Exec VP)*
R. Steven Cadogan *(Sr VP-Federal Programs)*
Phillip Justice *(Sr VP-Comml Programs & Consulting Practice)*

THE NEWCOURTLAND LIFE PROGRAM
6970 Germantown Ave, Philadelphia, PA 19119-2114
Tel.: (215) 951-4242   PA
Web Site:
   http://www.newcourtlandlife.org
Year Founded: 2006
Sales Range: $25-49.9 Million
Emp.: 110
Elder Care Services
N.A.I.C.S.: 624120
Linda Kurian *(Dir-Medical)*
Andrew Seibert *(CFO)*
Marcia Edge *(Dir-Education)*
Donald Levesque *(Treas)*
Venus Connors *(Dir-Clinical Svcs)*

THE NEWTRON GROUP INC.
8183 W El Cajon Dr, Baton Rouge, LA 70815-8035
Tel.: (225) 927-8921   LA
Web Site:
   http://www.thenewtrongroup.com
Year Founded: 1973
Sales Range: $250-299.9 Million
Emp.: 2,510
Electrical & Industrial Contractors; Installation & Repair Instrumentation
N.A.I.C.S.: 238210
Newton Thomas *(CEO)*
John Schempf *(Pres)*
Tami Misuraca *(CFO)*
Mark Richardson *(Mgr-Corp Safety)*
Steve Cherco *(Mgr-Quality Assurance & Quality Control)*
Vince Thibodaux *(Mgr-Com-Net Svcs)*
Rock Thompson *(Mgr-Executive Aviation)*
John Smith *(Pres-Newtron)*
Mike Defee *(Mgr-Newtron Beaumont)*
Nick Parsons *(Mgr-Newtron-California Bay Area)*
Kevin Singleton *(Mgr-Newtron Electrical Svcs)*
Walter Jetton *(Mgr-Newtron Heat Trace)*
Trey Ellis *(Mgr-Newtron Mechanical)*
Chad Beard *(Pres-NGI National Constructors)*
Michael Redd *(Mgr-NGI Engrg & Automation)*
Brian Bordelon *(Pres-Triad Electric & Controls)*
Eric Coco *(Mgr-Triad Electric & Controls-Houston)*

THE NEWTRON GROUP INC.

The Newtron Group Inc.—(Continued)
Subsidiaries:

Com-Net Services, LLC (1)
7786 S Commerce Ave, Baton Rouge, LA 70815
Tel.: (225) 928-1231
Web Site: http://www.comnetserv.com
Communication Service
N.A.I.C.S.: 517810
Vince Thivodux (VP)

NGI National Constructors, L.L.C. (1)
8183 W El Cajon Dr, Baton Rouge, LA 70815
Tel.: (225) 927-8921
Emp.: 100
Construction Engineering Services
N.A.I.C.S.: 541330
John Schempf (Mgr)

NGI Technical Services, L.L.C. (1)
8646 Kiowa Dr, Baton Rouge, LA 70815
Tel.: (225) 927-8921
Web Site:
http://www.triadcontrolsystems.com
Emp.: 40
Electrical Engineering Services
N.A.I.C.S.: 541330
Michael Redd (Mgr)

Newtron Inc. (1)
8183 W El Cajon Dr, Baton Rouge, LA 70815-8035 (100%)
Tel.: (225) 927-8921
Web Site: http://www.thenewtrongroup.com
Sales Range: $10-24.9 Million
Emp.: 50
Electrical Work
N.A.I.C.S.: 238210

Newtron Mechanical, L.L.C. (1)
1640 Industrial Park Dr, Nederland, TX 77627
Tel.: (409) 727-2469
Sales Range: $10-24.9 Million
Emp.: 2
Mechanical Engineering Services
N.A.I.C.S.: 541330

Triad Control Systems Inc. (1)
8646 Kiowa Dr, Baton Rouge, LA 70815-8064
Tel.: (225) 927-1043
Web Site:
http://www.triadcontrolsystems.com
Sales Range: $10-24.9 Million
Emp.: 25
Process Control Instruments
N.A.I.C.S.: 334513
Michael Red (Gen Mgr)
Brian Savoy (Mgr-Ops)

Triad Electric & Controls Inc. (1)
2288 N Airway Dr, Baton Rouge, LA 70815-8064 (100%)
Tel.: (225) 923-0604
Web Site: http://www.thenewtrongroup.com
Sales Range: $25-49.9 Million
Emp.: 400
Electrical Contractor
N.A.I.C.S.: 811210
Jay J. Rush (Pres)

THE NIELLO COMPANY

150 Automall Dr, Roseville, CA 95661
Tel.: (916) 334-6300
Web Site: http://www.niello.com
Year Founded: 1963
Sales Range: $25-49.9 Million
Emp.: 600
New Car Whslr
N.A.I.C.S.: 441110
Vince Gregory (Gen Mgr)
Melinda Levy-Storms (Mgr-Admin)
Gail Stevens (Owner)
Richard Niello Jr. (Pres)

THE NIELSEN NORMAN GROUP

48105 Warm Springs Blvd, Fremont, CA 94539-7498
Tel.: (415) 685-4230   CA
Web Site: http://www.nngroup.com

Year Founded: 1998
Sales Range: $1-9.9 Million
Emp.: 12
Computer Consulting & Research Services
N.A.I.C.S.: 541519
Jakob Nielsen (Co-Founder & Principal)
Luice Hwang (Dir-Consulting Svcs & Events)
Don Norman (Co-Founder & Principal)
Kara Pernice (Mng Dir)
Bruce Tognazzini (Principal)
Hoa Loranger (VP)

THE NIEMEYER CORPORATION

19 S Newtown St, Newtown Square, PA 19073
Tel.: (610) 356-2672
Web Site:
http://www.mowersonline.com
Sales Range: $10-24.9 Million
Emp.: 25
Lawn Machinery & Equipment Sales
N.A.I.C.S.: 423820
Karl W. Niemeyer (Pres)

THE NORD CENTER

6140 S Broadway, Lorain, OH 44053
Tel.: (440) 233-7232   OH
Web Site: http://www.nordcenter.org
Year Founded: 1960
Sales Range: $10-24.9 Million
Emp.: 282
Behavioral Healthcare Services
N.A.I.C.S.: 623220
Jack Holt (Dir-Info Svcs)
Lori Berencsi (Dir-Billing & Fin Intake)
Judy Hyde (Dir-CPST Svcs)
Malcolm L. Peel (Pres)
William Richardson (CFO & Chief Admin Officer)
Sharon Thornton (Coord-Clinical Svcs, Africancentric & SAMI)
Melissa Mack (Coord-Quality Assurance)
Rebecca Jones (Chief Clinical Officer-Interim & Dir-Intake & Counseling)
Michael Rivera (Mgr-Facilities & Maintenance)
Roseann Harper (Coord-Partial Hospitalization)
Rebecca Opel (Coord-Sexual Assault Svcs)
Anna Colwell (Dir-Supported Employment)
Franca Curci-Winiasz (Officer-Clients Rights)
Frank Balcik (Dir-Food Svcs)

THE NORTH ATLANTIC MARINE GROUP

570 Harbor Side St Ste 101, Woodbridge, VA 22191
Tel.: (703) 491-0800
Web Site:
http://www.virginiayachts.com
Rev.: $32,000,000
Emp.: 5
Boat Dealers
N.A.I.C.S.: 441222
Laura Gore (Controller)

THE NORTH CAROLINA PARTNERSHIP FOR CHILDREN, INC.

1100 Wake Forest Rd, Raleigh, NC 27604
Tel.: (919) 821-7999   NC
Web Site: http://www.smartstart.org
Year Founded: 1993
Sales Range: $75-99.9 Million
Emp.: 57

Child Care Services
N.A.I.C.S.: 624110
Cindy Watkins (Pres)
Ellen Preston (Dir-Fin)
Susan Clark (Mgr-Monitoring)
Heather Strickland (Dir-Comm)
Diane Umstead (Dir-Early Childhood Sys)
J. Zachary Everhart (Treas)
Nancy H. Brown (Chm)
Robert L. Eagle (Vice Chm)
James Dodson (COO)
Matthew McKeown (Co-Founder)
Devonya Govan-Hunt (Co-Founder & CEO)
Laura Hitt (Officer-Compliance)
Donna White (VP)

THE NORTH HIGHLAND COMPANY

3333 Piedmont Rd Ste 1000, Atlanta, GA 30305
Tel.: (404) 233-1015
Web Site:
http://www.northhighland.com
Year Founded: 1992
Sales Range: $25-49.9 Million
Emp.: 220
Provider of Management & Technology Consulting Services
N.A.I.C.S.: 541611
Dan Reardon (Chm)
Anne Game (Mng Dir)
Matthew Klein (Mng Dir, COO & Chief Mktg Officer)
Alex Bombeck (CEO)
Mary Slaughter (Chief People Officer)
Patrick Ray (Gen Counsel & VP)
Michael Han (VP-Strategy-Dallas)
John Norkus (Mng Dir)
Kevin Burkhart (VP-Los Angeles)
Jeffrey McMahon (Mng Dir)
Scott Rainey (Principal)
Charles Vivian (VP)
Marty Brennan (VP)
Troy Sands (VP)
Dwight Specht (VP-Data & Analytics)
Michael Hollar (VP-Data & Analytics-West Reg)
Angela Navarro (Sr VP-Ops)
Kimberly Currier (Sr VP)
Lauren Childers (Mng Dir & CFO)
Rochelle Rivas (Head-Indus Dev)
Barbara Ray (Mng Dir & Pres-Client Svcs)
Micail Samiere (VP-Healthcare-Nashville)
Katie Argus (VP-Fin)
Helen Baxter (VP-Life Sciences-London)

THE NORTH WARD CENTER, INC.

346 Mount Prospect Ave, Newark, NJ 07104
Tel.: (973) 481-0415   NJ
Web Site:
http://www.northwardcenter.org
Year Founded: 1971
Sales Range: $10-24.9 Million
Emp.: 273
Community Health Care Services
N.A.I.C.S.: 621498
Rashard Casey (Dir-Youth Dev & Recreation)
Sung Yi (CFO)
Adrianne Davis (Co-Founder & Exec Dir)
Bruno Tedeschi (Dir-Comm)
Albio Sires (Pres)
Stephen N. Adubato Sr. (Co-Founder)

THE NORTHEAST HEALTH GROUP INC

2 Bala Plz, Bala Cynwyd, PA 19004

Tel.: (215) 346-6454   MA
Year Founded: 1995
Sales Range: $25-49.9 Million
Emp.: 690
Health Care Srvices
N.A.I.C.S.: 622110

THE NORTHWEST COMPANY

49 Bryant Ave, Roslyn, NY 11576
Tel.: (516) 484-6996
Web Site:
http://www.thenorthwest.com
Rev.: $20,100,000
Emp.: 130
Sports Team & Entertainment Branded Blankets & Throws Mfr
N.A.I.C.S.: 424350
Michael Busser (CFO)
Ross Auerbach (Pres & CEo)
Glenn Auerbach (Exec VP)
Marc Friedman (COO)
Stanley Mieszkowski (Exec VP-Sls & Mktg)
Sandy Karoll (Exec VP-Production & Plng)

THE NORTHWEST GROUP

28265 Beck Rd Ste C2, Wixóm, MI 48393
Tel.: (248) 349-9480   MI
Web Site:
http://www.nwestgroup.com
Year Founded: 1959
Rev.: $1,000,000
Emp.: 8
Fiscal Year-end: 12/31/04
N.A.I.C.S.: 541810
Tom Graham (Owner)
Dave Nelson (Gen Mgr)
Paul Van Kirk (Dir-Creative)
Corey Beals (Acct Exec)

THE NORTHWESTERN MUTUAL LIFE INSURANCE COMPANY

720 E Wisconsin Ave, Milwaukee, WI 53202
Tel.: (414) 271-1444   WI
Web Site:
http://www.northwesternmutual.com
Year Founded: 1857
Rev.: $28,482,000,000
Assets: $272,167,000,000
Liabilities: $245,436,000,000
Net Worth: $26,731,000,000
Earnings: $783,000,000
Emp.: 7,000
Fiscal Year-end: 12/31/18
Life & Disability Income Long Term Care Insurance, Annuities & Mutual Funds Services
N.A.I.C.S.: 524113
John Edward Schlifske (Chm, Pres & CEO)
Todd M. Jones (CFO & Exec VP)
Aditi Javeri Gokhale (Chief Strategy Officer, Pres-Retail Investments, Exec VP & Head-Institutional Investments)
Nicholas E. Brathwaite (Bd of Trustees, Executives)
John Mitchell Grogan (Chief Insurance Officer & Exec VP)
Timothy John Gerend (Chief Distribution Officer & Exec VP)
Raymond J. Manista (Chief Legal Officer, Chief Compliance Officer, Sec & Exec VP)
Christian W. Mitchell (Chief Customer Officer & Exec VP)
Don J. Robertson (Chief HR Officer & Exec VP)
Lynn Marie Bowser (Mng Dir)
Laura Deaner (Chief Info Security Officer)
Jennifer Brase (Mng Partner-Omaha)

COMPANIES

Macauley Hill *(Mng Dir)*
Michael G. Carter *(Exec VP)*
Jeff Sippel *(CIO & Exec VP)*

Subsidiaries:

Frank Russell Company (1)
1301 2nd Ave 18th Fl, Seattle, WA 98101
Tel.: (206) 505-7877
Web Site: http://www.russell.com
Emp.: 1,900
Holding Company; Alternative Investment Management, Advisory & Implementation Services
N.A.I.C.S.: 551112
James G. Polisson *(CEO-Exchange-Traded Funds)*
Joseph Gelly *(Mng Dir-Institution-Russell Investments Canada)*

Subsidiary (Domestic):

Russell Implementation Services, Inc. (2)
1301 2nd Ave 18th Fl, Seattle, WA 98101
Tel.: (206) 505-7877
Web Site: http://www.russell.com
Emp.: 950
Transition Management Services
N.A.I.C.S.: 522320

Subsidiary (Non-US):

Russell Investment Group Ltd (2)
level 13 188 quay street, Auckland, 1010, New Zealand
Tel.: (64) 9 357 6633
Web Site: http://www.russell.co.nz
Investment Management Service
N.A.I.C.S.: 523940
Alister Van der Maas *(Mng Dir)*

Russell Investment Group Private Limited (2)
1 Raffles Place, Tower 1 #24-00, Singapore, 048616, Singapore
Tel.: (65) 6880 5900
Web Site: http://www.russell.com
Sales Range: $50-74.9 Million
Emp.: 10
Investment Management Service
N.A.I.C.S.: 523940
Mengat Lin *(Mng Dir)*

Russell Investment Group Pty Limited (2)
L 29 135 King St, Sydney, 2000, NSW, Australia
Tel.: (61) 2 9229 5111
Emp.: 190
Investment Management Service
N.A.I.C.S.: 523940
Peter Gunning *(CEO-Asia Pacific)*
Tan Ying *(Pres/Gen Mgr-Investments Mgmt-Shanghai)*

Russell Investment Management Ltd (2)
Level 29 135 King Street, Sydney, 2000, NSW, Australia
Tel.: (61) 2 9229 5111
Web Site: http://www.russell.com
Sales Range: $100-124.9 Million
Emp.: 160
Investment Management Service
N.A.I.C.S.: 523940

Russell Investments Canada Limited (2)
200 Bay St North Tower Suite 1200, PO Box 476, Toronto, M5J 2J2, ON, Canada
Tel.: (416) 362-8411
Web Site: https://russellinvestments.com
Investment Management Service
N.A.I.C.S.: 523940
Kate El-Hillow *(Pres)*
Vernon Barback *(COO)*
Steve Belgrad *(CFO)*
Peter Gunning *(Vice Chm)*
Jenny Proctor *(Chief HR Officer)*
Howard Surloff *(Chief Legal Officer)*
Al Caesar *(Chief Strategy Officer)*
Jodie Hampshire *(Mng Dir)*
Brad Jung *(Pres)*
Kelly Mainelli *(Mng Dir)*
John McMurray *(Chief Risk Officer)*

Russell Investments Korea Limited (2)
19F Two IFC 10 Gukjegeumyung-ro, Youngdeungpo-gu, Seoul, 150-945, Korea (South)
Tel.: (82) 2 6137 6900
Web Site: http://www.russell.com
Emp.: 5
Investment Management Service
N.A.I.C.S.: 523940

LearnVest Inc. (1)
113 University Pl 5th Fl, New York, NY 10003
Tel.: (212) 675-6711
Web Site: http://www.learnvest.com
Personalized Financial Planning Services
N.A.I.C.S.: 519290
Alexa von Tobel *(Founder & CEO)*
John Gardner *(CFO)*
Ainslie Simmonds *(COO)*
Kelly Leyden *(VP-People)*
Stephany Kirkpatrick *(VP-Ops & Fin Advice)*

Northwestern Long Term Care Insurance Company (1)
720 E Wisconsin Ave, Milwaukee, WI 53202 (100%)
Tel.: (414) 271-1444
Web Site: http://www.northwesternmutual.com
General Insurance Services
N.A.I.C.S.: 524298

Northwestern Mutual Atlantic Benefit Group (1)
1 Beacon St Fl 25, Boston, MA 02108
Tel.: (617) 742-8900
Web Site: http://www.john-mara.com
Sales Range: $75-99.9 Million
Emp.: 110
Insurance Agents, Nec
N.A.I.C.S.: 524298

Northwestern Mutual Investment Services, LLC (1)
720 E Wisconsin Ave, Milwaukee, WI 53202 (100%)
Tel.: (414) 271-1444
Financial Investment Services
N.A.I.C.S.: 523999
William Taylor *(VP-Fin Plng)*

OJO Labs, Inc. (1)
720 Brazos St #110, Austin, TX 78701
Tel.: (512) 456-8292
Web Site: http://landing.ojo.me
Data Science, Engineering & Marketing
N.A.I.C.S.: 518210
David Rubin *(Co-founder & Chief Strategy Officer)*
John Berkowitz *(Co-founder & CEO)*
Chris Heller *(Chief Real Estate Officer)*
Karen Starns *(Chief Mktg Officer)*

Subsidiary (Domestic):

WolfNet Technologies, LLC (2)
600 Highway 169 S Ste 1100, Saint Louis Park, MN 55401-1206
Tel.: (612) 342-0088
Web Site: http://www.wolfnet.com
Broker Reciprocity, Property Search, WordPress Websites & Plugins, MLS Data Standardization & Property Search
N.A.I.C.S.: 531390
Joel MacIntosh *(CEO)*

Russell Investments Limited (1)
Rex House 10 Regent Street, London, SW1Y 4PE, United Kingdom
Tel.: (44) 207 024 6000
Web Site: http://www.russell.com
Emp.: 150
Investment Management Service
N.A.I.C.S.: 523940
Van Luu *(Head-Currency & Fixed Income Strategy)*
Joseph Linhares *(Head-EMEA)*
Julian Brown *(Dir-Consultant Rels)*
Jim Leggate *(Head-Institutional-UK & Middle East)*

The Russo Financial Group (1)
875 3rd Ave 23rd Fl, New York, NY 10022
Tel.: (212) 867-8989
Web Site: http://nyc.nmfn.com
Sales Range: $10-24.9 Million
Emp.: 150
Insurance Agents
N.A.I.C.S.: 524210

Robert Rabold *(COO)*
Matt Russo *(Mng Partner)*

THE NORTON COMPANY
3200 E Camelback Rd Ste 389, Phoenix, AZ 85018-2328
Tel.: (602) 954-8812 AZ
Year Founded: 1955
Sales Range: $50-74.9 Million
Emp.: 3
Agricultural Services
N.A.I.C.S.: 111998

THE NORWOOD COMPANY INC.
375 Technology Dr, Malvern, PA 19355
Tel.: (610) 240-4400 NJ
Web Site: http://www.norwoodco.com
Year Founded: 1975
Sales Range: $10-24.9 Million
Emp.: 90
Nonresidential Construction
N.A.I.C.S.: 236220
John E. Farrell *(Pres & CEO)*

THE NOVA GROUP
17055 S Dalton Ave Ste 1, Los Angeles, CA 90247
Tel.: (310) 217-8868
Web Site: http://www.tng.bz
Sales Range: $25-49.9 Million
Emp.: 7
Electrical Apparatus & Equipment
N.A.I.C.S.: 423610
Michael Ikeda *(Partner)*
Sherry Yudt *(Partner)*

THE NPD GROUP, INC.
900 W Shore Rd, Port Washington, NY 11050-4624
Tel.: (516) 625-0700 NY
Web Site: http://www.npd.com
Year Founded: 1953
Market Information Services
N.A.I.C.S.: 541910
Tod Johnson *(Chm)*
Karyn Schoenbart *(CEO)*
Tom Lynch *(CFO)*
Susan Pechman *(CMO)*
Tim Bush *(Pres-Comml Bus-Americas)*
Steve Coffey *(Chief Innovation Officer)*
Virginia Grande *(Chief HR Officer)*
Avi Halutz *(CIO)*
Don Unser *(Pres-Retail)*
Jeremy Allen *(Grp Pres-Product & Checkout)*
Gerhard Hausruckinger *(Grp Pres-Europe & Asia Pacific)*
Darren Person *(CIO-Global)*
Bob O'Brien *(Sr VP-Global)*
Dan Hess *(Chief Product Officer)*
Ricardo Solar *(Sr VP-Media Entertainment Practice)*
Kim Magnus *(Sr VP-Canada)*
Joanne Hageman *(Pres-t U.S. Entertainment Sector & Latin America)*
Robert Taylor *(Sr VP-Enterprise Sys)*
Larissa Jensen *(VP)*
Lori Monaco *(Pres-Beauty)*
Susan Merrill *(Pres-Apparel Practice-US)*
Joanne Sackett *(Pres-Softlines Sector)*
Cecilia Manget *(Head-Foodservice-Europe)*

Subsidiaries:

Electronic Entertainment Design & Research (1)
2075 Corte Del Nogal Ste B, Carlsbad, CA 92011
Tel.: (760) 579-7120
Web Site: http://www.eedar.com

THE NULMAN GROUP

Marketing Consulting Services
N.A.I.C.S.: 541613

LGI Network (1)
375 Route 10 E, Randolph, NJ 07869
Tel.: (973) 659-0333
Web Site: http://www.npd.com
Marketing Consulting Services
N.A.I.C.S.: 541613

Leisure Trends Group, LLC (1)
1680 38th St, Boulder, CO 80301
Tel.: (303) 786-7900
Web Site: http://www.leisuretrends.com
Marketing Consulting Services
N.A.I.C.S.: 541613
Jim Kelley *(Pres)*
Julia Clark Day *(VP-Sls & Mktg)*
Jason Gee *(VP-Retail Sls Tracking)*
Greg Shoenfeld *(Mgr-Retails Rels)*

NPD DisplaySearch LLC (1)
2350 Mission College Blvd Ste 705, Santa Clara, CA 95054
Tel.: (408) 418-1900
Web Site: http://www.displaysearch.com
Marketing Consulting Services
N.A.I.C.S.: 541613
Paul Semenza *(Sr VP-Analyst Svcs)*

NPD Information Consulting (Shanghai) Co., Ltd. (1)
Room 301 Sheng Gao International Building No 137 Xian Xia Road, Shanghai, 200051, China
Tel.: (86) 21 6275 3222
Web Site: http://www.npdchina.com
Marketing Consulting Services
N.A.I.C.S.: 541613
Jade Hsueh *(Sr Mgr-Sls & Mktg)*

NPD Japan Ltd. (1)
Shinagawa Center Bldg 13F 3-23-17 Takanawa, Minato-ku, Tokyo, 108-0074, Japan
Tel.: (81) 3 5798 7303
Web Site: http://www.displaysearch-japan.com
Marketing Consulting Services
N.A.I.C.S.: 541613
Satoshi Matsuno *(Pres)*
Shoichi Hiramatsu *(Dir-Sls & Mktg)*

The NPD Group Ltd (1)
Broadway Studios 20 Hammersmith Broadway, London, W6 7AF, United Kingdom
Tel.: (44) 2082371300
Web Site: http://www.npdgroup.co.uk
Marketing Consulting Services
N.A.I.C.S.: 541613

npdgroup deutschland GmbH (1)
Rathsbergstrasse 17, 90411, Nuremberg, Germany
Tel.: (49) 911 8918
Web Site: http://www.npdgroup.de
Marketing Consulting Services
N.A.I.C.S.: 541613
Andreas Lauszat *(Sr Mgr-Acct)*

THE NRP GROUP, LLC
5309 Transportation Blvd, Cleveland, OH 44125
Tel.: (216) 475-8900
Web Site: http://www.nrpgroup.com
Year Founded: 1995
Sales Range: $75-99.9 Million
Emp.: 450
Single-Family & Multi-Family Housing Construction; Property Management
N.A.I.C.S.: 236115
J. David Heller *(Co-Founder)*
Alan F. Scott *(Founder)*

Subsidiaries:

NRP Contractors LLC (1)
5309 Transportation Blvd, Cleveland, OH 44125
Tel.: (216) 475-8900
Web Site: http://www.nrpgroup.com
Sales Range: $50-74.9 Million
Emp.: 100
New Construction, Single-Family Houses
N.A.I.C.S.: 236115
Andrew Tanner *(CFO & VP)*

THE NULMAN GROUP

THE NULMAN GROUP

The Nulman Group—(Continued)

100 Davidson Ave Ste 205, Somerset, NJ 08873
Tel.: (732) 560-9566   NJ
Year Founded: 1979
Sales Range: $10-24.9 Million
Emp.: 8
Advetising Agency
N.A.I.C.S.: 541810
Philip R. Nulman *(CEO & Dir-Creative)*
Frank Pish *(Sr Dir-Art)*
Helen Nardone *(Assoc Dir-Art)*
Claire Curry *(Gen Mgr)*
Laura Boyer *(Sr Acct Supvr)*
Humphrey Wilson *(Acct Exec)*

THE NUTTING COMPANY, INC.
1500 Main St, Wheeling, WV 26003
Tel.: (304) 233-0100   WV
Web Site: http://www.nuttingcompany.com
Year Founded: 1890
Holding Company; Newspaper & Magazine Publisher; Professional baseball Club Owner & Operator
N.A.I.C.S.: 551112
Robert M. Nutting *(CEO)*
Duane Wittman *(CFO)*
Bill Nutting *(VP)*
Cameron Nutting Williams *(Dir-Strategic Initiatives & Ops)*
Mera Kutrovac *(Gen Counsel)*

Subsidiaries:

Pittsburgh Baseball Holdings, Inc. (1)
PNC Park 115 Federal St PO Box 7000, Pittsburgh, PA 15212
Tel.: (412) 321-2827
Web Site: http://www.pirates.com
Holding Company; Professional Baseball Club
N.A.I.C.S.: 551112
Robert M. Nutting *(Chm)*
Frank Coonelly *(Pres)*
Bryan Stroh *(Gen Counsel & Sr VP-Bus Affairs)*

Subsidiary (Domestic):

Pittsburgh Baseball Partnership (2)
PNC Park 115 Federal St, Pittsburgh, PA 15212
Tel.: (412) 323-5000
Web Site: http://www.mlb.com
Sales Range: $10-24.9 Million
Emp.: 100
Professional Baseball Club
N.A.I.C.S.: 711211
Robert M. Nutting *(Chm)*
Bryan Stroh *(Gen Counsel & Sr VP-Bus Affairs)*
Travis Williams *(Pres)*
John Baker *(Dir-Coaching & Player Dev)*
Ben Cherington *(Gen Mgr)*

Seven Springs Mountain Resort, Inc. (1)
777 Waterwheel Dr, Champion, PA 15622-4007
Tel.: (814) 352-7782
Web Site: http://www.7springs.com
All-Seasons Resort Operator
N.A.I.C.S.: 721110
Eric Mauck *(CEO)*
Katie Buchan *(Comm Mgr)*
Lauri Jones *(Dir-Winter Svcs)*

Unit (Domestic):

Hidden Valley Resort (2)
1 Craighead Dr, Hidden Valley, PA 15502-3900
Tel.: (814) 443-8000
Web Site:
  http://www.hiddenvalleyresort.com
Golf & Skiing Resort Operator
N.A.I.C.S.: 713910
Rachel Powel *(Mgr-Resort Sls)*
Eric Mauck *(CEO)*

The Ogden Newspapers, Inc. (1)
1500 Main St, Wheeling, WV 26003
Tel.: (304) 233-0100
Web Site: http://www.ogdennews.com
Holding Company; Newspaper & Magazine Publisher
N.A.I.C.S.: 551112
Robert M. Nutting *(Pres & CEO)*
Duane Wittman *(CFO)*
G. Ogden Nutting *(Publr)*
William C. Nutting *(VP)*
Dave Frisch *(Dir-Tech)*
Lori Figurski *(Dir-Adv)*
Mike Kernik *(Dir-HR)*
John McCabe *(Dir-Editorial)*
Cameron Nutting Williams *(Dir-Strategic Initiatives& Ops)*
Mera Kutrovac *(Gen Counsel)*
Michael Christman *(Publr)*
Charles Jarvis *(Publr)*

Subsidiary (Domestic):

Adirondack Publishing Co. Inc. (2)
54 Broadway, Saranac Lake, NY 12983
Tel.: (518) 891-2600
Web Site:
  http://www.adirondackdailyenterprise.com
Sales Range: $10-24.9 Million
Emp.: 32
Newspaper Publishers
N.A.I.C.S.: 513110

Elkins Inter-Mountain Co. Inc. (2)
520 Railroad Ave, Elkins, WV 26241-3861   (100%)
Tel.: (304) 636-2121
Web Site: http://www.theintermountain.com
Sales Range: $10-24.9 Million
Emp.: 78
Newspaper Publishers
N.A.I.C.S.: 513110
Dave Ickes *(Mgr-Press)*
Joyce Becker *(Dir-Svc)*
Stephanie Gilmore *(Mgr-Sls)*
Heather Henline *(Gen Mgr)*

Emmetsburg Publishing Co. (2)
1122 Broadway Ste B, Emmetsburg, IA 50536-2440   (100%)
Tel.: (712) 852-2323
Web Site: http://www.emmetsburgnews.com
Sales Range: $10-24.9 Million
Emp.: 9
Newspaper Publishers
N.A.I.C.S.: 513110
Dan McCain *(Publr & Gen Mgr)*

Estherville Publications Inc. (2)
10 N 7th St, Estherville, IA 51334-2232
Tel.: (712) 362-2622
Web Site:
  http://www.esthervilledailynews.com
Sales Range: $10-24.9 Million
Emp.: 10
Newspaper Publishers
N.A.I.C.S.: 513110
Glen Caron *(Publr)*

Fort Wayne Newspapers, Inc. (2)
600 W Main St, Fort Wayne, IN 46802-1498
Tel.: (260) 461-8444
Web Site: http://www.fortwayne.com
Sales Range: $25-49.9 Million
Emp.: 350
Newspaper Publishers
N.A.I.C.S.: 513110
Michael Christman *(Pres & CEO)*
Lori Fritz *(Dir-Sls & Mktg)*

Unit (Domestic):

The Journal Gazette (3)
600 W Main St, Fort Wayne, IN 46802
Tel.: (260) 461-8519
Web Site: http://www.fortwayne.com
Sales Range: $25-49.9 Million
Emp.: 15
Newspapers
N.A.I.C.S.: 513110
Julie Inskeep *(Publr)*
Lisa Green *(Asst Mng Editor-Local News)*
Mike Roeger *(Editor-Copy)*

The News-Sentinel (3)
600 W Main St, Fort Wayne, IN 46802
Tel.: (260) 461-8444
Web Site: http://www.news-sentinel.com
Sales Range: $25-49.9 Million
Emp.: 55
Newspapers

N.A.I.C.S.: 513110

Subsidiary (Domestic):

Marshalltown Newspaper Inc. (2)
135 W Main St, Marshalltown, IA 50158-5843
Tel.: (641) 753-6611
Web Site: http://www.timesrepublican.com
Newspaper Publishers
N.A.I.C.S.: 513110
Michael Schlesinger *(Publr)*
Ross Thede *(Editor-Sports)*
Clayton Steil *(Production Mgr)*
Steven Plain *(Dir-Creative Svcs)*
Deanna Davis *(Asst Dir-Adv)*
Randy Cutright *(Dir-Circulation)*
Jeff Hutton *(Editor)*
Linda R. Gould *(Dir-Mktg & Adv)*
LeAnn Siemens *(Mgr)*

Minot Daily News (2)
301 4th St SE, Minot, ND 58701
Tel.: (701) 857-1900
Web Site: http://www.minotdailynews.com
Sales Range: $10-24.9 Million
Emp.: 100
Newspaper Publishers
N.A.I.C.S.: 513110
Amy Boyle *(Mgr-Bus)*
Sarah Burhans *(Coord-Adv & Pre-Print)*
Jim Hart *(Dir-Adv)*
Kent Olson *(Mng Editor)*
Dan McDonald *(Publr)*

Unit (Domestic):

Morning Journal (2)
308 Maple St, Lisbon, OH 44432
Tel.: (330) 424-9541
Web Site:
  http://www.morningjournalnews.com
Newspaper Publishers
N.A.I.C.S.: 513110
Larry Dorschner *(Publr)*
Beth Todd *(Controller)*

Subsidiary (Domestic):

Observer Publishing Company (2)
122 S Main St, Washington, PA 15301
Tel.: (724) 222-2200
Web Site: http://www.observer-reporter.com
Newspaper Publishers
N.A.I.C.S.: 513110

Ogden Newspapers of Ohio Inc. (2)
320 Nelson St, Tiffin, OH 44883-8956
Tel.: (419) 448-3200
Web Site: http://www.advertiser-tribune.com
Sales Range: $10-24.9 Million
Emp.: 78
Newspaper Publishers
N.A.I.C.S.: 513110
Chris Dixon *(Dir-Adv)*
Tappan Rodgers *(Pres & Gen Mgr)*

Ogden Newspapers of Pennsylvania Inc. (2)
352 6th St, Lewistown, PA 17044-1213   (100%)
Tel.: (717) 248-6741
Web Site: http://www.lewistownsentinel.com
Sales Range: $10-24.9 Million
Emp.: 70
Newspaper Publishers
N.A.I.C.S.: 513110
Ruth Eddy *(Publr)*

Ogden Publications, Inc. (2)
1503 SW 42nd St, Topeka, KS 66609-1265   (100%)
Tel.: (785) 274-4300
Web Site: http://www.ogdenpubs.com
Rev: $29,900,000
Emp.: 125
Magazine Publisher
N.A.I.C.S.: 513120
Brandy Ernzen *(Brand Mgr)*
John Rockhold *(Mng Editor-Online)*
Rod Peterson *(Mgr-Adv)*
Elizabeth Granada *(Coord-Mktg)*

Subsidiary (Domestic):

Capper's Insurance Service Inc. (3)
1503 SW 42nd St, Topeka, KS 66609-1214   (100%)
Tel.: (785) 274-4300
Web Site: http://www.cappersinsurance.com

Sales Range: $50-74.9 Million
Emp.: 30
Health Insurance Services
N.A.I.C.S.: 524210
Bob Legault *(Dir-Sls)*
Joe Bowman *(Mgr-Field Ops)*
Sandy Flowers *(Office Mgr)*
Bill Uhler *(Gen Mgr)*

Mother Earth News (3)
1503 SW 42nd St, Topeka, KS 66609
Tel.: (785) 274-4300
Web Site: http://www.motherearthnews.com
Sales Range: $25-49.9 Million
Emp.: 100
Magazine Publisher
N.A.I.C.S.: 513120
Rebecca Martin *(Editor-Rural Lifestyles)*

Subsidiary (Domestic):

Sun-Gazette Company Inc. (2)
252 W 4th St, Williamsport, PA 17701-6102
Tel.: (570) 326-1551
Web Site: http://www.sun-gazette.com
Sales Range: $10-24.9 Million
Emp.: 100
Newspaper Publishers
N.A.I.C.S.: 513110

The Alpena News Publishing Co. Inc. (2)
130 Park Pl, Alpena, MI 49707
Tel.: (989) 354-3111
Web Site: http://www.thealpenanews.com
Sales Range: $10-24.9 Million
Emp.: 55
Newspaper Publishers
N.A.I.C.S.: 513110
Bill Spear *(Pres)*

The Breeze Corporation (2)
2510 Del Prado Blvd, Cape Coral, FL 33904-5750
Tel.: (239) 574-1110
Web Site: http://www.flguide.com
Sales Range: $25-49.9 Million
Emp.: 150
Newspaper Publishers
N.A.I.C.S.: 513110

Unit (Domestic):

The Daily News (2)
215 E Ludington St, Iron Mountain, MI 49801
Tel.: (906) 774-2772
Web Site:
  http://www.ironmountaindailynews.com
Emp.: 30
Newspaper Publishers
N.A.I.C.S.: 513110
Betsy Bloom *(Mng Editor)*
Corky Deroeck *(Publr & Dir-Adv)*

Subsidiary (Domestic):

The Journal Publishing Co. Inc. (2)
207 W King St, Martinsburg, WV 25401-3211
Tel.: (304) 263-8931
Web Site: http://www.journal-news.net
Sales Range: $25-49.9 Million
Emp.: 170
Newspaper Publishers
N.A.I.C.S.: 513110
Art Taylor *(Mgr-Ops-Creative Svcs & Comml Printing)*
Maria Lorensen *(Dir-Dev)*

Unit (Domestic):

The Lock Haven Express (2)
9-11 W Main St, Lock Haven, PA 17745-1217
Tel.: (570) 748-6791
Web Site: http://www.lockhaven.com
Sales Range: $10-24.9 Million
Emp.: 30
Newspaper Publishers
N.A.I.C.S.: 513110
Robert O. Rolley *(Publr)*

The Marietta Times (2)
700 Channel Ln, Marietta, OH 45750-2300
Tel.: (740) 373-2121
Web Site: http://www.mariettatimes.com
Newspaper Publishers
N.A.I.C.S.: 513110

Jennifer Houtman (Editor & Publr)
Patti Patton (Office Mgr)
Janet Dye (Mgr)
Joe Tranquill (Dir-Circulation)
Claire Hogue-Heiby (Editor-Copy)

The Shopper's Guide (2)
2510 Del Prado Blvd S, Cape Coral, FL 33904-5750
Tel.: (239) 544-1110
Sales Range: $10-24.9 Million
Emp.: 10
Newspaper Publishers
N.A.I.C.S.: 513110

The Times Leader (2)
200 S 4th St, Martins Ferry, OH 43935-1312
Tel.: (740) 633-1131
Web Site: http://www.timesleaderonline.com
Sales Range: $10-24.9 Million
Emp.: 75
Newspaper Publishers
N.A.I.C.S.: 513110
Robert Kapral (Exec Editor-Sports)
Jennifer Compston-Strough (Mng Editor)

Subsidiary (Domestic):

Uniontown Newspapers Inc. (2)
8 E Church St 18, Uniontown, PA 15401-3563
Tel.: (724) 439-7500
Web Site: http://www.heraldstandard.com
Newspapers
N.A.I.C.S.: 513110
Val Laub (VP & Publr)
Mark O'Keefe (Exec Editor)
Maureen Hranec (Dir-Adv)
Rick K. King (Controller)
Linda Esposito-Toth (Dir-Circulation)
Joanne G. Hunt (Dir-Interactive Media)
Albert B. Sloan (Dir-Production)

Unit (Domestic):

Wetzel Chronicle (2)
1100 3rd St, New Martinsville, WV 26155-1500
Tel.: (304) 455-3300
Web Site: http://www.wetzelchronicle.com
Sales Range: $10-24.9 Million
Emp.: 10
Newspaper Publishers
N.A.I.C.S.: 513110
Brian Clutter (Publr)

Subsidiary (Domestic):

Wheeling Newspapers, Inc. (2)
1500 Main St, Wheeling, WV 26003
Tel.: (304) 233-0100
Web Site: http://www.theintelligencer.net
Newspaper Publishers
N.A.I.C.S.: 513110
Perry Nardo (Gen Mgr)

William B. Collins Co., Inc. (2)
8 E Fulton St, Gloversville, NY 12078-3227
Tel.: (518) 725-8616
Web Site: http://www.leaderherald.com
Sales Range: $10-24.9 Million
Emp.: 100
Newspaper Publishers
N.A.I.C.S.: 513110
Tim Fonda (Mng Editor)
Toni Mosconi (Mgr-Circulation)
Chad Fleck (Mgr-Sys)
Brenda Anich (District Mgr)
James Cornell (Mgr-Bus)
Steve Herron (Publr)
Tim Vanaernam (Mgr-Production)

THE NYHART COMPANY INC.
8415 Allison Pointe Way Ste 300, Indianapolis, IN 46250
Tel.: (317) 845-3500
Web Site: http://www.nyhart.com
Year Founded: 1943
Sales Range: $10-24.9 Million
Emp.: 75
Medical Insurance Claim Processing
N.A.I.C.S.: 524292
Daryl J. Dean (Chm)
Thomas L. Totten (CEO & Actuary)
Lisa Hague (Controller)

THE O'BRIEN & GERE COMPANIES
333 W Washington St, Syracuse, NY 13202
Tel.: (315) 437-6100   DE
Year Founded: 1985
Sales Range: $25-49.9 Million
Emp.: 800
Provider of Consulting Engineering, Lab Analysis, Construction Management & Operations Services
N.A.I.C.S.: 541330
Gary D. Cannerelli (VP)
Ed Zawadzki (VP-Fin)
Mark Distler (VP)
Kendrick Jaglal (Sr Dir-Technical)

Subsidiaries:

Natural Resource Technology, Inc. (1)
N27W23713 Paul Rd Ste D, Pewaukee, WI 53072
Tel.: (262) 523-9000
Web Site: http://www.naturalrt.com
Sales Range: $1-9.9 Million
Emp.: 40
Scientific & Technical Consulting Services
N.A.I.C.S.: 541690
Joseph Ridgway (Engr-Environmental)
Clark Crosby (VP & Mgr-Bus)
Rick Fox (VP)
Laurie Parsons (Pres)

O'Brien & Gere Inc. of North America (1)
5000 Brittonfield Pkwy, East Syracuse, NY 13057-9200
Tel.: (315) 437-6400
Rev.: $5,467,626
Emp.: 400
Management Services
N.A.I.C.S.: 541611

Subsidiary (Domestic):

O'Brien & Gere Technical Services Inc. (2)
5000 Brittonfield Pkwy, East Syracuse, NY 13057-9200
Tel.: (315) 437-6400
Sales Range: $25-49.9 Million
Emp.: 300
Industrial Buildings & Warehouses
N.A.I.C.S.: 236220

O'Brien & Gere Laboratories, Inc. (1)
18 Link Dr, Binghamton, NY 13904
Tel.: (607) 232-5300
Rev.: $3,250,949
Emp.: 33
Engineeering Services
N.A.I.C.S.: 541715
Frank DeOrio (Mgr)

THE O'CARROLL GROUP
300 E McNeese Ste 2B, Lake Charles, LA 70605
Tel.: (337) 478-7396   LA
Web Site: http://www.ocarroll.com
Year Founded: 1978
Sales Range: Less than $1 Million
Emp.: 4
N.A.I.C.S.: 541810
Pam Doucet (Dir-Media & Acct Mgr)
Peter J. O'Carroll Jr. (Pres & Dir-Creative)

THE O'CONNELL COMPANIES, INCORPORATED
800 Kelly Way, Holyoke, MA 01040
Tel.: (413) 534-5667   MA
Web Site:
http://www.theoconnellcompanies.com
Year Founded: 1879
Sales Range: $150-199.9 Million
Emp.: 470
Holding Company; Construction Management & General Contractor Services
N.A.I.C.S.: 551112

James Sullivan (Pres)
Albert Bean (Mgr-IT)

Subsidiaries:

Appleton Corporation (1)
800 Kelly Way Ste 200, Holyoke, MA 01040-5015   (100%)
Tel.: (413) 536-8048
Web Site: http://www.appletoncorp.net
Rev.: $3,975,000
Emp.: 139
Real Estate Agents & Managers
N.A.I.C.S.: 531210
Paul Stelzer (Pres)

Appleton Security Corp. (1)
57 Suffolk St Ste 200, Holyoke, MA 01040-5015
Tel.: (413) 536-8048
Web Site: http://www.appletoncorp.net
Sales Range: $10-24.9 Million
Emp.: 100
Providers of Security Guard Services
N.A.I.C.S.: 561613
Paul Stelzer (Pres)

Daniel O'Connell's Sons Inc. (1)
480 Hampden St, Holyoke, MA 01040-3309
Tel.: (413) 534-5667
Web Site: http://www.oconnells.com
Sales Range: $25-49.9 Million
Emp.: 222
Industrial Buildings & Warehouses
N.A.I.C.S.: 236210
Tom Walsh (Dir-Bus Dev)
Frank Amaro (Dir-HR)

O'Connell Development Group Inc. (1)
480 Hampden St, Holyoke, MA 01040
Tel.: (413) 534-0243
Sales Range: $10-24.9 Million
Emp.: 30
Land Developers & Construction Consultants
N.A.I.C.S.: 237210
Andrew Crystal (VP)

O'Connell Properties Inc. (1)
480 Hampden St, Holyoke, MA 01040-3309
Tel.: (413) 534-5667
Web Site: http://www.oconnel.com
Rev.: $680,000
Emp.: 30
Subdividers & Developers
N.A.I.C.S.: 237210

The O'Connell Companies, Incorporated - Utilities Division (1)
6 Progress Ave, Nashua, NH 03062
Tel.: (603) 594-3082
Web Site: http://www.oconnell.com
Emp.: 2
Construction Engineering Services
N.A.I.C.S.: 541330
Dennis Fitzpatrick (Pres)

Western Builders Inc. (1)
73 Pleasant St, Granby, MA 01033-3321
Tel.: (413) 467-9171
Sales Range: $10-24.9 Million
Emp.: 15
Nonresidential Construction
N.A.I.C.S.: 236220
Bryan Hughes (Pres)

THE O'CONNOR GROUP
3700 Horizon Dr, King of Prussia, PA 19406
Tel.: (484) 325-5900
Web Site: http://www.tocgrp.com
Year Founded: 2007
Sales Range: $1-9.9 Million
Emp.: 50
Human Resource Consulting Services
N.A.I.C.S.: 541612
Marcia Zaruba-O'Connor (Pres & CEO)
Amy Cobb (Mgr-Ops)
Barbara Rader (Mgr-Client Success)
Meghan Popoleo (Dir-Sls & Mktg)
Amanda Haugh (Dir-Talent Acquisition)

THE O'GARA GROUP, INC.
9113 LeSaint Dr, Fairfield, OH 45014
Tel.: (513) 881-9800   OH
Web Site:
http://www.ogaragroup.com
Year Founded: 1982
Sales Range: $25-49.9 Million
Emp.: 1,450
Security, Safety & Defense Products & Services
N.A.I.C.S.: 561621
Wilfred T. O'Gara (Pres & CEO)
Rick Holman (Sr VP-Ops)
Kelly Dollins (VP-Trng & Ops)
Dominic Hunter (CFO)
Michael Reynolds (VP & Gen Mgr)

THE O'NEIL GROUP COMPANY, LLC
6 N Tejon Ste 501, Colorado Springs, CO 80903
Tel.: (719) 445-5050
Web Site:
http://www.theoneilgroupco.com
Year Founded: 2008
Real Estate Management & Development Services
N.A.I.C.S.: 531390
Ron Voss (Gen Counsel)
Kevin O'Neil (CEO)
Maury A. Keller (CFO)
Jon Lee (Dir-Fin)
Ingrid Richter (Dir-Economic Dev)

Subsidiaries:

OneDev LLC (1)
455 Pikes Peak Ave Ste 308, Colorado Springs 80903
Tel.: (719) 445-5050
Web Site: https://onedev.com
Data Processing, Hosting & Related Services
N.A.I.C.S.: 518210

Subsidiary (Domestic):

Systems Engineering & Management, Co. (2)
1430 Vantage Ct, Vista, CA 92081
Tel.: (760) 727-7800
Web Site: http://www.semco.com
Sales Range: $1-9.9 Million
Emp.: 70
Radio & Television Broadcasting & Wireless Communications Equipment Mfr
N.A.I.C.S.: 334220
William M. Tincup (Pres)
Doug O'Cull (VP-Bus & Product Dev)
Michael Samuels (Dir-Mktg & Sls)

Space Ground System Solutions, Inc. (1)
4343 Fortune Pl, Melbourne, FL 32904
Tel.: (321) 956-8200
Web Site: https://www.sgss.com
Engineeering Services
N.A.I.C.S.: 541330
Robert S. Tormala (Pres)
Brian Davis (Treas)
Maury A. Keller (VP)
Kenneth W. O'Neil (Chm)
David Buckman (Sec)

THE OAKLAND RAIDERS, L.P.
1220 Harbor Bay Pkwy, Alameda, CA 94502-6501
Tel.: (510) 864-5000   CA
Web Site: http://www.raiders.com
Year Founded: 1960
Sales Range: $50-74.9 Million
Emp.: 100
Professional Football Franchise
N.A.I.C.S.: 711211
Marc Badain (Pres)
Mark Davis (Owner)
Jon Gruden (Dir-College Scouting)
Mike Mayock (Gen Mgr)
Ken Norton Jr. (Coord-Defensive)

THE OAKVIEW COMPANIES, INC.

THE OAKVIEW COMPANIES, INC.

The Oakview Companies, Inc.—(Continued)
1981 G Ave, Red Ak, IA 51566-4474
Tel.: (712) 623-5561   IA
Year Founded: 1978
Sales Range: $10-24.9 Million
Emp.: 80
Nonresidential Construction
N.A.I.C.S.: 236220
Richard C. Bulkeley *(Chm)*

Subsidiaries:

Oakview Construction, Inc.   (1)
1981 G Ave, Red Oak, IA 51566-4474
Tel.: (712) 623-5561
Web Site: http://www.oakviewconst.com
Nonresidential Construction
N.A.I.C.S.: 236220
Rick Watts *(Pres-Comml Div)*

THE OAKWOOD GROUP
1100 Oakwood Blvd, Dearborn, MI 48124
Tel.: (313) 561-7740
Web Site: http://www.theoakwoodgroup.com
Sales Range: $25-49.9 Million
Emp.: 450
Automotive Stampings
N.A.I.C.S.: 336370
Ryan Bousamra *(Engr-Dev)*
Patty Longo *(Mgr-HR)*
Tom Perkins *(Dir-Fin)*
Susan Skelly *(Sr Acct Mgr)*
Donald Smith *(Exec VP)*
Nick Podges *(Engr-Dev)*

THE OCTOBER COMPANY, INC.
51 Ferry St, Easthampton, MA 01027
Tel.: (413) 527-9380   MA
Web Site: http://www.octobercompany.com
Sales Range: $10-24.9 Million
Emp.: 200
Manufactures Of Furniture Parts, Metal
N.A.I.C.S.: 332999
James Thompson *(Gen Mgr)*

THE ODOM CORPORATION
11400 SE 8th St Ste 300, Bellevue, WA 98004
Tel.: (425) 456-3535   DE
Web Site: http://www.odomcorp.com
Year Founded: 1934
Sales Range: $450-499.9 Million
Emp.: 1,400
Wholesale Beverage Distr
N.A.I.C.S.: 424490
William Odom *(Exec VP)*

THE OHIO HIGH SCHOOL ATHLETIC ASSOCIATION
4080 Roselea Pl, Columbus, OH 43214
Tel.: (614) 267-2502   OH
Web Site: http://www.ohsaa.org
Year Founded: 1907
Sales Range: $10-24.9 Million
Emp.: 70
Athletic Association
N.A.I.C.S.: 813990
Tim Stried *(Dir-Info Svcs)*
Todd Boehm *(Comptroller)*
Jeff Jordan *(Sr Dir-Fin & Acctg)*
Doug Foote *(Pres-Southwest)*
Jerry Snodgrass *(Exec Dir)*

THE OHIO HOSPITAL ASSOCIATION
155 E Broad St Ste 301, Columbus, OH 43215-3640
Tel.: (614) 221-7614   OH
Web Site: http://www.ohiohospitals.org

Year Founded: 1915
Sales Range: $10-24.9 Million
Emp.: 67
Health Care Srvcs
N.A.I.C.S.: 622110
James Guliano *(VP-Quality Programs)*
Amy Andres *(Sr VP-Quality & Data)*
Mary Gallagher *(Exec VP)*
Ryan Biles *(Sr VP-Health Economics & Policy)*
Scott Borgemenke *(Sr VP-Advocacy)*
Chip Hubbs *(CEO)*

THE OHIO MOULDING CORPORATION
30396 Lakeland Blvd, Wickliffe, OH 44092-1748
Tel.: (440) 944-2100   OH
Web Site: http://www.omcoform.com
Year Founded: 1955
Sales Range: $50-74.9 Million
Emp.: 150
Owns & Operates Custom Roll-Forming Facilities
N.A.I.C.S.: 332312
Clint Cassese *(CFO)*
Robert Stephenson *(VP-Engrg)*
Trish Carleton *(Dir-Mktg)*
Gary Schuster *(Pres & COO)*

Subsidiaries:

Midwest Roll Forming & Manufacturing, Inc.   (1)
1 Arnolt Dr, Piercetown, IN 46562-9641   **(100%)**
Tel.: (574) 594-2100
Web Site: http://www.omcoform.com
Sales Range: $10-24.9 Million
Emp.: 60
Steel Foundries
N.A.I.C.S.: 331513
Gary Schuster *(Pres)*

The Ohio Moulding Corporation - OMCO Solar Division   (1)
4550 W Watkins St, Phoenix, AZ 85043
Tel.: (602) 233-9787
Web Site: http://www.omcosolar.com
Solar Equipment Mfr
N.A.I.C.S.: 334413
Todd Owen *(Mgr)*

THE OKONITE COMPANY
102 Hilltop Rd, Ramsey, NJ 07446
Tel.: (201) 825-0300   NJ
Web Site: http://www.okonite.com
Year Founded: 1878
Sales Range: $350-399.9 Million
Emp.: 1,100
Insulated Wires & Cables Mfr
N.A.I.C.S.: 332618
Bruce Sellers *(VP-Sls & Mktg)*

THE OLD GLOBE
1363 Old Globe Way, San Diego, CA 92101-1696
Tel.: (619) 231-1941   CA
Web Site: http://www.theoldglobe.org
Year Founded: 1937
Sales Range: $10-24.9 Million
Emp.: 644
Theater
N.A.I.C.S.: 711110
Barry Edelstein *(Dir-Artistic)*
Amy E. Allison *(Gen Mgr)*
Dave Henson *(Dir-Mktg & Comm)*
Todd Schultz *(Dir-Dev)*
Llewellyn Crain *(Dir-Dev)*
Vicki L. Zeiger *(Chm)*
Timothy J. Shields *(Mng Dir)*

THE OLD TRAIL PRINTING CO., INC.
100 Fornoff Rd, Columbus, OH 43207
Tel.: (614) 443-4852

Web Site: http://www.oldtrailprinting.com
Year Founded: 1928
Sales Range: $10-24.9 Million
Emp.: 100
Commercial Printing Services
N.A.I.C.S.: 323111
Mary M. Held *(CEO)*

THE OLDHAM GROUP
2056 N Republic St, Springfield, IL 62702
Tel.: (217) 528-4649
Web Site: http://www.oldhamgroup.com
Sales Range: $10-24.9 Million
Emp.: 60
Printing Trades Machinery, Equipment & Supplies
N.A.I.C.S.: 423830
Nancy Lucca *(Pres)*

THE OLIVER GROUP, INC.
13500 Oliver Station Ct, Louisville, KY 40245
Tel.: (502) 241-2292   KY
Web Site: http://www.olivergroup.com
Year Founded: 1984
Rev.: $2,700,000
Emp.: 16
Management Consulting Services
N.A.I.C.S.: 541611
Jennifer O. Mackin *(CEO)*
Scott T. Kiefer *(VP)*
Bruce McKay *(Dir-St. Louis Market)*
Andrew Ferguson *(Exec Dir-Creative)*
Brian Cooper *(Chief Creative Officer)*
Tom Cox *(Pres)*

THE OLSON COMPANY
3010 Old Ranch Pkwy Ste 100, Seal Beach, CA 90740
Tel.: (562) 596-4770
Web Site: http://www.olsonhomes.com
Sales Range: $10-24.9 Million
Emp.: 75
Single-Family Housing Construction
N.A.I.C.S.: 236115
Stephen E. Olson *(Chm)*

THE OMAHA THEATER COMPANY
2001 Farnam St, Omaha, NE 68102
Tel.: (402) 345-4852   NE
Web Site: http://www.omaha-theater.com
Year Founded: 1949
Theatrical, Musical & Performance Arts Events & Venues Guides
N.A.I.C.S.: 711310
Grant Hilgenkamp *(Dir-Tech)*

THE OMNIA GROUP INC.
1501 W Cleveland St Ste 300, Tampa, FL 33606
Tel.: (813) 254-9449
Web Site: http://www.omniagroup.com
Year Founded: 1985
Sales Range: $1-9.9 Million
Emp.: 40
Behavioral Assessment & Employment Consulting Services
N.A.I.C.S.: 541618
Heather Caswell *(Pres)*
Kim Busse *(Mgr-Key Relationship)*
Wendy Sheaffer *(Sr VP-Ops)*

THE ONE-PAGE COMPANY INC.
233 Post St 4th Fl, San Francisco, CA 94108
Tel.: (415) 781-7243   DE
Year Founded: 2011
Sales Range: $1-9.9 Million

Cloud-Based Human Resources Software Platform Developer & Publisher
N.A.I.C.S.: 541511
Joanna Riley *(Founder, CEO & CFO)*

THE ONESTAR FOUNDATION
9011 Mountain Ridge Dr Ste 100, Austin, TX 78759
Tel.: (512) 287-2000   TX
Web Site: http://www.onestarfoundation.org
Year Founded: 2003
Sales Range: $1-9.9 Million
Emp.: 19
Community Welfare Services
N.A.I.C.S.: 813319

THE ONYX GROUP
1199 N Fairfax St Ste 600, Alexandria, VA 22314
Tel.: (703) 548-6699
Web Site: http://www.onyxgroup.com
Year Founded: 1982
Sales Range: $1-9.9 Million
Emp.: 37
Architectural Services
N.A.I.C.S.: 541310
Philip W. Rush *(CEO)*
Al McCoubrey *(Pres)*
Steve Lettau *(Mgr-Hawaii Program)*
Andrew Goldwater *(CFO)*

THE OPERAND GROUP II LLC
234 James St, Barrington, IL 60010
Tel.: (312) 513-3558   IL
Web Site: http://www.theoperandgroup.com
Emp.: 100
Portfolio Management Services
N.A.I.C.S.: 523999

Subsidiaries:

Atlantic Duct Cleaning, Inc.   (1)
22875 Bryant Crt Ste 120, Sterling, VA 20166
Tel.: (703) 435-4485
Web Site: http://www.atlanticductcleaning.com
Sales Range: $1-9.9 Million
Emp.: 26
Residential & Commercial Duct Cleaning Services
N.A.I.C.S.: 333415
Thomas R. Keys *(Pres)*
David Doyle *(Sr Project Mgr)*
Corrie Mason *(Mgr-Bus Dev)*

THE OPPORTUNITY ALLIANCE
50 Monument Sq, Portland, ME 04101
Tel.: (207) 874-1175   ME
Web Site: http://www.opportunityalliance.org
Year Founded: 1965
Sales Range: $25-49.9 Million
Emp.: 694
Community Action Services
N.A.I.C.S.: 624190
Craig Given *(VP-IT)*
Dawn Ouellette *(CFO)*
Janet LaFlamme *(Sr VP-HR)*

THE OPTICAL SOCIETY OF AMERICA, INC.
2010 Massachusetts Ave NW, Washington, DC 20036
Tel.: (202) 223-8130   NY
Web Site: http://www.osa.org
Year Founded: 1916
Sales Range: $25-49.9 Million
Emp.: 183
Optical Industry Association
N.A.I.C.S.: 813910
Elizabeth A. Rogan *(CEO)*
Elizabeth Nolan *(Chief Publ Officer)*
Sean Bagshaw *(COO & CIO)*

Melissa Russell *(Chief Indus Rels Officer)*
Chad Stark *(Chief Meetings Officer)*
Philip Russell *(Pres)*
Stephen D. Fantone *(VP)*
Ryan Strowger *(Chief Events & Indus Officer)*

THE OPTIONS CLEARING CORP.
125 S Franklin St Ste 1200, Chicago, IL 60606-1028
Tel.: (312) 322-6200
Web Site: http://www.theocc.com
Year Founded: 1975
Sales Range: $250-299.9 Million
Emp.: 400
Clears & Regulates Options Trade
N.A.I.C.S.: 523999
John Davidson *(CEO)*
Jean Cawley *(Sr VP)*
Craig S. Donohue *(Exec Chm)*
Luke Moranda *(Sr VP)*
John Fennell *(Chief Risk Officer & Exec VP)*
David Ridgway *(Sr VP-Enterprise Risk Mgmt)*
David Hoag *(CIO & Sr VP)*
Mark Morrison *(Chief Security Officer & Sr VP)*
Timothy Dwyer *(Sr VP-Strategic Sys)*
Vishal Thakkar *(Sr VP & Head-Enterprise Risk Mgmt)*
Janet Angstadt *(Gen Counsel & Exec VP)*
Pat Hickey *(Sr VP-Product & Bus Dev)*
Saqib Jamshed *(Sr VP-Model Risk Governance)*
Sandeep Maira *(First VP & Head-Risk Solution Delivery & Support)*
Dan Busby *(COO)*
Mike Hansen *(Chief Clearing & Settlement Svcs Officer)*

THE OREGON COMMUNITY FOUNDATION
1221 SW Yamhill St Ste 100, Portland, OR 97205
Tel.: (503) 227-6846   OR
Web Site: https://www.oregoncf.org
Year Founded: 1973
Sales Range: $150-199.9 Million
Emp.: 83
Community Foundation
N.A.I.C.S.: 813211
Elizabeth Carey *(CFO-Portland & VP)*
Nancy Bales *(Exec Dir)*
Kathleen Cornett *(VP-Grants & Programs-Portland)*
Art Frank *(Dir-Tech Svcs-Portland)*
Max Williams *(Pres & CEO)*
Jenn Columbus *(Dir-Northern Willamette Valley)*
Johanna Thoeresz *(Chief Dev Officer-Portland)*
Sheila Murty *(VP-Ops-Portland)*
Sonia Worcel *(Chief Community Impact Officer)*
Stephanie Swanson *(Dir-Mktg & Comm)*
Mariann Hyland *(VP-People & Culture)*

THE OREGON HISTORICAL SOCIETY
1200 SW Park Ave, Portland, OR 97205
Tel.: (503) 222-1741   OR
Web Site: http://www.ohs.org
Year Founded: 1898
Sales Range: $1-9.9 Million
Emp.: 72
Historical Resource Conservation Services

N.A.I.C.S.: 712110
Kerry Tymchuk *(Exec Dir)*
Dwight Peterson *(Dir-IT & Security)*
Sue Metzler *(Dir-Dev)*
Sheri Neal *(CFO)*
Lisa Noah *(COO)*
Helen Louise *(Dir-Museum)*
Jamieson Grabenhorst *(Sec)*
Carl Christoferson *(VP)*

THE ORIGINAL HONEYBAKED HAM CO.
405 Broadway, Saugus, MA 01906
Tel.: (781) 233-9000
Web Site: http://www.honeybakedham.com
Sales Range: $10-24.9 Million
Emp.: 12
Meat Markets, Including Freezer Provisioners
N.A.I.C.S.: 459420
Stephen McHugh *(Pres)*

THE ORIGINAL KEVIN GUIDRY PRODUCE MARKET, INC.
3619 Moss St, Lafayette, LA 70507
Tel.: (337) 269-4726
Rev.: $11,500,000
Emp.: 60
Fresh Fruit & Vegetable Merchant Whslr
N.A.I.C.S.: 424480
Johnathan Guidry *(VP)*
Kevin Guidry *(Pres)*

THE ORIGINAL MATTRESS FACTORY
4930 State Rd, Cleveland, OH 44134
Tel.: (216) 661-8388
Web Site: http://www.originalmattress.com
Rev.: $16,600,000
Emp.: 100
Mattresses & Foundations
N.A.I.C.S.: 337910
Ronald E. Trzcinski *(Pres & Partner)*
Perry Doermann *(Controller)*
Jim Carlton *(Mgr-Store)*
Tom Kessler *(Mgr)*

THE ORLANDO BAKING COMPANY INC.
7777 Grand Ave, Cleveland, OH 44104-3061
Tel.: (216) 361-1872   OH
Web Site: http://www.orlandobaking.com
Year Founded: 1872
Sales Range: $125-149.9 Million
Emp.: 325
Bread, Cake & Related Products
N.A.I.C.S.: 311812
Nicholas Orlando *(Co-Pres)*
Chester Orlando *(Co-Pres)*
John C. Orlando *(Owner)*

THE OROGEN GROUP
1 Rockefeller Plz Ste 3020, New York, NY 10020
Tel.: (212) 332-4580
Web Site: http://orogengroup.com
Financial Services
N.A.I.C.S.: 523999
Vikram Shankar Pandit *(Chm & CEO)*

Subsidiaries:

Westcor Land Title Insurance Company   (1)
875 Concourse Pkwy S Ste 200, Maitland, FL 32751
Tel.: (702) 251-5228
Web Site: http://www.wltic.com
Regional Title Insurance Underwriter
N.A.I.C.S.: 524127
Scott Chandler *(COO)*
Mary O'Donnell *(Pres & CEO)*
Susan Green *(Dir-Comm)*

THE ORVIS COMPANY, INC.
178 Conservation Way, Sunderland, VT 05250
Tel.: (802) 362-3622   VT
Web Site: http://www.orvis.com
Year Founded: 1856
Sales Range: $250-299.9 Million
Emp.: 1,500
Mail Order of Sporting Goods, Gifts & Sportswear
N.A.I.C.S.: 459110
David D. Perkins *(Vice Chm)*
Leigh H. Perkins *(Chm & CEO)*
William R. McLaughlin *(Pres)*
Dave Finnegan *(VP-Tech & Interactive)*

Subsidiaries:

The Orvis Company   (1)
1711 Blue Hills Dr, Roanoke, VA 24012-8602
Tel.: (540) 345-6789
Web Site: http://www.orvis.com
Sales Range: $25-49.9 Million
Emp.: 550
Sporting Goods Mfr
N.A.I.C.S.: 339920
Robert J. Bean *(CFO, COO & VP)*

THE OSAWATOMIE AGENCY INC.
601 Main St, Osawatomie, KS 66064
Tel.: (913) 755-3811   KS
Financial Holding Company
N.A.I.C.S.: 551112
Gregg P. Lewis *(Pres)*

Subsidiaries:

First Option Bank   (1)
601 Main St, Osawatomie, KS 66064
Tel.: (913) 755-3811
Web Site: http://www.firstoptionbank.com
Banking Services
N.A.I.C.S.: 522110
Katie Stoecker *(Branch Mgr)*
Blake Heid *(Pres & CEO)*

THE OSBORN
101 Theall Rd, Rye, NY 10580
Tel.: (914) 925-8000   NY
Web Site: http://www.theosborn.org
Year Founded: 1892
Sales Range: $25-49.9 Million
Emp.: 428
Retirement Community
N.A.I.C.S.: 623311
Mark R. Zwerger *(CEO)*

THE OSBORNE ASSOCIATION, INC.
809 Westchester Ave, Bronx, NY 10455
Tel.: (718) 707-2600   NY
Web Site: http://www.osborneny.org
Year Founded: 1933
Sales Range: $10-24.9 Million
Emp.: 325
Community Welfare Services
N.A.I.C.S.: 624190
Elizabeth Gaynes *(Exec Dir)*
Carolina Cordero Dyer *(CFO)*
Frederik R. L. Osborne *(Vice Chm)*
Jeffrey G. Smith *(Chm)*
Victor F. Germack *(Treas)*
Zelma Weston Henriques *(Sec)*

THE OSCAR W. LARSON COMPANY INC.
10100 Dixie Hwy, Clarkston, MI 48348-2414
Tel.: (248) 620-0070   MI
Web Site: http://www.larsonco.com
Year Founded: 1946
Sales Range: $25-49.9 Million
Emp.: 300
Specialty Trade Contractors
N.A.I.C.S.: 238990

Bruce F. Larson *(Pres)*
James C. Lintol *(Exec VP)*
Bill O'Brien *(CFO)*

THE OSTERKAMP GROUP
1350 E Philadelphia St, Pomona, CA 91769
Tel.: (909) 590-8200
Web Site: http://www.osterkampgrp.com
Rev.: $21,754,192
Emp.: 100
Holding Company
N.A.I.C.S.: 484230
Hank Osterkamp *(Exec VP)*
Steve Pilcher *(VP)*
Anthony H. Osterkamp Jr. *(Pres & CEO)*

Subsidiaries:

Dedicated Fleet Systems, Inc.   (1)
1350 E Philadelphia St, Pomona, CA 91766
Tel.: (909) 590-8200
Web Site: http://www.osterkampgrp.com
Rev.: $11,475,916
Emp.: 75
Local Trucking Services
N.A.I.C.S.: 484110

Frontier Transportation Inc.   (1)
3577 Philadelphia St, Chino, CA 91710
Tel.: (909) 590-8245
Web Site: http://www.osterkampgrp.com
Rev.: $10,622,734
Emp.: 37
Local Trucking Services
N.A.I.C.S.: 484110

Osterkamp Trucking Inc.   (1)
1350 E Philadelphia St, Pomona, CA 91769
Tel.: (909) 590-8200
Web Site: http://www.osterkampgrp.com
Rev.: $21,600,000
Emp.: 35
Provider of Interstate & Intrastate Trucking Services
N.A.I.C.S.: 484230
Hank Osterkamp *(Pres)*

THE OUSSET AGENCY, INC.
20475 Hwy 46 W Ste 180-602, Spring Branch, TX 78070
Tel.: (830) 885-5130   TX
Web Site: http://www.getousset.com
Year Founded: 1982
Sales Range: $25-49.9 Million
Emp.: 6
N.A.I.C.S.: 541810
John M. Ousset *(Founder)*
Margaret A. Ousset *(VP & Dir-Mktg)*

THE OXFORD INVESTMENT GROUP, INC.
9404 Genesee Ave Ste 200, La Jolla, CA 92037
Tel.: (858) 458-1122
Web Site: http://www.oxfordinvestmentgroup.com
Year Founded: 1985
Privater Equity Firm
N.A.I.C.S.: 523999
Selwyn Isakow *(Founder & CEO)*
Michael J. Baltosiewich *(CFO)*
James Niu *(Mng Dir)*

THE P.A. HUTCHISON COMPANY
400 Penn Ave, Mayfield, PA 18433
Tel.: (570) 876-4560
Web Site: http://www.pahutch.com
Year Founded: 1911
Rev.: $23,600,000
Emp.: 148
Books Printing
N.A.I.C.S.: 323117

THE P.A. HUTCHISON COMPANY

The P.A. Hutchison Company—(Continued)
Erin Jones (Dir-Sls & Admin)
Janet Elvis (Mgr)
Christian P. Hutchison (Pres)

THE PABLOVE FOUNDATION
6607 W Sunset Blvd, Los Angeles, CA 90028-7103
Tel.: (323) 657-5557   CA
Web Site: http://www.pablove.org
Year Founded: 2008
Sales Range: $1-9.9 Million
Emp.: 15
Grantmaking Services
N.A.I.C.S.: 813219
Raul Lorenzana (Program Mgr-Pablove Shutterbugs)
Ashley Lough (Mgr-Events)
Jane Cheung (VP-Programs)
Bart Verry (VP-Dev & Comm)
Michael Orendy (Fin Dir & Dir-Ops)
Eva Schlomann (Sr Program Mgr-Pablove Shutterbugs)
Jeff Castelaz (Co-Founder & Chm)
Jo Ann Thrailkill (Co-Founder, Pres & CEO)
Caroline Merrill (Mgr-Dev)
Brynne Zaniboni (Mgr-Mktg & Comm)
Jeff Castelaz (Co-Founder & Chm)
Jo Ann Thrailkill (Co-Founder, Pres & CEO)
Jane Cheung (VP-Programs)
Bart Verry (VP-Dev & Comm)
Michael Orendy (Fin Dir & Dir-Ops)

THE PACKAGING HOUSE, INC.
6330 N Pulaski Rd, Chicago, IL 60646-4512
Tel.: (773) 286-1888   IL
Web Site: http://www.tphinc.com
Year Founded: 1965
Sales Range: $10-24.9 Million
Emp.: 45
Mfr of Corrugated & Fiber Boxes
N.A.I.C.S.: 322211
Philip Schmidt (Pres)

THE PACKER GROUP INC.
1950 N Washington St, Naperville, IL 60563
Tel.: (630) 505-5722
Web Site: http://www.packereng.com
Rev.: $21,600,000
Emp.: 100
Engineeering Services
N.A.I.C.S.: 541330
Charlotte Sartain (Sec & VP-Fin)
Kenneth Packer (Chm & CEO)
Edward M. Caulfield (Pres)

THE PADDED WAGON INC.
163 Exterior St, Bronx, NY 10451
Tel.: (718) 585-9445
Web Site:
  http://www.thepaddedwagon.com
Rev.: $10,000,000
Emp.: 100
Provider of Moving & Storage Services
N.A.I.C.S.: 484110
Eddie Dowling (Pres)
Frances Notarnicola (Office Mgr)

THE PAGE SEED CO.
1A Green St, Greene, NY 13778-1108
Tel.: (607) 656-4107
Web Site: http://www.pageseed.com
Year Founded: 1896
Sales Range: $1-9.9 Million
Emp.: 50
Garden, Flower & Lawn Seeds Whslr
N.A.I.C.S.: 424910
Jefferey Serko (VP-Sls)

THE PAIGE GROUP
258 Genesee St Ste 204, Utica, NY 13502
Tel.: (315) 733-2313
Web Site: http://www.paigegroup.com
Year Founded: 1967
Sales Range: $10-24.9 Million
Emp.: 12
Full Service
N.A.I.C.S.: 541810
Christine Shields (VP & Dir-Media)
Nancy Pattarini (Pres & CEO)
Claude Schuyler (VP & Sr Dir-Creative)
Carrie McMurray (VP-Plng)
Susan Evans (Assoc Dir-Creative)
Lori Beckman (Project Mgr)
Barbara Majka (Dir-Ops)
Allison Damiano (Acct Mgr)
Ann Martel (Coord-Traffic & Admin)
Allison Damiano-DeTraglia (VP-Acct Svcs)
Diane Stirling (Dir-Strategic Comm)

THE PALEY CENTER FOR MEDIA
25 W 52nd St, New York, NY 10019
Tel.: (212) 621-6600
Web Site: http://www.paleycenter.org
Year Founded: 1976
Sales Range: $10-24.9 Million
Emp.: 150
Museum Chronicling the History of Television & Radio
N.A.I.C.S.: 712110
Frank A. Bennack Jr. (Chm)
Diane Lewis (Exec VP-Programming)
Gustave M. Hauser (Vice Chm)
Maureen J. Reidy (Pres & CEO)
David Schoer (Exec VP-Fin & Ops)
William S. Paley (Founder)
Susan Madden (Sr VP-Dev)
David S. Weinberg (VP-Bus & Legal Affairs)
Kathryn Thompson (VP-Corp Partnership)
Jamitha Fields (VP-Dev & Client Svcs)
Jennifer Joyce (VP-Mktg, Comm & Guest Svcs)
Jordan Ryder (VP-Indus Programming)

THE PALISADES GROUP LLC
11755 Wilshire Blvd Ste 1700, Los Angeles, CA 90025
Tel.: (424) 280-7560   DE
Web Site:
  http://www.palisades.us.com
Year Founded: 2012
Sales Range: $300-349.9 Million
Financial Investment Advisory & Asset Management Services
N.A.I.C.S.: 523940
Matt Mustich (Head-Asset Mgmt)
Nirvan Ghosh (Sr Portfolio Mgr)
Sally Kelly (CFO)
Haseeb Rahman (Dir-Trading & Analytics)
Caleb Reed (Dir-Data Science)
Leyla Mamedova (head-Transaction Mgmt)
Ken Rideout (Head-Bus Dev)
Jack L. Macdowell Jr. (Chief Investment Officer)

THE PALMER-DONAVIN MANUFACTURING COMPANY, INC.
3210 Centerpoint Dr, Columbus, OH 43123
Tel.: (614) 317-0100   DE
Web Site:
  http://www.palmerdonavin.com
Year Founded: 1907
Sales Range: $150-199.9 Million
Emp.: 300
Retail of Lumber Plywood & Millwork Building Matter
N.A.I.C.S.: 423310
Robyn Pollina (CEO)
Ron Calhoun (Pres & COO)
Robert Hudgins (VP-Fin)

Subsidiaries:

Diamond Hill Plywood Company (1)
600 E Broad St, Darlington, SC 29532-2900
Tel.: (843) 393-2803
Web Site:
  http://www.diamondhillplywood.com
Sales Range: $10-24.9 Million
Emp.: 35
Wholesale Plywood & Other Building Materials
N.A.I.C.S.: 423310
James H. Ramsey (Exec VP)
Kennedy Breeden (CFO)
Sherman Ramsey (Founder)

THE PAPE GROUP, INC.
355 Goodpasture Is Rd, Eugene, OR 97401-2119
Tel.: (541) 683-5073
Web Site: http://www.pape.com
Year Founded: 1990
Industrial Machinery & Equipment
N.A.I.C.S.: 423830
Dan Hollingsheag (Pres)
Don Rowland (Mgr-Health & Safety)
Shaun Swift (Dir-Info Sys)

Subsidiaries:

BlueLine Rental (1)
3820 E Winslow, Phoenix, AZ 85040
Tel.: (602) 454-7368
Web Site: http://www.bluelinerental.com
Sales Range: $10-24.9 Million
Emp.: 30
Material Handing & Construction Equipment Sales
N.A.I.C.S.: 423830

Bobcat West (1)
29550 Airport Rd, Eugene, OR 97440
Tel.: (541) 689-7407
Web Site: http://www.bobcatwest.com
Compact Construction Equipment Dealer
N.A.I.C.S.: 423830

Engineered Products (1)
9883 40th Ave S, Seattle, WA 98118
Tel.: (206) 394-8300
Web Site: http://www.eppape.com
Sales Range: $1-9.9 Million
Emp.: 40
Warehouse, Storage, Conveyance & Allied Products
N.A.I.C.S.: 423830
Dave Salman (Pres)

Industrial Finance Co., Inc. (1)
355 Goodpasture Rd, Eugene, OR 97401
Tel.: (541) 683-5073
Web Site: http://www.pape.com
Sales Range: $50-74.9 Million
Emp.: 100
Personal Credit Institution Services
N.A.I.C.S.: 522291
Randy Neuman (Gen Mgr)

Pape D.W., Inc. (1)
7909 N Upland Dr, Portland, OR 97203
Tel.: (503) 286-6400
Web Site: http://www.ditchwitchnw.com
Trencher, Vibratory Plow & Horizontal Directional Drilling Equipment Sales
N.A.I.C.S.: 423830
Steve Jergentz (Gen Mgr)
Rob Weaver (Mgr-Fin)

Subsidiary (Domestic):

Ditch Witch Equipment Co. Inc. (2)
929 Stillwater Rd, West Sacramento, CA 95605
Tel.: (916) 371-6000
Web Site: http://www.ditchwitchwest.com
Mining Machinery & Equipment Whslr & Distr
N.A.I.C.S.: 423810
Robert Kilgour (Co-Pres)

Pape Kenworth (1)
550 NE Columbia Blvd, Portland, OR 97211-1402
Tel.: (503) 240-6282
Web Site: http://www.papekenworth.com
Sales Range: $50-74.9 Million
Emp.: 80
New & Used Truck Dealership
N.A.I.C.S.: 441227
Mike Pati (Gen Mgr)
Cameron Thornburg (Supvr-Body Shop)
Alan Link (Supvr-Svc)

Subsidiary (Domestic):

Pape Kenworth (2)
4300 Hadley Dr, Central Point, OR 97502
Tel.: (541) 772-5211
Web Site: http://www.papekenworth.com
Sales Range: $25-49.9 Million
Emp.: 14
Truck & Truck Parts Sales & Service
N.A.I.C.S.: 441330
Gary Neal (Mgr)

Pape Machinery, Inc. (1)
355 Goodpasture Is Rd Ste 300, Eugene, OR 97401-2119
Tel.: (541) 683-5073
Web Site: http://www.papemachinery.com
Sales Range: $10-24.9 Million
Emp.: 160
Provider of Construction & Mining Machinery Services
N.A.I.C.S.: 423830
Rodger Spears (Pres)
Hal Hansen (Dir-Sls)

Subsidiary (Domestic):

Hobi Outdoor Power Equipment (2)
1810 NE Stephens St, Roseburg, OR 97470
Tel.: (541) 673-7567
Emp.: 10
Construction Equipment Distr
N.A.I.C.S.: 423810
Pat Gaffney (Mgr)

Branch (Domestic):

Pape Machinery (2)
1425 NE Columbia Blvd, Portland, OR 97211-1672
Tel.: (503) 289-1103
Web Site: http://www.papemachinery.com
Mfr of Construction & Mining Machinery
N.A.I.C.S.: 423810
Scot Boatright (Gen Mgr)
Jim Smith (Reg Mgr-Svc)
Russell Paradis (Mgr-Rental)

Pape Machinery (2)
3607 20th St E, Tacoma, WA 98424-1704   (100%)
Tel.: (253) 922-8718
Web Site: http://www.papemachinery.com
Construction & Mining Machinery
N.A.I.C.S.: 423810
Larry Phillips (Gen Mgr)

Pape Material Handling (1)
29550 Airport Rd, Eugene, OR 97402
Tel.: (541) 689-7478
Web Site: http://www.papemh.com
Lift Truck Service & Support Network
N.A.I.C.S.: 811310
Terry McCabe (Gen Mgr)
Mike Kienle (Supvr-Sls Admin)

Subsidiary (Domestic):

Globe-Bay Area Forklift (2)
4040 3rd St, San Francisco, CA 94124-2129
Tel.: (415) 647-6990
Web Site: http://www.globeforklift.com
Scientific & Technical Consulting Services
N.A.I.C.S.: 541690
John Walsh (Owner)

THE PARENT COMPANY, INC.
241 Wilson Pike Cir, Brentwood, TN 37027
Tel.: (615) 221-7000
Web Site:
  http://www.theparentco.com
Year Founded: 1984
Sales Range: $100-124.9 Million
Emp.: 50

Commercial & Office Building, New Construction
N.A.I.C.S.: 236220
Til Bourland (Pres)

THE PARK BANK
1815 Greenway Cross, Madison, WI 53713
Tel.: (608) 278-2801
Web Site: http://www.parkbank.com
Year Founded: 1966
Sales Range: $10-24.9 Million
Emp.: 250
State Savings Banks, Not Federally Chartered
N.A.I.C.S.: 522180
Erik Wilhelm (Controller)
Scott Ducke (Sr VP-Bus Dev)
Mike Leibundgut (VP-HR)
Darwin Lynde (Sr VP-Credit Admin)
Chad R. Armstrong (Pres)
James H. Hegenbarth (CEO)
James R. Imhoff Jr. (Chm)

THE PARK CIRCLE MOTOR CO.
1829 Reisterstown Rd, Baltimore, MD 21208-6320
Tel.: (410) 484-0600   MD
Year Founded: 1921
Sales Range: $150-199.9 Million
Emp.: 10
Holding Company
N.A.I.C.S.: 523150
Jeffrey A. Legum (Pres & CEO)
Thomas J. Karwacki (Treas & Sec)

THE PARKSITE GROUP
1563 Hubbard Ave, Batavia, IL 60510-1419
Tel.: (630) 761-9490   IL
Web Site: http://www.parksite.com
Year Founded: 1971
Rev: $41,996,070
Emp.: 400
Lumber, Plywood & Millwork-Wood Panelling, Solid Surface Material & Counter-Top Material
N.A.I.C.S.: 423310
Ron Heitzman (Pres & CEO)
Robert Higgins (Sr VP-Sls)

Subsidiaries:

Parksite Plunkett-Webster   (1)
1 W Ave Ste 217, Larchmont, NY 10538
Tel.: (914) 834-8461
Web Site: http://www.parksite.com
Sales Range: $25-49.9 Million
Emp.: 225
Mfr & Distr of Hardwood, Softwood & Building Materials
N.A.I.C.S.: 423310

THE PARQUET GROUP
189 S Orange Ave Ste 850, Orlando, FL 32801
Tel.: (407) 425-0300
Web Site: http://www.parquetgroup.com
Sales Range: $1-9.9 Million
Service Industry Consulting Services
N.A.I.C.S.: 541611
Rick Van Warner (Pres & Principal)
Joe Kefauver (Sr Partner & Principal)
Franklin Coley (Partner)

Subsidiaries:

Parquet Public Affairs, LLC   (1)
189 S Orange Ave Ste 850, Orlando, FL 32801
Tel.: (407) 425-0300
Web Site: http://www.parquetpa.com
Public Relations
N.A.I.C.S.: 541820
Joe Kefauver (Mng Partner & Principal)
Jenifer Fuller Jessep (Partner)

Shannon McAleavey (Partner)
Carson Chandler (Partner)
Rachel Moalli (Mgr-Pub Affairs)

THE PARTNERS GROUP, LTD.
11740 SW 68th Pkwy Ste 200, Portland, OR 97223
Tel.: (503) 241-9550
Web Site: http://www.tpgrp.com
Year Founded: 1999
Sales Range: $1-9.9 Million
Emp.: 48
Insurance Consulting Services
N.A.I.C.S.: 524210
Bruce Kerr (Co-Founder)
Doreen Barnhouse (VP-Ops)
Roderick Cruickshank (Pres & CEO)
Jake Shafer (CFO)
Craig Pankow (Mng Dir-Comml Insurance Div)
Nicole Pond (Partner-Retirement Plan Svcs)
Emily Roselle (Acct Mgr)
Gary Alton (Mng Partner-Employee Benefits)
John Woolley (Dir-Wealth Mgmt)
Austin Early (Acct Exec-Comml Insurance)
Tim Anderson (Dir-IT)
Joanne Sweeney (Mng Dir-Private Client Svcs)

THE PASHA GROUP
4040 Civic Ctr Dr Ste 350, San Rafael, CA 94903
Tel.: (415) 927-6400
Web Site: http://www.pashagroup.com
Year Founded: 1947
Sales Range: $25-49.9 Million
Emp.: 455
Provider of Maritime, Automotive & Freight Forwarding Transportation Services
N.A.I.C.S.: 483113
John Pasha (Sr VP-Pasha Automotive Svcs)
Amy Sherburne Manning (Gen Counsel & Sr VP)
Charles D. Patton (Sr VP)
Christine Irvine (Sr VP-HR & Payroll)
David Beckerman (Sr VP-IT Svcs)
James Britton (CFO)
John Kreisler (Sr VP-Pasha Distr Svcs)
Michael Caswell (Sr VP)
Missy Donnelly (Sr VP-Govt Re-Location Svcs)
George W. Pasha III (Chm)
George Pasha IV (Pres & CEO)

Subsidiaries:

Gateways International Inc.   (1)
2030 1st Ave Ste 200, Seattle, WA 98121-1212
Tel.: (206) 728-5990
Web Site: http://www.gatewaysinternational.com
Sales Range: $10-24.9 Million
Emp.: 20
Freight Transportation Arrangement
N.A.I.C.S.: 488510

Pasha Distribution Services LLC   (1)
8050 Veterans Memorial Pkwy, Saint Peters, MO 63376
Tel.: (636) 978-8100
Web Site: http://www.pashadistributionservices.com
Emp.: 14
Logistics Consulting Servies
N.A.I.C.S.: 541614

Pasha Stevedoring & Terminals L.P.   (1)
802 S Fries Ave Berth 176-179, Wilmington, CA 90744
Tel.: (310) 835-9869
Web Site: http://www.psterminals.com
Marine Cargo Handling Services

N.A.I.C.S.: 488320
David Vanwaardenburg (VP-Maritime Ops)

The Pasha Group - Automotive and Logistics Division   (1)
4040 Civic Center Dr Ste 350, San Rafael, CA 94903
Tel.: (415) 927-6400
Logistics Consulting Servies
N.A.I.C.S.: 541614
Carol Kresse (Controller)

THE PASSION GROUP
600 Cookman Ave, Asbury Park, NJ 07712
Tel.: (732) 897-1111
Web Site: http://www.thepassiongroup.com
Sales Range: $1-9.9 Million
Emp.: 8
Event Marketing & Management
N.A.I.C.S.: 541613
Richie Tarzian (Pres)

THE PASTA HOUSE CO.
700 New Ballas Rd, Saint Louis, MO 63141
Tel.: (314) 535-6644   CO
Web Site: http://www.pastahouse.com
Year Founded: 1974
Sales Range: $50-74.9 Million
Emp.: 2,500
Owns & Operates Restaurants
N.A.I.C.S.: 722511
Joseph A. Fresta (Founder)
John Harris (CFO)
Sam Garanzini (VP)
Jennifer Duerfahrd (Dir-Mktg)
Roger Bastar (Supvr-Ops)

Subsidiaries:

The Pasta House Company Franchises, Inc.   (1)
1143 Macklind Ave, Saint Louis, MO 63110-1440   (100%)
Tel.: (314) 535-6644
Web Site: http://www.pastahouse.com
Restaurant Franchise
N.A.I.C.S.: 533110

THE PASTENE COMPANIES, LTD.
330 Tpke St Ste 100, Canton, MA 02021-2357
Tel.: (781) 830-8200   MA
Web Site: http://www.pastene.com
Year Founded: 1874
Sales Range: $75-99.9 Million
Emp.: 50
Importer of Foods & Wines
N.A.I.C.S.: 424410
Christopher Tosi (Chm)
Mark Tosi (Pres)
John Franciosa (CFO)

Subsidiaries:

Pastene Inc.   (1)
9101 De L, Ville d'Anjou, H1J2X9, QC, Canada
Tel.: (514) 353-7997
Web Site: http://www.pastene.ca
Sales Range: $10-24.9 Million
Emp.: 8
Packaged Food Product Mfr & Whslr
N.A.I.C.S.: 424420
Vincent Tangredi (Gen Mgr)

THE PATIENT RECRUITING AGENCY
6207 Bee Caves Rd Ste 288, Austin, TX 78746
Tel.: (512) 345-7788
Web Site: http://www.tprausa.com
Year Founded: 1999
Rev: $12,000,000
Emp.: 30
Advetising Agency
N.A.I.C.S.: 541810

Lance Nickens (Pres)
Todd B. Sanders (CTO)
Carl T. Wibbenmeyer (Exec VP)

THE PATRON SPIRITS COMPANY
6670 S Vly View, Las Vegas, NV 89118-4516
Tel.: (702) 262-9446   NV
Web Site: http://www.patronspirits.com
Year Founded: 1989
Sales Range: $10-24.9 Million
Emp.: 30
Alcoholic Beverages Mfr
N.A.I.C.S.: 312140
Dave Lowren (CFO)
John Paul DeJoria (Founder)
Greg Cohen (Dir-Corp Comm)
Adrian Parker (VP-Global Mktg-Patron)

THE PEABODY ESSEX MUSEUM
161 Essex St, Salem, MA 01970
Tel.: (978) 745-9500   MA
Web Site: http://www.pem.org
Year Founded: 1992
Sales Range: $50-74.9 Million
Emp.: 306
Museums
N.A.I.C.S.: 712110
Dan L. Monroe (CEO)
Jay Finney (CMO)
Derek O'Brien (Dir-Creative Svcs)
Robert Monk (Dir-Facilities)
Steven Mallory (Mgr-Historic Structures & Landscapes)
Robert N. Shapiro (Chm)

THE PEACH FOUNDATION
1098 Marlin Ave, Foster City, CA 94404
Tel.: (650) 525-1188   CA
Web Site: http://www.peachfoundationusa.org
Year Founded: 2001
Sales Range: $1-9.9 Million
Emp.: 2
Education & Art Promotion Services
N.A.I.C.S.: 711310

THE PECAN DELUXE CANDY COMPANY INC.
2570 Lone Star Dr, Dallas, TX 75212-6308
Tel.: (214) 631-3669   TX
Web Site: http://www.pecandeluxe.com
Year Founded: 1950
Sales Range: $25-49.9 Million
Emp.: 200
Flavoring Extracts & Syrups-Flavorings for Ice Cream & Yogurt
N.A.I.C.S.: 311930
Bennie Brigham (Chm)
Jeff French (Dir-Dairy Sls-North America)
Jay Brigham (Pres & CEO)
Keith Hurd (Controller)
Steve Dunlop (VP-Bus Dev-Asia)

THE PECK-HANNAFORD & BRIGGS CO. INC.
4670 Chester Ave, Cincinnati, OH 45232
Tel.: (513) 681-4600   OH
Web Site: http://www.peckhannafordbriggs.com
Year Founded: 1936
Sales Range: $10-24.9 Million
Emp.: 150
Provider of Plumbing, Heating & Air-conditioning Services
N.A.I.C.S.: 238220

THE PECK-HANNAFORD & BRIGGS CO. INC.

U.S. PRIVATE

The Peck-Hannaford & Briggs Co. Inc.—(Continued)

James Briggs (Pres)
Jerry Govert (Sr VP)

Subsidiaries:

Peck-Hannaford & Briggs Service Corp. (1)
4673 Spring Grove Ave, Cincinnati, OH 45232-1919
Tel.: (513) 681-1200
Web Site:
http://www.peckhannafordbriggs.com
Sales Range: $10-24.9 Million
Emp.: 35
Provider of Plumbing, Heating & Air-Conditioning Services
N.A.I.C.S.: 238220

THE PEDRO COMPANIES, INC.

797 Belmont Ln E, Saint Paul, MN 55117-2205
Tel.: (651) 224-9491   MN
Web Site:
http://www.pedrocompanies.com
Year Founded: 1914
Sales Range: $75-99.9 Million
Emp.: 100
Stock, Industrial Carrying Cases, Tools, Shipping & Business Cases Mfr
N.A.I.C.S.: 316990
Eugene Pedro (Owner & CEO)
Carl Pedro Jr. (Pres)

THE PEEBLES CORPORATION

2020 Ponce de Leon Blvd Ste 907, Coral Gables, FL 33134
Tel.: (305) 993-5050   DC
Web Site:
http://www.peeblescorp.com
Year Founded: 1983
Commercial & Institutional Real Estate Investment, Development & Building Construction Services
N.A.I.C.S.: 236220
R. Donahue Peebles (Founder, Chm & CEO)
Katrina L. Peebles (Principal & Dir-Creative)
Gregory P. Cola (Dir-Acq & Investments)
Adriana Aragon Echevarria (Dir-Mktg & Comm)
R. Lee Hodges (Dir-Dev-Southeast Reg)
Chris Leng Smith (Dir-Dev-Northeast Reg)
Rochelle R. Carroll (Assoc Dir-Corp Rels)
Lowell D. Plotkin (Gen Counsel)

THE PEELLE COMPANY

3373 Nesconset Hwy Ste, Hauppauge, NY 11788
Tel.: (905) 846-4545
Web Site: http://www.peelledoor.com
Sales Range: $10-24.9 Million
Emp.: 100
Elevators & Equipment Mfr
N.A.I.C.S.: 333921
Michael Ryan (VP-Sls)
Henry E. Peelle III (Pres)

Subsidiaries:

Peelle Asia Pacific, Pte. Ltd. (1)
Blk 326 Ubi Avenue 1 Unit 08-689, Singapore, 400326, Singapore
Tel.: (65) 9830 2212
Elevator Mfr
N.A.I.C.S.: 333921

The Peelle Company Ltd. (1)
195 Sandalwood Parkway West, Brampton, L7A 1J6, ON, Canada
Tel.: (905) 846-4545
Web Site: https://www.peelledoor.com
Elevator Mfr
N.A.I.C.S.: 333921

THE PEGASUS GROUP

1148 Alpine Rd Ste 100, Walnut Creek, CA 94596-4444
Tel.: (925) 930-0810
Web Site:
http://www.pegasusgroup.net
Sales Range: $10-24.9 Million
Emp.: 25
Property Management Company
N.A.I.C.S.: 531210
Dwight W. Davis (Pres)
William Schmicker (Partner)
Tim Davis (Dir-Acq)
Margaret Martin (Exec VP-Property Mgmt)
Paula Shorf (Exec VP-Acctg)
Phil Jones (Asst Dir-Acq)

THE PENN COMPANIES

2577 Interplex Dr Ste A, Trevose, PA 19053
Tel.: (215) 632-7800   PA
Web Site:
http://www.pennemblem.com
Year Founded: 1945
Sales Range: $200-249.9 Million
Emp.: 500
Mfr & Distr of Personalization & Identification Products
N.A.I.C.S.: 313310
Jon Joseph (Sr VP-Sls & Bus Dev)
Keane Hoffman (Dir-Div Sls & Svc)
David Braun (Dir-Div Sls & Svc)
Phil Pogue (Dir-Sls)
Rich Hirsh (Mgr-Natl Acct Direct Sls)
Aaron Singh (Mgr-Tech Support)
Bob Wiberg (VP-Mfg)
Michelle Burgess (Mgr-Direct Sls Customer Svc)
Debbie Martinenza (Mgr-Customer Support)

Subsidiaries:

Penn Emblem Co. (1)
11199 Inland Ave, Mira Loma, CA 91752
Tel.: (951) 681-8000
Web Site: http://www.pennemblem.com
Sales Range: $25-49.9 Million
Emp.: 80
Mfr of Emblems
N.A.I.C.S.: 314999
G. Ramirez (Gen Mgr)
Liz Hathaway (Mgr-Creative-Mktg Dept)
Beatrice Gonzalez (Acct Mgr-Direct Sls-West Coast)

The Penn Companies - ImprintsUSA (1)
10909 Dutton Rd, Philadelphia, PA 19154-9979
Tel.: (888) 521-1255
Web Site: http://www.imprintsusa.com
Cartridge Toner Whslr
N.A.I.C.S.: 424120

THE PENN MUTUAL LIFE INSURANCE COMPANY

600 Dresher Rd, Horsham, PA 19044
Tel.: (215) 956-8000   PA
Web Site:
http://www.pennmutual.com
Year Founded: 1847
Rev.: $3,231,252,000
Assets: $33,164,151,000
Liabilities: $29,201,098,000
Net Worth: $3,963,053,000
Earnings: $333,392,000
Emp.: 1,761
Fiscal Year-end: 12/31/18
Fire Insurance Services
N.A.I.C.S.: 524113
Eileen C. McDonnell (Exec Chm)
David M. O'Malley (Pres & CEO)
Thomas H. Harris (Chief Distr Officer & Exec VP)
Susan T. Deakins (Co-CFO & Exec VP)
Raymond Caucci (Sr VP-Product Mgmt & Underwriting)
Greg Driscoll (CIO & Sr VP-Svc Ops)
Dave Raszeja (Co-CFO & Sr VP)
Victoria Robinson (Chief Ethics & Compliance Officer & Sr VP)
Ann-Marie Mason (Chief Legal Officer)
Bill Bell (VP-Advanced Sls)
Jennifer Dorfmeister (Head-Independent Distr)

Subsidiaries:

Hornor, Townsend & Kent, Inc. (1)
600 Dresher Rd, Horsham, PA 19044-2204 (100%)
Tel.: (215) 957-7300
Web Site: http://www.htk.com
Sales Range: $25-49.9 Million
Emp.: 40
Broker/Dealer
N.A.I.C.S.: 523150
Tim Donahue (Pres & CEO)
Rob Kaehler (Chief Compliance Officer & Asst VP)

Janney Montgomery Scott LLC (1)
1717 Arch St, Philadelphia, PA 19103 (100%)
Tel.: (215) 665-6000
Web Site: http://www.janney.com
Sales Range: $250-299.9 Million Investment
N.A.I.C.S.: 523150
Karen Shakowske (Sr VP & Dir-Mktg & Corp Comm)
Timothy C. Scheve (CEO)
Douglas Scales (Co-Mng Dir-Institutional Credit Sls-New York)
Meredith Contente (Mng Dir-Credit Res-New York)
Allison Sylvin (Dir-Institutional Taxable Fixed Income-New York)
Jeffrey Smith (Sr VP & Mgr-Washington)
George Keith (Sr VP & Mgr-Complex)
Anthony Miller (Pres)
Joe Timmins (Sr VP & Dir-HR)
Gregory B. McShea (Gen Counsel & Sr VP)
John Kline (Exec VP-Wealth Mgmt-Raleigh)
Michael Slaymaker (VP-Wealth Mgmt)
Norman L. Oremland (Sr VP-Wealth Mgmt-Washington)
M. Villani Villani (Sr VP-Wealth Mgmt-Bethlehem)
Matt Dragal (VP-Janney Bank Funding & Investor Solutions Grp)
Cliff K. Booth (Head-Investment Banking)
Joseph D. Culley Jr. (Sr VP & Head-Capital Markets Grp)
David Lau (Mng Dir-Equity Capital Markets)
Pat Fagan (Mng Dir-Institutional Equity Sls Trading)
Mitchel Penn (Mng Dir-Equity Res)
Martin Schamis (Head-Wealth Plng-Wealth Mgmt Div)
Chris Johnson (Mgr-Advisor Mktg & Comm)
Mark Anderson (Mng Dir)
Cricket Barlow (Dir-Institutional CD Sls)
Jeffrey Bertoni (Dir-Fixed Income Sls)
John Otis (Dir-Mortgage Trading)
Wayne A. Seaton (Mng Dir-Pub Fin)
Terrell Wilson (Dir-Generalist Sls Grp)
Vince Montesano (Mng Dir-Chicago)
Stephen Yamane (Mng Dir-Boston)
Nick Lampone (Head-Trading & Sls Trading)
Jessica Landis (Dir-Fin Plng)
Mark Margiotta (Mgr-Retail Compliance)
Matthew Giammarinaro (Dir-Fixed Income Sls)
Christopher Gorman (Dir-Fixed Income Sls)
Gregory Lobo (Dir-Fixed Income Sls)
Richard Smith (Dir-Fixed Income Sls)
Karen L. Shakoske (Sr VP & Head-Mktg & Corp Comm)
John Putrino (Mng Dir-Real Estate Investment Banking Grp)
Anne Lurton (Sr VP & Mgr-Complex-Washington)
Kevin J. Reed (Pres-Private Client Grp & Exec VP)
Edward A. Bartlett (First VP-Wealth Mgmt & Mgr-Harrisonburg)
Jason Bender (Mgr-Ponte Vedra Beach)
Noah Doyle (Sr VP)
Charles Princiotto (VP)
Andrew M. Maddaloni (Head-Equities)
Dan Wantrobski (Dir-Research)
Davina DeMark (Mgr-Diversity & Inclusion Programs)
Sean Gallagher (Mng Dir-Infrastructure Investment Banking Grp)
Justin Ausher (Dir-Fixed Income Sls-Chicago)
Mary Jane Darby (Mng Dir & Head-Higher Education & Not-For-Profit Advisory)
Robert Kanzer (Mng Dir-Higher Education & Not-For-Profit Advisory-New York)
Mari Monahan (Mng Dir-Fixed Income Sls-New York)
James Still (Dir-Higher Education & Not-For-Profit Advisory-New York)
Andy Ballou (Head-Institutional Equity Sls-New York)
Katherine O'Brien (VP-Institutional Equity Sls-Boston)
Hany Farag (VP-Wealth Mgmt-New York)
Sheldon Ferriss (VP-Wealth Mgmt-Bedminster)
Ronald H. Holmes (Sr VP-Wealth Mgmt-Holmes Riley Wealth Advisors)
Whitney E. Riley (First VP-Wealth Mgmt-Holmes Riley Wealth Advisors)
Gary Halter (Sr VP-Wealth Mgmt-Glastonbury)
Daniel Mickley (First VP-Wealth Mgmt-Columbus Grandview)
Matthew Kroehler (Exec VP-Wealth Mgmt-KSF Wealth)
Lee Springer (First VP-Wealth Mgmt-KSF Wealth)
Paul Pitsironis (First VP-Melville)
Michael Hricko (CFO & Sr VP)
Margolit Hillsberg (Chief HR Officer & Sr VP)
John C. Yackel (Exec VP & Head-Wealth Mgmt)
Andrew M. Kistler III (Sr VP & Mgr-Southeast)
Jerome F. Lombard Jr. (Pres-Private Client Grp)

Subsidiary (Domestic):

FIG Partners LLC (2)
1475 Peachtree St NE Ste 800, Atlanta, GA 30309
Tel.: (404) 601-7200
Web Site: http://www.figpartners.com
Financial Investment Advisory Services
N.A.I.C.S.: 523150
Greg Gersack (Sr Mng Principal & Co-Head-Investment Banking)
Geoffrey Hodgson (CEO)
Christopher Marinac (Sr Mng Principal & Dir-Res)
Bill Henningson (Assoc Dir-Institutional Sls)
Alex Krasutsky (Head-Equity Sls & Trading)
Sloan Deerin (Principal-Investment Banking-Mid Atlantic)
Matthew Veneri (Mng Principal & Co-Head-Investment Banking)
Timothy R. Chrisman (Chm)
Troy Carlson (Sr VP & Head-Corp & Private Client Svcs)
Adam Desmond (Founder)

Penn Insurance & Annuity Co. (1)
600 Dresher Rd, Horsham, PA 19044-2204 (100%)
Tel.: (215) 956-8000
Web Site: http://www.penninsurance.com
Sales Range: $50-74.9 Million
Emp.: 150
Life Insurance
N.A.I.C.S.: 531120
Aileen Mconneoo (CEO)

THE PENNSYLVANIA COALITION AGAINST DOMESTIC VIOLENCE

3605 Vartan Way Ste 101, Harrisburg, PA 17110
Tel.: (717) 545-6400   PA
Web Site: http://www.pcadv.org
Year Founded: 1976
Sales Range: $25-49.9 Million
Emp.: 35
Domestic Violence Prevention Services

COMPANIES

N.A.I.C.S.: 813410
Susan Higginbotham (Exec Dir)
Michelle Robinson-Ritter (Pres)

THE PENNSYLVANIA EMPLOYEES BENEFIT TRUST FUND
150 S 43rd St, Harrisburg, PA 17111
Tel.: (717) 561-4750 PA
Web Site: http://www.pebtf.org
Year Founded: 1988
Sales Range: $900-999.9 Million
Emp.: 144
Employee Benefit Fund Services
N.A.I.C.S.: 525120
Kathryn Farley (CEO & Exec Dir)
Robert Bickford (CFO)
Nancy Murphy (COO)
Joseph Sassano (CIO)
Gerald Anastasio (Dir-HR)
Kelly Powell Logan (Sec)
Christy Leo (Dir-Comm)
David Fillman (Chm)

THE PENROD COMPANY INC.
2809 S Lynnhaven Rd Ste 350, Virginia Beach, VA 23452-8500
Tel.: (757) 498-0186 VA
Web Site: http://www.thepenrodcompany.com
Year Founded: 1986
Sales Range: $125-149.9 Million
Emp.: 50
Provider of Lumber, Plywood & Millwork Services
N.A.I.C.S.: 423310
Edward A. Heidt (Chm & CEO)
Carl Gade (Pres & COO)
Karsten Nielsen (VP-Sls)
Stewart P. Mitchell (CFO)

THE PEOPLE'S BANK
305 E Jefferson St, Ripley, MS 38663
Tel.: (662) 837-8191
Web Site: http://www.peoplesripley.com
Sales Range: $10-24.9 Million
Emp.: 70
State Commercial Banks
N.A.I.C.S.: 522110
Bobby P. Martin (Pres)
Ricky Settlemires (Sr VP)
Mary Childs (Pres & CEO)

THE PEOPLES BANK CO. INC.
112-114 W Main St, Coldwater, OH 45828
Tel.: (419) 678-2385
Web Site: http://www.pbcbank.com
Sales Range: $10-24.9 Million
Emp.: 75
State Commercial Banks
N.A.I.C.S.: 522110
Jack A. Hartings (Pres & CEO)

THE PEOPLES STATE BANK
601 E Temperance St, Ellettsville, IN 47429
Tel.: (812) 876-2228
Web Site: http://www.peoples-bank.com
Year Founded: 1904
Sales Range: $10-24.9 Million
Emp.: 120
Provider of State Commercial Banks
N.A.I.C.S.: 522110
Alain T. Bouvier (VP)
Lon Stevens (Pres)
Susie Knust (Sr VP)
Johnny Lindsey (Exec VP)
Ashley Hazelrig (Mgr-Bridgeport)
Randy Goodman (VP)
Tim Risen (VP)
Chris Roberge (Chm)
Julie Lindsey (Sec)

THE PEPPER GROUP
220 N Smith St Ste 406, Palatine, IL 60067
Tel.: (847) 963-0333
Web Site: http://www.peppergroup.com
Year Founded: 1994
Sales Range: $1-9.9 Million
Emp.: 16
Advetising Agency
N.A.I.C.S.: 541810

THE PERFECT PUREE OF NAPA VALLEY, LLC.
2700 Napa Vly Corporate Dr Ste L, Napa, CA 94558
Tel.: (707) 261-5100
Web Site: http://www.perfectpuree.com
Year Founded: 1988
Sales Range: $10-24.9 Million
Emp.: 19
Fruit Puree Mfr
N.A.I.C.S.: 311942
Michele Lex (Dir-Mktg)
Tracy Hayward (Founder & Pres)

THE PERFORMANCE COMPANIES INC.
5053 Broadway, Gary, IN 46409
Tel.: (219) 887-6514
Web Site: http://www.performancep.com
Year Founded: 1917
Rev.: $5,000,000
Emp.: 200
Provider of Builder Maintenance & Janitorial Services; Sales of Janitorial Supplies
N.A.I.C.S.: 561720
Michael Saks (VP)
Paula Broutman (Pres)

Subsidiaries:

Performance Plus (1)
2106 S Franklin St, South Bend, IN 46613-2120 (100%)
Tel.: (574) 234-1151
Web Site: http://www.performancep.com
Sales Range: $10-24.9 Million
Emp.: 50
Provider of Air Filter Repair Service
N.A.I.C.S.: 561720
Terry Morse (Gen Mgr)

THE PERKINS + WILL GROUP, LTD.
The Wrigley Bldg 410 N Michigan Ave Ste 1600, Chicago, IL 60611-3603
Tel.: (312) 755-0770 DE
Web Site: http://www.perkinswill.com
Year Founded: 1935
Sales Range: $25-49.9 Million
Emp.: 2,500
Architecture & Design Services
N.A.I.C.S.: 541310
Phil Harrison (CEO-Atlanta)
Meg Brown (Chief Talent Officer-Washington)
Brodie Stephens (Gen Counsel)
Peter Busby (Principal)
Allison Held (CMO)
Murali Selvaraj (CIO)
Tyson Curcio (COO)
Gabrielle Bullock (Dir-Diversity-Global)
D'Arcy Arthurs (Mng Dir-Toronto)
Eric Aukee (Mng Dir-Toronto)
Gina Berndt (Mng Dir)
Robert Brown (Mng Dir-Chicago)
William Harris (Mng Dir-New York)
Tim Wolfe (Principal)
Jennifer Carzoli (Assoc Principal)
Andrew Mowat (Dir-Ops)
Lisa Killaby (Principal & Dir-Workplace Strategy)
Gautam Sundaram (Assoc Principal-Urban Design Practice-Boston)
Dana Waymire (CFO)
Ralph Johnson (Member-Mgmt Bd)
Kay Kornovich (Member-Mgmt Bd)
Jean Mah (Member-Mgmt Bd)
Richard Marshall (Member-Mgmt Bd)
Jessica Figenholtz (Assoc Principal-Higher Education Practice)
Aimee Eckmann (Principal-PreK-12 Education Practice)
Adana Johns (Assoc Principal-Science & Tech Practice)
Andrew Hausmann (Assoc Principal)
Remi Isaacs (Assoc Principal)
Kami Kinkaid (Assoc Principal)
Sarah Rege (Principal)

Subsidiaries:

Perkins + Will - Research Triangle Park (1)
Legacy Tower 411 W Chapel Hill St Ste 200, Durham, NC 27701
Tel.: (919) 433-5300
Web Site: http://www.freelon.com
Sales Range: $1-9.9 Million
Emp.: 40
Architectural Services
N.A.I.C.S.: 541310

Perkins + Will - Washington, DC (1)
1250 24th St NW Ste 800, Washington, DC 20037
Tel.: (202) 737-1020
Web Site: http://www.perkinswill.com
Sales Range: $25-49.9 Million
Emp.: 76
Interior Design & Architectural Services
N.A.I.C.S.: 541410
Chris Morrison (Mng Dir & Principal)
Carl Knutson (Principal & Dir-Design)
Kendall Wilson (Principal & Dir-Interior Design)
Tim Bakos (Principal & Dir-Ops)
Joshua Rubin (Dir-Technical)
Daniel Moore (Principal)
Edward Feiner (Principal)
Laura Morris (Mng Principal)
Paul Harney (Principal)
Thomas Butcavage (Principal)

THE PERRY COMPANY
500 S Vly Mills Dr, Waco, TX 76711
Tel.: (254) 756-2139 TX
Web Site: http://www.perry-co.com
Year Founded: 1946
Sales Range: $50-74.9 Million
Emp.: 25
Mfr & Distributor of Pickup Truck Accessories & Farm Implements
N.A.I.C.S.: 333111
Jeff Weaver (Pres)

Subsidiaries:

Pickup Outfitters (1)
220 Lk Air Dr, Waco, TX 76710
Tel.: (254) 399-9416
Sales Range: $1-9.9 Million
Emp.: 4
Retail Pickup Truck Accessories
N.A.I.C.S.: 333111
Jay Ehret (CEO)

THE PERRYMAN COMPANY
213 Vandale Dr, Houston, PA 15342
Tel.: (724) 746-9390 PA
Web Site: http://www.perrymanco.com
Year Founded: 1988
Emp.: 410
Titanium Product Mfr
N.A.I.C.S.: 332999
Frank Perryman (Pres & CEO)
James T. Perryman Sr. (Founder & Chm)

Subsidiaries:

The Perryman Co. - Pittsburgh Plant (1)
149 S Johnson Rd, Houston, PA 15342
Tel.: (724) 745-7272
Web Site: http://www.perrymanco.com
Emp.: 150
Forged Metal Products Mfr
N.A.I.C.S.: 332111
Frank L. Perryman (Pres)

THE PERSIMMON GROUP LLC
11 E 5th St Ste 300, Tulsa, OK 74103
Tel.: (918) 592-4121
Web Site: http://www.thepersimmongroup.com
Year Founded: 2004
Sales Range: $1-9.9 Million
Emp.: 22
Business Consultancy Services
N.A.I.C.S.: 541614
Bill Fournet (Founder, Pres & CEO)
Shane Cox (VP-Govt Svcs)
Josh Miller (Dir-Bus Dev)
Jill Nickerson (Dir-TPG Speakers)
Amy Joy (VP-Fin)
Kris Reynolds (VP-Project Mgmt)

THE PERT GROUP
270 Farmington Ave Ste 200, Farmington, CT 06032
Tel.: (860) 242-2005
Web Site: http://www.thepertgroup.com
Sales Range: $10-24.9 Million
Emp.: 99
Marketing Research & Public Opinion Polling Services
N.A.I.C.S.: 541910
Dale Lersch (CEO & Principal)
Doug Guion (Pres)
Gigi Ryan (Exec VP & Principal)

THE PERVO PAINT COMPANY
4225 Solano Ave, Napa, CA 94558-1611
Tel.: (323) 758-1147 CA
Year Founded: 1929
Sales Range: $50-74.9 Million
Emp.: 50
Commercial, Industrial & Traffic Paints, Acrylic Emulsion-Alkyds Mfr
N.A.I.C.S.: 325510
Brad DeRuiter (Pres-Pervo Paint & Owner)
Scott Shannon (VP-Sls & Mktg)
Diana Reyes (VP-Ops)
Nick Perera (CFO)

THE PET LOSS CENTER - AUSTIN LLC
2215 W Pipeline Rd, Euless, TX 76040
Tel.: (817) 283-7297
Web Site: http://www.thepetlosscenter.com
Year Founded: 2014
Sales Range: $1-9.9 Million
Emp.: 96
Pet Cremation Services
N.A.I.C.S.: 812220
Peter A. Gudmundsson (CEO)

THE PETE STORE, LLC
5100 Holabird Ave, Baltimore, MD 21224
Web Site: http://www.thepetestore.com
Truck Sales
N.A.I.C.S.: 441227
John C. Arscott (Pres & CEO)

Subsidiaries:

The Peterbilt Store - Knoxville (1)
5218 Rutledge Pike, Knoxville, TN 37924
Tel.: (865) 546-9553
Web Site: http://www.thepetestore.com
Sales Range: $25-49.9 Million
Emp.: 150
Retailer of Trucks & Tractors

THE PETE STORE, LLC

The Pete Store, LLC—(Continued)
N.A.I.C.S.: 423110
John Arscott (Pres)

THE PETER GROUP, INC.
7 N Columbus Blvd, Philadelphia, PA 19106-1422
Tel.: (215) 592-8303   PA
Year Founded: 1991
Sales Range: $10-24.9 Million
Emp.: 50
N.A.I.C.S.: 541810
Joseph Delago (CEO)
John Hoey (Pres)

Subsidiaries:

Topak Marketing Inc. (1)
7 N Columbus Blvd, Philadelphia, PA 19106-1422 (100%)
Tel.: (215) 574-8307
Web Site: http://www.merchantcircle.com
N.A.I.C.S.: 541810
John Hoey (Pres)
Paulette Scarry (HR Dir)

THE PETROLEUM ALLIANCE OF OKLAHOMA
500 NE 4th St Ste 200, Oklahoma City, OK 73104
Tel.: (405) 942-2334   OK
Web Site: https://www.thepetroleumalliance.com
Year Founded: 1955
Oil & Natural Gas Producer Association
N.A.I.C.S.: 221210
Jeff Wilson (VP-Govt Affairs)
Brian Woodard (VP-Regulatory Affairs)
Avery Smith (VP-Dev)
Phillip Browder (Mgr-Safety & Membership Benefits)
Lauren Burnett (Dir-Events)
A. J. Ferate (VP-Regulatory Affairs)
Mindy Huffman (Coord-Membership & Mktg)
Natalie Kinmonth (Dir-Bus Dev)
James Roller (VP-Legislative Affairs)
Ellis Stromberg (Mgr-Admin & Registration)

THE PEW CHARITABLE TRUSTS
1 Commerce Sq 2005 Market St Ste 2800, Philadelphia, PA 19103-7077
Tel.: (215) 575-9050   PA
Web Site: http://www.pewtrusts.org
Year Founded: 2002
Sales Range: $250-299.9 Million
Emp.: 860
Grantmaking Services
N.A.I.C.S.: 813211
Melissa Skolfield (Sr VP-Comm)
Joshua S. Reichert (Exec VP)
Tamera Luzzatto (Sr VP)
Janice Bogash (Chief Admin Officer & Sr VP)
Sally O'Brien (Sr VP)
Susan K. Urahn (Chief Program Officer & Exec VP)
Frazierita D. Klasen (VP)
Linda Bartlett (CFO & Sr VP)
Esther Berg (Officer-Comm)
Michael Dimock (Pres-Pew Res Center)
Ernesto Fernandez Monge (Officer-Reducing Harmful Fishing Subsidies)

Subsidiaries:

Pew Research Center (1)
1615 L St NW Ste 700, Washington, DC 20036
Tel.: (202) 419-4300
Public Opinion Research
N.A.I.C.S.: 541910

Michael Dimock (VP-Res)
Elizabeth Mueller Gross (VP)
Paul Taylor (VP-Special Projects)
James Bell (Dir-Intl Survey Res)
Alan Cooperman (Dir-Religion Res)
Claudia Dean (Dir-Res Practices)
Carroll Doherty (Dir-Political Res)
Scott Keeter (Dir-Survey Res)
Vidya Krishnamurthy (Dir-Comm)
Mark Hugo Lopez (Dir-Hispanic Res)
Amy Mitchell (Dir-Journalism Res)
Kim Parker (Dir-Social Trends Res)
Richard Wike (Dir-Global Attitudes Res)
James G. McMillan (Acting Pres)

THE PHELPS GROUP
12121 Bluff Creek Dr Ste 200, Los Angeles, CA 90094
Tel.: (310) 752-4400   CA
Web Site: http://www.thephelpsgroup.com
Year Founded: 1981
Sales Range: $50-74.9 Million
Emp.: 80
Advertising Services
N.A.I.C.S.: 541810
Joe Phelps (Founder & Chm)
Ed Chambliss (CEO)
Tony Stern (Chief Creative Officer)
Kristen Bergevin (VP-PR)

Subsidiaries:

Copia Creative, Inc. (1)
3122 Santa Monica Blvd Ste 203, Santa Monica, CA 90404-2511
Tel.: (310) 826-7422
Web Site: http://www.copiacreative.com
Sales Range: $10-24.9 Million
Emp.: 15
Advertising Agencies
N.A.I.C.S.: 541810

THE PHIA GROUP LLC
163 Bay State Dr, Braintree, MA 02184
Tel.: (718) 535-5600
Web Site: http://www.phiagroup.com
Year Founded: 1999
Rev: $3,300,000
Emp.: 75
Claims Adjusting
N.A.I.C.S.: 524291
Marta Butkiewicz (Acct Mgr)
Jennifer McCormick (VP-Consulting)

THE PHILADELPHIA BOURSE, INC.
120 Sallitt Dr Ste A, Stevensville, MD 21666
Tel.: (410) 604-3780   DE
Year Founded: 1979
Sales Range: $75-99.9 Million
Emp.: 5
Holding Company
N.A.I.C.S.: 238210
McBee Butcher (Chm)
John Hozik (Pres & CEO)
Jonathan Butcher (Director)
Howard Butcher IV (VP)

Subsidiaries:

E.C. Ernst South East (1)
3320 Vineland Rd Ste B, Orlando, FL 32811-6452 (100%)
Tel.: (407) 839-5088
Electrical Contracting
N.A.I.C.S.: 238210

E.C. Ernst, Inc. (1)
132 Log Canoe Cir, Stevensville, MD 21666
Tel.: (301) 350-7770
Web Site: http://www.ecernst.com
Emp.: 9
Electrical Contracting
N.A.I.C.S.: 238210
James Hegarty (CFO & Controller)
Tom Booze (Sr VP)

Sensenich Propeller Manufacturing Co., Inc. (1)

14 Citation Ln, Lancaster, PA 17601 (100%)
Tel.: (717) 569-0435
Web Site: http://www.sensenich.com
Sales Range: $1-9.9 Million
Mfr & Sales Of Airplane Propellers
N.A.I.C.S.: 811310

Sensenich Wood Propeller Co., Inc. (1)
2008 Wood Ct, Plant City, FL 33563 (100%)
Tel.: (813) 752-3711
Web Site: http://www.sensenichprop.com
Sales Range: $10-24.9 Million
Mfr, Sales & Service of Wood Airplane & Air Boat Propellers
N.A.I.C.S.: 811310
Donald Rowell (Pres)
Terry Griffe (Gen Mgr-Aluminum Propeller)

THE PHILADELPHIA CONTRIBUTIONSHIP
210 S 4th St, Philadelphia, PA 19106
Tel.: (215) 627-1752
Web Site: http://www.1752.com
Year Founded: 1752
Sales Range: $125-149.9 Million
Emp.: 200
Holding Company
N.A.I.C.S.: 551112
Scott Mahaley Jenkins (Chm)
Kevin L. Tate (CFO, Treas, VP & Asst Sec)
Stephen A. McGowan (Controller, Asst Treas & Asst VP)
Stacey M. Manzo (Asst VP-Customer Svcs & Corp Sec)
Christopher S. Strohl (VP-Underwriting)
Kathy Morris-Rosati (Asst VP-HR)
John E. Barry (Mgr-Facilities)
J. Ransley Lennon (VP-IT)
Brenda J. Peremes (VP-Claims)
Alan M. Pakula (Chief Actuary & VP)
Christopher C. Oehrle (VP-Mktg & Agency Rels)
Thomas Greenfield (Pres & CEO)

Subsidiaries:

ADS Security L.P. (1)
3001 Armory Dr Ste 100, Nashville, TN 37204-3711
Web Site: http://www.adssecurity.com
Electrical Contractor
N.A.I.C.S.: 238210
Eliza Kitchens (Mgr-Huntsville Office)
Tom Cooney (Sr VP-Western Reg)
Paul Dyson (VP-Acq)
John Cerasuolo (Pres)
Victor Chapman (VP-Acq)
Craig Leyers (Sr VP-Sls & Mktg)

Subsidiary (Domestic):

Central Carolina Security (2)
1142 N Horner Blvd, Sanford, NC 27330-9444
Web Site: http://www.centralcarolinasecurity.com
Electrical Apparatus & Equipment, Wiring Supplies & Related Equipment Merchant Whslr
N.A.I.C.S.: 423610
Nelson McDonald (Owner)

Vector Security, Inc. (1)
2000 Ericsson Dr, Warrendale, PA 15086
Tel.: (724) 741-2200
Web Site: http://www.vectorsecurity.com
Emp.: 100
Insurance Services
N.A.I.C.S.: 524298
Pamela J. Petrow (Pres & CEO)
Michael T. Grady (Exec VP)
Leslie D. Baker (VP-HR)
Vince R. DiValerio (VP-Acq)
Thomas P. Helisek (VP-Info Sys)
John F. Madden (VP-Authorized Dealer Div)
Art A. Miller (VP-Mktg)
Anita C. Ostrowski (VP-Central Station Svcs)
Chuck Thropp (CFO)

U.S. PRIVATE

THE PHILADELPHIA FOUNDATION
1234 Market St Ste 1800, Philadelphia, PA 19107
Tel.: (215) 563-6417   PA
Web Site: http://www.philafound.org
Year Founded: 1918
Sales Range: $25-49.9 Million
Emp.: 38
Community Development Services
N.A.I.C.S.: 624190
Betsy Anderson (Dir-Comm)
Matt Charles (Mgr-Acct)
Pedro A. Ramos (Pres & CEO)
Laura Solomon (Founder)
Liz Kenney (CFO)
Lois Gabin-Legato (Chief Advancement Officer & VP-Institutional Advancement)

THE PHILADELPHIA ORCHESTRA ASSOCIATION
The Atlantic Bldg 260 S Broad St 16th Fl, Philadelphia, PA 19102
Tel.: (215) 893-1900
Web Site: http://www.philorch.org
Sales Range: $10-24.9 Million
Emp.: 110
Music Producer
N.A.I.C.S.: 711130
Mario Mestichelli (CFO, Treas & VP)
Allison Vulgamore (Pres & CEO)
Karen M. Tomlinson (Dir-HR)
Richard B. Worley (Chm)
Lisa Bullard (Dir-Mktg)
Kathleen Curtis (Sr Mgr-Acctg)
Maura Deming (Sr Dir-Individual Giving)
Rachele Armstrong (Mgr)
Travis Wells (Dir-Touring & Ops)
Sarah Miller Coulson (Sec)
Ezra Wiesner (Mng Dir)
Bradford Wm. Voigt (VP)
Janice Hay (VP)
Jeremy Rothman (VP)

Subsidiaries:

Peter Nero & the Philly Pops (1)
260 S Broad St 16th Fl, Philadelphia, PA 19102
Tel.: (215) 893-1900
Web Site: http://www.phillypops.com
Sales Range: $10-24.9 Million
Emp.: 5
Symphony Orchestra
N.A.I.C.S.: 711130

The Philadelphia Orchestra (1)
1 S Broad St 14th Fl, Philadelphia, PA 19107
Tel.: (215) 893-1900
Web Site: http://www.philorg.org
Sales Range: $10-24.9 Million
Emp.: 72
Philharmonic Orchestra
N.A.I.C.S.: 711130
Allison Vulgamore (Pres & CEO)
Marilyn Rife (Mgr-Orchestra Personnel)

THE PHILADELPHIA PARKING AUTHORITY INC.
3101 Market St, Philadelphia, PA 19104-2807
Tel.: (215) 683-9600   PA
Web Site: http://www.philapark.org
Year Founded: 1950
Sales Range: $75-99.9 Million
Emp.: 1,500
Automobile Parking Services
N.A.I.C.S.: 812930
Ernie Rodriguez (Dir-Procurement)

THE PHILADELPHIA PROTESTANT HOME
6500 Tabor Ave, Philadelphia, PA 19111
Tel.: (215) 697-8000   PA
Web Site: http://www.pphfamily.org
Year Founded: 1890
Sales Range: $25-49.9 Million

COMPANIES

Emp.: 596
Continuing Care Retirement Community Operator
N.A.I.C.S.: 623311
Jan Walters (*Dir-Independent Living Mktg*)
Barry Fineman (*Dir-Personal Care mktg*)
Maryann Cassizzi (*Sr Dir-Care Mgmt & Admissions*)
Richard D. Soltan (*Vice Chm*)
W. Russell Koerwer (*Chm*)
Andrew J. Fennell (*Treas*)
Anthony L. Manzo (*Pres & CEO*)
David E. Heilman (*Sec*)
James P. Bodine (*Exec VP*)
William Davis (*CFO*)

THE PHILLIES, L.P.
Citizens Bank Park 1 Citizens Bank Way, Philadelphia, PA 19148
Tel.: (215) 463-6000 PA
Web Site:
http://www.philadelphia.phillies.mlb.com
Year Founded: 1893
Emp.: 200
Professional Baseball Club
N.A.I.C.S.: 711211
David Montgomery (*Chm*)
David Buck (*Sr VP-Mktg & Adv Sls*)
Mike DiMuzio (*Dir-Ops-Ballpark*)
Brian Lamoreaux (*Dir-Info Sys*)
John Weber (*VP-Ticket Sls & Ops*)
Rob MacPherson (*Dir-Corp Partnerships*)
Michael G. Ciccotti (*Dir-Medical Svcs*)
Michael Stiles (*COO & Exec VP*)
Joe Giles (*Dir-Ballpark Enterprises & Bus Dev*)
Susan Ingersoll Papaneri (*Dir-Baseball Admin*)
Steve Noworyta (*Asst Dir-Player Dev*)
Frank Coppenbarger (*Dir-Team Travel & Clubhouse Svcs*)
Karen Wright Dice (*Dir-Payroll Svcs*)
Debbie Nocito (*Mgr-Client Svcs & Alumni Rels*)
Kurt Funk (*VP-Mktg Programs & Events*)
Chris Long (*Dir-Entertainment*)
Scott Brandreth (*Dir-Mdsg*)
Jo-Anne Levy-Lamoreaux (*Mgr-Adv & Internet Svcs*)
Dan Stephenson (*Dir-Video Production*)
Tina Urban (*Dir-Graphic Production*)
Kathy Killian (*VP-HR & Customer Svcs*)
Christopher Pohl (*Dir-Ticket Tech & Dev*)
Tom Mashek (*Mgr-Suite Sls & Svcs*)
Phil Feather (*Dir-Ticket Svcs & Intern Program*)
Eric Tobin (*Dir-Ops-Events*)
Sal DeAngelis (*Dir-Ops-Security*)
Kevin Steinhour (*Mgr-Visiting Clubhouse*)
John Nickolas (*CFO & VP*)
Bonnie D. Clark (*VP-Comm*)
Pat Gillick (*Pres*)
JoAnn Marano (*Dir-HR & Benefits*)
Leila Graham-Willis (*Mgr-Special Events*)
Gordon Lakey (*Dir-Major League Scouting*)
Tom Sullivan (*Mgr-Adv Sls*)
Brian Mahoney (*Dir-Adv Sls*)
Dan O'Rourke (*Mgr-Equipment & Umpire Svcs*)
Michael Harris (*Dir-Mktg & Special Projects*)
Mark DiNardo (*Dir-Brdcst & Video Svcs*)
Rob Brooks (*Mgr-Brdcst*)
Scott Palmer (*Dir-Pub Affairs*)
Greg Casterioto (*Dir-Baseball Comm*)
John Brazer (*Dir-Publicity*)
Derek Schuster (*Dir-Sls*)
Mike Holdren (*Mgr-Season Ticket Svcs*)
Bill Wilson (*Mgr-Sls Ops*)
Kevin Beale (*Dir-Suite Sls & Client Svcs*)
Ken Duffy (*Mgr-Ticket Ops*)
Lori Loughlin (*Mgr-Ticket Vault Svcs*)
Sharon Nelson (*Mgr-Box Office Ops*)
Joe Jordan (*Dir-Player Dev*)
Benny Looper (*Asst Gen Mgr-Player Personnel*)
Leslie Safran (*Assoc Gen Counsel*)
Andy MacPhail (*Pres-Delegate*)
Rick Strouse (*Gen Counsel & VP*)
Mike Ondo (*Dir-Pro Scouting*)
Sophie Riegel (*Mgr-Player Rels & Charities*)
Mike Carson (*Controller*)
James Trout (*Dir-Mktg Svcs & Events*)
Matt Klentak (*Gen Mgr*)
Brian Barber (*Dir-Amateur Scouting*)

Subsidiaries:

Clearwater Threshers (1)
601 N Old Coachman Rd, Clearwater, FL 33765-2321 **(100%)**
Tel.: (727) 442-8496
Web Site: http://www.threshersbaseball.com
Sales Range: $10-24.9 Million
Emp.: 18
Baseball Team
N.A.I.C.S.: 321999

THE PHOENIX LEARNING GROUP, INC.
1990 E Lohman Ave Ste 102, Las Cruces, NM 88001
Tel.: (314) 569-0211 DE
Web Site: http://www.phoenixlearninggroup.com
Year Founded: 1973
Sales Range: $75-99.9 Million
Emp.: 4
Educational Media, Video, Film, CD-Rom & Book Publisher
N.A.I.C.S.: 512110
Bill Copeland (*Controller*)

Subsidiaries:

BFA Educational Media (1)
141 Millwell Dr Ste A, Saint Louis, MO 63043 **(100%)**
Tel.: (314) 569-0211
Web Site:
http://www.phoenixlearninggroup.com
Sales Range: $10-24.9 Million
Emp.: 3
Educational Films
N.A.I.C.S.: 512110
Andy Amir-Fazli (*Office Mgr*)

Coronet/MTI (1)
141 Millwell Dr Ste A, Maryland Heights, MO 63043
Tel.: (314) 569-0211
Web Site:
http://www.phoenixlearninggroup.com
Sales Range: $10-24.9 Million
Educational & Training Films & Video Tapes
N.A.I.C.S.: 512110
Kathy Longsworth (*VP-Mktg*)
William Copeland (*VP-Acctg*)

Phoenix Films & Video (1)
2349 Chaffee Dr, Saint Louis, MO 63146-3306
Tel.: (314) 569-0211
Web Site:
http://www.phoenixlearninggroup.com
Sales Range: $10-24.9 Million
Educational Films
N.A.I.C.S.: 512110
Heinz Gelles (*Pres*)

Phoenix Learning Resources (1)
1366 Kingsley Dr, Warminster, PA 18974
Tel.: (215) 674-4080
Web Site:
http://www.phoenixlearninggroup.com
Sales Range: $10-24.9 Million
Publisher of Educational Materials
N.A.I.C.S.: 513130
Rod Orth (*Mgr-Sls*)

THE PHOENIX MEDIA/COMMUNICATIONS GROUP
150 Chestnut St, Providence, RI 02903
Tel.: (617) 536-5390
Web Site:
http://www.corp.thephoenix.com
Year Founded: 1966
Rev.: $100,000,000
Emp.: 200
Regional Newspaper & Magazine Publisher & Radio Station Operator
N.A.I.C.S.: 513110
Stephen M. Mindich (*Chm & Publr*)
Bradley M. Mindich (*Pres*)

Subsidiaries:

People2people Group Inc. (1)
126 Brookline Ave, Boston, MA 02215 **(100%)**
Tel.: (617) 450-8671
Web Site: http://www.people2people.com
Rev.: $18,000,000
Emp.: 50
Online Personal Ad & Dating Services
N.A.I.C.S.: 513199

THE PHONE SHOPPE
677A Washington St, Norwood, MA 02062
Tel.: (781) 762-8800
Year Founded: 1988
Sales Range: $25-49.9 Million
Emp.: 100
Car Whslr
N.A.I.C.S.: 441110
Michael Digiandomenico (*Owner*)

THE PICERNE GROUP, INC.
5000 Birch St E Tower Ste 600, Newport Beach, CA 92660
Tel.: (949) 487-6262 DE
Web Site:
http://www.picernegroup.com
Year Founded: 1988
Residential Land Subdividers & Developers
N.A.I.C.S.: 523999
Kenneth A. Picerne (*Founder, Chm & Pres*)
Jon Demorest (*Sr Mng Dir*)
Gregory G. Nakahira (*Chief Investment Officer*)
Christopher M. Davis (*Mng Dir-Southwest States Dev*)
John Colletti (*Dir-Dev*)
Derek Picerne (*Dir-Dev*)
Eric A. Donnelly (*Exec VP-Construction*)
Diane Murphy (*Exec VP*)
Heather D. Derlin (*Exec VP-Asset Mgmt*)
Forrest E. Newhall Jr. (*Sr VP-Fin*)

THE PICTSWEET COMPANY
10 Pictsweet Dr, Bells, TN 38006-0199
Tel.: (731) 663-7600 DE
Web Site:
http://www.pictsweetfarms.com
Year Founded: 1945
Frozen Vegetables Mfr & Whslr
N.A.I.C.S.: 311411
Kevin Schwab (*Sr VP-Sls & Mktg*)
David Everson (*Sr VP-Bus Dev*)

THE PIKE COMPANY INC.
1 Cir St, Rochester, NY 14607-1007
Tel.: (585) 271-5256 NY

Web Site:
http://www.thepikecompany.com
Year Founded: 1985
Sales Range: $25-49.9 Million
Provider of Construction Services
N.A.I.C.S.: 236220
William Tehan (*Pres*)
Rufus M. Judson (*CEO*)
Mauricio F. Riveros (*Chief Innovation Officer*)
Thomas F. Judson Jr. (*Chm*)

Subsidiaries:

BCI Construction Inc. (1)
20 Loudonville Rd, Albany, NY 12204
Tel.: (518) 371-5900
Residential Remodeler
N.A.I.C.S.: 236118
Jim Mahoney (*Mgr-Safety, Resource & Logistics*)
Lynne Fitzgerald (*Asst Project Mgr*)

THE PILOT LLC
145 W Pennsylvania Ave, Southern Pines, NC 28387
Tel.: (910) 692-7271
Web Site: http://www.thepilot.com
Newspaper Publishers
N.A.I.C.S.: 513110
David Woronoff (*Publr*)
Andie Rose (*Creative Dir*)
Darlene Stark (*Dir-Circulation*)
Jim Dodson (*Editor*)
John A. Nagy (*Editor*)
Kit McKinley (*Gen Mgr*)

Subsidiaries:

Red Hand Media, LLC (1)
5435 77 Ctr Dr Ste 50, Charlotte, NC 28217-0711
Tel.: (704) 523-6987
Web Site: http://www.businessnc.com
Sales Range: $1-9.9 Million
Emp.: 16
Business Magazine Publisher
N.A.I.C.S.: 513120
Ben Kinney (*Publr*)

THE PINELLAS COUNTY EMERGENCY MEDICAL SERVICES AUTHORITY
12490 Ulmerton Rd, Largo, FL 33774
Tel.: (727) 582-2000
Web Site:
http://www.sunstarems.com
Sales Range: $25-49.9 Million
Emp.: 600
Ambulance Service
N.A.I.C.S.: 621910
Craig Hare (*Dir-EMS*)

THE PINES AT DAVIDSON
400 Avinger Ln, Davidson, NC 28036
Tel.: (704) 896-1100 NC
Web Site:
http://www.thepinesatdavidson.org
Year Founded: 1983
Sales Range: $10-24.9 Million
Emp.: 301
Community Care Services
N.A.I.C.S.: 624190
David C. Rainey (*VP & Dir-Fin Svcs*)
Carolyn Picton (*Dir-Sls & Mktg*)
Motria Procyk (*Dir-Dev*)
Lorraine Terry (*Dir-Health Svcs*)
Steven H. Jewell (*Pres & Exec Dir*)
Karen Frazier (*Asst Dir-Fin Svcs*)
Judy Green (*Dir-Health Svcs*)
Stephanie Clontz (*Dir-Social Svcs*)
Chad Lauderbaugh (*Dir-Culinary & Dining Svcs*)
Scott Chinery (*Dir-Plant Svcs*)
Amy Smith (*Dir-Wellness Activities & Transportation*)

THE PINES AT WHITING
509 Rt 530, Whiting, NJ 08759
Tel.: (866) 622-5037 NJ

THE PINES AT WHITING

The Pines at Whiting—(Continued)
Web Site:
http://www.thepinesatwhiting.org
Year Founded: 1989
Sales Range: $10-24.9 Million
Emp.: 327
Elderly People Housing Assistance Services
N.A.I.C.S.: 623312
Eric Ghaul (CEO)
Wendy Harshaw (Dir-Sls)
Georgina Bavais (CFO)

THE PIONEER GROUP, INC.
115 N Michigan Ave, Big Rapids, MI 49307
Tel.: (231) 796-4831
Web Site:
http://www.pioneergroup.com
Year Founded: 1862
Sales Range: $10-24.9 Million
Newspaper, Shopping Guide & Telephone Directory Publisher; Commercial Printing Services
N.A.I.C.S.: 513110
Jack Batdorff (Chm)
John A. Batdorff II (Pres & CEO)

Subsidiaries:

The Manistee News Advocate (1)
75 Maple St, Manistee, MI 49660
Tel.: (231) 723-3592
Web Site: http://news.pioneergroup.com
Sales Range: $1-9.9 Million
Emp.: 30
Newspaper & Shopping Guides Publisher
N.A.I.C.S.: 513110
Michelle Graves (Mng Editor)

The Pioneer Newspaper (1)
115 N Michigan Ave, Big Rapids, MI 49307
Tel.: (231) 796-4831
Web Site:
http://www.bigrapidsnewsnews.com
Newspaper Publishers
N.A.I.C.S.: 513110
Jim Crees (Editor-in-Chief)
Whitney Gronski-Buffa (Assoc Editor)
Justin McKee (Coord-Multimedia)

THE PIPCO COMPANIES LTD.
1409 W Altorfer Dr, Peoria, IL 61615-1918
Tel.: (309) 692-4060
Web Site: http://www.pipco-co.com
Year Founded: 1958
Sales Range: $25-49.9 Million
Emp.: 75
Provider of Plumbing, Heating & Air Conditioning Services
N.A.I.C.S.: 238220
Scott J. Cicciarelli (Exec VP)

THE PIPE LINE DEVELOPMENT COMPANY
870 Canterbury Rd, Cleveland, OH 44145
Tel.: (440) 871-5700
Web Site: http://www.plidco.com
Year Founded: 1949
Sales Range: $10-24.9 Million
Emp.: 90
Fabricated Pipe & Pipe Fitting Mfr
N.A.I.C.S.: 332996

THE PITTSBURGH BAGEL FACTORY INC.
5825 Ellsworth Ave Ste 1, Pittsburgh, PA 15232-1771
Tel.: (412) 362-6666
Sales Range: $10-24.9 Million
Emp.: 216
Baked Goods Mfr
N.A.I.C.S.: 311811
David Feldstein (Pres)

THE PLACEMAKING GROUP
505 14th St 5th Fl, Oakland, CA 94612
Tel.: (510) 835-7900
Web Site:
http://www.placemakinggroup.com
Sales Range: $10-24.9 Million
Emp.: 12
Advetising Agency
N.A.I.C.S.: 541810
Dennis Erokan (Pres)
Irvin Hamilton (Sr VP)
Barbara Irias (VP)
Dianne Newton-Shaw (Acct Supvr)
Miraim Schaffer (Acct Mgr)
Jannah Lyon (Dir-Creative)

THE PLANNING COUNCIL
5365 Robin Hood Rd Ste 700, Norfolk, VA 23513
Tel.: (757) 622-9268
Web Site:
http://www.theplanningcouncil.org
Year Founded: 1941
Sales Range: $10-24.9 Million
Human Life Improvement Services
N.A.I.C.S.: 624190
Valerie Langhorne (Treas)
J. Gail Nicula (Co-Vice Chm)
Greg Grootendorst (Chm)
Oneiceia Howard (Sec)
Angela Kellam (Pres & CEO)
Julie Dixon (Sr Dir-Plng & Program Dept)
Cynthia Powell (Dir-HR & Org Dev)
Kimberly Malone (CFO)
Richard D. Knox Jr. (Co-Vice Chm)

THE PLASENCIA GROUP, INC.
1 N Dale Mabry Hwy Ste 1000, Tampa, FL 33609
Tel.: (813) 932-1234
Web Site: http://www.tpghotels.com
Year Founded: 1993
Sales Range: $25-49.9 Million
Emp.: 22
Hotel Consulting & Investing
N.A.I.C.S.: 541611
Lou Plasencia (Chm & CEO)
Richard Conti (Sr Mng Dir)
Robert Wiemer (Sr VP-Southwest Reg)
Orlando Plasencia (Chief Admin Officer)
Paul Williams (VP)
Nicholas Plasencia (VP-Tampa)
Christopher Plasencia (VP)
Joseph T. Corcoran (VP)
Tony M. Haddad (Mgr-Sr Asset)
Jodie Orozco (Partner & VP-Mktg)
Dexter Wood (Sr Mng Dir-New England)

Subsidiaries:

TPG Development Management Consultants (1)
529 Colonel Dewees Rd Ste 300, Wayne, PA 19087
Tel.: (610) 902-9901
Hotel Consulting
N.A.I.C.S.: 541611

THE PLASTEK GROUP
2425 W 23rd St, Erie, PA 16506-2920
Tel.: (814) 878-4400
Web Site:
http://www.plastekgroup.com
Year Founded: 1956
Sales Range: $400-449.9 Million
Emp.: 1,800
Designer & Manufacturer of Consumer Packaging & Personal Care Products
N.A.I.C.S.: 326199
Joseph J. Prischak (Chm)
Scott Ross (Engr-Quality)
Michael Liberatore (Gen Mgr)

Subsidiaries:

Master Mold (1)
2425 W 23rd St, Erie, PA 16506-2920 (100%)
Tel.: (814) 878-5500
Web Site: http://www.plastekgroup.com
Sales Range: $10-24.9 Million
Emp.: 30
Injection Molding Of Plastics
N.A.I.C.S.: 333511

Penn Erie Division (1)
2315 W 23rd St, Erie, PA 16506-2918 (100%)
Tel.: (814) 878-4602
Web Site: http://www.theplastekgroup.com
Sales Range: $10-24.9 Million
Emp.: 30
Mfr of Plastic Injection Molding
N.A.I.C.S.: 333511
Sue Dolas (Controller)
Tom Hartline (Gen Mgr)

Plastek Industries, Inc. (1)
2425 W 23rd St, Erie, PA 16506-2920
Tel.: (814) 878-4400
Web Site: http://www.plastek.com
Sales Range: $25-49.9 Million
Emp.: 300
Mfr of Consumer Products
N.A.I.C.S.: 326199

Plastek UK Ltd (1)
Crown Farm Way, Forrest Town, Mansfield, NG19 0FT, Nottinghamshire, United Kingdom
Tel.: (44) 1623 662233
Web Site: http://www.plastekuk.com
Sales Range: $25-49.9 Million
Emp.: 150
Plastics Product Mfr
N.A.I.C.S.: 326199
Michel Shaw (Gen Mgr)

Spectrum Molding (1)
2425 W 23rd St, Erie, PA 16506-2920 (100%)
Tel.: (814) 878-4400
Web Site: http://www.plastek.com
Sales Range: $25-49.9 Million
Emp.: 250
Injection Molding Of Plastics
N.A.I.C.S.: 326199

The Plastek Group - Engineered Plastics Division (1)
3001 W 15th St, Erie, PA 16505
Tel.: (814) 878-4400
Plastics Product Mfr
N.A.I.C.S.: 326199

The Plastek Group - Plastek do Brasil Division (1)
Rod Eng Ermenio de Oliveira Penteado SP 75 s/n Km 58 2, Indaiatuba, 13337-300, SP, Brazil
Tel.: (55) 19 3885 8200
Web Site: http://www.plastekbrasil.com.br
Plastic Injection Molding Machine Mfr
N.A.I.C.S.: 333248

Triangle Tool Co. (1)
3230 W 22nd St, Erie, PA 16506-2308
Tel.: (814) 878-4703
Web Site: http://www.trianglemachinery.com
Sales Range: $10-24.9 Million
Emp.: 75
Plastic Injection Molding, Tool & Die
N.A.I.C.S.: 333511

THE PLASTRIDGE AGENCY, INC.
820 NE 6th Ave, Delray Beach, FL 33483
Tel.: (561) 276-5221
Web Site: http://www.plastridge.com
Sales Range: $10-24.9 Million
Emp.: 95
Insurance Agents
N.A.I.C.S.: 524210
Thomas E. Lynch (Co-Owner)
Connor C. Lynch (Co-Owner)
Patrick Lacy (VP-Personal & Comml Lines)
Brendan T. Lynch (CFO)

U.S. PRIVATE

THE PLATT BROTHERS & COMPANY, INC.
2670 So Main St, Waterbury, CT 06721
Tel.: (203) 753-4194
Web Site: http://www.plattbros.com
Year Founded: 1830
Sales Range: $10-24.9 Million
Emp.: 100
Deep-Drawn Metal Part Mfr
N.A.I.C.S.: 331491
David Mieczkowski (Pres)
James Goggins (CFO)

Subsidiaries:

Manhattan American Terrazzo Strip Company Inc. (1)
Old Rd 421, Staley, NC 27355 (100%)
Tel.: (336) 622-4247
Web Site:
http://www.manhattanamerican.com
Rev: $1,400,000
Emp.: 20
Design & Manufacture Terrazzo Flooring
N.A.I.C.S.: 327390

Newmark Medical Components Inc. (1)
2670 S Main St, Waterbury, CT 06706
Tel.: (203) 753-1158
Medical Equipment Distr
N.A.I.C.S.: 423450

THE PLAZA CLUB
112 E Pecan St, San Antonio, TX 78205-1414
Tel.: (210) 227-4191
Web Site: http://mycentreclub.com
Year Founded: 1973
Private Membership Business Club & Restaurant Operator
N.A.I.C.S.: 713910
Melani Espinoza (Accountant)
Paula Doris (Dir-Private Event)
Janette Surrett (Dir-Membership)

THE PLAZA GROUP INC.
1177 West Loop S Ste 1450, Houston, TX 77027
Tel.: (713) 266-0707
Web Site:
http://www.theplazagrp.com
Year Founded: 1994
Petrochemical Distr
N.A.I.C.S.: 424690
Ray Heinen (Controller)
Randy E. Velarde (Pres)
Jerry Dunn (Sr VP)

THE PLEXUS GROUPE, INC.
21805 Field Pkwy Ste 300, Deer Park, IL 60010
Tel.: (847) 307-6100
Web Site:
http://www.plexusgroupe.com
Year Founded: 1990
Insurance Brokerage & Consulting Services
N.A.I.C.S.: 524298
Mark Matuscak (Partner)
Matthew McKenna (CFO)
Dave Demas (VP-Bus Dev)
Wes Hornsby (VP-Bus Dev-Dallas)
Kari Fredrick (VP-HR)
Walter R. Fawcett III (CEO)

Subsidiaries:

Cher A Bumps & Associates, Inc. (1)
2601 NW Expwy Ste 1000W, Oklahoma City, OK 73112
Tel.: (405) 840-3033
Web Site: http://www.cabainc.com
Employee Benefit Consulting Firm
N.A.I.C.S.: 541612
Cher Bumps (Founder)

THE PLYMOUTH ROCK CO.
695 Atlantic Ave, Boston, MA 02111

COMPANIES

Tel.: (617) 720-1620
Web Site: http://www.prac.com
Year Founded: 1982
Sales Range: $100-124.9 Million
Emp.: 500
Auto Insurance Company
N.A.I.C.S.: 524210
James M. Stone (Chm)

Subsidiaries:

695 Atlantic Avenue Company, LLC (1)
695 Atlantic Ave Fl 3, Boston, MA 02111
Tel.: (617) 330-9488
Real Estate Manangement Services
N.A.I.C.S.: 531390

Bunker Hill Insurance Company (1)
695 Atlantic Ave, Boston, MA 02111
Tel.: (617) 956-1775
Web Site: http://www.bunkerhillins.com
Emp.: 30
General Insurance Services
N.A.I.C.S.: 524210
Bill Martin (CEO)

Subsidiary (Domestic):

Bunker Hill Insurance Casualty Company (2)
695 Atlantic Ave, Boston, MA 02111
Tel.: (617) 956-1777
Web Site: http://www.bunkerhillins.com
Health Insurance Services
N.A.I.C.S.: 524114
Curt Troutman (VP)

Mt. Washington Assurance Corporation (1)
81 Hall St Fl 2, Concord, NH 03301-3488 (100%)
Tel.: (603) 224-6288
Web Site: http://www.mwac.com
Sales Range: $25-49.9 Million
Emp.: 15
Fire Marine & Casualty Insurance
N.A.I.C.S.: 524126
Dan Reardon (Gen Mgr)

Pilgrim Insurance Company (1)
695 Atlantic Ave, Boston, MA 02111
Tel.: (617) 956-6000
Web Site: http://www.pilgrimins.com
Emp.: 40
General Insurance Services
N.A.I.C.S.: 524210
William Hartranft (Pres)
Barry Tagen (VP-Ops)
Patrick W. Avery (Mgr-Claims)
Joseph L. Mullen (Controller)
Mike Bredy (Mgr-Underwriting)

Plymouth Rock Management Company of New Jersey (1)
200 Connell Dr Ste 3000, Berkeley Heights, NJ 07922
Tel.: (908) 790-7885
Real Estate Manangement Services
N.A.I.C.S.: 531390

Shared Technology Services Group Inc. (1)
695 Atlantic Ave, Boston, MA 02111
Tel.: (617) 720-1620
Web Site: http://www.stsgi.com
Real Estate Manangement Services
N.A.I.C.S.: 531390
Denise Verrier (Gen Mgr)

THE POCA VALLEY BANKSHARES

7033 Charleston Rd, Walton, WV 25286
Tel.: (304) 577-6611 WV
Web Site: http://www.pocavalleybank.com
Year Founded: 1908
Sales Range: $10-24.9 Million
Emp.: 100
Banking Services
N.A.I.C.S.: 522110
Robert N. Rowsey (Sr VP)
Linda Ashley (Pres)

THE POINT COMMUNITY DEVELOPMENT CORPORATION

940 Garrison Ave, Bronx, NY 10474
Tel.: (718) 542-4139 NY
Web Site: http://www.thepoint.org
Year Founded: 1994
Sales Range: $1-9.9 Million
Emp.: 30
Youth Development Services
N.A.I.C.S.: 624110
Danny R. Peralta (Exec Mng Dir)
Carey Clark (Dir-Visual Arts)
Rebecca Rosado (Program Mgr & Community Organizer)
Angela A. Tovar (Dir-Community Dev)
Moises Marquez (Mgr-Facilities)
Sarah C. Lee (Treas)
Svati Lelyveld (Sec)

THE POINT GROUP

5949 Sherry Ln Ste 1800, Dallas, TX 75225-8084
Tel.: (214) 378-7970
Web Site: http://www.thepointgroup.com
Year Founded: 1996
Emp.: 40
Holding Company; Marketing Communications
N.A.I.C.S.: 551112
Heidi McKinley (Pres-PR)
Ann Peebles Rimkus (VP-Strategy)
Brenda Hurtado (COO)
Martha Cook (VP-PR)
Beth Wilbins (Pres)
Ruth Baron (Sr VP)

Subsidiaries:

FORTE Group Inc. (1)
333 W Wacker Dr Lobby Ste, Chicago, IL 60606
Tel.: (312) 757-4944
Web Site: http://fortegrp.com
Emp.: 300
IT Talent for IT Outsourcing, Staffing & Consulting, Offshore Development, Test Automation, Maintenance & Ongoing Support
N.A.I.C.S.: 561311
Steve Kreynin (Founder)
Larry Fedin (Partner-Forte New York)
Vera Kimmi (VP-Global Delivery)
Aleksandr Shakhnovich (Technical Mgr-E-Commerce)
Svetlana Dovidovich (Dir-Ops & Fin)
Marina Perla (VP-Sls & Mktg)
Tatiana Strugalskaya (Mng Dir-Belarus)
Sergii Kutuzov (Mng Dir-Ukraine)
Michael Makishima (CFO)
Mikael Carlsson (CEO)

THE POLLY HILL ARBORETUM

809 State Rd, West Tisbury, MA 02575
Tel.: (508) 693-9426 DE
Web Site: http://www.pollyhillarboretum.org
Year Founded: 1996
Sales Range: $10-24.9 Million
Emp.: 15
Botanical Garden
N.A.I.C.S.: 712130
Timothy M. Boland (Exec Dir)
Susan Wasserman (Sec)

THE POSSE FOUNDATION, INC.

14 Wall St Ste 8A-60, New York, NY 10005
Tel.: (212) 405-1691 NY
Web Site: http://www.possefoundation.org
Year Founded: 1989
Sales Range: $10-24.9 Million
Emp.: 130
Educational Support Services
N.A.I.C.S.: 611710
Rico Blancaflor (VP-Strategic Projects)
Matthew Fasciano (COO)
Jonathan Garcia (Mgr-IT)
Hedy Roma (VP-Dev)
Deborah Bial (Founder & Pres)

THE POST COMPANY

333 Northgate Mile, Idaho Falls, ID 83401
Tel.: (208) 522-1800
Web Site: http://www.postregister.com
Sales Range: $25-49.9 Million
Emp.: 175
Newspapers, Publishing & Printing
N.A.I.C.S.: 513110
Roger Plothow (Publr & Editor)

THE POST GROUP PRODUCTION SUITES

1415 Cahuenga Blvd, Los Angeles, CA 90028
Tel.: (323) 822-4400
Web Site: http://postgroup.com
Year Founded: 1979
Emp.: 200
Motion Picture Production Services
N.A.I.C.S.: 512191
Alan Chalfin (CFO)
Celena Martirossian (VP)
Deniece Frick (Ops Mgr)
Jenna Johnson (Coord-Client Care)

THE POWER HOUSE, INC.

10233 S Dolfield Rd, Owings Mills, MD 21117
Tel.: (844) 384-7290
Web Site: http://www.thepowerhouseinc.com
Year Founded: 1979
Thermoelectric Devices
N.A.I.C.S.: 334413
S. John Blumenthal (Pres)

THE PPA GROUP, LLC

11149 Research Blvd Ste 375, Austin, TX 78759
Tel.: (512) 501-3635
Web Site: http://www.theppagroup.com
Year Founded: 2005
Rev.: $3,500,000
Emp.: 68
Real Estate Agency
N.A.I.C.S.: 531210
Monte Lee-Wen (Pres & CEO)
Nalie Lee-Wen (CFO)

THE PR CONSULTING GROUP, INC.

45 Broadway Ste 3140, New York, NY 10006
Tel.: (212) 683-8100 NY
Web Site: http://www.prcg.com
Year Founded: 1982
Sales Range: $1-9.9 Million
Emp.: 13
Public Relations Agency
N.A.I.C.S.: 541820
James F. Haggerty (Pres & CEO)
Rachel Serlin (Acct Exec)
Jon Coifman (Mng Dir)
Sean Gammon (Acct Supvr)

Subsidiaries:

The PR Consulting Group, Inc.-Los Angeles (1)
801 S Figueroa St Ste 1050, Los Angeles, CA 90017
Tel.: (212) 683-8100
Public Relations Agency
N.A.I.C.S.: 541820

The PR Consulting Group, Inc.-Washington (1)
45 Broadway Ste 3140, Washington, DC 10006
Tel.: (212) 683-8100

Web Site: http://www.prcg.com
Emp.: 7
Public Relations Agency
N.A.I.C.S.: 541820
James F. Haggerty (Pres & CEO)
Sean Hughes (Acct Supvr)

THE PR GROUP, INC.

1130 Commodore St, Clearwater, FL 33755
Tel.: (727) 447-4992
Web Site: http://www.theprgroup.com
Year Founded: 1993
Emp.: 10
Public Relations Agency
N.A.I.C.S.: 541820
Vicki Southard (Co-Founder & Pres)
Steve Town (Co-Founder & Dir-Creative)
Ciara Sibbick (Publr)
Moriah Camenker (Publr)

THE PRAEDIUM GROUP LLC

825 3rd Ave 36th Fl, New York, NY 10022
Tel.: (212) 224-5600
Web Site: http://www.praediumgroup.com
Year Founded: 1991
Real Estate Investment Services
N.A.I.C.S.: 531390
A. Floyd Lattin (Co-Founder & Principal)
Russell Appel (Co-Founder & Principal)
Robert Murray (Mng Dir)
Christopher F. Hughes (Principal)
Ronald W. Strobl (CFO & Chief Compliance Officer)
King Lee (Chief Acctg Officer)
Mason Sleeper (Principal)
Shelly Baldwin (Dir-Bus Dev)
Peter Calatozzo (Mng Dir)
Adam McGovern (VP & Gen Counsel)

THE PREDICTIVE INDEX LLC

16 Laurel Ave, Wellesley, MA 02481
Tel.: (781) 235-8872
Year Founded: 2014
Holding Company
N.A.I.C.S.: 551112
Daniel Muzquiz (Chm & Pres)
Mike Zani (CEO)
Alisa Sheyn (Sr VP-Product)
Jennifer Moebius (VP-Mktg)
Drew Fortin (Chief Growth Officer)

Subsidiaries:

PI Southeast LLC (1)
101 Station Dr, Westwood, MA 02090
Tel.: (781) 493-7535
Web Site: http://www.predictiveindex.com
Workforce Assessment Platform
N.A.I.C.S.: 561311
John McGuiness (CFO)
Greg Barnett (VP-R&D)
Jackie Dube (VP-People Ops)
Todd Lingle (VP-Global Talent Acq)
Matt Poepsel (VP-Product Mgmt)
Chris Buontempo (Dir-Legal Affairs)

Subsidiary (Domestic):

Waterhouse Group, Inc. (2)
1467 Walnut Creek Dr, Fleming Island, FL 32003
Tel.: (904) 862-2666
Web Site: http://www.waterhousegroup.com
Scientific & Technical Consulting Services
N.A.I.C.S.: 541690
Steve Waterhouse (Pres)
Brett Unzicker (Gen Mgr)

THE PREMIER GROUP, INC.

955 Broadway, Denver, CO 80204
Tel.: (303) 997-5085
Web Site: http://www.thepremiergroupus.com
Year Founded: 2008
Sales Range: $1-9.9 Million

THE PREMIER GROUP, INC.   U.S. PRIVATE

The Premier Group, Inc.—(Continued)
Emp.: 14
Employee Placement
N.A.I.C.S.: 561311
Dara Johnson (Pres)
JeriLynn Keeley (Branch Mgr)

THE PRESIDENT COUNTRY CLUB INC.
2300 Presidential Way, West Palm Beach, FL 33401-1510
Tel.: (561) 686-4700
Web Site:
   http://www.presidentcc.com
Sales Range: $1-9.9 Million
Emp.: 80
Country Club & Golf Course
N.A.I.C.S.: 713910
Ray Finch (Gen Mgr)
Lori Owenby (Controller)
Scott Mailloux (Dir-Golf)
George Elmore (Pres)

THE PRESIDIO GROUP LLC
12 Funston Ave Ste B, San Francisco, CA 94129
Tel.: (415) 449-2500
Web Site:
   http://www.thepresidiogroup.com
Financial Services
N.A.I.C.S.: 523999
Brodie Cobb (Founde & CEO)
George Karolis (Pres)
Keith R. Style (Mng Dir)
Nate Klebacha (Mng Dir)

THE PRESTON PARTNERSHIP, LLC
South Terraces Bldg 115 Perimeter Center Pl Ste 650, Atlanta, GA 30346
Tel.: (770) 396-7248
Web Site:
   http://www.theprestonpartnership.com
Year Founded: 1995
Sales Range: $1-9.9 Million
Emp.: 49
Architectural, Landscaping & Interior Design Services
N.A.I.C.S.: 541310
Thomas D. Dickinson (CIO-Atlanta)
Sue Locke (Accountant)
Andrew P. Preston (CFO-Atlanta)
Dennis S. Galindo (Principal-Plng-Atlanta)
Edsel J. Arnold (Principal-Design-Atlanta)
Robert N. Preston (Principal-Atlanta)
David Yung (Principal)
Richard Kilpatrick (Principal-Atlanta)
Chandra K. Cherry (Principal-Interior Design)
Steven M. Middendorf (Principal-Landscape Architecture)
Steve Byerly (VP-Strategic Initiatives-Atlanta)
Tim Williamson (Principal-Atlanta)
Warren Boatman (Principal-Atlanta)

THE PRETESTING COMPANY, INC.
376 Warwick Ave, Tenafly, NJ 07666
Tel.: (201) 569-4800
Web Site: http://www.pretesting.com
Market Research Services
N.A.I.C.S.: 541910
Lee Weinblatt (CEO)
Dan Morris (Pres)

THE PRICE COMPANIES, INC.
218 Midway Rte, Monticello, AR 71655
Tel.: (870) 367-9751
Web Site:
   http://www.thepricecompanies.com

Year Founded: 1965
Sales Range: $10-24.9 Million
Emp.: 300
Wood Processing Services
N.A.I.C.S.: 321113
Tommy Smith (CFO)

THE PRICE GROUP, INC.
1801 Broadway, Lubbock, TX 79401-3015
Tel.: (806) 763-5033
Web Site:
   http://www.pricegroupinc.com
Year Founded: 1972
Sales Range: $10-24.9 Million
Emp.: 23
Advetising Agency
N.A.I.C.S.: 541810
Phil Price (Pres)
Linda Weddle (VP & Controller)
Mike Meister (VP & Dir-Co-Creative)
Pam Sharpe (VP & Media Dir)

THE PRIMARY GROUP, INC.
2180 W State Rd 434 Ste 4160, Longwood, FL 32779
Tel.: (407) 869-4111
Web Site:
   http://www.theprimarygroup.com
Year Founded: 1990
Sales Range: $1-9.9 Million
Emp.: 10
Executive Placement & Consulting Services
N.A.I.C.S.: 541612
Paul Cresho (Owner & Pres)
Barbara Volz (Mng Dir & Sr VP)
Leigh Milwee (VP)

THE PRINTER WORKS INC.
39980 Eureka Dr, Newark, CA 94560-4810
Tel.: (510) 670-2700
Web Site:
   http://www.theprinterworks.com
Sales Range: $10-24.9 Million
Emp.: 28
Computer Printers Mfr
N.A.I.C.S.: 423430
Stephen Roberts (Founder & Pres)

THE PRITZKER GROUP - CHICAGO, LLC
111 S Wacker Dr Ste 4000, Chicago, IL 60606
Tel.: (312) 447-6000   DE
Web Site:
   http://www.pritzkergroup.com
Private Equity, Venture Capital & Asset Management Firm
N.A.I.C.S.: 523999
Anthony N. Pritzker (Co-Founder & Mng Partner-Los Angeles)
J. B. Pritzker (Co-Founder & Mng Partner)
Chris Girgenti (Mng Partner-Venture Capital)
Matthew McCall (Partner-Venture Capital)
Adam Koopersmith (Partner-Venture Capital)
Gabe Greenbaum (Partner-Venture Capital)
Sonia Sahney Nagar (VP-Venture Capital)
Peter Liu (VP)
David Schonthal (Operating Partner)
Craig Wortmann (Operating Partner)
Pat Basu (Venture Partner)
Ty Findley (VP)
Mirirai Sparks (Coord)
Ashley Shind (Coord)

Subsidiaries:

Bardstown Bourbon Company, LLC (1)

1500 Pkwy Dr, Bardstown, KY 40004
Tel.: (502) 233-4769
Web Site:
   http://www.bardstownbourbon.com
Food & Beverage Mfr
N.A.I.C.S.: 312140
Mark W. Erwin (Pres & CEO)
Jeff Hopmayer (Mng Partner)
Peter Loftin (Founder & Chm)
John Hangrove (COO)

The Pritzker Group - LA, LLC (1)
11150 Santa Monica Blvd Ste 1500, Los Angeles, CA 90025
Tel.: (310) 575-9400
Web Site: http://www.pritzkergroup.com
Private Equity & Venture Capital Firm
N.A.I.C.S.: 523999
Anthony N. Pritzker (Founder & Mng Partner)
Michael Dal Bello (Partner-Healthcare Investment-Private Capital)
Peter Liu (VP-Venture Capital)

Division (Domestic):

PPC Investment Partners LP (2)
111 S Wacker Dr Ste 4050, Chicago, IL 60606
Tel.: (312) 447-6050
Web Site: http://www.ppcpartners.com
Equity Investment Firm
N.A.I.C.S.: 523999
Gregg A. Kaplan (Operating Partner)
Tony Pritzker (Chm & CEO)
Paul Carbone (Pres & Mng Partner)
Stephanie Paine (CFO & Chief Admin Officer)
Brad West (Chief Compliance Officer & Gen Counsel)
Ryan Roberts (Partner-Investment-Svcs)
Michael Dal Bello (Investment Partner-Healthcare)
Brian Baxter (Controller)
Chris Brannan (Asst Gen Counsel)
Silvia Yim (Mgr-HR)
David Baker (Principal-Ops Grp)
Ceron Rhee (Principal-Healthcare)
Chris Trick (Partner-Investment)
Kaitlyn Desai (VP-Manufactured Products)
Jeff Carlson (Dir-Tech)
David Gau (Partner & Head-Ops)
Benjamin Barry (VP-Svcs)

Holding (Domestic):

Aurorium Holdings LLC (3)
201 N Illinois St Ste 1800, Indianapolis, IN 46204
Tel.: (317) 247-8141
Web Site: https://www.aurorium.com
Chemicals Mfr
N.A.I.C.S.: 325998
John Van Hulle (CEO)
Faye Freeman (Pres)

Subsidiary (Domestic):

Centauri Technologies, LP (4)
5200 Underwood Rd, Pasadena, TX 77507
Tel.: (281) 474-4675
Sales Range: $1-9.9 Million
Emp.: 20
Basic Organic Chemical Mfr
N.A.I.C.S.: 325199
Kyle Killebrew (Principal)
Alan Peterson (Engr-Maintenance)
Wesley Batts (Coord-Logistics)

Holding (Domestic):

C.H. Guenther & Son, LLC (3)
2201 Broadway, San Antonio, TX 78215
Tel.: (210) 227-1401
Web Site: http://www.chg.com
Dry & Frozen Grain Based Food, Sauces & Gravies Mfr
N.A.I.C.S.: 311211
Dale W. Tremblay (Exec Chm)
Stephen T. Phillips (Sr VP-Corp Svcs)
Thomas A. McRae (Gen Counsel & Sr VP)
Eric Stockl (COO & Sr VP)
Janelle M. Skyes (CFO, Treas & Sr VP)
Kelly Crouse (Chief Comml Officer & Sr VP)
John Buckles (Pres & CEO)

Subsidiary (Domestic):

Baldinger Baking, LP (4)
1256 Phalen Blvd, Saint Paul, MN 55106

Tel.: (651) 224-5761
Web Site: http://www.baldingerbakery.com
Commercial Bakeries
N.A.I.C.S.: 311812
Bob Baldinger (Gen Partner)
Steve Baldinger (CEO)

Plant (Domestic):

C.H. Guenther & Son, Inc. - Pioneer Flour Mill (4)
129 E Guenther St, San Antonio, TX 78204
Tel.: (210) 227-1401
Web Site: http://www.chg.com
Flour Milling Services
N.A.I.C.S.: 311211

Subsidiary (Non-US):

Guenther Bakeries UK Limited (4)
Hareshill Road Heywood, Manchester, OL10 2TN, Lancs, United Kingdom
Tel.: (44) 1706 367676
Web Site: http://www.chg.com
Bakery Products Mfr
N.A.I.C.S.: 311821

Subsidiary (Domestic):

Pioneer Frozen Foods LLC (4)
627 Big Stone Gap, Duncanville, TX 75137
Tel.: (972) 298-4281
Bread, Cake & Related Products Mfr
N.A.I.C.S.: 311812
Dale W. Tremblay (Pres & CEO)

Pizza Blends Inc. (4)
1541 Vernon St N, Kansas City, MO 64116
Tel.: (816) 842-8244
Web Site: http://www.pizzablends.com
Prepared Flour Mixes & Doughs Mfr
N.A.I.C.S.: 311824

Tribeca Oven, Inc. (4)
447 Gotham Pkwy, Carlstadt, NJ 07072
Tel.: (201) 935-8800
Web Site: http://www.tribecaoven.com
Commercial Bakery
N.A.I.C.S.: 311812

Subsidiary (Non-US):

Trousdale Limited (4)
17 Wildmere Road, Banbury, OX16 3JU, Oxon, United Kingdom
Tel.: (44) 1295 251000
Bakery Products Mfr
N.A.I.C.S.: 311821

Subsidiary (Domestic):

Williams Foods LLC (4)
13301 W 99th St, Lenexa, KS 66215-1348
Tel.: (913) 888-4343
Web Site: http://www.williamsfoods.com
Dry Seasoning & Canned Food Mfr
N.A.I.C.S.: 311942

Holding (Domestic):

Entertainment Cruises Inc. (3)
455 N Cityfront Plaza Dr Ste 2600, Chicago, IL 60611
Tel.: (312) 321-7600
Web Site:
   http://www.entertainmentcruises.com
Sales Range: $100-124.9 Million
Operator of Harbor Cruise Ships
N.A.I.C.S.: 487210
Kenneth Svendsen (CEO)

Subsidiary (Domestic):

Spirit Cruises LLC (4)
561 Light St, Baltimore, MD 21202
Tel.: (410) 347-5552
Web Site: http://www.spiritcruises.com
Sales Range: $25-49.9 Million
Emp.: 35
Harbor Cruise Reservation Services
N.A.I.C.S.: 487210

Unit (Domestic):

Spirit of Boston (5)
200 Seaport Blvd Ste 75, Boston, MA 02210
Tel.: (617) 748-1499
Web Site: http://www.spiritofboston.com
Sales Range: $10-24.9 Million
Harbor Cruise Ship Operator
N.A.I.C.S.: 487210

COMPANIES — THE PRITZKER GROUP - CHICAGO, LLC

Spirit of Chicago (5)
NBC Tower 455 N Cityfront Plaza Dr Ste 2600, Chicago, IL 60611
Tel.: (312) 321-7600
Web Site: http://www.spiritofchicago.com
Harbor Cruise Ship Operator
N.A.I.C.S.: 487210

Spirit of New York (5)
Pier 61 Chelsea Piers W 23rd St Ste 200, New York, NY 10011
Tel.: (212) 727-7735
Web Site: http://www.entertainmentcruises.com
Harbor Cruise Ship Operator Service
N.A.I.C.S.: 487210
Nilda Braacero (Gen Mgr)

Spirit of Norfolk (5)
109 E Main St Ste 500, Norfolk, VA 23510
Tel.: (757) 625-1463
Web Site: http://www.spiritofnorfolk.com
Sales Range: $10-24.9 Million
Harbor Cruise Ship Operator
N.A.I.C.S.: 487210

Spirit of Philadelphia (5)
123 Chestnut St Ste 402, Philadelphia, PA 19106
Tel.: (215) 923-4354
Web Site: http://www.spiritofphiladelphia.com
Sales Range: $10-24.9 Million
Harbor Cruise Ship Operator
N.A.I.C.S.: 487210
Theresa Cinalli (Mgr-Admin)

Spirit of Washington (5)
580 Water St SW, Washington, DC 20024
Tel.: (202) 479-4577
Web Site: http://www.spiritofwashington.com
Sales Range: $10-24.9 Million
Harbor Cruise Ship Operator
N.A.I.C.S.: 487210

Holding (Domestic):

KabaFusion Holdings, LLC (3)
17777 Ctr Ct Dr N Ste 550, Cerritos, CA 90703-9337
Tel.: (562) 860-6015
Web Site: http://www.kabafusion.com
Drugs & Druggists' Sundries Merchant Whslr
N.A.I.C.S.: 424210
Michael Rigas (Chief Clinical Officer)

Subsidiary (Domestic):

KabaFusion - Michigan (4)
31555 Industrial Rd Ste 200, Livonia, MI 48150-1850
Tel.: (734) 425-2550
Health Care Srvices
N.A.I.C.S.: 621610

Holding (Domestic):

PECO Pallet, Inc. (3)
2 Bridge St Ste 210, Irvington, NY 10533 (100%)
Tel.: (914) 376-5444
Web Site: http://www.pecopallet.com
Sales Range: $1-9.9 Million
Emp.: 17
Equipment Rental/Leasing
N.A.I.C.S.: 532490
Tom Kuczmarski (CFO)
Lisa Vegso (Chief Comml Officer)
Joseph Dagnese (CEO)
Ken Chazotte (CIO)
Jeff Euritt (Sr VP-Svc)
Adrian Potgieter (Sr VP-Sls)
Roberto Sobrino (VP-Bus Dev & Ops)
Mike Greene (Sr VP-Network Plng & Transportation)
Eric Sobanski (Sr VP-Ops)

PLZ Corp. (3)
2651 Warrenville Rd Ste 300, Downers Grove, IL 60515
Tel.: (800) 332-9000
Web Site: https://www.plzcorp.com
Aerosol Products Mfr
N.A.I.C.S.: 325998
Gary Hendrickson (Interim CEO)
Kevin Rule (CFO)

Subsidiary (Domestic):

220 Laboratories Inc. (4)
2375 3rd St, Riverside, CA 92507
Tel.: (951) 683-2912
Web Site: http://www.220labs.com
Rev.: $16,281,385
Emp.: 150
Cosmetic Preparations
N.A.I.C.S.: 325620
Ian Fishman (Pres)
Robyn Reid (Dir-Product Innovation)
Anthony Jackson (Mgr-Shipping)
Evangeline Raguindin (Mgr-QA & Regulatory Affairs)
Konrad Krauss (Mgr-Quality & Regulatory)
Nesbit Misquitta (Mgr-Pur)
Russell Hosking (Mgr-Admin)
Michael Herzog (VP-Ops)
Jim Laing (Mgr-Plant Engrg)

Liquid Technologies, Inc. (4)
14510 Monte Vista Ave, Chino, CA 91710
Tel.: (909) 393-9475
Web Site: http://www.liquidtek.com
Sales Range: $1-9.9 Million
Emp.: 30
Toilet Preparation Mfr
N.A.I.C.S.: 325620

Mansfield-King LLC (4)
6501 Julian Ave, Indianapolis, IN 46219
Tel.: (317) 788-0750
Web Site: http://www.mansfieldking.com
Sales Range: $1-9.9 Million
Emp.: 45
Personal Care Products Manufacturer
N.A.I.C.S.: 325620
Charles R. Haywood (Owner & Pres)
Tom Lehman (Exec VP)

Plaze, Inc. (4)
105 Bolte Ln, Saint Clair, MO 63077
Tel.: (636) 629-3400
Web Site: http://www.plaze.com
Contract Packaging Services
N.A.I.C.S.: 325998
Hugh Davison (VP-Sls)
Dennis Bullock (VP-Pur)
Bob Thornton (VP-Ops)

Precise Packaging, Inc. (4)
300 Riggenbach Rd, Fall River, MA 02720
Tel.: (508) 677-2600
Corrugated & Solid Fiber Box Mfr
N.A.I.C.S.: 322211
Matt Levesque (Dir-Ops)

Sprayway, Inc. (4)
1005 S Westgate Ave, Addison, IL 60101
Tel.: (630) 628-3000
Web Site: http://www.spraywayinc.com
Aerosol Cleaning Products Mfr
N.A.I.C.S.: 325612
Matt Keller (Mgr-Corp Accts)

The Claire Manufacturing Company (4)
2651 Warrenville Rd, Downers Grove, IL 60515
Tel.: (630) 543-7600
Web Site: http://www.clairemfg.com
Aerosol Products Mfr
N.A.I.C.S.: 325612

The Penray Companies, Inc. (4)
440 Denniston Ct, Wheeling, IL 60090-4731
Tel.: (847) 459-5000
Web Site: http://www.penray.com
Automotive Chemicals & Heavy-Duty Fuel Additives Mfr
N.A.I.C.S.: 325998
Howard Laga (Pres)
David Sholtis (CEO)

Holding (Domestic):

Plaskolite, LLC (3)
1770 Joyce Ave, Columbus, OH 43219-1026
Tel.: (614) 294-3281
Web Site: http://www.plaskolite.com
Sales Range: $100-124.9 Million
Emp.: 530
Acrylic Sheets Mfr
N.A.I.C.S.: 326130
James Dunn (Chm)
Richard Larkin (CFO)
Mark Grindley (VP-Ops)
Doug Nielsen (Treas)
Josh Keck (Plant Mgr-Conversion Facility)
Mitchell Grindley (Pres & CEO)
Jason Gorham (Controller)
Jack Black (Exec VP-Sls & Mktg)
Gordon Jankulovski (Dir-Coated Products)
John Szlag (Co-Pres)

Subsidiary (Domestic):

MXL Industries, Inc. (4)
1764 Rohrerstown Rd, Lancaster, PA 17601-2320
Tel.: (717) 569-8711
Web Site: http://www.mxl-industries.com
Optical Quality Injection Molding Services; Mold Design & Construction; Abrasion-Resistant Protective Coatings, Marine Coatings; Recreational Eyewear
N.A.I.C.S.: 333514
Jude D. Krady (Chief People Officer)
Sean R. Bitts (CMO)
Thomas J. Ulaky (Mgr-Quality Assurance)
Jim Eberle (Pres & CEO)

Holding (Domestic):

ProAmpac LLC (3)
12025 Tricon Rd, Cincinnati, OH 45246
Tel.: (513) 671-1777
Web Site: http://www.proampac.com
Holding Company; Flexible Packaging Products Mfr & Whslr
N.A.I.C.S.: 551112
Gregory R. Tucker (CEO)
Vince Musacchio (Pres-Global Flexibles)
Hesam Tabatabaei (Dir-Res, Innovation & Tech)
Millie Nuno (Dir-Mktg)
Sal Pellingra (VP-Global Application & Innovation)
Ann Marie Braker (VP-HR)
Rita Cox (Pres-Flexibles Products Div)

Subsidiary (Domestic):

APC Paper Co. Inc. (4)
131 Sullivan St, Claremont, NH 03743
Tel.: (603) 542-0411
Web Site: http://www.apcpapergroup.com
Sales Range: $10-24.9 Million
Emp.: 60
Paper Milling Services
N.A.I.C.S.: 322120
Tom Moore (Pres)
Brian Caisse (Mgr-Mill)

Ampac Holdings, LLC (4)
12025 Tricon Rd, Cincinnati, OH 45246
Tel.: (513) 671-1777
Web Site: http://www.ampaconline.com
Holding Company; Packaging Products Mfr & Whslr
N.A.I.C.S.: 551112
Gregory R. Tucker (CEO)
Millie Nuno (Mktg Dir)

Subsidiary (Non-US):

Ampac Flexibles AG (5)
Industrie Neuhof 5, 3422, Kirchberg, Switzerland
Tel.: (41) 34 448 44 44
Web Site: http://www.proampac.com
Plastic & Paper Bag Whslr
N.A.I.C.S.: 322220

Ampac Flexibles GmbH (5)
Daimlerstrasse 5, 71735, Eberdingen, Germany
Tel.: (49) 7042 9526 0
Web Site: http://www.ampaconline.de
Plastic & Paper Bag Mfr
N.A.I.C.S.: 326111

Subsidiary (Domestic):

Gateway Packaging Company LLC (4)
20 Central Industrial Dr Northgate Industrial Park, Granite City, IL 62040
Tel.: (618) 451-0010
All Other Converted Paper Product Mfr
N.A.I.C.S.: 322299

Polyfirst Packaging, Inc. (4)
2261 Innovation Way, Hartford, WI 53027
Tel.: (262) 673-6888
Web Site: http://www.polyfirst.com
Sales Range: $1-9.9 Million
Emp.: 100
Specialty Plastic Bag Mfr
N.A.I.C.S.: 326111
Ed Logue (VP-Bus Dev)
Steve Randazzo (CEO)
King Coles (Pres)
Dave Corey (COO & Plant Mgr)
Curtis Yorkey (VP-Sls & Admin)

Prolamina Corporation (4)
132 N Elm St, Westfield, MA 01086
Tel.: (413) 562-2315
Web Site: http://www.prolamina.com
Packaging Products Mfr
N.A.I.C.S.: 322220
Tim French (COO)
Matt Conlin (VP-Sls)

Subsidiary (Non-US):

Rapid Action Packaging Ltd. (4)
107 Mortlake High Street, London, SW14 8HQ, United Kingdom
Tel.: (44) 20 8392 8320
Web Site: http://www.rapuk.com
Packaging & Labeling Services
N.A.I.C.S.: 561910
Graham Williams (CEO)

Subsidiary (Domestic):

Specialty Packaging, Inc. (4)
3250 W Seminary Dr, Fort Worth, TX 76133
Tel.: (800) 284-7722
Web Site: http://specialtypackaginginc.com
Sales Range: $1-9.9 Million
Emp.: 70
Paper Mill Services
N.A.I.C.S.: 322120
Hank Dorris (Pres)
Mike Homan (Mgr-Sls)
Herman Chenevert (Mgr-Ops)

TULSACK, Inc. (4)
10405 E 55th Pl, Tulsa, OK 74146
Tel.: (918) 664-0664
Web Site: http://www.tulsack.com
Emp.: 200
Paper & Coated Paper Shopping Bags Mfr
N.A.I.C.S.: 322220
Tim Tackett (Dir-Maintenance & Facilities)

Trinity Packaging Corporation (4)
55 Innsbruck Dr, Buffalo, NY 14227
Tel.: (914) 273-4111
Plastic Packaging Products Mfr
N.A.I.C.S.: 326111
Thomas Zink (Dir-Pur)
John Matthews (Mgr-IT)

Vitex Packaging Group (4)
1137 Progress Rd, Suffolk, VA 23434
Tel.: (757) 538-3115
Web Site: http://www.vitexpackaging.com
Packaging Materials Mfr; Paper Lamination, Printing & Converting Services
N.A.I.C.S.: 323111
Mike Moore (VP-Sls & Mktg)
Debbie Wiggins (Mgr-Customer Svc)
Sandy Arulf (VP-Quality & Technical Svcs)
Mike DeGrandis (CFO)
Rich Juliano (VP-Ops)
Scott Silverstein (VP-New Bus Dev)

Holding (Domestic):

Sugar Foods Corporation (3)
950 3rd Ave Fl 21, New York, NY 10022-2890
Tel.: (212) 753-6900
Web Site: http://www.sugarfoods.com
Sales Range: $150-199.9 Million
Emp.: 500
Sugar Substitutes Supplier
N.A.I.C.S.: 325199
Donald G. Tober (Chm)
Jack Vivinetto (CFO)
Richard Ticknor (VP-Mktg)
Marty Wilson (CEO)
Andrea Brule (Pres)

Subsidiary (Domestic):

Mrs. Cubbison's Kitchen, LLC (4)
7240 E Gage Ave, City of Commerce, CA 90040 (80%)
Tel.: (562) 231-1699
Web Site: http://www.mrscubbisons.com
Sales Range: $1-9.9 Million
Emp.: 100
Croutons, Poultry Dressing & Other Food Products Mfr
N.A.I.C.S.: 311812

Holding (Domestic):

Technimark LLC (3)
180 Commerce Pl, Asheboro, NC 27203-0515
Tel.: (336) 498-4171

THE PRITZKER GROUP - CHICAGO, LLC

U.S. PRIVATE

The Pritzker Group - Chicago, LLC—(Continued)
Web Site: http://www.technimark.com
Sales Range: $450-499.9 Million
Emp.: 1,600
Injection Molding Plastic Products Mfr & Whslr
N.A.I.C.S.: 326199
Donald F. Wellington (Founder & Chm)
Kevin Hedspeth (Sr VP-Global Tech & Dev)
Kris Peavy (Chief Comml Officer)
Brad Wellington (CEO)

Valicor Environmental Services, LLC (3)
1045 Reed Rd, Monroe, OH 45050
Tel.: (513) 733-4666
Web Site: https://www.valicor.com
Environmental Services
N.A.I.C.S.: 562219
Steve Hopper (CEO)

Subsidiary (Domestic):

Usher Enterprises, Inc. (4)
9000 Roselawn St, Detroit, MI 48204
Tel.: (313) 834-7055
Web Site: http://www.usheroil.com
Sales Range: $1-9.9 Million
Emp.: 40
Recyclable Material Merchant Whslr
N.A.I.C.S.: 423930
Matthew Usher (Pres)
Lori-Anne Usher (VP)

Holding (Domestic):

Valicor Environmental Technologies, LLC (3)
1701 W 54th Ln, Denver, CO 80221
Tel.: (720) 540-7716
Web Site: http://www.valicor.com
Non-Hazardous Wastewater Treatment Services
N.A.I.C.S.: 562219
Rich Goodwin (Reg Dir-Ops)
Duke Gates (Gen Mgr)
Bill Hinton (Chief Comml Officer)

Subsidiary (Domestic):

Affiliated Wastewater Environmental Services, LLC (4)
1701 W 54th Pl, Denver, CO 80221
Tel.: (720) 540-7716
Rev.: $1,472,000
Emp.: 8
All Other Miscellaneous Waste Management Services
N.A.I.C.S.: 562998

Agricultural Services, Inc. (4)
7600 Alumax Dr, Texarkana, TX 75501-0400
Tel.: (903) 832-4790
Web Site: http://www.asicompanies.com
Sales Range: $1-9.9 Million
Emp.: 35
Remediation Services
N.A.I.C.S.: 562910
John Norton (VP)

THE PRITZKER ORGANIZATION, LLC

150 N Riverside Plz Ste 3200, Chicago, IL 60606
Tel.: (312) 873-4900 DE
Web Site: http://www.pritzkerorg.com
Year Founded: 1997
Holding Company; Merchant Banking
N.A.I.C.S.: 551112
Thomas J. Pritzker (Chm & CEO)
Joe Gleberman (Mng Dir)

Subsidiaries:

Crown Health Care Laundry Services (1)
3805 Al Hwy 41, Selma, AL 36701-7855
Web Site: http://www.crownlaundry.com
All Other Miscellaneous Ambulatory Health Care Services
N.A.I.C.S.: 621999
Bill Sopp (Mgr)

Lithko Contracting LLC (1)
2958 Crescentville Rd, West Chester, OH 45069
Tel.: (513) 564-2000
Web Site: http://www.lithko.com
Sales Range: $25-49.9 Million
Emp.: 1,500
Concrete Contractor & Construction Services
N.A.I.C.S.: 238110
Robert Strobel (Pres & CEO)
Perry Hossfeld (VP-Ops)
Brian Albanese (VP-Fin Ops, Mergers & Acquisitions)
Rob Kief (Dir-Safety)
Ben Cutting (CFO)

TMS International Corporation (1)
Southside Works Bldg 1 3rd Fl 2835 E Carson St, Pittsburgh, PA 15203 (100%)
Tel.: (412) 678-6141
Web Site: https://www.tmsinternational.com
Sales Range: $1-4.9 Billion
Emp.: 4,300
Iron & Steel Mills & Ferroalloy Manufacturing
N.A.I.C.S.: 331110
Jason Pritzker (Exec Chm)
Kirk D. Peters (CFO & Sr VP)
J. David Aronson (Pres/COO-Raw Matl & Optimization Grp)
Raymond S. Kalouche (Chm, Pres, CEO, COO, Exec VP, Sr VP, VP-Plng & Ops & Gen Mgr)
Peter Macaluso (Gen Counsel, Sec & Sr VP)

Subsidiary (Domestic):

Stein, LLC (2)
1929 E Royalton Rd, Broadview Heights, OH 44147
Tel.: (440) 526-9301
Web Site: http://www.steininc.com
Sales Range: $25-49.9 Million
Emp.: 19
Iron Ore Recovery From Open Hearth Slag
N.A.I.C.S.: 331110
Douglas Huffnagel (Area Mgr)
Paul Longville (Mgr)

Subsidiary (Domestic):

KT Grant, Inc. (3)
3073 Route 66, Export, PA 15632
Tel.: (724) 468-4700
Web Site: http://www.kt-grantinc.com
Emp.: 100
Custom Engineered & Standard Earth Moving Equipment, Rental Or Leasing
N.A.I.C.S.: 333120
Dawn Hilty (VP)
Scott Rubright (Plant Mgr)
John Wargofchik (VP)

Subsidiary (Non-US):

TMS International Services UK Limited (2)
Scotter Road South Bottesford, Scunthorpe, DN17 2BU, North Lincolnshire, United Kingdom
Tel.: (44) 1724 867595
Web Site: http://www.tms.com
Emp.: 66
Business Support Services
N.A.I.C.S.: 561499
Marco Grazina (Mng Dir)

Subsidiary (Domestic):

Hanson Resource Management Limited (3)
Scotter Road South Bottesford, Scunthorpe, DN17 2BU, United Kingdom
Tel.: (44) 1724 289884
Electrical Equipment Installation Services
N.A.I.C.S.: 238210

Subsidiary (Domestic):

TMS International, LLC (2)
SouthSide Works Bldg 1 3rd Fl 2835 E Carson St, Pittsburgh, PA 15203
Tel.: (412) 678-6141
Web Site: http://www.tmsinternational.com
Sales Range: Less than $1 Million
Steel Mills Operating Services
N.A.I.C.S.: 331110
Raymond S. Kalouche (Co-Pres & CEO)
J. David Aronson (Co-Pres & COO-Raw Material & Optimization Grp)
Jonathan M. Fingeret (Gen Counsel, Sec & Sr VP)
Kirk D. Peters (CFO & Sr VP)

Subsidiary (Non-US):

Tube City IMS Belgium BVBA (2)
J F Kennedylaan 51, Gent, 1942, Belgium
Tel.: (32) 9 349 63 09
Web Site: http://www.tmsinternational.com
Emp.: 50
Steel Mills Operating Services
N.A.I.C.S.: 561499
Mark Marquette (Mgr)

Tube City IMS Canada Limited (2)
275 Sherman Ave N, Hamilton, L8L 6N2, ON, Canada
Tel.: (905) 549-5100
Web Site: http://www.tubecityims.com
Sales Range: $50-74.9 Million
Emp.: 7
Metal Mining Services
N.A.I.C.S.: 213114
Russell Moore (Mgr-Site)

Tube City IMS France Centre S.A.S. (2)
Industeel Le Creusot Site Du Bre 56 Rue Clemenceau, Le Creusot, 71200, France
Tel.: (33) 385788958
Steel Process & Production Support Services
N.A.I.C.S.: 331513

Tube City IMS Holding B.V. (2)
Prins Bernhardplein 200, Amsterdam, 1097 JB, Noord-Holland, Netherlands
Tel.: (31) 205214777
Investment Management Service
N.A.I.C.S.: 523999

Tube City IMS Kosice s.r.o. (2)
Vstupny Areal U S Steel, Kosice, 04454, Slovakia
Tel.: (421) 556734677
Web Site: http://www.tmsinternational.sk
Emp.: 40
Steel Mills Operating Services
N.A.I.C.S.: 331110
Brinc Curtin (Gen Mgr)

Tube City IMS Servicios de Mexico S. de R.L. de C.V. (2)
Zaragoza No 1000 Monterrey Centro, Monterrey, 64000, Nuevo Leon, Mexico
Tel.: (52) 8183455963
Steel Process & Production Support Services
N.A.I.C.S.: 331513
Elisa Porcayo (Gen Mgr)

Tube City IMS South Africa (Pty) Ltd. (2)
Building 2 Ext 34 Stone Ridge Office Park, Kempton Park, 1313, South Africa
Tel.: (27) 828798371
Steel Products Mfr
N.A.I.C.S.: 331110

Tube City IMS Taiwan Limited (2)
Rm A4 21F-1 No 6 Siwei 3rd Rd, Lingya District, Kaohsiung, 80250, Taiwan
Tel.: (886) 73326088
Web Site: http://www.tubecityims.com
Steel Mills Operating Services
N.A.I.C.S.: 561499

Tube City IMS Trinidad Limited (2)
Mediterranean Dr, Po Box 1146, Couva, Trinidad & Tobago
Tel.: (868) 6362862
Steel Mill Engineering Services
N.A.I.C.S.: 331513

Tube City IMS de Mexico S. de R.L. de C.V. (2)
Zaragoza No 1000 Ofna 209 Centro, Monterrey, 64000, Nuevo Leon, Mexico
Tel.: (52) 8183455963
Steel Mills Operating Services
N.A.I.C.S.: 331110

THE PROCACCIANTI GROUP

1140 Reservoir Ave, Cranston, RI 02920
Tel.: (401) 946-4600
Web Site: http://www.procgroup.com
Sales Range: $1-4.9 Billion
Emp.: 8,000
Real Estate Investment Company
N.A.I.C.S.: 525990
Elizabeth Procaccianti (COO)
Paul Sacco (Pres & Chief Dev Officer-TPG Hotels & Resorts)
James A. Procaccianti (Pres & CEO)
Gregory D. Vickowski (CFO)

THE PRODUCE EXCHANGE INCORPORATED

7407 S Frnt Rd, Livermore, CA 94550
Tel.: (925) 454-8700 CA
Web Site: http://www.tpeonline.com
Year Founded: 1979
Sales Range: $125-149.9 Million
Emp.: 340
Fresh Fruits & Vegetables
N.A.I.C.S.: 424480
Sam Jones (Pres)
Peggy Francois (Acct Mgr)
Marty Mazzanti (Chm)

THE PROFESSIONAL BASKETBALL CLUB, LLC

208 Thunder Dr, Oklahoma City, OK 73102
Tel.: (405) 208-4800
Web Site: http://www.nba.com
Year Founded: 2006
Sales Range: $25-49.9 Million
Emp.: 150
Holding Company; Professional Basketball Teams
N.A.I.C.S.: 551112
Clayton I. Bennett (Chm)

Subsidiaries:

Oklahoma City Thunder (1)
208 Thunder Dr, Oklahoma City, OK 73102
Tel.: (405) 605-4306
Web Site: http://www.nba.com
Sales Range: $10-24.9 Million
Emp.: 100
Professional Basketball Team
N.A.I.C.S.: 711211
Clayton I. Bennett (Chm)
Danny Barth (Chief Admin Officer & Exec VP)
Brian M. Byrnes (Sr VP-Sls & Mktg)
Pete Winemiller (VP-Guest Rels)
Paul Rivers (Dir-Basketball Tech)
Marc St. Yves (Mgr-Equipment & Trng Facility)
Donnie Strack (VP-Human & Player Performance)
Ayana Clinton (Coord-Video)
Ryan O'Toole (Acct Exec-Bus Dev)
Christine Berney (VP-Community Rels)
Dan Mahoney (VP-Brdcst & Corp Comm)
Dawn Turner (Dir-Mktg & Brand Mgmt)

THE PROFESSIONAL GOLFERS ASSOCIATION OF AMERICA

100 Ave of The Champions, Palm Beach Gardens, FL 33418
Tel.: (561) 624-8400
Web Site: http://www.pga.org
Sales Range: $10-24.9 Million
Emp.: 175
Sports Clubs, Managers & Promoters
N.A.I.C.S.: 711320
Sandy Cross (Sr VP-Diversity)
Peter Bevacqua (CEO)
Suzy Whaley (Pres)

THE PROFESSIONAL LANDLORDS, LLC

4702 Old Spanish Trl, Houston, TX 77021
Tel.: (713) 224-7368
Web Site: http://www.rentterswarehouse.com
Year Founded: 2013
Sales Range: $1-9.9 Million
Emp.: 14

COMPANIES

Real Estate Manangement Services
N.A.I.C.S.: 531390
Jim Youngblood (Partner)
Clyde Adams (Partner)
Mark Zimmerman (COO)
Richard Drake II (CEO & Partner)

THE PROSPER GROUP CORPORATION
150 W Market St Ste 500, Indianapolis, IN 46204
Tel.: (317) 886-4438
Web Site:
http://www.prospergroupcorp.com
Year Founded: 2006
Sales Range: $10-24.9 Million
Emp.: 36
Digital Marketing Services
N.A.I.C.S.: 541613
Kristen Luidhardt (Co-Founder & Pres)
Kurt Luidhardt (Co-Founder & VP)
Jeff Vreeland (VP-Client Svcs)
Andrew Finnan (VP-Digital Strategy)
Todd Harris (VP-Sls & Mktg)

THE PROTECTOSEAL COMPANY
225 Foster Ave, Bensenville, IL 60106-1631
Tel.: (630) 595-0800
Web Site:
http://www.protectoseal.com
Sales Range: $10-24.9 Million
Emp.: 100
Mfr of Safety Equipment For Handling, Storing & Dispensing Flammable Liquids
N.A.I.C.S.: 922160
Michael King (VP & Controller)
Carol Beem (Mgr-Mktg Comm)
John McDonough (Mgr-Mktg Support)
Ken Nosek (Mgr-Midwest Reg)

THE PROUD COMPANY
600 Bursca Dr Ste 602, Bridgeville, PA 15017
Tel.: (412) 838-0230
Web Site: http://www.proudco.com
Year Founded: 1993
Sales Range: $1-9.9 Million
Emp.: 15
Engineeering Services
N.A.I.C.S.: 541330
Chuck Short (Dir-Network Solutions)
Christopher Ulam (Mgr-Ops)
Joseph Veltri (Mgr-Repairs & Returns)
Mark D. Proud Sr. (Pres)

THE PUBLIC THEATER
425 Lafayette St, New York, NY 10003
Tel.: (212) 539-8500
Web Site:
http://www.publictheater.org
Year Founded: 1962
Rev.: $12,918,251
Emp.: 100
Theatrical Production Services
N.A.I.C.S.: 711110
Patricia D. Fili-Krushel (Vice Chm)
Oskar Eustis (Dir-Artistic)
Patrick Willingham (Exec Dir)
Rachel Pivnick (CFO)
Jeremy Adams (Gen Mgr)
Arielle Tepper Madover (Chm)
Zach Buchwald (Sec)
Patricia Huie (CFO)
Kevin Abbott (Mng Partner)

THE PULSE NETWORK, INC.
Tel.: (781) 688-8000   NV
Web Site: http://www.tpni.com
Year Founded: 2011
Emp.: 100
Digital Media Services
N.A.I.C.S.: 541810

THE QUANDEL GROUP INC.
3003 N Frnt St Ste 203, Harrisburg, PA 17110
Tel.: (717) 657-0909   PA
Web Site: http://www.quandel.com
Year Founded: 1882
Rev.: $35,000,000
Emp.: 100
Nonresidential Construction
N.A.I.C.S.: 236220
Noble C. Quandel Jr. (CEO)
Chris Bushey (CFO)
Joseph Mastrippolito (Pres & COO)
Stan Hendricks (COO-Preconstruction)
Gregory Quandel (Pres & COO)

Subsidiaries:

The Quandel Construction Group, Inc.   (1)
3003 N Frnt St Ste 203, Harrisburg, PA 17110
Tel.: (717) 657-0909
Web Site: http://www.quandel.com
Sales Range: $25-49.9 Million
Emp.: 80
Nonresidential Construction
N.A.I.C.S.: 236220
Noble C. Quandel Jr. (CEO)
Cindy Heath (Coord-Mktg)
James Kostecky (Exec VP)

The Quandel Group, Minersville   (1)
401 Jones St, Minersville, PA 17954-1214   (100%)
Tel.: (570) 544-4400
Sales Range: $10-24.9 Million
Emp.: 5
N.A.I.C.S.: 236220
Chris Bushey (CFO)

THE QUAY CORPORATION, INC.
7101 N Capitol Dr, Lincolnwood, IL 60712
Tel.: (847) 676-4233
Web Site: http://www.quaycorp.net
Year Founded: 1982
Sales Range: $10-24.9 Million
Emp.: 35
Cheese Mfr
N.A.I.C.S.: 311513
Margaret Cuellar (VP & Sec)

THE QUEEN'S HEALTH SYSTEMS
1301 Punchbowl St, Honolulu, HI 96813
Tel.: (808) 691-5900   HI
Web Site: http://www.queens.org
Year Founded: 1985
Sales Range: $25-49.9 Million
Emp.: 69
Health Care Srvices
N.A.I.C.S.: 622110
Keala Peters (Dir-Strategic Mktg)
Jason Chang (COO & Exec VP)
Art Ushijima (Pres & CEO)
Stacey Tokairin (Exec VP-Property Mgmt & Bus Dev)
Brian Yoshii (CIO & VP)
Carol Shimada (Dir-Sys Total Rewards)
Charie Lee Wicklund (Dir-Internal Audit)
Dan Yousey (Dir-IT Project Mgmt Office)

THE QUEENSBORO SHIRT COMPANY
1400 Marstellar St, Wilmington, NC 28401
Tel.: (910) 251-1251
Web Site:
http://www.queensboro.com
Year Founded: 1981
Rev.: $15,200,000
Emp.: 150
Retail Mail Order House Pleating & Stitching Services
N.A.I.C.S.: 458110
Fred Meyers (Founder & Chm)

THE QUEST BUSINESS AGENCY, INC.
2150 W 18th St Ste 202, Houston, TX 77008
Tel.: (713) 956-6569   TX
Web Site: http://www.tqba.com
Year Founded: 1981
Sales Range: $10-24.9 Million
Emp.: 9
Advertising Agencies
N.A.I.C.S.: 541810
Alan D. Vera (Owner)
Carol Frenza (Controller)

THE QUEST GROUP, INC.
9300 Wade Blvd Ste 320, Frisco, TX 75035-2175
Tel.: (972) 731-0021
Web Site: http://www.quest-grp.com
Year Founded: 2002
Sales Range: $1-9.9 Million
Emp.: 245
Recruits Nurses for Acute-Care Hospitals
N.A.I.C.S.: 561311
Neil Brady (Founder & CEO)
Tyler Richardson (Mgr-Ops)

THE QUIKRETE COMPANIES, LLC
1 Securities Centre 3490 Piedmont Rd Ste 1300, Atlanta, GA 30305-4811
Tel.: (404) 634-9100
Web Site: http://www.quikrete.com
Year Founded: 1940
Sales Range: $100-124.9 Million
Emp.: 2,500
Cement & Concrete Product Mfr
N.A.I.C.S.: 327320
Dennis Winchester (Exec VP)
Chad Corley (Dir-PR)

Subsidiaries:

Colorado Best Block, LLC   (1)
8227 Blakeland Dr, Littleton, CO 80125
Tel.: (303) 791-3334
Web Site: http://www.coloradobestblock.com
Sales Range: $25-49.9 Million
Emp.: 35
Construction Materials Distr
N.A.I.C.S.: 423320
Bruce Otten (Gen Mgr)

Forterra, Inc.   (1)
511 E John Carpenter Fwy 6th Fl, Irving, TX 75062
Tel.: (469) 458-7973
Web Site: http://www.forterrabp.com
Rev.: $1,858,270,000
Assets: $1,774,033,000
Liabilities: $1,454,966,000
Net Worth: $319,067,000
Earnings: $116,317,000
Emp.: 1,434
Fiscal Year-end: 12/31/2021
Holding Company; Pipe & Precast Product Mfr
N.A.I.C.S.: 551112
Lori M. Browne (Gen Counsel & Exec VP)
Vikrant Bhatia (Pres-Water Pipe & Products)
Sean Hasan (Dir-Sls-Western)
Jeff Arnold (VP & Gen Mgr-Oklahoma)
Todd Keppler (VP & Gen Mgr-Iowa)
Shaun Slotterback (Dir-Ops-Arizona)
Joel Mich (VP-Engrg & Quality-Minnesota)
Bart Dooley (Mgr-Sls-North Texas)
Chad Wiemers (Sr Mgr-Sls)
Chance Hemerda (Mgr-Specialty Sls)
Charles Jordan (Dir-Precast Ops)
Cody Felps (Mgr-Sls)
David Matocha (Engr-Technical Res)
Dennis Moore (Dir-Gravity Ops-Texas)
Gary Robertson (Mgr-Sls)
Jeff Killin (VP-Strategic Accts)
Jeff Moeller (Sr Mgr-Sls)
Kyle Dickerson (Mgr-Sls-North Texas)
Kyle Nelson (Mgr-Sls-North Texas)
Charlie R. Brown II (CFO & Exec VP)
Karl H. Watson Jr. (CEO)

QUIKRETE Holdings, Inc.   (1)
5 Concourse Pkwy Ste 1900, Atlanta, GA 30328
Tel.: (404) 634-9100
Holding Company
N.A.I.C.S.: 551112
Will Magill (CEO)

Quikrete   (1)
6950 Stevenson Blvd, Fremont, CA 94538
Tel.: (510) 490-4670
Web Site: http://www.quikrete.com
Sales Range: $10-24.9 Million
Emp.: 100
Concrete Products
N.A.I.C.S.: 327390

Quikrete of Virginia   (1)
3712 Cook Blvd, Chesapeake, VA 23320
Tel.: (757) 547-9411
Rev.: $55,000,000
Emp.: 40
Dry Mixture Concrete
N.A.I.C.S.: 327999

THE R. LANG COMPANY
8240 W Doe Ave, Visalia, CA 93291
Tel.: (559) 651-0701   CA
Web Site: http://www.rollaway.com
Year Founded: 1967
Rev.: $14,000,000
Emp.: 100
Mfr of Screen Doors & Windows
N.A.I.C.S.: 332321
Richard A. Lang (Pres)

THE R.A. SIEGEL COMPANY
1370 Discovery Industrial Ct, Mapleton, GA 30126
Tel.: (404) 355-2952   GA
Web Site: http://www.rasiegel.com
Year Founded: 1950
Sales Range: $10-24.9 Million
Emp.: 120
Wholesale Floor Covering
N.A.I.C.S.: 423220

THE R.E. KRUG CORPORATION
190 Oliver St, North Tonawanda, NY 14120
Tel.: (716) 692-2305   NY
Web Site: http://www.rekrug.com
Year Founded: 1980
Sales Range: $10-24.9 Million
Emp.: 12
Provider of Architectural Glass & Metal Engineering
N.A.I.C.S.: 238150
Erik Chretien (Owner & Pres)

THE R.J. MARSHALL COMPANY
26776 W 12 Mile Rd, Southfield, MI 48034-7807
Tel.: (248) 353-4100   MI
Web Site:
http://www.rjmarshallco.com
Year Founded: 1978
Sales Range: $75-99.9 Million
Emp.: 85
Industrial Mineral & Chemical Mfr & Distr
N.A.I.C.S.: 325180
Richard J. Marshall (Co-Founder & CEO)
Joan Marshall (Co-Founder & Exec VP)
Dan Mahlmeister (VP)
Larry Blake (Exec Dir-North American Sls)

THE R.J. MARSHALL COMPANY

The R.J. Marshall Company—(Continued)

Subsidiaries:

The R.J. Marshall Company Europe BVBA (1)
Industriezone Leuvensebaan, 208A Hal 3A, Antwerp, 2820, Putte, Belgium **(100%)**
Tel.: (32) 15228030
Web Site: http://www.rjmarshall.com
Sales Range: $1-9.9 Million
Emp.: 1
Specialty Fillers Mfr
N.A.I.C.S.: 322230
Hilde De Bal (Office Mgr)

THE R.L. BRYAN COMPANY
301 Greystone Blvd, Columbia, SC 29202
Tel.: (803) 779-3560
Web Site: http://www.rlbryan.com
Sales Range: $10-24.9 Million
Emp.: 156
Commercial Printing, Lithographic
N.A.I.C.S.: 323111
Christopher D. Christiansen (CEO)

THE RADOS COMPANIES
2002 E McFadden Ave, Santa Ana, CA 92705-4766
Tel.: (714) 835-4612 CA
Web Site: http://www.radoscompanies.com
Sales Range: $15-24.9 Billion
Emp.: 50
Heavy Engineering Construction Company & Holding Company
N.A.I.C.S.: 237310
Stephen S. Rados (Co-Pres)
Jack Oiknine (VP-Engrg)
Jeff Clutter (Controller)

Subsidiaries:

RADOS EQUIPMENT CORPORATION (1)
13570 Benson Ave, Chino, CA 91710
Tel.: (909) 591-3931
Construction Engineering Services
N.A.I.C.S.: 541330

REC Equipment Corp. (1)
2002 E McFadden Ave, Santa Ana, CA 92705-4766
Tel.: (714) 835-4612
Web Site: http://www.radoscompanies.com
Sales Range: $10-24.9 Million
Emp.: 38
Heavy Engineering Construction & Equipment Services
N.A.I.C.S.: 532412
Walter Rados (Co-Pres)

Steve P. Rados, Inc. (1)
2002 E McFadden Ave, Santa Ana, CA 92705-4766
Tel.: (714) 835-4612
Web Site: http://www.radoscompanies.com
Sales Range: $10-24.9 Million
Emp.: 38
Heavy Engineering Construction
N.A.I.C.S.: 237310
Walter Rados (Co-Pres)

Universal Management Corp. (1)
2002 E McFadden Ave, Santa Ana, CA 92705-4766
Tel.: (714) 835-4612
Sales Range: $10-24.9 Million
Emp.: 38
Heavy Engineering Construction Management Services
N.A.I.C.S.: 561110
Steve Rados (CEO)

THE RAHWAY SAVINGS INSTITUTION
1500 Irving St, Rahway, NJ 07065
Tel.: (732) 388-1800
Web Site: http://www.rsibanking.com
Year Founded: 1851
Sales Range: $10-24.9 Million
Emp.: 70
Banking Services
N.A.I.C.S.: 522180
Russell Taylor (Pres & CEO)

THE RAINMAKER GROUP VENTURES, LLC.
4550 N Point Pkwy Ste 400, Alpharetta, GA 30022
Tel.: (678) 578-5700
Web Site: http://www.letitrain.com
Sales Range: $10-24.9 Million
Emp.: 100
Profit Optimization Services
N.A.I.C.S.: 525990
Bruce Barfield (Co-Founder)
Tammy Farley (Co-Founder & Pres)
Amar Duggasani (Chief Strategy Officer)
Mark Sohl (VP-Tech Ops)
Dom Beveridge (Exec VP-Demand Generation)
David O'Donohoe (Sr VP-Hospitality Sls)
Ellis Connolly (VP-Hospitality Sls-San Diego)
Matt Curry (Head-Sls)

THE RALPH J. STOLLE COMPANY
2099 N Waynesville Rd, Oregonia, OH 45054
Tel.: (513) 932-8664 OH
Year Founded: 1944
Sales Range: $10-24.9 Million
Emp.: 6
Metal Stamping
N.A.I.C.S.: 332119
William Falknor (Pres)

Subsidiaries:

The Sheffer Corporation (1)
6990 Cornell Rd, Cincinnati, OH 45242-3025 **(100%)**
Tel.: (513) 489-9770
Web Site: http://www.sheffercorp.com
Fluid Power Cylinders & Actuators
N.A.I.C.S.: 333995
Jeffrey R. Norris (Pres & CEO)
Randy Logsdon (VP-Customer Svc)
Jim Jones (Controller)

THE RAMEY AGENCY LLC
3100 N State St Ste 300, Jackson, MS 39216
Tel.: (601) 898-8900 MS
Web Site: http://www.tra.net
Year Founded: 1985
Rev: $32,000,000
Emp.: 38
Business-To-Business, Consumer Marketing, Consumer Publications, E-Commerce, Public Relations, Sales Promotion, Strategic Planning
N.A.I.C.S.: 541810
Chris Ray (CEO & Partner)
Jim Garrison (Partner & COO)
Terry Tanner (VP & Dir-Media)
Jack Garner (Pres & Partner)
Melanie Jeffreys (VP & Fin Dir)
Wes Williams (VP & Dir-Creative)
Josh Schooler (Assoc Dir-Creative)
Kathy Potts (VP & Dir-Acct Mgmt)
Beth Kitchings (Sr Acct Exec)
Anne Lauren Fratesi (Acct Exec)
Allison Watts (Assoc Dir-Art)
Philip Wilson (Sr VP & Exec Dir-Creative)

Subsidiaries:

The Ramey Agency (1)
1322 Hardwood Trail, Cordova, TN 38016
Tel.: (901) 761-3685
Web Site: http://www.rameyagency.com
Fiscal Year-end: 12/31/2004
N.A.I.C.S.: 541810
Terry Tanner (VP & Dir-Media)

The Ramey Agency (1)
590 Madison Ave, New York, NY 10022

Tel.: (212) 521-4391
N.A.I.C.S.: 541810

The Ramey Agency (1)
3100 N State St Ste 300, Jackson, MS 39216
Tel.: (404) 962-4412
Web Site: http://www.rameyagency.com
N.A.I.C.S.: 541810
Chris Ray (CEO & Partner)
Jack Garner (Pres & Partner)

THE RAMS CLUB
450 Skipper Bowles Dr, Chapel Hill, NC 27599
Tel.: (919) 843-2000 NC
Web Site: http://www.ramsclub.com
Year Founded: 1938
Sales Range: $25-49.9 Million
Emp.: 28
Scholarship Facilitation Services
N.A.I.C.S.: 813211
Diane Aldridge (CFO)
Kim Jones (Dir-Special Events)
Nick Fulton (Dir-The Annual Fund)
Gary Burns (Dir-Major Gift)
Brian Bersticker (Dir-Member Svcs)
Brian Chacos (Dir-Scholarship Donor Dev & Student-Athlete Rels)
Lowry Caudill (Chm)
Milt Petty (Treas)
Todd Pope (Vice Chm)
Carrie Truax (Asst Dir-Member Svcs)
Dawn McPherson (Dir-Campaign Ops)
Don McCauley (Dir-Scholarship Donor Rels)
Eric Montross (Dir-Major Gift)
Ginny French (Dir-Carolina Athletic Hospitality)
Grant Leiendecker (Dir-Major Gifts)
John Montgomery (Exec Dir)
Willem Bokhoven (Dir-Annual Fund)

THE RAND CORPORATION
1776 Main St, Santa Monica, CA 90401-3208
Tel.: (310) 393-0411
Web Site: http://www.rand.org
Research Services
N.A.I.C.S.: 541715
Michael Januzik (CFO)
Jeffrey Wasserman (VP, Dir-Health & Professor)
V. Darleen Opfer (VP & Dir-Education)
Bo R. Hoehn (Sr VP-Res & Analysis)
Rekha Chiruvolu (Chief Diversity Officer & Exec Dir-Diversity, Equity, and Inclusion)
Michele Colon (VP-Workplace Svcs & Real Estate)
Jennifer Gould (VP-Communications & External Affairs)
Curt Havard (CIO)
Christine Lanoie-Newman (Chief Dev Officer & VP-Development)
Melissa Rowe (VP-Global Res Talent)
Nancy Staudt (VP)
James S. Chow (VP)
Walter S. Hussey (VP)
Jim Mitre (VP)
Barry Pavel (VP)
Sally Sleeper (VP-Army Res Division & Dir)
Michelle Woods (VP)
Hans Pung (Pres-Europe)
Michael E. Leiter (Chm)
Robert M. Case (Gen Counsel, Sec & VP)
Lester Arnold Sr. (Chief HR Officer & VP)
Jason Matheny (Pres & CEO)
Anita Chandra (VP)
Andrew Dowse (Dir-Australia)

THE RANDALL GROUP INC.
9500 SW Barbur Blvd Ste 300, Portland, OR 97219-5466
Tel.: (503) 245-1131 OR
Web Site: http://www.randallgroup.com
Year Founded: 1993
Sales Range: $25-49.9 Million
Emp.: 309
Provider of Apartment Building Operation Services
N.A.I.C.S.: 531110
Randy Norgart (Pres)
Kirk Bass (Controller)
Ron Koos (VP)

Subsidiaries:

CTL Management Inc. (1)
9500 SW Barbur Blvd Ste 300, Portland, OR 97219-5410 **(100%)**
Tel.: (503) 245-1255
Web Site: http://www.ctlmanagement.com
Sales Range: $10-24.9 Million
Emp.: 50
Provider of Real Estate Agency Services
N.A.I.C.S.: 531210
Jason Dowd (Pres)

Focus Commercial, Inc. (1)
9500 SW Barbur Blvd Ste 300, Portland, OR 97219
Tel.: (503) 452-5545
Web Site: http://www.focuscommercial.randallgroup.com
Emp.: 3
Real Estate Management Services
N.A.I.C.S.: 531210
Sales Range: $10-24.9
Jason Dowd (Pres)

Scott Acceptance Corporation (1)
9500 Southwest Barbur Blvd, Portland, OR 97219-5466 **(100%)**
Tel.: (503) 245-1224
Sales Range: $50-74.9 Million
Emp.: 25
Provider of Loan Broker Services
N.A.I.C.S.: 522310

THE RATNER COMPANIES
1577 Spring Hill Rd Ste 500, Vienna, VA 22182-2223
Tel.: (703) 269-5400
Web Site: http://www.ratnerco.com
Year Founded: 1974
Sales Range: $200-249.9 Million
Emp.: 10,000
Hair Salon Chain Owner & Operator Services
N.A.I.C.S.: 812112
Dennis Ratner (Co-Founder & CEO)
Ann Ratner (Co-Founder)

Subsidiaries:

The Hair Cuttery (1)
1577 Spring Hill Rd Ste 500, Vienna, VA 22182
Tel.: (703) 883-0800
Web Site: http://www.haircuttery.com
Sales Range: $10-24.9 Million
Beauty Salon Services
N.A.I.C.S.: 812112
Dennis Ratner (Co-Founder)
Ann Ratner (Co-Founder)
Eric A. Bakken (Pres & CEO)

The Ratner Companies - ColorWorks Division (1)
2564 Solomons Island Rd, Annapolis, MD 21401-3710
Tel.: (410) 571-0585
Web Site: http://www.bubblesalons.com
Hair, Nail & Skin Care Services
N.A.I.C.S.: 812112

THE REAL ESTATE GROUP, LLC
1112 F Eden Way N, Chesapeake, VA 23320
Tel.: (757) 410-8500
Web Site: http://www.realestategrp.com
Year Founded: 2003
Sales Range: $10-24.9 Million

COMPANIES

Real Estate Agency
N.A.I.C.S.: 531210
Gary Lundholm (Co-Founder)
Joseph Auzenne (Co-Founder)
Steven Edwards (Co-Founder & Dir-Trng)

THE REAL HIP-HOP NETWORK, INC.
1455 Pennsylvania Ave NW Ste 400, Washington, DC 20004
Tel.: (202) 379-3115   DE
Web Site: http://www.rhn.tv
Year Founded: 2010
Emp.: 4
Cable Television Broadcasting
N.A.I.C.S.: 516120
Atonn F. Muhammad (Chm & CEO)
Abdul Aquil Muhammad (Vice Chm & Chief Security Officer)

THE RECORD-JOURNAL PUBLISHING COMPANY
11 Crown St, Meriden, CT 06450-5713
Tel.: (203) 235-1661   CT
Web Site: http://www.record-journal.com
Year Founded: 1867
Sales Range: $10-24.9 Million
Emp.: 200
Newspaper Publishing Services
N.A.I.C.S.: 513110
Eliot C. White (Publr)

THE REDONDO BEACH EDUCATIONAL FOUNDATION
409 N Pacific Coast Hwy Ste 310, Redondo Beach, CA 90277
Tel.: (310) 954-2004   CA
Web Site: http://www.rbef.org
Year Founded: 1992
Sales Range: $1-9.9 Million
Emp.: 77
Child Educational Services
N.A.I.C.S.: 624110
Kristen Byard (Dir-Admin)
Ted Craddock (Pres)
Sally House Miller (VP)
Monika L. McCarthy (Sec)
Sandra Fuchs (Treas)

THE REDSTONE COMPANIES, L.P.
109 N Post Oak Ln Ste 200, Houston, TX 77024
Tel.: (713) 266-1899   TX
Web Site: http://www.trccapitalpartners.com
Sales Range: $10-24.9 Million
Emp.: 50
Holding Company; Private Equity, Hospitality & Real Estate
N.A.I.C.S.: 551112
Pam Hayes (CFO & Exec VP)
Kellie Jenks (VP-Investments)
Steven D. Lerner (Pres & CEO)

Subsidiaries:

Redstone Companies Hospitality, LLC   (1)
109 N Post Oak Ln Ste 200, Houston, TX 77024
Tel.: (713) 266-1899
Web Site: http://www.redstonecompanieshospitality.com
Hotel, Golf Course, Fitness Center & Health Spa Properties Investment Management
N.A.I.C.S.: 523940
Mark Yanke (Pres & CEO)
Al Gallo (CFO & Sr VP)
Evan Johansen (Sr VP-Bus Dev)
Gina Harrell (Sr VP-HR)
Kim Phillips (VP-Mktg & Special Projects)
Eric Terry (VP-Dev-Sls & Mktg)

Holding (Domestic):

The Houstonian Golf & Country Club   (2)
12600 Houstonian Dr, Houston, TX 77469
Tel.: (281) 494-4244
Web Site: http://www.houstoniangolf.com
Hotels & Motels
N.A.I.C.S.: 713910
Natalie Nielson (Mgr-Trellis Spa)
Greg Nielson (Mng Dir)
John Kennedy (Gen Mgr)
Matt Austin (Sr VP-HR)
Rich Gustke (Dir-Creative)
Jeff Hemric (Sr Mgr-IT)
Maria Holler (Mgr-Mktg)
Tom Ivers (CIO)
Scott Koester (VP-Product Mgmt)
Douglas Lee (Dir-Fin)
Ray McDonald (Exec VP)
Carrie Seddon (Dir-Production)
William Ivers Sr. (CEO)

THE REDWOOD EMPIRE FOOD BANK
3990 Brickway Blvd, Santa Rosa, CA 95403
Tel.: (707) 523-7900   CA
Web Site: http://www.refb.org
Year Founded: 1987
Sales Range: $25-49.9 Million
Emp.: 63
Community Food Services
N.A.I.C.S.: 624210
Jean Larson (COO)
David Goodman (Exec Dir)
Jon Griffith (VP)
Rebecca La Londe (Treas)
Eric McHenry (Sec)
Justin Hofmann (Coord-Inventory)
Steve Armstrong (Dir-Ops & Logistics)
Jen Oberti (Mgr-Corp & Community Rels)
Itzul Gutierrez (Mgr-Program)
Pete Golis (Pres)

THE REDWOOD GROUP, LLC
5920 Nall Ave Ste #400, Mission, KS 66202
Tel.: (816) 979-1786
Web Site: http://theredwoodgroup.com
Year Founded: 2010
Commodities Company; Customized Supply Chain Solutions, Food & Feed Ingredient Supply, Energy & Energy Input Supply & Grain Merchandising
N.A.I.C.S.: 311999
Mike Kincaid (Pres)

Subsidiaries:

Ceres Commodities, LLC   (1)
329 E 4th St, Newport, KY 41071
Tel.: (859) 371-1484
Web Site: http://ceresag.com
Whol Grain
N.A.I.C.S.: 424510

THE REHANCEMENT GROUP, INC.
11911 Freedom Dr Ste 910, Reston, VA 20190
Tel.: (703) 450-4176
Web Site: http://www.rehancement.com
Sales Range: $1-9.9 Million
Emp.: 60
Business Research & Development Services
N.A.I.C.S.: 541720
David S. Baker (CEO)
Bento I. Polzak (VP)

THE REINALT-THOMAS CORPORATION
20225 N Scottsdale Rd, Scottsdale, AZ 85255

Tel.: (480) 606-6000   MI
Web Site: https://www.discounttire.com
Year Founded: 1960
Sales Range: $1-4.9 Billion
Emp.: 28,292
Tire Dealers
N.A.I.C.S.: 441340
Gary Van Brunt (Vice Chm)
Dean Butler (Sr VP-Pur)
Christian Roe (CFO)
Timothy J. Schafer (Exec VP)
Jess Stine (Sr VP-Store Ops)
Michael Zuieback (Chm)
Dean Muglia (CEO)

THE REINFORCED EARTH COMPANY
12001 Sunrise Valley Dr Ste 400, Reston, VA 20191
Web Site: http://www.reinforcedearth.com
Year Founded: 1971
Retaining Wall Systems, Reflective & Absorptive Sound Walls, Precast Arches & Slope Stabilization Systems Constructor
N.A.I.C.S.: 237990
Kim Britton (Mgr-HR)

Subsidiaries:

The Reinforced Earth Company   (1)
1660 Hotel Cir N Ste 304, San Diego, CA 92108-2803
Tel.: (619) 688-2400
Sales Range: $10-24.9 Million
Emp.: 10
Engineeering Services
N.A.I.C.S.: 331210

THE REISER GROUP
3201 Danville Blvd Ste 180, Alamo, CA 94507
Tel.: (925) 314-9800
Web Site: http://www.reisergroup.com
Year Founded: 1999
Sales Range: $10-24.9 Million
Emp.: 15
Sales & Marketing Services for Real Estate Developers
N.A.I.C.S.: 531390
Tom Reiser (Pres)
Paul Renker (VP-Sls & Mktg)
Peter Gillis (VP-Ops)
Teresa Routt (Dir-Ops)

THE RELATED COMPANIES, L.P.
60 Columbus Cir, New York, NY 10023
Tel.: (212) 421-5332   NY
Web Site: http://www.related.com
Year Founded: 1972
Sales Range: $25-49.9 Million
Emp.: 400
Holding Company; Residential & Commercial Real Estate Properties Acquisition, Development & Management Services
N.A.I.C.S.: 551112
Stephen Millard Ross (Founder & Chm)
Bruce L. Warwick (Vice Chm)
Kenneth P. Wong (COO & Dir-Dev-Intl)
Michael J. Brenner (Exec VP)
Richard L. O'Toole (Exec VP)
Stephen Earle (Sr VP & Dir-Creative)
Nick Anderson (VP-Related Midwest)
Warren Dauber (VP)
MaryAnn Osborn (VP-Sls)
David Zussman (CFO)
Ron Parker (CEO-Related Restaurant Group)
Bruce A. Beal Jr. (Pres)
Jeff T. Blau (CEO & Partner)

THE RELATED COMPANIES, L.P.

Subsidiaries:

KSW, Inc.   (1)
37-16 23rd St, Long Island City, NY 11101
Tel.: (718) 361-6500
Web Site: http://www.kswmechanical.com
Sales Range: $50-74.9 Million
Emp.: 41
Heating, Ventilation, Air-Conditioning & Plumbing Supplies Whslr & Installation Services
N.A.I.C.S.: 423730
James F. Oliviero (Gen Counsel)
Richard W. Lucas (CFO)
Vincent Terraferma (COO)
Al Schroeder (VP & Chief Engr)

Subsidiary (Domestic):

KSW Mechanical Services, Inc.   (2)
37-16 23rd St, Long Island City, NY 11101-3518
Tel.: (718) 361-6500
Web Site: http://www.kswmechanical.com
Sales Range: $25-49.9 Million
Heating & Air Conditioning Supply & Installation
N.A.I.C.S.: 238220
Al Schroeder (VP & Chief Engr)

LR Development Company LLC   (1)
350 W Hubbard Ste 300, Chicago, IL 60654
Tel.: (312) 595-7400
Web Site: http://www.relatedmidwest.com
Emp.: 75
Residential & Commercial Real Estate Properties Acquisition, Development & Management Services
N.A.I.C.S.: 237210
Curt R. Bailey (Pres)
Don Biernacki (Sr VP-Construction)
Jacques Sandberg (VP)
Nick Anderson (VP-Acq & Dev)
Michael Ellch (VP-Dev)
Marron Kilworth (Dir-Ops)
Ann Thompson (Sr VP-Architecture & Design)
Tricia Van Horn (VP-Mktg & Comm)

Related Beal, LLC   (1)
177 Milk St, Boston, MA 02109
Tel.: (617) 451-2100
Web Site: http://www.relatedbeal.com
Emp.: 35
Real Estate Development Services
N.A.I.C.S.: 531390
Bruce A. Beal (Chm)
Stephen N. Faber (Exec VP)
Kimberly Sherman Stamler (Pres)
Mark P. Biondi (Sr VP)
Maxwell O. Cassidy (Sr Project Mgr-Construction)
Hassan Afzali (VP-Engrg)
Dean S. Leventman (Dir-Fin Analysis)
Brian M. Radomski (VP-Construction)
Michael P. Tammaro (VP-Brokerage & Valuation)

Related California, LLC   (1)
18201 Von Karman Ave Ste 900, Irvine, CA 92612
Tel.: (949) 660-7272
Web Site: http://www.relatedcalifornia.com
Real Estate Development Services
N.A.I.C.S.: 531390
William A. Witte (Chm & CEO)
Steve Sherman (CFO)
Frank Cardone (COO & Pres-Affordable)
Steven Wraight (Dir-Design)
Greg Vilkin (Pres-Urban Residential)
Gino Canori (Exec VP-Dev)
Susan Smartt (Exec VP-Dev)
Meea Kang (Sr VP)

Related China Limited   (1)
Room 2906 29F Chong Hing Finance Center, 288 Nanjing West Road, Shanghai, 200003, China
Tel.: (86) 2160809000
Web Site: http://www.related.com
Residential & Commercial Real Estate Properties Acquisition, Development & Management Services
N.A.I.C.S.: 237210

Related Fund Management LLC   (1)
2515 McKinney Ave Ste 950, Dallas, TX 75201
Tel.: (972) 656-2850
Web Site: http://www.related.com

THE RELATED COMPANIES, L.P.

The Related Companies, L.P.—(Continued)
Emp.: 23
Investment Advisory Services
N.A.I.C.S.: 523940
Peter Murray (CEO)

Related Group (1)
315 S Biscayne Blvd, Miami, FL 33131
Tel.: (305) 460-9900
Web Site: http://www.relatedgroup.com
Real Estate Manangement Services
N.A.I.C.S.: 531390
Adolfo Henriques (Vice Chm)
Jorge M. Perez (Founder, Chm & CEO)
Matthew J. Allen (COO & Exec VP)
Carlos Rosso (Pres-Condominium Dev Div)
Jeffery Hoyos (Sr VP)
Sonia Figueroa (VP-Dev)
Patrick Campbell (VP)
James M. Werbelow (Sr VP-Construction)
Betsy Mccoy (Gen Counsel & VP)
Lissette Calderon (Pres-Intl & Strategic Projects)
Allison Goldberg (Dir-Mktg)
Patricia M. Hanna (Dir-Art)
Steve Patterson (Pres & CEO-Related Dev)
Albert Milo Jr. (Principal & Sr VP-Related Urban Dev)

Related Management Company, L.P. (1)
423 W 55th St 9th Fl, New York, NY 10019
Tel.: (212) 319-1200
Web Site: http://www.related.com
Sales Range: $10-24.9 Million
Emp.: 100
Residential & Commercial Property Management Services
N.A.I.C.S.: 531312
Jeffrey I. Brodsky (Pres)

Related Retail, L.P. (1)
60 Columbus Cir, New York, NY 10023
Tel.: (212) 801-1000
Web Site: http://www.related.com
Sales Range: $10-24.9 Million
Emp.: 45
Retail Shopping Center Property Development Services
N.A.I.C.S.: 237210
Glenn A. Goldstein (Pres)

Related Sales LLC (1)
60 Columbus Cir, New York, NY 10023
Tel.: (212) 801-3900
Web Site: http://www.related.com
Luxury Residential Real Estate Agency
N.A.I.C.S.: 531210

Related Urban Development, L.P. (1)
60 Columbus Cir, New York, NY 10023
Tel.: (212) 801-1000
Web Site: http://www.related.com
Sales Range: $50-74.9 Million
Emp.: 200
Large-Scale Mixed-Use Real Estate Development Services
N.A.I.C.S.: 237210
Kenneth A. Himmel (Pres & CEO)

THE REMBAR COMPANY, LLC
67 Main St PO Box 67, Dobbs Ferry, NY 10522
Tel.: (914) 693-2620
Web Site: http://www.rembar.com
Year Founded: 1950
Emp.: 20
Refractory Metal Powders, Pastes & Flakes
N.A.I.C.S.: 331221
Walter Pastor (Pres & VP-Sls)
Rob Peters (Mgr-Quality Control)
Frank Firor (Chm & CEO)
Audra Haase (VP-Fin)
Hal Rostad (Mgr-Sls)
Gannett Ries (Mgr-Production)
Mike Misch (Mgr-Shipping)
Tom DeRentilis (Engr-Sls)
Jim DeLong (Dir-Sls)
Dave Gordon (Engr-Sls)

THE REMI GROUP, LLC.
11325 N Community House Rd Ste 300, Charlotte, NC 28277
Tel.: (704) 602-0828
Web Site: http://www.theremigroup.com
Year Founded: 2002
Sales Range: $25-49.9 Million
Emp.: 86
Equipment Maintenance Programs for Electronic Devices Not Utilizing Service Technicians
N.A.I.C.S.: 811210
Daniel Schuster (Founder & CEO)
Brent Howison (Pres)
Robert Fleischacker (VP, Gen Counsel & Chief Compliance Officer)
Brian Landon (Dir-HR)
Michael Van Derveer (Chief Production Officer)
Laura Barclift (COO)
Dana Upshaw (Chief Revenue Officer)
Van Miller (CFO)

THE REMODELING COMPANY
100 Cummings Ctr Ste 327J, Beverly, MA 01915
Tel.: (781) 861-6400
Web Site: http://www.theremodelingco.com
Year Founded: 1998
Sales Range: $1-9.9 Million
Emp.: 17
Residential Building Remodeling Services
N.A.I.C.S.: 236118
Melissa Smith (Mgr-Ops)
Steve Daigneau (Mgr-Production)

THE RENAISSANCE GROUP LLC
25260 Montane Dr W, Golden, CO 80401-8508
Tel.: (303) 221-8338
Year Founded: 1996
Sales Range: $25-49.9 Million
Emp.: 2
Privater Equity Firm
N.A.I.C.S.: 523999
Gregory C. Mosher (Principal)

THE RENCO GROUP INC.
1 Rockefeller Plz 29th Fl, New York, NY 10020
Tel.: (212) 541-6000
Web Site: https://www.rencogroup.net
Year Founded: 1980
Sales Range: $1-4.9 Billion
Emp.: 15,000
Offices of Other Holding Companies
N.A.I.C.S.: 551112
Ira Leon Rennert (Founder)

Subsidiaries:

AM General LLC (1)
105 N Niles Ave, South Bend, IN 46617
Tel.: (574) 237-6222
Web Site: http://www.amgeneral.com
Sales Range: $25-49.9 Million
Emp.: 1,500
High-Mobility Vehicles Mfr; Owned 70% by MacAndrews & Forbes Holding Inc. & 30% by Renco Group Inc.
N.A.I.C.S.: 336992
James J. Cannon (Pres & CEO)
R. Andrew Hove (Pres & CEO)
Christopher P. Vanslager (Exec VP-US Defense)
Claudia Gast (Sr VP-Strategy & Corp Dev)
John P. Chadbourne (Sr VP-DC Ops)
Kevin A. Rahrig (Exec VP-Comml)
Mark Minne (Chief Admin Officer & VP)
Nguyen Trinh (Exec VP-Defense-Intl)
Robert Gold (CFO & Exec VP)
Stephen Zink (COO & Exec VP)
Tricia Sherick (Gen Counsel & Exec VP)

Subsidiary (Domestic):

AM General Aftermarket Fulfillment and Training Center (2)
5448 Dylan Dr, South Bend, IN 46628
Tel.: (574) 237-6222
Specialized Vehicle Mfr
N.A.I.C.S.: 336211

AM General Technology and Engineering Center (2)
1399 Pacific Dr, Auburn Hills, MI 48326
Tel.: (574) 237-6222
Specialized Vehicles Designer & Mfr
N.A.I.C.S.: 336211

General Engine Products LLC (2)
2000 Watkins Glen Dr, Franklin, OH 45005
Tel.: (937) 704-1800
Engine Products Mfr
N.A.I.C.S.: 333618

Plant (Domestic):

Mishawaka Manufacturing Campus (2)
13200 McKinley Hwy, Mishawaka, IN 46545
Tel.: (574) 237-6222
Specialized Vehicle Mfr
N.A.I.C.S.: 336211

Baron Drawn Steel Corp. (1)
10221 Capital St, Oak Park, MI 48237-3103
Tel.: (734) 354-8100
Sales Range: $25-49.9 Million
Emp.: 35
Cold Drawn Steel Bars & Coils
N.A.I.C.S.: 331221

Doe Run Peru S.R.L. (1)
Av Victor Andres Belaunde 147 Torre 3 Piso 9 San Isidro, Lima, 27, Peru
Tel.: (51) 1 215 1200
Web Site: http://www.doerun.com.pe
Sales Range: $25-49.9 Million
Emp.: 60
Metal Ore Mining Services
N.A.I.C.S.: 212290
Edwin Escalante (Mgr-Comml)

Subsidiary (US):

Fabricated Products, Inc. (2)
3201 Lower River Rd Bldg 2575 WW Ste 7, Vancouver, WA 98660
Tel.: (360) 695-5949
Fabricated Metal Product Mfr & Distr
N.A.I.C.S.: 423510

Renfro Corporation (1)
661 Linville Rd, Mount Airy, NC 27030-3101
Tel.: (336) 719-8000
Web Site: http://www.renfro.com
Sales Range: $250-299.9 Million
Emp.: 4,500
Socks Mfr
N.A.I.C.S.: 315120
Stan Jewell (Pres & CEO)
David Dinkins (CFO & Exec VP)

Subsidiary (Non-US):

Renfro BV (2)
Schweitzerlaan 16-A, 1187 JD, Amstelveen, Netherlands
Tel.: (31) 2020 51020
Web Site: http://www.renfro.com
Emp.: 4
Footwear Distr
N.A.I.C.S.: 424340
Paul Bos (Gen Mgr & Dir-Fin)

Renfro Canada Inc. (2)
250 Admiral Blvd, Mississauga, L5T 2N6, ON, Canada
Tel.: (905) 795-3130
Web Site: http://www.renfro.com
Emp.: 30
Footwear Distr
N.A.I.C.S.: 424340
Brian Grant (VP-Sls & Gen Mgr)

Renfro India Pvt Ltd. (2)
The Chambers Office No 403 Near Ganapati Temple, Viman Nagar, Pune, 411014, India
Tel.: (91) 20 30552300
Web Site: http://www.renfroindia.com
Emp.: 900
Socks Mfr
N.A.I.C.S.: 315120

Renfro Japan (2)
Sompo Japan Gotanda Kyodo Building 7F 2-3-1 Higashi Gotanda, Shinagawa, Tokyo,
141 0022, Japan
Tel.: (81) 3 6721 9497
Footwear Whslr
N.A.I.C.S.: 424340
Ryota Takahashi (Gen Mgr)

Renfro Mexico, S.A. de C.V. (2)
Mesa de Leon No 112 Parque Carr Km 28.5 Sta Rosa, Jauregui Mexico Tec de San Lu, Queretaro, 76220, Mexico
Tel.: (52) 442 242 0403
Web Site: http://www.renfro.com
Emp.: 42
Footwear Distr
N.A.I.C.S.: 424340
Fernando Cartagena (Mgr-Mktg)

The Doe Run Company (1)
1801 Park 270 Dr Ste 300, Saint Louis, MO 63146-4020 (100%)
Tel.: (314) 453-7100
Web Site: http://www.doerun.com
Sales Range: $250-299.9 Million
Emp.: 50
Lead Production & Recycling
N.A.I.C.S.: 212230
Sharon Gietl (CIO)
J. Ross Conner (VP-Metals & Exploration)
Matthew Wohl (Pres & CEO)
Mark Coomes (VP-HR & Community Rels)
Steve Batts (VP-HR & Ops)
Lou Magdits (Dir-Raw Matls)
Jose Hansen (VP-Sls & Mktg)
Mark Yingling (VP-Environmental, Health & Safety)
Anthony Staley (Gen Mgr-Metals Div)
Dianne Whitaker (Dir-HR)
Tony Bogolin (CFO, Treas & Exec VP-Fin & HR)
Tammy Stankey (Dir-Comm)
Crystal Saling (Gen Counsel & VP-Law)
Brian Mangogna (COO & VP-Ops)
Michael Montgomery (VP-Environment, Health & Safety)

Unarco Material Handling, Inc. (1)
701 16th Ave E, Springfield, TN 37172-3305 (100%)
Tel.: (615) 384-3531
Web Site: http://www.unarcorack.com
Sales Range: $25-49.9 Million
Emp.: 750
Warehouse Storage Systems Mfr
N.A.I.C.S.: 333248
Paul Neal (CFO)
John Fyke (VP-Pur)

THE RENFREW CENTERS INC.
475 Spring Ln, Philadelphia, PA 19128
Tel.: (215) 482-5353
Web Site: http://www.renfrewcenter.com
Rev.: $19,000,000
Emp.: 750
Women's Mental Health Services
N.A.I.C.S.: 622310
Samuel E. Menaged (Founder & Pres)

THE RENOVATOR'S SUPPLY, INC.
Renovators Old Mill, Millers Falls, MA 01349
Tel.: (413) 423-3559
Web Site: http://www.rensup.com
Year Founded: 1978
Sales Range: $25-49.9 Million
Emp.: 120
Mail Order Internet Services: Hardware, Plumbing & Lighting
N.A.I.C.S.: 332510
Claude Jeanloz (Pres)
Mike Gordon (Mgr-Mfg)

THE RESERVES NETWORK INC.
22021 Brookpark Rd, Fairview Park, OH 44126
Tel.: (866) 876-2020
Web Site: http://www.trnstaffing.com
Year Founded: 1984
Sales Range: $10-24.9 Million

COMPANIES

Emp.: 125
Staffing, Training & Human Resource Management Services
N.A.I.C.S.: 561320
Don Stallard *(Founder & Chm)*
Gordon Friedrich *(VP)*
Patrick Durant *(Dir-Sls)*
Amy Gerrity *(Pres)*
Kelly Burke *(VP)*
Neil Stallard *(CEO)*
Brandon Thimke *(Dir-Comm)*
Nick Stallard *(CFO)*
Brad Qua *(Sr VP-Specialty Groups)*

Subsidiaries:

TempWise, Inc. (1)
110 S Magnolia Ave, Tampa, FL 33606
Tel.: (813) 258-4101
Web Site: http://www.tempwise.com
Sales Range: $1-9.9 Million
Emp.: 5
Temporary Help Service
N.A.I.C.S.: 561320
Lee Rachelson *(Reg Dir)*

The FocIS Group LLC (1)
22021 Brookpark Rd, Fairview Park, OH 44126
Tel.: (440) 779-4800
Web Site: http://www.thefocisgroup.com
Emp.: 50
Information Technology Consulting Services
N.A.I.C.S.: 541618
Don Shadrake *(VP)*

The Professional Search Group (1)
22021 Brookpark Rd, Fairview Park, OH 44126
Tel.: (440) 779-5684
Web Site: http://www.TheProSearchGroup.com
Employment Placement Agency
N.A.I.C.S.: 561311

THE RESOURCE GROUP INTERNATIONAL LTD.
1700 Pennsylvania Ave NW Ste 560, Washington, DC 20006
Tel.: (202) 289-9898
Web Site: http://www.trgworld.com
Business Process Outsourcing & Investment Services
N.A.I.C.S.: 561499
Zia Chishti *(Co-Founder, Chm, CEO & Partner)*
Mark Ayling *(Mng Dir)*
Nadeem Elahi *(Mng Dir)*
Mohammed Khaishgi *(Co-Founder & Partner)*
Shuja Keen *(Mng Dir)*
Pat Costello *(Mng Dir & Gen Counsel)*
Hasnain Aslam *(Co-Founder, Partner & Chief Investment Officer)*

Subsidiaries:

IBEX Limited (1)
Crawford House 50 Cedar Avenue, Hamilton, HM11, Bermuda
Tel.: (441) 2956500
Web Site: http://www.ibex.co
Rev.: $443,662,000
Assets: $274,287,000
Liabilities: $193,628,000
Net Worth: $80,659,000
Earnings: $2,847,000
Emp.: 24,243
Fiscal Year-end: 06/30/2021
Technology Service Provider
N.A.I.C.S.: 541512
Julie Casteel *(CMO & Chief Strategic Accounts Officer)*
Paul Inson *(Chief People Officer)*
Robert Dechant *(CEO)*
Taylor C. Greenwald *(CFO)*
David Afdahl *(COO)*
Christy O'Connor *(Chief Legal Officer, Gen Counsel & Asst Sec)*
Bruce Dawson *(Chief Sls Officer & Chief Client Svcs Officer)*
Mohammed Khaishgi *(Chm)*
Andreas Wilkens *(CTO)*

Subsidiary (Non-US):

IBEX Global Solutions Limited (2)
2nd Floor Castlemead, Lower Castle Street, Bristol, BS1 3AG, United Kingdom
Tel.: (44) 1275344344
Web Site: http://www.ibexglobal.com
Business Process Outsourcing Services
N.A.I.C.S.: 561422
Karl Gabel *(CFO)*
Vickie Leslie *(Sr VP-Global Performance Support)*
Robert Dechant *(CEO)*
Jim Ferrato *(CIO)*
Bruce Dawson *(Chief Sls & Client Svcs Officer)*
Rosemary Hanratty *(Sr Dir-Mktg)*

THE RESPONSE SHOP, INC.
7486 La Jolla Blvd Ste 164, La Jolla, CA 92037
Tel.: (858) 735-7646
Web Site: http://www.responseshop.com
Year Founded: 2000
Sales Range: Less than $1 Million
Emp.: 12
Direct Marketing, Full Service, Radio, T.V.
N.A.I.C.S.: 541810
Marla Hoskins *(Founder & Pres)*
Jean B. Hall *(Copywriter)*
Peter Hochstein *(Copywriter)*
Sam Auster *(Pres-Auster Productions)*
Kate McCarthy *(Dir-Art)*
Deborah Schatten *(Copywriter)*

THE RETAIL BUS TOUR, INC.
98 SE Atlantic Ave Ste 2, Delray Beach, FL 33483
Tel.: (561) 353-0151
Web Site: http://www.retailbustour.com
Sales Range: $1-9.9 Million
Emp.: 8
Tour Operator
N.A.I.C.S.: 561520
Gary Broidis *(Partner)*
Stuart Hodes *(Mng Dir)*

THE RETAIL OUTSOURCE
75 Valencia Ave Ste 800, Coral Gables, FL 33134
Tel.: (305) 539-3810
Web Site: http://www.theretailoutsource.com
Year Founded: 2000
Sales Range: $1-9.9 Million
Emp.: 150
Consulting, Outsourced Staffing & Management Operations
N.A.I.C.S.: 541618
Brett Beveridge *(Pres, Founder & CEO)*
Tyler Mahler *(COO)*
Michael Faulk *(VP-Fin)*
Maylen Santana *(Dir-HR)*

THE RETIREMENT SYSTEMS OF ALABAMA
201 S Union St, Montgomery, AL 36104
Web Site: http://www.rsa-al.gov
Assets: $40,705,173,000
Liabilities: $1,284,949,000
Net Worth: $39,420,224,000
Fiscal Year-end: 09/30/20
State Pension Fund Administrations Services
N.A.I.C.S.: 524292
David G. Bronner *(CEO)*
Diane E. Scott *(CFO & Chief Accountant)*

Subsidiaries:

CNHI, LLC (1)
201 Monroe St Ste 450, Montgomery, AL 36104
Tel.: (334) 293-5800
Web Site: http://www.cnhi.com
Newspaper Publishers
N.A.I.C.S.: 513110
Donna J. Barrett *(Pres & CEO)*
Chris Cato *(CFO)*
Steve McPhaul *(COO)*
Matthew Gray *(Gen Counsel)*

Unit (Domestic):

Commercial-News (2)
17 WN St, Danville, IL 61832-5765 **(100%)**
Tel.: (217) 446-9444
Web Site: http://www.commercial-news.com
Sales Range: $10-24.9 Million
Emp.: 15
Newspaper Publishing
N.A.I.C.S.: 513110
Amy Winter *(Publr)*

Commonwealth Journal Inc. (2)
110 E Mount Vernon St 112, Somerset, KY 42501-1411
Tel.: (606) 678-8191
Web Site: http://www.somerset-kentucky.com
Rev.: $3,000,000
Emp.: 54
Publishing & Distribution of Newspapers
N.A.I.C.S.: 513110
Steve Cornelius *(Editor-Sports)*
Paula Jones *(Office Mgr-Bus)*
Jeff Neal *(Editor)*
Michael McCleery *(Publr)*
Mark Walker *(Gen Mgr)*

Community Holdings Of Kentucky LLC (2)
123 W 5th St, London, KY 40741-1837
Tel.: (606) 878-7400
Web Site: http://www.sentinel-echo.com
Sales Range: $25-49.9 Million
Emp.: 33
Newspaper Publishing
N.A.I.C.S.: 513110
Judy McCowan *(Mgr-Bus)*
Kathy Jones *(Mgr-Adv)*
Mark Walker *(Gen Mgr)*
Erin Cox *(Editor)*

Eagle-Tribune Publishing Company Inc. (2)
100 Turnpike St, North Andover, MA 01845-5033
Tel.: (978) 946-2000
Web Site: http://www.eagletribune.com
Sales Range: $25-49.9 Million
Emp.: 522
Newspaper Publishers
N.A.I.C.S.: 513110
Mark Zappala *(VP-Adv)*
Steve Milone *(Dir-Audience Dev)*
John Gregory *(Dir-IT)*

Subsidiary (Domestic):

Derry Publishing Co. Inc. (3)
46 W Broadway, Derry, NH 03038-2329
Tel.: (603) 437-7000
Web Site: http://www.derrynews.com
Sales Range: $25-49.9 Million
Emp.: 10
Newspaper Publishers
N.A.I.C.S.: 513110
Bruce Slichko *(Mgr-Circulation)*
Mark Zappala *(VP-Adv)*
Steve Pare *(Dir-Retail Adv)*

Haverhill Gazette (3)
100 Turnpike St, North Andover, MA 01845
Tel.: (978) 946-2000
Web Site: http://www.hgazette.com
Sales Range: $25-49.9 Million
Emp.: 15
Newspaper Publishers
N.A.I.C.S.: 513110
Karen Andreas *(Publr)*
Mark Zappala *(VP-Adv)*
Sean McKenna *(Dir-Retail Adv)*
Bill Cantwell *(Editor)*

Unit (Domestic):

Lockport Union Sun & Journal (2)
135 Main St, Lockport, NY 14094
Tel.: (716) 439-9222
Web Site: http://www.lockportjournal.com

THE RETIREMENT SYSTEMS OF ALABAMA

Sales Range: $10-24.9 Million
Emp.: 30
Daily Newspaper Except Sunday
N.A.I.C.S.: 513110
Cheryl Phillips *(Dir-Ops)*
Diana Henry *(Mgr-Bus)*
Joyce Miles *(Editor-City)*
Matt Winterhalter *(Mng Editor)*
Mark Scheer *(Editor-News)*

McAlester News-Capital & Democrat (2)
500 S 2nd St, McAlester, OK 74501
Tel.: (918) 423-1700
Web Site: http://www.mcalesternews.com
Sales Range: $10-24.9 Million
Emp.: 30
Daily (Except Saturday) & Sunday Newspaper
N.A.I.C.S.: 513110
Reina Owens *(Gen Mgr)*
James Beaty *(Mng Editor)*
Kevin Harvison *(Editor-Photo)*
Julie Everly *(Supvr-Office)*
Adrian O'Hanlon III *(Editor)*

Mineral Wells Index Inc. (2)
300 SE 1st St, Mineral Wells, TX 76067-5331 **(100%)**
Tel.: (940) 325-4465
Web Site: http://www.mineralwellsindex.com
Sales Range: $10-24.9 Million
Emp.: 4
Newspaper Publishing
N.A.I.C.S.: 513110

North Georgia Newspaper Group (2)
308 S Thornton Ave, Dalton, GA 30720-8268
Tel.: (706) 217-6397
Sales Range: $10-24.9 Million
Emp.: 125
Newspapers
N.A.I.C.S.: 513110
William Bronson *(Publr)*

Ottumwa Courier (2)
213 E 2nd St, Ottumwa, IA 52501-2902
Tel.: (641) 684-4611
Web Site: http://www.ottumwacourier.com
Sales Range: $10-24.9 Million
Emp.: 50
Newspaper Publishing
N.A.I.C.S.: 513110

Press-Republican (2)
170 Margaret St, Plattsburgh, NY 12901
Tel.: (518) 561-2300
Web Site: http://www.pressrepublican.com
Sales Range: $10-24.9 Million
Emp.: 125
Newspaper Publishers
N.A.I.C.S.: 513110
Lamiaa Elshafay *(Dir-Ops)*
Scott Bresett *(Mgr-Circulation)*
Joe LoTemplio *(Editor-in-Chief)*
Ben Rowe *(Editor-Night)*
Joey LaFranca *(Editor-Sports)*

The Daily Item (2)
200 Market St, Sunbury, PA 17801
Tel.: (570) 286-5671
Web Site: http://www.dailyitem.com
Sales Range: $10-24.9 Million
Emp.: 200
Newspapers
N.A.I.C.S.: 513110
David R. Hilliard *(Editor-Digital)*
Lori Seebold *(Mgr-Adv Svcs)*
Fred Scheller *(Publr)*
Dennis Lyons *(Editor)*
Bill Bowman *(Mng Editor)*
John Zaktansky *(Mng Editor)*
Eric Pehowic *(Editor-News & Weekend)*
Kurt Ritzman *(Editor-Sports)*
Joe Sylvester *(Editor-Danville News)*

The Daily Southerner (2)
504 W Wilson St, Tarboro, NC 27886-4239
Tel.: (252) 823-3106
Web Site: http://www.dailysoutherner.com
Sales Range: $10-24.9 Million
Emp.: 8
Job Printing And Newspaper Publishing Combined
N.A.I.C.S.: 513110

The Daily Star (2)
102 Chestnut St, Oneonta, NY 13820
Tel.: (607) 432-1000

THE RETIREMENT SYSTEMS OF ALABAMA

The Retirement Systems of Alabama—(Continued)

Web Site: http://www.thedailystar.com
Sales Range: $10-24.9 Million
Emp.: 50
Newspaper Publishers
N.A.I.C.S.: 513110
Denielle Ziemba Cazzolla (Editor)
Sean Lewis (Mgr-Retail Adv)
Robert Cairns (Mng Editor)
Greg Klein (Editor-Copy)
Jared Bomba (Editor-Sports)
Justin Vernold (Editor-Copy)
Pam Ferguson (Mgr-Audience Dev)
Valerie Secor (Dir-Adv)
Christine Benson (Mgr-Classified Adv)
Lonny Chin (Mgr-Multimedia Campaign)
Tracy Bender (Mgr-Creative Svcs)

The Journal-Register (2)
170 E Ave, Lockport, NY 14094 (100%)
Tel.: (585) 798-1400
Web Site: http://www.journal-register.com
Sales Range: $10-24.9 Million
Emp.: 5
Publishers of Evening Newspapers Except Saturday & Newspaper Publisher
N.A.I.C.S.: 513110

The Tribune-Democrat (2)
425 Locust St, Johnstown, PA 15901 (100%)
Tel.: (814) 532-5050
Web Site: http://www.tribdem.com
Rev.: $17,000,000
Emp.: 216
Newspaper Publishers
N.A.I.C.S.: 513110
Louis Gjurich (Controller)
Mary Anne Rizzo (Dir-Adv)
Renee Carthew (Editor-News)
Steve Sindleri (Dir-Production)

The Union-Recorder (2)
165 Garrett Way, Milledgeville, GA 31061 (100%)
Tel.: (478) 452-0567
Web Site: http://www.unionrecorder.com
Sales Range: $10-24.9 Million
Emp.: 45
Newspaper Printing & Publishing Service
N.A.I.C.S.: 541512
Keith Barlow (Publr)
Natalie Davis Linder (Editor)
Melissa Miller (Mgr-Circulation)
Keith Justice (Dir-Production)
Tiffany Jones (Bus Mgr)

Traverse City Record-Eagle (2)
120 W Front St, Traverse City, MI 49684
Tel.: (231) 946-2000
Web Site: http://www.record-eagle.com
Sales Range: $10-24.9 Million
Emp.: 140
Newspaper Publishers
N.A.I.C.S.: 513110
Brian Steele (Mgr-Design Center)
Paul Heidbreder (Publr)
Dan Nielsen (Editor-Bus)

Division (Domestic):

cnhi-can (2)
3500 Colonnade Pkwy Ste 600, Birmingham, AL 35243
Tel.: (205) 298-7100
Web Site: http://www.cnhi-can.com
Emp.: 70
Media Buying Agency
N.A.I.C.S.: 541830

THE REUTLINGER COMMUNITY FOR JEWISH LIVING

4000 Camino Tassajara, Danville, CA 94506
Tel.: (925) 648-2800 CA
Web Site: http://www.rcjl.org
Year Founded: 1994
Sales Range: $10-24.9 Million
Emp.: 211
Elder Care Services
N.A.I.C.S.: 623312
Richard Goldstein (Pres & Pres)
Steven Wolfe (Sec & Sec)
Larry Kaufman (Treas)
Phil Friedman (VP)
Carol Goldman (Dir-Activity Program)
Betty Rothaus (Dir-Artist-in,Residence)
Claddy Dennis (Bus Mgr)
Sonia Gonzalez (Dir-Dietary)
Troy Beaton (Dir-Residential Care)
Karen Kelleher (Dir-Traditions)
Janice Corran (Exec Dir)
Ja Zimmer (CEO)
Jay Zimmer (Pres & CEO)

THE REYNOLDS & REYNOLDS COMPANY

1 Reynolds Way, Dayton, OH 45430
Tel.: (937) 485-2000
Web Site: http://www.reyrey.com
Year Founded: 1866
Automotive Web Solutions Provider & Associated Software Developer
N.A.I.C.S.: 518210
Bob Brockman (Chm & CEO)
Tommy Barras (Pres & COO)

Subsidiaries:

TradeMotion, LLC
2190 Carmel Valley Rd Ste D, Del Mar, CA 92014
Tel.: (858) 461-4418
Web Site: http://www.trademotion.com
Online Automotive Parts Distr
N.A.I.C.S.: 518210
Shawn Lucas (Pres)

THE REYNOLDS & REYNOLDS COMPANY

1 Reynolds Way, Kettering, OH 45430
Tel.: (937) 485-2000
Web Site: http://www.reyrey.com
Year Founded: 1866
Sales Range: $1-4.9 Billion
Emp.: 6,000
Computer Software & Services for Automotive Retailers
N.A.I.C.S.: 541512
Trey Hiers (VP-Mktg)
Jerry Kirwan (Sr VP & Gen Mgr-Reynolds Document Svcs)
Jon Strawsburg (VP)

Subsidiaries:

DCS Group plc (1)
Clarendon House, Clarendon Square, Leamington Spa, CV32 5QJ, Warks, United Kingdom
Tel.: (44) 1926 488 200
Web Site: http://www.dcsgroup.co.uk
Sales Range: $50-74.9 Million
Emp.: 584
Information Technology Services for Automotive Industry
N.A.I.C.S.: 541512

Reyna Capital Corporation (1)
1 Reynolds Way, Dayton, OH 45430
Tel.: (937) 485-2955
Web Site: http://www.reyrey.com
Rev.: $17,320,000
Leasing of Computer Products & Services to Automobile Dealers
N.A.I.C.S.: 532420

Reynolds & Reynolds (Canada) Ltd. (1)
2-3800B Laird Road, PO Box 22, Mississauga, L5L 0B2, ON, Canada
Tel.: (905) 606-2800
Web Site: http://www.reyrey.com
Sales Range: $25-49.9 Million
Emp.: 200
Business Forms & Electronic Data Processing Services
N.A.I.C.S.: 323111

Reynolds and Reynolds B.V. (1)
Mercurion 10-12, Postbus 2028, Zevenaar, 6903 PZ, Netherlands
Tel.: (31) 316 58 28 10
Web Site: http://www.reyrey.nl
Emp.: 50
Computer Software Development Services
N.A.I.C.S.: 541511
Hang Nederzeen (Mgr)

Xpressdocs Partners, Ltd. (1)
4901 N Beach St, Fort Worth, TX 76137
Tel.: (866) 977-3627
Web Site: http://www.xpressdocs.com
Graphic Design Services
N.A.I.C.S.: 541430
Jim Wright (CEO)
Darrin Rayner (Exec VP)
Jeremy Donelan (CFO)
Rob Shaw (VP-Ops)
Chasity Torti (VP- Client Svcs)
Jed Richards (VP-Premedia & Workflow Svcs)
Eric Arnold (VP-Sls & Bus Dev)

iMakeNews, Inc. (1)
7400 Wilshire Place Dr, Houston, TX 77040
Tel.: (937) 485-8030
Web Site: http://www.imninc.com
Sales Range: $1-9.9 Million
Emp.: 100
Email Software Publisher
N.A.I.C.S.: 513210
Ben Levitan (CEO)

THE RHODE ISLAND FOUNDATION

1 Union Station, Providence, RI 02903
Tel.: (401) 274-4564 RI
Web Site: http://www.rifoundation.org
Year Founded: 1916
Sales Range: $75-99.9 Million
Emp.: 49
Grantmaking Services
N.A.I.C.S.: 813211
James S. Sanzi (Sr VP-Dev)
John Barnett (CFO & VP-Fin)
Jennifer Reid (Controller)
Arianne Corrente (VP-Comm & Mktg)
Katie Murray (Dir-Evaluation & Learning)
Jessica David (Exec VP-Strategy & Community Investments)
Frank Cerilli (VP-HR)
Jenny Pereira (VP-Grant Programs)

THE RHODE ISLAND QUALITY INSTITUTE

50 Holden St Ste 300, Providence, RI 02908
Tel.: (401) 276-9141 RI
Web Site: http://www.riqi.org
Year Founded: 2001
Sales Range: $1-9.9 Million
Health Care Srvices
N.A.I.C.S.: 622110
Charlie Dansereau (Dir-IT)
Richard H. Leclerc (Chm)
Laura L. Adams (Pres & CEO)
Stephen J. Farrell (Treas & Sec)
Michelle Dexter (Dir-HR)
Dawn Dunn (Dir-Fin & Grants Mgmt)
Michael R. Dwyer (Dir-Risk Mgmt & Compliance)
Elaine Fontaine (Dir-Data Quality & Analytics)
Darlene Morris (Dir-Center for Improvement Science)
Scott Young (Dir-Bus Strategy & Consumer Svcs)

THE RICCIARDI GROUP CORP.

200 Varick St Ste 910, New York, NY 10014
Tel.: (917) 634-4772
Web Site: http://www.thericciardigroup.com
Year Founded: 2014
Sales Range: $1-9.9 Million
Emp.: 10
Business Management Consulting Services
N.A.I.C.S.: 541611
Marisa Ricciardi (Founder & CEO)
Karma Von Burg (Sr VP-Client Strategy)

U.S. PRIVATE

Jason Brown (Creative Dir)
Claudine Lorme (Creative Dir)
Bianca West (Creative Dir)

THE RICE COMPANY

3721 Douglas Blvd Ste 375, Roseville, CA 95661
Tel.: (916) 784-7745
Web Site: http://www.riceco.com
Sales Range: $250-299.9 Million
Emp.: 30
Rice, Grain, By-Products & Other Agricultural Commodities Trading Services
N.A.I.C.S.: 424510
J. K. Kapila (Pres)

THE RICHARD E. JACOBS GROUP, LLC

25425 Center Ridge Rd, Cleveland, OH 44145
Tel.: (440) 871-4800 OH
Web Site: http://www.rejacobsgroup.com
Year Founded: 1955
Sales Range: $10-24.9 Million
Emp.: 50
Real Estate Development Services
N.A.I.C.S.: 531120
Tom Novak (Controller)
Judson E. Smith (Chm)
Douglas L. Miller (Pres & CEO)
Michael R. Johnson (VP-Construction)

Subsidiaries:

Jacobs Real Estate Services LLC (1)
25425 Center Ridge Rd, Cleveland, OH 44145
Tel.: (440) 871-4800
Web Site: http://www.jresgroup.com
Sales Range: $10-24.9 Million
Emp.: 30
Real Estate Management Services
N.A.I.C.S.: 531210
James F. Eppele (Pres & CEO)
William R. Hansen (Gen Counsel, Sec & Exec VP)
John L. Klayman (VP-Office Leasing)
Cindy A. Greiner (VP-Office Leasing)
Kristine M. McGivney (Treas)
Carl F. Frey (Dir-Engrg)
Thomas G. Novak (Controller)

THE RICHARDS GROUP, INC.

2801 N Central Expy Ste 100, Dallas, TX 75204-3663
Tel.: (214) 891-5700 TX
Web Site: http://www.richards.com
Year Founded: 1976
Rev.: $1,280,000,000
Emp.: 630
Advertising Services
N.A.I.C.S.: 541810
Scot Dykema (CFO)
Jimmy Baldwin (Head-Creative Grp & Dir-Art)
Glenn Dady (CEO)
Lynda Hodge (Head-Creative Grp & Dir-Art)
Jeff Hopfer (Head-Creative Grp & Dir-Art)
Terence Reynolds (Head-Creative Grp & Dir-Art)
Gary Gibson (Head-Creative Grp & Dir-Art)
John Baker (Dir-Brand Plng)
Christopher Owens (Dir-Brand Plng)
Craig Anderson (Head-Creative Grp & Dir-Art)
Jimmy Bonner (Head-Creative Grp & Dir-Art)
Dave Snell (Dir-Brand Plng)
Tim Tone (Head-Creative Grp & Dir-Art)
Matt Butcher (Dir-Brand Plng)

COMPANIES

Brian Nadurak (Head-Creative Grp & Dir-Art)
Randy Bradshaw (Principal)
Shane Altman (Head-Creative Grp & Dir-Art)
Todd McArtor (Head-Creative Grp & Dir-Art)
Chris Ferrel (Dir-Digital Strategy)
Gary Anderson (Mgr-Production)
Jayr Sotelo (Head-Motion Graphics Grp)
Joe Wilson (Head-Project Mgmt Grp)
Roddy McGinnis (Head-Quality Control Grp)
Nikki Wilson (Chief Talent & Culture Officer)
Trevor Monteiro (Head-Brand Media)
Sue Batterton (Chief Creative Officer)
Patrick J. Murray Jr. (Head-Creative Grp & Dir-Art)

Subsidiaries:

Latitude (1)
2801 N Central Expy, Dallas, TX 75204
Tel.: (214) 696-7900
Sales Range: $10-24.9 Million
Emp.: 14
Advertising Services
N.A.I.C.S.: 541810
Anah Olah (Dir-Studio)
Pat Hartman (Mgr-Adv Production)

RBMM (1)
7007 Twin Hills Ste 200, Dallas, TX 75231
Tel.: (214) 987-6500
Web Site: http://www.rbmm.com
Rev.: $20,000,000
Emp.: 20
Advertising Services
N.A.I.C.S.: 541810
Brian Boyd (Principal)
Jeff Barfoot (Mng Principal, Principal & Dir-Creative)
Lindsey Phaup (Principal)
Philip Smith (Principal)

Richards Partners (1)
2801 Nrth Expwy, Dallas, TX 75204-6430
Tel.: (214) 891-5700
Web Site: http://www.richardspartners.com
Rev.: $10,000,000
Emp.: 25
Advertising Services
N.A.I.C.S.: 541810
Stacie Barnett (Mng Principal)
George McCane (Principal)
Ruth Miller Fitzgibbons (Principal)

Richards/Lerma (1)
8750 N. Central Expwy, Dallas, TX 75231-6437
Tel.: (214) 891-5700
Web Site: http://www.richardslerma.com
Advertising Services
N.A.I.C.S.: 541810
Stan Richards (Principal)
Pete Lerma (Principal)
Stephanie Hoefken (Dir-PR)
Quim Gil (Principal & Dir-Brand Plng)
Salma Gottfried (Principal & Dir-Brand Mgmt)
Miguel Moreno (Dir-Brand Creative)
Aldo Quevedo (Principal & Dir-Creative)

The Richards Group, Inc. (1)
6085 Lake Forest Dr Ste 105, Atlanta, GA 30328
Tel.: (770) 384-4756
Emp.: 1
Advertising Services
N.A.I.C.S.: 541810

THE RICHARDS ORGANIZATION
14 Calvert St, Harrison, NY 10528-3213
Tel.: (914) 835-3111 NY
Year Founded: 1982
Rev.: $22,750,000
Emp.: 30
Advetising Agency
N.A.I.C.S.: 541810
Jim Richards (Pres)
Suzanne Milone (Mgr-Acctg)

Michael Lamy (Art Dir)
Sally Slater (Dir-Brdcst & Copywriter)
Peggy Robinson (Dir-Pub Rel & Copywriter)
Tina Maltese (VP-Adv)
N. Richards (Acct Supvr)
T. Wyker (Acct Supvr)
Anne Marie Ruggiero (Acct Supvr)
Jennifer Kelly (Acct Supvr)
Pam Sacchetillo (Acct Mgr)
Gina Romanello (Acct Mgr)

THE RICHMAN GROUP DEVELOPMENT CORPORATION
777 W Putnam Ave, Greenwich, CT 06830
Tel.: (203) 869-0900
Web Site:
http://www.therichmangroup.com
Year Founded: 1987
Property Developer, Manager & Owner; Mortgage Lender
N.A.I.C.S.: 237210
Kristin Miller (Pres-Dev)
Stephen M. Daley (Exec VP)
Jason Wilber (Exec VP)
Jon Caputo (Dir-Architectural & Construction Svcs)
James Hussey (CFO)
Luke Daniels (Pres-California)
Richard Paul Richman (Founder & Chm)
Joanne D. Flanagan (Gen Counsel)
David Salzman (Pres-Richman Real Estate Investment)
Brian P. Myers (Pres-Richman Asset Mgmt)
William W. Traylor (Pres-Richman Housing Resources)
Kim Pardoe (Sr VP)
Peter McHugh (Exec VP)
Michael Ramires (Exec VP)
Richard McCauley (Exec VP)
William T. Fabbri (Pres-Florida)
Will Cureton (Pres-Southwest)
Jennifer Ambrosecchia (Exec VP-Dev Corp)
Rick Westberg (Exec VP-California)
Kristen Gucwa-Fuechslin (Exec VP-Mktg)
Theresa Eastwood Davis (Exec VP-Ops)
Chad Wood (Sr VP-Physical Assets & Risk Mgmt)

Subsidiaries:

The Richman Group of Florida, Inc. (1)
477 S Rosemary Ave Ste 301, West Palm Beach, FL 33401
Tel.: (561) 832-1114
Web Site: http://www.therichmangroup.com
Emp.: 6
Property Developer, Manager & Owner
N.A.I.C.S.: 237210
Todd Fabbri (Exec VP)
Gina K. Dodge (Sec)
Joanne D. Flanagan (Gen Counsel)
James Hussey (CFO)
Richard Paul Richman (Founder & Chm)
Michael Stefan Jr. (VP)

THE RIDGE COMPANY
1535 S Main St, South Bend, IN 46613
Tel.: (574) 234-3143 IN
Web Site: http://www.ridgeap.com
Year Founded: 1928
Sales Range: $50-74.9 Million
Emp.: 200
Automotive Parts & Accesories Retailer
N.A.I.C.S.: 441330
James E. Goodhew (Pres)
Mark Goodhew (VP)

THE RIESE ORGANIZATION
560 5th Ave, New York, NY 10036
Tel.: (212) 563-7440
Web Site:
http://www.rieserestaurants.com
Year Founded: 1940
Sales Range: $150-199.9 Million
Emp.: 100
Restaurant Management Services
N.A.I.C.S.: 541611
Dennis Riese (Chm & CEO)

Subsidiaries:

National Restaurant Management, Inc. (1)
560 5th Ave, New York, NY 10036
Tel.: (212) 563-7440
Sales Range: $200-249.9 Million
Manages Restaurants; Restaurant & Real Estate Company
N.A.I.C.S.: 722511
Dennis Riese (Pres & CEO)
Ann Martinez (Controller)

Subsidiary (Domestic):

Charlio's (2)
560 5th Ave, New York, NY 10036-3901
Tel.: (212) 563-7440
Restaurant Chain
N.A.I.C.S.: 722511

THE RIGHTER COMPANY, INC.
2424 Harrison Rd, Columbus, OH 43204
Tel.: (614) 272-9700
Web Site:
http://www.rightercompany.com
Sales Range: $10-24.9 Million
Emp.: 70
Construction Engineering Services
N.A.I.C.S.: 237310
David M. Righter (Pres)

THE RIVERSIDE COMPANY
45 Rockefeller Ctr 630 5th Ave Ste 400, New York, NY 10111
Tel.: (212) 265-6575
Web Site:
https://www.riversidecompany.com
Year Founded: 1988
Emp.: 300
Privater Equity Firm
N.A.I.C.S.: 523999
Bela Szigethy (Co-CEO)
Stewart A. Kohl (Co-CEO)
Anne F. Hayes (Sr Partner)
Brian Sauer (Partner)
Loren Schlachet (Mng Partner)
Eric Feldman (CIO)
George Cole (Mng Partner)
Hal Greenberg (Founding Partner)
Jeffrey Gordon (Mng Partner)
Damien Gaudin (Partner-Europe)
Rafael Alvarez-Novoa (Partner-Europe)
Sean Ozbolt (Mng Partner)
Steven E. Rodgers (Executives)
Steven E. Rodgers (Executives)
Bart Thielen (CFO)
Ervin Cash (Operating Partner)
Gary Schlegel (Fin Dir)

Subsidiaries:

ARCOS LLC (1)
445 Hutchinson Ave Ste 700, Columbus, OH 43235
Tel.: (614) 396-5500
Web Site: http://www.arcos-inc.com
Application Development Services
N.A.I.C.S.: 541511
Mitchell B. McLeod (Founder)
William J. Brackett (VP-Svcs & Support)
Robert Stinsa (VP-Sls)
Ted Schneider (CTO)
Nancy Bohman (VP-Mktg)
Michael Brubaker (VP-Sls)
Ross D.S. Fuller (Pres)
Odus Wittenburg (CEO)

Adventures in Advertising Franchise Inc (1)
800 Winneconne Ave, Neenah, WI 54957
Tel.: (800) 460-7836
Web Site: http://www.advinadv.com
Sales Range: $25-49.9 Million
Emp.: 45
Marketing Solutions
N.A.I.C.S.: 541613

American Hospice LLC (1)
50 N Laura St Ste 1800, Jacksonville, FL 32202
Tel.: (904) 493-6745
Web Site: http://www.americanhospice.com
Hospice Care Services
N.A.I.C.S.: 621610
Jeffrey Preuss (CEO)

Unit (Domestic):

Embracing Hospice (2)
5775 Peachtree Dunwoody Rd Ste D580, Atlanta, GA 30342
Tel.: (404) 659-0110
Web Site: http://www.americanhospice.com
Emp.: 15
Hospice Care Services
N.A.I.C.S.: 623110
Diana Sparks (Exec Dir)

Frontier Hospice (2)
221 N I 35 Service Rd Ste D, Moore, OK 73160
Tel.: (405) 789-2913
Hospice Care Services
N.A.I.C.S.: 623110

Hospice of Arizona (2)
19820 N 7th Ave Ste 130, Phoenix, AZ 85027
Tel.: (602) 678-1313
Hospice Care Services
N.A.I.C.S.: 623110
Tonnie Martell (Gen Mgr)

Hospice of New Jersey (2)
400 Broadacres Dr, Bloomfield, NJ 07003
Tel.: (973) 893-0818
Web Site:
http://www.hospiceofnewjersey.com
Hospice Care Services
N.A.I.C.S.: 623110
Lillian Pliner (Exec Dir)

Hospice of Virginia (2)
1700 Bayberry Ct, Richmond, VA 23226
Tel.: (804) 281-0451
Hospice Care Services
N.A.I.C.S.: 623110
Beth McNeil (Exec Dir)

American Service Company (1)
20 Fort St, Quincy, MA 02169
Tel.: (617) 471-5953
Web Site:
http://www.americanservicecompany.com
Rev.: $4,700,000
Emp.: 35
Electrical Contractor
N.A.I.C.S.: 238210
Pamela Meehan (Treas)

Anitox Corp (1)
1055 Progress Cir, Lawrenceville, GA 30043-4646
Tel.: (678) 376-1055
Web Site: http://www.anitox.com
Pharmaceuticals Product Mfr
N.A.I.C.S.: 325412
Rick Phillips (CEO)
Dave Smith (CFO)
Mark Eblin (Chm)
Enrique Montiel (Dir-Nutrition & Live Production)
Tom Glomsky (Chief Revenue Officer)

Arrowhead Electrical Products, Inc. (1)
3787 95th Ave NE Ste 250, Blaine, MN 55014
Tel (763) 255-2555
Web Site: http://www.arrowheadep.com
Automobile Parts Distr
N.A.I.C.S.: 423120
Chris Nelson (Supvr-Shipping)
Rich Bartlett (VP-Customer Svc)
Jim Applegate (Gen Mgr-West Coast Distr)
Paul Lavoie (Gen Mgr-East Coast Distr)
Robert Diamond (Gen Mgr-Canadian Distr)

THE RIVERSIDE COMPANY

U.S. PRIVATE

The Riverside Company—(Continued)

Subsidiary (Domestic):

Ariens Specialty Brands, LLC (2)
401 S Wright Rd, Janesville, WI 53546
Tel.: (608) 373-2797
Web Site: http://www.awdirect.com
Outdoor Power Equipment Supplier
N.A.I.C.S.: 423440
Vicki L. Leinbach (CIO)

Division (Domestic):

AW Direct, Inc. (3)
401 S Wright Rd, Janesville, WI 53546
Tel.: (608) 373-2797
Web Site: http://www.awdirect.com
Towing & Service Vehicle Accessories Supplier
N.A.I.C.S.: 441330

Ben Meadows Company (3)
PO Box 5277, Janesville, WI 53547-5277
Tel.: (800) 241-6401
Web Site: http://www.benmeadows.com
Emp.: 100
Environmental & Forestry Management Equipment Retailer
N.A.I.C.S.: 459999
Gary Clark (Gen Mgr)

Gempler's (3)
PO Box 5175, Janesville, WI 53547-5175
Tel.: (608) 662-3301
Web Site: http://www.gemplers.com
Agricultural & Horticultural Equipment & Supplies Retailer
N.A.I.C.S.: 459999

Subsidiary (Domestic):

Atlantic International Distributors, Inc. (2)
5061 Ste A Shawland Rd, Jacksonville, FL 32254
Tel.: (904) 725-5202
Web Site: http://www.aidtractor.com
Automobile Parts Distr
N.A.I.C.S.: 423440
Sissy Warnock (Dir-Global Supply Chain)
Chris Harper (Mgr-Acct Sls)
Chris Schoolcraft (Mgr-Ops)
Joe Keppel (Dir-Sls & Mktg)

Be Green Packaging LLC (1)
800 Presidio Ste B, Santa Barbara, CA 93101
Tel.: (805) 456-6088
Web Site: http://www.begreenpackaging.com
Emp.: 20
Packaging Product Mfr & Distr
N.A.I.C.S.: 326199
Ron Blitzer (CEO)
Capp Raisin (Dir-Bus Dev)

Plant (Domestic):

Be Green Packaging LLC - South Carolina Mfg Facility (2)
4452 Grays Hwy Cypress Ridge Industrial Park, Ridgeland, SC 29936
Tel.: (843) 400-4092
Packaging Products Mfr
N.A.I.C.S.: 326199

Brand Muscle, Inc. (1)
233 S Wacker Dr Ste 4400, Chicago, IL 60606
Web Site: http://www.brandmuscle.com
Software Distr
N.A.I.C.S.: 423430
Clarke Smith (Chief Strategy Officer)
Raymond Trantina (Pres-Wine, Sprits, Beer & Distr Div)
Chris Hesburgh (Exec VP-Client Svc)
Mike Marchetti (Exec VP-Consumer Brands)
Elizabeth Journell (Sr VP-Sls)
Jason Tabeling (Exec VP-Product Strategy)

Buildout, Inc. (1)
222 S Riverside Plz #810, Chicago, IL 60606
Tel.: (312) 525-8941
Web Site: http://www.buildout.com
Commercial Real Estate & Deal Management Software
N.A.I.C.S.: 513210

Kris Krisco (Chief Customer Officer)

Subsidiary (Domestic):

McLabs, LLC (2)
1644 Platte St Fl 4, Denver, CO 80202
Tel.: (888) 633-6424
Web Site: http://www.apto.com
Real Estate Brokerage Software Development Services
N.A.I.C.S.: 541511
Tanner McGraw (Founder & CEO)
Jennifer Panning (CFO)

CertaSite Grand Rapids LLC (1)
54 Monument Cir Ste 807, Indianapolis, IN 46204
Tel.: (463) 777-8710
Web Site: http://www.certasitepro.com
Fire & Life Safety Company
N.A.I.C.S.: 922160
Jeff Wyatt (CEO)

Subsidiary (Domestic):

Craynon Fire Protection, Inc. (2)
2801 Thunderhawk Ct, Dayton, OH 45414
Tel.: (937) 395-1453
Web Site: http://www.craynonfireprotection.com
Fire Protection Product Services & Distr
N.A.I.C.S.: 922160
Tom Doty (VP)
Ron Caplinger (Pres)

Fire Systems Professionals, LLC (2)
4110 Demorest Rd, Grove City, OH 43123
Tel.: (614) 875-9959
Web Site: http://www.firesystemspro.com
Rev: $3,290,000
Emp.: 5
Electrical Apparatus & Equipment, Wiring Supplies & Related Equipment Merchant Whslr
N.A.I.C.S.: 423610
Ron Lapping (Mgr)

Starfire Systems, Inc. (2)
9825 S 54th St, Franklin, WI 53132
Tel.: (414) 448-0100
Web Site: http://www.starfiresys.com
Electronic & Precision Equipment Repair & Maintenance
N.A.I.C.S.: 811210
Darrel Malek (Pres)

Corporate Visions, Inc. (1)
3875 Hopyard Rd Ste 370, Pleasanton, CA 94588
Tel.: (415) 464-4400
Web Site: http://www.corporatevisions.com
Marketing & Sales Messaging, Tools & Training Products & Services
N.A.I.C.S.: 541618
Tim Riesterer (Chief Strategy Officer)
Erik Peterson (CEO)
Gloria Fan (CFO)
Jennifer Zick (Exec VP-Mktg)
Nicci Nesmith Hammerel (Dir-Content Consulting)
Paul F. Murphy (Chm)
Steven Cumbow (CFO)
Mike Finley (Chief Customer Officer)

Subsidiary (Domestic):

Primary Intelligence Inc. (2)
11778 Election Road Ste 120, Draper, UT 84020
Tel.: (801) 838-9600
Web Site: http://www.primary-intel.com
Rev: $9,000,000
Emp.: 60
Custom Computer Programming Services
N.A.I.C.S.: 541511
Ken Allred (Founder & CEO)
Mike Brose (VP-Sls)
Rob Allen (VP-Tech)
Lance Davis (VP-Bus Dev)
Jesyca Hauer (Coord-Scheduling)
Tiffany Larsen (Mgr-HR)
Mark Larson (Dir-Art)
Melissa Short (VP-Product Mgmt)

Crioestaminal-Saude e Tecnologia SA (1)
Biocant Park Nucleo 4 Lote 2, 3060-197, Cantanhede, Portugal
Tel.: (351) 231 305 060
Web Site: http://www.crioestaminal.pt
Emp.: 40

Biotechnology Research & Development Services
N.A.I.C.S.: 541714
Andrea Domes (Gen Mgr)

DF King Worldwide (1)
48 Wall St 22nd Fl, New York, NY 10005
Tel.: (212) 826-7000
Web Site: http://www.king-worldwide.com
Sales Range: $25-49.9 Million
Holding Company; Corporate Governance & Shareholder Management Services
N.A.I.C.S.: 551112
Oliver Niedermaier (Founder)
Hugh Morrison (Exec VP-Fin Comm)
Anthony Biondo (CIO)
Mark Wilson (CEO)
M. Asher F. Richelli (Head-Proxy Solicitation)

Eemax, Inc. (1)
400 Captain Neville Dr, Waterbury, CT 06705
Tel.: (203) 267-7890
Web Site: http://www.eemax.com
Tankless Hot Water Heaters Mfr
N.A.I.C.S.: 335220
Aaron Siegel (VP-Bus Dev & Strategic Accts)
Mark Smola (Mgr-Quality Assurance)
Jens Bolleyer (VP & Gen Mgr)
Chris Hayden (Mgr-Engrg)

Subsidiary (Domestic):

Ecosmart US, LLC (2)
3315 NW 167th St, Miami, FL 33056-4254
Tel.: (305) 623-7900
Web Site: http://www.ecosmartus.com
Sales Range: $10-24.9 Million
Emp.: 8
Tankless Water Heater Mfr
N.A.I.C.S.: 335220

Experient (1)
2500 Enterprise Pkwy E, Twinsburg, OH 44087
Tel.: (330) 425-8333
Web Site: http://www.experient-inc.com
Sales Range: $25-49.9 Million
Emp.: 83
Meeting Planner Services
N.A.I.C.S.: 541618
Michael Guerriero (Pres)
Jeff Fugate (Sr VP-Sls & Mktg)
David Beckett (Sr VP-Ops)
Nancy DeBrosse (Sr VP-Strategic Acct Mgmt)
Jamie Murdock (VP-Sls)
Dee Blakeney (VP-Event Plng)
Mike Godsey (Sr VP-Market Dev)
Thad Lurie (VP-Bus Intelligence & Performance)

FoodLogiQ, LLC (1)
2655 Meridian Pkwy, Durham, NC 27713
Tel.: (866) 492-4468
Web Site: https://www.foodlogiq.com
Software Development
N.A.I.C.S.: 513210
Katy Jones (CEO)

Subsidiary (Domestic):

Esha Research Inc. (2)
4747 Skyline Road South, Salem, OR 97306
Tel.: (503) 585-6242
Web Site: http://www.esha.com
Rev: $2,000,000
Emp.: 10
Software Publisher
N.A.I.C.S.: 513210
Craig W. Bennett (CEO)
David Hands (VP)
Jim Kearns (Dir-Technical)
Scott Hadsall (Mgr-Sls)

Frenchies Modern Nail Care (1)
10106 W San Juan Way, Littleton, CO 80127-6332
Tel.: (303) 390-9900
Web Site: http://www.frenchiesnails.com
Nail Salons
N.A.I.C.S.: 812113

G&H Orthodontics (1)
2165 Earlywood Dr, Franklin, IN 46131
Tel.: (317) 346-6655
Web Site: http://www.ghwire.com

Orthodontic Product Mfr & Distr
N.A.I.C.S.: 339114
John Voskuil (CEO)

GiveAnything.com, Inc. (1)
Empire State Bldg Ste 3920 350 5th Ave, New York, NY 10118
Tel.: (212) 689-1200
Web Site: http://www.corporaterewards.com
Management Consulting Services
N.A.I.C.S.: 541618
G. Edward Brookshire (Founder & Chm)
Steve Lien (CFO)
Tom Silk (Exec VP-Sls & Mktg)

H-D Advanced Manufacturing Company (1)
2418 Greens Rd, Houston, TX 77032
Tel.: (346) 219-0320
Web Site: http://www.h-dam.com
Holding Company
N.A.I.C.S.: 551112
Dale B. Mikus (CFO & Sr VP)
Michael Vincent (Pres & CEO)
Tom Hicks (Chm)

Holding (Domestic):

Firstmark Corp. (2)
2200 Georgetowne Dr Ste 300, Sewickley, PA 15143
Tel.: (724) 759-2850
Web Site: http://www.firstmarkcorp.com
Mfr of Components & Sub-Assemblies for Aerospace & Defense Applications
N.A.I.C.S.: 334511
William H. Coogan Jr. (CEO)

Subsidiary (Domestic):

Aircraft Belts, Inc. (3)
1176 Telecom Dr, Creedmoor, NC 27522-8294
Tel.: (919) 956-4395
Web Site: http://www.aircraftbelts.com
Sales Range: $1-9.9 Million
Emp.: 21
Aircraft Safety Restraints Mfr
N.A.I.C.S.: 336413
Rick O'Quinn (Sls Mgr)

Centroid, Inc. (3)
111 E Ames Ct, Plainview, NY 11803
Tel.: (516) 349-0070
Web Site: http://www.centroidinc.com
Sales Range: $1-9.9 Million
Emp.: 24
Electronic Components Mfr
N.A.I.C.S.: 334419
Matt Isley (Pres)

Firstmark Aerospace Corporation (3)
1176 Telecom Dr, Creedmoor, NC 27522-8294
Tel.: (919) 956-4200
Web Site: http://www.firstmarkaerospace.com
Precision Electronic, Electromagnetic & Mechanical Components & Systems Mfr
N.A.I.C.S.: 334419
Derek Ashcroft (Program Mgr)
David Devine (Exec VP)

Twin Commander Aircraft LLC (3)
1176 Telecom Dr, Creedmoor, NC 27522-8294
Tel.: (919) 956-4300
Web Site: http://www.twincommander.com
Aircraft Original Equipment Parts Mfr & Repair Services
N.A.I.C.S.: 336413
Allen Goad (Pres)

Holding (Domestic):

Overton Chicago Gear Inc. (2)
530 S Westgate Dr, Addison, IL 60101-4525
Tel.: (630) 543-9570
Web Site: http://www.oc-gear.com
Engineering Components & Industrial Gear Products Mfr
N.A.I.C.S.: 333612
Louis Ertel (CEO)
Kevin Walsh (VP-Ops)
Don Brown (CEO)

Sungear, Inc. (2)
8535-G Arjons Dr, San Diego, CA 92126
Tel.: (858) 549-3166
Web Site: http://www.sungearinc.com

COMPANIES

THE RIVERSIDE COMPANY

Emp.: 50
Aerospace Gear Mfr
N.A.I.C.S.: 336413
John Gizicki *(Founder)*
James Wilson *(Dir-Mfg)*
Paul M. Scott *(Dir-Quality Assurance)*

It's Just Lunch International LLC (1)
75400 Gerald Ford Dr Ste 124, Palm Desert, CA 92211
Tel.: (760) 779-0101
Web Site: http://www.itsjustlunch.com
Match Making & Dating Services
N.A.I.C.S.: 561499

Junior Sports Corporation (1)
55 Hospital Ctr Commons, Hilton Head Island, SC 22926
Tel.: (843) 785-2444
Web Site: http://www.ijga.com
Golf Training Services
N.A.I.C.S.: 713910

Justrite Manufacturing Company, LLC (1)
2454 E Dempster St, Des Plaines, IL 60016
Tel.: (847) 298-9250
Web Site: http://www.justritemfg.com
Sales Range: $25-49.9 Million
Safety Containment System Mfr
N.A.I.C.S.: 332313

Plant (Domestic):

Justrite Manufacturing Company (2)
3921 Dewitt Ave, Mattoon, IL 61938
Tel.: (217) 234-7486
Web Site: http://www.justritemfg.com
Sales Range: $25-49.9 Million
Emp.: 120
Safety Equipment for Handling Flammable Liquids Mfr
N.A.I.C.S.: 332431

Subsidiary (Domestic):

National Marker Company (2)
100 Providence Pike, North Smithfield, RI 02876
Tel.: (401) 762-9700
Web Site: http://www.nationalmarker.com
Sign Mfr
N.A.I.C.S.: 339950
Michael Black *(Pres)*

Keepsake Quilting, Inc. (1)
12 Main St, Center Harbor, NH 03226
Tel.: (603) 253-8148
Web Site: http://www.keepsakequilting.com
Sales Range: $10-24.9 Million
Emp.: 130
Quilting Fabrics & Supplies Mail Order Services
N.A.I.C.S.: 459130

Keycast Ljungby AB (1)
Stalgatan 2, PO Box 320, SE 341 26, Ljungby, Sweden
Tel.: (46) 37288340
Web Site: http://www.keycast.nu
Sales Range: $50-74.9 Million
Emp.: 50
Industrial Component Mfr
N.A.I.C.S.: 333310

Division (Domestic):

Combi Wear Parts (2)
Frasaregatan 2, PO Box 205, SE 681 24, Ljungby, Sweden
Tel.: (46) 550410550
Web Site: http://www.combiparts.com
Sales Range: $50-74.9 Million
Emp.: 70
Industrial Component Mfr
N.A.I.C.S.: 333310
Fredrik Ivansson *(Mng Dir)*

Subsidiary (Domestic):

Keycast Kohlswa AB (2)
Bruksgatan Kolsva Bruksomradet, PO Box 950, 731 10, Kolsva, Sweden
Tel.: (46) 22153000
Web Site: http://www.onekeycast.com
Steel Casting Services
N.A.I.C.S.: 331513
Fredrik Ivansson *(CEO)*
Acke Berg von Linde *(Dir-Sls)*

Keycast Meko AB (2)
Sadelvagen 5, 302 62, Halmstad, Sweden
Tel.: (46) 35 144 800
Web Site: http://www.keycast.se
Steel Casting Services
N.A.I.C.S.: 331513

Lighthouse Business Information Solutions, LLC (1)
5700 Harper Dr NE Ste 430, Albuquerque, NM 87109
Tel.: (505) 798-0900
Web Site: http://www.lhbis.com
Sales Range: $1-9.9 Million
Emp.: 12
Business Consulting Services
N.A.I.C.S.: 541618
Bryan Handing *(Principal)*
Florian Griego *(Mgr-Bus Dev)*

Logically, Inc. (1)
63 Marginal Way 4th Fl, Portland, ME 04101
Tel.: (866) 946-9638
Web Site: http://www.logically.com
Information Technology Consulting & Outsourcing Services
N.A.I.C.S.: 541690
Michael Williams *(Chief Strategy Officer)*
Michelle Accardi-Petersen *(CEO)*
Karl Noone *(CFO)*
Joshua Skeens *(COO)*

Subsidiary (Domestic):

Carolinas IT, LLC (2)
1600 Hillsborough St, Raleigh, NC 27605
Tel.: (919) 856-2300
Computer System Design Services
N.A.I.C.S.: 541512

Halski Systems, LLC (2)
210 Washington St NW, Gainesville, GA 30501-3672
Tel.: (770) 536-2276
Web Site: http://www.halski.com
Computer System Design Services
N.A.I.C.S.: 541512
Lewis Halski *(Pres)*

Network Support Company, LLC (2)
7 Kenosia Ave, Danbury, CT 06810
Tel.: (203) 744-2274
Web Site: http://www.network-support.com
Data Processing, Hosting & Related Services
N.A.I.C.S.: 518210
James Kennedy *(Founder & CEO)*
Alan Chandler *(Dir-Client Svcs)*
Chris Morton *(Dir-Technical Svcs)*
Donna Tomascak *(Mgr-HR)*
Liz Caswell *(Dir-Ops)*
Nancy Toussaint *(Mgr-Acctg)*

Sullivan Data Management, Inc. (2)
1520B Front St, Yorktown Heights, NY 10598-3626
Tel.: (914) 962-1573
Web Site: http://www.sullivandata.com
Computer System Design Services
N.A.I.C.S.: 541512
Glenn Sullivan *(Co-Founder)*

MEC3 Optima srl (1)
Via Gaggio 72, 47832, San Clemente, Rimini, Italy
Tel.: (39) 0541 859411
Web Site: http://www.mec3.com
Frozen Dessert Mfr & Distr
N.A.I.C.S.: 311520
Donata Sabbatini *(Mgr-Quality Control)*
Elena Emendatori *(Mgr-Pur & Indus Programming)*
Luciano Carestiato *(Plant Mgr)*
Cristina Tosi *(Mgr-Mktg)*
Gian Maria Emendatori *(Exec Mgr-Sls)*
Maurizio Raggi *(Gen Mgr)*
Alessandro Pagnini *(Mgr-Lean Production)*
Simone Annese *(Dir-Sls)*
Carlo Vanni *(Supvr-R&D)*

Mansell Group, Inc. (1)
3630 Peachtree Rd NE Ste 900, Atlanta, GA 30326
Tel.: (404) 995-8600
Web Site: http://www.mansellgroup.com
Sales Range: $1-9.9 Million
Emp.: 50
Marketing Software
N.A.I.C.S.: 513210
Alan Mance *(CEO)*

Midnite Express Inc. (1)
8801 Beilanca Ave, Los Angeles, CA 90045
Tel.: (310) 330-2300
Web Site: http://www.mnx.com
Courier & Logistics Services
N.A.I.C.S.: 541614
Richard Mickowski *(Mgr-Gateway)*

National Flavors, LLC (1)
3680 Stadium Park Way, Kalamazoo, MI 49009
Tel.: (269) 344-3640
Web Site: http://www.nationalflavors.com
Spice & Extract Mfr
N.A.I.C.S.: 311942

Subsidiary (Domestic):

GSB & Associates, Inc. (2)
3115 Cobb Intl Blvd NW, Kennesaw, GA 30152-4354
Tel.: (770) 424-1886
Web Site: http://www.gsbflavorcreators.com
Spice & Extract Mfr
N.A.I.C.S.: 311942
Corinne Baskin *(Pres)*

ONITelecom - Infocomunicacoes, S.A. (1)
Av Prof Dr Cavaco Silva A1-A2, 2740 296, Porto Salvo, Portugal **(60.9%)**
Tel.: (351) 210005300
Web Site: http://www.oni.pt
Sales Range: $200-249.9 Million
Voice, Data & Internet Services
N.A.I.C.S.: 517111

Omnigo Software LLC (1)
10430 Baur Blvd, Saint Louis, MO 63132
Tel.: (866) 421-2374
Web Site: http://www.omnigo.com
Computer System Design Services
N.A.I.C.S.: 541512
Nicholas Kehoe *(Chief Strategy Officer)*
Jim Clayman *(Sr VP-Mktg)*
Mark Heinen *(CFO)*
Rohit Chhabra *(Chief Product Officer)*
Gary Rock *(Chief Revenue Officer)*
Jarret Winkelman *(Dir-Products)*
Kevin Lafeber *(CEO)*
Damian Starosielsky *(CTO)*

Subsidiary (Domestic):

Incident Response Technologies, Inc. (2)
4582 S Ulster St Ste 1325, Denver, CO 80237
Tel.: (720) 221-7394
Web Site: http://www.irtsoftware.com
Emergency & Relief Services
N.A.I.C.S.: 624230
Jarret Winkelman *(Pres)*

Operating Tax Systems, LLC (1)
3924 Clock Pointe Trl, Stow, OH 44224
Tel.: (877) 445-2058
Web Site: http://www.ots.net
Tax Recovery Services
N.A.I.C.S.: 561440
Andrew Jackson *(Mgr-IT)*
Casey Dorman *(Dir-HOS Compliance)*
Chuck Farone *(Gen Mgr)*
Eric Shriver *(Dir-Tax & Licensing)*
Alyson Arnold Seaman *(Mgr-Bus Dev)*

PFB Corp. (1)
2891 Sunridge Way NE Suite 300, Calgary, T1Y 7K7, AB, Canada
Tel.: (403) 569-4300
Web Site: https://pfbcorp.com
Rev.: $105,448,215
Assets: $79,406,114
Liabilities: $30,931,351
Net Worth: $48,474,762
Earnings: $12,845,038
Emp.: 439
Fiscal Year-end: 12/31/2020
Holding Company
N.A.I.C.S.: 551112
Robert Graham *(CEO)*
Red Ortega *(CIO)*
David Carr *(Pres-Plasti-Fab)*

Subsidiary (US):

Insulspan, LLC (2)
9012 E US Hwy 223, Blissfield, MI 49228 **(100%)**
Tel.: (517) 486-4844
Web Site: https://www.insulspan.com
Sales Range: $50-74.9 Million
Emp.: 95
Roofing Siding & Insulation Material Whslr
N.A.I.C.S.: 423330

Plant (Non-US):

Insulspan, LLC - Delta Plant (3)
600 Chester Rd Annacis Business Pk, Delta, V3M 5V8, BC, Canada
Tel.: (604) 540-0600
Emp.: 20
Insulated Building Products Mfr
N.A.I.C.S.: 326140
Jeff Verhoeven *(Gen Mgr)*

Subsidiary (Domestic):

Plasti-Fab Ltd. (2)
300 2891 Sunridge Way NE, Calgary, T1Y 7K7, AB, Canada
Tel.: (403) 569-4300
Web Site: https://www.plastifab.com
Sales Range: $25-49.9 Million
Emp.: 35
Plastic Mfr
N.A.I.C.S.: 326199
Jack Hoogstraten *(Mgr-Plasti-Fab Product)*
Jim Whalen *(Mgr-Tech Mktg)*
Greg Doren *(Mgr-Advantage Product)*

Plant (Domestic):

Plasti-Fab Ltd. - Crossfield Plant (3)
802 McCool Street, Crossfield, T0M 0S0, AB, Canada
Tel.: (403) 946-5622
Web Site: https://www.plastifab.com
Sales Range: $25-49.9 Million
Emp.: 18
Insulated Building Materials Mfr
N.A.I.C.S.: 339999

Plasti-Fab Ltd. - Delta Plant (3)
679 Aldford Avenue Annacis Ind Est, Delta, V3M 5P5, BC, Canada
Tel.: (604) 526-2771
Web Site: https://www.plastifab.com
Sales Range: $25-49.9 Million
Emp.: 325
Polystyrene Product Mfr
N.A.I.C.S.: 325211

Subsidiary (US):

Poly Foam, Inc. (2)
116 Pine St S, Lester Prairie, MN 55354
Tel.: (320) 395-2551
Web Site: http://www.polyfoaminc.com
Sales Range: $1-9.9 Million
Emp.: 75
Mfg Plastic Products Mfg Plastic Foam Prdts Mfg Plstc Material/Resin Mfg Packaging Paper/Film
N.A.I.C.S.: 326199

Riverbend Timber Framing, LLC (2)
245 N Jipson St, Blissfield, MI 49228
Tel.: (517) 486-4844
Web Site: http://www.riverbendtf.com
Emp.: 20
Timber Frames Mfr & Distr
N.A.I.C.S.: 321911

Paradigm Tax Group (1)
3200 N Central Ave, Phoenix, AZ 85012
Tel.: (602) 393-9689
Web Site: http://www.paradigmtax.com
Property Tax Consulting Services
N.A.I.C.S.: 921130
Frank Giglio *(CFO)*
Mark Wanic *(CEO)*
Brian Elkins *(CTO)*

Pareto Corporation (1)
1 Concorde Gate Ste 200, Toronto, M2J 5C2, ON, Canada
Tel.: (416) 494-7745
Web Site: http://www.pareto.ca
Sales Range: $50-74.9 Million
Marketing Programs & Incentive Campaigns Implementation
N.A.I.C.S.: 541613

Parker Products, LLC (1)
3020 W Lancaster Ave, Fort Worth, TX 76107
Tel.: (817) 336-7441
Web Site: http://www.parkerproducts.com

# THE RIVERSIDE COMPANY — U.S. PRIVATE

The Riverside Company—(Continued)
Ice Cream, Frozen Dessert & Associated Confectioneries Mfr
N.A.I.C.S.: 311520
Greg Hodder (Pres)

PharmMD Solutions, LLC (1)
5200 Maryland Way Ste 200, Brentwood, TN 37027
Tel.: (615) 346-0880
Web Site: http://www.pharmmd.com
Emp.: 120
Medication Therapy Management Services
N.A.I.C.S.: 621498
Doug Berry (CFO)
Jeff Goodman (Chm)
Kent M. Holdcroft (Sr VP-Sls & Mktg)
Robert Yeager (CEO)
Cyndi Barham-Sloas (VP-Quality & Star Ratings Improvement)
Chris Geppi (VP-Bus Dev-Midwest & Southeast)
Mackey Long (VP-Bus Dev-West & Northwest)
Victor Mattingly (CTO)
Stuart C. McWhorter (Co-Founder)
Joe Porter (VP-Bus Dev-Midwest & Northeast)
Kempton Presley (VP-Bus Info Solutions & Client Performance)
Chris Schickling (VP-Bus Dev-Southwest & Upper Midwest)
Samuel W. Bartholomew III (Co-Founder & Pres)

Physicians Pharmacy Alliance, Inc. (1)
118 Mackenan Dr Ste 200, Cary, NC 27511
Tel.: (888) 772-6871
Web Site: http://www.physicianspharmacy.com
Health Care Srvces
N.A.I.C.S.: 621491
F. Bartow Hester (Sr VP-Sls & Bus Dev)
Gail Stallings (Sr VP-HR)
Pete A. Stark (CEO)
Susan Goldstein Mackin (Sr VP-Client Svcs)
Dennis M. Cole (Sr VP-Ops)
Deanna McFadden (Chief Compliance & Quality Officer)

Porcelain Products Co., Ltd (1)
225 N Patterson St, Carey, OH 43316
Tel.: (419) 396-7621
Web Site: http://www.ppcinsulators.com
Sales Range: $100-124.9 Million
Mfr of Electrical Porcelain Insulator Products
N.A.I.C.S.: 327110

ProVelocity LLC (1)
2793 Skyline Ct Ste B, Grand Junction, CO 81506
Tel.: (970) 255-0103
Web Site: https://www.provelocity.com
Software Publisher
N.A.I.C.S.: 513210

Reima Oy (1)
Jamintie 14, 38701, Kankaanpaa, Finland
Tel.: (358) 20 759 5800
Web Site: http://www.reima.fi
Emp.: 100
Children Apparel Retailer
N.A.I.C.S.: 458110

Safetec Compliance Systems (1)
501 SE Columbia Way, Vancouver, WA 98661
Tel.: (360) 567-0280
Web Site: http://www.safetec.net
Sales Range: $1-9.9 Million
Emp.: 19
Custom Computer Programming Services
N.A.I.C.S.: 541511
Jim Frohlich (Pres & CEO)

Sencore, Inc. (1)
3200 Sencore Dr, Sioux Falls, SD 57107-0729
Tel.: (605) 339-0100
Web Site: http://www.sencore.com
Sales Range: $25-49.9 Million
Emp.: 130
Mfr of Electronic Test Equipment
N.A.I.C.S.: 334515
Bruce Hasche (Controller)
Thomas Stingley (Pres)

Joe Sucharda (VP-Mktg & Per-Sls Engrg)
Jeff Briden (VP-Engrg)
Dana Nachreiner (VP-Ops)

Sport Court International Inc. (1)
939 S 700 West, Salt Lake City, UT 84104
Tel.: (801) 972-0260
Web Site: http://www.sportcourt.com
Rev.: $28,063,000
Emp.: 120
Modular Athletic Flooring & Golf Surfaces
N.A.I.C.S.: 326113
Andrew Gettig (VP-Intl Bus)
Joel McCausland (Dir-Sport Court Products)

TICONTRACT GmbH (1)
Heisinger Str 12, 87437, Kempten, Germany
Tel.: (49) 8315758580
Web Site: http://www.ticontract.com
Emp.: 60
Software Development Services
N.A.I.C.S.: 541511

The Database Marketing Agency LLC (1)
12655 SW Center St 100 Cascade Plz W, Beaverton, OR 97005-1600
Tel.: (503) 597-0088
Web Site: http://www.dmacorporation.com
Emp.: 50
Marketing Research & Consulting Services
N.A.I.C.S.: 541613
Greg Hutzell (Exec VP-Strategic Client Svcs Div)
Pisarn Leungpathomaram (Exec VP-IDM Tech Div)
Jeff Dwornicki (VP & Fin Mgr-IDM)
Preeti Shrestha (VP & Mgr-IDM Dev)
Reggie Beason (Sr VP & Mgr-Client Dev)
Naseer Nasim (Pres & CEO)
John Kish (Chm)
Hal Barnabas (CFO)
Niles Bay (COO)
David Helmick (Sr VP-Sls)

The Riverside Company - Cleveland Office (1)
Terminal Twr 50 Public Sq 29th Fl, Cleveland, OH 44113
Tel.: (216) 344-1040
Web Site: http://www.riversidecompany.com
Sales Range: $50-74.9 Million
Emp.: 50
Privater Equity Firm
N.A.I.C.S.: 523999
Stewart A. Kohl (Co-CEO)
Jeffrey A. Goodman (Operating Partner)
Ron Sansom (Mng Partner-Global)
Coleen Becker (Office Mgr)
George Benson (Partner-Operating)
Christine Croissant (Mng Dir-Mktg & IR)
Keith Davisson (Mng Dir-Comm & Mktg)
Doug England (Dir-Fin)
Tim Gosline (Partner)
Graham Hearns (Mng Dir)
Alan Peyrat (Partner)
Peggy Roberts (Mng Partner)
Cheryl Strom (Reg Dir)
Joe Lee (Partner)
Jennifer Boyce (Chief Compliance Officer & Gen Counsel)
Joe Manning (Partner)
Dave Tiley (Sr Partner-Operating)
Antonio Cabral (Mng Partner)
Russell Leupold (Dir-Project Mgmt)
Stephanie Barbera (Coord-Origination)
Lynda Barr (Dir-Fin)
Erick Bronner (Head-Fundraising & IR-Global)
Bela Szigethy (Co-CEO)
Allison Cole (Mng Dir & Head-Fundraising & IR-Global)

The Riverside Company - Dallas Office (1)
3333 Lee Pkwy Ste 200, Dallas, TX 75219-5111
Tel.: (214) 871-9640
Web Site: http://www.riversidecompany.com
Privater Equity Firm
N.A.I.C.S.: 523999
Suzanne B. Kriscunas (Mng Partner)
Linda Jackson (Office Mgr)
Mike Michienzi (Sr Operating Partner)
Stephanie Barbera (Coord-Origination)
Stuart Baxter (Partner)

Thibaut, Inc. (1)
480 Frelinghuysen Ave, Newark, NJ 07114
Tel.: (973) 643-1118
Web Site: http://www.thibautdesign.com
Sales Range: $25-49.9 Million
Emp.: 55
Wallpaper Designer, Mfr & Distr
N.A.I.C.S.: 424950
Stacy Senior Allan (Dir-Mktg)

Tropikal Bahce ve Evcil Hayvan Urunleri A.S. (1)
K Bakkalkoy Sevinc Sok No 5 Kat 7-8, Atasehir, 34750, Istanbul, Turkiye
Tel.: (90) 216 306 66 60
Web Site: http://www.tropikalpet.com.tr
Pet Food Product Mfr & Distr
N.A.I.C.S.: 311111
Izzet Saban (CEO)

U.S. Lawns Inc. (1)
6700 Forum Dr Ste 150, Orlando, FL 32821
Tel.: (407) 246-1630
Web Site: http://www.uslawns.com
Sales Range: $10-24.9 Million
Emp.: 30
Landscaping Services & Franchiser
N.A.I.C.S.: 561730
Ken Hutcheson (Pres)
Mike Fitzpatrick (VP)
Pam Dolan (Dir-Bus Mgmt)
Brandon Moxam (VP)
Carol Beeler (Mgr-Comm & Mktg)

Y international Co., Ltd. (1)
5-22-26 Honcho Y international building, Shiki, 353-0004, Saitama, Japan
Tel.: (81) 48 471 1513
Web Site: http://www.ysroad.net
Sports Bicycle Mfr & Distr
N.A.I.C.S.: 336991
Takahiko Ito (Pres & CEO)
Yasuo Yoshida (Chm)
Asazo Yoshida (Founder)

iAutomation, Inc. (1)
10 Larsen Way, North Attleboro, MA 02763
Tel.: (508) 699-7411
Web Site: http://www.i-automation.com
Industrial Automation Component Mfr
N.A.I.C.S.: 333248
Charles Williams (CEO)

THE RIVERSTONE GROUP, LLC
800 E Canal St Ste 1900, Richmond, VA 23219
Tel.: (804) 643-4200
Holding Company
N.A.I.C.S.: 551112
William H. Goodwin Jr. (CEO & COO)

Subsidiaries:

Sea Pines Resort, LLC (1)
32 Greenwood Dr, Hilton Head Island, SC 29928-4510
Tel.: (843) 785-3333
Web Site: http://www.seapines.com
Sales Range: $50-74.9 Million
Emp.: 375
Resort, Hotel & Recreational Facility
N.A.I.C.S.: 721110
Chris Beck (Dir-Golf Sls)
Mark Goodwin (Dir-Grp Sls, Catering & Conference Svcs)
Mary Doyle (Dir-Mktg)

THE RIVETT GROUP LLC — SD
1910 8th Ave NE, Aberdeen, SD 57401-3207
Tel.: (605) 229-8685
Web Site: http://www.rivettgroup.com
Year Founded: 1993
Sales Range: $50-74.9 Million
Emp.: 30
Franchise Motel Owner & Operator
N.A.I.C.S.: 721110
Ron Rivett (Chm)
Loren Steele (Vice Chm & CEO)
Joel Albright (CFO & Controller)
Paul Pettit (Exec VP-Ops)

THE RK GROUP, LLC
1220 E Commerce, San Antonio, TX 78205
Tel.: (210) 223-2680
Web Site: http://www.therkgroup.com
Year Founded: 1946
Sales Range: $10-24.9 Million
Emp.: 800
Large Scale Food Service Contractors & Catering Services
N.A.I.C.S.: 722310
Laurie Ontjes (VP-Illusions Rentals & Designs)
Greg Kowalski (Pres & CEO)
Sonya Villarreal (Mgr-Sls-Rush Catering)
Allison Whitt (Asst Dir-Sls)
John Kiehle (VP-Mktg & Comm)

Subsidiaries:

Catering By Rosemary, Inc. (1)
1220 E Commerce St, San Antonio, TX 78205
Tel.: (210) 223-2680
Web Site: http://www.rosemarycatering.com
Sales Range: $10-24.9 Milllion
Emp.: 50
Business & Social Catering Services
N.A.I.C.S.: 722320
Paul Nix (VP-Sls)

Circa Destination Management Company (1)
1220 E Commerce, San Antonio, TX 78250
Tel.: (210) 224-0926
Web Site: http://www.circadmc.com
Luxury Transportation Distr
N.A.I.C.S.: 485320
Lauren Abbl (Gen Mgr-Natl)
Kerin Croft (Acct Exec)

The RK Group West, LLC (1)
225 N 32nd Pl, Phoenix, AZ 85034
Tel.: (602) 231-9321
Web Site: http://continentalcateringaz.com
Sales Range: $1-9.9 Million
Emp.: 50
Business & Social Catering Services
N.A.I.C.S.: 722320

THE RK LOGISTICS GROUP, INC.
41707 Christy St, Fremont, CA 94538-4195
Tel.: (408) 942-9226
Web Site: http://www.rklogisticsgroup.com
General Management Consulting Services
N.A.I.C.S.: 541611
Keoki Kalune (VP)
Christopher Shepard (VP)
Rock Magnan (Pres)

Subsidiaries:

On Time Trucking, Inc. (1)
921 Conklin St, Farmingdale, NY 11735
Tel.: (631) 694-1154
Web Site: https://www.ontimetrucking.com
Sales Range: $1-9.9 Million
Emp.: 85
General Freight Trucking, Local
N.A.I.C.S.: 484110
Daniel Leitgeb (Pres)

THE RLJ COMPANIES, LLC — DE
3 Bethesda Metro Ctr Ste 1000, Bethesda, MD 20814
Tel.: (301) 280-7700
Web Site: https://rljcompanies.com
Holding Company
N.A.I.C.S.: 551112
Robert Louis Johnson (Founder & Chm)
H. Van Sinclair (Pres, CEO & Gen Counsel)
Ernita F. Thomas (Sr VP & Controller)

Subsidiaries:

RLJ Equity Partners LLC (1)
7315 Wisconsin Ave Ste 900, Bethesda, MD 20814
Tel.: (240) 744-7856

Web Site: http://www.rljequitypartners.com
Privater Equity Firm
N.A.I.C.S.: 523999
Jerry Lavell Johnson *(Founder)*
Rufus H. Rivers *(Partner)*
Nigel M. Howard *(Partner)*
T. Otey Smith *(Partner)*

Joint Venture (Domestic):

Flow Service Partners (2)
725 Cool Springs Blvd., Suite 600, Franklin, TN 37067
Tel.: (502) 558-1264
Web Site: https://www.flowservice.com
HVAC Plumbing & Refrigeration Services
N.A.I.C.S.: 238220
Michael Epperson *(CEO)*

Subsidiary (Domestic):

R. Brooks Mechanical, Inc. (3)
PO Box 1090, Rising Sun, MD 21911
Tel.: (410) 658-0822
Web Site: http://www.rbrooksmechanical.com
Plumbing, Heating & Air-Conditioning Contractors
N.A.I.C.S.: 238220

Joint Venture (Domestic):

LAI International, Inc. (2)
708 W 22nd St, Tempe, AZ 85282
Tel.: (480) 968-6228
Web Site: http://www.laico.com
Sales Range: $25-49.9 Million
Emp.: 250
Precision-Finished Components & Subassemblies Mfr
N.A.I.C.S.: 332999
Stewart Cramer *(Pres)*
Vinnie Caliendo *(CFO)*
John Rogers *(VP & COO)*
Darcy Dodge *(VP-Strategic Markets & Products)*
Jim Corrao *(CIO)*
Joe Beauchemin *(Dir-Quality)*
Patrick J. Gruetzmacher *(Pres & CEO)*
Michael Koesling *(VP-Engrg)*
Gary Thornton *(VP-HR)*
Kevin McGlinch *(CFO)*

Branch (Domestic):

LAI International, Inc.-Minneapolis (3)
7645 Baker St NE, Minneapolis, MN 55432
Tel.: (763) 780-0060
Web Site: http://www.laico.com
Sales Range: $10-24.9 Million
Emp.: 35
Precision-Finished Components & Subassemblies Mfr
N.A.I.C.S.: 332999
Patrick J. Gruetzmacher *(Pres)*

LAI International, Inc.-Westminster (3)
1110 Business Pkwy S, Westminster, MD 21157
Tel.: (410) 857-0770
Web Site: http://www.laico.com
Sales Range: $10-24.9 Million
Emp.: 50
Precision-Finished Component & Subassemble Mfr
N.A.I.C.S.: 332999
Steve Jones *(Mgr-Site)*

Holding (Domestic):

Naylor, LLC (2)
5950 NW 1st Pl, Gainesville, FL 32607
Tel.: (352) 332-1252
Web Site: http://www.naylor.com
Sales Range: $25-49.9 Million
Emp.: 500
Advertising Agencies
N.A.I.C.S.: 541810
Tara Ericson *(Sr VP-Member Comm)*
Craig Judt *(VP-Tech & Production)*
Dave Bornmann *(CMO)*
John Kilchenstein *(Sr Dir-Bus Dev)*
Joe Rosensteel *(VP-Digital Product Dev)*
John Schwallie *(CFO)*
Christine Shaw *(Pres & CEO)*
Heather Swanson *(Exec VP-Association Mgmt)*

Ogle School Management LLC (2)
2200 W Park Row Dr, Arlington, TX 76013
Tel.: (817) 460-8181
Web Site: http://www.ogleschool.edu
Cosmetology Schools Operator
N.A.I.C.S.: 611511
John Blair *(Pres & CEO)*
Kim Layton *(VP-Education)*
Aaron McCardell *(VP-Mktg & Admission)*
Neil Amari *(CFO)*
Jeff Chiarelli *(Exec Dir-Mktg)*

Virteva LLC (2)
6110 Golden Hills Dr, Golden Valley, MN 55416
Tel.: (800) 847-8382
Web Site: http://www.virteva.com
IT Services & IT Consulting
N.A.I.C.S.: 561499
Dan Rosedahl *(VP & Gen Mgr)*

RLJ Lodging Trust (1)
3 Bethesda Metro Ctr Ste 1000, Bethesda, MD 20814
Tel.: (301) 280-7777
Web Site: https://www.rljlodgingtrust.com
Rev.: $1,193,662,000
Assets: $4,978,225,000
Liabilities: $2,549,579,000
Net Worth: $2,428,646,000
Earnings: $41,925,000
Emp.: 76
Fiscal Year-end: 12/31/2022
Hotel Real Estate Investment Trust
N.A.I.C.S.: 525990
Robert Louis Johnson *(Co-Founder & Exec Chm)*
Leslie D. Hale *(Pres & CEO)*
Kate B. Henriksen *(CIO)*
Christopher A. Gormsen *(Chief Acctg Officer & Sr VP)*
Anita Cooke Wells *(Sec & Sr VP-Admin)*
Thomas J. Bardenett *(COO & Exec VP)*
Craig Amos *(Exec VP)*
Chad D. Perry *(Gen Counsel)*
Cartarwa Jones *(Sr VP)*
Nikhil Bhalla *(Treas)*
Thomas J. Baltimore Jr. *(Co-Founder)*
Sean M. Mahoney *(CFO & Exec VP)*

Subsidiary (Domestic):

RLJ Lodging Trust L.P. (2)
3 Bethesda Metro Ctr Ste 1000, Bethesda, MD 20814
Tel.: (301) 280-7777
Web Site: http://www.rljlodgingtrust.com
Home Management Services
N.A.I.C.S.: 721111
Leslie D. Hale *(Pres & CEO)*
Sean Mahoney *(CFO, Treas & Exec VP)*
Tom Bardenett *(Exec VP-Asset Mgmt)*
Jeffrey Dauray *(Sr VP-Acquisition)*
Christopher A. Gormsen *(Chief Acctg Officer)*
Frederick D. McKalip *(Gen Counsel & Sr VP)*
Anita Cooke Wells *(Sec & Sr VP-Admin)*

RLJ-McLarty-Landers Automotive Holdings, LLC (1)
425 W Capitol Ave Ste 3600, Little Rock, AR 72201
Tel.: (501) 232-4156
Web Site: http://www.rmlauto.com
Holding Company; Car Dealerships Operator
N.A.I.C.S.: 551112
Paul Hart *(CFO)*
Thomas F. McLarty III *(Vice Chm)*

THE ROADSTER SHOP
28775 N Rte 83, Mundelein, IL 60060
Tel.: (847) 949-7637
Web Site: https://roadstershop.com
Emp.: 100
Automotive Customization Services
N.A.I.C.S.: 811111

Subsidiaries:

Aeromotive, Inc. (1)
7805 Barton St, Lenexa, KS 66214
Tel.: (913) 647-7300
Web Site: http://www.aeromotiveinc.com
Rev.: $3,028,048
Emp.: 15
All Other Motor Vehicle Parts Mfr

N.A.I.C.S.: 336390
Jeff Stacy *(VP)*
Steve Matusek *(Pres)*
Phillip VanBuskirk *(Natl Sls Mgr)*

THE ROBERT BAKER COMPANIES
1700 Mtn Rd, West Suffield, CT 06093
Tel.: (860) 668-7371
Web Site: http://www.robertbaker.com
Sales Range: $25-49.9 Million
Emp.: 200
Holding Company
N.A.I.C.S.: 424930

Subsidiaries:

Robert W. Baker Nursery Inc. (1)
1700 Mountain Rd, West Suffield, CT 06093
Tel.: (860) 668-7371
Web Site: http://www.robertbaker.com
Rev.: $45,300,000
Emp.: 100
Flower & Plant Whslr
N.A.I.C.S.: 424710

Subsidiary (Domestic):

Atlantic Tree Nursery, Inc. (2)
1700 Mountain Rd, West Suffield, CT 06093
Tel.: (860) 668-7371
Web Site: http://www.robertbaker.com
Wholesale Grower of Caliper Shade Trees & Large Evergreens
N.A.I.C.S.: 111421

Medford Nursery, Inc. (2)
560A Eayrestown Red Lion Rd, Medford, NJ 08055
Tel.: (609) 267-8100
Sales Range: $25-49.9 Million
Emp.: 100
Whslr of Flowers
N.A.I.C.S.: 424930
Alex Salvi *(Gen Mgr)*

Northern Nurseries, Inc. (2)
1695 King St, Enfield, CT 06082
Tel.: (860) 623-9697
Sales Range: $25-49.9 Million
Emp.: 10
Whslr of Flowers
N.A.I.C.S.: 424930
Jim Barnes *(Gen Mgr)*

Division (Domestic):

Winfield Nursery, Inc. (3)
1320 Mountain Rd, West Suffield, CT 06093
Tel.: (860) 668-5225
Landscaping; Wholesaler of Flowers & Other Plants
N.A.I.C.S.: 424930
Diana Hammond *(Office Mgr)*

Subsidiary (Domestic):

Robert Baker, Inc. (2)
1700 Mtn Rd, West Suffield, CT 06093
Tel.: (860) 668-7371
Web Site: http://www.robertbaker.com
Whslr of Flowers
N.A.I.C.S.: 424930
Fred Platt *(Sr Mgr-Special Accts)*

THE ROBERTS GROUP, INC.
PO Box 5810, Huntsville, AL 35810
Tel.: (256) 922-1114
Web Site: http://www.crystalmtnwater.com
Sales Range: $10-24.9 Million
Emp.: 25
Bottled Water Mfr
N.A.I.C.S.: 312112
Terry L. Roberts *(Pres)*
Julia Hansch *(Sr Acct Exec)*

THE ROBERTSON GROUP, INC.
2275 Research Blvd Ste 500, Rockville, MD 20850
Tel.: (410) 822-7090
Web Site: http://www.rgp-inc.com
Rev.: $2,700,000

Emp.: 35
Administrative Management & General Management Consulting Services
N.A.I.C.S.: 541611
Nicole Robertson *(Owner & Pres)*

THE ROBINS AND MORTON GROUP
400 Shades Creek Pkwy, Birmingham, AL 35209
Tel.: (205) 870-1000
Web Site: http://www.robinsmorton.com
Year Founded: 1946
Sales Range: $600-649.9 Million
Emp.: 300
Nonresidential Construction Services
N.A.I.C.S.: 236220
Zane Williams *(Superintendent-Field)*
Brian McCord *(Coord-Employee Benefits)*
Sheldon Monroe *(Mgr-Safety Div)*
Paul Hantzis *(Sr Project Mgr-Charlotte)*
Paul Meyerer *(Project Mgr-Charlotte)*
Graham Whitley *(Project Mgr-Charlotte)*

THE ROCK CREEK GROUP, LP
1133 Connecticut Ave NW, Washington, DC 20036
Tel.: (202) 331-3400
Web Site: http://www.therockcreekgroup.com
Year Founded: 2002
Investment Advisory Services
N.A.I.C.S.: 523940
Sudhir Krishnamurthi *(Sr Mng Dir)*
George Milanovic *(VP)*
Ryan Lynch *(VP)*
Alifia Doriwala *(Mng Dir)*
Alberto Fassinotti *(Mng Dir)*
Kerneth LaPlace *(Mng Dir)*
Kerneth G. Lay *(Sr Mng Dir)*
Maryam Mashayekhi *(Mng Dir)*
Sherri Rossoff *(Mng Dir & Chief Compliance Officer)*
Antonio Sierra *(Mng Dir)*
Ronald van der Wouden *(Mng Dir)*
Afsaneh M. Beschloss *(Founder & CEO)*

THE ROCKET COMPANY
PO Box 1918, Cumming, GA 30028
Tel.: (678) 679-6410
Web Site: http://www.therocketcompany.com
Year Founded: 2008
Sales Range: $1-9.9 Million
Emp.: 9
Coaching & Practical Resources for Church Leaders & Pastors
N.A.I.C.S.: 611430
Karen Isbell *(Dir-Content)*
Becca Harper *(Controller)*

THE ROCKFORD GROUP
216 Congers Rd Bldg 2, New City, NY 10956
Tel.: (845) 624-1322
Web Site: http://www.rockfordgroup.com
Sales Range: Less than $1 Million
Emp.: 4
N.A.I.C.S.: 541810
Michael Zack *(Pres)*

THE ROGERS COMPANY
7550 Tyler Blvd, Mentor, OH 44060
Tel.: (440) 951-9200
Web Site: http://www.therogersco.com
Year Founded: 1945
Exhibit Designers
N.A.I.C.S.: 561920

THE ROGERS COMPANY

The Rogers Company—(Continued)
Jeremy Goodman (Ops Mgr)
Subsidiaries:

Expo Services, a Rogers Company LLC (1)
1601 S Rainbow Blvd, Las Vegas, NV 89146
Tel.: (800) 544-3880
Web Site: http://www.exposervices.com
Convention & Trade Show Organizers
N.A.I.C.S.: 561920

THE ROMWEBER COMPANY
4 S Park Ave, Batesville, IN 47006-0191
Tel.: (812) 934-3485
Web Site:
http://www.romwebermarketplace.com
Year Founded: 1879
Sales Range: $75-99.9 Million
Emp.: 250
Mfr of Furniture
N.A.I.C.S.: 337122

THE ROOTO CORPORATION
3505 W Grand River Ave, Howell, MI 48843-7604
Tel.: (517) 546-8330
Web Site:
http://www.rootocorporation.com
Sales Range: $10-24.9 Million
Emp.: 15
Drain Cleaning Chemicals Mfr
N.A.I.C.S.: 325612
Joon S. Moon (Pres)

THE ROSE HILLS FOUNDATION
225 S Lake Ave Ste 1250, Pasadena, CA 91101
Tel.: (626) 696-2220
Web Site:
http://www.rosehillsfoundation.org
Year Founded: 1950
Sales Range: $10-24.9 Million
Emp.: 6
Grantmaking Services
N.A.I.C.S.: 813211
Ingrid Hillebrand (Office Mgr & Mgr-Grants)

THE ROSEN GROUP
135 W 20th St Ste 402, New York, NY 10011
Tel.: (212) 255-8455
Web Site:
http://www.rosengrouppr.com
Year Founded: 1984
Sales Range: Less than $1 Million
Emp.: 21
Public Relations Agency
N.A.I.C.S.: 541820
Lori S. Rosen (Founder & Pres)
Shawna Seldon McGregor (VP)

THE ROSEWOOD CORPORATION
2101 Cedar Springs Rd Ste 1600, Dallas, TX 75201
Tel.: (214) 849-9000
Web Site: https://rosewd.com
Year Founded: 1976
Investment Firm & Holding Company
N.A.I.C.S.: 551112
Sinead Clifford Soesbe (Gen Counsel & Sr VP)
John Dziminski (Pres)
Loren Greaves (CFO & Sr VP)
Jed Nau (Sr VP & Sr Counsel)
Subsidiaries:

Rosewood Acquisition Corporation (1)
2101 Cedar Springs Rd Ste 1600, Dallas, TX 75201
Tel.: (202) 387-5400
Web Site: http://www.rosewoodpi.com
Investment Services
N.A.I.C.S.: 523940
G. T. Barden (Mng Dir)
Derry Burns (Dir)
Marquez Bela (Dir)
Briton Burge (Principal)

Holding (Domestic):

Heckethorn Manufacturing Company, Inc. (2)
2005 Forrest St, Dyersburg, TN 38024-3683
Tel.: (731) 285-3310
Web Site: http://www.hecomfg.com
Sales Range: $100-124.9 Million
Emp.: 400
Mfr of Automotive Component Parts; U-Bolts & Muffler Clamps
N.A.I.C.S.: 336390
Gary Whittle (VP-Engrg)
Tim McKinney (VP-Pur & Matls)
Alvin Cagle (Engr-Mfg)
David Haddock (Mgr-R&D)
Doug Grace (CFO)
Jared Lee (Engr-Mfg)
Tim Masek (Pres & CEO)
Trudy Lutrell (Mgr-Customer Svc)
Woody Woodward (Dir-Quality)

Petroleum Equipment Co., Inc. (2)
541 Hwy 49 S, Richland, MS 39218
Tel.: (601) 932-9100
Web Site:
http://www.petroleumequipmentco.com
Sales Range: $1-9.9 Million
Emp.: 25
Petroleum Equipment Distr
N.A.I.C.S.: 423830
Forrest Rhemann (Pres)

SSB Holdings, Inc. (2)
4300 FM 2225, Quitman, TX 75783-3529
Tel.: (903) 878-7513
Web Site: http://www.proteclab.com
Dietary & Nutritional Supplements Mfr & Whslr
N.A.I.C.S.: 325412

Joint Venture (Domestic):

States Industries, LLC (2)
29545 E Enid Rd, Eugene, OR 97402
Tel.: (541) 688-7871
Web Site: http://www.statesind.com
Sales Range: $75-99.9 Million
Mfr of Plywood, Hardwood Or Hardwood Faced Panels
N.A.I.C.S.: 321211
Mike Taylor (Pres)
Milena Lodestein-Riel (Mgr-Value stream)
David Bell (Mgr-Mktg)
Kristee Neumann (Mgr-HR)
Mario Serra (Dir-OEM Sls)

Subsidiary (Domestic):

Drawer Box Specialties Inc. (3)
1482 N Batavia St, Orange, CA 92867
Tel.: (714) 744-4247
Web Site: http://www.dbsdrawers.com
Sales Range: $10-24.9 Million
Emp.: 75
Custom Drawer Mfr
N.A.I.C.S.: 423310

Holding (Domestic):

Stationserv Holdings, LLC (2)
2101 Cedar Springs Rd Ste 1600, Dallas, TX 75201
Tel.: (214) 849-9000
Holding Company
N.A.I.C.S.: 551112
Eric A. Reisner (CEO)

Subsidiary (Domestic):

The Southern Co., Inc. (3)
3101 Carrier St, Memphis, TN 38116
Tel.: (901) 345-2531
Rev.: $7,400,000
Emp.: 35
Business to Business Electronic Markets
N.A.I.C.S.: 425120
Eric M. Scott (Pres)
Jason Scott (Treas)

THE ROSS AGENCY
201 Gibraltar Rd Ste 149, Horsham, PA 19044
Tel.: (888) 815-7536
Year Founded: 1962
Rev.: $10,000,000
Emp.: 18
Automotive
N.A.I.C.S.: 541810
Susan Burg (Dir-Bus Devel)
Jessica Mandes (Dir-Creative)

THE ROUGH NOTES COMPANY, INC.
11690 Technology Dr, Carmel, IN 46032-5600
Tel.: (317) 582-1600
Web Site: http://www.roughnotes.com
Year Founded: 1878
Sales Range: $75-99.9 Million
Emp.: 20
Insurance Magazines & Insurance Information Services Publisher
N.A.I.C.S.: 513120
Eric Hall (Exec VP-Adv & Dir-Natl Sls)
Samuel W. Berman (COO & Exec VP)
Dick Schoeninger (VP-Adv-East Coast)
Teri Cotton Santos (Chief Compliance & Risk Officer & Sr VP)

THE ROWMAN & LITTLEFIELD PUBLISHING GROUP, INC.
4501 Forbes Blvd Ste 200, Lanham, MD 20706-4310
Tel.: (301) 459-3366
Web Site: http://www.rowman.com
Sales Range: $100-124.9 Million
Emp.: 500
Holding Company; Academic, Reference & General Interest Books & Materials Publisher
N.A.I.C.S.: 551112
Rob McCreadie (Dir-HR)
Deborah Hudson (Sr Mgr-Mktg)
Linda May (VP-Mktg & Sls)
Carla Quental (VP-Customer Svc-RLPG)
Robert Marsh (COO)
Jessica Wetzel (Mgr-Convention)
Claudia Buttler (Mgr-Mktg)
Kicheko Driggins (Mgr-Online Mktg)
Paul Konowitch (Pres/CEO-Sundance Newbridge)
Jared Hughes (Sr Mgr-Library Mktg)
Karin Cholak (Sr Mgr-Mktg)
Dave Horvath (Sr Mgr-Mktg-Lexington Books)
Julie E. Kirsch (Publr & VP)
Tom Koerner (Publr-Education Issues & VP)
Susan McEachern (VP)
Mike Cornell (VP-Ops-Blue Ridge Summit)
Oliver Gadsby (Pres-Academic & Pro Div)
Michael Lippenholz (CFO)
Stephen Driver (VP-Production)

Subsidiaries:

Bernan Press (1)
15200 NBN Way, Blue Ridge Summit, PA 17214
Tel.: (301) 459-7666
Web Site: http://www.bernan.com
Government Publications Distr
N.A.I.C.S.: 424920
Veronica Dove (Mgr-Mktg)

Gooseberry Patch (1)
4501 Forbes Blvd Ste 200, Lanham, MD 20706
Web Site: http://www.gooseberrypatch.com
Cookbook Publisher
N.A.I.C.S.: 513130

Jo Ann Martin (Co-Founder)
Vickie Hutchins (Co-Founder)

National Book Network, Inc. (1)
4501 Forbes Blvd Ste 200, Lanham, MD 20706
Tel.: (301) 459-3366
Web Site: http://www.nbnbooks.com
Book Retailer & Distr
N.A.I.C.S.: 459210
James E. Lyons (Pres & CEO)
Les Petriw (Mng Dir-Canadian Div & Dir-Intl Sls)
Dennis Hayes (Dir-Special Markets)
Sylvia Williams (Dir-Sls Admin)
Mike Cornell (VP-Ops)
Tom Hunt (Dir-Publr Acctg)
Richard Lowe (Dir-Acct Mgmt)
Ron Powers (VP-Digital Publ)
Barbara Taylor (Coord-Sls)
Jason Brockwell (VP-Sls)

Newbridge Educational Publishing (1)
33 Boston Post Rd W Ste 440, Marlborough, MA 01752
Tel.: (508) 571-6500
Web Site: http://www.newbridgeonline.com
Sales Range: $25-49.9 Million
Emp.: 150
Publisher of Non-Fiction Science & Social Studies Books
N.A.I.C.S.: 513199
Paul Konowitch (Pres & CEO)

Rowman & Littlefield Publishers, Inc. (1)
4501 Forbes Blvd Ste 200, Lanham, MD 20706
Tel.: (301) 459-3366
Web Site: http://www.rowman.com
Sales Range: $25-49.9 Million
Emp.: 110
Academic, Reference & General Interest Book & Journal Publisher
N.A.I.C.S.: 513130
Kimberly Lyons (Sr Mgr-Mktg)
Clare Cox (Dir-Rights & Permissions)
Claudia Buttler (Mgr-Mktg)
Karin Cholak (Sr Mgr-Mktg)
Kicheko Driggins (Mgr-Online Mktg)
George Franzak (CFO)
Dave Horvath (Sr Mgr-Mktg)
Deborah Hudson (Mgr-Mktg)
Jared Hughes (Sr Mgr-Library Mktg)
Robert Marsh (Exec VP-Fin & Ops)
Jessica Wetzel (Mgr-Convention)

Scarecrow Press, Inc. (1)
4501 Forbes Blvd Ste 200, Lanham, MD 20706-4310
Tel.: (301) 459-3366
Web Site: http://www.scarecrowpress.com
Sales Range: $25-49.9 Million
Emp.: 140
Reference & Professional Books
N.A.I.C.S.: 513130

University Press of America, Inc. (1)
4501 Forbes Blvd Ste 200, Lanham, MD 20706-4310
Tel.: (301) 459-3366
Web Site: http://www.rowman.com
Rev.: $26,900,000
Emp.: 120
Academic Publishing; Reference Books
N.A.I.C.S.: 513130
James E. Lyons (Pres)
George Franzak (CFO)
Rob McCradie (VP-HR)

THE ROYAL HEALTH GROUP LLC
329 Washington St, Hanover, MA 02061
Tel.: (781) 659-4901
Web Site:
http://www.royalhealthgroup.com
Year Founded: 1997
N.A.I.C.S.:
Jonathan Mamary (Gen Counsel & VP)
James S. Mamary Sr. (Founder & Pres)
Subsidiaries:

J & B PARTNERSHIP LLP (1)
209 County Rd, North Falmouth, MA 02556
Tel.: (508) 563-5913

Nursing Care Facility Operator
N.A.I.C.S.: 623110

Mashpee Acquisition LLC (1)
161 Falmouth Rd, Mashpee, MA 02649-2662
Tel.: (508) 477-2490
Nursing Care Facilities Services
N.A.I.C.S.: 623110
Mary Ann Liatsis *(Exec Dir)*

THE ROZIER MERCANTILE COMPANY
2 E Saint Maries St, Perryville, MO 63775
Tel.: (573) 547-6521 MO
Web Site: http://www.roziers.com
Year Founded: 1903
Sales Range: $10-24.9 Million
Emp.: 88
Holding Company; Grocery, Hardware, Electronics, Greeting Cards, Shoes & Apparel Stores Owner & Operator
N.A.I.C.S.: 551112
James E. Lottes *(Pres)*

THE RUBIN GROUP, INC.
Tel.: (954) 467-3993
Web Site: http://www.rubingroup.com
Year Founded: 1992
Governmental Consulting Services
N.A.I.C.S.: 541618
William David Rubin *(Pres)*
Heather L. Turnbull *(VP)*

THE RUBY GROUP
330 Route 17A, Goshen, NY 10924
Tel.: (845) 651-3800
Web Site: http://www.rubygrp.com
Year Founded: 2006
Sales Range: $10-24.9 Million
Emp.: 15
Real Estate Development Services
N.A.I.C.S.: 531390
Pete Berman *(CEO)*

THE RUDOLPH/LIBBE COMPANIES
6494 Latcha Rd, Walbridge, OH 43465-9738
Tel.: (419) 241-5000 OH
Web Site: http://www.rlcos.com
Year Founded: 1955
Sales Range: $200-249.9 Million
Emp.: 1,500
Holding Company; Construction
N.A.I.C.S.: 236220
Scott W. Libbe *(Exec VP)*

Subsidiaries:

GEM Energy LLC. (1)
6842 Commodore Dr, Walbridge, OH 43465
Tel.: (419) 720-2700
Web Site: http://www.gemenergy.com
Energy Consulting Services
N.A.I.C.S.: 541690
Bill Alexander *(Pres)*
Stephanie Andrews *(Project Coord-Solar)*
Jeremy Damstra *(Dir-Svc Sls-Svc Grp)*
Lisa O'Neill *(Mgr-Customer Customer Assurance, Review & Evaluation)*
Tom Ulmer *(VP-Sls-Northeast Ohio)*
Jason Manders *(Mgr-Bus Dev)*

GEM Industrial, Inc. (1)
6842 Commodore Dr, Walbridge, OH 43465-9765 (100%)
Tel.: (419) 666-6554
Web Site: http://www.gemindustrial.com
Sales Range: $25-49.9 Million
Emp.: 100
Mechanical, Electrical, Boilermaker & Machinery Installation Contractors
N.A.I.C.S.: 238220

ProcedureLink, LLC (1)
6842 Commodore Dr, Walbridge, OH 43465
Tel.: (419) 720-2763
Web Site: http://www.procedurelink.com
Business Management Consulting Services
N.A.I.C.S.: 541611

Resource Mechanical Insulation LLC (1)
47461 Clipper St, Plymouth, MI 48170
Tel.: (734) 455-0600
Web Site: http://www.gemincorporated.com
Building Equipment Contracting Services
N.A.I.C.S.: 238290
Nancy Paquette *(Office Mgr)*

Rudolph/Libbe Properties, Inc. (1)
7255 Crossley Ste 101, Toledo, OH 43617-1504 (100%)
Tel.: (419) 534-6555
Web Site: http://www.rudolphlibbe.com
Sales Range: $1-9.9 Million
Emp.: 24
Real Estate Development; Financing
N.A.I.C.S.: 237210
Andy Rush *(Controller)*

Rudolph/Libbe, Inc. (1)
6494 Latcha Rd, Walbridge, OH 43465-9738 (100%)
Tel.: (419) 241-5000
Web Site: http://www.rudolphlibbe.com
Sales Range: $125-149.9 Million
Emp.: 186
General Contractors-Commercial & Institutional
N.A.I.C.S.: 236220
Brian P. Zientek *(Controller)*
Timothy Alter *(Pres)*
Michelle Dean *(Mgr-Bus Dev)*
Keith St. John *(Dir-IT)*
Jim Russell *(Project Mgr)*
Rod Bowe *(VP-Real Estate)*
Jeff Schaller *(Exec VP)*
Justin Rossi *(VP-Preconstruction Ops)*
Mat Arnold *(Exec Dir-Preconstruction Ops)*

THE RUHLIN COMPANY
6931 Rdg Rd, Sharon Center, OH 44274
Tel.: (330) 239-2800 OH
Web Site: http://www.ruhlin.com
Year Founded: 1915
Sales Range: $50-74.9 Million
Emp.: 500
Provider of General Contracting & Construction Services
N.A.I.C.S.: 236220
James L. Ruhlin *(Pres & CEO)*
Russell Gregory *(Treas)*
Brian Miller *(Controller)*
Michael L. Deiwert *(VP)*
Matt English *(Project Mgr-Structural Div)*

THE RUSCOE COMPANY
485 Kenmore Blvd, Akron, OH 44301-1013
Tel.: (330) 253-8148 OH
Web Site: http://www.ruscoe.com
Year Founded: 1946
Sales Range: $1-9.9 Million
Emp.: 46
Adhesive Mfr & Distr
N.A.I.C.S.: 325520
Betty Pfaff *(Treas, Sec & Dir-HR)*
Larry Musci *(Mgr-Sls & Mktg)*
Paul Michalec *(Pres)*

THE RYAN COMPANIES, LLC
1700 S Powerline Rd Ste H, Deerfield Beach, FL 33442-3025
Tel.: (954) 427-5599 WI
Web Site: http://www.theryancompanies.com
Year Founded: 1985
Sales Range: $25-49.9 Million
Emp.: 75
Excavation Work
N.A.I.C.S.: 238910
William H. Ryan *(Pres)*
Mike Shepper *(Controller)*
Joe Burke *(Exec VP)*

Subsidiaries:

Ryan Incorporated Mining (1)
1700 S Powerline Rd Ste H, Deerfield Beach, FL 33442
Tel.: (954) 427-5599
Web Site: http://www.ryanfl.com
Mining Construction Services
N.A.I.C.S.: 237990

Ryan Sales & Service, Inc. (1)
1700 S Powerline Rd Ste H, Deerfield Beach, FL 33442
Tel.: (954) 427-5599
Web Site: http://www.theryancompanies.com
Sales Range: $25-49.9 Million
Emp.: 10
Highway, Heavy & Site Construction
N.A.I.C.S.: 236210

Ryangolf Corporation (1)
614 S Military Trl, Deerfield Beach, FL 33442
Tel.: (954) 571-2088
Web Site: http://www.ryangolf.com
Golf Course Construction Services
N.A.I.C.S.: 237990
Fidel J. Garcia *(Pres & CEO)*
Larry Hughes *(VP-Ops)*
Jack K. Daughaerty *(VP-Ops)*
Liz Garrido *(CFO, Treas & Sec)*

THE S.M. STROLLER CORPORATION
105 Technology Dr Ste 190, Broomfield, CO 80021
Tel.: (303) 546-4300
Web Site: http://www.stoller.com
Sales Range: $75-99.9 Million
Emp.: 900
Cleans Up & Manages Sites Contaminated by Nuclear Waste
N.A.I.C.S.: 562112
Nicolas Lombardo *(Pres)*

THE SAGE GROUP
601 4th St Ste 312, San Francisco, CA 94107
Tel.: (415) 512-8200
Web Site: http://www.thesagegroup.com
Year Founded: 2003
Sales Range: $10-24.9 Million
Emp.: 62
Advertising Services
N.A.I.C.S.: 541810
Cara France *(CEO)*
Chris Yelton *(COO)*
Barbara Caylor *(VP-Bus Dev & Client Mgmt)*
Melanie Vest *(VP-Bus Dev & Client Mgmt)*
Sandy Minella *(VP-Bus Dev & Client Mgmt)*

THE SAINT LOUIS BREWERY, LLC.
2100 Locust St, Saint Louis, MO 63103
Tel.: (314) 241-2337
Web Site: http://www.schlafly.com
Year Founded: 1989
Sales Range: $10-24.9 Million
Emp.: 100
Brewery Mfr
N.A.I.C.S.: 312120
Dan Kopman *(Co-Founder & Chm)*
James Pendegraft *(CEO)*
Keith Moszczenski *(CFO & COO)*
Christian Fregin *(Controller & Mgr-Supply Chain)*
Emily Parker *(Head-Brewing Ops)*
Matt McFarland *(Mgr-Pkg)*
Charles Orear *(Mgr-Schlafly Bottleworks)*
Augie Altenbaumer *(Mgr-Tap Room Brewery)*

THE SALEM GROUP
2 Transam Plz Dr, Oakbrook Terrace, IL 60181-4823
Tel.: (630) 932-7000 IL
Web Site: http://www.saleminc.com
Year Founded: 1992
Sales Range: $25-49.9 Million
Emp.: 800
Staffing Services
N.A.I.C.S.: 561320
Dan Caraher *(Exec VP)*
Cary Boss *(Controller)*
Jennifer Mandala *(Mgr-Staffing)*
Sharon Fairbanks *(Supvr-Acctg)*
Steve Sorensen *(Branch Mgr)*

THE SALVAJOR COMPANY
4530 E 75th Ter, Kansas City, MO 64132-2081
Tel.: (816) 363-1030 MO
Web Site: http://www.salvajor.com
Year Founded: 1944
Sales Range: $50-74.9 Million
Emp.: 50
Commercial Waste Disposers & Waste Handling Systems Mfr
N.A.I.C.S.: 333310
Chris Hohl *(Pres)*
Don Misenhelter *(VP-Ops)*
George C. Hohl *(Pres)*
Jim Ottmer *(Mgr-Sls-Natl)*

THE SAMUEL MILLS DAMON ESTATE
999 Bishop St Ste 2800, Honolulu, HI 96813
Tel.: (808) 536-3717
Sales Range: $10-24.9 Million
Emp.: 13
Commercial & Industrial Building Operation
N.A.I.C.S.: 531120

THE SAN DIEGO MUSEUM OF ART
1450 El Prado Balboa Park, San Diego, CA 92112-2107
Tel.: (619) 232-7931 CA
Web Site: http://www.sdmart.org
Year Founded: 1935
Sales Range: $1-9.9 Million
Emp.: 141
Art Museum
N.A.I.C.S.: 712110
Roxana Velasquez *(Exec Dir)*
Dieter Fenkart-Froeschl *(COO)*

Subsidiaries:

Museum of Photographic Arts (1)
1649 El Prado, San Diego, CA 92101
Tel.: (619) 238-7559
Web Site: http://www.mopa.org
Sales Range: $1-9.9 Million
Emp.: 25
Museums And Art Galleries, Nsk
N.A..C.S.: 712110

THE SAN JOSE GROUP LTD.
233 N Michigan Ave 24 Fl, Chicago, IL 60601
Tel.: (312) 565-7000 IL
Web Site: http://www.thesanjosegroup.com
Year Founded: 1981
Sales Range: $25-49.9 Million
Emp.: 35
Advetising Agency
N.A.I.C.S.: 541810
George L. San Jose *(Pres & COO)*

THE SANBORN MAP COMPANY, INC.
1935 Jamboree Dr Ste 100, Colorado Springs, CO 80920-5398
Tel.: (866) 726-2676 DE
Web Site: http://www.sanborn.com
Map Publishing & Mapping Services
N.A.I.C.S.: 513199
John Copple *(Pres & CEO)*
Jason Caldwell *(VP-Bus Dev & Sls)*

THE SANBORN MAP COMPANY, INC.

The Sanborn Map Company, Inc.—(Continued)

Brad Arshat *(Dir-Strategic Accounts Northeast Region)*
Krysia Sapeta *(Dir-Strategic Accounts Southeast Region)*
Scott Faust *(Dir-Strategic Accounts Western Region)*
Chris Genovese *(Gen Mgr-Property & Facility Data Project Mgmt Office)*
Kate Hickey *(COO)*
Morgen Healy *(Gen Mgr-AppGeo Div)*
Richard Butgereit *(CIO)*
Jamie Curtin *(Exec VP-Strategy & Bus Dev)*

Subsidiaries:

Applied Geographics, Inc. (1)
24 School St Ste 500, Boston, MA 02108-5113
Tel.: (512) 922-2674
Web Site: http://www.appgeo.com
Custom Computer Programming Services
N.A.I.C.S.: 541511
Richard K. Grady *(Pres)*
Katie Crawford *(Acct Mgr)*
Sarah Joyce *(Coord-Sls & Mktg Support)*
Maurice Khollman *(Mgr-Product Sls)*
Michael Terner *(Exec VP)*

THE SANIBEL CAPTIVA TRUST COMPANY

2460 Palm Rdg Rd, Sanibel, FL 33957
Tel.: (239) 472-8300
Web Site:
http://www.sancaptrustco.com
Rev.: $750,000,000
Emp.: 32
Trust & Investment Services
N.A.I.C.S.: 523999
S. Albert D. Hanser *(Founder & Chm)*
Richard A. Botthof *(Vice Chm)*
Terence M. Igo *(CEO)*
Craig J. Holston *(COO)*
Beth Weigel *(Exec VP & Dir-Client Svcs & Trust Ops)*
Steven V. Greenstein *(Exec VP)*
Cherry W. Smith *(Exec VP)*
Timothy P. Vick *(Sr VP & Dir-Res)*
Ian N. Breusch *(Chief Investment Officer)*

Subsidiaries:

Sanibel Captiva Investment Advisers, Inc. (1)
980 N Michigan Ave Ste 1400, Chicago, IL 60611
Tel.: (312) 214-3555
Web Site: http://www.scia-capital.com
Investment & Advisory Services
N.A.I.C.S.: 523999
Pat Dorsey *(Pres)*

The Naples Trust Company (1)
5920 Goodlette Frank Rd, Naples, FL 34109
Tel.: (239) 774-4000
Web Site:
http://www.naplestrustcompany.com
Emp.: 13
Trust & Investment Services
N.A.I.C.S.: 523999
Carol B. Boyd *(Pres)*
Ian N. Breusch *(Portfolio Mgr)*
Terence M. Igo *(CEO)*

The Tampa Bay Trust Company (1)
4488 Boy Scout Blvd Ste 425, Tampa, FL 33607
Tel.: (813) 915-6202
Web Site:
http://www.tampabaytrustcompany.com
Emp.: 6
Trust & Investment Services
N.A.I.C.S.: 523999
Terence M. Igo *(CEO)*
Donald Jowdy *(Sr VP & Sr Portfolio Mgr)*
Carla Porcaro Powers *(VP)*
Lori Mobley *(Corp Sec & VP)*
Michael R. Dreyer *(Co-Pres)*
Judy Bricker *(Sr VP & Dir-Mktg & PR)*

Ian N. Breusch *(VP & Portfolio Mgr)*
Huck Harris *(Sr VP-Family Office Svcs-Winter Haven)*
Craig J. Holston *(COO)*
Timothy P. Vick *(Sr VP & Dir-Res)*
Louis N. Pappas *(VP-Family Office Svcs)*
Hood Craddock *(Dir-Family Office Svcs)*
Peter Knize *(Sr VP-Trust Admin)*

THE SARPES GROUP, INC.

296 Ocean Blvd, Golden Beach, FL 33160
Tel.: (305) 792-7900 FL
Year Founded: 2002
Holding Company; Specialty Sleep Aid Bottled Water Mfr & Whslr
N.A.I.C.S.: 551112
Rachmil Lekach *(Pres & CEO)*
David Lekach *(CEO-Dream Products)*

THE SARUT GROUP

780 Humboldt St, Brooklyn, NY 11222
Tel.: (718) 387-7484
Web Site: http://www.sarut.com
Year Founded: 1979
Rev.: $5,000,000
Emp.: 30
Giftware Whslr
N.A.I.C.S.: 424990
Frederic Rambaud *(Owner)*

THE SAVINGS BANK

357 Main St, Wakefield, MA 01880
Tel.: (781) 224-5341
Web Site:
http://www.tsbawake24.com
Year Founded: 1869
Sales Range: $50-74.9 Million
Emp.: 140
Banking Services
N.A.I.C.S.: 522110
Robert J. DiBella *(Pres & CEO)*
Raichelle L. Kallery *(Officer-Retail Banking & Exec VP)*
Patricia A. O'Brien *(Sr VP-HR)*
Bruce G. Donovan *(VP-Branch Admin)*
Frederick P. Maloof *(Officer-Comml Banking & VP)*
Peter W. Johnston *(Officer-Comml Banking & Sr VP)*
Allyson Houghton *(Coord-Mktg)*
Tes Mercedat *(Mgr-South Lynnfield)*
Michael R. Barrett *(Chm)*
Denise Carbone *(CFO, Treas & Sr VP)*
Maria F. Melo *(Sr VP & Mgr-Sys)*
Jeff P. D'Alessandro *(Officer-Retail Lending & Sr VP)*
Kathleen M. Conary *(Sr VP-Compliance & Audit)*
Nick Kefalas *(Officer-Comml Banking & VP)*
David J. Fama *(Asst VP)*

Subsidiaries:

First Financial Trust, N.A. (1)
351 Main St, Wakefield, MA 01880
Tel.: (617) 658-7600
Web Site: http://www.firstfinancialtrust.com
Sales Range: $1-9.9 Million
Emp.: 12
Investment Services
N.A.I.C.S.: 523999
Joseph A. Giovino *(Officer-Investment & Exec VP)*
Janice M. Casoli *(Officer-Trust & VP)*
James D. Hohman *(Officer-Investment & Sr VP)*
Peter C. Armbruster *(Officer-Trust & Sr VP)*
Rick Ciolino *(Officer-Investment & VP)*
Brendan M. Szocik *(Pres & CEO)*
Kathryn Boyle *(Chief Fiduciary Officer & VP)*

THE SAVINGS BANK OF ROCKVILLE

25 Park St, Vernon Rockville, CT 06066-3211
Tel.: (860) 871-1858 CT
Web Site:
http://www.rockvillebank.com
Year Founded: 1858
Sales Range: $25-49.9 Million
Emp.: 350
Banking Services
N.A.I.C.S.: 523999
William Crawford *(Pres)*

THE SAVOGRAN COMPANY

259 Lenox St, Norwood, MA 02062-3417
Tel.: (781) 762-5400 MA
Web Site: http://www.savogran.com
Year Founded: 1872
Sales Range: $75-99.9 Million
Emp.: 20
Paint & Varnish Remover, Cleaners, Compounders, Spackling Products, Liquid Paint Remover, Wallpaper Remover, Waterless Hand Cleaner, Tile Repairer, Crack Filler, Wood Putty & Brush Cleaner Mfr
N.A.I.C.S.: 325510
Steve McLean *(VP-Sls)*
Mark Monique *(Pres)*
Janice Jonson *(Treas)*

THE SAWTOOTH GROUP

25 Bridge Ave Ste 203, Red Bank, NJ 07701
Tel.: (732) 945-1004
Web Site:
http://www.sawtoothgroup.com
Year Founded: 1988
Emp.: 75
Advetising Agency
N.A.I.C.S.: 541810
Kristi Bridges *(Pres, Partner, Chief Creative Officer & Creative Dir)*
Anne-Marie Connors *(Controller)*
Patricia A. Little *(Mng Partner)*
Bill Schmermund *(CEO & Partner)*
Kristi Bridges *(Partner & Creative Dir)*
Jamie Caprio *(Dir-Strategic Plng)*
Patricia A. Little *(Mng Partner)*

THE SCHAECHTER ADVERTISING AGENCY

34 Connecticut Blvd, East Hartford, CT 06108-3014
Tel.: (860) 289-0304
Year Founded: 1959
Sales Range: Less than $1 Million
Emp.: 5
N.A.I.C.S.: 541810
Harry B. Schaechter *(Pres)*
Richard Wilton *(Art Dir)*
Ida Smith *(Production Mgr)*

THE SCHAEFER GROUP, INC.

1500 Humphrey Ave, Dayton, OH 45410
Tel.: (937) 253-3342
Web Site:
http://www.theschaefergroup.com
Sales Range: $10-24.9 Million
Emp.: 350
Boiler & Furnace Contractors
N.A.I.C.S.: 238220
Richard Schaefer *(CEO)*
Mike Flinn *(VP)*
John Miltenberger *(Dir-HR)*
Frank Maher *(Dir-Safety)*
Cheryl Morgan *(Mgr-Acctg)*
Doug Williamson *(Engr-Sls)*
David White *(Mgr-Natl Sls)*
Steve Wieser *(Mgr-Traffic)*

THE SCHAFER COMPANY INC.

Hwy 301 N I 95, Hamer, SC 29547
Tel.: (843) 774-2411 SC
Web Site: http://www.pedroland.com

Year Founded: 1973
Sales Range: $125-149.9 Million
Emp.: 400
Holding Company; Restaurant & Motel Owner & Operator
N.A.I.C.S.: 551112
Alan Schafer *(Chm & CEO)*

Subsidiaries:

Ace-Hi Inc. (1)
Hwy 301 N Dillon, Hamer, SC 29547
Tel.: (843) 774-6620
Rev.: $1,200,000
Emp.: 6
Provider of Outdoor Advertising Services
N.A.I.C.S.: 541850

Blenheim Bottlers Inc. (1)
PO Box 8, Hamer, SC 29547
Tel.: (843) 774-0322
Sales Range: $10-24.9 Million
Emp.: 5
Mfr of Ginger Ale
N.A.I.C.S.: 424490

Pedro Land Inc. (1)
I-95 Hwy 301-501, Hamer, SC 29547
Tel.: (843) 774-2411
Web Site: http://www.pedroland.com
Rev.: $48,200,000
Emp.: 300
Amusement Services
N.A.I.C.S.: 713110

South of the Border Restaurant Inc.
Hwy 301, Hamer, SC 29547
Tel.: (843) 774-2411
Sales Range: $10-24.9 Million
Emp.: 50
Provider of Dining Places
N.A.I.C.S.: 713110
Timmy Townesend *(Gen Mgr)*

The Border Court Inc. (1)
3346 Hwy 301, Hamer, SC 29547
Tel.: (843) 774-2411
Web Site:
http://www.thesouthoftheborder.com
Rev.: $10,000,000
Emp.: 26
Provider of Hotel & Motel Services
N.A.I.C.S.: 441110

THE SCHIMBERG GROUP INC.

40 S Pineapple Ave Ste 101, Sarasota, FL 34236
Tel.: (941) 894-6888
Web Site: http://www.theschim.com
Year Founded: 2004
Sales Range: $1-9.9 Million
Emp.: 5
Architectural & Interior Design Services
N.A.I.C.S.: 541310
Barron Schimberg *(Owner)*
Patricia Morrison Schimberg *(Principal)*
Todd Anderson *(Project Mgr)*

THE SCHOCKMAN LUMBER COMPANY, INC.

342 W Columbus St, Saint Henry, OH 45883
Tel.: (419) 678-4198 OH
Web Site:
http://www.schockmanlumber.com
Year Founded: 1990
Sales Range: $1-9.9 Million
Emp.: 10
Lumber, Plywood, Millwork & Wood Panel Merchant Whslr
N.A.I.C.S.: 423310
Jeff Bruns *(Pres)*
Kevin Leugers *(Mgr-Acct)*
Beth Westgerdes *(Mgr-Acct)*

Subsidiaries:

Iverson's Lumber Company Inc. (1)
1664 N Milford Rd, Highland, MI 48357-3806
Tel.: (248) 889-4910
Web Site: http://www.iversonslumber.com

COMPANIES

Sales Range: $10-24.9 Million
Emp.: 45
Lumber & Other Building Materials
N.A.I.C.S.: 423310

THE SCHULTZ ORGANIZATION, LLC
1540 Chestnut St, Emmaus, PA 18049
Tel.: (610) 967-2141
Web Site: http://www.schultzorg.com
General Construction Firm
N.A.I.C.S.: 236220
Jess Kronenwetter *(Field Engr)*

Subsidiaries:

Nyleve Bridge Corp. (1)
1540 Chestnut St, Emmaus, PA 18049
Tel.: (610) 965-3083
Web Site: http://www.nylevebridgecorp.com
Bridge Construction & Rehabilitation & Heavy Concrete Work
N.A.I.C.S.: 237310

THE SCHWAN FOOD COMPANY
115 W College Dr, Marshall, MN 56258
Tel.: (507) 532-3274 MN
Web Site: http://www.theschwanfoodcompany.com
Year Founded: 1952
Sales Range: $1-4.9 Billion
Emp.: 22,000
Frozen Food Mfr & Distr
N.A.I.C.S.: 311412
Brian Sattler *(Gen Counsel & Exec VP-Bus Svcs)*
Julie Francis *(COO)*
Dimitrios P. Smyrnios *(CEO)*
Robin Galloway *(CFO & Exec VP-Fin)*
Kathy Persian *(CIO & Sr VP)*
Jeff Erickson *(Chm)*
Chuck Blomberg *(Mgr-Comm)*
Tony Puri *(Exec VP- SFC Global Supply Chain)*
Marvin Schwan *(Founder)*
Roberto Rios *(CMO)*
Scott F. Peterson *(Chief HR Officer & Exec VP)*

Subsidiaries:

Schwan's Bakery Inc (1)
2900 Rolling Pin Ln Ste A, Suwanee, GA 30024 **(100%)**
Tel.: (678) 482-3339
Web Site: http://www.schwans.com
Sales Range: $150-199.9 Million
Emp.: 500
Dessert Mfr & Distr
N.A.I.C.S.: 311813

Schwan's Consumer Brands, Inc. (1)
6395 Karen St, Marlette, MI 48453
Tel.: (989) 635-7501
Frozen Food Retailer
N.A.I.C.S.: 445298
April Anslinger *(Chief Growth Officer & Sr VP)*

Schwan's Food Service, Inc. (1)
115 W College Dr, Marshall, MN 56258
Tel.: (507) 532-3274
Web Site: http://www.schwansfoodservice.com
Frozen Food & Meal Distr
N.A.I.C.S.: 424420
Craig Claude *(Mgr-Culinary Svcs)*
Ciaran Duffy *(Mgr-Culinary Svcs)*
Kit Kiefer *(Dir-Culinary Svcs)*
Peter Genna *(Mgr-Culinary Svcs)*
Trevor Bynum *(Pres)*

Schwan's Home Service, Inc. (1)
115 W College Dr, Marshall, MN 56258
Tel.: (507) 532-3274
Web Site: http://www.schwans.com
Frozen Food Retailer
N.A.I.C.S.: 445298

THE SCHWARTZBERG COMPANIES
4 W Red Oak Ln Ste 201, White Plains, NY 10604
Tel.: (914) 390-4300
Web Site: http://www.schwartzbergcompanies.com
Sales Range: $75-99.9 Million
Emp.: 500
Holding Company; Nursing Care Facilities Owner
N.A.I.C.S.: 551112

Subsidiaries:

Cypress Health Care Management (1)
4 W Red Oak Ln, White Plains, NY 10604
Tel.: (914) 390-4300
Web Site: http://www.cypresshealthcare.net
Sales Range: $10-24.9 Million
Emp.: 100
Nursing Care Facilities
N.A.I.C.S.: 623110
Harris Schwartzberg *(Pres)*

THE SCOTTSDALE CO.
4200 Gulf Shore Blvd N, Naples, FL 34103
Tel.: (239) 261-6100 FL
Web Site: http://www.lutgert.com
Property Developer & Manager
N.A.I.C.S.: 237210
Scott Lutgert *(Chm)*
Howard B. Gutman *(Pres)*
Michael T. Hoyt *(Sr VP)*
Kurt Lutgert *(VP)*
David Crowley *(CFO)*
Barbara Cunningham *(Controller)*
Joe Consolino *(Mgr-IT)*
Erik Lutgert *(VP)*
Rebecca Randolph *(Coord-HR)*

Subsidiaries:

Premier Commercial, Inc. (1)
27400 Riverview Ctr Blvd Ste 4, Bonita Springs, FL 34134
Tel.: (239) 992-1200
Web Site: http://www.premcomm.com
Sales Range: $10-24.9 Million
Emp.: 10
Real Estate Broker
N.A.I.C.S.: 531210
Dougall McCorkle *(Sr VP-Comml Real Estate)*
Thomas A. Bringardner Jr. *(Pres & CEO)*

THE SCOULAR COMPANY
13660 California St, Omaha, NE 68154
Tel.: (402) 342-3500 NE
Web Site: https://www.scoular.com
Year Founded: 1892
Sales Range: $1-4.9 Billion
Emp.: 1,400
Grain & Field Bean Merchant Wholesalers
N.A.I.C.S.: 424510
Marshall E. Faith *(Vice Chm)*
John Heck *(Sr VP-Omaha-Nebraska)*
Roger Barber *(CFO)*
Todd McQueen *(Sr VP-Omaha-Nebraska)*
Robert Ludington *(Sr VP & Gen Mgr-Kansas)*
Kurt Peterson *(VP-Minnesota)*
Julie Heiliger *(Dir-Brand Mktg & Corp Comm)*
Jeff Schreiner *(CIO)*
Megan Belcher *(Gen Counsel & Sr VP)*
Bryan Wurscher *(VP/Gen Mgr/Mgr-Special Crops Bus)*
Joshua Mellinger *(Dir-Sustainability)*
Melissa Matczak *(Sr Mgr-Corp Comm)*

Subsidiaries:

Northwest Farm Food Cooperative, Inc. (1)
1370 S Anacortes St, Burlington, WA 98233
Tel.: (360) 757-4225
Sales Range: $1-9.9 Million
Emp.: 17
Farm Supplies Merchant Whslr
N.A.I.C.S.: 424910
Glade Wilkinson *(Dir)*

The Scoular Co. - Minneapolis Corporate Office (1)
250 Marquette Ave Ste 1050, Minneapolis, MN 55401
Tel.: (612) 335-8205
Web Site: http://www.scoular.com
Sales Range: $25-49.9 Million
Emp.: 80
Buying, Selling, Storing, Handling & Transporting Agricultural Products
N.A.I.C.S.: 424510
John Messerich *(Sr VP & Gen Mgr)*
Kurt Peterson *(Chief HR Officer)*

The Scoular Co. - Overland Park Corporate Office (1)
10801 Mastin St Ste 800, Overland Park, KS 66210
Tel.: (913) 338-1474
Web Site: http://www.scoular.com
Sales Range: $25-49.9 Million
Emp.: 20
Agriculture Product Distr
N.A.I.C.S.: 424510
Robert Ludington *(Sr VP & Gen Mgr)*

THE SCRNEN FOUNDATION
1 Rockefeller Plz Ste 31, New York, NY 10020-2102
Tel.: (212) 977-6900 NY
Year Founded: 1975
Sales Range: $10-24.9 Million
Grantmaking Services
N.A.I.C.S.: 813211
Jane F. Clark *(Pres)*
Kevin S. Moore *(Treas & VP)*
Kathleen F. Kestler *(Sec)*
Richard C. Vanison *(Asst Treas)*

THE SCRUGGS COMPANY INC.
4679 Old Hwy 41 N, Hahira, GA 31632
Tel.: (229) 242-2388
Web Site: http://www.scruggscompany.com
Rev.: $34,146,971
Emp.: 200
Highway & Street Paving Contractor
N.A.I.C.S.: 237310
Mary Wisenbaker *(VP)*

THE SEAGATE HOTEL & SPA
1000 E Atlantic Ave, Delray Beach, FL 33483
Tel.: (561) 665-4800
Web Site: http://www.theseagatehotel.com
Sales Range: $1-9.9 Million
Emp.: 80
Hotel & Spa
N.A.I.C.S.: 721110
E. Anthony Wilson *(Pres & CEO)*
Cathy McNellen *(Mgr-Catering)*
William J. Sander III *(Gen Mgr)*

THE SECURITY TITLE GUARANTEE CORP
6 S Calvert St, Baltimore, MD 21202
Tel.: (410) 727-4456
Web Site: http://www.esecuritytitle.com
Year Founded: 1952
Rev.: $14,936,232
Emp.: 41
Guarantee Of Titles
N.A.I.C.S.: 524127
Theodore Rogers *(Pres & CEO)*
William C. Rogers Jr. *(Chm)*

THE SEGAL GROUP, INC.

THE SEER GROUP LLC
2725 152nd Ave NE, Redmond, WA 98052
Tel.: (425) 678-1780
Web Site: http://www.theseergroupllc.com
Heating, Ventilation & Air Conditioning Services
N.A.I.C.S.: 238220
Darrin Erdahl *(Founder & CEO)*

Subsidiaries:

Coffman & Company Group (1)
11919 I 70 Frontage Rd N Ste 122, Wheat Ridge, CO 80033
Tel.: (303) 366-1112
Web Site: http://www.hvacrepairdenverco.com
Electrical Contractor
N.A.I.C.S.: 238210

Western Heating and Air Conditioning Inc. (1)
4980 N Bradley St Ste B, Garden City, ID 83714-1478
Tel.: (208) 375-6101
Web Site: http://www.westernhvac.com
Plumbing, Heating & Air-Conditioning Contractors
N.A.I.C.S.: 238220
Candy Sinclair *(Mgr-HR)*

THE SEGAL GROUP, INC.
333 W 34th St, New York, NY 10001
Tel.: (212) 251-5000 DE
Web Site: http://www.segalco.com
Sales Range: $75-99.9 Million
Emp.: 300
Holding Company; Benefits & Human Resources Consulting Services
N.A.I.C.S.: 551112
David Blumenstein *(Pres & CEO)*
Kathryn L. Bakich *(Sr VP)*
Joseph A. Locicero *(Chm)*
John Gingell *(Chief Practice Officer-Chicago)*
Jim Sokol *(CIO & Sr VP)*
Stuart Wohl *(Sr VP-Washington)*
Jesse M. Rivera *(VP)*
John Flynn *(COO-Hartford)*
Richard S. Hiss *(Sr VP & Natl Dir-Content, Mktg & Sls Support)*
Guy Lester *(VP & Dir-Mktg)*
Helene Dankner *(Chief People Officer & Sr VP)*
Margery Friedman *(Gen Counsel & Sr VP)*
Ricardo DiBartolo *(CFO & Sr VP)*
Susanne Antonucci *(Mgr-Production)*
Mitchell Bramstaedt *(Sr VP-Chicago)*
Andrew D. Sherman *(Dir-Public Sector Market-Natl)*
Randolph Carter *(Sr VP)*
Howard B. Goldsmith *(Sr VP & Mgr-New York)*
Andrew Kaplan *(VP & Specialist-Pub Sector Comm)*
Edward Kaplan *(Sr VP)*
Stuart Lerner *(Sr VP-Admin)*
Lydia Moore *(VP)*
Kim Nicholl *(Sr VP)*
Serena Simons *(Sr VP)*
Elliot Susseles *(Sr VP)*

Subsidiaries:

Segal Advisors, Inc. (1)
333 W 34th St 5th Fl, New York, NY 10001-2402
Tel.: (212) 251-5000
Web Site: http://www.segalmarco.com
Emp.: 40
Investment Advisory Services
N.A.I.C.S.: 523940
Timothy R. Barron *(Chief Investment Officer)*
John DeMairo *(Pres & CEO)*
Seth Almaliah *(Sr VP)*
Frank Carofano *(Sr VP & Dir-Investment Ops & Tech)*
Michael Joyce *(Sr VP)*

THE SEGAL GROUP, INC.

The Segal Group, Inc.—(Continued)
Jeffrey Boucek *(Sr VP & Dir-Pub Fund Consulting)*
John Marco *(Sr VP)*
Frank Picarelli *(Sr VP)*
Marc Procek *(Sr VP)*
Richard Ranallo *(Sr VP)*
Julian Regan *(Sr VP)*
Nick Trella *(Sr VP)*
Michael C. Wright *(Sr VP)*

Subsidiary (Domestic):

RogersCasey, Inc. **(2)**
1 Parklands Dr, Darien, CT 06820-3627
Tel.: (203) 656-5900
Web Site: http://www.rogerscasey.com
Sales Range: $75-99.9 Million
Emp.: 100
Investment Consultants
N.A.I.C.S.: 523940
Ryen Sherman *(VP-Manhattan)*

Segal Benz **(1)**
275 9th St, San Francisco, CA 94103
Tel.: (415) 913-7805
Web Site: http://www.benzcommunications.com
Emp.: 58
HR & Employee Benefits Communications, Custom Websites & Print Campaigns
N.A.I.C.S.: 541612
Jennifer Benz *(Sr VP-Comm)*
Isabelle Englund-Geiger *(Sr VP-Comm)*
Caroline Lowry *(Sr Project Mgr)*
Michelle Lyn *(Sr Project Mgr)*
Phoebe Snow *(Office Mgr)*
Libby DeMeo *(COO)*
Randolph B. Carter *(Sr VP)*

Segal Select Insurance Services, Inc. **(1)**
333 W 34th St, New York, NY 10001-2402
Tel.: (212) 251-5000
Web Site: http://www.segalselect.com
General Insurance Services
N.A.I.C.S.: 524210
Diane R. McNally *(Sr VP)*

Sibson Consulting, LLC **(1)**
33 W 34th St, New York, NY 10001 **(100%)**
Tel.: (212) 251-5901
Web Site: http://www.sibson.com
Sales Range: $10-24.9 Million
Emp.: 16
Benefits, Compensation & Human Resources Consulting Services
N.A.I.C.S.: 541612
Michael O'Malley *(VP)*
Daniel G. Fries *(Sr VP)*
Erin Burns *(VP & Dir-Publ)*
Susanne Antonucci *(Mgr-Production)*

Branch (Domestic):

Sibson Consulting, LLC - Los Angeles **(2)**
10880 Wilshire Blvd Ste 850, Los Angeles, CA 90024
Tel.: (310) 231-1700
Web Site: http://www.sibson.com
Benefit Compensation & Human Resource Consulting Services
N.A.I.C.S.: 541612

Sibson Consulting, LLC - Princeton **(2)**
1009 Lenox Dr Ste 115, Lawrence, NJ 08648-2321
Tel.: (609) 520-2700
Web Site: http://www.segalco.com
Benefits, Compensation & Human Resources Consulting Services
N.A.I.C.S.: 541612

Sibson Consulting, LLC - Raleigh **(2)**
1100 Crescent Green Dr Ste 103, Cary, NC 27518
Tel.: (919) 233-1220
Web Site: http://www.sibson.com
Benefits, Compensation & Human Resources Consulting Services
N.A.I.C.S.: 541612
Jim Kochanski *(Sr VP)*

The Segal Company (Eastern States), Inc. **(1)**
333 West 34th St, New York, NY 10001-2402
Tel.: (212) 251-5000
Web Site: http://www.segalco.com
Benefits, Compensation & Human Resources Consulting Services
N.A.I.C.S.: 541612
Joseph A. LoCicero *(Pres & CEO)*

The Segal Company, Ltd. **(1)**
45 St Clair Ave West, Toronto, M4V 1K9, ON, Canada **(100%)**
Tel.: (416) 969-3960
Web Site: http://www.segalco.com
Sales Range: $10-24.9 Million
Emp.: 21
Information Technology Consulting Firm
N.A.I.C.S.: 541511

THE SEGERDAHL CORPORATION

1351 S Wheeling Rd, Wheeling, IL 60090
Tel.: (847) 541-1080 IL
Web Site: http://www.sg360.com
Year Founded: 1956
Sales Range: $100-124.9 Million
Emp.: 200
Offset Printing & Binding of Text Books, Catalogs & Direct Mail Stuffers
N.A.I.C.S.: 323111
Richard Joutras *(Pres & CEO)*
Paul White *(Exec VP)*
Bruce Rush *(Dir-Engrg)*
Hans Kollinger *(Sr VP-Sls)*
John Romita *(VP-Mfg)*

Subsidiaries:

Data Service Solutions, Inc. **(1)**
401 E South Frontage Rd, Bolingbrook, IL 60440
Tel.: (815) 254-2110
Web Site: http://www.datserv.com
Sales Range: $1-9.9 Million
Emp.: 25
Technical Printing Services
N.A.I.C.S.: 323111
John James *(Gen Mgr)*
Wesley Biggs *(VP-Sls)*

SG360 **(1)**
385 Gilman Ave, Wheeling, IL 60090
Tel.: (847) 850-8800
Web Site: http://www.sg360.com
Emp.: 400
Digital & Offset Printing Services
N.A.I.C.S.: 323111
John Wallace *(Interim Pres & Interim CEO)*

THE SEIBELS BRUCE GROUP, INC.

1501 Lady St, Columbia, SC 29201
Tel.: (803) 748-2000 SC
Web Site: http://www.seibels.com
Year Founded: 1869
Sales Range: $50-74.9 Million
Emp.: 264
Multiple Line Property & Casualty Insurance; Servicing Carrier; Managing General Agent; Brokerage Services
N.A.I.C.S.: 524126
Matt P. McClure *(Gen Counsel & VP)*
Stephen Harding *(VP-Insurance Mgmt Svcs)*
Rex W. Huggins *(Chm & CEO)*
Adrian E. Brown *(Chief Risk Officer)*
Clarence E. Lee *(VP-Catastrophe Ops & Property Claims)*
Nan D. Brunson *(COO)*
Ron Giomi *(VP-Litigation & Liability Claims-Seibels Claims Solutions, Inc.)*
Dester J. Terry *(Pres/Chief Claims Officer-Seibels Claims Solutions)*
Julie McKenna *(VP-Bus Dev)*
Steven Hastings *(VP-Claims)*
Alyssa Rockwell *(Asst VP-Sls & Mktg)*
Pam Ringquist *(Chief People Officer)*
Rao Tadepalli *(CIO)*
Jim Brophy *(Asst VP-Pricing & Vendor Mgmt)*
Hope Broadway *(VP-HR)*
Sree Putta *(Asst VP-Product Implementation)*
Mike Gilmer *(VP-Claims)*
Kellie Reid *(VP-Compliance & Underwriting)*
Laura M. Spells *(CFO)*
Jody Hawkins *(VP-IT Ops)*
Jeff Karam *(VP-IT Ops)*

Subsidiaries:

America's Flood Services, Inc. **(1)**
2941 Sunrise Blvd Ste 100, Rancho Cordova, CA 95742-7203 **(100%)**
Tel.: (803) 748-2000
Web Site: http://www.americasflood.com
Sales Range: $50-74.9 Million
Emp.: 30
Insurance
N.A.I.C.S.: 524210

Catawba Insurance Company **(1)**
1501 Lady St, Columbia, SC 29201 **(100%)**
Tel.: (803) 748-2000
Sales Range: $125-149.9 Million
Emp.: 200
Property & Casualty Insurance
N.A.I.C.S.: 524128
Nan D. Brunson *(Pres & CEO)*

Insurance Network Services, Inc. **(1)**
1501 Lady St, Columbia, SC 29201-3401 **(100%)**
Tel.: (803) 748-2000
Web Site: http://www.claims-ins.com
Sales Range: $50-74.9 Million
Emp.: 155
Provider of Fire, Marine & Casualty Insurance
N.A.I.C.S.: 524291

Seibels, Bruce & Company **(1)**
1501 Lady St, Columbia, SC 29201 **(100%)**
Tel.: (803) 748-2000
Web Site: http://www.seibelsbruce.com
Sales Range: $75-99.9 Million
Emp.: 260
Insurance Managing General Agent
N.A.I.C.S.: 524126

THE SEIDEN GROUP

708 3rd Ave 13th Fl, New York, NY 10017
Tel.: (212) 223-8700
Web Site: http://www.seidenadvertising.com
Year Founded: 1995
Rev.: $90,000,000
Emp.: 43
Advertising Agencies, Brand Development, Consulting, Full Service, New Product Development, Planning & Consultation
N.A.I.C.S.: 541810
Matthew Seiden *(Pres & CEO)*
Steve Feinberg *(Chief Creative Officer)*
Susan Small-Weil *(Chief Plng Officer)*
Shari Bronson *(Mng Dir)*
Patrick Lupinski *(Mng Dir)*

THE SEIDLER COMPANY, LLC

4640 Admiralty Way Ste 1200, Marina Del Rey, CA 90292
Tel.: (213) 683-4622 DE
Web Site: http://www.sepfunds.com
Year Founded: 1992
Privater Equity Firm
N.A.I.C.S.: 523999
Leonard Lee *(Partner)*
Christopher L. Eastland *(Partner)*
Jonelle Jue *(CFO)*
Tristan Burns *(Controller)*
Eric O'Brien *(VP)*
Scott Yingling *(VP)*

Subsidiaries:

Fitness International, LLC **(1)**
2600 Michelson Dr Ste 600, Irvine, CA 92612-4406
Tel.: (949) 255-7330
Web Site: http://www.lafitness.com
Sales Range: $1-4.9 Billion
Health & Fitness Club Operator
N.A.I.C.S.: 713940
Louis Welch *(CEO)*

Monahan Products, LLC **(1)**
60 Sharp St, Hingham, MA 02043
Tel.: (844) 823-3132
Web Site: http://www.uppababy.com
Toys & Childrens Vehicle Mfr
N.A.I.C.S.: 339930
Bob Monahan *(Founder & Owner)*

Subsidiary (Domestic):

Thorley Industries LLC **(2)**
40 24th St 3rd Fl, Pittsburgh, PA 15222
Tel.: (412) 434-8380
Web Site: http://www.4moms.com
Sales Range: $25-49.9 Million
Emp.: 180
Toys & Childrens Vehicle Mfr
N.A.I.C.S.: 339930
Florian Hunziker *(COO)*
David Trabulsi *(VP-Product Dev & Ops)*

Rawlings Sporting Goods Co., Inc. **(1)**
510 Maryville University Dr Ste 110, Saint Louis, MO 63141
Tel.: (314) 819-2800
Web Site: http://www.rawlings.com
Athletic Equipment, Apparel & Sporting Goods Mfr
N.A.I.C.S.: 339920
Michael Zlaket *(Pres)*

Subsidiary (Non-US):

Rawlings Canada Inc. **(2)**
131 Savanah Oak Dr, Brantford, N3V 1E8, ON, Canada
Tel.: (519) 750-1380
Web Site: http://www.rawlings.com
Sporting Goods Whslr
N.A.I.C.S.: 423910
Randy Beatty *(Gen Mgr)*

Subsidiary (Domestic):

Worth Inc. **(2)**
510 Maryville University Dr Ste 110, Saint Louis, MO 63141
Tel.: (314) 819-2800
Web Site: http://www.worthsports.com
Baseball & Softball Equipment Mfr
N.A.I.C.S.: 339920

THE SEMBLER COMPANY

5858 Central Ave St, Saint Petersburg, FL 33707
Tel.: (727) 384-6000
Web Site: http://www.sembler.com
Year Founded: 1962
Sales Range: $10-24.9 Million
Emp.: 100
Shopping Center Construction
N.A.I.C.S.: 236220
Brent Sembler *(Vice Chm)*
Greg Sembler *(Co-Chm)*
Craig Sher *(Co-Chm)*
Ron Wheeler *(CEO)*
Sue Harker *(VP-Property Mgmt)*
Sean Davis *(Chief Investment Officer)*
Steve Althoff *(Sr VP-Leasing & Property Mgmt)*
J. P. Guzzardo *(VP-Dev)*
Josh Beyer *(Sr VP-Dev)*
Jon Graber *(Mgr-Real Estate)*
Laurie Cable *(Dir-People & Culture)*

Subsidiaries:

Bay Walk **(1)**
Ste 310 146 2nd St N, Saint Petersburg, FL 33701-3361
Tel.: (727) 824-8888
Web Site: http://www.baywalkstpete.com
Shopping Complex
N.A.I.C.S.: 459910

THE SENIOR LIVING FOUNDATION INC

COMPANIES

THE SHURTLEFF & ANDREWS CORP.

4488 N Shallowford Rd Ste 103,
Dunwoody, GA 30338
Tel.: (770) 399-9988   GA
Year Founded: 2008
Sales Range: $10-24.9 Million
Emp.: 370
Elder Care Services
N.A.I.C.S.: 624120
Steve Pickin *(Chm)*
Winston Allen Porter III *(Mng Dir)*

THE SEYDEL COMPANIES
244 John B Brooks Rd, Pendergrass,
GA 30567
Tel.: (706) 693-2266   GA
Web Site: http://www.seydel.com
Year Founded: 1919
Sales Range: $75-99.9 Million
Emp.: 110
Holding Company; Manufacturers,
Developers & Marketers of Textile
Process Chemicals
N.A.I.C.S.: 424690
Maria White *(Controller)*
Steve Adams *(Pres)*

Subsidiaries:

Chemol Company, Inc.   (1)
2300 Randolph Ave, Greensboro, NC
27406-2908
Tel.: (336) 333-3050
Sales Range: $10-24.9 Million
Emp.: 30
Fat & Oil Related Chemicals
N.A.I.C.S.: 325180
William Newlin *(Product Mgr)*
Fred Willams *(Pres)*

Seydel International, Inc.   (1)
244 John B Brooks Rd, Pendergrass, GA
30567
Tel.: (706) 693-2266
Web Site: http://www.seydel.com
Supplier of Specialty Chemicals to International Textile & Paper Producer Mfr
N.A.I.C.S.: 424690

Seydel-Woolley & Company   (1)
244 John B Brooks Rd, Pendergrass, GA
30567
Tel.: (706) 693-2266
Web Site: http://www.seydel.com
Sales Range: $10-24.9 Million
Emp.: 40
Produce Processing Compounds for Textile
Mill Mfr
N.A.I.C.S.: 424690
Lynn Rose *(Pres)*

THE SHAMROCK COMPANIES INC.
24090 Detroit Rd, Westlake, OH
44145
Tel.: (440) 899-9510
Web Site:
http://www.shamrockcompanies.net
Sales Range: $50-74.9 Million
Emp.: 150
Business Forms
N.A.I.C.S.: 424120
Robert E. Troop *(Chm)*
Tim Connor *(CEO)*
Sai Totapally *(Dir-IT)*
Gary A. Lesjak *(CFO)*
Bob De Garmo *(Pres)*

Subsidiaries:

The Shamrock Company   (1)
24090 Detroit Rd, Westlake, OH 44145-1513
Tel.: (410) 238-0125
Web Site: http://www.shamrockacq.com
Sales Range: $25-49.9 Million
Printing Broker
N.A.I.C.S.: 561790

THE SHAND GROUP
1482 E Valley Rd Ste 474, Santa
Barbara, CA 93108
Tel.: (805) 969-1068
Web Site:
http://www.theshandgroup.com
Sales Range: $10-24.9 Million
Emp.: 30
Advertising Agencies
N.A.I.C.S.: 541810
Bobby Shand *(Pres & Principal)*
Chris Weakley *(Sr VP)*
Joe Long *(VP-Mktg)*
Angelique Rothermel *(VP-Client Svcs)*

THE SHAW GROUP INC.
4171 Essen Ln, Baton Rouge, LA
70809
Tel.: (225) 932-2500   LA
Web Site: https://theshawgrp.com
Year Founded: 1986
Prefab Piping Systems Mfr; Bending
& Shaping Steel Pipe; Specialty Pipe
Fittings; Design & Engineering Services; Industrial Building Construction
N.A.I.C.S.: 326122
Don Stokes *(Pres-Construction & Maintenance Grp)*
Mike Childers *(Pres & CEO)*

Subsidiaries:

Field Services, Inc.   (1)
135 Palm St, Canton, GA 30115
Tel.: (770) 345-9277
Web Site: http://www.fieldservices.com
Testing Laboratories
N.A.I.C.S.: 541380
Charm Derrick *(Office Mgr)*

KP Shaw, LLC   (1)
5575 Old Jacksonville Hwy, Tyler, TX
75703
Tel.: (903) 534-9155
Web Site: http://www.kpengineering.com
Engineeering Services
N.A.I.C.S.: 541330
William E. Preston *(Pres & CEO)*

Manufacturas Shaw South America,
C.A.
Zona Industrial Avenida Principal, Pimera
Etapa, Maracaibo, 4004, Venezuela
Tel.: (58) 2617360153
Emp.: 32
Engineeering Services
N.A.I.C.S.: 541330
Gianfranco Occupati *(Gen Mgr)*

Shaw Alloy Piping Products, LLC   (1)
740 N Market St, Shreveport, LA 71107
Tel.: (318) 674-9860
Sales Range: $25-49.9 Million
Emp.: 200
Mfr of Stainless, Alloy, Carbon, High Yield & Chrome Steel Fittings for the Power & Process Industries
N.A.I.C.S.: 332996
Ben Arnold *(Mgr)*

Shaw Environmental &
Infrastructure   (1)
13 British American Blvd Ste 1, Latham, NY
12110
Tel.: (518) 783-1996
Sales Range: $75-99.9 Million
Integrated Solid Waste Services
N.A.I.C.S.: 541690

Subsidiary (Domestic):

American Plastic Pipe and Supply,
L.L.C.   (2)
725 S Friendship Dr, New Concord, OH
43762   (100%)
Tel.: (740) 826-7900
Emp.: 15
Supplier of Pipe, Valves, Fittings, Specialty Items, Pumps & Pre-Fabricated Geomembrane Liners to the Landfill Industry
N.A.I.C.S.: 326122
Don Hershman *(Gen Mgr)*

LFG Specialties, L.L.C.   (2)
16406 E Us Route 224, Findlay, OH
45840   (100%)
Tel.: (419) 424-4999
Web Site: http://www.lfgspecialties.com
Landfill Gas Recovery Systems Designer & Mfr
N.A.I.C.S.: 333413

Shaw Group UK Limited   (1)
Stores Road, Derby, DE21 4BG,
Derbyshire, United Kingdom   (100%)
Tel.: (44) 1332 291122
Sales Range: $50-74.9 Million
Emp.: 100
Pipework Systems & Repair & Maintenance
Services Supplier
N.A.I.C.S.: 332996
Trevor Nuttall *(Mgr-Technical Svcs)*
Derek Shipley *(Mgr-Ops)*
Allan Latham *(Dir-Engrg)*

Subsidiary (Domestic):

The Shaw Group UK Pension Plan
Limited   (2)
Stores Road, Derby, DE21 4BG, United
Kingdom
Tel.: (44) 1332291122
Pension Funding
N.A.I.C.S.: 525110
Mark Phillips *(Mng Dir)*

Shaw Lancas, C.A.   (1)
Avenida Intercomunal, Ali Primera Judibana, Judibana, Estado Falcon, Venezuela
Tel.: (58) 2692460584
Engineering Services
N.A.I.C.S.: 541330

Shaw NAPTech, Inc.   (1)
210 E 700 S, Clearfield, UT 84015
Tel.: (801) 773-7300
Sales Range: $75-99.9 Million
Emp.: 350
Fabricator of Industrial Piping Systems &
Engineered Piping Modules
N.A.I.C.S.: 332996

Shaw Process Fabricators, Inc.   (1)
4150 S Sherwood Forest Blvd Ste 210, Baton Rouge, LA 70816-4605
Tel.: (318) 387-0212
Pipe Fabricator & Cold Bending Machine
Mfr
N.A.I.C.S.: 332996

Shaw SSS Fabricators, Inc.   (1)
7012 Hwy 1 S, Addis, LA 70710-2031
Tel.: (225) 749-3165
Structural Steel Fabrication
N.A.I.C.S.: 332312
Fachin Singh *(Gen Mgr)*
Jarrod Smith *(Project Mgr)*

THE SHEAKLEY GROUP
1 Sheakley Way Ste 100, Cincinnati,
OH 45246-3751
Tel.: (513) 771-2277
Web Site: http://www.sheakley.com
Sales Range: $10-24.9 Million
Emp.: 400
Benefit Administration & Consultation
For Workers Compensation, Managed Care For Workers Compensation, Unemployment & Pension
N.A.I.C.S.: 541612
Larry Sheakley *(CEO)*

THE SHELTERING ARMS
385 Centennial Olympic Park Dr, Atlanta, GA 30313
Tel.: (404) 523-2767   GA
Web Site:
http://www.shelteringarmsfor
kids.com
Year Founded: 1888
Sales Range: $25-49.9 Million
Emp.: 770
Child Educational Support Services
N.A.I.C.S.: 611710
Blythe Keeler Robinson *(Pres & CEO)*
DaShana Jelks *(VP-Fin)*
Martha Abbott-Shim *(Sec)*
Jeff Kammerer *(Chm)*
Helen Cease *(Treas)*
Leona Rapelye *(Vice Chm)*
Diane Bellem *(VP-Programs)*
Michael Davis *(VP-Strategic Initiatives & Partnerships)*
Norman Hill *(VP-HR)*
Michele Schmitt *(VP-Ops)*
Cristel Williams *(VP-Dev & Comm)*

THE SHEPHERD CHEMICAL COMPANY, INC.
4900 Beech St, Cincinnati, OH
45212-2316
Tel.: (513) 731-1110
Web Site: http://www.shepchem.com
Year Founded: 1916
Sales Range: $25-49.9 Million
Emp.: 205
Mfr of Industrial Inorganic Chemicals
N.A.I.C.S.: 325180
Tom Shepherd *(CEO)*

THE SHERIDAN GROUP INC
2045 Pontius Ave, Los Angeles, CA
90025
Tel.: (310) 575-0664
Web Site:
http://www.sheridaninc.com
Sales Range: $10-24.9 Million
Emp.: 35
Furniture Retailer
N.A.I.C.S.: 449110
Dannine Sheridan *(Pres)*
Terri Bianco *(VP)*

THE SHERWOOD GROUP, INC.
111 Deer Lake Rd Ste 100, Deerfield,
IL 60015
Tel.: (847) 480-9080   IL
Web Site: http://www.sherwood-group.com
Year Founded: 1979
Sales Range: $1-9.9 Million
Emp.: 82
Association Management Services
N.A.I.C.S.: 541611
John R. Waxman *(Pres)*
Richard Koepke *(Acct Exec)*
Gregory L. Schultz *(VP)*
Liz Freyn *(VP-Meeting & Convention Svcs)*
Scott M. Freeman *(CFO & COO)*
Jill Hronek *(Dir-Mktg Comm)*
Beth Kampner *(Dir-Info Sys)*
Kismet Saglam *(Dir-Education Svcs)*

THE SHIPYARD BREWING COMPANY
86 Newbury St, Portland, ME 04101
Tel.: (207) 761-0807
Web Site: http://www.shipyard.com
Year Founded: 1994
Sales Range: $10-24.9 Million
Emp.: 75
Brewery
N.A.I.C.S.: 312120
Fred Forsley *(Pres & Co-Owner)*
Alan Pugsley *(Master Brewer & Co-Owner)*
Bruce Forsley *(Dir-Sls & Mktg)*

THE SHURTLEFF & ANDREWS CORP.
1875 W 500 S, Salt Lake City, UT
84104-3508
Tel.: (801) 973-9096
Web Site: http://www.shurtleff-slc.com
Year Founded: 1949
Sales Range: $10-24.9 Million
Emp.: 5
Industrial Buildings & Warehouses
N.A.I.C.S.: 236210
Rich Mitchell *(Controller)*

Subsidiaries:

American Sales Company, Inc.   (1)
1845 W 500 S, Salt Lake City, UT
84104-3508   (100%)

THE SHURTLEFF & ANDREWS CORP.

The Shurtleff & Andrews Corp.—(Continued)
Tel.: (801) 973-8828
Sales Range: $10-24.9 Million
Emp.: 1
Provider of Industrial Machinery & Equipment
N.A.I.C.S.: 423830
Rich Mitchell (Controller)

THE SIEBENTHALER CO.
3001 Catalpa Dr, Dayton, OH 45405-1745
Tel.: (937) 274-1154 OH
Web Site:
http://www.siebenthaler.com
Year Founded: 1870
Sales Range: $1-9.9 Million
Emp.: 100
Landscape Nursery Services; Nursery Stock Retailer
N.A.I.C.S.: 561730
Robert J. Siebenthaler (Chm)
John Lee (Treas)
Jeff Siebenthaler (Pres)

THE SIEGEL GROUP
12080 Ventura Pl Ste A, Studio City, CA 91604
Tel.: (818) 255-3600 CA
Web Site:
http://www.siegelcompanies.com
Year Founded: 2001
Sales Range: $10-24.9 Million
Emp.: 200
Buys, Rehabilitates & Manages or Sells Commercial & Residential Properties
N.A.I.C.S.: 531390
Stephen Siegel (Co-Founder & CEO)
Ned L. Siegel (Co-Founder & Pres)
Chigozie Amadi (CFO)

THE SIEMON COMPANY
101 Siemon Company Dr, Watertown, CT 06795
Tel.: (860) 945-4200
Web Site: http://www.siemon.com
Year Founded: 1903
Sales Range: $25-49.9 Million
Emp.: 630
Mfr of Thermoformed Finished Plastic Products
N.A.I.C.S.: 326199
John A. Siemon (VP-Engrg)
Henry Siemon (Pres & CEO)
Charlie Maynard (Product Mgr-Fiber Optic)

THE SIGNAL GROUP, LLC
22285 Roethel Dr, Novi, MI 48375
Tel.: (248) 896-8587 MI
Web Site: http://www.solidsignal.com
Year Founded: 2002
Professional Media Equipment Retailer & Information Services
N.A.I.C.S.: 449210
Jerry Chapman (Founder)

THE SILVERCREST CENTER FOR NURSING AND REHABILITATION
144-45 87th Ave, Briarwood, NY 11435
Tel.: (718) 480-4000 NY
Web Site: http://www.silvercrest.org
Year Founded: 1990
Sales Range: $50-74.9 Million
Emp.: 604
Nursing Care Services
N.A.I.C.S.: 623110
Penny Blakely (Mgr)
Cynthia Alston (Mgr)
Adrienne Channer (Mgr)
Myrlene Michel (Mgr)
Margaret Farah (Mgr)
Nsini Udo (Coord-Clinical Care)
Ann Marie Phillips (Coord-Clinical Care)
Delita Lawrence (Coord-Clinical Care)
Andrea Gibbon (Coord-Clinical Care)
Clara Rankin-Gamboa (Coord-Clinical Care)

THE SIMON KONOVER COMPANY
342 N Main St Ste 200, West Hartford, CT 06117
Tel.: (860) 570-2000
Web Site:
http://www.simonkonover.com
Year Founded: 1957
Sales Range: $100-124.9 Million
Emp.: 600
Real Estate Owner, Developer & Investor
N.A.I.C.S.: 531311
James Wakim (Pres & COO)
Simon Konover (Founder)
Elizabeth G. Judd (Pres-Comml Corp)
Marie Mazzotta (Pres-Residential Corp)

Subsidiaries:
Konover Commercial Corporation (1)
342 N Main St, West Hartford, CT 06117
Tel.: (860) 570-2000
Commercial Real Estate Management & Construction
N.A.I.C.S.: 531312
Kathleen Waterman (Sr Mgr-Property)

Konover Hotel Corporation (1)
c/o Simon Konover Company 342 N Main St, West Hartford, CT 06117
Tel.: (860) 570-2000
Web Site: http://www.simonkonover.com
Home Management Services
N.A.I.C.S.: 531312
Peter H. Mason (Exec VP)

Konover Residential Corporation (1)
342 N Main St, West Hartford, CT 06117
Tel.: (860) 570-2000
Apartment Leasing & Management
N.A.I.C.S.: 531110

Konover South, LLC (1)
431 Fairway Dr, Deerfield Beach, FL 33441
Tel.: (954) 354-8282
Web Site: http://www.konoversouth.com
Emp.: 16
Real Estate Management & Development
N.A.I.C.S.: 531311
David Coppa (CEO)
Trey Patton (CFO)
Agustin Amaro (Dir-Construction)
Jacob E. Gerb (Gen Counsel)
Christopher Smith (Sr Mgr-Property)
Jeffrey Williams (Exec VP-Dev & Construction)

Simon Konover Development Corporation (1)
342 N Main St, West Hartford, CT 06117
Tel.: (860) 570-2000
Web Site: http://www.simonkonover.com
Emp.: 400
Commercial & Retail Development
N.A.I.C.S.: 237210
Bradford H. Wainman (Sr VP)

THE SINGER GROUP
1926 Greentree Rd, Cherry Hill, NJ 08003
Tel.: (856) 489-7380
Web Site:
http://www.thesingergroup.com
Sales Range: $10-24.9 Million
Emp.: 45
Merchandising Services to Military Personnel
N.A.I.C.S.: 424990
Evan Singer (Pres)

THE SISTERS OF THE THIRD ORDER OF ST. FRANCIS
530 NE Glen Oak Ave, Peoria, IL 61603-3100
Tel.: (309) 655-2645 IL
Web Site:
http://www.franciscansisterspeoria.org
Year Founded: 1877
Sales Range: $200-249.9 Million
Emp.: 5,000
Religious Organizations
N.A.I.C.S.: 813110
Rose Therese (Dir-Vocation)

Subsidiaries:
OSF HealthCare System (1)
800 NE Glen Oak Ave, Peoria, IL 61603-3200 (100%)
Tel.: (309) 655-2000
Web Site: http://www.osfhealthcare.org
Non-Profit Healthcare Organization; Hospitals, Long-Term Care Facilities & Nursing Colleges Operator
N.A.I.C.S.: 621610
Judith Ann Duvall (Chm)
Robert Sehring (CEO)
A. J. Querciagrossa (Pres)
Lois Bentler-Lampe (Chief Nursing Officer & VP-Clinical Ops)
Paul Arco (Coord-Media Rels-North)

THE SKI MARKET LTD. INC.
265 Winters St 2nd Fl, Waltham, MA 02451-1107
Tel.: (781) 890-1212 MA
Web Site: http://www.skimarket.com
Year Founded: 1958
Sales Range: $25-49.9 Million
Emp.: 200
Ski Specialty Shop
N.A.I.C.S.: 459110
Robert L. Ferguson (Chm & Treas)

THE SKY FACTORY, LC.
801 N 18th St, Fairfield, IA 52556
Tel.: (641) 472-1747
Web Site:
http://www.theskyfactory.com
Year Founded: 2002
Rev.: $3,900,000
Emp.: 34
SkyCeilings & Virtual Windows Mfr
N.A.I.C.S.: 238320
Bill Witherspoon (Founder)

THE SLANE COMPANY LLC
261 W Johnstown Rd, Columbus, OH 43230
Tel.: (614) 475-3331
Web Site:
http://www.theslanecompany.com
Sales Range: $10-24.9 Million
Emp.: 7
Commercial & Office Building Contractors
N.A.I.C.S.: 236220
Daniel M. Slane (Owner & Pres)

THE SMITH & OBY COMPANY
7676 Northfield Rd, Walton Hills, OH 44146
Tel.: (440) 735-5333 OH
Web Site:
http://www.smithandoby.com
Year Founded: 1898
Sales Range: $10-24.9 Million
Emp.: 80
Heating, Ventilation, Air Conditioning & Plumbing System Design, Fabrication, Installation & Contractor Services
N.A.I.C.S.: 238220
Ted E. Macfarlane (CFO & Treas)
Michael A. Brandt (Pres & CEO)
Jake Wattenbarger (Gen Mgr)

Subsidiaries:
The Smith & Oby Service Co. (1)
7676 Northfield Rd, Walton Hills, OH 44146
Tel.: (440) 735-5333
Web Site: http://www.smithandoby.com
Sales Range: $10-24.9 Million
Emp.: 20
Heating, Ventilation, Air Conditioning & Plumbing Maintenance Contractor Services
N.A.I.C.S.: 238220
Matthew P. Kittelberger (Gen Mgr)

THE SMITH CENTER
361 Symphony Park Ave, Las Vegas, NV 89106
Tel.: (702) 749-2012 NV
Web Site:
http://www.thesmithcenter.com
Year Founded: 1996
Sales Range: $25-49.9 Million
Emp.: 72
Art Center Operator
N.A.I.C.S.: 711310
Candy Schneider (VP-Education & Outreach)
Richard A. Johnson (VP)
Suzanne Chabre (VP-Mktg Comm)
Paul Beard (COO & VP)

THE SMITHERS GROUP
121 S Main St Ste 300, Akron, OH 44308
Tel.: (330) 762-7441
Web Site: http://www.smithers.com
Year Founded: 1925
Holding Company
N.A.I.C.S.: 551112
J. Michael Hochschwender (CEO)
Nathaniel Leonard (Pres-Rapra & Pira)
James Popio (VP-North America-Smithers Rapra)
Matt Kent (Dir-Technical-Smithers Rapra Tire & Wheel Test Center-Ravenna)
Susan Shepherd (Pres)
Michael A. Dorato (Exec VP-Avanza Toxicology Svcs)
Ira S. DuBey (Pres-Pharmaceutical Dev Svcs Div)
Jeanette Preston (Pres-Quality Assessments)
Rav Lally (Mng Dir-Information)
Mark Shackelford (Mgr-Bus Dev-Tire & Wheel-North America)
Meletios Roussis (Mgr-Bus Dev-Pharmaceutical Dev Svcs)
Glenn Goldney (Exec VP-Sls & Mktg)
Gus Zieske (VP-Environmental Risk Sciences-North America)

Subsidiaries:
Pira International Limited (1)
Cleeve Road, Leatherhead, KT22 7RU, United Kingdom
Tel.: (44) 1372802000
Web Site: http://www.smithers.com
Sales Range: $10-24.9 Million
Emp.: 90
Packaging, Paper & Print Industry Consulting Services
N.A.I.C.S.: 541618

Smithers Avanza (1)
15 Firstfield Rd, Gaithersburg, MD 20878
Tel.: (240) 364-6360
Web Site: http://www.smithersavanza.com
Sales Range: $10-24.9 Million
Emp.: 75
Drug Development Services
N.A.I.C.S.: 325412
Steven Godin (Chief Scientific Officer)
Carol S. Spicer (Exec Dir-Quality, Compliance & Support Svcs)
Robert L. Moore (Dir-Bus Dev-Bioanalytical Svcs)
Hope Aubin (Dir-Mktg)
Ira DuBey (Exec VP-Bioanalytical Svcs)
Nadia Kulagina (Dir-Science-Bioanalytical Svcs)
Brian Hoffpauir (Dir-Ops-Bioanalytical Svcs)
Lyric Boyle (Dir-Bus Dev-Smithers Avanza Toxicology Svcs)
Michael Dorato (Exec VP-Smithers Avanza Toxicology Svcs)

COMPANIES

Smithers Scientific Services, Inc. (1)
425 W Market St, Akron, OH 44303
Tel.: (330) 762-7441
Web Site: http://www.smithers-scientific.com
Sales Range: $25-49.9 Million
Emp.: 250
Product Testing Laboratories
N.A.I.C.S.: 541380

THE SMITHTOWN LIBRARY

1 N Country Road, Smithtown, NY 11787
Tel.: (631) 360-2480   NY
Web Site: http://www.smithlib.org
Year Founded: 2002
Sales Range: $10-24.9 Million
Emp.: 195
Library
N.A.I.C.S.: 519210
Robert Lusak (Dir-Library)
Anthony J. Monteleone (Pres)

THE SNYDER GROUP

9255 Doheny Rd, Los Angeles, CA 90069
Tel.: (310) 858-0444
Web Site: http://www.snyder-group.com
Year Founded: 1990
Sales Range: Less than $1 Million
Emp.: 2
N.A.I.C.S.: 541810
Art Snyder (Owner)

THE SNYDER GROUP, INC.

PO Box 1022, Kittanning, PA 16201
Tel.: (724) 548-8101   PA
Emp.: 445
Investment Holding Company
N.A.I.C.S.: 551112
David E. Snyder (Pres & CEO)

Subsidiaries:

Snyder Associated Companies, Inc. (1)
1 Glade Pk E, Kittanning, PA 16201
Tel.: (724) 548-8101
Sales Range: $650-699.9 Million
Emp.: 2,000
Holding Company; Natural Resource Mining, Construction & Horticulture
N.A.I.C.S.: 551112
Dan Boylestein (Controller)

Subsidiary (Domestic):

Allegheny Mineral Corporation (2)
1 Glade Pk E, Kittanning, PA 16201
Tel.: (724) 548-8101
Limestone Mining
N.A.I.C.S.: 212312
Charles H. Snyder Jr. (Chm)

C.H. Snyder Company (2)
1 Glade Park Dr, Kittanning, PA 16201
Tel.: (724) 548-8101
Web Site: http://www.snydercos.com
Sales Range: $25-49.9 Million
Emp.: 5
Bituminous Coal Mining
N.A.I.C.S.: 212115
Daniel Boylstein (Controller)

Snyder Brothers, Inc. (2)
1 Glade Park E, Kittanning, PA 16201
Tel.: (724) 548-8101
Web Site: http://www.snyderbrothersinc.com
Natural Gas & Crude Oil Extraction Natural Gas Marketing Services
N.A.I.C.S.: 211120

Affiliate (Domestic):

Sylvan Inc. (2)
90 Glade Dr, Kittanning, PA 16201
Tel.: (724) 543-3900
Web Site: http://www.sylvaninc.com
Sales Range: $100-124.9 Million
Emp.: 10
Fungal Technology Services
N.A.I.C.S.: 111411

Monir K. Elzalaki (Pres-Sylvan America)
Mark P. Wach (VP & Dir-Res)
Mark A. Snyder (Chm)
Mel O'Rourke (Mng Dir-Europe)

Subsidiary (Domestic):

The Bauer Company, Inc. (2)
119 Ruth Hill Rd, Worthington, PA 16262
Tel.: (724) 297-3200
Web Site: http://www.bauerblock.com
Concrete Block Mfr
N.A.I.C.S.: 327331

THE SOCIETY OF SAINT ANDREW, INC.

3383 Sweet Hollow Rd, Big Island, VA 24526-8517
Tel.: (434) 299-5956   VA
Web Site: http://www.endhunger.org
Year Founded: 1984
Rev: $17,028,070
Earnings: ($3,608)
Emp.: 55
Fiscal Year-end: 12/31/18
Hunger Relief Services
N.A.I.C.S.: 624210
Harriet Bryan (Sec)
Randy Beardsworth (Chm)
Sheila Carden (Vice Chm)

THE SOFTWARE CONSTRUCTION CO. INC.

1024 S Greenville Ave Ste 160, Allen, TX 75002
Tel.: (214) 495-7387   TX
Web Site: http://www.advanceddataspectrum.com
Year Founded: 1996
Sales Range: $10-24.9 Million
Emp.: 14
Data & Document Management Solutions
N.A.I.C.S.: 513210
Clint Carter (Pres)

Subsidiaries:

Peladon Software Inc. (1)
6050 Santo Rd Ste 140, San Diego, CA 92124
Tel.: (858) 300-0960
Web Site: http://www.peladonsoftware.com
Sales Range: $10-24.9 Million
Emp.: 8
Data Services Software Developer
N.A.I.C.S.: 334610

THE SOFTWARE DEVELOPMENT AND TESTING COMPANY, INC.

5114 Balcones Woods Dr Ste 307-406, Austin, TX 78759
Tel.: (512) 331-0222
Web Site: http://www.customdevelopmentandtesting.com
Sales Range: $1-9.9 Million
Software Developer & Other Computer Related Services
N.A.I.C.S.: 513210
Chris Maggio Jr. (Pres & CEO)

THE SOLUTIONSDEVELOPERS CORPORATION

45240 Business Crt Ste 400, Dulles, VA 20166
Tel.: (703) 471-8310
Web Site: http://www.armaturecorp.com
Year Founded: 2000
Rev: $3,100,000
Emp.: 25
Custom Computer Programming Services
N.A.I.C.S.: 541511

Jonathan Bransky (Mgr)
Irwin Lazar (Mgr)
Theodore Ritter (Mgr)
David McTaggart (VP)

THE SOMMERS COMPANY

1000 Sommers Blvd, Richmond Hill, GA 31324-8817
Tel.: (912) 756-5423
Year Founded: 1976
Sales Range: $10-24.9 Million
Emp.: 40
Gasoline & Grocery Services
N.A.I.C.S.: 457120
Jackie M. Sommers (Pres)

THE SOURCE, LLC

3637 N Lk Harbor Ln, Boise, ID 83703
Tel.: (208) 368-0520
Web Site: http://www.thesourcestore.com
Year Founded: 1999
Sales Range: $1-9.9 Million
Fashion Apparel & Accessory Retailer
N.A.I.C.S.: 458110
Mike Hodge (Founder & CEO)
Mike Brown (Partner)

THE SOURCING GROUP LLC

77 Water St, New York, NY 10005
Tel.: (646) 572-7520
Web Site: http://www.thesourcinggroup.com
Sales Range: $25-49.9 Million
Emp.: 50
Various Business Services
N.A.I.C.S.: 561499
Joseph Falcone (Pres)

THE SOUTH BEND CLINIC, LLP

211 N Eddy St, South Bend, IN 46617
Tel.: (574) 234-8161   IN
Web Site: http://www.southbendclinic.com
Sales Range: $75-99.9 Million
Emp.: 575
Real Estate Managers
N.A.I.C.S.: 621111
Paul Meyer (Exec Dir)
Lisa Wine (Controller)
LeAnne Goble (Sr Dir-HR)
Pat Wagner (Supvr-AR)

Subsidiaries:

Allied Physicians of Michiana, LLC (1)
130 S Main St Ste 250, South Bend, IN 46601-1817
Web Site: http://www.apom.com
Other Accounting Services
N.A.I.C.S.: 541219
Carol Mills (Mgr)

THE SOUTHERN MULCH COMPANY, LLC

2994 Fairfoest Clevedale Rd, Spartanburg, SC 29301
Tel.: (864) 587-1875   SC
Web Site: http://www.southernmulch.com
Year Founded: 2003
Sales Range: $10-24.9 Million
Mulch Products Distr
N.A.I.C.S.: 424910
Christian Swensen (Pres)
Richard Bruner (Mgr-Sls-Bulk Matls)

THE SOUTHWESTERN COMPANY

2451 Atrium Way, Nashville, TN 37214-5102
Tel.: (615) 391-2500   TN

Web Site: http://www.southwestern.com
Year Founded: 1855
Sales Range: $350-399.9 Million
Emp.: 788
Publisher & Sales of Reference Books
N.A.I.C.S.: 561990
Spencer Hays (Chm)
Dan Moore (Pres)
Lee McCroskey (Mgr-Mktg)
John Davis (Pres-Great American Opportunities)

Subsidiaries:

Great American Opportunities, Inc. (1)
2451 Atrium Way, Nashville, TN 37214
Web Site: http://www.southwesternfundraising.com
Fundraising Programs
N.A.I.C.S.: 926110
John Di Dio (Dir-Program)

THE SOWLES COMPANY

700 Canterbury Rd, Shakopee, MN 55379
Tel.: (651) 287-9700   MN
Web Site: http://www.sowles.com
Year Founded: 1961
Sales Range: $200-249.9 Million
Emp.: 200
Steel Erection Contractor
N.A.I.C.S.: 238120
Dan Sowles (CEO)
Sture Berg (Sec & VP-Admin)
Gary Lewerer (Pres & COO)
Sheila Stenseth (Treas & Controller)
Brian Kaufhold (Project Mgr)
Paul Jirik (Project Mgr)

Subsidiaries:

Northwest Tower Cranes (1)
700 Canterbury Rd, Shakopee, MN 55379-1840
Tel.: (952) 698-9735
Web Site: http://www.sowles.com
Emp.: 20
Tower Crane & Construction Elevator Rental Services
N.A.I.C.S.: 238990
Dan Sowles (CEO)

Sowles Company (1)
302 S 24th St, Billings, MT 59101-4325   (100%)
Tel.: (406) 248-4361
Web Site: http://www.sowles.com
Sales Range: $10-24.9 Million
Emp.: 60
Steel Erection Contractor
N.A.I.C.S.: 238120
Daniel C. Sowles (CEO)
John Dahl (Project Mgr)
Mark Fjosne (Project Mgr)
Richard Hellquist (Project Mgr)
Jonathan Hoback (Project Mgr)
Gary Lewerer (Pres)
Erik Paulson (Project Mgr)
Jake Treptau (Project Mgr)

Sowles Company (1)
2160 NE 240th Unit B, Wood Village, OR 97060   (100%)
Tel.: (503) 661-9693
Web Site: http://www.sowles.com
Sales Range: $25-49.9 Million
Steel Erection Contractor Services
N.A.I.C.S.: 238120
Chad Swanson (Project Mgr)
Brian Kaufhold (VP)
John Dahl (VP & Area Mgr)
Mark Fjosne (Superintendent-Field & Project Mgr)
Richard Hellquist (Superintendent-Field & Project Mgr)
Erik Paulson (Superintendent-Field & Project Mgr)
Dan Sowles (Pres & CEO-Midwest)
Jake Treptau (Superintendent-Field & Project Mgr)
Brian Riggs (Mgr-Rocky Mountain)

The Sowles Company—(Continued)

Valley Building Products Company (1)
302 S 24th St, Billings, MT 59101-4325
Tel.: (406) 252-2884
Sales Range: $10-24.9 Million
Emp.: 1
Engineering Consulting Services
N.A.I.C.S.: 541330
Brian Rigg (Gen Mgr)

THE SPARK AGENCY, INC.
6600 Manchester Ave, Saint Louis, MO 63139
Tel.: (314) 206-7700 — DE
Web Site: http://www.switch.us
Sales Range: $25-49.9 Million
Emp.: 130
Advetising Agency
N.A.I.C.S.: 541810
Michael O'Neill (CEO)
Ann Castellano (Chief Creative Officer)
Jeremy Lueders (Editor-Motion Graphics & Design)
Shelley Hibdon (Dir-HR)

THE SPECIALISTS INC.
4414 E Speedway Blvd, Tucson, AZ 85712
Tel.: (520) 326-2455
Web Site: http://www.az-specialists.com
Year Founded: 1986
Sales Range: $10-24.9 Million
Emp.: 80
Installer of Audio/Video for Automobiles & Home Theaters: Automotive Audio/Security Retailer
N.A.I.C.S.: 441330
Charles E. Weisel (Pres)
Debbie Weisel (Dir-Mktg)

THE SPEED ART MUSEUM
2035 S 3rd St, Louisville, KY 40208
Tel.: (502) 634-2700 — KY
Web Site: http://www.speedmuseum.org
Year Founded: 1933
Sales Range: $10-24.9 Million
Emp.: 104
Art Museum Operator
N.A.I.C.S.: 712110
David Cannon Knopf (CFO)
Steven Bowling (Dir-Mktg & Comm)
Michael Grisanti (Treas)
Martha Winans Slaughter (Chm)
Anne Taylor (Chief Engagement Officer)
Alan Kamei (Treas)
Brian Wells (Chief Dev Officer)

THE SPINX COMPANY INC.
1414 E Washington St, Greenville, SC 29607-1841
Tel.: (864) 233-5421 — SC
Web Site: http://www.myspinx.com
Year Founded: 1973
Sales Range: $50-74.9 Million
Emp.: 700
Gasoline Service Stations
N.A.I.C.S.: 457120
Stewart Spinks (Chm & CEO)
Steven Zisser (Controller)
Stan Storti (Pres)

THE SPORTS FACILITIES ADVISORY
600 Cleveland St Ste 910, Clearwater, FL 33755
Tel.: (727) 474-3845
Web Site: http://www.sportadvisory.com
Sales Range: $10-24.9 Million
Emp.: 25

Sports Management Consulting & Advisory Services
N.A.I.C.S.: 541618
Dev Pathik (Founder & CEO)
Jason Clement (Partner)
Eric Sullivan (Principal)
Evan Eleff (Partner & COO)
Karla Spivey (Mgr-HR)
Jack Adams (VP-Sports Facilities Mgmt)
Ashley Whittaker (VP-Bus Dev & Mktg)
Toney Vicars (CFO)

THE SPRINGS COMPANY
104 E Spring St, Lancaster, SC 29721
Tel.: (803) 286-3055 — SC
Web Site: http://www.springsco.com
Year Founded: 1887
Sales Range: $150-199.9 Million
Emp.: 20
Management Services Company
N.A.I.C.S.: 524210
Harry B. Emerson (Sr VP)

Subsidiaries:

S.E. Huffman Corp. (1)
1050 Huffman Way, Clover, SC 29710-1400
Tel.: (803) 222-4561
Web Site: http://www.huffman-llc.com
Sales Range: $25-49.9 Million
Mfr of Grinders, CNC, Lasers & Waterjet Cutting Systems
N.A.I.C.S.: 333517
Robert McBurney (VP-Admin & Controller)

Springfield Manufacturing LLC (1)
901 Ultra Dr, Clover, SC 29710-8653 (50%)
Tel.: (803) 222-9600
Web Site: http://www.scottspringfield.com
Sales Range: $10-24.9 Million
Waterjet Parts Production
N.A.I.C.S.: 333517
Mitchell O. Miller (Pres)

THE SQUIRES GROUP INC
608 Melvin Ave Ste 101, Annapolis, MD 21401-1369
Tel.: (410) 224-7779
Web Site: http://www.squiresgroup.com
Year Founded: 1994
Rev.: $21,100,000
Emp.: 115
Computer System Design Services
N.A.I.C.S.: 541512
Nancy Squires (CEO)
Eric Galasso (Pres)
Apurva Shah (Dir-Mktg & Ops)
Mike Parker (Controller)
Berry Sprague (Acct Mgr)
Tarry Lalonde (Mgr-Program-Mid Atlantic)
Paul Noble (Sr Mgr-Resource)

THE SSI GROUP, INC.
4721 Morrison Dr, Mobile, AL 36609
Tel.: (251) 345-0000
Web Site: http://www.thessigroup.com
Year Founded: 1988
Sales Range: $25-49.9 Million
Emp.: 335
Information Technology Services
N.A.I.C.S.: 541511
James M. Lyons (Pres & CEO)
Mark M. Blossom (Chief Data Ops Officer)
Eric Nilsson (CTO)
Mike Freeman (Chief Growth Officer)
Deborrah Short Rodrick (Chief Outcomes Officer)
Tom Turi (Chief Payer Officer)
Jay Colfer (COO)

THE ST. HENRY BANK

231 E Main St, Saint Henry, OH 45883
Tel.: (419) 678-2358 — OH
Web Site: http://www.sthenrybank.com
Year Founded: 1905
Sales Range: $10-24.9 Million
Emp.: 25
Banking Services
N.A.I.C.S.: 522110
John F. Romer (Chm & CEO)
David J. Romer (Pres)
Bonnie Garrison (Mgr-Maria Stein & Loan Officer)
Matt Lammers (Officer-Risk & Compliance)
Jaime Knapke (Head-Customer Svc)
Randy Bruns (Loan Officer)
Ryan C. Lange (Loan Officer)
Julie Uhlenhake (Supvr-Ops)
Chad Guggenbiller (Chief Relationship Officer)

THE ST. PETERSBURG FREE CLINIC, INC.
863 3rd Ave N, Saint Petersburg, FL 33701
Tel.: (727) 821-1200 — FL
Web Site: http://www.stpetersburgfreeclinic.org
Year Founded: 1970
Sales Range: $1-9.9 Million
Emp.: 39
Individual & Family Social Services & Medical Clinic
N.A.I.C.S.: 624190
Beth Houghton (Exec Dir)
Debbie Sokolov (Dir-Dev)
Gina Ruiz (Dir-Comm)
Hope Woodson (Dir-Health Center)
Jennifer Yeagley (CEO)

THE STAFFING GROUP LTD.
125 Townpark Dr Ste 300, Kennesaw, GA 30144
Tel.: (678) 881-0834 — NV
Web Site: http://www.staffinggroupltd.com
Year Founded: 2012
TSGL—(OTCBB)
Sales Range: $1-9.9 Million
Emp.: 14
Electromagnetic Field, Microwave, Electrical & Ionizing Detection Consulting Services
N.A.I.C.S.: 541690
Sam Leyva (Founder & CEO)
Michael Leyva (COO & Mgr-Payroll)
Sheila Leyva (Dir-Human Resources)

Subsidiaries:

EmployUS, LLC (1)
720 Clearview Pkwy Ste A, Metairie, LA 70001
Tel.: (504) 525-7944
Web Site: http://www.employusllc.com
Sales Range: $10-24.9 Million
Emp.: 3,000
Staffing Services
N.A.I.C.S.: 561311
Brent Callais (Pres)
Brian McLoone (COO)
John Guerineau (Controller)

THE STAFFING RESOURCE GROUP, INC.
405 N Reo St, Tampa, FL 33609
Tel.: (813) 872-7707
Web Site: http://www.srg-us.com
Year Founded: 2007
Sales Range: $1-9.9 Million
Emp.: 20
Staffing Services
N.A.I.C.S.: 561311
Britt Massing (Co-Founder & Pres)
Matt Spanke (Co-Founder & COO)
Chris Elam (CEO)

THE STAGE FUND, LLC
3000 Lawrence St Ste 124, Denver, CO 80205
Tel.: (720) 638-1642
Web Site: http://www.stagefund.com
Year Founded: 2009
Ventrue Capital & Private Equity Firm
N.A.I.C.S.: 523999
Daniel Frydenlund (Chm & CEO)
Ingrid Alongi (Gen Partner)

Subsidiaries:

Haystack Mountain Goat Dairy, Inc. (1)
1121 Colorado Ave Ste A, Longmont, CO 80501
Tel.: (720) 494-8714
Web Site: http://www.haystackgoatcheese.com
Sales Range: $1-9.9 Million
Emp.: 25
Goat Farming
N.A.I.C.S.: 112420
Chuck Hellmer (Pres & Gen Mgr)
John Scaggs (Dir-Sls & Mktg)

Needle, Inc. (1)
14864 Pony Express Rd, Bluffdale, UT 84065
Tel.: (801) 858-0868
Web Site: http://www.needle.com
Sales Range: $10-24.9 Million
Emp.: 70
Software Publisher
N.A.I.C.S.: 513210
Stephanie Walsh (VP-Community)
Tim Stewart (VP-Engrg)
Christian Matsumori (VP-Product)
Jeff Adcock (Sr VP-Strategic Alliances)
Scott Pulsipher (Pres & COO)
Kristen Knight (Sr VP-Client Success & Community)
Levi Miller (VP-Engrg)
Brandon Anderson (CEO)

Worklete, Inc. (1)
1423 Broadway Ste 134, Oakland, CA 94612
Web Site: http://www.worklete.com
Software Development Services
N.A.I.C.S.: 541511
Benjamin Kanner (Co-Founder & CEO)
John Leo Post (Co-Founder & VP-Product)
James Rowley (CTO)

THE STANLEY MEDICAL RESEARCH INSTITUTE
10605 Concord St Ste 206, Kensington, MD 20895
Tel.: (301) 571-0760 — MD
Web Site: http://www.stanleyresearch.org
Year Founded: 2001
Sales Range: $25-49.9 Million
Emp.: 22
Disease Research Services
N.A.I.C.S.: 813212
Shen Zhong (Mgr-Info Sys)
Maree J. Webster (Exec Dir)
E. Fuller Torrey (Assoc Dir-Research)

THE STANWICH CLUB, INC.
888 North St, Greenwich, CT 06831
Tel.: (203) 869-0555 — CT
Web Site: http://www.stanwich.com
Year Founded: 1963
Sales Range: $10-24.9 Million
Emp.: 184
Country Club
N.A.I.C.S.: 713910
Michael Summa (Dir-Golf)
Scott Niven (Mgr-Property)
Peter J. Tunley (COO & Gen Mgr)
Lori J. Stalowicz (Controller)

THE STAPLEX COMPANY, INC.
777 5th Ave, Brooklyn, NY 11232
Tel.: (718) 768-3333 — NY
Web Site: http://www.staplex.com
Year Founded: 1949
Sales Range: $50-74.9 Million

COMPANIES

Emp.: 20
Automatic Electric Stapling Machines & Electric Mail Openers Mfr
N.A.I.C.S.: 333310
Greg Pauls *(Mgr-Mktg & Adv)*

Subsidiaries:

Air Sampler Div. (1)
777 5th Ave, Brooklyn, NY 11232-1695
Tel.: (718) 768-3333
Web Site: http://www.staplex.com
Sales Range: $10-24.9 Million
Mfr of Air Sampling Equipment, Asbestos Air Samplers
N.A.I.C.S.: 333413
Doug Butler *(VP-Sls)*

THE STAR-JOURNAL PUBLISHING CORP.

825 W 6th St, Pueblo, CO 81003
Tel.: (719) 544-3520
Web Site: http://www.chieftain.com
Sales Range: $10-24.9 Million
Emp.: 256
Commercial Printing & Newspaper Publishing Combined
N.A.I.C.S.: 513110
Robert Hudson *(Mgr-Adv)*
Marvin Laut *(Gen Mgr)*

THE STARCO GROUP, INC.

3137 E 26th St, Vernon, CA 90058
Tel.: (323) 266-7111   CA
Web Site:
  http://ww.thestarcogroup.com
Year Founded: 1973
Sales Range: $1-9.9 Million
Emp.: 75
Industrial Machinery Mfr
N.A.I.C.S.: 333248
John Burnett *(VP-Starco Enterprises)*
Ross Sklar *(CEO)*
Darin Brown *(Exec VP-Ops)*

Subsidiaries:

Chase Products Co. (1)
19th St Gardner Rd, Broadview, IL 60153
Tel.: (708) 865-1000
Web Site: http://www.chaseproducts.com
Rev: $7,500,000
Emp.: 38
Farm Machinery & Equipment Mfr
N.A.I.C.S.: 333111
Carl Svendsen *(Founder)*

THE STARFISH FOUNDATION

PO Box 3696, Wichita Falls, TX 76301
Tel.: (940) 631-1985   TX
Web Site:
  http://www.thestarfishfoundation.net
Year Founded: 2007
Sales Range: $1-9.9 Million
Welfare Service Centers
N.A.I.C.S.: 624190
Dennis J. Cady *(Founder)*

THE STEAMSHIP AUTHORITY

1 RailRd Ave, Woods Hole, MA 02543
Tel.: (508) 548-5011
Web Site:
  http://www.steamshipauthority.com
Sales Range: $50-74.9 Million
Emp.: 550
Provider of Intraport Transportation Services
N.A.I.C.S.: 483212
Carl R. Walker *(Dir-Maintenance & Engrg)*
Mark Rozum *(Treas & Comptroller)*
Steven M. Sayers *(Gen Counsel)*
Robert B. Davis *(Gen Mgr)*
Sean F. Driscoll *(Dir-Comm)*
Alison Fletcher *(Dir-Shoreside Ops)*
Mark Amundsen *(Dir-Marine Ops)*

THE STELLAR GROUP INC.

2900 Hartley Rd, Jacksonville, FL 32257-8221
Tel.: (904) 260-2900   FL
Web Site: http://www.stellar.net
Year Founded: 1985
Sales Range: $500-549.9 Million
Emp.: 640
Construction Engineering & Architectural Services
N.A.I.C.S.: 236220
Michael S. Santarone *(Pres & COO)*
Todd Allsup *(VP-Corp Sls)*
Phil Hinrichs *(VP-Risk Mgmt)*
Richard Lovelace *(Sr VP-Comml Svcs)*
Clint Pyle *(CFO & Sr VP)*
Brian E. Kappele *(Exec VP-Food & Beverage Facility Svcs)*
Michael Wodrich *(Gen Counsel & Sr VP)*
Jeff D. Williams *(Sr VP-Refrigeration Svcs)*
Scott Mark *(Sr VP-Food Mfg & Logistics)*
Wyatt Payne *(VP-Field Svcs, Quality & Safety Grp)*
Ronald H. Foster Jr. *(Chm & CEO)*

Subsidiaries:

Star Fabricators (1)
2989 Imeson Park Blvd, Jacksonville, FL 32218
Tel.: (904) 260-2900
Construction Manufacturing Services
N.A.I.C.S.: 332312

Stellar Energy Americas, Inc. (1)
3015 Hartley Rd, Jacksonville, FL 32257
Tel.: (904) 260-2044
Emp.: 90
Construction Engineering Services
N.A.I.C.S.: 541330
Curtis Lovelace *(VP-Project Dev)*
Alan Culpepper *(Gen Mgr)*
Jason Combs *(Controller)*
Craig Kedrowski *(VP-Ops-Global)*
Malcolm Koros *(Mgr-Engrg)*
Steve Hawkins *(VP-Svcs-Global)*
Peter Gibson *(CEO)*
Mark Jones *(Dir-Application Engrg)*

Stellar Energy Asia (1)
2/F No 2 Nongzhanguan, Beili Chaoyang District, Beijing, 100125, China
Tel.: (86) 10 6462 0909
Energy Consulting Services
N.A.I.C.S.: 541690

Stellar Energy MENA (1)
Business Central Towers Tower B 3802, PO Box 49434, Dubai Media City, Dubai, United Arab Emirates
Tel.: (971) 4 454 8530
Energy Consulting Services
N.A.I.C.S.: 541690

THE STEPHENS GROUP, LLC

100 River Bluff Dr Ste 500, Little Rock, AR 72202
Tel.: (501) 377-3401
Web Site:
  http://www.stephensgroup.com
Year Founded: 1933
Privater Equity Firm
N.A.I.C.S.: 523999
Ronald M. Clark *(COO)*
Elizabeth Stephens Campbell *(Founder & Co-Chm)*
Craig D. Campbell *(Vice Chm)*
Robert L. Schulte *(CFO)*
W. Kent Sorrells *(Mng Dir)*
Aaron Clark *(Mng Dir)*
Tim Trzebiatowski *(VP)*
Debbie Evans Blough *(Chief Admin Officer & VP)*
Christopher E. Kauffman *(VP-Fin & Acctg)*
Grant Jones *(Mng Dir)*
Mark Steenhoek *(Principal-Ops)*
Witt Stephens *(Co-Chm & CEO)*
Allie Laborde *(Principal-Bus Dev)*
Jens Talbert *(VP)*
Whit Kilgroe *(Gen Counsel)*
Bobby L. Martin *(Operating Partner)*

Subsidiaries:

Kele, Inc. (1)
3300 Brother Blvd, Memphis, TN 38133
Tel.: (877) 826-9045
Web Site: http://www.kele.com
Building Automation Products Distr
N.A.I.C.S.: 238210
Richard Campbell *(Exec Chm)*
Danny Lyons *(CEO)*
Rob Benson *(Pres-Comml)*
Mike DeLacluyse *(Pres-Industrial)*

Subsidiary (Domestic):

Lesman Instrument Company (2)
135 Bernice Dr, Bensenville, IL 60106
Tel.: (630) 595-8400
Web Site: http://www.lesman.com
Sales Range: $10-24.9 Million
Emp.: 33
Distr; Process Control Instrument
N.A.I.C.S.: 334519
Mike DeLacluyse *(Pres)*

Micontrols Inc. (2)
6516 5th Pl S, Seattle, WA 98108
Tel.: (206) 767-0140
Web Site: http://www.micontrols.com
Warm Air Heating Equipment & Supplies
N.A.I.C.S.: 423730
Steve Roe *(Pres)*
Randy Sneesby *(Acct Exec-Comml Products)*
Siao Ling Kok *(Controller)*
Tom Bissonnette *(Acct Exec-Comml Products)*

Temperature Control Systems, Inc. (2)
10315 Brockwood Rd, Dallas, TX 75238
Tel.: (214) 343-1444
Web Site:
  http://www.temperaturecontrolsystems.net
Wholesales Temperature Control Systems
N.A.I.C.S.: 423730

Pearlman Group (1)
3950 Steve Reynolds Blvd, Norcross, GA 30093
Tel.: (800) 969-5561
Metal Cutting Tools, Stone Fabrication Tools & Equipment
N.A.I.C.S.: 333120
Dan Davidenko *(CEO)*

Division (Domestic):

GranQuartz, L.P. (2)
3950 Steve Reynolds Blvd, Norcross, GA 30093
Tel.: (770) 621-9777
Web Site: http://www.granquartz.com
Hardware Stores
N.A.I.C.S.: 444140
Jerry Ramirez *(Sls Mgr-South Central District)*
David Coy *(Branch Mgr)*

Subsidiary (Domestic):

Power Rental & Sales, LLC. (2)
3653A Trousdale Dr, Nashville, TN 37204-4518
Tel.: (615) 837-1450
Web Site: http://www.prsconcrete.com
Sales Range: $1-9.9 Million
Emp.: 15
Contractor Equipment & Supply Distr
N.A.I.C.S.: 423810
Brent Cornelius *(Co-Founder)*
John McCarthy *(Co-Founder)*

vXchnge Holdings, LLC (1)
1580 W. Cleveland St, Tampa, FL 33606
Web Site: http://www.vxchnge.com
Software Mfr & Data Center Services
N.A.I.C.S.: 423430
Keith Olsen *(Chm & CEO)*
George Pollock *(CFO, Treas & Sr VP)*
Ali Marashi *(CTO & Sr VP-Engrg)*
Charles Browning *(Sr VP-Ops)*
Ernest Sampera *(Sr VP-Sls & Mktg)*
Tom Banta *(Sr VP-Product Mgmt & Dev)*

THE STEPHENZ GROUP, INC.

75 E Santa Clara St Ste 900, San Jose, CA 95113-1319
Tel.: (408) 286-9899
Web Site: http://www.stephenz.com
Year Founded: 1981
Sales Range: $10-24.9 Million
Emp.: 28
Advertising Agencies, Brand Development, Business-To-Business, Full Service, High Technology, Interactive Agencies, Internet/Web Design, Strategic Planning/Research
N.A.I.C.S.: 541810
Barbara E. Zenz *(Pres & CEO)*
Stephanie Paulson *(VP & Dir-Creative)*
Barbara Sater *(VP-Strategic Svcs)*
Jan Knight *(Grp Acct Dir)*
Judy Jordan *(Bus Dev Mgr)*
Angela Diffly *(Sr PR Supvr)*
Scott Brendel *(Sr Acct Mgr)*
Phillip Kim *(Assoc Dir-Creative)*
Meitra Chahidi *(Mgr-Media)*

THE STERLING GROUP, L.P.

9 Greenway Plz Ste 2400, Houston, TX 77046-0909
Tel.: (713) 877-8257   TX
Web Site: http://www.sterling-group.com
Year Founded: 1982
Privater Equity Firm
N.A.I.C.S.: 523940
John D. Hawkins *(Partner)*
Gary L. Rosenthal *(Partner)*
Kent Wallace *(Partner)*
Christopher Ahearn *(Operating Partner-Comml)*
Gregory L. Elliott *(Partner)*
Brian Henry *(Partner)*
Bradley Staller *(Partner)*
Erin M. Arnold *(Mng Dir)*
Gary H. Torgow *(Founder & Chm)*

Subsidiaries:

Apply-A-Line, LLC (1)
175 Roy Rd SW Bldg C, Pacific, WA 98047
Tel.: (253) 299-1200
Web Site: http://www.applyaline.com
Pavement Marking Services
N.A.I.C.S.: 237310
Terry Buol *(Treas & Sec)*
Mike Liljestrom *(Pres)*

Aquatic Co. (1)
1521 N Cooper Ste 500, Arlington, TX 76011
Tel.: (800) 945-2726
Web Site: http://www.aquaticbath.com
Bathware & Shower Products Mfr
N.A.I.C.S.: 326191
Mike Hasey *(Reg Sls Mgr-Northwest)*
Mike Pugh *(Reg Sls Mgr-Pacific Southwest)*
Kevin Brown *(Reg Sls Mgr-Midwest)*
Jeremy Sharpe *(Reg Sls Mgr-Southwest)*
George Stewart *(Reg Sls Mgr-Southeast)*
Harry Schaefer *(Reg Sls Mgr-Mideast)*
Chuck Stoebe *(Reg Sls Mgr-Northeast)*

Artisan Design Group, LLC (1)
3401 Olympus Blvd, Ste 450, Dallas, TX 75019
Tel.: (682) 324-9402
Web Site: http://www.artisandesigngroup.us
Holding Company; Flooring Designer, Retailer & Contractor
N.A.I.C.S.: 551112
Steven N. Margolius *(CEO)*
Dan Shear *(CFO)*
Doug Davis *(Pres, COO & VP-Sls)*

Subsidiary (Domestic):

Arlun, Inc. (2)
6250 Corporate Dr, Colorado Springs, CO 80919-1979
Tel.: (719) 599-4175
Web Site: http://www.arlun.com
Floor Laying Services
N.A.I.C.S.: 238330

Atlanta West Carpets, LLC (2)
1850 Westfork Dr, Lithia Springs, GA 30122

THE STERLING GROUP, L.P.

The Sterling Group, L.P.—(Continued)
Tel.: (770) 941-1700
Web Site: http://www.atlwest.com
Floor Covering Stores
N.A.I.C.S.: 449121

Builders Alliance LLC (2)
3801 Hannegan Rd, Bellingham, WA 98226
Tel.: (360) 738-9000
Web Site: http://www.buildersalliance.com
Clay Building Material & Refractories Mfr
N.A.I.C.S.: 327120
Mark Hopkins *(Project Mgr)*
Drew Orem *(Co-Pres)*
Mike Werner *(Co-Pres)*

Distinctive Kitchens & Baths, Inc. (2)
1217 Clint Moore Rd, Boca Raton, FL 33487
Tel.: (561) 997-9400
Web Site: http://www.distinctivekb.com
Sales Range: $10-24.9 Million
Emp.: 36
Kitchens & Baths
N.A.I.C.S.: 337110
Adam Canter *(Pres)*
Rene Travieso *(Dir-Ops)*
Phil Ackerman *(Dir-Sls)*

Dixie Carpet Installations Inc. (2)
13510 S Gessner, Missouri City, TX 77489
Tel.: (281) 261-6334
Web Site: http://www.dixiecarpet.com
Carpet & Upholstery Cleaning Services
N.A.I.C.S.: 561740

Floors Inc. (2)
200 Bank St, Southlake, TX 76092
Tel.: (817) 421-8787
Web Site: http://www.floorsinc.com
Flooring Coverings Designer, Retailer & Installation Services
N.A.I.C.S.: 423220
Ron Johnson *(CFO)*
Larry Barr *(Pres & CEO)*

Great Floors, LLC (2)
524 E Sherman Ave, Coeur D'Alene, ID 83814
Tel.: (208) 765-6014
Web Site: http://www.greatfloors.com
Sales Range: $125-149.9 Million
Emp.: 20
Flooring Contractors
N.A.I.C.S.: 238330
Doug Chadderdon *(Pres)*
Ken Chadderdon *(VP)*
Jim McGee *(Co-Founder & CFO)*
Jim McKay *(VP-Sls & Dir-Multifamily Sls)*
Mike Nelson *(COO)*
Teresa Gavin *(Dir-Mktg)*
L. John Parker *(Dir-Insurance Sls & Svc)*
Curt Shewmake *(Dir-Store Ops)*
Debbie Tott *(Dir-Trng)*
Will Osborne *(Sr VP-Ops)*

Images Flooring, Inc. (2)
1820 W Evans Ave, Englewood, CO 80110
Tel.: (303) 937-9221
Web Site: http://www.imagesflooring.com
Poured Concrete Foundation & Structure Contractors
N.A.I.C.S.: 238110

Malibu Acceptance Corp. (2)
2077 N Collins Blvd Ste 100, Richardson, TX 75080
Tel.: (972) 422-9013
Flooring Installation Contractor
N.A.I.C.S.: 238330
Wayne Joseph *(Pres & CEO)*

Markraft Cabinets Inc. (2)
2705 Castle Creek Ln, Wilmington, NC 28401-5840
Tel.: (910) 793-0202
Web Site: http://www.markraft.com
Cabinets, Kitchen
N.A.I.C.S.: 444180
Joseph Jacobus *(Chm & CEO)*
Cee Edwards *(Pres & Gen Mgr)*

Metro Carpets, LLC (2)
1525 Elm Hill Pike, Nashville, TN 37210
Tel.: (615) 228-6477
Web Site: http://www.metrocarpets.com
Home Furnishing Whslr
N.A.I.C.S.: 449129

Nonn's Flooring Inc. (2)
7550 Graber Rd, Middleton, WI 53562
Tel.: (608) 836-8833
Web Site: http://www.nonns.com
Floor Laying & Floor Work
N.A.I.C.S.: 238330
Jeff Nehmer *(Mgr-Comml Sls)*
Adam Nonn *(CEO)*

Pacific Carpets, Inc. (2)
17752 Metzler Ln, Huntington Beach, CA 92647-6245
Tel.: (714) 842-9115
Web Site: http://www.pacificcarpets.com
Flooring Contractors
N.A.I.C.S.: 238330
Fred Ferrari *(CEO)*

Value Plus Flooring, Inc. (2)
3109 Neil Armstrong Blvd, Saint Paul, MN 55121
Tel.: (651) 454-9344
Web Site: http://www.valueplusflooring.com
Building Finishing Contractors
N.A.I.C.S.: 238390
Dana Johnson *(Sr Project Mgr)*

Vintage Design Inc. (2)
25200 Commercentre Dr, Lake Forest, CA 92630
Tel.: (949) 900-5400
Web Site: http://www.vintagedesigninc.com
Flooring Contractors
N.A.I.C.S.: 238330
Timothy Buckley *(Founder)*

WCCV Floor Coverings, LLC (2)
4535 State Rd, Peninsula, OH 44264
Tel.: (330) 688-0114
Web Site: http://www.wccv.com
Flooring Products Design & Installation Services
N.A.I.C.S.: 449121

Aurora Jet Center (1)
14357 Keil Rd NE, Aurora, OR 97002
Tel.: (503) 678-1336
Web Site: http://www.aurorajetcenter.com
Rev: $1,010,000
Emp.: 10
Other Airport Operations
N.A.I.C.S.: 488119
Josh Lewis *(Mgr)*

Capitol Wholesale Fence Company, Inc. (1)
1200 Lebanon Pike, Nashville, TN 37210
Tel.: (615) 244-4923
Web Site: http://www.capitolwholesale.com
Ornamental & Architectural Metal Work Mfr
N.A.I.C.S.: 332323
Lisa Harrison *(CEO)*
Chad Mitchell *(Branch Mgr)*
David Cuffman *(Branch Mgr)*
Greg Adams *(Branch Mgr)*
Ron McClurg *(Branch Mgr)*

Construction Supply Group (1)
800 E Union Ave Ste 110, Denver, CO 80237
Tel.: (877) 426-7337
Web Site: http://www.constructionsupplygroup.com
Construction Materials, Accessories & Tools Distr
N.A.I.C.S.: 423390
Mitch Wiliams *(Pres & CEO)*
Tom Leahy *(Sr VP-Supplier Relationship & Dev)*
John Vanderberg *(Sr VP-Integration & Special Projects)*
Lisa Scinta *(Sr VP-Ops)*
Mike Lang *(Sr VP-Bus Dev)*
Shane Dryanski *(Sr VP-Project Mgmt)*
Greg Hanson *(CFO)*
Kevin Brown *(CIO)*

Subsidiary (Domestic):

All-Tex Supply Inc. (2)
3351 N Pan Am Expressway, San Antonio, TX 78219
Tel.: (512) 837-0977
Web Site: https://www.whitecap.com
Other Construction Material Merchant Whslr
N.A.I.C.S.: 423390
Donald Hendrix *(Gen Mgr)*

Best Materials, LLC (2)
2338 N 33rd Ave, Phoenix, AZ 85009
Tel.: (602) 272-8128

Web Site: http://www.bestmaterials.com
Lumber, Plywood, Millwork & Wood Panel Merchant Whslr
N.A.I.C.S.: 423310

Border Construction Specialties, LLC (2)
3880 E Broadway Rd, Phoenix, AZ 85040
Tel.: (602) 437-1900
Web Site: http://www.bordercorp.com
Construction Materials Distr
N.A.I.C.S.: 423320
Brian Saker *(Pres & CEO)*
Andy Anderson *(Mgr-Border Tucson)*
Ryan Gearhart *(Mgr-Border Flagstaff)*
Ricardo Yvellez *(Mgr-Border El Paso)*
Barry Correll *(VP-Ops)*

Subsidiary (Domestic):

Carter-Waters LLC (3)
6803 W 64th St Ste 300 Bldg 6, Overland Park, KS 66202
Tel.: (816) 471-2570
Web Site: http://www.carter-waters.com
Emp.: 500
Construction Materials, Accessories & Tools Distr
N.A.I.C.S.: 423710
Tim Cadden *(VP-Sls-Heavy Highway)*

Stetson Building Products, LLC (3)
2205 Bell Ave, Des Moines, IA 50321
Tel.: (515) 243-6286
Web Site: http://www.stetsonbuildingproducts.com
Emp.: 115
Construction Product Distr
N.A.I.C.S.: 423320
John Willmore *(CFO)*
Marte Cook *(Pres)*
Vicky Strand *(Mktg Mgr)*
Dean Cooper *(VP-Sls)*

Williams Equipment & Supply Company (3)
3821 New Getwell Rd, Memphis, TN 38118
Tel.: (901) 775-2275
Web Site: http://www.williamsequipment.com
Construction & Mining Machinery
N.A.I.C.S.: 423810
Gregg McIntyre *(Pres & CEO)*
Gordon McIntyre *(Pres & CEO)*
Jeff Hayes *(Mgr-Purchasing)*
Daniel Smith *(Dir-Ops)*
Mike Wainscott *(Mgr-Credit)*

Subsidiary (Domestic):

Brock White Company LLC (2)
2575 Kasota Ave, Saint Paul, MN 55108-1504
Tel.: (651) 647-0950
Web Site: http://www.brockwhite.com
Emp.: 100
Construction & Building Materials Distr
N.A.I.C.S.: 423320
Brian Hanson *(Dir-Ops & Safety Compliance)*
Dennis Ehlert *(Dir-Mktg)*
Ted McArthur *(Treas & VP-Fin)*
George White *(VP-Sls & Mktg)*
Jane Gilbert *(Mgr-HR)*

Construction Materials Ltd. (2)
4350 Northern Blvd, Montgomery, AL 36110
Tel.: (334) 272-8200
Web Site: http://www.constructionmaterialsltd.com
Sales Range: $25-49.9 Million
Emp.: 133
Provider of Lumber, Plywood & Millwork Services
N.A.I.C.S.: 423310
John Crews *(Pres)*
Greg Crews *(VP)*
David Cahoon *(Mgr-Birmingham-Alabama)*
Mike Elmore *(Controller)*

Holdfast Technologies, LLC (2)
12026 Lower Vly Pike, Medway, OH 45341
Tel.: (877) 423-2562
Web Site: http://www.holdfast.com
Construction Materials Whslr
N.A.I.C.S.: 423390
Daniel J. Hilty *(Founder)*

Hub Construction Specialties, Inc. (2)
379 S I St, San Bernardino, CA 92410-2409

Tel.: (909) 889-0161
Web Site: http://www.hubhasit.com
Construction & Mining Services
N.A.I.C.S.: 423810
Robert Gogo *(Pres)*
Dave Bukowski *(Mgr-Rental)*
John Warren *(Mgr-Sls)*
Stan Gilson *(Mgr-Sls)*
Tom Holod *(Mgr-Ops)*

Masonpro, Inc. (2)
43300 7 Mile Rd, Northville, MI 48167
Tel.: (248) 347-3824
Web Site: http://www.masonpro.com
Foundation, Structure & Building Exterior Contractors
N.A.I.C.S.: 238190

Spec West, Inc. (2)
3855 Taylor Rd, Loomis, CA 95650
Tel.: (916) 660-0140
Web Site: https://www.whitecap.com
Sheet Metal Work Mfg
N.A.I.C.S.: 332322

Titan Construction Supply, Inc. (2)
250 Edison Way, Reno, NV 89502
Tel.: (775) 351-2201
Web Site: https://www.whitecap.com
Building Material Dealers
N.A.I.C.S.: 444180

Destin Jet (1)
1001 Airport Rd, Destin, FL 32541-2915
Tel.: (850) 424-6890
Web Site: http://www.destinjet.com
Emp.: 25
Airport Operations
N.A.I.C.S.: 488119
Greg Donovan *(Mgr)*

Elkhart Brass Manufacturing Company, Inc. (1)
1302 W Beardsley Ave, Elkhart, IN 46514
Tel.: (574) 295-8330
Web Site: http://www.elkhartbrass.com
Sales Range: $10-24.9 Million
Firefighting Apparatus Mfr
N.A.I.C.S.: 332999
Gregg Brennecke *(VP-Ops)*
Eric Combs *(VP-Product Dev Div)*
Sean O'Connell *(VP-Fin Div)*
Scott Warbritton *(VP-Indus Sls Div)*
Troy Turley *(Dir-Info Sys)*
Ray Bell *(Mgr-Southeast)*
Rachele Benn *(Coord-Event)*
Mike Dupay *(VP-Mktg Div)*
Bill Haushalter *(VP-Bus Dev Div)*
Chris Martin *(Mgr-Municipal Product)*
Toh Meng *(VP-Emergency & Indus)*
Jim North *(Mgr-Corp Commodity)*
Tim Pratt *(Mgr-Strategic Sourcing)*
Norbe Puroll *(Mgr-Central)*
Paul Albinger Jr. *(Dir-Sls)*

Enovate Medical, LLC (1)
1152 Park Ave, Murfreesboro, TN 37129
Tel.: (618) 896-1652
Web Site: https://www.enovatemedical.com
Retails Mobile & Wall-Mounted Clinical Workstations & Other Point-of-Care Products to Health Care Industries
N.A.I.C.S.: 335999
Doug Gallacher *(VP-Sls)*
Bob Brolund *(CEO)*
Dan R. Jandura *(VP-Ops)*
Mark Dalen *(VP-Tech)*
Kevin Bridges *(VP-Mktg & Bus Dev)*
Kim Trapp *(VP-HR)*

Ergotron, Inc. (1)
1181 Trapp Rd, Saint Paul, MN 55121-1325
Tel.: (651) 681-7600
Web Site: http://www.ergotron.com
Ergonomic Mounting & Mobility Products for Computers Mfr
N.A.I.C.S.: 334118
Craig Thomas *(VP-Mfg & Ops)*
Jim Orrock *(VP-Product Dev)*
David Denham *(VP-Mktg-Global)*
Charles Christ *(CTO)*
Chad Severson *(CEO)*
Peter Martin *(VP-North America-Sls)*
Lisa Nied *(VP-Ops)*
Jason Schlicht *(VP-Ergotron Custom)*
Mike Schaefer *(VP-Engrg & Innovation)*
Dena Mayne *(CMO)*
Phil Kelaart *(Exec VP-Supply Chain Ops-Global)*
David Kemp *(Chief Sls Officer & Exec VP)*

COMPANIES

Subsidiary (Non-US):

Ergotron Nederland B.V. (2)
Beeldschermweg 3, 3821 AH, Amersfoort, Netherlands **(100%)**
Tel.: (31) 334545600
Web Site: http://www.ergotron.com
Computer & Equipment Stands Mfr
N.A.I.C.S.: 423430
Jonathan Pyenson (Sr VP-EMEA Bus Ops)
Kleopatra Kivrakidou (Mktg Mgr-Channel-EMEA)

Fence Supply, Inc. (1)
435 E Highway 80, Mesquite, TX 75182
Tel.: (972) 226-0004
Web Site: http://www.fencesupplyinc.com
Sales Range: $1-9.9 Million
Emp.: 10
Lumber, Plywood, And Millwork, Nsk
N.A.I.C.S.: 423310
Freddie C. Brown (Founder & CEO)
Christopher S. Brown (Pres)

Merchants Metals, Inc. (1)
400 N Sam Houston Pkwy E Ste 1200, Houston, TX 77060
Tel.: (281) 372-3800
Web Site: http://www.merchantsmetals.com
Sales Range: $600-649.9 Million
Emp.: 1,140
Fence & Gate Products Mfr & Distr
N.A.I.C.S.: 332618
Andrea Hogan (CEO)

North American Industrial Services, Inc. (1)
1240 Saratoga Rd, Ballston Spa, NY 12020
Tel.: (518) 885-1820
Web Site: http://www.naisinc.com
Sales Range: $1-9.9 Million
Emp.: 300
Industrial Cleaning Services
N.A.I.C.S.: 333248
Jon Hodges (Founder, Chm & CEO)

PK Contracting, Inc. (1)
1965 Barrett Dr, Troy, MI 48084
Tel.: (248) 362-2130
Web Site: http://www.pkcontracting.com
Sales Range: $1-9.9 Million
Emp.: 50
Painting/Paper Hanging Contractor
N.A.I.C.S.: 238320
Chris Shea (CEO)
Aden Shea (VP)

Polychem Corporation (1)
6277 Heisley Rd, Mentor, OH 44060
Tel.: (800) 548-9557
Web Site: http://www.polychem.com
Sales Range: $25-49.9 Million
Strapping Machines Mfr
N.A.I.C.S.: 316990
Brian Jeckering (Pres & CEO)

Randall Manufacturing, LLC (1)
722 Church Rd, Elmhurst, IL 60126
Tel.: (630) 782-0001
Web Site: http://www.randallmfg.com
Rev.: $9,700,000
Emp.: 60
All Other Motor Vehicle Parts Mfr
N.A.I.C.S.: 336390

Stripe-A-Zone, Inc. (1)
2714 Sherman St, Grand Prairie, TX 75051
Tel.: (972) 647-2714
Web Site: http://www.stripe-a-zone.com
Sales Range: $10-24.9 Million
Emp.: 45
Painting & Wall Covering Contractors
N.A.I.C.S.: 238320
David Q. Sargent (Pres)
Chuck Dratwick (Mgr-Ops)
Danny Wood (Gen Mgr)
Jim Blanchat (Asst Mgr-Production)
Jay Green (Project Mgr)
Laurie Schroeder (Office Mgr)
Adam Ross (Mgr-Sls)
Kevin Kelly (Mgr-East Texas)

Subsidiary (Domestic):

Griffin Pavement Striping, Inc. (2)
2383 Harrison Rd, Columbus, OH 43204
Tel.: (614) 276-2622
Web Site: http://www.griffinpavementstriping.com
Foundation, Structure & Building Exterior Contractors
N.A.I.C.S.: 238190
Shawn Bremer (Sr Project Mgr)

Time Manufacturing Company (1)
7601 Imperial Dr, Waco, TX 76702-0368
Tel.: (254) 399-2100
Web Site: http://www.timemfg.com
Vehicle-Mounted Aerial Lift Designer, Mfr & Distr
N.A.I.C.S.: 333998
Don Fratus (Dir-Customer Svc)
Jack Jeffrey (Dir-Sls-North & South America)
Paul B. Rugh (Dir-Strategic Accts)
Charles Wiley (CEO)

Subsidiary (Domestic):

Versalift Northwest, LLC. (2)
3770 Brooklake Rd, Salem, OR 97305
Tel.: (971) 701-2500
Web Site: https://northwest.versalift.com
Electric Utility, Telecommunications, Tree care, Municipal & Contractor Fleet Services
N.A.I.C.S.: 237130

Subsidiary (Domestic):

Aspen Aerials, Inc. (3)
4303 W 1st St, Duluth, MN 55807
Tel.: (218) 624-1111
Web Site: http://www.aspenaerials.com
Bridge Specialty Equipment Mfr
N.A.I.C.S.: 333248

MAP Rentals, Inc. (3)
614 E Hanover Rd, Graham, NC 27253
Tel.: (336) 228-1722
Construction & Mining Equipment Whslr
N.A.I.C.S.: 423810

West Star Aviation LLC (1)
2 Airline Ct, East Alton, IL 62024
Web Site: http://www.weststaraviation.com
Aircraft Maintenance & Repair Services
N.A.I.C.S.: 488190
Marty Rhine (VP-Sls)
Rodger Renaud (Pres)
Kraig Meyer (Dir-EHS)
Debi Cunningham (VP-Mktg)
Matthew DeLellis (CFO)
Vince Ruscitti (Program Mgr-Govt Affairs)
Jim Rankin (CEO)
Allen McReynolds (COO)

Subsidiary (Domestic):

Avant Aerospace, LLC (2)
720 Industrial Blvd Ste 500, Grapevine, TX 76051-8642
Tel.: (817) 416-0110
Web Site: http://avantaero.org
Transportation Equipment Whslr
N.A.I.C.S.: 423860
Stephanie Simpson (Office Mgr)
Peter McKerman (Sr VP-Parts)
John Hardy (Dir-Aerospace)
Jay Roever (Sls Mgr)
Danny Hoosier (Mgr-Materials)
Laura Strauss (Mgr-Mktg)

Jet East Corporate Aviation, LLC (2)
18 W Piper Ave, Trenton, NJ 08628
Tel.: (215) 937-9020
Web Site: http://www.jeteastgama.com
Engineeering Services
N.A.I.C.S.: 541330

THE STEVEN STYLE GROUP
106 W 32nd St Ste 600, New York, NY 10001
Tel.: (212) 465-1290
Web Site: http://www.stylegroup.com
Sales Range: Less than $1 Million
Emp.: 5
N.A.I.C.S.: 541810
Steven Style (Pres & CEO)

THE STEVENS & LEE COMPANIES, LLC
111 N 6th St, Reading, PA 19601
Tel.: (610) 478-2000 **PA**
Web Site:
https://www.stevenslee.com
Year Founded: 2024
Holding Company; Legal, Investment Banking, Financial Advisory & Government Consulting Services
N.A.I.C.S.: 551112

Subsidiaries:

Stevens & Lee, P.C. (1)
111 N 6th St, Reading, PA 19603-0679
Tel.: (610) 478-2000
Web Site: http://www.stevenslee.com
Sales Range: $100-124.9 Million
Emp.: 280
Law firm
N.A.I.C.S.: 541110
Joseph M. Harenza (Chm)
Ernie Choquette (Pres)

THE STOLLER GROUP
7401 SW Washo Ct Ste 200, Tualatin, OR 97062-8343
Tel.: (503) 612-1414 **OR**
Web Site:
http://www.expresspersonel.com
Year Founded: 1982
Sales Range: $10-24.9 Million
Emp.: 190
Human Resource Solutions
N.A.I.C.S.: 561320
William H. Stoller (Vice Chm & Pres)
Suzanne Meyers (Mgr-Credit)
Merrilyn MaGee (Coord-Front Office)
Julie Moore (Acct Mgr)

THE STONE GROUP, INC.
1025 Thimblegate Ct, Johns Creek, GA 30022
Tel.: (770) 361-1870 **GA**
Web Site: http://www.stonegroup-inc.com
Year Founded: 1999
Sales Range: $1-9.9 Million
Information Technology Systems Design & Consulting Services
N.A.I.C.S.: 541512
Thomas Neal Stone (Founder & CEO)

THE STRATFORD-CAMBRIDGE GROUP CO.
1058 Maple St Ste 200, Plymouth, MI 48170
Tel.: (734) 667-3867 **MI**
Web Site:
http://www.stratfordcambridgegroup.com
Year Founded: 1953
Investment Services
N.A.I.C.S.: 523940
Steve Ellis (Mng Dir)

Subsidiaries:

Fluid Air Controls LLC (1)
32613 Folsom, Farmington Hills, MI 48336 **(100%)**
Tel.: (248) 478-3330
Web Site: http://www.flairline.com
Emp.: 15
Pneumatic & Light Duty Hydraulic Cylinders & Components Mfr
N.A.I.C.S.: 333995
Pete Coulder (VP)

Speedgrip Chuck, Inc. (1)
2000 Industrial Pkwy, Elkhart, IN 46516
Tel.: (574) 294-1506
Web Site: http://www.speedgrip.com
Precision Workholding Equipment Mfr
N.A.I.C.S.: 333515
James Runyon (Mgr-Sls)
Barry Neilson (Dir-Engrg)

Division (Domestic):

Cameron (2)
200 E Industrial Pkwy, Elkhart, IN 46515
Tel.: (574) 294-1506
Web Site: http://www.speedgrip.com
Precision Workholding Equipment Mfr
N.A.I.C.S.: 333515

THE STRAWHECKER GROUP, LLC
11605 Miracle Hills Dr Ste 302, Omaha, NE 68154
Tel.: (833) 690-1301 **NE**
Web Site: https://thestrawgroup.com
Emp.: 100
Management Consulting Services
N.A.I.C.S.: 541618

Subsidiaries:

Global Netwatch, Inc. (1)
10846 Old Mill Rd, Omaha, NE 68154
Tel.: (402) 333-5900
Web Site: http://www.globalnetwatch.com
Rev.: $2,232,000
Emp.: 12
Data Processing, Hosting & Related Services
N.A.I.C.S.: 518210
Bradley Mellott (Chm & CEO)

THE STRIP DEVELOPMENT, INC.
1812 W Sunset Blvd, Saint George, UT 84770
Tel.: (435) 619-3638 **UT**
Land Developer
N.A.I.C.S.: 237210
Alexandra Green (Treas & Sec)
Adrian Morrisette (Chm & Pres)

THE STRONG
1 Manhattan Sq Dr, Rochester, NY 14607
Tel.: (585) 263-2700 **NY**
Web Site:
http://www.museumofplay.org
Year Founded: 1968
Sales Range: $10-24.9 Million
Emp.: 348
Museums
N.A.I.C.S.: 712110
Steven Dubnik (Pres & CEO)

THE STUDY ABROAD FOUNDATION
1100 W 42nd St Ste 385, Indianapolis, IN 46208
Tel.: (317) 925-2943 **IN**
Web Site:
http://www.studyabroadfoundation.org
Year Founded: 2000
Sales Range: $10-24.9 Million
Emp.: 11
Educational Support Services
N.A.I.C.S.: 611710
Mary Ann Stanley (Mgr-Acct Bus)
Chris Hartley (Mgr-Student Acct)
Carol Carmody (Exec Dir)
David Gray (Chm & Co-CEO)
John Belcher (Pres & Co-CEO)
Thomas Roberts (Sec)
Molly Carmody (Coord-Program)
Daniel Shen (Dir-SAF Mainland China)
Dominique Luthringer (Dir-SAF Taiwan)
Zach Simon (Coord-Program)
Brett Rumminger (Dir-SAF Japan)
Henry Oh (Dir-SAF Mainland China)

THE STURGESS COMPANY
901 Dover Dr Ste 110, Newport Beach, CA 92660-5514
Tel.: (949) 646-3879 **CA**
Year Founded: 1990
Sales Range: $10-24.9 Million
Emp.: 5
Advetising Agency
N.A.I.C.S.: 541810
John C. Sturgess (Pres)
Robert Brocke (Creative Dir)
Doug Henry (Art Dir)
Mary Thomas (PR Dir)

THE STURM FINANCIAL GROUP, INC.

The Sturgess Company—(Continued)

THE STURM FINANCIAL GROUP, INC.
3033 E 1st Ave Ste 200, Denver, CO 80206
Tel.: (303) 394-5005
Web Site: http://www.anbbank.com
Banking Services
N.A.I.C.S.: 525920
Donald Sturm *(Chm)*
Susan Sturm *(Vice Chm)*

Subsidiaries:

ANB Bank (1)
3033 E First Ave, Denver, CO 80206
Tel.: (303) 394-5100
Web Site: http://www.anbbank.com
Rev: $72,433,000
Assets: $2,057,632,000
Liabilities: $1,879,683,000
Net Worth: $177,949,000
Earnings: $11,760,000
Emp.: 503
Fiscal Year-end: 12/31/2013
State Commercial Banks
N.A.I.C.S.: 522110
Koger L. Propst *(CEO)*
Donald Sturm *(Chm)*
Susan Sturm *(Vice Chm, CFO & Exec Officer)*
Matthew Baldner *(Pres-Denver Metro)*
David Wright *(Pres-Boulder Banking Center)*
Tom Ashley *(Pres-Southern Colorado)*
Kevin Paintner *(Pres-Wyoming)*
Scott Peterson *(Pres-Food & Agribus)*
Vance A. Wagner *(Pres-Western Colorado)*

Community First Data Services (1)
3033 E First Ave, Denver, CO 80206
Tel.: (303) 394-5100
Web Site: http://www.anbbank.com
Sales Range: $10-24.9 Million
Emp.: 20
Data Processing & Financial Preparation Services
N.A.I.C.S.: 518210
Donald Sturm *(Chm & CEO)*
Steve Griego *(CIO)*
John Fiedler *(Reg Pres)*

THE SU-DAN CORPORATION
1853 Rochester Industrial Ct, Rochester Hills, MI 48309-3336
Tel.: (248) 651-6035
Web Site: http://www.su-dan.com
Year Founded: 1966
Sales Range: $10-24.9 Million
Emp.: 260
Precision Metal Stampings, Technical Plastic Insert, Injection & Over Molding, Welding, Riveting, Staking, Spinning & Assembly
N.A.I.C.S.: 336370
Sandra Heins *(Mgr-Customer Svc)*

THE SUDDATH COMPANIES
815 S Main St, Jacksonville, FL 32207-9050
Tel.: (904) 390-7100
Web Site: http://www.suddath.com
Year Founded: 1919
Sales Range: $400-449.9 Million
Emp.: 1,630
Moving & Relocation Services
N.A.I.C.S.: 484210
Stephen M. Suddath *(Pres)*
Elizabeth Spradley *(Sr VP-HR)*
James G. Barnett *(Treas & VP)*
Barry S. Vaughn *(Vice Chm)*
Michael J. Brannigan *(Pres & CEO)*
Frank P. Senatore *(Pres-Network Ops)*
Len O'Neill *(CIO & Sr VP)*
Mark Scullion *(Pres-Workplace Solutions)*
Darren Cook *(VP & Gen Mgr-Los Angeles)*
Joanna Aman *(Chief Compliance Officer, Gen Counsel & VP)*
Steve Von Oetinger *(VP & Gen Mgr-Miami)*
Mark Burchell *(Chief Comml Officer)*
Bob Fruchterman *(Sr VP-Intl Logistics)*
Kevin Gannon *(CFO & Exec VP)*
Tom Ruede *(VP-Sls)*
Barbara Suddath Strickland *(Sec & VP)*
Scott Kelly *(Pres-Govt Svcs)*
Scott Perry *(COO-Moving & Logistics)*
Brad Liddie *(Sr VP-Global Logistics)*

Subsidiaries:

Centra Worldwide, Inc. (1)
3030 Old Ranch Pkwy Ste 400, Seal Beach, CA 90740-2752 (100%)
Tel.: (714) 903-3520
Web Site: http://www.centraworld.com
Sales Range: $10-24.9 Million
Emp.: 25
Web-Based Distribution & Logistics Management Programs
N.A.I.C.S.: 541511

Lexicon Relocation (1)
815 S Main St, Jacksonville, FL 32207-9050
Tel.: (904) 858-1255
Web Site: http://www.temporarylodging.com
Sales Range: $10-24.9 Million
Emp.: 30
Relocation Services
N.A.I.C.S.: 488510
Bob Packard *(VP-Ops)*
Carole Thompson *(VP & Gen Mgr)*
Robert Giese *(Dir-Bus Tech Integration)*
Kevin Russell *(Sr VP-Client Engagements)*
Andrew J. Brombosz *(VP-Global Bus Dev)*
Spring Zhou *(Dir-Asia Pacific)*
Avrom Goldberg *(Mng Dir & Sr VP-Asia Pacific & EMEA)*
Craig Donovan *(Sr VP-Global Network Integration & Real Estate Svcs)*
Fadia Kek *(Sr VP-Ops & Client Svcs)*
Judi Coffey *(VP-Client Svcs-Cincinnati)*
Debbie Maupin *(Sr VP-Global Sls)*

Subsidiary (Non-US):

Lexicon Relocation Ltd. (2)
James House 27-35 London Road, Newbury, RG14 1JL, Berkshire, United Kingdom
Tel.: (44) 1635271271
Web Site: http://www.lexiconrelocation.com
Relocation Services
N.A.I.C.S.: 488510
Damon Ward *(Mng Dir-EMEA & VP-Client Svcs)*
Richard Lucas *(Dir-Bus Dev-EMEA)*

PenserSC (1)
11001 Pritchard Rd, Jacksonville, FL 32219
Tel.: (904) 345-3956
Web Site: http://www.suddath.com
Logistics Consulting Services
N.A.I.C.S.: 541614
Melissa Davis *(Coord-Logistics)*
Regina Raulerson *(Dir-Customer Svc)*

Sentry Household Shipping Inc (1)
815 S Main St, Jacksonville, FL 32207-9050
Tel.: (904) 858-1200
Web Site: http://www.suddathinternational.com
Sales Range: $25-49.9 Million
Emp.: 200
Moving & Relocation Services
N.A.I.C.S.: 488510
Stephen Crooks *(Pres)*

Suddath Global Logistics, LLC (1)
161 W Victoria St Ste 220, Long Beach, CA 90805
Tel.: (310) 762-2676
Web Site: http://www.suddathlogistics.com
Logistics Consulting Services
N.A.I.C.S.: 541614
Tom Ruede *(VP-Sls)*
Daniel DeSoto *(Pres)*
Sam Sharp *(Sr VP-Contract Logistics)*
Bob Fruchterman *(Sr VP-Intl Logistics)*
Bob Thomas *(Exec VP-Ops-North America)*

Suddath Relocation Systems Inc (1)
815 S Main St, Jacksonville, FL 32207-1802
Tel.: (904) 390-7100
Web Site: http://www.suddath.com
Sales Range: $25-49.9 Million
Emp.: 210
Transport & Storage of Household Goods
N.A.I.C.S.: 484210
Barry S. Vaughn *(CEO)*
Tim Evans *(VP & Gen Mgr)*
Scott O'Neill *(VP-Sls-Pacific Northwest)*
Joanna Aman *(Gen Counsel & VP)*
Michael J. Brannigan *(Pres & CEO)*
Elizabeth Spradley *(Sr VP-HR)*

Subsidiary (Domestic):

Suddath Relocation Systems of Arizona LLC (2)
3600 E 36th St, Tucson, AZ 85713
Tel.: (520) 720-0130
Web Site: http://www.horizonmoves.com
Sales Range: $25-49.9 Million
Emp.: 200
Moving & Relocation Services
N.A.I.C.S.: 484110
Rick Shelley *(Dir-Sls)*
Troy Mannan *(VP & Gen Mgr)*

Branch (Domestic):

Suddath Relocation Systems of Arizona - Phoenix (3)
1717 E Rairdan Ln, Phoenix, AZ 85034
Tel.: (602) 910-3054
Web Site: http://www.horizonmoves.com
Moving & Relocation Services
N.A.I.C.S.: 484210
Paula Olson *(Coord-Natl Accts)*

Subsidiary (Domestic):

Suddath Relocation Systems of Atlanta, Inc. (2)
2600 Pinemeadow Ct, Duluth, GA 30096
Tel.: (770) 872-0844
Web Site: http://www.suddath.com
Emp.: 100
Logistics Consulting Services
N.A.I.C.S.: 541614
Chris Perry *(VP & Gen Mgr)*

Suddath Relocation Systems of Charlotte, LLC (2)
1520 Tar Heel Rd, Charlotte, NC 28208
Tel.: (704) 820-4348
Web Site: http://www.suddath.com
Logistics Consulting Services
N.A.I.C.S.: 541614
Monty Miller *(VP & Gen Mgr)*

Suddath Relocation Systems of Ft. Lauderdale, Inc. (2)
1900 SW 43rd Ter, Deerfield Beach, FL 33442
Tel.: (954) 596-4000
Web Site: http://www.suddathftlauderdale.com
Emp.: 50
Household Goods Moving Services
N.A.I.C.S.: 484210
Steve Suddath *(Pres)*

Suddath Relocation Systems of Houston, Inc. (2)
5301 Polk St Bldg 14, Houston, TX 77023
Tel.: (713) 924-6999
Web Site: http://www.suddathhouston.com
Logistics Consulting Services
N.A.I.C.S.: 541614
Paul Drury *(Asst Gen Mgr)*

Suddath Relocation Systems of Maryland, Inc. (2)
1710 Crossroads Dr, Odenton, MD 21113
Tel.: (410) 874-1010
Web Site: http://www.suddathmaryland.com
Emp.: 50
Logistics Consulting Services
N.A.I.C.S.: 541614

Suddath Relocation Systems of Milwaukee, LLC (2)
N8 W22270 Johnson Dr, Waukesha, WI 53186
Tel.: (262) 347-4518
Emp.: 75
Logistics Consulting Services

U.S. PRIVATE

N.A.I.C.S.: 541614
Mike Hansen *(Gen Mgr)*

Suddath Relocation Systems of Minnesota, LLC (2)
7100 Washington Ave S, Eden Prairie, MN 55344
Tel.: (612) 213-3887
Web Site: http://www.suddathrelocation.com
Logistics Consulting Services
N.A.I.C.S.: 541614

Subsidiary (Domestic):

Suddath Relocation Systems of the Twin Cities, LLC (3)
7100 Washington Ave S, Eden Prairie, MN 55344-3512
Tel.: (952) 944-6550
Web Site: http://www.barrettmoving.com
Emp.: 60
Trucking & Storage Services
N.A.I.C.S.: 484210
Randy Koepsell *(Pres)*
Laura Langer *(Mgr-HR)*
John Orme *(VP-Sls)*

Subsidiary (Domestic):

Suddath Relocation Systems of Northern California, LLC (2)
2071 Ringwood Ave Ste D, San Jose, CA 95131
Tel.: (408) 600-0005
Web Site: http://www.suddath.com
Emp.: 200
Logistics Consulting Services
N.A.I.C.S.: 541614
Gene Kopecky *(Pres)*

Suddath Relocation Systems of Oregon LLC (2)
9611 NE Sunderland Rd, Portland, OR 97211
Tel.: (503) 288-6565
Web Site: http://www.suddathrelocation.com
Emp.: 35
General Freight Trucking & Warehousing Services
N.A.I.C.S.: 484121
Tim Evans *(VP & Gen Mgr)*
Scott O'Neill *(VP-Sls-Pacific Northwest)*

Suddath Relocation Systems of Orlando, Inc. (2)
4850 L B McLeod Rd, Orlando, FL 32811
Tel.: (407) 843-6683
Web Site: http://www.suddathorlando.com
Logistics Consulting Services
N.A.I.C.S.: 541614
B B Flynn *(Asst Gen Mgr)*

Suddath Relocation Systems of St. Petersburg, Inc. (2)
4756 122nd Ave N, Clearwater, FL 33762
Tel.: (727) 573-0000
Web Site: http://www.suddathtampa.com
Logistics Consulting Services
N.A.I.C.S.: 541614
Gary Paul *(Gen Mgr)*

Suddath Relocation Systems of Texas, Inc. (2)
1990 N State Hwy 360, Grand Prairie, TX 75050
Tel.: (972) 660-5600
Web Site: http://www.suddathdallas.com
Emp.: 100
Logistics Consulting Services
N.A.I.C.S.: 541614
Kathy Meredith *(Coord-Move)*

Suddath Van Lines Inc. (2)
8743 Western Way, Jacksonville, FL 32256
Tel.: (904) 256-5540
Web Site: http://www.suddath.com
Sales Range: $25-49.9 Million
Emp.: 75
Moving & Relocation Services
N.A.I.C.S.: 484210
Roy Hines *(Gen Mgr)*

Division (Domestic):

Suddath Van Lines, Inc. - Kent (3)
7819 S 206th St, Kent, WA 98032
Tel.: (253) 518-8800
Web Site: http://www.suddathrelocation.com
Emp.: 65
Freight Truck Operator

N.A.I.C.S.: 484121
Jay Keen (Gen Mgr)

Suddath Transportation Services, Inc. (1)
815 S Main St, Jacksonville, FL 32207 (100%)
Tel.: (904) 858-1234
Sales Range: $10-24.9 Million
Emp.: 25
Freight Forwarding, Logistics, Warehousing & Multimodal Transportation
N.A.I.C.S.: 488510
Bob Thomas (Exec VP-North American Ops)
Peggy Kemery (Controller)
Tom Ruede (VP-Sls)
Daniel DeSoto (Pres)

Withers/Suddath Van Lines, Inc. (1)
6900 NW 74th Ave, Miami, FL 33166-2825 (100%)
Tel.: (305) 885-8161
Web Site: http://www.suddath.com
Sales Range: $10-24.9 Million
Emp.: 33
Moving Services
N.A.I.C.S.: 484121
Rick Noel (Gen Mgr)

THE SUN BELT CONFERENCE
1500 Sugar Bowl Dr, New Orleans, LA 70112
Tel.: (504) 299-9066 LA
Web Site:
http://www.sunbeltsports.org
Year Founded: 1976
Sales Range: $10-24.9 Million
Emp.: 13
Sport Event Organizer
N.A.I.C.S.: 711310
Kathy Keene (COO)
Scott Connors (Dir-Compliance)
Travis Llewellyn (Dir-Electronic Media)
Herbert L. Carter III (CFO)
Dominick Giambrone Jr. (Dir-Championships)

THE SUNDT COMPANIES, INC.
2015 W River Rd Ste 101, Tucson, AZ 85704
Tel.: (520) 750-4600 AZ
Web Site: http://www.sundt.com
Year Founded: 1890
Sales Range: $700-749.9 Million
Emp.: 1,350
Holding Company; Commercial, Institutional, Industrial & Infrastructure Engineering Construction Services
N.A.I.C.S.: 551112
David S. Crawford (CEO)
Mike Hoover (Pres)
Dan Haag (Chief Admin Officer & Sr VP)
Kevin M. Burnett (CFO & Sr VP)
Ronald R. Stuff (Gen Counsel, Officer-Corp Compliance & Sr VP)
Tom Case (COO, Exec VP & Mgr-Civil Grp)

Subsidiaries:

Sundt Construction, Inc. (1)
2620 S 55th St, Tempe, AZ 85282-1903 (100%)
Tel.: (480) 293-3000
Web Site: http://www.sundt.com
Sales Range: $50-74.9 Million
Emp.: 697
Commercial, Institutional, Industrial & Infrastructure Engineering Construction Services
N.A.I.C.S.: 237990
Daniel Haag (Chief Admin Officer & Sr VP)
Rich Keil (Pres-Industrial Grp)
Ron R. Stuff (Officer-Compliance, Gen Counsel & Sr VP)
Ian McDowell (VP & Dir-Tucson Reg)
Teri Jones (Pres-Building Grp)
James Geer (Sr VP & Mgr-Pub Private Partnership Grp)
Ed Segovia (VP & Dir-Gen Contractor's Building Grp-California)
Nathan Griggs (Engr-Civil Project)
Brian Van Vleet (Project Mgr-Civil)

Branch (Domestic):

Sundt Construction, Inc. - Irvine Office (2)
41 Corporate Park Ste 310, Irvine, CA 92606
Tel.: (949) 468-5309
Web Site: http://www.sundt.com
Emp.: 10
Commercial, Institutional, Industrial & Infrastructure Engineering Construction Services
N.A.I.C.S.: 237990

Sundt Construction, Inc. - Sacramento Office (2)
2850 Gateway Oaks Dr Ste 450, Sacramento, CA 95833-4334
Tel.: (916) 830-8000
Web Site: http://www.sundt.com
Sales Range: $10-24.9 Million
Emp.: 30
Commercial, Institutional, Industrial & Infrastructure Engineering Construction Services
N.A.I.C.S.: 237990
Dan Haag (Chief Admin Officer & Sr VP)
Paul Sprecco (Mgr-Safety-Building Grp)
Ed Segovia (VP & Reg Dir-General Contractor's Building Grp)
Tim Spence (VP & Reg Dir-Northern California)
Nicolas Cho (Engr-Field)
Arthur Yurov (Engr-Field)
Dorian Martinez (Engr-Field)

Sundt Construction, Inc. - San Antonio Office (2)
911 Central Pkwy N Ste 375, San Antonio, TX 78232
Tel.: (210) 276-2760
Commercial, Institutional, Industrial & Infrastructure Engineering Construction Services
N.A.I.C.S.: 237990
Teri Jones (Pres-Building Grp)
Joe Dooley (VP & Reg Mgr-Transportation)
Amber Simonson (Project Mgr-Building Grp-Fort Worth)

Sundt Construction, Inc. - San Diego Office (2)
1660 Hotel Cir N Ste 400, San Diego, CA 92108
Tel.: (619) 321-4800
Web Site: http://www.sundt.com
Sales Range: $100-124.9 Million
Commercial Commercial Industrial & Infrastructure Engineering Construction Services
N.A.I.C.S.: 237990
Ryan Nessen (VP & Ops Mgr-California District)
Ferdinand Benito (Mgr-Quality Control)

THE SUNFLOWER GROUP
14001 Marshall Dr, Lenexa, KS 66215
Tel.: (913) 890-0900 PA
Web Site:
http://www.sunflowergroup.com
Year Founded: 1978
Sales Range: $100-124.9 Million
Emp.: 131
Advertising Agency Services
N.A.I.C.S.: 541810
Thomas Hughey (Sr Mgr-Market Res)
Patrick Carr (Sr VP)

Subsidiaries:

The Sunflower Group (1)
150 N Wacker Dr #2650, Chicago, IL 60606-1609
Tel.: (312) 337-7086
Web Site: http://www.sunflowergroup.com
Emp.: 3
Direct Marketing, Event Marketing, Sales Promotion
N.A.I.C.S.: 541810

The Sunflower Group (1)
5310 Village Pkwy, Bentonville, AR 72758
Tel.: (479) 464-7396
Web Site: http://www.sunflowergroup.com
Emp.: 5
Advertising Agencies
N.A.I.C.S.: 541810

The Sunflower Group (1)
101 Merritt 7 Upper Level, Norwalk, CT 06851
Tel.: (203) 750-9604
Web Site: http://www.sunflowergroup.com
Emp.: 1
Retail Services
N.A.I.C.S.: 541810
Dorathy Balsano (Exec VP-Agency Svcs)
Pete Reininga (Sr VP-Mktg & Strategy)

THE SUNRIDER CORPORATION
1625 Abalone Ave, Torrance, CA 90501-2860
Tel.: (310) 781-3808 UT
Web Site: http://www.sunrider.com
Year Founded: 1982
Sales Range: $25-49.9 Million
Emp.: 450
Pharmaceuticals & Toiletries Distr
N.A.I.C.S.: 325412
Tei-Fu Chen (Co-Founder & Chm)
Sunny Beutler (CEO)
Oi-Lin Chen (Co-Founder)
Dirk Hobgood (CFO)
Sam Lee (Gen Mgr-China)

THE SUPPLY ROOM COMPANIES INC.
14140 N Washington Hwy, Ashland, VA 23005-4810
Tel.: (804) 412-1200
Web Site:
http://www.thesupplyroom.com
Year Founded: 1991
Sales Range: $25-49.9 Million
Emp.: 221
Supplier of Stationery & Office Supplies
N.A.I.C.S.: 424120
Susan Tait (Acct Mgr)
Patricia Barber (Pres & CEO)

Subsidiaries:

Open Plan Systems, Inc. (1)
4700 Deepwater Terminal Rd, Richmond, VA 23234
Tel.: (804) 275-2468
Web Site: http://www.openplan.com
Rev.: $129,207,000
Emp.: 110
Remanufacture, Restore & Market Modular Office Work Stations
N.A.I.C.S.: 423210
Jay Bryson (Dir-Sls)
Pamela Williams (CEO)
Dean Williams (COO)

THE SUPPORTING CAST, INC.
148 Madison Ave, New York, NY 10016
Tel.: (212) 532-8888 NY
Web Site:
http://www.supportingcast.com
Rev.: $10,000,000
Emp.: 30
Temporary Help Service
N.A.I.C.S.: 561320
Denise Jakeway (CEO)
Phillip Jakeway III (Pres)

Subsidiaries:

DeltaForce Personnel Services, Inc. (1)
10 E 40th St, New York, NY 10016
Tel.: (212) 725-2100
Web Site: http://www.deltaforcelegal.com
Rev.: $1,300,000
Emp.: 17
Legal Professional Employment Placement Agency
N.A.I.C.S.: 561311
Denise Jakeway (CEO)
Nicole Gable (Dir-Bus Dev)
Liz Mahr (Office Mgr)
Philip E. Jakeway III (VP)

THE SUTPHEN CORPORATION
7000 Columbus Marysville Rd, Amlin, OH 43002-9782
Tel.: (614) 889-1005 OH
Web Site: http://www.sutphen.com
Year Founded: 1890
Sales Range: $10-24.9 Million
Emp.: 140
Motor Vehicles & Car Bodies
N.A.I.C.S.: 336120
Drew Sutphen (Pres)
Ken Creese (Dir-Sls)

THE SWARM AGENCY, INC.
204 Clear Springs Ln, Peachtree City, GA 30269
Tel.: (404) 334-7030 GA
Year Founded: 2009
Marketing & Advertising Services
N.A.I.C.S.: 541870

THE SWARTHMORE GROUP, INC.
1650 Arch St Ste 2100, Philadelphia, PA 19103
Tel.: (215) 557-9300 DE
Web Site:
http://www.swarthmoregroup.com
Year Founded: 1991
Sales Range: $1-4.9 Billion
Emp.: 14
Investment Advisory Firm
N.A.I.C.S.: 561611
Paula R. Mandle (CEO & Chief Compliance Officer)
Glenn E. Becker (Pres)
Denise Caruso (Controller)
Gwenn M. Melcher (Mgr-Client Svcs)
Kurt W. Brunner (Sr Portfolio Mgr-Equity)
Daniel H. Cook (Portfolio Mgr-Equity)
Lester Rich (Portfolio Mgr-Equity)
John B. DeLaney (Sr Portfolio Mgr-Fixed Income)
Grace X. Schaffer (Portfolio Mgr-Fixed Income)
Erin H. Lockard (Mgr-Mktg)

THE SWEET LAKE LAND & OIL CO. LLC
PO Box 997, Lake Charles, LA 70602
Tel.: (337) 439-4041
Sales Range: $10-24.9 Million
Emp.: 75
Minerals & Agricultural
N.A.I.C.S.: 523999
Olan Menard (Gen Mgr)
Karl Zimmermann (Mgr-Mktg)
Mary Leach Werner (VP)
Claude Leach Jr. (CEO)

THE SWEET LIFE ENTERPRISES
2350 Pullman St, Santa Ana, CA 92705
Tel.: (949) 261-7400
Web Site:
http://www.freshstartbakeries.com
Rev.: $20,000,000
Emp.: 100
Doughs & Batters
N.A.I.C.S.: 311211

THE SWEET SHOP USA
1316 Industrial Rd, Mount Pleasant, TX 75455
Tel.: (817) 332-7941
Web Site:
http://www.econfections.com
Sales Range: $1-9.9 Million
Emp.: 110
Candy Mfr
N.A.I.C.S.: 311352
Brian Webb (Dir-Sls-Natl)
Matt Kelley (CFO)

THE SWEET SHOP USA

The Sweet Shop USA—(Continued)
Lauren Schuchman (Head-Sls)
Kate Neill (Dir-Comm)
Paul Prince (Founder & CEO)

THE SWIFT GROUP, LLC
12100 Sunset Hills Rd Ste 310, Reston, VA 20190
Tel.: (571) 470-2701
Web Site: https://theswiftgroup.com
Year Founded: 2019
Information Technology & Services
N.A.I.C.S.: 519290
Holton Yost (Pres & CEO)

THE T.L.C. GROUP, LTD.
751 N Bolingbrook Dr Ste 20, Clarendon Hills, IL 60440-5304
Tel.: (630) 789-8894
Web Site: http://www.tlcgroupltd.com
Landscape Architectural Services
N.A.I.C.S.: 541320
Stephen J. Gay (Dir-Ops)

THE TAMPA CLUB
101 E Kennedy Blvd Ste 4200, Tampa, FL 33602
Tel.: (813) 229-6028
Web Site: http://www.thetampaclub.com
Year Founded: 1981
Restaurant & Club
N.A.I.C.S.: 722511
Sandy Callahan (Pres)
Bruce Narzissenfeld (Treas)
Robie Addams (Sec)

THE TANEY CORPORATION
5130 Allendale Ln, Taneytown, MD 21787-2104
Tel.: (410) 756-6671   MD
Web Site: http://www.taneystair.com
Year Founded: 1958
Sales Range: $75-99.9 Million
Emp.: 90
Mfr of Wood Stairs & Wood Stair Parts
N.A.I.C.S.: 321918
Jeff Glass (Pres & Co-Owner)
Brian Glass (VP)
Eric Glass (Co-Owner & CEO)

THE TASI GROUP
10100 Progress Way, Harrison, OH 45030
Tel.: (513) 202-5182
Web Site: http://www.tasigroup.com
Measuring Systems Mfr
N.A.I.C.S.: 334519
John T. McKenna (Pres)

Subsidiaries:

Signalfire Telemetry Inc.   (1)
43 Broad St, Hudson, MA 01749-2558
Tel.: (978) 212-2868
Web Site: http://www.signal-fire.com
Professional, Scientific & Technical Services
N.A.I.C.S.: 541990
Scott Keller (CEO & Sec)

THE TELEPHONE CENTRE, INC.
1204 Oakland Ave, Greensboro, NC 27403-2743
Tel.: (336) 574-3000
Web Site: http://www.telectr.com
Sales Range: $10-24.9 Million
Emp.: 275
Market Analysis & Research
N.A.I.C.S.: 541910
Mitchell Capano (Pres & CEO)
Maria Rose (VP-Ops)

THE TEMPLE FOUNDATION
9229 Arlington Blvd, Fairfax, VA 22031
Tel.: (703) 591-8993   VA
Year Founded: 1965
Sales Range: $25-49.9 Million
Emp.: 444
Lifecare Retirement Community Operator
N.A.I.C.S.: 623311
Priscilla Kneisley (Dir-Health Svcs)
Christie Billings (Dir-Home Health)
Norwu Howard-Wesson (Dir-Nursing)
Cathy Renkiewicz (Dir-Rehabilitation)

THE TENNESSEE CREDIT UNION
1400 8th Ave S, Nashville, TN 37203
Tel.: (615) 244-1910   TN
Web Site: http://www.ttcu.org
Year Founded: 1950
Sales Range: $1-9.9 Million
Credit Union Operator
N.A.I.C.S.: 522130
Michael D. Martin (Pres & CEO)
Lisa Carlisle (Mgr-Bus Dev)
James Hall (Vice Chm)
Edith P. Jordan (Sec)
H. Woodard Pigg Jr. (Treas)

THE TERLATO WINE GROUP
2401 Waukegan Rd, Bannockburn, IL 60044
Tel.: (847) 604-8900   DE
Web Site: http://www.terlatowinegroup.com
Year Founded: 1946
Sales Range: $25-49.9 Million
Emp.: 600
Importing, Marketing & Distribution of Wine
N.A.I.C.S.: 424820
William A. Terlato (Pres & CEO)
Anthony J. Terlato II (Chm)

Subsidiaries:

Alderbrook Winery   (1)
2306 Magnolia Dr, Healdsburg, CA 95448
Tel.: (800) 405-5987
Web Site: http://www.alderbrook.com
Emp.: 15
Wine Mfr
N.A.I.C.S.: 312130

Chimney Rock Winery   (1)
5350 Silverado Trl, Napa, CA 94558
Tel.: (800) 257-2641
Web Site: http://www.chimneyrock.com
Emp.: 19
Wine Mfr
N.A.I.C.S.: 312130
Elizabeth Vianna (Gen Mgr)

Rutherford Hill Winery   (1)
200 Rutherford Hill Rd, Rutherford, CA 94573
Tel.: (707) 963-1871
Web Site: http://www.rutherfordhill.com
Wine Mfr
N.A.I.C.S.: 312130

Sanford Winery   (1)
5010 Santa Rosa Rd, Lompoc, CA 93436
Tel.: (805) 735-5900
Web Site: http://www.sanfordwinery.com
Wine Mfr
N.A.I.C.S.: 312130
Steve Fennell (Gen Mgr)

Terlato Wines   (1)
900 Armour Dr, Lake Bluff, IL 60044
Tel.: (847) 604-8900
Web Site: http://www.terlatovineyards.com
Rev.: $26,000,000
Emp.: 60
Wines, Beers & Spirits Imports & Distr
N.A.I.C.S.: 424820
Anthony J. Terlato II (Reg Mgr-Premier)
John A. Terlato (Vice Chm)
Philip Tardy (VP-Sls-Central)
Bill Terlato (CEO)

Terlato Wines International Inc.   (1)
900 Armour Dr, Lake Bluff, IL 60044
Tel.: (847) 604-8900
Web Site: http://www.terlatowines.com

Wine Mfr
N.A.I.C.S.: 312130
Anthony J. Terlato (Chm)
William A. Terlato (CEO)
John A. Terlato (Vice Chm)
David Lane (Pres & COO)
Edward J. Pitlik (CFO)
Michael Perlberg (Chief Legal Officer)

THE THINK TANK
1801 N Lamar Blvd, Austin, TX 78701-1051
Tel.: (512) 499-8811
Web Site: http://www.t-3.com
Year Founded: 1989
Emp.: 145
Advertising & Public Relations Agency
N.A.I.C.S.: 541810
Gay Warren Gaddis (CEO)
Jay Suhr (Chief Creative Officer & Sr VP)
Chris Wooster (Exec Dir-Creative)
Marie Bevione (Chief Talent Officer & VP)
Bryan Noguchi (VP & Exec Dir-Media)
Jennifer Mollo (Sr VP & Dir-Client Svcs)
Jane Crisan (Mng Dir-NY & Sr VP)
Yumi Prentice (Mng Dir-SF & Sr VP)
Bernard Briggs (CTO)
Rick Doerr (Chief Client Officer)
Donald Smith (Sr Mgr-Bus Dev)
Ben Gaddis (Pres)
Keith Johnston (COO)
Jim Firestone (Chief Strategy Officer)
Dillon Nugent (Dir-Client Svcs)
Marshall Wright (Dir-Connections)
Taylor Hight (Grp Acct Dir)

Subsidiaries:

The Think Tank   (1)
126 5th Ave 15th Fl, New York, NY 10011
Tel.: (212) 404-7045
Web Site: http://www.t-3.com
Emp.: 13
Advertising & Public Relations Agency
N.A.I.C.S.: 541810

The Think Tank   (1)
576 Folsom St, San Francisco, CA 94105
Tel.: (415) 983-0815
Advertising & Public Relations Agency
N.A.I.C.S.: 541810
Tamara Weinman (Mng Dir)

THE THOMAS KINKADE COMPANY
18635 Sutter Blvd, Morgan Hill, CA 95037
Tel.: (877) 412-7467   DE
Web Site: http://www.thomaskinkade.com
Sales Range: $100-124.9 Million
Emp.: 385
Artwork & Art Memorabilia Mfr & Whslr
N.A.I.C.S.: 459920
Robert Murray (Gen Counsel, Sec & VP)
John Hastings (CEO)
Mark Mickelson (Owner)
Patrick Kinkade (VP)

THE THOMAS MONAHAN COMPANY INC.
202 N Oak St, Arcola, IL 61910-1425
Tel.: (217) 268-4955   IL
Web Site: http://www.thomasmonahan.com
Year Founded: 1922
Sales Range: $10-24.9 Million
Emp.: 25
Industrial Handle Mfr
N.A.I.C.S.: 332510
Thomas F. Monahan (Pres)

THE THOMPSON COMPANIES
120 Royall St, Canton, MA 02021-1028
Tel.: (781) 828-8800   MA
Web Site: http://www.thompsondayton.com
Year Founded: 1922
Rev.: $100,000,000
Emp.: 500
Primary Metal Industries
N.A.I.C.S.: 331221
Mary L. Ryan (Chm & CEO)
Edward J. Ryan (Pres)

Subsidiaries:

Arrow Thompson Metals, Inc.   (1)
6880 Troost Ave, North Hollywood, CA 91605-6126
Tel.: (818) 765-0522
Web Site: http://www.thompsonsteelco.com
Sales Range: $10-24.9 Million
Emp.: 20
Stainless Flat Steel Products Mfr
N.A.I.C.S.: 423510
Hank Williams (Plant Mgr)

Optimal Steel Service LLC   (1)
6880 Troost Ave, North Hollywood, CA 91605
Tel.: (818) 765-0522
Web Site: http://www.thompsonsteelco.com
Sales Range: $25-49.9 Million
Emp.: 34
Steel Products Mfr
N.A.I.C.S.: 332322
Henry Williams (Plant Mgr)

Thompson Dayton Steel Service   (1)
3911 Dayton Park Dr, Dayton, OH 45414
Tel.: (937) 236-6940
Flat Rolled & Strip Steel Mfr
N.A.I.C.S.: 331221
Jim Fletcher (Gen Mgr)

Plant (Domestic):

Thompson Dayton Steel Service - Paulding   (2)
815 W Gasser Rd, Paulding, OH 45879-8765
Tel.: (800) 452-1690
Web Site: http://www.thompsonsteelco.com
Sales Range: $25-49.9 Million
Emp.: 50
Rolled Steel Mfr
N.A.I.C.S.: 331221
Doug Fiske (Gen Mgr)
Amy Wilhem (Office Mgr)

Thompson Dayton Steel Service - Roseville   (2)
27840 Groesbeck Hwy, Roseville, MI 48066
Tel.: (586) 775-6804
Web Site: http://www.thompsonsteelco.com
Sales Range: $25-49.9 Million
Emp.: 7
Rolled Steel Mfr
N.A.I.C.S.: 331221
Edward J. Ryan (Pres)

THE THOMPSON COMPANY
12225 Greenville Ave Ste 440, Dallas, TX 75243-9335
Tel.: (972) 699-3800
Year Founded: 1958
Rev.: $1,500,000
Emp.: 15
Single-Family Housing Construction
N.A.I.C.S.: 811114
Dean Renkes (Pres)
Amir Khanzabe (Dir-Tax)

Subsidiaries:

Thompson Realty Corporation   (1)
1600 N Collins Blvd Ste 1500, Richardson, TX 75080-3692
Tel.: (972) 644-2400
Web Site: http://www.thompson-realty.com
Sales Range: $25-49.9 Million
Emp.: 20
Commercial Construction
N.A.I.C.S.: 236115
Tod L. Radford (Treas & VP-Fin)
Victor Aguilar (Dir-Ops)

COMPANIES

Cherrilyn Barnard *(Mgr-Property)*
Barbara Bennett *(VP-Office Leasing)*
Taylor Field *(VP-Property & Construction Mgmt)*

THE THYMES, LLC
629 9th St SE, Minneapolis, MN 55414
Tel.: (612) 338-4471
Web Site: http://www.thymes.com
Miscellaneous Nondurable Goods Merchant Whslr
N.A.I.C.S.: 424990
Sherry Osterhaus *(Mgr-HR)*

Subsidiaries:

DesirePath Mississippi LLC (1)
1010 Lynn Lane W, Starkville, MS 39759
Web Site: http://www.aspenbaycandles.com
Sales Range: $1-9.9 Million
Emp.: 65
Mfr of High-End Specialty Candles
N.A.I.C.S.: 238990
Tom Reed *(Pres & Owner)*
Valerie Hicks *(Office Mgr)*

Division (Domestic):

DPM Fragrance (2)
1010 Lynn Lane W, Starkville, MS 39759
Tel.: (662) 324-2231
Web Site: http://www.dpmfragrance.com
Sales Range: $1-9.9 Million
High-End Specialty Candles
N.A.I.C.S.: 339999
Casey Wesson *(Dir-Sls & Mktg)*

THE TICKET EXPERIENCE, LLC
2222 Bissonnet Ste 202, Houston, TX 77005
Web Site: http://www.theticketexperience.com
Year Founded: 2007
Sales Range: $1-9.9 Million
Emp.: 5
Travel Arrangement & Reservation Services
N.A.I.C.S.: 561599
Patrick Ryan *(Partner)*
Celine Dion *(Mgr)*

THE TIMBERMEN, INC.
PO Box 107, Thomson, GA 30807
Tel.: (706) 465-3506
Web Site: http://www.timbermen.net
Year Founded: 1972
Sales Range: $10-24.9 Million
Emp.: 143
Wood Container & Pallet Mfr
N.A.I.C.S.: 321920
Sammy McCorkle *(Gen Mgr)*
Josh Stephens *(Mgr-Sls)*
Teddie Love *(Mgr-Personnel)*
Jim Hicks Sr. *(Founder)*

THE TIME GROUP INC.
11433 Cronridge Dr, Owings Mills, MD 21117-3528
Tel.: (410) 727-5525
Web Site: http://www.thetimegroup.com
Year Founded: 1986
Sales Range: $10-24.9 Million
Emp.: 110
Property Management Services
N.A.I.C.S.: 531210
Mark M. Caplan *(Pres & CEO)*

THE TIN BOX COMPANY
216 Sherwood Ave, Farmingdale, NY 11735
Tel.: (631) 845-1600
Web Site: http://www.tinboxco.com
Rev.: $47,600,000
Emp.: 230
Tinware Products Mfr & Distr
N.A.I.C.S.: 332439
Lloyd Roth *(Pres)*

THE TIRE RACK INC.
7101 Vorden Pkwy, South Bend, IN 46628
Tel.: (574) 287-2345
Web Site: http://www.tirerack.com
Year Founded: 1979
Sales Range: $1-9.9 Million
Emp.: 400
High-Performance Wheels & Tires Online Distr
N.A.I.C.S.: 423130
Pete Veldman *(Founder)*
Matt Edmans *(Dir-Mktg)*

THE TOBACCO HUT INC.
5826 Maple St, Omaha, NE 68104-4140
Tel.: (402) 551-5592
Year Founded: 1992
Sales Range: $10-24.9 Million
Emp.: 9
Tobacco Stores & Stands
N.A.I.C.S.: 459991
Denny Teig *(Pres)*

THE TODAY SHOW CHARITABLE FOUNDATION INC.
30 Rockefeller Plz Ste 380E, New York, NY 10112
Tel.: (212) 664-3157
Year Founded: 2001
Sales Range: $25-49.9 Million
Emp.: 2
Community Welfare Services
N.A.I.C.S.: 624190
Cathy Lavaty *(VP)*
Antoinette Machiaverna *(Pres)*
Anthony Gannon *(Treas)*

THE TODD GROUP, INC.
5017 Haines Rd N, Saint Petersburg, FL 33714
Tel.: (727) 526-6459
Web Site: http://www.tommytoddlandscape.com
Year Founded: 1982
Sales Range: $1-9.9 Million
Emp.: 20
Landscaping Services
N.A.I.C.S.: 561730
Thomas N. Todd *(Pres)*
Michael Todd *(VP)*

THE TOKARZ GROUP ADVISERS, LLC
287 Bowman Ave 2nd Fl, Purchase, NY 10577
Tel.: (914) 701-0310
Web Site: http://www.ttga.com
Year Founded: 2002
Closed-End Investment Advisory & Portfolio Management Services
N.A.I.C.S.: 523940
Jaclyn Shapiro-Rothchild *(Sec & VP)*
James D. Lynch *(Mng Dir-Portfolio Investments)*
Patrick Mullins *(Controller)*
Kevin M. Byrne *(Chief Compliance Officer)*

THE TOLEDO ZOOLOGICAL SOCIETY
2700 Broadway St, Toledo, OH 43609
Tel.: (419) 385-5721
Web Site: http://www.toledozoo.org
Year Founded: 1982
Sales Range: $25-49.9 Million
Zoo Operator
N.A.I.C.S.: 712130
Rick Payeff *(Dir-Facilities & Plng)*
Mary Fedderke *(Dir-Institutional Advancement)*
Nancy L. Foley *(Dir-HR)*
Sue Bagdonas *(Dir-Fin)*

Dennis Schnurbusch *(Dir-Visitor Svcs)*
John Jones *(VP)*
William McDonnell *(Sec)*
Elaine Canning *(Treas)*
Jeff Sailer *(CEO & Exec Dir)*
Ron Fricke *(Deputy Dir)*
Pamela S. Hershberger *(Pres)*

THE TOP DIE CASTING CO. INC.
13910 Dearborn Ave, South Beloit, IL 61080-9473
Tel.: (815) 389-2599
Web Site: http://www.topdie.com
Year Founded: 1977
Sales Range: $10-24.9 Million
Emp.: 140
Aluminum Die-Castings
N.A.I.C.S.: 331523
Floyd McCurdy *(Pres)*
Brad Lindmark *(Gen Mgr-Sls)*
Jay Dexl *(Reg Mgr-Sls)*

THE TOPOCEAN GROUP
2727 Workman Mill Rd, Whittier, CA 90601
Tel.: (562) 908-1688
Web Site: http://www.topocean.com
Rev.: $50,000,000
Emp.: 170
Freight Forwarding & Logistics Services
N.A.I.C.S.: 488510
Grace Lin *(Mng Dir)*
Robert Wang *(Pres)*
Andy Wang *(VP)*

THE TORRINGTON SAVINGS BANK INC.
129 Main St, Torrington, CT 06790-5207
Tel.: (860) 496-2152
Web Site: http://www.torringtonsavings.com
Year Founded: 1868
Sales Range: $25-49.9 Million
Emp.: 80
Provider of Banking Services
N.A.I.C.S.: 522180
Patricia G. Gangloff *(VP-Info Security)*
Miles C. Borzilleri *(Officer-Trust & Sr VP)*
Jeffrey Geddes *(Sr VP-Residential & Consumer Lending)*
Paul F. Reardon *(VP-Audit)*
Robert J. Salvatore *(VP-Ops)*
Althea B. Haberern *(VP-Mortgage Servicing)*
Lesa A. Vanotti *(CFO, Treas & Sr VP)*
John E. Janco *(Pres & CEO)*
John Scarritt *(VP-Comml Lending)*

THE TOWNSEND CORPORATION
1015 W Jackson St, Muncie, IN 47305
Tel.: (765) 468-3007
Web Site: http://www.thetownsendcorp.com
Year Founded: 1939
Sales Range: $1-4.9 Billion
Emp.: 1,800
Energy, Industrial & Defense Industries Services
N.A.I.C.S.: 221118
Gary Townsend *(Chm & CEO)*
Phillip E. Chambers *(Pres & COO)*
Abi Bath *(Dir-Emergency Svcs & Mktg Specialist)*

Subsidiaries:

Eco-Pak, LLC (1)
9211 E Jackson St Selma, Muncie, IN 47383 **(100%)**

Tel.: (765) 287-2093
Web Site: http://www.ecopakllc.com
Custom Blending & Repackaging Services for Industrial Vegetation Management
N.A.I.C.S.: 562998
Nick Hoffman *(Mgr-Sls & Mktg)*

Kelley Electric Company (1)
PO Box 428, Kennett, MO 63857-0428 **(100%)**
Tel.: (573) 888-5395
Web Site: http://www.kelleyelec.com
Sales Range: $10-24.9 Million
Emp.: 79
Electrical Work Contractors
N.A.I.C.S.: 238210
Gary Marchbanks *(Project Mgr)*

N.G. Gilbert Corporation (1)
1015 W Jackson St, Muncie, IN 47305 **(100%)**
Tel.: (765) 468-3007
Web Site: http://www.townsendcorporation.com
Electric Power Utilities Construction
N.A.I.C.S.: 335311
Amy Townsend *(CEO)*

ROW-Care LLC (1)
101 S Main St, Parker City, IN 47368 **(100%)**
Tel.: (765) 468-3007
Web Site: http://www.thetownsendcorp.com
Vegetative Clearance & Maintenance Services Exclusively to the Pipeline Industry
N.A.I.C.S.: 562998
Jack Moore *(Office Mgr)*

Townsend Tree Service (1)
101 S Main St, Parker City, IN 47368 **(100%)**
Tel.: (765) 468-3007
Web Site: http://www.thetownsendcorp.com
Sales Range: $75-99.9 Million
Emp.: 1,700
Tree-Trimming, Clearance & Integrated Vegetation Management Services
N.A.I.C.S.: 562998
Preston Mills *(Area Mgr)*
Mick Saulman *(VP-Reg)*

THE TRADEMARK COMPANY
344 Maple Ave W Ste 151, Vienna, VA 22180
Tel.: (800) 906-8626
Web Site: http://www.thetrademarkcompany.com
Year Founded: 2003
Sales Range: $1-9.9 Million
Emp.: 15
Trademark & Brand Protection Services
N.A.I.C.S.: 561499
Matthew H. Swyers *(Founder)*

THE TRAINING ASSOCIATES (TTA)
287 Turnpike Rd 3 Fl, Westborough, MA 01581-2807
Tel.: (508) 890-8500
Web Site: http://www.thetrainingassociates.com
Year Founded: 1994
Sales Range: $10-24.9 Million
Emp.: 90
IT Trainer Staff & Consulting Services
N.A.I.C.S.: 611430
Maria Melfa *(Pres & CEO)*
Andrea Turner *(Sr VP-Learning & Engagement)*
Justin Barrett *(Dir-Contracts & Compliance)*
Pietro Curini *(VP-Info Sys)*
Liz Malone *(Controller)*
Jason R. Murphy *(VP-Learning Strategy)*
Lynne Wagner *(Dir-Mktg Programs)*
Frank McNamara *(Gen Counsel)*
Kara Murphy *(Mgr-Sls Ops)*
Judy Melfa *(Founder & Treas)*
Jasmine Martirossian *(VP-Mktg)*

THE TRAINING ASSOCIATES (TTA)   U.S. PRIVATE

The Training Associates (TTA)—(Continued)
Sarah Lindberg (Dir-Learning & Dev)
Michael J. Noble (COO)
Kim Schofield (Mgr-Talent Recruitment)

THE TRANSITION COMPANIES LLC
5080 Spectrum Dr Ste 310W, Addison, TX 75001
Tel.: (972) 450-3100
Web Site: http://www.transitioncompanies.com
Year Founded: 1988
Sales Range: $1-9.9 Million
Emp.: 53
Business Research & Development Services
N.A.I.C.S.: 541720
Gene Sartin (Pres & CEO)
Michael Ryan (Exec VP)
R. Michael Allen (Sr Mng Dir)
Richard D. Parker (Exec Dir-Ops)

THE TRAVEL HAMMOCK INC.
8136 Monticello Ave, Skokie, IL 60076
Tel.: (847) 763-0005
Web Site: http://www.grandtrunk.com
Year Founded: 2001
Sales Range: $1-9.9 Million
Emp.: 12
Travel Accessory Distr
N.A.I.C.S.: 423910
Kevin Kaiser (Founder)
Andy Stroman (Partner)

Subsidiaries:

Alite Designs, Inc. (1)
2505 Mariposa St, San Francisco, CA 94110-1424
Tel.: (415) 651-8899
Web Site: http://www.alitedesigns.com
Outdoor Power Equipment Stores
N.A.I.C.S.: 444230
Tae Kim (Founder)

THE TREATMENT AND LEARNING CENTERS, INC.
2092 Gaither Rd Ste 100, Rockville, MD 20850
Tel.: (301) 424-5200   MD
Web Site: http://www.ttlc.org
Year Founded: 1956
Sales Range: $10-24.9 Million
Emp.: 280
Disability Assistance Services
N.A.I.C.S.: 624120
Suellyn Sherwood (CFO)
Bill McDonald (Pres)
James LaGrone (Treas)
Michael Cogan (VP)
Patricia A. Ritter (Exec Dir)

THE TROXEL COMPANY
11495 Hwy 57 W, Moscow, TN 38057
Tel.: (901) 877-6875
Web Site: http://www.troxel.com
Rev.: $48,000,000
Emp.: 200
Steel Tubing
N.A.I.C.S.: 331210
Bobby N. Rowlett (Pres)
Bruce Miller (VP-Fin)

THE TRUMP ORGANIZATION, INC.
725 5th Ave, New York, NY 10022
Tel.: (212) 832-2000   NY
Web Site: http://www.trump.com
Sales Range: $5-14.9 Billion
Emp.: 15,000
Holding Company; Real Estate, Hospitality, Investment & Licensing Assets
N.A.I.C.S.: 551112
Allen Weisselberg (CFO)
Eric F. Trump (Exec VP-Dev & Acq)
Alan Garten (Gen Counsel)
Donald J. Trump Jr. (Trustee)

Subsidiaries:

Trump International Golf Club, Inc. (1)
3505 Summit Blvd, West Palm Beach, FL 33406
Tel.: (561) 682-0700
Web Site: http://trumpinternationalpalmbeaches.com
Sales Range: $1-9.9 Million
Emp.: 70
Golf Courses & Country Clubs
N.A.I.C.S.: 713910
Janine Gill (Dir-HR)
John Nieporte (Pres)

Trump International Hotels Management LLC (1)
725 5th Ave, New York, NY 10022
Web Site: http://www.trumphotels.com
Luxury Hotel Administrative Services
N.A.I.C.S.: 561110
Eric Danziger (CEO)

Subsidiary (Domestic):

Trump Central Park West Corp. (2)
1 Central Park W, New York, NY 10023
Tel.: (212) 299-1000
Web Site: http://www.trumphotels.com
Sales Range: $10-24.9 Million
Luxury Hotel Operator
N.A.I.C.S.: 721110
Suzie Mills (Gen Mgr)
Prince A. Sanders (Gen Mgr)

Trump National Golf Club, LLC (1)
339 Pine Rd, Briarcliff Manor, NY 10510
Tel.: (914) 944-0900
Web Site: http://www.trumpnationalwestchester.com
Sales Range: $1-9.9 Million
Emp.: 50
Golf Courses & Country Clubs
N.A.I.C.S.: 713910
Lauren Papile (Controller)
Brian Lynch (Gen Mgr)

Trump Organization LLC (1)
725 5th Ave, New York, NY 10022
Tel.: (212) 832-2000
Web Site: http://www.trump.com
Investment & Business Development Services
N.A.I.C.S.: 523999

Division (Domestic):

Trump International Realty (2)
108 Central Park S, New York, NY 10019
Tel.: (212) 247-7100
Web Site: http://www.trumpinternationalrealty.com
Luxury Residential & Commercial Real Estate Brokerage Services
N.A.I.C.S.: 531210
Jodie Widaseck (Mng Dir)

Unit (Domestic):

Trump Palace (3)
200 E 69th St, New York, NY 10021
Tel.: (212) 247-7100
Web Site: http://www.trumppalace.com
Lessors of Residential Buildings & Dwellings
N.A.I.C.S.: 531110

THE TRUSS COMPANY, INC.
2802 142nd Ave E, Sumner, WA 98390
Tel.: (253) 863-5555
Web Site: http://www.thetrussco.com
Year Founded: 1985
Sales Range: $10-24.9 Million
Emp.: 75
Mfr of Engineered Wood Roof & Floor Trusses
N.A.I.C.S.: 321215
Nancy Russell (Sec)

Subsidiaries:

Tri County Truss (1)
Bay View Industrial Park 15599 Ashten Rd, Burlington, WA 98233-3662
Tel.: (360) 757-8500
Web Site: http://www.tricountytruss.com
Emp.: 100
Provider of Structural Wood Services
N.A.I.C.S.: 321215
Craig Mackay (Pres)

THE TRUST FOR PUBLIC LAND
101 Montgomery St 9th Fl, San Francisco, CA 94104
Tel.: (415) 495-4014
Web Site: http://www.tpl.org
Year Founded: 1972
Sales Range: $100-124.9 Million
Emp.: 400
Conservation Services
N.A.I.C.S.: 924120
William B. Rogers (Pres & CEO)
Page Knudsen Cowles (Chm)
Adrian Benepe (Sr VP & Dir-City Park Dev)
Raymond Christman (Sr VP & Dir-Mid-South Div)
Sean Connolly (CMO & Sr VP)
Ernest Cook (Sr VP & Dir-Conservation)
Jeff Danter (Sr VP & Dir-Atlantic Seaboard Div)
Kathy DeCoster (Sr VP & Dir-Federal Affairs)
M. Holly Haugh (Gen Counsel & Sr VP)
Cindy Scherer (CFO & Sr VP)
Brenda Schick (VP & Dir-Conservation Transactions)
Barbara Smith (VP & Sr Dir-HR)
Tim Wohlgenant (Sr VP)
Stephen N. Lackey (Dir-Philanthropy)
Lea Hong (Dir-Hawaii)

THE TRUSTEES OF RESERVATIONS
200 High St 4th Fl, Boston, MA 02110
Tel.: (978) 921-1944   MA
Web Site: http://www.thetrustees.org
Year Founded: 1891
Sales Range: $10-24.9 Million
Emp.: 695
Land Conservation & Historic Preservation Services
N.A.I.C.S.: 813312
Barbara Erickson (Pres & CEO)
Matt Montgomery (CMO)
Jocelyn Forbush (VP-Program Leadership)
Jennifer Ryan (Dir-Policy)
Ed Wilson (VP-Strategic Dev & Social Enterprise)
Noah Schneiderman (Chief Fin & Admin Officer)
Alicia Leuba (VP-East)

THE TWISTER GROUP, INC.
1547 Brandon Rd, Glenview, IL 60025
Tel.: (847) 478-1450
Web Site: http://www.thetwistergroup.com
Sales Range: $1-9.9 Million
Emp.: 6
Online Retailer of Discount Electronics, Appliances, Games & Radios
N.A.I.C.S.: 423430
Eugene Pritsker (Pres)

THE TYONEK NATIVE CORPORATION
1689 C St Ste 219, Anchorage, AK 99501-5131
Tel.: (907) 272-0707   AK
Web Site: http://www.tyonek.com
Year Founded: 1973
Sales Range: $1-9.9 Million
Holding Company
N.A.I.C.S.: 551112
Alicia Casteel (VP-HR)
Connie Downing (Chief Admin Officer)
Sharon Williford (VP)
Leo Barlow (CEO)
Bart Garber (Pres)
Stephen Gair (CFO)
Angie Constantine (Treas, VP & Asst Sec)
Billy Stephan (Vice Chm)
Heather Hudson (Gen Counsel)

Subsidiaries:

Tyonek Construction Group, Inc. (1)
1689 C St Ste 219, Anchorage, AK 99501-5131
Tel.: (907) 272-0707
Web Site: http://www.tyonek.com
Holding Company; Civil & Energy Infrastructure Engineering & Construction Services
N.A.I.C.S.: 551112
Don Standifer Sr. (Pres)

Tyonek Manufacturing Group, Inc. (1)
229 Palmer Rd, Madison, AL 35758   (100%)
Tel.: (256) 258-6200
Web Site: https://www.tyonek.com
Holding Company; Mechanical & Electrical Components Mfr & Specialty Fabrication Services
N.A.I.C.S.: 551112
Carl Runyon (VP-Special Programs)
Paul Stein (Mgr-Bus Dev-Mfg)
Doug Baker (Dir-Bus Dev)

Tyonek Services Group, Inc. (1)
229 Palmer Rd, Madison, AL 35758
Tel.: (256) 258-6200
Web Site: http://tsgi.tyonek.com
Holding Company; Aviation Maintenance, Information Technology & Cybersecurity Training Support Services
N.A.I.C.S.: 551112
Steve Adlich (Pres)
Andy Gignilliat (Sr Program Mgr-Aviation)

Subsidiary (Domestic):

Tyonek Services Overhaul Facility-Stennis, LLC (2)
7095 Roscoe Turner Rd Hangar C, Kiln, MS 39556
Tel.: (228) 467-2000
Avionics Systems Integration Services
N.A.I.C.S.: 336411

THE UHLMANN COMPANY
1009 Central St, Kansas City, MO 64105
Tel.: (816) 221-8200   DE
Web Site: http://www.heckerceresota.com
Year Founded: 1951
Sales Range: $25-49.9 Million
Emp.: 14
Producer & Distr of Grocery Flour; Investments & Real Estates
N.A.I.C.S.: 311211
Stanley P. Cyphers (CFO & Exec VP)
John W. Uhlmann (VP)
Judy Rasmussen (Mgr-Sls-Food Svcs)
Paul Uhlmann III (Pres & CEO)

THE ULMAN CANCER FUND FOR YOUNG ADULTS
1215 E Fort Ave, Baltimore, MD 21230
Tel.: (410) 964-0202   MD
Web Site: http://www.ulmanfund.org
Year Founded: 1997
Sales Range: $1-9.9 Million
Emp.: 25
Cancer Patient Wellness Services

N.A.I.C.S.: 813212
Brock Yetso *(Pres & CEO)*
Brian Satola *(COO)*
Diana Ulman *(Co-Founder)*
Doug Ulman *(Co-Founder)*
Jessica Tanner *(Sec)*
Christopher Sproule *(Vice Chm)*
Andrew Veliuona *(Chm)*
Katie Norton *(Dir-Dev)*

THE ULUM GROUP
1416 Williamette St, Eugene, OR 97401
Tel.: (541) 302-6620
Web Site: http://www.ulum.com
Year Founded: 1995
Sales Range: Less than $1 Million
Emp.: 10
Event Planning & Marketing, Government/Political/Public Affairs, Media Relations, Public Relations
N.A.I.C.S.: 541820
Patrick Walsh *(CEO)*

THE UNGAR GROUP
333 N Michigan Ave Ste 2234, Chicago, IL 60601
Tel.: (312) 541-0000
Web Site: http://www.ungargroup.com
Year Founded: 1987
Sales Range: $10-24.9 Million
Emp.: 7
Full Service
N.A.I.C.S.: 541810
Tom Ungar *(Pres & Chief Creative Officer)*
Maria G. Allen *(Dir-Media)*
Mete Moran *(Interactive Designer)*
Laurie Teidel *(Office Mgr)*

THE UNICORN GROUP
25B Hanover Rd, Florham Park, NJ 07932
Tel.: (973) 360-0611
Web Site: http://www.unicornhro.com
Year Founded: 1995
Sales Range: $25-49.9 Million
Emp.: 2
Investment Company
N.A.I.C.S.: 525990
Frank Diassi *(Chm & CEO)*

Subsidiaries:

Unicorn HRO (1)
2605 Meridian Pkwy Ste 105, Durham, NC 27713-2294 **(100%)**
Tel.: (919) 544-5008
Web Site: http://www.unicornhro.com
Sales Range: $10-24.9 Million
Sales & Development of Financial & Human Resource Applications for IBM Midrange Computers
N.A.I.C.S.: 541715
Edward J. Gettings *(Sr VP-Ops)*
Alice Williams *(Dir-Client Svcs)*
Frank Diassi *(Chm & CEO)*
Cal McGrath *(VP-Product Mgmt)*
Karen Pearsall *(Dir-Outsource Products & Svcs)*
Michelle Steiner *(Dir-Client Bus Solutions)*
Joseph H. Toss *(Dir-Product Dev)*

Unicorn HRO (1)
25 Hanover Rd B, Florham Park, NJ 07932-1410
Tel.: (973) 360-0688
Web Site: http://www.softwareplus.com
Sales Range: $10-24.9 Million
Sales & Development of Financial Payroll & Human Resources Software Mfr
N.A.I.C.S.: 541512
Frank P. Diassi *(Chm & CEO)*
Timothy M. Diassi *(Sr VP-Acquisitions & Partnerships)*
Edward J. Gettings *(Sr VP-Product Dev & Ops)*

THE UNION CLUB OF THE CITY OF NEW YORK
101 E 69th St, New York, NY 10021
Tel.: (212) 734-5400 NY
Web Site: http://www.theunionclub.com
Year Founded: 1940
Sales Range: $10-24.9 Million
Emp.: 175
Social Club
N.A.I.C.S.: 813410
Erika Kitano *(Mgr-Banquet)*
Humphrey Feliciano *(Controller)*
Jean Pierre David *(Gen Mgr)*

THE UNION GROUP
405 Pleasant St Bldg Ste 12, Fall River, MA 02721
Tel.: (508) 676-8580
Web Site: http://www.theuniongroup.com
Year Founded: 1909
Sales Range: $25-49.9 Million
Emp.: 20
Custom Loose-leaf Binder Business Form Software Packaging & Indexes Mfr
N.A.I.C.S.: 323111
Elliot Comenitz *(Pres)*
Bruce Comenitz *(VP)*
Lynne Medeiros *(Controller)*

Subsidiaries:

Elbe-Cesco Inc. (1)
405 Pleasant St Bldg 12, Fall River, MA 02722
Tel.: (508) 676-8580
Web Site: http://www.theuniongroup.com
Sales Range: $10-24.9 Million
N.A.I.C.S.: 323111
Bruce Comenitz *(Plant Mgr)*

Metropolitan Loose Leaf (1)
405 Pleasant St 12 Bldg, Fall River, MA 02721
Tel.: (508) 676-8580
Web Site: http://www.uniongroup.com
Sales Range: $10-24.9 Million
Emp.: 25
N.A.I.C.S.: 323111
Bruce Comenitz *(Pres)*

Union Printing (1)
649 Alden St, Fall River, MA 02722
Tel.: (508) 676-8580
Web Site: http://www.uniongroup.com
Sales Range: $10-24.9 Million
N.A.I.C.S.: 323111

THE UNION LEAGUE CLUB
38 E 37th St, New York, NY 10016
Tel.: (212) 685-3800 NY
Web Site: http://www.unionleagueclub.org
Year Founded: 1863
Sales Range: $10-24.9 Million
Emp.: 160
Social Club
N.A.I.C.S.: 813410
Richard Y. Newton III *(Exec Dir)*

THE UNITED COMPANY
1005 Glenway Ave, Bristol, VA 24201
Tel.: (276) 466-3322 VA
Web Site: http://www.unitedco.net
Year Founded: 1971
Sales Range: $300-349.9 Million
Emp.: 500
Coal Mining, Oil Drilling, Real Estate & Financial Services; Manufacturer of Movable Walls
N.A.I.C.S.: 213112
James W. McGlothlin *(Chm & CEO)*

Subsidiaries:

Scratch Golf Company (1)
60 Hilton Head National Dr, Bluffton, SC 29910-4885
Tel.: (843) 815-4653
Web Site: http://www.scratch-golf.com
Sales Range: $10-24.9 Million
Emp.: 50
Owner of Golf Courses
N.A.I.C.S.: 713910

THE UNITED GROUP
175 Camponelli Dr, Braintree, MA 02185
Tel.: (781) 348-8000 MA
Year Founded: 1934
Sales Range: $200-249.9 Million
Emp.: 755
Wine & Distilled Beverages Whslr & Distr
N.A.I.C.S.: 424820
Dave Roberts *(Vice Chm & CEO)*
Mark Fisher *(Pres-Mktg & Sls)*

Subsidiaries:

Best Brands Beverage Inc. (1)
3 Deerfield Dr, Canastota, NY 13032-4752
Tel.: (315) 463-5005
Sales Range: $10-24.9 Million
Emp.: 7
Distr of Beer And Ale
N.A.I.C.S.: 424810

THE UNITED SERVICE ORGANIZATIONS, INC.
PO Box 96860, Washington, DC 20077-7677
Web Site: https://www.uso.org
Year Founded: 1941
Recreational Support Services
N.A.I.C.S.: 721214

THE UNITED STATES PONY CLUBS INC.
4041 Iron Works Pkwy, Lexington, KY 40511
Tel.: (859) 254-7669 KY
Web Site: http://www.ponyclub.org
Year Founded: 1954
Sales Range: $1-9.9 Million
Emp.: 19
Horse Care Services
N.A.I.C.S.: 711211
Karen Clark *(Dir-Fin & Admin)*
Aileen Gordon *(Mgr-Content & Data)*
Shelley Mann *(Dir-Mktg & Comm)*
Deb Kirsch *(Treas)*
Nancy Pittman *(Chm & Pres)*
Debbie McLeod *(VP-Activities)*
Jennifer Sweet *(VP-Reg Admin)*
Lorelei Coplen *(Sec)*

THE UNITED TEACHERS OF DADE
2200 Biscayne Blvd, Miami, FL 33137
Tel.: (305) 854-0220 FL
Web Site: http://www.utofd.com
Year Founded: 1961
Sales Range: $10-24.9 Million
Emp.: 45
Educational Support Services
N.A.I.C.S.: 611710
Kristi Alger *(Accountant)*
Jason Joseph *(Dir-Comm & Community Engagement)*
Randy Biro *(Project Mgr-Academic Advancement)*
Gladys Podnar *(Dir-Fin & Ops)*
Jeffrey Redmon *(Dir-Member Svcs)*

THE UNIVERSITY BOOK STORE
711 State St, Madison, WI 53703-1017
Tel.: (608) 257-3784 WI
Web Site: http://www.uwbookstore.com
Year Founded: 1894
Sales Range: $75-99.9 Million
Emp.: 80
College Book Stores; School Supplies
N.A.I.C.S.: 459210
Pat McGowan *(Pres)*
Kim Fredrickson *(Controller)*
Kevin Phelps *(VP)*

THE UNIVERSITY OF OKLAHOMA COLLEGE OF MEDICINE
941 Stanton L Young Blvd, Oklahoma City, OK 73104-5042
Tel.: (405) 271-2265
Web Site: http://www.oumedicine.com
Year Founded: 1900
Emp.: 1,000
Medical College
N.A.I.C.S.: 611310
M. Dewayne Andrews *(Exec Dean & VP-Health Affairs)*
Barish Edil *(Chm)*

THE UNREAL AGENCY
52 Broad St 3rd Fl, Keyport, NJ 07735
Tel.: (732) 888-0055
Web Site: http://www.theunrealagency.com
Year Founded: 2001
Sales Range: Less than $1 Million
Emp.: 10
Advetising Agency
N.A.I.C.S.: 541810
Craig Bocchiaro *(CEO)*

THE UPPER DECK COMPANY, LLC
5909 Sea Otter Pl, Carlsbad, CA 92010
Tel.: (760) 929-6500 CA
Web Site: http://www.upperdeck.com
Year Founded: 1988
Sales Range: $75-99.9 Million
Emp.: 90
Sports & Non-Sports Trading Cards & Posters Mfr
N.A.I.C.S.: 323111
Jason Masherah *(Pres)*

THE UPPER ROOM
1908 Grand Ave, Nashville, TN 37212-2129
Tel.: (615) 340-7200 TN
Web Site: http://www.upperroom.org
Year Founded: 1935
Sales Range: $10-24.9 Million
Emp.: 200
Publisher of Spiritual Formation Resources
N.A.I.C.S.: 513120
Charles Carahan *(CFO)*

THE UPTURN, INC.
4695 MacArthur Ct Ste 1430, Newport Beach, CA 92660
Tel.: (949) 475-9086
Web Site: http://www.theupturn.com
Sales Range: $125-149.9 Million
Online Real Estate Matchmaking Exchange
N.A.I.C.S.: 531390
Jeffrey M. Eckman *(CEO)*
Stefania Mitrano *(Exec Dir-Projects & Client Svcs)*
Scott Shunk *(Exec VP-Strategy & Bus Dev)*
Bernard DeCunha *(Exec VP & Gen Mgr)*

THE UTE MOUNTAINEER, LTD.
308 S Mill St, Aspen, CO 81611
Tel.: (970) 925-2849
Web Site: http://www.utemountaineer.com
Year Founded: 1977

THE UTE MOUNTAINEER, LTD.

The Ute Mountaineer, Ltd.—(Continued)

Sales Range: $1-9.9 Million
Emp.: 27
Ret Sport Goods/Bicycles Ret Misc Apparel/Access Ret Shoes
N.A.I.C.S.: 459110
Robert Wade (Co-Owner)
Ruth Wade (Co-Owner)

Subsidiaries:

Neptune Mountaineering, Inc. (1)
633 S Broadway St Ste A, Boulder, CO 80305
Tel.: (303) 499-8866
Web Site:
 http://www.neptunemountaineering.com
Sales Range: $1-9.9 Million
Emp.: 20
Sporting Goods Retailer
N.A.I.C.S.: 459110
Diane Diangeissinger (VP)
Jen Mull (CEO)

THE UTICA SYMPHONY ORCHESTRA

261 Genesee St, Utica, NY 13501
Tel.: (315) 732-5146
Sales Range: Less than $1 Million
Emp.: 75
Symphony Orchestra
N.A.I.C.S.: 711320
Charles Schneider (Dir-Music)

THE VALLEY CADILLAC CORP.

3100 Winton Rd S, Rochester, NY 14623
Tel.: (585) 427-8400
Web Site:
 http://www.valleycadillac.com
Sales Range: $25-49.9 Million
Emp.: 61
Automobiles, New & Used
N.A.I.C.S.: 441110
Dan Merrick (Controller)
Edward T. Meagher Sr. (CEO)

THE VALLEY ENDOSCOPY CENTER, L.P.

18425 Burbank Blvd Ste 525, Tarzana, CA 91356
Tel.: (818) 708-6050
Sales Range: $50-74.9 Million
Emp.: 15
Outpatient Surgical Center
N.A.I.C.S.: 621498
Susan Fischer (Office Mgr)

THE VALLEY GROUP, INC.

3610 78th Ave W, Rock Island, IL 61201-7333
Tel.: (309) 787-0292
Web Site:
 http://www.valleyconstruction.com
Year Founded: 1990
Sales Range: $10-24.9 Million
Emp.: 55
Holding Company; Infrastructure & Building Construction Services
N.A.I.C.S.: 551112
John Hass (Chm)
James Hass (Vice Chm)

Subsidiaries:

Valley Construction Company (1)
3610 78th Ave W, Rock Island, IL 61201-7333 (100%)
Tel.: (309) 787-0292
Web Site: http://www.valleyconstruction.com
Highway & Street Construction
N.A.I.C.S.: 237310
Greg Hass (Pres & CEO)
Adam Hass (VP)

THE VAN HOOF COMPANIES

2525 N Casaloma Dr, Appleton, WI 54913
Tel.: (920) 830-5050
Web Site: http://www.vanhoof.com
Year Founded: 1966
Sales Range: $350-399.9 Million
Emp.: 1,500
Holding Company for Paper Product Manufacturing & Warehousing & Distribution Operations
N.A.I.C.S.: 493110
Robert Schroeder (Pres)

Subsidiaries:

Fulfillment Specialists of America (1)
675 Brighton Beach Rd, Menasha, WI 54952
Tel.: (920) 751-7692
Packaging Services
N.A.I.C.S.: 561910

Superior Specialties, Inc. (1)
2525 N Casaloma Dr, Appleton, WI 54913
Tel.: (920) 560-6262
Web Site: http://www.superspec.com
Sales Range: $25-49.9 Million
Emp.: 200
Mfr of Seamless Background Papers for the Photographic & Display Industries
N.A.I.C.S.: 322220
James Smith (Gen Mgr)

Warehouse Specialists, Inc. (1)
1160 N Mayflower Dr, Appleton, WI 54913
Tel.: (920) 830-5000
Web Site: http://www.wsinc.com
Rev.: $18,100,000
Emp.: 70
Warehousing & Distribution Services
N.A.I.C.S.: 493110
Robert Schroeder (Pres & CEO)
Rob Kriewaldt (Dir-Mktg)
Andrew Chisel (Dir-Org Dev)

THE VAN METRE COMPANIES

9900 Main St Ste 500, Fairfax, VA 22031
Tel.: (703) 425-2600
Web Site:
 http://www.vanmetrecompanies.com
Year Founded: 1955
Sales Range: $150-199.9 Million
Emp.: 300
Provider of Real Estate Development & Management Services
N.A.I.C.S.: 531210
Richard J. Rabil (Vice Chm, Pres & CEO)

THE VANGUARD GROUP, INC.

100 Vanguard Blvd, Malvern, PA 19355
Tel.: (610) 669-1000
Web Site: http://www.vanguard.com
Year Founded: 1975
Sales Range: $5-14.9 Billion
Emp.: 13,000
Mutual Fund Company
N.A.I.C.S.: 525910
Tim J. Buckley (Chm & CEO)
James M. Norris (Head-Intl)
John T. Marcante (Mng Dir-IT)
Chris D. McIsaac (Head-Plng & Dev)
Karin A. Risi (Mng Dir-Retail Investor Grp)
Martha G. King (Mng Dir-Institutional Investor Grp)
Thomas M. Rampulla (Mng Dir-Fin Advisor Svcs)
Michael Rollings (CFO)
Juan Hernandez (Head-Mexico)
Yan Pu (Head-Investment Mgmt Grp-China)
Daniel Reyes (Head-Investment Strategy Grp-Asia-Pacific)
Axel Lomholt (Head-ETFs-Intl)
Lauren Valente (Chief HR Officer)
John Galloway (Head-Investment Stewardship-Global)
Anne Robinson (Mng Dir & Gen Counsel)

Subsidiaries:

Vanguard Brokerage Services (1)
100 Vanguard Blvd, Malvern, PA 19355-0741
Tel.: (610) 669-1000
Web Site: http://www.vanguard.com
Brokerage Services
N.A.I.C.S.: 523150

Vanguard Investments (1)
100 Vanguard Blvd, Malvern, PA 19355
Tel.: (610) 669-4572
Web Site: http://www.vanguard.com
Sales Range: $50-74.9 Million
Emp.: 100
Underwriting & Other Financial Investment Services
N.A.I.C.S.: 523999

Vanguard Investments Australia Ltd. (1)
Level 34 Freshwater Place 2 Southbank Boulevard, Southbank, 3006, VIC, Australia
Tel.: (61) 388883888
Web Site:
 http://www.vanguardinvestments.com.au
Sales Range: $50-74.9 Million
Emp.: 200
Investment Services
N.A.I.C.S.: 523150
Kim Petersen (CIO-Asia Pacific)
Frank Kolimago (Mng Dir)
Charles Thompson (Co-CFO)
Johanna Platt (Co-CFO)
Lucy Carr (Head-HR)

THE VELOCITY GROUP, INC.

4393 Digital Way, Mason, OH 45040
Tel.: (513) 701-9124
Web Site: http://www.velocityfast.com
Engineeering Services
N.A.I.C.S.: 541330
Bill Jarvis (Pres)

Subsidiaries:

Fehrman Tool & Die Inc. (1)
8824 Clay Pike, Byesville, OH 43723-9695
Tel.: (740) 685-2637
Web Site: http://www.ftdinc.com
Special Die & Tool, Die Set, Jig & Fixture Mfr
N.A.I.C.S.: 333514
Delbert Fehrman (Pres)

THE VENICE AUCTION COMPANY, INC.

1250 US 41 Bypass S, Venice, FL 34285
Tel.: (941) 485-4964
Web Site:
 http://www.veniceauction.com
Year Founded: 1985
Sales Range: $1-9.9 Million
Emp.: 9
Home Furniture & Home Accessories
N.A.I.C.S.: 449129
Joe LaRaviere (Owner)

THE VERMONT COMMUNITY FOUNDATION

3 Court St, Middlebury, VT 05753
Tel.: (802) 388-3355
Web Site: http://www.vermontcf.org
Year Founded: 1986
Sales Range: $10-24.9 Million
Emp.: 30
Community Action Services
N.A.I.C.S.: 624190
Jane Kimble (Mgr-Building)
Patrick H. Berry (VP-Philanthropy)
Lydia Brownell (Sr Mgr-Fund & Contract)
Meg Seely (Sec)
Tim Volk (Chm)
Felipe Rivera (VP-Comm)
Dan Smith (Pres & CEO)
Stacie Fagan (VP-Philanthropy)
Adam Bornstein (Mgr-Mission Investment)

THE VERNDALE CORPORATION

266 Summer St, fl 7, Boston, MA 02210
Tel.: (617) 399-8777
Web Site: http://www.verndale.com
Year Founded: 1998
Rev.: $4,100,000
Emp.: 38
Computer Programming Services
N.A.I.C.S.: 541511
Sean Scollin (Co-Founder & Partner)
Chris Pisapia (Co-Founder & Partner)
Matt Pisapia (Mng Dir)
Joe Zarrett (Co-Founder, Pres & Partner)
Ryan Clark (Sr VP-North American Sls)
Ryan Moltenbrey (Exec VP-Sls & Mktg)
Lisa Waters (Exec VP-Agency & Partner Alliances)
Keith LaFerriere (CEO)

THE VERNON COMPANY

604 W 4th St N Newton, Newton, IA 50208
Tel.: (641) 792-9000
Web Site:
 http://www.vernonpromotions.com
Year Founded: 1902
Sales Range: $150-199.9 Million
Emp.: 500
Promotional Products, Ad Specialties & Specific Incentives & Premiums Mfr & Distr
N.A.I.C.S.: 541890
Chris Vernon (Pres & CEO)

Subsidiaries:

Dunlap Manufacturing Co. (1)
PO Box 248, Unionville, MO 63565-0248 (100%)
Tel.: (660) 947-2455
Web Site: http://www.dun-lap.com
Sales Range: $10-24.9 Million
Emp.: 25
Mfr of Pressure Sensitive Signs & Advertising Specialties
N.A.I.C.S.: 323111

The Vernon Company - Vernon Display Graphics Division (1)
145 Commerce Rd, Carlstadt, NJ 07072
Tel.: (201) 935-7117
Web Site:
 http://www.vernondisplaygraphics.com
Emp.: 50
Graphic Design & Printing Services
N.A.I.C.S.: 541430
Andrew Gabriel (CEO)

The Vernon Graphics Group (1)
604 W 4th St N, Newton, IA 50208
Tel.: (800) 743-7545
Digital & Screened Graphic Product Mfr
N.A.I.C.S.: 339999

Vernon Promotions (1)
1 Promotion Pl, Newton, IA 50208
Tel.: (817) 933-4733
Web Site: http://www.vernonpromotions.com
Sales Range: $25-49.9 Million
Emp.: 300
Customized Merchandise Mfr
N.A.I.C.S.: 339999
Dave Regan (Mgr-Sls)

THE VESTCOR COMPANIES

3030 Hartley Rd Ste 310, Jacksonville, FL 32257
Tel.: (904) 260-3030
Web Site: http://www.vestcor.com
Year Founded: 1983
Residential Construction
N.A.I.C.S.: 236115
Steve Moore (Pres)
Jason Floyd (CFO)
John Darrell Rood (Founder & Chm)

THE VIA GROUP LLC

619 Congress St, Portland, ME 04101-5598
Tel.: (207) 221-3000
Web Site: http://www.vianow.com
Year Founded: 1993
Sales Range: $75-99.9 Million
Emp.: 70
Brand Development, Communications, Graphic Design, Planning & Consultation
N.A.I.C.S.: 541810
John Coleman *(Founder & Chm)*
Greg Smith *(Chief Creative Officer)*
David Burfeind *(Chief Strategy Officer)*
Teddy Stoecklein *(Dir-Creative)*
Ivan Salazar *(CFO)*
Leeann Leahy *(CEO)*
Bobby Hershfield *(Chief Creative Officer)*

THE VILLAGE AT MORRISONS COVE
429 S Market St, Martinsburg, PA 16662
Tel.: (814) 793-2104 PA
Web Site: http://www.villageatmorrisonscove.org
Year Founded: 1903
Sales Range: $10-24.9 Million
Emp.: 423
Lifecare Retirement Community Operator
N.A.I.C.S.: 623311
Corey Jones *(CEO)*
Kathleen Dombrosky *(CFO)*
Cindy Wareham *(Chm)*
Ramon Burket *(Vice Chm)*
Shirley Lingenfelter *(Sec)*

THE VILLAGE BANK
307 Auburn St, Auburndale, MA 02466
Tel.: (617) 527-6090
Web Site: http://www.village-bank.com
Sales Range: $800-899.9 Million
Emp.: 75
State Commercial Banks
N.A.I.C.S.: 523999
Kenneth C. Brennan *(Chm)*
Craig D. Bell *(Founder & Chm)*
Jeffrey Tucker *(Sr VP-Ops & IT)*
Richard White *(Treas & VP-Acctg)*
Susan Paley *(VP-Community Rels)*
Eileen Colella *(Asst VP-Loan Servicing)*
Lilly Trainor *(Asst VP-Trng)*
Sharon M. Dillon *(Asst VP)*
Jill Rousseau *(Asst VP)*
Joseph De Vito *(Pres & CEO)*
Eric D. Boecher *(CFO)*
Andrew S. Franklin *(Sr VP-Lending)*
John L. Karacalidis *(Sr VP-Enterprise Risk)*
Elizabeth R. MacLellan *(Sr VP-Compliance)*
Lisa Boccabella *(VP-BSA)*
Denise Leonard *(VP-Retail Lending)*
Patricia A. MacNeil *(VP)*
James Farina *(Asst VP-Bus Dev)*
Anna M. Lemieux *(Asst VP-Project Mgmt)*
Nicole E. Sloan *(Asst Treas & Mgr Bus-Process)*
Slater Cram *(Asst Treas & Mgr-Auburndale)*
D. Mark Loveless *(Asst Treas & Mgr-Newtonville)*
Laura Tannous *(Asst Treas & Mgr-Nonantum)*
John Tarpinian *(Asst VP-Comml Lending)*
JoAnn M. Jirichian *(Mgr-Nonantum & Asst Treas)*
Reilly Cavanaugh *(Mgr-Newton Centre)*
Susan Zacharer *(Asst VP)*
Roy I. Barzel *(Chief Credit Officer & Exec VP)*
David C. Pennybaker Jr. *(VP-Comml Lending)*
Christy F. Quesenbery *(Exec VP-Ops)*

THE VILLAGE FAMILY SERVICES
6736 Laurel Canyon Blvd Ste 200, North Hollywood, CA 91606
Tel.: (818) 755-8786 CA
Web Site: http://www.thevillagefs.org
Year Founded: 1997
Sales Range: $10-24.9 Million
Emp.: 135
Individual & Family Support Services
N.A.I.C.S.: 624190
Krista Brown *(VP-Admin)*
Charles Robbins *(VP-Comm & Dev)*
Ivonne Wolovich *(VP-Fin)*
Krista Gonzalez *(Dir-Compliance & Risk Mgmt)*
Deborah Hoffman *(Dir-Outpatient Svcs)*
Diego Edber *(Sec)*
Irma Seilicovich *(COO)*
Hugo C. Villa *(CEO)*
Adik Parsekhian *(Dir-Quality Assurance)*
Diana Redeemer *(Dir-Foster Care-ITFC & Adoptions)*
Lynda Aguilar *(Dir-Wraparound)*
Zachery Scott *(VP-Dev & Comm)*

THE VILLAGE FOR FAMILIES & CHILDREN, INC.
1680 Albany Ave, Hartford, CT 06105
Tel.: (860) 236-4511 CT
Web Site: http://www.thevillage.org
Year Founded: 1809
Sales Range: $25-49.9 Million
Emp.: 523
Child & Family Support Center
N.A.I.C.S.: 624190
Galo A. Rodriguez *(Pres & CEO)*
Donna Jolly *(Chief Comm Officer)*
Hector Glynn *(VP-Programs)*
Ashley Dorin *(Dir-Medical)*
Martin Morrissey *(CFO)*
Tammy Freeberg *(Assoc VP-Strategy & Plng)*

THE VILLAGE NETWORK
3011 Akron Rd, Wooster, OH 44691
Tel.: (330) 264-3232 OH
Web Site: http://www.thevillagenetwork.org
Year Founded: 1946
Sales Range: $25-49.9 Million
Emp.: 310
Behavioral Healthcare Services
N.A.I.C.S.: 623220
Richard Rodman *(COO)*
Bel Klockenga *(CFO)*
David Paxton *(Chief Clinical Officer)*
Tim Homan *(VP-Advancement)*
Lynn Moomaw *(Dir-Ops)*
Richard Graziano *(Pres & CEO)*
Scott Allen *(Chm)*
Todd Gordon *(Chief Admin Officer)*

THE VILLAGES
2405 N Smith Pike, Bloomington, IN 47404
Tel.: (812) 332-1245 IN
Web Site: http://www.villages.org
Year Founded: 1986
Sales Range: $10-24.9 Million
Emp.: 431
Individual & Family Support Services
N.A.I.C.S.: 624190
Michael North *(Treas)*
Eileen Williams *(Sec)*
Rhonda Yoder Breman *(Chm)*
Daniel Phair *(Vice Chm)*

THE VILLAGES, FLORIDA INC.
1000 Lake Sumter Landing, The Villages, FL 32162
Tel.: (352) 753-2270
Web Site: http://www.thevillages.com
Sales Range: $900-999.9 Million
Emp.: 890
Real Estate Retirement Communities
N.A.I.C.S.: 237210
H. Gary Morse *(CEO)*

THE VIRGINIA HOME
1101 Hampton St, Richmond, VA 23220
Tel.: (804) 359-4093 VA
Web Site: http://www.thevirginiahome.org
Year Founded: 1894
Sales Range: $10-24.9 Million
Emp.: 288
Disability Assistance Services
N.A.I.C.S.: 624120
Jean Benson *(First VP)*
Barbara Reames *(VP)*
Suzanne Wilson *(Asst Sec)*
Joan Buhrman *(VP)*
Mary Frances Gravitt *(VP)*

THE VISTRIA GROUP, LP
300 E Randolph St Ste 4030, Chicago, IL 60601
Tel.: (312) 626-1101
Web Site: http://www.vistria.com
Privater Equity Firm
N.A.I.C.S.: 523999
Harreld N. Kirkpatrick III *(Co-CEO & Sr Partner)*
Mark A. Green *(Operating Partner)*
Phil Alphonse *(Sr Partner)*
Mike Castleforte *(Partner)*
Amy ChristensenP *(Partner)*
Tom Duffy *(CFO & Partner)*
Jon Maschmeyer *(Partner)*
Adnan Nisar *(Partner)*
Marcelus Decoulode *(Principal)*
Nick Potter *(VP)*
Bruce Hampton *(VP)*
Sara Bernardi *(Head-Office Svcs & Events)*
Stephanie Solomon *(Dir-Fin)*
Matt Schulz *(Principal)*
Jo Samuels *(Partner)*
Martin H. Nesbitt *(Co-CEO & Sr Partner)*

Subsidiaries:

Apollo Education Group, Inc. (1)
4025 S Riverpoint Pkwy, Phoenix, AZ 85040
Tel.: (480) 966-5394
Web Site: http://www.apollo.edu
Holding Company; Online Higher Education Program Services
N.A.I.C.S.: 551112
Anthony Miller *(Chm)*
Gregory W. Cappelli *(CEO)*

Subsidiary (Domestic):

Institute for Professional Development (2)
17 Hathaway Pl, Glen Ridge, NJ 07028
Tel.: (973) 777-4200
Web Site: https://www.ipd2.com
Educational Consulting Services
N.A.I.C.S.: 541618

University of Phoenix, Inc. (2)
4035 S Riverpoint Pkwy, Phoenix, AZ 85040
Tel.: (602) 254-0086
Web Site: https://www.phoenix.edu
Colleges & Universities
N.A.I.C.S.: 611310

Steve Gross *(CMO)*
Raghu Krishnaiah *(COO)*
Srini Medi *(Gen Counsel & Sr VP)*
Cheryl Naumann *(Chief HR Officer)*
Eric Rizzo *(Sr VP-Govt Affairs)*
Jamie Smith *(CIO)*
Ruth Veloria *(Chief Strategy Officer & Chief Customer officer)*
John Woods *(Chief Academic Officer)*
Blair Westblom *(CFO)*

Western International University, Inc. (2)
1601 W Fountainhead Pkwy, Tempe, AZ 85282
Investment Services
N.A.I.C.S.: 523999

Edmentum, Inc. (1)
5600 W 83rd St Ste 300 8200 Tower, Bloomington, MN 55437-1000
Tel.: (952) 832-1000
Web Site: http://www.edmentum.com
Sales Range: $50-74.9 Million
Emp.: 300
Online Educational Resource Software Publisher
N.A.I.C.S.: 513210
Jamie Candee *(CEO)*
Dave Adams *(Chief Academic Officer)*
Stacey Herteux *(VP-HR)*
Paul Johansen *(CTO)*
Richard Whalley *(Mng Dir)*
Mark McEachen *(Chm)*
Erin Cassady-Dorion *(Mgr-Bus Dev)*
Marcus Lingenfelter *(Sr VP-Strategic Initiatives & Partnerships)*
Karen Barton *(Sr VP-Res & Design)*
Jason Scherschligt *(VP-Product Strategy & Experience)*
Christy Spivey *(VP-Curriculum & Assessment Dev)*
Marty Thomas *(VP-Svcs)*
Cheryl Dodge *(Chief Product Officer)*
Frank Jalufka *(CFO)*
Amanda Kocon *(Chief Strategy Officer)*

Subsidiary (Domestic):

Apex Learning, Inc. (2)
1215 Fourth Ave Ste 1500, Seattle, WA 98161
Tel.: (206) 381-5600
Web Site: http://www.apexlearning.com
Sales Range: $1-9.9 Million
Emp.: 55
Education Services
N.A.I.C.S.: 611699
Todd Mahler *(Chief Product Officer)*
Chris Porter *(CEO)*
Wade Pfeiffer *(CFO)*
Jean Sharp *(Chief Academic Officer)*

Archipelago Learning, Inc. (2)
3232 McKinney Ave Ste 400, Dallas, TX 75204
Tel.: (214) 397-0794
Sales Range: $125-149.9 Million
Emp.: 377
Web-Based Educational Software Retailer
N.A.I.C.S.: 449210

Subsidiary (Domestic):

Educationcity Inc. (3)
55 S Main St Ste 271, Naperville, IL 60540-8044
Tel.: (800) 995-5410
Web Site: http://www.educationcity.com
Educational Support Services
N.A.I.C.S.: 611710
Matt Drakard *(Co-Founder)*

Help at Home, LLC (1)
1 N State St Ste 800, Chicago, IL 60602
Tel.: (312) 663-4244
Web Site: http://www.helpathome.com
Emp.: 25,000
In-Home Health Care Services
N.A.I.C.S.: 621610
Tim O'Rourke *(Pres)*

Subsidiary (Domestic):

Excel Companion Care, Inc. (2)
1240 Old York Rd Ste 201, Warminster, PA 18974-2013
Tel.: (215) 675-4701
Web Site: http://www.excelcompanioncare.com

THE VISTRIA GROUP, LP

U.S. PRIVATE

The Vistria Group, LP—(Continued)
Emp.: 600
In-Home Non-Medical Care Services
N.A.I.C.S.: 624120
Joshua Drebes (Co-Founder)
John Gifford (Co-Founder)

Open Systems Healthcare, Inc. (2)
1818 Market St Ste 1105, Philadelphia, PA 19103
Tel.: (215) 399-1400
Web Site:
http://www.opensystemshealthcare.com
Sales Range: $50-74.9 Million
Women Healthcare Services
N.A.I.C.S.: 621610
Charles Hill (Pres & CEO)
Ian Cooper (VP-Sls)
Kate Kolodey (VP-Ops & HR)
Erin Brown (Dir-HR)
Sara Stevens (Dir-Ops)

MGT of America Consulting LLC (1)
4320 West Kennedy Blvd, Tampa, FL 33609
Tel.: (813) 327-4717
Web Site: https://www.mgtconsulting.com
Emp.: 100
Management Consulting Services
N.A.I.C.S.: 523940

Subsidiary (Domestic):

MGT of America, LLC (2)
3800 Esplanade Way Ste 210, Tallahassee, FL 32311
Tel.: (850) 386-3191
Web Site: http://www.mgtofamerica.com
Emp.: 120
Technical & Scientific Consulting Services
N.A.I.C.S.: 541690
Brad Burgess (Exec VP)
Ed Humble (VP-Education)
A. Traviesa (Chm & CEO)
Robert Holloway (Dir-Sls Ops)

Pantherx Specialty, LLC (1)
24 Summit Park Dr, Pittsburgh, PA 15275
Tel.: (412) 547-3483
Web Site: https://www.pantherxrare.com
Sales Range: $25-49.9 Million
Pharmaceuticals Product Mfr
N.A.I.C.S.: 325412
Timothy Davis (Sr VP-Special Project)
Austin Russian (VP-Program Management)
Robert Snyder (Pres)

SCA Pharmaceuticals, LLC (1)
8821 Knoedl Ct, Little Rock, AR 72205-4600
Tel.: (501) 312-2800
Web Site:
http://www.sterilecompoundingusa.com
Drugs & Druggists' Sundries Merchant Whslr
N.A.I.C.S.: 424210
Heather L. Mason (Chm)
Matt Graves (Exec VP)
Gene Graves (Founder)
Matt White (Dir-Pharmacy Ops)
Rich Colucciello (VP-Fin & HR)
Heather L. Mason (Chm)
Scott Luce (CEO)

THE VIVIAN BEAUMONT THEATER, INC.
1285 Ave Of Americas, New York, NY 10019-6064
Tel.: (212) 362-7600 NY
Web Site: http://www.lct.org
Year Founded: 1979
Sales Range: $50-74.9 Million
Emp.: 894
Art Event Promoter
N.A.I.C.S.: 711310
J. Tomilson Hill (Chm)
Eric M. Mindich (Pres)
Brooke Garber Neidich (Vice Chm)
Leonard Tow (Vice Chm)
Elizabeth I. Peters (Sec)
Andre Bishop (Dir-Producing Artistic)
Adam Siegel (Mng Dir)
Hattie K. Jutagir (Exec Dir-Dev & Plng)
Jessica Niebanck (Gen Mgr)
Meghan Lantzy (Assoc Gen Mgr)

Alex Mustelier (Mgr-Facilities)
Mike Assalone (Assoc Mgr-Facilities)
Jeffrey G. Hamlin (Mgr-Production)
Paul Smithyman (Mgr-Production)
Rachel Norton (Assoc Dir-Dev)
Karin Schall (Mgr-Special Events)
Sheilaja Rao (Mgr-Patron Program)
David S. Brown (Dir-Fin)
Susan Knox (Controller)
Stacy Valentine (Mgr-Sys)
Linda Mason Ross (Dir-Mktg)
Kati Koerner (Dir-Education)
Alexandra Lopez (Assoc Dir-Education)
Mike Adank (Office Mgr)
Bartlett Sher (Dir-Resident)
Daniel Swee (Dir-Casting)
Matthew Markoff (Mgr)
Jessica Perlmeter Cochrane (Mgr)
Josh Lowenthal (Mgr)
Rheba Flegelman (Mgr-House)
Bill Cannon (Mgr-House)
Robert A. Belkin (Asst Treas)
Lynn Bowling (Supvr-Wardrobe)
John W. Rowe (Treas)

THE VOCATIONAL DEVELOPMENT FOUNDATION
1943 SE 6th Ave, Portland, OR 97214
Tel.: (503) 238-6115 OR
Year Founded: 2000
Sales Range: $10-24.9 Million
Vocational Rehabilitation Services
N.A.I.C.S.: 624310
Michael M. Miller (Pres)
Karl F. Koch (Treas & Sec)

THE VOLCKER ALLIANCE
560 Lexington Ave Ste 16B, New York, NY 10022
Tel.: (212) 218-7893 NY
Web Site:
http://www.volckeralliance.org
Year Founded: 2012
Sales Range: $10-24.9 Million
Emp.: 15
Civic & Social Organization
N.A.I.C.S.: 813410
Amy Smitherman (Dir-Fin & HR)
Gaurav Vasisht (Dir-Fin Regulation Program)
William Glasgall (Dir-State & Local Program)
Paul A. Volcker (Founder & Chm)
Anthony J. Dowd (Treas)
William Bradley (Vice Chm)
Thomas W. Ross Sr. (Pres)

THE VOLLRATH COMPANY LLC
1236 N 18th St, Sheboygan, WI 53081-3201
Tel.: (920) 457-4851 WI
Web Site: http://www.vollrathco.com
Year Founded: 1874
Sales Range: $150-199.9 Million
Emp.: 800
Mfr of Stainless Steel Smallware, Utensils & Equipment, Plastic Serving Utensils, Medical Products & Deep-Drawn Components
N.A.I.C.S.: 339910
Paul Bartelt (Pres & CEO)
Katharine Mizla (Mgr-Consultant Sls)
Christina Wegner (VP-Mktg)

Subsidiaries:

Acry Fab Inc. (1)
1236 N 18th St, Sheboygan, WI 53081
Tel.: (608) 837-0045
Acrylic Product Mfr
N.A.I.C.S.: 325220
Ralph Shillingburg (Mgr-Ops)

Albers Mechanical Contractors, Inc. (1)
200 W Plato Blvd, Saint Paul, MN 55107-2045
Tel.: (651) 224-5428
Web Site: http://www.albersco.com
Sales Range: $1-9.9 Million
Sheet Metal Fabrication Services
N.A.I.C.S.: 332999
Chuck Albers (Owner & Pres)
Charles Albers (CEO)

CORSAIR DISPLAY SYSTEMS, LLC (1)
5560 Airport Rd, Canandaigua, NY 14424
Tel.: (585) 396-3480
Web Site: http://www.corsairdisplay.com
Sales Range: $10-24.9 Million
Emp.: 25
Display Unit Mfr
N.A.I.C.S.: 337215
Michael Komendat (Mgr-Mktg)
Cindy Main (Mgr-Mfg)

PW Stoelting, L.L.C. (1)
502 Highway 67, Kiel, WI 53042
Tel.: (920) 894-2293
Web Site: http://www.stoelting.com
Sales Range: $25-49.9 Million
Emp.: 300
Food Service Equipment Sales
N.A.I.C.S.: 423440
David Kettler (Head-HR)

VOLLRATH DE MEXICO S. DE R.L. DE C.V. (1)
Periferico Sur No 7980 Edificio 4-E, Col Santa Maria Tequepexpan, 45600, Tlaquepaque, Jalisco, Mexico
Tel.: (52) 3331336767
Web Site: http://www.vollrathco.com
Sales Range: $10-24.9 Million
Emp.: 10
Oral Care Product Sales
N.A.I.C.S.: 423450

VOLLRATH EUROPE B.V. (1)
Beneluxbaan 7, PO Box 165, 5121DC, Rijen, Netherlands
Tel.: (31) 161870005
Web Site: http://www.vollrathco.com
Sales Range: $10-24.9 Million
Emp.: 8
Kitchenware Product Whslr
N.A.I.C.S.: 445298
Taco Wijbenga (Mgr-Sls)

Vollrath Shanghai Trading Limited (1)
500 Zhang Yang Road, Pudong, 200122, Shanghai, China
Tel.: (86) 2150589580
Foodservice Equipment Mfr
N.A.I.C.S.: 333241

THE VPS COMPANIES INC.
310 Walker St, Watsonville, CA 95076-4525
Tel.: (831) 724-7551 CA
Web Site: http://www.innfoods.com
Year Founded: 1966
Sales Range: $25-49.9 Million
Emp.: 200
Producer of Packaged Frozen Goods
N.A.I.C.S.: 424420

Subsidiaries:

Central Cold Storage Corporation (1)
13526 Blackie Rd, Castroville, CA 95012-3212
Tel.: (831) 633-4011
Web Site:
http://www.centralcoldstorage.com
Sales Range: $10-24.9 Million
Emp.: 100
Provider of Refrigerated Warehousing & Storage Services
N.A.I.C.S.: 424420
Norm Long (Pres)
Tim Heffernan (Pres)

Food Service Systems Inc. (1)
275 Westridge Dr, Watsonville, CA 95076
Tel.: (831) 761-6255
Web Site: http://www.innfoods.com
Emp.: 8

Frozen Food Distr
John Pengelly (Pres)

Inn Foods Inc. (1)
310 Walker St, Watsonville, CA 95076-4525
Tel.: (831) 724-2026
Web Site: http://www.innfoods.com
Sales Range: $10-24.9 Million
Emp.: 40
Producer of Packaged Frozen Goods
N.A.I.C.S.: 424420

National Custom Packing Inc. (1)
13526 Blackie Rd, Castroville, CA 95012-3212
Tel.: (831) 633-0203
Web Site: http://www.innfoods.com
Sales Range: $10-24.9 Million
Emp.: 80
Custom Packaging & Refrigeration Services of Meat, Poultry & Vegetables
N.A.I.C.S.: 424420

Valley Packing Service Inc. (1)
310 Walker St, Watsonville, CA 95076-4525
Tel.: (831) 724-7551
Sales Range: $10-24.9 Million
Emp.: 10
Producer of Packaged Frozen Goods
N.A.I.C.S.: 424420

THE W.B. WOOD COMPANY
225 Park Ave S, New York, NY 10003
Tel.: (212) 206-9500 NJ
Web Site: http://www.wbwood.com
Year Founded: 1905
Sales Range: $10-24.9 Million
Emp.: 60
Office Furnishings Contractor
N.A.I.C.S.: 423210
Richard Mines (Pres)

THE W.L. MAY COMPANY
1120 SE Madison St, Portland, OR 97214-3618
Tel.: (503) 231-7000 OR
Web Site: http://www.wlmay.com
Year Founded: 1923
Sales Range: $10-24.9 Million
Emp.: 90
Major Appliance Parts, Heating & Cooling Supplies & Equipment Distr
N.A.I.C.S.: 423620
Stuart Sharman (Pres & CEO)

THE WAGGONERS TRUCKING
5220 Midland Rd, Billings, MT 59101
Tel.: (406) 248-1919 MT
Web Site:
http://www.waggonerstrucking.com
Year Founded: 1951
Sales Range: $75-99.9 Million
Emp.: 300
Freight Truck Transportation Services
N.A.I.C.S.: 484121
David D. Waggoner (Pres)
Dennis Martin (Dir-HR)
Mary Waggoner (Treas & Sec)
Wayne Waggoner (Founder)
Caroline Phillips (CFO)

THE WAGNER COMPANIES, INC.
10600 W Brown Deer Rd, Milwaukee, WI 53224
Tel.: (414) 214-0444
Web Site:
http://www.wagnercompanies.com
Rev.: $18,000,000
Emp.: 160
Pipe Fitting Mfr
N.A.I.C.S.: 541211
Robert A. Wagner (Chm & CEO)
Steve Engebregsten (VP)
Anthony R. Goodings (Dir-Sls)

THE WAGNER SMITH COMPANY

3178 Encrete Ln, Dayton, OH 45439-1902
Tel.: (937) 298-7481   OH
Web Site: http://www.wagner-ind.com
Year Founded: 1917
Sales Range: $25-49.9 Million
Emp.: 250
Providers of Electrical Services
N.A.I.C.S.: 238210
Donna Goss *(Controller)*

THE WALDINGER CORPORATION
2601 Bell Ave, Des Moines, IA 50321-1120
Tel.: (515) 284-1911
Web Site: http://www.waldinger.com
Year Founded: 1986
Sales Range: $300-349.9 Million
Emp.: 1,200
Plumbing, Heating, Air Conditioning & Construction Products & Services
N.A.I.C.S.: 238220
Thomas Koehn *(CEO)*
Dave Miller *(Sr VP)*
Wendy Gray *(Dir-Corp Comm)*
Brian Worth *(CFO)*

THE WALKING COMPANY HOLDINGS, INC.
519 Lincoln County Pkwy, Lincolnton, NC 28092
Tel.: (828) 695-2800   DE
Web Site: http://www.thewalkingcompany.com
Footwear Retailer, Catalog Sales & Electronic Commerce
N.A.I.C.S.: 458210
Jeffrey Cowen *(Sr VP-Production)*
David R. Wolf *(Sr VP-Mktg)*
Matthew D. Lux *(VP-Real Estate)*
Michael Walker *(Sr VP)*

Subsidiaries:

The Walking Company, Inc.   (1)
2475 Townsgate Ste 200, Westlake Village, CA 91361
Tel.: (805) 496-3005
Web Site: http://www.thewalkingcompany.com
Sales Range: $100-124.9 Million
Emp.: 40
Shoes & Accessories Retailer
N.A.I.C.S.: 458210
Mike Grenley *(CEO)*

THE WALL COMPANY
1476 W Harvard Ave, Gilbert, AZ 85233
Tel.: (602) 453-9255
Web Site: http://www.thewallco.com
Year Founded: 1991
Sales Range: $10-24.9 Million
Emp.: 165
Concrete Finishing Services
N.A.I.C.S.: 238140
Scott McDonald *(Pres)*

THE WALLING COMPANY, INC.
6103 N 90th St, Omaha, NE 68134-1902
Tel.: (402) 571-9600
Web Site: http://www.thewallingcompany.com
Sales Range: $75-99.9 Million
Emp.: 10
Industrial Process Furnaces & Ovens
N.A.I.C.S.: 423830
Bob Henrichs *(Pres-Sls)*
Don Miller *(VP-Outside Sls-Nebraska)*
Larry Stacy *(VP-Outside Sls-Iowa)*

Subsidiaries:

The Walling Co., Inc.   (1)
1621 NW 70th Pl, Ankeny, IA 50023-9042
Tel.: (515) 289-4500

Web Site: http://www.thewallingcompany.com
Sales Range: $25-49.9 Million
Emp.: 6
Industrial Process Furnaces & Ovens
N.A.I.C.S.: 423830

THE WALNUT GROUP
312 Walnut St Ste 1151, Cincinnati, OH 45202
Tel.: (513) 651-3300
Web Site: http://www.thewalnutgroup.com
Sales Range: $25-49.9 Million
Emp.: 13
Privater Equity Firm
N.A.I.C.S.: 523999
James M. Gould *(Mng Gen Partner)*
Frederic H. Mayerson *(Founder, Chm & Mng Gen Partner)*
R. Scott Barnes *(CFO)*
Daniel C. Staton *(Mng Gen Partner)*

THE WALSH GROUP
929 W Adams St, Chicago, IL 60607-3021
Tel.: (312) 563-5400   IL
Web Site: https://www.walshgroup.com
Year Founded: 1898
Sales Range: $5-14.9 Billion
Emp.: 8,000
Offices of Other Holding Companies
N.A.I.C.S.: 551112
Daniel J. Walsh *(Co-Chm)*
Roy Epps *(Sr VP-Water & Wastewater)*
David Casey *(Pres-Heavy Civil)*
Mike Whelan *(Pres-Building Div)*
Matthew Walsh Sr. *(Co-Chm)*

Subsidiaries:

Archer Western Contractors   (1)
2410 Paces Ferry Rd Ste 600, Atlanta, GA 30339
Tel.: (404) 495-8700
Web Site: http://www.walshgroup.com
Sales Range: $700-749.9 Million
Emp.: 70
General Contracting; Construction Management & Design Services
N.A.I.C.S.: 236220
Don Gillis *(VP)*

R&L Brosamer Inc.   (1)
1777 Oakland Blvd Ste 300, Walnut Creek, CA 94596
Tel.: (925) 627-1700
Web Site: http://www.walshgroup.com
Sales Range: $100-124.9 Million
Emp.: 40
General Contractor, Highway & Street Construction
N.A.I.C.S.: 237310

Walsh Construction Co. of Illinois   (1)
929 W Adams St, Chicago, IL 60607
Tel.: (312) 563-5400
Web Site: http://www.walshgroup.com
Sales Range: $350-399.9 Million
Emp.: 500
General Construction Services
N.A.I.C.S.: 236210
Daniel J. Walsh *(Co-Pres)*
Nick Fawell *(Dir-Bus Dev)*
Sean Walsh *(Co-Pres)*
Matthew Walsh Jr. *(Chm)*

THE WALTON FAMILY FOUNDATION, INC.
PO Box 2030, Bentonville, AR 72712
Tel.: (479) 464-1570   DE
Web Site: http://www.waltonfamilyfoundation.org
Year Founded: 1987
Sales Range: $100-124.9 Million
Emp.: 125
Grantmaking Services
N.A.I.C.S.: 813211

Bob Smith *(Dir-Acctg & Ops)*
Naccaman Williams *(Dir-Special Projects)*
Karen Minkel *(Dir-Home Reg Program)*
Marc Sternberg *(Dir-K-12 Education Program)*
Lisa Montez *(Gen Counsel)*
Frances Woodard *(Dir-People)*
Matthew Carr *(Dir-Strategy, Learning & Evaluation)*
Moira Mcdonald *(Dir-Environment Program)*
Chelsea Peters *(Chief Strategy Officer)*
Caryl M. Stern *(Exec Dir)*

THE WARD GROUP
5750 Genesis Court Ste 220, Dallas, TX 75034
Tel.: (972) 818-4050
Web Site: http://www.mediastewards.com
Advertising Services
N.A.I.C.S.: 541810
Shirley Ward *(CEO)*
Rob Enright *(Pres)*
Robin Cox *(Supvr-Media)*
Brad Hagstrom *(VP-Bus Dev)*
Lacy Edwards *(Acct Exec)*
James Pruitt *(Coord-Digital Media)*

THE WAREHOUSE STORE FIXTURE COMPANY
84 Progress Ln, Waterbury, CT 06705
Tel.: (203) 575-0111
Web Site: http://www.restaurantcity.com
Sales Range: $10-24.9 Million
Emp.: 40
Commercial Equipment Merchant Whslr
N.A.I.C.S.: 423440
Roy Silverman *(VP)*
David Silverman *(Treas & Sec)*
Judith Silverman *(Pres)*

THE WARMINGTON GROUP
3090 Pullman St, Costa Mesa, CA 92626-5901
Tel.: (714) 557-5511   CA
Web Site: http://www.warmingtonhomes.com
Year Founded: 1972
Sales Range: $350-399.9 Million
Emp.: 300
Construction Services
N.A.I.C.S.: 237210
Sara Banta *(Owner)*

Subsidiaries:

Bayport Mortgage - Las Vegas   (1)
8363 W Sunset Rd Ste 200, Las Vegas, NV 89113-2210
Tel.: (702) 876-2994
Mortgage Brokerage Services
N.A.I.C.S.: 522310

Bayport Mortgage - Sacramento   (1)
2901 Douglas Blvd Ste 230, Roseville, CA 95661-4247
Tel.: (916) 791-5001
N.A.I.C.S.: 236220

Chateau Interiors & Design   (1)
10 Bunsen, Irvine, CA 92618
Tel.: (949) 679-3100
Sales Range: $50-74.9 Million
Emp.: 48
Interior Decorators
N.A.I.C.S.: 449121
Rob Robinson *(Coord-Trng & Tech)*

The Warmington Group - Northern California Division Office   (1)
2400 Camino Ramon Ste 234, San Ramon, CA 94583
Tel.: (925) 866-6700

Web Site: http://www.warmingtonhomes.com
Sales Range: $25-49.9 Million
Emp.: 13
New Home Construction
N.A.I.C.S.: 237210
Matt Tingler *(Pres)*

Warmington Properties, Inc.   (1)
3090 Pullman St, Costa Mesa, CA 92626
Tel.: (714) 557-5511
Web Site: http://www.warmingtonpropertiesinc.com
Emp.: 14
Real Estate Manangement Services
N.A.I.C.S.: 531390
Greg Oberling *(Pres)*

Warmington Residential   (1)
3090 Pullman St, Costa Mesa, CA 92626
Tel.: (714) 557-5511
Web Site: http://www.homesbywarmington.com
Real Estate Manangement Services
N.A.I.C.S.: 531390
Maribel Maciel *(Mgr-Contract Admin)*
Jennifer Bell *(Dir-Adv)*
Jay Deckard *(Project Mgr-Southern California)*
Bob Dressler *(Controller)*

THE WARRIOR GROUP, INC.
1624 Falcon Dr Ste 100, De Soto, TX 75115
Tel.: (972) 228-9955
Web Site: http://www.warrior-group.net
Year Founded: 1997
Sales Range: $100-124.9 Million
Emp.: 57
Modular Construction
N.A.I.C.S.: 236210
Gail Warrior-Lawrence *(Pres & CEO)*
Phil Slingerland *(COO)*
Betty Floyd *(CFO)*
Susan Johnson *(Chief Dev Officer)*

THE WASH TUB
2208 NW Loop 410, San Antonio, TX 78230
Tel.: (210) 493-8822   TX
Web Site: http://www.washtub.com
Year Founded: 1986
Car Wash Operators
N.A.I.C.S.: 811192
Matt Vizza *(Pres & CEO)*

THE WASHINGTON CONSULTING GROUP INC.
4915 Auburn Ave Ste 301, Bethesda, MD 20814
Tel.: (301) 656-2330
Web Site: http://www.washcg.com
Sales Range: $25-49.9 Million
Emp.: 500
Technical Industry Consulting
N.A.I.C.S.: 541330
Ned S. Reese *(VP-Air Traffic Programs)*
Jeff Griffith *(Exec VP)*
Armando C. Chapelli Jr. *(Founder, Chm & CEO)*

THE WATKINS COMPANY INC.
181 E 56th Ave Ste 600, Denver, CO 80216-1766
Tel.: (303) 292-0500   CO
Year Founded: 1986
Sales Range: $25-49.9 Million
Emp.: 240
Gasoline Service Stations
N.A.I.C.S.: 457120
Sue Vanderberg *(Pres)*

THE WATKINS COMPANY INC.
11601 Otter Creek S, Mabelvale, AR 72103
Tel.: (501) 217-7400
Year Founded: 1971
Sales Range: $10-24.9 Million

THE WATKINS COMPANY INC.

The Watkins Company Inc.—(Continued)
Emp.: 100
Provider of Commercial Art & Graphic Design Services
N.A.I.C.S.: 541430
Richard Taylor Watkins (Pres)
Steve Fike (CFO)

THE WAY TO HAPPINESS FOUNDATION INTERNATIONAL
201 E Broadway, Glendale, CA 91205
Tel.: (818) 254-0600   CA
Web Site: http://www.thewaytohappiness.org
Year Founded: 1984
Sales Range: $1-9.9 Million
Emp.: 22
Community Action Services
N.A.I.C.S.: 624190
Joni Ginsberg (Pres)
Tom Burpee (Sec)
Nadja Lehmann (Treas)

THE WECK CORPORATION
1220 3rd Ave Fl 1, New York, NY 10021-5104
Tel.: (212) 517-6300   NY
Web Site: http://www.gracioushome.com
Year Founded: 1963
Sales Range: $50-74.9 Million
Emp.: 300
Provider of Retail Housewares
N.A.I.C.S.: 449129
Jordan Smilowitz (VP)
Ivan Zubin (Controller)

THE WEEKS-LERMAN GROUP LLC
5838 Page Pl, Maspeth, NY 11378-2235
Tel.: (718) 803-5000
Web Site: http://www.weekslerman.com
Year Founded: 1996
Sales Range: $75-99.9 Million
Emp.: 225
Mfr of Stationery & Office Supplies
N.A.I.C.S.: 424120
Cindy Ciaccio (COO & VP)
Cindi Cordo-Gutkowski (Mgr-Customer Svc)

THE WEINSTEIN ORGANIZATION, INC.
1 S Wacker Dr Ste 1670, Chicago, IL 60606-4670
Tel.: (312) 214-2900   IL
Web Site: http://www.weinsteinorg.com
Year Founded: 1992
Sales Range: $10-24.9 Million
Emp.: 16
Advetising Agency
N.A.I.C.S.: 541810
Mark J. Weinstein (Pres)
Janelle Schenher (Supvr-Acct)
Julie Determann (Supvr-Acct)
Kyla Herbes (Dir-Creative)
Bhavesh Patel (Dir-IT)

THE WELFONT COMPANIES INC.
601 N Ashley Dr Ste 600, Tampa, FL 33602
Tel.: (813) 226-2099
Web Site: http://www.welfont.com
Year Founded: 2014
Sales Range: $10-24.9 Million
Emp.: 51
Real Estate Development Services
N.A.I.C.S.: 531210

Shawn Marcell (CEO)
Michael Surowiec (CFO)
Mike Mehaffey (COO)
Rachel Shelley (Exec VP-Real Estate)
Amy Stevenson (Exec VP-Brokerage & Transactions)

THE WELK GROUP INC.
300 Rancheros Dr Ste 450, San Marcos, CA 92069
Tel.: (760) 749-3000   CA
Web Site: http://www.welkresorts.com
Year Founded: 1955
Sales Range: $100-124.9 Million
Emp.: 1,350
Vacation & Timeshare Properties
N.A.I.C.S.: 721214

Subsidiaries:
Welk Resorts San Diego   (1)
8860 Lawrence Welk Dr, Escondido, CA 92026   (100%)
Tel.: (760) 749-3000
Web Site: http://www.welksandiego.com
Sales Range: $25-49.9 Million
Emp.: 200
Vacation Properties, Sales & Rentals
N.A.I.C.S.: 531311
Sean Coogan (Gen Mgr)

THE WELLSPRING GROUP
4 Research Dr Ste 402, Shelton, CT 06484
Tel.: (203) 261-1515
Web Site: http://www.wellspringrp.com
Year Founded: 2001
Sales Range: $10-24.9 Million
Emp.: 75
Information Technology Staffing & Consulting Services
N.A.I.C.S.: 561311
Amy Dain (Co-Founder & Co-Mng Partner)
Melissa Peirce (Co-Founder & Co-Mng Partner)

THE WEST END LUMBER COMPANY
4520 W 130th St, Cleveland, OH 44135
Tel.: (216) 671-1133   OH
Web Site: http://www.westendlumber.com
Year Founded: 1896
Sales Range: $10-24.9 Million
Emp.: 16
Supplier of Lumber
N.A.I.C.S.: 423310
Warren P. Coleman Jr. (Pres)

THE WESTERN GROUP
4025 NW Express Ave, Portland, OR 97210-1401
Tel.: (503) 222-1644
Web Site: http://www.thewesterngroup.com
Year Founded: 1967
Sales Range: $10-24.9 Million
Emp.: 300
Provider of Wire Products & Sheet Metal
N.A.I.C.S.: 332618
Tom Holtz (Controller)
Zanley F. Galton III (Pres)

THE WESTERN PENNSYLVANIA CONSERVANCY
800 Waterfront Dr, Pittsburgh, PA 15222
Tel.: (412) 288-2777   PA
Web Site: http://www.paconserve.org
Year Founded: 1931
Sales Range: $10-24.9 Million
Environmental Conservation Services

N.A.I.C.S.: 813312
Stephen G. Robinson (Vice Chm)
Susan Fitzsimmons (Chm)
Thomas D. Saunders (Pres & CEO)
David E. Barensfeld (Sec)
Daniel S. Nydick (Treas)
Cynthia Carrow (VP-Govt & Community Rels)
Constance Eads (CFO & VP)
Shaun Fenlon (VP-Land Conservation)
Genny McIntyre (VP-Institutional Advancement)
Lynda Waggoner (VP & Dir-Fallingwater)

THE WESTERN STATE BANK
1500 E Kansas Ave, Garden City, KS 67846
Tel.: (620) 275-4128
Web Site: http://www.wsbks.com
Year Founded: 1973
Sales Range: $10-24.9 Million
Emp.: 55
Commercial Banking Services
N.A.I.C.S.: 522110
Leonard Herman (VP)
Joe Burnside (VP)
Kim Partin (VP)
J. P. Arellano (Officer-Bank Physical Security & VP)
Lorita J. Frey (CEO)
Renee Cheramy (Asst VP)
Blanca Corral (Asst VP)
Jeremy Curlo (Asst VP)
Bebe Denney (Asst VP)
Katie Gates (Asst VP)
Anita Hernandez (Asst VP)
Melissa Morrow (Asst VP)
Don Linville (Sr VP-Internal Audit)
Jason Drohman (Sr VP-Ops & IT)
Lisa Donat (VP)

THE WESTERVELT COMPANY
1400 Jack Warner Pkwy NE, Tuscaloosa, AL 35404-1002
Tel.: (205) 562-5000   DE
Web Site: http://www.westervelt.com
Year Founded: 1884
Sales Range: $150-199.9 Million
Emp.: 2,000
Lumber Milling Mfr
N.A.I.C.S.: 321113
Gary Dailey (CFO & VP-Fin)
Alicia D. Cramer (VP-Bus Dev)
Jim King (VP & Gen Mgr-Forest Resources)
Brian Luoma (Pres & CEO)
Ray Robbins (Gen Counsel, Sec & VP)

Subsidiaries:
Resolution Packaging   (1)
33 Burgin St, Marion, NC 28752
Tel.: (828) 652-5511
Web Site: http://www.rocktenn.com
Sales Range: $25-49.9 Million
Emp.: 240
Packaging Products
N.A.I.C.S.: 322212

Westervelt Realty   (1)
1400 Jack Warner Pkwy, Tuscaloosa, AL 35404   (100%)
Tel.: (205) 562-5531
Web Site: http://www.westerveltrealty.com
Sales Range: $50-74.9 Million
Emp.: 150
Commercial & Residential Real Estate Sales & Management
N.A.I.C.S.: 531320
Tom Chambers (VP)
Michael O'Neal (Mgr-Land Dev)

THE WESTWOOD GROUP, INC.
720 I St SE, Washington, DC 20003
Tel.: (202) 667-0091

Sales Range: $1-9.9 Million
Emp.: 35
Management Consulting for Federal Government Clients
N.A.I.C.S.: 921190
Pamela H. Frank (Pres)

THE WHEELING CORPORATION INC.
100 1st St E, Brewster, OH 44613-1202
Tel.: (330) 767-3401   DE
Web Site: http://www.wlerwy.com
Year Founded: 1990
Sales Range: $25-49.9 Million
Emp.: 350
Railroad & Line-Haul Operating Services
N.A.I.C.S.: 482111
Larry R. Parsons (Chm & CEO)
James I. Northcraft (VP-Transportation)
Kasey O'Connor (VP-Engrg)
Gregory J. Levy (VP-Mktg)
Linda Patterson (Dir-Car Acctg)
Tammie Herring (Mgr-Accts Payable)
Donna L. Phillips (CFO)
Marc Masters (Dir-IT)
Justin Crues (Dir-Market-Petroleum)
Becky Himmel (Dir-Pur)
Jodi Specht (Dir-Revenue Acctg)
Jeffery A. Davis (Dir-Transportation)
Jonathan Chastek (Exec VP)
Sara Ehman (Mgr-Customer Svc)
Alec Jarvis (VP-Law & Govt Rels)
Drew A. Nelson (VP-Mktg & Sls)

Subsidiaries:
Akron Barberton Cluster Railway Company, Inc.   (1)
43 2nd St SW, Barberton, OH 44203-2619
Tel.: (330) 767-7221
Web Site: http://www.wlerwy.com
Sales Range: $10-24.9 Million
Emp.: 8
Switching & Terminal Services
N.A.I.C.S.: 488210
Les Ashley (Gen Mgr)

Wheeling & Lake Erie Railway Co., Inc.   (1)
100 1st St SE, Brewster, OH 44613
Tel.: (330) 767-3401
Sales Range: $10-24.9 Million
Emp.: 75
Provider of Railroad & Line-Haul Operating Services
N.A.I.C.S.: 482111
Larry R. Parsons (CEO)
Joe Burley (Mgr-HR)

THE WHITAKER COMPANIES, INC.
1200 Enclave Pkwy Ste 200, Houston, TX 77077
Tel.: (281) 870-1000
Web Site: http://www.whitakercompanies.com
Sales Range: $10-24.9 Million
Emp.: 70
Medical Help Service
N.A.I.C.S.: 561320
Bruce Whitaker (Owner, Pres & CEO)
Carol Wenom (VP-Trng & Organizational Dev)

Subsidiaries:
Whitaker Technical   (1)
10375 Richmond Ave Ste 1700, Houston, TX 77042
Tel.: (281) 870-1000
Web Site: http://www.whitaker.com
Technical Staffing Services
N.A.I.C.S.: 561311
Bruce Whitaker (CEO)
Carol Wenom (Gen Mgr)

THE WHITE BUFFALO SALOON, LLC

5377 McIntosh Rd, Sarasota, FL 34233
Tel.: (941) 927-6655
Web Site:
http://www.thewbsaloon.com
Sales Range: $1-9.9 Million
Emp.: 80
Bar & Grill
N.A.I.C.S.: 722511
Mike Evanoff *(Owner)*

THE WHITE FAMILY COMPANIES, INC.
2 River Pl Ste 444, Dayton, OH 45405
Tel.: (937) 220-6394   OH
Web Site: http://www.whitecars.com
Year Founded: 1932
Sales Range: $300-349.9 Million
Emp.: 1,800
New & Used Car Dealerships Owner & Operator
N.A.I.C.S.: 441110
Tim White *(Pres)*

THE WHITE OAK GROUP, INC.
5665 Northside Pkwy Ste 500, Atlanta, GA 30328
Tel.: (404) 875-9994
Web Site:
http://www.thewhiteoakgroup.com
Investment Management Service
N.A.I.C.S.: 523940
Christopher C. Melton *(Founder, Chm & CEO)*

Subsidiaries:

Prism Spectrum Holdings LLC   (1)
4000 Triangle Ln Ste 160, Export, PA 15632
Tel.: (724) 325-3330
Web Site: http://www.alloygroup.com
Remediation Services
N.A.I.C.S.: 562910
Luke Novomesky *(VP)*
Shawn P. Regan *(CEO)*

Subsidiary (Domestic):

Copper Environmental Consulting, LLC   (2)
406 E Park Ave Ste 2, Anaconda, MT 59711
Tel.: (406) 563-2700
Web Site: http://www.copperenv.com
Environmental Consulting Services
N.A.I.C.S.: 541620
Dave McCarthy *(Founder)*
Jim Jonas *(Principal)*

Dec-Tam Corporation   (2)
50 Concord St, North Reading, MA 01864
Tel.: (978) 470-2860
Web Site: http://www.dectam.com
Sales Range: $10-24.9 Million
Emp.: 65
Asbestos Removal & Encapsulation
N.A.I.C.S.: 562910
Brian Fitz Simmons *(CEO)*
Bruce Sullivan *(Project Mgr)*

THE WHITESTONE GROUP, INC.
4100 Regent St Ste C, Columbus, OH 43219
Tel.: (614) 501-7007   OH
Web Site:
http://www.whitestonegroup.us
Year Founded: 2000
Sales Range: $10-24.9 Million
Emp.: 388
Security System Services
N.A.I.C.S.: 561621
Pamela Gentile *(COO)*
Jeff LaRe *(Exec VP)*
John D. Clark Sr. *(Pres & CEO)*

THE WHITING-TURNER CONTRACTING COMPANY
300 E Joppa Rd, Baltimore, MD 21286
Tel.: (410) 821-1100   MD
Web Site: https://www.whiting-turner.com
Year Founded: 1909
Sales Range: $1-4.9 Billion
Emp.: 4,255
Commercial & Institutional Building Construction
N.A.I.C.S.: 236220
Brent Voyles *(VP)*
Chris Martinson *(VP)*
Jack DaSilva *(Sr VP-Allentown)*
Paul Schmitt *(Sr VP-Las Vegas)*
Espen Brooks *(VP-Dallas)*
Keith Douglas *(Sr VP-Atlanta)*
Kevin Shields *(VP)*
Jack Stackalis *(VP-Sacramento)*
Steven Likins *(VP-San Diego)*
Tavio Darchangelo *(Mgr-Los Angeles)*
Vijay Daniel *(VP-Phoenix)*
Richard L. Vogel Jr. *(Sr VP-Columbia)*
Len Cannatelli Jr. *(Sr VP-Irvine)*

THE WHOLE PERSON, INC.
3710 Main St, Kansas City, MO 64111
Tel.: (816) 561-0304   MO
Web Site:
http://www.thewholeperson.org
Year Founded: 1978
Sales Range: $10-24.9 Million
Disability Assistance Services
N.A.I.C.S.: 624120
Rick O'Neal *(Pres)*
Mike Wiley *(COO)*
Lisa Cherry *(Dir-Payroll Admin)*
Tim Sandusky *(Mgr-Quality Assurance)*
Monique Todd *(Dir-HR)*
Julie De Jean *(CEO)*
Jim Keeney *(CFO)*
Jim Johnson *(Mgr-Consumer Directed Svcs)*
Jay Robertson *(Mgr-Employment Svcs)*
Debbie Housh *(Treas-Interim & Sec)*
Genny Manly-Klocek *(VP)*
Melanie Middlebrook *(Dir-Fin)*
Gabi Collins *(Mgr-Transition Svcs, Info & Referral)*
Terri Goddard *(Mgr-Resource Dev & Community Rels)*
Kim Krueger *(Mgr-Mktg & Comm)*
Erik Nelson *(Mgr-Social Enterprise)*
Donnette Fayne *(Mgr-Youth & Adult Support Svcs)*

THE WHOLESALE HOUSE INC.
503 W High St, Hicksville, OH 43526-1037
Tel.: (419) 542-7739   OH
Web Site: http://www.twhouse.com
Year Founded: 1978
Sales Range: $25-49.9 Million
Emp.: 100
Electronic Parts & Equipment Whslr
N.A.I.C.S.: 423690

THE WICKS GROUP OF COMPANIES, LLC
400 Park Ave, New York, NY 10022-9420
Tel.: (212) 838-2100   NY
Web Site: http://www.wicksgroup.com
Year Founded: 1989
Investment Services
N.A.I.C.S.: 523999
Craig B. Klosk *(Founder & Mng Partner)*
Daniel M. Kortick *(Mng Partner)*
Max Von Zuben *(Mng Partner)*
Daniel L. Black *(Mng Partner)*
Andreia Santos de Araujo *(Dir-Ops & Acctg)*
Irina I. Krasik *(VP)*
Thomas P. Kearney III *(Principal)*

Subsidiaries:

Antenna International   (1)
15 River Rd Ste 15B, Wilton, CT 06897
Tel.: (203) 523-0320
Web Site:
http://www.antennainternational.com
Audio & Multimedia Equipment Mfr
N.A.I.C.S.: 334310
Christopher Bazley *(Sr VP-Sls-Global)*
Gordon Montgomery *(CMO & Exec VP)*
Jeff Pierne *(CFO & Exec VP)*

Bisnow LLC   (1)
7 World Trade Ctr 46th Fl, New York, NY 10007
Tel.: (202) 293-0370
Web Site: http://www.bisnow.com
Sales Range: $10-24.9 Million
Emp.: 70
News & Information for Commercial Real Estate
N.A.I.C.S.: 519290
Mike Ponticelli *(VP-Sls)*
Devin Crone *(Asst Controller)*
Jaime Rome *(Coord-Events)*
Mike Vigario *(VP-Fin)*
Liz Keevil *(VP-Email Mktg)*
Alex Funaro *(CTO)*
Will Friend *(CEO)*
Francesco Decamilli *(COO)*

Bonded Services Group Limited   (1)
Units 4-5 Space Waye, Feltham, TW14 0TH, Middlesex, United Kingdom
Tel.: (44) 2088977973
Web Site: https://www.bonded.com
Emp.: 40
Investment Management Service
N.A.I.C.S.: 523940
John Reeves *(Mng Dir)*

CFM Religion Publishing Group, LLC   (1)
8805 Governor's Hill Dr Ste 400, Cincinnati, OH 45249
Tel.: (513) 931-4050
Web Site:
http://www.cfmreligionpublishing.com
Magazine Publisher
N.A.I.C.S.: 513120

EZShield, Inc.   (1)
9920 Franklin Sq Dr Ste 250, Nottingham, MD 21236
Tel.: (888) 439-7443
Web Site: http://www.ezshield.com
Software Publisher
N.A.I.C.S.: 513210
John Evans *(Exec VP-Sls)*
Dale Dabbs *(Pres & CEO)*
Rich Scott *(Chief Revenue Officer)*
Angela Murphy *(COO)*
Michael Catanzarita *(CFO)*
Darrell Laffoon *(CTO)*
Heidi Daitch *(Chief Strategy Officer)*
Donna Parent *(CMO)*

Jobson Healthcare Information LLC   (1)
100 Ave of the Americas 9th Fl, New York, NY 10013-1689
Tel.: (212) 274-7000
Web Site: http://www.jmihealth.com
Healthcare Information & Marketing Services Publisher
N.A.I.C.S.: 513120
Jeffrey MacDonald *(CEO)*
Marc Ferrara *(CEO-Info Svcs Grp)*
Jeff Levitz *(Sr VP-Ops)*
Michael R. Lemon *(Sr VP-CME Compliance)*
Lorraine Orlando *(Sr VP-HR)*

Subsidiary (Domestic):

International Center for Postgraduate Medical Education, LLC   (2)
179 Graham Rd Ste E, Ithaca, NY 14850-1141
Tel.: (607) 257-5860
Web Site: http://www.icpme.us
Sales Range: $25-49.9 Million
Emp.: 9
Medical Education Services
N.A.I.C.S.: 519290

JHI Optical Group   (2)
100 Avenue of the Americas, New York, NY 10013
Tel.: (212) 274-7000
Magazine Publisher
N.A.I.C.S.: 513120

Jobson Medical Information LLC   (2)
100 Avenue of the Americas 9th Fl, New York, NY 10013
Tel.: (212) 274-7000
Magazine Publisher
N.A.I.C.S.: 513120
Pierre Gascon *(Dir-Network & Sys Svcs)*
Bill Scott *(Pres-ECP Bus Svcs)*
Breanna Benz *(Assoc Editor)*
Derek Winston *(CFO)*
James Spina *(Editor-In-Cheif)*
Marge Axelrad *(Sr VP & Dir-Editorial & Optical)*

Subsidiary (Domestic):

Frames Data Inc.   (3)
100 Avenue of the Americas 9th Fl, New York, NY 10013
Tel.: (212) 274-7132
Web Site: http://www.framesdata.com
Ophthalmic Goods Whslr
N.A.I.C.S.: 423460
Lenor Fowler *(Dir-Sls)*
Candi Dooley *(Mgr-Licensing Acct)*
Tom Doyle *(Dir-Key Accts)*
Daniel Lehrhaupt *(Mgr-Client Svcs)*
Nichola Liboro *(Coord-Mktg)*
Judith Michael *(Sr VP-Bus Ops)*
Lisa Rosenberg *(Designer-Graphic)*
Joshua Wasserman *(Sr Mgr-Mktg)*
Hunter Noell *(Mgr-Bus Dev)*

Subsidiary (Domestic):

Jobson Professional Publications Group   (2)
11 Campus Blvd Ste 100, Newtown, PA 18940-1761
Tel.: (610) 492-1000
Periodicals
N.A.I.C.S.: 513130

Jobson Publishing Corporation   (2)
367 Inverness Pkwy Ste 215, Englewood, CO 80112-5891
Tel.: (303) 799-1930
Web Site: http://www.jmihealth.com
Periodicals
N.A.I.C.S.: 541690

Post Graduate Institute for Medicine (PIM)   (2)
367 Inverness Pkwy Ste 215, Englewood, CO 80112
Tel.: (303) 799-1930
Web Site: http://www.pimed.com
Sales Range: $25-49.9 Million
Periodicals
N.A.I.C.S.: 513120
Michael R. Lemon *(Pres)*
Trace Hutchison *(Dir-Medical Education)*
Allison Hughes *(Dir-Ops)*
Samantha Mattiucci *(Mng Dir & Dir-Medical Education)*

Postgraduate Healthcare Education, LLC   (2)
777 Passaic Ave Ste 380, Clifton, NJ 07012
Tel.: (973) 777-9513
Web Site: http://www.jhihealth.com
Health Care Srvices
N.A.I.C.S.: 621999

alert Marketing, Inc.   (2)
160 Chubb Ave Ste 304, Lyndhurst, NJ 07071
Tel.: (201) 623-0961
Web Site: http://www.alertmarketing.com
Health Care Srvices
N.A.I.C.S.: 621999
Dave Leyden *(Pres)*
Bruce Birtwell *(Sr VP-Sls & Mktg)*
Ethan Armstrong *(Mgr-Acct-Sls)*
Susan Benner *(Mgr-Acct-Sls)*
Peter Coyne *(Mgr-Acct-Sls)*
Lynn Gale *(Mgr-Acct-Sls)*
Kevin Kingree *(Mgr-Acct-Sls)*
Brian Miller *(Mgr-Acct-Sls)*
Sharilyn Anton *(Mgr-Acct-Sls)*
Wendy Waerness *(Mgr-Acct-Sls)*

THE WICKS GROUP OF COMPANIES, LLC

U.S. PRIVATE

The Wicks Group of Companies, LLC—(Continued)

Standard Publishing Group LLC (1)
8805 Governor's Dr Ste 400, Cincinnati, OH 45249
Tel.: (513) 931-4050
Web Site: http://www.standardpub.com
Sales Range: $75-99.9 Million
Publishes, Prints & Distributes Religious & Educational Materials
N.A.I.C.S.: 513130
Stewart McMeking (VP-Trade Sls)

Wilks Broadcast Group, LLC (1)
6470 E Johns Crossing Ste 450, Duluth, GA 30097
Tel.: (678) 240-8976
Web Site:
http://www.wilksbroadcastgroup.com
Radio Broadcasting Services
N.A.I.C.S.: 516110
Jeff Wilks (CEO)
Stephen Bradshaw (CFO)
Jeff Sanders (Exec VP-Programming)

THE WILDER COMPANIES
800 Boyleston St Ste 1300, Boston, MA 02115
Tel.: (617) 247-9200   MA
Web Site: http://www.wilderco.com
Year Founded: 1990
Sales Range: $75-99.9 Million
Emp.: 50
Provider of Real Estate Management & Leasing Services
N.A.I.C.S.: 531210
Andrew T. Lagrega (Principal)
David J. Mallen (Principal)
Thomas Wilder (Principal)
Shelley M. Anderson (Dir-New Bus Dev)
Angelo Russo (VP-Fin)
Jill Crouch (Mgr-HR)
Courtney Dobrowolski (Coord-Leasing & Mktg)
Eileen Boylen (Mgr-Construction)
Brian Cosentino (VP-Acq)

THE WILDLIFE CENTER OF VIRGINIA
1800 S Delphine Ave, Waynesboro, VA 22980
Tel.: (540) 942-9453   VA
Web Site:
http://www.wildlifecenter.org
Year Founded: 1982
Sales Range: $1-9.9 Million
Emp.: 26
Wildlife Preservation Services
N.A.I.C.S.: 813312
Randy Huwa (Exec VP)
Elizabeth Brooks (Office Mgr)
Lee Campbell (Co-Treas)
Kurt Plowman (Sec)
Neysa Simmers (Chm)
Dale Bateman (Co-Treas)
Edward Clark Jr. (Founder & Pres)

THE WILL GROUP, INC.
401 S Carlton Ave, Wheaton, IL 60187
Tel.: (630) 462-0230
Web Site: https://thewillgroup.com
Year Founded: 1986
Emp.: 100
Lighting Fixtures & Electrical Products Mfr; Lighting Consultant & Electrical Contractors
N.A.I.C.S.: 238210
Joshua Davis (Pres)
Steve L. Davis (Chm)

Subsidiaries:

TWiG Technologies, LLC (1)
401 S Carlton Ave, Wheaton, IL 60187
Tel.: (630) 462-0230
Web Site: https://www.twigtechnologies.com
Field Engineering Services
N.A.I.C.S.: 541330
Joshua Davis (Founder)

Subsidiary (Domestic):

Ruettiger, Tonelli & Associates, Inc. (2)
2174 Oneida St, Joliet, IL 60435
Tel.: (815) 744-6600
Web Site: http://www.ruettigertonelli.com
Rev.: $3,950,000
Emp.: 50
Geophysical Surveying & Mapping Services
N.A.I.C.S.: 541360

THE WILL-BURT CO., INC.
169 S Main St, Orrville, OH 44667-1801
Tel.: (330) 682-7015   OH
Web Site: http://www.willburt.com
Year Founded: 1901
Sales Range: $100-124.9 Million
Emp.: 250
Pneumatic Telescoping Mast & Accessories Mfr
N.A.I.C.S.: 332710
Jeffry O. Evans (Chm)
Bruce Inzetta (VP-Fin)
Richard J. Lewin (Pres & CEO)

Subsidiaries:

Antenna Mast Incorporated (1)
169 S Main St, Orrville, OH 44667
Tel.: (330) 682-7015
Mast System Mfr
N.A.I.C.S.: 321999

Integrated Tower Systems, Inc. (1)
2703 Dawson Rd, Tulsa, OK 74110
Tel.: (918) 749-8535
Web Site: http://www.itstowers.com
Mobile Tower & Mast System Mfr
N.A.I.C.S.: 237130

Will-Burt Advanced Composites, Inc. (1)
356 Collins Blvd, Orrville, OH 44667
Tel.: (330) 684-5286
Mast System Mfr
N.A.I.C.S.: 321999

THE WILLAMETTE VALLEY COMPANY
1075 Arrowsmith St, Eugene, OR 97402
Tel.: (541) 484-9621   OR
Web Site: http://www.wilvaco.com
Year Founded: 1952
Sales Range: $50-74.9 Million
Emp.: 350
Synthetic Patch, Polyurethane Fillers, Epoxies, Adhesive Fillers & Extenders Mfr; Equipment Mfr for Wood Products Industry
N.A.I.C.S.: 423840
John Harrison (CEO)
Tony Vukfich (VP)
John Murray (Pres)
Bob Halligan (COO)
Rob Loomis (Mgr-Bus-Performance Products & Railroad)

Subsidiaries:

Canadian Willamette Industries, Inc. (1)
19081 27 Avenue, Surrey, V35 5T1, BC, Canada   (100%)
Tel.: (604) 540-1111
Web Site: http://canadianwillamette.com
Sales Range: $10-24.9 Million
Emp.: 15
Synthetic Patching Products, Primers, Paints, Sealants & Adhesive Extenders Mfr
N.A.I.C.S.: 325510

Tapel Willamette Inc. S.A. (1)
Av Estero La Posada 3625 Parque Industrial Coronel, Coronel, Chile
Tel.: (56) 41 2928 100
Web Site: http://www.tapel.cl
Emp.: 50
Wood Coating Mfr
N.A.I.C.S.: 325510
Mauricio Antonio Sola Perez (Mgr-Site)

The Willamette Valley Company - Idaho Milling and Grain Division (1)
430 W 445 N, Malad City, ID 83252
Tel.: (208) 766-2206
Emp.: 12
Flour Mfr
N.A.I.C.S.: 321999
Kerry Phillips (Gen Mgr)

The Willamette Valley Company - MIDWEST DIVISION (1)
1549 Hwy 2, Two Harbors, MN 55616
Tel.: (218) 834-3922
Wood Coating Mfr
N.A.I.C.S.: 325510

The Willamette Valley Company - PRE-TEC Division (1)
990 Owen Loop N, Eugene, OR 97402
Tel.: (541) 484-2368
Web Site: http://www.pre-tec.com
Industrial Automation Equipments Mfr
N.A.I.C.S.: 333248
Rufus Burton (Mgr-Sls & Mktg)
Martin Holland-Bak (Engr-Product Dev)

The Willamette Valley Company - Southern Division Louisiana (1)
100 Dixie Mae Dr, Pineville, LA 71361
Tel.: (318) 640-5077
Web Site: http://www.wilvaco.com
Sales Range: $25-49.9 Million
Emp.: 25
Mfr of Synthetic Patching Products, Primers, Paints, Sealers, Adhesive Extenders & Coated Abrasives
N.A.I.C.S.: 423840
Donny Arrington (Gen Mgr)

The Willamette Valley Company - WESTERN DIVISION (1)
660 McKinley St, Eugene, OR 97402
Tel.: (800) 333-9826
Wood Coating Mfr
N.A.I.C.S.: 325510

The Willamette Valley Company - WVCO Wood Products Division (1)
1830 Central Blvd, Centralia, WA 98531
Tel.: (360) 736-9999
Emp.: 22
Wood Product Distr
N.A.I.C.S.: 423310
Don Colman (Plant Mgr)

The Willamette Valley Company - Southern Division Georgia (1)
6662 Marbut Rd, Lithonia, GA 30058   (100%)
Tel.: (770) 482-7700
Web Site: http://www.wilvaco.com
Sales Range: $25-49.9 Million
Emp.: 30
Synthetic Patching Product Primer Paint Sealer Adhesive Extender & Coated Abrasive Distr
N.A.I.C.S.: 423840
Peter Kinkeaz (Mgr-Ops)

THE WILLIAMS CAPITAL GROUP, L.P.
650 5th Ave 9th Fl, New York, NY 10019
Tel.: (212) 830-4500
Web Site: http://www.willcap.com
Sales Range: $25-49.9 Million
Emp.: 50
Financial Services
N.A.I.C.S.: 523999
Patrick Wo (CFO)
Christopher J. Williams (Founder)

Subsidiaries:

Cordova, Smart & Williams, LLC (1)
570 Fashion Ave Rm 504, New York, NY 10018-1659
Tel.: (212) 920-3700
Web Site: http://www.csandw.com
Sales Range: $75-99.9 Million
Emp.: 9
Private Equity Firm
N.A.I.C.S.: 523999

Joint Venture (Domestic):

H2O Plus, LLC (2)
845 W Madison St, Chicago, IL 60607
Tel.: (312) 850-9283
Sales Range: $75-99.9 Million
Water-Based Skincare Products Mfr & Distr
N.A.I.C.S.: 325620
Joy Chen (Pres & CEO)

THE WILLS GROUP, INC.
6355 Crain Hwy, La Plata, MD 20646-4267
Tel.: (301) 932-3600   MD
Web Site: http://www.willsgroup.com
Year Founded: 1926
Sales Range: $125-149.9 Million
Emp.: 300
Retailer of Petroleum & Convenience Store Products
N.A.I.C.S.: 457120
J. Blacklock Wills (Exec Chm)
Wendy Jackson (Area Mgr)
Kenneth Halperin (CFO & Exec VP-Fin & Admin)
Mark Samuels (Exec VP-Convenience Retailing)
Rayma Alexander (Dir-Corp Comm)
Julian Blackie Wills III (Pres & CEO)

Subsidiaries:

Dash In Food Stores, Inc. (1)
6355 Crain Hwy, La Plata, MD 20646
Tel.: (301) 932-3663
Web Site: http://www.dashin.com
Convenience Store Operator
N.A.I.C.S.: 457110

SMO Motor Fuels, Inc. (1)
6355 Crain Hwy, La Plata, MD 20646
Tel.: (301) 932-3600
Web Site: http://www.willsgroup.com
Petroleum Distr
N.A.I.C.S.: 424720

Southern Maryland Oil, Inc. (1)
109 N Maple Ave, La Plata, MD 20646
Tel.: (800) 492-3420
Web Site: http://www.smoenergy.com
Heating Oil Distr
N.A.I.C.S.: 424720
Joe Wills (Pres)

THE WILSON COMPANY
655 N Franklin St Ste 2200, Tampa, FL 33602
Tel.: (813) 281-8888
Web Site:
http://www.wilsoncompany.com
Year Founded: 1980
Sales Range: $50-74.9 Million
Emp.: 350
Real Estate Development & Management
N.A.I.C.S.: 237210
Carolyn Wilson (Pres)

THE WILSON GROUP KW23, LLC
147 Delta Dr, Pittsburgh, PA 15238
Tel.: (412) 586-7191
Web Site:
http://www.thewilsongroup.com
Year Founded: 2012
Sales Range: $10-24.9 Million
Emp.: 41
Printing Services
N.A.I.C.S.: 513110
Derrick Wilson (Pres & CEO)
Sally Andreaco (COO)
Jeff Jeffers (VP-Sls)
Douglas Beck (Dir-Bus Dev)
Deseia A. Carter (Mgr-Ops)

THE WILSON HOLDING COMPANY
655 N Franklin St Ste 2200, FL 33602
Tel.: (813) 281-8888
Web Site:

Year Founded: 1980
Rev.: $18,100,000
Emp.: 250
Provider of Real Estate Development Services
N.A.I.C.S.: 237210
Carolyn Wilson (Pres)

Subsidiaries:

Wilson Construction Company (1)
655 N Franklin St Ste 2200, Tampa, FL 33602
Tel.: (813) 288-8882
Web Site: http://www.wilsoncompany.com
Rev.: $630,000
Emp.: 200
Commercial & Office Building Construction Services
N.A.I.C.S.: 236220

Wilson Management Company (1)
655 N Franklin St Ste 2200, Tampa, FL 33602
Tel.: (813) 281-8888
Web Site: http://www.wilsoncompany.com
Rev.: $11,000,000
Emp.: 175
Residential Building Operator
N.A.I.C.S.: 531120
Carolyn Wilson (Pres)

THE WIMBLEY GROUP, INC.
1100 N Arlington Hts Rd Ste 210, Itasca, IL 60143-3111
Tel.: (630) 775-7500   IL
Year Founded: 1987
Rev.: $30,000,000
Emp.: 22
African-American Market, Consumer Marketing
N.A.I.C.S.: 541810
Lita K. Wimbley (Pres & Office Mgr)
Zeline K. Bates (Media Dir)
Anna Morris (Dir-Creative)
Charles L. Wimbley Jr. (Pres)

THE WINDWARD DESIGN GROUP, INC.
1130 Commerce Blvd N, Sarasota, FL 34243
Tel.: (941) 359-0890   FL
Web Site: http://www.windwarddesigngroup.com
Year Founded: 1995
Sales Range: $10-24.9 Million
Emp.: 100
Outdoor Furniture
N.A.I.C.S.: 337122
David Peace (Pres)
Carrie Morales (VP)
Danny Peace (VP)

THE WINE CLUB INC.
1431 S Village Way Ste A, Santa Ana, CA 92705-4700
Tel.: (714) 835-6485
Web Site: http://www.thewineclub.com
Year Founded: 1985
Sales Range: $10-24.9 Million
Emp.: 22
Provider of Wine
N.A.I.C.S.: 445320
Byron Glover (Mgr-Santa Clara)
Jim Hammer (Gen Mgr)

THE WINE GROUP, INC.
4596 S Tracy Blvd, Tracy, CA 95377
Tel.: (415) 986-8700   CA
Web Site: http://www.thewinegroup.com
Year Founded: 1981
Sales Range: $300-349.9 Million
Emp.: 100
Holding Company; Vineyard & Winery Owner & Operator
N.A.I.C.S.: 551112
Al Bentley (Supvr-Bottling)
Brian Vos (CEO)

Darin Miller (VP-Supply Chain Plng)
John Quinlivan (Sr VP-Sls)
Lou D'Ambrosio (Sr VP)
Ryan Taylor (Supvr-Maintenance)
Sarah Andrews (Mgr-Continual Improvement)
Debra Charest (Mgr)
Dave Johnson (Exec VP-Fin)
Jeff Dubiel (CMO)
Melanie Amezaga (Mgr)
Paul Weidenfeller (Mgr-IT Ops)
Deo Singh (Mgr-Quality)
Fred Barron (Sr Dir-Tech)
Sudhir Kumar (VP-Tech)
Eben Gillette (VP-Mktg)

Subsidiaries:

Benziger Family Winery LLC (1)
1883 London Ranch Rd, Glen Ellen, CA 95442
Tel.: (707) 935-3000
Web Site: http://www.benziger.com
Sales Range: $50-74.9 Million
Emp.: 70
Winery
N.A.I.C.S.: 312130
Joaquin Corona (Mgr-Estate Vineyard)
Mark Burningham (Gen Mgr-North Coast Ops)
Chris Benziger (VP-Trade Rels)
Lalo Avalos (Office Mgr-Vineyard)
Jeffery Landolt (Mgr-Estate Properties Vineyard)

Corbett Canyon Vineyards (1)
2195 Corbett Canyon Rd, Arroyo Grande, CA 93420-6910
Tel.: (805) 544-5800
Web Site: http://www.corbettcanyon.com
Sales Range: $10-24.9 Million
Emp.: 20
Production of Wine
N.A.I.C.S.: 312130

Mogen David Wine Corp. (1)
85 Bourne St, Westfield, NY 14787-0543
Tel.: (716) 326-3151
Sales Range: $10-24.9 Million
Emp.: 60
Mfr of Wines
N.A.I.C.S.: 312130
David Kent (CEO)

THE WINEBOW GROUP, LLC
4800 Cox Rd Ste 300, Glen Allen, VA 23060
Tel.: (804) 752-3670   DE
Web Site: http://www.winebow.com
Year Founded: 2014
Holding Company; Wine & Distilled Beverage Distr
N.A.I.C.S.: 551112
Dean K. Ferrell (Pres & CEO)
Erle Martin (Exec VP-Wholesale-West)
Arjun Dewan (Exec VP-Wholesale-East)
Ian Downey (Exec VP-Winebow Imports)
Richard Driscoll (Exec VP-Supplier Rels)
Mike Levine (CIO & Sr VP)
Kristy Heady (Sr VP-HR)
Brad Mayer (Sr VP-Mktg)

Subsidiaries:

Country Vintner of WV (1)
11 Dunn White Rd, Lewisburg, WV 24901
Tel.: (304) 645-5522
Web Site: http://www.countryvintner.com
Beer, Wine & Liquor Stores
N.A.I.C.S.: 445320

Grape Beginnings, Inc. (1)
14827 Richards Dr W, Hopkins, MN 55345
Tel.: (952) 933-7290
Web Site: http://www.grapebeginnings.org
Sales Range: $1-9.9 Million
Emp.: 10
Wine & Distilled Alcoholic Beverage Merchant Whslr
N.A.I.C.S.: 424820

Negociants USA Inc. (1)
Devlin Rd, Napa, CA 94558
Tel.: (707) 259-0993
Web Site: http://www.negociants.com
Wine Whslr
N.A.I.C.S.: 424820

Purple Feet Wines, LLC (1)
N29 W23810 Woodgate Ct W, Pewaukee, WI 53072
Tel.: (262) 970-7200
Web Site: http://www.purplefeetwines.net
Sales Range: $1-9.9 Million
Emp.: 30
Wine & Distilled Beverage Distr
N.A.I.C.S.: 424820
Melanie Denhart (VP & Gen Mgr)

Quality Wine & Spirits, Inc. (1)
2279 Defoor Hills Rd NW, Atlanta, GA 30318
Tel.: (404) 367-9463
Web Site: http://www.qwine.com
Sales Range: $10-24.9 Million
Emp.: 80
Wine & Distilled Alcoholic Beverage Distr
N.A.I.C.S.: 424820
Dee Herb (Dir-Bus Dev-Coastal Territory)
Bill Yorks (Dir-IT & Pur)
Geoff Gilbertson (Sls Mgr-Key Accts)
Ted Bergquist (VP-Sls)
Michael McNeill (Dir-Wine Education)
Chris Luke (Dir-Bus Dev-Atlanta)
Jon J. George (Sr VP & Gen Mgr)

The Henry Wine Group (1)
4301 Industrial Way, Benicia, CA 94510-1180
Tel.: (707) 745-8500
Web Site: http://www.henrywinegroup.com
Wine Distr
N.A.I.C.S.: 424820
Edward Hogan (Pres & CEO)
Warner Henry (Owner & Chm)

The Stacole Company, Inc. (1)
1822 SW 2nd St, Pompano Beach, FL 33069
Tel.: (954) 861-2520
Web Site: http://www.stacolewines.com
Sales Range: $1-9.9 Million
Emp.: 40
Wine & Distilled Beverage Distr
N.A.I.C.S.: 424820
Al Schoester (Mgr-Traffic)
Ron VanStone (Mgr-Warehouse)
Thomas Johnson (Mgr-Central & North Florida District)
Laura DePasquale (Sr VP & Gen Mgr)

Vintage Wines, LLC (1)
2700 S River Rd Ste 200, Des Plaines, IL 60018
Tel.: (773) 596-2800
Web Site: http://www.winebow.com
Sales Range: $1-9.9 Million
Wine & Distilled Beverage Distr
N.A.I.C.S.: 424820
Jennifer Crowley (VP & Gen Mgr)

Winebow, Inc. (1)
75 Chestnut Ridge Rd, Montvale, NJ 07645-1820
Tel.: (201) 445-0620
Web Site: http://www.winebow.com
Wine & Distilled Beverage Distr
N.A.I.C.S.: 424820
Leonardo LoCascio (Sr VP)
Vinny Chiaramonte (Exec VP-Imports)
Scott Ades (Co-COO & Exec VP)
Richard Driscoll (Exec VP-Supplier Rels)
Kristy Heady (Sr VP-HR)
Teresa Low (Sr VP-Mktg & PR)
David Townsend (Co-COO & Exec VP)

THE WINIFRED MASTERSON BURKE REHABILITATION HOSPITAL, INC.
785 Mamaroneck Ave, White Plains, NY 10605
Tel.: (914) 597-2500
Web Site: http://www.burke.org
Year Founded: 1915
Sales Range: $25-49.9 Million
Rehabilitation Services
N.A.I.C.S.: 624310
John Ryan (Exec Dir)
Barry Jordan (Asst Dir-Medical)

Chris Dal Ceredo (Dir-Amputee & Orthopedic Program)
Lisa Edelstein (Dir-Stroke Program)
Rachel Feld-Glazman (Dir-Neuro Programs)
Pam Jones (Dir-Cardiopulmonary Program)
Elizabeth Dominick (Program Dir-Neurological Program)
Stephanie Campbell (Asst Dir-Nursing)
Cathleen Brooks (Mgr-Nurse)
Kate Holzel (Mgr-Nurse)
Marlene Rose (Mgr-Nurse)
Donald E. Foley (Chm)
Robert J. Baldoni (Vice Chm)
Tracey A. Bogart (Asst Sec)
Wilfred A. Finnegan (Treas)
Ben Gilbert (VP-Outpatient Svcs)
Anthony B. Gioffre III (Sec)

Subsidiaries:

Burke Rehabilitation Hospital (1)
785 Mamaroneck Ave, White Plains, NY 10605
Tel.: (914) 597-2500
Web Site: http://www.burke.org
Rev.: $430,212
Real Estate Managers & Hospital Care Facilities
N.A.I.C.S.: 531210
Michael J. Daly (Vice Chm)
Charles V. Glennon (Sec)
Justin Hill (Dir-Brain Injury Rehabilitation Program)
Pasquale Fonzetti (Dir-Memory Evaluation & Treatment Svc)
Tracey A. Bogart (Asst Sec)
Wilfred A. Finnegan (Treas)
Jeffrey Menkes (Pres & CEO)
Mooyeoon Oh-Park (Chief Medical Officer & Sr VP)
Scott Edelman (CFO & Sr VP)
Valerie Vermiglio-Kohn (Chief Nursing Officer & VP-Nursing)
Anthony B. Gioffre III (Partner)

THE WINSTON CO.
2837 Anthony Ln S, Minneapolis, MN 55418
Tel.: (612) 789-7800
Web Site: http://www.thewinstoncompany.com
Rev.: $12,141,982
Emp.: 23
Packing, Industrial
N.A.I.C.S.: 423840
Tom Coppo (Pres)

THE WINSTON-SALEM FOUNDATION
751 W 4th St Ste 200, Winston Salem, NC 27101-2702
Tel.: (336) 725-2382   NC
Web Site: http://www.wsfoundation.org
Year Founded: 1919
Sales Range: $25-49.9 Million
Emp.: 26
Community Foundation
N.A.I.C.S.: 813211
Lisa Purcell (Exec VP)
Cici Fulton (Dir-Mktg & Comm)
David Gore (Dir-IT & Tech)
Eliza Walmsley (Mgr-Comm & Program)
Todd Slate (VP-Fin & Admin)
Scott Wierman (Pres)
Brittney Gaspari (Dir-Grants)
Jonathan Halsey (Dir-Community Engagement)
Sabrina Slade (Dir-Womens Fund)

THE WINTHROP CORPORATION
440 Wheelers Farms Rd, Milford, CT 06461
Tel.: (203) 783-4400

THE WINTHROP CORPORATION

U.S. PRIVATE

The Winthrop Corporation—(Continued)

Web Site: http://www.wisi.com
Investment Management & Financial Advisory Services
N.A.I.C.S.: 523999
Laura Petrucci *(CEO)*

THE WIRENUT
6395 E Platte Ave, Colorado Springs, CO 80915
Tel.: (719) 227-0500
Web Site: http://www.thewirenut.com
Year Founded: 2004
Sales Range: $1-9.9 Million
Emp.: 30
Electrical Repair & Installation Services
N.A.I.C.S.: 238210
Robert Urban *(Co-Owner & VP)*
Trent Urban *(Co-Owner & Mgr-Ops)*
Angela Neuhaus *(Dir-First Impressions)*

THE WISE CO. INC.
5828 Shelby Oaks Dr, Memphis, TN 38134
Tel.: (901) 388-0155
Web Site: http://www.wiseseats.com
Sales Range: $25-49.9 Million
Emp.: 18
Vehicle Furniture
N.A.I.C.S.: 336360
Mike Monroe *(Pres)*

THE WISE OPTICAL VISION GROUP
4 Executive Blvd, Yonkers, NY 10701-6822
Tel.: (914) 376-9800
Year Founded: 1981
Sales Range: $25-49.9 Million
Emp.: 140
Contact Lens Distr
N.A.I.C.S.: 423490

THE WITTERN GROUP
8040 University Blvd, Des Moines, IA 50325
Tel.: (515) 277-5397
Web Site: http://www.vending.com
Year Founded: 1986
Sales Range: $25-49.9 Million
Emp.: 520
Holding Company
N.A.I.C.S.: 561990
Phil Masters *(VP-Natl Acct)*
David Tweedale *(Mgr-Network)*
Chris Crawford *(Mgr-Sls-Natl)*
Matt Herr *(Engr-Mfg)*
Jim Kinning *(Gen Mgr)*
Brian Retterath *(Mgr-Production Control)*
Connie Laverrenz *(Supvr-Customer Svc)*
Ron Harter *(Dir-Matls)*
Paul Knode *(Supvr-Powder Coat)*
Ray Lantz *(VP-Fin)*

Subsidiaries:

Inland Finance Company (1)
8040 University Blvd, Des Moines, IA 50325-1118
Tel.: (515) 271-8380
Web Site: http://www.wittern.com
Sales Range: $10-24.9 Million
Emp.: 20
Mfr of Automatic Vending Machines
N.A.I.C.S.: 333310
Francis A. Wittern Jr. *(Chm)*

Subsidiary (Domestic):

Fawn Engineering Corp. (2)
8040 University Blvd, Des Moines, IA 50325-1118
Tel.: (515) 274-3641
Web Site: http://www.fawnvendors.com
Emp.: 400

Mfr of Automatic Vending Machines
N.A.I.C.S.: 333310
John Bruntz *(Pres)*
Francis A. Wittern Jr. *(Chm & CEO)*

Fawn Vending Systems, Inc. (2)
8040 University Blvd, Clive, IA 50325-1118
Tel.: (515) 274-3641
Web Site: http://www.vending.com
Sales Range: $10-24.9 Million
Emp.: 12
Retailer of Commercial Equipment
N.A.I.C.S.: 333310

Selectivend Inc. (2)
8040 University Blvd, Des Moines, IA 50325-1118
Tel.: (515) 274-3641
Web Site: http://www.vending.com
Sales Range: $10-24.9 Million
Emp.: 4
Mfr of Automatic Vending Machines
N.A.I.C.S.: 333310
John Scofield *(VP)*
Heidi Chica *(Pres)*

U-Select-It Corporation (2)
8040 University Blvd, Des Moines, IA 50325-1118
Tel.: (515) 274-3641
Web Site: http://www.uselectit.com
Provider of Service Establishment Equipment
N.A.I.C.S.: 423440
Mark Craigmile *(Controller)*
Alejandro Castillo *(Mgr-Technical Svc-Latin America)*

THE WITTERS CONSTRUCTION COMPANY
1040 SE 14th St, Miami, FL 33157
Tel.: (305) 887-9471   FL
Web Site: http://www.witters.com
Year Founded: 1932
Sales Range: $10-24.9 Million
Emp.: 10
Commercial & Office Buildings, Renovation & Repair
N.A.I.C.S.: 236220
Brent C. Nagel *(Pres & CEO)*
Luisa E. Suarez *(CFO & Controller)*

THE WM. POWELL COMPANY
2503 Spring Grove Ave, Cincinnati, OH 45214-1729
Tel.: (513) 852-2000   OH
Web Site: http://www.powellvalves.com
Year Founded: 1846
Sales Range: $50-74.9 Million
Emp.: 50
Valves & Engineering Specialties Mfr
N.A.I.C.S.: 332911
Randy Cowart *(Pres & CEO)*
Brandy Cowart *(Exec VP)*
Jeff Thompson *(CFO & Sr VP-Fin)*
Jim Hengehold *(Sr VP-Engrg & Quality Control)*
Sally Sand *(Sr VP & Gen Mgr-Orangeburg Facility)*
Jeff Sizer *(Mgr-Bus Dev & Customer Svc-Intl)*
Kate Boggs *(Mgr-Capital Project Mgmt & Sls)*
Jimmy Buck *(Mgr-Southeast)*
Tim Fries *(VP-Sls & Mktg-North America & Intl)*
Todd Kaiser *(VP-Supply Chain Mgmt)*

Subsidiaries:

The Starflo Corporation (1)
940 Crosscreek Rd SE, Orangeburg, SC 29115
Tel.: (803) 536-9660
Sales Range: $10-24.9 Million
Emp.: 35
Mfr of Industrial Valves
N.A.I.C.S.: 332911

The Starflo Corporation (1)
1568 Joe Rogers Jr Blvd, Manning, SC 29102-9765
Tel.: (803) 473-4046

Sales Range: $10-24.9 Million
Emp.: 45
Mfr of Industrial Valves
N.A.I.C.S.: 332919

THE WOLF MACHINE CO.
5570 Creek Rd, Cincinnati, OH 45242-4004
Tel.: (513) 791-5194
Web Site: http://www.wolfmachine.com
Year Founded: 1888
Sales Range: $50-74.9 Million
Emp.: 40
Cloth & Meat Cutting Machines & Equipment Mfr
N.A.I.C.S.: 333248
Ken Park *(CFO)*

THE WOLF ORGANIZATION, LLC
20 W Market St, York, PA 17401
Tel.: (800) 388-9653
Web Site: http://www.wolfhomeproducts.com
Year Founded: 1843
Cabinetry, Decking & Exterior Building Products Mfr
N.A.I.C.S.: 337110
Craig Danielson *(Pres & CEO)*

Subsidiaries:

Carstin Brands, Inc. (1)
520 E 2nd, Arthur, IL 61911
Tel.: (217) 543-3331
Web Site: http://carstinbrands.com
Plastics Plumbing Fixture Mfr
N.A.I.C.S.: 326191
MaryAnn Wright *(Mgr-Customer Svc-Solid Surface, Stone Div)*

THE WONDERFUL COMPANY LLC
11444 W Olympic Blvd, Los Angeles, CA 90064
Tel.: (310) 966-5700   DE
Web Site: https://www.wonderful.com
Year Founded: 1979
Sales Range: $1-4.9 Billion
Emp.: 10,000
Offices of Other Holding Companies
N.A.I.C.S.: 551112
Stewart Resnick *(Co-Founder)*
Lynda Resnick *(Co-Founder)*
Michael Perdigao *(Pres-Agency)*
Darren Moran *(Chief Creative Officer)*
Bobby Pearce *(Chief Creative Officer-Agency)*

Subsidiaries:

Fiji Water Company LLC (1)
11444 W Olympic Blvd Ste 210, Los Angeles, CA 90064
Tel.: (310) 312-2850
Web Site: http://www.fijiwater.com
Sales Range: $25-49.9 Million
Emp.: 50
Supplier of Bottled Water
N.A.I.C.S.: 312112
David Ricanati *(Pres)*

Interflora British Unit (1)
Interflora House Watergate, Sleaford, NG34 7TB, Lincolnshire, United Kingdom
Tel.: (44) 1529 416591
Web Site: http://www.interflora.co.uk
Sales Range: $125-149.9 Million
Emp.: 230
Online Flowers & Gifts Retailer
N.A.I.C.S.: 459310
Kirsty Gaunt *(Mgr-Affiliate & Partnership)*

Justin Vineyards & Winery LLC (1)
11680 Chimney Rock Rd, Paso Robles, CA 93446
Tel.: (805) 238-6932
Web Site: http://www.justinwine.com
Sales Range: $25-49.9 Million
Emp.: 50
Winery
N.A.I.C.S.: 312130

Steve Lister *(Mgr-Sls)*

Subsidiary (Domestic):

Lewis Cellars (2)
4101 Big Ranch Rd, Napa, CA 94558-1406
Tel.: (707) 255-3400
Web Site: http://www.lewiscellars.com
Wineries
N.A.I.C.S.: 312130
Randy Lewis *(Owner)*

Neptune Pacific Agency Australia Pty. Limited (1)
Level 12 45-47 York Street, Sydney, 2000, NSW, Australia
Tel.: (61) 2 9235 2999
Web Site: http://www.neptunepacific.com
Sales Range: $25-49.9 Million
Emp.: 150
Freight Shipping Services
N.A.I.C.S.: 483111
Bill MacDonald *(Gen Mgr)*

POM Wonderful LLC (1)
11444 W Olympic Blvd, Los Angeles, CA 90064
Tel.: (310) 966-5800
Web Site: http://www.pomwonderful.com
Sales Range: $150-199.9 Million
Emp.: 60
Pomegranate Processor & Distr
N.A.I.C.S.: 311411
Lynda Resnick *(Owner)*

Suterra LLC (1)
20950 NE Talus Pl, Bend, OR 97701
Tel.: (541) 388-3688
Web Site: http://www.suterra.com
Sales Range: $25-49.9 Million
Emp.: 55
Pest Control; Provider of Products & Services to the Commercial, Agriculture & Consumer Markets
N.A.I.C.S.: 561710
Cheyne Detwiler *(Mgr-Ops)*

Teleflora LLC (1)
11444 W Olympic Blvd, Los Angeles, CA 90064-1549
Tel.: (310) 966-5700
Web Site: http://www.teleflora.com
Sales Range: $75-99.9 Million
Emp.: 700
Flowers by Wire Service; Floral Products
N.A.I.C.S.: 459310
Jeff Bennett *(Pres)*
Jim Talarico *(CIO)*
David Dancer *(Exec VP & Head-Mktg)*

Subsidiary (Non-US):

Petals Network Pty. Ltd. (2)
PO Box 341, Armidale, 2350, NSW, Australia
Tel.: (61) 2 6774 9200
Web Site: http://www.petals.com.au
Emp.: 20
Florist Shop Franchisor & Operator
N.A.I.C.S.: 459310

Wonderful Citrus LLC (1)
1901 S Lexington St, Delano, CA 93215
Tel.: (661) 720-2400
Web Site: http://www.wonderfulcitrus.com
Sales Range: $50-74.9 Million
Emp.: 550
Orange Growing; Juice Processing; Packing
N.A.I.C.S.: 111310
David Krause *(Pres)*
Zak Laffite *(Chief Sls Officer)*

Subsidiary (Domestic):

I. Kunik Company (2)
2000 Industrial Dr, McAllen, TX 78504-4003
Tel.: (956) 686-4324
Web Site: http://www.ikunik.com
Emp.: 200
Producers & Distr of Fruits & Vegetables. Also Imports & Sales of Persian Limes
N.A.I.C.S.: 445230
Carlos Ponce de Leon *(Mgr-Pur)*

Division (Domestic):

Wonderful Citrus Packing LLC (2)
702 E Interstate 2, Mission, TX 78572
Tel.: (956) 598-6800
Web Site: http://www.riograndejuice.com
Citrus Juice Processor

N.A.I.C.S.: 424480
Dodson Galloway *(Dir-Ops)*
Justin Simpson *(Dir-Quality Assurance)*
Jay Madden *(Dir-Sls)*
Boyd Beasley *(Dir-Sls)*
Ninfa Sepulveda *(Fin Mgr & Controller)*
Norma Perez *(Supvr-Acctg)*
Abel Razo *(Supvr-Pur)*

Wonderful Pistachios & Almonds LLC (1)
13654 Hawaii 33, Lost Hills, CA 93249
Tel.: (661) 797-6500
Web Site: http://www.wonderfulpistachiosandalmonds.com
Sales Range: $150-199.9 Million
Emp.: 1,000
Pistachios & Almonds Farming
N.A.I.C.S.: 111335
Dave Blanchat *(VP-Ops)*

THE WOOD AGENCY
7550 IH 10 W Ste 510, San Antonio, TX 78229
Tel.: (210) 474-7400
Web Site: http://www.thewoodagency.com
Year Founded: 1987
Sales Range: $10-24.9 Million
Emp.: 14
Advertising Agencies
N.A.I.C.S.: 541810
Kathy Bellamy *(Dir-Media)*

THE WOOSTER BRUSH COMPANY
604 Madison Ave, Wooster, OH 44691-4764
Tel.: (330) 264-4440   OH
Web Site: http://www.woosterbrush.com
Year Founded: 1851
Sales Range: $150-199.9 Million
Emp.: 570
Paint Brushes, Roller Applicators & Accessory Item Mfr
N.A.I.C.S.: 339994
Scott Rutledge *(VP-Mktg)*

Subsidiaries:

The Wooster Brush Company - Reno (1)
4960 Joule St, Reno, NV 89510-0650
Tel.: (775) 856-1950
Web Site: http://www.woosterbrush.com
Sales Range: $25-49.9 Million
Emp.: 15
Distr of Paint Brushes, Paint Rollers & Accessory Items
N.A.I.C.S.: 424950

THE WORKPLACE, INC.
350 Fairfield Ave, Bridgeport, CT 06604
Tel.: (203) 610-8500   CT
Web Site: http://www.workplace.org
Year Founded: 1983
Sales Range: $10-24.9 Million
Emp.: 125
Workforce Development Services
N.A.I.C.S.: 561311
Nestor Leon *(VP-Ops)*
Gino Venditti *(Chief Admin Officer)*
Adrienne Parkmond *(Exec VP)*

THE WORLD BANK GROUP
1818 H St NW, Washington, DC 20433-0001
Tel.: (202) 473-1000
Web Site: http://www.worldbankgroup.org
Year Founded: 1944
Sales Range: $1-4.9 Billion
Emp.: 9,000
Economic Development Organization
N.A.I.C.S.: 813990
Jorge Familiar Calderon *(VP-Latin America & Caribbean)*
Leonard McCarthy *(VP-Institutional Integrity)*
Cyril Muller *(VP-Europe & Central Asia)*
Axel van Trotsenburg *(VP-Latin America & Caribbean)*
Sheila Redzepi *(VP-External & Corp Rels)*
Shaolin Yang *(Chief Administrative Officer & Mng Dir)*
Joaquim Levy *(CFO & Mng Dir)*
Victoria Kwakwa *(Reg VP)*
Paul Romer *(Sr VP)*
Shubham Chaudhuri *(Dir-Afghanistan)*
Sandie Okoro *(Gen Counsel & Sr VP)*
Tahseen Sayed Khan *(Dir-Caribbean)*
Tatiana Proskuryakova *(Dir-Central Asia)*
Pascale Helene Dubois *(VP-Integrity)*
Ellen Goldstein *(Dir-Cambodia, Burma & Laos)*
Aparna S. *(Exec Dir)*
Makhtar Diop *(VP-Infrastructure)*
Annette Dixon *(VP-South Asia)*
Karin Finkelston *(VP-Portfolio Mgmt)*
Mohamed Gouled *(VP-Risk & Fin Sustainability)*
Keith Hansen *(VP-Sustainable Dev)*
Bernard Lauwers *(VP-Institutional Integrity)*
Hiroshi Naka *(VP)*
Hartwig Schafer *(VP-Themes-Global)*
Yvonne Tsikata *(Sec & VP)*
Laura Tuck *(VP-Sustainable Dev)*
Jan Walliser *(VP-Themes-Global)*
Ferid Belhaj *(VP-Middle East & North Africa)*
Hafez Ghanem *(VP-Africa)*
Marina Wes *(Dir-Egypt, Yemen & Djibouti)*
Shahid Ashraf Tarar *(Chm)*
Jorge Familiar *(VP-Fin & Acctg Unit)*
David R. Malpass *(Pres)*
Martin Raiser *(Dir-China, Mongolia & Korea)*
Marie Francoise Marie-Nelly *(Dir-South Africa, Namibia, Lesotho, Botswana & Eswatini)*
Ceyla Pazarbasioglu *(VP-Equitable Growth, Finance & Institutions)*
Carlos Felipe Jaramillo *(VP-Latin America & Caribbean)*
Auguste Tanoa Kouame *(Dir-India)*

Subsidiaries:

International Finance Corporation (1)
2121 Pennsylvania Ave NW, Washington, DC 20433
Tel.: (202) 473-1000
Web Site: http://www.ifc.org
Rev.: $1,853,000,000
Assets: $77,525,000,000
Liabilities: $55,250,000,000
Net Worth: $22,275,000,000
Earnings: $1,010,000,000
Emp.: 4,015
Fiscal Year-end: 06/30/2013
International Economic Development Lending & Financing Services
N.A.I.C.S.: 813219
Desmond Dodd *(Head-Comm-South Africa)*
Adriana Gomez *(Officer-Comm)*
John McNally *(Officer-Comm)*
Jingdong Hua *(VP-Treasury & Syndications)*
Nena Stoiljkovic *(VP-Asia & Pacific)*
Ethiopis Tafara *(Gen Counsel & VP-Legal, Compliance Risk & Sustainability)*
Maria Kozloski *(Chief Investment Officer & Head-Global)*
Philippe Le Houerou *(CEO)*
Nikunj Jinsi *(Head-Venture Capital-Global)*
Nicholas Vickery *(Portfolio Mgr-Global)*
Judith Green *(Mgr-Caribbean)*
Walid Labadi *(Mgr-Egypt, Libya & Yemen)*
Gabriel Goldschmidt *(Dir-Latin America & Caribbean)*
Nicolas Marquier *(Mgr-Singapore)*
Vivek Pathak *(Dir-East Asia & The Pacific)*
Luc Grillet *(COO-Latin America & Caribbean)*

Subsidiary (Domestic):

IFC Asset Management Company (2)
2121 Pennsylvania Ave NW, Washington, DC 20433
Tel.: (202) 473-9478
Emp.: 40
Investment Management Service
N.A.I.C.S.: 523940
Gavin Wilson *(CEO)*

Multilateral Investment Guarantee Agency (1)
1818 H St NW, Washington, DC 20433
Tel.: (202) 458-2538
Web Site: http://www.miga.org
Sales Range: $50-74.9 Million
Emp.: 130
Financial Management Services
N.A.I.C.S.: 523940
Ana-Mita Betancourt *(Gen Counsel-Legal Affairs & Claims Grp)*
Edith Quintrell *(Grp Dir-Ops)*
Keiko Honda *(CEO & Exec VP)*
Merli Margaret Baroudi *(Dir-Economics & Sustainability)*
Subramaniam Vishwanathan Iyer *(COO & VP)*

THE WORLD COMPANY
645 New Hampshire St, Lawrence, KS 66044-2243
Tel.: (785) 843-1000   KS
Web Site: http://www.ljworld.com
Year Founded: 1905
Sales Range: $10-24.9 Million
Emp.: 380
Newspaper Publishers
N.A.I.C.S.: 513110
Kathleen Johnson *(Mgr-Adv)*
Scott Stanford *(Publr)*
Dolph C. Simons Jr. *(Chm-Lawrence Journal-World)*

Subsidiaries:

WorldWest Limited Liability Company (1)
645 New Hampshire St, Lawrence, KS 66044-2243
Tel.: (785) 832-7100
Web Site: http://www.ljworld.com
Newspaper Publishers
N.A.I.C.S.: 513110
Dan C. Simons *(Co-CEO)*
Dolph C. Simons III *(Co-CEO)*

Unit (Domestic):

Craig Daily Press (2)
466 Yampa Ave, Craig, CO 81625
Tel.: (970) 824-7031
Web Site: http://www.craigdailypress.com
Newspaper Publishers
N.A.I.C.S.: 513110
Renee Campbell *(Publr)*

Payson Roundup (2)
708 N Beeline Hwy, Payson, AZ 85541
Tel.: (928) 474-5251
Web Site: http://www.paysonroundup.com
Emp.: 17
Newspaper Publishers
N.A.I.C.S.: 513110
Julie Williams *(Mgr-Ops)*
Pia Wyer *(Mgr-Digital Media)*
Peter Aleshire *(Editor-Consulting Publications)*
Patty Behm *(Mgr-Circulation)*
Gary Tackett *(Gen Mgr)*
Brian Kramer *(Publr)*

Steamboat Pilot & Today (2)
32 10th St Ste C1-C, Steamboat Springs, CO 80487
Tel.: (970) 879-1502
Web Site: http://www.steamboatpilot.com
Emp.: 50
Newspaper Publishers
N.A.I.C.S.: 513110
Lisa Schlichtman *(Editor)*
Steve Balgenorth *(Dir-Circulation)*

THE WORLD OF MINIATURE BEARS, INC.
7356 NW 34th St, Miami, FL 33122
Tel.: (305) 592-7970
Web Site: http://www.minibear.com
Sales Range: $10-24.9 Million
Emp.: 5
Stuffed Bears Mfr & Distr
N.A.I.C.S.: 339930
Theresa Yang *(Founder)*

THE WORTH COMPANY
214 Sherman Ave, Stevens Point, WI 54481-5847
Tel.: (715) 344-6081
Web Site: http://www.worthco.com
Year Founded: 1942
Sales Range: $50-74.9 Million
Emp.: 80
Mfr of Fishing Tackle & Leisure Time Products
N.A.I.C.S.: 339920
David Worth *(Pres & CEO)*
Denny Rosenthal *(Dir-Intl Sls & Customer Svc)*
Kristin Crass *(VP)*

THE WOW FACTOR, INC.
11330 Ventura Blvd, Studio City, CA 91604
Tel.: (818) 755-4400   CA
Web Site: http://www.wowfactor.net
Year Founded: 1993
Rev.: $1,300,000
Emp.: 12
Fiscal Year-end: 12/31/06
Multimedia Productions
N.A.I.C.S.: 512110
Donald Blanton *(Pres & CEO)*
Anthony Hudacs *(Editor, Production Mgr & Animator)*
Billy Moran *(VP-Production)*
Josh Harris *(Mgr-Tech)*

THE WRIGHT GROUP
19201 120th Ave NE Ste 100, Bothell, WA 98011-9512
Tel.: (215) 295-3814
Web Site: http://www.thewrightgroup.net
Book Publishers
N.A.I.C.S.: 513130
James Cushing *(Pres)*

THE YALE CLUB OF NEW YORK CITY
50 Vanderbilt Ave, New York, NY 10017
Tel.: (212) 716-2100   NY
Web Site: http://www.yaleclubnyc.org
Year Founded: 1897
Sales Range: $25-49.9 Million
Emp.: 351
Clubhouse Operator
N.A.I.C.S.: 813410
Kevin O'Brien *(Dir-Food & Beverage)*
Alan K. Dutton *(Gen Mgr)*

THE YOUNG ENTREPRENEURS ACADEMY INC.
175 Corporate Woods Ste 130, Rochester, NY 14623
Tel.: (585) 272-3535   NY
Web Site: http://www.yeausa.org
Year Founded: 2004
Sales Range: $1-9.9 Million
Emp.: 150
Entrepreneur Business & Support Services
N.A.I.C.S.: 541611
Jenna Moonan *(Mgr-Client Svcs)*
Sara Bukowiec *(Dir-Ops)*
Gayle Jagel *(Founder, Pres & CEO)*

THE YUCAIPA COMPANIES LLC

THE YUCAIPA COMPANIES LLC

The Yucaipa Companies LLC—(Continued)
9130 W Sunset Blvd, Los Angeles, CA 90069-7002
Tel.: (310) 789-7200 DE
Web Site: http://www.yucaipaco.com
Year Founded: 1986
Sales Range: $200-249.9 Million
Emp.: 75
Investment Holding Company
N.A.I.C.S.: 551112
Frank Quintero (Principal)
Norice Rice (Principal)

Subsidiaries:

Fresh & Easy Neighborhood Market Inc (1)
2120 Park Pl # 200, El Segundo, CA 90245-4741
Tel.: (310) 341-1200
Web Site: http://www.freshandeasy.com
Sales Range: $800-899.9 Million
Emp.: 5,000
Grocery Chain
N.A.I.C.S.: 445110
Darcey Harraka (Mgr-DSD)
Amir Agam (Chief Restructuring Officer)

Independent Talent Group Ltd. (1)
Oxford House 76 Oxford Street, London, W1D 1BS, United Kingdom
Tel.: (44) 2076366565
Web Site: http://www.independenttalent.com
Sales Range: $10-24.9 Million
Artist Entertainment & Media Talent & Literary Agency
N.A.I.C.S.: 711410

Piccadilly Restaurants, LLC (1)
3232 Sherwood Forest Blvd, Baton Rouge, LA 70816-2218
Tel.: (225) 296-8351
Web Site: http://www.piccadilly.com
Sales Range: $300-349.9 Million
Cafeteria-Style Restaurant Operator
N.A.I.C.S.: 722514
Patrick R. Prudhomme (VP)

THE YUMA COMPANIES

1177 W Loop S Ste 1825, Houston, TX 77027
Tel.: (713) 968-7068
Web Site: http://www.yumacompanies.com
Sales Range: $10-24.9 Million
Emp.: 30
Provider of Oil & Gas Exploration Services
N.A.I.C.S.: 213112
Paul Nckinney (Pres)

THE ZABEL COMPANIES, LLC

4201 Congress St Ste 125, Charlotte, NC 28209
Tel.: (704) 973-9934 NC
Web Site: http://www.zabelcompanies.com
Private Investment Firm
N.A.I.C.S.: 523999
Bill Lunsford (Pres)
Rich Jones (Partner)

Subsidiaries:

K.G. Motors, Inc. (1)
202 Daniel Zenker Dr, Big Flats, NY 14814-8944
Tel.: (607) 562-2877
Web Site: http://www.notubes.com
Sporting Goods Retailer
N.A.I.C.S.: 459110
Mike Bush (Pres)
Clayton Goldsmith (Mgr-OE)

Medical Packaging, Inc. (1)
8 Kings Ct, Flemington, NJ 08822
Tel.: (609) 466-8991
Web Site: http://www.medpak.com
Sales Range: $1-9.9 Million
Emp.: 15
Pharmaceutical Packaging & Labeling Equipment Mfr
N.A.I.C.S.: 423830
Andy Bartels (Pres & CEO)

THE ZIEGLER COMPANIES, INC.

1 N Wacker Dr Ste 2000, Chicago, IL 60606
Tel.: (312) 263-0110 WI
Web Site: http://www.ziegler.com
Year Founded: 1902
Sales Range: $50-74.9 Million
Emp.: 262
Holding Company; Financial Services
N.A.I.C.S.: 523150
Gary P. Engle (Sr Mng Dir-Fin)
Jeffrey C. Vredenbregt (Mng Dir & CFO)
Angelique A. David (Exec Mng Dir, COO & Gen Counsel)
Scott Winter (Mng Dir-Healthcare Fin)
Daniel J. Hermann (Pres, CEO & Head-Investment Banking)
Kevin L. Strom (Exec Mng Dir & Head-Capital Markets)
Dave Kolzow (Chief Admin Officer-Investment Banking)
William D. McGuire (Chm)
Mark A. Baumgartner (Chief Credit Officer)
Christine S. McCarty (CMO)
James M. Bushman (Chief Compliance Officer)
Robert Moats (Sr Mng Dir & Head-Wealth Mgmt)
Kim I. Marshall (First VP)
Nick Corrente (VP)
Mathews J. Andrews (Sr VP & Mgr-West Bend & Sheboygan)
Donald A. Carlson Jr. (Vice Chm, Sr Mng Dir & Head-Capital Markets)

Subsidiaries:

Ziegler & Co. (1)
735 North Water St Ste 1000, Milwaukee, WI 53202-4298 (100%)
Tel.: (414) 978-6400
Web Site: http://www.ziegler.com
Sales Range: $100-124.9 Million
Emp.: 105
Bond Underwriter, Dealer in Bonds, Commercial Papers, Brokerage
N.A.I.C.S.: 326199
Gary P. Engle (Sr Mng Dir-Fin & Res)
Thomas R. Paprocki (CEO)
M. P. McDaniel (Mng Dir-Sls)
Rob Hellman (VP)
Matt Andrews (Sr VP)

Unit (Domestic):

Church & School Financing (2)
250 E Wisconsin Ave Ste 1900, Milwaukee, WI 53202-4298
Tel.: (414) 978-6400
Web Site: http://www.zieglerloan.com
Sales Range: $125-149.9 Million
Emp.: 50
Health Care Srvices
N.A.I.C.S.: 221111
Scott Rolfs (Mng Dir)
John R. Biggar (CFO & Exec VP)
Tom Paprocki (CFO)

Institutional Trading, Money Management Office (2)
250 E Wisconsin Ave Ste 2000, Milwaukee, WI 53202-4232
Tel.: (414) 978-6400
Web Site: http://www.ziegler.com
Sales Range: $1-4.9 Billion
Emp.: 70
N.A.I.C.S.: 522299

Ziegler Capital Markets Group (1)
200 S Wacker Dr Ste 2000, Chicago, IL 60606-4617 (100%)
Tel.: (312) 263-0110
Web Site: http://www.zeigler.com
Sales Range: $25-49.9 Million
Emp.: 60
Health Care & Public Finance Underwriting
N.A.I.C.S.: 523910
D. J. Hermann (Mng Dir)
D.M. Kolzow (VP-Ops)
Christian DeCaro (Sr VP-Mktg)
John H. Dinkins (Mng Dir)

Andrew Belsky (VP)
Kevin Strom (Sr Mng Dir)
Donald A. Carlson Jr. (Vice Chm)

THE ZIMMERMAN AGENCY LLC

1821 Miccosukee Commons Dr, Tallahassee, FL 32308-5433
Tel.: (850) 668-2222 FL
Web Site: http://www.zimmerman.com
Year Founded: 1987
Sales Range: $10-24.9 Million
Emp.: 150
Advetising Agency
N.A.I.C.S.: 541810
Carrie Zimmerman (Founder & CEO)
John Nicholas (VP-Media Activation)
Sheila Simpson (VP-HR)

THE ZIMMERMAN GROUP

21940 Minnetonka Blvd, Excelsior, MN 55331
Tel.: (952) 470-8830 MN
Web Site: http://www.thezimmermangroup.com
Year Founded: 1984
Rev.: $10,000,000
Emp.: 10
Advetising Agency
N.A.I.C.S.: 541810
Jim Zimmerman (Pres)
Kathy Ashpole (VP)
Greg Johnson (VP & Dir-Creative)

THE ZIPPERTUBING COMPANY

13000 S Broadway, Los Angeles, CA 90061-1120
Tel.: (310) 527-0488 CA
Web Site: http://www.zippertubing.com
Year Founded: 1957
Sales Range: $75-99.9 Million
Emp.: 35
Jacketing & Shielding Materials Mfr
N.A.I.C.S.: 326199
Terry Plummer (Pres)

Subsidiaries:

Accessible Products Company - Techlite Insulation Division (1)
2122 W 5th Pl, Tempe, AZ 85281
Tel.: (480) 967-8888
Web Site: http://www.techlite.net
Sales Range: $10-24.9 Million
Insulation Material Mfr
N.A.I.C.S.: 325211
Dave Winzlick (Gen Mgr)

Aero-Model Inc. (1)
2122 W 5th Pl, Tempe, AZ 85281
Tel.: (480) 726-7519
Web Site: http://www.aero-model.com
Model Aircraft Component Retailer
N.A.I.C.S.: 334419

The Zippertubing Company - ZT Automotive Division (1)
2122 W 5th Pl, Tempe, AZ 85281
Tel.: (866) 441-8308
Web Site: http://www.ztautomotive.com
Wire & Cable Mfr
N.A.I.C.S.: 335929

The Zippertubing Company - ZipTape Label ID Systems Division (1)
2122 W 5th Pl, Tempe, AZ 85281
Tel.: (480) 966-2999
Web Site: http://www.ziptape.com
Emp.: 40
Label Mfr
N.A.I.C.S.: 561910
David Wenzlick (Gen Mgr)

Zipper Technik GmbH (1)
Wernher-von-Braun-Strasse 3, 63263, Neu-Isenburg, Germany
Tel.: (49) 610273870
Web Site: http://www.zipper-technik.de

Sales Range: $10-24.9 Million
Harness Tool Mfr
N.A.I.C.S.: 332999
Frank Reusswig (Mng Dir)

Zippertubing (Japan), Ltd. (1)
3-2-8 Takatsukadai, Nishi-ku, Hyogo, 6512-271, Kobe, Japan
Tel.: (81) 789914171
Web Site: http://www.ztj.co.jp
Sales Range: $10-24.9 Million
Wire & Cable Mfr
N.A.I.C.S.: 335929
Yoshihiko Tsuchihashi (Pres)
Mitsuru Kurata (Mng Dir)
Norifumi Fukuda (Auditor)
Yoshinori Hashimoto (Auditor)

THE ZISES GROUP

230 Park Ave Ste 1000, New York, NY 10169
Tel.: (212) 777-7888
Year Founded: 1963
Sales Range: Less than $1 Million
Emp.: 3
N.A.I.C.S.: 541810
Anita Micossi (Treas & Media Dir)

THE ZLOTNICK GROUP

14 Woodland Rd, West Caldwell, NJ 07006-6519
Tel.: (973) 454-8536 NY
Year Founded: 1999
Rev.: $15,000,000
Emp.: 11
Brand Development, Business-To-Business, Communications, Consumer Marketing, Print, Public Relations, Strategic Planning, T.V.
N.A.I.C.S.: 541810
Jan Zlotnick (CMO)
Melanie Kartzman (CFO)
Jay Shaw (Brand Planner)
Gloria Eng (Brand Planner & Ethnography)
Marija Miljkovic (Dir-Design & Art)
Jhan Snyder (Dir-Special Events)
Christina Strong (Acct Mgr)
Emma Gunn (Media Planner)
Retla Nairb (Media Strategist)
Colin Ochel (Web Designer)

THE ZRIKE COMPANY INC.

7 Fir Bldg 2, Oakland, NJ 07436
Tel.: (201) 651-5158
Sales Range: $10-24.9 Million
Emp.: 15
China
N.A.I.C.S.: 423220
David G. Zrike (Pres)
Raymond W. Zrike Sr. (Founder & Chm)

THEA & SCHOEN, INC.

380 Allwood Rd, Clifton, NJ 07012-1702
Tel.: (973) 472-4720
Web Site: http://www.theaschoeninc.com
Year Founded: 1930
Sales Range: $10-24.9 Million
Emp.: 65
Electrical Apparatus & Equipment Whslr
N.A.I.C.S.: 423610
Stephanie Peterson (Dir-Mktg)

THEATRE COMMUNICATIONS GROUP, INC.

520 8th Ave 24th Fl, New York, NY 10018-4156
Tel.: (212) 609-5900
Web Site: http://www.tcg.org
Sales Range: $10-24.9 Million
Emp.: 50
American Theatre Promoter; Books Publisher
N.A.I.C.S.: 813920

COMPANIES

Jennifer Cleary *(Dir-Membership)*
Laurie Baskin *(Dir-Res, Policy & Collective Action)*
Emilya Cachapero *(Dir-Artistic Programs)*
Kitty Suen *(Dir-Creative)*
Carol Van Keuren *(Dir-Adv)*
Teresa Eyring *(Exec Dir)*
Kevin Moriarty *(Chm)*
Tim Jennings *(Treas)*
Joseph P. Benincasa *(Pres & CEO)*
Ellen Richard *(Exec Dir)*
Larissa FastHorse *(Sec)*
Ed Herendeen *(Dir-Producing)*
Chris Jennings *(Exec Dir)*
Michael S. Rosenberg *(Mng Dir)*
Allison Whitehall *(Mgr-Dev)*
Gus Schulenburg *(Dir-Comm & Community Engagement)*
Rebecca Marzalek-Kelly *(Assoc Dir-Membership)*
Robin Schlinger *(CFO)*
Adrian Budhu *(COO)*
Meghan Pressman *(Mng Dir)*
Rebecca Hopkins *(Mng Dir)*

THEATRE DEVELOPMENT FUND
520 8th Ave Ste 801, New York, NY 10018-6507
Tel.: (212) 912-9770   NY
Web Site: http://www.tdf.org
Year Founded: 1967
Sales Range: $10-24.9 Million
Emp.: 193
Fundraising Services
N.A.I.C.S.: 561499
Eric Sobel *(Dir-Fin)*
David LeShay *(Dir-Mktg & PR)*
Daniel Renner *(Dir-Education)*
Joy Cooper *(Dir-Dev)*
Stephen Cabral *(Dir-Costume Collection)*
Ginger Bartkoski Meagher *(Assoc Dir-Education)*
Anne Trites *(Dir-Dev)*
Lisa Carling *(Dir-TDF Accessibility Programs)*
Allie Relihan *(Mgr-Education & Community Programs)*
Michael Naumann *(Mng Dir)*
Doug Smith *(Dir-Internet Svcs & New Media)*
Julian Christenberry *(Dir-Ticket Programs)*
Emily Travis *(Mgr-Mktg)*

THEATRE FOR A NEW AUDIENCE
262 Ashland Pl, Brooklyn, NY 11217
Tel.: (212) 229-2819
Web Site: http://www.tfana.org
Year Founded: 1979
Sales Range: $25-49.9 Million
Emp.: 20
Theatre Production
N.A.I.C.S.: 711110
Dorothy Ryan *(VP & Sec)*
Jeffrey Horowitz *(Founder & Pres)*
Theodore C. Rogers *(Chm)*
Gloria Messinger *(Sec)*
Robert Buckholz *(Vice Chm)*

THEATRE MANAGEMENT INC.
1798 S Woodland Blvd, Deland, FL 32720
Tel.: (386) 736-6830
Web Site: http://www.epictheaters.com
Sales Range: $10-24.9 Million
Emp.: 6
Motion Picture Theater Operator
N.A.I.C.S.: 512131
Frank Demarsh *(Pres)*

THEBLAZE INC.
1133 Avenue of the Americas 34th Fl, New York, NY 10036
Tel.: (212) 520-1518
Web Site: http://www.theblaze.com
Year Founded: 2012
Sales Range: $75-99.9 Million
Support Services
N.A.I.C.S.: 561499
Omar Rodriguez *(Sr VP-Sls)*
Stewart Padveen *(Pres)*
Leon Wolf *(Mng Editor)*
Chris Gannett *(Sr VP-Mktg)*

THEDIRECTORY.COM, INC.
2701 N Rocky Point Dr Ste 950, Tampa, FL 33607
Tel.: (727) 417-7807   UT
Web Site: http://www.thedirectory.com
Year Founded: 1983
Sales Range: $1-9.9 Million
Emp.: 14
Online Business Directory Publisher
N.A.I.C.S.: 513140
Scott Gallagher *(Chm, Pres, CEO, CFO, Principal Acctg Officer & Sec)*

THEIPGUYS.NET LLC
7250 Metro Blvd Ste 200, Edina, MN 55439
Tel.: (952) 960-1000
Web Site: https://www.onenetglobal.com
Year Founded: 1995
Emp.: 100
Managed Telecom, IT & Cybersecurity Solutions
N.A.I.C.S.: 541512
Subsidiaries:

Ecessa Corporation   (1)
10900 Red Circle Dr, Minnetonka, MN 55343
Tel.: (763) 694-9949
Web Site: http://www.ecessa.com
Data Communication Products Mfr
N.A.I.C.S.: 334220
Scott Fluegge *(Gen Mgr)*

JDL Technologies, Inc.   (1)
10900 Red Circle Dr, Minnetonka, MN 55343
Tel.: (952) 946-1810
Web Site: http://www.jdltech.com
Sales Range: $25-49.9 Million
Emp.: 15
Provider of Network Design, Specification, Integration & Training Services for the K-12 Education Market
N.A.I.C.S.: 423430

Subsidiary (Domestic):
Twisted Technologies, Inc.   (2)
400 Galleria Pkwy Ste 1500, Atlanta, GA 30339
Tel.: (404) 202-1517
Web Site: http://www.twistedtechnologies.com
Software Solutions
N.A.I.C.S.: 513210
Mark Mancini *(Founder & CEO)*

THEIS PRECISION STEEL INC.
300 Broad St, Bristol, CT 06010
Tel.: (860) 585-6610
Web Site: http://www.theis-usa.com
Sales Range: $25-49.9 Million
Design & Production of Engineered Steel
N.A.I.C.S.: 331221
Paul Ashton *(Engr-Facility)*

THEISEN VENDING INC.
2335 Nevada Ave N, Minneapolis, MN 55427-3609
Tel.: (612) 827-5588
Web Site: http://www.theisenvending.com
Sales Range: $10-24.9 Million
Emp.: 60
Coin-Operated Amusement Devices
N.A.I.C.S.: 445132
Thomas N. Theisen *(Pres)*
Daniel Wright *(Controller)*
Anita Bennett *(Gen Mgr-Kiddie Ride Mall Leasing)*
Dale Lund *(Gen Mgr-Vending & Amusement)*

THELADDERS.COM, INC.
137 Varick St 8th Fl, New York, NY 10013
Tel.: (646) 453-1800
Web Site: http://www.theladders.com
Year Founded: 2003
Sales Range: $100-124.9 Million
Emp.: 305
Publisher Of Online Job Newsletters
N.A.I.C.S.: 561311
Marc Cenedella *(Founder, Chm & CEO)*

THELEN INC.
1112 N Euclid Ave, Bay City, MI 48706
Tel.: (989) 684-2980
Web Site: http://www.thinkthelen.com
Sales Range: $25-49.9 Million
Emp.: 40
Sales of New & Used Automobiles
N.A.I.C.S.: 441110
Joe Thelen *(Gen Mgr)*
Pat Thelen *(Gen Mgr)*
Mike Thelen *(Gen Mgr)*

THELEN SAND & GRAVEL INC.
28955 W State Rte 173, Antioch, IL 60002
Tel.: (847) 662-0760
Web Site: http://www.thelensg.com
Rev.: $42,000,000
Emp.: 70
Construction Sand & Gravel
N.A.I.C.S.: 212321
Steven Thelen *(Pres & CEO)*

THELMA LAGER & ASSOCIATES
3015 Glendale Blvd, Los Angeles, CA 90039-1832
Tel.: (323) 664-2177
Year Founded: 1964
Sales Range: $10-24.9 Million
Emp.: 2
Advertising Agencies, Children's Market, Direct Marketing, E-Commerce, Magazines, Merchandising, Planning & Consultation, Print, Publicity/Promotions
N.A.I.C.S.: 541810
Thelma Lager *(Owner)*
Lee Jones *(Media Dir)*

THEO KALOMIRAKIS THEATERS
535 Dean St, Brooklyn, NY 11217
Tel.: (212) 244-2404
Web Site: http://www.tktheaters.com
Sales Range: $10-24.9 Million
Emp.: 12
Home Theater Design Services
N.A.I.C.S.: 541410
Theo Kalomirakis *(Pres)*
James Theobald *(VP-Sls & Mktg)*

THEOCHEM LABORATORIES, INC.
7373 Rowlett Pk Dr, Tampa, FL 33610
Tel.: (813) 237-6463   FL
Web Site: http://www.theochem.com
Year Founded: 1963
Sales Range: $100-124.9 Million

THEOREM INC.

Emp.: 150
Sanitation Goods Mfr
N.A.I.C.S.: 325612
Elisabeth Theofilos *(VP)*
Angela Harder *(VP-Acctg & Info Svcs)*
John Theofilos *(CEO)*
Ken Gilbank *(Supvr-Inventory Control)*
Subsidiaries:

Theochem Laboratories, Inc.   (1)
3780 Browns Mill Rd SE, Atlanta, GA 30354-2927   (100%)
Tel.: (404) 767-7526
Web Site: http://www.timeproducts.com
Sales Range: $10-24.9 Million
Emp.: 25
Detergents Mfr
N.A.I.C.S.: 325611
John Liljenquist *(Gen Mgr)*

THEODORE PRESSER CO.
588 N Gulph Rd, King of Prussia, PA 19406
Tel.: (610) 592-1222   DE
Web Site: http://www.presser.com
Year Founded: 1883
Sales Range: $50-74.9 Million
Emp.: 50
Distr & Publisher of Printed Music
N.A.I.C.S.: 512230
Dewight Munroe *(Dir-Mktg)*
John Howell *(CFO)*
Sonya Kim *(Pres & CEO)*
F. Hayden Connor *(Chm)*
Subsidiaries:

Beekman Music, Inc.   (1)
588 N Gulph Rd, King of Prussia, PA 19406
Tel.: (610) 592-1222
Music Publishers
N.A.I.C.S.: 513140

Elkan-Vogel Inc.   (1)
1 Presser Place, Bryn Mawr, PA 19010-3490
Tel.: (610) 525-3636
Music Publishers
N.A.I.C.S.: 513140

John Church Co.   (1)
588 N Gulph Rd, King of Prussia, PA 19406
Tel.: (610) 592-1222
Sales Range: $25-49.9 Million
Emp.: 35
Music Publishers
N.A.I.C.S.: 513140

Mercury Music Corporation   (1)
1 Presser Pl, Bryn Mawr, PA 19010-3490
Tel.: (610) 525-3636
Music Publisher & Distr
N.A.I.C.S.: 512230

Oliver Ditson Co.   (1)
1 Presser Pl, Bryn Mawr, PA 19010-3490
Tel.: (610) 525-3636
Music Publishers
N.A.I.C.S.: 513140

THEOREM INC.
383 Main St Ste 101, Chatham, NJ 07928
Tel.: (973) 665-1700
Web Site: http://www.theoreminc.net
Year Founded: 2002
Sales Range: $25-49.9 Million
Emp.: 700
Marketing Related Software & Services
N.A.I.C.S.: 541613
Jay Kulkarni *(Founder & CEO)*
Jack Demetris *(Sr VP-Bus Dev & Strategy)*
Reem Al-Basri *(Head-Digital Media Strategy)*
Subsidiaries:

Theorem Creations   (1)
241 W Charleston Blvd Ste 175, Las Vegas, NV 89102

THEOREM INC.   U.S. PRIVATE

Theorem Inc.—(Continued)
Tel.: (702) 838-7283
Web Site: http://www.theoremcreations.com
Creative Services
N.A.I.C.S.: 541430

Theorem Espanol (1)
Calle Pedro Ignacio Espaillat Esq Independencia 655, Gazcue, Santo Domingo, Dominican Republic
Tel.: (809) 682 4039
Web Site: http://www.theoremcreations.com
Emp.: 95
Marketing Related Software & Services
N.A.I.C.S.: 541613

Theorem India Pvt. Ltd. (1)
23/4 D Rajagopala Road Sanjaynagar Main Road, Bengaluru, 560 094, India
Tel.: (91) 80 43471600
Web Site: http://www.theoreminc.net
Emp.: 150
Marketing Related Software & Services
N.A.I.C.S.: 541613
Bhaskar Kalale (VP)

THEORY ONE
PO Box 789762, Wichita, KS 67278-9762
Tel.: (316) 652-2277
Year Founded: 2009
Sales Range: $10-24.9 Million
Emp.: 55
New Car Whslr
N.A.I.C.S.: 441110
Harold Johnson (CEO)
Michael Stevens (Pres)

THEPRINTERS.COM
3500 E College Ave, State College, PA 16801
Tel.: (814) 237-7600
Web Site: http://www.theprinters.com
Year Founded: 1973
Sales Range: $10-24.9 Million
Emp.: 75
Graphic Design, Printing, Mailing & Fulfillment Services
N.A.I.C.S.: 541430
Raymond Caravan (CEO)

THER-A-PEDIC MIDWEST INC.
2350 5th St, Rock Island, IL 61201
Tel.: (309) 788-0401
Web Site: http://www.thebettinggroup.com
Rev.: $18,000,000
Emp.: 67
Mattresses, Innerspring & Box Spring
N.A.I.C.S.: 337910
Jeffrey Sherman (Pres)
Jerry Irey (Controller)

THERAPEDIC ASSOCIATES, INC.
103 College Rd E 2nd Fl, Princeton, NJ 08540
Tel.: (609) 720-0700
Web Site: http://www.therapedic.com
Year Founded: 1957
Sales Range: $200-249.9 Million
Emp.: 4
Mfr of Mattresses
N.A.I.C.S.: 337121
Norman Rosenblatt (Chm)
Gerry Borreggine (Pres & CEO)
Sheryl Friedman (Office Mgr)

Subsidiaries:

Therapedic Associates, Inc. - The Bed Factory (1)
25 Copsey Place, PO Box 71090, Avondale, Auckland, New Zealand
Tel.: (64) 98282259
Web Site: http://www.thebedfactory.co.nz
Mattress Mfr
N.A.I.C.S.: 337910

THERAPEUTIC FAMILY LIFE
5810 Trade Center Dr Ste 500, Austin, TX 78744
Tel.: (512) 451-7310
Web Site: http://www.tflife.org
Year Founded: 1993
Sales Range: $10-24.9 Million
Emp.: 106
Foster Care Services
N.A.I.C.S.: 624110
Leon J. Smith (Exec Dir)
Jeffrey Smith (Dir-Ops)

THERAPY SOURCE, INC.
5215 Militia Hill Rd Ste A, Plymouth Meeting, PA 19462-1276
Tel.: (484) 342-2000
Web Site: http://www.txsource.net
Year Founded: 2001
Sales Range: $1-9.9 Million
Emp.: 10
Physical, Occupational & Psychological Therapy
N.A.I.C.S.: 621340
Stacey Cartagenova (Owner & CEO)
Neil McGettigan (Mgr-Bus Dev)
Jason Montagna (Dir-Fin)
Tracyl Sipp (Mgr-TheraWeb Clinical)
Rachel Ostafi (Dir-Mktg)

THERAPYSITES.COM LLC
1035 Parl St Suite 400, Boulder, CO 80302
Tel.: (866) 288-2771
Web Site: http://www.therapysites.com
Year Founded: 2007
Sales Range: $1-9.9 Million
Emp.: 36
Builds, Optimizes & Hosts Websites for Mental Health Professionals
N.A.I.C.S.: 541810
Denise Marshall (Coord-Bus Dev)
Ryan King (Mgr-Tech Support)

THERM, INC.
1000 Hudson St Ext, Ithaca, NY 14850
Tel.: (607) 272-8500
Web Site: http://www.therm.com
Year Founded: 1935
Sales Range: $200-249.9 Million
Emp.: 200
Mfr of Machine Parts
N.A.I.C.S.: 336412
Leo McGratten (Controller)

THERM-O-LINK INC.
10513 Freedom St, Garrettsville, OH 44231
Tel.: (330) 527-2124
Web Site: http://www.tolwire.com
Sales Range: $25-49.9 Million
Emp.: 118
Nonferrous Wiredrawing & Insulating
N.A.I.C.S.: 335929
Richard B. Thompson (Co-Founder)
Donna Pishotti (Mgr-Credit)
Kevin Ryan (Mgr-Corp Quality & R&D)
John Archer (Mgr-IS)
Tom Brest (Mgr-Sls)

THERMA-SEAL ROOFS INC.
1011 Fairfield Dr, West Palm Beach, FL 33407
Tel.: (561) 848-0333
Rev.: $11,600,000
Emp.: 150
Roofing Contractors
N.A.I.C.S.: 238160
Dave Wilken (Pres)

THERMAL & MECHANICAL EQUIPMENT, LLC
1423 E Richey Rd, Houston, TX 77073
Tel.: (713) 688-8834
Web Site: http://www.tmec.com
Year Founded: 1986
Sales Range: $25-49.9 Million
Emp.: 20
Mfr of Industrial Heat Exchange Equipment
N.A.I.C.S.: 423830
Russell Braden (Pres)

THERMAL EDGE, INC.
1751 Hurd Dr, Irving, TX 75038
Tel.: (972) 580-0200
Web Site: http://www.thermal-edge.com
Sales Range: $1-9.9 Million
Emp.: 50
Industrial Valve Mfr
N.A.I.C.S.: 332911
Andrew Cohen (Pres)
Dan Valentino (Mgr-Sls-Eastern Territory)

THERMAL MECHANICS INC.
715 Goddard Ave, Chesterfield, MO 63005
Tel.: (636) 532-1110
Web Site: http://www.thermalmechanics.com
Rev.: $25,000,000
Emp.: 75
Warm Air Heating & Air-Conditioning Equipment & Supplies Merchant Whslr
N.A.I.C.S.: 423730
David Rich (Owner & Pres)
Michael Fallon (CFO)

THERMAL PAPER DIRECT INC.
380 Franklin Tpke, Mahwah, NJ 07430
Tel.: (201) 684-1733
Web Site: http://www.thermalpaperdirect.com
Year Founded: 2005
Sales Range: $1-9.9 Million
Emp.: 10
Paper Roll Products
N.A.I.C.S.: 322299
David Mindich (Pres)

THERMAL SUPPLY INC.
717 S Lander St, Seattle, WA 98134
Tel.: (206) 624-4590
Web Site: http://www.thermalsupply.com
Rev.: $40,000,000
Emp.: 32
Refrigeration Equipment & Supplies
N.A.I.C.S.: 423740
Dan Monroe (Owner)
Michael Monroe (Co-Pres)
Tom Nunamacher (Reg Mgr)
Tony Rogers (Branch Mgr)

THERMAL WINDOWS INC.
12805 E 31st St, Tulsa, OK 74146
Tel.: (918) 663-7580
Web Site: http://www.thermalwindows.com
Year Founded: 1980
Sales Range: $10-24.9 Million
Emp.: 200
Designer & Producer of Windows & Frames
N.A.I.C.S.: 332321
Dennis Lane (Pres)
Brent Ragsdale (Owner)
Jorge Chavez (Mgr-IT)
Mark Shiew (Project Mgr)

THERMALCAST, LLC
15 Coppage Dr, Worcester, MA 01603
Tel.: (508) 791-5594
Web Site: http://www.thermalcast.com
Sales Range: $10-24.9 Million
Emp.: 230
Aluminum Die-Castings
N.A.I.C.S.: 331523

THERMICO INC.
3405 Centennial Dr Ste 2, Midland, MI 48642
Tel.: (989) 496-2927
Web Site: http://www.thermico.com
Sales Range: $10-24.9 Million
Emp.: 200
Building Insulation Services
N.A.I.C.S.: 238310
Mark A. Thompson (Pres)

THERMO ELECTRIC COMPANY, INC.
1193 McDermott Dr, West Chester, PA 19380
Tel.: (610) 692-7990
Web Site: http://www.te-direct.com
Year Founded: 1941
Sales Range: $25-49.9 Million
Emp.: 70
Temperature Sensor Mfr
N.A.I.C.S.: 334513
Ralph Vuoncino (Mgr-Corp Quality Control & Documentation)

THERMO FLUIDS INC.
8925 E Pima Ctr Pkwy Ste 105, Scottsdale, AZ 85258-4409
Tel.: (602) 272-2400
Web Site: http://www.thermofluids.com
Used Oil Recycling Services
N.A.I.C.S.: 423930
Todd J. Bogart (Chief Mktg Officer)
Amy Tuggle (Dir-HR)

THERMO KING CENTRAL CAROLINAS, LLC
6633 Statesville Rd, Charlotte, NC 28269
Tel.: (704) 596-2652
Web Site: http://www.tkcentralcarolinas.com
Rev.: $15,000,000
Emp.: 68
Provider of Air Conditioning Equipment
N.A.I.C.S.: 423730
Peter Holland (Pres)

THERMO KING CHRISTENSEN INC.
7508 F St, Omaha, NE 68127
Tel.: (402) 331-6116
Web Site: http://www.tkcweb.com
Rev.: $25,456,708
Emp.: 45
Refrigeration Units, Motor Vehicles
N.A.I.C.S.: 423740
Don Kasier (Pres)

THERMO KING OF INDIANA INC.
817 S Tibbs Ave, Indianapolis, IN 46241
Tel.: (317) 247-4002
Web Site: http://www.tkoi.com
Sales Range: $10-24.9 Million
Emp.: 35
Automotive Supplies & Parts
N.A.I.C.S.: 423120
Dan Bartholomew (Pres)

THERMO KING QUAD CITIES INC.
3900 81st Ave W, Rock Island, IL 62101
Tel.: (309) 787-6177

COMPANIES

Web Site:
http://www.biz.50below.com
Rev.: $12,100,000
Emp.: 30
Refrigeration Equipment & Supplies
N.A.I.C.S.: 423740
John Deitrick (Pres)

THERMO KING SALES & SERVICE, INC.
1951 Old Hwy 8 NW, Saint Paul, MN 55112-1826
Tel.: (651) 633-2820 MN
Web Site: http://www.thermoking.com
Year Founded: 1966
Sales Range: $10-24.9 Million
Emp.: 50
Provider of Refrigeration Equipment & Supplies
N.A.I.C.S.: 423740
Jerry Burk (Controller)

THERMO TELECOM PARTNERS, LLC
1735 19th St Ste 200, Denver, CO 80202
Tel.: (303) 294-0690
Web Site:
http://www.thermocapitalpartners.com
Sales Range: $250-299.9 Million
Holding Company
N.A.I.C.S.: 551112
James Monroe III (Partner)
James F. Lynch (Mng Dir)

THERMO-TECH PREMIUM WINDOWS & DOORS, INC.
1120 38th Ave NE, Sauk Rapids, MN 56379
Tel.: (320) 529-4012
Web Site: http://www.ttwindows.com
Year Founded: 1953
Sales Range: $10-24.9 Million
Emp.: 120
Metal Window & Door Mfr
N.A.I.C.S.: 332321
Michael Kutay (Pres)

THERMO-TWIN INDUSTRIES INC.
1155 Allegheny Ave, Oakmont, PA 15139
Tel.: (412) 826-1000
Web Site: http://www.thermotwin.com
Year Founded: 1972
Sales Range: $10-24.9 Million
Emp.: 180
Metal Storm Doors & Windows Mfr
N.A.I.C.S.: 332321
Joseph Palermo (Pres & CEO)

THERMOCOPY OF TENNESSEE INC.
3505 Sutherland Ave, Knoxville, TN 37919
Tel.: (865) 524-1124
Web Site:
http://www.thermocopy.com
Sales Range: $1-9.9 Million
Emp.: 63
Office Equipment
N.A.I.C.S.: 423420
Stephen Sumner (Pres)
Mark Denicola (CFO & Exec Dir-Sls & Mktg)

THERMOPATCH CORPORATION
2204 Erie Blvd E, Syracuse, NY 13224
Tel.: (315) 446-8110
Web Site:
http://www.thermopatch.com
Year Founded: 1987
Sales Range: $25-49.9 Million
Emp.: 60
Mfr of Metal Figures
N.A.I.C.S.: 339940
Tom Depuit (Pres)
Sharon Wescott (Sec)

THERMORETEC CORP.
300 Baker Ave Ste 302, Concord, MA 01742-2131
Tel.: (978) 371-1422 DE
Year Founded: 1986
Sales Range: $125-149.9 Million
Emp.: 1,000
Waste Management Company
N.A.I.C.S.: 562219
Robert Dunlap (Pres & COO)
Mary Livingston (Dir-HR)
Dan Donovan (CFO)

THERMOS L.L.C.
475 N Martingale Rd Ste 1100, Schaumburg, IL 60173
Tel.: (847) 439-7821 DE
Web Site: http://www.thermos.com
Year Founded: 1904
Steel & Glass Vacuum Ware; Foam Containers; School Lunch Kits; Ice Chests & Jugs; Foam Insulated Coolers; Insulated Coffee Carafes Mfr
N.A.I.C.S.: 332439
Rick Dias (Pres & COO)

Subsidiaries:

Canadian Thermos Products, Inc. (1)
370 King St W Ste 302, Toronto, M5V 1J9, ON, Canada (100%)
Tel.: (416) 757-6231
Web Site: http://www.thermosbrand.ca
Sales Range: $25-49.9 Million
Emp.: 13
Insulated Jugs, Chests, Lunch Kits, Vacuumware, Barbeques
N.A.I.C.S.: 326199

Lifefactory, Inc. (1)
3 Harbor Dr #200, Sausalito, CA 94965
Tel.: (415) 729-9820
Web Site: http://www.lifefactory.com
Reusable Glass Beverage & Food Storage Products Mfr
N.A.I.C.S.: 327213

Thermos (China) Housewares Co. Ltd.
No 55 Jin Yang Road Kunshan Development Zone He Feng Complete, Industrial Area, Kunshan, Jiangsu, China
Tel.: (86) 512 5767 9888
Thermoware Mfr
N.A.I.C.S.: 332439

Thermos (Singapore) Pte Ltd (1)
16 Arumugam Road 06-05 LTC Building D, Singapore, 409961, Singapore
Tel.: (65) 6749 4100
Web Site: http://www.thermos.com.sg
Thermoware Mfr
N.A.I.C.S.: 423990

Thermos Hong Kong Ltd. (1)
Unit 705 7/F Grandtech Centre No 8 On Ping Street, Shek Mun, Hong Kong, China (Hong Kong)
Tel.: (852) 2608 0880
Web Site: http://www.thermos.com.hk
Sales Range: $10-24.9 Million
Emp.: 40
Food Service Equipment Whslr
N.A.I.C.S.: 423440

Thermos K.K. (1)
2F Taiyo-Nissan Bldg 1-16-7 Nishi-Shinbashi, Minato-Ku, Tokyo, 105-8404, Japan
Tel.: (81) 3 3500 0800
Web Site: http://www.thermos.jp
Thermoware Distr
N.A.I.C.S.: 423990

Thermos Pty. Ltd. (1)
15-16 Walker Place, Wetherill Park, 2164, NSW, Australia (100%)
Tel.: (61) 297564311
Web Site: http://www.thermos.com

Sales Range: $25-49.9 Million
Emp.: 10
Sales of Housewares
N.A.I.C.S.: 449121

Top Thermo Mfg. (Malaysia) SDN. BHD (1)
Lot 64565 4 1/2 Mi Jalan Kebun Section 36, Shah Alam, 40470, Selangor Darul Ehsan, Malaysia (100%)
Tel.: (60) 351613196
Web Site: http://www.thermos.com
Sales Range: $50-74.9 Million
Emp.: 636
Mfr & Sales of Housewares
N.A.I.C.S.: 335210
Toru Goto (Mng Dir)

THERMOSET INC.
10605 N Baehr Rd, Mequon, WI 53092
Tel.: (262) 242-1430
Web Site:
http://www.thermosetinc.com
Year Founded: 1975
Sales Range: $10-24.9 Million
Emp.: 50
Friction Material, Made From Powdered Metal
N.A.I.C.S.: 332117
Robert Neitzel (Engr-Design)
John McGourthy Jr. (Pres)

THERMWELL PRODUCTS CO., INC.
420 Rte 17 S, Mahwah, NJ 07430
Tel.: (201) 684-4400 NJ
Web Site: http://www.frostking.com
Year Founded: 1910
Sales Range: $100-124.9 Million
Emp.: 1,500
Mfr of Hardware & Weatherstrip Products Under Brand Name Frost King
N.A.I.C.S.: 326113
Jeff Adler (VP-IT)

Subsidiaries:

Filmco Industries Inc. (1)
99 5th Ave, Paterson, NJ 07524-1105 (100%)
Tel.: (973) 357-2250
Web Site: http://www.filmco.com
Sales Range: $10-24.9 Million
Emp.: 20
Mfr of Plastic Sheets & Drop Cloths
N.A.I.C.S.: 322220

Lever Manufacturing Corp. (1)
420 Rte 17 S, Mahwah, NJ 07430
Tel.: (201) 684-4400
Web Site: http://www.levercorp.com
Sales Range: $10-24.9 Million
Emp.: 25
Roll Slitter & Bias Binding Machinery Designer & Mfr
N.A.I.C.S.: 333248
William M. Corbett (VP & Gen Mgr)
Don Bower (Mgr-Parts)

THERMWOOD CORPORATION
904 Buffaloville RD, Dale, IN 47523-9057
Tel.: (812) 937-4476
Web Site:
https://www.thermwood.com
Year Founded: 1969
Sales Range: $10-24.9 Million
Emp.: 90
Machine Tools & Routers Mfr & Distr for Woodworking, Plastics, Aerospace, Boating & Auto Industries
N.A.I.C.S.: 333517

Subsidiaries:

Akela Ltd. (1)
The Old Fire Station Pandy Park Aberkenfig, Bridgend, CF32 9RE, South Wales, United Kingdom (100%)
Tel.: (44) 8453456732
Web Site: http://www.akelaltd.com

THEWEBDIGEST CORP.

Sales Range: $10-24.9 Million
Emp.: 2
Mfr & Distr of Machine Tools & Routers for Woodworking, Plastics, Aerospace, Boating & Auto Industries
N.A.I.C.S.: 333515

THESIS, INC.
505 NW Couch St Ste 300, Portland, OR 97209
Tel.: (503) 221-6200
Web Site: http://www.eroi.com
Year Founded: 2002
Sales Range: $1-9.9 Million
Digital Marketing Services
N.A.I.C.S.: 541613
Ryan Buchanan (Founder & CEO)
Matt Popkes (VP-Strategy)
Andy Bowen (Mgr-Email Campaign)
Angelee Stenson (Office Mgr)
Becky Duncan (Mgr-Email Campaign)
Caitlin Leonard (Mgr-Acct)
Christina Davis (Mgr-Acct)
Grady Marold (Project Mgr)
Karen Butler-Kennedy (Accountant)
Kat Shapka (Mgr-Acct)
Kimberley Catchpole (Mgr-Acct)
Laurie Seibold (Sr Mgr-Acct)
Liz Goodin (Mgr-Acct)
Louisa Rekasi (Sr Project Mgr)
Mackenzie Harrington (Mgr-Acct)
Megan Trevarthen (Project Mgr)
Molly Leaf (Mgr-Acct)
Nadya Ighani (Coord-Acct)
Pat Rice (Mgr-Acct)
Rachael Klicka (Mgr-Acct)
Sara Reilly (Sr Mgr-Acct)
Sarah Lembcke (Mgr-Acct)
Stephen Hammill (Dir-Mktg Tech)
Tatiana Mac (Dir-Art)
Umi Francis (Sr Project Mgr)

Subsidiaries:

Bonfire Marketing Company (1)
3530 N Vancouver Ave Ste 200, Portland, OR 97227
Tel.: (503) 334-2071
Web Site: http://www.thinkbonfire.com
Sales Range: $1-9.9 Million
Digital Marketing Services
N.A.I.C.S.: 541613
Ryan Lewis (Founder & Pres)
Marion Olsen (VP-Ops)
Garrett Ira (VP-Strategy)
Cheyenne Allott (Mgr-Acct)
Aaron Colter (Mgr-Acct)
Vanessa Hammer (Mgr-Traffic)
Brody Lowe (Mgr-Creative)
Allison Rick (Mgr-Acct)
Jenny Le (Mgr-Events & Ops)
Melinda Lease (Mgr-Bus Process)
Keegan Meyer (Mgr-Community)
Jenn Tibbett (Dir-Editorial)
Si Robins (Acct Dir)
Jeff Wester (Dir-Creative)
Troy O'Bryan (VP-Strategic Growth)
Priscilla Converse (Mgr-Acct)
Manu Grossi (Sr Mgr-Acct)
Greg Hessong (Sr Mgr-Acct)

THEUT PRODUCTS INC.
73408 Van Dyke Rd, Romeo, MI 48065-3214
Tel.: (586) 752-4541 MI
Web Site:
http://www.theutproductsinc.com
Year Founded: 1957
Sales Range: $25-49.9 Million
Emp.: 100
Lumber & Other Building Materials Distr
N.A.I.C.S.: 444180
Edwin C. Theut Jr. (VP)

THEWEBDIGEST CORP.
7076 Spyglass Ave, Parkland, FL 33076
Tel.: (954) 599-3672 FL
Year Founded: 2007

TheWebDigest Corp.—(Continued)
Internet Informational Portal Operator
N.A.I.C.S.: 519290
Roland Breton *(Pres)*
Peter M. Burgess *(Chm & COO)*

THEXTON MANUFACTURING COMPANY, INC.
6539 Cecilia Cir, Edina, MN 55439
Tel.: (952) 831-4171
Web Site: http://www.thexton.com
Year Founded: 1907
Sales Range: $10-24.9 Million
Emp.: 15
Automotive Service Tools, Testers & Repair Items Designer, Mfr & Supplier
N.A.I.C.S.: 332216
Brian Tichy *(Pres)*
Dennis Harder *(VP-Product Engrg)*
Tom Wolfe *(VP-Ops)*
Karen Paul *(Mgr-Customer Svc)*
Ross Tichy *(VP-Sls & Mktg)*

THI INC.
900 Clancy Ave NE, Grand Rapids, MI 49503
Tel.: (616) 458-1538
Web Site: http://www.thierica.com
Rev.: $10,200,000
Emp.: 40
Machine & Other Job Shop Work
N.A.I.C.S.: 332710
Forrest Frank *(Pres)*

Subsidiaries:

Thierica Equipment Corporation (1)
3147 N Wilson Ct NW, Grand Rapids, MI 49534
Tel.: (616) 453-6570
Web Site: http://www.thieqip.com
Machine & Other Job Shop Work
N.A.I.C.S.: 332710
Lou McGough *(Gen Mgr)*
Dominic Zerilli *(Mgr-Sls)*

THIELE KAOLIN COMPANY
520 Kaolin Rd, Sandersville, GA 31082-1056
Tel.: (478) 552-3951
Web Site: http://www.thielekaolin.com
Year Founded: 1946
Sales Range: $300-349.9 Million
Emp.: 540
Kaolin Clay Mining, Processing & Blending for Kaolin Coating & Filler Pigments
N.A.I.C.S.: 212323
Scott Ahrens *(Mgr-Sls-North American)*
Paul R. Kirschling *(Pres)*
Mike Markillie *(VP-Sls, Mktg & Technical Svcs)*

Subsidiaries:

Piedmont Minerals (1)
520 Kaolin Rd, Sandersville, GA 31082
Tel.: (478) 552-3951
Sales Range: $25-49.9 Million
Emp.: 10
Kaolin Mining & Processing
N.A.I.C.S.: 551112

THIELEN IDEACORP
970 Van Ness, Fresno, CA 93721
Tel.: (559) 252-2500
Web Site: http://www.thielenideacorp.com
Year Founded: 1969
Rev.: $22,072,000
Emp.: 34
Advetising Agency
N.A.I.C.S.: 541810
Michel C. Thielen *(CEO)*
Donald C. Emery *(Exec VP)*
Cynthia Fidel *(Dir-Client Svcs)*
Darren Riley *(VP-Ops)*
Ursula Thielen *(CFO)*
Linda Sommers *(VP & Dir-Media Svcs)*
Douglas P. Morris *(Creative Dir)*
Charles Looney *(Sr Acct Mgr)*
Blair Looney *(Sr Acct Mgr)*
Jennifer Fitzgerald *(Media Planner & Media Buyer)*
Michelle Cortes *(Project Mgr)*

THIELSCH ENGINEERING, INC.
195 Frances Ave, Cranston, RI 02910-2211
Tel.: (401) 467-6454
Web Site: http://www.thielsch.com
Year Founded: 1984
Rev.: $34,300,000
Emp.: 500
Provider of Engineering Services, Technical Services & Various Other Professional, Consulting & Testing Services
N.A.I.C.S.: 541330
Thomas E. Lent *(Pres & CEO)*
Trent Theroux *(VP-Fin)*
Ara Nalbandian *(VP-Pro & Engrg)*
Peter Kennefick *(VP-Field Engrg)*

Subsidiaries:

ALCO Engineering, Inc. (1)
195 Frances Ave, Cranston, RI 02910-2212 (100%)
Tel.: (401) 467-6454
Web Site: http://www.thielsch.com
Sales Range: $10-24.9 Million
Emp.: 19
Water & Wastewater Treatment Plant Support Services
N.A.I.C.S.: 541330

BAL Laboratory (1)
185 Frances Ave, Cranston, RI 02910-2211 (100%)
Tel.: (401) 467-6454
Web Site: http://www.thielsch.com
Sales Range: $10-24.9 Million
Emp.: 3
Environmental & Public Health Microbiology Testing Services
N.A.I.C.S.: 541720
Darlene Caspuano *(Dir-Lab)*

ESS Laboratory (1)
185 Frances Ave, Cranston, RI 02910-2211 (100%)
Tel.: (401) 461-7181
Web Site: http://www.thielsch.com
Sales Range: $10-24.9 Million
Emp.: 35
Provider of Analytical Testing of Water, Wastes, Soil, Sludge & Debris
N.A.I.C.S.: 541330
Laurel Stoddard *(Dir-Laboratory)*

RISE Group, Inc. (1)
1341 Elmwood Ave, Cranston, RI 02910
Tel.: (401) 784-3700
Web Site: https://www.riseengineering.com
Engineering, Laboratory, Consulting & Field Services
N.A.I.C.S.: 561499
Vincent R. Graziano *(Pres & CEO)*

Subsidiary (Domestic):

Air Masters HVAC Services of New England, Inc. (2)
59 Turner St, Fall River, MA 02720-2517
Tel.: (508) 672-7993
Web Site: http://www.airmastershvac.net
Plumbing, Heating & Air-Conditioning Contractors
N.A.I.C.S.: 238220
Michael Medeiros Sr. *(Pres)*
Michael Medeiros Jr. *(Head-Controls Div)*
Josh Medeiros *(Dir-Ops)*

Rise Engineering, Inc. (2)
1341 Elmwood Ave, Cranston, RI 02910-3821
Tel.: (800) 422-5365
Web Site: http://www.riseengineering.com
Sales Range: $10-24.9 Million
Emp.: 50
Energy Management Services for Commercial, Industrial, Institutional & Residential Building Owners & Managers
N.A.I.C.S.: 541690
Vincent R. Graziano *(Pres)*

Water Management Services Division (1)
195 Frances Ave, Cranston, RI 02910-2211 (100%)
Tel.: (401) 467-6454
Web Site: http://www.thielsch.com
Sales Range: $10-24.9 Million
Emp.: 15
Water Meter Installation, Testing & Repair Services
N.A.I.C.S.: 541611
Bill Hinton *(Gen Mgr)*

THIES & TALLE MANAGEMENT CO.
470 W 78th St 260, Chanhassen, MN 55317
Tel.: (952) 949-2200
Web Site: http://www.thiestalle.com
Sales Range: $10-24.9 Million
Emp.: 250
Nonresidential Building Operators
N.A.I.C.S.: 531120
Kenneth R. Talle *(Pres)*
Mary Russell *(Mgr-Property)*

THINK BROWNSTONE INC.
201 Fayette St, Conshohocken, PA 19428
Web Site: http://www.thinkbrownstone.com
Year Founded: 2007
Sales Range: $1-9.9 Million
Emp.: 20
Design Software
N.A.I.C.S.: 513210
Carl White *(Co-Founder & CEO)*
Brian McIntire *(Co-Founder)*
Russ Starke *(Exec VP)*
Kimberly Blessing *(Sr Dir-Tech Consulting & Software Dev)*

THINK FINANCE, INC.
4150 International Plz Ste 400, Fort Worth, TX 76109
Tel.: (817) 546-2700
Web Site: http://www.thinkfinance.com
Sales Range: $500-549.9 Million
Emp.: 450
Financial Software Development Services
N.A.I.C.S.: 541511
Bill Kontgis *(CIO)*
Martin Wong *(CEO)*
Nina Vitagliano *(CFO)*
Ranga Kothamasu *(Chief Risk Officer)*
Matthew Hargrove *(COO)*
Stephen Costas *(Gen Counsel)*
Tom Carter *(VP-Bus Dev)*

THINK INK MARKETING & DIRECT MAIL SERVICES, INC.
16692 Burke Ln, Huntington Beach, CA 92647
Tel.: (714) 841-2041
Web Site: http://www.thinkinkmarketing.com
Year Founded: 1991
Sales Range: $1-9.9 Million
Emp.: 25
Direct Mail Advertising Services
N.A.I.C.S.: 541860
Craig Dickhout *(Pres & CEO)*
Lindsay Dickhout *(VP)*
Manny Jurado *(Mgr-Production)*
Crystal O'Brien *(Mgr-Accts)*
Eric Garcia *(VP-Bus Dev)*
Lois Willingham *(Mgr-Sls & Mktg)*
Ted Lonnberg *(Sr VP-Sls)*
Tim Owen *(Exec Dir-Sls)*

THINK INK, INC.
8101 Cessna Ave, Gaithersburg, MD 20879
Tel.: (301) 963-7481
Web Site: http://www.thinkink.com
Year Founded: 2001
Sales Range: Less than $1 Million
Emp.: 7
Printing Systems Ink & Supplies Mfr
N.A.I.C.S.: 325910
Dave Loos *(Owner & CEO)*
Lisa White *(Gen Mgr)*

THINK! INC.
1750 W Superior Ste 100, Chicago, IL 60622
Tel.: (312) 850-1190
Web Site: http://www.e-thinkinc.com
Year Founded: 1996
Sales Range: $1-9.9 Million
Emp.: 17
Sales Management Consulting Services
N.A.I.C.S.: 541613
Carrie Welles *(VP-Global Customer Mgmt)*

THINKING GREEN
170 S Green Valley Pkwy Ste 300, Henderson, NV 89012
Tel.: (702) 202-0068
Web Site: http://www.thinkinggreen-usa.com
Year Founded: 2013
Farm Product Mfr & Distr
N.A.I.C.S.: 111419
Richard Ham *(Founder, Chm, Pres, CEO & Treas)*
Carla Ham *(Sec)*

THINKINGMAN.COM NEW MEDIA
1970 Hanalima St D102, Lihue, HI 96766-8928
Tel.: (808) 652-9243
Web Site: http://www.thinkingman.com
Sales Range: Less than $1 Million
Emp.: 3
Web Design, Programming & Public Relations
N.A.I.C.S.: 541890
Adam Prall *(Mgr-Bus)*

THINKPATH INC.
9080 Springboro Pike Ste 300, Miamisburg, OH 45342
Tel.: (937) 291-8374
Web Site: http://www.thinkpath.com
Year Founded: 1975
Engineeering Services
N.A.I.C.S.: 541330
Kelly Hankinson *(CFO)*
Robert J. Trick *(Pres & COO)*

THINSOLUTIONS
9150 South Hills Blvd Ste 125, Cleveland, OH 44147
Tel.: (216) 685-3000
Web Site: http://www.thinsolutions.com
Year Founded: 1997
Sales Range: $1-9.9 Million
Emp.: 38
Custom Computer Programming Services
N.A.I.C.S.: 541511
Michael J. Fischer *(CEO)*
Brandon Bergan *(Dir-Client Rels)*
Nathaniel Fisher *(Dir-Client Svcs)*
Barbara Hemsath *(Dir-Admin)*
John Rowland *(CTO)*
Brian Limkemann *(Mgr-Dev Grp)*

THIONVILLE LABORATORIES INC.

COMPANIES

5440 Pepsi St, New Orleans, LA 70123
Tel.: (504) 733-9603
Web Site:
http://www.thionvillenola.com
Sales Range: $10-24.9 Million
Emp.: 50
Testing Laboratories
N.A.I.C.S.: 541715
Paul Thionville (Pres)

THIRD COST TERMINALS
1871 Mykawa, Pearland, TX 77581
Tel.: (281) 412-0275
Web Site:
http://www.3cterminals.com
Rev.: $38,128,152
Emp.: 200
Specialized Storage for the Petrochemical Industry
N.A.I.C.S.: 424720
Jim Clawson (Pres)

THIRD DOOR MEDIA INC.
279 Newtown Tpke, Redding, CT 06896
Tel.: (203) 664-1350
Web Site:
http://www.thirddoormedia.com
Sales Range: $1-9.9 Million
Emp.: 30
Marketing Consulting Services
N.A.I.C.S.: 541613
Sean Moriarty (Partner & VP-Sls)
Chris Sherman (Partner & VP-Programming)
Claire Schoen (VP-Mktg Svcs)
Michelle Robbins (Sr VP-Content & Mktg Tech)
Karen DeWeese (VP-Event Ops)
Sarah Power (Dir-Bus Dev)
Chris Elwell (CEO & Partner)
Katie Gausepohl (Dir-Fin)
Allison Jones (Mgr-Mktg)
Ed Kuryluk (Sr Mgr-Mktg Svcs)
Elisabeth Osmeloski (VP-Audience Dev)
Kyle Pouliot (Mgr-Community)
Tracey Rosato (Mgr-Client Svcs & Ops)
Mary Warley (Dir-Sls)
Monica Wright (VP-Audience Engagement)
Edna Chavira (Dir-Campaign Mgmt)
Diane Vincent (Mgr-Acct Receivable)
Pamela Parker (Exec Editor-Features)
Marc Sirkin (VP-ECommerce & Mktg)

THIRD LAW SOURCING
3700 Crestwood Pkwy, Duluth, GA 30096
Tel.: (404) 592-1380
Web Site: http://www.3rdlaw.com
Sales Range: $1-9.9 Million
Emp.: 20
Business Research & Development Services
N.A.I.C.S.: 541720
Scott Drobes (Mng Partner)

THIRD LEAF PARTNERS
155 Sansome St Ste 610, San Francisco, CA 94104
Tel.: (415) 830-3870
Web Site:
http://www.thirdleafpartners.com
Investments in Winery, Hospitality & Lifestyle Brands
N.A.I.C.S.: 523999
Aaron D. Faust (Mng Partner)
Alexander G. Pagon (Mng Partner)
John Micek (Mng Partner)

Subsidiaries:

WineBid.com, Inc. (1)
755 Skwy Ct, Napa, CA 94558
Tel.: (707) 226-5893
Web Site: http://www.winebid.com
Wine Mfr
N.A.I.C.S.: 312130
Nate Cluett (Dir-IT)

THIRD POINT LLC
390 Park Ave, New York, NY 10022
Tel.: (212) 715-6707
Web Site: http://www.thirdpoint.com
Sales Range: $15-24.9 Billion
Investment Services & Advisor
N.A.I.C.S.: 523940
Daniel S. Loeb (Founder, CEO & Chief Investment Officer)
Josh Targoff (Partner, COO & Gen Counsel)
Ian Wallace (Partner)

THIRD SECTOR NEW ENGLAND, INC.
89 South St Ste 700, Boston, MA 02111
Tel.: (617) 523-6565   MA
Web Site: http://www.tsne.org
Year Founded: 1959
Sales Range: $10-24.9 Million
Emp.: 391
Community Action Services
N.A.I.C.S.: 813319
Rodney Byrd (Mgr-HR)
Neil Currie (Mgr-IT)
Andrew Cox-Stavros (CFO)
Phil Audier (Controller)
Heather Harker (Dir-Programs)
Lyn Freundlich (Dir-HR)
Lee Swislow (Interim CEO)
Tammy Dowley-Blackman (Pres)

THIRD SECURITY, LLC
The Governor Tyler 1881 Grove Ave, Radford, VA 24141
Tel.: (540) 633-7900   VA
Web Site:
http://www.thirdsecurity.com
Sales Range: $25-49.9 Million
Emp.: 50
Equity Investment Firm
N.A.I.C.S.: 523999
Randal J. Kirk (CEO & Sr Mng Dir)
Robert M. Patzig (Sr Mng Dir & Chief Investment Officer)
Marcus E. Smith (Sr Mng Dir, Chief Compliance Officer & Gen Counsel)
Julian P. Kirk (Mng Dir)
Jason H. Gabriel (Mng Dir)
Scott R. Horner (Mng Dir)
Betty J. Davis (VP-Taxation)
Clifton R. Herndon II (Mng Dir & Controller)
Doit Leon Koppler II (Mng Dir & Treas)

THIRD SUN SOLAR & WIND POWER, LTD.
340 W State St Ste 25, Athens, OH 45701
Tel.: (740) 597-3111
Web Site: http://www.third-sun.com
Year Founded: 2000
Rev.: $3,700,000
Emp.: 28
Plumbing Heating Air-Conditioning Contractors
N.A.I.C.S.: 238220
Geoff Greenfield (Pres)

THIRD WAVE SYSTEMS, INC.
6475 City W Pkwy, Eden Prairie, MN 55344
Tel.: (952) 832-5515   MN
Web Site:
http://www.thirdwavesys.com
Year Founded: 1993
Sales Range: $10-24.9 Million
Emp.: 30

Simulation Software Distr
N.A.I.C.S.: 423430
Kerry J. Marusich (Founder & Pres)
Lisa A. Ferris (COO)
Amanda Taylor (Mgr-HR)
Brian Becker (Mgr-Engrg)

THIRLBY AUTOMOTIVE INC.
231 E 8th St, Traverse City, MI 49684
Tel.: (231) 947-8120
Web Site:
http://www.thirlbyautomotive.com
Sales Range: $100-124.9 Million
Emp.: 1,200
Sales of Automotive Supplies & Parts
N.A.I.C.S.: 423120
Julie Strait (VP)

THIRSTY BEAR BREWING CO. LLC
661 Howard St, San Francisco, CA 94105
Tel.: (415) 974-0905
Web Site: http://www.thirstybear.com
Sales Range: $10-24.9 Million
Emp.: 100
Brewery Mfr
N.A.I.C.S.: 312120
Ronald Silberstein (Founder & Owner)
Aleksandra Grozdanic (Mgr)
Timothy Mullin (Gen Mgr)

THIS LIFE, INC.
20 Jay St Ste 932 9th Fl, Brooklyn, NY 11201
Tel.: (202) 906-0436   DE
Web Site:
http://www.howaboutwe.com
Year Founded: 2010
Online Dating Site
N.A.I.C.S.: 519290
Brian Schechter (Co-Founder)
Rose Levy (Dir-PR)
Aaron Schildkrout (Co-Founder)

Subsidiaries:

Nerve.com, Inc. (1)
520 Broadway, New York, NY 10012-4436
Tel.: (212) 625-9914
Web Site: http://www.nerve.com
Sales Range: $1-9.9 Million
Emp.: 20
Online Magazine
N.A.I.C.S.: 513120

THISMOMENT, INC.
222 Kearny St Ste 500, San Francisco, CA 94108
Tel.: (415) 684-7040
Web Site:
http://www.thismoment.com
Social Content Management Software
N.A.I.C.S.: 513210
Ankarino Lara (Co-Founder & Chief Product Officer)
Sharon Le Duy (Sr VP-Legal & HR)

Subsidiaries:

Position2, Inc. (1)
2880 Lakeside Dr Ste 131, Santa Clara, CA 95054
Tel.: (650) 618-8900
Web Site: http://www.position2.com
Sales Range: $10-24.9 Million
Emp.: 100
Search Engine Optimization & Social Media Marketing
N.A.I.C.S.: 541613
Vinod Nambiar (Founder & Mng Dir)
Niraj Swarup (Mng Dir-Client Success)
Sajjan Kanukolanu (VP-Delivery-Global)

THOGUS PRODUCTS COMPANY
33490 Pin Oak Pkwy, Avon Lake, OH 44012

Tel.: (440) 933-8850
Web Site: http://www.thogus.com
Year Founded: 1950
Sales Range: $1-9.9 Million
Emp.: 58
Plastics Product Mfr
N.A.I.C.S.: 326199

Subsidiaries:

Proto Plastics Inc. (1)
316 Park Ave, Tipp City, OH 45371-5371
Tel.: (937) 667-8416
Web Site: http://www.protoplastics.com
Plastics Product Mfr
N.A.I.C.S.: 326199
David Gagnon (Mgr-Production)

THOMA BRAVO, L.P.
150 N Riverside Plz Ste 2800, Chicago, IL 60606
Tel.: (312) 254-3300   DE
Web Site:
http://www.thomabravo.com
Year Founded: 2008
Emp.: 45,000
Private Equity Firm
N.A.I.C.S.: 523999
A. J. Rohde (Sr Partner)
Holden Spaht (Mng Partner)
Lee M. Mitchell (Mng Partner)
Carl D. Thoma (Founder & Mng Partner)
Orlando Bravo (Founder & Mng Partner)
Robert Sayle (Partner)
Erwin Mock (Mng Dir & Head-Capital Markets)
Tara Gadgil (Partner)
Andrew Almeida (Partner)
Mike Hoffmann (Partner)
Peter Stefanski (Partner)
Hudson Smith (Partner)
Scott Crabill (Mng Partner)
George Jaber (Principal)
Seth Boro (Executives)
Matt LoSardo (VP)
Oliver Thym (Partner)
Brendan Fox (Sr VP & VP)
Amy Coleman Redenbaugh (Mng Dir & CFO)
Mary Amundson (Mgr-Acctg)
Jeanine Calabrese (VP-Acctg-Firm)
Cynthia Clarke (CIO)
McKenzie Collins (Coord-IR)
Alexis Czaja (Sr VP-HR)
Dariusz Dziurdzik (VP-Acctg & Tax)
Shari Huisman (Chief Acctg Officer & Sr Dir)
Caitlin Howard (VP-Acctg & Tax)
Andy Lueke (Sr VP, VP-Tax & Acctg & Head-Tax)
Kristy Pike (VP & Controller-Equity Funds)
Sandra Popovic (Ops Mgr-Credit Funds)
Christina Roitto (VP-IT Governance & Program Mgmt)
Steven Schwab (Chief Compliance Officer, Sr Dir & Deputy Gen Counsel)
Matthew Smith (VP-Valuation)
Vito Giuliani (Operating Partner)
Seth Boro (Mng Partner)
Jamie Hutter (Principal)
Cody Cowan (VP)
Brian Jaffee (Partner)

Subsidiaries:

ABC Financial Services, Inc. (1)
8320 Hwy 107, Sherwood, AR 72120
Tel.: (501) 515-5000
Web Site: http://www.abcfinancial.com
Health Club Management Services
N.A.I.C.S.: 541219
Paul Schaller (Vice Chm)
Mike Escobedo (Chief Customer Officer)
Lee Washington (CIO)

THOMA BRAVO, L.P.

U.S. PRIVATE

Thoma Bravo, L.P.—(Continued)
Bob Whisnant (VP)
Jill Dozier (Chief Svcs Officer)
Daniel Pack (VP-Product Mgmt)
Kyle Garner (Chief Sls Officer)
Jennifer Hutchinson (Dir-PR & Events)
Bill Davis (CEO)
Khal Rai (COO)
Ryon Packer (Chief Product Officer)
Rachana Jain (Chief People Officer)
Ashok Pinto (CTO)
Cristine Kao (CMO)
David Dye (CFO)
Kelly Card (Chief Engagement Officer)

Apryse Software Inc. (1)
500-838 West Hastings Street, Vancouver, V6C 0A6, BC, Canada
Tel.: (604) 730-8989
Web Site: https://apryse.com
Document Processing Computer Application Developer
N.A.I.C.S.: 541511
Ivan Nincic (Co-Founder & CTO)
Brian Cannon (VP-Fin)
Michael Hobkirk (VP-Legal)
Randall Isaac (VP-Sls)
Louisa Yeung (VP-Corp Dev)
Cassidy Smirnow (CEO)

Subsidiary (US):

Activepdf, Inc. (2)
27405 Puerta Real Ste 100, Mission Viejo, CA 92691
Tel.: (949) 582-9002
Web Site: http://www.activepdf.com
Sales Range: $1-9.9 Million
Emp.: 20
Custom Computer Programming
N.A.I.C.S.: 541511
Tim Sullivan (CEO)
Aaron Schnarr (Mgr-Technical)
Dorothy Schaller (Controller-Fin)
Jay Schlarb (COO)
Leo Lu (Mgr-IT)
Michelle Petsche (Mgr-HR)
Mike Kadell (Mgr-Product)
Nicole Diaz (CTO)
Derek Gerber (Dir-Global Mktg)
Jason Bittick (Dir-Sls)

BCL Technologies (2)
3031 Tisch Way Ste 1000, San Jose, CA 95128
Tel.: (408) 557-2080
Web Site: http://www.bcltechnologies.com
Document Conversion Software Developer
N.A.I.C.S.: 541511
Hassan Alam (Pres & CEO)

Lead Technologies, Inc. (2)
1201 Greenwood Clfs, Charlotte, NC 28204
Tel.: (704) 332-5532
Web Site: http://www.leadtools.com
Rev.: $7,800,000
Emp.: 80
Custom Computer Programming Services
N.A.I.C.S.: 541511
Richard Little (Co-Founder)
Moe Daher (Co-Founder)

Windward Studios, Inc. (2)
11990 Grant St Ste 550, Northglenn, CO 80233
Tel.: (303) 499-2544
Web Site: http://www.windwardreports.com
Sales Range: $1-9.9 Million
Emp.: 20
Custom Computer Programming Services
N.A.I.C.S.: 541511
David Thielen (Pres & CEO)
Anuleka Bilhanan (Dir-Software Dev)
Nancy Bodnar (Dir-People)
Patrick Bates (Dir-Mktg)
Ryan Fligg (Dir-Product Mgmt)

Autodata Solutions, Inc. (1)
345 Saskatoon Street, London, N5W 4R4, ON, Canada
Tel.: (519) 451-2323
Web Site: http://www.autodatasolutions.com
Sales Range: $25-49.9 Million
Emp.: 500
Automotive Content, Research, Software Tools & Technology Implementation Services for Automobile Companies
N.A.I.C.S.: 513210
Gregory T. Perrier (Pres & CEO)

Bluesight, Inc. (1)
1800 Duke St. Suite 108, Alexandria, VA 22314
Tel.: (586) 548-2432
Web Site: https://bluesight.com
Software Develoment

Subsidiary (Domestic):

Medacist Solution Group, LLC (2)
PO Box 892, Cheshire, CT 06410
Web Site: http://www.medacist.com
Computer Related Services
N.A.I.C.S.: 541519
Rick Hartenstein (Dir-Pharmacy Svcs)

Bottomline Technologies Inc. (1)
100 International Dr Ste 200, Portsmouth, NH 03801-6808
Tel.: (603) 436-0700
Web Site: https://www.bottomline.com
Rev.: $471,403,000
Assets: $815,728,000
Liabilities: $359,494,000
Net Worth: $456,234,000
Earnings: $(16,288,000)
Emp.: 2,344
Fiscal Year-end: 06/30/2021
Laser Check Printing, Electronic Payment, Check Fraud Avoidance & Electronic Remittance Software Systems Developer
N.A.I.C.S.: 513210
Paul J. Fannon (Mng Dir-Global Bus Solutions)
Craig S. Saks (Pres & CEO)
Stephanie B. Lucey (Chief People Officer)
Eve Aretakis (CTO)
Darrell Riekena (CIO)
Chuck Garner (CFO)
Mandy Miller (Chief Customer Officer)

Subsidiary (Domestic):

Nexus Systems, Inc. (2)
6400 Arlington Blvd Ste 1000, Falls Church, VA 22042
Tel.: (703) 524-9101
Web Site: http://www.nexussystems.com
Sales Range: $1-9.9 Million
Emp.: 50
Software Development Services
N.A.I.C.S.: 541511
Thomas Coolidge (CEO)
John Bruno (CFO)

Calabrio, Inc. (1)
400 1st Ave N Ste 300, Minneapolis, MN 55401
Tel.: (763) 592-4600
Web Site: http://www.calabrio.com
Emp.: 700
Software Development Services
N.A.I.C.S.: 541511
Joel Martins (CTO)
Ross Daniels (CMO)
Kris McKenzie (Sr VP-Sls-Intl)
Matt Matsui (Chief Product Officer)
Doug Lang (Sr VP-Customer Success)
Miska Suves (Sr VP-HR)
Olle During (Sr VP-Calabrio Intl)
Tim Klein (Sr VP-Corp Dev)
Daniel Maier (Chief Revenue Officer)
Ryan Toben (Sr VP-Customer Success & Sls Ops)
Kevin Jones (CEO)

Calypso Technology, Inc. (1)
595 Market St Ste 1800, San Francisco, CA 94105
Tel.: (415) 530-4000
Web Site: http://www2.calypso.com
Financial Software Developer
N.A.I.C.S.: 513210
Tej Sidhu (CTO)
Jonathan D. Walsh (Chief Admin Officer)
Corinne Grillet (Chief Customer Officer)
Andrew Coll (CFO)
Dennis Belford (Mng Dir-Sub Saharan Africa)
Mayank Shah (Sr Dir-Corp Strategy & Planning)
Jim Fiesel (Mng Dir-Americas)
Boon Huat Lee (Mng Dir-Asia Pacific)
Maroun Tabet (Mng Dir-Continental Europe)
Edmond Tehini (Mng Dir-Middle East)
Olivier Vinciguerra (Mng Dir-Northern Europe, Middle East & Africa)
Didier Bouillard (CEO)
Sameh Fouad (Dir-Middle East, Africa & Turkey)

Subsidiary (Non-US):

Calypso Technology Deutschland GmbH (2)
Eurotheum Frankfurt Neue Mainzer Strasse 66-68 11th Floor, 60311, Frankfurt, Germany
Tel.: (49) 69667780650
Web Site: http://www.calypso.com
Sales Range: $10-24.9 Million
Emp.: 24
Software Distr
N.A.I.C.S.: 423430
Anoop Sonpar (Reg Mgr-Sls)

Calypso Technology K.K. (2)
2-3 Kojimachi Chiyoda-ku, Tokyo, 102-0083, Japan
Tel.: (81) 352141800
Web Site: http://www.calypso.com
Software Sales & Distr
N.A.I.C.S.: 423430

Calypso Technology Ltd (2)
6th Floor One New Change, London, EC4M 9AF, United Kingdom
Tel.: (44) 2078262500
Sales Range: $10-24.9 Million
Emp.: 70
Software Sales & Distr
N.A.I.C.S.: 423430

Calypso Technology Private Limited (2)
1 Phillip St 13 Fl, Singapore, 048692, Singapore
Tel.: (65) 63721121
Web Site: http://www.calypso.com
Emp.: 25
Software Sales & Distr
N.A.I.C.S.: 423430

Calypso Technology Pty Ltd (2)
Australia Square Tower Level 20 Suite 2004 264 George Street, Sydney, 2000, NSW, Australia
Tel.: (61) 290461700
Web Site: http://www.calypso.com
Sales Range: $10-24.9 Million
Emp.: 20
Software Sales
N.A.I.C.S.: 423430
Alex York (VP)

Calypso Technology S.A. (2)
106/108 rue de La Boetie, Paris, 75008, France
Tel.: (33) 144501399
Web Site: http://www.calypso.com
Sales Range: $10-24.9 Million
Software Sales & Distr
N.A.I.C.S.: 423430

Command Alkon Corp (1)
1800 International Park D Ste 400, Birmingham, AL 35243
Tel.: (205) 879-3282
Web Site: http://www.commandalkon.com
Computer Software Development & Applications
N.A.I.C.S.: 541511
Michael Wilson (Dir-Mktg)
Phil Ramsey (CEO)
Mark Harris (Mgr-Sls-Americas)
Andrew Ellis (CFO)
Charles Evans (CTO & VP-Engrg)
Doug Moore (VP-Cloud Platform)
Martin Willoughby (Chief Product Officer & Exec VP-Bus Dev)
Jeff Newlin (Chief Revenue Officer)

ConnectWise, Inc. (1)
4925 Independence Pkwy Ste 400, Tampa, FL 33634
Tel.: (813) 935-7100
Web Site: http://www.connectwise.net
Sales Range: $25-49.9 Million
Emp.: 245
Local Area Networks, Web Site Development & Internet Hosting
N.A.I.C.S.: 517810
Jason Magee (CEO)
Geoffrey Willison (COO)
Brad Surminsky (CFO)
Clint Maddox (Chief Revenue Officer)
Steve Cochran (CTO)
Jeff Bishop (Chief Product Officer)
Jennifer Locklear (Chief Talent Officer)
Scott Marshall (Sr VP-Mktg)
Steve Farnan (Sr VP-Sls-North America)
Gregg Lalle (Sr VP-Intl Sls & Strategy)
Craig Fulton (Chief Customer Officer)
Amy Lucia (CMO)

Subsidiary (Domestic):

Sienna Group, LLC (2)
9644 Linebaugh Ave, Tampa, FL 33626
Tel.: (800) 792-6421
Web Site: http://www.siennasecure.com
All Other Support Services
N.A.I.C.S.: 561990
William Wagner (Owner)

Continuum Managed Services LLC (1)
99 High St 31 Fl, Boston, MA 02110-2310
Tel.: (866) 223-7394
Web Site: http://www.continuum.net
Information Technology Consulting Services
N.A.I.C.S.: 541512
Michael George (CEO)
Steve Cardillo (VP-Corp Dev)
John Mandel (Sr VP-Engrg)
Ai-Li Lim (Sr VP-HR)
Fielder Hiss (VP-Product)
Tina McNulty (VP-Mktg)

Cority Software Inc. (1)
250 Bloor Street East 9th Floor, BOx 15, Toronto, M4W 1E6, ON, Canada
Tel.: (416) 863-6800
Web Site: http://www.cority.com
Software Services
N.A.I.C.S.: 513210
Mark Wallace (Pres & CEO)
Atish Ghosh (CTO)
Mark Wallace (Pres & CEO)

Subsidiary (US):

Axion Health Inc. (2)
11001 W 120th Ave #315, Broomfield, CO 80021
Software Publishing Services
N.A.I.C.S.: 541511

Enviance, Inc. (2)
5780 Fleet St Ste 200, Carlsbad, CA 92008
Tel.: (760) 496-0200
Web Site: http://www.enviance.com
Environmental Compliance Software Developer
N.A.I.C.S.: 513210
Lawrence P. Goldenhersh (Founder)
Ben Archibald (VP-Pro Svcs)
Craig Ross (CFO)
John Sinnott (CTO)
Amanda Smith (VP-Product Mgmt)

Subsidiary (Domestic):

Actio Software Corp. (3)
30 International Dr Suite 201-203, Portsmouth, NH 03801 (100%)
Tel.: (603) 433-2300
Web Site: http://www.actio.net
Sales Range: $1-9.9 Million
Emp.: 200
SaaS Enterprise Compliance Solutions & Software Development for Environmental Regulatory Compliance
N.A.I.C.S.: 513210
Rob Friedman (Dir)
Chris Nowak (Dir-Bus Dev)
Kal Kawar (Exec VP)

Remedy Interactive, Inc. (3)
1 Harbor Dr Ste 200, Sausalito, CA 94965
Tel.: (415) 332-6433
Web Site: http://remedyinteractive.com
Application Service Provider
N.A.I.C.S.: 541511
Patricia Flores (Project Mgr)
Kim Weiss (CEO)
Erik Anderson (Head-Global Sls)
Tom Burke (CFO)
Daniel Cassidy (Head-Cutomer Supporrt)
Irene White (Head-Mktg)

Coupa Software Incorporated (1)
1855 S Grant St, San Mateo, CA 94402
Tel.: (650) 931-3200

Web Site: https://www.coupa.com
Rev.: $725,289,000
Assets: $3,193,179,000
Liabilities: $2,299,601,000
Net Worth: $893,578,000
Earnings: ($379,039,000)
Emp.: 3,076
Fiscal Year-end: 01/31/2022
Software Publisher
N.A.I.C.S.: 513210
Raja Hammoud (Exec VP-Products)
Raymond M. Martinelli (Chief People Officer)
Leagh Turner (CEO)
Alicia Allen (CFO)
Dean Bain (Sr VP & Gen Mgr-Supply Chain)
Fang Chang (Chief Product Officer)
Kevin Iaquinto (CMO)
Stephen Knipe (COO & Sr VP-Revenue Ops)
Salvatore Lombardo (CTO & Chief Product Officer)
Craig Newfield (Chief Legal Officer)
Arjun Ramaratnam (Chief Dev Officer)
George Riding (Sr VP-Fin Plng & Analysis)
Mike Schanker (Exec VP-Strategy)
Rich Slipec (Mng Dir)
Amy Sweeney (CIO)
Susan Tohyama (Chief HR Officer)

Subsidiary (Domestic):

ConnXus, Inc. (2)
5155 Financial Way Ste 3, Mason, OH 45040
Tel.: (513) 204-2873
Web Site: http://www.connxus.com
Business Support Services
N.A.I.C.S.: 561499

Subsidiary (Non-US):

Coupa Deutschland GmbH (2)
An der Welle 4, 60322, Frankfurt am Main, Germany
Tel.: (49) 6975938481
Software Development Services
N.A.I.C.S.: 541511

Coupa EMEA (2)
90 Long Acre, Covent Garden, London, WC2E 9RZ, United Kingdom
Tel.: (44) 207 203 2043
Software Publisher
N.A.I.C.S.: 513210

Coupa Software India Private Limited (2)
ICC Trade Towers 3rd Floor B Wing Senapati Bapat Road, Pune, 411016, Maharashtra, India
Tel.: (91) 7030930857
Software Development Services
N.A.I.C.S.: 541511

Coupa Software Switzerland AG (2)
Guterstrasse 133, 4053, Basel, Switzerland
Tel.: (41) 613678700
Computer Software Development Services
N.A.I.C.S.: 541511

Subsidiary (Domestic):

Exari Group, Inc. (2)
745 Boylston St 2nd Fl, Boston, MA 02116
Tel.: (617) 938-3777
Web Site: http://www.exari.com
Cloud Based Contract Lifecycle Management Solutions
N.A.I.C.S.: 513210

Hiperos, LLC (2)
3040 Route 22 W Ste 110, Branchburg, NJ 08876
Tel.: (908) 981-0080
Web Site: http://www.hiperos.com
Software Publisher
N.A.I.C.S.: 513210

LLamasoft Inc. (2)
201 S Division St Ste 300, Ann Arbor, MI 48104
Tel.: (734) 418-3119
Web Site: http://www.llamasoft.com
Software Publisher
N.A.I.C.S.: 513210
Don Hicks (Co-Founder & Chm)

Subsidiary (Non-US):

Simeno Holding AG (2)
Guterstrasse 133, 4002, Basel, Switzerland
Tel.: (41) 613678700
Web Site: http://www.simeno.com
Software Development Services
N.A.I.C.S.: 541511
Udo Grunhoff (Founder)

Darktrace Plc (1)
Maurice Wilkes Building St Johns Innovation Park Cowley Road, Cambridge, CB4 0DS, United Kingdom
Tel.: (44) 08081893465
Web Site: https://www.darktrace.com
Rev.: $545,430,000
Assets: $751,865,000
Liabilities: $488,352,000
Net Worth: $263,513,000
Earnings: $58,958,000
Emp.: 2,200
Fiscal Year-end: 06/30/2023
Information Technology Services
N.A.I.C.S.: 541512
Chris Kozup (CMO)
Poppy Gustafsson (CEO)
Denise Walter (Chief Revenue Officer)
Jack Stockdale OBE (CTO)
Max Heinemeyer (Chief Product Officer)
Nick Trim (Chief Ops Officer)
Cathy Graham (CFO)

Subsidiary (Non-US):

Darktrace Colombia S.A.S. (2)
Cra 16 97-46 Torre 1 piso 6, Bogota, Colombia
Tel.: (57) 3184245555
Cybersecurity Artificial Intelligence Services
N.A.I.C.S.: 561990

Darktrace GmbH (2)
Sonnenstrasse 15, 80331, Munich, Germany
Tel.: (49) 8925552985
Software Development Services
N.A.I.C.S.: 541511

Subsidiary (Domestic):

Darktrace Holdings Limited (2)
Maurice Wilkes Building Cowley Road, Cambridge, CB4 0DS, United Kingdom
Tel.: (44) 1223394100
Cyber Security Services
N.A.I.C.S.: 541512

Subsidiary (Non-US):

Darktrace Ireland Limited (2)
38 Upper Mount Street, Dublin, 2, Ireland
Tel.: (353) 19693232
Industrial Infrastructure Services
N.A.I.C.S.: 541420

Darktrace Japan KK (2)
Level 15 Cerulean Tower 26-1 Sakuragaoka-cho, Shibuya-ku, Tokyo, 150-8512, Japan
Tel.: (81) 354565537
Cybersecurity Artificial Intelligence Services
N.A.I.C.S.: 561990

Darktrace Mexico, S.A. de C.V. (2)
Boulevard Manuel Avila Camacho No 76 PB Colonia Lomas de Chapultepec, Alcaldia Miguel Hidalgo, 11000, Mexico, Mexico
Tel.: (52) 5570050956
Cybersecurity Artificial Intelligence Services
N.A.I.C.S.: 561990

Darktrace S.a.S. (2)
38 Av des Champs-Elysees, 75008, Paris, France
Tel.: (33) 140738485
Software Development Services
N.A.I.C.S.: 541511

Darktrace Singapore Pte. Ltd. (2)
23 Church St Level 7 Capital Square, Singapore, 049481, Singapore
Tel.: (65) 68045010
Cybersecurity Artificial Intelligence Services
N.A.I.C.S.: 561990

EQS Group AG (1)
Karlstr 47, 80333, Munich, Germany (98%)
Tel.: (49) 89444430
Web Site: https://www.eqs.com
Rev.: $61,685,898
Assets: $229,480,677
Liabilities: $143,209,099
Net Worth: $86,271,578
Earnings: ($8,142,003)
Emp.: 565
Fiscal Year-end: 12/31/2021
Online Communication Services
N.A.I.C.S.: 517121
Achim Weick (Founder, CEO & Member-Exec Bd)
Christian Pfleger (COO & Member-Exec Bd)
Andre Silverio Marques (CFO & Member-Exec Bd)
Marcus Sultzer (Chief Revenue Officer & Member-Exec Bd)
Anka Lappoehn (Chief Product Officer)
Juan Antonio Galan Martinez (CTO)
Stefan Berg (Chief Strategy Officer)
Christina Jahn (Mgr-Corp PR)

Subsidiary (Domestic):

Business Keeper GmbH (2)
Bayreuther Strasse 35, 10789, Berlin, Germany
Tel.: (49) 3088774440
Cloud Based Software Services
N.A.I.C.S.: 518210

Subsidiary (Non-US):

EQS Asia Limited (2)
14/F Amber Commercial Building 70-74 Morrison Hill Road, Wan Chai, Hong Kong, China (Hong Kong)
Tel.: (852) 28935622
Holding Company Services
N.A.I.C.S.: 551112
Trish Kong (Sr Mgr-Acct)

EQS Group AG (2)
Hardturmstrasse 11, 8005, Zurich, Switzerland
Tel.: (41) 417630050
Online Communication Services
N.A.I.C.S.: 517810

Subsidiary (US):

EQS Group Inc. (2)
20 W 22nd St Ste 408, New York, NY 10010
Tel.: (212) 335-0664
Online Communication Services
N.A.I.C.S.: 517810
Marco Goldberg (Mng Dir)

Subsidiary (Non-US):

EQS Group Ltd. (2)
76 Cannon Street, London, EC4N 6AE, United Kingdom
Tel.: (44) 2031413940
Online Communication Services
N.A.I.C.S.: 517810
Viviane Joynes (Mng Dir)

EQS Group SAS (2)
3 rue Tronchet, 75008, Paris, France
Tel.: (33) 143148510
Online Communication Services
N.A.I.C.S.: 517810
Dorian Losch (Project Mgr)

EQS Web Technologies Pvt. Ltd. (2)
Suite 1 5th Floor Centre A Alapatt Heritage Building MG Road, Kochi, 682035, India
Tel.: (91) 4844868001
Online Communication Services
N.A.I.C.S.: 517810

Eqs Group GmbH (2)
Siebensterngasse 31/8, 1070, Vienna, Austria
Tel.: (43) 14170880
Cloud Based Software Services
N.A.I.C.S.: 518210

Eqs Group S.R.L. (2)
Corso Vercelli 40, 20145, Milan, Italy
Tel.: (39) 0289041045
Emp.: 600
Cloud Based Software Services
N.A.I.C.S.: 518210

EquityStory RS, LLC (2)
Ermolaevskiy Per 27, 123001, Moscow, Russia
Tel.: (7) 4951145242
Online Communication Services
N.A.I.C.S.: 517810

Everbridge, Inc. (1)
25 Corporate Dr Ste 400, Burlington, MA 01803
Tel.: (781) 373-9800
Web Site: https://go.everbridge.com
Rev.: $448,788,000
Assets: $1,025,885,000
Liabilities: $723,576,000
Net Worth: $302,309,000
Earnings: ($47,305,000)
Emp.: 1,593
Fiscal Year-end: 12/31/2023
All Other Telecommunications
N.A.I.C.S.: 517810
David E. Rockvam (CFO)
Scott Burnett (Sr VP-Ops)
Patrick Brickley (Exec VP)
Tracy Reinhold (Chief Security Officer)
Sheila Carpenter (CIO)
Shirley Devlin-Lebow (Chief Acctg Officer)
David Alexander (CMO)
Bryan Barney (Chief Product Officer)
Haibei Wang (CTO)
John Di Leo (Chief Revenue Officer)
Noah F. Webster (Chief Legal Officer)
Stefica Divkovic (Sr VP)
Paul Robinson (Sr VP)

Subsidiary (Non-US):

Everbridge Asia Pte. Ltd. (2)
Tel.: (65) 31578893
Software Development Services
N.A.I.C.S.: 541511

Everbridge Europe Limited (2)
6 De Grey Square De Grey Road, Colchester, CO4 5YQ, Essex, United Kingdom
Tel.: (44) 8000350081
Internet Telecommunication Services
N.A.I.C.S.: 517810

Everbridge Finland OY (2)
Konepajankuja 1, FI-00510, Helsinki, Finland
Tel.: (358) 452655263
Software Development Services
N.A.I.C.S.: 541511

Everbridge France SAS (2)
75 Boulevard Haussmann, 75008, Paris, France
Tel.: (33) 142685098
Software Application Services
N.A.I.C.S.: 541511

Everbridge Norway AS (2)
Innspurten 15 Helsfyr Atrium, 0663, Oslo, Norway
Tel.: (47) 23501600
Software Application Services
N.A.I.C.S.: 541511

Subsidiary (Domestic):

NC4 Public Sector, LLC (2)
100 N Sepulveda Blvd, El Segundo, CA 90245
Tel.: (949) 265-9307
Web Site: http://www.everbridge.com
Prepackaged Software
N.A.I.C.S.: 513210

Subsidiary (Non-US):

Previstar Private Limited (2)
Unit No 604 DN 51 Merlin Infinite Building Sector - V, Salt Lake City, Kolkata, 700091, West Bengal, India
Tel.: (91) 9903021124
Software Development Services
N.A.I.C.S.: 541511

Respond Beheer B.V. (2)
Sportweg 15, 5037 AC, Tilburg, Netherlands
Tel.: (31) 135321001
Software Development Services
N.A.I.C.S.: 541511
John van Laerhoven (Exec Dir)

SnapComms Limited (2)
Level 1 159 Hurstmere Road, Takapuna, Auckland, 0622, New Zealand
Tel.: (64) 99503360
Web Site: https://www.snapcomms.com
Software Development Services
N.A.I.C.S.: 541511

SnapComms UK Limited (2)
6 De Grey Square De Grey Road,

THOMA BRAVO, L.P.

U.S. PRIVATE

Thoma Bravo, L.P.—(Continued)
Colchester, CO4 5YQ, Essex, United Kingdom
Tel.: (44) 2033553152
Software Development Services
N.A.I.C.S.: 541511

Subsidiary (Domestic):

SnapComms, Inc. (2)
155 N Lake Ave 9th Fl, Pasadena, CA 91101
Tel.: (805) 715-0300
Software Development Services
N.A.I.C.S.: 541511

Subsidiary (Non-US):

Techwan SA (2)
Route de Cossonay 194, 1020, Renens, Switzerland
Tel.: (41) 217850280
Web Site: https://www.techwan.com
Software Development Services
N.A.I.C.S.: 541511

UMS ApS (2)
Lyskaer 3, 2730, Herlev, Denmark
Tel.: (45) 48163700
Software Development Services
N.A.I.C.S.: 541511

UMS OY (2)
Konepajankuja 1, 00510, Helsinki, Finland
Tel.: (358) 401251428
Software Development Services
N.A.I.C.S.: 541511

Unified Messaging Systems AS (2)
Innspurten 15 0663, 0663, Oslo, Norway
Tel.: (47) 23501600
Software Development Services
N.A.I.C.S.: 541511

Subsidiary (Domestic):

xMatters, Inc. (2)
12647 Alcosta Blvd Ste 425, San Ramon, CA 94583-4439
Tel.: (925) 226-0300
Web Site: http://www.xmatters.com
Custom Computer Programming Services
N.A.I.C.S.: 541511
David Andrews *(Product Dir-Mktg)*
Mike Desai *(VP-Corp & Global Bus Dev)*
George Biry *(Dir-Channels & Alliances-EMEA)*
Dave Reardon *(Sr VP-Worldwide Sls)*
Samantha Loveland *(VP-Client Success)*
Troy McAlpin *(CEO)*

ForgeRock, Inc. (1)
201 Mission St Ste 2900, San Francisco, CA 94105
Tel.: (415) 599-1100
Web Site: https://www.forgerock.com
Rev.: $217,512,000
Assets: $494,180,000
Liabilities: $178,014,000
Net Worth: $316,166,000
Earnings: ($66,272,000)
Emp.: 923
Fiscal Year-end: 12/31/2022
Software Development Services
N.A.I.C.S.: 541511
David DeWalt *(Vice Chm)*

Foundation Software, Inc. (1)
17800 Royalton Rd, Strongsville, OH 44136
Tel.: (330) 220-8383
Web Site: http://www.foundationsoft.com
Sales Range: $1-9.9 Million
Emp.: 58
Software Publisher
N.A.I.C.S.: 513210
Frederick Ode *(Founder)*
David Poduska *(Dir-Dev)*
Mike Ode *(Pres & CEO)*

Subsidiary (Domestic):

Mccormick Systems, Inc. (2)
149 W Boston St, Chandler, AZ 85225-9514
Tel.: (480) 831-8214
Web Site: http://www.mccormicksys.com
Sales Range: $1-9.9 Million
Emp.: 35
Prepackaged Software Services Custom Computer Programming

N.A.I.C.S.: 513210
Todd McCormick *(Owner & Pres)*

Greenphire, Inc. (1)
640 Freedom Business Ctr Dr Ste 201, King of Prussia, PA 19406
Tel.: (215) 948-9251
Web Site: http://www.greenphire.com
Sales Range: $1-9.9 Million
Emp.: 42
Clinical Payment Processing Services
N.A.I.C.S.: 522320
Samuel Whitaker *(Co-Founder)*
Jennifer Peters *(Co-Founder & Chief Experience Officer)*
Laura Remaker *(VP-HR)*
Kyle Cunningham *(VP-Product Mgmt)*
Neil Rotherham *(Exec Dir)*
Wayne Baker *(Chief Comml Officer)*
Jim Murphy *(CEO)*
Sue Vestri *(CFO)*
Dave Espenshade *(VP-CRO Partnerships)*
Claudine Paccio *(COO)*
Alan Matuszak *(CTO)*

Subsidiary (Domestic):

Gray Consulting Inc. (2)
833 Chestnut East 12th Fl, Philadelphia, PA 19107
Tel.: (215) 413-2034
Web Site: https://www.clincierge.com
Rev.: $7,000,000
Emp.: 50
Other Management Consulting Services
N.A.I.C.S.: 541618
Kathy Murphy *(Pres)*
Scott Gray *(CEO)*
Brent Snyder *(Dir-Info Sys)*
Joyce Wooden *(Mgr-Client Svcs)*
Trish Maguire *(Mgr-Client Svcs)*
Zac Carr *(Mgr-Client Svcs)*

Hyland Software, Inc. (1)
28500 Clemens Rd, Westlake, OH 44145
Tel.: (440) 788-5000
Web Site: http://www.hyland.com
Sales Range: $50-74.9 Million
Emp.: 1,660
Enterprise Content Management Software Developer
N.A.I.C.S.: 513210
Chris Hyland *(CFO & Exec VP)*
Noreen Kilbane *(Chief Admin Officer & Exec VP)*
Tim Pembridge *(Gen Counsel, Sec & VP)*
George Angelato *(VP-Quality Assurance)*
Alfonso Zubizarreta *(VP-Intl Strategy)*
Bill Priemer *(Pres & CEO)*
Debbie Connelly *(VP-HR)*
Brenda Kirk *(Sr VP-Corp Strategy & Product)*
Bill Filion *(VP-Software Dev)*
Drew Chapin *(VP-Mktg)*
Ed McQuiston *(Chief Comml Officer & Exec VP)*
Ken Malone *(VP-Technical Support)*
John Phelan *(VP-Info Sys)*
Dan Wilson *(Assoc VP-Dev)*
Sam Babic *(Assoc VP-Dev)*
Bill Kavanaugh *(Assoc VP-Sls)*
Nancy Person *(Assoc VP-Acctg & Fin)*
Patrick Mulcahy *(VP-Cloud Svcs)*
Valt Vesikallio *(Sr VP-Svcs-Global)*

Subsidiary (Domestic):

Alfresco Software, Inc. (2)
100 Worcester St Ste 203, Wellesley, MA 02466
Tel.: (617) 963-0372
Web Site: http://www.alfresco.com
Document Management Software Publisher
N.A.I.C.S.: 513210
John Newton *(Founder & CTO)*
Brigid MacDonald *(Chief People Officer & Chief Culture Officer)*
Tony Grout *(Chief Product Officer)*
Steve Buonaiuto *(CFO)*
Ken Tacelli *(Chief Revenue Officer)*
Kamil Chaudhary *(Gen Counsel & VP)*
Heather Guntrum *(Customer Success Officer)*

Subsidiary (Non-US):

Alfresco Software Limited (3)
Bridge Ave The Place, Maidenhead, SL6 1AF, United Kingdom
Tel.: (44) 1628 876 600

Web Site: http://www.alfresco.com
Document Management Software Publisher
N.A.I.C.S.: 513210
John Newton *(Founder & CTO)*

Subsidiary (Domestic):

Computer Systems Company, Inc. (2)
17999 Foltz Pkwy, Strongsville, OH 44149
Tel.: (440) 546-4272
Sales Range: $10-24.9 Million
Emp.: 110
Enterprise Information Management & Business Process Automation Solutions
N.A.I.C.S.: 334610

Division (Domestic):

Computer Systems Company, Inc. - Healthcare Consulting Services Division (3)
14888 Foltz Pkwy, Strongsville, OH 44149
Tel.: (440) 546-4272
Assists Healthcare Providers with Identifying & Implementing Sustainable, Financially Advantageous Process Improvements
N.A.I.C.S.: 541513

Unit (Domestic):

R4, LLC (3)
17999 Foltz Pkwy, Strongsville, OH 44149
Tel.: (440) 546-4272
Sales Range: $10-24.9 Million
Emp.: 12
Ultrasound Information Systems
N.A.I.C.S.: 513210

Group (Domestic):

The CSC Group of Michigan (3)
3425 Belle Chase Way, Lansing, MI 48911
Tel.: (517) 393-8610
Enterprise Information Management & Business Process Automation Solutions
N.A.I.C.S.: 334610

Subsidiary (Domestic):

Hyland LLC (3)
28500 Clemens Rd, Westlake, OH 44145
Tel.: (440) 788-5000
Web Site: http://www.hyland.com
Content Management Software Solutions Services
N.A.I.C.S.: 513210
William Priemer *(Pres & CEO)*
Ed McQuiston *(Chief Comml Officer & Exec VP)*
John Phelan *(Chief Product Officer & Exec VP)*
Noreen Kilbane *(Chief Admin Officer & Exec VP)*
Tim Pembridge *(Chief Legal Officer & Exec VP)*
Razvan Atanasiu *(VP-Healthcare Engrg)*
Sam Babic *(Chief Innovation Officer & Sr VP)*
Drew Chapin *(CMO & VP)*
Debbie Connelly *(Chief People Officer & Sr VP)*
Scott Dwyer *(Sr VP-Product & Strategic Plng)*
Bill Kavanaugh *(VP-Sls)*
Ken Malone *(Sr VP-Global Customer Success)*
Nancy Person *(CFO & Exec VP)*
Chris Winczewski *(VP-Corp Strategy & Plng)*

Subsidiary (Non-US):

Hyland Software Germany GmbH (3)
Steinplatz 2 4th Floor, Charlottenburg, 10623, Berlin, Germany
Tel.: (49) 30600610
Web Site: http://www.hyland.com
Software Development Services
N.A.I.C.S.: 541511

Imprivata, Inc. (1)
10 Maguire Rd Bldg 1 Ste 125, Lexington, MA 02421-3120
Tel.: (781) 674-2700
Web Site: http://www.imprivata.com
Custom Computer Programming Services
N.A.I.C.S.: 541511

David Ting *(CTO)*
Geoff Hogan *(Sr VP-Corp & Bus Dev)*
Sean P. Kelly *(Chief Medical Officer)*
Carina Edwards *(Sr VP-Customer Experience)*
Kelliann McCabe *(Chief People Officer)*
John Milton *(Gen Counsel & VP)*
Aaron Miri *(CIO & VP-Govt Rels)*
Gus Malezis *(Pres & CEO)*
Adam Bangle *(VP-Intl Sls)*
Mark Nesline *(Sr VP-Engrg)*
Barbara Dumery *(Sr VP-Product Mgmt)*
Dean Mericka *(Sr VP-WW Sls)*
Rob Egan *(Sr VP-Mktg)*
Jim Carr *(CFO)*

Subsidiary (Domestic):

FairWarning LLC (2)
13535 Feather Sound Dr Ste 600, Clearwater, FL 33762-2259
Tel.: (727) 576-6700
Web Site: http://www.fairwarning.com
Sales Range: $1-9.9 Million
Emp.: 50
Healthcare Security Software Publisher
N.A.I.C.S.: 513210
Kurt J. Long *(Founder & CEO)*
M. Shane Whitlatch *(VP-Enterprise)*
Frank DePrisco *(VP-Global Customer Ops)*
Chris Arnold *(VP-Product Mgmt & Engrg)*
Tim Nolan *(Sr Mgr-Implementation)*
Jennifer Sherwood *(Mgr-Implementation)*
Christian Merhy *(VP-Mktg)*
Tim Dunn *(Exec VP-Intl Bus Dev)*
Scott Baker *(Dir-Solution Sls-North America)*
Brad Price *(Sr Mgr-Software Implementation)*
Christine Horodecki *(Mgr-Customer Success)*
Teresa Parks *(VP-Ops)*
Ed Holmes *(CEO)*

Subsidiary (Non-US):

FairWarning SARL (3)
9/11 allee de l'Arche, Courbevoie, 92671, Paris, La Defense, France
Tel.: (33) 6 26 26 84 67
Web Site: http://www.fairwarning.com
Security Software Publisher
N.A.I.C.S.: 513210

Instructure, Inc. (1)
6330 S 3000 E Ste 700, Salt Lake City, UT 84121
Tel.: (801) 869-5007
Web Site: http://www.instructure.com
Rev.: $258,473,000
Assets: $367,500,000
Liabilities: $221,943,000
Net Worth: $145,557,000
Earnings: ($80,819,000)
Emp.: 1,397
Fiscal Year-end: 12/31/2019
Learning Management Software Development Services
N.A.I.C.S.: 541511
Steve Kaminsky *(CFO)*
Joshua L. Coates *(Chm)*
S. David Burggraaf *(Sr VP-Engrg)*
Matthew A. Kaminer *(Chief Legal Officer)*
Jeff Weber *(Exec VP-People & Places)*
Melissa Loble *(Chief Customer Experience Officer)*
Kenny Nicholl *(Gen Mgr-EMEA)*
Jared Stein *(VP-Higher Education Product Strategy)*
Frank Maylett *(Exec VP-Global & Head-Sls)*
John Knotwell *(Gen Mgr-Bridge)*
Chris Benwell *(Sr VP-Canvas Sls)*
Christopher Bradman *(Gen Mgr-APAC)*
Steve Daly *(CEO)*
Shiren Vijiasingam *(Chief Product Officer)*

Subsidiary (Non-US):

Instructure Global Limited (2)
Rivington House 82 Great Eastern St, London, EC2A 3JF, United Kingdom
Tel.: (44) 8003584330
Web Site: https://www.canvasvle.co.uk
Educational Software Publisher
N.A.I.C.S.: 513210

J.D. Power (1)
3200 Park Center Dr 13th Fl, Costa Mesa, CA 92626 **(100%)**
Tel.: (714) 621-6200

COMPANIES — THOMA BRAVO, L.P.

Web Site: http://www.jdpower.com
Marketing Information Services
N.A.I.C.S.: 541910
Finbarr O'Neill (Pres)
Keith Webster (Sr VP & Gen Mgr-Fin & Svc Indus Div-Global)
Joseph DaMour (Sr VP-Fin & CFO)
Bernardo Rodriguez (Chief Digital Officer)
Doug Betts (Sr VP-Global Automotive Ops & Gen Mgr)
Thomas King (Sr VP-Data & Analytics)
Lindsay Rush (VP & CTO)
Rochelle Matson (VP-HR)
Jay Meyers (VP-Analytical Ctr-Res Div)
Kyle Schmitt (Mng Dir-Insurance Practice-Global)
David C. Habiger (CEO)
David C. Habiger (Pres & CEO)

LogRhythm, Inc. (1)
4780 Pearl East Cir, Boulder, CO 80301
Tel.: (303) 413-8745
Web Site: http://www.logrhythm.com
Security Software Publisher
N.A.I.C.S.: 513210
Phillip Villella (Founder)
James Carder (Chief Security Officer & VP-Labs)
Barry Capoot (CFO)
Kish Dill (Chief Customer Officer)
Melissa Garza (Chief People Officer)
Mitzi Hunter (CMO)
Mike Dalgleish (VP-Sls-Americas)
David Rizzo (CTO)
David Kluzak (Chief Revenue Officer)
Andrew Hollister (Chief Info Security Officer)
Chris O'Malley (CEO)

Majesco (1)
412 Mount Kemble Ave Ste 110C, Morristown, NJ 07960
Tel.: (973) 461-5200
Web Site: http://www.majesco.com
Rev.: $146,445,000
Assets: $159,515,000
Liabilities: $52,902,000
Net Worth: $106,613,000
Earnings: $9,680,000
Emp.: 2,403
Fiscal Year-end: 03/31/2020
Software Development & Consulting Services
N.A.I.C.S.: 541511
Allan I. Grafman (Chm)
Edward Ossie (COO)
Denise Garth (Sr VP-Strategic Mktg)
Prateek Kumar (Exec VP-Sls-Global)
Manish D. Shah (Pres & Chief Product Officer)
Mallinath Sengupta (Exec VP & Head-Delivery, Consulting & Support Svcs)
Adam Elster (CEO)
James Miller (Chief Revenue Officer)
Norman Carroll (CEO-Exaxe)
Melissa Blankenbaker (Chief HR Officer)
Lauren Holmes (CIO)
Joe Aho (CFO)
Laura Tillotson (Dir-Mktg Comm & Creative Svcs)
Ravi Krishnan (CTO)

Subsidiary (Domestic):

Agile Technologies, LLC (2)
685 Route 202/206, Bridgewater, NJ 08807
Tel.: (908) 253-9550
Web Site: http://www.agiletech.com
Sales Range: $1-9.9 Million
Emp.: 50
Information Technology Consulting Services
N.A.I.C.S.: 541690
William Freitag (CEO)
Robert Buhrle (Partner)

Decision Research Corp. (2)
1600 Kapiolani Blvd Ste 900, Honolulu, HI 96814
Tel.: (808) 949-8316
Web Site: http://www.decisionresearch.com
Rev.: $5,000,000
Emp.: 43
Custom Computer Programming Services
N.A.I.C.S.: 541512
Darren Horn (VP-Sls & Mktg)

INSPRO TECHNOLOGIES CORPORATION (2)
1510 Chester Pike Ste 400 Baldwin Tower, Eddystone, PA 19022
Tel.: (484) 654-2200
Web Site: http://www.inspro.com
Rev.: $14,892,216
Assets: $8,565,280
Liabilities: $6,884,718
Net Worth: $1,680,562
Earnings: ($1,194,735)
Emp.: 50
Fiscal Year-end: 12/31/2019
Life & Health Insurance Software Products
N.A.I.C.S.: 513210
Anthony R. Verdi (Pres, CEO, CFO, COO & Asst Sec)
Patricia Dauch (VP-Product Mgmt)
Jacqueline Marshall (VP-Professional Svcs Ops)
Kevin Nelson (Head-Tech)
Francis L. Gillan III (VP & Controller)

Subsidiary (Domestic):

InsPro Technologies, LLC (3)
1510 Chester Pike 400 Baldwin Tower, Eddystone, PA 19022
Tel.: (610) 872-6135
Web Site: http://www.inspro.com
Computer Programming Services
N.A.I.C.S.: 541511
Mike Lanniccari (VP-Technical Support & ASP Hosting Svcs)

Subsidiary (Domestic):

Utilant LLC (2)
155 Chandler St Ste 6, Buffalo, NY 14207
Tel.: (815) 301-8258
Web Site: http://www.utilant.com
Computer System Design Services
N.A.I.C.S.: 541512
Andrew Worral (VP-Dev)
Greg Osborne (Sr VP-Sls)
Rob Mikulec (Chief Revenue Officer)
Patrick Davis (Founder & CEO)

Medallia, Inc. (1)
575 Market St Ste 1850, San Francisco, CA 94105
Tel.: (650) 321-3000
Web Site: http://www.medallia.com
Rev.: $477,221,000
Assets: $1,401,649,000
Liabilities: $893,408,000
Net Worth: $508,241,000
Earnings: ($148,656,000)
Emp.: 2,037
Fiscal Year-end: 01/31/2021
Software Publisher
N.A.I.C.S.: 513210
Mikael Ottosson (CTO & Exec VP)
Leslie J. Stretch (Pres & CEO)
Jimmy Duan (Chief Customer Officer & Exec VP)
Sarika Khanna (Chief Product Officer & Exec VP)
Rory Cameron (Exec VP-Mid Market & Corp Dev)
Drew Grasham (Gen Counsel & Exec VP)
Mary Ainsworth (Chief People Officer & Exec VP)
Nick Thomas (Exec VP)
Elizabeth Carducci (Chief Revenue Officer & Exec VP)
Steve Vierra (Sr VP-Channels, Alliances Bus & Global Partnerships)
Rene Carayol (Exec VP-Environmental Social & Governance)
Henson Gawliu (Chief Digital & Demand Generation Officer & Sr VP)
Bill Staikos (Sr VP-Indus Solutions)
Roxanne Oulman (CFO & Exec VP)

Subsidiary (Non-US):

CheckMarket BV (2)
Parklaan 126, 2300, Turnhout, Belgium
Tel.: (32) 14700703
Web Site: http://www.checkmarket.com
Computer Software Services
N.A.I.C.S.: 541511

Cooladata Ltd. (2)
30 Tuval Street, Ramat Gan, 5252242, Israel
Tel.: (972) 5038632218
Web Site: http://www.cooladata.com
Computer Software Services
N.A.I.C.S.: 541511
Guy Greenberg (CEO)
Eyal Drori (VP-R&D)
Hagit Ben Shoshan (VP-Customer Success & Data Science)

Crowdicity Limited (2)
19-21 Hatton Garden, London, EC1N 8BA, United Kingdom
Tel.: (44) 2038808383
Web Site: http://www.crowdicity.com
Computer Software Services
N.A.I.C.S.: 541511
Rob Wilmot (Founder & CEO)

Living Lens Enterprise Limited (2)
49 Jamaica Street, Merseyside, Liverpool, L1 0AH, United Kingdom
Tel.: (44) 1516017383
Web Site: http://livinglens.tv
Information Technology Services
N.A.I.C.S.: 541511

Medallia Argentina (2)
Humboldt 1550 Office 313, Buenos Aires, 1414, Argentina
Tel.: (54) 11 6091 7590
Web Site: http://www.medallia.com
Software Publisher
N.A.I.C.S.: 513210

Medallia Australia Pty. Ltd. (2)
20 Martin Place Level 14, Sydney, 2000, NSW, Australia
Tel.: (61) 292581204
Software Publisher
N.A.I.C.S.: 513210
Jared McMahon (Acct Dir)

Medallia Digital Ltd. (2)
7 Jabotinsky Street, Ramat Gan, 5252007, Israel
Tel.: (972) 37404478
Software Publisher
N.A.I.C.S.: 513210

Medallia France SARL (2)
64-66 Rue des Archives, 75003, Paris, France
Tel.: (33) 185640850
Software Publisher
N.A.I.C.S.: 513210
Jerome Comin (Sls Dir)

Medallia GmbH (2)
Mullerstrasse 27, 80469, Munich, Germany
Tel.: (49) 8926205668
Software Publisher
N.A.I.C.S.: 513210

Medallia Singapore Pte. Ltd. (2)
109 North Bridge Road Level 5, Singapore, 179097, Singapore
Tel.: (65) 67976201
Software Publisher
N.A.I.C.S.: 513210
Robin Prince (Sls Dir)

Medallia Spain S.L.U. (2)
Paseo de la Castellana 77, 28046, Madrid, Spain
Tel.: (34) 919041960
Computer Software Services
N.A.I.C.S.: 541511

Medallia UK (2)
80 Cheapside, London, EC2V 6EE, United Kingdom
Tel.: (44) 2039002121
Web Site: http://www.medallia.com
Software Publisher
N.A.I.C.S.: 513210

Middleton Technology Limited (2)
Kenyon Lane, Middleton, Manchester, M24 2GT, United Kingdom
Tel.: (44) 1616435116
Web Site: http://www.middtech.com
Computer Software Services
N.A.I.C.S.: 541511

Neural Technology Limited (2)
Bedford Road, Petersfield, GU32 3QA, Hampshire, United Kingdom
Tel.: (44) 1730260256
Computer Software Services
N.A.I.C.S.: 541511

Subsidiary (Domestic):

Omnichannel Solutions, LLC (2)
200 Spectrum Center Dr Ste 300, Irvine, CA 92618
Tel.: (202) 555-1212
Web Site: http://www.omnichannelsol.com
Business Process Outsourcing Services
N.A.I.C.S.: 541611

Promoter.IO Inc. (2)
110 E Houston St 6th Fl, San Antonio, TX 78205
Web Site: http://www.promoter.io
Computer Software Services
N.A.I.C.S.: 541511
Chad Keck (Founder & CEO)

StellaService, Inc. (2)
75 Broad St Ste 1010, New York, NY 10004
Tel.: (212) 366-1483
Web Site: http://www.stellaservice.com
Emp.: 70
Computer Software Development Services
N.A.I.C.S.: 541511
Jordy Leiser (Co-Founder & CEO)
John Ernsberger (Co-Founder & Sr VP-Global Client Svcs)
David Blanke (CFO)
Bill Hilliard (Sr VP-Sls)
Bill Beckler (VP-Engrg)

Subsidiary (Domestic):

ICC/Decision Services (3) (100%)
30 Galesi Dr Ste 108, Wayne, NJ 07470
Tel.: (973) 890-8611
Web Site: http://www.iccds.com
Sales Range: $1-9.9 Million
Emp.: 37
Marketing Research Service
N.A.I.C.S.: 541910
David Rich (CEO & Pres)
Kevin Leifer (VP-Client Success)
Mark Kutt (Dir-IT)
Nanette Brown (Exec VP & Gen Mgr)
Patty Rivers (Dir-HR & Fin)

Subsidiary (Domestic):

Strikedeck, Inc. (2)
400 Concar Dr, San Mateo, CA 94402
Tel.: (408) 513-3020
Web Site: http://www.strikedeck.com
Computer Software Services
N.A.I.C.S.: 541511
Shreesha Ramdas (Co-Founder & CEO)
Shabd Vaid (Co-Founder & CTO)
Sudha Subramanian (Head-Product)
Michael Cormier (VP-Ops)
Sonia Siganporia (Mktg Dir)

Virtual Hold Technology, LLC (2)
3875 Embassy Pkwy Ste 350, Akron, OH 44333
Tel.: (330) 670-2200
Web Site: http://www.vhtcx.com
Contact Center Virtual Queuing Solutions
N.A.I.C.S.: 541519
Matt DiMaria (CEO & Pres)
Matt Moller (Sr VP-Tech)
Thomas Jameson (Exec VP-Worldwide Sls)
Jim Bokar (Dir-Fin & Admin/Controller)
Kevin Shinseki (VP-Product Mgmt)
Nick Kennedy (VP-Customer Care)
Jaime Bailey (VP-Mktg)
Chris Swansiger (VP-Sls Ops)
Jeremy Starcher (VP-Cloud Strategy)
Walter Lash (Dir-Bus Consultation)

Voci Technologies, Inc. (2)
Burns White Ctr Ste 100 48 26th St, Pittsburgh, PA 15222
Tel.: (412) 621-9310
Web Site: http://www.vocitec.com
Software Development Services
N.A.I.C.S.: 541511
David Garrod (Gen Counsel)
John Kominek (Founder & CTO)
Michael Coney (Sr VP & Gen Mgr)
Wayne Ramprashad (Chief Product Officer)
Yasir Bugrara (Sls Dir)
Stephanie DiPaolo (Mktg Dir)
Tim Wallick (VP-Ops)

Zingle, Inc. (2)
2270 Camino Vida Roble Ste K, Carlsbad, CA 92011
Web Site: http://www.zingle.com
Computer Software Services
N.A.I.C.S.: 541511
Ford Blakely (Founder & CEO)
Jeremy Boatman (Product Dir)

MedeAnalytics, Inc. (1)
5858 Horton St Ste 475, Emeryville, CA 94608
Tel.: (510) 379-3300
Web Site: http://www.medeanalytics.com

THOMA BRAVO, L.P.

U.S. PRIVATE

Thoma Bravo, L.P.—(Continued)
Web-Hosted Business Analytics for Healthcare Providers & Payers
N.A.I.C.S.: 541519
Amy Ferretti *(Sr VP-Mktg)*
Ping Zhang *(CTO & Sr VP-Product Innovation)*
David Weiss *(Chm)*
Jim Hagan *(CFO)*
Emmet O'Gara *(Sr VP & Gen Mgr-Prayer Solutions)*
Paul Kaiser *(CEO)*
Kerry Martin *(Sr VP-Sls-Atlanta)*
Anne Perez *(Sr Dir-Mktg)*
Cindi Carter *(Chief Security Officer)*
Neal Schwartz *(COO)*
Scott Hampel *(Chief Product Officer)*
Tyler Downs *(CTO)*

Subsidiary (Domestic):

MedeAnalytics, Inc. (2)
501 W President George Bush Hwy Ste 250, Richardson, TX 75080
Tel.: (469) 916-3300
Web Site: http://www.medeanalytics.com
Healthcare Software Mfr
N.A.I.C.S.: 513210
Paul Kaiser *(CEO)*
Tyler Downs *(CTO)*
James Hagan *(CFO)*
Scott Hampel *(Chief Product Officer)*
Kerry Martin *(Sr VP-Sls)*
David Weiss *(Chm)*
Rosie Goddard *(Officer-Privacy & VP-Legal Counsel)*
Scott Checkoway *(CIO)*

MeridianLink, Inc. (1)
3560 Hyland Ave Ste 200, Costa Mesa, CA 92626
Tel.: (714) 708-6950
Web Site: https://www.meridianlink.com
Rev.: $288,046,000
Assets: $1,059,157,000
Liabilities: $480,066,000
Net Worth: $579,091,000
Earnings: $1,294,000
Emp.: 751
Fiscal Year-end: 12/31/2022
Software Developer
N.A.I.C.S.: 541511
Timothy Nguyen *(Founder & Chief Strategy Officer)*
Nicolaas Vlok *(CEO)*
Devesh Khare *(Chief Product Officer)*
Elizabeth Rieveley *(Chief People Officer)*
Dean Germeyer *(Chief Customer Officer)*
Suresh Balasubramanian *(CMO)*
Richard Scheig *(Chief Sls Officer)*
Erik Schneider *(Sr VP)*
Kayla Dailey *(Gen Counsel)*
Edward H. McDermott *(Chm)*
Nicolaas Vlok *(CEO)*
Laurence E. Katz *(Pres)*
Elias Olmeta *(CFO & Principal Acctg Officer)*

Subsidiary (Domestic):

Beanstalk Networks, LLC (2)
314 Clematis St, West Palm Beach, FL 33401
Tel.: (561) 655-6418
Web Site: https://www.openclose.com
Custom Computer Programming Services
N.A.I.C.S.: 541511
Jason Regalbuto *(CEO & CTO)*
James P. Kelly *(Pres)*

Motus, LLC (2)
2 Financial Ctr 60 S St, Boston, MA 02111
Tel.: (888) 312-0788
Web Site: http://www.motus.com
Vehicle Management & Reimbursement Platform
N.A.I.C.S.: 525990
Phong Nguyen *(CEO)*
Craig Powell *(Pres & CEO)*
Kristen Dooley *(COO & Chief People Officer)*
Karen O'Byrne *(CFO)*
Tim Brown *(Chief Corp Dev Officer)*
Danielle Lackey *(Chief Legal Officer)*
JD Miller *(Chief Revenue Officer)*
Todd Gebski *(Chief Strategy Officer)*
Heidi Skatrud *(Sr VP-Product Mgmt)*
Amanda Pettengill *(VP-Ops)*
Dennis Stevens *(VP-Enterprise Acct Mgmt)*

Joe Mocco *(VP-Admin)*
G. William McKinzie *(Chm)*
Jon Bernstein *(VP-Product Mgmt-Payments)*
Candice Helm *(VP-Product Mgmt-Vehicle)*
John Petrucelli *(VP-Product Line Mgmt-Sustainability)*
Ryon Packer *(Chief Product Officer)*

Subsidiary (Domestic):

Runzheimer International LLC (2)
1 Runzheimer pkwy, Waterford, WI 53185
Web Site: http://www.runzheimer.com
Administrative Management & General Management Consulting Services
N.A.I.C.S.: 541611

Wireless Analytics, LLC (2)
230 North St Suite 4, Danvers, MA 01923
Tel.: (978) 762-0900
Web Site: http://www.wirelessanalytics.com
Mobile Expense Management Firm
N.A.I.C.S.: 541618
Erik M. Eames *(Co-Founder & CEO)*
Paul Knittle *(Dir-Strategic Accts)*
Carl F. Jahn *(Co-Founder & CTO)*

Nearmap Ltd. (1)
Level 4 Tower One International Towers 100 Barangaroo Avenue, Sydney, 2000, NSW, Australia
Tel.: (61) 280760700
Web Site: https://www.nearmap.com
Rev.: $87,714,964
Assets: $183,639,653
Liabilities: $74,339,585
Net Worth: $109,300,068
Earnings: ($14,419,696)
Emp.: 300
Fiscal Year-end: 06/30/2021
Geospatial Mapping
N.A.I.C.S.: 541360

Subsidiary (Domestic):

Nearmap Pty. Ltd. (2)
Level 4 Tower One International Towers 100 Barangaroo Avenue, Barangaroo, 2000, NSW, Australia
Tel.: (61) 28 076 0700
Web Site: https://www.nearmap.com
Sales Range: $25-49.9 Million
Emp.: 10
Geospatial Media Services
N.A.I.C.S.: 541370

NextGen Healthcare, Inc. (1)
18111 Von Karman Ave Ste 600, Irvine, CA 92612
Tel.: (949) 255-2600
Rev.: $596,350,000
Assets: $627,674,000
Liabilities: $204,596,000
Net Worth: $423,078,000
Earnings: $1,618,000
Emp.: 2,655
Fiscal Year-end: 03/31/2022
Holding Company; Healthcare Information Technology Products & Services
N.A.I.C.S.: 551112
David William Sides *(CEO)*

Subsidiary (Domestic):

Gennius, Inc. (2)
PO Box 391937, Cambridge, MA 02139
Tel.: (781) 290-4744
Web Site: http://www.gennius.com
Healthcare Support Services
N.A.I.C.S.: 561990

HealthFusion Holdings, Inc. (2)
100 N Rios Ave, Solana Beach, CA 92075
Tel.: (858) 523-2120
Emp.: 62
Holding Company
N.A.I.C.S.: 551112

HealthFusion, Inc. (2)
100 N Rios Ave, Solana Beach, CA 92075
Tel.: (858) 523-2120
Web Site: http://www.healthfusion.com
Emp.: 200
Develops Web-based Cloud Computing Software for Physicians, Hospitals & Medical Billing Services
N.A.I.C.S.: 513210

Mirth, LLC (2)

611 Anton Blvd Ste 500, Costa Mesa, CA 92626
Tel.: (714) 389-1200
Web Site: http://www.mirth.com
Healthcare Support Services
N.A.I.C.S.: 561990

Subsidiary (Non-US):

NextGen Healthcare India Pvt. Ltd. (2)
Pritech Park SEZ Block 14B 4th Floor Outer Ring Rd, Bellandur, Bengaluru, 560103, India
Tel.: (91) 8049072400
Community Health Services
N.A.I.C.S.: 621498

Subsidiary (Domestic):

NextGen Healthcare Information Systems, LLC (2)
795 Horsham Rd, Horsham, PA 19044 **(100%)**
Tel.: (215) 657-7010
Web Site: http://www.nextgen.com
Sales Range: $75-99.9 Million
Emp.: 400
Healthcare Industry Software & Technological Support Services
N.A.I.C.S.: 513210

Subsidiary (Domestic):

Matrix Management Solutions, LLC (3)
5200 Stoneham Rd Ste 210, North Canton, OH 44720
Tel.: (330) 470-3700
Web Site: http://www.matrixmso.com
Sales Range: $1-9.9 Million
Emp.: 30
Revenue Cycle Management, Healthcare IT Training & Support Services
N.A.I.C.S.: 561499
Suhaasa Krishna *(Founder & CEO)*

Branch (Domestic):

NextGen Healthcare Information Systems, LLC - Atlanta (3)
3340 Peachtree Rd NE Ste 150, Atlanta, GA 30326-1200
Tel.: (770) 998-0500
Web Site: http://www.nextgen.com
Sales Range: $25-49.9 Million
Emp.: 500
Medical & Dental Practice Management Software Developer & Marketer
N.A.I.C.S.: 513210

Subsidiary (Domestic):

OTTO Health, LLC (2)
2300 Central Ave Ste D, Boulder, CO 80301
Tel.: (720) 510-2910
Web Site: http://www.ottohealth.com
Healtcare Services
N.A.I.C.S.: 621999
Michael Guese *(Founder & Chm)*

QSI Management, LLC (2)
18111 Von Karman Ave Ste 700, Irvine, CA 92612-0199
Tel.: (949) 255-2600
Healthcare Software Development Services
N.A.I.C.S.: 541511

The Poseidon Group, Inc. (2)
2451 Cumberland Pkwy Ste 3512, Atlanta, GA 30339
Tel.: (404) 261-0401
Web Site: http://www.poseidongroup.com
Sales Range: $10-24.9 Million
Emp.: 12
Custom Computer Programming Services
N.A.I.C.S.: 541511

ViaTrack Systems, LLC (2)
2840 Hillcreek Dr, Augusta, GA 30909
Tel.: (706) 869-9960
Web Site: http://www.viatrack.com
Emp.: 20
Healthcare Software Development Services
N.A.I.C.S.: 541511

PEC Safety Operations LLC (1)
233 General Patton Ave, Mandeville, LA 70471

Tel.: (985) 892-8177
Web Site: http://www.pecsafety.com
Risk Managemeng Srvices
N.A.I.C.S.: 541611
Elizabeth Haley *(Dir-Regulatory Outreach)*
Colby Lane *(CEO)*

Subsidiary (Domestic):

Veriforce, LLC (2)
1575 Sawdust Rd Ste 600, The Woodlands, TX 77380
Tel.: (281) 404-7102
Web Site: http://www.veriforce.com
Computer Software Developer
N.A.I.C.S.: 513210
Jessica Renard *(Mgr-Compliance)*

Ping Identity Holding Corp. (1)
1001 17th St Ste 100, Denver, CO 80202
Tel.: (303) 468-2900
Web Site: https://www.pingidentity.com
Rev.: $299,449,000
Assets: $1,178,033,000
Liabilities: $436,628,000
Net Worth: $741,405,000
Earnings: ($64,391,000)
Emp.: 1,247
Fiscal Year-end: 12/31/2021
Holding Company
N.A.I.C.S.: 551112
Michael Fosnaugh *(Chm)*
Raj Dani *(CFO)*
Shalini Sharma *(Chief Legal Officer)*
Aaron Lapoint *(Chief Admin Officer & Chief HR Officer)*
Peter Barker *(Chief Product Officer)*
Rakesh Thaker *(Chief Dev Officer)*

Subsidiary (Non-US):

Ping Identity Canada Inc. (2)
600 - 564 Beatty Street, Vancouver, V6B 2L3, BC, Canada
Tel.: (604) 697-7040
Web Site: https://www.pingidentity.com
Software Services
N.A.I.C.S.: 541511

Ping Identity France, SAS (2)
7 Rue Leo Delibes, Paris, 75016, France
Tel.: (33) 186264316
Identity Security Services
N.A.I.C.S.: 541511

Ping Identity Israel, Ltd. (2)
Ef al St 25 11th Floor, Petach Tikva, 4951125, Israel
Tel.: (972) 37500620
Identity Security Services
N.A.I.C.S.: 541511

Ping Identity UK Limited (2)
New Penderel House 8th Floor 283-288 High Holborn, London, WC1V 7HP, United Kingdom
Tel.: (44) 2071909105
Identity Security Services
N.A.I.C.S.: 541511
Phil Allen *(VP-EMEA)*

Symphonic Software Limited (2)
Atholl House 51 Melville Street, Edinburgh, EH3 7HL, United Kingdom
Tel.: (44) 1312902318
Web Site: http://www.symphonicsoft.com
Information Technology Services
N.A.I.C.S.: 541511
Judith Halkerston *(Chm)*
Derick James *(Founder & CEO)*
Niall Burns *(Co-Founder & CTO)*
Steven Holmes *(Head-Architecture)*
Daniel McCarragher *(Engr-Software)*

Proofpoint, Inc. (1)
925 W Maude Avenue, Sunnyvale, CA 94085
Tel.: (408) 517-4710
Web Site: http://www.proofpoint.com
Rev.: $1,050,010,000
Assets: $2,498,710,000
Liabilities: $2,056,966,000
Net Worth: $441,744,000
Earnings: ($163,809,000)
Emp.: 3,658
Fiscal Year-end: 12/31/2020
Email Security & Data Loss Prevention Services
N.A.I.C.S.: 513210
Marcel DePaolis *(Co-Founder & CTO)*
David Knight *(Exec VP & Gen MgrSecurity Products)*

COMPANIES
THOMA BRAVO, L.P.

Darren Lee *(Exec VP/Gen Mgr-Compliance & Digital Risk Bus Unit)*
Michael Yang *(Gen Counsel, Sec & Sr VP)*
Sumit Dhawan *(CEO)*
Ryan Kalember *(Exec VP-Cybersecurity Strategy)*
Lyn Campbell *(Exec VP-Customer Success & IT)*
Jason Hurst *(Sr VP-Corp Dev)*
Blake P. Salle *(Chief Revenue Officer)*
Alan LeFort *(Sr VP & gen Mgr-Security Awareness Training Products)*
Jason Starr *(VP-IR)*
Remi Thomas *(CFO)*
Gary L. Steele *(Co-Founder)*
Michael Frendo *(CTO-Engrg)*

Subsidiary (Domestic):

Armorize Technologies, Inc. (2)
5201 Great America Pkwy Ste 320, Santa Clara, CA 95054
Tel.: (877) 634-7660
Web Security; Web Malware Monitoring, Vulnerability Assessment & Web Scanning
N.A.I.C.S.: 513210

Subsidiary (Non-US):

CLOUDMARK LABS SARL (2)
41 Boulevard Des Capucines, 75002, Paris, France
Tel.: (33) 180480820
Web Site: http://www.cloudmark.com
Advanced Threat Services
N.A.I.C.S.: 541512

Subsidiary (Domestic):

Cloudmark, Inc. (2)
128 King St 2nd Fl, San Francisco, CA 94107
Tel.: (415) 946-3800
Web Site: http://www.cloudmark.com
Threat Protection & Electronic Messaging Security Products
N.A.I.C.S.: 541512
Angela Knox *(Sr VP-Engrg)*
Debra Kladis *(VP-Sls Ops)*
Kevin San Diego *(VP-Product Mgmt)*
Mike Reading *(Sr VP-Support & Technical Svcs)*
Lori Cho *(VP-Ops)*
Paul Buttle *(Sr VP-Worldwide Sls)*

NetCitadel, Inc. (2)
2513 E Charleston Rd Ste 100, Mountain View, CA 94043
Tel.: (650) 564-4285
Data Protection & Security Services
N.A.I.C.S.: 561621

Subsidiary (Non-US):

PROOFPOINT GMBH (2)
Zeppelinstr 73, 81669, Munich, Germany
Tel.: (49) 8945835370
Advanced Threat Services
N.A.I.C.S.: 541512

Proofpoint Canada Inc. (2)
210 King Street East Suite 400, Toronto, M5A 1J7, ON, Canada
Tel.: (647) 436-1036
Email Security & Data Loss Prevention Services
N.A.I.C.S.: 513210

Proofpoint Email Solutions GmbH (2)
Landsberger Strasse 302, 80687, Munich, Germany
Tel.: (49) 89 90 405 464
Email Security & Data Loss Prevention Services
N.A.I.C.S.: 513210

Proofpoint Japan KK (2)
Shiroyama Trust Tower 34F 4-3-1, Toranomon Minato-ku, Tokyo, 105-6034, Japan
Tel.: (81) 364025041
Web Site: http://www.proofpoint.com
Emp.: 1,800
Email Security & Data Loss Prevention Services
N.A.I.C.S.: 513210

Proofpoint Limited (2)
100 Brook Drive, Green Park, Reading, RG2 6UJ, Berkshire, United Kingdom
Tel.: (44) 118 402 5900
Web Site: http://www.proofpoint.com
Email Security & Data Loss Prevention Services
N.A.I.C.S.: 513210

Proofpoint NI Ltd. (2)
Cyber House 11 Weavers Court Linfield Road, Belfast, BT12 5GH, Northern Ireland, United Kingdom
Tel.: (44) 844 800 8456
Web Site: http://essentials.proofpoint.com
Email Security & Data Loss Prevention Services
N.A.I.C.S.: 513210

Proofpoint Netherlands B.V. (2)
Strawinsylaan 4117 4th Floor, 1077 XZ, Amsterdam, Netherlands
Tel.: (31) 1184025900
Network Security Services
N.A.I.C.S.: 561621

Proofpoint Singapore Pte. Ltd. (2)
Suntec Tower 2 9 Temasek Boulevard 31F, Singapore, 038989, Singapore
Tel.: (65) 6559 6128
Web Site: http://www.proofpoint.com
Email Security & Data Loss Prevention Services
N.A.I.C.S.: 513210

Subsidiary (Domestic):

Sendmail, Inc. (2)
6475 Christie Ave Ste 400, Emeryville, CA 94608
Tel.: (510) 594-5400
Web Site: http://www.sendmail.com
Sales Range: $25-49.9 Million
Emp.: 120
Designs & Develops Software Solutions for Internet Mail
N.A.I.C.S.: 513210

Subsidiary (Non-US):

Sendmail KK (3)
8th Fl Shiodome sprior Bldg 7-10 Shinbashi 1-chome Minato, Tokyo, 105-0004, Japan
Tel.: (81) 355370371
Web Site: http://www.sendmail.co.jp
Internet Mail Solutions
N.A.I.C.S.: 423430

Sendmail S.A.R.L (3)
64 rue Tocqueville, 75017, Paris, France
Tel.: (33) 143182222
Sales Range: $10-24.9 Million
Emp.: 3
Provider of Internet Mail Solutions
N.A.I.C.S.: 517810

Sendmail, Ltd. (3)
Lakeside House 1 Furzeground Way Stockley Park, Uxbridge, UB11 1BD, Middlesex, United Kingdom
Tel.: (44) 207 112 7015
Web Site: http://www.sendmail.com
Internet Mail Solutions
N.A.I.C.S.: 517810

Subsidiary (Domestic):

Socialware, Inc. (2)
6500 River Pl Blvd Bldg V Ste 400, Austin, TX 78730
Tel.: (512) 329-8880
Web Site: http://www.socialware.com
Software Development Services
N.A.I.C.S.: 513210

Wombat Security Technologies, Inc. (2)
3030 Penn Ave, Pittsburgh, PA 15201
Tel.: (412) 621-1484
Security Software & Services
N.A.I.C.S.: 513210
Joe Ferrara *(Gen Mgr)*
Norman Sadeh *(Founder)*
Lorrie Cranor *(Founder)*
Amy Baker *(VP-Mktg)*
Tom Sands *(VP-Engrg)*

QAD Inc. (1)
100 Innovation Pl, Santa Barbara, CA 93108
Tel.: (805) 566-6000
Web Site: http://www.qad.com
Rev.: $307,865,000
Assets: $350,787,000
Liabilities: $221,321,000
Net Worth: $129,466,000
Earnings: $11,065,000
Emp.: 1,930
Fiscal Year-end: 01/31/2021
Developer & Supplier of Integrated Business Software & Services in the Open Systems Environment
N.A.I.C.S.: 513210
Edward A. Boclair *(Sr VP-Sls-Global)*
Kara L. Bellamy *(Chief Acctg Officer, Sr VP & Controller)*
Anton Chilton *(CEO)*
Tony J. Winter *(CTO)*
Leif Petersen *(CIO)*
Bill Keese *(Sr VP-R&D)*
Charlie Eggerding *(Sr VP-Automotive Strategic Accounts)*
Eugenio Riveroll *(Sr VP-Latin America)*
Kaye Swanson *(Chief People Officer)*
Carter Lloyds *(CMO & Sr VP)*
Stefan De Haar *(Sr VP-Asia Pacific)*
Steve Gardner *(Sr VP-EMEA)*
Robin Riordan *(Sr VP-Consulting & Transformation Svcs)*
Michael Brunnick *(Sr VP-North America)*
Michael McGrattan *(Sr VP-Svc Delivery-Global)*

Subsidiary (Non-US):

Allocation Network GmbH (2)
Arabellastrasse 17, 81925, Munich, Germany
Tel.: (49) 892782570
Web Site: http://www.allocation.net
Software Publisher
N.A.I.C.S.: 513210
Bernhard Soltmann *(Mng Dir)*
Andreas Vollmann *(Mng Dir)*
Andreas Prohaska *(Mng Dir)*

Subsidiary (Domestic):

CEBOS, Ltd. (2)
5936 Ford Ct Ste 203, Brighton, MI 48116
Tel.: (810) 534-2222
Web Site: http://www.cebos.com
Administrative & General Management Consulting Services
N.A.I.C.S.: 541611

Subsidiary (Non-US):

DynaSys S.A.S. (2)
Espace Europeen de l'Entreprise Immeuble Le Skansen, 3 Allee de Stockholm, 67300, Schiltigheim, France
Tel.: (33) 388191414
Web Site: http://www.dys.com
Software Development Services
N.A.I.C.S.: 513210

PT QAD Asia Indonesia (2)
Pqm Building Jl Cempaka Putih Tengah 17C no 7A, Jakarta, 10510, Indonesia
Tel.: (62) 214206340
Software Development Services
N.A.I.C.S.: 513210
Tantik Rahaju *(Dir-Svcs)*

Precision Software Limited (2)
Dublin The Hubble 7 Ardee Road, Rathmines, Dublin, D06 RX85, Ireland
Tel.: (353) 14060700
Web Site: http://www.precisionsoftware.com
Software Development Services
N.A.I.C.S.: 513210
Paul Murphy *(VP-R&D)*
Vivienne Gleeson *(Partner-HR Bus)*
Jerry Peck *(VP-Product Strategy)*
Brendan Kerlin *(VP-Consulting & Transformation Svcs)*
Chris Caouette *(VP-Sls & Mktg)*
Corey Rhodes *(Pres)*

QAD (Thailand) Ltd. (2)
CW Tower A 23rd Floor 90 Ratchadapisek Road, Huaykwang, Bangkok, 10310, Thailand (100%)
Tel.: (66) 22029369
Web Site: http://www.qad.com
Software Development Services
N.A.I.C.S.: 513210

QAD Australia Pty Ltd. (2)
Level 1 City Views Business Park 67 Epping Road, Macquarie Park, 2113, NSW, Australia (100%)
Tel.: (61) 298573000
Web Site: http://www.qad.com
Sales Range: $10-24.9 Million
Emp.: 60
Software Development Services
N.A.I.C.S.: 513210
Pamela Meyer Lopker *(Pres)*

QAD Bilgisayer Yazilim Ltd. (2)
Ozce Business Center Hal Cd No 3 Kat 12, Icerenkoy, 8110, Istanbul, Turkiye
Tel.: (90) 2165725595
Sales Range: $100-124.9 Million
Provider of Software
N.A.I.C.S.: 334610

QAD Brasil Ltda. (2)
Praca General Gentil Falca 108 - Conj 52 Brooklin, Sao Paulo, 04571-150, Brazil
Tel.: (55) 1135292700
Software Development Services
N.A.I.C.S.: 513210

QAD Brazil Ltda. (2)
Praca General Gentil Falcao 108 - Conj 52 Brooklin, Sao Paulo, 04571-011, Sao Paulo, Brazil (100%)
Tel.: (55) 1135292700
Web Site: http://www.qad.com
Sales Range: $1-9.9 Million
Emp.: 30
Software Development Services
N.A.I.C.S.: 513210

QAD China Ltd. (2)
Floor 3 North Tower Building No 9 20th in Lujiazui, Software Park lane 91 on Ershan Road Pudong, Shanghai, 200127, China
Tel.: (86) 2161823600
Software Development Services
N.A.I.C.S.: 513210
Kitty He *(Mgr-Mktg & Channel Program)*

QAD China, Inc. (2)
Floor 3 North Tower Building No 9 20th in Lujiazui Software Park, Lane 91 on Ershan Road Shanghai, Pudong, 200127, China (100%)
Tel.: (86) 2161823600
Web Site: http://www.qad.com.cn
Sales Range: $25-49.9 Million
Emp.: 150
Integrated Business Software Services
N.A.I.C.S.: 513210
Pamela Meyer Lopker *(Pres)*

QAD Europe (Ireland) Limited (2)
Clive House National Technological Park, Plassey, Limerick, V94 HN4N, Ireland
Tel.: (353) 61213600
Software Development Services
N.A.I.C.S.: 513210

QAD Europe GmbH (2)
Dr Kulz-Ring 15, 01067, Dresden, Germany (100%)
Tel.: (49) 35188899931
Web Site: http://www.qad.com
Sales Range: $10-24.9 Million
Emp.: 20
Software Development Services
N.A.I.C.S.: 513210

QAD Europe Lda. (2)
Centro De Negocios Do Freixieiro Edificio, De Quental 236 Rm 1 103/104, 4455-586, Oporto, Portugal (100%)
Tel.: (351) 229984280
Web Site: http://www.qad.com
Sales Range: $1-9.9 Million
Emp.: 3
Provider of Computer Software
N.A.I.C.S.: 334610

QAD Europe Limited (2)
Sir Stanley Clarke House 7 Ridgeway, Quinton Business Park, Birmingham, B32 1AF, West Midlands, United Kingdom
Tel.: (44) 1215066500
Web Site: http://www.qad.com
Software Development Services
N.A.I.C.S.: 513210

QAD Europe N.V./S.A. (2)
Luchthavenlei 7B, 2100, Deurne, Antwerp, Belgium (100%)
Tel.: (32) 32861221
Web Site: http://www.qad.com
Sales Range: $10-24.9 Million
Emp.: 20
Software Development Services
N.A.I.C.S.: 513210

THOMA BRAVO, L.P.

U.S. PRIVATE

Thoma Bravo, L.P.—(Continued)

QAD Europe S.A.S. (2)
Colisee Gardens 8 avenue de l'Arche, 4 Rue De Charenton, Courbevoie, Cedex, France **(100%)**
Tel.: (33) 187158009
Web Site: http://www.qad.com
Software Development Services
N.A.I.C.S.: 513210

QAD Europe S.L. (2)
Avda Diagonal 567 2nd Floor, 08029, Barcelona, Spain
Tel.: (34) 933272000 **(100%)**
Web Site: http://www.qad.com
Software Development Services
N.A.I.C.S.: 513210

QAD India Private Limited (2)
301 3rd Floor Techniplex - I Techniplex Complex Off Veer Savarkar, Flyover Goregaon West, Mumbai, 400 062, Maharashtra, India **(100%)**
Tel.: (91) 2240989999
Web Site: http://www.qad.com
Sales Range: $25-49.9 Million
Emp.: 180
Software Development Services
N.A.I.C.S.: 513210

QAD Ireland Limited (2)
Hamilton House National Technology Park, National Technological Park, Limerick, Ireland **(100%)**
Tel.: (353) 61213600
Web Site: http://www.qad.com
Saas Erp Developer Services
N.A.I.C.S.: 513210

QAD Italy S.r.l. (2)
Via Amedei 6, Milan, MI, Italy **(100%)**
Tel.: (39) 0282951358
Web Site: http://www.qad.com
Sales Range: $10-24.9 Million
Emp.: 60
Software Development Services
N.A.I.C.S.: 513210

QAD Japan Inc. (2)
Frontier Onarimon 7F 3-25-33 Nishi-Shinbashi, Minato-ku, Tokyo, 105-0003, Japan
Tel.: (81) 357338011
Software Development Services
N.A.I.C.S.: 513210

QAD Japan, Inc. (2)
Frontier Onarimon 7F 3-25-33, Nishi-Shinbashi Minato-ku, Tokyo, 105-0003, Japan **(100%)**
Tel.: (81) 357338011
Web Site: http://www.qad.co.jp
Sales Range: $10-24.9 Million
Emp.: 24
Software Development Services
N.A.I.C.S.: 513210
Ichiro Shibata (Chm)

QAD Netherlands B.V. (2)
Boeingavenue 56, 1119 PE, Schiphol-Rijk, Netherlands **(100%)**
Tel.: (31) 206547200
Web Site: http://www.qad.com
Sales Range: $10-24.9 Million
Emp.: 70
Software Development Services
N.A.I.C.S.: 513210

QAD Polska Sp. z o.o. (2)
ul Legnicka 55f, 54-203, Wroclaw, Poland **(100%)**
Tel.: (48) 713803000
Web Site: http://www.qad.com
Software Development Services
N.A.I.C.S.: 513210

QAD Singapore Pte Ltd. (2)
71 Ubi Road 1 05-41 Oxley Bizhub, Singapore, 408732, Singapore **(100%)**
Tel.: (65) 67024855
Web Site: http://www.qad.com.sg
Sales Range: $1-9.9 Million
Emp.: 10
Software Development Services
N.A.I.C.S.: 513210

QAD Sistemas Integrados Casa de Software, S.A. de C.V. (2)
Newton 27, Col Polanco, Mexico, 11560, DF, Mexico **(100%)**

Tel.: (52) 5552798800
Web Site: http://www.qad.com
Sales Range: $10-24.9 Million
Emp.: 48
Developer & Supplier of Integrated Business Software & Services in the Open Systems Environment
N.A.I.C.S.: 541511

QAD Sistemas Integrados Servicios de Consultoria, S.A. de C.V. (2)
Newton 27 Col Polanco, 11560, Mexico, Mexico **(100%)**
Tel.: (52) 5552798800
Web Site: http://www.qad.com
Sales Range: $10-24.9 Million
Emp.: 46
Software Development Services
N.A.I.C.S.: 513210

QAD United Kingdom (2)
Waterfront Business Park, Waterfront West Dudley Road, Brierley Hill, DY5 1LX, West Midlands, United Kingdom **(100%)**
Tel.: (44) 1384487700
Web Site: http://www.qad.com
Sales Range: $10-24.9 Million
Emp.: 70
Software Development Services
N.A.I.C.S.: 513210

Qlik Technologies Inc. (1)
21 S Gulph Rd Ste 500, King of Prussia, PA 19406
Tel.: (888) 828-9768
Web Site: http://www.qlik.com
Sales Range: $600-649.9 Million
Emp.: 5,000
Software Developer & Publisher
N.A.I.C.S.: 513210
Dennis E. Johnson (CFO)
Timothy J. MacCarrick (Treas)
Deborah Cleary Lofton (Gen Counsel, Sec & VP)
Mark C. Thurmond (Exec VP-Worldwide Sls & Svcs)
Rick Jackson (CMO)
Mike Potter (Sr VP-Global Res & Dev)
Lynn Carino (VP-Global Employment & Compliance)
Mike Capone (CEO)
Arun Balasubramanian (Mgr-India)
Julian Quinn (VP-Asia Pacific)

Subsidiary (Non-US):

QlikTech International AB (2)
Scheelevagen 24-26, SE-223 63, Lund, Sweden
Tel.: (46) 102097500
Software Publisher
N.A.I.C.S.: 513210
Chris Jones (Exec VP-Sls)

Division (Non-US):

Attunity Ltd. (3)
16 Atir Yeda Street Atir Yeda Industrial Park, Kfar Saba, 4464321, Israel
Tel.: (972) 98993000
Web Site: http://www.attunity.com
Rev: $86,249,000
Assets: $112,269,000
Liabilities: $38,369,000
Net Worth: $73,900,000
Earnings: $5,957,000
Emp.: 298
Fiscal Year-end: 12/31/2018
Technology Solutions for Integrating Disparate Data Sources, Legacy & Mainframe Applications
N.A.I.C.S.: 541511
Dror Harel-Elkayam (CFO & Sec)
Itamar Ankorion (Chief Mktg Officer)
Erez Zeevi (Exec VP-R&D & Technical Ops-Global)
Paul Kelly (Exec VP-Sls-EMEA)
Byron Yeung (VP-Asia Pacific)
Stephen Foster (Exec VP-Sls-Americas)

Subsidiary (Non-US):

Attunity (Hong Kong) Ltd. (4)
Unit 10E Neich Tower 128 Gloucester Road, Wanchai, China (Hong Kong) **(100%)**
Tel.: (852) 27569233
Web Site: http://www.attunity.com.hk
Technology Solutions for Integrating Disparate Data Sources, Legacy & Mainframe Applications

N.A.I.C.S.: 334610

Attunity (UK) Limited (4)
3000 Hillswood Drive, Hillswood Business Park, Chertsey, KT16 0RS, Surrey, United Kingdom **(100%)**
Tel.: (44) 1932 895024
Technology Solutions for Integrating Disparate Data Sources, Legacy & Mainframe Applications
N.A.I.C.S.: 334610
Paul Kelly (VP-Sls-EMEA)

Subsidiary (US):

Attunity Inc. (4)
70 Blanchard Rd, Burlington, MA 01803
Tel.: (781) 730-4070
Web Site: http://www.attunity.com
Technology Solutions for Integrating Disparate Data Sources, Legacy & Mainframe Applications
N.A.I.C.S.: 334610

Subsidiary (Domestic):

Attunity Israel (1992) Ltd (4)
16 Atir Yeda Street 5th Floor kfar saba, Kfar Netter, 4464321, Israel
Tel.: (972) 98993000
Real Time Data Management Software Development Services
N.A.I.C.S.: 541511
Shimon Alon (CEO)

Subsidiary (Non-US):

QlikTech Italy S.r.l. (2)
Via Dante n 15, 20123, Milan, Italy
Tel.: (39) 0289653000
Web Site: http://www.qlik.com
Emp.: 40
Software Development Services
N.A.I.C.S.: 541511
Rosagrazia Bombimi (VP)

Quorum Business Solutions, Inc. (1)
811 Main St Ste 2000, Houston, TX 77002
Tel.: (713) 430-8600
Web Site: http://www.qbsol.com
Sales Range: $10-24.9 Million
Emp.: 350
Energy Sector Software Developer & Consulting Services
N.A.I.C.S.: 513210
Bruce Wartell (CTO)
R. Scott Leeds (Co-Founder, Chm & CEO)
Perry Turbes (Pres)
Jessica Sumners (Office Mgr)
Rick Piacenti (CFO)
Eric Hazeldine (Exec VP)
Olivier Thierry (CMO)
Michael Hart (Exec VP)
Joe Norris (Exec VP)
David Townsend (VP)
Jason Webster (VP)
Jess Porter (VP)
Shawn Cutter (VP)
Tyson Greer (VP)
Jan Manning (CIO)
Paul Langenbahn (CEO)

Subsidiary (Domestic):

EnergyIQ LLC (2)
2329 W Main St Ste 300, Littleton, CO 80120
Tel.: (303) 790-0919
Web Site: http://www.energyiq.info
Information Management Solutions Provider
N.A.I.C.S.: 541618
Steve Cooper (Pres & CEO)
Mike Haden (CTO)
Mike Skeffington (COO)
Amelia Webster (VP-Product Mgmt)
Brandon Schroeder (VP-Bus Dev)

Subsidiary (Domestic):

petroWEB, Inc. (3)
5500 Greenwood Plz Blvd Ste 130, Greenwood Village, CO 80113
Tel.: (303) 308-9100
Web Site: http://www.petroweb.com
Custom Computer Programming Services
N.A.I.C.S.: 541511
Darcy Vaughan (Co-Founder)
Gina Godfrey (Co-Founder & CEO)
Jeff Wadsworth (Exec VP-Ops)

Branch (Domestic):

Quorum Business Solutions, Inc. - Dallas (2)
1420 W Mockingbird Ln Ste 700, Dallas, TX 75247
Tel.: (214) 630-6442
Web Site: http://www.qbsol.com
Energy Sector Software Developer & Consulting Services
N.A.I.C.S.: 513210
Bruce Wartell (Founder & CTO)
Perry Turbes (Pres & CEO)
Michael Hart (Exec VP)
Eric Hazeldine (Exec VP)
Lindsey Herndon (VP-Goodgion)
Joe Norris (Exec VP)
Rick Piacenti (CFO)
Olivier Thierry (CMO)

Subsidiary (Domestic):

WellEz Information Management, LLC (2)
11931 Wickchester, Ln Ste 102, Houston, TX 77043-4501
Tel.: (281) 584-9200
Web Site: http://www.wellez.com
General Management Consulting Services
N.A.I.C.S.: 541611
Charles Jeffrey (Pres)

RealPage, Inc. (1)
2201 Lakeside Blvd, Richardson, TX 75082
Tel.: (214) 273-6671
Web Site: http://www.realpage.com
Property Management Software Developer
N.A.I.C.S.: 513210
Stephen T. Winn (CEO)
Michael Britti (Exec VP-Mergers & Acquisitions & Emerging Markets)
Vinit Doshi (COO)
Titina Ott Adams (Chief Customer Officer)
Dana S. Jones (Pres & CEO)

Subsidiary (Domestic):

A.L. Wizard, Inc. (2)
11230 Sorrento Valley Rd Ste 220, San Diego, CA 92121
Tel.: (858) 457-0566
Web Site: http://www.alwizard.com
Sales Range: $10-24.9 Million
Emp.: 7
Assisted Living Services
N.A.I.C.S.: 623312

American Utility Management, Inc. (2)
3062 N Central Ave, Chicago, IL 60634-5310
Tel.: (773) 237-7667
Web Site: http://www.aum-inc.com
Ambulatory & Health Care Services
N.A.I.C.S.: 621999
Viga Cossel (Founder)

Axiometrics LLC (2)
14800 Landmark Blvd Ste 640, Dallas, TX 75254
Tel.: (214) 953-2242
Web Site: http://www.axiometrics.com
Apartment & Student Housing Research, Market Intelligence & Analysis Services
N.A.I.C.S.: 541910

Buildium, LLC (2)
3 Ctr Plz Ste 400, Boston, MA 02108
Tel.: (617) 600-0448
Web Site: http://www.buildium.com
Sales Range: $1-9.9 Million
Emp.: 30
Property Management Software Development Services
N.A.I.C.S.: 541511
Dimitris Georgakopoulos (Co-Founder)
Michael Monteiro (Co-Founder)
Patrick Rubeski (VP-Engrg)
Jessica Steinberg (Mgr-Customer Care)
Chris Litster (CEO)
Jeff Belanger (VP-People & Culture)
Michelle Burtchell (VP-Mktg)
Ben Nadol (VP-Fin)
Deirdre O'Driscoll (CFO)
Kim Rose (VP-Customer Success)
Piyum Samaraweera (VP-Product Mgmt)
Mark Brierley (Product Mgr)
Lauren Mason (Mgr-Field Mktg)

Investor Management Services, LLC (2)

COMPANIES

THOMA BRAVO, L.P.

4001 Yancey Rd Ste C200, Charlotte, NC 28217
Web Site:
 http://www.info.investormanagementservices.com
Real Estate Firm Services
N.A.I.C.S.: 531390

Subsidiary (Non-US):

Kigo Rental Systems, S.L. (2)
Carrer de Provenca 388, 08025, Barcelona, Spain
Tel.: (34) 931980697
Software Development Services
N.A.I.C.S.: 541511

Subsidiary (Domestic):

Kigo, Inc. (2)
2628 Maxwell St, Philadelphia, PA 19152
Tel.: (215) 717-7223
Web Site: http://www.kigo.net
Software Development Services
N.A.I.C.S.: 541511

Modern Message, Inc. (2)
750 N Saint Paul St Ste 1230, Dallas, TX 75201
Tel.: (214) 238-4200
Web Site: http://www.modernmessage.com
Emp.: 55
Application Software Development Services
N.A.I.C.S.: 541511
John Hinckley *(Co-Founder & CEO)*
Michael Ivey *(Co-Founder & COO)*
Audrey Springer *(Chief Client Officer)*
Daniel Miller *(CTO)*

Multifamily Technology Solutions, Inc. (2)
343 Sansome St Ste 700, San Francisco, CA 94104
Tel.: (800) 689-5388
Web Site: http://www.mynewplace.com
Online Residential Property Rental Services
N.A.I.C.S.: 561439

NWP Services Corporation (2)
535 Anton Blvd Ste 1100, Costa Mesa, CA 92626
Tel.: (949) 253-2500
Web Site: http://www.nwp.com
Emp.: 500
Utility Management Services
N.A.I.C.S.: 522320

On-Site Manager, Inc. (2)
2201 Lakeside Blvd, Richardson, TX 75082
Tel.: (866) 266-7483
Web Site: http://www.on-site.com
Support Services
N.A.I.C.S.: 561990
Thomas Herrington *(CEO)*

OpsTechnology, Inc. (2)
140 Geary St 5th Fl, San Francisco, CA 94104
Tel.: (415) 222-6996
Expense Management Software Publisher
N.A.I.C.S.: 513210

Subsidiary (Non-US):

PEX Software Australia Pty. Ltd. (2)
246 Pacific Highway, Crows Nest, 2065, NSW, Australia
Tel.: (61) 284583325
Software Development Services
N.A.I.C.S.: 541511

PEX Software Limited (2)
14th Floor The Tower Building 11 York Road, London, SE1 7NX, United Kingdom
Tel.: (44) 2034322105
Web Site: http://www.pexsoftware.com
Software Development Services
N.A.I.C.S.: 541511
Philip Evans *(Mng Dir)*

Subsidiary (Domestic):

PropertyPhotos.com LLC (2)
2201 Lakeside Blvd, Richardson, TX 75082
Tel.: (972) 820-3000
Web Site: http://www.propertyphotos.com
Commercial Photography Services
N.A.I.C.S.: 541922
Sheena Pabari *(VP-Content Svcs)*
Debi Cole Williams *(VP-Ops & Content Svcs)*
Michael Prior *(Mgr-Photography)*
Kevin Wilson *(Production Mgr-Video & Photography)*
Emily Kelp *(Mgr-Content Svcs)*
Katie King *(Mgr-Interactive Site Maps & Process Improvement)*

Propertyware, Inc. (2)
343 Sansome St Ste 825, San Francisco, CA 94105
Tel.: (415) 455-2400
Web Site: http://www.propertyware.com
Property Management Software Publisher
N.A.I.C.S.: 513210

RealPage Payments Services LLC (2)
4000 International Pkwy, Carrollton, TX 75007-1951
Tel.: (972) 820-3188
Emp.: 5
Credit Union
N.A.I.C.S.: 522130

Rentlytics, Inc. (2)
77 Geary St, San Francisco, CA 94108
Web Site: http://www.rentlytics.com
Software Development Services
N.A.I.C.S.: 541511
Justin Alanis *(Founder & CEO)*
Steve Dyrdahl *(VP-Engrg & Product)*
Roger Muckenfuss *(VP-Customer Success)*
Ted Connolly *(Dir-Professional Svcs & Product Solutions)*

Senior-Living.com, Inc. (2)
8521 Leesburg Pike Ste 350, Vienna, VA 22182
Tel.: (703) 887-2191
Web Site: http://www.seniorliving.net
Assisted Living Services
N.A.I.C.S.: 623312

SailPoint Technologies Holdings, Inc. (1)
11120 4 Points Dr Ste 100, Austin, TX 78726
Tel.: (512) 346-2000
Web Site: https://www.sailpoint.com
Rev.: $438,954,000
Assets: $1,159,840,000
Liabilities: $755,601,000
Net Worth: $404,239,000
Earnings: $(61,634,000)
Emp.: 1,676
Fiscal Year-end: 12/31/2021
Information Technology Support Services
N.A.I.C.S.: 541612
William Gregory Bock *(Chm)*
Christopher G. Schmitt *(Gen Counsel)*
Abby Payne *(Chief People Officer)*
Meredith Blanchar *(Sr VP-Customer Success)*
Matt Mills *(Pres-Field Ops-Worldwide)*
Steve Bradford *(Sr VP-EMEA)*
Wendy Wu *(CMO)*
Mark McClain *(Founder & CEO)*
Brian Carolan *(CFO)*
Gary Nafus *(Chief Sls Officer)*
Nina Somerville *(Sr VP-Sales)*
Ben Cody *(Sr VP-Product Mgmt)*
Rex Booth *(Chief Information Security Officer)*
Sreeveni Kancharla *(CIO)*

Sailpoint Technologies, Inc. (1)
11305 Four Points Dr Bldg 2 Ste 100, Austin, TX 78730
Tel.: (512) 346-2000
Web Site: http://www.sailpoint.com
Sales Range: $100-124.9 Million
Emp.: 250
Identity & Access Management Software & Solutions
N.A.I.C.S.: 513210
William Gregory Bock *(Chm)*
Mark D. McClain *(Co-Founder & CEO)*
Christopher G. Schmitt *(Gen Counsel)*
Grady K. Summers *(Exec VP-Product)*
Darran Rolls *(CTO)*
Kevin Cunningham *(Co-Founder & Pres)*
Dave Hendrix *(Sr VP-Client Svcs)*
Dave Hildebrand *(Sr VP-Engrg)*
Michael Michael D'Eath *(VP-Corp Bus Dev)*
Troy Donley *(VP-North American Sls)*
Paul Trulove *(VP-Product Mgmt)*
Harry Gould *(VP-Worldwide Alliances & channels)*
Kevin Hansel *(CIO)*
Sarah Van Sicklen *(Mgr-Contracts)*

Subsidiary (Non-US):

Osirium Technologies PLC (2)
Theale Court 11-13 High Street, Theale, Reading, RG7 5AH, Berkshire, United Kingdom
Tel.: (44) 1183242444
Web Site: http://www.osirium.com
Rev.: $1,948,158
Assets: $7,858,667
Liabilities: $6,330,136
Net Worth: $1,528,531
Earnings: $(3,400,377)
Emp.: 46
Fiscal Year-end: 12/31/2020
Software Development Services
N.A.I.C.S.: 541511
David Guyatt *(Co-Founder & CEO)*
Kev Pearce *(Co-Founder & Dir-Tech Services)*
Simon Lee *(Chm)*
Rupert Hutton *(CFO)*
Andy Harris *(CTO)*

Subsidiary (Domestic):

Osirium Limited (3)
Theale Court 11-13 High St, Theale, Reading, RG7 5AH, Berkshire, United Kingdom
Tel.: (44) 1183242444
Software Development Services
N.A.I.C.S.: 541511
David Guyatt *(Co-Founder & CEO)*
Simon Lee *(Chm)*
Rupert Hutton *(CFO)*
Andy Harris *(CTO)*
Stuart McGregor *(Sls Dir)*

Segall Bryant & Hamill LLC (1)
10 S Wacker Dr Ste 3500, Chicago, IL 60606
Tel.: (312) 474-1222
Web Site: http://www.sbhic.com
Lessors of Residential Buildings & Dwellings
N.A.I.C.S.: 531110
Paul Alan Lythberg *(COO & Chief Compliance Officer)*

SolarWinds, Inc. (1)
7171 SW Pkwy Bldg 400, Austin, TX 78735
Tel.: (512) 682-9300
Web Site: http://www.solarwinds.com
Emp.: 2,500
Corporate IT & Network Infrastructure Services
N.A.I.C.S.: 541519
Douglas G. Hibberd *(Pres-Bus Ops & Exec VP)*
J. Barton Kalsu *(CFO & Exec VP)*
Jason W. Bliss *(Gen Counsel, Sec & Exec VP)*
Darren Beck *(CMO & Exec VP)*
Joe Kim *(CTO & Exec VP-Engrg)*
John Pagliuca *(Exec VP & Gen Mgr)*
David Gardiner *(Exec VP-Core IT)*
Rohini Kasturi *(Chief Product Officer & Exec VP)*
Tim Brown *(Chief Info Security Officer & VP-Security)*
Andrea Webb *(Chief Customer Officer & Sr VP)*

Subsidiary (Domestic):

Librato, Inc. (2)
535 Mission St Ste 2100, San Francisco, CA 94105
Web Site: http://www.librato.com
Software Development Services
N.A.I.C.S.: 513210
Michelle Urban *(Dir-Mktg)*
Dan Stondin *(Co-Founder & Dir-Design)*
Nik Wekwerth *(Dir-Customer Success)*
Joe Ruscio *(Co-Founder & CTO)*
Matt Sanders *(Dir-Engrg)*
Mike Heffner *(Co-Founder & Dir-Engrg)*

Loggly, Inc. (2)
535 Mission St 14th Fl, San Francisco, CA 94105
Tel.: (512) 498-6011
Web Site: http://www.loggly.com
Software Publisher
N.A.I.C.S.: 513210
Vinh Nguyen *(Principal Engr)*

Subsidiary (Non-US):

Pingdom AB (2)
Kopparbergsvagen 8 5th Floor, 722 13, Vasteras, Sweden
Tel.: (46) 20889858
Web Site: http://www.pingdom.com
Website Monitoring Software Publisher
N.A.I.C.S.: 513210

SolarWinds MSP UK Ltd. (2)
The Vision Building, 20 Green Market, Dundee, DD1 4QB, United Kingdom
Tel.: (44) 1382309040
Web Site: http://www.logicnow.com
Software Services
N.A.I.C.S.: 513210
John Pagliuca *(Pres)*
J. P. Jauvin *(Sr VP-Sls & Customer Ops)*
August Wehrmann *(VP-Engrg)*
Mike Cullen *(VP-Sls & Customer Retention)*
Frank Colletti *(VP-Worldwide Sls)*
Leo Sanchez *(VP-Worldwide Customer Support)*
Mike Adler *(Chief Tech & Product Officer)*

Subsidiary (Domestic):

SolarWinds Worldwide, LLC (2)
7171 SW Pkwy Bldg 400, Austin, TX 78735
Tel.: (512) 682-9300
Web Site: http://www.solarwinds.com
IT Management Software Services
N.A.I.C.S.: 423430

Stamps.com Inc. (1)
1990 E Grand Ave, El Segundo, CA 90245
Tel.: (310) 482-5800
Web Site: http://www.stamps.com
Rev.: $757,980,000
Assets: $1,297,299,000
Liabilities: $323,180,000
Net Worth: $974,119,000
Earnings: $178,665,000
Emp.: 1,482
Fiscal Year-end: 12/31/2020
Online Postage & Mailing Services
N.A.I.C.S.: 491110
J. R. Veingkeo *(Chief Acctg Officer)*
Nathan Jones *(CEO)*
Charles Goodman *(Chm)*

Subsidiary (Domestic):

Auctane LLC (2)
3800 N Lamar Blvd Ste 220, Austin, TX 78756
Tel.: (512) 485-4282
Web Site: http://www.shipstation.com
Software Development Services
N.A.I.C.S.: 541511
Albert Ko *(CEO)*
Gene Austin *(Chm)*

Interapptive, Inc. (2)
1 Memorial Dr 20th Fl, Saint Louis, MO 63102
Tel.: (417) 283-8548
Web Site: http://www.shipworks.com
Shipping Software Publisher
N.A.I.C.S.: 513210
Wes Clayton *(Founder)*

Subsidiary (Non-US):

MetaPack Ltd (2)
200 Grays Inn Road, London, WC1X 8XZ, United Kingdom
Tel.: (44) 207 843 6720
Web Site: http://www.metapack.com
Web-Based Delivery Management Services
N.A.I.C.S.: 513210
Patrick Wall *(Founder)*
Tom Forbes *(VP-Customer Delivery & Intl)*
John Clem *(Gen Mgr)*
Bruce Fair *(Chief Revenue Officer)*
Steve Homan *(CTO)*
Ton Ter Laak *(Gen Mgr-Europe)*
Marcin Wojcicki *(Co-Founder)*
Chris Mackie *(VP-Customer Success)*

Subsidiary (US):

Abol Software, Inc. (3)
413 Creekstone Rdg, Woodstock, GA 30188
Tel.: (678) 494-3172
Web Site: http://www.abolsoft.com
Emp.: 20
Computer & Computer Peripheral Equipment & Software Merchant Whslr
N.A.I.C.S.: 423430

THOMA BRAVO, L.P.

Thoma Bravo, L.P.—(Continued)
Maik Goettel *(Pres)*
Christina Wysocki *(Mgr-Implementation & Support)*

Subsidiary (Non-US):

MetaPack Far East Limited (3)
Room 1701 17th Floor China Merchant Building 303-307 Des Voeux Road, Central, China (Hong Kong)
Tel.: (852) 97297726
Software Development Services
N.A.I.C.S.: 541511

MetaPack Germany GmbH (3)
Bahnhofstrasse 37, 53359, Rheinbach, Germany
Tel.: (49) 2226 157 468 0
Software Development Services
N.A.I.C.S.: 541511

Subsidiary (US):

MetaPack Holdings USA, Inc. (3)
413 Creekstone Rdg, Woodstock, GA 30188
Software Development Services
N.A.I.C.S.: 541511

Subsidiary (Non-US):

MetaPack Poland Sp. z o.o. (3)
ul Kostrzynska 4, 65-127, Zielona Gora, Poland
Tel.: (48) 68 412 77 00
Web Site: http://www.metapack.com
Software Development Services
N.A.I.C.S.: 541511

MetaPack Software SAS (3)
7 rue Meyerbeer, 75009, Paris, France
Tel.: (33) 670238002
Software Development Services
N.A.I.C.S.: 541511

Metapack France Sas (3)
31 rue La Boetie, 75008, Paris, France
Tel.: (33) 1 45 22 75 13
Web Site: http://www.metapack.fr
Glass Accessory Mfr
N.A.I.C.S.: 327215

Subsidiary (Domestic):

PSI Systems, Inc. (2)
323 N Mathilda Ave, Sunnyvale, CA 94085-4207
Tel.: (650) 321-2640
Web Site: http://www.endicia.com
Postage Software Solutions
N.A.I.C.S.: 513210
Amine Khechfe *(Founder)*

ShipEngine Inc. (2)
4009 Marathon, Austin, TX 78756
Tel.: (512) 485-4282
Web Site: http://www.shipengine.com
Software Development Services
N.A.I.C.S.: 541511

Subsidiary (Non-US):

ShipStation Limited (2)
One Lyric Square, London, W6 0NB, United Kingdom
Tel.: (44) 2080685522
Software Development Services
N.A.I.C.S.: 541511

Talend Inc. (1)
5150 El Camino Real Ste C-31, Los Altos, CA 94022
Tel.: (650) 539-3200
Web Site: http://www.talend.com
Sales Range: $1-9.9 Million
Emp.: 95
Open Source Integration Software
N.A.I.C.S.: 513210
Ashley Stirrup *(CMO)*
Christal Bemont *(CEO)*
Krishna Tammana *(CTO)*
Bertrand Diard *(Founder)*
Francois Mero *(Sr VP-Sls-EMEA)*
Michael Pickett *(VP-Bus Dev & Partner Ecosys)*
Fergal McDonnell *(Reg VP-Emerging Markets)*
Barbara Cadigan *(Sr VP-People)*
Chris Taylor *(VP-Corp Comm)*
Adam Meister *(CFO)*

Helen Larcos *(Mgr-Channel & Alliances-Australia & New Zealand)*
Steve Singer *(Mgr-Australia & New Zealand)*
Stu Garrow *(Sr VP-Sls & Gen Mgr-Asia Pacific)*
Simon Burgoyne *(Acct Exec-Strategic-New Zealand)*
Jeff Lambert *(Chief Legal Officer)*

Subsidiary (Non-US):

Talend Beijing Technology Co., Ltd. (2)
Rm 1101-1107 T2 Sung Dong An Office Building No138 Wangfujing Street, Dongcheng District, Beijing, 100004, China
Tel.: (86) 10 6526 7475
Web Site: http://www.talend.com
Open Source Integration Software Development Services
N.A.I.C.S.: 513210
R. Nicolas *(Dir-Tech)*

Talend GmbH (2)
Baunscheidtstrasse 17, 53113, Bonn, Germany
Tel.: (49) 2287637760
Web Site: http://www.talend.com
Open Source Integration Software Services
N.A.I.C.S.: 513210

Talend GmbH (2)
Servatiusstrasse 53, 53175, Bonn, Germany
Tel.: (49) 228 76 37 76 0
Open Source Integration Software
N.A.I.C.S.: 513210

Talend GmbH (2)
Hohenlindner Strasse 11b, 85622, Feldkirchen, Germany
Tel.: (49) 89 944 0275 0
Web Site: http://www.talend.com
Open Source Integration Software
N.A.I.C.S.: 513210

Talend GmbH (2)
Jahnstrasse 3, 40215, Dusseldorf, Germany
Tel.: (49) 211 5426 8650
Open Source Integration Software
N.A.I.C.S.: 513210

Talend KK (2)
ARK Hills South Tower 3F 1-4-5 Roppongi, Minato-ku, Tokyo, 106-0032, Japan
Tel.: (81) 3 6427 6370
Web Site: http://www.talend.com
Open Source Integration Software
N.A.I.C.S.: 513210

Talend Ltd (2)
Berkshire House Queen Street, Maidenhead, SL6 1NF, Berkshire, United Kingdom
Tel.: (44) 1628 640160
Open Source Integration Software
N.A.I.C.S.: 513210

Talend SA (2)
5-7 rue Salomon de Rothschild, 92150, Suresnes, France
Tel.: (33) 189961460
Web Site: http://www.talend.com
Rev: $287,471,000
Assets: $419,730,000
Liabilities: $411,005,000
Net Worth: $8,725,000
Earnings: ($79,582,000)
Emp.: 1,397
Fiscal Year-end: 12/31/2020
Open Source Integration Software
N.A.I.C.S.: 513210

Trader Corporation (1)
405 The West Mall Suite 110, Etobicoke, M9C 5J1, ON, Canada
Tel.: (416) 784-5200
Web Site: http://www.go.trader.ca
Automotive, General Merchandise & Employment Publications & Website Publisher
N.A.I.C.S.: 513199
Sebastian Baldwin *(Pres & CEO)*
Gerry O'Reilly *(CFO)*
Steve Maidment *(Chief Digital Officer)*
Jody Gill *(Chief Sls Officer)*
Jill Hadfield *(Chief Product Officer)*
Ian MacDonald *(CMO)*

Subsidiary (Domestic):

LesPAC Network Inc. (2)

1721 rue Saint-Patrick Bureau 104, Montreal, H3K 3G9, QC, Canada
Tel.: (514) 282-8767
Web Site: http://www.lespac.com
Sales Range: $25-49.9 Million
Emp.: 10
Online Classified Advertising Services
N.A.I.C.S.: 541890
Claude Roy *(CEO)*
Paul Bourque *(VP)*

UserTesting, Inc. (1)
660 4th St Ste 246, San Francisco, CA 94107
Tel.: (650) 567-5616
Web Site: https://www.usertesting.com
Rev: $147,398,000
Assets: $283,128,000
Liabilities: $133,449,000
Net Worth: $149,679,000
Earnings: ($50,721,000)
Emp.: 783
Fiscal Year-end: 12/31/2021
Software Development Services
N.A.I.C.S.: 541511
Andy MacMillan *(Pres, CEO & Chm)*
Jon Pexton *(CFO)*
Kaj Van de Loo *(CTO)*
Michelle Huff *(CMO)*
Matt Zelen *(COO)*

Veracode, Inc. (1)
65 Network Dr, Burlington, MA 01803
Tel.: (339) 674-2500
Web Site: http://www.veracode.com
Internet Security Applications
N.A.I.C.S.: 513210
Christien Rioux *(Co-Founder)*
Chris Wysopal *(Co-Founder & CTO)*
Chris Eng *(VP-Security Res)*
Samskriti Y. King *(CEO)*
Ellen Nussbaum *(Sr VP-Svcs)*
Mike McGuinness *(Exec VP-Sls)*
Leslie Bois *(VP-Global Channel & Alliances)*
Elana Anderson *(Chief Mktg Officer)*

Subsidiary (Non-US):

Veracode Ltd (2)
36 Queen Street, London, EC4R 1BN, United Kingdom
Tel.: (44) 20 3761 5501
Web Site: http://www.veracode.com
Internet Security Applications
N.A.I.C.S.: 513210

THOMA INC.
520 Fellowship Rd Ste B-208, Mount Laurel, NJ 08054
Tel.: (856) 608-6887
Web Site: http://www.thomainc.com
Sales Range: $10-24.9 Million
Emp.: 15
Laboratory Equipment Distr
N.A.I.C.S.: 423490
Brian Thoma *(Pres)*
Jim Hickman *(Project Mgr)*
Dave Kimball *(Dir-Engrg)*

THOMAS & KING INC.
249 E Main St, Lexington, KY 40507-1330
Tel.: (859) 254-2180
Web Site: http://www.tandk.com
Year Founded: 1988
Sales Range: $200-249.9 Million
Emp.: 6,000
Restaurant
N.A.I.C.S.: 722511
Mike Scanlon *(Pres & CEO)*
Christy Metcalfe *(VP-Mktg)*
Bill Hilliard *(Gen Counsel, Sr Exec VP & Chief Dir-Dev)*

THOMAS & MARKER CONSTRUCTION COMPANY
2084 US Hwy 68 S, Bellefontaine, OH 43311
Tel.: (937) 599-2160
Web Site:
http://www.thomasmarker.com
Rev: $14,800,000
Emp.: 100
Industrial Buildings, New Construction

N.A.I.C.S.: 236210
Randall K. Marker *(Pres)*

THOMAS & SKINNER, INC.
1120 E 23rd St, Indianapolis, IN 46205-4508
Tel.: (317) 923-2501
Web Site: http://www.thomas-skinner.com
Year Founded: 1901
Sales Range: $10-24.9 Million
Emp.: 150
Mfr of Permanent Magnets & Permanent Magnet Assemblies; Silicon Iron Electric Laminations
N.A.I.C.S.: 332999
Vernon A. Detlef *(Pres)*
Neil Moehring *(Controller)*

Subsidiaries:

Ceramic Magnetics, Inc. (1)
16 Law Dr, Fairfield, NJ 07004
Tel.: (973) 227-4222
Web Site: http://www.cmi-ferrite.com
Sales Range: $10-24.9 Million
Emp.: 42
Provider of Magnetic Ferrites
N.A.I.C.S.: 327110
Tom Muench *(Mgr-Matls Production Processing)*
Amit Patel *(Mgr-Sls, Engrg & IT)*

THOMAS & SONS DISTRIBUTORS
840 S Front St, Coos Bay, OR 97420
Tel.: (541) 267-3483
Web Site:
http://www.thomasandsonsinc.net
Rev: $18,100,000
Emp.: 150
Freight Distribution
N.A.I.C.S.: 488510

Subsidiaries:

Arnold J Thomas & Son Inc (1)
840 S Frnt St, Coos Bay, OR 97420
Tel.: (541) 267-3483
Web Site:
http://www.thomasandsonsinc.com
Rev: $2,700,000
Emp.: 35
Trucking Except Local
N.A.I.C.S.: 484121
Aaron Thomas *(Owner)*

THOMAS BENNETT & HUNTER INC.
70 John St, Westminster, MD 21157
Tel.: (410) 848-9030
Web Site:
http://www.tbhconcrete.com
Sales Range: $10-24.9 Million
Emp.: 100
Ready Mixed Concrete
N.A.I.C.S.: 327320
Kevin W. Beaver *(Pres)*
Stanley W. Arnold *(Treas)*
John E. Alexander *(VP)*
L. Glenn Keith *(VP)*
Kevin Bowers *(Mgr-Production)*

THOMAS BROTHERS FOODS, LLC.
1852 Gold Hill Rd, Asheboro, NC 27203
Tel.: (336) 672-0337
Web Site:
http://www.thomasbrothersham.com
Year Founded: 1958
Sales Range: $10-24.9 Million
Emp.: 25
Meat & Meat Product Whslr
N.A.I.C.S.: 424470
Ricky Thomas *(Mgr)*
Deborah Kinney *(Mgr)*
H. Franklin Thomas Jr. *(Mgr)*

COMPANIES
THOMAS H. LEE PARTNERS, L.P.

THOMAS BROTHERS HAM CO. INC.
1852 Gold Hill Rd, Asheboro, NC 27203
Tel.: (336) 672-0337
Web Site:
http://www.thomasbrothersham.com
Sales Range: $10-24.9 Million
Emp.: 23
Meat Processing Services
N.A.I.C.S.: 424470
Frank Thomas *(Partner)*

THOMAS CONVEYOR COMPANY
555 N Burleson Blvd, Burleson, TX 76028-2907
Tel.: (817) 295-7151   TX
Web Site:
http://www.thomasconveyor.com
Year Founded: 1953
Rev.: $22,000,000
Emp.: 100
Bulk Material Conveyors, Screw Conveyors, Bucket Elevators & Drag Conveyors Mfr
N.A.I.C.S.: 333922
Buzz Grant *(Gen Mgr)*

THOMAS D. MANGELSEN, INC.
13303 F St, Omaha, NE 68137
Tel.: (402) 330-0132
Web Site: http://www.mangelsen.com
Sales Range: $75-99.9 Million
Emp.: 100
Photographic Services
N.A.I.C.S.: 541921
Thomas D. Mangelsen *(Owner)*
Mike Campisi *(Pres)*

THOMAS D. WOOD AND COMPANY
9100 S Dadeland Blvd Ste 700, Miami, FL 33156
Tel.: (305) 447-7823
Web Site: http://www.tdwood.com
Year Founded: 1987
Sales Range: $1-9.9 Million
Emp.: 30
Mortgage Banking
N.A.I.C.S.: 522310
Steven Hayes Wood *(COO)*
Marshall G. Smith *(Exec VP)*
Patrick Harrington *(Sr VP)*
Bradford Cox *(Sr VP-Sarasota)*
Jeff Schnupp *(VP-Orlando)*
Marcella Schmidt *(VP-Miami)*
Martha E. O'Grady *(Mgr-Investor Acctg-Miami)*
Martha B. Vega *(Coord-Loan Closing-Miami)*
Patrick Madore *(Sr VP-Boca Raton)*
Thomas D. Wood Sr. *(Chm)*
Thomas D. Wood Jr. *(Pres)*

Subsidiaries:

Thomas D. Wood and Company   (1)
9100 S Dadeland Blvd Ste 700, Miami, FL 33156
Tel.: (407) 937-0470
Web Site: http://www.tdwood.com
Mortgage Banking
N.A.I.C.S.: 522310
Jeff Schnupp *(VP)*

Thomas D. Wood and Company   (1)
1000 Corporate Dr Ste 100, Fort Lauderdale, FL 33334
Tel.: (954) 233-6024
Mortgage Banking
N.A.I.C.S.: 522310

Thomas D. Wood and Company - Sarasota   (1)
6751 Professional Pkwy West Ste 105, Sarasota, FL 34240
Tel.: (941) 552-9731

Web Site: http://www.tdwood.com
Commercial Mortgage Banking Firm
N.A.I.C.S.: 522310
Bradford A. Cox *(Sr VP)*

THOMAS E. STRAUSS INC.
2811 Lincoln Hwy E, Ronks, PA 17572
Tel.: (717) 687-6621   PA
Web Site:
http://www.millerssmorgasbord.com
Year Founded: 1929
Sales Range: $10-24.9 Million
Emp.: 300
Family Restaurants Owner & Operator
N.A.I.C.S.: 722511
Albert Duncan *(CEO)*
Donald Trout *(Pres)*
Randy Hessner *(Mgr-HR)*

THOMAS ELECTRONICS INC.
100 Riverview Dr, Wayne, NJ 07470
Tel.: (973) 696-5200
Web Site:
http://www.thomaselectronics.com
Rev.: $10,400,000
Emp.: 100
Cathode Ray Tubes, Including Rebuilt
N.A.I.C.S.: 334419

THOMAS ENGINEERING COMPANY
7024 Northland Dr N, Minneapolis, MN 55428
Tel.: (763) 533-1501
Web Site:
http://www.thomasengineering.com
Sales Range: $10-24.9 Million
Emp.: 50
Metal Stamping
N.A.I.C.S.: 332119
Sulien Thomas *(CEO)*

THOMAS ENGINEERING INC.
575 W Central Rd, Hoffman Estates, IL 60192-1937
Tel.: (847) 358-5800   IL
Web Site: http://www.thomaseng.com
Year Founded: 1959
Sales Range: $75-99.9 Million
Emp.: 100
Designer of Pharmaceutical Tablet Presses & Coater Packaging Machinery Punche & Die Mfr
N.A.I.C.S.: 333248
Chrysa Beck *(Supvr-Customer Svc)*
Joel Gray *(Pres)*
Nick Alfano *(Project Mgr)*

Subsidiaries:

Service Industries LLC   (1)
3885 Industrial Ave, Rolling Meadows, IL 60008
Tel.: (847) 392-1652
Web Site: http://www.serviceindustries.biz
Industrial Machinery Distr
N.A.I.C.S.: 423830

Triangle Metals Inc.   (1)
2500 Harrison Ave, Rockford, IL 61108
Tel.: (815) 398-0280
Web Site: http://www.trianglemetalsusa.com
Fabricated Structural Metal Mfr
N.A.I.C.S.: 332312
Jocelyn Painter *(Gen Mgr)*

THOMAS FORD SALES INC.
211 Rantoul St, Beverly, MA 01915
Tel.: (978) 922-0059
Web Site: http://www.thomasford.com
Year Founded: 1969
Sales Range: $10-24.9 Million
Emp.: 48
Car Whslr
N.A.I.C.S.: 441110
Jeffrey Klein *(Principal)*
Steven Leary *(Owner)*

THOMAS G. GALLAGHER, INC.
109 Smith Pl, Cambridge, MA 02138
Tel.: (617) 661-7000
Web Site: http://www.tggallagher.com
Year Founded: 1940
Sales Range: $50-74.9 Million
Emp.: 130
Plumbing, Heating & Air-Conditioning Contractors
N.A.I.C.S.: 238220
Kevin J. Potter *(VP)*
Brian T. Potter *(Pres & CEO)*
Gary Eason *(CFO)*
Shawn Guertin *(VP-Ops)*

THOMAS GLOVER ASSOCIATES, INC.
13891 Asheville Hwy, Inman, SC 29349
Tel.: (864) 473-1200   SC
Web Site:
http://www.tgasolutions.com
Year Founded: 1980
Sales Range: $1-9.9 Million
Emp.: 6
Fiscal Year-end: 12/31/15
Computer System Design Services
N.A.I.C.S.: 541512
Thomas E. Glover Jr. *(Owner)*

THOMAS H. BOYD MEMORIAL HOSPITAL
800 School St, Carrollton, IL 62016
Tel.: (217) 942-6946   IL
Web Site: http://www.boydhcs.org
Year Founded: 1940
Sales Range: $10-24.9 Million
Emp.: 173
Health Care Srvices
N.A.I.C.S.: 622110
Deborah Campbell *(CEO)*
Gwenda Berry *(Dir-Medical Records)*

THOMAS H. LEE PARTNERS, L.P.
100 Federal St, Boston, MA 02110
Tel.: (617) 227-1050   MA
Web Site: http://www.thl.com
Year Founded: 1974
Privater Equity Firm
N.A.I.C.S.: 523999
Scott M. Sperling *(Co-Pres & Co-CEO)*
James C. Carlisle *(Mng Dir)*
Jeff T. Swenson *(Mng Dir)*
Charles P. Holden *(Mng Dir)*
Soren L. Oberg *(Mng Dir)*
Gregory A. White *(Mng Dir)*
Shari H. Wolkon *(Mng Dir)*
Joshua M. Nelson *(Mng Dir & Head-Healthcare Vertical)*
Todd M. Abbrecht *(Executives)*
Megan M. Preiner *(Dir)*
Jay H. Bhatt *(Mng Dir)*
Gregory Maxon *(Mng Dir)*
Mark Bean *(Principal)*
Mark L. Benaquista *(Mng Dir)*
Mark A. Garcia *(VP)*
Laura A. Grattan *(Mng Dir)*
Tyler D. Griffith *(Dir)*
Matthew L. Hooks *(VP)*
Michael Kaczmarek *(Dir)*
Cliff Longley *(Principal)*
Michael McDonnell *(VP)*
Vicente Piedrahita *(Dir)*
Salvador Quinonez *(VP)*
Gazal Sikand *(Principal)*
Robert W. Spies *(Principal)*
Douglas A. Haber *(Mng Dir)*
Jagjit P. Singh *(Dir)*
Shahab Vagefi *(Mng Dir-Healthcare Vertical)*
Michael A. Bell *(Mng Dir)*

Joshua M. Nelson *(Mng Dir & Head-Healthcare)*
Megan M. Preiner *(Mng Dir)*
Ganesh B. Rao *(Mng Dir)*
Thomas Martin Hagerty *(Mng Dir)*
Anthony J. DiNovi *(Co-Pres)*

Subsidiaries:

Abacus Data Systems, Inc.   (1)
4850 Eastgate Mall, San Diego, CA 92121-1977
Tel.: (858) 452-4280
Web Site: http://www.abacusnext.com
Management Software & Data Hosting
N.A.I.C.S.: 541511
Mike Skelly *(CFO)*
Chris Cardinal *(Exec VP-Software Engrg)*
Thomas Schoessow *(VP-Tech Infrastructure)*
Eric Hart *(Gen Counsel)*
Scott Johnson *(CEO)*

Subsidiary (Domestic):

Results Software LLC   (2)
620 Herndon Pkwy Ste 350, Herndon, VA 20170
Tel.: (703) 713-9100
Web Site: http://www.results-software.com
Software Publisher
N.A.I.C.S.: 513210
Sam Saab *(Founder & Exec VP-Product)*

AgencyPort Insurance Services, Inc.   (1)
51 Sleeper St Fl 8, Boston, MA 02210-1284
Web Site: http://www.agencyport.com
Sales Range: $25-49.9 Million
Specialty Software & Web-based Solutions for Property & Casualty Insurers
N.A.I.C.S.: 541511
Curt Stevenson *(CEO)*
Jeanette Tweed *(CFO)*
Norm Baker *(CTO)*
Dave Fielding *(Sr VP-Pro Svcs)*
Fil Firmani *(Sr VP-Product & Strategy)*
Julie Howe *(Sr VP-Mktg & Comm)*
Chris Stone *(Gen Counsel & Sr VP)*
Drew Tripp *(Sr VP-Sls)*
Allan L. Egbert Jr. *(CTO)*

Agiliti, Inc.   (1)
11095 Viking Dr, Eden Prairie, MN 55344   (100%)
Tel.: (952) 893-3200
Web Site: https://www.agilitihealth.com
Rev.: $1,121,292,000
Assets: $2,444,107,000
Liabilities: $1,497,782,000
Net Worth: $946,325,000
Earnings: $30,212,000
Emp.: 5,500
Fiscal Year-end: 12/31/2022
Holding Company
N.A.I.C.S.: 551112
Thomas Leonard *(CEO)*
Bettyann Bird *(Chief Strategy Officer & Exec VP)*
Robert L. Creviston *(Sr VP-HR)*
Scott A. Christensen *(Chief Acctg Officer, Sr VP, VP & Controller)*
Lee M. Neumann *(Gen Counsel, Exec VP & Sr VP)*
Matthew E. McCabe *(Treas, Sr VP & VP-Fin)*
Derrick Johnson *(COO & Sr VP)*
Kate Kaiser *(Sr VP & --Corporate Communications & Investor Relations)*
Matt Neale *(CIO & Sr VP-Information Technology)*
Heidi Drafall *(Sr VP-Quality)*

Subsidiary (Domestic):

Agiliti Health, Inc.   (2)
2020 E 28th St, Minneapolis, MN 55407
Tel.: (952) 893-3200
Web Site: https://www.agilitihealth.com
Rev.: $565,246,000
Assets: $744,958,000
Liabilities: $812,617,000
Net Worth: ($67,659,000)
Earnings: ($31,552,000)
Emp.: 2,662
Fiscal Year-end: 12/31/2018
Medical Equipment Leasing
N.A.I.C.S.: 532283

THOMAS H. LEE PARTNERS, L.P.

Thomas H. Lee Partners, L.P.—(Continued)
Robert L. Creviston *(Chief HR Officer)*
Thomas J. Leonard *(CEO)*

Federal Street Acquisition Corp. (2)
100 Federal St 35th Fl, Boston, MA 02110
Tel.: (617) 227-1050
Sales Range: $1-9.9 Million
Emp.: 6
Investment Services
N.A.I.C.S.: 523999
Tom Leonard *(CEO)*
Jim Pekarek *(CFO)*
Lee Neumann *(Gen Counsel & Sr VP)*

Mobile Instrument Service & Repair, Inc. (2)
333 Water Ave, Bellefontaine, OH 43311
Tel.: (937) 592-5025
Web Site: http://www.mobileinstrument.com
Repair Services
N.A.I.C.S.: 811210
Jeff Duffy *(Mgr-Repair Center)*
Kim Hassel *(Supvr-Customer Svc)*

SizeWise Rentals, L.L.C. (2)
8601 Monrovia St, Lenexa, KS 66215
Tel.: (800) 814-9389
Web Site: http://www.sizewise.com
Medical, Dental & Hospital Equipment & Supplies Merchant Whslr
N.A.I.C.S.: 423450
Trever Frickey *(Principal)*
Andrew Baron *(Reg VP)*
Mary Nell Westbrook *(CMO & Exec VP)*
Craig Ruster *(Reg VP)*
Brian Frickey *(CEO)*

AmeriLife Group, LLC (1)
2650 McCormick Dr, Clearwater, FL 33759
Tel.: (727) 726-0726
Web Site: http://www.amerilife.com
Life & Health Insurance Services
N.A.I.C.S.: 524210
Scott Perry *(Chm & CEO)*
Mike Vietri *(Chief Distr Officer)*
Nathan Hightower *(Chief Legal Officer & Chief Admin Officer)*
Jim Quinn *(CFO)*
Nick Hildenbrand *(Principal-Mktg Grp)*
Doug Stovall *(Vice Principal-Mktg Grp)*
Kiersten Burstiner *(Chief HR Officer)*
Tim Calvert *(COO)*
Galya Appell *(Sr VP-Strategy & Innovation)*
David Paul *(Sls Dir-Natl-Simplified Issue Life)*
Ovi Vitas *(CMO)*
Kelly Atkinson *(Sr VP-Brand Mgmt & Creative Svcs)*
Rhonda Fenner *(Sr VP-Ops Transformation)*
Bob Yates *(VP-Distr, Analytics & Data)*
Brad Shelton *(Sr VP-Product Innovation)*
Patrick Fleming *(Exec VP-Product Innovation & Corp Actuary)*
Greg Etchison *(VP-Medicare Supplement & Specialty Health)*
Scotty Elliott *(Pres-Life & Health Brokerage Distr)*
Ford Stokes *(Sr VP-Annuity Mktg)*

Subsidiary (Domestic):

Dallas Financial Wholesalers (2)
7512 San Jacinto Pl Ste 100, Plano, TX 75024
Tel.: (972) 788-1128
Web Site: http://www.ronrawlings.com
Insurance Agencies & Brokerages
N.A.I.C.S.: 524210
Ron W. Rawlings *(Owner)*

Ceridian Corporation (1)
3311 E Old Shakopee Rd, Minneapolis, MN 55425-1640 (68%)
Tel.: (952) 853-8100
Web Site: https://www.ceridian.com
Sales Range: $1-4.9 Billion
Emp.: 100,000
Payroll Processing & Human Resource Services
N.A.I.C.S.: 541214
Lisa Sterling *(Chief People & Culture Officer)*
Eric Glass *(Exec VP)*
Noemie Heuland *(Exec VP)*
Steve Holdridge *(Pres)*
Joe Korngiebel *(Exec VP)*
Bill McDonald *(Exec VP)*
Stephen Moore *(Mng Dir)*
Wendy Muirhead *(Mng Dir)*
Carrie Rasmussen *(CIO)*
Susan Tohyama *(Exec VP)*
Erik Zimmer *(Exec VP)*
David Ossip *(CEO)*

Unit (Domestic):

Ceridian Benefits Services (2)
3201 34th St S, Saint Petersburg, FL 33711
Tel.: (952) 853-8100
Web Site: http://www.ceridian.com
Sales Range: $200-249.9 Million
Benefits Services
N.A.I.C.S.: 541214

Fogo de Chao (Holdings) Inc. (1)
14881 Quorum Dr Ste 750, Dallas, TX 75254
Tel.: (972) 960-9533
Web Site: http://www.fogodechao.com
Restaurant Operators
N.A.I.C.S.: 722511
Larry Johnson *(Chm)*
Kristen Knauer *(Mgr-Sls)*
Barry McGowan *(CEO)*

Hawkeye Energy Holdings LLC (1)
224 S Bell Ave, Ames, IA 50010-2523 (80%)
Tel.: (515) 233-5577
Sales Range: $75-99.9 Million
Methanol Mfr
N.A.I.C.S.: 551112

Intelligent Medical Objects, Inc. (1)
9600 W Bryn Mawr Ave. Ste 100, Rosemont, IL 60018
Tel.: (847) 272-1242
Web Site: https://www.imohealth.com
Computer Related Services
N.A.I.C.S.: 541519
Ann Barnes *(CEO)*

Material Handling Systems, Inc. (1)
131 Griffin Wy, Washington, KY 40047
Tel.: (502) 636-0690
Web Site: http://www.mhsglobal.com
Industrial Material Handling Systems Designer, Mfr, Whslr & Installation Services
N.A.I.C.S.: 333922
Scott McReynolds *(CEO)*

Subsidiary (Domestic):

MHS Distribution & Fulfillment, LLC (2)
4260 Trotters Way, Alpharetta, GA 30004
Tel.: (678) 226-1120
Web Site: http://www.mhsglobal.com
Material Handling & Sortation Services
N.A.I.C.S.: 541614
Bob Cobak *(Pres)*
Kyle Hester *(VP-Ops)*
Brian Ulanch *(VP-Sls)*

Party City Holdco, Inc. (1)
80 Grasslands Rd, Elmsford, NY 10523 (54.51%)
Tel.: (914) 345-2020
Web Site: http://www.partycity.com
Rev.: $2,171,060,000
Assets: $2,711,900,000
Liabilities: $2,629,186,000
Net Worth: $82,714,000
Earnings: ($6,528,000)
Emp.: 6,400
Fiscal Year-end: 12/31/2021
Holding Company; Party Supplies Retailer
N.A.I.C.S.: 551112

Subsidiary (Domestic):

Party City Holdings, Inc. (2)
80 Grasslands Rd, Elmsford, NY 10523
Tel.: (914) 345-2020
Rev.: $2,271,257,000
Assets: $3,374,393,000
Liabilities: $2,557,770,000
Net Worth: $816,623,000
Earnings: $70,766,000
Emp.: 7,313
Fiscal Year-end: 12/31/2014
Holding Company; Party Supplies Mfr, Distr & Retailer
N.A.I.C.S.: 551112
James M. Harrison *(CEO)*
Gregg A. Melnick *(Pres)*
Michael A. Correale *(CFO)*

Subsidiary (Domestic):

Amscan Inc. (3)
80 Grasslands Rd Ste 4, Elmsford, NY 10523
Tel.: (914) 345-2020
Web Site: http://www.amscan.com
Sales Range: $25-49.9 Million
Cups & Paper Mfr
N.A.I.C.S.: 322219
James M. Harrison *(Pres)*
Anthony Pepe *(Mgr-Facilities)*

Subsidiary (Domestic):

Anagram International, Inc. (4)
7700 Anagram Dr, Eden Prairie, MN 55344-7305
Tel.: (952) 949-5600
Web Site: http://www.anagramballoons.com
Sales Range: $50-74.9 Million
Emp.: 380
Foil Balloons Mfr
N.A.I.C.S.: 326299
James Plutt *(Pres)*

Factory Card & Party Outlet Corp. (4)
2727 W Diehl Rd, Naperville, IL 60563-8720
Tel.: (630) 579-2000
Web Site: http://www.factorycard.com
Sales Range: $200-249.9 Million
Party Supplies, Greeting Cards, Gift Wrap, Balloons & Other Special Occasion Merchandise Mfr & Retailer
N.A.I.C.S.: 459420

Subsidiary (Domestic):

Factory Card Outlet of America Ltd. (5)
2727 Diehl Rd, Naperville, IL 60563
Tel.: (630) 579-2000
Sales Range: $75-99.9 Million
Sales of Greeting Cards & Party Supplies
N.A.I.C.S.: 459420

Subsidiary (Domestic):

Gags & Games Inc. (4)
35901 Veronica St, Livonia, MI 48150
Tel.: (734) 591-1717
Novelty Store Retailer
N.A.I.C.S.: 459420

Party City Corporation (4)
25 Green Pond Rd Ste 1, Rockaway, NJ 07866
Tel.: (973) 983-0888
Web Site: http://www.partycity.com
Sales Range: $125-149.9 Million
Retailer of Party Supplies
N.A.I.C.S.: 459420
Gregg A. Melnick *(Pres-Party City Retail Grp)*
Jim Fogler *(VP-Bus Dev-South Burlington)*

Print Appeal, Inc. (4)
11220 Pagemill Rd, Dallas, TX 75243 (60%)
Tel.: (972) 699-0100
Web Site: http://www.printappeal.com
Commercial Printing Mfr & Whlsr
N.A.I.C.S.: 323111
Jon Hendricks *(Pres)*

Ya Otta Pinata (4)
PO Box 18387, Anaheim, CA 92817
Tel.: (714) 972-2626
Web Site: http://www.pinatapeople.com
Pinata Mfr
N.A.I.C.S.: 339910

Sam Levin Inc. (1)
301 Fitzhenry Rd, Smithton, PA 15479-8715
Tel.: (724) 872-2050
Web Site: http://www.levinfurniture.com
Furniture Store Operator
N.A.I.C.S.: 449110
Chris Pelcher *(Chief Merchandising Officer & Exec VP)*

World of Floors, Inc. (1)
43665 Utica Rd, Sterling Heights, MI 48314
Tel.: (586) 353-1790
Web Site: http://www.worldoffloors.com
Sales Range: $1-9.9 Million
Emp.: 10
Floor Covering Store Distr

N.A.I.C.S.: 449121

THOMAS INTERIOR SYSTEMS INC.
476 Brighton Dr, Bloomingdale, IL 60108
Tel.: (630) 980-4200
Web Site: http://www.thomasinterior.com
Year Founded: 1977
Sales Range: $25-49.9 Million
Emp.: 50
Office Furniture
N.A.I.C.S.: 423210
Thomas S. Klobucher *(Owner & CEO)*
Paul Klobucher *(Pres)*

THOMAS INVESTMENTS INC.
936 Grand Ave, Beattyville, KY 41311
Tel.: (606) 464-3651   KY
Rev.: $48,000,000
Emp.: 10
Holding Company; Property Investments
N.A.I.C.S.: 551112
Barbara Thomas *(Treas & Sec)*
Michael Thomas *(Pres)*

THOMAS J. FINNEGAN COMPANY
27 S Perry St, Vandalia, OH 45377
Tel.: (937) 890-5215   OH
Web Site:
http://www.thomasfinnegan.com
Year Founded: 1974
Sales Range: $10-24.9 Million
Heating, Air Conditioning & Ventilation Equipment & Supplies Whslr
N.A.I.C.S.: 423730
Thomas J. Finnegan *(Pres)*

THOMAS J. O'BEIRNE & CO. INC.
37 Woodland Rd, Roseland, NJ 07068
Tel.: (973) 364-1600
Web Site: http://www.tjobeirne.com
Rev.: $10,276,388
Emp.: 21
Nonresidential Construction
N.A.I.C.S.: 236220
Thomas J. O'Beirne *(Pres)*
Mary Dino *(Office Mgr)*

THOMAS J. PAYNE MARKET DEVELOPMENT
865 Woodside, San Mateo, CA 94401-1611
Tel.: (650) 340-8311
Web Site: http://www.tjpmd.com
Year Founded: 1986
Sales Range: $1-9.9 Million
Emp.: 2
Public Relations Agencies
N.A.I.C.S.: 541820
Thomas J. Payne *(Pres)*

Subsidiaries:

Thomas J. Payne Market Development (1)
4508 Oak Valley Rd, Cross Plains, WI 53528
Tel.: (608) 236-2909
Web Site: http://www.tjpmd.com
Emp.: 1
Marketing & Public Relations
N.A.I.C.S.: 541820

THOMAS JAMES HOMES, INC.
26880 Aliso Viejo Pkwy Ste 100, Aliso Viejo, CA 92656
Tel.: (949) 481-7026   DE
Year Founded: 2021
Emp.: 251

COMPANIES

Holding Company
N.A.I.C.S.: 551112
Thomas Beadel *(Founder & Chm)*
James Mead *(CEO)*
James Simpson *(CTO)*
Anne Lee Benedict *(Chief Legal Officer & Sec)*
Steve Kalmbach *(Pres & COO)*
Bill Welsh *(CFO)*

THOMAS JEFFERSON FOUNDATION INC.
PO Box 316, Charlottesville, VA 22902
Tel.: (434) 984-9806 VA
Year Founded: 1923
Sales Range: $25-49.9 Million
Emp.: 452
Historical Site Preservation Services
N.A.I.C.S.: 712120
Leslie G. Bowman *(Pres)*
Joshua J. Scott *(Dir-Dev)*
Kenneth I. Mitchell *(Asst VP)*
Gary L. Sandling *(VP-Visitor Svcs & Programs)*
Susan R. Stein *(VP)*

THOMAS L. CARDELLA & ASSOCIATES INC
4515 20th Ave SW, Cedar Rapids, IA 52404
Tel.: (319) 730-4000
Web Site:
  http://www.tlcassociates.com
Year Founded: 2007
Sales Range: $10-24.9 Million
Emp.: 880
Telemarketing Services
N.A.I.C.S.: 561422
Thomas L. Cardella *(Pres & CEO)*
Gary Kaufman *(Sr VP-Fin)*

THOMAS MEDIA GROUP, LLC
13900 Conlan Cir Ste 240, Charlotte, NC 28277
Tel.: (704) 752-9800
Sales Range: $10-24.9 Million
Emp.: 3
N.A.I.C.S.: 541810
Thomas Hager *(CEO)*
Charlene Sloan *(Controller)*
Beverly Brown *(Office Mgr)*

THOMAS P. CARNEY INC.
2490 Village Rd, Langhorne, PA 19047
Tel.: (215) 757-3308
Web Site:
  http://www.thomaspcarneyinc.com
Sales Range: $10-24.9 Million
Emp.: 12
Commercial & Office Building, New Construction
N.A.I.C.S.: 236220
Robert V. Carney *(Pres)*
John Czuba *(Controller)*
Daniel Driscoll *(Project Mgr)*

THOMAS PETROLEUM, INC.
3053 Hwy 49, West Helena, AR 72390
Tel.: (870) 572-7353 AR
Year Founded: 1976
Sales Range: $10-24.9 Million
Emp.: 130
Petroleum Products Whslr; Owner & Operator of Convenience Stores
N.A.I.C.S.: 424720

THOMAS PUBLISHING COMPANY LLC
5 Penn Plz, New York, NY 10001-1810
Tel.: (212) 695-0500 DE
Web Site:
  http://www.thomaspublishing.com
Year Founded: 1898
Sales Range: $100-124.9 Million
Emp.: 300
Trade Reference Publisher
N.A.I.C.S.: 513140
Jose E. Andrade *(Co-Chm)*
Carl T. Holst-Knudsen *(Co-Chm)*
Ivy J. Molofksy *(VP-HR)*
Tony Uphoff *(Pres & CEO)*
Amy Kim *(Chief Revenue Officer)*
Hans Wald *(CTO)*
Mark Holst-Knudsen *(Pres-Enterprise Solutions)*
Travis J. Sherbine *(Exec VP-Product)*

Subsidiaries:

INCOM Co., Ltd. (1)
Plaza Edogawabashi 1-23-6 Sekiguchi
Bunkyo-ku, Tokyo, 112-8712, Japan
Tel.: (81) 332607871
Sales Range: $25-49.9 Million
Emp.: 20
Trade Reference Sources
N.A.I.C.S.: 513140
Ichiro Suzuki *(Pres)*

Managing Automation (1)
5 Penn Plz 9th Fl, New York, NY 10001
Tel.: (212) 695-0500
Web Site:
  http://www.managingautomation.com
Sales Range: $50-74.9 Million
Online & Print Publisher
N.A.I.C.S.: 513199
Jose Andrade *(Pres)*

Thomas Endustriyel Medya Yayincilik ve Paz. Ltd. (1)
Sadikoglu Plaza 5 No 65, 34722, Istanbul, Turkiye
Tel.: (90) 216 550 86 80
Industrial Book Publisher
N.A.I.C.S.: 513130

Thomas Industrial Media GmbH (1)
Friedrich Strasse 5, 45525, Hattingen, Germany (100%)
Tel.: (49) 2324919504
Web Site: http://www.tr-online.de
Sales Range: $10-24.9 Million
Emp.: 3
Publisher of Product Information Journals
N.A.I.C.S.: 513120

Thomas Industrial Media SARL (1)
120 Rue Jean Jaures, Levallois-Perret, 92300, Paris, France
Tel.: (33) 1 47 56 20 18
Sales Range: $10-24.9 Million
Emp.: 4
Book Publishers
N.A.I.C.S.: 513130
Orhan Erenberk *(Mng Dir)*

Thomas Industrial Media srl (1)
Centro Commerciale Milano San Felice 44, 20090, Segrate, Milan, Italy
Tel.: (39) 02 7030 631
Web Site: http://www.tim-europe.com
Sales Range: $10-24.9 Million
Emp.: 10
Book Publishers
N.A.I.C.S.: 513130
Christian Pons *(Gen Mgr)*

Thomas Industrial Network Advertising (1)
5 Penn Plz, New York, NY 10001
Tel.: (212) 629-2100
Web Site: http://www.thomaspublishing.com
Business Publications, Direct Marketing, Exhibit/Trade Shows, Graphic Design, Industrial, Internet/Web Design, Logo & Package Design, Print, Publicity/Promotions
N.A.I.C.S.: 513140
Mark Holst-Knudsen *(Pres)*

Thomas International Advertising Co. (Beijing), Ltd. (1)
Room 708 Coal Tower, 35 Heping Street, Beijing, 100013, China
Tel.: (86) 1084261278
Trade Reference Sources
N.A.I.C.S.: 513140

Thomas International Publishing Co. India Private Limited (1)
1-G Bharat Nagar Estate, New Friends Colony, New Delhi, 110025, India
Tel.: (91) 11 4004 1100
Web Site: http://www.thomex.com
Trade Reference Sources Publisher
N.A.I.C.S.: 513140

Thomas International Publishing Company, Inc. (1)
5 Penn Plz, New York, NY 10001
Tel.: (212) 613-3441
Web Site: http://www.tipco.com
Industrial Book Publisher
N.A.I.C.S.: 513130

Thomas Publishing Company LLC - MADE2SPEC (1)
5 Penn Plz, New York, NY 10001
Tel.: (212) 695-0500
Web Site: http://www.made2spec.com
Sales Range: $25-49.9 Million
Emp.: 150
Online Information Services
N.A.I.C.S.: 519290
Walter Koopalethes *(Gen Mgr)*

Thomas Register of American Manufacturers (1)
5 Penn Plz, New York, NY 10001-1810
Tel.: (212) 695-0500
Web Site: http://www.thomasnet.com
Sales Range: $50-74.9 Million
Thomas Register Publishing
N.A.I.C.S.: 541910
Jose E. Andrade *(Chm)*
Carl T. Holst-Knudsen *(Pres)*
Rita Lieberman *(Dir-Mktg Comm)*
Ivy Molofsky *(VP-HR)*

Thomas Technology Solutions Inc. (1)
1 Progress Dr, Horsham, PA 19044-3502 (100%)
Tel.: (215) 682-5000
Web Site:
  http://www.thomastechsolutions.com
Online Database Services
N.A.I.C.S.: 323120

Division (Non-US):

Thomas Technology Solutions (UK) Ltd. (2)
1st Fl Lee House 109 Hammersmith Rd, London, W14 0QH, United Kingdom
Tel.: (44) 2070707550
Web Site:
  http://www.thomastechsolutions.com
Sales Range: $25-49.9 Million
Emp.: 4
Provider of Information Management; Online Database Services & CD-ROM Information Retrieval Development
N.A.I.C.S.: 517810

Thomas/Lund Publicacoes Industriais Ltda. (1)
Rua Brigaderio Tobias 356, 6 Andar, Sao Paulo, 01032-901, Brazil
Tel.: (55) 11 3327 4404
Trade Reference Sources
N.A.I.C.S.: 513140

THOMAS RAWLINGS GROUP INC.
5050 Forbes Blvd, Lanham, MD 20706
Tel.: (240) 260-0460
Sales Range: $10-24.9 Million
Emp.: 75
Insulation Services
N.A.I.C.S.: 238310
Steve Shegogue *(Pres)*

Subsidiaries:

TBN Associates Inc. (1)
5050 Forbes Blvd, Lanham, MD 20706-4404
Tel.: (301) 937-5544
Rev.: $11,327,042
Emp.: 70
Asbestos Removal & Encapsulation
N.A.I.C.S.: 562910

Thomas Rawlings Associates (1)
11262 Old Baltimore Pike, Beltsville, MD 20705
Tel.: (301) 937-5544
Sales Range: $1-9.9 Million
Insulation, Buildings
N.A.I.C.S.: 238310

THOMAS REPROGRAPHICS, INC.
600 N Central Expy, Richardson, TX 75080-5316
Tel.: (972) 231-7161 TX
Web Site:
  http://www.thomasprintworks.com
Year Founded: 1956
Emp.: 563
Printing Services
N.A.I.C.S.: 323111
Bryan C. Thomas *(Pres & CEO)*
Terry Witt *(Dir-Mgmt Info Sys)*
Jack Haynes *(Asst Controller)*
Nancy Riddell *(Mgr-Store)*
Todd Rohani *(Mgr-Store)*
Brianna Long *(Mktg Dir)*
Metz Curtis *(Mgr-Tech & Product Analysis)*
Linda Carter *(District Mgr)*
Thomas Lechner *(Mgr-Large Color Format)*
LT Temple *(Mgr-Store)*

Subsidiaries:

Dynamic Reprographics, Inc. (1)
304 E 3rd St, Austin, TX 78701
Tel.: (512) 474-8842
Web Site:
  http://www.dynamicreprographics.com
Rev.: $2,333,333
Emp.: 20
Commercial Lithographic Printing Services
N.A.I.C.S.: 323111
Cora Brown *(Mgr-Ops)*

THOMAS SCIENTIFIC, LLC
1654 High Hill Rd At 295, Swedesboro, NJ 08085
Tel.: (856) 467-2000
Web Site: http://www.thomassci.com
Year Founded: 1900
Rev.: $50,000,000
Emp.: 150
Scientific & Engineering Equipment & Supplies
N.A.I.C.S.: 611810
Ricardo Martofel *(VP-Sls-Intl)*
Noelle Trader *(Acct Mgr)*
Nick Kennish *(Acct Mgr-Reseller)*
Stan Haas *(Pres & CEO)*
Lynn Calpeter *(Chm)*

Subsidiaries:

Day Associates, Inc. (1)
1968 Lakeview Ave, Dracut, MA 01826
Tel.: (978) 957-4519
Web Site: http://www.daysupply.com
Rev.: $2,280,000
Emp.: 11
Safety & Industrial Products Distr
N.A.I.C.S.: 423840
Michelle Desmarais *(Treas)*
William A. Day *(Pres)*

North Central Instruments, Inc. (1)
7125 Northland Ter N Ste 100, Brooklyn Park, MN 55428
Tel.: (763) 559-3008
Web Site: http://www.ncimicro.com
Sales Range: $10-24.9 Million
Emp.: 24
Office Supplies & Stationery Stores
N.A.I.C.S.: 459410
Brad Johnson *(Pres)*

Quintana Associates, Inc. (1)
177 Ferry Rd, Haverhill, MA 01835
Tel.: (800) 499-1000
Web Site: https://www.quintanasupply.com
Rev.: $4,854,900
Emp.: 20
Business to Business Electronic Markets
N.A.I.C.S.: 425120
Michael A. Quintana *(Pres)*

THOMAS SIGN & AWNING CO., INC.

Thomas Sign & Awning Co., Inc.—(Continued)

THOMAS SIGN & AWNING CO., INC.
4590 118th Ave N, Clearwater, FL 33762
Tel.: (727) 573-7757
Web Site:
    http://www.thomassign.com
Year Founded: 1969
Sales Range: $10-24.9 Million
Emp.: 200
Signs & Awnings Mfr
N.A.I.C.S.: 339950
Priscilla G. Thomas (Pres)

THOMAS SOMERVILLE CO. INC.
16155 Trade Zone Ave, Upper Marlboro, MD 20774-8733
Tel.: (301) 390-9575
Web Site: http://www.tsomerville.com
Year Founded: 1860
Sales Range: $125-149.9 Million
Emp.: 480
Plumbing Fixtures, Equipment & Supplies
N.A.I.C.S.: 423720
Pat McGowan (Pres)
Scott Weir (VP-Pur)

THOMAS SUPPLY COMPANY INC.
721 Liberty St, Marion, SC 29571
Tel.: (843) 423-1781
Web Site:
    http://www.thomassupply.com
Sales Range: $10-24.9 Million
Emp.: 38
Electrical Apparatus & Equipment
N.A.I.C.S.: 423610
Richard Skipper (Pres)

THOMAS WEST INC.
470 Mercury Dr, Sunnyvale, CA 94085
Tel.: (408) 481-9200
Web Site:
    http://www.thomaswest.com
Sales Range: $10-24.9 Million
Emp.: 40
Towels, Dishcloths & Dust Cloths
N.A.I.C.S.: 314120
Ken Ponder (VP-Sls & Mktg)

THOMAS WOOD PRESERVING INC.
1964 Murff Dr, Elliott, MS 38926
Tel.: (662) 226-2350
Sales Range: $10-24.9 Million
Emp.: 50
Wood Preserving
N.A.I.C.S.: 321114
Brent Thomas (Pres)

THOMAS, MCNERNEY & PARTNERS II, LLC
12527 Central Ave NE Ste 297, Minneapolis, MN 55434
Tel.: (612) 465-8679   DE
Web Site: http://www.tm-partners.com
Year Founded: 2004
Sales Range: $25-49.9 Million
Emp.: 11
Health Care Venture Capital Firm
N.A.I.C.S.: 523999
Kathleen A. Tune (Partner)
Susan J. Haedt (CFO)
Jason M. Brown (Partner)
Robert C. Perry (Dir-IR)
Eric Aguiar (Partner)
James E. Thomas (Partner)
Eric Aguiar (Partner)

THOMASSEN AMCOT INTERNATIONAL, LLC.
6628 Bryant Irvin Rd, Fort Worth, TX 76132-4216
Tel.: (817) 263-3270
Web Site:
    http://www.thomassenamcot.com
Year Founded: 1992
Sales Range: $10-24.9 Million
Emp.: 2
Electric Power Generation Services
N.A.I.C.S.: 221118
Rick Williamson (Sr Mng Partner)
Bart Zaino (Partner & Dir-Global Sls)

THOMASSON COMPANY
1007 Saint Francis Dr, Philadelphia, MS 39350
Tel.: (601) 656-5555   MS
Web Site:
    http://www.thomassoncompany.com
Year Founded: 1972
Utility Poles Mfr
N.A.I.C.S.: 321999
Patricia T. Thomasson (CEO)
Randy Deweese (VP-Ops)
Jane Thomas (Sec & Treas)
Brent Gray (Pres)
Helen Thomasson (Treas)

THOMASTECH, LLC
620 E Smith Rd Enterprise Ctr Ste D, Medina, OH 44256
Tel.: (330) 225-3117
Web Site:
    http://www.thomastechllc.com
Year Founded: 2007
Sales Range: $1-9.9 Million
Emp.: 21
Hardware Providing Services
N.A.I.C.S.: 513210
Trent Thomas (Founder)

THOMASTON SAVINGS BANK
203 Main St, Thomaston, CT 06787
Tel.: (860) 283-4373
Web Site: http://www.tsbdan.com
Sales Range: $10-24.9 Million
Emp.: 100
Federal Savings Bank
N.A.I.C.S.: 522180
Mark S. Graveline (VP)

THOMASVILLE TOYOTA USED CARS
14724 US Hwy 19 S, Thomasville, GA 31757
Tel.: (229) 228-0554
Web Site:
    http://www.thomasvilletoyota.com
Year Founded: 1991
Rev.: $3,500,000
Emp.: 15
New Car Dealers
N.A.I.C.S.: 441110
Lee Graham (Gen Mgr)
Chris Matchett (Co-Owner, Partner & Gen Mgr)
Gregg Isaac (Co-Owner)

Subsidiaries:

Thomasville Ford Lincoln Mercury   (1)
1515 E Jackson St, Thomasville, GA 31792
Tel.: (229) 226-5133
Web Site: http://www.thomasvillefordlm.com
Sales Range: $25-49.9 Million
Emp.: 45
New & Used Automobile Distr
N.A.I.C.S.: 441110
Chris Matchett (Mng Partner)
Brian Bralich (Gen Mgr)

THOMPSON & BENDER LLC
1192 Pleasantville Rd, Briarcliff Manor, NY 10510
Tel.: (914) 762-1900   NY

Web Site: http://www.thompson-bender.com
Sales Range: $10-24.9 Million
Emp.: 15
Advertising & Public Relations Agency
N.A.I.C.S.: 541820
Dean Bender (Pres)
Geoffrey Thompson (Chm)
Jennifer Bannan (Dir-Adv & Mktg)

THOMPSON & CO. PUBLIC RELATIONS
600 Barrow St Ste 400, Anchorage, AK 99501
Tel.: (907) 561-4488
Web Site:
    http://www.thompsonpr.com
Year Founded: 1989
Sales Range: $10-24.9 Million
Emp.: 14
Public Relations
N.A.I.C.S.: 541820
Gary Scott (VP & Dir-New Media)
Jennifer Thompson (Pres & CEO)
Meghan Aftosmis (VP-New York)
Ariel Walsh Amand (Dir-Ops-Anchorage)
Emily Kurn (Sr Acct Exec & Dir-Art)
Abby Cooper (Acct Exec)
Alexis Isaacs (Acct Exec-New York)

Subsidiaries:

Thompson & Co. New York   (1)
44 W 28th St 8th Fl, New York, NY 10001   (100%)
Tel.: (646) 794-4281
Web Site: http://www.thompsonpr.com
Public Relations
N.A.I.C.S.: 541820

THOMPSON & COMPANY MARKETING COMMUNICATIONS
50 Peabody Pl, Memphis, TN 38103-3667
Tel.: (901) 527-8000   TN
Web Site: http://www.thompson-co.com
Year Founded: 1977
Rev.: $30,000,000
Emp.: 40
Advetising Agency
N.A.I.C.S.: 541810
Robert F. Vornbrock (Vice Chm & COO)
Julian Smith (CTO)
Ralph Berry (Pres)
Bob Winkler (CFO)
Roger Puls (Sr Mgr-Production)
David Dasenbrock (Sr VP-Media & Dir-Acct Plng)
Grant Joiner (Pres-Sports Mktg Div)
Earl Keister (Dir-Creative)
Michael H. Thompson Sr. (CEO)

Subsidiaries:

Disciple Design   (1)
390 S Main St, Memphis, TN 38103
Tel.: (901) 386-4299
Web Site: http://www.discipledesign.com
Emp.: 6
N.A.I.C.S.: 541810
Craig Thompson (Pres & Dir-Creative)
Mary Jones (Mgr-Office & Traffic)
David Terry (Assoc Dir-Creative & Sr Designer)

Thompson & Berry   (1)
50 Peabody Pl 4th Fl, Memphis, TN 38103-3699
Tel.: (901) 527-8000
Emp.: 6
N.A.I.C.S.: 541820
Ralph Berry (Pres)
Bob Phillips (VP-PR)
Abby More (Acct Exec)

THOMPSON & JOHNSON EQUIPMENT CO.
6926 Fly Rd, East Syracuse, NY 13057
Tel.: (315) 437-2881
Web Site:
    http://www.thompsonandjohnson.com
Rev.: $24,418,681
Emp.: 300
Materials Handling Machinery
N.A.I.C.S.: 423830
Dave Schneckenburger (Pres)
Bill MacBlane (VP-Fin)
Jim Antoine (Mgr-Ops)
Shaun Harrington (Mgr-Sls)
Jason Piaquadio (Mgr-Svc-Albany)

THOMPSON & PECK INC.
1412 Whalley Ave, New Haven, CT 06515
Tel.: (203) 787-6781
Web Site:
    http://www.thompsonandpeck.com
Year Founded: 1928
Sales Range: $25-49.9 Million
Emp.: 25
Insurance Agents
N.A.I.C.S.: 524210
Stanley F. Prymas (Pres)
Susan Redente (VP)

THOMPSON AUTOMOTIVE GROUP INC.
40 Swamp Rd, Doylestown, PA 18901
Tel.: (215) 340-3900
Web Site:
    http://www.1800thompson.com
Year Founded: 1986
Sales Range: $50-74.9 Million
Emp.: 500
Automobiles, New & Used
N.A.I.C.S.: 441110
Steve McCloskey (Controller)
Danny Szarka (Mgr-Collision Center)

Subsidiaries:

Thompson Toyota Inc.   (1)
50 W Swamp Rd, Doylestown, PA 18901
Tel.: (215) 345-9460
Web Site: http://www.1800thompson.com
Rev.: $57,000,000
Emp.: 450
Car Dealership
N.A.I.C.S.: 441110
Julius Libutti (Gen Mgr)
Laura Widder (Specialist-Vehicle Exchange)
Mike Fink (Mgr-Pre-Owned Sls)
Paul Hagan (Mgr-Sls)
Steve Tagye (Mgr-Sls)
John H. Thompson Sr. (Owner & Pres)

THOMPSON BRANDS LLC
80 South Vine St, Meriden, CT 06451
Tel.: (203) 235-2541
Web Site:
    http://www.thompsonchocolate.com
Sales Range: $10-24.9 Million
Emp.: 150
Candy & Other Confectionery Products Mfr
N.A.I.C.S.: 311340
Gene Dunkin (CEO)
Robert Lis (COO)
Elise Lenz (Mgr-Mktg)

THOMPSON BROOKS, INCORPORATED
375 Rhode Island St, San Francisco, CA 94103
Tel.: (415) 581-2600
Web Site:
    http://www.thompsonbrooks.com
Year Founded: 1990
Rev.: $17,500,000
Emp.: 45
Construction Services
N.A.I.C.S.: 238170

COMPANIES

Bruce Clymer *(Pres)*
Clifton B. Shoolroy *(CFO)*
Judith Thompson *(Founder & CEO)*
Greg Hall *(Exec VP)*

THOMPSON BUILDERS CORPORATION
250 Bel Marin Keys Blvd Bldg A, Novato, CA 94949-5727
Tel.: (415) 456-8972   CA
Web Site: http://www.tbcorp.com
Year Founded: 1988
Sales Range: $125-149.9 Million
Commercial, Institutional & Multi-Family Residential Construction Services
N.A.I.C.S.: 236220
Paul Thompson *(Pres)*
Vicki Fowler Nance *(CFO)*
Paul Petri *(Mgr-Heavy Civil Area)*
Laurie Weyl *(Office Mgr & Mgr-HR)*
Lee Jones *(VP-Estimating)*
Joe Hass *(Sr VP)*
Clayton Fraser *(VP-Bus Dev)*

Subsidiaries:

WBB Management Company, Inc.   (1)
250 Bell Marin Keys Blvd Bldg A, Novato, CA 94949
Tel.: (415) 456-8972
Construction Management Services
N.A.I.C.S.: 236220
Paul Thompson *(Pres)*

THOMPSON CHILD & FAMILY FOCUS
6800 Saint Peters Ln, Matthews, NC 28105
Tel.: (704) 536-0375   NC
Web Site: http://www.thompsoncff.org
Year Founded: 1887
Sales Range: $10-24.9 Million
Emp.: 434
Child Care Services
N.A.I.C.S.: 624110
Allison Todd *(Chief Program Officer-Clinical Svcs)*
Steve Brace *(CFO)*
Cathy Cloud *(Chief HR Officer)*
Danny Whitley *(Sr VP-Facilities)*
Gilbert Galle *(Vice Chm)*
Alexandra Reardon *(Chief Dev Officer)*
Anthony Jones *(COO)*
Matt Dillworth *(Chief Clinical Officer)*
Patrick Vaca *(VP-Strategic Dev)*
Sherri Grace *(Sr VP-Fin)*
Kirby D. Shealy III *(Sec)*

THOMPSON COBB BAZILIO ASSOCIATES PC
1101 15th St NW Ste 400, Washington, DC 20005
Tel.: (202) 737-3300
Web Site: http://www.tcba.com
Rev.: $17,621,194
Emp.: 200
Accounting, Auditing & Bookkeeping
N.A.I.C.S.: 541219
Barbara Knowles *(Controller)*
Nuhailita Iddrisu *(Mgr-Audit)*
Sam Arthur *(Dir-IT Assurance & Control)*

THOMPSON COBURN LLP
1 US Bank Plz, Saint Louis, MO 63101-1693
Tel.: (314) 552-6000
Web Site: https://www.thompsoncoburn.com
Emp.: 380
Law firm
N.A.I.C.S.: 541199
Lacey Searfoss *(Partner)*
Bill Rowe *(Dir-Bus Dev)*

Kathleen Dunagin *(Dir-Library Svcs)*
Anne Schuster *(Chief Mktg Officer)*
Evan R. Goldfarb *(Partner)*
Laura M. Jordan *(Partner)*
Todd A. Rowden *(Partner-Chicago)*
Barry M. Weisz *(Partner-Los Angeles)*
Roman P. Wuller *(Partner)*
Kurt E. Reitz *(Partner-Southern Illinois)*
Adrienne Clair *(Partner)*
Natalie Ikhlassi *(Partner)*
Jesse Halpern *(Partner)*
Matt Finke *(CFO)*
James Inendino *(Partner-Real Estate Practice-Chicago)*
James Shreve *(Partner-Chicago)*
Norma Jackson *(Dir-Diversity & Inclusion)*
Felicia Williams *(Partner)*
Tonya Oliver Rose *(Partner)*
R. Nelson Williams *(Partner)*
Nicole Jobe *(Partner)*
Sara Chamberlain *(Partner)*
Erica Rancilio *(Partner-Energy Practice-Washington)*

THOMPSON CREEK WINDOW COMPANY
5000 Philadelphia Way, Lanham, MD 20706
Tel.: (301) 306-5290
Web Site: http://www.thompsoncreek.com
Year Founded: 1980
Rev.: $24,200,000
Emp.: 161
Plastics Product Mfr
N.A.I.C.S.: 326199
Brian Wuest *(VP)*
Rick Wuest *(CEO)*
Martha Williams *(CFO)*
John Mitchell *(VP-Mfg & Engrg)*

THOMPSON DISTRIBUTION COMPANY, INC.
2225 N College Ave, Indianapolis, IN 46205
Tel.: (317) 923-2581
Web Site: http://www.thomdist.com
Rev.: $7,000,000
Emp.: 10
Plumbing & Heating Equipment & Supplies, Hydronics, Merchant Whslr
N.A.I.C.S.: 423720
John T. Thompson *(Pres & CEO)*
Dexter Thompson *(Dir-Sls & Ops)*
Marcus Johnson *(Mgr-Inside Sls & Pur)*

Subsidiaries:

Goodpasture Motor Company, Inc.   (1)
3415 Lee Hwy, Bristol, VA 24202
Tel.: (276) 669-0311
Web Site: http://www.goodpasturemotor.com
Automobile Whslr
N.A.I.C.S.: 423110
Eddie Ingle *(Gen Mgr-Svc Dept)*
Mike Lucas *(Gen Mgr-Parts)*
Ben Chapman *(Mgr-Territory)*
Frank Goodpasture III *(Pres)*
Frank Goodpasture Jr. *(CEO)*
Frank Goodpasture IV *(Mgr-Territory)*

THOMPSON DISTRIBUTION, LLC
203 Lynnwood Blvd, Nashville, TN 37205
Tel.: (615) 277-2970   TN
Web Site: https://tdco.us
Year Founded: 2018
Investment Holding Company
N.A.I.C.S.: 551112
John Thompson *(CEO)*

Subsidiaries:

MTA Distributors, LLC   (1)

555 Hickory Hills Blvd, Whites Creek, TN 37189-9244
Tel.: (615) 299-8777
Web Site: https://www.mtadistributors.com
Sales Range: $1-9.9 Million
Emp.: 48
Commercial Rental Equipment Distr
N.A.I.C.S.: 423810
John Thompson *(CEO)*

Thompson Truck Group, LLC   (1)
4550 Rutledge Pike, Knoxville, TN 37914
Tel.: (865) 637-4881
Web Site: https://www.thompsontruckgroup.com
New & Used Commercial Truck Dealer
N.A.I.C.S.: 441227
John Thompson *(CEO)*

THOMPSON ELECTRIC, INC.
PO Box 414, Mabelvale, AR 72103
Tel.: (501) 455-0555
Web Site: http://www.thompson-electric.com
Year Founded: 1983
Electrical Contractor
N.A.I.C.S.: 238210
Terri Thompson *(Pres)*
Keith Thompson *(VP & Gen Mgr)*

THOMPSON ENERGY
745 Collage Dr, Dalton, GA 30720
Tel.: (706) 278-5818
Sales Range: $10-24.9 Million
Emp.: 325
Convenience Store
N.A.I.C.S.: 445131
Dianne Thompson *(CFO)*

THOMPSON HINE LLP
3900 Key Ctr 127 Public Sq, Cleveland, OH 44114-1291
Tel.: (216) 566-5500
Web Site: http://www.thompsonhine.com
Year Founded: 1893
Sales Range: $150-199.9 Million
Emp.: 501
Legal Advisory Services
N.A.I.C.S.: 541110
George J. Walsh III *(Executives)*
Anthony C. White *(Co-Partner)*
Robert M. Curry *(Co-Partner)*
Thomas A. Aldrich *(Co-Partner)*
Deborah Z. Read *(Mng Partner)*
Frank R. DeSantis *(Partner)*
Robert F. Ware *(Partner)*
Frank A. LaManna *(COO)*
Stephen J. Walsh *(CIO)*
Michael E. Goldberg *(CFO)*
George M. Holobinko *(Dir-Ops & Facilities)*
William T. Garcia *(Dir-Legal Project Mgmt)*
James B. Aronoff *(Partner)*
Russell J. Rogers *(Partner)*
Stephen B. Schrock *(Partner)*
Devin A. Barry *(Partner-Environmental Practice Grp)*
Tony J. Hornbach *(Partner-Bus Litigation Practice Grp-Cincinnati)*
Art Licygiewicz *(Partner-Intellectual Property Practice Grp)*
Garrett A. Nail *(Partner-Bus Restructuring, Creditors Rights & Bankruptcy)*
Todd M. Schild *(Partner-Corp Transactions & Securities Practice Grp)*
Jonathan A. Olick *(Partner-Real Estate Practice)*
David D. Watson *(Partner-Corp Transactions & Securities Practice)*
Andy Colon *(Chief Talent Officer)*
Pingshan Li *(Partner-Corp Transactions & Securities Practice)*
Cassandra Borchers *(Partner)*
Elizabeth H. Blattner *(Partner)*
Mark Lunn *(Partner-Intl Trade Practice)*

THOMPSON INDUSTRIAL SERVICES, LLC

Marvin T. Griff *(Partner-Corp Transactions & Securities Practice-Washington)*
E. J. Joswick *(Partner-Intellectual Property Practice-Atlanta)*
John B. Kopf III *(Partner-Bus Litigation Practice Grp-Columbus)*

THOMPSON HOSPITALITY INC.
505 Huntmar Park Dr Ste 350, Herndon, VA 20170
Tel.: (703) 964-5500
Web Site: http://www.thompsonhospitality.com
Year Founded: 1992
Sales Range: $150-199.9 Million
Emp.: 2,400
Provider of Contract Food Services
N.A.I.C.S.: 722511
Maurice Jenoure *(COO)*
Warren M. Thompson *(Chm & Pres)*

THOMPSON INDUSTRIAL SERVICES, LLC
104 N Main St, Sumter, SC 29150
Tel.: (803) 773-8005
Web Site: http://www.thompsonindustrialservices.com
Year Founded: 1986
Commercial & Industrial Construction & Maintenance, Architectural Services, Industrial Cleaning, Industrial Supply Distribution & Commercial & Industrial HVAC Services
N.A.I.C.S.: 561210
Carl Wise *(Sr Mgr-Bus Dev)*

Subsidiaries:

Thompson Construction Group   (1)
100 N Main St, Sumter, SC 29150 **(100%)**
Tel.: (803) 773-8005
Web Site: http://www.thompsonconstructionsouth.com
Emp.: 2,500
Construction & Maintenance Services to Industrial, Commercial & Government Clients
N.A.I.C.S.: 236220
Greg A. Thompson *(Pres & CEO)*

Division (Domestic):

Thompson Construction Group   (2)
6550 Ward Ave, North Charleston, SC 29406 **(100%)**
Web Site: http://www.thompsonsoutheast.com
Emp.: 20
Construction Services
N.A.I.C.S.: 236210
Greg A. Thompson *(Pres & CEO)*

Thompson HVAC   (1)
705 Seaboard St, Myrtle Beach, SC 29577 **(100%)**
Tel.: (843) 773-8005
Web Site: http://www.thompsonhvac.com
Heating, Ventilation & Air Conditioning (HVAC) Installation & Repair for Commercial & Industrial Clients
N.A.I.C.S.: 333415
Alan Bass *(Reg Mgr)*

Thompson Industrial Supply   (1)
87 Shaw St, Sumter, SC 29153 **(100%)**
Tel.: (803) 775-7723
Web Site: http://www.thompsonindustrialsupply.com
Lubricants, Janitorial Supplies, Filtration & Reclamation Products Mfr
N.A.I.C.S.: 324191
Geri Thompson *(Founder)*
Chuck Hinds *(Mgr-Technical Svc)*
Philip Sawyer *(Gen Mgr)*
Daly Ward *(Controller)*

Thompson Turner Construction   (1)
100 N Main St, Sumter, SC 29150 **(100%)**
Tel.: (803) 773-8005
Web Site: http://www.thompsonturner.com
New Construction & Renovation Services
N.A.I.C.S.: 236220

THOMPSON INDUSTRIAL SERVICES, LLC

Thompson Industrial Services, LLC—(Continued)
Hal L. Turner *(VP)*
H. Paige Carlton *(Dir-Bus Dev)*

Division (Domestic):

Thompson Turner Construction (2)
6550 Ward Ave, North Charleston, SC
29406 (100%)
Tel.: (800) 628-7141
Web Site: http://www.thompsonturner.com
Emp.: 50
New Construction & Renovation Services
N.A.I.C.S.: 236117
Hal L. Turner *(Reg Mgr & VP)*
James K. Davis Jr. *(Engr)*

Thompson Turner Construction (2)
1116 Henderson St Ste 200, Columbia, SC
29201 (100%)
Tel.: (803) 933-9337
Web Site: http://www.thompsonturner.com
New Construction & Renovation Services
N.A.I.C.S.: 236210

TiGroup (1)
1116 Henderson St Ste 200, Columbia, SC
29201 (100%)
Tel.: (803) 933-9337
Web Site: http://www.tigrouparchitects.com
Architectural Services, New Construction &
Renovation & Restoration Projects
N.A.I.C.S.: 541310
Hal L. Turner *(Engr)*

THOMPSON INDUSTRIAL SUPPLY INC.
10222 6th St, Rancho Cucamonga,
CA 91730
Tel.: (909) 941-8881
Web Site: http://www.tismc.com
Year Founded: 1969
Sales Range: $10-24.9 Million
Emp.: 75
Supplier of Bearings, Sprockets &
Chains
N.A.I.C.S.: 423840
Gary R. Thompson *(Pres)*
Carolyn Burns *(Mgr-Acctg)*
Chuck Hatfield *(Mgr-Store)*

THOMPSON INSURANCE GROUP
896 Broadway E, Providence, RI
02914
Tel.: (401) 434-7203
Web Site:
 http://thompsoninsurancegroup.net
Insurance Services
N.A.I.C.S.: 524298
Kenneth Thompson *(CEO)*

Subsidiaries:

Lezaola Thompson Insurance,
Inc. (1)
896 Broadway, East Providence, RI 02914
Tel.: (401) 434-7203
Web Site: http://www.lezaola-ins.com
Insurance Related Activities
N.A.I.C.S.: 524298
Kenneth Thompson *(Owner)*

Mercier & Kosinski Insurance,
Inc. (1)
1009 Smithfield Ave, Lincoln, RI 02865-2707
Tel.: (401) 274-4043
Web Site: http://www.mkiagency.com
Insurance Agencies & Brokerages
N.A.I.C.S.: 524210

THOMPSON INTERNATIONAL INC.
5840 Airline Rd, Henderson, KY
42420-9561
Tel.: (270) 826-3751
Web Site:
 http://www.thompsoninternatio
 nal.com
Year Founded: 1951
Sales Range: $75-99.9 Million
Emp.: 75

Rotary Drilling Tool Mfr
N.A.I.C.S.: 423830
Clifford H. Thompson *(Pres & CEO)*
Elizabeth Thompson *(Exec VP)*
Doug Black *(Product Mgr-Drilco)*
Don Thompson Jr. *(Exec VP)*

THOMPSON MACHINERY COMMERCE CORPORATION
1245 Bridgestone Pkwy, La Vergne,
TN 37086-3510
Tel.: (615) 256-2424   TN
Web Site:
 http://www.thompsonmachinery.com
Year Founded: 1943
Sales Range: $100-124.9 Million
Emp.: 450
Construction & Mining Machinery
Sales, Leases & Rentals
N.A.I.C.S.: 423810
James B. Ezzell *(CFO, Treas, Sec & Exec VP)*
DeWitt C. Thompson IV *(Chm)*
DeWitt C. Thompson V *(Pres)*

THOMPSON MARKETING
70 NE Loop 410 Ste 750, San Antonio, TX 78216
Tel.: (210) 349-9925
Web Site:
 http://www.thompsonagency.com
Year Founded: 1976
Rev.: $17,200,500
Emp.: 10
Advetising Agency
N.A.I.C.S.: 541810
Matt Mohr *(Owner)*
Kelly Griffin *(Acct Coord)*
John Boggess *(VP-Comm)*

THOMPSON MEDIA GROUP LLC
805 15th St NW 3rd Fl, Washington,
DC 20005
Tel.: (202) 872-4000   DE
Web Site: http://www.thompson.com
Year Founded: 2011
Multi-Platform Publishing & Information Services
N.A.I.C.S.: 513199

Subsidiaries:

Thompson Publishing Group (1)
805 15th St NW 3rd Fl, Washington, DC
20005-2207
Tel.: (202) 872-4000
Web Site: http://www.thompson.com
Sales Range: $25-49.9 Million
Emp.: 100
Commercial & Institutional Publisher & Information Services
N.A.I.C.S.: 513199

THOMPSON PETROLEUM CORP.
325 N Saint Paul St Ste 4300, Dallas,
TX 75201
Tel.: (214) 953-1177
Sales Range: $10-24.9 Million
Emp.: 100
Producer of Crude Petroleum
N.A.I.C.S.: 211120
Christy Thompson *(VP)*

THOMPSON PRODUCTS, INC.
310 Kenneth Welch Dr, Lakeville, MA
02347-1374
Tel.: (508) 946-4500   MA
Web Site:
 http://www.thompsonproducts.com
Year Founded: 1906
Sales Range: $25-49.9 Million
Emp.: 150
Converted Paper Products
N.A.I.C.S.: 322299
Ruth Correia *(Controller)*
Scott Slater *(Pres & CEO)*

THOMPSON PUMP AND MANUFACTURING CO., INC.
4620 City Ctr Dr, Port Orange, FL
32129
Tel.: (386) 767-7310
Web Site:
 http://www.thompsonpump.com
Year Founded: 1970
Sales Range: $25-49.9 Million
Emp.: 225
Pumps Mfr
N.A.I.C.S.: 333914
William F. Thompson *(Pres)*
Shawn Mackey *(CFO)*
Majid Tavakoli *(VP-Product)*
John Farrell *(VP-Sls)*

THOMPSON SALES CO.
1555 E Independence St, Springfield,
MO 65804
Tel.: (417) 866-6611
Web Site:
 http://www.thompsonsales.com
Sales Range: $25-49.9 Million
Emp.: 120
Automobiles, New & Used
N.A.I.C.S.: 441110
Milt Thompson *(Chm)*
Lynn Thompson *(Owner & Pres)*

THOMPSON SCHOOL BOOK DEPOSITORY
39 NE 24th St, Oklahoma City, OK
73105
Tel.: (405) 525-9458
Web Site:
 http://www.thompsonschool
 book.com
Year Founded: 1955
Rev.: $14,000,000
Emp.: 20
Book, Periodical & Newspaper Merchant Whslr
N.A.I.C.S.: 424920
John Thompson *(Pres)*
Betty O'Brien *(Mgr-Ops)*
Patsy Dukes *(Sec)*

THOMPSON STREET CAPITAL MANAGER LLC
120 S Central Ave Ste 600, Saint
Louis, MO 63105
Tel.: (314) 727-2112   DE
Web Site: https://www.tscp.com
Year Founded: 2000
Privater Equity Firm
N.A.I.C.S.: 523999
Robert Dunn *(Mng Partner)*
James A. Cooper *(Mng Partner)*
Elizabeth Borow *(Mng Dir)*
Neal J. Berman *(Mng Dir)*
Vincent E. Warrick *(Mng Dir)*
Jack Senneff *(Mng Dir)*
Kelly Wittenbrink *(VP)*
Brian Kornmann *(Mng Dir)*
Bradley Strahorn *(Dir-Ops)*
Craig Albrecht *(Mng Dir)*
Jesse Klein *(Dir)*
Becky Lopez *(VP)*
Brandon Muirhead *(Dir)*
Joe Amadio *(Dir)*
Rick Clifton *(Dir)*
Stefan Sigurdson *(VP)*
Clayton Milburn *(VP)*
Joe St. Geme *(Dir)*
J.C. Wetzel *(Dir)*
Harry Holiday III *(COO)*

Subsidiaries:

BCM One, Inc. (1)
521 5th Ave 14th Fl, New York, NY 10175
Tel.: (800) 543-4226
Web Site: http://www.bcmone.com
Sales Range: $25-49.9 Million
Emp.: 56

U.S. PRIVATE

Technology Integration Services & Communications Technologies & Solutions
N.A.I.C.S.: 541511
Frank Ahearn *(Co-Founder & Co-CEO)*
Geoff Bloss *(CEO)*
John Cunningham *(Co-Founder & Co-CEO)*
Jay Monaghan *(COO)*
Douglas Fechter *(CFO)*
Paula Como Kauth *(Sr Dir-Mktg)*
Pete Zarras *(Head-Microsoft Cloud Practice)*

Subsidiary (Domestic):

CoreDial, LLC (2)
Hillcrest I 751 Arbor Way Ste 150, Blue
Bell, PA 19422
Tel.: (215) 297-4400
Web Site: http://www.coredial.com
Cloud Telecommunications Platform Developer & Services
N.A.I.C.S.: 518210
Alan Rihm *(CEO)*
Warren Barratt *(CFO)*
Ken Lienemann *(Chief Revenue Officer)*
Jennifer Nading *(Sr VP-Ops)*

Subsidiary (Domestic):

eZuce, Inc. (3)
5 Central Sq Ste 302, Stoneham, MA
02180
Tel.: (978) 296-1005
Web Site: http://www.ezuce.com
Software Publisher
N.A.I.C.S.: 513210
David Grazio *(VP-Mktg & Channels)*

Subsidiary (Domestic):

Flowroute, LLC (2)
1218 3rd Ave Ste 600, Seattle, WA 98101
Tel.: (206) 641-8000
Web Site: http://www.flowroute.com
Telecommunication Servicesb
N.A.I.C.S.: 517810
Dan Rubins *(VP-Engrg)*

NexVortex Inc. (2)
510 Spring St Ste 250, Herndon, VA 20170
Tel.: (703) 579-0200
Web Site: http://www.nexvortex.com
Sales Range: $1-9.9 Million
Telecommunication Services Provider
N.A.I.C.S.: 541618
Frederick R. Fromm *(Pres & CEO)*
Wes Rogers *(Founder & COO)*
Mike Nowak *(VP-Sls)*
Deb Matthews *(VP-Customer Experience)*

Bradley Morris Inc. (1)
1825 Barrett Lakes Blvd Ste 300, Kennesaw, GA 30144
Tel.: (770) 794-8318
Web Site: http://www.bradley-morris.com
Emp.: 50
Human Resources & Executive Search
Consulting Services
N.A.I.C.S.: 541612
Bill Scott *(VP-Mktg & Comm)*
Tim Best *(CEO)*
Anthony Morris *(CFO)*

Cequel Data Centers, LLC (1)
520 Maryville Centre Dr Ste 300, Saint
Louis, MO 63141
Tel.: (314) 594-1300
Holding Company; Information Technology
Data Centers Operator
N.A.I.C.S.: 551112
Jerald L. Kent *(Chm)*

Subsidiary (Domestic):

TierPoint, LLC (2)
520 Maryville Centre Dr Ste 300, Saint
Louis, MO 63141
Tel.: (877) 859-8437
Web Site: http://www.tierpoint.com
Information Technology Data Centers Operator
N.A.I.C.S.: 518210
Jerald L. Kent *(Chm)*
Andy Stewart *(Chief Strategy Officer)*
Wendy Knudsen *(Chief Legal Officer & Exec VP)*
Dennis Jesielowski *(COO)*
Jeff Bertocci *(Sr VP-Svc Delivery)*
Rob Carter *(Sr VP-Solutions Engrg)*
Rob Fewkes *(VP-Cloud Tech)*

COMPANIES

THOMPSON STREET CAPITAL MANAGER LLC

Terry Morrison *(Sr VP-Tech)*
Keith Markley *(Sr VP-Ops)*
Robert Hicks *(Sr VP-Ops)*
David Foster *(VP-Data Center Facilities)*
Robert Lupo *(Gen Mgr-Facility & Ops-Jacksonville)*
Keith Waldrup *(VP-Sls-Missouri & Kentucky)*
Bret Dupuis *(VP-Sls-Illinois, Indiana, Michigan & Ohio)*
John Holland *(Sr VP-Sls)*
Tyler Holley *(VP-Sls-Jacksonville)*
Paige Dirscherl *(Sr Acct Exec)*
Linda Bailey *(VP-HR)*
Bob Desantis *(Chief Acctg Officer)*
Shea Long *(Sr VP-Products)*
Paul Mazzucco *(Chief Security Officer)*
Octavio Morales *(Sr VP-Ops)*
Miranda Smith *(Acct Exec)*
David Haggerty *(VP-Sls-Wisconsin & Minnesota)*
Dan Capra *(Reg VP-Sls)*
Dick Weisberg *(VP-Sls-Pacific Northwest)*
Jeff Waide *(VP-Charlotte)*
Tony Rossapi *(Chief Revenue Officer & Exec VP)*
Kenny Ash *(VP-Channel)*
Mary E. Meduski *(Pres & CFO)*

Connecticut Electric, Inc. (1)
100 W 11th St #100, Anderson, IN 46016
Tel.: (765) 608-5230
Web Site: http://www.connecticut-electric.com
Sales Range: $25-49.9 Million
Designer, Mfr & Distr of Electrical Components
N.A.I.C.S.: 334419
Bruce Dunham *(Mgr-Sls-Natl)*

ControlScan, Inc. (1)
11475 Great Oaks Wy Ste 300, Atlanta, GA 30022
Tel.: (800) 825-3301
Web Site: http://www.controlscan.com
Cyber Security Consulting Services
N.A.I.C.S.: 541511
Mark Carl *(CEO)*
Schane Simpsob *(COO)*
Jim Ealy *(Exec VP-Direct Sls)*
Steve VanHandel *(CFO)*
Brad McArthur *(CTO)*

Detroit Tool & Engineering Company (1)
1107 Springfield Rd, Lebanon, MO 65536
Tel.: (417) 532-2141
Web Site: http://www.dtengineering.com
Specialty Machine & Automated System Mfr
N.A.I.C.S.: 333248
Matt Fanelli *(Mgr-Svc Dept)*

Domaille Engineering, LLC (1)
7100 Dresser Dr NE, Rochester, MN 55906
Tel.: (507) 281-0275
Web Site: http://www.domailleengineering.com
Emp.: 200
Precision Engineering Solutions, Supply Chain Management & Manufacturing Services
N.A.I.C.S.: 332710
Timothy E. Kane *(Pres)*
Dean A. Krueger *(VP-Bus Dev)*

Subsidiary (Domestic):

Tech Manufacturing, LLC (2)
45 Cooperative Way, Wright City, MO 63390
Tel.: (636) 745-9477
Web Site: http://www.techmanufacturing.com
Aircraft Equipment Mfr
N.A.I.C.S.: 336413
Jerry Halley *(Exec VP & Chief Engr)*
Tony Delf *(COO & Exec VP)*
Charles Stout *(Pres)*
Frank Kimball *(Sr VP-Sls)*
Dan Bertschmann *(Mgr-QA)*

Freddy's Frozen Custard LLC (1)
260 N Rock Rd Ste 200, Wichita, KS 67206
Tel.: (316) 260-8282
Web Site: http://www.freddysusa.com
Food Store Operator
N.A.I.C.S.: 445298
Scott Redler *(Co-Founder & COO)*
Ben Simon *(Dir-Ops)*
Markus K. Scholler *(VP-Franchise Dev)*
Randy Simon *(Co-Founder & CEO)*

Iracore International, Inc. (1)
3430 E 13h Ave, Hibbing, MN 55746
Tel.: (218) 263-8831
Web Site: http://www.irproducts.com
Sales Range: $50-74.9 Million
Pipeline & Industrial Equipment Elastomeric Protective Coatings Mfr
N.A.I.C.S.: 326299
James Skalski *(CFO & Comptroller)*
Christopher Liesmaki *(COO & VP)*

Subsidiary (Domestic):

Industrial Rubber Applicators, Inc. (2)
3804 E Beltline, Hibbing, MN 55746
Tel.: (218) 263-8831
Web Site: http://www.irproducts.com
Emp.: 100
Pipeline Elastomeric Protective Coatings Mfr
N.A.I.C.S.: 326299
James Skalski *(CFO)*

Irathane Systems, Inc. (2)
3516 E 13th Ave, Hibbing, MN 55746-2338
Tel.: (218) 262-5211
Web Site: http://www.iracore.com
Sales Range: $10-24.9 Million
Industrial Equipment Elastomeric Protective Coatings Mfr
N.A.I.C.S.: 326150
James Skalski *(CFO)*
Rick Brouwer *(Pres)*

Isto Biologics, Inc. (1)
45 South St, Hopkinton, MA 01748
Tel.: (314) 995-6049
Web Site: http://www.istobiologics.com
Emp.: 24
Research & Development Lab
N.A.I.C.S.: 541715
Don Brown *(CEO)*
Brian Barnes *(CTO & Chief Innovation Officer)*
Davis Adkisson *(Chief Scientific Officer)*
John Mitchell *(CFO)*

Subsidiary (Domestic):

Advanced Biologics, LLC (2)
555 Corporate Dr Ste 260, Ladera Ranch, CA 92694-2175
Tel.: (561) 715-0187
Web Site: http://www.advancedbiologics.com
Chemicals Mfr
N.A.I.C.S.: 325412
Scott Cadotte *(VP-Sls & Mktg)*
Amit Govil *(Pres)*

MediaRadar, Inc. (1)
252 W 37th St Ste 1001, New York, NY 10018
Tel.: (646) 652-7000
Web Site: http://www.mediaradar.com
Software Publisher
N.A.I.C.S.: 513210
Jesse Keller *(Co-Founder & CTO)*

Montana Silversmiths, Inc. (1)
Ste 1 Sterling Ln, Columbus, MT 59019
Tel.: (406) 322-4555
Web Site: http://www.montanasilversmiths.com
Sales Range: $10-24.9 Million
Designer of American West Influenced Buckle Jewelry & Lifestyle Product Mfr
N.A.I.C.S.: 339910
David Stimmel *(CFO)*
Rick Ruebusch *(CEO)*

Subsidiary (Domestic):

Big Sky Carvers Inc. (2)
308 East Main St, Manhattan, MT 59741
Tel.: (406) 284-3193
Web Site: http://www.bigskycarvers.com
Decoy & Decorative Wood Products Carver
N.A.I.C.S.: 339920

PKWARE, Inc. (1)
201 E Pittsburgh Ave, Milwaukee, WI 53204
Tel.: (414) 289-9788
Web Site: http://www.pkware.com
Custom Computer Programming Services
N.A.I.C.S.: 541511
Phil Katz *(Founder)*
Tammy McCormack *(VP-HR)*
Matt Little *(VP-Product Dev)*

Rick Hofmann *(VP-Sls-North America Channel)*
Spencer Kupferman *(CEO)*
Matt Zomboracz *(CFO)*
Sarah Fellner *(VP-Global Mktg)*
Tonya Cannady *(Pres & Chief Revenue Officer)*
Craig Irwin *(VP-Sls)*
Mike Wood *(VP-Product Mgmt)*
Marc Punzirudu *(CTO-Field)*

Subsidiary (Domestic):

Dataguise, Inc. (2)
39650 Liberty St Ste 400, Fremont, CA 94538
Tel.: (510) 824-1036
Web Site: http://www.dataguise.com
Rev.: $1,000,000
Emp.: 25
Security System Services
N.A.I.C.S.: 561621
Venkat Subramanian *(CTO)*
Ron Miles *(VP-Intl Sls)*
Duncan Brown *(Dir-Res)*
Manmeet Singh *(Co-Founder & CEO)*
Adrian Booth *(Co-Founder & VP)*
J. T. Sison *(VP-Mktg & Bus Dev-Worldwide)*
James Emmons *(VP-Global Sls)*
Subra Ramesh *(VP-Engrg)*

PestCo Holdings, LLC (1)
7676 Forsyth Blvd Ste 2700, Clayton, MO 63105-4146
Tel.: (314) 727-2112
Web Site: https://pestcoholdings.com
Holding Company; Residential & Commercial Pest Control Services
N.A.I.C.S.: 551112
Jay Keating *(CEO)*

Subsidiary (Domestic):

Alliance Commercial Pest Control, Inc. (2)
1 Steven Ave, Tinton Falls, NJ 07724
Tel.: (732) 747-3200
Web Site: http://www.alliancepestservices.com
Exterminating & Pest Control Services
N.A.I.C.S.: 561710
Brett Madden *(Principal)*

Ecoteam, LLC (2)
3900 Valley View Ln, Irving, TX 75062
Tel.: (972) 232-7400
Web Site: https://www.ecoteam.com
Exterminating & Pest Control Services
N.A.I.C.S.: 561710
Jonathan Polenz *(Pres)*

Subsidiary (Domestic):

Envirotrol Pest Solutions LLC (3)
12114 Dover St, Houston, TX 77031
Tel.: (281) 498-6007
Web Site: https://www.envirotrolhouston.com
Exterminating & Pest Control Services
N.A.I.C.S.: 561710

Subsidiary (Domestic):

Live Oak Pest Control Inc. (2)
8819 Brae Park Dr, San Antonio, TX 78249-3841
Tel.: (210) 647-5110
Exterminating & Pest Control Services
N.A.I.C.S.: 561710

PestCo, LLC (2)
7676 Forsyth Blvd Ste 2700, Clayton, MO 63105
Tel.: (314) 727-2112
Pest Control Services
N.A.I.C.S.: 561710
Jay Keating *(CEO)*
Patrick Polenz *(Dir-Southwest Reg)*

Pointe Pest Control-ID LLC (2)
1324 N Liberty Lake Rd Ste 226, Liberty Lake, WA 99019
Tel.: (509) 590-4100
Web Site: http://www.pointepest.com
Commercial Pest Management Services
N.A.I.C.S.: 561710
Jacob Borg *(Founder)*

Pointe Pest Control-IL, LLC (2)
1275 W Roosevelt Rd Ste 118, West Chicago, IL 60185-4816

Tel.: (630) 231-0717
Web Site: http://www.pointepestcontrol.net
Exterminating & Pest Control Services
N.A.I.C.S.: 561710
Prince Cunningham *(Mgr)*

Receivables Management Partners, LLC (1)
1809 N Broadway St, Greensburg, IN 47240
Tel.: (765) 228-7790
Web Site: http://www.receivablesmp.com
Collection Agencies
N.A.I.C.S.: 561440
Doug Marcum *(CIO)*
Randy Tempest *(Chief Sls Officer)*
Mark Schabel *(CEO)*
Steve Gayheart *(COO)*
Clay Callicoat *(CFO)*
Noelle Ten-Eyck *(Officer-Compliance)*

SmartProcure, Inc. (1)
700 W Hillsboro Blvd Ste 4-100, Deerfield Beach, FL 33441-1619
Web Site: http://www.smartprocure.us
Data Processing, Hosting & Related Services
N.A.I.C.S.: 518210
Jeff Rubenstein *(Co-Founder, Chm & CEO)*
Jack Siney *(Co-Founder & Chief Revenue Officer)*
Nate Haskins *(Pres & COO)*

Subsidiary (Domestic):

Fedmine LLC (2)
13708 Ginkgo Ter, Rockville, MD 20850-5431
Tel.: (301) 279-7575
Web Site: http://www.fedmine.us
Software Publisher
N.A.I.C.S.: 513210
Ashok Mehan *(Founder & CEO)*

Stone Panels, Inc. (1)
2945 FM 1431 W, Marble Falls, TX 78654
Tel.: (469) 635-5000
Web Site: http://www.stonepanels.com
Sales Range: $10-24.9 Million
Natural Stone Panel Mfr
N.A.I.C.S.: 327991
Harry Jefferson *(CFO)*
Donald Schroeder *(Mgr-Eastern Reg)*
Tim Friedel *(Pres & CEO)*
Jeanne VerDugt *(VP-Ops)*

Transnetyx, Inc. (1)
8110 Cordova Rd Ste 119, Cordova, TN 38016
Tel.: (901) 507-0476
Web Site: http://www.transnetyx.com
Emp.: 30
Genetic Testing Laboratories
N.A.I.C.S.: 541380
Robert Bean *(Pres)*
Ryan Yanase *(Mgr-Sls-North America)*
Suzanne Welshans *(Controller)*
Jeanie Wolaver *(VP-Dev & QA)*
Mike Gahan *(VP-Ops)*
John Minnick *(VP-IT)*

Subsidiary (Domestic):

Brainbits LLC (2)
1139 N MacArthur Blvd, Springfield, IL 62702-2314
Tel.: (217) 789-9313
Web Site: http://www.brainbitsllc.com
Professional Equipment & Supplies Merchant Whslr
N.A.I.C.S.: 423490
Gregory Brewer *(Owner)*

Laragen Incorporated (2)
10601 Virginia Ave Ste B, Culver City, CA 90232-3517
Tel.: (310) 280-0804
Web Site: http://www.laragen.com
Professional, Scientific & Technical Services
N.A.I.C.S.: 541990

Vector Laboratories, Inc. (1)
30 Ingold Rd, Burlingame, CA 94010
Tel.: (650) 697-3600
Web Site: http://www.vectorlabs.com
Medical Equipment & Device Mfr
N.A.I.C.S.: 339112
Jim Whitehead *(Founder)*
Lisa V. Sellers *(CEO)*

THOMPSON STREET CAPITAL MANAGER LLC — U.S. PRIVATE

Thompson Street Capital Manager LLC—(Continued)

WeVideo, Inc. (1)
480 San Antonio Rd Ste 210, Mountain View, CA 94040
Tel.: (650) 397-5026
Web Site: http://www.wevideo.com
Emp.: 11
Video Editing Software Development Services
N.A.I.C.S.: 541511
Jostein Svendsen *(Co-Founder & CEO)*
Bjorn Rustberggaard *(Co-Founder & COO)*
Krishna Menon *(CTO)*
Sarah Lerche Carpenter *(VP-Fin & Admin)*

THOMPSON TECHNOLOGIES, INC.
200 Galleria Pkwy Ste 1100, Atlanta, GA 30339
Tel.: (770) 794-8380
Web Site: http://www.thompsontalent.com
Year Founded: 1995
Sales Range: $10-24.9 Million
Emp.: 186
Information Technology Services
N.A.I.C.S.: 513210
David Thompson *(Founder & CEO)*
Tim Smith *(Pres)*
Jim Calise *(VP-Fin & Admin)*
Ari Waller *(VP-Recruiting)*

THOMPSON THRIFT DEVELOPMENT, INC.
901 Wabash Ave Ste 300, Terre Haute, IN 47807
Tel.: (812) 235-5959
Web Site: http://www.thompsonthrift.com
Year Founded: 1986
Sales Range: $75-99.9 Million
Emp.: 175
Construction Engineering Services
N.A.I.C.S.: 237990
John Thompson *(CEO-Construction)*
Henry Stadler *(Sr VP-Ops)*
John Vyverberg *(COO)*
R. Matthew Neff *(Exec Dir)*
Dan Sink *(Pres & CFO)*
Aimee O'Connor *(COO)*
Kurt Stahl *(COO-Construction)*
Paul Thrift *(CEO)*

THOMPSON TRACTOR COMPANY
2401 Pinson Hwy, Birmingham, AL 35217
Tel.: (205) 841-8601   AL
Web Site: http://www.thompsontractor.com
Year Founded: 1957
Sales Range: $450-499.9 Million
Emp.: 1,500
Sales & Servicer of Heavy Machinery
N.A.I.C.S.: 423810
Tom McGough *(VP-Fin)*
Michael D. Thompson *(Pres)*
Mike Rooney *(Exec VP & Gen Mgr)*
Tommy Riggs *(Mgr-Used Parts)*
Charlie Stevens *(VP-Earthmoving Sls)*

Subsidiaries:

Thompson Tractor Company - Thompson Truck Source Division (1)
2401 Pinson Vly Pkwy, Tarrant, AL 35217-2051
Tel.: (877) 642-6002
Web Site: http://www.thompsontractor.com
Truck Trailer Mfr
N.A.I.C.S.: 336212

THOMPSON'S HONDA
101 S 1st St, Terre Haute, IN 47807
Tel.: (812) 232-1111
Web Site: http://www.thompsonshonda.com
Sales Range: $10-24.9 Million
Emp.: 42
Car Whslr
N.A.I.C.S.: 441110
Richard Jaeger *(Owner)*

THOMPSON-DURKEE COMPANY INC.
11 Brooks Dr, Braintree, MA 02184
Tel.: (617) 782-6200
Rev.: $15,471,447
Emp.: 27
Plumbing & Hydronic Heating Supplies
N.A.I.C.S.: 423720
Peter Castoldi *(Pres)*

THOMSEN GROUP LLC
1303 43rd St, Kenosha, WI 53140
Tel.: (262) 652-3662
Web Site: http://www.lcthomsen.com
Sales Range: $10-24.9 Million
Emp.: 15
Sanitary Equipment Mfr
N.A.I.C.S.: 333241

THOMSON MACCONNELL CADILLAC, INC.
2820 Gilbert Ave, Cincinnati, OH 45206-1206
Tel.: (513) 221-5600
Web Site: http://www.thomsonmacconnell.com
Year Founded: 1953
Sales Range: $75-99.9 Million
Emp.: 100
Provider of Auto Sales, Service & Leasing
N.A.I.C.S.: 441110
Chris MacConnell *(Pres)*
Tim MacConnell *(Treas)*
Mary Puckett *(Controller)*
Emily Coots *(Mgr-Leasing)*
Neil Diemler *(Mgr-Parts)*
C. J. MacConnell *(Gen Mgr-Sls)*

THOMSON MOTOR CENTRE INC.
2158 Washington Rd, Thomson, GA 30824
Tel.: (706) 597-0062
Web Site: http://www.jeepcheap.com
Sales Range: $25-49.9 Million
Emp.: 86
Automobile Sales
N.A.I.C.S.: 441110
Irvin L. Grant *(Owner)*

THOMSON PLASTICS, INC.
130 Quality Dr NW, Thomson, GA 30824
Tel.: (706) 595-0658
Web Site: http://www.thomsonplastics.com
Year Founded: 1995
Sales Range: $10-24.9 Million
Emp.: 300
Plastics Pipe & Pipe Fitting Mfr
N.A.I.C.S.: 326122
Tom Talboys *(Dir-Engrg & Sls)*

THOMSON PROPERTIES INC.
9400 McKnight Rd Ste 207, Pittsburgh, PA 15237
Tel.: (412) 364-1146
Web Site: http://www.thomsonproperties.net
Sales Range: $10-24.9 Million
Emp.: 16
Provider of Property Management Services
N.A.I.C.S.: 237210
Alfred E. Thomson *(Pres)*

Subsidiaries:

850 Thorn St Inc (1)
9400 McKnight Rd Ste 207, Pittsburgh, PA 15237
Tel.: (412) 364-1146
Sales Range: $10-24.9 Million
Emp.: 1
Real Estate Services
N.A.I.C.S.: 531190

Thomson Homes Inc (1)
9400 McKnight Rd Ste 207, Pittsburgh, PA 15237
Tel.: (412) 364-1146
Web Site: http://www.thomsonproperties.net
Sales Range: $10-24.9 Million
Emp.: 12
Condominium Construction
N.A.I.C.S.: 236117

THOMVEST VENTURES LLC
138 S Park St, San Francisco, CA 94107
Tel.: (415) 329-8400   DE
Web Site: https://www.thomvest.com
Investment Management Service
N.A.I.C.S.: 523999

Subsidiaries:

Thomvest Asset Management Ltd. (1)
138 S Park St, San Francisco, CA 94107
Tel.: (415) 329-8400
Financial Services
N.A.I.C.S.: 523999
Eugene Siklos *(Pres)*

Holding (Non-US):

Liminal BioSciences Inc. (2)
440 Armand-Frappier Boulevard Suite 300, Laval, H7V 4B4, QC, Canada   (100%)
Tel.: (450) 781-0115
Web Site: https://www.liminalbiosciences.com
Rev.: $313,694
Assets: $39,473,067
Liabilities: $11,148,272
Net Worth: $28,324,794
Earnings: $486,578
Emp.: 43
Fiscal Year-end: 12/31/2022
Biopharmaceutical Product Mfr
N.A.I.C.S.: 325412
Jonathan M. Rothberg *(Founder & Chm)*
Patrick Sartore *(Pres)*
Bruce Pritchard *(CEO)*
N. Nicole Rusaw *(CFO)*

Subsidiary (US):

ProMetic BioSciences (USA), Inc. (3)
155 Willowbrook Blvd Ste 460, Wayne, NJ 07470
Tel.: (973) 812-9880
Pharmaceutical Marketer, Distr & Sales
N.A.I.C.S.: 424210

Subsidiary (Domestic):

ProMetic BioSciences Inc. (3)
500 Cartier Blvd W Ste 150, Laval, H7V 5B7, QC, Canada
Tel.: (450) 781-0115
Pharmaceutical Preparation Mfr
N.A.I.C.S.: 325412
G. F. Kym Anthony *(Chm)*

Subsidiary (Non-US):

ProMetic BioSciences Ltd (3)
The Freeport, Ballasalla, IM9 2AP, Isle of Man
Tel.: (44) 1624821450
Web Site: http://www.prometicbiosciences.com
Sales Range: $25-49.9 Million
Emp.: 17
Biopharmaceutical Mfr
N.A.I.C.S.: 325412

ProMetic BioSciences Ltd - Enabling Technology (3)
211 Cambridge Science Park, Milton Road, Cambridge, CB4 0WA, United Kingdom
Tel.: (44) 1223420300

Web Site: http://www.prometicbiosciences.com
Sales Range: $25-49.9 Million
Emp.: 50
Biopharmaceutical Products Research & Development
N.A.I.C.S.: 541714

Subsidiary (US):

ProMetic BioTherapeutics, Inc. (3)
1330 piccard Dr Ste 201, Rockville, MD 20850
Tel.: (301) 917-6320
Web Site: http://www.prometic.com
Emp.: 50
Therapeutics Mfr
N.A.I.C.S.: 325412

THOR-LO, INC.
2210 Newton Dr, Statesville, NC 28677-4850
Tel.: (704) 872-6522
Web Site: http://www.thorlo.com
Year Founded: 1952
Sales Range: $25-49.9 Million
Emp.: 265
Socks Mfr
N.A.I.C.S.: 315120
Rick Mende *(Acct Dir-UK)*

THORBURN ASSOCIATES INC
20880 Baker Rd, Castro Valley, CA 94546-8399
Tel.: (510) 886-7826
Web Site: http://www.ta-inc.com
Year Founded: 1992
Sales Range: $1-9.9 Million
Emp.: 19
Engineeering Services
N.A.I.C.S.: 541330
Lisa A. Thorburn *(Pres)*

THORLABS INC.
56 Sparta Ave, Newton, NJ 07860
Tel.: (973) 579-7227
Web Site: http://www.thorlabs.com
Year Founded: 1989
Sales Range: $10-24.9 Million
Emp.: 600
Photonics Products Mfr
N.A.I.C.S.: 334516
Alex Cable *(Pres & CEO)*
Jacob Slate *(Coord-RMA)*

THORNE ELECTRIC COMPANY
1558 Candish Ln, Chesterfield, MO 63017
Tel.: (636) 532-5753
Rev.: $10,351,780
Emp.: 1
Cleaning & Maintenance Equipment & Supplies
N.A.I.C.S.: 423850

THORNE MANAGEMENT INC.
1440 Franklin Ave, Salem, OH 44460
Tel.: (330) 337-9526
Rev.: $25,800,000
Emp.: 10
Independent Supermarket
N.A.I.C.S.: 445110
Bill Thorne *(CEO)*

THORNE RESEARCH, INC.
25820 Hwy 2 W, Sandpoint, ID 83864
Tel.: (208) 263-1337
Web Site: http://www.thorne.com
Rev.: $10,000,000
Emp.: 250
Pharmaceutical Preparation Mfr
N.A.I.C.S.: 325412
Scott Wheeler *(CFO)*

THORNHILL GM SUPERSTORE INC.

COMPANIES

US Route 119 Trace Fork Rd, Chapmanville, WV 25508
Tel.: (304) 855-4100
Web Site:
http://www.thornhillgmsuperstore.com
Sales Range: $25-49.9 Million
Emp.: 56
New & Used Automobile Sales
N.A.I.C.S.: 441110

THORNHILL SECURITIES, INC.
336 S Congress Ste 200, Austin, TX 78704
Tel.: (512) 472-7171
Web Site:
http://www.thornhillsecurities.com
Year Founded: 1985
Rev.: $11,000,000
Emp.: 8
Security Brokerage Services
N.A.I.C.S.: 523150
F. Gabriel Thornhill *(Pres & Chief Compliance Officer)*
Linda Arredondo *(Head-Ops)*
Shannon Hadley *(VP)*
Kathy McGuire *(Chief Compliance Officer)*

THORNTON & STEFANOVICH INC.
1615 Sunset Ave, Clinton, NC 28328
Tel.: (910) 592-2133
Web Site: http://www.gotoyota.com
Sales Range: $10-24.9 Million
Emp.: 40
Sell & Service New & Used Automobiles
N.A.I.C.S.: 441110
S. D. Stefanovich *(Pres)*
Chris Fann *(Gen Mgr)*
Nicholas Autry *(Asst Mgr-Sls)*

THORNTON-TOMASETTI, INC.
120 Broadway, New York, NY 10271-0016
Tel.: (917) 661-7800   NY
Web Site:
http://www.thorntontomasetti.com
Year Founded: 1949
Architectural Services
N.A.I.C.S.: 541310
Andrew Goldbaum *(COO)*
Aine M. Brazil *(Vice Chm)*
Najib Abboud *(Mng Principal)*
Benjamin Howes *(VP & Dir-Application Dev)*
Michael Squarzini *(Co-CEO)*
Peter DiMaggio *(Co-CEO)*
Wayne Stocks *(Pres)*
Gary Panariello *(Mng Dir-San Francisco)*

Subsidiaries:

Weidlinger Associates Inc.   (1)
40 Wall St 19th Fl, New York, NY 10005
Tel.: (212) 367-3000
Web Site: http://www.wai.com
Rev.: $10,000,000
Emp.: 250
Engineeering Services
N.A.I.C.S.: 541330
Raymond Daddazio *(Pres)*

THOROUGHBRED RESEARCH GROUP, INC.
1941 Bishop Ln Ste 1017, Louisville, KY 40218
Tel.: (502) 459-3133
Web Site: http://www.torinc.net
Year Founded: 1975
Rev.: $10,000,000
Emp.: 166
Market Analysis & Research Services
N.A.I.C.S.: 541910
Steve Alsbury *(Pres)*
James Lunger *(VP-Data Analytics)*

Harold Busack *(CFO)*
Brian Trammell *(VP-DP)*
Victor Walsh *(VP-Bus Dev)*
John Wolak *(VP-Programming)*
Nancy Alsbury *(VP-Operational Resources)*
Brad Larson *(VP-Mktg)*
Mary Lea Quick *(Dir-Qualitative Res)*
Tim Alex *(Dir-Online Programming)*
David A. Bryant *(VP-Healthcare Res)*
Janelle Cambron-Mellott *(Dir-Res Design & Analytics)*
Tim Wirtz *(Dir-Field Ops)*
Don Ludemann *(Dir-Software Engrg)*
Jeff Samulowitz *(Dir-Res)*

THOROUGHBRED SOFTWARE INTERNATIONAL
46 Vreeland Dr, Skillman, NJ 08558
Tel.: (732) 560-1377   NJ
Web Site: http://www.tbred.com
Year Founded: 1982
Computer Software Development
N.A.I.C.S.: 541511
John L. Johnson *(CEO)*
Kathy Kennedy *(Ops Mgr)*
Mark Lewis *(VP-Sls & Mktg)*
Bill Clarke *(Pres)*
Kevin Koskela *(VP-Applications & Scvs)*

THORP & COMPANY
355 Alhambra Cir Ste 800, Coral Gables, FL 33134-5006
Tel.: (305) 446-2700
Web Site: http://www.thorpco.com
Year Founded: 1988
Sales Range: $1-9.9 Million
Emp.: 8
Public Relations Agency
N.A.I.C.S.: 541820
Patricia Thorp *(Pres)*
Laurie Wilson *(Office Mgr)*

THORPE ELECTRIC SUPPLY INC.
27 Washington St, Rensselaer, NY 12144
Tel.: (518) 462-5496
Web Site:
http://www.thorpeelectric.com
Rev.: $16,643,971
Emp.: 35
Wire & Cable
N.A.I.C.S.: 423610
Thomas Gammel *(Co-Owner & Pres)*
Cynthia Vona-Jones *(Controller)*

THORSON GMC TRUCK BUICK MOTOR COMPANY, INC.
3456 E Colorado Blvd, Pasadena, CA 91107
Tel.: (626) 795-8851
Web Site:
http://www.thorsonmotorcenter.com
Year Founded: 1991
Sales Range: $50-74.9 Million
Emp.: 80
Car Whslr
N.A.I.C.S.: 441110
John Delorme *(CEO)*

THORSTAD CHEVROLET INC.
1702 S Park St, Madison, WI 53713
Tel.: (608) 256-0281
Sales Range: $25-49.9 Million
Emp.: 120
Automobiles, New & Used
N.A.I.C.S.: 441110
Ronald C. Thorstad *(Pres)*
Thomas S. Thorstad *(Gen Mgr)*
Bill Gower *(Mgr-Fin)*
Kenn Bumpke *(Mgr-Fin)*
Keith Burleigh *(Gen Mgr-Sls)*
Ken Kovacic *(Mgr-Used Vehicle)*

THOS. S. BYRNE, INC.
2601 Scott Ave Ste 300, Fort Worth, TX 76103
Tel.: (817) 335-3394
Web Site: http://www.tsbyrne.com
Sales Range: $100-124.9 Million
Emp.: 100
Commercial & Office Building, New Construction
N.A.I.C.S.: 236220
Jason Potter *(Controller)*
Dillard Coates *(Controller, Chief Admin Officer & Sr VP)*
Martin Lehman *(VP-Ops)*
Tracey Hart *(Dir-HR)*

THQ INC.
29903 Agoura Rd, Agoura Hills, CA 91301
Tel.: (818) 871-5000   DE
Web Site: http://www.thq.com
Year Founded: 1990
Sales Range: $800-899.9 Million
Emp.: 1,088
Interactive Entertainment Software Developer, Publisher & Distr
N.A.I.C.S.: 334610
Kevin Kraff *(VP-Global Brand Mgmt)*

Subsidiaries:

THQ (UK) Limited   (1)
Block A Dukes Court Duke Street, Woking, GU21 5BH, Surrey, United Kingdom
Tel.: (44) 1483724500
Video Game Publisher
N.A.I.C.S.: 449210

THQ Entertainment GmbH   (1)
Kimplerstrasse 278, 47807, Krefeld, Germany   (100%)
Tel.: (49) 215141890
Web Site: http://www.thq.de
Sales Range: $75-99.9 Million
Mfr, Designer & Distr of Computer Software & Games
N.A.I.C.S.: 339930

THQ France S.a.r.l.   (1)
32 Paradis Street, 75010, Paris, France
Tel.: (33) 145239980
Video Game Developer
N.A.I.C.S.: 449210

THRALL ENTERPRISES, INC.
180 N Stetson Ave Ste 3020, Chicago, IL 60601-6845
Tel.: (312) 621-8200   IL
Web Site: http://www.nazdar.com
Sales Range: $200-249.9 Million
Emp.: 10
Holding Company; Industrial Supplies, Printing Ink
N.A.I.C.S.: 423840
Erik Reed *(Mgr-Regulatory Compliance)*
Nancy Haller *(Treas & VP)*

Subsidiaries:

Naz-Dar Company   (1)
5444 E Ave Unit B, Countryside, IL 60525   (100%)
Tel.: (913) 422-1888
Web Site: http://www.nazdar.com
Sales Range: $25-49.9 Million
Emp.: 200
Silk Screen Process Inks, Equipment & Supplies
N.A.I.C.S.: 423840
J. Jeffrey Thrall *(CEO)*
Michael P. Fox *(Pres)*

Division (Domestic):

Nazdar Company - Nazdar Consulting Services Division   (2)
8501 Hedge Lane Ter, Shawnee, KS 66227
Tel.: (913) 422-1888
Web Site: http://www.nazdarconsulting.com
Sales Range: $25-49.9 Million
Color Management Consulting Services
N.A.I.C.S.: 541690

Nazdar Company - Nazdar SourceOne Division   (2)
8501 Hedge Lane Ter, Shawnee, KS 66227-3290
Tel.: (888) 578-5713
Web Site: http://www.sourceoneonline.com
Printing Equipment & Supplies Retailer
N.A.I.C.S.: 423830
Mike Xos *(Gen Mgr)*

Subsidiary (Non-US):

Nazdar Ltd.   (2)
Barton Road, Heaton Mersey, Stockport, SK4 3EA, United Kingdom
Tel.: (44) 161 442 2111
Web Site: http://www.nazdar.com
Printing Ink Mfr
N.A.I.C.S.: 325910
James Mc Donald *(VP-Mktg)*

THRALOW, INC.
216 W 6th St, Duluth, MN 55806-2551
Tel.: (218) 728-7953
Web Site: http://www.binoculars.com
Year Founded: 2000
Sales Range: $10-24.9 Million
Emp.: 40
Binoculars, Telescopes & Other Optical Goods Whslr
N.A.I.C.S.: 456130
Eric Dormanen *(VP-Opers)*
Larry Whalen *(Dir-IT)*

THREATTRACK SECURITY, INC.
311 Park Pl Blvd Ste 300, Clearwater, FL 33759
Tel.: (727) 324-0001
Web Site: http://www.threattrack.com
Year Founded: 1994
Sales Range: $75-99.9 Million
Emp.: 400
Security Software
N.A.I.C.S.: 513210
John Lyons *(Pres)*

THREE CHIMNEYS FARM
PO Box 114, Midway, KY 40347
Tel.: (859) 873-7053
Web Site:
http://www.threechimneys.com
Sales Range: $10-24.9 Million
Emp.: 110
Horses & Equine Production Services
N.A.I.C.S.: 112920
Case Clay *(Pres)*

THREE COUNTY VOLKSWAGEN CORP
701 Riverside Ave, Lyndhurst, NJ 07071
Tel.: (201) 933-8383
Web Site:
http://www.threecountyvw.com
Sales Range: $10-24.9 Million
Emp.: 55
Sales of New & Used Automobiles
N.A.I.C.S.: 441110
Robert A. Senior *(Pres)*
Scott R. Senior *(VP)*
Joe Bulna *(Mgr-Fin)*

THREE D METALS INC.
5462 Innovation Dr, Valley City, OH 44280
Tel.: (330) 220-0451
Web Site:
http://www.threedmetals.com
Year Founded: 1972
Rev.: $30,839,215
Emp.: 100
Strip, Metal
N.A.I.C.S.: 423510
David D. Dickens *(Founder)*

THREE D METALS INC.

U.S. PRIVATE

Three D Metals Inc.—(Continued)
Subsidiaries:
Three D Metals Canada, Inc. (1)
110 Lancing Drive Building 2 Unit 2, Hamilton, L8W 3A1, ON, Canada (100%)
Tel.: (905) 286-9876
Web Site: https://threedmetals.com
Sales Range: $10-24.9 Million
Emp.: 10
Strip, Metal
N.A.I.C.S.: 331221

THREE DOG LOGISTICS
3012 Dunglow Rd Ste 300, Baltimore, MD 21222
Tel.: (410) 284-5494
Web Site:
  http://www.threedoglogistics.com
Year Founded: 2005
Sales Range: $1-9.9 Million
Emp.: 8
Mail Services & Transportation Management System
N.A.I.C.S.: 561431
John Kennedy (Founder & CEO)
Dan Meyerpeter (Exec VP-Ops)
Tina Siatkowski (Dir-Client Svcs)
Kelly Spore (Dir-Bus Dev)
Yvette Diamond (COO)

THREE J'S DISTRIBUTING, INC.
16251 SE 98th Ave, Clackamas, OR 97015
Tel.: (503) 657-1211
Web Site: http://www.3js.com
Year Founded: 1985
Sales Range: $10-24.9 Million
Emp.: 35
Bakery Product Distr
N.A.I.C.S.: 424420
John R. Jon (Mgr)
Kelly Edwards (Controller)
Florin Ionescu (VP-Ops)

THREE L INC.
12235 Robin Blvd, Houston, TX 77045-4826
Tel.: (713) 434-7600
Web Site: http://www.3l.com
Sales Range: $10-24.9 Million
Emp.: 20
Petroleum Bulk Stations
N.A.I.C.S.: 424710
Andrew S. Leach (Pres)

THREE LOWER COUNTIES COMMUNITY SERVICES, INC.
32033 Beaver Run Dr, Salisbury, MD 21804
Tel.: (410) 749-1015   MD
Web Site: http://www.tlccs.org
Year Founded: 1994
Sales Range: $25-49.9 Million
Emp.: 411
Community Health Care Services
N.A.I.C.S.: 621498
Christopher LaBarge (VP)
Elizabeth Walker (Treas)

THREE M TOOL & MACHINE, INC.
8155 Richardson Rd, Commerce Township, MI 48390
Tel.: (248) 363-1555
Web Site: http://www.three-m.com
Year Founded: 1971
Sales Range: $10-24.9 Million
Precision Machinery Mfr & Distr
N.A.I.C.S.: 332721
Michael A. Medwid (Pres)
Sharon Medwid (Owner)
Christine Brime (Project Coord)
Mark Bresnahan (Plant Mgr)

Toby Barbrey (Mgr-Quality)
Lori Holland (Controller)
Erika Miu (Mgr-Acctg & IT)

THREE NOTCH ELECTRIC MEMBERSHIP CORP.
116 W 2nd St, Donalsonville, GA 39845
Tel.: (229) 524-5377
Web Site:
  http://www.threenotchemc.com
Year Founded: 1938
Sales Range: $25-49.9 Million
Emp.: 51
Electric Power Distribution Services
N.A.I.C.S.: 221122
Carlton O. Thomas (Pres & CEO)
Mike Torrance (VP-Engrg)
Heather L. Mathis (Supvr-DP)
Enoch Benefield (Coord-Safety)

THREE RIVERS COMMUNITY FOUNDATION
1333 Columbia Park Trl Ste 310, Richland, WA 99352
Tel.: (509) 735-5559   WA
Web Site: http://www.3rcf.org
Year Founded: 1999
Sales Range: $1-9.9 Million
Emp.: 2
Grantmaking Services
N.A.I.C.S.: 813211
Carrie Green (Sec)
Dale Burgeson (Treas)
Tim Anderson (Vice Chm)
Matt Hammer (Chm)

THREE RIVERS ELECTRIC COOP
1324 E Main St, Linn, MO 65051
Tel.: (573) 644-9000
Web Site:
  http://www.threeriverselectric.com
Sales Range: $10-24.9 Million
Emp.: 60
Distribution, Electric Power
N.A.I.C.S.: 221122
Tom Werdenhause (Pres & Gen Mgr)
Ted Neuner (Supvr-Engrg)
Bill Wibberg (Coord-Safety & Pur)
Kloeppel Roger (Head-Engrg)
Thayne Barton (Mgr-Admin Svcs)

THREE RIVERS FS COMPANY
217 Northside Rd, Earlville, IA 52041
Tel.: (563) 923-2315
Web Site:
  http://www.threeriversfs.com
Sales Range: $25-49.9 Million
Emp.: 85
Feed & Farm Supply
N.A.I.C.S.: 459999
Dave Kirsch (CEO)
Mark Feldman (CFO)
Gary Lahr (Chm)
Gary Kregel (Vice Chm)
Jim Kelchen (Treas & Sec)

THREE RIVERS LAND TRUST, INC.
204 E Innes St Ste 280, Salisbury, NC 28144
Tel.: (704) 647-0302   NC
Web Site:
  http://www.threeriverslandtrust.org
Sales Range: $1-9.9 Million
Emp.: 6
Land Conservation Services
N.A.I.C.S.: 813312
Jason A. Walser (Exec Dir)
Joe Morris (Dir-Dev)
Lynn Raker (Sec)
Bob Pendergrass (Treas)
Edward P. Norvell (VP)
Darrell Hancock (Pres)

Subsidiaries:
Sandhills Area Land Trust (1)
140 SW Broad St Ste A, Southern Pines, NC 28387-5405
Tel.: (910) 695-4323
Web Site: http://www.sandhillslandtrust.org
Research & Development in Biotechnology
N.A.I.C.S.: 541714
Nancy Talton (Exec Dir)

THREE RIVERS ORTHOPEDIC & SPINE PRODUCTS, INC.
5103 Center Dr Ste A, Latrobe, PA 15650-5203
Tel.: (724) 520-1600
Web Site: http://www.3riv.com
Year Founded: 1970
Sales Range: $10-24.9 Million
Emp.: 89
Medical Device Distr
N.A.I.C.S.: 423450
Craig Liberatore (Pres)
Mike Lynch (Dir-Sls-Recon)
Troy Keefer (Dir-Sls-Full Line)
Dan Huggins (Dir-Ops)
John Lennert (Mgr-Warehouse-Pennsylvania)

THREE RIVERS TRUCKING, INC.
2300 W Willow St, Long Beach, CA 90810
Tel.: (562) 432-0628   CA
Web Site:
  http://www.threeriverstrucking.com
Year Founded: 1988
Rev.: $12,500,000
Emp.: 30
Contract Haulers
N.A.I.C.S.: 484121
Imelda Castillo (Coord-Export)
Bruce White (Pres)

THREE WAY
42505 Christy St, Fremont, CA 94538
Tel.: (408) 748-3929
Web Site: http://www.threeway.com
Year Founded: 1954
Rev.: $42,106,000
Emp.: 90
Freight Transportation Arrangement
N.A.I.C.S.: 484110
Andoni Isasi (Mgr-Customer Svcs)
Kevin Scherer (Pres)

THREE WIRE SYSTEMS, LLC
3130 Fairview Park Dr Ste 425, Falls Church, VA 22042
Tel.: (703) 776-9731
Web Site:
  http://www.threewiresys.com
Sales Range: $10-24.9 Million
Emp.: 30
Computer System Design Services
N.A.I.C.S.: 541512
Dan Frank (CEO)
Mike Fabling (Sr VP-Tech Solutions)
Jennifer Roseman-Farabaugh (Exec VP-Military & Veteran Programs)
Bill Ogletree (CFO & Exec VP)
Gregory Feldman (Pres)
Ryan Latreille (CTO)
Kitty Nix (Sr VP-Strategy & Dev)
Phil De-Bodene (Sr VP-Bus Dev)
Paul Averna (Sr VP-Enterprise Sls)
Serena Bliss (Chief Info Security Officer)
Jan Patterson (VP-Admin)
Jennifer Christman (Pres-MyAdvisor)
Courtney Conroy (Dir-HealthCare)
Keith Foley (Sr Dir-Civilian)
John Meier (Sr VP-Tech)
John Wells (Sr Dir-Engrg & Delivery)

THRESHOLD ENTERPRISES, LTD.

23 Janis Way, Scotts Valley, CA 95066
Tel.: (831) 438-6851
Web Site:
  http://www.thresholdenterprises.com
Sales Range: $25-49.9 Million
Emp.: 600
Nutritional Formulations Mfr & Distr
N.A.I.C.S.: 325412
Diana Krentz (Mgr-Sls Office)
James Loveless (Mgr-Inventory Control)
Alea Lampman (Mgr-Pur)

Subsidiaries:
Source Naturals (1)
23 Janis Way, Scotts Valley, CA 95066
Tel.: (831) 438-1144
Web Site: http://www.sourcenaturals.com
Sales Range: $25-49.9 Million
Emp.: 450
Nutritional Formulations Mfr
N.A.I.C.S.: 325412
Ira Goldberg (CEO)

THRESHOLD FOUNDATION
PO Box 29903, San Francisco, CA 94129-0903
Tel.: (415) 561-6400   NY
Web Site:
  http://www.thresholdfoundation.org
Year Founded: 1982
Sales Range: $1-9.9 Million
Fundraising Organization
N.A.I.C.S.: 813211
Reid Williams (Treas)
Anne Irwin (Sec)
Terrence Meck (Pres)

THRESHOLD REHABILITATION SERVICES, INC.
1000 Lancaster Ave, Reading, PA 19607
Tel.: (610) 777-7691   PA
Web Site: http://www.trsinc.org
Year Founded: 1965
Sales Range: $10-24.9 Million
Emp.: 470
Disability Assistance Services
N.A.I.C.S.: 624120
Linda Groff (Dir-Behavioral Health)
Kathy Bell (Dir-Employment & Community Dev)
Heidi Shaffer (Dir-HR)

THRESHOLD VENTURES III, L.P.
2882 Sand Hill Rd #150, Menlo Park, CA 94025
Tel.: (650) 233-9000   DE
Web Site: http://www.threshold.vc
Year Founded: 1985
Privater Equity Firm
N.A.I.C.S.: 523999
Stephen T. Jurvetson (Founder)
Andreas Stavropoulos (Partner)
Josh Stein (Mng Partner)
Heidi Roizen (Partner)
Emily Melton (Mng Partner)
William Bryant (Partner)

THRIFTWAY INC.
1501 Davies St, Owensboro, KY 42303
Tel.: (270) 684-9438
Rev.: $13,000,000
Emp.: 38
Lumber & Other Building Materials
N.A.I.C.S.: 423310
Kristen Hardesty (Coord-Adv)
Rick Baker (Mgr-Store)
Kenneth V. Lawson Jr. (Pres)

THRIFTY DRUG STORES, INC.
6055 Nathan Ln N Ste 200, Plymouth, MN 55442-1675
Tel.: (763) 513-4300

Web Site: http://www.thriftywhite.com
Year Founded: 1995
Sales Range: $75-99.9 Million
Emp.: 1,300
Pharmaceutical Product Whslr
N.A.I.C.S.: 424210
Marilyn Thelen *(Pres)*
Dan Stout *(Mgr)*
Saeed Sassan *(Owner)*

THRIFTY OIL CO.
13116 Imperial Hwy, Santa Fe Springs, CA 90670-4836
Tel.: (562) 921-3581   CA
Year Founded: 1963
Sales Range: $75-99.9 Million
Emp.: 50
Real Estate & Management Services
N.A.I.C.S.: 531120
Ted Orden *(Chm & Pres)*
Barry Berkett *(Exec VP)*
Moshe Sassover *(Sr VP)*

Subsidiaries:

Golden West Refining Company   (1)
13116 Imperial Hwy, Santa Fe Springs, CA 90670   **(100%)**
Tel.: (562) 921-3581
Real Estate And Land Development
N.A.I.C.S.: 324110
Ted Orden *(Pres)*

THRIFTY SUPPLY CO.
13212 NE 16th St B Ste 312, Bellevue, WA 98005
Tel.: (425) 641-8073
Web Site: http://www.thriftysupply.com
Sales Range: $10-24.9 Million
Emp.: 35
Plumbing & Hydronic Heating Supplies
N.A.I.C.S.: 423720
Herman Gorelick *(Owner)*
Peter Natale *(Mgr-IT)*

THRILLIST MEDIA GROUP, INC.
560 Broadway Ste 605, New York, NY 10012-3938
Tel.: (212) 966-2263
Web Site: http://www.thrillist.com
Year Founded: 2004
Sales Range: $50-74.9 Million
Emp.: 200
Online Newsletter Services
N.A.I.C.S.: 513199
Adam Rich *(Co-Founder)*
Benjamin Lerer *(Co-Founder)*
Anthony Shneck *(Editor-Health)*
Nicole Caldwell *(Editor-Sex & Dating)*

THRIVE LIFE, LLC
691 S Auto Mall Dr, American Fork, UT 84003
Tel.: (801) 756-9902
Web Site: http://www.thrivelife.com
Year Founded: 2004
Sales Range: $25-49.9 Million
Emp.: 176
Food Storage System Distr
N.A.I.C.S.: 423740
Steve Palmer *(Founder)*
Amy Palmer *(Founder)*
Jason Budge *(Founder)*
Lindsay Budge *(Founder)*
Jason Norton *(Pres)*
Jeremy Taeoalii *(COO)*
Eric Morgan *(VP-Mktg)*
Sebastian Nilsson *(VP-Fin)*

THRIVE MORTGAGE LLC
4819 Williams Dr, Georgetown, TX 78633
Tel.: (512) 930-7888
Web Site: https://www.thrivemortgage.com
Emp.: 100
Financial Services
N.A.I.C.S.: 522310

Subsidiaries:

American Mortgage Service Company   (1)
415 Glensprings Dr # 203, Cincinnati, OH 45246
Tel.: (513) 421-9600
Web Site: http://www.americanhomelending.com
Sales Range: $1-9.9 Million
Emp.: 70
Real Estate Credit
N.A.I.C.S.: 522292
Dan Hickman *(Mgr-Sls)*
Vivian Moore *(Mgr-HR)*
Dave Osburg *(Branch Mgr)*
Rich Phillips *(Sr VP & Reg Mgr-Sls)*

THRIVE WORLD WIDE, INC.
647 Main St Ste 500, Lake Geneva, WI 53147
Tel.: (855) 889-2929
Web Site: http://www.thriveworldwide.com
Year Founded: 2005
Web-based Software Development Services
N.A.I.C.S.: 541511
Bruce T. Dugan *(CEO)*

THRIVENT FINANCIAL FOR LUTHERANS FOUNDATION
625 4th Ave S, Minneapolis, MN 55415-1624   MN
Web Site: http://www.thrivent.com
Year Founded: 1917
Sales Range: $5-14.9 Billion
Emp.: 2,300
Fraternal Benefit Society
N.A.I.C.S.: 813410
Paul R. Johnston *(Gen Counsel & Sec)*
Susan Oberman Smith *(Chief Actuary)*
Mary Nease *(Chief HR Officer)*
David S. Royal *(Chief Investment Officer)*
Bonnie E. Raquet *(Chm)*

Subsidiaries:

Newman Financial Services, LLC   (1)
6636 Cedar Ave S Ste 100, Richfield, MN 55423
Tel.: (612) 454-4400
Web Site: http://www.newmanltc.com
Long Term Care Insurance Services
N.A.I.C.S.: 524210
Andrea Meger *(Head-Ops, Fin & HR)*
Craig Roers *(Head-Mktg)*
Lori Gubash *(Dir-Sls-Natl)*
Jason Bonk *(Mgr-Case)*
Naomi Phakeovilay *(Mgr-Case)*

Thrivent Financial Investor Services Inc.   (1)
625 4th Ave S, Minneapolis, MN 55415-1624
Tel.: (612) 340-4030
Web Site: http://www.thrivent.com
Security Brokers
N.A.I.C.S.: 523150
Karen Hansis Larson *(VP & Gen Mgr)*

Thrivent Investment Management Inc.   (1)
625 4th Ave S, Minneapolis, MN 55415-1624
Tel.: (612) 340-7348
Web Site: http://www.thrivent.com
Sales Range: $100-124.9 Million
Emp.: 900
Securities Brokerage & Investment Advisory Services
N.A.I.C.S.: 523150
Karen Hansis Larson *(VP)*

Thrivent Life Insurance Company   (1)
625 4th Ave S, Minneapolis, MN 55415-1624
Tel.: (612) 340-8352
Web Site: http://www.thrivent.com
Sales Range: $200-249.9 Million
Emp.: 1,000
Life Insurance Products & Services
N.A.I.C.S.: 524113
Bradford L. Hewitt *(Pres & CEO)*

Thrivent Trust Company   (1)
4321 Ballard Rd, Appleton, WI 54919-0001
Web Site: http://www.thriventtrust.com
Trust Services
N.A.I.C.S.: 523991
Gary Bell *(Mng Dir-Ronald Blue Trust-Nashville)*
Zack Fulmer *(Mng Dir-Ronald Blue Trust-Orlando)*
Chris Scotchler *(Mng Dir-Ronald Blue Trust-Seattle)*
Brian Shepler *(Pres/Exec VP-Client Svcs-Ronald Blue Trust)*

THRU THE BIBLE RADIO NETWORK
1146 E Green St, Pasadena, CA 91106
Tel.: (626) 795-4145   CA
Web Site: http://www.ttb.org
Year Founded: 1967
Sales Range: $10-24.9 Million
Emp.: 18
Christian Ministry Services
N.A.I.C.S.: 813110
Gregg Harris *(VP)*
Leo Karlyn *(Chm & CEO)*

THRUSH AIRCRAFT, INC.
300 Old Pretoria Rd, Albany, GA 31721
Tel.: (229) 883-1440   GA
Web Site: http://www.thrushaircraft.com
Year Founded: 1958
Sales Range: $10-24.9 Million
Emp.: 280
Aircraft Mfr
N.A.I.C.S.: 336411
Mike Pierce *(Dir-Contract & Plng)*
Payne Hughes *(Pres)*
Eric Rojek *(VP-Sls)*
Diane Davis *(Dir-HR)*
Stan Logue *(CFO)*

THRUSTMASTER OF TEXAS, INC.
6900 Thrustmaster Dr, Houston, TX 77041
Tel.: (713) 937-6295
Web Site: http://www.thrustmastertexas.com
Sales Range: $75-99.9 Million
Emp.: 120
Marine Propulsion & Thruster Mfr
N.A.I.C.S.: 333618
Jack Chancellor *(Mgr-Sls-US)*
Rob Watson *(Mgr-Mktg)*
Bart Pols *(Dir-Sls-Asia Pacific)*
Derek James Kirkup *(Gen Mgr)*
Wim La Maitre *(Gen Mgr)*
Joshua Soong *(Gen Mgr)*
Andre Araujo *(Mgr-Sls)*
Daniel He *(Mgr-Sls-China-Natl)*
Melvin Yuen *(Mgr-Sls-Singapore)*
Bert Alt *(Gen Mgr)*
Jon Holvik *(Exec VP-Bus Dev-Dynamic Positioning Sys)*

THRUWAY FASTENERS INC.
2910 Niagara Falls Blvd, North Tonawanda, NY 14120-1140
Tel.: (716) 694-1434   NY
Web Site: http://www.thruwayfasteners.com
Year Founded: 1959
Sales Range: $25-49.9 Million
Emp.: 185
Distr of Hardware & Adhesives

N.A.I.C.S.: 423710
Pete Jenkins *(Pres)*
Patrick Gallagher *(Mgr-Quality Control)*
Russ Bowman *(Mgr-Quality)*
Mike Coad *(Gen Mgr)*
Stephanie Worden *(Office Mgr)*
Gerald Pullano *(CFO)*
Paul G. Lemke Sr. *(Chm)*

THUMANN, INC.
670 Dell Rd Ste 1, Carlstadt, NJ 07072
Tel.: (201) 935-3636
Web Site: http://www.thumanns.com
Year Founded: 1949
Sales Range: $50-74.9 Million
Emp.: 200
Meat Processing
N.A.I.C.S.: 311612
Tom Lewandowski *(Dir-Mktg & Sls)*
John Zelekowski *(Mgr-Production)*

THUMB BANCORP, INC.
7254 Michigan Ave, Pigeon, MI 48755   MI
Web Site: http://www.thumb.bank
Year Founded: 1995
Sales Range: $10-24.9 Million
Emp.: 77
Bank Holding Company
N.A.I.C.S.: 551111
Benjamin F. Schott *(Pres & CEO)*

Subsidiaries:

Thumb Bank & Trust   (1)
7254 Michigan Ave, Pigeon, MI 48755
Tel.: (989) 453-3113
Web Site: http://www.thumb.bank
Sales Range: $10-24.9 Million
Federal Savings Bank
N.A.I.C.S.: 522180
Mary Buda *(Sr VP & Head-Mortgage Lending)*
Michael LePage *(Pres-Thumb Area)*
Benjamin F. Schott *(Pres & CEO)*
Michelle Hill *(CFO & Exec VP)*
Debbie Deering *(Sr VP-HR)*
Bob Thomas *(Pres-Bay Area)*
John James Hempton II *(Chief Lending Officer & Exec VP)*

THUMB CELLULAR LTD. PARTNERSHIP
82 S Main St, Pigeon, MI 48755
Tel.: (989) 453-4333
Web Site: http://www.thumbcellular.com
Sales Range: $10-24.9 Million
Emp.: 41
Cellular Telephone Services
N.A.I.C.S.: 517112
Tammy Taylor *(Acct Mgr-Huron County)*
Lisa Calahan *(Acct Mgr-Sanilac County)*
Tracy Schuette *(Acct Mgr-Huron County)*
Corky Dean *(Mgr-Key Acct-Tuscola County)*

THUMB ELECTRIC COOP OF MICHIGAN
2231 E Main St, Ubly, MI 48475
Tel.: (989) 658-8571
Web Site: http://www.tecmi.coop
Sales Range: $10-24.9 Million
Emp.: 33
Electric Power Distr
N.A.I.C.S.: 221122
Dallas Braun *(Gen Mgr)*

THUMBTACK, INC.
454 Natoma St, San Francisco, CA 94103
Tel.: (415) 779-2191

THUMBTACK, INC.

Thumbtack, Inc.—(Continued)
Web Site: http://www.thumbtack.com
Sales Range: $10-24.9 Million
Emp.: 35
Internet Professional Services Directory Publisher
N.A.I.C.S.: 513140
Marco Zappacosta *(Co-Founder & CEO)*
Jonathan Swanson *(Co-Founder & Pres)*
Dan Birken *(Dir-Engrg)*
Sander Daniels *(Co-Founder)*
Raghavendra Prabhu *(Dir-Engrg)*
Alexander Kojevnikov *(Engr-Software)*
Benjamin Anderson *(Engr-Software)*
Jeffrey Lock *(Mgr-Product)*
Jenny Cook *(Mgr-Learning & Dev)*
Jeremy Mikkola *(Engr-Software)*
Tommy Saylor *(Engr-Software)*
Yue Zhao *(Mgr-Product)*
Noam Lovinsky *(VP-Product)*
Matteo Vianello *(Dir-Creative)*
Melanie Margolin *(Chief Legal Officer)*
Larry Roseman *(CFO)*
Jeff Grant *(COO)*
Nikhil Bobde *(CTO)*
P.J. Linarducci *(Chief Product Officer)*
Jelena Djordjevic *(VP-People)*
Llibert Argerich *(CMO)*
Mark Poston *(Chief Comml Officer)*

THUNDER TECH INC.
3635 Perkins Ave Studio 5 SW, Cleveland, OH 44114
Tel.: (216) 391-2255
Web Site:
  http://www.thundertech.com
Year Founded: 1999
Sales Range: $1-9.9 Million
Emp.: 35
Advetising Agency
N.A.I.C.S.: 541810
Marc Theodore *(Mgr-Ops)*

THUNDERBIRD LLC
1501 Oakton St, Elk Grove Village, IL 60007
Tel.: (847) 718-9300
Web Site:
  http://www.thunderbirdllc.com
Year Founded: 1999
Investment Holding Company
N.A.I.C.S.: 551112
John Newell *(Co-Founder & Partner)*
Kevin Prunsky *(Co-Founder & Partner)*
Phillip G. Kretekos *(Pres)*

Subsidiaries:

Bright Plastics, Inc. (1)
4833 High Point Rd, Greensboro, NC 27407
Tel.: (336) 668-3636
Web Site: http://www.brightplastics.com
Rev.: $9,000,000
Emp.: 70
All Other Plastics Product Mfr
N.A.I.C.S.: 326199
Kirk Sparks *(Pres)*
Steve Bright *(CEO)*
Kate Bryant *(Mgr-Quality & Trng)*
Todd Poteat *(VP-Mfg)*
Joe Vest *(VP-Engrg & Logistics)*
Jeff Larrimore *(Controller)*

F&B Mfg. LLC (1)
4245 N 40th Ave, Phoenix, AZ 85019-3512
Tel.: (602) 272-3900
Web Site: http://www.fbmfg.com
Sales Range: $25-49.9 Million
Emp.: 120
Fabricated Metal Parts & Sub-Assemblies Mfr
N.A.I.C.S.: 332999
Misty Reynolds *(Mgr-Sls)*

MPR Plastics Inc. (1)
1551 Scottsdale Ct Unit Ste 100, Elgin, IL 60123
Tel.: (847) 468-9950
Web Site: http://www.mprplastics.com
Plastic Injection Molded Parts & Assemblies Mfr & Distr
N.A.I.C.S.: 326199
Donald Wessendorf *(Mgr-Tool Room)*

Metal Impact LLC (1)
1501 Oakton St, Elk Grove Village, IL 60007-2101
Tel.: (847) 718-9300
Web Site: http://www.metalimpact.com
Sales Range: $25-49.9 Million
Emp.: 300
Contract Aluminum Impact Extrusion & Cold-Forged Steel Products Mfr
N.A.I.C.S.: 331318
John Newell *(Partner)*
Kevin Prunsky *(Partner)*

THUNDERCAT TECHNOLOGY, LLC
1775 Wiehle Ave Ste 101, Reston, VA 20190
Tel.: (703) 657-7050
Web Site:
  http://www.thundercattech.com
Year Founded: 2008
Information Technology Consulting Services
N.A.I.C.S.: 541690
Thomas J. Deierlein *(CEO)*
Keith McMeans *(Founder & Gen Mgr)*
Andrew Donnelly *(Principal)*
David Schlosser *(COO)*
Daniel Schneider *(Dir-Cyber Security Sls)*

THUNDERMIST HEALTH CENTER
191 Social St 9th Fl, Woonsocket, RI 02895
Tel.: (401) 767-4161
Web Site:
  http://www.thundermisthealth.org
Year Founded: 1969
Sales Range: $25-49.9 Million
Emp.: 469
Health Care Center Association
N.A.I.C.S.: 813910
David Bourassa *(Chief Medical Officer)*
Jeanne LaChance *(Pres & CEO)*
Matthew Roman *(COO)*
Timothy Henry *(Chm)*

THURLAND REAY FAMILY INVESTMENT CO.
2100 N Kolb Rd, Tucson, AZ 85715
Tel.: (520) 298-2391
Web Site:
  http://www.reaysranchinvestors.com
Rev.: $38,871,629
Emp.: 450
Grocery Store Operator
N.A.I.C.S.: 456191
Gordon Reay *(Pres)*
Rod Herbert *(CFO)*

THURMAN HOTEL CONSULTANTS
1808 James L Redman Pkwy #313, Plant City, FL 33563
Tel.: (877) 790-5002
Web Site:
  http://www.thurmanhotelconsultants.com
Sales Range: $10-24.9 Million
Emp.: 6
Hotel Sales, Reputation Management & Online Support Consulting Services
N.A.I.C.S.: 541611
Gwen Thurman *(CEO)*
Cusic Daniels *(Pres)*
Kristina Gildersleeve *(Mgr-ECommerce & Social Media)*

THURSTON AUTO PLAZA
2800 N State St, Ukiah, CA 95482-3028
Tel.: (707) 462-8817
Web Site:
  http://www.thurstonautoplaza.com
Year Founded: 1990
Sales Range: $10-24.9 Million
Emp.: 50
Car Whslr
N.A.I.C.S.: 441110
Jason Thurston *(Gen Mgr)*

THURSTON GROUP, LLC
225 W Washington St Ste 1575, Chicago, IL 60606
Tel.: (312) 255-0077
Web Site:
  http://www.thurstongroup.com
Year Founded: 1986
Privater Equity Firm
N.A.I.C.S.: 523999
Patrick J. Hayes III *(CEO)*
Willard C. McNitt III *(Principal)*
John E. McGovern III *(Principal)*

Subsidiaries:

ARC Health Holdings, LLC (1)
25800 Science Park Dr Ste 210, Beachwood, OH 44122
Tel.: (800) 339-3903
Web Site: https://archealthpartners.com
Mental Health Care Services
N.A.I.C.S.: 621112
Vince Morra *(CEO)*

Subsidiary (Domestic):

Advanced Psychiatric Group, P.A (2)
721 N Magnolia Ave, Orlando, FL 32803
Tel.: (407) 423-7149
Web Site: https://www.apghealth.com
Freestanding Ambulatory Surgical & Emergency Centers
N.A.I.C.S.: 621493

The Ross Center for Anxiety & Related Disorders, LLC (2)
5225 Wisconsin Ave NW, Washington, DC 20015
Tel.: (202) 363-1010
Web Site: http://www.rosscenter.com
Offices of All Other Miscellaneous Health Practitioners
N.A.I.C.S.: 621399
Beth Salcedo *(Dir-Medical)*

THWING-ALBERT INSTRUMENT COMPANY
14 W Collings Ave, West Berlin, NJ 08091
Tel.: (856) 767-1000
Web Site:
  http://www.thwingalbert.com
Year Founded: 1899
Sales Range: $50-74.9 Million
Emp.: 45
Advanced Testing Instruments Mfr
N.A.I.C.S.: 334519
Joseph Raab *(Pres)*
Brenda Fisher *(Mgr-Mktg)*
Steve Berg *(VP-Sls & Mktg)*

Subsidiaries:

Thwing-Albert Netherlands (1)
Postbus 30030, 1339 GS, Almere, Netherlands (100%)
Tel.: (31) 365352721
Web Site: http://www.thwing-albert.nl
Sales Range: $10-24.9 Million
Emp.: 5
Instruments
N.A.I.C.S.: 334513

THYBONY WALLCOVERINGS INC.
5424 N Clark St, Chicago, IL 60640
Tel.: (773) 463-3050
Web Site: http://www.thybony.com
Year Founded: 1886

U.S. PRIVATE

Sales Range: $75-99.9 Million
Emp.: 120
Mfr & Distr of Wall Coverings
N.A.I.C.S.: 424950
James D. Thybony *(Pres)*
Bo Pruski *(VP-Fin)*
Robin Thybony *(VP-Sls)*

TIAX LLC
35 Hartwell Ave, Lexington, MA 02421-3102
Tel.: (781) 879-1200
Web Site: http://www.tiaxllc.com
Year Founded: 1886
Sales Range: $100-124.9 Million
Emp.: 301
Technology & Product Development; Environmental, Health & Safety Consulting; Management Consulting Services
N.A.I.C.S.: 541330
Kenan Sahin *(Founder, Pres & CTO)*

Subsidiaries:

Camx Power LLC (1)
35 Hartwell Ave, Lexington, MA 02421-3102
Tel.: (781) 879-1285
Primary Battery Mfr
N.A.I.C.S.: 335910

TIBA PARKING LLC
5126 S Royal Atlanta Dr, Tucker, GA 30084
Tel.: (770) 491-7586
Web Site: http://www.tibaparking.com
Parking & Facility Management Services
N.A.I.C.S.: 561210
Matty Roter *(CTO)*

Subsidiaries:

Signature Control Systems, LLC (1)
405 N Brice Rd, Blacklick, OH 43004
Tel.: (614) 864-2222
Web Site: http://www.signaturecontrols.com
Sales Range: $1-9.9 Million
Emp.: 42
Wholesales & Installs Parking Control Devices
N.A.I.C.S.: 423610
Jon Bowsher *(Owner & Pres)*
Shawn Page *(CTO)*

TIBBETTS LUMBER CO., LLC
3300 Fairfield Ave S, Saint Petersburg, FL 33712
Tel.: (727) 322-1403
Web Site:
  http://www.tibbettslumber.com
Sales Range: $10-24.9 Million
Emp.: 150
Lumber & Building Materials Retailer
N.A.I.C.S.: 423310
Juan Quesada *(Pres)*

Subsidiaries:

D & M Truss Co. Inc. (1)
2620 W Michigan Ave, Pensacola, FL 32526
Tel.: (850) 944-5546
Web Site: http://www.dmtruss.com
Sales Range: $1-9.9 Million
Emp.: 33
Truss Mfr
N.A.I.C.S.: 321215
Steve McGowan *(Pres)*

Florida Forest Products, LLC (1)
1975 20th Ave SE, Largo, FL 33771
Tel.: (727) 585-2067
Web Site: http://www.ffptruss.com
Sales Range: $1-9.9 Million
Emp.: 35
Truss Mfr
N.A.I.C.S.: 321215
Rick Cashman *(Owner)*
Ron Hott *(Mgr-Production)*
Dona Skinner *(Controller)*
Ralph Del Valle *(Mgr-Sls)*

COMPANIES

TIBERSOFT CORPORATION
1900 W Park Dr Ste 180, Westborough, MA 01581-3919
Tel.: (508) 898-9555
Web Site: http://www.tibersoft.com
Year Founded: 1996
Sales Range: $1-9.9 Million
Food Cost Control Systems for the Foodservices Industry
N.A.I.C.S.: 334519
Christopher W. Martin (CEO)
Mary Wilson (Founder & VP-Fin & Ops)

TIBERTI ORGANIZATION
1806 Industrial Rd, Las Vegas, NV 89102
Tel.: (702) 248-4000
Web Site: http://www.tiberti.com
Sales Range: $10-24.9 Million
Emp.: 12
Management & Construction Services & Mfr of Fences
N.A.I.C.S.: 238990
Renaldo Tiberti (Pres)

Subsidiaries:

J. A. Tiberti Construction Co., Inc. (1)
1806 Industrial Rd, Las Vegas, NV 89102 (100%)
Tel.: (702) 248-4000
Web Site: http://www.tiberti.com
Rev.: $12,200,000
Emp.: 10
Provider of Commercial & Office Building Construction
N.A.I.C.S.: 236220

The Tiberti Fence Company (1)
4975 Rogers St, Las Vegas, NV 89118
Tel.: (702) 382-7070
Web Site: http://www.tibertifence.com
Fence Construction
N.A.I.C.S.: 238990

TIBOR MACHINE PRODUCTS INC.
7400 W 100 Pl, Bridgeview, IL 60455-1504
Tel.: (708) 499-3700
Web Site: http://www.tibormachine.com
Year Founded: 1968
Sales Range: $10-24.9 Million
Emp.: 170
Mfr of Industrial Machinery
N.A.I.C.S.: 332710
Mark A. Lindemulder (Pres & CEO)
Jerry Stockton (Exec VP)

TIC INTERNATIONAL CORPORATION
11590 N Meridian St Ste 600, Carmel, IN 46032
Tel.: (317) 580-8686
Web Site: http://www.tici.com
Year Founded: 1951
Rev.: $1,000,000
Emp.: 45
Pension & Retirement Plan Consultants
N.A.I.C.S.: 524298
James Schreiber (Pres)

TIC PROPERTIES, LLC
777 Lowndes Hill Rd Bldg 3 Ste 110, Greenville, SC 29607
Tel.: (864) 672-4842
Web Site: http://www.ticpropertiesmanagement.com
Year Founded: 2001
Sales Range: $150-199.9 Million
Emp.: 20
Real Estate Services
N.A.I.C.S.: 531390

Josh A. Workman (COO)
Barry L. Gruebbel (Pres)

Subsidiaries:

Banker Exchange, LLC (1)
555 N Pleasantburg Dr Ste 110, Greenville, SC 29607
Tel.: (864) 271-1449
Tax Intermediary
N.A.I.C.S.: 541213

TIC TOC
4006 E Side Ave, Dallas, TX 75226
Tel.: (214) 416-9300
Web Site: http://www.tictoc.com
Year Founded: 1974
Advetising Agency
N.A.I.C.S.: 541810
Paul Gittemeier (CEO)
Julia Shifflett (Pres)
Amy Burrows (VP-Client Svcs)
Maria Koch (Creative Dir)
Alex Watson (VP-New Bus Dev)
Michael Ramsey (VP-Client Svcs)
Susie Aleman (VP-Client Svcs)
Steven Kearl (Acct Dir)
Chelsea Bilbia (Acct Mgr)
Dan Gittemeier (Sls Dir)
Haylee Vieregg (Acct Mgr)
Courtney Baptiste (Acct Mgr)
Diana Harley (Controller)

TICK DATA, INC.
10134 Colvin Run Rd Ste G, Great Falls, VA 22066-1841
Tel.: (703) 757-1370
Web Site: http://www.tickdata.com
Year Founded: 1984
Electronic Stock Pricing Information
N.A.I.C.S.: 519290
Thomas N. Falkenberry (Pres)

TICKET ALTERNATIVE, LLC
1369 Spring St NW, Atlanta, GA 30309
Tel.: (404) 897-2384
Web Site: http://www.ticketalternative.com
Year Founded: 2004
Sales Range: $1-9.9 Million
Emp.: 55
Boutique Ticketing Software
N.A.I.C.S.: 513210
Iain Bluett (Pres)

TICKETCITY INC.
5912 Balcones Dr Ste 102, Austin, TX 78731-4289
Tel.: (512) 472-5797
Web Site: http://www.ticketcity.com
Year Founded: 1990
Sales Range: $25-49.9 Million
Emp.: 39
Ticket Broker
N.A.I.C.S.: 425120
Randy Cohen (CEO)
Clark Kothlow (CFO)
Zach Anderson (Pres)
Rafael Rivas (VP-Sls & Chief Strategy Officer)

TICKETLEAP INC.
2401 Walnut St Ste 502, Philadelphia, PA 19103
Tel.: (215) 525-1300
Web Site: http://www.ticketleap.com
Year Founded: 2003
Sales Range: $1-9.9 Million
Emp.: 22
Ticket Reservation Services
N.A.I.C.S.: 561599
Christopher Stanchak (Founder & Chm)
Tim Raybould (Pres & CEO)

TICKETNETWORK, INC.

75 Gerber Rd E, South Windsor, CT 06074
Tel.: (860) 644-4000
Web Site: http://www.ticketnetwork.com
Year Founded: 2002
Online Ticketing Services
N.A.I.C.S.: 561599
Donald J. Vaccaro (Co-Founder & CEO)
Douglas J. Kruse (Co-Founder & CTO)

Subsidiaries:

ScoreBig.com (1)
75 Gerber Rd S Ste 116, South Windsor, CT 06074
Tel.: (877) 726-7324
Web Site: http://www.scorebig.com
Online Ticketing Services
N.A.I.C.S.: 561599

TICKETS FOR KIDS CHARITIES
139 Freeport Rd, Pittsburgh, PA 15215
Tel.: (412) 781-5437 PA
Web Site: http://www.ticketsforkids.org
Year Founded: 2002
Sales Range: $1-9.9 Million
Emp.: 9
Child Welfare Services
N.A.I.C.S.: 624110
Chris Anderson (Mgr-Ticket Rels)
Meryl Hellring (Dir-Dev & Comm)
Carolyn L. Falk (Program Dir)
Jason J. Riley (Exec Dir)
Bruce B. Weiner (Chm & Pres)
George L. Stewart II (VP)

TICKETZOOM.COM
336 Bon Air Ctr #486, Greenbrae, CA 94904
Tel.: (800) 323-7329
Web Site: http://www.ticketzoom.com
Year Founded: 2005
Sales Range: $10-24.9 Million
Emp.: 6
Online Reseller of Event Tickets
N.A.I.C.S.: 711320
Robert Gavin (Chm & CEO)

TICO TITANIUM INC.
30150 S Wixom Rd, Wixom, MI 48393
Tel.: (248) 446-0400
Web Site: http://www.ticotitanium.com
Emp.: 125
Provider of Metal Products
N.A.I.C.S.: 423510
James D. Morell (CFO)
Lynn A. Brace (Gen Mgr)
Jeffrey A. White (Pres)

TICOMIX, INC.
5642 N 2nd St, Loves Park, IL 61111
Tel.: (779) 423-6200 IL
Web Site: http://www.ticomix.com
Year Founded: 1999
Sales Range: $10-24.9 Million
Emp.: 40
Custom Software & Information Technology Support Services
N.A.I.C.S.: 541519
Timothy N. Ancona (CEO)
John Manna (VP-Sls-Aptris-Northern Reg)
Kevin Reichley (VP-Sls-CRM)
David Achilli (Dir-Network Svcs)
Brian Huber (Dir-Pro Svcs)
Mike Roberts (VP-Mktg)
Steven J. Horvath (VP-Advisory Svcs)
Phyllis Ginestra (CFO)

TIDE ROCK HOLDINGS, LLC

TICOMO VALLEY CORP
475 E Badillo St, Covina, CA 91723
Tel.: (626) 967-1779
Web Site: http://www.mastersrealestate.com
Rev.: $10,200,000
Emp.: 18
Real Estate Agents & Managers
N.A.I.C.S.: 531210
Jose Pastora (Pres)
Maria Baran (Sec-Escrow)

TICON, INC.
5836 Fayetteville Rd Ste 201, Durham, NC 27713
Tel.: (919) 484-1060 NC
Web Site: http://www.ticonproperties.com
Rev.: $14,000,000
Emp.: 40
Operator of Apartment Buildings
N.A.I.C.S.: 531110
W. Jack McGhee (Pres)

TIDAL POWER SERVICES, LLC.
4202 Chance Ln, Rosharon, TX 77583
Tel.: (281) 710-9150
Web Site: http://www.tidalpowerservices.com
Year Founded: 2002
Sales Range: $10-24.9 Million
Emp.: 50
Eletric Power Generation Services
N.A.I.C.S.: 221118
Dennis Janak (Pres)

TIDE PETROLEUM CORP.
700 Louisiana St Ste 3950, Houston, TX 77002
Tel.: (832) 390-2635 NV
Web Site: http://www.tidepetroleum.com
Year Founded: 2014
Oil & Gas Exploration
N.A.I.C.S.: 211120
John L. Smoot (CEO & CFO)

TIDE ROCK HOLDINGS, LLC
1953 San Elijo Ave #203, Cardiff, CA 92007
Web Site: http://www.tiderockholdings.com
Privater Equity Firm
N.A.I.C.S.: 523999
Ryan Peddycord (CEO)
Brooks Kincaid (Pres)

Subsidiaries:

Bayless Engineering, Inc. (1)
26100 Avenue Hall, Valencia, CA 91355
Tel.: (661) 257-3373
Web Site: http://www.baylessengineering.com
Rev.: $5,295,039
Emp.: 135
All Other Miscellaneous Fabricated Metal Product Mfr
N.A.I.C.S.: 332999
Earl Bayless (Founder)
Robert Lummus (CEO)

Cal Micro Recycling (1)
1541 Brooks St, Ontario, CA 91762-3619
Tel.: (909) 467-4800
Web Site: http://www.onestoprecycler.com
Recyclable Material Merchant Whslr
N.A.I.C.S.: 423930

Plastics Design & Manufacturing, Inc. (1)
6284 S Nome Ct, Centennial, CO 80111
Tel.: (303) 768-8380
Web Site: http://www.plasticsdesign-mfg.com
Sales Range: $1-9.9 Million
Emp.: 52
Custom Thermoformer
N.A.I.C.S.: 326199

TIDE ROCK HOLDINGS, LLC   U.S. PRIVATE

Tide Rock Holdings, LLC—(Continued)
Michael Engler (CEO)
Trent Cunningham (Pres)

Pro-Active Engineering, Inc. (1)
350 Business Park Dr, Sun Prairie, WI 53590
Tel.: (608) 837-7838
Web Site: http://www.proactivepcb.com
Rev.: $3,000,000
Emp.: 20
Engineeering Services
N.A.I.C.S.: 541330
Toby Klusmeyer (Founder,Pres & CEO)

Specialized Coating Services (1)
42680 Christy St, Fremont, CA 94538
Tel.: (510) 226-8700
Web Site: http://www.speccoat.com
Sales Range: $1-9.9 Million
Emp.: 17
Bare Printed Circuit Board Mfr
N.A.I.C.S.: 334412
Ed Branco (CTO)
Rick Ramirez (Pres)

Triad Service Solutions, Inc (1)
8257 Southpark Cir, Littleton, CO 80120
Tel.: (303) 744-8285
Web Site: http://www.triadservices.biz
Rev.: $5,000,000
Emp.: 24
Other Chemical & Allied Products Merchant Whslr
N.A.I.C.S.: 424690
Michael E. Bondi (Pres)

TIDELAND ELECTRIC MEMBERSHIP CORPORATION
25831 US Hwy 264 E, Pantego, NC 27860
Tel.: (252) 943-3046
Web Site: http://www.tidelandemc.com
Sales Range: $25-49.9 Million
Emp.: 100
Distr of Electric Power
N.A.I.C.S.: 221122
Myra Beasley (Mgr-HR)
Heidi Jernigan Smith (Mgr-Corp Comm)
Wayne Brackin (Dir-Safety)
Ben Beagle (Mgr-Ops)
Bill Waters (Mgr-IT)
Paul Spruill (CEO)

TIDELANDS FORD - LINCOLN
9387 Ocean Hwy, Pawleys Island, SC 29585-7596
Tel.: (843) 237-3673
Web Site: http://www.tidelands.net
Year Founded: 1995
Sales Range: $10-24.9 Million
Emp.: 29
Car Whslr
N.A.I.C.S.: 441110
John Paglio (Pres)

TIDEPOOL PROJECT
555 Bryant St Ste 429, Palo Alto, CA 94301
Tel.: (650) 353-2352   CA
Web Site: http://www.tidepool.org
Year Founded: 2012
Rev.: $1,130,759
Assets: $94,968
Liabilities: $198,899
Net Worth: ($103,931)
Earnings: ($559,842)
Emp.: 6
Fiscal Year-end: 06/30/14
Health Care Technology Support Services
N.A.I.C.S.: 621999
Brandon Arbiter (VP-Product & Bus Dev)
Howard Look (Founder, Pres & CEO)
Steve McCanne (CTO)

TIDES
PO Box 29198, San Francisco, CA 94129-0198
Tel.: (415) 561-6400   CA
Web Site: http://www.tides.org
Year Founded: 2005
Sales Range: $10-24.9 Million
Emp.: 139
Community Welfare Services
N.A.I.C.S.: 624190
Kriss Deiglmeier (CEO)
Judith Hill (CFO)
Amanda Keton (Dir-Legal)
Kim Sarnecki (Dir-Admin & Real Estate)
Patti Robinson (Dir-HR)
Deepak Puri (VP-Strategic Alliances)
Jason Wingard (Chm)

TIDEWATER DIRECT LLC
300 Tidewater Dr, Centreville, MD 21617
Tel.: (410) 758-1500
Web Site: http://www.tidewaterdirect.com
Year Founded: 1959
Rev.: $12,400,000
Emp.: 100
Commercial Lithographic Printing
N.A.I.C.S.: 323111
Ken Boone (Pres)
April Mackenzie (Controller)
Aurthur Kudner III (Mgr-Sls)

Subsidiaries:

American Direct LLC (1)
3501 Duncanwood Ln, Baltimore, MD 21213-4003
Tel.: (443) 772-0922
Printing Services for Personalized Letters, Direct Mail Forms & Cut Sheets
N.A.I.C.S.: 323111

TIDEWATER EQUIPMENT COMPANY
7303 Blythe Island Pkwy, Brunswick, GA 31523-6254
Tel.: (912) 265-8760
Web Site: http://www.tidewaterequip.com
Year Founded: 1947
Sales Range: $25-49.9 Million
Emp.: 6
Logging Equipment & Supplies
N.A.I.C.S.: 423810
Earl Tarry (Controller)
John Carrillo (Mgr-Fin)

TIDEWATER HOLDINGS, INC.
6305 NW Old Lowr River Rd, Vancouver, WA 98660
Tel.: (360) 693-1491   DE
Web Site: http://www.tidewater.com
Year Founded: 1996
Sales Range: $25-49.9 Million
Emp.: 250
Freight Transportation by Water
N.A.I.C.S.: 483211
Kelly Larson (Mgr-Fin Analysis)
Stan Smith (Mgr-IT & QA)
Marc Schwartz (Mgr-Maintenance & Engrg)
Aaron Degodny (Chief Comml Officer & VP)

Subsidiaries:

Sundial Marine Tug & Barge Works Inc. (1)
5605 NE Sundial Rd, Troutdale, OR 97060-9504
Tel.: (503) 667-1974
Sales Range: $10-24.9 Million
Emp.: 100
Mfr & Repair of Ships
N.A.I.C.S.: 336611

Tidewater Barge Lines Inc. (1)
6305 NW Old Lowr River Rd, Vancouver, WA 98660-1068   (100%)
Tel.: (360) 693-1491
Web Site: http://www.tidewater.com
Rev.: $60,000,000
Emp.: 55
Provider of Freight Transportation by Water
N.A.I.C.S.: 483211
Bob Curcio (CEO)
Myron Reising (CFO)

Tidewater Terminal Company Inc. (1)
6305 NW Old Lowr River Rd, Vancouver, WA 98660-7103   (100%)
Tel.: (360) 693-1491
Web Site: http://www.tidewater.com
Sales Range: $10-24.9 Million
Emp.: 75
Provider of Special Warehousing & Storage
N.A.I.C.S.: 493190
Andy Stephens (VP-Bus Dev & Terminals)

TIDEWATER PIZZA TIME INC.
905 W 21st St, Norfolk, VA 23517
Tel.: (757) 456-0010
Web Site: http://www.chanellospizza.com
Rev.: $20,000,000
Emp.: 6
Pizza Restaurant
N.A.I.C.S.: 722513
Juliette Chanel (Pres)

TIDEWATER TRANSIT CO., INC.
Hwy 70 W, Kinston, NC 28504
Tel.: (252) 523-4103
Web Site: http://www.tidewater-transit.com
Rev.: $12,900,000
Emp.: 50
Contract Haulers
N.A.I.C.S.: 484121
Kim Tucker (CFO)
James Bailey (Mgr-Quality Control)
Joe Clay Jones (Mgr-Comml Acct)
David Edgerton (Dir-Safety)
Silas Martin (Supvr-Shop)
Kendra Warren (VP-Admin)
Michael Ling (Dir-IT)
Ricky Johnson (Mgr-Ops)
Don Greenwaldt (Dir-Trng)
Jim Notarfrancesco (Mgr-Ops)
Todd Lindquist (Mgr-Ops)
John Williams (VP-Bus Dev)
Dave Arnold (VP-Ops)

TIDEWELL HOSPICE INC.
5955 Rand Blvd, Sarasota, FL 34238
Tel.: (941) 552-7500
Web Site: http://www.tidewell.org
Sales Range: $50-74.9 Million
Emp.: 800
Hospice Care Services
N.A.I.C.S.: 621610
Gerry Radford (Pres & CEO)
Stephen A. Leedy (Chief Medical Officer)
Jan Miller (Chm)

TIDWELL GROUP, LLC
2001 Park Pl N Ste 900, Birmingham, AL 35203
Tel.: (205) 822-1010
Web Site: http://www.tidwellgroup.com
Sales Range: $10-24.9 Million
Emp.: 40
Accounting & Auditing Services
N.A.I.C.S.: 541211
J. Barry Tidwell (Mng Partner)
Todd Fentress (Mng Partner-Office)
Aram Moore (Partner)
Kevin Allmandinger (Partner)

TIE DOWN ENGINEERING, INC.
5901 Wheaton Dr, Atlanta, GA 30336-2625
Tel.: (404) 344-0000   GA
Web Site: http://www.tiedown.com
Year Founded: 1971
Sales Range: $10-24.9 Million
Emp.: 250
Mfr of Fabricated Structural Metal
N.A.I.C.S.: 332312
Chuck MacKarvich (Chm)
Merrill Sutton (VP-Mktg-OEM Trailer)
Shirley Davenport (Exec VP-Sls)
David Maxey (VP-Sls & Mktg)

TIENDAS LA GLORIA INC.
6 W Ernesto Ramos Antonini St, Mayaguez, PR 00680
Tel.: (787) 834-0450
Rev.: $23,000,000
Emp.: 100
Shoe Stores
N.A.I.C.S.: 458210
Ramon Vidal Nadal (Pres)
Epiosanio Vidal Cruz (VP)

TIENDAS LA GRAN VIA INC.
167 Ave De Diego, Arecibo, PR 00612
Tel.: (787) 878-3396
Web Site: http://www.lagranviapr.com
Rev.: $22,798,536
Emp.: 240
Sales of Men's & Boys' Clothing
N.A.I.C.S.: 458110
Joaquin Gutierrez (Pres)
Enrique Ledo (VP)

TIER 1 PERFORMANCE SOLUTIONS, LLC
100 E RiverCenter Blvd Ste 100
Tower 2, Covington, KY 41011
Tel.: (859) 415-1000   KY
Web Site: http://www.tier1performance.com
Year Founded: 2002
Sales Range: $10-24.9 Million
Emp.: 200
Business Consulting Services
N.A.I.C.S.: 541611
Greg Harmeyer (Co-Founder, CEO & Partner)
Kevin Moore (Co-Founder & Partner)
Normand Desmarais (Co-Founder, Chm & Partner)
Jerry Hamburg (VP-Solution Svcs)
Kerry Headley (Mng Dir)
Anna Wolf (CFO)
Brian Lapthorn (VP-Market Dev)
Jim Feniello (CTO)
John Drugo (Mng Dir-Bus Dev)
John Perkins (Mng Dir)
Karen Nelson (Mng Dir-People Ops)
Mark Renneker (Dir-Market Dev)
Michael Fortin (Mng Dir)
Jack Calhoun (Mng Dir)
Amy Fox (Mng Dir)
Brandee Abel (Mng Dir)
Jim Ruberg (Mng Dir-Organizational Evolution)
Katie Frey (Mng Dir-Strategic Change Capability Lead)
Stu Rodgers (Mng Dir)

Subsidiaries:

Bottom-Line Performance, Inc. (1)
4022 Arbor Lane, New Palestine, IN 46163
Tel.: (317) 861-7281
Web Site: http://www.bottomlineperformance.com
Sales Range: $1-9.9 Million
Emp.: 29
Project Development Services
N.A.I.C.S.: 541511
Leanne Batchelder (VP-Client Rels)
Jennifer Bertram (Dir-Instructional Design)
Kirk Boller (Co-Founder & CFO)
Sharon Boller (Co-Founder, Pres & CEO)
Steven Boller (Dir-Mktg)

Centurion Systems, Inc. (1)

2310 Pk Lake Dr NE Suite 300, Atlanta, GA 30345 **(100%)**
Tel.: (404) 929-3301
Web Site: http://www.centurionsys.com
Rev.: $1,800,000
Emp.: 100
Custom & Performance Improvement Solutions for the Retail Industry
N.A.I.C.S.: 513210
Jerry Leverette (Founder & Pres)
Marijana Bratic (Project Mgr)

Rapid Learning Deployment, LLC (1)
1775 Woodstock Rd Ste 300, Roswell, GA 30075
Tel.: (770) 874-1190
Web Site: http://www.rapidld.com
Sales Range: $1-9.9 Million
Emp.: 17
Professional Development Learning Center Operator
N.A.I.C.S.: 611691
James M. Everidge (Founder, Pres & CEO)
Chris Terry (Founder & VP-Consulting Ops)
C. Reed Jones (Founder)
Will Avery (Founder)
Shivakumar Venkatakrishna (Dir-Tech Solutions)
Tony Alexander (Dir-Consulting)
Steve Owens (Founder)

TIER ONE PARTNERS
29 Turning Mill Rd, Lexington, MA 02420
Tel.: (781) 861-5249
Web Site: http://www.tieronepr.com
Year Founded: 2003
Sales Range: $1-9.9 Million
Emp.: 18
Public Relations Agency
N.A.I.C.S.: 541820
Marian Sly Hughes (Mng Partner)
Sue Parente (Mng Partner)
Kathy Wilson (Founder & Mng Partner)
Laureen McGowan Sanderson (Partner)
Sarah Mees (Sr Acct Dir)
Matt McCarthy (Acct Mgr)
Allison Salzberg (Sr Acct Dir)
Celena Fine (VP)

TIER-RACK CORPORATION
425 Sovereign Ct, Ballwin, MO 63011
Tel.: (636) 527-0700
Web Site: http://www.tierrack.com
Sales Range: $10-24.9 Million
Emp.: 11
Mfr of Wooden Shelves
N.A.I.C.S.: 337126
Charles Scott Teneyck (Pres)
Alan Lajeunesse (Reg Mgr-Sls)
Mike Mudd (Mgr-Sls)
Todd Windes (Reg Mgr-Sls)
Ward Wilson (VP-Fin)

TIER10
13825 Sunrise Valley Dr Ste 150, Herndon, VA 20171
Tel.: (703) 552-4140
Web Site: http://www.tier10.com
Year Founded: 2008
Sales Range: $10-24.9 Million
Emp.: 53
Advertising & Marketing Consulting Services
N.A.I.C.S.: 541613
Scott Rodgers (Co-Founder & Chief Creative Officer)
Scott Fletcher (Co-Founder & VP-Acct Svcs)

TIERRA, INC
7351 Temple Ter Hwy, Tampa, FL 33637
Tel.: (813) 989-1354
Web Site: http://www.tierraeng.com
Year Founded: 1992
Rev.: $11,000,000
Emp.: 81
Engineering Consulting Services
N.A.I.C.S.: 541330
Raj Krishnasamy (Owner)
Luis Mahiquez (Pres)
Chris Federick (Dir-HR)
Dominique Bennett (Mgr-Fin)

TIES
1667 Snelling Ave N, Saint Paul, MN 55108
Tel.: (651) 999-6000
Web Site: http://www.ties.k12.mn.us
Sales Range: $10-24.9 Million
Emp.: 70
Computer Software Development & Applications for Educational Use
N.A.I.C.S.: 541511
Betty Schweizer (CEO)
Mark Gamelin (Mgr-Sys Consulting)
Caroline Little (Coord-Education Tech)
Mario Jara (Engr-Network)

TIES.COM
10372 Stanford Ave Ste Q, Garden Grove, CA 92840
Web Site: http://www.ties.com
Year Founded: 1998
Sales Range: $1-9.9 Million
Emp.: 12
Neck Ties & Scarves
N.A.I.C.S.: 458110
Omar Sayyed (Owner)

TIETGENS ENTERPRISES INC.
707 Brass Lantern Pl, Brentwood, TN 37027-6212
Tel.: (615) 373-0769
Rev.: $15,500,000
Emp.: 170
Operator of Grocery Stores
N.A.I.C.S.: 445110
Ed Tietgen (Pres)

TIFCO INDUSTRIES INC.
21400 US Hwy 290, Cypress, TX 77429-3394
Tel.: (281) 571-6000 **TX**
Web Site: http://www.tifco.com
Year Founded: 1961
Sales Range: $50-74.9 Million
Emp.: 325
Provider of Industrial Supplies
N.A.I.C.S.: 423840
Robert B. Brown (Pres & CEO)
Larry Duke (VP)
Cheryl Schumann (Mgr-Acctg & Benefits)

TIFFANY CONSTRUCTION COMPANY
PO Box 9790, Phoenix, AZ 85060
Tel.: (602) 276-2414
Web Site: http://www.tiffanyconst.com
Sales Range: $10-24.9 Million
Emp.: 75
Provider of Heavy Construction Services
N.A.I.C.S.: 236210
John Tiffany (VP)
Courtney Stockstill (Sr Project Mgr)
Lyndon Larson (CFO)

TIFFANY MOTOR COMPANY INC.
300 Gateway Dr, Hollister, CA 95023
Tel.: (831) 637-4461
Web Site: http://www.tiffanyford.com
Rev.: $22,900,000
Emp.: 23
Automobiles, New & Used
N.A.I.C.S.: 441110
Leyton Selix (Gen Mgr)

TIFFIN PAPER COMPANY
265 6th Ave, Tiffin, OH 44883
Tel.: (419) 447-2121
Web Site: http://www.tpcfoodservice.com
Sales Range: $25-49.9 Million
Emp.: 50
Supplier of Foodservice & Janitorial Maintenance
N.A.I.C.S.: 424130
Thomas M. Maiberger (Chm, Pres & CEO)

TIFORP INC.
2512 Quakertown Rd, Pennsburg, PA 18073
Tel.: (215) 679-2300
Web Site: http://www.nationalautostores.com
Year Founded: 1969
Sales Range: $25-49.9 Million
Emp.: 200
Automotive Parts
N.A.I.C.S.: 441330

TIGER ANALYTICS LLC
2350 Mission College Blvd Ste 495, Santa Clara, CA 95054
Tel.: (408) 508-4430
Web Site: http://www.tigeranalytics.com
Year Founded: 2011
Sales Range: $10-24.9 Million
Emp.: 250
Software Development Services
N.A.I.C.S.: 541511
Mahesh Kumar (Co-Founder & CEO)
Pradeep Gulipalli (Co-Founder & Chief Delivery Officer)
Kishor Gummaraju (Chief Customer Officer)

TIGER COMMISSARY SERVICES, INC.
176 County Rd 406, Jonesboro, AR 72404
Tel.: (870) 932-1907 **AR**
Web Site: http://www.tigercommissary.com
Year Founded: 1998
Sales Range: $1-9.9 Million
Emp.: 100
Computer System Design Services
N.A.I.C.S.: 541512
Chad Niell (CEO)
Debbie Harrison (Specialist-Payroll)
Roger Josam (Dir-Ops)
Pam Niell (Pres)
Christie Prestridge (Specialist-AP & AR)

TIGER CORRECTIONAL SERVICES
176 County Rd 406, Jonesboro, AR 72404
Tel.: (870) 932-1907
Web Site: http://www.tigercommissary.com
Sales Range: $10-24.9 Million
Emp.: 73
Software Development Services
N.A.I.C.S.: 541511
Chad Niel (CEO)
Pam Niell (Pres)
Ray Culpepper (CFO)
Stephen Newberry (Mgr-Software Dev)
Tim Ponder (Pres-Food Svcs Div)
Riley VanHorn (Dir-Mktg)
Roger Josam (Mgr-Ops)
Patti Davis (Reg Dir-Food Svcs Div)
Brad Blaylock (Mgr-Technical Support)
Matt Bennett (Mgr-Distr Center)
Sara Trimarchi (Coord-Food Svc)
JoAnn Cooper (Coord-Food Svc Trng)
Hal Wyatt (Dir-HR)
Phillip Reid (Dir-Sls)
Keith Reed (Dir-Tech)
Kevin Edwards (Mgr-Food Svc District)
Jeannie Tyler (Mgr-Food Svc District)
Angie York (Project Mgr)
Karen Hinson (Reg Mgr-Food Svc)

TIGER DISTRIBUTORS INC.
910 Cosmo Ln, Jackson, NJ 08527-5432
Tel.: (732) 965-1000
Web Site: http://www.tigersnacks.com
Sales Range: $10-24.9 Million
Emp.: 29
Whslr of Potato Chips
N.A.I.C.S.: 424450
Robert E. Stahl (Chm)
Joanne Hensley (Pres)

TIGER DRYLAC USA INC.
1261 East Belmont St, Ontario, CA 91761
Tel.: (909) 930-9100
Web Site: http://www.tiger-coatings.com
Year Founded: 1984
Sales Range: $250-299.9 Million
Emp.: 1,000
Paint & Coating Mfr
N.A.I.C.S.: 325510
Oliver Ortner (CIO)
Thomas Knoll (Mng Dir)

TIGER ENTERPRISES INC.
205 E Race St, Kingston, TN 37763
Tel.: (865) 376-9494
Web Site: http://www.oldcapitaltravel.com
Sales Range: $1-9.9 Million
Emp.: 1
Petroleum Bulk Stations
N.A.I.C.S.: 424710
John Robinson (Pres)

TIGER FITNESS INC.
6350 Castle Dr, Mason, OH 45040
Tel.: (513) 321-1442
Web Site: http://www.tigerfitness.com
Year Founded: 2001
Sales Range: $1-9.9 Million
Emp.: 10
Nutritional Supplements
N.A.I.C.S.: 456191
Chad Vordem Esche (CEO)
Jon Briscoe (COO)

TIGER GLOBAL MANAGEMENT LLC
9 W 57th St 35th Fl, New York, NY 10019
Tel.: (212) 984-8847
Web Site: https://www.tigerglobal.com
Year Founded: 2001
Investment Services
N.A.I.C.S.: 523999
Neil Schwartz (Chief Compliance Officer)
Alexander Captain (Mng Dir)
Joseph A. Marovich (Head-Ops)
Neeraj Chandra (Mng Dir)
Anil Crasto (COO)
Vishnu Varma (CTO)
Jason Lenga (Partner-Ops)
Lee Jared Fixel (Partner)
Feroz Dewan (Mng Partner)
Charles Payson Coleman III (Mng Partner)

TIGER INFORMATION SYSTEMS INC.

TIGER INFORMATION SYSTEMS INC.

Tiger Information Systems Inc.—(Continued)
120 Broadway 10th Fl, New York, NY 10271
Tel.: (212) 412-0600   NY
Web Site: http://www.tigerinfo.com
Year Founded: 1982
Sales Range: $10-24.9 Million
Emp.: 75
Provider of Temporary Employment & IT Training
N.A.I.C.S.: 611420
Alvaro Castro (Dir-IT)
Alexander Foster (Mgr-Acctg)

TIGER INFRASTRUCTURE PARTNERS LP
717 5th Ave, New York, NY 10022
Tel.: (212) 201-2180
Web Site: http://www.tigerinfrastructure.com
Privater Equity Firm
N.A.I.C.S.: 523940
Emil William Henry Jr. (Founder, CEO & Mng Partner)

Subsidiaries:

Granite Comfort, LP   (1)
717 Fifth Ave, New York, NY 10022
Tel.: (212) 201-2180
Web Site: http://www.granitecomfort.com
Residential HVAC & Plumbing Contractors
N.A.I.C.S.: 238220
Alison Albrecht (VP-Mktg)
Alex Black (Founder)

Subsidiary (Domestic):

Green Air Care Group Inc.   (2)
1584 Barclay Blvd, Buffalo Grove, IL 60089
Web Site: http://www.greenaircare.com
Air Conditioning Contractor Services
N.A.I.C.S.: 238220
Michael Vaynshteyn (Project Mgr)
Larry Kichatay (Pres)
Erik Babayev (Dir-Installation)

TIGER NATURAL GAS, INC.
1422 E 71st St Ste J, Tulsa, OK 74136-5060
Tel.: (918) 491-6998
Web Site: http://www.tigernaturalgas.com
Year Founded: 1991
Sales Range: $125-149.9 Million
Emp.: 21
Natural Gas Distribution Services
N.A.I.C.S.: 221210
Lori Nalley (Owner & Pres)
Johnathan Burris (Mgr)
Todd Campbell (Dir-Gas Supply)
Jim Isenhour (VP-Natl Accts & Comml Sls)

TIGER OPTICS LLC
250 Titus Ave, Warrington, PA 18976
Tel.: (215) 343-6600
Web Site: http://www.tigeroptics.com
Year Founded: 1999
Rev.: $4,900,000
Emp.: 45
Instruments, Measuring, Displaying, Controlling Industrial Process Variables & Related Products Mfr
N.A.I.C.S.: 334513
Lisa Bergson (Founder & CEO)

TIGERCONNECT, INC.
2110 Broadway, Santa Monica, CA 90404
Tel.: (310) 401-1820
Web Site: http://www.tigerconnect.com
Year Founded: 2010
Software Publisher
N.A.I.C.S.: 513210
Sumeet Bhatia (Head-Tech)
Kirk Kirkman (Pres-Client Org)

Kelli Castellano (CMO)
Brad Brooks (Founder & CEO)
John Elms (Chief Product Officer)

Subsidiaries:

Critical Alert Systems, LLC   (1)
4901 Belfort Rd Ste 130, Jacksonville, FL 32256
Tel.: (877) 265-8266
Web Site: http://www.criticalalert.com
Security System Services
N.A.I.C.S.: 561621
Laurie Brochu (Sr VP-Fin)
Mary Bradshaw (VP-Pro Svcs & Product Delivery)
Lynne D. Haley (VP-Sys Dev)
Suzanne West (Dir-Clinical Svcs)
Dave Sokalski (CFO)
Wil Lukens (Gen Mgr-Nurse Call Hardware Unit)

TIGERGPS.COM, LTD.
20 Constitution Blvd S, Shelton, CT 06484
Tel.: (203) 922-7620
Web Site: http://www.tigergps.com
Year Founded: 2001
Sales Range: $10-24.9 Million
Emp.: 8
GPS Navigation Equipment & Accessories Sales
N.A.I.C.S.: 441330
Derek Kleinow (CEO)

TIGERLOGIC CORPORATION
1532 SW Morrison St Ste 200, Portland, OR 97205
Tel.: (503) 488-6988   DE
Web Site: http://www.tigerlogic.com
Year Founded: 2000
Emp.: 60
Computer Software Development Services
N.A.I.C.S.: 513210
Justin Garrity (Pres)

Subsidiaries:

TigerLogic France   (1)
47 Boulevard de Charonne, 75011, Paris, France
Tel.: (33) 1 55 28 99 99
Web Site: http://www.tigerlogic.com
Emp.: 4
Computer Software Sales & Support
N.A.I.C.S.: 423430
Alain Teboul (Mng Dir)

TigerLogic Germany GmbH   (1)
Langenhorner Chaussee 40, 22335, Hamburg, Germany
Tel.: (49) 40 53 28 72 11
Web Site: http://www.tigerlogic.com
Emp.: 7
Computer Software Sales & Support
N.A.I.C.S.: 423430
Atsushi Godai (Gen Mgr)

TigerLogic UK, Ltd.   (1)
Mitford House, Benhall, Saxmundham, IP17 1JS, Suffolk, United Kingdom
Tel.: (44) 1728 603011
Web Site: http://www.tigerlogic.com
Emp.: 15
Computer Software Sales & Support
N.A.I.C.S.: 423430
Bob Whiting (Gen Mgr)

TIGHE & BOND, INC.
53 Southampton Rd, Westfield, MA 01085-5308
Tel.: (413) 562-1600
Web Site: http://www.tighebond.com
Year Founded: 1911
Emp.: 340
Engineeering Services
N.A.I.C.S.: 541330
John A. Bologna (VP-Bldg Svcs Business Line)
Michael Toto (Grp Mgr-Mechanical, Electrical & Plumbing)
F. Adam Yanulis (VP-Bus Dev)

Margo Armstrong (Dir-HR)
Brandee Nelson (Project Mgr-Red Hook)
Marc Richards (Principal)
Peter Grabowski (Principal)
Robert Belitz (Pres & CEO)
William Hardy (COO)
Tracy Adamski (VP)
Dana Huff (Principal & Dir-Client Sector)
Jeffrey Arps (Principal-Environmental Scientist)
Stephen Seigal (Principal)
Peter Valinsk (Principal)
Francis Hoey III (Principal)

Subsidiaries:

Coastal Engineering Co. Inc.   (1)
260 Rt 6a, Orleans, MA 02653
Tel.: (508) 255-6511
Web Site: http://www.coastalengineeringcompany.com
Rev.: $3,800,000
Emp.: 35
Engineeering Services
N.A.I.C.S.: 541330
David J. Michniewicz (VP)
Suzanne M. Sullivan (CFO & Treas)
Bradford M. Malo (Principal)
John G. Schnaible (Principal)

Halvorson Design Partnership   (1)
25 Kingston St, Boston, MA 02111-2200
Tel.: (617) 536-0380
Web Site: http://www.halvorsondesign.com
Landscape Architectural & Designing Services
N.A.I.C.S.: 541320
Deborah D. Whelan (CFO & Principal)
Cynthia W. Smith (Principal & VP)
Charles P. Kozlowski (VP)
Robert R. Uhlig (Pres, CEO & Principal)
Craig C. Halvorson (Founder & Principal)
Kelly Auld (Dir-Mktg)

TIGHE WAREHOUSING & DISTRIBUTION
481 Wildwood Ave, Woburn, MA 01801
Tel.: (781) 939-0925
Web Site: http://www.tighe-co.com
Rev.: $17,571,570
Emp.: 125
General Warehousing & Storage
N.A.I.C.S.: 493110
John F. Tighe (Pres & CEO)

TIHATI PRODUCTIONS LTD., INC.
3615 Harding Ave Ste 506, Honolulu, HI 96816-3757
Tel.: (808) 735-0292
Web Site: http://www.tihati.com
Year Founded: 1971
Sales Range: $900-999.9 Million
Emp.: 825
Entertainers & Entertainment Groups
N.A.I.C.S.: 711190
Cha Thompson (Owner)
Hoku Damaso (Mgr-Entertainment)
Ben Taaca (Mgr-Lounge Entertainment)
Jeanne Nakagawa (VP & Dir-Sls & Mktg)

TIKI RESTAURANT, LOUNGE & MARINA, INC.
3212 Mary Walker Dr, Gautier, MS 39553
Tel.: (228) 497-1591
Sales Range: $10-24.9 Million
Emp.: 250
Family Restaurant Operating Services
N.A.I.C.S.: 722511
Norma Thornton (VP)
Edward H. Thornton (Pres)
John J. Thornton (VP)
Walter M. Thornton Jr. (Treas & Sec)

TILE & CARPET TOWN EAST INCORPORATED
3195 Erie Blvd E, De Witt, NY 13214
Tel.: (315) 446-9100
Web Site: http://www.carpetone.com
Sales Range: $10-24.9 Million
Emp.: 47
Floor Covering Stores
N.A.I.C.S.: 449121
Harold Shapiro (Pres)

TILE CONTRACTORS SUPPLY COMPANY
3065 Trotters Pkwy, Alpharetta, GA 30004
Tel.: (770) 569-5232
Web Site: http://www.traditionsintile.com
Year Founded: 1936
Sales Range: $10-24.9 Million
Emp.: 70
Distr of Tile & Stone
N.A.I.C.S.: 423320
Richard P. Morley (Pres)

TILE IMPORTS LLC
5800 E Jewell Ave, Denver, CO 80224
Tel.: (303) 759-1919
Web Site: http://www.capcotile.com
Year Founded: 1977
Sales Range: $10-24.9 Million
Emp.: 100
Ceramic Wall & Floor Tile Whslr
N.A.I.C.S.: 327120
Clyde Smith (Mgr-Pur)
Meredith Cole (Dir-Sls)

TILE WEST INC.
11 Hamilton Dr, Novato, CA 94949
Tel.: (415) 382-7550
Web Site: http://www.tilewestinc.com
Year Founded: 1968
Sales Range: $10-24.9 Million
Emp.: 50
Provider of Tile Installation Services
N.A.I.C.S.: 238340
Wayne Jackson (Superintendent)

TILIA HOLDINGS LLC
111 S Wacker Dr Ste 4960, Chicago, IL 60606
Tel.: (312) 535-0225
Web Site: http://www.tiliallc.com
Private Equity
N.A.I.C.S.: 523999
Johannes Burlin (Co-Founer & Co-CEO)

Subsidiaries:

FlexXray LLC   (1)
3751 New York Ave Ste 130, Arlington, TX 76014-4404
Tel.: (817) 453-3539
Web Site: http://www.flexxray.com
Food Inspection & Recovery Services
N.A.I.C.S.: 561499
Kevin Fritzmeyer (CEO)
Chris Keith (VP-Sls & Customer Svc)

TILLAGE CONSTRUCTION L.L.C.
2635 Choctaw Dr, Baton Rouge, LA 70805
Tel.: (225) 356-1700
Web Site: http://www.tillageconstruction.com
Sales Range: $10-24.9 Million
Emp.: 23
Construction Engineering Services
N.A.I.C.S.: 237990
Ken Tillage (Co-Founder)
Keith A. Tillage (Co-Founder)

TILLAMOOK COUNTY CREAMERY ASSOCIATION

COMPANIES

4165 Hwy 101 N, Tillamook, OR 97141-7770
Tel.: (503) 815-1300   OR
Web Site:
http://www.tillamookcheese.com
Year Founded: 1909
Sales Range: $250-299.9 Million
Emp.: 470
Mfr of Cheddar Cheese, Ice Cream, Butter & Whey Powder Products
N.A.I.C.S.: 311513
Patrick Criteser (Pres & CEO)

Subsidiaries:

Tillamook Cheese Inc.   (1)
1400 NW 22nd Ave Ste 100, Portland, OR 97210
Tel.: (503) 639-5512
Web Site: http://www.tillamook.com
Sales Range: $10-24.9 Million
Emp.: 90
Sales of Cheddar Cheese, Ice Cream, Butter & Whey Powder
N.A.I.C.S.: 424410
David Booth (VP-Sls & Mktg)
Patrick Criteser (Pres & CEO)

TILLEMAN MOTOR COMPANY
4514 US Hwy 2W, Havre, MT 59501
Tel.: (406) 265-7865
Web Site:
http://www.tillemanmotor.com
Sales Range: $25-49.9 Million
Emp.: 45
Car Whslr
N.A.I.C.S.: 441110
Craig Tilleman (Principal)

TILLERY CAPITAL LLC
7013 Willow Trace Ln, Weddington, NC 28104-6804
Tel.: (704) 258-9885
Web Site:
http://www.tillerycapital.com
Privater Equity Firm
N.A.I.C.S.: 523999
Chris Weidenhammer (Mng Partner)
Richard Fetter (Partner)
James Buck (Partner)

Subsidiaries:

Electromedical Products International, Inc.   (1)
2201 Garrett Morris Pkwy, Mineral Wells, TX 76067-9034
Tel.: (940) 328-0788
Web Site: http://www.alpha-stim.com
Electromedical Apparatus Mfr & Distr
N.A.I.C.S.: 334510
Tonja Trammell (Dir-Ops & Govt Svcs)
Daniel L. Kirsch (Chm)
Tracey B. Kirsch (Pres)
Scott Elder (VP & Corp Counsel)
Raymond Chan (VP-Engrg)
Jeffrey A. Marksberry (Chief Science & Clinical Officer)

TILLERY CHEVROLET GMC INC.
1400 US Rte 66 W, Moriarty, NM 87035
Tel.: (505) 832-4431
Web Site: http://www.tillerycars.com
Rev.: $19,000,000
Emp.: 38
New & Used Automobiles
N.A.I.C.S.: 441110
Glen Tillery (Pres & Gen Mgr)
Gayle Tillery Pedrick (Treas & Sec)
Gena Tillery Hoagland (Controller)
Hi Tillery (Mgr-Fleet Sls)

TILLMAN, ALLEN, GREER
1305 Lakes Pkwy Ste 119, Lawrenceville, GA 30043
Tel.: (770) 236-8703
Web Site:
http://www.tillmanallengreer.com
Year Founded: 1998

Sales Range: $10-24.9 Million
Emp.: 20
Advetising Agency
N.A.I.C.S.: 541810
David Greer (Owner)
David Giles (Creative Dir)

TILSON HR, INC.
1530 American Way Ste 200, Greenwood, IN 46143
Tel.: (317) 885-3838
Web Site: http://www.tilsonhr.com
Year Founded: 1995
Sales Range: $10-24.9 Million
Emp.: 35
Provider of Outsourcing Services
N.A.I.C.S.: 541611
Brent Tilson (Pres & CEO)
Rob Glass (Sr Dir-IT Sys & Infrastructure)
John A. Bush (Dir-IT Dev)
Scott Ingram (Dir-Client Svcs)
Stephen Palamara (VP-Sls)
Nick Vivaldi (Dir-HR)

TILSON TECHNOLOGY MANAGEMENT
245 Commercial St Ste 203, Portland, ME 04101
Tel.: (207) 591-6427
Web Site: http://www.tilsontech.com
Year Founded: 1996
Sales Range: $1-9.9 Million
Emp.: 100
IT & Telecommunications Consulting Services
N.A.I.C.S.: 541690
Joshua Broder (CEO)
Doreen Bell (Dir-Bus Sys)
Mike Svigelj (Controller)
Alda Licis (VP-Infrastructure Dev)
Jason Burns (CIO)

TILT CREATIVE + PRODUCTION, LLC
23 S 13th St Ste 301, Richmond, VA 23219
Tel.: (804) 346-3232   VA
Web Site: http://www.tiltcp.com
Year Founded: 2018
Digital Content Marketing & Production Services
N.A.I.C.S.: 541810
Ron Carey (Founder & CEO)
Dave Trownsell (Founder & Pres)
Stacy Murphy (Founder & COO)
Christina Grelich (Mgr-Office)
Dave Parrish (Dir-Creative)
Constance Eisele (Sr Dir-Art)
Denise Bobadilla (Controller)
Ellen Carlton (Dir-Strategy)
Jessica Nickens (Dir-Fin & Ops)
Dontrese Brown (Chief Growth Officer & Exec VP)

Subsidiaries:

Marketing Arts Corporation   (1)
1 Shockoe Plz, Richmond, VA 23219
Tel.: (804) 915-3690
Web Site: http://www.s2content.com
Digital Marketing Agency
N.A.I.C.S.: 541810
Ron Carey (Pres)
Hugh Callahan (VP & Creative Dir)
Kevin Power (Dir-Tech)

TILTED KILT PUB & EATERY!
17 N Wabash Ave, Chicago, IL 60602
Tel.: (312) 269-5580
Web Site: http://www.TiltedKilt.com
Year Founded: 2003
Sales Range: $1-9.9 Million
Emp.: 78
Sports Bar
N.A.I.C.S.: 722410

Ron Lynch (Pres)
Mark Hanby (VP-Dev)
Eddie Goitia (CFO)
Mercedes Contreras (Dir-Mktg)

TILTON EQUIPMENT COMPANY
189 Lafayette Rd, Rye, NH 03870-6103
Tel.: (603) 964-6560
Web Site:
http://www.tiltonequipment.com
Year Founded: 1969
Sales Range: $10-24.9 Million
Emp.: 120
Outdoor Power Equipment Products Distr
N.A.I.C.S.: 423830
David B. Tilton (Pres)

TIM CASTELLAW AUTOMOTIVE
920 Hwy 51 Bypass, Dyersburg, TN 38024
Tel.: (731) 285-2500   TN
Web Site: http://tryuscars.com
Emp.: 100
Automobile Dealership
N.A.I.C.S.: 441110
Tim Castellaw (Owner)

TIM O'BRIEN HOMES, INC.
N27 W24075 Paul Ct, Pewaukee, WI 53072
Tel.: (262) 542-5750
Web Site:
http://www.timobrienhomes.com
Year Founded: 2007
Sales Range: $25-49.9 Million
Emp.: 50
Residential Building Construction Services
N.A.I.C.S.: 236117
Tim O'brien (Owner)

TIM WHITEHEAD CHRYSLER DODGE JEEP RAM
PO Box 310717, Enterprise, AL 36331-0717
Tel.: (334) 347-8906
Web Site:
http://www.timwhiteheadjeep.com
Sales Range: $10-24.9 Million
Emp.: 55
Car Whslr
N.A.I.C.S.: 441110
Tim Whitehead (Owner)

TIM'S BUICK PONTIAC GMC TOYOTA
1006 Commerce Dr, Prescott, AZ 86305
Tel.: (928) 445-7350
Web Site: http://www.timsauto.com
Sales Range: $25-49.9 Million
Emp.: 150
Automobiles, New & Used
N.A.I.C.S.: 441110
Tim Coury (Owner)

TIMBER INDUSTRIES INC.
600 Fairmount Ave Ste 206, Baltimore, MD 21286
Tel.: (410) 823-8300
Web Site:
http://www.timberindustries.com
Rev.: $20,000,000
Emp.: 5
Pallets, Wood
N.A.I.C.S.: 423310
Annette Walter (Pres)
Danielle Sutphen (Dir-Bus Dev)

TIMBER PRODUCTS COMPANY, LP

TIMBERLAND HARVESTERS INC.

305 S 4th St, Springfield, OR 97477-0055
Tel.: (541) 291-4993   OR
Web Site:
http://www.timberproducts.com
Year Founded: 1967
Sales Range: $150-199.9 Million
Emp.: 1,100
Lumber Mfr & Distr
N.A.I.C.S.: 321113
Patrick Nosler (Mgr-Territory Sls)
Greg Koehn (Mgr-Territory Sls)
Mike Lyon (Mgr-Territory Sls)
Lin Thompson (Mgr-Territory Sls)
Steve Killgore (CEO)
David Gonyea (Chm)
Mark Avery (COO)

Subsidiaries:

TP Associates Inc.   (1)
305 S 4th St, Springfield, OR 97477
Tel.: (541) 747-3321
Rev.: $10,000
Emp.: 80
Payroll Accounting Service
N.A.I.C.S.: 541214
Joseph Gonyea (CEO)

TP Trucking LLC   (1)
5630 Table Rock Rd, Central Point, OR 97502
Tel.: (541) 664-4776
Web Site: http://www.tptrucking.com
Sales Range: $10-24.9 Million
Emp.: 110
Trucking Service
N.A.I.C.S.: 484121
Scott Kimmons (Mgr-Maintenance)

Timber Products Co.   (1)
305 S 4th St, Springfield, OR 97477-0055   (100%)
Tel.: (541) 291-4993
Web Site: http://www.timberproducts.com
Sales Range: $10-24.9 Million
Emp.: 5
Importers of Wholesale Hardwoods Distr
N.A.I.C.S.: 423310

Timber Products Company   (1)
106 E B St, Iron Mountain, MI 49801
Tel.: (906) 779-2000
Web Site: http://www.timberproducts.com
Rev.: $43,000,000
Emp.: 2
Provider of Veneer Stock & Hardwood
N.A.I.C.S.: 321211

TIMBERFENCE CAPITAL PARTNERS, LLC
133 N Winter St 2nd Fl, Midway, KY 40347
Tel.: (859) 846-4637
Web Site:
http://www.timberfencecp.com
Privater Equity Firm
N.A.I.C.S.: 523999
Michael S. Michalisin (Co-Founder & Mng Partner)

Subsidiaries:

Bob Mickler's, Inc.   (1)
1093 W High St, Lexington, KY 40508-3113
Tel.: (859) 925-3814
Web Site: http://www.bobmicklers.com
Other Clothing Stores
N.A.I.C.S.: 458110
Julie Mickler (Pres)

TIMBERLAND HARVESTERS INC.
619 Beams Dr, Eufaula, AL 36027
Tel.: (334) 687-6000
Web Site:
http://www.timberharvesters.com
Sales Range: $10-24.9 Million
Emp.: 80
Wooden Logs & Timber
N.A.I.C.S.: 113310
Lanier J. Edwards (Pres)
William T. Vancil (VP)
John Edwards (Treas & Sec)

TIMBERLINE FASTENERS, INC.

Timberline Fasteners, Inc.—(Continued)

TIMBERLINE FASTENERS, INC.
6195 Clermont St, Commerce City, CO 80022-3124
Tel.: (303) 287-5555
Web Site:
http://www.timberlinefasteners.com
Year Founded: 1923
Bolts, Threaded Products & Fasteners Distr
N.A.I.C.S.: 423710
Russell Doran (Pres)

TIMBERLINE FOREST PRODUCTS LLC
16044 SW 2nd St, Sherwood, OR 97140-9329
Tel.: (503) 590-5485
Web Site:
http://www.timberlineforestprod.com
Sales Range: $10-24.9 Million
Emp.: 20
Provider of Building Services & Products
N.A.I.C.S.: 423310
Tim Allred (Owner & Mgr)

TIMBERLINE LAND CO. INC.
150 E Arlington Blvd Ste E, Greenville, NC 27858
Tel.: (252) 355-9288
Sales Range: $10-24.9 Million
Emp.: 15
Provider of Land Clearing Contracting Services
N.A.I.C.S.: 236210
Clifford Brown (Pres)

TIMBERLINE PLASTICS, INC.
6195 Clermont St, Commerce City, CO 80022-3124
Tel.: (303) 289-2557
Web Site:
http://www.timberlineplastics.com
Year Founded: 1987
Sales Range: $10-24.9 Million
Emp.: 16
Industrial Plastics, Plastic Pipes, Fittings, Tank & Valves Distr
N.A.I.C.S.: 423840
Charles Folsom (Owner & Gen Mgr)
Sam Adams (Sls Mgr-Outside Sls)
Mark Speros (Mgr-Ops)

TIMBERLINE, LLC
235 Warehouse Rd, Henderson, NC 27536
Tel.: (252) 492-6144
Web Site:
http://www.timberlinellc.com
Year Founded: 1972
Rev.: $3,200,000
Emp.: 25
Wood Container & Pallet Mfr
N.A.I.C.S.: 321920
Gary Norberg (Owner)

TIMBERTECH, INC.
8796 Moeller Dr, Harbor Springs, MI 49740
Tel.: (231) 348-2750 MI
Web Site: http://www.timbertech.net
Year Founded: 1985
Commercial Printing & Lithographic Services
N.A.I.C.S.: 323111
John Phillips (Pres)
Deborah Baker (Owner)

TIMBES & YEAGER, LLC
605 Belair Blvd Ste 11, Mobile, AL 36606
Tel.: (251) 471-8433 AL

Year Founded: 1940
Rev.: $2,500,000
Emp.: 5
Fiscal Year-end: 12/31/04
N.A.I.C.S.: 541810
Shirley Dean (Media Buyer)
Sheryll Yeager Hall (Owner)

TIMBIL MECHANICAL CORP
68 Fanny Rd, Boonton, NJ 07005
Tel.: (973) 263-5273
Web Site:
http://www.timbilmechanical.com
Sales Range: $10-24.9 Million
Emp.: 50
Plumbing, Heating, Air-Conditioning
N.A.I.C.S.: 238220
William J. Ross (Founder & Pres)
Tim Ross (VP & Superintendent)
Anthony Ciavatta (Controller)
John Roumes (Project Mgr)
Julia Campanella (Office Mgr)
Kevin Steinberg (Project Mgr)
Scott Paine (Mgr-Procurement)
William M. Ross Sr. (CEO)

TIME DEFINITE SERVICES INC.
1360 Madeline Ln Ste 300, Elgin, IL 60124
Tel.: (847) 531-4500
Web Site:
http://www.timedefinite.com
Year Founded: 1990
Sales Range: $10-24.9 Million
Emp.: 135
Freight Transportation Arrangement
N.A.I.C.S.: 488510
Michael Suarez (Pres)
Bill Schanck (Dir-Bus Dev)

TIME EQUITIES, INC.
55 5th Ave 15th Fl, New York, NY 10003
Tel.: (212) 206-6000
Web Site:
http://www.timeequities.com
Sales Range: $10-24.9 Million
Emp.: 135
Commercial Real Estate Investment & Management Services
N.A.I.C.S.: 525990
Francis Greenburger (Founder & CEO)
Robert Kantor (Pres & COO)
Philip Brody (Gen Counsel)
Dorothy Biondo (Controller)
Paul Gottsegen (Mgr-Exec Asset & Acq-Canada & US)

TIME MOVING & STORAGE INC.
116 Church St, Freeport, NY 11520
Tel.: (718) 855-1700
Web Site:
http://www.timemoving.com
Rev.: $10,180,684
Emp.: 45
Local Trucking with Storage
N.A.I.C.S.: 484110
J Kevin Gilgan (Pres)

TIME TIMER LLC
7707 Camargo Rd, Cincinnati, OH 45243
Web Site: http://www.timetimer.com
Year Founded: 2002
Sales Range: $1-9.9 Million
Emp.: 6
Electronic Products Mfr
N.A.I.C.S.: 334419
Jan Rogers (Owner)

TIME ZONE MULTIMEDIA
4770 Murphy Canyon Rd, San Diego, CA 92111

Tel.: (858) 569-4000
Web Site:
http://www.timezonemultimedia.com
Sales Range: $1-9.9 Million
Emp.: 100
Multimedia & Internet Video Production Services
N.A.I.C.S.: 541519
Lenny Magill (CEO)

TIMEC COMPANY, INC.
155 Corp Pl, Vallejo, CA 94590-6968
Tel.: (707) 642-2222 CA
Web Site: http://www.timec.com
Year Founded: 1971
Sales Range: $200-249.9 Million
Emp.: 800
Provider of Refinery & Oilfield Maintenance Services; Manufacturer of Related Equipment
N.A.I.C.S.: 237990
Lou Hall (Sr VP-Ops)

TIMELY ADVERTISING, INC.
601 Bound Brook Rd Ste 100, Middlesex, NJ 08846-2155
Tel.: (732) 424-0100 NJ
Year Founded: 1975
Sales Range: Less than $1 Million
Emp.: 5
N.A.I.C.S.: 541810
Steven C. Pell (Pres, Creative Dir & Acct Exec)
Michael McDarby (Dir-Media)
Chris Medallis (Dir-Art)

TIMERACK INC.
400 E Rincon St, Corona, CA 92879
Tel.: (951) 284-1500
Web Site: http://www.timerack.com
Electronics Stores
N.A.I.C.S.: 449210
Adam Day (Pres & CEO)
Gregory Javins (Exec VP)

TIMES HOLDING CO.
490 1st Ave S, Saint Petersburg, FL 33701
Tel.: (727) 893-8111 FL
Web Site: http://www.tampabay.com
Year Founded: 1959
Sales Range: $10-24.9 Million
Emp.: 500
Holding Company; Newspaper & Periodical Publisher
N.A.I.C.S.: 551112
Paul C. Tash (Chm, Pres & CEO)
Jana L. Jones (CFO)
Andrew P. Corty (Exec Dir)

Subsidiaries:

Tampa Bay Newspapers, Inc. (1)
9911 Seminole Blvd, Seminole, FL 33772
Tel.: (727) 397-5563
Web Site: http://www.tbnweekly.com
Sales Range: $10-24.9 Million
Emp.: 30
Newspaper Publishers
N.A.I.C.S.: 513110
Dan Autrey (Pres & Publr)
David Brown (Mgr-Production)
Suzette Porter (Editor-Pinellas)
Jay Rey (Dir-Adv Sls)
Bob McClure (Editor-Beach Beacon)
Tiffany Razzano (Editor-Seminole Beacon)
Wendy Edwards (Mgr-Classified Sls)
Tom Germond (Editor-Belleair Bee & Dunedin Beacon & Exec Editor-TBN)
Logan Mosby (Editor-Clearwater Beacon)

Times Publishing Company (1)
490 1st Ave S, Saint Petersburg, FL 33701-4204
Tel.: (727) 893-8111
Web Site: http://www.tampabay.com
Sales Range: $150-199.9 Million
Newspaper & Magazine Publisher
N.A.I.C.S.: 513110
Paul C. Tash (Chm & CEO)
Jana L. Jones (CFO & VP)

Neil Brown (Editor & VP)
Joe DeLuca (Publr & VP)
Bruce Faulmann (VP-Sls & Mktg)
Andrew P. Corty (Sec & VP)
Conan Gallaty (Chief Digital Officer)

Unit (Domestic):

Tampa Bay Times (2)
490 1st Ave S, Saint Petersburg, FL 33701-4204
Tel.: (727) 893-8111
Web Site: http://www.tampabay.com
Newspaper Publishers
N.A.I.C.S.: 513110
Paul C. Tash (Chm, Pres & CEO)
Sebastian Dortch (Editor-Metro)
Nancy Waclawek (Dir-Corp Giving)
Tim Nickens (Editor-Editorials)
Neil Brown (Editor)
Joseph Childs (Mng Editor-Tampa Bay)
Jeanne Grinstead (Deputy Mng Editor)
Bill Stevens (Editor-North Suncoast)
Jounice Nealy-Brown (Dir-Comm)
Jennifer Orsi (Mng Editor)
Mike Sherman (Editor-Sports)
Chris Tisch (Editor-Audience)
Jeff Harrington (Editor-Bus)
Graham Brink (Editor-Editorials)
Allison Ross (Editor-State Govt & Politics)
Emily L. Mahoney (Editor-Political)

Subsidiary (Domestic):

Trend Magazines, Inc. (2)
490 1st Ave S, Saint Petersburg, FL 33701-4204
Tel.: (727) 821-5800
Web Site: http://www.floridatrend.com
Statewide Business & Financial Publication
N.A.I.C.S.: 513120
John Annunziata (Mng Editor)
Gary Bernloehr (Dir-Art)
Jill South (Dir-Production)
Barbara Goodman (Deputy Dir-Lands & Recreation)

TIMES JOURNAL INC.
580 S Fairground St SE, Marietta, GA 30060
Tel.: (770) 428-9411
Web Site: http://www.mdjonline.com
Sales Range: $25-49.9 Million
Emp.: 160
Publisher of Newspapers
N.A.I.C.S.: 513110
Otis A. Brumby Jr. (Publr)

Subsidiaries:

Morgan County Citizen (1)
259 N 2nd St, Madison, GA 30650
Tel.: (706) 342-7440
Web Site:
http://www.morgancountycitizen.com
Newspaper Publishers
N.A.I.C.S.: 513110
Patrick Yost (Publr)

TIMES OIL CORPORATION
1500 E Main St, Lincolnton, NC 28093
Tel.: (704) 735-2198
Web Site: http://www.timesoil.com
Sales Range: $25-49.9 Million
Emp.: 275
Fuel Oil Dealers
N.A.I.C.S.: 457210
Elgin Clark (Dir-Maintenance)
Dan M. Boyd III (Pres)

TIMES SQUARE PROPERTIES
468 4th Ave S, Saint Petersburg, FL 33701
Tel.: (727) 895-5298
Web Site:
http://www.timessquareproperties.com
Sales Range: $1-9.9 Million
Apartment Building & Commercial Property Leasing, Management & Investment Services
N.A.I.C.S.: 531110
Maryann Lynch (Owner)

COMPANIES

TIMES-SHAMROCK, INC.
149 Penn Ave Fl 5, Scranton, PA 18503
Tel.: (570) 346-6555
Web Site:
http://www.timesshamrock.com
Sales Range: $10-24.9 Million
Emp.: 300
Radio Broadcasting Stations
N.A.I.C.S.: 516110
William R. Lynett *(Pres)*
Mark Hoover *(Mktg Dir)*
Dave Mehall *(Mgr-Sls)*
Mitch Dolan *(COO)*
Steve Borneman *(Gen Mgr)*
Leo Flynn *(Dir-Production-Cluster)*

Subsidiaries:

Towanda Printing Co. (1)
116 Main St, Towanda, PA 18848
Tel.: (570) 265-2151
Web Site: http://www.thedailyreview.com
Newspapers, Publishing & Printing
N.A.I.C.S.: 513110
Melanie Featherson *(Mgr-Bus Office)*

TIMESHARE RELIEF, INC.
2239 W 190th St, Torrance, CA 90504
Web Site:
http://www.timesharereliefnow.com
Year Founded: 2004
Sales Range: $50-74.9 Million
Emp.: 150
Time Share Services
N.A.I.C.S.: 561599
David MacMillan *(Co-Founder & Pres)*
Cindy Martin MacMillan *(Co-Founder & VP)*
Marcus Gillette *(Sr VP-Sls)*
David Halpern *(CEO)*
Alessandra Luas *(Dir-Acctg)*

TIMESHARES BY OWNER
8810 Commodity Cir Ste 16, Orlando, FL 32819
Tel.: (321) 329-3120
Web Site:
http://www.timesharesbyowner.com
Year Founded: 1998
Sales Range: $10-24.9 Million
Emp.: 300
Database of Timeshares
N.A.I.C.S.: 561599
Jeffrey Frantz *(Owner)*

TIMMONS & COMPANY, INC.
1753 Kendarbren Dr, Jamison, PA 18929
Tel.: (267) 483-8220   PA
Web Site:
http://www.timmonsandcompany.com
Year Founded: 1974
Sales Range: Less than $1 Million
Emp.: 10
Web Marketing & Print Advertising
N.A.I.C.S.: 541810
Rich Timmons *(Founder)*
Frank Bradley *(VP-Acct Svcs)*
Bob Kent *(Pres)*
Neil Samuels *(VP-Strategic Plng)*
Bryl Villanueva *(Dir-Mktg & Emerging Channels)*

TIMMONS GROUP, INC.
1001 Boulders Pkwy Ste 300, Richmond, VA 23225-5512
Tel.: (804) 200-6500
Web Site: http://www.timmons.com
Engineeering Services
N.A.I.C.S.: 541330
Lowell Ballard *(Dir-Geospatial Solutions)*
Brian Bortell *(Pres & CEO)*

Paul Trapp *(Dir-Infrastructure Svcs)*
Vince Doherty *(CFO)*
Nate Groover *(Mgr-Economic Dev)*

Subsidiaries:

Robert H. Vogel Engineering, Inc. (1)
3300 North Ridge Rd Ste 110, Ellicott City, MD 21043
Tel.: (410) 461-7666
Web Site: http://www.vogeleng.com
Engineeering Services
N.A.I.C.S.: 541330
Robert H. Vogel *(Owner)*

TIMMONS INTERNATIONAL INC.
7605 Coliseum Blvd, Alexandria, LA 71303
Tel.: (318) 448-6211
Web Site:
http://www.timmonstruckcenter.com
Year Founded: 1983
Sales Range: $25-49.9 Million
Emp.: 30
Sales of New & Used Trucks, Tractors & Trailers
N.A.I.C.S.: 441110
John Timmons *(Pres)*
Billy Timmons *(VP)*

TIMONEER STRATEGIC PARTNERS, LLC
1215 NOTTINGHAM Rd, Newport Beach, CA 92660
Tel.: (949) 525-2008   DE
Web Site:
https://www.timoneersp.com
Year Founded: 2019
Emp.: 100
Private Equity
N.A.I.C.S.: 523999
Ben Frazier *(Mng Dir)*

Subsidiaries:

Solid Restoration Inc. (1)
912 S Andreasen Dr Ste 111, Vista, CA 20774-8900
Tel.: (760) 724-0454
Carpet & Upholstery Cleaning Services
N.A.I.C.S.: 561740
Shirley Gonzales *(Mgr)*

TIMONIUM TOYOTA INCORPORATED
10401 York Rd, Cockeysville, MD 21030
Tel.: (410) 666-8900
Web Site:
http://www.billkiddstoyota.com
Sales Range: $50-74.9 Million
Emp.: 100
Automobiles, New & Used
N.A.I.C.S.: 441110
William F. Kidd *(Owner)*

TIMOTHY F. PASCH INC.
2645 Carnegie Rd, York, PA 17402
Tel.: (717) 757-4859
Web Site:
http://www.paschenterprises.com
Sales Range: $10-24.9 Million
Emp.: 45
New Construction, Single-Family Houses
N.A.I.C.S.: 236115
Timothy Pasch *(Pres)*

TIMOTHY OFF HEATING & AIR CONDITIONING
835 Lincoln Ave Ste A1, West Chester, PA 19380
Tel.: (610) 314-7030
Web Site:
http://www.timothyoffheating.com
Year Founded: 2002
Sales Range: $1-9.9 Million

Emp.: 11
Heating & Air Conditioning
N.A.I.C.S.: 238220
Timothy Off *(Owner)*
Kim Morlock *(Office Mgr)*

TIMOTHY P. DE MARTINI AUTO SALES
625 Idaho Maryland Rd, Grass Valley, CA 95945
Tel.: (530) 272-1921
Web Site: http://www.rvdeals.net
Rev.: $26,051,898
Emp.: 28
Recreational Vehicle Dealers
N.A.I.C.S.: 441210
Jay Griffin *(Mgr-Sls)*

TIMPTE INDUSTRIES INC.
700 Broadway Ste 800, Denver, CO 80203
Tel.: (303) 839-1900
Web Site: http://www.timpte.com
Year Founded: 1970
Rev.: $19,700,000
Emp.: 200
Holding Company
N.A.I.C.S.: 336212
Scott Samek *(VP-Western Ops)*
Perry Rittenbach *(Sr VP-Sls)*
Ray Boyer *(Mgr-Parts)*
Paul Lunde *(Branch Mgr-Sls)*
Lonnie Wright *(Mgr-Svc)*
Spencer Weeks *(Branch Mgr-Sls)*

TIMSAMLEE ASSOCIATES INC.
13033 NE Jacksonville Rd, Sparr, FL 32192
Tel.: (352) 622-7063
Web Site:
http://www.sparrbuilding.com
Rev.: $12,000,000
Emp.: 40
Lumber & Other Building Materials
N.A.I.C.S.: 423310
Samuel B. Howard *(Pres)*
Tracey Herst *(Office Mgr)*

TIN ROOF SOFTWARE LLC
600 Peachtree St NE Ste 3910, Atlanta, GA 30308
Tel.: (404) 926-6387
Web Site:
http://www.tinroofsoftware.com
Year Founded: 2014
Sales Range: $25-49.9 Million
Emp.: 215
Software Development Services
N.A.I.C.S.: 541511
Daniel Gore *(Founder & Pres)*

TINCHER-WILLIAMS CHEVROLET, INC.
698 S Laurel Rd, London, KY 40744
Tel.: (606) 864-5790
Web Site:
http://www.tincherwilliamschevrolet.com
Sales Range: $10-24.9 Million
Emp.: 50
Car Whslr
N.A.I.C.S.: 441110
Jerry Howard *(Gen Mgr)*
Etta Faye Jackson *(Bus Mgr)*
Edward L. Tincher *(Owner & Pres)*
Mike Wyatt *(Gen Mgr-Sls)*

TINDALL CORPORATION
3076 N Blackstock Rd, Spartanburg, SC 29301
Tel.: (864) 576-3230
Web Site: http://www.tindallcorp.com
Sales Range: $125-149.9 Million
Emp.: 250

TINICUM ENTERPRISES, INC.

Design, Manufacture & Erection of Precast, Prestressed Concrete Systems
N.A.I.C.S.: 327390
Cheryl O. Lang *(CFO & VP)*
Gregory F. Force *(Pres & CEO)*
Rob Smith *(VP/Gen Mgr-Georgia)*
Barry Phillips *(Mgr-Sls)*
Chuck Wynings *(VP & Gen Mgr-Virginia Div)*
David Britt *(VP/Gen Mgr-South Carolina)*
Chris Gibbs *(Dir-Mktg)*
Tim Welborn *(Plant Mgr-South Carolina)*
William Lowndes IV *(Chm)*

TINDELL'S INC.
7751 Norris Fwy, Knoxville, TN 37938-4226
Tel.: (865) 922-7751   TN
Web Site: http://www.tindells.com
Year Founded: 1963
Sales Range: $50-74.9 Million
Emp.: 180
Provider of Lumber
N.A.I.C.S.: 423310
F. Carl Tindell *(Chm)*
Johan Vantrlburg *(Pres)*
Roger Bates *(Controller)*

TINGUE, BROWN & CO.
535 N Midland Ave, Saddle Brook, NJ 07663-5505
Tel.: (201) 796-4490
Web Site: http://www.tingue.com
Year Founded: 1938
Sales Range: $25-49.9 Million
Emp.: 267
Service Establishment Equipment Mfr
N.A.I.C.S.: 423850
Ty Acton *(Pres)*
David M. Tingue *(CEO)*

Subsidiaries:

Talley Machinery Corporation (1)
7009 Cessna Dr, Greensboro, NC 27409-9792   (100%)
Tel.: (336) 664-0012
Web Site: http://www.talleymachinery.com
Sales Range: $10-24.9 Million
Emp.: 8
Commercial Laundry Equipment Mfr
N.A.I.C.S.: 333310

Tingue, Brown & Co. (1)
309 Dividend Dr, Peachtree City, GA 30269-1907   (100%)
Tel.: (863) 294-2718
Sales Range: $25-49.9 Million
Emp.: 70
Provider of Piece Goods & Notions
N.A.I.C.S.: 424310
Patty Jordano *(Office Mgr)*

TINICUM ENTERPRISES, INC.
990 Stewart Ave Ste 580, Garden City, NY 11530-4822
Tel.: (212) 446-9300   DE
Web Site: https://www.tinicum.com
Investment Holding Company
N.A.I.C.S.: 551112
Eric M. Ruttenberg *(Mng Partner)*
John F. Keane *(CFO)*
Michael Donner *(Partner)*

Subsidiaries:

Tinicum Incorporated (1)
800 3rd Ave 40th Fl, New York, NY 10022
Tel.: (212) 446-9300
Web Site: http://www.tinicum.com
Equity Investment Firm
N.A.I.C.S.: 523999
Eric M. Ruttenberg *(Mng Partner)*

Holding (Domestic):

Astrodyne Corporation (2)
36 Newburgh Rd, Hackettstown, NJ 07840
Tel.: (908) 850-5088

TINICUM ENTERPRISES, INC.

U.S. PRIVATE

Tinicum Enterprises, Inc.—(Continued)
Web Site: http://www.astrodynetdi.com
Electric Power Adapters, Converters & Other Components Designer, Mfr & Distr
N.A.I.C.S.: 335999
Mark Petty *(Chm)*
Chris Viola *(CEO)*

Subsidiary (Domestic):

Jerome Industries Corp. (3)
730 Division St, Elizabeth, NJ 07201
Tel.: (908) 353-5700
Web Site: http://www.astrodynetdi.com
Electronic Components Designer & Mfr
N.A.I.C.S.: 334419

LCR Electronics, Inc. (3)
9 S Forest Ave, Norristown, PA 19401
Tel.: (610) 278-0840
Web Site: http://www.lcr-inc.com
Electronic Component Designer & Mfr
N.A.I.C.S.: 334419

Radius Power Inc. (3)
22895 Eastpark Dr, Yorba Linda, CA 92887
Tel.: (714) 289-0055
Web Site: http://www.radiuspower.com
Electronic Filter Mfr
N.A.I.C.S.: 334419

Holding (Domestic):

Consolidated Aerospace Manufacturing LLC (2)
630 E Lambert Rd, Brea, CA 92821-4119
Tel.: (714) 990-4121
Web Site: http://www.camaerospace.com
Fittings, Hardware & Fastening Solutions for Aircraft & Aerospace Industries
N.A.I.C.S.: 332510
Mark Gordon *(CEO)*
Bill Carrigan *(COO)*

Subsidiary (Domestic):

Aerofit, LLC (3)
1425 S Acacia Ave, Fullerton, CA 92831-5317
Tel.: (714) 521-5060
Web Site: http://www.aerofit.com
Fluid Power Valve & Fitting Systems Mfr
N.A.I.C.S.: 332912
David Beddome *(Pres)*
Alicia Rojas *(Mgr-Sls-Inside)*

Bristol Industries LLC (3)
630 E Lambert Rd, Brea, CA 92821-4119
Tel.: (714) 990-4121
Web Site: http://www.bristol-ind.com
Sales Range: $10-24.9 Million
Emp.: 185
Aerospace Fasteners Mfr
N.A.I.C.S.: 332722
Wendy Guerts *(Mgr-HR)*
Brad Hamblin *(Dir-Sls)*
Scott Wood *(Pres)*
Richard Martinez *(Dir-Ops)*
Mark Johnson *(Mgr-Production)*

Moeller Manufacturing & Supply, Inc. (3)
805 E Cerritos Ave, Anaheim, CA 92805
Tel.: (714) 999-5551
Web Site: http://www.camaerospace.com
Hardware Mfr
N.A.I.C.S.: 332510

Voss Industries, LLC (3)
2168 W 25th St, Cleveland, OH 44113-4115
Tel.: (216) 771-7655
Web Site: http://www.vossind.com
Sales Range: $100-124.9 Million
Emp.: 300
Mfr of Clamps & Couplings & Ducting Components for Aviation & Aerospace Industries
N.A.I.C.S.: 332510
John Fritskey *(VP-Engrg)*

Holding (Domestic):

F+W Media, Inc. (2)
10151 Carver Rd Ste 200, Blue Ash, OH 45242
Tel.: (513) 531-2690
Web Site: http://www.fwcommunity.com
Sales Range: $75-99.9 Million
Magazine & Book Publisher
N.A.I.C.S.: 513130

David Nussbaum *(Chm & CEO)*
Stacie Berger *(VP-Comm)*
Kenneth S. Kharbanda *(CFO)*

Subsidiary (Domestic):

Adams Media Corporation (3)
57 Littlefield St, Avon, MA 02322
Tel.: (508) 427-7100
Web Site: http://www.adamsmedia.com
Sales Range: $10-24.9 Million
Paperback Book Publisher
N.A.I.C.S.: 513130

Creative Crafts Group LLC (3)
741 Corp Cir Ste A, Golden, CO 80401
Tel.: (303) 215-5600
Web Site: http://www.creativecraftsgroup.com
Sales Range: $25-49.9 Million
Craft Periodicals Publisher
N.A.I.C.S.: 513120
Tina Battock *(VP & Publr)*

Division (Domestic):

F&W Publications - Books (3)
4700 E Galbraith Rd, Cincinnati, OH 45236
Tel.: (513) 531-2690
Web Site: http://www.fwpublications.com
Sales Range: $25-49.9 Million
Book Publishers
N.A.I.C.S.: 513130

Subsidiary (Domestic):

I.D. Magazine (3)
38 E 29th St 3rd Fl, New York, NY 10016-8942
Tel.: (212) 447-1400
Web Site: http://www.idonline.com
Rev.: $7,000,000
Emp.: 25
Magazine, ID Products & Handbooks Distr
N.A.I.C.S.: 513120

Krause Publications, Inc. (3)
700 E State St, Iola, WI 54990-0001
Tel.: (715) 445-2214
Web Site: http://www.krause.com
Sales Range: $75-99.9 Million
Emp.: 200
Publisher of Books & Magazines Focusing on Hobbies, Collectibles, Crafts, Sewing, Hunting, Fishing & The Construction Trade
N.A.I.C.S.: 513120
Amy Myer *(VP-HR)*
David Nussbaum *(Pres)*
Phil Graham *(VP-Production)*

Holding (Domestic):

Penn Engineering & Manufacturing Corp. (2)
5190 Old Easton Rd, Danboro, PA 18916
Tel.: (215) 766-8853
Web Site: http://www.penn-eng.com
Sales Range: $75-99.9 Million
Specialty Fastener Mfr
N.A.I.C.S.: 332722
Richard Davies *(Treas & Asst Sec)*
Charles W. Grigg *(Chm)*
Mark Petty *(Pres & CEO)*
Peter C. George *(CEO)*

Plant (Domestic):

PennEngineering & Manufacturing Corp. (3)
2400 Lowery St, Winston Salem, NC 27101
Tel.: (336) 777-1346
Web Site: http://www.pemnet.com
Sales Range: $50-74.9 Million
Screw Machine Product Mfr
N.A.I.C.S.: 332722
Robert Gentile *(Gen Mgr)*

Division (Domestic):

PennEngineering Fastening Technologies (3)
5190 Old Easton Rd, Danboro, PA 18916
Tel.: (215) 766-8853
Web Site: http://www.pemnet.com
Sales Range: $125-149.9 Million
Emp.: 250
Self-Clinching Fasteners Mfr
N.A.I.C.S.: 332510
Leon Attarian *(Dir-Mktg)*
Mark Petty *(CEO)*

Subsidiary (Domestic):

Sherex Fastening Solutions, LLC (3)
1400 Commerce Pkwy, Lancaster, NY 14086
Tel.: (716) 681-6250
Web Site: http://www.sherex.com
Sales Range: $1-9.9 Million
Emp.: 25
Hardware Merchant Whslr
N.A.I.C.S.: 423710
Andrew Johnson *(Principal)*
Adam Pratt *(Pres & Pres-ATLAS)*
Alex Hsiao *(Gen Mgr-Sherex Taiwan)*

Holding (Domestic):

TSL Engineered Products, LLC (2)
12430 Tesson Ferry Rd Ste 313, Saint Louis, MO 63128
Tel.: (314) 821-5665
Web Site: http://www.tsl-llc.com
Holding Company
N.A.I.C.S.: 551112
Drew Ladau *(CEO)*

Holding (Domestic):

Continental Disc Corporation (3)
3160 W Heartland Dr, Liberty, MO 64068-3385
Tel.: (816) 792-1500
Web Site: http://www.contdisc.com
Sales Range: $25-49.9 Million
Emp.: 170
Industrial Valves & Pipes Mfr
N.A.I.C.S.: 332911
Connie Darnell *(Mgr-Sls)*
Steven Breid *(VP-Sls & Mktg)*
Debbie Fields *(Mgr-Acctg)*
Dylan Marksman *(Reg Mgr-Sls)*
Ben Cox *(Pres)*

Dexter Magnetic Technologies, Inc. (3)
1050 Morse Ave, Elk Grove Village, IL 60007-5110
Tel.: (847) 956-1140
Web Site: http://www.dextermag.com
Magnets & Magnetic Products Mfr & Distr
N.A.I.C.S.: 334416
Bob Brinley *(Pres & CEO)*

Division (Domestic):

Dexter Magnetic Technologies, Inc. - Syosset (4)
1050 Morse Ave, Elk Grove Village, IL 60007
Tel.: (847) 956-1140
Web Site: http://www.dextermag.com
Magnets & Magnetic Products Mfr
N.A.I.C.S.: 334610

Holding (Domestic):

Groth Corporation (3)
13650 N Promenade Blvd, Stafford, TX 77477
Tel.: (281) 295-6800
Web Site: http://www.grothcorp.com
Sales Range: $25-49.9 Million
Emp.: 60
Industrial Supplies
N.A.I.C.S.: 332911
Steven Breid *(VP-Sls & Mktg)*
Betty Jurado *(Mgr-Admin Svcs)*
Freddy Weatherford *(Product Mgr-Biogas)*
Jeff Owens *(Supvr-Production)*

Holding (Domestic):

Watlow Electric Manufacturing Company (2)
12001 Lackland Rd, Saint Louis, MO 63146
Tel.: (314) 878-4600
Web Site: http://www.watlow.com
Sales Range: $1-4.9 Billion
Emp.: 2,500
Mfr & Designer of Electric Heating Units, Temperature Controls & Sensors, Power Switching Devices & Controls for Industrial & Commercial Machinery & Equipment
N.A.I.C.S.: 333994
Peter Desloge *(CEO)*
Craig Dennis *(Product Mgr)*
Jim Rowland *(VP-Ops)*
Rob Gilmore *(CEO)*

Subsidiary (Domestic):

Component Re-Engineering Company, Inc. (3)
1600 Wyatt Dr Ste 11, Santa Clara, CA 95054
Tel.: (408) 562-4000
Semiconductor & Related Device Mfr
N.A.I.C.S.: 334413

Subsidiary (Non-US):

Watlow Australia Pty. Ltd. (3)
4 No 57 Sharps Rd, Tullamarine, 3043, VIC, Australia (100%)
Tel.: (61) 393356449
Web Site: http://www.watlow.com
Heating & Electrical Equipment Mfr
N.A.I.C.S.: 333414

Subsidiary (Domestic):

Watlow Engineering (3)
2800 Brookview Dr, Burnsville, MN 55337 (100%)
Tel.: (314) 878-7820
Web Site: http://www.watlow.com
Sales Range: $10-24.9 Million
Emp.: 11
Heating Equipment Mfr & Sales
N.A.I.C.S.: 333414

Holding (Non-US):

Watlow France S.A.R.L. (3)
Tour D'Asnieres 4 Avenue Laurent Cely, Asnieres-sur-Seine, 92606, France (100%)
Tel.: (33) 1 4132 7970
Web Site: http://www.watlow.fr
Sales Range: $25-49.9 Million
Emp.: 5
Sales & Marketing of Industrial Heaters, Sensors & Controllers
N.A.I.C.S.: 423720
Franck Rofengoltz *(Gen Mgr)*

Watlow GmbH (3)
Industriegebiet Heidig Lauchwasenstrasse 1, Postfach 1165, Kronau, 76709, Germany (100%)
Tel.: (49) 72539400100
Web Site: http://www.watlow.de
Sales Range: $25-49.9 Million
Emp.: 80
Mfr of Heating Elements
N.A.I.C.S.: 333994

Subsidiary (Domestic):

Watlow Heater Technology Center (3)
909 Horan Dr, Fenton, MO 63026 (100%)
Tel.: (636) 349-5123
Web Site: http://www.watlow.com
Sales Range: $10-24.9 Million
Emp.: 21
Corporate Research & Development
N.A.I.C.S.: 541715
Lou Steinhauser *(VP-New Product Dev)*

Holding (Non-US):

Watlow Japan Ltd. (3)
Shikoku Building Annex 9th Floor 1 14 4 Uchikanda, Chiyoda-ku, Tokyo, 101-0047, Japan (100%)
Tel.: (81) 335186630
Web Site: http://www.watlow.com
Sales Range: $25-49.9 Million
Emp.: 4
Sales Office
N.A.I.C.S.: 425120
Chad Merryman *(CEO)*

Watlow Limited (3)
Robey Close Linby Industrial Estate, Linby, Nottingham, NG15 8AA, United Kingdom (100%)
Tel.: (44) 1159640777
Web Site: http://www.watlow.co.uk
Sales Range: $25-49.9 Million
Emp.: 15
Mfg., Sales & Marketing of Heating Elements
N.A.I.C.S.: 423720

Subsidiary (Domestic):

Watlow Polymer Technologies, Inc. (3)

2101 Pennsylvania Dr, Columbia, MO
65202-1937 **(100%)**
Tel.: (573) 474-9402
Web Site: http://www.watlow.com
Sales Range: $25-49.9 Million
Emp.: 400
Heater Mfr
N.A.I.C.S.: 333414
Peter Desloge *(Chm & CEO)*

Watlow Richmond (3)
5710 Kenosha St, Richmond, IL
60071-9411 **(100%)**
Tel.: (815) 678-2211
Web Site: http://www.watlow.com
Sales Range: $25-49.9 Million
Emp.: 278
Heaters, Sensors & Controller Mfr
N.A.I.C.S.: 334513

Holding (Non-US):

Watlow Singapore Pte. Ltd. (3)
16Ayer Rajah Crescent 06-03/04, Ayer Rajah Industrial Estate, Singapore, 139965, Singapore **(100%)**
Tel.: (65) 67739488
Web Site: http://www.watlow.com.sg
Sales Range: $25-49.9 Million
Emp.: 50
Sales & Marketing Office
N.A.I.C.S.: 423720

Subsidiary (Domestic):

Watlow St. Louis, Inc. (3)
12001 Lackland Rd, Saint Louis, MO
63146 **(100%)**
Tel.: (314) 878-4600
Web Site: http://www.watlow.com
Sales Range: $25-49.9 Million
Emp.: 450
Electric Heating Units
N.A.I.C.S.: 333414
Chris Mallow *(Product Mgr)*

Holding (Non-US):

Watlow Taiwan Corporation (3)
10F-1 No 189 Chi-Shen 2nd Road, Chi Sen 2nd Rd, Kaohsiung, 801, Taiwan **(100%)**
Tel.: (886) 72885168
Web Site: http://www.watlow.com
Sales Range: $25-49.9 Million
Emp.: 7
Sales & Marketing Office
N.A.I.C.S.: 423720
Miao Yuqing *(Gen Mgr)*

Subsidiary (Domestic):

Watlow Winona, Inc. (3)
1241 Bundy Blvd, Winona, MN
55987-4873 **(100%)**
Tel.: (507) 454-5300
Web Site: http://www.watlow.com
Sales Range: $25-49.9 Million
Emp.: 300
Electronic Controls Mfr
N.A.I.C.S.: 334512

Division (Domestic):

Watlow Columbia, Inc. (4)
2101 Pennsylvania Dr, Columbia, MO
65202-1937 **(100%)**
Tel.: (573) 474-9402
Web Site: http://www.watlow.com
Sales Range: $50-74.9 Million
Emp.: 380
Mfr of Flexible & Ceramic Fiber Heaters
N.A.I.C.S.: 333994
Randy Schmitz *(Plant Mgr)*

Watlow Hannibal (4)
6 Industrial Loop Rd, Hannibal, MO
63401-0975 **(100%)**
Tel.: (573) 221-2816
Web Site: http://www.watlow.com
Sales Range: $25-49.9 Million
Emp.: 300
Electric Heating Units Mfr
N.A.I.C.S.: 333994
Steve Rhoads *(Gen Mgr)*

Holding (Non-US):

Watlow de Mexico S.A. de C.V. (3)
Av Fundicion 5, Col Parques Industriales, Queretaro, 76130, Qro, Mexico **(100%)**
Tel.: (52) 4422176235

Web Site: http://www.watlow.com
Sales Range: $25-49.9 Million
Emp.: 74
Cartridge Heaters Mfr & Resale Office
N.A.I.C.S.: 333414

TINITRON, INC.
6501 NW Croeni Rd, Hillsboro, OR
97124
Tel.: (503) 533-4400
Web Site: http://www.tinitron.com
Year Founded: 2002
Sales Range: $1-9.9 Million
Emp.: 35
Miscellaneous Electrical Equipment & Component Mfr
N.A.I.C.S.: 335999
Srinivasan Seshadri *(CEO)*
David Fulton *(Mgr-Bus Dev)*
Mary Kleve *(Controller)*

TINIUS OLSEN, INC.
1065 Easton Rd, Horsham, PA
19044-8009
Tel.: (215) 675-7100   PA
Web Site: http://www.tiniusolsen.com
Year Founded: 1880
Sales Range: $10-24.9 Million
Emp.: 110
Testing & Balancing Machines, Instruments & Equipment Mfr
N.A.I.C.S.: 334519
Cheryl Spinieo *(Mgr-Customer Svc-Global)*

Subsidiaries:

Tinius Olsen, Ltd. (1)
6 Perrywood Business Park Honeycrock Lane, Salfords, RH1 5DZ, Surrey, United Kingdom
Tel.: (44) 1737 765001
Sales Range: $10-24.9 Million
Emp.: 60
Industrial Equipment & Machinery Mfr
N.A.I.C.S.: 332999
Mark Youings *(Mng Dir)*

TINKER FEDERAL CREDIT UNION
4140 W I 40, Oklahoma City, OK
73108
Tel.: (405) 732-0324
Web Site: http://www.tinkerfcu.org
Year Founded: 1946
Rev.: $90,298,858
Emp.: 397
State Credit Union
N.A.I.C.S.: 522130
Susan Rogers *(Sr VP-HR)*
Christie A. Porter *(Sr VP-Compliance)*
David Willis *(COO & Exec VP)*
Billie Houston *(CFO & Exec VP)*
Donna Haines *(Sr VP-Lending)*
Lisa Leeper *(Sr VP-Ops)*
Michael D. Kloiber *(Pres & CEO)*
Patrick J. Yager *(Chief Risk Officer & Exec VP)*
Grant Woldum *(CIO & Exec VP)*
Linda K. Ellis *(Gen Counsel)*
Brenda Peddycoart *(Sr VP)*
Matthew Stratton *(Sr VP-Mktg)*
Edgar Medina *(Asst VP & Mgr-Capitol Hill)*
Eldon Overstreet *(Vice Chm)*
Rodney Walker *(Sec)*
Sheila Jones *(Treas)*
Tiffany Broiles *(Chm)*
Connie Wall *(Sr VP-Lending)*

TINSLEY ADVERTISING
2000 S Dixie Hwy Ste 201, Miami, FL
33133-2451
Tel.: (305) 856-6060   FL
Web Site: http://www.tinsley.com
Year Founded: 1974
Sales Range: $10-24.9 Million
Emp.: 57
N.A.I.C.S.: 541810

James P. Flanagan *(Pres)*
Dorn Martell *(Exec VP & Dir-Creative)*
Sofie Vilar-Frary *(VP & Controller)*
Scott Sussman *(VP & Dir-Media)*
Rick Balter *(Exec VP & Dir-Ops)*
Maureen Flanagan *(VP)*
John Underwood *(Sr VP & Acct Supvr)*
Casey Lunsford *(VP & Controller)*
Rick Blitman *(Assoc Dir-Creative)*
Giovanny Gutierrez *(Dir-Interactive)*
Korryn Warner *(Sr Dir-Art)*
Julian Samper *(Dir-Art)*

TINT WORLD
2629 Weston Rd, Weston, FL 33331
Tel.: (954) 385-0049
Web Site: http://www.tintworld.com
Year Founded: 1962
Sales Range: $1-9.9 Million
Emp.: 86
Automotive Window Tinting & Detailing
N.A.I.C.S.: 441330
Charles J. Bonfiglio *(Pres & CEO)*
Jeanette Bonfiglio *(CFO)*
John Marsh *(VP-Store Ops)*
Jeremy Doran *(Ops Mgr)*
Kelly Wruck *(Dir-Franchise Ops)*
Chris Hejda *(Mgr-Acctg)*
Jonathan Norman *(Chief Investment Officer)*

TINY TOTS THERAPY INC.
551 Park Ave Ste 4, Scotch Plains,
NJ 07076
Tel.: (908) 380-7715
Web Site:
  http://www.tinytotstherapy.com
Year Founded: 1997
Sales Range: $1-9.9 Million
Emp.: 15
Pediatric Therapy Services
N.A.I.C.S.: 621112
Rebecca Dean *(Pres)*

TIOGA PIPE SUPPLY CO. INC.
2450 Wheatsheaf Ln, Philadelphia,
PA 19137
Tel.: (215) 831-0700
Web Site: http://www.tiogapipe.com
Sales Range: $75-99.9 Million
Emp.: 133
Steel Pipe & Tubing Mfr & Distr
N.A.I.C.S.: 423510
Andy Keiser *(Pres)*
David Keiser *(VP)*
Bennett Keiser *(VP)*

TIONA TRUCK LINE INC.
102 West Ohio St Fl 3, Butler, MO
64730
Tel.: (660) 679-4197
Sales Range: $10-24.9 Million
Emp.: 5
Trucking Service
N.A.I.C.S.: 484121

TIP TOP CANNING COMPANY
505 S 2nd St, Tipp City, OH 45371
Tel.: (937) 667-3713
Web Site:
  http://www.tiptopcanning.com
Year Founded: 1924
Sales Range: $10-24.9 Million
Emp.: 150
Fruit & Vegetable Canning Services
N.A.I.C.S.: 311421
Joe Carner *(Gen Mgr)*
Cynthia Timmer *(Mgr-Sls)*

TIP TOP CONSTRUCTION CORP
5064 Estate Mount Welcome, Christiansted, VI 00820
Tel.: (340) 773-5252

Web Site: http://www.tiptopvi.com
Sales Range: $10-24.9 Million
Emp.: 80
Provider of Renovation & Repair of Commercial & Office Buildings
N.A.I.C.S.: 236220
Percy Hollins Jr. *(Pres)*

TIP TOP POULTRY, INC.
327 Wallace Rd, Marietta, GA 30062-3573
Tel.: (770) 973-8070   GA
Web Site:
  http://www.tiptoppoultry.com
Sales Range: $400-449.9 Million
Emp.: 1,200
Poultry Processing Cooking & Deboning Mfr
N.A.I.C.S.: 311615
Kyle Vance *(Dir-Sls)*
Candace Turner *(VP-Sls)*
Graham Kirkman *(Dir-Sls-Foodservice)*

Subsidiaries:

New Market Poultry, LLC (1)
145 E Old Cross Rd, New Market, VA
22844
Tel.: (540) 740-4260
Web Site: http://www.newmarketpoultry.com
Emp.: 570
Poultry Product Mfr & Distr
N.A.I.C.S.: 311615
Jason Shiflett *(Mgr-Supply Chain)*

Tip Top Poultry, Inc. - Rockmart Facility (1)
479 Nathan Dean Pkwy, Rockmart, GA
30153
Tel.: (770) 973-8070
Web Site: http://www.tiptoppoultry.com
Poultry Product Mfr
N.A.I.C.S.: 311615
Brad Restess *(CEO)*

TIPMONT RURAL ELECTRIC MEMBERSHIP CORPORATION
403 S Main St, Linden, IN 47955
Tel.: (800) 726-3953   IN
Web Site: http://www.tipmont.org
Year Founded: 1938
Sales Range: $50-74.9 Million
Emp.: 71
Electric Power Distr
N.A.I.C.S.: 221122
Corey Willis *(Mgr-Tech & Comm)*
Chadd Jenkins *(Mgr-Ops & Engrg)*
Deb Morris *(Mgr-Fin & Admin)*
Debbie Schavietello *(Dir-HR)*
Kirk Alter *(Treas & Sec)*
Ron Holcomb *(CEO)*
Robert Baker *(VP)*

TIPOTEX CHEVROLET, INC.
1600 N Expwy 77/83, Brownsville, TX
78521
Tel.: (956) 541-3131
Web Site:
  http://www.tipotexchevrolet.com
Year Founded: 1934
Sales Range: $10-24.9 Million
Emp.: 105
Car Whslr
N.A.I.C.S.: 441110
S. Mark Roberts *(VP & Gen Mgr)*

TIPPETT STUDIO, INC
2741 10th St, Berkeley, CA 94710
Tel.: (510) 649-9711   CA
Web Site: http://www.tippett.com
Year Founded: 1984
Sales Range: $1-9.9 Million
Emp.: 47
Prerecorded Compact Disc (except Software), Tape & Record Reproducing
N.A.I.C.S.: 334610

TIPPETT STUDIO, INC

Tippett Studio, Inc—(Continued)
Julie Tippett (VP)
Jules Roman (Pres & CEO)
Sanjay Das (CTO)

TIPPING POINT COMMUNITY
220 Montgomery St Ste 850, San Francisco, CA 94104
Tel.: (415) 348-1240   CA
Web Site: http://www.tippingpoint.org
Year Founded: 2004
Sales Range: $10-24.9 Million
Emp.: 35
Fundraising Services
N.A.I.C.S.: 561499
Chris James (Chm)
Daniel Lurie (Founder & CEO)
Kelly Bathgate (Dir-Strategic Partnerships)
Bryan Malong (Dir-Project)
Annie Ulevitch (COO)
Carol Jin (Dir-Fin & Ops)
Jake Hobson (Dir-Individual Giving)
Karina Moreno (Mng Dir-Programs)
Alex Briscoe (Mng Dir)
Liz Givens (VP-Dev Strategy)

TIPPING POINT SOLUTIONS, INC.
7000 S Yosemite St Ste 280, Centennial, CO 80112
Tel.: (303) 353-0440
Web Site: http://www.tp-solutions.com
Year Founded: 2011
Sales Range: $1-9.9 Million
Emp.: 36
Computer Training Services
N.A.I.C.S.: 611420
Rick Schmidt (Pres & CEO)

TIPSY ELVES LLC
624 Broadway Ste 405, San Diego, CA 92101
Tel.: (877) 578-0702
Web Site: http://www.tipsyelves.com
Sales Range: $1-9.9 Million
Online Sweater Retailer
N.A.I.C.S.: 424350
Nicklaus Morton (Founder)

TIPTON & MAGLIONE INC.
1010 Northern Blvd Ste 208, Great Neck, NY 11021
Tel.: (516) 466-0093
Web Site: http://www.tiptonandmaglione.com
Sales Promotion
N.A.I.C.S.: 541810
Martin Maglione (Pres)
Edward Maglione (Dir-Client Svcs & Partner)
Jowill Woodman (Dir-Creative & Partner)

TIPTON HONDA
889 Arnele Ave, El Cajon, CA 92020
Tel.: (619) 440-1000
Web Site: http://www.tiptonhonda.com
Year Founded: 1985
Sales Range: $25-49.9 Million
Emp.: 115
Car Whslr
N.A.I.C.S.: 441110
Michael Peterson (Pres)
Corey Taft (Mgr-Sls)

TIRE AND OIL INC.
201 S Main St, Saluda, SC 29138
Tel.: (864) 445-2611
Sales Range: $1-9.9 Million
Emp.: 15
Petroleum Bulk Stations
N.A.I.C.S.: 424710
Joe L. Shealy (Pres)

TIRE DEN INC.
202 Industrial Dr, Rock Springs, WY 82901
Tel.: (307) 382-4700
Web Site: http://www.thetireden.com
Year Founded: 1975
Sales Range: $10-24.9 Million
Emp.: 35
Home Supply Whslr
N.A.I.C.S.: 441330
Joe Agostini (Owner)

TIRE GROUP INTERNATIONAL, LLC
7500 NW 35 Ter, Miami, FL 33122-1201
Tel.: (305) 696-0096   FL
Web Site: http://www.tiregroup.com
Year Founded: 1992
Sales Range: $100-124.9 Million
Emp.: 95
Tires & Tubes Distr
N.A.I.C.S.: 423130
Orlando Delgado (COO)
Lito Roitman (VP-Category Sls)
Craig Hancock (CFO)
Joaquin Gonzalez Jr. (Pres)

TIRE GUYS INC.
2409 4th Ave N, Billings, MT 59101
Tel.: (406) 245-4006   MT
Web Site: http://www.tirerama.com
Year Founded: 1977
Automotive Tires
N.A.I.C.S.: 441340
Jacob Cassidy (Pres)

TIRE'S WAREHOUSE, INC.
240 Teller St, Corona, CA 92879
Tel.: (951) 808-9055   CA
Web Site: http://www.tireswarehouse.com
Year Founded: 1969
Sales Range: $10-24.9 Million
Automobile Tires & Tubes Whslr
N.A.I.C.S.: 441340
Eric Helmle (CEO)
Gino Tagliaferri (Mgr-Comml Sls & Mktg)
Dan King (Pres)
Garrett Webb (Project Mgr)
Andy Franko (Mgr-Sls)

TIREMAXX INC.
2555 Dorr St, Toledo, OH 43607
Tel.: (419) 531-8473
Web Site: http://www.tiremaxx.biz
Sales Range: $10-24.9 Million
Emp.: 50
Automotive Tires
N.A.I.C.S.: 441340

TIRESOLES OF BROWARD INC.
1865 S Powerline Rd, Deerfield Beach, FL 33442
Tel.: (561) 585-9427
Web Site: http://www.tiresoles.com
Year Founded: 1998
Sales Range: $10-24.9 Million
Emp.: 65
Distr of Tires & Tubes
N.A.I.C.S.: 423130
Abby Stafford (CFO)
Stephen Stafford (Pres)

TIS INC.
5005 N State Rd 37, Bloomington, IN 47404
Tel.: (812) 332-3207
Web Site: http://www.tisbook.com
Year Founded: 1980
Sales Range: $25-49.9 Million
Emp.: 200
Provider of Book Services
N.A.I.C.S.: 459210

Tim Tishner (CEO)
Chuck Webber (CFO)
Pam Farris (Mgr-HR)

TISCHLER FINER FOODS INC.
9118 Broadway Ave, Brookfield, IL 60513
Tel.: (708) 485-3222
Web Site: http://www.tischlerfinerfoods.com
Sales Range: $10-24.9 Million
Emp.: 70
Operator of Grocery Stores
N.A.I.C.S.: 445110
Ma Joan (Mgr-Bakery)

TISCHLER UND SOHN USA LIMITED
6 Suburban Ave, Stamford, CT 06901
Tel.: (203) 674-0600
Web Site: http://www.tischlerwindows.com
Sales Range: $10-24.9 Million
Emp.: 30
Mfr of Doors, Windows & Wood Products
N.A.I.C.S.: 444110
Timothy Carpenter (Pres)
Stefan Precht (VP-Project Mgmt)

TISHCON CORP.
50 Sylvestoor Ste, Westbury, NY 11590-4907
Tel.: (516) 333-3050   NY
Web Site: http://www.tishcon.com
Year Founded: 1977
Sales Range: $100-124.9 Million
Emp.: 500
Pharmaceutical Preparations
N.A.I.C.S.: 325412
Vipin Patel (Founder)

TISHMAN SPEYER PROPERTIES LP
45 Rockseller Plz, New York, NY 10111
Tel.: (212) 715-0300   NY
Web Site: http://www.tishmanspeyer.com
Year Founded: 1978
Sales Range: $50-74.9 Million
Emp.: 500
Subdividers & Developers/Real Estate & Acquisitions
N.A.I.C.S.: 531210
Jerry I. Speyer (Chm)
Michael P. M. Spies (Sr Mng Dir & Head-Europe & India)
David N. Augarten (Sr Mng Dir-Global Portfolio Mgmt)
Paul A. Galiano (Sr Mng Dir & Head-Acq, Dispositions & Capital Markets)
Steven R. Wechsler (Sr Mng Dir & Head-US Acq, Dispositions & Equity Capital Markets)
Michael B. Benner (Sr Mng Dir & Gen Counsel)
John R. Miller (Sr Mng Dir & Dir-Southern California)
Russell Makowsky (Sr Mng Dir & CFO)
Robert Jeffrey Speyer (Pres & CEO)
Carl D. Shannon (Sr Mng Dir & Dir-Northern California)
Benoit Delacour (Mng Dir-Design & Construction-Paris)
Christopher Ahrenkiel (Mng Dir-Leasing)
Gregory Conen (Mng Dir-Leasing)
Jeffrey Chod (Mng Dir-Acq & Dev)
Luiz Ceotto (Mng Dir-Design & Construction-Brazil)
Matthew Biss (Mng Dir-Design & Construction-San Francisco)
Melissa Chia (Mng Dir & Chief Compliance Officer)

U.S. PRIVATE

Michelle A. Adams (Mng Dir-Pub Affairs)
Volkmar Agthe (Mng Dir-Design & Construction-Europe & Turkey)

Subsidiaries:

Beijing Fraser Suites Real Estate Management Co., Ltd   (1)
12 Jin Tong Xi Road, Chaoyang, Beijing, 100020, China
Tel.: (86) 1059086000
Web Site: http://beijing.frasershospitality.com
Real Estate Manangement Services
N.A.I.C.S.: 531390

TISSUE BANKS INTERNATIONAL
815 Park Ave, Baltimore, MD 21201
Tel.: (410) 752-3800   MD
Web Site: http://www.tbionline.org
Year Founded: 1983
Sales Range: $25-49.9 Million
Emp.: 284
Eye & Tissue Banking Services
N.A.I.C.S.: 621991

TISTA SCIENCE AND TECHNOLOGY CORP
9210 Corporate Blvd Ste 410, Rockville, MD 20850
Tel.: (301) 571-9398
Web Site: http://www.tistatech.com
Year Founded: 2006
Sales Range: $10-24.9 Million
Emp.: 110
It Consulting
N.A.I.C.S.: 541690
Ahmed R. Ali (Chm & Pres)
Paul Egermeier (CEO)
Marion Devoe (Mng Partner)
Elvis Moreland (VP-Cybersecurity)

TITAN
850 3rd Ave, New York, NY 10022
Tel.: (212) 644-6200
Year Founded: 2001
Sales Range: $450-499.9 Million
Emp.: 700
Full Service Advertising
N.A.I.C.S.: 541810
Donald R. Allman (Vice Chm)
Craig Abolt (CFO & Exec VP)
Jamie Lowe (Chief Sls Officer & Exec VP)
Scott E. Goldsmith (Chief Comml Officer & Exec VP)
Chris Pezzello (Mgr-Sls)
Stephen Hillwig (Sr VP & Dir-Ops-North America)
Mike Collins (VP & Gen Mgr)
Dave Etherington (Chief Strategy Officer & Exec VP)
Margit Kittridge (VP & Head-Digital)
Anne Weiner (Acct Exec)
Natalie Gilliland (Coord-Sls)
Rolando Cantu (Mgr-Ops)

Subsidiaries:

Control Group, Inc.   (1)
233 Broadway 21st Fl, New York, NY 10279
Tel.: (212) 343-2525
Web Site: http://www.controlgroup.com
Sales Range: $10-24.9 Million
Emp.: 45
Computer System Design Services
N.A.I.C.S.: 541512
Michael O'Neil (CTO)
Dan Doctoroff (Chm)
Steven Gray (Pres-Online People Search Properties)
Kris Kibak (Co-Founder)
Joey Rocco (Co-Founder)
Kristle Khoury (Dir-Mktg & PR)

Titan Outdoor   (1)
719 2nd Ave Ste 425, Seattle, WA 98104
Tel.: (206) 762-2531
N.A.I.C.S.: 541810

COMPANIES

Titan Worldwide (1)
195 State St 4th Fl, Boston, MA 02109
Tel.: (781) 356-2009
Emp.: 13
N.A.I.C.S.: 541810

Pamela Quadros (VP & Gen Mgr)
Tammi Boggan (Mgr-Sls)

Titan Worldwide (1)
1 Harmon Plz 8th Fl, Secaucus, NJ 07094
Tel.: (973) 439-5621
Emp.: 40
N.A.I.C.S.: 541810

Titan Worldwide (1)
121 S Broad St Ste 1200, Philadelphia, PA 19107-4545
Tel.: (215) 281-1980
Web Site: http://www.titanoutdoor.com
Sales Range: $10-24.9 Million
Emp.: 27
N.A.I.C.S.: 541810
Jon Roche (Gen Mgr)

TITAN CLOUD SOFTWARE, LLC
1006 Flagpole Ct Ste 104, Brentwood, TN 37027
Tel.: (615) 372-6000
Web Site: http://www.titancloud.com
Software Publisher
N.A.I.C.S.: 513210
David Freese (Pres & CEO)
Chris Brock (CFO)
Rob Boughton (VP-Mktg & Sls)
Amanda Bennett (Dir-Compliance & Software Svcs)
Meredith Bagdazian (Dir-Mktg)
David Beechum (Dir-Tech & Software)
Clay Moore (Sr Product Mgr)
John Donnelly III (Chief Revenue Officer)

Subsidiaries:

JMM Management Group, LLC (1)
2496 Technology Dr, Elgin, IL 60124
Tel.: (855) 888-0276
Web Site: http://www.jmmglobal.com
Emp.: 10
Storage Tank Management & Regulatory Compliance Solutions
N.A.I.C.S.: 541618
Jon M. Marinas (Pres & CEO)
Greg Kieca (Dir-IT Solutions & Mgr-Info Svcs)
Michael Pepe (Dir-Sls-Natl)

TITAN CONSULTING LLC
101 Smith Dr Ste 8, Cranberry, PA 16066
Tel.: (724) 779-7911
Web Site: http://www.us-titan.com
Year Founded: 2002
Sales Range: $1-9.9 Million
Emp.: 38
It Consulting
N.A.I.C.S.: 541690
John Barnyk (Owner)

TITAN HOA MANAGEMENT, LLC
1631 E Vine St Ste 300, Kissimmee, FL 34744
Tel.: (407) 705-2190
Web Site: http://www.titanhoa.com
Sales Range: $1-9.9 Million
Emp.: 15
Home Owners' Association Management & Other Real Estate Services
N.A.I.C.S.: 531390
Domingo Sanchez (Pres & CEO)
Lisa Siders (Mgr-Acctg)
Tony Wait (Dir-Org Dev)
Lori Dann (Mgr-Acctg)

TITAN INDUSTRIES INCORPORATED
Hwy 30 E, Paxton, NE 69155
Tel.: (308) 239-4281
Web Site: http://www.titanpipe.com
Sales Range: $10-24.9 Million
Emp.: 38
Water Quality Monitoring & Control Systems
N.A.I.C.S.: 334513

TITAN OIL & GAS, INC.
7521 W Lake Meade Blvd Ste 300, Las Vegas, NV 89128
Tel.: (702) 562-4315
Web Site: http://www.titanoilinc.com
Year Founded: 2008
Sales Range: Less than $1 Million
Oil & Gas Exploration Services
N.A.I.C.S.: 211120
Michal Gnitecki (Pres)

TITAN ROOFING INC.
70 Orange St, Chicopee, MA 01013
Tel.: (413) 536-1624
Web Site: http://www.titanroofing.com
Year Founded: 1978
Sales Range: $75-99.9 Million
Emp.: 450
Roofing Contractors
N.A.I.C.S.: 238160
Fred Pazmino (Pres)
Tony Pazmino (VP-Ops)

TITAN SEO INC.
16855 W Bernardo Dr Ste 125, San Diego, CA 92127
Web Site: http://www.titan-seo.com
Year Founded: 2004
Sales Range: $1-9.9 Million
Emp.: 18
Advetising Agency
N.A.I.C.S.: 541810
Danny Shepherd (Founder & CEO)
Mike Tretinjak (VP)
Jesus Parrilla (VP-Intl Bus Strategy)

TITAN STEEL CORP.
2500-B Broening Hwy, Baltimore, MD 21224
Tel.: (410) 631-5200
Web Site: http://www.titansteel.com
Year Founded: 1946
Sales Range: $75-99.9 Million
Emp.: 85
Steel Processor & Distributor
N.A.I.C.S.: 423510

TITANIUM FABRICATION CORPORATION
110 Lehigh Dr, Fairfield, NJ 07004-3013
Tel.: (973) 227-5300
Web Site: http://www.tifab.com
Year Founded: 1972
Sales Range: $75-99.9 Million
Emp.: 100
Fabrication of Titanium & other Reactive Materials for Industries
N.A.I.C.S.: 332313
Dan Williams (VP-Strategic Accounts)
William J. Brownlee (Mgr-Materials & Distr)

Subsidiaries:

Titanium Fabrication Corporation - Phoenix Group Division (1)
5121 Hiltonview Rd, Houston, TX 77086
Tel.: (832) 375-1800
Fabricated Titanium Mfr
N.A.I.C.S.: 331491

Titanium, LTD. (1)
5055 Rue Levy, Saint Laurent, H4R 2N9, QC, Canada
Tel.: (514) 334-5781
Web Site: http://www.tifab.com
Sales Range: $10-24.9 Million
Emp.: 30
Fabricator of Reactive Metals
N.A.I.C.S.: 332999

Daniel Lefebvre (Controller)

TITANIUM HEALTHCARE, INC.
2100 McKinney Ave Ste 1780, Dallas, TX 75201
Tel.: (469) 606-4521
Sales Range: Less than $1 Million
Emp.: 64
Investment Services
N.A.I.C.S.: 523999
Kamran Nezami (Chm)
Chris Mashburn (COO)
Debbie Woods (CMO)

TITANIUM INDUSTRIES, INC.
18 Green Pond Rd, Rockaway, NJ 07866
Tel.: (973) 983-1185
Web Site: http://www.titanium.com
Year Founded: 1972
Sales Range: $125-149.9 Million
Emp.: 100
Nonferrous Metal Extruding Services
N.A.I.C.S.: 331491
Brett S. Paddock (Pres & CEO)
Greg Himstead (VP-Sls & Mktg)
Regis Baldauff (Dir-Indus Mktg)
Mary Downes (Dir-Medical Mktg)
Mark Miscavage (Dir-QA & Safety)
Richard Brousseau (Gen Mgr)
Gary Martin (Gen Mgr)
Carl Joseph (Gen Mgr-Europe)
Tom Deming (Mgr-Facilities)
Thomas Ziert (Mgr-Sls)
Vasanth Kini (Mng Dir)
Craig Simpson (Mng Dir-Europe)

TITLE FIRST AGENCY, INC.
250 E Town St, Columbus, OH 43215
Tel.: (614) 224-9207
Web Site: http://www.titlefirst.com
Year Founded: 1956
Sales Range: $50-74.9 Million
Emp.: 150
Provider of Title Insurance
N.A.I.C.S.: 524127
Susan M. Temple (Gen Counsel & Exec VP)
Dirk Cantrell (Pres, CEO & Treas)
Jonathan Iseman (VP)

TITSCH & ASSOCIATES ARCHITECTS, INC.
1591 Hayley Ln, Fort Myers, FL 33907
Tel.: (239) 936-4875
Web Site: http://www.t-a-architects.com
Sales Range: $1-9.9 Million
Emp.: 9
Architectural Services
N.A.I.C.S.: 541310
James Titsch (Owner)

TIVERSA, INC.
606 Liberty Ave, Pittsburgh, PA 15222
Tel.: (724) 940-9030
Web Site: http://www.tiversa.com
Year Founded: 2003
Rev.: $1,000,000
Emp.: 100
P2P Cyberintelligence Services
N.A.I.C.S.: 541511
Robert Boback (CEO)
Anju S. Chopra (CIO)
Maxwell D. Rieck (CFO)

Subsidiaries:

Corporate Armor, Inc. (1)
13739 Steele Creek Rd Suite 201, Charlotte, NC 28273-7138 (100%)
Tel.: (704) 583-9973
Web Site: http://www.corporatearmor.com
Emp.: 80

TJOD COMPANY INC.

Reseller of Business-to-Business Technology Infrastructure Wireless, Security & Data Storage Products
N.A.I.C.S.: 561621
Thomas H. Schiffers (Pres)

TIVOLI ENTERPRISES INC.
603 Rogers St, Downers Grove, IL 60515
Tel.: (630) 968-1600
Web Site: http://www.classiccinemas.com
Sales Range: $10-24.9 Million
Emp.: 300
Motion Picture Theater
N.A.I.C.S.: 512131
Willis G. Johnson (Pres)
Chris Johnson (VP)
Matt Galvan (Mgr)
Michael Schindler (Gen Mgr)
Dominic Kirschbaum (Mgr)

TIVOLI HOMES OF SARASOTA
32 S Osprey Ave Ste 203, Sarasota, FL 34236
Tel.: (941) 954-0355
Web Site: http://www.tivolihomes.com
Year Founded: 1979
Sales Range: $1-9.9 Million
Emp.: 4
Residential Construction
N.A.I.C.S.: 236115
Gary Johnson (Pres)

TIVOLI PARTNERS
309 E Morehead St Ste 290, Charlotte, NC 28202
Tel.: (704) 295-6800
Web Site: http://www.tivolipartners.com
Year Founded: 1998
Rev.: $20,500,000
Emp.: 6
N.A.I.C.S.: 541810
Lisa Bell (Owner & Chief Creative Officer)
Steve Bell (VP-Ops)
Janine Rogers (VP-Client Svcs)

TIZIANI & WHITMYRE, INC.
Sharon Commerce Ctr 2 Commercial St, Sharon, MA 02067
Tel.: (781) 793-9380
Web Site: http://www.tizinc.com
Year Founded: 1991
Sales Range: $125-149.9 Million
Emp.: 20
Marketing Agency
N.A.I.C.S.: 541810
Robert O. Tiziani (CEO)
John Nero (VP-PR & Integrated Svcs)
Fred Martins (VP & Dir-Creative)
Scott Segel (Controller)
Richard Whitmyre (Pres)
Don Goncalves (Sr VP)
Christopher Martin (VP & Dir-Creative)

TJM PROPERTIES, INC.
5801 Ulmerton Rd Ste 200, Clearwater, FL 33760
Tel.: (727) 683-1200
Web Site: http://www.tjmproperties.us
Year Founded: 1979
Sales Range: $50-74.9 Million
Emp.: 20
Real Estate Brokerage & Management Services
N.A.I.C.S.: 531210
Terence J. McCarthy (Pres)
David C. Jones (VP-Ops)
Dale Schooley (Dir-Acq)

TJOD COMPANY INC.
8620 Baltimore Natl Pike, Ellicott City, MD 21043

TJOD COMPANY INC.

TJOD Company Inc.—(Continued)
Tel.: (410) 461-5000
Web Site:
  http://www.odonnellhonda.com
Sales Range: $25-49.9 Million
Emp.: 120
New & Used Car Dealers
N.A.I.C.S.: 441110
Sherry Price *(Mgr-Acctg)*
Brian Schwenk *(Gen Mgr)*
Thomas O'Donnell Jr. *(Pres)*

TJR PROCUREMENT, LLC
2907 W Bay to Bay Blvd Ste 203, Tampa, FL 33629
Tel.: (813) 574-2200
Web Site: http://www.tjrglobal.com
Sales Range: $1-9.9 Million
Emp.: 20
Electronic Components & Related Hardware Distr
N.A.I.C.S.: 423690
Tim Johnson *(Co-Owner & Dir-Ops)*
John Crotty *(Co-Owner)*

TJS DEEMER DANA LLP
1004 Hillcrest Pkwy, Dublin, GA 31021
Tel.: (478) 272-2030
Web Site: http://www.tjsdd.com
Year Founded: 2013
Emp.: 70
Accounting Firm
N.A.I.C.S.: 541211
Arthur Dana *(Partner)*
Tracy G. Sharkey *(Partner)*
Scotty C. Jones *(Partner)*

Subsidiaries:

TJS & Company, LLC (1)
1004 Hillcrest Pkwy, Dublin, GA 31021
Tel.: (478) 272-2030
Web Site: http://www.tjsdd.com
Emp.: 25
Accounting Firm
N.A.I.C.S.: 541211
Tracey G. Sharkey *(CEO & Partner)*
Scotty C. Jones *(Partner)*
Rhonda M. Norris *(Partner)*
Robyn T. Tanner *(Partner)*

TJS Deemer Dana - Duluth (1)
2905 Premiere Pkwy Ste 100, Duluth, GA 30097
Tel.: (678) 242-1300
Web Site: http://www.tjsdd.com
Accounting Firm
N.A.I.C.S.: 541211

TK6, INC.
5905 Johns Rd, Tampa, FL 33634-4452
Tel.: (813) 249-3399
Web Site:
  http://www.cesinternational.com
Rev.: $13,816,277
Emp.: 7
Telecommunications Equipment Mfr
N.A.I.C.S.: 423690
Thomas Brunette *(Pres & CEO)*

TKG-STORAGEMART PARTNERS PORTFOLIO, LLC
215 N Stadium Blvd Ste 207, Columbia, MO 65202
Tel.: (573) 443-3233 MO
Web Site: http://www.storage-mart.com
Year Founded: 1974
Storage Facility Operator
N.A.I.C.S.: 531130
Mike Burnam *(CEO)*
Chris Burnam *(Pres-StorageMart)*

Subsidiaries:

StorageMart Partners L.L.C. (1)
2506 W Worley St, Columbia, MO 65203
Tel.: (800) 547-4674

Web Site: https://www.storage-mart.com
Storage Units
N.A.I.C.S.: 531130

Subsidiary (Domestic):

Highland Mini Storage (2)
8615 Marbach Rd, San Antonio, TX 78227-2346
Tel.: (210) 670-2242
Web Site:
  http://www.highlandministorage.com
Lessors of Miniwarehouses & Self-Storage Units
N.A.I.C.S.: 531130
Marggie Pardon *(Mgr)*

TKO APPAREL, INC.
1175 NE 125th St Ste 102, Miami, FL 33161
Tel.: (305) 891-1107 FL
Web Site: http://www.tkoapparel.com
Year Founded: 1996
Sales Range: $10-24.9 Million
Emp.: 80
Clothing Mfr
N.A.I.C.S.: 314999
J K. Tate *(Pres)*

TKO MILLER, LLC
788 N Jefferson St Ste 550, Milwaukee, WI 53202
Tel.: (414) 375-2660
Web Site: http://www.tkomiller.com
Year Founded: 2015
Investment Services
N.A.I.C.S.: 523150
Timothy Oleszczuk *(Mng Dir)*

TL CANNON CORPORATION
220 Ponte Vedra Park Dr, Ponte Vedra Beach, FL 32082
Tel.: (904) 273-9558
Web Site: http://tlcannon.com
Sales Range: $10-24.9 Million
Emp.: 18
Investor
N.A.I.C.S.: 523999
David A. Stein *(Co-Founder & Chm)*
Ritch Mabry *(CFO & VP)*
Matthew J. Fairbairn *(Co-Founder & Pres)*

TL MACHINE.
14272 Commerce Dr, Garden Grove, CA 92843
Tel.: (714) 554-8809
Web Site: http://www.tlmachine.com
Sales Range: $10-24.9 Million
Emp.: 90
Precision Turned Product Mfr
N.A.I.C.S.: 332721
Thanh Ly *(Co-Founder & Pres)*
Quang Ly *(Co-Founder & Mgr-Facility)*
Tuyen Ly *(Co-Founder & VP-Sls & Mktg)*

TL VENTURES INC.
435 Devon Park Dr 700 Bldg, Wayne, PA 19087
Tel.: (610) 971-1515 DE
Web Site: http://www.tlventures.com
Year Founded: 1988
Rev.: $1,500,000,000
Emp.: 40
Venture Capital Investment Firm
N.A.I.C.S.: 523999
Mark J. DeNino *(Mng Dir)*
Robert N. Verratti *(Partner-Operating)*
Robert J. McParland *(Partner-Fin)*
Janet L. Stott *(CFO)*
Robert E. Keith Jr. *(Mng Dir)*

TLA ENTERTAINMENT GROUP, INC.
234 Market St, Philadelphia, PA 19106

Tel.: (215) 733-0608
Web Site: http://www.tlavideo.com
Sales Range: $25-49.9 Million
Emp.: 175
Sales & Rentals of Video Tapes & DVDs
N.A.I.C.S.: 532282
Raymond Murray *(Pres)*
Claire Brown-Kohler *(CFO)*
Brian Sokel *(Mng Dir)*

TLA INC.
2009 Roane St, Richmond, VA 23222
Tel.: (804) 321-4444
Web Site: http://www.tla-va.com
Rev.: $10,000,000
Emp.: 15
Air Conditioning Equipment
N.A.I.C.S.: 423730
David Anderson Jr. *(Gen Mgr)*

TLC BEATRICE INTERNATIONAL HOLDINGS INC.
9 W 57th St Fl 39, New York, NY 10019-2701
Tel.: (212) 756-8900 DE
Year Founded: 1987
Sales Range: $25-49.9 Million
Emp.: 800
Ice Cream & Frozen Desserts
N.A.I.C.S.: 311520
Loida Nicolas Lewis *(CEO)*

TLC DIVERSIFIED INC.
2719 17th St E, Palmetto, FL 34221
Tel.: (941) 722-0621
Web Site:
  http://www.tlcdiversified.com
Year Founded: 1985
Sales Range: $25-49.9 Million
Emp.: 80
Water & Wastewater Infrastructure
N.A.I.C.S.: 237110
Thurston Lamberson *(Co-Founder)*
Joanne Lamberson *(Co-Founder)*

TLC ELECTRONICS, INC.
18 Long Lake Rd, Saint Paul, MN 55115
Tel.: (651) 488-2933
Year Founded: 1984
Sales Range: $1-9.9 Million
Emp.: 80
Electronic Components Mfr
N.A.I.C.S.: 334419
Jeff Haselhorst *(Acct Mgr)*
Steven Olson *(Dir-Mktg)*
Jon Crofford *(Owner & CEO)*

Subsidiaries:

Schuster Electronics Inc. (1)
11320 Grooms Rd, Cincinnati, OH 45242
Tel.: (513) 489-1400
Web Site: http://www.schusterusa.com
Rev.: $19,403,798
Emp.: 30
Electronic Parts & Equipment
N.A.I.C.S.: 423690
Theodore W. Ludeke *(Owner)*
John Pellep *(Controller & Mgr-Ops)*
Mike Fine *(Pres)*

TLC ENGINEERING FOR ARCHITECTURE, INC.
255 S Orange Ave Ste 1600, Orlando, FL 32801-3463
Tel.: (407) 841-9050 FL
Web Site: http://www.tlc-engineers.com
Sales Range: $25-49.9 Million
Emp.: 300
Architectural & Engineering Services
N.A.I.C.S.: 541330
Brett McKinstry *(Pres)*
Michael Sheerin *(Chm & CEO)*
Mark A. Gelfo *(VP)*
Robert D. Danner *(VP)*

Bill Daly *(CFO, Treas & Sec)*
Gary Krueger *(VP)*
Emily Crews *(Principal-Jacksonville)*
Dominic Cacolici *(Principal & Sr Project Engr-Mechanical)*
Cole Parkinson *(Principal)*
James D. Ferris *(COO)*

TLC HEALTH NETWORK
845 Routes 5 & 20, Irving, NY 14081
Tel.: (716) 951-7000 NY
Web Site: http://www.tlchealth.org
Year Founded: 2002
Sales Range: $50-74.9 Million
Emp.: 788
Health Care Srvices
N.A.I.C.S.: 622110
Timothy Cooper *(Chm)*
John Galati *(Exec VP)*
John Eichner *(CFO)*
Ray Merrick *(VP)*
Scott Butler *(COO)*

TLC TECHNOLOGIES, INC.
5800 Pennsylvania 378 458, Center Valley, PA 18034
Tel.: (610) 770-9052
Web Site:
  http://www.tlctechnologies.net
Year Founded: 1997
Custom Computer Programming Services
N.A.I.C.S.: 541511

TLD ACQUISITION CO. LLC
3528 Volmer Ave, City of Commerce, CA 90040
Tel.: (310) 324-5111
Web Site: http://www.triple-l.com
Year Founded: 2001
Sales Range: $25-49.9 Million
Emp.: 65
Restaurant & Bar Equipment & Supplies Whslr & Distr
N.A.I.C.S.: 424490
Mario Ernst *(CEO)*
Michael Dodo *(Pres)*
Jamie Purcell *(Controller)*

TLG MULTICULTURAL COMMUNICATIONS
21 Tamal Vista Blvd Ste 135, Corte Madera, CA 94925
Tel.: (415) 927-1010
Year Founded: 2003
Rev.: $12,000,000
Emp.: 10
Full Service, Hispanic Marketing
N.A.I.C.S.: 541810
Diana Putterman *(Dir-Acct Mngmt & Dir-Strategic Plng)*
Mary Yang *(Dir-Creative)*
Angelica Contreas *(Dir-Media)*
Andrea Castro *(Project Mgr)*

TLH ENTERPRISES INC.
200 N 13th St Ste 210, Corsicana, TX 75110
Tel.: (903) 872-3242
Year Founded: 1985
Sales Range: $10-24.9 Million
Emp.: 200
Provider of Television & Furniture Rental
N.A.I.C.S.: 532210
Mike Harwood *(CEO)*
Mike Kahler *(VP-Ops)*
Kathy Marr *(Controller)*
Chris Higgs *(Pres)*

TLI ENTERPRISES INC.
1842 Sabre st, Hayward, CA 94545
Tel.: (510) 538-3304

COMPANIES

Web Site:
http://www.thermionics.com
Sales Range: $25-49.9 Million
Emp.: 30
Vacuum Pumps, Laboratory
N.A.I.C.S.: 333248
John J. Trujillo (Chm)

TLINGIT HAIDA TRIBAL BUSINESS CORPORATION
201 Cordova St, Douglas, AK 99801
Tel.: (907) 463-7139
Business Services to Promote Economic Development of Indian Tribe
N.A.I.C.S.: 561499
Richard J. Rinehart Jr. (CEO)

Subsidiaries:

KIRA, Inc. (1)
2595 Canyon Blvd Ste 240, Boulder, CO 80302 (100%)
Tel.: (303) 402-1526
Web Site: http://www.kira.com
Sales Range: $50-74.9 Million
Emp.: 1,000
Facilities Support Services; Management & Maintenance Services of Government Facilities
N.A.I.C.S.: 561210
Carlos A. Garcia (Founder & Pres)

T&H Services, LLC (1)
9097 Glacier Hwy, Juneau, AK 99801 (100%)
Tel.: (907) 209-9094
Web Site: http://www.thservicesllc.com
Facilities Support Services
N.A.I.C.S.: 561210
Robert Hamilton (Gen Mgr)
Richard J. Rinehart Jr. (CEO)

TLINGIT-HAIDA REGIONAL HOUSING AUTHORITY
5446 Jenkins Dr, Juneau, AK 99801
Tel.: (907) 780-6868 AR
Web Site: http://www.thrha.org
Year Founded: 1973
Sales Range: $10-24.9 Million
Emp.: 195
Housing Assistance Services
N.A.I.C.S.: 624229
Craig Moore (VP-Plng & Dev)
Jocelyn Ramirez (VP-Ops & Tribal Svcs)
Joyce Niven (VP-Admin)
Irene Tupou (Mgr-Fin)
Norton Gregory (Mgr-Housing Svcs)
Carla Mahosky (Accountant)
Merrilee Mosher (Accountant)
Gloria Eyon (Accountant-Grant)
Louise Kadinger (Coord-Energy Programs)
Tasha McKoy (Coord-Mktg, Media & Comm)
Lorilyn Swanson (Mgr-Fireweed)
Robert Reimer (Mgr-Maintenance)
Lorena Gray (Office Mgr)
Lorraine DeAsis (Officer-Budget)
Angela Lewis (Officer-Inventory)
Mary Elsner (Officer-Loan)
Charlie Horvath (Project Coord)
Roy Carte (Supvr-Field Rep)
Kari Metz (Supvr-Housing Svcs)

TLX TECHNOLOGIES, LLC
N27 W23727 Paul Rd, Pewaukee, WI 53072
Tel.: (262) 970-8660 WI
Web Site: http://www.tlxtech.com
Year Founded: 1996
Sales Range: $1-9.9 Million
Emp.: 25
Electro-Mechanical Solenoid Devices
N.A.I.C.S.: 335999
Neil Karolek (Pres & CEO)
Derek Dahlgren (Dir-Quality & Mfg Engrg)
Kat Goetz (Controller)
Wayne Groth (Mgr-Sls)
Alex Doll (Engr-Quality)
Boyd Schindler (Mgr-Engrg)
Phil D'Acquisto (Mgr-Quality)

TM ADVERTISING, LLC
3030 Olive St #400, Dallas, TX 75219
Tel.: (972) 556-1100 DE
Web Site: http://www.tm.com
Year Founded: 1934
Advertising Services
N.A.I.C.S.: 541810
Becca Weigman (CEO)
Kim Moss (Chief Strategy Officer-Comm)
Jeff Kempf (Chief Digital Officer)
Wade Alger (Chief Creative Officer)

TM AVIATION INC.
17039 Kencon Dr 3rd Fl, Cornelius, NC 28031
Tel.: (704) 359-0007
Web Site: http://www.cfsjets.com
Sales Range: $75-99.9 Million
Emp.: 4
Aircraft, Self-Propelled
N.A.I.C.S.: 441227
Tom W. McCune (CEO)
Mitchell McCune (Pres)

TM SYSTEMS, LLC
4119 W Burbank Blvd, Burbank, CA 91505
Tel.: (818) 306-5300
Web Site: http://www.tm-systems.com
Sales Range: $10-24.9 Million
Emp.: 12
Language Customization Software
N.A.I.C.S.: 541512
Ken Lorber (Pres & CEO)

Subsidiaries:

Kitchen Inc. (1)
265 NE 24th St Ste 401, Miami, FL 33137
Tel.: (305) 415-6200
Web Site: http://www.thekitchen.tv
Cable Television Services
N.A.I.C.S.: 516210
Ken Lorber (Pres & CEO)
Deeny Kaplan (Exec VP)
Don Denkhaus (Chm & CFO)

TM5 PROPERTIES, LP
1580 Copperfield Pkwy, College Station, TX 77845
Tel.: (979) 703-1979 TX
Web Site: http://www.tm5properties.com
Year Founded: 2010
Sales Range: $1-9.9 Million
Emp.: 5
Real Estate Brokerage Services
N.A.I.C.S.: 531210
Terrence Murphy (CEO)

TMB INDUSTRIES INC.
980 N Michigan Ave Ste 1900, Chicago, IL 60611
Tel.: (312) 280-2565
Web Site: http://www.tmbindustries.com
Year Founded: 1989
Sales Range: $25-49.9 Million
Emp.: 50
Privater Equity Firm
N.A.I.C.S.: 523999
Camillo M. Santomero (Mng Dir)
Joseph R. Ponteri (Mng Dir)
Michael D. Wilson (Mng Dir)
Kelly L. Bodway (Mng Dir)

Subsidiaries:

Prospect Foundry, LLC (1)
1225 Winter St NE, Minneapolis, MN 55413-2604
Tel.: (612) 331-9282
Web Site: http://www.prospectfdry.com
Sales Range: $25-49.9 Million
Construction, Mining & Agricultural Equipment Castings Mfr
N.A.I.C.S.: 331511
Bob Gruidl (Mgr-Quality)
Darrin Carlson (Pres & CEO)

Stainless Foundry & Engineering Inc. (1)
5110 N 35th St, Milwaukee, WI 53209-5303
Tel.: (414) 462-7400
Web Site: http://www.stainlessfoundry.com
Sales Range: $25-49.9 Million
Steel Foundry
N.A.I.C.S.: 331513

TMC FOODS LLC
116 Bertrand Dr, Lafayette, LA 70506
Tel.: (337) 289-6890
Sales Range: $10-24.9 Million
Emp.: 726
Fast Food Restaurant Operator
N.A.I.C.S.: 722513

TMC GROUP INC.
300 Oak St, Pembroke, MA 02359-1984
Tel.: (781) 829-0530
Web Site:
http://www.tmcgroupusa.com
Rev.: $25,000,000
Emp.: 103
Gifts & Novelties
N.A.I.C.S.: 561499
Dickie Richardson (Owner)

TMC HEALTHCARE
5301 E Grant Rd, Tucson, AZ 85712
Tel.: (520) 327-5461 AZ
Web Site: http://www.tmcaz.com
Year Founded: 2005
Sales Range: $10-24.9 Million
Medical Association
N.A.I.C.S.: 813920
Frank R. Marini (CIO & Sr VP)
Michael J. Duran (Chief Dev Officer & VP)
Tim Hartin (Chief Legal Officer & Sr VP)

TMC SERVICES, INC.
19 National Dr, Franklin, MA 02038
Tel.: (508) 966-3737
Web Site: http://www.hazmatt.com
Rev.: $10,548,783
Emp.: 60
Environmental Remediation Services
N.A.I.C.S.: 221320
Anthony Cichetti (Supvr-Field Svc)
Jim Connolly (Project Mgr)
MaryLouise McDonald (Mgr-Accts Receivable)

TMF HEALTH QUALITY INSTITUTE
5918 W Courtyard Dr Ste 300, Austin, TX 78730-5036
Tel.: (512) 329-6610 TX
Web Site: http://www.tmf.org
Year Founded: 1971
Sales Range: $25-49.9 Million
Emp.: 322
Health Care Srvices
N.A.I.C.S.: 622110
Robert B. Morrow (Chm)
Starr West (Treas & Sec)
Steven L. Gates (Vice Chm)

TMG ENERGY CORP.
555 Theodore Fremd Ave Ste C-200, Rye, NY 10580
Tel.: (914) 925-0300 NV
Web Site:
http://www.tmgenergysystems.com
Year Founded: 2011
Sales Range: $25-49.9 Million
Emp.: 3
Energy Efficiency & Alternative Energy Solutions; Heat Reclamation Systems
N.A.I.C.S.: 221118
Edward Miller (Pres, CEO, CFO, Chief Acctg Officer, Treas & Sec)

TML INTERGOVERNMENTAL RISK POOL
1821 Rutherford Ln No 100, Austin, TX 78754
Tel.: (512) 491-2300
Web Site: http://www.tmlirp.org
Rev.: $114,538,405
Emp.: 165
Loss Prevention Services Insurance
N.A.I.C.S.: 524298
Allan Romer (Mgr-Personnel)
Richard Dorsey (Mgr-Member Svcs)
Carol Loughlin (Exec Dir)
David Reagan (Gen Counsel)

TMP INTERNATIONAL, INC.
1711 W Greentree Dr Ste 212, Tempe, AZ 85284-2717
Tel.: (480) 491-7070 DE
Web Site: http://www.spawn.com
Year Founded: 1994
Sales Range: $10-24.9 Million
Emp.: 100
Comic Books & Related Items Publisher; Toys Mfr; Filmed Entertainment
N.A.I.C.S.: 339930
Todd McFarlane (Founder)
Debbie Ziola (CFO)
Rae Brown (VP-Fin)
Suzy Thomas (Mgr-Intl Pub)

Subsidiaries:

McFarlane Toys (1)
1711 W Greentree Dr Ste 208, Tempe, AZ 85284
Tel.: (480) 491-7070
Sales Range: $10-24.9 Million
Emp.: 60
Toy Mfr
N.A.I.C.S.: 339930
Matt Connelly (Exec Dir-Mktg & Licensing)
David Hughes (Pres-Sls)
John Shobe (VP-Sls)
Carmen Bryant (Exec Dir-PR & Mktg)
Tanya Visano (Exec VP-Bus Dev & Licensing-Global)
Todd McFarlane (Founder & CEO)
Jen Cassidy (Dir-Licensing)

Todd McFarlane Entertainment (1)
1711 W Greentree Dr Ste 208, Tempe, AZ 85284
Tel.: (480) 491-7070
Web Site: http://www.spawn.com
Sales Range: $10-24.9 Million
Animated Television, Feature Films, Music Videos & Electronic Gaming Products
N.A.I.C.S.: 339930

Todd McFarlane Productions (1)
1711 W Greentree Dr Ste 208, Tempe, AZ 85284
Tel.: (480) 491-7070
Web Site: http://www.mcfarlane.com
Sales Range: $10-24.9 Million
Emp.: 65
Comic Books & Magazines
N.A.I.C.S.: 339930
Todd McFarlane (Pres)

TMS MANAGEMENT GROUP, INC.
13825 ICOT Blvd Ste 613, Clearwater, FL 33760
Tel.: (727) 545-2100
Web Site:
http://www.tmsmanagement
group.com
Year Founded: 2005
Sales Range: $10-24.9 Million
Emp.: 120
Non-Emergency Medical Transportation Services
N.A.I.C.S.: 488490

TMS MANAGEMENT GROUP, INC.

TMS Management Group, Inc.—(Continued)
David McDonald (Pres)
Darryl Minardi (VP)
Lionel D. Martinez (CFO)
Nicholas A. Cambas (Sec)
Chad Barr (Exec VP-Ops)
Lisa Bacot (Dir-Bus Dev)
Tony Thomas (CTO)

TMT ACQUISITION CORP.
500 5th Ave Ste 938, New York, NY 10110
Tel.: (347) 627-0058
Year Founded: 2021
Emp.: 2
Investment Services
N.A.I.C.S.: 523999
Linan Gong (Chm)
Dajiang Guo (CEO)
Jichuan Yang (CFO)

TMT LOGISTICS INC.
PO Box 148, Neffs, PA 18065
Tel.: (484) 894-0300
Web Site: http://www.tmtloginc.com
Year Founded: 1999
Sales Range: $1-9.9 Million
Emp.: 10
Logistics & Transportation
N.A.I.C.S.: 488510
Karen Zaleski (Pres)

TMW ENTERPRISES INC.
101 W Big Beaver Rd Ste 800, Troy, MI 48084
Tel.: (248) 844-1410   DE
Web Site: http://www.tmwent.com
Real Estate Investment & Private Equity Firm
N.A.I.C.S.: 523999
Robert T. Howard (Pres & CEO)
Paul Oster (CFO & Treas)
Douglas S. Soifer (VP)
Janine R. Vrabel (Mgr-HR)
Margaret Bargardi (Mgr-Office Mgmt)

Subsidiaries:

FabEnCo, Inc.   (1)
2002 Karbach St, Houston, TX 77092
Tel.: (713) 686-6620
Web Site: http://www.fabenco.com
Sales Range: $10-24.9 Million
Metal Safety Gate Mfr
N.A.I.C.S.: 332323
David H. LaCook (CEO)
Donald Henderson (Exec VP)
Scott Friedman (Sls Mgr)
Donna Dennis (Controller)
Philippe Suhas (Chm)

TN-K ENERGY GROUP INC.
649 Sparta Hwy Ste 102, Crossville, TN 38571
Tel.: (931) 707-9599   DE
Sales Range: Less than $1 Million
Emp.: 1
Oil & Gas Exploration Services
N.A.I.C.S.: 211120
Ken Page (Chm, Pres, CEO & Sec)

TNEMEC COMPANY INC.
6800 Corp Dr, Kansas City, MO 64120
Web Site: http://www.tnemec.com
Sales Range: $125-149.9 Million
Emp.: 77
Coating, Air Curing
N.A.I.C.S.: 325510
Mark Thomas (VP-Mktg)
Chase Bean (Pres)
Terry Wallace (VP-Bus Dev & Customer Experience)

TNG WORLDWIDE, INC.
29683 WK Smith Dr Lyon Tech Park, New Hudson, MI 48165
Tel.: (248) 347-7700
Web Site: http://www.tngworldwide.com
Year Founded: 1985
Cosmetics & Personal Care Products Mfr & Distr
N.A.I.C.S.: 456199
Larry Gaynor (Pres & CEO)
Teresa Gaynor (VP)
Debra Herr-Dempsey (Dir-Stores)
Edmond Verbeke (VP-Hospitality)
Lindsay Mishock (Dir-Education)
Vince Ferrera (Dir-Outside Sls)
Dawn Kuhn (CFO)
Jim DiMarco (VP-Mktg)
Gaye Wanner (VP-Logistics)
Julie Szostak (Dir-Tech Solutions)
Matt Mellendorf (Dir-eCommerce)

TNH SPECIALTY PHARMACY II
15211 Vanowen St Ste 301, Van Nuys, CA 91405
Tel.: (818) 988-1288
Web Site: http://www.tnhpharmacy.com
Year Founded: 2009
Sales Range: $25-49.9 Million
Emp.: 20
Pharmaceutical Product Whslr
N.A.I.C.S.: 424210
Andreana Bruner (Acct Mgr)

TNT INC.
43980 Mahlon Vail Cir Ste 303, Temecula, CA 92592
Tel.: (951) 302-0816
Web Site: http://www.tnt-inc.com
Sales Range: $10-24.9 Million
Emp.: 20
Provider of Freight Forwarding Services
N.A.I.C.S.: 488510
Karen Rodriguez (Mng Dir)

TNT PETROLEUM INC.
171 Carleton Ave, East Islip, NY 11730
Tel.: (631) 581-6983
Rev.: $18,000,000
Emp.: 5
Petroleum Bulk Stations & Terminals
N.A.I.C.S.: 424710
Tamer Azaz (Pres)

TNT POWER WASH, INC.
3220 Toy Rd, Groveport, OH 43125
Tel.: (614) 444-8686
Web Site: http://www.tntpowerwash.com
Year Founded: 1990
Sales Range: $1-9.9 Million
Emp.: 70
Powerwashing Services
N.A.I.C.S.: 238990
Seth Bromberg (Pres)
Jason Mellott (Mgr-Body Shop)
Jeff Price (Dir-Ops)
Steve Long (Mgr-Sls)
Alicia Alexander (Mgr-Acct)
Cassidy Turley (Mgr-Property)
Martin Brower (Supvr-Transportation)

TO BOOT NEW YORK INC.
43-30 24th St, Long Island City, NY 11101
Tel.: (718) 392-8711
Web Site: http://www.toboot.com
Sales Range: $10-24.9 Million
Emp.: 10
Sales of Shoes
N.A.I.C.S.: 458210
Charles R. Steakley (CEO)
Adam Derrick (Owner)

TOAD HOLLOW VINEYARDS, INC.
4024 Westside Rd, Healdsburg, CA 95448-3814
Tel.: (707) 431-1441
Web Site: http://www.toadhollow.com
Emp.: 100
Office Administrative Services
N.A.I.C.S.: 561110

TOBACCO MERCHANTS ASSOCIATION OF THE UNITED STATES, INC.
1121 Situs Court, Ste 370, Raleigh, NC 27606
Tel.: (919) 917-7449   DE
Web Site: http://www.tma.org
Year Founded: 1915
Business Associations
N.A.I.C.S.: 813910
Chris Greer (CEO & Pres)
Robert Crosby (VP & CFO)
Taco Tuinstra (VP & Chief Content Officer)
Elise Rasmussen (VP-Sls & Mktg)
Darryl Johnson (VP & COO)

TOBACCO SUPERSTORES INC.
3550 Commerce Rd, Forrest City, AR 72335
Tel.: (870) 633-0099
Web Site: http://www.tobaccosuper.com
Rev.: $11,300,000
Emp.: 600
Owners & Operators of Tobacco Stores & Stands
N.A.I.C.S.: 459991

TOBAHMAOZ, INC.
94 E Canyon Rd PO Box 32, Mayfield, UT 84643
Tel.: (435) 610-1987   WY
Year Founded: 2012
Sales Range: $10-24.9 Million
Emp.: 2
Plant-Based Medical Products Mfr
N.A.I.C.S.: 325411
Alan R. Josselyn (Chm & CEO)
Craig S. Cheney (Sec)
Leonard M. Stillman Jr. (CFO & Treas)

TOBE DIRECT
9700 Park Plz Ave Ste 210, Louisville, KY 40241
Tel.: (502) 423-9898
Web Site: http://www.tobedirect.com
Year Founded: 1988
Sales Range: $10-24.9 Million
Emp.: 49
Advertising Agency
N.A.I.C.S.: 541810
John Tobe (Founder & CEO)
Angela Farmer (VP-Strategic Outsourcing)
Brad Craig (Mgr-Data Dept)
Rob Baraban (Mgr-Ops)
Mike Rule (Mgr-Postal Affairs)
Mike Romer (VP-Sls & Mktg)

TOBY/O, INC.
6781 E Outlook Dr, Tucson, AZ 85756-9409
Tel.: (520) 886-8548
Sales Range: $1-9.9 Million
Emp.: 20
Animal Feed Mfr
N.A.I.C.S.: 311119
Lisa Newman (VP)
Marcy Merin (Pres)
Rob Carr (COO)
Linda Pillings (Office Mgr)

TOC HOLDINGS CO.
2737 W Commodore Way, Seattle, WA 98199
Tel.: (206) 285-2400   WA
Year Founded: 1930
Sales Range: Less than $1 Million
Emp.: 6
Holding Company
N.A.I.C.S.: 551112
Raymond G. Stromer (Treas, Sec & Controller)
Theone K. Scholl-Tollefson (VP)

TOCQUIGNY DESIGN, INC.
401 Congress Ave Ste 1700, Austin, TX 78701
Tel.: (512) 532-2800
Web Site: http://www.tocquigny.com
Year Founded: 1980
Sales Range: $10-24.9 Million
Emp.: 44
Advertising Agency
N.A.I.C.S.: 541810
Yvonne Tocquigny (CEO)
Tracy Bramlet (Dir-Acct Svcs)
Amy Fenwick (Sr Dir-Client Engagement)
Matt Rand (Exec Creative Dir)

TODAI FRANCHISING LLC
19481 San Jose Ave, City of Industry, CA 91748-1435
Tel.: (909) 869-7727
Web Site: http://www.todai.com
Sales Range: $25-49.9 Million
Emp.: 30
Seafood Buffet Restaurant Franchise
N.A.I.C.S.: 722511
Danny Kim (CEO)

TODAY'S BUSINESS PRODUCTS
12985 Snow Rd, Cleveland, OH 44130
Tel.: (216) 267-5000
Web Site: http://www.todaysbusinessproducts.com
Year Founded: 1984
Sales Range: $10-24.9 Million
Emp.: 35
Office Supply & Furniture Distr.
N.A.I.C.S.: 424120
Richard C. Voigt (Pres)
John Quinones (VP)
Debbie Vodan (Office Mgr)

TODAY'S GROWTH CONSULTANT, INC.
212 Slalom Ct, Minooka, IL 60447
Web Site: http://www.todaysgrowthconsultant.com
Year Founded: 2009
Sales Range: $1-9.9 Million
Emp.: 20
Builds & Purchases Revenue Generating Authority Websites
N.A.I.C.S.: 541512
Ken Courtright (CEO)
Todd Krause (CIO)
Allen Wilterdink (COO)

TODAY'S OFFICE INC.
717 W 7th St, Little Rock, AR 72201
Tel.: (501) 375-5050
Web Site: http://www.todaysofficeinc.com
Sales Range: $10-24.9 Million
Emp.: 30
Office Furniture
N.A.I.C.S.: 449110
Art Bowren (VP-Sls-Little Rock)
Rocky Brown (VP-Ops-Little Rock)
Leah Thompson (Sr Acct Exec)
Jason Moles (Pres)
Marvin Moles (CEO)

TODD & SARGENT, INC.

2905 SE 5th St, Ames, IA 50010-9760
Tel.: (515) 232-0442
Web Site: http://www.tsargent.com
Year Founded: 1961
Sales Range: $50-74.9 Million
Emp.: 300
Provider of Industrial Building Construction Services
N.A.I.C.S.: 236220
Lee M. Sargent (Chm)
Paul J. Sondgeroth (Sr VP-Ops)
Bryan Coussens (VP-Engrg)
Jon Sargent (CEO)
James Bucher (CFO)
Stephen Smith (COO)
Rori Bouchard (Pres-Canada)

Subsidiaries:

Sargent Metal Fabricating (1)
650 Arrasmith Trl, Ames, IA 50010-5600 (100%)
Tel.: (515) 232-1535
Rev.: $2,000,000
Emp.: 28
Custon Metal Fabrication
N.A.I.C.S.: 332312

TODD AND CASSANELLI INC.
69 Water St, Torrington, CT 06790
Tel.: (860) 482-5591
Web Site:
http://www.burnsbrooksmcneil.com
Sales Range: $25-49.9 Million
Emp.: 60
Provider of Insurance Services
N.A.I.C.S.: 524210

TODD ENTERPRISES INC.
747 Middle Neck Rd Ste 103, Great Neck, NY 11024
Tel.: (516) 773-8087
Web Site: http://www.toddent.com
Year Founded: 1985
Sales Range: $10-24.9 Million
Emp.: 35
CD-ROM & DVD Network Solutions Supplier
N.A.I.C.S.: 334111
Bob Bell (Gen Mgr)

TODD HARRIS CO. INC.
2 Sutton Pl, Edison, NJ 08817
Tel.: (732) 287-4443
Web Site: http://www.toddharris.com
Year Founded: 1974
Rev.: $10,000,000
Emp.: 50
Sales of Swimming Pool & Hot Tub Products
N.A.I.C.S.: 561790
Frank Rajs (Pres)

TODD WADENA ELECTRIC COOPERATIVE
550 Ash Ave NE, Wadena, MN 56482
Tel.: (218) 631-3120
Web Site:
http://www.oddwadena.coop
Year Founded: 1940
Sales Range: $10-24.9 Million
Emp.: 28
Electricity Provider Association
N.A.I.C.S.: 813910
Robin Doege (Pres, CEO & Mgr-Ops)
Lisa Graba Meech (Fin Mgr)

TODD WENZEL CHEVROLET
3156 Highland Dr, Hudsonville, MI 49426
Tel.: (616) 669-6683
Web Site:
http://www.toddwenzel.com
Year Founded: 1998
Sales Range: $25-49.9 Million
Emp.: 50

Sales of New & Used Automobile Service & Parts
N.A.I.C.S.: 441110
Denese Bykstra (Comptroller)
Todd Wenzel (Owner, Pres & CEO)
Todd Halsey (Dir-Fixed Ops)

TODD-FORD MANAGEMENT INC.
1914 Breeden Ave Ste 100, San Antonio, TX 78212-2148
Tel.: (210) 732-9791
Year Founded: 1985
Rev.: $904,243
Emp.: 4
Plumbing; Heating & Air-conditioning
N.A.I.C.S.: 238220
Jon G. Ford (CEO)
Thomas Ford (Treas & Sec)

Subsidiaries:

Todd-Ford Inc. (1)
202 Wildrose Ave, San Antonio, TX 78209-3815
Tel.: (210) 732-9791
Sales Range: $25-49.9 Million
Mechanical Contracting
N.A.I.C.S.: 238220

Todd-Ford Sheetmetal Inc. (1)
1914 Breeden Ave Ste 200, San Antonio, TX 78212-2148 (100%)
Tel.: (210) 732-9791
Sales Range: $10-24.9 Million
Provider of Sheet Metal Work
N.A.I.C.S.: 238220

TODEY MOTOR CO. INC.
1345 N Oxnard Blvd, Oxnard, CA 93030
Tel.: (805) 983-6800
Web Site: http://www.todey.com
Sales Range: $75-99.9 Million
Emp.: 20
New & Used Automobile Sales
N.A.I.C.S.: 441110
Dan Gates (VP)

TODINO ENGINEERING SALES INC.
15 Higgins Unit 301, Smithfield, RI 02917
Tel.: (401) 233-9501
Web Site:
http://todinoengineering.com
Year Founded: 1956
Sales Range: $10-24.9 Million
Emp.: 2
Sales of Electronic Parts & Equipment
N.A.I.C.S.: 423690
Steve Hague (Pres)

TOENSMEIER ADJUSTMENT SERVICE
10 Duff Rd Ste 401, Pittsburgh, PA 15235
Tel.: (412) 242-7489
Web Site: http://www.toensmeier.net
Year Founded: 1947
Sales Range: $25-49.9 Million
Emp.: 50
Provider of Claim-Adjustment Services
N.A.I.C.S.: 524211
Donald M. Maury (Pres & CEO)

TOFT DAIRY, INC.
3717 Venice Rd, Sandusky, OH 44870
Tel.: (419) 625-4376
Web Site: http://www.toftdairy.com
Year Founded: 1900
Sales Range: $10-24.9 Million
Emp.: 52
Milk & Icecream Product Mfr & Distr
N.A.I.C.S.: 112120

Eugene H. Meisler (Pres)
Sandy Bodi (Mgr-Personnel)
Charles M. Meisler (Treas)

TOG MANUFACTURING CO., INC.
1454 S State St, North Adams, MA 01247
Tel.: (413) 664-6711
Web Site:
http://www.togmanufacturing.com
Year Founded: 1970
Machine Shops
N.A.I.C.S.: 332710
Keith Kupiec (Plant Mgr)

TOGORUN
1285 Ave of the Americas 5th Fl, New York, NY 10019
Tel.: (646) 651-4001
Web Site: http://www.togorun.com
Year Founded: 1993
Public Relations Agency
N.A.I.C.S.: 541820
Gloria M. Janata (Pres & CEO)

TOHATSU AMERICA CORPORATION
2005 Vly View Ln Ste 200, Farmers Branch, TX 75234
Tel.: (214) 420-6440
Web Site: http://www.tohatsu.com
Year Founded: 1922
Sales Range: $10-24.9 Million
Emp.: 20
Outboard Boat Motor Mfr & Distr
N.A.I.C.S.: 333618
Hiroshi Wakayabashi (Pres)

Subsidiaries:

Nissan Marine & Power Products (1)
2005 Valley View Ln Ste 200, Farmers Branch, TX 75234
Tel.: (214) 420-6440
Web Site: http://www.nissanmarine.com
Outboard Boat Motor Mfr & Distr
N.A.I.C.S.: 333618
Jim Morgenthaler (Gen Mgr)

TOHOPEKALIGA WATER AUTHORITY
951 Martin Luther King Blvd, Kissimmee, FL 34741
Tel.: (407) 944-5000
Web Site: http://www.tohowater.com
Year Founded: 2003
Sales Range: $50-74.9 Million
Emp.: 226
Water Supply & Irrigation Systems
N.A.I.C.S.: 221310
Rodney Anderson (CFO)
Alexender Green (Comptroller)
Brian L. Wheeler (Exec Dir)
Bruce R. Van Meter (Chm)
Tom E. White (Sec)

TOKENEX, LLC
3825 NW 166th St Ste C1, Edmond, OK 73012
Tel.: (877) 316-4544
Web Site: http://www.tokenex.com
Year Founded: 2010
Sales Range: $1-9.9 Million
Emp.: 20
Software Programming Services
N.A.I.C.S.: 541511
Alex Pezold (Founder & CEO)

TOLBERT ENTERPRISES INC.
1500 Miracle Strip Pkwy SE, Fort Walton Beach, FL 32548
Tel.: (850) 243-9161
Web Site: http://www.ramadafwb.com
Sales Range: $10-24.9 Million
Emp.: 150
Franchise Owner of Resort Hotels
N.A.I.C.S.: 721110

Jessica Francis (Gen Mgr)

TOLEDO ENGENERING COMPANY INC.
3400 Executive Pkwy, Toledo, OH 43606
Tel.: (419) 537-9711
Web Site: http://www.teco.com
Sales Range: $25-49.9 Million
Emp.: 400
Glass Making Machinery: Blowing, Molding & Forming
N.A.I.C.S.: 333248
Fred C. Paulsen (Pres & COO)

TOLEDO FINANCE CORP.
112 Tenaha St, Center, TX 75935-3839
Tel.: (936) 598-2776
Web Site: http://www.toledocorp.com
Year Founded: 1967
Sales Range: $25-49.9 Million
Emp.: 95
Personal Credit Institutions
N.A.I.C.S.: 522291
Jason Buddin (Pres)
Adraín Buddin (VP)
Lisa Barbee (VP-Admin)
Brad Davis (Pres)
Kirk Dillon (VP-Ops)

TOLEDO MUSEUM OF ART
2445 Monroe St, Toledo, OH 43697
Tel.: (419) 255-8000
Web Site:
http://www.toledomuseum.org
Year Founded: 1901
Sales Range: $25-49.9 Million
Emp.: 381
Art Museum Operator
N.A.I.C.S.: 712110
Cynthia B. Thompson (Vice Chm)
Dennis G. Johnson (Sec)
John S. Szuch (Treas)
Sara Jane DeHoff (Vice Chm)
Mary Siefke (CFO)
Mike Deetsch (Dir-Education)
Lynn Miller (Dir-HR)
Amy Gilman (Assoc Dir)
Adam Levine (CEO & Dir-Edward Drummond & Florence Scott Libbey)
Anne Bennett (CIO)
Todd Ahrens (Dir-Dev)
Candice L. Harrison (Dir-Comm)
Halona Norton-Westbrook (Dir-Collections)
James R. Meador (Dir-Protective Svcs)
Patricia L. O'Toole (Dir-Fin)
Kristina Crystal (Chief Revenue Officer)
John S. Stanley (Dir-Special Projects)
Jennifer McCary (Chief People & Culture Officer)
David K. Welles Jr. (Chm)

TOLEDO SYMPHONY
1838 Parkwood Ave Ste 310, Toledo, OH 43614
Tel.: (419) 246-8000
Web Site:
http://www.toledosymphony.com
Sales Range: $25-49.9 Million
Emp.: 100
Symphony Orchestra
N.A.I.C.S.: 711130
Kathleen Carroll (Pres & CEO)
Randi Dier (VP-Fin)
Keith McWatters (Gen Mgr)
Tim Lake (Mgr-Production)

TOLEDO WEB SHOP
3450 W Central Ave Ste 136, Toledo, OH 43606
Tel.: (567) 225-5920

Toledo Web Shop—(Continued)
Web Site:
http://www.toledowebshop.com
Year Founded: 1999
Sales Range: $1-9.9 Million
Web Design & Internet Marketing
N.A.I.C.S.: 541519
Patrick L. Pylypuik (Pres & CEO)
Lonnie Nitschke (Dir-Ops)
Caleb Bryant (Dir-Search)
Dan Dotson (Mgr-Direct Mktg)
Mary Alkilani (Mgr-Mktg)

TOLL COMPANY
3005 Niagara Ln N, Plymouth, MN 55447
Tel.: (763) 551-5300
Web Site: http://www.tollgas.com
Year Founded: 1945
Sales Range: $10-24.9 Million
Emp.: 60
Gases, Compressed & Liquefied; Welding Supplies
N.A.I.C.S.: 424690
Jim Quicksell (Pres)

TOLLEFSON'S RETAIL GROUP INC.
2100 S Broadway, Minot, ND 58701
Tel.: (701) 852-5231
Sales Range: $25-49.9 Million
Emp.: 100
Retailer of Carpets
N.A.I.C.S.: 449121
Todd Nelson (Controller)

TOLLMAN SPRING COMPANY INC.
91 Enterprise Dr, Bristol, CT 06010
Tel.: (860) 583-1326
Web Site: https://tollmanspring.com
Year Founded: 1945
Sales Range: $10-24.9 Million
Emp.: 100
Mfr of Steel Springs
N.A.I.C.S.: 332613
Richard Zinc (Pres)
Matt Zink (CEO)

TOLMAR, INC.
701 Centre Ave, Fort Collins, CO 80526
Tel.: (970) 212-4500
Web Site: http://www.tolmar.com
Pharmaceutical Research & Development Services
N.A.I.C.S.: 325412
Mike Duncan (CEO)
Nancy Elstad (Dir-Clinical Ops)
Wendi Young (Dir-Analytical Dev)
William Griffith (Asst Controller)
Annette Bruntz (Controller)
Jeff Sieranski (Dir-Engrg & Facilities)
Ann Gauntlett (Mgr-Clinical Trials)
Eva Petrecca (Mgr-Clinical Trials)
Tracy Milburn (Mgr-Analytical Dev)
Vicki Gorum (Mgr-Warehouse)

Subsidiaries:

TOLMAR Pharmaceuticals, Inc. (1)
475 Half Day Rd Ste 200, Lincolnshire, IL 60069
Tel.: (224) 880-5770
Web Site: http://www.tolmar.com
Pharmaceuticals Whslr
N.A.I.C.S.: 424210

Tolmar Pharmaceuticals, Inc. (1)
2579 Midpoint Dr, Fort Collins, CO 80525 (100%)
Tel.: (970) 482-5868
Drug Delivery Systems
N.A.I.C.S.: 325412

TOLUNAY-WONG ENGINEERS, INC.
10710 S Sam Houston Pkwy W Ste 100, Houston, TX 77031
Tel.: (713) 722-7064
Web Site: http://www.tweinc.com
Year Founded: 1993
Rev.: $19,700,000
Emp.: 157
Engineeering Services
N.A.I.C.S.: 541330
Patrick J. Kenney (VP-Southeast Reg)
William R. Tobin (Sr VP)

TOM + CHEE
133 E Court St, Cincinnati, OH 45202
Tel.: (513) 721-2433
Web Site:
http://www.tomandchee.com
Sales Range: $1-9.9 Million
Emp.: 70
Sandwich Shop
N.A.I.C.S.: 722513
Trew Quackenbush (Pres)
Corey Ward (Founder)

TOM AHL BUICK GMC
2525 Allentown Rd, Lima, OH 45805
Tel.: (419) 228-2345
Web Site:
http://www.tomahlbuickgmc.com
Sales Range: $25-49.9 Million
Emp.: 160
Car Whslr
N.A.I.C.S.: 441110
Thomas Ahl (Owner & Pres)
Vince Downing (Gen Mgr)
Sharon Dukes (Office Mgr)
Tammy Pelletier (Office Mgr)

TOM BUSH REGENCY MOTORS INC.
9850 Atlantic Blvd, Jacksonville, FL 32225-6536
Tel.: (904) 725-0911
Web Site: http://www.tombush.com
Year Founded: 1970
Sales Range: $100-124.9 Million
Emp.: 211
New & Used Car Dealers
N.A.I.C.S.: 441110
Robert Hudson (Gen Mgr-Sls)
Telis Assimenios (COO & Gen Mgr)

Subsidiaries:

Tom Bush Motors Inc. (1)
9850 Atlantic Blvd, Jacksonville, FL 32225-6536 (100%)
Tel.: (904) 725-0911
Web Site: http://www.tombush.com
Sales Range: $25-49.9 Million
New & Used Car Dealers
N.A.I.C.S.: 441110

Tom Bush Volkswagen Inc. (1)
9850 Atlantic Blvd, Jacksonville, FL 32225-6536
Tel.: (904) 725-0911
Web Site: http://www.tombush.com
Sales Range: $25-49.9 Million
New & Used Car Dealers
N.A.I.C.S.: 441110

TOM CLARK CHEVROLET INC.
1063 Long Run Rd Route 48, McKeesport, PA 15132
Tel.: (412) 751-2900
Web Site:
http://www.tomclarkchevy.com
Year Founded: 1987
Sales Range: $25-49.9 Million
Emp.: 94
Car Whslr
N.A.I.C.S.: 441110
Thomas E. Clark Sr. (Owner)

TOM FITTS TOBACCO CO INC.
222 S Florida St, Pine Bluff, AR 71601
Tel.: (870) 534-8565
Rev.: $15,200,000
Emp.: 18
Tobacco & Tobacco Product Merchant Whslr
N.A.I.C.S.: 424940
John Hauge (Pres)
Lisa Hauge (Treas & Sec)

TOM GEORGE YACHT GROUP
343 Causeway Blvd Ste 210, Dunedin, FL 34698
Tel.: (727) 734-8707
Web Site: http://www.tgyg.com
Emp.: 15
Yacht Sales, Management, Construction Management & Chartering Services
N.A.I.C.S.: 441222
Tom George (Pres)
Debbie Carbery (Office Mgr)

TOM GRADDY ENTERPRISES INC.
700 Ruskin Dr, Forest Park, GA 30297
Tel.: (404) 363-8390
Web Site:
http://www.vanguardtrucks.com
Sales Range: $10-24.9 Million
Emp.: 75
New & Used Trucks, Tractors & Trailers
N.A.I.C.S.: 441110
Thomas Graddy (Pres)

TOM HESSER AUTO GROUP
1001 N Washington Ave, Scranton, PA 18509-2917
Tel.: (570) 343-1221
Web Site:
http://www.tomhesserchevrolet.com
Sales Range: $25-49.9 Million
Emp.: 75
Car Dealership Owner & Operator
N.A.I.C.S.: 441110
Dean L. Hesser (Pres)

Subsidiaries:

Tom Hesser Chevrolet/BMW Inc. (1)
1001 N Washington Ave, Scranton, PA 18509
Tel.: (570) 343-1221
Web Site: http://www.tomhesser.com
Automobiles, New & Used
N.A.I.C.S.: 441110
Dean L. Hesser (Pres)

TOM JOHNSON INVESTMENT MANAGEMENT, LLC (TJIM)
201 Robert S Kerr Ste 510, Oklahoma City, OK 73102
Tel.: (405) 236-2111
Web Site: http://www.tjim.com
Year Founded: 1983
Sales Range: $150-199.9 Million
Emp.: 11
Independent Investment Management Services
N.A.I.C.S.: 523940
Lori A. Calfy (Sr VP & Chief Compliance Officer)
Richard H. Parry (Pres & Chief Investment Officer)
Douglas A. Haws (VP & Portfolio Mgr)
Steven G. Schenk (VP & Portfolio Mgr)
Edward L. Schrems (VP & Portfolio Mgr)
Nicholas J. Pointer (VP & Portfolio Mgr)

TOM JONES FORD
23454 W US Hwy 85, Buckeye, AZ 85326
Tel.: (623) 386-4429
Web Site:
http://www.tomjonesfordinc.com
Sales Range: $10-24.9 Million
Emp.: 40
New Car Dealers
N.A.I.C.S.: 441110
Tom G. Jones (Principal)
Scotty McMillan (Mgr-Svc)
Jay Ballard (Dir-Fin & Gen Mgr-Sls)
Justine Campos (Mgr-Fin)
Adam Spooner (Mgr-Sls)
J. J. Mahalek (Dir-Fleet)
Joel Russell (Mgr-Parts)

TOM JONES INC.
2320 Birmingham Hwy, Montgomery, AL 36108
Tel.: (334) 263-6681
Sales Range: $10-24.9 Million
Emp.: 10
Petroleum Bulk Stations
N.A.I.C.S.: 424710
Lisa J Stevens (Office Mgr)
Annette Watson (Co-Pres)
Leslie Watson Jr. (Co-Pres)

TOM JONES INC.
41 21 28th St, Long Island City, NY 11101
Tel.: (212) 707-7717
Web Site: http://www.searlenyc.com
Year Founded: 1962
Sales Range: $10-24.9 Million
Emp.: 40
Retailer of Women's & Men's Apparel
N.A.I.C.S.: 561499
Searle Blatt (Pres)
Alice Blatt (VP)
Farokh Hirjibehebin (Controller)
Rick Weinstein (Dir-Sls & Mktg)

TOM LANGE COMPANY, INC.
755 Apple Orchard Rd, Springfield, IL 62703-5746
Tel.: (217) 786-3300
Web Site: http://www.tomlange.com
Year Founded: 1962
Sales Range: $100-124.9 Million
Emp.: 200
Fresh Fruits & Vegetables
N.A.I.C.S.: 424480
Phil Gumper (Chm & CEO)
Josh McKey (CFO)

TOM LIGHT CHEVROLET
738 N Earl Rudder Fwy, Bryan, TX 77802-2914
Tel.: (979) 776-7000
Web Site: http://www.tomlight.com
Year Founded: 1972
Sales Range: $10-24.9 Million
Emp.: 65
Car Whslr
N.A.I.C.S.: 441110
Tommy Light (Owner)
Tim Light (Pres)
Randy Miller (Dir-Svc)

TOM LOFTUS INC.
809 Steve Hawkins Pkwy, Marble Falls, TX 78654
Tel.: (830) 693-6477
Web Site: http://www.austinturf.com
Sales Range: $10-24.9 Million
Emp.: 53
Construction & Mining Machinery
N.A.I.C.S.: 423810
Tom Loftus (Pres)
Margaret Loftus (Sec)
Harry Jukes (Dir-Ops)
Chad Mobley (Dir-Sls)
Nathan New (CFO)
Ben Davis (Mgr-CWP Sls & Comml)
Kenny Sierra (Mgr-Corp Svc)
Ben Rutland (Mgr-Ops-North Texas)

Jim Newkirk (Mgr-Govt Sls & Fort Worth Acct)
Gene Sueltenfuss (Mgr-Acctg)
Gary Stephensen (Mgr-Svc-North Texas)
Jeff Coleman (Mgr-Acct-East Texas)
Gus Furlong (Mgr-Comml Svc)
Terry Harris (Mgr-Acct-Central Texas)
Jon Manning (Mgr-Acct-Dallas)
Jessie Hunt (Mgr-Acct-West Texass)

TOM LOPES DISTRIBUTING INC.
1790 S 10th St, San Jose, CA 95112
Tel.: (408) 292-1041   CA
Web Site: http://www.lubeoil.com
Year Founded: 1956
Premium Quality Petroleum Products; Gasoline & Diesel Marketing, Lubricants & Petrochemicals
N.A.I.C.S.: 424720
Steve Lopes (Pres)
Jeff Lopes (VP)
Jack Scott (Controller)
Lee Curry (Gen Mgr)
Kristine Le (Mgr-Credit)

TOM MASANO INC.
1600 Lancaster Ave, Reading, PA 19607
Tel.: (610) 775-0311   PA
Web Site: http://www.tommasano.com
Year Founded: 1920
Sales Range: $10-24.9 Million
Emp.: 250
Car Dealership Owner & Operator
N.A.I.C.S.: 441110
John Massano (Pres)

TOM NEHL TRUCK CO.
417 Edgewood Ave S, Jacksonville, FL 32254
Tel.: (904) 389-3653
Web Site: http://www.tomnehl.com
Sales Range: $50-74.9 Million
Emp.: 150
Trucks, Tractors & Trailers: New & Used
N.A.I.C.S.: 441110
Steve Bacalis (Pres)
Wanda Cotter (Comptroller)
Kelly Amburgey (Comptroller)

TOM O'BRIEN CHRYSLER JEEP GREENWOOD
750 US 31 N, Greenwood, IN 46142
Tel.: (317) 881-6791
Sales Range: $10-24.9 Million
Emp.: 70
Car Whslr
N.A.I.C.S.: 441110
Tom Miller (Pres)

TOM PECK FORD OF HUNTLEY, INC.
13900 Automall Dr, Huntley, IL 60142-8024
Tel.: (847) 669-6060
Web Site: http://www.tompeckford.com
Sales Range: $10-24.9 Million
Emp.: 50
Car Whslr
N.A.I.C.S.: 441110
Mike Zell (Mgr-Used Car)
Maureen Garcia (Office Mgr)
Tom Peck Sr. (Pres)

TOM RANDALL DISTRIBUTING CO.
415 Sugar St, Layton, UT 84041
Tel.: (801) 544-3466
Web Site: http://www.tomrandalldist.com
Rev.: $18,000,000
Emp.: 75
Convenience Store
N.A.I.C.S.: 445131
Brad Randall (Pres)

TOM ROUSH INC.
525 W David Brown Dr, Westfield, IN 46074
Tel.: (317) 896-5561
Web Site: http://www.tomroush.com
Year Founded: 1972
Rev.: $44,533,124
Emp.: 62
Automobiles, New & Used
N.A.I.C.S.: 441110
Thomas A. Roush (Owner & Pres)
Jeff Roush (VP)
Steve Reynolds (Controller)

TOM STINNETT HOLIDAY RV CENTER INC.
520 Marriott Dr, Clarksville, IN 47129-3054
Tel.: (812) 282-7718   IN
Web Site: http://www.stinnettrv.com
Year Founded: 1979
Sales Range: $10-24.9 Million
Emp.: 60
Recreational Vehicle Dealers
N.A.I.C.S.: 441210
Paul Cunningham (Gen Mgr)

TOM WESSEL CONSTRUCTION CORP.
4940 Lakewood Ranch Blvd N Ste 110, Sarasota, FL 34240
Tel.: (941) 365-1145
Web Site: http://www.tomwesselconstruction.com
Year Founded: 1992
Sales Range: $1-9.9 Million
Emp.: 5
General Contractors
N.A.I.C.S.: 236220
Thomas J. Wessel (Pres)
Scott Herman (Sr Project Mgr)
Mike Rice (VP)
Gary Elwick (VP)

TOM WHEAT LANDSCAPING
1522 Poleline Rd, Davis, CA 95618
Tel.: (530) 756-6490
Sales Range: $10-24.9 Million
Emp.: 35
New Car Whslr
N.A.I.C.S.: 441110
Donald Thpmpson (Owner)

TOM YATES PETROLEUM CO. INC.
1300 E Saunders St, Laredo, TX 78041
Tel.: (956) 723-3626
Rev.: $10,200,000
Emp.: 8
Distr of Petroleum Products
N.A.I.C.S.: 424710
Thomas H. Yates Jr. (Pres)

TOM'S FOOD MARKETS INC.
1311 S Division St, Traverse City, MI 49684
Tel.: (231) 946-6395   MI
Web Site: http://www.toms-foodmarkets.com
Year Founded: 1946
Sales Range: $25-49.9 Million
Emp.: 20
Operator of Grocery Stores
N.A.I.C.S.: 445110
Daniel Deering (CEO)

TOM'S FORD INC.
200 Hwy 35 S, Keyport, NJ 07735
Tel.: (732) 264-1600
Web Site: http://www.tomsford.com
Sales Range: $25-49.9 Million
Emp.: 100
New & Used Car Dealers
N.A.I.C.S.: 441110
Robert Lyttle (Pres)
Larry Doremus (Gen Mgr)

TOM'S TRUCK CENTER INC.
1008 E 4th St, Santa Ana, CA 92701
Tel.: (714) 835-8350
Web Site: http://www.ttruck.com
Rev.: $59,931,283
Emp.: 150
Sales of New & Used Trucks, Tractors & Trailers
N.A.I.C.S.: 441110
Brad Skarsten (Mgr-Sls)
Chuck Seymour (Controller)
Steve Regets (Mgr-Sls-Fleet)
George P. Heidler Jr. (Pres)

TOM, DICK & HARRY ADVERTISING
350 W Erie 2nd Fl, Chicago, IL 60654
Tel.: (312) 327-9500
Web Site: http://www.tdhadvertising.com
Year Founded: 2002
Rev.: $30,000,000
Emp.: 21
Advertising Agencies
N.A.I.C.S.: 541810
Greg Reifel (Mng Partner)
Michael Herlehy (Creative Partner)
Bob Volkman (Creative Partner)
David Yang (Founder, Owner & Creative Partner)
Don Brashears (Mng Partner)
Thomas Richie (Dir-Creative)
John Candelaria (Dir-Creative)
Taylor LeCroy (Sr Dir-Art)
Jared El-Mofty (Copywriter)

TOMAHAWK LOG & COUNTRY HOMES, INC.
2285 County L, Tomahawk, WI 54487
Tel.: (715) 453-3265
Web Site: http://www.tomahawklog.com
Prefabricated Wood Building Mfr
N.A.I.C.S.: 321992
Tom Wyles (Pres & CEO)
Charlotte Wyles (CFO)
Justin Rigney (Coord-Design)
Nick Schmit (Mgr-Mill)
Troy Gullo (Mgr-Sls-Natl)

TOMAHAWK STRATEGIC SOLUTIONS LLC
1225 17th Ave S, Nashville, TN 37212
Tel.: (615) 431-3700
Web Site: http://www.tomahawkstrategicsolutions.com
Year Founded: 2014
Sales Range: $1-9.9 Million
Emp.: 50
Education Services
N.A.I.C.S.: 611710
Keith Walawender (CEO)
Mike Biller (Pres & COO)
Matt Coufalik (Sr VP)
Kahler Macphail (VP)
Peter O'Connell (VP)

TOMAR INDUSTRIES, INC.
300 Commerce Dr, Freehold, NJ 07728
Tel.: (732) 780-2200   NJ
Web Site: http://www.tomarind.com
Year Founded: 1968
Sales Range: $10-24.9 Million
Emp.: 25
Janitorial & Packaging Products Distr
N.A.I.C.S.: 424130
Ruth Casey (Mgr-Pur)
Thomas Field Sr. (CEO)
Thomas Field Jr. (Pres)

Subsidiaries:

Willgain Enterprises, Inc.   (1)
262 Lackland Dr E, Middlesex, NJ 08846
Tel.: (732) 271-3400
Web Site: http://www.willgain.com
Packaging Material Distr
N.A.I.C.S.: 423840
Kevin Willmann (Founder & CEO)

TOMARCO CONTRACTOR SPECIALTIES
148 48 Northam St, La Mirada, CA 90638
Tel.: (714) 523-1771
Web Site: http://www.tomarco.com
Sales Range: $10-24.9 Million
Emp.: 60
Hand Tools
N.A.I.C.S.: 423710
Keith Watkins (Pres)

TOMASSO BROTHERS INC.
1 Liberty Sq Ste 5, New Britain, CT 06051
Tel.: (860) 224-9977
Web Site: http://www.thetomassogroup.com
Rev.: $12,600,000
Emp.: 60
Commercial & Office Building Contractors
N.A.I.C.S.: 236220
William A. Tomasso (Pres)
Michael W. Tomasso (Principal)
J. Leo Gagne (CFO & COO)

TOMBELL CHEVROLET INC.
800 Alabama St, Redlands, CA 92373
Tel.: (909) 793-2681
Web Site: http://www.tombellchevy.com
Sales Range: $200-249.9 Million
Emp.: 102
Automobiles, New & Used
N.A.I.C.S.: 441110
Tom Bell (Pres)
Jim Devor (Mgr-Parts)

TOMBIGBEE ELECTRIC POWER ASSOCIATION
1346 Auburn Rd, Tupelo, MS 38804
Tel.: (662) 842-7635
Web Site: http://www.tombigbeeelectric.com
Sales Range: $25-49.9 Million
Emp.: 132
Distribution, Electric Power
N.A.I.C.S.: 221122
William Long (Gen Mgr)
Bruce Williams (Office Mgr)

TOMCO2 EQUIPMENT COMPANY
3340 Rosebud Rd, Loganville, GA 30052
Tel.: (770) 979-8000
Web Site: http://www.tomcoequipment.com
Year Founded: 1970
Sales Range: $10-24.9 Million
Emp.: 115
CO_2 Products & Services
N.A.I.C.S.: 332313
Lynn G. Brown (CFO)
Bill Wiggins (VP-Technical Svcs)
Vicky Crowe (Coord-Mktg & Sls)
Ken Mercer (Dir-Ops)
Jeff Hering (Gen Mgr-Fire Sys)

TOMLINSON/ERWIN-LAMBETH, INC.

TOMLINSON/ERWIN-LAMBETH, INC.

Tomlinson/Erwin-Lambeth, Inc.—(Continued)
201 E Holly Hill Rd, Thomasville, NC 27360-5819
Tel.: (336) 472-5005
Web Site:
http://www.tomlinsonerwinlambeth.com
Year Founded: 1901
Sales Range: $50-74.9 Million
Emp.: 100
Upholstered Furniture Mfr
N.A.I.C.S.: 337121
W.R. Lambeth (Pres)

Subsidiaries:

Directional Furniture (1)
201 E Hollyhill Rd, Thomasville, NC 27360
Tel.: (336) 472-5005
Sales Range: $10-24.9 Million
Emp.: 80
Furniture Mfr
N.A.I.C.S.: 337121

Unit (Domestic):

Carter Furniture (2)
201 E Hollyhill Rd, Thomasville, NC 27360
Tel.: (336) 475-8000
Web Site: http://www.carterfurniture.com
Rev.: $10,000,000
Emp.: 80
Retailer of Household Furniture
N.A.I.C.S.: 337121

TOMMIE VAUGHN MOTORS INC.
1201 N Shepherd Dr, Houston, TX 77008
Tel.: (713) 869-4661
Web Site:
http://www.tommievaughnsford.com
Sales Range: $125-149.9 Million
Emp.: 200
Automobiles, New & Used
N.A.I.C.S.: 441110
Rick Camp (Mgr-Fin)
Jim Janke (Gen Mgr)
Brenda McGaffie (Mgr-Credit)
Joe Blair (Controller)
Mike Cooley (Mgr-Svcs)

TOMMY BARTLETT, INC.
560 Wisconsin Dells Pkwy, Wisconsin Dells, WI 53965
Tel.: (608) 254-2525
Web Site:
http://www.tommybartlett.com
Year Founded: 1948
Sales Range: $75-99.9 Million
Emp.: 150
Operator of Water Show
N.A.I.C.S.: 713990
Thomas M. Diehl (Co-Owner, Pres & Gen Mgr)
Margaret Diehl (Exec VP)
Mark Schilling (VP-Ops & Gen Mgr)
Jill C. Diehl (Exec VP & Asst Gen Mgr)
Joey Lincicum (VP-Production)
Kristi Meister (VP-Admin)

TOMMY BROOKS OIL COMPANY
1400 S Gloster St, Tupelo, MS 38801
Tel.: (662) 842-1135
Web Site: http://www.brooksoil.com
Year Founded: 1966
Rev.: $24,000,000
Emp.: 70
Distr of Petroleum Products
N.A.I.C.S.: 424710
Thomas L. Brooks (Pres)
Lee Brooks (Controller)

TOMMY HOUSE TIRE COMPANY
340 E Macon St, Decatur, IL 62523
Tel.: (217) 423-2690

Web Site:
http://www.tommyhousetire.com
Sales Range: $10-24.9 Million
Emp.: 80
Tire Recapping
N.A.I.C.S.: 811198
John House (VP)
Beth Austin (Pres)

TOMMY'S QUALITY USED CARS
424 State St, Guthrie, KY 42234
Tel.: (270) 483-0386
Web Site:
http://www.tommysusedcars.com
Sales Range: $10-24.9 Million
Emp.: 15
Used Car Dealerships
N.A.I.C.S.: 441110
Angels Gates (Mgr-Fin)

TOMPKINS INDUSTRIES, INC.
1912 E 123rd, Olathe, KS 66061
Tel.: (913) 764-8088
Web Site:
http://www.tompkinsind.com
Sales Range: $100-124.9 Million
Emp.: 196
Hardware & Plastic Mfr
N.A.I.C.S.: 326199
Keith Skinner (Mgr-Charlotte)
Angie Gump (Mgr-Portland)
Dan Turnbull (Branch Mgr)
Mike Kerr (Mgr-Rancho Cucamonga)
Frank Ezzio (Branch Mgr-Des Moines)
Bryan Restorick (Mgr-Twinsburg)
Bill Hartman (Mgr-Des Moines)
Gabriel Moore (Asst Mgr-Customer Svc-Twinsburg)
Heath Sullivan (Mgr-Houston)
Jeff Hegwood (Mgr-Pella)
Jeremy Swanson (Mgr-Elkhart)
Nancy Scheiterle (Mgr-Kansas City)
Sean McGuinness (Gen Mgr-Mississauga)
Steve Roman (Asst Mgr-Customer Svc-Kansas City)

TOMS RIVER LINCOLN MERCURY MAZDA, INC.
PO Box 5056, Toms River, NJ 08754
Tel.: (732) 341-2900
Year Founded: 1990
Sales Range: $25-49.9 Million
Emp.: 50
New Car Dealers
N.A.I.C.S.: 441110
Michael Maffucci (Gen Mgr)

TOMS-PRICE CO.
303 E Front St, Wheaton, IL 60187
Tel.: (630) 668-7878
Web Site: http://www.tomsprice.com
Rev.: $11,200,000
Emp.: 50
Furniture Retailer
N.A.I.C.S.: 449110
John Troller (Controller)
Scott Price (Pres)

TOMSHEEHAN WORLDWIDE
645 Penn St, Reading, PA 19601-3408
Tel.: (610) 478-8448
Web Site:
http://www.tomsheehan.com
Year Founded: 1989
Sales Range: $1-9.9 Million
Emp.: 13
Advertising Agencies, Asian Market, Brand Development, Business Publications, Business-To-Business, Collateral & Communications
N.A.I.C.S.: 541810

Tom Sheehan (Principal & Dir-Creative)
Sandra Reber (Supvr-Creative Svcs)

Subsidiaries:

tomsheehan worldwide (1)
3001 N Rocky Point Dr E Ste 200, Tampa, FL 33607 (100%)
Tel.: (727) 498-7797
Web Site: http://www.tomsheehan.com
Marketing & Public Relations
N.A.I.C.S.: 541820
Scott Boie (VP-Bus Dev)

TONAQUINT DATA CENTERS, INC.
1108 W 1600 S Ste D, Saint George, UT 84770
Tel.: (435) 628-6164
Web Site: http://tonaquint.com
Year Founded: 2000
All Other Support Services
N.A.I.C.S.: 561990
Matt Hamlin (CEO)

Subsidiaries:

Fiberpipe, Inc. (1)
10215 W Emerald St Ste 160, Boise, ID 83704
Tel.: (208) 331-3232
Web Site: http://www.fiberpipe.net
Sales Range: $1-9.9 Million
Emp.: 13
Wired Telecommunication Services
N.A.I.C.S.: 517810
Ken Birch (Founder)

TONAR INDUSTRIES INC.
419 Franklin Ave, Rockaway, NJ 07866
Tel.: (973) 586-9000
Web Site: http://www.tonar.com
Year Founded: 1973
Sales Range: $10-24.9 Million
Emp.: 17
Electronic Parts & Equipment
N.A.I.C.S.: 423690
Perry Fox (Pres)
Barry Sokol (Mgr-Outside Sls)

TONAWANDA COKE CORP
3875 River Rd, Tonawanda, NY 14150
Tel.: (716) 876-6222
Web Site:
http://www.tonawandacoke.com
Year Founded: 1978
Sales Range: $10-24.9 Million
Emp.: 130
Foundry Coke Mfr
N.A.I.C.S.: 324199
J. Crane (Owner & CEO)
Michael Durkin (CFO)

TONE PRODUCTS INC.
2129 N 15th Ave, Melrose Park, IL 60160
Tel.: (708) 681-3660
Web Site:
http://www.toneproducts.com
Rev.: $12,264,085
Emp.: 40
Provider of Flavoring Syrups
N.A.I.C.S.: 311930
Timothy Evon (Pres & CEO)
Matt Claus (Dir-Pur)
William Hamen (CFO)
Mike Evon (Dir-HR)

TONER CABLE EQUIPMENT INC.
969 Horsham Rd, Horsham, PA 19044
Tel.: (215) 675-2053
Web Site: http://www.tonercable.com
Year Founded: 1971
Sales Range: $10-24.9 Million
Emp.: 30

Dist of Control & Signal Wire & Cable
N.A.I.C.S.: 423610
Jim Dee (Mgr-Warehouse & Shipping)
Kathy Gray (Asst Mgr-Credit)
Tony Scarcelli (VP-Admin)
Art McWilliams (Mgr-Credit)
B. J. Toner (Pres)
Allen Morgan (Mgr-Sls UK)
Kathleen Wyatt (Mgr-Tradeshow)
Ted Tozzi (Dir-Engrg)
Karen Knight (Mgr-Credit)
Steve Deasey (Mgr-Sls)

Subsidiaries:

Toner Cable Equipment UK Ltd (1)
Unit 1 Portman Ctr, 37 45 Portman Rd, Reading, RG3 01EA, United Kingdom
Tel.: (44) 1189596116
Web Site: http://www.tonercable.com
Sales Range: $10-24.9 Million
Emp.: 2
Mfr of Control & Signal Wire & Cable
N.A.I.C.S.: 331318

TONERS PLUS OFFICE PRODUCTS
657 W Harvard St, Glendale, CA 91204
Tel.: (818) 548-8815
Web Site:
http://www.tonersplusinc.com
Year Founded: 1996
Sales Range: $10-24.9 Million
Emp.: 6
Office Supplies & Stationery Stores
N.A.I.C.S.: 459410
Shahin Azizi (Pres)

TONGLI PHARMACEUTICALS (USA), INC.
42-60 Main St Apt 6F, Flushing, NY 08540
Tel.: (212) 842-8837
Year Founded: 1999
Pharmaceutical Product Mfr & Distr
N.A.I.C.S.: 325412
Mingli Yao (Chm & CEO)

TONI & GUY USA, INC.
2311 Midway Rd, Carrollton, TX 75006
Tel.: (972) 931-1567
Web Site: http://www.toniguy.com
Sales Range: $200-249.9 Million
Emp.: 500
Haircare Products; Hair Salons
N.A.I.C.S.: 812112
Bruno Mascolo (Pres)

TONKA BAY EQUITY PARTNERS LLC
301 Carlson Pkwy Ste 325, Minnetonka, MN 55305
Tel.: (952) 345-2030   MN
Web Site:
http://www.tonkabayequity.com
Year Founded: 1998
Rev.: $350,000,000
Emp.: 25
Privater Equity Firm
N.A.I.C.S.: 523999
Cary Musech (Partner)
Peter Kooman (Partner)
Steve Soderling (Partner)
Shane Slominski (Partner)
Molly Simmons (Principal)
Jane King (Dir-Fin)
Pam Milliren (Dir-Admin)
Kam Kielhorn (Principal)

Subsidiaries:

Corporate Technologies LLC (1)
6210 Bury Dr, Minneapolis, MN 55346
Tel.: (952) 715-3600
Web Site: https://www.gocorptech.com
Information Technology Services

COMPANIES

TOOL-SMITH COMPANY, INC.

N.A.I.C.S.: 541512
Elam Baer *(CEO)*

Subsidiary (Domestic):

NuMSP LLC (2)
200 Broadacres Dr Ste 200, Bloomfield, NJ 07003
Tel.: (800) 381-9383
Web Site: https://www.numsp.com
Managed IT & Cybersecurity Solutions
N.A.I.C.S.: 541511

Subsidiary (Domestic):

Info-Link Technologies, Inc. (3)
601 Pittsburgh Ave, Mount Vernon, OH 43050
Tel.: (740) 393-3100
Web Site: http://www.infolinktechnologies.net
Computer System Design Services
N.A.I.C.S.: 541512
Tim Theophilus *(Pres)*
Ben Rule *(VP)*
Ivan Rollit *(Dir-Svcs)*
Zachary Beougher *(Ops Mgr-ITA)*
Christopher Keller *(Chief Engr & Mgr-Network)*
Harrison Thorp *(Engr-IT Svcs)*
Robert Adkins *(Engr-IT Svcs)*
Carlton Walters *(Engr-IT Svcs)*
Brad Zearott *(Engr-IT Svcs)*
Joe Forster *(Supvr-Svc Center)*
Philip Kraus *(Mktg Dir)*

J & J Technical Services, Inc. (3)
1510 Barbara Loop SE, Rio Rancho, NM 87124
Tel.: (505) 896-2969
Web Site: http://www.jandjtech.com
Computer & Software Stores
N.A.I.C.S.: 449210
John Freienmuth *(CEO)*
Martin Watterstrom *(CTO)*
Brian Wilson *(Mgr-Svc)*

Netfusion, Inc. (3)
1017 N La Cienega Blvd Ste 320, Los Angeles, CA 90046
Tel.: (323) 606-7600
Web Site: http://www.netfusion.com
Professional, Scientific & Technical Services
N.A.I.C.S.: 541990
Dave Watts *(Pres)*

Network Medics, Inc. (3)
1200 Washington Ave S Ste 300, Minneapolis, MN 55415
Tel.: (612) 315-7100
Web Site: https://www.networkmedics.com
Limited-Service Restaurants
N.A.I.C.S.: 722513

Realize Information Technology LLC (3)
3303 S Harvard Ave Ste D, Tulsa, OK 74135
Tel.: (918) 508-2228
Web Site: http://www.realizetech.com
Interurban & Rural Bus Transportation
N.A.I.C.S.: 485210
Jeff Woods *(Owner)*

Salient IT Inc. (3)
1050 Opportunity Dr Ste 180, Roseville, CA 95678
Tel.: (916) 800-2748
Web Site: http://www.salientit.com
Computer System Design Services
N.A.I.C.S.: 541512
David Hanjiev *(Founder)*

Swift Systems, Inc. (3)
7340 Executive Way Ste M, Frederick, MD 21704
Tel.: (301) 682-5100
Web Site: https://www.swiftsystems.com
Data Processing, Hosting & Related Services
N.A.I.C.S.: 518210

Quick Cable Corporation (1)
3700 Quick Dr, Franksville, WI 53126-0509
Tel.: (262) 824-3100
Web Site: http://www.quickcable.com
Sales Range: $10-24.9 Million
Mfr & Distr of Connectors, Cable, Cable Assemblies & Tools for Energy Storage Industry

N.A.I.C.S.: 335931
Kenneth Bons *(VP-Sls & Mktg)*
Justin Leonsteiner *(Mgr-OEM Sls)*

Subsidiary (Non-US):

Quick Cable Canada Limited (2)
6395 Kestrel Road, Mississauga, L5T 1Z5, ON, Canada
Tel.: (905) 362-1606
Web Site: http://www.quickcable.com
Mfr & Distr of Connectors, Cable, Cable Assemblies & Tools for Energy Storage Industry
N.A.I.C.S.: 335931
Warren DiMarco *(Gen Mgr)*

Standard Locknut, LLC (1)
1045 E 169th St, Westfield, IN 46074
Tel.: (317) 399-2252
Web Site: http://www.standard-miether.com
Bearings Accessory Mfr
N.A.I.C.S.: 332991
Matt Lesher *(CFO)*
Stuart Jara *(Pres)*
David Zimmer *(Pres)*

The Resort Company (1)
1847 Ski Time Sq, Steamboat Springs, CO 80477 (100%)
Tel.: (970) 879-8000
Web Site: http://www.theresortcompany.com
Hotel & Ski Resort Operator
N.A.I.C.S.: 721110
Robert E. Milne *(Pres)*

TONNER DOLL COMPANY, INC.
401 Wall St, Kingston, NY 12401
Tel.: (845) 339-9537 NY
Web Site: http://www.tonnerdoll.com
Year Founded: 1991
Sales Range: $10-24.9 Million
Doll Designer, Mfr, Whslr & Online Retailer
N.A.I.C.S.: 339930
Robert Tonner *(Founder, CEO & Designer)*
Jack Kralik *(VP)*

TONOGA INC.
136 Coonbrook Rd, Petersburg, NY 12138
Tel.: (518) 658-3202 DE
Web Site: http://www.4taconic.com
Year Founded: 1961
PTFE & Silicone Coated Fabrics, Tapes & Belts Mfr
N.A.I.C.S.: 313320
Andrew G. Russell *(Chm)*

TONSA AUTOMOTIVE INC.
30 Seaview Blvd, Port Washington, NY 11050
Tel.: (516) 299-4404
Web Site: http://www.tonsa.com
Rev.: $12,322,652
Emp.: 25
Automotive Supplies
N.A.I.C.S.: 561499
Santo Muradian *(Pres)*

TONY DOMIANO AUTO DEALERSHIPS
900 Carbondale Hwy RR 6, Archbald, PA 18403
Tel.: (570) 876-6000
Web Site: http://www.tonydomiano.com
Sales Range: $50-74.9 Million
Emp.: 20
Automobiles, New & Used
N.A.I.C.S.: 441110
Anthony R. Domiano Sr. *(Pres)*
Anthony R. Domiano Jr. *(VP)*

TONY GULLO MOTORS OF TEXAS, INC.
500 I 45 S, Conroe, TX 77304
Tel.: (936) 539-9191 TX
Web Site: http://www.gullotoyota.com

Sales Range: $25-49.9 Million
Emp.: 115
Automobiles; New & Used
N.A.I.C.S.: 441110
Philip Sharp *(Mgr-Internet)*
Anthony Gullo Sr. *(Pres)*
Tony Gullo Jr. *(VP)*

TONY MARTERIE & ASSOCIATES
28 Liberty Ship Way, Sausalito, CA 94965-2018
Tel.: (415) 331-7150 CA
Web Site: http://www.blastforward.info
Year Founded: 1984
Women's Clothing Mfr
N.A.I.C.S.: 315250
Tony Marterie *(Founder)*

TONY VOLKSWAGEN
94-1299 Ka Uka Blvd, Waipahu, HI 96797
Tel.: (808) 680-7170
Web Site: http://www.tonyvolkswagen.com
Sales Range: $10-24.9 Million
Emp.: 66
Car Whslr
N.A.I.C.S.: 441110
Angela Henry *(Mgr-Customer Rels)*
Stan Masamitsu *(Pres)*

TONY'S EXPRESS INC.
10613 Jasmine St, Fontana, CA 92337
Tel.: (909) 427-8700
Web Site: http://www.tony-express.com
Year Founded: 1954
Sales Range: $10-24.9 Million
Emp.: 125
Provider of Trucking Services
N.A.I.C.S.: 484122
George Raluy *(Pres & Co-Owner)*
Ken Fasola *(VP-Ops)*
Terry Jacob *(Mgr-Sls)*
Elizabeth Guerrero *(Mgr-HR)*

TONY'S SEAFOOD LTD
5215 Plank Rd, Baton Rouge, LA 70805
Tel.: (225) 357-9669
Web Site: http://www.tonyseafood.com
Sales Range: $100-124.9 Million
Emp.: 185
Seafood Markets
N.A.I.C.S.: 445250
Bill Pizzolato *(Pres)*

TOOF COMMERCIAL PRINTING
670 S Cooper St, Memphis, TN 38104
Tel.: (901) 274-3632
Web Site: http://www.toofprinting.com
Rev.: $17,000,000
Emp.: 110
Commercial Printing & Lithographic Services
N.A.I.C.S.: 323111
Stillman McFadden *(Pres)*

TOOJAY'S MANAGEMENT CORP.
3654 Georgia Ave, West Palm Beach, FL 33405
Tel.: (561) 659-9011
Web Site: http://www.toojays.com
Sales Range: $50-74.9 Million
Emp.: 1,300
Deli Restaurant Owner & Operator
N.A.I.C.S.: 722511
Dennis Snuszka *(VP-Food & Beverage)*

Alan Nuckles *(VP-Pur)*
Dave Diamond *(Dir-IT)*
Sharon Polinski *(VP-HR)*
Jim Vinz *(CEO)*
Kevin Gagnon *(Chief Acctg Officer & VP-Fin)*
Scott Nietschmann *(COO)*
Robin Y. Bayless *(VP-Mktg)*
Tony Rispoli *(Gen Mgr-Hallandale Beach)*
Peter Crowley *(Gen Mgr-Boynton Beach)*

TOOL KING
11111 W Ave, Denver, CO 80215
Tel.: (303) 922-5551 CO
Year Founded: 1978
Sales Range: $75-99.9 Million
Emp.: 50
Distr of Tools
N.A.I.C.S.: 444140
Donald Cohen *(Pres, CEO & CFO)*
Bruce Sompolski *(Dir-Mktg)*
Ben Skigen *(VP-E-Commerce)*
Matt Sime *(Asst Mgr-Retail Store)*

TOOL MART INC.
13721 S Gessner Ste 200, Missouri City, TX 77489
Tel.: (713) 222-8665
Web Site: http://www.toolmarthou.com
Sales Range: $10-24.9 Million
Emp.: 25
Distr of Industrial Machinery & Equipment
N.A.I.C.S.: 423830
Alan Soutar *(Pres)*

TOOL STEEL SERVICE, INC.
7333 S 76th Ave, Bridgeview, IL 60455
Tel.: (708) 458-7878
Web Site: http://www.toolsteel.com
Year Founded: 1961
Sales Range: $50-74.9 Million
Emp.: 80
Mfr of Steel Products
N.A.I.C.S.: 423510
Lee Miller *(Chm & Pres)*
Laurie Vogler *(Controller)*
Mary Dulik *(Office Mgr)*

TOOL TECH, INC.
4901 Urbana Road, Springfield, OH 45502
Tel.: (937) 399-4333
Web Site: http://www.tooltech.com
Sales Range: $10-24.9 Million
Special Die & Tool, Die Set, Jig & Fixture Mfr
N.A.I.C.S.: 333514
Mike Schneider *(Pres)*

Subsidiaries:

Cameron Tool Corp. (1)
1800 Bassett St, Lansing, MI 48915
Tel.: (517) 487-3671
Web Site: http://www.camerontool.com
Sales Range: $1-9.9 Million
Emp.: 62
Special Die & Tool, Die Set, Jig & Fixture Mfr
N.A.I.C.S.: 333514
Brian Mendyk *(Dir-Sls)*
Kathy Bracey *(Exec VP-Fin)*
Carey Oberlin *(Mgr-HR)*
Keith Krupsky *(Mgr-IT)*

TOOL-SMITH COMPANY, INC.
1300 4th Ave S, Birmingham, AL 35233
Tel.: (205) 323-2576
Web Site: http://www.toolsmith.ws
Rev.: $15,000,000
Emp.: 50
Pumps & Pumping Equipment

4185

TOOL-SMITH COMPANY, INC.   U.S. PRIVATE

Tool-Smith Company, Inc.—(Continued)
N.A.I.C.S.: 423830
William Otis Smith Jr. (Pres & CEO)

TOOLBARN.COM, INC.
7820 L St, Omaha, NE 68127
Tel.: (402) 597-3850
Web Site: http://www.toolbarn.com
Year Founded: 1999
Sales Range: $1-9.9 Million
Emp.: 33
Online Tool Sales
N.A.I.C.S.: 459999
Dan Williams (CEO)
Scott Reiss (Controller)
Matt Griffith (Dir-QA & Optimization)
Chad Wiese (Mgr-IT)
Patrick Kinchler (Dir-Supply Chain)
Russ Seveera (Supvr-Warehouse)
Shane Murphy (Dir-e-Commerce)

TOOLING SPECIALISTS INC.
33 E Fayette St, Latrobe, PA 15650
Tel.: (724) 539-2534
Rev.: $13,650,712
Emp.: 80
Machine Shop, Jobbing & Repair
N.A.I.C.S.: 332710
Theodore Prettiman (Pres)
Sue Trout (Sec)

TOOLWATCH CORP.
10303 E Dry Creek Rd, Englewood, CO 80112
Tel.: (303) 799-0272
Web Site: http://www.toolwatch.com
Year Founded: 1991
Sales Range: $1-9.9 Million
Emp.: 20
Custom Computer Programming Services
N.A.I.C.S.: 541511
Denise Shelton (VP-Pro Svcs)
Jay Martin (CEO)

Subsidiaries:

Busybusy, Inc. (1)
475 S Donlee Dr, Saint George, UT 84770
Tel.: (435) 414-8598
Web Site: https://www.busybusy.com
Software Services
N.A.I.C.S.: 541511
Isaac Barlow (CEO)

TOOLWIRE, INC.
7031 Koll Ctr Pkwy Ste 220, Pleasanton, CA 94566
Tel.: (925) 227-8500
Web Site: http://www.toolwire.com
Year Founded: 1998
Sales Range: $10-24.9 Million
Emp.: 29
Computer Training
N.A.I.C.S.: 611420
John Valencia (Pres & CEO)
John Catanzaro (Exec VP-Engrg)
Cameron D. Crowe (Exec VP-Sls & Mktg)
David James Clarke IV (VP-Learning Solutions)

TOOT'N TOTUM FOOD STORES LLC
1201 S Taylor St, Amarillo, TX 79101
Tel.: (806) 373-4351
Web Site: http://www.tootntotum.com
Year Founded: 1950
Sales Range: $75-99.9 Million
Emp.: 600
Operator of Convenience Stores
N.A.I.C.S.: 445131
Andrew Mitchell (VP-Supply & Transportation)

TOOTIE PIE COMPANY, INC.
129 Industrial Dr, Boerne, TX 78006
Tel.: (210) 737-6600
Web Site: http://www.tootiepieco.com
Year Founded: 2005
Sales Range: $1-9.9 Million
Emp.: 34
Pie Mfr
N.A.I.C.S.: 311813

TOP BRANDS, INC.
5739 Green Vly Ct, Oshkosh, WI 54904-6546
Tel.: (920) 236-2800
Web Site: http://www.top-brands.com
Year Founded: 1961
Sales Range: $50-74.9 Million
Emp.: 25
Promotional Marketing Services, Product & Specialty Customization, Warehousing, Packaging Services & Certificate Programs
N.A.I.C.S.: 541890
Norma Knollenberg (Pres & CEO)
Richard Knollenberg (VP-Fin)

TOP CLASS ACTIONS LLC
11201 N Tatum Blvd Ste 300, Phoenix, AZ 85028-6039
Web Site: http://www.topclassactions.com
Year Founded: 2008
Sales Range: $1-9.9 Million
Emp.: 25
Law firm
N.A.I.C.S.: 541110
Scott Hardy (Pres)
Sarah Mirando (VP-Ops)
Steve Williams (VP-Strategy)
Courtney Jorstad (Editor-in-Chief)

TOP EGG
702 S Elevator St, Okawville, IL 62271
Tel.: (618) 243-5293
Web Site: http://www.topag.net
Year Founded: 1920
Grain Retailer & Whslr
N.A.I.C.S.: 424510
Lloyd Strubhart (Mgr-Credit)
Shawn Meier (Mgr-Feed-Trenton)
Scott Harre (Mgr-Grain Dept)
Dave Wilke (Mgr-Lumberyard)
Lonny Schultz (Mgr-Trucking-Trenton)
Steve Meentemeyer (Sec)

Subsidiaries:

TOP AG Cooperative (1)
401 E Kentucky St, Trenton, IL 62293
Tel.: (618) 224-7332
Web Site: http://www.topag.net
Rev.: $17,025,595
Emp.: 25
Grain Retailer & Whslr
N.A.I.C.S.: 424510
Kevin Hartkemeyer (Gen Mgr)
Steve Meentemeyer (Sec)
Brian Kunz (Pres)

TOP FLIGHT, INC.
1300 Central Ave, Chattanooga, TN 37408-1515
Tel.: (423) 266-8171
Web Site: http://www.topflightpaper.com
Year Founded: 1920
Sales Range: $100-124.9 Million
Emp.: 250
Mfr of School Supplies & Envelopes
N.A.I.C.S.: 322230
E. Montgomery Robinson (Pres & Treas)
Douglas Berg (VP-Sls & Mktg)
James Skipper (Dir-IS)
Mike Carlin (Reg Mgr-Sls)

TOP FLITE CONSTRUCTION INC.
364 S Smith Rd Ste 101, Tempe, AZ 85281
Tel.: (480) 804-0920
Web Site: http://www.tfci.net
Rev.: $19,164,021
Emp.: 60
Structural Steel Erection
N.A.I.C.S.: 238120
Dan Selton (Pres)

TOP FLITE FINANCIAL, INC.
123 E Grand River Ave, Williamston, MI 48895
Tel.: (517) 655-2140
Web Site: http://www.tffinc.net
Year Founded: 2002
Sales Range: $10-24.9 Million
Emp.: 230
Mortgage Broker & Lender
N.A.I.C.S.: 522310
Timothy Baise (Co-Founder)
Tracie Baise (Co-Founder)
Jason Bottiglia (Branch Mgr)
Kurt Gallert (Branch Mgr)
Tim Enbody (Mgr-Sls)

TOP GUN SALES PERFORMANCE
5155 Financial Way, Mason, OH 45040
Tel.: (513) 770-0870
Web Site: http://www.topgunsps.com
Year Founded: 1990
Sales Range: $1-9.9 Million
Emp.: 54
Marketing Consulting Services
N.A.I.C.S.: 541613
J. Stephen Osborne (Founder & CEO)
David Kessinger (VP-Ops)
Ephriam Swafford (VP-Sls)

TOP HITS INC.
360 Hastings Ln, Buffalo Grove, IL 60089
Tel.: (847) 537-1690
Web Site: http://www.tophitsmusic.com
Sales Range: $10-24.9 Million
Emp.: 10
Video Cassettes, Accessories & Supplies Distributor
N.A.I.C.S.: 423990
Todd Rosenbaum (COO)
Kevin Rosenbaum (Pres & CFO)

TOP METAL BUYERS INC.
808 Walnut Ave, East Saint Louis, IL 62201
Tel.: (618) 271-0824
Web Site: http://www.topmetalbuyers.com
Sales Range: $10-24.9 Million
Emp.: 40
Junk & Scrap
N.A.I.C.S.: 423930
Norman Schultz (Co-Owner)

TOP RX INC.
2950 Brother Blvd, Bartlett, TN 38133-4012
Tel.: (901) 373-9314
Web Site: http://www.toprx.com
Year Founded: 1987
Sales Range: $25-49.9 Million
Emp.: 200
Sales of Drugs Proprietaries & Sundries
N.A.I.C.S.: 424210
Kenny King (CEO)
Anne Tetreault (Mgr-Compliance)

TOP SHELF SPIRITS & WINE
1042 Princeton, Marina Del Rey, CA 90292
Tel.: (310) 306-6800
Web Site: http://www.topshelfbottlingandbeverages.com
Sales Range: $50-74.9 Million
Emp.: 5
Beverage Bottling Services
N.A.I.C.S.: 312112
Todd Graham (Chm)

TOP VALUE FABRICS INC.
401 W Carmel Dr, Carmel, IN 46032
Tel.: (317) 844-7496
Web Site: http://www.tvfinc.com
Year Founded: 1974
Sales Range: $10-24.9 Million
Emp.: 55
Piece Goods & Other Fabrics
N.A.I.C.S.: 424310
Bob Burns (VP)
Robert Hinsch (VP)
Ken Siecinski (Mgr-Program, Active & Outerwear)
Michael Compton (Mgr-Bus Dev)
Jeff Nonte (Dir-Print Media)
Karen Stuerenberg (Dir-Mktg)
Tad Calahan (CFO & VP)
Chris Fredericks (Pres)

TOPA EQUITIES LTD, INC.
1800 Ave of the Stars Ste 1400, Los Angeles, CA 90067-4216
Tel.: (310) 203-9199
Web Site: http://www.topa.com
Year Founded: 1962
Sales Range: $800-899.9 Million
Emp.: 2,000
Holding Company
N.A.I.C.S.: 424810
Brenda Seuthe (CFO)
Darren Bell (VP & Dir-Leasing)
Bill Anderson (Chm & CEO)

Subsidiaries:

Topa Insurance Company (1)
24025 Park Sorrento Ste 300, Calabasas, CA 91302
Tel.: (310) 201-0451
Web Site: http://www.topains.com
Sales Range: $50-74.9 Million
Emp.: 80
Insurance Brokers
N.A.I.C.S.: 524126
Diana Daubenspeck (Asst VP-Internal Audit)
Tammy Nichols Schwartz (Mgr-Personal Lines)
William Robinson (VP-HR)
Chuck Williamson (Controller & Asst VP)
Tina Epstein Abrams (Asst VP-Comml Wholesale Brokerage)
Cynthia Morrison (CFO & Sr VP)
Judith Provencher (Sr VP-Claims-Calabasas)
Pete Sanchez (VP-Claims)
Brian Schween (CIO & Sr VP)
John E. Anderson (Founder)
Olive Chang (VP-Reinsurance)
Denise Pavlov (Chief Underwriting Officer)
Delaney O'Brien (Dir-Mktg & Comm)
Geoffrey Griffard (Dir-Fin Plng & Analysis)
Ben Rozema (Dir-Programs)
Michael Day (Pres & CEO)
Bill Anderson (Chm)
Susan Pavone (VP-Underwriting)

Subsidiary (Domestic):

Dorchester Insurance Company (2)
67 Dronningens Gade St, Charlotte Amalie, VI 00804
Tel.: (340) 776-9063
Sales Range: $50-74.9 Million
Emp.: 7
General Insurance Services
N.A.I.C.S.: 524210
Esther Ledee (Gen Mgr)
Theresa Fabela (Pres)

Four Corners Insurance Services (2)
4751 N 15th St, Phoenix, AZ 85014
Tel.: (602) 280-9500
Web Site: http://www.4cis.com
Automobile Insurance Services
N.A.I.C.S.: 524126

COMPANIES

Bill Marr *(Exec VP)*

Nevada Pacific Insurance Services (2)
4055 Spencer St Ste 236, Las Vegas, NV 89119
Tel.: (800) 574-5121
Web Site: http://www.nevpacins.com
General Insurance Services
N.A.I.C.S.: 524210
Donna Hart *(Supvr-Office Svcs)*

Topa Insurance Services (2)
5185 Dronningens Gade Ste 2, Charlotte Amalie, VI 00802-6400
Tel.: (340) 777-8844
Sales Range: $50-74.9 Million
Emp.: 13
General Insurance Services
N.A.I.C.S.: 524210
Esther Ledee *(Gen Mgr)*

Topa Management Company (1)
1800 Avenue of the Stars Ste 1400, Los Angeles, CA 90067
Tel.: (310) 203-9199
Web Site: http://www.topamanagement.com
Emp.: 30
Real Estate Management Services
N.A.I.C.S.: 531390
Jim Brooks *(Pres)*
Jeanne Lazar *(CFO & VP)*
Darren Bell *(VP-Leasing)*
Robin N. Platt *(Reg VP)*

Topa Properties, Ltd. (1)
Dronningens Gade Ste 1 Palm Passage 2nd Fl, Saint Thomas, VI 00802
Tel.: (340) 774-8175
Web Site: http://www.topavi.com
Sales Range: $10-24.9 Million
Emp.: 10
Real Estate Management Services
N.A.I.C.S.: 531390
Steve Morton *(Pres)*
Christine Thompson *(Dir-Ops)*

TOPAZ LIGHTING CORP
925 Waverly Ave, Holtsville, NY 11742
Tel.: (631) 758-5507
Web Site: http://www.topaz-usa.com
Rev: $40,305,332
Emp.: 47
Light Bulbs & Electric Supplies
N.A.I.C.S.: 423610
Russ Burroughs *(Pres)*
Ken Jones *(VP)*
James H. McLaughlin *(Mgr-Sls)*
Carrie Schwabacher *(VP-Sls)*
Greg Griswold *(Sls Dir-New York, New Jersey & Pennsylvania)*

TOPAZ SYSTEMS, INC.
650 Cochran St Ste 6, Simi Valley, CA 93065
Tel.: (805) 520-8282
Web Site: http://www.topazsystems.com
Sales Range: $10-24.9 Million
Emp.: 35
Mfr of Electronic Signature Solutions & Software
N.A.I.C.S.: 513210
Anthony E. Zank *(Pres & CEO)*
Josh Burkett *(Mgr-Engrg)*

TOPCO HOLDINGS INC.
150 NW Point Blvd, Elk Grove Village, IL 60007
Tel.: (847) 676-3030   WI
Web Site: http://www.topco.com
Year Founded: 1944
Sales Range: $200-249.9 Million
Emp.: 400
Holding Company; Perishables Equipment & Supplies Mfr
N.A.I.C.S.: 424410
Steven K. Lauer *(Pres & CEO)*
Kenneth Guy *(Sr VP-Acct Mgmt)*
Daniel Mazur *(Sr VP)*
Ian Grossman *(Sr VP)*

Subsidiaries:

Topco Associates LLC (1)
7711 Gross Point Rd, Skokie, IL 60077-2615   (86%)
Tel.: (847) 676-3030
Web Site: http://www.topco.com
Provider of Perishables, Equipment & Supplies for Wholesale Retail & Food Service Industries
N.A.I.C.S.: 424410
Thomas G. Frey *(CFO & Exec VP)*
David P. Picarillo *(Sr VP-Indirect Spend)*
James E. Goers *(Sr VP-Member Svcs & Natl Brands)*
Randall J. Skoda *(Pres & CEO)*
Paul Randle *(VP-Acct Mgmt)*
Andrew J. Broccolo *(Gen Counsel & Sr VP)*
Danell O'Neill *(VP-Corp Comm)*
Christopher Hooks *(Chm-Ops & Exec VP)*
Anjani Bhargava *(Chief HR Officer & Sr VP)*
Adam Schoor *(Mgr-Corp Comm)*
Christine Heffernan *(Sr VP-Center Store)*
David Negron *(VP-Meat, Seafood, Deli & Bakery)*
Clint Johnson *(VP-Center Store Ops)*

World Brands Inc. (1)
7711 Gross Pt Rd, Skokie, IL 60077-2615
Tel.: (847) 676-3030
Provider of Food, Drugs, Beauty Aids & Household Products
N.A.I.C.S.: 424410

World Classics (1)
7711 Gross Point Rd, Skokie, IL 60077-2615
Tel.: (847) 676-3030
Rev: $41,000
Provider of Perishables, Equipment & Supplies For Wholesale Retail & Food Service Industries
N.A.I.C.S.: 459110

TOPCRAFT PRECISION MOLDERS, INC.
301 Ivyland Rd, Warminster, PA 18974
Tel.: (215) 441-4700
Web Site: http://www.topcraft.com
Rev: $16,954,034
Emp.: 75
Injection Molding of Plastics Mfr
N.A.I.C.S.: 326199
Oscar Musitano *(Pres)*

TOPDEK, INC.
2926 NW 72nd Ave, Miami, FL 33122-1308
Tel.: (305) 599-0006   FL
Web Site: http://www.topdek.com
Year Founded: 1989
Sales Range: $10-24.9 Million
Emp.: 16
Computers, Peripherals & Software
N.A.I.C.S.: 423430
Fred Chuang *(Pres)*

TOPETE/STONEFIELD, INCORPORATED
325 W Encanto Blvd # B, Phoenix, AZ 85003-1110
Tel.: (602) 254-8780
Web Site: http://www.topete-stonefield.com
Year Founded: 1986
Sales Range: Less than $1 Million
Emp.: 4
Advetising Agency
N.A.I.C.S.: 541810
Liz Topete-Stonefield *(Pres & CEO)*
Emilio Espinosa *(VP-Latin America)*
Don Donner *(Office Mgr)*

TOPFLIGHT CORPORATION
277 Commerce Dr, Glen Rock, PA 17427
Tel.: (717) 227-5400   PA
Web Site: http://www.topflight.com
Year Founded: 1943
Sales Range: $75-99.9 Million
Emp.: 100

Printed Pressure-Sensitive Adhesive Materials for Electronic Switches; Labels & Nameplates
N.A.I.C.S.: 322220
Brad Harner *(VP-Sls & Mktg)*
Brian Litvak *(Plant Mgr)*
Tonya Nye *(Dir-Ops)*
Craig McClenachan *(Pres)*

TOPFLIGHT GRAIN COOPERATIVE INC.
400 E Bodman St, Bement, IL 61813-1202
Tel.: (217) 678-2261   IL
Web Site: http://www.topflightgrain.com
Year Founded: 1998
Sales Range: $100-124.9 Million
Emp.: 45
Grain & Seed Beans
N.A.I.C.S.: 424510
Pam Jarboe *(Asst Mgr)*
Eric Clements *(Mgr-Ops)*
Scott Docherty *(Gen Mgr)*
Gloria Litwiller *(Branch Mgr)*
Evan Brewbaker *(Branch Mgr)*
Jon Carr *(Branch Mgr)*
Jacob Quaid *(Branch Mgr)*
Vanessa Stinson *(Branch Mgr)*
Andrew Hanes *(Mgr-Branch & Safety)*
Derrick Bruhn *(Mgr-Grain Mdsg)*
Jack Warren *(Mgr-Ops-Central Reg)*
Larry Ackerman *(Mgr-Ops-Northern)*
Gerry Lolling *(Mgr-Ops-Western)*
Todd Steinberg *(Mgr-Western Div)*

TOPICA, INC.
PO Box 32480, San Francisco, CA 94134
Tel.: (415) 344-0800
Web Site: http://www.topica.com
Sales Range: $10-24.9 Million
Emp.: 90
Email Marketing Software & Solutions
N.A.I.C.S.: 513210
Max Henry *(CEO)*
Jeffery Lee *(CFO)*
Walid Ezzeddine *(VP-Customer Success)*
Lindsay McMurdo *(VP-Mktg)*

TOPICS ENTERTAINMENT INC.
3405 Lind Ave SW, Renton, WA 98057
Tel.: (425) 656-3621
Web Site: http://www.topics-ent.com
Year Founded: 1990
Sales Range: $50-74.9 Million
Emp.: 26
Publisher of Educational Software & Spoken Word Audio Products; Distributor of Specialty Videos
N.A.I.C.S.: 423990
Greg James *(Founder & CEO)*
Duayne Zeigler *(Pres)*

TOPLINE FINANCIAL CREDIT UNION
9353 Jefferson Hwy, Maple Grove, MN 55369
Tel.: (763) 391-9494
Web Site: http://www.toplinecu.com
Year Founded: 1935
Rev: $13,175,652
Emp.: 82
Credit Union Services
N.A.I.C.S.: 522130
Thomas Smith *(Pres & CEO)*
Mick Olson *(CFO & Sr VP-Fin)*
Jim Kaster *(Chm)*
Christine Maros *(Sr VP-Member Svc & Ops)*
Bill Hnath *(Sec)*
Joan Molenaar *(Treas)*
Alan Sonnenburg *(Chief Lending Officer & Sr VP-Lending)*

TOPRANK ONLINE MARKETING

Vicki Roscoe Erickson *(Sr VP-Mktg & Comm)*
Kent Engler *(Sr VP-Member Svcs & Branch Ops)*

TOPLINE IMPORTS, INC.
13150 SE 32nd St, Bellevue, WA 98005-4436
Tel.: (425) 643-3003   WA
Web Site: http://www.reportshoes.com
Year Founded: 1980
Sales Range: $75-99.9 Million
Emp.: 90
Whslr of Shoes
N.A.I.C.S.: 424340
Richard A. Philby *(COO)*

Subsidiaries:

Taiwan Topline, Inc. (1)
3F-2 No 367 Kung Yi Road, Taichung, Taiwan
Tel.: (886) 4 2328 2250
Footwear Distr
N.A.I.C.S.: 424340

Topline Footwear China, Ltd. (1)
Dongguan Economy & Trade Centre Guangchang Road, Dingshan Village Hojie Town, Dongguan, Guangdong, China
Tel.: (86) 769 221 6652
Footwear Distr
N.A.I.C.S.: 424340

TOPLINGO DEVELOPMENT, INC.
1 Parliament Pl, Irvine, CA 92694
Tel.: (949) 222-0301
Web Site: http://www.toplingo.com
Year Founded: 2001
Sales Range: $1-9.9 Million
Emp.: 20
Software Publisher, Website Design & Marketing
N.A.I.C.S.: 513210
Jason Berry *(CEO)*

TOPPER INDUSTRIAL INC.
1729 E Frontage Rd, Sturtevant, WI 53177
Tel.: (262) 886-6931
Web Site: http://www.topperindustrial.com
Rev: $13,000,000
Emp.: 52
Fabricated Structural Metal Mfr
N.A.I.C.S.: 332312
Rob Wrixton *(Gen Mgr)*

TOPPINO'S INC.
Mile Marker 8 5 US Hwy 1, Key West, FL 33040
Tel.: (305) 296-5606
Web Site: http://www.charleytoppinoandsons.com
Sales Range: $10-24.9 Million
Emp.: 70
Underground Utility Construction
N.A.I.C.S.: 237310
Frank P. Toppino *(Pres)*
Patrick Ortega *(Project Mgr)*

TOPRANK ONLINE MARKETING
4032 Shoreline Dr Ste 1, Spring Park, MN 55384
Tel.: (952) 400-0194
Web Site: http://www.toprankmarketing.com
Sales Range: $10-24.9 Million
Emp.: 20
Internet Marketing & Public Relations Services
N.A.I.C.S.: 541613
Susan Misukanis *(Co-Founder & Pres)*
Lee Odden *(Co-Founder & CEO)*
Jolina Pettice *(VP)*

TOPRANK ONLINE MARKETING

TopRank Online Marketing—(Continued)
Alexis Hall *(Dir-Client Accts)*
Amie Krone *(Dir-Ops & HR)*
Ashley Zeckman *(Dir-Agency Mktg)*
Evan Prokop *(Mgr-Digital Mktg)*
Jesse Pickrain *(Mgr-Content Mktg)*
Shaya Clark *(Coord-Ops)*
Knute Sands *(Mgr-Content Mktg)*

TOPS HOLDING II CORPORATION
6363 Main St, Williamsville, NY 14221
Tel.: (716) 635-5000   DE
Web Site: http://www.topsmarkets.com
Sales Range: $1-4.9 Billion
Emp.: 14,800
Holding Company; Supermarkets Owner & Operator
N.A.I.C.S.: 551112
John Persons *(Pres & COO)*
Frank Curci *(Chm & CEO)*

Subsidiaries:

Tops Holding LLC   (1)
6363 Main St, Williamsville, NY 14221
Tel.: (716) 635-5000
Sales Range: $1-4.9 Billion
Emp.: 100
Holding Company
N.A.I.C.S.: 551112
Kevin Darrington *(COO)*
John Persons *(Sr VP-Ops)*
Frank Curci *(Chm, Pres & CEO)*
Jack Barrett *(Sr VP-HR & Asst Sec)*
Diane Colgan *(VP-Sls & Mktg)*
Lynne Burgess *(Gen Counsel, Sec & Sr VP)*
David Langless *(Interim CFO)*

TOPS PRODUCTS
184 Shuman Blvd Ste 130, Naperville, IL 60563
Tel.: (502) 286-3411
Web Site: http://www.tops-products.com
Office Supplies & Stationery Stores
N.A.I.C.S.: 459410
Bill Bowes *(VP)*

Subsidiaries:

Redi-Tag Corp.   (1)
51 Century Blvd, Ste 100, Nashville, TN 37214
Tel.: (714) 226-9596
Web Site: http://www.reditag.com
Rev.: $3,792,000
Emp.: 16
Coated & Laminated Paper Mfr
N.A.I.C.S.: 322220
Karen Whistler *(Pres)*

TOPS SOFTWARE, LLC
5540 Rio Vista Dr, Clearwater, FL 33760
Tel.: (727) 756-8587
Web Site: http://www.topssoft.com
Computer & Computer Peripheral Equipment & Software Merchant Whslr
N.A.I.C.S.: 423430
Dan Doering *(Sr Acct Exec)*
Mike Hardy *(CEO)*
Vishnu Sharma *(Head-Fin Svcs Grp)*

Subsidiaries:

Sharma & Associates, Inc.   (1)
5810 S Grant St, Hinsdale, IL 60521
Tel.: (630) 655-4630
Web Site: http://www.sharma-associates.com
Engineeering Services
N.A.I.C.S.: 541330
Vinaya Sharma *(Founder & Pres)*
Anand Prabhakaran *(VP-Engrg)*
Vishnu Sharma *(Founder& Pres)*

TOPS STAFFING, LLC
600 Davidson Rd, Pittsburgh, PA 15239
Tel.: (412) 798-0779
Web Site: http://www.topsjobs.com
Year Founded: 1987
Sales Range: $10-24.9 Million
Emp.: 20
Temporary Staffing
N.A.I.C.S.: 561320
Mary Dvorsky *(Pres)*
Joseph Johnston *(VP-Ops)*
Frank Ily *(Mgr-Bus Dev)*

TOPSON DOWNS OF CALIFORNIA, INC.
3840 Watseka Ave, Culver City, CA 90232
Tel.: (310) 558-0300
Web Site: http://www.topsondowns.com
Year Founded: 1971
Sales Range: $350-399.9 Million
Emp.: 346
Apparels Mfr
N.A.I.C.S.: 315990
Robert Salka *(Pres)*
Erika Rodas *(Coord-Production)*
Ingrid Zambrano *(Product Mgr)*
Kevin Castle *(Mgr-HR & Payroll)*

TOPSOURCE INC.
100 S Pine Island Rd Ste 200, Plantation, FL 33324
Web Site: http://www.topsource.com
Year Founded: 2005
Sales Range: $1-9.9 Million
Emp.: 25
Temporary & Permanent Employment Placement
N.A.I.C.S.: 561311
Gil Bonwitt *(Pres)*

TOPSPIN PARTNERS, L.P.
1 Station Plz Ste 2B, Mamaroneck, NY 10543
Tel.: (914) 834-7370   DE
Web Site: http://www.topspinpartners.com
Year Founded: 2000
Privater Equity Firm
N.A.I.C.S.: 523999
Leigh J. Randall *(Mng Partner)*
Ojas Vahia *(Partner)*
Stephen Parks *(Partner)*
Jason Wargon *(VP-Fin)*
Josh Shaw *(Operating Partner)*

Subsidiaries:

Polder Products, LLC   (1)
195 Christian St, Oxford, CT 06478-1252
Tel.: (203) 888-9208
Web Site: http://www.polder.com
High Quality Mfr of Durable Home Goods
N.A.I.C.S.: 423990
Rob Curran *(Mgr-Sls Div)*

Remedy Health Media, LLC   (1)
330 Madison Ave 35th Fl, New York, NY 10017
Tel.: (212) 695-2223
Web Site: http://www.remedyhealthmedia.com
Online Health Information & Technology Services
N.A.I.C.S.: 519290
Erica Hembree *(CFO)*
Paul Gartner *(CTO & Exec VP-Engrg)*
Mike Collins *(Exec VP-Sls)*
Lindsey Guenther *(Exec VP-Strategy & Partnerships)*
Demian Perry *(VP-Product)*
Michael A. Cunnion *(CEO)*

Subsidiary (Domestic):

The HealthCentral Network, Inc.   (2)
2111 Wilson Blvd Ste 330, Arlington, VA 22201
Tel.: (703) 302-1040
Web Site: http://www.healthcentral.com

Online Medical Information Provider
N.A.I.C.S.: 519290

Texas Family Fitness LLC   (1)
11501 Custer Rd Ste 104, Frisco, TX 75053
Tel.: (469) 215-2185
Web Site: http://www.texasfamilyfitness.com
Fitness Center
N.A.I.C.S.: 713940
Brooks Johnson *(District Mgr)*

The Tiffen Company LLC   (1)
90 Oser Ave, Hauppauge, NY 11788-3886
Tel.: (631) 273-2500
Web Site: http://www.tiffen.com
Sales Range: $10-24.9 Million
Holding Company; Consumer & Professional Photographic Filters & Other Accessories Mfr & Distr
N.A.I.C.S.: 551112
Steven Tiffen *(Pres & CEO)*
Mike Cannata *(COO)*

Subsidiary (Non-US):

Tiffen International Ltd.   (2)
Pinewood Studios Prlongadaon Santa Fe 1115 Eastside Complex, Howes Lane, Iver Heath, SL0 0NH, United Kingdom   (100%)
Tel.: (44) 8701001220
Web Site: http://www.tiffeninternational.com
Emp.: 9
Consumer & Professional Photographic Equipment & Accessories Distr
N.A.I.C.S.: 423410
Robin Thwaites *(Dir-Intl Sls)*

Subsidiary (Domestic):

Tiffen Manufacturing Corp.   (2)
90 Oser Ave, Hauppauge, NY 11788-3886   (100%)
Tel.: (631) 273-2500
Web Site: http://www.tiffen.com
Consumer & Professional Photographic Filters & Other Accessories Mfr
N.A.I.C.S.: 333310
Steven D. Tiffen *(Pres & CEO)*

TOPSPOT INTERNET MARKETING
515 Post Oak Blvd Ste 300, Houston, TX 77027
Tel.: (713) 933-0449
Web Site: http://www.topspotims.com
Sales Range: $1-9.9 Million
Emp.: 80
Internet Management Consulting Services
N.A.I.C.S.: 541613
David Underwood *(Pres)*
Whitney Kane *(Dir-Client Svcs)*
Aaron Efland *(Engr-Web Analytics)*
Megan Sunday *(Project Mgr)*
Tim Doyle *(VP-Sls & Mktg)*
Jessica Arias *(Controller-Fin)*
Jeff Montgomery *(Co-Founder-TopSpot Internet Marketing & Sr VP-Sls)*
Anita Perez *(VP-Ops)*

TOPSTEPTRADER, LLC
130 S Jefferson St Ste 200, Chicago, IL 60661
Web Site: http://www.topsteptrader.com
Year Founded: 2012
Sales Range: $1-9.9 Million
Financial Services
N.A.I.C.S.: 523999
Jay Rudman *(CEO & Chief Growth Officer)*
Michael Patak *(Founder & Chief Vision Officer)*
Melissa Footlick *(COO)*

TORCH ENERGY ADVISORS INCORPORATED
1331 Lamar Ave Ste 1450, Houston, TX 77010
Tel.: (713) 650-1246
Web Site: http://www.teai.com
Sales Range: $25-49.9 Million

U.S. PRIVATE

Emp.: 42
Investment Services
N.A.I.C.S.: 523999
David A. Love *(VP-Bus Dev)*

TORCH TECHNOLOGIES
4035 Chris Dr Ste C, Huntsville, AL 35802
Tel.: (256) 319-6000
Web Site: http://www.torchtechnologies.com
Year Founded: 2002
Sales Range: $25-49.9 Million
Emp.: 475
Engineeering Services
N.A.I.C.S.: 541715
Bill Roark *(CEO)*
Don Holder *(Founder)*
Sue Clark *(CFO)*
Joe Hill *(CTO)*
Scott Parker *(COO)*
John Watson *(Pres)*

TORCO TERMITE & PEST CONTROL COMPANY, LLC
4301 Donlyn Kimberly Office Park, Columbus, OH 43232
Tel.: (877) 638-7173   OH
Web Site: http://www.torcotermite.com
Year Founded: 1934
Pest & Bug Control
N.A.I.C.S.: 561710
J. Edward Breen *(Pres)*

Subsidiaries:

Giddy-Up-Go Termite & Pest Control, Inc.   (1)
1625 Sandalwood Pl, Columbus, OH 43229-3657
Tel.: (614) 840-9299
Web Site: http://www.giddyupgo.com
Pest, Termite & Bed Bug Control
N.A.I.C.S.: 561710
Davis De Clouet *(Owner)*

TORCON, INC.
328 Newman Springs Rd, Red Bank, NJ 07701
Tel.: (732) 704-9800   NJ
Web Site: http://www.torcon.com
Year Founded: 1965
Sales Range: $350-399.9 Million
Emp.: 250
Construction Management, General Construction & Project Consultants
N.A.I.C.S.: 541618
Joseph A. Torcivia *(Co-Pres)*
Steve G Mauer *(Sr VP)*
Philip Fischer *(CFO)*
Richard Estrin *(Sr VP)*
Dennis Schettino *(Sr VP)*
Benedict J. Torcivia Jr. *(Co-Pres)*

TORESCO ENTERPRISES
170 Rte 22 E, Springfield, NJ 07081
Tel.: (973) 467-2900   CO
Web Site: http://www.1800autoland.com
Sales Range: $150-199.9 Million
Emp.: 692
Car Dealership
N.A.I.C.S.: 561110
Donald Toresco *(Pres)*
Cheryl Giles *(Controller)*

TORGERSON PROPERTIES INC.
103 15th Ave NW Ste 200, Willmar, MN 56201
Tel.: (320) 235-7207
Web Site: http://www.torgersonproperties.com
Year Founded: 1929
Sales Range: $25-49.9 Million
Emp.: 1,500
Provider of Hotel Services

N.A.I.C.S.: 721110
Thomas R. Torgerson *(Chm & CEO)*
Mitch Peterson *(COO)*
Kathy Aamot *(Chief Admin Officer)*
Sheryl D. Walton *(CFO)*
Pete Bromelkamp *(Sr VP-HR)*
Joel Vogler *(Sr VP-Hotel Ops)*
Dennis Wallenta *(Sr VP-Hotel Ops)*
Teresa Runke *(Dir-Admin & Acctg)*
Marlene Kubasch *(Dir-Admin & Acctg)*
Paul Carlson *(Dir-Internal Auditing)*
Gene Lubbers *(Dir-IT)*
Rebecca Gross *(Dir-Sls Support)*
Bob Smith *(Sr VP-Facilities Maintenance)*
Dee Anne Osborne *(Sr VP-Sls & Mktg)*
Jessica Kloss *(VP-ECommerce Strategies)*
Larry Eisenberg *(VP-Restaurant Ops)*
Mike Lamoureux *(VP-Restaurant Ops)*
John Cox *(VP-Revenue Mgmt Strategies)*

TORGO, LTD.
415 W Wall Ste 2000, Midland, TX 79701
Tel.: (432) 685-0277
Web Site: http://www.ortloff.com
Holding Company
N.A.I.C.S.: 551112

Subsidiaries:

Ortloff Engineers, Ltd. (1)
415 W Wall Ave Ste 2000, Midland, TX 79701-4442
Tel.: (432) 685-0277
Web Site: http://www.ortloff.com
Sales Range: $10-24.9 Million
Emp.: 25
Natural Gas Cryogenic Processing & Sulfur Recovery Technology Services
N.A.I.C.S.: 541330
John D. Wilkinson *(Pres & CEO)*
Hank M. Hudson *(Mgr-Sulfur Tech & LNG Licensing)*
Joe Lynch *(Mgr-Gas Processing Licensing)*
Steve Munden *(Mgr-Bus Dev)*

TORK PRODUCTS, INC.
4125 N Clinton St, Fort Wayne, IN 46805
Tel.: (260) 482-7713
Web Site: http://www.torkproducts.com
Rev.: $10,000,000
Emp.: 11
Electrical Apparatus & Equipment, Wiring Supplies & Related Equipment Merchant Whslr
N.A.I.C.S.: 423610
Bernie Becker *(Mgr-Electronics)*
Mike Schulte *(VP)*
Larry Shaffer *(VP)*

TORKE COFFEE ROASTING COMPANY
3455 Paine Ave, Sheboygan, WI 53081-8457
Tel.: (920) 458-4114 WI
Web Site: http://www.torkecoffee.com
Year Founded: 1941
Sales Range: $25-49.9 Million
Emp.: 30
Provider of Coffee Roasting & Production Services
N.A.I.C.S.: 311920
Ward J. Torke *(Chm & CEO)*
Allen R. Berchem *(VP-Fin & Pur)*
Jay Torke *(Pres & COO)*

TORKZADEH LAW FIRM, PLC
811 Wilshire Blvd Ste 1700, Los Angeles, CA 90017
Tel.: (310) 935-1111
Web Site: http://www.torklaw.com
Year Founded: 2012
Sales Range: $1-9.9 Million
Emp.: 31
Law Firm
N.A.I.C.S.: 541110
Reza Torkzadeh *(Founder)*

TORME LAURICELLA
847 Sansome St, San Francisco, CA 94111
Tel.: (415) 956-1791
Web Site: http://www.torme.com
Year Founded: 1983
Sales Range: $10-24.9 Million
Emp.: 13
Marketing & Public Relations
N.A.I.C.S.: 541820
Deborah J. Lauricella *(Pres & Dir-Creative)*
Margaret Torme *(Owner)*
Alexis Cohen *(VP)*

TORMEE CONSTRUCTION INC.
PO Box 7921, Shrewsbury, NJ 07702
Tel.: (732) 747-3231
Web Site: http://www.tormee.com
Sales Range: $10-24.9 Million
Emp.: 8
Commercial & Office Building Contractors
N.A.I.C.S.: 236220
W. Scott Havard *(Pres)*
Diane Meyer *(Office Mgr)*

TORN & GLASSER INC.
18933 S Reyes Ave, Compton, CA 90221
Tel.: (213) 627-6496
Web Site: http://www.tornandglasser.com
Rev.: $23,000,000
Emp.: 15
Provider of Dried Fruits
N.A.I.C.S.: 424490
Robert Glasser *(Pres)*
Bob Torn *(VP)*
Michael Fletcher *(Mgr-IT)*
Freddy Alanis *(Mgr-EHS)*
Hector Lopez *(Mgr-Pur)*
William Large *(Acct Mgr)*

TORO DATA LABS, INC.
32 Mandalay Pl S, San Francisco, CA 94080
Tel.: (352) 642-4078 DE
Web Site: https://www.bigeye.com
Year Founded: 2019
Software Development Services
N.A.I.C.S.: 513210
Kyle Kirwan *(Founder & CEO)*

Subsidiaries:

Data Advantage Group, Inc. (1)
604 Mission St Ste 700, San Francisco, CA 94105
Tel.: (415) 947-0400
Web Site: http://www.dag.com
Sales Range: $1-9.9 Million
Emp.: 15
Prepackaged Software Whol Computer Software
N.A.I.C.S.: 513210
Geoff Rayner *(CEO)*

TORO PETROLEUM CORP.
308 W Market St, Salinas, CA 93901-1420
Tel.: (831) 375-5178 CA
Web Site: http://www.toropetroleum.com
Year Founded: 1974
Rev.: $35,000,000
Emp.: 65
Petroleum Product Distr
N.A.I.C.S.: 424720
Brian Hill *(VP)*
Jonathon Bohlman *(Pres)*
Mark Elliott *(CFO)*

TORO-AIRE INC.
1708 W Mahalo Pl, Compton, CA 90220
Tel.: (310) 632-6000
Web Site: http://www.toroaire.com
Sales Range: $10-24.9 Million
Emp.: 16
Air Conditioning Equipment
N.A.I.C.S.: 423730
David McIntyre *(Pres)*

TORPEDO SPECIALTY WIRE INC.
1115 Instrument Dr, Rocky Mount, NC 27804
Tel.: (252) 977-3900
Web Site: http://www.torpedowire.com
Sales Range: $10-24.9 Million
Emp.: 100
Wire & Fabricated Wire Products Mfr
N.A.I.C.S.: 331222
Loren D. Ota *(Pres)*
Carol Dees *(CFO)*
Hal McConnell *(VP-Ops)*
Vanessa Pierce *(Mgr-IT)*

TORQ CORPORATION
32 W Monroe St, Bedford, OH 44146
Tel.: (440) 232-4100 OH
Web Site: http://www.torq.com
Year Founded: 1950
Sales Range: $1-9.9 Million
Emp.: 35
Centrifugal & Stationary Switch Mfr
N.A.I.C.S.: 335999
John Taylor *(Pres)*

TORQTEK DESIGN & MANUFACTURING, LLC
4500 Leeds Ave Ste 112, Charleston, SC 29405
Tel.: (843) 745-1523 DE
Web Site: http://www.torqtekusa.com
Year Founded: 1995
Motor Vehicle Drivetrain Parts & Systems Designer, Developer & Mfr
N.A.I.C.S.: 333612
Friedemann Strasser *(CEO)*
Armin Laicher *(CFO)*
Bahman Haghshanas *(Exec VP-Engrg, Sls & Pur)*
Nikolaus Andriaschko *(Sr Mgr-Ops)*
Floyd Lancaster *(Mgr-Timing Gear Sls & Metallurgical Heat Treat)*
Anita Thompkins *(Mgr-HR)*
Lisa Hernandez *(Mgr-Supply Chain-NAFTA)*

TORQUE CAPITAL GROUP, LLC
437 Madison Ave 33rd Fl, New York, NY 10022
Tel.: (212) 705-0164 DE
Web Site: http://www.torquecap.com
Year Founded: 2010
Privater Equity Firm
N.A.I.C.S.: 523999
Joseph Parzick *(Mng Partner)*
Jonathan Saltzman *(Mng Dir)*
James Rosseau *(Operating Partner)*
Terry Culmone *(Partner)*

Subsidiaries:

Brake Parts Inc LLC (1)
4400 Prime Pkwy, McHenry, IL 60050
Tel.: (815) 363-9000
Web Site: http://www.brakepartsinc.com
Motor Vehicle Brake System Components Mfr
N.A.I.C.S.: 336340
David Overbeeke *(Pres & CEO)*
Kristin Grons *(Mgr-Mktg)*
Brian Kirts *(VP-Sls)*
Chip Hudson *(Mgr-Police Fleet-Natl)*
H. T. Chang *(VP-Product Dev, Engrg, R&D & Quality)*
Paul Ferrandino *(Chief Comml Officer)*
Sam Rusenovich *(Dir-Customer Experience)*
Edward West *(Gen Counsel, Sec & VP)*
Jeff Wawrzyniak *(Chief Legal Officer)*

Cablecraft Motion Controls LLC (1)
2110 Summit St, New Haven, IN 46774-9524
Tel.: (260) 749-5105
Web Site: http://www.cablecraft.com
Sales Range: $25-49.9 Million
Emp.: 250
Motion Control Products Mfr
N.A.I.C.S.: 334519
Christopher Carmien *(CFO)*
Thomas Wenger *(Mgr-Ops)*
Miles Stepney *(Mgr-IT)*
Tom Crone *(Pres & CEO)*
Robert Koontz *(VP-Sls & Mktg-Global)*

Branch (Domestic):

Cablecraft Motion Controls LLC (2)
4401 S Orchard St, Tacoma, WA 98466-6619 (100%)
Tel.: (253) 475-1080
Web Site: http://www.cablecraft.com
Sales Range: $25-49.9 Million
Emp.: 120
Mfr of Push-Pull Cable Assemblies, Manual Transmission Shift Systems, Levers & Related Cable Hardware
N.A.I.C.S.: 334519

Subsidiary (Domestic):

Radial Bearing Corp. (2)
21 Taylor St, Danbury, CT 06810
Tel.: (203) 744-0323
Web Site: http://www.radialbearing.com
Rev.: $2,333,333
Emp.: 30
Ball & Roller Bearing Mfr
N.A.I.C.S.: 332991
Stephen Papish *(Pres)*

Remy Power Products, LLC (1)
4400 Prime Pkwy, McHenry, IL 60050
Tel.: (815) 363-9000
Web Site: http://www.remyautomotive.com
Automotive Starters & Alternators Mfr
N.A.I.C.S.: 336320
Kristin Grons *(Mktg Mgr)*
Dave Nichols *(Pres)*
Darwin Moen *(VP-Sls)*

Subsidiary (Domestic):

Maval Industries LLC (2)
1555 Enterprise Pkwy, Twinsburg, OH 44087
Web Site: http://www.mavalgear.com
Motor Vehicle Parts Mfr
N.A.I.C.S.: 336390
John Dougherty *(VP-Sls & Mktg)*
Jon Statler *(Founder)*

TORRE & BRUGLIO INC.
850 Featherstone Rd, Pontiac, MI 48342
Tel.: (248) 452-9292
Web Site: http://www.torreandbruglio.com
Year Founded: 1980
Rev.: $28,000,000
Emp.: 500
Landscape Contractors
N.A.I.C.S.: 561730
Francisco Torre Jr. *(Pres)*

TORRENT RESOURSES INC
1509 E Elwood St, Phoenix, AZ 85040
Tel.: (602) 268-0785
Web Site: http://www.torrentresources.com
Rev.: $10,000,000
Emp.: 100
Drainage System Construction
N.A.I.C.S.: 236210
Stephen Detommaso *(Pres)*

TORRES INSURANCE AGENCY, INC.

Torres Insurance Agency, Inc.—(Continued)

TORRES INSURANCE AGENCY, INC.
257 Hampden St, Chicopee, MA 01013
Tel.: (413) 452-4100
Web Site:
http://www.torresinsurance.com
Year Founded: 1983
Insurance Agencies & Brokerages
N.A.I.C.S.: 524210
Ana Torres (Owner)
Octavio Torres (Pres)

TORREY HILLS TECHNOLOGIES, LLC
6370 Lusk Blvd Ste F111, San Diego, CA 92121
Tel.: (858) 558-6666
Web Site:
http://www.torreyhillstech.com
Sales Range: $1-9.9 Million
Emp.: 11
Metal Product Distr
N.A.I.C.S.: 423510
Ken Kuang (Pres & CEO)

TORRID INC.
18501 E San Jose Ave, City of Industry, CA 91748
Tel.: (626) 667-1002   DE
Web Site: http://www.torrid.com
Year Founded: 2015
Sales Range: $600-649.9 Million
Emp.: 1,317
Women's Apparel Retailer
N.A.I.C.S.: 424350
Liz Munoz (CEO)
Kate Horton (Sr VP-Mdsg & Mktg)
Stefan Kaluzny (Chm)
George Wehlitz Jr. (CFO)

TORRINGTON SUPPLY COMPANY, INCORPORATED
100 N Elm St, Waterbury, CT 06702
Tel.: (203) 756-3641   CT
Web Site: http://www.torrco.com
Year Founded: 1932
Sales Range: $1-9.9 Million
Emp.: 186
Plumbing & Piping Equipment Distr
N.A.I.C.S.: 423720
Joel S. Becker (Chm & CEO)
Nancy Becker (Owner & VP)

Subsidiaries:

Commercial Heating Supply   (1)
25 Rachel Dr, Stratford, CT 06615
Tel.: (203) 386-1611
Web Site: http://www.commercialheat.com
Electrical Apparatus & Related Equipment Merchant Whslr
N.A.I.C.S.: 423610
Roy Freedman (Owner)

TORRMETAL CORPORATION
12125 Bennington Ave, Cleveland, OH 44135
Tel.: (216) 671-1616   OH
Web Site: http://www.torrmetal.com
Year Founded: 1972
Sales Range: $1-9.9 Million
Emp.: 20
High Production Metal, Precision Stampings & Dies Mfr
N.A.I.C.S.: 332119
Patrick Sheehan (Pres)
Becky Almodovar (Office Mgr)
Bill Ross (Acct Mgr)
Mark D. Hoyt (Mgr-Production)
Paul Christensen (Mgr-Tooling)

TORRY HARRYS INC.
536 Fayette St, Perth Amboy, NJ 08861
Tel.: (732) 442-0049

Web Site:
http://www.frozenshrimp.com
Year Founded: 1985
Sales Range: $25-49.9 Million
Emp.: 10
Seafood Importer & Whslr
N.A.I.C.S.: 424460
Ravi Chander (Pres)

TORTILLA KING INC.
PO Box 763, Moundridge, KS 67107
Tel.: (620) 345-2674
Web Site: http://www.tortillaking.com
Year Founded: 1992
Sales Range: $10-24.9 Million
Emp.: 140
Tortilla Mfr
N.A.I.C.S.: 311830
Juan Guardiola (Mgr)

TORTILLERIA ATOTONILCO INC.
1707 W 47th St FL 4, Chicago, IL 60609
Tel.: (773) 523-0800
Web Site:
http://www.tortilleriaatotonilco.com
Rev.: $16,400,000
Emp.: 36
Crackers, Cookies & Bakery Products
N.A.I.C.S.: 424490
Oscar Munoz (Owner)

TORTUGA TRADING INC.
2240 Encinitas Blvd Ste D-228, Encinitas, CA 92024
Tel.: (760) 271-5457
Web Site:
http://www.tortugatrading.com
Year Founded: 2004
Antique Dealer & Movie Prop Supplier
N.A.I.C.S.: 459510
Sean E. Rich (Pres & CEO)

TORY BURCH LLC
11 W 19th St 7th Fl, New York, NY 10011
Tel.: (212) 683-2323   DE
Web Site: http://www.toryburch.com
Year Founded: 2004
Women's Fashion Apparel Designer, Distr & Retailer
N.A.I.C.S.: 458110
Robert Isen (Pres-Bus Dev & Chief Legal Officer)
Reepal Shah (CFO)
Tory Burch (Chm)
Keisha Smith (COO)
Stefano Sutter (Pres-Europe & Middle East)
Pierre-Yves Roussel (CEO)

TOTAL ACTION AGAINST POVERTY
302 2nd St, Roanoke, VA 24011
Tel.: (540) 345-6781
Web Site: http://www.tapintohope.org
Rev.: $16,675,176
Emp.: 350
Community & Social Services
N.A.I.C.S.: 813319
Angela Penn (VP-Dev)
Annette Lewis (Sr VP-Programs)
Owen Schultz (VP-Dev & Plng)
Pete Clark (Dir-Property Mgmt & Maintenance)

TOTAL ADMINISTRATIVE SERVICES CORPORATION
2302 International Ln, Madison, WI 53704
Tel.: (608) 241-1900
Web Site: http://www.tasconline.com
Rev.: $15,100,000
Emp.: 240

Scientific & Technical Consulting Services
N.A.I.C.S.: 541690
Daniel N. Rashke (Owner & CEO)
Ken Odom (Exec VP-Acqs & Alliances)
Pam Reynolds (Chief Dev Officer)
Andy Bartel (Exec VP-Grp Sls)
Jim Gowan (Chief Sls Officer)
Steve Cable (COO)
Micheal Herman (Exec VP-Bus Conversion)
Christian Rosenstock (Exec VP-Bus Dev)
Karl Richards (Exec VP-Bus Tech Svcs)
Brad Hoffman (Exec VP-Customer Svc)
Rick Allen (Exec VP-Pub Sector & Strategic Markets)

TOTAL APPLIANCE & AIR CONDITIONING REPAIRS, INC.
1015 SW 10th Ave, Hallandale, FL 33009
Tel.: (954) 454-6801   FL
Web Site:
http://www.totalappliance.net
Year Founded: 1970
Sales Range: $1-9.9 Million
Emp.: 115
Appliance Repair Services
N.A.I.C.S.: 811412
Robert Southard (VP)

TOTAL BEVERAGE SOLUTION
1671 Belle Isle Ave Ste 125, Mount Pleasant, SC 29464-8338
Tel.: (843) 881-0761
Web Site:
http://www.totalbeveragesolution.com
Sales Range: $1-9.9 Million
Emp.: 3
Supplier of Wine, Beer & Spirits to Distributors
N.A.I.C.S.: 424810
Dave Pardus (CEO)
Brittany Cooper (Coord-Mktg)
Jessie Haggerty (Mgr-Mktg Capability & Trade Dev)
Krystin Kilman (Coord-Sls Ops)
Lisa Funston (Mgr-Compliance)
Marina Terzieva (Mgr-Acctg)
Morgan Condon (Mgr-Brand Design & Dev)
Tom Rose (VP-Sls & Mktg)

TOTAL CAR FRANCHISING CORP.
125 Daytona St, Conway, SC 29526
Tel.: (843) 347-8818   SC
Web Site:
http://www.colorsonparade.com
Year Founded: 1988
Sales Range: $1-9.9 Million
Emp.: 17
Automotive Body, Paint & Interior Repair & Maintenance
N.A.I.C.S.: 811121
Catherine Lowery (VP)
Jeffrey Cox (Pres)

TOTAL CARE
5232 Witz Dr, North Syracuse, NY 13212-6501
Tel.: (315) 234-5900   NY
Web Site: http://www.totalcareny.com
Year Founded: 1988
Sales Range: $125-149.9 Million
Health Care Srvices
N.A.I.C.S.: 622110
John DiPaola (COO)

TOTAL COMFORT SOLUTIONS LLC

U.S. PRIVATE

2904 Melrose St, Walla Walla, WA 99362-9525
Tel.: (509) 956-4764
Web Site:
http://www.comfortrightdayornight.com
Emp.: 20
Steam & Air-Conditioning Supply
N.A.I.C.S.: 221330
Terry Hall (Owner & Mgr-Sls)
Maureen Hall (Owner & Mgr-Acctg)

Subsidiaries:

Schaefer Refrigeration Inc.   (1)
2929 E Isaacs Ave, Walla Walla, WA 99362-9306
Tel.: (509) 525-2076
Web Site:
http://www.schaeferrefrigeration.com
Wholesale Trade Agents & Brokers
N.A.I.C.S.: 425120
Mindy Schmerer (Sec)

TOTAL COMMUNICATIONS GROUP
122 E 42nd St, New York, NY 10168-0002
Tel.: (212) 949-3400
Year Founded: 1981
Rev.: $10,000,000
Emp.: 10
Media Buying Services
N.A.I.C.S.: 541830
Jerry Wolff (Pres)
Sandra Crystal (VP)

TOTAL COMMUNICATIONS INC.
333 Burnham St, East Hartford, CT 06108
Tel.: (860) 282-9999
Web Site: http://www.totalcomm.com
Sales Range: $100-124.9 Million
Emp.: 120
Telephone Equipment
N.A.I.C.S.: 423690
John Gunning (Mgr-Pur)
Eric Scrivano (Acct Mgr-Major)
Erich Pilatti (Mgr-Customer Svc)
Jeff May (Mgr-Engrg & Sls)
Terri Warren (Mgr-Network Svc)
Mike Godbout (Mgr-Sys Maintenance)

TOTAL COMMUNITY ACTION, INC.
1420 S Jefferson Davis Pkwy, New Orleans, LA 70056
Tel.: (504) 872-0334   LA
Web Site: http://www.tca-nola.org
Year Founded: 1964
Sales Range: $25-49.9 Million
Community Action Services
N.A.I.C.S.: 624190
Thelma Harris French (Pres & CEO)
James Singleton (Chm)
Victor Gordon (Vice Chm)

TOTAL CONCEPTS OF DESIGN, INC.
1054 S Taylor Mill Rd, Scottsburg, IN 47170-6908
Tel.: (812) 752-6534
Web Site:
http://www.totalconceptsofdesign.com
Year Founded: 1993
Sales Range: $10-24.9 Million
Emp.: 80
Urethane & Foam Product Mfr
N.A.I.C.S.: 326150
Karen Mayer-Sebastian (Mgr-Pur)
Jeff Mills (Mgr-Sls)
Travis Brock (Mgr-Production)
Pete Curlin (Acct Mgr)

TOTAL DOLLAR MANAGEMENT EFFORT LTD

1 Pleasant Ave, Port Washington, NY 11050-2201
Tel.: (212) 689-4477
Web Site: http://www.totaldollar.com
Sales Range: $10-24.9 Million
Emp.: 24
Insurance Brokers
N.A.I.C.S.: 524210
Arthur Buhr *(Pres)*
C. J. Patzelt *(Mgr-Acctg Dept)*

TOTAL ENGINEERING INC.
9344 Lanham Severn Rd Ste 200, Lanham, MD 20706
Tel.: (301) 459-7484
Web Site:
 http://www.totalengineering.biz
Year Founded: 1993
Rev.: $42,500,000
Emp.: 154
Engineeering Services
N.A.I.C.S.: 541330
Greg Deweese *(CFO)*
Pablo Osorio *(Pres)*

TOTAL EQUIPMENT COMPANY
400 5th Ave, Coraopolis, PA 15108
Tel.: (412) 269-0999
Web Site:
 http://www.totalequipment.com
Year Founded: 1983
Sales Range: $10-24.9 Million
Emp.: 75
Provider of Compressors
N.A.I.C.S.: 423830
Michael Weir *(Pres)*

TOTAL EXPERT INC
1600 Utica Ave S Ste 600, Saint Louis Park, MN 55416
Tel.: (952) 977-8620
Web Site: http://www.totalexpert.com
Year Founded: 2012
Sales Range: $1-9.9 Million
Software Development Services
N.A.I.C.S.: 541511
Josh Jabs *(CTO)*
Joe Welu *(Founder & CEO)*
Charles Wyatt *(CFO)*
Sue Woodard *(Chief Customer Officer)*
Anna Klombies *(Chief People Officer)*
Matt Tippets *(Chief Product Officer)*
Chad Gaydos *(Pres)*

TOTAL FOODS CORPORATION
282 Rail Rd Ave, Greenwich, CT 06830
Tel.: (203) 661-9090 MI
Web Site: http://www.totalfood.com
Year Founded: 1971
Sales Range: $10-24.9 Million
Emp.: 6
Provider of Wholesale Grocery Services
N.A.I.C.S.: 424410

TOTAL HOCKEY, INC.
5833 Suemandy Dr, Saint Peters, MO 63376
Tel.: (636) 397-6370 MO
Web Site: http://www.totalhockey.com
Year Founded: 1999
Sales Range: $25-49.9 Million
Emp.: 310
Hockey Equipment Retailer
N.A.I.C.S.: 459110
Michael Benoit *(Pres & CEO)*
Susan O'Leary *(CFO)*
George McNichols *(Dir-Real Estate)*

TOTAL INSIGHT, LLC
328 1st Ave NW, Hickory, NC 28601
Tel.: (828) 485-5240 NC
Web Site: http://www.totalinsight.com
Emp.: 250

Holding Company; Supply Chain Management Solutions
N.A.I.C.S.: 551112
Chris Baltz *(Pres & CEO)*
Clay Gentry *(VP-Logistics Ops)*
Eric Lail *(VP-Continuous Improvement)*
John Richardson *(Dir-Supply Chain Analytics)*

TOTAL LENDER SOLUTIONS, INC.
10505 Sorrento Valley Rd, Ste. 125, San Diego, CA 92121
Tel.: (866) 535-3736 NV
Web Site:
 https://totallendersolutions.com
Emp.: 100
Foreclosure Trustee
N.A.I.C.S.: 531390
Randy Newman *(Founder & CEO)*

Subsidiaries:

Mortgage Lender Services, Inc. (1)
4401 Hazel Ave, Fair Oaks, CA 95628
Tel.: (916) 962-3453
Web Site:
 http://www.mtglenderservices.com
Rev.: $1,100,000
Emp.: 10
Real Estate Credit
N.A.I.C.S.: 522292
Marsha Townsend *(CFO)*
Sara Berens *(Mgr)*

TOTAL LIVING NETWORK
2880 Vision Ct, Aurora, IL 60506
Tel.: (630) 801-3838 IL
Web Site: http://www.tln.com
Year Founded: 1973
Sales Range: $200-249.9 Million
Emp.: 75
Christian Television Broadcasting Stations
N.A.I.C.S.: 516120
Jerry K. Rose *(Pres & CEO)*
Rich Grant *(Dir-HR)*

TOTAL MECHANICAL, INC.
W234 N2830 Paul RD, Pewaukee, WI 53072
Tel.: (262) 523-2500
Web Site: http://www.total-mechanical.com
Year Founded: 1968
Sales Range: $10-24.9 Million
Emp.: 300
Commercial & Residential Heating & Air Conditioning Systems
N.A.I.C.S.: 423730
Dennis J. Braun *(Pres & CEO)*
Timothy J. Braun *(Exec VP)*
Licia C. Stretch *(COO)*
Jonathon M. Friske *(VP-Fire Protection Div)*
Thomas J. Jacobi *(VP-Indus Div)*
Brian M. Hoernke *(VP-Plumbing Div)*
Dennis M. Anderson *(VP-Electrical Div)*
Andrew Boeck *(VP-Comml HVAC Div)*
Robert Kannegiesser *(VP-Residential Div)*

TOTAL MEDIA
2550 Middle Rd Ste 502, Bettendorf, IA 52722
Tel.: (563) 344-9034
Web Site:
 http://www.totalmediaqc.com
Year Founded: 1994
Sales Range: Less than $1 Million
Emp.: 7
Advetising Agency
N.A.I.C.S.: 541810
Gene Smith *(Owner)*
Ty Thomson *(Acct Supvr)*

TOTAL MORTGAGE SERVICES, LLC
185 Plains Rd, Milford, CT 06460
Tel.: (203) 876-2200
Web Site:
 http://www.totalmortgage.com
Sales Range: $1-9.9 Million
Emp.: 118
Direct Mortgage Lending Services
N.A.I.C.S.: 522310
Joe Antos *(Acct Exec)*
Brett Balisciano *(Mgr-Closing)*
Bill Schettler *(VP)*

TOTAL OFFICE PLANNING SERVICES
134 W 29th St 5th Fl, New York, NY 10001
Tel.: (212) 290-8555
Web Site:
 http://www.topsinstallation.com
Year Founded: 1985
Sales Range: $10-24.9 Million
Emp.: 35
Installer of Office Furniture
N.A.I.C.S.: 238990
James Fenimore *(Co-Founder)*
Frank Sapienza *(Co-Founder)*
Mike Mercurio *(Project Mgr)*

TOTAL PROMOTIONS
1340 Old Skokie Rd, Highland Park, IL 60035
Tel.: (847) 831-9500 IL
Web Site:
 http://www.totalpromote.com
Year Founded: 1976
Sales Range: $1-9.9 Million
Emp.: 25
Sales Promotion
N.A.I.C.S.: 541810
Howard Wolff *(Pres)*
Felice Gertz *(Mgr-Natl Sls)*

TOTAL QUALITY LOGISTICS INC.
4289 Ivy Pointe Blvd, Cincinnati, OH 45245
Tel.: (513) 831-2600
Web Site: https://www.tql.com
Year Founded: 1997
Sales Range: $1-4.9 Billion
Emp.: 10,000
Freight Transportation Arrangement
N.A.I.C.S.: 488510
Kenneth Oaks *(CEO)*
Tracy Burnett *(Sr Mgr-HR)*

TOTAL RECOVERY GROUP, LLC
3030 E 55th St, Cleveland, OH 44127
Tel.: (216) 271-0581
Web Site: http://www.gmtow.com
Sales Range: $50-74.9 Million
Emp.: 200
Specialized Towing & Heavy Haul Services; Bulk, Refrigerated & Dry Van Transportation Services
N.A.I.C.S.: 488410
Craig Stacy *(Owner & Pres)*

Subsidiaries:

G&M Towing & Recovery, LLC (1)
3030 E 55th St, Cleveland, OH 44127
Tel.: (216) 271-0581
Web Site: http://www.gmtow.com
Sales Range: $1-9.9 Million
Emp.: 30
Motor Vehicle Towing Services
N.A.I.C.S.: 488410

Wills Trucking Inc. (1)
3185 Columbia Rd, Richfield, OH 44286-9622
Tel.: (330) 659-9381

Sales Range: $25-49.9 Million
Emp.: 120
Wast Materials Trucking Services
N.A.I.C.S.: 484121

TOTAL RESOURCE MANAGEMENT, INC.
510 King St, Alexandria, VA 22314
Tel.: (703) 548-4285
Web Site: http://www.trmnet.com
Rev.: $7,200,000
Emp.: 97
Educational Support Services
N.A.I.C.S.: 611710
Don Omura *(CEO)*
Jagadisan Shivakumar *(Pres)*

Subsidiaries:

Idcon Incorporated (1)
7200 Falls Of Neuse Rd, Raleigh, NC 27615
Tel.: (919) 847-8764
Web Site: http://www.idcon.com
Rev.: $3,000,000
Emp.: 8
Administrative Management & General Management Consulting Service
N.A.I.C.S.: 541611
Christer Idhammar *(Founder, Partner & VP)*
Tor Idhammar *(CEO & Pres)*

TOTAL SERVICE SUPPLY INC.
2505 Jane St, New Iberia, LA 70563
Tel.: (337) 365-5954
Web Site:
 http://www.totalservicesupply.com
Sales Range: $10-24.9 Million
Emp.: 12
Oil Well Machinery, Equipment & Supplies
N.A.I.C.S.: 423830
Rashid Shamsie *(Pres)*
Ron Richard *(Treas & Sec)*

TOTAL SPORTS MEDIA, INC.
5662 Calle Real 231, Goleta, CA 93117
Tel.: (805) 308-9151 WY
Web Site:
 http://www.totalsportsmedia.com
Year Founded: 2008
TSMI—(OTCBB)
Sales Range: Less than $1 Million
Emp.: 2
Digital Media & Technology Services
N.A.I.C.S.: 518210

TOTAL STAFFING SOLUTIONS INC.
4 S 100 Rt 59 Ste 17, Naperville, IL 60563
Tel.: (630) 836-2200
Web Site: http://www.4tssi.com
Sales Range: $10-24.9 Million
Emp.: 50
Temporary Help Service
N.A.I.C.S.: 561320
Craig Kelly *(Pres)*

TOTAL SYSTEMS TECHNOLOGY INC.
65 Terence Dr, Pittsburgh, PA 15236
Tel.: (412) 653-7690
Web Site: http://www.tst5k.com
Rev.: $20,100,000
Emp.: 10
Polytetrafluoroethylene Resins & Teflon Mfr
N.A.I.C.S.: 325211
Charles Piscatelli *(Pres)*
Tom Sullivan *(Gen Mgr)*

TOTAL TELCO SPECIALIST INC.
602 W Southern Ave, Orange, CA 92865
Tel.: (714) 484-8266

TOTAL TELCO SPECIALIST INC.   U.S. PRIVATE

Total Telco Specialist Inc.—(Continued)
Web Site: http://www.totaltelco.net
Sales Range: $10-24.9 Million
Emp.: 42
Telecommunication Equipment Repair
N.A.I.C.S.: 811210
Earl Darway (Pres)
Phil Calkins (VP)

TOTAL TEMPERATURE INSTRUMENTATION, INC.
35 Green Mountain Dr, South Burlington, VT 05403
Tel.: (802) 863-0085
Web Site: http://www.instrumart.com
Year Founded: 1988
Emp.: 20
Industrial Equipment Whsr
N.A.I.C.S.: 423830
Robert M. Berman (Pres & CEO)
Rebecca Nichol (Mgr-HR)

TOTAL TOOL SUPPLY INC.
315 N Pierce St, Saint Paul, MN 55104
Tel.: (651) 646-4055
Web Site: http://www.totaltool.com
Year Founded: 1977
Rev.: $24,769,558
Emp.: 80
Cable & Wire
N.A.I.C.S.: 423510
R. Douglas Jordan (Owner)
Mark Smith (Mgr-Ops)
Ryan Brunner (Mgr-Customer Svc)
Jayme Reinisch (CFO)

Subsidiaries:

Total Tool Supply Inc., Crane & Hoist Division   (1)
315 N Pierce St, Saint Paul, MN 55104
Tel.: (651) 646-4055
Web Site: http://www.totaltool.com
Sales Range: $25-49.9 Million
Designers, Manufacturers, Suppliers & Repairers Of Cranes, Crane Components & Hoists
N.A.I.C.S.: 423510
Sara Preimesberger (Mgr-Mktg)

TOTAL TRANSPORTATION CONCEPT
8728 Avaition Blvd, Inglewood, CA 90301
Tel.: (310) 337-0515
Web Site: http://www.totaltrans.com
Sales Range: $10-24.9 Million
Emp.: 22
Freight Forwarding
N.A.I.C.S.: 488510
James DeArruda (Pres)
Victor Caceres (Mgr-Export)

TOTAL TRUCK PARTS INC.
6545 Wallis Rd, West Palm Beach, FL 33413-1700
Tel.: (561) 684-3332
Web Site: http://www.totaltruckparts.net
Sales Range: $10-24.9 Million
Emp.: 70
Truck Equipment & Parts
N.A.I.C.S.: 441330
Jamie Deans (Mgr-Fort Pierce)

TOTAL VALUE RV
25610 County Rd 4, Elkhart, IN 46514-5947
Tel.: (574) 262-4460
Web Site: http://www.totalvaluerv.com
Sales Range: $25-49.9 Million
Emp.: 40
Recreational Vehicle Whslr
N.A.I.C.S.: 441210
Hank Schrock (Owner)
Jeffrey Lemmon (Mgr-Mktg)

TOTAL-WESTERN, INC.
8049 Somerset Blvd, Paramount, CA 90723
Tel.: (562) 220-1450   CA
Web Site: http://www.total-western.com
Year Founded: 1972
Sales Range: $25-49.9 Million
Industrial Engineering & Construction Services
N.A.I.C.S.: 237990
Payman Farrokhyar (Pres)
Lou Hall (VP-Ops)

TOTALLY TICKETS INC.
210 36th Ave SW, Norman, OK 73072
Tel.: (405) 801-2871
Web Site: http://www.totallytickets.com
Year Founded: 2000
Rev.: $5,600,000
Emp.: 9
Retail Ticket Agent
N.A.I.C.S.: 711320
Michael Fletcher (Pres)

TOTALPAAS, INC.
10776 Argonaut Ln, Jackson, CA 95642
Tel.: (650) 887-5018
Web Site: http://www.totalpaas.com
Year Founded: 2009
Support Services to Media Companies
N.A.I.C.S.: 561499
Tami Tran (CEO)

TOTEM ELECTRIC OF TACOMA INC.
2332 S Jefferson Ave, Tacoma, WA 98402-1405
Tel.: (253) 383-5022   WA
Web Site: http://www.totemelectric.com
Year Founded: 1960
Sales Range: $50-74.9 Million
Emp.: 70
Electrical Work
N.A.I.C.S.: 238210
Scott Stephens (Pres)
John Stephens (Treas & Sec)
Mark Stephens (VP)

TOTH BUICK-GMC
3300 S Arlington Rd, Akron, OH 44312
Tel.: (330) 644-3400
Web Site: http://www.tothakron.com
Year Founded: 1972
Sales Range: $25-49.9 Million
Emp.: 42
New Car Whslr
N.A.I.C.S.: 441110
Steve Toth (Gen Mgr)
George Toth (Mgr-Svc)
Edward T. Toth (Owner & Pres)

TOTH INDUSTRIES, INC.
5102 Enterprise Blvd, Toledo, OH 43612
Tel.: (419) 729-4669
Web Site: http://www.tothindustries.com
Year Founded: 1955
Sales Range: $10-24.9 Million
Emp.: 70
Machine Shop Operator
N.A.I.C.S.: 332710
Richard J. Toth (VP-Ops)
Bernard J. Toth (Founder)

TOTH, INC.
86 Baker Ave Ext Ste 230, Concord, MA 01742
Tel.: (617) 252-0787   MA

Web Site: http://www.toth.com
Year Founded: 1983
Sales Range: $75-99.9 Million
Emp.: 40
Advetising Agency
N.A.I.C.S.: 541810
Robert Fouhy (Grp Acct Dir)
Margaret Royston (Gen Mgr)
Yvonne Barriga (Sr Producer)
Bob Fouhy (Grp Acct Dir)
Thatcher Adams (Exec Dir-Creative)

TOTRAMA SUPERMARKET INC.
Hartford Ave Rte 6, North Scituate, RI 02857
Tel.: (401) 934-2283
Web Site: http://www.brigidos.com
Year Founded: 1946
Sales Range: $10-24.9 Million
Emp.: 75
Supermarket
N.A.I.C.S.: 445110
Edie Langlais (Mng Dir)

TOTSY MANUFACTURING COMPANY, INC.
1 Bigelow St, Holyoke, MA 01040-0509
Tel.: (413) 536-0510   MA
Year Founded: 1930
Sales Range: $75-99.9 Million
Emp.: 10
Mfr of Dolls, Doll Clothing & Accessories
N.A.I.C.S.: 423920
Barry Schulman (VP)

TOTTEN TUBES, INC.
500 Danlee St, Azusa, CA 91702
Tel.: (626) 812-0220   CA
Web Site: http://www.tottentubes.com
Year Founded: 1955
Sales Range: $75-99.9 Million
Emp.: 100
Marketer of Steel Pipes & Tubing
N.A.I.C.S.: 423510
Tracy Totten (Pres)

TOTUS PRO DEO
4698 Alvarado Canyon Rd Ste K, San Diego, CA 92120
Tel.: (619) 582-4571   CA
Web Site: http://www.all4godcatholic.com
Year Founded: 2004
Sales Range: $1-9.9 Million
Emp.: 3
Youth Ministry Services
N.A.I.C.S.: 813110
Margie Rapp (Exec Dir)

TOUCAN INC.
1275 8th St, Arcata, CA 95521
Tel.: (707) 822-6662
Web Site: http://www.tomasjewelry.com
Year Founded: 1980
Sales Range: $10-24.9 Million
Emp.: 105
Jewelry
N.A.I.C.S.: 423940
Tom Perrett (Pres)

TOUCHETTE REGIONAL HOSPITAL
5900 Bond Ave, Centerville, IL 62207
Tel.: (618) 332-3060   IL
Web Site: http://www.touchette.org
Year Founded: 1992
Sales Range: $50-74.9 Million
Emp.: 628
Health Care Srvices
N.A.I.C.S.: 622110
Thomas Mikkelson (COO & VP-Medical Affairs)

Larry McCulley (CEO)
John Majchrzak (CFO)
Sulbrena Day (COO)

TOUCHSTONE BEHAVIORAL HEALTH
15648 N 35th Ave, Phoenix, AZ 85053
Tel.: (866) 207-3882   AZ
Web Site: http://www.touchstonebh.org
Year Founded: 1969
Sales Range: $10-24.9 Million
Emp.: 212
Behavioral Healthcare Services
N.A.I.C.S.: 621420
Frank Saverino (Dir-Clinical Svcs)
Linda Warne (Dir-HR)
Steve Ginsberg (CEO)
Dion Foreman (Chm)
Helena Whitney (Vice Chm)
John Lincoln (Treas)
Martha Zhan (CFO & COO)

TOUCHSTONE ENERGY COOPERATIVE, INC.
4301 Wilson Blvd, Arlington, VA 22203
Tel.: (703) 907-5500   VA
Web Site: http://www.touchstoneenergy.com
Electric Power Cooperatives Association
N.A.I.C.S.: 813990
Nicholas Pascale (Gen Counsel)
Roger Meader (Chm)
Lynn Moore (Exec Dir)

Subsidiaries:

Egyptian Electric Cooperative Association   (1)
1005 W Broadway, Steeleville, IL 62288
Tel.: (618) 965-3434
Web Site: http://www.eeca.coop
Sales Range: $10-24.9 Million
Emp.: 45
Electric Power Cooperative Association
N.A.I.C.S.: 813910

National Rural Electric Cooperative Association   (1)
4301 Wilson Blvd, Arlington, VA 22203-1867
Tel.: (703) 907-5500
Web Site: https://www.electric.coop
Emp.: 600
Electric Power Supply Services
N.A.I.C.S.: 221122
Jim Matheson (CEO)
Jeffrey Connor (COO)
Peter Baxter (Sr VP-Insurance & Fin Svcs)
Kirk Johnson (Sr VP-Govt Rels)
Veneicia Lockhart (Sr VP-Fin)
Rich Meyer (Gen Counsel & Sr VP)
J. Scott Peterson (Sr VP-Comm)
Michele Rinn (Sr VP-HR)
Danielle Sieverling (Chief Compliance Officer, Chief Risk Officer & VP)
Jim Spiers (Sr VP-Bus & Tech Strategies)
Tracey Steiner (Sr VP-Education & Trng)
Dan Waddle (Sr VP-Intl)

Taylor Electric Cooperative   (1)
N1831 State Hwy 13, Medford, WI 54451
Tel.: (715) 678-2411
Web Site: http://www.taylorelectric.org
Electric Power Cooperative Association
N.A.I.C.S.: 813910
Michael Schaefer (Pres & CEO)
Brian Kulas (Chm)
Chuck Zenner (Vice Chm)

Wabash Valley Power Association Inc.   (1)
722 N High School Rd, Indianapolis, IN 46214
Tel.: (317) 481-2800
Web Site: http://www.wvpa.com
Rev.: $735,472,000
Assets: $931,866,000
Liabilities: $135,146,000
Net Worth: $796,720,000
Earnings: $20,000,000

COMPANIES

Emp.: 60
Fiscal Year-end: 12/31/2013
Electric Power Cooperative Association
N.A.I.C.S.: 813910
Katherine A. Joyce (VP-Member & Corp Rels)
Jeffrey A. Conrad (CFO)
M. Keith Thompson (VP-Power Production)
Lee R. Wilmes (VP-Power Supply)
Randolph G. Holt (Gen Counsel)
Gregory E. Wagoner (VP-Transmission Ops)
Curtis E. Taylor (VP-Technical Svcs)
Jay C. Bartlett (Pres & CEO)
Bill Conley (Pres & CEO)
Bruce Goslee (CEO)
Mark Batman (Pres & CEO)
Mark Leu (Gen Mgr)
Michael Burrow (Pres & CEO)
Peter Kollinger (Pres & CEO)
Philip H. High (Mgr)
Ron Raypole (Pres & CEO)

TOUCHSTONE MERCHANDISE GROUP, LLC
7200 Industrial Row Dr, Mason, OH 45040
Tel.: (513) 741-0400
Web Site: http://tmgideas.com
Promotional Products & Marketing Solutions
N.A.I.C.S.: 541890
Derek Block (CEO)
David Mills (Creative Dir)

Subsidiaries:

Freestyle Marketing, LLC (1)
16099 N 82nd St Ste B2A, Scottsdale, AZ 85260
Tel.: (480) 998-9878
Web Site: http://www.freestylemktg.com
Sales Range: $1-9.9 Million
Emp.: 20
Promotional Specialty Service
N.A.I.C.S.: 541890

TOUCHSUITE
1081 Holland Dr, Boca Raton, FL 33487
Tel.: (800) 793-3250
Web Site: http://www.touchsuite.com
Year Founded: 2007
Sales Range: $10-24.9 Million
Emp.: 45
Inventory Software Developer for Businesses
N.A.I.C.S.: 513210
Michael DePinto (Exec VP)
Sam Zietz (Founder & CEO)
Richard Feldman (Chief Corp Dev Officer)
Ira Bornstein (COO)
Jack B. Lynn (COO)

TOUCHUPDIRECT, LLC
7622 Van Nuys Blvd, Van Nuys, CA 91405
Tel.: (818) 600-8160
Web Site: http://www.touchupdirect.com
Year Founded: 2012
Sales Range: $1-9.9 Million
Emp.: 16
Automotive Paint Retailer
N.A.I.C.S.: 441330
Uri Thatcher (CEO)

TOUGH MUDDER LLC
15 MetroTech Center 7th Fl, Brooklyn, NY 11201
Tel.: (718) 643-6171
Web Site: http://www.toughmudder.com
Year Founded: 2010
Sales Range: $75-99.9 Million
Emp.: 154
Obstacle-Course Race Organizer
N.A.I.C.S.: 711320

Will Dean (Founder & CEO)
Don Baxter (CFO)
Mark Darbon (Sr VP-Ops)
Simon Massie-Taylor (Sr VP-Comm)

TOURNAMENT GOLF FOUNDATION
6775 SW 111th Ave Ste 100, Beaverton, OR 97008-5378
Tel.: (503) 626-2711 OR
Year Founded: 1990
Sales Range: $1-9.9 Million
Emp.: 9
Golf Event Organizer
N.A.I.C.S.: 711310
Rob Neal (Exec Dir)
Doug Hamilton (VP)
Rick Meyer (Chm)
Tom Maletis (Pres)
Ray Grubbs (Treas & Sec)

TOURS ON LOCATION INC
555 8th Ave, New York, NY 10018
Tel.: (212) 683-2027
Web Site: http://www.screentours.com
Year Founded: 1999
Rev: $3,600,000
Emp.: 24
Tour Operator
N.A.I.C.S.: 561520
Georgette Blau (Pres & CEO)

TOUTON HOLDINGS LTD
129 W 27th St, New York, NY 10001
Tel.: (212) 255-0674
Web Site: http://www.touton.com
Sales Range: $25-49.9 Million
Emp.: 60
Winery
N.A.I.C.S.: 424820
Guillaume Touton (Pres)
Neil Amoruso (Exec VP)

Subsidiaries:

Monsieur Touton Selection Ltd. (1)
129 W 27th St 9th Fl, New York, NY 10001
Tel.: (212) 255-0674
Web Site: http://www.mtouton.com
Rev: $27,526,578
Emp.: 50
Winery
N.A.I.C.S.: 424820
Michael Hogan (Gen Mgr)

TOWBIN AUTOMOTIVE ENTERPRISES
5550 W Sahara Ave, Las Vegas, NV 89146
Tel.: (702) 253-7000
Web Site: http://www.smartcenterlasvegas.com
Automobile Dealership
N.A.I.C.S.: 441110
Carolynn Towbin (Pres)

TOWEL TRACKER, LLC
2100 Nelson Ave SE, Grand Rapids, MI 49507
Tel.: (616) 325-2060
Web Site: http://www.toweltracker.com
Year Founded: 2009
Sales Range: $1-9.9 Million
Emp.: 13
Tracking System Services
N.A.I.C.S.: 517810
Steven Molewyk (Founder & COO)
Matthew Cheng (CEO)
Michael Pemberton (Mgr-Customer Experience)

TOWER ARCH CAPITAL LLC
14034 S 145 E Ste 300 Draper, Draper, UT 84020
Tel.: (801) 997-5808
Web Site: http://www.towerarch.com

Sales Range: Less than $1 Million
Privater Equity Firm
N.A.I.C.S.: 523999
Aubrey Burnett (Principal)
Tom Feveryear (CFO & Chief Compliance Officer)
Jim Allred (VP)
David Calder (Principal)
Christian Little (Mgr-Tax)
James McKean (VP)
Kathy Mickelson (Office Mgr)
Rhett Neuenschwander (Partner)
David Parkin (Partner)
Steve Smith (VP)
Ryan Stratton (Partner)
David Topham (Partner)

TOWER CANCER RESEARCH FOUNDATION
9090 Wilshire Blvd Ste 350, Beverly Hills, CA 90211
Tel.: (310) 299-8470 CA
Web Site: http://www.towercancerfoundation.org
Year Founded: 1996
Sales Range: $1-9.9 Million
Emp.: 12
Cancer Research Services
N.A.I.C.S.: 813212
Brooke Poklemba (Dir-Special Events)
Linda David (CEO)
Jim Surmeian (Mgr-Acctg)
Nancy Mishkin (Chm)
Solomon Hamburg (Pres)
David Ruderman (Treas)
Elizabeth Drucker (Sec)
Fred Rosenfelt (VP-Scientific Affairs)

TOWER CLEANING SYSTEMS INC.
1880 Markley St, Norristown, PA 19401-2977
Tel.: (610) 278-9000 PA
Year Founded: 1988
Sales Range: $10-24.9 Million
Emp.: 240
Building Maintenance Services
N.A.I.C.S.: 561720
David A. Gansky (CEO)
Adam Beck (COO)
Jason Griska (CFO)
Phil Whitmoyer (Mgr-Facilities)

TOWER FORD
124 S Middle Neck Rd, Great Neck, NY 11021
Tel.: (516) 466-6400
Web Site: http://www.towerford.net
Year Founded: 1992
Sales Range: $10-24.9 Million
Emp.: 50
New Car Dealers
N.A.I.C.S.: 441110
Larry Orlando (Pres)

TOWER HEALTH
420 S 5th Ave, Reading, PA 19611
Tel.: (484) 628-8000 PA
Web Site: http://www.towerhealth.org
Year Founded: 1982
Health Care Services Organization
N.A.I.C.S.: 813910
Thomas Work (Chm)
P. Sue Perrotty (Interim Pres)

Subsidiaries:

CHHS Hospital Company, LLC (1)
8835 Germantown Ave, Philadelphia, PA 19118
Tel.: (215) 248-8200
Web Site: http://chestnuthill.towerhealth.org
Hospital Operator
N.A.I.C.S.: 622110
John Cacciamani (CEO)
T. Ramsey Thorp (Vice Chm)

TOWER HEALTH

Coatesville Hospital Corporation (1)
201 Reeceville Rd, Coatesville, PA 19320
Tel.: (610) 383-8000
Web Site: http://brandywine.towerhealth.org
Healtcare Services
N.A.I.C.S.: 622110
Paul Martone (COO & VP)
Jeff Hunt (Pres & CEO)
Kenneth Doroski (Chm)
Tom Tracy (Vice Chm)

Phoenixville Hospital Company, LLC (1)
140 Nutt Rd, Phoenixville, PA 19460
Tel.: (610) 983-1000
Web Site: https://phoenixville.towerhealth.org
Health Care Srvices
N.A.I.C.S.: 622110

Pottstown Hospital Company, LLC (1)
1600 E High St, Pottstown, PA 19464
Tel.: (610) 327-7000
Web Site: https://pottstown.towerhealth.org
Health Care Srvices
N.A.I.C.S.: 622110

Reading Hospital (1)
420 S 5th Ave, Reading, PA 19611
Tel.: (484) 628-8000
Web Site: http://reading.towerhealth.org
Hospital Operator
N.A.I.C.S.: 622110

Southern Berks Regional Emergency Medical Services, Inc. (1)
769 Mountain View Rd, Reading, PA 19607
Tel.: (610) 775-1041
Web Site: http://www.sbrems.com
Rev: $2,532,963
Assets: $226,132
Liabilities: $620,368
Net Worth: ($394,236)
Earnings: ($74,089)
Emp.: 80
Fiscal Year-end: 12/31/2014
Emergency Medical Services
N.A.I.C.S.: 621910
Malcolm Cole (Exec Dir)
George Mang (Controller)
Edward Michalik (Pres)

St. Christopher's Hospital for Children, LLC (1)
160 E Erie Ave, Philadelphia, PA 19134
Tel.: (215) 427-5000
Web Site: http://www.stchristophershospital.com
Children's Hospitals
N.A.I.C.S.: 622110
Ronald Dreskin (CEO-Interim)

Subsidiary (Domestic):

SCHC Pediatric Anesthesia Associates, L.L.C. (2)
3601 A St, Philadelphia, PA 19134-1043
Tel.: (215) 427-5293
Web Site: http://www.stchristopher.com
Medical Devices
N.A.I.C.S.: 622110

SCHC Pediatric Associates, LLC (2)
3601 A St, Philadelphia, PA 19134-1095
Tel.: (215) 427-8881
Medical Devices
N.A.I.C.S.: 622110

St. Christopher's Pediatric Urgent Care Center, L.L.C. (2)
500 Old York Rd Ste 250, Jenkintown, PA 19046
Tel.: (215) 572-5300
Health Care Srvices
N.A.I.C.S.: 621999

West Grove Hospital Company, LLC (1)
1015 W Baltimore Pike, West Grove, PA 19390
Tel.: (610) 869-1000
Web Site: http://jennersville.towerhealth.org
Health Care Srvices
N.A.I.C.S.: 622110
Steve Tullman (Pres & CEO)
Raymond Kovalski (Chm)
Robert Romain (Vice Chm)

Subsidiary (Domestic):

Jennersville Family Medicine, LLC (2)

TOWER HEALTH

Tower Health—(Continued)

390 Vineyard Way Bldg 501, West Grove, PA 19390
Tel.: (610) 869-0953
Web Site: http://www.towerhealth.org
Health Care Srvices
N.A.I.C.S.: 621111

TOWER HILL INSURANCE GROUP

7201 NW 11th Pl, Gainesville, FL 32605
Tel.: (352) 332-8800
Web Site: http://www.thig.com
Sales Range: $25-49.9 Million
Emp.: 500
Provider of Home & Auto Insurance
N.A.I.C.S.: 524210
Ashley Kennedy *(Mgr-Community)*
Brittney Mattair *(Project Mgr)*
Charmy Gray *(Dir-Ops)*
Jacqui Wilke Meyer *(Asst VP-Regulatory Compliance)*
Jane Johnson *(VP-Mktg)*
Janice Goldacker *(Acct Mgr-Agency)*
Kimberly Iriarte *(CFO)*
Laura Marin *(Sr VP-Actuarial)*
Patricia Lerch Walker *(Mgr-Claims-AVP)*
Pedro Quiroga *(Asst VP & Dir-Claims Trng)*
Rebecca Rodriguez *(Mgr-Ops)*
Ric Gwin *(Asst VP-HR)*
Dave Polson *(Asst VP-Claims)*
Jeffrey Michell *(Asst VP-Sys)*
Michael Wyrick *(Atty-Claims)*
Donna Gonzalez *(Dir-CSU)*
Peggy Levins *(Mgr-Help Desk)*
Michelle Hack *(Supvr-Claims)*
Nancy Weber *(Supvr-Claims)*
Tammy Rieger *(VP-Personal Lines Underwriting)*

TOWER INDUSTRIES INC.

2951 E La Palma Ave, Anaheim, CA 92806
Tel.: (714) 630-6981
Web Site: http://www.towerindustries.net
Year Founded: 1968
Sales Range: $10-24.9 Million
Emp.: 150
Provider of Metal Stamping Services
N.A.I.C.S.: 332710
Richard Slater *(VP)*

Subsidiaries:

Allied Mechanical (1)
1720 S Bon View, Ontario, CA 91761
Tel.: (909) 947-2723
Web Site: http://www.alliedmech.com
Sales Range: $10-24.9 Million
Emp.: 126
Metal Stamping Services
N.A.I.C.S.: 332710
Michael Shelton *(Pres)*

Allied Pacific (1)
2951 E La Palma Ave, Anaheim, CA 92806
Tel.: (714) 630-8145
Web Site: http://www.allied-pacific.com
Provider of Metal Stamping Services
N.A.I.C.S.: 332710

TOWER MANUFACTURING CORPORATION

25 Reservoir Ave, Providence, RI 02907
Tel.: (401) 467-7550
Web Site: http://www.towermfg.com
Sales Range: $10-24.9 Million
Emp.: 125
Electric Switches
N.A.I.C.S.: 335931
Louis Shatkin *(Pres)*
Robert Oliver *(Mgr-Quality Assurance)*
Carmen Nunez *(Coord-Production)*
Walter Carty *(Mgr-Matl)*
Michael Mertler *(Chief Engr)*

TOWER MOTOR CO. INC.

505 S Broadway, Coos Bay, OR 97420
Tel.: (541) 267-2118
Web Site: http://www.towerford.com
Sales Range: $10-24.9 Million
Emp.: 50
Automobiles; New & Used
N.A.I.C.S.: 441110
Charles L. Day *(Owner)*
Matt Larson *(Mgr-Svcs)*

TOWER REALTY PARTNERS, INC.

2600 Maitland Center Pkwy Ste 225, Maitland, FL 32751
Tel.: (407) 659-0120
Web Site: http://www.towerrealtypartners.com
Year Founded: 1987
Sales Range: $1-9.9 Million
Emp.: 12
Commercial Real Estate Investment & Management Services
N.A.I.C.S.: 212312
Tiffany Zullo *(Dir-Leasing)*
Pung Jeffers *(VP-Investments)*

TOWER ROCK STONE COMPANY INC.

250 W Sand Bank Rd, Columbia, IL 62236-1044
Tel.: (618) 281-4106
Web Site: http://www.luhr.com
Year Founded: 1972
Sales Range: $25-49.9 Million
Emp.: 200
Provider of Crushed & Broken Limestone
N.A.I.C.S.: 212312
Michael Luhr *(Pres)*

TOWER THREE PARTNERS, LLC

2 Sound View Dr, Greenwich, CT 06830
Tel.: (203) 485-5800
Web Site: http://www.towerthreepartners.com
Investment Management Service
N.A.I.C.S.: 523940
Debra Bricker *(CFO & Chief Compliance Officer)*
Michael Khutorsky *(Principal)*

Subsidiaries:

Facet Technologies, LLC (1)
3900 N Commerce Dr, Atlanta, GA 30344
Tel.: (770) 590-6464
Web Site: http://www.facetmed.com
Medical Device Mfr & Distr
N.A.I.C.S.: 339112
Kevin Seifert *(Chm)*
Don Jackson *(VP-Fin-Info Sys)*
Howard Baker *(VP-Quality & Regulatory Affairs)*

TOWERBROOK CAPITAL PARTNERS, L.P.

Park Ave Twr 65 E 55th St, New York, NY 10022
Tel.: (212) 699-2200
Web Site: http://www.towerbrook.com
Year Founded: 2001
Privater Equity Firm
N.A.I.C.S.: 523999
Neal Moszkowski *(Co-Founder & Co-Chm)*
Ramez Sousou *(Co-Founder & Co-CEO)*
Jonathan D. Bilzin *(Mng Dir)*
Jennifer Ternoey Glassman *(Mng Dir & CFO)*
Evan Goldman *(Mng Dir)*
Glenn Miller *(Mng Dir & Gen Counsel-North America)*
Ian R. Sacks *(Mng Dir)*
Christoph Lueneburger *(Mng Dir)*
Karim Saddi *(Mng Dir)*
Filippo Cardini *(Mng Dir, COO & Gen Counsel)*
Shannon Barton *(Sr Principal)*
Josh Bernath *(Principal)*
Edouard Peugeot *(Principal)*
David Winokur *(Sr Principal)*
Pamela Yu *(Principal & Dir-Tax Compliance)*
Andrew Rolfe *(Mng Dir & Head-Private Equity-USA)*
Jose Arellano *(Mng Dir)*
Guy Cartwright *(Mng Dir)*
Nicolas Chavanne *(Mng Dir)*
Alicia Corbin *(Sr Principal-IR)*
Fahd Elkadiri *(Principal)*
Matthew Gerber *(Mng Dir & Gen Counsel-Europe)*
Winston Ginsberg *(Mng Dir)*
Joseph Knoll *(Mng Dir)*
Lisa Kirschner *(Principal & Controller)*
Ronald van Loo *(Mng Dir)*
Elsie Umpierre *(Office Mgr)*

Subsidiaries:

AA PLC (1)
Fanum House Basing View, Basingstoke, RG21 4EA, Hampshire, United Kingdom
Tel.: (44) 3705448866
Web Site: https://www.theaacorporate.com
Rev.: $1,305,042,000
Assets: $2,511,714,000
Liabilities: $4,585,353,600
Net Worth: ($2,073,639,600)
Earnings: $114,109,200
Emp.: 7,536
Fiscal Year-end: 01/31/2020
Roadside Assistance Services
N.A.I.C.S.: 561990
Edmund King *(Pres)*
Rick Haythornthwaite *(Chm)*
Jakob Pfaudler *(CEO)*
Thomas Mackay *(CFO)*
Louise Benford *(Chief People Officer)*

Subsidiary (Domestic):

Drivetech (UK) Limited (2)
Fanum House Basing View, Basingstoke, RG21 4EA, Hampshire, United Kingdom
Tel.: (44) 1256610907
Web Site: http://www.drivetech.co.uk
Driver Training Services
N.A.I.C.S.: 611692
Charlie Norman *(Mng Dir)*
Ian Dudley *(Dir-IT)*
Sarah Homer *(Head-Fin)*
Colin Paterson *(Head-Mktg)*
Tanya Hills *(Head-Bus Ops)*

Aernnova Aerospace Corporation S.A. (1)
Leonardo da Vinci 13, Parque Tecnologico de Alava, 01510, Minano, Spain
Tel.: (34) 945 185 600
Web Site: http://www.aernnova.com
Rev.: $789,786,995
Fiscal Year-end: 12/31/2018
Aerostructures & Aircraft Components Designer, Mfr & Distr
N.A.I.C.S.: 336413
Juan Ignacio Gandasegui *(Chm & CEO)*
Pedro Fuente Arce *(Vice Chm)*
Hipolito Suarez Gutierrez *(Sec)*

ECIT AS (1)
Rolfsbuktveien 4A, 1364, Fornebu, Norway
Tel.: (47) 22721414
Web Site: https://www.ecit.com
Rev.: $317,568,816
Assets: $348,143,359
Liabilities: $174,210,235
Net Worth: $173,933,124
Earnings: $16,072,418
Emp.: 2,602
Fiscal Year-end: 12/31/2023
Information Technology Services
N.A.I.C.S.: 541512
Peter Lauring *(Founder)*
Thomas Plenborg *(Chm)*
Jes Schjotler *(VP)*
Mads Skovgaard *(CFO)*
Pedro Fasting *(Deputy Chm)*

Subsidiary (Domestic):

3C Technology AS (2)
Drapen 16, 3036, Drammen, Norway
Tel.: (47) 32856700
Web Site: https://3ctechnology.no
Teaching & Communication Digital Solution Services
N.A.I.C.S.: 541810

Abaci AS (2)
Autorisert Regnskapsforerselskap Martin Linges Vei 25, 1364, Fornebu, Norway
Tel.: (47) 67141030
Web Site: https://www.abaci.no
Accounting Software Development Services
N.A.I.C.S.: 541219

Argus Kreditt AS (2)
Kartverksveien 5, 3510, Honefoss, Norway
Tel.: (47) 32116990
Web Site: https://www.arguskreditt.no
Emp.: 6
Credit Information & Advice Services
N.A.I.C.S.: 522320

Subsidiary (Non-US):

Credite Consulting AB (2)
Lustgardsgatan 19, 112 51, Stockholm, Sweden
Tel.: (46) 840021240
Web Site: https://www.credite.se
Accounting & Counselling Services
N.A.I.C.S.: 541512

ECIT Account A/S (2)
Friis Hansens Vej 5, Jylland, 7100, Vejle, Denmark
Tel.: (45) 75863750
Information Technology Support Services
N.A.I.C.S.: 541512

ECIT Advisory AB (2)
Grev Turegatan 14, 114 46, Stockholm, Sweden
Tel.: (46) 854507530
Information Technology Support Services
N.A.I.C.S.: 541512

ECIT Aros A/S (2)
Rudolfgardsvej 1B, 8260, Viby, Denmark
Tel.: (45) 51430033
Finance & Consulting Services
N.A.I.C.S.: 541690

Subsidiary (Domestic):

ECIT Autogear AS (2)
Rolfsbuktveien 4A, 1364, Fornebu, Norway
Tel.: (47) 21080260
Information Technology Support Services
N.A.I.C.S.: 541512

ECIT Capstone AS (2)
Rolfsbuktveien 4A, 1364, Fornebu, Norway
Tel.: (47) 22040550
Information Technology Support Services
N.A.I.C.S.: 541512

ECIT Consulta AS (2)
Glynitveien 27, 1400, Ski, Norway
Tel.: (47) 48310500
Information Technology Consultancy Services
N.A.I.C.S.: 541512

ECIT Lillehammer AS (2)
Kirkegata 45, 2609, Lillehammer, Norway
Tel.: (47) 97050900
Information Technology Support Services
N.A.I.C.S.: 541512

ECIT Marketing AS (2)
Hvamsvingen 7, 2013, Skjetten, Norway
Tel.: (47) 90992497
Advertising Buying & Marketing Services
N.A.I.C.S.: 541830

ECIT Normann & Oygarden AS (2)
Stromsbusletta 9B, 4847, Arendal, Norway
Tel.: (47) 37073030
Information Technology Support Services
N.A.I.C.S.: 541512

ECIT Peritus AS (2)
Bjornstjerne Bjornsonsgate 110, 3044, Drammen, Norway

Tel.: (47) 93264310
Web Site: https://www.peritus.no
Emp.: 15
Information Technology Consulting Services
N.A.I.C.S.: 541512

ECIT Rad & Regnskap AS (2)
Holmaveien 20, 1339, Voyenenga, Norway
Tel.: (47) 21627000
Emp.: 60
Accounting & Financial Consulting Services
N.A.I.C.S.: 541690

Subsidiary (Non-US):

ECIT Services AB (2)
Lustgardsgatan 19, 112 51, Stockholm, Sweden
Tel.: (46) 840021240
Information Technology Support Services
N.A.I.C.S.: 541512

ECIT Solutions A/S (2)
Rudolfgardsvej 1B, 8260, Viby, Denmark
Tel.: (45) 77341334
Information Technology Security Services
N.A.I.C.S.: 541512

Subsidiary (Domestic):

ECIT Solutions DI AS (2)
Eidsvagbakken 1, 5105, Bergen, Norway
Tel.: (47) 55333770
Information Technology Support Services
N.A.I.C.S.: 541512

ECIT Solutions ITS AS (2)
Grenseveien 21, 4313, Sandnes, Norway
Tel.: (47) 51816380
Information Technology Services
N.A.I.C.S.: 541512

ECIT Solutions One AS (2)
Rolfsbuktveien 4A, 1364, Fornebu, Norway
Tel.: (47) 92200200
Information Technology Support Services
N.A.I.C.S.: 541512

Subsidiary (Non-US):

ECIT Solutions Pro AB (2)
Runstensgatan 5, 582 78, Linkoping, Sweden
Tel.: (46) 104051100
Web Site: https://www.ecitshop.se
Computer Software Development Services
N.A.I.C.S.: 541511

Subsidiary (Domestic):

ECIT Stord AS (2)
Kunnskapshuset Sae 134, 5417, Stord, Norway
Tel.: (47) 53456300
Information Technology Support Services
N.A.I.C.S.: 541512

ECIT Trondheim AS (2)
Vegamot 8B, 7049, Trondheim, Norway
Tel.: (47) 72909272
Information Technology Support Services
N.A.I.C.S.: 541512

ECIT Veiby Akonto AS (2)
Hvervenmoveien 49, 3511, Honefoss, Norway
Tel.: (47) 32123212
Information Technology Support Services
N.A.I.C.S.: 541512

Ecit Aktivapluss AS (2)
Grenseveien 21, 4313, Stavanger, Norway
Tel.: (47) 51850960
Information Technology Support Services
N.A.I.C.S.: 541512

Ecit Wlcom As (2)
Industrivegen 23A, 2039, Jessheim, Norway
Tel.: (47) 63912000
Web Site: https://www.wlcom.no
Emp.: 194
Accounting & Payroll Services
N.A.I.C.S.: 541214

Enklerestart.No As (2)
Espehaugen 32, 5258, Bergen, Norway
Tel.: (47) 2135
Web Site: https://enklerestart.no
Finance & Information Technology Services
N.A.I.C.S.: 541512

Subsidiary (Non-US):

Intect ApS (2)
Horkaer 12A, 2730, Herlev, Denmark
Tel.: (45) 71991122
Web Site: https://www.intect.io
Payroll Management Software Development Services
N.A.I.C.S.: 541214

Subsidiary (Domestic):

Isonor IT AS (2)
Rolfsbuktveien 4 A, 1364, Fornebu, Norway
Tel.: (47) 22040550
Web Site: https://www.isonor.no
Emp.: 5
Information Technology Support Services
N.A.I.C.S.: 541512

Subsidiary (Non-US):

Modern Ekonomi Sverige AB (2)
Sigurdsgatan 7 A, 721 30, Vasteras, Sweden
Tel.: (46) 214703600
Web Site: https://www.modernekonomi.se
Emp.: 130
Financial Investment Services
N.A.I.C.S.: 523999

Norian Accounting AB (2)
Lofstroms Alle 7, 172 66, Sundbyberg, Sweden
Tel.: (46) 854661000
Web Site: https://www.norian.se
Accounting & Payroll Automation Services
N.A.I.C.S.: 541214

Norian Accounting Oy (2)
Ohjelmakaari 10, 40500, Jyvaskyla, Finland
Tel.: (358) 942454520
Web Site: https://www.norian.fi
Outsourcing & Software Robotic Services
N.A.I.C.S.: 561110

Norian Accounting Sp. z o.o. (2)
Grudziadzka 46-48, 87-100, Torun, Poland
Tel.: (48) 224612630
Web Site: https://www.norian-accounting.pl
Accounting & Payroll Automation Services
N.A.I.C.S.: 541214

Norian Accounting UAB (2)
Konstitucijos pr 21c Quadrum North, LT-08130, Vilnius, Lithuania
Tel.: (370) 64554876
Web Site: https://www.norian.lt
Accounting & Payroll Automation Services
N.A.I.C.S.: 541214

Subsidiary (Domestic):

Norian Regnskap AS (2)
Stortingsgata 2, 0158, Oslo, Norway
Tel.: (47) 22911350
Web Site: https://www.norian.no
Accounting & Property Management Services
N.A.I.C.S.: 531312

Subsidiary (Non-US):

PA Kompetens Lon AB (2)
Singelgatan 7, 212 28, Malmo, Sweden
Tel.: (46) 406076230
Web Site: https://www.pakompetens.se
Emp.: 2,000
Payroll Outsourcing Services
N.A.I.C.S.: 561110

Subsidiary (Domestic):

Partner Regnskap AS (2)
Grenseveien 21, 4313, Sandnes, Norway
Tel.: (47) 51850960
Web Site: https://partnerregnskap.no
Accounting & Counselling Services
N.A.I.C.S.: 541219

Subsidiary (Non-US):

Pramo Ekonomi & Data AB (2)
Singelgatan 7, 212 28, Malmo, Sweden
Tel.: (46) 40490390
Web Site: https://www.pramo.se
Information Technology Support Services
N.A.I.C.S.: 541512

Subsidiary (Domestic):

XACCT Accounting AS (2)
Sorkedalsveien 6, 0369, Oslo, Norway
Tel.: (47) 40637349
Web Site: https://www.xacct.no
Emp.: 45
Accounting & Payroll Services
N.A.I.C.S.: 541214

Subsidiary (Non-US):

Xtracon A/S (2)
Olbycenter 5 1 sal, 4600, Koge, Denmark
Tel.: (45) 46350902
Web Site: https://www.xtracon.dk
Information Technology Support Services
N.A.I.C.S.: 541512

Equity Group Investments, LLC (1)
2 N Riverside Plz Ste 600, Chicago, IL 60606
Tel.: (312) 454-1800
Web Site: http://www.egizell.com
Holding Company
N.A.I.C.S.: 551112
Philip G. Tinkler *(CFO & COO)*
Robert S. Silberman *(Mng Dir)*

Holding (Domestic):

Rewards Network Inc. (2)
2 N Riverside Plz Ste 950, Chicago, IL 60606
Tel.: (312) 521-6767
Web Site: http://www.rewardsnetwork.com
Restaurant Dining & Hotels Awards Programs
N.A.I.C.S.: 561499
Edmond I. Eger III *(CEO)*
Shane Kern *(CFO)*
John Leen *(Chief Sls Officer & Sr VP)*
Andrei Utkin *(CMO)*
Hunt Kingsbury *(VP-Corp Dev)*
Chris Razniewski *(VP-People)*
Jeanne Steinback *(VP-Software Delivery)*
Mike Tegtmeyer *(VP-IT & Security)*
Kevin Dulsky *(Sr VP-Bus Dev & Partnerships)*
Steve Freiberg *(Chm)*

Subsidiary (Domestic):

iDine (3)
2 N Riverside Plz Ste 200, Chicago, IL 60606
Tel.: (312) 521-6767
Web Site: http://www.idine.com
Restaurant Dining & Entertainment Promotions
N.A.I.C.S.: 812990

Infopro Digital SAS (1)
Antony Parc 2-10 place du General de Gaulle, BP 20156, La Croix de Berny, 92 186, Antony, Cedex, France
Tel.: (33) 1 77 92 92 92
Web Site: http://www.infopro-digital.com
Sales Range: $500-549.9 Million
Emp.: 3,200
Professional Information, Multimedia Software & Print Publication Services
N.A.I.C.S.: 513210
Christophe Czajka *(Founder & Exec Chm)*
Julien Elmaleh *(CEO)*
Isabelle Andre *(CEO-Media & Trade Shows Brands)*
Stephane Deplus *(CFO)*
Manon Rossetti *(Deputy CEO-Publ, Training, Markets & Events)*
Celine Ruat *(Grp Head-HR)*
Sajid Fayyaz *(CTO)*

Subsidiary (Non-US):

Docu Group Deutsche Holding GmbH (2)
Arnulfstr 124, 80636, Munich, Germany
Tel.: (49) 892351937 50
Web Site: http://www.docugroup.info
Construction Industry Business to Business Publishing Services
N.A.I.C.S.: 513199
Christophe Czajka *(Mng Dir)*
Julien Elmaleh *(Mng Dir)*

Subsidiary (Domestic):

Bauverlag BV GmbH (3)
Avenwedderstr 55, 33311, Gutersloh, Germany
Tel.: (49) 5241802791
Web Site: http://www.bauverlag.de

Architecture & Construction Industry Information Publisher
N.A.I.C.S.: 519290
Michael Voss *(CEO)*
Ahmet Kocabiyik *(Dir-HR)*

Subsidiary (Non-US):

Haynes Publishing Group PLC (2)
Sparkford, Yeovil, BA22 7JJ, Somerset, United Kingdom
Tel.: (44) 1963440635
Web Site: http://www.haynes.co.uk
Instructional Book, Manual & Video Publisher
N.A.I.C.S.: 513130
Eddie Bell *(Chm)*
James T. Bunkum *(COO)*
Jeremy Yates-Round *(Mng Dir-Haynes Consumer)*
Alex Kwarts *(CTO)*
Jean H. C. Haynes *(CEO)*
Richard S. Barker *(Sec & Dir-Grp Fin)*
Dean Eddies *(Mgr-Sls-Natl)*
Shaun Merritt *(Mgr-Natl Acct-Motorcycle Trade, Trade Sls-South East)*
Leanne Bramley *(Mgr-Field & Trade Sls-East Midlands, Central & Northern UK)*
James Cole *(Mgr-Field & Trade Sls-West Midlands, Wales & South West)*
Peter Van der Galien *(Mng Dir-Professional Bus)*
Simon Stafford *(Mgr-Field & Trade Sls Scotland-Northern England & Ireland)*

Subsidiary (US):

Haynes North America, Inc (3)
859 Lawrence Dr, Newbury Park, CA 91320
Tel.: (805) 498-6703
Web Site: http://www.haynes.com
Books Publishing Services
N.A.I.C.S.: 513130
Dan Benhardus *(CFO & Sr VP)*

Subsidiary (Domestic):

J H Haynes & Co Ltd (3)
Yeovil, Somerset, BA22 7JJ, United Kingdom
Tel.: (44) 1963440635
Web Site: http://www.haynes.co.uk
Sales Range: $25-49.9 Million
Emp.: 75
Book Publisher & Distr
N.A.I.C.S.: 513130
Jeremy Haynes-Round *(Mng Dir)*

Subsidiary (US):

Odcombe Press LP (3)
1299 Bridgestone Pkwy, La Vergne, TN 37086
Tel.: (615) 793-5414
Web Site: http://www.haynes.com
Sales Range: $25-49.9 Million
Emp.: 60
Printing Services
N.A.I.C.S.: 323117
Nigel Clenns *(VP-Ops)*

Subsidiary (Domestic):

Vivid Automotive Data (UK) Ltd (3)
Ground Fl N Barn, Broughton Hall Business Park, Skipton, BD23 3AE, Yorkshire, United Kingdom
Tel.: (44) 1756794393
Sales Range: $25-49.9 Million
Emp.: 4
Database Management Services
N.A.I.C.S.: 541513

Subsidiary (Non-US):

Vivid Italia srl (3)
Strada San Luigi 27, I 10043, Orbassano, Italy
Tel.: (39) 0119040768
Database Management Services
N.A.I.C.S.: 541513

ProSight Global, Inc. (1)
412 Mt Kemble Ave Ste 300, Morristown, NJ 07960
Tel.: (973) 532-1900
Web Site: http://www.prosightspecialty.com
Rev.: $817,090,000
Assets: $3,050,712,000
Liabilities: $2,426,744,000
Net Worth: $623,968,000

TOWERBROOK CAPITAL PARTNERS, L.P.

TowerBrook Capital Partners, L.P.—(Continued)
Earnings: $22,228,000
Emp.: 351
Fiscal Year-end: 12/31/2020
General Insurance Services
N.A.I.C.S.: 524210
Vivienne Zimmermann *(Chief Customer Experience Officer)*
Frank D. Papalia *(Chief Legal Officer)*
Kari Hilder *(Chief HR Officer)*
Lee Kraemer *(Chief Actuary Officer)*
Anthony S. Piszel *(CFO)*
Erin Cullen *(Pres-Customer Segment)*
Darryl Siry *(COO & CTO)*
Ric Victores *(Chief Sls & Mktg Officer)*
Joe Finnegan *(Pres-Customer Segment)*
Rob Bednarik *(Pres-Customer Segment)*
Donna Biondich *(Chief Claims Officer)*
Lee Lloyd *(Officer-Field Ops)*
Kevin Topper *(Pres-Customer Segment)*
Nico Santini *(Chief Investment Officer)*
Jeff Arricale *(Head-Capital Markets)*
Darryl Siry *(COO & CTO)*
Jonathan Ritz *(CEO)*
Stan Galanski *(Chm)*
Hunter Morgan *(Sr VP-Excess Casualty)*
Tim Ryan *(Pres)*
Christine Doherty *(VP)*
Philip Yung *(VP)*
Keith Lavigne *(Sr VP-Exec Liability)*

TowerBrook Capital Partners (U.K.) L.L.P. (1)
1st James Market Carlton Street, London, SW1Y4AH, United Kingdom
Tel.: (44) 2074512020
Web Site: http://www.towerbrook.com
Privater Equity Firm
N.A.I.C.S.: 523999
Matthew Gerber *(Mng Dir & Gen Counsel)*

True Religion Apparel, Inc. (1)
2263 E Vernon Ave, Vernon, CA 90058
Tel.: (323) 266-3072
Web Site:
http://www.truereligionbrandjeans.com
Denim Apparel Mfr, Designer & Marketer
N.A.I.C.S.: 315250
Allen Onyia *(Dir-Artistic)*
Gene Davis *(Chm)*

Subsidiary (Domestic):

Guru Denim, Inc. (2)
1888 Rosecrans Ave, Manhattan Beach, CA 90266
Tel.: (323) 266-3072
Web Site: http://www.truereligion.com
Sales Range: $650-699.9 Million
Clothing Mfr.
N.A.I.C.S.: 458110
Jeffrey Lubell *(CEO)*

Subsidiary (Non-US):

True Religion Brand Jeans Germany GmbH (2)
Weizenmuhlenstrasse 21, 40221, Dusseldorf, Germany
Tel.: (49) 2111714990
Fashion Apparel Mfr & Distr
N.A.I.C.S.: 458110

True Religion Brand Jeans Italy, s.r.l. (2)
Via Morimondo 5, Milan, 20143, Italy
Tel.: (39) 028137359
Fashion Apparel Mfr & Distr
N.A.I.C.S.: 458110

True Religion Brand Jeans U.K. Limited (2)
27 Kingly Street 2nd Floor, London, W1B 5QE, United Kingdom
Tel.: (44) 2072406208
Fashion Apparel Mfr & Distr
N.A.I.C.S.: 458110

True Religion Japan K.K. (2)
Sunrise Aoyama 301 2-13-2 Minami-Aoyama, Minato-Ku, Tokyo, 107-0062, Japan
Tel.: (81) 345802772
Fashion Apparel Mfr & Distr
N.A.I.C.S.: 458110

TOWERCO

5000 Valleystone Dr Ste 200, Cary, NC 27519
Tel.: (919) 469-5559
Web Site: http://www.towerco.com
Year Founded: 2004
Sales Range: $100-124.9 Million
Emp.: 25
Wireless Communications Tower Mfr
N.A.I.C.S.: 517112
Richard Byrne *(CEO)*
Scot Lloyd *(COO)*
Tina White *(Project Mgr-Collocation)*
Jen Courtemanche *(VP-Property Mgmt)*

TOWERDATA, INC.

33 Irving Pl 3rd Fl, New York, NY 10003
Tel.: (646) 742-1771
Web Site: http://www.towerdata.com
Year Founded: 2001
Software Publisher
N.A.I.C.S.: 513210
Jeremy Lizt *(Co-Founder & VP-Engrg)*
Tom Burke *(CEO)*

Subsidiaries:

FreshAddress, LLC (1)
36 Crafts St, Newton, MA 02458
Tel.: (617) 965-4500
Web Site: http://www.freshaddress.com
Email Marketing Services
N.A.I.C.S.: 541860
Austin Bliss *(Co-Founder & Pres)*
Bill Kaplan *(Co-Founder & CEO)*
Janis Garland *(Dir-Bus Ops)*
Jon Tejeda *(Dir-Sls)*
Suzanne Shaughnessy *(Dir-Strategic Solutions)*
Nicole Campbell *(VP-Client Svcs)*

TOWLIFT INC.

1395 Valley Belt Rd, Cleveland, OH 44131
Tel.: (216) 749-6800
Web Site: http://www.towlift.com
Year Founded: 1965
Sales Range: $50-74.9 Million
Emp.: 300
Whslr of Materials Handling Machinery
N.A.I.C.S.: 423830
David H. Cannon *(Pres)*
David Bongorno *(VP-Plng & Fin)*
Matt Adams *(Pres)*

TOWN & COUNTRY BANCORP INC.

1925 S MacArthur Blvd, Springfield, IL 62704
Tel.: (217) 787-3100
Web Site: http://www.townandcountrybank.com
Year Founded: 1962
Sales Range: $10-24.9 Million
Emp.: 150
Provider of Banking Services
N.A.I.C.S.: 522110
David E. Kirschner *(Chm)*
Doug Cheatham *(CFO & Exec VP)*
Joe Pauk *(Exec VP-Ops & Tech)*
Grant Franklin *(Exec VP-Sls)*
Jason Barth *(Exec VP-Talent)*
Micah Bartlett *(Pres & CEO)*

Subsidiaries:

Town & Country Bank Springfield (1)
1925 S MacArthur Blvd, Springfield, IL 62704
Tel.: (217) 787-3100
Web Site:
http://www.townandcountrybank.com
Sales Range: $1-9.9 Million
Emp.: 21
Provider of Banking Services
N.A.I.C.S.: 522110

TOWN & COUNTRY BANCORP, INC.

524 S 30th St, Quincy, IL 62301-3604
Tel.: (217) 222-0015
Web Site:
http://www.tcbankmidwest.com
Banking Services
N.A.I.C.S.: 522110
Shelby Tonnies *(VP)*
Gary Penn *(Pres & CEO-Quincy)*
Linda Bradshaw *(Exec VP & Trust Officer)*
Jennilee Carper *(Sr VP-Quincy & La-Belle)*
Kelly Miller *(VP-Quincy)*
Trevor Beck *(VP-Quincy)*
Dana Sharpe *(VP-Quincy)*

TOWN & COUNTRY BANK & TRUST COMPANY

201 N 3rd St, Bardstown, KY 40004
Tel.: (502) 348-3911
Web Site: http://www.mytcbt.com
Rev.: $13,871,000
Emp.: 100
State Commercial Banks
N.A.I.C.S.: 522110
Raffo Wimsett *(CEO)*
David Greenwell *(Chief Credit Officer & Exec VP)*

TOWN & COUNTRY CEDAR HOMES

04740 Skop Rd, Boyne Falls, MI 49713
Tel.: (800) 968-3178
Web Site:
http://www.cedarhomes.com
Year Founded: 1947
Sales Range: $10-24.9 Million
Emp.: 30
Modular Housing Construction
N.A.I.C.S.: 321992

TOWN & COUNTRY CO-OP

813 Clark Ave, Ashland, OH 44805
Tel.: (419) 281-2153
Web Site: http://www.tc-coop.com
Year Founded: 2002
Sales Range: $1-9.9 Million
Emp.: 200
Agricultural & Petroleum Products
N.A.I.C.S.: 115116
Al Holdren *(CEO)*
John Steiner *(Chm)*
Earl Stitzlein *(Sec)*
William Walter *(Vice Chm)*
Jean Bratton *(COO)*
Pat Place *(Mgr-Retail)*
Brian Amstutz *(CFO)*
Gary Besancon *(Mgr-Ops-Smithville-Agronomy)*
Bill Rohrbaugh *(Mgr-Feed-Corporate-Energy)*
Deb Froelich *(Mgr-Credit)*
Bob Mole *(Mgr-Ashland-Fuel-Delivery)*
Matt Fugate *(Mgr-Ashland-Propane)*

TOWN & COUNTRY CO-OP INC.

427 W Henry St, Wooster, OH 44691
Tel.: (330) 264-9925
Web Site:
http://www.townandcountry.coop
Sales Range: $10-24.9 Million
Emp.: 5
Grain Distribution
N.A.I.C.S.: 424510
Al Holdren *(Pres)*

TOWN & COUNTRY CREDIT UNION

615 S Broadway, Minot, ND 58701

Tel.: (701) 852-2018
Web Site:
http://www.townandcountry.org
Year Founded: 1939
Sales Range: $10-24.9 Million
Emp.: 132
Credit Union
N.A.I.C.S.: 522130
Raymond Kopp *(Vice Chm)*
Randy Arneson *(Treas & Sec)*
Jeremiah Kossen *(Pres & CEO)*
Trevor Keney *(Chief Retail Officer & Sr VP)*
Mark Larson *(Sr VP-Bus Lending)*
Tyler Neether *(VP-Bus Lending)*

TOWN & COUNTRY DISTRIBUTORS

1050 Ardmore Ave, Itasca, IL 60143
Tel.: (630) 250-0590
Web Site: http://www.tcbeer.com
Rev.: $31,600,000
Emp.: 150
Beer & Other Fermented Malt Liquors
N.A.I.C.S.: 424810
Lawrence S. Sowa *(Pres)*
Glenn Niezgoda *(Mgr-Sls)*
Adam Stephan *(Gen Mgr-Sls)*
John M. Holland *(CEO)*
Jon Jahnke *(Gen Mgr)*
Rebecca Pray *(VP-Mktg)*

TOWN & COUNTRY FORD INC.

6015 Preston Hwy, Louisville, KY 40219-1317
Tel.: (502) 964-8131
Web Site:
http://www.fordlouisville.com
Sales Range: $50-74.9 Million
Emp.: 1,000
Sales of Automobiles
N.A.I.C.S.: 441110
Ray Duran *(Treas)*
William Hays Jr. *(Pres & CEO)*

TOWN & COUNTRY HONDA

19400 SE McLoughlin Blvd, Gladstone, OR 97027
Tel.: (866) 802-3620
Web Site:
http://www.tchondagladstone.com
Sales Range: $50-74.9 Million
Emp.: 75
Automobile Dealership
N.A.I.C.S.: 441110
Chris Martinez *(Mgr-Sls)*
Sam Miller *(Mgr-Sls)*

TOWN & COUNTRY LANDSCAPE SUPPLY CO.

3900 W 167th St, Harvey, IL 60426
Tel.: (708) 596-7200
Web Site: http://rrmulchandsoil.com
Sales Range: $10-24.9 Million
Emp.: 30
Brick, Stone & Other Landscape Related Material
N.A.I.C.S.: 423320
Dale Habenicht *(Pres)*
Joe Land *(COO)*

TOWN & COUNTRY MARKET INC.

2208 NW Market St Ste 507, Seattle, WA 98107
Tel.: (206) 784-7064
Web Site: http://www.central-market.com
Rev.: $120,000,000
Emp.: 7
Provider of Grocery Services
N.A.I.C.S.: 445110
Larry Nakata *(Pres)*

TOWN & COUNTRY SERVICES

COMPANIES

220 LaSalle St, Tonica, IL 61370
Tel.: (815) 442-3415
Web Site:
http://www.towncountryservices.com
Year Founded: 1919
Sales Range: $1-9.9 Million
Emp.: 20
Air Conditioning Contractors & Systems
N.A.I.C.S.: 333415
Luke Weiden *(VP)*

TOWN AND COUNTRY SUPERMARKETS, INC.
PO Box 748, Salem, MO 65560
Tel.: (573) 729-3455
Web Site: http://www.tcmarkets.com
Sales Range: $75-99.9 Million
Emp.: 500
Owner & Operator of Grocery Stores
N.A.I.C.S.: 445110
Dennis Gott *(Pres)*

TOWN FAIR TIRE CENTERS INC.
460 Coe Ave, East Haven, CT 06512
Tel.: (203) 467-8600
Web Site: http://www.townfair.com
Sales Range: $25-49.9 Million
Emp.: 60
Sales of Automotive Tires
N.A.I.C.S.: 441340
Kathryn Tutino *(VP & Controller)*

TOWN MANAGEMENT CORP
3330 Dundee Rd Ste S1, Northbrook, IL 60062-2327
Tel.: (847) 635-0000
Web Site:
http://www.townmanagement.com
Rev.: $27,100,000
Emp.: 90
Operative Builders
N.A.I.C.S.: 236117

TOWN MOTOR CAR CORPORATION
135 S Dean St, Englewood, NJ 07631
Tel.: (201) 568-5200
Web Site: http://www.town-motors.com
Sales Range: $25-49.9 Million
Emp.: 150
Automobiles, New & Used
N.A.I.C.S.: 441110
Robert F. Siebold *(Pres)*

TOWN NORTH MAZDA
307 S Central Expy, Richardson, TX 75080-6307
Tel.: (972) 231-6370
Web Site:
http://www.townnorthmazda.com
Year Founded: 1974
Sales Range: $10-24.9 Million
Emp.: 52
Car Whslr
N.A.I.C.S.: 441110
Donny Bobo *(Gen Mgr)*
Max C. Wedell *(Pres)*
Alex Tsvang *(Mgr-Sls)*

TOWN PUMP, INC.
600 S Main St, Butte, MT 59701-2534
Tel.: (406) 497-6700 MT
Web Site: http://www.townpump.com
Year Founded: 1953
Sales Range: $1-4.9 Billion
Emp.: 2,600
Operator of Gas Stations & Convenience Stores
N.A.I.C.S.: 457120

Mary Kenneally *(Co-Founder, Treas & Sec)*
Thomas F. Kenneally Sr. *(Co-Founder, Pres & CEO)*

TOWN SPORTS INTERNATIONAL HOLDINGS, INC.
1250 Old Dixie Hwy, Vero Beach, FL 32960
Tel.: (772) 563-0905 DE
Web Site:
http://www.mysportsclubs.com
Year Founded: 2004
Rev.: $466,760,000
Assets: $794,278,000
Liabilities: $882,623,000
Net Worth: ($88,345,000)
Earnings: ($18,558,000)
Emp.: 1,900
Fiscal Year-end: 12/31/19
Holding Company; Fitness & Recreational Sports Centers Owner & Operator
N.A.I.C.S.: 551112
Patrick Dennis Walsh *(Chm & CEO)*
Phillip Juhan *(CFO)*

Subsidiaries:

Boutique Fitness, LLC (1)
1441 SW Chanl Ave Ste 104, Bend, OR 97702
Tel.: (541) 550-7822
Women's Clothing Store Operator
N.A.I.C.S.: 458110

Palm Beach Sports Club, LLC (1)
4540 Donald Ross Rd, Palm Beach Gardens, FL 33410
Tel.: (561) 799-1515
Health Club & Physical Fitness Services
N.A.I.C.S.: 713940

TSI - Lucille 38th Avenue, LLC (1)
13539 38th Ave, Flushing, NY 11355
Tel.: (718) 321-0100
Health Club & Physical Fitness Services
N.A.I.C.S.: 713940

TSI - Lucille 42nd Street, LLC (1)
50 E 42nd St, New York, NY 10017
Tel.: (212) 682-8421
Health Club & Physical Fitness Services
N.A.I.C.S.: 713940
Michell Bencosme *(Mgr-Customer Svc)*

TSI - Lucille 89th Street, LLC (1)
430 89th St, Brooklyn, NY 11209
Tel.: (718) 680-8200
Health Club & Physical Fitness Services
N.A.I.C.S.: 713940
Jennyne Jean *(Mgr-Customer Svc)*

TSI - Lucille Astoria, LLC (1)
32-62 Steinway St, Astoria, NY 11103
Tel.: (718) 626-6464
Health Club & Physical Fitness Services
N.A.I.C.S.: 713940

TSI - Lucille Austin Street, LLC (1)
7020 Austin St, Forest Hills, NY 11375
Tel.: (718) 261-2350
Health Club & Physical Fitness Services
N.A.I.C.S.: 713940
Elayne Rodriguez *(Gen Mgr)*

TSI - Lucille Bayshore, LLC (1)
1850 Sunrise Hwy, Bay Shore, NY 11706
Tel.: (631) 206-2122
Health Club & Physical Fitness Services
N.A.I.C.S.: 713940

TSI - Lucille Bronx, LLC (1)
2449 Morris Ave, Bronx, NY 10468
Tel.: (718) 329-3441
Health Club & Physical Fitness Services
N.A.I.C.S.: 713940

TSI - Lucille Clifton, LLC (1)
1075 Bloomfield Ave, Clifton, NJ 07012
Tel.: (973) 249-2966
Health Club & Physical Fitness Services
N.A.I.C.S.: 713940

TSI - Lucille Commack, LLC (1)
6534 Jericho Tpke, Commack, NY 11725
Tel.: (631) 864-0167

TOWN SPORTS INTERNATIONAL HOLDINGS, INC.

Health Club & Physical Fitness Services
N.A.I.C.S.: 713940

TSI - Lucille Holbrook, LLC (1)
5801 Sunrise Hwy, Holbrook, NY 11741
Tel.: (631) 319-1975
Health Club & Physical Fitness Services
N.A.I.C.S.: 713940
Marilyn Zdrakas *(Mgr)*

TSI - Lucille Jersey City, LLC (1)
338 Central Ave, Jersey City, NJ 07307
Tel.: (201) 217-0708
Health Club & Physical Fitness Services
N.A.I.C.S.: 713940

TSI - Lucille Kings Highway, LLC (1)
925 Kings Hwy, Brooklyn, NY 11223
Tel.: (718) 339-0990
Health Club & Physical Fitness Services
N.A.I.C.S.: 713940

TSI - Lucille Ralph Avenue, LLC (1)
1950 Ralph Ave, Brooklyn, NY 11234
Tel.: (718) 444-2623
Health Club & Physical Fitness Services
N.A.I.C.S.: 713940

TSI - Lucille Rockville Centre, LLC (1)
298 Sunrise Hwy, Rockville Centre, NY 11570
Tel.: (516) 766-8443
Health Club & Physical Fitness Services
N.A.I.C.S.: 713940

TSI - Lucille St. Nicholas Avenue, LLC (1)
1387 Saint Nicholas Ave, New York, NY 10033
Tel.: (212) 927-8376
Health Club & Physical Fitness Services
N.A.I.C.S.: 713940

TSI - Lucille Valley Stream, LLC (1)
225 W Merrick Rd, Valley Stream, NY 11580
Tel.: (516) 536-5153
Health Club & Physical Fitness Services
N.A.I.C.S.: 713940
Kathy Russello *(Mgr)*

TSI - Northridge, LLC (1)
19456 Nordhoff St, Northridge, CA 91324
Tel.: (818) 772-8900
Health Club & Physical Fitness Services
N.A.I.C.S.: 713940
Racheli Maman *(Mgr-Sls)*

TSI - Peacock, Port St. Lucie, LLC (1)
250 NW Peacock Blvd, Port Saint Lucie, FL 34986
Tel.: (772) 878-7662
Health Club & Physical Fitness Services
N.A.I.C.S.: 713940

TSI - Placentia, LLC (1)
860 N Rose Dr, Placentia, CA 92870
Tel.: (714) 993-6003
Health Club & Physical Fitness Services
N.A.I.C.S.: 713940

TSI - San Jose, LLC (1)
950 El Paseo de Saratoga, San Jose, CA 95130
Tel.: (408) 865-1400
Health Club & Physical Fitness Services
N.A.I.C.S.: 713940

TSI - Studio City, LLC (1)
12050 Ventura Blvd, Studio City, CA 91604
Tel.: (818) 760-0526
Health Club & Physical Fitness Services
N.A.I.C.S.: 713940

TSI - Topanga, LLC (1)
6600 Topanga Canyon Blvd, Canoga Park, CA 91303
Tel.: (818) 710-7606
Health Club & Physical Fitness Services
N.A.I.C.S.: 713940

TSI - Torrance, LLC (1)
2755 E Pacific Coast Hwy, Torrance, CA 90505
Tel.: (310) 891-2237
Health Club & Physical Fitness Services
N.A.I.C.S.: 713940

TSI - US Highway, Jupiter, LLC (1)
201 N US Hwy 1, Jupiter, FL 33477

Tel.: (561) 743-3700
Health Club & Physical Fitness Services
N.A.I.C.S.: 713940

TSI - Valencia, LLC (1)
24245 Magic Mountain Pkwy, Valencia, CA 91355
Tel.: (661) 286-0229
Health Club & Physical Fitness Services
N.A.I.C.S.: 713940

TSI - Westlake, LLC (1)
30770 Russell Ranch Rd, Westlake Village, CA 91362
Tel.: (805) 496-9978
Health Club & Physical Fitness Services
N.A.I.C.S.: 713940

TSI 1231 3rd Avenue, LLC (1)
1231 3rd Ave, New York, NY 10021
Tel.: (212) 232-0050
Health Club & Physical Fitness Services
N.A.I.C.S.: 713940

TSI 30 Broad Street, LLC (1)
30 Broad St, New York, NY 10005
Tel.: (212) 482-4800
Health Club & Physical Fitness Services
N.A.I.C.S.: 713940

TSI 555 6th Avenue, LLC (1)
555 6th Ave, New York, NY 10011
Tel.: (917) 382-5573
Health Club & Physical Fitness Services
N.A.I.C.S.: 713940

TSI Astor Place, LLC (1)
4 Astor Pl, New York, NY 10003
Tel.: (917) 877-1400
Health Club & Physical Fitness Services
N.A.I.C.S.: 713940

TSI Bradford, LLC (1)
3 Ferry St, Bradford, MA 01835
Tel.: (978) 521-4949
Web Site: http://www.bostonsportsclubs.com
Health Club & Physical Fitness Services
N.A.I.C.S.: 713940

TSI Hell's Kitchen, LLC (1)
355 W 49th St, New York, NY 10019
Tel.: (917) 521-6666
Web Site: http://www.tmplgym.com
Health Club & Physical Fitness Services
N.A.I.C.S.: 713940

TSI Methuen, LLC (1)
116 Pleasant Valley St, Methuen, MA 01844
Tel.: (978) 738-4653
Health Club & Physical Fitness Services
N.A.I.C.S.: 713940
Eric Lever *(Dir-Reg Ops)*

TSI Peabody, LLC (1)
194 Newbury St, Peabody, MA 01960
Tel.: (978) 536-0777
Health Club & Physical Fitness Services
N.A.I.C.S.: 713940
John Bushnell *(Mgr-Reg Sls)*

TSI Salisbury, LLC (1)
191 Elm St, Salisbury, MA 01952
Tel.: (978) 462-5662
Health Club & Physical Fitness Services
N.A.I.C.S.: 713940
Stephanie Bearse *(Dir-Fitness)*

TSI-LIV Condado, LLC (1)
103 Ave De Diego, San Juan, PR 00911
Tel.: (787) 303-4849
Health Club & Physical Fitness Services
N.A.I.C.S.: 713940

TSI-LIV Guaynabo, LLC (1)
Calle Parkside 2, Guaynabo, PR 00969
Tel.: (787) 302-5238
Health Club & Physical Fitness Services
N.A.I.C.S.: 713940

Town Sports International, LLC (1)
5 Penn Plaza 4th Fl, New York, NY 10001 (100%)
Tel.: (212) 246-6700
Web Site: http://www.mysportsclubs.com
Sales Range: $25-49.9 Million
Emp.: 100
Fitness & Recreational Sports Centers Owner & Operator
N.A.I.C.S.: 713940

Subsidiary (Domestic):

Fitcorp Private Fitness Centers (2)

TOWN SPORTS INTERNATIONAL HOLDINGS, INC.
U.S. PRIVATE

Town Sports International Holdings, Inc.—(Continued)
800 Boylston St Ste 2475, Boston, MA 02199
Tel.: (617) 375-5600
Web Site: http://www.fitcorp.com
Rev.: $12,700,000
Emp.: 25
Physical Fitness Facilities Operator
N.A.I.C.S.: 713940

TSI Alexandria, LLC (2)
3654 King St, Arlington, VA 22301-1908
Tel.: (703) 933-3777
Fitness Club Operator
N.A.I.C.S.: 713940

TSI Ardmore, LLC (2)
34 W Lancaster Ave, Ardmore, PA 19003
Tel.: (610) 645-7600
Fitness Club Operator
N.A.I.C.S.: 713940

TSI Clarendon, LLC (2)
2800 Clarendon Blvd, Arlington, VA 22201
Tel.: (703) 465-2828
Web Site: http://www.mysportsclub.com
Fitness & Recreational Sports Club Operator
N.A.I.C.S.: 713940

TSI East 86, LLC (2)
151 E 86th St, New York, NY 10028
Tel.: (212) 860-8630
Web Site: http://www.neworksportsclub.com
Fitness Club Operator
N.A.I.C.S.: 713940

TSI Mahwah, LLC (2)
10 Edison Rd, Mahwah, NJ 07430-3131
Tel.: (201) 848-0015
Web Site: http://www.nysc.com
Fitness & Recreational Sports Club Operator
N.A.I.C.S.: 713940

TSI Princeton, LLC (2)
301 N Harrison St Ste 9A, Princeton, NJ 08540-3526
Tel.: (609) 921-6985
Web Site: http://www.mysportsclubs.com
Emp.: 20
Fitness & Recreational Sports Club Operator
N.A.I.C.S.: 713940

TSI Springfield, LLC (2)
215 Morris Ave, Springfield, NJ 07081-1211
Tel.: (973) 376-3776
Web Site: http://www.mysportsclubs.com
Fitness & Recreational Sports Club Operator
N.A.I.C.S.: 713940

TSI West Caldwell, LLC (2)
913 Bloomfield Ave, Caldwell, NJ 07006
Tel.: (973) 808-8411
Web Site: http://www.townsportsinternational.com
Fitness & Recreational Sports Club Operator
N.A.I.C.S.: 713940

TOWNE BANCORP, INC.
3158 E Baseline Rd, Mesa, AZ 85204
Tel.: (480) 346-7551
Holding Company
N.A.I.C.S.: 551112
Rick S. Meikle (CEO)

TOWNE HOLDINGS INC.
24805 US Hwy 20 W, South Bend, IN 46628-5911
Tel.: (574) 233-3183
Web Site: http://www.towneair.com
Year Founded: 1994
Sales Range: $75-99.9 Million
Emp.: 2,000
Freight Transportation Services
N.A.I.C.S.: 484121
Tom Downey (Pres & CEO)
Jerry Scott (VP-HR)
Kim Sheridan-Rohasek (COO)

Subsidiaries:

Towne Air Freight Inc. (1)
24805 US Hwy 20, South Bend, IN 46628-5911
Tel.: (574) 233-3183
Web Site: http://www.towneair.com
Sales Range: $100-124.9 Million
Emp.: 275
Trucking
N.A.I.C.S.: 484121

TOWNE HYUNDAI
3170 Route 10 W, Denville, NJ 07834
Tel.: (973) 366-7777
Web Site: http://www.townehyundai.com
Rev.: $12,000,000
Emp.: 25
Car Dealership
N.A.I.C.S.: 441110
Eddie Pagan (Gen Mgr-Sls)
Ken Goss (Mgr-Svc)
Ben Lanterman (Mgr-Parts)

TOWNE PROPERTIES
1055 St Paul Pl, Cincinnati, OH 45202-6042
Tel.: (513) 381-8696   OH
Web Site: http://www.towneproperties.com
Year Founded: 1961
Sales Range: $50-74.9 Million
Emp.: 1,000
Real Estate Development & Management
N.A.I.C.S.: 531210
Phil Montanus (Partner)
Marvin Rosenberg (Partner)

TOWNECRAFT HOMEWARES, LLC
1 De Boer Dr, Glen Rock, NJ 07452
Tel.: (800) 977-7687
Web Site: http://www.townecraft.com
Year Founded: 1947
American made Cookware & Related Kitchen Accessories Distr
N.A.I.C.S.: 332215
Rafael A. Ramirez (Pres & CEO)

Subsidiaries:

Kitchen Fair (1)
4300 Amon Carter Blvd Ste 100, Fort Worth, TX 76155
Tel.: (262) 626-2121
Web Site: http://www.kitchenfair.com.mx
Direct Sales Of Cast Aluminum Cookware And Accessories
N.A.I.C.S.: 722511
Luis Rey (Pres)

TOWNECRAFT, INC.
1 De Boer Dr, Glen Rock, NJ 07452-3301
Tel.: (201) 445-9700   NJ
Web Site: http://www.townecraft.com
Year Founded: 1944
Sales Range: $100-124.9 Million
Emp.: 300
Cookware Distr
N.A.I.C.S.: 423220
Paul J. Ando (VP-Mktg & Adv)
John Dimaria (VP-Sls)
Ralph A. Ramirez (Pres & CEO)

TOWNER COUNTY MEDICAL CENTER
Hwy 281 N, Cando, ND 58324
Tel.: (701) 968-4411   ND
Web Site: http://www.tcmedcenter.org
Year Founded: 1992
Sales Range: $10-24.9 Million
Emp.: 193
Health Care Srvices
N.A.I.C.S.: 622110
Tammy Larson (CFO)

TOWNES TELECOMMUNICATIONS
Jct Hwy 82 and 29, Lewisville, AR 71845
Tel.: (870) 921-4224
Web Site: http://www.townes.net
Sales Range: $10-24.9 Million
Emp.: 20
Local Telephone Communications
N.A.I.C.S.: 517121
Larry Charles Townes (Pres & CEO)
Robert Bridges (Head-Security)

TOWNHOMES MANAGEMENT, INC.
407 E Livingston Ave, Columbus, OH 43215
Tel.: (614) 228-3578   OH
Year Founded: 1962
Sales Range: $1-9.9 Million
Emp.: 3
Land Subdivision Services
N.A.I.C.S.: 237210
Darrell L. Spegal (COO)

TOWNLEY INC.
389 5th Ave Rm 1100, New York, NY 10016-3320
Tel.: (212) 779-0544   NJ
Web Site: http://www.townleygirl.com
Year Founded: 1953
Sales Range: $10-24.9 Million
Emp.: 20
Teen Cosmetics
N.A.I.C.S.: 424210
Abraham Safdieh (CEO)
Seelena Jagarnauth (VP-Fin)

TOWNLEY MANUFACTURING COMPANY
110 SE 110th St Rd, Candler, FL 32111
Tel.: (352) 687-3001
Web Site: http://www.townley.net
Rev.: $22,000,000
Emp.: 165
Mining Machinery
N.A.I.C.S.: 333131
Toro Townley (Pres)

TOWNSEND
4540 Ambassador Caffery Pkwy Ste C-110, Lafayette, LA 70508
Tel.: (337) 216-7502
Web Site: http://www.townsendla.com
Sales Range: $1-9.9 Million
Emp.: 32
Health Care Srvices
N.A.I.C.S.: 621610
Kevin Jordan (COO)
Michael Handley (Founder & CEO)

TOWNSEND CAPITAL, LLC
11311 McCormick Rd Ste 470, Hunt Valley, MD 21031
Tel.: (410) 321-1900
Web Site: http://www.townsendcapital.com
Privater Equity Firm
N.A.I.C.S.: 523999
Josh Ferguson (VP)

TOWNSEND FORD INC.
5801 McFarland Blvd E, Tuscaloosa, AL 35405
Tel.: (866) 399-9140
Web Site: http://www.tuscaloosafordal.com
New & Used Car Dealer
N.A.I.C.S.: 441110
Adam Stetler (Gen Mgr)
Betty Hartley (Controller)

TOWNSEND OIL CO. INC.
3 Oak St, Beverly, MA 01915
Tel.: (978) 283-2000   MA
Web Site: http://townsendoil.com
Year Founded: 1925
Sales Range: $10-24.9 Million
Emp.: 10
Sellers of Fuel Oil
N.A.I.C.S.: 457210
Mark J. Townsend (Pres)
Richard Gouleg (Controller)

TOXCO INC.
Ste A 125 E Commercial St, Anaheim, CA 92801-1214
Tel.: (714) 278-9211
Web Site: http://www.toxco.com
Year Founded: 1984
Sales Range: $100-124.9 Million
Emp.: 90
Hazardous Waste Collection & Disposal
N.A.I.C.S.: 562211
Steve Kinsbursky (CEO)
David Eaker (VP-Metals)
Kathy Bruce (Sr VP-British Columbia Ops)
Ed Green (Sr VP-Ohio Ops)
Natan Gleizer (VP-Europe)
Paul Schneider (Dir-Mktg-Kinsbursky Brother)

TOYOS CLINIC
1720 E Reelsoot, Union City, TN 38261
Tel.: (731) 660-3937
Web Site: http://www.toyosclinic.com
Sales Range: $50-74.9 Million
Emp.: 26
Eye Care
N.A.I.C.S.: 621320
Rolando Toyos (Founder & Dir-Medical)

TOYOTA CENTER
2136 Sunset Blvd, West Columbia, SC 29169
Tel.: (803) 796-6650
Web Site: http://www.toyotacenter.com
Sales Range: $10-24.9 Million
Emp.: 75
Car Whslr
N.A.I.C.S.: 441110
Bob Klose (Gen Mgr)

TOYOTA OF BOWLING GREEN
2398 Scottsville Rd, Bowling Green, KY 42104
Tel.: (270) 843-4321
Web Site: http://www.toyotaofbowlinggreen.com
Year Founded: 1982
Car Dealership
N.A.I.C.S.: 441110
Eric Carr (Gen Sls Mgr)
Dave Stumbo (Owner & Pres)
Matt Stumbo (Mgr-Sls)
Joey Cooke (Bus Mgr)
Shirley Lee (Controller)
Jimmy White (Mgr-Used Car)
Kevin Sanson (Dir-Svc & Parts)
Courtney Miller (Mgr-Internet)
Melissa Guy (Office Mgr)
John Watt (Mgr-Parts)

TOYOTA OF DES MOINES
1650 SE 37th St, Grimes, IA 50111
Tel.: (515) 276-4911
Web Site: http://www.toyotadm.com
Rev.: $26,300,000
Emp.: 160
New Car Dealers
N.A.I.C.S.: 441110
Rob Bierma (Mgr-New Car)
Paul Vannausdle (Mgr-Sls)

TOYOTA OF EASLEY

COMPANIES

5643 Calhoun Memorial Hwy, Easley, SC 29640
Tel.: (864) 855-2233
Web Site:
http://www.toyotaofeasley.com
Year Founded: 1981
Sales Range: $10-24.9 Million
Emp.: 75
New Car Dealers
N.A.I.C.S.: 441110
Tommy Norris *(Principal)*
Ryan Norris *(Principal)*
Larry Shaw *(Comptroller)*
Corey Arnold *(Mgr-Inventory & Trng)*
Janet Bobo *(Mgr-Customer Rels)*
David Garrett *(Mgr-Used Truck Sls)*
Chris Hall *(Mgr-Bus)*
Tim McGaha *(Mgr-Sls-New Car)*
Michael Muldoon *(Mgr-Svc)*
Chad Ratliff *(Mgr-Sls-New Car)*
Don Wolf *(Mgr-Bus)*
Michael Mundy *(Dir-Internet)*
Alex Johnson *(Mgr-Parts-Columbus)*

TOYOTA OF GLENDALE
1260 S Brand Blvd, Glendale, CA 91204
Tel.: (818) 244-4196
Web Site:
http://www.toyotaofglendale.com
Sales Range: $25-49.9 Million
Emp.: 99
New Car Dealers
N.A.I.C.S.: 441110
Anna Nathan *(Mgr-Fleet)*
Jesse Rivas *(Mgr-Sls Desk)*

TOYOTA OF GREENVILLE
2686 Laurens Rd, Greenville, SC 29607
Tel.: (864) 288-3535
Web Site:
http://www.toyotaofgreenville.com
Year Founded: 1995
Sales Range: $125-149.9 Million
Emp.: 140
Used Car Whslr
N.A.I.C.S.: 441120
Mike Oleary *(Gen Mgr)*

TOYOTA OF HATTIESBURG, INC.
1620 W Pine St, Hattiesburg, MS 39401
Tel.: (601) 544-9630
Web Site:
http://www.toyotahattiesburg.com
Year Founded: 1975
Sales Range: $10-24.9 Million
Emp.: 51
Car Whslr
N.A.I.C.S.: 441110
Alton Pierce *(Gen Mgr)*

TOYOTA OF IRVING INC.
1999 W Airport Fwy, Irving, TX 75062
Tel.: (972) 258-1200
Web Site: http://www.toyota-irving.com
Year Founded: 1968
Sales Range: $50-74.9 Million
Emp.: 150
Car Dealership
N.A.I.C.S.: 441110
Vernon Schoemaker *(Pres)*
David Schoemaker *(VP)*
Barbara Schoemaker *(Treas & Sec)*
Randy Helgason *(Controller)*

TOYOTA OF LOUISVILLE, INC.
6514 Dixie Hwy, Louisville, KY 40258
Tel.: (502) 935-1433
Web Site:
http://www.toyotaoflouisville.com
Year Founded: 1956
Sales Range: $10-24.9 Million
Emp.: 97
Car Whslr
N.A.I.C.S.: 441110
Dennis Fante *(Pres)*
Dick Swope *(CEO)*

TOYOTA OF MELBOURNE
24 N Harbor City Blvd, Melbourne, FL 32935
Tel.: (321) 254-8888
Web Site:
http://www.toyotaofmelbourne.com
Year Founded: 2006
Sales Range: $150-199.9 Million
Emp.: 150
New Car Dealers
N.A.I.C.S.: 441110
Christopher Heinze *(Gen Mgr)*
Brenda Novaro *(Controller)*

TOYOTA OF MORRISTOWN
169 Ridgedale Ave, Morristown, NJ 07960
Tel.: (973) 540-1111
Web Site:
http://www.toyotaofmorristown.com
Sales Range: $25-49.9 Million
Emp.: 150
Retailer of New & Used Cars
N.A.I.C.S.: 441110
Anthony Ferrara *(Owner & Gen Mgr)*
Jonathan Brauer *(Owner & Principal)*
Tim Ryan *(Mgr-Sls)*
James Brath *(Mgr-Toyota Parts)*

TOYOTA OF PASADENA
3600 E Foothill Blvd, Pasadena, CA 91107-6001
Tel.: (626) 795-9787
Web Site:
http://www.toyotapasadena.com
Year Founded: 1993
Sales Range: $10-24.9 Million
Emp.: 52
Car Whslr
N.A.I.C.S.: 441110
John Symes *(Pres)*
Win Phelps *(Mgr-Parts)*
Steve Ganz *(Mgr-Svc)*

TOYOTA OF REDLANDS
921 New York St, Redlands, CA 92374-2939
Tel.: (909) 307-1325
Year Founded: 1983
Sales Range: $25-49.9 Million
Emp.: 94
New Car Whslr
N.A.I.C.S.: 441110
Adam Garvey *(Mgr-BDC & Dir-Internet)*

TOYOTA OF RIVERSIDE INC.
7870 Indiana Ave, Riverside, CA 92504
Tel.: (951) 687-1622
Web Site:
http://www.toyotaofriverside.com
Sales Range: $10-24.9 Million
Emp.: 109
Car Whslr
N.A.I.C.S.: 441110
Marshall Gordon *(Gen Mgr)*

TOYOTA OF RUNNEMEDE
99 S Black Horse Pike, Runnemede, NJ 08078
Tel.: (856) 939-3400
Web Site:
http://www.toyotaofrunnemede.com
Year Founded: 1978
Sales Range: $50-74.9 Million
Emp.: 75
Car Whslr
N.A.I.C.S.: 441110
Lou Hernandez *(Gen Mgr)*

TOYOTA OF TRI-CITIES
6321 W Canal Dr, Kennewick, WA 99336
Tel.: (509) 735-0977
Web Site:
http://www.toyotaoftricities.com
Year Founded: 1997
Sales Range: $10-24.9 Million
Emp.: 65
New Car Dealers
N.A.I.C.S.: 441110
John Manterola *(Gen Mgr)*
Mark Troup *(Mgr-Sls)*
Bill Bolton *(Mgr-Bus)*
David Cook *(Mgr-Inventory Control)*
Cindy Flagg *(Mgr-Bus)*
Jim Lehuta *(Mgr-Sls & Leasing)*
Ron Owens *(Gen Mgr-Sls)*

TOYOTA ON NICHOLASVILLE
2100 Lexington Rd, Nicholasville, KY 40356
Tel.: (859) 887-4200
Web Site:
http://www.toyotaonnicholasville.com
Sales Range: $25-49.9 Million
Emp.: 150
Owner & Operator of Car Dealerships
N.A.I.C.S.: 441110
Lance Royalty *(Dir-Internet Sls)*
Suzanne Chapman *(Asst Mgr-Svc)*
Rob Khalas *(Dir-Fin)*

TOYOTA RENT-A-CAR
3124 Bristol Hwy, Johnson City, TN 37601
Tel.: (423) 282-2241
Sales Range: $10-24.9 Million
Emp.: 42
New Car Whslr
N.A.I.C.S.: 441110
Benjamin Royal *(Mgr)*
Daniel Johnson *(Gen Mgr)*

TOYOTA SCION OF GOLDSBORO
301 N Oak Forest Rd, Goldsboro, NC 27534-8349
Tel.: (919) 778-3232
Web Site:
http://www.toyotaofgoldsboro.com
Year Founded: 1997
Sales Range: $10-24.9 Million
Emp.: 610
Car Whslr
N.A.I.C.S.: 441110
Richard Hardin *(Mgr-Sls-New Car)*
Ben Rodriguez *(Pres)*
Julie Pickett *(Office Mgr)*

TOYOTA SCION OF SAN BERNARDINO
765 Showcase Dr N, San Bernardino, CA 92408
Tel.: (909) 571-5082
Web Site: http://www.toyotasb.com
Sales Range: $25-49.9 Million
Automobile Dealership
N.A.I.C.S.: 441110
Eli Rivera *(Gen Sls Mgr)*

TOYOTA SOUTH, INC.
961 4 Mile Rd, Richmond, KY 40475
Tel.: (859) 624-1313
Web Site:
http://www.toyotasouth.com
Sales Range: $10-24.9 Million
Emp.: 60
Car Whslr
N.A.I.C.S.: 441110
Stephen B. Gates *(Pres)*
Charlie Johnson *(Gen Mgr)*
Jennifer Johnson *(Mgr-Customer Rels)*
John Muncie *(Controller)*

TPC HOLDINGS, INC.

TOYOTA TOWN OF STOCKTON
2150 E Hammer Ln, Stockton, CA 95210
Tel.: (209) 473-2513
Web Site:
http://www.toyotaofstockton.com
Sales Range: $10-24.9 Million
New & Used Car Dealer
N.A.I.C.S.: 441110
Jason Kim *(Gen Mgr)*
Nick Aninag *(Dir-Fin)*

TOYOTA WALNUT CREEK, INC.
2100 North Broadway, Walnut Creek, CA 94596-0628
Tel.: (925) 933-7440
Web Site: http://www.toyotawc.com
Year Founded: 1969
Sales Range: $25-49.9 Million
Emp.: 160
Car Whslr
N.A.I.C.S.: 441110
John Schafer *(VP)*
Owen Schafer *(Owner)*

TOZOUR ENERGY SYSTEMS, INC.
3606 Horizon Dr, King of Prussia, PA 19406-1401
Tel.: (610) 962-1600
Web Site:
http://www.tozourtrane.com
Year Founded: 1979
Plumbing, Heating & Air-Conditioning Contractors
N.A.I.C.S.: 238220
Daeen Salam *(Gen Mgr-Tozour Automation)*
Doug Tozour *(Chm & CEO)*
Kevin Duffy *(Pres)*
David Wagner *(CFO)*
Frank Rhea *(Exec VP-Energy & Contracting)*
Bill Artosky *(VP-Sls & Energy)*
Frank Laster *(Dir-HVAC Parts and Supplies)*
Lauren Schmitz *(Mgr-HR)*

TP ORTHODONTICS INC.
100 Ctr Plz, La Porte, IN 46350
Tel.: (219) 785-2591   IN
Web Site: http://www.tportho.com
Year Founded: 1979
Sales Range: $25-49.9 Million
Emp.: 430
Dental Equipment & Supply Services
N.A.I.C.S.: 339114
Randy Hoover *(Supvr-Tool & Die)*

TP RACING L.L.L.P.
1501 W Bell Rd, Phoenix, AZ 85023-3411
Tel.: (602) 942-1101   AZ
Web Site:
http://www.turfparadise.com
Year Founded: 1956
Sales Range: $125-149.9 Million
Emp.: 400
Thoroughbred Horse Racing
N.A.I.C.S.: 711212
Jerry Simms *(Owner)*
Dave Johnson *(VP & Gen Mgr)*
Patty Chakour *(CFO)*
Tony Toporek *(Dir-Television Ops)*
Vince Francia *(Gen Mgr)*
Frank Abbate *(Dir-Mutuels)*
Serena Simms *(Dir-Sls)*

TPC HOLDINGS, INC.
505 Capital St, Lewiston, ID 83501
Tel.: (208) 743-9411   ID
Web Site: https://tpcprinting.com
Year Founded: 1997

TPC HOLDINGS, INC.

TPC Holdings, Inc.—(Continued)
Sales Range: $10-24.9 Million
Emp.: 250
Holding Company; Newspaper Publisher
N.A.I.C.S.: 551112
Justin Ralston (Controller)
Nathan Alford (Gen Mgr)

Subsidiaries:

Moscow Pullman Daily News (1)
409 S Jackson St, Moscow, ID 83843
Tel.: (208) 882-5561
Web Site: http://www.dnews.com
Rev.: $5,916,000
Emp.: 60
Newspaper Publishers
N.A.I.C.S.: 513110
Lee Rozen (Mng Editor)
Nathan Alford (Publr & Editor)
Mark V. Bryan (Dir-Circulation)
Angela Kay (Dir-Adv)
Bill McKee (Editor-Bus)
Justin Ralston (CFO)

Tribune Publishing Company (1)
505 Capital St, Lewiston, ID 83501
Tel.: (208) 743-9411
Web Site: http://www.lmtribune.com
Newspaper Publishers
N.A.I.C.S.: 513110
Nathan Alford (Publr & Editor)
Lori Gaskill (Mgr-HR)
Mark V. Bryan (Dir-Circulation)
Craig Clohessy (Mng Editor)
Doug Bauer (Dir-Mktg)

TPG TELEMANAGEMENT INC.
11161 Mill Vly Rd, Omaha, NE 68154-3933
Tel.: (402) 933-0214
Web Site: http://www.tpginc.com
Sales Range: $10-24.9 Million
Emp.: 202
Custom Computer Programming Services
N.A.I.C.S.: 541511
Lisa Defalco (CEO)
Scott Keller (Pres)

TPH ACQUISITION, LLLP
10321 Fortune Pkwy, Jacksonville, FL 32256-3678
Tel.: (904) 731-3034
Web Site:
    http://www.thepartshouse.com
Year Founded: 1997
Sales Range: $75-99.9 Million
Emp.: 215
Motor Vehicle Supplies & New Parts
N.A.I.C.S.: 423120
David Miller (COO)
Jay Acree (Dir-IT & Mktg)
Richard Kilpatrick (VP-Fleet & Contract Sls)
Chase Baxley (VP-Product & Supply Chain)

Subsidiaries:

Cold Air Distributors Warehouse of
Florida Inc. (1)
3053 Industrial 31st St, Fort Pierce, FL 34946
Tel.: (772) 466-3036
Web Site: http://www.coldairdistributors.com
Rev.: $21,000,000
Emp.: 170
Distr of Automotive Supplies & Parts
N.A.I.C.S.: 423120

The Parts Pros Automotive Warehouse, Inc. (1)
701 Manatee Avenue East, Bradenton, FL 34203
Tel.: (941) 758-8848
Sales Range: $1-9.9 Million
Auto Supply Stores
N.A.I.C.S.: 441230

White Brothers Auto Supply, Inc. (1)
356 Walnut St, Macon, GA 31201
Tel.: (478) 745-1162
Web Site: http://www.whitebros.net
Sales Range: $10-24.9 Million
Emp.: 20
Automotive Supplies & Parts
N.A.I.C.S.: 423120
Russ Wagers (Head-Counter Sls)
Richard W. White Jr. (Pres)

TPI BILLING SOLUTIONS
9525A E 51st St, Tulsa, OK 74145
Tel.: (918) 664-0144
Web Site: http://www.tpisys.com
Year Founded: 1991
Sales Range: $10-24.9 Million
Emp.: 62
Printing, Mailing & Billing Services
N.A.I.C.S.: 561499
Geri Emrick (Mgr-Bus Processes)

TPI CORP.
114 Roscoe Fitz Rd, Gray, TN 37615
Tel.: (423) 477-4131
Web Site: http://www.tpicorp.com
Rev.: $75,500,000
Emp.: 600
Electric Heating Units & Devices, Industrial
N.A.I.C.S.: 333994
Nicole Burke (Exec Dir)
Roger Perkins (Controller)
Terry Tipton (Engr-Indus)

Subsidiaries:

Fostoria Industries, Inc. (1)
114 Roscoe Fitz Rd, Johnson City, TN 37615-3436
Tel.: (419) 435-9201
Web Site: http://www.fostoriaindustries.com
Sales Range: $25-49.9 Million
Emp.: 160
Industrial Lighting; Industrial Ovens; Industrial, Commercial & Residential Heating
N.A.I.C.S.: 333415
J.M. Burkett (HR Dir)

TR CUTLER, INC.
3032 S Oakland Forest Dr Ste 2803, Fort Lauderdale, FL 33309-5684
Tel.: (954) 682-6200
Web Site: http://www.trcutlerinc.com
Year Founded: 1998
Sales Range: $25-49.9 Million
Emp.: 42
Public Relations Agency
N.A.I.C.S.: 541820
Thomas R. Cutler (Founder & CEO)
Rich McGrath (VP-Ops)

Subsidiaries:

Manufacturing Affinity Program (1)
3032 S Oakland Forest Dr Ste 2803, Fort Lauderdale, FL 33309
Tel.: (954) 486-7562
Web Site: http://www.trcutlerinc.com
Rev.: $20,000,000
Public Relations Agency
N.A.I.C.S.: 541820

TRABON PRINTING COMPANY INC.
420 E Bannister Rd, Kansas City, MO 64131
Tel.: (816) 361-6279
Web Site:
    http://www.trabongroup.com
Sales Range: $10-24.9 Million
Emp.: 150
Provider of Lithographic Printing Services
N.A.I.C.S.: 323111
George Gillam (Plant Mgr)
Charlie Willis (Supvr-Maintenance-Mktg Svcs Grp)

TRAC-WORK INC.
3801 N I-45, Ennis, TX 75119
Tel.: (972) 875-6565
Web Site: http://www.trac-work.com
Sales Range: $25-49.9 Million
Emp.: 150
Provider of Railroad & Railway Roadbed Construction Services
N.A.I.C.S.: 236210
Daniel G. Wallen (Pres & CEO)
Ericka Allen (Mgr-HR)
Doug Rhea (Area Mgr)

TRACE SERVICES INC.
230 Stanton Ave, Pittsburgh, PA 15209-2732
Tel.: (412) 821-8310
Web Site:
    http://www.traceservices.com
Rev.: $11,000,000
Emp.: 15
Provider of Remote Meter Reading Services
N.A.I.C.S.: 561990
Daniel Desta (Gen Mgr)

TRACE WORLDWIDE CORP.
421 Via Chico, Palos Verdes Estates, CA 90274-1309
Tel.: (310) 791-5500
Web Site: http://www.traceww.com
Year Founded: 1987
Sales Range: $10-24.9 Million
Emp.: 100
Mfr of Aircraft & Space Vehicle Supplies & Parts
N.A.I.C.S.: 423860
John Douglass (Pres & CEO)
Luc Neyrinck (Mng Dir)
Robert Mabli (Exec VP)
Emiko Kadowaki (Gen Mgr)
Vladimir Tsiplakov (Dir-Tech)
Martin Hacker (Mng Dir-Europe)
Irina Rabinovich (Dir-Bus Dev)
John P. Pavlanto (Mng Dir)
Nigel Hands (Mgr-Sls)

TRACE-A-MATIC CORPORATION
21125 Enterprise Ave, Brookfield, WI 53045
Tel.: (262) 797-7300
Web Site:
    http://www.traceamatic.com
Sales Range: $25-49.9 Million
Emp.: 130
Mfr of Industrial Machinery
N.A.I.C.S.: 332710
Thorsten Wienss (Pres)
Allen Larsen (Controller)

TRACEGUARD TECHNOLOGIES, INC.
330 Madison Ave, New York, NY 10017
Year Founded: 2002
Software Development Services
N.A.I.C.S.: 541511
Udi Ganani (CEO)

TRACEN TECHNOLOGIES, INC.
9720 Capital Ct Ste 401, Manassas, VA 20110
Tel.: (703) 368-3499
Web Site: http://www.tracen.com
Sales Range: $10-24.9 Million
Emp.: 14
Custom Computer Programming Services
N.A.I.C.S.: 541511
Deanna Davidson (Pres)
Jason Davidson (Founder)
Marlene Johnson (Dir-Ops)

TRACESECURITY INC.
6300 Corporate Blvd Ste 200, Baton Rouge, LA 70808
Tel.: (225) 612-2121
Web Site:
    http://www.tracesecurity.com

U.S. PRIVATE

Year Founded: 2003
Sales Range: $10-24.9 Million
Emp.: 50
Security Compliance & Risk Management Services
N.A.I.C.S.: 541611
Peter Stewart (Pres & CEO)
Jim Stickley (Founder)
Paul McCown (CFO & COO)
Dariel LeBoeuf (Exec VP-Sls & Mktg)
Jason Wells (VP-Products & Customer Success)
Ryan Castle (VP-Tech)

TRACEY ROAD EQUIPMENT INC.
6803 Manlius Center Rd, East Syracuse, NY 13057-3912
Tel.: (315) 437-1471 NY
Web Site: http://www.traceyroad.com
Year Founded: 1978
Sales Range: $50-74.9 Million
Emp.: 225
Construction Services & Mining Machinery
N.A.I.C.S.: 423810
Gerald W. Tracey (Pres & Treas)
Debbie Tracey (VP)
Bill Allman (Gen Mgr)
Bob Coon (Mgr-Truck Svc)
Dick Ridings (Dir-Equipment Sls & Fin-Syracuse)
Kevin Williamson (Gen Mgr-Parts)
Art Ospelt (Mgr-Ops-Binghamton)
Bryan Winters (Mgr-Svc-Albany)
Dave Holzwarth (Mgr-Truck Sls-Syracuse)
Dave Renzi (Mgr-Parts-Albany)
Jeff Guyer (Mgr-Equipment Svc-Syracuse)
Jerry Tracey (Pres)
Neil Kessler (Mgr-Parts-Syracuse)
Nick Skiba (Mgr-Truck Svc-Binghamton)
Scott Thayer (Dir-Compact Sls-Syracuse)
Terry Bush (Mgr-Equipment Svc-Binghamton)

TRACHTE BUILDING SYSTEMS INC.
314 Wilburn Rd, Sun Prairie, WI 53590
Tel.: (608) 837-7899 WI
Web Site: http://www.trachte.com
Year Founded: 1901
Sales Range: $10-24.9 Million
Emp.: 100
Prefabricated Metal Buildings & Components Mfr
N.A.I.C.S.: 332311
Jeff Seefeldt (Pres & CEO)
Pamela Klute (VP-HR)
John Whalen (VP-Engrg)

Subsidiaries:

Roof Mart, LLC (1)
7380 Highway 18, Vernon, AL 35592-4844
Tel.: (205) 695-0141
Web Site: http://www.roofmartllc.com
Rev.: $1,100,000
Emp.: 5
Mfg Prefabricated Metal Buildings
N.A.I.C.S.: 332311
Robert McNees (CEO)

Trac-Rite Door Inc. (1)
314 Wilburn Rd, Sun Prairie, WI 53590
Tel.: (608) 837-7899
Web Site: http://www.tracrite.com
Sales Range: $10-24.9 Million
Emp.: 15
Metal Doors, Sash & Trim Mfr
N.A.I.C.S.: 332321
Chris O'Hearn (Mgr-Natl Sls)

TRACINDA CORPORATION

COMPANIES

150 S Rodeo Dr Ste 250, Beverly Hills, CA 90212
Tel.: (310) 271-0638 NV
Year Founded: 1969
Sales Range: $1-4.9 Billion
Emp.: 10
Holding Company
N.A.I.C.S.: 551112
Anthony L. Mandekic *(Treas & Sec)*

TRACK DATA CORPORATION
1122 Coney Island Ave, Brooklyn, NY 11230
Tel.: (718) 522-7373
Web Site: http://www.trackdata.com
Year Founded: 1981
Sales Range: $1-9.9 Million
Emp.: 4
Web-Based Software Development Platforms
N.A.I.C.S.: 513210
Marty Kaye *(CEO & CFO)*
Barry Hertz *(CTO)*

TRACK ENTERTAINMENT
32 Union Sq E Ste 4c, New York, NY 10003-3223
Tel.: (212) 921-2100
Web Site:
   http://www.trackentertainment.com
Year Founded: 2004
Rev.: $29,100,000
Emp.: 109
Independent Artists, Writers & Performers
N.A.I.C.S.: 711510
Andrew Fox *(Principal)*
Lee Heiman *(Principal)*

TRACO ADVERTISING, INC.
PO Box 2187, Tulsa, OK 74102-2187
Tel.: (918) 591-2180 OK
Web Site: http://www.oralroberts.com
Year Founded: 1969
Sales Range: $1-9.9 Million
Emp.: 160
Religious Promotions & Publicity Events
N.A.I.C.S.: 541810
Michael Bernard *(Pres)*
Helen Montgomery *(Office Mgr)*

TRACTION CORPORATION
1349 Larkin St, San Francisco, CA 94109
Tel.: (415) 962-5823
Web Site: http://www.tractionco.com
Year Founded: 2001
Sales Range: $1-9.9 Million
Emp.: 40
Advetising Agency
N.A.I.C.S.: 541810
Adam Kleinberg *(CEO)*
Theo Fanning *(Dir-Creative)*
Paul Giese *(Dir-Tech)*
Jabeen Yusuf *(Dir-Strategy)*
Luigi Imperatore *(CFO)*
Sidney Burrows *(Dir-Client Svcs)*
Jessica Baum *(Dir-Media)*
Brian Hovis *(Sr Partner & Head-Performance Mktg)*

TRACTION WHOLESALE CENTER
1515 Pkwy Ave, Trenton, NJ 08628
Tel.: (609) 771-9383
Web Site: http://www.tractiontire.com
Rev.: $16,718,255
Emp.: 12
Sales of Tires & Tubes
N.A.I.C.S.: 423130
Joseph E. O'Donnell Jr. *(Pres)*

TRACTOR & EQUIPMENT COMPANY
5336 Airport Hwy, Birmingham, AL 35212
Tel.: (205) 591-2131 AL
Web Site: http://www.tractor-equipment.com
Year Founded: 1943
Sales Range: $350-399.9 Million
Emp.: 550
Sales of Tractors & Equipment
N.A.I.C.S.: 423810
Chris Lucas *(VP-Info Sys)*
Tim Tipton *(VP-Product Support Mktg)*
Jeff Roberts *(Mgr-Adv)*
Hugh Stith *(VP & Reg Mgr-Sls-Georgia)*
DeVaughn Pettit *(Reg Mgr-Sls-Georgia)*
James W. Steele Jr. *(CFO & VP)*

Subsidiaries:

Tractor & Equipment Company (1)
5732 Frontage Rd, Forest Park, GA 30297 **(100%)**
Tel.: (404) 366-0693
Web Site: http://www.tractorequipment.com
Sales Range: $25-49.9 Million
Emp.: 34
General Construction Machinery & Equipment
N.A.I.C.S.: 423810
James Stracener *(Pres)*

TRACTOR CENTRAL LLC
5704 State Rd 93, Eau Claire, WI 54701
Tel.: (715) 833-9690 WI
Web Site:
   http://www.tractorcentral.com
Year Founded: 1986
Sales Range: $10-24.9 Million
Emp.: 115
Farm & Garden Machinery Mfr
N.A.I.C.S.: 423820
Sigfried Weiss *(Gen Mgr)*
Jennifer Schneider *(Coord-Whole Goods)*
Jason Wirth *(Mgr-Parts)*
Joe Weber *(Mgr-Sls-AG)*

Subsidiaries:

Tractor Central (1)
N6387 State Hwy 25, Durand, WI 54736 **(100%)**
Tel.: (715) 672-8915
Web Site: http://www.tractorcentral.com
Sales Range: $10-24.9 Million
Emp.: 30
John Deere Agricultural Products, Equipment & Services Distr
N.A.I.C.S.: 333111

Tractor Central - Mondovi (1)
994 E Main St, Mondovi, WI 54755
Tel.: (715) 926-3891
Web Site: http://tractorcentral.com
Farm & Garden Machinery Distr
N.A.I.C.S.: 423820

TRACTOR TRAILER SUPPLY CO.
2525 Natural Bridge Ave, Saint Louis, MO 63107
Tel.: (314) 241-3072
Web Site: http://www.tts.com
Sales Range: $10-24.9 Million
Emp.: 50
Truck Equipment & Parts
N.A.I.C.S.: 441330
Tom Bley *(Pres & Dir-Mktg)*

TRACTORBEAM
325 S Central Expy, Dallas, TX 75201
Tel.: (214) 747-5400
Web Site:
   http://www.tractorbeam.com
Year Founded: 1997
Sales Range: $10-24.9 Million

Emp.: 10
Brand Development, Fashion/Apparel
N.A.I.C.S.: 541810
Peter Benanti *(Principal)*
Kelly Smith *(CFO)*

TRACY EVANS LTD. INC.
151 W Rosecrans Ave, Gardena, CA 90248
Tel.: (310) 851-4772
Web Site: http://www.tracyevans.com
Year Founded: 1986
Sales Range: $50-74.9 Million
Emp.: 185
Provider of Women's & Misses' Outerwear
N.A.I.C.S.: 315210

TRACY INDUSTRIES INC.
22421 Gilberto Ste A, Rancho Santa Margarita, CA 92688-2104
Tel.: (949) 858-7002 CA
Year Founded: 1997
Sales Range: $25-49.9 Million
Emp.: 800
Lawn & Garden Services
N.A.I.C.S.: 561730
Michael Tracy *(Pres)*
Susan Telfair *(Mgr-Customer Svc)*
William J. Grunwald *(Gen Counsel)*

Subsidiaries:

Park West Landscape (1)
22421 Gilberto Ste A, Rancho Santa Margarita, CA 92688 **(100%)**
Tel.: (949) 858-7002
Web Site:
   http://www.parkwestlandscape.com
Sales Range: $10-24.9 Million
Emp.: 40
Commercial Landscaping Services
N.A.I.C.S.: 236210
Robert Allgaier *(Acct Mgr)*
Scott Schmidt *(Dir-Pur)*
Alan Gross *(Mgr-Fleet Fuel)*
Lisa Polizzi *(Office Mgr)*
Cynthia Olea *(Office Mgr-Pur)*
Dave Kratt *(Project Mgr)*

Park West Landscape Inc. (1)
11415 Hwy 2, Brighton, CO 80603-7100
Tel.: (303) 289-1988
Sales Range: $10-24.9 Million
Emp.: 100
Commercial Landscaping
N.A.I.C.S.: 561730

Park West Landscape Inc. (1)
5375 Cameron St Ste G, Las Vegas, NV 89118-2221
Tel.: (702) 248-8999
Web Site:
   http://www.parkwestlandscape.com
Sales Range: $10-24.9 Million
Emp.: 50
Provider of Lawn & Garden Services
N.A.I.C.S.: 561730

Tracy & Ryder Landscape Inc. (1)
5375 Cameron St Ste G, Las Vegas, NV 89118-2221 **(100%)**
Tel.: (702) 248-6336
Web Site:
   http://www.parkwestlandscape.com
Sales Range: $75-99.9 Million
Provider of Lawn & Garden Services
N.A.I.C.S.: 561730
Mike Anibal *(Branch Mgr)*

TRACY TOYOTA SCION
2895 Naglee Rd, Tracy, CA 95304-7307
Tel.: (209) 834-1111
Web Site: http://www.tracytoyota.com
Year Founded: 2000
Sales Range: $75-99.9 Million
Emp.: 103
Car Whslr
N.A.I.C.S.: 441110
Cynthia Taylor *(Mgr-Customer Rels)*
Steve Haworth *(Gen Mgr)*

TRACY VOLKSWAGEN
686 Iyannough Rd Route 132, Hyannis, MA 02601
Tel.: (508) 775-3049
Web Site: http://www.tracyvw.com
Year Founded: 1968
Sales Range: $10-24.9 Million
Emp.: 50
New Car Dealers
N.A.I.C.S.: 441110
James Helgerson *(Gen Mgr-Sls)*
John Backman *(Mgr-Sls)*
Kayla Wilcox *(Mgr-Fin)*

TRACY VOLKSWAGEN, INC.
686 Iyannough Rd, Hyannis, MA 02601
Tel.: (508) 775-3049
Web Site: http://www.tracyvw.com
Sales Range: $25-49.9 Million
Emp.: 50
Owner & Operator of Car Dealerships
N.A.I.C.S.: 441120
Jay H. Tracy *(Co-Owner & Co-Pres)*
Brad Tracy *(Co-Owner & Co-Pres)*
Darlene Webb *(Controller & Mgr-HR)*

TRADA
1023 walnut St, Boulder, CO 80302
Tel.: (877) 871-1835
Web Site: http://www.trada.com
Year Founded: 2008
Sales Range: $10-24.9 Million
Emp.: 75
Online Advertising & Marketing
N.A.I.C.S.: 541890
Matt Harada *(CEO)*
Emily Pieper *(Controller)*

TRADAVO INC
AFC Bldg 900 S Kipling Pkwy, Lakewood, CO 80226
Web Site: http://www.tradavo.com
Year Founded: 2006
Sales Range: $1-9.9 Million
Emp.: 12
Organic Food Products & Beverages Mfr & Whslr
N.A.I.C.S.: 424420
Bobby Martyna *(Pres & CEO)*
Tom Furphy *(Founder & Chm)*

TRADE AM INTERNATIONAL INC.
6045 Atlantic Blvd, Norcross, GA 30071-1304
Tel.: (770) 263-6144 TX
Web Site: http://www.tradeam.com
Year Founded: 1986
Sales Range: $10-24.9 Million
Emp.: 100
Provider of Home Furnishings
N.A.I.C.S.: 423220
Ashutosh Ladha *(Pres)*

TRADE FAIR CORP.
30-08 30th Ave, Astoria, NY 11102
Tel.: (718) 728-9484
Web Site: http://www.tradefairny.com
Sales Range: $10-24.9 Million
Emp.: 54
Independent Supermarket
N.A.I.C.S.: 445110
Frank Jaber *(Pres)*

Subsidiaries:

Kamal Corp. (1)
3012 30th Ave Ste 210, Astoria, NY 11102
Tel.: (718) 721-2437
Web Site: http://www.tradefairny.com
Independent Supermarket
N.A.I.C.S.: 445110

TRADE ONLY DESIGN LIBRARY
1150 Kapp Dr, Clearwater, FL 33765

Trade Only Design Library—(Continued)

Tel.: (727) 441-2060 FL
Web Site: http://www.todl.com
Year Founded: 1997
Sales Range: $1-9.9 Million
Emp.: 32
Trade Buyer's Online Product Library
N.A.I.C.S.: 517810
Lynn Molter (Acct Mgr)
Kathleen Rocchio (Acct Mgr)

TRADE PRESS PUBLISHING CORP.

2100 W Florist Ave, Milwaukee, WI 53209
Tel.: (414) 228-7701
Web Site: http://www.tradepress.com
Rev.: $16,000,000
Emp.: 58
Trade Journal Publisher
N.A.I.C.S.: 513120
Robert Wisniewski (Pres & CEO)
Tim Rowe (VP-Mktg)
Wendy Melnick (Mgr-Production)

TRADE PRODUCTS CORP

12124 Popes Head Rd, Fairfax, VA 22030
Tel.: (703) 502-9000
Web Site: http://www.tradeproductscorp.com
Sales Range: $50-74.9 Million
Emp.: 10
Provider of Furniture
N.A.I.C.S.: 423210
Allyn I. Richert (Pres)
Brent Neilson (Gen Mgr)

TRADE THE MARKETS

401 Congress Ave Ste 1540, Austin, TX 78701
Tel.: (512) 266-8659
Web Site: http://www.tradethemarkets.com
Year Founded: 2003
Sales Range: $1-9.9 Million
Emp.: 14
Online Trading, Video Training & Mentorship Applications
N.A.I.C.S.: 523150
Hubert Senters (VP)

TRADE WINGS, INC.

Pease International Tradeport 130 International Dr, Portsmouth, NH 03801
Tel.: (603) 766-7000 NH
Web Site: http://www.tradewings.com
Year Founded: 1996
Sales Range: $10-24.9 Million
Emp.: 39
Telecommunications Consulting Services
N.A.I.C.S.: 541690
Todd Adelman (Founder & CEO)
Michael Johnson (COO)
Lisa Clark (CMO)
Jim Merecki (VP-Fin)
Dan McCarthy (Dir-Global Svc Ops)
Ian Saalfield (Dir-Software Engrg)
Billy Balfour (Dir-Bus Dev)
Ulla Neunzert (Mng Dir)

TRADEHOME SHOE STORES, INC.

8300 97th St S, Cottage Grove, MN 55016-4341
Tel.: (651) 459-8600 MN
Web Site: http://www.tradehome.com
Year Founded: 1991
Sales Range: $200-249.9 Million
Emp.: 350
Sales of Shoes
N.A.I.C.S.: 458210

Patrick Teal (Pres)
Brian Wilkinson (VP-Mdsg)
Stacy Robjent (Treas & Controller)

TRADEMARK HARDWARE INC.

100 Rt 59 Unit 120, Suffern, NY 10901
Tel.: (845) 388-1300
Web Site: http://www.tmhardware.com
Year Founded: 2012
Sales Range: $1-9.9 Million
Emp.: 13
Door Hardware Mfr & Distr
N.A.I.C.S.: 332510
Yanky Drew (Owner)

TRADEMARK RECRUITING INC.

100 S Ashley Dr Ste 1470, Tampa, FL 33602
Tel.: (813) 472-7200
Web Site: http://www.trademark1.net
Year Founded: 2000
Sales Range: $1-9.9 Million
Emp.: 26
Human Resources & Executive Search Consulting Services
N.A.I.C.S.: 541612
Michael Carideo (Partner-IT)
A. James Tagg (Partner-Fin & Acctg)
Randy Williams (Mng Dir-Pro Svcs)

TRADEONE

11149 Research Blvd Ste 400, Austin, TX 78759
Tel.: (512) 343-2002 TX
Web Site: http://www.tradeone.com
Year Founded: 1997
Marketing & Promotional Services
N.A.I.C.S.: 541611
Evelyn Nugent (Exec VP)
Brent David (Acct Mgr)

TRADERPLANET.COM, LLC

5807 Old Pasco Rd Ste 100, Wesley Chapel, FL 33544
Tel.: (813) 973-3456
Web Site: http://www.traderplanet.com
Sales Range: $1-9.9 Million
Financial Education Website
N.A.I.C.S.: 519290
Lane Mendelsohn (Pres)

TRADERS & FARMERS BANK

819 20th St, Haleyville, AL 35565
Tel.: (205) 486-5263
Web Site: http://www.tradersandfarmersbank.com
Year Founded: 1906
Rev.: $22,655,000
Emp.: 85
Provider of Banking Services
N.A.I.C.S.: 522110
Rickey McCreless (CEO)
Donny Hood (Exec VP)
Will Walker (Chm & Pres)
Bret Whiteside (Sr VP)
Billy McNutt (Exec VP)
Rita Pearson (Exec VP)
Albert Partridge (Pres-Addison)
E. F. Walker Jr. (Vice Chm)

TRADES UNLIMITED

322 Hermitage Ave, Nashville, TN 37210
Tel.: (615) 360-0099
Web Site: http://www.tradesunlimitedusa.com
Year Founded: 2002
Sales Range: $10-24.9 Million
Emp.: 200

Staffing Services for the Construction Industry
N.A.I.C.S.: 561311
John Stallworth (Founder, Pres & CEO)

TRADESHIFT INC.

612 Howard St Ste 100, San Francisco, CA 94105
Tel.: (800) 381-3585 DE
Web Site: http://www.tradeshift.com
Year Founded: 2009
Emp.: 800
Business Software Developer
N.A.I.C.S.: 513210
Christian Lanng (Co-Founder & CEO)
Mikkel Hippe Brun (Co-Founder & Sr VP-APAC)
Gert Sylvest (Co-Founder & Gen Mgr-Frontiers)
Thijs Stalenhoef (Sr VP-Global Product)
Carrie Dolan (CFO)
James Stirk (Head-Enterprise Sls-Europe, Middle East & Africa & Asia Pacific)
Christophe Bodin (Chief Revenue Officer)
Harry Ronaldson (Dir-Corp Comm)

Subsidiaries:

Merchantry, Inc. (1)
355 Lexington Ave 4th Fl, New York, NY 10017
Tel.: (646) 588-4910
Web Site: http://www.merchantry.com
Software Publisher
N.A.I.C.S.: 513210
Jean Barmash (VP-Engrg)
Rick Watson (CEO)
John Carles (COO)

TRADESOURCE INC.

205 Hellene Rd Ste 211, Warwick, RI 02886
Tel.: (401) 384-6148
Web Site: http://www.tradesource.com
Rev.: $55,000,000
Emp.: 40
Employment Agencies
N.A.I.C.S.: 561311
James Ferry (Pres & CEO)
Gordon Sigman (CFO)
David Dedman (Mgr-Metro Hartford Area)

TRADETEC SKYLINE

1136 N Garfield St, Lombard, IL 60148
Tel.: (630) 629-9317
Web Site: http://www.ttskyline.com
Year Founded: 1999
Sales Range: $10-24.9 Million
Emp.: 47
Amusement & Recreation Industries
N.A.I.C.S.: 713990
Ken Buckman (CEO)
Troy Trice (Owner & Co-Pres)
Cory Preis (Dir-Ops)
Abby Georgacopoulos (Dir-Mktg)
Jeff Meyer (CFO)
Bill Dierberger (Co-Pres)
Tim Brengman (VP-Ops)
Dave Bouquet (VP-Sls & Bus Dev)

TRADETHEMARKETS.COM

401 Congress Ave Ste 1540, Austin, TX 78701
Tel.: (512) 266-8659
Web Site: http://www.TradeTheMarkets.com
Year Founded: 1999
Rev.: $4,300,000
Emp.: 14
Computer & Electronic Devices Mfr
N.A.I.C.S.: 334112

John Carter (Pres)

TRADEWINDS MECHANICAL SERVICES, LLC.

3511 NE 22nd Ave Ste 100, Fort Lauderdale, FL 33308-6261
Tel.: (603) 778-4807
Year Founded: 1995
Rev.: $17,200,000
Emp.: 104
Plumbing, Heating & Air-Conditioning Contractors
N.A.I.C.S.: 238220
Judi Sewall (Gen Mgr)
Steve Sewall (Pres & Gen Mgr)

TRADEX INTERNATIONAL, INC.

5300 Tradex Pkwy, Cleveland, OH 44102
Tel.: (216) 651-4788 OH
Web Site: http://www.tradexgloves.com
Year Founded: 1988
Sales Range: $50-74.9 Million
Emp.: 50
Disposable Glove Mfr
N.A.I.C.S.: 423990
Saji Daniel (Founder)

TRADING POST MANAGEMENT COMPANY, LLC

490 Sparrow Dr, Shepherdsville, KY 40165-5472
Tel.: (502) 955-5622 KY
Web Site: http://www.tphomes.com
Year Founded: 1946
Mobile Home Dealers
N.A.I.C.S.: 459930
Christopher L. Richter (Co-Owner & Pres)
Steve M. Richter (Co-Owner)
Tracy Stearman (Mgr-HR)
Criss Pruitt (Mgr-Sls)

TRADING TECHNOLOGIES INTERNATIONAL, INC.

222 S Riverside Plz Ste 1100, Chicago, IL 60606
Tel.: (312) 476-1000 IL
Web Site: http://www.tradingtechnologies.com
Sales Range: $10-24.9 Million
Emp.: 250
Investment Trading Software Developer & Publisher
N.A.I.C.S.: 513210
Robbie McDonnell (Exec VP-Global Sls)
Brian Mehta (CMO)
Mike Mayhew (CIO)
Michael Kraines (CFO)
Russ Cotton (COO)
Craig Mohan (Chief Growth Officer)
Tim Geannopulos (Chm & CEO)

TRADITIONAL BAKERY INC.

2040 W Vista, Springfield, MO 65807
Tel.: (417) 889-8282
Web Site: http://www.panerabread.com
Rev.: $15,027,209
Emp.: 1,500
Retail Bakeries
N.A.I.C.S.: 311811
Brian Carney (Pres)
David Tuthill (Asst Gen Mgr)

Subsidiaries:

Traditional Bakery Inc. (1)
3638 N Frnt St, Fayetteville, AR 72703
Tel.: (479) 587-1188
Web Site: http://www.traditionalbakery.com
Rev.: $1,200,000
Emp.: 25
Retail Bakeries
N.A.I.C.S.: 311811

COMPANIES

TRADITIONAL BANCORPORATION
49 W Main St, Mount Sterling, KY 40353
Tel.: (859) 498-0414
Web Site: http://www.traditionalbank.com
Sales Range: $25-49.9 Million
Emp.: 198
Bank Holding Company
N.A.I.C.S.: 522110
Bill Bramblett *(Pres)*

Subsidiaries:

Traditional Bank, Inc. (1)
49 W Main St, Mount Sterling, KY 40353
Tel.: (859) 498-0414
Web Site: http://www.traditionalbank.com
Sales Range: $50-74.9 Million
Emp.: 70
Provider of Banking Services
N.A.I.C.S.: 522110
William M. Alverson *(CEO)*
Dan Mason *(Chief Lending Officer)*
Shawn Woolum *(Officer-Loan)*
William B. Bramblett *(Chm)*
Anthony C. Baker *(Pres)*
Grover A. Carrington *(Vice Chm)*
E. Daniel Duzyk *(Sec)*
Dana Adamson *(Dir-Sls & Mktg)*
Mike Hendrix *(CFO)*
Elaine Highley *(Dir-HR)*
Bill Potter *(Sr VP-Retail Banking)*

TRADITIONAL JEWELERS INC.
817 Newport Center Dr, Newport Beach, CA 92660
Tel.: (949) 721-9010
Web Site: http://www.traditionaljewelers.com
Sales Range: $10-24.9 Million
Emp.: 40
Jewelry Stores
N.A.I.C.S.: 458310
Nick Vega *(Mgr)*

TRADITIONAL SERVICE CORPORATION
1415 N Rock Rd, Derby, KS 67037-3740
Tel.: (316) 788-2828 KS
Web Site: http://www.smithfamilymortuaries.com
Holding Company; Funeral Homes & Cemeteries Owner & Operator
N.A.I.C.S.: 551112
Reba J. Smith *(Founder)*
Justin C. Smith *(Pres)*
Kim Foster *(Controller-Fin)*
Carol Mobley *(Office Mgr)*

Subsidiaries:

Traditional Service Company, LLC (1)
1415 N Rock Rd, Derby, KS 67037
Tel.: (316) 788-2828
Web Site: http://www.smithfamilymortuaries.com
Emp.: 12
Funeral Homes & Cemeteries Operator
N.A.I.C.S.: 812210
Justin C. Smith *(Pres)*
Kim Foster *(Controller-Fin)*
Jackie Hartman *(Dir-Advance Plng & After Care)*
Carol Mobley *(Office Mgr)*

Subsidiary (Domestic):

Reflection Pointe Cemetery, Inc. (2)
3201 S Webb Rd, Wichita, KS 67210-1886
Tel.: (316) 618-9898
Web Site: http://www.reflectionpointeks.com
Funeral Home, Cemetery & Crematory Operator
N.A.I.C.S.: 812220

TRAEGER PELLET GRILLS LLC
445 SW Ridder Rd, Wilsonville, OR 97070
Tel.: (800) 872-3437
Web Site: http://www.traegergrills.com
Year Founded: 1985
Sales Range: $10-24.9 Million
Emp.: 100
Pellet Grill Mfr
N.A.I.C.S.: 335220
Jeremy Andrus *(CEO)*

TRAFFIC & PARKING CONTROL CO., INC.
5100 W Brown Deer Rd, Brown Deer, WI 53223
Tel.: (262) 814-7000
Web Site: http://www.tapconet.com
Year Founded: 1956
Sales Range: $25-49.9 Million
Emp.: 150
Traffic & Parking Control Products Mfr
N.A.I.C.S.: 334513
John Kugel *(Co-Owner & Pres)*
Rick Bergholz *(Co-Owner & Mgr-Sls)*
Justin Jablonski *(Mgr-Production)*
Jason Kugel *(Div Mgr)*
Joanne Conrad *(Mgr-Sls-Digital)*
Andrew Bergholz *(VP-Sls)*
Dave Meyer *(Mgr-Key Accts)*
Scott Plouff *(Mgr-Sls-Michigan, Minnesota & Wisconsin)*

Subsidiaries:

Adaptive Micro Systems LLC (1)
7840 N 86th St, Milwaukee, WI 53224
Tel.: (414) 357-2020
Web Site: http://www.adaptivedisplays.com
Intercommunication Systems, Electric
N.A.I.C.S.: 531190
Dennis Thums *(Pres)*
Mike Heltemes *(Engr-Sls-OEM)*
Russell Groth *(Mgr-Info Sys)*
Dake Wang *(Engr-Mechanical Design)*
Jialock Wong *(Mgr-Engrg-Asia Div)*

TRAFFIC CONTROL DEVICES INC.
242 N Westmonte Dr, Altamonte Springs, FL 32714-3344
Tel.: (407) 869-5300 FL
Web Site: http://www.trafficcontroldevices.com
Year Founded: 1978
Sales Range: $50-74.9 Million
Emp.: 200
Electrical Work
N.A.I.C.S.: 238210
Steve Cockman *(Pres)*
Bill Good *(Office Mgr)*
Fred Horn *(Project Mgr)*

TRAFFIC PLANNING & DESIGN, INC.
2500 E High St Ste 650, Pottstown, PA 19464
Tel.: (610) 326-3100
Web Site: http://www.trafficpd.com
Year Founded: 1989
Sales Range: $1-9.9 Million
Emp.: 120
Engineeering Services
N.A.I.C.S.: 541330
Don Jacobs *(Exec VP)*
Shawn Glick *(CFO, Principal & Sec)*
Matthew Hammond *(Exec VP)*
Kevin L. Johnson *(Pres)*
Tony Dougherty *(Principal)*
Craig Mellott *(Principal)*
Eric Ostimchuk *(Principal)*
Rob Prophet *(Principal)*
Matt Hickson *(Principal)*

Subsidiaries:

Traffic Planning & Design Inc. (1)
812 W Hamilton St Ste 402, Allentown, PA 18101
Tel.: (610) 625-4242
Web Site: http://www.trafficpd.com
Sales Range: $1-9.9 Million
Emp.: 35
Engineeering Services
N.A.I.C.S.: 541330

TRAFON GROUP
Mercado Central Edificio C 1229, Puerto Nuevo, PR 00920
Tel.: (787) 783-0011
Web Site: http://www.trafongroup.com
Year Founded: 2009
Sales Range: $10-24.9 Million
Emp.: 187
Real Estate & Shopping Centers; Food & Beverage, Mfr, Processing & Distr; Commercial & Residential Development; Landscaping & Sod Services
N.A.I.C.S.: 531390
Carlos Trapaga Fonalledas *(Pres & CEO)*
Leyda E. Fresse Gonzalez *(VP-Admin)*
David Valle *(Sr VP)*
Federico Trapaga Fonalledas *(VP-Ops)*

Subsidiaries:

Packers Provision Co. of Puerto Rico Inc. (1)
Bldg 1229 Mercado Central, Puerto Nuevo, PR 00920
Tel.: (787) 783-0011
Web Site: http://www.trafongroup.com
Meats & Meat Products
N.A.I.C.S.: 424470
Carlos Trabaga *(CEO)*

Subsidiary (Domestic):

Caribbean International Foods Corporation (2)
9 Bldg C Mercado Central, San Juan, PR 00936
Tel.: (787) 783-6011
Frozen Food Distr & Logistics
N.A.I.C.S.: 424420

Provisiones Legrand Inc. (2)
1229 Bldg C Mercado Central, Puerto Nuevo, PR 00920
Tel.: (787) 783-0011
Web Site: http://www.trafongroup.com
Grocery 7 Food Services
N.A.I.C.S.: 424410

TRAILER BOSS
7821 Martin Way E, Olympia, WA 98516-5708
Tel.: (360) 923-2135
Web Site: http://www.trailerbossonline.com
Truck, Utility Trailer & RV Rental & Leasing
N.A.I.C.S.: 532120
Arv Corliss *(Mgr-Sls)*

TRAILER BRIDGE, INC.
10405 New Berlin Rd E, Jacksonville, FL 32226-2291
Tel.: (904) 751-7100 DE
Web Site: http://www.trailerbridge.com
Year Founded: 1991
Sales Range: $100-124.9 Million
Emp.: 133
Integrated Trucking & Marine Freight Services Encompassing Lower 48 States & Puerto Rico & Dominican Republic
N.A.I.C.S.: 488510
Chad Switzer *(Dir-Fin Plng & Analysis)*
Jacob Wegrzyn *(VP & Gen Mgr-Caribbean)*
John Wroby *(COO)*
Mitch Luciano *(CEO)*
Indie B. Bollman *(VP-Corp Dev)*
Steven Grguric *(Mgr-Brokerage-Cincinnati)*
Scott Russell *(Dir-IT)*
Jose Javier Mendez *(Dir-Maintenance & Security)*
James Raulerson *(Dir-Safety & Risk Mgmt)*
Satoshi Griffin *(Dir-Pricing & Freight Forwarding)*
Aida Sabic *(Mgr-Atlanta)*
Tony Kvasnicka *(Mgr-Vessel Ops)*
Amanda Lucas *(Asst VP-Customer Experience)*
Adela Hysaj *(Dir-Acct Mgmt)*
Eric Masotti *(VP-Logistics)*
Mark Ryan *(Dir-Truck Ops)*
Scott Douthitt *(Mgr-Houston)*
Gregg Molchan *(Mgr-Harrisburg)*
Josh Hoefker *(Mgr-Minneapolis)*
Ilona Fischer *(Dir-Mktg)*
William G. Gotimer Jr. *(Gen Counsel & Exec VP)*
J. Edward Morley *(VP-Ops)*

TRAILER PARK
6922 Hollywood Blvd 12th Fl, Hollywood, CA 90028
Tel.: (310) 845-3000 CA
Web Site: http://www.trailerpark.com
Year Founded: 1991
Sales Range: $10-24.9 Million
Emp.: 500
Advertising Agencies
N.A.I.C.S.: 541810
Matthew Brubaker *(CEO/Dir-Creative-Film Entertainment)*
Doug Troy *(CFO & COO)*
Jane Lopez *(VP-HR)*
Kevin Van Belois *(Pres-Content)*
Dana Flowers *(Sr VP & Dir-Creative-Theatrical & Home Entertainment)*
George Anderson *(Pres-Creative Svcs)*
John McMahon *(Pres/Gen Mgr-Art Machine)*
Jeremy Kaplan *(Pres-Art Machine & Dir-Creative)*
Bernie Del Carpio *(Sr VP & Dir-Creative-Television)*
Mike Tankel *(Sr VP-Mktg Innovation)*
Scott Lowy *(VP-Content)*
Steven Bruno *(VP-Creative Svcs)*
John Ryan *(VP-Post Production)*
Jennifer Kline *(VP-Creative & Dir-Television A/V)*
Luis Miranda *(Dir-Strategy Grp)*
Jason Zammit *(Dir-Live Theatrical Mktg)*
Simon Peck *(Mng Dir)*
Zihla Salinas *(CEO)*
Howard Moggs *(Sr VP & Dir-Dev)*

Subsidiaries:

Goodness Mfg. (1)
6922 Hollywood Blvd 12th Fl, Los Angeles, CA 90028
Tel.: (310) 845-3035
Web Site: http://www.trailerpark.com
Advertising Agencies
N.A.I.C.S.: 541810
Rick Eiserman *(CEO)*

TRAILER SOURCE INC.
4060 Patterson Ave, Winston Salem, NC 27105-2249
Tel.: (336) 661-7858
Web Site: http://www.trailersource.us
Sales Range: $10-24.9 Million
Emp.: 5
Provider of New & Used Trailers & Trucks
N.A.I.C.S.: 441110
Brian Kennedy *(Owner & Pres)*

TRAILER WHEEL & FRAME COMPANY

Trailer Wheel & Frame Company—(Continued)

TRAILER WHEEL & FRAME COMPANY
8222 Interstate 45 N, Houston, TX 77037-3608
Tel.: (281) 931-7777   TX
Web Site: http://www.trailerwheel.com
Sales Range: $75-99.9 Million
Emp.: 35
Whslr & Retailer of Truck Trailers, Accessories & Parts
N.A.I.C.S.: 441330
Bernard Vlahakis *(Pres & CEO)*
Glenda Vlahakis *(Treas & Sec)*
John Vlahakis *(Gen Mgr)*

TRAILINER CORP.
2169 E Blaine St, Springfield, MO 65803-5176
Tel.: (417) 866-7258   MO
Web Site: http://www.trailiner.com
Year Founded: 1982
Sales Range: $50-74.9 Million
Emp.: 400
Trucking Service
N.A.I.C.S.: 484230
H. E. Whitener *(CEO)*
Kelly Isom *(CFO)*
Amber Edmondson *(Pres)*

TRAILSIDE CAMPERS RV SALES, INC.
700 R D Mize Rd, Grain Valley, MO 64029
Tel.: (816) 229-2257
Web Site: http://www.trailsiderv.net
Sales Range: $10-24.9 Million
Emp.: 35
Recreational Vehicle Whslr
N.A.I.C.S.: 441210
Stephen Francis *(Mgr)*

TRAILWOOD TRANSPORTATION INC.
4825 Mustang Cir, Saint Paul, MN 55112
Tel.: (763) 783-2903
Web Site: http://www.trailwoodtransportation.com
Rev.: $13,000,000
Emp.: 90
Refrigerated Products Transport
N.A.I.C.S.: 484230

TRAIN SIGNAL INC.
152 W Ctr Ct, Schaumburg, IL 60195
Tel.: (847) 776-8800
Web Site: http://www.trainsignal.com
Year Founded: 2002
Rev.: $3,900,000
Emp.: 40
Computer Training
N.A.I.C.S.: 611420
Scott Skinger *(Founder & Pres)*
Kasia Grabowska *(Mgr-Website)*
Gary Eimerman *(Dir-Product Dev)*
Iman Jalali *(Dir-Sls & Mktg)*

TRAINER COMMUNICATIONS
5000 Hopyard Rd Ste 125, Pleasanton, CA 94588
Tel.: (925) 271-8200
Web Site: http://www.trainercomm.com
Sales Range: $1-9.9 Million
Emp.: 15
Public Relations Agency
N.A.I.C.S.: 541820
Ross Perich *(VP-Client Svcs)*
Karen Poli *(VP-Fin & Ops)*
Gary Good *(VP-Net Telecom Wireless)*
Tisa Penny *(Acct Coord)*

Joe Franscella *(Dir)*
Angela Griffo *(Sr Dir)*
Brad Langley *(Gen Mgr)*

TRAINING AND RESEARCH FOUNDATION
5150 W Goldleaf Cir, Los Angeles, CA 90056
Tel.: (310) 412-4195   CA
Web Site: http://www.trfhs.org
Year Founded: 1968
Sales Range: $10-24.9 Million
Emp.: 249
Community Welfare Services
N.A.I.C.S.: 624190
Reginald Brown *(VP)*
Henry Knawls *(Chm)*
Margarita Uyere *(Vice Chm)*
Shirley Dionzon *(Treas)*

TRAINING TOWARD SELF-RELIANCE, INC.
2500 Canoe Ripple Rd, Sligo, PA 16255
Tel.: (814) 358-2472   PA
Web Site: http://www.ttsrinc.com
Year Founded: 2001
Sales Range: $10-24.9 Million
Disability Assistance Services
N.A.I.C.S.: 624120
Yvonne Buzard *(Co-Sec)*
Denise Babcock *(Co-Sec)*
Josh Altman *(Chief Compliance Officer)*
Leslie Johnson *(Dir-Fiscal)*

TRAININGFOLKS
501 Cascade Pointe Ln Ste 101, Cary, NC 27513-5787
Tel.: (919) 535-8548
Web Site: http://www.trainingfolks.com
Year Founded: 1997
Sales Range: $75-99.9 Million
Emp.: 27
Corporate Training Services
N.A.I.C.S.: 611430
Steve Davis *(Mng Dir-Tech Solutions)*
Kate Banning *(VP-Fin Ops)*
Matthew Davis *(Co-Founder & CEO)*
Saqib Hassan *(Co-Founder & Pres)*
Owen Davis *(Mng Dir-US Ops)*

TRAINOR GRAIN & SUPPLY CO.
13201 N 2753 E Rd, Forrest, IL 61741-9535
Tel.: (815) 832-5512   IL
Web Site: http://www.trainorgrainandsupply.com
Year Founded: 1957
Sales Range: $10-24.9 Million
Emp.: 40
Grain, Feed & Chemical Fertilizer Distr
N.A.I.C.S.: 424510
John A. Trainor *(Pres)*

TRAJECTOR, INC.
410 SW 140th Ter, Newberry, FL 32669
Tel.: (352) 282-0782   DE
Web Site: https://www.trajector.com
Year Founded: 2021
Emp.: 1,341
Software Development Services
N.A.I.C.S.: 541511
James S. Hill *(Co-CEO, Co-Founder & Chm)*
Gina G. Uribe *(Co-Founder)*
Richard S. Blaser *(Co-CEO)*
Kevin M. Frain *(CFO)*
Phusit Tom Pongpat *(Pres & Sec)*

TRAJEN INC.

5901 Philip J Rhoads Ave # 14, Bethany, OK 73008-7007
Tel.: (979) 260-4000
Web Site: http://www.trajen.com
Sales Range: $75-99.9 Million
Emp.: 12
Aircraft Fueling Services
N.A.I.C.S.: 424720
Dan Bucaro *(Pres)*

TRAM DATA, LLC
4119 C Mauchunk Rd, Coplay, PA 18037
Web Site: http://www.replacemycontacts.com
Year Founded: 2007
Sales Range: $1-9.9 Million
Emp.: 12
Online Contact Lens Retailer
N.A.I.C.S.: 456130
Todd Messinger *(Pres)*

TRAMAC CORPORATION
Unit 3 12 Orben Dr, Landing, NJ 07850-1800
Tel.: (973) 887-7700
Web Site: http://www.tramac.com
Year Founded: 1967
Sales Range: $10-24.9 Million
Emp.: 5
General Construction Machinery & Equipment
N.A.I.C.S.: 423810
Gary Hesseltine *(VP)*

TRAMMO, INC.
8 W 40th St Fl 12, New York, NY 10018-2307
Tel.: (212) 223-3200   DE
Web Site: https://www.trammo.com
Year Founded: 1965
Sales Range: $5-14.9 Billion
Emp.: 150
Petroleum & Petroleum Products Merchant Wholesalers (except Bulk Stations & Terminals)
N.A.I.C.S.: 424720
Edward G. Weiner *(Pres & CEO)*
Oliver K. Stanton *(Owner & Sr VP)*
Dudley Cox *(Sr VP)*
Louis Epstein *(Gen Counsel & Sr VP)*
Vildan Bekirov *(Exec VP & Head-Sulfur Div)*
Christophe Savi *(Sr VP & Head-NH3 Div)*
William E. Markstein *(CFO & Sr VP)*
Nicholas J. Wilson *(Chief Risk Officer & VP)*
Sarah Terrell *(Sr VP-Trading)*

Subsidiaries:

Sea-3 Inc.   (1)
1111 Bagby Ste 2510, Houston, TX 77002
Tel.: (713) 650-6520
Web Site: http://www.sea3.com
Sales Range: $25-49.9 Million
Emp.: 30
Fertilizers, Fertilizer Raw Materials & Ammonia
N.A.I.C.S.: 212390

Subsidiary (Domestic):

Sea-3 of Florida Inc.   (2)
3606 Pendola Point Rd, Tampa, FL 33619
Tel.: (813) 241-0550
Sales Range: $25-49.9 Million
Emp.: 10
Propane Supplier
N.A.I.C.S.: 424720
Kevin Wertman *(Gen Mgr)*

T/A Terminals, Inc.   (1)
1994 Old Grace Rd, Meredosia, IL 62665
Tel.: (217) 584-1472
Emp.: 5
Fertilizer & Petrochemical Product Distr
N.A.I.C.S.: 424720
Todd Clayton *(Office Mgr)*

U.S. PRIVATE

Trammo AG   (1)
Riverside Towers Kosmodamianskaya emb 52, Building 4 10th Floor, Moscow, 115054, Russia
Tel.: (7) 4952585622
Web Site: http://www.trammo.com
Sales Range: $10-24.9 Million
Emp.: 15
Fertilizers, Fertilizer Raw Materials & Ammonia
N.A.I.C.S.: 325311

Trammo AG   (1)
Business Center AFD Building A 34 Al-Farabi Ave Office Rooms #236-239, Almaty, 050043, Kazakhstan
Tel.: (7) 727 356 3500
Web Site: http://www.trammo.com
Emp.: 4
Fertilizer & Ammonia Distr
N.A.I.C.S.: 424690
Askarov Marus *(Gen Mgr)*

Trammo Gas Domestic   (1)
1111 Bagby Ste 2510, Houston, TX 77002
Tel.: (713) 289-5900
Web Site: http://www.trammogas.com
Sales Range: $10-24.9 Million
Emp.: 20
Liquid Petroleum Gases Merchandising & Trading
N.A.I.C.S.: 424720
Sondra Reed *(Office Mgr)*

Trammo Gas International, Inc.   (1)
320 Park Ave, New York, NY 10022-6987
Tel.: (212) 223-3200
Liquefied Petroleum Gas Supplier
N.A.I.C.S.: 424720

Trammo India Pvt. Limited   (1)
Unit No O-503 A 5th Fl Salcon Rasvilas D-1 District Centre Saket, New Delhi, 110017, India
Tel.: (91) 11 4711 5225
Web Site: http://www.trammo.com
Fertilizer Mfr & Soft Commodities Distr
N.A.I.C.S.: 424690
Vimal Thareja *(VP)*

Trammo Ltd.   (1)
Whittaker House Whittaker Avenue, Richmond, TW9 1EH, Surrey, United Kingdom
Tel.: (44) 2088226680
Crude Oil & Oil Products
N.A.I.C.S.: 211120

Trammo Maghreb S.A.R.L.   (1)
89 Av Habib Bourguiba Imm Ariana Palace Bureau 3-2 3eme etage, Ariana, 2080, Tunis, Tunisia
Tel.: (216) 70722019
Crude Petroleum & Natural Gas Supplier
N.A.I.C.S.: 424720

Trammo Petroleum, Inc.   (1)
1111 Bagby Ste 1920, Houston, TX 77002
Tel.: (713) 289-8900
Web Site: http://www.transammonia.com
Crude Oil & Oil Products
N.A.I.C.S.: 424720

Trammo Pte Ltd.   (1)
12 Marina Boulevard 26-03 Marina Bay Financial Centre Tower 3, Singapore, 18982, Singapore
Tel.: (65) 6220 0700
Web Site: http://www.trammo.com
Sales Range: $10-24.9 Million
Emp.: 30
Fertilizer & Petrochemical Supplier
N.A.I.C.S.: 424690
Pushkar Jamnerkar *(VP & Gen Mgr)*

Trammochem   (1)
19 Old Kings Hwy S, Darien, CT 06820   (100%)
Tel.: (203) 655-7770
Web Site: http://www.trammochem.com
Sales Range: $10-24.9 Million
Emp.: 15
Petrochemicals Traders
N.A.I.C.S.: 424720
Lorraine Kelly *(Mgr-Ops)*

Trammochem A.G.   (1)
Bahnhofstrasse 1, CH-8852, Altendorf, Switzerland
Tel.: (41) 554511444
Sales Range: $10-24.9 Million
Emp.: 11
Petrochemicals

COMPANIES / TRANS-BRIDGE LINES, INC.

Trans East Trading (Korea) Ltd. (1)
0-302 Seocho-Trapalce Seocho-Dong, Seocho-Gu, Seoul, 137-923, Korea (South)
Tel.: (82) 2 6204 7350
Fertilizer & Petrochemical Supplier
N.A.I.C.S.: 424690

Transammonia (Shanghai) Trading Co., Ltd. (1)
Beijing Silver Tower No 2 North Rd, Dong San Huan, Chao Yang District, Beijing, 10027, China
Tel.: (86) 1064106580
Web Site: http://www.transammonia.com
Fertilizers, Fertilizer Raw Materials & Ammonia Mfr
N.A.I.C.S.: 325311

Transammonia AG (1)
Jerusalem Commercial Centre 5th Fl, PO Box 815409, Shmeisani, Amman, 11180, Jordan
Tel.: (962) 6 568 3570
Web Site: http://www.trammo.com
Nitrogeneous Fertilizer Mfr & Supplier
N.A.I.C.S.: 325311

Transammonia AG (1)
Plaza Chase 18th Floor Jalan Jendral Sudirman Kav 21, Jakarta, 12920, Indonesia
Tel.: (62) 21 2934 7909
Emp.: 8
Fertilizer & Ammonia Distr
N.A.I.C.S.: 424690
Lily Augustine (Office Mgr)

Transammonia B.V. (1)
Oudlandstraatje 25, 4838 BL, Breda, Netherlands
Tel.: (31) 765209099
Sales Range: $10-24.9 Million
Emp.: 2
Fertilizers, Fertilizer Raw Materials & Ammonia
N.A.I.C.S.: 325311

Transammonia Dis Ticaret Limited Company (1)
Ebulula Mardin Cad Meydan Sok Mermerler Sitesi No16 D13, Akatlar, Istanbul, 80600, Turkiye
Tel.: (90) 2123582224
Sales Range: $10-24.9 Million
Emp.: 4
Fertilizer & Ammonia Distr
N.A.I.C.S.: 424690
Iatender Istener (Gen Mgr)

Transammonia Internacional Representacoes Ltda. (1)
Av Angelica 2163 13 andar conj 135, Consolacao, 1227200, Sao Paulo, Brazil
Tel.: (55) 11 3154 1616
Sales Range: $10-24.9 Million
Emp.: 4
Fertilizer & Ammonia Distr
N.A.I.C.S.: 424690
Mauro Bergerman (Gen Mgr)

Transammonia Ltd. (1)
1 Berkeley Street, London, W1J 8DJ, United Kingdom
Tel.: (44) 2070169991
Web Site: http://www.transammonia.com
Fertilizers, Fertilizer Raw Materials & Ammonia
N.A.I.C.S.: 325311

Transammonia S.A.R.L. (1)
38 Rue Jean Mermoz, 75008, Paris, France
Tel.: (33) 58183380
Fertilizers, Fertilizer Raw Materials & Ammonia
N.A.I.C.S.: 325311

TRAMZ HOTELS INC.
776 Mountain Blvd Ste 200, Watchung, NJ 07069
Tel.: (908) 753-7400
Web Site: http://www.tramzhotels.com
Year Founded: 1987
Rev.: $18,500,000
Emp.: 37
Provider of Hotel Services
N.A.I.C.S.: 721110
Tarrunumn Murad (CEO)
Subsidiaries:
Comfort Inn (1)
6491 Thompson Rd, Syracuse, NY 13206
Tel.: (315) 437-0222
Sales Range: $1-9.9 Million
Emp.: 20
Hotel
N.A.I.C.S.: 721110
Regan Grubka (Gen Mgr)

TRANAX TECHNOLOGIES INC.
30984 Santana St, Hayward, CA 94544-7058
Tel.: (510) 770-2227
Rev.: $32,350,122
Emp.: 27
Provider of Automatic Teller Machines
N.A.I.C.S.: 334118
Dan Carillo (Controller)
Bill Dunn (VP-Sls)
Dominic DiBlasio (VP-Fin Products)
Kwon Lee (Pres & CEO)

TRANCOS, INC.
6800 Koll Center Pkwy Ste 170, Pleasanton, CA 94566-7044
Tel.: (650) 364-3110   CA
Web Site: http://www.trancos.com
Year Founded: 1999
Sales Range: $1-9.9 Million
Emp.: 35
Lead Generation & Customer Acquisition Services
N.A.I.C.S.: 541511
Brian Nelson (CEO)
Laure Majcherczyk (COO)
Judit Rigo (Coord-Acct)
Subsidiaries:
CoregMedia (1)
6800 Koll Centre Pkwy Ste 170, Pleasanton, CA 94566
Tel.: (650) 364-3110
Web Site: http://www.coregmedia.com
Lead Generation & Marketing Services
N.A.I.C.S.: 541613
Craig Bougas (Reg Mgr)

TRANDES CORPORATION
4601 Presidents Dr Ste 360, Lanham, MD 20706
Tel.: (301) 459-0200
Web Site: http://www.trandes.com
Year Founded: 1972
Sales Range: $10-24.9 Million
Emp.: 10
Custom Computer Programming Services
N.A.I.C.S.: 541511
Janine Carran (Dir-HR)

TRANS AMERICAN TRUCKING SERVICE
115 Saint Nicholas Ave, South Plainfield, NJ 07080
Tel.: (908) 755-9000
Web Site: http://www.transamer.com
Rev.: $12,101,423
Emp.: 17
Provider of Trucking Services
N.A.I.C.S.: 484121
Ronald McGraw (Pres)
Joe Bartlinski (Dir-Safety)
Chris Corcoran (Mgr-Ops)
Anne Esposito (Office Mgr)

TRANS EXPEDITE, INC.
7 Founders Blvd Ste E, El Paso, TX 79906
Tel.: (915) 779-9100   TX
Web Site: http://www.trans-expedite.com
Year Founded: 2001
Sales Range: $25-49.9 Million
Emp.: 182
Freight Transportation Arrangement
N.A.I.C.S.: 488510
Keeli Jernigan (Pres & CEO)
Lourdes Bonilla-Jones (Dir-HR)
Estella Ortega (Supvr-Ops)
Michael Strohacker (Mgr-Sls)
Mike Stires (Acct Mgr)
Pablo Gonzalez (Mgr-Warehouse)

TRANS INNS MANAGEMENT INC.
4111 Andover Rd Ste 110-W, Bloomfield Hills, MI 48302
Tel.: (248) 489-4333
Web Site: http://www.transinns.com
Year Founded: 1981
Sales Range: $25-49.9 Million
Emp.: 300
Hotel Management & Investment
N.A.I.C.S.: 721110
Daniel Vosotas (Chm & CEO)

TRANS MACHINE TECHNOLOGIES
920 Brenner St NE, Salem, SC 27101
Tel.: (336) 778-9306
Web Site: http://www.trans-machine.com
Precision Machined Components Mfr
N.A.I.C.S.: 332721
Barry Leonard (CEO)
Subsidiaries:
Wright Metal Products, Inc. (1)
690 Duncan Reidville Rd, Duncan, SC 29334
Tel.: (864) 949-3741
Structural Steel & Precast Concrete Contractors
N.A.I.C.S.: 238120

TRANS NATIONAL GROUP SERVICES
2 Charlesgate W, Boston, MA 02215-3540
Tel.: (617) 262-9200   MA
Year Founded: 1974
Sales Range: $10-24.9 Million
Emp.: 24
Telecommunications
N.A.I.C.S.: 517810
Steve Belkin (Chm)
William Weidlein (Vice Chm)
Felix Riccio (Sr VP-Dev)
Marianne Kelly (Controller & Mgr-Farm)

TRANS PACIFIC BANCORP
88 St Ste 750, San Francisco, CA 94108
Tel.: (415) 543-3377
Web Site: http://www.ttnb.com
Sales Range: $10-24.9 Million
Emp.: 30
National Commercial Banks
N.A.I.C.S.: 551111
Crystal Huadle (Controller)
Dennis J. Daly Sr. (Chm)
Subsidiaries:
Trans Pacific National Bank (1)
55 2nd St Ste 100, San Francisco, CA 94105
Tel.: (415) 543-3377
Web Site: http://www.tpnb.com
Sales Range: $1-9.9 Million
Emp.: 40
National Commercial Banks
N.A.I.C.S.: 522110
Dennis Jang (CFO & Exec VP)
Robert F. Lussier (Pres & CEO)
Erick A. Kostuchek (Exec VP-Comml Banking)
Hector Hernadez (VP)
Gwendolyn J. Wong (Chief Credit Officer & Exec VP)
Denis J. Daly Jr. (Chm)

TRANS STATES AIRLINES INC.
11495 Natural Bridge Rd No 340, Bridgeton, MO 63044-2325
Tel.: (314) 222-4300   MO
Web Site: http://www.transstates.net
Year Founded: 1983
Sales Range: $250-299.9 Million
Emp.: 2,500
Provider of Air Transportation Services
N.A.I.C.S.: 481111
David Hayes (Gen Counsel & VP)
Richard A. Leach (Pres & CEO)
Fred Oxley (COO)
Al Blosse (VP)
Matt Conrad (Dir-Safety)
Shonn Clark (Dir-Inflight Svc)
John Wilk (Dir-Quality Assurance)

TRANS WORLD ASSURANCE INC.
885 S El Camino Real, San Mateo, CA 94402-2310
Tel.: (650) 348-2300   CA
Web Site: http://www.transworldassurance.com
Year Founded: 1962
Sales Range: $25-49.9 Million
Emp.: 22
Provider of Life Insurance
N.A.I.C.S.: 524113
Charles Royal (Pres)
Jennifer Catney (Office Mgr)
Earl Bartlett Jr. (Chm)

TRANS WORLD MARKETING CORP.
360 Murray Hill Pkwy, East Rutherford, NJ 07073-2109
Tel.: (201) 935-5565   NJ
Web Site: http://www.transworldmarketing.com
Year Founded: 1976
Sales Range: $10-24.9 Million
Emp.: 100
Signs & Advertising Specialties
N.A.I.C.S.: 339950
Gerry Molitor (Exec VP-Sls & Mktg)
James Cavaluzzi (Chm)

TRANS WORLD RADIO INC.
300 Gregson Dr, Cary, NC 27511-6444
Tel.: (919) 460-3700   NJ
Web Site: http://www.twr.org
Year Founded: 1952
Sales Range: $25-49.9 Million
Emp.: 500
Radio Broadcasting Stations
N.A.I.C.S.: 516110
Steve Hippe (CFO)
Debbi Moninger (Dir-HR)

TRANS-ATLANTIC MOTORS INC.
107 Myrtle Ave, Stamford, CT 06902
Tel.: (203) 359-2632
Web Site: http://www.stamfordvolvo.com
Rev.: $17,600,000
Emp.: 40
Car Dealership
N.A.I.C.S.: 441110
Chris Riley (Pres)
Kurt Riley (VP)

TRANS-BRIDGE LINES, INC.
2012 Industrial Dr, Bethlehem, PA 18017
Tel.: (610) 868-6001
Web Site: http://www.transbridgelines.com
Year Founded: 1941
Sales Range: $10-24.9 Million
Emp.: 200

TRANS-BRIDGE LINES, INC.

Trans-Bridge Lines, Inc.—(Continued)
Bus Charter Services
N.A.I.C.S.: 485510
Tom JeBran *(Pres)*
Roy Riche *(Controller)*

TRANS-GLOBAL PRODUCTS INC.
111 S Armenia Ave Ste 101, Tampa, FL 33609-3307
Tel.: (813) 839-9060
Web Site: http://www.transglobalproducts.com
Year Founded: 1982
Sales Range: $25-49.9 Million
Emp.: 6
Provider of Packaged, Frozen Fish
N.A.I.C.S.: 424420
Mac Chen *(Pres & CEO)*

TRANS-GLOBAL SOLUTIONS INC.
11811 I 10 E Ste 630, Houston, TX 77029
Tel.: (713) 453-0341
Web Site: http://www.tgsgroup.com
Year Founded: 1975
Sales Range: $10-24.9 Million
Emp.: 325
Rail Logistics Services
N.A.I.C.S.: 541614
William Scott *(VP)*

Subsidiaries:
Trans-Global Solutions, Inc. (1)
1735 W Cardinal Dr, Beaumont, TX 77705
Tel.: (409) 727-4801
Web Site: http://www.tgsgroup.com
Sales Range: $10-24.9 Million
Emp.: 18
Rail Logistic Services
N.A.I.C.S.: 541614
Will Scott *(VP)*
Johnny Pavlica *(Dir-Ops)*
Matt Fleming *(VP-Bus Dev)*
Chris Warner *(Mgr-Locomotive Fleet)*

TRANS-INDIA PRODUCTS, INC.
3330 A Coffey Ln, Santa Rosa, CA 95403
Tel.: (707) 544-0298
Web Site: http://www.shikai.com
Sales Range: $1-9.9 Million
Emp.: 15
Cosmetics Mfr
N.A.I.C.S.: 325620
Jason Sepp *(VP)*

TRANS-LEASE GROUP
200 Highland Ave, Needham, MA 02494
Tel.: (781) 329-4400
Web Site: http://www.westwoodcottage.com
Rev: $16,100,000
Emp.: 20
Contract Haulers
N.A.I.C.S.: 484121
Carol Gray McCarthy *(Pres)*

TRANS-MATIC MFG.
300 E 48th St, Holland, MI 49423-5301
Tel.: (616) 820-2500
Web Site: http://www.transmatic.com
Year Founded: 1968
Sales Range: $25-49.9 Million
Emp.: 300
Metal Stamping
N.A.I.C.S.: 336370
Patrick A. Thompson *(Pres)*
Steve Patterson *(CFO & Controller)*
Bryan Claerbaut *(Controller)*

TRANS-MED USA INC.
31 Progress Ave, Tyngsboro, MA 01879
Tel.: (978) 649-1970
Web Site: http://www.transmed-usa.com
Sales Range: $10-24.9 Million
Emp.: 9
Medical Equipment & Supplies
N.A.I.C.S.: 423450
Ebrahim Masalehdan *(Pres)*

TRANS-OVERSEAS CORPORATION
28000 Goddard Rd, Romulus, MI 48174
Tel.: (734) 946-8750
Web Site: http://www.trans-overseas.com
Year Founded: 1978
Sales Range: $10-24.9 Million
Emp.: 40
Foreign Freight Forwarding
N.A.I.C.S.: 488510
James Gannon *(Pres)*
Joe Karnykowski *(Controller)*
Susan Dysarczyk *(Supvr-Ops)*

TRANS-RESOURCES, INC.
200 W 57th St, New York, NY 10119
Tel.: (212) 515-4100
Sales Range: $500-549.9 Million
Emp.: 1,000
Holding Company
N.A.I.C.S.: 551112
William Dowd *(Pres, CEO & COO)*
Gail Glazebrook *(Controller)*

Subsidiaries:
Elgo Irrigation Ltd. (1)
4 Shoham St, PO Box 3147, Business industrial Park, Caesarea, 38900, Israel
Tel.: (972) 49111442
Web Site: http://www.elgo.co.il
Sales Range: $25-49.9 Million
Emp.: 80
Mfr of Irrigation & Sprinkler Systems
N.A.I.C.S.: 221310
Avi Shemesh *(CEO)*
Uria Feuchtwanger *(Chm)*

Haifa Chemicals Ltd. (1)
Industrial Zone, Haifa Bay, Haifa, 26120, Israel
Tel.: (972) 74 7373737
Web Site: http://www.haifa-group.com
Sales Range: $25-49.9 Million
Emp.: 650
Potassium Nitrate Mfr
N.A.I.C.S.: 325311
Jeules Crump *(Pres)*
Nadav Shachar *(Deputy Chm & CEO)*
Tamir Kadashi *(CFO)*
Nathan Feldman *(VP-Mktg & Sls)*
Amihai Zaider *(VP-Ops)*
Daniel Yakir *(VP-Bus Dev)*
Nir Yitzhaki *(VP-Resources)*
Yoel Nitzany *(VP-Supply Chain)*

Subsidiary (US):
Haifa North America Incorporated (2)
307 Cranes Roost Blvd Ste 2030, Altamonte Springs, FL 32701
Tel.: (407) 862-6400
Web Site: http://www.haifachem.com
Sales Range: $50-74.9 Million
Emp.: 20
Agricultural Fertilizer Distr
N.A.I.C.S.: 424910
Marc Lebl *(Mgr)*

TRANS-SYSTEM INC.
7405 S Hayford Rd, Cheney, WA 99004-9633
Tel.: (509) 623-4000
Web Site: http://www.trans-system.com
Year Founded: 1972
Sales Range: $100-124.9 Million
Emp.: 900
Trucking Service
N.A.I.C.S.: 484121
James C. Williams *(Chm & CEO)*
Ted Rehwald *(VP)*
Gary R. King *(Pres & CFO)*

Subsidiaries:
Driver Training & Solutions, LLC. (1)
7405 S Hayford Rd, Cheney, WA 99004
Tel.: (509) 777-0073
Web Site: http://www.drivertrainingandsolutions.com
Truck Driver Training Services
N.A.I.C.S.: 611519

James J. Williams Bulk Service Transport, Inc. (1)
16702 E Euclid Ave, Spokane, WA 99216-1821
Tel.: (509) 928-8171
Web Site: http://www.jjwilliams.com
Sales Range: $10-24.9 Million
Emp.: 40
Provider of Trucking Services
N.A.I.C.S.: 484121
James C. Williams *(Pres)*
Francis McGee *(Mgr-Traffic)*

System Transport Inc. (1)
7405 S Hayford Rd, Cheney, WA 99004-9633
Tel.: (509) 623-4000
Web Site: http://www.systemtrans.com
Sales Range: $75-99.9 Million
Emp.: 110
Trucking Except Local
N.A.I.C.S.: 484121
James C. Williams *(Chm & CEO)*

T-W Transport, Inc. (1)
7405 S Hayford Rd, Cheney, WA 99004-9633
Tel.: (509) 623-4000
Web Site: http://www.twtrans.com
Rev.: $17,900,000
Emp.: 155
Trucking Except Local
N.A.I.C.S.: 484121
James C. Williams *(CEO)*

TWT Refrigerated Service (1)
7405 S Hayford Rd, Cheney, WA 99004
Tel.: (509) 623-4004
Web Site: http://www.twtrans.com
Emp.: 150
Refrigerated Product Transportation Services
N.A.I.C.S.: 484220
Brian Love *(Mgr-Logistics)*

TRANS-TEX FABRICATING CO., INC.
105 Humble Ave, San Antonio, TX 78225
Tel.: (210) 924-4431
Web Site: http://www.trans-tex.com
Year Founded: 1989
Sales Range: $10-24.9 Million
Emp.: 75
Blast Furnaces, Steel Mills & Alloy Mfr
N.A.I.C.S.: 331110
John C. Schuepbach *(Pres & CEO)*
Alyssa Schuepbach *(Mgr-Acctg)*
Andrew Lozano *(Controller)*
Adrian Augustin *(Gen Mgr)*
Troy Pawelek *(Gen Mgr)*
Dale Dennis *(Mgr-Sls)*
Don Jackson *(Project Mgr)*
Paul Allen *(Dir-Indus Fabrication)*
Al Davis *(Mgr-Detailing)*
Shannon Whalen *(Mgr-Bus Dev)*
Bud Smith *(Mgr-Sls)*
Paula Rae *(Project Mgr)*

TRANS-TRADE, INC.
4450 W Walnut Hill Ln Ste 100, Irving, TX 75038
Tel.: (972) 456-1581
Web Site: http://www.transtrade.com
Sales Range: $25-49.9 Million
Emp.: 60
Shipping & Logistics Services

U.S. PRIVATE

N.A.I.C.S.: 488510
Matthew Moseley *(VP-Fin)*
Chris Condon *(CEO)*

Subsidiaries:
Trans-Trade, Inc. (1)
9664 Oak Crossing rd Ste-200, Orlando, FL 32837
Tel.: (407) 438-5499
Web Site: http://www.transtrade.com
Sales Range: $10-24.9 Million
Emp.: 8
Freight Forwarding Services
N.A.I.C.S.: 488510
Chris Condon *(CEO)*

TRANS-WEST INC.
20770 E I-76 Frontage Rd, Brighton, CO 80603
Tel.: (303) 289-3161
Web Site: http://www.transwest.com
Sales Range: $150-199.9 Million
Emp.: 100
Sales of New & Used Trucks, Tractors & Trailers
N.A.I.C.S.: 441110
Kyle Brophy *(Mgr-Parts)*

TRANSACTION ASSOCIATES, INC.
5 Wheeling Ave Unit B, Woburn, MA 01801
Tel.: (781) 895-1100
Web Site: http://www.transactionassoc.com
Year Founded: 1990
Sales Range: $1-9.9 Million
Emp.: 50
Transportation Software Development Services
N.A.I.C.S.: 541511
Cindy Frene *(Principal)*
Rob Tassinari *(VP)*
Trisha Morris *(Coord-Verizon Transportation)*

TRANSACTION PUBLISHERS, INC.
35 Berrue Cir, Piscataway, NJ 08854
Tel.: (732) 445-2280
Web Site: http://www.transactionpub.com
Year Founded: 1962
Scholarly Books, Annuals & Journals In Various Social Sciences Disciplines Including International Relations, Economics, Government & Public Policy, Psychology, Ethnic & Urban Studies & Communications
N.A.I.C.S.: 513120
Mary E. Curtis *(Chm & Pres)*
Michael Celletto *(Sec)*
Bruce Carl Meyers *(Mgr-Production)*

TRANSACTTOOLS, INC.
100 Wall St Bsmt 2, New York, NY 10005-3733
Tel.: (212) 244-5551
Year Founded: 2000
Sales Range: $1-9.9 Million
Emp.: 27
Software For Financial Messaging Connectivity
N.A.I.C.S.: 517810
Sam Johnson *(CEO)*

TRANSAERO INC.
35 Melville Park Rd Ste 100, Melville, NY 11747
Tel.: (631) 752-1240
Web Site: http://www.transaeroinc.com
Rev.: $68,455,000
Emp.: 40
Aircraft Equipment & Supp
N.A.I.C.S.: 423860

COMPANIES

Perry K. Youngwall *(Pres & CEO)*
Johan Eriksson *(Reg Mgr)*
Lance Homan *(VP-Sls)*
Michael Osterloh *(Dir-Military Sls)*
Dan Moss *(Mgr-Airline Sls)*
William Koshansky *(Mgr-Reg Sls-Aviation Life Support-Eastern US)*

TRANSAM TRUCKING INC.
15910 South Hwy 169, Olathe, KS 66062-3800
Tel.: (913) 782-5300   MO
Web Site:
http://www.transamtruck.com
Year Founded: 1987
Sales Range: $75-99.9 Million
Emp.: 800
Trucking Service
N.A.I.C.S.: 484121
Russ McElliott *(Pres)*
Diana Thorston *(Dir-Fixed Assets)*
Max Loehr *(Exec VP-Sls)*
John Jacobson Jr. *(Pres)*

TRANSAMERICA EXPRESS LOGISTICS, LLC
980 9th St 16th Fl, Sacramento, CA 95814
Web Site:
http://www.transamericaexp.com
Year Founded: 2015
Sales Range: $100-124.9 Million
Emp.: 22
Freight Transportation Services
N.A.I.C.S.: 488510
Paul Virdi *(Pres)*

TRANSCARE NEW YORK INC.
1 Metrotech Ctr Ste 2000 20th Fl, Brooklyn, NY 11201
Tel.: (718) 763-8888
Web Site: http://www.transcare.com
Sales Range: $50-74.9 Million
Emp.: 2,400
Ambulance Service
N.A.I.C.S.: 621910
Peter Wolf *(CEO)*

Subsidiaries:

Transcare of Maryland Inc   (1)
1125 Desoto Rd, Baltimore, MD 21223
Tel.: (410) 242-2279
Web Site: http://www.transcare.com
Rev.: $7,700,000
Emp.: 175
Ambulance Service
N.A.I.C.S.: 621910
Brian Nevins *(Gen Mgr)*

TRANSCEND MEDIA LLC
1 International Pl 27th Fl, Boston, MA 02110
Web Site:
http://www.transcendmedia.com
Year Founded: 2009
Sales Range: $1-9.9 Million
Emp.: 107
Advertising Agency & Marketing Consulting
N.A.I.C.S.: 541810
Jason Nauman *(Founder & CEO)*
Chris Hoyt *(CFO)*

TRANSCENDENT INVESTMENT MANAGEMENT
18305 Biscayne Blvd Ste 402, Aventura, FL 33160
Tel.: (305) 871-7841
Web Site: http://www.timgmt.com
Sales Range: $1-9.9 Million
Real Estate Private Equity Firm
N.A.I.C.S.: 523999
Jordan Kavana *(Founder & CEO)*

TRANSCEPTA LLC
135 Columbia Ste 202, Aliso Viejo, CA 92656

Tel.: (949) 382-2840
Web Site: http://www.transcepta.com
Sales Range: $1-9.9 Million
Electronic Invoicing Solutions
N.A.I.C.S.: 561499
Ray Parsons *(Pres & CEO)*
Mitch Baxter *(VP-Strategic Accts)*
Shan Haq *(VP-Corp Strategy & Dev)*
Dave Berkus *(Chm)*
Lloyd Wendland *(VP-Engrg)*

TRANSCHEM, INC.
5963 La Pl Ct Ste 104, Carlsbad, CA 92008
Tel.: (760) 431-6310
Web Site:
http://www.wesellchemicals.com
Year Founded: 1988
Sales Range: $10-24.9 Million
Emp.: 7
Chemical & Allied Product Whslr
N.A.I.C.S.: 424690
David Krome *(Pres)*
Jeremy Krome *(COO)*
Amanda Krome *(Dir-Supply Chain Mgmt)*
Allen Brecht *(Mgr-Natl Sls)*
Barbi Krome *(Treas)*
Adam Egelhoff *(Mgr-Global Accts)*

TRANSCO INC.
55 E Jackson Blvd, Chicago, IL 60604-4100
Tel.: (312) 427-2818   DE
Web Site:
http://www.transcoproducts.com
Year Founded: 1936
Sales Range: $50-74.9 Million
Emp.: 450
Contracting Services
N.A.I.C.S.: 332812
Charles Anderson *(CEO)*
Edward Wolbert *(Pres)*
Gerry Shaffer *(Controller)*
Bernardo Figueiredo *(Project Mgr)*
Bruce Alpha *(VP)*
Dan Hanson *(VP-Ops)*
John Solon *(Mgr-Project Implementation)*
Mark Detwiler *(Project Mgr)*
Nick Hawkins *(Project Mgr)*
Orie Barnes *(Mgr-Quality Assurance)*

Subsidiaries:

Advance Thermal Corp.   (1)
548 York Rd, Bensenville, IL 60106   **(100%)**
Tel.: (630) 595-5150
Web Site:
http://www.advancethermalcorp.com
Sales Range: $10-24.9 Million
Emp.: 50
Blanket Insulation
N.A.I.C.S.: 327993
Joseph Pirogovsky *(Pres)*
Cheryl Bellinger *(Gen Mgr)*

Transco Products Inc.   (1)
200 N Lasalle St, Chicago, IL 60601-4100   **(100%)**
Tel.: (312) 427-2818
Web Site: http://www.transcoproducts.com
Sales Range: $10-24.9 Million
Emp.: 40
Insulation Contractor; Fire Protection Products
N.A.I.C.S.: 332812
John Solon *(Mgr-Project Implementation)*
Bruce Alpha *(VP)*
Mark Detwiler *(Project Mgr)*
Edward Wolbert *(Pres & CEO)*

Transco Products Inc. - TPI Fabrication Facility   (1)
1215 E 12th St, Streator, IL 61364
Tel.: (815) 672-2197
Nuclear Power Plant Equipment Mfr
N.A.I.C.S.: 332313

Transco Railway Products, Inc   (1)
901 N Lk Ave, Miles City, MT 59301

Tel.: (406) 232-1527
Web Site: http://www.transcorailway.com
Sales Range: $10-24.9 Million
Emp.: 70
Railroad Car Repair
N.A.I.C.S.: 488210

TRANSCO LEASING INC.
60 Transco Park Dr, Russellville, AR 72802
Tel.: (479) 967-5700
Web Site:
http://www.transcolines.com
Rev.: $16,100,000
Emp.: 300
Provider of Trucking Services
N.A.I.C.S.: 484121
Mike Standridge *(Dir-Maintenance)*
E. Wayne Bookout *(Sr VP)*
Sue Edwards *(Office Mgr)*
Allen Massey *(Dir-Safety)*
Michael Bar *(Pres & CEO)*

TRANSCO UNION OFFICE
257 Water St, Augusta, ME 04330
Tel.: (207) 622-6252   DE
Web Site: http://www.trans-co.com
Year Founded: 1962
Rev.: $27,760,603
Emp.: 450
Office Equipment Solutions
N.A.I.C.S.: 337214
Anne Vallee-Portorella *(Pres)*
Tom Vallee *(Mgr-Warehouse)*

TRANSCOASTAL CORPORATION
4975 Voyager Dr, Dallas, TX 75237
Tel.: (972) 818-0720   DE
Web Site: http://www.transcoastal.net
Year Founded: 1998
Sales Range: $1-9.9 Million
Emp.: 21
Oil & Gas Production
N.A.I.C.S.: 213112

Subsidiaries:

TransCoastal Corporation of Texas   (1)
17304 Preston Rd, Dallas, TX 75252
Tel.: (972) 818-0720
Web Site: http://www.transcoastal.net
Sales Range: $50-74.9 Million
Emp.: 14
Support Activities for Oil & Gas Operations
N.A.I.C.S.: 213112
Stuart Hagler *(CEO)*

TRANSCOMMUNICATIONS INC.
6125 Preservation Dr, Chattanooga, TN 37416
Tel.: (423) 553-5200
Web Site: http://www.transcard.com
Rev.: $24,820,685
Emp.: 50
Telephone Communication Services
N.A.I.C.S.: 517121
Craig Fuller *(CEO)*
David Samples *(CTO)*
Kevin Martin *(Chief Legal Officer & Exec VP-Compliance)*
Greg Bloh *(Pres)*
Mark Patterson *(CFO)*

TRANSCON BUILDERS INC.
25250 Rockside Rd, Bedford, OH 44146
Tel.: (440) 439-2100   OH
Web Site:
http://www.transconbuilders.com
Year Founded: 1957
Sales Range: $10-24.9 Million
Emp.: 40
Providers of Residences for Older Persons, Multi-Family Living, Commercial Office Space, Contract Builders & Land Development

N.A.I.C.S.: 531110
Fred Rzepka *(Pres)*
Peter Rzepka *(Chm)*
Paul Wilms *(CFO & Controller)*
Jeff Breha *(VP)*

TRANSCONTINENTAL CORPORATION
420 E Carrillo St, Santa Barbara, CA 93101
Tel.: (805) 963-6851
Rev.: $18,300,000
Emp.: 30
Provider of Real Estate Development
N.A.I.C.S.: 481219

TRANSCORR LLC
4901 W 96th St, Indianapolis, IN 46268
Tel.: (317) 879-3900
Web Site: http://www.transcorr.com
Year Founded: 1983
Sales Range: $25-49.9 Million
Emp.: 80
Provider of Trucking Services
N.A.I.C.S.: 484121
Steve Harris *(Pres)*
Gregg Eddy *(Owner)*
Jim Davidson *(Controller)*
Emma Hegmyer *(Dir-Accts Payable)*

TRANSCRIPT PHARMACY, INC.
2506 Lakeland Dr Ste 201, Jackson, MS 39232
Tel.: (601) 420-4041
Web Site:
http://www.transcriptpharmacy.com
Year Founded: 2002
Rev.: $14,100,000
Emp.: 14
Retail Drugs & Sundries
N.A.I.C.S.: 456110
Clifton Osbon *(Pres)*
John T. Barrett *(VP)*

TRANSDUCERS DIRECT, LLC
12115 Ellington Ct, Cincinnati, OH 45249
Tel.: (513) 583-9491   OH
Web Site:
http://www.transducersdirect.com
Year Founded: 1999
Sales Range: $10-24.9 Million
Emp.: 20
Transducers, Sensors & Other Industrial Components Mfr
N.A.I.C.S.: 334419
Rob Matthes *(Pres)*

TRANSFER ENTERPRISES, INC.
10045 Red Run Blvd Ste 140, Owings Mills, MD 21117
Tel.: (443) 334-8840   DE
Year Founded: 2013
Transfer Agent Services
N.A.I.C.S.: 561499
Jerry Gruenbaum *(Pres, CEO, CFO, Chief Acctg Officer & Treas)*
David Mathias *(Sec)*

TRANSFER MARKETING INC.
1025 French Rd, Buffalo, NY 14227
Tel.: (716) 668-4054
Rev.: $14,200,000
Emp.: 7
Bond Brokers
N.A.I.C.S.: 424410

TRANSFINDER CORPORATION
440 State St, Schenectady, NY 12305
Tel.: (518) 377-3609
Web Site: http://www.transfinder.com

TRANSFINDER CORPORATION

Transfinder Corporation—(Continued)
Year Founded: 1988
Rev.: $4,500,000
Emp.: 67
Computer Peripheral Equipment & Software Merchant Whlslr
N.A.I.C.S.: 423430
Antonio Civitella *(Pres & CEO)*
Greg P. Zibro *(VP-Bus Dev)*
Frank Gazeley *(VP-Client Rels)*
Rachel Shayne *(Mgr-Client Projects)*
Brad McGinnis *(Acct Exec-Austin & Texas)*
Caitlyn Sheil *(Dir-Software Dev)*
Robb Snyder *(Dir-Mktg)*

TRANSFORM HOLDCO LLC
3333 Beverly Rd, Hoffman Estates, IL 60179
Tel.: (847) 286-2500   DE
Web Site: http://www.transformco.com
Year Founded: 2018
Holding Company
N.A.I.C.S.: 551112
Neeraj Karhade *(CFO)*
Kathy Mayor *(CMO)*
Dave Shellenberger *(VP-Mktg Plng)*

Subsidiaries:

Transform SR Brands LLC   (1)
5407 Trillium Blvd, Hoffman Estates, IL 60192
Tel.: (847) 286-2500
Web Site: https://www.sears.com
Online Department Store Operator
N.A.I.C.S.: 455110

TRANSFORM-X, INC.
6969 E Sunrise Dr Ste 100, Tucson, AZ 85750
Tel.: (520) 512-5299
Year Founded: 2017
Software & Hardware Technologies for Satellite & RF Communications
N.A.I.C.S.: 541519
Daniel Hodges *(Pres)*

Subsidiaries:

DragonWave-X   (1)
362 Terry Fox Drive, Ottawa, K2K 2P5, ON, Canada
Tel.: (613) 599-9991
Web Site: https://dragonwavenetworks.com
Sales Range: $25-49.9 Million
Broadband Wireless Microwave Equipment Developer, Mfr & Marketer
N.A.I.C.S.: 334220

Subsidiary (Non-US):

DragonWave Mexico S.A. de C.V.   (2)
Avenida Las Colonias 1 Int 17-B Fracc Residencial Casa Blanca, Colonia Jardines de Atizapan, Zaragoza, CP 52978, Mexico
Tel.: (52) 1 55 5406 2318
Broadband Wireless Microwave Equipment Mfr & Marketer
N.A.I.C.S.: 334220

TRANSFORMATION ADVISORS GROUP, LLC
1616 Anderson Rd Ste 223, McLean, VA 22102-1602
Tel.: (703) 224-8831
Web Site: http://www.taateam.com
Year Founded: 2006
Emp.: 100
Information Technology Services & Program Management Consulting
N.A.I.C.S.: 519290
Campbell P. Shannon *(Owner & CEO)*
Jennifer Kudla *(Chief Admin Officer)*

Subsidiaries:

M-Cubed Information Systems, Inc.   (1)
1616 Anderson Rd #430, McLean, VA 22102
Tel.: (703) 224-8831
Web Site: http://www.mcubedinfo.com
Rev.: $7,000,000
Emp.: 200
Environmental Protection Services
N.A.I.C.S.: 541620
LaVerne Evans *(Mgr-HR)*
Paul Hodges *(Engr-Lead Sys & Software)*

TRANSFORMATION SYSTEMS, INC.
2011 Crystal Dr Ste 400, Arlington, VA 22202
Tel.: (703) 682-6853
Web Site: http://www.transformationsystems.com
Year Founded: 1994
Rev.: $4,000,000
Emp.: 20
Business & Management Consulting Services
N.A.I.C.S.: 561990
Marta Wilson *(Founder & CEO)*
Betty Cruise *(CFO)*
Robert Wilson *(COO)*
Altyn Clark *(Chief Solutions Officer)*
Garry Coleman *(Exec VP-Marine Corps Programs)*
Shawn James *(VP-Strategic Dev)*

TRANSFORMATIONAL CPG ACQUISITION CORP.
6 St Johns Ln, New York, NY 10013
Tel.: (646) 450-6720   DE
Year Founded: 2021
Investment Services
N.A.I.C.S.: 523999
Daryl G. Brewster *(CEO)*
Charles A. Norris *(Chm)*
Nadim Barakat *(Co-Pres)*
Woody Boueiz *(Co-Pres)*
Richard A. Kassar *(CFO)*

TRANSGLOBAL COMMUNICATIONS INC.
3505 N Roxboro St, Durham, NC 27704
Tel.: (919) 479-2121
Web Site: http://www.transglobalcomm.com
Emp.: 25
Telephone & Telephone Equipment Installation
N.A.I.C.S.: 238210
Shirley A. White *(CEO & VP)*
Linda Campman *(Mgr-Ops)*

TRANSGLOBAL GAS & OIL COMPANY
10904A McBride Ln, Knoxville, TN 37932-3221
Tel.: (865) 777-2162
Sales Range: $10-24.9 Million
Emp.: 200
Operator of Gas Stations & Convenience Stores
N.A.I.C.S.: 424720
Chuck Baine *(Pres)*

TRANSHUMANCE HOLDING COMPANY INC.
2530 River Plz Dr Te 200, Sacramento, CA 95833
Tel.: (530) 758-3091   CA
Web Site: http://www.superiorfarms.com
Year Founded: 1964
Premium Lamb Products Producer & Marketer
N.A.I.C.S.: 311611
Les Oesterreich *(Chm & CEO)*

TRANSICO INCORPORATED
880 Columbia St, Brea, CA 92821
Tel.: (714) 835-6000   CA
Web Site: http://www.eecoswitch.com
Year Founded: 1947
Sales Range: $1-9.9 Million
Emp.: 20
Electronics Mfr
N.A.I.C.S.: 335314
Wen-Hu Tu *(Chm)*
Dane Hoiberg *(Pres & CEO)*
Steve Potter *(VP-Fin)*
Richard Soden *(VP-Mktg & Sls)*

Subsidiaries:

EECO   (1)
880 Columbia St, Brea, CA 92821 **(100%)**
Tel.: (714) 835-6000
Web Site: http://www.eecoswitch.com
Mfr Of Electro Mechanical Switches
N.A.I.C.S.: 335314

EECO Switch (UK)   (1)
Unit 5 Hazlewell Court Bar Road, Lolworth, CB23 8DS, Cambs, United Kingdom **(100%)**
Tel.: (44) 1954781818
Web Site: http://www.eecoswitch.co.uk
Sales Range: $1-9.9 Million
Emp.: 2
Mfr & Distr of Electro-Mechanical Switches, Rubber Keypads & Hi-Tech Lead-Free, Double Sided, STH Printed Circuit Boards
N.A.I.C.S.: 334412
Dane Hoiberg *(Mng Dir)*

TRANSIT MEDIA GROUP
14067 Hoppe Dr, Rancho Cucamonga, CA 91739
Tel.: (909) 581-0887
Web Site: http://www.tm-g.com
Year Founded: 2003
Sales Range: $1-9.9 Million
Emp.: 10
Media Buying Services
N.A.I.C.S.: 541830
Michael Scafuto *(CEO)*

TRANSIT SYSTEMS INC.
999 Old Eagle School Rd Ste 114, Wayne, PA 19087
Tel.: (610) 971-1830
Web Site: http://www.transitsystems.com
Year Founded: 1989
Sales Range: $1-9.9 Million
Emp.: 25
Freight Transportation Arrangement
N.A.I.C.S.: 488510
Chris Smith *(CEO)*
Troy Bausinger *(Dir-Sls)*

TRANSITCENTER, INC.
1 Whitehall St 17th Fl, New York, NY 10001
Tel.: (646) 395-9555   NY
Web Site: http://www.transitcenter.com
Year Founded: 2000
Sales Range: $25-49.9 Million
Emp.: 97
Public Transportation Services
N.A.I.C.S.: 813319
Jennifer Elam *(Mgr-Grants & Ops)*
Jon Orcutt *(Dir-Comm & Advocacy)*

TRANSITION CAPITAL PARTNERS LTD.
1909 Woodall Rodgers Fwy Ste 575, Dallas, TX 75201
Tel.: (214) 978-3800
Web Site: http://tcplp.com
Year Founded: 1993
Private Investment Firm
N.A.I.C.S.: 523999
Dan Patterson *(Chm)*
Keith Driscoll *(Mng Dir)*
Colin Patrick *(CFO)*
Andy Foskey *(Mng Partner)*
Jason Faucett *(Mng Dir)*

TRANSITION HOUSE
425 E Cota St, Santa Barbara, CA 93101
Tel.: (805) 966-9668   CA
Web Site: http://www.transitionhouse.com
Year Founded: 1986
Sales Range: $1-9.9 Million
Emp.: 49
Family & Child Care Services
N.A.I.C.S.: 624190
Kathleen Baushke *(Exec Dir)*
Debbie Michael *(Program Dir)*
Mike Zaragoza *(Dir-Facilities)*
Heather Stevenson *(Dir-Grants & Dev)*
Natalie Graves *(Fin Dir)*
Kathryn Dinkin *(Sec)*
Andrew Gardner *(Treas)*
Gayla Visalli *(VP)*
Jim Buckley *(Pres)*

TRANSITIONAL SERVICES FOR NEW YORK, INC.
10-16 162nd St, Whitestone, NY 11357
Tel.: (718) 746-6647   NY
Web Site: http://www.tsiny.org
Year Founded: 1974
Sales Range: $10-24.9 Million
Emp.: 392
Behavioral Healthcare Services
N.A.I.C.S.: 621420
Daniel Donoghue *(COO)*
Larry S. Grubler *(CEO)*
Stanley L. Corfman *(CFO)*

TRANSITIONS GROUP INC.
116 Cleveland St, Wichita, KS 67214
Tel.: (316) 263-5750
Web Site: http://www.transitionsgroup.net
Rev.: $16,985,761
Emp.: 40
Furniture Rental
N.A.I.C.S.: 532289
Piper Ayala *(VP-Housing)*
Brent Dorrah *(Pres)*
Brendan Hogan *(VP-Furniture Options)*
William R. Jackson *(Founder & Chm)*

TRANSLATIONS.COM
3 Park Ave 39th Fl, New York, NY 10016-5902
Tel.: (212) 689-1616
Web Site: http://www.translations.com
Sales Range: $1-9.9 Million
Emp.: 5,000
Globalization Technology & Services
N.A.I.C.S.: 541930
Phil Shawe *(Pres & CEO)*
Roy B. Trujillo *(COO)*
Tim Coughlin *(VP-Sls)*
Jacques Barreau *(VP-Media & Interactive Entertainment)*
Matt Hauser *(Sr VP)*
Keith Brazil *(Sr VP-Tech)*
Lisa Chan *(Sr VP)*

Subsidiaries:

Translations.com   (1)
160 Spear St Ste 1100, San Francisco, CA 94105
Tel.: (212) 689-5555
Provider of Globalization Technology & Services
N.A.I.C.S.: 449210
Mike McPherson *(Dir-Client Svcs)*
Eduardo D'Antonio *(VP & Gen Mgr)*
Tim Coughlin *(VP-Sls)*
Marc Johnson *(Gen Mgr-Ops)*
Hsueh-Fu Ku *(Product Mgr)*

TRANSLINK SHIPPING INC.

COMPANIES

15020 Bothell Way NE No 100, Seattle, WA 98155
Tel.: (206) 363-8888
Web Site:
http://www.translinkshipping.com
Rev.: $11,500,000
Emp.: 12
Provider of Trans-Oceanic Freight Transportation
N.A.I.C.S.: 483111
Sam Chen (Pres)
Barb Johnson (Gen Mgr)
Carl Baak (Branch Mgr)

TRANSMARKET GROUP INC.
550 West Jackson Blvd Ste 1300, Chicago, IL 60661
Tel.: (312) 284-5500
Web Site:
http://www.transmarketgroup.com
Rev.: $14,600,000
Emp.: 85
Futures Brokers & Dealers, Commodity
N.A.I.C.S.: 523160
Jim McCormick (Pres & CEO)
Eric Meier (COO)
Ray Cahnman (Chm)
Thomas R. O'Brien (CFO)

TRANSMEDIA GROUP
240 W Palmetto Park Rd Ste 300, Boca Raton, FL 33432
Tel.: (561) 750-9800
Web Site:
http://www.transmediagroup.com
Year Founded: 1981
Sales Range: $1-9.9 Million
Emp.: 14
Public Relations
N.A.I.C.S.: 541820
Thomas J. Madden (Founder & CEO)
Angela Madden (CFO & VP)
Adrienne Mazzone (Pres)
Cassandra Cardenas (Dir-Creative)
Lisa Armoyan (Pres-Model & Talent Div)
Alexandra Flugel (VP-Social Media & PR)
Adam Furman (Dir-SEO & SEM)
Gabriela Vega (Dir-PR)
Steve Sloane (Dir-Media Buying)
Tim Stergiou-Allen (VP-PR)
Rebecca Shpektor (Dir-PR)
Dawn Kimball (Exec VP-Dallas)
Catherine deHaan (Exec VP-PR, Mktg & Video Production)

TRANSMEDICS, INC.
200 Minuteman Rd Ste 302, Andover, MA 01810
Tel.: (978) 552-0900 DE
Web Site:
http://www.transmedics.com
Year Founded: 1998
Sales Range: $10-24.9 Million
Emp.: 82
Organ Transplantation Medical Device Mfr & Marketer
N.A.I.C.S.: 339112
Waleed H. Hassanein (Founder, Pres & CEO)
Tamer I. Khayal (CMO)
John Sullivan (VP-Engrg)
Neal Beswick (VP-Bus Dev)
Marienne Sanders (VP-Global Mktg)
Jacqueline Sneve (VP-Healthcare Economics & Reimbursement)
John Carey (VP-Ops)
Christine Brauer (VP-Regulatory Affairs)

TRANSMISSION & FLUID EQUIPMENT COMPANY
6912 Trafalgar Dr, Fort Wayne, IN 46803
Tel.: (260) 493-3223 IN
Web Site: http://www.tfedirect.com
Year Founded: 1964
Sales Range: $10-24.9 Million
Emp.: 40
Provider of Power Transmission Equipment & Apparatus
N.A.I.C.S.: 423840
Robert Hughes (Treas)
Chris Hughes (Pres)
Al Linsdey (Controller)

TRANSNATIONAL FOODS
1110 Brickell Ave Ste 808, Miami, FL 33131
Tel.: (305) 365-9652
Web Site:
http://www.transnationalfoods.com
Year Founded: 2002
Sales Range: $50-74.9 Million
Emp.: 18
Professional Scientific & Technical Services
N.A.I.C.S.: 541990
Ignacio Sangronis (CMO)
Marcelo Young (CEO)
Juan Iribarne (CFO)
Francisco Young (Exec VP)
Brett Barcelona (Exec VP-New Bus)
Amandah Martin (VP-Sls-Confectionary)
Bryan Nichols (VP-Sls)
Jim Stephenson (VP-Sls)

TRANSOM CAPITAL GROUP, LLC
100 N Pacific Coast Hwy Ste 1725, El Segundo, CA 90245
Tel.: (424) 293-2818 DE
Web Site:
http://www.transomcap.com
Year Founded: 2008
Private Equity Firm Services
N.A.I.C.S.: 523999
Ken Firtel (Founder & Mng Partner)
Russ Roenick (Co-Founder & Mng Partner)
James Oh (Partner)
T. Y. Schultze (Mng Partner)
Nathan Dastic (CFO)
Steve Kim (Principal)
Andres Meza (VP-Ops)
Brendan Hart (VP-Ops)
Rob Randolph (VP-Fin Ops)
Chris Baddon (VP-Bus Dev)
James Whittle (VP-Bus Dev)
Nishant Bubna (VP-Bus Dev)

Subsidiaries:

A.T. Cross Company (1)
299 Promenade St, Providence, RI 02865
Tel.: (401) 335-8242
Web Site: http://www.cross.com
Fine Writing Instruments & Accessories Mfr, Distr & Online Retailer
N.A.I.C.S.: 339940
Mahoney Kevin (CFO)
Michael Foley (COO)

Subsidiary (Non-US):

A.T. Cross (France) S.A. (2)
5 Avenue Georges Bataille, 60330, Le Plessis-Belleville, France
Tel.: (33) 172190490
Web Site: http://www.cross.com
Fine Writing Instruments Distr & Online Retailer
N.A.I.C.S.: 424120

A.T. Cross Limited (2)
Ballinasloe Enterprise Centre, Ballinasloe, 02865-3749, Galway, Ireland
Tel.: (353) 90 963 1400
Web Site: http://www.cross.com
Fine Writing Instruments Distr & Online Retailer
N.A.I.C.S.: 424120

A.T. Cross Limited (2)
Cross House Unit 14 Windmill Trading Estate Thistle Road, Luton, LU1 3XJ, Bedfordshire, United Kingdom
Tel.: (44) 1582422793
Web Site: http://www.cross.com
Fine Writing Instruments Distr & Online Retailer
N.A.I.C.S.: 424120

Subsidiary (Domestic):

Sheaffer Pen & Art Supply Co. (2)
299 Promenade St, Providence, RI 02908
Tel.: (800) 346-3736
Web Site: http://www.sheaffer.com
Fountain Pens, Ballpoint Pens, Writing Instruments, Cartridge Pens, Mechanical Pencils, Desk Sets & Calligraphy Pens Mfr
N.A.I.C.S.: 339940

Aden & Anais, Inc (1)
55 Washington St Ste 702, Brooklyn, NY 11201
Tel.: (718) 801-8432
Web Site: http://www.adenandanais.com
Sales Range: $25-49.9 Million
Emp.: 90
Baby Clothing Store Operator
N.A.I.C.S.: 458110
Raegan Moya-Jones (Founder)
Jennifer Mederos (Dir-Creative)
Andrea Veiga (Mng Dir)
Scott Schreistein (Dir-Art)
Ciara Beggan (CFO)
Danielle Beale (Dir-Mktg-Global)

Subsidiary (Domestic):

BreathableBaby, LLC (2)
1593 Wexford Cir, Eagan, MN 55122-2569
Tel.: (651) 994-6519
Web Site: http://www.breathablebaby.com
Clothing, Textile & Accessory Mfr
N.A.I.C.S.: 325998

Blue Microphones, LLC (1)
5706 Corsa Ave Ste 102, Westlake Village, CA 91362-4057
Tel.: (818) 879-5200
Web Site: http://www.bluemic.com
Sales Range: $1-9.9 Million
Emp.: 35
Microphones & Audio Accessories Designer & Mfr
N.A.I.C.S.: 334310
Martins Saulespurins (Co-Founder & Dir-R&D)
John Maier (CEO)

Bravo Sports Corporation (1)
12801 Carmenita Rd, Santa Fe Springs, CA 90670
Tel.: (562) 484-5100
Web Site: http://www.bravosportscorp.com
Sales Range: $25-49.9 Million
Emp.: 110
In-Line Skating Wheels & Accessories & Portable Canopy Mfr
N.A.I.C.S.: 339920
Leo Pais (CEO)
Jeff Balaban (Sr VP-Sls-Specialty)
Drew Brassard (CIO & VP-Ops)
Mark Heineken (Chief Brand Officer)
Patrick Enright (Sr-VP-Sls)
Kyle Brookey (Dir-Sls)
Dave Davenport (Product Mgr-Helmets & Protective Gear)
Steve Segvich (CFO)

Subsidiary (Domestic):

Sector 9, Inc. (2)
5893 Oberlin Dr Ste 100, San Diego, CA 92121
Tel.: (858) 408-0083
Web Site: http://www.sector9.com
Sales Range: $1-9.9 Million
Emp.: 50
Sporting & Athletic Goods Mfr
N.A.I.C.S.: 339920
Dave Kimkiewicz (Co-Owner)

Variflex Inc. (2)
12801 Carmenita Rd, Santa Fe Springs, CA 90605
Tel.: (562) 484-5100
Web Site: http://www.bravosportscorp.com
Sales Range: $25-49.9 Million
Emp.: 110
Inline Skates, Skateboards, Recreational Safety Helmets, Athletic Protective Equipment, Snowboards, Portable Instant Canopies & Springless Trampolines Distr
N.A.I.C.S.: 423910

BridgeTower Media, LLC (1)
222 S Ninth St Ste 900, Minneapolis, MN 55402
Tel.: (612) 317-9420
Web Site: http://www.bridgetowermedia.com
Broadcast Media Services
N.A.I.C.S.: 541910
Adam Reinebach (Pres & CEO)
Hal Cohen (Exec VP)
Candice Hoppe (VP-HR)
Kathryn Ross (Publr)
Lisa Blossman (Grp Publr)
Tammy Overcash (VP-Fin & Acctg)
Jen Kahn (Dir-Mktg, Strategy & Analytics)
Vincent Velasquez (VP-Events)
Liz Irwin (VP-Creative Svcs)
Sheila Long O'Mara (Exec Editor-Furniture Today)
Tom Callahan (CFO)

Galleher LLC (1)
9303 Greenleaf Ave, Santa Fe Springs, CA 90670-3029
Tel.: (562) 356-4885
Web Site: http://www.galleher.com
Sales Range: $50-74.9 Million
Emp.: 110
Wood Flooring Products Distr
N.A.I.C.S.: 321918
Jeff Hamar (Chm)
Todd Hamar (Sr VP)
Rick Coates (COO)
Jim Whitney (CFO & Sr VP)
Ted Kozikowski (Pres & CEO)
Jim Harrington (VP-Mktg & Brand Strategy)
Irina Slonim (Controller)

Subsidiary (Domestic):

Trinity Hardwood Distributors, Inc. (2)
110 Oregon Ave, Dallas, TX 75203
Tel.: (214) 948-3001
Web Site: http://www.trinityhardwood.net
Whol Homefurnishings
N.A.I.C.S.: 423220
Jon Roy Reid (Founder & Pres)

Virginia Tile Company, LLC (2)
28320 Plymouth Rd, Livonia, MI 48150
Tel.: (248) 649-4422
Web Site: http://www.virginiatile.com
Rev.: $2,880,000
Emp.: 6
Brick, Stone & Related Construction Material Merchant Whslr
N.A.I.C.S.: 423320
Lynne Moran (Mgr-Michigan Showroom Ops)

Gene Juarez Salons LLC (1)
3633 136th Pl SE Ste 200, Bellevue, WA 98006
Tel.: (425) 748-1400
Web Site: http://www.genejuarez.com
Sales Range: $50-74.9 Million
Emp.: 1,300
Salon & Spa Operator
N.A.I.C.S.: 812112
Bonnie Guiton Hill (VP-HR)
Jerry Ahern (VP-Education)
Scott Missad (CEO)

Midwest Center for Stress & Anxiety, LLC (1)
106 N Church St Ste 200, Oak Harbor, OH 43449
Tel.: (419) 898-4357
Web Site: http://www.stresscenter.com
Sales Range: $1-9.9 Million
Emp.: 35
Stress, Anxiety & Depression Self-Help Products & Support Services
N.A.I.C.S.: 624190
Lucinda Bassett (Pres)

Scantron Corporation (1)
1313 Lone Oak Rd, Eagan, MN 55121-1334 (100%)
Tel.: (949) 639-7500
Web Site: http://www.scantron.com
Sales Range: $100-124.9 Million
Emp.: 50
Automated Data Entry & Collection Equipment & Related Supplies Designer, Developer, Mfr & Marketer
N.A.I.C.S.: 333310

TRANSOM CAPITAL GROUP, LLC

U.S. PRIVATE

Transom Capital Group, LLC—(Continued)

Kevin Brueggeman (CEO)
Nikki Eatchel (Chief Assessment Officer & Sr VP)
Cathy Pickoski (Sr VP-Sls & Mktg)
Bryan Reel (CTO & Sr VP)
Maria Incrocci (VP-Psychometrics)
Jay Whitchurch (Pres)

Division (Domestic):

P&L Technology, Inc. (2)
4211 S 143rd Cir, Omaha, NE 68137
Tel.: (402) 330-9580
Web Site: http://www.pltechnology.com
Information Technology Services
N.A.I.C.S.: 541512
Scott Wilson (Dir-Tech Ops)

Scantron Corporation - Data Management Solutions (2)
1313 Lone Oak Rd, Eagan, MN 55121 (100%)
Tel.: (651) 683-6000
Web Site: http://www.scantron.com
Scannable Data Collection Services & Products Mfr
N.A.I.C.S.: 333310

TRANSON MEDIA LLC
995 Market St, San Francisco, CA 94103
Tel.: (415) 621-9830
Web Site:
  http://www.victoriousseo.com
Year Founded: 2014
Sales Range: $1-9.9 Million
Emp.: 50
Website Development Services
N.A.I.C.S.: 541511
Michael Transon (CEO)

TRANSONIC COMBUSTION, INC.
461 Calle San Pablo, Camarillo, CA 93012
Tel.: (805) 484-5540
Web Site:
  http://www.tscombustion.com
Year Founded: 2006
Sales Range: $1-9.9 Million
Emp.: 14
Fuel Injector Production
N.A.I.C.S.: 541720
Wolfgang Bullmer (CEO)

TRANSOURCE INC.
8700 Triad Dr, Colfax, NC 27235
Tel.: (336) 996-6060
Web Site:
  http://www.transourcetrucks.com
Rev.: $26,000,000
Emp.: 50
Retailer of Trucks
N.A.I.C.S.: 441110
James E. Bland (Pres)
Justin Underwood (Mgr-Leasing)
Scott Hunt (Mgr-Acctg)
Brian Causer (Dir-Parts Ops)
Michael Wolfe (Mgr-Fin)

TRANSOURCE SERVICES CORP
2405 W Utopia Rd, Phoenix, AZ 85027
Tel.: (623) 879-8882
Web Site: http://www.transource.com
Sales Range: $10-24.9 Million
Emp.: 25
Computers Sales
N.A.I.C.S.: 541519
Ann Ting (CEO)

TRANSPAC IMPORTS INC.
1050 Aviator Dr, Vacaville, CA 95688
Tel.: (707) 452-0600
Web Site: http://www.shoptii.com
Year Founded: 1995
Sales Range: $10-24.9 Million
Emp.: 90
Vitreous China, Fine Earthenware & Pottery Product Mfr
N.A.I.C.S.: 327110
Jesse Ma (Owner & Pres)
Lisa Campisano (Dir-Acct Svcs)

TRANSPERFECT GLOBAL, INC.
3 Park Ave 39th Floor, New York, NY 10016
Tel.: (212) 689-5555   DE
Web Site:
  http://www.transperfectglobal.com
Sales Range: $450-499.9 Million
Emp.: 4,600
Holding Company; Professional Services & Technologies
N.A.I.C.S.: 551112
Phil Shawe (Founder, Pres & CEO)
Brooke Christian (Exec VP-Global Sls & Mktg & Chief Sls Officer)
Stewart I. Edison (Pres-TransPerfect Deposition Services)
Kaarin Gordon (VP-Tech Solutions-TransPerfect Life Sciences)
Edgar Vargas-Castaneda (VP-Growth Strategies & Bus Optimization)
Annika Rynger (Dir-Bus Dev)

Subsidiaries:

TransPerfect Legal Solutions (1)
3 Park Ave 39th Fl, New York, NY 10016
Tel.: (212) 689-5555
Web Site: http://www.transperfectlegal.com
Legal & Patent Business Development
N.A.I.C.S.: 541199
Eric Elting (Dir-Global Legal Bus Dev)
Daniel S. Meyers (Pres-Info Governance)
Stefan Nigam (Dir-Consulting & Info Governance-Europe, Middle East & Africa)
Phil Shawe (Pres & CEO)

Subsidiary (Domestic):

TransPerfect Document Management, Inc. (2)
40 Exchange Pl 15th Fl, New York, NY 10007
Tel.: (212) 269-2200
Web Site: http://www.transperfectlegal.com
Reprographic & Litigation Services
N.A.I.C.S.: 561410
Phil Shawe (CEO)
Andrew Kwon (Mgr-Hosting)

TransPerfect Translations International Inc. (1)
3 Park Ave 39th Fl, New York, NY 10016
Tel.: (212) 689-5555
Web Site: http://www.transperfect.com
Translation Services
N.A.I.C.S.: 541930
Mark Peeler (VP-Quality Assurance, Compliance & Standardization)
Kevin Obarski (VP-Sls-US)
Michael Sank (VP-Corp Dev)
Phil Shawe (Co-Founder, Pres & CEO)
Jessica Eker (Sr VP)
Jin Lee (VP-Global Production)
Mark Hagerty (CTO)
Matt Hauser (VP-Content Solutions)
Yu-Kai Ng (CIO)
Dominique Hourant (VP-Strategic Accts-Barcelona)

TRANSPLY INC.
1005 Vogelsong Rd, York, PA 17404
Tel.: (717) 767-1005
Web Site: http://www.transply.com
Year Founded: 1972
Sales Range: $10-24.9 Million
Emp.: 73
Industrial Supplies
N.A.I.C.S.: 423840
Brian Gross (Pres)
Susan Crone (VP-HR)

TRANSPORT DISTRIBUTION COMPANY
5357 E 7th St, Joplin, MO 64801
Tel.: (417) 624-3814
Web Site: http://www.gotdc.com
Year Founded: 1984
Rev.: $20,810,825
Emp.: 140
Household Goods Transport
N.A.I.C.S.: 484210
Larry Kloeppel (Pres)

TRANSPORT DRIVERS INC.
3540 7th Bridges Dr Ste 300, Woodridge, IL 60517
Tel.: (630) 766-2721
Web Site:
  http://www.transportdrivers.com
Sales Range: $25-49.9 Million
Emp.: 30
Truck Driving Services
N.A.I.C.S.: 561320
John Urman (CFO)
Ronald P. Formento Sr. (Chm & Pres)

TRANSPORT EXPRESS LLC
3275 Mike Collins Dr, Eagan, MN 55121
Tel.: (651) 452-5306
Web Site:
  http://www.transportexpress.com
Year Founded: 1991
Sales Range: $1-9.9 Million
Emp.: 9
Freight Transportation & Logistics Services
N.A.I.C.S.: 488510
J. Nick Schultheis (Principal-Admin)

TRANSPORT INVESTMENTS, INC.
100 Industry Dr, Pittsburgh, PA 15275-1014
Tel.: (412) 788-8878   DE
Web Site:
  http://www.transportinvestment.com
Year Founded: 1988
Sales Range: $350-399.9 Million
Holding Company; Freight Transportation Services
N.A.I.C.S.: 551112
Douglas B. McAdams (Founder, Pres & CEO)
Michael J. Pellicci (CFO)
R. Bruce McAdams (Pres)

Subsidiaries:

Aetna Freight Lines, Inc. (1)
100 Industry Dr, Pittsburgh, PA 15275-1014
Tel.: (412) 490-7777
Web Site:
  http://www.transportinvestments.com
Freight Transportation Services
N.A.I.C.S.: 488510
Jeffrey F. Kollar (Pres)

Air Transport, Inc. (1)
100 Industry Dr, Pittsburgh, PA 15275-1014
Tel.: (412) 788-8878
Web Site: http://transportinvestments.com
Freight Transportation Services
N.A.I.C.S.: 488510
David N. Hartman (Pres)

Greentree Transportation Company (1)
100 Industry Dr, Pittsburgh, PA 15275-1014
Tel.: (412) 788-3680
Web Site:
  http://www.transportinvestments.com
Freight Transportation Services
N.A.I.C.S.: 488510
Douglas Bruce McAdams (Exec VP)
Kenneth E. Slafka (Pres)
Ronald R. Miller (Fin Mgr)

Jones Motor Group, Inc. (1)
654 Enterprise Dr, Limerick, PA 19468
Tel.: (610) 948-7900
Web Site: http://www.jonesmotor.com
Holding Company; Freight Transportation Services
N.A.I.C.S.: 551112

Subsidiary (Domestic):

Jones Motor Co., Inc. (2)
654 Enterprise Dr, Limerick, PA 19468
Tel.: (610) 948-7900
Web Site: http://www.jonesmotor.com
Freight Transportation Services
N.A.I.C.S.: 488510
Kenneth J. Lacy (Pres)
Larry Nestor (VP)

Marathon Transport, Inc. (1)
100 Industry Dr, Pittsburgh, PA 15275-1014
Tel.: (412) 788-8878
Web Site:
  http://www.transportinvestments.com
Freight Transportation Services
N.A.I.C.S.: 488510
Daniel S. Singer (Pres)

TRANSPORT LEASING COMPANY LLP
1901 Benefis Ct, Great Falls, MT 59405
Tel.: (406) 727-7500
Web Site:
  http://www.transystemsllc.com
Year Founded: 1942
Sales Range: $50-74.9 Million
Emp.: 100
Truck Rental Services
N.A.I.C.S.: 532120

TRANSPORT LEASING/CONTRACT
6160 Summit Dr N Ste 500, Minneapolis, MN 55430-2252
Tel.: (763) 585-7000
Web Site:
  http://www.tlccompanies.com
Sales Range: $350-399.9 Million
Emp.: 75
Temporary Truck Driver Placement Services
N.A.I.C.S.: 561320
Bill Benson (CFO)
Tim Coughlin (Pres & CEO)
Rod Jordan (Gen Counsel, Sec & VP-HR)

TRANSPORT REFRIGERATION INC.
3964 Packerland Dr, De Pere, WI 54115
Tel.: (920) 339-5700
Web Site:
  http://www.thermokinggreenbay.com
Rev.: $36,000,000
Emp.: 45
Provider of Refrigerated Transportation Services
N.A.I.C.S.: 423740
Rebecca Cayo (Office Mgr)
Rick Holeman (Acct Mgr)

TRANSPORT REFRIGERATION OF SOUTH DAKOTA INC.
5700 N Seubert Ave, Sioux Falls, SD 57104-0501
Tel.: (605) 332-3861
Web Site: http://www.keizerco.com
Year Founded: 2001
Sales Range: $10-24.9 Million
Emp.: 16
Repair & Sales of Refrigeration Units
N.A.I.C.S.: 811412
Shane Keizer (VP)

TRANSPORT SERVICES INC.
10499 Royalton Rd, Cleveland, OH 44133
Tel.: (440) 582-4900
Web Site:
  http://www.transportservices.net
Year Founded: 1976
Sales Range: $10-24.9 Million
Emp.: 39
Trailer Rental

TRANSPORT SPECIALISTS INCORPORATED
12130 Best Pl, Cincinnati, OH 45241
Tel.: (513) 771-2220
Web Site: http://www.tktransport.net
Year Founded: 1971
Sales Range: $10-24.9 Million
Emp.: 54
Truck Equipment & Parts
N.A.I.C.S.: 441330
Jake Jennings *(Pres)*
Glenn Martin *(Controller)*

TRANSPORT TOPICS PUBLISHING GROUP
950 N Glebe Rd Ste 210, Arlington, VA 22203-4654
Tel.: (703) 838-1770
Web Site: http://www.ttnews.com
Year Founded: 1933
Sales Range: $75-99.9 Million
Emp.: 150
National Weekly Business Newspaper of Trucking Industry
N.A.I.C.S.: 513110
Brian Kelly *(Mgr-Creative Svcs)*
Debra Devine *(Mgr-Production)*
Neil Abt *(Dir-Editorial)*
Scott Smith *(Dir-Circulation)*
Tara McClelland *(Mgr-Mktg)*

TRANSPORTATION & TRANSIT ASSOCIATES, LLC
1 William K Jackson Ln, Hornell, NY 14843
Tel.: (607) 324-0216
Web Site: http://www.ttallc.com
Rev.: $27,778,962
Emp.: 300
Re-builder & Assembler of Rail Transit Vehicles, Systems & Components
N.A.I.C.S.: 332312
Dave Sharma *(Pres)*

TRANSPORTATION COMMUNICATIONS UNIONIAM
3 Research Pl, Rockville, MD 20850
Tel.: (301) 948-4910
Year Founded: 1899
Sales Range: $25-49.9 Million
Emp.: 251
Transportation Support Services
N.A.I.C.S.: 561510
Robert A. Scardelletti *(Pres)*
Russell C. Oathout *(Treas & Sec)*
Richard A. Johnson *(VP)*
Ronald Kloos *(VP)*
Joel Parker *(VP)*

TRANSPORTATION CONSULTANTS OF AMERICA, INC.
36-40 37th St Ste 201, Long Island City, NY 11101
Tel.: (212) 481-2727
Web Site: http://www.qualitytca.com
Year Founded: 1998
Sales Range: $25-49.9 Million
Emp.: 140
Provider of Courier Services
N.A.I.C.S.: 561499
Julius F. DeVito *(Pres & CEO)*
John Scarola *(Exec VP)*
Rocco DeVito *(VP-Ops)*
Sandy Ganz *(CFO)*
Star Line *(Controller)*

TRANSPORTATION DESIGN & MANUFACTURING CO.
13000 Farmington Rd, Livonia, MI 48150-4209
Tel.: (734) 525-1068
Web Site: http://www.tdmco.com
Year Founded: 1999
Sales Range: $10-24.9 Million
Emp.: 194
Provider of Motor Vehicles & Car Bodies
N.A.I.C.S.: 336110

TRANSPORTATION EQUIPMENT SALES CORP. (TESCO)
6401 Seaman Rd, Oregon, OH 43616-7230
Tel.: (419) 836-2835
Web Site: http://www.tescobus.com
Sales Range: $10-24.9 Million
Emp.: 100
Sales of Busses
N.A.I.C.S.: 423110
Diane Krueger *(Sec)*
Noel E. Graham Sr. *(Pres & CEO)*
Noel E. Graham Jr. *(Mgr-Used Sls)*

TRANSPORTATION GENERAL INC.
3251 Washington Blvd, Arlington, VA 22201
Tel.: (703) 525-0900
Web Site: http://www.fairfaxredtopcab.com
Sales Range: $10-24.9 Million
Emp.: 250
Provider of Transportation Services
N.A.I.C.S.: 484110
Neal C. Nichols *(Pres)*
Charles King *(VP)*
John Zarbo *(Gen Mgr)*
Katy Korb *(CFO)*
Keith Ahn *(VP)*
Von Pelot *(Dir-Sls & Mktg)*

TRANSPORTATION LEASING CO.
7215 E 46th St, Tulsa, OK 74145
Tel.: (918) 622-8400
Web Site: http://www.hvsu.com
Sales Range: $10-24.9 Million
Emp.: 25
Passenger Car Leasing
N.A.I.C.S.: 532112
Charles W. Harris *(Pres)*

TRANSPORTATION RESOURCE PARTNERS, LP
2555 S Telegraph Rd, Bloomfield Hills, MI 48302
Tel.: (248) 648-2101
Web Site: http://www.trpfund.com
Year Founded: 2003
Sales Range: $1-9.9 Million
Emp.: 62
Miscellaneous Financial Investment Activities
N.A.I.C.S.: 523999
Dave Mitchell *(Mng Dir)*

TRANSPORTATION SERVICES, INC.
18165 Telegraph Rd, Romulus, MI 48174
Tel.: (734) 282-4444
Web Site: http://www.tsitrucks.com
Sales Range: $10-24.9 Million
Emp.: 50
Trucking Except Local
N.A.I.C.S.: 484121
A. J. Pellegrino *(Founder)*
David Dubach *(Exec VP-Sls)*
Cheryl Damron *(Mgr-Collections)*
William Gennaro *(Dir-Ops)*
Bernie Frascarelli *(Mgr-Shop)*
Mike Zavislak *(CFO & COO)*
Jesse Lopez *(Dir-Maintenance)*
Gustavo Sifuentes *(Dir-Operation-Intl)*
Pat Cardenas *(Dir-Safety)*
Joann Plopan *(Mgr-Customer Svc)*
Carlos Sepulveda *(Mgr-Ops)*
David Trueblood *(Mgr-Ops-Northern)*
Chris Giermanski *(VP-Intl Ops)*
John Lawrence *(VP-Pricing & Contracts)*

Subsidiaries:

TSI Equipment Inc. (1)
18165 Telegraph Rd, Romulus, MI 48174
Tel.: (734) 282-4444
Truck Leasing, Without Drivers
N.A.I.C.S.: 532120

TRANSPORTATION SOLUTIONS GROUP, LLC.
400 N Noble St, Chicago, IL 60622
Tel.: (312) 738-5500
Web Site: http://www.tsgsolutions.com
Rev.: $48,800,000
Emp.: 80
Freight Transportation Arrangement
N.A.I.C.S.: 488510
Ashley Larson *(Mgr-Ops Staff)*
R. J. Whidman *(Mgr)*
Eric Rempel *(CTO)*

TRANSPORTATION WORLDWIDE INC.
16930 Park Row, Houston, TX 77084
Tel.: (281) 492-7717
Web Site: http://www.tww.net
Rev.: $11,000,000
Emp.: 16
Foreign Freight Forwarding
N.A.I.C.S.: 488510
Kay Arny *(Mgr-Ops)*
Michael Feigleson *(VP)*

TRANSTECH SOLUTIONS, INC.
843 N Rainbow Blvd Unit 1175, Las Vegas, NV 89107
Tel.: (866) 998-6920
Year Founded: 2011
Medical Transcription Services
N.A.I.C.S.: 561499
Christopher Weinhaupl *(Pres, CEO, CFO, Treas & Sec)*

TRANSTELCO HOLDING, INC.
500 W Overland Ave Ste 310, El Paso, TX 79901
Tel.: (915) 534-8100
Web Site: http://www.transtelco.net
Year Founded: 2001
Telecommunication Servicesb
N.A.I.C.S.: 517810
Edgar Mosti *(VP-Network Svcs-Wholesale)*
Miguel Fernandez *(CEO)*

Subsidiaries:

Maxcom Telecomunicaciones, S.A.B. de C.V. (1)
Tel.: (52) 5547701170
Web Site: https://www.ri.maxcom.com
Rev.: $45,592,515
Assets: $147,551,328
Liabilities: $106,928,469
Net Worth: $40,622,860
Earnings: ($26,196,201)
Emp.: 232
Fiscal Year-end: 12/31/2020
Local, Long Distance, Internet, VoIP & Public Telephony Services
N.A.I.C.S.: 517111
Javier Molinar Horcasitas *(Vice Chm)*
Carlos Muriel Gaxiola *(Chm)*
Rodrigo Castro Wright *(Head-IR)*
Erik Gonzalez Laureano *(Co-CEO & VP-Fin)*
Javier Ramon Guerrero *(Co-CEO & VP-Comml Strategy)*
Armando Jorge Rivero Laing *(VP-Admin & Legal)*

Neutrona Networks International LLC (1)
1951 NW 7th Ave 600 6th Fl, Miami, FL 33136
Tel.: (305) 728-8500
Web Site: http://www.neutrona.com
Wired Telecommunications Carriers
N.A.I.C.S.: 517111
Luciano Salata *(Pres & COO)*

TRANSTEX LLC
8219-100 NW Blvd, Indianapolis, IN 46278
Tel.: (877) 960-2644
Web Site: https://transtex-llc.com
Truck Transportation
N.A.I.C.S.: 336999

Subsidiaries:

U.S. Liner Company (1)
19 Leonberg Rd, Cranberry Township, PA 16066
Tel.: (724) 776-4044
Web Site: http://www.uslco.com
Glass-Reinforced Thermoplastic Composite Products Mfr
N.A.I.C.S.: 326199

TRANSWEST PARTNERS
2850 E Skyline Dr Ste 200, Tucson, AZ 85718
Tel.: (520) 544-4000
Web Site: http://www.transwest.us
Year Founded: 1988
Sales Range: $10-24.9 Million
Emp.: 300
Commercial Real Estate Services
N.A.I.C.S.: 531190
Randal G. Dix *(Partner & VP)*
Michael J. Hanson *(Pres & Partner)*

TRANSWHEEL CORPORATION
3000 Yeoman Way, Huntington, IN 46750-9003
Tel.: (260) 358-8660
Web Site: http://www.transwheel.com
Rev.: $22,000,000
Emp.: 215
Provider of Motor Vehicle Wheel Reconditioning
N.A.I.C.S.: 336390
Jhon Withmore *(Mgr-HR)*
Dave Roth *(Dir-Pur)*
Mike Mader *(Supvr-Production)*

TRANSWOOD CARRIERS INC.
2565 Saint Marys Ave, Omaha, NE 68105
Tel.: (402) 346-8092
Web Site: http://www.transwood.com
Year Founded: 1928
Sales Range: $200-249.9 Million
Emp.: 500
Provider of Trucking Services
N.A.I.C.S.: 484121
Bill Sawin *(VP-Compliance & Ops)*

Subsidiaries:

Leasco Inc (1)
2565 St Marys Ave, Omaha, NE 68101
Tel.: (402) 346-8092
Web Site: http://www.transwood.com
Sales Range: $10-24.9 Million
Emp.: 50
Provider of Trucking Services
N.A.I.C.S.: 532120
Bill Sawin *(VP)*

Transwood Inc. (1)
2565 Saint Marys Ave, Omaha, NE 68105
Tel.: (402) 346-8092
Web Site: http://www.transwood.com
Provider of Trucking Services
N.A.I.C.S.: 484110
Brian Wood *(Pres)*

Subsidiary (Domestic):

Kane Transport, Inc. (2)
40925 403rd Ave, Sauk Centre, MN 56738
Tel.: (320) 352-2762
Web Site: http://www.kanetransport.com
General Freight Trucking Services

TRANSWOOD CARRIERS INC. U.S. PRIVATE

Transwood Carriers Inc.—(Continued)
N.A.I.C.S.: 484110
Robert Kane (CEO)
Pat Kane (Mgr-Terminal)

Transwood Logistics Inc (1)
2565 Saint Marys Ave, Omaha, NE 68105
Tel.: (402) 346-8092
Rev.: $2,000,000
Emp.: 50
Provider of Trucking Services
N.A.I.C.S.: 484110
Brian Wood (Pres & CEO)
Mark Penry (Controller)

TRANSWORLD ADVERTISING, INC.
3684 N Wickham Rd Ste C, Melbourne, FL 32935
Tel.: (321) 259-7737
Web Site: http://www.transworldadvertising.com
Year Founded: 1981
Sales Range: $10-24.9 Million
Emp.: 11
Advertising Agencies, Newspaper, Recruitment, Restaurant
N.A.I.C.S.: 541810
Teri Burcham (Pres)

TRANSWORLD BUSINESS ADVISORS OF COLORADO LLC
215 S Wadsworth Blvd Ste 550, Lakewood, CO 80226
Tel.: (720) 259-5099
Web Site: http://www.tworld.com
Year Founded: 2013
Sales Range: $1-9.9 Million
Emp.: 18
Financial Consulting Services
N.A.I.C.S.: 541611
Jessica Fialkovich (Co-Founder & Pres)
Albert Fialkovich (Co-Founder & Mng Partner)
Ali Elman (Dir-Ops)
Rachael Holstein (Mktg Mgr)
Lindsey Hayden (Coord-Mktg & Sls)

TRANSYLVANIA COMMUNITY HOSPITAL, INC.
Hospital Dr, Brevard, NC 28712
Tel.: (828) 884-9111
Web Site: http://www.trhospital.org
Sales Range: $25-49.9 Million
Emp.: 600
Health Care Srvices
N.A.I.C.S.: 622110
Mark Emory (VP-HR)
Theresa Parker (Mgr-Fin)
Gwen McKinney (Chief Compliance Officer)
Ronald A. Paulus (Pres & CEO)
Bobbie Young (Co-Chm)
John McCoy (Co-Chm)
Ken Stonebraker (Co-Chm)
Lee Lattimore (Treas & Sec)
Roswell S. Bowers (Co-Chm)
Tim Blenco (Vice Chm)

TRANSYSTEMS LLC
1901 Benefis Ct, Great Falls, MT 59405
Tel.: (406) 727-7500
Web Site: http://www.transystemsllc.com
Year Founded: 1942
Sales Range: $150-199.9 Million
Emp.: 1,000
Bulk Commodities Transporter
N.A.I.C.S.: 484110
Pat Rice (Co-Pres)
Scott Lind (Co-Pres)
Dan Brennan (VP-IT & Revenue Equipment)
John Zimmermann (VP)

Todd Herman (Asst VP-Kansas City)
F. Allen Smith (VP-St. Louis)
Kevin Thibault (VP-Southeast)
Brian Krul (VP-Pittsburgh)
Alex Stone (VP-Atlanta)
Todd Thalmann (VP-Kansas City)
Tanya Lindquist (Asst VP-Houston)

Subsidiaries:

Transystems (1)
505 14th St Ste 1000, Oakland, CA 94612
Tel.: (510) 271-7970
Web Site: http://www.transystemsllc.com
Logistics Supply Chain Management
N.A.I.C.S.: 541614
Kit Wong (Principal)
Kenneth Kerr (Asst VP)

Transystems LLC (1)
220 St Charles Way Ste 150, York, PA 17402
Tel.: (717) 854-3861
Construction Management Services
N.A.I.C.S.: 236220
Alex Houseal (VP-Northeast)

Transystems LLC - Idaho Division (1)
419 Shoup Ave W, Twin Falls, ID 83301
Tel.: (208) 734-8050
Web Site: http://www.transystemsllc.com
Emp.: 500
General Freight Trucking Services
N.A.I.C.S.: 484121
Kevin Iversen (Gen Mgr)

Transystems LLC - Minnesota Division (1)
83901 County Road 21, Renville, MN 56284
Tel.: (320) 329-3400
General Freight Trucking Services
N.A.I.C.S.: 484121

Transystems LLC - Red River Valley Division (1)
2211 S Washington St Ste A, Grand Forks, ND 58201
Tel.: (701) 746-0389
General Freight Trucking Services
N.A.I.C.S.: 484121

TRANUM AUTO GROUP
5620 S Gen Bruce Dr, Temple, TX 76502
Tel.: (254) 773-4548
Web Site: http://www.tranumauto.com
Sales Range: $10-24.9 Million
Emp.: 30
New & Used Car Dealers Service & Parts
N.A.I.C.S.: 441110
Anna Kessler (Principal)

TRANZACT TECHNOLOGIES INC.
360 W Butterfield Rd Ste 400, Elmhurst, IL 60126
Tel.: (630) 833-0890
Web Site: http://www.tranzact.com
Rev.: $37,900,000
Emp.: 80
Transportation Management Solutions
N.A.I.C.S.: 513210
Jean Regan (Pres)
Michael A. Regan (Co-Founder & chief relationship development officer)
Leonard Turnbull (Coord-EDI)
David Bungum (VP-Mktg & Sls Dev)
Mike Everett (Mgr-Implementation)
Kevin Mosciano (Dir-Logistics)
Mike Brown (Sr VP-Client Svcs)

TRAP ROCK INDUSTRIES, INC.
PO Box 419, Kingston, NJ 08528
Tel.: (609) 924-0300
Web Site: http://www.traprock.com
Rev.: $34,800,000

Emp.: 350
Provider of Concrete Products
N.A.I.C.S.: 327390
Brian Murphy (Mgr-Construction)
Dawn Crutchley (Office Mgr-Construction Div)
Gloria Morgan (Mgr-Credit)
George M. Conway Jr. (Sec)

TRAPP FAMILY LODGE, INC.
700 Trapp Hill Rd, Stowe, VT 05672
Tel.: (802) 253-8511
Web Site: http://www.trappfamily.com
Year Founded: 1962
Sales Range: $75-99.9 Million
Emp.: 200
Provider of Resort Hotel Services
N.A.I.C.S.: 721110
Johannes Von Trapp (Pres)

TRAPP TECHNOLOGY, INC.
7360 E Acoma Dr Ste 2, Scottsdale, AZ 85260
Web Site: http://www.trapptechnology.com
Year Founded: 2007
Sales Range: $1-9.9 Million
Emp.: 48
Information Technology Consultation Services
N.A.I.C.S.: 519290
Chris Hunt (Mgr-Ops)
David Trapp (Founder & CEO)
Ashley Capps (Mgr-Comm)
Jim Mapes (Chief Info Security Officer)

Subsidiaries:

Brinkster Communications Corporation (1)
2600 N Central Ave 11th Fl, Phoenix, AZ 85004 (100%)
Tel.: (480) 388-3777
Web Site: http://www.brinkster.com
Data Hosting & Management Services
N.A.I.C.S.: 518210
Jared Stauffer (Founder & CEO)
Nathaniel Kemberling (CTO & Exec VP)
Jason Boffo (VP-Sls & Bus Dev)

TRATON CORP.
720 Kennesaw Ave, Marietta, GA 30060-3119
Tel.: (770) 427-9064
Web Site: http://www.tratonhomes.com
Year Founded: 1971
Sales Range: $10-24.9 Million
Emp.: 46
Provider of Real Estate Development Services
N.A.I.C.S.: 237210
Milburn Poston (Founder & Pres)
Josh Hilscher (VP-Sls & Mktg)

TRAU & LOEVNER INCORPORATED
838 Braddock Ave, Braddock, PA 15104
Tel.: (412) 361-7700
Web Site: http://www.trau-loevner.com
Rev.: $16,925,568
Emp.: 111
Screen Printing Services
N.A.I.C.S.: 323113
Steven Loevner (Pres)

TRAUBE TENT COMPANY, INC.
510 DD Rd, Columbia, IL 62236
Tel.: (618) 281-8368
Web Site: http://www.traubetent.com
Year Founded: 1938
Rev.: $4,600,000
Emp.: 45
Consumer Goods Rental

N.A.I.C.S.: 532289
John Traube (Pres)
Patty Franklin (Office Mgr)
Steve Traube (Owner)

TRAVAGLINI ENTERPRISES, INC.
276 North St, Meadville, PA 16335
Tel.: (814) 724-4880
Year Founded: 1979
Sales Range: $10-24.9 Million
Restaurant Operators
N.A.I.C.S.: 722511
Donald Fagley (Pres)
Jennifer E. Lipps (VP)
Kristine R. Presho (Sec & Treas)

TRAVCO INC.
2851 S Parker Rd Ste 510, Aurora, CO 80014
Tel.: (303) 755-6565
Web Site: http://www.travco1.com
Rev.: $26,532,772
Emp.: 120
Computer Related Consulting Services
N.A.I.C.S.: 541512
Francois Plouffe (VP)

TRAVCO SERVICES INC.
416 W San Ysidro Blvd Ste J, San Ysidro, CA 92173-2423
Tel.: (212) 624-9194
Web Site: https://www.sanborns.com
Year Founded: 1948
Insurance Agencies & Brokerages
N.A.I.C.S.: 524210
Jessica Gonazalez (Mgr)

TRAVEL & TRANSPORT INC.
2120 S 72nd St, Omaha, NE 68124-2366
Tel.: (402) 399-4500
Web Site: http://www.travelandtransport.com
Year Founded: 1946
Sales Range: $25-49.9 Million
Emp.: 600
Provider of Travel Agency Services
N.A.I.C.S.: 561510
William H. Tech (Chm)
Michael P. Kubasik (CIO & Exec VP)
Timothy J. Fleming (Pres & COO)
Kevin M. O'Malley (CEO)
Michael J. King (Gen Counsel & Sr VP)
Nancy J. Miller (Sr VP-Ops)
Nancy L. Rissky (Sr VP-Acct Mgmt)
Jeff Cain (Sr VP-Specialty Divisions)
Thomas Chermack (Chief Innovation Officer)
Josh Weiss (CFO)
Tim Krueger (CTO)

Subsidiaries:

TripLingo, LLC (1)
744 Saint Charles Ave NE, Atlanta, GA 30345
Tel.: (404) 333-8355
Web Site: http://www.triplingo.com
Custom Computer Programming Services
N.A.I.C.S.: 541511

TRAVEL ALL RUSSIA LLC
2300 N Pershing Dr Ste 202, Arlington, VA 22201
Tel.: (703) 276-6674
Web Site: http://www.travelallrussia.com
Year Founded: 2007
Sales Range: $1-9.9 Million
Emp.: 10
Travel Agency & Tour Operator

N.A.I.C.S.: 561510
Slava Shirokov (CEO)
Natalia Pakhomova (Gen Mgr)

TRAVEL EXCHANGE
32 Thread Needle Ln, Stamford, CT 06902
Tel.: (203) 961-1900
Web Site:
http://www.travelexchange.net
Rev.: $18,100,000
Emp.: 50
Travel & Tour Operating Agencies
N.A.I.C.S.: 561510
Barbara Herrott (Pres)
Carrie Negrinelli (Dir-Grp & Meetings)
Tom Mullen (Dir-Edgewood Div)

TRAVEL HOLDINGS, INC.
220 E Central Pkwy Ste 4010, Altamonte Springs, FL 32701
Tel.: (407) 215-7465
Web Site:
http://www.travelholdings.com
Year Founded: 2004
Sales Range: $10-24.9 Million
Emp.: 114
Travel & Tour Services
N.A.I.C.S.: 561599
Uri Argov (Pres & CEO)
Lauren Volcheff (Exec VP-Global Sls)
Dermot Quigley (Exec VP-PRB Dev & Product Integration)
Michael McIntyre (CFO)
Wendy E. Friedberg (Chief Legal Officer)
Asi Ginio (COO)
Jason Soss (Pres-Global Bus Dev)

TRAVEL INCORPORATED
4355 River Green Pkwy, Duluth, GA 30096-2572
Tel.: (770) 291-4100
Web Site: http://www.travelinc.com
Year Founded: 1979
Sales Range: $25-49.9 Million
Emp.: 375
Travel Management
N.A.I.C.S.: 561510
Wil L. Brown (CEO)
Mike Brown (Pres)
Tina Haney (CFO)

TRAVEL LEADERS GROUP, LLC
119 W 40th St, New York, NY 10018
Tel.: (800) 335-8747   DE
Web Site:
http://www.travelleaders.com
Year Founded: 1984
Holding Company; Travel Agencies & Travel Arrangement Services
N.A.I.C.S.: 551112
Michael Batt (Founder & Chm)
Roger Block (Pres-Travel Leaders Network)
Stephen McGillivray (CMO)
J. D. O'Hara (Pres)
Ninan Chacko (CEO)
Peter Vlitas (Sr VP-Airline Rels)
Gabriel Rizzi (Chief Sls Officer & Pres-Travel Leaders Corp)
Shaun Malay (VP-Airline Rels)
Steve DeLorenzo (CFO)
Jennifer de la Cruz (VP-PR & Comm)
Dina Ruden (Sr VP-PR & Comm)
John Lovell (Pres-Travel Leaders Network & Leisure Grp)
Jason Oshiokpekhai (Mng Dir-UK)

Subsidiaries:

Andrew Harper, LLC   (1)
4214 Medical Pkwy Ste 200, Austin, TX 78756
Tel.: (512) 904-7320
Web Site: http://www.andrewharper.com
High End Travel Agency, Publishing & Services Firm
N.A.I.C.S.: 561510
Dana Such (VP-Membership & Mktg)

Barrhead Travel Service Limited   (1)
190-194 Main Street Barrhead, Glasgow, G78 1SL, United Kingdom
Tel.: (44) 871 226 2673
Web Site: http://www.barrheadtravel.co.uk
Travel Agency Services
N.A.I.C.S.: 561510
Bill Munro (Founder)
Jacqueline Dobson (Pres)

Nexion   (1)
6565 N MacArthur Blvd Ste 400, Irving, TX 75039-2468
Tel.: (800) 747-6813
Web Site: http://www.nexion.com
Sales Range: $250-299.9 Million
Emp.: 60
Support Services for Travel Agencies
N.A.I.C.S.: 561499
Jackie Friedman (Pres)

Protravel International Inc.   (1)
515 Madison Ave 10th Fl, New York, NY 10022-5403
Tel.: (212) 755-4550
Web Site: http://www.protravelinc.com
Sales Range: $750-799.9 Million
Emp.: 700
Travel Agencies
N.A.I.C.S.: 561510
Michele Capaccio (COO)
Mickey Weill (VP-Bus Dev)
Peter Vlitas (Sr VP-Airline Rels)
Andy Pesky (Sr VP-Leisure Sls & Mktg)
Becky Powell (COO & Gen Mgr)
Gail Grimmett (Pres-Luxury Brands)

Branch (Domestic):

Protravel   (2)
6100 Glades Rd Ste 214, Boca Raton, FL 33434-4371
Tel.: (561) 483-4220
Web Site: http://www.protravelinc.com
Sales Range: $25-49.9 Million
Emp.: 21
Travel Agencies
N.A.I.C.S.: 561510
Patrick Fragale (Pres)

Division (Domestic):

Protravel/Austin   (2)
6801 Jericho Tpke Ste 100, Syosset, NY 11791
Tel.: (516) 465-1000
Web Site: http://www.protravelinc.com
Sales Range: $100-124.9 Million
Emp.: 60
Travel Agencies
N.A.I.C.S.: 561510
Stewart Austin (Dir-Client Reporting)

Travel Leaders Franchise Group, LLC   (1)
3033 Campus Dr Ste W 320, Plymouth, MN 55441
Tel.: (952) 914-6952
Web Site: http://www.travelleaders.com
Sales Range: $150-199.9 Million
Emp.: 100
Holding Company; Travel Agency Franchisor & Operator
N.A.I.C.S.: 551112
Roger E. Block (Pres)
John Brehm (VP-Franchise Dev)

Affiliate (Domestic):

Market Square Travel LLC   (2)
13756 83rd Way N, Maple Grove, MN 55369
Tel.: (763) 231-8870
Web Site: http://www.tvlleaders.com
Sales Range: $50-74.9 Million
Emp.: 22
Travel Agency
N.A.I.C.S.: 561510
David Lovick (Pres)

Travel Leaders of Charleston   (1)
1132 Oakland Market Rd, Mount Pleasant, SC 29466-8219
Tel.: (843) 881-1181
Web Site:
http://www.travelleadersofcharleston.com
Travel Agencies
N.A.I.C.S.: 561510
Sharon Knight (Owner)

Tzell Travel Group   (1)
119 W 40th St 14th Fl, New York, NY 10018
Tel.: (212) 944-2121
Web Site: http://www.tzell.com
Sales Range: $1-4.9 Billion
Corporate Travel Services
N.A.I.C.S.: 561599
Barry Liben (Chm)
Willie Lynch (CFO)
Jerry Behrens (Exec VP)
Cindy Schlansky (Sr VP)
Sara Sessa (VP-West Coast Ops)
Christopher Griffin (VP-Bus Dev & Acct Mgmt)
Monty Swaney (VP-Ops)
Gina Gabbard (VP-Leisure Sls)
Christina Gambini (VP-Hotel Programs & Dev)

Vacation.com, Inc.   (1)
1650 King St Ste 450, Alexandria, VA 22314-2747
Tel.: (703) 535-5505
Web Site: http://www.vacation.com
Sales Range: $10-24.9 Million
Emp.: 75
Online Travel Agent Network
N.A.I.C.S.: 561510
Lauraday Kelley (VP-Conference & Corp)
John Lovell (Pres)
Stephen McGillivray (CMO)
Scott Ackerman (Sr VP-Product Dev)
Jim Nathan (VP-Mktg)
Bernadette Stark (VP-Conference, Events & Trng)
Karin Viera (VP-Sls)
Kevin Weisner (Sr VP-Sls)

TRAVEL MANAGEMENT PARTNERS INC.
3128 Highwoods Blvd Ste 110, Raleigh, NC 27604
Tel.: (919) 782-3810   NC
Web Site: http://www.tmptravel.com
Year Founded: 1992
Sales Range: $25-49.9 Million
Emp.: 127
Provider of Travel Agency Services
N.A.I.C.S.: 561510
John Lewis (Pres & CEO)
Wanda Shankle (COO)

TRAVEL NETWORK VACATION CENTRAL
560 Sylvan Ave, Englewood Cliffs, NJ 07632
Tel.: (201) 567-8500
Web Site:
http://www.travelnetwork.com
Year Founded: 1979
Sales Range: $75-99.9 Million
Emp.: 233
Holding Company: Travel & Marketing Services
N.A.I.C.S.: 561599
Derek Brent (Pres)

Subsidiaries:

The Travel Network   (1)
560 Sylvan Ave, Englewood Cliffs, NJ 07632   (100%)
Tel.: (201) 567-8500
Web Site: http://www.travelnetwork.com
Travel Franchises
N.A.I.C.S.: 561599
Derek Brent (Pres)

Vacation Central   (1)
560 Sylvan Ave Ste 3230, Englewood Cliffs, NJ 07632   (100%)
Tel.: (201) 567-8500
Web Site: http://www.vacationcentral.net
Full Service Travel Agency
N.A.I.C.S.: 561510

TRAVEL NURSE ACROSS AMERICA, LLC
5020 Northshore Dr Ste 2, North Little Rock, AR 72118   AR
Web Site: http://www.nurse.tv
Year Founded: 1999
Sales Range: $10-24.9 Million
Emp.: 225
Healthcare Staffing Agency
N.A.I.C.S.: 561320
Gene Scott (Pres & CEO)
Chris Glover (COO & Gen Counsel)
Jean Cook (CFO)
Kathy Kerstiens (Sr VP-Client Svcs)
Rose Fulton (Sr VP-Recruitment)

TRAVEL SPIKE, LLC
3300 Highlands Pkwy Ste 120, Smyrna, GA 30082
Tel.: (404) 835-2704
Web Site: http://www.travelspike.com
Sales Range: $10-24.9 Million
Emp.: 20
Education, Email, Internet/Web Design, Media Buying Services, Media Planning, Multimedia, Public Relations, Strategic Planning/Research, Travel & Tourism
N.A.I.C.S.: 541810
Ryan Bifulco (Founder & CEO)
Howard Koval (Exec VP)
Ori Klein (CTO)
David Bowman (VP-Sls)
Inna Shamis (VP-Corp Comm)
John Oliver (Sr VP-Bus Dev)

TRAVEL STATION
380 Ice Ctr Ln Ste C, Bozeman, MT 59715
Tel.: (406) 587-8747
Web Site:
http://www.thetravelstation.com
Year Founded: 1984
Sales Range: $1-9.9 Million
Emp.: 10
Travel Agency
N.A.I.C.S.: 561510
Edward Schmidt (Pres)

Subsidiaries:

Cook Travel Station   (1)
1844 Broadwater Ave Ste 8, Billings, MT 59102
Tel.: (406) 245-6291
Web Site: http://www.thetravelstation.com
Emp.: 4
Travel Agency
N.A.I.C.S.: 561510
Edward Schmidt (Pres)

TRAVEL TRIPPER, LLC
370 Lexington Ave Ste 1601, New York, NY 10017
Tel.: (212) 683-6161
Web Site:
http://www.traveltripper.com
Software Publisher
N.A.I.C.S.: 513210
P. J. McIntyre (Sr Dir-Sls)
Gautam Lulla (CEO)

Subsidiaries:

Pegasus Solutions Companies   (1)
4141 N Scottsdale Rd Ste 200, Scottsdale, AZ 85251
Tel.: (480) 624-6000
Web Site: http://www.pegasus.io
Hotel & Travel Industry Reservation, Electronic Data Distribution, Business Intelligence & Operational Support Services
N.A.I.C.S.: 518210
Sean Lenahan (CEO)
Phil Steitz (CTO)
John M. Henricksen (CFO)
Ges Doran (COO)
Rainer Gruber (Exec VP)
Donna Jackson (VP-Customer Support)
Tommy Crutchfield (VP-Product Dev)

TRAVEL-ON LTD., INC.

TRAVEL-ON LTD., INC.

Travel-On Ltd., Inc.—(Continued)
9000 Virginia Manor Rd Ste 201, Beltsville, MD 20707
Tel.: (240) 387-4000 — MD
Web Site: http://www.tvlon.com
Year Founded: 1974
Sales Range: $10-24.9 Million
Emp.: 60
Provider of Travel Agency Services
N.A.I.C.S.: 561510
Karen Dunlap (CEO)
Pat Sullivan (VP-Sls & Mktg)
Claire Simmons (VP-Special Interest Grp)
Dave Cahan (VP)
Edie Grosz (Dir-Ops & Tech)
Amy Dunn Ripley (Mgr-Acctg & MIS)
Marcia Goldman (Mgr-Special Projects)
Niki Yianilos (Mgr-Travel Place Bethesda)
Mary Bonuccelli (Mgr-Travel Place Manassas)
Karen Kephart (Mgr-Travel Place Potomac)
Elizabeth Farmer (VP-Client Solutions)
Dick A. Nabors (VP-Global Sls & Mktg)

TRAVELER'S RV SALES
295 Kietzke Ln, Reno, NV 89502-1414
Tel.: (775) 329-3441
Web Site: http://www.travelersrv.com
Year Founded: 1997
Rev: $12,000,000
Emp.: 40
Recreational Vehicle Dealers
N.A.I.C.S.: 441227
Dana Bailey (Founder)

TRAVELERS MARKETING LLC
47 Church St Ste 301, Wellesley, MA 02482
Tel.: (781) 416-5000
Web Site: http://www.travelersmarketing.com
Year Founded: 1997
Sales Range: $10-24.9 Million
Emp.: 13
Advetising Agency
N.A.I.C.S.: 541810
Cynthia Lore (CFO)

TRAVELERS RENTAL CO. INC.
230 Porter St, Boston, MA 02128
Tel.: (617) 634-0006
Web Site: http://www.dollar.com
Rev.: $30,070,928
Emp.: 120
Passenger Car Rental
N.A.I.C.S.: 532111
Doug Perry (Controller)

TRAVELHOST, INC.
433 E Lascolinas Blvd Ste 1065, Dallas, TX 75039
Tel.: (972) 556-0541
Web Site: http://www.travelhost.com
Year Founded: 1967
Sales Range: $75-99.9 Million
Emp.: 60
Publisher of Travel Information Online & Offline
N.A.I.C.S.: 513199
James E. Buerger (Founder & Chm)
Al Schoenberg (Gen Mgr-Production)
Ginger Roberson (Dir-Fin)
Scott Holmes (Dir-IT)
Erin Boyle (Dir-Creative)
Joe Shocklee (Dir-Market Dev)
William Schroeder (Pres & CEO)
Maria Andrew (Publr-Kansas City)

TRAVELING COACHES, INC
2805 Dallas Pkwy Ste 150, Plano, TX 75093
Tel.: (214) 742-6224 — TX
Web Site: http://www.travelingcoaches.com
Year Founded: 1995
Sales Range: $10-24.9 Million
Emp.: 33
Software Training Services
N.A.I.C.S.: 611420
Gina Buser (CEO)
Frank Barnard (Dir-Ops & Client Svc)
Jennifer Korba (Mgr-Production-Learning Dev)
Joe Buser (Dir-Bus Dev)
Kellie Chandler (Mgr-Project Talent & Logistics)
Kimberley Smith (Project Mgr)
Lyndi Lockhart (Acct Mgr)
Tracie Beck (Dir-Fin)
Amy Manint (Acct Exec)
Cindy Mitchell (Mgr-Product Dev)

TRAVELNET SOLUTIONS, INC.
9900 Hemingway Ave S, Cottage Grove, MN 55016
Tel.: (651) 757-4900 — MN
Web Site: http://www.travelnetsolutions.com
Year Founded: 1999
Sales Range: $1-9.9 Million
Emp.: 29
Travel Agencies, Nsk
N.A.I.C.S.: 561510

TRAVERS & COMPANY INC.
979 Third Ave, New York, NY 10022
Tel.: (212) 888-7900
Web Site: http://www.traversinc.com
Rev.: $16,322,381
Emp.: 15
Fabrics, Yarns & Knit Goods
N.A.I.C.S.: 424990

TRAVERS REALTY CORP.
550 S Hope St Ste 2600, Los Angeles, CA 90071
Tel.: (213) 683-1500 — CA
Web Site: http://www.traversrealty.com
Year Founded: 1978
Sales Range: $1-9.9 Million
Emp.: 30
Commercial Real Estate Broker
N.A.I.C.S.: 531210
James N. Travers (Founder & Chm)
Akeel Ghelani (Dir-IT)
Dennis E. Smith (Mng Dir & Exec VP)
George Katunich (Principal)
Howard B. Feuerstein (Principal)
Jeffrey D. Mintz (Principal)
Linda Eng (Sr VP)
Erlinda J. Tan (Controller)
Mark D. Rauch (Sr VP)
Steven N. Eyler (Principal)
Stewart E. Niles (Sr VP)
Guy H. Eisner (VP)
W. Lawson Martin III (Mng Principal)

Subsidiaries:

Travers Realty Corp. (1)
840 Newport Ctr Dr Ste 770, Newport Beach, CA 92260
Tel.: (949) 644-5900
Commercial Real Estate Broker
N.A.I.C.S.: 531210
Randall S. Parker (Pres)
Matt Wiley (Sr VP)
Reynolds T. McCabe (Mng Dir & Exec VP)
Stacy N. Garcia (VP)
Steven T. Card (Mng Dir & Exec VP)

Travers Realty Corp. (1)
2929 E Camelback Rd Ste 130, Phoenix, AZ 85016
Tel.: (602) 753-0300
Commercial Real Estate Broker
N.A.I.C.S.: 531210

Travers Realty Corp. (1)
55 2nd St Ste 1975, San Francisco, CA 94105
Tel.: (415) 685-4240
Commercial Real Estate Broker
N.A.I.C.S.: 531210

Travers Realty Corp. (1)
11111 Santa Monica Blvd Ste 650, Los Angeles, CA 90025
Tel.: (310) 966-8030
Commercial Real Estate Broker
N.A.I.C.S.: 531210

TRAVERS TOOL COMPANY INC.
128-15 26th Ave, Flushing, NY 11354-1147
Tel.: (718) 886-7200
Web Site: http://www.travers.com
Year Founded: 1924
Sales Range: $10-24.9 Million
Emp.: 130
Mfr of Metalworking Tools & Industrial Supplies
N.A.I.C.S.: 423840
Barry Zolot (Chm)
Bruce Zolot (Pres)

TRAVERSE CITY AUTO PLAZA INC.
1301 S Garfield Ave, Traverse City, MI 49686
Tel.: (231) 941-0700
Web Site: http://www.traversemotors.com
Sales Range: $10-24.9 Million
Emp.: 60
Automobiles, New & Used
N.A.I.C.S.: 441110
Otto Belovich (Pres)

TRAVERSE CITY FILM FESTIVAL
PO Box 4064, Traverse City, MI 49685
Tel.: (231) 392-1134 — MI
Web Site: http://www.traversecityfilmfestival.org
Year Founded: 2005
Sales Range: $1-9.9 Million
Emp.: 15
Film Festival Organizer
N.A.I.C.S.: 711310
Michael Moore (Founder & Pres)
John Robert Williams (Co-Founder)

TRAVERSE POINTE PARTNERS LLC
55 E Monroe 32nd Fl, Chicago, IL 60603
Tel.: (312) 754-8200
Web Site: http://www.traversepointe.com
Privater Equity Firm
N.A.I.C.S.: 523940
Michael Simon (Mng Principal)

TRAVERTINE, INC.
1325 E 35th Pl Ste 100, Tulsa, OK 74120
Tel.: (918) 583-5210
Web Site: http://www.travertine-elevator.com
Year Founded: 1998
Sales Range: $10-24.9 Million
Emp.: 60
Goods Repair & Maintenance Services
N.A.I.C.S.: 811490
Christine Lamber (Pres)
Scott Lambert (VP)
Laurie Price (Mgr-Corp Acctg)

U.S. PRIVATE

TRAVIS BUSINESS SYSTEMS INC.
4211 N Barnes Ave, Oklahoma City, OK 73112
Tel.: (405) 848-1797
Web Site: http://www.travisvoice.com
Year Founded: 1988
Sales Range: $50-74.9 Million
Emp.: 50
Office Equipments & Dictating Machines Whslr
N.A.I.C.S.: 423420
David Mccoin (Intern Mgr)
Greg Mantia (VP)
Randy Cope (CFO)
Greg Mante (CEO)

Subsidiaries:

Digital Transcription System, Inc. (1)
135 N Cedar Branch Way Ste 111, Mustang, OK 73064
Tel.: (405) 948-9200
Web Site: http://www.dtsok.com
Rev.: $610,000
Emp.: 5
Secretarial & Typing Service
N.A.I.C.S.: 561410
Joe Jackson (Pres)

TRAVIS CREDIT UNION
1 Travis Way, Vacaville, CA 95687
Tel.: (707) 449-4700 — CA
Web Site: http://www.traviscu.org
Year Founded: 1951
Sales Range: $100-124.9 Million
Emp.: 538
Credit Union Operator
N.A.I.C.S.: 522130
Patricia Moreno (Chm)
Mary Coburn (Sec)
Tom Kulinski (Treas)
Deborah Aspling (Vice Chm)
Karl Goin (VP-Mktg)
Barry Nelson (Pres & CEO)
John Shelby (Mgr-Bus Banking Grp)
Dena Rothmann (Chief Retail Officer & Sr VP-Experience)

TRAVIS INDUSTRIES INC.
4800 Harbour Pointe Blvd SW, Mukilteo, WA 98275-5458
Tel.: (425) 609-2500
Web Site: http://www.lopistoves.com
Year Founded: 1983
Sales Range: $25-49.9 Million
Emp.: 350
Wood & Coal Burning Stoves Mfr
N.A.I.C.S.: 333414
K. Rumens (Pres & Gen Mgr)
Melodie Kauf (Mgr-Sls)
Perry Ranes (Mgr-Sls-Natl)

TRAVIS MEATS INC.
PO Box 670, Powell, TN 37849-0670
Tel.: (865) 938-9051
Web Site: http://www.travismeats.com
Year Founded: 1935
Sales Range: $25-49.9 Million
Emp.: 145
Mfr of Portioned Food Products for Restaurants, Retail & Healthcare Industries
N.A.I.C.S.: 424420
William Trevors (Pres)
Steve Harris (VP)

TRAVIS TILE SALES INC.
3811 Airport Blvd, Austin, TX 78722
Tel.: (512) 478-8705
Web Site: http://www.travistile.com
Rev.: $13,000,000
Emp.: 32
Provider of Clay & Ceramic Tile
N.A.I.C.S.: 423320
Mike Hamer (Gen Mgr)
Jim Wynn (Mgr-San Antonio)
Ronnie Tyler (Pres)

COMPANIES

TRAX INTERNATIONAL CORPORATION
8337 W Sunset Rd Ste 250, Las Vegas, NV 89113
Tel.: (702) 216-4455
Web Site: http://www.traxintl.com
Year Founded: 1979
Sales Range: $50-74.9 Million
Emp.: 1,200
Government Services Contractor
N.A.I.C.S.: 541715
F. Craig Wilson *(Pres & CEO)*
Pamela Hormell *(CFO)*
Christopher Campbell *(Dir-HR)*

TRAX TECHNOLOGIES, INC.
909 Lake Carolyn Pkwy Ste 260, Irving, TX 75039   AZ
Web Site: http://www.traxtech.com
Year Founded: 1993
Sales Range: $10-24.9 Million
Emp.: 300
Software Development Services
N.A.I.C.S.: 541511
Josh Bouk *(Chief Revenue Officer)*
Steven C. Beda *(Exec VP-Customer Solutions & Advisory)*
Liz Murray *(CFO)*
Daman Wood *(COO)*
George Santillan *(CTO)*
Bill Strogis *(Chief Revenue Officer)*
Blake Tablak *(CEO)*

TRAY, INC.
681 Hollins Ferry Rd Ste A, Glen Burnie, MD 21061
Web Site: http://www.traypml.com
Sales Range: $10-24.9 Million
Emp.: 32
Printing & Mailing Service
N.A.I.C.S.: 323111
Brian Burlace *(Pres)*
Paul Gillespie *(VP-Sls)*
John Long *(CFO)*

TRAYER PRODUCTS, INC.
541 E Clinton St, Elmira, NY 14901-2553
Tel.: (607) 734-8124
Web Site: http://www.trayerproducts.com
Year Founded: 1929
Sales Range: $100-124.9 Million
Emp.: 225
Mfr of Automobile Shackles, Pins & Bolts, Shock Absorber & Stabilizer Links
N.A.I.C.S.: 332722
Tony A. Desocio *(Mgr-Mktg)*

TRAYLOR BROTHERS, INC.
835 N Congress Ave, Evansville, IN 47715-2452
Tel.: (812) 477-1542   IN
Web Site: http://www.traylor.com
Year Founded: 1946
Sales Range: $450-499.9 Million
Emp.: 400
Provider of Contracting & Construction Services
N.A.I.C.S.: 237990
Glen R. Traylor *(Dir)*
Don Bartow *(VP)*
Thomas W. Traylor Jr. *(VP)*

Subsidiaries:

Traylor Mining, LLC (1)
405 Urban St Ste 210, Lakewood, CO 80228
Tel.: (303) 988-8821
Mine Development & Management Services
N.A.I.C.S.: 213114

TRAYLOR CHEMICAL & SUPPLY CO.
1911 Traylor Blvd, Orlando, FL 32804-4713
Tel.: (407) 422-6151   FL
Web Site: http://www.traylorchemical.com
Year Founded: 1952
Sales Range: $75-99.9 Million
Emp.: 48
Whslr of Agricultural Chemicals
N.A.I.C.S.: 424910
James R. Pindell *(Midwest Reg Mgr)*
Kenneth A. Zielinski *(Upper Midwest Reg Mgr)*

TRC COMPANIES, INC.
21 Griffin Road, North Windsor, CT 06095
Tel.: (860) 298-9692   DE
Web Site: https://www.trccompanies.com
Year Founded: 1969
Emp.: 100
Environmental Engineering & Consulting Services
N.A.I.C.S.: 541620
Christopher P. Vincze *(Chm & CEO)*
Ed Myszka *(Pres-Power Sector)*
Laura Ramey *(Chief People Officer)*
Jason S. Greenlaw *(CFO)*
Mark Robbins *(Pres-Environmental Sector)*
Marc Faecher *(Chief Risk Officer)*
Rajeev Gollarahalli *(CIO & Chief Digital Officer)*
Todd Wager *(Pres-Infrastructure)*
Nik Krishnamurthy *(Chief Growth Officer)*
David Tiernan *(Sr VP & Dir-Strategic Growth)*
Phedora Rosiclair *(Mgr-Comm)*

Subsidiaries:

American Environmental Consultants, Inc. (1)
814 Broad St, Weymouth, MA 02189
Tel.: (781) 337-0016
Web Site: http://www.americanenviron.com
Environmental Consulting Services
N.A.I.C.S.: 541618
Mark A. McMullen *(Principal)*
Greg Hatch *(Partner)*
Michael Mccaffrey *(Principal)*

Blue Oak Energy, Inc. (1)
1560 Drew Ave, Davis, CA 95618
Tel.: (530) 747-2026
Web Site: http://www.blueoakenergy.com
Sales Range: $10-24.9 Million
Emp.: 50
Photovoltaic Solar Energy System Mfr
N.A.I.C.S.: 335999
Tobin Booth *(Founder)*
Danny Lee *(VP-Bus Dev)*
Ryan Zahner *(VP-Ops)*
Cherie Garrett *(VP-Fin)*
Zack Zoller *(Dir-Engrg)*
Tim Brown *(Mgr-Construction)*
Kelly Birkes *(Dir-Civil Engrg)*
William Stanton *(VP-Engrg)*

ESS Group, Inc. (1)
78 Carranza Rd, Vincentown, NJ 08088
Tel.: (609) 268-1200
Web Site: http://www.colonial-chemical.com
Sales Range: $1-9.9 Million
Emp.: 65
Pharmaceutical Preparation Mfr
N.A.I.C.S.: 325412
James Egan *(CEO)*
Eric Wegelius *(Bus Dir)*

Environmental Partners, Inc. (1)
1180 NW Maple St Ste 310, Issaquah, WA 98027
Tel.: (425) 395-0010
Web Site: http://www.epi-wa.com
Sales Range: $1-9.9 Million
Emp.: 21
Management Consulting Services
N.A.I.C.S.: 541618
Tom Elsemore *(Principal & Gen Mgr)*

Gladstein, Neandross & Associates LLC (1)

TRC WORLDWIDE ENGINEERING, INC.

3015 Main St Ste 300, Santa Monica, CA 90405
Tel.: (310) 314-1934
Web Site: http://www.gladstein.org
Sales Range: $1-9.9 Million
Emp.: 15
Scientific & Technical Consulting Services
N.A.I.C.S.: 541690
Sarah Gallagher *(Dir-Marketing-Events)*
Cliff Gladstein *(Pres)*
Dee Olomajeye *(Mgr-Human Resources)*
Erik Neandross *(CEO)*
Jarrod Kohout *(Dir-Project)*
Jonathan Leonard *(Sr VP)*
Katherine Engel *(Program Mgr)*
Scott Sadler *(Sr Project Mgr)*
Sean Turner *(COO)*
Tony Quist *(VP)*

Ijus, LLC (1)
1612 Prosser Ave Suite 200, Kettering, OH 45409
Tel.: (937) 347-5438
Engineering Services, Nsk
N.A.I.C.S.: 541330

TRC Albuquerque (1)
4221 A Balloon Park Rd NE, Albuquerque, NM 87109
Tel.: (505) 761-0099
Web Site: http://www.trcsolutions.com
Electric Consulting Services
N.A.I.C.S.: 541618

TRC Companies, Inc. - Cincinnati (1)
11231 Cornell Park Dr, Cincinnati, OH 45242
Tel.: (513) 489-2255
Web Site: http://www.trcsolutions.com
Engineering Consulting Services
N.A.I.C.S.: 541618

TRC Companies, Inc. - Mount Laurel (1)
16000 Commerce Pkwy, Mount Laurel, NJ 08054
Tel.: (856) 273-1224
Web Site: http://www.trcsolutions.com
Construction Contractors & Engineering Services
N.A.I.C.S.: 541330

TRC Companies, Ltd. (1)
175-185 Grays Inn Road, London, WC1X 8UE, United Kingdom
Tel.: (44) 2078120620
Web Site: http://www.trcsolutions.com
Environmental Consulting Services
N.A.I.C.S.: 541620
Will Nitch-Smith *(Dir-Ops)*

TRC Engineers Inc. (1)
1430 Broadway, New York, NY 10018
Tel.: (212) 221-7822
Web Site: http://www.trcsolutions.com
Engineering Consulting Services
N.A.I.C.S.: 541330

Subsidiary (Domestic):

Caltrop Corporation (2)
4371 Latham St Ste 101, Riverside, CA 92501
Tel.: (909) 931-9331
Web Site: http://www.caltrop.com
Engineeering Services
N.A.I.C.S.: 541330
David Saber *(VP)*

TRC Engineers LLC (1)
249 Western Ave, Augusta, ME 04330
Tel.: (207) 621-7000
Web Site: http://www.trcsolutions.com
Engineering & Environmental Consulting Services
N.A.I.C.S.: 541330

TRC Environmental Corporation (1)
21 Griffin Rd N, Windsor, CT 06095-1568
Tel.: (860) 298-9692
Web Site: http://www.trcsolutions.com
Environmental Engineering & Consulting Services
N.A.I.C.S.: 541690

Branch (Domestic):

TRC Environmental - Laramie (2)
605 Skyline Rd, Laramie, WY 82070-8909
Tel.: (307) 742-3843

Web Site: http://www.trcsolutions.com
Environmental Engineering & Consulting Services
N.A.I.C.S.: 541690
Scott Kamber *(Principal & Sr Project Mgr)*

TRC Software (1)
10680 White Rock Rd, Rancho Cordova, CA 95670
Tel.: (916) 366-0683
Web Site: http://www.trcbridgedesignsoftware.com
Bridge Design Software & Services
N.A.I.C.S.: 541330

United Sciences Testing Inc. (1)
5475 William Flynn Hwy, Gibsonia, PA 15044-9624
Tel.: (724) 449-9700
Web Site: http://www.ustirata.com
Veterinary Services
N.A.I.C.S.: 541940
Mike Brown *(Mgr)*

Utility Support Systems Inc. (1)
2976 Chapel Hill Rd Ste 100, Douglasville, GA 30133
Tel.: (770) 947-4272
Utility Engineering Services
N.A.I.C.S.: 541330

TRC GLOBAL SOLUTIONS, INC.
1042 E Juneau Ave, Milwaukee, WI 53202
Tel.: (414) 226-4200   WI
Web Site: http://www.trcgs.com
Year Founded: 1987
Sales Range: $25-49.9 Million
Emp.: 100
International & Government Relocation Services
N.A.I.C.S.: 484210
Paul G. Hailsmaier *(Founder & Chm)*
Sarah Larson *(VP-Org Dev)*
Jerry Funaro *(VP-Global Mktg)*
Sean Lickver *(Exec VP)*
Craig Mueller *(VP-Global Bus Dev & Client Rels)*
Amy Kust *(Controller)*
Rafe MacDonald *(Sr Dir-Global Expense Mgmt)*
Jeremiah Blakeley *(Dir-Global Acct Mgmt)*
Chris Grundy *(Dir-Ops)*
Craig Vuoso *(VP-Client Fin & Tech)*

TRC STAFFING SERVICES, INC.
115 Perimeter Center Pl NE S Terraces Ste 850, Atlanta, GA 30346-1249
Tel.: (770) 399-0213   GA
Web Site: http://www.trcstaffing.com
Year Founded: 1980
Sales Range: $200-249.9 Million
Emp.: 600
Provider of Staffing Services
N.A.I.C.S.: 561320
Brian Robinson *(Pres & CEO)*
Conrad Helms *(Exec VP)*
Craig Kumpf *(CFO & Sr VP)*
Kimberly Huffman *(VP-Sls-Greater Atlanta)*
Nancy Wright Whatley *(VP-Franchise Ops-Natl)*
Eric Adams *(VP-Delivery & Implementation)*
Roy Cannon *(Founder)*

TRC WORLDWIDE ENGINEERING, INC.
217 Ward Cir, Brentwood, TN 37027
Tel.: (615) 661-7979
Web Site: http://www.trcww.com
Year Founded: 1989
Emp.: 100
Engineeering Services
N.A.I.C.S.: 541330

4215

TRC WORLDWIDE ENGINEERING, INC.

TRC Worldwide Engineering, Inc.—(Continued)
Surendra Ramanna *(Chm & CEO)*
Barry Kasselman *(Principal)*
Jennifer Giralo *(Mgr-Bus Dev-Phoenix)*
Marcia Alvarado *(Engr-Structural)*
Lisa D'Addio *(Mgr-Bus Dev)*

TREADMILLDOCTOR.COM, INC.
3508 Tchulahoma Rd, Memphis, TN 38118
Tel.: (901) 683-5292   TN
Web Site: http://www.treadmilldoctor.com
Year Founded: 1998
Rev.: $3,100,000
Emp.: 34
Fitness Equipment Maintenance Repair Services
N.A.I.C.S.: 811490
Jon Stevenson *(VP)*
Clark Stevenson *(CEO)*

TREADWELL CORPORATION
341 Railroad St, Thomaston, CT 06787-1667
Tel.: (860) 283-8251   DE
Web Site: http://www.treadwellcorp.com
Year Founded: 1896
Sales Range: $50-74.9 Million
Emp.: 42
Mfr of Oxygen Generators for U.S. Navy Submarines
N.A.I.C.S.: 336611
Kevin Dunphy *(Controller)*
Kyle Loseke *(Dir-Ops)*

TREASURE COAST BOATING CENTER, INC.
420 SW Federal Hwy, Stuart, FL 34994
Tel.: (772) 287-9800   FL
Web Site: http://www.tcboating.com
Year Founded: 1996
Sales Range: $10-24.9 Million
Emp.: 8
Boat Dealers
N.A.I.C.S.: 441222
Thomas Cuber *(Pres)*

TREASURE ISLAND CORP.
3300 Las Vegas Blvd S, Las Vegas, NV 89109-8916
Tel.: (702) 894-7111
Web Site: http://www.treasureisland.com
Sales Range: $500-549.9 Million
Emp.: 4,500
Hotel & Casino Properties
N.A.I.C.S.: 721120
Jeff Dennis *(Gen Mgr-Beverage)*
Najam Khan *(Exec VP & Gen Mgr)*
Kim Phelps *(Mgr-Casino Mktg)*
Marie Adams *(Supvr-Reservations)*

TREASURE ISLAND FOOD MARTS INC.
3460 N Broadway St, Chicago, IL 60657-2516
Tel.: (773) 327-4265   IL
Web Site: http://www.tifoods.com
Year Founded: 1964
Sales Range: $200-249.9 Million
Emp.: 700
Provider of Retail Grocery Services
N.A.I.C.S.: 445110
Sarah Rising *(Mgr-Media Comm)*
Maria A. Kamberos *(Pres & CEO)*
Christ Nicholas Kamberos Jr. *(VP-Dev)*

TREAT AMERICA FOOD SERVICES, INC.
8500 Shawnee Mission Pkwy Ste 100, Merriam, KS 66202
Tel.: (913) 384-4900
Web Site: http://www.treatamerica.com
Year Founded: 1987
Sales Range: $125-149.9 Million
Emp.: 1,200
Food Service Management Services
N.A.I.C.S.: 722514
Linda Harp *(Mgr-Restaurant)*
Pauline Pfannenstiel *(Gen Mgr)*
Lauren Roesner *(Mgr-Chef)*
John Mitchell Jr. *(Pres)*

Subsidiaries:

Treat America Food Services, Inc. - Indianapolis   (1)
2120 S Meridian St, Indianapolis, IN 46225
Tel.: (317) 899-1234
Web Site: http://www.treatamerica.com
Sales Range: $25-49.9 Million
Emp.: 220
Food Management, Vending, Catering, Coffee & Beverage Services
N.A.I.C.S.: 445132
Todd Milby *(Gen Mgr)*

Treat America Omaha   (1)
3200 S 60th St, Omaha, NE 68106-3743
Tel.: (402) 553-4000
Web Site: http://www.treatamerica.com
Sales Range: $50-74.9 Million
Emp.: 400
Catering & Vending Machine Services
N.A.I.C.S.: 445132

TREAT ENTERTAINMENT INC.
3101 Clairmont Rd NE, Atlanta, GA 30329
Tel.: (404) 214-4300
Rev.: $21,600,000
Emp.: 200
Toys & Hobby Goods & Supplies
N.A.I.C.S.: 711320

TREATCO, INC.
2300 N Broadway St, Wichita, KS 67219
Tel.: (316) 265-7900
Web Site: http://www.treatco.com
Sales Range: $10-24.9 Million
Emp.: 70
Dog Food Mfr
N.A.I.C.S.: 311111
Brenda Thomas *(VP-Sls & Mktg)*

TREATMENT EQUIPMENT COMPANY
Ste 101 6220 Campbell Rd, Dallas, TX 75248-1363
Tel.: (972) 931-1116
Web Site: http://www.tectx.com
Year Founded: 1986
Rev.: $15,000,000
Emp.: 7
Mfr Representatives of Water & Waste Water Treatment Equipment
N.A.I.C.S.: 423830
Bruce S. Smith *(Owner & Pres)*
Janice Fuqua *(Office Mgr)*

TREBBIANNO LLC
19 W 34th St Fl 7, New York, NY 10001
Tel.: (212) 868-2770
Rev.: $30,000,000
Emp.: 40
Mfr of Leather Handbags
N.A.I.C.S.: 316110
Terry McCormick *(Pres & Partner)*
Tony Cheng *(Pres)*
Maria Som *(Mgr-Production)*
Milagros Arana *(Dir-Ops & Logistics)*
Nicole Redden *(Mgr-Production)*
Victoria Maresco *(Sr Acct Exec)*

TREBOL MOTORS CORPORATION
Ave Kennedy Corner Orquidea, San Juan, PR 00920
Tel.: (787) 793-2828
Web Site: http://www.trebolmotors.com
Rev.: $15,000,000
Emp.: 35
Automobiles
N.A.I.C.S.: 441110
Gonzalez Ricardo *(Pres)*

TREBOR INC.
100 Matawan Rd Ste 220, Matawan, NJ 07747
Tel.: (732) 335-4255
Web Site: http://www.trebor.com
Year Founded: 1971
Sales Range: $100-124.9 Million
Emp.: 27
Industrial & Personal Service Paper
N.A.I.C.S.: 424130
Richard Repoli *(VP)*
Joe Lamb *(Controller)*
Robert Glidden Jr. *(CEO)*

TRECEK CHEVROLET OLDSMOBILE GEO
1350 E Wisconsin St, Portage, WI 53901
Tel.: (608) 742-7155
Web Site: http://www.trecek.com
Sales Range: $10-24.9 Million
Emp.: 48
Car Whslr
N.A.I.C.S.: 441110
Don Hughes *(Mgr-Svc)*

TREDIT TIRE & WHEEL COMPANY, INC.
3305 Charlotte Ave, Elkhart, IN 46517-1150
Tel.: (574) 293-0581
Web Site: http://www.tredittire.com
Sales Range: $10-24.9 Million
Emp.: 75
Tires & Wheels Distr
N.A.I.C.S.: 423130
Terry O'Rourke *(Pres)*
Tim Ball *(VP-Sls)*
Jen Sailor *(VP-Fin)*
Ron Pike *(Pres)*

TREDROC TIRE SERVICES
2450 Lunt Ave, Elk Grove Village, IL 60007
Tel.: (224) 265-4070
Web Site: http://www.tredroc.com
Emp.: 10,000
Tire Sales, Retreading & Repair Services
N.A.I.C.S.: 441340
Glen Parks *(CFO)*
John C. Boynton *(CEO)*

Subsidiaries:

Tredroc Tire Services   (1)
1325 N 31st Ave, Melrose Park, IL 60160-2907
Tel.: (708) 681-5363
Web Site: http://www.tredroc.com
Tire Sales, Retreading & Repair Services
N.A.I.C.S.: 441340
Michael Quig *(Gen Mgr)*

Tredroc Tire Services   (1)
875 Ralston Rd, Machesney Park, IL 61115-1609
Tel.: (815) 636-8000
Web Site: http://www.tredroc.com
Rev.: $2,500,000
Emp.: 17
Tire Sales, Retreading & Repair Services
N.A.I.C.S.: 441340
Clark Bucher *(Mgr)*

Tredroc Tire Services   (1)
2505 Thornwood St SW, Wyoming, MI 49519
Tel.: (616) 538-3800
Web Site: http://www.tredroc.com

Sales Range: $10-24.9 Million
Emp.: 40
Tire Sales, Retreading & Repair Services
N.A.I.C.S.: 441340
Dan Taylor *(Reg Mgr)*

TREE BRAND PACKAGING, INC.
7971 Graham Rd, Denver, NC 28037
Tel.: (704) 483-0719
Web Site: http://www.treebrand.com
Year Founded: 1991
Sales Range: $10-24.9 Million
Emp.: 75
Wood Container & Pallet Mfr
N.A.I.C.S.: 321920
Mike Helms *(VP)*
Al Helms *(Founder & Chm)*
Chris Helms *(Pres)*

TREE MEDIC, LLC
2900 N Government Way 229, Coeur d'Alene, ID 83815
Tel.: (208) 755-2349   ID
Year Founded: 2004
Tree & Shrub Care
N.A.I.C.S.: 111421
Ryan W. Wichman *(Owner)*

Subsidiaries:

Specialty Tree Services, LLC   (1)
3901 W Industrial Ave, Coeur d'Alene, ID 83815
Tel.: (208) 659-8400
Web Site: http://www.specialtytree.com
Landscaping Services
N.A.I.C.S.: 561730

TREE TOP, INC.
220 E 2nd Ave, Selah, WA 98942-0248
Tel.: (509) 698-1430   WA
Web Site: http://www.treetop.com
Year Founded: 1960
Sales Range: $100-124.9 Million
Emp.: 1,156
Fruit Juices Mfr
N.A.I.C.S.: 311411
Tom Hurson *(Pres & CEO)*
Dwaine Brown *(CIO & VP-Information Svcs)*
Gary Price *(VP-Ops)*
Scott Washburn *(VP-HR)*
Jim Divis *(Chm)*
John Howard Gebbers *(Treas & Sec)*
Craig Green *(CFO & VP-Fin)*
Alan Groff *(Vice Chm)*

Subsidiaries:

Northwest Naturals LLC   (1)
11805 N Creek Pkwy S Ste A-104, Bothell, WA 98011
Tel.: (425) 881-2200
Web Site: http://www.nwnaturals.com
Emp.: 30
Fruit Juice Concentrate & Sweetener Mfr
N.A.I.C.S.: 311411
Tom Hurson *(VP)*
Courtney Doolin *(Mgr-Food Safety)*

Tree Top, Inc. - Medford Oregon Plant   (1)
690 S Grape St, Medford, OR 97501
Tel.: (541) 772-5653
Sales Range: $50-74.9 Million
Emp.: 200
Fruit Sauce Mfr
N.A.I.C.S.: 311423
John Bradley *(Supvr-Safety & Environmental)*

Tree Top, Inc. - Oxnard California Plant   (1)
1250 E 3rd St, Oxnard, CA 93030
Tel.: (805) 483-3030
Fruit Puree & Concentrate Mfr
N.A.I.C.S.: 311930

Tree Top, Inc. - Prosser Plant   (1)
2780 Lee Rd, Prosser, WA 99350-0071
Tel.: (509) 786-2926

Sales Range: $25-49.9 Million
Emp.: 125
Fruit Juice Concentrate Mfr
N.A.I.C.S.: 311411

Tree Top, Inc. - Ross Plant (1)
101 S Railroad Ave, Selah, WA 98942
Tel.: (509) 698-1432
Sales Range: $25-49.9 Million
Emp.: 100
Processed Fruit Product Mfr
N.A.I.C.S.: 311421

Tree Top, Inc. - Selah Plant (1)
205 S Railroad Ave, Selah, WA 98942
Tel.: (509) 698-1430
Web Site: http://www.treetop.com
Sales Range: $50-74.9 Million
Emp.: 200
Processed Fruit Product Mfr
N.A.I.C.S.: 311421
Jason Simpson (Plant Mgr)

Tree Top, Inc. - Wenatchee Plant (1)
3981 Chelan HwyHwy, Wenatchee, WA 98801-0231
Tel.: (509) 663-8583
Web Site: http://www.treetop.com
Sales Range: $50-74.9 Million
Emp.: 150
Processed Fruit Product Mfr
N.A.I.C.S.: 311421

Tree Top, Inc. - Woodburn Oregon Plant (1)
1440 Silverton Rd, Woodburn, OR 97071
Tel.: (503) 982-9931
Sales Range: $25-49.9 Million
Emp.: 100
Food Products Mfr
N.A.I.C.S.: 311930

TREEFROG DATA SOLUTIONS
1980 N Atlantic Ave Ste 402, Cocoa Beach, FL 32931
Tel.: (321) 783-5667
Web Site:
  http://www.treefrogdatasolution.com
Year Founded: 1998
Sales Range: $1-9.9 Million
Emp.: 50
Medical Claims Processing
N.A.I.C.S.: 524291
Deborah DeLeo (Pres)

TREEHOUSE ISLAND INC.
622 E Washington St Ste 240, Orlando, FL 32801
Tel.: (800) 928-2130
Web Site: http://teamtreehouse.com
Sales Range: $25-49.9 Million
Web Design & Development Training
N.A.I.C.S.: 611420
Ryan Carson (CEO)
Rich Pettit (Controller)
Faye Bridge (Mgr-Community)
Michael Watson (CFO & COO)
Londa Quisling (Chief Product Officer)
Michael Fox (Chief Risk Officer)
Tommy Morgan (VP-Engrg)

TREELINE, INCORPORATED
599 N Ave Ste 6, Wakefield, MA 01880
Tel.: (781) 876-8100
Web Site: http://www.treeline-inc.com
Year Founded: 2001
Rev.: $2,000,000
Emp.: 18
Business Products & Services
N.A.I.C.S.: 561439
Daniel Fantasia (Pres & CEO)
Howard Schor (COO)

TREEN BOX & PALLET CORP.
1950 St Rd Ste 400, Bensalem, PA 19020
Tel.: (215) 639-5100   PA
Web Site: http://treenpallet.com
Sales Range: $25-49.9 Million
Emp.: 50
Holding Company; Wood Container & Pallet Mfr
N.A.I.C.S.: 551112
George P. Geiges (Co-Pres)
Charles Hicks (CFO)
Keith Geiges (Co-Pres)
Subsidiaries:

Treen Box & Pallet, Inc. (1)
1950 St Rd Ste 400, Bensalem, PA 19020
Tel.: (215) 639-5100
Web Site: http://www.treenboxandpallet.com
Wood Container & Pallet Mfr
N.A.I.C.S.: 321920
John Walton (Mgr)
Keith Geiges (Co-Pres)
Steve Geiges (Partner)

TREES N TRENDS INC.
3229 Old Benton Rd, Paducah, KY 42003
Tel.: (270) 441-3300
Web Site:
  http://www.treesntrends.com
Sales Range: $50-74.9 Million
Emp.: 400
Artificial Flowers
N.A.I.C.S.: 459999
Joe L. Wallace (Pres)

TREESAP FARMS, LLC
5151 Mitchelldale Ste B2, Houston, TX 77092
Tel.: (713) 613-5600   TX
Web Site:
  http://www.treetownusa.com
Year Founded: 2001
Tree Growing Services
N.A.I.C.S.: 111421
Jonathan Saperstein (CEO)
David Kirby (Exec VP)
Jeffrey Pettit (CFO)
Mark Marriott (Sr VP-Ops-Northwest Div)
Terri Cook (Sr VP-HR)
Bud Summers (COO)
Subsidiaries:

Village Nurseries Wholesale LLC (1)
1589 N Main St, Orange, CA 92867
Tel.: (714) 279-3100
Web Site: http://www.villagenurseries.com
Nursery Stock
N.A.I.C.S.: 424930
David House (Pres & CEO)

TREESOURCE INDUSTRIES, INC.
8277 Center St SW, Tumwater, WA 98501
Tel.: (360) 352-1548   OR
Year Founded: 1983
Sales Range: $75-99.9 Million
Emp.: 250
Producer of Soft & Hardwood Lumber, Wood Products & By-products
N.A.I.C.S.: 321113

TREFZ & TREFZ INC.
753 Broad St Ste 901, Augusta, GA 30901
Tel.: (706) 722-4516
Web Site: http://www.arbys.com
Sales Range: $25-49.9 Million
Emp.: 500
Fiscal Year-end: 12/31/14
Fast Food Restaurants
N.A.I.C.S.: 722513
Oren Trefz (Pres)
Paul Trefz (VP)

TREFZ CORPORATION
10 Middle St Ste 17, Bridgeport, CT 06604
Tel.: (203) 367-3621
Web Site:
  http://www.trefzproperties.com
Sales Range: $25-49.9 Million
Emp.: 20
Operator of Fast-Food Restaurants
N.A.I.C.S.: 541219
Maria Carlos (Mgr-HR & Mktg)
Robert Hull (CFO & Sr VP)

TREGARON MANAGEMENT, LLC
300 Hamilton Ave Ste 400, Palo Alto, CA 94301
Tel.: (650) 403-2080   DE
Web Site:
  http://www.tregaroncapital.com
Year Founded: 2001
Privater Equity Firm
N.A.I.C.S.: 523999
J. R. Matthews (Mng Dir)
Todd Collins (Mng Dir)
John Thornton (Mng Dir)
David Pickerd (VP)
Lauren Glazebrook (Mgr-Bus Dev)
Subsidiaries:

Fun-Brands of Tempe, LLC (1)
17767 N Perimeter Dr Ste B 117, Scottsdale, AZ 85255
Tel.: (480) 371-1200
Web Site: http://www.fun-brands.com
Sales Range: $100-124.9 Million
Emp.: 50
Holding Company; Family Entertainment Facilities Franchisor
N.A.I.C.S.: 551112
Susan Fickes (VP-Fin)
Ron Stilwell (VP-Ops-BounceU)
Jeff Smith (Dir-Ops-Fun Brands Carousel)
Subsidiary (Domestic):

BU Holdings, LLC (2)
1860 W University Dr Ste 108, Tempe, AZ 85281
Tel.: (480) 371-1200
Web Site: http://www.bounceu.com
Family Entertainment Facilities Franchisor
N.A.I.C.S.: 533110

Fun-Brands HQ Carousel, LLC (2)
1860 W University Dr Ste 108, Tempe, AZ 85281
Tel.: (480) 371-1200
Web Site: http://www.hqcarousels.com
Double-Decker Carousel Unit Franchisor
N.A.I.C.S.: 533110

TREHEL CORPORATION
1376 Tiger Blvd Ste 104, Clemson, SC 29631
Tel.: (864) 654-6582
Web Site: http://www.trehel.com
Year Founded: 1982
Sales Range: $25-49.9 Million
Emp.: 80
Provider of General Contracting Services
N.A.I.C.S.: 236220
James Neal Workman (Owner)
Linda Cowart (CFO)
Will Huff (Pres)

TREJO OIL CO. INC.
7227 E Baseline Rd Ste 109, Mesa, AZ 85206
Tel.: (480) 833-1199
Web Site: http://www.trejofuels.com
Rev.: $14,600,000
Emp.: 23
Petroleum Bulk Stations
N.A.I.C.S.: 424710
Cameron Trejo (Mgr)

TREK BICYCLE CORPORATION
801 W Madison St, Waterloo, WI 53594-1379
Tel.: (920) 478-2191   WI
Web Site: http://www.trekbikes.com
Year Founded: 1976
Sales Range: $550-599.9 Million
Emp.: 1,500
Bicycle Mfr
N.A.I.C.S.: 336991
John P. Burke (Pres & CEO)
Subsidiaries:

Electra Bicycle Company, LLC (1)
3275 Corporate View Suite A, Vista, CA 92081
Tel.: (760) 607-2453
Web Site: http://www.electrabike.com
Sales Range: $1-9.9 Million
Emp.: 25
Motorized Bikes Mfr
N.A.I.C.S.: 423910
Robin Vallaire (Creative Dir)
Elayne Fowler (Mktg Dir)

TREKKER TRACTOR, LLC
12601 W Okeechobee Rd, Miami, FL 33018
Tel.: (305) 821-2273
Web Site:
  http://www.trekkertractor.com
Sales Range: $1-9.9 Million
Construction Equipment Distr
N.A.I.C.S.: 423810
Jose Ramirez (Owner & CEO)

TRELLANCE, INC.
7650 W Courtney Campbell Causeway Ste 900, Tampa, FL 33607
Tel.: (888) 930-2728
Web Site: http://www.trellance.com
Year Founded: 1989
Credit Union
N.A.I.C.S.: 522130
Bill Lehman (Sr VP-Managed Svcs)
Subsidiaries:

On Approach LLC (1)
3455 Plymouth Blvd Ste 200, Plymouth, MN 55447
Tel.: (763) 557-7118
Web Site: http://www.onapproach.net
Electronics Stores
N.A.I.C.S.: 449210
Marwa Massoud (CEO)

TRELLIS EARTH PRODUCTS, INC.
9125 SW Ridder Rd Ste D, Wilsonville, OR 97070
Tel.: (503) 582-1300   NV
Web Site: http://www.trellisearth.com
Year Founded: 2006
Sales Range: $1-9.9 Million
Emp.: 38
Bio-Plastic Products Mfr
N.A.I.C.S.: 326199
Brian Dresbeck (Mgr-Legal & Compliance)
Patrick Lahmann (VP-Mfg)
Subsidiaries:

Trellis Bioplastics (1)
2213 Killion Ave, Seymour, IN 47274
Tel.: (812) 672-4995
Web Site: http://www.trellisbioplastic.com
Bioplastics Mfr
N.A.I.C.S.: 326199
Patrick Lahmann (VP-Mfg)

TREMBLY ASSOCIATES INC.
119 Quincy St NE, Albuquerque, NM 87108
Tel.: (505) 266-8616
Web Site: http://www.trembly.com
Rev.: $20,000,000
Emp.: 6
Electronic Parts & Equipment
N.A.I.C.S.: 423690
Gary Mulryan (Pres-Sls & Head Engr)
John Hoen (Engr-Utah)
Bill Toon (Engr-Arizona)

TREMONT COOPERATIVE GRAIN CO

TREMONT COOPERATIVE GRAIN CO

Tremont Cooperative Grain Co—(Continued)
112 N W St, Tremont, IL 61568
Tel.: (309) 925-4981
Web Site: http://www.tremont.coop
Sales Range: $25-49.9 Million
Emp.: 9
Grain Elevators
N.A.I.C.S.: 424510
Donald Stuber (Pres)

TREMONT GROUP, INC.
201 E St, Woodland, CA 95776
Tel.: (530) 662-5442
Web Site: http://www.tremontag.com
Year Founded: 1990
Sales Range: $10-24.9 Million
Emp.: 96
Distr of Farm Supplies
N.A.I.C.S.: 532490
Johnnie Council (VP)
Larry Chillemi (CFO)
Leslie F. Lyman (Chm)

TREMONT HOMES INC.
4008 Louetta Rd #256, Spring, TX 77388
Tel.: (832) 673-2000
Web Site:
   http://www.tremonthomes.com
Sales Range: $25-49.9 Million
Emp.: 26
Single-Family Housing Construction
N.A.I.C.S.: 236115
Sam Parrott (VP-Construction)

TRENCH SHORING COMPANY
206 N Central Ave, Los Angeles, CA 90220
Tel.: (310) 327-5554
Web Site:
   http://www.trenchshoring.com
Sales Range: $10-24.9 Million
Emp.: 12
Construction & Mining Machinery
N.A.I.C.S.: 423810
Thomas E. Malloy (Owner)
Kevin Malloy (Pres)

TREND HEALTH PARTNERS LLC
20 Wight Ave Ste 150, Hunt Valley, MD 21030
Tel.: (443) 689-2700
Web Site:
   https://www.trendhealthpartner.com
Emp.: 100
Healthcare Credit Balance Management & Payment Services
N.A.I.C.S.: 522320

Subsidiaries:

Advent Health Partners, Inc.   (1)
301 Plus Park Blvd, Nashville, TN 37217
Tel.: (605) 331-3492
Web Site: http://www.adventhp.com
Sales Range: $1-9.9 Million
Emp.: 75
Software Development Services
N.A.I.C.S.: 541511
Bri Brown (VP-Mktg)
Mark Thienel (CEO)

TREND TECHNOLOGIES, LLC
4626 Eucalyptus Dr, Chino, CA 91710
Tel.: (909) 597-7861
Web Site:
   http://www.trendtechnologies.com
Year Founded: 2003
Metal Stamping Mfr; Sheet Metal Fabricator
N.A.I.C.S.: 326199
Ron Begin (Mgr-IT)

TRENDHR SERVICES
5133 FM 549 S, Rockwall, TX 75032
Tel.: (214) 553-5505   TX

Web Site: http://www.trendhr.com
Year Founded: 1997
Sales Range: $50-74.9 Million
Emp.: 38
Personnel Outsourcing
N.A.I.C.S.: 561311
Dan W. Bobst (Founder & CEO)

TRENDS INTERNATIONAL LLC
5188 W 74th St., Indianapolis, 46268, IN
Tel.: (91) 8003544639
Web Site:
   https://trendsinternational.com
Year Founded: 1987
Publisher : posters, calendars, stickers & social stationery products & Mfg.
N.A.I.C.S.: 513199

Subsidiaries:

Art.com Inc.   (1)
2100 Powell St 13th Fl, Emeryville, CA 94608
Tel.: (510) 879-4700
Web Site: http://www.art.com
Sales Range: $25-49.9 Million
Emp.: 150
Online Posters, Art Prints & Phototgraphs Retailer & Custom Framing
N.A.I.C.S.: 459999

TRENDWOOD INC.
120 E Watkins St, Phoenix, AZ 85004
Tel.: (602) 416-7800
Web Site: http://www.trendwood.com
Rev: $24,272,019
Emp.: 220
Wood Household Furniture
N.A.I.C.S.: 337122
Dan Ragland (Pres)
Don Knight (VP)

TRENT BOX MFG. CO., INC.
PO Box 2650, Trenton, NJ 08691
Tel.: (609) 587-7515
Sales Range: $25-49.9 Million
Emp.: 20
Corrugated & Solid Fiber Box Mfr
N.A.I.C.S.: 322211
Carl A. Angelini (Owner)

TRENT CAPITAL PARTNERS, LLC
2640 Golden Gate Pkwy Ste 105, Naples, FL 34105
Tel.: (239) 302-6680   DE
Web Site: http://trentequity.com
Year Founded: 2010
Emp.: 100
Privater Equity Firm
N.A.I.C.S.: 523999
Raymond J. Desrocher Jr. (Partner)

Subsidiaries:

Alloy Holdings, LLC   (1)
160 Niantic Ave, Providence, RI 02907
Tel.: (401) 353-7500
Web Site: http://www.leesmorvillogroup.com
Precious Metal Components & Finished Jewelry Designer, Mfr & Whslr
N.A.I.C.S.: 331492
Todd R. Morvillo (Co-Pres & Head-Morvillo Precision Products)
Rich Powers (Chm)
Charles Morvillo (Co-Pres & Head-Lee's Mfg)

Subsidiary (Domestic):

Checon, LLC   (2)
30 Larsen Way, North Attleboro, MA 02763
Tel.: (508) 809-5112
Web Site: https://checon.com
Electrical Contact & Contact Materials Mfr
N.A.I.C.S.: 335999
D. Allen Conaway (Pres)

Subsidiary (Domestic):
Umicore Electrical Materials USA Inc.   (3)
527 Pleasant St Bldg 11, Attleboro, MA 02703
Tel.: (508) 838-2064
Web Site: https://jim-em.umicore.com
Emp.: 100
Metal Recycling Services
N.A.I.C.S.: 562920

TRENT, INC.
201 Leverington Ave, Philadelphia, PA 19127
Tel.: (215) 482-5000
Web Site: http://www.trentheat.com
Year Founded: 1927
Sales Range: $10-24.9 Million
Emp.: 15
Heated Industrial Equipment, Folded & Formed Electric Elements Mfr
N.A.I.C.S.: 333994
L.J. Silverthorn (Pres)

TRENTON MARINE CENTER PERFORMANCE GROUP, INC.
1501 Lamberton St, Trenton, NJ 08611
Tel.: (609) 392-7275
Web Site:
   http://www.trentonmarine.com
Sales Range: $10-24.9 Million
Emp.: 23
Boat Whslr
N.A.I.C.S.: 441222
Gerald L. Tipton (Pres)

TRENTON SYSTEMS INC
1725 Macleod Dr, Lawrenceville, GA 30043
Tel.: (770) 287-3100
Web Site:
   http://www.trentonsystems.com
Year Founded: 1989
Integrated Computer Systems Mfr
N.A.I.C.S.: 334118

Subsidiaries:

Trenton Technology Inc.   (1)
2007 Beechgrove Pl, Utica, NY 13501
Tel.: (315) 797-7534
Board Level Products & Integrated Computer Systems Mfr
Albert Mazloom (Gen Counsel & VP)
Ed Wheeler (Dir-Mfg Engrg)
Stuart Baunoch (Mgr-Inventory)

TRENTON WATER WORKS
PO Box 528, Trenton, NJ 08603-0528
Tel.: (609) 989-3044
Web Site: http://www.trentonnj.org
Sales Range: $10-24.9 Million
Emp.: 177
Provider of Water Supply Services
N.A.I.C.S.: 221310
Reno Cassarini (Engr-Supervising)
William Mitchell (Superintendent-Water Treatment Plant)

TRENWA, INC.
1419 Alexandria Pike, Fort Thomas, KY 41075-3530
Tel.: (859) 781-0831
Web Site: http://www.trenwa.com
Year Founded: 1968
Sales Range: $10-24.9 Million
Emp.: 47
Precast Concrete Trench System Mfr
N.A.I.C.S.: 327390
Keith Riggs (Chm & CEO)
George Schurr (Pres & COO)
Steve Wahlbrink (VP-Sls)
Kara McCormick (Mgr-Acctg & HR)
Kim Greene (Engr-Sls)
Austin Riggs (Engr-Sls)

U.S. PRIVATE

TREPCO IMPORTS & DISTRIBUTION LTD.
1201 E Lincoln, Madison Heights, MI 48071
Tel.: (248) 546-3661
Web Site: http://www.trepco.com
Sales Range: $10-24.9 Million
Emp.: 52
Wholesale Distributors of Tobacco Products
N.A.I.C.S.: 424940
Albert D. Paulus (Chm & Pres)

TREPOINT BARC
170 Columbus Ave Ste 120, San Francisco, CA 94133-5146
Tel.: (415) 967-7514   CA
Web Site: http://www.barcsf.com
Year Founded: 1989
Sales Range: $25-49.9 Million
Emp.: 25
Sales Promotion
N.A.I.C.S.: 541810
John Anthony Randazzo (Partner, Sr VP & Mgmt Supvr)
Felix Lam (Partner, CFO & Sr VP)
Brian Gillespie (VP)
John Koch (Dir-Creative)
Heather O'Donnell (Dir-Plng)
Bill Carmody (CEO)
Brian De La Torre (Exec VP-Creative)
Len Devanna (Exec VP-Account Svc & Gen Mgr)
Molly Reynolds (Pres-Public Rels)
Marc Sirkin (Pres-Trepoint Tech & VP-Strategy)
Bert Stouffer (Exec VP-Prod & Gen Mgr-Kansas Office)
John Randazzo Sr. (Pres, CEO & Vice Chm)

Subsidiaries:

TrepointBarc   (1)
98 Cuttermill Rd Ste 479 N, Great Neck, NY 11021
Tel.: (516) 453-5000
Web Site: http://www.trepoint.com
Sales Range: $1-9.9 Million
Emp.: 15
Advetising Agency
N.A.I.C.S.: 541810
Bill Carmody (CEO)
James L. Paterek (Chm)
Brian De La Torre (Exec VP-Creative)
Bert Stouffer (Exec VP-Production & Gen Mgr-Kansas Office)
Eric Salas (Exec VP-Acct Svcs)
John Randazzo (Vice Chm)
Len Devanna (Pres)
Molly Reynolds (Exec VP-Content Mktg)

TRES HERMANOS, INC.
6801 Pacific Blvd, Huntington Park, CA 90255
Tel.: (323) 585-1618   CA
Sales Range: $10-24.9 Million
Emp.: 30
Family Clothing Stores
N.A.I.C.S.: 458110
Monir Awada (Chm)

TRESCH ELECTRICAL COMPANY
1026 Machin Ave, Novato, CA 94945
Tel.: (415) 897-2125   CA
Sales Range: $10-24.9 Million
Emp.: 65
General Electrical Contractor & Appliance Sales
N.A.I.C.S.: 238210
Mani Majano (Pres)
Maureen Tresch (CEO)

TRESSA, INC.
2711 Circleport Dr, Erlanger, KY 41018-1080
Tel.: (859) 525-1300   OH

COMPANIES

Web Site: http://www.tressa.com
Year Founded: 1969
Sales Range: $150-199.9 Million
Emp.: 500
Provider of Hair-Care Preparations
N.A.I.C.S.: 325620
Jim Cooper (Dir-Ops)

TREVARROW INC.
1295 N Opdyke Rd, Auburn Hills, MI 48326
Tel.: (248) 377-2300   MI
Web Site:
  http://www.trevarrowinc.com
Year Founded: 1928
Sales Range: $25-49.9 Million
Emp.: 50
Distr of Electrical Appliances
N.A.I.C.S.: 423620
Bruce Trevarrow (Pres)
Janina Murdock (Reg Mgr-Sls)

TREVDAN INC.
PO Box 28, Chester Springs, PA 19425-0028
Tel.: (610) 458-8500   PA
Web Site: http://www.trevdan.com
Year Founded: 1982
Sales Range: $10-24.9 Million
Emp.: 100
Provider of Lumber Products
N.A.I.C.S.: 423310
Larry Kanavy (Founder, Pres & Treas)
Tim J. Kanavy (VP)

TREW MARKETING
4301 W William Cannon Dr Ste 150 #238, Austin, TX 78749
Tel.: (512) 410-7337
Web Site:
  http://www.trewmarketing.com
Year Founded: 2008
Sales Range: $1-9.9 Million
Advertising Agencies
N.A.I.C.S.: 541810
Rebecca Geier (Co-Founder & CEO)
Wendy Covey (Co-Founder & COO)
Denise Goluboff (Sr Mgr-Web)
Irene Bearly (Mgr-Technical Mktg)
Laura Lee Daigle (Designer)
Lee Chapman (Acct Dir)
Ryan Gardner (Coord-Mktg)
Stephanie Logerot (Mgr-Inbound Mktg)
Kristi Bjornaas (Mgr-Market Inbound)

TREX ENTERPRISES CORPORATION
10455 Pacific Ctr Ct, San Diego, CA 92121
Tel.: (858) 646-5300
Web Site:
  http://www.trexenterprises.com
Sales Range: $25-49.9 Million
Emp.: 100
Commercial Physical Research
N.A.I.C.S.: 541715
Kenneth Y. Tang (Chm & CEO)
Debbie Doyle (CFO & VP)

Subsidiaries:

Loea Communications Corp.   (1)
10455 Pacific Center Ct, San Diego, CA 92121
Tel.: (858) 646-5700
Web Site: http://www.loeacom.com
Rev.: $1,300,000
Emp.: 12
Cellular Telephone Services
N.A.I.C.S.: 517112
Debbie Doyle (CFO)

TREXIN CONSULTING LLC
601 Carlson Pkwy 10th Fl, Minneapolis, MN 55305
Tel.: (952) 745-4529

Web Site: http://www.trexin.com
Year Founded: 2005
Sales Range: $1-9.9 Million
Emp.: 32
It Consulting
N.A.I.C.S.: 541690
Marvin Richardson (Mng Dir)
Dale Anderson (Mng Dir)
Robert Bloyd (Mng Dir)
Warren Golla (Mng Dir)
Jon Waddell (Co-Founder & CTO)
Doren Jacobs (Mng Principal)
Matt Anderson (Sr Principal)
Bhoopendra Singh (Partner)
Chris Bloomer (Partner)
Aaron Drinkwine (Principal)
Andy Way (Sr Principal)
Arif Khan (Sr Principal)
Ashley Anthonsen (Principal)
Ashwin Manepalli (Sr Principal)
Asif Karim (Principal)
Brent Mavity (Principal)
Claire Patel (Principal)
Erica Maltby (Principal)
Gayle Kowalski (Principal)

TREXTEL, LLC
1955 Evergreen Blvd Ste 200, Duluth, GA 30096
Tel.: (678) 578-7900   GA
Web Site: http://www.trextel.com
Year Founded: 2007
Sales Range: $10-24.9 Million
Emp.: 118
Information Technology Services
N.A.I.C.S.: 541512
Jason Morrow (CEO)
Craig Henry (Exec VP-Strategic Partnerships)
Joe Macchiarella (Exec VP-Ops)

TREYNOR BANCSHARES, INC.
15 E Main St, Treynor, IA 51575
Tel.: (712) 487-3000   IA
Web Site: http://www.tsbg.com
Year Founded: 1982
Sales Range: $10-24.9 Million
Bank Holding Company
Joshua M. Guttau (CEO)
Brett Werner (Chief Investment Officer)
Wendi Stane (Officer-Credit Ops)
Edward Kentch (Officer-CRA)

Subsidiaries:

State Bank of Arcadia, Inc.   (1)
131 W Main St, Arcadia, WI 54612
Tel.: (608) 323-3331
Web Site: http://www.rkdbank.com
Sales Range: $1-9.9 Million
Emp.: 30
Commericial Banking
N.A.I.C.S.: 522110
Janet M. Mueller (Sr VP-Arcadia)
Kevin P. Manley (Pres)
Nancy M. Lettner (Exec VP-Arcadia)

The Bank of Tioga   (1)
7 N Main St, Tioga, ND 58852
Tel.: (701) 664-3388
Web Site: http://www.thebankoftioga.com
Sales Range: $1-9.9 Million
Emp.: 25
Commericial Banking
N.A.I.C.S.: 522110
David A. Grubb (Pres-Market)
Judy D. Odegaard (Officer-BSA & VP)
Harlan Germundson (Officer-Relationship & VP)
Debbie Axtman (VP-Personal Banking)
Deb McClelland (VP-Personal Banking)

Treynor State Bank   (1)
15 E Main St, Treynor, IA 51575
Tel.: (712) 487-3000
Web Site: http://www.tsbank.com
Sales Range: $10-24.9 Million
Emp.: 68
Commericial Banking

N.A.I.C.S.: 522110
Michael K. Guttau (Chm)
Joshua M. Guttau (CEO)
Judith A. Guttau (Sec & Dir-Community Reinvestment)
Eugene W. Young (Pres & Exec VP)
Christy Baker (COO)
Glen Fleming (CIO)
Mark Sorfonden (Chief Credit Officer)
Kevin Forristall (Chief Risk Officer)
Pete Boothby (Chief Talent Mgmt Officer)
Kelsey Stupfell (Officer-Client Experience)
Chris Graham (CFO & Controller)
Angela Avis (Dir-HR)
Frank Wellenstein (Sr VP-Wealth Mgmt & Trust)
Corine Fox (VP-Personal Banking)
Christine Blum (Pres-Market)
Debra Brown (Asst VP & Mgr-Atlantic)
Mike Burchett (VP-Credit Admin)
Mary Jewell (VP-Wealth Mgmt & Trust)
Jim Koch (VP-Wealth Mgmt & Trust Admin)
Sandy Mass (VP-Wealth Mgmt & Trust)
Melissa Peterson (Dir-Mktg)
Cecilia Silba (Asst VP & Mgr-West Broadway)
Brett Werner (Dir-Analytics)

TRG HOLDINGS, LLC
1700 Pennsylvania Ave NW Ste 560, Washington, DC 20006
Tel.: (202) 289-9898
Web Site: http://www.trgworld.com
Sales Range: $450-499.9 Million
Emp.: 3,000
Holding Company
N.A.I.C.S.: 551112
Zia Chisti (Chm & Sr Partner)
Mohammed Khaishgi (COO & Sr Partner)
Hasnain Aslam (Sr Partner)
Nadeem Elahi (Mng Dir)

TRG MANAGEMENT LP
Park Ave Twr 65 E 55th St 15th Fl, New York, NY 10022
Tel.: (212) 984-2900   DE
Web Site:
  http://www.rohatyngroup.com
Year Founded: 2002
Emerging Market Asset Management Services
N.A.I.C.S.: 523940
Nicolas Rohatyn (CEO & Partner)
Vladimir Krin (Chief Risk Officer, CIO & Partner)
Warren Master (CTO, Chief Security Officer & Mng Dir)
Roberto Chute (Partner-Buenos Aires)
Harold Chatelus (Dir)

Subsidiaries:

Capital Advisors Partners Asia Pte. Ltd.   (1)
1 Temasek Ave 30-02, Singapore, 039192, Singapore   (60%)
Tel.: (65) 66320480
Web Site: http://www.capasia.com
Rev.: $400,000,000
Emp.: 15
Infrastructure Private Equity Investment Management Services
N.A.I.C.S.: 523940
Ziehan Adnan (Office Mgr)
Johan Bastin (CEO)
Craig Martin (Mng Partner & Head-SEASAF)
Devarshi Das (Sr Dir & Co-Head-Infrastructure Investment Fund)
Burcu Seslioglu (VP-Investment)

Subsidiary (Non-US):

Capital Advisors Partners Asia Sdn. Bhd.   (2)
Lot 17 4 Level 17 Menara Milenium 8 Jalan Damanlela, Damansara Heights, 50490, Kuala Lumpur, Malaysia
Tel.: (60) 320938942
Web Site: http://www.cap-asia.net

TRG MANAGEMENT LP

Sales Range: $125-149.9 Million
Infrastructure Private Equity Investment Management Services
N.A.I.C.S.: 523940

Ethos Private Equity (Proprietary) Limited   (1)
35 Fricker Road, Illovo, 2196, South Africa
Tel.: (27) 113287400
Web Site: http://www.ethos.co.za
Privater Equity Firm
N.A.I.C.S.: 523999
Andre Roux (CEO & Partner)
Craig Dreyer (CFO & Partner)
Anthonie de Beer (Partner)
Stuart MacKenzie (Partner)
Bill Ashmore (Partner)
Christo Roos (Partner)
Garry Boyd (Partner)
Ngalaah Chuphi (Partner & Head-IR)
Shaun Zagnoev (Partner)
Jos van Zyl (COO & Partner)
Sebotsa de Bruyn (Partner)
Richard Fienberg (Partner-Value Creation)
Peter Hayward-Butt (Partner)
Walter Hirzebruch (Partner)
Jonathan Matthews (Partner)
Michael Jensen (Partner)
Phillip Myburgh (Mng Partner)
Edward Pitsi (Mng Partner-Mid Market)
Timothy Souter (Partner)
Glynn Potgieter (Principal)
Joao Rodrigues (Principal-Value Add)
Richard Hardy (Principal)
Tabane Matheolane (Principal)
Titi Sekhukhune (Principal)

Holding (Domestic):

AutoZone Retail and Distribution (Pty) Ltd   (2)
111 Mimetes Road, Cape Town, 2094, South Africa
Tel.: (27) 861122111
Web Site: http://www.autozone.co.za
Automotive Part Whslr
N.A.I.C.S.: 423120
Johan Adendorff (Mgr-Fin)

RTT Group (Pty) Ltd   (2)
ACSA Park CNR Jones & Springbok Road, Bartlett, Boksburg, 1469, South Africa
Tel.: (27) 861367786
Web Site: http://www.rtt.co.za
Emp.: 3,000
Logistics Consulting Servies
N.A.I.C.S.: 541614
Gerhard van Zyl (Branch Mgr)

Joint Venture (Domestic):

Torre Industries Limited   (2)
11Avalon Road West Lake View Ext 11, Modderfontein, 1609, South Africa
Tel.: (27) 119237000
Web Site: http://www.torreindustries.com
Investment Holding Company
N.A.I.C.S.: 551112
Shivan Mansingh (CFO)
Jon Hillary (CEO)
Sean Graham (Sec)

Subsidiary (Non-US):

Kanu Equipment Congo Limited   (3)
Rue de Kinsoundi Quartier Wharf, Pointe Noire, Congo, Republic of
Tel.: (242) 6 438 7619
Web Site: http://www.kanuequipment.com
Construction Equipment Distr
N.A.I.C.S.: 423810

Kanu Equipment Cote'Ivoire Limited   (3)
Yopougon Zone Industrielle 30, BP 115, Abidjan, 30, Cote d'Ivoire
Tel.: (225) 57923797
Web Site: http://www.kanuequipment.com
Construction Equipment Distr
N.A.I.C.S.: 423810

Kanu Equipment Ghana Limited   (3)
House no 38/24 George Walker Bush Highway, Dzorwulu, Accra, Ghana
Tel.: (233) 207 252 598
Web Site: http://www.kanuequipment.com
Construction Equipment Distr
N.A.I.C.S.: 423810

Kanu Equipment Liberia Ltd.   (3)

TRG MANAGEMENT LP

TRG Management LP—(Continued)
Sinkor Old Road, PO Box 1858, Monrovia, 1000, Liberia
Tel.: (231) 777 55 56 77
Web Site: http://www.kanuequipment.com
Construction Equipment Distr
N.A.I.C.S.: 423810

Kanu Equipment Sierra Leone (3)
117 Wilkinson Road, Freetown, Sierra Leone
Tel.: (232) 99 00 18 00
Web Site: http://www.kanuequipment.com
Construction Equipment Distr
N.A.I.C.S.: 423810

Subsidiary (Domestic):

Torre Holdings (Pty) Ltd. (3)
461 Flower Close Greenhills Industrial Estate, Tunney Extension 9, Germiston, South Africa
Tel.: (27) 11 822 8782
Web Site: http://www.safrench.co.za
Holding Company; Industrial & Automotive Equipment & Components Mfr & Distr
N.A.I.C.S.: 551112

Subsidiary (Domestic):

Torre Parts and Components (4)
59 Merino Avenue, City Deep, Johannesburg, 2049, South Africa
Tel.: (27) 116272500
Web Site: http://www.torreparts.com
Holding Company; Automotive & Industrial Components Mfr
N.A.I.C.S.: 551112

Subsidiary (Domestic):

Torre Automotive (Pty) Limited (5)
76 White Road, Retreat, Cape Town, 7945, South Africa
Tel.: (27) 217106800
Web Site: http://www.torreparts.com
Aftermarket Automotive Components Mfr
N.A.I.C.S.: 336390

Subsidiary (Domestic):

Tractor and Grader Supplies (Pty) Ltd (3)
11 Avalon Road Westlake View Ext 11, Modderfontein, 1609, Gauteng, South Africa
Tel.: (27) 11 392 7533
Web Site: http://www.tags.co.za
Industrial Machinery & Equipment Distr
N.A.I.C.S.: 423830

Holding (Domestic):

Twincare Group (2)
Building 3 Bryanston Gate 170 Curzon Road, Private Bag X85, Bryanston, 2021, South Africa
Tel.: (27) 117997111
Web Site: http://www.twincaregroup.co.za
Emp.: 133
Cosmetic Product Distr
N.A.I.C.S.: 424210
Joanne Gould (COO)

Twinsaver Group (2)
Building 3 Bryanston Gate 170 Curzon Rd, Sandton, South Africa
Tel.: (27) 860777111
Web Site: http://www.twinsavergroup.co.za
Emp.: 7
Tissue Products Mfr, Marketer & Distr
N.A.I.C.S.: 322120
Garth Towell (CEO)
Chevonne Wilkins (Mktg Dir)
Dion De Graaff (COO-Strategic Growth)
Evelyn De Wee (Dir-HR)
Joanne Gould (COO-Tissue)
Mervyn Pillay (Dir-IT & Fin)
Paul Richards (Dir-Customer Mgmt & Sls)
Sean Nieuwenhuys (Dir-Ops)
Simon Ndimande (Dir-Supply Chain)
Kevin Kistan (CEO)

Universal Industries Corporation (Pty) Limited (2)
2nd Floor 2 Melrose Boulevard, Melrose Arch, Johannesburg, 2076, South Africa
Tel.: (27) 114622110
Web Site: http://www.universalindustries.co.za

Display Cases & Polyurethane Insulated Panels Mfr
N.A.I.C.S.: 423740

Subsidiary (Domestic):

Colcab (Pty) Ltd. (3)
Buttskop Rd, Blackheath, 7580, Cape Town, Western Province, South Africa
Tel.: (27) 219072800
Web Site: http://www.colcab.co.za
Sales Range: $25-49.9 Million
Emp.: 250
Refrigerated Display Cabinets Mfr
N.A.I.C.S.: 333415
Ian Harries (Dir-Sls & Mktg)
Keith Reeves (Dir-HR)
Rainer Faustmann (Dir-Production)

Insulated Structures (1989) (Pty) Limited (3)
CGIS Building 12 Brunel Road, Tulisa Park, Johannesburg, 2197, Gauteng, South Africa
Tel.: (27) 114622130
Web Site: http://www.insulatedstructures.co.za
Sales Range: $50-74.9 Million
Emp.: 150
Panels & Refrigerated Cabinets Mfr & Supplier
N.A.I.C.S.: 333415

Macadams International (Pty) Ltd. (3)
Macadams Business Park School St, Blackheath, Cape Town, 7581, Western Cape, South Africa
Tel.: (27) 219071000
Web Site: http://www.macadams.co.za
Sales Range: $50-74.9 Million
Emp.: 300
Bakery Equipment Mfr
N.A.I.C.S.: 333241
Karien Donnelly (Mgr-Sls)

TRI - COUNTY BEVERAGE
2651 E 10 Mile Rd, Warren, MI 48126-3410
Tel.: (586) 757-4900
Web Site: http://www.tricountybeverage.com
Year Founded: 1958
Sales Range: $25-49.9 Million
Emp.: 100
Supplier of Beer & Ale
N.A.I.C.S.: 445320
Walter J. Wolpin (Pres & Treas)
Bill Pappas (Mgr-Sls)
Kevin O'Connor (Mgr-Sls)
Steve Smith (Mgr-Sls)

TRI CENTRAL CO-OP
104 N Michigan, Ashkum, IL 60911
Tel.: (815) 698-2327
Web Site: http://www.tricentralcoop.com
Sales Range: $10-24.9 Million
Emp.: 11
Grain Elevators
N.A.I.C.S.: 424510

TRI CITY DISTRIBUTORS LP
523 FM 306, New Braunfels, TX 78130
Tel.: (830) 625-0422
Web Site: http://www.tricitybud.com
Rev.: $15,000,000
Emp.: 75
Beer & Other Fermented Malt Liquors
N.A.I.C.S.: 424810
S. Scott Brown (Pres & Owner)
Boyd Anderson (VP)

TRI CITY FOODS INC.
150 N Oliver St, Wichita, KS 67208
Tel.: (316) 685-1324
Rev.: $15,694,540
Emp.: 12
Provider of Restaurant Services
N.A.I.C.S.: 722513
Theodore A. Swan (Pres)

TRI CITY PAVING INC.
13504 Haven Rd, Little Falls, MN 56345
Tel.: (320) 632-5435
Web Site: http://www.tri-citypaving.com
Sales Range: $10-24.9 Million
Emp.: 140
Highway & Street Construction Contracting Services
N.A.I.C.S.: 237310
John Surma (Pres)
Daniel Surma (VP)
Susan Houdek (Office Mgr)

TRI CITY RENTAL
255 Washington Ave Ext, Albany, NY 12205
Tel.: (518) 862-6600
Web Site: http://www.tricityrentals.com
Sales Range: $10-24.9 Million
Emp.: 20
Apartment Building Operator
N.A.I.C.S.: 531110
Julie Knox (Mgr-Sls & Mktg)
Tim Owens (Gen Mgr)

TRI COASTAL DESIGN GROUP INC
40 Harry Shupe Blvd, Wharton, NJ 07885
Tel.: (973) 560-0300
Web Site: http://www.tricoastaldesign.com
Year Founded: 1990
Rev.: $100,000,000
Emp.: 200
Gift Sets & Accessories Mfr
N.A.I.C.S.: 424120
Marvin Stutz (Pres)
Ronald Fiore (CFO)
Michael Mastrangelo (VP & Treas)

TRI COUNTY AIR CONDITIONING & HEATING, INC.
1080 Enterprise Ct, Nokomis, FL 34275
Tel.: (941) 485-2222
Web Site: http://www.tricountyair.com
Year Founded: 1977
Sales Range: $10-24.9 Million
Emp.: 86
Air Conditioning, Heating & Solar Contractor
N.A.I.C.S.: 238220
William S. Swanson (Owner & Pres)

TRI COUNTY COMMUNITY ACTION AGENCY, INC.
110 Cohansey St, Bridgeton, NJ 08302
Tel.: (856) 451-6330
Web Site: http://www.gatewaycap.org
Year Founded: 1987
Rev.: $33,200,000
Emp.: 400
Child Care & Social Services
N.A.I.C.S.: 624190
John Washington (Chm)
Edward Bethea (Founder, COO & Exec VP)
Albert Kelly (CEO)

TRI COUNTY FARMERS EQUIPMENT
209 Parks St, Newbern, TN 38059
Tel.: (731) 627-2541
Web Site: http://tricountyfarmersequip.com
Sales Range: $10-24.9 Million
Emp.: 30
Agricultural Equipment Repair Services
N.A.I.C.S.: 811310
James Hendrix (Pres)

U.S. PRIVATE

TRI COUNTY OFFICE FURNITURE
230 Santa Barbara St, Santa Barbara, CA 93101
Tel.: (805) 564-4060
Web Site: http://www.tcof.com
Sales Range: $10-24.9 Million
Emp.: 25
Office Furniture
N.A.I.C.S.: 449110
Bryan Burnell (Partner)
Mike Young (Partner)
Jennifer Escobar (Mgr-Pur)
Melva Hatchard (Acct Mgr)

TRI COUNTY WHOLESALE DISTRIBUTORS INC.
1120 Oak Hill St, Youngstown, OH 44502-6404
Tel.: (330) 743-3101   OH
Year Founded: 1997
Sales Range: $10-24.9 Million
Emp.: 40
Alcoholic Beverage Distr
N.A.I.C.S.: 424820
Steve Eisenburg (Pres)

Subsidiaries:

R.L. Lipton Wholesalers Inc. (1)
250 Seco Rd, Monroeville, PA 15146-1420   (100%)
Tel.: (412) 380-9380
Sales Range: $10-24.9 Million
Emp.: 30
Distr of Tobacco Products
N.A.I.C.S.: 424940

The Anchor Cigar & Candy Company Inc. (1)
537 Williamson Ave, Youngstown, OH 44502-2068
Tel.: (330) 744-4443
Sales Range: $10-24.9 Million
Emp.: 30
Distr of Tobacco & Candy Products
N.A.I.C.S.: 424450

TRI DAL LTD.
540 Commerce St, Southlake, TX 76092-9113
Tel.: (817) 481-2886
Web Site: http://www.tridal.com
Year Founded: 1995
Sales Range: $25-49.9 Million
Emp.: 208
Provider of Water, Sewer & Utility Lines
N.A.I.C.S.: 237110
Steve Hendricks (Dir-Mktg)
Phillip Hutchings (Project Mgr)
Scott Carr (Supvr-Survey Field)

TRI RINSE, INC.
1400 S 2nd St, Saint Louis, MO 63104
Tel.: (314) 647-8338   MO
Web Site: http://www.tri-rinse.com
Year Founded: 1981
Sales Range: $1-9.9 Million
Emp.: 48
Environment Services, Including Container Disposal, Hazardous Waste Removal, Above & Underground Tank Cleaning & Recycling
N.A.I.C.S.: 562211
Tim Shocklee (Founder & CEO)
Mike Kamrath (Mgr-Sls-Containers & Pkg)
Ben Perkins (Mgr-Indus Cleaning)
Mike Morgan (Owner)

TRI STAR ENERGY, LLC
1740 Ed Temple Blvd, Nashville, TN 37208
Tel.: (615) 313-3600   DE
Web Site: http://www.tri-staris.com
Petroleum Products Producer & Retailer; Convenience Stores Operator

COMPANIES

N.A.I.C.S.: 424720
R. Jeffrey Williams (CFO)
Steve Hostetter (CEO & COO)
Charlton Bell (Sr VP-Facilities)
Mohamed Makky (VP-Wholesale Ops)
Rob Jewell (VP-Comml Fueling)
Christy Cox (VP-HR)
Ken Buettner (VP-IT)
Dawn Boulanger (VP-Mktg)
Rick Hamilton (VP-Retail Ops)

Subsidiaries:

Consumers Gasoline Stations, Inc. (1)
904 8th Ave S, Nashville, TN 37203-4720
Tel.: (615) 259-3226
Sales Range: $150-199.9 Million
Emp.: 420
Gasoline & Market Stations
N.A.I.C.S.: 457120

Dailys (1)
1740 Ed Temple Blvd, Nashville, TN 37208-1850
Tel.: (615) 313-3600
Sales Range: $50-74.9 Million
Operator of Convenience Stores
N.A.I.C.S.: 445120

TRI STAR FREIGHT SYSTEM INC.
5407 Mesa Dr, Houston, TX 77028
Tel.: (713) 631-1095
Web Site: http://www.tristarfreightsys.com
Rev.: $18,526,001
Emp.: 29
Provider of Transportation Services
N.A.I.C.S.: 484210
Bill Roehr (Exec VP-Ops)
Kevin Garrison (VP & Mgr-Intermodal)
Keith Garrison (Treas)
Jeff Schoch (Mgr-Store-Retail)
Jim Price (Mgr-Baltimore)
Paul McKinney (Mgr-Charleston)
Sheila Davis (Mgr-Sls)

TRI STAR METALS INC.
375 Village Dr, Carol Stream, IL 60188-1828
Tel.: (630) 462-7600
Web Site: http://www.tristarmetals.com
Year Founded: 1988
Sales Range: $25-49.9 Million
Emp.: 25
Steel Mfr & Distr
N.A.I.C.S.: 423510
Jay Mandel (Pres)
Jim Roach (Mgr-Mktg)
Peter Walter (VP-Sls & Aluminum)

TRI STATE DISTRIBUTORS INC.
550 E 1st Ave, Spokane, WA 99202
Tel.: (509) 455-8300
Web Site: http://www.tristatedistributors.com
Year Founded: 1975
Sales Range: $50-74.9 Million
Emp.: 48
Electrical Appliances, Televisions & Radios Distr
N.A.I.C.S.: 423620
Don Dickson (Co-Pres-Washington)
Gary Dickson (Co-Pres)
Randy German (Sec & Comptroller)
Jim Hornback (Gen Mgr)
Lon Madsen (Gen Mgr)
Ron Mindemann (Mgr-Sls-Appliances)
Dustin Perasso (Gen Mgr)
Greg Truchot (Gen Mgr & Mgr-Sls & Appliances)
Danyal Lowe (Mgr-Credit)

TRI STATE SUPPLY COMPANY, INC.
371 W Chestnut St, Washington, PA 15301-4615
Tel.: (724) 225-8311 PA
Web Site: http://www.tssab.com
Year Founded: 1968
Sales Range: $10-24.9 Million
Emp.: 50
Mfr of Electrical Apparatus & Equipment
N.A.I.C.S.: 423610
James D. Van Zandt (Pres & CEO)
Mike Warco (CFO)
Bill Roedler (Mgr-Counter Sls)
Jeff Van Zandt (VP)
Doug Miller (Dir-Pur)

TRI SUPPLY COMPANY
3685 Martin Luther King Pkwy, Beaumont, TX 77705
Tel.: (409) 835-7966
Web Site: http://trisupplyhometeam.com
Sales Range: $10-24.9 Million
Emp.: 11
Exterior Building Materials
N.A.I.C.S.: 423310
John R. Raykovich (Pres)
Jason Bush (Mgr-Svc)
Jessica Castrejon (Asst Mgr)
Jeffery Foreman (Gen Mgr)

TRI TECH CONSTRUCTION CORP.
34 S 30th St, Keokuk, IA 52632
Tel.: (319) 524-9002
Web Site: http://www.tritechconstruction.com
Sales Range: $10-24.9 Million
Emp.: 40
Provider of Industrial Buildings & New Construction Services
N.A.I.C.S.: 238220
Jerry Fett (Dir-Safety)

TRI TECH LABORATORIES, INC.
1000 Robins Rd, Lynchburg, VA 24504
Tel.: (434) 845-7073 DE
Web Site: http://www.tritechlabs.com
Year Founded: 1919
Health & Beauty Aid Contract Mfr
N.A.I.C.S.: 325620
Lisa Coffey (Mgr-HR)

TRI TOOL INC.
3041 Sunrise Blvd, Rancho Cordova, CA 95742-6502
Tel.: (916) 288-6100
Web Site: http://www.tritool.com
Year Founded: 1972
Rev.: $16,000,000
Emp.: 100
Provider of Metal Cutting Tools
N.A.I.C.S.: 333517
George J. Wernette (Pres)
Troy Todd (VP-Global Sls & Field Svcs)
Chris Belle (CEO)
George J. Wernette III (Founder & Chm)

Subsidiaries:

Tri Tool International (1)
3041 Sunrise Blvd, Rancho Cordova, CA 95742-6502
Tel.: (916) 288-6100
Web Site: http://www.tritool.com
Sales Range: $25-49.9 Million
Machine Tools, Metal Cutting Type
N.A.I.C.S.: 333517

Tri Tool Power Services, Inc. (1)
4694 Aviation Pkwy Ste S, Atlanta, GA 30349
Tel.: (404) 763-3011
Web Site: http://www.tritool.com
Machine Tools, Metal Cutting Type
N.A.I.C.S.: 333517
George J. Wernette (Pres)

TRI-AM RV CENTER
5441 NE Jacksonville Rd, Ocala, FL 34479
Tel.: (352) 732-6269
Web Site: http://www.triamrv.com
Rev.: $18,000,000
Emp.: 20
Recreational Vehicle Dealers
N.A.I.C.S.: 441210
Russ Perkins (Pres)

TRI-AUTO ENTERPRISES, LLC
7225 Georgetown Rd, Indianapolis, IN 46268
Tel.: (317) 644-5700
Web Site: http://www.triauto.com
Year Founded: 2001
Sales Range: $10-24.9 Million
Emp.: 59
Automotive Print Marketing
N.A.I.C.S.: 541810
Scott Hill (Co-Founder)
Andy Medley (Dir-Mktg Bus)

TRI-CHEM, INC.
681 Main St Bldg 24, Belleville, NJ 07109-3461
Tel.: (973) 751-9200 DE
Web Site: http://www.trichem.com
Year Founded: 1948
Sales Range: $100-124.9 Million
Emp.: 5
Mfr of Fabric Paints, Silk Screened Fabric & Molded Plastic
N.A.I.C.S.: 336991
Andrew D. McKnight (Pres & CEO)
R.Y. Keegan (Treas)

TRI-CITY COMMUNITY ACTION PROGRAM INC.
110 Pleasant St, Malden, MA 02148
Tel.: (781) 322-4125 MA
Year Founded: 1978
Sales Range: $10-24.9 Million
Emp.: 105
Anti-Poverty Advocacy Services
N.A.I.C.S.: 813319
Gabriella Snyder-Stelmack (Pres)
Charlie Harak (Treas)
D. Matthew Dugan (VP)
Philip Bronder-Giroux (Exec Dir)

TRI-CITY ELECTRIC CO.
6225 N Brady St, Davenport, IA 52806
Tel.: (563) 322-7181 IA
Web Site: http://www.tricityelectric.com
Year Founded: 1895
Sales Range: $25-49.9 Million
Emp.: 700
Electrical Work Services
N.A.I.C.S.: 238210
Steve Maine (Project Mgr)

Subsidiaries:

COMET Technologies USA, Inc. - ebeam Technologies (1)
8700 Hillandale Rd, Davenport, IA 52806-9619
Tel.: (563) 285-7411
Web Site: http://www.ebeamtechnologies.com
Emp.: 85
Electron Beam Equipped Systems Mfr
N.A.I.C.S.: 333998
Karl Swanson (VP-Sls-Global)
Terry Thompson (Gen Mgr)

TRI-CITY ELECTRICAL CONTRACTORS, INC.
430 West Dr, Altamonte Springs, FL 32714
Tel.: (407) 788-3500 FL
Web Site: http://www.tcelectric.com
Year Founded: 1958
Sales Range: $100-124.9 Million
Emp.: 600
Electrical Contracting & Communication Services
N.A.I.C.S.: 238210
Charles W. McFarland (CFO & Sr VP-Admin)
F. Rance Borderick (VP-Residential & Multifamily)
Tom Lancione (Mgr-Facility)
Kevin Neal (Mgr-Svc & Comm-Central Florida)
H. L. Eidel (Founder & CEO)
Dino Martinez (Mgr-Estimating Comml-Tampa)
Michael Germana (CFO)
Jack A. Olmstead (Pres)

Subsidiaries:

Tri-City Electrical Contractors, Inc. - Tampa Division (1)
5910 Hartford St, Tampa, FL 33619
Tel.: (813) 622-7180
Electrical Contracting Services
N.A.I.C.S.: 238210
Jack Olmstead (Pres)
Wayne Stewart (Project Mgr)

TRI-CITY FORD INC.
912 S Van Buren Rd, Eden, NC 27288
Tel.: (336) 623-2185
Web Site: http://www.tricityford.net
Sales Range: $10-24.9 Million
Emp.: 40
Car Whslr
N.A.I.C.S.: 441110
Kevin Coates (Gen Mgr)

TRI-CITY MEATS INCORPORATED
1346 N Hickory Ave, Meridian, ID 83642
Tel.: (208) 884-2600
Web Site: http://www.tricitymeats.com
Year Founded: 1967
Sales Range: $10-24.9 Million
Emp.: 50
Meats & Meat Products Whslr & Distr
N.A.I.C.S.: 424470
Gary Goodwin (Mgr-Sls)

TRI-CON INC.
7076 W Port Arthur Rd, Beaumont, TX 77705
Tel.: (409) 835-2237
Web Site: http://www.triconinc.org
Sales Range: $10-24.9 Million
Emp.: 150
Provider of Petroleum Products
N.A.I.C.S.: 424720
Samir Sarkis (CEO)
Lynn Fazio (Mgr-Retail Fuels)
Ron Nicklas (Mgr-Ops)
Brian Limbocker (Mgr-Mktg)

TRI-CONSTRUCTION COMPANY, INC.
5550 Hwy 332 E, Freeport, TX 77541
Tel.: (979) 233-7211
Web Site: http://www.tri-con.com
Year Founded: 1971
Sales Range: $10-24.9 Million
Emp.: 130
Other Heavy & Civil Engineering Construction Services
N.A.I.C.S.: 237990
Lisa Bundick Woods (CFO)
Sherry Seffens (Office Mgr)

TRI-COUNTIES ASSOCIATION FOR THE DEVELOPMENTALLY DISABLED — U.S. PRIVATE

TRI-COUNTIES ASSOCIATION FOR THE DEVELOPMENTALLY DISABLED—(Continued)

TRI-COUNTIES ASSOCIATION FOR THE DEVELOPMENTALLY DISABLED
520 E Montecito St, Santa Barbara, CA 93103
Tel.: (805) 962-7881   CA
Year Founded: 1968
Sales Range: $200-249.9 Million
Emp.: 322
Developmental Disability Assistance Services
N.A.I.C.S.: 623210
Lorna Owens (CFO)
Omar Noorzad (Exec Dir)
Dominic Namnath (Dir-Info Svcs)
Patricia Forgey (Dir-Community Dev)
Frank Bush (Dir-Svcs & Supports)
Rachel Huff (Treas & VP)
Robin Rosso (Sec)
Robyn Adkins (Pres)

TRI-COUNTY BUILDING SUPPLIES
1001 Boughtay Rd, Pleasantville, NJ 08232
Tel.: (609) 646-0950
Web Site: http://www.tcbsi.com
Sales Range: $25-49.9 Million
Emp.: 104
Provider of Wallboard, Paneling, Roofing & Siding
N.A.I.C.S.: 444110
Stephen A. Gross (Pres)
Patrick Finnerty (Gen Mgr)

TRI-COUNTY COMMUNICATIONS COOPERATIVE, INC.
417 5th Ave N, Strum, WI 54770
Tel.: (715) 695-2691   WI
Web Site: http://www.tcc.coop
Year Founded: 1961
Sales Range: $10-24.9 Million
Emp.: 34
Telecommunication Servicesb
N.A.I.C.S.: 517810
Cheryl Rue (CEO & Gen Mgr)

TRI-COUNTY ELECTRIC COOP
600 NW Pkwy, Azle, TX 76020
Tel.: (817) 444-3201
Web Site: http://www.tcectexas.com
Rev.: $80,287,409
Emp.: 145
Distr of Electric Power
N.A.I.C.S.: 221122
Craig Knight (Exec VP & Gen Mgr)
Phil Colvin (Controller)
David Kliment (Mgr-Member Svcs)

TRI-COUNTY ELECTRIC COOP
7973 E Grand River Ave, Portland, MI 48875
Tel.: (517) 647-7554
Web Site: http://www.homeworks.org
Rev.: $22,899,024
Emp.: 72
Distribution, Electric Power
N.A.I.C.S.: 221122
Mark Kappler (Gen Mgr)

TRI-COUNTY ELECTRIC COOP
PO Box 626 31110 Cooperative Way, Rushford, MN 55971
Tel.: (507) 864-7783
Web Site: http://www.tec.coop
Sales Range: $10-24.9 Million
Emp.: 54
Distr of Electric Power
N.A.I.C.S.: 221122
Brian Krambeer (Pres & CEO)
Kaye Bernard (CFO & VP-Fin & Admin)
Ted Kjos (VP-Mktg)
Chad Chaffee (VP-Sys Ops)

TRI-COUNTY ELECTRIC COOP
2862 W US90, Madison, FL 32340
Tel.: (850) 973-2285
Web Site: http://www.tcec.com
Sales Range: $10-24.9 Million
Emp.: 70
Electric Power Distr
N.A.I.C.S.: 221122
Stephanie Carroll (Mgr-Member Svcs & Admin)

TRI-COUNTY ELECTRIC COOPERATIVE INC.
200 Bailey Ranch Rd, Aledo, TX 76008
Tel.: (817) 444-3201
Web Site: http://www.tcectexas.com
Electric Power Distr
N.A.I.C.S.: 221122
Melissa Watts (CFO)
Nichole Eshbaugh (CTO)

TRI-COUNTY ELECTRIC COOPERATIVE, INC.
3906 Broadway St, Mount Vernon, IL 62864-2224
Tel.: (618) 244-5151   IL
Web Site: http://www.tricountycoop.com
Year Founded: 1938
Sales Range: $25-49.9 Million
Emp.: 57
Provider of Electric Services
N.A.I.C.S.: 221122
Marcia Scott (Gen Mgr)
Bruce Barkau (Dir-Member Svcs)
Dennis Ivers (Dir-Engrg)
Tom Marlow (Office Mgr)

TRI-COUNTY ELECTRIC MEMBERSHIP CORP
310 W Clinton St, Gray, GA 31032
Tel.: (478) 986-8100
Web Site: http://www.tri-countyemc.com
Year Founded: 1939
Sales Range: $25-49.9 Million
Emp.: 60
Cooperative Distr of Electric Power
N.A.I.C.S.: 221122
Dawn Haskins (CFO & Sr Exec VP)
Tommy Noles (Treas & Sec)
Greg Mullis (Sr VP & VP-Corp Svcs)
Brenda P. Green (Chm)
Keith Brooks (VP-Ops)
Lee Marsh (VP-Distr Svcs)
Ray Grinberg (CEO)

TRI-COUNTY ELECTRIC MEMBERSHIP CORP.
405 College St, Lafayette, TN 37083
Tel.: (615) 666-2111
Web Site: http://www.tcemc.org
Sales Range: $50-74.9 Million
Emp.: 145
Distr of Electric Power
N.A.I.C.S.: 221122
Paul Thompson (VP & Gen Mgr)
Jimmy Beecham (Dir-Engrg)
Glenn Hale (Dir-Fin & Admin)
Ralph Law (Dir-Ops)
Tammy Dixon (Mgr-Mktg)
Russell Cherry (Mgr-Pur)
Bret Carver (Pres)
Ray Goad (Treas & Sec)

TRI-COUNTY RURAL ELECTRIC CO
22 N Main St, Mansfield, PA 16933
Tel.: (570) 662-2175
Web Site: http://www.tri-countyrec.com
Rev.: $23,747,396
Emp.: 80
Electric Power Distribution
N.A.I.C.S.: 221122

Barbara Johnson (Dir-Fin)
John Lykens (Dir-Engrg & Ops)

TRI-COUNTY TRUCK COMPANY
555 Sandy Cir, Oxnard, CA 93036
Tel.: (805) 485-6551
Year Founded: 1965
Sales Range: $10-24.9 Million
Emp.: 9
Truck Transportation Services
N.A.I.C.S.: 488510
Louis A. Marietta (Pres)
Dean Marietta (CFO & Controller)

TRI-COUNTY-PETROLEUM
1630 E Clay St, Colusa, CA 95932
Tel.: (530) 458-2555
Rev.: $12,228,070
Emp.: 2
Petroleum Products
N.A.I.C.S.: 424720

TRI-DAM PROJECT
PO Box 1158, Pinecrest, CA 95364-0158
Tel.: (209) 965-3996
Web Site: http://www.tridamproject.com
Sales Range: $10-24.9 Million
Emp.: 21
Waste Treatment Services
N.A.I.C.S.: 221310
Tom Ruhl (Supvr-Maintenance)
Dan Pope (Gen Mgr)
Ron Berry (Asst Gen Mgr)

TRI-ELECTRONICS INC.
6231 Calumet Ave, Hammond, IN 46324
Tel.: (219) 931-6850
Web Site: http://www.tri-electronics.com
Sales Range: $10-24.9 Million
Emp.: 100
Mobile Telephone Equipment
N.A.I.C.S.: 423690
James V. Donovan (VP)
Thomas F. Donovan (Pres)
Angela Smith (Mgr)

TRI-FORCE CONSULTING SERVICES, INC.
650 N Cannon Ave Business Center, Lansdale, PA 19446
Tel.: (215) 362-2611
Web Site: http://www.triforce-inc.com
Year Founded: 2000
Sales Range: $1-9.9 Million
Emp.: 30
Custom Software & Mobile Application Development, Network Support Services & Website Design & Development
N.A.I.C.S.: 541511
Manish Gorawala (Pres, Founder, CTO & CEO)

TRI-FORD INC.
12610 State Rte 143, Highland, IL 62249
Tel.: (618) 654-2122
Web Site: http://www.triford.com
Year Founded: 1969
Sales Range: $10-24.9 Million
Emp.: 65
Car Dealership
N.A.I.C.S.: 441110
Scott Novak (Gen Mgr)
Eric Rehkemper (Principal)
Josh Lynn (Mgr-Sls)

TRI-GAS & OIL CO. INC.
3941 Federalsburg Hwy, Federalsburg, MD 21632
Tel.: (410) 754-8184

Web Site: http://www.trigas-oil.com
Rev.: $38,600,000
Emp.: 95
Provider of Petroleum Products
N.A.I.C.S.: 424720
John Dalina (Dir-Wholesale & Transport)
Kristin Taylor (Mgr-Retail Billing)
Earl Slacum (Mgr-Safety)

TRI-JAY TIRE DISTRIBUTORS INC.
755 11th Ave SE, Hickory, NC 28602
Tel.: (828) 328-1191
Web Site: http://www.knmtireonline.com
Sales Range: $25-49.9 Million
Emp.: 60
Tire Whslr
N.A.I.C.S.: 423130
George Moore (Pres & CEO)

TRI-LIFT INC.
180 Main St, New Haven, CT 06512
Tel.: (203) 467-1686
Web Site: http://www.triliftinc.com
Year Founded: 1968
Sales Range: $10-24.9 Million
Emp.: 40
Provider of Leasing, Sales & Service of Trucks
N.A.I.C.S.: 532120
Cathy Pond (Mgr-HR)
Paul Fournier (Mgr-Warranty)
Edward Angelino (Mgr-Ops)
Mike Keefe (Gen Mgr)
Robert Vincent (Mgr-Sls)
Scott Sample (Mgr-Sls)

TRI-MEATS INC.
17 W 662 Butterfield Rd Ste 200, Oakbrook Terrace, IL 60181
Tel.: (630) 705-2800
Web Site: http://www.trimeats.com
Sales Range: $75-99.9 Million
Emp.: 20
Distr of Meats & Meat Products
N.A.I.C.S.: 424470
Richard P. Smurawski (Pres & CEO)

TRI-MET
4012 SE 17th Ave, Portland, OR 97202
Tel.: (503) 962-7505
Web Site: http://www.trimet.org
Sales Range: $250-299.9 Million
Emp.: 2,653
Bus Line Operations
N.A.I.C.S.: 485113
Tim McHugh (CIO)
Steve Witter (Mgr)
Bernie Bottomly (Exec Dir-Pub Affairs)
Dee Brookshire (Exec Dir-Fin & Admin)
Doug Kelsey (COO)
Harry Saporta (Exec Dir-Safety & Security)
Randy Stedman (Exec Dir-Labor Rels & HR)
Sam Marra (Exec Dir-Maintenance Ops)
Shelley Devine (Interim Gen Mgr)
Bruce Warner (Pres)
T. Allen Bethel (VP)
Mark Dorn (Exec Dir-Engrg, Construction & Plng)

TRI-MODAL DISTRIBUTION SERVICES
2011 E Carson St, Carson, CA 90810
Tel.: (310) 522-5506
Web Site: http://www.trimodal.com
Rev.: $19,056,209
Emp.: 18
Provider of Trucking Services

N.A.I.C.S.: 484110
Greg Owen (Pres)
Mike Kelso (Exec VP)
Bill Owen (Chm)

TRI-NORTH BUILDERS INC.
2625 Research Park Dr, Fitchburg, WI 53711
Tel.: (608) 271-8717 WI
Web Site: http://www.tri-north.com
Year Founded: 1981
Sales Range: $200-249.9 Million
Emp.: 200
Renovation & Repair of Commercial Buildings
N.A.I.C.S.: 236220
Carl Hardy (VP-Retail Construction)
Randy Danielson (Pres-Retail Construction)

TRI-S ENVIRONMENTAL SERVICES INC.
25 Pinney St, Ellington, CT 06029-3812
Tel.: (860) 875-2110
Web Site: http://www.tri-senvironmental.com
Waste Remediation & Transportation Services
N.A.I.C.S.: 562211

TRI-SIGNAL INTEGRATION, INC.
15853 Monte St 101 102, Sylmar, CA 91342
Tel.: (818) 566-8558
Web Site: http://www.tri-signal.com
Sales Range: $10-24.9 Million
Emp.: 150
Designer, Installer & Servicer of Customized Low Voltage Systems
N.A.I.C.S.: 561621
Robert McKibben (Pres)
Rett Hicks (Exec VP)
Mike Swisher (COO)
Dennis Furden (CFO)
Tom Kommer (Sr VP)

TRI-STAR CABINET & TOP CO.
1000 S Cedar Rd, New Lenox, IL 60451
Tel.: (815) 485-2564
Web Site: http://www.tristarcabinets.com
Year Founded: 1966
Sales Range: $10-24.9 Million
Emp.: 62
Custom Wood Cabinetry Mfr
N.A.I.C.S.: 337110
Kathleen Lenci (VP)
Paulette Wilda (Owner)

TRI-STAR ENGINEERING, INC.
35640 Beattie Dr, Sterling Heights, MI 48312
Tel.: (586) 978-0435 MI
Web Site: http://www.tristarengineering.com
Year Founded: 1990
Sales Range: $25-49.9 Million
Emp.: 8
Engineeering Services
N.A.I.C.S.: 541330
Janice Dalfovo-Dawson (Pres)

TRI-STAR FORD-MERCURY, INC.
930 Rte 22 Hwy W, Blairsville, PA 15717
Tel.: (888) 248-2119 PA
Web Site: http://www.tri-starford.com
Year Founded: 2006
Sales Range: $25-49.9 Million
Car Whslr
N.A.I.C.S.: 441110

Kevin B. Sergent (Owner)

TRI-STAR MARINE INTERNATIONAL, INC.
10500 NE 8th St, Bellevue, WA 98004
Tel.: (425) 688-1288
Web Site: http://www.trimarinegroup.com
Year Founded: 1971
Commercial Fishing & Fish Processing
N.A.I.C.S.: 114111
Renato Curto (Chm)
Steve Farno (CFO)

Subsidiaries:

Tri-Marine Fish Company (1)
220 Cannery St, San Pedro, CA 90731-7308
Tel.: (310) 547-1144
Web Site: http://www.trimarinegroup.com
Sales Range: $25-49.9 Million
Emp.: 250
Fish & Seafood Whslr & Distr
N.A.I.C.S.: 424460
Renato Curto (Pres & CEO)

TRI-STAR PLASTICS CORPORATION
906 Boston Tpke, Shrewsbury, MA 01545
Tel.: (508) 845-1111
Web Site: http://www.tstar.com
Rev.: $13,500,000
Emp.: 55
Plastics Products Mfr & Distr
N.A.I.C.S.: 424610
Richard Cedrone (CEO)
David Mello (Pres)
Brian Parath (Branch Mgr)

TRI-STAR PLASTICS INC.
1915 Via Burton, Anaheim, CA 92806
Tel.: (714) 533-7360
Web Site: http://www.tri-starplastics.com
Year Founded: 1974
Sales Range: $10-24.9 Million
Emp.: 105
Injection Molding Of Plastics
N.A.I.C.S.: 326199
Earl Thorn (Mgr-Assembly Dept)
Robert Gomez (VP)
Harry Thummar (Controller)

TRI-STAR SEMI TRUCK & TRAILER SERVICES, LLC
2727 Edgewood Ave N, Jacksonville, FL 32254
Tel.: (904) 589-0333
Web Site: http://www.ttristarjax.com
Year Founded: 2000
Automotives Repair Services And Assistance
N.A.I.C.S.: 811114
LuAnn Altendorf (Mgr-Office)
Clay Glisson (Pres & CEO)

TRI-STATE ADVERTISING CO., INC.
307 S Buffalo St, Warsaw, IN 46580-4304
Tel.: (574) 267-5178 IN
Year Founded: 1948
Sales Range: $10-24.9 Million
Emp.: 8
Advetising Agency
N.A.I.C.S.: 541810
Clayton R. Kreicker (Pres)
Barbara Bolles (Controller)
T.J. Hartman (Sr VP)
April Menzie (Dir-Creative)
Cindy Ronk (Traffic Mgr)
Amber Hartman (Mgr-Pub Rel)

TRI-STATE ARMATURE & ELECTRIC WORKS, INC.
330 G E Patterson Ave, Memphis, TN 38126
Tel.: (901) 527-8412 TN
Web Site: http://www.tristatearmature.com
Year Founded: 1920
Sales Range: $25-49.9 Million
Emp.: 225
Provider of Electrical Contracting Services, Electrical Supplies & Repair of Electric Motors
N.A.I.C.S.: 423610
Cresta Kain (Coord-PC)
Marian Starks (Sec)
John Pate (Mgr-Bus Dev)
Art Frey (Controller & Mgr-Credit)
Jim Cox (Mgr-Acct)
Tyler Jenkins (Mgr-Warehouse)
Sharon Card (Sec & Mgr-Admin Svcs)
Brandon Spencer (Accountant)
Jerry Hatcher Jr. (VP)

Subsidiaries:

Electric Motor Service (1)
1420 Hwy 51 Bypass E, Dyersburg, TN 38024
Tel.: (731) 285-6241
Web Site: http://www.tsarm.com
Sales Range: $10-24.9 Million
Emp.: 10
Provider of Electric Motor Services
N.A.I.C.S.: 423610

Madison Electric Service (1)
29 Miller Ave, Jackson, TN 38305
Tel.: (731) 668-5922
Web Site: http://www.tsarm.com
Sales Range: $10-24.9 Million
Emp.: 8
Provider of Electric Repair Services
N.A.I.C.S.: 423610

Tri-State Electric of Corinth (1)
1605 Sawyer Rd, Corinth, MS 38835-1268
Tel.: (662) 287-2451
Sales Range: $10-24.9 Million
Emp.: 7
Provider of Electric Repair Services
N.A.I.C.S.: 811310
Ronnie Loeffel (CEO)

Tri-State Electric of Jonesboro (1)
4712 E Highland Dr, Jonesboro, AR 72401
Tel.: (870) 935-9362
Web Site: http://www.tsarm.com
Emp.: 30
Provider of Electric Repair Services
N.A.I.C.S.: 459999
Tim Houston (Branch Mgr)

TRI-STATE AUTO AUCTION LLC
1911 Hwy 80 S, Cuba City, WI 53807
Tel.: (608) 744-2020
Web Site: http://www.tsaaonline.com
Sales Range: $25-49.9 Million
Emp.: 90
Provider of Automobile Auction Services
N.A.I.C.S.: 423110
Jerry Brogley (Pres)
Helen Brogley (Grp VP)

TRI-STATE BANK OF MEMPHIS
180 S Main St, Memphis, TN 38101
Tel.: (901) 525-0384
Web Site: http://www.tristatebank.com
Year Founded: 1946
Sales Range: $1-9.9 Million
Emp.: 67
Commericial Banking
N.A.I.C.S.: 522110
Joyce A. McGhee (COO & Exec VP)
Carolyn B. Walker (Asst VP)
Christine Munson (CEO)

Lucy Y. Shaw (Chm)
Cheryl Hurst (Asst VP & Mgr-Retail Sls)
Michael Gaines (Branch Mgr-Sls)
Angela McGowan (Branch Mgr-Sls)
Felecia S. Robinson (Branch Mgr-Sls)
Latonya M. Gray (Controller & Asst VP)
Pamela Venson Jones (VP-HR)
Jesse H. Turner Jr. (Pres)
Archie Willis III (Vice Chm)

TRI-STATE BUILDING MATERIALS
4515 Hwy 95, Bullhead City, AZ 86426
Tel.: (928) 763-6696
Web Site: http://www.tristateace.com
Rev.: $13,554,747
Emp.: 52
Home Center Operator
N.A.I.C.S.: 444110
D. Michael Paul (Pres & CEO)

TRI-STATE CONSTRUCTION, INC.
350 106th Ave NE, Bellevue, WA 98004
Tel.: (425) 455-2570 WA
Web Site: http://www.tristatecon.com
Year Founded: 1964
Sales Range: $25-49.9 Million
Emp.: 250
Highway & Street Construction
N.A.I.C.S.: 237310
Kristy MacMillan (Controller)

TRI-STATE DIESEL INC.
1 Depot Hill Rd, Enfield, CT 06082
Tel.: (860) 627-8030
Web Site: http://www.tristatekw.com
Sales Range: $25-49.9 Million
Emp.: 80
New & Used Dealer of Trucks, Tractors & Trailers
N.A.I.C.S.: 441110
Scott Pagliughi (Pres)
Monte Kroh (CFO)

TRI-STATE DISTRIBUTORS INC.
1104 Pullman Rd, Moscow, ID 83843
Tel.: (208) 882-4555
Web Site: http://www.t-state.com
Sales Range: $10-24.9 Million
Emp.: 120
Sporting Goods Whslr
N.A.I.C.S.: 459110
Mary Connelly (VP-HR)
Bob Schmidt (VP-Sls)

TRI-STATE DISTRIBUTORS INCORPORATED
2500 Hwy 17 S, Royston, GA 30662
Tel.: (706) 245-6164
Web Site: http://www.tri-statedistributors.com
Rev.: $22,572,409
Emp.: 150
Doors & Windows Mfr
N.A.I.C.S.: 423310
Steve Williams (CEO)
Joe Walden (VP)

TRI-STATE ENTERPRISES INC.
5412 S 24th St, Fort Smith, AR 72901
Tel.: (479) 646-6121
Web Site: http://www.tri-stateonline.com
Year Founded: 1977
Sales Range: $100-124.9 Million
Emp.: 43
Automotive Supplies & Parts
N.A.I.C.S.: 423120

TRI-STATE ENTERPRISES INC.   U.S. PRIVATE

Tri-State Enterprises Inc.—(Continued)
Tristan Taylor (Owner & CEO)
Kevin Rice (Mgr-Internet Sls)
Robert Pesiri (COO)

TRI-STATE ENVELOPE CORPORATION
20th and Market St, Ashland, PA 17921
Tel.: (570) 875-0433   PA
Web Site:
http://www.tristateenvelope.com
Year Founded: 1966
Sales Range: $25-49.9 Million
Emp.: 500
Mfr of Envelopes
N.A.I.C.S.: 322230
Frank Decarlo (CFO)

TRI-STATE FOREST PRODUCTS
2105 Sheridan Ave, Springfield, OH 45505
Tel.: (937) 323-6325
Web Site: http://www.tsfpi.com
Rev.: $26,431,244
Emp.: 70
Distr of Lumber, Plywood & Millwork
N.A.I.C.S.: 423310
Thomas Latham (Pres)
Rob Latham (Mgr-Springfield)
Dan Kelly (Mgr-Sls)
Thomas Berghouse (CFO)
Kirk Westerbeck (Branch Mgr)
Vickey Stegner (COO & Exec VP)
Joe Farr (Mgr-Commodity Sls)
Ron Gamble (VP)

TRI-STATE GARDEN SUPPLY INC.
RR 38 PO Box 184, Eau Claire, PA 16030
Tel.: (724) 867-1711
Web Site:
http://www.gardenscapeinc.com
Sales Range: $10-24.9 Million
Emp.: 150
Farm Supplies
N.A.I.C.S.: 424910
Dave Kasmoch (Pres)
Edna Kasmoch (VP)

TRI-STATE GENERATION AND TRANSMISSION ASSOCIATION, INC.
1100 W 116th Ave, Westminster, CO 80234
Tel.: (303) 452-6111   CO
Web Site: https://www.tristate.coop
Year Founded: 1932
Rev.: $1,533,571,000
Assets: $4,913,649,000
Liabilities: $933,109,000
Net Worth: $3,980,540,000
Emp.: 1,105
Fiscal Year-end: 12/31/22
Wholesale Electricity
N.A.I.C.S.: 221118
Todd E. Telesz (CFO & Sr VP)
Rick Gordon (Chm & Pres)
Julie Kilty (Sec)
Stuart Morgan (Treas)
Matt M. Brown (Asst Sec)
Timothy Rabon (Vice Chm)
Duane D. Highley (CEO)
Scott Wolfe (Asst Sec)
Subsidiaries:

Colowyo Coal Company L.P.   (1)
5731 State Hwy 13, Meeker, CO 81641
Tel.: (970) 824-4451
Emp.: 320
Eletric Power Generation Services
N.A.I.C.S.: 221118

TRI-STATE INDUSTRIAL GROUP
7608 N Harvey Ave, Oklahoma City, OK 73116
Tel.: (405) 341-3043
Web Site: http://www.tsig.com
Year Founded: 1983
Sales Range: $50-74.9 Million
Emp.: 202
Infrastructure & Project Management Services
N.A.I.C.S.: 236220
Gary E. Allison (CEO)
Brad Martin (VP-Strategic Dev)
Louis Watts (VP-Indus Products & Svcs)
David Mayfield (CFO)
David Sellers (Dir-Bus Dev)
Debbie Mick (Dir-HR)
Lori Mason (Controller)

TRI-STATE JOINT FUND
25 Research Dr, Milford, CT 06460
Tel.: (203) 876-3110   CT
Year Founded: 1968
Sales Range: $75-99.9 Million
Emp.: 15
Health Benefit Services
N.A.I.C.S.: 525120
Dennis Raymond (Co-Chm)
Dennis McGuire (Co-Chm)
Patricia Sandillo (Exec Dir)

TRI-STATE MACHINE, INC.
3301 McColloch St, Wheeling, WV 26003
Tel.: (304) 234-0170
Web Site: http://www.tri-statemachine.com
Rev.: $13,500,000
Emp.: 113
Machine Shops
N.A.I.C.S.: 332710
Dean E. Miller (Treas & VP)
Walter C. Moskey (Pres)
Ray A. Byrd (Sec)

TRI-STATE MEMORIAL HOSPITAL & MEDICAL CAMPUS
1221 Highland Ave, Clarkston, WA 99403
Tel.: (509) 758-5511   WA
Web Site:
http://www.tristatehospital.org
Year Founded: 1955
Sales Range: $50-74.9 Million
Emp.: 529
Health Care Srvices
N.A.I.C.S.: 622110
Donald J. Wee (CEO)
Dave Hagen (Pres)
Jack Seeh (Treas & Sec)

TRI-STATE MOTOR TRANSIT CO.
8141 E 7th St, Joplin, MO 64801
Tel.: (417) 624-3131   MO
Web Site: http://www.tsmtco.com
Year Founded: 1929
Trucking & Storage Facilities
N.A.I.C.S.: 484121
Glen Garrett (Chm & Pres)
David Bennett (Exec VP)
Jim Wingfield (Exec VP-Risk Mgmt)

TRI-STATE OIL COMPANY, INC.
129 Chancellor Dr, Belle Chasse, LA 70037
Tel.: (504) 394-5530
Web Site: http://www.tristateoil.com
Sales Range: $10-24.9 Million
Emp.: 45
Petroleum Product Distr
N.A.I.C.S.: 424710
Jean Cosse (Office Mgr)

TRI-STATE PETROLEUM CORPORATION
PO Box 4006, Wheeling, WV 26003
Tel.: (304) 277-3232
Web Site:
http://www.fueledbytristate.com
Sales Range: $25-49.9 Million
Emp.: 200
Delivery of Home Heating Fuels & Gasoline
N.A.I.C.S.: 424710

TRI-STATE PETROLEUM INC.
1400 Channel Rd, Marshall, MN 56258
Tel.: (507) 532-4343
Rev.: $12,500,000
Emp.: 85
Petroleum Bulk Stations
N.A.I.C.S.: 424710
Ted Haugen (Pres)

TRI-STATE SURGICAL SUPPLY & EQUIPMENT LTD.
409 Hoyt St, Brooklyn, NY 11231
Tel.: (718) 624-1000
Web Site:
http://www.tristatesurgical.com
Rev.: $14,000,000
Emp.: 150
Whslr of Surgical Equipment & Supplies
N.A.I.C.S.: 423450
George Hoffman (Pres)
Moshe Spira (Mgr-Pur)

TRI-STATE TRUCK & EQUIPMENT, INC.
5250 Midland Rd, Billings, MT 59101-6324
Tel.: (406) 245-3188
Web Site: http://www.tste.com
Sales Range: $10-24.9 Million
Emp.: 25
Supplier of Construction & Mining Machinery
N.A.I.C.S.: 423810
Thomas W. Zimmer (Pres)
John Sibert (Mgr-Svc)
Mike Weidler (Mgr-Parts)
Art Logan (Mgr-Truck Sls)

TRI-STATE TRUCK CENTER, INC.
494 E EH Crump Blvd, Memphis, TN 38126-4620
Tel.: (901) 947-5000   TN
Web Site: http://www.tri-statemack.com
Year Founded: 1945
Sales Range: $200-249.9 Million
Emp.: 250
Sales & Leasing of New & Used Trucks, Tractors & Trailers
N.A.I.C.S.: 423110
Rodney A. Maddox (Chm & CEO)
James D. Maddox (Pres)
Earl Triplett (VP-Parts)
Steve Dupuis (VP-Sls & Mktg)
Jason McAlister (CFO, Treas & Sec)
Subsidiaries:

Tri-State Leasing   (1)
494 EH Crump Blvd, Memphis, TN 38126-4620   (100%)
Tel.: (901) 947-5000
Web Site: http://www.tristatetruck.com
Sales Range: $25-49.9 Million
Emp.: 100
Commercial Trucks
N.A.I.C.S.: 423110

TRI-STATE WINDOW & DOOR FACTORY, INC.
120 Mount Prospect Ave, Clifton, NJ 07013
Tel.: (973) 471-5500
Web Site:
http://www.tristatewindowandsiding.com
Door & Window Products Mfr
N.A.I.C.S.: 444110
Andreas Kypreos (Pres)

TRI-STATE WINDOW FACTORY, CORP.
360 Marcus Blvd, Deer Park, NY 11729
Tel.: (631) 242-9600
Web Site:
http://www.tristatewindowfactory.com
Sales Range: $1-9.9 Million
Emp.: 75
Plastics Product Mfr
N.A.I.C.S.: 326199
John Kypreos (Pres)

TRI-VALLEY MINOR HOCKEY ASSOCIATION
PO Box 2821, Dublin, CA 94568
Tel.: (925) 452-7825   CA
Web Site:
http://www.trivalleyminorhockey.com
Year Founded: 1970
Sales Range: $1-9.9 Million
Hockey Association
N.A.I.C.S.: 711211
Cameron Higley (VP)
Steve Zonner (Dir-Sports Medicine)
Johanna Asher (Dir-Girls Programs)
Chris Candelaria (Treas)
Anjie Stevenson (Dir-Parent Reps & Travel)
Mike Holmes (Dir-Coaches)
Dave Curtis (First VP)
Cory Linteo (Mgr-Equipment)
Joey Miller (Dir-High School Programs)
Bryan Long (Co-Treas)
Katie King (Sec)

TRI-VALLEY OPPORTUNITY COUNCIL, INC.
102 N Broadway, Crookston, MN 56716
Tel.: (218) 281-5832   MN
Web Site: http://www.tvoc.org
Year Founded: 1965
Sales Range: $10-24.9 Million
Emp.: 782
Community Development Services
N.A.I.C.S.: 813410
Heidi Simmons (Sr Dir-Programs)
Jason Carlson (CEO)
Cynthia Pic (Dir-Transportation Programs)
Laurie Coleman (Dir-Head Start, Child & Family Programs)
Leroy Vonasek (Chm)
Mark Kroulik (Vice Chm)
Shawna Peterson (Sec)
Don Diedrich (Treas)

TRI-VALLEY TRANSPORT & STORAGE
5481 Brisa St, Livermore, CA 94550
Tel.: (925) 373-0511
Year Founded: 1985
Sales Range: $10-24.9 Million
Emp.: 100
Provider of Relocation, Transportation & Storage Services
N.A.I.C.S.: 484110
Scott Harvey (VP-Sls-Mktg)

TRI-WEST LTD.
12005 Pike St, Santa Fe Springs, CA 90670-2964
Tel.: (562) 692-9166
Web Site: http://www.triwestltd.com

Year Founded: 1981
Sales Range: $75-99.9 Million
Emp.: 295
Distr of Home Furnishings
N.A.I.C.S.: 423220
Tony Geiger *(CEO)*
David White *(Mgr-Sls & Mktg)*
Larry Johnson *(Mgr-Sls & Mktg)*
Naser Long *(Mgr-IT)*
Nicolas Rodriguez *(Controller)*
Sandy Elicker *(Mgr-Pur)*

Subsidiaries:

Tri-West of Hawaii Inc. (1)
94-440 Koaki St, Waipahu, HI 96797-2874
Tel.: (808) 678-0002
Web Site: http://www.triwestltd.com
Sales Range: $10-24.9 Million
Emp.: 11
Floor Covering Distr
N.A.I.C.S.: 423220

TRI-WIN
4301 Simonton Rd Ste 100, Dallas, TX 75244
Tel.: (214) 826-2244
Web Site: http://www.tri-win.com
Year Founded: 1995
Rev.: $6,800,000
Emp.: 52
Direct Mail Advertising Services
N.A.I.C.S.: 541860
Robin Fish *(VP)*
Scott Fish *(Founder & CEO)*

TRI-WIRE ENGINEERING SOLUTIONS, INC.
890 E St, Tewksbury, MA 01876
Tel.: (978) 452-7474
Web Site: http://www.triwire.net
Year Founded: 1999
Rev.: $36,500,000
Emp.: 513
Power, Communication Line & Related Structures Construction
N.A.I.C.S.: 237130
John Wade *(CEO)*

TRIA BEAUTY, INC.
4160 Dublin Blvd Ste 200, Dublin, CA 94568
Tel.: (925) 452-2500 DE
Web Site: http://www.triabeauty.com
Year Founded: 2003
Sales Range: $25-49.9 Million
Emp.: 100
Hair Removal Device Mfr
N.A.I.C.S.: 339112
Harvey I. Liu *(Sr VP-Engrg)*
Charles Bracher *(Dir-Independent)*
Peter Wyles *(Pres & CEO)*
Michael R. Lopez *(Co-COO)*
Pat Reichert *(Dir-Optical Engrg)*
Nicole Landberg *(Mng Dir-North America)*
Heather Tanner *(Sr Dir-Clinical, Regulatory & Quality Affairs)*
Jessica Raefield *(Sr Dir-HR-Global)*
Dave Youngquist *(Sr Dir-Product Design & Mechanical Engrg)*
Jiyoung Choi *(VP & Gen Mgr-Asia-Pacific)*
Jim Quinn *(VP-Global Ops)*

TRIA CAPITAL PARTNERS, LLC
5005 LBJ Fwy Ste 425, Dallas, TX 75244
Tel.: (214) 251-8310
Web Site: https://triacapitalpartners.com
Investment Services
N.A.I.C.S.: 523999

TRIAD COMPONENTS GROUP
1675 Pioneer Way Ste C, El Cajon, CA 92020
Tel.: (619) 873-2277
Web Site: http://www.triadcomponentsgroup.com
Year Founded: 1999
Sales Range: $1-9.9 Million
Emp.: 50
N.A.I.C.S.:
Jason Kalb *(Natl Sls Mgr)*

TRIAD FOODS GROUP
191 Waukegan Rd Ste 300 N Field, Winnetka, IL 60093
Tel.: (847) 441-9696
Rev.: $175,000,000
Emp.: 12
Holding Company
N.A.I.C.S.: 551112
John Stewart *(CEO)*
Brian Brucker *(COO)*

Subsidiaries:

Creekstone Farms, Inc. (1)
2129 Port Royal Rd, Campbellsburg, KY 40011-7408
Tel.: (502) 845-0399
Meat Farm
N.A.I.C.S.: 115210

TRIAD FREIGHTLINER OF GREENSBORO INC.
6420 Burnt Poplar Rd, Greensboro, NC 27409
Tel.: (336) 668-0911
Web Site: http://www.triadfreightliner.com
Sales Range: $100-124.9 Million
Emp.: 110
Trailers for Trucks Mfr
N.A.I.C.S.: 423110
Larry Tysinger *(Pres)*
Penny Laginess *(CFO)*
Joel Pegram *(Mgr-Svcs)*
J. R. Harrelson *(Mgr-Svcs)*

TRIAD MACHINERY INC.
18200 NE River Side Pkwy, Portland, OR 97230-4311
Tel.: (503) 254-5100 OR
Web Site: http://www.triadmachinery.com
Year Founded: 1992
Sales Range: $10-24.9 Million
Emp.: 100
Construction Equipment Dealership
N.A.I.C.S.: 423810
Doug Summer *(Pres)*

TRIAD MANUFACTURING, INC.
4321 Semple Ave, Saint Louis, MO 63120-2241
Tel.: (314) 381-5280 MO
Web Site: http://www.triadmfg.com
Sales Range: $10-24.9 Million
Custom Fixture & Store Display Mfr
N.A.I.C.S.: 337215
Robert Hardie *(CEO)*
Jeff Finkelstein *(CFO)*
David Caito *(Pres)*

TRIAD MARKETING INC.
16911 Grays Bay Blvd, Wayzata, MN 55391-2922
Tel.: (952) 476-2006
Web Site: http://www.haverhills.com
Year Founded: 1967
Sales Range: Less than $1 Million
Emp.: 2
Retail Mail Order
N.A.I.C.S.: 459999
Paul Harris *(Pres)*
Lance A. Humphreys *(Mgr)*

TRIAD MECHANICAL INC.
1419 NE Lombard Pl, Portland, OR 97211-4061
Tel.: (503) 289-9000
Web Site: http://www.triadpdx.com
Sales Range: $25-49.9 Million
Emp.: 18
Mechanical Contractor
N.A.I.C.S.: 238220
Nicholas Scovill *(Pres)*

TRIAD METAL PRODUCTS COMPANY INC.
12990 Snow Rd, Parma, OH 44130
Tel.: (216) 676-6505
Web Site: http://www.triadmetal.com
Year Founded: 1945
Sales Range: $10-24.9 Million
Emp.: 125
Provider of Metal Stampings
N.A.I.C.S.: 332119
Richard E. Basista *(Pres)*

TRIAD PACKAGING DESIGN & DISPLAY INC.
100 Industrial Dr, Bristol, TN 37620
Tel.: (423) 764-5195 NC
Web Site: http://www.triadpkg.com
Sales Range: $10-24.9 Million
Emp.: 80
Supplier of Corrugated Boxes
N.A.I.C.S.: 322211
A. Lee Shillito Jr. *(Pres & CEO)*

Subsidiaries:

Triad Packaging, Inc. Athens, Alabama (1)
113 Durham Dr, Athens, AL 35611
Tel.: (256) 232-7949
Sales Range: $1-9.9 Million
Emp.: 40
Corrugated Box Mfr & Distr
N.A.I.C.S.: 322211
Patrick Jacklin *(Gen Mgr)*

TRIAD PLASTICS INC.
3 Oratam Rd, Saddle River, NJ 07458
Tel.: (201) 825-7000 NJ
Web Site: http://www.triadplasticsinc.com
Year Founded: 1975
Sales Range: $25-49.9 Million
Emp.: 11
Mfr of Plastics Resins
N.A.I.C.S.: 424610
Stand Walters *(Pres)*

TRIAD SEMICONDUCTOR
1760 Jones Town Rd, Winston Salem, NC 27103
Tel.: (336) 774-2150
Web Site: http://www.triadsemi.com
Year Founded: 2002
Sales Range: $1-9.9 Million
Emp.: 55
Semiconductor Devices Mfr
N.A.I.C.S.: 334413
Aubrey Mayfield *(Dir-Applications Engrg)*

TRIAD TECHNOLOGIES
985 Falls Creek Dr, Vandalia, OH 45377
Tel.: (937) 832-2861
Web Site: http://www.triadtechnologies.com
Rev.: $10,500,000
Emp.: 60
Industrial Fittings
N.A.I.C.S.: 423830
Doug Wissman *(Pres)*
Chris Hansen *(Engr-Sls)*
Dustin Meyer *(Engr-Electromechanical)*

TRIAD TRANSPORT INC.
1630 Diesel Ave, McAlester, OK 74501
Tel.: (918) 426-4751
Web Site: http://www.triadtransport.com
Sales Range: $10-24.9 Million
Emp.: 350
Provider of Trucking Services
N.A.I.C.S.: 484121
John Titsworth *(Pres)*
Davey Wilkett *(VP)*
Philip G. Desimone *(COO)*

TRIAD WEB DESIGN
3100 Spring Forest Rd Ste 120, Raleigh, NC 27616
Tel.: (919) 878-4530
Web Site: http://www.triadwebdesign.com
Year Founded: 2002
Sales Range: $1-9.9 Million
Emp.: 150
Web Designer
N.A.I.C.S.: 541512
John Hammond *(Gen Mgr-Ops)*
Geeta Punjabi *(Exec VP)*
Rupesh Narvekar *(CEO)*

TRIAD, INC.
3286 Hoffman Norton Rd NW, Warren, OH 44483
Tel.: (330) 847-6597
Web Site: http://www.triad-online.com
Sales Range: $10-24.9 Million
Emp.: 85
Telephone Equipment Repair
N.A.I.C.S.: 811210
William Patrick Soltis *(Pres)*

TRIAD-FABCO INC.
1325 Baker Rd, High Point, NC 27263
Tel.: (336) 861-4195
Web Site: http://www.triadfabcoindustries.com
Sales Range: $10-24.9 Million
Emp.: 90
Plastic Foam Products Mfr
N.A.I.C.S.: 326150
Steve Sherrell *(Office Mgr)*

TRIAGE STAFFING INC.
11133 O S, Omaha, NE 68144
Tel.: (402) 331-1617
Web Site: http://www.triagestaff.com
Year Founded: 2006
Sales Range: $10-24.9 Million
Emp.: 300
Placement of Medical Professionals
N.A.I.C.S.: 561311
Tyler Pieper *(Principal)*
John Maaske *(Principal)*
Carla Vigness *(Mgr-Acct)*
Erik Mockelstrom *(Gen Mgr)*
Marc Jergovic *(Mgr-Acct)*
Brad McClatchey *(Principal)*
Mike Burke *(CFO)*

TRIAL SOLUTIONS OF TEXAS LLC
14655 NW Freeway, Houston, TX 77040
Tel.: (713) 462-6464
Web Site: http://www.cloudninediscovery.net
Year Founded: 2002
Sales Range: $1-9.9 Million
Emp.: 20
Software Services
N.A.I.C.S.: 449210
William H. David III *(CTO)*
Brad Jenkins *(Pres & CEO)*
Michael Heslop *(VP-Computer Forensics & Electronic Discovery Svc)*
Clint Lehew *(VP-Sls)*

TRIALCO INC.
900 E 14th St Route 30, Chicago Heights, IL 60411
Tel.: (708) 757-4200
Web Site: http://www.trialco.net

TRIALCO INC.

Trialco Inc.—(Continued)
Sales Range: $75-99.9 Million
Emp.: 50
Provider of Secondary Aluminum Smelting & Refining
N.A.I.C.S.: 331314
Jay Armstrong *(Pres-Quality Control)*
Jim Dee *(CFO)*
Mike Bailey *(Supvr-Laboratory)*
Gary Smith *(Plant Mgr & Supvr-Production)*
Timothy Falk *(Mgr-Ops)*
Mike Priller *(Supvr-Production)*

TRIAN FUND MANAGEMENT, L.P.
280 Park Ave 41st Fl, New York, NY 10017
Tel.: (212) 451-3000   DE
Web Site: http://www.trianpartners.com
Sales Range: $75-99.9 Million
Emp.: 40
Investment Management Service
N.A.I.C.S.: 523940
Peter William May *(Co-Founder, Pres & Partner)*
Nelson Peltz *(Co-Founder, CEO & Partner)*
Brian L. Schorr *(Chief Legal Officer)*
Joshua D. Frank *(Partner & Co-Chief Investment Officer)*
Brian M. Baldwin *(Partner & Head-Res)*
Edward P. Garden *(Co-Founder)*

TRIANGLE AGGREGATES LLC.
784 Bay Martin Rd, Jackson, AL 36545
Tel.: (251) 246-3781
Web Site: http://www.triagg.com
Sales Range: $300-349.9 Million
Emp.: 10
Construction Sand & Gravel Mining Services
N.A.I.C.S.: 212321
Buzz Chinnis *(Pres)*
Benny Chinnis *(VP)*
Brad Coaker *(Plant Mgr-Ops)*

TRIANGLE AUTO CENTER, INC.
1841 N State Rd 7, Hollywood, FL 33021-3895
Tel.: (954) 966-2150
Web Site: http://www.toyotaofhollywood.com
Sales Range: $75-99.9 Million
Emp.: 195
Automobile Dealers
N.A.I.C.S.: 441110
Craig Zinn *(CEO)*

TRIANGLE BRASS MANUFACTURING COMPANY, INC.
1351 Rocky Point Dr, Oceanside, CA 92056
Tel.: (323) 262-4191   CA
Web Site: http://www.trimcohardware.com
Year Founded: 1949
Sales Range: $50-74.9 Million
Emp.: 110
Architectural Door Hardware Mfr
N.A.I.C.S.: 332510
Anita Call *(Controller)*
Ron Verbeck *(Mgr-Sls-Natl)*
Jason Bennett *(Pres & CEO)*
Adam Matusz *(VP)*

TRIANGLE CAR WASH INC.
973 E Main St, Palmyra, PA 17078
Tel.: (717) 838-7125   PA
Web Site: http://www.trianglecarwashes.com
Year Founded: 1964
Sales Range: $50-74.9 Million
Emp.: 200
Owner & Operator of Car Washes
N.A.I.C.S.: 811192
Frederick Frattaroli *(Pres)*
David Barto *(Controller)*

TRIANGLE CHEMICAL CO. INC.
117 Preston Court, Macon, GA 31210
Tel.: (478) 743-1548
Web Site: http://www.trianglecc.com
Year Founded: 1955
Sales Range: $10-24.9 Million
Emp.: 200
Distr of Farm Supplies
N.A.I.C.S.: 424910
Eugene Maddux *(Pres)*
Aaron Belcher *(VP-Credit Mgr)*

TRIANGLE CONTRACTORS INC.
104 Lenoir Rd, Morganton, NC 28655
Tel.: (828) 432-0025
Web Site: http://www.trianglecontractors.com
Year Founded: 1977
Sales Range: $10-24.9 Million
Emp.: 100
Warm Air Heating & Air Conditioning Contractors
N.A.I.C.S.: 238220
Issac E. Fisher *(Pres)*
Robbie Killian *(Project Mgr)*
Buddy Fisher *(Pres)*
Don Mask *(VP-Field Ops)*

TRIANGLE DISTRIBUTING COMPANY
12065 Pike St, Santa Fe Springs, CA 90670-2964
Tel.: (562) 699-3424   CA
Web Site: http://www.abwholesaler.com
Year Founded: 1957
Sales Range: $100-124.9 Million
Emp.: 140
Producer & Retailer of Beer & Other Fermented Malt Liquors
N.A.I.C.S.: 424810
Donald Heimark *(Chm)*
Michael J. Crow *(VP-Fin)*
Craig Ewing *(Office Mgr)*

TRIANGLE ELECTRIC COMPANY
29787 Stephenson Hwy, Madison Heights, MI 48071-2334
Tel.: (248) 399-2200   MI
Web Site: http://www.trielec.com
Year Founded: 1923
Sales Range: $10-24.9 Million
Emp.: 250
Electrical Contracting Services
N.A.I.C.S.: 238210
Neil Whiteley *(Dir-Fin)*
Roy C. Martin Jr. *(Pres & CEO)*
Roy C. Martin Sr. *(Chm)*

TRIANGLE ENTERPRISES INC.
3630 Cairo Rd, Paducah, KY 42001
Tel.: (270) 443-2424
Web Site: http://www.triangle-co.com
Sales Range: $10-24.9 Million
Emp.: 130
Provider of Building Insulation Services
N.A.I.C.S.: 238310
Lance Morgan *(Controller)*
Dale Heath *(Mgr-Safety)*
J. P. Kelly *(Pres)*

TRIANGLE GRADING & PAVING INC.
1521 Huffman Mill Rd, Burlington, NC 27215-8815
Tel.: (336) 584-1745   NC
Web Site: http://www.trianglegradingpaving.com
Year Founded: 1986
Sales Range: $25-49.9 Million
Emp.: 250
Highway & Street Construction
N.A.I.C.S.: 237310
Gray Kirkpatrick *(Treas & VP)*

TRIANGLE MANUFACTURING CO. INC.
116 Pleasant Ave, Saddle River, NJ 07458
Tel.: (201) 825-1212
Web Site: http://www.trianglemfg.com
Sales Range: $100-124.9 Million
Emp.: 130
Machine & Other Job Shop Work
N.A.I.C.S.: 332710
Neal Strohmeyer *(Pres)*

TRIANGLE NORTH HEALTHCARE FOUNDATION, INC.
726 S Garnett St, Henderson, NC 27536
Tel.: (252) 430-8643   NC
Web Site: http://www.tnhfoundation.org
Year Founded: 1987
Sales Range: Less than $1 Million
Grantmaking Services
N.A.I.C.S.: 813211
Val T. Short *(Exec Dir)*
Eddie Ferguson *(Sec)*
Vanessa Jones *(Vice Chm)*
Ruth Jones Brummitt *(Asst Treas)*
Mike Brafford *(Treas)*
Roddy Drake *(Chm)*

TRIANGLE PACKAGE MACHINERY CO.
6655 W Diversey Ave, Chicago, IL 60707-2239
Tel.: (773) 889-0200
Web Site: http://www.trianglepackage.com
Year Founded: 1923
Sales Range: $75-99.9 Million
Emp.: 250
Packaging Machinery Mfr
N.A.I.C.S.: 333993
Bryan Muskat *(Pres)*
Ralph Hernandez *(VP-Sls & Mktg)*
Gene Gallagher *(Mgr-Sls-Southwest)*
David Hart *(Mgr-Sls-Southeast)*
John Cooke *(Sls Dir)*
N'Gai Merrill *(COO)*

TRIANGLE SALES INC.
15300 W 110th St, Lenexa, KS 66219
Tel.: (913) 541-1800
Web Site: http://www.trianglesales.com
Sales Range: $10-24.9 Million
Emp.: 18
Warm Air Heating & Air Conditioning
N.A.I.C.S.: 423730
Brenda Strauss *(Treas)*

TRIANGLE SERVICES, INC.
10 5th St, Valley Stream, NY 11581
Tel.: (516) 561-1700   NY
Web Site: http://www.triangleservices.com
Year Founded: 1960
Sales Range: $1-4.9 Billion
Emp.: 2,700
Building Maintenance Services
N.A.I.C.S.: 561720

Lonnie Fine *(Pres & CEO)*
Steve Lobasso *(CFO)*

TRIANGLE SYSTEMS INC.
601 W 26th St, New York, NY 10001
Tel.: (212) 505-8900
Web Site: http://www.idxcorporation.com
Sales Range: $25-49.9 Million
Emp.: 10
Office & Store Showcases & Display Fixtures
N.A.I.C.S.: 337126
Scott Norvell *(Gen Mgr-St. Louis)*
Terry Schultz *(CEO)*
Scott Stewart *(VP-Continuous Improvement)*
Fritz Baumgartner *(CFO)*
John Podrebarac *(VP-HR)*
Mark Pritchard *(Exec VP-Strategic Bus Dev)*
Dennis Dugan *(VP-Estimating)*
Jim Comarata *(Exec VP-Bus Dev)*
Dave Anderson *(VP-Quality Assurance)*
Lin Lin Courtois *(VP-MKtg & Comm)*
Keenan Keenan Lersch *(Dir-IT)*
Tom DeLaitsch *(Gen Mgr-Baltimore)*
Mat Crowther *(VP-Ops)*
Mayur Patadia *(Gen Mgr-Chicago)*
Jeff Ouyang *(Mng Dir-China)*
Rob Cox *(Gen Mgr-Seattle)*
Mark Fletcher *(Dir-Ops-Intl)*
Randy Roark *(Gen Mgr-North Carolina)*
David Mueller *(Gen Mgr-Louisville)*
Brian Bylykbashi *(Gen Mgr-Toronto)*

TRIANGLE TELEPHONE COOP ASSOCIATION
2121 US Hwy 2 NW, Havre, MT 59501
Tel.: (406) 394-7807
Web Site: http://www.triangle.com
Sales Range: $10-24.9 Million
Emp.: 125
Local Telephone Communications
N.A.I.C.S.: 517121
Mark Majors *(Supvr-Acctg)*

TRIANGLE TOOL CORPORATION
8609 W Port Ave, Milwaukee, WI 53224-3427
Tel.: (414) 357-7117
Web Site: http://www.triangletoolcorp.com
Year Founded: 1982
Sales Range: $25-49.9 Million
Emp.: 150
Special Dies, Tools, Jigs & Fixtures Mfr
N.A.I.C.S.: 333514
Daniel Gouge *(VP-Sls)*
Walt Grannen *(Engr-Tech Sls)*
Jordan Balcerzak *(Engr-Design)*

Subsidiaries:

A-1 Tool Corporation (1)
1425 Armitage Ave, Melrose Park, IL 60160-1424   (100%)
Tel.: (708) 345-5000
Web Site: http://www.a1toolcorp.com
Rev: $10,949,415
Emp.: 70
Special Dies, Tools, Jigs & Fixtures
N.A.I.C.S.: 333511
Jeff Luther *(Pres)*
Ken Trenhaile *(Mgr-Engrg)*

TRIANGLE TRUSS INC.
6740 W Germann Rd Ste 5036, Chandler, AZ 85226
Tel.: (480) 990-8253
Year Founded: 1983
Sales Range: $25-49.9 Million
Emp.: 267

COMPANIES

Truss Mfr
N.A.I.C.S.: 321215
Ray Hingson (CFO)
Jeffrey T. Campbell (Pres)

TRIANON HOTEL CO.
3401 Bay Commoms Dr, Bonita Springs, FL 34134
Tel.: (239) 948-4400
Web Site: http://www.trianon.com
Sales Range: $1-9.9 Million
Emp.: 38
Hotel Owner & Operator
N.A.I.C.S.: 721110
Thomas J. Longe (Pres & CEO)
Darren Robertshaw (VP-Hospitality)

TRIARC LTD
2914 S Cushman Ave, Tacoma, WA 98409
Tel.: (253) 627-8488
Sales Range: $10-24.9 Million
Emp.: 26
Electrical Apparatus & Equipment
N.A.I.C.S.: 423610
Joe Borrelli (Pres)

TRIBAL FUSION, INC.
2200 Powell St Ste 600, Emeryville, CA 94608
Tel.: (510) 250-5500
Web Site: http://www.tribalfusion.com
Year Founded: 2000
Emp.: 175
Advetising Agency
N.A.I.C.S.: 541810
Alex Saldanha (CTO)

TRIBAL LAW AND POLICY INSTITUTE
8235 Santa Monica Blvd Ste 211, West Hollywood, CA 90046
Tel.: (323) 650-5467   CA
Year Founded: 1996
Sales Range: $1-9.9 Million
Emp.: 17
Civic & Social Organization
N.A.I.C.S.: 813410
Gerald Gardner (Exec Dir)
Abby Abinanti (Pres)
Margrett Oberly Kelley (Treas & Sec)
David Raasch (VP)

TRIBBLE & STEPHENS CONSTRUCTORS LIMITED
580 Westlake Park Blvd Ste 1500, Houston, TX 77079-2662
Tel.: (713) 465-8550   TX
Web Site: http://www.tribblestephens.com
Year Founded: 1968
Sales Range: $100-124.9 Million
Emp.: 240
Provider of Commercial & Industrial Contracting Services
N.A.I.C.S.: 236220
James H. Stephens (Founder & Gen Mgr)
Gary R. Kelley (Pres, COO & Partner)
Tim Baker (Project Dir-T&S Florida)
Van Martin (Chm & CEO)

TRIBE
2100 Riveredge Pkwy Ste 710, Atlanta, GA 30328
Tel.: (404) 256-5858
Web Site: http://www.tribeinc.com
Sales Range: Less than $1 Million
Emp.: 7
Corporate Communications, Corporate Identity, Women
N.A.I.C.S.: 541810
Elizabeth Cogswell Baskin (CEO & Dir-Creative)
Jennifer Bull (Pres & Acct Dir)
Lindsay Podrid (Dir-Creative)
Alexis Snell (Sr Acct Mgr)
Amanda Jones (Acct Coord)

TRIBE 9 FOODS LLC
2901 Progress Rd, Madison, WI 53716
Tel.: (608) 257-7216
Web Site: http://www.tribe9foods.com
Year Founded: 2017
All Other Specialty Food Stores
N.A.I.C.S.: 445298
Brian Durst (Chm & CEO)

Subsidiaries:

Carlas Pasta Inc.   (1)
50 Talbot Ln, South Windsor, CT 06074
Tel.: (860) 436-4042
Web Site: http://www.carlaspasta.com
Sales Range: $1-9.9 Million
Emp.: 75
Dry Pasta Mfr
N.A.I.C.S.: 311824
Carla Squatrito (Founder & Pres)
Kevin Kearney (Dir-Ops)
Laura Kelly (Mgr-Pur)
Venu Guddera (Dir-Quality Assurance)
John Koch (Mgr-Sls-Mid South)
Mary Beth Rossi (Mgr-Customer Svc)
Frank Neville (Mgr-Sls-Mid Atlantic)
Jeff Block (Mgr-Sls-Northeast)
Keith Branham (Mgr-Sls-Mid Central)
Jack Dauray (Dir-Sls & Mktg)
Sergio Squatrito (VP-Ops)
Sandro Squatrito (VP-Bus Dev)

TRIBE MEDIA CORP.
3250 Wilshire Blvd Ste 1250, Los Angeles, CA 90010
Tel.: (213) 368-1661   CA
Year Founded: 1986
Sales Range: $1-9.9 Million
Emp.: 30
News Publishing Services
N.A.I.C.S.: 513110
Susan Freudenheim Core (Editor)
Adam Levine (CFO)
Peter Lowy (Chm)
Robert Eshman (Editor)
David Suissa (Pres)
Leon C. Janks (Sec)

TRIBECA FILM INSTITUTE INC.
375 Greenwich St, New York, NY 10013
Tel.: (212) 274-8080
Web Site: http://www.tribecafilminstitute.org
Year Founded: 2002
Global Awareness & New York Economic Revitalization Promoter Utilizing the Power of Film
N.A.I.C.S.: 512199
Robert De Niro (Co-Chm)
Jane Rosenthal (Co-Chm)
David Earls (Mng Dir)
Alberta Arthurs (Vice Chm)
Daniel Su (Dir-Tech)
Jose Rodriguez (Dir-Documentary Programs)
Opeyemi Olukemi (Sr Dir-Interactive Programs)
Amy Hobby (VP-Artist programs)
Vee Bravo (VP-Education)
Katherine Cheairs (Dir-Tribeca Teaches)

TRIBECA FLASHPOINT MEDIA ARTS ACADEMY
28 N Clark St Ste 500, Chicago, IL 60602
Tel.: (312) 332-0707
Web Site: http://www.tfa.edu
Year Founded: 2007
Sales Range: $10-24.9 Million
Emp.: 103
Digital Media Arts Programs
N.A.I.C.S.: 611310
Erik Parks (CFO)
Jill Geimer (Sr VP-HR & Career Svcs)

TRIBECA TECHNOLOGY SOLUTIONS INC.
150 Broadway Ste 1014, New York, NY 10038
Tel.: (212) 203-4970
Year Founded: 2004
Rev.: $34,400,000
Emp.: 38
Electronic Parts Equipment Merchant Whslr
N.A.I.C.S.: 423690
Greg Jones (Controller)

TRIBLES INC.
16200 Queens Ct, Upper Marlboro, MD 20774
Tel.: (301) 430-6100
Web Site: http://www.tribles.com
Rev.: $32,100,000
Emp.: 100
Household Appliance Parts
N.A.I.C.S.: 423620
Michael C. Almeida (CFO)
Tim Cassidy (Branch Mgr)

TRIBRIDGE RESIDENTIAL, LLC
1575 Northside Dr NW Bldg 100 Ste 200, Atlanta, GA 30318
Tel.: (404) 352-2800   GA
Web Site: http://www.tribridgeresidential.com
Real Estate Investment, Development & Property Management Services
N.A.I.C.S.: 531390
Robert H. West (Pres & Partner)
Lee Walker (Mng Partner)
Steve Broome (Mng Partner)
Jim Schroder (Partner & CFO)
Katherine Mosley (VP-Dev)
Andy Green (VP-Acq)
Yates Dunaway (VP-Acq)
Annie Asdal (VP-Investments)
Virginia Vicory (VP-Ops)
Seth Otey (VP-Ops)
Brian Brantley (Dir-IT)
Christina Thornton (VP-Acctg)
Monique Mitchell-Norman (Dir-Talent Dev)
Tiffany Crutchley (Dir-Mktg)

Subsidiaries:

Tribridge Residential Property Management Advisors, LLC   (1)
1575 Northside Dr NW Bldg 100 Ste 200, Atlanta, GA 30318-4235
Tel.: (404) 352-2800
Residential Property Management Services
N.A.I.C.S.: 531311
Kristyn Monticup (Pres)

TRIBUNE PUBLISHING COMPANY
560 W Grand Ave, Chicago, IL 60654
Tel.: (312) 222-9100   DE
Web Site: http://www.tribpub.com
Year Founded: 2013
Rev.: $746,250,000
Assets: $548,154,000
Liabilities: $246,752,000
Net Worth: $301,402,000
Earnings: ($39,012,000)
Emp.: 2,865
Fiscal Year-end: 12/27/20
Holding Company; Newspaper & Periodical Publisher & Distr; News Syndication Services
N.A.I.C.S.: 551112
Terry Jimenez (Pres & CEO)
Michael Norman Lavey (CFO-Interim, Chief Acctg Officer & Controller)

Subsidiaries:

Blue Lynx Media, LLC   (1)
Convergence Office Ctr Ste 800 B 2501 S State Hwy 121 Bus, Lewisville, TX 75067
Tel.: (469) 528-9000
Web Site: http://www.bluelynxmedia.com
Business Support Services
N.A.I.C.S.: 561110
David Silko (VP-Ops)

Builder Media Solutions, LLC   (1)
435 N Michigan Ave, Chicago, IL 60611
Tel.: (312) 222-4377
Web Site: http://www.buildermediasolutions.com
Newspaper Publishers
N.A.I.C.S.: 513110

California Community News Corporation   (1)
5091 4th St, Irwindale, CA 91706   (100%)
Tel.: (626) 472-5297
Sales Range: $50-74.9 Million
Emp.: 350
Newspaper & Magazine Printer & Distr
N.A.I.C.S.: 322120
Durga Bhoj (Mgr)

Chicago Tribune Company, LLC   (1)
160 N Stetson Ave, Chicago, IL 60601
Tel.: (312) 222-3232
Web Site: http://www.chicagotribune.com
Emp.: 3,000
Holding Company; Newspaper & Magazine Publisher; News Syndication Services
N.A.I.C.S.: 551112
Par Ridder (Gen Mgr)
Colin McMahon (Editor-in-Chief)
Christine Taylor (Mng Editor)

Unit (Domestic):

Chicago Tribune   (2)
160 N Stetson Ave, Chicago, IL 60601
Tel.: (312) 222-3232
Web Site: http://www.chicagotribune.com
Newspaper Publishers
N.A.I.C.S.: 513110
Colin McMahon (Editor-in-Chief)
Par Ridder (Gen Mgr)
Christine Taylor (Mng Editor)

Subsidiary (Domestic):

Chicagoland Publishing Company   (2)
435 N Michigan Ave 1100, Chicago, IL 60611   (100%)
Tel.: (312) 222-8999
Magazine Publisher
N.A.I.C.S.: 513120

Unit (Domestic):

Chicago Magazine   (3)
160 N Stetson Ave 4th Fl, Chicago, IL 60601
Tel.: (312) 222-8999
Web Site: http://www.chicagomag.com
Emp.: 55
Magazine Publisher
N.A.I.C.S.: 513120
Susanna Homan (Publr & Editor-in-Chief)
Terrance Noland (Exec Editor)
Katherine Bryja Shady (Dir-Design)
David McAninch (Editor-Features)
Lauren Williamson (Sr Editor)
Tal Rosenberg (Editor-Culture)
Amy Cavanaugh (Editor-Dining)
Matt Pollock (Sr Editor-Digital)
D. S. Shin (Editor-Social Media Video)
Emily Johnson (Deputy Dir-Design)
Michael Zajakowski (Dir-Photo)
Jessica Sedgwick (Art Dir)
Robert Loerzel (Editor-Contributing Copy)
Amy Schroeder (Editor-Contributing Copy)
Tom Kadzielawski (Mgr-Prepress & Design)
Megan Holbrook (Dir-Adv)
Diana Vdovets (Dir-Ops)
Patti Augustyn (Sr Acct Mgr)
Julia Carter (Sr Acct Mgr)
Valeria Coric (Sr Acct Mgr)
Jacqueline Simon (Sr Acct Mgr)
Kimberly Steinback (Sr Acct Mgr)
Liza Sweitzer (Sr Acct Mgr)
Kelly Zech (Mgr-Marketplace Adv)
Gina E. Pucci (Mktg Dir)
Michele De Venuto (Sr Dir-Fin)

TRIBUNE PUBLISHING COMPANY

Tribune Publishing Company—(Continued)

Subsidiary (Domestic):

Hoy Publications, LLC (2)
435 N Michigan Ave, Chicago, IL
60611-4066 **(100%)**
Tel.: (312) 527-8400
Web Site: http://www.tribpub.com
Newspaper Publishers
N.A.I.C.S.: 513110

Tribune Direct Marketing, Inc. (2)
505 NW Ave, Northlake, IL 60614
Tel.: (708) 836-2700
Web Site: http://www.tribunedirect.com
Emp.: 215
Direct Mail Advertising Services
N.A.I.C.S.: 541860

Branch (Domestic):

Tribune Direct Marketing (3)
5091 4th St, Irwindale, CA 91706
Tel.: (626) 472-5293
Web Site: http://www.tribunedirect.com
Sales Range: $1-9.9 Million
Emp.: 20
Direct Mail Advertising & Marketing Services
N.A.I.C.S.: 541860
Kristin Ranta *(Gen Mgr-West)*
Timothy Street *(Gen Mgr)*

Forum Publishing Group, Inc. (1)
6501 Nob Hill Rd, Tamarac, FL 33321
Tel.: (954) 596-5650
Web Site: http://www.forumpubs.com
Sales Range: $50-74.9 Million
Emp.: 112
Newspaper & Magazine Publisher
N.A.I.C.S.: 513110

Unit (Domestic):

South Florida Parenting (2)
6501 Nob Hill Rd, Tamarac, FL 33321
Tel.: (954) 747-3050
Web Site:
http://www.southfloridaparenting.com
Sales Range: $25-49.9 Million
Emp.: 12
Magazine Publisher
N.A.I.C.S.: 513120

McClatchy-Tribune Information Services (1)
435 N Michigan Ave St 1500, Chicago, IL
60611 **(50%)**
Tel.: (202) 383-6095
Web Site: http://www.mctinfoservices.com
Sales Range: $25-49.9 Million
Emp.: 100
News Wire Services
N.A.I.C.S.: 516210
Rapier Copeland *(Dir-IT)*

Orlando Sentinel Communications Company (1)
633 N Orange Ave, Orlando, FL 32801
Tel.: (407) 420-5000
Web Site: http://www.orlandosentinel.com
Sales Range: $100-124.9 Million
Emp.: 1,500
Newspaper Publishers
N.A.I.C.S.: 513110
Nancy A. Meyer *(Publr & Gen Mgr)*
Roger Simmons *(Mng Editor)*
Cassie Armstrong *(Dir-Content)*
Lisa Cianci *(Dir-Content & News)*
John Cutter *(Dir-Content, Ops & Standards)*
Iliana Limon Romero *(Dir-Content & Sports)*
Mark Skoneki *(Dir-Content & Economy)*
Mike Lafferty *(Sr Editor-Opinions)*
Kathleen Christiansen *(Editor-Content)*
Buddy Collings *(Editor-Content & Varsity Sports)*
Pam Dowd *(Editor-Sys)*
David Georgette *(Editor-Content & Sports)*
Charles King *(Sr Editor-Content, Photo & Video)*
Steven Lemongello *(Sr Editor-Content-Politics)*
Tiffini Theisen *(Editor-Content-Digital)*
Richard Tribou *(Sr Editor-Content-Digital)*
Jeff Weiner *(Sr Editor-Content-Justice & Safety)*

Sun-Sentinel Company (1)
333 SW 12th Ave, Deerfield Beach, FL
33442
Tel.: (954) 356-4000
Web Site: http://www.sun-sentinel.com
Sales Range: $100-124.9 Million
Emp.: 1,500
Newspaper Publishers
N.A.I.C.S.: 513110
Julie Anderson *(Editor-in-Chief)*
Rosemary O'Hara *(Editor-Editorial Page)*
David Schutz *(Dir-Content, Digital & Audience)*
Kathy Laskowski *(Dir-Content, Politics & Health News)*
Gretchen Day-Bryant *(Dir-Content, Entertainment & Features)*
David Selig *(Sr Editor-Digital)*
Sean Pitts *(Dir-Photography)*

The Baltimore Sun Company (1)
300 E Cromwell St, Baltimore, MD 21230
Tel.: (410) 332-6100
Web Site: http://www.baltimoresun.com
Sales Range: $100-124.9 Million
Emp.: 1,000
Newspaper Publishers
N.A.I.C.S.: 513110
Jay Judge *(Editor-Market & Dir-Content & Community News)*

Subsidiary (Domestic):

Baltimore Sun Media Group (2)
501 N Calvert St, Baltimore, MD 21278
Tel.: (410) 332-6000
Web Site:
http://www.baltimoresunmediagroup.com
Newspaper Publishers
N.A.I.C.S.: 513110
Sharon Nevins *(VP-Adv)*
D. J. Lamdin *(Dir-Premium Accounts)*
Kimberly Lansaw *(Dir-Premium Accounts)*
Shawn Hyatt *(Dir-Premium Accounts)*
Brian Price *(Dir-Adv & Media Sls)*
Chris Delapaz *(Gen Mgr-Digital Ad Sls)*
Marty Padden *(Mgr-Media Sls)*
Michelle Wagner *(Mgr-Media Sls)*
Nhan Ngo *(Sr Mgr-Digital Ops & Strategy)*
Sara Maniatty Kirby *(Mgr-Events & Special Section)*
Thom Maytas *(Mgr-Media Sls Local Retail East Team)*
Todd Frederick *(Dir-Adv & Media Sls)*

Homestead Publishing Co. (2)
139 N Main St Ste 203, Bel Air, MD
21014-8800 **(100%)**
Tel.: (410) 838-4400
Web Site: http://www.theaegis.com
Sales Range: $75-99.9 Million
Emp.: 160
Newspaper Publishers
N.A.I.C.S.: 513110

The Daily Press, Inc. (1)
703 Mariners Row, Newport News, VA
23606
Tel.: (757) 247-4600
Web Site: http://www.dailypress.com
Sales Range: $50-74.9 Million
Emp.: 600
Newspaper Publishers
N.A.I.C.S.: 513110
Kris Worrell *(Exec Editor)*
Jeff Reece *(Dir-Content & News)*
Kevin Goyette *(Dir-Content & News Ops)*
Erica Smith *(Dir-Content, Digital, Features & Sports)*
N. Pham *(Editor-Visuals)*
Jamesetta M. Walker *(Editor-Features)*
Jami Frankenberry *(Editor-Sports)*

Subsidiary (Domestic):

Virginia Gazette Companies, LLC (2)
1430 High St 504 Ironbound Rd, Williamsburg, VA 23188
Tel.: (757) 220-1736
Web Site: http://www.vagazette.com
Sales Range: $50-74.9 Million
Emp.: 55
Newspaper Publishers
N.A.I.C.S.: 513110

The Hartford Courant Company (1)
285 Broad St, Hartford, CT 06115
Tel.: (860) 241-6200
Web Site: http://www.courant.com
Sales Range: $50-74.9 Million
Emp.: 500
Newspaper Publishers
N.A.I.C.S.: 513110

Unit (Domestic):

Fairfield County Weekly (2)
285 Broad St, Hartford, CT 06115
Tel.: (860) 241-6200
Web Site: http://www.fairfieldweekly.com
Emp.: 15
Newspaper Publishers
N.A.I.C.S.: 513110

Hartford Advocate (2)
121 Wawarme Ave, Hartford, CT 06114
Tel.: (860) 548-9300
Web Site: http://www.hartfordadvocate.com
Emp.: 25
Newspaper Publishers
N.A.I.C.S.: 513110

Valley Advocate (2)
115 Conz St, Northampton, MA 01061
Tel.: (413) 584-5000
Web Site: http://www.valleyadvocate.com
Emp.: 15
Newspaper Publishers
N.A.I.C.S.: 513110
Dave Eisenstadter *(Editor)*
Colleen McGrath *(Sls Mgr)*

The Morning Call, Inc. (1)
101 N 6th St, Allentown, PA 18105
Tel.: (610) 820-6500
Web Site: http://www.mcall.com
Sales Range: $50-74.9 Million
Emp.: 900
Newspaper Publishers
N.A.I.C.S.: 513110
James Feher *(VP-Adv)*
Kimberly Riggins *(Gen Mgr-Stats Digital)*
John Misinco *(Dir-Content & Audience Engagement)*
Mike Hirsch *(Dir-Content & Opinion)*
Craig Larimer *(Dir-Content & Entertainment)*
Andy Schwartz *(Dir-Content & Sports)*

The Virginian-Pilot (1)
150 W Varmvaltom Ave, Norfolk, VA
23510 **(100%)**
Tel.: (757) 446-9000
Web Site: http://contact.pilotonline.com
Publishing
N.A.I.C.S.: 513110
Kate Wiltrout *(Editor-Military)*
Trudy Grace *(Mgr-Mktg-Call Center)*
Kris Worrell *(Exec Editor)*
Kevin Goyette *(Editor-Production & Dir-Content)*
Jeff Reece *(Dir-Content)*
Kelly Till *(VP-Adv)*
Shaun Fogarty *(Gen Mgr-Stats Digital)*
Jami Frankenberry *(Editor-Sports)*
Jamesetta M. Walker *(Editor-Features)*
N. Pham *(Dir-Photography)*
Matthew Cahill *(Editor-Copy)*
Joe Kacik *(Editor-Sports Copy & Layout)*

Tribune 365, LLC (1)
435 N Michigan Ave Ste 510, Chicago, IL
60611-4066
Tel.: (312) 527-8118
Web Site: http://www.trb365.com
Sales Range: $25-49.9 Million
Emp.: 35
Newspaper Advertising Sales
N.A.I.C.S.: 541890

Tribune Content Agency, LLC (1)
560 W Grand Ave, Chicago, IL 60654
Tel.: (312) 527-8078
Web Site:
http://www.tribunecontentagency.com
Newspaper Publishers
N.A.I.C.S.: 513110

Tribune Publishing Company, LLC (1)
3305 Huntington Ave, Newport News, VA
23607
Tel.: (757) 245-3737
Newspaper Publishers
N.A.I.C.S.: 513110
Timothy P. Knight *(CEO)*
David Dreier *(Chm)*
Timothy E. Ryan *(Pres)*

Tribune Washington Bureau, LLC (1)

U.S. PRIVATE

1100 Vermont Ave Nw, Washington, DC
20005-6327
Tel.: (202) 824-8200
Newspaper Publishers
N.A.I.C.S.: 513110

TRIBUNE-REVIEW PUBLISHING COMPANY
622 Cabin Hill Dr, Greensburg, PA
15601-1657
Tel.: (724) 834-1151 PA
Web Site: http://www.tribune-review.com
Year Founded: 1924
Sales Range: $400-449.9 Million
Emp.: 1,500
Publisher of Newspapers
N.A.I.C.S.: 513110
Ray A. Hartung *(CFO & Dir-Corp Acct)*
Ralph Martin *(Pres & CEO)*
Bill Cotter *(Dir-Adv)*

TRIBUS ENTERPRISES, INC.
155 Haas Dr, Englewood, OH 45322
Tel.: (509) 992-4743 WA
Web Site: http://www.tribususa.com
Year Founded: 2017
Rev.: $199,653
Assets: $2,626,983
Liabilities: $1,177,439
Net Worth: $1,449,544
Earnings: ($1,127,899)
Fiscal Year-end: 03/31/21
Tool Mfr & Distr
N.A.I.C.S.: 333517
Kendall Bertagnole *(Pres, CEO & CFO)*

TRICAL INC.
8770 Hwy 25, Hollister, CA 95023
Tel.: (831) 637-0195
Web Site: http://www.trical.com
Rev.: $11,400,000
Emp.: 125
Agricultural Chemical Distr
N.A.I.C.S.: 325320
Dean Storkan *(Pres)*
Carla Talavera *(Sec)*
Jeanette Whorley *(Mgr-HR)*
Mardel Belotinsky *(Mgr-Registration)*
Kas Filice *(Mgr-Pur)*
Mark Cicairos *(Mgr-Info Sys)*

TRICAP CHICAGO, LLC
171 N Aberdeen St Ste 400, Chicago,
IL 60607
Tel.: (312) 725-9440
Web Site: http://www.tricapres.com
Year Founded: 2007
Sales Range: $10-24.9 Million
Emp.: 50
Property Management Services
N.A.I.C.S.: 531311
Bryan Pritchard *(Founder & CEO)*
Suzanne Hopson *(Dir-Property Mgmt)*
Max Keate *(Fin Dir)*
Leena Agase *(Mgr-Community Sls)*

TRICE MEDICAL, INC
40 Gen Warren Blvd Ste 100,
Malvern, PA 19355
Tel.: (610) 989-8080
Web Site:
http://www.tricemedical.com
Year Founded: 2012
Emp.: 59
High Technology Clinical Apparatus
Mfr
N.A.I.C.S.: 334510
Mark Foster *(Pres & CEO)*

Subsidiaries:

S.E.G-Way Orthopaedics, Inc. (1)
5205 Avenida Encinas Ste C, Carlsbad, CA
92008-4366
Tel.: (760) 929-0313

Surgical & Medical Instrument Mfr
N.A.I.C.S.: 339112

Tenex Health Inc. (1)
26902 Vista Ter, Lake Forest, CA 92630
Tel.: (949) 454-7500
Web Site: http://www.tenexhealth.com
Health & Allied Services
N.A.I.C.S.: 456110
Jagi Gill *(Founder & Chief Scientific Officer)*
William Maya *(Pres & CEO)*
Chuck Grant *(Chm)*
Jeremy Stitcher *(Dir-Sls-US)*
Mike Steen *(Gen Mgr)*
Rom Papadopoulos *(Interim CFO)*

TRICENTIS USA CORP.
2570 W El Camino Real Ste 540,
Mountain View, CA 94040
Tel.: (650) 383-8329
Web Site: http://www.tricentis.com
Year Founded: 2007
Sales Range: $1-9.9 Million
Emp.: 1,000
Software Development Services
N.A.I.C.S.: 541511
Kevin B. Thompson *(Chm & CEO)*
David Gardiner *(Exec VP-DevOps & Gen Mgr-DevOps)*
Wolfgang Platz *(Founder & Chief Strategy Officer)*
Dave Keil *(COO)*
Mike Vandiver *(CFO)*
Grigori Melnik *(Chief Product Officer)*
Chris Collins *(Chief Customer Officer)*
Jen Lucas *(Chief People Officer)*
Amanda Borichevsky *(Chief Legal Officer & Gen Counsel)*
Darren Beck *(CMO)*
Suhail Ansari *(CTO)*

Subsidiaries:

Tx3 Services, LLC (1)
980 Harvest Dr Ste 205, Blue Bell, PA 19422
Web Site: http://www.tx3services.com
Sales Range: $1-9.9 Million
Emp.: 33
Software Development Services
N.A.I.C.S.: 541511
Jason Tepfenhardt *(Co-Founder & Mng Partner)*
Eric Toburen *(Co-Founder & Mng Partner)*
Henry Farris *(CTO)*
Laurie Canning *(CFO)*

TRICKETT HONDA
1823 Gallatin Pike N, Madison, TN 37115-2016
Tel.: (615) 868-1870
Web Site:
  http://www.trickketthonda.com
Year Founded: 1972
Sales Range: $25-49.9 Million
Emp.: 90
Car Whslr
N.A.I.C.S.: 441110
R. L. Page *(Dir-Parts & Svc)*
Reed Trickett *(Pres)*
Dennis Logan *(Mgr-HR)*

TRICKEY JENNUS INC.
5300 W Cypress St, Tampa, FL 33607
Tel.: (813) 831-2325
Web Site:
  http://www.trickeyjennus.com
Sales Range: $10-24.9 Million
Emp.: 8
Advetising Agency
N.A.I.C.S.: 541810
Kathie Comella *(COO)*
Teresa Costa *(VP-Strategy)*
Chris Elmore *(Assoc Dir-Creative)*
Alicia Gregory *(VP-Acct Svc)*
Tom Jennus *(Chief Creative Officer & Exec VP)*
Colleen Trickey *(Pres)*
Brittani Tramontana *(Dir-Art)*

TRICO ELECTRIC CO-OP.
85600 W Tangerine Rd, Marana, AZ 85653-8973
Tel.: (520) 744-2944   AZ
Web Site: http://www.trico.org
Year Founded: 1945
Sales Range: $150-199.9 Million
Emp.: 83
Distr of Electric Power
N.A.I.C.S.: 221122
Charles B. DeSpain *(VP)*
L. Nick Buckelew *(Treas)*
Barbara Stockwell *(Sec)*
Marsha Johnson *(Mgr-Mktg)*

TRICO ENTERPRISES LLC.
6430 T R 348, Millersburg, OH 44654
Tel.: (330) 674-1157
Year Founded: 2007
Sales Range: $1-9.9 Million
Emp.: 22
Fiscal Year-end: 12/31/11
Woodworking Machinery
N.A.I.C.S.: 333243

TRICO EQUIPMENT SERVICES LLC
551 N Harding Hwy, Vineland, NJ 08360-8719
Tel.: (856) 697-1414
Web Site:
  http://www.tricoequipment.com
Year Founded: 1952
Sales Range: $1-9.9 Million
Emp.: 50
Construction & Mining Machinery Sales & Rental
N.A.I.C.S.: 423810
Joseph Pustizzi Jr. *(Pres)*

TRICO MARINE SERVICES, INC.
3200 Southwest Fwy Ste 2950, Houston, TX 77027-7579
Tel.: (713) 780-9926   DE
Sales Range: $600-649.9 Million
Emp.: 1,780
Marine Support Services to the Oil & Gas Industries
N.A.I.C.S.: 488320
David Michael Wallace *(VP-Bus Dev & COO)*
John Castellano *(Chief Restructuring Officer)*

Subsidiaries:

Coastal Inland Marine Services Ltd. (1)
3rd Fl Katia Gardens Plot 1676, Oladele Olashore Street, Victoria Island, Lagos, Nigeria
Tel.: (234) 14620563
Web Site: http://www.tricomarine.com
Sales Range: $100-124.9 Million
Marine Transport Services
N.A.I.C.S.: 488510

Eastern Marine Services Limited (1)
Room 1008-1010 10F Building B, No 317 Xianxia Road, Shanghai, 200051, China
Tel.: (86) 62706737
Web Site: http://www.emsl.com.cn
Sales Range: $250-299.9 Million
Offshore Oil & Gas Exploration, Production Support & Pipeline Construction Services; Owned 51% by China Oilfield Services Limited & 49% by Trico Marine Services, Inc.
N.A.I.C.S.: 213112

Servicios de Apoyo Maritimo de Mexico, S. de R.L. de C.V. (1)
Apartado Postal 81 Calle 35 69 Colonia Centro, Ciudad del Carmen, Campeche, Mexico
Tel.: (52) 938 382 2492
Web Site: http://www.tricomarine.com
Sales Range: $100-124.9 Million
Marine Support Services
N.A.I.C.S.: 488510
Scott Worthington *(Gen Mgr)*

Trico Marine Assets, Inc. (1)
3200 Southwest Freeway Ste 2950, Houston, TX 77027   **(100%)**
Tel.: (713) 780-9926
Sales Range: $100-124.9 Million
Emp.: 10
Marine Transportation Services
N.A.I.C.S.: 488320

Subsidiary (Domestic):

Trico Marine International, Inc. (2)
10001 Woodloch Forest Dr Ste 610, The Woodlands, TX 77380   **(100%)**
Tel.: (713) 780-9926
Sales Range: $100-124.9 Million
Marine Transport Services
N.A.I.C.S.: 488320

Trico Marine Operators, Inc. (1)
10001 Woodloch Forest Dr, Houston, TX 77380   **(100%)**
Tel.: (713) 780-9926
Web Site: http://www.tricomarine.com
Sales Range: $100-124.9 Million
Cargo Vessel Operator
N.A.I.C.S.: 488320

Trico Servicos Maritimos Ltda. (1)
Rua Dr Borman 43/1103, Centro, 24020-320, Niteroi, RJ, Brazil
Tel.: (55) 212613 4476
Web Site: http://www.tricomarine.com
Sales Range: $100-124.9 Million
Marine Services
N.A.I.C.S.: 488510

TRICO USA, LLC.
120 Southampton St, Boston, MA 02118
Tel.: (617) 427-9351
Web Site:
  http://www.foodpakexpress.com
Sales Range: $10-24.9 Million
Emp.: 50
General Line Grocery Whslr
N.A.I.C.S.: 424410
Gary Wong *(Mgr)*

TRICOLOR AUTO GROUP
545 E John Carpenter Fwy Ste 945, Irving, TX 75062
Tel.: (214) 269-7777
Web Site:
  http://www.tricolorauto.net.com
Year Founded: 2007
Sales Range: $50-74.9 Million
Emp.: 210
Used Car Dealers
N.A.I.C.S.: 441120
Daniel Chu *(Founder, Chm & CEO)*

TRICOR AMERICA, INC.
717 Airport Blvd, South San Francisco, CA 94080
Tel.: (650) 877-3650
Web Site: http://www.tricor.com
Sales Range: $50-74.9 Million
Emp.: 870
Provider of Air Courier Services
N.A.I.C.S.: 492110
Chee B. Louie *(Pres)*
Andy Sun *(Controller & Mgr-Acctg)*
Garrick Louie *(VP)*

TRICOR, INC.
230 W Cherry St, Lancaster, WI 53813
Tel.: (608) 723-6441   WI
Year Founded: 1982
Sales Range: $1-9.9 Million
Emp.: 100
Insurance Agencies & Brokerages
N.A.I.C.S.: 524210
Bruce Fritz *(Treas)*

TRICORE INC.
117 N Gold Dr Bldg 1, Robbinsville, NJ 08691
Tel.: (609) 918-2668
Web Site: http://www.tricorepcm.com

Year Founded: 2001
Sales Range: $1-9.9 Million
Emp.: 25
HR Outsourcing & Benefits Administration
N.A.I.C.S.: 541612
Dave Fried *(Founder & CEO)*
Wayne R. Lynn *(Sec)*
Steve Tessler *(Pres-Ops-New York)*

TRICORE REFERENCE LABORATORIES
1001 Woodward Pl NE, Albuquerque, NM 87102
Tel.: (505) 938-8922   NM
Web Site: http://www.tricore.org
Year Founded: 2004
Sales Range: $50-74.9 Million
Medical Laboratory Operator
N.A.I.C.S.: 621511
Michael J. Crossey *(Pres & CEO)*
Bill Baker *(CIO)*
Christina Goleman *(Chief Bus Dev Officer)*
Kent Gordon *(CFO)*
Nicholas E. Dayan *(Chief HR Officer)*
Dina Hannah *(Chief Compliance Officer)*
William Remillard *(Chief Technical Officer)*
David G. Grenache *(Chief Scientific Officer)*
Robin Divine *(Chm)*

TRIDENT CAPITAL, INC.
400 S El Camino Real Ste 300, San Mateo, CA 94402
Tel.: (650) 289-4400
Web Site: http://www.tridentcap.com
Year Founded: 1993
Sales Range: $25-49.9 Million
Emp.: 24
Privater Equity Firm
N.A.I.C.S.: 523999
Arneek Multani *(Sr Mng Dir)*
Alberto Yepez *(Co-Founder & Mng Dir)*
Donald R. Dixon *(Mng Dir)*
John H. Moragne *(Co-Founder & Mng Dir)*
John Reardon *(Mng Dir)*
Michael Derrick *(CFO-Admin)*
Gustavo Alberelli *(Mng Dir)*
Howard Zeprun *(COO-Fin & Admin)*
Myrna M. Soto *(Partner)*

Subsidiaries:

Trident Capital (1)
325 Riverside Ave, Westport, CT 06880
Tel.: (203) 222-4594
Web Site: http://www.tridentcap.com
Sales Range: $50-74.9 Million
Emp.: 8
Privater Equity Firm
N.A.I.C.S.: 523999

TRIDENT CONTRACT MANAGEMENT
2918 Marketplace Dr Ste 206, Madison, WI 53719
Tel.: (608) 276-1900
Web Site: http://www.trident-it.com
Year Founded: 2003
Rev.: $8,800,000
Emp.: 10
Computer & Office Machine Repair & Maintenance
N.A.I.C.S.: 811210
Brett Armstrong *(CFO)*

TRIDENT MARKETING
1930 N Poplar St, Southern Pines, NC 28387
Tel.: (910) 693-3000
Web Site:
  http://www.tridentmarketing.com
Year Founded: 1986

TRIDENT MARKETING

Trident Marketing—(Continued)
Sales Range: $10-24.9 Million
Emp.: 500
Management Consulting Services
N.A.I.C.S.: 541613
Robert R. Bouse *(Dir-Resort Ops)*
Steven R. Baldelli *(CEO)*
Marina Craven *(Controller)*
David Petsolt *(CMO)*
Gerhard Renner *(CFO)*
Richard Craven *(Exec VP)*
Robert Dawson *(COO)*
Rick Treadway *(VP-Sls)*
Tommy Thompson *(VP-Sls & Home Svcs)*
Scott Snyder *(Mktg Dir & Home Svcs)*
James Reed *(Mgr-Telemarketing)*
Kevin Kelly *(Dir-IT Ops)*
Steve Katz *(Dir-Affiliate Mktg)*
Shelley Burnett *(Sr Mgr-Ops)*
Rhob Elliott *(Enterpirise Architect)*
James Ford *(Mktg Mgr-Travel Resorts)*
Wilson Gilliam *(Mgr-Construction)*
Marjorie Gray *(Dir-Partner Relations)*
Callip Hall *(Mgr-Bus Fin)*
Kendrick Jackson *(Sr Mgr-Sls)*

TRIDENT MICROSYSTEMS, INC.
1170 Kifer Rd, Sunnyvale, CA 94086-5303
Tel.: (408) 962-5000   DE
Web Site:
http://www.tridentmicro.com
Year Founded: 1987
Sales Range: $550-599.9 Million
Emp.: 1,522
Holding Company; Semiconductor & Printed Circuit Assemblies Mfr
N.A.I.C.S.: 551111
Peter Jen *(Sr VP-Opers)*
Saeid Moskelani *(Exec VP-R&D)*
Richard H. Janney *(Principal Acctg Officer, VP & Controller)*
Shekhar Khandekar *(VP-Bus Integration & Quality)*
Shirley B. Olerich *(VP-HR)*
Dirk Wieberneit *(Sr VP & Gen Mgr-TV Bus Unit)*
J. Duane Northcutt *(CTO)*

Subsidiaries:

NG Microsystems India Pvt. Ltd. (1)
Information Technology Park Nagawara Village, Kasaba Hobli, Bengaluru, 560045, Karnafaka, India   **(100%)**
Tel.: (91) 8040240000
Web Site: http://www.tridentmicro.com
Electrical, Semiconductor & Printed Circuits
N.A.I.C.S.: 334413

Trident Microelectronics, Ltd. (1)
6F No 1 Alley 30 Lane 358 Rui-Guang Road, Neihu District, Taipei, Taiwan
Tel.: (886) 226577686
Sales Range: $100-124.9 Million
Emp.: 150
Electrical, Semiconductor & Printed Circuits
N.A.I.C.S.: 334413

Trident Microsystems (Europe) B.V. (1)
Laan van Diepenvoorde 23, 5582, Waalre, Netherlands   **(100%)**
Tel.: (31) 40 272 9999
Web Site: http://www.tridentmicro.com
Electrical, Semiconductor & Printed Circuits
N.A.I.C.S.: 334413

Trident Microsystems (Europe) GmbH (1)
Frankenthaler Strasse 2, 81539, Munich, Germany   **(100%)**
Tel.: (49) 89548450
Web Site: http://www.tridentmicro.com
Electrical, Semiconductor & Printed Circuits
N.A.I.C.S.: 334413

Trident Microsystems (Far East) Ltd. (1)
Unit 05-07, 19/F, Tower III, Enterprise Sq,, 9 Sheung Yuet Road, Kowloon Bay, Kowloon, China (Hong Kong)   **(100%)**
Tel.: (852) 27569666
Web Site: http://www.tridentmicro.com
Sales Range: $10-24.9 Million
Emp.: 10
Sales, Operations & Technical Support for Trident's Asian Customers
N.A.I.C.S.: 423430

Trident Microsystems (Japan) GK (1)
Philips Bldg 13-37 Kohnan 2-chome, Minato-ku, Tokyo, 108 8507, Japan
Tel.: (81) 3 3740 5171
Web Site: http://www.tridentmicro.com
Electrical, Semiconductor & Printed Circuits
N.A.I.C.S.: 423690

Trident Microsystems (Korea) Ltd. (1)
6th Floor Dongyang Life Insurance BD 271-1 Seohyeon-dong, Seongnam, 463 824, Gyeonggi-do, Korea (South)
Tel.: (82) 317083101
Web Site: http://www.entropic.com
Emp.: 10
Electrical, Semiconductor & Printed Circuits
N.A.I.C.S.: 423690
Kane Kim *(Country Mgr)*

TRIDENT PRECISION MANUFACTURING INC.
734 Salt Rd, Webster, NY 14580
Tel.: (585) 265-2010
Web Site:
http://www.tridentprecision.com
Rev.: $12,700,000
Emp.: 150
Provider of Metal Stamping Services
N.A.I.C.S.: 332119
Nicholas Juskiw *(Pres & CEO)*
Dan Nuijens *(Plant Mgr)*
Julie Bedford *(Mgr-Mgmt Info Sys)*
Ted Thompson *(Engr-Quality)*

TRIDENT SEAFOODS CORPORATION
5303 Shilshole Ave NW, Seattle, WA 98107
Tel.: (206) 783-3818   WA
Web Site:
https://www.tridentseafoods.com
Year Founded: 1973
Sales Range: Less than $1 Million
Emp.: 9,000
Seafood Product Preparation & Packaging
N.A.I.C.S.: 311710
Chuck Bundrant *(Founder)*
Christine Garvey *(VP-Natl Accts)*

Subsidiaries:

LFS Inc. (1)
851 Coho Way, Bellingham, WA 98225-2067   **(100%)**
Tel.: (360) 734-3336
Web Site: http://www.lfsinc.com
Sales Range: $10-24.9 Million
Emp.: 50
Marine Supplies
N.A.I.C.S.: 423910

Louis Kemp Seafood Company (1)
2001 Butterfield Rd, Downers Grove, IL 60515
Tel.: (630) 512-1000
Web Site: http://www.louiskemp.com
Sales Range: $50-74.9 Million
Emp.: 500
Mfr of Seafood Products
N.A.I.C.S.: 311710

TRIDENT STEEL CORP.
12825 Flushing Meadows Dr Ste 110, Saint Louis, MO 63131-1837
Tel.: (800) 777-9687   MO
Web Site: http://www.tridentsteel.com
Year Founded: 1978

Sales Range: $75-99.9 Million
Emp.: 20
Provider of Metals Services
N.A.I.C.S.: 423510
Kevin Beckmann *(Pres)*
Mark Lewandowski *(Controller)*
Hope Snow *(VP-Line Pipe)*

TRIDENT TRANSPORT, LLC
1428 Chestnut St Ste 114, Chattanooga, TN 37402
Tel.: (423) 805-3705
Web Site:
http://www.tridenttransport.com
Year Founded: 2013
Sales Range: $25-49.9 Million
Emp.: 51
Freight Broker & Logistic Services
N.A.I.C.S.: 488510
Mark Harrell *(COO)*
Heath Haley *(CEO)*

TRIDEUM CORP.
555 Discovery Dr Ste 150, Huntsville, AL 35806
Tel.: (256) 704-6100   AL
Web Site: http://www.trideum.com
Year Founded: 2005
Sales Range: $1-9.9 Million
Emp.: 73
Engineeering Services
N.A.I.C.S.: 541330
Van Sullivan *(CEO)*
Serena Forbes *(Dir-Contracts & Admin)*
Matt Spruill *(Mgr-Ops)*
Favio Lopez *(Pres & COQ)*
Wayne Cline *(Dir-Bus Dev)*

TRIDYNE PROCESS SYSTEMS, INC.
80 Allen Rd, South Burlington, VT 05403-7801
Tel.: (802) 863-6873
Web Site: http://www.tridyne.com
Sales Range: $50-74.9 Million
Emp.: 8
Industrial Instrument Mfr
N.A.I.C.S.: 333998
Susith Wijetunga *(Pres)*
Emmy Madigan *(Office Mgr)*

TRIER & COMPANY
156 2nd St, San Francisco, CA 94105
Tel.: (415) 285-6147
Web Site:
http://www.triercompany.com
Year Founded: 2001
Sales Range: $1-9.9 Million
Marketing Services
N.A.I.C.S.: 541613
Beth Trier *(Founder & Mng Dir)*
Liz Gebhardt *(Sr VP-Strategic Dev)*
Harker Harker *(VP-Digital Mktg)*
Fanny Kim *(VP-Content Mktg Practice)*
Alicia Nieva-Woodgate *(VP-Media Rels)*

TRIERWEILER CONSTRUCTION & SUPPLY CO. INC.
406 E 29th St, Marshfield, WI 54449-5300
Tel.: (715) 387-8451   WI
Year Founded: 1947
Sales Range: $25-49.9 Million
Emp.: 160
Highway & Street Construction
N.A.I.C.S.: 237310
Kari Erdman *(Pres)*

Subsidiaries:

Heavy & Highway Inc. (1)
406 E 29th St, Marshfield, WI 54449-5300   **(100%)**

Tel.: (715) 387-8451
Sales Range: $25-49.9 Million
Emp.: 5
Heavy Construction Equipment Rental
N.A.I.C.S.: 532412
Steve Trierweiler *(Gen Mgr)*

TRIFECTA TECHNOLOGIES, INC.
5012 Medical Ctr Cir, Allentown, PA 18106
Tel.: (610) 530-7200   PA
Web Site: http://www.trifecta.com
Year Founded: 1991
Sales Range: $10-24.9 Million
Emp.: 100
Software Development Services
N.A.I.C.S.: 541511
Andrew Derr *(COO & Sr VP)*
Doug Pelletier *(Pres)*

TRIFLO INTERNATIONAL, INC.
1000 FM 830, Willis, TX 77318
Tel.: (936) 856-8551
Web Site: http://www.triflo.com
Year Founded: 1979
Sales Range: $10-24.9 Million
Emp.: 60
Industrial Machinery Equipment Whslr
N.A.I.C.S.: 423830
Jerry Turk *(Pres)*

TRIFUSION, LP
2550 N Mays, Round Rock, TX 78665
Tel.: (512) 310-1000   TX
Year Founded: 2003
Sales Range: $1-9.9 Million
Emp.: 57
Information Technology Services
N.A.I.C.S.: 541512
Corey Bell *(CEO)*

TRIGATE CAPITAL, LLC
750 N St Paul Str Ste 900, Dallas, TX 75201
Tel.: (214) 220-2274
Web Site:
http://www.trigatecapital.com
Sales Range: $25-49.9 Million
Emp.: 13
Real Estate Investment Services
N.A.I.C.S.: 523999
John Merns *(Dir-Asset Mgmt)*
Jason Obenhaus *(VP)*
Keith Schneider *(VP)*
James Vetter *(CFO)*
Judy Champion *(Office Mgr)*
Josh Wakeman *(VP-Fin & Acctg)*

TRIGG LABORATORIES, INC.
28650 Braxton Ave, Valencia, CA 91355
Tel.: (661) 775-3100
Web Site:
http://www.triggdigitalimages.com
Year Founded: 1989
Sales Range: $10-24.9 Million
Emp.: 70
Toilet Preparation Mfr
N.A.I.C.S.: 325620
Jennifer Martsolf *(VP-Mktg)*
Luis Hernandez *(Coord-Shipping)*

TRIGGER POINT TECHNOLOGIES
5321 Industrial Oaks Blvd Ste 110, Austin, TX 78735
Tel.: (512) 300-2804
Web Site: http://www.tptherapy.com
Year Founded: 2002
Sales Range: $1-9.9 Million
Emp.: 40
Exercise Equipment
N.A.I.C.S.: 459110

U.S. PRIVATE

COMPANIES

Cassidy Phillips *(Founder & CEO)*
Hank Coleman *(VP-TriggerPoint)*
Tim Kneip *(Mgr-Facilities)*

TRIGREEN EQUIPMENT LLC
1776 TriGreen Dr, Athens, AL 35611
Tel.: (256) 233-0339   AL
Web Site:
   http://www.trigreenequipment.com
Year Founded: 2006
Sales Range: $25-49.9 Million
Emp.: 300
Farm & Outdoor Power Equipment Retailer
N.A.I.C.S.: 444230
Shannon Norwood *(Mgr-Integrated Solutions)*

TRIHYDRO CORPORATION
1252 Commerce Dr, Laramie, WY 82070
Tel.: (307) 745-7474
Web Site: http://www.trihydro.com
Sales Range: $25-49.9 Million
Emp.: 411
Scientific & Technical Consulting Services
N.A.I.C.S.: 541690
Jeff Hostetler *(CIO)*
Derek Mitchum *(Mgr-Bus Information Product & Svcs)*
Jack G. Bedessem *(Pres & COO)*
Keith M. Marcott *(Sr VP)*
Deby Forry *(CFO & VP-Risk Mgmt)*
Josh Dorrell *(Sr VP-Tech Svcs & Solutions)*

TRILANTIC CAPITAL MANAGEMENT L.P.
399 Park Ave 39th Fl, New York, NY 10022
Tel.: (212) 607-8450   DE
Web Site: http://www.trilantic.com
Emp.: 100
Fund Management Services
N.A.I.C.S.: 523940
Charles Ayres *(Chm & Mng Partner-North America)*
Jeremy Lynch *(Co-Pres & Partner)*
James Manges *(Co-Pres & Partner)*
Li Zhang *(Partner)*
Elliot Attie *(Partner/CFO-Trilantic North America & Principal)*

Subsidiaries:

Nixon, Inc.   (1)
701 S Coast Hwy, Encinitas, CA 92024   **(48.5%)**
Tel.: (760) 944-0900
Web Site: http://www.nixonnow.com
Sales Range: $25-49.9 Million
Emp.: 50
Watches & Accessories
N.A.I.C.S.: 423940
Andy Laats *(Co-Founder & Chm)*
Michael Villa *(Gen Mgr)*
Dallas Hill *(Mgr-Svcs Center)*
Gary Morton *(Controller)*
Michel Murciano *(Mgr-Mktg)*
Tom Jones *(VP-Global Mktg & Creative)*
Chad DiNenna *(Co-Founder & Exec VP-Brand)*
Timothy Mack *(Sr VP-Direct to Consumer)*
Megan Brunner *(Dir-Mktg-North America)*
Nancy Dynan *(Pres)*

Subsidiary (Non-US):

Nixon Europe S.A.R.L.   (2)
185 Avenue de Pascouaou, Soorts-Hossegor, 40150, France
Tel.: (33) 558435917
Web Site: http://www.nixon.com
Sales Range: $25-49.9 Million
Emp.: 25
Watch & Parts Distr
N.A.I.C.S.: 423940
Franck Corbery *(Head-Mktg)*
Nick Stowe *(CEO)*

Outdoor Living Supply LLC   (1)
325 Alliance Place NE, Rochester, MN 55906
Tel.: (888) 657-4769
Web Site: http://www.outdoorlivingsupply.net
Outdoor Design Supplies Distr
N.A.I.C.S.: 541320
Brian Price *(CEO)*
Kathy Granger *(Mktg Dir)*
Daniel Edwards *(Mgr-Area Dev)*

Subsidiary (Domestic):

Apache Stone LLC   (2)
3900 E Cheyenne Ave, Las Vegas, NV 89115-3277
Tel.: (702) 651-0001
Web Site: http://www.apachestone.com
Other Building Material Dealers
N.A.I.C.S.: 444180
Samuel Henry *(Mgr)*

Garden Supply Hardscapes   (2)
2662 Monterey Hwy, San Jose, CA 95111
Tel.: (408) 971-7600
Web Site:
   http://www.gardensupplyhardscapes.com
Other Building Material Dealers
N.A.I.C.S.: 444180
Cesar Cayotzy *(Mgr)*

Geo. Schofield Co. Inc.   (2)
831 E Main St, Bridgewater, NJ 08807
Tel.: (732) 356-0858
Web Site: http://www.geoschofield.com
Sales Range: $10-24.9 Million
Emp.: 20
Aggregate
N.A.I.C.S.: 423320
Bill Newel *(Pres & CEO)*

Norristown Brick Inc.   (2)
741 Forrest Ave, Norristown, PA 19403
Tel.: (610) 844-9450
Web Site: http://www.norristownbrick.com
Clay Building Material & Refractories Mfr
N.A.I.C.S.: 327120
Bob Defrancisco *(Controller)*

Tahoe Sand & Gravel Inc.   (2)
1096 Industrial Ave, South Lake Tahoe, CA 96150-3600
Tel.: (530) 541-6862
Web Site: http://www.tahoesandgravel.com
Brick, Stone & Related Construction Materials Distr
N.A.I.C.S.: 423320

Quickparts.com, Inc.   (1)
620 S Industrial Way, Seattle, WA 98108
Tel.: (206) 203-1430
Web Site: https://www.quickparts.com
Sales Range: $25-49.9 Million
Emp.: 25
Ecommerce Services
N.A.I.C.S.: 522320
Ziad Abou *(CEO)*

Subsidiary (Domestic):

Laser Reproductions Inc.   (2)
950E Taylor Station Rd, Gahanna, OH 43230
Tel.: (614) 552-6905
Web Site: http://www.laserrepro.com
Sales Range: $1-9.9 Million
Product Development Services
N.A.I.C.S.: 323111
Cary Green *(Owner & Pres)*

Xcentric Mold & Engineering, LLC   (2)
25190 Terra Industrial Dr, Chesterfield, MI 48051
Tel.: (586) 598-4636
Web Site: http://www.xcentricmold.com
Rev.: $1,500,000
Emp.: 15
Plastics Product Mfr
N.A.I.C.S.: 326199
Damon Weaver *(Co-Founder & Gen Mgr)*
Pierre Viaud-Murat *(Sr VP-Sls)*
Brendan Weaver *(Co-Founder & Exec VP)*
Tom Neill *(VP-Ops)*
Matt McIntosh *(CEO)*

RoadSafe Traffic Systems, Inc.   (1)
8750 W Bryn Mawr Ave Ste 400, Chicago, IL 60631
Tel.: (773) 724-3300
Web Site: http://www.roadsafetraffic.com
Emp.: 1,000
Pavement Marking, Road Sign Installation & Traffic Control Services
N.A.I.C.S.: 488490
David Meirick *(Pres & CEO)*

Subsidiary (Domestic):

A Cone Zone, Inc.   (2)
120 N Joy St, Corona, CA 92879-1320
Tel.: (951) 734-2887
Web Site: http://www.aconezone.com
Security Guards & Patrol Services
N.A.I.C.S.: 561612
Elaine Norland *(Owner)*

All Star Striping LLC   (2)
1255 W 2550 S Ste B, Ogden, UT 84401-3237
Tel.: (801) 399-0099
Web Site: http://www.allstarstriping.com
Highway, Street & Bridge Construction
N.A.I.C.S.: 237310

BC Cannon Co. Inc.   (2)
PO Box 3889, Greenville, SC 29608-9608
Tel.: (864) 235-1255
Web Site: http://www.bccannon.com
Highway, Street & Bridge Construction
N.A.I.C.S.: 237310
Dede Vaughn Cannon *(CEO)*

Bay Area Barricade Service, Inc.   (2)
1861 Arnold Ind Way, Concord, CA 94520
Tel.: (925) 686-1089
Web Site: http://www.babsinc.com
Sales Range: $1-9.9 Million
Emp.: 12
Miscellaneous Durable Goods Merchant Whslr
N.A.I.C.S.: 423990
Barbara Songster *(Pres)*

Highway Supply, LLC   (2)
6221 Chappell Rd NE, Albuquerque, NM 87113
Tel.: (505) 345-8295
Web Site: http://www.highwaysupply.net
Sales Range: $1-9.9 Million
Emp.: 35
Highway And Street Construction
N.A.I.C.S.: 237310
Denis Riddiford *(Principal)*

Liddell Brothers, Inc.   (2)
600 Industrial Dr, Halifax, MA 02338
Tel.: (781) 293-2100
Web Site: http://www.liddellbrothers.com
Rev.: $2,700,000
Emp.: 25
Sign Mfr
N.A.I.C.S.: 339950

Western Remac, Inc.   (2)
1740 International Pkwy, Woodridge, IL 60517
Tel.: (630) 972-7770
Web Site: http://www.westernremac.com
Rev.: $5,333,333
Emp.: 43
Sign Mfr
N.A.I.C.S.: 339950
Jill Longoria *(Owner & CEO)*

Sunbelt Solomon Services, LLC   (1)
103 W Main St, Solomon, KS 67480
Tel.: (785) 655-2191
Web Site: http://www.solomoncorp.com
Rev.: $43,475,041
Emp.: 260
Voltage Regulating Transformers, Electric Power
N.A.I.C.S.: 335311
Phillip E. Hemmer *(Pres & Mgr-Ops)*

Subsidiary (Domestic):

Valley Transformer Co   (2)
21318 E Gilbert Ave, Otis Orchards, WA 99027
Tel.: (509) 926-1725
Rev.: $3,948,000
Emp.: 6
Electrical Apparatus & Equipment; Wiring Supplies & Related Equipment Merchant Whslr
N.A.I.C.S.: 423610
Kerry Riccardi *(Owner)*

Trilantic Capital Partners LLP   (1)
35 Portman Square, London, W1H 6LR, United Kingdom

TRILOGIC OUTDOOR

Tel.: (44) 20 3326 8600
Web Site: http://www.trilantic.com
Privater Equity Firm
N.A.I.C.S.: 523999
Vittorio Pignatti-Morano *(Chm & Partner)*

TRILINK ENERGY, INC.
326 South High St, Columbus, OH 43221
Tel.: (614) 388-8868   OH
Year Founded: 2008
Oil & Gas Exploration Services
N.A.I.C.S.: 211120
John E. Rayl *(Pres & Treas)*
Charles A. Koenig *(Sec)*

TRILLACORPE CONSTRUCTION
30100 Telegraph Rd Ste 366, Bingham Farms, MI 48025
Tel.: (248) 433-0585
Web Site:
   http://www.trillacorpeconstruction.com
Sales Range: $25-49.9 Million
Emp.: 14
Government & Military Building Construction Services
N.A.I.C.S.: 236210
Frank Campanaro *(CEO)*
Laurence Goss *(COO)*
Joseph Pica *(Sr VP)*

TRILLIANT INCORPORATED
1100 Island Dr Ste 201, Redwood City, CA 94065
Tel.: (650) 204-5050
Web Site: http://www.trilliantinc.com
Smart Grid Communication Equipment Mfr
N.A.I.C.S.: 334290
Andy White *(Pres & CEO)*
Tricie Damaso *(VP-HR)*

TRILLIUM CORPORATION
1329 N State St Ste 201, Bellingham, WA 98225-4754
Tel.: (360) 676-9400
Web Site: http://www.trilliumcorp.com
Year Founded: 1974
Sales Range: $100-124.9 Million
Emp.: 3
Provider of Timber Products
N.A.I.C.S.: 423990
David Syre *(Founder & Chm)*
Jonathan Syre *(Pres & CEO)*

TRILLIUM FAMILY SERVICES
3415 SE Powell Blvd, Portland, OR 97202
Tel.: (503) 234-9591   OR
Web Site: http://www.trilliumfamily.org
Year Founded: 1998
Sales Range: $25-49.9 Million
Emp.: 833
Child & Family Care Services
N.A.I.C.S.: 624190
Rich Blum *(VP-Bus Dev & Provider Rels)*
Kim Scott *(Pres & CEO)*
Keith Cheng *(Chief Medical Officer)*
Sandy Boyle *(Chief Strategy Officer)*
Stan Sawicki *(Chief Dev Officer)*
Savannah Paz *(Vice Chm)*
MaryBeth Cruz *(Sec)*
Mike Larson *(Treas)*
Jamie Vandergon *(Sr VP)*
Lisa Kane *(Chief Admin Officer)*
Logan Lynn *(Chief Comm Officer)*

TRILOGIC OUTDOOR
801 Brickwell Ave 9th Fl, Miami, FL 33131
Tel.: (305) 347-5156
Web Site:
   http://www.trilogicoutdoor.com
Advetising Agency

TRILOGIC OUTDOOR

Trilogic Outdoor—(Continued)
N.A.I.C.S.: 541810
Irene Fernandez (Coord-Mktg)

TRILOGY CAPITAL GROUP, LLC
990 Biscayne Blvd Ste 1203, Miami, FL 33132
Tel.: (786) 749-1221
Web Site: http://www.trilogy-capital.com
Year Founded: 2002
Financial Advisory Services
N.A.I.C.S.: 523940
Alfonso J. Cervantes (Chm)
Darren Minton (CEO)
Ronald Scott (Pres & CFO)
David Demarest (VP-Bus Dev)
Orestes Jimenez (VP-Fin)

TRILOGY COMMUNICATIONS, INC.
2910 Hwy 80 E, Pearl, MS 39208-3409
Tel.: (601) 933-7500　　DE
Web Site: http://www.trilogyrf.com
Year Founded: 1985
Mfr of Wires & Cables
N.A.I.C.S.: 335929
S. Shinn Lee (Chm & CEO)

TRILOGY EYE MEDICAL GROUP INC.
100 East California Bvd, Pasadena, CA 91105
Tel.: (626) 269-5348
Web Site:
　http://www.acuityeyegroup.com
Medical Ophthalmology Care Services
N.A.I.C.S.: 622110
Tom S. Chan (Founder)

Subsidiaries:

Schultz Eye Clinic　　(1)
81893 Doctor Carreon Blvd Ste 2, Indio, CA 92201-5592
Tel.: (760) 342-9991
Web Site:
　http://www.schultzeyecareclinic.com
Offices of Optometrists
N.A.I.C.S.: 621210
Rosalia Cervera (Office Mgr)

TRIM NUTRITION INC.
1245 N Hercules Ave, Clearwater, FL 33761
Tel.: (888) 666-4212
Web Site:
　http://www.trimnutrition.com
Year Founded: 2008
Sales Range: $1-9.9 Million
Emp.: 12
Developer of Pharmaceutical & Nutritional Weight Loss & Detox Products
N.A.I.C.S.: 325412
Brent Agin (Founder)

TRIMACO LLC
2300 Gateway Centre Blvd Ste 200, Morrisville, NC 27560-9669
Tel.: (919) 433-4010
Web Site: http://www.trimaco.com
Sales Range: $25-49.9 Million
Emp.: 250
Paint Sundries Mfr & Whslr
N.A.I.C.S.: 325510
Charles Cobaugh (VP)
Maria Costello (VP & Gen Mgr)
David C. May II (Principal)

Subsidiaries:

Trimaco LLC　　(1)
2814 Ram Bay Rd, Manning, SC 29102-8376
Tel.: (803) 473-5370
Web Site: http://www.trimaco.com

Sales Range: $25-49.9 Million
Emp.: 155
Painting Material Mfr
N.A.I.C.S.: 314910

Trimaco LLC　　(1)
3333 Washington Ave, Saint Louis, MO 63103-1118
Tel.: (314) 534-5005
Web Site: http://www.trimaco.com
Sales Range: $10-24.9 Million
Emp.: 6
Canvas & Related Product Distr
N.A.I.C.S.: 325510
Dale Niemeyer (Office Mgr)

TRIMAR CONSTRUCTION, INC.
1720 W Cass St, Tampa, FL 33606
Tel.: (813) 258-5524
Web Site:
　http://www.trimarconstruction.com
Year Founded: 1996
Sales Range: $10-24.9 Million
Emp.: 10
Commercial Construction
N.A.I.C.S.: 236220
William J. Wagner (Pres)
Richard M. Chapman (VP)

TRIMARAN CAPITAL PARTNERS, LLC
1325 Avenue of the Americas 25th Fl, New York, NY 10019
Tel.: (212) 616-3700　　DE
Web Site:
　http://www.trimarancapital.com
Year Founded: 1995
Privater Equity Firm
N.A.I.C.S.: 523999

Subsidiaries:

El Pollo Loco Holdings, Inc.　　(1)
3535 Harbor Blvd Ste 100, Costa Mesa, CA 92626
Tel.: (714) 599-5000
Web Site: https://www.elpolloloco.com
Rev.: $468,664,000
Assets: $592,301,000
Liabilities: $341,605,000
Net Worth: $250,696,000
Earnings: $25,554,000
Emp.: 4,362
Fiscal Year-end: 12/27/2023
Holding Company; Restaurant Operator
N.A.I.C.S.: 551112
Elizabeth Williams (CEO)
Ira M. Fils (CFO)
Jill Adams (CMO)
Maria Hollandsworth (Interim Pres, Interim CEO & COO)
Ira M. Fils (CFO, Principal Acctg Officer & Exec VP)

Subsidiary (Domestic):

El Pollo Loco Inc.　　(2)
3535 Harbor Blvd Ste 100, Costa Mesa, CA 92626
Tel.: (714) 599-5000
Web Site: http://www.elpolloloco.com
Sales Range: $350-399.9 Million
Emp.: 3,600
Mexican Food Restaurant Operator
N.A.I.C.S.: 722513
Michael G. Maselli (Chm)
Heather Gardea (VP-R&D)
Laurance Roberts (CFO)
Kay Bogeajis (COO)
Jennifer Jaffe (Chief People Officer & Sr VP)
Hector A. Munoz (Chief Mktg Officer)
Brian Wallunas (VP-Digital Mktg)

TRIMARK DIGITAL, LLC
611 Tucker St, Raleigh, NC 27603
Tel.: (919) 785-2275
Web Site:
　http://www.trimarkdigital.com
Year Founded: 2006
Sales Range: $1-9.9 Million
Emp.: 12
Digital Marketing Services

N.A.I.C.S.: 541613
Randy Goins (Founder & CEO)
Tansy OBryant (Exec Dir-Organic Search)

TRIMAX BUILDING PRODUCTS
2600 W Roosevelt Rd, Chicago, IL 60608
Tel.: (312) 491-2500　　NV
Web Site: http://www.trimaxbp.com
Year Founded: 2006
Sales Range: $25-49.9 Million
Plastic Lumber Products Mfr
N.A.I.C.S.: 325211

TRIMEDYNE, INC.
Tel.: (949) 951-3800　　NV
Web Site: https://www.trimedyne.com
Year Founded: 1980
TMED—(OTCIQ)
Emp.: 40
Surgical Laser Mfr
N.A.I.C.S.: 334510
Marshall A. Loeb (Chm & Chief Scientific Officer)

TRIMFIT, INC.
501 Cambria Ave, Bensalem, PA 19020
Tel.: (215) 781-0600　　PA
Web Site: http://www.trimfit.com
Year Founded: 1924
Sales Range: $100-124.9 Million
Emp.: 300
Socks, Hosiery, Tights & Stretch Wear Mfr
N.A.I.C.S.: 315120
Martin B. Kramer (Chm)
Arnold A. Kramer (Pres)
Harry Schultz (Controller)
Robert Rickus (Controller)

Subsidiaries:

Trimfit Company Limited　　(1)
3170 Orlando Dr Unit 3, Mississauga, L4V 1R5, ON, Canada　　(100%)
Tel.: (905) 678-1212
Sales Range: $25-49.9 Million
Emp.: 10
Mfr of Womens Hosiery
N.A.I.C.S.: 315120

TRIMFOOT CO., LLC
115 Trimfoot Ter, Farmington, MO 63640
Tel.: (573) 756-6616
Web Site: http://www.trimfootco.com
Rev.: $22,000,000
Emp.: 60
Children's Shoes & Dance Footwear Distr
N.A.I.C.S.: 424340
Gail Gail Guemmer (Brand Mgr)
Linda Nickelson (Mgr-HR)
Mike Wolo (VP-Sourcing)

TRIMGEN CORPORATION
34 Loveton Cir Ste 210, Sparks, MD 21152
Tel.: (410) 472-1100
Web Site: http://www.trimgen.com
Year Founded: 1999
Genetic Testing Laboratory Services
N.A.I.C.S.: 541380

TRIMIN SYSTEMS INC.
St 1E 2277 Hwy 36 W, Saint Paul, MN 55113-3804
Tel.: (651) 636-7667
Web Site:
　http://www.triminsystems.com
Sales Range: $10-24.9 Million
Emp.: 35
Sales of Computer Software Products
N.A.I.C.S.: 541512
Bill Metzger (Pres)

TRIMON INC.
5180 Pacheco Blvd, Martinez, CA 94553
Tel.: (925) 798-6330
Web Site:
　http://www.monumentcarparts.com
Sales Range: $10-24.9 Million
Emp.: 45
Automotive Supplies & Parts
N.A.I.C.S.: 423120
Tim Archer (Pres)

TRIMS UNLIMITED
4525 Wilshire Blvd Ste 205, Los Angeles, CA 90010
Tel.: (323) 939-3008
Web Site:
　http://www.trimsunlimited.com
Year Founded: 1985
Rev.: $4,600,000
Emp.: 6
Advertising & Marketing
N.A.I.C.S.: 424990
Susan Roth (Pres & CEO)

TRIMTEX CO. INC.
65 Railroad Ave Ste 3, Ridgefield, NJ 07657-2130
Tel.: (570) 326-9135　　PA
Web Site: http://www.trimtex.com
Year Founded: 1919
Sales Range: $50-74.9 Million
Emp.: 20
Braided, Knitted & Woven Trimmings & Tapes; Functional Braids, Specification Tapes & Braids; Coatings & Finishing of Trims
N.A.I.C.S.: 313220
Larry Epstein (Pres & CEO)

TRINCHERO FAMILY ESTATES
100 Main St, Saint Helena, CA 94574-2166
Tel.: (707) 963-3104　　CA
Web Site: http://www.tfewines.com
Year Founded: 1890
Sales Range: $200-249.9 Million
Emp.: 500
Wine Mfr
N.A.I.C.S.: 312130
Bob Torkelson (Pres & CEO)

Subsidiaries:

Rebel Wine Co. LLC　　(1)
100 Saint Helena Hwy S, Saint Helena, CA 94574
Tel.: (866) 584-2697
Web Site: http://www.banditwines.com
Wine Distr
N.A.I.C.S.: 424820

TRINET INTERNET SOLUTIONS, INC.
108 Discovery, Irvine, CA 92618
Tel.: (949) 442-8900
Web Site:
　http://www.trinetsolutions.com
Year Founded: 1995
Sales Range: $50-74.9 Million
Emp.: 50
Advertising Services
N.A.I.C.S.: 541810
John Carley (Founder, Pres & CEO)
Ron Weber (COO)
Monica Hunt (Mgr-Ops)

Subsidiaries:

Trinet Internet Solutions, Inc.　　(1)
1423 Powhatan Bldg 1, Alexandria, VA 22314
Tel.: (703) 548-8900
Web Site: http://www.trinetsolutions.com
Sales Range: $10-24.9 Million
Emp.: 25
N.A.I.C.S.: 541810

COMPANIES

TRINIDAD AREA HEALTH ASSOCIATION
410 Benedicta Ave, Trinidad, CO 81082
Tel.: (719) 846-9213 CO
Web Site: http://www.msrhc.org
Year Founded: 1969
Sales Range: $25-49.9 Million
Emp.: 231
Health Care Srvices
N.A.I.C.S.: 622110
Sandy Sphar *(Chief Nursing Officer)*
Lori Silva *(Dir-HR)*

TRINIDAD/BENHAM HOLDING CO
3650 S Yosemite St 300, Denver, CO 80237
Tel.: (303) 220-1400
Web Site: http://www.trinidadbenham.com
Rev.: $33,700,000
Emp.: 700
Holding Company
N.A.I.C.S.: 551112
Gary Peters *(CFO)*
Troy Hansen *(Controller)*
Keith Love *(Mgr)*

Subsidiaries:

Trinidad/Benham Corp. (1)
3650 S Yosemite Ste 300, Denver, CO 80237-8007
Tel.: (303) 220-1400
Web Site: http://www.trinidadbenham.com
Sales Range: $75-99.9 Million
Emp.: 74
Dried Beans, Lentils, Peas, Rice & Popcorn Whslr
N.A.I.C.S.: 424510

TRINITAS REGIONAL MEDICAL CENTER
225 Williamson St, Elizabeth, NJ 07202
Tel.: (908) 994-5000 NJ
Web Site: http://www.trinitashospital.org
Year Founded: 2000
Sales Range: $300-349.9 Million
Emp.: 3,118
Health Care Srvices
N.A.I.C.S.: 622110
Judy Comitto *(CIO & VP-Info Svcs)*
William McHugh *(Chief Medical Officer & Dir-Medical)*
Nancy M. DiLiegro *(Chief Clinical Officer & VP-Clinical Ops & Physician Svcs)*
Karen E. Lumpp *(CFO & Sr VP-Fin)*
Mary McTigue *(Chief Nursing Officer & VP-Patient Care Svcs)*
Grant Knaggs *(Chief Strategy Officer)*
Sam Germana *(Gen Counsel & VP-Legal Affairs)*
Gary S. Horan *(Pres & CEO)*
Barry Levinson *(Treas & Sec)*
Ricardo Rodriguez *(VP)*
James McCreath *(VP-Behavioral Health & Psychiatry)*
Glenn Nacion *(VP-HR)*
Doug Harris *(VP-Mktg & PR)*

TRINITE INC.
1860 Howe Ave, Mountain View, CA 94129-2254
Tel.: (650) 210-2010
Sales Range: $10-24.9 Million
Emp.: 15
Employment Agencies
N.A.I.C.S.: 561311
Lori D. Kwan *(Pres)*
Steve Houghton *(Mgr-Bus Dev)*

TRINITY BUILDING & CONSTRUCTION MANAGEMENT CORP.
1 Jewel Dr Ste 322, Wilmington, MA 01887
Tel.: (781) 938-0008
Web Site: http://www.trinitybuildingusa.com
Sales Range: $25-49.9 Million
Emp.: 30
Commercial Building Construction
Engineering Services
N.A.I.C.S.: 236220
Matthew Kilty *(Pres)*
Paul Mancini *(Exec VP-Bus Ops)*
David Story *(Exec VP-Field Ops)*
Mark Dettenrieder *(Dir-Estimating)*
Joseph Crowley *(Sr Project Mgr)*
Frank Gazzola *(Project Mgr)*
Jen Poskon *(Project Mgr)*
Tim Rogovich *(Project Mgr)*
Mike Russo *(Sr Project Mgr)*
Timothy Karl *(Sr Project Mgr-New York)*

TRINITY CAPITAL CORP.
475 Sansome St 19th Fl, San Francisco, CA 94111
Tel.: (415) 956-5174
Web Site: http://www.trinitycapital.com
Rev.: $23,949,224
Emp.: 82
Provider of Machinery & Equipment Leasing & Financing
N.A.I.C.S.: 522220
Norma Arias *(VP)*
Kyle Brown *(Pres & Chief Investment Officer)*
Bob D'Acquisto *(Mng Dir-Originations-Northern California)*
Phil Gager *(Mng Dir-Originations-Boston)*
Andrew Ghannam *(Mng Dir-Tech Lending)*

TRINITY CARPET BROKERS INC.
625 Charles Wat, Medford, OR 97501
Tel.: (541) 770-2800
Web Site: http://www.trinitycarpet.com
Rev.: $11,000,000
Emp.: 22
Floor Covering Stores
N.A.I.C.S.: 449121
John Chism *(CEO)*

Subsidiaries:

Trinity Carpet Inc. (1)
6327 Sw Capitol Hwy Ste C, Portland, OR 97239-2190
Tel.: (503) 283-2223
Mfr of Carpet & Flooring
N.A.I.C.S.: 423220

TRINITY COMMERCIAL SERVICES, INC.
90 SW 8th St Ste 271, Miami, FL 33130
Tel.: (305) 358-0777
Web Site: http://rchic4.wix.com
Sales Range: $1-9.9 Million
Financial & Other Business Services
N.A.I.C.S.: 525990
Julio C. Verona *(Mng Partner)*
Raul Chico *(Mng Partner)*

TRINITY CONSULTING, INC.
38345 W 10 Mile Rd Ste 3700, Farmington Hills, MI 48335
Tel.: (248) 477-8400
Web Site: http://www.trinity-world.com
Year Founded: 2000
Rev.: $6,600,000
Emp.: 40
Computer Related Consulting Services
N.A.I.C.S.: 541512

TRINITY ENVIRONMENTAL SERVICES, L.L.C
13443 Hwy 71 W, Bee Cave, TX 78738
Tel.: (512) 421-8520 TX
Web Site: http://trinityenv.com
Year Founded: 1999
Commercial Waste Disposal Services
N.A.I.C.S.: 562219
Charles Welch *(Sr VP-Mktg & Bus Dev)*
Diego Rubio *(Pres)*
Ryan Stephen *(Sr VP-Fin & Strategy)*
Cody Childers *(Sls Mgr-West Texas)*

TRINITY FOREST INDUSTRIES INC.
205 W Hurst Blvd, Hurst, TX 76053
Tel.: (817) 268-2441
Web Site: http://www.trinityforest.com
Year Founded: 1981
Sales Range: $10-24.9 Million
Emp.: 15
Lumber, Plywood & Millwork
N.A.I.C.S.: 423310
Keith Cortez *(Mgr-Ops & Mgr-Product)*

TRINITY GLASS INTERNATIONAL INC.
33615 1st Way S, Federal Way, WA 98003
Tel.: (253) 875-6700
Web Site: http://www.trinityglass.com
Rev.: $18,200,000
Emp.: 400
Mfr of Cut & Engraved Glass Products
N.A.I.C.S.: 327215
Johnny Ham *(Pres)*
Bong Jun Choi *(Supvr-Ops-Overseas)*
Jin Kim *(Coord-Import & Export)*

TRINITY GRAPHIC USA, INC.
885 Tallevast Rd, Sarasota, FL 34243
Tel.: (941) 355-2636 FL
Web Site: http://www.trinitygraphic.com
Year Founded: 1967
Sales Range: $1-9.9 Million
Emp.: 50
Commercial Graphic Design Services
N.A.I.C.S.: 323111
Robert Smithson *(Chm)*

TRINITY HEALTH CORPORATION
20555 Victor Pkwy, Livonia, MI 48152
Tel.: (734) 343-1000 MI
Web Site: https://www.trinity-health.org
Year Founded: 1976
Sales Range: $5-14.9 Billion
Emp.: 86,000
Healthcare Services Organization
N.A.I.C.S.: 813910
Michael R. Holper *(Sr VP-Internal Audit & Compliance)*
Michael A. Slubowski *(Pres & CEO)*
Larry Warren *(Interim COO)*
Dan Roth *(Chief Clinical Officer)*
Daniel P. Isacksen Jr. *(CFO & Exec VP)*
Edmund F. Hodge *(Chief HR Officer & Exec VP)*
Julie Spencer Washington *(CMO, Chief Comm Officer, Chief Customer Experience Officer & Exec VP)*
Ray Anderson *(Chief Strategy Officer & Exec VP)*
Cornie R. Francis *(Chief Mission Integration Officer & Exec VP)*

Subsidiaries:

Holy Cross Health System (1)
3575 Moreau Ct, South Bend, IN 46628-4320
Tel.: (574) 233-8558
Provider of Healthcare Services
N.A.I.C.S.: 622110

Loyola University Health System (1)
2160 S 1st Ave, Maywood, IL 60153
Tel.: (708) 216-5140
Web Site: http://www.loyolamedicine.org
Health Care Organization
N.A.I.C.S.: 813920
Blaine Petersen *(CFO)*
David W. Hecht *(Chief Medical Officer & Exec VP-Clinical Affairs)*
John B. Hart *(Chief Integrity Officer & VP)*
Vicky Piper *(Chief HR Officer & Sr VP)*
Lori Price *(Chief Nursing Officer & Pres-Gottlieb Memorial Hospital)*
Jill M. Rappis *(Gen Counsel & Sr VP)*
Chad Whelan *(Pres-Loyola University Medical Center)*
Daniel J. Post *(Exec VP-Strategy & Bus Dev)*
Mary Elizabeth Cleary *(Pres-MacNeal Hospital)*
Shawn P. Vincent *(Pres & CEO)*
Chris M. Gonzalez *(Chm-Dept of Urology)*
Glyn R. Morgan *(Dir-Intra Abdominal Transplant)*
Manmeet S. Taneja *(VP-Fin & Academic)*
Jennifer Scheeringa *(Reg VP-Case Mgmt & Utilization Mgmt)*

Subsidiary (Domestic):

Loyola University Medical Center (2)
2160 S 1st Ave, Maywood, IL 60153
Web Site: http://www.loyolamedicine.org
General Hospital
N.A.I.C.S.: 622110
Chad Whelan *(Pres)*
Karen Anderson *(VP)*
Joshua Lee *(Chief Medical Officer)*
Gregory Ozark *(VP-Graduate Medical Education)*
Donna Halinski *(VP-Clinical Affairs)*
Pradipta Komanduri *(VP-Clinical Svcs)*
Timothy M. Carrigan *(Chief Nursing Officer)*

MacNeal Hospital (2)
3249 S Oak Park Ave, Berwyn, IL 60402
Tel.: (708) 783-9100
Web Site: http://www.macnealhospital.org
General Hospital
N.A.I.C.S.: 622110

Mercy General Health Partners (1)
1500 E Sherman Blvd, Muskegon, MI 49442-2407
Tel.: (231) 672-2000
Web Site: http://www.mghp.com
Sales Range: $50-74.9 Million
Emp.: 1,700
Acute Care Hospital
N.A.I.C.S.: 813319
Greg Loomis *(CEO)*

Mercy Medical Center - North Iowa (1)
1000 4th St SW, Mason City, IA 50401-2800
Tel.: (641) 422-7000
Web Site: http://www.mercynorthiowa.com
Sales Range: $200-249.9 Million
Emp.: 2,500
Hospital
N.A.I.C.S.: 622110

Mercy Medical Center - Sioux City (1)
801 5th St, Sioux City, IA 51101
Tel.: (712) 279-2010
Web Site: http://www.mercysiouxcity.com
Sales Range: $50-74.9 Million
Emp.: 1,200
Hospital
N.A.I.C.S.: 624110
Milt Avery *(Chm)*
Mary Hendriks *(Dir-Mission Integration)*
Allison Gibler *(Dir-Risk & Safety)*

TRINITY HEALTH CORPORATION

U.S. PRIVATE

Trinity Health Corporation—(Continued)
Rod Schlader (Interim CEO)
Beth Hughes (Pres)
Michael Espirito (Treas & Sec)
Lawrence Volz (Chief Medical Officer)
Mark Abraham (Pres)

Riverbend Medical Group (1)
1029 N Rd Ste 6, Westfield, MA 01085-9715
Tel.: (413) 523-0900
Web Site: http://www.riverbendmedical.com
Freestanding Ambulatory Surgical & Emergency Centers
N.A.I.C.S.: 621493
Kathy Young (Mgr)

Saint Joseph Mercy Health System (1)
5301 McAuley Dr, Ypsilanti, MI 48197-0995 (100%)
Tel.: (734) 712-3456
Web Site: http://www.stjoeshealth.org
Sales Range: $200-249.9 Million
Emp.: 4,000
Health Care Srvices
N.A.I.C.S.: 621111
Robin Damschroder (COO-St. Joseph Mercy Ann Arbor & St. Joseph Mercy Livingston)
Ane McNeil (Chief HR Officer)
Rob Casalou (Pres & CEO)
Michael Gusho (CFO-Reg)
Jacquelynn Lapinski (Dir-Process Excelence-Reg)
Mary O'Neill (Chief Integrity & Compliance Officer)
Steve Paulus (VP-Strategy-Reg)
Fran Petonic (VP-Dev-Reg)
Michele Szczypka (CMO & Chief Comm Officer)
Mary Boyd (Chief Integration Officer)
David Ripple (Chief Dev Officer)
Joyce Young (Chief Nursing Officer-Reg)
Kelly Smith (Chief Strategy Officer)
Michael Sanderl (Chief Mission Officer)
Paul Harkaway (Chief Accountable Care Officer)
Rosalie Tocco-Bradley (Chief Clinical Officer)
Sally Guindi (Gen Counsel)

Unit (Domestic):

St. Joseph Mercy Oakland (2)
44405 Woodward Ave, Pontiac, MI 48341-2985
Tel.: (248) 858-3000
Hospital
N.A.I.C.S.: 622110

St. Joseph Mercy Port Huron (2)
2601 Electric Ave, Port Huron, MI 48060-6587 (100%)
Tel.: (810) 985-1500
Web Site: http://www.mercyporthuron.com
Sales Range: $25-49.9 Million
Emp.: 750
Health Care Center
N.A.I.C.S.: 622110

St. Agnes Medical Center (1)
1303 E Herndon Ave, Fresno, CA 93720
Tel.: (559) 450-3000
Web Site: http://www.samc.com
Sales Range: $200-249.9 Million
Emp.: 3,500
Health Care Srvices
N.A.I.C.S.: 622110
Nancy Hollingsworth (Co-Pres & CEO)
Robert Oliver (VP)
Kim Meeker (COO)
Michael Prusaitis (CFO)
Stacy Vaillancourt (Chief Admin Officer)
W. Eugene Egerton (Chief Medical Officer)
A. Thomas Ferdinandi Jr. (Co-Pres)

St. Alphonsus Regional Medical Center (1)
1055 N Curtis Rd, Boise, ID 83706-1352
Tel.: (208) 367-2121
Web Site: http://www.saintalphonsus.org
Sales Range: $75-99.9 Million
Emp.: 3,000
Health Care
N.A.I.C.S.: 622110
Kristen Micheletti (Dir-Mktg & Comm)
Matthew Godfrey (Dir-Ops)
Linda Martin (Mgr-Family Center)

Melissa Clark (Mgr-Recruitment & Employment)
Corinne Smith (Mgr-RN)

Trinity Continuing Care Services (1)
39500 Orchard Hill Pl Ste 400, Novi, MI 48375-5371
Tel.: (248) 305-7600
Sales Range: $10-24.9 Million
Emp.: 40
Health Insurance
N.A.I.C.S.: 623312

Trinity Health Plans (1)
20555 Victor Pkwy, Livonia, MI 48152-7018
Tel.: (734) 343-1000
Web Site: http://www.trinity-health.org
Sales Range: $75-99.9 Million
Emp.: 1,200
Parent Company of Healthcare Facilities
N.A.I.C.S.: 541611

TRINITY HEALTH SYSTEM INC.
380 Summit Ave, Steubenville, OH 43952-2667
Tel.: (740) 283-7349 OH
Web Site: http://www.trinityhealth.com
Year Founded: 1996
Sales Range: $75-99.9 Million
Emp.: 1,761
Health Services
N.A.I.C.S.: 541611
Fred Brower (Pres & CEO)
Keith Murdock (Dir-Community Rels & Dev)
Matt Grimshaw (CEO-Market)

TRINITY HUNT MANAGEMENT, L.P.
2001 Ross Ave Ste 4250, Dallas, TX 75201
Tel.: (214) 777-6600 DE
Web Site: http://www.trinityhunt.com
Private Equity Investment Firm
N.A.I.C.S.: 523999
Daniel S. Dross (Co-Founder, Mng Partner & Sr Partner)
Peter J. Stein (Co-Founder & Sr Partner)
Scott H. Colvert (Partner-Origination)
Cheryl L. Small (CFO)
Mike Steindorf (Partner)
Blake Apel (Mng Partner)
Garrett Greer (Partner)
Ryan Horstman (CFO & COO)
Satchel Park (VP & Dir-Res)
John Oakes (Principal)
George Morgan (Principal)

Subsidiaries:

America's Auto Auction Inc. (1)
219 N Loop 12, Irving, TX 75062
Tel.: (972) 445-1044
Web Site: http://www.jaxaa.com
New & Used Car Dealers
N.A.I.C.S.: 441120
Ben Lange (Pres & CEO)
Chuck Tapp (CEO)

Argano, LLC (1)
6100 W Plano Pkwy Ste 1800, Plano, TX 75093
Web Site: http://argano.com
Business & Technology Services
N.A.I.C.S.: 561499
Chip Register (CEO)
Kent Herring (CFO)

Subsidiary (Domestic):

aMind Solutions, LLC. (2)
3201 Danville Blvd Ste 155, Alamo, CA 94507
Tel.: (925) 804-6139
Web Site: http://www.amindsolutions.com
Buiness & Technology Consulting Firm
N.A.I.C.S.: 541611
Billy Hunt (Pres & CEO)
Sharad Mitra (COO)
Robert Wing (CTO)
Don Nanneman (VP-Mktg)

Doug Cummings (VP-Sls, North America)
John Nielson (Dir-South America)
Steve Sindelar (Dir-Delivery)

Bresslergroup, Inc. (1)
2400 Market St # 1, Philadelphia, PA 19103
Tel.: (215) 561-5100
Web Site: http://www.bresslergroup.com
Rev.: $3,808,000
Emp.: 17
Surgical & Medical Instrument Mfr
N.A.I.C.S.: 339112
Peter Bressler (Founder)
Keith S. Karn (Dir-User Res & Interaction Design)
Mathieu Turpault (Mng Partner & Dir-Design)
Jason Zerweck (Engr-Mechanical)
Takiyah Felder (Mgr-Production)

Coker Group Holdings, LLC (1)
2400 Lakeview Pkwy Ste 400, Alpharetta, GA 30009
Tel.: (678) 832-2000
Web Site: https://www.cokergroup.com
Sales Range: $10-24.9 Million
Emp.: 90
Health Care Consulting Services
N.A.I.C.S.: 621999
Max Reiboldt (Chm)
Justin Chamblee (Sr VP & Dir-Ops)
Jeffery Daigrepont (Sr VP)
Mark Reiboldt (VP)
Matt Jensen (Sr Mgr-Fin Svcs-San Diego)
Christopher Kunney (Sr VP-Atlanta)

Dataprise, Inc (1)
9600 Blackwell Rd Ste 400, Rockville, MD 20850
Tel.: (301) 945-0700
Web Site: http://www.dataprise.com
Rev.: $14,000,000
Emp.: 280
Computer Systems Design & Related Services
N.A.I.C.S.: 541511
Scott R. Gordon (VP-Tech Svcs)
David E. Eisner (Pres & CEO)
Christian Fulmino (Sr VP-Merger & Acq)

Subsidiary (Domestic):

Performance Enhancements Inc. (2)
5435 Airport Rd, Boulder, CO 80301
Tel.: (303) 786-7474
Web Site: http://www.pei.com
Rev.: $2,737,000
Emp.: 17
Data Processing, Hosting & Related Services
N.A.I.C.S.: 518210

Reboot Networks LLC (2)
11835 W Olympic Blvd Ste 435e, Los Angeles, CA 90064
Tel.: (310) 451-3445
Web Site: http://www.rebootnetworks.com
Infrastructure Design, Staff Augmentation, Managed Services, Project Management, Maintenance & Monitoring Services
N.A.I.C.S.: 519290
Daniel W. Dickenson (CEO & Principal)
Jeremy J. Fitzgerald (COO & Principal)
Brandon Pearce (Mgr-Client Svcs)
Steve Lewis (CEO)

Tomar Computer Integration, Inc. (2)
5241 Cleveland St, Virginia Beach, VA 23462
Tel.: (757) 499-6761
Web Site: http://www.360itpartners.com
Sales Range: $1-9.9 Million
Emp.: 21
Computer System Design Services
N.A.I.C.S.: 541512
Martin Joseph (CEO)
Aaron Frketich (COO)
Jasmin Rebultan (CFO)
Reuben D. Mendez (VP-HR & Community Dev)
Ken Peacock (Acct Mgr)
Mike Myers (Mgr-Shop & Engr-Field)
Jim Muhlenbruch (Sr Engr-Network)
Joe Aksel (Project Mgr)
Chris Mosier (Sr Engr-Sys)
Esther Macdonald (Coord-Customer Svc)
Justin Carter (CTO)
Kevin Greene (Sr Engr-Sys)
Kirsten Conti (Mgr-Mktg)
Peter Glanville (Sr Engr-Sys)
Reid Corbett (Sr Engr-Sys)

Dayspring Restoration, LLC (1)
533 W Franklin St, Missoula, MT 59801
Tel.: (406) 543-6070
Web Site: http://www.dayspringrestoration.com
Sales Range: $1-9.9 Million
Emp.: 24
Commercial & Institutional Building Construction Services
N.A.I.C.S.: 236220
Mark Springer (Pres)

Depo Holdings, LLC (1)
13101 Northwest Fwy Ste 210, Houston, TX 77040
Web Site: http://www.lexitaslegal.com
Holding Company; Court Reporting, Deposition & Medical Record Retrieval Services
N.A.I.C.S.: 551112
Gary Buckland (CEO)
Zack Miller (Chief Admin Officer)
Stan Mason (CFO)
Aaron Brown (Sr VP-Sls & Mktg)

Subsidiary (Domestic):

Phipps Reporting, Inc. (2)
1615 Forum Pl Ste 500, West Palm Beach, FL 33401-2318
Web Site: http://www.phippsreporting.com
Temporary Help Service
N.A.I.C.S.: 561320
Christine Phipps (Pres & CEO)
Robert Klupt (Dir-Client Dev)

IMS Consulting & Expert Services, LLC (1)
4400 Bayou Blvd Ste 4, Pensacola, FL 32503
Tel.: (850) 473-2500
Web Site: http://www.ims-expertservices.com
Expert Witness Searches & Litigation Consulting
N.A.I.C.S.: 541199
Bill Wein (CEO)
Steven Hickson (CFO)
Chris Sizemore (VP-Client Svcs)

Subsidiary (Domestic):

The Focal Point, LLC (2)
1999 Harrison St Ste 1350, Oakland, CA 94612
Tel.: (510) 208-1760
Litigation Consulting Services
N.A.I.C.S.: 541199

Improving Holdings, LLC (1)
5445 Legacy Dr Ste 100, Plano, TX 75024
Tel.: (214) 613-4444
Web Site: http://www.improving.com
Technology Consulting & Training Services
N.A.I.C.S.: 541690
Curtis A. Hite (Chm, Chm & CEO)
Ken Howard (VP-Consulting)
Kristin Kacir (Dir-Mktg)
Mark Kovacevich (Mng Dir-USA North Reg)
Devlin Liles (Chief Consulting Officer)
David O'Hara (Pres-Dallas)
Tim Rayburn (VP-Consulting)
Susan Fojtasek (Sr VP)
Gabriela Garza-Ramos (VP-Recruiting)
Don McGreal (VP-Training)
Kristin Johnson (VP-Mktg)

Subsidiary (Domestic):

Code Authority, LLC (2)
3001 Dallas Pkwy Ste 500, Frisco, TX 75034
Tel.: (214) 774-4262
Web Site: http://www.codeauthority.com
Software Design & Development Services
N.A.I.C.S.: 541511
Jason W. Taylor (Founder & Pres)

Object Partners, Inc. (1)
100 N 6th St Ste 302A, Minneapolis, MN 55403
Tel.: (612) 746-1580
Web Site: http://www.objectpartners.com
Sales Range: $1-9.9 Million
Emp.: 43
Computer System Design Services
N.A.I.C.S.: 541512
Chris Spurgat (Pres)
Colleen Peterson (VP-Bus Ops)
Jason Umerski (Partner-Object)
Ehren Seim (COO)

COMPANIES

The Willow Group, Inc. (2)
8201 Norman Center Dr, Minneapolis, MN 55437
Tel.: (952) 897-3550
Web Site: http://www.willowg.com
Sales Range: $1-9.9 Million
Emp.: 30
Management & IT Consulting Services
N.A.I.C.S.: 541611
Barbara J. Gurstelle *(Sr VP-Consulting Svcs)*
Leroy G. Thydean *(Pres & CEO)*

iTexico LLC (2)
4807 Spicewood Springs Rd Bldg 2 Ste 220, Austin, TX 78759
Tel.: (512) 551-2773
Web Site: http://www.itexico.com
Application Software Development Services
N.A.I.C.S.: 541511
Abhijeet Pradhan *(Co-Founder & CTO)*
Adriana Reid *(Mgr-Global Ops)*
Anurag Kumar *(Co-Founder & CEO)*
Cindy Swenson *(Project Mgr)*
David Sandoval *(Mgr-Creative Delivery)*

Keste, LLC (1)
6100 W Plano Pkwy Ste 1800, Plano, TX 75093
Tel.: (214) 778-2100
Web Site: http://www.keste.com
Sales Range: $10-24.9 Million
Emp.: 28
Custom Computer Programming Services
N.A.I.C.S.: 541511
Srirama Ayyeppen *(Pres)*
Howard Moore *(CEO)*
Vince Casarez *(Sr VP-Tech)*

Lone Star Fasteners, L.P. (1)
24131 W Hardy Rd, Spring, TX 77373
Tel.: (281) 353-1191
Web Site: http://www.lonestarfasteners.com
Sales Range: $125-149.9 Million
High Performance Specialty Fasteners & Gaskets Mfr
N.A.I.C.S.: 339991
Dwayne Clarke *(COO & CFO)*
Phillip Contella *(Mgr-Sls)*

Subsidiary (Non-US):

Lone Star Leeds Limited (2)
Unit 2 Airedale Industrial Estate, Kitson Road, Leeds, LS10 1NT, United Kingdom
Tel.: (44) 1132056020
Web Site: http://www.lwdeng.com
Sales Range: $25-49.9 Million
Emp.: 100
Oil, Gas & Petrochemical Specialty Gaskets, Valves & Actuator Components & Surface Coatings Mfr
N.A.I.C.S.: 339991
Craig Hebden *(Mng Dir)*

LoneStar Fasteners Europe Limited (2)
Universal Point Steelmans Road, Wednesbury, WS10 9UZ, W Midlands, United Kingdom
Tel.: (44) 121 435 0009
Web Site: http://www.lonestargroup.com
Standard & Specialty Fasteners & Gaskets Mfr
N.A.I.C.S.: 339991

RepEquity Inc. (1)
1211 Connecticut Ave NW Ste 250, Washington, DC 20036
Tel.: (202) 654-0800
Web Site: http://req.co
Digital Marketing Agency
N.A.I.C.S.: 541810
Tripp Donnelly *(Pres)*
Kyong Choe *(COO & CFO)*
Eric Gilbertsen *(Chief Client Officer)*
Robert Fardi *(Exec VP-Strategic Dev & Partnerships)*
Elizabeth Shea *(Exec VP-Public Rels)*
Katie Hanusik *(Exec VP-Pub Rels)*
Kenny Rufino *(Sr VP & Creative Dir)*
Katie Garrett *(Sr VP-Client Svcs)*
Steve Wanczyk *(Sr VP-Digital Mktg)*

Subsidiary (Domestic):

Internet Marketing Inc. (2)
10620 Treena St Ste 250, San Diego, CA 92131
Web Site: http://www.internetmarketinginc.com
Sales Range: $1-9.9 Million
Emp.: 40
Integrated Online Marketing Services for Midsize & Larger Businesses Worldwide
N.A.I.C.S.: 541613
Brandon Fishman *(Co-Founder)*
Ben Norton *(Pres & COO)*
Devon Gardner *(Dir-Social Media)*
Jason Brigham *(CEO)*
Dan Romeo *(CFO)*
Justin Cohen *(Co-Founder, Pres & Principal)*

Branch (Domestic):

Internet Marketing Inc. (3)
8170 W Sahara Ave Ste 204, Las Vegas, NV 89117 (100%)
Tel.: (702) 835-6986
Web Site: http://www.internetmarketinginc.com
Sales Range: $1-9.9 Million
Emp.: 25
Full Service Interactive Marketing
N.A.I.C.S.: 541613
Justin Cohen *(Pres)*

Subsidiary (Domestic):

SpeakerBox Communications, LLC (2)
8603 Westwood Centre Dr 4th Fl, Vienna, VA 22182
Tel.: (703) 287-7800
Web Site: http://www.speakerboxpr.com
Sales Range: $10-24.9 Million
Emp.: 20
Media Relations, Strategic Planning/Research
N.A.I.C.S.: 541820
Elizabeth Shea *(Pres & CEO)*
Lisa Throckmorton *(Exec VP)*
Katie Hanusik *(VP)*
Pete Larmey *(Sr Acct Dir)*
Cristina Upston *(Dir-HR)*

Rotorcraft Services Group, Inc. (1)
3901 N Main St Hangar 2-S, Fort Worth, TX 76106
Tel.: (817) 625-0192
Web Site: http://www.rotorcraftservices.com
Helicopter Modification, Component Overhaul, Specialty Products Manufacture & Design Engineering Services
N.A.I.C.S.: 811310
Brian Nerney *(Chm & CEO)*

Division (Domestic):

RSG Aviation (2)
3901 N Main St Hngr 2 S, Fort Worth, TX 76106-2752
Tel.: (817) 625-0192
Rev.: $1,800,000
Emp.: 100
Fiscal Year-end: 12/31/2006
Helicopter Engineering, Modification, Maintenance & Equipment Repair Services
N.A.I.C.S.: 811210

Veracity Research Co. (1)
111 Dallas St, Argyle, TX 76226-2360
Web Site: http://www.vrcinvestigations.com
Investigation Services
N.A.I.C.S.: 561611
Lance Foster *(Co-Founder & Pres)*

Subsidiary (Domestic):

Probe Information Services, LLC (2)
3835 N Freeway Blvd Ste 228, Sacramento, CA 95834
Tel.: (800) 397-6517
Web Site: http://www.probeinfo.com
Emp.: 100
Investigation Services
N.A.I.C.S.: 561611

TRINITY LOGISTICS INC.
50 Fallon Ave, Seaford, DE 19973
Web Site: http://www.trinitylogistics.com
Year Founded: 1979
Sales Range: $250-299.9 Million
Emp.: 200
Third Party Logistics & Transportation
N.A.I.C.S.: 541614
Jeff Banning *(CEO)*
Jay McCutcheon *(VP-Mktg)*
Billy Banning *(Pres)*

TRINITY MANOR INC.
PO Box 7070, Pasadena, CA 91109-7070
Tel.: (323) 258-3512 CA
Year Founded: 2004
Sales Range: $1-9.9 Million
Emp.: 5
Elderly Housing Services
N.A.I.C.S.: 624229
Robert Rentto *(Sec)*
Emil J. Wohl *(Pres)*

TRINITY PRIVATE EQUITY GROUP, LLC
925 S Kimball Ave Ste 100, Southlake, TX 76092
Tel.: (817) 310-2900 TX
Web Site: http://www.trinitypeg.com
Privater Equity Firm
N.A.I.C.S.: 523999
Daniel Meader *(Mng Partner)*
Sanjay Chandra *(Mng Partner)*

Subsidiaries:

eLearning Brothers, LLC (1)
732 E Utah Vly Dr Ste 130, American Fork, UT 84003
Tel.: (801) 796-8323
Web Site: http://www.eLearningBrothers.com
Sales Range: $1-9.9 Million
Emp.: 32
Online Learning & Development Services
N.A.I.C.S.: 611691
Andrew Scivally *(Co-Founder & CEO)*
Curtis Morley *(Pres)*
Todd Cummings *(Dir-Custom Dev)*
Scott Condie *(Partner-Custom Solutions)*
John Blackmon *(CTO)*

Subsidiary (Domestic):

Edulence Corporation (2)
79 Madison Ave 15th Fl, New York, NY 10016
Tel.: (212) 792-5800
Web Site: http://www.Edulence.com
Sales Range: $1-9.9 Million
Emp.: 15
Web Search Portal Operator
N.A.I.C.S.: 519290
Jon Tota *(CEO)*
Peter Getchell *(VP-Sls)*
Moki Goyal *(VP-Product Dev)*
Carolyn Haggerty *(VP-Bus Mgmt)*
Yoomi Chun *(VP-Mktg & Dir-Creative)*
Karlene Readinger *(Acct Mgr)*
Megan Niffenegger *(Project Mgr)*
Cindy Tanton *(Dir-Monitoring & Evaluation-Trng)*
Harry Altman *(Acct Exec)*
Joey Davenport *(Chief Dev Officer & Principal)*
Laurie Ann Thorne *(Dir-Ops)*

Division (Domestic):

The Game Agency LLC (2)
470 West Ave Ste 2011, Stamford, CT 06902
Tel.: (212) 931-8552
Web Site: http://www.thegameagency.com
Sales Range: $1-9.9 Million
Emp.: 32
Game Development Services
N.A.I.C.S.: 513210
Stephen Baer *(Mng Partner & Head-Creative)*
Joseph McDonald *(Founder, Mng Partner & Head-Production)*
Richard Lowenthal *(Mng Partner & Head-Bus Ops)*
Jordan Duvall *(Mgr-Support)*
J. D. Fox *(Mgr-Ops)*
James Lange *(Mgr-Tech)*

Subsidiary (Domestic):

Trivantis Corporation (2)
400 Fairway Dr Ste 101, Deerfield Beach, FL 33441
Tel.: (513) 929-0188
Web Site: http://www.trivantis.com
Software Publisher
N.A.I.C.S.: 513210
Jennifer Valley *(Community Mgr)*
Laura Silver *(Dir-Product Mgmt)*

TRINITY PRODUCTS INC.
1969 W Terra Ln, O'Fallon, MO 63366
Tel.: (636) 639-5244
Web Site: http://www.trinityinc.com
Rev.: $27,000,000
Emp.: 88
Iron & Steel Mills
N.A.I.C.S.: 331110
Vince Hasen *(VP)*
Robert Griggs *(Founder & Pres)*
Bryan Davis *(Mgr-Sls)*

TRINITY REAL ESTATE SOLUTIONS, INC.
4851 Lyndon B Johnson Fwy Ste 410, Dallas, TX 75244
Tel.: (972) 865-0200 TX
Web Site: http://www.trinityonline.com
Year Founded: 2003
Sales Range: $1-9.9 Million
Emp.: 35
Real Estate Services, Including Inspection & Appraisal Services
N.A.I.C.S.: 541350
Brad Meyer *(Pres & CEO)*
Chris Wood *(VP-Inspection Svcs)*
Jerry Sattler *(VP)*
Steve Fontaine *(VP-Svcs)*

TRINITY SOLAR, INC.
2211 Allenwood Rd, Wall, NJ 07719
Tel.: (732) 780-3779 NJ
Web Site: http://www.trinity-solar.com
Year Founded: 1994
Sales Range: $50-74.9 Million
Emp.: 400
Designs, Installs & Services Photovoltaic Solar Systems for Home & Business Owners
N.A.I.C.S.: 238220
Thomas Pollock *(Co-Founder & CEO)*
William Pollock *(Co-Founder & Pres)*
Joshua Beach *(Asst Mgr-Reg Sls)*

TRINITY STERILE
201 Kiley Dr, Salisbury, MD 21801
Tel.: (410) 860-5123
Web Site: http://www.trinitysterile.com
Year Founded: 2004
Rev.: $22,300,000
Emp.: 89
Plastics Product Mfr
N.A.I.C.S.: 326199
Abrar Solatch *(Pres & CEO)*
Mike Viner *(Dir-Special Products & Projects)*
Mike Thomason *(Acct Mgr-Natl)*
Stacey Nichols *(Acct Mgr-Natl)*

TRINITY TECHNOLOGIES, INC.
4633 Old Ironsides Dr 330, Santa Clara, CA 95054
Tel.: (408) 986-0500
Web Site: http://www.trinity-tech.com
Sales Range: $1-9.9 Million
Emp.: 10
Semiconductor Devices Whslr & Distr
N.A.I.C.S.: 334413
Paris Greenwood *(Partner)*
Mike Lewis *(Partner)*
Mark Powers Sr. *(Founder & CEO)*

TRINITY TECHNOLOGY GROUP, INC.
3701 Pender Dr Ste 320, Fairfax, VA 22030
Tel.: (703) 345-1660

TRINITY TECHNOLOGY GROUP, INC.   U.S. PRIVATE

Trinity Technology Group, Inc.—(Continued)
Web Site:
http://www.trinitytechnology
group.com
Year Founded: 2002
Sales Range: $10-24.9 Million
Emp.: 190
Security Support Services
N.A.I.C.S.: 561612
Elizabeth Parker *(Dir-HR)*
Mark Harding *(COO)*
Ted London *(Mng Dir)*
Stephen Williamson *(Chief Innovation Officer)*
Greg Vas Nunes *(CEO)*
Bruce Anneaux *(CTO)*

TRINITY TRANSPORT, INC.
1201 Bridgeville Hwy, Seaford, DE 19973
Tel.: (302) 337-3900
Year Founded: 1979
Sales Range: $10-24.9 Million
Emp.: 63
Provider of Freight Transportation Arrangement Services
N.A.I.C.S.: 488510
Jeffrey E. Banning *(Pres & CEO)*
Richie Smith *(Mgr-Opers)*
Doug Potvin *(CFO)*
Greg Massey *(VP-Corp Risk)*

TRINITY VALLEY ELECTRIC COOP
1800 Hwy 243 E, Kaufman, TX 75142
Tel.: (972) 932-2214
Web Site: http://www.tvec.net
Sales Range: $50-74.9 Million
Emp.: 185
Distr of Electric Power
N.A.I.C.S.: 221122
Jerry Boze *(Pres & CEO)*
Tim Craig *(Mgr-Engrg)*
Bryan Wood *(CFO)*
Donna Hindman *(Mgr-HR)*

Subsidiaries:

Trinity Valley Electric Coop (Athens Office)   (1)
909 W Larkin St, Athens, TX 75752-1270
Tel.: (903) 675-5688
Web Site: http://www.tvec.net
Sales Range: $50-74.9 Million
Emp.: 100
Distr of Electric Services
N.A.I.C.S.: 221118
Ian Flemming *(Branch Mgr)*
Jerry Boze *(CEO & Gen Mgr)*

Trinity Valley Electric Coop (Cedar Creek Sub-Office)   (1)
1012 W Main Ste 102, Gun Barrel City, TX 75156
Tel.: (903) 713-4400
Sales Range: $25-49.9 Million
Emp.: 100
Distr of Electric Services
N.A.I.C.S.: 582490
Joe Boze *(Gen Mgr)*

TRINITY VENTURES
2480 Sand Hill Rd Ste 200, Menlo Park, CA 94025-7113
Tel.: (650) 854-9500
Web Site:
http://www.trinityventures.com
Sales Range: $350-399.9 Million
Emp.: 200
Venture Capital Investment Firm
N.A.I.C.S.: 523999
Lawrence K. Orr *(Gen Partner)*
Gus Tai *(Venture Partner)*
Dan Scholnick *(Gen Partner)*
Patricia Nakache *(Gen Partner)*
Karan Mehandru *(Gen Partner)*
Anjula Acharia-Bath *(Partner)*
Schwark Satyavolu *(Gen Partner)*
Nina Labatt *(COO & Gen Partner)*
Noel Fenton *(Partner)*
Patricia Nakache *(Gen Partner)*
John Lin *(Assoc Partner)*
Patricia Nakache *(Gen Partner)*
Ajay Chopra *(Gen Partner)*

TRINITY WHOLESALE DISTRIBUTORS, INC.
11034 Lincoln Hwy E, New Haven, IN 46774
Tel.: (260) 493-2574
Web Site:
http://www.trinityhomecenter.com
Year Founded: 1962
Rev.: $13,900,000
Emp.: 20
Lighting; Plumbing; Electrical
N.A.I.C.S.: 423720
Kevin Walsh *(Pres)*
Sharon Welch *(VP & Controller)*

TRINITY YACHTS, LLC
13085 Seaway Rd, Gulfport, MS 39503-4607
Tel.: (228) 276-1000
Web Site:
http://www.trinityyachts.com
Sales Range: $100-124.9 Million
Emp.: 425
Yacht Builder & Retailer
N.A.I.C.S.: 336612
Felix Sabates Jr. *(Chm)*
John Dane III *(Pres)*
William S. Smith III *(COO)*

TRIO ADVERTISING. DESIGN. SOLUTIONS
1130 Industry Dr, Seattle, WA 98188
Tel.: (253) 856-8746
Web Site: http://www.trioads.com
Year Founded: 2003
Sales Range: $25-49.9 Million
Emp.: 10
Education, Full Service, Government/Political/Public Affairs
N.A.I.C.S.: 541810
Jeff Quint *(Partner & Acct Dir)*
Dennis Brooks *(CFO & Partner)*

TRIO PACKAGING CORP
90 13th Ave Ste 11, Ronkonkoma, NY 11779
Tel.: (631) 588-0800
Web Site:
http://www.triopackaging.com
Year Founded: 1975
Sales Range: $10-24.9 Million
Emp.: 60
Flexible Packaging Services
N.A.I.C.S.: 333993
John Bolla *(Pres)*
Diane Trio *(Mgr-Accts Receivable)*

TRIO TRUCKING INC.
7750 Reinhold Dr, Cincinnati, OH 45237
Tel.: (513) 679-7100
Web Site:
http://www.trioenterprises.com
Sales Range: $10-24.9 Million
Emp.: 75
Trucking Service
N.A.I.C.S.: 484121
Carvel E. Simmons *(Pres)*
Dean Spade *(Dir-Intermodal Ops)*

TRIO, INC.
20 E Center Ave, Denver, CO 80209
Tel.: (303) 663-1285
Web Site: http://www.triodesign.com
Year Founded: 1999
Interior Design Services
N.A.I.C.S.: 541410
Angela Harris *(Principal & Creative Dir)*

Subsidiaries:

Design Lines, Inc.   (1)
7555 E Hampden Ave Ste 400, Denver, CO 80231
Tel.: (720) 347-9333
Web Site: http://www.designlinesinc.com
Interior Design Services
N.A.I.C.S.: 541410
Sandy E. Saul *(CEO)*

TRIOAK FOODS, INC.
103 W Railroad St, Oakville, IA 52646
Tel.: (319) 766-2230
Web Site: http://www.trioak.com
Year Founded: 1951
Sales Range: $10-24.9 Million
Emp.: 300
Provider of Farm Supplies
N.A.I.C.S.: 424510
Randy Pflum *(Pres & CEO)*
Robert G. McCulley *(Chm)*
Dennis Breder *(CFO)*
Fred Bakerink *(Mgr-Mill Maintenance)*
Brian Blake *(Dir-HR)*
Adam Daniel *(Mgr-Live Production Logistics)*
Kenney Dixon *(Mgr-GDU & Internal Transport)*
Andrew Forbes *(Controller)*
Tom Gall *(Mgr-Genetics & Multiplication)*
Tom Marker *(Mgr-Sow Production)*
Kristen Moore *(Mgr-Comm)*
Al Muhlenbruck *(Mgr-Mktg & PR)*
Tom Parchert *(Mgr-Grain & Milling Ops)*
Matt Smith *(Mgr-Finishing Production)*
Terry Vogel *(Mgr-Regulatory & Oklahoma Facilities-Colorado)*
John McCulley Jr. *(VP)*

TRIOSE, INC.
2001 State Hill Rd Ste-205, Wyomissing, PA 19610
Tel.: (866) 241-2268
Web Site: http://www.triose.com
Year Founded: 1999
Sales Range: $10-24.9 Million
Emp.: 60
Hospital Freight Management, Supply Chain Consulting & Logistics Management for Medical Research & Health Care Networks
N.A.I.C.S.: 541614
Carl Joyner *(Founder & CEO)*
Ira Tauber *(Pres)*
Tom Wengrowski *(Exec VP)*
Melanie Gittens *(VP-East)*
Tracy Leatherman *(VP-Sls)*
Gerald Gerry Romanelli *(Exec VP-Bus Dev)*

TRIOSIM CORPORATION
2111 N Sandra St, Appleton, WI 54911
Tel.: (920) 968-0800
Web Site: http://www.triosim.com
Pulp Mill
N.A.I.C.S.: 322110
Ray McIntosh *(Exec VP-Mfg)*
Kurt Bramer *(Pres-Mfg)*
James Hickman *(CEO)*
Bruce Truskowski *(COO)*
Dave Louden *(CFO)*
David Bryant *(Exec VP-Sls)*
Scott Bowman *(Pres-Svcs)*
Glen Kowalski *(VP-Tech Svcs)*

Subsidiaries:

Mtr Martco, LLC   (1)
3350 Yankee Rd, Middletown, OH 45044
Tel.: (513) 424-5307
Paper Industries Machinery
N.A.I.C.S.: 333243

TRIPIFOODS INC.
1427 William St, Buffalo, NY 14206-1807
Tel.: (716) 853-7400
Web Site: http://www.tripifoods.com
Year Founded: 1958
Sales Range: $25-49.9 Million
Emp.: 222
Convenience Store Supplier
N.A.I.C.S.: 424410
Greg Tripi *(Pres)*

TRIPLAY, INC.
215 Lexington Ave Ste 1702, New York, NY 10016
Tel.: (212) 372-6019
Web Site: http://www.triplay.com
Cloud Services
N.A.I.C.S.: 541519
Tamir Koch *(Founder & CEO)*
Lior Solomon *(VP-R&D)*
Matt Downing *(CMO)*

Subsidiaries:

eMusic.com Inc.   (1)
244 5th Ave Ste 2070, New York, NY 10001   (100%)
Tel.: (212) 201-9240
Web Site: http://www.emusic.com
Digital Music Distr
N.A.I.C.S.: 512290
Lara Peterson *(Dir-CRM)*

TRIPLE A SERVICES INC.
2637 S Throop St, Chicago, IL 60608
Tel.: (312) 225-5040
Web Site:
http://www.tripleaservices.com
Sales Range: $25-49.9 Million
Emp.: 12
Mobile Caterers & Food Service
N.A.I.C.S.: 722320
Thomas A. Whennen *(Pres-Vending & Food Svc)*
Scott Whennen *(Pres-Catering Div)*
Dave Frisco *(Gen Mgr)*
Thomas J. Whennen Sr. *(Founder)*

TRIPLE B CORP
4103 2nd Ave S., Seattle, WA 98134
Tel.: (206) 625-1412
Web Site:
http://www.charliesproduce.com
Year Founded: 1978
Sales Range: $1-9.9 Million
Emp.: 12
Fresh Fruit & Vegetable Merchant Whslr
N.A.I.C.S.: 424480

TRIPLE B FORWARDERS, INC.
1511 Glen Curtis St, Carson, CA 90746
Tel.: (310) 604-5840
Web Site: http://www.tripleb.com
Sales Range: $10-24.9 Million
Emp.: 100
Freight Forwarding Services
N.A.I.C.S.: 488510
Rick Beliveau *(Pres)*
Dante Octaviano *(Controller)*

TRIPLE CITIES ACQUISITION LLC
76 Frederick St, Binghamton, NY 13901
Tel.: (607) 723-7481
Rev.: $28,000,000
Emp.: 60
Distr of Trucks
N.A.I.C.S.: 423110
Mike Venuti *(Pres)*
Stanley Polhamus *(Controller)*

TRIPLE H FOOD PROCESSORS INCORPORATED
5821 Wilderness Ave, Riverside, CA 92504
Tel.: (951) 352-5700
Web Site: http://www.triplehfoods.com
Rev.: $16,000,000
Emp.: 45
Canned Fruits & Specialties
N.A.I.C.S.: 311421
Thomas G. Harris Jr. (Pres)

TRIPLE H SPECIALTY CO. INC.
60 W Coffee St, Hazlehurst, GA 31539
Tel.: (912) 375-7723
Web Site: http://www.tripleh.com
Year Founded: 1972
Sales Range: $10-24.9 Million
Emp.: 25
Electrical Supplies
N.A.I.C.S.: 423610
Charles W. Shepard (Pres)
Tim Taylor (CEO)

TRIPLE J ENTERPRISES, INC.
PO Box 6066, Tamuning, GU 96931
Tel.: (671) 646-9126
Web Site: http://www.carsguam.com
Sales Range: $100-124.9 Million
Emp.: 400
Holding Company; Car Dealership Owner & Operator; Food Services
N.A.I.C.S.: 551112
Robert H. Jones (Founder)
Jeffrey Jones (Pres)
Jay Jones (Sr VP)
Christopher L. C. Duenas (CFO)
Nathan Taimanglo (Dir-HR)
Kristine R. Lujan (VP-Mktg)

TRIPLE LEAF TEA, INC.
434 N Canal St Unit 5, South San Francisco, CA 94080
Tel.: (650) 588-8258
Web Site: http://www.tripleleaf-tea.com
Sales Range: $10-24.9 Million
Emp.: 12
Tea Production Services
N.A.I.C.S.: 311920
Johnson Lam (Pres)
Mary Anne Schlosser (VP-Mktg & Sls)

TRIPLE M ROOFING CORP.
914 NW 19th Ave, Fort Lauderdale, FL 33311-6938
Tel.: (954) 524-7000
Web Site: http://www.triplemroofing.com
Sales Range: $10-24.9 Million
Emp.: 40
Roofing Contractors
N.A.I.C.S.: 238160
Thomas Milanese (Pres)
Pete Milanese (VP & Project Mgr)

TRIPLE P PACKAGING & PAPER PRODUCTS, INC.
20 Burke Dr, Brockton, MA 02301
Tel.: (508) 588-0444
Web Site: http://www.ppppack.com
Sales Range: $10-24.9 Million
Emp.: 25
Whslr of Packaging Materials
N.A.I.C.S.: 561910
Richard Shaughnessy (Pres)
Gregory O'Connell (VP)
Paul Kotchian (Mgr-Quality)
Margie Verissimo (Office Mgr & Controller)

Scott Doody (Mgr-Logistics)
Bob Dow (Mgr-Foam)
Richard Ferrini (Plant Mgr)

TRIPLE S AIR SYSTEMS, INC.
80 Raynor Ave, Ronkonkoma, NY 11779
Tel.: (631) 580-7460
Web Site: http://www.triplesair.com
Year Founded: 1995
Sales Range: $10-24.9 Million
Emp.: 64
Plumbing, Heating & Air-Conditioning Contract Services
N.A.I.C.S.: 238220
Steve Benkovsky (Pres)

TRIPLE S PETROLEUM COMPANY INC.
4911 E 7th St, Austin, TX 78702-5020
Tel.: (512) 385-2020   TX
Web Site: http://www.sssfuel.com
Year Founded: 1988
Sales Range: $10-24.9 Million
Emp.: 500
Supplier of Petroleum
N.A.I.C.S.: 424720
Ford Smith (Pres)
Cody Douglas (Controller)

TRIPLE S TIRE CO. INC.
405 S 9th St, Elwood, IN 46036
Tel.: (765) 552-5765
Web Site: http://www.triplestire.com
Sales Range: $10-24.9 Million
Emp.: 50
Tires & Tubes Mfr
N.A.I.C.S.: 423130
Richard Stanley (Pres)
Deb Chalfant (Mgr)

TRIPLE S&P, INC.
9135 58th Dr E, Bradenton, FL 34202
Tel.: (941) 776-1211
Web Site: http://www.dixiesouthern.com
Year Founded: 1976
Sales Range: $10-24.9 Million
Emp.: 100
Steel & Plate Work Mfr
N.A.I.C.S.: 331110
Stan Kinnett (Pres & CEO)
Pascal Logue (VP-Ops)
Charissa Putnam (CFO)
Gene Sweet (Sr Mgr-Sls & Estimating)
Shawntel Carlton (Mgr-Admin Ops)

TRIPLE T TRANSPORT, INC.
PO Box 649, Lewis Center, OH 43035
Tel.: (740) 657-3244
Web Site: http://www.triplettransport.com
Year Founded: 1998
Rev.: $74,900,000
Emp.: 42
Freight Transportation Arrangement
N.A.I.C.S.: 488510
Thomas A. Sanfilippo (Pres)
Darin Puppel (Pres)
Jem Kellar (Coord-Transportation)
David Santisi (VP-Sls)
Terry McKenzie (VP-Sls)
Rick Duskey (Coord-Sls-Natl)

TRIPLE V INC.
403 S Church Ave, Louisville, MS 39339-2921
Tel.: (662) 773-5951   MS
Year Founded: 1977
Sales Range: $50-74.9 Million
Emp.: 350
Grocery Stores
N.A.I.C.S.: 445110

E.L. Vowell (Pres)
Todd Vowell (Owner)

TRIPLE-I INVESTMENTS INC.
6330 Lamar Ave Ste 230, Shawnee Mission, KS 66202-4286
Tel.: (913) 563-7200   MO
Web Site: http://www.triplei.com
Year Founded: 1971
Sales Range: $50-74.9 Million
Emp.: 400
Management Consulting Services
N.A.I.C.S.: 541611

Subsidiaries:

Triple-I Corp   (1)
6330 Lamont Ste 230, Overland Park, KS 66202
Tel.: (913) 262-6500
Web Site: http://www.triplei.com
Sales Range: $25-49.9 Million
Emp.: 250
Provider of Management Consulting & E-Business Services
N.A.I.C.S.: 541618

Triple-I of Colorado Inc.   (1)
5445 DTC Pkwy., Ste. P4, Denver, CO 80111-3059
Tel.: (303) 721-0900
Sales Range: $10-24.9 Million
Emp.: 50
Management Consulting Services
N.A.I.C.S.: 541618

TRIPLE-S STEEL HOLDINGS INC.
6000 Jensen Dr, Houston, TX 77026
Tel.: (713) 697-7105   TX
Web Site: http://www.sss-steel.com
Holding Company
N.A.I.C.S.: 551112
Gary Stein (CEO)

Subsidiaries:

AAP Metals, LLC   (1)
811 Regal Row, Dallas, TX 75247
Tel.: (214) 357-6161
Web Site: http://www.arbormetals.com
Rev.: $6,249,000
Emp.: 35
Metal Stamping
N.A.I.C.S.: 332119
William Sultzbaugh (Pres)

Alamo Iron Works, Inc.   (1)
943 AT&T Ctr Pkwy, San Antonio, TX 78219
Tel.: (210) 223-6161
Web Site: http://www.aiwdirect.com
Steel Product Distr
N.A.I.C.S.: 423510
Micheal Pawlik (Mgr-Inside Sls)

Branch (Domestic):

Alamo Iron Works - Brownsville   (2)
2771 Robindale, Brownsville, TX 78526
Tel.: (956) 831-4291
Rev.: $15,000,000
Emp.: 54
Steel & Industrial Products Distr
N.A.I.C.S.: 423510
Robert Caceres (Dir-Ops)

Borrmann Metal Center, Inc.   (1)
110 W Olive Ave, Burbank, CA 91502
Tel.: (818) 846-7171
Web Site: http://www.borrmannmetalcenter.com
Rev.: $7,500,000
Emp.: 24
Metal Service Centers & Other Metal Merchant Whslr
N.A.I.C.S.: 423510
Jane Borrmann (CEO)
Bob Persson (Co-Pres)
Joel Silver (Mgr-Pur)

Intsel Steel   (1)
11310 W Little York Rd, Houston, TX 77041
Tel.: (713) 937-9500
Web Site: http://www.saxon-clark.com
Rev.: $96,000,000
Emp.: 200
Steel Products Mfr

N.A.I.C.S.: 423510
Mike Livergood (VP-Ops)

R&S Steel Company Inc.   (1)
8573 Ulster St, Denver, CO 80022
Tel.: (303) 321-9660
Web Site: http://www.rssteel.com
Sales Range: $10-24.9 Million
Emp.: 70
Structural Steel Products
N.A.I.C.S.: 423510

Triple-S Steel Supply Co. Inc.   (1)
6000 Jensen Dr, Houston, TX 77026-1113
Tel.: (713) 697-7105
Web Site: http://www.sss-steel.com
Sales Range: $25-49.9 Million
Emp.: 230
Steel Whslr
N.A.I.C.S.: 423510
Bruce D. Stein (Chm)
Adam Vieyra (Mgr-Export Sls)
Paul Kruppa (VP-Ops)
Joe Mignona (Gen Mgr)

Tube Supply, LLC   (1)
5169 Ashley Ct, Houston, TX 77041
Tel.: (713) 466-4130
Web Site: http://www.tubesupply.com
Sales Range: $200-249.9 Million
Emp.: 75
Metal Tubing & Bar Products Distr
N.A.I.C.S.: 423510

Subsidiary (Domestic):

Marco Steel & Aluminum Inc.   (2)
11524 County Rd 128 W, Midland, TX 79711
Tel.: (432) 563-5051
Web Site: http://www.marcosteel.com
Sales Range: $10-24.9 Million
Emp.: 20
Metals Service Centers & Offices
N.A.I.C.S.: 423510
Jay Roberts (Gen Mgr-Lubbock)
Brad Blake (Gen Mgr)

TRIPLE/S DYNAMICS, INC.
1031 S Haskell Ave, Dallas, TX 75223
Tel.: (214) 828-8600
Web Site: http://www.sssdynamics.com
Year Founded: 1888
Sales Range: $10-24.9 Million
Emp.: 100
Mfr of Dry Bulk Material Handling Equipment
N.A.I.C.S.: 333922
Celie Reid (Mgr-Sls & Mktg)
Kenneth Everill (Pres)
James F. Sullivan Sr. (Chm)

TRIPLEPOINT PRIVATE VENTURE CREDIT INC.
2755 Sand Hill Rd Ste 150, Menlo Park, CA 94025
Tel.: (650) 854-2090   MD
Year Founded: 2019
Rev.: $61,643,000
Assets: $480,585,000
Liabilities: $195,950,000
Net Worth: $284,635,000
Earnings: $37,874,000
Fiscal Year-end: 12/31/22
Investment Services
N.A.I.C.S.: 523940
James P. Labe (Chm & CEO)
Sajal K. Srivastava (Pres, Chief Investment Officer, Treas & Sec)
Brandon R. Campbell (Interim CFO & Controller)

TRIPLETT INC.
429 N Ohio St, Salina, KS 67401-2402
Tel.: (785) 823-7839   KS
Web Site: http://www.24-7stores.com
Year Founded: 1963
Sales Range: $10-24.9 Million
Emp.: 80
Gasoline Service Stations

TRIPLETT INC.

Triplett Inc.—Continued
N.A.I.C.S.: 457120
Judd Bircher (Treas & Sec)
Jaime Kelsey (Mgr)
Paul Haase (Dir-IT)
Butch Stucky (VP)

TRIPLETT OFFICE ESSENTIALS
3553 109th St, Des Moines, IA 50322
Tel.: (515) 270-9150
Web Site: http://www.tripletts.com
Rev.: $19,000,000
Emp.: 45
Office Supplies
N.A.I.C.S.: 424120
Richard Triplett (Pres & CEO)
Sue Triplett (Treas & Sec)
Tom Triplett (VP)

TRIPLEX INC.
1122 Kress St, Houston, TX 77020-7417
Tel.: (713) 672-7521
Web Site: http://www.triplex-inc.com
Year Founded: 1958
Sales Range: $75-99.9 Million
Emp.: 120
Industrial Supplies
N.A.I.C.S.: 423840
Marcus Northrup (Pres & CEO)

TRIPP ENTERPRISES INC.
250 Greg St, Sparks, NV 89431
Tel.: (775) 355-7552
Web Site: http://www.trippnv.com
Sales Range: $25-49.9 Million
Emp.: 90
Provider of Synthetic Resin Finished Products
N.A.I.C.S.: 326199
Warren W. Tripp (Pres & Owner)
Ken Juenke (Mgr-Electronic Sys)
Ray Duer (Mgr-Engrg)
Howie Tune (Mgr-Sls)

TRIPPE MANUFACTURING COMPANY
1111 W 35th St, Chicago, IL 60609-1404
Tel.: (773) 869-1111
Web Site: http://www.tripplite.com
Year Founded: 1922
Sales Range: $150-199.9 Million
Emp.: 400
Surge Suppressors & Other Power Protection Equipment for Computers
N.A.I.C.S.: 334419
Glen Haeflinger (Pres)
Shane Kilfoil (Sr VP-Sls-Global)
Bryn Morgan (VP-Sls-Intl)

TRIPPIES INC.
1515 Brookville Crossing Way, Indianapolis, IN 46239
Tel.: (740) 884-4434
Web Site: http://www.obiwholesale.com
Year Founded: 1947
Sales Range: $10-24.9 Million
Emp.: 14
Giftware & Pottery Sales
N.A.I.C.S.: 424990
Tim Chocklette (CEO)

TRIS PHARMA, INC.
2031 US Hwy 130, Monmouth Junction, NJ 08852
Tel.: (732) 940-2800
Web Site: http://www.trispharma.com
Year Founded: 2000
Pharmaceutical Developer & Mfr
N.A.I.C.S.: 325412
Barry Herman (Chief Medical Officer)
Ketan B. Mehta (Founder & CEO)

Thomas Englese (Chief Comml Officer)
Alfred C. Liang (VP-R&D)
Anthony Amato (Exec VP-Bus Dev-Generics Div)
Marc Lesnick (Chief Dev Officer)

TRISH MCEVOY LTD.
430 Commerce Blvd, Carlstadt, NJ 07072-3013
Tel.: (201) 559-9234
Web Site: http://www.trishmcevoy.com
Sales Range: $25-49.9 Million
Emp.: 82
Cosmetics Mfr & Retailer
N.A.I.C.S.: 325620
Trish McEvoy (Pres)

TRISOME FOODS, INC.
72 Portsmouth Ave, Stratham, NH 03885
Tel.: (603) 773-5800
Web Site: http://www.trisomefoods.com
Sales Range: $10-24.9 Million
Emp.: 5
Fish & Seafood Whslr
N.A.I.C.S.: 424460
Robert J. Fitzsimmons (Founder)

TRISSEL, GRAHAM & TOOLE INC.
220 Emerson Pl Ste 200, Davenport, IA 52801-1633
Tel.: (563) 322-3521
Web Site: http://www.tgtinsurance.com
Year Founded: 1896
Sales Range: $25-49.9 Million
Emp.: 50
Provider of Insurance Services
N.A.I.C.S.: 524210

TRISTAR ENTERPRISES, LLC
300 E Valley Dr, Bristol, VA 24201
Web Site: http://www.tristarclean.com
Year Founded: 1937
Vacuum Cleaner Mfr & Distr
N.A.I.C.S.: 335210

TRISTAR HOLDINGS INC.
4010 Airline Dr, Houston, TX 77022-4114
Tel.: (713) 691-0005
Web Site: http://www.tristarholdings.com
Rev.: $22,000,000
Emp.: 4
Provider of Investment Services
N.A.I.C.S.: 523999
Hazem Megerisi (Exec VP-Bus Dev)
Masaud Baaba (Pres)

Subsidiaries:
Omega III Investment Co. (1)
4010 Airline Dr, Houston, TX 77022-4114
Tel.: (713) 691-0005
Web Site: http://www.tristarholdings.com
Sales Range: Less than $1 Million
Real Estate Investment Services
N.A.I.C.S.: 523999
Omar Megerisi (CEO)

Tristar Web Graphics Inc (1)
4010 Airline Dr, Houston, TX 77022
Tel.: (713) 691-0005
Web Site: http://tristarholdings.com
Printing Services
N.A.I.C.S.: 323111

Tristar Web Solutions, Inc. (1)
2800 Post Oak Blvd 5310, Houston, TX 77056
Tel.: (713) 496-4623
Web Design & Development Services
N.A.I.C.S.: 541511

TRISTAR INSURANCE GROUP, INC.
100 Oceangate Ste 700, Long Beach, CA 90802
Tel.: (562) 495-6600
Web Site: http://www.tristarrisk.com
Insurance Provider & Services
N.A.I.C.S.: 524298
Tom Veale (Pres)

Subsidiaries:
Aspen Risk Management Group (1)
2727 Camino Del Rio S, San Diego, CA 92108
Tel.: (503) 699-4732
Web Site: http://www.aspenrmg.com
Human Resource Consulting Services
N.A.I.C.S.: 541612
Steve Thompson (Principal)

TRISTAR MANAGING GENERAL AGENCY
5408 W Plano Pkwy, Plano, TX 75093
Tel.: (972) 713-0315
Web Site: http://www.tristarmga.net
Sales Range: $25-49.9 Million
Emp.: 13
Provider of Insurance Services
N.A.I.C.S.: 524210
Melissa Harral (Controller)

TRISTAR PRODUCTS INC.
492 Rte 46 E, Fairfield, NJ 07004
Tel.: (973) 575-5400
Web Site: http://www.tristarproductsinc.com
Year Founded: 1993
Sales Range: $10-24.9 Million
Emp.: 30
Celebrity-Endorsed Consumer Goods Marketing & Sales
N.A.I.C.S.: 424990
Ed Hendrick (Controller)
Lynda Gentile (Dir-Creative)
Paul DiLonardo (VP-Sls)
Joe Urbay (Dir-Intl Sls)

TRISTAR RISK MANAGEMENT INC.
2835 Temple Ave, Long Beach, CA 90806
Tel.: (562) 506-0300
Web Site: http://www.tristarrisk.com
Rev.: $10,172,166
Emp.: 45
Provider of Insurance Inspection & Investigation Services
N.A.I.C.S.: 524298
Curt Crockett (VP & Reg Mgr)
James Soto (VP & Reg Mgr)
Dennis Hoppe (Mgr-Claims)
Ian Stewart (Mgr-Audit & Compliance)
Flerida Astacio (Supvr-Claims)
Richard Thibault (Gen Counsel)
Lydia Hsiao (Mgr-Brand)

TRISTATE HVAC EQUIPMENT LLP
1 Resource Dr, West Conshohocken, PA 19428
Tel.: (610) 825-4770
Web Site: http://www.tristatehvac.com
Rev.: $20,000,000
Emp.: 44
Warm Air Heating Equipment & Supplies
N.A.I.C.S.: 423730
Michael Porter (Mgr-Sls)
Robert Lowry (Engr-Sls)
Andrew Doble (Mgr-Engrg Sls)

TRISTATE MACHINERY, INC.

U.S. PRIVATE

129 Wheeling Rd, Wheeling, IL 60090-4807
Tel.: (847) 520-4420
Web Site: http://www.tristatemachinery.com
Year Founded: 1986
Sales Range: $10-24.9 Million
Emp.: 10
Industrial Equipment Whsr
N.A.I.C.S.: 423830
Tim Doran (Pres)

TRISTRATA INC.
307 College Rd E, Princeton, NJ 08540-6608
Tel.: (609) 520-0715
Web Site: http://www.neostrata.com
Rev.: $25,700,000
Emp.: 70
Cosmetics; Holding Company
N.A.I.C.S.: 424210
Leanne Catlin (VP)
Dennis Reilly (VP-Fin)
Mark Steele (CEO)

Subsidiaries:
Tristrata Technology Inc (1)
1105 N Market St Ste 1300, Wilmington, DE 19801
Tel.: (302) 427-3819
Web Site: http://www.neostrata.com
Rev.: $150,000
Patent Owners & Lessors
N.A.I.C.S.: 533110

TRITEC BUILDING COMPANY INC.
45 Research Way Ste 100, East Setauket, NY 11733
Tel.: (631) 751-0300
Web Site: http://www.tritecrealestate.com
Year Founded: 1986
Sales Range: $100-124.9 Million
Emp.: 80
Provider of Nonresidential Construction
N.A.I.C.S.: 236220
Robert T. Coughlan (Chm)
Christopher Kelly (Dir-Mktg)
Martin A. DePasquale (VP-Preconstruction Svcs)
Sandra Eavens (VP-Asset Mgmt)

TRITEN CORPORATION
3657 Briar Pk, Houston, TX 77042
Tel.: (832) 214-5000
Web Site: http://www.triten.com
Sales Range: $200-249.9 Million
Emp.: 125
Provider of Steel Plate
N.A.I.C.S.: 541618
John Scott Arnoldy (Chm & CEO)

TRITIUM PARTNERS, LLC
221 W 6th St Ste 700, Austin, TX 78701
Tel.: (512) 493-4100
Web Site: http://www.tritiumpartners.com
Privater Equity Firm
N.A.I.C.S.: 523999
Phil Siegel (Mng Partner)
David Lack (Mng Partner)

TRITON CAPITAL PARTNERS LIMITED
566 W Lake St Ste 235, Chicago, IL 60661
Tel.: (312) 575-0190
Web Site: http://www.tritoncap.com
Year Founded: 2000
Private Equity & Investment Banking Services
N.A.I.C.S.: 523999

COMPANIES

David J. Asmann *(Co-Founder & Co-CEO)*
Gregory J. Nowlin *(Co-Founder & Co-CEO)*

TRITON COMMERCE, LLC
1828 Marshall St NE Ste 14B, Minneapolis, MN 55418
Tel.: (651) 321-0578
Web Site:
  http://www.tritoncommerce.com
Year Founded: 2012
Sales Range: $1-9.9 Million
Emp.: 22
Digital Marketing Services
N.A.I.C.S.: 541810
Corey Kelly *(CEO)*
Nick Kelly *(Chief Design Officer)*
Caryn Butler *(COO)*
Matt Ashley *(VP-Client Ops)*
Shianne Verness *(Dir-Mktg & Strategy)*

TRITON CONSOLIDATED, INC.
1500 S Interstate 35 E Ste 181, Lancaster, TX 75146-3362
Tel.: (214) 686-4400
Web Site: http://www.usatriton.com
Holding Company
N.A.I.C.S.: 551112
Perry Jasin *(CEO)*
Derald Armstrong *(COO)*

Subsidiaries:

Apple Fabrication Company (1)
815 Mercury Ave, Duncanville, TX 75137
Tel.: (972) 298-9898
Web Site: http://www.applefabrication.com
Rev.: $2,646,000
Emp.: 14
All Other Industrial Machinery Mfr
N.A.I.C.S.: 333248
Jack Green *(Pres)*

TRITON CORP.
857 W State St, Hartford, WI 53027
Tel.: (262) 670-6514
Web Site:
  http://www.tritontrailers.com
Year Founded: 1975
Sales Range: $10-24.9 Million
Emp.: 80
Trailers & Trailer Equipment
N.A.I.C.S.: 336214
Michelle Livingston *(Controller)*
Rochelle Priesgen *(Pres & CEO)*
Tony Priesgen *(Exec VP)*

TRITON DIVING SERVICES, LLC
3421 N Causeway Blvd Ste 601, Metairie, LA 70002
Tel.: (504) 846-5056   LA
Web Site: http://www.tritondiving.net
Year Founded: 1999
Sales Range: $25-49.9 Million
Emp.: 200
Specialty Diving & Marine Oil & Gas Support Services
N.A.I.C.S.: 541990
Mark J. Jeansonne *(Pres)*
Matt Blalock *(Acct Mgr-Special Projects)*
Bill Folse *(Dir-HSE)*

TRITON INDUSTRIES, INC.
1020 N Kolmar Ave, Chicago, IL 60651-3343
Tel.: (773) 384-3700   IL
Web Site:
  http://www.tritonindustries.com
Year Founded: 1961
Sales Range: $75-99.9 Million
Emp.: 150
Metal Stampings & Fabrications; Electronic Enclosures
N.A.I.C.S.: 332119

Brent Wortell *(Pres & CEO)*

TRITON MARINE CONSTRUCTION
5405 Constants Dr SW, Bremerton, WA 98312
Tel.: (360) 373-7090
Web Site: http://www.triton-marine.com
Year Founded: 1987
Sales Range: $25-49.9 Million
Emp.: 150
Provider of Marine Construction Services
N.A.I.C.S.: 236210
Nordlund Chris *(Project Mgr)*
Jon Archer *(Pres)*
Dave Rolfs *(Project Mgr & Project Engr)*
Paul Johnson *(Mgr-Construction)*

TRITON MARKETING COMPANY
8255 Dunwoody Pl, Atlanta, GA 30350
Tel.: (770) 992-7088   GA
Year Founded: 1992
Sales Range: $50-74.9 Million
Emp.: 250
Owner & Operator of Gasoline Station & Convenience Store Chains
N.A.I.C.S.: 457120
Mark Bevill *(VP-Fin)*
Mark Barron *(VP-Mktg)*

TRITON PACIFIC CAPITAL PARTNERS LLC
6701 Center Dr 14th Fl, Los Angeles, CA 90045
Tel.: (310) 943-4990
Web Site:
  http://www.tritonpacific.com
Year Founded: 1996
Sales Range: $25-49.9 Million
Emp.: 13
Privater Equity Firm
N.A.I.C.S.: 523999
Ivan Faggen *(Mng Partner)*
Craig J. Faggen *(CEO)*
Joseph I. Davis *(Mng Partner-Healthcare)*
Thomas M. Scott *(Mng Partner)*
Sean D. Gjos *(Operating Partner)*
Brian D. Buehler *(Partner)*
Jill Tregillis *(CFO)*

Subsidiaries:

Myprint Corp. (1)
2772 Main St, Irvine, CA 92614
Tel.: (949) 261-0333
Sales Range: $25-49.9 Million
Offset Printing
N.A.I.C.S.: 323111

TRITON SERVICES INC.
2016 Industrial Dr, Annapolis, MD 21401-2942
Tel.: (301) 809-6834
Web Site: http://www.tritonsvc.com
Rev.: $17,020,000
Emp.: 190
Electron Tubes
N.A.I.C.S.: 334419
Ray Kwong *(Chm)*
Steve Groninga *(Sr Program Mgr)*
Ted Gamester *(Chief Technical Officer)*

TRITON SUBMARINES, LLC
9015 17th Pl, Vero Beach, FL 32966
Tel.: (772) 770-1995
Web Site: http://www.tritonsubs.com
Year Founded: 2007
Sales Range: $1-9.9 Million
Emp.: 25
Submarine Mfr

N.A.I.C.S.: 336612
L. Bruce Jones *(CEO)*
Patrick Lahey *(Pres)*

TRITON SYSTEMS INC.
200 Tpke Rd, Chelmsford, MA 01824
Tel.: (978) 250-4200
Web Site:
  http://www.tritonsystems.com
Year Founded: 1992
Sales Range: $10-24.9 Million
Emp.: 37
Technology Products Development Services
N.A.I.C.S.: 541380
Bill Altergott *(Exec VP)*
Arjan Giaya *(VP)*
Ross Haghighat *(Chm, Pres, CEO & Mng Partner)*
Anant Singh *(Exec VP-New Applications Ventures)*
David Model *(COO)*
Ken Mahmud *(Exec VP)*
Robert Miller *(VP-Fin)*
Sonja Hansen *(VP-HR)*
Tyson Lawrence *(VP-Engineered Sys)*

Subsidiaries:

VOmax (1)
76 Industrial Dr, Northampton, MA 01060
Tel.: (413) 584-0065
Web Site: http://www.vomax.com
Sales Range: $1-9.9 Million
Emp.: 30
Cycling Apparel Mfr
N.A.I.C.S.: 315250
Robert Miller *(Mgr-Fin)*

TRITON TECHNOLOGIES, INC.
115 Plymouth St, Mansfield, MA 02048
Tel.: (508) 230-7300
Web Site:
  http://www.tritontechnology.com
Year Founded: 2001
Sales Range: $10-24.9 Million
Emp.: 170
Direct Response Sales Services
N.A.I.C.S.: 541613
Matthew Bock *(VP-Bus Dev)*
Andy Bank *(CFO)*
Debbie Cohen Skelton *(CIO)*
S. Jay Nalli *(CEO)*

TRIUMPH CAPITAL, L.P.
445 Park Ave Fl 10, New York, NY 10022
Tel.: (212) 551-3636   DE
Sales Range: $10-24.9 Million
Emp.: 2
Venture Capital Company
N.A.I.C.S.: 523910
Michael Nugent *(Gen Partner)*

TRIUMPH ENTERPRISES INC
8000 Westpark Drive, McLean, VA 22102
Tel.: (703) 563-4400
Web Site: http://www.triumph-enterprises.com
Year Founded: 2005
Sales Range: $10-24.9 Million
Emp.: 130
Technical Consulting
N.A.I.C.S.: 541990
Shane Thrailkill *(Chm & CEO)*
Brandy Wicks *(VP-Strategy)*
Mark O'Donnell *(Chief Growth Officer)*

TRIUMPH HIGHER EDUCATION GROUP, LLC
150 N Martingale Rd, Ste 300, Schaumburg, IL 60173
Tel.: (224) 698-2150

TRIVE CAPITAL INC.

Web Site:
  https://triumpheducation.com
Year Founded: 2010
E-Learning Providers
N.A.I.C.S.: 611710

Subsidiaries:

Gecko Hospitality Inc (1)
16880 McGregor Blvd Ste 102, Fort Myers, FL 33908
Tel.: (239) 690-7006
Web Site: http://www.geckohospitality.com
Sales Range: $1-9.9 Million
Emp.: 2
Hospitality Staffing Services
N.A.I.C.S.: 561320
Robert Krzak *(Founder & Pres)*
Andrea Hudon *(Partner-Franchise)*

TRIVE CAPITAL INC.
2021 McKinney Ave Ste 1200, Dallas, TX 75201
Tel.: (214) 499-9715   DE
Web Site: http://www.trivecapital.com
Year Founded: 2012
Privater Equity Firm
N.A.I.C.S.: 523999
Conner Searcy *(Mng Partner)*
Jonathan Nunnaley *(Chief Compliance Officer & Head-Special Projects)*
Steve Yoost *(Partner & COO)*
Blake Bonner *(Partner)*
Chris Zugaro *(Partner)*
David Stinnett *(Partner)*
Shravan Thadani *(Partner)*
Trevor Johnston *(Gen Counsel)*

Subsidiaries:

Earthlink, LLC. (1)
1439 Peachtree St, Atlanta, GA 30309
Tel.: (404) 815-0770
Web Site: http://www.earthlink.net
Wired Telecommunication Services
N.A.I.C.S.: 517111
Leon Hounshell *(Chief Product Officer)*
Chris Roy *(Exec VP-Bus Dev)*

Subsidiary (Domestic):

Nextera Communications LLC (2)
7115 Forthun Rd Ste 100, Baxter, MN 56425
Tel.: (218) 818-6400
Web Site: http://www.nextera.net
Data Processing, Hosting & Related Services
N.A.I.C.S.: 518210
Greg Arvig *(Pres & CEO)*

One Ring Networks, Inc. (2)
2030 Powers Ferry Rd SE Ste 200, Atlanta, GA 30339
Tel.: (404) 303-9900
Web Site: http://www.oneringnetworks.com
Administrative Management & General Management Consulting Service
N.A.I.C.S.: 541611
John Jenkins *(CEO)*
Kris Maher *(VP-Sls)*
Sotheara Leang *(VP-Ops)*

Subsidiary (Domestic):

Skyriver Communications, Inc. (3)
7310 Miramar Rd Ste 600, San Diego, CA 92126
Tel.: (858) 812-5280
Cable And Other Pay Television Services
N.A.I.C.S.: 517810
Saeed Khorami *(Pres & CEO)*

Subsidiary (Domestic):

QX Networking & Design, Inc. (2)
333 W Vine St Ste 1210, Lexington, KY 40507
Tel.: (859) 255-1928
Web Site: http://www.qx.net
Wireless Telecommunications Carriers
N.A.I.C.S.: 517112
Zachary Murray *(Pres)*

Forward Slope, Inc. (1)

TRIVE CAPITAL INC.

Trive Capital Inc.—(Continued)
3935 Harney St Ste 100, San Diego, CA 92110
Tel.: (619) 299-4400
Web Site: http://www.forwardslope.com
Sales Range: $1-9.9 Million
Emp.: 25
Software Programming Applications
N.A.I.C.S.: 541511
Carlos Persichetti *(CEO)*

Subsidiary (Domestic):

Soar Technology, Inc. (2)
3600 Green Ct Ste 600, Ann Arbor, MI 48105
Tel.: (734) 327-8000
Web Site: http://www.soartech.com
Sales Range: $1-9.9 Million
Emp.: 40
Computer System Design Services
N.A.I.C.S.: 541512
Andrew Dallas *(VP-Federal Sys)*
Katherine Harding *(COO & Exec VP)*
Mike van Lent *(CEO)*

KARMAN Missile & Space Systems Company (1)
2632 Saturn St, Brea, CA 92821
Tel.: (714) 996-8178
Web Site: http://karmanmss.com
Metallic & Composite Flight Hardware & Sub-assemblies Mfr
N.A.I.C.S.: 336415
Tony Koblinski *(CEO)*

Subsidiary (Domestic):

Systima Technologies, Inc. (2)
6500 Harbour Heights Pkwy, Mukilteo, WA 98275
Tel.: (425) 487-4020
Web Site: http://www.systima.com
Computer System Design Services
N.A.I.C.S.: 541512
Peter Hayden *(Mgr-Quality)*
Tom Prenzlow *(Pres)*

NxEdge, Inc. (1)
7500 W Mossy Cup St, Boise, ID 83709
Tel.: (208) 362-7200
Web Site: https://nxedge.com
Electrical Equipment & Component Mfr
N.A.I.C.S.: 335999

Rubicon Bakery LLC (1)
154 S 23rd St, Richmond, CA 94804-2804
Tel.: (510) 779-3010
Web Site: http://www.rubiconbakery.com
Commercial Bakeries
N.A.I.C.S.: 311812
Leslie Crary *(Co-Founder)*
Andrew Stoloff *(Co-Founder)*

Subsidiary (Domestic):

Just Desserts, Inc. (2)
550 85th Ave, Oakland, CA 94621
Tel.: (510) 567-2900
Web Site: http://www.justdesserts.com
Rev.: $14,000,000
Emp.: 30
Dessert & Bakery Products Mfr
N.A.I.C.S.: 311813
Christian Bernal *(Coord-Pur)*
Jonathan McLeod *(Dir-Ops)*
Miguel Vargas *(Mgr-Supply Chain)*
Leighton Mue *(VP-Fin & Controller)*
Terry Watson *(VP-Culinary)*
John Wohlgemuth *(VP-Ops)*
Julie Scully *(Mgr-Sls-North America)*
David Purvis *(Mgr-Bus Dev)*
David Baffoni *(VP-Engrg & Production)*
Dean Gold *(VP-Sls)*
Anthony Zamudio *(Sls Dir)*

SSW Holding Company, Inc. (1)
1100 West Park Rd, Elizabethtown, KY 42701
Tel.: (270) 769-5526
Web Site: http://www.sswholding.net
Holding Company; Miscellaneous Fabricated Wire Products Mfr
N.A.I.C.S.: 551112
Paul Kara *(Chm)*
Mark Gritton *(Pres & CEO)*

Subsidiary (Domestic):

American Appliance Products, Inc. (2)
345 Chemwood Dr, Newport, TN 37821
Tel.: (423) 625-2072
Bar, Rod & Wire Products Mfr
N.A.I.C.S.: 331110

Collis Inc. (2)
2005 S 19th St, Clinton, IA 52732-3288 (100%)
Tel.: (563) 242-1797
Mfr of Fabricated Wire Products
N.A.I.C.S.: 332618

Premier Manufacturing Corporation (2)
867 Premier Way, Henderson, TN 38340
Tel.: (731) 989-3700
Fabricated Steel Wire Products Mfr
N.A.I.C.S.: 332618

Southern Steel & Wire Co. LLC (2)
5101 1/2 Old Greenwood Rd, Fort Smith, AR 72901 (100%)
Tel.: (479) 646-1651
Mfr of Fabricated Wire Products
N.A.I.C.S.: 332618

Straits Steel & Wire Company (2)
902 N Rowe St #1, Ludington, MI 49431-1495 (100%)
Tel.: (231) 843-3416
Sales Range: $10-24.9 Million
Emp.: 75
Mfr of Fabricated Wire Products
N.A.I.C.S.: 332618

Seven Aces Limited (1)
79 Wellington Street West Suite 1630, PO Box 138, Toronto, M5K 1H1, ON, Canada
Tel.: (416) 477-3400
Web Site: http://www.sevenaces.com
Rev.: $59,713,046
Assets: $72,464,155
Liabilities: $80,977,664
Net Worth: ($8,493,509)
Earnings: ($3,341,799)
Fiscal Year-end: 12/31/2018
Investment Services
N.A.I.C.S.: 523999
Manu K. Sekhri *(CEO)*
Chad Williams *(Chm)*
Ryan Bouskill *(CFO)*

Subsidiary (US):

Lucky Bucks LLC (2)
5745 Ninth Ave, Countryside, IL 60525
Tel.: (773) 213-9137
Emp.: 4
Privater Equity Firm
N.A.I.C.S.: 551112
Mark Donahue *(Mgr)*

Holding (Domestic):

AM/PM Property Management, Inc. (3)
16882 Gothard St Ste E, Huntington Beach, CA 92647-5472
Tel.: (714) 963-4500
Web Site: http://www.ampmproperties.com
Digital Gaming Terminal Operator
N.A.I.C.S.: 713120
Kenny Y. Bae *(Pres)*

American Amusements LLC (3)
120 Northwood Dr, Atlanta, GA 30342
Tel.: (678) 949-9782
Sales Range: Less than $1 Million
Emp.: 2
Digital Gaming Terminal Operator
N.A.I.C.S.: 713120
Murad Manjiyani *(Admin Sec)*

Ten Entertainment Group plc (1)
Aragon House University Way Cranfield Technology Park, Cranfield, Bedford, MK43 0EQ, United Kingdom
Tel.: (44) 2034410700
Web Site: http://www.tegplc.co.uk
Rev.: $91,674,612
Assets: $352,111,105
Liabilities: $305,863,088
Net Worth: $46,248,016
Earnings: $5,437,669
Emp.: 1,410
Fiscal Year-end: 12/26/2021
Ten Pin Bowling Center Operator
N.A.I.C.S.: 713950
Antony Smith *(CFO)*
Graham Blackwell *(CEO)*

Trive Capital Management LLC (1)
2021 McKinney Ave Ste 1200, Dallas, TX 75201
Tel.: (214) 499-9715
Web Site: http://www.trivecapital.com
Private Equity Investment Management Firm
N.A.I.C.S.: 523940
Desmond Henry *(Mng Dir)*
Dan Lenahan *(Mng Dir)*
Jonathan Nunnaley *(CFO)*
Steve Yoost *(Gen Counsel)*

Vitesse Systems (1)
37955 Central Ct, Newark, CA 94560
Tel.: (510) 790-2300
Web Site: https://vitessesys.com
Thermal & Microwave Solutions Provider
N.A.I.C.S.: 334419
Matthew Alty *(CEO)*

Subsidiary (Domestic):

California Brazing Company (2)
37955 Central Ct, Newark, CA 94560
Tel.: (510) 790-2300
Web Site: http://www.californiabrazing.com
Thermal Management Devices, Heat Exchangers & Industrial Equipment Mfr
N.A.I.C.S.: 332811
Ron Lustig *(Dir-Bus Dev)*

Custom Microwave, Inc. (2)
24 Boston Ct, Longmont, CO 80501
Tel.: (303) 651-0707
Web Site: http://www.custommicrowave.com
Rev.: $3,333,333
Emp.: 30
Radio & Television Broadcasting & Wireless Communications Equipment Mfr
N.A.I.C.S.: 334220
Clancy Lee-Yow *(Pres)*
Bryce Fox *(Engr-Mechanical Design Test)*

TRIVEST PARTNERS, LP
550 S Dixie Hwy Ste 300, Coral Gables, FL 33146
Tel.: (305) 858-2200
Web Site: http://www.trivest.com
Year Founded: 1981
Privater Equity Firm
N.A.I.C.S.: 523999
David Gershman *(Partner & Gen Counsel)*
Troy D. Templeton *(Mng Partner)*
Forest T. Wester *(Mng Partner-Mid-Market)*
Russ Wilson *(Mng Partner-Discovery)*
Todd V. Jerles *(Partner-Ops)*
Brian Connell *(Partner-Mid-Market)*
Amir Mirheydar *(Partner-TGIF)*
Steve Reynolds *(Partner-Mid-Market)*
Jacob Roche *(Principal-Mid- Market)*
Dan Rogan *(CFO)*
Chris Berton *(VP-Bus Dev)*
Tony Hill *(Principal-Bus Dev)*
Mario Masrieh *(Principal)*
Hans Grunwaldt *(VP-Portfolio Support Grp)*
Ryan Parker *(CMO)*
Robert Crapsey *(Dir-Bus Dev-Gulf Coast)*
Lori Cunningham *(Dir-Bus Dev-Midwest)*
Jamie Elias *(Mng Partner-TGIF)*
Greg Irons *(VP-Mid-Market)*
Patrick Komendant *(VP-Mid-Market)*
Yan Levinski *(VP-Mid-Market)*
Spencer Ledwith *(VP-Mid-Market)*
Mac Lothrop *(Dir-Bus Dev-Northeast)*
Jamie Lukaszewski *(Dir-Fin-PSG)*
Tarek Mohamed *(VP-Mid-Market)*
Stephanie Mooney *(Dir-Bus Dev-Canada/PNW)*
Yonatan Naymark *(VP)*
Herby Raymond *(VP-Discovery)*
Jared Roberts *(Dir-Bus Dev-West)*
Alissa Walker *(VP-Mid-Market)*
Reid Terry *(Dir-Talent-PSG)*
Justin Spears *(Dir-Bus Dev-Southeast)*
Neel Sheth *(Asst Gen Counsel)*

Jonathan Schonfeld *(VP-TGIF)*
Allison Gracer *(Dir-Environmental, Social, and Governance)*
Jorge Gross Jr. *(Mng Partner-Control Funds)*
Jamie Elias *(Mng Partner/Mng Partner-TGIF)*

Subsidiaries:

ABC/Amega Inc. (1)
500 Seneca St Ste 400, Buffalo, NY 14204-1963
Tel.: (716) 885-4444
Web Site: https://www.abc-amega.com
Sales Range: $10-24.9 Million
Emp.: 110
Provider of Adjustment & Collection Services
N.A.I.C.S.: 561440
David I. Herer *(CEO)*
Paul F. Catalano *(Pres & COO)*
Robert Gagliardi *(Dir-Mktg & Member Svcs Grp)*
Paul Grolemund *(VP-Credit Svcs)*
Rosanne Battaglia *(Asst Dir-Member Grp Svcs)*
Robert M. States *(CFO & Exec VP)*
Michael Meyers *(Dir-Sys & Member Svcs)*
Michele Gerst *(VP-Outsourcing-Global)*
Domenic DiLoreto *(Sr VP-Bus Dev)*
Tracey Wild *(VP-Legal Collections)*
Virginia Sheflin *(Mgr-First Party)*
Pam Melling *(Chm)*
Dalene Lawson *(Vice Chm)*
Debbie Heinrich *(Treas)*

ASA Safety Supply (1)
300 Petty Rd, Lawrenceville, GA 30043
Tel.: (770) 496-1033
Web Site: https://www.asasafetysupply.com
Rev.: $2,100,000
Emp.: 12
Industrial Machinery & Equipment Merchant Whslr
N.A.I.C.S.: 423830
Burrell Patch *(Pres)*
Ken Calhoun *(Mgr-Sls)*

Dal, Inc. (1)
300 E Madison Ave, Clifton Heights, PA 19018
Tel.: (610) 623-1400
Web Site: http://www.dalcollects.com
Rev.: $1,638,100
Emp.: 25
Collection Agencies
N.A.I.C.S.: 561440
Dominick A. Longhi *(Pres)*

Ellery Homestyles, LLC (1)
295 5th Ave, New York, NY 10016
Tel.: (212) 684-5364
Web Site: http://www.elleryhomestyles.com
Sales Range: $10-24.9 Million
Home Fashion Product Mfr & Distr
N.A.I.C.S.: 423220
Sandy McNeil *(Sr VP-Sls & Mdsg)*

J.E.S. Restaurant Equipment, Inc. (1)
2108 Hwy 72 W, Greenwood, SC 29649
Tel.: (864) 223-8222
Web Site: http://www.jesrestaurantequipment.com
Commercial Equipment Merchant Whslr
N.A.I.C.S.: 423440
Natasha Riggs Smith *(Dir-ECommerce)*
Carl Stanley *(Mgr-Sls)*

Miami Beef Company Inc. (1)
4870 NW 157th St, Hialeah, FL 33014-6486
Tel.: (305) 620-4562
Web Site: http://www.miamibeef.com
Fresh & Frozen Meat Products Distr
N.A.I.C.S.: 424470
Robert Young *(CEO)*

Subsidiary (Domestic):

Devault Packing Company, Inc. (2)
1 Devault Ln, Devault, PA 19432
Tel.: (610) 644-2536
Web Site: http://www.devaultfoods.com
Sales Range: $75-99.9 Million
Emp.: 120
Meat Processing Services
N.A.I.C.S.: 311612
Carl L. Sorzano *(CFO)*

COMPANIES

Hofmann Sausage Co., Inc. (2)
6196 Eastern Ave, Syracuse, NY 13211
Tel.: (315) 437-7257
Web Site: http://www.hofmannsausage.com
Rev.: $6,666,666
Emp.: 30
Animal, except Poultry, Slaughtering
N.A.I.C.S.: 311611
Janice Rappazzo (Office Mgr)

Onepath Systems, LLC (1)
2053 Franklin Way, Marietta, GA 30067
Tel.: (678) 355-0555
Web Site: http://www.onepathsystems.com
Information Technology Consulting Services
N.A.I.C.S.: 541512
Richard Collins (VP-Engrg)
Mike Cotrone (CTO)
Bill Demarest (Exec VP)
Tommy Mullins (VP-Sls)
Chris Lewis (VP-Building Tech)
Ben Balsley (CEO)
Michelle Dunford (VP-HR)
Steven Gilbert (Sr VP-Field Svcs)
Patrick Kinsella (VP-IT & Transformation)
Brian Kirsch (VP-Sls)
Eddie Lanham (Exec VP-Solutions Design)
Greg Sweeney (VP-Sls)
Sean Vojtasko (Exec VP-Advanced Tech & Managed Svcs)
Bob Von Sprecken (Sr VP-Residential Security & Home Automation Svcs)

Quatrro Business Support Services, Inc. (1)
1850 Pkwy Pl Ste 1100, Marietta, GA 30067
Tel.: (866) 622-7011
Web Site: https://www.quatrrobss.com
Emp.: 1,300
Outsourcing & Offshoring Consulting Services
N.A.I.C.S.: 541690
C. M. Sharma (Chm & CEO)

Subsidiary (Domestic):

USWired Incorporated (2)
2107 N 1st St Ste 250, San Jose, CA 95131
Tel.: (408) 432-1144
Web Site: http://www.uswired.com
Sales Range: $1-9.9 Million
Emp.: 36
Information Technology Support Services
N.A.I.C.S.: 541512
Aaron Arutunian (Principal)
Casey Shem (Engr-Sys)
Arnulfo Gonzalez (Engr-IT Support Sys)

Thermal Concepts, LLC (1)
2201 College Ave, Davie, FL 33317
Tel.: (954) 472-4465
Web Site: https://thermalconcepts.com
Heating, Ventilation & Air-Conditioning Services
N.A.I.C.S.: 238220
Larry Maurer (Founder & CEO)

Subsidiary (Domestic):

Irvine Mechanical, Inc. (2)
1500 N Orange Blossom Trl, Orlando, FL 32804
Tel.: (407) 839-3630
Sales Range: $1-9.9 Million
Emp.: 26
Plumbing, Heating & Air-Conditioning Contractors
N.A.I.C.S.: 238220
Robert Irvine (Pres)

Unosquare LLC (1)
1800 Blankenship Rd Ste 200, West Linn, OR 97068
Tel.: (503) 722-3480
Web Site: http://www.unosquare.com
Engineeering Services
N.A.I.C.S.: 541330
Giancarlo Di Vece (CEO)

Subsidiary (Domestic):

Airship, LLC (2)
101 12th St S Ste 101, Birmingham, AL 35233
Tel.: (205) 530-5441
Web Site: http://www.teamairship.com
Sales Range: $1-9.9 Million
Emp.: 50
Software Development Services

N.A.I.C.S.: 541511
Trent Kocurek (Co-Founder & CEO)
Adam Aldrich (Co-Founder & Pres)
Luke Richardson (VP)

Catalystux Holdings, Inc. (2)
1700 S El Camino Real Ste 404, San Mateo, CA 94402
Web Site: http://www.catalystux.com
Sales Range: $1-9.9 Million
Emp.: 50
Computer Software Analysis & Design Services
N.A.I.C.S.: 541511
Paul Giurata (CEO)
Kevin Growney (Partner & VP-User Experience)
Zach Brown (Partner & VP-Tech Svcs)

TRIWAYS LOGISTICS USA INC.
11938 S La Cienega Blvd, Hawthorne, CA 90250
Tel.: (310) 643-8888
Web Site: http://www.triways.com
Sales Range: $10-24.9 Million
Emp.: 8
Freight Forwarding
N.A.I.C.S.: 488510
Bobby Teoh (Pres)
Raul Blanco (Controller)
Kevin Ngai (Export Mgr)
Peter Lai (Gen Mgr)
Peter Ferrari (Mng Dir)
Greg McKay (Mng Dir)
Felix Poon (Mng Dir)

TRM EQUITY LLC
24 Frank Lloyd Wright Dr Ste H322, Ann Arbor, MI 48105
Tel.: (248) 890-5225
Web Site: https://www.trmequity.com
Year Founded: 2019
Emp.: 100
Privater Equity Firm
N.A.I.C.S.: 522320
Jeffrey Stone (Mng Dir)

Subsidiaries:

Innovative Hearth Products LLC (1)
1769 Lawrence St E, Russellville, AL 35654
Tel.: (615) 925-3417
Web Site: http://www.ihp.us.com
Mfr of Wood-Burning & Gas-Fired Fireplaces, Fireplace Inserts, Stoves & Chimney Systems
N.A.I.C.S.: 327390

Plant (Domestic):

Innovative Hearth Products (2)
1502 14th St NW, Auburn, WA 98001
Tel.: (253) 735-1100
Wood & Pellet-Fueled Stoves Mfr
N.A.I.C.S.: 333414
Mark Klein (Pres & CEO)

WDC Acquisition LLC (1)
1746 Commerce Rd, Creston, IA 50801
Tel.: (641) 782-8521
Web Site: https://www.wellmandynamics.com
Emp.: 350
Magnesium & Aluminum Castings Mfr
N.A.I.C.S.: 331523

TRM INC.
2599 Charlotte Hwy, Mooresville, NC 28117-9463
Tel.: (704) 660-7660
Web Site: http://www.transolid.com
Year Founded: 1993
Sales Range: $25-49.9 Million
Emp.: 500
Hardwood Veneer & Plywood Furniture
N.A.I.C.S.: 321211
Robbie Wiltsher (VP)

Subsidiaries:

Transolid, Inc. (1)
125 Linwood Veneer Rd, Linwood, NC 27299-9521
Tel.: (704) 660-7660
Web Site: http://www.transolid.com
Rev.: $1,300,000
Emp.: 35
Partitions & Fixtures for Kitchens & Bathroom Sinks
N.A.I.C.S.: 337126

TROFHOLZ TECHNOLOGIES, INC.
2207 Plaza Dr Ste 100, Rocklin, CA 95765
Tel.: (916) 577-1903
Web Site: http://www.tti-tech.com
Sales Range: $10-24.9 Million
Emp.: 125
Systems Integration & Technology Solutions
N.A.I.C.S.: 541512
Yvonne Glenn (Founder, Owner & CEO)
David Raymond (VP-Bus Dev)
Brenna Pedone (VP-Fin & Admin)

TROJAN ELECTRONIC SUPPLY CO., INC.
15 Middleburgh St, Troy, NY 12180
Tel.: (518) 274-4481
Web Site: http://www.trojanelectronics.com
Sales Range: $1-9.9 Million
Emp.: 5
Electronics Distr
N.A.I.C.S.: 423620
Herb Page (Owner & Pres)

TROLEX CORP.
55 57 Bushes Ln, Elmwood Park, NJ 07407
Tel.: (201) 794-1359
Web Site: https://www.zonefirst.com
Year Founded: 1964
Sales Range: $1-9.9 Million
Emp.: 40
Air-Conditioning & Warm Air Heating Equipment & Commercial & Industrial Refrigeration Equipment Mfr
N.A.I.C.S.: 333415
Richard Foster (Pres)

Subsidiaries:

Zonex Inc (1)
5622 Engineer Dr, Huntington Beach, CA 92649
Tel.: (714) 898-9963
Web Site: http://www.zonexsystems.com
Sales Range: $1-9.9 Million
Emp.: 50
Relay & Industrial Control Mfr
N.A.I.C.S.: 335314
Jeff Osheroff (Pres)
Joseph Siegmund (VP)
Cheryl Geller (Office Mgr)

TROLLANDTOAD.COM
250 American Greeting Card Rd, Corbin, KY 40701
Tel.: (859) 280-3235
Web Site: http://www.trollandtoad.com
Year Founded: 1994
Sales Range: $10-24.9 Million
Emp.: 175
Retailer of Out-of-Print, Collectibles & Single Unit & Current Games & Accessories
N.A.I.C.S.: 459120
Jathan Shupe (Dir-IT)
Jon Huston (Pres)
Lana Huston (Owner)
Shawn Gambel (CFO)

TROMA ENTERTAINMENT INC.
3640 11th St, Long Island City, NY 11106
Tel.: (718) 391-0110

TRONICOM CORP.

Web Site: http://www.troma.com
Rev.: $9,000,000
Emp.: 50
Producer & Distr of Motion Pictures
N.A.I.C.S.: 512110
Lisa Borhoum (Dir-Intl Sls)

TRONE BRAND ENERGY, INC.
1823 Eastchester Dr Ste A, High Point, NC 27265-9402
Tel.: (336) 886-1622
Web Site: http://www.tronebrandenergy.com
Year Founded: 1982
Advertising Agencies
N.A.I.C.S.: 541810
Rick Morgan (CFO)
Martin Buchanan (Exec Dir-Creative)
Douglas Barton (Pres)
Eric Tessau (VP-Digital Ops)
Gary Towning (Exec VP-Digital Strategy & Svcs)
Robin Yontz (VP & Creative Dir)
Nicole Donoghue (VP-Acct Mgmt & Media)
Jeremy Glover (Dir-Digital Tech)
Angi Wesson (Dir-Social Media & Public Rels)

TRONEX INTERNATIONAL INC.
300 International Dr, Mount Olive, NJ 07828
Tel.: (973) 335-2888
Web Site: http://www.tronexcompany.com
Year Founded: 1989
Sales Range: $10-24.9 Million
Emp.: 50
Disposable Personal Protective Equipment
N.A.I.C.S.: 339113
Donald Chu (Pres & CEO)

TRONICOM CORP.
6437 Manchester Ave, Saint Louis, MO 63139
Tel.: (314) 645-6200
Year Founded: 1983
Sales Range: $10-24.9 Million
Emp.: 200
Communications Specialization
N.A.I.C.S.: 238210
Kurt Canova (Pres)

Subsidiaries:

Tech Electronics, Inc. (1)
6437 Manchester Ave, Saint Louis, MO 63139
Tel.: (314) 645-6200
Web Site: http://www.techelectronics.com
Emp.: 300
Safety & Communication Systems Sales & Installation
N.A.I.C.S.: 238210
Kurt S. Canova (Pres)
James Canova (Founder & Chm)
Craig Lubbers (CFO)
John Maniaci (Exec VP)
Laura Wasson (Dir-Healthcare)
Chris Wilhelm (Exec Dir-Construction)
Michael Scott (Dir-IT-Corp)
Emily Patterson (VP-HR)
Alex Wasson (Dir-Fire & Security Technologies)
Steven Lee (Acct Mgr-Healthcare Strategic-Kansas City)

Subsidiary (Domestic):

Tech Electronics of Colorado, LLC (2)
1351 W 121st Ave, Denver, CO 80234
Tel.: (303) 438-8088
Sales Range: $1-9.9 Million
Emp.: 28
Fire Alarm Systems Mfr
N.A.I.C.S.: 334290
Rich Salacinski (Project Mgr)

TRONICOM CORP.

Tronicom Corp.—(Continued)

Tech Electronics of Columbia, Inc. (2)
1406 Rangeline St, Columbia, MO 65201
Tel.: (573) 875-1516
Web Site: http://www.techelectronics.com
Sales Range: $1-9.9 Million
Emp.: 15
Safety & Communication Systems Sales & Installation
N.A.I.C.S.: 238210
John Pile (Mng Dir)

Tech Electronics of Illinois, LLC (2)
417 Olympia Dr, Bloomington, IL 61704
Tel.: (309) 874-2700
Web Site: http://www.techelectronics.com
Safety & Communication Systems Sales & Installation
N.A.I.C.S.: 238210
Paul Maier (Mng Dir)

Tech Electronics of Indiana, LLC (2)
2350 Executive Dr, Indianapolis, IN 46241
Tel.: (317) 241-8324
Web Site: http://www.techelectronics.com
Safety & Communication Systems Sales & Installation
N.A.I.C.S.: 238210

TROON ENTERPRISES INC.
16441 N 90th St Ste 100, Scottsdale, AZ 85260
Tel.: (480) 626-4300   AZ
Web Site: http://www.trooninc.com
Year Founded: 2001
Sales Range: $25-49.9 Million
Emp.: 11
Commercial Builder
N.A.I.C.S.: 236220
Ray W. Garcia (Pres & CEO)

TROON GOLF L.L.C.
15044 N Scottsdale Rd Ste 300, Scottsdale, AZ 85254
Tel.: (480) 606-1000   AZ
Web Site: http://www.troongolf.com
Year Founded: 1990
Golf Course Management Services
N.A.I.C.S.: 541611
Dana R. Garmany (Chm & CEO)
Bruce Glasco (COO & Mng Dir-Intl Div)
Cindy Anderson (VP-Clubhouse Design & Dev)
Scott Van Newkirk (Sr VP-Bus Dev-Global)
Jim Bellington (Sr VP-Troon Ops & Dev)
Darrell Morgan (VP-Ops)
Timothy S. Schantz (Pres)
Jay McGrath (Chief Admin Officer & Exec VP)
Ron Despain (VP-Golf Course Dev)
Mike Ryan (Sr VP-Troon Golf Ops)
Carl Bielstein (VP-Ops)
Ruth Engle (CFO & Exec VP)
Jim McLaughlin (Sr VP-Troon Prive Ops)
Kris Strauss (VP-Sls & Mktg)
Rick Gepilano (VP-Tech)
Jim Richerson (Sr VP-Bus Dev)
Greg Leisher (VP-Bus Dev)
Robin Evans (VP-Construction & Agronomy-Middle East)
John Bartilomo (VP-Food & Beverage Ops)
Pete Wong (VP-HR)
Justin Herr (VP-Membership Sls)
Bill O'Brien (VP-Ops)
D. J. Flanders (VP-Ops)
Phillip Martin (VP-Ops)
Ricardo Catarino (VP-Ops)
Guy Sugden (VP-Ops, Sls & Mktg)
Rob Manning (VP-Program Office-Global)
Brian Hampson (VP-Science & Agronomy)
Sarah Lang (VP-Taxation-Global)

Subsidiaries:

Cliff Drysdale Management, LLC (1)
625 Mission Vly Rd, New Braunfels, TX 78132
Tel.: (830) 625-5911
Web Site: http://www.cliffdrysdale.com
Fitness & Recreational Sports Centers
N.A.I.C.S.: 713940
Cliff Drysdale (Founder & Pres)
Donald Henderson (Pres & CEO)
Jamie Graham (CFO)
Kimberly Arena (VP-Sls & Mktg)
Scott Colebourne (VP-Ops)
Scott McCulloch (VP-Ops)

Honours Golf Company, LLC (1)
1960 Stonegate Dr, Birmingham, AL 35242
Tel.: (205) 298-0001
Web Site: http://www.honoursgolf.com
Emp.: 60
Golf Course Owner & Operator
N.A.I.C.S.: 713910
Robert B. Barrett (CEO)
Gary D. Spivey (CFO & VP)
Phil Oakes (VP-HR)
Matt Hurley (VP-Ops)
Jim DeReuil (VP-Agronomy)
Kelly Olshove Newman (Dir-Mktg)
Don Shirey (VP-Bus Dev)
Mike Ryan (VP-Ops)
Evan Godfrey (Reg Mgr-Ops)

Indigo Golf Partners, LLC (1)
8300 Boone Blvd Ste 350, Vienna, VA 22182
Tel.: (703) 761-1444
Web Site: http://www.billycaspergolf.com
Sales Range: $350-399.9 Million
Emp.: 3,000
Golf Course
N.A.I.C.S.: 713910
Peter M. Hill (Co-Founder, Chm & CEO)
Robert C. Morris (Co-Founder)
R. Joseph Goodrich (Exec VP)
Joseph D. Livingood (Sr VP-Ops)
Bill Rehanek (Sr VP-Ops)
Bryan Bielecki (VP-Agronomy)
Mike Cutler (VP-Bus Dev)
Douglas White (VP-Bus Dev)
Marnie Boyer (Chief Acctg Officer & VP-Fin)
Stephen Nicholson (Dir-Acctg)
Sandra Colareta (Dir-Contracts & Risk Mgmt)
Nick Bednar (Dir-Ops-Central)
Steve Simoneaux (Dir-Sls-Natl)
Tom Reilly (Dir-Talent Mgmt)
Tony Cianci (Sr VP-Ops)
Joel Gohlmann (Sr VP-Ops)
Katie Barongan (VP-HR)
Kyle Ragsdale (VP-Ops)
Danny Ackerman (Gen Mgr-Golf Ops)

Unit (Domestic):

Buffalo Groupe LLC (2)
12700 Sunrise Vly Dr Ste 300, Reston, VA 20197
Tel.: (703) 761-1444
Web Site:
http://www.buffalocommunications.com
Product Publicity & Brand Recognition Marketing Services
N.A.I.C.S.: 541613
Kyle Ragsdale (CEO)

Subsidiary (Domestic):

Rawle Murdy Associates, Inc. (3)
960 Morsan Dr 300, Charleston, SC 29403
Tel.: (843) 577-7327
Web Site: http://www.rawlemurdy.com
Sales Range: $450-499.9 Million
Public Relations Agency
N.A.I.C.S.: 541820
Bruce D. Murdy (Mng Dir)

TROOPSDIRECT
2400 Camino Ramon Ste 105, San Ramon, CA 94583
Tel.: (877) 978-7667   CA
Web Site: http://www.troopsdirect.org
Year Founded: 2010
Sales Range: $1-9.9 Million
Deployed Military Support Services
N.A.I.C.S.: 812990
Juliet Calvin (Sec)
Aaron Negherbon (Pres & Exec Dir)
Gary Negherbon (Treas)

TROPAR MFG. CO., INC.
5 Vreeland Rd, Florham Park, NJ 07932-1505
Tel.: (973) 822-2400   NJ
Web Site: http://www.airflyte.com
Year Founded: 1959
Sales Range: $50-74.9 Million
Emp.: 90
Trophies, Plaques & Gift Awards & Clocks Mfr
N.A.I.C.S.: 339910
Steve Wannemacher (Mgr-Pur)

Subsidiaries:

Tropar Mfg. Co., Inc. (1)
2313 N Preston St, Ennis, TX 75119-7717   (100%)
Tel.: (972) 875-5831
Web Site: http://www.airflyte.com
Sales Range: $10-24.9 Million
Emp.: 17
Mfr of Awards
N.A.I.C.S.: 339910

Tropar Mfg. Co., Inc. (1)
839 N Central Ave, Wood Dale, IL 60191-1219
Tel.: (708) 343-3200
Web Site: http://www.tropar.com
Mfr of Awards & Promotional Products
N.A.I.C.S.: 332322

TROPEX PLANT SALES LEASING & MAINTENANCE, INC.
3220 Whitfield Ave, Sarasota, FL 34243
Tel.: (941) 351-2864
Web Site: http://www.tropex.com
Year Founded: 1981
Sales Range: $1-9.9 Million
Emp.: 45
Landscaping Services
N.A.I.C.S.: 561730
Charlie Lenger (Owner)

TROPHY HOLDINGS INC.
487 Edward H Ross Dr, Elmwood Park, NJ 07407-3118
Tel.: (201) 475-8888   DE
Year Founded: 1995
Sales Range: $75-99.9 Million
Emp.: 275
Holding Company
N.A.I.C.S.: 423940
David Hoffman (Chm)
George Ercolino (CFO)
Donald Greene (Controller)
Vincent Cariello (Pres)
Tom Ferrigno (Dir-IS)

Subsidiaries:

Freeman Products (1)
487 Edward H Ross Dr, Elmwood Park, NJ 07407-3118
Tel.: (201) 475-8888
Web Site:
http://freemanproductsworldwide.com
Sales Range: $10-24.9 Million
Emp.: 35
Trophy Parts; Zinc Diecasting & Plastic Molding; Gifts & Engravers Supplies
N.A.I.C.S.: 423940

TROPHY NISSAN, INC.
5031 N Galloway Ave, Mesquite, TX 75150-1557
Tel.: (972) 613-2200
Web Site:
http://www.trophynissan.com
Year Founded: 1998
Sales Range: $50-74.9 Million
Emp.: 230
New Car Whslr
N.A.I.C.S.: 441110
Jennifer Carroll (Gen Mgr)

TROPHY NUT CO.
320 N 2nd St, Tipp City, OH 45371
Tel.: (937) 667-8478

U.S. PRIVATE

Web Site: http://www.trophynut.com
Sales Range: $25-49.9 Million
Emp.: 100
Processor of Dried, Dehydrated, Salted & Roasted Nuts
N.A.I.C.S.: 311911
Robert Bollinger (Pres)
David Henning (Controller)
Bob Wilke (VP-Sls)

TROPIC FISH & VEGETABLE CENTER INC.
2312 Kamehameha Hwy Ste E, Honolulu, HI 96819
Tel.: (808) 591-2936   HI
Web Site:
http://www.tropicfishhawaii.com
Year Founded: 1951
Sales Range: $25-49.9 Million
Emp.: 80
Fish & Seafoods
N.A.I.C.S.: 424460
Shawn Tanoue (Pres & COO)

Subsidiaries:

Konafish Company Inc. (1)
73 4776 Kanalani St Ste 8, Kailua Kona, HI 96740-2625
Tel.: (808) 326-7708
Web Site: http://www.hilofish.com
Sales Range: $10-24.9 Million
Emp.: 15
Fish & Seafoods
N.A.I.C.S.: 424460

TROPIC SUPPLY INC.
1001 Sawgrass Corporate Pkwy, Sunrise, FL 33323
Tel.: (954) 835-6010
Web Site:
http://www.tropicsupply.com
Year Founded: 1973
Sales Range: $10-24.9 Million
Emp.: 56
Air Conditioning & Ventilation & Duct Work Contractor
N.A.I.C.S.: 423730
Charles F. Del Vecchio (Pres)

TROPICAL BLOSSOM HONEY CO, INC.
106 N Ridgewood Ave, Edgewater, FL 32132
Tel.: (386) 428-9027   FL
Web Site:
http://www.tropicbeehoney.com
Year Founded: 1940
Sales Range: $10-24.9 Million
Emp.: 15
Honey Mfr
N.A.I.C.S.: 311999
John Douglas McGinnis (Pres)

TROPICAL CHEESE INDUSTRIES, INC.
PO Box 1357, Perth Amboy, NJ 08862-1357
Tel.: (732) 442-4898
Web Site:
http://www.tropicalcheese.com
Year Founded: 1981
Sales Range: $25-49.9 Million
Emp.: 150
Cheese Mfr
N.A.I.C.S.: 311513
Clint Carter (VP)
Roberto Encarnacion (Dir-IT)
Maria Luisa Jimenez (Mgr-HR)
Alex Quiles (Mgr-Production)
Leonardo Rojas (Mgr-Quality Assurance & Quality Control)
Pedro Mendez (Mgr-IT)

TROPICAL NUT & FRUIT CO
1100 Continental Blvd, Charlotte, NC 28273
Tel.: (704) 588-0400

Web Site:
http://www.tropicalfoods.com
Year Founded: 1977
Sales Range: $25-49.9 Million
Emp.: 130
Specialty Food Items
N.A.I.C.S.: 424490
John Bauer *(Pres)*

TROUT UNLIMITED INC.
1700 N Moore St Ste 2005, Arlington, VA 22209-2793
Web Site: https://www.tu.org
Year Founded: 1959
Water Resource Management Services
N.A.I.C.S.: 813312

TROUT-BLUE CHELAN, INC.
100 Highway 150, Chelan, WA 98816
Tel.: (509) 682-2591   WA
Web Site: http://www.chelanfruit.com
Sales Range: $150-199.9 Million
Emp.: 800
Packer & Shipper of Export Apples
N.A.I.C.S.: 115114
Phyllis Gleasman *(Dir-Safety)*

TROUTLODGE, INC.
12000 McCutcheon Rd, Bonney Lake, WA 98391
Tel.: (253) 863-0446   WA
Web Site: http://www.troutlodge.com
Year Founded: 1945
Finfish Farming & Fish Hatchery Operator
N.A.I.C.S.: 112511
Keith Drynan *(CEO)*

TROUTMAN PEPPER HAMILTON SANDERS LLP
600 Peachtree St Ste 3000, Atlanta, GA 30308
Tel.: (800) 255-8752
Web Site:
https://troutmanemerge.com
Emp.: 100
Officess of Layers
N.A.I.C.S.: 541110

TROUTMAN SANDERS LLP
600 Peachtree St NE Ste 5200, Atlanta, GA 30308
Tel.: (404) 885-3000
Web Site:
http://www.troutmansanders.com
Year Founded: 1897
Sales Range: $350-399.9 Million
Emp.: 620
Law firm
N.A.I.C.S.: 541110
Kevin Buchan *(Dir-Tech Svcs)*
Maureen Theresa Callahan *(Partner)*
Richard Gerakitis *(Partner)*
Larry A. Cerutti *(Partner)*
Ashley Z. Hager *(Partner)*
Andrea L. Rimer *(Partner)*
Dewitt R. Rogers *(Partner)*
Pete Robinson *(Partner)*
Thomas E. Reilly *(Partner)*
Scott A. Farrow *(Partner)*
William M. Droze *(Partner)*
Douglas D. Salyers *(Partner)*
Jaime L. Theriot *(Partner & Gen Counsel-Atlanta)*
Matthew F. Roberts *(Partner)*
John Hamilton *(Partner)*
Adam C. Kobos *(Partner)*
M. Chadwick Stackhouse *(Partner)*
Stephen C. Hall *(Partner)*
J. Michael Childers *(Partner)*
Justin Boose *(Partner)*
Keith J. Barnett *(Partner)*
Lara L. Skidmore *(Partner)*
Neil S. Kessler *(Partner)*
Randy E. Brogdon *(Partner)*
Stephen C. Piepgrass *(Partner)*
Stephen D. Rosenthal *(Partner)*
Steven J. Hewitson *(Partner)*
David M. Chaiken *(Partner)*
Amy Williams *(Partner-Fin Svcs Litigation-Charlotte)*
Maura Connell Brandt *(CMO)*
Sallie A. Daniel *(Chief Dev & Diversity Officer)*
Mindy Schwartz *(Chief HR Officer)*
Robert D. Seabolt *(COO)*
Lee Tremlett Williams *(CFO)*
David Meadows *(Partner-Bus Litigation)*
Charles Sensiba *(Partner-Energy Practice-Washington)*
Roman Hernandez *(Partner-Labor & Employment Practice-Portland)*
Matt Bowsher *(Partner-Multifamily Housing Fin Practice)*
Lindsey Crawford *(Partner-Multifamily Housing Fin Practice)*
Brooks Smith *(Mng Partner-Richmond)*
Robb Willis *(Chm-Troutman Sanders Strategies)*
Kalama Lui-Kwan *(Partner-Fin Svcs Litigation Practice-San Francisco)*
Michael D. Hobbs Jr. *(Partner)*
W. Brinkley Dickerson Jr. *(Partner)*
Roger S. Reigner Jr. *(Partner)*
Christopher G. Browning Jr. *(Partner)*
James B. Manley Jr. *(Partner-Litigation)*

TROUTWINE AUTO SALES, INC.
9 N Main St, Arcanum, OH 45304
Tel.: (937) 692-8373
Web Site:
http://www.troutwineautosales.com
Sales Range: $10-24.9 Million
Emp.: 30
Car Whslr
N.A.I.C.S.: 441110
David Reed *(Mgr-Svc)*
Justin Troutwine *(Sec & Treas)*
F. Scott Troutwine *(VP)*

TROWBRIDGE ENTERPRISES
2606 Chanticleer Ave, Santa Cruz, CA 95065
Tel.: (831) 476-3815
Web Site: http://www.gopalace.com
Year Founded: 1949
Rev.: $11,784,032
Emp.: 45
Stationery & Office Supplies Distr & Retailer
N.A.I.C.S.: 424120
Roy Trowbridge *(Co-Owner)*
Gary Trowbridge *(Co-Owner)*
Peggy Paylow *(Mgr-Comml Sls & Mktg)*
Frank H. Trowbridge III *(Co-Owner)*

TROY CORPORATION
8 Vreeland Rd, Florham Park, NJ 07932-0955
Tel.: (973) 443-4200
Web Site: http://www.troycorp.com
Year Founded: 1950
Sales Range: $75-99.9 Million
Emp.: 100
Mfr of Industrial Fungicides, Bactericides, Specialty Chemicals for Paints, Inks, Adhesives, Caulks, Sealants, Textiles & Metal Working Fluids
N.A.I.C.S.: 325199
Donald A. Shaw *(Sr VP-AMEAI & Regulatory Affairs)*
Robert Okin *(VP & Controller)*
Jan Scott Beck *(Gen Counsel & VP)*
W. Brian Smith *(COO & Exec VP)*
Ulf Becker *(Mng Dir-Europe)*
Christopher E. Smith *(VP-Mfg & Engrg)*

Subsidiaries:

TROY CHEMICAL COMPANY Sp. z o.o.   (1)
ul Krolowej Marysienki 9/4, 02-954, Warsaw, Poland
Tel.: (48) 226517066
Sales Range: $10-24.9 Million
Emp.: 3
Industrial Additive Distr
N.A.I.C.S.: 424690
Jaroslaw Kania *(Reg Mgr-Sls)*

TROY FRANCE S.A.R.L.   (1)
ZAC Paris Nord 2 66 rue des Vanesses Bat L2, 93420, Villepinte, France
Tel.: (33) 148 177 610
Sales Range: $10-24.9 Million
Emp.: 2
Industrial Additive Distr
N.A.I.C.S.: 424690
Christophe Laubignat *(Gen Sls Mgr)*

Troy Biosciences, Inc.   (1)
113 S 47th Ave, Phoenix, AZ 85043
Tel.: (602) 233-9047
Web Site: http://www.troybiosciences.com
Pesticide Mfr
N.A.I.C.S.: 325320
Mark Gwillim *(Pres)*

Troy Chemical Company B.V.   (1)
Uiverlaan 12e, PO Box 132, 3145 XN, Maassluis, Netherlands
Tel.: (31) 10 592 7494
Web Site: http://www.troy.com
Sales Range: $10-24.9 Million
Emp.: 15
Industrial Additive Distr
N.A.I.C.S.: 424690
Roland Burgers *(Dir-Fin & Admin-Europe)*

Troy Chemical Company Limited   (1)
2600-160 Elgin Street, Ottawa, K1P 1C3, ON, Canada
Tel.: (905) 451-8346
Web Site: http://www.troycorp.com
Emp.: 6
Chemical Products Mfr
N.A.I.C.S.: 325320
Walter Loveis *(Office Mgr)*

Troy Chemical Corporation   (1)
1 Avenue L, Newark, NJ 07105
Tel.: (973) 589-2500
Web Site: http://www.troycorp.com
Chemical Products Mfr
N.A.I.C.S.: 325320

Troy Chemie GmbH   (1)
Freundallee 9A, 30173, Hannover, Germany
Tel.: (49) 511 8998 830
Web Site: http://www.troycorp.com
Sales Range: $10-24.9 Million
Emp.: 40
Industrial Additive Distr
N.A.I.C.S.: 424690
Katrin Stickdorn *(Mgr-Supply Chain)*

TROY GROUP INC.
940 S Coast Dr Ste 260, Costa Mesa, CA 92626-7719
Tel.: (714) 241-4760   CA
Web Site: http://www.troygroup.com
Year Founded: 1982
Sales Range: $25-49.9 Million
Emp.: 115
Computer Peripheral Equipment; Printer Electronic Internet Business to Business
N.A.I.C.S.: 541512
Patrick J. Dirk *(CEO)*
John Hodgson *(VP & Gen Mgr)*
Baris Vural *(VP-Sls)*
Ryan Rotillio *(CFO)*

Subsidiaries:

TROY Healthcare Solutions   (1)
3 Bryan Dr, Wheeling, WV 26003
Tel.: (304) 232-0899
Web Site: http://www.troygroup.com
Emp.: 120
Computer Peripheral Equipment Whslr
N.A.I.C.S.: 423430
John Hodgson *(VP & Gen Mgr)*

Troy Group, Inc.   (1)
Unit 101 1550 Hartley Ave, Coquitlam, V3K 7A1, BC, Canada   (100%)
Tel.: (604) 517-2300
Integrated Computer Systems
N.A.I.C.S.: 541512

TROY INDUSTRIAL SOLUTIONS LLC
70 Cohoes Rd, Watervliet, NY 12189
Tel.: (518) 272-4920
Web Site:
http://www.troyindustrialsolutions.com
Sales Range: $10-24.9 Million
Emp.: 63
Industrial Supplies
N.A.I.C.S.: 423840
Karen E. Smith *(Chm & Treas)*
David R. Barcomb *(VP)*
Jason Smith *(Pres)*
Michael Moran *(Gen Mgr-Watervliet New York Facility)*

Subsidiaries:

Motors & Drives LLC   (1)
262A Quarry Rd, Milford, CT 06460
Tel.: (203) 877-5828
Web Site: http://www.motorsanddrives.com
Electrical Apparatus & Related Equipment Merchant Whslr
N.A.I.C.S.: 423610
Edward H. Cowern *(Mgr-New England)*

TROY NISSAN INC.
110 Hwy 231 N, Troy, AL 36081
Tel.: (334) 566-7357
Web Site:
http://www.troynissaninc.com
Rev.: $10,000,000
Emp.: 25
New & Used Automobiles
N.A.I.C.S.: 441110
Duane Webb *(Pres)*

TROY TUBE & MANUFACTURING, CO.
50100 E Russell Schmidt Blvd, Chesterfield, MI 48051
Tel.: (586) 949-8700
Web Site: http://www.troytube.com
Sales Range: $10-24.9 Million
Emp.: 120
Pipe Fitting Mfr
N.A.I.C.S.: 332996
John Maniaci *(Pres)*

TROY-ALAN CHEVROLET
217 Grove City Rd, Slippery Rock, PA 16057
Tel.: (724) 794-2240
Web Site:
http://www.troyalancars.com
Rev.: $14,000,000
Emp.: 30
New & Used Automobile Sales
N.A.I.C.S.: 441110
Alan Strezeski *(Pres)*

TROYER FOODS, INC.
17141 State Rd 4, Goshen, IN 46528-6674
Tel.: (574) 533-0302   IN
Web Site: http://www.troyers.com
Year Founded: 1948
Sales Range: $125-149.9 Million
Emp.: 240
Wholesale Fresh & Frozen Poultry; Beef; Pork; Other Food Products
N.A.I.C.S.: 424470
Paris Ball-Miller *(Pres)*

TROYRESEARCH
947 E Johnstown Rd Ste 242, Gahanna, OH 43230
Tel.: (740) 549-9700
Web Site:
http://www.troyresearch.com

TROYRESEARCH   U.S. PRIVATE

TroyResearch—(Continued)

Year Founded: 1997
Sales Range: $1-9.9 Million
Emp.: 7
Market Research Services for Entertainment & Media Companies
N.A.I.C.S.: 541910
Bill Troy (Pres)
James Young (Dir-Sys Tech)

TROZZOLO COMMUNICATIONS GROUP

802 Broadway Ste 300, Kansas City, MO 64105
Tel.: (816) 842-8111
Web Site: http://www.trozzolo.com
Year Founded: 1989
Rev.: $42,000,000
Emp.: 40
Advetising Agency
N.A.I.C.S.: 541810
Angelo R. Trozzolo (Pres)
Pasquale Trozzolo (CEO)
Tina Wheeler (Acct Mgr-Prairie Dog Div)
Becky Blades (Chm)
Jon Ratliff (VP & Acct Grp Dir)
Joe Davidson (Chief Admin Officer)
Shawna Samuel (VP)
Jill Brooks (Mgr-Creative Svcs)
Jeff Madden (Acct Supvr)
Morgan Johnson (Acct Supvr)
Lisa Phillips (Mgr-Pro Practices)
Tara Schroeder (Acct Mgr)
Jenny Stasi (Acct Supvr)
Sarah Davis (Acct Supvr)
Paul Behnen (Exec Creative Dir)
Rachel Lupardus (CFO & COO)

Subsidiaries:

Prairie Dog/TCG   (1)
802 Broadway Ste 300, Kansas City, MO 64105
Tel.: (816) 822-3636
Web Site: http://www.pdog.com
Advertising, Health Care
N.A.I.C.S.: 541810
Phil Smith (Exec Dir-Creative)
Jerry Hobbs (Exec VP)
Laura Lynch (VP & Creative Dir)
Denise Crossen (VP-Acct)
Rachel Rahe (Sr Acct Mgr)
Tina Wheeler (Acct Mgr)
Lisa Smith (Acct Mgr)

TRP RESTAURANT ENTERPRISES, INC.

1514 US Hwy 70 W, Garner, NC 27529
Tel.: (919) 772-9772   NC
Web Site:
http://www.ragazzisitalian.com
Casual Italian Restaurant Operator
N.A.I.C.S.: 722511

TRT HOLDINGS, INC.

4001 Maple Ave, Dallas, TX 75219
Tel.: (214) 283-8500   DE
Web Site:
http://www.omnihotelsandresorts.com
Year Founded: 1950
Sales Range: $800-899.9 Million
Investment Holding Company
N.A.I.C.S.: 551112
James D. Caldwell (CEO)
Amanda Lewis (VP & Sr Counsel)
Jeanette Vloitos (VP & Sr Counsel)
Janett O'Dwyer (VP-Acctg)
Mike Popejoy (Sr VP-Energy)
Michael G. Smith (Gen Counsel & Sr VP-Real Estate)
Michael Frantz (VP-Investments)
Blake Rowling (Pres)

Subsidiaries:

Gold's Gym International, Inc.   (1)
4001 Maple Ave Ste 200, Dallas, TX 75219
Tel.: (214) 574-4653
Web Site: http://www.goldsgym.com
Rev.: $25,989,000
Emp.: 100
Holding Company; Fitness Center Operator & Franchisor
N.A.I.C.S.: 551112
Dave Reiseman (Dir-Comm)
Adam Zeitsiff (CIO)
Craig Sherwood (Sr VP-Franchising)
Brandon Bean (CEO)
Konstantinos Pappous (COO)
Jolynda Ward (Sr VP-HR)

Omni Hotels Management Corporation   (1)
4001 Maple Ave, Dallas, TX 75219
Tel.: (972) 871-5600
Web Site: http://www.omnihotels.com
Sales Range: $400-449.9 Million
Emp.: 18,000
Holding Company; Hotels & Resorts Operator
N.A.I.C.S.: 551112
James D. Caldwell (Pres & CEO)
Joy Rothschild (Chief HR Officer)
Peter Strebel (Pres)
Manuel Deisen (Gen Mgr)
Daniel Surette (VP-Sls)
Matthew Adams (Exec VP-Ops)
Andrew Rubinacci (Sr VP-Revenue Mgmt & Global Distr)
Ken Barnes (CIO)
Kurt Alexander (CFO)

Subsidiary (Domestic):

Omni Barton Creek, Inc.   (2)
8212 Barton Club Dr, Austin, TX 78735
Tel.: (512) 329-4000
Web Site: http://www.bartoncreek.com
Hotel & Resort Operator
N.A.I.C.S.: 721110
James Walsh (VP & Gen Mgr)
Terasa Whitten Rivera (Dir-Conference Svcs)
Kevin Newbolt (Dir-Food & Beverage)
Eddie Brammer (Dir-Revenue)
Libby L. Nations (Dir-Sls & Mktg)
Jeremy Lander (Dir-Grp Sls)
Crystal Ma (Mgr-HR)
Tara Cruz (Dir-Travel Indus Sls)
Whitney Hueber Hodges (Sls Mgr-Catering)
Cory Christian (Dir-Reservations)
Kristen Green (Mktg Mgr)
Carissa Smith (Dir-Sls & Mktg)
Bob Peckenpaugh (Mng Dir)
Zan Miller (Dir-Revenue Mgmt)
Greg Schneider (Pres)
Delfin Ortiz (Mgr-Luxurious Hill Country Property)
Laurean Love (Mgr-Resort Events)
Rodrigo Ibanez (Dir-Rooms)
Michael Hammes (Dir-Food & Beverage)
Sylvia Deer (Dir-Assoc Svcs)
Spencer Cody (Dir-Golf Ops)

Omni Grove Park, LLC   (2)
290 Macon Ave, Asheville, NC 28804-3711
Tel.: (828) 252-2711
Web Site: http://www.groveparkinn.com
Hotel & Resort Operator
N.A.I.C.S.: 721110
Simon Andres (Dir-Golf)

Omni Homestead, Inc.   (2)
7696 Sam Snead Hwy, Hot Springs, VA 24445
Tel.: (540) 839-1766
Web Site: http://www.thehomestead.com
Hotel & Resort Operator
N.A.I.C.S.: 721110
Lynn Swann (Dir-Mktg & Comm)
Kevin Phenegar (Dir-Food & Beverage)
Wayne Kearney (Dir-Resort Sls)
Donald Warlitner (Dir-Restaurants)
Angela Roberts (Dir-Conference Svcs)
Joseph Miller (Mgr-Guest Svcs)
Jeffrey Ford (Dir-Sls)
David Jurcak (Mng Dir)
James Caldwell (Co-CEO)
Michael Deitemeyer (Co-CEO)

Omni La Costa Resort & Spa, LLC   (2)
2100 Costa Del Mar Rd, Carlsbad, CA 92009
Tel.: (760) 438-9111

Web Site: http://www.lacosta.com
Hotel & Resort Operator
N.A.I.C.S.: 721110
John Anderson (Dir-Sls)

Omni Rancho Las Palmas, LLC   (2)
41-000 Bob Hope Dr, Rancho Mirage, CA 92270-4497
Tel.: (760) 568-2727
Web Site: http://www.rancholaspalmas.com
Hotel & Resort Operator
N.A.I.C.S.: 721110
Markie Mullins (Dir-Revenue Mgmt)

TRU COMMUNITY CARE

2594 Trailridge Dr E, Lafayette, CO 80026
Tel.: (303) 449-7740   CO
Web Site: http://www.trucare.org
Year Founded: 1977
Sales Range: $10-24.9 Million
Emp.: 250
Community Care Services
N.A.I.C.S.: 621498
Scott Gresser (CFO & VP)
Beth Davis (VP-Bus Dev)
Pat Mehnert (Interim CEO)
Annette Mainland (VP-Philanthropy)
Bob Thorn (VP-Senior Care)
Denise Hendrickson (VP-Clinical Svcs)
Shirley Huang (Dir-Medical)
Carlene Crall (VP-HR)
Cynthia Werner (Exec Dir-Hospice of Northern Colorado)
Rick Romeo (Chm)

TRU INDEPENDCE LLC

15350 SW Sequoia Pkwy Ste 250, Portland, OR 97224
Tel.: (971) 371-3444
Web Site: http://www.tru-ind.com
Investment Advisory & Wealth Management Services
N.A.I.C.S.: 523999
Craig Stuvland (CEO & Pres)

Subsidiaries:

Pure Portfolios Holdings, LLC   (1)
15350 SW Sequoia Pkwy Ste 250, Portland, OR 97224
Tel.: (877) 261-0015
Web Site: http://www.pureportfolios.com
Privater Equity Firm
N.A.I.C.S.: 523999
Nik Schuurmans (Founder)

Subsidiary (Domestic):

Northwest Wealth Advisors LLC   (2)
1800 Blankenship Rd Ste 130 W Linn, Portland, OR 97068
Tel.: (503) 478-6632
Web Site: http://www.nwwealthadvisors.com
Management Consulting Services
N.A.I.C.S.: 541618
Mark Neil (Pres)

TRU-POWER INC.

22520 Temescal Canyon Rd, Corona, CA 92883
Tel.: (951) 277-3180
Web Site: http://www.trupower.com
Rev.: $15,000,000
Emp.: 22
Lawn & Garden Machinery & Equipment Distr
N.A.I.C.S.: 423820
Cash Smith (Gen Mgr)

TRUARC PARTNERS, L.P.

545 Madison Ave, New York, NY 10022
Tel.: (212) 508-3300   DE
Web Site: https://truarcpartners.com
Year Founded: 2021
Venture Capital & Private Equity Firm
N.A.I.C.S.: 523999
John A. Pless (Mng Partner)
Alan H. Mantel (Co-Mng Partner)

Subsidiaries:

AI Fire, LLC   (1)
3760 Kilroy Airport Way Ste 600, Long Beach, CA 90806
Tel.: (562) 444-0301
Web Site: http://www.aifire.com
Fire & Life Safety Services
N.A.I.C.S.: 922160
Michael Lloyd (CEO)

Subsidiary (Domestic):

Impact Fire Services, LLC   (2)
1 Chisholm Trail Rd, Ste 330, Round Rock, TX 78681
Tel.: (800) 862-1301
Web Site: http://impactfireservices.com
Fire Protection & Safey Services
N.A.I.C.S.: 922160
Michael Lloyd (CEO)

Subsidiary (Domestic):

Queen City Fire Equipment, Inc.   (3)
552 Ave D Suite 20, Williston, VT 05495
Tel.: (800) 322-7999
Web Site: http://www.fireprotec.com
Rev.: $2,000,000
Emp.: 15
Service Establishment Equipment & Supplies Merchant Whslr
N.A.I.C.S.: 423850

Subsidiary (Domestic):

Legacy Fire Protection, Inc.   (2)
592 Ctr St, Ludlow, MA 01056
Tel.: (413) 589-0672
Web Site:
http://www.legacyfireprotection.com
Site Preparation Contractor
N.A.I.C.S.: 238910
Joseph Brosseau (Pres)

P & J Sprinkler Company, Inc.   (2)
67 Main St, Willimantic, CT 06226
Tel.: (860) 456-0515
Web Site: http://www.pjsprinkler.com
Plumbing Services
N.A.I.C.S.: 238220

BlackHawk Industrial Distribution, Inc. (1)
1501 SW Expressway Dr, Broken Arrow, OK 74012
Tel.: (918) 610-4700
Web Site: http://www.bhid.com
Sales Range: $300-349.9 Million
Emp.: 525
Holding Company; Industrial Supplies Distribution
N.A.I.C.S.: 551112
Bill Scheller (CEO)
James MacEachern (CFO)
Stephen Burns (CIO)
Robert Miller (Sr VP-Sls & Dev)
Heather Riggs (Dir-Supplier Dev)
James Cote (Sr VP-Natl Acct Bus Solutions)
Robert Koch (Sr VP-Engineered Solutions)
George Schwenk (VP-HR)
Ian Hartman (VP-Supply Chain & Logistics)
Chris Bignell (VP-Customer Experience)

Branch (Domestic):

BlackHawk Industrial - Omaha   (2)
11651 S 154th St, Omaha, NE 68138
Tel.: (402) 734-1991
Web Site: http://www.bhid.com
Industrial Machinery & Equipment Distr
N.A.I.C.S.: 423830
Bill Scheller (CEO)

Subsidiary (Domestic):

BlackHawk Industrial - Peoria   (2)
1506 W Luthy Dr, Peoria, IL 61615
Tel.: (309) 692-2666
Web Site: http://blackhawkid.com
Industrial Machinery & Equipment Distr
N.A.I.C.S.: 423830
James Cote (Sr VP)

Branch (Domestic):

BlackHawk Industrial - Springfield   (2)
40 Bowles Rd, Agawam, MA 01001
Tel.: (413) 739-3885.

COMPANIES

Web Site: http://www.blackhawkid.com
Metal Cutting Tool Distr
N.A.I.C.S.: 423830
Derek Upson (Dir-Bus Dev)

Subsidiary (Domestic):

Duncan Industrial Solutions Inc. (2)
3450 S MacArthur Blvd, Oklahoma City, OK 73179-7638
Tel.: (405) 688-2300
Web Site: http://www.duncanindustrial.com
Industrial Machinery & Equipment Merchant Whslr
N.A.I.C.S.: 423830
Mark Pittman (VP-Sls & Mktg)

Fluid Service Corporation (2)
4703 Dresser Dr, Janesville, WI 53546
Tel.: (608) 757-0500
Web Site: http://www.fluidservicecorp.com
Sales Range: $1-9.9 Million
Emp.: 13
Fluid Management Machinery Distr
N.A.I.C.S.: 423830
John Schumacher (Pres)

Jarvis Supply Co., Inc. (2)
405 W 115th Ave Unit 5, Northglenn, CO 80234
Tel.: (303) 744-2355
Web Site: http://www.jarvissupply.com
Industrial Tools Distr
N.A.I.C.S.: 423840
George Hoff (Mgr)

MT Supply, Inc. (2)
3505 Cadillac Ave Bldg K, Costa Mesa, CA 92626
Tel.: (714) 641-9007
Industrial Machinery & Equipment Merchant Whslr
N.A.I.C.S.: 423830

Packaging Incorporated (2)
7200 93rd Ave N Ste 190, Brooklyn Park, MN 55445
Tel.: (952) 935-3421
Web Site: http://www.packinc.com
Packaging, Fastening Supplies & Strapping Tools Whslr & Distr
N.A.I.C.S.: 423710
Duane Buck (Dir-Ops)
Christine Voss (Sec-Admin)
Jackie Brown (Mgr-Pur)

Tool Fabrication Corporation (2)
2940 N 117th St, Milwaukee, WI 53222
Tel.: (414) 453-5030
Web Site: http://www.toolfab.com
Sales Range: $1-9.9 Million
Emp.: 22
Machine Tool Accessories Distr
N.A.I.C.S.: 423830
Jaci Alyea (Mgr-Customer Svc & Acctg)
Jeff Hesse (Pres)
Scott Vielgut (Mgr-Production & Technical)
Mark Vielgut (Engr-Design)

Tool Service Corporation (2)
2942 N 117th St, Milwaukee, WI 53222
Tel.: (414) 476-7600
Web Site: http://www.toolservice.com
Sales Range: $10-24.9 Million
Industrial Supplies Distr
N.A.I.C.S.: 423840
L. Abbrederis (Mgr-Mktg)
Janice Shandel (Controller)
Mike Wettstein (Branch Mgr)

Cascade Drilling, L.P. (1)
17270 Woodinville-Redmond Rd Building A 777, Woodinville, WA 98072
Tel.: (425) 527-9700
Web Site: http://www.cascadedrilling.com
Environmental, Geotechnical & Mining Drilling Services
N.A.I.C.S.: 213114
Timothy Smith (Pres & CEO)
John Murnane (Dir-Mktg & Comm)
Michael Gray (VP-Technical Svcs)
Gary Crueger (VP-Safety & Admin)
Todd Marti (VP-Sls & Mktg)
Tyler Kopet (CFO)
Timothy S. Cechini (VP-Drilling Ops-West)

Subsidiary (Domestic):

TerraTherm, Inc. (2)
151 Suffolk Ln, Gardner, MA 01440
Tel.: (978) 730-1200
Web Site: http://www.terratherm.com
Emp.: 70
Thermal Remediation Services
N.A.I.C.S.: 562910
James P. Galligan (VP-Projects)
David B. Allworth (CFO)
Gorm Heron (CTO & Sr VP)
Michael Gentry (Mgr-Corp Safety & Compliance)

Subsidiary (Domestic):

Current Environmental Solutions LLC (3)
15399 Cranes Mill Rd, Canyon Lake, TX 78133
Tel.: (830) 899-2626
Web Site: http://www.cesiweb.com
Soil & Groundwater Remediation Solutions
N.A.I.C.S.: 562910
William Heath (COO & VP)
Joe Pezzullo (Pres)

Subsidiary (Domestic):

Vironex Technical Services LLC (2)
3 Owls Nest Rd, Wilmington, DE 19807
Tel.: (302) 661-1400
Web Site: http://www.vironex.com
Sales Range: $1-9.9 Million
Environmental Field Services
N.A.I.C.S.: 541620
Alan Livadas (Pres)
Todd Hanna (Dir-Ops)
Jose Suarez (Natl Contracts Officer)
Kelley Marsilii (Controller)
Eliot Cooper (Dir-Remediation Support Svcs)
Frank Stolfi (Dir-Advanced Site Characterization Svcs)

Efficient Collaborative Retail Marketing Company LLC (1)
27070 Miles Rd Ste A, Solon, OH 44139
Tel.: (440) 498-0500
Web Site: http://www.ecrm.marketgate.com
Promotional Data Syndication & Analysis Solutions
N.A.I.C.S.: 513210
Greg Farrar (CEO)
Brian Nelson (CFO)
Joseph Tarnowski (VP-Content)
Charlie Bowlus (Founder)
Christina Fallon (Dir-Retail Sls)
Mike Kennedy (Dir-Sys Infrastructure)
Rick Andersen (VP-Software Dev)
Ken Nicolai (Dir-Intl Dev)
Matias Oseroff (Mgr-Sls-Intl)
Craig Chmielowicz (Sr VP-Intl)
Kurt Repola (Sr VP-Mktg)
Melinda Young (Sr VP-Gen Mdse)
Michael Castillo (Sr VP-Pharmacy & Medical Markets)
Sarah Davidson (Sr VP-Food & Beverage)
Tarina Wren (Sr VP-HR)
Tony Giovanini (Sr VP-Health & Beauty Care)
Wayne Bennett (Sr VP-Retail)

Electric Guard Dog, LLC (1)
550 Assembly St 5th Fl, Columbia, SC 29201
Tel.: (800) 432-6391
Web Site: http://www.electricguarddog.com
Monitored Electric Security Fence Systems
N.A.I.C.S.: 561621
Nathan Leaphart (CFO)
Randy Mullis (Dir-Field Ops)
Joseph Bury (Dir-Tech)
Michael Pate (Dir-Bus Dev & Compliance)
Cindy Williams (Dir-Bus Dev & Compliance)
Michael Dorrington (VP-Sls & Mktg)
Josh Ott (Sls Mgr)
Joseph Quesenberry (Reg Dir-Sls-Southeast)
Crystal Gurtisen (Mgr-Installation)
Jennifer Dorward (Mgr-Customer Svc)
Mark Wesley (CEO)
John Kenny (Chm)

Feradyne Outdoors LLC (1)
101 Main St, Superior, WI 54880
Tel.: (800) 282-4868
Web Site: http://www.feradyne.com
Hunting & Archery Equipment Designer, Mfr & Whslr
N.A.I.C.S.: 339920
Jon Syverson (Chief Comml Officer)
Craig Tinsley (VP-Ops)

Todd Seyfert (Pres & CEO)
Aaron Van Rossum (Mgr-Sls Ops)
Chris James (VP-Sls-Natl Accts)
Peter K. Shea (Chm)

Subsidiary (Domestic):

Field Logic, Inc. (2)
1230 Poplar Ave, Superior, WI 54880
Tel.: (715) 395-9955
Web Site: http://www.fieldlogic.com
Sales Range: $1-9.9 Million
Emp.: 75
Sporting & Athletic Goods Mfr
N.A.I.C.S.: 339920
Larry Pulkrabek (Pres)
Wanda Grew-Jasken (Dir-HR)
Phil Matson (Dir-Ops)
Tom Hadrava (Mgr-IT)

Tru-Fire Corp. (2)
722 State St, Fond Du Lac, WI 54937
Tel.: (920) 923-6866
Web Site: http://www.trufire.com
Sales Range: $10-24.9 Million
Emp.: 25
Archery Hunting Products Mfr
N.A.I.C.S.: 339920

HCTec Partners LLC (1)
7105 S Springs Dr Ste 208, Franklin, TN 37067
Tel.: (615) 577-4030
Web Site: http://www.hctecpartners.com
Sales Range: $75-99.9 Million
Emp.: 500
Healthcare IT, Health Information Management & Staffing Solutions
N.A.I.C.S.: 541519
William Bartholomew (Founder)

Branch (Domestic):

HCTec Partners (2)
4605 E Galbraith Rd Ste 200, Cincinnati, OH 45236
Tel.: (513) 985-6400
Web Site: http://www.hctecpartners.com
Emp.: 260
Human Resource Consulting Services
N.A.I.C.S.: 541612
Terry L. Correll (Pres-Recruiting Ops)
Steve Schott (COO)
William Bartholomew (CEO)

Ideal Clamp Products, Inc. (1)
8100 Tridon Dr, Smyrna, TN 37167-6603
Tel.: (615) 459-5800
Web Site: http://idealtridon.com
Specialty & Custom Clamping Products Mfr
N.A.I.C.S.: 332999
Bruce Bowater (VP-New Bus Dev)
Rick Stepien (CEO)

Subsidiary (Domestic):

Campbell Fittings, Inc. (2)
310 S Washington St, Boyertown, PA 19512
Tel.: (610) 367-6916
Web Site: http://www.campbellfittings.com
Metal Valve & Pipe Fitting Mfr
N.A.I.C.S.: 332919
Thomas J. Paff (Pres)
Dave Street (Chief Engr)

Ideal Clamp Products, Inc.-Brownsville (2)
7765 Padre Is Hwy Ste 500, Brownsville, TX 78521-5625
Tel.: (956) 838-5488
Web Site: http://www.idealtridon.com
Clamps, Bands, Buckle & Motor Vehicle Parts
N.A.I.C.S.: 336390

Tridon Inc. (2)
8100 Tridon Dr, Smyrna, TN 37167-6603
Tel.: (615) 459-5800
Web Site: http://www.stant.com
Hose Clamps Mfr
N.A.I.C.S.: 332510
Mike Priddy (Plant Mgr)

ZSI-Foster, Inc. (2)
45065 Michigan Ave, Canton, MI 48188
Tel.: (734) 844-0055
Web Site: http://www.zsi-foster.com
Clamping & Coupling Products Mfr
N.A.I.C.S.: 332913

TRUARC PARTNERS, L.P.

Subsidiary (Domestic):

Hydra-Zorb Co. (3)
1751 Summit Dr, Auburn Hills, MI 48326
Tel.: (248) 373-5151
Web Site: http://www.hydra-zorb.com
Specialty & Custom Clamping Products Mfr
N.A.I.C.S.: 332999
Robert Dodge (CEO)

Meyer Laboratory, Inc. (1)
2401 NW Jefferson St, Blue Springs, MO 64015
Tel.: (816) 228-4433
Web Site: http://www.meyerlab.com
Sales Range: $1-9.9 Million
Emp.: 65
Miscellaneous Chemical Product & Preparation Mfr
N.A.I.C.S.: 325998
Art Kurth (Pres)
Mike Miller (Pres)

Molded Devices, Inc. (1)
740 W Knox Rd, Tempe, AZ 85284
Tel.: (951) 509-6918
Web Site: http://www.moldeddevices.com
Sales Range: $1-9.9 Million
Emp.: 45
Plastics Product Mfr
N.A.I.C.S.: 326199
Elaine Robles (Office Mgr & Mgr-Acctg)
Jack Slinger (Pres & CEO)

Subsidiary (Domestic):

Dempsey Industries, Inc. (2)
802 N 4th St, Miamisburg, OH 45342
Tel.: (937) 866-2345
Web Site: http://www.dempseyind.com
Sales Range: $1-9.9 Million
Emp.: 34
Plastisol Moldings & Coatings Services
N.A.I.C.S.: 333511
Duane Estes (VP)

Southwest Mold, Inc. (2)
740 W Knox Rd, Tempe, AZ 85284
Tel.: (480) 785-9100
Web Site: http://moldeddevices.com
Dies, Tools, Jigs, Fixtures & Other Plastic Products Mfr
N.A.I.C.S.: 333511

Prototek Holdings LLC (1)
244 Burnham Intervale Road, Contoocook, NH 03229
Tel.: (800) 403-9777
Web Site: https://www.prototek.com
Emp.: 300
Metal Fabrication Mfr.
N.A.I.C.S.: 332312
Bill Gress (CEO)

Subsidiary (Domestic):

Prototype Solutions Group (2)
1621 Indianhead Dr, Menomonie, WI 54751
Tel.: (715) 235-0156
Web Site: http://www.protosg.com
Rev.: $2,333,333
Emp.: 20
Industrial Pattern Mfr
N.A.I.C.S.: 332999

Snow Phipps Group, LLC (1)
667 Madison Ave 18th Fl, New York, NY 10065
Tel.: (212) 508-3300
Venture Capital & Private Equity
N.A.I.C.S.: 523999
Peter K. Shea (Operating Partner)
Ian Kendall Snow (CEO & Partner)
Gary Spitz (Mng Dir-Fin Ops)
John Kenny (Operating Partner)
Gerald E. Sheehan (Mng Dir)
Paul Chellgren (Operating Partner)
Campbell Langdon (Operating Partner)
John Schweig (Operating Partner)
J. Alexander Forrey (VP)
Max Wein (VP)
John L. Zacharias (VP)
Ogden Phipps II (Co-Founder & Partner)
Philip S. Kemp Jr. (Mng Dir & Head-IR)

Teasdale Foods, Inc. (1)
901 Packers St, Atwater, CA 95301
Tel.: (209) 356-2352
Web Site: http://www.teasdalefoods.com
Food Processing

TRUARC PARTNERS, L.P.

TruArc Partners, L.P.—(Continued)
N.A.I.C.S.: 311421
Paula Demuria *(Chief Customer Officer)*
Chris Kiser *(CEO)*
Curtis Rhine *(CFO)*
Jerry Cook *(Exec VP & Gen Mgr)*
Corey Hoerning *(COO)*
Cale Nelson *(CMO)*

Subsidiary (Domestic):

Mesa Foods, LLC (2)
3701 W Magnolia Ave, Louisville, KY 40211
Tel.: (502) 772-2500
Web Site: http://www.mesafds.com
Emp.: 350
Tortillas, Tortilla Chips, Flat Bread & Pizza Crusts Mfr
N.A.I.C.S.: 311830
Sherrie Weber *(Mgr-HR)*

Rudy's Food Products, Inc. (2)
2115 E Belt Line Rd, Carrollton, TX 75006
Tel.: (214) 634-7839
Web Site: http://www.rudystortillas.com
Tortilla Products Mfr
N.A.I.C.S.: 311830
Joe R. Guerra *(VP)*
Louis Guerra *(CEO)*
Dionicio Casas *(Mgr-Warehouse)*

ZeroChaos, LLC (1)
420 S Orange Ave Ste 600, Orlando, FL 32801
Tel.: (407) 770-6161
Web Site: http://www.zerochaos.com
Sales Range: $75-99.9 Million
Emp.: 1,400
Contract Labor Services & Workforce Management Solutions
N.A.I.C.S.: 561320
Sue Ann Leone *(Sr VP-Sls)*
Doug Goin *(Chief Admin Officer)*
Sally Kauffman *(Sr VP-Quality Mgmt & Customer Svc)*
Matthew Levine *(COO)*
Ted Blankenship *(CFO)*
Bill Tayler *(Gen Counsel)*
Helen Seigfried *(Exec VP & Mng Dir-EMEA)*
Lisa Quattrini *(Exec VP-Enterprise Solutions-North America)*
Patricia Braa *(Exec VP-Bus Solutions & Svcs Delivery)*
Ken Lawrence *(Sr VP-Security & IT Ops)*
Nancy Hecker *(Sr VP-Product Dev)*
Gary Jones *(Sr VP-Bus Solutions-EMEA)*
Jim Burke *(CEO)*
Gordon Coburn *(Chm)*

TRUAX CORPORATION
4221 SW Research Way, Corvallis, OR 97333-1069
Tel.: (541) 758-1500
Year Founded: 1979
Rev.: $106,000,000
Emp.: 250
Dealers of Liquefied Petroleum Gas
N.A.I.C.S.: 457210
John Truax *(Pres)*
Deryl Fackrell *(Mgr-IT)*

TRUCCHIS MARKETS
1062 Broadway, Raynham, MA 02767-1944
Tel.: (508) 824-7515
Web Site: http://www.trucchis.com
Year Founded: 1928
Sales Range: $50-74.9 Million
Emp.: 500
Owner of Retail Supermarkets
N.A.I.C.S.: 445110
James Trucchi *(Pres)*
William Trucchi *(VP)*

TRUCK CENTER INCORPORATED
1007 Intl Dr, Tupelo, MS 38804
Tel.: (662) 842-3401
Web Site: http://www.summittruckgroup.com
Sales Range: $10-24.9 Million
Emp.: 46
New & Used Car Dealers

N.A.I.C.S.: 441110
Goynn Franklin *(Treas)*
Tim Raper *(Mgr-IT)*
David McGinnis *(Mgr-Svc)*

TRUCK CENTERS INC.
2280 Formosa Rd, Troy, IL 62294-3170
Tel.: (618) 667-3454 IL
Web Site: http://www.truckcentersinc.com
Year Founded: 1970
Sales Range: $100-124.9 Million
Emp.: 1,000
Truck Repairs & Sales
N.A.I.C.S.: 441330
M. John Hopkins *(CEO-Troy)*
Mary Deuser *(Sec)*
Steve Bartels *(Mgr-Parts)*
Brian Jubelt *(Mgr-Svc Ops)*

TRUCK CITY OF GARY INC.
PO Box 64800, Gary, IN 46401-0800
Tel.: (219) 949-8595 IN
Web Site: http://www.truckcityofgary.com
Year Founded: 1946
Sales Range: $10-24.9 Million
Emp.: 60
Commercial Trucks Leasing Services
N.A.I.C.S.: 423110
Paul Davis *(VP)*
Gerri Davis-Parker *(Pres)*
Crystal Frost-Doeing *(Controller)*

TRUCK COUNTRY INC.
3201 Hwy 61 151, Dubuque, IA 52003
Tel.: (563) 556-3773 WI
Web Site: http://www.truckcountry.com
Sales Range: $75-99.9 Million
Emp.: 100
Freight Liner Operation
N.A.I.C.S.: 423110
Michael R. McCoy *(Chm & Pres)*
William Arnold *(Treas)*
John R. McCoy *(VP)*
Brian McCoy *(VP-Ops)*

TRUCK ENTERPRISES INCORPORATED
3440 S Main St, Harrisonburg, VA 22801
Tel.: (540) 564-6900
Web Site: http://www.truckenterprises.com
Rev.: $82,300,000
Emp.: 100
Provider of New & Used Trucks, Tractors & Trailers
N.A.I.C.S.: 441110
Kim Smith *(Mgr-Fin)*
Dennis Brooks *(Mgr-Svc)*
Earl Krantz *(Mgr-Parts)*

TRUCK EQUIPMENT INC.
680 Potts Ave, Green Bay, WI 54304
Tel.: (920) 494-7451
Web Site: http://truckequipinc.com
Sales Range: $10-24.9 Million
Emp.: 40
Trailer Parts & Accessories
N.A.I.C.S.: 423120
Nick Willems *(Mgr-Parts)*
Ron Heim *(Gen Mgr-Parts & Pur)*

TRUCK LEASE SERVICES, INC.
4350 Idlewild Industrial Dr, Winston Salem, NC 27105
Tel.: (336) 661-1355
Year Founded: 1987
Rev.: $9,500,000
Emp.: 65
Logistics & Transportation

N.A.I.C.S.: 484110
Wanda R. Butner *(Pres)*
David P. Butner *(Treas & Sec)*
Wanda Butner *(Owner & Pres)*
Lori Lawson *(Mgr-Shop)*
Don Felder *(VP-Transportation)*
Danny A. Hepler II *(Dir-Bus Unit)*

TRUCK LIGHTHOUSE
425 W 10th St, San Pedro, CA 90731
Tel.: (310) 547-9946
Web Site: http://www.thelighthouseinc.com
Rev.: $15,000,000
Emp.: 10
Distr of Motor Vehicle Supplies & New Parts
N.A.I.C.S.: 423120
Robert Sumich *(Pres)*
Sergio Narvaez *(Branch Mgr-San Diego)*
Kimberly Sumich *(Mgr-Credit)*
Ann Palacios *(CFO)*
Michael Boyd *(Branch Mgr-West Sacramento)*
Joe Mannina *(Branch Mgr-Hayward)*

TRUCK ONE, INC.
140 Everett Ave, Newark, OH 43055
Tel.: (740) 349-9258
Web Site: http://www.truckone.net
Year Founded: 1947
Rev.: $10,954,414
Emp.: 25
Provider of Truck Transportation Services
N.A.I.C.S.: 484121
Jay Windgardner *(Pres)*
Dave Dawley *(Mgr-Bus Dev)*

TRUCK PARTS AND EQUIPMENT CO.
2272 Larkin Cir, Sparks, NV 89431
Tel.: (775) 359-8840
Web Site: http://www.peterbilttpe.com
Rev.: $57,992,021
Emp.: 57
Provider of Truck Leasing, Sales & Service
N.A.I.C.S.: 522220
Mike Altimus *(Gen Mgr)*

TRUCK SALES & SERVICE INC.
3429 Brightwood Rd, Midvale, OH 44653
Tel.: (740) 922-3412
Web Site: http://www.trksls.com
Sales Range: $50-74.9 Million
Emp.: 165
Truck & Semi Truck Sales & Service
N.A.I.C.S.: 423110
Rod Rafael *(Pres)*
Ryan Rafael *(Acct Mgr)*

TRUCK TRAILER & EQUIPMENT INC.
1670 Hwy 80 E, Pearl, MS 39208
Tel.: (601) 939-7873
Web Site: http://www.trucktrailerequipment.com
Sales Range: $10-24.9 Million
Emp.: 35
Provider of New & Used Truck Trailers
N.A.I.C.S.: 423110
James W. Fielder *(Owner)*

TRUCK WORLD INC.
6813 Commerce Dr, Hubbard, OH 44425-3086
Tel.: (330) 448-2210 OH
Web Site: http://www.truckworldinc.com
Year Founded: 1956
Sales Range: $10-24.9 Million

U.S. PRIVATE

Emp.: 80
Producer & Retailer of Gasoline, Fuel Oils, Lubricants & Bulk Petroleum Products; Operator of Full Service Truck Stop Convenience Stores
N.A.I.C.S.: 457120
J. Gary Burke *(Pres)*
Barry Brocker *(CFO)*

TRUCKEE GAMING LLC
PO Box 160, Verdi, NV 89439
Tel.: (775) 246-9696
Web Site: https://www.truckeegaming.com
Year Founded: 2013
Casino Gambling & Gaming, Recreation, Hospitality
N.A.I.C.S.: 713290

Subsidiaries:

Rail City Casino (1)
2121 Victorian Ave, Sparks, NV 89431-4130
Tel.: (775) 359-9440
Web Site: http://www.railcity.com
Casino, Eating & Recreational Services
N.A.I.C.S.: 713290

TRUCKEE-TAHOE LUMBER CO
10242 Church St, Truckee, CA 96161
Tel.: (530) 587-9211
Web Site: http://www.ttlco.com
Rev.: $16,000,000
Emp.: 40
Lumber Yard
N.A.I.C.S.: 444110
Ruth Cross *(Sec)*
Andrew Cross *(Pres)*
Joshua Chaplin *(Mgr-Dispatch)*

TRUCKS & PARTS OF TAMPA INC.
1015 S 50th St, Tampa, FL 33619
Tel.: (813) 247-6637
Web Site: http://www.trucks.com
Sales Range: $10-24.9 Million
Emp.: 209
Provider of Trucks, Tractors & Trailers & Parts
N.A.I.C.S.: 423110
Bruce Goldenberg *(Exec VP)*
Blake Hamilton *(Mgr-Municipal Sls)*

TRUCKS FOR YOU, INC.
PO Box AH 3250 N 32nd St, Muskogee, OK 74402-7030
Tel.: (918) 687-7708 OK
Web Site: http://www.trucksforyou.com
Year Founded: 1984
Sales Range: $25-49.9 Million
Emp.: 600
Trucking Service
N.A.I.C.S.: 484121
Dewey Grigsby *(Pres)*
Joe Irwin *(Mgr-Risk)*

TRUCKS-E-QUIP INC.
8913 Martin Luther King Blvd, Tampa, FL 33610-7309
Tel.: (813) 621-8605
Web Site: http://www.trucksequip.com
Sales Range: $1-9.9 Million
Trucks, Trailers & Construction Equipment Sales
N.A.I.C.S.: 441227
Carl Larson *(Pres)*

TRUCKWAY LEASING INC.
1745 Dreman Ave, Cincinnati, OH 45223-2434
Tel.: (513) 541-7700
Web Site: http://www.truckwayleasing.com
Year Founded: 1988
Sales Range: $10-24.9 Million
Emp.: 130

COMPANIES

Truck Rental & Leasing Services
N.A.I.C.S.: 532120
Ron Horstman *(Pres)*
Shawn Watson *(Mgr-Sls)*
Robert Jones *(VP-Fin)*
Dan Arnold *(Mgr-HR)*

TRUCO ENTERPRISES INC.
10515 King William Dr, Dallas, TX 75220
Tel.: (972) 869-4600
Web Site:
http://www.trucoenterprises.com
Sales Range: $10-24.9 Million
Emp.: 40
Provider of General Merchandise
N.A.I.C.S.: 424990
Niki Wolpmann *(CFO)*
David L. Silver *(Pres)*
Lisa Walsh *(CEO)*
David Lowe *(Chm)*

TRUCO INC.
3033 W 44th St, Cleveland, OH 44113
Tel.: (216) 631-1000
Web Site: http://www.truco-inc.com
Rev.: $15,741,888
Emp.: 15
Waterproofing Compounds
N.A.I.C.S.: 324122
Christopher Hoskins *(Pres)*

TRUDEAU DISTRIBUTING COMPANY
25 Cliff Rd W Ste 115, Burnsville, MN 55337
Tel.: (952) 882-8295
Web Site:
http://www.trudeaudistributing.com
Year Founded: 1981
Sales Range: $50-74.9 Million
Emp.: 180
Bakery Product Distr
N.A.I.C.S.: 311811
Lee Regensburger *(VP-Sls)*
Sieg Buck *(CEO)*
Jason Dugan *(CFO)*
John Radmann *(Mgr-Warehouse)*

TRUDELL TRAILERS OF GRAND RAPIDS, INC.
2049 Creamery Rd, De Pere, WI 54115
Tel.: (616) 530-2100
Web Site:
http://www.trudelltrailers.com
Year Founded: 2006
Rev.: $60,000,000
Emp.: 122
New & Used Trailer Whslr
N.A.I.C.S.: 336212
David Turbiville *(Treas)*
Ken Trudell *(Pres)*
Virginia Trudell *(Sec)*
Brian Pratt *(Dir-Svc Ops)*

Subsidiaries:

Michigan Trailer Service Inc. (1)
4350 Clyde Park Ave SW, Grand Rapids, MI 49509
Tel.: (616) 534-1515
Web Site: http://www.trudelltrailers.com
Sales Range: $1-9.9 Million
Emp.: 25
Trailer Repair
N.A.I.C.S.: 811114

TRUDY'S TEXAS STAR INC.
409 W 30th St, Austin, TX 78745
Tel.: (512) 477-2935
Web Site: http://www.trudys.com
Year Founded: 1977
Restaurant Services
N.A.I.C.S.: 722511

Nancy Bebko *(Mgr)*
Patrick Fortson *(Gen Mgr)*
Jesse Moore *(Supvr-Kitchen)*

TRUE COLORS STUDIO
1300 W Arrowhead Rd, Duluth, MN 55811-2218
Tel.: (218) 722-7696
Sales Range: $10-24.9 Million
Emp.: 165
Pharmaceutical Product Whslr
N.A.I.C.S.: 424210
Mike Groth *(Gen Mgr)*
Dawn J. Janousek *(Mgr)*
Steven Preston *(Owner & Pres)*

TRUE COMPANIES
455 N Poplar, Casper, WY 82601-1758
Tel.: (307) 237-9301
Web Site: http://www.truecos.com
Year Founded: 1948
Sales Range: $150-199.9 Million
Emp.: 700
Oil & Gas Extraction & Distribution; Trucking & Warehousing; Oil Pipelines
N.A.I.C.S.: 486110
Ken White *(Mgr-Personnel)*
H. A. TRUE *(Owner)*
David L. TRUE *(VP)*

Subsidiaries:

Belle Fourche Pipeline Co. (1)
895 W River Cross Rd, Casper, WY 82601-1758
Tel.: (307) 237-9301
Web Site: http://www.truecos.com
Petroleum Pipe Lines
N.A.I.C.S.: 486110

Black Hills Trucking Co. (1)
455 N Poplar 82601, Casper, WY 82602-2360
Tel.: (307) 237-9301
Rev.: $7,339,000
Emp.: 68
Trucking
N.A.I.C.S.: 484121

Eighty Eight Oil Co. (1)
455 North Poplar, Casper, WY 82601
Tel.: (307) 237-9301
Web Site: http://www.truecos.com
Sales Range: $25-49.9 Million
Emp.: 10
Real Estate Manangement Services
N.A.I.C.S.: 531390
Tony Martin *(Mgr-Credit)*

Toolpusher Supply Co. (1)
455 N Poplar St, Casper, WY 82601
Tel.: (307) 237-9301
Sales Range: $150-199.9 Million
Tubular Mfr & Distr
N.A.I.C.S.: 331210
David True *(Pres)*

True Drilling Co. (1)
455 N Poplar St, Casper, WY 82601
Tel.: (307) 237-9301
Web Site: http://www.truedrilling.com
Sales Range: $25-49.9 Million
Emp.: 100
Crude Petroleum & Natural Gas
N.A.I.C.S.: 213111

True Oil Co. (1)
PO Box 2360, Casper, WY 82602-2360
Tel.: (307) 237-9301
Web Site: http://www.trueco.com
Crude Petroleum & Natural Gas
N.A.I.C.S.: 211120

True Ranches (1)
455 N Poplar, Casper, WY 82601-1758
Tel.: (307) 237-9301
Web Site: http://www.truecos.com
Emp.: 200
Ranches & Farms
N.A.I.C.S.: 112111
Tony Martin *(Mgr-Credit)*

TRUE DIGITAL SECURITY, INC.
1401 Forum Way Ste 100, West Palm Beach, FL 33401
Tel.: (561) 835-8351
Web Site:
http://www.truedigitalsecurity.com
Security Consulting Services
N.A.I.C.S.: 541690
Michael Oglesby *(VP-Security Svcs Ops)*
Jerald Dawkins *(Chief Info Security Officer)*
Rory V. Sanchez *(CEO)*
Dominic Schulte *(Pres)*
Kat Ray *(VP-Human Capital & Admin)*
Rebecca Montanez *(VP-Fin)*
Sam J Ruggeri *(Exec VP)*
Heath Gieson *(VP-Ops)*
Scott Williamson *(VP-Info Svcs)*

TRUE FABRICATIONS
154 N 35th St, Seattle, WA 98103
Tel.: (206) 624-3195
Web Site:
http://www.truefabrications.com
Year Founded: 2004
Sales Range: $10-24.9 Million
Emp.: 80
Wine & Spirits Accessories
N.A.I.C.S.: 423620
Dhruv Agarwal *(Mng Dir)*
Jennifer Miller *(Mgr-Product Dev & Branding)*
Tina Saloutos *(Mgr-Supply Chain)*
Abbie Carlson *(Reg Mgr-Sls)*
Lauren Austin *(Acct Mgr-New Bus)*

TRUE FITNESS TECHNOLOGY INC.
865 Hoff Rd, O'Fallon, MO 63366-1900
Tel.: (636) 272-7100
Web Site: http://www.truefitness.com
Year Founded: 1981
Sales Range: $75-99.9 Million
Emp.: 75
Commercial & Consumer Treadmills & Fitness Equipment Mfr
N.A.I.C.S.: 339920
Frank Trulaske *(Founder & CEO)*
Matthew Hacker *(VP)*
Serena Hoelscher *(Mgr-Shipping)*
Ward Petito *(COO)*
Sally Matheson *(Chief Mktg Officer)*

TRUE GREEN CAPITAL MANAGEMENT LLC
315 Post Rd W, Westport, CT 06880
Tel.: (855) 335-5900
Web Site:
https://truegreencapital.com
Year Founded: 2011
Investment Services
N.A.I.C.S.: 523999
Panos Ninios *(Co-Founder & Mng Partner)*
Bo Wiegand *(Co-Founder & Partner)*

TRUE HOME VALUE, INC.
5611 Fern Valley Rd, Louisville, KY 40228-1055
Tel.: (502) 968-2020
Web Site:
http://www.truehomevalue.com
Year Founded: 1998
Sales Range: $50-74.9 Million
Windows, Doors & Other Building Materials Mfr & Dealer
N.A.I.C.S.: 444180
Charles L. Smith *(CEO)*

Subsidiaries:

Leingang Home Center (1)
2601 Twin City Dr, Mandan, ND 58554
Tel.: (701) 663-7966
Web Site: http://www.leingang.com

TRUE NORTH ENERGY, LLC

Sales Range: $25-49.9 Million
Emp.: 90
Home Remodeling Services
N.A.I.C.S.: 444110

Paragon Door Designs, Inc. (1)
7845 National Tpke Unit 150, Louisville, KY 40214
Tel.: (502) 363-2188
Web Site: http://www.paragondoor.com
Sales Range: $1-9.9 Million
Emp.: 28
Window & Door Mfr
N.A.I.C.S.: 332321

Rolox Inc. (1)
2321 NE Independence Ave Ste A, Lees Summit, MO 64064-2363
Tel.: (816) 765-3060
Web Site: http://www.rolox.com
Sales Range: $1-9.9 Million
Emp.: 70
Replacement Door & Window Mfr
N.A.I.C.S.: 332321
David Chiarelli *(Owner)*

THV Compozit Windows & Doors (1)
3601 30th Ave NW, Mandan, ND 58554-1356
Tel.: (800) 669-2020
Web Site: http://www.thv.com
Sales Range: $1-9.9 Million
Emp.: 70
Window Mfr & Distr
N.A.I.C.S.: 332321
Charles L. Smith *(CEO)*

Thomas Construction Inc. (1)
4761 Earth City Expy, Bridgeton, MO 63044
Tel.: (314) 739-1111
Web Site:
http://www.thomasconstruction.com
Rev.: $27,000,000
Emp.: 225
Replacement Window & Door Mfr
N.A.I.C.S.: 236118

TRUE INFLUENCE, LLC
8000 Towers Crescent Dr 13th Fl, Vienna, VA 22182
Tel.: (301) 365-6600
Web Site:
http://www.trueinfluence.com
Sales Range: $1-9.9 Million
Marketing Automation Software
N.A.I.C.S.: 513210
Brian Giese *(CEO)*
Radhakrishnan Maniyani *(CTO)*
Ken Stout *(Chief Revenue Officer)*
Craig Weiss *(COO)*
Shana Deane *(VP-Sls-East)*
Mike Rogers *(Sr VP)*
Michael VanPatten *(CFO)*

TRUE MEDIA
500 Business Loop 70 W, Columbia, MO 65203
Tel.: (573) 443-8783
Web Site:
http://www.truemediaservices.com
Year Founded: 2005
Sales Range: $10-24.9 Million
Emp.: 125
Media Buying Agency
N.A.I.C.S.: 541830
Jack Miller *(CEO)*
Carolle Sutter *(Dir-Media-Canada)*
Stephanie Padgett *(Sr VP-Media Ops)*
Bruce Neve *(Pres-Canada)*
Michele Cropp *(Assoc Dir-Media)*
Candice Rotter *(Sr VP-Media Ops)*
Chris Actis *(Pres-US)*

TRUE NORTH ENERGY, LLC
10346 Brecksville Rd, Brecksville, OH 44141
Tel.: (440) 792-4200
Web Site: http://www.truenorth.org
Sales Range: $1-9.9 Million
Emp.: 12
Gasoline Service Stations

TRUE NORTH ENERGY, LLC U.S. PRIVATE

True North Energy, LLC—(Continued)
N.A.I.C.S.: 457120
Brad Hayden (Mgr)
Char Salmons (Gen Mgr-Retail Ops)
Dina Bowen (Mgr)
Fran Cook (Mgr)
Greg Wood (Mgr)
John Guzdanski (CFO)
Kathy Gorski (Mgr)
Keith A. McIntyre (VP-Dealers)
Kim Crippen (Mgr)
Mark E. Lyden (Pres)
Roberta Varner (Mgr)
Tom Grady (Mgr)
Ryan Howard (COO)

Subsidiaries:

Schmuckal Oil Company Inc. (1)
1516 Barlow St, Traverse City, MI 49686-4315
Tel.: (231) 946-2800
Web Site: http://www.schmuckaloil.com
Gasoline Service Stations
N.A.I.C.S.: 457120
Paul Schmuckal (Pres)
Jerry Olshansky (Gen Mgr-Wholesale Ops)

TRUE NORTH EQUIPMENT CO.
5101 Gateway Dr, Grand Forks, ND 58203-1109
Tel.: (701) 746-4436
Web Site:
http://www.truenorthequipment.com
Farm & Garden Machinery & Equipment Merchant Whslr
N.A.I.C.S.: 423820
John Oncken (Owner & VP)

TRUE NORTH HOTEL GROUP, INC.
7300 W 110th St Ste 990, Overland Park, KS 66210
Tel.: (913) 345-6400
Web Site:
http://www.truenorthhotels.com
Sales Range: $10-24.9 Million
Emp.: 850
Home Management Services
N.A.I.C.S.: 721110
Richard Merkel (Pres & COO)
Gary Liebergen (CFO)
Brad Wiens (Chief Dev Officer & Exec VP)
Jerry Culkin (VP-Ops)
Linda Rhodes (Mgr-HR)
Joe Novak (VP-Sls & Mktg)
Maura Peeler (Reg VP-Ops)
Kristen VonFosson (Dir-Market-Sls)
Karen Thomas (Controller)
Mike Egan (Reg VP-Sls)
Michael Watson (Gen Mgr-Fairfield Inn & Suites-Leavenworth)

TRUE NORTH INC.
630 Third Ave 12th Fl, New York, NY 10017
Tel.: (212) 557-4202
Web Site:
http://www.truenorthinc.com
Year Founded: 1994
Sales Range: $25-49.9 Million
Emp.: 45
Advertising Agencies
N.A.I.C.S.: 541810
Tom Goosmann (Chief Creative Officer)
Garen Karnikian (Assoc Dir-Analytics)
Rehan Iqbal (Assoc Dir-Media)
Norma Wisnevitz (CEO)
Andrew Sheldon (Co-Founder)
Jess Fowle (Co-Founder)
Christian Hills (Creative Dir)
Fiona O'Sullivan (Creative Dir)

Subsidiaries:

True North Interactive (1)
417 Montgomery St Ste 900, San Francisco, CA 94104
Tel.: (415) 732-0301
Emp.: 3
N.A.I.C.S.: 541810

TRUE NORTH RECRUITING, LLC
70 NE Loop 410 Ste 850, San Antonio, TX 78216
Tel.: (210) 798-5888 TX
Web Site: http://www.truenorth-us.com
Year Founded: 2004
Sales Range: $1-9.9 Million
Emp.: 8
Financial Staffing Services
N.A.I.C.S.: 561320
Jay Lucas (Founder & CEO)
Denise Bradford (Dir-Talent Delivery)
Mike Shumard (Mgr-Bus Dev)
Kevin Krisko (Mgr-IT Bus Dev)

TRUE TEMPER SPORTS, INC.
8275 Tournament Dr Ste 200, Memphis, TN 38125-8871
Tel.: (901) 746-2006 DE
Web Site: http://www.truetemper.com
Sales Range: $25-49.9 Million
Emp.: 692
Golf Shafts & Bicycle Parts Mfr
N.A.I.C.S.: 339920
Jason A. Jenne (CFO)
Chad Hall (Dir-Mktg)
Jeremy Erspamer (Pres & CEO)
Jerry Scott (Dir-Lacrosse Products)
Lorne Smith (Mgr-Global Sls)

TRUE VENTURES
575 High St Ste 400, Palo Alto, CA 94301
Tel.: (650) 319-2150
Web Site:
http://www.trueventures.com
Year Founded: 2005
Venture Capital
N.A.I.C.S.: 523999
Puneet Agarwal (Partner)
Phil Black (Co-Founder)
John Callaghan (Co-Founder)
Tony Conrad (Co-Founder, CEO & Partner)
Om Malik (Partner-Venture)
Toni Schneider (Partner-Venture)
Jim Stewart (CFO)
Adam DAugelli (Partner)
Amanda Mann (Controller)
Jeff Veen (Partner)
Rohit Sharma (Partner)
Ulrike Kellmereit (VP-Fin)
Kevin Rose (Partner-Venture)
Amy Errett (Venture Partner)
Jonathan D. Callaghan (Founder)

TRUE VIEW REALTY PARTNERS ONE LP
11233 Shadow Creek Pkwy Ste 400, Pearland, TX 77584
Tel.: (832) 230-5108
Year Founded: 2004
Sales Range: $1-9.9 Million
Emp.: 93
Private Equity Real Estate
N.A.I.C.S.: 531390
Taseer A. Badar (Pres)

TRUE WIND CAPITAL MANAGEMENT, L.P.
Four Embarcadero Center Suite 2350, San Francisco, CA 94111
Tel.: (415) 780-9975
Web Site:
http://www.truewindcapital.com
Year Founded: 2015

Privater Equity Firm
N.A.I.C.S.: 523999
Adam Clammer (Co-Founder)
Jamie Greene (Co-Founder)
Rufina A. Adams (CFO)
Sean Giese (Principal)
David Hirsch (VP)
Stephanie Portillo (Mgr-Office)
Scott W. Wagner (Head-Strategic Capital)
William Heldfond (Executives)

Subsidiaries:

ARI Network Services, Inc. (1)
10850 W Park Pl Ste 1200, Milwaukee, WI 53224
Tel.: (414) 973-4300
Web Site: http://www.arinet.com
Business-to-Business E-Commerce Solutions
N.A.I.C.S.: 541690
Robert A. Ostermann (CTO)
Robert Jones (VP-Sls)
Nancy Bennett (Mgr-Mktg)

Subsidiary (Non-US):

ARI Europe B.V. (2)
Schipholweg 101L, Leiden, 2316 XC, Netherlands
Tel.: (31) 715248030
Web Site: http://www.arinet.nl
Digital Marketing Services
N.A.I.C.S.: 513210

TRUE WIRELESS, INC
12657 Alcosta Blvd Ste 450, Berkley, CA 94707
Tel.: (925) 362-9600 CA
Web Site:
http://www.truewireless.com
Year Founded: 2004
Sales Range: $1-9.9 Million
Emp.: 27
Cellular & Other Wireless Telecommunications
N.A.I.C.S.: 517112
Robert Chamberlin (Founder & CEO)
Steve Carter (VP-Sls & Bus Dev)
Paul Diekmann (Pres-Southern California)
Michael Furminger (Dir-Bus Dev)
Don Anderson (Dir-Bus Dev)
Jim Salsman (Dir-Bus Dev)
Danielle Price (Dir-Bus Dev)
Gwen Garris (Mng Dir)

TRUE.COM
5215 N O'Connor Ste 1600, Irving, TX 75039
Tel.: (972) 402-4802
Web Site: http://www.true.com
Sales Range: $10-24.9 Million
Emp.: 100
Online Dating Services
N.A.I.C.S.: 812990
Ruben Buell (Pres)
Cornell McGee (CMO & Exec VP)
Ted Sinclair (CFO)
David Reid (Chief Legal Officer)
Terra Gray (VP-Govt Affairs)
John Aldredge (Project Mgmt Officer)

TRUEBLOOD OIL CO. INC.
11792 N US Hwy 41, Farmersburg, IN 47850
Tel.: (812) 696-5151
Web Site:
http://www.truebloodoil.com
Rev: $18,601,121
Emp.: 7
Lubricating Oils & Greases
N.A.I.C.S.: 424720
Ted L. Trueblood (Pres)
Kathy Copeland (Controller)

TRUECORE BEHAVIORAL SOLUTIONS, LLC
3109 W Dr Martin Luther King Jr Blvd Ste 650, Tampa, FL 33607
Tel.: (813) 514-6275 VA
Web Site:
http://www.truecorebehavioral.com
Year Founded: 2017
Youth Secure Services
N.A.I.C.S.: 624110
Jeanne Walters (CFO)
Rodney Brockenbrough (COO)
Jeanne Walters (CFO)
Eric Jonas (VP-HR)
Mellissa Longo (Gen Counsel)
Michael Baglivio (Chief Research Officer)
Mary Frances Magan (Chief Compliance Officer)
Peter Plant (Sr VP)
Dahlia Kaplan (Chief Clinical Officer)
Katherine Jackowski (Chief Analytics Officer)
Bridget Goodrich (Dir-Staff Dev & Training)
Antonio Bratcher (Dir-Tennesse State)
Michael Pelletier (Chief Dev Officer)

TRUEFFECT, INC.
10170 Church Ranch Way Ste 300, Westminster, CO 80021-5490
Tel.: (303) 438-9597
Web Site: http://www.trueffect.com
Year Founded: 2002
Sales Range: $10-24.9 Million
Emp.: 56
Internet Advertising Services
N.A.I.C.S.: 541810
Robert Hess (Exec VP-Bus Dev)
Dave Hinton (CEO)
Jad Nehme (CTO)
Khristin Dickey (VP-Acct Mgmt)
Kurt DeMarais (Exec VP)
Tony Dipaolo (CFO & COO)

TRUELEARN, LLC
109 Professional Park Dr Ste 200, Mooresville, NC 28117
Tel.: (866) 475-4777
Web Site: http://truelearn.com
Year Founded: 2013
Digital Learning Services
N.A.I.C.S.: 611710
Joshua Courtney (Founder & Exec Chm)
Kevin Sayar (CEO)

Subsidiaries:

Picmonic, Inc. (1)
515 E Grant St, Phoenix, AZ 85004
Tel.: (480) 499-0887
Web Site: http://www.picmonic.com
Ambulatory Health Care Services
N.A.I.C.S.: 621999
Ron Robertson (Founder & CEO)

TRUELOVE & MACLEAN INC.
PO Box 268, Watertown, CT 06795-0268
Tel.: (203) 574-2240 CT
Web Site: http://www.truelove-maclean.com
Year Founded: 1944
Sales Range: $75-99.9 Million
Emp.: 165
Mfr of Deep Drawn Eyelets & Progressive Metal Stampings
N.A.I.C.S.: 332119
Mike Malec (Mgr-Tooling)

TRUENORTH COMPANIES L.C.
500 1st St SE, Cedar Rapids, IA 52401-1901
Tel.: (319) 364-5193 IA
Web Site:
https://truenorthcompanies.com
Year Founded: 2001
Insurance & Financial Services
N.A.I.C.S.: 524126

COMPANIES

Duane Smith *(CEO)*
Dave Verhille *(Mng Partner)*
Ty Kimble *(Reg Dir-Specialist)*
Marcia Strasburger *(Acct Mgr)*
Patti Seda *(VP-HR)*
Jason Smith *(CEO)*
Trent Tillman *(Pres)*

Subsidiaries:

Gateway Insurance Services, Inc. (1)
404 Rocksylvania Ave, Iowa Falls, IA 50126
Tel.: (641) 648-4275
Web Site: http://www.gisiowa.com
General Insurance Agency
N.A.I.C.S.: 524210
Monica Danner *(Acct Mgr-Comml)*

Jewell Insurance Associates, Inc. (1)
8480 E Orchard Rd Ste 6200, Greenwood Village, CO 80111
Tel.: (303) 740-8101
Insurance Agencies & Brokerages
N.A.I.C.S.: 524210

TRUENORTH STEEL INC.
702 13th Ave E, West Fargo, ND 58078
Tel.: (701) 492-4466
Web Site: http://www.truenorthsteel.com
Emp.: 500
Steel Products Mfr
N.A.I.C.S.: 332323
Dan Kadrmas *(Pres)*
Ole Rommesmo *(CEO)*
Lisa Reich *(CFO)*

Subsidiaries:

Fargo Tank & Steel Co. (1)
4401 Main Ave, Fargo, ND 58103
Tel.: (701) 282-2345
Web Site: http://www.rommesmo.com
Sales Range: $10-24.9 Million
Emp.: 140
Building Materials Mfr
N.A.I.C.S.: 423310
Dan Kadrmas *(Pres)*
Ole Rommesmo Jr. *(Owner)*

TrueNorth Steel - Billings (1)
1510 S 30th St W, Billings, MT 59102-6735
Tel.: (406) 656-2253
Web Site: http://www.truenorthsteel.com
Sales Range: $25-49.9 Million
Emp.: 115
Fabricated Structural Metal Mfr
N.A.I.C.S.: 332312

TrueNorth Steel - Blaine (1)
3575 85th Ave NE, Saint Paul, MN 55126-1186
Tel.: (763) 780-1760
Web Site: http://www.truenorthsteel.com
Fabricated Steel Product Mfr
N.A.I.C.S.: 332999
Dick Keiser *(Mgr)*

TrueNorth Steel - Huron (1)
220 4th St NW, Huron, SD 57350
Tel.: (605) 352-8643
Web Site: http://www.truenorthsteel.com
Emp.: 25
Sheet Metal Work Mfg
N.A.I.C.S.: 332322
Rod Bult *(Mgr-Safety)*

TrueNorth Steel - Mandan (1)
2522 Memorial Hwy, Mandan, ND 58554
Tel.: (701) 663-0321
Web Site: http://www.truenorthsteel.com
Emp.: 50
Fabricated Structural Metal Mfr
N.A.I.C.S.: 332312
Bruce Maragos *(Mgr-Stair Div)*

TRUENORTHLOGIC
8180 S 700 E Ste 250, Sandy, UT 84070-0571
Tel.: (801) 453-0136
Web Site: http://www.truenorthlogic.com
Year Founded: 2000
Rev.: $3,700,000

Emp.: 33
Custom Computer Programming Services
N.A.I.C.S.: 541511
Jeanette Hammock *(Founder & CEO)*
Eric Jensen *(CTO)*

TRUEPOINT COMMUNICATIONS, LLC
14800 Landmark Blvd Ste 250, Dallas, TX 75254
Tel.: (972) 380-9595 TX
Web Site: http://www.truepointagency.com
Year Founded: 2006
Sales Range: $1-9.9 Million
Emp.: 19
Media Advertising Services
N.A.I.C.S.: 541840
Jessica Nunez *(Founder & Pres)*

TRUEPOINT INC.
4901 Hunt Rd Ste 200, Cincinnati, OH 45242
Tel.: (513) 792-6648 OH
Web Site: http://www.truepointinc.com
Year Founded: 1990
Sales Range: $1-9.9 Million
Emp.: 20
Investment Management & Wealth Planning
N.A.I.C.S.: 523940
Elizabeth B. Niehaus *(Principal)*
Alexandra H. Ollinger *(Principal)*
Scott M. Barbee *(Principal-Wealth Advisory Svcs)*
Katrina M. Hartsel *(Principal)*
Ryan J. Klekar *(Principal)*
Ginger Ittenbach *(Principal & Specialist-Tax)*
Steve Condon *(Pres & Principal)*
Christine L. Carleton *(Principal)*
Heather M. Spencer *(Principal)*
John S. Evans *(Principal)*
Thomas E. Bentley *(Principal & Specialist-Estate Plng)*
Eric Ross *(Principal & Specialist-Fin Plng)*
Christopher M. Meyer *(Principal & Specialist-Investment)*
Scott Keller *(Principal & Specialist-Investment)*
Wayne A. Lippert Jr. *(Principal)*

TRUFOODS LLC
666 5th Ave Ste 27 B, New York, NY 10103
Tel.: (212) 359-3600 DE
Web Site: http://www.trufoods.com
Year Founded: 1969
Rev.: $75,000,000
Emp.: 300
Operates & Licenses Specialty Restaurants
N.A.I.C.S.: 722511
Robert J. Bagnell *(CFO)*
Anthony Leone *(COO)*
Gary Occhiogrosso *(Interim Pres & Chief Dev Officer)*
Jeff Auerbach *(Dir-Mktg)*

Subsidiaries:

Wall Street Deli, Inc. (1)
666 Fifth Ave 27th Fl, New York, NY 10103
Tel.: (212) 359-3600
Web Site: http://www.wallstreetdeli.com
Quick Service, Delicatessen-Style Restaurant Chain Operator
N.A.I.C.S.: 722511

TRUFUSION, LLC
2240 Corporate Cir Ste 160, Henderson, NV 89074
Tel.: (702) 786-0090
Web Site: http://www.trufusion.com
Year Founded: 2013

Sales Range: $1-9.9 Million
Emp.: 649
Fitness Club Operator
N.A.I.C.S.: 713940
Mike Borden *(Co-Founder)*
Martin Hinton *(Co-Founder)*

TRUGREEN LIMITED PARTNERSHIP
860 Ridge Lake Blvd, Memphis, TN 38120-9421
Tel.: (901) 681-1800
Web Site: http://www.trugreen.com
Year Founded: 1974
Sales Range: $900-999.9 Million
Emp.: 12,000
Lawn Care Services
N.A.I.C.S.: 561730
David W. Martin *(VP-Sourcing & Acctg)*
John Compton *(Chm)*
John Cowles *(Pres & CEO)*
Anthony Conversa *(Chief Growth Officer)*
Ayman Taha *(CIO)*
Michael B. Sims *(CFO & Sr VP)*
Rebecca Schoepfer *(Chief HR Officer)*

Subsidiaries:

EG Systems, LLC (1)
320 Eagle Crest Dr, Evansville, IN 47715
Web Site: http://www.actionpest.com
Emp.: 70
Pest Control Services
N.A.I.C.S.: 561710
Kevin Pass *(Founder)*
Keith Smith *(COO)*
Sara McKinney *(Dir-Mktg)*

Trugreen Companies LLC (1)
4141 North 27th St, Lincoln, NE 68521
Tel.: (402) 477-0303
Rev.: $6,000,000
Emp.: 25
Landscaping Services
N.A.I.C.S.: 561730

Subsidiary (Domestic):

LawnAmerica, Inc. (2)
5129 S 110th East Ave, Tulsa, OK 74146
Tel.: (918) 249-5296
Web Site: http://www.lawnamerica.com
Sales Range: $1-9.9 Million
Emp.: 60
Landscaping & Lawn Care Services
N.A.I.C.S.: 561730
Brad Johnson *(Founder)*
Benjamin Allen *(COO)*
Paul Reimers *(Pres)*

TRUITT & WHITE
642 Hearst Ave, Berkeley, CA 94710
Tel.: (510) 841-0511
Web Site: http://www.truittandwhite.com
Year Founded: 1946
Sales Range: $25-49.9 Million
Emp.: 100
Other Building Material Retailer
N.A.I.C.S.: 444180
Joel Trestrail *(Mgr)*

TRULITE GLASS & ALUMINUM SOLUTIONS, LLC
800 Fairway Dr Ste 200, Deerfield Beach, FL 33441
Tel.: (954) 724-1775 FL
Web Site: http://www.trulite.com
Year Founded: 1978
Mirrors, Architectural Laminated Glass & Fabricated Glass Products Mfr
N.A.I.C.S.: 332321
Ron Biberdorf *(Mgr-All Glass Entrance)*
Sean Cooney *(Mgr-Metal)*
Paul Mahedy *(Reg VP)*

TRULITE GLASS & ALUMINUM SOLUTIONS, LLC

Matt Sampsel *(Reg Mgr-Sls)*
Kevin Yates *(CEO)*
Todd Golditch *(Co-Founder & Mng Partner)*

Subsidiaries:

American Insulated Glass, LLC (1)
3965 E Conley Rd, Conley, GA 30288
Tel.: (404) 361-9154
Web Site: http://www.aiglass.com
Specialty Glass Products Mfr & Whslr
N.A.I.C.S.: 327211
Richard Freeman *(Founder)*
Shane Ellerbee *(Production Mgr)*
Holly Bowie *(Mgr-HR)*
William Blair *(CEO)*
Clint Blair *(Pres)*

Arch Ohio, Inc. (1)
297 Ascott Pkwy, Cuyahoga Falls, OH 44223
Tel.: (330) 923-3726
Web Site: http://www.archaluminum.net
Sales Range: $25-49.9 Million
Emp.: 105
Aluminum & Specialty Glass Products Mfr
N.A.I.C.S.: 327211

Super Sky Products Enterprises, LLC (1)
10301 N Enterprise Dr, Mequon, WI 53092-4639
Tel.: (262) 242-2000
Web Site: http://www.supersky.com
Sales Range: $125-149.9 Million
Emp.: 100
Skylights Mfr & Installation Services
N.A.I.C.S.: 327211
Cindy Selig *(Coord-Mktg)*
Claude Keshemberg *(CFO & VP)*
Curtis Groeschel *(Project Mgr)*
Eric Dahm *(Project Mgr)*
Dick Poklar *(Dir-Ops)*
Jeff Pfluger *(Project Mgr)*
Tim Staats *(Dir-Engrg)*
Dan Stiller *(Mgr-Pur)*
Todd Wilde *(Project Mgr)*
Ryan Navis *(Project Mgr)*
Julie Guetzke *(Mgr-Tech Sls & Estimating)*
Gregory Kraft *(Dir-Fabrication)*
Jamie Imbery *(Asst Mgr-Production Engrg)*
Jason Sprague *(Project Mgr)*
Jeff Parmann *(Mgr-Production Engrg)*
Julia Brock *(Project Mgr)*
Althea Erfourth *(Coord-Ops)*
Ann Willman *(Mgr-HR)*
Pete Archambeau *(Coord-Matl)*
Larry Grassmann *(Dir-Sls)*
Brian Thomas *(Pres)*

Trudeco (1)
2395 Setterlin Dr, Columbus, OH 43228-9499
Tel.: (614) 876-1057
Web Site: http://www.trulite.com
Sales Range: $10-24.9 Million
Emp.: 50
Specialty Custom Decorative Glass for Windows, Doors & Decoration Mfr
N.A.I.C.S.: 327215
Jerry Hackler *(Branch Mgr)*

Trulite Glass & Aluminum Solutions, LLC - Atlanta (1)
605 Stonehill Dr, Atlanta, GA 30336
Tel.: (404) 346-7900
Tempered Glass Mfr
N.A.I.C.S.: 327211

Trulite Glass & Aluminum Solutions, LLC - Cheswick (1)
100 Business Center Dr, Cheswick, PA 15024-1069
Tel.: (724) 274-9050
Sales Range: $25-49.9 Million
Architectural Glass Distr
N.A.I.C.S.: 423390
Dickey Clinton *(Pres)*

Trulite Glass & Aluminum Solutions, LLC - Grenada (1)
501 Govan St, Grenada, MS 38901
Tel.: (662) 226-5551
Web Site: http://www.trulite.com
Flat Glass Mfr
N.A.I.C.S.: 327211
Wayne Smith *(Branch Mgr)*

TRULITE GLASS & ALUMINUM SOLUTIONS, LLC

Trulite Glass & Aluminum Solutions, LLC—(Continued)

Trulite Glass & Aluminum Solutions, LLC - New Berlin (1)
5700 S Moorland Rd, New Berlin, WI 53151
Tel.: (800) 432-8132
Web Site: http://www.trulite.com
Glass for Commercial Use Mfr
N.A.I.C.S.: 327211
Joe Hawley (Branch Mgr)

TRULY NOLEN OF AMERICA INC.
3636 E Speedway Blvd, Tucson, AZ 85716-4018
Tel.: (520) 327-3447 AZ
Web Site: http://www.trulynolen.com
Year Founded: 1955
Sales Range: $25-49.9 Million
Emp.: 1,047
Disinfecting & Pest Control Services
N.A.I.C.S.: 561710
Steven Scott Nolen (Pres)

TRUMAN ARNOLD COMPANIES
100 Crescent Ct Ste 1600, Dallas, TX 75201
Tel.: (214) 884-2660 TX
Web Site:
 http://www.thearnoldcos.com
Year Founded: 1964
Sales Range: $1-4.9 Billion
Emp.: 520
Retail Service Stations & Sales of Wholesale Petroleum Products
N.A.I.C.S.: 424720
Greg Arnold (Chm & CEO)

Subsidiaries:

TAC Energy (1)
100 Crescent Ct Ste 1600, Dallas, TX 75201
Web Site: http://www.thearnoldcos.com
Fuel Distr
N.A.I.C.S.: 424720
Carl Nelson (Mgr-Sls-Natl)
Chad Hebert (Gen Mgr-Sls)
Josh Long (Mgr-Sls)
Casey Bostain (Mgr-Sls)
Clayton Wilson (Mgr-Sls)
Fred Sloan (COO & VP)
Mark Anderle (Dir-Supply & Trading)

Subsidiary (Domestic):

IPC (USA) Inc. (2)
4 Hutton Ctr Dr Ste 700, Santa Ana, CA 92707
Energy, Metals And Minerals Company
N.A.I.C.S.: 212290

Mutual Oil Co. Inc. (2)
863 Crescent St, Brockton, MA 02302
Tel.: (508) 583-5777
Petroleum Distr
N.A.I.C.S.: 424720
Edward A. Rachins (Pres)

TRUMARK FINANCIAL CREDIT UNION
1000 Northbrook Dr, Trevose, PA 19053-8496
Tel.: (215) 953-5300 PA
Web Site:
 http://www.trumarkonline.org
Year Founded: 1939
Sales Range: $1-9.9 Million
Emp.: 425
Credit Union
N.A.I.C.S.: 522130
Hugh T. Bray (Pres)
R. Terence Brunt (Sec)
Wayne J. Goodwin (Treas)
Christine Woods (VP-PR & Govt Affairs)
Mark Holder (Asst VP & Mgr-North)
Elizabeth Kaspern (Sr VP-Retail Sls)
Randi Marmer (Asst VP-Community Rels)

Richard F. Stipa (CEO)
Karen Sweeney (Chief HR Officer & Sr VP)
Leonard V. Doughty III (VP)

TRUMBULL INDUSTRIES INC.
400 Dietz Rd NE, Warren, OH 44483
Tel.: (330) 393-6624
Web Site: http://www.trumbull.com
Rev.: $88,710,837
Emp.: 1,000
Plumbing & Heating Supplies
N.A.I.C.S.: 423720
Murray Miller (Pres)
Sam H. Miller (VP)
Ken Miller (VP)

TRUMP PAVILION FOR NURSING AND REHABILITATION
89-40 135th St, Jamaica, NY 11418
Tel.: (718) 206-5000 NY
Web Site:
 http://www.trumppavilion.org
Year Founded: 1972
Sales Range: $25-49.9 Million
Emp.: 274
Nursing & Rehabilitation Services
N.A.I.C.S.: 623110
Noreen Bock (Dir-Social Work)
Ilene Wood (Coord-Rehabilitation)

TRUMPET LLC
2803 St Philip St, New Orleans, LA 70119
Tel.: (504) 525-4600
Web Site:
 http://www.trumpetgroup.com
Year Founded: 1997
Rev.: $26,000,000
Emp.: 30
N.A.I.C.S.: 541810
Pat McGuiness (Founder & Partner)
Robbie Vitrano (Pres & Principal)
Matt McGuiness (VP-& Dir-Creative)
Malcolm Schwarzenbach (Dir-Brand Study)
Nathan Calhoun (Dir-Art)
Alicia Mora (Acct Supvr)
Laura Higley (Acct Exec)
Emily Good (Asst Acct Exec)
David Manders (Asst Acct Exec)

TRUPAL MEDIA, INC.
1205 Lincoln Ave Ste 220, Miami Beach, FL 33139
Tel.: (954) 882-7951 FL
Year Founded: 2014
Rev.: $49,481
Assets: $1,035
Liabilities: $947,374
Net Worth: ($946,339)
Earnings: ($200,396)
Fiscal Year-end: 03/31/18
Online Games Publishing Services
N.A.I.C.S.: 541511
Panayis Palexas (Chm, Pres, CEO, CFO, Treas & Sec)

TRUPAY
810 Park Pl, Mishawaka, IN 46545
Tel.: (574) 256-5751
Web Site: http://www.trupay.com
Sales Range: $1-9.9 Million
Emp.: 39
Payroll Processing Services
N.A.I.C.S.: 541214
Mark Rutledge (Pres)
Miriam Shaffer (Principal & Exec VP)
Chris Sharp (Exec VP-Sls & Mktg)
Jack Wilkinson (Dir-Mktg)
Mike Rutledge (Acct Mgr-North Central Indiana)
Scott Holland (Principal & Exec VP-Fin)

TRUPOINT INC.
415 Bellbrook Ave, Xenia, OH 45385
Tel.: (937) 372-3541
Web Site: http://www.trupointe.com
Sales Range: $25-49.9 Million
Emp.: 200
Feed & Farm Supply
N.A.I.C.S.: 459999
Gordon Wallace (CEO)

TRUS-WAY, INC.
3901 NE 68th St, Vancouver, WA 98661
Tel.: (360) 750-1470
Web Site: http://www.trusway.com
Rev.: $12,100,000
Emp.: 120
Roof Truss Mfr
N.A.I.C.S.: 321215
Mark S. Turner (Pres)
Kenneth T. Carty (Treas & Sec)

TRUSANT TECHNOLOGIES, LLC.
6011 University Blvd Ste 400, Ellicott City, MD 21043-6107
Tel.: (410) 997-5400
Web Site: http://www.trusant.com
Year Founded: 2002
Rev.: $4,100,000
Emp.: 22
Computer Related Consulting Services
N.A.I.C.S.: 541512
Cindy Cacace (Engr-Software)

TRUSS SYSTEMS, INC.
1642 US Hwy 641 N, Benton, KY 42025-7462
Tel.: (270) 527-2601
Sales Range: $10-24.9 Million
Emp.: 7
Truss Mfr
N.A.I.C.S.: 321215
Darren Dodson (Pres)

TRUSS TECH INDUSTRIES INC.
4883 Roy Carlson Blvd B, Buford, GA 30518
Tel.: (770) 271-1347
Web Site:
 http://www.trusstechind.com
Year Founded: 1987
Sales Range: $10-24.9 Million
Emp.: 60
Mfr of Trusses & Wooden Roofs
N.A.I.C.S.: 321215
Alec Asgari (Pres)
Jay Asgari (VP-Production)
Bobby Asgari (VP-Sls & Engrg)

TRUSS-PRO'S, INC.
10954 424th Ave, Britton, SD 57430
Tel.: (605) 448-2202
Web Site: http://www.truss-pros.com
Year Founded: 1988
Sales Range: $10-24.9 Million
Emp.: 75
Truss Mfr
N.A.I.C.S.: 321215
Luke Kraft (Owner)

TRUSSBILT, LLC.
2375 Ariel St N, Maplewood, MN 55109
Tel.: (651) 633-6100
Web Site: http://www.trussbilt.com
Year Founded: 1926
Sales Range: $25-49.9 Million
Emp.: 130
Wood Window & Door Mfr
N.A.I.C.S.: 321911
Rob Henderson (Sr Project Mgr)
Brad Schotzko (Mgr-Sls & Mktg)
Kent Winkelman (Sr Project Mgr)
Eric Christensen (VP-Fin & Admin)

U.S. PRIVATE

TRUSSES UNLIMITED INC.
2167 W 18th St, Jacksonville, FL 32209
Tel.: (904) 355-6611
Web Site:
 http://www.lumberunlimited.com
Rev.: $17,923,627
Emp.: 170
Millwork
N.A.I.C.S.: 423310
Kenneth Kuester (Owner)
Paige Halley (Mgr-Sls)
Stan Kell (Gen Mgr)
Dave Myers (VP)

TRUSSVILLE GAS & WATER DEPARTMENTS
127 Mtn St, Trussville, AL 35173
Tel.: (205) 655-3211
Web Site: http://www.trussville.com
Rev.: $32,600,000
Emp.: 80
Natural Gas Distr
N.A.I.C.S.: 221210
Pat Sims (Sec)
William H. Wingate (Gen Mgr)

TRUSSWAY LTD.
9411 Alcorn St, Houston, TX 77093-6753
Tel.: (713) 691-6900 TX
Web Site: http://www.trussway.com
Year Founded: 1995
Sales Range: $200-249.9 Million
Emp.: 600
Structural Wood Members
N.A.I.C.S.: 321215
Jeff Tucker (Mgr-Plng)
Randy Ives (Dir-IT)
Rene Pena (Mgr-Ops)
Jeff Smith (Pres & CEO)
David Pogue (VP-Sls & Mktg)
Shane McCullough (Mgr-Ops)

TRUST COMPANIES OF AMERICA, INC.
201, Ctr Rd Ste 2, Venice, FL 34285
Tel.: (941) 493-3600 FL
Year Founded: 1993
Trust Services
N.A.I.C.S.: 525920
Suzanne Thacker (Coord-Compliance)
R.G. Caldwell Jr. (Pres & CEO)

Subsidiaries:

Caldwell Trust Company (1)
1400 Center Rd, Venice, FL 34292
Tel.: (941) 999-3376
Web Site: http://www.ctrust.com
Rev.: $600,000,000
Emp.: 20
Trust Services
N.A.I.C.S.: 525920
Sheryl Vieira (Asst VP-Mktg)
Susan D. Hines (Trust Officer & VP)
Jan Miller (Exec VP)
Wendy L. Fishman (Officer-Trust & Exec VP)
Alan Blair (Trust Officer & VP)
Scott T. Antritt (Officer-Trust & VP)
Ashley R. Harrison (Asst VP-Ops)
James F. Gabbert (Chm)
Leonard Nagel (CTO & Sr VP)
Suzanne B. Thacker (Coord-Compliance)
J. Chris McGee (Chief Investment Officer)
Tony Blasini (VP-Employee Benefits)
John Tufaro (Dir-Employee Benefits Dept)
Gina B. Jordan (Officer-Trust & Sr VP)
Sandra L. Pepper (Officer-Trust & Sr VP)
R. G. Caldwell Jr. (Pres & CEO)
H. Lee Thacker Jr. (Officer-Trust, Sec & Sr Exec VP)

TRUST HOSPITALITY LLC
806 Douglas Rd 4th Fl, Coral Gables, FL 33134
Tel.: (305) 537-7040

Web Site:
http://www.trusthospitality.com
Rev.: $81,000,000
Emp.: 600
Hotel Management
N.A.I.C.S.: 721110
Richard Millard (Chm & CEO)
Patrick Goddard (Pres & COO)
Michael Register (Partner & Head-Dev)
Dave MacRae (VP-Fin)
Teri Merritt (VP-Mktg)

TRUSTAFF, INC.
4270 Glendale Milford Rd, Cincinnati, OH 45242
Tel.: (513) 272-3999   OH
Web Site: http://www.trustaff.com
Year Founded: 2002
Sales Range: $50-74.9 Million
Emp.: 800
Women Healthcare Services
N.A.I.C.S.: 561320
Jerry Ball (Acct Mgr-Nursing)
Dave Hartman (Mgr-Housing & Travel)
Jeffrey Schoepf (Dir-Sls & Recruiting)
Pam Oliver (VP)
Kara Tudor (VP-Travel Nursing)
Gregg Harris (Chief Admin Officer)
Amy Hehman (Dir-HR)
Larry Hoelscher (VP)
Amber Keller (Coord-Compliance)
Sarah Gilbert (Coord-Billing)
Chanah Winter (Asst Acct Mgr)
Julie Fischer (Acct Mgr)
Rupreet Narula (Acct Mgr)
Trista Myers (Acct Mgr)
Gregg Fitzgerald (Acct Mgr)
Ben Sanchez (Acct Mgr)
Kristina Stoddart (Coord-HR)

TRUSTE
835 Market St Ste 800, San Francisco, CA 94103-1905
Tel.: (415) 520-3490
Web Site: http://www.truste.com
Year Founded: 1997
Sales Range: $1-9.9 Million
Emp.: 150
Online Privacy Services
N.A.I.C.S.: 541519
Tim Sullivan (CFO)
Chris Babel (CEO)
Dave Deasy (VP-Mktg)
Ken Okumura (VP-Engrg)
Kevin Trilli (VP-Product)
Ken Parnham (Mng Dir)
Ray Everett (Dir-Product Mgmt)
Elizabeth Blass (VP-Client Svcs)
Josh Harris (Dir-Policy)
Joanne Furtsch (Dir-Product & Policy)
Hilary Wandall (Chief Data Governance Officer & Gen Counsel)
Eleanor Treharne-Jones (Sr VP-Sls & Consulting)
Park Allen (VP-HR)

TRUSTED HEALTH PLAN, INC.
1100 New Jersey Ave SE Ste 840, Washington, DC 20003
Tel.: (202) 821-1100
Web Site: http://www.trustedhp.com
Health Plan Services
N.A.I.C.S.: 524114
Thomas Duncan (CEO)
Cleveland Slade (CFO)
Scott Pickens (COO)
Thomas Scully (Chm)

TRUSTED SUPPLY CHAIN PARTNERS
1625 Baker Dr, Ossian, IN 46777
Web Site: http://www.trustedmfg.com
Year Founded: 1991
Rev.: $5,000,000
Emp.: 45
Metals Mfr
N.A.I.C.S.: 423510
Lane Gerber (CEO)
Cheryl Gerber (Owner)
Michael Gerber (Owner)

TRUSTMARK MUTUAL HOLDING COMPANY
400 Field Dr, Lake Forest, IL 60045
Tel.: (847) 615-1500
Web Site: http://www.trustmarkinsurance.com
Year Founded: 1913
Sales Range: $900-999.9 Million
Emp.: 6,200
Holding Company
N.A.I.C.S.: 551112
Phil Goss (CFO & Sr VP)
David D. Weick (Chm)
Alex N. Moral (Sr VP)
John K. Anderson (Sr VP-Starmark, Managed Care & Strategic Growth Ventures)
Dan Simpson (CIO & Sr VP)
Jerry Hitpas (Sr VP-Investments & Risk Mgmt)
Kristin Zelkowitz (Chief HR Officer & Sr VP)
Steve Auburn (Gen Counsel, Sec & VP)
Kevin Slawin (CEO)
Dan Busiel (Chief Investment Officer & Sr VP)
Bill Gould (Pres & COO)

Subsidiaries:

Coresource Inc.   (1)
400 Field Dr, Lake Forest, IL 60045-4809
Tel.: (847) 604-9200
Web Site: http://www.coresource.com
Sales Range: $25-49.9 Million
Emp.: 15
Provider of Insurance Services
N.A.I.C.S.: 524114
Clare Smith (CFO & VP)
Nancy Eckrich (Pres & CEO)
Bob Wolfkiel (Pres-Northeast)
Steve Horvath (VP-Product Dev & Mktg)
Dave Kenney (VP-HR)
Lloyd Sarrel (COO)
Brooke Terry (CIO)
Kim Fiori (Pres-Central)
Ben Frisch (Pres-West)

Health Fitness Corporation   (1)
1700 W 82nd St Ste 200, Bloomington, MN 55431
Tel.: (952) 831-6830
Web Site: http://www.healthfitness.com
Sales Range: $75-99.9 Million
Emp.: 100
Health Improvement Program Services
N.A.I.C.S.: 923120
Paul Lotharius (Pres & CEO)
Steve Alavi (CFO)
Brian Harrigan (Sr VP-Sls & Dev)
Jen Smith (VP-Client Strategy & Growth)
Mark Totts (Sr VP-Solution Dev)
Ann Wyatt (VP-Program Mgmt & Engagement)
Andy Jacobson (Dir-Strategic Comm)
Mark Dogadalski (COO)

Starmark   (1)
400 Field Dr, Lake Forest, IL 60045-4809
Tel.: (847) 615-1313
Web Site: http://www.starmarkinc.com
Health & Life Insurance Services
N.A.I.C.S.: 524114

TRUSTPOINT INTERNATIONAL, LLC
3200 Cobb Galleria Pkwy Ste 200, Atlanta, GA 30339
Tel.: (404) 592-1872   GA
Web Site: http://www.trustpointintl.com
Year Founded: 2008
Sales Range: $25-49.9 Million
Emp.: 230

Law firm
N.A.I.C.S.: 541199
Mark Hawn (CEO)
Steve Simeone (CFO)
Ki Yun Hwang (COO-Review Svcs)
Phil Shellhaas (VP-eDiscovery Svcs)

Subsidiaries:

Alderson Reporting Co., Inc.   (1)
1111 14th St NW, Washington, DC 20005
Tel.: (202) 289-2260
Web Site: http://www.aldersonreporting.com
Court Reporting & Stenotype Services
N.A.I.C.S.: 561492
Christopher J. Gaskill (Dir-Bus Dev-Washington)
Joe Bradley (Dir-Resource Dev)
Liz Murphy (Dir-Bus Dev-Washington)
Amy Derr (Dir-Resource Dev-Washington)
Ariel Rayman (Exec Dir)
Cassandra Kowal (Dir-Resource Dev)
Joshua Fanning (Mgr-Federal Hearings)
Marvin Dumas (Dir-Bus Dev)

Kelly Law Registry   (1)
999 West Big Beaver Rd, Troy, MI 48084
Tel.: (248) 362-4444
Sales Range: $10-24.9 Million
Emp.: 48
Law Firm Employment Placement Services
N.A.I.C.S.: 561311

inWhatLanguage, LLC   (1)
3007 S W Temple Ste L, Salt Lake City, UT 84115
Tel.: (801) 618-3450
Web Site: http://www.inwhatlanguage.com
Sales Range: $1-9.9 Million
Emp.: 23
Software Development Services
N.A.I.C.S.: 541511
Cody Broderick (Founder & CEO)

TRUSTTEXAS BANK
121 E Courthouse Sta, Cuero, TX 77954
Tel.: (361) 275-2345
Web Site: http://www.trusttexasbank.com
Sales Range: $10-24.9 Million
Emp.: 60
Federal Savings & Loan Associations
N.A.I.C.S.: 522180
Jay Howard (Pres)
Sara Teague (Exec VP)
Susan Frels (Sr VP-HR)
Sean Garcia (Mgr & Asst VP)

TRUSWOOD INC.
8816 Running Oak Dr, Raleigh, NC 27617
Tel.: (919) 787-8787
Web Site: http://www.truswood.com
Sales Range: $10-24.9 Million
Emp.: 75
Wood Building Components
N.A.I.C.S.: 321215
Richard Watts (Pres)
Bill Jeffery (Mgr-Sls)

TRUVERIS, INC.
2 Park Ave Ste 1500, New York, NY 10016
Tel.: (800) 430-1430
Web Site: http://www.truveris.com
Year Founded: 2009
Sales Range: $25-49.9 Million
Emp.: 118
Health Care Srvices
N.A.I.C.S.: 621498
Joanne Biscardi (Sr VP-Life Sciences)
Michael Napolitano (Sr VP-Payer Sls)
Nanette Oddo (Pres & CEO)
Paige Northup (Mktg Mgr-Strategic)

TRUWEST CREDIT UNION
1667 N Priest Dr, Tempe, AZ 85281
Tel.: (480) 441-5900   AZ
Web Site: http://www.truwest.org

Year Founded: 1952
Sales Range: $25-49.9 Million
Emp.: 256
Credit Union
N.A.I.C.S.: 522130
Chris Kearney (CIO & Sr VP)
Alan Althouse (Pres & CEO)
Jeff Peabody (CMO & Sr VP)
Gary Bernard (COO & Exec VP)
Mark Hunton (VP-Member Bus Lending)
Farid Farbod (Chief Lending Officer & Sr VP)

TRY-IT DISTRIBUTING CO. INC.
4155 Walden Ave, Lancaster, NY 14086-1512
Tel.: (716) 651-3551
Web Site: http://www.tryitdist.com
Lessors of Nonresidential Buildings
N.A.I.C.S.: 531120
Eugene P. Vukelic (CEO)

Subsidiaries:

Saratoga Eagle Sales & Services   (1)
45 Duplainville Rd, Saratoga Springs, NY 12866
Tel.: (518) 581-7377
Beverages Mfr
N.A.I.C.S.: 424820
Jeff Vukelic (Pres)

Subsidiary (Domestic):

Plattsburgh Distributing Co., Inc.   (2)
217 Sharron Ave, Plattsburgh, NY 12901
Tel.: (518) 561-3800
Web Site: http://www.plattsburghdistributing.com
Sales Range: $1-9.9 Million
Emp.: 20
Beer & Ale Merchant Whslr
N.A.I.C.S.: 424810
John Fisher (Owner & Pres)
Jim Cring (Mgr)
Tina Olsen (Mgr-Inventory)

TRYCERA FINANCIAL, INC.
18100 Von Karman Ave Ste 850, Irvine, CA 92612
Tel.: (949) 705-4480   NV
Web Site: http://www.trycera.com
Year Founded: 2004
Sales Range: Less than $1 Million
Emp.: 4
Financial Services
N.A.I.C.S.: 522320
Ray A. Smith (Pres & CEO)
Matthew Richards (Chm)
Carl Giese (VP-Credit Svcs)
Shampa Mitra-Reddy (Gen Counsel & VP-Bus Dev)

TRYKO PARTNERS, LLC
1608 Rt 88, Brick, NJ 08724
Tel.: (732) 961-9991
Web Site: http://www.tryko.com
Year Founded: 1989
Emp.: 3,800
Real Estate Investment Services
N.A.I.C.S.: 523940
Yitzchok Rokowsky (CEO)
Chad Buchanan (Chief Investment Officer)
Yonah Kohn (Pres)
Uri Kahanow (Dir-Acq)
Ari Holtz (CFO)

Subsidiaries:

Hopkins Manor Ltd.   (1)
610 Smithfield Rd, North Providence, RI 02904
Tel.: (401) 353-6300
Web Site: http://www.hopkinsmanor.com
Nursing Care Facilities
N.A.I.C.S.: 623110
Lawrence S. Gates (Sec)

TRYKO PARTNERS, LLC

Tryko Partners, LLC—(Continued)

Marquis Health Services (1)
635 Duquesne Blvd, Brick, NJ 08723
Tel.: (732) 903-1900
Web Site: http://www.mhslp.com
Healthcare Investment Firm Services
N.A.I.C.S.: 523940
Norman Rokeach (CEO)
Barry Munk (COO)
Adam Goldman (VP-HR & Employee Engagement-LNHA)
Jennifer M. Hertzog (VP-Mktg & Bus Dev-Mid-Atlantic Reg)
Dina Harman (VP-Clinical Svcs)
Andrea Gele (VP-Case Mgmt)
Yogesh V. Viroja (Chief Medical Officer & VP-Medical Affairs)
Sharon Donaghue (Sr VP-Ops-New England)

TRYLON SMR
41 East 11th St, New York, NY 10003
Tel.: (212) 725-2295
Year Founded: 1990
Sales Range: $1-9.9 Million
Emp.: 14
Public Relations Agency
N.A.I.C.S.: 541820
Lloyd Trufelman (Pres & CEO)

TRYON DISTRIBUTING CO. LLC
4701 Stockholm Ct, Charlotte, NC 28273
Tel.: (704) 334-0849
Web Site: http://www.tryondist.com
Sales Range: $10-24.9 Million
Emp.: 85
Wine Distr
N.A.I.C.S.: 424820
Brad Johnston (Pres)
Steve Davis (District Mgr-Off Premise)
Don Helton (VP-Ops)
Kerry Smith (Mgr-Northern Coastal)
Brent Hinson (Controller)
Rodney Plachy (Dir-Trng & Sls)
Brooke Heavner (Mgr-Acct)
Stephanie Winslow (Mgr-HR)
Leslie Eldredge (Mgr-Off Premise District)
Derek Sides (Mgr-On Premise District)
Chris Mincey (Mgr-Statewide Beer Brand)
Randy Clower (Mgr-Statewide Wine Brand)
Shelley Granger (Mgr-Statewide Wine Brand)
Jim Litton (Mgr-StatewideOff Premise)
Dale Cannon (Mgr-Triangle Area)
Angie Packer (Owner & Sr VP)
Max Perkins (VP-Sls)

TRYSPORTS, LLC
1903 Towne Centre Blvd, Mount Pleasant, SC 29464
Tel.: (843) 849-9292
Web Site: http://www.trysports.com
Year Founded: 2003
Rev.: $3,000,000
Emp.: 50
Sporting Goods Retailer
N.A.I.C.S.: 459110
James M. Kirwan (Owner)

TRYSTAR, LLC
2917 Industrial Dr, Faribault, MN 55021
Tel.: (507) 333-3990
Web Site: http://www.trystar.com
Year Founded: 1992
Sales Range: $10-24.9 Million
Emp.: 50
Wiring Device Mfr
N.A.I.C.S.: 335931
Pamela Dahl (CFO & Sec)

Subsidiaries:

Cyber Sciences Inc. (1)
715 Richard Rd, Murfreesboro, TN 37129-1164
Tel.: (615) 890-6709
Web Site: http://www.cyber-sciences.com
Computer Related Services
N.A.I.C.S.: 541519
Lee Wallis (Mgr)

Oztek Corp. (1)
11 Continental Blvd Unit B, Merrimack, NH 03054
Tel.: (603) 546-0090
Web Site: http://www.oztekcorp.com
Electrical Equipment & Component Mfr
N.A.I.C.S.: 335900
John O'Connor (Pres & CEO)

TS RECREATIONAL, INC.
1682 US Hwy 10 E, Detroit Lakes, MN 56501
Tel.: (218) 844-3033 MN
Web Site: http://www.recreationalsalvage.com
Year Founded: 1995
Sales Range: $1-9.9 Million
Used Recreation Equipment Auctioneer
N.A.I.C.S.: 459999
Todd Simison (Owner)

Subsidiaries:

TS Dock & Lift Services (1)
1682 Hwy 10 E, Detroit Lakes, MN 56501
Tel.: (218) 844-3033
Web Site: http://www.tsdockandlift.com
Dock Dealer & Maintenance Services
N.A.I.C.S.: 459999
Todd Simison (Gen Mgr)

TSA CONSULTING GROUP, INC.
15 Yacht Club Dr NE, Fort Walton Beach, FL 32548
Tel.: (850) 244-7308 FL
Web Site: http://www.tsacg.com
Year Founded: 1997
Sales Range: $10-24.9 Million
Emp.: 10
Retirement Plan Compliance & Administration Services
N.A.I.C.S.: 541611
Kevin Hensley (COO & Sr VP)
Sherry Marcolongo (Dir-Corp Comm)
Brad Hope (Chief Revenue Officer & Exec VP)
Joseph E. Rollins Jr. (Pres & CEO)

TSAMOUTALES STRATEGIES
225 S Adams St Ste 200, Tallahassee, FL 32301
Tel.: (850) 294-4009
Web Site: http://www.tsamoutales.com
Year Founded: 2009
Sales Range: $1-9.9 Million
Government Relations, Business Development & Management Consulting Services
N.A.I.C.S.: 541618
Frank N. Tsamoutales (Pres)
Sarah Huckabee Sanders (VP)
Daphne E. Gilbert (Dir-Admin)

TSAWORLD INC.
3011-B Adriatic Ct, Norcross, GA 30071
Tel.: (770) 417-2323
Web Site: http://www.tsaworld.com
Year Founded: 1999
Rev.: $7,500,000
Emp.: 27
Office Equipment Merchant Whslr
N.A.I.C.S.: 423420
James J. Spall (Pres)

TSAY CORPORATION

Hwy 68 N of Espanola, San Juan Pueblo, NM 87566
Tel.: (505) 747-0700
Web Site: http://www.tsay.com
Year Founded: 1990
Sales Range: $75-99.9 Million
Emp.: 800
Holding Company; Commercial Building Construction
N.A.I.C.S.: 551112
Deborah Carrillo (CFO)
Ron Lovato (CEO)
Bruce Fraser (Gen Mgr)

Subsidiaries:

Tsay Construction & Services, LLC (1)
Hwy 68 N of Espanola PO Box 1079, San Juan Pueblo, NM 87566
Tel.: (505) 747-2495
Sales Range: $10-24.9 Million
Emp.: 60
Construction & Support Services
N.A.I.C.S.: 236220

TSB BANK
695 E Ave, Lomira, WI 53048
Tel.: (920) 269-7777
Web Site: http://www.tsbbanking.com
Year Founded: 1905
Sales Range: $50-74.9 Million
Emp.: 35
Retail & Commercial Banking Services
N.A.I.C.S.: 522180
Ryan J. Mueller (VP)
Becky L. Feucht (COO & VP)
Donna Cooper (CEO)

TSB BANKSHARES, INC.
695 E Ave, Lomira, WI 53048
Tel.: (920) 269-7777 WI
Web Site: http://www.tsbbanking.com
Year Founded: 1997
Sales Range: $25-49.9 Million
Emp.: 20
Bank Holding Company
N.A.I.C.S.: 551111
Thomas M. O'Connor (Chm & CEO)

TSB SERVICES INC.
1 N Main St PO Box 386, Spencer, NY 14883-0386
Tel.: (607) 589-7000
Web Site: http://www.tiogabank.com
Sales Range: $10-24.9 Million
Emp.: 103
Bank Holding Company
N.A.I.C.S.: 551111
Robert M. Fisher (Pres & CEO-Tioga State Bank)
Anne E. McKenna (Sr VP-Fin & Control)
George J. Bowen (Chief Lending Officer & Sr VP-Tioga State Bank)
Jennifer Moraczewski (Sr VP-Ops & Tech)
Christopher P. Powers (Sr VP-HR)
Lisa J. Welch (Chief Credit Officer & Sr VP)

Subsidiaries:

Tioga State Bank (1)
1 Main St, Spencer, NY 14883
Tel.: (607) 659-5125
Web Site: http://www.tiogabank.com
Sales Range: $50-74.9 Million
Emp.: 100
Provider of Banking Services
N.A.I.C.S.: 522110
Robert M. Fisher (Pres & CEO)
Anne E. McKenna (Sr VP-Fin)
George J. Bowen (Chief Lending Officer & Sr VP)
Christopher P. Powers (Sr VP-HR)
Lisa J. Welch (Chief Credit Officer & Sr VP)

TSC ACQUISITION CORP.

1100 Glendon Ave Ste 905, Los Angeles, CA 90024
Tel.: (310) 696-4001 DE
Year Founded: 2006
Sales Range: $25-49.9 Million
Telecommunication Servicesb
N.A.I.C.S.: 517810
Nathan Johnson (CEO)

TSE
108 5th Ave NW, Arlington, MN 55307
Tel.: (507) 964-2237
Web Site: http://www.tseinc.net
Year Founded: 1972
Sales Range: $10-24.9 Million
Emp.: 260
Molded Cable Assemblies for Electronics
N.A.I.C.S.: 334419
Kirk Mikkelsen (Dir-Engrg)
Mike Checketts (Dir-QA & RA & Tech)
Larry Gillard (Dir-Sls & Mktg)

TSE INDUSTRIES INC.
4370 112th Ter N, Clearwater, FL 33762-4902
Tel.: (727) 573-7676 FL
Web Site: http://www.tse-industries.com
Year Founded: 1961
Sales Range: $25-49.9 Million
Emp.: 200
Mfr of Plastic Products
N.A.I.C.S.: 326199
Robert R. Klingel (Chm, Pres & CEO)
Gary A. Reese (VP-Sls-EPD)
Diane M. Klingel (VP)
David J. Tottle (CFO & Treas)

TSG CONSUMER PARTNERS LLC
600 Montgomery St Ste 2900, San Francisco, CA 94111-3420
Tel.: (415) 217-2300 DE
Web Site: http://www.tsgconsumer.com
Year Founded: 1987
Privater Equity Firm
N.A.I.C.S.: 523999
Charles Esserman (Founder, Chm & CEO)
Pierre LeComte (Mng Dir)
Blythe Jack (Mng Dir)
Michael Layman (Mng Dir)
Monica Chase (Mng Dir & Head-IR)
Diane Miles (CEO-TSG Beauty & Partner-Operating)
Colin Welch (Mng Dir)
Edward Wong (Principal)
Adam Hemmer (Sr VP)
Jessica Duran (Mng Dir, CFO & Chief Compliance Officer)
Rana Mogannam (Office Mgr)
Jessica Tarabay (Mgr-Tax)
Melissa Tison (Controller)
Charles Esserman (CEO, Co-Founder & Chm)
James O'Hara (Pres)
Daniel Costello (Mng Dir)
Alex Gilmore (VP)
James L. O'Hara (Pres)
Hadley Mullin (Sr Mng Dir)

Subsidiaries:

Backcountry.com, Inc. (1)
2607 S Decker Lake Blvd Ste 150, Salt Lake City, UT 84119
Tel.: (801) 973-4553
Web Site: http://www.backcountry.com
Outdoor & Country Clothing Retailer
N.A.I.C.S.: 459999
Jim Holland (Founder)
Peter Eischeid (Exec VP-Product & Engrg)
Pete Labore (COO)
Jon Armitage (CMO)

COMPANIES

Thomas Jeon *(Gen Counsel & Exec VP-HR)*
Diana Seung *(Exec VP-Merchandising)*
Girish Satya *(CFO-Global)*
Melanie Cox *(CEO)*

CorePower Yoga, LLC (1)
3001 Brighton Blvd Ste 269, Denver, CO 80216
Tel.: (866) 441-9642
Web Site: http://www.corepoweryoga.com
Sales Range: $50-74.9 Million
Fitness Facility Operator
N.A.I.C.S.: 713940
Chad Kilpatrick *(CFO)*
Christine Mosher *(Dir-Retail Ops)*

Duckhorn Wine Company (1)
1000 Lodi Ln, Saint Helena, CA 94574
Tel.: (707) 963-7108
Web Site:
  http://www.duckhornwinecompany.com
Winery
N.A.I.C.S.: 312130
Daniel Duckhorn *(Chm & Co-Founder)*
Margaret Duckhorn *(Co-Founder)*
Alex Ryan *(Pres & CEO)*
Zach Rasmuson *(COO & Sr VP)*
Lori Beaudoin *(CFO & Sr VP)*
Carol Reber *(CMO, Chief Business Dev Officer & Sr VP)*
Pete Przybylinski *(Sr VP-Sls & Strategy)*
Sean Sullivan *(Gen Counsel, Sr VP & Head-M&A)*

Subsidiary (Domestic):

KB Wines, LLC (2)
220 Morris St, Sebastopol, CA 95472
Tel.: (707) 823-7430
Web Site: http://www.kostabrowne.com
Alcoholic Beverages Mfr
N.A.I.C.S.: 312130
Dan Kosta *(Founder)*
Micheal Browne *(Founder)*

LuckyVitamin LLC (1)
555 N Ln Ste 6050, Conshohocken, PA 19428
Tel.: (610) 635-0474
Web Site: http://www.luckyvitamin.com
Health & Wellness Product Distr
N.A.I.C.S.: 456191
Steve Cone *(Dir-IT)*
Deanne Cunningham *(Mgr-Data Maintenance)*
Sam Wolf *(Founder & CEO)*

Nuun & Co., Inc. (1)
800 Maynard Ave S Ste 102, Seattle, WA 98134
Tel.: (206) 219-9237
Web Site: http://www.nuun.com
Sales Range: $1-9.9 Million
Emp.: 16
Mfr of Dissolvable Electrolyte Tablets
N.A.I.C.S.: 312111
Tyler Smith *(Dir-Sls Sports Specialty)*
Kevin Rutherford *(CEO)*

Pabst Brewing Company (1)
10635 Santa Monica Blvd Ste 350, Los Angeles, CA 90025
Web Site: http://pabstbrewingco.com
Sales Range: $50-74.9 Million
Beer Mfr
N.A.I.C.S.: 312120
Eugene Kashper *(Chm)*
Lyssa Reynolds *(VP-HR)*
Matt Bruhn *(Chief Mktg Officer)*
Ron Kane *(Chief Supply Chain Officer)*
Brian Smith *(Chief Sls Officer)*
Eric Tis *(CFO)*
Rob Urband *(Chief Legal Officer)*
Paul Chibe *(CEO)*

Paige Denim (1)
3040 E Ana St, Rancho Dominguez, CA 90221
Tel.: (310) 733-2100
Web Site: http://www.paigeusa.com
Men's & Women's Jeans Designer, Distr & Online Retailer
N.A.I.C.S.: 424350
Paige Adams-Geller *(Founder & Dir-Creative)*

TSG Consumer Partners LLC - New York Office (1)
712 5th Ave 46st Fl, New York, NY 10019
Tel.: (212) 265-4111
Web Site: http://www.tsgconsumer.com
Sales Range: $50-74.9 Million
Emp.: 60
Privater Equity Firm
N.A.I.C.S.: 523999
Edward Wong *(VP)*
David Anderson *(Mng Dir-IR)*
Kelly Pease *(VP)*

TSG INC.
1400 Welsh Rd, North Wales, PA 19454-1906
Tel.: (215) 628-2000   PA
Web Site:
  http://www.tsgcombeau.com
Year Founded: 1901
Sales Range: $25-49.9 Million
Emp.: 200
Paper Mills
N.A.I.C.S.: 322120
Michael Goldman *(Plant Mgr)*

TSHIRTBORDELLO.COM
6900 Phillips Hwy Ste 51, Jacksonville, FL 32216
Tel.: (904) 758-3320
Web Site:
  http://www.tshirtbordello.com
Sales Range: $1-9.9 Million
Emp.: 5
Online Tee Shirt & Related Products Retailer
N.A.I.C.S.: 424350
Don Myers *(Owner & CEO)*

TSI
102 F Ctr Blvd, Marlton, NJ 08053
Tel.: (856) 988-9900   NJ
Web Site: http://www.tsirep.com
Year Founded: 1931
Sales Range: $75-99.9 Million
Emp.: 12
Electronic Components Distr
N.A.I.C.S.: 459910
Jim Macchione *(VP)*
Peter Thomas *(Co-Owner & Pres)*

TSI GLOBAL COMPANIES
700 Fountain Lakes Blvd, Saint Charles, MO 63301
Tel.: (636) 949-8889
Web Site: http://www.tsi-global.com
Year Founded: 1987
Sales Range: $25-49.9 Million
Emp.: 110
Construction Services
N.A.I.C.S.: 238170
Robert T. Bray *(Owner)*

TSI GRAPHICS INC.
1300 S Raney, Effingham, IL 62401
Tel.: (217) 347-7733
Web Site: http://www.tsigraphics.com
Rev.: $10,000,000
Emp.: 50
Typographic Composition
N.A.I.C.S.: 323120
Ralph E. Hoffman *(CEO)*
Richard A. Whitsitt *(Pres)*

TSI HEALTHCARE, INC
101 Europa Dr Ste 200, Chapel Hill, NC 27517
Tel.: (919) 929-8251
Web Site:
  http://www.tsihealthcare.com
Year Founded: 1997
Sales Range: $10-24.9 Million
Emp.: 77
IT Software & Consulting
N.A.I.C.S.: 513210
Glenn Dickson *(COO)*
David M. Dickson Jr. *(Founder, Pres & CEO)*

TSI HOLDING COMPANY
999 Executive Pkwy Dr Ste 202, Saint Louis, MO 63141
Tel.: (314) 628-6030
Web Site: http://www.tsiholding.com
Sales Range: $10-24.9 Million
Emp.: 6
Pipe & Tubing, Steel
N.A.I.C.S.: 423510
John C. Hauck *(CEO)*
Craig J. Iammarino *(Exec VP)*
Annette M. Eckerle *(CFO & Sr VP)*

Subsidiaries:

Miami Air International, Inc. (1)
5000 NW 36th St Ste 307, Miami, FL 33122
Tel.: (305) 876-3600
Web Site: http://www.miamiair.com
Passenger Air Transportation Services
N.A.I.C.S.: 481211
Armando Martinez *(Sr Dir-Safety & Security)*
Kurt Kamrad *(Pres & CEO)*
Mirella Quadri *(Dir-HR)*
Rafael Dovarganes *(VP-Bus Ops)*
Sheila Britt *(Acct Exec)*
Jennifer Cook *(Dir-Sls)*
Uganda Dawkins *(Acct Exec)*
Carla Manechini *(Acct Exec)*

TSI HOLDINGS, LLC
2200 Cassens Dr, Fenton, MO 63026
Tel.: (636) 349-1233
Web Site: http://tsiholdingsllc.com
Sales Range: $10-24.9 Million
Emp.: 100
Flame Retardent Chemicals Mfr
N.A.I.C.S.: 325998
Joseph T. Neubauer *(Gen Mgr)*
Allen Thorpe *(Mgr-Quality Assurance)*
David O'Bryant *(Mgr-Quality Control)*

TSI INCORPORATED
500 Cardigan Rd, Shoreview, MN 55126-3903
Tel.: (651) 490-2860   MT
Web Site: http://www.tsi.com
Year Founded: 1961
Sales Range: $75-99.9 Million
Emp.: 800
Precision Instrument Mfr
N.A.I.C.S.: 334519
Kevin Krause *(VP)*
Chris Zimick *(Dir-IT)*
Ricky Holm *(Project Mgr-Engrg)*
Todd Campbell *(Engr-Electrical)*
Steve Kerrigan *(Engr-Design)*

Subsidiaries:

MSP Corporation (1)
5910 Rice Creek Pkwy Ste 300, Shoreview, MN 55126
Tel.: (651) 287-8100
Web Site: http://www.mspcorp.com
Sales Range: $1-9.9 Million
Emp.: 33
Scientific Equipment Supplier
N.A.I.C.S.: 541990
William Dick *(Mgr-Product)*

TSI AB (1)
Lindberghs Gata 9, Arlanda Stad, 195 61, Stockholm, Sweden   (100%)
Tel.: (46) 859513230
Web Site: http://www.tsi.com
Sales Range: $25-49.9 Million
Emp.: 11
Precision Instruments Sales & Service
N.A.I.C.S.: 334519

TSI France, Inc. (1)
Europarc Bat D Technopole De Chateau Gombert, F 13013, Marseilles, France   (100%)
Tel.: (33) 491955008
Web Site: http://www.tsi.com
Sales Range: $10-24.9 Million
Emp.: 5
Precision Instruments Sales & Service
N.A.I.C.S.: 334519

TSI GmbH (1)
Neukoellner Strasse 4, 52068, Aachen, Germany   (100%)
Tel.: (49) 241523030
Web Site: http://www.tsi.com
Sales Range: $25-49.9 Million
Emp.: 20
Precision Instruments Sales & Service
N.A.I.C.S.: 332721

TSI Instrument (Beijing) Co.,Ltd. (1)
Unit 1201 Pan-Pacific Plaza No 12 A Zhongguancun South Avenue, Haidian District, Beijing, 100081, China
Tel.: (86) 10 8219 7688
Precision Measurement Product Mfr & Whslr
N.A.I.C.S.: 332721

TSI Instruments India Private Limited (1)
3rd Floor Sri Sai Heights 447 17th Cross 17th Main Sector 4 HSR Layout, Bengaluru, 560034, India
Tel.: (91) 80 67877200
Web Site: http://www.tsi.com
Sales Range: $10-24.9 Million
Emp.: 8
Precision Measurement Product Mfr & Whslr
N.A.I.C.S.: 332721
Sachin Gokak *(Country Mgr)*

TSI Instruments Ltd. (1)
Stirling Road, High Wycombe, HP12 3ST, Bucks, United Kingdom
Tel.: (44) 1494459200
Web Site: http://www.tsiinc.co.uk
Sales Range: $10-24.9 Million
Emp.: 50
Precision Instruments Sales & Service
N.A.I.C.S.: 811210
Mark Crooks *(Reg Mgr-Sls)*

TSI Instruments Singapore Pte Ltd. (1)
150 Kampong Ampat 05-05 KA Centre, Singapore, 368324, Singapore
Tel.: (65) 65956388
Web Site: http://www.tsi.com
Sales Range: $10-24.9 Million
Emp.: 13
Precision Measurement Product Whslr
N.A.I.C.S.: 332721
Edward Chow *(Gen Mgr)*

Tekran Instruments Corporation (1)
330 Nantucket Boulevard, Toronto, M1P 2P4, ON, Canada
Tel.: (416) 449-3084
Web Site: http://www.tekran.com
Sales Range: $10-24.9 Million
Emp.: 20
Environmental Monitoring Equipment Mfr
N.A.I.C.S.: 334513
Karl Wilber *(Exec VP & Gen Mgr)*

TSK PARTNERS, INC.

TSK PARTNERS, INC.
1533 E 12th St, Erie, PA 16511
Tel.: (814) 459-4495
Web Site:
  http://www.mcinnesrolledrings.com
Year Founded: 1992
Sales Range: $10-24.9 Million
Emp.: 84
Iron & Steel Forging Services
N.A.I.C.S.: 332111
Timothy M. Hunter *(Pres & CEO)*
John Christie *(Gen Mgr-Sls)*
Christine Crotty *(CFO)*
Paul Janicke *(VP-Ops)*
Shawn O'Brien *(VP-Sls & Mktg)*

Subsidiaries:

McInnes Rolled Rings (1)
1533 E 12th St, Erie, PA 16511-1747
Tel.: (814) 459-4495
Web Site:
  http://www.mcinnesrolledrings.com
Seamless Rolled Rings Mfr
N.A.I.C.S.: 332111
Paul Janicke *(VP-Ops)*
Christine Crotty *(CFO)*
Timothy M. Hunter *(Pres & CEO)*
John Christie *(Gen Mgr-Sls)*
Jeremy Plummer *(Gen Mgr-Ops)*

TSL COMPANIES

TSL Companies—(Continued)

TSL COMPANIES
10001 S 152nd St, Omaha, NE 68138
Tel.: (402) 895-6692
Web Site: http://www.4tsl.com
Sales Range: $10-24.9 Million
Emp.: 60
Provider of Truck Transportation Services
N.A.I.C.S.: 488510
Tom Hastings (Pres)
Erik Wiegert (VP)
Mike Contreras (VP)
Brooklynne Rosado (Acct Mgr)

Subsidiaries:

Rail Intermodel Specialists (1)
10001 S 152nd St, Omaha, NE 68138
Tel.: (402) 895-6980
Web Site: http://www.onlinelogistics.com
Transportation Agents & Brokers
N.A.I.C.S.: 488510
Tom Hastings (Owner & Pres)

TranSpec Leasing Inc. (1)
10001 S 152nd St, Omaha, NE 68138
Tel.: (402) 895-8096
Web Site: http://www.onlinelogistics.com
Truck Lessor
N.A.I.C.S.: 532120
Tom Hastings (Pres)

Transportation Specialists Ltd. (1)
10001 S 152nd St, Omaha, NE 68138
Tel.: (402) 895-9610
Web Site: http://www.4tsl.com
Rev.: $4,000,000
Emp.: 48
Contract Haulers
N.A.I.C.S.: 484121
Tom Hastings (Pres)

Truck Track Logistics Ltd. (1)
10001 S 152nd St, Omaha, NE 68138
Tel.: (402) 895-8096
Web Site: http://www.4tsl.com
Sales Range: $10-24.9 Million
Truck Transportation Brokers
N.A.I.C.S.: 488510

TSL LTD.
5217 Monroe St, Toledo, OH 43623
Tel.: (419) 843-3200
Sales Range: $25-49.9 Million
Emp.: 2,495
Trucking Service
N.A.I.C.S.: 561320
Jim Newsome (VP)

TSS TECHNOLOGIES INCORPORATED
1201 Hill Smith Dr, Cincinnati, OH 45215
Tel.: (513) 772-7000
Web Site: http://www.tsstech.com
Year Founded: 1948
Sales Range: $10-24.9 Million
Emp.: 110
Machine Shop, Jobbing & Repair
N.A.I.C.S.: 332710
Greg Freese (Engr-Application)
Brenda Harmon (Engr-Quality)
Erika Jacobs (Coord-Pur)
Ron Zeilman (Assoc Dir)
Marc Drapp (CEO)
Shirish Pareek (Chm)

TSS-RADIO
344 N Ogden Ave, Chicago, IL 60607-1508
Tel.: (773) 772-4340
Web Site: http://www.tss-radio.com
Year Founded: 2005
Sales Range: $1-9.9 Million
Emp.: 12
Satellite Radio & Accessories Online Retail
N.A.I.C.S.: 449210
Taylor Mitchell (Co-Founder)

TST INC.
11601 Etiwanda Ave, Fontana, CA 92337-6929
Tel.: (951) 685-2155
Web Site: http://www.tst-inc.com
Year Founded: 1976
Sales Range: $10-24.9 Million
Emp.: 300
Secondary Nonferrous Metals
N.A.I.C.S.: 331314
Robert A. Stein (Owner)
Andrew Stein (CEO)
Jim Davidson (Controller)

Subsidiaries:

TST Inc. - STANDARD METALS Division (1)
2032 E 220th St, Long Beach, CA 90810
Tel.: (310) 835-0115
Aluminum Product Mfr & Distr
N.A.I.C.S.: 331523

TSUNAMI MARKETING
2469-C Puu Rd, Kalaheo, HI 96741
Tel.: (808) 332-7992
Web Site: http://www.tsunamimarketing.com
Year Founded: 1991
Sales Range: Less than $1 Million
Emp.: 5
Advetising Agency
N.A.I.C.S.: 541810
Robert Rekward (Creative Dir)
Valerie Rekward (Owner)
Teresa Caries (Office Mgr)

TSYMMETRY, INC.
1101 Penn Ave NW Ste 850, Washington, DC 20004
Tel.: (202) 480-2020
Web Site: http://www.tsymmetry.com
Year Founded: 1999
Sales Range: $10-24.9 Million
Emp.: 85
Computer System Design Services
N.A.I.C.S.: 541512
Philip Lowit (Co-Founder & CEO)
David Lowit (Co-Founder & Chm)
Jessica Jewart (Sr Mgr-Resource)

TT OF COLUMBIA, INC.
106 S James Campbell Blvd, Columbia, TN 38401-4324
Tel.: (931) 380-0800
Web Site: http://www.chryslerdodgejeeprramofcolumbia.com
Sales Range: $10-24.9 Million
New & Used Car Dealer
N.A.I.C.S.: 441110
Eddie Collier (Owner)

TTC GROUP, INC.
310 Lexington Ave Ste 10H, New York, NY 10016
Tel.: (646) 290-6400
Web Site: http://www.ttcominc.com
Sales Range: $1-9.9 Million
Emp.: 9
Public Relations
N.A.I.C.S.: 541820
Victor J. Allgeier (Pres)
David Reynolds (Partner)
Jim Kirkwood (CEO)

TTC INNOVATIONS
3281 Avenida De Sueno, Carlsbad, CA 92009
Tel.: (913) 268-4400
Web Site: http://www.ttcinnovations.com
Year Founded: 2001
Sales Range: $1-9.9 Million
Emp.: 65
Professional Training Services
N.A.I.C.S.: 611430
Debbie Wooldridge (Pres)

TTC MARKETING SOLUTIONS
3945 N Neenah Ave, Chicago, IL 60634
Tel.: (773) 545-0407
Web Site: http://www.callttc.com
Year Founded: 1984
Sales Range: $25-49.9 Million
Emp.: 300
Inbound & Outbound Telemarketing
N.A.I.C.S.: 561422
Mary Shanley (Pres)
Noreen Shanley (VP)
Bob Aloisio (VP-Sls & Mktg)

Subsidiaries:

Telemarketing Co., Inc. (1)
3945 N Neenah Ave, Chicago, IL 60634
Tel.: (773) 545-0407
Web Site: http://www.ttcmarketingsolutions.com
Sales Range: $10-24.9 Million
Telemarketing Services
N.A.I.C.S.: 561422

TTCP MANAGEMENT SERVICES, LLC.
3600 American Blvd W., Ste 150, Bloomington, MN 55431
Tel.: (952) 540-4500
Web Site: https://www.ttcapitalpartners.com
Private Equity
N.A.I.C.S.: 523940

Subsidiaries:

Propio Language Services, LLC. (1)
10801 Mastin St. #580, Overland Park, KS 66210
Tel.: (913) 381-3143
Web Site: http://www.propio-ls.com
Sales Range: $1-9.9 Million
Emp.: 70
Language Interpretation Services
N.A.I.C.S.: 541930
Joe Fackrell (Founder & Partner)
Douglas Judd (Partner-Fin & Ops)
Brian Simkins (Partner-IT)
Robert Campbell (Partner-Strategy & Bus Dev)

Subsidiary (Domestic):

Telelanguage Inc. (2)
514 SW 6th Ave, Portland, OR 97204-1624
Tel.: (503) 535-2176
Web Site: http://www.telelanguage.com
Translation & Interpretation Services
N.A.I.C.S.: 541930

United Language Group, Inc. (2)
315 E Lake Ste #301, Wayzata, MN 55391
Tel.: (612) 916-6060
Language Service Provider
N.A.I.C.S.: 611630
Tim Kubicek (Sr Dir-Fin & Acctg)
Nicholas McMahon (CEO)

Subsidiary (Domestic):

KJ International Resources Ltd. (3)
800 Washington Ave N Ste 905, Minneapolis, MN 55401-1195
Tel.: (612) 288-9494
Web Site: http://www.kjinternational.com
Translation & Interpretation Services
N.A.I.C.S.: 541930
Kristen Giovanis (Co-founder & CEO)
Janna Lundberg (Co-founder)

TTCU THE CREDIT UNION
3720 E 31st St, Tulsa, OK 74135
Tel.: (918) 744-7158
Web Site: http://www.ttcu.com
Year Founded: 1934
Rev.: $97,700,000
Assets: $1,885,000,000
Liabilities: $499,000,000
Net Worth: $1,386,000,000
Earnings: $21,800,000
Fiscal Year-end: 12/31/18
Financial Credit Union
N.A.I.C.S.: 522130

Shelby Beil (CFO & CTO)
Tim Lyons (Pres & CEO)
Clark Ogilvie (Chm)
Saundra Ford (Treas & Sec)
Steve Pittman (Vice Chm)
Chuck Chastain (Chief Sls & Ops Officer)
Jerry Hoopert (Sr VP-Facilities)
Stephanie Jones (Chief Strategy Officer)
Liz Stidham (Sr VP-Branch Ops)
Celia Armstrong (Sr VP-HR)
Dan Newberry (Sr VP-Lending)
Andy Tripp (Sr VP-Tech)
Donita Quesnel (VP-Mktg)

TTG EQUIPMENT, LLC
5068 E 100 N, Bluffton, IN 46714
Tel.: (800) 876-9351
Web Site: http://www.ttgequipment.com
Year Founded: 2019
Turf & Utility Equipment Dealer
N.A.I.C.S.: 336110
Shawn Scott (Mgr-Parts)

Subsidiaries:

Tri Green Tractor, LLC (1)
1002 S Sycamore St, Flora, IN 46929
Tel.: (574) 967-4164
Web Site: http://www.trigreentoytractor.com
Sales Range: $10-24.9 Million
Emp.: 40
Fiscal Year-end: 12/31/2014
Agricultural Machinery & Equipment
N.A.I.C.S.: 423820
Jason Pearson (Pres)
Karen East (Controller)

Troxel Equipment Co. (1)
5068 E 100 N, Bluffton, IN 46714
Tel.: (260) 565-3659
Web Site: http://www.troxelequipment.com
Sales Range: $10-24.9 Million
Emp.: 60
Farm & Garden Machinery Equipment Whslr
N.A.I.C.S.: 423820
Roger Reinhard (Mgr-Sls)
Brad Schoeff (Mgr-Parts)
Bob Maller (Mgr-Svc)
Mike Hill (Mgr-Set Up Shop)
Bob Bittner (Mgr-Turf Svc)
Cathy Montel (Mgr-Parts)
Dave Swenson (Mgr-Parts)
Jay Rubrake (Mgr-Svc)
Pat Caley (Mgr-Svc)
Ryan Neuenschwander (Mgr-Turf)

TTI HOLDINGS INC.
5205 Adamo Dr, Tampa, FL 33619
Tel.: (813) 623-2675
Web Site: http://www.tti-fss.com
Sales Range: $25-49.9 Million
Emp.: 175
Mfr of Metal Tanks
N.A.I.C.S.: 332420

Subsidiaries:

Florida Miscellaneous Structural Products (1)
2710 E 5th Ave, Tampa, FL 33605
Tel.: (813) 241-4261
Web Site: http://www.fsstructural.com
Sales Range: $10-24.9 Million
Architectural Metalwork
N.A.I.C.S.: 332323
Bill Dumelle (Gen Mgr)

General Engineering Corp (1)
5205 Adamo Dr, Tampa, FL 33619
Tel.: (813) 626-6246
Web Site: http://www.tampatank.com
Sales Range: $10-24.9 Million
Emp.: 50
Structural Steel Erection
N.A.I.C.S.: 238120

Tampa Tank & Welding Inc. (1)
5205 Adamo Dr, Tampa, FL 33619
Tel.: (813) 623-2675
Web Site: http://www.tampatank.com

Sales Range: $10-24.9 Million
Emp.: 15
Metal Tank Mfr
N.A.I.C.S.: 332420
Elizabeth Rice (Mgr-HR)
Diana Torres (Mgr-HR)

TTI, INC.
2263 Hwy B, Eden, WI 53019
Tel.: (920) 477-4364
Web Site: http://www.ttitrucking.com
Sales Range: $10-24.9 Million
Emp.: 250
General Freight Trucking, Long-Distance, Truckload
N.A.I.C.S.: 484121
William Timblin (Pres)

TTIK INC.
3541 Challenger St, Torrance, CA 90503
Tel.: (310) 303-3600   CA
Web Site:
  http://www.pcscsecurity.com
Year Founded: 1983
Access Control Management Software Designer & Mfr
N.A.I.C.S.: 335999
Subsidiaries:

Proprietary Control Systems Corp.   (1)
3541 Challenger St, Torrance, CA 90503
Tel.: (310) 638-0400
Web Site: http://www.pcscsecurity.com
Rev.: $12,500,000
Emp.: 49
Burglar Alarm Apparatus Mfr
N.A.I.C.S.: 334290
Al Portal (Dir-Sls)
Mas Kosaka (Pres & CEO)
Henry Asao (VP-Ops)

Security Innovations Inc   (1)
3541 Challenger St, Torrance, CA 90503
Tel.: (310) 303-3600
Rev.: $430,000
Emp.: 5
Security Control Equipment & Systems
N.A.I.C.S.: 561621

TTS, LLC
11000 Frisco St Ste 100, Frisco, TX 75033
Tel.: (214) 778-0800
Web Site: http://www.tts-us.com
Sales Range: $250-299.9 Million
Emp.: 85
Transportation Services
N.A.I.C.S.: 488999
Andy Cole (Pres & CEO)
Dennis Farnsworth (CFO & Exec VP)
Jeffrey R. Brashares (Sr VP-Sls & Natl Accts)
Robert Ebinger (VP-Agency Dev)
Jeffrey Vielhaber (COO)
Christi Fox (VP & Controller)

TTT WEST COAST INC.
1840 Victory Blvd, Glendale, CA 91201-2558
Tel.: (818) 972-0500
Web Site: http://www.extratv.com
Year Founded: 1993
Sales Range: $25-49.9 Million
Emp.: 212
Motion Picture Production
N.A.I.C.S.: 512110
Tommy Post (Gen Mgr)

TTX CO.
101 N Wacker Dr, Chicago, IL 60606-1784
Tel.: (312) 853-3223   DE
Web Site: http://www.ttx.com
Year Founded: 1955
Sales Range: $900-999.9 Million
Emp.: 1,400
Mfr & Supplier of Specialty & Standardized Railroad Freight Cars
N.A.I.C.S.: 488210
Patrick B. Loftus (Sr VP-Law & Admin)
Thomas F. Wells (Pres & CEO)
Bruce G. Schinelli (CIO & VP-IT)
Patrick J. Casey (VP-Fleet Mgmt)
Brian Powers (VP-HR)
Victoria A. Dudley (CFO, Treas & VP)

TTX HOLDINGS INC.
1155 S Neenah Ave, Sturgeon Bay, WI 54235
Tel.: (920) 743-6568
Web Site: http://www.therma-tron-x.com
Rev.: $28,383,140
Emp.: 160
Industrial Furnaces & Ovens
N.A.I.C.S.: 333994
John N. Acker (Chm & CEO)
Subsidiaries:

Therma-Tron-X Inc   (1)
1155 S Neenah Ave, Sturgeon Bay, WI 54235
Tel.: (920) 743-6568
Web Site: http://www.therma-tron-x.com
Rev.: $20,800,000
Emp.: 146
Industrial Furnaces & Ovens
N.A.I.C.S.: 333994

TUALATIN SLEEP PRODUCTS INC.
12225 SW Myslony St, Tualatin, OR 97062
Tel.: (503) 692-5510
Web Site: http://www.englander.com
Sales Range: $10-24.9 Million
Emp.: 130
Mfr & Distributor of Mattresses
N.A.I.C.S.: 337910
Melissa Sprowls (Mgr-Customer Svc)
Kristina Westlake (Supvr-Sewing Dept)

TUALITY HEALTHCARE
335 SE 8th Ave, Hillsboro, OR 97123
Tel.: (503) 681-1111   OR
Web Site: http://www.tuality.org
Year Founded: 1954
Sales Range: $150-199.9 Million
Community Health Care Services
N.A.I.C.S.: 621498
Tim Fleischmann (CFO & Treas)
Eunice Rech (Chief Clinical Officer)
Charles Rosenblatt (Vice Chm)
Fred Nachtigal (Chm)
Manuel Berman (Pres & CEO)
Sonney Sapra (CIO & Dir-Info Sys)
Cheryl Gebhart (Chief HR Officer)
Leslie Hallick (Sec)

TUBA CITY REGIONAL HEALTH CARE CORPORATION
167 N Main St, Tuba City, AZ 86045
Tel.: (928) 283-2501   AZ
Web Site: http://www.tchealth.org
Year Founded: 2002
Sales Range: $150-199.9 Million
Emp.: 1,200
Community Health Care Services
N.A.I.C.S.: 622110
Christopher Curley (Pres)
Kimberlee Williams (Treas)
Tincer Nez Sr. (VP)

TUBBY'S SUB SHOPS, INC.
30551 Edison Dr, Roseville, MI 48066
Tel.: (586) 293-5099   MI
Web Site: http://www.tubby.com
Year Founded: 1968
Sandwich Shops Operator & Franchisor
N.A.I.C.S.: 722513
Robert Paganes (CEO)
Bill Kiryakoza (Exec VP)
Subsidiaries:

Just Baked Shop LLC   (1)
31805 Glendale, Livonia, MI 48150
Tel.: (734) 367-0729
Web Site: http://www.justbakedshop.com
Sales Range: $1-9.9 Million
Retail Cupcake Kiosks Operator & Franchisor
N.A.I.C.S.: 445251
Erin Mireles (Mgr-Topping & Packing)

TUBE ART DISPLAYS INC.
11715 SE 5th St, Bellevue, WA 98005
Tel.: (206) 223-1122   WA
Web Site: http://www.tubeart.com
Year Founded: 1946
Sales Range: $10-24.9 Million
Emp.: 100
Mfr of Electric Signs
N.A.I.C.S.: 339950
Pam Larin (Controller)
Frank Dupar III (Pres)

TUBE DUDE, LLC
26 N Blvd of the Presidents, Sarasota, FL 34236
Tel.: (941) 735-6009
Web Site: http://www.tube-dude.com
Sales Range: $1-9.9 Million
Emp.: 12
Art Gallery & Store
N.A.I.C.S.: 712110
Scott Gerber (Founder & CEO)

TUBE FABRICATION INDUSTRIES, INC.
130 E Industrial Blvd, Logansport, IN 46947
Tel.: (574) 753-6377
Web Site:
  http://www.tubefabricationindustries.com
Emp.: 40
Automotive Anti-Vibration Devices & Tube Fabrication Products for Agriculture, Lawn & Garden & Furniture Industries Mfr
N.A.I.C.S.: 332996
Julie Ellis (Pres)
Douglas Smith (Plant Mgr)
Joyce Rusnak (Mgr-R&R Saw Div)

TUBE FORGINGS OF AMERICA INC.
5200 NW Frnt Ave, Portland, OR 97210
Tel.: (503) 241-0716
Web Site:
  http://www.tubeforgings.com
Rev.: $12,900,000
Emp.: 175
Mfr of Pipe Fittings
N.A.I.C.S.: 332996
Tammy Beeler (Mgr-Inside Sls)
Mark Brand (Mgr-Natl Sls-Western & Northeast Reg)
Patrick Benavides (VP & Gen Mgr)
Gary Browning (Mgr-IT)

TUBE PROCESSING CORP.
604 E Legrande, Indianapolis, IN 46203
Tel.: (317) 787-1321
Web Site: http://www.tubeproc.com
Year Founded: 1940
Sales Range: $50-74.9 Million
Emp.: 500
Mfr Fabricated Pipe & Fittings
N.A.I.C.S.: 332996
Howard Beeson (VP)
Tracy Gerth (VP-HR)
Howard Brandenburg (Mgr-Sls)
Steven Dreyer (Controller)

TUBE SPECIALTIES CO. INC.
1459 NW Sundial Rd, Troutdale, OR 97060
Tel.: (503) 618-8823
Web Site:
  http://www.tubespecialties.com
Sales Range: $50-74.9 Million
Emp.: 215
Steel Fabrication Services
N.A.I.C.S.: 332996
Peter Schubert (Mgr-Sys Dev)

TUBELITE COMPANY INC.
102 Semoran Commerce Pl, Apopka, FL 32703
Tel.: (201) 641-1011   NJ
Web Site: http://www.tubelite.com
Year Founded: 1920
Sales Range: $25-49.9 Million
Emp.: 230
Supplier of Sign, Screen Printing & Digital Printing Services
N.A.I.C.S.: 423420
Greg McCarter (Pres & COO)
Steve Mikkelson (Mgr-Quality)
Mike Peters (Mgr-Client Dev)
Kelly Townsend (Mgr-Client Dev)
Subsidiaries:

Tubelite Company Inc.   (1)
102 Semoran Commerce Pl, Apopka, FL 32703-4670
Tel.: (407) 884-0477
Web Site: http://www.tubelight.com
Sales Range: $10-24.9 Million
Emp.: 50
Supplier of Sign, Screen Printing & Digital Printing Services
N.A.I.C.S.: 423420
Greg McCarter (Pres & COO)
Steven Jaffe (Gen Mgr)
Terry Sessions (Branch Mgr)

Tubelite Company Inc.   (1)
10700 Twin Lakes Pkwy, Charlotte, NC 28269   (100%)
Tel.: (704) 875-3117
Web Site: http://www.tubelite.com
Sales Range: $10-24.9 Million
Emp.: 23
Supplier of Sign, Screen Printing & Digital Printing Services
N.A.I.C.S.: 423420
Tim Mastin (Gen Mgr)

Tubelite Company Inc.   (1)
1224 Refugee Ln, Columbus, OH 43207-2112
Tel.: (614) 443-9734
Web Site: http://www.tubelite.com
Sales Range: $10-24.9 Million
Emp.: 24
Supplier of Sign, Screen Printing & Digital Printing Services
N.A.I.C.S.: 423420
Dan Brown (Gen Mgr)

Tubelite Company Inc.   (1)
3111 Bellbrook Dr, Memphis, TN 38116
Tel.: (901) 396-8320
Web Site: http://www.tubelite.com
Sales Range: $10-24.9 Million
Emp.: 34
Supplier of Sign Screen Printing & Digital Printing Services
N.A.I.C.S.: 423420
Kevin McCarter (Gen Mgr)

Tubelite Company Inc.   (1)
3875 Culligan Ave Unit H, Indianapolis, IN 46218   (100%)
Tel.: (317) 352-9366
Web Site: http://www.tubelite.com
Sales Range: $10-24.9 Million
Emp.: 10
Supplier of Sign, Screen Printing & Digital Printing Services
N.A.I.C.S.: 423420
Boyd Grace (Gen Mgr)

TUBELITE COMPANY INC.

Tubelite Company Inc.—(Continued)

Tubelite Company Inc. (1)
7310 W Roosevelt St Bldg 2 Ste 36, Phoenix, AZ 85043 (100%)
Tel.: (602) 484-0122
Web Site: http://www.estore.tubelite.com
Sales Range: $10-24.9 Million
Emp.: 6
Supplier of Sign, Screen Printing & Digital Printing Services
N.A.I.C.S.: 423430

TUBES INC.
9401 Telge Rd, Houston, TX 77095
Tel.: (281) 858-8300
Web Site: http://www.tubes-inc.com
Sales Range: $10-24.9 Million
Emp.: 100
Whslr of Industrial Heat Exchange Equipment
N.A.I.C.S.: 423830
Michael S. Amburn (Pres)
Steward Travis (Controller)
Mike Coleman (Exec VP)
James Laperouse (Exec VP-Sls)

TUBETECH INC.
900 E Taggart St, East Palestine, OH 44413
Tel.: (330) 426-9476
Web Site: http://www.tubetechnorthamerica.com
Sales Range: $10-24.9 Million
Emp.: 35
Provider of Metal Tubes
N.A.I.C.S.: 331210
Stephen D. Oliphant (CEO)
Jon Roscow (Pres)

TUBULAR & EQUIPMENT SERVICES, LLC
4307 E US Hwy 160, Independence, KS 67301
Tel.: (620) 331-7384
Web Site: http://www.sealtitelining.com
Line Pipe Systems & Used Equipment Mfr
N.A.I.C.S.: 326122
Terry Werner (Pres)

TUBULAR INSTRUMENTATION & CONTROLS LP
15151 Summer Meyer St, Houston, TX 77041
Tel.: (832) 467-3110
Web Site: http://www.tubingservices.com
Stainless Steel Tubing Mfr
N.A.I.C.S.: 331210
Darryll Holmes (Mgr-Tendering)

TUBULAR SERVICES LP
1010 McCarty Dr, Houston, TX 77029-2426
Tel.: (713) 675-6212
Web Site: http://www.tubularservices.com
Year Founded: 1954
Sales Range: $10-24.9 Million
Emp.: 200
Service of Pipes & Tubular Goods
N.A.I.C.S.: 213112
Robert Sherrill (CFO & VP)
Rick Hickman (Pres)
Norma Jimenez (Mgr-Inventory-Houston)

Subsidiaries:

Tubular Services LP - Jacintoport Plant (1)
2030 Jacintoport Blvd, Houston, TX 77015
Tel.: (281) 452-4353
Threaded Tubular Pipe Mfr
N.A.I.C.S.: 332996
Rick Hickman (Pres)

Tubular Services LP - McCarty Tubing Plant (1)
1010 McCarty Dr, Houston, TX 77029
Tel.: (713) 675-6212
Threaded Tubular Pipe Mfr
N.A.I.C.S.: 332996

TUBULAR TEXTILE MACHINERY, INC.
113 Woodside Dr, Lexington, NC 27292
Tel.: (336) 956-6444
Web Site: http://www.navisglobal.com
Year Founded: 1929
Textile Machinery Mfr & Whslr
N.A.I.C.S.: 423830
William J. Motchar (Pres & CEO)
Thomas Redden (CFO)
R. Craige Murray (Exec VP-Ops)
Mark West (VP-Engrng)

Subsidiaries:

Gaston Systems, Inc. (1)
200 S Main St, Stanley, NC 28164
Tel.: (704) 263-6000
Web Site: http://www.gastonsystems.com
Rev.: $1,600,000
Emp.: 17
Coated & Laminated Paper Mfr
N.A.I.C.S.: 322220
Christoph Aurich (Gen Mgr)
Gary Harris (Pres)

TUCKER ALBIN & ASSOCIATES, INC.
1702 N Collins Ste 100, Richardson, TX 75080
Tel.: (877) 455-4572
Web Site: http://www.tuckeralbin.com
Year Founded: 2009
Sales Range: $1-9.9 Million
Emp.: 71
Commercial Debt Collection & Asset Recovery Services
N.A.I.C.S.: 561440
Allen Humphris (CEO)

TUCKER CHRYSLER JEEP, INC.
902 N Saginaw St, Durand, MI 48429
Tel.: (989) 288-2666
Web Site: http://www.tuckerchryslerjeepdodge.net
Year Founded: 1967
Sales Range: $10-24.9 Million
Emp.: 17
Car Whslr
N.A.I.C.S.: 441110
Sue Tucker (Owner)

TUCKER COUNTY COMMISSION
211 1st St Ste 307, Parsons, WV 26287
Tel.: (304) 478-2866
Web Site: http://www.tuckercountycommission.com
County Commissioners
N.A.I.C.S.: 921110
Michael Rosenau (Pres)

Subsidiaries:

Tucker County Solid Waste Authority, Inc. (1)
284 Landfill Rd, Davis, WV 26260
Tel.: (304) 259-4867
Web Site: http://www.tuckercountycommission.com
Waste Collection
N.A.I.C.S.: 562111
Carol Helmick (Office Mgr)

TUCKER OIL COMPANY INC.
1001 Idlelwild Blvd, Columbia, SC 29201
Tel.: (803) 779-9538
Web Site: http://www.tuckeroil.com
Rev.: $17,000,000
Emp.: 200
Liquefied Petroleum Gas Distr
N.A.I.C.S.: 424720
David Tucker (Pres)

TUCKER PAVING, INC.
PO Box 1759, Winter Haven, FL 33882
Tel.: (863) 299-2262
Web Site: http://www.tuckerpaving.com
Sales Range: $10-24.9 Million
Emp.: 49
Construction Materials Whslr
N.A.I.C.S.: 423320
Larry D. Tucker (Pres)
Matt Greene (VP-Construction)
Clettus Greene (VP)

TUCKER-DAVIS TECHNOLOGIES, INC.
11930 Research Cir, Alachua, FL 32615
Tel.: (386) 462-9622
Web Site: http://www.tdt.com
Year Founded: 1989
Sales Range: $1-9.9 Million
Emp.: 30
Medical Device Mfr
N.A.I.C.S.: 339112
Timothy J. Tucker (Pres)

Subsidiaries:

Optima Neuroscience, Inc. (1)
11930 Research Cir, Alachua, FL 32615
Tel.: (352) 371-8281
Web Site: http://www.optimaneuro.com
Medical Device Mfr
N.A.I.C.S.: 339112
Timothy J. Tucker (Pres)
Ryan T. Kern (CEO)
Deng-Shan Shiau (VP-Scientific Affairs)

TUCKER/HALL, INC.
1 Tampa City Ctr Ste 2760, Tampa, FL 33602
Tel.: (813) 228-0652
Web Site: http://www.tuckerhall.com
Year Founded: 1990
Sales Range: $1-9.9 Million
Emp.: 20
Public Relations & Communications Services
N.A.I.C.S.: 541820
Jeffrey W. Tucker (Founder)
Thomas Hall (Chm)
Darren Richards (COO)
Guy Hagen (VP)
John Finotti (VP)
Keith Rupp (VP)
William E. Carlson Jr. (Pres)

TUCKERTON LUMBER CO. INC.
200 N Blvd, Surf City, NJ 08008
Tel.: (609) 494-2111
Web Site: http://www.tlcnj.com
Year Founded: 1932
Rev.: $25,000,000
Emp.: 25
Provider of Building Supplies
N.A.I.C.S.: 444110
Claire Laird (Founder, Owner & Pres)

TUCSON AIRPORT AUTHORITY INC.
7005 S Plumer Ave, Tucson, AZ 85756
Tel.: (520) 573-4844
Web Site: http://www.flytucson.com
Year Founded: 1948
Sales Range: $25-49.9 Million
Emp.: 300
Airports, Flying Fields & Services
N.A.I.C.S.: 488119

Bonnie Allin (Pres & CEO)
Richard Woehrmann (Dir-Internal Audit)
Tina Moore (Dir-Plng, Dev Programs & Regulatory Compliance)
Danette Bewley (COO & VP-Ops & Projects)

TUCSON DODGE, INC.
4220 E 22nd St, Tucson, AZ 85711-5337
Tel.: (520) 745-1000
Web Site: http://www.tucsondodgearizona.com
Sales Range: $25-49.9 Million
Emp.: 95
Car Whslr
N.A.I.C.S.: 441110
Cynthia Gray (Mgr-Sls)
Ed Motzkin (Gen Mgr)

TUCSON EMBEDDED SYSTEMS, INC.
5620 N Kolb Rd Ste 160, Tucson, AZ 85750
Tel.: (520) 575-7283
Web Site: http://www.tucsonembedded.com
Year Founded: 1997
Sales Range: $10-24.9 Million
Emp.: 95
Systems & Software Engineering Support
N.A.I.C.S.: 541519
Antonio Procopio (Co-Founder & Exec VP)
Chris Fox (Sr VP)
Dennis Kenman (Co-Founder, COO & Exec VP)
Sean Mulholland (Co-Founder & CEO)

Subsidiaries:

Precise Systems, Inc. (1)
46591 Expedition Dr Ste 200, Lexington Park, MD 20653
Tel.: (301) 862-5006
Web Site: http://www.goprecise.com
Sales Range: $25-49.9 Million
Emp.: 165
Information Technology Services
N.A.I.C.S.: 541512
Tom Curtis (CEO)
Scott Pfister (Pres & COO)
Joe Marino (VP-Navy Programs)
Clark Hutchinson (VP-Ops-Southeast)
Anne Welfare (Dir-Contracts)
Kevin Adams (Dir-Technical Dev)
Christina Payne (Dir-HR & Recruitment)
Matt Orsino (VP-Bus Dev)
Angela Rothwell (VP-Fin & Acctg)
Lindy Kirkland (VP-Marine Programs)
Pete Williams (VP-Tech)
Hank Vanderborght (COO)

TUCSON SYMPHONY ORCHESTRA
2175 N 6th Ave, Tucson, AZ 85705-5606
Tel.: (520) 792-9155
Web Site: http://www.tucsonsymphony.org
Sales Range: $10-24.9 Million
Emp.: 110
Symphony Orchestra
N.A.I.C.S.: 711130
Shawn A. Campbell (Mgr-Ticketing Svcs)
G. Mark Sandberg (Mgr-Production Stage)
George Hanson (Dir-Music)
Andrea Dillenburg (Chief Acctg Officer & VP-Fin)
Jeremy Softley (Dir-Ops)
Michael Becker (Principal)
Letitia Bryant (Principal)
James Karrer (Principal)
Alexander Lipay (Principal)

Johanna Lundy *(Principal)*
Joseph Rousos-Hammond *(Principal)*
Thomas J. McKinney *(Pres & CEO)*
Cecile Follansbee *(Chm)*

TUDOR INVESTMENT CORPORATION
1275 King St, Greenwich, CT 06831
Tel.: (203) 863-6700   DE
Web Site: http://www.tudor.com
Sales Range: $10-24.9 Million
Emp.: 150
Investment Advice
N.A.I.C.S.: 523940
John DiStefano *(Mgr-Property)*
Benjamin Randol *(VP)*
Jocelyn Rose *(VP-Facilities Mgmt)*
Bruce Townsend *(VP & Mgr-Global Ops)*
Brad Williams *(Mng Dir & Head-Product Dev)*
Brandon Sica *(VP)*
Joseph Intagliata *(VP)*
Oleg Olovyannikov *(CTO)*
Clayton Otto *(Head-Treasury Ops)*
Victor Calaba *(Mng Dir)*
Louise Zarrilli *(Mng Dir)*
Ryan Capilupi *(Portfolio Mgr)*
Ronald Elkhoury *(Portfolio Mgr)*
Dmitriy Genkin *(Portfolio Mgr)*
Dudley Hoskin *(Portfolio Mgr)*
Dan Pelletier *(Portfolio Mgr)*
Bob Uljua *(VP-Aviation)*
Sapna Kapil *(Mgr-IT Audit)*
Sally Waugh *(VP)*
Matthew Luizza *(VP & Controller-Functional)*
Emil M. Dabora *(Portfolio Mgr)*

Subsidiaries:

Tudor Capital Australia Pty. Ltd.   (1)
Ste 11 2-3 Shore Bldg, 13 Hickson Rd, Sydney, 2000, NSW, Australia
Tel.: (61) 290806906
Investment Advice
N.A.I.C.S.: 523940

Tudor Capital Europe LLP   (1)
Yew Tree Bottom Road, Epsom, KT18 5XT, Surrey, United Kingdom
Tel.: (44) 208 786 3900
Financial Management Services
N.A.I.C.S.: 523999
Ashwin Ranganathan *(Partner & Mng Dir)*

TUDOR RANCH, INC.
93-400 Hammond Rd, Mecca, CA 92254
Tel.: (760) 396-2134
Web Site: http://www.tudorranch.com
Year Founded: 1960
Sales Range: $10-24.9 Million
Emp.: 35
Grape Distr
N.A.I.C.S.: 111332
Joseph Tudor *(Co-Owner & Dir-Ops)*

TUERFF-DAVIS ENVIROMEDIA
1717 W 6th St Ste 400, Austin, TX 78703
Tel.: (512) 476-4368
Year Founded: 1997
Sales Range: $10-24.9 Million
Emp.: 36
Public Relations Agency
N.A.I.C.S.: 541820
Kevin Tuerff *(Pres & Principal)*

TUFENKIAN IMPORT/EXPORT VENTURES, INC.
919 3rd Ave, New York, NY 10022-3902
Tel.: (212) 475-2475
Web Site: http://www.tufenkiancarpets.com
Sales Range: $25-49.9 Million
Emp.: 35
Carpet Whslr
N.A.I.C.S.: 423220
James F. Tufenkian *(Pres)*
Eric Jacobsen *(CFO & COO)*

TUFF SHED, INC.
1777 S Harrison St Ste 600, Denver, CO 80210-3931
Tel.: (800) 369-8833   CO
Web Site: http://www.tuffshed.com
Year Founded: 1980
Sales Range: $25-49.9 Million
Emp.: 300
Construction of Storage Buildings & Garages
N.A.I.C.S.: 321992
Tom Saurey *(Founder)*

Subsidiaries:

Home Brands, LLC   (1)
300 Constitution Ave Ste 200, Portsmouth, NH 03801
Tel.: (603) 431-8489
Web Site: http://www.shedsusa.com
Distr of Pine Storage Sheds
N.A.I.C.S.: 321992

TUFFCARE INC.
4999 E La Palma Ave, Anaheim, CA 92807
Tel.: (714) 632-3999
Web Site: http://www.tuffcare.com
Year Founded: 1989
Sales Range: $10-24.9 Million
Emp.: 16
Sales of Hospital Equipment & Furniture
N.A.I.C.S.: 423450
Joseph Chang *(Pres)*

TUFFY ADVERTISING
7150 Granite Cir, Toledo, OH 43617
Tel.: (419) 865-6900   OH
Web Site: http://www.tuffy.com
Year Founded: 1970
Sales Range: $10-24.9 Million
Emp.: 35
Automotive, House Agencies
N.A.I.C.S.: 541810
Roger Hill *(Pres & CEO)*
Bob Bresler *(VP-Tuffy Associates)*
Karen Vellequette *(CFO-Tuffy Associates Corp)*

TUFFY ASSOCIATES CORPORATION
7150 Granite Cir, Toledo, OH 43617
Tel.: (419) 865-6900   OH
Web Site: http://www.tuffy.com
Year Founded: 1970
Sales Range: $50-74.9 Million
Emp.: 45
Automobile Maintenance Services
N.A.I.C.S.: 811121
Karen Vellequette *(CFO)*

Subsidiaries:

Car-X Associates Corp.   (1)
1375 E Woodfield Rd Ste 500, Schaumburg, IL 60173
Tel.: (847) 273-8938
Web Site: http://www.carx.com
Sales Range: $10-24.9 Million
Emp.: 14
Automotive Repair Services
N.A.I.C.S.: 811114

Subsidiary (Domestic):

Car-X Auto Service, Inc.   (2)
9507 Page Ave, Saint Louis, MO 63132
Tel.: (314) 428-0002
Web Site: http://www.carx.com
Sales Range: $10-24.9 Million
Provider of Automotive Repair Services
N.A.I.C.S.: 811114
John Keeley *(VP)*

TUFTCO CORPORATION
2318-2320 Holtzclaw Ave, Chattanooga, TN 37408
Tel.: (423) 698-8601
Web Site: http://www.tuftco.com
Sales Range: $10-24.9 Million
Emp.: 150
Provider of Textile Machinery
N.A.I.C.S.: 333248
Steve Frost *(Pres)*
Mike Bishop *(VP-Res-Tufting Machine Div)*
Bill Fowler *(VP-Sls)*
Steve Martin *(Dir-Mktg)*
Mike Minter *(Exec VP)*
Kevin Whiteside *(Pres-Tufting Machine Div)*

TUGWELL OIL CO. INC.
8368 Old Brownsville Rd, Brunswick, TN 38014
Tel.: (901) 386-1827
Year Founded: 1925
Sales Range: $10-24.9 Million
Emp.: 9
Petroleum Terminal
N.A.I.C.S.: 424710
Wesley Tugwell *(Owner)*

TUI LIFESTYLE, LLC
18000 State Rd 9, Miami, FL 33162
Tel.: (305) 652-0232
Web Site: http://www.tuilifestyle.com
Sales Range: $10-24.9 Million
Emp.: 40
Interior Design Services
N.A.I.C.S.: 541410
Michael Gabbett *(Pres)*

TUKAIZ LLC
2917 Latoria Ln, Franklin Park, IL 60131
Tel.: (847) 455-1588
Web Site: http://www.tukaiz.com
Year Founded: 1963
Marketing Communication Products & Services
N.A.I.C.S.: 541810
John Quinto Defino *(Mng Dir & VP)*
Christopher M. Calabria *(CFO, Mng Dir & VP)*
Daniel Defino *(Mng Dir & VP)*
Frank Defino Sr. *(Founder & Mng Dir)*
Frank Defino Jr. *(Mng Dir & VP)*

Subsidiaries:

Dr. Graphx   (1)
1751 W Grand Ave, Chicago, IL 60622
Tel.: (312) 553-4357
Web Site: http://www.drgraphx.com
Graphic Design Services
N.A.I.C.S.: 541430
Mike Mages *(Pres)*

TUKATECH INC.
5462 Jillson St, Los Angeles, CA 90040
Tel.: (323) 726-3836
Web Site: http://www.tukatech.com
Year Founded: 1997
Rev.: $40,000,000
Emp.: 20
Apparel Design Software
N.A.I.C.S.: 513210
Ram Sareen *(Founder & CEO)*
Marta Maiandi *(Dir-Europe)*
Martin Bailey *(Pres-Tukaweb)*

TULALIP TRIBES
6406 Marine Dr, Tulalip, WA 98271
Tel.: (360) 651-4000   WA
Web Site:
  http://www.tulaliptribes.com
Year Founded: 1940
Sales Range: $150-199.9 Million
Emp.: 700
Cable & Other Pay Television Services
N.A.I.C.S.: 516210
Glen Gobin *(Vice Chm)*
Misty Napeahi *(Treas)*
Jared Parks *(Sec)*
Michelle Gettsy *(Mng Dir-Bus Ops)*
Wendy Fryberg *(Mng Dir-Regulatory Affairs)*
Shawneen Zackuse *(Mng Dir-Community Enrichment)*
Norma Razote *(Mng Dir-Health Svcs)*
Teri Gobin *(Chm)*

Subsidiaries:

Tulalip Casino   (1)
10200 Quil Ceda Blvd, Tulalip, WA 98271   (100%)
Tel.: (360) 716-6000
Web Site: http://www.tulalipresortcasino.com
Sales Range: $200-249.9 Million
Amusement & Recreation Services
N.A.I.C.S.: 713290
Ken Kettler *(Pres)*

TULARE COUNTY ASSOCIATION OF REALTORS, INC.
2424 E Vly Oaks Dr, Visalia, CA 93292
Tel.: (559) 627-1776
Web Site: http://www.tcmls.org
Year Founded: 1852
Emp.: 1,000
Real Estate Association
N.A.I.C.S.: 531390
Darcy Staberg *(Pres)*

TULIP CORPORATION
14955 E Salt Lake Ave, City of Industry, CA 91746-3133
Tel.: (626) 968-9680   CA
Web Site: http://www.tulipcorp.com
Year Founded: 1976
Sales Range: $150-199.9 Million
Emp.: 25
Mfr of Plastic Containers & Molded Plastic Products
N.A.I.C.S.: 326199
Fred Teshinsky *(Pres)*

Subsidiaries:

P.H.I. Division   (1)
14955 Salt Lake Ave, City of Industry, CA 91746
Tel.: (626) 968-9680
Web Site: http://www.phihydraulics.com
Sales Range: $25-49.9 Million
Custom Poly Bag Mfr
N.A.I.C.S.: 326111

Tulip Corp., Milwaukee Div.   (1)
714 E Keefe Ave, Milwaukee, WI 53212-1615
Tel.: (414) 963-3120
Web Site: http://www.tulipproducts.com
Sales Range: $25-49.9 Million
Mfr of Plastic Products
N.A.I.C.S.: 326199
Al Schmidt *(Sr VP-Sls & Mktg)*

Tulip Molded Plastics Corp - Niagara Falls Div.   (1)
3125 Highland Ave, Niagara Falls, NY 14305
Tel.: (414) 963-3120
Web Site: http://www.tulipcorp.com
Custom Injection Molded Plastics Mfr
N.A.I.C.S.: 326199
John Signore *(Gen Mgr-Engineered Resin)*
Rob Johnson *(Mgr)*
Bill Banaszak *(Engr-Quality)*

TULLY CONSTRUCTION CO., INC.
127-50 Northern Blvd, Flushing, NY 11368
Tel.: (718) 446-7000
Web Site:
  http://www.tullyconstruction.com
Sales Range: $25-49.9 Million
Emp.: 450

TULLY CONSTRUCTION CO., INC.   U.S. PRIVATE

Tully Construction Co., Inc.—(Continued)
Highway & Street Construction Services
N.A.I.C.S.: 237310
Dan James (CFO)

TULLY RINCKEY PLLC
441 New Karner Rd, Albany, NY 12205
Tel.: (518) 218-7100
Web Site: http://www.tullylegal.com
Year Founded: 2003
Sales Range: $10-24.9 Million
Emp.: 75
Law firm
N.A.I.C.S.: 541110
Mathew B. Tully (Founder, Partner & Atty)
Greg T. Rinckey (Founder, Partner & Atty)
Barbara J. King (Partner)
Graig Cortelyou (COO)
Kim Tully (Dir-Educational Advisement)
Jennifer J. Corcoran (Partner)
Darren M. Swetz (Partner & Atty)
Peter J. Pullano (Mng Partner & Atty)
Robert J. Rock (Mng Partner & Atty)
Donna Williams Rucker (Deputy Mng Partner & Atty)
Brandon Delaney (Mgr-Helpdesk)
Cheri L. Cannon (Mng Partner & Atty)
Donald E. Kelly (Mng Partner)
JoAnne Perniciaro (Dir-Client Svcs)
Ken R. Twinam (CIO)
Marc A. Skipp (CFO)
Shirley C. Favata (Mgr-HR)
Steven L. Herrick (Mng Partner)
Gregory F. Greiner (Partner & Atty)
Anthony J. Kuhn (Mng Partner-Buffalo)
Karen Veronica DeFio (Partner-Trust & Estates Law Practice Grp)
John C. Doherty (Mng Partner)
Gerald D. Raymond (Partner)
Matt Welch (Dir-Ops & Strategic Dev)
Dave Russell (Mgr-Bus Ops)
Peter P. Charnetsky (Mng Partner-Binghamton)
Kevin H. Yeager (Partner)
Charles McCullough III (Partner)

TULLY-WIHR COMPANY
148 Whitcomb Ave, Colfax, CA 95713
Tel.: (530) 346-2649
Web Site: http://www.tullywihr.com
Sales Range: $10-24.9 Million
Emp.: 50
Provider of Lithographed Business Forms
N.A.I.C.S.: 323111
Gerry D. Knoll (Pres)
Douglas V. Dunn (COO & Partner)
Jim L. Knoll (Partner & VP)
Jerry Knoll (VP)

TULSA AIRPORT AUTHORITY
7777 E Apache St Rm A217, Tulsa, OK 74115
Tel.: (918) 838-5000
Web Site: http://www.tulsaairports.com
Sales Range: $25-49.9 Million
Emp.: 136
Provider of Airport Services
N.A.I.C.S.: 488119
Carl Remus (Deputy Dir-Admin & Fin)
Jeff Mulder (Dir-Airport)
Mike Kerr (Coord-Engrg Graphics)

TULSA POWER, INC
913 N Wheeling Ave, Tulsa, OK 74110
Tel.: (918) 584-1000
Web Site: http://www.tulsapower.com
Year Founded: 1998
Sales Range: $25-49.9 Million
Emp.: 225
Aluminum Rolling & Drawing
N.A.I.C.S.: 331318
Michael Spence (Pres)
Vinod Shirhatti (Dir-Sls & Mktg-Oil & Gas Indus)

TULSA RIG IRON INC.
4457 W 151st St, Kiefer, OK 74041
Tel.: (918) 321-3330
Web Site: http://www.tulsarigiron.com
Rev.: $14,404,692
Emp.: 50
Petroleum Industry Machinery
N.A.I.C.S.: 423830
Trevor Young (Pres)
John Donohue (VP-Ops)
Michael Sadler (Mgr-Natl Sls)

Subsidiaries:

Tulsa Trenchless Inc   (1)
4457 W 151st St, Kiefer, OK 74041
Tel.: (918) 321-3330
Web Site: http://www.tulsarigiron.com
Rev.: $630,000
Emp.: 2
Drilling Equipment, Excluding Bits
N.A.I.C.S.: 423830

TULSA ROUTE 66 MARATHON INC.
1611 S Utica Ave, Tulsa, OK 74104
Tel.: (918) 409-2828   OK
Year Founded: 2005
Sales Range: $1-9.9 Million
Marathon Event Organizer
N.A.I.C.S.: 711310
Jeff Frable (Treas)
Kim Hann (Sec)
Chris Lieberman (Exec Dir)

TUMAC LUMBER CO. INC.
805 SW Broadway Ste 600, Portland, OR 97205-3325
Tel.: (503) 226-6661   OR
Web Site: http://www.tumac.com
Year Founded: 1959
Sales Range: $300-349.9 Million
Emp.: 140
Lumber Plywood & Millwork
N.A.I.C.S.: 423310
Timothy Leipzig (CFO)
Brad McMurchie (Pres & CEO)

Subsidiaries:

Disdero Lumber Co. Inc.   (1)
12301 SE Carpenter Dr, Clackamas, OR 97015-0469   (100%)
Tel.: (503) 239-8888
Web Site: http://www.disdero.com
Sales Range: $10-24.9 Million
Emp.: 47
Lumber, Plywood & Millwork
N.A.I.C.S.: 423310

Pacific Architectural Products, Inc.   (1)
12301 SE Carpenter Dr, Clackamas, OR 97015
Tel.: (503) 239-8128
Web Site: http://www.panelguys.com
Sales Range: $1-9.9 Million
Emp.: 3
Building Materials Whslr
N.A.I.C.S.: 444180
Mike Johnson (Gen Mgr)

Specialty Wood Products Inc.   (1)
2790 Laredo St, Aurora, CO 80011-4611
Tel.: (303) 288-8484
Web Site: http://www.swp.net
Sales Range: $10-24.9 Million
Emp.: 20
Lumber & Other Building Materials
N.A.I.C.S.: 423310
Brian Reynolds (VP)
Josh Deguire (Pres)

Wood-Lam Structures Inc.   (1)
2828 SE 14th Ave, Portland, OR 97202-2204
Tel.: (503) 239-7276
Sales Range: Less than $1 Million
Emp.: 20
Installing Building Equipment
N.A.I.C.S.: 238290

TUMBLEWEED, INC.
2301 River Rd Ste 200, Louisville, KY 40206
Tel.: (502) 893-0323   DE
Web Site:
http://www.tumbleweedrestaurants.com
Year Founded: 1975
Sales Range: $75-99.9 Million
Emp.: 1,800
Operator & Franchiser of Full Service Restaurants
N.A.I.C.S.: 722511
Glennon F. Mattingly (CFO & VP)
Jan Malesh (Coord-Trng Ops)
Annette Hines (Supvr-Accts Payable)
Helen Taylor (Mgr-Acctg)
John East (Mgr)

TUMPEER CHEMICAL CO. INC.
522 N Hicks Rd, Palatine, IL 60067-3609
Tel.: (847) 358-5600   IL
Web Site:
http://www.tumpeerchemical.com
Year Founded: 1947
Sales Range: $10-24.9 Million
Emp.: 6
Chemicals & Allied Products
N.A.I.C.S.: 424690
Gerald L. Williams (CEO)

TUNHEIM PARTNERS
1100 Riverview Twr 8009 34th Ave S, Minneapolis, MN 55425
Tel.: (952) 851-1600
Web Site: http://www.tunheim.com
Year Founded: 1990
Sales Range: $1-9.9 Million
Emp.: 30
Public Relations Agency
N.A.I.C.S.: 541820
Kathryn H. Tunheim (CEO)
Lou Ann Olson (Exec VP)
Patrick Milan (Chief Creative Officer & Exec VP)
Brian Ortale (CFO)

TUNNELL CONSULTING
900 E 8th Ave Ste 106, King of Prussia, PA 19406
Tel.: (610) 337-0820
Web Site:
http://www.tunnellconsulting.com
Year Founded: 1962
Sales Range: $25-49.9 Million
Emp.: 66
Life Sciences Consultants To Pharmaceutical & Biotechnology Companies
N.A.I.C.S.: 541690
Robert Johnson (Grp VP)
Maryann Gallivan (Pres & CEO)
David Kromer (Grp VP-Program Dev)
Larry Frattura (CFO)
Jonathan Horn (Principal)

Subsidiaries:

Tunnell Consulting   (1)
6701 Democracy Blvd Ste 515, Bethesda, MD 20817   (100%)
Tel.: (240) 383-3033
Web Site: http://www.tunnellconsulting.com
Sales Range: $10-24.9 Million
Emp.: 40
Government Consulting
N.A.I.C.S.: 541690
Robert Johnson (Principal)
Conrad Heilman (Pres)

TUNSTALL CONSULTING, INC.
13153 N Dale Mabry Hwy Ste 200, Tampa, FL 33618
Tel.: (813) 968-4461
Web Site:
http://www.tunstallconsulting.com
Year Founded: 1980
Sales Range: $1-9.9 Million
Emp.: 25
Business Management Consulting Services
N.A.I.C.S.: 541611
A. Gordon Tunstall (Pres & CEO)
Benjamin McCullough (Mng Dir)

TUOHY FURNITURE CORPORATION
42 Saint Albans Pl, Chatfield, MN 55923
Tel.: (507) 867-4280
Web Site:
http://www.tuohyfurniture.com
Sales Range: $25-49.9 Million
Emp.: 170
Provider of Wooden Office Furniture
N.A.I.C.S.: 337211
Francis J. Tuohy (Chm)
Daniel J. Tuohy (Pres & CEO)
Greg Eichten (CFO)

TURAN-FOLEY MOTORS INC.
1123 Hwy 49 N, Gulfport, MS 39503
Tel.: (228) 539-7500
Web Site: http://www.turanfoley.com
Year Founded: 1955
Sales Range: $50-74.9 Million
Emp.: 128
Owner & Operator of Car Dealerships
N.A.I.C.S.: 441110
Richard T. Foley (Pres)
Mike Penny (Controller)
Paul Bozant (Gen Mgr-Sls)

TURANO BAKING COMPANY
6501 W Roosevelt Rd, Berwyn, IL 60402
Tel.: (708) 788-9220
Web Site: http://www.turano.com
Sales Range: $25-49.9 Million
Emp.: 500
Bakery Products
N.A.I.C.S.: 424490
Renato Turano (Co-Owner, Chm & CEO)
Sandra Battersby (VP-Fin & Controller)
Giancarlo Turano (Co-Owner & Exec VP-Sls & Mktg)
Umberto Turano (Co-Owner & Pres)

TURBINE
21 Charles St, Westport, CT 06880
Tel.: (203) 226-2400   CT
Year Founded: 1993
Rev.: $15,000,000
Emp.: 20
Advertising Agencies
N.A.I.C.S.: 541810
Jeff Vogt (Owner & Dir-Creative)
Rob Slosberg (Owner)
Kate Altmann (VP & Dir-Design)
Matt Songer (Sr Dir-Art)
Jessamyn Smith-Sokol (Acct Exec)
Stephanie Hazard (Sr VP-Bus Dev)

TURBINE DIAGNOSTIC SERVICES, INC.
13447 Byrd Dr, Odessa, FL 33556
Tel.: (727) 375-8700
Web Site:
http://www.turbinedoctor.com
Year Founded: 1998
Sales Range: $1-9.9 Million
Emp.: 19
Turbine Generator Repair Services
N.A.I.C.S.: 811412

COMPANIES

Ronald Rubrecht *(Pres)*

TURBINE GENERATOR MAINTENANCE, INC.
125 SW 3rd Pl Ste 300, Cape Coral, FL 33991
Tel.: (239) 573-1233
Web Site: http://www.turbinegenerator.com
Year Founded: 1985
Sales Range: $25-49.9 Million
Emp.: 49
Generator Repair & Service
N.A.I.C.S.: 811310
David Branton *(Pres & CEO)*
Robert Davis *(CFO)*
Tim Jones *(Project Mgr)*
Chris Fowler *(Project Mgr)*
Jeff Russell *(Mgr-Proposal)*
Jim Fitzmartin *(Dir-Safety)*
Mark Sherrill *(Dir-Steam Turbine Svcs)*
Ben Ingram *(Project Coord)*
Todd Feeley *(VP-Bus Dev)*

TURBO HOLDINGS INC.
2600 Main St, Sayreville, NJ 08872
Tel.: (732) 525-0101
Web Site: http://www.turboholdings.com
Year Founded: 1982
Sales Range: $10-24.9 Million
Emp.: 6
Supplier of Men's & Boys' Clothing
N.A.I.C.S.: 424350
Young In Chung *(Pres)*

TURBOCAM INTERNATIONAL
607 Calef Highway, Barrington, NH 03825
Tel.: (603) 905-0200
Web Site: http://www.turbocam.com
Year Founded: 1985
Rev.: $54,100,000
Emp.: 215
Turbine & Computer Programming Service Mfg
N.A.I.C.S.: 333611
John Bressoud *(Gen Mgr-Turbocam Mfg)*
Doug D. Patteson *(CFO)*
Marian Noronha *(Founder, Chm & Pres)*
Robert Bujeaud *(VP-Engrg Dev)*

TURBODYNE TECHNOLOGIES, INC.
250 W 57th St Ste 2328, New York, NY 10107
Tel.: (646) 308-1503 NV
Web Site: http://www.turbodyne.net
Year Founded: 1983
Engine Parts Mfr
N.A.I.C.S.: 336310

TURBONOMIC, INC.
500 Boylston St 7th Fl, Boston, MA 02116
Tel.: (844) 438-8872
Web Site: http://www.turbonomic.com
Year Founded: 2009
Automation Processing Services
N.A.I.C.S.: 513210
Ben Nye *(CEO)*
Shmuel Kliger *(Founder & Pres)*

Subsidiaries:

SevOne, Inc. (1)
500 Boylston St 7th Fl, Boston, MA 02116
Tel.: (302) 319-5400
Web Site: http://www.sevone.com
Sales Range: $1-9.9 Million
Emp.: 60
Mfr of Application-Aware, Network Performance Management Software for Various Industries
N.A.I.C.S.: 513210

Bruce Johnson *(Sr VP)*
Vess Bakalov *(CTO & Sr VP)*
Jack Sweeney *(CEO)*
Jim Melvin *(Sr VP-Mktg & Dev)*
Ed Zaval *(Sr VP-Global Svcs)*
Paul Ciesielski *(Chief Revenue Officer)*
Joseph Ghattas *(Mng Dir/VP-Sls-EMEA)*
Danny Smolders *(VP-Sls/Gen Mgr-Asia Pacific)*

TURBOTEC PRODUCTS, INC.
1404 Blue Hills Ave, Bloomfield, CT 06002-1348
Tel.: (860) 731-4200 UK
Web Site: http://www.turbotecproducts.com
Year Founded: 1978
Sales Range: $10-24.9 Million
Emp.: 127
Heat Exchanger & Fabricated Metal Component Mfr
N.A.I.C.S.: 332410
Robert Lieberman *(CFO & Treas)*
Fred Scheideman *(VP-Engrg)*
Donna Santomenno *(Mgr-Customer Svc)*
Craig Ellis *(Exec VP)*
Joe Lutz *(VP-HR)*

TURCHETTE ADVERTISING AGENCY LLC
9 Law Dr, Fairfield, NJ 07004
Tel.: (973) 227-8080
Web Site: http://www.turchette.com
Year Founded: 1950
Rev.: $11,000,000
Emp.: 10
N.A.I.C.S.: 541810
Michael Gavin *(Pres)*
James Gorab *(Exec VP)*
Deborah Ahneman-Gavin *(VP)*
Christopher McDonough *(VP & Dir-Creative)*
Joan McNally *(Dir-PR & Comm)*
Rhona Siciliano *(Asst VP & Dir-Media)*
Deborah Gavin *(Sr VP)*
Laurie Kneller *(Sr Acct Exec)*
Alysa McKenna *(Dir-PR & Comm)*

TURCK INC.
3000 Campus Dr, Plymouth, MN 55441
Tel.: (763) 553-7300
Web Site: http://www.turck.com
Sales Range: $25-49.9 Million
Emp.: 325
Provider of Electronic Switches
N.A.I.C.S.: 335314
Brad Beagle *(Dir-IT)*
Wolfgang Boss *(Mgr-Product Test & Improvement)*
Robert Dornbach *(Mgr-Configuration)*
Bernie Froberg *(Mgr)*
Sandy Fulton *(Mgr-Cable Design & Procurement)*
Susi Gramigni *(Mgr-Intl Sls)*
James Hill *(Engr-Cable Procurement)*
Scott Lipa *(Coord-Exhibit)*
Guy Nauman *(Supvr-Test)*
Jeffrey Ursell *(VP-Sls)*
Christopher Italiano *(Project Mgr-ERP)*
David Lagerstrom *(Pres & CEO)*
Bob Diem *(CFO)*
David Franke *(Dir-Dev)*
Sean Watts *(Engr-Mechanical Design-I)*
Donovan Dawson *(Mgr-Mechanical Div)*
Amanda Mansfield *(Partner-HR & Staffing)*
Abdi Ayanle *(Product Mgr)*
Brad Nielsen *(Reg Mgr-Sls)*
Tom Miller *(Engr-Compliance)*

TURCOTTE O'KEEFFE, INC.
215 Homewood Dr, Libertyville, IL 60048
Tel.: (847) 247-8827
Year Founded: 1996
Sales Range: Less than $1 Million
Emp.: 2
N.A.I.C.S.: 541810
Stephen O'Keeffe *(Dir-Creative, Acct Mgr & Print Producer)*
Jacquie Turcotte-O'Keeffe *(Owner)*

TUREC ADVERTISING ASSOCIATES, INC.
9272 Olive Blvd, Saint Louis, MO 63132
Tel.: (314) 993-1190 MO
Year Founded: 1976
Rev.: $1,900,000
Emp.: 12
Fiscal Year-end: 12/31/06
Advertising Agencies, Nsk
N.A.I.C.S.: 541810
Ben Turec *(Pres)*

TURELK INC.
3700 Santa Fe Ave Ste 200, Long Beach, CA 90810-2169
Tel.: (310) 835-3736 CA
Web Site: http://www.turelk.com
Year Founded: 1978
Sales Range: $10-24.9 Million
Emp.: 105
Provider of Nonresidential Construction Services
N.A.I.C.S.: 236220
Michael G. Turi *(Pres)*

TURF MERCHANTS, INC.
33390 Tangent Loop, Tangent, OR 97389
Tel.: (541) 926-8649
Web Site: http://www.turfmerchants.com
Year Founded: 1983
Sales Range: $10-24.9 Million
Emp.: 25
Turf Grass Seed Mfr & Distr
N.A.I.C.S.: 111998
Steven Tubbs *(Owner)*
John Cochran *(VP)*

TURF PRODUCTS CORPORATION
157 Moody Rd, Enfield, CT 06082
Tel.: (860) 763-3581
Web Site: http://www.turfproductscorp.com
Rev.: $60,000,000
Emp.: 70
Lawn Machinery & Equipment
N.A.I.C.S.: 423820
Frederick N. Zeytoonjian *(Chm & CEO)*
Tim Berge *(Mgr-Golf Irrigation Sls)*

TURF STAR INC.
2110 La Mirada Dr, Vista, CA 92083
Tel.: (760) 734-4200
Web Site: http://www.turfstar.com
Rev.: $60,000,000
Emp.: 100
Distr of Lawn Equipment
N.A.I.C.S.: 333111
Gene Warne *(CEO)*
Len Gregory *(Owner)*
Doug Dahl *(Mgr-Sls)*

TURFGRASS, LLC
46495 Humboldt Dr, Novi, MI 48377-2446
Tel.: (248) 437-1427 DE
Web Site: http://www.residex.com
Year Founded: 1970
Emp.: 200
Fertilizer & Turf Pesticides Mfr & Whslr

TURN/RIVER MANAGEMENT LLC

N.A.I.C.S.: 325314
Todd A. Griebe *(Pres)*
Janice Cronin *(VP-Fin)*

TURKEL
2871 Oak Ave, Coconut Grove, FL 33133-5207
Tel.: (305) 476-3500 FL
Year Founded: 1983
Sales Range: $25-49.9 Million
Emp.: 35
Advetising Agency
N.A.I.C.S.: 541810
Bruce Turkel *(CEO)*
Marlisa Shapiro *(Dir-Comm)*
Sara Saiz *(Mng Dir)*
Roberto S. Schaps *(Pres)*
Ginette Velasquez *(Acct Dir)*
Eblis Parera *(Mgr-IT)*
Zoila Cardoso *(Fin Mgr)*

TURLEY PUBLICATIONS INC.
24 Water St, Palmer, MA 01069
Tel.: (413) 283-8393
Web Site: http://www.turley.com
Rev.: $14,246,591
Emp.: 150
Publisher of Newspapers
N.A.I.C.S.: 513110
Patrick H. Turley *(Owner & Pres)*
Tim Kane *(Editor)*

TURLOCK IRRIGATION DISTRICT
333 E Canal Dr, Turlock, CA 95380
Tel.: (209) 883-8300
Web Site: http://www.tid.com
Sales Range: $300-349.9 Million
Emp.: 462
Provider of Electric Power Generation
N.A.I.C.S.: 221118
Casey Hashimoto *(Gen Mgr)*
Larry Gilbertson *(Asst Gen Mgr-Electrical Engrg & Ops)*
Brian LaFollette *(Asst Gen Mgr-Power Supply)*

TURN/RIVER MANAGEMENT LLC
535 Mission St, San Francisco, CA 94105
Tel.: (415) 858-0910 DE
Web Site: https://turnriver.com
Private Investment Firm
N.A.I.C.S.: 523999
Dominic Ang *(Mng Partner)*
Evan Ginsburg *(Partner)*
Chase Sorgel *(Operating Partner)*
Saied Amiry *(Operating Principal)*
Joanne Yuan *(VP-Investment)*
Alvin Ang *(VP-Ops)*
Jeff Kline *(VP-Sls)*
Jarrett Stringfellow *(Dir-Sls & Customer Success)*
Micah Fisher-Kirshner *(Dir-SEO & Content)*
Danny Zhang *(Dir-Paid Media)*
Julie Pellegrini *(VP-Fin)*
Kristen Swanson *(VP-Talent Mgmt)*
Taras Naumenko *(Dir-Cust Success)*

Subsidiaries:

Tufin Software Technologies Ltd. (1)
ToHa Tower, Tel Aviv, 6789205, Israel
Tel.: (972) 36128118
Web Site: https://www.tufin.com
Rev.: $110,949,000
Assets: $151,393,000
Liabilities: $97,072,000
Net Worth: $54,321,000
Earnings: ($36,926,000)
Emp.: 542
Fiscal Year-end: 12/31/2021
Software Development Services
N.A.I.C.S.: 541511
Reuven Kitov *(Co-Founder, Chm & CEO)*
Yoram Gronich *(Sr VP-Products and Engineering & VP-R&D)*

TURN/RIVER MANAGEMENT LLC

U.S. PRIVATE

Turn/River Management LLC—(Continued)
Raj Motwane *(Sr VP-Services and Operations & VP-Global Svcs & Support)*
Jack Wakileh *(CFO & Chief Revenue Officer)*
Raymond Brancato *(CEO & Chief Revenue Officer)*
Shay Dayan *(Sr VP-Products & Engineering)*
Scott Tucker *(CFO)*
Jeff Taylor *(COO)*
Jeffrey Wilmot *(Chief Revenue Officer)*
Tali Inbar *(VP-People & Culture)*
Christian Na *(Gen Counsel)*
Revital Gabay *(VP-Corporate Strategy)*
Dennis Behrens *(VP-Global Services & Support)*

TURN5, INC.
600 N Cedar Hollow Rd, Paoli, PA 19301
Tel.: (610) 251-1672
Web Site: http://www.turn5.com
Year Founded: 2003
Automobile Parts Distr
N.A.I.C.S.: 423110
Steve Voudouris *(Co-Founder & CEO)*
Andrew Voudouris *(Co-Founder & CMO)*

TURNBERRY HOMES
210 Jamestown Park Dr Ste 102, Brentwood, TN 37027
Tel.: (615) 376-7001
Web Site: http://www.turnberryhomes.com
Sales Range: $10-24.9 Million
Emp.: 15
Housing Construction Services
N.A.I.C.S.: 236117
Richard Bell *(Pres)*

TURNBERRY SOLUTIONS, INC
Gwynedd Hall 1777 Sentry Pkwy W Ste 401, Blue Bell, PA 19422
Tel.: (215) 654-9991
Web Site: http://www.turnberrysolutions.com
Year Founded: 2001
Rev.: $17,500,000
Emp.: 80
IT Services
N.A.I.C.S.: 334610
Joe Rose *(Co-Founder & Pres)*
Pete Davis *(Co-Founder & CTO)*

TURNBERRY, LTD.
19950 W Country Club Dr, Aventura, FL 33180
Tel.: (305) 937-6262 FL
Web Site: http://www.turnberry.com
Holding Company; Residential & Commercial Real Estate Investment, Development, Construction & Property Management Services
N.A.I.C.S.: 531311
Jeffrey Soffer *(Principal)*
Alan Philips *(Chief Branding Officer)*
Aly-Khan S. Merali *(Pres & CFO)*
Christopher J. Barone *(Chief Acctg Officer & Exec VP)*
Dan Riordan *(Pres-Residential Dev)*
Jeffrey L. Shonty *(Treas & VP)*
Kristofer Cooper *(Sr VP-HR)*
Lenny O'Neill *(Sr VP-Construction)*
Mario A. Romine *(Gen Counsel-Special Projects & Sr VP)*
Matthew Juall *(Sr VP-Fin & Asset Mgmt)*
Patrick Powers *(Sr VP-Soffer Family Office)*
Warren Jay Stamm *(Gen Counsel & Sr VP)*
Yamila Garayzar *(Sr VP-Mktg, Sponsorship & Retail)*

Subsidiaries:

Turnberry Associates (1)
Aventura Mall 19501 Biscayne Blvd Ste 400, Aventura, FL 33180
Tel.: (305) 937-6200
Web Site: http://www.turnberry.com
Residential & Commercial Real Estate Investment, Development & Property Management Services
N.A.I.C.S.: 531390

Holding (Domestic):

Turnberry Isle Resort & Spa (2)
19999 W Country Club Dr, Aventura, FL 33180
Tel.: (305) 932-6200
Web Site: http://www.turnberryislemiami.com
Sales Range: $50-74.9 Million
Emp.: 800
Luxury Hotel & Resort Operator
N.A.I.C.S.: 721110
Greg Flaherty *(Controller)*
William James *(Dir-Sls & Mktg)*
Valerie Peru *(Mgr-Natl Sls)*

TURNBRIDGE CAPITAL, LLC
100 Crescent Ct Ste 800, Dallas, TX 75201
Tel.: (214) 624-5010 TX
Web Site: http://www.turnbridgecapital.com
Privater Equity Firm
N.A.I.C.S.: 523999
Robert Horton *(Partner)*
Todd M. Tomlin *(Partner)*
C. Mitchell Cox *(Partner)*
David J. Graham *(Partner)*
J. Kent Sweezey *(Partner)*
John U. Clarke *(Chm & Partner)*

Subsidiaries:

Cimarron Energy, Inc. (1)
11025 Equity Dr Ste 200, Houston, TX 77041
Tel.: (844) 746-1676
Web Site: http://www.cimarron.com
Industrial Equipment Mfr
N.A.I.C.S.: 335999
John U. Clarke *(Chm)*
Richard Wilke *(CFO)*
Mike McMahon *(Sr Dir-Ops)*
Martin Hesse *(Dir-Sls)*
Brenda Truman *(Sr Dir-HSE)*
Narda Smith *(Controller)*
Jeff Wilson *(Dir-Mktg & Dev)*
Jeffrey L. Foster *(CEO)*

Subsidiary (Domestic):

Diverse Energy Systems LLC (2)
1301 McKinney Ste 330, McKinney, TX 77010
Tel.: (713) 358-7000
Web Site: http://www.des-co.com
Power Boiler & Heat Exchanger Mfr
N.A.I.C.S.: 332410
Chet Erwin *(CEO)*

Hy-Bon Engineering Company, Inc. (2)
2404 Commerce Dr, Midland, TX 79703
Tel.: (432) 697-2292
Web Site: http://www.hy-bon.com
Vent Gas Equipment Mfr & Distr
N.A.I.C.S.: 423830
Kenny Rice *(Mgr-Svc)*
James K. Sidebottom *(Sr VP-Tech Svcs)*
Inayat Virani *(Pres & CEO)*

Subsidiary (Domestic):

Electronic Design for Industry, Inc. (3)
100 Ayers Blvd, Belpre, OH 45714
Tel.: (740) 401-4000
Web Site: http://www.ediplungerlift.com
Emp.: 75
Industrial Controller Mfr
N.A.I.C.S.: 334513
Jay Pottmeyer *(VP)*
Richard Wynn *(Pres)*
Christy Blair *(Office Mgr)*
David Pouzar *(Engr-Embedded)*

Flare Industries, LLC (1)
16310 Bratton Ln Bldg 3 Ste 350, Austin, TX 78728
Tel.: (512) 836-9473
Web Site: http://www.flareindustries.com
Emp.: 200
Flare Systems, Thermal Oxidizers & Ignition Systems Designer, Mfr & Distr
N.A.I.C.S.: 333132
Ahmed Othman *(Gen Mgr)*
John U. Clarke *(Chm)*
Ben Smith *(CFO & VP)*
Mark Zyskowski *(Sr VP-Global Sls & Mktg)*

Subsidiary (Domestic):

Jordan Technologies, LLC (2)
5051 Commerce Crossings Dr, Louisville, KY 40229
Tel.: (502) 267-8344
Web Site: http://www.jordantech.com
Emp.: 200
Industrial Vapor Recovery Units & Air Filtration Products Designer, Mfr & Distr
N.A.I.C.S.: 333998
Saeid Rahimian *(Pres)*

TURNBULL LLC
3100 Viona Ave, Baltimore, MD 21230-3422
Tel.: (410) 789-1700 MD
Year Founded: 1946
Sales Range: $1-9.9 Million
Emp.: 60
Shipboard Furniture for the U.S. Navy, Coast Guard & Maritime Services Mfr & Distr
N.A.I.C.S.: 336611
Louis Frank *(VP-Ops)*

TURNBULL-WAHLERT CONSTRUCTION, INC.
5533 Fair Ln, Cincinnati, OH 45227
Tel.: (513) 731-7300
Web Site: http://www.turnbull-wahlert.com
Year Founded: 2002
Sales Range: $25-49.9 Million
Emp.: 60
Midwest Commercial Property Designer & Builder
N.A.I.C.S.: 236220
Stewart Turnbull *(Pres)*
Mark Thomas *(Project Mgr)*
Patrick Gilles *(VP)*

TURNER BROS TRUCKING LLC
2000 S May Ave, Oklahoma City, OK 73108
Tel.: (405) 680-5100
Web Site: http://www.turnerbros.com
Year Founded: 1933
Sales Range: $25-49.9 Million
Emp.: 500
Provider of Trucking Services
N.A.I.C.S.: 484121

TURNER CONSULTING GROUP, INC.
306 Florida Ave NW, Washington, DC 20001
Tel.: (202) 986-5533
Web Site: http://www.tcg.com
Year Founded: 1994
Sales Range: $10-24.9 Million
Emp.: 32
Custom Computer Programming Services
N.A.I.C.S.: 541511
Robert Buccigrossi *(CTO)*
David G. Cassidy *(VP)*
Daniel A. Turner *(Pres)*
Judith Axler Turner *(VP)*
Maureen Sullivan *(VP)*
Lisa Alferieff *(COO)*

TURNER DAIRY FARMS, INC.
1049 Jefferson Rd, Pittsburgh, PA 15235
Tel.: (412) 372-2211
Web Site: http://www.turnerdairy.net
Year Founded: 1930
Sales Range: $25-49.9 Million
Emp.: 165
Dairy Product Mfr & Whlsr
N.A.I.C.S.: 311511
Charles G. Turner *(Founder)*
Cathy Turner *(Mgr-HR)*

TURNER GAS COMPANY INC.
2825 W 500 S, Salt Lake City, UT 84104
Tel.: (801) 973-6886
Web Site: http://www.turnergas.com
Year Founded: 1939
Sales Range: $25-49.9 Million
Emp.: 65
Propane Whslr
N.A.I.C.S.: 424720
Ken Turner *(VP)*
James Turner *(VP)*

TURNER INDUSTRIAL SUPPLY CO.
5000 Orange Ave, Fort Pierce, FL 34947
Tel.: (772) 464-8600
Web Site: http://www.turind.com
Industrial Supplies Merchant Whslr
N.A.I.C.S.: 423840
Charles A. Turner *(Pres)*

TURNER INDUSTRIES GROUP, L.L.C.
8687 United Plz Blvd, Baton Rouge, LA 70809-7009
Tel.: (225) 922-5050 LA
Web Site: https://www.turner-industries.com
Year Founded: 1960
Sales Range: $1-4.9 Billion
Emp.: 20,000
Commercial & Institutional Building Construction Services
N.A.I.C.S.: 236220
Roland M. Toups *(Chm)*

Subsidiaries:

Harmony LLC (1)
2515 Leroy Stevens Rd, Mobile, AL 36695-8578
Tel.: (251) 639-0246
Sales Range: $10-24.9 Million
Emp.: 34
Construction Company
N.A.I.C.S.: 236210

Turner Equipment Division (1)
2865 Mason Ave, Baton Rouge, LA 70805-1231
Tel.: (225) 356-1301
Web Site: http://www.turner-industries.com
Emp.: 150
Construction Equipment Rental
N.A.I.C.S.: 532490

Turner Industries (1)
401 Jefferson Hwy, Jefferson, LA 70121-2514
Tel.: (504) 837-2063
Web Site: http://www.turnerindustries.com
Sales Range: $25-49.9 Million
Emp.: 20
Construction Company
N.A.I.C.S.: 532490
Jessica Boudreaux *(Asst Mgr-Billing)*
Warren Landry *(Exec VP-Pipe Fabrication Div)*
Jim Doolittle *(Mgr-Bus Sys)*
Antoine Simon *(Mgr-Cost)*
Quinn Guidry *(Mgr-HR & Personnel)*
Jack Groemer *(Mgr-Procurement Pipe Fabrication Div)*
Darrel King *(Mgr-Safety)*
Will Arnold *(Mgr-Safety)*
Scott Gautreau *(Mgr-Tech)*
Monique Goldman *(Office Mgr)*
Sylvia Delcambre *(Office Mgr)*

COMPANIES
TURQUOISE COUNCIL OF AMERICANS & EURASIANS

Thomas Turner *(Pres)*
Bob Pearson *(Pres-Pipe Fabrication Div)*
Barry Barker *(Project Mgr)*
Frank Hardison *(Project Mgr)*
Phil Gauthreaux *(Project Mgr)*
John Higdon *(Project Mgr-Controls)*
Albert Swarts *(Supvr-I&E Maintenance)*
Dwain Hebert *(Supvr-Maintenance)*
Eric Williams *(Supvr-Safety)*
David Guitreau *(VP)*
Troy Bergeron *(VP)*

Turner Industries (1)
2005 Industrial Park, Beaumont, TX 77704-1029 **(100%)**
Tel.: (409) 722-8031
Web Site: http://www.turnerindustries.com
Sales Range: $200-249.9 Million
Emp.: 1,000
Special Trade Contractors & Industrial Construction Maintenance
N.A.I.C.S.: 236210
Keith Rost *(Gen Mgr)*

Turner Industries Group L.L.C. (1)
3850 Pasadena Blvd, Pasadena, TX 77503 **(100%)**
Tel.: (713) 477-7440
Web Site: http://www.turnerindustriesgroup.com
Sales Range: $50-74.9 Million
Emp.: 175
Construction Company
N.A.I.C.S.: 236220
John Golashesky *(VP)*
Tim Drake *(Mgr-Estimating)*

Turner Industries Group L.L.C. (1)
2346 Swisco Rd, Sulphur, LA 70665 **(100%)**
Tel.: (337) 882-6980
Web Site: http://www.turnerindustries.com
Sales Range: $25-49.9 Million
Emp.: 50
Special Trade Contractors & Industrial Construction Maintenance
N.A.I.C.S.: 236118
Thomas H. Turner *(Vice Chm- & CEO)*
David Frank *(VP-Ops)*

Turner Industries Group LLC Pipe Fabrication Div (1)
1100 Nasa Rd 1 Ste 504, Houston, TX 77058
Tel.: (713) 995-6822
Web Site: http://www.ips10.com
Sales Range: $125-149.9 Million
Emp.: 1,100
Carbon & Alloy Part Fabrication
N.A.I.C.S.: 423720

Turner Industries Group, L.L.C. - Corpus Christi Facility (1)
8601 IH 37 Access Rd, Corpus Christi, TX 78409
Tel.: (361) 248-3005
Sales Range: $25-49.9 Million
Emp.: 150
Fabricated Structural Metal Mfr
N.A.I.C.S.: 332312
David Arreola *(Gen Mgr-Constructions)*

Turner Industries Group, L.L.C. - Decatur Facility (1)
127 Old Hwy 24, Decatur, AL 35601
Tel.: (256) 584-0004
Web Site: http://www.turnerindustries.com
Emp.: 170
Fabricated Structural Metal Mfr
N.A.I.C.S.: 332312
David Amos *(Mgr-Acctg-Decatur)*

Turner Industries Group, L.L.C. - Houston Facility (1)
3850 Pasadena Blvd, Pasadena, TX 77503
Tel.: (713) 477-7440
Web Site: http://www.turner-industries.com
Industrial Building Construction Services
N.A.I.C.S.: 236210
Glenn Cook *(Project Mgr)*

Turner Industries Group, L.L.C. - Port Allen Facility (1)
1700 S Westport Dr, Port Allen, LA 70767
Tel.: (225) 381-9422
Fabricated Structural Metal Mfr
N.A.I.C.S.: 332312

Turner Maintenance Corporation (1)
8687 United Plz, Baton Rouge, LA 70809-2750 **(100%)**
Tel.: (225) 922-5050
Web Site: http://www.turner-industries.com
Sales Range: $700-749.9 Million
Emp.: 15,000
N.A.I.C.S.: 562910
Thomas Turner *(Owner)*

Turner Scaffolding Services (1)
2865 E Mason Ave, Baton Rouge, LA 70805-1231 **(100%)**
Tel.: (225) 356-1301
Sales Range: $25-49.9 Million
Emp.: 15
Construction Equipment Rental
N.A.I.C.S.: 532490
Mike Morain *(VP)*

TURNER KIA
4201 Chambers Hill Rd, Harrisburg, PA 17111
Tel.: (717) 564-2240
Web Site: http://www.turnerautos.com
Sales Range: $10-24.9 Million
Emp.: 50
Owner & Operator of Car Dealerships
N.A.I.C.S.: 441110
Lee C. Turner *(Owner & Pres)*
Thomas Priese *(Treas & Sec)*

TURNER LABORATORIES, INC.
2445 N Coyote Dr Ste 104, Tucson, AZ 85745-1236
Tel.: (520) 882-5880   AZ
Web Site: http://www.turnerlabs.com
Year Founded: 1988
Sales Range: $1-9.9 Million
Emp.: 10
Environmental Consulting Firm
N.A.I.C.S.: 541380
Michael McGovern *(Pres)*

TURNER MACHINE COMPANY, INC.
1433 Salem Pkwy, Salem, OH 44460-1070
Tel.: (330) 332-5821
Web Site: http://www.turnermachineco.com
Year Founded: 1934
Machine Fabrication; Supplier of Straightener Equipment for Tubes, Bars & Shapes
N.A.I.C.S.: 332710
Roy A. Page *(Pres)*
Neill McLachlan *(Owner)*

TURNER SUPPLY COMPANY
250 N Royal St, Mobile, AL 36602
Tel.: (251) 438-5581   AL
Web Site: http://www.turnersupply.com
Year Founded: 1905
Sales Range: $10-24.9 Million
Emp.: 250
Provider of Industrial Supplies
N.A.I.C.S.: 423840
Theresa Bishop *(Mgr-Inside Sls)*
Tommy Thompson *(Exec VP)*
Christopher Pratt *(VP-Birmingham)*

TURNER'S OUTDOORS, INC.
11738 San Marino Ste A, Rancho Cucamonga, CA 91730
Tel.: (909) 923-3009   CA
Web Site: http://www.turners.com
Year Founded: 1971
Sales Range: $25-49.9 Million
Emp.: 300
Sporting Goods
N.A.I.C.S.: 459110
Bill Ortiz *(VP-Ops)*
Gene Lumsden *(Pres & CEO)*

TURNINGPOINT GLOBAL SOLUTIONS
1355 Piccarda Dr Ste 250, Rockville, MD 20850
Tel.: (301) 795-1616
Web Site: http://www.tpgsi.com
Year Founded: 2002
Sales Range: $10-24.9 Million
Emp.: 85
Information Technology Consulting Services
N.A.I.C.S.: 541512
S. Shivacharan *(CEO)*
David R. Hughes *(Founder & Mng Partner)*
Michael Edwards *(VP-Federal Delivery)*
Silvio Renzi *(VP-Comml Svcs)*
Tsippora Rosenberg *(VP-Engrg Federal Telecom Practice)*
Dorothy Fera *(Dir-Fin & Contracts)*

TURNKEY TECHNOLOGIES, INC.
2500 Main St Ext Ste 10, Sayreville, NJ 08872
Tel.: (732) 553-9100   PA
Web Site: http://www.turnkeytechnologies.com
Year Founded: 1991
Sales Range: $75-99.9 Million
Emp.: 20
Radio Paging & Intercom Systems Distr
N.A.I.C.S.: 423690
Craig Badrick *(Pres)*
Chris Krehel *(Mgr-Svc Contracting-Natl)*

TURNPIKE FORD INC.
US 61 MacCorkle Ave SE, Marmet, WV 25315
Tel.: (304) 925-0431
Web Site: http://www.turnpikeford.com
Rev.: $31,400,000
Emp.: 43
Automobiles, New & Used
N.A.I.C.S.: 441110
Alex Parsons *(Pres)*
Diane Harold *(Bus Mgr)*
Randy Reed *(Mgr-Fin)*
Steve Parsons *(VP)*
Jimmy Marker *(Mgr-Sls)*

TURNSPIRE CAPITAL PARTNERS LLC
575 Madison Ave Ste 1006, New York, NY 10022
Tel.: (212) 605-0271
Web Site: http://www.turnspirecap.com
Private Equity
N.A.I.C.S.: 523999
Ilya Koffman *(Mng Partner)*

TURNSTILE PUBLISHING COMPANY
1500 Park Center Dr, Orlando, FL 32835
Tel.: (407) 563-7000
Web Site: http://www.turnstilemediagroup.com
Year Founded: 1990
Sales Range: $10-24.9 Million
Emp.: 98
Newspaper & Magazine Publisher
N.A.I.C.S.: 513120
Armand Cimaroli *(Dir-Events)*
Patti Green *(VP)*
Craig Horan *(Mng Editor)*
Diana Rodriquez *(Mgr-Acctg)*
Robin Daily *(Dir-Production)*

TURNSTONE CAPITAL MANAGEMENT LLC
15 Riverside Ave, Westport, CT 06880
Tel.: (203) 416-6581
Web Site: http://www.turnstonecapital.com
Sales Range: $25-49.9 Million
Emp.: 5
Investment Management Service
N.A.I.C.S.: 523999
Marc J. La Magna *(Founder & Mng Partner)*
Craig Samuel *(Co-Operating Partner)*
Richard Blue *(Co-Operating Partner)*

TURNTIDE TECHNOLOGIES INC.
1295 Forgewood Ave, Sunnyvale, CA 94089
Tel.: (877) 776-8470
Web Site: https://turntide.com
Emp.: 100
Industrial Machinery Mfr
N.A.I.C.S.: 333310
Ryan Morris *(CEO)*
Chris Pennison *(Sr VP-Strategic Ops)*
Subsidiaries:

Royal de Boer Stalinrichtingen B.V. (1)
Vestaweg 5, Postbus 1512, 8901 BV, Leeuwarden, Netherlands
Tel.: (31) 582332000
Web Site: http://www.deboerstal.com
Sales Range: $25-49.9 Million
Emp.: 100
Dairy Industry Machinery Mfr & Whslr
N.A.I.C.S.: 333111

TURNUPSEED ELECTRIC SERVICE, INC.
1580 S K St, Tulare, CA 93274
Tel.: (559) 686-1541   CA
Web Site: http://www.turnupseed.com
Year Founded: 1995
Sales Range: $25-49.9 Million
Emp.: 200
Electrical & Contracting Services
N.A.I.C.S.: 238210
David Turnupseed *(Pres)*

TURPIN DODGE OF DUBUQUE
90 John F Kennedy Rd, Dubuque, IA 52002
Tel.: (563) 583-5781
Web Site: http://www.turpindodgeofdubuque.net
Year Founded: 1953
Sales Range: $10-24.9 Million
Emp.: 48
Owner & Operator of Car Dealership
N.A.I.C.S.: 441110
Patrick Turpin *(Owner)*

TURQUINO EQUITY LLC
7601 River Rd Ste 919, North Bergen, NJ 07047
Tel.: (610) 564-5574
Web Site: http://www.turquinoequity.com
Private Equity Services
N.A.I.C.S.: 523999
Andrew Hidalgo *(Mng Partner)*
Matthew Hidalgo *(Mng Partner)*

TURQUOISE COUNCIL OF AMERICANS & EURASIANS
Galleria Tower 1 2700 Post Oak Blvd Ste 1750, Houston, TX 77056
Tel.: (713) 622-9200   TX
Web Site: http://www.tcae.org
Year Founded: 2009
Sales Range: $1-9.9 Million
Emp.: 4
Civic & Social Organization
N.A.I.C.S.: 813410
Bilal Eksili *(Pres & CEO)*

TURQUOISE HEALTH & WELLNESS, INC.

TURQUOISE HEALTH & WELLNESS, INC.—(Continued)

TURQUOISE HEALTH & WELLNESS, INC.
202 E Earll Dr Ste 200, Phoenix, AZ 85012
Tel.: (602) 553-7300 NM
Year Founded: 2013
Sales Range: $10-24.9 Million
Emp.: 260
Behavioral Healthcare Services
N.A.I.C.S.: 623220
Doris Vaught (CFO)
Thomas McKelvey (CEO)
Wayne Hochstrasser (Chm)
Ron Smith (Sec)

TURRI'S ITALIAN FOODS, INC.
16695 Common Rd, Roseville, MI 48066
Tel.: (586) 773-6010
Web Site: http://www.turrisitalianfoods.com
Year Founded: 1949
Sales Range: $10-24.9 Million
Emp.: 90
Frozen Specialty Food Mfr
N.AI.C.S.: 311412
Ron Cupp (Mgr-Sanitation)
Kevin Najor (Mgr-Pur)
Nora Allor (Office Mgr)
Susan Schrade (Mgr-HR)
Willy Jacobs (Mgr-Natl Sls)

TURSSO COMPANIES INCORPORATED
223 Plato Blvd E, Saint Paul, MN 55107
Tel.: (651) 222-8445
Web Site: http://www.tursso.com
Sales Range: $10-24.9 Million
Emp.: 90
Offset Printing
N.A.I.C.S.: 323111
Dennis Tursso (Owner)
John Erickson (VP-Sls & Mktg)
Earl Otte (Dir-IS)

TURTLE & HUGHES, INC.
1900 Lower Rd, Linden, NJ 07036-6519
Tel.: (732) 574-3600 NJ
Web Site: http://www.turtle.com
Year Founded: 1923
Sales Range: $500-549.9 Million
Emp.: 325
Electrical & Industrial Distr
N.A.I.C.S.: 423610
Jayne Millard (Exec Chm & Co-CEO)
Luis Valls (Co-CEO)
Chris Rausch (CFO)
Kevin Doyle (COO)
Luke Supak (Mgr-Indus Switchgear-Houston)
Jim Bailey (Mgr-Credit-New York)
Dan Fongaro (Dir-Internal Audit)
Caldwell Hart (Chief Procurement Officer & Sr VP-Supply Chain)
Robert Courcy (VP-Gulf Reg)
Teesee Murray (Chief Strategy Officer)
Aram Marandyan (VP-Sls-Los Angeles)
Dan Pinshaw (Branch Mgr-Los Angeles)

Subsidiaries:

Forest Hills Electrical Supply, Inc. (1)
3607 Washington St, Boston, MA 02130
Tel.: (617) 983-9920
Web Site: http://www.fhelectrical.com
Rev.: $10,000,000
Emp.: 15

Electrical Apparatus & Equipment, Wiring Supplies & Related Equipment Merchant Whslr
N.A.I.C.S.: 423610
Dennis L. Albert (Pres)

Mid Island Electrical Sales Corp. (1)
59 Mall Dr, Commack, NY 11725
Tel.: (631) 864-4242
Web Site: http://www.turtle.com
Rev.: $27,148,257
Emp.: 55
Electrical Supplies
N.A.I.C.S.: 423610

TURTLE MOUNTAIN BAND OF CHIPPEWA INDIANS INC.
Hwy 5, Belcourt, ND 58316
Tel.: (701) 477-2600 ND
Web Site: http://www.tmbci.net
Year Founded: 1972
Sales Range: $50-74.9 Million
Emp.: 500
Hotel
N.A.I.C.S.: 721120

Subsidiaries:

Uniband Enterprises (1)
PO Box 1059 Hwy 5 W, Belcourt, ND 58316
Tel.: (701) 477-6445
Web Site: http://www.uniband.com
Rev.: $44,161,128
Emp.: 20
Data Processing & Preparation
N.A.I.C.S.: 518210

TURTLE SURVIVAL ALLIANCE FOUNDATION
1989 Colonial Pkwy, Fort Worth, TX 76110
Tel.: (817) 759-7262 TX
Web Site: http://www.turtlesurvival.org
Year Founded: 2004
Sales Range: $1-9.9 Million
Animal Welfare Services
N.A.I.C.S.: 813312
Walter Sedgwick (Treas)
Rick Hudson (Pres)
Dwight Lawson (VP)
Jim Breheny (Exec VP & Gen Dir)
Patricia Koval (Chm)

TURTLE WAX, INC.
2250 W Pinehurst Blvd Ste 150, Addison, IL 60101
Tel.: (630) 455-3700 IL
Web Site: http://www.turtlewax.com
Year Founded: 1944
Sales Range: $150-199.9 Million
Emp.: 450
Car Care Products Mfr
N.A.I.C.S.: 325612
Michele Johannes (Brand Mgr)
Tina Brendemuehl (Coord-Customer Svc)

TURTLEDOVE CLEMENS, INC.
1230 SW 1st Ave Ste 200, Portland, OR 97204-3200
Tel.: (503) 226-3581
Web Site: http://www.turtledove.com
Year Founded: 1941
Sales Range: $10-24.9 Million
Emp.: 12
Advertising, Communications, Consumer Marketing, Food Service, Graphic Design, Health Care, Leisure, Planning & Consultation, Public Relations, Restaurant, Travel & Tourism
N.A.I.C.S.: 541810
Jay Clemens (Owner)
Linda Higgons (Exec VP)
Stuart Sammuelson (Acct Mgr)
Brooke Jones (Production Mgr)
Jeff Bernius (Sr Dir-Art)

Sandra Carpenter (Acct Mgr)
Jackie Hensel (Media Buyer)
Ken Howard (Mgr-Interactive)

TUSCALOOSA HYUNDAI, INC.
2502 Skyland Blvd E, Tuscaloosa, AL 35405
Tel.: (205) 409-2077
Web Site: http://www.tuscaloosahyundai.com
Sales Range: $10-24.9 Million
Emp.: 55
New Car Dealers
N.A.I.C.S.: 441110
Barry Buckner (Pres & Gen Mgr)
David Clements (Mgr-Sls)
Brooke Meissner (Office Mgr)
Jimmy Oswalt (Mgr-Svc)
Shane Deason (Mgr-Collision Center)
Jason Estes (Mgr-Parts)
Jessica Browning (Asst Mgr-Svc)
Bobby Perkins (Mgr-Svc-Columbus)
Matt Strickland (Mgr-Used Car)

TUSCANY PAVERS
402 W Broadway Ste 400, San Diego, CA 92101
Tel.: (760) 877-3060
Web Site: http://www.tuscanypavers.com
Year Founded: 1991
Sales Range: $1-9.9 Million
Emp.: 12
Designs & Installs Paving Stones
N.A.I.C.S.: 327991
Jay Erdos (Dir-Mktg)

TUSCARORA YARNS INC.
8760 E Franklin St, Mount Pleasant, NC 28124-8788
Tel.: (704) 436-6527 NC
Web Site: http://www.tuscarorayarns.com
Year Founded: 1899
Sales Range: $50-74.9 Million
Emp.: 500
Acrylic, Polyester, Cotton & Rayon Yarns Mfr
N.A.I.C.S.: 313110

TUSCOLA COUNTY ROAD COMMISSION
1733 Mertz Rd, Caro, MI 48723
Tel.: (989) 673-2128
Web Site: http://www.tuscolaroad.org
Rev.: $11,048,091
Emp.: 60
Highway & Street Maintenance
N.A.I.C.S.: 237310
Mike Tuckey (Dir-Fin)
Michele Zawerucha (Engr-Highway)

TUSTIN BUICK GMC
1 Auto Center Dr, Tustin, CA 92782
Tel.: (866) 362-9920
Web Site: http://www.tustingmc.com
Year Founded: 1953
Rev.: $114,000,000
Emp.: 69
Automobiles, New & Used Dealer
N.A.I.C.S.: 441110

TUSTIN MECHANICAL SERVICES (LEHIGH VALLEY), LLC.
2555 Industry Ln, Norristown, PA 19403
Tel.: (610) 539-8200
Web Site: http://www.thetustingroup.com
Emp.: 50
Plumbing, Heating & Air-Conditioning Contractors
N.A.I.C.S.: 238220
James Sasser (Pres)
John Heloskie (Engr-Sls)

U.S. PRIVATE

Subsidiaries:

Tilley Fire Equipment Company Inc (1)
280 N Broad St, Doylestown, PA 18901
Tel.: (215) 345-8066
Web Site: http://www.tilleyfire.com
Emp.: 75
Fire Protection Systems
N.A.I.C.S.: 561621
Michael B. Tilley (Pres)

TUSTIN TOYOTA
36 Auto Center Dr, Tustin, CA 92782-8407
Tel.: (714) 832-3111
Web Site: http://www.tustintoyota.com
Year Founded: 1983
Sales Range: $25-49.9 Million
Emp.: 220
Car Dealership Owner & Operator
N.A.I.C.S.: 441110
Glenn Kashima (Dir-Svc)

TUTERA GROUP INC.
7611 State Line Rd No 301, Kansas City, MO 64114
Tel.: (816) 444-0900
Web Site: http://www.tutera.com
Sales Range: $25-49.9 Million
Emp.: 50
Non-Residential Construction Services
N.A.I.C.S.: 236220
Joseph C. Tutera (Pres)

Subsidiaries:

Investment Properties and Management (1)
7611 Sta Line Rd Ste 301, Kansas City, MO 64114
Tel.: (816) 444-0900
Web Site: http://www.tutera.com
Rev.: $160,000
Emp.: 100
Real Estate Managers
N.A.I.C.S.: 531210
Joseph C. Tutera (Pres)

TUTHILL CORP
1660 Blue Mtn Dr, Palmerton, PA 18071
Tel.: (610) 826-7700
Web Site: http://www.skibluemt.com
Year Founded: 1977
Sales Range: $10-24.9 Million
Emp.: 25
Ski Lodge
N.A.I.C.S.: 721199
Bruce Ebert (VP)
Diane R. Tuthill (Sec)
Hidie Lutz (Mgr-Mktg)

TUTHILL CORPORATION
8500 S Madison St, Burr Ridge, IL 60527-6284
Tel.: (630) 382-4900 DE
Web Site: http://www.tuthill.com
Year Founded: 1892
Sales Range: $300-349.9 Million
Industrial Pumps, Blowers, Quick Connective Couplings, Control Linkage Components & Push-Pull Cables Mfr
N.A.I.C.S.: 333611
Garry Johnson (Dir-Strategic Sourcing)
Phil Dalen (Mgr-Data Govt)
Chad Gabriel (Brand Dir-Seismic)
Brad Boyd (VP-Sls-Pump Grp)
Steven Westfall (Pres & CEO)

Subsidiaries:

TUTHILL MEXICO, S RL CV (1)
Chula Vista No 305 Col Linda Vista, Guadalupe, Nuevo Leon, Mexico
Tel.: (52) 8183030025
Web Site: http://www.es.tuthill.com

COMPANIES

Pump & Pumping Equipment Mfr
N.A.I.C.S.: 333914

Tuthill Corporation Pump Group (1)
12500 S Pulaski Rd, Alsip, IL 60803-1911
Tel.: (708) 389-2500
Web Site: http://www.tuthill.com
Sales Range: $10-24.9 Million
Emp.: 130
Rotary Pumps & Plugs Mfr
N.A.I.C.S.: 333914
Ruth Nelson (Pres)

Tuthill Fill-Rite Division (1)
8825 Aviation Dr, Fort Wayne, IN 46809-9630
Tel.: (260) 747-7529
Web Site: http://www.tuthill.com
Sales Range: $25-49.9 Million
Emp.: 185
Mfr of Electric & Hand-Operated Gasoline Pumps, Meters & Electronic Fuel Control Systems
N.A.I.C.S.: 333914
Jeff Morris (Controller)

Tuthill Plastics Group (1)
2050 Sunnydale Blvd, Clearwater, FL 33765-1201 (100%)
Tel.: (727) 446-8593
Web Site: http://www.tuthill.com
Sales Range: $10-24.9 Million
Emp.: 50
Mfr of Injection Molded Plastics
N.A.I.C.S.: 326199
Richard Curtin (Pres)
Ralph Guthrie (Mgr-Quality)

Tuthill Transfer Systems (1)
8825 Aviation Dr, Fort Wayne, IN 46809
Tel.: (260) 747-7529
Web Site: http://www.tuthill.com
Sales Range: $25-49.9 Million
Emp.: 300
Fluid Handling Equipment Mfr
N.A.I.C.S.: 333310
Adam Potts (Engr-Machining)
Jay Boester (Mgr-Sls-Chemical Pumps & Meters-Natl)
Carlos Limardo (Product Mgr-South America)
Jennifer Stevens (Product Mgr)
Denise Lewis (Dir-Tactical Plng)
Paul Pike (Mgr-Strategic Sourcing)

Tuthill UK Ltd (1)
Birkdale Close, Manners Industrial Estate, Ilkeston, DE7 8YA, Derbyshire, United Kingdom
Tel.: (44) 1159325226
Web Site: http://www.tuthill.com
Sales Range: $10-24.9 Million
Emp.: 45
Pumps Mfr
N.A.I.C.S.: 333914
Michael Weigl (Dir-Sls)

TUTHILL FINANCE
60 Katona Dr, Fairfield, CT 06824
Tel.: (203) 335-5600
Web Site: http://www.tuthillfinance.com
Sales Range: $25-49.9 Million
Emp.: 4
Mortgage Banker
N.A.I.C.S.: 522292
Jeffrey Wain (Pres)

TUTTLE GROUP INC.
1859 Summit Commerce Pk, Twinsburg, OH 44087
Tel.: (330) 487-5200
Web Site: http://www.spencerprodco.com
Year Founded: 1954
Sales Range: $10-24.9 Million
Emp.: 55
Whslr of Industrial Nuts, Bolts, Screws & Fasteners
N.A.I.C.S.: 423840
Joseph Double (CFO)
Ralph Art (Mgr-Quality)
Bryan Stock (VP)
Jim Tuttle (VP)

Subsidiaries:

Spencer Products Co. Inc. (1)
1859 Summit Commerce Park, Twinsburg, OH 44087
Tel.: (330) 487-5200
Web Site: http://www.spencerprodco.com
Sales Range: $10-24.9 Million
Emp.: 21
Industrial Fasteners
N.A.I.C.S.: 423840
Joe Double (Controller)
David Tuttle (Treas & Sec)
Bryns Stock (VP)

TUTTLE-CLICK AUTOMOTIVE GROUP
40 Auto Center Dr, Irvine, CA 92618
Tel.: (949) 472-7400 CA
Web Site: http://www.tuttleclick.com
Year Founded: 1953
Sales Range: $200-249.9 Million
Emp.: 500
Car Distr
N.A.I.C.S.: 441110
Chris Cotter (Pres)

Subsidiaries:

Holmes Tuttle Ford, Inc. (1)
660 W Auto Mall Dr, Tucson, AZ 85705-6009
Tel.: (520) 292-3600
Web Site: http://www.holmestuttleford.com
Sales Range: $25-49.9 Million
Emp.: 225
Retail Sales of New & Used Cars
N.A.I.C.S.: 441110
Corey Goffer (Mgr-Parts)
Scott Jones (Mgr-Svc)
Jason Davis (Mgr-Svc)

TUTTLE-CLICK COLLISION CENTER
800 W Auto Mall Dr, Tucson, AZ 85705-6013
Tel.: (520) 884-4100
Web Site: http://www.jimclick.com
Year Founded: 1995
Sales Range: $150-199.9 Million
Emp.: 750
Car Whslr
N.A.I.C.S.: 441110
Jim Click (Owner)
Joe Diaz (Mgr)
Sam Khayat (Exec VP)
Ed Yashar (CFO)

TUXEDO JUNCTION INC.
120 Earhart Dr, Williamsville, NY 14221
Tel.: (716) 633-2400
Web Site: http://www.tuxedojunction.com
Sales Range: $25-49.9 Million
Emp.: 200
Retailer of Men's & Boys' Clothing
N.A.I.C.S.: 424350
Mike Bristol (Exec VP)
Joe Terranova (VP-Sls)
Nancy Macdonald (Dir-Mktg)

TV EARS
2701 Via Orange Way Ste 1, Spring Valley, CA 91978-1702
Tel.: (619) 797-1605
Web Site: http://www.tvears.com
Year Founded: 1998
Sales Range: $10-24.9 Million
Emp.: 30
Electronic Parts & Equipment Merchant Whslr
N.A.I.C.S.: 423690
George Dennis (CEO)

TV SPECIALISTS INC.
180 E 2100 S Ste 104, Salt Lake City, UT 84115
Tel.: (801) 486-7555

Web Site: http://www.tvspecialists.com
Sales Range: $10-24.9 Million
Emp.: 23
Provider of Industrial & Commercial Sales
N.A.I.C.S.: 423620
Jerry Bollinger (Pres)
Steve Bollinger (VP)
Ted Bollinger (Mgr-Sls)

TV, INC.
2465 Northside Dr Ste 1704, Clearwater, FL 33761
Tel.: (310) 985-1229
Year Founded: 1987
Sales Range: $10-24.9 Million
Emp.: 12
N.A.I.C.S.: 541810
William Thompson (CEO)

Subsidiaries:

TV, Inc. (1)
Gronhogen 1409D SE-380 65 Oland, Stockholm, 1409D, Sweden
Tel.: (46) 485 661 212
N.A.I.C.S.: 541810
Kenneth Forsman (Gen Mgr-European Markets)
William Thompson (Pres & CEO)
Elia Grando Mattiazzi (Dir-Client Svcs)

TVA COMMUNITY CREDIT UNION
1010 Reservation Rd, Muscle Shoals, AL 35662
Tel.: (256) 386-3000 AL
Web Site: http://www.tvaccu.com
Year Founded: 1936
Sales Range: $10-24.9 Million
Credit Union
N.A.I.C.S.: 522130
Kimball R. Burkett (Pres & CEO)
Sammy Clements (Exec VP)
Rhonda Cabler (CFO)
Lewis Frederick (Chrm)
Frances Weatherford (Sec & Treas)
Alyssa Bole (Mktg Dir)
Amy McCormack (VP-Lending Svcs)
Tammie Aday (VP & Sr Loan Officer)
Larry Softley Jr. (Vice Chm)

TVAX BIOMEDICAL, INC.
8006 Reeder St, Lenexa, KS 66214
Tel.: (913) 492-2221 DE
Web Site: http://www.tvaxbiomedical.com
Sales Range: Less than $1 Million
Emp.: 6
Cancer Treatment Cell-Based Immunotherapies Researcher, Developer & Mfr
N.A.I.C.S.: 541715
Frank P. Holladay (Co-Founder)

TVC CAPITAL LLC
11452 El Camino Real Ste 450, San Diego, CA 92130
Tel.: (858) 704-3261
Web Site: http://www.tvccapital.com
Sales Range: $25-49.9 Million
Emp.: 5
Privater Equity Firm
N.A.I.C.S.: 523999
Steven J. Hamerslag (Mng Partner)
Jeb S. Spencer (Mng Partner)

TVO GROUPE
180 N Michigan Ave Ste 2120, Chicago, IL 60601
Tel.: (312) 500-8833
Web Site: http://www.tvogroupe.com
Rev.: $4,000,000,000
Real Estate Investment & Property Services
N.A.I.C.S.: 531390

Wayne Vandenburg (Co-Founder)
Russell A. Vandenburg (Co-Founder)
David L. Vandenburg (Chief Investment Officer & Principal)
Stephen Beltran (Principal & Head-Property Ops)

Subsidiaries:

TVO North America (1)
221 N Kansas St 16th Fl, El Paso, TX 79901
Tel.: (915) 778-7500
Web Site: http://www.tvonorthamerica.com
Sales Range: $10-24.9 Million
Emp.: 52
Real Estate Support Services
N.A.I.C.S.: 531390
Kevin Stasiewicz (Head-Asset Mgmt)
Russell A. Vandenburg (CEO)

TVO REALTY PARTNERS
70 E Lk St Ste 600, Chicago, IL 60601
Tel.: (312) 553-1133
Web Site: http://www.tvogroupe.com
Year Founded: 1983
Sales Range: $25-49.9 Million
Emp.: 300
Provider of Real Estate Services
N.A.I.C.S.: 237210
Wayne A. Vandenburg (Chm & CEO)
David L. Vandenburg (Pres, Mng Dir & Principal)

TW PERRY ENTERPRISES, INC.
8519 Connecticut Ave, Chevy Chase, MD 20815
Tel.: (301) 840-9600
Web Site: http://www.twperry.com
Year Founded: 1911
Sales Range: $10-24.9 Million
Emp.: 300
Building Materials Distr
N.A.I.C.S.: 444110
Gary Bowman (CEO)
Mike Moore (VP-Matls Mgmt)
Doug Kelly (VP-Sls & Mktg)
Elisa Kerneklian (Dir-HR)
Edward J. Quinn Jr. (Chm)

TWC AVIATION, INC.
16700C Roscoe Blvd, Van Nuys, CA 91406
Tel.: (818) 441-0100
Web Site: http://www.twcaviation.com
Year Founded: 1996
Sales Range: $50-74.9 Million
Emp.: 253
Aircraft Management & Consulting Services
N.A.I.C.S.: 336413
Robert J. Oliver (Dir-Ops)
Edward Frank (Gen Mgr)
Chris Battagllia (Sr VP-Charter Svcs)
Alan Ause (CFO)

TWD & ASSOCIATES INC.
2800 S Shirlington Rd Ste 400, Arlington, VA 22206
Tel.: (703) 820-9777
Web Site: http://www.twd.com
Year Founded: 1986
Rev.: $14,326,430
Emp.: 300
Provider of Computer Integrated Systems Design Services
N.A.I.C.S.: 541512
Larry A. Besterman (Pres & CEO)
Mary Gostel (VP-Bus Dev)
Mike Lee (COO)
Woody Hume (VP-Tech Sls)
Rodney Martin (Sr VP-Corp Dev)
Jennifer Luce (VP-Capture & Proposal)
Ashwin Karkera (VP-Civilian Agency Programs)

TWD & ASSOCIATES INC.

TWD & Associates Inc.—(Continued)
Chris Ackerman (VP-Collaboration & Cloud Solutions)
Steve Estwick (VP-Navy & Marine Corps Programs)

TWEDDLE LITHO COMPANY
24700 Maplehurst Dr, Clinton Township, MI 48036-1336
Tel.: (586) 307-3700
Web Site: http://www.tweddle.com
Year Founded: 1954
Sales Range: $100-124.9 Million
Emp.: 200
Provider of Printing & Technical Authoring Services
N.A.I.C.S.: 323111
Dan Titus (Exec VP-Fin)
Andrew Tweddle (Pres)
Eric Taylor (Dir-Pur)
Scott Thomasson (VP-Ford Team)

TWEET-GAROT MECHANICAL INC.
2545 Larsen Rd, Green Bay, WI 54303
Tel.: (920) 498-0400
Web Site: http://www.tweet-garot.com
Rev.: $33,000,000
Emp.: 225
Mechanical Contractor
N.A.I.C.S.: 238220
Michael Sturdivant (Exec VP)
Christopher Howald (CEO)
Hope Voigt (COO)
Greg Weinfurter (VP-Central Wisconsin Acct)
Mark Hill (VP-Green Bay Acct)

TWELVE CONSULTING GROUP, INC.
575 SE 9th St Ste 70, Minneapolis, MN 55414
Tel.: (612) 383-2208
Web Site: http://www.twelvecg.com
Year Founded: 2013
Sales Range: $1-9.9 Million
Emp.: 44
Information Technology Consulting Services
N.A.I.C.S.: 541690
Jill King (Co-CEO & Partner)
Josh King (Co-CEO)
John Wihtol (Principal)
Megan Henderson (Head-Internal Ops)
Ralph Blanco (Office Mgr)

TWELVE NYC
45 Main St Ste 615, Brooklyn, NY 11201
Tel.: (212) 244-5221
Web Site: http://www.twelvenyc.com
Year Founded: 2005
Sales Range: $1-9.9 Million
Label Printing Services
N.A.I.C.S.: 561910
Katie Conovitz (Founder & CEO)

TWELVE POINTS WEALTH MANAGEMENT, LLC
Damon Mill Sq 9 Pond Ln Ste 3A, Concord, MA 01742
Tel.: (978) 318-9500
Web Site: http://www.twelvepointswealth.com
Year Founded: 2014
Sales Range: $1-9.9 Million
Emp.: 17
Financial Management Services
N.A.I.C.S.: 541611
Dave Clayman (Co-Founder & CEO)
Francesca Federico (Co-Founder & Principal)
Manny Frangiadakis (Co-Founder & Principal)
Kimberly Van Winkle (Chief Compliance Officer & Dir-Ops)
Igor Tiguy (Dir-Plng Svcs)

TWENTY FIRST CENTURY LP
825 3rd Ave Fl 4, New York, NY 10022-9524
Tel.: (201) 569-3400
Web Site: http://www.tfclpi.com
Rev.: $20,600,000
Emp.: 20
Fast-Food Restaurant, Chain
N.A.I.C.S.: 722513
Dorothy Kornblith (Pres)
Daniel E. Penni (Principal-Endowment)
Daniel E. Penni (Principal-Endowment)

TWENTY FOUR SEVEN, INC.
425 NE 9th Ave, Portland, OR 97232
Tel.: (503) 222-7999
Web Site: http://www.twentyfour7.com
Year Founded: 1995
Rev.: $13,700,000
Emp.: 20
Advertising & Marketing
N.A.I.C.S.: 541810
Jennifer Brothers (Gen Mgr)
Lori Alkana (Mgr-HR)
Mimi Lettunich (Owner)
Jon Roy (Dir-Creative)
Ray Wilson (Mgr-Project)
Emory Welcher (Office Mgr)

Subsidiaries:
Twenty Four Seven (1)
250 Hudson St 11th Fl, New York, NY 10013
Tel.: (212) 300-6222
N.A.I.C.S.: 541810
Lora Churcher (Sr Brand Mgr)
Mike Lettunich (Owner)

TWENTY-FIRST CENTURY GRAIN PROCESSING COOPERATIVE
PO Box 239, Canyon, TX 79015
Tel.: (806) 258-7227
Sales Range: $25-49.9 Million
Emp.: 45
Flour Mfr
N.A.I.C.S.: 311212
Lynn Randle (CEO)

TWENTY/TWENTY WORLDWIDE HOSPITALITY, LLC
60 Seagate Dr Ste 1704, Naples, FL 34103
Tel.: (239) 384-9050
Web Site: http://www.twentytwentyworldwide.com
Year Founded: 1996
Sales Range: $1-9.9 Million
Hospitality Management & Consulting Services
N.A.I.C.S.: 541611
Fred Hirschovits (Pres)

TWG BENEFITS, INC.
400 Skokie Blvd Ste 415, Northbrook, IL 60062
Tel.: (847) 296-2045
Web Site: http://www.twgbenefits.com
Year Founded: 1995
Sales Range: $1-9.9 Million
Retirement Benefit Valuation & Recordkeeping Services
N.A.I.C.S.: 524292
Haskel B. Weiss (Pres)
Adam Weiss (VP)

Subsidiaries:
General Pension Planning Corp. (1)
2912 Springboro W Ste 105, Dayton, OH 45439-1674
Tel.: (937) 298-3908
Web Site: http://www.generalpension.com
Sales Range: $1-9.9 Million
Emp.: 25
Retirement Pension Plan Consulting & Recordkeeping Services
N.A.I.C.S.: 541618
Steve Scrudder (Pres)

TWI GROUP, INC.
4480 S Pecos Rd, Las Vegas, NV 89121-3612
Tel.: (702) 691-9000
Web Site: http://www.twiglobal.com
Year Founded: 1973
Sales Range: $10-24.9 Million
Emp.: 80
Freight Transportation Arrangement
N.A.I.C.S.: 488510
Greg Keh (Exec VP)
Jay Cease (Dir-Ops)
Stephen J. Barry Jr. (Chm & CEO)

Subsidiaries:
TWI Group Inc. (1)
2000 Argentia Road Suite 450 Plaza 4, Mississauga, L5N 1W1, ON, Canada
Tel.: (905) 812-1124
Web Site: http://www.twigroup.com
Emp.: 1
Freight Transportation Arrangement
N.A.I.C.S.: 488510

TWIDDY AND COMPANY REALTORS
1181 Duck Rd, Duck, NC 27949
Tel.: (252) 261-3521
Web Site: http://www.twiddy.com
Year Founded: 1978
Sales Range: $50-74.9 Million
Real Estate Brokers & Agents
N.A.I.C.S.: 531210
Douglas A. Twiddy (Founder)

TWILIGHT TECHNOLOGY, INC.
325 N Shepard St, Anaheim, CA 92806
Tel.: (714) 257-2257
Web Site: http://www.twilighttechnology.com
Year Founded: 1996
Obsolete Semiconductor & Memory Module Mfr
N.A.I.C.S.: 334413
Randy Greene (Pres & CEO)
Akon Essien (Sr Mgr-Ops)

Subsidiaries:
Twilight Now, LLC (1)
325 N Shepard St, Anaheim, CA 92806
Tel.: (714) 257-2257
Semiconductor Mfr & Whslr
N.A.I.C.S.: 334413
Randy Greene (Co-CEO)
Aaron Goodridge (Co-CEO)

TWIN BRIDGES TRUCK CITY INC.
2250 W 76th St, Davenport, IA 52806
Tel.: (563) 355-2631
Web Site: http://www.twinvm.com
Rev.: $15,052,201
Emp.: 150
Turck Sales
N.A.I.C.S.: 423110
Jim Street (Mgr-Parts)
Sue Jarvis (Pres)

TWIN CITIES AD
701 4th Ave S Ste 500, Minneapolis, MN 55415
Tel.: (612) 605-0729
Year Founded: 2007
Sales Range: $1-9.9 Million

Emp.: 21
Advertising Agencies
N.A.I.C.S.: 541810
Johannes Marliem (Founder & CEO)
Robert Christenson (Owner)
Robert Gerving (VP-Sales)

TWIN CITIES FINANCIAL SERVICES
330 E Broadway, Maryville, TN 37804
Tel.: (865) 977-5900
Web Site: http://www.cbbcbank.com
Sales Range: $10-24.9 Million
Emp.: 90
State Commercial Banks
N.A.I.C.S.: 522110
Joe Bruce (Founder)
Susan Philips (VP)
Al Grubb (Exec VP)
Bob Carroll (Sr Exec VP)
Gaynell Lawson (Pres & CEO)
Mike Baker (Pres)
Perry Roberts (VP)
Marilyn Cobble (VP & Mgr-Comml Relationship)
Paul Hodge (Asst VP)

TWIN CITIES PUBLIC TELEVISION, INC.
172 E 4th St, Saint Paul, MN 55101
Tel.: (651) 222-1717
Web Site: http://www.tpt.org
Year Founded: 1955
Sales Range: $10-24.9 Million
Emp.: 150
Television Broadcasting Station
N.A.I.C.S.: 516120
James R. Pagliarini (Pres & CEO)
Gerry Richman (VP)
Jenny Masters-Wolfe (Sr VP-HR & Org Effectiveness)
Elaine Powell (Sr Mgr-Station Rels & Client Svcs)
Sally Mullen (Chm)
Melissa Wright (Gen Counsel)
Donna Zimmerman (Sr VP-Govt & Community Rels)

TWIN CITY CHRISTIAN HOMES, INC.
7645 Lyndale Ave S Ste 110, Richfield, MN 55423
Tel.: (612) 861-2799
Web Site: http://www.tcchomes.org
Rev.: $11,098,686
Emp.: 192
Adult Housing Services
N.A.I.C.S.: 925110
Barbara Kuhlman (Dir-Ops)
Chris Schmidt (Dir-Fin)
Nancy Starr (Exec Dir)

TWIN CITY CONCRETE PRODUCTS CO.
2025 Center Pointe Blvd Ste 300, Mendota Heights, MN 55120
Tel.: (651) 688-9116
Web Site: http://www.twincityconcrete.com
Year Founded: 1957
Sales Range: $10-24.9 Million
Emp.: 100
Concrete Products Mfr
N.A.I.C.S.: 423320
Hammon T. Becken (CEO)

TWIN CITY DIE CASTINGS CO.
1070 SE 33rd Ave, Minneapolis, MN 55414-2707
Tel.: (651) 645-3611
Web Site: http://www.tcdcinc.com
Year Founded: 1919
Sales Range: $50-74.9 Million
Emp.: 100

Aluminum, Zinc & Magnesium Die Castings Mfr
N.A.I.C.S.: 331523
Douglas Harmon *(CEO)*
Greg Hansen *(Pres & COO)*
Ron Barse *(Dir-Continuous Improvement)*
Todd Olson *(CFO)*

Subsidiaries:

Twin City Die Castings Co. (1)
122 Cessna St NW, Watertown, SD 57201-5611 **(100%)**
Tel.: (605) 886-9448
Web Site: http://www.pcdcinc.com
Sales Range: $10-24.9 Million
Emp.: 62
Mfr of Zinc & Aluminum Die Castings
N.A.I.C.S.: 331523

Twin City Die Castings Co. - WATERTOWN FACILITY (1)
122 Cessna St NW, Watertown, SD 57201
Tel.: (605) 886-9448
Web Site: http://www.tcdcinc.com
Aluminum Die-Castings Mfr
N.A.I.C.S.: 331523
John Maratea *(Mgr-Production)*

TWIN CITY FAN COMPANIES, LTD.
5959 Trenton Ln N, Minneapolis, MN 55442-3237
Tel.: (763) 551-7500   MN
Web Site: http://www.twincityfan.com
Year Founded: 1973
Sales Range: $200-249.9 Million
Emp.: 1,000
Mfr & Retailer of Propeller Fans & Power Roof Ventilators
N.A.I.C.S.: 333413
Michael Barry *(Pres)*
Chuck Barry *(CEO)*

Subsidiaries:

Aerovent (1)
5959 Trenton Ln N, Minneapolis, MN 55442-3237
Tel.: (763) 551-7500
Web Site: http://www.aerovent.com
Emp.: 200
Ventilation Equipment Mfr
N.A.I.C.S.: 333413
Sherry Fredrickson *(Mgr-HR)*

Azen Manufacturing Pte. Ltd. (1)
NO 8 Tuas Link 1, Singapore, 638593, Singapore
Tel.: (65) 6261 0277
Web Site: http://www.azen.com.sg
Ventilation Equipment Mfr
N.A.I.C.S.: 333413
Meng Tan Chee *(Mgr-Engrg)*

Clarage (1)
202 Commerce Way, Pulaski, TN 38478
Tel.: (931) 363-2667
Web Site: http://www.clarage.com
Sales Range: $10-24.9 Million
Emp.: 45
Mfr of Air Pollution Control & Acid Gas Removal Systems, Wet & Dry Scrubbers, Fabric Filters, Mechanical Dust Collectors & Dampers & Fans
N.A.I.C.S.: 333413
Michael Barry *(Pres)*
Eranga Devasurendra *(Mgr-Engrg)*
Mike Thornton *(Coord-Safety & Maintenance)*

NADI Airtechnics Private Limited (1)
Gate No 3 Door No 57-58 Thattanmkulam Road, Madhavaram, Chennai, 600 060, India
Tel.: (91) 4425532212
Web Site: http://www.nadiindia.com
Industrial Fans Mfr
N.A.I.C.S.: 333413

Unit (Domestic):

NADI Airtechnics Private Limited - Unit 4 (2)
Gate no 3 Door no 57-58 Thattanmkulam Road, Madhavaram, Chennai, 600060, India
Tel.: (91) 44 25532419
Industrial Fans Mfr
N.A.I.C.S.: 333413
J. B. Kambar *(Mng Dir)*

TCF Vzduchotechnika ltd. (1)
Prumyslova 920, 38301, Prachatice, Czech Republic
Tel.: (420) 388 317 302
Web Site: http://www.tcf.cz
Sales Range: $10-24.9 Million
Emp.: 55
Industrial Fans Mfr
N.A.I.C.S.: 333413
Jiri Maly *(Gen Mgr)*

Twin City Fan & Blower (1)
5959 Trenton Ln N, Minneapolis, MN 55442
Tel.: (763) 551-7600
Web Site: http://www.tcf.com
Industrial Fans Mfr
N.A.I.C.S.: 333413
Charles L. Barry *(CEO)*
Michael Barry *(Pres & COO)*
Andy Bosscher *(Product Mgr-Sls)*

Twin City Holland Industries (1)
944 S Farragut, Davenport, IA 52808
Tel.: (563) 323-2797
Web Site: http://www.tcholland.com
Emp.: 25
Aluminum Die-Castings Mfr
N.A.I.C.S.: 331523
Amber Payne *(Office Mgr)*

Twin City Ventco (1)
5959 Trenton Ln N, Minneapolis, MN 55442-3237
Tel.: (763) 551-7600
Web Site: http://www.tcventco.com
Emp.: 500
Centrifugal Fan Mfr
N.A.I.C.S.: 333413

TWIN CITY FOODS, INC.
10120 269th Pl NW, Stanwood, WA 98292
Tel.: (206) 515-2400   WA
Web Site: http://www.twincityfoods.com
Year Founded: 1945
Sales Range: $25-49.9 Million
Emp.: 350
Processor of Frozen Vegetables
N.A.I.C.S.: 311411
Roger O. Lervick *(Chm & CEO)*
John Lervick *(Pres & COO)*
Rob Watson *(Mgr-Export & Indus Sls)*

TWIN CITY HARDWARE COMPANY
723 Hadley Ave N, Oakdale, MN 55128
Tel.: (651) 735-2200
Web Site: http://www.twincityhardware.com
Sales Range: $10-24.9 Million
Emp.: 80
Hardware
N.A.I.C.S.: 423710
George H. Boomer *(Owner & Pres)*
Steve Kilibarda *(Project Mgr)*

TWIN CITY MAZDA
3234 Airport Hwy, Alcoa, TN 37701
Tel.: (865) 970-2977
Web Site: http://www.twincitymazda.com
Year Founded: 1956
Sales Range: $10-24.9 Million
Emp.: 40
New Car Whslr
N.A.I.C.S.: 441110
Brian Scates *(VP)*
Charles Stephens *(Mgr)*

TWIN CITY SECURITY, INC.
519 Coon Rapids Blvd, Minneapolis, MN 55433
Tel.: (763) 784-4160   MN
Web Site: http://www.twincitysecurity.com
Sales Range: $10-24.9 Million
Emp.: 3
Security Guard Services
N.A.I.C.S.: 561612
Donna Shrider *(Pres)*

TWIN CITY TRACTOR & EQUIPMENT INC.
7200 Landers Rd, North Little Rock, AR 72117
Tel.: (501) 834-9999
Web Site: http://www.gocapeq.com
Year Founded: 1987
Sales Range: $10-24.9 Million
Emp.: 20
Sale of General Construction Machinery & Equipment
N.A.I.C.S.: 423810
Deanna Mahoney *(CFO)*

TWIN CITY TRAILER SALES & SERVICE, INC.
1220 Baucun Industrial Dr, North Little Rock, AR 72117
Tel.: (501) 568-2185
Web Site:
http://www.twincitytrailer.com
Rev.: $17,000,000
Emp.: 35
Trailer Repair & Sales
N.A.I.C.S.: 811114
James H. Glover *(Pres & Owner)*

TWIN CITY WIRE, INC.
3350 Dodd Rd, Eagan, MN 55121
Tel.: (651) 454-8835
Web Site: http://www.tcwire.com
Sales Range: $10-24.9 Million
Emp.: 100
Wire Cloth & Woven Wire Products
N.A.I.C.S.: 332618
John Groess *(CFO)*

TWIN COUNTY ELECTRIC POWER ASSOCIATION
900 E Ave N, Hollandale, MS 38748
Tel.: (662) 827-2262
Web Site: http://www.twincoepa.com
Rev.: $14,900,000
Emp.: 49
Distribution, Electric Power
N.A.I.C.S.: 221122

TWIN LAKES TELEPHONE COOP. CORP.
200 Telephone Ln, Gainesboro, TN 38562
Tel.: (931) 268-2151
Web Site: http://www.twlakes.net
Sales Range: $10-24.9 Million
Emp.: 128
Local Telephone Communications
N.A.I.C.S.: 517121
Bridget Betcher *(Mgr-Acctg)*
Larry Stafford *(Pres)*
Jonathan West *(Gen Mgr)*
Gary Flynn *(Pres)*

TWIN LIQUORS
1000 E 41st St Ste 810, Austin, TX 78751
Tel.: (512) 451-7400
Web Site: http://www.twinliquors.com
Wine & Distilled Beverages
N.A.I.C.S.: 424820
David Jabour *(Pres)*

Subsidiaries:

Sigels Beverages LP (1)
2960 Anode Ln, Dallas, TX 75220
Tel.: (214) 350-1271
Web Site: http://www.sigels.com
Beer, Wine & Liquor Stores
N.A.I.C.S.: 445320

Al Miller *(CFO)*
Debbie Safford *(Dir-HR)*
David Waddington *(Dir-Wine)*
Dulcie Price *(Mgr-Wholesale)*
Eric Moore *(Dir-Wine)*

TWIN OAKS COMMUNITY SERVICES INC.
770 Woodlane Rd, Mount Holly, NJ 08060
Tel.: (609) 267-5928   NJ
Web Site: http://www.twinoakscs.org
Year Founded: 1962
Sales Range: $50-74.9 Million
Emp.: 1,201
Individual & Family Support Services
N.A.I.C.S.: 624190
Narsimha Pinninti *(Chief Medical Officer)*
Sheri Bell *(Chief HR Officer)*
Derry Holland *(COO-Adult Svcs)*
Qindi Shi *(CFO)*

TWIN POINT CAPITAL, LLC
860 Washington St 6th Fl., New York, NY 10014
Web Site:
http://www.twinpointcap.com
Year Founded: 2015
Private Equity
N.A.I.C.S.: 523999

Subsidiaries:

TESSCO Technologies, Inc. (1)
11126 McCormick Rd, Hunt Valley, MD 21031-1494
Tel.: (410) 229-1000
Web Site: https://www.tessco.com
Rev.: $417,544,800
Assets: $202,513,300
Liabilities: $126,590,200
Net Worth: $75,923,100
Earnings: ($2,700,800)
Emp.: 530
Fiscal Year-end: 03/27/2022
Wireless Communications Products Distr
N.A.I.C.S.: 423690
Dave Eckelbarger *(CEO)*
David Young *(CFO)*
Kelly Mavias *(VP-National Carrier Sls & Business Development)*
Steve Schiech *(VP-Commercial Sls)*
Steve Marshner *(VP-CFD Systems Engrg, Operations, Logistics, and QMS)*
Justin Seda *(VP & Controller)*
Anu Gupta *(VP-E & Commerce)*
Andrew Sapitowicz *(VP-Bus Analytics & PMO)*
Thomas Callahan *(VP-Infrastructure, Security, and Operations)*
Ryan Smith *(VP-Talent Acquisition & Human Resources)*

TWIN RIVER NATIONAL BANK
201 2nd St, Asotin, WA 99402
Tel.: (509) 243-8847
Web Site:
http://www.twinriverbank.com
Emp.: 30
Commericial Banking
N.A.I.C.S.: 522110
Jody Servatius *(Pres & CEO)*
Jackie Hough *(Mgr-Dev & R&E)*
Kathy Brown *(Mgr)*

TWIN RIVERS GROUP INC.
302 Maelist St, Fayetteville, AR 72703
Tel.: (479) 444-8898   AR
Web Site: http://www.twinriver.com
Year Founded: 1997
Sales Range: $100-124.9 Million
Emp.: 1,400
Packaged Frozen Food Distr
N.A.I.C.S.: 424420
Maynor Anderson *(Chm)*
Matt Duffy *(Pres)*

Subsidiaries:

Anderson & Fryer Exports Inc. (1)

TWIN RIVERS GROUP INC.

U.S. PRIVATE

Twin Rivers Group Inc.—(Continued)
1 Colt Sq, Fayetteville, AR 72703
Tel.: (479) 444-8898
Sales Range: $10-24.9 Million
Emp.: 34
Distr of Packaged Frozen Goods
N.A.I.C.S.: 424420

Twin Rivers Foods Inc. (1)
1 Colt Sq, Fayetteville, AR 72703
Tel.: (479) 444-8898
Web Site: http://www.twinrivers.com
Sales Range: $10-24.9 Million
Emp.: 25
Processor of Poultry
N.A.I.C.S.: 311615
Matt Duffy (COO)

Twin Rivers Packaging Inc. (1)
1 Colt Sq, Fayetteville, AR 72703
Tel.: (479) 444-8898
Web Site: http://www.twinriversfoods.com
Sales Range: $10-24.9 Million
Emp.: 36
Provider of Building Operation Services
N.A.I.C.S.: 311615
Matt Duffy (Mng Dir)

TWIN RIVERS PAPER COMPANY
707 Sable Oaks Dr Ste 010, South Portland, ME 04106
Tel.: (207) 523-2350
Web Site: http://www.twinriverspaper.com
Year Founded: 2010
Sales Range: $25-49.9 Million
Emp.: 667
Paper Products Mfr
N.A.I.C.S.: 322120
Tony Rigelman (VP-Sls)
John Reichert (COO)
Tim Lowe (Chm)
Robert Snyder (CEO)

TWIN RIVERS PLUMBING INC.
1525 Irving Rd, Eugene, OR 97402
Tel.: (541) 688-1444
Web Site: http://www.twinrp.com
Sales Range: $10-24.9 Million
Emp.: 30
Plumbing Contractor
N.A.I.C.S.: 238220
Richard Gerber (Co-Owner & Pres)
Sandra Gerber (Co-Owner)
Shannon Moore (Controller)
Gerry Bush (Project Mgr)

TWIN STATE INC.
3541 E Kimberly Rd, Davenport, IA 52807
Tel.: (563) 359-3624
Web Site: http://www.twinstateinc.com
Sales Range: $10-24.9 Million
Emp.: 250
Phosphatic Fertilizers
N.A.I.C.S.: 325312
Gary Mills (Branch Mgr)
Marry Britton (Office Mgr)

TWIN STATE TRUCKS INC.
3016 S Eastman Rd, Longview, TX 75602
Tel.: (903) 758-3351
Web Site: http://www.plilerinternational.com
Sales Range: $10-24.9 Million
Emp.: 75
International Truck Dealership
N.A.I.C.S.: 423830
Darrell Pliler (Owner & Pres)

TWIN TIER HOSPITALITY, LLC
1100 Crocker Rd Ste 2R, Westlake, OH 44145
Tel.: (440) 617-2350
Web Site: http://www.twintierhospitality.com
Year Founded: 1997
Hotel Services
N.A.I.C.S.: 721110
Satish Duggal (Pres & CEO)
Robert Trammell (COO)
Jogesh Shah (CFO)

TWIN TOWERS
5343 Hamilton Ave, Cincinnati, OH 45224
Tel.: (513) 853-2000 OH
Year Founded: 1899
Sales Range: $25-49.9 Million
Nursing Care Services
N.A.I.C.S.: 623110
James Lay (Exec Dir)

TWIN TOWERS TRADING, INC.
10 Sta St, Englishtown, NJ 07726
Tel.: (732) 786-8010 NJ
Web Site: http://www.twintowerstrading.com
Year Founded: 1994
Sales Range: $1-9.9 Million
Emp.: 15
General Merchandise Retailer
N.A.I.C.S.: 455219
Ann Cellie (Office Mgr)
Jeff Brandon (Pres & CEO)

TWINCO AUTOMOTIVE WAREHOUSE, INC.
4635 Willow Dr, Medina, MN 55340
Tel.: (763) 478-2360 MN
Web Site: http://www.twincoromax.com
Year Founded: 1962
Sales Range: $10-24.9 Million
Emp.: 60
Whslr of Automotive Parts & Accessories
N.A.I.C.S.: 423120

Subsidiaries:

Zecol Inc. (1)
4635 Willow Dr, Hamel, MN 55340-9528
Tel.: (763) 478-2360
Web Site: http://www.twincoromax.com
Rev.: $2,000,000
Emp.: 15
Mfr of Polishing Wax for Autos, Automotive & Industrial Chemicals, Sootout & Lubaid Diesel Additive
N.A.I.C.S.: 423120

TWINCO INC.
145 Ellicott Rd, West Falls, NY 14170
Tel.: (716) 655-1171 NY
Web Site: http://www.twincoinc.com
Year Founded: 1969
Food, Beverage & Pharmaceutical Industry Sanitation Machinery Fabricator & Whslr
N.A.I.C.S.: 333998
Robert N. Hopkins (Founder & CEO)
Neil Hopkins (Pres)
Ken Cox (Mgr-Engrg)
Ron Eiseman (Ops Mgr)
James Meholick (Sls Mgr)

TWINING INC.
2883 E Spring St Ste 300, Long Beach, CA 90806
Tel.: (562) 426-3355
Web Site: http://www.twininglabs.com
Sales Range: $10-24.9 Million
Emp.: 150
Engineering, Testing & Inspection for Landmark Project Sites
N.A.I.C.S.: 237990
Steve Schiffer (VP)
Rob Ryan (Pres)
Amy Owens (Dir-HR)

Subsidiaries:

DRP Consulting, Inc. (1)
17962 Cowan St, Irvine, CA 92614
Tel.: (949) 307-5188
Web Site: http://www.drpconsulting.com
Sales Range: $1-9.9 Million
Data Processing, Hosting & Related Services
N.A.I.C.S.: 518210

TWINSTAR CREDIT UNION
PO Box 718, Olympia, WA 98507-0718
Tel.: (360) 357-9917 WA
Web Site: http://www.twinstarcu.com
Year Founded: 1937
Sales Range: $50-74.9 Million
Emp.: 412
Credit Union
N.A.I.C.S.: 522130
Kimberly Peterson (CFO & VP)
Jeff Kennedy (Pres)
Rebecca Breen (Chief Retail Officer & VP)
Elkan Wollenberg (CTO & VP)
Matthew Devlin (VP-Mktg & Bus Dev)

TWIST INC.
47 S Limestone St, Jamestown, OH 45335
Tel.: (937) 675-9581
Web Site: http://www.twistinc.com
Year Founded: 1971
Sales Range: $10-24.9 Million
Emp.: 200
Precision Mechanical Springs Mfr
N.A.I.C.S.: 332613
Joe W. Wright (Pres)
Tim Dillon (Engr-Electrical & Controls)
Jim Church (Engr-Mechanical)
Bruce Biery (Mgr-Sls)
Don Maynard (Project Mgr)

TWIST INVESTMENT CORPORATION
9440 Santa Monica Blvd Ste 301, Beverly Hills, CA 90210
Tel.: (310) 878-8490 DE
Year Founded: 2021
Investment Services
N.A.I.C.S.: 523999
Sean V. Madnani (Founder, Chm & CEO)
Mary L. Dotz (CFO & COO)

TWISTED SCHOLAR, INC.
3241 35th Ave SW, Seattle, WA 98126
Tel.: (206) 254-9215
Web Site: http://www.twistedscholar.com
Sales Range: Less than $1 Million
Emp.: 5
Videos for Broadcast & Home Video Distribution Producer
N.A.I.C.S.: 512110
Marty Riemer (Co-Founder)
Michael A. Stusser (Co-Founder)
Mark Goodnow (Dir-Photography)
Patrick McGlone (Project Mgr)

TWM INDUSTRIES
899 Cherry Ave, San Bruno, CA 94066
Tel.: (650) 583-6491 CA
Web Site: http://www.twmindustries.com
Year Founded: 1974
Rev.: $10,302,017
Emp.: 20
Franchise Fast-Food Restaurants Owner & Operator
N.A.I.C.S.: 722513
Be Wierdsma (Founder & Partner)
Tom Thompson (Founder & Partner)
Stella Thompson (Founder & Partner)
Jeff Casaretto (Partner)
Gene Ciufo (Partner)
Beverly Ciufo (Partner)

TWO FARMS, INC.
3611 Roland Ave, Baltimore, MD 21211-2408
Tel.: (410) 889-0200
Web Site: http://www.royalfarms.com
Year Founded: 1929
Sales Range: $100-124.9 Million
Emp.: 1,000
Gasoline Service Stations & Convenience Stores
N.A.I.C.S.: 445131
John Kemp (Pres)
Franklin Fontanazza (CFO)
Ed Stronski (Mgr-Mktg)

TWO RIVER GROUP HOLDINGS, LLC
689 5th Ave 12th Fl, New York, NY 10022
Tel.: (212) 871-7900 DE
Web Site: http://www.tworiver.com
Sales Range: $10-24.9 Million
Emp.: 12
Venture Capital Holding Company
N.A.I.C.S.: 551112
David M. Tanen (Partner)

Subsidiaries:

Two River Group Management, LLC (1)
689 5th Ave 12th Fl, New York, NY 10022
Tel.: (212) 871-7900
Web Site: http://www.tworiver.com
Equity Investment & Portfolio Management Services
N.A.I.C.S.: 523999
David M. Tanen (Partner)
Joshua A. Kazam (Co-Founder)
Arie Belldegrun (Chm & Partner)

TWO RIVERS CONSUMERS COOP ASSOCIATION
200-300 S D St, Arkansas City, KS 67005
Tel.: (620) 442-2360
Web Site: http://www.tworiversks.com
Sales Range: $25-49.9 Million
Emp.: 35
Grains
N.A.I.C.S.: 424510
Kevin Kelly (Gen Mgr)

TWO RIVERS COOPERATIVE
109 S St, Pella, IA 50219
Tel.: (641) 628-4167
Web Site: http://www.tworivers.coop
Sales Range: $10-24.9 Million
Emp.: 35
Fertilizer & Fertilizer Materials
N.A.I.C.S.: 424910
Tracy Gathman (Gen Mgr)
Matt Van Weelden (Mgr-Agronomy)

TWO RIVERS WATER & FARMING COMPANY
999 18th St Ste 3000, Denver, CO 80202
Tel.: (303) 222-1000 CO
Web Site: http://www.2riverswater.com
Year Founded: 2002
TURV—(OTCBB)
Sales Range: $10-24.9 Million
Emp.: 3
Water Storage & Distribution Services
N.A.I.C.S.: 221310

Subsidiaries:

Water Redevelopment Company (1)
3025 S Parker Rd Ste 140, Aurora, CO 80014
Tel.: (303) 222-1000
Web Site: http://www.waterredev.com
Water Redevelopment Services
N.A.I.C.S.: 221310
Wayne Harding (CEO)
Bill Gregorak (CFO & Sec)

TWO SIGMA INVESTMENTS, LP
100 Ave of the Americas 16th Fl, New York, NY 10013
Tel.: (212) 625-5700
Web Site: http://www.twosigma.com
Year Founded: 2001
Rev.: $46,000,000,000
Emp.: 1,200
Investment Management
N.A.I.C.S.: 523150
John Overdeck *(Co-Founder & Co-Chm)*
David Siegel *(Co-Founder & Co-Chm)*
Nobel Gulati *(Mng Dir)*
Eric Schaffer *(Chief HR Officer)*
Mark Roth *(Mng Dir & Head-Architecture)*
Bill Squier *(Chief Security Officer & Sr VP)*
Andrew Janian *(CIO)*
Jeffrey Wecker *(CTO & Head-Engrg)*

TWO TECHNOLOGIES, INC.
419 Sargon Way, Horsham, PA 19044
Tel.: (215) 441-5305   PA
Web Site: http://www.2t.com
Year Founded: 1987
Industrial & Commercial Hand-Held Computer & Terminal Designer, Mfr & Whslr
N.A.I.C.S.: 334118
David Young *(Pres & CEO)*
Joan Rickards *(Exec VP-Sls & Mktg)*
Roger Mick *(Exec VP-Engrg)*

TWO WEST, INC.
514 W 26th St 2nd Fl, Kansas City, MO 64108
Tel.: (816) 471-3255
Web Site: http://www.twowest.com
Year Founded: 1997
Sales Range: $10-24.9 Million
Emp.: 35
Advetising Agency
N.A.I.C.S.: 541810
Scott Burditt *(COO)*
Ethan Whitehill *(Founder & CEO)*

TWO'S COMPANY INC.
500 Saw Mill River Rd, Elmsford, NY 10523-1023
Tel.: (914) 664-2277
Web Site:
http://www.twoscompany.com
Sales Range: $10-24.9 Million
Emp.: 125
Gifts & Novelties
N.A.I.C.S.: 339910
Roberta Gottlieb *(CEO)*
Tom Gottlieb *(Pres)*

TWO-STATE CONSTRUCTION COMPANY, INC.
2292 Washington Rd, Thomson, GA 30824
Tel.: (706) 595-2863
Web Site: http://www.twostate.com
Year Founded: 1970
Sales Range: $10-24.9 Million
Emp.: 100
Provider of Construction Services
N.A.I.C.S.: 236220
James L. Poston *(Pres & VP-Roofing)*
Joyce Strother *(Mgr-Project Correspondence)*
Grady Suller *(Controller)*

TWO-WAY COMMUNICATIONS INC.
1704 Justin Rd, Metairie, LA 70001
Tel.: (504) 835-7722
Web Site: http://www.twowayusa.com
Sales Range: $10-24.9 Million
Emp.: 33
Communications Equipment
N.A.I.C.S.: 423690

TWOADAY OIL, INC.
4828 Park Glen Rd, Minneapolis, MN 55416
Tel.: (800) 711-0442   NV
Year Founded: 2013
Oil Well Drilling
N.A.I.C.S.: 213111
William Hudlow *(Pres, CEO, CFO, Principal Acctg Officer & Sec)*

TWOTON INC.
1743 Rohrerstown Rd, Lancaster, PA 17601
Tel.: (717) 569-5791
Sales Range: $25-49.9 Million
Emp.: 1,500
Franchise Owner of Fast-Food Restaurants
N.A.I.C.S.: 722513
William Harrington *(CEO)*
Gerald Mitchell *(Pres)*
Shelly Casper *(Asst Mgr)*
Katherine Burris *(Mgr)*
Ian Blair *(Mgr-Restaurant)*
Garry Gearheart *(Mgr-Restaurant)*
Esseff Linda *(Mgr-Mktg)*
Pam Wolf *(Mgr)*
Rita Camodeca *(Office Mgr)*
Crinnion Dave *(Gen Mgr)*

TWS PARTNERSHIP LLC
1040 Holland Dr, Boca Raton, FL 33487-2759
Tel.: (561) 997-5417
Privater Equity Firm
N.A.I.C.S.: 523999
Warren Struhl *(Mng Partner)*
Warren Struhl *(Mng Partner)*
Subsidiaries:

Successories.com LLC   (1)
1040 Holland Dr, Boca Raton, FL 33487
Tel.: (561) 962-3507
Web Site: http://www.successories.com
Inspirational Calendars, Posters & Accessories Mfr
N.A.I.C.S.: 323111

Subsidiary (Domestic):

Awards.com LLC   (2)
1040 Holland Dr, Boca Raton, FL 33487
Tel.: (407) 265-2001
Rev.: $10,000,000
Emp.: 50
Trophies & Plaques Mfr
N.A.I.C.S.: 459999

TWSCO
5515 W Ritchie, Houston, TX 77066
Tel.: (281) 880-4444
Web Site: http://www.twsco.com
Rev.: $22,000,000
Emp.: 30
Welding Machinery & Equipment
N.A.I.C.S.: 423830
Scott Chenoweth *(Pres)*
Blake Felton *(VP-Sls)*
Lee Chenoweth *(Exec VP-Sls)*
Keith Finke *(CFO)*
Dan Chenoweth *(Chm)*

TXEX ENERGY INVESTMENTS, LLC
12140 Wickchester Ln Ste 100, Houston, TX 77079
Tel.: (832) 200-3792   TX
Emp.: 100
Investment Services
N.A.I.C.S.: 523999
Subsidiaries:

Retailco, LLC   (1)
12140 Wickchester Ln Ste 100, Houston, TX 77079
Tel.: (832) 200-3792
Investment Services
N.A.I.C.S.: 523999

TXRB HOLDINGS, INC.
2595 Preston Rd Ste 100, Frisco, TX 75034
Tel.: (972) 334-0700   TX
Web Site:
http://www.texasrepublicbank.com
Bank Holding Company
N.A.I.C.S.: 551111
David Baty *(Pres & CEO)*
Subsidiaries:

Texas Republic Bank, N.A.   (1)
2595 Preston Rd, Frisco, TX 75034
Tel.: (972) 334-0700
Web Site: http://www.texasrepublicbank.com
Sales Range: $10-24.9 Million
Emp.: 50
Commericial Banking
N.A.I.C.S.: 522110
Pamela Folkman *(VP)*
David Baty *(Pres & CEO)*
Jerrica Anderson *(Officer-Compliance & VP)*
Larry Bowman *(CFO)*
Tim Cantrell *(Vice Chm)*
John Henderson *(Treas & VP)*
Carly Hollaway *(Asst VP)*
Maureen McGuire *(Officer-Ops & Exec VP)*
Kaili Parde *(Mgr-Ops)*
Kim Sale *(Asst VP)*
Kathy Selvidge *(Asst VP)*
Mike Sweet *(Asst VP)*
Charles Rolfe Jr. *(Chm)*

TY INC.
PO Box 5377, Oak Brook, IL 60522
Tel.: (630) 920-1515   DE
Web Site: http://www.ty.com
Year Founded: 1933
Sales Range: $750-799.9 Million
Emp.: 630
Mfr of Stuffed Toys
N.A.I.C.S.: 423920
Richard Jeffery *(CFO)*

TYCORE BUILT LLC
2360 Dousman St, Green Bay, WI 54303
Tel.: (920) 662-0303
Web Site: http://www.tycorebuilt.com
Year Founded: 2003
Sales Range: $10-24.9 Million
Emp.: 6
Building Construction Services
N.A.I.C.S.: 236116
Wade Micoley *(Owner)*

TYGA-BOX SYSTEMS, INC.
501 7th Ave Fl 18, New York, NY 10018
Tel.: (212) 398-3809
Web Site: http://www.tygabox.com
Year Founded: 1994
Sales Range: $10-24.9 Million
Emp.: 13
Commercial, Industrial Machinery, Equipment Rental & Leasing
N.A.I.C.S.: 532490
Martin Spindel *(Pres)*
Nadine Cino *(CEO)*

TYGAR MANUFACTURING, INC.
425 Wilbanks Dr, Ball Ground, GA 30107
Tel.: (770) 345-6625
Web Site: http://www.tygarmfg.com
Sales Range: $10-24.9 Million
Emp.: 10
Decorative Landscaping
N.A.I.C.S.: 541320
Mark Crosswell *(Pres)*

TYGON PEAK CAPITAL
200 Vesey St 24th Fl, New York, NY 10281
Tel.: (646) 952-8626
Web Site:
https://www.tygonpeakcapital.com
Year Founded: 2016
Privater Equity Firm
N.A.I.C.S.: 523999
Haran Narulla *(Mng Partner)*
Subsidiaries:

Voice Comm, LLC   (1)
175 Derousse Ave, Ste 100, Pennsauken, NJ 08110
Tel.: (856) 317-0620
Web Site: https://www.myvoicecomm.com
Electronic Parts & Equipment Merchant Whslr
N.A.I.C.S.: 423690

TYLDIN CORP.
1771 Brighton Henrietta Town Line Rd, Rochester, NY 14623-2505
Tel.: (585) 328-4720
Sales Range: $10-24.9 Million
Emp.: 30
Automobile Tires & Tubes
N.A.I.C.S.: 423130
Tony Sagona *(Pres)*
Andy Caruso *(Mgr-Sls-Reg)*

TYLER 2 CONSTRUCTION, INC.
5400 Old Pineville Rd, Charlotte, NC 28217
Tel.: (704) 527-3031
Web Site:
http://www.tyler2construction.com
Year Founded: 1983
Sales Range: $10-24.9 Million
Emp.: 22
Non-Residential Building Contractor
N.A.I.C.S.: 236210
Kathryn B. Tyler *(CEO)*
Lynne Ferretti *(VP-Ops)*
Dale Fite *(Pres)*

TYLER AUTOMOTIVE INC.
1810 S 11th St, Niles, MI 49120
Tel.: (269) 683-1710
Web Site: http://www.tylers.com
Sales Range: $50-74.9 Million
Emp.: 40
Car Dealership Owner & Operator
N.A.I.C.S.: 441110
Scott Tyler *(Owner)*
Paula Wilkinson *(Controller)*
John Jolley *(Mgr-Fin)*

TYLER BUILDING SYSTEMS, L.P.
3535 Shiloh Rd, Tyler, TX 75707
Tel.: (903) 561-3000
Web Site:
http://www.tylerbuilding.com
Year Founded: 1971
Rev.: $16,000,000
Emp.: 80
Mfr, Sales & Installation of Metal Building Systems
N.A.I.C.S.: 332311
R. C. Curtis *(Pres)*
W. B. Curtis *(Mgr-Ops)*
Mark Bounds *(Mgr-Fin)*
Greg Pirtle *(Plant Mgr)*

TYLER EQUIPMENT CORPORATION
251 Shaker Rd, East Longmeadow, MA 01028
Tel.: (413) 525-6351
Web Site:
http://www.tylerequipment.com
Rev.: $11,200,000
Emp.: 55
Construction & Mining Machinery
N.A.I.C.S.: 423810

TYLER EQUIPMENT CORPORATION
U.S. PRIVATE

Tyler Equipment Corporation—(Continued)
Fred Smith *(Mgr-Svc)*
Shirley Worlund *(Mgr-Pur)*
Lawrence Drapeau *(Dir-Ops)*
M. Brooke Tyler III *(Pres)*

TYLER FORD
2626 S Southwest Loop 323, Tyler, TX 75701-0754
Tel.: (903) 597-9331
Web Site: http://www.tylerford.com
Year Founded: 1998
Sales Range: $25-49.9 Million
Emp.: 200
Car Whslr
N.A.I.C.S.: 441110
Dave Capps *(Owner)*
Dave Cox *(Partner)*
David Irwin *(Mng Partner)*
Steve Covington *(Mgr-Svc)*

TYLER MOUNTAIN WATER COMPANY
159 Harris Dr, Poca, WV 25159
Tel.: (304) 755-8400
Web Site:
http://www.tylermountainwater.com
Rev.: $20,000,000
Emp.: 196
Mineral or Spring Water Bottling
N.A.I.C.S.: 424490
Richard Merrill *(Pres & CEO)*
William Bell *(Exec Vp)*
Dave Riddick *(Dir-Ops)*
Karen Minnich *(Controller)*

TYLER STAFFING SERVICES INC.
750 Hammond Dr NE Bldg 9, Atlanta, GA 30328
Tel.: (404) 250-0919   GA
Web Site:
http://www.chasestaffing.com
Year Founded: 1979
Sales Range: $50-74.9 Million
Emp.: 200
Employment Services
N.A.I.C.S.: 561311
Roy F. Abernethy *(Pres)*

TYLER'S JEFFERSON MOTORS
PO Box 1770, Mount Vernon, IL 62864-0055
Tel.: (618) 242-0334
Year Founded: 1951
Sales Range: $10-24.9 Million
Emp.: 30
Car Whslr
N.A.I.C.S.: 441110
Michael Tyler *(Owner)*

TYLERS AUTOMOTIVE INC.
1102 S 11th St, Niles, MI 49120
Tel.: (269) 684-8200
Web Site: http://www.tylers.com
Year Founded: 1999
Sales Range: $25-49.9 Million
Emp.: 50
Car Dealership
N.A.I.C.S.: 441110
Paula Wilkinson *(Controller)*

TYMCO INTERNATIONAL LTD.
225 E Industrial Blvd, Waco, TX 76705
Tel.: (254) 799-5546
Web Site: http://www.tymco.com
Sales Range: $10-24.9 Million
Emp.: 140
Civil Engineering Services
N.A.I.C.S.: 237310
Kenneth Young *(Principal)*

TYMPHANY CORP.
1050 Northgate Dr ste 400, San Rafael, CA 94903
Tel.: (415) 526-5780
Web Site: http://www.tymphany.com
Year Founded: 2002
Sales Range: $10-24.9 Million
Audio Transducers & Acoustical Engineering Customization Services
N.A.I.C.S.: 334310
Ed Boyd *(CEO)*
Tom Jacoby *(Corp Dev Officer)*
Stuart Croxford *(Mng Dir-Asia Ops)*
Alex Kroworz *(Dir-Europe-Sls)*

Subsidiaries:

Hymnario - EAW (HK) Limited   (1)
Unit 1706 17F Hewlett Center, 54 Hoi Yuen Road, Kwun Tong, China (Hong Kong)   (100%)
Tel.: (852) 27970268
Emp.: 30
Durable Goods Whslr
N.A.I.C.S.: 423990
William Pang *(Mgr)*

Tymphany-China   (1)
Tymphany Industrial AreaXinLian Village, XinXu HuiYang District, 516 223, Huizhou, Guangdong, China
Tel.: (86) 7523533555
Audio & Speaker Mfr
N.A.I.C.S.: 334310

Tymphany-Hong Kong   (1)
Room 1307-8 Dominion Centre, 43-59, Queens Road East, 516 223, Wanchai, China (Hong Kong)
Tel.: (852) 7523530222
Audio Speakers Mfr
N.A.I.C.S.: 334310

TYNAN'S VOLKSWAGEN, INC.
700 S Havana St, Aurora, CO 80012
Tel.: (303) 343-8180
Web Site:
http://www.tynansvolkswagen.com
Sales Range: $10-24.9 Million
Emp.: 80
New & Used Car Dealer
N.A.I.C.S.: 441110
Denise Dennis *(Mgr-Svc)*

TYNDALE ADVISORS, LLC
4100 S Houston Levee Rd, Collierville, TN 38017
Tel.: (901) 205-9075   TN
Web Site:
http://www.tyndaleadvisors.com
Year Founded: 2010
Investment Advisory & Asset Management Services
N.A.I.C.S.: 523940
Boyden Moore *(Pres & Chm-CNRG)*
David Mills *(CFO & VP)*
Elizabeth Brown *(Dir-HR)*
Paul Comeau *(Dir-HR-Ops)*
Craig Cowart *(Pres-Fulcrum Retail Grp & VP-Tyndale Advisors)*
Jordan Hughes *(Brand Mgr)*
John Sieggreen *(Pres-CNRG)*

Subsidiaries:

Central Network Retail Group, LLC   (1)
3753 Tyndale Dr Ste 102, Memphis, TN 38125
Tel.: (901) 205-9075
Web Site: http://www.cnrgstores.com
Holding Company; Hardware & Lumber Home Centers
N.A.I.C.S.: 551112
Jimmy R. Smith *(Co-Founder, Chm & Partner)*
Boyden Moore *(Co-Founder, Pres & Partner)*
Douglas A. Gregory *(Partner)*
David Mills *(CFO)*
John Sieggreen *(Ops Mgr)*
Chris Freader *(Mgr-Supply Chain)*

Subsidiary (Domestic):

Elliott's Hardware, Inc.   (2)
2300 Coit Rd, Plano, TX 75075
Tel.: (972) 312-0700
Web Site: http://www.elliottshardware.com
Sales Range: $10-24.9 Million
Emp.: 200
Hardware & Home Centers Operator
N.A.I.C.S.: 444110
Jerre B. Elliott *(Founder)*

Habersham Hardware & Distributing Company   (2)
232 Larkin St, Cornelia, GA 30531
Tel.: (706) 778-2224
Web Site:
http://www.habershamacehardware.com
Sales Range: $10-24.9 Million
Emp.: 100
Hardware & Lumber Home Centers Operator
N.A.I.C.S.: 444110
Stan Crump *(Gen Mgr)*

Hiawassee Hardware & Building Supply, Inc.   (2)
139 Main St N, Hiawassee, GA 30546
Tel.: (706) 896-3617
Web Site:
http://www.hiawasseehardware.com
Hardware, Gardening Supplies & Home Improvement Products Store Operator
N.A.I.C.S.: 444110
H. Dan ParisJr. *(Pres)*

Unit (Domestic):

LumberJack Building Centers   (2)
3470 Pointe Tremble Rd, Algonac, MI 48001
Tel.: (810) 794-4921
Web Site: http://www.lumber-jack.com
Sales Range: $10-24.9 Million
Lumber & Other Building Materials Centers Operator
N.A.I.C.S.: 444110

Subsidiary (Domestic):

Marvin's, LLC   (2)
7480 Pkwy Dr Ste 100, Leeds, AL 35094
Tel.: (205) 702-7305
Web Site:
http://www.marvinsbuildingmaterials.com
Emp.: 30
Building Material & Home Center Operator
N.A.I.C.S.: 444110
Junior Breasseale *(Mgr-Albertville)*
Don Simmer *(Mgr-Calera)*
Tony Adams *(Mgr-Eufaula)*
Wade Braden *(Mgr-Tupelo)*
Jay Marby *(Mgr-Meridian)*
John Mark Shell *(Mgr-Greenville)*
Michelle Bell *(Mgr-Gadsden)*

McLendon Hardware, Inc.   (2)
440 Rainier Ave S, Renton, WA 98057-2401
Tel.: (425) 235-3555
Web Site: http://www.mclendons.com
Lumber & Other Building Materials; Hardware, Lighting & Plumbing Fixtures & Housewares
N.A.I.C.S.: 444140
Steve Judd *(Mgr)*
Leah Mills *(Dir-HR)*
David Murphy *(Mgr)*

Unit (Domestic):

Morrison Terrebonne Lumber Center   (2)
605 Barataria Ave, Houma, LA 70360-4320
Tel.: (985) 879-1597
Web Site: http://www.lumbercenter.com
Sales Range: $1-9.9 Million
Emp.: 35
Lumber Dealer
N.A.I.C.S.: 444180
Doug Gregory *(CEO)*

NFL Home Center   (2)
913 US Hwy 98, Daphne, AL 36526-4127
Tel.: (251) 626-0727
Web Site: http://www.nflhomecenter.com
Sales Range: $1-9.9 Million
Home Center Operator
N.A.I.C.S.: 444110
Brad Hembree *(Mgr-Store-Daphne)*

Subsidiary (Domestic):

Parkrose Hardware, Inc.   (2)
10625 NE Sandy Blvd, Portland, OR 97220
Tel.: (503) 256-3103
Web Site: http://www.parkrosehardware.com
Sales Range: $10-24.9 Million
Hardware Store Operator
N.A.I.C.S.: 444140
Bryan Ableidinger *(Pres)*

Subsidiary (Domestic):

Parkrose Hardware Washington, Inc.   (3)
16509 SE 1st St, Vancouver, WA 98684
Tel.: (360) 693-7881
Web Site: http://www.parkrosehardware.com
Hardware Store Operator
N.A.I.C.S.: 444140
Bryan Ableidinger *(Pres)*

Subsidiary (Domestic):

Taylor-Foster Hardware, Inc.   (2)
15 E Main St, Manchester, GA 31816-2114
Tel.: (706) 846-3138
Web Site:
http://www.taylorfosterhardware.com
Sales Range: $1-9.9 Million
Emp.: 15
Hardware Store Operator
N.A.I.C.S.: 444140

Town & Country Hardware Stores, LLC   (2)
157 Chatham Downs Dr, Chapel Hill, NC 27517
Tel.: (919) 969-1400
Web Site: http://www.tchardware.com
Hardware Store Operator
N.A.I.C.S.: 444140

W.T. Harvey Lumber Co., Inc.   (2)
800 15th St, Columbus, GA 31901-1935
Tel.: (706) 322-8204
Web Site: http://www.harveylumber.com
Sales Range: $25-49.9 Million
Emp.: 35
Lumber & Home Centers Operator
N.A.I.C.S.: 444110
Bailey Gross *(Mgr-Ops)*

TYNDALE HOUSE PUBLISHERS, INC.
351 Exec Dr, Carol Stream, IL 60188
Tel.: (630) 668-8300   DE
Web Site: http://www.tyndale.com
Year Founded: 1962
Sales Range: $100-124.9 Million
Emp.: 250
Bibles, Religious Books, Videos, Audios, Periodicals & Calendars
N.A.I.C.S.: 513130
Mark D. Taylor *(Chm-Bd)*
Doug Knox *(VP)*
Paul Matthews *(CFO)*
Jeff Johnson *(COO)*

TYNDALL FEDERAL CREDIT UNION INC.
3109 Minnesota Ave, Panama City, FL 32405
Tel.: (850) 769-9999
Web Site: http://www.tyndallfcu.org
Rev.: $39,100,000
Emp.: 288
Credit Union
N.A.I.C.S.: 522130
James Warren *(Pres & CEO)*
Joy Williams *(Mgr-Loan Servicing Dept)*
Mindy Porep Rankin *(Chm)*
Shalla Phelps Jefcoat *(Sec)*
Lucy R. Lewis *(Treas)*
Richard Millett *(Vice Chm)*
James Davis *(Chief HR Officer & Sr VP)*

TYP RESTAURANT GROUP INC.
9523 Culver Blvd, Culver City, CA 90232

Tel.: (310) 842-8300
Web Site:
http://www.tendergreens.com
Year Founded: 2006
Sales Range: $25-49.9 Million
Emp.: 450
Restaurant Management Services
N.A.I.C.S.: 722511
Erik Oberholtzer *(Co-Founder)*
Matt Lyman *(Co-Founder)*
David Dressler *(Co-Founder)*
Lina O'Connor *(Dir-Fin)*
Cynthia Yilmaz *(Dir-People Svcs)*

TYPHOON TOUCH TECHNOLOGIES, INC.
1700 7th Ave Ste 2100, Seattle, WA 98101
Tel.: (206) 407-2538   NV
Web Site:
http://www.typhoontouchtech.com
Year Founded: 2005
Sales Range: $400-449.9 Million
Music Downloading Services
N.A.I.C.S.: 512230
Raymond P. Tellini *(Pres, CEO, CFO & Sec)*

TYR EQUITY, INC.
PO Box 1571, Cumming, GA 30028
Tel.: (706) 421-3140   GA
Web Site: http://www.tyrequity.com
Year Founded: 2018
Emp.: 1
Money Lending Services
N.A.I.C.S.: 522390
Ryan Schadel *(Pres, CEO, CFO, Chief Acctg Officer, Treas & Sec)*

TYREE OIL INC.
1355 W 1st Ave, Eugene, OR 97402
Tel.: (541) 687-0076
Web Site: http://www.tyreeoil.com
Sales Range: $25-49.9 Million
Emp.: 28
Fuel Oil
N.A.I.C.S.: 424720
Nick Lawlor *(CFO)*
Lisa Irving *(Controller)*
Tim Reed *(Mgr-Sls)*
Ryan Weaver *(Mgr-Oil Ops)*
Brian Otto *(Branch Mgr)*
Brandon Prentice *(Gen Mgr)*

TYREE ORGANIZATION, LTD
208 Route 109, Farmingdale, NY 11735
Tel.: (631) 249-3150
Web Site: http://www.tyreeorg.com
Rev.: $109,418,923
Emp.: 175
Environmental Cleanup Services
N.A.I.C.S.: 562910
Scott Newman *(Controller)*
Subsidiaries:

Tyree Maintenance Co. Inc.   (1)
208 Rte 109, Farmingdale, NY 11735
Tel.: (631) 249-3150
Web Site: http://www.tyreeorg.com
Sales Range: $50-74.9 Million
Service Station Equipment Installation, Maint. & Repair
N.A.I.C.S.: 238990
Stephen J. Tyree *(Pres)*

TYRES INTERNATIONAL INC.
4637 Allen Rd, Stow, OH 44224-1037
Tel.: (330) 374-1000
Web Site: http://www.tyres1.com
Year Founded: 1968
Rev.: $33,787,826
Emp.: 45
Tires & Tubes
N.A.I.C.S.: 423130

Thomas Babb *(Pres)*
Crystal Kramer *(Coord-AP)*
Mike Bezbatchenko *(VP)*

TYREX GROUP, LTD.
12317 Technology Blvd Ste 200, Austin, TX 78727
Tel.: (512) 835-1200
Web Site: http://www.tyrexmfg.com
Sales Range: $25-49.9 Million
Emp.: 300
Current-Carrying Wiring Devices
N.A.I.C.S.: 335931
Andrew Cooper *(Partner & Principal)*
Kevin Alwell *(Controller)*
Reina Wiatt *(Controller-Megladon Mfg Grp)*
Subsidiaries:

Megladon Manufacturing Group   (1)
12317 Technology Blvd, Austin, TX 78727
Tel.: (512) 491-0006
Web Site: http://www.tyrexmfg.com
Rev.: $7,045,221
Emp.: 30
Fiber Optic Cable (Insulated)
N.A.I.C.S.: 335921

SebeRex Group Ltd.   (1)
Ste 100 12317 Technology Blvd, Austin, TX 78727-6134
Tel.: (512) 445-4758
Provides Cable & DSL Services
N.A.I.C.S.: 335931

TyRex Engineering Group   (1)
12317 Technology Blvd Ste 200, Austin, TX 78727
Tel.: (512) 835-1200
Web Site: http://www.tyrexmfg.com
Sales Range: $10-24.9 Million
Emp.: 100
Offers Engineering Services
N.A.I.C.S.: 335931

iRex Group Ltd.   (1)
12317 Technology Blvd Ste 200, Austin, TX 78727
Tel.: (512) 835-1200
Web Site: http://www.irexmfg.com
Sales Range: $10-24.9 Million
Emp.: 100
Custom Cable, DSL & Flash Production
N.A.I.C.S.: 335931
Matt Ache *(Pres)*
Keith Smith *(Controller)*
Gary Wojcik *(Mgr-Ops)*

TYRHOLM BIG R STORES
6225 S 6th St, Klamath Falls, OR 97603
Tel.: (541) 882-5540
Web Site: http://www.bigroregon.com
Rev.: $27,349,412
Emp.: 43
Country General Stores
N.A.I.C.S.: 455219
Steven Tyrholm *(Owner)*

TYRRELL-DOYLE CHEVROLET CO.
2142 W Lincoln Way, Cheyenne, WY 82001
Tel.: (307) 634-2540
Web Site:
http://www.tyrrelldoylechevrolet.com
Rev.: $30,000,000
Emp.: 65
New & Used Car Dealers
N.A.I.C.S.: 441110
Dave Doyle *(Pres)*
Rocky Lincoln *(Mgr)*

TYRRELL-MARXEN CHEVROLET OLDSMOBILE CADILLAC INC.
1118 W Hwy 66, Flagstaff, AZ 86001
Tel.: (928) 774-2794
Web Site: http://www.tyrrell-marxen.com
Sales Range: $10-24.9 Million

Emp.: 75
Automobiles, New & Used
N.A.I.C.S.: 441110
Terry Marxen *(Pres)*
Mike Kentera *(Mgr-Parts)*

TYRRELLTECH, INC.
9045 Maier Rd Ste A, Laurel, MD 20723
Tel.: (240) 568-4080
Web Site: http://www.tyrrelltech.com
Year Founded: 1997
Rev.: $4,200,000
Emp.: 11
Other Computer Peripheral Equipment Mfr
N.A.I.C.S.: 334118
Michael Fambro *(Mgr-Production)*
Craig Tyrrell *(Pres)*

TYSENS COUNTRY GROCERY INC.
325 N Halleck St, Demotte, IN 46310
Tel.: (219) 987-2141
Web Site:
http://www.tysensgrocery.com
Rev.: $10,300,000
Emp.: 100
Grocery Stores, Independent
N.A.I.C.S.: 445110

TZ FINANCIAL COMPANY
11107 W Olympic Blvd, Los Angeles, CA 90064
Tel.: (310) 479-1666
Rev.: $25,800,000
Emp.: 50
Bank Holding Company
N.A.I.C.S.: 551111

TZP GROUP LLC
7 Times Sq Ste 4307, New York, NY 10036
Tel.: (212) 398-0300   NY
Web Site: http://www.tzpgroup.com
Year Founded: 2007
Privater Equity Firm
N.A.I.C.S.: 523999
Samuel L. Katz *(Mng Partner)*
Vladimir M. Gutin *(Partner)*
Daniel H. Galpern *(Partner)*
Sheera Michael *(CFO & Chief Acctg Officer)*
Paul Davis *(Partner)*
Dan Gaspar *(Partner)*
Daniel Balzora *(Principal)*
Kenneth S. Esterow *(Partner)*
Maggie Prager *(Principal)*
Robert S. Schwartz *(Partner)*
Tiffany Shatzkes *(Chief Compliance Officer)*
Rodney Eshelman III *(Partner)*
William H. Hunscher Jr. *(Partner)*
Subsidiaries:

Awareness Technologies, Inc.   (1)
1391 Post Rd E, Westport, CT 06880
Web Site:
http://www.awarenesstechnologies.com
Sales Range: $1-9.9 Million
Emp.: 35
Custom Computer Programming Services
N.A.I.C.S.: 541511
Brad Miller *(Chm)*

Thing 5, LLC   (1)
138 Longmeadow St, Longmeadow, MA 01106
Tel.: (413) 241-2519
Web Site: http://www.thing5.com
Wired Telecommunications Carriers
N.A.I.C.S.: 517111
David Thor *(Mgr)*

Subsidiary (Domestic):

Innflux LLC   (2)
850 W Jackson Blvd Ste 250, Chicago, IL 60607
Tel.: (312) 850-3399

Web Site: http://www.innflux.com
Software Publisher
N.A.I.C.S.: 513210
Chris Drinkall *(VP-Installation & Tech Support)*

U & S SERVICES, INC.
233 Fillmore Ave Ste 11, Tonawanda, NY 14150-2316
Tel.: (716) 693-4490
Web Site:
http://www.usservicesinc.com
Sales Range: $10-24.9 Million
Emp.: 50
Computer Equipment & Software Whslr
N.A.I.C.S.: 423430
Russell Stuber *(Pres)*
Dan Faes *(Treas & Mgr-Field Ops)*
Randy Urschel *(VP)*

U-FREIGHT AMERICA INC.
320 Corey Way, South San Francisco, CA 94080
Tel.: (650) 583-6527
Web Site: http://www.ufreight.com
Rev.: $16,400,000
Emp.: 50
Freight Forwarding
N.A.I.C.S.: 488510
Eugine Boyer *(Dir Gen)*
Simon Wong *(Chm-Hong Kong)*

U-SAVE PHARMACY OF DAWSON COUNTY, LLC
603 N Washington St, Lexington, NE 68850
Tel.: (308) 324-6325   NE
Web Site: http://www.usaverx.co
Sales Range: $1-9.9 Million
Pharmacy & Gift Shop Operator
N.A.I.C.S.: 456110
Travis Maloley *(Co-Owner)*
Mark Vogt *(Co-Owner)*

U-SAVE-IT PHARMACY, INC.
2112 Palmyra Rd, Albany, GA 31701
Tel.: (229) 439-4939   GA
Web Site:
http://www.usaveitpharmacy.com
Sales Range: $10-24.9 Million
Pharmacies Operator
N.A.I.C.S.: 456110
Paula Norman *(CFO & Sec)*

U.N.X. INCORPORATED
707 E Arlington Blvd, Greenville, NC 27858-5810
Tel.: (252) 756-8616   NC
Web Site: http://www.unxinc.com
Year Founded: 1958
Sales Range: $25-49.9 Million
Emp.: 200
Polishes Detergents & Sanitation Goods Mfr
N.A.I.C.S.: 325612
Angela Vess *(Coord-Bid)*
John Brick *(Dir-Athletic Sls)*
David Barbe *(Dir-Engrg)*

U.S. AIRMOTIVE GSE
5439 NW 36th St, Miami Springs, FL 33166
Tel.: (305) 885-4992
Web Site:
http://www.usairmotivegse.com
Year Founded: 1963
Rev.: $10,200,000
Emp.: 20
Aircraft & Parts Supplier
N.A.I.C.S.: 336412
Anthony Kruszewski *(Chm)*
Frank Bortunk *(Pres)*

U.S. AIRPORTS FLIGHT SUPPORT LLC

U.S. Airports Flight Support LLC

U.S. Airports Flight Support LLC—(Continued)
1295 Scottsville Rd, Rochester, NY 14624-3128
Tel.: (585) 527-6835 NY
Web Site: http://www.usairports.com
Year Founded: 1996
Sales Range: $25-49.9 Million
Emp.: 90
Provider of Ground Support for Corporate & Private Airflights & Charter Services
N.A.I.C.S.: 481112
Anthony J. Costello (Chm & CEO)

U.S. ASSETS GROUP
1800 2nd St Ste 806, Sarasota, FL 34236
Tel.: (941) 378-3983
Web Site:
http://www.usassetsgrp.com
Sales Range: $1-9.9 Million
Emp.: 14
Residential Real Estate Developer
N.A.I.C.S.: 237210
Tom Brown (Principal)
Steve Brown (Principal)

U.S. AXLE, INC.
275 Shoemaker Rd, Pottstown, PA 19464-6433
Tel.: (610) 323-3800 PA
Web Site: http://www.usaxle.com
Year Founded: 1920
Sales Range: $50-74.9 Million
Emp.: 40
Shafts & Axle Shafts Mfr
N.A.I.C.S.: 332710
Ernie Inmon (Pres)
Jim Kraus (Controller)
Ken Harrison (Mgr-Mfg Engrg)
Patrick Solley (Engr-Mfg)
Rich Frye (Mgr-Pur)
Ken Krauss (Pres & COO)

U.S. BAND & ORCHESTRA SUPPLIES, INC.
1400 Ferguson Ave, Saint Louis, MO 63133
Tel.: (314) 727-4512 MO
Year Founded: 1999
Emp.: 50
Musical Instrument Mfr & Distr
N.A.I.C.S.: 339992
Gail Rose (Sr VP-Credit)
Mark Ragin (Founder & CEO)

Subsidiaries:

St. Louis Music, Inc. (1)
1400 Ferguson Ave, Saint Louis, MO 63133
Tel.: (314) 727-4512
Web Site: http://www.stlouismusic.com
Sales Range: $50-74.9 Million
Emp.: 45
Musical Instruments & Accessories Mfr & Sales
N.A.I.C.S.: 339992
Patrick R. Stevenson (VP-Sls)

U.S. BOTTLERS MACHINERY COMPANY
11911 Steele Creek Rd, Charlotte, NC 28273-3773
Tel.: (704) 588-4750 NC
Web Site: http://www.usbottlers.com
Year Founded: 1912
Sales Range: $50-74.9 Million
Emp.: 85
Bottling & Packaging Equipment Mfr
N.A.I.C.S.: 333993
Emil Popa (Dir-Sls)
Henry Pie (VP-Mfg)

U.S. BRONZE FOUNDRY & MACHINE, INC.
18649 Brake Shoe Rd, Meadville, PA 16335
Tel.: (814) 337-4234
Web Site: http://www.usbfmi.com
Rev.: $16,100,000
Emp.: 45
Provider of Copper Smelting & Refining Services
N.A.I.C.S.: 331420
Thomas Seringer (VP-Mktg)

Subsidiaries:

Lubrite Technologies (1)
18649 Brake Shoe Rd, Meadville, PA 16335
Tel.: (814) 337-4234
Web Site:
http://www.lubritetechnologies.com
Rev.: $2,700,000
Emp.: 15
Self Lubricating Bearing Mfr & Distr
N.A.I.C.S.: 332991
Dan Higham (Pres)
Tom Seringer (VP)

New Frontier Industries Inc. (1)
18649 Brake Shoe Rd, Meadville, PA 16335
Tel.: (814) 337-4234
Web Site: http://www.usbfmi.com
Sales Range: $1-9.9 Million
Copper Smelting & Refining
N.A.I.C.S.: 331420
Dan Higam (Pres)

U.S. CARGO, INC.
2036 E Williams Rd, Columbus, OH 43207
Tel.: (614) 552-2746
Web Site: http://www.us-cargo.com
Sales Range: $10-24.9 Million
Emp.: 13
Cargo & Courier Services
N.A.I.C.S.: 492110
Ralph E. Richter Jr. (Pres & CEO)

Subsidiaries:

United States Cargo & Courier Service, Inc. (1)
2036 E Williams Rd, Columbus, OH 43207
Tel.: (614) 449-2854
Web Site: http://www.us-cargo.com
Sales Range: $10-24.9 Million
Courier Services, Except By Air
N.A.I.C.S.: 492110
Bobbi Nayygross (Exec VP)
Ralph E. Richter Jr. (Pres)

U.S. CHINA MINING GROUP, INC.
15310 Amberly Dr Ste 250, Tampa, FL 33647
Tel.: (626) 581-8878 NV
Web Site:
http://www.uschinamining.com
Year Founded: 2001
Sales Range: $1-9.9 Million
Emp.: 92
Coal Mining Services
N.A.I.C.S.: 212115
Hongwen Li (Pres & CEO)
Guoqing Yue (Chm)
Tony Peng (CFO & Sec)

U.S. COMPANIES, INC.
17210 Campbell Rd Ste 100 W, Dallas, TX 75252
Tel.: (214) 891-3300
Rev.: $10,000,000
Crude Petroleum Production
N.A.I.C.S.: 211120
Max Williams (Chm)

U.S. COTTON, LLC
590 Laser Rd, Rio Rancho, NM 87124
Tel.: (505) 892-2269 OH
Web Site: http://www.uscotton.com
Year Founded: 1976
Sales Range: $150-199.9 Million
Emp.: 700
Mfr of Cotton Balls, Swabs, Tissues, Foot Insoles & Other Health & Beauty Aids
N.A.I.C.S.: 325620
Anthony Thomas (Pres & CEO)
Jeanne Ramaeker (Sec)
Cecelia Meade (CFO)

U.S. DRY CLEANING SERVICES CORPORATION
PO Box 13489, Mesa, AZ 85216
Tel.: (949) 734-7310
Web Site:
http://www.usdrycleaning.com
Sales Range: $10-24.9 Million
Emp.: 450
Laundry & Dry Cleaning Stores & Operations
N.A.I.C.S.: 812320
Alexander M. Bond (Chm & CEO)
Timothy N. Stickler (Chief Legal Officer & Chief Admin Officer)

Subsidiaries:

Tuchman Cleaners Inc. (1)
1430 Sadlier Cir W Dr, Indianapolis, IN 46239
Tel.: (317) 545-4321
Web Site: http://www.tuchmancleaners.com
Rev.: $5,700,000
Emp.: 25
Dry Cleaning, Collecting & Distributing Services
N.A.I.C.S.: 812320
Bill Wall (Reg Mgr)

U.S. EAGLE CORPORATION
582 Progress St, Elizabeth, NJ 07201
Tel.: (908) 351-5700 DE
Rev.: $50,000,000
Emp.: 5
Holding Company
N.A.I.C.S.: 551112
Frank Dela Ferra (CFO)
Scott K. Westphal (Chm, Sec & VP)
D. Thompson (Treas)

Subsidiaries:

Eagle One Golf Products (1)
1340 N Jefferson St, Anaheim, CA 92807
Tel.: (714) 983-0050
Web Site: http://www.eagleonegolf.com
Sales Range: $10-24.9 Million
Recycled Plastic & Rubber Products for Golf Courses, Parks, Tennis Courts & Other Outdoor Recreation Facilities
N.A.I.C.S.: 423990

U.S. ENDOWMENT FOR FORESTRY & COMMUNITIES, INC.
908 E North St, Greenville, SC 29601
Tel.: (864) 233-7646 DE
Web Site:
http://www.usendowment.org
Year Founded: 2006
Sales Range: $10-24.9 Million
Emp.: 11
Forest Conservation Services
N.A.I.C.S.: 813312
Peter Stangel (Sr VP)
Alan McGregor (VP)
Michael Goergen (Dir-P3 Nano)
Signe Cann (CFO)
Cameron Tommey (Dir-Legal & Prog Compliance)
Carlton N. Owen (Pres & CEO)
Florence Colby (Mgr-Org Support)

U.S. ENERGY DEVELOPMENT CORPORATION
2350 N Forest Rd, Getzville, NY 14068
Tel.: (716) 636-0401
Web Site: http://www.usedc.com
Year Founded: 1980
Sales Range: $50-74.9 Million
Emp.: 85
Drilling Oil & Gas Wells
N.A.I.C.S.: 213111

Jordan M. Jayson (CEO)
Douglas K. Walch (Pres)
Lynne M. Stewart (Controller)
Matthew P. Iak (Exec VP)

U.S. ENERGY TECHNOLOGIES, INC.
14370 Myford Rd Ste 100, Irvine, CA 92606
Tel.: (714) 617-8800 CA
Web Site:
http://www.uslightingtech.com
Year Founded: 1992
Sales Range: $10-24.9 Million
Holding Company; Lighting & Other Energy Technologies Developer & Mfr
N.A.I.C.S.: 551112
Richard Ham (Pres)
Alexander Ham (VP-Ops)

Subsidiaries:

U.S. Lighting Tech (1)
14370 Myford Rd Ste 100, Irvine, CA 92606
Tel.: (714) 617-8800
Web Site: http://www.uslightingtech.com
Sales Range: $10-24.9 Million
Emp.: 30
Energy Efficient Lighting Products
N.A.I.C.S.: 335132

U.S. FIDUCIARY SERVICES, INC.
801 Warrenville Rd Ste 500, Lisle, IL 60532
Tel.: (888) 647-4282
Web Site:
http://www.usfiduciaryservices.com
Holding Company
N.A.I.C.S.: 551112
Michael Welgat (Pres & CEO)

U.S. FINANCIAL SERVICES, LLC
30 Two Bridges Rd, Fairfield, NJ 07004
Tel.: (973) 882-3600
Web Site: http://www.usfsc.com
Portfolio Management
N.A.I.C.S.: 523940
Gerard T. Papetti (Owner)
Matthew DeFelice (Mng Dir)

Subsidiaries:

BMH Investment Group, LLC (1)
150 S Pearl St Ste 1150, Albany, NY 12202-1832
Tel.: (518) 894-2510
Web Site:
http://www.bmhinvestmentgroup.com
Other Financial Vehicles
N.A.I.C.S.: 525990
Richard Bolio (Pres)

U.S. GREEN BUILDING COUNCIL, INC.
2101 L St NW Ste 500, Washington, DC 20037
Tel.: (202) 828-7422 DC
Web Site: http://www.usgbc.org
Year Founded: 1993
Sales Range: $50-74.9 Million
Emp.: 337
Community Action Services
N.A.I.C.S.: 624190
Susan Dorn (Gen Counsel)
Roger Limoges (Sr VP-Market Transformation & Dev)
Marc Heisterkamp (VP-Strategic Relationships)
Lisa Revitte (COO)
Aaron Bernstein (Chm)
Fiona Cousins (Co-Vice Chm)
S. Richard Fedrizzi (Founder)
Chrissa Pagitsas (Treas & Sec)
Bob Fox (Co-Vice Chm)
Peter Templeton (Pres & CEO)
Doug Gatlin (Sr VP)

Rachel Gutter *(Sr VP-Knowledge)*
Sarah Alexander *(VP-Certification)*
Kate Hurst *(VP-Community, Conferences & Events)*
Vincent Chiusano *(VP-Customer Experience)*
Jennifer Druliner *(VP-Governance)*
Rhiannon Jacobsen *(VP-Strategic Relationships)*
Melissa Baker *(VP-Technical Solutions)*
Heidi Kunka *(Dir-Central Pennsylvania)*
Kimberly Lewis *(Sr VP-Community Advancement, Conferences & Events)*
Jim Craig *(Sr VP-Strategic Fin Plng)*
David Gottfried *(Co-Founder)*
Jennifer Guslick *(Principal & Mgr-Acct)*
Taryn Holowka *(Sr VP-Mktg, Comm & Advocacy)*
Mike Italiano *(Co-Founder)*
Lisa Marshall *(Principal-Ecological Building Strategies)*
Rich Mintz *(VP-Sls)*
Timothy Peterson *(VP)*
Jamie Statter *(VP-Strategic Relationships)*
Gretchen Sweeney *(VP-LEED Implementation)*
David Witek *(Sr VP-Fin, Ops & Admin)*

U.S. INSPECT, INC.
3650 Concorde Pkwy Ste 100, Chantilly, VA 20151
Tel.: (703) 293-1400
Web Site: http://www.usinspect.com
Year Founded: 1986
Rev.: $26,000,000
Emp.: 200
Provider of Home Inspection Services
N.A.I.C.S.: 541380
Keith S. Fimian *(Founder & Chm)*
Christopher C. Greene *(CFO)*
Edward E. How III *(Gen Counsel, Sec & VP)*

U.S. INTERNATIONAL MEDIA
1201 Alta Loma Rd, Los Angeles, CA 90069-2403
Tel.: (310) 482-6700
Web Site: http://www.usintlmedia.com
Year Founded: 2005
Sales Range: $10-24.9 Million
Emp.: 250
Media Buying Agency
N.A.I.C.S.: 541830
Dennis F. Holt *(Chm & CEO)*
Jack Silver *(Exec VP-Client Svcs)*
Alicia Nelson *(Pres-Broadcast Media Ops)*
Dot DiLorenzo *(Exec VP-Strategy & Res)*
Elizabeth Kelly *(Exec VP & Dir-Broadcast Media)*
Ryan McArthur *(Exec VP)*
Sherry Catchpole *(Exec VP-Ops)*
Leila Winick *(Exec VP-US Multicultural Grp)*
Eran Goren *(Pres & Chief Digital Officer)*
Russell Zingale *(Pres-Eastern)*
Steve Berger *(Pres-Patriot Media Grp)*
Mike Haggerty *(Sr VP-Client Svcs)*
Benson Hausman *(Chief Growth Officer & Exec VP)*

U.S. LABORATORIES
2 Jonathan Dr, Brockton, MA 02301
Tel.: (508) 583-2000
Web Site: http://www.us-labs.com
Rev.: $10,700,000

Emp.: 220
Mobile Laboratory & Radiology Services
N.A.I.C.S.: 621512
Rachel Carey *(Controller)*
Lynne Morley *(Mgr-Billing)*
Tracey Agrella *(Mgr-Client Svcs)*

U.S. LEGAL SUPPORT, INC.
16825 Northchase Dr Ste 900, Houston, TX 77060-6004
Tel.: (713) 653-7100   TX
Web Site: http://www.uslegalsupport.com
Legal Support & Litigation Services
N.A.I.C.S.: 541199
Charles F. Schugart *(Founder)*
Peter J. Giammanco *(Founder)*
Carrie Cosenza *(Sr VP-Enterprise Sls)*
April Orlando *(Sr VP-Key Acct Mgmt)*
Karen S. Gann *(Sr VP-Local Sls)*
Myke Hawkins *(Chief Comml Officer & Exec VP)*
Rick E. Levy *(Sr VP-Court Reporter Rels)*
Jimmie R. Bridwell *(CEO)*
Chris Vickery *(COO & Exec VP)*
Jessica M. Frost *(Chief HR Officer & Sr VP)*
Theresa Bridwell *(VP-Ops-Records)*

Subsidiaries:

DecisionQuest, Inc.   (1)
21515 Hawthorne Blvd Ste 720, Torrance, CA 90503
Tel.: (310) 618-9600
Web Site: http://www.decisionquest.com
Title Abstract & Settlement Offices
N.A.I.C.S.: 541191
Anthony Falzon *(Dir-Online Res)*

Subsidiary (Domestic):

Trial Partners, Inc.   (2)
5670 Wilshire Blvd Ste 850, Los Angeles, CA 90036
Tel.: (323) 653-3330
Web Site: http://www.trial-partners.com
Litigation Consulting Services
N.A.I.C.S.: 541199
J. Lee Meihls *(Pres)*
Mark R. Phillips *(VP)*

Medrecs, Inc.   (1)
805 Lenora St Fl 2, Seattle, WA 98121
Tel.: (206) 624-1420
Web Site: http://www.medrecs.com
Sales Range: $1-9.9 Million
Emp.: 60
Law firm
N.A.I.C.S.: 541199
Forrest Allard *(Founder & Pres)*

Sclafani Williams Court Reporters, Inc.   (1)
402 S Kentucky Ave Ste 390, Lakeland, FL 33801   (100%)
Tel.: (863) 688-5000
Web Site: http://www.swcourtreporters.com
Sales Range: $1-9.9 Million
Emp.: 18
Court Reporting & Stenotype Services
N.A.I.C.S.: 561492
Frieda Williams *(Pres)*

Trial Exhibits, Inc.   (1)
1177 W Cass St, Tampa, FL 33606
Tel.: (206) 920-4219
Web Site: http://www.trialexhibitsinc.com
Law firm
N.A.I.C.S.: 541199

U.S. LOGISTICS, INC.
PO Box 225, Elizabeth, NJ 07207
Tel.: (908) 289-9081   DE
Web Site: http://www.uslogistics.us
Emp.: 140
Holding Company; Freight Forwarding Services
N.A.I.C.S.: 551112

Subsidiaries:

U.S. Express, Inc.   (1)
145-43 226th St, Springfield Gardens, NY 11413
Tel.: (718) 978-0200
Web Site: http://www.us-express.com
Sales Range: $10-24.9 Million
Freight Transportation Arrangement Services
N.A.I.C.S.: 488510
Jack Jacobsen *(Exec VP)*
Chris Trizano *(Mgr-Acctg)*
Carole Murray *(Pres)*

U.S. MERCHANTS FINANCIAL GROUP, INC.
1118 S La Cienega Blvd, Los Angeles, CA 90035
Tel.: (310) 855-1946
Sales Range: $150-199.9 Million
Emp.: 1,500
Provider of Packaging & Labeling Services
N.A.I.C.S.: 551112
Jeff Green *(Pres)*

U.S. METALS POWDERS INC.
408 US Hwy 202, Flemington, NJ 08822-6020
Tel.: (908) 782-5454   NY
Sales Range: $50-74.9 Million
Emp.: 50
Mfr of Metallic Powders & Pigments
N.A.I.C.S.: 332117
Klyde C. Ramsey *(Pres)*

U.S. MICRO CORPORATION
7000 Highlands Pkwy SE Ste 160, Smyrna, GA 30082
Tel.: (770) 437-0706
Web Site: http://www.usmicrocorp.com
Sales Range: $10-24.9 Million
Emp.: 45
Computer Wholesaler
N.A.I.C.S.: 423430
Jason Terrell *(Dir-Ops)*
Matt Gillis *(Mgr-IT)*
Robert A. Krauss *(Sr VP-Sls-United States)*

Subsidiaries:

USM Capital, Inc.   (1)
Ste 400 690 Dorval Dr, Oakville, L6K 3W7, ON, Canada
Tel.: (905) 849-3529
Sales Range: $10-24.9 Million
Emp.: 15
Computer Equipment Leasing Services
N.A.I.C.S.: 532420

U.S. MUNICIPAL SUPPLY, INC.
Route 26 S, Huntingdon, PA 16652
Tel.: (814) 627-4671
Web Site: http://www.usmuni.com
Sales Range: $10-24.9 Million
Emp.: 60
Whslr of Construction & Mining Machinery
N.A.I.C.S.: 423810
Paul Statler *(Pres)*
Robert Puchalla *(Controller)*
Alvah Adam *(VP)*
Gary Wright *(VP)*

U.S. NATIONAL WHITEWATER CENTER, INC.
5000 Whitewater Center Pkwy, Charlotte, NC 28214
Tel.: (704) 391-3900
Web Site: http://www.usnwc.org
Sales Range: $10-24.9 Million
Emp.: 675
Community Care Services
N.A.I.C.S.: 624190
Jeffrey T. Sheldon *(CFO & COO)*
Jeffrey T. Wise *(CEO & Exec Dir)*

U.S. NAVAL INSTITUTE
291 Wood Rd, Annapolis, MD 21402
Tel.: (410) 268-6110
Web Site: http://www.usni.org
Sales Range: $10-24.9 Million
Emp.: 100
Proceedings & Naval History Magazines & Books Publisher; Seminars for the Advancement of Issues Related to National Security
N.A.I.C.S.: 513130
Thomas Cutler *(Dir-Pro Publ)*
Rick Russell *(Dir-Naval Institute Press)*
Peter H. Daly *(CEO)*
Brian Walker *(Mgr-Inventory, Exhibits & Special Sls)*
Robin Noonan *(Mgr-Mktg)*

U.S. NEWS & WORLD REPORT, L.P.
450 W 33rd St, New York, NY 10001-2603
Tel.: (212) 716-6800   NY
Web Site: http://www.usnews.com
Year Founded: 1933
Sales Range: $150-199.9 Million
Emp.: 500
Weekly News Magazine of National & International Affairs
N.A.I.C.S.: 513120
Peter M. Dwoskin *(Gen Counsel & Sr VP-Strategic Dev)*
Brian Kelly *(Dir-Editorial)*
Karen S. Chevalier *(COO)*
Phyllis A. Panza *(Dir-Adv Svcs)*
Margaret Mannix *(Exec Editor)*
Gary Emerling *(Sr Editor-News)*
Kim Castro *(Chief Content Officer & Editor)*
Kim Heneghan *(VP & Gen Mgr-Money Products)*
Bill Holiber *(Pres & CEO)*
Jada Graves *(Mng Editor-BrandFuse)*
Chad Smolinski *(Chief Product Officer)*
Chris DiCosmo *(Sr VP-Education & Gen Mgr-News)*
David Lawrence *(Founder)*
Eric Gertler *(Chm)*
Neil Maheshwari *(CFO)*
Thomas H. Peck *(Sr VP-Plng)*
Stephanie Salmon *(VP-Data & Information Strategy)*
Yingjie Shu *(Sr VP-Tech)*
Lori Overstreet *(VP & Gen Mgr-Education)*
Kate O'Donnell *(VP-Comm)*

U.S. PAVEMENT SERVICES INC.
39 Industrial Pkwy, Woburn, MA 01801
Tel.: (781) 932-4722
Web Site: http://www.uspavement.com
Year Founded: 1985
Sales Range: $25-49.9 Million
Emp.: 120
Pavement & Seal Coating Services
N.A.I.C.S.: 324121
Michael J. Musto *(Pres)*

U.S. PREMIUM BEEF, LLC
12200 N Ambassador Dr, Kansas City, MO 64163
Tel.: (816) 713-8800   DE
Web Site: http://www.uspremiumbeef.com
Year Founded: 1996
Rev.: $365,729,000
Assets: $343,990,000
Liabilities: $11,718,000
Net Worth: $332,272,000
Earnings: $359,497,000
Emp.: 7

U.S. Premium Beef, LLC—(Continued)
Fiscal Year-end: 12/25/21
Beef Cattle Processing & Marketing Services
N.A.I.C.S.: 311612
Stanley D. Linville (CEO)
Mark R. Gardiner (Chm)
Tracy Thomas (VP-Mktg)
Danielle D. Imel (Treas & Sr VP)
Brian Bertelsen (VP-Field Ops)
Jerry L. Bohn (Sec)
Scott J. Miller (CFO)
Lisa Phillips (Dir-Ops)
Joe M. Morgan (Vice Chm)

U.S. PRESS, LLC
1628 James P Rodgers Dr, Valdosta, GA 31601-6569
Tel.: (229) 244-5634
Web Site: http://www.uspress.com
Year Founded: 1981
Direct Mail Printing Services
N.A.I.C.S.: 323111
Kent A. Buescher (Co-Founder)
Dawn C. Buescher (Co-Founder)

U.S. RARE EARTHS, INC.
5600 Tennyson Pkwy Ste 240, Plano, TX 75024
Tel.: (972) 294-7116   NV
Web Site:
 http://www.usrareearths.com
Emp.: 1
Mineral Exploration Services
N.A.I.C.S.: 212290
Kevin Michael Cassidy (CEO & Chief Acctg Officer)

U.S. RENAL CARE, INC.
5851 Legacy Cir Ste 900, Plano, TX 75024
Tel.: (214) 736-2700   AR
Web Site:
 http://www.usrenalcare.com
Year Founded: 2000
Emp.: 180
Kidney Dialysis Centers
N.A.I.C.S.: 621492
J. Christopher Brengard (Founder)
Charla Williams (Sr VP-Revenue Cycle Mgmt)
Jack F. Egan (Exec VP-Fin)
Jack N. Harrington (Sr VP-Real Estate & Dev)
James D. Shelton (CFO & Exec VP)
Lauren McDowell (Sr VP-HR)
Stephen Pirri (Pres)
Thomas L. Weinberg (Gen Counsel & Exec VP)
David Eldridge (Sr VP-Fin)
Geoffrey A. Block (Sr VP-Clinical Res & Medical Affairs)
Bradley Stoltz (Exec VP-Ops)
Brett Kirstein (Chief Revenue Officer & Sr VP)
Cameron Thompson (Exec VP-Ops)
David Adams (Sr VP-Managed Care)
Debbie Mitchell-Taylor (Sr VP-Ops)
Mike Huguelet (Chief Dev Officer & Exec VP)
Tim Thomasson (CIO & Sr VP-IT)
Mary Dittrich (Interim CEO & Chief Medical Officer)
Andy Johnston (COO)
Mark Caputo (Chm)
Subsidiaries:
Ambulatory Services of America, Inc.   (1)
320 Seven Springs Way Ste 220, Brentwood, TN 37027
Tel.: (615) 250-1799
Web Site: http://www.asaambulatory.com
Alternate Site Healthcare Services
N.A.I.C.S.: 621999

U.S. SOYBEAN EXPORT COUNCI
16305 Swingley Ridge Rd Ste 200, Chesterfield, MO 63017
Tel.: (636) 449-6400   DE
Web Site: http://www.ussec.org
Year Founded: 2005
Sales Range: $25-49.9 Million
Emp.: 130
Soybean Export Association
N.A.I.C.S.: 813910
Jim Sutter (CEO)
Ed Beaman (Chief Operating Officer)
Brent Babb (Reg Dir)

U.S. SPACE & ROCKET CENTER
1 Tranquility Base, Huntsville, AL 35805
Tel.: (256) 837-3400
Web Site:
 http://www.rocketcenter.com
Space Related Instruction & Camp Services
N.A.I.C.S.: 712110
Claudia Jones (Dir-Special Events)
Jason Lanier (Dir-Plng & Logistics)
Vickie Henderson (VP-HR)
Brenda Perez (Controller)
Daniel Karb (Dir-Catering)
Kay Taylor (Dir-Education)
Louie Ramirez (CFO)
Tom White (Dir-Sls & Custom)
Katie Anderson (Dir-Museum Ops)
Rachael Samples (Mgr-Guest Svcs)
Susan Moore (Mgr-Mdse)
Betty Burdick (Volunteer Coord)
Ed Stewarts (Dir-Exhibits)
Chris Myers (Dir-Space Camps Programs)
Chelsea Scott Montgomery (Dir-Training & Dev)
Quineth Moon (Dir-Aviation Challenge)
Anthony Greer (Dir-Robotics & Cyber Camp Programs)
Holly Ralston (Exec Dir-Education Foundation)
Joseph Vick (Mgr-Museum Educ)
Pat Ammons (Dir-Comm)
Margie Phillips (Mgr-Pub Rels)
Sara Vowell (Mgr-Sls & Outreach)
Deborah Barnhart (CEO)
Brenda Carr (VP-Dev)
Celia Lee (Dir-Protocol & Community Rels)

U.S. TEXTILES LLC
9540 W 62nd St, Merriam, KS 66203
Tel.: (913) 660-0995
Web Site:
 http://www.ustextilesonline.com
Year Founded: 2001
Sales Range: $1-9.9 Million
Emp.: 6
Linen & Apparel Textiles
N.A.I.C.S.: 812331

U.S. TRANSLATION COMPANY
320 W 200 S 3 Fl, Salt Lake City, UT 84101
Tel.: (801) 393-5300
Web Site:
 http://www.ustranslation.com
Sales Range: $1-9.9 Million
Emp.: 9
Language Translation Agency
N.A.I.C.S.: 541930
David Utrilla (Founder & Pres)
Kathy Sprouse (Project Mgr)
Gordon Kirkham (Mgr-Contract)
Doug Bingham (Mgr-Bus Dev)
Zach Jacob (Mgr-Mktg Comm & PR)

U.S. VENTURE, INC.
425 Better Way, Appleton, WI 54915
Tel.: (920) 739-6101   WI
Web Site: http://www.usventure.com
Year Founded: 1951
Gasoline & Fuel Oil; Plumbing & Heating; Express Convenience Stores; Tires; Industrial Heating & Air Whslr
N.A.I.C.S.: 424710
John Schmidt (Pres & CEO)
Mike Koel (Pres-U.S. Gain)
Scott Hanstedt (Dir-Sls-U.S. Gain)
Subsidiaries:
Design Air   (1)
1010 W Kennedy Ave, Kimberly, WI 54136-2202
Tel.: (920) 739-7005
Web Site: http://www.designair.com
Sales Range: $25-49.9 Million
Emp.: 50
Whslr of Heating & Cooling Products & Services
N.A.I.C.S.: 423730
Southwest Transport, Co.   (1)
137 Hillsborough St, Hartford, MI 49057
Tel.: (269) 621-6216
Sales Range: $1-9.9 Million
Emp.: 20
Water & Sewer Line & Related Structures Construction
N.A.I.C.S.: 237110
Gerald Heppler (Treas)
U.S. AutoForce   (1)
425 Better Way, Appleton, WI 54915
Tel.: (920) 739-6101
Web Site: http://www.usautoforce.com
Sales Range: $25-49.9 Million
Emp.: 200
Automotive Tires, Parts & Lubricants Distr
N.A.I.C.S.: 441330
John Schmidt (Pres)
Brian Decker (Mgr-Mktg)
Subsidiary (Domestic):
Pacific Tire Distributors   (2)
2750 N Hayden Island Dr, Portland, OR 97217
Tel.: (503) 247-7115
Web Site:
 http://www.pacifictiredistributors.com
Rev.: $3,500,000
Emp.: 20
Tire & Tube Merchant Whslr
N.A.I.C.S.: 423130
Chris Roberg (Pres)
U.S. Custom Manufacturing   (1)
424 S Washington St, Kimberly, WI 54136
Tel.: (920) 735-8238
Web Site:
 http://www.uscustommanufacturing.com
Sales Range: $10-24.9 Million
Emp.: 25
Metal Tubing Supply & Forming Services
N.A.I.C.S.: 332114
U.S. Lubricants   (1)
425 S Washington St, Kimberly, WI 54136
Tel.: (920) 735-8298
Web Site: http://www.uslube.com
Sales Range: $10-24.9 Million
Emp.: 25
Custom Lubricant Blending Services
N.A.I.C.S.: 324191
Albert Selker (Gen Mgr)
Tony Springer (Gen Mgr)
Unit (Domestic):
U.S. OilChek   (2)
422 S Washington St, Kimberly, WI 54136
Tel.: (920) 831-8839
Web Site: http://www.usoilcheck.com
Oil Analysis & Predictive Maintenance Services
N.A.I.C.S.: 541380
Scott Vanevenhoven (Mgr-Laboratory)
Jim Stevens (Dir-Tech)
U.S. Oil   (1)
425 Better Way, Appleton, WI 54915
Tel.: (920) 739-6101
Web Site: http://www.usventure.com
Emp.: 300
Petroleum Services & Products Whslr
N.A.I.C.S.: 424710
Sherry Bevers (Mgr-Customer Svc)
John Schmidt (Pres & CEO)
Subsidiary (Domestic):
Combined Oil Co.   (2)
100 Tri-State International Ste 140, Lincolnshire, IL 60069
Tel.: (847) 444-0792
Web Site: http://www.combinedoil.com
Petroleum Product Distr
N.A.I.C.S.: 424720
Division (Domestic):
U.S. Oil - Cheboygan Terminal   (2)
311 N B St, Cheboygan, MI 49721-1250
Tel.: (231) 627-6411
Sales Range: $25-49.9 Million
Emp.: 5
Petroleum Refining
N.A.I.C.S.: 324110
U.S. Petroleum Equipment   (1)
558 Carter Ct, Kimberly, WI 54136
Tel.: (920) 735-8287
Web Site:
 http://www.uspetroleumequipment.com
Sales Range: $10-24.9 Million
Emp.: 40
Fuel Delivery Systems Installation Services
N.A.I.C.S.: 541330
Terry Jandrey (Gen Mgr)
Sherri Gates (Mgr-Svc)
Bruce Uitenbroek (Coord-Sls)
Todd Broeckel (Coord-Sls)
Pat Schmidt (Coord-Estimating & Parts)
U.S. Venture, Inc. - Express Convenience Centers Division   (1)
606 Dousman St, Green Bay, WI 54303
Tel.: (920) 433-9650
Web Site:
 http://www.expressconvenience.com
Convenience Store Operator
N.A.I.C.S.: 457110
Tracy Williams-Prince (Mgr-Mktg)

U.S. WHOLESALE PIPE AND TUBE, INC.
3351 Grand Blvd, Holiday, FL 34690
Tel.: (727) 945-9060
Web Site: http://www.usw.com
Year Founded: 1963
Sales Range: $25-49.9 Million
Emp.: 45
Metal Pipe & Tube Distr & Mfr
N.A.I.C.S.: 423130
Ed Rachel (Pres & CEO)
J. R. Baker (COO)
Robert Posavec (CFO)
Milo Coppes (Mgr-Sls)

U.W. MARX CONSTRUCTION COMPANY, INC.
20 Gurlay Ave, Troy, NY 12182
Tel.: (518) 272-2541   NY
Web Site: http://www.uwmarx.com
Year Founded: 1954
Sales Range: $25-49.9 Million
Emp.: 300
Nonresidential Construction
N.A.I.C.S.: 236220
Peter B. Marx (Pres)
Bill Shannon (Exec Dir-Sls & Mktg)
Chuck Dollard (Dir-Mktg)
Jeff West (VP)
Khristopher Fitzgerald (Chief Sustainability Officer)

UA LOCAL UNION 669 ROAD SPRINKLER FITTERS
7050 Oakland Mills Rd Ste 200, Columbia, MD 21046
Tel.: (410) 381-4300
Web Site:
 https://www.sprinklerfitters669.org
Year Founded: 1915
Emp.: 15,000
Educational Support Services
N.A.I.C.S.: 611710

COMPANIES

UB GREENSFELDER LLP
1660 W 2nd St Ste 1100, Cleveland, OH 44113-1448
Tel.: (216) 583-7000
Web Site: http://www.ulmer.com
Year Founded: 1908
Emp.: 181
Law firm
N.A.I.C.S.: 541110
John M. Alten *(Partner & Atty)*
Thomas L. Anastos *(Partner & Atty)*
Lewis T. Barr *(Partner & Atty)*
Jeffrey Baddeley *(Partner & Atty)*
Jennifer Lawry Adams *(Partner)*
David Pope *(Partner-Chicago)*
David T. Meehan *(Partner & Atty)*
Paul M. Ulrich *(Partner & Atty)*
Andrew Owen *(Partner-Columbus)*
Seth Voit *(Partner-Cincinnati)*
Scott Kadish *(Mng Partner)*
Eric Robbins *(Chm-IP & Tech Grp)*
Amanda Martinsek *(Partner)*
Jeffrey S. Dunlap *(Chm-Bus Litigation Practice Grp)*
Rachael L. Rodman *(Partner)*
John Bennett *(Partner)*
Kevin McLaughlin *(Pres & CEO)*

Subsidiaries:

Greensfelder, Hemker & Gale, P.C. (1)
10 S Broadway Ste 2000, Saint Louis, MO 63102
Tel.: (314) 241-9090
Web Site: http://www.greensfelder.com
Emp.: 147
Law firm
N.A.I.C.S.: 541110
George J. Leontsinis *(Atty)*
Joseph R. Meives *(Atty)*
Walter L. Wittenberg *(Atty)*
Dennis G. Collins *(Atty)*
Gary A. Eberhardt *(Atty)*
Caitlin M. Schweppe *(Atty)*
Katherine L. Anderson *(Atty)*
Christopher A. Pickett *(Chief Diversity Officer)*
Heather Henry *(COO)*
Timothy Thornton *(CEO)*
Matthew E. Cohn *(Partner-Chicago)*
John L. Senica *(Atty-Bus Svcs Practice Grp-Chicago)*
Mollie Farrell *(Dir-Pro Dev)*
Carmen White *(Mgr-Diversity & Inclusion)*
Sanja Ord *(Assoc Atty)*
Kevin F. O'Malley *(Atty)*
Risa McMahon *(Dir-Bus Dev)*
John Suermann Jr. *(Assoc Atty)*

UBEE INTERACTIVE, INC.
8085 S Chester St Ste 200, Englewood, CO 80112 CA
Web Site: http://www.ubeeinteractive.com
Year Founded: 1996
Broadband Products & Services
N.A.I.C.S.: 334118
Maria Popo *(Pres-Americas)*
Leonard Kao *(Sr VP-Enterprise Resource Mgmt)*
Jackie Yang *(VP-Ops)*

Subsidiaries:

AirWalk Communications, Inc. (1)
1830 N Greenville Ave, Richardson, TX 75081
Tel.: (972) 638-9400
Web Site: http://www.airwalkcom.com
Sales Range: $1-9.9 Million
Emp.: 27
Small Cell Technologies Mfr
N.A.I.C.S.: 334290
Serge Pequeux *(CEO)*

UBICARE
284 Amory St G-101, Boston, MA 02130
Tel.: (617) 524-8861
Web Site: http://www.ubicare.com
Year Founded: 2002
Sales Range: $1-9.9 Million
Emp.: 20
Electronic Communication Services
N.A.I.C.S.: 541990
Betsy Weaver *(Founder, Pres & CEO)*
Bill Lindsay *(Exec VP-Content, UI & Product)*
Debra Zalvan *(Exec VP)*
Jo Charest *(Mgr-Client Success)*
Tom Raleigh *(VP-Bus Dev)*
Chris Turner *(CTO)*

UBIQUITY MANAGEMENT, L.P.
5700 W 112th St Ste 500, Overland park, KS 66211
Web Site: http://ubiqpartners.com
Private Infrastructure Investment Firm
N.A.I.C.S.: 523999
Christian Scharosch *(Mng Partner)*
Ajay Ghanekar *(Mng Partner)*
Jamie Earp *(Mng Partner)*

Subsidiaries:

Millennium Telcom, LLC (1)
4800 Keller Hicks Rd, Keller, TX 76244
Tel.: (817) 745-2000
Web Site: http://www.1scom.com
Sales Range: $1-9.9 Million
Emp.: 35
Telecommunications Resellers
N.A.I.C.S.: 517121
Andy Slote *(Gen Mgr)*
B. Ken Carter *(Gen Mgr)*

UC SAN DIEGO HEALTH
200 W Arbor Dr, San Diego, CA 92103
Tel.: (858) 657-7000
Web Site: https://health.ucsd.edu
Emp.: 100
General Hospitals & Related Healthcare Facilities Owner & Operator
N.A.I.C.S.: 622110
Patty Maysent *(CEO)*

Subsidiaries:

Alvarado Hospital Medical Center, Inc. (1)
6655 Alvarado Rd, San Diego, CA 92120
Tel.: (619) 287-3270
Web Site: https://www.alvaradohospital.com
General Medical Services
N.A.I.C.S.: 622110
Sara D. Turner *(Reg Dir-HR)*
Robin Gomez *(CEO)*
Larry Emdur *(Chief Medical Officer)*
Marilyn Sharp *(CFO)*
Peggy Tilley *(Dir-Medical & Surgical)*
Lorena Villegas *(Dir-Telemetry)*
Natalie Dumont *(Dir-Critical Care Svcs)*
Michael Brislin *(Dir-Perioperative Svcs)*
Rhonda Thomas *(Dir-Medical Staff Svcs)*
Vishnu Duvuuru *(Reg Dir-IT)*
Raven Lopez *(Dir-Nutritional Svcs)*
Sandy Gergen *(Dir-Imaging & Cardiology)*
Janice Bowman *(Dir-Social Svcs & Case Mgmt)*
Ben Macapugay *(Reg Mgr-Mktg)*
Lori Turgeon *(Dir-Emergency Svcs)*
Shirlee Meadows *(Dir-Patient Access)*
Joanna Cox *(Dir-Patient Fin Svcs)*
Jane Schmoll *(Dir-Environmental Svcs & Volunteers)*
Sacha Ridgway *(Chief Nursing Officer)*
Kenneth Glover *(Mgr-Plant Ops & Security)*
Sandy Galeski *(Dir-Distr & Central Supply)*
John Stauffer *(Dir-Performance Improvement)*
Elizabeth Pina *(Mgr-Lab Svcs)*
Dan Peterson *(Dir-Pharmacy Svcs)*
Mollie Nunn *(Dir-Infection Control)*
Durand Hartin *(Reg Mgr-Security)*
Jay Flaherty *(Reg Dir-Rehabilitation Svcs)*
Annie Hodges *(Dir-Bus Dev)*
Jeri Chaldekas *(Dir-Pulmonary Svcs)*
Audra Burton *(Dir-Medical & Surgical Svcs)*
Pearl Bautista *(Sr Dir-Care Specialty Svcs Reg)*
Mohammed Ahmed *(Dir-Health Information Mgmt)*

Subsidiary (Domestic):

Alvarado Hospital, LLC (2)
6655 Alvarado Rd, San Diego, CA 92120
Tel.: (619) 287-3270
Web Site: http://www.alvaradohospital.com
Sales Range: $75-99.9 Million
Emp.: 1,000
Hospital Services
N.A.I.C.S.: 622110
Brian Kleven *(CFO)*
Jim Scull *(Dir-Lab Svcs)*

UCA GROUP COMPONENT SPECIALTY INC.
412 N State St, Elgin, IL 60123
Tel.: (847) 742-4400
Web Site: http://www.ucagroup.com
Year Founded: 1983
Rev.: $14,429,277
Emp.: 80
Machine Shop, Jobbing & Repair Services
N.A.I.C.S.: 332710
Nand Kumar *(VP)*
Andy Nuggehalli *(Controller)*

Subsidiaries:

Accu-Cast Inc. (1)
1911 Crutchfield St, Chattanooga, TN 37406-2404
Tel.: (423) 622-4344
Web Site: http://www.eaccucast.com
Sales Range: $10-24.9 Million
Emp.: 50
Mfr of Investment Casting
N.A.I.C.S.: 331512
Patrick Rush *(Mgr-Ops)*

Component Specialty, Inc. (1)
2144 Royal Ln, Dallas, TX 75229
Tel.: (214) 738-6746
Web Site: http://www.ucagroup.com
Industrial Machinery Mfr
N.A.I.C.S.: 333248

General Technology, Inc. (1)
412 N State St, Elgin, IL 60123
Tel.: (847) 742-8870
Sales Range: $10-24.9 Million
Emp.: 75
Machine Shop, Jobbing & Repair
N.A.I.C.S.: 332710

Total Outsource, Inc. (1)
1875 Big Timber Rd Ste A, Elgin, IL 60123
Tel.: (630) 872-5000
Web Site: http://www.totaloutsource.com
Emp.: 3
Information Technology Consulting Services
N.A.I.C.S.: 541512
Amarnath Nuggehalli *(CEO)*

Subsidiary (Domestic):

PC Products & Services Inc (2)
1875 Big Timber Rd Ste B, Elgin, IL 60123
Tel.: (847) 888-8400
Web Site: http://www.pcproducts.com
Computer Peripheral Equipment Distr
N.A.I.C.S.: 423430
Patrick Boghra *(CEO)*

Subsidiary (Non-US):

Syntax Soft-Tech Pvt. Ltd. (2)
16 30th Cross Opp Sagar Hospital 4th T Block Jayanagar, Bengaluru, 560 041, India
Tel.: (91) 80 41380700
Web Site: http://www.syntaxsoft.com
Emp.: 40
Information Technology Consulting Services
N.A.I.C.S.: 541512
P. Prashant *(COO)*
S. Srivatsa *(CMO)*
K. V. Subramaniyan *(CTO)*

Tantra Infosolutions Pvt. Ltd. (2)
32-F Veerasandra Industrial Area Hosur Road, Bengaluru, 560 100, India
Tel.: (91) 80 28020800
Web Site: http://www.tantrainfosolutions.com
Emp.: 300
Information Technology Consulting Services
N.A.I.C.S.: 541512

UCI HEALTH

Amar Nuggehalli *(Dir-Fin & Ops)*
Mysore S. Sudheendra *(CTO)*
N. B. Nandkumar *(CEO)*

UCA HOLDINGS INC.
2 Town Sq Blvd Ste 310, Asheville, NC 28803
Tel.: (828) 210-8120
Web Site: http://www.stonypoint.com
Sales Range: $100-124.9 Million
Emp.: 5
Aircraft Engines & Engine Parts
N.A.I.C.S.: 336412
Kenneth E. Glass *(Chm)*

Subsidiaries:

Turbine Engine Components Textron, Inc. (1)
334 Beechwood Rd Ste 304, Fort Mitchell, KY 41017
Tel.: (859) 426-0090
Aerospace Equipment Mfr
N.A.I.C.S.: 336413
Anthony Smith *(VP-Mktg & Bus Dev)*

Subsidiary (Domestic):

TECT Aerospace, Inc. (2)
300 W Douglas Ste 100, Wichita, KS 67202
Tel.: (316) 425-3638
Aerospace Equipment Mfr
N.A.I.C.S.: 336413

Utica Corporation (1)
2 Halsey Rd, Whitesboro, NY 13492
Tel.: (315) 768-8072
Aircraft Engines & Engine Parts
N.A.I.C.S.: 336412
Donna Prentice *(Mgr-HR)*

UCA SYSTEMS INC.
9 Whippany Rd, Whippany, NJ 07981
Tel.: (973) 887-2758
Web Site: http://www.ucasystems.com
Year Founded: 1996
Sales Range: $100-124.9 Million
Emp.: 75
Computer Hardware Analysis
N.A.I.C.S.: 334310
Faisal Syed *(CEO)*

UCBH HOLDINGS, INC.
555 Montgomery St, San Francisco, CA 94111
Tel.: (415) 315-2800 DE
Web Site: http://www.ibankunited.com
Year Founded: 1998
Sales Range: $650-699.9 Million
Emp.: 1,542
Bank Holding Company
N.A.I.C.S.: 551111

Subsidiaries:

UCB Asset Management, Inc. (1)
555 Montgomery St, San Francisco, CA 94111
Tel.: (415) 315-2800
Sales Range: $125-149.9 Million
Emp.: 250
Professional Investment Management Services
N.A.I.C.S.: 523940

UCI CONSTRUCTION INC.
261 Arthur Rd, Martinez, CA 94553
Tel.: (925) 370-9808
Web Site: http://www.uciconstruction.com
Sales Range: $10-24.9 Million
Emp.: 125
Provider of Plumbing, Heating & Air Conditioning Contracting Services
N.A.I.C.S.: 238220
Tom Weatherford *(Pres)*

UCI HEALTH
101 The City Dr. S, Orange, CA 92868

UCI Health—(Continued)

Tel.: (714) 456-7890
Web Site: https://www.ucihealth.org
Year Founded: 1976
Emp.: 4,102
Hospitals & Health Care
N.A.I.C.S.: 621610

Subsidiaries:

Fountain Valley Regional Hospital & Medical Center, Inc. (1)
17100 Euclid St, Fountain Valley, CA 92708
Tel.: (714) 966-7200
Web Site:
   https://www.fountainvalleyhospital.com
Sales Range: $200-249.9 Million
Hospital
N.A.I.C.S.: 622110
Robert B. Shappley (COO)
Scott Killion (CFO)
Paulette Heitmeyer (Chief Nursing Officer)
Anna Aguilar (Chief HR Officer)

Subsidiary (Domestic):

Specialty Surgery Center at Fountain Valley Regional Hospital, L.L.C. (2)
11190 Warner Ave Ste 212, Fountain Valley, CA 92708-4019
Tel.: (714) 427-0880
Web Site:
   http://www.fountainvalleysurgerycenter.com
Health Care Srvices
N.A.I.C.S.: 621999

Lakewood Regional Medical Center, Inc. (1)
3700 E S St, Lakewood, CA 90712
Tel.: (562) 531-2550
Web Site:
   https://www.lakewoodregional.com
Sales Range: $10-24.9 Million
Hospital
N.A.I.C.S.: 622110
Yvonne Roddy-Sturm (Chief Nursing Officer)
Eric Delgado (CFO)
Kim Pensenstadler (Chief Strategy Officer)
Mary Okuhara (Chief HR Officer)
Michael Paul Amos (COO)
Matthew Sandoval (Chief Quality Officer)
Michelle Skipper (Chief HR Officer)
Scott Killion (CFO)

Los Alamitos Medical Center, Inc. (1)
3751 Katella Ave, Los Alamitos, CA 90720
Tel.: (562) 598-1311
Web Site:
   https://www.losalamitosmedctr.com
Sales Range: $50-74.9 Million
Hospital
N.A.I.C.S.: 622110

Placentia-Linda Hospital, Inc. (1)
1301 N Rose Dr, Placentia, CA 92870
Tel.: (714) 993-2000
Web Site: https://www.placentialinda.com
Sales Range: $25-49.9 Million
Hospital
N.A.I.C.S.: 622110
Fred Valtairo (Chief Operating & Quality Officer)
Rhonda Sausedo (Chief Nursing Officer)
Keslie Blackwell (CFO)
Rosa Chiacchierarelli (Compliance Officer)
Cindy Greenberg (Chrm)
Beth Haney (Vice Chm)
Ken Ryan (Sec)
Michele Severson (Exec Dir)
Rosa Chiacchierarelli (Compliance Officer)
Ken Ryan (Sec)
Michele Severson (Exec Dir)

Subsidiary (Domestic):

Anaheim Hills Medical Imaging, L.L.C. (2)
781 S Weir Canyon Rd Ste 185, Anaheim, CA 92808
Tel.: (714) 282-8160
Web Site: http://www.anaheimhillsmri.com
Emp.: 5
Medical Imaging Services
N.A.I.C.S.: 621511

UCKELE HEALTH NUTRITION

5600 Silberhorn Hwy, Blissfield, MI 49228
Tel.: (517) 486-4341
Web Site: http://www.uckele.com
Year Founded: 1962
Sales Range: $10-24.9 Million
Emp.: 50
Pharmaceutical Preparation Mfr
N.A.I.C.S.: 325412
Michael Uckele (Pres & CEO)
Tanya Macbeth (Dir-Safety & Mgr-HR)
Sarah Aubry (Controller)
Mary Isley (Coord-Mktg)

UCS

1834 Ferguson Ln Ste 1000, Austin, TX 78754
Tel.: (512) 385-6600
Web Site:
   http://www.ucscompanies.com
Year Founded: 1999
Sales Range: $1-9.9 Million
Emp.: 69
Carpet & Rug Cleaning Services
N.A.I.C.S.: 561740
Ben Wells (CFO)
Eric Maxwell (VP)
Max Rhorer (Mgr-Carpet Cleaning-Austin)
Craig Campbell (Project Mgr)

UCSF MEDICAL CENTER

505 Parnassus Ave, San Francisco, CA 94143
Tel.: (415) 476-1000
Web Site: https://www.ucsfhealth.org
Hospitals & Healtcare Services
N.A.I.C.S.: 622110

UDG, INC.

2600 N Central Expy Ste 500, Richardson, TX 75080
Tel.: (972) 788-9242   CO
Web Site:
   http://www.urbandesigngroup.com
Architectural & Interior Design Services
N.A.I.C.S.: 541310
Donald C. Buenger (Pres, CEO & Principal-Atlanta Studio)
Raymond R. Kahl (Principal)
Ronald D. Armstrong (Principal)
John M. Novack Jr. (Founder & Principal)

Subsidiaries:

UDG, Inc. - Atlanta Studio (1)
3475 Piedmont Road NE Ste 1200, Atlanta, GA 30305
Tel.: (770) 444-9630
Web Site: http://www.urbandesigngroup.com
Architectural & Interior Design Services
N.A.I.C.S.: 541310

Affiliate (Domestic):

EquiTrust USA (2)
3475 Piedmont Rd NE Ste 1200, Atlanta, GA 30305
Tel.: (404) 996-5838
Real Estate Investment Trust
N.A.I.C.S.: 525990

UEBELHOR & SONS

972 Wernsing Rd, Jasper, IN 47546
Tel.: (812) 482-2222
Web Site: http://www.uebelhor.com
Year Founded: 1929
Sales Range: $25-49.9 Million
Emp.: 100
Car Whslr
N.A.I.C.S.: 441110
Ed Schroeder (Mgr-Bus)
Tony Uebelhor (Owner)

UEBELHOR DEVELOPMENT INC.

1005 N Chestnut St, Huntingburg, IN 47542
Tel.: (812) 683-2833
Sales Range: $10-24.9 Million
Emp.: 9
Provider of Fuel Oil
N.A.I.C.S.: 424710
Steve Uebelhor (Gen Mgr)

UENO, LLC

1263 Mission St Fl 3, San Francisco, CA 94103
Tel.: (415) 813-7553
Web Site: http://www.ueno.co
Year Founded: 2014
Sales Range: $10-24.9 Million
Advertising Agency Services
N.A.I.C.S.: 541810
Haraldur Thorleifsson (Pres & CEO)

UES, INC.

4401 Dayton Xenia Rd, Dayton, OH 45432-1894
Tel.: (937) 426-6900   OH
Web Site: http://www.ues.com
Year Founded: 1973
Sales Range: $10-24.9 Million
Emp.: 200
Hi-Technology Research & Development
N.A.I.C.S.: 541511
Nina Joshi (Pres & CEO)

UFG GROUP, INC.

2121 Titus Pkwy, West Palm Beach, FL 33411
Tel.: (561) 868-1358
Web Site:
   http://www.unitedfranchisegroup.com
Holding Company; Franchise Development Services
N.A.I.C.S.: 551112
Ray W. Titus (Founder & CEO)
Tony Foley (VP-Sls-Global)
David Baxter (COO)
Todd Newton (Gen Counsel)
Jill Klein (Gen Counsel)
Mary Mills (Dir-Mktg)
Sarah Griner (Controller)
Paula Mercer (VP-Shared Svcs)
Jason Anderson (CTO)
Evan Foster (Dir-Global)

Subsidiaries:

Sign-A-Rama Inc. (1)
2121 Vista Pkwy, West Palm Beach, FL 33411-2706
Tel.: (561) 640-5570
Web Site:
   http://www.unitedfranchisegroup.com
Sales Range: $10-24.9 Million
Emp.: 100
Sign Franchise Services
N.A.I.C.S.: 533110
Ray W. Titus (Founder & CEO)
A. J. Titus (Pres)

UFOOD RESTAURANT GROUP, INC.

22 A St, Burlington, MA 01803
Tel.: (516) 316-7420   NV
Web Site: http://www.ufoodgrill.com
Year Founded: 2006
Restaurant Operator & Franchisor
N.A.I.C.S.: 722511
Irma Norton (CFO)
Salvatore Rincione (CEO)
Walter Pomerleau (VP-Ops & Mktg)
Bob DiBartolomeo (VP-Franchise Dev)
Kathryn Kaufman (Dir-Ops & Trng)

UFS BANCORP

49 Church St, Whitinsville, MA 01588
Tel.: (508) 234-8112   MA

Web Site: http://www.unibank.com
Year Founded: 1998
Rev.: $69,356,000
Assets: $1,762,615,000
Liabilities: $1,618,533,000
Net Worth: $144,082,000
Earnings: $10,289,000
Emp.: 257
Fiscal Year-end: 12/31/18
Bank Holding Company
N.A.I.C.S.: 551111

Subsidiaries:

UniBank for Savings (1)
49 Church St, Whitinsville, MA 01588
Tel.: (508) 234-8112
Web Site: http://www.unibank.com
Sales Range: $50-74.9 Million
Emp.: 228
Federal Savings Bank
N.A.I.C.S.: 522180
Wendy Brown (VP)
Timothy P. Wickstrom (Chm)
Lemonia Mironidis (VP & Branch Mgr-Customer Rels)
Michael Stone (VP & Branch Mgr-Customer Rels)
Jamie How (VP & Mgr-Consumer Lending)
Ryan D. Landry (Asst VP)
Joseph Vettese (Mgr-Milford)

UGENIUS TECHNOLOGY, LLC.

9950 S 300 W, Sandy, UT 84070
Tel.: (801) 619-5200
Year Founded: 2007
Sales Range: $10-24.9 Million
Computer Technology Development Services
N.A.I.C.S.: 541511
Kurt Forsberg (Dir-Client Svcs)
Travis Lafleur (VP-Engrg)
Gene Pranger (Founder & CEO)
Jed Taylor (Pres & COO)
Joseph Ward (Dir-Creative Svcs)

UHL TRUCK SALES INC.

13450 Hwy 135 NE, Palmyra, IN 47164
Tel.: (812) 364-6101   IN
Web Site:
   http://www.uhltrucksales.com
Year Founded: 1953
Sales Range: $10-24.9 Million
Emp.: 90
Sales of New & Used Trucks, Tractors & Trailers
N.A.I.C.S.: 441110
John Shireman (Gen Mgr)
Bobby Chinn (Mgr-Whole Sale & Retail Truck)

UHRIG CONSTRUCTION INC.

1700 N 5th St, Reading, PA 19601
Tel.: (610) 373-1612
Web Site:
   http://www.uhrigconstruction.com
Year Founded: 2001
Sales Range: $1-9.9 Million
Emp.: 20
General Contracting Specialists in Commercial, Industrial & Residential Construction
N.A.I.C.S.: 236220
Donald M. Uhrig (Pres & Owner)

UHSOME, LLC

3104 N Armenia Ave Ste 2, Tampa, FL 33607
Tel.: (813) 466-2435
Web Site: http://www.uhsome.com
Sales Range: $25-49.9 Million
Emp.: 10
Search Engine Optimization & Digital Media Marketing
N.A.I.C.S.: 541890
Lisa Poole (Member-Mgmt Bd)
Abdulaziz Alzamel (Member-Mgmt Bd)

COMPANIES

Chris Arnoldi (Founder & CEO)
Milan Kostadinovic (Dir-Design)
Mirjana Perovic (Dir-Adv)
Jay Wheaton (Head-Res)
Chris Abbott (Dir-Applications)
Louie Paez (Dir-Ops)

UHY ADVISORS, INC.
30 S Wacker Dr Ste 2850, Chicago, IL 60606-7413
Tel.: (312) 578-9600
Web Site: http://www.uhy-us.com
Sales Range: $150-199.9 Million
Emp.: 1,800
Accounting, Auditing & Bookkeeping Services
N.A.I.C.S.: 541219
Anthony P. Frabotta (Chm)
Harold Mohn (Mng Dir-UHY Advisors Mid-Atlantic MD, Inc.)
Robert Scope (Mng Dir-UHY Advisors MI, Inc.)
Mehmet Sengulen (Mng Dir-UHY Advisors NY, Inc.)
Mike Duska (Sr Mgr-Atlanta)
George Crane (Principal-FLVS & Bus Valuation Svcs Practice-New York)
Jeremy Falendysz (Dir-Corp Fin)
Chelsea Belmonte (Mgr-Internal Audit, Risk & Compliance Practice)
Steve McCarty (CEO)
Mark Witte (Partner-Albany)
Lance Haynes (VP-Fin)

UHY LLP
4 Tower Pl Executive Park 7th Fl, Albany, NY 12203
Tel.: (518) 674-9539
Web Site: https://uhy-us.com
Emp.: 100
Accounting Firm
N.A.I.C.S.: 541211

Subsidiaries:

Paresky Flitt & Company, LLP (1)
14 W Plain St, Wayland, MA 01778
Tel.: (508) 650-1122
Web Site: http://www.pareskyflitt.com
Offices of Certified Public Accountants
N.A.I.C.S.: 541211
Lee D. Paresky (Partner)
Mike Okenquist (Co-Mng Partner-Wayland)
David Lorenzi (Co-Mng Partner-Wayland)

UINTAH BASIN MEDICAL CENTER
250 W 300 N, Roosevelt, UT 84066
Tel.: (435) 722-4691 UT
Web Site: http://www.ubmc.org
Year Founded: 2003
Sales Range: $50-74.9 Million
Emp.: 710
Health Care Srvices
N.A.I.C.S.: 622110
Brent H. Hales (CFO)
Roger Marett (VP-Physician Recruitment)
Jim Marshall (Pres & CEO)

UJA FEDERATION OF NEW YORK
130 E 59th St, New York, NY 10022
Tel.: (212) 980-1000
Web Site: https://www.ujafedny.org
Year Founded: 1917
Educational Support Services
N.A.I.C.S.: 611710

UJENA SWIMWEAR AND FASHION
2544 Leghorn St, Mountain View, CA 94043
Tel.: (650) 948-8901
Web Site: http://www.ujena.com
Year Founded: 1984
Sales Range: $1-9.9 Million
Emp.: 35
Swimwear, Casual & Active Wear Mfr & Retailer
N.A.I.C.S.: 458110
Lisa Anderson-Wall (Pres)

UK HEALTHCARE GOOD SAMARITAN HOSPITAL
310 S Limestone, Lexington, KY 40508-3008
Tel.: (859) 226-7000
Web Site: http://www.samaritanhospital.com
Year Founded: 1866
Sales Range: $25-49.9 Million
Emp.: 550
Hospital
N.A.I.C.S.: 622110
Lanny Adkins (Coord-Clinical)

Subsidiaries:

Samaritan Physical Therapy (1)
125 E Maxell, Lexington, KY 40508
Tel.: (859) 225-1218
Sales Range: $10-24.9 Million
Emp.: 3
General Medical & Surgical Hospitals
N.A.I.C.S.: 621340

UKAS BIG SAVER FOODS INC.
4260 Charter St, Vernon, CA 90058
Tel.: (323) 582-7222
Web Site: http://www.bigsaverfoods.com
Rev.: $65,000,000
Emp.: 425
Grocery Store Operator
N.A.I.C.S.: 445110
Malini Solanki (VP)
Uka Solanki (Pres & CEO)

UKG INC.
2250 N Commerce Pkwy, Weston, FL 33326
Web Site: https://www.ukg.com
Year Founded: 2020
Emp.: 13,000
Software Development Services
N.A.I.C.S.: 541511
Patricia Wadors (Chief People Officer)
Liz McCarron (Chief Legal Officer)
Jennifer Morgan (CEO)
John Butler (CFO)
Mustapha Kebbeh (chief security officer)

UKIAH FORD
1170 S State St, Ukiah, CA 95482-6411
Tel.: (707) 468-0091
Web Site: http://www.ukiahford.org
Year Founded: 1989
Sales Range: $10-24.9 Million
Emp.: 34
Car Whslr
N.A.I.C.S.: 441110
Rob Haskell (Mgr-Parts Dept)

UKPEAGVIK INUPIAT CORPORATION
1250 Agvik St, Barrow, AK 99723
Tel.: (907) 852-4460 AK
Web Site: http://www.uicalaska.com
Year Founded: 1973
Sales Range: $300-349.9 Million
Emp.: 3,000
Native American Investment Holding Company
N.A.I.C.S.: 551112
Price E. Brower (Chm)
Beverly J. Shontz Eliason (Treas)
Walt George (CFO)
Lloyd Kanayurak (VP)
Ethel Akpik (Dir-HR)
Josiah Patkotak (Vice Chm)
Delbert J. Rexford (Pres & CEO)
Jeevan Pokharel (COO)
Terry W. Moore (Sr VP-Ops & UIC Govt Svcs)
Clayton Arterburn (Sr VP-Comml Ops)
Ned T. Arey Sr. (Vice Chm)
Richard Ungarook Sr. (Sec)

Subsidiaries:

Bowhead Manufacturing Company, LLC (1)
1525 Perimeter Pkwy NW Ste 210, Huntsville, AL 35806
Tel.: (256) 382-3260
Web Site: http://www.bowheadsupport.com
Trailer-Mounted Fuel & Water Pump Mfr
N.A.I.C.S.: 333996
Tim Howell (Gen Mgr)

HME Construction, Inc. (1)
6801 N W Old Lower River Rd, Vancouver, WA 98660-1062
Tel.: (360) 695-4553
Heavy & Civil Engineering Construction
N.A.I.C.S.: 237990
Greg Speyer (Gen Mgr)

UIC Commercial Services, LLC (1)
6700 Arctic Spur Rd, Anchorage, AK 99518
Tel.: (907) 677-8299
Web Site: https://uicalaska.com
Holding Compay; Design, Architecture, Construction, Environmental, Oil & Gas support, Marine Transport & Logistics Services
N.A.I.C.S.: 551112

Subsidiary (Domestic):

UMIAQ, LLC (2)
6700 Arctic Spur Rd, Anchorage, AK 99518
Tel.: (907) 677-8220
Web Site: http://www.uicprofessionalservices.com
Architectural, Engineering, Surveying & Construction Project Management Services
N.A.I.C.S.: 541990
Richard S. Reich (Gen Mgr)
Edith Vorderstrasse (Mgr-Resource Dev Div)
Wiley Wilhelm (Mgr-Design Div)
Richard Rearick (Mgr-Architecture Dept)
Ken Robbins (Mgr-Municipal Svcs Div)
Jeff Wilson (Mgr-Oilfield Svcs)
Michael Wolski (Mgr-Engrg Dept)
Ken Pinard (Mgr-Surveying & Mapping Dept)
Cindy Shake (Mgr-Mktg & Comm)

UIC Technical Services, LLC (1)
4900 Seminary Rd Ste 1200, Alexandria, VA 22311
Tel.: (703) 413-4226
Web Site: http://www.bowheadsupport.com
Holding Company; Technical Support Services
N.A.I.C.S.: 551112
Steve Darner (Pres-Products & Solutions Grp)
Anton Geisz (Sr Dir-Ops, Info & Tech Grp)

UKRAINIAN NATIONAL ASSOCIATION, INC.
2200 Route 10, Parsippany, NJ 07054
Tel.: (973) 292-9800 NJ
Web Site: http://www.ukrainiannationalassociation.org
Year Founded: 1894
Sales Range: $25-49.9 Million
Financial Support Services
N.A.I.C.S.: 523999
Michael Koziupa (First VP)
Stefan Kaczaraj (Pres)
Eugene Oscislawski (Second VP)
Myron Groch (Dir-Canada)
Christine E. Kozak (Sec)

UKROP'S HOMESTYLE FOODS, LLC.
2001 Maywill St Ste 100, Richmond, VA 23230
Tel.: (804) 340-3000
Web Site: http://www.ukropshomestylefoods.com
Year Founded: 2010
Sales Range: $10-24.9 Million
Emp.: 390
Food Products Mfr
N.A.I.C.S.: 311999
Robert S. Ukrop (Pres & CEO)
Julie Bishop (Dir-Product Dev & Quality)
Patrick Hadden (Mgr-Food Safety)
Debbie Kunkel (Office Mgr)

ULBRICH STAINLESS STEEL & SPECIAL METALS, INC.
153 Washington Ave, North Haven, CT 06473-1191
Tel.: (203) 239-4481 CT
Web Site: http://www.ulbrich.com
Year Founded: 1924
Sales Range: $150-199.9 Million
Emp.: 700
Rerolled Stainless Steel Strip & Special Metal Strip; Wire, Round, Flat, Shaped Wire
N.A.I.C.S.: 331221
Christian Ulbrich (CEO)

Subsidiaries:

Diversified Ulbrich of Canada (1)
150 New Huntington Road Unit 1, Woodbridge, L4H 4N4, ON, Canada (100%)
Tel.: (416) 663-7130
Web Site: http://www.diversifiedulbrich.ca
Sales Range: $50-74.9 Million
Emp.: 22
Stainless Steel Distr
N.A.I.C.S.: 423510
Etienne Chouinard (Gen Mgr)

Diversified Ulbrich of Canada (1)
20 Hymus Blvd, Pointe-Claire, H9R 1C9, QC, Canada (100%)
Tel.: (514) 694-6522
Sales Range: $75-99.9 Million
Emp.: 30
N.A.I.C.S.: 332618
Etienne Chouinard (Mgr-Canada)

Ulbrich Asia Metals Malaysia Sdn Bhd (1)
Plot 36E Lorong Perindustrian Bukit Minyak 6, 14100, Penang, Malaysia
Tel.: (60) 4 508 5986
Sales Range: $10-24.9 Million
Emp.: 10
Stainless Steel Supplier
N.A.I.C.S.: 423510

Ulbrich Precision Flat Wire, Inc. (1)
692 Plant Rd, Westminster, SC 29693
Tel.: (864) 647-6087
Web Site: http://www.ulbrich.com
Emp.: 220
Precision Flat Wire Mfr & Distr
N.A.I.C.S.: 331221

Ulbrich Precision Special Metals (Suzhou) Co., Ltd. (1)
Building 2 Wei Xin Road WeiTing Zone, Suzhou, 215121, Jiangsu, China
Tel.: (86) 512 6262 5833
Sales Range: $10-24.9 Million
Emp.: 10
Stainless Steel & Metal Distr
N.A.I.C.S.: 423510

Ulbrich Shaped Wire, Inc. (1)
55 Defco Park Rd, North Haven, CT 06473-1129 (100%)
Tel.: (203) 239-4481
Web Site: http://www.ulbrich.com
Sales Range: $10-24.9 Million
Emp.: 70
Stainless Steel & Nickel Alloy Wire
N.A.I.C.S.: 331222
Jay Cei (Pres & COO)
Vivtor Diamato (Mgr-Fin)

Ulbrich Solar Technologies Oregon LLC (1)
22975 NW Evergreen Pkwy Ste 404, Hillsboro, OR 97124
Tel.: (503) 597-6880
Stainless Steel Products Distr

ULBRICH STAINLESS STEEL & SPECIAL METALS, INC.

U.S. PRIVATE

Ulbrich Stainless Steel & Special Metals, Inc.—(Continued)
N.A.I.C.S.: 423510

Ulbrich Solar Technologies, Inc. (1)
692 Plant Rd, Westminster, SC 29693
Tel.: (864) 647-6087
Web Site: http://www.pvribbon.com
Sales Range: $25-49.9 Million
Emp.: 146
PV Ribbon Mfr & Distr
N.A.I.C.S.: 332999
Ed Treglia *(Mng Dir)*

Ulbrich Specialty Strip Mill (1)
1 Dudley Ave, Wallingford, CT 06492-4457 **(100%)**
Tel.: (203) 269-2507
Web Site: http://www.ulbrich.com
Sales Range: $25-49.9 Million
Emp.: 200
Reroll Metal
N.A.I.C.S.: 331221

Ulbrich of California, Inc. (1)
5455 E Home Ave, Fresno, CA 93727-2106 **(100%)**
Tel.: (559) 456-2310
Web Site: http://www.ulbrich.com
Sales Range: $10-24.9 Million
Emp.: 30
Service Center And Stainless Steel Distribution
N.A.I.C.S.: 423510
Christian Ulbrich *(Vice Chm & COO)*
Tom Leblanc *(Gen Mgr)*

Ulbrich of Illinois, Inc. (1)
12340 S Laramie Ave, Alsip, IL 60803
Tel.: (708) 489-9500
Web Site: http://www.ulbrich.com
Sales Range: $10-24.9 Million
Emp.: 70
Service Center
N.A.I.C.S.: 423510
Ed Brandt *(Gen Mgr)*

Ulbrich of New England (1)
153 Washington Ave, North Haven, CT 06473-1119
Tel.: (203) 239-4481
Web Site: http://www.ulbrich.com
Sales Range: $10-24.9 Million
Emp.: 60
Stainless Steel Mfr
N.A.I.C.S.: 332618

Ulbrinox (1)
Avenida La Canada 25 Parque Industrial Bernardo Quintana, Queretaro, Mexico
Tel.: (52) 4422215500
Web Site: http://www.ulbrinox.com.mx
Sales Range: $75-99.9 Million
Emp.: 30
Glass, Door, Plumbing Fixture Retailer
N.A.I.C.S.: 444180
Christian Ulbrich *(CEO)*
Jay Cei *(COO)*

ULINE, INC.
12575 Uline Dr, Pleasant Prairie, WI 53158
Tel.: (847) 473-3000   DE
Web Site: https://www.uline.com
Year Founded: 1980
Sales Range: $400-449.9 Million
Emp.: 9,000
Industrial & Personal Service Paper Merchant Wholesalers
N.A.I.C.S.: 424130
Elisabeth Uihlein *(Pres)*
Mike Mally *(Sr Mgr-Mdsg)*
Bruce L. Peterson *(CIO)*
Melissa Thompson *(Controller)*
Andy Park *(Dir-Distr)*
Mackenzie Bestold *(Mgr-Customer Acq)*
Melanie Freeman *(Mgr-Mdse)*
Matt Charnon *(Product Mgr)*
Stephanie Conrardy *(Product Mgr)*
Robert Holst *(Product Mgr)*
Jason Miller *(Product Mgr)*
Justin Wisneski *(Product Mgr)*
Frank Unick *(CFO)*
Harry Vosganian *(Dir-Freight)*
Dan Schlagenhaft *(Mgr-Sls-Natl)*
Cindy Hahn *(Project Mgr-IT)*
Elizabeth Tenner *(Sr Dir-Creative)*
Sara Jaramillo *(Sr Mgr-Circulation)*
Brian Uihlein *(VP-Mdsg)*
Duke Uihlein *(VP)*
Richard E. Uihlein *(CEO)*
Dick Uihlein *(CEO)*

ULLA POPKEN LTD.
12201 Long Green Pk, Glen Arm, MD 21057
Tel.: (410) 592-9190
Web Site: http://www.ullapopken.com
Sales Range: $10-24.9 Million
Emp.: 50
Women's Clothing Retailer
N.A.I.C.S.: 458110

ULLAND BROTHERS INC.
1634 Hwy 210, Carlton, MN 55718-8176
Tel.: (218) 384-4266   MN
Web Site: http://www.ulland.com
Year Founded: 1954
Sales Range: $25-49.9 Million
Emp.: 200
Highway & Street Construction
N.A.I.C.S.: 237310
Michael Welch *(Pres)*
Lance Strandberg *(CFO-Cloquet)*
Orlin Ofstad *(Exec VP-Hibbing)*
Jeff Carlson *(VP-Albert Lea)*

ULLICO INC.
1625 Eye St NW, Washington, DC 20006
Tel.: (202) 682-0900
Web Site: http://www.ullico.com
Year Founded: 1927
Rev: $269,198,000
Assets: $4,097,495,000
Liabilities: $3,924,229,000
Net Worth: $173,266,000
Earnings: $31,216,000
Fiscal Year-end: 12/31/18
Insurance Holding Company
N.A.I.C.S.: 551112
Joseph J. Hunt *(Chm)*
Edward M. Smith *(Pres & CEO)*
David J. Barra *(CFO & Sr VP)*
Herbert A. Kolben *(Sr VP-Real Estate Investment Grp & Union Labor Life Insurance)*
Brian J. Hale *(COO & Sr VP)*
Patrick McGlone *(Chief Compliance Officer, Gen Counsel & Sr VP)*
Joseph R. Linehan *(Pres-Ulico Investment Advisors & Ullico Investment Company)*
Sean McGarvey *(Treas & Sec)*
Larry J. Paradise *(VP-Grp Sls)*
Tina J. Fletcher *(Pres-Ullico Casualty Grp, Inc)*
Robert Ship *(VP-Midwest Reg)*
William H. Weeks *(VP-Northwest Reg)*
Stephanie Whalen *(Pres-The Union Labor Life Insurance Company)*
Kerrie Lowery *(VP-Ops)*

Subsidiaries:

Hope Utilities (1)
184 Shuman Blvd Ste 300, Naperville, IL 60563
Tel.: (844) 488-0530
Web Site: http://hopeutilities.com
Utility Services; Natural Gas & Water & Waste Wastewater Utilities
N.A.I.C.S.: 221210
Morgan O'Brien *(CEO)*

Subsidiary (Domestic):

Hope Gas, Inc. (2)
48 Columbia Blvd, Clarksburg, WV 26301
Tel.: (304) 623-8600
Natural Gas Distr
N.A.I.C.S.: 221210

Subsidiary (Domestic):

Southern Public Service Co, Inc. (3)
1075 Main St, Milton, WV 25541
Tel.: (304) 743-1700
Sales Range: $1-9.9 Million
Emp.: 21
Natural Gas Distr
N.A.I.C.S.: 221210
Theresa Williamson *(DP)*

Student Transportation Inc. (1)
3349 Highway 138 Building A, Ste C, Wall Township, NJ 07719
Tel.: (732) 280-4200
Web Site: https://ridesta.com
School & Charter Bus Transportation Services
N.A.I.C.S.: 485410
Patrick J. Walker *(CFO)*
Patrick Vaughan *(CEO)*
Gene Kowalczewski *(COO)*
Kirk Wilkie *(Sr VP-Central & Western Operations)*

Subsidiary (Domestic):

Student Transportation of America, Inc. (2)
3349 Hwy 138 Bldg B Ste D, Wall, NJ 07719-9671
Web Site: http://www.ridesta.com
School & Charter Bus Transportation Services
N.A.I.C.S.: 485410
Denis J. Gallagher *(VP-Ops)*
Shelly Hall *(Sr VP-Health & Safety)*

Subsidiary (Domestic):

Rick Bus Company, Inc. (3)
1399 Lower Ferry Rd, Ewing, NJ 08618
Tel.: (609) 392-7550
School Buses
N.A.I.C.S.: 485510

Subsidiary (Non-US):

Student Transportation of Canada, Inc. (3)
160 Saunders Road Unit 6, Barrie, L4N 9A4, ON, Canada
Tel.: (705) 721-2626
Web Site: http://www.ridestc.com
Student Transportation
N.A.I.C.S.: 485410

Subsidiary (Domestic):

Parkview Transit (4)
95 Forhan Ave, Newmarket, L3Y 8X6, ON, Canada
Tel.: (905) 775-5331
Web Site: http://www.parkviewtransit.ca
School Bus Transportation Services
N.A.I.C.S.: 485113

The Union Labor Life Insurance Co. (1)
8403 Colesville Rd, Silver Spring, MD 20910 **(100%)**
Tel.: (202) 682-0900
Web Site: http://www.ullico.com
Rev.: $348,000,000
Emp.: 645
Insurance
N.A.I.C.S.: 524113
Ed Smith *(Sr Exec VP)*
Mark Zinsmeister *(Mgr-HR)*

ULLICO Casualty Company (1)
1625 Eye St NW, Washington, DC 20006
Tel.: (202) 682-0900
Web Site: http://www.ullico.com
Sales Range: $25-49.9 Million
Emp.: 40
Property & Casualty Insurance
N.A.I.C.S.: 524126

ULLICO Inc. (1)
PO Box 6900, Corona, CA 92878-5131 **(100%)**
Tel.: (951) 279-0073
Rev.: $6,000,000
Emp.: 7
Property Damage Insurance
N.A.I.C.S.: 524126

ULLICO Indemnity (1)
1625 Eye St NW, Washington, DC 20006 **(100%)**
Tel.: (202) 682-0900
Sales Range: $25-49.9 Million
Emp.: 10
Excess & Surplus Lines Reinsurer
N.A.I.C.S.: 524126
Karen Micklish *(Dir-Compensation & HRIS)*

ULLICO Investment Advisors, Inc. (1)
8403 Colesville Rd 13FL, Silver Spring, MD 20910 **(100%)**
Tel.: (202) 682-7927
Web Site: http://www.ullico.com
Sales Range: $50-74.9 Million
Emp.: 80
Investment Managment Company
N.A.I.C.S.: 523940
Cathy Humphrey *(COO)*

ULLICO Mortgage Corporation (1)
1625 Eye St N W, Washington, DC 20006
Tel.: (800) 431-5425
Insurance Brokerage Services
N.A.I.C.S.: 524210

Ulico Standard of America Casualty Company (1)
1625 Eye St NW, Washington, DC 20006
Tel.: (202) 682-0900
Property & Casualty Insurance Services
N.A.I.C.S.: 524126

Ullico Casualty Group, Inc. (1)
1625 Eye St NW, Washington, DC 20006
Tel.: (888) 315-3352
Property & Casualty Insurance Services
N.A.I.C.S.: 524126
Ed Titus *(VP-Surety)*
Daniel Aronowitz *(Pres)*
Michael Cundiff *(Asst VP)*
Dennis Ferretti *(Mgr-Underwriting)*
Mike Hall *(Mgr-Underwriting)*

Ullico Investment Company, Inc. (1)
1625 Eye St NW, Washington, DC 20006-4061
Tel.: (800) 431-5425
Investment Management Service
N.A.I.C.S.: 523940

Union Standard of America Life Insurance Co. (1)
1625 Eye St NW, Washington, DC 20006-1461 **(100%)**
Tel.: (202) 682-0900
Web Site: http://www.ullico.com
Life Insurance & Health Products
N.A.I.C.S.: 524114

Zenith Administrators, Inc. (1)
5565 Sterrett Pl Ste 210, Columbia, MD 21044-2604 **(100%)**
Tel.: (410) 884-1440
Web Site: http://www.zenithtpa.com
Rev.: $46,000,000
Emp.: 700
Provider of Administrative Services
N.A.I.C.S.: 525110
Kathy Brennan *(Asst Mgr-Client Svcs)*

ULLIMAN SCHUTTE CONSTRUCTION LLC
9111 Springboro Pike, Miamisburg, OH 45342
Tel.: (937) 910-9900
Web Site: http://www.ullimanschutte.com
Sales Range: $150-199.9 Million
Emp.: 300
Waste Water & Sewage Treatment Plant Construction
N.A.I.C.S.: 237110
Herbert T. Schutte *(CEO)*
Cynthia Martin *(CFO)*

ULLMAN DEVICES CORPORATION
664 Danbury Rd, Ridgefield, CT 06877-2720
Tel.: (203) 438-6577
Web Site: http://www.ntplx.net
Year Founded: 1935
Sales Range: $50-74.9 Million
Emp.: 40

Work Inspection Mirrors, Magnetic Tools, Piston Ring Compressors, Screw Starters
N.A.I.C.S.: 332216
Edward Coleman (Pres)

ULLMAN OIL, INC.
9812 E Washington St, Chagrin Falls, OH 44023-5486
Tel.: (440) 543-5195 OH
Web Site: http://www.ullmanoil.com
Year Founded: 1966
Sales Range: $125-149.9 Million
Emp.: 42
Fuel Dealer & Petroleum Product Whslr
N.A.I.C.S.: 457210
Kim Ullman (Pres)

Subsidiaries:

Swiss Valley Oil Co.   (1)
9812 E Washington St, Chagrin Falls, OH 44023
Tel.: (330) 852-4631
Web Site: http://www.ullmanoil.com
Rev.: $15,000,000
Emp.: 12
Fuel Dealers
N.A.I.C.S.: 457210

ULRICH MOTOR COMPANY
1130 W 16th St, Pella, IA 50219-7577
Tel.: (641) 628-2184
Web Site: http://www.ulrichford.com
Year Founded: 1935
Sales Range: $10-24.9 Million
Emp.: 40
Car Whslr
N.A.I.C.S.: 441110
Charles VanderWaal (Co-Owner)
Marla VanderWaal (Co-Owner)
Todd Vander Waal (Gen Mgr)

ULSTER ELECTRIC SUPPLY CO. INC.
9 Cornell St, Kingston, NY 12401
Tel.: (845) 331-5653
Web Site:
   http://www.ulsterelectric.com
Sales Range: $10-24.9 Million
Emp.: 20
Electrical Apparatus & Equipment
N.A.I.C.S.: 423610
Barry Gruberg (Pres & CEO)

ULSTER SAVINGS BANK
180 Schwenk Dr, Kingston, NY 12401-2940
Tel.: (845) 338-6322 NY
Web Site:
   http://www.ulstersavings.com
Year Founded: 1851
Sales Range: $50-74.9 Million
Emp.: 300
Federal Savings Institutions
N.A.I.C.S.: 522180
Debra Benn (Mgr-Woodstock)
Kristin Bauer (Mgr-New Paltz)
Jose Lemus (Mgr-Newburgh)
Michael Janasiewicz (Asst VP-Ops)
Ann M. Marrott (Sec)
William Calderara (Pres & CEO)
Anique Morrison (Officer-Comml Bus)

ULTA-LIT TECHNOLOGIES INC.
1989 Johns Dr, Glenview, IL 60025-1615
Tel.: (847) 729-4022
Web Site:
   http://www.lightkeeperpro.com
Year Founded: 1996
Sales Range: $1-9.9 Million
Emp.: 10
Product that Repairs LED Light Sets
N.A.I.C.S.: 335139

John DeCosmo (Pres)
Jerry Cepa (VP)
Linda Barrientos (Mgr-Sls & Mktg)
Connie Bergstrom (Controller)

ULTIMATE ACQUISITION PARTNERS, L.P.
321 West 84th Ave Ste A, Thornton, CO 80260
Tel.: (303) 412-2500
Sales Range: $700-749.9 Million
Emp.: 3,500
Investment Services; Electronics Stores
N.A.I.C.S.: 523999
Mark J. Wattles (Owner, Chm & CEO)
Mark D. Shapiro (CFO)
Jim Pearse (Pres)

ULTIMATE EVERCARE HOLDINGS, LLC
3440 Preston Rdg Rd Ste 650, Alpharetta, GA 30005
Tel.: (770) 570-5000 DE
Year Founded: 2012
Holding Company; Wardrobe, Home & Pet Care Sanitation Products Mfr
N.A.I.C.S.: 551112
Robert B. Kay (Chm & CEO)

Subsidiaries:

The Evercare Company   (1)
3440 Preston Ridge Rd Ste 650, Alpharetta, GA 30005-5455
Tel.: (770) 570-5000
Web Site: http://www.evercare.com
Sales Range: $100-124.9 Million
Emp.: 200
Wardrobe, Home & Pet Care Products Mfr & Distr
N.A.I.C.S.: 339999
Mike Ortale (VP-Sls)
Dave Stauffer (Controller)
Jarrod Streng (VP-Mktg)
Tim Young (CMO & VP-Mktg & Bus Dev)
Mary Ogg (Dir-HR)
Robert Bruce Kay (Chm & CEO)

ULTIMATE JETCHARTERS, INC.
6061 W Airport Dr, North Canton, OH 44720
Tel.: (330) 497-3344 OH
Web Site:
   http://www.ultimatejetcharters.com
Year Founded: 1984
Private Charter & Jet Services
N.A.I.C.S.: 488119
Eddie Moneypenny (Dir-Sls & Mktg)
Dave Parsons (Dir-Ops)

ULTIMATE NURSING SERVICES OF IOWA, INC.
6750 Westown Pkwy Ste 115, West Des Moines, IA 50266-7716
Tel.: (515) 280-2160
Web Site:
   http://www.ultimatenursing.com
Year Founded: 1995
Rev.: $8,100,000
Emp.: 350
Nursing Care Facilities
N.A.I.C.S.: 623110
Connie Anderson (Pres)

ULTIMATE PRECISION METAL PRODUCTS
200 Finn Ct, Farmingdale, NY 11735
Tel.: (631) 293-6330
Web Site:
   http://www.ultimateprecision.com
Year Founded: 1971
Sales Range: $10-24.9 Million
Emp.: 80
Stamping Metal
N.A.I.C.S.: 332119

Michael Mallia (CEO)

ULTIMATE RACK, INC.
5600 Tennyson Pkwy Ste 330, Plano, TX 75024
Tel.: (972) 608-4300 NV
Web Site:
   http://www.ultimaterackinc.com
Year Founded: 2010
Emp.: 2
Bicycle Vehicle Mounted Racks Mfr
N.A.I.C.S.: 336991
Robert Oblon (Chm & CEO)
Kevin Bobryk (Pres & COO)

ULTIMATE SUPPORT SYSTEMS INC.
5836 Wright Dr, Loveland, CO 80538
Tel.: (970) 493-4488
Web Site:
   http://www.ultimatesupport.com
Sales Range: $10-24.9 Million
Emp.: 50
Bicycle Stand Mfr
N.A.I.C.S.: 336991
Mike Belitz (CEO)
Doug Towne (Bus Dir)

ULTIMATE TECHNOLOGIES GROUP, INC.
8594 E 116th St, Fishers, IN 46038
Tel.: (317) 214-8710
Web Site:
   http://www.ultimatetechnologies
   group.com
Year Founded: 2017
Investment Companies
N.A.I.C.S.: 523999
William F. O'Brien (Pres)
Tiffany O'Brien (Owner)

Subsidiaries:

Electronic Evolutions, Inc.   (1)
525 Congressional Blvd, Carmel, IN 46032-5647
Tel.: (317) 848-7503
Web Site:
   http://www.electronicevolutions.com
Radio, Television & Other Electronics Stores
N.A.I.C.S.: 449210
Daniel Knotts (Pres)
Lee Bellomy (CTO)
Julie Knotts (CEO)
Tami Koch (VP-Sls & Mktg)
Heather Sarber (VP-Fin)

ULTIMATE TECHNOLOGY CORPORATION
100 Rawson Rd, Victor, NY 14564-1170
Tel.: (585) 924-9500 NY
Web Site: http://www.utcretail.com
Year Founded: 1988
Sales Range: $10-24.9 Million
Emp.: 100
Point of Sale Displays, Terminals, Keyboards & Peripheral Devices Mfr
N.A.I.C.S.: 334118
Samuel J. Villanti (Pres & CEO)
Karen L.F. Palmer (CFO & VP)
Randy Hems (VP-Hardware Solutions)

ULTIMO SOFTWARE SOLUTIONS, INC.
2860 Zanker Rd Ste 203, San Jose, CA 95134
Tel.: (408) 943-1490 CA
Web Site: http://www.ultimosoft.com
Year Founded: 2003
Sales Range: $1-9.9 Million
Emp.: 125
Software Services
N.A.I.C.S.: 541511

Subhash Pasumarthy (Pres & Co-CEO)
Smita Pasumarthy (Co-CEO & Exec VP)

ULTRA ADDITIVES INC.
1455 Broad St Ste 3, Bloomfield, NJ 07003
Tel.: (973) 279-1306
Sales Range: $10-24.9 Million
Emp.: 55
Paints & Paint Additives
N.A.I.C.S.: 325510
Jean Schaefle (Pres)
Frank Portaro (VP)

ULTRA INC.
504 Jenson Ave SE, Watertown, SD 57201
Tel.: (605) 882-1555
Web Site:
   http://www.connectingpoint.biz
Sales Range: $50-74.9 Million
Emp.: 50
Computer & Software Stores
N.A.I.C.S.: 449210
Bryan Waege (Pres)

ULTRA POWER CORP.
85 Kaufman Rd, Monticello, NY 12701
Tel.: (845) 794-4200
Sales Range: $10-24.9 Million
Emp.: 12
Fuel Oil
N.A.I.C.S.: 424720
Michael Hochman (Pres & CEO)
Michael Card (Controller)

ULTRA TECHNOLOGIES INC.
2750 Killarney Dr Ste 207, Woodbridge, VA 22192-4124
Tel.: (703) 897-9000 MD
Web Site: http://www.ultra-tech.com
Year Founded: 1986
Sales Range: $10-24.9 Million
Emp.: 55
Provider of Computer Systems Analyst & Design Services
N.A.I.C.S.: 541512
Beauford White (Pres & CEO)

ULTRA WHEEL COMPANY INC.
570A N Gilbert St, Fullerton, CA 92833-2549
Tel.: (714) 994-1444
Web Site: http://www.ultrawheel.com
Year Founded: 1984
Rev.: $41,400,000
Emp.: 30
Mfr of Motor Vehicle Parts & Accessories
N.A.I.C.S.: 336390
James Smith (Pres)

Subsidiaries:

Dallas Wheels & Accessories Inc.   (1)
1668 Sands Pl SE, Marietta, GA 30067-8765
Tel.: (817) 640-7575
Sales Range: $10-24.9 Million
Emp.: 5
Motor Vehicle Supplies & New Parts
N.A.I.C.S.: 423120

ULTRA-CHEM INC.
8043 Flint St, Lenexa, KS 66214
Tel.: (913) 492-2929
Web Site: http://www.ultra-cheminc.com
Sales Range: $10-24.9 Million
Emp.: 150
Mfr of Chemicals & Allied Products
N.A.I.C.S.: 424690

ULTRA-CHEM INC.

Ultra-Chem Inc.—(Continued)
Patricia A. Crane (VP)
Tim Mc Candless (Controller)
John P. Crane Sr. (Pres)

ULTRAEX, INC.
2633 Barrington Ct, Hayward, CA 94545
Tel.: (510) 723-3760   CA
Web Site: http://www.ultraex.com
Year Founded: 1983
Courier & Messenger Service
N.A.I.C.S.: 561499
Bill Carlson (Mgr-Bus Dev)

ULTRAFAB INC.
1050 Hook Rd, Farmington, NY 14425
Tel.: (585) 924-2186
Web Site: http://www.ultrafab.com
Rev.: $23,832,715
Emp.: 264
Manufactures Weather Stripping
N.A.I.C.S.: 313110
Robert C. Horton (Chm & CEO)
Tom Hare (CFO & VP-Fin)
Rich Arvidson (Chief Engr)
Alan DeMello (Pres)

ULTRAFLEX SYSTEMS INC.
1578 Sussex Tpke Bldg 4, Randolph, NJ 07869
Tel.: (973) 627-8608   NJ
Web Site: http://www.ultraflexx.com
Year Founded: 1984
Sales Range: $10-24.9 Million
Emp.: 35
Textile Mill
N.A.I.C.S.: 313210
Frank Salek (CFO)
Matt Loede (Dir-Mktg & Product Dev)
John Schleicher Jr. (CEO)

ULTRAMATICS, INC.
720 Brooker Creek Blvd Ste 220, Oldsmar, FL 34677
Tel.: (813) 891-0300
Web Site: http://www.ultramatics.com
Year Founded: 2001
Sales Range: $1-9.9 Million
Emp.: 50
Custom Computer Programing Related Service
N.A.I.C.S.: 541511
Sarazanan Seshadri (Founder, Chm & CTO)
Sri Sridharan (CEO)
Susan Gork (Acct Mgr)
Michael Higney (Mgr-HR)

ULTRASOURCE LLC
1414 W 29th St, Kansas City, MO 64108-3604
Tel.: (816) 753-2150   MO
Web Site: http://www.ultrasourceusa.com
Year Founded: 1883
Sales Range: $75-99.9 Million
Emp.: 70
Packaging Machines, Machinery Equipment & Supplies for Meat Handling, Commercial Kitchens, Sausage Makers, Locker Plants, Food Retailers, Laboratories & Automated Production Lines
N.A.I.C.S.: 333993
John D. Starr (Owner)
Steve Kingeter (Pres)
Scott Lickteig (Engr-Mechanical Design)
Chris Isom (CEO)

ULTRATEC, INC.
450 Science Dr, Madison, WI 53711
Tel.: (608) 238-5400

Web Site: http://www.ultratec.com
Rev.: $28,700,000
Emp.: 300
Telephone Apparatus Mfr
N.A.I.C.S.: 334210
Robert M. Engelke (Founder & Pres)
Pam Holmes (Dir-Construction & Reg Affairs & Cap Tel Customer Svc)

ULTROID TECHNOLOGIES, INC.
3140 W Kennedy Blvd Ste 103, Tampa, FL 33609
Tel.: (727) 898-0717
Web Site: http://www.ultroid.com
Sales Range: $1-9.9 Million
Emp.: 20
Medical Device Mfr
N.A.I.C.S.: 339112

ULYSSES MANAGEMENT, LLC
1 Rockefeller Plz 20th Fl, New York, NY 10020
Tel.: (212) 455-6237
Web Site: http://www.ulyssesmgmt.com
Year Founded: 1997
Rev.: $1,000,000,000
Emp.: 90
Privater Equity Firm
N.A.I.C.S.: 523999
Paul D. Barnett (Mng Dir-Private Equity Grp)
Toby Rando (Mng Dir)

Subsidiaries:

Ice House America, LLC   (1)
13901 Sutton Park Dr S Bldg A Ste 100, Jacksonville Beach, FL 32224
Tel.: (904) 241-7535
Web Site: http://www.icehouseamerica.com
Sales Range: $1-9.9 Million
Emp.: 27
Consumer Goods Rental
N.A.I.C.S.: 532289
Michael Little (VP-Sls & Mktg)
Mark Mueller (CFO)
Troy Doom (CEO)

UM HOLDINGS LIMITED
56 Haddon Ave, Haddonfield, NJ 08033-2438
Tel.: (856) 354-2200   NJ
Web Site: http://www.umholdings.com
Year Founded: 1973
Rev.: $44,000,000
Emp.: 450
Medical Providers Services
N.A.I.C.S.: 551112
Joan P. Carter (Co-Founder & Pres)
John Aglialoro (Co-Founder & Chm)

Subsidiaries:

Cutler-Owens International Ltd. Inc.   (1)
40 E 52nd St, New York, NY 10022-5911
Tel.: (212) 688-4222
Web Site: http://www.gymsource.com
Fitness Equipment
N.A.I.C.S.: 459110
Ed Pryts (VP-Sls & Mktg)
Danny Musico (Partner-Strategic)

EHE, Inc.   (1)
10 Rockefeller Plz 4th FL, New York, NY 10020-1903   (100%)
Tel.: (212) 332-3700
Sales Range: $10-24.9 Million
Emp.: 100
Provides Physical Examination Services to Corporate Clients & Individuals
N.A.I.C.S.: 621999
Susan Spear (Sr VP-Medical Affairs)
Tanla Elliot (Chief Medical Officer)
Shaun Francis (Chm)
David Levy (CEO)

UMASS MEMORIAL HEALTH CARE, INC.
365 Plantation St Biotech One, Worcester, MA 01605
Tel.: (508) 334-1000
Web Site: http://www.umassmemorialhealthcare.org
Health Care Srvices
N.A.I.C.S.: 621399
Eric Dickson (Pres & CEO)

UMATILLA ELECTRIC COOPERATIVE INC.
750 W Elm Ave, Hermiston, OR 97838
Tel.: (541) 567-6414   OR
Web Site: http://www.umatillaelectric.com
Year Founded: 1937
Sales Range: $25-49.9 Million
Emp.: 78
Electronic Services
N.A.I.C.S.: 221122

UMBC TRAINING CENTERS
6996 Columbia Gateway Dr Ste 100, Columbia, MD 21046
Tel.: (443) 692-6600
Web Site: http://www.umbctraining.com
Sales Range: $1-9.9 Million
Emp.: 24
Professional Training Services
N.A.I.C.S.: 611430
Gib Mason (COO & VP-Fin & Admin)
Jon Lau (CTO & VP)
Carolyn Boehm (Dir-Trng Ops)
Homer Minnick (Dir-Center for Cybersecurity Trng)

UMBRA INC.
1705 Broadway St, Buffalo, NY 14212-2030
Tel.: (716) 892-8852   NY
Web Site: http://www.umbra.com
Year Founded: 1984
Sales Range: $25-49.9 Million
Emp.: 200
Wholesale of Home Furnishings
N.A.I.C.S.: 423220
Les Mandelbaum (Founder & Pres)

UMC ACQUISITION CORP.
10807 Stanford Ave, Lynwood, CA 90262-1837
Tel.: (310) 886-1750   DE
Web Site: http://www.universalmold.com
Year Founded: 1994
Sales Range: $10-24.9 Million
Emp.: 260
Metal Products & Services
N.A.I.C.S.: 331491
Dominick Baione (Chm)
James Baione (Pres)

Subsidiaries:

Anaheim Extrusion Co. Inc.   (1)
1330 N Kraemer Blvd, Anaheim, CA 92816
Tel.: (714) 630-3111
Web Site: http://www.anaheimextrude.com
Sales Range: $10-24.9 Million
Emp.: 75
Provider of Aluminum Extruded Products
N.A.I.C.S.: 331318

Universal Molding Company Inc.   (1)
10807 Stanford Ave, Lynwood, CA 90262-1837
Tel.: (310) 886-1750
Web Site: http://www.universalmold.com
Metal Products & Services
N.A.I.C.S.: 331491

Subsidiary (Domestic):

RACO Interior Products, Inc.   (2)
7354 Denny Rd Ste 100, Houston, TX 77055-2623
Tel.: (323) 264-1670

U.S. PRIVATE

Web Site: http://www.racointeriors.com
Interior Aluminum Doors, Frames & Wall Systems Mfr
N.A.I.C.S.: 332321
Abbie Scheliga (Project Mgr)

Universal Molding Extrusion Co.   (1)
9151 Imperial Hwy, Downey, CA 90242-2808   (100%)
Tel.: (562) 940-0300
Web Site: http://www.universalmold.com
Sales Range: $10-24.9 Million
Emp.: 29
Provider of Aluminum Extruded Products
N.A.I.C.S.: 331318

Subsidiary (Domestic):

International Extrusion Corp.   (2)
202 Singleton Dr, Waxahachie, TX 75165-5012
Tel.: (972) 937-7032
Web Site: http://www.intlextrusion.com
Aluminum Extrusions Mfr
N.A.I.C.S.: 331318
Mitch Whitehead (Gen Mgr)

International Window Corp.   (2)
1551 E Orangethorpe, Fullerton, CA 92831
Tel.: (562) 928-6411
Web Site: http://www.intlwindow.com
Mfr of Aluminum & Vinyl Residential Window & Doors
N.A.I.C.S.: 332321

Subsidiary (Domestic):

International Window Corp. - Northern California   (3)
30526 San Antonio St, Hayward, CA 94544-7102
Tel.: (510) 487-1122
Web Site: http://www.intlwindow.com
Mfr of Aluminum & Vinyl Residential Windows & Doors
N.A.I.C.S.: 332321
Rick Johnson (Gen Mgr)

UMI COMPANY, INC.
1520 S 5th St, Hopkins, MN 55343
Tel.: (952) 935-8431
Web Site: http://www.spantek.com
Sales Range: $25-49.9 Million
Emp.: 100
Metal Products Mfr
N.A.I.C.S.: 332119
David R. Carlsen (CEO)
Brian Beich (CFO)

Subsidiaries:

UMI Company, Inc. - Spantek Division   (1)
1520 S 5th St, Hopkins, MN 55343
Tel.: (952) 935-8431
Web Site: http://www.spantek.com
Fabricated Structural Metal Mfr
N.A.I.C.S.: 332312
Mike Gilboy (Gen Mgr)

Plant (Domestic):

UMI Company, Inc. - MINNEAPOLIS PLANT   (2)
1520 S 5th St, Hopkins, MN 55343
Tel.: (952) 935-8431
Emp.: 28
Fabricated Structural Metal Mfr
N.A.I.C.S.: 332312

UMINA BROS INC.
1601 E Olympic Blvd Ste 405, Los Angeles, CA 90021-1936
Tel.: (213) 622-9206   CA
Web Site: http://www.umina.com
Year Founded: 1973
Sales Range: $10-24.9 Million
Emp.: 60
Fresh Fruits & Vegetables
N.A.I.C.S.: 424480
Richard Flamminio (Pres)
Victor Grosso (Controller)
James Monarrez (Asst Controller)

UMLAUT

123 Townsend St Ste 100, San Francisco, CA 94107
Tel.: (415) 777-0123
Web Site:
http://www.umlautfilms.com
Sales Range: $10-24.9 Million
Emp.: 12
Production, Production (Ad, Film, Broadcast), T.V.
N.A.I.C.S.: 541890
Gina LoCurcio *(Exec Producer)*
Heather Gibbons *(Gen Mgr)*

UMPQUA DAIRY PRODUCTS CO. INC.
333 SE Sykes Ave, Roseburg, OR 97470-3414
Tel.: (541) 672-2638 OR
Web Site:
http://www.umpquadairy.com
Year Founded: 1930
Sales Range: $25-49.9 Million
Emp.: 156
Fluid Milk
N.A.I.C.S.: 311511
Douglas Feldkamp *(Pres)*
Steve Feldkamp *(COO)*
Marty Weaver *(Dir-Sls-Mktg)*

UMPQUA INSURANCE AGENCY INC.
808 SE Lane Ave, Roseburg, OR 97470
Tel.: (541) 672-3348
Web Site:
http://www.umpquainsurance.com
Rev.: $14,000,000
Emp.: 20
Insurance Agents, Brokers & Service
N.A.I.C.S.: 524210
Brian R. Pargeter *(Owner & Pres)*
Rick Holland *(Branch Mgr-Adv)*
Jason Pargeter *(Owner)*

UMSI INCORPORATED
125 Lincoln Blvd, Middlesex, NJ 08846-1060
Tel.: (732) 805-0200
Web Site: http://www.umsiinc.com
Year Founded: 1966
Sales Range: $1-9.9 Million
Emp.: 3
Magic Supplies Mail Order
N.A.I.C.S.: 459120
Robert Bokor *(Pres)*

UNA VEZ MAS, LP
703 McKinney Ave Ste 240, Dallas, TX 75202
Tel.: (214) 754-7008
Year Founded: 2002
Sales Range: $1-9.9 Million
Emp.: 70
Television Broadcasting
N.A.I.C.S.: 516120
Roel Medina *(VP & Gen Mgr-Houston)*
Susan Kretschmar *(VP-Sls)*

UNACAST, INC.
152 E Putnam Ave., Cos Cob, CT 06807-9984
Tel.: (646) 300-0708
Web Site: https://www.unacast.com
Year Founded: 2014
IT System Data Services
N.A.I.C.S.: 513210
Thomas Walle *(Co-Founder & CEO)*
Subsidiaries:

Gravy Analytics, Inc. (1)
45610 Woodland Rd Ste 100, Dulles, VA 20166
Tel.: (703) 840-8850
Web Site: http://www.gravyanalytics.com
Sales Range: $1-9.9 Million
Advertising Agency Services
N.A.I.C.S.: 541810
Jeff White *(Pres)*

UNADILLA SILO COMPANY INC.
18 Clifton St, Unadilla, NY 13849-3361
Tel.: (607) 369-9341 NY
Web Site: http://www.unalam.com
Year Founded: 1906
Emp.: 50
Laminated Wood Arches & Beams Mfr
N.A.I.C.S.: 321215
Subsidiaries:

Unadilla Laminated Products (1)
18 Clifton St, Unadilla, NY 13849
Tel.: (607) 369-9341
Web Site: http://www.unalam.com
Sales Range: $25-49.9 Million
Emp.: 65
Provider of Laminated Products
N.A.I.C.S.: 321215
Craig Van Cott *(Pres)*

UNAKA COMPANY INC.
1500 Industrial Rd, Greeneville, TN 37745
Tel.: (423) 639-1171 TN
Web Site: http://www.unaka.com
Year Founded: 1989
Sales Range: $10-24.9 Million
Emp.: 120
Provider of Special Food Preparation, Warehousing & Distribution Services
N.A.I.C.S.: 311991
Robert Austin Jr. *(CEO)*
Subsidiaries:

Crown Point Ltd. (1)
118 S Cypress St, Mullins, SC 29574-3004
Tel.: (843) 464-8165
Web Site: http://www.crownpt.com
Sales Range: $10-24.9 Million
Emp.: 9
Supplier of Farm Supplies
N.A.I.C.S.: 424590
Kevin Gates *(Pres)*

Sopakco Inc. (1)
102 Coile St, Greeneville, TN 37745
Tel.: (423) 639-1163
Web Site: http://www.sopakcotn.com
Sales Range: $10-24.9 Million
Emp.: 50
Provider of Food Preparation Services
N.A.I.C.S.: 493190
Larry Schofield *(Mgr-Safety)*

UNBOUNDED SOLUTIONS
1180 W Peachtree St Nw Ste 600, Atlanta, GA 30309-3483
Tel.: (678) 754-9994 GA
Web Site:
http://www.theunbounded.com
Year Founded: 2000
Sales Range: $1-9.9 Million
Emp.: 50
Information Technology Services & Software Consulting in Enterprise Content Management, Enterprise Application Integration & Customer Relations Management
N.A.I.C.S.: 541690
Vik Thadani *(Founder & CEO)*
Bill Sengstacken *(VP-Mktg)*
Aman Vohra *(COO)*
Olga Bogachek *(Mgr-HR)*

UNCAS MANUFACTURING COMPANY
150 Niantic Ave, Providence, RI 02907-3118
Tel.: (401) 944-4700 RI
Web Site: http://www.uncas.com
Year Founded: 1911
Sales Range: $75-99.9 Million
Emp.: 150
Costume Jewelry Mfr
N.A.I.C.S.: 339910
Michael Britto *(VP-Fin)*
John Corsini *(Owner)*
Subsidiaries:

Uncas (HK) Company Ltd. (1)
Room 1708-1712 Sterling Centre 11 Cheung Yue Street, Lai Chi Kok, Hong Kong, China (Hong Kong)
Tel.: (852) 27390003
Jewelry Mfr
N.A.I.C.S.: 339910

UNCLAIMED FREIGHT COMPANY LLC
2260 Industrial Dr Unit 1, Bethlehem, PA 18017-2163
Tel.: (610) 974-8194
Web Site:
http://www.unclaimedfreight.us
Rev.: $17,100,000
Emp.: 12
Furniture Retailer
N.A.I.C.S.: 449110

UNCLE CHARLEY'S SAUSAGE CO.
1135 Industrial Park Rd, Vandergrift, PA 15690
Tel.: (724) 845-3302
Web Site:
http://www.unclecharleyssausage.com
Year Founded: 1988
Sales Range: $10-24.9 Million
Emp.: 45
Sausage Mfr
N.A.I.C.S.: 311612
Charley Armitage *(CTO)*

UNCLE LEE'S TEA INC.
11020 Rush St, South El Monte, CA 91733-3547
Tel.: (626) 350-3309
Web Site: http://www.unclelee.com
Year Founded: 1988
Sales Range: $1-4.9 Billion
Emp.: 35
Tea Production Services
N.A.I.C.S.: 311920
James O'Young *(Sr VP)*
Johnathen Lee *(Sr VP)*

UNCLE WALLY'S LLC
41 Natcon Dr, Shirley, NY 11967
Tel.: (631) 205-0455 NY
Web Site:
http://www.unclewallys.com
Muffin Whslr & Marketing Services
N.A.I.C.S.: 424490

UND SPORTS FACILITIES INC.
1 Ralph Engelstad Arena Dr, Grand Forks, ND 58203-2205
Tel.: (701) 777-4930 ND
Year Founded: 2002
Sales Range: $10-24.9 Million
Sport Facility Maintenance Services
N.A.I.C.S.: 561210
Michael Bergeron *(CFO)*
Jody Hodgson *(Gen Mgr)*
Alice Brekke *(VP)*
Aron Anderson *(Treas & Sec)*
Earl Strinden *(Pres)*

UNDERGROUND ELEPHANT INC.
600 B St Ste 1300, San Diego, CA 92101
Tel.: (858) 815-5324
Web Site: http://www.undergroundelephant.com
Year Founded: 2008
Sales Range: $1-9.9 Million
Emp.: 75
Online Marketing Services
N.A.I.C.S.: 541613
Jason Kulpa *(CEO)*
Keola Malone *(CTO)*
Mike Norman *(Chief Strategic Officer)*
James Riebel *(Exec VP-Bus Dev)*
William Huff *(CFO)*

UNDERGROUND PRINTING
260 Metty Dr Ste G, Ann Arbor, MI 48103
Tel.: (734) 665-2692
Web Site:
http://www.undergroundshirts.com
Year Founded: 2003
Sales Range: $1-9.9 Million
Emp.: 60
Custom Designed & Screen Print Shirts
N.A.I.C.S.: 323113
Ryan Gregg *(Co-Owner & CEO)*
Rishi Narayan *(Co-Owner)*

UNDERGROUND SPECIALISTS INC.
570 SW 16 Terr Bldg 1500, Pompano Beach, FL 33069
Tel.: (954) 782-8740
Web Site: http://www.usicable.com
Sales Range: $10-24.9 Million
Emp.: 186
Utility Wiring Installation
N.A.I.C.S.: 238210
Richard Jenkins *(Pres)*

UNDERRINER BUICK, INC.
1834th Ave N, Billings, MT 59101
Tel.: (406) 252-5101 MT
Web Site:
http://www.underrinermotors.com
Year Founded: 1947
Sales Range: $25-49.9 Million
Emp.: 80
New & Used Automobiles Sales & Leasing
N.A.I.C.S.: 441110
Bill Underriner *(Pres)*

UNDERSCORE MARKETING LLC
163 West 23rd St 3rd Fl, New York, NY 10011
Tel.: (212) 647-8436
Web Site:
http://www.underscoremarketing.com
Year Founded: 2002
Rev.: $11,700,000
Customer Relationship Management, Electronic Media, Integrated Marketing, Media Buying Services, Media Planning, Paid Searches, Podcasting, Search Engine Optimization, Web (Banner Ads, Pop-ups, etc.)
N.A.I.C.S.: 541830
Tom Hespos *(Chm, Pres & Partner)*
Lauren Boyer *(Partner & Chief Global Strategist)*

UNDERSCORE.VC MANAGEMENT CO. LLC
45 School St 2nd FL, Boston, MA 02108
Tel.: (617) 303-0064 DE
Web Site: https://underscore.vc
Emp.: 100
Investment Services
N.A.I.C.S.: 523999
Richard Dulude *(Co-Founder & Partner)*
John Pearce *(Co-Founder & Partner)*

UNDERWATER CONSTRUCTION CORP.
110 Plains Rd, Essex, CT 06426
Tel.: (860) 767-8256 CT

UNDERWATER CONSTRUCTION CORP.

Underwater Construction Corp.—(Continued)
Web Site: http://www.uccdive.com
Year Founded: 1979
Sales Range: $10-24.9 Million
Emp.: 125
Contracting Services
N.A.I.C.S.: 236210
John Lawton (Pres)
Linda Tower (Sec)
Ray Palumbo (CFO & COO)

UNDERWOOD BROS INCORPORATED
3747 E S Ave, Phoenix, AZ 85040
Tel.: (602) 437-2690
Web Site:
http://www.aaalandscape.com
Sales Range: $10-24.9 Million
Emp.: 225
Landscape Contractors
N.A.I.C.S.: 561730
Robert Underwood (Co-Owner & CEO)
Richard K. Underwood (Co-Owner, Pres & Gen Mgr-Southern Arizona)

UNDERWOOD CHEVROLET-BUICK, INC.
1017 US 12, Clinton, MI 49236
Tel.: (517) 456-4181
Year Founded: 1941
Sales Range: $10-24.9 Million
Emp.: 45
Car Whslr
N.A.I.C.S.: 441110
Charley Rebottaro (Gen Mgr)

UNDERWRITERS LABORATORIES INC.
333 Pfingsten Rd, Northbrook, IL 60062-2096
Tel.: (847) 272-8800
Web Site: http://www.ul.org
Year Founded: 1894
Product Safety Testing Services
N.A.I.C.S.: 541380
Christian Anschuetz (Chief Digital Officer & Sr VP)
Gitte Schjotz (Pres-Retail & Industry)
Adrian Groom (Chief HR Officer & Sr VP)
Jason Fischer (Sr VP & Gen Mgr-Field Svcs)
Patrick Boyle (Chief Learning Officer & Sr VP)
Weifang Zhou (Pres-UL Consumers)
Kathy Seegebrecht (CMO & Sr VP)
Sajeev Jesudas (Pres-Intl Ops)
Lynn H. Hancock (Chief Program Officer & Sr VP)
Jackie McLaughlin (Chief Legal Officer & Sr VP)
Ryan Robinson (CFO & Sr VP)
Karriem Shakoor (CIO & Sr VP)
James M. Shannon (Chm)

Subsidiaries:

ChemADVISOR, Inc. (1)
811 Camp Horne Rd Ste 200 Stone Quarry Crossing, Pittsburgh, PA 15237
Tel.: (412) 847-2000
Web Site: http://www.ul.com
Scientific & Technical Consulting Services & Compliance Solutions for Chemical Manufacturing Industry
N.A.I.C.S.: 541690

Consumer Testing Laboratories, Inc. (1)
2601 SE Otis Corley Dr, Bentonville, AR 72712
Tel.: (479) 286-2300
Web Site: http://www.consumertesting.com
Product Testing Laboratories
N.A.I.C.S.: 541715

Leslie Ryver (Mgr-Color Tech)
Steven Mansfield (Dir-Textile Testing Laboratory)
Terry Yost (Mgr-Chemistry Laboratory)

Futuremark Oy (1)
Niittytaival 13, Espoo, 02200, Finland
Tel.: (358) 407667466
Web Site: http://www.futuremark.com
Emp.: 4
Computer Performance Software & Hardware Developer
N.A.I.C.S.: 513210

Subsidiary (US):

Futuremark Corporation (2)
47173 Benecia St, Fremont, CA 94538
Tel.: (408) 614-2026
Web Site: http://www.futuremark.com
Computer Performance Software & Hardware Developer
N.A.I.C.S.: 513210

InfoGard Laboratories (1)
709 Fiero Ln Ste 25, San Luis Obispo, CA 93401
Tel.: (805) 783-0810
Web Site: http://www.infogard.com
Sales Range: $1-9.9 Million
Emp.: 41
Information Technology Security Testing Services
N.A.I.C.S.: 541380
Steve Weymann (Engr-Security-Bus Dev)
Douglas Biggs (CTO)
Adam Hardcastle (Program Mgr-PTS)
Marc Ireland (Program Mgr-FIPS)
Melanie Springer (Chief Bus Officer)
Mark Shin (COO)

Lighting Sciences Inc. (1)
7826 E Evans Rd, Scottsdale, AZ 85260
Tel.: (480) 991-9260
Web Site: http://www.lightingsciences.com
Rev: $1,863,000
Emp.: 9
Engineeering Services
N.A.I.C.S.: 541330
Sajeev Jesudas (Pres-Verification Svcs)

National Analysis Center, Inc. (1)
2365 Vista Pkwy Ste 1, West Palm Beach, FL 33411-2783
Tel.: (561) 615-2622
Web Site:
http://www.nationalanalysiscenter.com
Testing Laboratories
N.A.I.C.S.: 541380
Joe Murphy (VP-Bus Dev)
Stephen Raxter (Dir-Bluetooth Testing)
Jim Lipsit (Pres, Co-Founder & Co-Owner)
Dan Lipsit (Exec VP-Ops, Co-Founder & Co-Owner)
Martin Hochman (Exec VP, Co-Founder & Co-Owner)
James C. Massey (Exec VP, Co-founder & Co-Owner)

PureWorks, Inc. (1)
730 Cool Springs Blvd Ste 400, Franklin, TN 37067
Tel.: (615) 367-4404
Web Site: http://www.puresafety.com
Sales Range: $10-24.9 Million
Emp.: 125
Software Services
N.A.I.C.S.: 611699
Ben Scott (Mgr-IT)
William A. Grana Jr. (Pres & CEO)

The Wercs, Ltd. (1)
23 British American Blvd, Latham, NY 12110
Tel.: (518) 640-9200
Web Site: http://www.thewercs.com
Sales Range: $10-24.9 Million
Emp.: 80
Software Tools & Services
N.A.I.C.S.: 513210

UL De Mexico, S.A. De C.V. (1)
Blas Pascal 205, Los Morales, 11510, Mexico, Mexico (100%)
Tel.: (52) 5530005400
Web Site: http://www.ul-mexico.com
Sales Range: $75-99.9 Million
Emp.: 50
Product Testing Services
N.A.I.C.S.: 541380

Eli Puszkar (Gen Mgr)

UL India Private Ltd. (1)
135 1st Fl Titanium, Airport Rd, Bengaluru, 560 017, India (100%)
Tel.: (91) 8025204400
Web Site: http://www.ul-asia.com
Sales Range: $10-24.9 Million
Emp.: 100
Product Safety Testing Services
N.A.I.C.S.: 541380

UL International (Netherlands) B.V. (1)
Westervoortsedijk 60, 6827 AT, Arnhem, Netherlands (100%)
Tel.: (31) 263764800
Web Site: http://www.ul-europe.com
Sales Range: $10-24.9 Million
Emp.: 80
Product Safety Testing Services
N.A.I.C.S.: 541380
Matthijs Huisman (Mng Dir)

UL International (Sweden) AB (1)
Stormbyvagen 2-4 Spanga Ctr, 163 29, Spanga, Sweden (100%)
Tel.: (46) 87954370
Web Site: http://www.ul.com
Sales Range: $10-24.9 Million
Emp.: 5
Provider of Product Safety Testing Services
N.A.I.C.S.: 541380

UL International (UK) Ltd. (1)
Wonersch House The Guildway, Old Portsmouth Rd, Guildford, GU3 1LR, Surrey, United Kingdom (100%)
Tel.: (44) 483302130
Sales Range: $10-24.9 Million
Emp.: 60
Provider of Product Safety Testing Services
N.A.I.C.S.: 541380

UL International Demko A/S (1)
Borupvang 5A, PO Box 514, Ballerup, DK 2750, Denmark (100%)
Tel.: (45) 44856565
Web Site: http://www.ul.com
Sales Range: $10-24.9 Million
Emp.: 100
Provider of Product Safety Testing Services
N.A.I.C.S.: 541380
Mette Peterson (Mng Dir)

UL International France S.A. (1)
Espace Technologique Route de Lorme des Merisiers Batiment Explorer, Saint-Aubin, 91190, France (100%)
Tel.: (33) 160198800
Web Site: http://www.ul-europe.com
Sales Range: $10-24.9 Million
Emp.: 66
Provider of Product Safety Testing Services
N.A.I.C.S.: 541380
Patrick Leclerc (Gen Mgr)

UL International Germany GmbH (1)
Frankfurter Strasse 229, D 63263, Neu-Isenburg, Hessen, Germany (100%)
Tel.: (49) 61023690
Web Site: http://www.ul-europe.com
Sales Range: $10-24.9 Million
Emp.: 100
Provider of Product Safety Testing Services
N.A.I.C.S.: 541380
Jose Leon (Mng Dir)

UL International Italia S.r.l. (1)
Via Archimede 42, 20864, Agrate Brianza, MI, Italy (100%)
Tel.: (39) 0396410101
Sales Range: $10-24.9 Million
Emp.: 100
Provider of Product Safety Testing Services
N.A.I.C.S.: 541380

UL International Italia S.r.l. (1)
Zn Ind Predda Niedda, 71000, Sassari, Italy (100%)
Tel.: (39) 0792636600
Web Site: http://www.ul.it
Sales Range: $10-24.9 Million
Emp.: 15
Provider of Product Safety Testing Services
N.A.I.C.S.: 541380

UL International Ltd. (1)
18th Floor Delta House 3 On Yiu Street, Sha Tin, NT, China (Hong Kong) (100%)

U.S. PRIVATE

Tel.: (852) 22769898
Sales Range: $100-124.9 Million
Emp.: 200
Product Safety Testing Services
N.A.I.C.S.: 541380
Mickey Yu (VP-Global)

UL International New Zealand Limited (1)
21 Tarndale Grove, Albany, 632, Auckland, New Zealand
Tel.: (64) 94153355
Web Site: http://www.newzealand.ul.com
Sales Range: $10-24.9 Million
Emp.: 23
Product Safety & Certification Services
N.A.I.C.S.: 541380
Ken Wilson (Gen Mgr)

Subsidiary (Domestic):

UL International New Zealand Ltd (2)
10 Vanadium Place, Middletown, Christchurch, 8024, New Zealand (100%)
Tel.: (64) 39404400
Web Site: http://newzealand.ul.com
Product Safety & Certification Services
N.A.I.C.S.: 541380
Ken Wilson (Gen Mgr)
Paul Deverall (Mgr-Certification & Fin)

UL Japan, Inc. (1)
4383 326 Asama Cho Ise Shi, Mie, 516 0021, Japan (100%)
Tel.: (81) 596246717
Web Site: http://www.ulapex.jp
Sales Range: $75-99.9 Million
Emp.: 100
Product Safety Testing Services
N.A.I.C.S.: 541380

UL Korea Ltd. (1)
Gangnam Finance Center 737 Yeoksam-dong, Kangnam-gu, Seoul, 135-984, Korea (South) (100%)
Tel.: (82) 220099000
Web Site: http://www.ulk.co.kr
Sales Range: $100-124.9 Million
Emp.: 200
Provider of Product Safety Testing Services
N.A.I.C.S.: 541380
James M. Kurtz (Mng Dir)
Eunyoung Koh (Dir-Fin)

UL Services (Malaysia) Sdn. Bhd. (1)
17 1st Floor Jalan USJ 10/1G, 47620, Subang Jaya, Selangor, Malaysia (100%)
Tel.: (60) 356325922
Web Site: http://www.ul-asia.com
Sales Range: $75-99.9 Million
Emp.: 12
Provider of Product Safety Testing Services
N.A.I.C.S.: 541380
Douglas Chin (Mgr-Sls)

Underwriters Laboratories AG (1)
Ringstrasse 1, 8603, Schwerzenbach, Switzerland
Tel.: (41) 43 355 4020
Safety Consulting Services
N.A.I.C.S.: 541690

Underwriters Laboratories of Canada (1)
7 Underwriters Road, Toronto, M1R 3A9, ON, Canada
Tel.: (416) 757-3611
Web Site: http://www.canada.ul.com
Sales Range: $100-124.9 Million
Emp.: 150
Offices of Product Safety Testing Services
N.A.I.C.S.: 541380
Keith Williams (Pres & Gen Mgr)

Branch (Domestic):

Underwriters Laboratories of Canada - Vancouver Branch (2)
130-13775 Commerce Parkway, Richmond, V6V 2V4, BC, Canada
Tel.: (604) 214-9555
Web Site: http://www.canada.ul.com
Product Safety Testing Services
N.A.I.C.S.: 541380

UNDERWRITERS SAFETY AND CLAIMS, INC.

1700 E Point Pkwy, Louisville, KY 40223
Tel.: (502) 244-1343
Web Site: http://www.uscky.com
Year Founded: 1941
Rev.: $28,000,000
Emp.: 350
Provider of Insurance Services
N.A.I.C.S.: 524210
Scott Ferguson *(Exec VP)*
Jim Johnson *(Controller)*

UNEEDA DOLL COMPANY, LTD.
227 Red Bud Cir, Henderson, NC 27536
Tel.: (252) 438-6888
Web Site: http://www.uneedadoll.com
Year Founded: 1917
Sales Range: $1-9.9 Million
Emp.: 50
Mfr & Distr of Dolls
N.A.I.C.S.: 423920

UNETTE CORPORATION
1578 Sussex Tpke Ste 400, Randolph, NJ 07869-1833
Tel.: (973) 328-6800   NJ
Web Site: http://www.unette.com
Year Founded: 1955
Sales Range: $10-24.9 Million
Emp.: 80
Tube & Pouch Filling & Contract Filling of Liquids & Creams
N.A.I.C.S.: 326199
Joseph R. Hark *(Pres)*
Chris Doscher *(VP-Fin)*

UNEX MANUFACTURING, INC.
691 New Hampshire Ave, Lakewood, NJ 08701
Tel.: (732) 928-2800
Web Site: http://www.unex.com
Year Founded: 1964
Industrial Carton Flow Track Mfr
N.A.I.C.S.: 333922
Brian Neuwirth *(VP-Sls & Mktg)*
Drew LaFrennie *(Mgr-Inside Sls Support)*

UNGER COMPANY
12401 Berea Rd, Cleveland, OH 44111-1617
Tel.: (216) 252-1400   OH
Web Site: http://www.ungerco.com
Year Founded: 1920
Sales Range: $75-99.9 Million
Emp.: 24
Wholesale Distributor of Bakery & Deli Packaging Boxes & Containers
N.A.I.C.S.: 424130
John O'Neill *(Mgr-Warehouse)*

UNGER FABRIK LLC
1515 E 15th St, Los Angeles, CA 90021-2711
Tel.: (213) 222-1010
Web Site: http://www.ungerfabrik.com
Sales Range: $10-24.9 Million
Emp.: 60
Athletic Clothing & Sportswear Mfr
N.A.I.C.S.: 315250
Dede Venegas *(COO)*
Ralph Guerra *(Dir-Mgmt Info Sys)*
Gina Turney *(Acct Exec)*

UNI HOSIERY CO. INC.
1911 E Olympic Blvd, Los Angeles, CA 90021
Tel.: (323) 846-9900
Web Site: http://www.unihosiery.com
Rev.: $34,166,787
Emp.: 130
Hosiery Mfr
N.A.I.C.S.: 315120
Kenny Chung *(VP)*

UNI-CAST, INC.
11 Industrial Dr, Londonderry, NH 03053-2011
Tel.: (603) 625-5761
Web Site: http://www.uni-cast.com
Year Founded: 1965
Sales Range: $25-49.9 Million
Emp.: 105
Aluminum Castings
N.A.I.C.S.: 331523
Jose Martinez *(Gen Mgr)*

UNI-WORLD CAPITAL, L.P.
52 Vanderbilt Ave Ste 401, New York, NY 10017-3851
Tel.: (212) 612-9170
Web Site:
  http://www.uniworldcapital.com
Privater Equity Firm
N.A.I.C.S.: 523999
Christopher P. Fuller *(Mng Partner)*
Erik S. Miller *(Partner)*
Mark Deutsch *(Partner)*
Richard Moreau *(Partner)*

Subsidiaries:

Drake Manufacturing Service Co., LLC   (1)
4371 N Leavitt Rd NW, Warren, OH 44485
Tel.: (330) 847-7291
Web Site: http://www.drakemfg.com
Sales Range: $10-24.9 Million
Emp.: 90
Machine Tool Replacement & Repair Parts, Metal Cutting Types
N.A.I.C.S.: 333517
James L. Vosmik *(CEO)*
Stig Mowatt-Larssen *(CTO)*
Donna Cavalier *(Mgr-HR)*
Jacci Ferenczy *(Supvr-Sls Admin)*
Timothy Young *(CMO)*
William Royals *(COO)*
Michael Katafiasz *(CFO)*
Nancy Halliday *(Mktg Mgr)*
Ken Kamimura *(Sls Mgr-Natl)*
Andy Zhang *(Sls Mgr-China)*

Pittsburgh Brewing Company   (1)
3340 Liberty Ave, Pittsburgh, PA 15201-1321
Tel.: (412) 682-7400
Web Site:
  http://www.pittsburghbrewingco.com
Sales Range: $50-74.9 Million
Brewery
N.A.I.C.S.: 312120
Brian Walsh *(Pres & CEO)*

UNIBAR MAINTENANCE SERVICES
4325 Concourse Dr, Ann Arbor, MI 48108
Tel.: (734) 769-2600   MI
Web Site: http://www.unibarinc.com
Year Founded: 1985
Sales Range: $10-24.9 Million
Emp.: 990
Provider of Contract Janitorial Services
N.A.I.C.S.: 561720
G. J. Davis *(Pres & CEO)*
John J. McManus *(COO)*
Chris Wilson *(Mgr-Mktg)*

UNICABLE INCORPORATED
511 S Harbor Blvd Ste I, La Habra, CA 90631-9374
Tel.: (562) 383-9278
Web Site: http://www.unicable.com
Sales Range: $10-24.9 Million
Emp.: 5
Wire & Cable
N.A.I.C.S.: 423610
T. C. Tseng *(Pres)*

UNICARS HONDA
78-970 Varner Rd, Indio, CA 92203-9710
Tel.: (760) 345-7555
Web Site:
  http://www.unicarshonda.com
Year Founded: 1989
Sales Range: $10-24.9 Million
Emp.: 61
New Car Whslr
N.A.I.C.S.: 441110
Andreas Mozoras *(Principal)*

UNICELL HOLDINGS INC.
725 Primer Blvd Ste 215, Sanford, FL 32771
Tel.: (407) 330-9696
Web Site:
  http://www.thesharmagroup.com
Rev.: $19,000,000
Emp.: 6
Paper Mills
N.A.I.C.S.: 322120
Brij Sharma *(CFO & VP)*
Girish Sharma *(Pres)*

UNICO PROPERTIES INC.
1215 4th Ave Ste 600, Seattle, WA 98161-1084
Tel.: (206) 628-5050
Web Site: http://www.unicoprop.com
Year Founded: 1952
Sales Range: $150-199.9 Million
Emp.: 100
Real Estate Agents & Managers
N.A.I.C.S.: 531210
Brian Pearce *(Exec VP-Real Estate Svcs)*
Jonas Sylvester *(Pres)*
Julie Currier *(VP-Dev)*
Quentin W. Kuhrau *(Chm & CEO)*
Andrew Cox *(Sr VP & Dir-Puget Sound & Nashville Markets)*
Ty Barker *(VP-Real Estate Svcs)*
Russ Davis *(VP-Real Estate Svcs)*
Chrissy Schrader *(Dir-Real Estate Svcs)*
Ned Carner *(VP-Acq)*
Jackie Costigan *(Sr VP-Dev)*
Scott Brucker *(Sr VP-Asset Mgmt)*
Courtney Jolicoeur *(CFO)*
Robert Penney *(Sr VP-Acq)*
Mike Lemker *(VP-Corp Compliance)*

UNICOIN INC.
228 Park Ave S 16065, New York, NY 10003
Tel.: (212) 216-0001   DE
Web Site: https://www.unicoin.com
Year Founded: 2015
Rev.: $23,213,963
Assets: $25,035,662
Liabilities: $49,921,362
Net Worth: ($24,885,700)
Earnings: ($32,623,856)
Fiscal Year-end: 12/31/22
Asset Management Services
N.A.I.C.S.: 523999
Alexandre P. Konanykhine *(CEO)*
Silvina Moschini *(Co-Founder)*

UNICOM GLOBAL, INC.
15535 San Fernando Mission Blvd UNICOM Plz Ste 310, Mission Hills, CA 91345
Tel.: (818) 838-0606   CA
Web Site:
  http://www.unicomglobal.com
Holding Company
N.A.I.C.S.: 551112
Corry S. Hong *(Founder & CEO)*

Subsidiaries:

Macro 4 Ltd.   (1)
The Orangery Turners Hill Road, Worth, Crawley, RH10 4SS, West Sussex, United Kingdom
Tel.: (44) 1293872000
Web Site: http://www.macro4.com
Sales Range: $50-74.9 Million
Emp.: 240
Computer Software
N.A.I.C.S.: 334610
Lynda Kershaw *(Mgr-Mktg)*

Subsidiary (Non-US):

Macro 4 (Benelux) NV/SA   (2)
Pa Bopro Business Center, Zandvoortstraat C27/00, 2800, Mechelen, Belgium
Tel.: (32) 15747480
Web Site: http://www.macro4.com
Sales Range: $10-24.9 Million
Emp.: 6
Computer Software
N.A.I.C.S.: 334610
Ilse Borremans *(Country Mgr)*

Macro 4 (France) SARL   (2)
63 bis rue de Sevres, 92100, Boulogne, France
Tel.: (33) 141033250
Web Site: http://www.macro4.com
Computer Software
N.A.I.C.S.: 334610

Macro 4 AG   (2)
Zurcherstrasse 61, 8800, Thalwil, Switzerland
Tel.: (41) 17234000
Web Site: http://www.macro4.ch
Computer Software
N.A.I.C.S.: 334610

Macro 4 GmbH   (2)
Humboldstrasse 12, Aschheim, 85609, Germany
Tel.: (49) 896100970
Web Site: http://www.macro4.de
Sales Range: $10-24.9 Million
Emp.: 20
Computer Software
N.A.I.C.S.: 334610

Subsidiary (US):

Macro 4 Inc.   (2)
800 Lanidex Plz, Parsippany, NJ 07054
Tel.: (973) 526-3900
Web Site: http://www.macro4.com
Sales Range: $10-24.9 Million
Emp.: 10
Computer Software
N.A.I.C.S.: 334610

Subsidiary (Non-US):

Marco 4 Srl   (2)
Via Monzese 76, 20090, Segrate, Italy
Tel.: (39) 022131941
Web Site: http://www.macro4.it
Sales Range: $25-49.9 Million
Emp.: 100
Computer Software
N.A.I.C.S.: 334610

UNICOM Global Iberia, S.A.   (2)
Calle Tizona 1 Planta 3, Majadahonda, 28220, Madrid, Spain
Tel.: (34) 914430220
Web Site: http://www.unicomglobal.com
Computer Software
N.A.I.C.S.: 513210

SoftLanding Systems, Inc.   (1)
1 Vose Farm Rd Ste 110, Peterborough, NH 03458
Tel.: (603) 924-8818
Web Site: http://www.softlanding.com
Custom Computer Programing Computer Related Services
N.A.I.C.S.: 541511

UNICOM Engineering, Inc.   (1)
25 Dan Rd, Canton, MA 02021-2817   (100%)
Tel.: (781) 332-1000
Web Site:
  http://www.unicomengineering.com
Sales Range: $250-299.9 Million
Emp.: 200
Information Technology Application Platforms, Appliances & Deployment Services
N.A.I.C.S.: 541519
Austin Hipes *(VP-Engrg)*
Jeff Hudgins *(VP-Svcs-Global)*
Robert Sheriff *(VP-Bus Ops)*
William O'Connell *(VP-Lean Enterprise)*
Keith Paul *(VP-Bus Mgmt Sys)*
Rusty Cone *(Gen Mgr)*

UNICOM GLOBAL, INC.

UNICOM Global, Inc.—(Continued)

UNICOM Government, Inc. (1)
2553 Dulles View Dr Ste 100, Herndon, VA 20171-5219
Tel.: (703) 502-2000
Web Site: http://www.unicomgov.com
Emp.: 455
Infrastructure Technology Solutions
N.A.I.C.S.: 423430
Corry Hong (CEO)
Steve Levine (Sr VP-Federal Sls & Mktg)
Rusty Cone (Gen Mgr)

UNICOM Systems Inc. (1)
15535 San Fernando Mission Blvd UNICOM Plz Ste 310, Mission Hills, CA 91345
Tel.: (818) 838-0606
Web Site: http://www.unicomglobal.com
Emp.: 20
Computer Software Development & Applications Services
N.A.I.C.S.: 541511
Corry S. Hong (Pres & CEO)
Larry Lawler (CTO)
Paul Hillbourne (Chief Architect & Dir-Emerging Tech)
Gerard R. Kilroy (Gen Counsel & VP-Bus Dev)
Rick Crunelle (Dir-Mktg-Intl)
Neil Watt (CFO)
Jim Fisher (Dir-Intl Ops)

iET Solutions, LLC (1)
25 Dan Rd, Canton, MA 02021
Web Site: http://www.iet-solutions.com
Sales Range: $1-9.9 Million
Emp.: 2
Information Technology & Software Asset Management Services
N.A.I.C.S.: 541519
Corry S. Hong (Pres & CEO)

illustro Systems International, LLC (1)
3210 Oaklawn Ave Ste 558, Dallas, TX 75219
Tel.: (214) 800-8900
Web Site: http://www.illustro.com
Sales Range: $1-9.9 Million
Computer Mainframe Application Modernization Services
N.A.I.C.S.: 541511

UNICOMP INC.
2665 North First St Ste 102, San Jose, CA 95134
Tel.: (408) 577-1263
Web Site: http://www.unicompincorp.com
Rev.: $34,254,983
Emp.: 15
Computer Related Consulting Services
N.A.I.C.S.: 541512
Faramarsz Fouladian (Pres)

UNICOMP, INC.
510 Henry Clay Blvd, Lexington, KY 40505
Tel.: (859) 233-2130   CO
Web Site: http://www.pckeyboard.com
Year Founded: 1985
Sales Range: $25-49.9 Million
Emp.: 231
Retail E-Business Solutions, Customer Activated Wireless Devices & Software Solutions for Companies, Resellers & System Integrators
N.A.I.C.S.: 334118
Neil Muyskens (Pres)

UNICON INTERNATIONAL INC.
241 Outerbelt St, Columbus, OH 43213
Tel.: (614) 861-7070
Web Site: http://www.unicon-intl.com
Sales Range: $10-24.9 Million
Emp.: 98
Computer Related Consulting Services
N.A.I.C.S.: 541512

Peichen Jane Lee (Pres & CEO)
Michael McAlear (VP)
Chris Anderson (VP)
Rich Johnston (Dir-IT Svcs)
Li-Hung David Lee (VP)

UNICORD CORPORATION
12010 S Paulina St, Calumet Park, IL 60827-5318
Tel.: (708) 385-7999
Web Site: http://www.unicordcorp.com
Mfr of Rope & Cordage Products
N.A.I.C.S.: 314994
Arman Moseni (Pres)

Subsidiaries:

Unicord International LLC (1)
145 Towery St, Guntown, MS 38849
Tel.: (662) 348-2246
Web Site: http://www.unicordcorp.com
Rope, Twine & Industrial Fiber Products Mfr & Distr
N.A.I.C.S.: 314994

Subsidiary (Domestic):

Plymkraft, Inc. (2)
479 Export Cir, Newport News, VA 23601-3750
Tel.: (757) 595-0364
Web Site: http://www.plymkraft.com
Sales Range: $25-49.9 Million
Emp.: 100
Mfr of Twisted Paper Products
N.A.I.C.S.: 322120

UNICORP NATIONAL DEVELOPMENTS, INC.
7940 Via Dellagio Way Ste 200, Orlando, FL 32819
Tel.: (407) 999-9985   FL
Web Site: http://www.unicorpusa.com
Year Founded: 1997
Sales Range: $1-9.9 Million
Emp.: 30
Land Development & Property Management
N.A.I.C.S.: 237210
Charles Whittall (Pres)
Amy Barnard (Dir-Legal Affairs)
Sam Beavers (Dir-Property Mgmt)

UNICOVER CORPORATION
1 Unicover Ctr, Cheyenne, WY 82008-0001
Tel.: (307) 771-3000   WY
Web Site: http://www.unicover.com
Year Founded: 1968
Sales Range: $100-124.9 Million
Emp.: 200
Mail Order Stamps, Coins & Collectors' Items Marketer & Distr
N.A.I.C.S.: 459999
Jan Loftin (Product Mgr)

UNIDEL FOUNDATION, INC.
PO Box 1146, Wilmington, DE 19899
Tel.: (302) 658-7691   DE
Year Founded: 1939
Sales Range: $25-49.9 Million
Grantmaking Services
N.A.I.C.S.: 813211
G. Arno Loessner (Treas & Sec)

UNIDEX GROUP INC.
1601 Glenlake Ave, Itasca, IL 60143
Tel.: (630) 438-6600
Web Site: http://www.unidexgroup.com
Sales Range: $50-74.9 Million
Emp.: 30
Packaging Company
N.A.I.C.S.: 423840
Jong Ho Kim (Pres)

UNIDINE CORPORATION
1000 Washington St Ste 510, Boston, MA 02118
Tel.: (617) 467-3700
Web Site: http://www.unidine.com
Year Founded: 2001
Sales Range: $25-49.9 Million
Emp.: 1,000
Food & Dining Management Services
N.A.I.C.S.: 722310
Richard B. Schenkel (Pres & CEO)
David B. Silva (CFO)

UNIFI FINANCIAL, INC.
PO Box 12747, San Antonio, TX 78212
Tel.: (830) 879-2331   TX
Year Founded: 2022
Investment Services
N.A.I.C.S.: 523999

UNIFIED AIRCRAFT SERVICES INC.
1571 S Lilac Ave, Bloomington, CA 92316
Tel.: (909) 877-0535
Rev.: $20,217,675
Emp.: 15
Packing Services for Shipping
N.A.I.C.S.: 488991
Ben C. Warren (Pres)

UNIFIED COMMERCE GROUP
390 Broadway 3rd Fl, New York, NY 10013
Web Site: http://www.unifiedcommercegroup.com
Holding Company
N.A.I.C.S.: 551112
Dustin Jones (Co-Founder & CEO)
Greg Freihofner (Co-Founder & CFO)

Subsidiaries:

GREATS Brand, Inc. (1)
101 N 10th St Ste 309, Brooklyn, NY 11249
Web Site: https://www.greats.com
Online Footwear Distr
N.A.I.C.S.: 458210

Modasuite Inc. (1)
160 St-Viateur East Suite 613, Montreal, H2T 1A8, QC, Canada
Tel.: (855) 376-5625
Web Site: http://www.frankandoak.com
Emp.: 110
Men's Clothing Retailer
N.A.I.C.S.: 458110
Hicham Ratnani (Co-Founder & COO)
Ethan Song (Co-Founder & CEO)

UNIFIED DEVELOPMENT, INC.
16690 Swingley Rdg Rd Ste 260, Chesterfield, MO 63017
Tel.: (636) 532-4424   MO
Web Site: http://www.unidev.com
Year Founded: 1990
Sales Range: $1-9.9 Million
Emp.: 60
Software Developer
N.A.I.C.S.: 513210
Greg Alexander (Owner & CEO)
Steve Thomas (VP)
Mike Winebright (VP-Dev)
Andrea Bemis (VP-Software Dev)
Gregg Dieckhaus (Dir-Product Dev-Mobile & Java Tech)
Kym Bohl (Mgr-Project)

Subsidiaries:

The Net Impact (1)
16690 Swingley Ridge Rd Ste 260, Chesterfield, MO 63017
Tel.: (636) 458-7772
Web Site: http://www.unidev.com
Emp.: 40
Web Marketing Services
N.A.I.C.S.: 541613
Lauren Williamson (Acct Mgr-Web Mktg)

U.S. PRIVATE

UNIFIED FINANCIAL SERVICES, INC.
2353 Alexandria Dr, Lexington, KY 40504
Tel.: (859) 422-0347   DE
Web Site: http://www.unified.com
Sales Range: $25-49.9 Million
Emp.: 126
Holding Company; Financial Trust, Retirement & Investment Advisory Services
N.A.I.C.S.: 551112
Jack H. Brown (Chief Acctg Officer)
Calvin Lui (Pres & Chief Strategy Officer)
Jason Beckerman (Co-Founder & CEO)
Roger Clark (CFO)
Sheldon Owen (Co-Founder & Chm)

Subsidiaries:

Commonwealth Premium Finance Corporation (1)
220 Lexington Green Cir Ste 600, Lexington, KY 40503
Tel.: (859) 245-2500
Sales Range: $25-49.9 Million
Emp.: 5
Insurance Premium Financing Services
N.A.I.C.S.: 525990

Unified Trust Company, N.A. (1)
2353 Alexandria Dr Ste 100, Lexington, KY 40504   (100%)
Tel.: (859) 296-4407
Web Site: http://www.unifiedtrust.com
Sales Range: $25-49.9 Million
Emp.: 50
Financial Trust Services
N.A.I.C.S.: 523991
Kevin Avent (Mng Dir-Wealth Mgmt)
Marty Lautner (CFO)
Justin Morgan (Mng Dir-Plan Admin & Svc)
Christina Crawford (Chief Risk Officer)
Gregory Kasten (Founder & CEO)

UNIFIED HOUSING FOUNDATION, INC.
1603 Lyndon B Johnson Fwy Ste 300, Dallas, TX 75234
Tel.: (214) 750-8845   TX
Web Site: http://www.unifiedhousing.com
Year Founded: 1997
Sales Range: $50-74.9 Million
Building Construction Services
N.A.I.C.S.: 236115
Robert Neil Crouch (Pres & Treas)
Martha C. Stephens (Sec & Exec VP)
Brad Kyles (Gen Mgr)

UNIFIED INDUSTRIES INC.
6551 Loisdale Ct Ste 400, Springfield, VA 22150-1854
Tel.: (703) 922-9800
Web Site: http://www.uii.com
Year Founded: 1973
Sales Range: $10-24.9 Million
Emp.: 65
Systems Engineering, Computer Related
N.A.I.C.S.: 541512
Tom Callahan (VP)

UNIFIED MARINE INC.
1190 Old Asheville Hwy, Newport, TN 37821
Tel.: (423) 613-1400   FL
Web Site: http://www.seasense.com
Year Founded: 1984
Sales Range: $1-9.9 Million
Emp.: 35
Mfr & Importer of Sporting & Recreation Goods
N.A.I.C.S.: 423910
David Nirenberg (CEO)
Larry Churchwell (Mgr-Ops)

COMPANIES

UNIFIED MARINE, INC.
25270 Bernwood Dr Unit 7, Bonita Springs, FL 34135
Tel.: (239) 594-7997 FL
Web Site: http://www.seasense.com
Year Founded: 1984
Emp.: 25
Marine Accessories Mfr
N.A.I.C.S.: 423910
Doug Morichika (Gen Mgr)

UNIFIED PACKAGING, INC.
1187 E 68th Ave, Denver, CO 80229
Tel.: (303) 733-1000 CO
Web Site: http://www.unifiedbinders.com
Year Founded: 1991
Sales Range: $10-24.9 Million
Emp.: 45
Blank Book & Looseleaf Binder Mfr
N.A.I.C.S.: 323111
Doug Miller (Owner)

UNIFIED PORT OF SAN DIEGO
3165 Pacific Hwy, San Diego, CA 92101-1128
Tel.: (619) 686-6200 CA
Web Site: http://www.portofsandiego.org
Year Founded: 1962
Sales Range: $125-149.9 Million
Emp.: 600
Nonresidential Building Operators
N.A.I.C.S.: 531120
Michelle Corbin (Dir-HR)
Shirley Grothen (Dir-Equal Opportunity Mgmt)

UNIFIED RESOURCES IN DISPLAY
40 Bourgiht, Kenilworth, NJ 07033
Tel.: (908) 272-1112
Web Site: http://www.urindisplay.com
Year Founded: 1986
Rev.: $15,000,000
Emp.: 128
Displays & Cutouts Mfr
N.A.I.C.S.: 339950
Dennis Polvere (Pres)
Dean Polvere (VP)
John Pillarella (Controller)

UNIFIED SIGNAL, INC. DE
Web Site: https://www.unifiedsignal.com
Year Founded: 1996
UNSI—OTCBB
Sales Range: $1-9.9 Million
Communication Service
N.A.I.C.S.: 517112
Peter V. Sperling (Chief Product Officer)
Paris W. Holt (CEO)
Jaime Campbell (Dir-Bus Dev)

UNIFIEDCOMMUNICATIONS.COM
2075 E Governors Cir, Houston, TX 77092 TX
Web Site: http://www.unifiedcommunications.com
Sales Range: $10-24.9 Million
Emp.: 32
Telecommunication Device Distr
N.A.I.C.S.: 423690
Jason Herbst (CEO)
Mark Grimes (VP)

UNIFIEDONLINE, INC.
4126 Leonard Dr, Fairfax, VA 22030
Tel.: (571) 287-2388
Year Founded: 1969
Wireless & Fiber Broadband Services
N.A.I.C.S.: 517211

Robert M. Howe III (Chm, Pres & Sec)

UNIFOCUS, LP.
2455 McIver Ln, Carrollton, TX 75006
Tel.: (972) 512-5000
Web Site: http://www.unifocus.com
Year Founded: 1998
Sales Range: $10-24.9 Million
Emp.: 84
Data Processing Services
N.A.I.C.S.: 518210
Mark S. Heymann (Chm & CEO)
Robert Anderson (Controller)
Barry Kaplan (Sr VP-Org Dev)
George Harth (VP-Org Effectiveness)
Beth Mahler (Dir-Mktg)
David Phillips (Exec VP-Bus Dev)
Brett S. Kilpatrick (Chief Revenue Officer)
Denise Senter (Chief Mktg Officer)

UNIFOIL CORPORATION
12 Daniel Rd E, Fairfield, NJ 07004-2536
Tel.: (973) 244-9900 NJ
Web Site: http://www.unifoil.com
Year Founded: 1971
Sales Range: $75-99.9 Million
Emp.: 100
Mfr of Aluminum Coated Paper, Paperboard & Laminators
N.A.I.C.S.: 322220
Joseph Funicelli (Pres & CEO)
Bob Gallino (Dir-Tech)

UNIFORMED SERVICES BENEFIT ASSOCIATION
10895 Grandview Dr Ste 350, Overland Park, KS 66210
Tel.: (913) 327-5500
Web Site: http://www.usba.com
Sales Range: $50-74.9 Million
Emp.: 45
Fire Insurance Services
N.A.I.C.S.: 524298

UNIGEN CORPORATION
45388 Warm Springs Blvd, Fremont, CA 94539
Tel.: (510) 668-2088 CA
Web Site: http://www.unigen.com
Year Founded: 1991
Sales Range: $10-24.9 Million
Emp.: 200
Semiconductors & Related Devices
N.A.I.C.S.: 334413
Paul W. Heng (Pres & CEO)
Julie Huang (Mgr-Product Mktg)
Joshua McCulloch (Mgr-Demand)
Tina Vyas (Engr-Mfg)
Pam Morgan (Mgr-HR)
Philip Au (Engr-Mfg Test)
Simon Tam (Engr-Mechanical Process)
Ivan Lee (Engr-Mgmt Info Sys)
Shawn Aung (Engr-Test)
Ron Katen (Controller)
Kristen Young (Dir-Sls)

UNIGROUP, INC.
1 Premier Dr, Fenton, MO 63026
Tel.: (636) 305-5000
Web Site: http://www.unigroupinc.com
Year Founded: 1987
Sales Range: $1-4.9 Billion
Emp.: 1,350
Transportation & Freight Services
N.A.I.C.S.: 484210
Brent Stottlemyre (Pres-Interim)

Subsidiaries:

Mayflower Transit, LLC (1)
1 Premier Dr, Saint Louis, MO 63026 (100%)

Tel.: (636) 305-4000
Web Site: http://www.mayflower.com
Sales Range: $50-74.9 Million
Emp.: 900
Trucking Except Local
N.A.I.C.S.: 484121
Mark Schrader (CFO)

Subsidiary (Domestic):

Best Mayflower (2)
1 Mayflower Dr, Fenton, MO 63026
Tel.: (636) 305-4000
General Freight Trucking Services
N.A.I.C.S.: 484110

Mayflower International Forwarding Inc.
1 Mayflower Dr, Fenton, MO 63026-2934
Tel.: (636) 305-4000
Web Site: http://www.mayflower.com
Rev.: $660,000
Emp.: 100
Trucking Except Local
N.A.I.C.S.: 484121

Mayflower Military Movers, LLC (2)
1 Mayflower Dr, Fenton, MO 63026
Tel.: (636) 305-6260
Container Trucking Services
N.A.I.C.S.: 484121

Northstar Van Lines (2)
1 Mayflower Dr, Fenton, MO 63026
Tel.: (636) 349-2891
Container Trucking Services
N.A.I.C.S.: 484110

Pilgrim Van Lines, LLC (2)
1 Mayflower Dr, Fenton, MO 63026
Tel.: (636) 305-4000
Relocation Services
N.A.I.C.S.: 484210

Stealth Mayflower Inc. (2)
1 Mayflower Dr, Fenton, MO 63026-2934
Tel.: (636) 305-4000
Web Site: http://www.mayflowertransit.com
Provider of Trucking Services
N.A.I.C.S.: 484121
Rich McClure (COO)
Patrick Larch (Pres)

Total Transportation Services, Inc. (1)
1 Premier Dr, Fenton, MO 63026-2989
Tel.: (636) 305-5000
Sales Range: $25-49.9 Million
Emp.: 200
Movers & Packers
N.A.I.C.S.: 532120

UniGroup Relocation (1)
1 Worldwide Dr, Saint Louis, MO 63026
Tel.: (636) 349-7222
Web Site: http://www.unigrouprelocation.com
Container Trucking Services
N.A.I.C.S.: 484121
Pat Baehler (Pres)

UniGroup Worldwide Logistics, LLC (1)
1 Premier Dr, Fenton, MO 63026
Tel.: (636) 305-4040
Web Site: http://www.unigrouplogistics.com
Logistics Management Consulting Services
N.A.I.C.S.: 541614

UniGroup Worldwide, Inc. (1)
1 Premier Dr, Fenton, MO 63026-1350 (100%)
Tel.: (636) 326-3100
Web Site: http://www.unigroupworldwide.com
Sales Range: $25-49.9 Million
Emp.: 900
Global Mobility Management
N.A.I.C.S.: 484210
Jim Powers (Pres)

United Mayflower Container Services, LLC (1)
399 E Industrial Park Dr, Manchester, NH 03109-5313
Tel.: (877) 670-6061
Web Site: http://www.unitedmayflower.com
Container Trucking Services
N.A.I.C.S.: 484110

United Van Lines, LLC (1)

1 United Dr, Fenton, MO 63026-2535 (100%)
Tel.: (636) 349-3900
Web Site: http://www.unitedvanlines.com
Sales Range: $25-49.9 Million
Emp.: 900
Household Moving Services
N.A.I.C.S.: 484210
Rich McClure (CEO)
Tom Duwel (VP)
Casey Ellis (COO)

UNILAVA CORPORATION
353 Sacramento St Ste 1500, San Francisco, CA 94111
Tel.: (415) 321-3490 VG
Web Site: https://www.unilava.com
Year Founded: 1975
Sales Range: $1-9.9 Million
Emp.: 17
Telecommunication Servicesb
N.A.I.C.S.: 517112
Baldwin Yung (Pres & CEO)
Dicken Yung (Chm)
Boaz Yung (Exec VP-Bus Dev & Tech)
Rodger D. Spainhower Sr. (Sec)

UNILIFE CORPORATION
250 Cross Farm Ln, York, PA 17406
Tel.: (717) 384-3400
Web Site: http://www.unilife.com
Sales Range: $10-24.9 Million
Emp.: 160
Safety Syringe Developers
N.A.I.C.S.: 339112
Stephen Allan (Sr VP-Strategic Plng)
Dan Adlon (Dir-Contract Product Dev)
Keith Bocchicchio (Dir-Tech)
Mary Katherine Wold (Chm)
J. Christopher Naftzger (VP-Legal Affairs)
Dennis P. Pyers (Interim CFO & Interim Chief Acctg Officer)
John C. Ryan (Pres & CEO)
Ian Hanson (COO & Sr VP)
Stephanie Walters (Gen Counsel, Sec & Sr VP)
Molly Weaver (Chief Compliance Officer & VP-Quality & Regulatory Affairs)

Subsidiaries:

Unilife Medical Solutions, Inc. (1)
250 Cross Farm Ln, York, PA 17406
Tel.: (717) 384-3400
Web Site: http://www.unilife.com
Emp.: 100
Medical Instrument Mfr
N.A.I.C.S.: 339112
Alan D. Shortall (Chm & CEO)

Unitract Syringe Pty Limited (1)
L 5 35 Clarence St, Sydney, 2000, NSW, Australia
Tel.: (61) 283466500
Sales Range: $25-49.9 Million
Emp.: 3
Medical Equipment Mfr
N.A.I.C.S.: 423450

UNILUX, INC.
59 N 5th St, Saddle Brook, NJ 07663-6113
Tel.: (201) 712-1266
Web Site: http://www.unilux.com
Year Founded: 1962
Sales Range: $10-24.9 Million
Emp.: 35
Strobe Lights for Industrial Surface Inspection, Film & Video Production & Special Applications Designer & Mfr
N.A.I.C.S.: 335139
Steven A. Hirsh (Chm)
Michael Simonis (Pres)

UNIMAC GRAPHICS
350 Michele Pl, Carlstadt, NJ 07072-2304
Tel.: (201) 372-1000 DE

UNIMAC GRAPHICS

Unimac Graphics—(Continued)
Web Site:
http://www.unimacgraphics.com
Sales Range: $10-24.9 Million
Emp.: 300
Commercial Lithographic Printing
N.A.I.C.S.: 561499
Bob Greene *(VP-Sls)*
Butch McNulty *(VP-Mfg)*
Dave Klaiss *(Exec VP)*
Jack Kapinos *(Dir-Pre-Media)*
Joseph Hoffmann *(VP-Mfg)*
Steve Esposito *(Dir-Bus Dev)*
James Cox *(VP)*
Michael Anzalone *(VP-Sls)*

Subsidiaries:

Command Web Offset Co. (1)
100 Castle Rd, Secaucus, NJ 07094-1602
Tel.: (201) 863-8100
Web Site: http://www.commandweb.com
Offset Printing
N.A.I.C.S.: 323111
Ed Karaway *(Mgr-Production)*

UNIMAC Packaging Group (1)
350 Michele Pl, Carlstadt, NJ 07072
Tel.: (201) 372-1000
Web Site: http://www.unimacpackaging.com
Packaging Services
N.A.I.C.S.: 561910

UNION BANK
1011 Red Banks Road, Greenville, NC 27858
Tel.: (252) 215-3030 NC
Web Site:
http://www.thelittlebank.com
Year Founded: 1998
Rev.: $33,942,000
Assets: $745,186,000
Liabilities: $666,992,000
Net Worth: $78,194,000
Earnings: $6,737,000
Emp.: 153
Fiscal Year-end: 12/31/18
Savings Bank
N.A.I.C.S.: 522180
V. Robert Jones *(Pres & CEO)*
Doyle M. Thigpen *(Sec)*
Susan W. Barrett *(COO & Exec VP)*
Anne R. Corey *(Chief Credit Officer)*
Crawford A. Knott *(Vice Chm)*
Amy F. Watts *(Officer-Credit)*
John E. Burns *(Chief Banking Officer)*
Robert Lee Burrows Jr. *(Chm)*

UNION BAY RISK ADVISORS LLC
116 Village Blvd, Ste 306, Princeton, NJ 08540
Tel.: (609) 454-8544
Web Site:
https://www.unionbayrisk.com
Insurance Agencies
N.A.I.C.S.: 524210
Patrick Sullivan *(Pres)*

Subsidiaries:

Farrell Insurance Associates, Inc. (1)
513 N Broad St, Lansdale, PA 19446
Tel.: (215) 631-9390
Web Site:
http://www.farrellinsuranceagency.com
Insurance Related Activities
N.A.I.C.S.: 524298
Chris Farrell *(VP)*

UNION BENEFITS TRUST
390 Worthington Rd Ste B, Westerville, OH 43082-8332
Tel.: (614) 508-2250 OH
Web Site: http://www.benefitstrust.org
Year Founded: 1993
Sales Range: $25-49.9 Million
Emp.: 5
Employee Benefit Association
N.A.I.C.S.: 813930

Claudia Williams Cherry *(Program Mgr)*
Kathleen Stewart *(Treas)*
Chris Mabe *(Chm)*
Kelly L. Phillips *(Dir-SPHR)*

UNION CITY NISSAN INC.
4080 Jonesboro Rd, Union City, GA 30291
Tel.: (770) 964-7162
Web Site:
http://www.nissanofunioncity.com
Automobiles, New & Used
N.A.I.C.S.: 441110
Nick Cantwell *(Mgr-Sls)*
Shamarr Gregory *(Dir-Internet Sls)*
James Hill *(Mgr-Sls)*
Linda Chambers *(Mgr-Rent-To-Own)*

UNION COMMUNITY HEALTH CENTER
260 E 188th St, Bronx, NY 10458
Tel.: (718) 220-2020 NY
Web Site: http://www.uchcbronx.org
Year Founded: 2000
Sales Range: $25-49.9 Million
Emp.: 135
Health Care Srvices
N.A.I.C.S.: 622110
Anne Spellman *(COO & Chief Nursing Officer)*
Nelson Eng *(CMO)*
Douglas L. York *(CEO)*

UNION COUNTY SAVINGS BANK
320 N Broad St, Elizabeth, NJ 07207
Tel.: (908) 354-4600
Sales Range: $25-49.9 Million
Emp.: 44
Provider of Banking Services
N.A.I.C.S.: 522180
Donald C. Sims *(Pres)*
Kathleen Doyle *(VP)*
Frank Zabita *(Treas)*

UNION GOSPEL MISSION
400 Bannon St, Sacramento, CA 95811
Tel.: (916) 447-3268 CA
Web Site: http://www.ugmsac.com
Year Founded: 1962
Sales Range: $1-9.9 Million
Emp.: 32
Christian Ministry Services
N.A.I.C.S.: 624221
Mike Blain *(Mgr-Warehouse)*
Tim Lane *(Exec Dir)*
Eileen Trussell *(Office Mgr)*
Scott Holman *(Fin & Acct Mgr)*
Tim Trenum *(Mgr-Food)*
Vince Harris *(Pres)*
Cindy Murphy *(Treas & Sec)*

UNION HEALTH CENTER
160 W 26th St 4th & 5th Fl, New York, NY 10001-6708
Tel.: (212) 924-2510 NY
Web Site:
http://www.unionhealthcenter.org
Year Founded: 1917
Sales Range: $10-24.9 Million
Emp.: 168
Health Care Srvices
N.A.I.C.S.: 622110
Keith Mestrich *(Treas)*

UNION HEALTH SERVICE, INC.
1634 W Polk St, Chicago, IL 60612
Tel.: (312) 423-4200 IL
Web Site: http://www.unionhealth.org
Sales Range: $50-74.9 Million
Voluntary Health Care Services
N.A.I.C.S.: 813212
W. Joe Garrett *(Exec Dir)*

UNION HOME MORTGAGE CORP.
8241 Dow Circle W, Strongsville, OH 44136
Tel.: (877) 846-4968
Web Site: https://www.uhm.com
Year Founded: 1970
Emp.: 100
Equal Housing Lender
N.A.I.C.S.: 522310
Bill Cosgrove *(Pres & CEO)*

Subsidiaries:

Amerifirst Financial Corporation (1)
950 Trade Centre Way Ste 400, Kalamazoo, MI 49002
Tel.: (269) 685-1441
Web Site: http://www.amerifirst.com
Real Estate Credit
N.A.I.C.S.: 522292
Dave Gahm *(Co-Founder & CEO)*
Mark Jones *(Co-Founder)*

UNION HOSPITAL
659 Boulevard St, Dover, OH 44622
Tel.: (330) 343-3311 OH
Web Site:
http://www.unionhospital.org
Year Founded: 1906
Sales Range: $100-124.9 Million
Emp.: 1,163
Health Care Srvices
N.A.I.C.S.: 622110
Diana L. Boyd *(VP-Nursing Svcs)*
Robert J. Craig *(VP-Professional Svcs)*
Darwin K. Smith *(VP-HR)*
Eugene A. Thorn III *(VP-Fin)*

UNION ICE LTD.
2970 E 50th St, Vernon, CA 90058
Tel.: (323) 277-1000
Web Site: http://www.unionice.com
Rev.: $14,391,197
Emp.: 120
Warehousing, Cold Storage Or Refrigerated
N.A.I.C.S.: 493120
Keith McMann *(Pres)*

UNION LEADER CORPORATION
100 William Loeb Dr, Manchester, NH 03109
Tel.: (603) 668-4321
Web Site:
http://www.theunionleader.com
Sales Range: $25-49.9 Million
Emp.: 335
Newspapers, Publishing & Printing
N.A.I.C.S.: 513110
Jim Normandin *(COO)*
Shannon Sullivan *(Mgr-Community Rels)*
Carl Perreault *(Dir-Ops-Online)*
Dirk Ruemenapp *(Exec VP)*

UNION METAL CORPORATION
1432 Maple Ave NE, Canton, OH 44705
Tel.: (330) 456-7653
Web Site: http://www.unionmetal.com
Sales Range: $50-74.9 Million
Emp.: 420
Fabricated Structural Metal
N.A.I.C.S.: 332312
Louis Capuano *(Mgr-Reg Sls)*
Timothy Francis *(Mgr-Sls-Utility Lighting)*
Greg Borocki *(Supvr-Quality Control)*
Randy Shaffer *(Dir-Engrg & Support Svcs)*
Kevin Spall *(Engr-Design)*
Tom Aber *(Dir-Bus Dev)*
Paul Irwin *(Mgr-Quality Control)*

U.S. PRIVATE

UNION MUTUAL FIRE INSURANCE CO.
139 State St, Montpelier, VT 05602
Tel.: (802) 223-5261
Web Site: http://www.umfic.com
Sales Range: $50-74.9 Million
Emp.: 60
Property Damage Insurance
N.A.I.C.S.: 524126
Lisa L. Keysar *(Pres & CEO)*
Jennifer P. Galfetti *(CFO & Treas)*
Gary H. Ouellette *(Exec VP)*
Robert Pembroke *(VP-IT)*
Pamela LaCount *(Asst VP-IT Dev)*

UNION PACIFIC RAILROAD EMPLOYEE HEALTH SYSTEMS INC.
1040 N 20200 W, Salt Lake City, UT 84116-1452
Tel.: (801) 595-4300
Web Site: http://www.uphealth.com
Year Founded: 1947
Sales Range: $25-49.9 Million
Emp.: 124
Pension, Health & Welfare Funds
N.A.I.C.S.: 525120
Dell Butterfield *(Pres)*
Pat Jensen *(Sec)*

UNION PARK AUTOMOTIVE GROUP, INC.
1704 Pennsylvania Ave, Wilmington, DE 19806
Tel.: (302) 658-7245
Web Site: http://www.unionpark.com
Sales Range: $25-49.9 Million
Emp.: 170
Car Whslr
N.A.I.C.S.: 441110
Jim Ursomarso *(Principal)*
Frank A. Ursomarso Jr. *(VP)*

UNION PARK CAPITAL
200 Newbury St, Boston, MA 02116
Tel.: (857) 254-1751
Web Site: http://www.union-park.com
Privater Equity Firm
N.A.I.C.S.: 523999
Morgan Jones *(Founder & Mng Partner)*
Peter McGuire *(Co-Partner)*
Brian McCafferty *(Co-Partner)*
Evan Stein *(Co-Partner)*
Michael Nestle *(VP)*
Jeff Steer *(VP-Talent)*

Subsidiaries:

Earth Networks, Inc. (1)
12410 Milestone Center Dr Ste 300, Germantown, MD 20876
Tel.: (301) 250-4000
Web Site: http://www.earthnetworks.com
Emp.: 144
Scientific & Technical Consulting Services
N.A.I.C.S.: 541690
Anuj Agrawal *(CMO)*

Exaktera LLC (1)
200 Newbury St, Boston, MA 02116
Tel.: (857) 254-1751
Web Site: http://www.exaktera.com
Electrical & Electronic Mfr
N.A.I.C.S.: 335999
Phil Martin *(CEO)*

Subsidiary (Domestic):

ProPhotonix Limited (2)
13 Red Roof Ln Ste 200, Salem, NH 03079
Tel.: (603) 893-8778
Web Site: http://www.prophotonix.com
Optical Subcomponents for Telecommunications Industry & Advance Illumination Systems for Machine Vision Industry
N.A.I.C.S.: 333310
Raymond Joseph Oglethorpe *(Chm)*
Timothy Paul Losik *(Pres & CEO)*
Simon Stanley *(Mng Dir-Ireland)*
Jeremy Lane *(Mng Dir-ProPhotonix UK)*
Edward Dolan *(CFO)*

Unit (Non-US):

ProPhotonix (3)
Sparrow Lane, Broad Oak, Hatfield, CM22 7BA, Herts, United Kingdom (100%)
Tel.: (44) 1279717170
Web Site: http://www.photonic-products.com
Sales Range: $100-124.9 Million
Emp.: 54
Custom Designed Laser Diode & Laser Assembly Mfr
N.A.I.C.S.: 335999
David McGuinness (Dir-Sls)
George Minott (Mgr-Sls-US East Coast)

ProPhotonix (3)
3020 Euro Business Park, Little Island, Co Cork, Ireland
Tel.: (353) 215001300
Web Site: http://www.prophotonix.com
Sales Range: $25-49.9 Million
Emp.: 60
LED-Based Illumination Products Mfr
N.A.I.C.S.: 335999

KPM Analytics, Inc. (1)
113 Cedar St, Milford, MA 01757
Tel.: (774) 462-6700
Web Site: http://www.pmanalytics.com
Privater Equity Firm
N.A.I.C.S.: 523999
Chris McIntire (CEO)
Rainer Roehrig (CFO)
Maurice Janssen (VP-Sls & Mktg)

Subsidiary (Domestic):

Smart Vision Works, LLC (2)
1345 N 1020 E, American Fork, UT 84003-3234
Tel.: (801) 592-7860
Web Site: http://www.smartvisionworks.com
Computer System Design Services
N.A.I.C.S.: 541512
Kirt Lillywhite (VP-R&D)
Chris Bryant (Pres)

UNION PEN COMPANY
PO Box 220, Hagaman, NY 12086 CT
Web Site:
    http://www.imprintsonline.com
Year Founded: 1904
Sales Range: $100-124.9 Million
Emp.: 140
Imprinted Promotional Products
N.A.I.C.S.: 561990

UNION POWER COOPERATIVE
1525 Rocky River Rd N, Monroe, NC 28110-7958
Tel.: (704) 289-3145 NC
Web Site: http://www.union-power.com
Year Founded: 1939
Sales Range: $25-49.9 Million
Emp.: 109
Electric Utility Distribution
N.A.I.C.S.: 221122
Jeremy Black (Mgr-IT Svcs)

UNION SANITARY DISTRICT
5072 Benson Rd, Union City, CA 94587-2508
Tel.: (510) 477-7500 CA
Web Site:
    http://www.unionsanitary.com
Year Founded: 1918
Sales Range: $25-49.9 Million
Emp.: 135
Sewerage Systems
N.A.I.C.S.: 221320
Michelle Powell (Coord-Comm)
Jennifer Toy (Pres)
Pat Kite (Sec)
Tom Handley (VP)

UNION SAVINGS & LOAN ASSOCIATION
353 Carandolet St, New Orleans, LA 70130
Tel.: (504) 522-5581
Year Founded: 1886

Savings Bank
N.A.I.C.S.: 522180
Stephen H. Schonberg (Pres & CEO)
Anthony S. Sciortino (Exec VP)

UNION SAVINGS BANK
226 Main St, Danbury, CT 06810-6635
Tel.: (203) 830-4200 CT
Web Site:
    http://www.unionsavings.com
Year Founded: 1866
Sales Range: $50-74.9 Million
Emp.: 250
Banking Services
N.A.I.C.S.: 522180
Cynthia C. Merkle (Pres & CEO)
Patricia A. Carlson (Sr VP & Mgr-Trust Dept)
John E. Celli (VP & Mgr-Investment Portfolio)
Susan E. Anderson (VP & Sr Mgr-Portfolio)
Jeff Levine (Chm)
Paul Bruce (CFO, Treas & Exec VP)
Peter Maher (Chief Lending Officer & Exec VP)
Joseph Morrissey (Sr VP & Head-Comml Lending)
Chris Daigle (Sr VP & Reg Mgr)
Shawn Gregory (VP & Mgr-Construction Lending)
Frederick F. Judd III (Exec VP-Wealth Mgmt)
Arnold E. Finaldi Jr. (Vice Chm)

UNION SAVINGS BANK
223 W Stephenson St, Freeport, IL 61032
Tel.: (815) 235-0800
Web Site:
    http://www.unionsavingsbank.com
Year Founded: 1883
Sales Range: $1-9.9 Million
Banking Services
N.A.I.C.S.: 522310
Albert Kersten (Sr VP)
Thomas A. Huber (Chm)

UNION SERVICE INDUSTRIES INC.
780 Rdg Lk Blvd Ste 102, Memphis, TN 38120
Tel.: (901) 683-4242
Sales Range: $10-24.9 Million
Emp.: 85
Warehousing Services
N.A.I.C.S.: 493130
Warren East (Pres & CEO)
Willis H. Willey III (Chm)

UNION SPECIAL CORPORATION
1 Union Special Plz, Huntley, IL 60142-7007
Tel.: (847) 669-5101 IL
Web Site:
    http://www.unionspecial.com
Year Founded: 1881
Industrial Sewing Machines Mfr & Automated Sewing Systems for Apparel Manufacturers
N.A.I.C.S.: 333248
Terence A. Hitpas (Pres & COO)

UNION SPORTSMEN'S ALLIANCE
235 Noah Dr Ste 200, Franklin, TN 37064
Tel.: (615) 831-6787 TN
Web Site:
    http://www.unionsportsmen.org
Year Founded: 2010
Sales Range: $1-9.9 Million
Emp.: 21

Conservation & Development Services
N.A.I.C.S.: 813312
Richard Trumka (Chm)
Scott Vance (CEO)
Brian Dowler (Dir-Membership, Mktg & Comm)
Forrest Parker (Dir-Conservation & Community Outreach)
Erik Frankl (COO)

UNION SPRING & MANUFACTURING CORP.
4268 Northern Pike Chamber of Commerce Bldg, Monroeville, PA 15146
Tel.: (412) 843-5900
Sales Range: $10-24.9 Million
Emp.: 50
Hot Formed Spring Services
N.A.I.C.S.: 332613
Ray Beacha (Pres)

UNION SQUARE VENTURES LLC
19 Bdwy 19th Fl, New York, NY 10010
Tel.: (212) 994-7880
Web Site: http://www.usv.com
Year Founded: 2003
Rev.: $450,000,000
Emp.: 12
Venture Capital
N.A.I.C.S.: 523150
Andy Weissman (Partner)
Albert Wenger (Partner)
John Buttrick (Partner)
Bradford R. Burnham (Founder & Mng Partner)
Rebecca Kaden (Gen Partner-Investment Team)
Nick Grossman (Partner)
Fred Wilson (Mng Partner)

UNION STATE BANCSHARES, INC.
204 Sherman St, Uniontown, KS 66779
Tel.: (620) 756-4305 KS
Web Site:
    http://www.unionstbank.com
Sales Range: $1-9.9 Million
Bank Holding Company
N.A.I.C.S.: 551111
Kenneth R. Holt (Pres)
Ken Holt (Mgr)

Subsidiaries:

Union State Bank (1)
204 Sherman St, Uniontown, KS 66779
Tel.: (620) 756-4305
Web Site: http://www.unionstbank.com
Sales Range: $1-9.9 Million
Commericial Banking
N.A.I.C.S.: 522110
Kenneth R. Holt (Pres)

UNION STATE BANK
201 W Court Ave, Winterset, IA 50273-1604
Tel.: (515) 462-2161 IA
Web Site: http://usbiowa.com
Year Founded: 1979
Rev.: $3,400,000
Emp.: 28
Commericial Banking
N.A.I.C.S.: 522110
Jeff Nolan (Pres & CEO)
Dave Koch (VP)

UNION STATION REDEVELOPMENT CORPORATION
10 G St NE Ste 504, Washington, DC 20002
Tel.: (202) 222-0271 DC
Web Site: http://www.usrcdc.com
Year Founded: 1983

Sales Range: $10-24.9 Million
Emp.: 6
Train Station Management Services
N.A.I.C.S.: 488210
Beverley K. Swaim-Staley (Pres & CEO)
Nzinga Baker (VP & Dir-Fin & Admin)

UNION TELEPHONE COMPANY INC.
850 N State Hwy 414, Mountain View, WY 82939
Tel.: (307) 782-6131 WY
Web Site: http://www.union-tel.com
Year Founded: 1914
Sales Range: $25-49.9 Million
Emp.: 170
Telephone Communications
N.A.I.C.S.: 517121
Howard D. Woody (Founder)
John D. Woody (CEO)

UNION TOWNSHIP ADULT COMMUNITY DEVELOPMENT CORPORATION
100 Frances Ct, Union, NJ 07083
Tel.: (908) 688-0565 NJ
Year Founded: 1978
Sales Range: $1-9.9 Million
Emp.: 12
Elder Care Services
N.A.I.C.S.: 623312
James Masterson (Pres)
Lula Young (VP)
Greg Muller (VP)
Jeannette Cantalupo (Treas)
Eugene O'Brien (Sec)

UNIONVALE COAL CO. INC.
210 E Main St, Ligonier, PA 15658-1318
Tel.: (724) 238-6601 DE
Year Founded: 1962
Sales Range: $10-24.9 Million
Emp.: 15
Coal & Other Minerals & Ores Mfr
N.A.I.C.S.: 423520
G Gray Garland (Chm)
Debra Oiler (Controller)

UNIPHARM INC.
350 5th Ave Ste 6500, New York, NY 10118
Tel.: (212) 594-3260
Web Site:
    http://www.unipharmus.com
Sales Range: $10-24.9 Million
Emp.: 12
Vitamin Preparations
N.A.I.C.S.: 325412
Ilya Sapritsky (Dir-Bus Dev)
Michael M. Tonucci (Mgr-Ops)
Chris Adamo (Gen Mgr)
Elena Prokhorova (Mgr-Ops)

UNIPRO FOODSERVICE INC.
2500 Cumberland Pkwy Ste 600, Atlanta, GA 30339-3932
Tel.: (770) 952-0871 DE
Web Site:
    http://www.uniprofoodservice.com
Year Founded: 1958
Sales Range: $100-124.9 Million
Emp.: 200
Dairy Products Distr
N.A.I.C.S.: 424430
Charlotte N. Phillips (Dir-HR)
Bill Golob (Mgr-IT)
Michele Beaman (Program Mgr)
Jim Zeck (VP)

UNIPROP, INC.
280 Daines St Ste 300, Birmingham, MI 48009
Tel.: (248) 645-9220 MI

UNIPROP, INC.

Uniprop, Inc.—(Continued)
Web Site: http://www.uniprop.com
Year Founded: 1970
Sales Range: $25-49.9 Million
Emp.: 350
Holding Company; Real Estate & Private Equity Investment
N.A.I.C.S.: 551112
Roger I. Zlotoff *(Pres)*
Paul M. Zlotoff *(Chm)*
Susann Kehrig *(VP-Fin & Controller)*

Subsidiaries:

Michigan Chandelier Company, LLC (1)
20855 Telegraph Rd, Southfield, MI 48033
Tel.: (248) 353-0510
Web Site: http://www.michand.com
Lighting Fixture Distr
N.A.I.C.S.: 423610
Ken Sanders *(Pres)*
John Testasecca *(Mgr-Sls)*

Uniprop Homes Inc. (1)
280 Daines St Ste 300, Birmingham, MI 48009
Tel.: (248) 645-9220
Web Site: https://www.uniprop.com
Sales Range: $1-9.9 Million
Emp.: 50
New & Used Mobile Home Seller
N.A.I.C.S.: 531210
Roger I. Zlotoff *(Pres)*
Roger Zlotoff *(Pres)*
Roger Zlotoff *(Pres)*

UNIQUE AIR SERVICES INC.
4515 19th St Court E, Bradenton, FL 34203
Tel.: (941) 377-0153
Web Site: http://www.uniqueservices.com
Sales Range: $10-24.9 Million
Emp.: 100
HVAC, Plumbing & Electrical
N.A.I.C.S.: 238220
Mike Montgomery *(Pres & CEO)*

UNIQUE BALANCE, INC.
557 Finegan Rd, Del Rio, TX 78840
Tel.: (830) 768-0057
Web Site: http://www.unique-balance.com
Sales Range: $10-24.9 Million
Emp.: 192
Window Mfr
N.A.I.C.S.: 332321
Dave Gurney *(Gen Mgr-Birmingham-UK)*
Dale Shuler *(Gen Mgr)*

UNIQUE DIGITAL TECHNOLOGY
10595 Westoffice Dr, Houston, TX 77042
Tel.: (713) 777-0447
Web Site: http://www.uniquedigital.com
Year Founded: 1986
Sales Range: $10-24.9 Million
Emp.: 20
Provider of Computer Related Engineering Services
N.A.I.C.S.: 541512
Stephanie Huffman *(Mgr-Inside Sls)*

UNIQUE LIMOUSINE, INC.
1900 Crooked Hill Rd, Harrisburg, PA 17110-9319
Tel.: (717) 233-4731
Web Site: http://www.uniquelimousine.com
Passenger Car Rental & Limousine Services
N.A.I.C.S.: 532111
Jim Salginger *(Owner)*

Subsidiaries:

At Your Service Limousines, Inc. (1)
3965 Roxton Ave, Los Angeles, CA 90008-2717
Tel.: (323) 299-7693
Web Site: http://www.yourservicelimos.com
Limousine Service
N.A.I.C.S.: 485320
Byron McKnight *(Pres)*

UNIQUE WHOLESALE DISTRIBUTORS, INC.
6811 NW 15th Ave, Fort Lauderdale, FL 33309
Tel.: (954) 975-0227
Web Site: http://www.uniquewholesale.net
Year Founded: 1980
Sales Range: $10-24.9 Million
Emp.: 90
Home Furnishing Merchant Whslr
N.A.I.C.S.: 423220
Christopher L. Collins *(CFO)*
Sal Nocera *(Dir-Sls)*

UNIQUE WINDOWS & DOORS
5550 Progress Rd, Indianapolis, IN 46241-4331
Tel.: (317) 337-9300
Web Site: http://www.uniquewindowanddoor.com
Rev.: $15,800,000
Emp.: 110
Window & Door Sales
N.A.I.C.S.: 444110
Robert D. Dillon *(Pres)*

UNIQUESOURCE
1007 N Front St, Harrisburg, PA 17110-0865
Tel.: (717) 236-3610 PA
Web Site: http://www.uniquesource.com
Year Founded: 1956
Sales Range: $1-9.9 Million
Emp.: 53
Disabled People Assistance Services
N.A.I.C.S.: 624120
Vincent M. Loose *(Pres & CEO)*
Perry Snyder *(CFO)*
Danette Blank *(Sec)*
Jonathan Fister *(Chm)*
Robert Garrett *(Treas)*

UNISA HOLDINGS INCORPORATED
6701 Nw 7th St Ste 125, Miami, FL 33126-6032
Tel.: (305) 591-9397 DE
Year Founded: 1973
Sales Range: $50-74.9 Million
Emp.: 220
Holding Company; Footwear Retail & Wholesale
N.A.I.C.S.: 551112
Grissel Hernandez *(Controller)*
Albert Salazar *(Mgr-Mgmt Info.Sys)*

Subsidiaries:

Coconut Enterprises Inc. (1)
6701 Nw 7th St Ste 125, Miami, FL 33126-6032
Tel.: (305) 591-9397
Web Site: http://www.unisa.com
Sales Range: $25-49.9 Million
Emp.: 5
Retailer of Shoes
N.A.I.C.S.: 458210

Coconuts in the Grove Inc. (1)
10814 Northwest 33rd St Ste 100, Miami, FL 33172-2190
Tel.: (305) 591-9397
Web Site: http://www.unisa.com
Sales Range: $25-49.9 Million
Emp.: 100
Retailer of Shoes
N.A.I.C.S.: 458210

Unisa (1)
8888 Howard Dr, Miami, FL 33166
Tel.: (305) 235-2085
Sales Range: $10-24.9 Million
Emp.: 6
Retailer of Shoes
N.A.I.C.S.: 458210

Unisa America Inc. (1)
10814 NW 33rd St Ste 100, Miami, FL 33172-2190
Tel.: (305) 591-9397
Web Site: http://www.shopunisa.com
Sales Range: $25-49.9 Million
Emp.: 10
Mfr of Footwear
N.A.I.C.S.: 424340

Unisa Europa Holdings Inc. (1)
6701 Nw 7th St Ste 125, Miami, FL 33126-6032
Tel.: (305) 591-9397
Sales Range: $10-24.9 Million
Emp.: 10
Mfr of Footwear
N.A.I.C.S.: 424340

Subsidiary (Non-US):

Unisa Europa SA (2)
Poligono XB Parcela 56, Xinorlet Monovar, 3649, Alicante, Spain
Tel.: (34) 966979610
Web Site: http://www.unisa-europa.com
Footwear Mfr
N.A.I.C.S.: 316210
Antonio Porta *(Gen Mgr)*

UNISHIPPERS ASSOCIATION INC.
7158 S Flsmidth Dr Ste 200, Salt Lake City, UT 84047
Tel.: (801) 487-0600
Web Site: http://www.unishippers.com
Year Founded: 1987
Sales Range: $200-249.9 Million
Emp.: 1,000
Provider of Shipping Services
N.A.I.C.S.: 561499
Steve Leavitt *(Pres)*
Kevin Lathrop *(CIO & Exec VP)*
Alison Smith *(VP-Ops)*
Dan Lockwood *(Exec Chm)*

UNISON CONSULTING, INC.
409 W Huron St Ste 400, Chicago, IL 60654
Tel.: (312) 988-3360
Web Site: http://www.unison-ucg.com
Year Founded: 1989
Sales Range: $10-24.9 Million
Emp.: 43
Aviation Consulting Services
N.A.I.C.S.: 541611
Anthony Drake *(Exec VP)*
Donald C. Arthur *(Principal)*
Sharon Sarmiento *(Principal)*

UNISON PACIFIC CORPORATION
1001 Bayhill Dr 2nd Fl, San Bruno, CA 94066
Tel.: (650) 877-0780 OH
Year Founded: 1979
Rev.: $10,000,000
Emp.: 275
Management Services
N.A.I.C.S.: 561110

Subsidiaries:

UniHorn, Inc. (1)
1001 Bayhill Dr, San Bruno, CA 94066
Tel.: (650) 877-0780
Rev.: $3,500,000
Emp.: 3
Custom Computer Programming Services
N.A.I.C.S.: 541511

Unison International Corp. (1)
1001 Bayhill Dr, San Bruno, CA 94066

Tel.: (650) 877-0780
Web Site: http://www.unison-group.com
Rev.: $4,100,000
Emp.: 9
Industrial Machinery & Equipment
N.A.I.C.S.: 423830

UNISON SYSTEMS, INC.
6130 Greenwood Plaza Blvd Ste 100, Greenwood Village, CO 80111
Tel.: (303) 623-8800
Web Site: http://www.unisonsystems.com
Year Founded: 1997
Sales Range: $10-24.9 Million
Emp.: 120
IT Consulting Services & Customized Software Applications
N.A.I.C.S.: 513210
Lukas Hurst *(Pres)*
Debbie Chrenen *(Dir-Ops)*

UNISOURCE SOLUTIONS INC.
8350 Rex Rd, Pico Rivera, CA 90660
Tel.: (562) 949-1111
Web Site: http://www.unisourceit.com
Sales Range: $10-24.9 Million
Emp.: 105
Mfr & Sales of Office Furniture
N.A.I.C.S.: 423210
Clem Mieto *(Controller)*
Allan Kennedy *(Acct Mgr)*
Rick Bartlett *(Pres)*
Jim Kastner *(CEO)*

UNISSANT, INC.
12310 Pinecrest Rd Ste 202, Reston, VA 20191
Tel.: (703) 889-8500
Web Site: http://unissant.com
Year Founded: 1999
Sales Range: $10-24.9 Million
Emp.: 85
Software Development & Consulting Services
N.A.I.C.S.: 541618
Manish Malhotra *(Chm & CEO)*
Jango Unwalla *(CMO)*
Eric T. Hartung *(CIO)*
David P. Dougherty *(Sr VP-Ops)*
Beth Hiatt *(COO)*
Jay Wright *(VP-Fin Svcs)*
Paul A. Aronhime *(VP-Bus Dev)*
Kenneth Bonner *(Exec VP-Federal Growth)*
Venkat Kodumudi *(CTO)*
Macon Hardy *(Sr VP-Bus Dev)*
Kimberly Finnegan *(Sr VP-Growth-Federal Health)*
Umme Hasnain *(Chief Admin Officer & Sr VP-Bus Ops)*
Davy Simanivanh *(Dir-Mktg & Comm)*
Craig Janus *(Chief Strategy & Revenue Officer)*
Ian Graham *(VP & Gen Mgr)*

UNISTAN INC.
5500 United Dr SE, Smyrna, GA 30082
Tel.: (678) 305-2000
Web Site: http://www.unitedistinc.com
Sales Range: $400-449.9 Million
Emp.: 1,300
Beer, Liquor, Wine & Non-Alcoholic Beverages
N.A.I.C.S.: 424810
Douglas J. Hertz *(Pres)*
Carolyn Aston *(Controller)*

Subsidiaries:

United Distributors, Inc. (1)
5500 United Dr, Smyrna, GA 30082-4755
Tel.: (678) 305-2000
Web Site: http://www.udiga.com
Sales Range: $50-74.9 Million
Emp.: 1,000
Wine, Beer, Liquor & Non-Alcoholic Beverages Distr
N.A.I.C.S.: 424820

COMPANIES

David Gregory *(Gen Mgr-Spirits)*
Pete Moraitakis *(Pres & COO)*
John Ramsaur *(Gen Mgr-Wine)*
Don Hovde *(CFO)*
Virginia Means *(Chief People Officer)*

Subsidiary (Domestic):

MBC United Wholesale LLC (2)
3181 Selma Hwy, Montgomery, AL 36108
Tel.: (334) 284-0550
Sales Range: $25-49.9 Million
Emp.: 200
Wine Distr
N.A.I.C.S.: 424820

UNISTAR FOODS, INC.
128 N Gibbs St, Pomona, CA 91769
Tel.: (909) 622-9611 CA
Web Site:
http://www.unistarfoodsinc.com
Year Founded: 1986
Rev.: $12,000,000
Emp.: 18
Meats & Meat Products
N.A.I.C.S.: 424470

UNISTAR PLASTICS LLC
5821 Citrus Blvd, Harahan, LA 70123
Tel.: (504) 738-8838
Web Site:
http://www.unistarplastics.com
Year Founded: 1986
Sales Range: $10-24.9 Million
Emp.: 28
Mfr of Plastics
N.A.I.C.S.: 322220
Greg Tan *(Pres)*
Donald Ward *(Dir-Sls & Mktg)*
Tina Roberts *(Mgr-Traffic)*
Nilo Martins Jr. *(Supvr-Maintenance)*

UNISTAR-SPARCO COMPUTERS INC.
7089 Ryburn Dr, Millington, TN 38053
Tel.: (901) 872-2272
Web Site: http://www.sparco.com
Year Founded: 1992
Sales Range: $25-49.9 Million
Emp.: 29
Computer Hardware & Software
N.A.I.C.S.: 423430
Soo Tsong Lim *(Pres)*

UNIT DROP FORGE CO., INC.
1903 S 62nd St, West Allis, WI 53219
Tel.: (414) 545-3000 WI
Web Site:
http://www.unitforgings.com
Provider of Forgings
N.A.I.C.S.: 332111
Paul Spitz *(VP-Sls & Mktg)*
Janis Pawlak *(Controller-Accts Payable)*
Jason Pofahl *(Mgr-Systems)*
Jim Knight *(Mgr-Engrg)*
Kristy Hunt *(Coord-Railroad Products & Outside Matl)*
Chris Westra *(VP-Mfg)*
Ronald Janzen *(Pres & Gen Mgr)*

UNITAS GLOBAL LLC
910 W Van Buren St Ste 605, Chicago, IL 60607
Tel.: (213) 785-6200
Web Site:
http://www.unitasglobal.com
Year Founded: 2011
Information Technology Services
N.A.I.C.S.: 519290
Patrick Shutt *(CEO)*
Grant Kirkwood *(Co-Founder & CTO)*
Bob Pollan *(CFO)*
Steve Neiger *(Chief Revenue Officer)*
Ian Gillott *(COO)*
Francesco Paola *(Chief Strategy Officer)*

Scott Walker *(Chief Marketing Officer)*
Farrah Kashef *(Co-Founder & VP-Strategic Partnerships & Alliances)*
Erik Salazar *(Co-Founder & VP-Comml Dev)*
Lawrence Lee *(Co-Founder, VP & Partner-Alliances)*
Paul Weinstein *(Chm)*
Kelvin Lai *(Chief Administrative Officer)*
Saam Dowlatshahi *(Sr VP-Global Ops & Integration Procurement)*
Joss Wynne Evans *(Head-Legal Affairs)*
Paco Diaz *(Chief Compliance Officer)*
Elaine Gilruth *(VP-Mktg)*
Janet Kim *(Sr VP-Fin)*
Frank Muscarello *(Chief Development Officer)*

UNITE HERE
275 7th Ave 16 Fl, New York, NY 10001-6708
Tel.: (212) 265-7000
Web Site: https://www.unitehere.org
Year Founded: 2004
Sales Range: $300-349.9 Million
Emp.: 1,100
Labor Union
N.A.I.C.S.: 813920
Pamela Vossenas *(Coord-Workplace Safety & Health)*
Andrea van den Heever *(Dir-Community Org Programs)*
Theresa McGuire *(Dir-Res Dept)*
Linda Muller *(Office Mgr)*
Enrique Fernandez *(Mgr-Bus)*
Peter Ward *(Mgr-Bus)*

UNITE HERE HEALTH
711 N Commons Dr, Aurora, IL 60598-0020
Tel.: (630) 236-5100 IL
Web Site:
http://www.unitherehealth.org
Year Founded: 1974
Sales Range: $800-899.9 Million
Emp.: 352
Health & Welfare Benefit Services
N.A.I.C.S.: 525120
Matthew Walker *(CEO)*
Dolores Michael *(COO)*
D. Taylor *(Chm)*
Jim DuPont *(Dir-Food Svc Div)*
Joel Vandevusse *(CFO)*

UNITED ABRASIVES INC.
185 Boston Post Rd, North Windham, CT 06256
Tel.: (860) 456-7131
Web Site:
http://www.unitedabrasives.com
Rev.: $21,400,000
Emp.: 300
Abrasive Products
N.A.I.C.S.: 327910
Aris Marziali *(Chm)*
Chris Comer *(Controller)*
Ron Gehen *(Dir-Sls-Central & North America)*
Michael Smyth *(Plant Mgr)*

UNITED ADMINISTRATIVE SERVICES
6800 Santa Teresa Blvd Ste 100, San Jose, CA 95119
Tel.: (408) 288-4400 CA
Web Site: http://www.uastpa.com
Year Founded: 1947
Pension Health & Welfare Funds
N.A.I.C.S.: 525110
David Andersen *(Owner & Pres)*
Debora Wolfe *(Sec)*
Sandy Stephenson *(VP-Admin)*

UNITED AG SERVICE INC.
129 Clifford St, Gorham, KS 67640
Tel.: (785) 637-5481
Web Site: http://www.unitedag.coop
Sales Range: $10-24.9 Million
Emp.: 42
Grain Elevators
N.A.I.C.S.: 424510
John Lapka Jr. *(Gen Mgr)*

UNITED AGRICULTURAL CO-OPERATIVE INC.
911 S Wharton St, El Campo, TX 77437
Tel.: (979) 543-6284
Web Site: http://www.unitedag.net
Sales Range: $25-49.9 Million
Emp.: 60
Agriculture Product Distr
N.A.I.C.S.: 424510
Jimmy N. Roppolo *(Gen Mgr)*
April Graves *(Controller)*

UNITED AIR CONDITIONING & HEATING COMPANY, INC.
13150 Belcher Rd S, Largo, FL 33773
Tel.: (727) 470-6803
Web Site:
http://www.unitedairconditioning.com
Year Founded: 1961
Warm Air Heating & Air Conditioning Contractor
N.A.I.C.S.: 238220

UNITED AIR-TEMP AC & HEATING
6900 Hill Park Dr, Lorton, VA 22079
Tel.: (703) 516-8316
Web Site:
http://www.unitedairtemp.com
Rev.: $14,609,760
Emp.: 200
Warm Air Heating & Air Conditioning Contractor
N.A.I.C.S.: 238220
Gabe Ivanescu *(CEO)*
Mike Giordano *(Pres)*
Ken Smith *(Mng Partner)*

UNITED ALLOY, INC.
4100 Kennedy Rd, Janesville, WI 53545
Tel.: (608) 758-4717
Web Site: http://www.unitedalloy.com
Year Founded: 1999
Sales Range: $10-24.9 Million
Emp.: 150
Fabricated Structural Metal Mfr
N.A.I.C.S.: 332312
Holly Backhaus *(COO)*
Michael Coyle *(VP-Engrg)*
Rick Sullivan *(Mgr-Facility)*
Jenna Newcomb *(Mgr-Production Control)*

UNITED ALUMINUM CORPORATION
100 United Dr, North Haven, CT 06473-3218
Tel.: (203) 239-5881 CT
Web Site:
http://www.unitedaluminum.com
Sales Range: $75-99.9 Million
Emp.: 150
Brazing Sheets, Aluminum Coiled Sheets & Strips Mfr
N.A.I.C.S.: 331315
John S. Lapides *(Pres)*

UNITED AMERICAN PETROLEUM CORP.
9600 Great Hills Trail Ste 150W, Austin, TX 78759
Tel.: (512) 852-7888 NV

UNITED AUTOMOBILE INSURANCE GROUP, INC.

Web Site:
http://www.unitedamericanpetroleum.com
Sales Range: Less than $1 Million
Emp.: 3
Oil & Gas Exploration Services
N.A.I.C.S.: 211120
Michael Douglas Carey *(Pres, CEO, CFO & Treas)*
Ryan Charles Hudson *(COO & Sec)*
Tula Cox *(Mgr-Acctg)*

UNITED ANIMAL HEALTH, INC.
4310 W State Rd 38 W, Sheridan, IN 46069
Tel.: (317) 758-4495 IN
Web Site: http://www.unitedanh.com
Year Founded: 1956
Sales Range: $300-349.9 Million
Emp.: 400
Livestock Feeds
N.A.I.C.S.: 311119
John Corbett *(Chm)*
Trent Torrance *(VP-Animal Nutrition & Health)*
Doug M. Webel *(Pres & CEO)*
Ellen Swisher Crabb *(Vice Chm)*
Steve D. Biddle *(VP)*

Subsidiaries:

Mid-Central Products LLC (1)
322 S main st, Sheridan, IN 46069
Tel.: (317) 758-2699
Web Site: http://www.mid-central.com
Emp.: 2
Farm Supplies Whslr
N.A.I.C.S.: 424910
Jan Powell *(Pres)*

United Pig Placement Services (1)
322 S Main St, Sheridan, IN 46069
Web Site: http://www.pigmover.com
Swine Management Services
N.A.I.C.S.: 541611
Scott Kosher *(Mgr)*

UNITED AUTO SUPPLY
450 Tracy St, Syracuse, NY 13204
Tel.: (315) 478-4242
Web Site:
http://www.unitedautosupply.com
Rev.: $13,325,515
Emp.: 100
Automotive Supplies & Parts
N.A.I.C.S.: 423120
Kim Discenza *(Controller)*
Chip Raven *(Gen Mgr)*
James Ranalli Jr. *(Pres)*

UNITED AUTO SUPPLY INC.
625 3rd St S, La Crosse, WI 54601
Tel.: (608) 784-9198
Web Site: http://www.uasparts.com
Sales Range: $10-24.9 Million
Emp.: 15
Automotive Supplies & Parts
N.A.I.C.S.: 423120

UNITED AUTOMOBILE INSURANCE GROUP, INC.
3909 NE 163rd St Ste 308, Miami, FL 33160
Tel.: (305) 940-5022 FL
Web Site: http://www.uaig.net
Year Founded: 2000
Sales Range: $350-399.9 Million
Emp.: 800
Automobile Insurance
N.A.I.C.S.: 524126
Richard Parrillo *(Pres)*
Abraham Estevez *(Dir-IT)*
Charles Grimsley *(Chief Legal Officer & Gen Counsel)*
George Tarsitano *(Sr VP-Mktg)*
Jack Ramirez *(COO)*
Juan Ferrer *(Sr VP-Ops)*
Paul Polacheck *(CFO)*
Sandra Iglesias *(Sr VP-Claims)*

UNITED BAKING CO., INC.

United Baking Co., Inc.—(Continued)

UNITED BAKING CO., INC.
41 Natcon Dr, Shirley, NY 11967
Tel.: (631) 205-0455 NY
Web Site:
http://www.unclewallys.com
Year Founded: 1993
Sales Range: $10-24.9 Million
Emp.: 74
Muffin Mfr & Whslr
N.A.I.C.S.: 311821
Louis Avignone (Pres & CEO)
Jim Farrell (Dir-Ops)

UNITED BANCSHARES, INC.
500 Virginia St E, Charleston, WV 25301
Tel.: (215) 351-4600 PA
Web Site:
http://www.irsolutions.snl.com
Year Founded: 1993
Sales Range: $1-9.9 Million
Bank Holding Company
N.A.I.C.S.: 551111
L. Armstead Edwards (Chm)
William B. Moore (Vice Chm)
Evelyn F. Smalls (Pres & CEO)
Brenda M. Hudson-Nelson (CFO & Exec VP)

Subsidiaries:

United Bank of Philadelphia (1)
The Graham Bldg 30 S 15th St Ste 1200, Philadelphia, PA 19102
Tel.: (215) 351-4600
Web Site: http://www.ubphila.com
Commericial Banking
N.A.I.C.S.: 522110
Dimitria Davenport (Asst VP-Compliance & Admin)
Evelyn F. Smalls (Pres & CEO)
Brenda M. Hudson-Nelson (CFO & Exec VP)
Norman W. Greene (Chief Risk Officer & VP)

UNITED BANK & TRUST COMPANY
400 Central Ave E, Hampton, IA 50441
Tel.: (641) 456-5587 IA
Web Site: http://www.ubtc.net
Year Founded: 1915
Sales Range: $10-24.9 Million
Emp.: 25
Personal, Commercial & Agricultural Banking & Trust Services
N.A.I.C.S.: 522110
Arlene K. Noss (COO & VP)
John J. Trewin (Pres & CEO)
Larry P. Miller (VP-Ag Lending)
Rebecca J. Strother (VP-Mktg & Ops)
Andrea Jones (Officer-Personal Banking)
Barbara J. Swanson (Officer-Personal Banking)
Brenda M. Bradley (Officer-Personal Banking)
Grant Petersen (VP)
Jane A. Weiland (Officer-Compliance & Consumer Loan)
Lynette F. Mossman (Officer-Loan)
Rick Rosburg (VP)
Shawn B. Loughren (VP)

UNITED BANK CORPORATION
308 Thomaston St, Barnesville, GA 30204
Tel.: (770) 358-7211
Web Site:
http://www.accessunited.com
Year Founded: 1981
Sales Range: $50-74.9 Million
Emp.: 368
Bank Holding Company
N.A.I.C.S.: 551111

Scott W. Swafford (COO)
Christopher C. Edwards (CIO)
Thomas L. Redding (CFO)
Allie E. Armistead (Sr VP)
Harry G. Kozee (Sr VP)
Jennifer W. Eavenson (Exec VP & Dir-HR)
Lisa J. Maxwell (Sr VP & Mgr-Ops)
Lori S. Tucker (Exec VP & Mgr-Retail Delivery)
Thomas W. Williams (Sr VP & Mgr-Compliance)
Travis J. Weed (Sr VP)
James J. Edwards Jr. (Co-Chm & CEO)
John W. Edwards Jr. (Co-Chm)

Subsidiaries:

United Bank (1)
685 Griffin St, Zebulon, GA 30295
Tel.: (770) 567-7211
Web Site: http://www.accessunited.com
Sales Range: $50-74.9 Million
Commercial Banking Services
N.A.I.C.S.: 522110
Christopher C. Edwards (CIO)
Douglas J. Tuttle (COO)
Thomas L. Redding (CFO)
Scott W. Swafford (Chief Credit Officer)
John W. Edwards Jr. (Chm)
J. Joseph Edwards Sr. (Vice Chm)
James J. Edwards Jr. (CEO)

UNITED BILT HOMES INCORPORATED
8500 Line Ave, Shreveport, LA 71106
Tel.: (318) 861-4572
Web Site: http://www.ubh.com
Sales Range: $10-24.9 Million
Emp.: 25
Speculative Builder, Single-Family Houses
N.A.I.C.S.: 236115
Donald R. Pitts (Pres)
Craig Young (Exec VP)

UNITED BIOMEDICAL INC.
25 Davids Dr, Hauppauge, NY 11788-2037
Tel.: (631) 273-2828 NY
Web Site:
http://www.unitedbiomedical.com
Sales Range: $25-49.9 Million
Emp.: 350
Develops Therapeutic, Vaccine & Diagnostic Products for Human & Veterinary Use
N.A.I.C.S.: 621511
Chang Yi Wang (Co-Founder, Chm & CEO)
Nean Hu (Co-Founder, Pres & CFO)
Fran Volz (Mgr-Bus Dev)

UNITED BRASS WORKS INC.
714 S Main St, Randleman, NC 27317
Tel.: (336) 498-2661
Web Site: http://www.ubw.com
Sales Range: $10-24.9 Million
Emp.: 130
Industrial Valves
N.A.I.C.S.: 332911
Michael Berkelhammer (Pres)
Liz Runkel (Controller)
Jim Sattler (Mgr-Sls)
Tommy Hall (Engr-Design)

UNITED BUILDING MAINTENANCE, INC.
165 Easy St, Carol Stream, IL 60188
Tel.: (630) 653-4848
Web Site: http://www.ubm-usa.com
Year Founded: 1979
Sales Range: $100-124.9 Million
Emp.: 1,000
Building Maintenance Services
N.A.I.C.S.: 561790

James S. Cabrera (Pres)

UNITED CABINET COMPANY, LLC
3650 Trousdale Dr, Nashville, TN 37204
Tel.: (615) 833-1961 TN
Web Site: http://www.kabinart.com
Year Founded: 1963
Emp.: 140
Wood Kitchen Cabinet Mfr
N.A.I.C.S.: 337110
David Gordon (Pres)

UNITED CANNABIS CORPORATION
301 Commercial Rd Unit D, Golden, CO 80401
Tel.: (303) 386-7104 CO
Web Site:
http://www.unitedcannabis.us
Year Founded: 2007
Rev.: $7,244,625
Assets: $12,893,232
Liabilities: $5,590,255
Net Worth: $7,302,977
Earnings: ($24,104,551)
Emp.: 65
Fiscal Year-end: 12/31/18
Business Support & Consulting Services to the Cannabis Industry
N.A.I.C.S.: 561499
John Walsh (CFO)

UNITED CAPITAL CONSULTANTS, INC.
3210 E Coralbell Ave, Mesa, AZ 85204
Tel.: (480) 666-4116 DE
Web Site:
http://www.ucconsultantsinc.com
Year Founded: 2016
Assets: $65,761
Liabilities: $50,000
Net Worth: $15,761
Earnings: ($48,907)
Fiscal Year-end: 12/31/21
Business Development & Management Consulting Services
N.A.I.C.S.: 541611
Clayton Patterson (Pres, CEO & Sec)
Harold Patterson (CFO & Treas)
Michael Brungard (Head-Project Engrg)
Supakon Lertmongkon (Head-Govt Rels)
Robert Buss (Head-Res & Compliance)
Lona King (Head-HR & Controller)

UNITED CAPITAL CORP.
United Capital Bldg 9 Park Pl 4th Fl, Great Neck, NY 11021
Tel.: (516) 466-6464 DE
Web Site:
http://www.unitedcapitalcorp.net
Year Founded: 1980
Sales Range: $100-124.9 Million
Emp.: 630
Real Estate Investment & Management Services, Hotel Operations & Engineering Products Mfr
N.A.I.C.S.: 531390
Anthony J. Miceli (CFO)
Michael J. Weinbaum (VP-Real Estate Ops)
Stephen Kronick (VP)
Gary A. Rosenberg (Corp Controller)
Rochelle Laufer (Gen Counsel)
Steve A. Lawrence (Mgr-Property)
Stacey A. O'Brien (Controller-Real Estate)
Michael McCurdy (VP-Hotel Ops)

Subsidiaries:

AFP Transformers, Inc. (1)

U.S. PRIVATE

206 Talmadge Rd, Edison, NJ 08817-2824 (100%)
Tel.: (732) 248-0305
Web Site: http://www.afp-transformers.com
Sales Range: $25-49.9 Million
Emp.: 50
Mfr of Transformers
N.A.I.C.S.: 335311
Greg Vongas (Pres)

Metal Textiles Corporation (1)
970 New Durham Rd, Edison, NJ 08818 (100%)
Tel.: (732) 287-0800
Web Site: http://www.metexcorp.com
Sales Range: $75-99.9 Million
Emp.: 200
Fabricated Wire Product Mfr
N.A.I.C.S.: 332618
Greg Vongas (Pres)

UNITED CAPITAL FUNDING CORP.
146 2nd St N Ste 200, Saint Petersburg, FL 33701
Tel.: (727) 894-8232 FL
Web Site: http://www.ucfunding.com
Year Founded: 1997
Sales Range: $1-9.9 Million
Emp.: 18
Nondepository Credit Intermediation
N.A.I.C.S.: 522299
Chris Youmans (Pres & Mng Partner)
Ivan Baker (CFO & Mng Partner)
Mark Mandula (CMO & Mng Partner)

UNITED CAPITAL MARKETS HOLDINGS, INC.
240 Crandon Blvd Ste 167, Key Biscayne, FL 33149
Tel.: (305) 365-0527 FL
Web Site:
http://www.unitedcapital.com
Year Founded: 1999
Sales Range: $150-199.9 Million
Emp.: 20
Financial & Investment Advisory Services
N.A.I.C.S.: 525990
Dennis Devaney (CEO)

UNITED CHARITABLE PROGRAMS
8201 Greesnboro Dr Ste 702, Tysons, VA 22102
Tel.: (571) 620-3000 VA
Web Site:
http://www.unitedcharitable.org
Year Founded: 2005
Sales Range: $10-24.9 Million
Grantmaking Services
N.A.I.C.S.: 813219
Marian H. Houk (Dir-Program Ops)
Katie Kern (Dir-Program Ops)
Julie L. Houk (Dir-Mktg)
David Koury (Controller)
Julia Healey (Dir-Fin)
Jan Ridgely (CEO)
Stacy Summit (Mgr-Acctg)
Melanie Macatangay (Program Coord)
Lyn Haston (Chm)
Bruce Mcclintock (Vice Chm)
Matteo Sabattini (Treas)
Dave Finnigan (Sec)

UNITED CHURCH HOMES AND SERVICES
100 Leonard Ave, Newton, NC 28658
Tel.: (828) 464-8264 NC
Web Site: http://www.uchas.org
Year Founded: 1961
Sales Range: $25-49.9 Million
Emp.: 753
Senior Living Center
N.A.I.C.S.: 624120

Lee Syria *(Pres & CEO)*
Aimee Reimann *(COO)*
J. Ray Deal *(Chm)*
Anthony J. Branch *(Treas)*
Mark L. Burns *(Sec)*
Gary Shull *(CFO)*
Linda J. Morris *(Vice Chm)*
Steve Paterson *(Chief Quality & Compliance Officer)*
Sarah Snell *(Sec)*
Cathy Cooper *(Chief HR Officer)*
Joy Cline *(Chief Mktg & PR Officer)*

UNITED CHURCH OF CHRIST HOMES, INC.
30 N 31st St, Camp Hill, PA 17011
Tel.: (717) 303-1502   PA
Web Site: http://www.ucc-homes.org
Year Founded: 1962
Sales Range: $50-74.9 Million
Emp.: 855
Lifecare Retirement Community Operator
N.A.I.C.S.: 623311
Stephen Horvath *(Pres & CEO)*
Laurence Kilpatrick *(CFO & VP-Fin)*
Beth McMaster *(COO & VP-Ops)*
Debra Keller *(Dir-HR)*
Victoria Velez *(Dir-PR & Dev)*

UNITED CLAIM SOLUTIONS, LLC
23048 N 15th Ave, Phoenix, AZ 85027
Web Site: http://www.valenzhealth.com
Year Founded: 2004
Sales Range: $1-9.9 Million
Emp.: 200
Health Care Srvices
N.A.I.C.S.: 621610
Rob Gelb *(CEO)*
Larry Eisel *(CFO)*
Amy Gasbarro *(COO)*
Ed Zwicker *(VP-IT)*
Pamela Burns *(VP-Bus Dev)*

Subsidiaries:

Certus Management Group   (1)
300 N Meridian St, Indianapolis, IN 46204
Tel.: (877) 884-6475
Web Site: http://www.certusmg.com
Stop-Loss Insurance Services
N.A.I.C.S.: 524298
Brad Lewis *(Principal, Pres & CEO)*
Beth Madden *(Principal & COO)*
Steve Butz *(Principal & Exec VP-Bus Dev)*
Greg Edwards *(Principal & Exec VP-Bus Dev)*

UNITED COLOR MANUFACTURING
660 Newtown Yardley Rd Ste 205, Newtown, PA 18940
Tel.: (215) 860-2165
Web Site: http://www.unitedcolor.com
Sales Range: $10-24.9 Million
Emp.: 22
Mfr of Dyes & Pigments
N.A.I.C.S.: 325130
Bill Kelly *(Mgr-Sls-Export)*
Thomas E. Nowakowski Sr. *(Pres)*

UNITED COM-SERVE
989 Plumas St, Yuba City, CA 95991
Tel.: (530) 740-1920   CA
Year Founded: 1983
Sales Range: $10-24.9 Million
Emp.: 358
Health Care Srvices
N.A.I.C.S.: 622110
L. Wayne Mills *(CFO)*
Chance White *(Chief Clinical Officer & Sr VP)*
Emma Nelson *(Dir-Fountains)*
Theresa Hamilton *(CEO)*
Janice S. Nall *(Asst Sec)*

UNITED COMMERCE CENTERS INC.
1720 E State Hwy 356, Irving, TX 75060
Tel.: (214) 352-1191
Web Site: http://www.ucci-autoparts.com
Year Founded: 1983
Sales Range: $10-24.9 Million
Automotive Parts & Equipments Whslr
N.A.I.C.S.: 441330
Juan Ruiz *(Mgr-Store)*
Steve Culver *(Sr VP)*

Subsidiaries:

New World International Inc.   (1)
1720 E Evan Blvd, Irving, TX 75060
Tel.: (214) 352-1191
Rev.: $1,500,000
Automobile Parts Distr
N.A.I.C.S.: 441330
Yao H. Tsai *(Pres)*
Manny Solocano *(Asst VP)*

UNITED COMMERCIAL TRAVELERS OF AMERICA
PO Box 159019, Columbus, OH 43215
Tel.: (614) 487-9680
Web Site: http://www.uct.org
Sales Range: $10-24.9 Million
Emp.: 100
Fraternal Accident & Health Insurance Organizations
N.A.I.C.S.: 525190
Linda Fisher *(Mgr-PR)*
Kevin C. Hecker *(VP & Controller)*
Ronald Ives *(VP-IT Svcs)*
Kate Chillinsky *(Mgr-Mktg)*

UNITED COMMUNICATION SYSTEMS
225 W Wacker Dr 7th FL, Chicago, IL 60606
Tel.: (312) 681-8300
Web Site: http://www.callone.com
Year Founded: 1992
Rev.: $15,000,000
Emp.: 100
Provides Telephone Communications
N.A.I.C.S.: 517121
Craig J. Foster *(CEO)*

UNITED COMMUNICATIONS CORPORATION
5800 7th Ave, Kenosha, WI 53140
Tel.: (262) 656-6360
Web Site: http://www.ucclocalmedia.com
Newspaper Publishers
N.A.I.C.S.: 513110
Lucy Brown *(CEO)*
Tom Yunt *(COO)*

UNITED COMMUNICATIONS GROUP
9737 Washingtonian Blvd, Gaithersburg, MD 20878
Tel.: (301) 287-2700   MD
Web Site: http://www.ucg.com
Year Founded: 1977
Sales Range: $75-99.9 Million
Emp.: 300
Publishing
N.A.I.C.S.: 513120
Jon Slabaugh *(Mng Dir-Bus Dev)*
Nancy Becker *(Partner)*
Todd Foreman *(CEO)*
Chris Dingee *(CFO)*
Shalisa Mohamed *(CIO)*
Mitchell Barlow *(CTO)*
Steve McVearry *(Gen Counsel)*

Subsidiaries:

CCMI   (1)
9737 Washingtonian Blvd Ste 200, Gaithersburg, MD 20878-7364
Tel.: (888) 275-2264
Web Site: http://www.ccmi.com
Telecommunication Servicesb
N.A.I.C.S.: 517810
Caroline Cooksey *(VP-Data & Res Ops)*
Ed Sullivan *(Dir-Product Mgmt)*
John Abernathy *(Dir-Bus Dev)*
Michael Yokay *(Pres)*
Samantha Schultheis *(Mgr-Mktg)*

DecisionHealth LLC   (1)
9737 Washingtonian Blvd Ste 200, Gaithersburg, MD 20878-7364
Tel.: (301) 287-2682
Web Site: http://www.decisionhealth.com
Business Support Services
N.A.I.C.S.: 561499
Corinne Kuypers-Denlinger *(VP-Product Mgmt)*
Steve Greenberg *(Pres)*
Tonya Nevin *(VP-Medical Practice Products & Solutions)*
Warren Hoppmeyer *(VP-Fin & Ops)*
Jettie Eddleman *(Dir-Quality & Education)*
Lindsey Harris *(Dir-Mktg)*

Kates-Boylston Publications   (1)
11300 Rockville Pike Ste 1100, Rockville, MD 20852
Web Site: http://www.kates-boylston.com
Publisher of Magazines, Directories, Books & Other Products for Funeral Services Market
N.A.I.C.S.: 513120
Thomas A. Parmalee *(Exec Dir)*
Amy Fidalgo *(Mgr-Mktg & Production)*
Allison Sullivan *(Publr)*
Megan Conway *(Dir-Art)*

UCG Information Services LLC   (1)
9737 Washingtonian Blvd Ste 200, Rockville, MD 20878
Tel.: (301) 287-2700
Web Site: http://www.ucg.com
Sales Range: $50-74.9 Million
Pamphlets: Publishing & Printing
N.A.I.C.S.: 513130
Jon Slabaugh *(Mng Dir-Bus Dev)*

Vantage Production, LLC.   (1)
10 Rte 35, Redbank, NJ 07701
Tel.: (800) 963-1900
Web Site: http://www.vantageproduction.com
Marketing Consulting Services
N.A.I.C.S.: 541613
Bill Bodnar *(Sr VP-Strategic Acct)*
Derek Egeberg *(Branch Mgr)*
Laura Smith *(Sr VP-Client Svcs)*
Mike Sepesi *(Co-CFO)*
Paul Zoukis *(CEO)*
Ryan Stillwell *(COO)*
Sally Bucciero *(Branch Mgr)*
Sue Woodard *(Pres & CEO)*
Todd K. Ballenger *(Exec VP-Bus & Product Dev)*
Anselon Harrington *(Branch Mgr)*
Jason Hauben *(Co-CFO)*
Shalisa Mohamed *(CTO)*
Timothy Murphy *(Exec VP-Sls)*

Wellesley Information Services, LLC   (1)
20 Carematrix Dr, Dedham, MA 02026
Tel.: (781) 751-8755
Web Site: http://www.wisinc.com
Emp.: 60
Book Publishers
N.A.I.C.S.: 513130
George Balerna *(VP-Sls)*
Sean Edwards *(Exec VP-Mktg)*
Jamie Bedard *(Pres & CEO)*
Raj Joshi *(CTO)*
Yolanda Maggi *(Exec VP-Events & Memberships)*
John McLaughlin *(VP-Mktg)*
John Carroll *(Chief Revenue Officer)*

UNITED COMMUNITY & FAMILY SERVICES INC.
34 E Town St, Norwich, CT 06360
Tel.: (860) 889-2375   CT
Year Founded: 1871
Sales Range: $25-49.9 Million
Emp.: 403

Health & Human Welfare Support Services
N.A.I.C.S.: 813311
Debbie Kievits *(Chm)*
Shiela Hayes *(Sec)*
Paul Mathieu *(Treas)*

UNITED COMMUNITY ACTION NETWORK
280 Kenneth Ford Dr, Roseburg, OR 97470
Tel.: (541) 672-3421   OR
Web Site: http://www.ucancap.org
Year Founded: 1969
Sales Range: $10-24.9 Million
Emp.: 282
Community Action Services
N.A.I.C.S.: 624190
Vicky Brown *(Chm)*
Keith Heck *(Vice Chm)*
Michael Fieldman *(Gen Mgr)*

UNITED COMMUNITY BANCORP, INC.
301 N Main St, Chatham, IL 62629-0138
Tel.: (217) 483-2491   DE
Year Founded: 1973
Bank Holding Company
N.A.I.C.S.: 551111
Robert Narmont *(Chm, Pres & CEO)*
Daniel J. Cook *(Chief Investment Officer)*
Tracy West *(Sr VP-Investments)*
Fred Jessup *(Exec VP-Lending & Community Markets)*
Todd Wise *(Pres/CEO-United Community Bank)*
Movita Campbell *(Exec VP-Retail Banking)*
Mary Midiri *(VP-HR)*
Steve Otten *(Pres-Comml Lending Market)*
Tisha Rooney *(Dir-Mktg)*

Subsidiaries:

Mercantile Bank   (1)
200 N 33rd St, Quincy, IL 62301
Tel.: (217) 223-7300
Web Site: http://www.mercantilebk.com
Sales Range: $10-24.9 Million
Emp.: 118
Commericial Banking
N.A.I.C.S.: 522110
Daniel J. Cook *(Chief Investment Officer, Sr Trust Officer & VP)*
F. Randy McFarland *(Sr VP & Trust Officer)*
Brett Hoover *(Sr VP & Dir-HR)*

Unit (Domestic):

Mercantile Bank - Mortgage Center   (2)
200 N 33rd St, Quincy, IL 62301
Tel.: (217) 223-7676
Web Site: http://www.mercantilebk.com
Emp.: 10
Mortgage Lending Services
N.A.I.C.S.: 522292
Shelley Miller *(VP-Mortgage Loans & Head-Mortgage Center)*

United Community Bank   (1)
301 N Main St, Chatham, IL 62629-0138
Tel.: (217) 483-2491
Web Site: http://www.ucbbank.com
Sales Range: $75-99.9 Million
Emp.: 463
Federal Savings Bank
N.A.I.C.S.: 522180
Robert Narmont *(Chm)*
Todd W. Wise *(Pres & CEO)*
Nan Carlen *(VP-Retail Sls)*

Subsidiary (Domestic):

Community Banc Mortgage Corporation   (2)
3200 W Iles Ave, Springfield, IL 62711
Tel.: (888) 821-7729
Web Site: http://www.bancmac.com
Emp.: 10

United Community Bancorp, Inc.—(Continued)

Mortgage Lending Services
N.A.I.C.S.: 522292
Mary Sexton (Sr VP)

UNITED COMMUNITY BANK OF WEST KENTUCKY, INC.
500 N Morgan St, Morganfield, KY 42437
Tel.: (270) 389-3232
Web Site: http://www.ucbwest.com
Year Founded: 2001
Commericial Banking
N.A.I.C.S.: 522110
Garland Certain (CEO)
Gwen Paris (Pres & Chief Credit Officer)
Jim Peak (Exec VP & CFO)
Angie Duncan (Sr VP-Bus Dev, Mktg &Comml Lender)
Tammy Belt (Chief Risk Officer& Sr VP-Info & Sys, Mktg)
Melanie Legate (Office Mgr & VP-Clay)
Travis Neitz (Office Mgr & Asst VP-Comml Lender)
Sandra Brock (VP & Mgr-Consumer Lending)
Chris Ellis (Mgr-IT)
Kristy Joiner (HR Officer)
Jona Moore (Asst VP & Mgr-Ops)
Kelly McBride (Asst VP-Internal Controller)
Tara Wright (Asst VP & Coord-Compliance)
Charity Wallace (Deposit Compliance & Security Officer)

UNITED COMMUNITY CENTER, INC.
1028 S 9th St, Milwaukee, WI 53204
Tel.: (414) 384-3100　WI
Web Site: http://www.unitedcc.org
Year Founded: 1970
Sales Range: $10-24.9 Million
Emp.: 261
Community Care Services
N.A.I.C.S.: 624190
Ricardo Diaz (Exec Dir)
Keith A. Kolb (Asst Treas)
Bill Schwartz (Treas)
Mary Alice Tierney (VP)
Cristy Garcia-Thomas (Sec)
Laura Gutierrez (Assoc Exec Dir)

UNITED COMMUNITY FINANCIAL
900 E Paris Ave SE, Grand Rapids, MI 49546
Tel.: (616) 559-7000
Web Site: http://www.unitedbankofmichigan.com
Year Founded: 1980
Sales Range: $25-49.9 Million
Emp.: 100
State Trust Companies Accepting Deposits, Commercial
N.A.I.C.S.: 522110
Arthur C. Johnson (Chm & Co-CEO)
Michael J. Manica (Pres & Co-CEO)
Brian Klaver (Sr VP)
Doris L. Drain (VP)
Mary E. Spray (VP)
Kenneth J. Stienstra (Sr VP)
John W. Figg (VP)
Paul Kramer (Exec VP)

Subsidiaries:

United Bank Insurance Agency (1)
1131 W Superior St, Wayland, MI 49348
Tel.: (269) 792-6730
Web Site: http://www.unitedbankinsurance.com
Sales Range: Less than $1 Million
Emp.: 10
Insurance Services

N.A.I.C.S.: 524210
Rosenn Wendt (Mgr)

United Bank of Michigan Inc (1)
900 E Paris Ave SE, Grand Rapids, MI 49546
Tel.: (616) 559-7000
Web Site: http://www.unitedbankofmichigan.com
Rev.: $20,024,000
Emp.: 70
State Trust Companies Accepting Deposits, Commercial
N.A.I.C.S.: 522110
Arthur C. Johnson (Chm)
Paul Kramer (Chief Lending Officer & Exec VP)
Brian Klaver (Sr VP)
Doris Drain (VP)
Joe Crittendon (VP)
Joe Manica (Sr VP)
John Figg (VP)
Ken Stienstra (Sr VP)
Mary Spray (VP)
Sue Rankin (VP)
Alice Doherty (Officer-Mortgage Loan)
Jennifer Ferguson (Officer-Mortgage Loan)
Shannan Smith (Officer-Mortgage Loan)

UNITED CONSTRUCTION & REALTY
123 S Linwood Ave, Appleton, WI 54914
Tel.: (920) 734-2651
Web Site: http://www.automotivesupplyco.com
Rev.: $12,000,000
Emp.: 25
Motor Vehicle Supplies & New Parts
N.A.I.C.S.: 423120
Case Wewerka (CEO)

UNITED CONSTRUCTION CO. INC.
5300 Mill St, Reno, NV 89502-2316
Tel.: (775) 858-8090　NV
Web Site: http://www.unitedconstruction.com
Year Founded: 1978
Sales Range: $10-24.9 Million
Emp.: 30
Industrial Buildings & Warehouse Construction Contractor
N.A.I.C.S.: 236210
Brandon Breach (CFO, Partner & VP)
Craig A. Willcut (Pres & Partner)

UNITED CONTRACTORS INC.
6678 Nw 62nd Ave, Johnston, IA 50131
Tel.: (515) 276-6162　IA
Web Site: http://www.unitedcontractors.net
Year Founded: 1959
Sales Range: $10-24.9 Million
Emp.: 60
Providers of Bridge Construction Contracts
N.A.I.C.S.: 237310
Steve Sandquist (Pres)
Brian Willem (Controller)

UNITED CONTRACTORS INC.
5562 Pendergrass Blvd, Great Falls, SC 29055-0268
Tel.: (803) 581-6000
Sales Range: $10-24.9 Million
Emp.: 225
Bridge Construction
N.A.I.C.S.: 237310
Carl Franseen (CFO)

UNITED CONTRACTORS MIDWEST, INC.
3151 Robbins Rd, Springfield, IL 62704
Tel.: (217) 546-6192　IL
Web Site: http://www.ucm.biz

Heavy Construction & Road Paving Services
N.A.I.C.S.: 324121
James W. Bruner (Pres)

Subsidiaries:

Freesen Inc. (1)
3151 Robbins Rd, Springfield, IL 62704
Tel.: (217) 546-6192
Sales Range: $25-49.9 Million
Emp.: 445
Asphalt Paving Services
N.A.I.C.S.: 237310

UNITED CONVEYOR CORPORATION
2100 Norman Dr W, Waukegan, IL 60085-6752
Tel.: (847) 473-5900　IL
Web Site: http://www.unitedconveyor.com
Year Founded: 1920
Sales Range: $10-24.9 Million
Emp.: 500
Provider of Industrial Equipment
N.A.I.C.S.: 332313
Douglas S. Basler (CEO)

UNITED COOPERATIVE
N7160 Raceway Rd, Beaver Dam, WI 53916-9315
Tel.: (920) 887-1756　WI
Web Site: http://www.unitedcooperative.com
Year Founded: 1936
Sales Range: $550-599.9 Million
Agricultural Services
N.A.I.C.S.: 424590
David A. Cramer (Treas)
Howard Bohl (Chm)
Robin Craker (Sec)
Gary Nolden (Vice Chm)

Subsidiaries:

United Cooperative (1)
140 Short St, Beaver Dam, WI 54634
Tel.: (608) 489-2231
Web Site: http://www.unitedcooperative.com
Sales Range: $50-74.9 Million
Emp.: 100
Feed & Farm Supply Whslr
N.A.I.C.S.: 424910
Norbert Schleicher (Mgr)

UNITED COOPERATIVE
1932 W 2nd St, Webster City, IA 50595
Tel.: (515) 832-6373
Web Site: http://www.unitedcoop.com
Sales Range: $25-49.9 Million
Emp.: 50
Grain Elevators
N.A.I.C.S.: 424510
Jack McGonegie (Controller)

UNITED COOPERATIVE SERVICES
3309 N Main St, Cleburne, TX 76033
Tel.: (817) 556-4000
Web Site: http://www.united-cs.com
Sales Range: $75-99.9 Million
Emp.: 150
Electric Power Distribution Co-op
N.A.I.C.S.: 221122
Raymond Beavers (CEO & Gen Mgr)
Landy Bennett (Sr VP-Member Svcs & Mktg)
Robert Bernhoft (VP-Information Sys & Tech)
Cameron Smallwood (COO)
Marty Haught (Chief Comm Officer)
Quentin Howard (Sr VP-Sys Engrg)
Tommy Cantrell (Treas & Sec)
Larry Bays (VP)
Patsy Dumas (Pres)

UNITED CORP.
4605 Tutu Park Mall Ste 200, Saint Thomas, VI 00802
Tel.: (340) 775-5646
Web Site: http://www.plavaextra.com
Sales Range: $50-74.9 Million
Emp.: 170
Supermarket
N.A.I.C.S.: 445110
Willie Hamed (Gen Mgr)

UNITED COUNSELING SERVICE
100 Ledge Hill Dr, Bennington, VT 05201
Tel.: (802) 442-5491　VT
Web Site: http://www.ucsvt.org
Year Founded: 1961
Sales Range: $10-24.9 Million
Emp.: 319
Mental Health Care Services
N.A.I.C.S.: 621420
Lorna W. Mattern (Exec Dir)
Jill Doyle (Dir-Fin & Ops)
Victor Martini (Dir-Community Rehabilitation & Emergency)
Leslie Addison (Dir-HR)
Roberta Lynch Carroll (VP)
Robert W. Thompson (Pres)
Nathaniel Marcoux (Treas)
Shawn Thibodeau (Dir-Facilities & Safety)
William Baldwin (Dir)
Betsy Rathbun-Gunn (Dir-Early Childhood Svcs Div)
Heidi French (Dir-Community Rels & Dev)
Dawn Danner (Dir-Dev Svcs)

UNITED CREDIT CORP.
718 23rd Ave, Meridian, MS 39301
Tel.: (601) 693-1304　MS
Year Founded: 1976
Rev.: $12,400,000
Emp.: 13
Small Licensed Loan Companies
N.A.I.C.S.: 522299
Davis Purvis (Pres)
Billy Carroll (Treas)

UNITED CUSTOMHOUSE BROKERS
540 E Alondra Blvd, Gardena, CA 90248
Tel.: (310) 988-7000
Web Site: http://www.unitedchb.com
Sales Range: $10-24.9 Million
Emp.: 18
Customhouse Brokers
N.A.I.C.S.: 488510
Young S. Chang (Pres)
Edward Chang (VP)
Linda Louie (VP)

UNITED DAIRY FARMERS, INC.
3955 Montgomery Rd, Cincinnati, OH 45212
Tel.: (513) 396-8700　OH
Web Site: http://www.udfinc.com
Year Founded: 1940
Sales Range: $5-14.9 Billion
Emp.: 75,300
Chain of Convenience Stores; Milk Processing, Ice Cream & Ices; Frozen Dairy Desserts
N.A.I.C.S.: 445131
Phyllis McCoy (Sec)
David Lindner (Dir-Mktg)
Brad Lindner (Pres & CEO)
Marilyn Mitchell (CFO)

UNITED DAIRY, INC.
300 N 5th St, Martins Ferry, OH 43935-1647
Tel.: (740) 633-1451　OH

Web Site: http://www.uniteddairy.com
Year Founded: 1973
Sales Range: $200-249.9 Million
Emp.: 440
Milk Processing Pasteurizing Homogenizing & Bottling Services
N.A.I.C.S.: 311511
George Wood (CFO)
Bill Suto (Plant Mgr)
Clare Cohen (Mgr-Sls & Customer Svc)
Ed Evans (Gen Mgr)
Tom McCombs (Mgr-Milk Procurement)
Ralph Calvacante (Controller)

Subsidiaries:

United Dairy (1)
508 Roane St, Charleston, WV 25302-2024
Tel.: (304) 344-2511
Web Site: http://www.drinkunited.com
Milk & Ice Cream Product Mfr
N.A.I.C.S.: 311511
John Duty (Gen Mgr)

UNITED DAIRYMEN OF ARIZONA
2008 S Hardy Dr, Tempe, AZ 85282-1211
Tel.: (480) 966-7211   AZ
Web Site: http://www.uda.coop
Year Founded: 1960
Sales Range: $100-124.9 Million
Emp.: 250
Dairy Products Mfr
N.A.I.C.S.: 311511
James Boyle (Pres)
Edward Boschma (Owner)
Tammy Baker (Gen Mgr-Adv)
Gayle Lindsey (VP-IT)

UNITED DATA TECHNOLOGIES, INC.
8825 NW 21 Ter, Doral, FL 33172
Tel.: (305) 882-0435
Web Site: http://www.udtonline.com
Year Founded: 1995
Sales Range: $75-99.9 Million
Emp.: 120
IT Services
N.A.I.C.S.: 519290
Daniel Rodriguez (CTO & VP-Tech Svcs)
Gerard Amaro (COO)
Henry Fleches (CEO)
Jacqueline Coleman (Mgr-PR)
Mike Sanchez (Chief Info Security Officer)
Guillermo A. Benites (VP-Fin Svcs)
Jeff Swords (Dir-Sls-Tennessee)

UNITED DEVELOPMENT FUNDING INCOME FUND V
1301 Municipal Way Ste 100, Grapevine, TX 76051
Tel.: (214) 370-8960   MD
Web Site: http://www.udfonline.com
Year Founded: 2003
Sales Range: Less than $1 Million
Real Estate Investment Trust
N.A.I.C.S.: 525990
Hollis M. Greenlaw (Co-Founder & CEO)
Michael K. Wilson (Pres)
Cara D. Obert (CFO)
Todd Etter (Co-Founder & Chm)
Melissa Youngblood (COO)
Ben L. Wissink (Pres-Land Dev)

UNITED DEVELOPMENT FUNDING IV
Tel.: (817) 835-0650   MD
Web Site: http://www.udfonline.com
Year Founded: 2008
UDFI—(OTCBB)
Real Estate Investment Trust
N.A.I.C.S.: 525990
Theodore Forest Etter Jr. (Co-Founder & Chm)

UNITED DRILLING INC.
62 Appletree Ln, Plumsteadville, PA 18949
Tel.: (215) 766-3745
Web Site: http://www.uniteddrilling.com
Sales Range: $10-24.9 Million
Emp.: 75
Provider of Elevator Drilling Services
N.A.I.C.S.: 238290
Gary Nonemacher (Pres)
Lynn Lorenz (Office Mgr)

UNITED EDUCATORS INC.
900 W N Shore Dr Ste 279, Lake Bluff, IL 60044-2235
Tel.: (847) 234-3700
Web Site: http://www.unitededucators.com
Rev.: $10,000,000
Emp.: 15
Book Publishing
N.A.I.C.S.: 513130
Diane Tracht (VP)

UNITED EDUCATORS INSURANCE, A RECIPROCAL RISK RETENTION GROUP, INC.
7700 Wisconsin Ave Ste 500, Bethesda, MD 20814
Tel.: (301) 907-4908
Web Site: http://www.ue.org
Year Founded: 1987
Rev.: $86,550,986
Emp.: 103
Insurance & Risk Management Products & Service Provider
N.A.I.C.S.: 524298
Janice M. Abraham (CEO)
Michael F. Horning (CFO & VP-Fin & Admin)
Robb Jones (Sr VP & Gen Counsel-Claims Mgmt)
Albert J. Beer (Vice Chm-Subscribers Advisory Bd)

UNITED EGG PRODUCERS
6455 E Johns Crossing, Johns Creek, GA 30097
Tel.: (770) 360-9220   GA
Web Site: http://www.unitedegg.org
Year Founded: 1968
Rev.: $19,000,000
Emp.: 7
Food Marketing Cooperative
N.A.I.C.S.: 813910
Chad Gregory (Pres & CEO)
Sherry Shedd (VP-Fin)
Larry Sadler (VP-Animal Welfare)

UNITED EL SEGUNDO INC.
17311 S Main St, Gardena, CA 90248
Tel.: (310) 323-3992
Web Site: http://www.unitedoilco.com
Sales Range: $10-24.9 Million
Emp.: 60
Gasoline & Petroleum Products Whslr
N.A.I.C.S.: 531210
Ronald Appel (Pres)
Jeff Appel (Treas & Sec)
Rhonda Wolf (Gen Counsel)

UNITED ELECTRIC CO. INC.
4333 Robards Ln, Louisville, KY 40218-4511
Tel.: (502) 459-5242   KY
Web Site: http://www.unitedelec.com
Year Founded: 1957
Sales Range: $1-9.9 Million
Emp.: 150
Electrical Work

N.A.I.C.S.: 238210
Edward Cassin (Project Mgr)
Larry Farrell (Gen Mgr & Project Mgr-Cincinnati)
Mark Hatcher (Mgr)
Phillip Harris (Project Mgr)
Joseph Heger (Project Mgr)
Rhonda Hand (Dir-Safety)
Jana Kohorst (Controller)
Anthony Hodges (Mgr-Louisville Warehouse)
Randy Knopf (Project Mgr-Cincinnati)
Ray Knapp (Project Mgr-Cincinnati)
Mike Moore (Project Mgr-Louisville)
Joe Kellams (Pres)

UNITED ELECTRIC CONTROLS COMPANY INC.
180 Dexter Ave, Watertown, MA 02472
Tel.: (617) 926-1000   MA
Web Site: http://www.ueonline.com
Year Founded: 1931
Sales Range: $75-99.9 Million
Emp.: 200
Mfr of Process Control Instruments
N.A.I.C.S.: 334513
David A. Reis (Owner)
Brian Hallahan (VP-Fin)
Rick Frauton (Product Mgr)
Luke Warren (Mgr-HR)

UNITED ELECTRIC COOPERATIVE, INC.
PO Box 688, Du Bois, PA 15801
Tel.: (814) 371-8570
Web Site: http://www.unitedpa.com
Sales Range: $10-24.9 Million
Emp.: 53
Distr of Electric Power
N.A.I.C.S.: 221122
Steve Long (Mgr-Engrg)
Leonard Hawkins (Mgr-Fin & Acctg)
Stephen A. Marshall (Chm)
Arden E. Owens (Treas & Sec)
Paula Pascuzzo (Mgr-HR)
Brenda Swartzlander (Pres & CEO)
Shane Farrell (Mgr-Ops)
Richard Heverley (Mgr-Mktg & Member Svcs)
Timothy D. Burkett (Vice Chm)
Richard A. Petrosky (Treas & Sec)

UNITED ELECTRIC SUPPLY COMPANY, INC.
10 Bellecor Dr, New Castle, DE 19720-1763
Tel.: (302) 322-3333   DE
Web Site: http://www.unitedelectric.com
Year Founded: 1965
Electrical Supply Wholesaler & Distributor
N.A.I.C.S.: 423610
Richard Stagliano (CFO & Sr VP)
Rick Freebery (VP-Vendor & New Svcs Dev)
Gayle Davis (VP-HR)
Mike Deneault (VP-Bus Dev)
Greg Sundberg (VP-Sls-Chesapeake)
Phil McCloud (VP-Sls-Delaware Valley)
Anthony Buonocore (Dir-Mktg)
Jordan Bauer (Sls Mgr-Maryland)
George Vorwick Jr. (Pres & CEO)

Subsidiaries:

Kovalsky-Carr Electric Supply Co, Inc. (1)
208 Saint Paul St, Rochester, NY 14604
Tel.: (585) 325-1950
Web Site: http://www.kovalskycarr.com
Sales Range: $1-9.9 Million
Emp.: 30

Electrical Apparatus & Equipment, Wiring Supplies & Related Equipment Merchant Whslr
N.A.I.C.S.: 423610

UNITED ELECTRICAL, RADIO & MACHINE WORKERS OF AMERICA
4 Smithfield St 9th Fl, Pittsburgh, PA 15222-2226
Tel.: (412) 471-8919   PA
Web Site: https://www.ueunion.org
Year Founded: 1936
Sales Range: $1-9.9 Million
Emp.: 61
Electrical Worker Association
N.A.I.C.S.: 813920
John Hovis (Co-Pres)

UNITED ENERGIES DEVELOPMENT CORPORATION
9454 Wilshire Blvd Ste 612, Beverly Hills, CA 90212
Tel.: (310) 888-1870   DE
Year Founded: 2015
Investment Services
N.A.I.C.S.: 523999
James Cassidy (Pres & Sec)
James McKillop (VP)

UNITED ENGINE & MACHINE COMPANY
1040 Corbett St, Carson City, NV 89706-0351
Tel.: (775) 882-7790   CA
Web Site: http://www.kb-silvolite.com
Year Founded: 1956
Sales Range: $150-199.9 Million
Emp.: 350
Mfr of Pistons & Engine Parts
N.A.I.C.S.: 336310
Keith Sulprizio (VP)
Glen Howard (Mgr-Natl Accts)

UNITED ENTERTAINMENT CORP.
3601 18th St S Ste 104, Saint Cloud, MN 56301-6012
Tel.: (320) 203-1003
Web Site: http://www.uecmovies.com
Sales Range: $10-24.9 Million
Emp.: 350
Video Tape Production
N.A.I.C.S.: 532282
Stacy Stellmach (Office Mgr)

UNITED ESOTERIC CORP.
7 Wheeling Ave Ste 2E, Woburn, MA 01801
Tel.: (781) 729-1700
Web Site: http://www.unitedesoterics.com
Year Founded: 2006
Sales Range: $1-9.9 Million
Emp.: 38
Physician Office Lab Services
N.A.I.C.S.: 621511
Craig Sockol (Founder & Pres)

UNITED FABRICARE SUPPLY INC.
1237 W Walnut St, Compton, CA 90220
Tel.: (310) 537-2096
Web Site: http://www.unitedfabricaresupply.com
Sales Range: $10-24.9 Million
Emp.: 69
Laundry & Dry Cleaning Equipment & Supplies
N.A.I.C.S.: 423850
Steve S. Hong (Pres & CEO)
Bo Gilbert (VP-Sls-Natl)
Kirby Schnebly (CFO & Exec VP)
Rod Benzon (Mgr-Sls)
Steve Echelberger (Mgr-Field Sls)

UNITED FABRICARE SUPPLY INC.

U.S. PRIVATE

United Fabricare Supply Inc.—(Continued)
Jae Park *(Dir-Korean Mktg)*
Doug Rowell *(Gen Mgr-San Francisco)*
Peter Kim *(Mgr-Field Sls)*
Jin Cho *(Mgr-Textile Div)*
Jim Zell *(Mgr-Warehouse-Las Vegas)*
Roger Higginbotham *(Mgr-Warehouse-San Diego)*
Tim Watanabe *(Mgr-Warehouse-San Francisco)*
Rob Frost *(VP & Gen Mgr)*
Eric Kim *(VP-San Diego)*

UNITED FACILITIES, INC.
603 N Main St, East Peoria, IL 61611-2023
Tel.: (309) 699-7271   IL
Web Site: http://www.unifac.com
Year Founded: 1953
Sales Range: $25-49.9 Million
Emp.: 350
Provider of General Warehousing & Storage Services
N.A.I.C.S.: 493110
Larry Yocum *(VP-Ops)*

UNITED FAMILY PRACTICE HEALTH CENTER
1026 W 7th St, Saint Paul, MN 55102
Tel.: (651) 241-1000   MN
Web Site:
  http://www.unitedfamilymedicine.org
Year Founded: 2003
Sales Range: $10-24.9 Million
Emp.: 109
Health Care Srvices
N.A.I.C.S.: 622110
David Bucher *(Dir-Medical)*
Jen Smith-Kristensen *(Dir-Quality)*
Melissa Parker *(COO)*
Steve Ficks *(CFO)*
Rebecca Norris *(Sec)*
Ken Schaefer *(Treas)*
George Baboila *(Chm)*
Kim Hyers *(Vice Chm)*
Brian Nasi *(CEO)*
Phuang-Giang Pham *(Dir-Dental)*
Lisa Stein *(Dir-Advancement)*

UNITED FARM INDUSTRIES INCORPORATED
405 E 24th St, Plainview, TX 79072
Tel.: (806) 293-5103
Year Founded: 1933
Sales Range: $10-24.9 Million
Emp.: 25
Retailer of Fertilizer & Fertilizer Materials
N.A.I.C.S.: 115112
Don James *(Pres)*

UNITED FARMERS COOPERATIVE
705 E 4th St, Winthrop, MN 55396
Tel.: (507) 647-6600
Web Site: http://www.ufcmn.com
Sales Range: $50-74.9 Million
Emp.: 280
Agricultural Cooperative
N.A.I.C.S.: 424510
Lorie Reinarts *(VP-Acctg)*
Todd Nelson *(Co-Chm)*
Jeff Franta *(Chm)*
Todd Kettner *(Sec)*
Ruth Bauer *(CFO)*
Greg Peton *(Chief Mktg Officer)*
Jason Tews *(VP-Grain)*
Steve LeBrun *(VP-Feed)*
Dave Eckhoff *(VP-Agronomy)*
Darv Turbes *(VP-Energy)*
Steve Spears *(VP-Consumer Goods & Hardware)*
Mitch Altermatt *(COO)*
Tyler Zollner *(VP-Equipment)*

UNITED FARMERS COOPERATIVE
2803 N Nebraska Ave, York, NE 68467
Tel.: (402) 362-0253
Web Site: http://www.ufcoop.com
Grain, Animal Feed, Fuel & Farming Supplies Wholesale Distr
N.A.I.C.S.: 424510
John Hild *(Mgr-Grain Acctg)*
Dennis Hoefer *(Dir-IT)*
Peggy Hopwood *(Mgr-Credit)*
Rhonda Johnson *(Office Mgr)*

UNITED FASHIONS OF TEXAS LTD.
4629 Macro Dr, San Antonio, TX 78218-5420
Tel.: (210) 662-7140   TX
Web Site:
  http://www.melrosestore.com
Year Founded: 1994
Sales Range: $50-74.9 Million
Emp.: 430
Women's Clothing Store
N.A.I.C.S.: 458110
Tzipora B. Yadin *(Pres)*
Koyt Everhart *(VP-Real Estate)*

UNITED FEATHER & DOWN INC.
414 E Golf Rd, Des Plaines, IL 60016-2234
Tel.: (847) 296-6610
Web Site: http://www.ufandd.com
Year Founded: 1974
Sales Range: $25-49.9 Million
Emp.: 200
Provider of Down & Feathers
N.A.I.C.S.: 424590
Mark Palmer *(Chm)*
Stephen Palmer *(Co-Pres)*
Brandon Palmer *(Co-Pres)*

UNITED FEDERAL CREDIT UNION
2807 S State St, Saint Joseph, MI 49085
Tel.: (269) 301-1232
Web Site: http://www.unitedfcu.com
Year Founded: 1949
Credit Union
N.A.I.C.S.: 522130
Terry O'Rourke *(Pres & CEO)*

Subsidiaries:

Edgewater Bancorp, Inc.   (1)
321 Main St, Saint Joseph, MI 49085
Tel.: (269) 982-4175
Web Site: http://www.edgewaterbank.com
Banking Holding Company
N.A.I.C.S.: 551111
Coleen S. Frens-Rossman *(CFO & Sr VP)*

Subsidiary (Domestic):

Edgewater Bank   (2)
321 Main St, Saint Joseph, MI 49085
Tel.: (269) 982-4175
Web Site: http://www.edgewaterbank.com
Sales Range: $25-49.9 Million
Emp.: 56
Federal Savings Bank
N.A.I.C.S.: 522180
Richard E. Dyer *(Pres & CEO)*
Coleen S. Frens-Rossman *(CFO & Sr VP)*
Cheryl Moeslein *(Sec & VP-Admin Svcs)*
James Higgins *(Chief Credit Officer & VP)*
Maria Kibler *(VP)*
Bobbi Smith *(VP)*
Tony Mandarino *(VP-Comml Lending)*

UNITED FEED COOP INC.
708 NW 2nd Ave, Okeechobee, FL 34972
Tel.: (863) 763-2145
Sales Range: $10-24.9 Million
Emp.: 9
Grain & Field Bean Merchant Whslr
N.A.I.C.S.: 424510
William Berman *(Pres)*

UNITED FINANCE CO.
515 E Burnside St, Portland, OR 97214
Tel.: (503) 232-5153   OR
Web Site:
  http://www.unitedfinance.com
Year Founded: 1922
Sales Range: $10-24.9 Million
Emp.: 22
Provider of Consumer Finance Companies
N.A.I.C.S.: 522291
Sam Bradbury *(Sr VP)*
Eric Young *(Branch Mgr)*

UNITED FINANCIAL OF ILLINOIS INC.
800 E Diehl Rd Ste 185, Naperville, IL 60563-8234
Tel.: (630) 955-0190   IL
Web Site:
  http://www.unitedfinancial.com
Year Founded: 1986
Sales Range: $25-49.9 Million
Emp.: 20
Provider of Financial Services
N.A.I.C.S.: 522299
William Gruber *(Pres)*
Lonnie Long *(VP & Mgr)*
Alan Riefenberg *(VP-Sls)*

UNITED FLEA MARKETS
7007 E 88th Ave, Henderson, CO 80640
Tel.: (720) 592-0260
Web Site:
  http://www.unitedfleamarkets.com
Flea Market Operators
N.A.I.C.S.: 459510
Robert Sieban *(Owner, Pres & CEO)*
Gene Berry *(VP-Fin & Controller)*

Subsidiaries:

J & J Flea Market   (1)
11661 Commerce Rd, Athens, GA 30607-2342
Tel.: (706) 613-2410
Web Site: http://www.jandjfleamarket.com
Flea Market Operators
N.A.I.C.S.: 459510
Pam Boggs *(Pres)*

Tanque Verde Enterprises, Inc.   (1)
4100 S Palo Verde Rd Tucson, Tucson, AZ 85714
Tel.: (520) 294-4252
Web Site: http://www.tanquerdeswap.com
Flea Market
N.A.I.C.S.: 445110

UNITED FOOD & COMMERCIAL WORKERS & EMPS ARIZONA HEALTH & WELFARE TRUST
2400 W Dunlap Ave Ste 250, Phoenix, AZ 85021-2811
Tel.: (602) 249-3582   AZ
Year Founded: 1968
Sales Range: $125-149.9 Million
Emp.: 1,279
Health & Welfare Fund Services
N.A.I.C.S.: 525120
James J. McLaughlin *(Chm)*

UNITED FOOD STORE INC.
900 Schofield Ln, Farmington, NM 87401-7431
Tel.: (505) 325-1959   NM
Web Site:
  http://www.vermeertexas.com
Year Founded: 1956
Sales Range: $25-49.9 Million
Emp.: 250
Convenience Store
N.A.I.C.S.: 445131

Bonnie Frazer *(Pres)*
Alan Frazer *(VP)*

UNITED FOR RESPECT EDUCATION FUND
2108 N St Ste 4231, Sacramento, CA 95816
Tel.: (510) 239-5037
Web Site:
  https://www.united4respectef.org
Year Founded: 2011
Educational Support Services
N.A.I.C.S.: 611710

UNITED FOREST PRODUCTS INC.
8345 Fairforest Rd, Spartanburg, SC 29303-1563
Tel.: (864) 503-0957   SC
Web Site:
  http://www.unitedforestinc.com
Year Founded: 1983
Sales Range: $50-74.9 Million
Emp.: 60
Wholesale Lumber Broker
N.A.I.C.S.: 541990
Jeff Davis *(Chm)*

UNITED FORMING INC.
470 Riverside Pkwy, Austell, GA 30168-7803
Tel.: (512) 243-0300   GA
Web Site:
  http://www.unitedforming.com
Year Founded: 1985
Sales Range: $10-24.9 Million
Emp.: 1,500
Concrete Forming
N.A.I.C.S.: 238110
Kevin Swanson *(Controller)*
Steve Lewis *(CEO)*

UNITED FREIGHT & LOGISTICS, LTD.
5902 Greens Rd, Humble, TX 77396
Tel.: (281) 441-1238   TX
Web Site: http://www.ufandl.com
Year Founded: 2002
Sales Range: $10-24.9 Million
Emp.: 43
Warehousing Brokerage & Logistical Management Services
N.A.I.C.S.: 541614
Wasem Demashkiah *(Pres)*
Michael Jundi *(VP & Gen Mgr)*

UNITED FREIGHT SERVICE INC.
641 E Watkins St, Phoenix, AZ 85004
Tel.: (602) 256-9470
Web Site: http://www.ufs.net
Sales Range: $10-24.9 Million
Emp.: 32
Textile Warehousing Services
N.A.I.C.S.: 493190
Nicholas Sblendorio *(Pres)*

UNITED FURNITURE INDUSTRIES
431 Hwy 41 E, Okolona, MS 38860
Tel.: (662) 447-5504
Web Site:
  http://www.unitedfurnitureindustries.com
Rev: $53,900,000
Emp.: 700
Living Room Furniture Mfr
N.A.I.C.S.: 337121
David Belford *(Owner)*
Sherrie Smith *(Mgr-Import)*

UNITED GAMING, LLC
18 Bellamy Ct, Stockbridge, GA 30281

Tel.: (678) 782-6969
Web Site:
http://www.unitedgamingllc.com
Year Founded: 2009
Amusement Machines Mfr
N.A.I.C.S.: 713290
Dhaval Doshi (CEO)

Subsidiaries:

Amusement Sales & Service Inc. (1)
5500 White Bluff Rd E, Savannah, GA 31405
Tel.: (912) 354-4881
Web Site:
http://www.amusementsalesandservice.com
Rev: $1,440,000
Emp.: 15
Amusement Arcade
N.A.I.C.S.: 713120
Rudy Bairas (Owner)

Star Coin Inc. (1)
54 Marshall Rd NE, Milledgeville, GA 31061-8223
Tel.: (478) 845-3290
Amusement & Theme Parks
N.A.I.C.S.: 713110
Jane Fofhee (CEO)

UNITED GLOBAL TECHNOLOGIES, INC.
10612 D Providence Rd Ste 320, Charlotte, NC 28277
Web Site:
http://www.ugtechnologies.com
Sales Range: $1-9.9 Million
Emp.: 42
Business Research & Development Services
N.A.I.C.S.: 541720
Elizabeth B. Bernstein (CEO & Sr VP-Bus Dev)
Jason R. Monastra (Sr VP-Ops & Delivery)

UNITED HARDWARE DISTRIBUTING CO.
5005 Nathan Ln N, Plymouth, MN 55442
Tel.: (763) 559-1800 MN
Web Site:
http://www.unitedhardware.com
Year Founded: 1945
Sales Range: $150-199.9 Million
Emp.: 310
Hardware, Tools, Plumbing & Ventilation Components, Electrical Components, Paint, Toys, Housewares, Motor Vehicle Supplies, School Supplies, Lawn & Garden Supplies Distr
N.A.I.C.S.: 423710
Lori Long (VP-Sys & Ops)
Alice Heroux (Dir-Customer Svc)

UNITED HARVEST LLC
900 Washington St Ste 700, Vancouver, WA 98660
Tel.: (360) 816-1920
Sales Range: $10-24.9 Million
Emp.: 30
Grain & Field Bean Merchant Whsl
N.A.I.C.S.: 424510
Chris D. Sol (Mgr-Accts Payable)
Bob Willis (Mgr-IP)
Mark Heidegger (Pres)

UNITED HELIUM, INCORPORATED
7109 E 2nd St Ste G, Scottsdale, AZ 85251
Tel.: (480) 949-2755 CO
Emp.: 4
Hydrocarbon Exploration
N.A.I.C.S.: 212390
Peter Trimarco (Pres)
Raymond S. Hobbs (CEO)

Gordon E. Dudley (Gen Counsel & Sec)
John F. Boyle (VP-Engrg & Ops)
Gordon LeBlanc (Chief Geologist)

UNITED HERITAGE CREDIT UNION
12208 N Mopac Expy, Austin, TX 78758
Tel.: (512) 435-4545 TX
Web Site: http://www.uhcu.org
Year Founded: 1957
Sales Range: $25-49.9 Million
Emp.: 259
Credit Union
N.A.I.C.S.: 522130
May Lofgreen (Chm)
James E. North (Treas & Sec)
Harold Keyes (Vice Chm)

UNITED HERITAGE MUTUAL LIFE INSURANCE COMPANY INC.
707 E United Heritage Ct, Meridian, ID 83642
Tel.: (208) 493-6100 DE
Web Site:
http://www.unitedheritage.com
Year Founded: 1934
Sales Range: $25-49.9 Million
Emp.: 130
Fire Insurance Services
N.A.I.C.S.: 523150
Richard E. Hall (Chm)
John Bellamy (VP-Mktg)
Shane Nelson (Dir-Mktg)
Robert J. McCarvel (Sr VP-Mktg)

UNITED HOME CARE SERVICES INC.
8400 NW 33rd St Ste 400, Miami, FL 33122
Tel.: (305) 716-0710
Web Site:
http://www.unitedhomecare.com
Year Founded: 1974
Sales Range: $25-49.9 Million
Emp.: 800
Women Healthcare Services
N.A.I.C.S.: 621610
Carlos Martinez (Pres & CEO)
Jacqueline Torre (VP-HR)
Roberta D'Angola (VP-Compliance)
Mary Ann Sprinkle (Sec)
Robert Rosenthal (Chm)
Armando Ferrer (Vice Chm)
Pablo J. Pino (Treas)
Roger Lopez (VP-Compliance)

UNITED INDUSTRIES
1900 E Central, Bentonville, AR 72712
Tel.: (479) 273-2924
Web Site: http://www.ultraboard.com
Year Founded: 1980
Sales Range: $25-49.9 Million
Emp.: 49
Urethane & Foam Product Mfr
N.A.I.C.S.: 326150
John Ferm (Pres)
Kent Ferm (VP)

UNITED ISRAEL APPEAL, INC.
25 Broadway Ste 1700, New York, NY 10004
Tel.: (212) 284-6900 NY
Year Founded: 1936
Sales Range: $200-249.9 Million
Emp.: 4
Social Welfare Services
N.A.I.C.S.: 525120
Pamela Zaltsman (CFO)

UNITED JUICE COMPANIES OF AMERICA, INC.
505 66th Ave SW, Vero Beach, FL 32968
Tel.: (772) 562-5442
Web Site:
http://www.lambethgroves.com
Sales Range: $10-24.9 Million
Emp.: 60
Fruit & Vegetable Canning Services
N.A.I.C.S.: 311421
Dan Petry (VP-Food Svc Sls)
Marc Craen (COO)

UNITED KENNEL CLUB, INC.
100 E Kilgore St, Portage, MI 49002
Tel.: (269) 343-9020 MI
Web Site: http://www.ukcdogs.com
Year Founded: 1898
Sales Range: $1-9.9 Million
Emp.: 50
Periodical Publishers
N.A.I.C.S.: 513120
Tanya Raab (VP)
Taylor Armstrong (Mgr-Customer Svc)
Leslie Cremin (Coord-Single Adv)
Kayla Deneau (Coord-Contracted Adv)
Allen Gingerich (Sr Dir-Hunting Events)
Sara Herbert (Sr Dir-Media & Promos)
Andrea Hunderman (Dir-Single Registration)
Melissa Mansfield (Coord-Production)
Angela Smith (Sr Dir-R&D)
Sydney Suwannarat (Sr Dir-Show Ops)

Subsidiaries:

American Field Publishing Company, Inc. (1)
542 S Dearborn St, Chicago, IL 60605-1508
Tel.: (312) 663-9797
Web Site: http://www.americanfield.com
Sales Range: $1-9.9 Million
Emp.: 16
Publisher Of Magazines No Printing On Site
N.A.I.C.S.: 513120
E. C. McBride (Pres)

UNITED LABORATORIES, INC.
320 37th Ave, Saint Charles, IL 60174-5414
Tel.: (630) 377-0900 DE
Web Site:
http://www.unitedlabsinc.com
Year Founded: 1964
Sales Range: $150-199.9 Million
Emp.: 340
Specialty Cleaning, Polishing & Sanitation Preparations Mfr; Specialty Chemicals Whslr
N.A.I.C.S.: 325612
Daniel E. Young (Chm & CEO)
Julie Benson (VP-Logistics)
Tom Bansch (CFO)

UNITED LANDMARK ASSOCIATES, INC.
3708 Swann Ave Ste 103, Tampa, FL 33609
Tel.: (813) 870-9519
Web Site:
http://www.unitedlandmark.com
Year Founded: 1985
Sales Range: $10-24.9 Million
Emp.: 15
Advetising Agency
N.A.I.C.S.: 541810
Donald J. Niederpruem (Pres)
Linda Altman (VP-Creative Svcs)
Barbara Lynch (Dir-Client Media)
Sally Suarez (Mgr-Ops)
Cameron Dilley (Creative Dir)
Irene Rodnizki (Sr Art Dir)
Jackie Smith (Dir-Air)
Loran Tripp (VP-Bus Dev & Strategy)
Heather Baker (Mgr-Acct)

Tricia Mason (Mgr-Acct)
Allison Rosoff (Dir-Brand)
Jaimie Frey (Asst Mgr-Acct)
Kyla Ross (Asst Mgr-Acct)
Michele Grimes (VP-Strategy)
Heather Richichi (Admin Officer)
Heather Pavliga (Sr Mgr-Strategy)
Shirley Pekarek (Controller)
Kristen Murphy (VP-Client Svcs)
Dave Wilson (Chief Mktg Officer)

UNITED LEGWEAR & APPAREL CO.
48 W 38th St, New York, NY 10018
Tel.: (212) 391-4143
Web Site:
http://www.unitedlegwear.com
Year Founded: 1998
Emp.: 100
Designs, Markets & Distributes Fashion Legwear for Men, Women & Children
N.A.I.C.S.: 458110
Isaac E. Ash (Founder, Pres & CEO)

Subsidiaries:

Wheat Group Inc. (1)
9950 Summers Ridge Rd, San Diego, CA 92121
Tel.: (858) 673-2070
Web Site: http://www.wheataccessories.com
Clothing Accessories Stores
N.A.I.C.S.: 458110
Chad Grismer (CEO & Co-Founder)
Kelly Grismer (Pres & Co-Founder)
Bryan Grismer (Chief Creative Officer & Principal)

UNITED LIGHTING AND SUPPLY CO.
121 Chestnut Ave SE, Fort Walton Beach, FL 32548
Tel.: (850) 244-8155
Web Site:
http://www.unitedlighting.com
Sales Range: $10-24.9 Million
Emp.: 40
Lighting Fixtures & Electrical
N.A.I.C.S.: 423610
James MacDonnell (Pres)
Jay MacDonnell (Controller)
Shiela Spaw (Mgr-AP)

UNITED LINEN SERVICES INC.
55 5th St E Ste 960, Saint Paul, MN 55101-1717
Tel.: (651) 227-9855
Sales Range: $10-24.9 Million
Emp.: 5
Power Laundries, Family & Commercial
N.A.I.C.S.: 812310
Phillip C. Foussard (Pres)

UNITED LUTHERAN PROGRAM FOR THE AGING, INC.
4545 N 92nd St, Wauwatosa, WI 53225
Tel.: (414) 464-3880 WI
Web Site: http://www.luthermanor.org
Year Founded: 1957
Sales Range: $25-49.9 Million
Emp.: 830
Elder Care Services
N.A.I.C.S.: 623312
Bette Diehl (CFO)
David J. Beinlich (VP-Admin)
Erika Tole (Dir-IT)

UNITED MAILING SERVICES, INC.
3625 N 126 St, Brookfield, WI 53005
Tel.: (262) 783-7868
Web Site:
http://www.unitedmailingservices.com
Rev: $20,000,000
Emp.: 175

UNITED MAILING SERVICES, INC.

United Mailing Services, Inc.—(Continued)
Direct Mail Advertising
N.A.I.C.S.: 541860
James Kolb *(CEO)*
Mark Kolb *(VP)*
Rob Scharmer *(Gen Mgr)*
Tom Diring *(Gen Mgr)*

UNITED MANUFACTURERS SUPPLIES, INC.
40 Banfi Plz, Farmingdale, NY 11735
Tel.: (516) 496-4430
Web Site: http://www.unitedmfrs.com
Rev.: $20,000,000
Emp.: 10
Hardware
N.A.I.C.S.: 423710
Tom Muscato *(VP-Sls & Mktg)*
Joseph Papa *(CEO)*

UNITED MARKETING GROUP LLC
250 E Devon Ave, Itasca, IL 60143
Tel.: (847) 240-2005
Web Site:
  http://www.unitedmarket.com
Sales Range: $50-74.9 Million
Emp.: 241
Catalog & Mail Order Houses
N.A.I.C.S.: 455219
Jarod Couch *(CFO)*
Jeffrey Harris *(CEO)*
Mike Byrne *(CTO)*

UNITED MARKETING GROUP, INC.
28 Calvert St, Harrison, NY 10528
Tel.: (914) 835-4600
Web Site: http://www.umgxray.com
Year Founded: 1985
Distributes Digital Solutions & Markets Digital Imaging Products, Including X-ray Products
N.A.I.C.S.: 423450

Subsidiaries:

UMG / Del Medical (1)
50 N Gary Ave Ste B, Roselle, IL 60172-1605 (100%)
Tel.: (847) 288-7000
Web Site: http://www.umgxray.com
Sales Range: $25-49.9 Million
Emp.: 100
Sales & Service of Medical Imaging Products
N.A.I.C.S.: 423450
JoEllen Lehman *(Mgr-Sys-MRP)*

UNITED MARKETING INC.
1801 W 4th St, Marion, IN 46952
Tel.: (765) 664-8657
Web Site:
  http://www.unitedmarketinginc.com
Rev.: $11,793,217
Emp.: 20
Motor Vehicle Supplies & New Parts
N.A.I.C.S.: 423120
Robert Kramer *(Pres)*
Jodi Kramer *(VP)*

UNITED MECHANICAL
11540 Plano Rd, Dallas, TX 75243
Tel.: (214) 341-2042
Web Site:
  http://www.unitedmechanical.com
Sales Range: $25-49.9 Million
Emp.: 178
Provider of Mechanical Contracting Services
N.A.I.C.S.: 238220
Jim Murdock *(Mgr)*

UNITED MECHANICAL INC.
8170-4 Mainline Pkwy, Fort Myers, FL 33912
Tel.: (239) 939-4502
Web Site: http://www.umihvac.com
Year Founded: 1987
Sales Range: $10-24.9 Million
Emp.: 19
Heating, Ventilation, Air Conditioning & Plumbing Contractor
N.A.I.C.S.: 238220
Michael A. Clark *(Pres)*
James Posey *(Dir-Safety)*
Don Pine *(VP)*

UNITED MECHANICAL, INC.
117 NE 38th Ter, Oklahoma City, OK 73105
Tel.: (405) 528-1234
Web Site:
  http://www.unitedmech.com
Sales Range: $25-49.9 Million
Emp.: 80
Plumbing, Heating, Air-Conditioning Repair & Maintenance Services
N.A.I.C.S.: 238220
Terry Longest *(Project Mgr)*
Tracy Bean *(Asst Project Mgr)*
Kyle Bellmon *(VP)*
Randy Corbin *(Project Mgr)*
Brad Stephens *(Mgr-Ops)*
Darryl Adams *(Project Mgr)*
George Christensen *(Project Mgr)*
J. R. Hile *(Pres & Gen Mgr)*
Jake Rutherford *(Project Mgr)*
Lane Shafer *(Mgr-Ops)*
Steve Yeagle *(Gen Mgr)*
Cynthia Garay *(VP & Gen Mgr)*
Jana Danker *(VP)*

Subsidiaries:

Air Temp Mechanical Services, Inc. (1)
360 Captain Lewis Dr, Southington, CT 06489
Tel.: (860) 953-8888
Web Site: http://www.ctairtemp.com
Appliance Repair & Maintenance Services
N.A.I.C.S.: 811412
Mark Conlogue *(VP)*

Subsidiary (Domestic):

Solo Mechanical Maintenance, Inc. (2)
50 Budney Rd, Newington, CT 06111
Tel.: (860) 667-7787
Web Site: http://www.solomech.com
Air Conditioning & Heating Equipment Maintenance Services
N.A.I.C.S.: 238220
Lev Solodovnik *(Founder & Pres)*

Donohue Commercial Service Inc. (1)
7676 E 46th Pl, Tulsa, OK 74145
Tel.: (918) 663-5353
Web Site:
  http://www.donohuecommercial.com
Rev.: $1,208,792
Emp.: 20
Heating & Air Conditioning Contractors
N.A.I.C.S.: 238220

UNITED MEDICAL SYSTEMS (DE), INC.
1700 W Park Dr, Westborough, MA 01581-3934
Tel.: (508) 870-6565   DE
Web Site: http://www.ums-usa.com
Emp.: 100
Mobile Health Care Services
N.A.I.C.S.: 621999
Jorgen Madsen *(CEO)*
Glenn A. Hetu *(Chief Dev Officer)*
Doug Stairs *(VP-Urology Sls)*
Bruce Pruden *(Dir-Urological Svcs)*
Lynn Lamburn *(Dir-Mktg)*
Joe Pelletiere *(Chm)*
Carol Straney *(Dir-Women's Health)*
Randy Whaley *(VP-Women's Health Div)*
Jim Kubic *(VP-Contracting)*
Johanna Porter *(Dir-HR)*

Stuart Tuthill *(VP-Bus Dev)*
Larry Woolhiser *(CFO)*
Matthew Gattuso *(Pres)*

UNITED MERCHANT SERVICES INC.
255 Rte 17, Hackensack, NJ 07601
Tel.: (201) 568-7600
Web Site:
  http://www.unitedmerchant.com
Year Founded: 1994
Sales Range: $50-74.9 Million
Emp.: 105
Payment Processing Services
N.A.I.C.S.: 522320
Jay Yoon *(Pres & CEO)*

UNITED METAL FABRICATORS, INC.
1316 Eisenhower Blvd, Johnstown, PA 15904-3307
Tel.: (814) 266-8726   PA
Web Site:
  http://www.umfmedical.com
Year Founded: 1955
Sales Range: $75-99.9 Million
Emp.: 110
Physicians & Hospital Furniture Mfr
N.A.I.C.S.: 337127
Elen Melvin *(Pres)*

UNITED METHODIST FAMILY SERVICES OF VIRGINIA, INC.
3900 W Broad St, Richmond, VA 23230
Tel.: (804) 353-4461   VA
Web Site: http://www.umfs.org
Year Founded: 1900
Sales Range: $10-24.9 Million
Emp.: 383
Child & Family Support Services
N.A.I.C.S.: 624190
Jay Ziehl *(Exec VP)*
Matt Lisagor *(VP-Fin)*
Marcy Johnson *(VP-Programs)*
Gary Duncan *(VP-Mktg & Dev)*
Adalay Wilson *(Assoc VP-Programs)*
Nancy Toscano *(VP-Strategy & Organizational Improvement)*
Laurie Dever *(VP-HR)*
Wade Puryear *(VP-Education)*
Margaret Hardy *(Vice Chm)*
Michael Giancaspro *(Sec)*
Bruce Whitehurst *(Chm)*

UNITED METHODIST PUBLISHING HOUSE
2222 Rosa L Parks Blvd, Nashville, TN 37228
Tel.: (615) 749-6000
Web Site:
  http://www.umpublishing.org
Sales Range: $100-124.9 Million
Emp.: 600
Book Publishing & Printing
N.A.I.C.S.: 513130
Neil M. Alexander *(Pres)*
Fred Allen *(Exec Dir)*
Joanie Catignani *(Mgr-Acctg)*
Mark Gibson *(Mgr-Bus Sys)*
Peggy Jennings *(Dir-Visual Mdse)*
Brian Maddy *(Mgr-Inventory Control & Distr)*
Robin Plunkett *(Mgr-Bus Sys)*
Christa Henning *(Mgr-Mktg Promotions)*
Robert Oda *(Mgr-Traffic)*

UNITED METHODIST RETIREMENT CENTER
1625 Center St NE, Salem, OR 97301
Tel.: (503) 585-6511   OR
Web Site: http://www.umrcsalem.org
Year Founded: 1909

U.S. PRIVATE

Sales Range: $1-9.9 Million
Emp.: 100
Christian Ministry Services
N.A.I.C.S.: 813110
Jim Hook *(Vice Chm)*
Cindy Hannum *(Treas & Sec)*
John D. Hawkins *(Chm)*

UNITED METHODIST RETIREMENT COMMUNITIES
805 W Middle St, Chelsea, MI 48118
Tel.: (734) 433-1000   MI
Web Site: http://www.umrc.com
Year Founded: 1906
Sales Range: $25-49.9 Million
Emp.: 466
Residential Support Services
N.A.I.C.S.: 623312
John Thorhauer *(Pres)*
Richard Lundy *(Treas)*
Stuart Main *(Sec)*
John Nixon III *(Chm)*

UNITED MIDWEST SAVINGS BANK, N.A.
101 S Main St, De Graff, OH 43318
Tel.: (937) 585-5861
Web Site: http://www.umwsb.com
Year Founded: 1889
Sales Range: $10-24.9 Million
Emp.: 120
Federal Savings Bank
N.A.I.C.S.: 522180
Edward N. Cohn *(Pres & CEO)*
Craig Street *(Chief Lending Officer & Exec VP)*
Michael Lerch *(CFO & COO)*
Rick Bates *(CIO)*
Judy K. Lease *(Chief Retail Banking Officer & VP)*
Jenny Flocken *(Sr VP-Comml Credit & Ops)*

UNITED MIGRANT OPPORTUNITY SERVICES, INC.
2701 S Chase Ave, Milwaukee, WI 53207
Tel.: (414) 389-6000   WI
Web Site: http://www.umos.org
Year Founded: 1965
Sales Range: $10-24.9 Million
Emp.: 753
Community Development Services
N.A.I.C.S.: 624190
Juan Jose Lopez *(Chm)*
Lupe Martinez *(Pres & CEO)*
Julio Guix *(Treas)*
Nedda Avila *(Sec)*
Maria Watts *(Vice Chm)*

UNITED MUSLIM RELIEF
1180 Cameron St, Alexandria, VA 22314
Tel.: (202) 370-6963   VA
Web Site: http://www.umrelief.org
Year Founded: 2010
Sales Range: $10-24.9 Million
Emp.: 7
Community Development Services
N.A.I.C.S.: 624190
Mohamed Ali *(Mgr-Comm)*
Omar Shahin *(VP-Fundraising)*
Oussama Mezoui *(VP-Programs)*
Shafi Khan *(VP-Special Proj)*
Abed Ayoub *(Pres & CEO)*
Aisha Hussain *(Coord-Ops)*
Khaled Falah *(Chm)*

UNITED NATIONAL CLOSE-OUT STORES, INC.
2404 E Sunrise Blvd, Fort Lauderdale, FL 33304
Tel.: (954) 524-3325   FL
Web Site: http://www.uncs.com
Sales Range: $10-24.9 Million
Emp.: 20

COMPANIES

Closeout Distr
N.A.I.C.S.: 424990
Brett Rose (Pres)
Todd Hartstone (CFO)

UNITED NATIONAL CORPORATION
601 S Minnesota Ave, Sioux Falls, SD 57104
Tel.: (605) 335-4000
Web Site: http://www.firstpremier.com
Sales Range: $700-749.9 Million
Emp.: 2,900
Bank Holding Company Commercial Bank
N.A.I.C.S.: 551111
Darrell Schmith (CFO & VP-Fin)
Dana Dykhouse (Pres)

Subsidiaries:

First Premier Bank (1)
601 S Minnesota Ave, Sioux Falls, SD 57104
Tel.: (605) 357-3000
Web Site: http://www.firstpremier.com
Sales Range: $50-74.9 Million
Emp.: 192
Commercial Banking Services
N.A.I.C.S.: 522110
Dana J. Dykhouse (CEO)
Dave Rozenboom (Pres)
T. Denny Sanford (Owner)

Premier Bankcard, LLC (1)
3820 N Louise Ave, Sioux Falls, SD 57107
Tel.: (605) 357-3440
Credit Card Issuing Services
N.A.I.C.S.: 522210

UNITED NATIONS DEVELOPMENT CORPORATION
2 United Nations Plz 27th Fl, New York, NY 10017
Tel.: (212) 888-1618
Web Site: http://www.undc.org
Year Founded: 1968
Sales Range: $25-49.9 Million
Emp.: 14
Community Action Services
N.A.I.C.S.: 925120
Frances Huppert (VP)
Kenneth Coopersmith (VP)
Robert Cole (Gen Counsel, Sec & Sr VP)
George Klein (Chm)
Jorge Ortiz (Treas & Controller)
Loida Diaz-de Jesus (VP)

UNITED NEGRO COLLEGE FUND, INC.
1805 7th St NW, Washington, DC 20001
Tel.: (703) 205-3400
Web Site: https://www.uncf.org
Year Founded: 1944
Sales Range: $150-199.9 Million
Emp.: 226
Financial Assistance to Students; Funds to Member & Historically Black Colleges & Universities
N.A.I.C.S.: 813319
LaJuan H. Lyles (Exec VP-People & Culture)
Maurice E. Jenkins (Chief Dev Officer & Exec VP)
Alfred G. Goldstein (Vice Chm)
Paulette Jackson (Sr VP-Dev-Natl & Ops)
Fred D. Mitchell (VP-Dev-Mid-Atlantic & Midwest Reg)
Michael L. Lomax (Pres & CEO)
Desiree C. Boykin (Gen Counsel)
Early Reese (COO)
Seth Bardu (CFO & Sr VP)
Lodriguez Murray (Sr VP-Pub Policy & Govt Affairs)
Larry A. Griffith Jr. (Sr VP-Programs & Student Svcs)
Milton H. Jones Jr. (Chm)

UNITED NOTIONS INC.
13800 Hutton Dr, Dallas, TX 75234
Tel.: (972) 484-8901
Web Site: http://www.unitednotions.com
Rev.: $14,700,000
Emp.: 65
Sewing Supplies & Notions
N.A.I.C.S.: 424310
Howard Marcus Dunn (Owner & Pres)
Bob Wallner (CFO & Controller)

UNITED OHANA, LLC
13355 Noel Rd Ste 1645, Dallas, TX 75240
Tel.: (972) 644-9494
Web Site: http://www.roysrestaurant.com
Full-Service Hawaiian Cuisine Restaurants Operator & Franchisor
N.A.I.C.S.: 722511
Richard Scott (Pres)
Sunil Dharod (Owner)

Subsidiaries:

Roy's of Baltimore, LLC (1)
720 B Aliceanna St, Baltimore, MD 21202
Tel.: (410) 659-0099
Web Site: http://www.roysrestaurant.com
Restaurant Operating Services
N.A.I.C.S.: 722511
Ryan Jones (Gen Mgr)

UNITED OIL CO.
17311 S Main St, Gardena, CA 90248-3131
Tel.: (310) 323-3992
Web Site: http://www.unitedoilco.com
Year Founded: 1977
Sales Range: $200-249.9 Million
Emp.: 600
Gasoline Service Stations
N.A.I.C.S.: 531210
Muhammed Zeman (Mgr-Acctg)

UNITED OIL CORP
1609 W Business 30, Columbia City, IN 46725
Tel.: (260) 244-6000
Web Site: http://www.unitedoilcorp.com
Year Founded: 1966
Sales Range: $10-24.9 Million
Emp.: 45
Provider of Heating Oil
N.A.I.C.S.: 424710
Joe Dorisey (Pres)

UNITED PACIFIC MORTGAGE CO., INC.
1 Spectrum Pointe Dr Ste 345, Lake Forest, CA 92630
Tel.: (877) 768-8081
Web Site: http://www.unipacmortgage.com
Sales Range: $75-99.9 Million
Emp.: 270
Mortgage Brokerage Services
N.A.I.C.S.: 522310
Wayner Lieser (Branch Mgr)
Diane Shankwiler (Branch Mgr)

UNITED PARADYNE CORPORATION
2415 Professional Pkwy, Santa Maria, CA 93455
Tel.: (805) 348-3150
Web Site: http://www.unitedparadyne.com
Sales Range: $10-24.9 Million
Emp.: 150
Aerospace Support Services
N.A.I.C.S.: 541611
Joseph Hasay (Pres & CEO)

UNITED PEOPLE POWER, INC.
656 Ave A Ste 22, Boulder City, NV 89005
Tel.: (702) 592-6134
Year Founded: 2011
Sales Range: $10-24.9 Million
Emp.: 1
Website Development
N.A.I.C.S.: 541519
Diana M. Hendricks (Chm, Pres & CEO)
Cynthia A. Taylor (Sec)
Shaun Hadley (CFO & Treas)
Rebel Brown (VP-Mktg & PR)
Dennis Myers (CIO & VP)
Richard Kaulfers (VP-IT)
Even I D. Rowell (VP-Graphics)

UNITED PET SUPPLY INC.
831 Little Britain Rd, New Windsor, NY 12553
Tel.: (845) 561-7770
Year Founded: 1977
Rev.: $15,000,000
Emp.: 6
Pet Supplies Distr
N.A.I.C.S.: 459910
Steven Zerilli (Pres)
Chris Brooks (VP)

UNITED PLANNING ORGANIZATION
301 Rhode Island Ave NW, Washington, DC 20001
Tel.: (202) 238-4609
Web Site: http://www.upo.org
Year Founded: 1962
Sales Range: $25-49.9 Million
Emp.: 469
Community Action Services
N.A.I.C.S.: 624190
Meseret Degefu (CFO & VP-Fin)
Andrea Thomas (Exec VP)
Dana Maurice Jones (Pres & CEO)
Ruth Hamilton (Sec)
Juan Jara (Treas)
Jacqueline Kinlow (Chm)

UNITED PLASTIC FABRICATING
165 Flagship Dr, North Andover, MA 01845
Tel.: (978) 975-4520
Web Site: http://www.unitedplastic.com
Year Founded: 1986
Emp.: 450
Mfr of Thermoformed Finished Plastics Products
N.A.I.C.S.: 326199
F. Joseph Lingel (Pres & CEO)
Michael Ashley (VP-Engrg)
Andrew Lingel (VP-Ops)
Neil Godin (Mgr-Production)

UNITED PLUMBING & HEATING SUPPLY CO.
9947 W Carmen Ave, Milwaukee, WI 53225
Tel.: (414) 464-5122
Web Site: http://www.unitedph.com
Sales Range: $10-24.9 Million
Emp.: 23
Industrial Plumming Supplies
N.A.I.C.S.: 423840
Chip Roska (Pres & Gen Mgr)

UNITED PLUMBING SUPPLY CO.
US Hwy 22 W End Ave, North Plainfield, NJ 07060
Tel.: (908) 757-3232
Sales Range: $10-24.9 Million
Emp.: 20
Plumbing & Hydronic Heating Supplies
N.A.I.C.S.: 423720

UNITED PLUMBING TECHNOLOGIES
1170 Main St, Newington, CT 06111-3030
Tel.: (860) 666-3342
Web Site: http://www.keeneymfg.com
Year Founded: 1923
Sales Range: $25-49.9 Million
Emp.: 350
Mfr of Plumbers Goods
N.A.I.C.S.: 332913
James Holden (Sr VP)

Subsidiaries:

Keeney Manufacturing Company (1)
1170 Main St, Newington, CT 06111
Tel.: (860) 666-3342
Web Site: http://www.plumbpak.com
Sales Range: $25-49.9 Million
Emp.: 70
Mfr Construction & Replacement Plumbing/Water Supply Products
N.A.I.C.S.: 332913
Chris Jeffers (Dir-Mktg)

UNITED PLYWOODS & LUMBER INC.
1640 Mims Ave SW, Birmingham, AL 35211
Tel.: (205) 925-7601
Web Site: http://www.unitedplywoods.com
Rev.: $29,187,004
Emp.: 37
Lumber; Plywood & Millwork
N.A.I.C.S.: 423310
John Mims (Chm)
Rick Eversole (VP-Sls & Mktg)

UNITED POWER INC.
500 Cooperative Way, Brighton, CO 80601-0929
Tel.: (303) 659-0551
Web Site: http://www.unitedpower.com
Year Founded: 1938
Electronic Services
N.A.I.C.S.: 221122
John Parker (CEO)
Laurie Rydwell (CFO)
Bryant Robbins (COO)

Subsidiaries:

Abound Solar, Inc. (1)
9586 E I-25 Frontage Rd, Longmont, CO 80504
Tel.: (970) 619-5386
Thin-film Cadmium Telluride Solar Modules Mfr
N.A.I.C.S.: 221114

UNITED PRAIRIE, LLC
929 County Rd 700 N, Tolono, IL 61880
Tel.: (217) 485-6000
Web Site: http://www.unitedprairie.com
Year Founded: 1996
Sales Range: $25-49.9 Million
Emp.: 40
Fertilizer, Seed & Crop Protection Chemicals Supplier
N.A.I.C.S.: 325314
Russ Dukeman (Coord-Sls)

UNITED PRECAST, INC.
PO Box 991 Roundhouse Ln, Mount Vernon, OH 43050
Tel.: (740) 393-1121
Web Site: http://www.unitedprecast.net
Year Founded: 1970
Sales Range: $50-74.9 Million

UNITED PRECAST, INC.   **U.S. PRIVATE**

United Precast, Inc.—Continued
Emp.: 245
Mfr & Sales of Concrete Products
N.A.I.C.S.: 327390
John D. Ellis (Pres & CEO)
William Canden (Mgr-Logistics, Dispatch & Collections)

UNITED PRODUCERS, INC.
8351 N High St Ste 250, Columbus, OH 43235
Tel.: (614) 433-2150
Web Site: http://www.uproducers.com
Year Founded: 1934
Sales Range: $75-99.9 Million
Emp.: 151
Marketers of Livestock; Financial, Risk Management & Production Management Services to Farmers
N.A.I.C.S.: 424520
Brad Warner (Comptroller)
Mike Bumgarner (Pres & CEO)
Clay Fredericks (Mgr-Dairy-Beef)

Subsidiaries:

Producers Credit Corporation   (1)
4809 S 114th St, Omaha, NE 68137
Web Site: http://www.producerscredit.com
Sales Range: $25-49.9 Million
Emp.: 30
Provider of Credit to Farmers for the Financing of Crop Input Machinery Livestock Construction & Real Estate Services
N.A.I.C.S.: 522299
Bob Siegel (VP-Credit)
John King (Officer-Bus Dev)

UNITED PRODUCTION & CONSTRUCTION SERVICES
4110 Coteau Rd, New Iberia, LA 70560-7663
Tel.: (337) 365-4400
Web Site: http://www.upcs-inc.com
Rev.: $12,100,000
Emp.: 5
Construction, Repair & Dismantling Services
N.A.I.C.S.: 213112
Charles Gunn (CEO)
Wayne Romero (Superintendent-Construction)

UNITED PRODUCTS DISTRIBUTORS INC.
1200 68th St, Baltimore, MD 21237-2517
Tel.: (410) 866-6800   MD
Web Site: http://www.updinc.com
Year Founded: 1973
Sales Range: $10-24.9 Million
Emp.: 65
Provider of Heating & Air Conditioning Services
N.A.I.C.S.: 423730
Ken Kaelin (CEO)
Herb Ruppert (CFO)
Linda Schoff (Sec)
Donna Pitz (Pres)
Richard Hicks (Mgr-Sls)

UNITED PROPANE GAS COMPANIES INC.
4200 Cairo Rd, Paducah, KY 42001
Tel.: (270) 442-5557
Web Site: http://www.upgas.com
Sales Range: $50-74.9 Million
Emp.: 250
Propane Gas
N.A.I.C.S.: 457210
Gorman Hines (Gen Mgr)

UNITED PROPERTIES
715 McGraw St, Bay City, MI 48707
Tel.: (989) 892-5593   MI
Year Founded: 1908
Sales Range: $75-99.9 Million

Emp.: 6
Operator & Manager of Shopping Centers
N.A.I.C.S.: 531120
Robert G. Koffman (Pres & CEO)
John R. Van Laan (Sr VP-Fin)
Brad W. Lavictor (Treas & VP)
Matt Oermann (Mgr-Dev)

UNITED RADIO INC.
5703 Enterprise Pkwy, East Syracuse, NY 13057-2905
Tel.: (315) 446-8700
Web Site: http://www.ursdealer.com
Rev: $30,000,000
Emp.: 210
Radio Repair Shop
N.A.I.C.S.: 811210
Arnold J. Rubenstein (Pres)
Jim Fitzgerald (Mgr-Customer Svcs)
Barbara Kearse (Coord-Intl Customs)

UNITED RADIO, INCORPORATED
3345 Point Pleasant Rd, Hebron, KY 41048
Tel.: (859) 371-4423
Web Site: http://www.bluestarinc.com
Year Founded: 1929
Sales Range: $75-99.9 Million
Emp.: 100
Distr of Barcoding Equipment
N.A.I.C.S.: 423440
Steve G. Cuntz (Pres & CEO)
Ryan Girbin (Controller)
Bill Nix (Dir-Global Channel Mktg & Sls)

UNITED READERS SERVICE LTD.
13400 Madison Ave, Lakewood, OH 44107
Tel.: (216) 228-1026
Web Site:
http://www.unitedreaders.com
Rev.: $15,000,000
Emp.: 80
Magazine Subscription Direct Sales
N.A.I.C.S.: 513120
Robert Anthony (Pres)

UNITED REAL ESTATE GROUP, LLC
5430 LBJ Frwy Ste 280, Dallas, TX 75240
Tel.: (877) 201-7640
Web Site:
http://www.UnitedRealEstate.com
Year Founded: 2011
Real Estate Services
N.A.I.C.S.: 531390
Dan Duffy (CEO)
Rick Haase (Pres-United Real Estate)
Leigh Ann Bogran (Dir-Strategic Project Mgmt-United Real Estate)

Subsidiaries:

Pearson Smith Realty, LLC   (1)
43777 Central Station Dr Ste 390, Ashburn, VA 20147
Tel.: (571) 386-1075
Web Site:
http://www.pearsonsmithrealty.com
Sales Range: $25-49.9 Million
Emp.: 12
Real Estate Manangement Services
N.A.I.C.S.: 531210
Eric Pearson (Founder & CEO)

Platinum Realty, LLC   (1)
9393 W 110th St Ste 170, Overland Park, KS 66210
Tel.: (913) 227-0798
Web Site:
https://www.movewithplatinum.com
Sales Range: $1-9.9 Million
Emp.: 650
Real Estate Services
N.A.I.C.S.: 531210

Scott DeNeve (Founder, Pres & CEO)
Unit (Domestic):

Platinum Realty R.E. Services   (2)
444 N Belleview Ave Ste 107, Gladstone, MO 64116
Tel.: (816) 994-8808
Web Site: http://www.movewithplatinum.com
Emp.: 15
Real Estate Services
N.A.I.C.S.: 531210
Scott G. DeNeve (Owner)

Virtual Properties Realty, LLC   (1)
2750 Premiere Pkwy, Duluth, GA 30097
Tel.: (770) 495-5050
Web Site:
http://www.virtualpropertiesrealty.com
Residential Property Management Services
N.A.I.C.S.: 531311
Steve Wagner (Co-Founder)
Karen Burks (Co-Founder)
Cathy McDaniel (Dir-Education)

UNITED RECORD PRESSING LLC
453 Chestnut St, Nashville, TN 37203-4894
Tel.: (615) 259-9396
Web Site: http://www.urpressing.com
Year Founded: 1949
Emp.: 150
Integrated Record Production/Distribution
N.A.I.C.S.: 512250
Mark Michael (Owner)

UNITED REFRIGERATION, INC.
11401 Roosevelt Blvd, Philadelphia, PA 19154-2102
Tel.: (215) 698-9100   PA
Web Site: http://www.uri.com
Year Founded: 1947
Rev.: $200,000,000
Emp.: 816
Distr & Wholesaler of Air Conditioning, Heating & Refrigeration Parts & Equipment
N.A.I.C.S.: 423740
Carmen Carosella (VP)
Linda Ceschan (Mgr-Ops Branch)
Bill Pimm (Reg Mgr)
Bruce Campbell (Acct Mgr-Natl)
Harkins Chris (Mgr-Warehouse)
Jim Warnock (Mgr-Refrigeration Product)
Joe White (Branch Mgr)
Mary Zenzen (Mgr-Pur)
Sue Smith (Mgr-Returns)
John H. Reilly Jr. (Pres)

Subsidiaries:

Bally Refrigerated Boxes, Inc.   (1)
135 Little 9 Dr, Morehead City, NC 28557-8483
Tel.: (252) 240-2829
Web Site: http://www.ballyrefboxes.com
Sales Range: $25-49.9 Million
Emp.: 200
Refrigeration & Heating Equipment Mfr
N.A.I.C.S.: 333415
Charles Jennings (Mgr-Facility)
Connie Carawan (Mgr-Inside Sls)
Lee Wilson (Supvr-Scheduling)

United Refrigeration of Canada Ltd.   (1)
130 Riviera Drive, Markham, L3R 5M1, ON, Canada
Tel.: (905) 479-1212
Emp.: 6
Refrigeration & Air Conditioning Equipment Distr
N.A.I.C.S.: 423740

UNITED RESTAURANT SUPPLY INC.
725 Clark Pl, Colorado Springs, CO 80915
Tel.: (719) 574-3200

Web Site:
http://www.urskitchens.com
Sales Range: $10-24.9 Million
Emp.: 26
Restaurant Equipment & Supplies
N.A.I.C.S.: 423440
Roger Boyles (Pres)

UNITED RIGGERS & ERECTORS INC.
4188 Vly Blvd, Walnut, CA 91789
Tel.: (909) 978-0400
Web Site:
http://www.unitedriggers.com
Sales Range: $25-49.9 Million
Emp.: 100
Machinery Installation
N.A.I.C.S.: 238290
Brian D. Kelley (CEO & CFO)
Ed Conner (Pres)
Larry D. Kelley (Sr VP)
Thomas J. Kruss (COO, Treas & Sec)

UNITED ROTARY BRUSH CORPORATION
15607 W 100th Ter, Shawnee Mission, KS 66219
Tel.: (913) 888-8450
Web Site: http://www.united-rotary.com
Sales Range: $10-24.9 Million
Emp.: 130
Mfr of Brushes
N.A.I.C.S.: 339994
Harry Vegter (Dir-Engrg)
Jeff Ghilani (Mgr-Sls)
Peter Gurney (Mgr-Sls)
Rob Hill (Mgr-Sls)
Jeff Purcell (Acct Mgr)

Subsidiaries:

United Rotary Brush   (1)
15607 W 100th Terr, Lenexa, KS 66219
Tel.: (913) 888-8450
Web Site: http://www.united-rotary.com
Emp.: 140
Brushes Mfr
N.A.I.C.S.: 339994

United Rotary Brush   (1)
8150 Business Way, Plain City, OH 43064
Tel.: (937) 644-3515
Web Site: http://www.united-rotary.com
Sales Range: $10-24.9 Million
Emp.: 35
Mfr of Brushes
N.A.I.C.S.: 339994

United Rotary Brush Corporation Eastern Division   (1)
8150 Business Way, Plain City, OH 43064
Tel.: (937) 644-3515
Web Site: http://www.united-rotary.com
Sales Range: $10-24.9 Million
Emp.: 15
Brushes Mfr
N.A.I.C.S.: 339994

United Rotary Brush Corporation of Canada   (1)
190 Saunders Road, Barrie, L4N 9A2, ON, Canada   (100%)
Tel.: (705) 737-3519
Web Site: http://www.unitedrotary.com
Sales Range: $10-24.9 Million
Emp.: 28
Mfr of Brushes
N.A.I.C.S.: 339994
Harry Vegter (Engr)

UNITED SALT CORPORATION
4800 San Felipe St, Houston, TX 77056-3908
Tel.: (713) 877-2600
Web Site: http://www.unitedsalt.com
Year Founded: 1970
Rev.: $62,500,000
Emp.: 392
Industrial Inorganic Chemicals
N.A.I.C.S.: 212390

COMPANIES

James O'Donnell (Pres)
Wayne Sneed (CFO)
Dennis Bradley (Plant Mgr)
Kyle Rash (VP-Ops)
Nancy Wimberly (Mgr-Customer Svc-AR)

Subsidiaries:

Alpha Automation Inc. (1)
4800 San Felipe St, Houston, TX 77056-3908
Tel.: (713) 877-8039
Sales Range: $10-24.9 Million
Emp.: 3
Computer Maintenance & Repair
N.A.I.C.S.: 811210
James O'Donnell (Pres)

Brinadd International Company Inc. (1)
4800 San Felipe St, Houston, TX 77056-3908
Tel.: (713) 877-2600
Sales Range: $10-24.9 Million
Emp.: 60
Chemicals & Allied Products
N.A.I.C.S.: 424690

Solar Petroleum Corp. (1)
4800 San Felipe St, Houston, TX 77056-3908
Tel.: (713) 877-2600
Sales Range: $25-49.9 Million
Emp.: 3
Drilling Oil & Gas Wells
N.A.I.C.S.: 213111

Sonar & Well Testing Services Inc. (1)
4800 San Felipe St, Houston, TX 77056-3908
Tel.: (713) 433-9597
Sales Range: $25-49.9 Million
Emp.: 5
Oil & Gas Field Services
N.A.I.C.S.: 213112

Texas Brine Company LLC (1)
4800 San Felipe St, Houston, TX 77056-3908
Tel.: (713) 877-2700
Web Site: http://www.texasbrine.net
Sales Range: $10-24.9 Million
Emp.: 36
Pipeline
N.A.I.C.S.: 486990
Bruce E. Martin (VP-Ops)

Texas United Chemical Company LLC (1)
4800 San Felipe St, Houston, TX 77056-3908
Tel.: (800) 554-8659
Web Site: http://www.tbc-brinadd.com
Sales Range: $10-24.9 Million
Emp.: 13
Industrial Inorganic Chemicals
N.A.I.C.S.: 325180

Texas United Supply Company Inc. (1)
4800 San Felipe St, Houston, TX 77056
Tel.: (713) 877-2600
Sales Range: $10-24.9 Million
Emp.: 2
Equipment Rental & Leasing
N.A.I.C.S.: 532490

United Brine Pipeline Company LLC (1)
4800 San Felipe St, Houston, TX 77056-3908
Tel.: (713) 877-1778
Sales Range: $10-24.9 Million
Emp.: 6
Transportation Services
N.A.I.C.S.: 488999

UNITED SAVINGS BANK
1510 Packer Ave, Philadelphia, PA 19145
Tel.: (215) 467-4300
Web Site: http://www.unitedsavingsbank.com
Year Founded: 1912
Sales Range: $10-24.9 Million
Emp.: 25
Banking Services
N.A.I.C.S.: 522180
Chad A. McGroarty (VP)
Nancy Marone (Asst VP)
Jacqueline Mellett (Branch Mgr)

UNITED SEAFOOD IMPORTS INC.
5500 1st Ave N, Saint Petersburg, FL 33710
Tel.: (727) 894-2661   FL
Year Founded: 1997
Sales Range: $10-24.9 Million
Emp.: 5
Supplier of Packaged Frozen Goods
N.A.I.C.S.: 424420
Dick Stowell (Pres)
Ron Arostegai (CFO)

UNITED SECURITY LIFE AND HEALTH INSURANCE COMPANY
6640 S Cicero Ave, Bedford Park, IL 60638
Tel.: (708) 475-6100
Web Site: http://www.uslandh.com
Sales Range: $100-124.9 Million
Emp.: 450
Provider of Insurance Services
N.A.I.C.S.: 524113
Sandy Horn (Pres & CEO)

Subsidiaries:

American Transit Insurance Company (1)
330 W 34th St Fl 10, New York, NY 10001
Tel.: (212) 857-8200
Web Site: http://www.american-transit.com
Sales Range: $100-124.9 Million
Emp.: 350
Provider of Insurance Agent Broker Services
N.A.I.C.S.: 524210

Subsidiary (Domestic):

United Security Life Insurance Co. (2)
6640 S Cicero Ave, Bedford Park, IL 60638
Tel.: (708) 475-6100
Web Site: http://www.ushandc.com
Rev.: $31,020,844
Emp.: 50
Fire Insurance Services
N.A.I.C.S.: 524113

UNITED SERVICE COMPANIES INC.
1550 S Indiana Ave, Chicago, IL 60605
Tel.: (312) 922-8558
Web Site: http://www.unitedhq.com
Sales Range: $25-49.9 Million
Emp.: 2,000
Provider of Janitorial Services
N.A.I.C.S.: 561720
Richard A. Simon (Pres & CEO)
Mike Graney (VP)
David Hill (CFO)
Bill Callaghan (VP)
Anthony D'Angelo (VP)
Paul Doerscheln (Gen Counsel)
Vicki Rosen-Sanetra (COO)

UNITED SERVICES AUTOMOBILE ASSOCIATION
9800 Fredericksburg Rd, San Antonio, TX 78288-0001
Tel.: (210) 531-8722   TX
Web Site: https://www.usaa.com
Year Founded: 1922
Sales Range: $15-24.9 Billion
Emp.: 28,000
Financial Planning, Insurance, Investment, Banking & Other Services Primarily to Military Personnel
N.A.I.C.S.: 524126
Wayne Peacock (Pres & CEO)
Amala Duggirala (CIO & Exec VP)
Juan Carlos Andrade (Chm-Advisory Panel)
Amala Duggirala (CIO & Exec VP)
Jeff Wallace (CFO & Exec VP)
Ameesh Vakharia (Chief Strategy Officer & Exec VP)
Bob Johnson (Chief Legal Officer, Gen Counsel & Exec VP)
Randy Termeer (Pres-Property & Casualty Insurance Grp)
James M. Zortman (Chm)
Brandon Carter (Pres-USAA Life Insurance Company)
Tami Cabaniss (Chief HR Officer & Exec VP)

Subsidiaries:

USAA Alliance Services Company (1)
9800 Fredericksburg Rd, San Antonio, TX 00078--245   (100%)
Tel.: (210) 498-2211
Web Site: http://www.usaa.com
Sales Range: $10-24.9 Million
Emp.: 150
Travel Agency,Banking,Earthlink
N.A.I.C.S.: 812990

USAA Federal Savings Bank (1)
10750 McDoermott Freeway, San Antonio, TX 78288-9876   (100%)
Tel.: (210) 531-8722
Web Site: http://www.usaa.com
Banking Services
N.A.I.C.S.: 522180
Josue Robles Jr. (CEO)
Wayne Peacock (Vice Chm)
G. Patrick Phillips (Bd of Dirs, Executives)

Subsidiary (Domestic):

USAA Acceptance, LLC (2)
10750 McDermott Fwy, San Antonio, TX 78288
Tel.: (210) 498-7479
Investment Services
N.A.I.C.S.: 523999
Brett Seybold (Pres, CEO, Treas, CFO & Controller)

USAA Relocation Services, Inc. (2)
10750 McDermott Freeway, San Antonio, TX 78288
Tel.: (210) 282-8132
Real Estate Brokerage Services
N.A.I.C.S.: 531210

USAA Savings Bank (2)
3773 Howard Hughes Pkwy, Las Vegas, NV 89169
Tel.: (702) 862-8891
Web Site: http://www.usaa.com
Commercial Banking Services
N.A.I.C.S.: 522110

USAA Insurance Agency Inc. (1)
9800 Fredericksburg Rd B-2e, San Antonio, TX 78288-0002
Tel.: (210) 498-2211
Automobile Insurance Services
N.A.I.C.S.: 524210

USAA Life General Agency Inc. (1)
1855 Telstar Rd, Colorado Springs, CO 80920-1005
Tel.: (800) 531-8000
Property & Casualty Insurance Services
N.A.I.C.S.: 524126

USAA Life Insurance Co. (1)
9800 Fredericksberg Rd, San Antonio, TX 78284-0001   (100%)
Tel.: (210) 498-8000
Web Site: http://www.usaa.com
Sales Range: $250-299.9 Million
Emp.: 1,000
Life Insurance
N.A.I.C.S.: 524130
Josue Robles Jr. (CEO)

USAA Real Estate Services (1)
100 S Ashley Dr, Tampa, FL 33602
Tel.: (813) 273-9300
Web Site: http://www.usrealco.com

Sales Range: $25-49.9 Million
Emp.: 2
Provider of Nonresidential Building Operating Services
N.A.I.C.S.: 531190
Kim Duncan (Office Mgr)

UNITED SERVICES INC.
1007 N Main St, Dayville, CT 06241
Tel.: (860) 774-2020   CT
Web Site: http://www.unitedservicesct.org
Year Founded: 1966
Sales Range: $10-24.9 Million
Emp.: 322
Behavioral Healthcare Services
N.A.I.C.S.: 623220
Mary Bromm (Sec)
Jeff Kramer (Chm)
Diane Manning (Pres & CEO)
Alexander Miano (Dir-Medical)
Robert Deverna (CFO & Sr VP)
Colleen Harrington (COO & VP)

UNITED SHIPPING SOLUTIONS
6900 S 900 E Ste 230, Midvale, UT 84047
Tel.: (801) 352-0012
Web Site: http://www.usshipit.com
Year Founded: 2002
Rev.: $74,200,000
Emp.: 12
Freight Transportation Services
N.A.I.C.S.: 488510
Robert Ross (VP)
Rick Derr (Mgr)

UNITED SHOE MACHINERY CORP.
32 Stevens St, Haverhill, MA 01830
Tel.: (978) 374-0303   DE
Web Site: http://www.usmcorporation.com
Year Founded: 1997
Sales Range: $10-24.9 Million
Emp.: 60
Supplier of Industrial Machinery & Equipment
N.A.I.C.S.: 423830
George Armstead (Mgr-Sls)
John Kozis (COO)
Margret Wolfendale (Controller)
Michael Taricano (Pres-USM)

UNITED SOUTH AND EASTERN TRIBES, INC.
711 Stewarts Ferry Pike Ste 100, Nashville, TN 37214
Tel.: (615) 872-7900   TN
Web Site: http://www.usetinc.org
Year Founded: 1969
Sales Range: $1-9.9 Million
Tribal Welfare Services
N.A.I.C.S.: 921150
Steve Adams (Controller)
Kitcki Carroll (Exec Dir)
Brian Patterson (Pres)
Cameron Chase (Coord-Health Program Evaluation)
Liz Malerba (Sec)
Tammy Fowler (Accountant)
Brandy Venuti (Coord-Special Projects)
Kate Grismala (Asst Dir-THPS)
Wanda Janes (Deputy Dir)
Jenna Middlebrooks (Dir-Dental Support Center)
Brandon Stephens (Dir-Dev)
Dee Sabattus (Dir-THPS)
Steve Terry (Sr Project Coord-Tribal Community Support)
Randy Noka (VP)
Jerry Pardilla (Dir-OERM)

UNITED SOUTH AND EASTERN TRIBES, INC.
U.S. PRIVATE

United South and Eastern Tribes, Inc.—(Continued)
B. Cheryl Smith (Treas)
Robert R. McGhee (VP)
Lynn Malerba (Sec)
Kirk E. Francis Sr. (Pres)

UNITED SOUTHERN BANK
2701 S Bay St, Eustis, FL 32726
Tel.: (352) 589-2121
Web Site: http://www.unitedsouthernbank.com
Year Founded: 1937
Sales Range: $10-24.9 Million
Emp.: 142
Provider of Banking Services
N.A.I.C.S.: 522110
Robert P. Adrid (Exec VP-Comml Banking)
Frank Munroe (VP)
Ivan Gonzalez (Mgr-Eustis)
G. Edward Clement (Chm)
Catherine Hanson (Vice Chm)

UNITED SPINAL ASSOCIATION
120-34 Queens Blvd Ste 320, Kew Gardens, NY 11415
Tel.: (718) 803-3782   NY
Web Site: http://www.unitedspinal.org
Year Founded: 1947
Sales Range: $10-24.9 Million
Emp.: 163
Spinal Cord Disorder Treatment Services
N.A.I.C.S.: 813920
Kleo J. King (Sr Dir-Accessibility Ops)
Ross Meglathery (Dir-VetsFirst)
Brian O'Connor (VP-Alliance Dev)
David C. Cooper (Chm)
Vincenzo Piscopo (Pres & CEO)
Dominic Marinelli (VP-Accessibility Svcs Program)

UNITED STAFFING ASSOCIATES
505 Higuera St, San Luis Obispo, CA 93401
Tel.: (805) 269-2677
Web Site: http://www.unitedwestaff.com
Rev.: $16,000,000
Emp.: 26
Staffing Services
N.A.I.C.S.: 561311
Debbie Allen (Mgr-Payroll & Acctg)
Mary Alpaugh (Mgr-Sls)
Mark Montanez (Mgr-HR & Corp)
Wendi Patterson (Dir-Mktg & Brand Dev)
Greg D. Elson (Dir-Comm & Tech)
Susan Elson (CFO)
Julie Camacho (VP)
David Elson (Pres)
Jorge Ramos (Dir-Bus Dev)
Norma White (Dir-Health & Safety)
William D. Hills (Gen Counsel & VP)
Juana Serrato (Mgr-Central California)
Michael Nursement (Mgr-Facilities)
Tracy Perez (Mgr-Oxnard Branch)
Donna Tarr (VP-Ops)
Shawnte Priest (VP-HR)

UNITED STAFFING SOLUTIONS INC.
2050 W 190 St Ste 201, Torrance, CA 90504
Tel.: (310) 305-9999
Web Site: http://www.ussinurses.com
Sales Range: $10-24.9 Million
Emp.: 40
Help Supply Services
N.A.I.C.S.: 561320
Parvez Gondal (CEO)

UNITED STARS INC.
1546 Henry Ave, Beloit, WI 53511-3668
Tel.: (608) 368-4625   WI
Web Site: http://www.ustars.com
Year Founded: 1936
Sales Range: $10-24.9 Million
Emp.: 20
Mfr of Steel, Copper, Carbon & Alloy, Aluminum, Titanium & Other High Alloy Content Raw Materials
N.A.I.C.S.: 331210
Roger W. West (Chm & CEO)

Subsidiaries:
GearTec, Inc.   (1)
4245 Hamann Pkwy, Willoughby, OH 44094-5623
Tel.: (440) 953-3900
Web Site: http://www.geartec.com
Sales Range: $1-9.9 Million
Custom Gear Mfr
N.A.I.C.S.: 333612
John E. Grazia (Pres)
Bill Stohr (Mgr-Ops & Engrg)
Betty Masitto (VP-Fin)

Precision Gears, Inc.   (1)
N13W24705 Bluemound Rd, Pewaukee, WI 53072
Tel.: (262) 542-4261
Web Site: http://www.precisiongears.com
Speed Changers, Drives, And Gears
N.A.I.C.S.: 333612
Mark Kaurich (VP)

The Electric Materials Company Inc.   (1)
50 S Washington St, North East, PA 16428-1508
Tel.: (814) 725-9621
Web Site: http://www.elecmat.com
Copper Rolling & Drawing Mfr
N.A.I.C.S.: 331420
Tony Newara (Mgr-Quality & Mfg Support)

United Gear & Assembly   (1)
1700 Livingstone Rd, Hudson, WI 54016-9365
Tel.: (715) 386-5867
Web Site: http://www.unitedindustries.com
Mfr of Motor Vehicle Parts & Accessories
N.A.I.C.S.: 334511
Michael Wodarck (CFO)

United Industries, Inc.   (1)
1546 Henry Ave, Beloit, WI 53511
Tel.: (608) 365-8891
Web Site: http://www.unitedindustries.com
Steel Pipe & Tube Mfr
N.A.I.C.S.: 331210
Greg Sturicz (Pres)
Lloyd J. Peterman (Dir-Intl)
Rodger Veneman (Mgr-Automotive)
Sharon Bruun (Mgr-Ornamental & Heat Exchanger)

United Stainless, Inc.   (1)
95 Lakeview Dr, Selmer, TN 38375
Tel.: (731) 645-8467
Steel Pipe & Tube Mfr
N.A.I.C.S.: 331210
Greg Sturicz (Gen Mgr)

United Stars Industries, Inc.   (1)
1546 Henry Ave, Beloit, WI 53511-3668   (100%)
Tel.: (608) 365-8891
Web Site: http://www.unitedindustries.com
Mfr Steel Pipe & Tubes
N.A.I.C.S.: 331210
Greg Sturicz (Pres)

UNITED STATES BAKERY
315 NE 10th Ave, Portland, OR 97232-2712
Tel.: (503) 731-5670   OR
Web Site: http://www.franzbakery.com
Year Founded: 1906
Commercial Bakery
N.A.I.C.S.: 311812
Bob Albers (CEO)

Subsidiaries:
Smith Cookie Company   (1)
1388 NE Hwy 99W, McMinnville, OR 97128
Tel.: (503) 472-5145
Cookie & Cracker Mfr
N.A.I.C.S.: 311821

United States Bakery - Portland Plant   (1)
340 NE 11th St, Portland, OR 97232
Tel.: (503) 232-2191
Web Site: http://www.franzbakery.com
Sales Range: $75-99.9 Million
Emp.: 500
Distr of Breads, Buns & Related Products
N.A.I.C.S.: 311812
Jim Kennison (Gen Mgr)

United States Bakery - Seattle, 6th Ave Plant   (1)
2901 6th Ave S, Seattle, WA 98134-2103
Tel.: (206) 682-2244
Web Site: http://www.franzbakery.com
Wholesale Bakery
N.A.I.C.S.: 311812

United States Bakery - Seattle, Weller Street Plant   (1)
2006 S Weller St, Seattle, WA 98144-2237
Tel.: (206) 726-7535
Web Site: http://www.franzbakery.com
Sales Range: $150-199.9 Million
Emp.: 900
Bakery
N.A.I.C.S.: 311812

United States Bakery - Springfield Plant   (1)
2000 Nugget Way, Springfield, OR 97403
Tel.: (541) 485-8211
Sales Range: $50-74.9 Million
Emp.: 300
Breads, Buns & Related Baked Products Distr
N.A.I.C.S.: 311811

UNITED STATES BARTENDER'S GUILD
2654 W Horizon Ridge Pkwy, Henderson, NV 89052
Tel.: (855) 655-8724   NV
Web Site: http://www.usbg.org
Year Founded: 2005
Sales Range: $1-9.9 Million
Emp.: 4
Professional Association
N.A.I.C.S.: 813920
Jodi Jordan (Fin Dir & Dir-Admin)
Sheila Rosario (Dir-Natl Programs)
Aaron Gregory Smith (Exec Dir)
Tiffany Soles (Mgr-Membership Admin)
David Nepove (Pres)
Kyle McHugh (VP)
Laura Cullen (Treas)
Nicola Riske (Sec)

UNITED STATES BEEF CORPORATION
4923 E 49th St, Tulsa, OK 74135
Tel.: (918) 665-0740
Web Site: http://www.usbeefcorp.com
Rev.: $147,041,870
Emp.: 70
Fast-Food Restaurant, Chain
N.A.I.C.S.: 722513
Brett Pratt (CEO)
Lori Pumphrey (CFO)
John R. Davis (Pres)

UNITED STATES BEVERAGE LLC
700 Canal St, Stamford, CT 06902
Tel.: (203) 961-8215
Web Site: http://www.unitedstatesbeverage.com
Sales Range: $10-24.9 Million
Emp.: 25
Beer & Other Fermented Malt Liquors
N.A.I.C.S.: 424810
Fred Gambke (COO-Natl Accts & Sls Dev)

Paul Moorehead (VP & Dir-Creative Mktg)
Joseph J. Fisch Jr. (Pres & CEO)

UNITED STATES BITCOIN AND TREASURY INVESTMENT TRUST
2 Park Ave 20th Fl, New York, NY 10016
Tel.: (917) 994-5119   DE
Year Founded: 2018
Investment Services
N.A.I.C.S.: 523999
William Joseph Herrmann (Mng Partner)

UNITED STATES BOX CORP.
14 Madison Rd Unit E, Fairfield, NJ 07004
Tel.: (973) 481-2000
Web Site: http://www.usbox.com
Mfr of Packing & Displays
N.A.I.C.S.: 322130
Tom Kossoff (Owner)

UNITED STATES BRASS & COPPER CO.
1401 Brook Dr, Downers Grove, IL 60515-1089
Tel.: (630) 629-9340   IL
Web Site: http://www.usbrassandcopper.com
Year Founded: 1925
Brass & Copper Products & Services Suppliers
N.A.I.C.S.: 423510
David J. Kavanaugh (Pres)

UNITED STATES BUILDING SUPPLY
4391 York St, Denver, CO 80216-3904
Tel.: (303) 991-1292
Web Site: http://www.usbsinc.com
Sales Range: $10-24.9 Million
Emp.: 45
Vinyl Siding Whslr
N.A.I.C.S.: 444110
Neil Hurta (VP)

UNITED STATES COACHWORKS INC.
35 Carlough Rd, Bohemia, NY 11716-2911
Tel.: (631) 567-7500   NY
Year Founded: 1994
Sales Range: $10-24.9 Million
Emp.: 188
Stretch Limousines Mfr
N.A.I.C.S.: 336110

UNITED STATES COAST GUARD
2100 Second St SW, Washington, DC 20593
Tel.: (202) 372-4620
Web Site: http://www.uscg.mil
Sales Range: $25-49.9 Million
Emp.: 100
Military Branch of the United States
N.A.I.C.S.: 523910
Angela Watson (Atty)

UNITED STATES DISTILLED PRODUCTS CO., INC.
1607 12th St S, Princeton, MN 55371-2300
Tel.: (763) 389-4903   MN
Web Site: http://www.usdp.com
Year Founded: 1976
Sales Range: $10-24.9 Million
Emp.: 130
Blended Liquors Mfr & Distr
N.A.I.C.S.: 312140

COMPANIES

Bradley P. Johnson *(Pres)*
Tammy Schuette *(Controller)*
Patricia Pelzer *(CFO)*
Mike Duggan *(CEO)*

UNITED STATES ENVIRONMENTAL PROTECTION AGENCY

Ariel Rios Bldg 1200 Pennsylvania Ave NW, Washington, DC 20460-0001
Tel.: (202) 272-0167
Web Site: http://www.epa.gov
Year Founded: 1970
Environmental Conservation Organization
N.A.I.C.S.: 813312
Andrew Wheeler *(Head-Admin)*
Henry Darwin *(Dir-Ops)*

UNITED STATES GEAR CORPORATION

1120 W 119th St, Chicago, IL 60643
Tel.: (773) 375-4900
Sales Range: $25-49.9 Million
Emp.: 32
Motor Vehicle Supplies & New Parts
N.A.I.C.S.: 333612
Mark Garfien *(Pres)*
Don Garfield *(Exec VP)*
Chatman Lempicki *(CFO)*

UNITED STATES GOLD AND TREASURY INVESTMENT TRUST

2 Park Ave 20th Fl, New York, NY 10016
Tel.: (212) 485-8922 DE
Year Founded: 2020
Investment Services
N.A.I.C.S.: 523999
William Herrmann *(Mng Partner)*

UNITED STATES HANG GLIDING & PARAGLIDING ASSOCIATION, INC.

1685 W Uintah St, Colorado Springs, CO 80904
Tel.: (719) 632-8300 CA
Web Site: http://www.ushpa.aero
Year Founded: 1974
Sales Range: $1-9.9 Million
Emp.: 8
Sport Promotion Services
N.A.I.C.S.: 711310
Beth Van Eaton *(Mgr-Ops)*
Julie Spiegler *(Program Mgr)*
Martin Palmaz *(Exec Dir)*

UNITED STATES HOMELAND INVESTIGATIONS INC

206 N Washington St, Alexandria, VA 22314
Web Site: http://www.ushii.com
Year Founded: 2003
Sales Range: $1-9.9 Million
Emp.: 15
Employee Background Screening
N.A.I.C.S.: 541612
Ashley McNeff *(CEO)*

UNITED STATES INFO SYSTEMS INC.

35 W Jefferson Ave, Pearl River, NY 10965
Tel.: (845) 358-7755
Web Site: http://www.usis.net
Rev.: $50,066,238
Emp.: 200
Communications Specialization
N.A.I.C.S.: 238210
Joseph R. Lagana *(Pres)*

UNITED STATES JUSTICE FOUNDATION

932 D St Ste 2, Ramona, CA 92065
Tel.: (760) 788-6624 CA
Web Site: http://www.usjf.net
Year Founded: 1979
Sales Range: $1-9.9 Million
Emp.: 18
Legal Support Services
N.A.I.C.S.: 541199
Norman Olney *(Pres)*
Randy Goodwin *(Treas)*
Darshan Brahmbhatt *(CFO)*
Floyd Brown *(Sec)*

UNITED STATES LUGGAGE COMPANY, LLC

400 Wireless Blvd, Hauppauge, NY 11788-3934
Tel.: (631) 434-7070 NY
Web Site: http://www.solo.net
Year Founded: 1982
Sales Range: $75-99.9 Million
Emp.: 40
Importer of Leather Attaches, Luggage & Portfolios
N.A.I.C.S.: 316690
Richard Krulik *(CEO)*
Lew Levy *(Sr VP)*
Amelia Mickaliger *(VP)*

Subsidiaries:

Briggs & Riley Travelware (1)
400 Wireless Blvd, Hauppauge, NY 11788-3934
Tel.: (631) 434-7722
Web Site: http://www.briggsriley.com
Sales Range: $10-24.9 Million
Emp.: 35
Luggage Importer & Distr
N.A.I.C.S.: 458320
Laura Ballereau *(Brand Mgr)*
Richard Krulik *(CEO)*
Carole Schnall *(VP-Admin)*
Georgene Rada *(VP-Product Design & Dev)*

UNITED STATES MARITIME ALLIANCE, LTD.

125 Chubb Ave Ste 350NC, Lyndhurst, NJ 07071
Tel.: (732) 404-2960 NJ
Web Site: http://www.usmx.com
Year Founded: 1997
Sales Range: $10-24.9 Million
Cargo Handling Services
N.A.I.C.S.: 488320
F. Paul De Maria *(VP-Labor Rels)*
Thomas P. Sullivan *(Dir-Labor Rels)*
David F. Adam *(Chm & CEO)*
Thomas J. Simmers *(Exec VP)*
Anissa Frucci *(VP)*
Beth Monica *(Sec)*
Anthony J. Dalonges *(Treas)*

UNITED STATES MEAT EXPORT FEDERATION INC.

1660 Lincoln St Ste2800, Denver, CO 80264
Tel.: (303) 226-7309 CO
Web Site: http://www.usmef.org
Year Founded: 1975
Sales Range: $100-124.9 Million
Emp.: 80
Business Associations
N.A.I.C.S.: 813910
Phil Seng *(Pres & CEO)*
Janel Domurat *(VP)*
John Hinners *(Dir-Membership)*
Joe Schuele *(Dir-Comml)*

UNITED STATES MINT

801 9th St NW, Washington, DC 20220-0012
Web Site: http://www.usmint.gov
Year Founded: 1792
Sales Range: $10-24.9 Million
Emp.: 2,800
Coins & Coin Related Products Mfr & Distr
N.A.I.C.S.: 921130
Tom Jurkowsky *(Dir-Corp Comm)*
Eric Anderson *(Sec)*
Ellen McCullom *(Plant Mgr-West Point)*
David Croft *(Assoc Dir-Mfg)*
J. Marc Landry *(Plant Mgr-Philadelphia)*
Annie Brown *(Assoc Dir-Workforce Solutions Dept)*
David Motl *(CFO)*
Jon Cameron *(Assoc Dir-Numismastic, Bullion & Coin Studies)*
April Stafford *(Mgr-Design Mgmt Div)*
David Jacobs *(Plant Mgr-San Francisco)*
Dick Peterson *(Deputy Dir-Mfg & Quality)*
Randall Johnson *(Acting Plant Mgr-Denver)*
Lauren Buschor *(CIO)*

UNITED STATES OIL & GAS CORPORATION

9322 3rd Ave Ste 475, Brooklyn, NY 11209
Tel.: (512) 464-1225 DE
Web Site: http://www.usaoilandgas.com
Year Founded: 1988
Sales Range: $10-24.9 Million
Emp.: 11
Oil & Gas Investment Services
N.A.I.C.S.: 523999
James Crimi *(Chm, Pres & CEO)*

UNITED STATES OLYMPIC COMMITTEE

27 S Tejon St, Colorado Springs, CO 80903
Tel.: (719) 632-5551
Year Founded: 1978
U.S. Arm of the International Olympic Committee
N.A.I.C.S.: 813990
Norman Bellingham *(COO)*
Nicole Deal *(Chief Security Officer)*
David Zodikoff *(CIO)*
Cathrine Erickson *(Dir-Track & Field-U.S. Paralympics)*
Susanne Lyons *(Chm)*
Sarah Hirshland *(CEO)*

UNITED STATES POLO ASSOCIATION, INC.

9011 Lake Worth Rd, Lake Worth, FL 33467
Tel.: (800) 232-8772 FL
Web Site: http://www.uspolo.org
Year Founded: 1890
Sales Range: $10-24.9 Million
Emp.: 25
Polo Association
N.A.I.C.S.: 813990
Jennifer Furlow *(Accountant)*
Kelly Vanderwerff *(Controller)*
Bob Puetz *(Exec Dir-Svcs)*
Peter Rizzo *(CEO)*
Susan C. Present *(CFO)*
Charles E. Weaver *(Chm)*
Daniel Walker *(Sec)*
Edward Campbell III *(Treas)*

UNITED STATES POSTAL SERVICE

475 L Enfant Plaza SW Ste 2P600, Washington, DC 20260-0600
Tel.: (202) 268-2000
Web Site: http://www.usps.com
Year Founded: 1971
Rev.: $71,154,000,000
Assets: $25,633,000,000
Liabilities: $97,165,000,000
Net Worth: ($71,532,000,000)
Earnings: ($8,813,000,000)
Emp.: 497,000
Fiscal Year-end: 09/30/19
Postal Service for the United States
N.A.I.C.S.: 491110
David Williams *(Chief Logistics & Processing Ops Officer & Exec VP)*
Jeff Adams *(VP-Corp Comm)*
Cara Greene *(VP & Controller)*
Dane Coleman *(Reg VP-Processing Ops-Eastern)*
Louis DeJoy *(CEO)*
Pritha Mehra *(CIO & Exec VP)*
Scott Bombaugh *(CTO & Exec VP)*
Isaac S. Cronkhite *(Chief HR Officer, Chief Processing Officer, Chief Distr Officer & Exec VP)*
Jacqueline Krage Strako *(Chief Commerce Officer, Chief Bus Solutions Officer & Exec VP)*
Steven Monteith *(CMO, Chief Customer Officer & Exec VP)*
Alan Caramella *(Officer-Judicial)*
Thomas J. Marshall *(Gen Counsel & Exec VP)*
Luke T. Grossmann *(Co-CFO, Exec VP & Sr VP-Fin & Strategy)*
Douglas Tulino *(Chief HR Officer & VP-Labor Rels)*
Joshua D. Colin *(Chief Retail Officer, Chief Delivery Officer & VP)*
Robert Cintron *(VP-Logistics)*
Linda Malone *(VP-Engrg Sys)*
Simon Storey *(VP-Human Resources)*
Jeffrey C. Johnson *(VP-Enterprise Analytics)*
Peter Pastre *(VP-Govt Rels & Pub Policy)*
Marc McCrery *(VP-IT)*
Randy Workman *(VP-Mail Entry & Payment Tech)*
Mark Guilfoil *(VP-Supply Mgmt)*
Derek T. Kan *(Governor)*
Roman Martinez IV *(Chm & Governor)*
Ambe F. McReynolds *(Governor & VP)*
Robert M. Duncan *(Governor)*
Anton G. Hajjar *(Governor)*
Ronald A. Stroman *(Governor)*
Daniel Tangherlini *(Governor)*
Joseph Corbett *(CFO & Exec VP)*

UNITED STATES REALTY & INVESTMENT COMPANY

450 7th Ave 45th Fl, New York, NY 10123-4599
Tel.: (212) 244-6650 NJ
Web Site: http://www.aetnarealty.com
Year Founded: 1927
Sales Range: $125-149.9 Million
Emp.: 700
Real Estate Investment & Asset Management Services
N.A.I.C.S.: 531390
Benjamin M. Braka *(VP)*

Subsidiaries:

Aetna Realty Financial Corp. (1)
450 7th Ave 45th Fl, New York, NY 10123
Tel.: (212) 244-6650
Web Site: http://www.aetnarealty.com
Real Estate Investment Financing Services
N.A.I.C.S.: 522299
Ivor Braka *(Chm & Pres)*
Gerald J. Valerius *(VP & Dir-Real Estate)*
David Braka *(VP)*
Benjamin M. Braka *(VP)*

UNITED STATES SEAFOODS, LLC

1801 Fairview Ave E Ste 100, Seattle, WA 98102
Tel.: (206) 763-3133
Web Site: http://www.unitedstatesseafoods.com

UNITED STATES SEAFOODS, LLC

United States Seafoods, LLC—(Continued)
Sales Range: $10-24.9 Million
Emp.: 500
Finfish Fishing Services & Seafood Distr
N.A.I.C.S.: 114111
Phil Gunsolus *(Dir-Fishery)*
Darrin Manor *(Dir-Ops)*
Udo G. Brossmann *(CFO)*
Matthew J. Doherty *(Pres)*

UNITED STATES SERVICE INDUSTRIES INC.
4330 EW Hwy Ste 200, Bethesda, MD 20814
Tel.: (202) 783-2030   DE
Web Site: http://www.ussiclean.com
Year Founded: 1912
Sales Range: $75-99.9 Million
Emp.: 2,200
Building Maintenance Services
N.A.I.C.S.: 561720
Tim Ruben *(Pres & CEO)*
Joel S. Felrice *(Sr VP)*
Zoe Epstein Hereford *(Sr VP)*

UNITED STATES SERVICES GROUP, LLC.
365 Canal St Ste 2520, New Orleans, LA 70130
Tel.: (504) 279-9930
Web Site: http://www.usesgroup.com
Rev.: $17,800,000
Emp.: 370
Facilities Support Services
N.A.I.C.S.: 561210
Barry Thibodeaux *(Pres & CEO)*
Thomas Sumner *(COO & Dir-Health & Safety)*
Thomas Bayham *(Chief Admin Officer)*
George Malvaney *(VP-Emergency Ops & Reg Mgr)*
Larry Lee *(VP & Reg Mgr)*
Bob Keesee *(Gen Mgr-Indus Ops)*
Herman Newell *(Reg Mgr-Emergency Ops)*
David Slauson *(Reg Mgr-Emergency Ops)*
Kate E. Mills *(Mgr)*
Scott Boudreaux *(Mgr-Bus Dev)*

UNITED STATES SOCIETY ON DAMS
1616 17th St Ste 483, Denver, CO 80202
Tel.: (303) 628-5430   CO
Web Site: http://www.ussdams.org
Year Founded: 1988
Sales Range: $1-9.9 Million
Dam Construction & Management Services
N.A.I.C.S.: 611430
Keith A. Ferguson *(Pres)*
John S. Wolfhope *(VP)*
Daniel L. Wade *(Treas & Sec)*

UNITED STATES STOVE COMPANY
227 Industrial Park Rd, South Pittsburg, TN 37380
Tel.: (423) 837-2100
Web Site: http://www.usstove.com
Rev.: $15,000,000
Emp.: 100
Manufacture & Distribute Furnaces, Domestic Steam Or Hot Water
N.A.I.C.S.: 333414
Richard Rogers *(Pres)*
John Hargis *(VP-Mfg)*
Kelly Brownfield *(Mgr-HR)*
Calvin Haggard *(VP-Sls)*

Subsidiaries:

Newmac Mfg. Inc.   (1)

208 Lancaster Crescent, Debert, B0M 1G0, NS, Canada
Tel.: (902) 662-3840
Web Site: https://newmacfurnaces.com
Industrial & Heating Equipment Mfr
N.A.I.C.S.: 423740

UNITED STATES SUGAR CORPORATION
111 Ponce de Leon Ave, Clewiston, FL 33440-3032
Tel.: (863) 983-8121   DE
Web Site: http://www.ussugar.com
Year Founded: 1931
Sales Range: $350-399.9 Million
Emp.: 2,000
Sugarcane & Orange Farming; Cane Sugar & Molasses Mfr & Whslr
N.A.I.C.S.: 111930
Judy C. Sanchez *(Dir-Corp Comm & Pub Affairs)*
Robert H. Buker *(CEO)*
Carl Stringer *(CIO)*
Malcolm S. Wade *(Sr VP-Corp Strategy & Bus Dev)*
Robert E. Coker *(Sr VP-Pub Affairs)*
Elaine Wood *(CFO & Sr VP)*
Ken McDuffie *(Sr VP-Agricultural Ops)*
Neil F. Smith *(Sr VP-Sugar Mfg)*
Ricke Kress *(Pres-Southern Gardens Citrus)*

Subsidiaries:

Bryant Sugar House   (1)
111 Ponce de Leon Ave, Clewiston, FL 33440-3032   (100%)
Tel.: (561) 924-5601
Web Site: http://www.ussugar.com
Sales Range: $550-599.9 Million
Sugar Production
N.A.I.C.S.: 311314

Clewiston Sugar House   (1)
111 Ponce De Leon Ave, Clewiston, FL 33440-3032
Tel.: (863) 983-8121
Web Site: http://www.ussugar.com
Sales Range: $450-499.9 Million
Sugar Production
N.A.I.C.S.: 111930

South Central Florida Express, Inc.   (1)
900 SW C Owens Ave, Clewiston, FL 33440-4901   (100%)
Tel.: (863) 983-3163
Web Site: http://www.ussugar.com
Sales Range: $10-24.9 Million
Emp.: 40
Producer of Sugar Cane & Raw Sugar Extracts; Processing of Citrus Fruits
N.A.I.C.S.: 482111

Southern Garden Citrus   (1)
1820 County Rd 833, Clewiston, FL 33440-1207   (100%)
Tel.: (863) 983-3030
Web Site: http://www.southerngarden.com
Sales Range: $100-124.9 Million
Emp.: 350
Citrus Processing Operation
N.A.I.C.S.: 115114
Mark Banky *(Mgr-Acctg)*

United Sugars Corp.   (1)
524 Center Ave, Moorhead, MN 56560
Tel.: (218) 236-4740
Web Site: http://www.unitedsugars.com
Rev.: $16,500,000
Emp.: 30
Beet Sugar Manufacturing
N.A.I.C.S.: 424590
Lee Glass *(Dir-Transportation)*
Christi Thielke *(Mgr-Customer Svc)*

UNITED STATES TELECOM ASSOCIATION
607 14th St NW Ste 400, Washington, DC 20005
Tel.: (202) 326-7300   DE
Web Site: http://www.ustelecom.org
Year Founded: 1897

Sales Range: $50-74.9 Million
Emp.: 40
Telecommunications Trade Association
N.A.I.C.S.: 813910
Mark Kulish *(CFO & Sr VP-Admin)*
Alan J. Roth *(Sr Exec VP)*
Jonathan Banks *(Sr VP-Law & Policy)*
Allison Remsen *(Exec VP)*
Jonathan Spalter *(Pres & CEO)*

UNITED STATES TRAFFIC NETWORK, LLC
3 Country View Rd, Malvern, PA 19355
Tel.: (484) 841-2400   DE
Year Founded: 2016
Traffic Information Reporting Services
N.A.I.C.S.: 519290

UNITED STATES WELDING, INC.
600 S Santa Fe Dr, Denver, CO 80223
Tel.: (303) 777-2475
Web Site: http://www.uswelding.com
Sales Range: $25-49.9 Million
Emp.: 54
Equipment Rental & Leasing
N.A.I.C.S.: 424690
Richard E. Lofgren *(Chm)*
Chane Kytle *(Mgr-Transportation)*

UNITED STATIONS RADIO NETWORKS INC.
25 W 45th St, New York, NY 10036
Tel.: (212) 869-1111
Web Site: http://www.usrn.com
Rev.: $1,600,000
Emp.: 21
Television Broadcasting
N.A.I.C.S.: 516120
Steven Tisi *(Sr Mgr-Morning Show Svcs)*
Neil Barry *(Exec Dir-Brand Sponsorships)*
Jim Higgins *(Pres)*
Greg Janoff *(Chief Revenue Officer)*
Nick Verbitsky *(Chm & CEO)*

UNITED STEEL INC.
164 School St, East Hartford, CT 06108
Tel.: (860) 289-2323
Web Site: http://www.unitedsteel.com
Sales Range: $25-49.9 Million
Emp.: 145
Fabricated Structural Metal
N.A.I.C.S.: 332312
Kenneth F. Corneau *(Pres)*
Mike Colt *(Dir-Safety)*
Lynn Caouette *(CFO)*

UNITED STEEL SERVICE, INC.
4500 Parkway Dr, Brookfield, OH 44403
Tel.: (330) 448-4057
Web Site: http://www.unitedsteelservice.com
Sales Range: $25-49.9 Million
Emp.: 100
Provider of Metals Services
N.A.I.C.S.: 423510
Morris I. Friedman *(Chm)*
Joel Miller *(Treas)*
Gary Komsa *(CFO)*
Steven Friedman *(Vice Chm)*

UNITED STRUCTURES OF AMERICA INC.
1912 Buschong St, Houston, TX 77039-1213
Tel.: (281) 442-8247   TX
Web Site: http://www.usabldg.com
Year Founded: 1980

Sales Range: $25-49.9 Million
Emp.: 520
Metal Buildings Services
N.A.I.C.S.: 332311
Brent Blackburn *(VP-Sls)*
Ron Fletcher *(Sr VP-Sls & Mktg)*
Richard F. Drake *(Pres & CEO)*

UNITED STUDENT AID FUNDS INC.
999 Crosspoint Blvd Ste 400, Indianapolis, IN 46256
Tel.: (317) 849-6510
Web Site: http://www.usafunds.org
Sales Range: $50-74.9 Million
Emp.: 43
Student Loan Marketing Association
N.A.I.C.S.: 921130
Stephen C. Ham *(CFO & Exec VP)*
Shital R. Patel *(CIO & Sr VP-Operational Support)*
Mark L. Pelesh *(Exec VP-Corp & Bus Dev)*
Craig P. Anderson *(Pres-Student Connections & Sr VP-Bus Dev)*
Larry A. Lutz *(Pres-Education at Work & Sr VP-Corp Dev)*
Alison R. Griffin *(Sr VP-External & Govt Rels)*
Thomas C. Dawson *(COO & Exec VP)*
A. Scott Fleming *(Sr VP-Strategy & Corp Dev)*
Terry Holloway *(Chief Talent Officer & Sr VP)*
Daryl A. Graham *(Sr VP-Philanthropy)*

UNITED SUPERMARKETS
600 E Broadway St, Altus, OK 73521
Tel.: (580) 482-1184
Web Site: http://www.unitedok.com
Sales Range: $125-149.9 Million
Emp.: 1,220
Supermarket Services
N.A.I.C.S.: 445110
Ruth Nichols *(Mgr-Bakery & Delivery)*
Art Zuniga *(Mgr-Meat)*
Michael Langham *(Mgr-Store)*

UNITED SUPPLY
8606 Darby Ave, Northridge, CA 91325-3312
Tel.: (818) 885-3783
Web Site: http://www.unitedsupply.com
Sales Range: $10-24.9 Million
Emp.: 25
Office Supplies & Equipment
N.A.I.C.S.: 424120

UNITED SURGICAL ASSISTANTS, INC.
12880 Commodity Pl, Tampa, FL 33626
Tel.: (813) 865-1340
Web Site: http://www.mysuspa.com
Year Founded: 1998
Sales Range: $1-9.9 Million
Emp.: 40
Employment Placement Services
N.A.I.C.S.: 561311
Maryann Hale *(CFO)*

UNITED SYSTEMS, INC.
5700 North Portland Ave Ste-201, Oklahoma City, OK 73112
Tel.: (405) 523-2162
Web Site: http://www.unitedsystemsok.com
Year Founded: 1984
Sales Range: $10-24.9 Million
Emp.: 30
Computer, Computer Peripheral Equipment & Software Whslr
N.A.I.C.S.: 423430

David Laase *(Mgr-Pro Svcs & Projects)*
Richard Brookhart *(Supvr-Support Svcs)*

UNITED TACTICAL SYSTEMS, LLC
28101 Ballard Dr Ste F, Lake Forest, IL 60045
Tel.: (260) 478-2500   DE
Web Site: http://www.pepperball.com
Year Founded: 1996
Emp.: 200
Weapons Mfr & Distr
N.A.I.C.S.: 332994
George Eurick *(CIO)*

UNITED TALENT AGENCY, INC.
9336 Civic Center Dr, Beverly Hills, CA 90210
Tel.: (310) 273-6700   CA
Web Site: http://www.unitedtalent.com
Year Founded: 1991
Sales Range: $1-9.9 Million
Emp.: 175
Talent Management
N.A.I.C.S.: 711410
Jim Berkus *(Chm)*
Jeremy Zimmer *(Founder & CEO)*
David Zedeck *(Head-Music-Worldwide)*
Jay Sures *(Vice Chm)*
Peter Goldberg *(Head-News & Brdcst)*
Joseph Kessler *(Head-IQ-Global)*
David Kramer *(Pres)*
Brent Weinstein *(Head-Digital Media)*
Rena Ronson *(Head-Independent Film Grp)*
Jim Meenaghan *(Partner)*
Rene Jones *(Partner)*
Rich Shuter *(Partner)*
David Spingarn *(Partner)*
Shanique Bonelli-Moore *(Exec Dir-Inclusion)*
Blair Kohan *(Head-HR-Global)*
Lyndsay Harding *(CFO)*
Seth Oster *(Chief Comm Officer-Global)*
Ashley Momtaheni *(Dir-Corp Comm)*
Alisann Blood *(Co-Head-Music Brand Partnerships-Los Angeles)*
Toni Wallace *(Co-Head-Music Brand Partnerships)*
Andrew Thau *(COO & Gen Counsel)*
Andrea Nelson Meigs *(Partner)*
Darnell O. Strom *(Partner & Head-Culture & Leadership Div)*
Jean-Rene Zetrenne *(Partner & Chief People Officer)*
Chris Pagano *(VP-Structured Fin & Gen Mgr)*
Richard A. Paul *(Partner-Agency & Head-Sports)*
Subsidiaries:

Greater Talent Network, Inc.   (1)
437 Fifth Ave 7th Fl, New York, NY 10016
Tel.: (212) 645-4200
Web Site: http://www.greatertalent.com
Sales Range: $1-9.9 Million
Emp.: 26
Lecture & Support Services
N.A.I.C.S.: 561499
Don Epstein *(CEO)*
Zachary Ares *(Dir-Digital Media)*
Kevin Bhatia *(Acct Exec)*
Jared Brodsky *(CTO)*
David Buchalter *(Sr VP & Gen Mgr-College Div)*
Rebecca Levine *(Acct Exec)*
Jennifer Peykar *(Dir-Bureau Rels)*
Alexander Pollock *(Acct Exec)*
Kristen Sena *(Chm)*
Michael Steele *(Sr VP & Mgr-Natl Sls)*

UNITED TEACHERS LOS ANGELES
3303 Wilshire Blvd 10th Fl, Los Angeles, CA 90010
Tel.: (213) 487-5560   CA
Web Site: http://www.utla.net
Year Founded: 1970
Sales Range: $25-49.9 Million
Emp.: 64
Educational Support Services
N.A.I.C.S.: 611710
Suzanne Spurgeon *(Dir-Comm)*
Diana Darty *(Dir-Support Svcs)*

UNITED THROUGH READING
11772 Sorrento Valley Rd Ste 125, San Diego, CA 92121
Tel.: (858) 481-7323   CA
Web Site: http://www.unitedthroughreading.org
Year Founded: 1989
Sales Range: $1-9.9 Million
Emp.: 16
Veteran Support Services
N.A.I.C.S.: 813410
Kara Dallman *(Sr Dir-Dev & Strategic Alliances)*
Kurt Schwend *(Dir-Tech)*
Samantha Hagan Lingad *(Program Mgr-Natl)*
Jeff Mader *(Vice Chm)*
Sean McHugh *(Chm)*
Douglas Stewart *(Sec)*
Tim Farrell *(CEO)*

UNITED TOOL & DIE COMPANY
1 Carney Rd, West Hartford, CT 06110
Tel.: (860) 246-6531
Web Site: http://www.utdco.com
Rev.: $12,471,342
Emp.: 110
Aircraft Engines & Engine Parts Mfr
N.A.I.C.S.: 336412

UNITED TOOL & FASTENER COMPANY
6320 N Shepherd, Houston, TX 77091
Tel.: (713) 692-2323
Web Site: http://www.unitedtoolandfastener.com
Sales Range: $10-24.9 Million
Emp.: 38
Distr of Fasteners & Related Industrial Products
N.A.I.C.S.: 423840
Bobby Williams *(Pres)*

UNITED TRANSPORTATION UNION INSURANCE ASSOCIATION
24950 Country Club Blvd Ste 340, North Olmsted, OH 44070-5333
Tel.: (216) 228-9400   OH
Web Site: http://www.utuia.org
Year Founded: 1970
Sales Range: $25-49.9 Million
Insurance Association
N.A.I.C.S.: 813910
Irma Collazo *(Dir-Billing Admin)*
Erin McKeever *(Asst Dir-Sls & Under Writing)*
Richard A. Kusnic *(Treas & Sec)*
Kenneth Laugel *(Pres)*

UNITED TUBE CORPORATION
960 Lake Rd, Medina, OH 44256
Tel.: (330) 725-4196
Web Site: http://www.unitedtube.com
Rev.: $11,000,000
Emp.: 6
Tubes, Wrought: Welded
N.A.I.C.S.: 331210

Jack Bretz *(VP)*

UNITED UNDERWRITERS INSURANCE
4956 N 300 W Ste 101, Provo, UT 84604
Tel.: (801) 226-2662
Web Site: http://www.uuinsurance.com
Rev.: $24,000,000
Emp.: 35
Insurance Provider
N.A.I.C.S.: 524210
Lynn Connelly *(CEO)*

UNITED UTILITY SUPPLY COOPERATIVE INC.
4515 Bishop Ln, Louisville, KY 40218-4507
Tel.: (502) 451-2430   KY
Web Site: http://www.uus.org
Year Founded: 1959
Sales Range: $10-24.9 Million
Emp.: 35
Electrical Apparatus & Equipment Services
N.A.I.C.S.: 423610
Tim Hargrove *(CFO)*
Bill Corum *(Pres)*

UNITED VALLEY BANK
211 Division Ave S, Cavalier, ND 58220
Tel.: (701) 265-8331
Web Site: http://www.uvbank.net
Year Founded: 1905
Emp.: 50
Commericial Banking
N.A.I.C.S.: 522110
Tim Siegle *(Co-Pres & CEO)*
Barry Hanson *(Exec VP)*
Karen Brown *(VP)*
Drew Olafson *(Co-Pres & CFO)*
Jean Johnson *(VP)*
Denelle Carrier *(Dir-Mktg)*
Corey Cleveland *(Sr VP)*
David Stewart *(VP)*
Jill Swanson *(Asst VP)*
Julie Hinschberger *(VP)*
Lloyd Wang *(VP)*
Lorri Sapa *(VP)*

UNITED VISION GROUP INC.
24 Link Dr, Rockleigh, NJ 07647-2504
Tel.: (201) 750-5650
Web Site: http://www.uv3store.com
Rev.: $30,829,929
Emp.: 100
Eyewear Mfr
N.A.I.C.S.: 456130
Hakan Ayanolu *(Mgr-IT)*
Subsidiaries:

Hudson River Inlay Inc.   (1)
No 4 207 Wembly Rd, New Windsor, NY 12553-5536
Tel.: (845) 567-4808
Web Site: http://www.hudsonriverinlay.com
Rev.: $5,660,371
Emp.: 12
Picture & Mirror Frames, Wood
N.A.I.C.S.: 339999
Jeff Nelson *(CEO)*

UNITED WAREHOUSE CO. INC.
1930 6th Ave S Ste 400, Seattle, WA 98134
Tel.: (206) 682-4535
Web Site: http://www.unitedwarehouses.com
Sales Range: $10-24.9 Million
Emp.: 20
General Warehousing & Storage
N.A.I.C.S.: 493110

Tom Herche *(Pres)*
Jim Teddy *(VP)*
Mitch Sullivan *(VP-Mktg)*

UNITED WAREHOUSE COMPANY
901 East 45th St N, Wichita, KS 67219
Tel.: (316) 712-1000
Web Site: http://www.unitedwarehouse.com
Sales Range: $10-24.9 Million
Emp.: 20
General Warehousing & Storage
N.A.I.C.S.: 493110
Brett Schaefer *(Pres)*

UNITED WATER SERVICES
2700 S Belmont Ave, Indianapolis, IN 46221-2009
Tel.: (317) 639-7000   IN
Web Site: http://www.unitedwater.com
Year Founded: 1993
Sales Range: $200-249.9 Million
Emp.: 2,500
Provider of Sewerage Systems
N.A.I.C.S.: 221320
Nadine Leslie *(Pres)*

UNITED WAY OF THE VIRGINIA PENINSULA
Two City Center 11820 Fountain Way Suite 206, Newport News, VA 23606
Tel.: (757) 873-9328
Web Site: http://www.uwvp.org
Civic & Social Organizations
N.A.I.C.S.: 813410
Thomas J. Cosgrove *(Chm)*
Subsidiaries:

United Way of Greater Mercer County, Inc.   (1)
3150 Brunswick Pike Ste 230, Lawrenceville, NJ 08648-2420
Tel.: (609) 896-1912
Web Site: http://www.uwgmc.org
Sales Range: $1-9.9 Million
Emp.: 17
Civic & Social Organizations
N.A.I.C.S.: 813410
Cheri H. Durst *(VP-Resource Dev)*
Denise Daniels *(Dir-Outreach & Volunteer Svcs)*
Megan Kirschner *(Dir-Community Outreach & Outcomes)*
Sandra Toussaint-Burgher *(Pres & CEO)*
Tarry Truitt *(Dir-Community Impact Programs)*

UNITED WAY WORLDWIDE
Tel.: (703) 836-7112   NY
Web Site: https://www.unitedway.org
Year Founded: 1932
Sales Range: $75-99.9 Million
Emp.: 256
Grantmaking Services
N.A.I.C.S.: 813211
Peggy Conlon *(Sec)*
Phillip N. Baldwin *(Treas)*
Robert Berdelle *(CFO & Exec VP)*
Jose Pedro Ferrao *(Sr VP-Intl Network)*
Steve Taylor *(Sr VP)*
Patricia Turner *(Gen Counsel & Sr VP)*
Juliette Tuakli *(Chm)*
Evan Hochberg *(Chief Strategy Officer)*
Paul DeBassio *(Exec VP-IR)*
Stan Little *(Chief Experience Officer)*

UNITED WESTERN COOP
222 E Lincoln Hwy, Missouri Valley, IA 51555
Tel.: (712) 642-3737
Web Site: http://www.uwcoop.com
Year Founded: 1918

United Western Coop—(Continued)
Sales Range: $25-49.9 Million
Emp.: 45
Provider of Agricultural Supplies
N.A.I.C.S.: 424510
Trent Sprecker (Gen Mgr)
Matt Earlywine (Pres)
Kevin Christensen (Controller)

UNITED WINDOW & DOOR MANUFACTURING
24-36 Fadem Rd, Springfield, NJ 07081
Tel.: (973) 912-0600
Web Site: http://www.unitedwindowmfg.com
Sales Range: $10-24.9 Million
Emp.: 275
Mfr Windows; Doors
N.A.I.C.S.: 332321
Gary Denoia (CFO)
Gregg Proscia (VP-Sls & Mktg)
Tim Viola (Mgr-Mktg)

UNITED WISCONSIN GRAIN PRODUCERS, LLC
W1231 Tessmann Dr, Friesland, WI 53935
Tel.: (920) 348-5016
Web Site: http://www.uwgp.com
Sales Range: $125-149.9 Million
Emp.: 48
Ethyl Alcohol Mfr
N.A.I.C.S.: 325193
Dan Wegner (Mgr-Commodity)
Barb Bontrager (Gen Mgr)
Eric Kuntz (Mgr-Production)
Dan Groh (Mgr-Process Improvement)
Marc Berger (Mgr-Safety)
Timothy Politano (Mgr-Quality Assurance)

UNITED-SOUTHERN WASTE MATERIAL CO
2800 W Illinois Ave, Dallas, TX 75233
Tel.: (214) 467-9100
Web Site: http://www.uswmco.com
Sales Range: $10-24.9 Million
Emp.: 100
Waste Rags
N.A.I.C.S.: 423930
Mike Levine (Pres)

UNITEDLEX CORPORATION
6130 Spring Pkwy Ste 300, Overland Park, KS 66211
Tel.: (913) 685-8900
Web Site: http://www.unitedlex.com
Year Founded: 2006
Sales Range: $25-49.9 Million
Emp.: 650
Technology Powered Legal Services & Business Solutions
N.A.I.C.S.: 561499
Daniel Reed (Founder & Chm)
Anup Bhasin (COO-India)
Dave Deppe (Pres)
Lata Setty (Chief Intellectual Property Officer)
Pavan Vaish (COO-Global)
Gerardo Herrera (CIO)
Ryan Reeves (Sr VP-US Ops)
Lorenzo Lleras (Sr VP-Immigration Svcs)
Eric Gonzales (Sr VP)
Jason Straight (Chief Privacy Officer & Sr VP)
Nancy A. Jessen (Sr VP)
Gabriel Buigas (Sr VP-Global Strategy & Digital Contracting Solutions)
Peter Krakaur (VP-Legal Bus Solutions Grp-Worldwide)
Christine Hasiotis (Sr VP & Deputy Gen Counsel)
James Schellhase (CEO)
Nicholas Hinton (CFO)
Timothy Gill (Chief Revenue Officer)
Susan Hammann (Dir-Strategic Comm)
Aaron Crews (Chief Product & Innovation Officer)
Elizabeth Bjork (CMO)

UNITEK INFORMATION SYSTEMS
4670 Automall Pkwy, Fremont, CA 94538
Tel.: (510) 249-1060
Web Site: http://www.unitek.com
Sales Range: $10-24.9 Million
Emp.: 50
Computer Related Consulting Services
N.A.I.C.S.: 541512
Meeta Ajmani (Mgr-Mktg)
Bahman Mozaffari (Engr-Network)
Eileen Phung (Coord-Healthcare Ops)
Varsha Sony (Coord-Trng & Ops)
Patrick Monk (Coord-Mktg)
Brian Schulman (Project Mgr)

UNITEK SOLVENT SERVICES INC.
91-125 Kaomi Loop, Kapolei, HI 96707-1711
Tel.: (808) 682-8284
Web Site: http://www.uniteksolvent.com
Year Founded: 1981
Sales Range: $10-24.9 Million
Emp.: 50
Recycling Services
N.A.I.C.S.: 532490
Sally Davis (VP)
Blain Yamagata (Pres)
Cleveland Tadiarca (Mgr-Maintenance)
Byron Manipon (Mgr-Ops)

UNITELLER FINANCIAL SERVICES
218 State Rt 17 N 402, Rochelle Park, NJ 07662
Tel.: (201) 345-2000 NJ
Web Site: http://www.uniteller.com
Year Founded: 1993
Rev.: $13,500,000
Emp.: 3
Telegraph & Other Communications
N.A.I.C.S.: 517111
L. Gutierrez (Pres & CEO)
Javier Zarate (Asst VP & Mgr-Acctg)

Subsidiaries:
Servicio Uniteller Inc (1)
218 State Rt 17 N, Rochelle Park, NJ 07662
Tel.: (201) 345-2000
Web Site: http://www.uniteller.com
Electronic Funds Transfer Network, Including Switching
N.A.I.C.S.: 522320

UNITIVE ELECTRONICS INC.
140 South Centre Ct Ste 600, Morrisville, NC 27560
Tel.: (919) 941-0606 NC
Web Site: http://www.amkor.com
Year Founded: 1996
Sales Range: $10-24.9 Million
Emp.: 250
Provider of Wafer-Level Packaging Solutions
N.A.I.C.S.: 334413
Ken Donahue (CEO)
Robert Lanzone (VP-Sls & Mktg)
David Hays (VP-Strategic Mktg-Bus Dev)
Robert McLaughlin (VP-Fin)
Arthur Bergens Jr. (CFO)

UNITIZE COMPANY INC.
1101 Negley Pl, Dayton, OH 45402
Tel.: (937) 277-8080
Web Site: http://www.unitize.com
Sales Range: $10-24.9 Million
Emp.: 20
Mechanical Contracting, Sheetmetal Work, Moving & Erecting,
N.A.I.C.S.: 238290
James R. Arnett Jr. (Chm)

Subsidiaries:
Orbit Movers & Erectors (1)
1101 Netley Pl, Dayton, OH 45402
Tel.: (937) 277-8080
Web Site: http://www.unitize.com
Heavy Machinery Rigging & Moving; Crane & Conveyor Installations
N.A.I.C.S.: 238290

Orbit Sheet Metal Co. Inc. (1)
1101 Negley Pl, Dayton, OH 45402
Tel.: (937) 277-8080
Web Site: http://www.unitize.com
Emp.: 25
Sheet Metal Contractors
N.A.I.C.S.: 238390
James Ornet (CEO)

S&D Osterfeld Mechanical Contractors (1)
1101 Negley Pl, Dayton, OH 45402
Tel.: (937) 277-8080
Web Site: http://www.unitize.com
Sales Range: $10-24.9 Million
Emp.: 3
Plumbing Contractor
N.A.I.C.S.: 238220
James R. Arnett Jr. (Chm)

UNITRON INC.
73 Mall Dr, Commack, NY 11725
Tel.: (631) 543-2000
Web Site: http://www.unitronusa.com
Year Founded: 1952
Sales Range: $10-24.9 Million
Emp.: 20
Industrial & Scientific Instruments Distr
N.A.I.C.S.: 423490
Brian Taub (Exec VP)

Subsidiaries:
Unitron Customized Systems (1)
73 Mall Dr, Commack, NY 11725
Tel.: (631) 589-6666
Industrial & Scientific Instruments
N.A.I.C.S.: 423490
Peter Indrigno (Sr VP)

Unitron Leisure Prods. (1)
73 Mall Dr, Commack, NY 11725
Tel.: (631) 589-6666
Web Site: http://www.unitronusa.com
Emp.: 8
Industrial & Scientific Instruments Distr
N.A.I.C.S.: 423490

UNITRONEX CORPORATION
612 Stetson Ave, Saint Charles, IL 60174
Tel.: (630) 587-0101
Web Site: http://www.unitronex.com
Year Founded: 1974
Sales Range: $10-24.9 Million
Emp.: 8
Electronic Parts
N.A.I.C.S.: 423690
Wanda Skonieczny (VP)

UNITRUST INDUSTRIAL CORP.
1329 Connecticut Ave NW, Washington, DC 20036
Tel.: (202) 833-2900
Sales Range: $10-24.9 Million
Emp.: 7
Groceries & Related Products
N.A.I.C.S.: 424490
Raj K. Mallick (Chm)

UNITUS COMMUNITY CREDIT UNION
PO Box 1937, Portland, OR 97207
Tel.: (503) 227-5571 OR
Web Site: http://www.unitusccu.com
Year Founded: 1937
Sales Range: $25-49.9 Million
Emp.: 281
Credit Union
N.A.I.C.S.: 522130
Laurie Kresl (Chief Mktg Officer & VP)
Greg Spear (CFO & Sr VP)
Gayle Evans (Chief HR Officer)
Jim Lewis (Vice Chm)
Susan Iggulden (Chm)
Steven Stapp (Pres & CEO)
Ronda Wagner (Asst VP-Consumer Lending)
Sarah Elmore (Asst VP-Loan Ops)
Karen Salman (Asst VP-Ops Support)
Blaine Bartholomew (Asst VP-Member Experience)
James Alexander (Chief Risk Officer & Sr VP)
Corlinda Wooden (Chief Retail Officer)

UNITY ALUMINUM, INC.
PO Box 2065, Ashland, KY 41105-2065
Tel.: (606) 420-4645
Web Site: https://www.unityal.com
Aluminum Mfr
N.A.I.C.S.: 331315
Craig Bouchard (Chm & CEO)
Blaine Holt (COO)

Subsidiaries:
NanoAl LLC (1)
260 Eliot St Ste 4A, Ashland, MA 01721
Tel.: (508) 433-6290
Web Site: http://www.nanoal.com
Research & Development in the Physical, Engineering & Life Sciences
N.A.I.C.S.: 541715
David C. Dunand (Founder)

UNITY ELECTRIC CO. INC.
65-45 Fresh Meadow Ln, Flushing, NY 11365-2011
Tel.: (718) 539-4300
Web Site: http://www.unityig.com
Year Founded: 1978
Sales Range: $75-99.9 Million
Emp.: 250
Electrical Work
N.A.I.C.S.: 238210

Subsidiaries:
Uni-Data Services, LLC (1)
65-21 Fresh Meadow Ln, Flushing, NY 11365
Tel.: (718) 445-5600
Electronic Services
N.A.I.C.S.: 238210

Unity Data & Electrical Services (1)
1076 Business Ln, Naples, FL 34110
Tel.: (239) 254-0000
Emp.: 42
Electronic Services
N.A.I.C.S.: 238210
Michael Scarpelli (Mng Dir & Sr VP)

Unity Electric LLC (1)
1 Madison St Bldg F, East Rutherford, NJ 07073-1605
Tel.: (973) 470-5700
Web Site: http://www.unityig.com
Rev.: $20,000,000
Emp.: 100
Electronic Services
N.A.I.C.S.: 238210

UNITY FINANCIAL LIFE INSURANCE COMPANY
4675 Cornell Rd Ste 160, Cincinnati, OH 45241
Tel.: (513) 247-0711

Web Site: http://www.uflife.com
Year Founded: 1993
Sales Range: $25-49.9 Million
Emp.: 40
Life Insurance
N.A.I.C.S.: 524113
Adam Goller (VP-Agency & Bus Analysts)

UNITY HEALTH - WHITE COUNTY MEDICAL CENTER
3214 E Race Ave, Searcy, AR 72143
Tel.: (501) 268-6121 AR
Web Site: http://www.wcmc.org
Year Founded: 1995
Emp.: 1,796
Community Health Care Services
N.A.I.C.S.: 621498
Ladonna Johnston (VP-Patient Svc)
Stuart Hill (Treas & VP)
Scotty Parker (Asst VP-Ancillary Svcs)

Subsidiaries:

National Healthcare of Newport, Inc. (1)
1205 McLain St, Newport, AR 72112
Tel.: (870) 523-8911
Web Site: http://www.harrishospital.com
Emp.: 225
Health Care Srvices
N.A.I.C.S.: 621498
Rebecca Pearrow (Mktg Dir)

UNITY HEALTH CARE, INC.
1220 12th St SE Ste 120, Washington, DC 20003
Tel.: (202) 715-7900 DC
Web Site: http://www.unityhealthcare.org
Year Founded: 1985
Sales Range: $75-99.9 Million
Emp.: 1,003
Health Care Srvices
N.A.I.C.S.: 622110
Aaronissa Alleyne (VP-HR)
Vincent A. Keane (Pres & CEO)
Janelle Goetcheus (Chief Medical Officer & Exec VP-Medical Affairs)
Ardell Butler (Exec VP-Ops & Fin)
Karin Werner (VP-Strategic Dev)
Diana Lapp (Deputy Chief Medical Office r& VP-Medical Admin)
Dianne Pledgie (Dir-Compliance)
Tracy Harrison (VP-Clinical Admin)
Oluwatoyin Abayomi (Deputy CFO & VP-Fin)
Aysha Corbett (Deputy Chief Medical Office r& VP-Quality Improvement)
Angelica Journagin (VP-Policy & Plng)
Edwin Jones (Sec)
Charles Barber (Treas)
Frederick Cooke (Vice Chm)
Jo Ann Smoak Mahone (Chm)
Angela Diop (VP-Information Sys)

UNITY HOUSE OF CAYUGA COUNTY, INC.
34 Wright Ave, Auburn, NY 13021
Tel.: (315) 253-6227 NY
Web Site: http://www.unityhouse.com
Year Founded: 1977
Sales Range: $10-24.9 Million
Mental Health Care Services
N.A.I.C.S.: 623220
Elizabeth Smith (Exec Dir)
Sue Morley (Dir-Mental Health Svcs & Programs)
Kelly Buck (Dir-Mktg & Dev)
Gary Fellows (Dir-Maintenance)
Diane Jurczak-Prue (Dir-Fin)
Sara Glauberman (Dir-HR)
Cindy Wilcox (Chm)
Andrew K. Cuddy (Vice Chm)
Bradley Chapman (Treas)

Amber Amidon (Officer-Compliance & Dir-Quality Assurance)
Darlene Podolak (COO)

UNITY HOUSE OF TROY, INC.
2431 6th Ave, Troy, NY 12180
Tel.: (518) 274-2607 NY
Web Site: http://www.unityhouseny.org
Year Founded: 1981
Sales Range: $10-24.9 Million
Emp.: 535
Community Development Services
N.A.I.C.S.: 624190
Chris Burke (CEO)
Patricia Dinkelaker (Dir-Org Dev)
Diane Cameron Pascone (Dir-Dev & Grants)
Stacy Faulisi (Dir-Fin)
Milinda J. Reed (Dir-HR)
James A. Slavin (Chm)
Jenny O'Neill (Treas)
Kathleen Koval (Sec)
Kathryn Allen (Vice Chm)

UNITY MANUFACTURING COMPANY
1260 N Clybourn Ave, Chicago, IL 60610
Tel.: (312) 943-5200 IL
Web Site: http://www.unityusa.com
Year Founded: 1918
Sales Range: $50-74.9 Million
Emp.: 100
Mfr & Designer of Automotive, Truck & Emergency Vehicle Lighting Systems & Products
N.A.I.C.S.: 336320
Louis E. Gross (Chm)
Timothy S. Gross (Pres)
Bill Koehler (Controller)
William Gross (VP-Markets)

UNITY MORTGAGE CORP.
7840 Roswell Rd Ste 301, Atlanta, GA 30350
Tel.: (770) 604-4000
Web Site: http://www.unitymortgage.com
Rev.: $23,400,000
Emp.: 80
Mortgage Banker
N.A.I.C.S.: 522292
Jack Quan (Pres & CEO)

UNITY PRINTING CO., INC.
5848 State Route 981, Latrobe, PA 15650
Tel.: (724) 537-5800
Web Site: http://www.unityprinting.com
Rev.: $4,200,000
Emp.: 20
Printing Services
N.A.I.C.S.: 323113
Brenda S. Ernette (Treas & Sec)
John Melle (Mgr-Ops)
Lisa Frederick (Pres)

Subsidiaries:

Stefano's Printing, Inc. (1)
266 Furnace Hill Rd, Dunbar, PA 15431
Tel.: (724) 277-8374
Web Site: http://www.stefanosprinting.com
Rev.: $1,064,000
Emp.: 7
Commercial Lithographic Printing Services
N.A.I.C.S.: 323111

UNITYPOINT HEALTH
1200 Pleasant St, Des Moines, IA 50309-1406
Tel.: (515) 241-6161 IA
Web Site: http://www.ihs.org
Year Founded: 1993
Sales Range: $1-4.9 Billion
Emp.: 18,375

Health Care Srvices
N.A.I.C.S.: 621399
Denny Drake (Officer-Compliance, Gen Counsel & Sr VP)
Linda Newborn (Sec-Quad Cities)
Katie Marchik (CFO-Trinity)
Emily Porter (VP-People Excellence)
Sabra Rosener (VP-Govt Rels)
Kara Dunham (VP-Fin)
Aric Sharp (VP-Accountable Care Org)
Randy Easton (Chm)
Mike Dewerff (CFO-Des Moines)
Matthew Kirschner (VP-Treasury)
Troy Caraway (Sr VP-Insurance Div)
Arthur Nizza (COO & Exec VP)
Tim Ahlers (Chief Operating & Fin Officer)
Chris Blair (Chief Admin Officer)
Marty Dorgan (Chief Quality Officer & VP-Quality & Safety)
Douglas Dorner (Chief Academic Officer)
Sue Erickson (Pres/CEO-Meriter)
Brian Jones (VP-Payor Innovation)
Dennis W. Linderbaum (Co-Pres)
Eric L. Lothe (COO-Des Moines & Sr VP)
Katie Pearson (Chief Strategy Officer & Sr VP)
W. Scott Reid (Co-Pres)
Gary Robb (Chief Pharmacy Officer)
Shari King (Interim VP-Ops-Marshalltown)
Jenni Friedly (Pres-Marshalltown)
Brian Schwering (Mgr-Environmental Svcs-Trinity Reg Medical Center)
Leah Glasgo (Pres/CEO-Fort Dodge)
Sue Thompson (Interim CEO)
Casey Greene (COO/VP-St. Luke's Hospital)
Sanjeeb Khatua (Pres/CEO-UnityPoint Clinic)
Theodore Townsend Jr. (Interim Pres/Interim CEO-Dubuque)

Subsidiaries:

Counseling Center & Blank Psychiatry (1)
6000 University Ave Ste 200, West Des Moines, IA 50266
Tel.: (515) 241-2300
Web Site: http://www.ihs.org
Sales Range: $10-24.9 Million
Emp.: 25
Psychiatric Services
N.A.I.C.S.: 622210
Eric Crowel (Pres)

Finley Tri-States Health Group, Inc. (1)
350 N Grandview Ave, Dubuque, IA 52001-6388
Tel.: (563) 582-1881
Health Care Srvices
N.A.I.C.S.: 621999

Iowa Lutheran Hospital Medical Education Foundation (1)
1200 Pleasant St, Des Moines, IA 50309-1406
Tel.: (515) 241-6212
Web Site: http://www.iowahealth.org
Medical Education Program Administrator
N.A.I.C.S.: 923110
Eric Crowell (Pres & CEO)

Penn Center Inc. (1)
2237 245th St, Delhi, IA 52223-8407
Tel.: (563) 922-2881
Web Site: http://www.unitypoint.org
Women Healthcare Services
N.A.I.C.S.: 622310

St. Luke's Health System, Inc. (1)
2720 Stone Park Blvd, Sioux City, IA 51104
Tel.: (712) 279-3500
Web Site: http://www.unitypoint.org
Health Care Srvices
N.A.I.C.S.: 621999
Susan Unger (Pres)
Mary Cronin (Assoc VP-Ops)

Subsidiary (Domestic):

Sacred Heart HealthCare System (2)
421 Chew St, Allentown, PA 18102
Tel.: (610) 776-4500
Web Site: http://www.slhn.org
Inpatient & Outpatient Services
N.A.I.C.S.: 622110

Trinity Health Systems, Inc. (1)
802 Kenyon Rd, Fort Dodge, IA 50501
Tel.: (515) 574-6676
Health Care Srvices
N.A.I.C.S.: 621999

UNIVERSAL 1 CREDIT UNION, INC.
1 River Park Dr, Dayton, OH 45409
Tel.: (937) 225-6800 OH
Web Site: http://www.u1cu.org
Year Founded: 1937
Sales Range: $10-24.9 Million
Financial Credit Union Services
N.A.I.C.S.: 522130
Ann M. Parrish (Treas & Exec VP-Fin)
Shannon R. Maloney (Exec VP-MIS & Corp Svcs)
Jessica Jones (VP-HR)
Loren A. Rush (Pres & CEO)
Alice M. Hensley (Sr VP-Member Svcs)
Lisa A. Carbaugh (Sr VP-Admin Svcs)

UNIVERSAL ACCOUNTING CENTER
5288 S Commerce Dr, Murray, UT 84107
Tel.: (801) 265-3777
Web Site: http://www.universalaccounting.com
Year Founded: 1979
Sales Range: $1-9.9 Million
Emp.: 8
Small-Business Accounting Instruction Services
N.A.I.C.S.: 611430
Roger Knecht (Pres)

UNIVERSAL ATHLETIC SERVICE, INC.
25 W Main St, Bozeman, MT 59715
Tel.: (406) 587-1220
Web Site: http://www.universalathletic.com
Emp.: 1,000
Athletic Goods
N.A.I.C.S.: 423910
Larry Aasheim (Co-Pres)
Paula Johnson (Controller)
Bret Chapman (Mgr-Footwear)
Lorri Olson (Mgr-HR)
Ben Petritz (Mgr)
Greg Miller (Co-Pres)
Gary Scheidecker (Mgr-Team Comml Sls)
Brian Pepper (Mgr-School Sls)

UNIVERSAL BANK
3455 Nogales St Fl 2, West Covina, CA 91792
Tel.: (626) 854-2818
Web Site: http://www.universalbank.com
Rev.: $33,513,000
Emp.: 60
Federal Savings Bank
N.A.I.C.S.: 522180
Frank Chang (Pres)
Johnson Huang (Mgr)
Shirley Pascal (Mgr & VP)
Edgar Gatchalian (VP)
Rudy Campos (Supvr-Branch Admin)

UNIVERSAL BIOENERGY, INC.

UNIVERSAL BIOENERGY, INC.

Universal Bioenergy, Inc.—(Continued)
18100 Von Karman Ave Ste 850, Irvine, CA 92612
Tel.: (949) 272-5677 NV
Web Site:
http://www.universalbioenergy.com
Year Founded: 2004
Sales Range: $50-74.9 Million
Emp.: 15
Biodiesel Producer
N.A.I.C.S.: 324199
Vince M. Guest *(Pres & CEO)*
Kenneth L. Harris *(Pres/CEO-NDR Energy Group)*
Rickey D. Hart *(Bus Dev Officer & Sr VP-NDR Energy Group)*
Gina Roy *(VP-Bus Dev-East)*

UNIVERSAL BLUEPRINT PAPER COMPANY, LLC
327 Bryan Ave, Fort Worth, TX 76104-2441
Tel.: (817) 332-9259 TX
Year Founded: 1982
Sales Range: $10-24.9 Million
Emp.: 50
Paper Coating & Converting Services
N.A.I.C.S.: 325992

UNIVERSAL BUILDERS SUPPLY, INC.
27 Horton Ave, New Rochelle, NY 10801-3408
Tel.: (914) 699-2400 DE
Web Site: http://www.ubs1.com
Year Founded: 1931
Sales Range: $25-49.9 Million
Emp.: 200
Mfr of Aluminum Scaffolding, Shoring, Material & Personnel Hoists & Towers
N.A.I.C.S.: 238990
Kevin O'Callaghan *(Chm & CEO)*
Cal O'Callaghan *(Safety Dir & EEO Coord)*
Chris Evans *(Pres)*
John Arvonio *(CFO & Sr VP)*

Subsidiaries:

Universal Builders Supply Ltd. (1)
85C Huntingdon Street, Saint Neots, Huntingdon, PE19 1DU, Cambs, United Kingdom
Tel.: (44) 1480 741579
Mfr of Aluminum Scaffolding, Shoring, Material & Personnel Hoists & Towers
N.A.I.C.S.: 532490

UNIVERSAL BUILDING SPECIALTIES INCORPORATED
210 Neptune Rd, Auburndale, FL 33823
Tel.: (863) 967-1131
Web Site: http://www.ubslumber.com
Year Founded: 1959
Sales Range: $10-24.9 Million
Emp.: 28
Wood Panel Whslr
N.A.I.C.S.: 423310
Edward R. Vila *(Pres)*
Thomas W. Moore *(Sec)*
Steven T. Moore *(CEO)*

UNIVERSAL BUSINESS SOLUTIONS, NA
90 John St 5th Fl, New York, NY 10038
Tel.: (212) 643-4808
Web Site: http://www.ubsna.com
Year Founded: 2006
Sales Range: $1-9.9 Million
Emp.: 26
Print Management Products & Services
N.A.I.C.S.: 323111
Abe Thomas *(Pres & CEO)*

UNIVERSAL CHEMICAL AND SUPPLY
607 Palm Dr, Hallandale, FL 33009
Tel.: (954) 454-9731
Rev.: $14,150,000
Emp.: 6
Chemicals, Industrial & Heavy
N.A.I.C.S.: 423830

UNIVERSAL CHEVROLET CO. INC.
105 Main St, Wendell, NC 27591
Tel.: (919) 365-6351
Web Site:
http://www.universalchevy.com
Sales Range: $10-24.9 Million
Emp.: 30
Automobiles, New & Used
N.A.I.C.S.: 441110
Paul White *(Pres)*
Allen White *(VP)*

UNIVERSAL COIN & BULLION LTD.
7410 Phelan Blvd, Beaumont, TX 77706
Tel.: (409) 835-1192
Web Site:
http://www.universalcoin.com
Sales Range: $250-299.9 Million
Emp.: 30
Coin Dealer
N.A.I.C.S.: 459999
Michael Fuljenz *(Pres)*

UNIVERSAL CONSOLIDATED SERVICES
1100 Poydras St Ste 1300, New Orleans, LA 70163
Tel.: (504) 561-5627
Web Site: http://www.universal-personnel.com
Sales Range: $10-24.9 Million
Emp.: 270
Temporary Help Service
N.A.I.C.S.: 561320
Michele Vignes *(Pres & CEO)*
Joseph C. Wink III *(Sec)*

UNIVERSAL CONSTRUCTION COMPANY, INC.
11200 W 79th St, Lenexa, KS 66214-1323
Tel.: (913) 342-1150 MO
Web Site:
http://www.universalconstruction.net
Year Founded: 1931
Sales Range: $75-99.9 Million
Emp.: 125
Provider of Construction & Contracting Services
N.A.I.C.S.: 236220
Steven P. Smith *(Pres)*
Bob Black *(Exec VP)*
John Shortall *(VP)*

UNIVERSAL CONSULTING SERVICES, INC.
3975 Fair Ridge Dr Ste 400 S, Fairfax, VA 22033
Tel.: (703) 591-5100
Web Site: http://www.universal-inc.net
Year Founded: 1993
Sales Range: $10-24.9 Million
Emp.: 125
Management Consulting Services
N.A.I.C.S.: 541611
Charu Dhumne *(Owner & Pres)*
Abhijit Dhumne *(Founder)*
Sachin Chandra *(VP-Tech & Bus Solutions)*
Erik Necciai *(Dir-Federal Acq Svcs)*

Luis Asqueri *(VP-Health & Bus Strategies)*
Bernie Poindexter *(Dir-Logistics)*
Jon Bolling *(VP-IT Ops & Dev)*

UNIVERSAL COOPERATIVES, INC.
1300 Corp Ctr Curve, Eagan, MN 55121
Tel.: (651) 239-1000 MN
Web Site: http://www.ucoop.com
Year Founded: 1972
Sales Range: $200-249.9 Million
Emp.: 390
International Farm Supply Cooperative; Agricultural Chemicals, Animal Health Products, Lubricating Oils, Baler Twine, Tractor, Truck & Passenger Tires, Automotive Accessories & Feed Additives Distr
N.A.I.C.S.: 423130
Terrance Bohman *(Pres & CEO)*
William Cubbage *(VP-Animal Health & Nutrition)*
L. Bryan Morrison *(VP-HR)*
Dennis Gyolai *(VP-Fin)*
Leon Westbrock *(Chm)*
Dale Halladay *(VP-Intl)*

Subsidiaries:

Bridon Cordage LLC (1)
909 16th St, Albert Lea, MN 56007-5307
Tel.: (507) 377-1601
Web Site: http://www.bridoncordage.com
Sales Range: $10-24.9 Million
Emp.: 127
Mfr of Twine & Cordage
N.A.I.C.S.: 314994
Jade Sherman *(Mgr-Mktg)*
Wade Carlson *(Mgr-QC)*

Filatures Et Corderies Ste. Germaine (1)
Immeuble Le Diesel 2 Impasse Rudolf DIESEL, 33692, Merignac, France
Tel.: (33) 5 56 28 13 08
Web Site: http://www.sainte-germaine.com
Farm Machinery & Equipment Mfr
N.A.I.C.S.: 333111

Universal Cooperatives, Inc - UCPA Chemical Plant (1)
1253 Independence Dr, Napoleon, OH 43545
Tel.: (419) 599-0010
Chemical Products Mfr
N.A.I.C.S.: 325998

UNIVERSAL DISPLAY & FIXTURES COMPANY INC.
726 E Hwy 121, Lewisville, TX 75057-4159
Tel.: (972) 420-0955 TX
Web Site: http://www.udfc.com
Year Founded: 1988
Sales Range: $10-24.9 Million
Emp.: 300
Partitions & Fixtures
N.A.I.C.S.: 337126
Dave Parker *(CEO)*

UNIVERSAL DYEING & PRINTING, INC.
2303 E 11th St, Los Angeles, CA 90021
Tel.: (213) 746-0818 CA
Web Site: http://www.udptextile.com
Year Founded: 1990
Rev.: $12,480,498
Emp.: 75
Printing, Manmade Fiber & Silk Broadwoven Fabrics
N.A.I.C.S.: 313310
Kee Sung Hwang *(Pres)*

UNIVERSAL E-BUSINESS SOLUTIONS
244 5th Ave 4th Fl, New York, NY 10001

U.S. PRIVATE

Tel.: (646) 706-4000
Web Site: http://www.uebiz.com
Sales Range: $25-49.9 Million
Emp.: 50
Electronic Business Consulting Services
N.A.I.C.S.: 541512
Anu Bhartiya *(Co-Founder & Co-Mng Partner)*
Marc Snyder *(Co-Founder & Co-Mng Partner)*
Raghav Manocha *(Engr-Voice)*
Anthony Cennami *(Sr VP)*

UNIVERSAL ENGINEERING SCIENCES, LLC
4205 Vineland Rd St L1, Orlando, FL 32811
Tel.: (407) 423-0504 FL
Web Site:
http://www.universalengineering.com
Engineering & Environmental Consulting Services
N.A.I.C.S.: 541330
Gary Elzweig *(Vice Chm & Chief Strategy Officer)*
Michael Burke *(Chm)*
Lauren Falcone *(VP-Corp Comm)*
Dave Witsken *(CEO)*
Benjamin P. Butterfield *(Gen Counsel)*
Lindsay Graham *(Dir-Mktg & Comm)*

Subsidiaries:

Alpha Testing, Inc. (1)
2209 Wisconsin St, Dallas, TX 75229
Tel.: (972) 620-8911
Web Site: http://www.alphatesting.com
Sales Range: $1-9.9 Million
Emp.: 110
Engineeering Services
N.A.I.C.S.: 541330
Brian Powell *(Pres)*
Chris Talamini *(Mgr-Environmental Svcs)*
Tony Janish *(Principal)*
Jeff Wilt *(Exec Principal)*
Ken Combs *(VP)*
Larry Goodrich *(Reg Mgr)*
Jeff Thomas *(CFO)*
Pat Stettner *(Principal)*

Carmichael Engineering, Inc. (1)
650 Oliver Rd, Montgomery, AL 36117
Tel.: (334) 213-5647
Web Site:
http://www.carmichaelengineering.com
Engineeering Services
N.A.I.C.S.: 541330
John Presley *(Reg Mgr-Technical Svcs)*
Steve Carmichael *(CEO)*
J. Stephen Carmichael *(Founder)*

GFA International, Inc. (1)
1215 Wallace Dr, Delray Beach, FL 33444
Tel.: (800) 226-7522
Web Site: http://teamgfa.com
Engineering Services
N.A.I.C.S.: 541330

InControl Technologies, Inc. (1)
14731 Pebble Bend Dr, Houston, TX 77068
Tel.: (281) 580-8892
Web Site: http://www.incontroltech.com
Sales Range: $1-9.9 Million
Emp.: 13
Scientific & Technical Consulting Services
N.A.I.C.S.: 541690
Lauren Grawey *(Project Mgr)*
Angela Marcon *(Pres)*
John C. Young *(Principal)*

McGinley & Associates, Inc. (1)
815 Maestro Dr Ste 202, Reno, NV 89511
Tel.: (775) 829-2245
Web Site: http://www.mcgin.com
Professional, Scientific & Technical Services
N.A.I.C.S.: 541990
Brian Giroux *(Principal)*

SUMMIT Engineering, Laboratory & Testing, P.C. (1)
3575 Centre Cir, Fort Mill, SC 29715
Tel.: (704) 504-1717

COMPANIES

UNIVERSAL MIND

Web Site: http://www.summit-companies.com
Sales Range: $1-9.9 Million
Emp.: 150
Engineeering Services
N.A.I.C.S.: 541330
Douglas Curley (Pres)

Universal Engineering Sciences (1)
4 Hargrove Grade Ste A, Palm Coast, FL 32137
Tel.: (386) 986-2122
Web Site: http://www.uesorl.com
Sales Range: $1-9.9 Million
Emp.: 17
Scientific & Technical Consulting Services
N.A.I.C.S.: 541690
Rick Rushner (Pres)
Phil Sutherland (Mgr)

Universal Engineering Sciences (1)
1748 Independence Blvd, Sarasota, FL 34234
Tel.: (941) 358-7410
Rev: $1,000,000
Emp.: 15
Fiscal Year-end: 12/31/2006
Commercial Physical Research
N.A.I.C.S.: 541720
Robert Gomez (Principal)

Universal Engineering Sciences (1)
3532 Maggie Blvd, Orlando, FL 32811-7404
Tel.: (407) 423-0504
Web Site:
  http://www.universalengineering.com
Engineeering Services
N.A.I.C.S.: 541330
Christiane Nelson (Asst Mgr-Construction Svcs)
Erin Murphy (Mgr-Mktg)
Melisse James (Mgr-Environmental Dept)
Kenneth Loihle (Mgr-Building Inspection-Southeast)
John Sullivan (Dir-Ops Optimization)
Brandy Agee (Asst Sls Mgr-Southeast)
Mike Ryan (Asst Sls Mgr-Southwest Florida)

UNIVERSAL ENGRAVING INC.
9090 Nieman Rd, Overland Park, KS 66214
Tel.: (913) 599-0600   KS
Web Site: http://www.ueigroup.com
Year Founded: 1982
Copper & Brass Engraving Dies Mfr
N.A.I.C.S.: 323120
Larry Hutchison (Pres & CEO)
Jim Hutchison (VP-Sls & Mktg)

UNIVERSAL FIBERS SYSTEMS LLC
14401 Industrial Park Rd, Bristol, VA 24202
Tel.: (276) 669-1161
Web Site:
  http://www.universalfibers.com
Sales Range: $50-74.9 Million
Emp.: 500
Organic Fibers, Noncellulosic
N.A.I.C.S.: 325220
Marcus Ammen (CEO)
Phil Harmon (Pres-Universal Fibers, Inc)

UNIVERSAL FIDELITY HOLDING CO., INC.
Ste 1120W 2601 NW Expressway St, Oklahoma City, OK 73112-7256
Tel.: (405) 415-2252
Sales Range: $25-49.9 Million
Emp.: 3
Holding Company
N.A.I.C.S.: 524114
Steve Hague (Pres & CEO)
Brent Haggard (Mng Partner)

Subsidiaries:

Universal Fidelity Life Insurance Co.   (1)
815 W Ash St, Duncan, OK 73534
Tel.: (580) 255-8530
Web Site: http://www.uflic.net

Sales Range: $50-74.9 Million
Life, Accident & Health Underwriter
N.A.I.C.S.: 524113

UNIVERSAL HEALTH CARE, INC.
100 Central Ave Ste 200, Saint Petersburg, FL 33701
Tel.: (727) 456-2900   FL
Web Site: http://www.univhc.com
Year Founded: 2002
Sales Range: $1-4.9 Billion
Emp.: 700
Direct Health & Medical Insurance Carriers
N.A.I.C.S.: 524114
Akshay Desai (Chm & CEO)
Mike Leavitt (Sec)
Jeff Ludy (CMO)
Sandip I. Patel (Chief Admin Officer & Gen Counsel)
Michael P. Holohan (COO)

UNIVERSAL HERBS INC.
33453 Western Ave, Union City, CA 94587
Tel.: (510) 324-2900
Web Site: http://www.herbspro.com
Year Founded: 2004
Sales Range: $1-9.9 Million
Emp.: 10
Herbal Supplements & Health Care Products
N.A.I.C.S.: 456191
Prasad Adavikolanu (Owner, Pres & CEO)

Subsidiaries:

Herbspro.com   (1)
1817 Addisonway, Hayward, CA 94544   (100%)
Tel.: (510) 324-2900
Web Site: http://www.herbspro.com
Online Herbal Supplement Sales
N.A.I.C.S.: 456191
Tanu Bhattacharya (Dir-Mktg & Ops)

UNIVERSAL HOME EXPERTS
9326 Kay Ln, Houston, TX 77064
Tel.: (713) 863-9311
Web Site:
  http://www.universalhomeexperts.com
Year Founded: 1992
Sales Range: $1-9.9 Million
Emp.: 22
Electrical & Air Conditioning Services & Repairs
N.A.I.C.S.: 335999
Ed Valot (Owner)

UNIVERSAL INDUSTRIAL PRODUCTS CO.
1 Coreway Dr, Pioneer, OH 43554-0628
Tel.: (419) 737-2324   DE
Web Site: http://www.soss.com
Year Founded: 1941
Sales Range: $1-9.9 Million
Emp.: 50
Universal Mower Blades, Construction Hinges, Stamping & Precision Grinding Metal Parts Mfr
N.A.I.C.S.: 332119
Neil Marko (Owner)
Randy Herriman (CFO)

UNIVERSAL INDUSTRIAL SALES, INC.
433 N 1030 W, Lindon, UT 84042
Tel.: (801) 785-0505
Web Site: http://www.uisutah.com
Year Founded: 1978
Emp.: 200
Fabricated Structural Metal Mfr
N.A.I.C.S.: 332312
Dan Hancock (Controller)

UNIVERSAL INDUSTRIES LLC
3455 W Reno Ste A, Las Vegas, NV 89118
Tel.: (702) 434-1694
Web Site:
  http://www.universalinds.com
Year Founded: 2008
Sales Range: $1-9.9 Million
Emp.: 8
Wholesale Distributor of Bed Frames, Mattresses & Dining & Living Room Sets
N.A.I.C.S.: 423210

UNIVERSAL INTERLOCK CORP.
950 New Durham Rd, Edison, NJ 08817
Tel.: (732) 650-9700
Web Site:
  http://www.gotokitchenexpo.com
Year Founded: 1987
Kitchen & Bath Cabinets Whslr & Distr
N.A.I.C.S.: 423310
Brian Gordon (CEO)

UNIVERSAL LANGUAGE SERVICE, INC.
925 110th Ave NE Ste A, Bellevue, WA 98004
Tel.: (425) 454-8072   WA
Web Site: http://www.ulsonline.net
Sales Range: $1-9.9 Million
Emp.: 12
Translation & Interpretation Services
N.A.I.C.S.: 541930
Elena Vasiliev (Pres)

UNIVERSAL LENDING CORPORATION
6775 E Evans Ave, Denver, CO 80224
Tel.: (303) 758-4969
Web Site: http://www.ulc.com
Sales Range: $25-49.9 Million
Emp.: 250
Mortgage Banker
N.A.I.C.S.: 522292
Brad Groves (CFO)
Carol Peterson (VP & Mgr-Production-Natl)
Carrie Goldman (Mgr-Wholesale Underwriting)
Doug Petz (Mgr-Secondary Mktg)
Gayle Campbell (VP-Underwriting)
Kaelyn Smith (Coord-Div)
Susan Perow (Mgr-Customer Accts)
Pete Lansing (Pres)
Terri Jowers (VP)
Susan Gumm (Branch Mgr)
T. J. Kennedy (Exec VP-Production)
Brian Hafner (Acct Exec-Wholesale-Montana-Wyoming)
Elizabeth Turra (Branch Mgr)

UNIVERSAL LIMITED
932 Alton Pkwy, Birmingham, AL 35173
Tel.: (205) 836-6053
Web Site:
  http://www.universalltd.com
Sales Range: $10-24.9 Million
Emp.: 300
Insulation, Buildings
N.A.I.C.S.: 238310
John E. Howell (Pres)
Joe Ragusa (Mgr-Safety)

UNIVERSAL MACHINE CO. OF POTTSTOWN
645 Old Reading Pike, Pottstown, PA 19464
Tel.: (610) 323-1810
Web Site: http://www.umc-oscar.com
Rev: $16,093,559

Emp.: 100
Machine & Other Job Shop Work
N.A.I.C.S.: 332710
Richard M. Francis Sr. (Pres)

UNIVERSAL MACOMB AMBULANCE SERVICE, INC.
37583 Mound Rd, Sterling Heights, MI 48310
Tel.: (586) 939-4350
Web Site:
  http://www.universalmacomb.com
Year Founded: 1957
Sales Range: $10-24.9 Million
Emp.: 130
Provider of Ambulance Transport Services
N.A.I.C.S.: 621910
Donald K. McLocklin (Owner)

UNIVERSAL MANUFACTURING COMPANY
405 Diagonal St, Algona, IA 50511-2001
Tel.: (515) 295-3557   NE
Web Site:
  http://www.universalmanf.com
Year Founded: 1947
Sales Range: $25-49.9 Million
Emp.: 102
Remanufacturer of Automotive Parts
N.A.I.C.S.: 337127
Darryl Anderson (Pres)
Trey Bajat (Dir-Supply Chain-Metal Works Mfg. Co.)

UNIVERSAL MANUFACTURING CORP.
318 Gidney St, Shelby, NC 28150-5978
Tel.: (704) 487-4359
Year Founded: 1970
Sales Range: $10-24.9 Million
Emp.: 15
Retail of Robes & Dressing Gowns
N.A.I.C.S.: 315250
Robert Brown (Controller)
Harvey Gossett (VP)
Dale Frost (Treas)

UNIVERSAL MEDIA INC.
4999 Louise Dr, Mechanicsburg, PA 17055
Tel.: (717) 795-7990
Web Site: http://www.umiusa.com
Year Founded: 1986
Emp.: 35
N.A.I.C.S.: 541830
Anne Carnathan (VP-Bus Dev)

UNIVERSAL METAL PRODUCTS INC.
29980 Lakeland Blvd, Wickliffe, OH 44092
Tel.: (440) 943-3040
Web Site:
  http://www.universalmetalproducts.com
Year Founded: 1946
Sales Range: $25-49.9 Million
Emp.: 115
Metal Stamping Mfr
N.A.I.C.S.: 332119
Hugh S. Seaholm (Pres & CEO)
Ted Rossman (Plant Mgr)
Dan Dorsey (Engr-Sls)
Doug Allen (VP-Sls & Mktg)
Gordon Daugherty (VP-Engrg)
Rick Kirby (VP-Matls)
Mick Shvorob (Plant Mgr)

UNIVERSAL MIND
94 N Elm St Ste 306, Westfield, MA 01085
Tel.: (413) 562-3630   MA

UNIVERSAL MIND

Universal Mind—(Continued)
Web Site:
http://www.universalmind.com
Year Founded: 2003
Sales Range: $10-24.9 Million
Emp.: 4
Designs & Builds Interactive Web-Based Applications using Adobe Technology
N.A.I.C.S.: 334610
Brett Cortese (Co-Founder)
David Tucker (Exec VP-Tech)

UNIVERSAL NUTRITION
3 Terminal Rd, New Brunswick, NJ 08901
Tel.: (732) 545-3130
Web Site:
http://www.universalnutrition.com
Rev.: $29,700,000
Emp.: 200
Vitamin, Nutrient & Hematinic Preparations For Human Use
N.A.I.C.S.: 323111
Erin Schiavino (Asst Dir-Art)
Tim Tantum (Dir-Sls)
Jason Budsock (Product Mgr)

UNIVERSAL OVERALL COMPANY
1060 W Van Buren St, Chicago, IL 60607-2920
Tel.: (312) 226-3336   DE
Web Site:
http://www.universaloverall.com
Year Founded: 1924
Sales Range: $75-99.9 Million
Emp.: 110
Supplier of Work Uniforms, Overalls & Coveralls
N.A.I.C.S.: 315250
Heather Eckerling (Dir-Sls & Adv)
Allen Farkas (Dir-Sls & Mktg)

UNIVERSAL PACKAGING SYSTEMS, INC.
6080 Jericho Tpk Ste 101, Commack, NY 11725-2850
Tel.: (909) 517-2442
Web Site: http://www.paklab.com
Sales Range: $100-124.9 Million
Emp.: 800
Packaging & Labeling Services
N.A.I.C.S.: 561910

Subsidiaries:

Diversapack, LLC   (1)
981 Joseph Beach Lowery Blvd, Atlanta, GA 30318
Tel.: (770) 874-8003
Packaging Services
N.A.I.C.S.: 561910
Andrew Young III (CEO & Chm)

Subsidiary (Domestic):

Universal Packaging Systems, Inc.   (2)
14570 Monte Vista Ave, Chino, CA 91710
Tel.: (909) 517-2442
Web Site: http://www.paklab.com
Sales Range: $25-49.9 Million
Packaging & Labeling Services
N.A.I.C.S.: 333993
Woody Allen (Pres)

UNIVERSAL PARAGON CORPORATION
150 Executive Park Blvd Ste 1180, San Francisco, CA 94134
Tel.: (415) 468-6676   DE
Web Site:
http://www.universalparagoncorp.com
Year Founded: 1987
Rev.: $13,400,000
Emp.: 400
Real Estate Developer; Hotels & Motels
N.A.I.C.S.: 721110
Howard Pearce (Project Mgr-Engrg)

Subsidiaries:

Tuntex Executive Park Inc.   (1)
150 Executive Park Blvd, San Francisco, CA 94134-3303
Tel.: (415) 468-6676
Sales Range: $10-24.9 Million
Emp.: 16
Nonresidential Building Operators
N.A.I.C.S.: 561320
How Chen (Pres)

UNIVERSAL PHOTONICS, INC.
85 Jetson Ln, Central Islip, NY 11722
Tel.: (516) 935-4000   NY
Web Site:
http://www.universalphotonics.com
Year Founded: 1926
Sales Range: $75-99.9 Million
Emp.: 100
Abrasives, Polishing Compounds, Machinery & Supplies Mfr & Distr for the Optical Industry
N.A.I.C.S.: 423490

Subsidiaries:

AquaBond Technologies, Inc.   (1)
5235 Mission Oaks Blvd Ste 300, Camarillo, CA 93010
Tel.: (805) 383-4008
Web Site:
http://www.aquabondtechnologies.com
Adhesive Mfr
N.A.I.C.S.: 325520

JH Rhodes Company, Inc.   (1)
4809 E Thistle Landing Dr Ste 100, Phoenix, AZ 85044
Tel.: (480) 346-7064
Web Site: http://www.jhrhodes.com
Emp.: 65
Polishing Pad Mfr
N.A.I.C.S.: 327910
Makoto Kozuma (Pres & CEO)

Plant (Domestic):

JH Rhodes Company, Inc. - Clinton Manufacturing Facility   (2)
3683 State Route 12B, Clinton, NY 13323
Tel.: (315) 853-8844
Polishing Pad Mfr
N.A.I.C.S.: 327910

Universal Photonics (Shenzhen) Co., Ltd.   (1)
Suite 1210-1211 Main Building Jinzhonghuan Business Building, Jintian Road Futian District, Shenzhen, 518048, China
Tel.: (86) 755 2584 9294
Surfacing Product Mfr
N.A.I.C.S.: 327910

Universal Photonics Far East, Inc   (1)
2F Uchisaiwaicho Kikaku Building 1-15-6 Nishi-Shimbashi, Minato-ku, Tokyo, 105-0003, Japan
Tel.: (81) 3 6205 4121
Surfacing Product Mfr
N.A.I.C.S.: 327910

Universal Photonics Hong Kong Limited   (1)
Suite 2408 24/F Lippo Centre Tower 2, Hong Kong, China (Hong Kong)
Tel.: (852) 9456 8628
Emp.: 1
Surfacing Product Mfr
N.A.I.C.S.: 327910

UNIVERSAL POLYMER & RUBBER LTD.
15730 S Madison Rd, Middlefield, OH 44062-0767
Tel.: (440) 632-1691
Web Site:
http://www.universalpolymer.com
Year Founded: 1970
Sales Range: $75-99.9 Million
Emp.: 60
Mfr of Polymers & Rubber
N.A.I.C.S.: 326299
Joe Colebank (Pres)
Wayne Read (CFO)

UNIVERSAL POOL CO. INC.
300 W Armory Dr, South Holland, IL 60473
Tel.: (708) 339-6060
Web Site:
http://www.shopthegreatescape.com
Rev.: $49,226,553
Emp.: 200
Swimming Pools, Equipment & Supplies
N.A.I.C.S.: 459999
Mark Rush (Pres)

UNIVERSAL POTASH CORPORATION
1300 E St, Fairport Harbor, OH 44077
Tel.: (440) 354-6500
Year Founded: 2001
Potash Mineral Mining Services
N.A.I.C.S.: 212390
Kevin Murphy (CEO)

UNIVERSAL POWER GROUP, INC.
488 S Royal Ln, Coppell, TX 75019
Tel.: (469) 892-1122   DE
Web Site: http://www.upgi.com
Year Founded: 1968
Batteries, Related Power Accessories & Security Accessories Supplier & Distr; Logistics & Supply Chain Management Services
N.A.I.C.S.: 423690

Subsidiaries:

Progressive Technologies, Inc.   (1)
331 Shellybrook Dr PO Box 950, Pilot Mountain, NC 27041-0950
Tel.: (336) 368-1375
Web Site: http://www.protechnologies.com
Sales Range: $25-49.9 Million
Emp.: 35
Battery Mfr
N.A.I.C.S.: 335910

UNIVERSAL PRINTING COMPANY
1234 S Kings Hwy Blvd, Saint Louis, MO 63110-2007
Tel.: (314) 771-6900   MO
Web Site:
http://www.universalprintingco.com
Year Founded: 1986
Sales Range: $25-49.9 Million
Emp.: 350
Lithographic Commercial Printing
N.A.I.C.S.: 323111
Joseph M. Ebel (Sec)
Janis A. Thouvenot (VP-Sls & Mktg)
Ryan Rigby (Coord-Production)
Robert C. Finkes (Controller)

UNIVERSAL PRODUCTS INC.
521 Industrial Rd, Goddard, KS 67052
Tel.: (316) 794-8601
Web Site: http://www.u-p.com
Year Founded: 1977
Sales Range: $25-49.9 Million
Emp.: 180
Printing Services
N.A.I.C.S.: 323111
Arla Dingman (Controller)
David Crumley (Dir-Quality Sys)

UNIVERSAL SELECT INC.
5915 Cedar Hills Blvd, Jacksonville, FL 32210
Tel.: (904) 786-1166

U.S. PRIVATE

Web Site: http://www.universalselect.com
Sales Range: $10-24.9 Million
Emp.: 320
Temporary Employee Services
N.A.I.C.S.: 561330
Dennis Jacob (Pres)

UNIVERSAL SEWING SUPPLY INC.
1011 E Park Indus Dr, Saint Louis, MO 63130-2641
Tel.: (314) 862-0800   MO
Web Site:
http://www.universalsewing.com
Year Founded: 1946
Sales Range: $10-24.9 Million
Emp.: 60
Industrial Supplies
N.A.I.C.S.: 423840
Philip Samuels (Pres)
Darrell Benton (Controller)
Michael Kelly (Mgr-IS)
Rick Giancola (Mgr-Facility)

UNIVERSAL SMARTCOMP, LLC
480 Johnson Rd Ste 200, Washington, PA 15301
Tel.: (877) 362-3391
Web Site:
http://www.universalsmartcomp.com
Year Founded: 2000
Sales Range: $100-124.9 Million
Emp.: 135
Physical Therapy Clinical Network Solutions
N.A.I.C.S.: 621340
Shannon Vissman (Chm & CEO)
Jan Richardson (Chief Clinical Officer)
Bernie Mccabe (Sr VP-Sls)
Leigh Ann Nedoma (VP-Ops)
Wayne P. Schmidt (VP-Clinical Svcs)

UNIVERSAL TECHNICAL RESOURCE SERVICES, INC.
950 N Kings Hwy Ste 208, Cherry Hill, NJ 08034
Tel.: (856) 667-6770
Web Site: http://www.utrs.com
Year Founded: 1985
Sales Range: $25-49.9 Million
Emp.: 175
Scientific & Technical Consulting Services
N.A.I.C.S.: 541690
Albert Zalcmann (Pres)
Steve George (Exec VP)
David Zalcmann (CFO)

Subsidiaries:

Gaum, Inc.   (1)
1080 US Highway 130, Robbinsville, NJ 08691
Tel.: (609) 586-0132
Web Site: http://www.gauminc.com
Sales Range: $1-9.9 Million
Emp.: 40
Industrial Machinery, Nec, Nsk
N.A.I.C.S.: 332710
Cheryl Gaum (Sec)
Bob Gaum (Pres)

RKR Hess Associates, Inc.   (1)
112 N Courtland St, East Stroudsburg, PA 18301
Tel.: (570) 421-1550
Web Site: http://www.rkrhess.com
Sales Range: $10-24.9 Million
Emp.: 15
Civil & Environmental Engineering Services
N.A.I.C.S.: 541330
Sam D'Alessandro (Mgr)

UNIVERSAL TELESERVICES LLC
2324 E. Bell Rd, Phoenix, AZ 85022
Tel.: (480) 606-0000
Web Site: http://www.calldms.com
Rev.: $30,000,000

Emp.: 50
Direct Selling Establishments
N.A.I.C.S.: 517111

UNIVERSAL THREAD GRINDING COMPANY
30 Chambers St, Fairfield, CT 06825
Tel.: (203) 336-1849   CT
Web Site: http://www.universal-thread.com
Year Founded: 1946
Sales Range: $50-74.9 Million
Emp.: 20
Precision Lead Screws Mfr
N.A.I.C.S.: 332722
Carl Linley (Treas)
William H. Everett Jr. (Pres)

UNIVERSAL TRAFFIC SERVICE
5500 International Pkwy S, Grand Rapids, MI 49512
Tel.: (616) 698-8038
Web Site: http://www.utsnet.com
Rev.: $27,496,827
Emp.: 90
Freight Transportation Arrangement
N.A.I.C.S.: 488510
Raymond D. Chester (Pres)
Julie Norman (Controller)
Ken Clark (Sr VP)
Bill Klotz (VP)
Christina Briggs (Dir-Traffic Svcs)
Sheila Lenhart (Acct Mgr)
Joel McCullough (Acct Mgr)
Jeff Mulder (Dir-Mktg)
Jessie Schelter (Acct Mgr)
Lamar Smith (Acct Mgr)
Charles McLanis (Acct Mgr)
Heidi Moreau (Acct Mgr)
Rose Crawford (Acct Mgr)
Brad Backhus (Mgr-Ops)

UNIVERSAL TRUCK & TRAILER SALES II LLC
3435 N Mccarty Dr, Houston, TX 77029
Tel.: (713) 678-7066
Web Site: http://www.universaltruck.com
Rev.: $14,000,000
Emp.: 9
Truck Tractor & Trailer Sales
N.A.I.C.S.: 441120
Charles Boone (Pres)

UNIVERSAL TURBINE PARTS, LLC
120 Grouby Airport Rd, Prattville, AL 36067
Tel.: (334) 361-7853   DE
Web Site: http://www.utpparts.com
Year Founded: 1993
Sales Range: $1-9.9 Million
Emp.: 48
Aftermarket Turboprop Aircraft Engine & Engine Parts Distr
N.A.I.C.S.: 423860
Joel Plake (CEO)

UNIVERSAL WAREHOUSE CO.
2850 Del Amo Blvd, Carson, CA 90221
Tel.: (310) 631-0800
Web Site: http://www.uwc-net.com
Sales Range: $10-24.9 Million
Emp.: 100
Provider of General Warehousing Services
N.A.I.C.S.: 493110
Don Grot (VP)
Subsidiaries:
ULS Express   (1)
PO Box 7547, Long Beach, CA 90807
Tel.: (310) 631-0800
Rev.: $160,000
Local Trucking without Storage
N.A.I.C.S.: 488510
Emy Elms (Office Mgr)

UNIVERSAL WARRANTY CORP.
PO Box 6855, Chicago, IL 60680
Tel.: (402) 333-9000
Web Site: http://www.universalwarranty.com
Rev.: $11,715,005
Emp.: 84
Loss Prevention Services Insurance
N.A.I.C.S.: 524298
Doug Frey (CFO & Sr VP-Fin & Admin)

UNIVERSAL WEATHER & AVIATION, INC.
8787 Tallyho Rd, Houston, TX 77061-3420
Tel.: (713) 378-2727
Web Site: http://www.universalweather.com
Year Founded: 1959
Rev.: $265,000,000
Emp.: 700
Flight Planning & Support Services
N.A.I.C.S.: 488190
C. Gregory Evans (Chm)
Ralph Vasami (CEO)
Tim Maystrik (Sr VP-Bus Dev)

UNIVERSAL WILDE
26 Dartmouth St, Westwood, MA 02090
Tel.: (781) 251-2700
Web Site: http://www.universalwilde.com
Emp.: 600
Marketing & Printing Services
N.A.I.C.S.: 323111
Bill Fitzgerald (Founder)
Jennifer MacAskill (VP-HR)
Stephen J. Flood (Pres & CEO)
Joe Musanti (CFO)
Kevin Molloy (Sr VP-IT)

UNIVERSAL WINDOW SOLUTIONS, LLC
2502 81st Pl E, Sarasota, FL 34243
Tel.: (941) 752-7473
Web Site: http://www.universalwindowsolutions.com
Year Founded: 1981
Sales Range: $1-9.9 Million
Emp.: 25
Windows, Doors & Hurricane Protection Products Installer & Distr
N.A.I.C.S.: 238130
Victor Phelps (Dir-Ops)
Rocky Smith (Co-Owner, Pres & Partner)
Bob Smith (Co-Owner)

UNIVERSAL YUMS LLC
9 Woodland Rd, Roseland, NJ 07068
Tel.: (973) 287-7393
Web Site: http://www.universalyums.com
Year Founded: 2014
Sales Range: $10-24.9 Million
Emp.: 50
Food Service
N.A.I.C.S.: 722310
Monique Bernstein (Co-Founder)
Eli Zauner (Co-Founder)

UNIVERSITIES RESEARCH ASSOCIATION, INC.
1140 19th St NW Ste 900, Washington, DC 20036
Tel.: (202) 293-1382   IL
Web Site: http://www.ura-hq.org
Year Founded: 1967
Sales Range: $300-349.9 Million
Emp.: 6
Research Facility
N.A.I.C.S.: 541720
Marta Cehelsky (Exec Dir)
Mary Egger (Gen Counsel)

UNIVERSITY AREA COMMUNITY DEVELOPMENT CORPORATION, INC.
14013 N 22nd St Ste A, Tampa, FL 33613
Tel.: (813) 558-5212   FL
Web Site: http://www.uacdc.org
Year Founded: 1997
Sales Range: $1-9.9 Million
Emp.: 20
Individual & Family Services
N.A.I.C.S.: 624190
Sarah Combs (CEO)
Martine Dorvil (Dir-Programs)
Albert Meza (Dir-Facilities & Asset Mgmt)
Gene Marshall (Chm)
Jaree Ervin (Chief Dev Officer)

UNIVERSITY BOOK STORE INC.
4326 University Way NE, Seattle, WA 98105
Tel.: (206) 634-3400
Web Site: http://www.ubookstore.com
Sales Range: $50-74.9 Million
Emp.: 300
Book Stores
N.A.I.C.S.: 459210
Julie Zommers (Dir-Fin & Admin)
Lara Konick-Mann (Dir-HR)
Louise Little (CEO)

UNIVERSITY CHRYSLER DODGE JEEP RAM OF FLORENCE
2354 Florence Blvd, Florence, AL 35630-2878
Tel.: (256) 766-7324
Web Site: http://www.universitychryslerdodgejeep.com
Year Founded: 2012
Sales Range: $10-24.9 Million
Emp.: 43
New Car Whslr
N.A.I.C.S.: 441110
Jeff Feltner (Gen Mgr)

UNIVERSITY CIRCLE INCORPORATED
10831 Magnolia Dr, Cleveland, OH 44106
Tel.: (216) 791-3900
Web Site: http://www.universitycircle.org
Sales Range: $1-9.9 Million
Emp.: 80
Tourism Destination
N.A.I.C.S.: 713110
Chris Ronayne (Pres)
Laura Kleinman (VP-Svcs)
Sheila O'Brycki (Sr Dir-District Svcs)
Jim Walton (VP-Fin & Admin)

UNIVERSITY CITY SCIENCE CENTER
3711 Market St Fl 8, Philadelphia, PA 19104
Tel.: (215) 966-6000
Web Site: http://www.sciencecenter.org
Year Founded: 1963
Sales Range: $10-24.9 Million
Emp.: 75

Real Estate Subdividers & Developers
N.A.I.C.S.: 541611
Saul Behar (Gen Counsel & VP)
Craig R. Carnaroli (Chm)
Lorraine G. LoPresti (VP-Fin & Admin)
Wenyong Wang (VP-Science & Tech)
Tracy S. Brala (VP-Ecosystem Dev)

UNIVERSITY CLUB OF MILWAUKEE
924 E Wells St, Milwaukee, WI 53202
Tel.: (414) 271-2222   WI
Web Site: http://www.uclubmke.com
Year Founded: 1898
Emp.: 70
Social & Civic Organization
N.A.I.C.S.: 813410
Julie Tolan (Sec & VP)
Jeff Podbielski (Controller & Mgr-HR)
Dan Aiello (Pres)
Mark Aasen (VP)
Carl Schmidt (Treas)
Greg Dick (COO & Gen Mgr)
Subsidiaries:
Tripoli Country Club, Inc.   (1)
7401 N 43rd St, Milwaukee, WI 53209
Tel.: (414) 351-7200
Web Site: http://www.tripolicc.com
Sales Range: $1-9.9 Million
Emp.: 150
Golf Courses & Country Clubs
N.A.I.C.S.: 713910
Timothy Stein (Dir-Food & Beverage)

UNIVERSITY CORP.
18111 Nordhoff St, Northridge, CA 91330
Tel.: (818) 677-5298
Web Site: http://www.csun.edu
Rev.: $11,981,238
Emp.: 200
Book Stores
N.A.I.C.S.: 516110
Rick Evans (Exec Dir)
Christine Matthew (Partner)

UNIVERSITY GAMES CORPORATION
2030 Harrison St, San Francisco, CA 94110-1310
Tel.: (415) 503-1600   CA
Web Site: http://www.ugames.com
Year Founded: 1985
Sales Range: $10-24.9 Million
Emp.: 40
Games & Toy Mfr
N.A.I.C.S.: 339930
A. Robert Moog (Co-Founder)
Cris Lehman (Co-Founder)
Subsidiaries:
Briarpatch Inc.   (1)
150 Essex St, Millburn, NJ 07041
Tel.: (973) 376-7002
Web Site: http://www.briarpatch.com
Sales Range: $1-9.9 Million
Emp.: 14
Childrens Games & Puzzles Mfr
N.A.I.C.S.: 339930
John Donofrio (Co-Founder & CEO)
Alex Fazio (VP-Sls)
University Games Australia   (1)
Level 1 Willoughby Rd, PO Box 296, Crows Nest, 2065, NSW, Australia
Tel.: (61) 294361016
Web Site: http://www.ugames.com.au
Sales Range: $10-24.9 Million
Emp.: 8
Games
N.A.I.C.S.: 339930
John Herbert (Mng Dir)
University Games Europe B.V.   (1)
Wethouder Sangersstraat 23, 6191 NA, Beek, Netherlands   (100%)
Tel.: (31) 644770690
Web Site: http://www.ug.nl
Sales Range: $10-24.9 Million
Emp.: 9
Games

UNIVERSITY GAMES CORPORATION U.S. PRIVATE

University Games Corporation—(Continued)
N.A.I.C.S.: 339930

University Games UK Ltd. (1)
Unit 3-4 The Business Centre The Courtyard Glory Park, Wooburn Moor, High Wycombe, HP10 0DG, United Kingdom
Tel.: (44) 3334050120
Web Site: http://www.university-games.co.uk
Sales Range: $10-24.9 Million
Emp.: 5
Game Product Mfr
N.A.I.C.S.: 339930
Adrian Whyles (Gen Mgr)

UNIVERSITY HEALTH CARE, INC.
301 SW Field, Madison, WI 53717
Tel.: (608) 263-7923   WI
Year Founded: 1984
Sales Range: $1-9.9 Million
Emp.: 36
Office Administrative Services
N.A.I.C.S.: 561110
Mike Dallman (Pres)

UNIVERSITY HEALTH SYSTEM
4502 Medical Dr, San Antonio, TX 78229
Tel.: (210) 358-4000
Web Site: http://www.universityhealthsystem.com
Sales Range: $800-899.9 Million
Emp.: 5,000
Hospital Owner & Operator
N.A.I.C.S.: 622110
Bryan Alsip (Chief Medical Officer & Exec VP)
Theresa De La Haya (Sr VP-Community Health & Clinical Prevention Programs)
Sergio Farrell (Sr VP-Ambulatory Svcs)
Roe Garrett (VP & Controller)
Sherry Johnson (VP-Integrity & Regulatory Svcs)
Leni Kirkman (VP-Strategic Comm & Patient Rels)
Bill Phillips (CIO & Sr VP)
Nancy Ray (Chief Nursing Officer & Sr VP)
Richard Rodriguez (VP-Assets & Property Mgmt)
Theresa Scepanski (Chief Admin Officer & Sr VP-Org Dev)
Allen Strickland (VP-Hospital Admin)
Roberto Villarreal (Sr VP-Res & Info Mgmt)
Edward Banos (COO & Exec VP)
Reed Hurley (CFO & Exec VP)
Daniel J. Snyder (CEO)
George B. Hernandez Jr. (Pres & CEO)

UNIVERSITY MEDICAL GROUP
1706 NW 24th Ave, Portland, OR 97296
Tel.: (503) 494-8423   OR
Year Founded: 1998
Sales Range: $10-24.9 Million
Emp.: 212
Health Care Educational Services
N.A.I.C.S.: 611710
Jessica Johnson (Mgr-Ops)
Jennifer Norrish (Mgr-Ops)
Tammy Bickle (Mgr-Ops)
Matthew L. Navigato (COO)
Thomas M. Heckler (CEO)

UNIVERSITY MOVING & STORAGE CO.
23305 Commerce Dr, Farmington Hills, MI 48335
Tel.: (248) 615-7000
Web Site: http://www.universitymoving.com
Year Founded: 1984
Rev: $20,117,568
Emp.: 200
Trucking Except Local
N.A.I.C.S.: 484121
Elise Benedict (Owner & CEO)
Bill Gray (Pres)
Tony Russo (VP-Bus Dev-HVP)

UNIVERSITY OF ARIZONA
1200 E University Blvd, Tucson, AZ 85721
Tel.: (520) 621-3237
Web Site: http://www.arizona.edu
Year Founded: 1885
Colleges & Universities
N.A.I.C.S.: 611310
Marvin J. Slepian (Professor-Medicine)
Andrew C. Comrie (Provost & Sr VP-Academic Affairs)
Jennifer Barton (Assoc VP-Res)
Gail Burd (Sr Vice Provost-Academic Affairs)
James S. Florian (Assoc VP-Institutional Analysis)
Andrew DuMont (Mgr-Exec Comm)
Barbara Bryson (VP-Strategic Plng & Analysis)
Mark Napier (Assoc Dir-Ops, Parking & Transportation)
Kendal Washington White (Asst VP-Student Affairs)
Karen Francis Begay (Asst VP-Tribal Rels)
James A. Hyatt (CFO & Interim Sr VP-Bus Affairs)
Michele Norin (CIO)
Melanie Tornquist (Coord-Specialty Trng-Medicine Education Office Dept)
Laura Todd Johnson (Gen Counsel & VP-Legal Affairs)
Melinda Burke (Pres-UA Alumni Association & VP-Alumni Rels)
Jon Dudas (Sec)
Joe G. N. Garcia (Sr VP-Health Sciences)
Teri Lucie Thompson (Sr VP-University Rels)
Shane Burgess (VP)
Greg Byrne (VP & Dir-Athletics)
Mike Proctor (VP-Global Initiatives)
Allison Vaillancourt (VP-HR & Institutional Effectiveness)
Joaquin Ruiz (VP-Innovation & Strategy)
Kimberly Andrews Espy (Sr VP-Res)
Raji Rhys (Chief Diversity Officer & Asst VP)
Mary Fleming (Coord-Academic Plng)
Anne Marx (Dir-Admin)
Nancy Stiller (Dir-Ombuds Program)
Laura Hunter (Mgr-Program & Res)
Shelley McGrath (Sr Dir-Academic Program & Transfer Coordination)
David Heeke (VP-Athletics)
R. Brooks Jeffery (Assoc VP-Res)
Jacob Rose (Mgr-Bus Dev)
Robert Robbins (Pres)
James H. Moore Jr. (Pres-UA Foundation)

Subsidiaries:

Ashford University LLC (1)
1310 19th Ave NW, Clinton, IA 52732
Tel.: (563) 242-4023
Web Site: http://www.ashford.edu
Sales Range: $75-99.9 Million
Degree-Granting University
N.A.I.C.S.: 611310
Craig Swenson (Pres & CEO)
Gregory L. Geoffroy (Chm)
Mary Jo Maydew (Vice Chm)
Jim Smith (Sr VP-Fin)
Katie Scheie (VP)

UNIVERSITY OF CALIFORNIA

SAN FRANCISCO MEDICAL CENTER
3330 Geary Blvd, San Francisco, CA 94118
Tel.: (415) 353-3155
Web Site: https://www.ucsfhealth.org
Sales Range: $1-9.9 Million
Emp.: 60
Women Healthcare Services
N.A.I.C.S.: 621610

Subsidiaries:

By the Bay Health (1)
17 E Sir Francis Drake Blvd, Larkspur, CA 94939
Tel.: (415) 927-2273
Web Site: http://www.hospicebythebay.org
Rev: $35,064,698
Assets: $30,181,851
Liabilities: $2,370,906
Net Worth: $27,810,945
Earnings: $6,468,460
Emp.: 311
Fiscal Year-end: 06/30/2012
Community Health Care Services
N.A.I.C.S.: 621498
Dennis A. Gilardi (Chm)
Kenneth Meislin (Vice Chm)
Michael R. Dailey (Treas)
Patricia Kendall (Sec)
Kitty Whitaker (CEO)
Denis Viscek (CFO)
David G. Zwicky (Dir-Bus Strategy)
Janet P. Evans (Dir-Dev)
Elizabeth Adamson (Dir-HR)
Ann Peronetto (Dir-Provider & Community Rels)
Wilmer E. Rivera (Dir-Quality Mgmt)
Molly Bourne (Dir-Medical)
Alan H. Margolin (Dir-Medical)
Sandee Wishon (Dir-Clinical Outreach)
James Mittelberger (Chief Medical Officer)

Subsidiary (Domestic):

Hope Hospice Inc. (2)
6500 Dublin Blvd Ste 100, Dublin, CA 94568
Tel.: (925) 829-8770
Web Site: http://www.hopehospice.com
Rev: $4,000,000
Emp.: 43
Women Healthcare Services
N.A.I.C.S.: 621610
Bob Boehm (CEO)
Craig Eicher (Pres)
James Wark (Sec)
Patrick Brown (Treas)
Patty Hefner (Mgr-Comm)

UNIVERSITY OF CHICAGO
5801 S Ellis Ave, Chicago, IL 60637
Tel.: (773) 702-1234
Web Site: http://www.uchicago.edu
Year Founded: 1890
Emp.: 20,000
Colleges & Universities
N.A.I.C.S.: 611310
James S. Crown (Chm)
Robert J. Zimmer (Pres)
David B. Fithian (Exec VP)
Joseph Neubauer (Chm)
Katherine Baicker (Provost & Professor-Harris School of Public)
Derek R. B. Douglas (VP-Civic Engagement)
Selwyn O. Rogers (Dir-Medicine Trauma Center)
Ivan Samstein (CFO & Sr VP)
Hays N. Golden (Mng Dir-Crime Lab and Education Lab)
Jeffrey A. Bluestone (Dir-Ben May Institute)
Javier A. Reyes (Interim Chancellor & Vice Chancellor-Academic Affairs)

Subsidiaries:

University of Chicago Medicine (1)
5841 S Maryland Avenue, Chicago, IL 60637
Tel.: (773) 702-1000
Web Site: http://www.uchospitals.edu
Sales Range: $1-4.9 Billion
General & Research Hospital
N.A.I.C.S.: 622110
Kenneth S. Polonsky (Exec VP-Medical Affairs)
Lorna Wong (Dir-Media Rels)
Ellen Feinstein (VP-Cancer Svcs)

Subsidiary (Domestic):

Ingalls Health System Inc. (2)
1 Ingalls Dr, Harvey, IL 60426
Tel.: (708) 333-2300
Web Site: http://www.ingalls.org
Medical Center
N.A.I.C.S.: 622110

Subsidiary (Domestic):

Ingalls Development Foundation Inc. (3)
1 Ingalls Dr, Harvey, IL 60426
Tel.: (708) 915-6369
Web Site: http://www.ingalls.org
Fund Raising & Social Services
N.A.I.C.S.: 813319
Kurt Johnson (Pres & CEO)

UChicago Medicine Ingalls Memorial (3)
1 Ingalls Dr, Harvey, IL 60426-3558
Tel.: (708) 333-2300
Web Site: http://www.ingalls.org
Offices & Clinics of Medical Doctors
N.A.I.C.S.: 622110
Scott Strausser (Sr VP-Bus Dev-Ingalls Health System)
Becky Jakymec (Mgr-Raiology)

University of Chicago Press (1)
1427 E 60th St, Chicago, IL 60637-2902
Tel.: (773) 702-7700
Web Site: http://www.press.uchicago.edu
Sales Range: $25-49.9 Million
Emp.: 200
Publisher of Academic Works
N.A.I.C.S.: 513199
John Kessler (Dir-Sls)
Levi Stahl (Dir-Mktg)
Karen Hyzy (Mgr-Customer Svc)
Priya Nelson (Editor)
Rachel Kelly Unger (Assoc Editor-Life Science, Cartography & Geography)
Scott Gast (Editor)

UNIVERSITY OF COLORADO HEALTH
2315 E Harmony Rd Ste 200, Fort Collins, CO 80528
Tel.: (970) 495-7000   CO
Web Site: http://www.pvhs.org
Year Founded: 1994
Sales Range: $500-549.9 Million
Emp.: 6,072
Health Care Srvices
N.A.I.C.S.: 622110
Shawn Evans (VP-Performance Excellence)
Stephanie A. Doughty (CFO)
Donna D. Poduska (Chief Nursing Officer)
Manny Rodriguez (CMO)
Jean Haynes (Chief Population Health Officer)
Kevin L. Unger (Pres & CEO)

Subsidiaries:

Integrity Urgent Care - East (1)
4323 Integrity Ctr Point, Colorado Springs, CO 80917
Tel.: (719) 591-2558
Web Site: http://www.uchealth.org
Emp.: 10
Health Practitioners
N.A.I.C.S.: 621399

Parkview Medical Center, Inc. (1)
400 W 16th St, Pueblo, CO 81003
Tel.: (719) 584-4000
Web Site: http://www.parkviewmc.com
General Medical & Surgical Hospitals
N.A.I.C.S.: 622110
Jon Riggs (CFO & VP-Fin)
Darrin Smith (Pres & CEO)

COMPANIES

UNIVERSITY OF CONNECTICUT COOPERATIVE CORPORATION
2075 Hillside Rd Unit 1019, Storrs, CT 06269
Tel.: (860) 486-3537
Web Site: http://www.uconncoop.com
Year Founded: 1975
Sales Range: $25-49.9 Million
Emp.: 150
College Book Store
N.A.I.C.S.: 459210
William Simpson (Pres)
Ashley N. Robinson (Dir-Residence Hall)
Douglas Goodstein (Dir-Residence Hall)
Brian Schwarz (Dir-Adv)
Jeffrey O. G. Ogbar (Chief Diversity Officer)
Thomas Agresta (Co-Dir-Health Info Biomedical Div)
Terry Monahan (Dir-Environmental, Health & Safety)
Joliana Yee (Dir-Residence Hall)
Mary Anne Rooke (Exec Dir-Tech Incubation Program)
Lori Hansen-Roy (Mgr-Cost Analysis)
Tyrell Ranger (Mgr-Facilities)
Ryan Bangham (Mgr-HR)
Steven Fletcher (Mgr-Tech Projects)
Rebecca Isenstein (Program Dir-Middle Eastern Studies-Judaic Center)
Tysen Kendig (VP-Comm)
Fotios Papadimitrakopoulos (Assoc Dir-IMS)
Marcia Firsick (Coord-Publicity & Mktg)
David Benedict (Dir-Athletics)

UNIVERSITY OF DREAMS, INC.
2221 Broadway St, Redwood City, CA 94063-1641
Tel.: (408) 358-9310
Web Site: http://www.summerinternships.com
Year Founded: 2000
Sales Range: $10-24.9 Million
Emp.: 55
College & University Internship Programs
N.A.I.C.S.: 611310
Eric Lochtefeld (Co-Founder & CEO)
Beth Lochtefeld (Co-Founder)
Danielle Normington (Co-Founder & COO)
Eric Normington (CMO)

UNIVERSITY OF KANSAS MEM CORP.
1301 Jayhawk Blvd, Lawrence, KS 66045
Tel.: (785) 864-4651
Web Site: http://www.kubookstore.com
Sales Range: $25-49.9 Million
Emp.: 287
College Book Store
N.A.I.C.S.: 459210
Janet Koehler (Asst Dir)
Liz Simpson (Mgr-Gen Mdse)
Teresa Ray (Mgr-Ops)
James Rourke (Mgr-Textbook & Asst Dir)

UNIVERSITY OF LOUISVILLE
2301 S 3rd St, Louisville, KY 40208
Tel.: (502) 852-5555
Web Site: http://www.llouisville.edu
Year Founded: 1789
Academic Institution
N.A.I.C.S.: 611310
Kim E. Schatzel (Pres)
Robert Caudill (Dir-Telemedicine & IT Programs)
Lori Stewart Gonzalez (Exec VP & Provost)
Mary Nixon (Chm)
Josh Heird (Dir-Athletic)

Subsidiaries:

KentuckyOne Health, Inc. (1)
200 Abraham Flexner Way, Louisville, KY 40202
Tel.: (502) 587-4011
Web Site: http://www.kentuckyonehealth.org
Health Care Srvices
N.A.I.C.S.: 622110
Sharon Hager (Co-Sec)
David Joos (VP-Access Mgmt & Transitions-Care)
Karen Veselsky (VP- Revenue Cycle)
Andrew Cline (Dir-Safety Svcs)
Richard A. Schultz (Chm)
Jane J. Chiles (Co-Chm)
Rick Mulia (Mng Dir-Sydney)
Avery Ching (Mng Dir)
Prafull Raheja (Mng Dir)
Neil Patil (Mng Dir)
Lisa Corum (Mng Dir)
Jianxia Wang (Mng Dir)
Bassel Alkhalil (Mng Dir)
Deepa Nidhiry (Mng Dir)
Vrinda Sardana (Mng Dir)
Elvin Rayford Jr. (Dir-Facilities Mgmt-PAS-FM)

UNIVERSITY OF MICHIGAN
500 S State St, Ann Arbor, MI 48109
Tel.: (734) 764-1817
Web Site: http://www.umich.edu
Year Founded: 1817
Colleges & Universities
N.A.I.C.S.: 611310
Stephen R. Forrest (VP-Res)
Sally J. Churchill (Sec & VP)
E. Royster Harper (VP-Student Life)
David R. Lampe (VP-Comm)
Jerry A. May (VP-Dev)
Suellyn Scarnecchia (Gen Counsel & VP)
James Hackett (Interim Dir-Athletic)
Kara Morgenstern (Interim Assoc VP & Deputy Gen Counsel)
Patricia Petrowski (Assoc VP & Deputy Gen Counsel)
Cynthia Kemner (Coord-Front Desk)
Kedra Ishop (Assoc VR- Enrollment Mgmt)
Laura McCaine Patterson (CIO & Assoc VP-IT Svcs)
Terrence J. McDonald (Dir-Bentley Historical Library)
Alan R. Saltiel (Dir-Life Sciences Institute)
Douglas L. Strong (CFO & Interim Exec VP)
Timothy G. Lynch (Gen Counsel & VP)
Cynthia H. Wilbanks (VP-Govt Rels)
Kallie Bila Michels (Chief Comm Officer & VP-Comm)
Robert Sellers (Chief Diversity Officer)
Kelli Trosvig (Co-CIO & VP-IT)
Aaron Powell (Interim Co-CIO & Interim VP)
Paul N. Courant (Exec VP-Academic Affairs & Interim Provost)
Angela Kujava (Mng Dir-Desai Accelerator)
Santa Ono (Pres)
Marschall S. Runge (CEO-Michigan Medicine, Exec VP-Medical Affairs & Medical School & Dean-Medical School)

Subsidiaries:

Sparrow Health System (1)
1215 E Michigan Ave, Lansing, MI 48912
Tel.: (517) 364-1000
Web Site: http://www.sparrow.org
Health Care Professional & Services Organization
N.A.I.C.S.: 813920
Joseph Ruth (COO & Exec VP)
Paula M. Reichle (CFO, Treas & Sr VP)
Thomas Bres (CIO, Chief Admin Officer & Sr VP)
James F. Dover (Pres & CEO)
John Pirich (Chm)
Michael Reinerth (Chief HR Officer & Sr VP)

Subsidiary (Domestic):

Edward W. Sparrow Hospital Association (2)
1215 E Michigan Ave, Lansing, MI 48912
Tel.: (517) 364-1000
Web Site: http://www.sparrow.org
Hospital Operator
N.A.I.C.S.: 622110
Alan R. Vierling (Pres)
Karen Kent VanGorder (Chief Medical & Quality Officer & Sr VP)
Amy Brown (Chief Nursing Officer & VP)
Denny Martin (Chief Medical Officer)
Tom Ostrander (VP-Ops)

Division (Domestic):

Sparrow Hospital - St. Lawrence Campus (3)
1210 W Saginaw St, Lansing, MI 48915
Tel.: (517) 364-1000
Web Site: http://www.sparrow.org
Outpatient Health Care Services
N.A.I.C.S.: 621498

Subsidiary (Domestic):

Sparrow Carson Hospital (2)
406 E Main St, Carson City, MI 48811
Tel.: (989) 584-3131
Web Site: http://www.sparrow.org
Medical & Surgical Services
N.A.I.C.S.: 622110
Bill Roeser (Pres)

Sparrow Clinton Hospital (2)
805 S Oakland St, Saint Johns, MI 48879
Tel.: (989) 227-3400
Web Site: http://www.sparrow.org
General Medical & Surgical Services
N.A.I.C.S.: 622110
Edward Bruun (Pres)

Sparrow Community Care (2)
3315 E Michigan Ave Ste 4, Lansing, MI 48912
Tel.: (517) 364-8600
Web Site: http://www.sparrow.org
Women Healthcare Services
N.A.I.C.S.: 621610
Kira Carter-Robertson (Pres)
Darwin Brewster (Exec Dir)

Sparrow Eaton Hospital (2)
321 E Harris St, Charlotte, MI 48813
Tel.: (517) 543-1050
Web Site: http://www.sparrow.org
Sales Range: $25-49.9 Million
Health Care Srvices
N.A.I.C.S.: 622110
Patrick Salow (Exec VP-Physician Svcs)
Patrick Sustrich (Exec Dir)

Sparrow Ionia Hospital (2)
3565 S State Rd, Ionia, MI 48846
Tel.: (616) 523-1400
Web Site: http://www.sparrow.org
General Medical & Surgical Services
N.A.I.C.S.: 622110
Bill Roeser (Pres)

Sparrow Specialty Hospital (2)
1215 E Michigan Ave, Lansing, MI 48912
Tel.: (989) 227-3400
Web Site: http://www.sparrow.org
Intensive Health Care Services
N.A.I.C.S.: 621610
Louis B. Little (Pres)

UNIVERSITY OF NEBRASKA FOUNDATION
1010 Lincoln Mall Ste 300, Lincoln, NE 68508
Tel.: (402) 458-1100

UNIVERSITY OF PITTSBURGH MEDICAL CENTER

Web Site: http://www.nufoundation.org
Sales Range: $50-74.9 Million
Emp.: 75
Fundraising Organization
N.A.I.C.S.: 561990
Keith D. Miles (Gen Counsel & Sr VP)
Joe Selig (Sr VP-UNL Dev)
Brian Hastings (Pres & CEO)
Dorothy Endacott (VP-Mktg Comm)
Mark Chronister (Chm)
Troy Wilhelm (CFO)

UNIVERSITY OF NEW HAMPSHIRE FOUNDATION
9 Edgewood Rd, Durham, NH 03824
Tel.: (603) 862-1000
Web Site: http://www.unh.edu
Year Founded: 1939
Rev.: $35,275,000
Assets: $242,874,000
Liabilities: $5,313,000
Net Worth: $237,561,000
Earnings: $18,503,000
Emp.: 120
Fiscal Year-end: 06/30/18
Fundraising Organization
N.A.I.C.S.: 561990
Deborah Dutton (Pres)
Brian S. McCabe (Chm)
Christine Carberry (Vice Chm)
Thomas C. Arrix (Sec)
Erik E. Gross (Treas & Assoc VP-Advancement)

UNIVERSITY OF OREGON BOOKSTORE
3895 E 19th Ave, Eugene, OR 97403
Tel.: (541) 346-4331
Web Site: http://www.uoduckstore.com
Sales Range: $10-24.9 Million
Emp.: 225
School Supplies Sportwear Computer Electronic
N.A.I.C.S.: 459410
Natalie Eggert (Mgr-HR)
Arlyn Schaufler (Gen Mgr)

UNIVERSITY OF PITTSBURGH MEDICAL CENTER
200 Lothrop St, Pittsburgh, PA 15213-2582
Tel.: (412) 647-8762
Web Site: http://www.upmc.com
Year Founded: 1893
General Admission Hospital Operator
N.A.I.C.S.: 622110
Leslie C. Davis (Pres & CEO)
G. Nicholas Beckwith III (Chm)

Subsidiaries:

H.C. Pharmacy Central, Inc. (1)
3175 E Carson St, Pittsburgh, PA 15203
Tel.: (412) 647-2240
Prescription & Proprietary Drugs Whslr & Distr
N.A.I.C.S.: 424210
Debbie L. Albin (Sr Dir-Ops)

UPMC Health Plan, Inc. (1)
US Steel Tower 600 Grant St, Pittsburgh, PA 15219
Tel.: (844) 220-4785
Web Site: http://www.upmchealthplan.com
Health Care Insurance Services
N.A.I.C.S.: 524114
Diane Holder (CEO)
Mary Beth Jenkins (COO & Chief Admin Officer)

UPMC Jameson (1)
1211 Wilmington Ave, New Castle, PA 16105
Tel.: (724) 658-9001
Web Site: http://www.upmcjameson.com
Hospital

University of Pittsburgh Medical Center—(Continued)
N.A.I.C.S.: 622110
Debra Perretta *(Dir-Quality Mgmt Svcs)*
Neil Chessin *(VP-Ops)*
Jane Beight *(Dir-Diagnostic Svcs)*
Lisa Lombardo *(Dir-PR & Mktg)*
James Aubel *(CFO)*
Ben Huffman *(Treas)*
Douglas D. Danko *(Pres & CEO)*
Frank Moses *(Vice Chm)*
Kenneth Romig *(Sec)*
Steve Warner *(Chm)*

UPMC Pinnacle (1)
409 S 2nd St, Harrisburg, PA 17104
Tel.: (717) 231-8900
Web Site: http://www.pinnaclehealth.org
Emp.: 11,000
Health Care Services Organization
N.A.I.C.S.: 813920
Philip W. Guarneschelli *(Pres & CEO)*
Christopher P. Markley *(Sec)*
John C. Hickey *(Chm)*
Doug Neidich *(Vice Chm)*
William Pugh *(Treas)*
John DeLorenzo *(Asst Sec)*

Subsidiary (Domestic):

UPMC Pinnacle Carlisle (2)
361 Alexander Spring Rd, Carlisle, PA 17015
Tel.: (717) 249-1212
Web Site: http://www.pinnaclehealth.org
Hospital Services
N.A.I.C.S.: 622110
David Steitz *(CEO)*
Jerry Clawson *(Dir-Matl Mgmt)*

UPMC Pinnacle Lancaster (2)
250 College Ave, Lancaster, PA 17603
Tel.: (717) 291-8211
Web Site: http://www.pinnaclehealth.org
Hospital Services
N.A.I.C.S.: 622110

UPMC Pinnacle Lititz (2)
1500 Highlands Dr, Lititz, PA 17543
Tel.: (717) 625-5000
Web Site: http://www.pinnaclehealth.org
Hospital Services
N.A.I.C.S.: 622110

UPMC Pinnacle Memorial (2)
325 S Belmont St, York, PA 17403
Tel.: (717) 843-8623
Web Site: http://www.pinnaclehealth.org
Hospital Operator
N.A.I.C.S.: 622110
Mike Gaskins *(Pres & Sec)*
William Pugh *(Treas)*
Christopher Markley *(Asst Sec)*

UPMC Somerset (1)
225 S Center Ave, Somerset, PA 15501
Tel.: (814) 443-5000
Web Site: http://www.somersethospital.com
Health Care Srvices
N.A.I.C.S.: 622110
Andrew Rush *(Pres-UPMC Somerset)*
David Bertoty *(Chief Nursing Officer)*
Krista Mathias *(Chm)*
Mark Bower *(Vice Chm)*
Tom Skelton *(Sec)*

UPMC Western Maryland Corporation (1)
12500 Willowbrook Rd, Cumberland, MD 21502
Tel.: (240) 362-0288
Web Site: http://www.wmhs.com
Health Programs & Services
N.A.I.C.S.: 621999
Pam Ackerman *(Mgr)*
Barry Ronan *(Pres)*
Nancy Adams *(COO & Sr VP)*

UNIVERSITY OF VIRGINIA PHYSICIANS GROUP
4105 Lewis & Clark Dr, Charlottesville, VA 22911
Tel.: (434) 295-1000
Web Site: http://www.upg.virginia.edu
Year Founded: 1979
Sales Range: $300-349.9 Million
Emp.: 600

Medical Billing & Bookkeeping Services
N.A.I.C.S.: 541219
Bradley Haws *(CEO)*
Beth Allen *(Treas & Dir-Fin)*
Beth C. Spilman *(Sec)*
Paul A. Levine *(Pres)*
William G. Shenkir *(Treas)*

UNIVERSITY OF WISCONSIN MEDICAL FOUNDATION
7974 UW Health Ct, Middleton, WI 53562
Tel.: (608) 833-6090
Web Site: http://www.uwdoctors.org
Year Founded: 1998
Sales Range: $75-99.9 Million
Emp.: 1,700
Billing & Bookkeeping Service
N.A.I.C.S.: 813920
Susan M. Ertl *(VP-Clinical Joint Ventures)*
Ralph Turner *(VP-Facilities & Support Svcs)*

UNIVERSITY PRODUCTS INC.
517 Main St, Holyoke, MA 01040
Tel.: (413) 532-3372
Web Site: http://www.universityproducts.com
Sales Range: $10-24.9 Million
Emp.: 80
Mfr of Library Cards & Paper Products
N.A.I.C.S.: 322299

UNIVERSITY VENTURES FUNDS MANAGEMENT LLC
303 Spring St, New York, NY 10013
Tel.: (212) 202-3100
Web Site: http://www.universityventures.com
Educational Investment Advice Services
N.A.I.C.S.: 523999
Ryan Craig *(Co-Founder & Mng Dir)*
Gregg Rosenthal *(Mng Dir)*
Troy Williams *(Mng Dir)*
Aanand Radia *(Mng Dir)*
Daniel S. Pianko *(Co-Founder & Mng Dir)*

Subsidiaries:

Avenica (1)
400 S Colorado Blvd 600, Denver, CO 80246
Tel.: (303) 257-6776
Web Site: http://www.gradstaff.com
Sales Range: $1-9.9 Million
Emp.: 9
Recruitment Services
N.A.I.C.S.: 541611
Jaclyn Schlaikjer *(VP)*

UNIVERSITY VOLKSWAGEN INC.
5150 Ellison NE, Albuquerque, NM 87109
Tel.: (505) 761-1900
Web Site: http://www.mastermarket.com
Sales Range: $25-49.9 Million
Emp.: 70
Automobiles, New & Used
N.A.I.C.S.: 441110
Selina Aragon *(Controller)*
Randy Price *(Pres)*

UNIVESCO INC.
2800 Dallas Pkwy Ste 100, Plano, TX 75093-4707
Tel.: (972) 836-8000 DE
Web Site: http://www.univesco.com
Year Founded: 1977
Sales Range: $10-24.9 Million
Emp.: 350

Provider of Real Estate Investment Services
N.A.I.C.S.: 531110
Robert Werra *(CEO)*
John Werra *(Pres)*
Paul Ivanoff *(VP)*
David R. Bower *(Gen Counsel)*

UNIVEX CORPORATION
3 Old Rockingham Rd, Salem, NH 03079-2133
Tel.: (603) 893-6191 DE
Web Site: http://www.univexcorp.com
Year Founded: 1948
Sales Range: $50-74.9 Million
Emp.: 75
Food Preparing Machines Mfr
N.A.I.C.S.: 333241
John Tsiakos *(Pres)*
Ines Smith *(Mgr-Sls & Admin)*

UNIVISTA INSURANCE CORPORATION
528 NW 7th Ave, Miami, FL 33136
Tel.: (305) 521-9152
Web Site: http://www.univistainsurance.com
Year Founded: 2009
Sales Range: $75-99.9 Million
Emp.: 1,114
Property Insurance Services
N.A.I.C.S.: 524126
Jose Gijon *(Mgr)*

UNIWEB INC.
222 Promenade Ave, Corona, CA 92879
Tel.: (951) 279-7999
Web Site: http://www.uniwebinc.com
Sales Range: $10-24.9 Million
Emp.: 120
Fixtures, Display, Office, Or Store: Except Wood
N.A.I.C.S.: 337126
Karl F. Weber *(Founder & CEO)*
Cynthia Weber Davidson *(Pres)*
John McDonnell *(VP-Admin)*
Tom Ohta *(Controller)*

UNIWELD PRODUCTS INC.
2850 Ravenswood Rd, Fort Lauderdale, FL 33312-4920
Tel.: (954) 584-2000 DE
Web Site: http://www.uniweld.com
Year Founded: 1953
Sales Range: $10-24.9 Million
Emp.: 253
Provider of Welding Services & Refrigeration Equipments
N.A.I.C.S.: 333992
Dragan Bukur *(Mgr-Engrg)*
David Foster *(Mng Dir)*
Chris Hebert *(Mgr-IT)*

UNIWELL CORPORATION
21172 Figueroa St, Carson, CA 90745
Tel.: (310) 782-8888
Year Founded: 1992
Sales Range: $10-24.9 Million
Emp.: 6
Subdividers & Developers, Nec
N.A.I.C.S.: 237210
Sidney Chen *(Pres)*
Kim Tjoe *(VP)*

UNIWORLD GROUP, INC.
1 Metro Ctr N 11th Fl, Brooklyn, NY 11201
Tel.: (212) 219-1600 NY
Web Site: http://www.uniworldgroup.com
Year Founded: 1969
Rev.: $90,000,000
Emp.: 150
N.A.I.C.S.: 541810

Gregory Edwards *(COO)*
Matilda Ivey *(Sr VP & Dir-Client Svcs)*
Melissa Davis *(VP & Dir-Digital Strategy & Innovation)*
Monique L. Nelson *(Chm & CEO)*
Emilio Ayala *(Grp VP & Creative Dir)*
Michelle Montague *(Sec)*
George Haynes *(VP, Gen Mgr & Dir-Grp Acct)*
Dan Tochterman *(VP-Digital Amplification Grp)*
Nakesha Holley *(VP-Integrated Comm)*

Subsidiaries:

Uniworld Group-Detroit (1)
1 Parklane Blvd Ste 1200 E, Dearborn, MI 48126
Tel.: (313) 203-1289
Emp.: 30
N.A.I.C.S.: 541810
Ed Boyd *(Sr VP & Dir-Client Ops)*

UNLEADED COMMUNICATIONS, INC.
1701 Commerce St, Houston, TX 77002
Tel.: (713) 874-8200
Web Site: http://www.ulcomm.com
Sales Range: $1-9.9 Million
Emp.: 44
Advertising Agencies
N.A.I.C.S.: 541810
Emmett Martin *(Pres)*
Paul Roland *(Dir-Online Mktg)*

UNLIMITED CONSTRUCTION SERVICES
1696 Haleukana St, Lihue, HI 96766
Tel.: (808) 245-7843
Web Site: http://www.unlimitedhawaii.com
Sales Range: $50-74.9 Million
Emp.: 35
Commercial & Office Building Contractors
N.A.I.C.S.: 236220
Jay Manzano *(Pres)*

UNLIMITED SERVICES OF WISCONSIN, INC.
170 Evergreen Rd, Oconto, WI 54153
Tel.: (920) 834-4418
Web Site: http://www.us-wire-harness.com
Sales Range: $200-249.9 Million
Emp.: 200
Wire Harness, Cable & Control Panel Assemblies Mfr
N.A.I.C.S.: 335929
William Kessenich *(Pres)*
Scott Newman *(CFO)*

Subsidiaries:

Trans World Connection (1)
173 Fastener Dr, Lynchburg, VA 24502
Tel.: (434) 525-0085
Sales Range: $10-24.9 Million
Emp.: 20
Harness Assemblies Mfr
N.A.I.C.S.: 334419

UNLIMITED SKY HOLDINGS, INC.
140 E Main St, Radford, VA 24141
Tel.: (540) 639-4121 VA
Year Founded: 2013
Real Estate Manangement Services
N.A.I.C.S.: 531390
Tokie Kinser *(Pres & CEO)*
Robert Chalnick *(CFO & Treas)*

UNO ALLA VOLTA, LLC.
242 Branford Rd, North Branford, CT 06471
Tel.: (203) 871-1000

COMPANIES

Web Site: http://www.unoallavolta.com
Year Founded: 2002
Rev.: $13,300,000
Emp.: 30
Retail Services
N.A.I.C.S.: 311811
Terri S. Alpert *(Founder & CEO)*

UNSDG ACQUISITION CORP.
1980 Festival Plaza Dr Summerlin S Ste 300, Las Vegas, NV 89135
Tel.: (702) 903-4265 DE
Year Founded: 2021
Investment Services
N.A.I.C.S.: 523999
James Boettcher *(Chm)*
Jeffrey Premer *(CEO)*
Joel Arberman *(CFO)*

UNTRACHT EARLY, LLC
325 Columbia Tpke Ste 202, Florham Park, NJ 07932
Tel.: (973) 408-6700
Web Site: http://www.untracht.com
Year Founded: 1993
Sales Range: $10-24.9 Million
Emp.: 95
Accounting & Tax Consulting Services
N.A.I.C.S.: 541219
Sandra Repetti *(Mgr)*
Dennis B. Murtha *(Sr Mgr-Assurance)*
Adam Doctor *(Sr Mgr-Assurance)*
Christopher Souza *(Sr Mgr-Tax)*
Stacy L. Palmer *(Sr Mgr-Tax)*
Alan H. Ackermann *(Principal)*
Barry S. Kleiman *(Principal)*
Elizabeth M. Gelson *(Principal)*
George J. Yager *(Principal)*
Karen Kerby *(Principal)*
Mark A. Soslow *(Principal)*
Olivia Campaniolo *(Mgr-Assurance)*
Phani Doddapaneni *(Mgr-Assurance)*
Richard A. Cagnetta *(Dir-Tax)*
Tracey B. Early *(Mng Principal)*

UNVERFERTH MANUFACTURING COMPANY INC.
18107 US 224 W, Kalida, OH 45853
Tel.: (419) 532-3121 OH
Web Site: http://www.unverferth.com
Year Founded: 1948
Sales Range: $25-49.9 Million
Emp.: 500
Sales of Farm Machinery & Equipment
N.A.I.C.S.: 333111
Jerry Ecklund *(Mgr-Adv)*
R. Steven Unverferth *(Chm)*
Brett Unverferth *(VP-Sls & Mktg)*
Larry Unverferth *(Pres)*
Richard Unverferth *(Founder)*

UNZ & COMPANY, INC.
333 Cedar Ave Bldg B Ste 2, Middlesex, NJ 08846-2400
Tel.: (732) 667-1020 DE
Web Site: http://www.unzco.com
Year Founded: 1879
Sales Range: $50-74.9 Million
Emp.: 9
Trainer of International Trade Compliance & Hazardous Materials; Publisher of Import/Export Forms, Placards & Software
N.A.I.C.S.: 611699
Daniel T. Scott *(Pres)*

UPARC, INC.
1501 N Belcher Rd, Clearwater, FL 33765
Tel.: (727) 799-3330
Web Site: http://www.uparc.com
Rev.: $13,200,000
Emp.: 270
Services for the Elderly & Persons with Disabilities
N.A.I.C.S.: 624120
Harry Jamieson *(Pres)*

UPCAP SERVICES, INC.
2501 14th Ave S, Escanaba, MI 49829
Tel.: (906) 786-4701 MI
Web Site: http://www.upcap.org
Year Founded: 1971
Sales Range: $10-24.9 Million
Emp.: 110
Community Action Services
N.A.I.C.S.: 624190
Bernard Lang *(Chm)*
Richard Aird *(Dir-Fin)*
Jonathan Mead *(Exec Dir)*
Jill Maki *(Vice Chm)*
Frank Stubenrauch *(Sec)*

UPCHURCH ELECTRIC SUPPLY CO.
2355 N Gregg Ave, Fayetteville, AR 72703
Tel.: (479) 521-2823
Web Site: http://www.upchurchelectrical.com
Sales Range: $10-24.9 Million
Emp.: 40
Electrical Apparatus & Equipment
N.A.I.C.S.: 423610
Doug Caughman *(Branch Mgr)*
Jeff Doty *(Branch Mgr-Inside Sls & Pur)*
David McConell *(Chm)*

UPCHURCH MANAGEMENT CO. INC.
1439 S Pompano Pkwy, Pompano Beach, FL 33069
Tel.: (954) 972-2004
Sales Range: $10-24.9 Million
Emp.: 10
Fast Food Restaurant Operator
N.A.I.C.S.: 722513
Roger Upchurch *(Pres)*
Cathie Clark *(Coord-Admin)*

UPDATA PARTNERS
2099 Pennsylvania Ave NW 8th Fl, Washington, DC 20006
Tel.: (202) 618-8750
Web Site: http://www.updata.com
Emp.: 35,000
Private Investment Firm
N.A.I.C.S.: 523999
Barry Goldsmith *(Gen Partner)*
Carter Griffin *(Gen Partner)*
Jon Seeber *(Gen Partner)*
John Burton *(Operating Partner)*
Ira Cohen *(Operating Partner)*
Greg Olear *(CFO)*
Braden Snyder *(VP)*
Dan Moss *(VP)*

Subsidiaries:

Ruby Receptionists (1)
805 SW Bdwy 900, Portland, OR 97205
Tel.: (866) 611-7829
Web Site: http://www.callruby.com
Virtual Office Receptionists
N.A.I.C.S.: 561110
Jill Nelson *(Founder & CEO)*
David De Rego *(CMO)*
Katharine Nester *(Chief Product & Technology Officer)*
Steve Severance *(VP-Engrg)*
Christina Burns *(VP-Svc)*
Jace Thompson *(CFO)*
Keith Nelson *(CIO)*
Diana Stepleton *(VP & Partner-Engagement)*

UPDATEPOWER CORPORATION
900 E Hamilton Ave Ste 100, Campbell, CA 95008
Tel.: (408) 717-4964
Web Site: http://www.updatepower.com
Year Founded: 1997
Corporate Sales & Marketing Solutions
N.A.I.C.S.: 561499
Gregory L. Migaki *(CEO)*
Amit Ghosh *(CTO)*
Michael Carey *(VP-Client Svcs)*
John Bosch *(VP-Ops)*
William Tietz *(CFO & VP-Fin)*

UPDATER INC.
19 Union Square W 12th Fl, New York, NY 10003
Tel.: (302) 636-5400 DE
Web Site: http://www.updater.com
Year Founded: 2011
Rev.: $2,235,405
Assets: $73,743,578
Liabilities: $3,260,289
Net Worth: $70,483,289
Earnings: ($13,676,399)
Emp.: 156
Fiscal Year-end: 12/31/17
Software Development Services
N.A.I.C.S.: 513210
David Greenberg *(Founder & CEO)*
Ryan Hubbard *(COO & CTO)*
Lindsey Dole *(Sr VP-People)*
James Pearson *(CFO)*

UPDEGRAFF VISION
1601 38th Ave N, Saint Petersburg, FL 33713
Tel.: (727) 551-2020 FL
Web Site: http://www.updegraffvision.com
Year Founded: 1996
Sales Range: $1-9.9 Million
Emp.: 25
Physicians Office
N.A.I.C.S.: 621111
Steven A. Updegraff *(Pres)*

UPFRONT HEALTHCARE SERVICES, INC.
500 W Madison St Suite 810, Chicago, IL 60661
Tel.: (312) 668-7946
Web Site: https://upfronthealthcare.com
Year Founded: 2016
Patient Engagement & Access platform
N.A.I.C.S.: 513210
Ben Albert *(Co-Founder & CEO)*
Carrie Kozlowski *(Co-Founder & COO)*

Subsidiaries:

PatientBond, LLC (1)
126 N York St Ste2, Elmhurst, IL 60126
Tel.: (630) 225-9450
Web Site: http://www.patientbond.com
Sales Range: $1-9.9 Million
Emp.: 100
Information Technology Development Services
N.A.I.C.S.: 541512
Anurag Juneja *(Pres & CEO)*
Casey Albertson *(Pres, COO & Sr VP-Acct Mgmt)*
David R. Floyd *(CTO)*
Mike Schiller *(Exec VP-Sls)*

UPFRONT VENTURES
1333 2nd St Ste 300, Los Angeles, CA 90067
Tel.: (310) 785-5100
Web Site: http://www.upfront.com
Year Founded: 1996
Rev.: $650,000,000
Emp.: 15
Venture Capital Investment Firm

UPHOLSTERY INTERNATIONAL, INC.

N.A.I.C.S.: 523999
Mark Suster *(Co-Mng Partner)*
Yves B. Sisteron *(Mng Partner)*
Dana Kibler *(CFO & VP)*
Gregory M. Bettinelli *(Partner)*
Aditi Maliwal *(Partner)*
Michael Carney *(Partner)*
Kara Nortman *(Co-Mng Partner)*

UPG ENTERPRISES LLC
1400 16th St Ste 250, Oak Brook, IL 60523
Tel.: (630) 822-7000
Web Site: http://upgllc.com
Year Founded: 2014
Investment Holding Company
N.A.I.C.S.: 551112
Paul Douglass *(Founder)*
Christopher G. Hutter *(Co-Founder)*

Subsidiaries:

Berg Steel Corp. (1)
4306 Normandy Ct, Royal Oak, MI 48073
Tel.: (248) 549-6066
Web Site: http://www.bergsteel.com
Sales Range: $1-9.9 Million
Emp.: 20
Metal Service Centers & Other Metal Merchant Whslr
N.A.I.C.S.: 423510
Kirk Havelock *(Gen Mgr)*
Anthony Trupiano *(Mgr-Traffic)*
Jeff Wonboy *(Mgr-Sls)*
Joe Smith *(Mgr-Production)*
Perry Morris *(Mgr-Plant)*
Scott Shown *(Mgr-Plant)*
Mark Berg *(CFO)*

Contractors Steel Company (1)
36555 Amrhein Rd, Livonia, MI 48150-1101
Tel.: (734) 464-4000
Web Site: http://www.contractorssteel.com
Sales Range: $1-9.9 Million
Emp.: 330
Mfr of Steel
N.A.I.C.S.: 423510
Donald R. Simon *(Pres & Treas)*
Steve Letnich *(COO)*

Lamination Specialties Corp. (1)
235 N Artesian Ave, Chicago, IL 60612-2148
Tel.: (312) 243-2181
Web Site: http://www.laminationspecialties.com
Metal Stamping
N.A.I.C.S.: 332119
Gregory Steves *(Ops Mgr)*
Vahe Ohanian *(Sr Dir-Tech Svcs)*
Irfan Khan *(Mgr-Quality)*
Marty Astorga *(Mgr-Pur)*

Maksteel (1)
7615 Torbram Rd, Mississauga, L4T 4A8, ON, Canada
Tel.: (905) 671-9000
Web Site: https://www.maksteel.com
Steel Industry
N.A.I.C.S.: 331110
Mike McKernan *(VP-Quality)*

Metalex LLC (1)
700 Liberty Dr, Libertyville, IL 60048
Tel.: (847) 362-5400
Web Site: http://www.industrial.metlx.com
Metal Fabrication Machine Shop
N.A.I.C.S.: 332999

UPHAM OIL & GAS COMPANY
999 Energy Ave, Mineral Wells, TX 76067
Tel.: (940) 325-4491
Web Site: http://www.uphamoilandgas.com
Sales Range: $10-24.9 Million
Emp.: 70
Crude Petroleum Production
N.A.I.C.S.: 213112
Paul Mcgettes *(Controller)*

UPHOLSTERY INTERNATIONAL, INC.

UPHOLSTERY INTERNATIONAL, INC. U.S. PRIVATE

Upholstery International, Inc.—(Continued)
22771 Citation Rd, Frankfort, IL 60423
Tel.: (708) 372-2726 DE
Furniture Reupholstering Services
N.A.I.C.S.: 811420
Ken Kovie (Pres, CFO & Treas)

UPLAND HILLS HEALTH, INC.
800 Compassion Way, Dodgeville, WI 53533-0800
Tel.: (608) 930-8000 WI
Web Site: http://www.uplandhillshealth.org
Year Founded: 1974
Sales Range: $25-49.9 Million
Emp.: 512
Health Care Srvices
N.A.I.C.S.: 622110
Karl Pustina (VP-Fin)
Lynn Hebgen (VP-Nursing)
Lisa Schnedler (Pres & CEO)

UPLIFT NUTRITION, INC.
575 Riverside Ave Ste 102, Westport, CT 06880
Tel.: (203) 513-9822 NV
Energy & Health Drinks
N.A.I.C.S.: 312111
Sean Martin (Pres)
David M. Baum (CFO & COO)

UPM PHARMACEUTICALS, INC.
501 5th St, Bristol, TN 37620
Tel.: (423) 989-8000
Web Site: http://www.upm-inc.com
Emp.: 265
Independent Contract Deolopment Services
N.A.I.C.S.: 325412
John M. Gregory (Chm)
James E. Gregory (CEO)
Mark M. Manno (Gen Counsel, Exec VP & Asst Sec)
Chris Curtin (COO)
John Bowles (Gen Counsel & VP)

UPMC WORKPARTNERS
600 Grant St, Pittsburgh, PA 15219
Web Site: http://www.workpartners.com
Year Founded: 1997
Health Care Insurance Provider
N.A.I.C.S.: 524114
David Weir (Pres)

Subsidiaries:

HCMS Group, LLC (1)
415 W 17th St Ste 250, Cheyenne, WY 82001
Tel.: (307) 638-0015
Web Site: http://www.hcmsgroup.com
Emp.: 65
Health Information & Consulting Services
N.A.I.C.S.: 541690
Harold Gardner (Founder)
Michel Simon (COO)

UPP TECHNOLOGY, INC.
1 Twr Ln Ste 1910, Oakbrook Terrace, IL 60181
Tel.: (630) 493-7899
Web Site: http://www.upp.com
Year Founded: 1984
Sales Range: $10-24.9 Million
Software Publisher
N.A.I.C.S.: 513210
Josh Vierling (Pres)
Jim Laverty (Gen Counsel & VP-Bus Dev)

UPPER CONNECTICUT VALLEY HOSPITAL
181 Corliss Ln, Colebrook, NH 03576
Tel.: (603) 237-4971 NH

Web Site: http://www.ucvh.org
Year Founded: 1969
Sales Range: $10-24.9 Million
Emp.: 154
Health Care Srvices
N.A.I.C.S.: 622110
E. Harlan Connary (Sec)
Greg Placy (Chm)
Jim Tibbetts (Treas)
Odette Crawford (Vice Chm)
Peter Gosline (Chief Admin Officer)

UPPER CUMBERLAND ELECTRIC MEMBERSHIP CORPORATION
138 Gordonsville Hwy, Carthage, TN 37030-1810
Tel.: (615) 735-2940 TN
Web Site: http://www.ucemc.com
Year Founded: 1938
Sales Range: $25-49.9 Million
Emp.: 135
Power Company
N.A.I.C.S.: 221122
Donnie Brooks (Dir-Ops)
Wayne E. Anderson (Dir-Engrg)
Jimmy Gregory (Gen Mgr)
Jerry K. Harper (Dir-Admin Svcs)
Cynthia Draper (Dir-Admin Svcs)
Eddie Thomas (Dir-JT & S & EP)
L. C. Grisham (Mgr-Carthage)
James Rony Myers (Mgr-Cookeville)
James West (VP)

UPPER DES MOINES OPPORTUNITY, INC.
101 Robins St, Graettinger, IA 51342
Tel.: (712) 859-3885 IA
Web Site: http://www.udmo.com
Year Founded: 1965
Sales Range: $10-24.9 Million
Emp.: 252
Community Care Services
N.A.I.C.S.: 624190
Elisa Umscheid (Dir-IT)
Carol Chicoine (Dir-Fiscal)
Connie Hurst (Dir-HR)
Jamey Whitney (Exec Dir)
Katie Cook (Dir-Ops)

UPPER EAST TENNESSEE HUMAN DEVELOPMENT AGENCY, INC.
PO Box 46, Kingsport, TN 37662
Tel.: (423) 246-6180 TN
Web Site: http://www.uethda.org
Year Founded: 1973
Sales Range: $10-24.9 Million
Emp.: 285
Community Support Services
N.A.I.C.S.: 624190
Lois Smith (Exec Dir)
Connie Shockley (Dir-Fin)

UPPER EDGE TECHNOLOGIES, INC.
201 Van Buren Ave, West Memphis, AR 72301
Web Site: http://www.upperedgetech.com
Year Founded: 2011
Sales Range: $1-9.9 Million
Emp.: 44
Electronic Parts Distr
N.A.I.C.S.: 423400
Chris Wilson (Owner)

UPPER LAKES COAL COMPANY INC.
1400 Bylsby Ave, Green Bay, WI 54303-3708
Tel.: (920) 432-2411 WI
Year Founded: 1983
Sales Range: $25-49.9 Million
Emp.: 11

Wholesale of Coal, other Minerals & Ores
N.A.I.C.S.: 423520
Paul Coppo (Pres & Treas)

UPPER LAKES FOODS INC.
801 Industry Ave, Cloquet, MN 55720-1635
Tel.: (218) 879-1265 MN
Web Site: http://www.upperlakesfoodsinc.com
Year Founded: 1967
Sales Range: $25-49.9 Million
Emp.: 350
Warehouse
N.A.I.C.S.: 424420
Dave Strang (Mgr-Supply & Equipment)

UPPER MIDWEST ORGAN PROCUREMENT ORGANIZATION, INC.
2225 West River Rd North, Minneapolis, MN 55411
Tel.: (651) 603-7800 MN
Web Site: http://www.life-source.org
Year Founded: 1987
Sales Range: $25-49.9 Million
Emp.: 149
Organ & Tissue Donation Services
N.A.I.C.S.: 621991
Peter Farstad (Chief Admin Officer)
Julie Zabloski (Dir-Donor Svcs Center & Tissue Svcs)
Susan Mau Larson (Dir-Pub Affairs)
Meg Rogers (Dir-Organ Procurement)
Kathy Geist (Dir-Hospital Svcs)
Susan Gunderson (CEO)

UPPER RANCH COMPANY LLC
135 W Main St Ste J, Aspen, CO 81611
Tel.: (970) 920-0036
Web Site: http://www.upperranchco.com
Year Founded: 2004
Sales Range: $1-9.9 Million
Emp.: 3
Business, Technology & Engineering Consulting
N.A.I.C.S.: 541611
Vlad Enache (CEO)

UPPER TRINITY REGIONAL WATER DISTRICT
PO Box 305, Lewisville, TX 75067-0305
Tel.: (972) 219-1228
Web Site: http://www.utrwd.com
Sales Range: $10-24.9 Million
Emp.: 70
Water Supply
N.A.I.C.S.: 221310
Thomas E. Taylor (Exec Dir)
Jan Morris (Mgr-Budget & Fin Plng Analysis)
Danny Hessell (Coord-Preventative Maintenance)
Bill Greenleaf (Dir-Fin & Bus Svc)

UPRINTING.COM
8000 Haskell Ave, Van Nuys, CA 91406
Tel.: (310) 575-4440
Web Site: http://www.uprinting.com
Year Founded: 1997
Sales Range: $25-49.9 Million
Emp.: 338
Business & Graphic Printing
N.A.I.C.S.: 323111
Ronnie Mesri (CEO)

UPSHUR RURAL ELECTRIC COOPERATIVE CORPORATION
1200 W Tyler St, Gilmer, TX 75644
Tel.: (903) 843-2536 TX
Web Site: http://www.urecc.coop
Year Founded: 1937
Sales Range: $75-99.9 Million
Emp.: 121
Electric Power Distr
N.A.I.C.S.: 221122
Frankie B. King (Pres)
Robert A. Walker Jr. (Gen Mgr)

UPSIGHT, INC.
501 Folsom St 1st Fl, San Francisco, CA 94105
Tel.: (415) 766-6500
Web Site: http://www.upsight.com
Year Founded: 2007
Mobile Marketing & Analytics
N.A.I.C.S.: 541519
Christopher Harris (Sr Mgr-Monetisation)
Javier Schoijet (Engr-Software)
Michael Morse (Architect-Principal Database & Performance)

UPSON ELECTRIC MEMBERSHIP CORPORATION
607 E Main St, Thomaston, GA 30286
Tel.: (706) 647-5475 GA
Web Site: http://www.upsonemc.com
Year Founded: 1937
Sales Range: $1-9.9 Million
Emp.: 27
Electric Power Distribution Services
N.A.I.C.S.: 221122
Neal Trice (Pres & CEO)

UPSON REGIONAL MEDICAL CENTER
801 W Gordon St, Thomaston, GA 30286
Tel.: (706) 647-8111 GA
Web Site: http://www.urmc.org
Year Founded: 1951
Sales Range: $75-99.9 Million
Emp.: 731
Medical Care Services
N.A.I.C.S.: 622110
Jason Gassett (Controller)
John H. Williams (CFO)
James J. Edwards Jr. (VP)
William H. Hightower IV (Pres)

UPSTACK, INC.
745 5th Ave, New York, NY 10151
Tel.: (917) 341-1344
Web Site: https://upstack.com
Year Founded: 2017
IT Services & IT Consulting Services; Cloud & Internet Services
N.A.I.C.S.:
Shawn Schmidt (Partner & Mng Dir)
John Bova (Partner & Mng Dir)
Christopher Trapp (CEO)
Ed Degenhart (Partner & Mng Dir)
Brent Killen (Partner)
Jonathan Watkins (Partner)

Subsidiaries:

Digital Planet Communications, Inc. (1)
1270 Northland Dr Ste 310, Saint Paul, MN 55120
Tel.: (651) 207-1300
Web Site: http://www.digitalplanetcommunications.com
Sales Range: $1-9.9 Million
Emp.: 10
Telecommunications Resellers
N.A.I.C.S.: 517121

LinkSource Technologies, LLC (1)
9281 Sierra College Blvd, Roseville, CA 95661
Tel.: (916) 757-1100

Web Site: http://www.linksource.com
Information Technology Consulting Services
N.A.I.C.S.: 541512
Tina Linn (Controller)
Curt Lewis (Founder & CEO)
Jason Newbold (Pres)
Chad Romine (VP-Bus Dev)
Mike Prachar (COO)
Frank Mastro (Dir-Sls)
Michelle Ulrich (Dir-Mktg & Trng)
Sherry Dutton (Dir-Ops)

Network One Solutions Inc. (1)
28202 Cabot Rd Ste 300, Laguna Niguel, CA 92677
Tel.: (949) 390-5790
Web Site:
http://www.networkonesolutions.com
Telecommunications Consulting Services
N.A.I.C.S.: 541690
Mike Stevens (Pres)

RDS Solutions LLC (1)
99 Grayrock Rd, Clinton, NJ 08809
Tel.: (908) 848-5385
Web Site: http://www.rdssolutions.com
Sales Range: $1-9.9 Million
Emp.: 10
Telecommunications Consultant
N.A.I.C.S.: 541618
John Vernick (Mng Partner)
Darren Jones (Mng Partner)

Subsidium Technologies Inc. (1)
1 Fairchild Sq Ste 101, Clifton Park, NY 12065
Tel.: (518) 899-1010
Web Site: http://www.subsidiumtech.com
Telecommunication Servicesb
N.A.I.C.S.: 517810
Frank Parisi (Acct Mgr)
Ken Daigle (Acct Mgr-Technical)

UPSTATE CEREBRAL PALSY
1020 Mary St, Utica, NY 13501
Tel.: (315) 724-6907   NY
Web Site: http://www.upstatecp.org
Year Founded: 1950
Sales Range: $75-99.9 Million
Emp.: 2,111
Community Care Services
N.A.I.C.S.: 624190
Dean Kelly (Second VP)
Paul Totaro (Treas)
Patrick Brennan (Asst Treas)
Ralph Imundo (Sec)
Tara Costello (VP-Behavioral Health Svcs)
Nancy Seller (Sr VP-Education Svcs)
Kathy Klosner (Chief Program Officer)
Lucy Rizzo (Chief Admin Officer)
Curt Pearsall Jr. (CFO)

UPSTATE ELECTRONIC WHOLESALERS
47 Jeanne Dr, Newburgh, NY 12550
Tel.: (845) 566-1600
Year Founded: 1985
Sales Range: $10-24.9 Million
Emp.: 38
Electrical Appliances Distr
N.A.I.C.S.: 423620
Leon Pearl (Pres)
Herman Gross (VP)
Diane Roberts (Controller)

UPSTATE MORTGAGE INC.
8 McKenna Commons Ct, Greenville, SC 29615
Tel.: (864) 232-3830
Web Site:
http://www.upstatemortgage.com
Year Founded: 1993
Loan Broker
N.A.I.C.S.: 522310
Valerie Lee (Pres & CEO)
James Breazeale (Sr Loan Officer)
Pam Gravlee (Sr Loan Officer)

UPSTATE NIAGARA COOPERATIVE, INC.
25 Anderson Rd, Buffalo, NY 14225-4905
Tel.: (716) 892-3156   NY
Web Site:
http://www.upstateniagara.com
Year Founded: 1965
Food & Beverage Cooperative
N.A.I.C.S.: 311511
Lawrence Webster (CEO)
Barbara Ellis (Mgr-HR)

UPSTATE PHARMACY, LTD.
40 North America Dr, West Seneca, NY 14224
Tel.: (716) 675-3784   NY
Web Site:
http://www.upstatepharmacy.com
Year Founded: 1998
Sales Range: $25-49.9 Million
Emp.: 60
Pharmacy Services
N.A.I.C.S.: 456110
Phillip Petonik (Pres)
Ted Kuzniarek (VP)
Phill Petoniak (Owner)

UPSTATE SHREDDING, LLC
1 Recycle Dr Tioga Indus Park, Owego, NY 13827-3213
Tel.: (607) 687-7777
Web Site:
http://www.upstateshredding.com
Sales Range: $750-799.9 Million
Scrap Metal Processing & Recycling
N.A.I.C.S.: 423930
Adam Weitsman (CEO)

UPTAKE TECHNOLOGIES, LLC
2045 W Grand Ave Ste B PMB 67705, Chicago, IL 60612
Tel.: (312) 242-2200
Web Site: https://www.uptake.com
Emp.: 100
Software Development Services
N.A.I.C.S.: 513210
Marie Wieck (Bd of Dirs, Executives)
Bradley A. Keywell (Founder & Exec Chm)

Subsidiaries:

Uptake Canada, Inc. (1)
Ste 800 1 Robert Speck Pkwy, Mississauga, L4Z 2G5, ON, Canada
Tel.: (905) 712-3840
Web Site: https://uptake-canada.us.hivebrite.com
Software Developer
N.A.I.C.S.: 513210

Subsidiary (Domestic):

Noble Iron Inc. (2)
291-7B Woodlawn Road West, Guelph, N1H 7L6, ON, Canada
Tel.: (519) 840-2123
Web Site: http://www.nobleiron.com
Rev.: $5,272,968
Assets: $4,948,250
Liabilities: $930,831
Net Worth: $4,017,418
Earnings: $209,302
Fiscal Year-end: 12/31/2021
Construction & Industrial Equipment Whslr & Rentals & Software Applications for Construction & Industrial Equipment Industry
N.A.I.C.S.: 532412
Nabil Kassam (Founder, Chm & CEO)

Division (US):

Noble Iron Texas (3)
505 Rankin Rd, Houston, TX 77073
Tel.: (281) 443-7667
Web Site: http://www.nobleiron.com
Construction Equipment Whslr & Rentals
N.A.I.C.S.: 532412

UPTOWN NETWORK, LLC
6609 Willow Park Dr, Naples, FL 34109
Tel.: (855) 577-7555
Web Site:
http://www.uptownnetwork.com
Sales Range: $25-49.9 Million
Software Publisher
N.A.I.C.S.: 513210
Jack Serfass (Co-Founder & CEO)
Edward J. Jones (Co-Founder & VP-Ops)
Nadine Serfass (Co-Founder & VP-Bus Dev)
Philip Turner (Co-Founder & VP-R&D)

UPWARD UNLIMITED
198 White Star Point, Spartanburg, SC 29301
Tel.: (864) 949-5700   SC
Web Site: http://www.upward.org
Year Founded: 1995
Sales Range: $10-24.9 Million
Emp.: 113
Christian Ministry Services
N.A.I.C.S.: 813110
Shane McKenzie (VP-Upward Recreation)

UPWORK GLOBAL INC.
441 Logue Ave, Mountain View, CA 94043
Tel.: (650) 316-7500   CA
Web Site: http://www.upwork.com
Year Founded: 2003
Holding Company; Workplace Talent Recruitment Platform Software Developer
N.A.I.C.S.: 551112
Hayden Brown (Sr VP-Product & Design)
Thomas H. Layton (Chm)
Brian Levey (Chief Bus Affairs & Legal Officer)
Stratis Karamanlakis (CTO)
Rich Pearson (Sr VP-Mktg)
Han Yuan (Sr VP-Engrg)
Eric Gilpin (Sr VP-Sls)

Subsidiaries:

Upwork Inc. (1)
655 Montgomery St Ste 490 Dept 17022, San Francisco, CA 94111-2676
Tel.: (650) 316-7500
Web Site: https://www.upwork.com
Rev.: $618,318,000
Assets: $1,080,245,000
Liabilities: $831,366,000
Net Worth: $248,879,000
Earnings: -$89,885,000)
Emp.: 850
Fiscal Year-end: 12/31/2022
Workplace Talent Recruitment Platform Software Developer
N.A.I.C.S.: 541511
Hayden Brown (Pres & CEO)
Brian Levey (Chief Legal Officer & Chief Bus Affairs Officer)
Melissa Waters (CMO)
Zoe Diamadi (Gen Mgr-Enterprise)
Sunita Solao (Chief People Officer)
Dave Bottoms (Gen Mgr-Marketplace)
Brandon Savage (Gen Mgr-Customer Experience & Trust)
Mohit Kumar (Gen Mgr)
Erica Gessert (CFO)
Andrew Rabinovich (VP & Head-AI & Machine Learning)
Paul Black (Chief Information Security Officer & VP-Engineering)

URAC
1220 L St NW Ste 400, Washington, DC 20005
Tel.: (202) 216-9010   DC
Web Site: http://www.urac.org
Year Founded: 1990
Sales Range: $10-24.9 Million
Emp.: 102
Health Care Management Services
N.A.I.C.S.: 621999

Marybeth Farquhar (VP-Quality, Res & Measurement)
Lois Elia (Sec)
George Furlong (Treas)
Peter Lund (Vice Chm)
Kylanne Green (Pres & CEO)
Alan B. Rosenberg (Chm)
Che Parker (VP-Sls & Mktg)
Deborah Smith (VP)
David Souders (VP-Fin & Admin)

URANIUM TRADING CORPORATION
2321 Rosecrans Ave Ste 3245, El Segundo, CA 90245
Tel.: (310) 906-2050   DE
Web Site:
http://www.uraniumtrading.com
Year Founded: 2018
Uranium Mining Services
N.A.I.C.S.: 212290
David Berklite (Co-Founder, Pres & CEO)
Markus Kemmerer (Co-Founder & CFO)
Joe Huber (Co-Founder & Chm)

URATA & SONS CEMENT COMPANY
3430 Luyung Dr, Rancho Cordova, CA 95742-6871
Tel.: (916) 638-5364
Web Site:
http://www.urataconcrete.com
Sales Range: $10-24.9 Million
Emp.: 300
Concrete Finishing Services
N.A.I.C.S.: 238140
John Bell (VP)

URBAN AFFAIRS COALITION
1207 Chestnut St, Philadelphia, PA 19107
Tel.: (215) 851-0110   PA
Web Site: http://www.uac.org
Year Founded: 1991
Sales Range: $25-49.9 Million
Emp.: 759
Management Consulting Services
N.A.I.C.S.: 541612
Kevin Satterthwaite (COO & CIO)
Beverly Woods (Dir-Economic Opportunity Div)
Arun Prabhakaran (Chief External Affairs Officer & VP)
Sandra Higginbotham-Briddell (Dir-HR)

URBAN APPAREL GROUP INC.
226 W 37th St, New York, NY 10018
Tel.: (212) 947-7009
Web Site:
http://www.urbanapparel.com
Rev.: $49,179,978
Emp.: 40
Sportswear, Women's
N.A.I.C.S.: 315250
Karen Camporeale (Pres)
Dave Dulinski (CFO)

URBAN COMMUNICATIONS
295 Madison Ave 40th Fl, New York, NY 10017
Tel.: (212) 471-3200   NY
Web Site:
http://urbancommunications.com
Year Founded: 1987
Sales Range: $10-24.9 Million
Emp.: 11
Publicity, Promotions & Radio
N.A.I.C.S.: 541830
Jay Levinson (CEO)
Tracey Bowden (Sr Acct Dir)

URBAN CONCRETE CON-

URBAN CONCRETE CON—(CONTINUED)

TRACTORS, LTD.
24114 Blanco Rd, San Antonio, TX 78258
Tel.: (210) 490-0090
Web Site: http://www.urbanconcrete.com
Sales Range: $25-49.9 Million
Emp.: 720
Concrete Finishing Services
N.A.I.C.S.: 238140
Ronnie Urbanczyk (VP)
Terry Urbanczyk (Pres)

URBAN ELEVATOR SERVICE, LLC
4830 W 16th St, Cicero, IL 60804
Tel.: (780) 656-5512
Web Site: http://www.urbanelevator.com
Building Equipment Contractors
N.A.I.C.S.: 238290
Mark Hertsberg (CEO)

Subsidiaries:

Urban Elevator Service CA LLC (1)
6915 Flanders Dr Ste B, San Diego, CA 92121
Tel.: (818) 436-6408
Building Equipment Installation & Service Contractors
N.A.I.C.S.: 238290
Pete Kasper (Principal & VP)

URBAN ENGINEERS INC.
530 Walnut St, Philadelphia, PA 19106-3619
Tel.: (215) 922-8080
Web Site: http://www.urbanengineers.com
Year Founded: 1960
Sales Range: $10-24.9 Million
Emp.: 200
Provider of Engineering Services
N.A.I.C.S.: 541330
Joseph P. McAtee (Dir-Support)
Bernard Carolan (CFO & Sr VP)
William T. Thomsen (Pres, CEO, COO & Sr VP-Svcs-Natl)
Kenneth Fulmer (Pres & CEO)
Scott J. Diehl (Engr-Traffic)
Meredith Clark (Dir-HR)
Carol Martsolf (VP & Dir-Trng)
Matthew C. Marquardt (COO & Sr VP-Vertical Svcs)
Mark Kinnee (COO-Horizontal Svcs & Sr VP)
Mike Leinheiser (VP)
Michael McAtee (VP & Mgr-Southwest)
Bill McGarrigel (VP & Gen Mgr-Transportation Plng & Design Svcs)
Tom Mitchell (VP & Gen Mgr-Natl Construction Consulting)
Tom Nodar (VP)
Jerry O'Neill (CFO & Sr VP)
Eric Sailer (Gen Counsel & VP)
Rick Simon (VP-Fin)
Ed Fronczkiewicz Jr. (Gen Counsel & VP)
John Holak Jr. (VP & Gen Mgr-Rail & Transit)

Subsidiaries:

John H. Robinson Testing Inc. (1)
1319 Sassafras St, Erie, PA 16501-1720
Tel.: (814) 453-5702
Web Site: http://www.robinsontesting.com
Sales Range: $10-24.9 Million
Emp.: 2
Engineeering Services
N.A.I.C.S.: 541330
George Willis (VP)

Urban Engineers of New York, P.C. (1)
403 Main St Ste 530, Buffalo, NY 14203
Tel.: (716) 856-9510
Web Site: http://www.urbanengineers.com
Sales Range: $10-24.9 Million
Emp.: 20
Engineeering Services
N.A.I.C.S.: 541330
Paul F. Parker (VP & Office Mgr)

URBAN EXPOSITIONS
1690 Roberts Blvd NW Ste 111, Kennesaw, GA 30144
Tel.: (678) 285-3976
Web Site: http://www.urban-expo.com
Sales Range: $10-24.9 Million
Emp.: 200
Trade Shows & Exhibitions
N.A.I.C.S.: 561920
Doug Miller (Pres)
Tim Von Gal (COO & Partner)
Barb Moreno (Dir-Conference)
Roger Schinkler (Dir-Creative Svcs)
Jo Mayer (Dir-Mktg)
Rich Ferrante (Dir-Sls)
Glenn Celentano (Dir-Sls & Ops)
Samantha Grimaldi (Mgr-Mktg & Conference)
Russ Turner (Mgr-Sls)
Jeannie Leggett (VP-Fin)
Mike Carlucci (VP-Sls)
Greg Topalian (CEO)
Jeff Dixon (CFO)
Ed Gallo (VP-Sls & Attendee Programs)
Liz Irving (VP-Mktg)
Tom Loughran (VP-Foodsvc)

URBAN FT GROUP, INC.
Tel.: (646) 661-1330
Web Site: http://www.urbanft.com
Year Founded: 2012
Core FineTech Mfr
N.A.I.C.S.: 334111
Richard Steggall (CEO)

URBAN HABITAT
1212 Broadway Ste 500, Oakland, CA 94612
Tel.: (510) 839-9510
Web Site: http://www.urbanhabitat.org
Year Founded: 2003
Sales Range: $1-9.9 Million
Emp.: 23
Community Welfare Services
N.A.I.C.S.: 624190
Bob Allen (Dir-Policy & Advocacy Campaigns)
Ellen Wu (Exec Dir)
Tony Roshan Samara (Program Dir-Land Use & Housing)
Carl Anthony (Founder)
Joe Brooks (Chm)
Arnold Perkins (Sec)
Tamar Dorfman (Treas)

URBAN HEALTH PLAN, INC.
1065 Southern Blvd, Bronx, NY 10459
Tel.: (718) 589-2440
Web Site: http://www.urbanhealthplan.org
Year Founded: 1974
Sales Range: $75-99.9 Million
Emp.: 818
Community Health Care Services
N.A.I.C.S.: 621498
Silva Umukoro (VP-Fin & Bus Mgmt)
Paloma Izquierdo-Hernandez (Pres & CEO)
Samuel De Leon (Chief Medical Officer & VP-Medical Affairs)
Rosa Agosto (Chief Talent & Learning Officer)
Daniel Figueras (CTO)
Edi Daley (Office Mgr-Medical Affairs)

URBAN INVESTMENT RE-

SEARCH CORP.
4201 W 36th St, Chicago, IL 60632
Tel.: (773) 650-1570
Web Site: http://www.uirc.com
Sales Range: $1-9.9 Million
Property Management & Investment
N.A.I.C.S.: 531312
Eric Warden (COO)
Isidor Cabiri (Mgr-Property)
Vincent Jadryev (Mgr-Property)
David Peluso (CMO)

URBAN LAND INSTITUTE
2001 L St NW Ste 200, Washington, DC 20036-4948
Tel.:
Web Site: https://www.uli.org
Year Founded: 1936
Educational Support Services
N.A.I.C.S.: 611710

URBAN LENDING SOLUTIONS LLC
Four Allegheny Ctr 6th Fl, Pittsburgh, PA 15212
Tel.: (412) 325-7046
Web Site: http://www.urban-ls.com
Year Founded: 1998
Sales Range: $50-74.9 Million
Emp.: 350
Mortgage Services
N.A.I.C.S.: 522310
Charles Sanders (CEO)
Elisa Sanders (Founder)
Jim Overton (CFO)
Michael Forgas (Chief Strategy Officer)

URBAN MINISTRY CENTER
945 N College St, Charlotte, NC 28206
Tel.: (704) 347-0278
Web Site: http://www.urbanministrycenter.org
Year Founded: 1993
Sales Range: $1-9.9 Million
Emp.: 40
Christian Ministry Services
N.A.I.C.S.: 813110
Jason Helms (Dir-Facilities)
Dale Mullennix (Exec Dir)
Liz Peralta (Dir-Dev)
Emily Helms (Accountant)
Caroline Chambre (Dir-HousingWorks)
Barbara L. Thomas (Dir-Neighbor Svcs)
Ben King (Mgr-Case)
John Feldman (Sec)
John Stubbs (VP)
Mike Clement (Pres)
Paul Duffy (Treas)

Subsidiaries:

Men's Shelter of Charlotte, Inc. (1)
1210 N Tryon St, Charlotte, NC 28206
Tel.: (704) 334-3187
Web Site: http://www.mensshelterofcharlotte.org
Sales Range: $1-9.9 Million
Homeless People Assistance Services
N.A.I.C.S.: 624221
Randall Hitt (Chief Engagement Officer)
Chuck Stauffer (Vice Chm)
Kristina Burke (Chm)
Jason Cipriani (Treas)
Liz Clasen-Kelly (CEO)
Nicole Higginbothem (Chief Talent Officer)
Don Kelly (CFO)
Veronica Ritchie (Chief Advancement Officer)
Stephanie Shatto (Chief Program Officer-Homeless Svcs)
Stephen McQueen (Chief Program Officer-Housing Svcs)
Trip R. Caldwell III (Sec)

URBAN NIRVANA

714 St Andrews Blvd, Charleston, SC 29407
Tel.: (843) 225-3007
Web Site: http://www.urbannirvana.com
Year Founded: 2000
Sales Range: $1-9.9 Million
Emp.: 224
Beauty Salons & Spas
N.A.I.C.S.: 812112
Susie McCrary (Founder)

URBAN OFFICE PRODUCTS, INC.
251 W 39th St 12th Fl, New York, NY 10018
Tel.: (718) 858-8100
Web Site: http://www.urbanofficeproducts.com
Year Founded: 1987
Sales Range: $1-9.9 Million
Emp.: 8
Office Furniture & Office Supplies
N.A.I.C.S.: 424120
Elizabeth Robin (Owner)

URBAN PARTNERS, LLC
304 South Broadway, Los Angeles, CA 90013
Tel.: (213) 437-0470
Web Site: http://www.urbanpartnersllc.com
Sales Range: $10-24.9 Million
Emp.: 20
Real Estate Investment & Development
N.A.I.C.S.: 531390
Matthew Burton (CFO)
Denise M. Mendoza (Office Mgr)
Paul N. Keller (Founding Principal & COO)

Subsidiaries:

Harbor Urban, LLC (1)
1411 4th Ave Ste 500, Seattle, WA 98101-2296
Tel.: (206) 876-3784
Web Site: http://www.harborurban.com
Sales Range: $10-24.9 Million
Emp.: 9
Real Estate Investment & Development
N.A.I.C.S.: 531390
Bob Krokower (CFO)
James L. Atkins (Principal & Mng Dir)

URBAN PREP ACADEMIES
420 N Wabash Ste 300, Chicago, IL 60611
Tel.: (312) 276-0259
Web Site: http://www.urbanprep.org
Year Founded: 2002
Sales Range: $10-24.9 Million
Emp.: 347
Educational Support Services
N.A.I.C.S.: 611710
Mary Pattillo (Vice Chm)
Joseph McCoy (Chm)
Darryl Cobb (Sec)
Tim King (Pres)

URBAN RENAISSANCE GROUP LLC
1425 4th Ave Ste 500, Seattle, WA 98101
Tel.: (206) 381-3344
Web Site: http://www.urbanrengroup.com
Year Founded: 2006
Emp.: 85
Real Estate Development Services
N.A.I.C.S.: 531120
Patrick Callahan (Founder & CEO)
John Bliss (Chief Investment Officer)
Kimberly Fuller (COO)
Vince Sheridan (VP-Dev)

Katarina Kueber *(Gen Mgr-Seattle Central Bus District)*
Mari Lim *(Asst Controller)*
Matt Bassist *(Dir-Leasing)*
Tony Silvestrini *(Dir-Construction)*
Holly Vetrone *(Dir-Ops)*
Renee Evans *(Dir-HR & Organizational Dev)*
Randy Bartl *(VP-Engrg)*
Matthew Simo *(VP-Acq)*
Troy Black *(CFO-Touchstone & Urban Renaissance Grp)*
Shawn Jackson *(VP & Gen Mgr-Seattle)*
Tom Kilbane *(VP & Gen Mgr-Portland)*
Jim Long *(VP-Engrg)*

Subsidiaries:

Touchstone Corporation (1)
1425 4th Ave Ste 200, Seattle, WA 98101
Tel.: (206) 381-3344
Web Site: http://www.touchstonenw.com
Real Estate Development Services
N.A.I.C.S.: 531120
A-P Hurd *(Pres & Chief Dev Officer)*

URBAN RESOURCE INSTITUTE

75 Broad St Ste 505, New York, NY 10004
Tel.: (646) 588-0030   NY
Web Site: http://www.urinyc.org
Year Founded: 1980
Sales Range: $10-24.9 Million
Emp.: 363
Human Service Organization
N.A.I.C.S.: 813410
Nathaniel M. Fields *(Pres & CEO)*
Jennifer White-Reid *(VP-Domestic Violence Programs)*
S. Scott Mason *(Gen Counsel & VP-Ops)*
Donovan Murray *(Sr VP-Fin)*
Vivian Y. Bright *(Vice Chm)*
Victoria Hernandez *(Chief Dev Officer)*
Whittaker Mack III *(Chm)*

URBAN RETAIL PROPERTIES, LLC

111 E Wacker Dr Ste 520, Chicago, IL 60601
Tel.: (312) 915-2000   DE
Web Site: http://www.urbanretail.com
Year Founded: 1972
Sales Range: $50-74.9 Million
Emp.: 400
Non-residential Property Developer & Manager
N.A.I.C.S.: 531312
Palmer W. Cameron *(Exec VP-Enviromental & Tech Svcs)*
David Johnson *(Exec VP & Dir-Mgmt)*
Joseph S. McCarthy *(CFO)*
Paul D. Motta *(COO)*
Gail M. Silver *(Sr VP-HR)*
Craig Delasin *(CEO)*
David Neuman *(Exec VP-Dev)*
Jim Roberts *(Sr VP & Dir-Mktg & Comm)*

URBAN SCIENCE, INC.

400 Renaissance Ctr Ste 3000, Detroit, MI 48243
Tel.: (313) 259-9900
Web Site: http://www.urbanscience.com
Sales Range: $75-99.9 Million
Emp.: 1,000
Retail Networking, Planning & Market Analysis
N.A.I.C.S.: 541618
Richard R. Widgren *(Treas & VP-Fin)*
James Anderson *(Founder, Pres & CEO)*

Sharif Farhat *(VP-Expert Analytical Svcs)*
Kevin Smith *(Mng Dir-Nashville)*
Robert Black *(Acct Dir-Renault & Nissan-Global)*
Paul Dillamore *(Mng Dir-UK)*
Rebecca Gualdoni *(Chief HR Officer)*
Elizabeth Klee *(CIO)*
Rod Wright *(COO)*
Frederique De Letter *(Dir-Global Acct)*
Jesus Tapia *(Mgr-Bus Dev)*
Tom Little *(Mng Dir-Detroit)*
Pedro de la Vega *(Mng Dir-Spain)*

URBAN STRATEGIES INC.

720 Olive St Ste 2600, Saint Louis, MO 63101
Tel.: (314) 421-4200   MO
Web Site: http://www.urbanstrategiesinc.org
Year Founded: 1978
Sales Range: $1-9.9 Million
Emp.: 84
Community Welfare Services
N.A.I.C.S.: 525120
Reinhard Baumgaertel *(Project Mgr-Assist)*
Esther U. Shin *(Co-Pres)*
Uma M. Murugan *(VP-Project)*
M. Wade Baughman *(Gen Counsel & Sr VP)*
Sandra M. Moore *(Co-Pres)*
Richard Baron *(Chm)*

URBAN STUDIO ARCHITECTS, INC.

1208 E Kennedy Blvd Ste 220, Tampa, FL 33602
Tel.: (813) 228-7301   FL
Web Site: http://www.urbanstudio.com
Year Founded: 1989
Sales Range: $1-9.9 Million
Emp.: 10
Architectural & Interior Design Services
N.A.I.C.S.: 541310
Brian Hammond *(Co-Founder & Principal)*
Michael Jacob *(Co-Founder & Mng Principal)*
Richard Zingale *(Co-Founder & Principal)*
Jeffrey Heidbreder *(Dir-Interior Design)*
Meredith Fisher *(Mgr-Mktg & Bus Dev)*

URBAN TANTRA INTERNATIONAL, INC.

1521 Alton Rd Ste 153, Miami Beach, FL 33139
Tel.: (305) 675-6302   NV
Web Site: http://www.urbantantra.net
Year Founded: 2009
Property Development Services
N.A.I.C.S.: 236220
Andrew McLaughlin *(Pres & Treas)*
Jill Butler *(Sec)*

URBANA COUNTRY CLUB

100 E Country Club Rd, Urbana, IL 61801
Tel.: (217) 344-8670
Web Site: http://www.urbanacountryclub.com
Year Founded: 1922
Sales Range: $1-9.9 Million
Emp.: 40
Golf Course & Country Club
N.A.I.C.S.: 713910
Thomas Wilsey *(Mgr-Banquet)*
Frank Fonte *(Dir-Golf)*

URBANDADDY, INC.

900 Broadway Ste 808, New York, NY 10003
Tel.: (212) 929-7905
Web Site: http://www.urbandaddy.com
Year Founded: 2005
Sales Range: $10-24.9 Million
Emp.: 105
Online Magazine Publisher
N.A.I.C.S.: 513120
Lance Broumand *(CEO)*
Caitlin Ganswindt *(Assoc Editor)*
Paul Underwood *(Dir-Editorial)*
Jon Bozak *(Mng Editor-Manero)*

URBANSTEMS INC.

1615 L St NW Ste 1230, Washington, DC 20036
Web Site: http://www.urbanstems.com
Year Founded: 2014
Sales Range: $10-24.9 Million
Flower Bouquet & Plant Distr
N.A.I.C.S.: 424930
Ana Mollinedo Mims *(CEO)*
Megan Darmody *(Sr Dir-Brand Mktg)*

URBIETA OIL CO.

9701 NW 89th Ave, Medley, FL 33178
Tel.: (305) 884-0008
Web Site: http://www.urbietaoil.com
Sales Range: $500-549.9 Million
Emp.: 30
Petroleum Product Distr
N.A.I.C.S.: 424720
Guillermo Urbieta *(Pres)*

URESCO CONSTRUCTION MATERIALS INC.

8246 S 194th St, Kent, WA 98032-1125
Tel.: (253) 395-1211   WA
Web Site: http://www.uresco.com
Year Founded: 1978
Sales Range: $10-24.9 Million
Emp.: 65
Distr of Lumber Plywood & Millwork
N.A.I.C.S.: 423310
Chad T. Moore *(Pres)*

URETEK USA INC.

13900 Humble Rd, Tomball, TX 77377
Tel.: (281) 351-7800
Web Site: http://www.uretekusa.com
Rev.: $16,000,000
Emp.: 50
Concrete Repair
N.A.I.C.S.: 238110
Brent Barron *(Pres & CEO)*
Amy Hyde *(Mgr-IT & Mktg)*

URGENT ACTION FUND FOR WOMEN'S HUMAN RIGHTS

660 13th St Ste 200, Oakland, CA 94612
Tel.: (415) 523-0360   CO
Web Site: http://www.urgentactionfund.org
Year Founded: 1997
Sales Range: $1-9.9 Million
Emp.: 10
Women Rights Protection Services
N.A.I.C.S.: 813311
Kate Kroeger *(Exec Dir)*
Shalini Eddens *(Dir-Programs)*
Caitlin Stanton *(Dir-Learning & Partnerships)*
Patricia Viseur Sellers *(Chm)*
Kamala Chandrakirana *(Vice Chm)*
Paulette Meyer *(Treas & Sec)*
Meerim Ilyas *(Officer-Program)*

URGENT CARE PARTNERS, INC.

310 4th Ave S, Minneapolis, MN 55415
Tel.: (877) 776-3639
Web Site: http://www.urgentcarepartners.com
Year Founded: 2015
Hospital & Health Care Services
N.A.I.C.S.: 622110
Brandon Robertson *(Mng Dir)*
Weston Johnson *(Chief Admin Officer)*

Subsidiaries:

Merchant Medicine, LLC (1)
2355 Fairview Ave N Ste 335, Saint Paul, MN 55113
Tel.: (651) 483-0450
Web Site: http://www.merchantmedicine.com
Offices of Physicians (except Mental Health Specialists)
N.A.I.C.S.: 621111
Tom Charland *(CEO)*

URGENT PLASTIC SERVICES INC.

2547 Product Dr, Rochester Hills, MI 48309
Tel.: (248) 852-8999
Web Site: http://www.3dimensional.com
Rev.: $10,393,765
Emp.: 110
Injection Molded Finished Plastics Products
N.A.I.C.S.: 326199
Douglas L. Peterson *(Pres)*
David Grache *(Plant Mgr)*
Alan Peterson *(VP)*

URGO HOTELS LP

6710A Rockledge Dr Ste 420, 20817, Bethesda, MD
Tel.: (301) 657-2130
Web Site: http://www.urgohotels.com
Year Founded: 1968
Sales Range: $600-649.9 Million
Emp.: 3,000
Hotels & Resorts Owner, Operator, Developer, Manager & Investor
N.A.I.C.S.: 721110
Kevin M. Urgo *(Chief Dev Officer & Mng Partner-Bus Dev, Treasury & Fin)*
Collin D. Urgo *(Sr VP-Ops)*
Phil Daniel *(Sr VP-Fin)*
Richard Riccio *(VP-Ops-US)*
Serge Primeau *(VP-Ops-Canada)*
Kyle Hamill *(VP-Sls & Mktg)*
Robert Spence *(VP-Quality Assurance)*
Ellen Wimsatt Cobb *(Dir-HR)*
Mathew Jalazo *(Dir-Dev)*
John J. Rish *(Reg Mgr)*
Donald J. Urgo Sr. *(Founder, Pres & CEO)*
Donald J. Urgo Jr. *(Mng Partner & Gen Counsel)*

URI, INC.

3635 Hayden Ave, Culver City, CA 90232-2458
Tel.: (310) 360-1212   CA
Web Site: http://www.uriglobal.com
Year Founded: 1996
Rev.: $26,000,000
Emp.: 20
Advetising Agency
N.A.I.C.S.: 541810
Xochitl Hwang *(Founder & CEO)*
Daniel Shin *(Pres)*
Gabriel J. Lee *(Acct Dir)*

URIGEN PHARMACEUTICALS, INC.

675 US Hwy 1 Ste B206, North Brunswick, NJ 08902

URIGEN PHARMACEUTICALS, INC.

U.S. PRIVATE

Urigen Pharmaceuticals, Inc.—(Continued)
Tel.: (732) 640-0160 DE
Web Site: http://www.urigen.com
Year Founded: 1997
Sales Range: Less than $1 Million
Urological Disorder Research & Pharmaceutical Development Services
N.A.I.C.S.: 325412
C. Lowell Parsons *(Founder & Chm)*
Dan B. Vickery *(Pres & COO)*

URM STORES, INC.
7511 N Freya St, Spokane, WA 99217-8004
Tel.: (509) 467-2620 WA
Web Site: http://www.urmstores.com
Year Founded: 1921
Sales Range: $450-499.9 Million
Emp.: 1,920
Cooperative; Wholesale Grocery Distributor; Retail Grocery Services
N.A.I.C.S.: 424510
Mike Winger *(VP-Store Dev)*
Paul Christianson *(VP-Procurement & Retail Svcs)*
Ray Sprinkle *(Pres & CEO)*
Kirk Rollings *(VP-Ops)*
Stan Hilbert *(CFO & Treas)*

Subsidiaries:

Harvest Foods (1)
506 N Mullan Rd, Spokane, WA 99206 (100%)
Tel.: (509) 922-3939
Web Site: http://www.harvestfoodsnw.com
Sales Range: $10-24.9 Million
Emp.: 8
Grocery Store Services
N.A.I.C.S.: 445110
Buzz Bellessa *(CEO)*

Peirone Produce Company (1)
9818 W Hallett Rd, Spokane, WA 99224
Tel.: (509) 838-3515
Web Site: http://www.peironeproduce.com
Sales Range: $10-24.9 Million
Emp.: 90
Fresh Produce Distr
N.A.I.C.S.: 424480
Mike Kamphaus *(Pres)*

Rosauers Supermarkets, Inc. (1)
1815 W Garland Ave, Spokane, WA 99205-2522
Tel.: (509) 326-8900
Web Site: http://www.rosauers.com
Sales Range: $25-49.9 Million
Emp.: 60
Supermarkets, Chain
N.A.I.C.S.: 445110
Jack Benfield *(Dir-Security)*
Cliff Rigsbee *(Pres & CEO)*

URM Development Corp. (1)
7511 N Freya St, Spokane, WA 99217-8004
Tel.: (509) 467-2620
Web Site: http://www.urmstores.com
Retailer-owned Business; Co-op
N.A.I.C.S.: 459999

URM Insurance Agency (1)
7511 N Freya St, Spokane, WA 99217-8004 (100%)
Tel.: (509) 467-2620
Web Site: http://www.urmstores.com
Sales Range: $25-49.9 Million
Emp.: 8
Insurance Agents
N.A.I.C.S.: 524210

URNERS INC.
4110 Wible Rd, Bakersfield, CA 93313
Tel.: (661) 396-8400
Web Site: http://www.urners.com
Sales Range: $10-24.9 Million
Emp.: 100
Electric Household Appliances, Major
N.A.I.C.S.: 449210
David H. Urner *(Pres)*
Barbara Smith *(Mgr-Credit)*
Dave Perkins *(Dir-Mktg)*

UROOJ LLC
301 Rt 17N Ste 800, Rutherford, NJ 07070
Tel.: (201) 933-7861 DE
Web Site: http://www.urooj.net
Year Founded: 2002
Sales Range: $10-24.9 Million
Emp.: 37
IT Short & Long-Term Staffing
N.A.I.C.S.: 561311
Riham Hassan *(Mgr-Ops)*

URSA FARMERS COOPERATIVE CO.
202 W Maple Ave, Ursa, IL 62376
Tel.: (217) 964-2111
Web Site: http://www.ursacoop.com
Sales Range: $50-74.9 Million
Emp.: 50
Grain Elevators
N.A.I.C.S.: 424510
Karen Voss *(Controller)*
Rich Gastler *(Pres-West Point)*
Kevin Cary *(Sec)*
Kevin Schrader *(Treas)*

URSA INFORMATION SYSTEMS INC.
890 W Elliot Rd Ste 107, Gilbert, AZ 85233
Web Site: http://www.opensourceintegrators.com
Year Founded: 2010
Sales Range: $1-9.9 Million
Emp.: 21
Information Technology Services
N.A.I.C.S.: 541512
Greg Mader *(Pres)*
Jennifer Campbell *(VP)*
Ronda Mader *(Mgr-Acctg)*
Balaji Kannan *(Mgr-Technical)*
Patrick Kittredge *(Project Mgr)*

URSANAV
616 Innovation Dr, Chesapeake, VA 23320
Tel.: (757) 312-0790
Web Site: http://www.ursanav.com
Year Founded: 2004
Rev.: $9,900,000
Emp.: 77
Engineeering Services
N.A.I.C.S.: 541330
Charles A. Schue III *(Co-Founder, Chm, Pres & CEO)*
Lori Smith *(Mgr-Proposal)*
Erik Johannessen *(VP-Bus Dev)*
Stephen Bartlett *(VP-Ops)*

URSCHEL LABORATORIES INCORPORATED
1200 Cutting Edge Dr, Chesterton, IN 46304
Tel.: (219) 464-4811 IN
Web Site: http://www.urschel.com
Year Founded: 1910
Sales Range: $100-124.9 Million
Emp.: 260
Machinery for Cutting, Chopping, Grinding & Mixing; Chemical Milling Machines
N.A.I.C.S.: 333241
Rick Urschel *(Pres & CEO)*

Subsidiaries:

Urschel (Thailand) Ltd. (1)
507 569 Soi Sathupradit 31 Sathupradit Rd, Kwaeng Choongnonsee Khet Yanna, Bangkok, 10120, Thailand
Tel.: (66) 22102705
Web Site: http://www.urschel.com
Sales Range: $10-24.9 Million
Emp.: 5
Food Products Machinery
N.A.I.C.S.: 333241

Urschel Asia Pacific Pte. Ltd. (1)
10 Tagore Lane, Singapore, 787473, Singapore (100%)
Tel.: (65) 62547757
Web Site: http://www.urschel.com
Sales Range: $10-24.9 Million
Emp.: 9
Food Products Machinery
N.A.I.C.S.: 333241
Christian Tan *(Gen Mgr)*

Urschel China Ltd. (1)
1F B10 No 449 Nu Jiang Bei Road, New Cao Yang Industry Zone, Shanghai, 200033, China
Tel.: (86) 2152653971
Web Site: http://www.urschel.net.cn
Sales Range: $10-24.9 Million
Emp.: 12
Food Products Machinery
N.A.I.C.S.: 333241
Forest Liu *(Mgr-Sls)*

Urschel Espana SL (1)
Avenida De Los Montes De Oca 19-Nav 1, San Sebastian De Los Reyes, 28703, Madrid, Spain
Tel.: (34) 91 002 31 02
Sales Range: $10-24.9 Million
Emp.: 3
Industrial Equipment & Machinery Mfr
N.A.I.C.S.: 332999

Urschel Hellas (1)
Agiou Konstantinou 13, Metamorphosis, 14452, Athens, Greece
Tel.: (30) 2102828989
Web Site: http://www.urschel.com
Sales Range: $10-24.9 Million
Emp.: 4
Food Products Machinery
N.A.I.C.S.: 333241

Urschel India Trading Private Limited (1)
Navale IT Zone Phase-2 S No 51/2 A/2 NH No 4, Narhe Gaon Taluka-Haveli, Pune, 411041, Maharashtra, India
Tel.: (91) 20 6680 3400
Food Processing Equipment Mfr
N.A.I.C.S.: 333241
Nitin Shilaskar *(Mgr-Sls)*

Urschel International Ltd. (1)
Meridian Business Park, Leicester, LE19 1QP, United Kingdom (100%)
Tel.: (44) 1162634321
Web Site: http://www.urschel.com
Sales Range: $10-24.9 Million
Emp.: 20
Food Products Machinery
N.A.I.C.S.: 333241
Robert Urschel *(Owner)*

Urschel International Ltd. (1)
Parc Technologique du Bois Chaland 8 Rue des Pyrénées, Lisses, 91090, France (100%)
Tel.: (33) 1 60 75 77 77
Web Site: http://www.urschel.com
Sales Range: $10-24.9 Million
Emp.: 12
Food Products Machinery
N.A.I.C.S.: 333241
Le Masle Florence *(Gen Mgr)*

Urschel International Ltd. (1)
Hogemaat 1, Wijk bij Duurstede, 3961 NC, Utrecht, Netherlands
Tel.: (31) 343575454
Web Site: http://www.urschel.com
Sales Range: $10-24.9 Million
Emp.: 9
Food Products Machinery
N.A.I.C.S.: 333241

Urschel International Ltd. (1)
Dieselstr 5, Ober Morlen, 61239, Hessen, Germany (100%)
Tel.: (49) 600291500
Web Site: http://www.urschel.com
Sales Range: $10-24.9 Million
Emp.: 6
Food Products Machinery
N.A.I.C.S.: 333241
Cristel K. Bhomer *(Branch Mgr)*

Urschel International Ltd. (1)
Largo Samwell Diniz n 1D, 1500-552, Lisbon, Portugal
Tel.: (351) 217710550
Web Site: http://www.urschel.com
Sales Range: $10-24.9 Million
Emp.: 3
Food Products Machinery
N.A.I.C.S.: 333241
Helena Gomes *(Mgr-Sls & Exhibitions-Intl)*

Urschel International Ltd. (1)
Steinegg Str 32, CH 8852, Altendorf, Switzerland (100%)
Tel.: (41) 554424800
Web Site: http://www.urschel.com
Sales Range: $10-24.9 Million
Emp.: 3
Food Products Machinery
N.A.I.C.S.: 333241

Urschel International Polska Sp. z o.o. (1)
Dluga 59, 05 530, Gora Kalwaria, Poland
Tel.: (48) 227271007
Web Site: http://www.urschel.com
Sales Range: $10-24.9 Million
Emp.: 6
Food Products Machinery
N.A.I.C.S.: 333241
Andrzej Jankowski *(Reg Mgr-Sls)*

Urschel Japan (1)
2 14 2 Sanno Grand Building Nagatacho, Chiyoda-Ku, Tokyo, 100 0014, Japan (100%)
Tel.: (81) 335063531
Web Site: http://www.urschelj.co.jp
Sales Range: $10-24.9 Million
Emp.: 10
Food Products Machinery
N.A.I.C.S.: 333241

Urschel Latinoamerica S.r.l. (1)
Edison 1205 Vila, A2124AAA, Gobernador Galvez, Santa Fe, Argentina
Tel.: (54) 341 3171400
Web Site: http://www.urschel.com
Sales Range: $10-24.9 Million
Emp.: 2
Industrial Equipment & Machinery Whslr
N.A.I.C.S.: 423830
Matias Mandel *(Gen Mgr)*

URWILER OIL & FERTILIZER INC.
Hwy 15 W, Laurel, NE 68745
Tel.: (402) 256-3177
Sales Range: $10-24.9 Million
Emp.: 30
Fertilizer & Fertilizer Materials
N.A.I.C.S.: 424910
Greg Urwiler *(Pres)*
Mitzi Urwiler *(Office Mgr)*

US 1 INDUSTRIES, INC.
336 W US Hwy 30 Ste 201, Valparaiso, IN 46385-5345
Tel.: (219) 476-1300 IN
Web Site: http://www.us1industries.com
Year Founded: 1946
Sales Range: $200-249.9 Million
Emp.: 90
Trucking Logistics & Management Distr
N.A.I.C.S.: 484230
Michael E. Kibler *(Pres & CEO)*
Harold E. Antonson *(CFO)*
David Antonson *(VP-Sls & Mktg)*

Subsidiaries:

ARL Network (1)
1155 Stoops Ferry Rd, Moon Township, PA 15108
Tel.: (800) 245-4722
Web Site: http://www.arlnetwork.com
Sales Range: $10-24.9 Million
Emp.: 60
Freight Transportation Services
N.A.I.C.S.: 484119
Ron Faherty *(Pres)*

Subsidiary (Domestic):

ARL Transport, LLC. (2)
1155 Stoops Ferry Rd, Moon Township, PA 15108
Tel.: (412) 264-6996

COMPANIES

Web Site: http://www.arlnetworks.com
Emp.: 50
Freight Transportation Services
N.A.I.C.S.: 484121
Tricia Gibson (Mgr-Ops)

America 1, LLC (1)
101 E town Pl Ste 120, Saint Augustine, FL 32092
Tel.: (219) 476-1390
Web Site:
http://www.america1.us1logistics.com
Sales Range: $10-24.9 Million
Emp.: 8
Freight Transportation Services
N.A.I.C.S.: 484121
Windy Gorch (Dir-Agent Svcs)

Blue & Grey Transportation (1)
341 Cedar Hill Dr, Birmingham, AL 35242-3179 (100%)
Tel.: (205) 674-3303
Sales Range: $25-49.9 Million
Emp.: 24
Flatbed Trucking Company
N.A.I.C.S.: 484122

Bruin Express Intermodal LLC (1)
12631 E Imperial Hwy Ste F-102, Santa Fe Springs, CA 90670
Tel.: (562) 282-0540
Web Site: http://www.bruinexpress.com
Transportation Services
N.A.I.C.S.: 488999

CAM Logistics, LLC (1)
336 W US Hwy 30 Ste 201, Valparaiso, IN 46385-5345
Tel.: (228) 539-1537
Logistics Consulting Services
N.A.I.C.S.: 541614

CAM Transport, LLC (1)
15487 Oak Ln Ste 200F, Gulfport, MS 39503-2664
Tel.: (803) 238-0414
Web Site: http://www.camtransportinc.com
Logistics Management Services
N.A.I.C.S.: 541614
Dorothy Wiggins (Dir-Safety)

Carolina Logistics (1)
950 Houston Northcutt Blvd Ste 100, Mount Pleasant, SC 29464 (100%)
Tel.: (843) 849-0451
Sales Range: $10-24.9 Million
Emp.: 30
Trucking Service
N.A.I.C.S.: 488510
Michael E. Kibler (Pres)

Carolina National Transportation LLC
950 Houston Northcutt Blvd Ste 100, Mount Pleasant, SC 29464 (100%)
Tel.: (843) 849-0451
Web Site:
http://www.carolinagrouponline.com
Sales Range: $25-49.9 Million
Emp.: 25
N.A.I.C.S.: 484122
Harold Antonson (Controller)

Freedom 1, LLC (1)
280 Business Park Cir Ste 406, Saint Augustine, FL 32095
Tel.: (219) 476-1304
Transport & Logistic Services
N.A.I.C.S.: 561110

Gulf Line Transportation (1)
950 Houston Northcutt Blvd Ste 100, Mount Pleasant, SC 29464 (100%)
Sales Range: $150-199.9 Million
N.A.I.C.S.: 484122

Harbor Bridge Intermodal Inc (1)
3720 W 74th St, Chicago, IL 60629
Tel.: (773) 581-1261
Web Site: http://www.harborbridge.com
Sales Range: $10-24.9 Million
Emp.: 8
Trucking & Transportation Services
N.A.I.C.S.: 484121
Jim Mellot (Gen Mgr)

ICG Logistics, LLC (1)
336 W US Hwy 30 Ste 201, Valparaiso, IN 46385
Tel.: (219) 476-1300
Web Site: http://www.us1industries.com

Emp.: 25
Logistics Consulting Servies
N.A.I.C.S.: 541614
Cindy Harris (Gen Mgr-HR)

Keystone Lines, Inc. (1)
Ste 201 336 W Us Highway 30, Valparaiso, IN 46385-5345 (100%)
Tel.: (219) 944-6116
Web Site: http://www.us1.com
Sales Range: $50-74.9 Million
Trucking
N.A.I.C.S.: 484121

Keystone Logistics, LLC (1)
1657 Commerce Dr Ste 9A, South Bend, IN 46628
Tel.: (574) 288-5555
Web Site: http://www.keystonelogistics.net
Logistics Consulting Servies
N.A.I.C.S.: 541614
Kenneth Cubberley (Pres)
Keith Stillson (Exec VP)

Patriot Logistics, Inc. (1)
4301 E Park Dr, Houston, TX 77028
Tel.: (713) 670-0072
Web Site: http://www.patriot-logistics.com
Sales Range: $10-24.9 Million
Emp.: 20
Logistics Consulting Servies
N.A.I.C.S.: 541614
Edwis Selph (Pres & CEO)

Risk Insurance Services of Indiana, Inc (1)
336 W US Hwy 30 Ste 201, Valparaiso, IN 46385
Tel.: (855) 306-4400
Web Site:
http://www.riskinsuranceservices.com
Sales Range: $25-49.9 Million
Emp.: 25
Automobile Insurance Services
N.A.I.C.S.: 524126
David Antonson (VP)

TC Services, Inc. (1)
336 W US Hwy 30 Ste 201, Valparaiso, IN 46385-5345 (100%)
Tel.: (219) 476-1300
Sales Range: $25-49.9 Million
Emp.: 25
Factoring & Financial Services
N.A.I.C.S.: 488490

US 1 Logistics, LLC (1)
200 Business Park Cir Ste 117, Saint Augustine, FL 32095
Tel.: (219) 476-1390
Web Site: http://www.us1logistics.com
Logistics & Transport Service Provider
N.A.I.C.S.: 488510

Subsidiary (Domestic):

Transport Leasing Systems, LLC. (2)
280 Business Park Cir, Saint Augustine, FL 32095
Tel.: (219) 476-1304
Freight Transportation Services
N.A.I.C.S.: 484121

US ACRYLIC INC.
1320 Harris Rd, Libertyville, IL 60048
Tel.: (847) 837-4800
Web Site: http://www.usacrylic.com
Year Founded: 1978
Sales Range: $10-24.9 Million
Emp.: 80
Plastic Kitchenware, Tableware & Houseware Mfr
N.A.I.C.S.: 326199
Jerry Lee (CEO)

US AIRCONDITIONING DISTRIBUTORS, INC.
16900 Chestnut St, City of Industry, CA 91748
Tel.: (626) 854-4500
Web Site: http://www.us-ac.com
Sales Range: $500-549.9 Million
Emp.: 400
Air Conditioning Distr
N.A.I.C.S.: 423730

John Staples (Pres & CEO)
John Scarsi (CFO & VP)
Ned Broadstreet (VP & Controller)
Craig Walker (Mgr-Customer Assurance)
Bernie Faller (Dir-Credit)
Debbie Garcia (Mgr-Credit)
Jack Scarsi (VP-Ops & Fin)
Doug Stewart (Mgr-Pur)
Margaret Holloway (Mgr-Accts Payable)

US AIRLINE PILOTS ASSOCIATION
200 E Woodlawn Rd Ste 250, Charlotte, NC 28217
Tel.: (877) 332-3342 NC
Web Site:
http://www.usairlinepilots.org
Year Founded: 2007
Sales Range: $10-24.9 Million
Emp.: 9
Pilot Association
N.A.I.C.S.: 813920
Stephen Bradford (VP)
Steve Smyser (Exec VP)
John Owens (Treas & Sec)

US ALLIANCE CORPORATION
1303 SW 1st American Pl Ste 200, Topeka, KS 66604
Tel.: (785) 228-0200 KS
Web Site:
https://www.usalliancecorporation.com
Year Founded: 2009
Rev.: $16,005,853
Assets: $118,298,297
Liabilities: $110,228,903
Net Worth: $8,069,394
Earnings: ($3,156,485)
Emp.: 11
Fiscal Year-end: 12/31/22
Fire Insurance Services
N.A.I.C.S.: 524113
Jack H. Brier (Chm, Pres & CEO)
Kurtis L. Scott (Treas)

Subsidiaries:

Dakota Capital Life Insurance Corporation (1)
107 W Main Ave Ste 325, Bismarck, ND 58501
Tel.: (701) 258-1499
Web Site: https://www.dakotacapitallife.com
Insurance Services
N.A.I.C.S.: 524113
Mike Anderson (Dir-Company Dev)
Dan Andre (Dir-Corp Dev)
Matt Andre (Dir-Corp Dev)
Rowdy Meyer (Mng Dir-Corp Dev)

US Alliance Life & Security Company (1)
1303 SW First American Pl Ste 200, Topeka, KS 66604
Tel.: (785) 228-0200
Web Site: https://www.usalliancelife.com
Insurance Services
N.A.I.C.S.: 524113
Rowdy Meyer (Mng Dir-Corp Dev)
Donald J. Schepker (Vice Chm)

US ALUMINUM SERVICES, CORP.
2211 W Washington St, Orlando, FL 32805
Tel.: (407) 237-3128
Web Site: http://www.us-aluminum.com
Sales Range: $1-9.9 Million
Emp.: 29
Aluminum Siding Installation Services
N.A.I.C.S.: 238170
Thiago Davila (CEO)

US APPRAISAL GROUP, INC.

US BIOSERVICES

200 S Wacker Dr Ste 3100, Chicago, IL 60606
Tel.: (312) 432-9300
Web Site:
http://www.usappraisalgroup.com
Year Founded: 2003
Sales Range: $1-9.9 Million
Emp.: 10
Real Estate Appraisal Services
N.A.I.C.S.: 531390
Dione Spiteri (Pres)

US AUTO GROUP LIMITED
34602 Woodward Ave, Birmingham, MI 48009
Tel.: (248) 645-5930
Web Site:
http://www.fredlaverycompany.com
Rev.: $178,712,776
Emp.: 60
New & Used Automobile Sales
N.A.I.C.S.: 441110
Frederick A. Lavery Jr. (Pres)

Subsidiaries:

Fred Lavery Company (1)
34602 Woodward Ave, Birmingham, MI 48009
Tel.: (248) 645-5930
Web Site: http://www.fredlaveryaudi.com
Rev.: $49,356,708
Automobiles, New & Used
N.A.I.C.S.: 441110
Frederick A. Lavery Jr. (Pres)

H.W. McKevitt Co. Inc. (1)
2700 Shattuck Ave, Berkeley, CA 94705
Tel.: (510) 848-2206
Web Site: http://www.mckevitt.com
Automobiles, New & Used
N.A.I.C.S.: 441110
David Adragna (Gen Mgr)

HW McKevitt Co. Inc. (1)
467 Marina Blvd, San Leandro, CA 94577
Tel.: (510) 895-5000
Web Site: http://www.mckevitt.com
Rev.: $49,630,096
Emp.: 50
Automobiles, New & Used
N.A.I.C.S.: 441110
Frederick Lavery (Pres)

Shrewsbury Motors Inc (1)
702 Shrewsbury Ave, Red Bank, NJ 07701
Tel.: (732) 741-8500
Web Site: http://www.shrewsbyvw.com
Rev.: $42,949,580
Emp.: 50
Automobiles, New & Used
N.A.I.C.S.: 441110
Jeff Anderson (Gen Mgr)

US Auto Group of Massachusetts (1)
43 N Beacon St, Watertown, MA 02472
Tel.: (617) 783-1300
Web Site: http://www.bostonvw.com
Sales Range: $25-49.9 Million
Emp.: 41
Automobiles, New & Used
N.A.I.C.S.: 441110
John J. Welch Jr. (Gen Mgr)

US AUTO SALES INC.
2875 University Pkwy, Lawrenceville, GA 30043
Tel.: (770) 962-9121
Web Site:
http://www.usautosalessuzuki.com
Year Founded: 1992
Rev.: $19,149,629
Emp.: 80
Automobiles, Used Cars Only
N.A.I.C.S.: 441120
Marvin Hewatt (Co-Owner)

US BIOSERVICES
3101 Gaylord Pkwy, Frisco, TX 75034
Tel.: (888) 518-7246 TX
Web Site:
http://www.usbioservices.com
Year Founded: 1994
Pharmaceuticals

US BIOSERVICES

US Bioservices—(Continued)
N.A.I.C.S.: 551112
Angela Ward (Pres)
Kevin James (VP-Payer Strategy)
Joy Gilbert (VP-Ops)
Randy Maloziec (VP-BioPharma Relations)
Amanda Winter (VP-Reimbursement, Quality & Learning & Dev)

US BUILDINGS LLC
355 Indus Park Dr, Boone, NC 28607
Tel.: (828) 264-6198
Web Site:
http://www.usbuildingsdirect.com
Rev.: $15,900,000
Emp.: 100
Contrustion of Prefabricated Buildings
N.A.I.C.S.: 444180
Subsidiaries:

Nation Funding Group Inc (1)
355 Industrial Park Dr Ste 123, Boone, NC 28607
Tel.: (828) 265-3303
Rev.: $260,000
Emp.: 4
Personal Credit Institutions
N.A.I.C.S.: 522291

US BULK TRANSPORT INC.
205 Pennbriar Dr, Erie, PA 16509
Tel.: (814) 824-9949
Web Site:
http://www.usbulktransport.com
Rev.: $25,361,587
Emp.: 20
Trucking Domestic
N.A.I.C.S.: 484121
Gary Goodelle (Pres)
James Uhrmacher (CFO)
Keith Warren (Mgr-Terminal)
Mary Ernst (Mgr-Terminal)
Gene Cobucci (Mgr-Credit)
Howard Weaver (Mgr-Terminal)
Christopher Kavala (Coord-Recruitment)

US CABLE GROUP
28 W Grand Ave, Montvale, NJ 07645
Tel.: (201) 930-9000
Web Site:
http://www.uscablegroup.com
Year Founded: 1975
Sales Range: $10-24.9 Million
Emp.: 4
Provider of Cable Services
N.A.I.C.S.: 541611
James D. Pearson (Pres & CEO)
Subsidiaries:

Smart City Networks LP (1)
28 W Grand Ave, Montvale, NJ 07645
Tel.: (201) 930-9000
Web Site: http://www.smartcity.com
Rev.: $18,000,000
Local Telephone Communications
N.A.I.C.S.: 517121

Subsidiary (Domestic):

Smart City Solutions, LLC (2)
3100 Bonnet Creek Rd, Lake Buena Vista, FL 32830
Tel.: (407) 828-6600
Web Site: http://www.smartcity.com
Sales Range: $1-9.9 Million
Business Consulting Services
N.A.I.C.S.: 541690

Smart City Telecommunications LLC (2)
3100 Bonnet Creek Rd, Lake Buena Vista, FL 32830 (100%)
Tel.: (407) 827-2000
Web Site: http://www.smartcitytelecom.com
Telephone Communications
N.A.I.C.S.: 517121

Martin Rubin (Pres & CEO)
James Schumacher (VP-Fin & Admin)
Carlos Palenzuela (VP-Engrg)

US Cable of Coastal Texas LP (1)
28 W Grand Ave Ste 10, Montvale, NJ 07645
Tel.: (201) 930-9000
Web Site: http://www.uscable.com
Rev.: $56,883,938
Cable Television Services
N.A.I.C.S.: 516210

US CAVALRY STORE INC.
2855 Centennial Ave, Radcliff, KY 40160
Tel.: (270) 351-1164
Web Site: http://www.uscav.com
Sales Range: $10-24.9 Million
Emp.: 90
Military Goods & Regalia
N.A.I.C.S.: 458110
James Leonard (CFO)

US CHROME CORPORATION
175 Garfield Ave, Stratford, CT 06615
Tel.: (203) 378-9622
Web Site: http://www.uschrome.com
Sales Range: $10-24.9 Million
Emp.: 7
Electroplating Of Metals Or Formed Products
N.A.I.C.S.: 332813
Robert Z. Reath (Chm)

US COAL CORPORATION
101 Helm St Ste 150, Lexington, KY 40505
Tel.: (859) 223-8820
Web Site: http://www.uscoalinc.com
Year Founded: 2006
Sales Range: $10-24.9 Million
Emp.: 200
Coal Mining Services
N.A.I.C.S.: 213113
Robert Gabbard (Pres & CEO)
Michael P. Windisch (CFO)

US DAIRY SYSTEMS INC.
1731 S Lincoln Ave, Jerome, ID 83338
Tel.: (208) 324-3213
Web Site:
http://www.automateddairy.com
Sales Range: $10-24.9 Million
Emp.: 100
Dairy Machinery & Equipment
N.A.I.C.S.: 423820
Jerry Higley (Owner & Pres)

US DESIGN & CONSTRUCTION CORP.
14900 Westheimer Rd Ste W, Houston, TX 77082-1625
Tel.: (281) 558-4000
Web Site: http://www.usdesign-const.com
Year Founded: 1973
Sales Range: $10-24.9 Million
Emp.: 10
Contractor of Commercial & Office Buildings; New Construction
N.A.I.C.S.: 236220
Peter Ferri (Pres)
David King (Mgr Project)
Terry Pratt (Dir-Construction)

US DESIGN & MILL, CORP.
380 Douglas Rd E Ste 8, Oldsmar, FL 34677-2947
Tel.: (813) 854-2321
Web Site:
http://www.usdesignmill.com
Year Founded: 1985
Sales Range: $10-24.9 Million
Emp.: 5
Cabinetry Mfr
N.A.I.C.S.: 321918

Terry D. Loche (Pres)
John J. Underwood (VP)

US DISMANTLEMENT LLC
2600 S Throop St, Chicago, IL 60608-5716
Tel.: (312) 328-1400
Web Site: http://www.usdllc.com
Year Founded: 1987
Sales Range: $10-24.9 Million
Emp.: 60
Wrecking Services
N.A.I.C.S.: 238910
Harry Gieschen (Owner)

US ENGINEERING COMPANY
3433 Roanoke Rd, Kansas City, MO 64111
Tel.: (816) 753-6969
Web Site:
http://www.usengineering.com
Sales Range: $100-124.9 Million
Emp.: 1,200
Mechanical Contractor
N.A.I.C.S.: 238220
Tim Moormeier (Pres)
Ken Glasbrenner (Controller & Mgr-Payroll)
Tyler Nottberg (Chm & CEO)

US ENTERPRISES INC.
225 Corey Ctr SE, Atlanta, GA 30312
Tel.: (404) 419-9700
Rev.: $11,000,000
Emp.: 25
Convenience Store Operator
N.A.I.C.S.: 445131
William E. Corey (Owner)
John Hahn (Dir-HR)

US EQUIPMENT CO. INC.
8311 Sorensen Ave, Santa Fe Springs, CA 90670-2125
Tel.: (323) 733-4733
Web Site:
http://www.usequipmentco.com
Sales Range: $10-24.9 Million
Emp.: 28
Compressors, Except Air Conditioning
N.A.I.C.S.: 423830
Kem Frkovich (Pres)

US EXP GROUP, INC.
160 Kerns Ave, Buffalo, NY 14211
Tel.: (716) 200-1162 NY
Year Founded: 2016
Emp.: 1
Psychological Healthcare Support Services
N.A.I.C.S.: 621112
Wenyi Yu (CEO)
Feng Li (Co-Founder & Dir-Corp)
Scott D. Marchant (Gen Counsel)
Jonathan J. Willard (CFO)

US FEDERAL CONTRACTOR REGISTRATION INC.
9400 4th St N Ste 111, Saint Petersburg, FL 33702
Tel.: (813) 775-2271
Web Site:
http://www.uscontractorregistration.com
Sales Range: $1-9.9 Million
Emp.: 40
Specialty Trade Contractor Services
N.A.I.C.S.: 238990
Eric M. Knellinger (Pres)

US FEDERAL PROPERTIES TRUST, INC.
4706 Broadway Ste 240, Kansas City, MO 64112
Tel.: (816) 531-2082 MD
Web Site: http://www.usfpco.com
Sales Range: $1-9.9 Million

U.S. PRIVATE

Emp.: 15
Real Estate Investment Services
N.A.I.C.S.: 525990
Richard Baier (Principal)
Chris Nelson (Dir-Property Mgmt)
Kristi Stuedle (Mgr-Transaction)
Krista McCray (Mgr-Acctg)

US FLEET TRACKING CORP.
2912 NW 156 St, Edmond, OK 73013
Tel.: (405) 749-1105
Web Site: http://www.usft.com
Year Founded: 2005
Rev.: $22,800,000
Emp.: 23
Marking Device Mfr
N.A.I.C.S.: 339940
Jerry Hunter (Founder & CEO)
Sam Sims (Dir-PR & Mktg)

US GLASS & ALUMINUM INC.
PO Box 1055, Rio Vista, CA 94571
Tel.: (925) 427-7100
Web Site: http://www.us-glass.com
Sales Range: $25-49.9 Million
Emp.: 70
Glass & Glazing Work
N.A.I.C.S.: 238150
John Brimmer (Pres)

US GOLF INC.
2130 Barranca Pkwy, Irvine, CA 92606-4940
Tel.: (949) 863-1293
Sales Range: $10-24.9 Million
Emp.: 10
Sports Equipment Retailer
N.A.I.C.S.: 459110

US GREENFIBER LLC
2500 Distribution St, Charlotte, NC 28203-5028
Tel.: (800) 666-4824
Web Site: http://www.greenfiber.com
Year Founded: 2000
Sales Range: $125-149.9 Million
Emp.: 250
Building, Insulating & Packaging Paperboard
N.A.I.C.S.: 322299

US GROUP INC.
20580 Hoover St, Detroit, MI 48205
Tel.: (313) 372-7900
Web Site:
http://www.usequipment.com
Sales Range: $10-24.9 Million
Emp.: 5
Industrial Machinery & Equipment
N.A.I.C.S.: 423830
Paul Simon (Chm & CEO)
Andrew Badai (Dir-Ops)

US GROWERS COLD STORAGE INC.
3141 E 44th St, Los Angeles, CA 90058
Tel.: (323) 583-3163
Web Site: http://www.usgrowers.com
Rev.: $16,612,251
Emp.: 142
Warehousing, Cold Storage Or Refrigerated
N.A.I.C.S.: 493120
Angelo Antoci (Pres)
Ralph Newton (Warehouse & Ops)

US HEALTH HOLDINGS LTD.
8220 Irving Rd, Sterling Heights, MI 48312
Tel.: (586) 826-4300
Web Site:
http://www.ushealthandlife.com
Sales Range: $10-24.9 Million
Emp.: 100
Medical Insurance Claim Processing
N.A.I.C.S.: 524292
Dan Gorczyca (Pres)

COMPANIES

Subsidiaries:

Automated Benefit Services (1)
8220 Irving Rd, Sterling Heights, MI 48312
Tel.: (586) 693-4300
Web Site: http://www.abs-tpa.com
Insurance Agents, Brokers & Service
N.A.I.C.S.: 524210
Tony Cooper (Dir-IT)

US Health and Life Insurance Co (1)
8220 Irving Rd, Sterling Heights, MI 48312
Tel.: (586) 826-4300
Web Site: http://www.ushealthandlife.com
Life Insurance
N.A.I.C.S.: 524113
Daniel Gorczyca (Pres)
Louis Lapiana (VP)

US HEALTHVEST LLC
32 Easth 57th St Ste 17, New York, NY 10022
Tel.: (866) 746-1707
Web Site:
  http://www.ushealthvest.com
Treatment Services
N.A.I.C.S.: 623220
Richard A. Kresch (Pres & CEO)

Subsidiaries:

Ridgeview Institute, Inc. (1)
3995 S Cobb Dr, Smyrna, GA 30080
Web Site: http://www.ridgeviewinstitute.com
Mental Health Services
N.A.I.C.S.: 621420
Amy Davis (Sec)
Frank Sartur (CEO)
Ruth Jenkins (CFO)

US HOLDINGS CORPORATION
3406 Lovers Ln, Dallas, TX 75225
Tel.: (214) 369-5600
Sales Range: $10-24.9 Million
Emp.: 1
Investment Holding Companies, Except Banks
N.A.I.C.S.: 551112
James Holcomb Jr. (Pres)

Subsidiaries:

Custom Coils Inc. (1)
101 Anvil St, Jacksonville, TX 75766
Tel.: (903) 586-3668
Web Site: http://www.customcoilsinc.com
Sales Range: $10-24.9 Million
Emp.: 65
Air Conditioning Condensers & Condensing Units
N.A.I.C.S.: 333415
Valerie Gatzka (Mgr-Quality Assurance)

US INFORMATION TECHNOLOGIES CORPORATION
4800 Westfields Blvd Ste 250, Chantilly, VA 20151
Tel.: (703) 229-6768
Web Site: http://www.usinfotech.com
Sales Range: $1-9.9 Million
Emp.: 120
Information Technology Services
N.A.I.C.S.: 541511
Joseph D. Morrone (Pres & CEO)
Theron Johnson (CTO & VP)
Keith Stone (Dir-Intelligence Programs)
Edwin Rosas (Dir-Healthcare)
Craig Proulx (Dir-Bus Dev)
John Fahy (Dir-Knowledge Transfer Programs)
Stephanie Hughes (Dir-Fin & Security)
Kimberly Folland (Dir-Recruiting)
Randy Lawson (Dir-Consulting)
Tarry Kirkland (Dir-Bus Dev)

US INTERACTIVE INC.
2005 De La Cruz Blvd Ste 195, Santa Clara, CA 95050
Tel.: (408) 863-7500
Web Site:
  http://www.usinteractive.com
Sales Range: $10-24.9 Million
Emp.: 300
Computer Related Consulting Services
N.A.I.C.S.: 541512
Sunil Mathur (Pres & CEO)

US INTERNET CORPORATION
12450 Wayzata Blvd Ste 315, Minnetonka, MN 55305
Tel.: (952) 253-3200
Web Site: http://www.usinternet.com
Year Founded: 1995
Sales Range: $10-24.9 Million
Emp.: 55
Internet & Hosting Services
N.A.I.C.S.: 517810
Joe Caldwell (Co-Founder)
Travis Carter (Founder & VP-Tech)
Kurt Lange (VP)

Subsidiaries:

Marix Technologies, Inc. (1)
12450 Wayzata Blvd Ste 121, Minnetonka, MN 55305
Tel.: (952) 253-3200
Web Site: http://www.marix.com
Sales Range: $10-24.9 Million
Emp.: 1
Enterprise Software
N.A.I.C.S.: 541511
Travis Carter (VP-Bus Dev)

US LED, LTD.
6807 Portwest Dr, Houston, TX 77024
Tel.: (713) 972-9191 TX
Web Site: http://www.usled.com
Year Founded: 2001
Sales Range: $1-9.9 Million
Emp.: 19
Mfr & Distr of Solid-State Light-Emitting Diode Products
N.A.I.C.S.: 335139
Ron Farmer (CEO)
John Allgood (Pres)
Ty Fox (Dir-Sls)
Sarah Farmer (Dir-Customer Svc)

US LETTER CARRIERS MUTUAL BENEFIT ASSOCIATION
100 Indiana Ave NW Ste 510, Washington, DC 20001
Tel.: (202) 638-4318
Web Site: http://www.nalc.org
Year Founded: 1895
Sales Range: $10-24.9 Million
Emp.: 25
Life Insurance Carrier
N.A.I.C.S.: 524113
Larry Winfield (Dir-Mktg)

US LOGISTICS LLC
901 Adams Crossing, Cincinnati, OH 45202
Web Site: http://www.uslfreight.com
Year Founded: 2009
Sales Range: $25-49.9 Million
Emp.: 10
Freight Brokering Agents
N.A.I.C.S.: 488510
Jeff Hiatt (Pres)
Doug Logeman (Exec VP)
Andrew Jackson (Mgr-Bus Dev)
Sarah Long (Controller)

US MARKERBOARD
270 Center St Unit F, Holbrook, MA 02343
Tel.: (781) 767-9544
Web Site:
  http://www.usmarkerboard.com
Year Founded: 2000
Rev: $6,800,000
Emp.: 21

Retail Services
N.A.I.C.S.: 311811
Brian Perkins (Product Mgr)
Steve Fleury (Mgr-Sls)
Chafiq Elbissouri (Mgr-Digital Mktg)

US MATERIALS HANDLING CORP.
2231 State Rte 5, Utica, NY 13502
Tel.: (315) 732-4111
Web Site:
  http://www.usmaterialshandling.com
Sales Range: $10-24.9 Million
Emp.: 47
Materials Handling Machinery
N.A.I.C.S.: 423830
Robert A. Payne (Founder & Controller)
Jon Payne (VP)

US MEDIA CONSULTING
1801 SW 3rd Ave 3rd Fl, Miami, FL 33129
Tel.: (305) 722-5500
Web Site:
  http://www.usmediaconsulting.com
Year Founded: 2003
Sales Range: $10-24.9 Million
Emp.: 20
Online & Print Advertising Consulting for Latin America, Caribbean & Hispanic Markets
N.A.I.C.S.: 541810
Bruno Almeida (CEO)
Tatiana Koike (Dir-Online Sls)
Lionel Guillioli (Dir-Central America & Caribbean & Reg Mgr-Adv Sls)
Francisco Pol (CFO)
Emerson Calegaretti (Chief Product Officer)
Ignacio Roizman (COO & CTO)

US MICRO PRODUCTS, INC.
6207 Bee Caves Rd Ste 330, Austin, TX 78746
Tel.: (512) 385-9000
Web Site:
  http://www.usmicroproducts.com
Year Founded: 1996
Sales Range: $10-24.9 Million
Emp.: 14
Engineered Display Products
N.A.I.C.S.: 423690
David Alben (CEO)

US MICRON LLC
15361 W 95th St, Lenexa, KS 66219
Tel.: (913) 888-7900
Web Site: http://www.micron-group.com
Sales Range: $10-24.9 Million
Emp.: 25
Commercial Nonphysical Research
N.A.I.C.S.: 541715
Esam Sidarous (VP-Clinical Ops)
Iain Simpson (Pres)

US NEWSPAPERS
5150 E La Palma Ave Ste 202, Anaheim, CA 92807
Tel.: (714) 693-9490
Web Site:
  http://www.usnewspapers.com
Sales Range: $25-49.9 Million
Media Buying Services
N.A.I.C.S.: 541830
Jim Trammel (Pres)

US NITTO
641 N Poplar St, Orange, CA 92868
Tel.: (714) 744-2622
Web Site: http://www.nubidet.com
Sales Range: $10-24.9 Million
Emp.: 18
Fasteners, Industrial: Nuts, Bolts, Screws, Etc,

US RESTAURANTS INC.

N.A.I.C.S.: 423840
Y. Josh Abe (Pres)
Law Winchester (Mgr-Natl Sls)

US PERISHABLES
7700 Edgewater Dr Suite 606, Oakland, CA 94621
Tel.: (866) 294-1189
Web Site:
  http://www.usperishables.com
Year Founded: 2008
Sales Range: $1-9.9 Million
Emp.: 15
Third-Party Logistics & Transportation of Perishable Foods
N.A.I.C.S.: 311991
Helen Camilletti (Mgr-Ops)

US PIZZA COMPANY
PO Box 251710, Little Rock, AR 72225
Tel.: (501) 280-0399 AR
Web Site: http://www.uspizzaco.net
Year Founded: 1972
Sales Range: $1-9.9 Million
Emp.: 240
Pizzeria & Restaurant
N.A.I.C.S.: 722513
Judy Waller (Owner)

US POLE LIGHTING CO.
660 W Ave O, Palmdale, CA 93551-3610
Tel.: (661) 233-2000 CA
Web Site: http://www.usaltg.com
Year Founded: 1984
Lamp Posts, Metal
N.A.I.C.S.: 335139
Joe Straus (Founder)

US POLYMERS INC.
1057 S Vail Ave, Montebello, CA 90640
Tel.: (323) 728-3023
Web Site:
  http://www.uspolymersinc.com
Rev.: $25,000,000
Emp.: 57
Aluminum Foundries
N.A.I.C.S.: 331318
Viken Ohanesian (CEO)
Ben Paparisto (Mgr-Ops)
John Paige (Controller)
Toni Love (Mgr-Acctg)

US RADIOLOGY SPECIALISTS, INC.
305 Church at NHills St Ste 1250, Raleigh, NC 27609
Tel.: (919) 763-1100
Web Site:
  http://www.usradiology.com
Radiation & Medical X-ray services
N.A.I.C.S.: 621511
John Perkins (CEO)

Subsidiaries:

Montclair Road Imaging, LLC (1)
924 Montclair Rd Ste 108, Birmingham, AL 35213
Tel.: (205) 592-4738
Web Site:
  http://www.imagesouthradiology.com
Sales Range: $1-9.9 Million
Emp.: 20
Offices of Physicians, Mental Health Specialists
N.A.I.C.S.: 621112
Tim Watkins (Principal)
Joseph Paul (Pres & Founder)
Paul Cote (COO & Founder)

US RESTAURANTS INC.
1780 Swede Rd, Blue Bell, PA 19422
Tel.: (610) 277-4200
Web Site:
  http://www.usrestaurantsinc.com
Sales Range: $25-49.9 Million

US RESTAURANTS INC.

US Restaurants Inc.—(Continued)
Emp.: 40
Family Restaurant Operator
N.A.I.C.S.: 722511
Steven M. Lewis (Founder & Pres)
Kathy Caputo (Office Mgr)
Michael Kadelski (CFO)

US SECURITY INC.
4544 NW 10th St, Oklahoma City, OK 73127
Tel.: (405) 917-5566
Web Site: http://www.ussecurity.com
Sales Range: Less than $1 Million
Emp.: 5
Security System Services
N.A.I.C.S.: 561621
Rick Ratliff (Pres)

US SERVICE GROUP, LLC
1030 Grand Blvd, Deer Park, NY 11729
Tel.: (888) 541-0044
Web Site: https://www.ussvs.com
Emp.: 100
Rigging & Machinery Moving Services
N.A.I.C.S.: 488999
Steve Laganas (Founder & CEO)

Subsidiaries:

Walker Crane & Rigging Corp. (1)
50 Farmington Vly Dr, Plainville, CT 06062
Tel.: (860) 793-9866
Web Site:
http://www.walkercraneandrigging.com
Oil & Gas Pipeline & Related Structures Construction
N.A.I.C.S.: 237120
Ken DiPaola (Engr-Sls)

US SPECIAL DELIVERY INC.
821 East Blvd, Kingsford, MI 49802
Tel.: (906) 774-1931
Web Site: http://www.usspecial.com
Year Founded: 1975
Sales Range: $10-24.9 Million
Emp.: 38
Trucking Service
N.A.I.C.S.: 484122
Terence Reed (Pres)
Sandra Philipps (Dir-HR)
Debra Lantagne (Mgr-Mgmt Info Sys)

US SUPPLY COMPANY INC.
50 Portland Rd, West Conshohocken, PA 19428
Tel.: (610) 828-5600
Web Site: http://www.ussupply.com
Rev.: $13,800,000
Emp.: 40
Plumbing & Hydronic Heating Supplies
N.A.I.C.S.: 423720
Douglas Hyman (Pres)

US TECH SERVICES INC.
3644 Meadowchase Dr, Marietta, GA 30062
Tel.: (770) 973-7070
Web Site: http://www.ustechsvcs.com
Rev.: $10,100,000
Emp.: 53
Industrial Machinery & Equipment
N.A.I.C.S.: 423830
Gary Conlan (Pres)

Subsidiaries:

Lisega South Inc. (1)
3644 Meadow Chase Dr, Marietta, GA 30062
Tel.: (770) 973-7070
Rev.: $110,000
Emp.: 2
Consulting Engineer
N.A.I.C.S.: 541330

US TECH SOLUTIONS INC.
101 Hudson St, Jersey City, NJ 07302
Tel.: (201) 524-9600
Web Site:
http://www.ustechsolutions.com
Year Founded: 2000
Sales Range: $10-24.9 Million
Emp.: 300
Global Consulting & Information Technology Services
N.A.I.C.S.: 541690
Manoj Agarwal (CEO)
Digant Vashi (VP)
Shaily Narnolia (Mgr-Resource)
Partha Usts (Mgr-Sls)

US TOOL GRINDING INC.
701 S Desloge Dr, Desloge, MO 63601
Web Site: http://www.ustg.net
Sales Range: $25-49.9 Million
Emp.: 500
Knife, Saw & Tool Sharpening & Repair
N.A.I.C.S.: 811411
Bruce Williams (Pres)
Michael Baugh (VP-Bus Dev)
Jim Galati (VP-Fin & Admin)
Annette Holloway (Mgr-Mktg & Customer Svc)
Brent Williams (VP-Ops)

US TRANSPORT
241 W 56th Ave, Denver, CO 80216
Tel.: (303) 297-9779
Web Site: http://www.us-transport.com
Rev.: $21,100,000
Emp.: 150
Building Materials Transport
N.A.I.C.S.: 484230
Michael T. Nelligan (Chm)

US VANADIUM LLC
7000 S Yosemite St, Englewood, CO 80112
Tel.: (888) 868-7489
Web Site:
http://www.highpurityvanadium.com
Specialty Vanadium Chemicals Producer
N.A.I.C.S.: 325998
Terry Perles (Dir)
Matthew Laper (Mgr-Ops)

Subsidiaries:

Evraz Stratcor, Inc. (1)
4285 Malvern Rd, Hot Springs, AR 71901-8504
Tel.: (501) 262-1270
Web Site: http://www.evrazstratcor.com
Emp.: 50
Specialty Alloys & Chemical Products Mfr
N.A.I.C.S.: 331110
David Miltenberger (Mgr-Sls-Specialty Products)
Lesa Jacob-Pollich (Mgr-Customer Svc)
Brandon Davis (CEO)

US VINYL MANUFACTURING CORP.
1766 Broomtown Rd, La Fayette, GA 30728
Tel.: (706) 638-8400
Web Site: http://www.usvinylmfg.com
Sales Range: $25-49.9 Million
Emp.: 50
Wallcovering
N.A.I.C.S.: 322220
Steve W. McCloud (Owner & Pres)
Nancy Linnenman (CFO)
Christi Young (Mgr-Ops)

US VR GLOBAL.COM INC.
923 E Valley Blvd Ste 103B, San Gabriel, CA 91776
Tel.: (626) 307-2273 DE
Year Founded: 2003
Assets: $3,264
Liabilities: $68,798
Net Worth: ($65,534)
Earnings: ($31,326)
Fiscal Year-end: 12/31/16
Consulting Services
N.A.I.C.S.: 541611

US WEB INCORPORATED
780 Pk Ave, Huntington, NY 11743
Tel.: (631) 427-5200
Sales Range: $25-49.9 Million
Emp.: 220
Provider of Commercial Printing Services
N.A.I.C.S.: 323111
John V. Busa (Pres)
Charles Lauricella (VP-Sls)
Michael Sommers (Controller)

US WORLDMEDS, LLC
4010 Dupont Cir Ste L-07, Louisville, KY 40207
Tel.: (502) 714-7800
Web Site:
http://www.usworldmeds.com
Year Founded: 2001
Sales Range: $25-49.9 Million
Emp.: 64
Pharmaceuticals Product Mfr
N.A.I.C.S.: 325412
Paul Breckinridge Jones (Founder & CEO)
George Digenis (Chief Scientific Officer)
Abeer M. Al-Ghananeem (VP-Scientific Affairs)
Glenn Esgro (VP-Sls & Managed Market)
Henry van den Berg (VP-Medical Affairs)
Brian Jackey (VP-Ops)
Stephanie Montgomery (VP-Fin)
H. Lee Warren Jr. (COO)

US YOUTH SOCCER
9220 World Cup Way, Frisco, TX 75033
Tel.: (800) 476-2237 TN
Web Site:
http://www.usyouthsoccer.org
Year Founded: 1983
Sales Range: $10-24.9 Million
Emp.: 35
Soccer Sport Organizer
N.A.I.C.S.: 713990
Jen Parker (Dir-Acctg & Fin)
Sam Snow (Dir-Coaching)
Todd Roby (Dir-Mktg & Comm)
Rob Martella (Dir-Ops)
Chris Branscome (CEO)
Dan Popp (Pres-Interim)
Delroy Ziadie (VP-Youth)

US-ANALYTICS SOLUTIONS GROUP, LLC
16301 Quorum Dr Ste 170B, Addison, TX 75001
Tel.: (214) 630-0081 TX
Web Site: http://www.us-analytics.com
Year Founded: 1999
Computer Related Services
N.A.I.C.S.: 541519
Scott Preszler (Pres & CEO)
Wayne Conrad (VP-Channels & Strategic Partnerships)
Chris Runyan (VP-Resource Mgmt)

US-CHINA BIOMEDICAL TECHNOLOGY, INC.
2 Park Plz Ste 400, Irvine, CA 92614
Tel.: (949) 679-3992 NV
Web Site: http://www.extong.com
Year Founded: 2010

UCBB—(OTCBB)
Assets: $77,487
Liabilities: $76,078
Net Worth: $1,409
Earnings: ($710,940)
Emp.: 5
Fiscal Year-end: 02/28/19
Medical Tourism & Services Company
N.A.I.C.S.: 622110
Qingxi Huang (Chm, Pres, CEO, CFO, Treas & Sec)

US-FEIWO AGRICULTURAL INDUSTRY INTERNATIONAL, INC.
699 Serramonte Blvd Ste 212, Daly City, CA 94015
Tel.: (650) 530-0699 CA
Web Site: http://www.usfeiwo.us
Year Founded: 2010
Fertilizer Production Equipment Exporter
N.A.I.C.S.: 423820
Haitao Liu (Chm, Pres & CEO)
Shuxia Wang (Sec)
Lihui Chen (CFO, Chief Acctg Officer & Treas)

US-HM STRAW CONSTRUCTION MATERIAL INT'L, INC.
699 Serramonte Blvd Ste 212, Daly City, CA 94015
Tel.: (650) 530-0699 CA
Year Founded: 2010
Construction Products & Equipment Exporter
N.A.I.C.S.: 423810
Guangtian Fu (Chm, Pres & CEO)
Yujie Fu (Sec)
Ying Deng (CFO, Chief Acctg Offcer & Treas)

US-NOBEL PRIMARY EDUCATION DEVELOPMENT INT'L, INC.
2500 E Colorado Blvd Ste 255, Pasadena, CA 91107
Tel.: (626) 568-8789 CA
Year Founded: 2012
International Quality Bilingual (Chinese & English) Educational Products for Children
N.A.I.C.S.: 611710
Raymond King Chung Wing (Chm, Pres & CEO)
Chi Kong Cheung (CFO, Chief Acctg Officer & Treas)
Wai Kin Fan (Sec)

US-PS ENERGYSAVE CONSTRUCTION MATERIAL INT'L, INC.
699 Serramonte Blvd Ste 212, Daly City, CA 94015
Tel.: (650) 530-0699 CA
Year Founded: 2010
Energy Efficient construction Materials Production Equipment Exporter
N.A.I.C.S.: 423810
Baoqing Dong (Chm, Pres & CEO)
Guanghui Zhang (Sec)
Xiuchun Bai (CFO, Chief Acctg Officer & Treas)

US-TQ BEVERAGE PRODUCTS INT'L, INC.
699 Serramonte Blvd Ste 212, Daly City, CA 94015
Tel.: (650) 530-0699 CA
Year Founded: 2010
Spring & Mineral Water Production Equipment Exporter
N.A.I.C.S.: 423830

COMPANIES

Anhui Li *(Chm, Pres & CEO)*
Libo An *(CFO, Chief Acctg Officer & Treas)*
Sisi Shang *(Sec)*

USA BABY
2222 FM 1960 W, Houston, TX 77090   IL
Web Site: http://www.usababy.com
Year Founded: 1975
Sales Range: $10-24.9 Million
Emp.: 580
Retailer of Baby Furniture
N.A.I.C.S.: 449129

USA BANK
211 Irving Ave, Port Chester, NY 10573
Tel.: (914) 939-3700
Commercial Banking Services
N.A.I.C.S.: 522110
Ronald A. Gentile *(CEO)*

USA CAPITAL MANAGEMENT, INC.
404 Ave Constitucion Ste 208, San Juan, PR 00901-2251
Tel.: (787) 900-5048   PR
Year Founded: 2014
Emp.: 1
Investment Services
N.A.I.C.S.: 523999
Richard Meruelo *(Pres, CEO, CFO & Sec)*

USA DEVELOPMENT CORP.
874 County St, Taunton, MA 02780
Tel.: (508) 822-9750
Rev.: $27,800,000
Emp.: 5
Real Estate Developers
N.A.I.C.S.: 237210

USA DIRECT HOLDINGS
912 14th St N, Jacksonville Beach, FL 32240-1467
Tel.: (904) 247-4801
Web Site:
   http://www.richboystoys.com
Year Founded: 1978
Sales Range: $700-749.9 Million
Emp.: 50
Computer Integrated Systems Design
N.A.I.C.S.: 541512

Subsidiaries:

USA Direct Computer Systems   (1)
PO Box 51425, Jacksonville Beach, FL 32240-1425   **(100%)**
Tel.: (404) 806-5403
Computer & Electronic Products Distr
N.A.I.C.S.: 541512

USA ENVIRONMENTAL, INC.
720 Brooker Creek Blvd Ste 204, Oldsmar, FL 34677
Tel.: (813) 343-6336   FL
Web Site: http://www.usatampa.com
Year Founded: 1998
Sales Range: $10-24.9 Million
Emp.: 200
Munitions & Explosives of Concern Remediation & Disposal Services
N.A.I.C.S.: 562211
Jonathan Chionchio *(Pres)*
Sarah Gambino *(Mgr-Mktg & Comm)*
David Conolly *(Mgr-Contracts)*
Jennifer Dorney *(Mgr-Acctg)*
Robin Miller *(VP-HR & Admin)*
Ron Bunnell *(CFO)*
Daphne Thoresen *(Mgr-Mktg Comm)*
Donald H. M. Shaw III *(Mgr-Projects)*

USA FINANCIAL MARKETING CORPORATION
6020 E Fulton St, Ada, MI 49301
Tel.: (616) 676-2288
Web Site:
   http://www.usafinancial.com
Year Founded: 1988
Sales Range: $50-74.9 Million
Emp.: 50
Financial Services
N.A.I.C.S.: 561499
Michael D. Walters *(Chm & CEO)*
Brent D. Enders *(Pres)*
Mark R. Mersman *(CMO)*
David D. Radde *(Exec VP-Mktg)*
Will Bachert *(CFO)*
Andrea McGrew *(Chief Compliance Officer & Chief Legal Officer)*
Justin Long *(Chief Sls Officer)*
Matt McGrew *(COO)*
Greg Lockwood *(CTO)*
Angela Schultz *(Exec VP-Logistics)*
Bruce Wisler *(VP-Bus Dev)*
Bryan Wirtz *(VP-Bus Dev)*
Cindy Garstka *(VP-Client Svcs)*

USA GYMNASTICS
130 E Washington St Ste 700, Indianapolis, IN 46204
Tel.: (317) 237-5050   IN
Web Site: http://www.usagym.org
Year Founded: 1964
Sales Range: $10-24.9 Million
Emp.: 67
Gymnastic Support Services
N.A.I.C.S.: 611620
Ava Gehringer *(Dir-Athlete)*
Gary Anderson *(Sec)*
Jim Morris *(Treas)*
Kelli Hill *(Dir-Natl Membership)*
Yoichi Tomita *(Dir-Natl Membership)*
Alicia Sacramone *(Dir-Athlete)*
Brooke Toohey *(Dir-Natl Membership)*
John Roethlisberger *(Dir-Athlete)*
Karl Heger *(Dir-Athlete)*
Michael Rodrigues *(Dir-Athlete)*
Peter Dodd *(Dir-Natl Membership)*
Tom Koll *(Dir-Natl Membership)*
Tom Meadows *(Dir-Natl Membership)*
Tom Forster *(Coord-High Performance-Women's Natl Team)*
Kathryn Carson *(Chm)*
Li Li Leung *(Pres & CEO)*
Edward Nyman *(Dir-Sports, Medicine & Science)*

USA HOCKEY, INC.
1775 Bob Johnson Dr, Colorado Springs, CO 80906-4090
Tel.: (719) 576-8724   CO
Web Site: http://www.usahockey.com
Year Founded: 1936
Rev.: $43,446,732
Assets: $23,317,998
Liabilities: $21,934,205
Net Worth: $1,383,793
Earnings: ($3,331,918)
Emp.: 116
Fiscal Year-end: 08/31/19
Hockey Promotion Services
N.A.I.C.S.: 711310
Scott Monaghan *(Sr Dir-Ops)*

USA LABS INC.
201 Alhambra Circle, Coral Gables, FL 33134-5107
Tel.: (305) 441-2444
Web Site: http://www.usalabs.com
Year Founded: 1984
Rev.: $26,000,000
Emp.: 25
Cosmetic Preparations
N.A.I.C.S.: 325620
Chuck Stokes *(Pres & CEO)*

Subsidiaries:

USA Labs Inc.   (1)
Ste 158 1 SE 3rd Ave, Miami, FL 33131-1714
Tel.: (305) 441-2444
Sales Range: $10-24.9 Million
Cosmetic Preparations
N.A.I.C.S.: 325620

USA MANAGED CARE ORGANIZATION
1250 S Capital Of Texas Hwy Bldg 3-500, West Lake Hills, TX 78746-6304
Tel.: (512) 306-0201   TX
Web Site: http://www.usamco.com
Year Founded: 1986
Sales Range: $100-124.9 Million
Emp.: 50
Insurance Agents & Brokers
N.A.I.C.S.: 524292
George E. Bogle *(Chm & CEO)*
Hilda Moreno *(Asst VP-Provider Contracting)*

Subsidiaries:

Atlas Administrators Inc.   (1)
PO Box 161748, Austin, TX 78716-1748
Tel.: (512) 306-0201
Web Site: http://www.atlasadmin.com
Sales Range: $25-49.9 Million
Emp.: 20
Claim Processing Services
N.A.I.C.S.: 524292

USA POULTRY & EGG EXPORT COUNCIL
2300 W Park Place Blvd Ste 100, Stone Mountain, GA 30087
Tel.: (770) 413-0006   GA
Web Site: http://www.usapeec.org
Year Founded: 1985
Sales Range: $10-24.9 Million
Emp.: 15
Poultry & Egg Export Association
N.A.I.C.S.: 813910
Greg Tyler *(VP-Mktg)*
Renan Zhuang *(Dir-Economic Analysis)*
Shelly McKee *(Dir-Technical Svcs)*
Marc Killebrew *(Chm)*
Joel Coleman *(Treas & Sec)*

USA PROPERTIES FUND, INC.
3200 Douglas Blvd Ste 200, Roseville, CA 95661
Tel.: (916) 773-6060
Web Site:
   http://www.usapropfund.com
Year Founded: 1988
Sales Range: $100-124.9 Million
Emp.: 200
Land Subdividing Services
N.A.I.C.S.: 237210
Geoffrey Brown *(Pres)*
Darren Bobrowsky *(Principal & Sr VP-Fin)*
Sean Reynolds *(Mgr-Dev)*
April Atkinson *(Exec VP-Property Mgmt)*

USA RESTAURANTS, INC.
1700 Pacific Ave Ste 2680, Dallas, TX 75201
Tel.: (214) 760-1000   NV
Year Founded: 2014
Restaurant Owner & Operator
N.A.I.C.S.: 722511
Jeffrey Love *(Chm & Pres)*
Tommy Hoang *(CEO)*

USA SUMMIT DISTRIBUTION, LLC.
6290 Northern Blvd, East Norwich, NY 11732
Tel.: (516) 628-8486
Web Site:
   http://www.usasummitorder.com
Year Founded: 2000
Sporting Equipment Distr
N.A.I.C.S.: 423910
Larry Locks *(CEO)*

USA SWIMMING
1 Olympic Plz, Colorado Springs, CO 80909
Tel.: (719) 866-4578   CO
Web Site:
   http://www.usaswimming.org
Year Founded: 2005
Sales Range: $25-49.9 Million
Emp.: 97
Fitness & Recreational Sports Centers
N.A.I.C.S.: 713940
Frank Busch *(Dir-National Team)*
Matthew Farrell *(CMO)*
James F. Harvey *(CFO)*
Pat Hogan *(Dir-Club Dev)*
Mary Jo Swalley *(VP-Admin)*
Jeff Gudman *(VP-Program Dev)*
David Berkoff *(VP-Technical)*
Tim Liebhold *(VP-Athletes)*
Kelly Otto *(Exec VP-Athletes)*
John Morse *(Sec)*
Stu Hixon *(Treas)*
Deborah Hesse *(Exec Dir)*
Lindsay Mintenko *(Dir-National Team Mng)*
Keenan Robinson *(Dir-Natl Team High Performance)*
Tim Hinchey *(Pres & CEO)*
Isabelle McLemore *(Sr Dir-Comm)*
Bob Vincent *(Chm)*

USA TECHNOLOGY SERVICES, LLC
501 Church St NE Ste 306, Vienna, VA 22180
Tel.: (703) 281-8901
Web Site:
   http://www.usatechnology.us
Year Founded: 2002
Rev.: $12,200,000
Emp.: 75
Electrical Equipment Merchant Whslr
N.A.I.C.S.: 423610
Michael P. Berard *(CEO)*
Kirk Price *(CFO & VP)*

USA TRIATHLON
5825 Delmonico Dr Ste 200, Colorado Springs, CO 80919
Tel.: (719) 597-9090   CO
Web Site: http://www.usatriathlon.org
Year Founded: 2012
Sales Range: $10-24.9 Million
Emp.: 83
Athlete Support Services
N.A.I.C.S.: 711219
Chuck Menke *(CMO)*
Sharon Carns *(Sr Mgr-Governance Affairs & HR)*
Mike Wien *(VP)*
Barry Siff *(Pres)*
Kevin Haas *(Treas)*
Kevin Sullivan *(Sec)*
Victoria Brumfiel *(Interim CEO)*
Scott Schnitzspahn *(Gen Mgr-High Performance)*

USA.NET, INC.
1155 Kelly Johnson Blvd Ste 300, Colorado Springs, CO 80920-3932
Tel.: (719) 265-2930   CO
Web Site: http://www.usa.net
Year Founded: 1998
Sales Range: $25-49.9 Million
Emp.: 65
Electronic Messaging Services
N.A.I.C.S.: 517810
Alan Hallberg *(CMO)*
Neal Watkins *(Chief Product Officer)*
Neil Medley *(COO)*

USAA REAL ESTATE COMPANY
9830 Colonnade Blvd Ste 600, San Antonio, TX 78230-2239

USAA REAL ESTATE COMPANY

USAA Real Estate Company—(Continued)
Tel.: (210) 641-8400   DE
Web Site: http://www.usaarealco.com
Year Founded: 1982
Sales Range: $10-24.9 Million
Emp.: 13,000
Real Estate Company
N.A.I.C.S.: 531390
Len O'Donnell (Pres & CEO)
Jim Hime (CFO)
Scott Stuckman (Head-Global Investors Grp)
Stanley Alterman (Exec Mng Dir-Asset Mgmt)
Pat Irwin (Chief Admin Officer)
Will McIntosh (Exec Mng Dir)
Sam Mitts (Exec Mng Dir-Office Asset Mgmt)
Bruce Petersen (Exec Mng Dir-Investments)
Steve Waters (Chief Legal Officer)
Ryan Krauch (Exec Mng Dir)

USABLE CORPORATION
601 S Gaines St, Little Rock, AR 72201
Tel.: (501) 378-2307   AR
Year Founded: 1948
Holding Company; Insurance Products & Services
N.A.I.C.S.: 551112
Calvin E. Kellogg (Pres)

Subsidiaries:

Life & Specialty Ventures, LLC   (1)
17500 Chenal Pkwy, Little Rock, AR 72223
Tel.: (501) 212-8852
Web Site: http://www.lsvusa.com
Holding Company; Life & Specialty Insurance Products & Services
N.A.I.C.S.: 551112
James F. Casey (Pres & CEO)
Julie Marshall (Exec VP-Partner Mgmt & Dev)
Edward Allan Murphy (Exec VP-Dental)
Solomon Brotman (VP-Clinical Ops-Natl)
Rich Macy (COO)
Danny Timblin (Chief Growth Officer)
Andrew Hottell (VP-Mktg & Strategic Plng)

Subsidiary (Domestic):

USAble Life Insurance Company   (2)
17500 Chenal Pkwy Ste 500, Little Rock, AR 72223
Tel.: (501) 375-7200
Web Site: http://www.usablelife.com
Life Insurance Products & Services
N.A.I.C.S.: 524113
James F. Casey (Pres & CEO)
John Moran (CFO & Exec VP-Fin)
Rich Macy (COO)
Brian Black (Gen Counsel & VP)
Julie Marshall (Exec VP-Partner Mgmt & Dev)
Edward Allan Murphy (Exec VP-Dental)
Chris Calos (Sr VP-Natl Grp Sls)
Andrew Hottell (VP-Mktg & Strategic Plan)
Steve Valenti (Chief Revenue Officer)

USAble MCO   (1)
601 S Gaines St, Little Rock, AR 72201
Tel.: (501) 378-2307
Web Site: http://www.usablemco.com
Workers' Compensation Management Services
N.A.I.C.S.: 524298

USAble Mutual Insurance Company   (1)
601 S Gaines St, Little Rock, AR 72201
Tel.: (501) 378-2307
Web Site: http://www.usablemutual.com
Health Insurance Products & Services
N.A.I.C.S.: 524114
Curtis Edwin Barnett (Pres & CEO)
Gray Donald Dillard (CFO & Treas)
David Bridges (Chief Admin Officer & Exec VP-Internal Ops)
Alicia Berkemeyer (Sr VP-Provider Network Services)
Calvin Eugene Kellogg (Chief Strategy Officer & Exec VP)

James Lee Douglass (Sec)
Steve Spaulding (Exec VP-Enterprise Networks)
Steve Abell (VP-Strategic Services)
Jim Bailey (Sr VP)
Judy Blevins (Sr VP-Enterprise Internal Ops)
Dan Bloodworth (VP-Alternate Payment Initiatives)
Richard Cooper (VP-HR)
David Greenwood (VP-Enterprise Business Intelligence)
Melvin Hardy (VP-IT)
Kim Henderson (VP-Information Systems)
David Jacobson (VP-Medicaid Strategy & Bus Dev)
Marcus James (VP-Claims Admin)
Hal Norman (VP-Customer Accounts & Membership)
Eric Paczewitz (VP-Corp Mktg)
Kathy Ryan (Sr VP-Information systems & Tech)
Wendy See (VP-Pharmacy & Primary Care Programs)
Phillip Sherrill (VP-Internal Control & Reporting)
Sam Vorderstrasse (VP-Actuarial Services)
Scott Winter (VP-Financial Services)
Mark Jansen (Chief Medical Officer & VP)
Max Greenwood (VP-Govt & Media Affairs)
Matthew Vannatta (VP-Consumer & Retail Markets)

Division (Domestic):

Arkansas Blue Cross and Blue Shield   (2)
601 S Gaines St, Little Rock, AR 72201
Tel.: (501) 378-2307
Web Site: http://www.arkansasbluecross.com
Health Insurance Products & Services
N.A.I.C.S.: 524114
Curtis Edwin Barnett (Pres & CEO)
Alicia Berkemeyer (Chief Health Mgmt Officer & Exec VP)

USABLENET, INC.
500 7th Ave 8th Fl, New York, NY 10018
Tel.: (212) 965-5388   DE
Web Site: http://www.usablenet.com
Year Founded: 2000
Sales Range: $50-74.9 Million
Emp.: 250
Mobile Communications Services
N.A.I.C.S.: 517810
Caity Tully (Mgr-Mktg)
Darcy Cottrell (Reg Dir)
Rodney Cummins (Project Mngr)
Chris Telander (Head-HR)

Subsidiaries:

Usablenet UK Ltd.   (1)
11A Curtain Road, London, EC2A 3LT, United Kingdom
Tel.: (44) 2036173200
Mobile Communications Services
N.A.I.C.S.: 517810

USAN, INC.
3080 Northwoods Cir, Norcross, GA 30071
Tel.: (770) 729-1449
Web Site: http://www.usan.com
Year Founded: 1989
Call Center Solutions
N.A.I.C.S.: 561422
Steven P. Walton (Pres & CEO)
Rocky Livingston (CIO)
Farid Shenassa (CTO)
Donny Jackson (Sr VP-Software Dev)
Loyd Olson (COO)
Steve Herlocher (Sr VP-Mktg)

USBID, INC.
2320 Commerce Park Dr, Palm Bay, FL 32905
Tel.: (321) 725-9565
Web Site: http://www.usbid.com
Year Founded: 1998
Internet Service Provider

N.A.I.C.S.: 517810
Gary Heyes (Pres & CEO)
Mark Caulfield (CFO & Controller)
Stephen Du Mont (Chm)

USC CONSULTING GROUP, LLC
3000 Bayport Dr Ste 1010, Tampa, FL 33607
Tel.: (813) 636-4004   DE
Web Site: http://www.usccg.com
Year Founded: 1968
Sales Range: $10-24.9 Million
Emp.: 150
Management Consulting Services
N.A.I.C.S.: 541618
George W. Coffey (Pres & CEO)
Richard W. Gross (Sr VP-Analysis & Bus Acq)
David W. Shouldice (Mng Dir-Global Mining & Metals Practice & VP)
David Riggs (Exec VP-Bus Dev)
Ted Buckles (Exec VP & Dir-Ops)
Joe Politoske (Partner, VP & Sr Acct Exec)

USC CREDIT UNION
3720 S Flower St CUB 1st Fl, Los Angeles, CA 90089
Tel.: (213) 821-7100   CA
Web Site: http://www.usccreditunion.org
Year Founded: 1973
Sales Range: $10-24.9 Million
Emp.: 66
Financial Management Services
N.A.I.C.S.: 522130
Christine Schwarz (VP-Real Estate Lending)
Richard E. McCormick (Assoc Dir-Maintenance, Special Events & Trams)

USC LLC
2320 124th Rd, Sabetha, KS 66534-9459
Web Site: http://www.uscllc.com
Farm & Garden Machinery & Equipment Merchant Whslr
N.A.I.C.S.: 423820
Tery Keene (Mgr)

USCUTTER INC.
17945 NE 65th St Ste 200, Redmond, WA 98052
Tel.: (425) 481-3555
Web Site: http://www.uscutter.com
Year Founded: 2005
Sales Range: $10-24.9 Million
Emp.: 28
Sign & Banner Supplies
N.A.I.C.S.: 339950
Karl Bowman (Pres)

USDIAGNOSTICS, INC.
2 Parade St, Huntsville, AL 35806
Tel.: (256) 534-4881
Web Site: http://www.usdiagnostics.com
Sales Range: $1-9.9 Million
Emp.: 21
Drug Testing Device Distr
N.A.I.C.S.: 423450
Larry Hartselle (Pres & CEO)
Brian Drake (Dir-Sls)
Pete Taft (Mgr-Warehouse & Shipping)
Pheaton Guinn (Dir-Mktg)

USE CREDIT UNION
10120 Pacific Heights Blvd Ste 100, San Diego, CA 92121
Tel.: (858) 795-6100   CA
Web Site: http://www.usecu.org
Year Founded: 1936
Sales Range: $25-49.9 Million

U.S. PRIVATE

Emp.: 208
Credit Union Operator
N.A.I.C.S.: 522130
Les Overman (Vice Chm)

USEM INC.
703 17th Ave NW, Austin, MN 55912
Tel.: (507) 433-1871
Web Site: http://www.useminc.com
Sales Range: $10-24.9 Million
Emp.: 40
Sales of New & Used Automobiles
N.A.I.C.S.: 441110
Tanner Asa (Gen Mgr)

USER CENTRIC COMMUNICATIONS
PO Box 411, New York, NY 10025
Tel.: (212) 748-3600
Web Site: http://www.usercentric.net
Year Founded: 1999
Sales Range: $10-24.9 Million
Emp.: 3
Scientific & Technical Consulting Services
N.A.I.C.S.: 541690
Simon Ginsberg (Founder & Pres)
Jodd Readick (Chm)
Eddie Davis (COO)

USER FRIENDLY HOME SERVICES, LLC
10200 Grogan's Mill Rd Ste 440, Woodland, TX 77380
Tel.: (877) 235-0708
Web Site: https://www.userfriendlyhomeservices.com
Plumbing Services
N.A.I.C.S.: 238220
Bruce Howard (CEO)

Subsidiaries:

Crestwood Plumbing, Inc.   (1)
6244 Old Lagrange Rd, Crestwood, KY 40014
Tel.: (502) 241-2101
Web Site: http://www.crestwoodplumbinginc.com
Rev.: $1,300,000
Emp.: 15
Site Preparation Contractor
N.A.I.C.S.: 238910

Falls Heating & Cooling, Inc.   (1)
461 Munroe Falls Ave, Cuyahoga Falls, OH 44221
Tel.: (330) 929-8777
Web Site: http://www.fallsheating.com
Sales Range: $1-9.9 Million
Emp.: 35
Plumbing, Heating, Air-Conditioning, Nsk
N.A.I.C.S.: 238220
Larry K. Burris (Pres)

USER INSIGHT, INC.
50 Glenlake Pkwy Ste 150, Atlanta, GA 30328
Tel.: (770) 391-1099
Web Site: http://www.userinsight.com
Year Founded: 2002
Rev.: $3,500,000
Emp.: 35
Computer System Design Services
N.A.I.C.S.: 541512
Kevin O'Connor (Pres & CEO)
Michele Hughes (Controller)

USERFUL CORPORATION
3001 Bishop Dr Ste 300, San Ramon, CA 94583
Tel.: (702) 290-8649
Web Site: http://www.userful.com
Year Founded: 2003
Sales Range: $1-9.9 Million
Emp.: 61
Software Development Services
N.A.I.C.S.: 541511
John Marshall (CEO)
Timothy Griffin (CTO)

COMPANIES

Prati Shrestha *(VP-Fin)*
Daniel Griffin *(VP-Mktg)*
Kevin Dillon *(VP-Channels & Alliances)*

USERVOICE, INC.
121 2nd St Fl 4, San Francisco, CA 94105
Tel.: (415) 309-1158
Web Site: http://www.uservoice.com
Year Founded: 2008
Sales Range: $10-24.9 Million
Emp.: 20
Software Publisher
N.A.I.C.S.: 513210
Richard White *(Founder & CEO)*
Joshua Rudd *(Dir-User Experience)*
Jonathan Novak *(CTO)*
Evan Hamilton *(Head-Community)*
Ted Choper *(Head-Customer Support)*
Des Traynor *(Co-Founder & VP-Customer Success)*
Jessica Semaan *(Mgr-Customer Svc Ops)*
Dwight Crow *(Product Mgr)*
Danny Bloomfield *(VP-Sls & Bus Dev)*

USF COLLECTIONS INC.
1385 Broadway Ste 1012A, New York, NY 10018-6001
Tel.: (212) 302-0280
Web Site: http://www.usfcollections.com
Sales Range: $10-24.9 Million
Emp.: 8
Importer & Distributor of Clothing
N.A.I.C.S.: 424350
Ranjit Khanna *(Pres)*
Kiran Rathod *(Mgr-Credit)*

USF FEDERAL CREDIT UNION
13302 USF Palm Dr, Tampa, FL 33612
Tel.: (813) 569-2000   FL
Web Site: http://www.usffcu.com
Year Founded: 1959
Credit Union
N.A.I.C.S.: 522130
Richard J. Skaggs *(Pres & CEO)*
Miles Strickland *(CFO & Sr VP)*
Deborah Clark *(CMO)*
Zachary Churchill *(VP-Lending)*
James Stock *(CTO)*

USFALCON, INC.
1 Copley Pkwy Ste 200, Morrisville, NC 27560
Tel.: (919) 388-3778
Web Site: http://www.usfalcon.com
Year Founded: 1999
Information Technology Services
N.A.I.C.S.: 541512
Peter von Jess *(Chm)*
Stephanie Martin *(VP-HR)*
Zannie Smith *(CEO)*
Jerry Tussing *(COO)*
Mark Cravens *(VP-Ops)*

USFI, INC.
500 W 140th St, Gardena, CA 90248
Tel.: (310) 768-1937
Web Site: http://www.usfifoods.com
Sales Range: $10-24.9 Million
Emp.: 45
Food Service Distr
N.A.I.C.S.: 424410
Gary T. Place *(Pres & CEO)*
Chris D. Lee *(Exec VP)*
Steven Choi *(VP)*
William Baek *(CFO)*
James Cho *(Dir-Pur)*
Larry Rosenberg *(Dir-Korea)*

USHER TRANSPORT INC.
3801 Shanks Ln, Louisville, KY 40216
Tel.: (502) 449-4000
Web Site: http://www.ushertransport.com
Rev.: $24,877,942
Emp.: 110
Contract Haulers
N.A.I.C.S.: 484121
Edward Watson *(CFO, Treas & Sec)*
Eric Mink *(Gen Mgr)*
Bill Usher *(Pres)*
Keith Judd *(Dir-Maintenance)*
Jesse Gosman *(Mgr-Sls & Recruiting)*

USHIP, INC.
205 Brazos St, Austin, TX 78701-4015
Tel.: (512) 773-7646
Web Site: http://www.uship.com
Year Founded: 2003
Sales Range: $1-9.9 Million
Emp.: 51
Website Facilitating Shipping Transportation
N.A.I.C.S.: 517810
Jay Manickam *(Co-Founder & VP-Strategy & Ops)*
Matt Chasen *(Co-Founder)*
Shawn Bose *(VP & Gen Mgr)*
Bob Bearden *(CFO)*
Heather Hoover-Salomon *(CEO)*
James J. Martell *(Exec Chm)*

USI SERVICES GROUP
51 Progress St, Union, NJ 07083
Tel.: (973) 376-6000   NJ
Web Site: http://www.usiservicesgroup.com
Year Founded: 1993
Sales Range: $25-49.9 Million
Emp.: 9,000
Building Maintenance Services
N.A.I.C.S.: 561720
Frederick Goldring *(Pres & CEO)*
Richard Goldring *(VP-Sls)*

USI TECHNOLOGIES, INC.
29219 Canwood St, Agoura Hills, CA 91301
Web Site: http://www.us.upsellit.com
Year Founded: 2005
Sales Range: $1-9.9 Million
Emp.: 44
Software Development Services
N.A.I.C.S.: 541511
Chris Wampler *(CEO)*

USI WIRELESS
12450 Wayzata Blvd Ste 121, Minnetonka, MN 55305-1926
Tel.: (952) 253-3262
Web Site: http://www.USIWireless.com
Year Founded: 1995
Sales Range: $1-9.9 Million
Emp.: 44
Internet Service Provider & Distr
N.A.I.C.S.: 449210
Sam H. Turner *(Mgr-Customer Support)*
Jacques Joubert *(Engr-Fiber-Optic Network)*

USI, INC.
98 Fort Path Rd, Madison, CT 06443
Tel.: (800) 282-9290   CT
Web Site: https://www.usi-laminate.com
Year Founded: 1975
Laminating Equipment & Supplies Mfr & Whslr
N.A.I.C.S.: 333310
Deborah H. Anderson *(Owner & Founder)*
Peter Gianacopolos *(Pres & CEO)*

USIBELLI COAL MINE, INC.
100 River Rd, Healy, AK 99743
Tel.: (907) 452-2625   AK
Web Site: http://www.usibelli.com
Year Founded: 1943
Sales Range: $10-24.9 Million
Emp.: 90
Miner of Bituminous Coal
N.A.I.C.S.: 212114
Lorali Simon *(VP-External Affairs)*
Glen Weaver *(CFO & VP-Fin)*
Alan Renshaw *(VP-Ops & Gen Mgr)*
Joseph E. Usibelli Jr. *(Pres)*

USIC, LLC
9045 River Rd Ste 300, Indianapolis, IN 46240
Tel.: (317) 575-7800
Web Site: http://www.usicllc.com
Sales Range: $250-299.9 Million
Emp.: 5,000
Utility Infrastructure Locating Services
N.A.I.C.S.: 541330
Jemmie Wang *(VP-Strategic Projects)*
Jim O'Malley *(CFO)*
Michael Johnson *(Chief Integration Officer)*
Timothy M. Seelig *(Sr VP-Mktg & Sls)*
Caryn Hildreth *(Dir-HR & Benefits)*
Amit Shankar *(CIO)*
Christa Harrell *(VP-HR)*
Trent Bowers *(Chief Comml Officer)*
Mike Ryan *(Pres & CEO)*
David Parker *(VP-Corp Affairs)*

Subsidiaries:

Blood Hound, LLC   (1)
750 Patricks Pl, Brownsburg, IN 46112
Tel.: (317) 858-9830
Web Site: http://www.bhug.com
Underground Utility Locating & Mapping Sevices
N.A.I.C.S.: 541370
Mark Mason *(Pres & CEO)*

Subsidiary (Domestic):

Subsurface Utility Imaging, LLC   (2)
9478 River Rd, Marcy, NY 13403-0000
Tel.: (315) 797-5194
Web Site: http://www.subsurfaceui.com
Surveying & Mapping Services
N.A.I.C.S.: 541370
James S. Thew *(Project Mgr)*

USLEGAL, INC.
3720 Flowood Dr, Jackson, MS 39232
Tel.: (601) 896-0180
Web Site: http://www.uslegalforms.com
Holding Company; Legal Services
N.A.I.C.S.: 551112
Frank D. Edens *(Founder & CEO)*
Carrie Anna Criado *(Chief Mktg & Comm Officer & Atty)*
Edward Tyler *(Dir-Partnership Alliances)*
Katie Edens *(CFO)*

Subsidiaries:

U.S. Legal Forms, Inc.   (1)
3720 Flowood Dr, Flowood, MS 39232
Tel.: (601) 896-0180
Web Site: http://www.uslegalforms.com
Sales Range: $1-9.9 Million
Emp.: 20
Legal Forms Publishing
N.A.I.C.S.: 323111
Frank D. Edens *(Founder & CEO)*

USM BUSINESS SYSTEMS, INC.
14175 Sullyfield Cir Ste 400, Chantilly, VA 20151
Tel.: (703) 263-0855
Web Site: http://www.usmsystems.com
Year Founded: 1999

Sales Range: $10-24.9 Million
Emp.: 200
Computer System Design Services
N.A.I.C.S.: 541512
Madan Kondayyagari *(Pres & CEO)*

USMETALS, INC.
4535 W Sahara Ave Ste 200, Las Vegas, NV 89102
Tel.: (702) 933-4034   NV
Year Founded: 2000
Sales Range: Less than $1 Million
Metal Mining
N.A.I.C.S.: 212290
Robert Dultz *(Chm, Pres, CEO & Acting CFO)*

USNR
1981 Schurman Way, Woodland, WA 98674
Tel.: (360) 225-8267
Web Site: http://www.usnr.com
Sawmill & Woodworking Equipment Mfr & Distr
N.A.I.C.S.: 333243
George Van Hoomissen *(Pres)*
John Reed *(Acct Mgr-Intl)*
Jeff Stephens *(Sr VP)*

Subsidiaries:

Inovec Inc.   (1)
1457 Westec Dr, Eugene, OR 97402
Tel.: (541) 485-7127
Web Site: http://www.inovec.com
Sales Range: $10-24.9 Million
Emp.: 55
Scanning, Optimization & Control Systems Mfr for the Forest Products Industry
N.A.I.C.S.: 541512

USNR   (1)
3550 - 45th Street SE, Salmon Arm, V1E 1X1, BC, Canada
Tel.: (250) 832-7116
Web Site: https://www.usnr.com
Sales Range: $10-24.9 Million
Emp.: 85
Sawmill & Wood Product Mfr & Distr
N.A.I.C.S.: 321113

USNY BANK
389 Hamilton St, Geneva, NY 14456
Tel.: (315) 789-1500
Web Site: http://www.usnybank.com
Year Founded: 2007
Emp.: 16
Commercial Banking Services
N.A.I.C.S.: 522110
R. Michael Briggs *(Pres & CEO)*
Michael Fratto *(VP)*
Christine M. Amos *(VP)*
Karen Luttrell *(VP-Compliance)*
Amy McNicholas *(VP-Credit Admin)*
Peter J. Principato *(VP & Mgr-Retail Lending)*
Rob Sollenne *(CFO)*
Heidi Westfall *(VP-Ops)*

USPP-TRI LAKES, LLC
6525 N Jerome Rd, Alma, MI 48801
Tel.: (989) 463-6445   DE
Web Site: https://www.trilakesllc.com
Investment Services
N.A.I.C.S.: 523999

Subsidiaries:

Barrick Enterprises Inc.   (1)
4307 Delemere Ct, Royal Oak, MI 48073-1809
Tel.: (248) 549-3737
Web Site: http://www.barrickent.com
Sales Range: $10-24.9 Million
Emp.: 30
Petroleum Products
N.A.I.C.S.: 424720
Robert L. Barrick *(Pres)*

USRG MANAGEMENT COMPANY, LLC

USRG MANAGEMENT COMPANY, LLC

USRG Management Company, LLC—(Continued)
2425 Olympic Blvd, Santa Monica, CA 90404
Tel.: (310) 586-3900
Web Site: http://www.usregroup.com
Year Founded: 2006
Sales Range: $1-9.9 Million
Emp.: 14
Renewable Energy Investment Firm
N.A.I.C.S.: 523999
James McDermott (Mng Dir)
Lee Bailey (Mng Dir)
Joshua Haacker (Mng Dir)
Jose Ordonez (Mng Dir)

USROBOTICS CORPORATION
1300 E Woodfield Rd Ste 506, Schaumburg, IL 60173
Tel.: (847) 874-2000
Web Site: http://www.usr.com
Rev.: $500,000,000
Emp.: 95
Modems, Monitors, Terminals & Disk Drives; Computers
N.A.I.C.S.: 449210
Evelina Kramer (Mgr-Ops Support)
Laura Avery (Mgr-Freight Audit & Accts Payable)
Marti Folena (Mgr-Trade & Compliance)

USS MIDWAY MUSEUM
910 N Harbor Dr, San Diego, CA 92101
Tel.: (619) 544-9600 CA
Web Site: http://www.midway.org
Year Founded: 1992
Sales Range: $10-24.9 Million
Emp.: 268
Historical Museum
N.A.I.C.S.: 712110
Joe Gursky (Dir-IT)
Philip Hamilton (CFO)
Liane Morton (Dir-HR)
Jim Nash (Dir-Docent Program)
Charles Nichols (Sr VP)
Malin Burnham (Vice Chm)
Carl Nank (VP-Supply Chain)
Kelly Oden-Prasser (Project Mgr-Dynamic Pricing Stakeholder Outreach)
Sam Attisha (VP-Business Dev & Pub Affairs)
Christopher Neils (Gen Counsel)
John Hawkins (Chm)
Vangie Burt Regan (Sec)
Vic Salazar (Pres & CEO)

UST GLOBAL INC.
5 Polaris Way, Aliso Viejo, CA 92656
Tel.: (949) 716-8757 DE
Web Site: http://www.ust-global.com
Year Founded: 1999
Computer Related Consulting Services
N.A.I.C.S.: 541512
Tony Velleca (Chief Information Security Officer)
Robert Dutile (Chief Comml Officer)
Krishna Sudheendra (CEO)
Arun Narayanan (Pres)
Alexander Varghese (Co-COO)
Manu Gopinath (Co-COO)
Sunil Balakrishnan (Chif Values Officer, & Head-Dev Center Ops-Global)
Catherine Gardner (Head-Global Legal Svcs)
Sunil Kanchi (CIO &Chief Investment Officer)
Paras Chandaria (Chm)
Kevin Adams (Pres-Healthcare Platform Solutions)
Trent Mayberry (Chief Digital Officer)
Niranjan Ram (CTO)
Diana Rosella (CFO)
Leslie Schultz (CMO)

Jose Aguilaniedo (Mng Dir-Spain & LATAM)
BG Moore (Pres-Xpanxion)
Stephe Raj (Gen Mgr-Digital Bus)
Anna Tassioula (Gen Mgr & Head-Global Fin Svcs Grp)
Yuval Wollman (Chief Cyber Officer & Mng Dir-Israel)
Sajesh Gopinath (Gen Mgr)
Gilroy Mathew (VP & Head-Semiconductor)
Anilal Ravi (Chief Product Officer)

Subsidiaries:

MobileComm Professionals, Inc. (1)
465 W President George Bush Hwy Ste 200, Richardson, TX 75080
Tel.: (972) 633-5100
Web Site: http://www.mcpsinc.com
Sales Range: $10-24.9 Million
Emp.: 300
Computer Integrated Systems Design
N.A.I.C.S.: 541512
Harvinder Cheema (CEO)

Pneuron Corp. (1)
5 Polaris Way, Aliso Viejo, CA 92656
Tel.: (949) 716-8757
Web Site: http://www.pneuron.com
Management Consulting Services
N.A.I.C.S.: 541618

Xpanxion, LLC (1)
333 N Point Ctr E Ste 270, Alpharetta, GA 30022
Tel.: (678) 867-0699
Web Site: http://www.xpanxion.com
Sales Range: $10-24.9 Million
Emp.: 500
Software Publishing Services
N.A.I.C.S.: 513210
David Stephens (CIO)
Nicholas Eurek (CFO)
S. Ramprasad (CEO-India Offshore Center)
Ronald Small (VP-Acct Svcs)
Cindy Westbrook (VP-Corp Ops)
Chris Artabeasy (Pres-Creative Svcs)
Prasanna Joshi (VP-Fin & Admin)
A. Leslie (Controller-Atlanta)
H. Tyson (Project Mgr-Nebraska Ops)
G. Pankaj (Mgr-Technical-India)
A. Gaurav (Assoc Mgr-Program-India)
E. Surendran (Engr-Quality Assurance-India)
Chad Sanders (COO)
Michael Halbert (VP-Sls-Atlanta)
Douglas Loo (Dir-ADA Compliance)
Kelly Barnes (VP-Rural Centers-Kearney)
Leslie Abrahamson (Sr VP-Fin)
Rahul Bhanose (Assoc VP)
Nathan Philippi (Dir-Quality Assurance)
Lance Rall (Sr Dir-Nebraska Ops)
Philip Sears (Dir-Kansas Ops)
Yogesh Thokal (Dir-Client Svcs)
Mason Wambolt (Dir-Colorado Ops)
Vincent Picerno (VP-Client Experience & Svcs)

UST MAMIYA
14950 FAA Blvd Ste 200, Fort Worth, TX 76155-2235
Tel.: (817) 267-2219 TX
Web Site: http://www.ustmamiya.com
Year Founded: 1991
Sales Range: $10-24.9 Million
Emp.: 35
Mfr of Carbon Fiber Golf Shafts & Premium Grips
N.A.I.C.S.: 339920
Lori Rice (VP-Ops Plng)

UT PHYSICIANS
7000 Fannin St Ste 1715, Houston, TX 77030
Tel.: (832) 325-7223
Web Site: http://www.utphysicians.com
Sales Range: $10-24.9 Million
Emp.: 30
Billing & Bookkeeping Service
N.A.I.C.S.: 541219
Andrew Casas (COO)

UTAH ASSOCIATED MUNICIPLE POWER SYSTEMS
155 N 400 W Ste 480, Salt Lake City, UT 84103
Tel.: (801) 566-3938
Web Site: http://www.uamps.com
Year Founded: 1980
Sales Range: $25-49.9 Million
Emp.: 45
Providers of Electrical Services
N.A.I.C.S.: 221118
Doug Hunter (CEO)
Scott Fox (CFO)
Ben Mitchell (Mgr-Ops & Maintenance)
Kelton Andersen (Dir-Power Metrics)
Marshall Empey (COO)
Mason Baker (Chief Legal Officer & Gen Counsel)
Nathan Hardy (Dir-Power Resources)
Ryan Huntington (Dir-Compliance)

UTAH DISASTER KLEENUP
13081 S Minuteman Dr, Draper, UT 84020-9236
Tel.: (801) 553-1010
Year Founded: 1977
Sales Range: $10-24.9 Million
Emp.: 93
Residential Remodeling Services
N.A.I.C.S.: 236118
Mark Goodmansen (Pres)
Trace Larsen (Dir-Ops)
Scott Oyler (Dir-Tech)

UTAH HOUSING CORPORATION
2479 S Lake Park Blvd, West Valley City, UT 84120-8217
Tel.: (801) 902-8200
Web Site: http://www.utahhousingcorp.org
Year Founded: 1977
Sales Range: $10-24.9 Million
Emp.: 64
Securities Brokerage Services
N.A.I.C.S.: 523150
Grant Whitaker (Pres & CEO)
Cleon P. Butterfield (CFO & Sr VP)
Jonathan Hanks (COO & Sr VP)
Claudia Ogrady (VP-Multifamily Fin)
Deon Spilker (Dir-Mortgage Banking)

UTAH MUNICIPAL POWER AGENCY INC.
75 W 300 N, Spanish Fork, UT 84660-1744
Tel.: (801) 798-7489 UT
Web Site: http://www.umpa.cc
Year Founded: 1980
Sales Range: $50-74.9 Million
Emp.: 20
Electronic Services
N.A.I.C.S.: 221118
Layne Burningham (Gen Mgr)

UTAH OFFICE OF TOURISM
Council Hall 300 N State St, Salt Lake City, UT 84114
Tel.: (801) 538-1030
Web Site: http://www.visitutah.com
Year Founded: 1953
Sales Range: $50-74.9 Million
Emp.: 25
Travel & Tourism Promoter
N.A.I.C.S.: 561591
Ben Dodds (Mgr-Special Projects)
Kelly Day (Mgr-Co-Op Mktg)
Tara Roner (Mgr-Bookstore-ZNHA)

UTAH PAPER BOX COMPANY INC.
920 S 700 W, Salt Lake City, UT 84104
Tel.: (801) 363-0093

U.S. PRIVATE

Web Site: http://www.upbslc.com
Rev.: $23,458,567
Emp.: 200
Folding Paperboard Boxes
N.A.I.C.S.: 322212
Paul B. Keyser (CEO)
Teri Jensen (VP)
Richard Severson (Controller)

UTAH SCIENTIFIC, INC.
4750 Wiley Post Way Ste 150, Salt Lake City, UT 84116-2810
Tel.: (801) 575-8801
Web Site: http://www.utahscientific.com
Sales Range: $50-74.9 Million
Emp.: 49
Mfr of Routers & Switchers for Broadcasting
N.A.I.C.S.: 334220
Tom Harmon (Chm)
David Burland (Pres & CEO)
Troy Davis (VP-Sls-North America)
Scott Barella (CTO)
Jim Barnhurst (Mgr-Technical Svc)
Mario Moreno (Engr-Field Svc)
Randy Rose (Dir-Sls Engrg)
John Bell (Mgr-Customer Svc)

UTAH STATE UNIVERSITY, SPACE DYNAMICS LABORATORY
1695 Research Pkwy, Logan, UT 84341
Tel.: (435) 797-4600
Web Site: http://www.sdl.usu.edu
Sales Range: $50-74.9 Million
Emp.: 500
Infrared Sensors, Solid State
N.A.I.C.S.: 334415
Brande Faupell (Exec Dir-HR)
James Taylor (Exec Dir-Uintah Basin Campus)

UTAH SYMPHONY & OPERA
Abavenel Hall 123 W South Temple, Salt Lake City, UT 84101-1496
Tel.: (801) 533-5626
Web Site: http://www.usuo.org
Year Founded: 1940
Sales Range: $10-24.9 Million
Emp.: 100
Symphony Orchestra & Opera Producer
N.A.I.C.S.: 711110
David S. Green (COO & Sr VP)
Paula Fowler (Dir-Education & Community Outreach)
Steve Hogan (CFO & VP-Fin)
Michelle Peterson (Mgr-Opera Artistic)
Jeff Bram (VP-Artistic Ops)
Anthony Tolokan (VP-Symphony Artistic Plng)
Paul Meecham (Pres & CEO)

UTAH TRANSIT AUTHORITY
669 W 200 S, Salt Lake City, UT 84101
Tel.: (801) 262-5626
Web Site: http://www.rideuta.com
Sales Range: $25-49.9 Million
Emp.: 2,062
Bus Line Operations
N.A.I.C.S.: 485113
Erika Shubin (Mgr-PR & Mktg)
Steve Meyer (Interim Exec Dir)
Mary DeLaMare-Schaefer (Reg Gen Mgr-Bus Unit-Timpanogos)
Robert McKinley (Chm)
Jeff Hawker (Vice Chm)
Sherrie Hall Everett (Vice Chm)
Nichol Bourdeaux (VP-External Rels)
Todd Provost (VP-Ops)

UTAH ZOOLOGICAL SOCIETY

2600 Sunnyside Ave, Salt Lake City, UT 84108
Tel.: (801) 584-1709
Year Founded: 1951
Sales Range: $10-24.9 Million
Emp.: 232
Zoological Museum Operator
N.A.I.C.S.: 712110
Paul M. Dougan (VP)
Partick Hogle (Treas)
Craig Dinsmore (Exec Dir)
James E. Hogle Jr. (Pres)

UTC OVERSEAS, INC.
370 W Passaic St Ste 3000, Rochelle Park, NJ 07662
Tel.: (201) 270-4600
Web Site: http://www.utcoverseas.com
Year Founded: 1989
Sales Range: $350-399.9 Million
Emp.: 80
International Logistics & Transportation Services
N.A.I.C.S.: 483111
Brian Posthumus (Chm)
Marco Poisler (Exec VP-Energy & Capital Projects)
Dean Temple (VP)
Hans Meyer (CEO)
Edward Vaz (CFO)
Mirko Knezevic (COO)
Rudy Steudel (Chief Bus Dev Officer)

Subsidiaries:

UTC ACCORD Logistics Australia Pty. Ltd. (1)
Unit 13 34-36 Ralph Street, Alexandria, 2015, NSW, Australia
Tel.: (61) 2 9669 2333
Web Site: http://www.accordlogistics.com.au
Logistics Consulting Servies
N.A.I.C.S.: 541614

UTC International Logistics Limited (1)
No 1 Huaihai Road M Huangpu District Room No 1501-1511, Shanghai, 200021, China
Tel.: (86) 21 63871286
Logistics Consulting Servies
N.A.I.C.S.: 541614

UTC Overseas (HK) Limited (1)
Flat 7B1 34/Floor Cable TV Tower 9 Hoi Shing Road Tsuen Wan, New Territories, Hong Kong, China (Hong Kong)
Tel.: (852) 27821001
Logistics Consulting Servies
N.A.I.C.S.: 541614

UTC Overseas (India) Pvt. Ltd. (1)
Old No 126 New No 257 4B Zafarullah Towers Angappan Naicken Street, Parry's Corner, Chennai, 600 001, India
Tel.: (91) 44 4215 5480
Web Site: http://www.utcoverseas.com
Emp.: 8
Logistics Consulting Servies
N.A.I.C.S.: 541614
Anand Purushothaman (Gen Mgr-Heavy Equipment)

UTC Overseas (Peru) S.A.C. (1)
Jr Bolognesi 235, Miraflores, Lima, 18, Peru
Tel.: (51) 1 243 6517
Logistics Consulting Servies
N.A.I.C.S.: 541614

UTC Overseas (Taiwan) Co., Ltd. (1)
5F No 36 Nanjiang W Rd, Taipei, 00103, Taiwan
Tel.: (886) 2 2556 2276
Logistics Consulting Servies
N.A.I.C.S.: 541614

UTC Overseas Bolivia SRL. (1)
Av Pirai Esquina Aruma Edificio Santa Monica Piso 1 Of 4, Santa Cruz, Bolivia
Tel.: (591) 3 327 2032
Logistics Consulting Servies
N.A.I.C.S.: 541614

UTC Overseas Brasil Ltda. (1)
Av Rio Branco 26 2nd Floor, 20090-001, Rio de Janeiro, Brazil
Tel.: (55) 21 3478 6000
Web Site: http://www.utcoverseas.com.br
Emp.: 10
Logistics Consulting Servies
N.A.I.C.S.: 541614
Boye Hansen (Branch Mgr)

UTC Overseas Colombia SAS (1)
Edif Centro Empresarial IV Ofc 401 Cra 13 No 94-A 44, Bogota, Colombia
Tel.: (57) 1 805 3046
Logistics Consulting Servies
N.A.I.C.S.: 541614

UTC Overseas Ecuador S.A. (1)
Av De Las Americas Y Av Isidro Ayora Aeropuerto Int'l J J De Olmedo, Edificio TAGSA 1er Piso, Guayaquil, Ecuador
Tel.: (593) 4 216 9112
Logistics Consulting Servies
N.A.I.C.S.: 541614

UTC Overseas GmbH (1)
Industriestrasse 12/12 a, 28199, Bremen, Germany
Tel.: (49) 421 5257 12 0
Web Site: http://www.utcoverseas.de
Logistics Consulting Servies
N.A.I.C.S.: 541614
Hans J. Meyer (Co-Mng Dir)
Jens Murken (Co-Mng Dir)
Stephan Prueser (Gen Mgr-Overseas)

UTC Overseas Inc. (1)
420 Doughty Blvd, Inwood, NY 11096
Tel.: (516) 239-7901
Web Site: http://www.utcoverseas.com
Rev.: $3,000,000
Emp.: 20
Freight Transportation Arrangement
N.A.I.C.S.: 488510
Edward Vaz (CFO)
Marian Clare (Branch Mgr)
Rudy Steudel (Chief Bus Dev Officer)
Mirko Knezevic (COO-Projects-Global)
Marco Poisler (COO-Energy & Capital Projects-Global)
Brian Posthumus (Chm)

UTC Overseas Ireland Ltd (1)
Swords Dublin Airport, Dublin, Ireland
Tel.: (353) 1 862 5544
Logistics Consulting Servies
N.A.I.C.S.: 541614

UTC Overseas Logistics Ltd (1)
10 Kozraktar Str V/2A-3, 1093, Budapest, Hungary
Tel.: (36) 1 445 1545
Logistics Consulting Servies
N.A.I.C.S.: 541614

UTC Overseas Ltd. (1)
13 Z Taghiyev Str Suite 402, Baku, AZ1005, Azerbaijan
Tel.: (994) 12 464 4019
Web Site: http://www.utcoverseas.com
Logistics Consulting Servies
N.A.I.C.S.: 541614

UTC Overseas OY (1)
Asiakkaankatu 3 3 Kerros, 00930, Helsinki, Finland
Tel.: (358) 9 759 2200
Logistics Consulting Servies
N.A.I.C.S.: 541614

UTC Overseas S de RL de CV (1)
Paseo De Las Palmas 731 ALTS 803-0 Col Lomas De Chapultepec, Deleg Miguel Hidalgo, 11000, Mexico, Mexico
Tel.: (52) 55 5005 6726
Logistics Consulting Servies
N.A.I.C.S.: 541614

UTC Overseas S.A. (1)
Av El Bosque Norte 0140 Of 23, Las Condes, Santiago, Chile
Tel.: (56) 2 242 9697
Logistics Consulting Servies
N.A.I.C.S.: 541614

UTC Overseas, AB (1)
Radhustorget 10 2nd Floor, 252 21, Helsingborg, Sweden
Tel.: (46) 42 26 76 60
Logistics Consulting Servies
N.A.I.C.S.: 541614

UTC UK Ltd (1)
Room 15F Manchester Int'l Office Center Styal Road, Manchester, M22 5WB, United Kingdom
Tel.: (44) 161 436 4555
Web Site: http://www.utcoverseas.co.uk
Emp.: 3
Logistics Consulting Servies
N.A.I.C.S.: 541614
Mark Kennedy (Country Mgr)
Zoey Byrne (Gen Mgr)

UTEC CONSTRUCTORS CORP.
7 Liberty Sq, Boston, MA 02109
Tel.: (617) 364-8960
Web Site: http://www.uteccorp.com
Sales Range: $50-74.9 Million
Emp.: 85
Fiscal Year-end: 12/31/15
Cable Laying Construction
N.A.I.C.S.: 237130
Joseph A. Gilmore (Pres & CEO)
Kevin McDononough (Superintendent)

UTEST INC.
153 Cordaville Rd Ste 205, Southborough, MA 01772
Tel.: (508) 480-9999
Web Site: http://www.utest.com
Year Founded: 2007
Sales Range: $10-24.9 Million
Emp.: 105
Software Testing Services
N.A.I.C.S.: 541519
Doron Reuveni (CEO)
Matt Johnston (CMO)
Fumi Matsumoto (CTO)
Roy Solomon (VP-Product Mgmt)

UTICA ENERGY, LLC.
4995 State Rd 91, Oshkosh, WI 54904
Tel.: (920) 230-3835
Web Site: http://www.uticaenergy.com
Year Founded: 2003
Sales Range: $100-124.9 Million
Emp.: 60
Ethyl Alcohol Mfr
N.A.I.C.S.: 325193
Dan Clark (Controller)
Phil Younger (Dir-Alternative Fuels)

UTICA ENTERPRISES, INC.
5750 New Kings St Ste-200, Troy, MI 48098
Tel.: (586) 726-4300
Web Site: http://www.uticaenterprises.com
Year Founded: 1977
Sales Range: $300-349.9 Million
Emp.: 1,500
Holding Company; Industrial Machine Tools & Metalworking Machinery Mfr & Engineering Services
N.A.I.C.S.: 551112
Stefan Wanczyk (Pres & CEO)
Pam Dybek (Mgr-Pur)
Thomas J. Carter (Chm)

Subsidiaries:

Advanced Boring & Tool Company (1)
26950 23 Mi Rd, Chesterfield, MI 48051-1911 (100%)
Tel.: (586) 598-9300
Sales Range: $10-24.9 Million
Emp.: 100
Boring & Machine Tool Metal Fabrication Services
N.A.I.C.S.: 332999
Sue Otts (Office Mgr)
Tom Winkel (Gen Mgr)

General Broach Company (1)
307 Salisbury St, Morenci, MI 49256-1043
Tel.: (517) 458-7555
Web Site: http://www.generalbroach.com
Sales Range: $25-49.9 Million
Emp.: 400
Broaching Machines & Tools Mfr
N.A.I.C.S.: 333517
Kerri Schmitz (Controller)

Utica Products, Inc. (1)
13231 23 Mile Rd, Shelby, MI 48315-2713
Tel.: (586) 726-4300
Sales Range: $25-49.9 Million
Emp.: 500
Provider of Metalworking Services
N.A.I.C.S.: 333519

UTICA GENERAL TRUCK CO. INC.
5636 Horatio St, Utica, NY 13502
Tel.: (315) 732-4300
Web Site: http://www.uticageneral.com
Sales Range: $10-24.9 Million
Emp.: 25
Trucks, Commercial
N.A.I.C.S.: 423110

UTICA NATIONAL INSURANCE GROUP
180 Genessee St, New Hartford, NY 13413
Tel.: (315) 734-2000
Web Site: http://www.uticanational.com
Year Founded: 1975
Sales Range: $250-299.9 Million
Emp.: 1,200
Holding Company
N.A.I.C.S.: 551112
J. Douglas Robinson (Chm & CEO)
Richard Creedon (Pres & COO)

Subsidiaries:

Graphic Arts Mutual Insurance Co. (1)
180 Gensee St, New Hartford, NY 13413
Tel.: (315) 734-2000
Web Site: http://www.uticanational.com
Sales Range: $200-249.9 Million
Insurance Service Provider
N.A.I.C.S.: 524126
Rich Creedon (Gen Mgr)

Republic Franklin Insurance Co. (1)
2 Easton Oval Ste 225, Columbus, OH 43219-1663
Tel.: (614) 823-5300
Web Site: http://www.uticanational.com
Sales Range: $75-99.9 Million
Emp.: 25
Commercial Insurance
N.A.I.C.S.: 524126
Ralph Laspina (Sr VP)

UNI-Service Operations Corporation (1)
180 Genesee St, New Hartford, NY 13413
Tel.: (315) 734-2000
Web Site: http://www.uticanational.com
Sales Range: $200-249.9 Million
Emp.: 800
Insurance Service Provider
N.A.I.C.S.: 524210

Utica Lloyds of Texas (1)
2435 N Central Expwy Ste 400, Richardson, TX 75080
Tel.: (972) 677-6700
Web Site: http://www.uticanational.com
Sales Range: $75-99.9 Million
Emp.: 45
Provider of Insurance Services
N.A.I.C.S.: 524126

Utica Mutual Insurance Company (1)
180 Genesee St, New Hartford, NY 13413-2299
Tel.: (315) 734-2000
Web Site: http://www.uticanational.com
Sales Range: $650-699.9 Million
Multiple-Line Property & Casualty Insurance
N.A.I.C.S.: 524126
J. Douglas Robinson (Chm)
Michael C. Austin (VP & Dir-Corp Comm)

UTICA NATIONAL INSURANCE GROUP

Utica National Insurance Group—(Continued)

Steven P. Guzski (Exec VP & Dir-HR & Facilities)
Richard P. Creedon (Pres & CEO)

Utica National Insurance Co. of Texas (1)
2435 N Central Expy Ste 400, Richardson, TX 75080
Tel.: (972) 677-6700
Web Site: http://www.uticanational.com
Sales Range: $75-99.9 Million
Emp.: 35
Provider of Insurance Services
N.A.I.C.S.: 524126
Brian McCulloch (Sr VP-Resident & Reg Mgr-Southwestern)

UTILI-COMM SOUTH, INC.
7045 Production Ct, Florence, KY 41042
Tel.: (859) 727-1815
Year Founded: 2000
Sales Range: $10-24.9 Million
Emp.: 230
Construction Engineering Services
N.A.I.C.S.: 237310
John Pudenz (Pres)

UTILITIES BOARD OF THE CITY OF FOLEY ALABAMA
413 E Laurel Ave, Foley, AL 36535
Tel.: (251) 943-5001
Web Site: http://www.rivierautilities.com
Sales Range: $50-74.9 Million
Emp.: 185
Provider of Electric & Cable Services; Distributor & Transmitter of Natural Gas; Supplier of Water & Wastewater
N.A.I.C.S.: 221118
Thomas L. DeBell (CEO)

UTILITIES BOARD OF TRUSSVILLE
127 Main St, Trussville, AL 35173
Tel.: (205) 655-3211
Web Site: http://www.trussville.com
Sales Range: $25-49.9 Million
Emp.: 53
Natural Gas Distribution
N.A.I.C.S.: 221210
Gordon Flynn (Chm)

UTILITIES DISTRICT OF WESTERN INDIANA REMC
1666 W State Hwy 54, Bloomfield, IN 47424
Tel.: (812) 384-4446   IN
Web Site: http://www.udwiremc.com
Year Founded: 1936
Sales Range: $25-49.9 Million
Emp.: 68
Electric Power Distr
N.A.I.C.S.: 221122
Brian Sparks (CEO)
Shane Smith (Mgr-Ops & Engrg)
Kim Todd (Mgr-Office Svcs)
Bill Watkins (Treas)
James S. Weimer (Pres)
James A. Jackson (VP)
Roger Shake (Sec)
Dough Chills (CEO)

UTILITIES, INC.
2335 Sanders Rd, Northbrook, IL 60062
Tel.: (847) 498-6440   IL
Web Site: http://www.uiwater.com
Year Founded: 1965
Sales Range: $75-99.9 Million
Emp.: 400
Water & Wastewater Processing Facilities Management
N.A.I.C.S.: 221310
Steve Lubertozzi (Pres)

UTILITY CONCIERGE, LLC
1755 Wittington Pl Ste 600, Dallas, TX 75234   TX
Web Site: http://www.utilityconcierge.com
Year Founded: 2009
Sales Range: $1-9.9 Million
Emp.: 50
Business Management Services
N.A.I.C.S.: 541611
Gabe Abshire (CEO)
Kevin Hockenjos (COO)
Ryan Miner (Sls Mgr)
Andrew Wilson (Ops Mgr)
Jordan Noble (Mgr-Trng)

UTILITY CONTRACTORS INC.
1930 S Hoover Ste 100, Wichita, KS 67209
Tel.: (316) 265-9506
Web Site: http://www.ucict.com
Sales Range: $10-24.9 Million
Emp.: 150
Heavy Construction
N.A.I.C.S.: 541611
Charles F. Grier (Pres & CEO)
Louise Gerwick (CFO)
Jeff Barley (VP-Construction Ops)
David B. Odell (VP-Project Dev)

UTILITY DYNAMICS CORPORATION
23 Commerce Dr, Oswego, IL 60543
Tel.: (630) 554-1722
Web Site: http://www.utilitydynamicscorp.com
Rev: $10,200,000
Emp.: 25
Electric Power Line Construction
N.A.I.C.S.: 237130
William J. Spencer (Pres)

UTILITY EQUIPMENT COMPANY
3739 State St, Bettendorf, IA 52722
Tel.: (563) 355-5376
Web Site: http://www.utilityequipementco.com
Rev: $25,900,000
Emp.: 50
Water Purification Equipment Distributors
N.A.I.C.S.: 423720
Michael Coryn (Pres)
Tom Coryn (VP)
Jeff Hines (Controller)

UTILITY HOLDINGS INC.
8755 Goodwood Blvd, Baton Rouge, LA 70806
Tel.: (225) 928-1000
Web Site: http://www.utilityholdings.com
Sales Range: $25-49.9 Million
Emp.: 10
Water Supply
N.A.I.C.S.: 221310
Mary Mitchell (Controller)

Subsidiaries:

Louisiana Water Company (1)
8755 Goodwood Blvd, Baton Rouge, LA 70806
Tel.: (225) 926-4081
Sales Range: $1-9.9 Million
Water Supply Services
N.A.I.C.S.: 221310

Utility Properties Inc. (1)
8755 Goodwood Blvd, Baton Rouge, LA 70806
Tel.: (225) 928-1000
Web Site: http://www.batonrougewater.com
Commercial & Industrial Building Operation
N.A.I.C.S.: 531120

UTILITY LINE SERVICES INC.
1302 Conshohocken Rd Ste 100, Conshohocken, PA 19428
Tel.: (610) 239-0900
Web Site: http://ulscorp.com
Sales Range: $25-49.9 Million
Emp.: 250
Water, Sewer & Utility Lines
N.A.I.C.S.: 237110
Austin A. Meehan (Pres)
Catherine Haas (Mgr-HR)
Paul Kaplan (Controller)

UTILITY ONE SOURCE L.P.
7701 Independence Ave, Kansas City, MO 64125
Tel.: (816) 241-4888   DE
Web Site: http://www.utility1source.com
Year Founded: 2015
Holding Company; Utility & Energy Equipment Mfr, Sales & Rental Services
N.A.I.C.S.: 551112
Chris Ragot (Chm)

Subsidiaries:

Load King, LLC (1)
701 E Rose St, Elk Point, SD 57025
Tel.: (605) 356-3301
Web Site: http://www.loadkingmfg.com
Specialized Trailer Whslr
N.A.I.C.S.: 336212
Richard Bodnar (Natl Sls Mgr & Mktg Mgr)
Jim Peterson (Gen Mgr)
Jeff Hess (Mgr-Engrg)
Misty Lee Jones (Controller)

MRT Manufacturing, Inc. (1)
12660 E Lynchburg Salem Tpke, Forest, VA 24551
Tel.: (434) 525-2929
Web Site: http://www.feva.net
Forestry Aerial Lift Truck Assembler & Whslr
N.A.I.C.S.: 333120
Bob Dray (VP-Sls & Mktg)
Mark Sharman (Pres & CEO)
Lauren Metz (Coord-HR)

TNT Equipment Sales & Rentals, LLC (1)
6677 Broughton Ave, Columbus, OH 43213
Tel.: (856) 786-7754
Web Site: http://www.tntequip.com
Utility Vehicles & Equipment Sales & Rental Services
N.A.I.C.S.: 423110
Tom Reilly III (Pres)

UCO Equipment, LLC (1)
4045 Hwy 5, Cabot, AR 72023-7309
Tel.: (501) 941-4330
Web Site: http://www.ucoequipment.com
Commercial Utility & Energy Vehicle & Equipment Whslr
N.A.I.C.S.: 423110
Rhonda Usery (Pres & CEO)
Billy Loney (Reg Mgr-Home Office)
Jim Usery (COO)
Jude Gordon (VP-Ops)

Utility Fleet Sales, Ltd. (1)
7200 Jack Newell Blvd S, Fort Worth, TX 76118
Tel.: (682) 200-6999
Web Site: http://www.utilityfleetsales.com
Remanufactured Utility Vehicle & Equipment Whslr
N.A.I.C.S.: 423110
Justin Bateman (Mgr-Sls)

UTILITY SALES & SERVICE, INC.
412 Randolph Dr, Appleton, WI 54913
Tel.: (920) 788-2699   WI
Web Site: http://www.utilityssi.com
Year Founded: 1993
Sales Range: $10-24.9 Million
Emp.: 50
Whol Industrial Equipment Ret New/Used Automobiles
N.A.I.C.S.: 423830

Andy Stefanek (Mgr-Matls)
Dennis Rassel (Mgr-Svc)
Tom Rose (Mgr-Parts)
Tom Harrmann (Mgr-Production)
Tom Saunders (VP & Mgr-Sls)
William Loehrke (Owner & Pres)

Subsidiaries:

Power Equipment Leasing Company (1)
605 Anderson Dr, Romeoville, IL 60446
Tel.: (815) 886-1776
Web Site: http://www.powerequipmentleasing.com
Rev: $1,900,000
Emp.: 15
Construction, Mining & Forestry Machinery & Equipment Rental & Leasing
N.A.I.C.S.: 532412
Steven Schroeder (Pres)

UTILITY SERVICE & SUPPLY INC.
401 Lawton Ave, Monroe, OH 45050
Tel.: (513) 539-7500
Web Site: http://www.utilitysupplies.com
Sales Range: $10-24.9 Million
Emp.: 20
Utilities Supplies
N.A.I.C.S.: 423830
David G. Beatty (Pres)
Mark Beatty (Treas & Sec)
Robert Keever (Controller)
Cindy Beatty (Mgr-Credit)
Jamie Baldridge (Mgr)
Joe Beatty (VP-Pur)
Bob Keever (Controller)

UTILITY TRAILER MANUFACTURING COMPANY, LLC
17295 E RailRd St, City of Industry, CA 91748
Tel.: (626) 965-1541   CA
Web Site: http://www.utilitytrailer.com
Year Founded: 1914
Sales Range: $600-649.9 Million
Emp.: 3,000
Commercial Trailers; Refrigerated Trailers; Flatbed Trailers; Dry Freight Vans; Tautliner Curtain Vans & Aftermarket Parts & Truck Bodies Mfr
N.A.I.C.S.: 336212
Paul F. Bennett (CEO)
Craig Bennett (Sr VP-Sls & Mktg)
Jeffrey Bennett (VP-Engrg)
Stephen Bennett (VP-Pur)
Larry Roland (Dir-Mktg)

Subsidiaries:

Utility Trailer Sales Southeast Texas Inc. (1)
4901 Blaffer St, Houston, TX 77026-1902
Tel.: (713) 674-8000
Web Site: http://www.utilitytrailers.com
Sales Range: $25-49.9 Million
Emp.: 140
Trailer Services
N.A.I.C.S.: 441330
Jon E. Loring (Pres & CEO)
Janet Huckabee (Controller)
Roger Gladden (VP)

UTILITY TRAILER SALES COMPANY ARIZONA
1402 N 22nd Ave, Phoenix, AZ 85009
Tel.: (602) 254-7213
Web Site: http://www.utilityaz.com
Sales Range: $10-24.9 Million
Emp.: 50
Generators
N.A.I.C.S.: 423610
Robert B. Cravens (Chm)
Alan Nash (Controller)
Doug Hansen (Mgr-Sls)
Stacy Massey (Mgr-Shop)
Tom Howard (Mgr-Parts)

UTILITY TRAILER SALES OF BOISE
7350 S Eisenman Rd, Boise, ID 83716
Tel.: (208) 482-5098
Web Site: http://www.utilityboise.com
Emp.: 100
Semi Trailer Parts, Truck Parts, Semi Trailer Service & Repair
N.A.I.C.S.: 423120

UTILITY TRAILER SALES OF CENTRAL CALIFORNIA
2680 S East Ave, Fresno, CA 93706
Tel.: (559) 237-2001
Web Site: http://www.utilitycc.com
Sales Range: $25-49.9 Million
Emp.: 140
Sales of Trailers & Industrial
N.A.I.C.S.: 423830
Kent Callahan (Coord-Sls)

UTILITY TRAILER SALES OF COLORADO LLC
9200 Brighton Rd, Denver, CO 80640
Tel.: (303) 295-1197
Web Site: http://www.utilitytrailer.net
Sales Range: $250-299.9 Million
Emp.: 50
Sales of New & Used Trailers For Trucks
N.A.I.C.S.: 423110
Jeff Martin (Pres)
Bill Hathorn (Gen Mgr)
Johnnie Smith (Gen Mgr)

UTILITY TRI-STATE INC.
15335 E Admiral Pl, Tulsa, OK 74116-2314
Tel.: (918) 437-0010   OK
Web Site: http://www.utilitytristate.com
Year Founded: 1987
Sales Range: $25-49.9 Million
Emp.: 50
Sales & Rental of Trailers
N.A.I.C.S.: 423110
Jeff Smith (Pres)
John Belie (VP)

UTILITY/KEYSTONE TRAILER SALES
1976 Auction Rd, Manheim, PA 17545
Tel.: (717) 653-9444
Web Site: http://www.utilitykeystone.com
Year Founded: 1978
Sales Range: $10-24.9 Million
Emp.: 48
Trucks, Tractors & Trailers: New & Used
N.A.I.C.S.: 441110
Stan Zeamer (Chm)
Bryan Zeamer (Pres)
Brian Von Stetten (Mgr-Svc)
Joe Ritchey (Mgr-New Sls)
Justin Barbush (Mgr-Parts)

UTOPIA, INC.
405 Washington Blvd Ste 203, Mundelein, IL 60060
Tel.: (847) 388-3600
Web Site: http://www.utopiainc.com
Year Founded: 2003
Rev.: $4,500,000
Emp.: 150
IT Services
N.A.I.C.S.: 541511
Arvind J. Singh (Co-Founder, Chm & CEO)
Peter Aynsley-Hartwell (CTO)
Narinder J. Singh (Co-Founder, Vice Chm & COO)
P. N. Subramanian (VP-HR-Global)
Rama Murthy Tenneti (Sr Dir-EAM)
Erast Wortel (Dir-EMEA)
Jonathan Budd (Dir-Sls-Canada)
Braden Slezak (Dir-Sls-US)
Ernie E. Dacho (Sr VP-Consulting Svcs)
Rich Anderson (VP)
Mike Jordan (VP-EAM Practice)
Alok Sharma (VP-Fin)
Randy Connelly (VP-Solutions & Delivery)
Stephen R. Kouba (Sr VP-Sls & Mktg)

UTXO ACQUISITION INC.
203 N LaSalle St Ste 2100, Chicago, IL 60601
Tel.: (713) 505-3208   DE
Year Founded: 2019
Emp.: 2
Investment Services
N.A.I.C.S.: 523999
Wei Huang (CEO)
Yuanyuan Huang (CFO & COO)

UW PROVISION COMPANY, INC.
2315 Pleasant View Rd, Middleton, WI 53562-4270
Tel.: (608) 836-7421   WI
Web Site: http://www.uwprovision.com
Year Founded: 1958
Sales Range: $75-99.9 Million
Fresh Meat Whslr
N.A.I.C.S.: 424470
Steven Kalscheur (Pres)

UWAJIMAYA INC.
4601 6th Ave, Seattle, WA 98108-1716
Tel.: (206) 624-3215   WA
Web Site: http://www.uwajimaya.com
Year Founded: 1928
Rev.: $67,731,914
Emp.: 400
Groceries
N.A.I.C.S.: 424410
Denise Moriguchi (CEO)
James Warjone (Chm)

UWORLD LLC
9111 Cypress Waters Blvd Ste 300, Dallas, TX 75019
Tel.: (713) ...
Web Site: https://www.uworld.com
Year Founded: 2003
E-Learning Providers
N.A.I.C.S.: 611710

V & A CONSULTING ENGINEERS, INC.
155 Grand Ave Ste 700, Oakland, CA 94612-3767
Tel.: (510) 903-6600
Web Site: http://www.vaengineering.com
Emp.: 100
Engineeering Services
N.A.I.C.S.: 541330
Bob Spetich (Gen Mgr-Utilities)

Subsidiaries:
Metzger & Willard, Inc.   (1)
8600 Hidden River Pkwy, Tampa, FL 33637
Tel.: (813) 977-6005
Web Site: http://www.metzgerwillard.com
Emp.: 100
Engineeering Services
N.A.I.C.S.: 541330
Nancy O. Metzger (Pres)

V & R DRYWALL, INC.
6064 Luckett Ct, El Paso, TX 79932
Tel.: (915) 774-0955
Web Site: http://www.vandrdrywall.webs.com
Year Founded: 1981
Sales Range: $10-24.9 Million
Emp.: 145
Drywall Installation Services
N.A.I.C.S.: 238310
Vicente Rodarte (Principal)

V BLOCKCHAIN GROUP INC.
4771 Sweetwater Blvd Ste 199, Sugar Land, TX 77479
Tel.: (713) 898-6818   TX
Year Founded: 2018
Assets: $263,858
Liabilities: $143,102
Net Worth: $120,756
Earnings: ($2,546)
Fiscal Year-end: 03/31/21
Investment Services
N.A.I.C.S.: 523999
Tian Jia (Pres, CEO, CFO & Sec)

V E C A ELECTRIC COMPANY INC.
PO Box 80467, Seattle, WA 98108-0467
Tel.: (206) 436-5200
Web Site: http://www.veca.com
Year Founded: 1946
Sales Range: $25-49.9 Million
Emp.: 150
Electrical Wiring Services
N.A.I.C.S.: 238210
Jutta Hood (Office Mgr)
Ted Rohwein (CEO)

V GROUP INC.
379 Princeton Hightstown Rd, Cranbury, NJ 08512
Tel.: (609) 371-9400
Web Site: http://www.vgroupinc.com
Year Founded: 1999
Sales Range: $1-9.9 Million
Emp.: 45
Custom Computer Programming Services
N.A.I.C.S.: 541511
Monika Rohila (Pres)
Vijay Kumar (CEO)

Subsidiaries:
Fernhill Beverage, Inc.   (1)
603 Seagave Dr Unit 163, Oceanside, CA 92054
Tel.: (619) 537-9310
Web Site: http://www.fernhillbev.com
Beverage Product Mfr
N.A.I.C.S.: 312111
David Roff (Pres, CEO, CFO, COO & Sec)

V&H, INC.
1505 S Central Ave, Marshfield, WI 54449-4904
Tel.: (715) 486-8800   WI
Web Site: http://www.vhtrucks.com
Year Founded: 1967
Sales Range: $10-24.9 Million
Emp.: 300
Retailer of Cars, Light Trucks, Heavy Trucks, Forestry Equipment & Building Material Handling Cranes
N.A.I.C.S.: 441110
Terry Frankland (Pres)
Dale Anderson (Dir-Parts 7 Svc)
A. L. Gauerke (Supvr-Crane & Equipment Parts)
Steve Biechler (Gen Mgr-Truck Ops)

V&J NATIONAL ENTERPRISES LLC
6933 W Brown Deer Rd, Milwaukee, WI 53223-2103
Tel.: (414) 365-9003   WI
Web Site: http://www.vjfoods.com
Year Founded: 1997
Sales Range: $25-49.9 Million
Emp.: 3,000
Restaurant
N.A.I.C.S.: 722511

Valerie Daniels-Carter (Pres & CEO)
John Daniels (Chm)
Tony Weiss (Controller)

V&N ADVANCED AUTOMATION SYSTEMS, LLC
415 Gus Hipp Blvd, Rockledge, FL 32955
Tel.: (321) 504-6440
Web Site: http://www.vnaas.com
Year Founded: 2004
Sales Range: $1-9.9 Million
Emp.: 15
Automated Vacuum Deposition Systems Mfr
N.A.I.C.S.: 333248
Jeff Budd (Project Mgr)
Phil Napolitano (VP)
Tito Visi (Pres)
Carlos Medina (Project Mgr)
Jason Gass (Dir-Engrg)

V&P NURSERIES INC.
14703 E Williams Field Rd, Queen Creek, AZ 85142
Tel.: (480) 917-9847
Web Site: http://www.vpnurseries.com
Rev.: $12,400,000
Emp.: 100
Whslr of Nursery Products
N.A.I.C.S.: 424930
Demetrios N. Vlachos (Pres)
Roger Rapanut (Mgr)

V&S MIDWEST CARRIERS CORP.
2001 Hyland Ave, Kaukauna, WI 54130
Tel.: (920) 766-9696
Web Site: http://www.vsmidwest.com
Rev.: $18,800,000
Emp.: 100
General Freight Trucking, Long-Distance, Truckload
N.A.I.C.S.: 484121
Don Dains (Project Coord-IT)
Dave Van Handel (Pres)
Marge Van Handel (VP)
Jeff Schramm (Dir-Safety)

V&V SUPREMO FOODS, INC.
2141 S Throop St, Chicago, IL 60608
Tel.: (312) 421-1020
Web Site: http://www.vvsupremo.com
Year Founded: 1964
Rev.: $41,000,000
Emp.: 160
Mfr of Mexican Style Foods
N.A.I.C.S.: 311513
Gilberto Villasenor (Co-Founder)
Ignacio Villasenor (Co-Founder)
Antonio Carmona (Sr Mgr-Production)
Brianna Ramirez-Smith (Supvr-CRM)
Efrain Sanoguet (Supvr-Warehouse)
Alan Hamann (Mgr-Quality Control & R&D)

V&W SUPPLY COMPANY
3320 2nd Ave S, Birmingham, AL 35222
Tel.: (205) 324-9521   AL
Web Site: http://www.vwsupply.com
Year Founded: 1968
Sales Range: $10-24.9 Million
Emp.: 55
Whslr of Plumbing & Hydronic Heating Supplies
N.A.I.C.S.: 423720
Lee Herritt (Pres)

V-EMPOWER, INC.
6800 Willow Creek Rd, Bowie, MD 20720
Tel.: (301) 805-9194
Web Site: http://www.v-empower.com

V-EMPOWER, INC.

V-Empower, Inc.—(Continued)
Year Founded: 2002
Sales Range: $1-9.9 Million
Emp.: 100
Security Applications & IT Solution Services
N.A.I.C.S.: 517810
Shukoor Ahmed (CEO)

Subsidiaries:
V-Empower Solutions Pvt., Ltd. (1)
10-1-17 Dana Chambers, Masab Tank, Hyderabad, 500 028, India
Tel.: (91) 4065581574
Web Site: http://www.vempower.com
Security Applications & IT Solution Services
N.A.I.C.S.: 541511

V-G SUPPLY COMPANY INC.

1400 Renaissance Dr Ste 309, Park Ridge, IL 60068
Tel.: (847) 635-1000
Web Site: http://www.vgsupply.com
Sales Range: $10-24.9 Million
Emp.: 15
Garden Supplies
N.A.I.C.S.: 424910
Tom Doll (VP-Ops)

V-SOFT CONSULTING GROUP, INC.

2115 Stanley Gault Pkwy Ste 200, Louisville, KY 40223
Tel.: (502) 425-8275
Web Site:
 http://www.vsoftconsulting.com
Year Founded: 1997
Rev.: $20,900,000
Emp.: 224
Computer System Design Services
N.A.I.C.S.: 541512
Purna B. Veer (Pres)
Dennis Engel (Dir-Natl Recruiting)
Michael Ross (Mktg Dir)
Doug Yates (Dir-Recruiting)
Geoffrey Ritter (Mgr-Bus Dev)
Bijal Shah (Mgr-HR)
Tanya Blocker (Mgr-Immigration)
John Hughes (Mgr-Sls-Natl)
Greg Daniel (Reg VP)
Ron Reeves (VP-Bus Solutions)
Jai Bokey (VP-Ops)
Satya Nandyala (VP-Resource Mgmt)
Adam Faris (VP-Fin)
Jared Mucciardi (Sr Mgr-Bus Dev)
Brianna Kolder (Coord-Sls & Recruiting)
Mike Lagger (Sr Mgr-Bus Dev)
SriRam Tadiboyina (Head-Practice Testing Center of Excellence)
Travis Arkon (Mgr-Recruiting Delivery)
Sue Danbom (Mgr-Trng)
Sean Keeley (Acct Mgr)
Shawn Moss (Engr-Network)
Jennifer Hegener (Dir-Recruiting-Chicago)
Parisa Amoozegar (Mgr-Bus Dev)
Mike Grendi (CFO)
Sanjay Kommera (CTO)
Kasey Tyring (Coord-Mktg)

V-TEK INCORPORATED

751 Summit Ave, Mankato, MN 56001
Tel.: (507) 387-2039 MN
Web Site: http://www.vtekusa.com
Year Founded: 1985
Sales Range: $10-24.9 Million
Emp.: 70
Tape & Reel Machines & M.A.C.H. Systems Mfr
N.A.I.C.S.: 334419
Dennis K. Siemer (Owner)
Dan Grode (Engr-Electrical)
Mitch Jacobs (Pres & CEO)
Mitch Jacob (Pres)

Subsidiaries:
Royce Instruments, Inc. (1)
831 Latour Ct Ste C, Napa, CA 94558
Tel.: (707) 255-9078
Web Site: http://www.royceinstruments.com
Sales Range: $1-9.9 Million
Emp.: 25
Instrument Mfr for Measuring & Testing Electricity & Electrical Signals
N.A.I.C.S.: 334515
Julie Adams (Dir-Sls-Worldwide)

V. ALEXANDER & CO. INC.

6555 Quinche Rd Ste 201, Memphis, TN 38119
Tel.: (901) 795-7761
Web Site: http://www.valexander.com
Year Founded: 1960
Sales Range: $10-24.9 Million
Emp.: 300
Supply Chain Management Services, Logistics Consulting & Freight Transportation Arrangement
N.A.I.C.S.: 488510
Michael Swett (COO & Exec VP)
Dan Collins (VP-Sls)
Brodie Foster (Controller)
Frances Gutt (VP-Import Ops)
Mike Barnett (CFO & Sr VP)
Randy Bradley (Mgr-Logistics & Ops)
Harry Buscher (Mgr-Exports)

Subsidiaries:
Worldbridge Logistics Inc. (1)
22 Century Blvd Ste 510, Nashville, TN 37214
Tel.: (615) 885-0020
Web Site:
 http://www.worldbridgelogistics.com
Freight Transportation & Logistics Services
N.A.I.C.S.: 484121
Michael Swett (COO & Exec VP)

V. J. CATALANO INC.

734 E Lake Ave Ste 2, Watsonville, CA 95076-3567
Tel.: (831) 728-1787
Web Site:
 http://www.imperialsalescompany.com
Sales Range: $25-49.9 Million
Emp.: 8
Fruits, Frozen
N.A.I.C.S.: 424420
Daniel R. Gibbs (Pres)

V. SUAREZ & COMPANY, INC.

Indus Pk 5 Rd Luchetti 300, Bayamon, PR 00961
Tel.: (787) 792-0725
Web Site: http://www.vsuarez.com
Year Founded: 1943
Sales Range: $500-549.9 Million
Emp.: 500
Beer & Other Fermented Malt Liquors
N.A.I.C.S.: 424430
Diego Suarez Sanchez (Chm)
Wallace Santos (VP)
Vicente Suarez Sanchez (Vice Chm)
Vicente Suarez (VP-Sls-Beverages)
Jose Brito (VP-Sls Provisions)
Mari Casellas (VP-Mktg)
Diego Suarez Jr. (Pres & CEO)

V.B. HOOK & CO., INC.

315 Wholesale Ln, West Columbia, SC 29172-3167
Tel.: (803) 799-0504 SC
Web Site: http://www.vbhook.com
Year Founded: 1935
Sales Range: $75-99.9 Million
Emp.: 40
Fruit & Vegetable Distr
N.A.I.C.S.: 424480
Gary Martin Hook (Pres)
Shonnie Thomas (Treas & Sec)

Subsidiaries:
V. B. Hook Vacuum Cooling Company (1)
315 Wholesale Ln, West Columbia, SC 29172
Tel.: (803) 794-2875
Fruit & Vegetable Canning Services
N.A.I.C.S.: 311421

V.F. GRACE INC.

605 E 13th Ave, Anchorage, AK 99501
Tel.: (907) 272-6431
Web Site: http://www.vfgrace.com
Year Founded: 1956
Sales Range: $10-24.9 Million
Emp.: 75
Whslr of Sporting Goods, Candy, Gardening, Health & Beauty Aids; Distributor of Seasonal Products
N.A.I.C.S.: 423910
Evelyn Rush (Treas, Sec & VP)
Kent Harrington (Gen Mgr)

V.L. RENDINA INC.

29 Midway Farms Ln, Lancaster, PA 17602-2670
Tel.: (717) 735-7500
Web Site:
 http://www.vlrendinainc.com
Year Founded: 1974
Sales Range: $10-24.9 Million
Emp.: 30
Commercial & Office Building, New Construction
N.A.I.C.S.: 236220

V.L.S SYSTEMS, INC.

4080 Lafayette Ctr Dr Ste 300, Chantilly, VA 20151
Tel.: (703) 953-3118
Web Site: http://www.vls-systems.com
Year Founded: 1995
Sales Range: $1-9.9 Million
Emp.: 184
IT Services
N.A.I.C.S.: 449210
Kris Nanda (Pres)
Tanu Govind (Mgr-HR & Ops)

V.R. PROPERTY MANAGEMENT

1360 S Carson St, Carson City, NV 89701
Tel.: (775) 884-4959
Sales Range: $10-24.9 Million
Emp.: 4
Convenience Store Operator
N.A.I.C.S.: 445131
Mohammed Ahmad (Pres)
Ajy Shamma (Controller)

V2 SYSTEMS, INC.

9104 Manassas Dr Unit P, Manassas, VA 20111
Tel.: (703) 361-4606
Web Site: http://www.v2systems.com
Year Founded: 1995
Rev.: $2,200,000
Emp.: 28
Information Technology, Outsourcing Solutions & Computer Support
N.A.I.C.S.: 811210
Erik Briceno (Pres & CEO)
Chris Waskowich (CIO)
Guy Hinkler (Founder)

V2SOFT, INC.

300 Enterprise Ct Ste 100, Bloomfield Hills, MI 48302
Tel.: (248) 904-1700 MI
Web Site: http://www.v2soft.com
Year Founded: 1998
Sales Range: $10-24.9 Million
Emp.: 400

U.S. PRIVATE

Custom Computer Programming Services
N.A.I.C.S.: 541511
Varchasvi Shankar (Pres)

V3 BROADSUITE, LLC

634 W 66th Ter, Kansas City, MO 64113
Tel.: (816) 200-2520 MO
Web Site: http://www.v3b.com
Sales Range: $1-9.9 Million
Marketing Consulting & Social Media Services
N.A.I.C.S.: 541613
Shelly Kramer (Founder & Chief Imagination Officer)
Katy Ryan Schamberger (Chief Content Officer)
Laura Seymour (Project Mgr)

V3 PRINTING CORPORATION

200 N Elevar St, Oxnard, CA 93030
Tel.: (805) 981-2600 CA
Web Site: https://printv3.com
Year Founded: 1959
Sales Range: $1-9.9 Million
Emp.: 80
Commercial Printing, Lithographic
N.A.I.C.S.: 323111
Michael Szanger (Pres, CEO & CFO)
Mike Szanger (Pres)

VA CONSULTING, INC.

17801 Cartwright Rd, Irvine, CA 92614
Tel.: (949) 474-1400 CA
Web Site:
 http://www.vaconsultinginc.com
Year Founded: 1973
Sales Range: $1-9.9 Million
Emp.: 82
Engineering Services, Nsk
N.A.I.C.S.: 541330
Max P. Vahid (CEO)
Don McDougald (VP)
Stan Ng (Engr-Design)
Keith Rutherfurd (VP-Traffic Engrg)
John Wolter (VP)
Michael S. Carter (CFO)

VA MORTGAGE CENTER.COM

2101 Chapel Plaza Ct Ste 107, Columbia, MO 65203
Tel.: (573) 268-3502
Web Site:
 http://www.vamortgagecenter.com
Year Founded: 2002
Sales Range: $10-24.9 Million
Emp.: 72
Mortgage Services
N.A.I.C.S.: 522310
Leigh Ann Wanserski (CFO)
Brock Bukowsky (Co-Owner)
Brant Bukowsky (Co-Owner)

VAAGEN BROTHERS LUMBER, INC.

565 W 5th Ave, Colville, WA 99114-2113
Tel.: (509) 684-5071 WA
Web Site:
 http://www.vaagenbros.com
Year Founded: 1950
Sales Range: $10-24.9 Million
Emp.: 170
Whslr of Lumber
N.A.I.C.S.: 321113
Duane Vaagen (Pres)
Josh Anderson (Mgr-Timber Resource)

VACATION HOME SWAP, INC.

112 N Curry St, Carson City, NV 89703
Tel.: (775) 321-8201 NV
Year Founded: 2009

Internet-Based Vacation Home Swapping Services
N.A.I.C.S.: 531390
William Henderson (Chm)
Frank J. Drechsler (Pres, CEO, CFO, Treas & Sec)

VACATION VILLAGES OF AMERICA, INC.
10300 SW Greenburg Rd Ste 465, Portland, OR 97223-5431
Tel.: (503) 601-2015
Web Site: http://www.v-v-a.com
Sales Range: $10-24.9 Million
Emp.: 200
Residential Property Management Services
N.A.I.C.S.: 531311
Doug Nealeigh (Pres)

VACATIONROOST GROUP INC.
90 400 W Ste 300, Salt Lake City, UT 84101
Tel.: (801) 559-3300
Web Site:
 http://www.vacationroost.com
Emp.: 250
Online Vacation Rental Services
N.A.I.C.S.: 721199
Jeff Berzolla (Gen Mgr-Consumer Brands)
Kristen Cherry (Dir-Market Mgmt)
Jeremy Griggs (Controller)
Myron Schram (CTO)
Rob Michalik (Chm)

Subsidiaries:

LeisureLink Inc. (1)
2795 E Cottonwood Pkwy, Salt Lake City, UT 84121
Tel.: (855) 840-2249
Web Site: http://www.leisurelink.com
Sales Range: $1-9.9 Million
Emp.: 25
Online Vacation Rental Services
N.A.I.C.S.: 561599
Andrew Bornstein (Dir-Mktg)

VACAVILLE HONDA
751 Orange Dr, Vacaville, CA 95687-3100
Tel.: (707) 449-5900
Web Site:
 http://www.vacavillehonda.com
Year Founded: 2004
Sales Range: $10-24.9 Million
Emp.: 50
New Car Whslr
N.A.I.C.S.: 441110
Kirk Thornhill (Principal)

VACCEX, INC.
6 Liberty Sq Ste 2381, Boston, MA 02109
Tel.: (452) 081-5802
Immunotherapy Product Mfr
N.A.I.C.S.: 325414
Per Horn (CEO)

VACCINEX, LP
1895 Mount Hope Ave, Rochester, NY 14620
Tel.: (585) 271-2700
Web Site: https://www.vaccinex.com
Rev.: $4,600,000
Emp.: 48
Research & Development in Biotechnology
N.A.I.C.S.: 541714
Maurice Zauderer (Pres)
Ernest Smith (Chief Scientific Officer & Sr VP-Res)
Raymond E. Watkins (COO & Sr VP)
John E. Leonard (Sr VP-Dev)

Steven P. Cobourn (CFO)
Jill Sanchez (CFO)
Elizabeth E. Evans (Sr VP)

VACCINOGEN, INC.
949 Fell St, Baltimore, MD 21231
Tel.: (410) 387-4000 MD
Web Site:
 http://www.vaccinogeninc.com
Year Founded: 2007
Emp.: 24
Pharmaceuticals Mfr
N.A.I.C.S.: 325412
Andrew L. Tussing (Chm, Pres & CEO)
Anders Ture Georg Halldin (Vice Chm)
Dinand van der Linde (Mng Dir-Bus Dev-Europe)
Peter Morsing (COO)
Jason D. Howard (Dir-Epitope-Based Vaccine Project)
Earl V. Miller (Dir-Fin & Controller)

VACHERIE MACHINE DIVISION
2990 Highway 20, Vacherie, LA 70090
Tel.: (225) 265-9200
All Other Miscellaneous Fabricated Metal Product Mfr
N.A.I.C.S.: 332999
Robin Hungerman (Gen Mgr)

VADATECH, INC.
11540 S Eastern Ave, Henderson, NV 89052
Tel.: (702) 896-3337 NV
Web Site: http://www.vadatech.com
Year Founded: 2004
Sales Range: $1-9.9 Million
Emp.: 11
Mfg Electronic Computers
N.A.I.C.S.: 334111
Saeed Karamooz (Pres)

Subsidiaries:

Radio Frequency Simulation Systems, Inc. (1)
2345 N Glassell St, Orange, CA 92865
Tel.: (714) 974-7377
Web Site: http://www.rfss-inc.com
Search, Detection, Navigation, Guidance, Aeronautical & Nautical System & Instrument Mfr
N.A.I.C.S.: 334511
Richard Damon (Pres & CEO)

VADEN HOLDING INC.
9393 Abercorn St, Savannah, GA 31406
Tel.: (912) 925-9393
Web Site:
 http://www.danvadenchevrolet.com
Sales Range: $75-99.9 Million
Emp.: 170
New & Used Car Dealers
N.A.I.C.S.: 532112
West Beaver (CFO)

VADEN'S ACOUSTICS & DRYWALL, INC.
8795 Harmon Rd, Fort Worth, TX 76177
Tel.: (817) 847-8822
Web Site:
 http://www.vadensacoustics.com
Year Founded: 1985
Sales Range: $10-24.9 Million
Emp.: 500
Plastering Services
N.A.I.C.S.: 238310
Shane Vaden (COO)
Leslie Vaden (Mgr-Production)
Harold R. Vaden Jr. (Owner & Pres)

VADTEK LLC.
1298 Jaycee Ct, Shawano, WI 54166

Tel.: (715) 524-6520
Web Site: http://www.vadtek.com
Rev.: $20,000,000
Emp.: 70
Electrical Apparatus & Equipment Wiring Supplies & Related Equipment Merchant Whslr
N.A.I.C.S.: 423610
Jody Anderson (Gen Mgr & Mgr-Production)

VAE INC.
12005 Sunrise Valley Dr Ste 202, Reston, VA 20191
Tel.: (703) 942-6727
Web Site: http://www.vaeit.com
Year Founded: 1998
Sales Range: $10-24.9 Million
Emp.: 150
Network & Systems Design Services
N.A.I.C.S.: 541511
Hailee Milko (Dir-HR & Ops)

VAGABOND FRANCHISE SYSTEM, INC.
3101 S Figueroa, Los Angeles, CA 90007
Tel.: (213) 746-1531 DE
Web Site:
 http://www.vagabondinn.com
Year Founded: 1998
Sales Range: $125-149.9 Million
Emp.: 650
Owner & Manager of Hotels
N.A.I.C.S.: 721110
Juan Sanchez-Llaca (Chm)
Jim Apostolis (VP-Info Sys)
Sandy Valentino (Dir-HR)
Les Biggins (CFO)
Bruce Weitzman (Pres & CEO)
Chuck Valentino (VP-Franchise Svc)
Erica Munguia (Dir-Guest Rels)

VAIL INDUSTRIES, INC.
49 Ohio St SW, Navarre, OH 44662-1143
Tel.: (330) 879-5653 OH
Web Site: http://www.vailpkg.com
Year Founded: 1972
Sales Range: $10-24.9 Million
Emp.: 50
Folding Paperboard Box Mfr
N.A.I.C.S.: 322212

Subsidiaries:

Massillon Container Co., Inc. (1)
49 Ohio St SW, Navarre, OH 44662-1143 (100%)
Tel.: (330) 879-5653
Web Site: http://www.vailpkg.com
Mfr of Corrugated Solid Fiber Boxes
N.A.I.C.S.: 322211
Benjamin Vail (Pres)

VAIL RUBBER WORKS, INC.
521 Langley Ave, Saint Joseph, MI 49085
Tel.: (269) 983-1595
Web Site: http://www.vailrubber.com
Year Founded: 1904
Sales Range: $75-99.9 Million
Emp.: 125
Rubber & Polyurethane Covered Rolls; Non-Woven Fiber Rolls; Molded Goods; Pulley Laggings for Industry; Roll Covers; New & Used; Millwright Services
N.A.I.C.S.: 326299
J. William Hanley (Pres)
Peter A. Fellows (VP-Tech Svcs & Gen Mgr)
Michael J. Hanley (VP-Sls)
Richard N. Mackie (VP-Fin)

VAIL SYSTEMS INC.
570 Lk Cook Rd Ste 400, Deerfield, IL 60015

Tel.: (312) 360-8245
Web Site: http://www.vailsys.com
Rev.: $11,000,000
Emp.: 60
Telephone Services
N.A.I.C.S.: 561421
Jim Whiteley (Founder & CEO)
Todd Whiteley (VP-Product Dev)
Beth McGinnis (VP-Client Svcs)
David Fruin (VP-Engrg)
Michael Bruening (VP-Ops)
Andrew Hap (VP-Svc Delivery)

VAL LIMITED
2601 S 70th St, Lincoln, NE 68506
Tel.: (402) 434-9350
Web Site: http://www.valentinos.com
Sales Range: $25-49.9 Million
Emp.: 25
Italian Restaurant
N.A.I.C.S.: 722511
A. Mike Aleisio (Exec VP)
Anthony O. Messineo Jr. (Pres)

VAL PORT DISTRIBUTORS INC.
45 S Rossler Ave, Buffalo, NY 14206
Tel.: (716) 825-7377
Web Site:
 http://valuhomecenters.com
Year Founded: 1968
Sales Range: $50-74.9 Million
Emp.: 800
Home Center Operator
N.A.I.C.S.: 444110
Michael Ervolina (Pres)

VAL SURF INC.
4810 Whitsett Ave, Valley Village, CA 91607
Tel.: (818) 769-6977
Web Site: http://www.valsurf.com
Sales Range: $100-124.9 Million
Emp.: 100
Surfing Equipment & Supplies
N.A.I.C.S.: 459110
Mark Richards (Pres)
Kurt Richards (VP)
Brandon Richards (Dir-Mktg)
Nathan Kaufman (Gen Mgr)

VAL VERDE HOSPITAL CORPORATION
801 Bedell Ave, Del Rio, TX 78840
Tel.: (830) 778-1749 TX
Web Site: http://www.vvrmc.org
Year Founded: 2000
Sales Range: $50-74.9 Million
Emp.: 531
Health Care Srvices
N.A.I.C.S.: 622110
Bonnie Henderson (Dir-Hospice)
John Furman (VP-Ops)
Tony Sotelo (Pres)

VAL VERDE WINERY
100 Qualia Dr, Del Rio, TX 78840
Tel.: (830) 775-9714
Web Site:
 http://www.valverdewinery.com
Year Founded: 1883
Sales Range: $10-24.9 Million
Emp.: 10
Wine Mfr
N.A.I.C.S.: 312130
Frank Qualia (Co-Founder)
Thomas Qualia (Owner)
Mary Qualia (Co-Founder)

VAL WARD CADILLAC, INC.
12626 Tamiami Trl S, Fort Myers, FL 33907
Tel.: (239) 939-2212 FL
Web Site:
 http://www.valwardautos.com
Year Founded: 1970

VAL WARD CADILLAC, INC.

Val Ward Cadillac, Inc.—(Continued)
Sales Range: $25-49.9 Million
Emp.: 100
New & Used Car Dealer
N.A.I.C.S.: 441110
Vince Verrico (Mgr-Sls-New Car)
Mark Harrell (Mgr-Sls-Pre-Owned)
Dave Ganger (Mgr-Sls-Internet)
Karen White (Dir-Fin)
Ned Kelly (Mgr-Collision Center)
Jeff Stahl (Mgr-Parts)
Don Behrens (Mgr-Accessories)
Dan Flynn (Mgr-Customer Rels)
April Buckley (Mgr-New Cadillac Bus)
Jeff Miller (Mgr-Internet Sls)
Jim Gedra (Gen Mgr)
Jimmy Lee Fleming (Mgr-Svcs)
Mike Holmes (Mgr-Pre Owned Sls)
Val Ward Jr. (Owner)

VAL-MATIC VALVE AND MANUFACTURING CORP.
905 S Riverside Dr, Elmhurst, IL 60126
Tel.: (630) 941-7600
Web Site: http://www.valmatic.com
Rev.: $20,000,000
Emp.: 96
Valves, Automatic Control
N.A.I.C.S.: 332911
Ed Gardner (Acct Mgr-OEM)

VALADOR, INC.
560 Herndon Pkwy Ste 300 159, Herndon, VA 20170
Tel.: (703) 435-9155
Web Site: http://www.valador.com
Year Founded: 2001
Sales Range: $10-24.9 Million
Emp.: 68
Management Consulting Services
N.A.I.C.S.: 541611
Kevin T. Mabie (Pres & CEO)
John Bacak (CFO & VP)
Donna Connell (VP)

VALBRIDGE PROPERTY ADVISORS, INC.
2240 Venetian Ct, Naples, FL 34109
Tel.: (239) 514-4646
Web Site: http://www.valbridge.com
Sales Range: $50-74.9 Million
Emp.: 600
Commercial Real Estate Valuation & Advisory Services
N.A.I.C.S.: 531390
Richard L. Armalavage (Pres, CEO & Sr Mng Dir)
Geri F. Armalavage (Chm & Sr Mng Dir)
David H. Brooks (Sr Mng Dir & VP)
Robert G. Beaumont (Sr Mng Dir)
Calvin Cummings (Sr Mng Dir)
Larry Colorito (Sr Mng Dir)
Karl Finkelstein (Sr Mng Dir)
Norman C. Hulberg (Sr Mng Dir)
Matthew J. Lubawy (Sr Mng Dir)
Timothy E. Mardell (Vice Chm & Sr Mng Dir)
Michael J. Naifeh (Sr Mng Dir)
Karlene R. Perry (Sr Mng Dir)
R. Matt Nobles (Mng Dir)
Reaves C. Lukens III (Sr Mng Dir)

Subsidiaries:
Schenberger, Taylor, McCormick & Jecker Inc. (1)
1306 Higuera St, San Luis Obispo, CA 93401-3122
Tel.: (805) 544-2472
Web Site: http://www.stmjappraisers.com
Offices of Real Estate Appraisers
N.A.I.C.S.: 531320

VALCO CINCINNATI INC.
411 Circle Fwy Dr, Cincinnati, OH 45246
Tel.: (513) 874-6550
Web Site: http://www.valcomelton.com
Sales Range: $10-24.9 Million
Emp.: 200
Measuring & Dispensing Pumps
N.A.I.C.S.: 333914
Gregory T. Amend (Chm)
Rich Centerford (Pres)
Emilio Ravelo (Engr-Mfg)

VALCO INSTRUMENTS CO., INC.
7811 W View Dr, Houston, TX 77055
Tel.: (713) 688-9345
Web Site: http://www.vici.com
Rev.: $35,400,000
Emp.: 250
Mfr of Components for Gas Chromatography, Liquid Chromatography & Flow Injection Analysis
N.A.I.C.S.: 334513
Stanley D. Stearns (Pres)

VALCOM ENTERPRISES INCORPORATED
120 Center St, Wilder, KY 41071
Tel.: (859) 655-4400
Web Site: http://www.veinet.com
Sales Range: $10-24.9 Million
Emp.: 115
Drywall
N.A.I.C.S.: 238310
George Steven (Controller)
David Markesbery (Project Mgr)
Todd Lafkas (VP-Ops)

VALCOM, INC.
5614 Hollins Rd, Roanoke, VA 24019
Tel.: (540) 563-2000
Web Site: http://www.valcom.com
Year Founded: 1977
Sales Range: $1-9.9 Million
Commercial & Institutional Paging, Intercom & Internet Protocol Products Mfr & Whslr
N.A.I.C.S.: 334290
Sharon Bowers (Dir-HR)
John W. Mason Sr. (Pres)

VALCOR ENGINEERING CORPORATION
2 Lawrence Rd, Springfield, NJ 07081-3121
Tel.: (973) 467-8400
Web Site: http://www.valcor.com
Year Founded: 1941
Sales Range: $75-99.9 Million
Emp.: 300
Solenoid & Manual Valves, Metering Pumps, Fluid Control Components, Pressure Regulators, Accumulators, Electromagnetic & Electronic Devices
N.A.I.C.S.: 335314
Paul Meyers (Dir-Aerospace Sls & Mktg)
Steven Gatcomb (Dir-Mktg & Nuclear Sls)

Subsidiaries:
Electroid Co (1)
45 Fadem Rd, Springfield, NJ 07081-3115 (100%)
Tel.: (973) 467-8100
Web Site: http://www.electroid.com
Sales Range: $10-24.9 Million
Emp.: 80
Electromagnetic & Pneumatic Device for Rotary Motion Control Mfr
N.A.I.C.S.: 335312
Steve Etter (Pres)
Steve DiGerolamo (Mgr-Clutches)

VALCOURT BUILDING SERVICES LLC
1600 Tyson Blvd Ste 950, McLean, VA 22102
Tel.: (703) 294-6202
Web Site: http://www.valcourt.net
Building Maintenance & Repair Services
N.A.I.C.S.: 561790
Jeffery T. Valcourt (Founder & Chm)
Eric Crabb (CEO)

Subsidiaries:
American Cleaning Systems, Inc. (1)
1745 E Jackson St, Phoenix, AZ 85034
Tel.: (602) 267-7600
Sales Range: $1-9.9 Million
Emp.: 50
Specialty Trade Contractors
N.A.I.C.S.: 238990
Barry Frankel (Pres)
Jamie Finn (Mgr-Acctg)
Shelley Lynn Frankel (Treas & Sec)

American National Skyline, Inc. (1)
614 Michigan St, Elmhurst, IL 60126
Tel.: (630) 941-8500
Web Site: http://www.ansi.com
Rev.: $1,240,000
Emp.: 40
Janitorial Services
N.A.I.C.S.: 561720
James Buczko (Pres)

Awnclean U. S. A., Inc. (1)
501 N Newport Ave, Tampa, FL 33606
Tel.: (813) 258-9344
Web Site: http://www.awnclean.com
Rev.: $1,160,000
Emp.: 14
Janitorial Services
N.A.I.C.S.: 561720

Jobs Building Services LLC (1)
7777 Parnell St, Houston, TX 77021
Tel.: (832) 255-4500
Web Site: http://www.jobs-amst.com
Commercial Facilities Maintenance & Restoration Services
N.A.I.C.S.: 561790
LaRue Coleman (Chm)
Eric Crabb (CEO)

Subsidiary (Domestic):
Exterior Diagnostic Services, Inc. (2)
811 Center St, Apex, NC 27502
Tel.: (919) 303-0448
Web Site: http://www.edswaterproofing.com
Rev.: $4,038,000
Emp.: 37
Janitorial Services
N.A.I.C.S.: 561720
Elda McGrath (Pres)
John McGrath (CFO)

Scottie's Building Services, LLC (2)
PO Box 821, Apex, NC 27502-0821
Tel.: (919) 303-8900
Web Site: http://www.scottiesbuildingservices.com
Other Services to Buildings & Dwellings
N.A.I.C.S.: 561790

Lupini Construction Inc. (1)
6081 Trenton Rd, Utica, NY 13502
Tel.: (315) 736-8809
Web Site: https://www.lupiniconstruction.com
Masonry Contractors
N.A.I.C.S.: 238140
Max Lupini (Pres)

South Shore Building Services, Inc. (1)
4208 E La Palma Ave, Anaheim, CA 92807
Tel.: (714) 646-0130
Web Site: http://www.southshoreinc.com
Sales Range: $1-9.9 Million
Emp.: 30
Janitorial Services
N.A.I.C.S.: 561720
Ty Eubanks (CEO)

VALDAK CORPORATION
1149 36th Ave S, Grand Forks, ND 58201
Tel.: (701) 746-8371
Web Site: http://www.valleydairy.com

U.S. PRIVATE

Year Founded: 1956
Rev.: $11,300,000
Emp.: 50
Convenience Store
N.A.I.C.S.: 445111
Monica Schmidt Musich (Pres)
Kathy Cummings (VP)

VALENCE MEDIA GROUP
c/o MRC - 9665 Wilshire Blvd 2nd Fl, Beverly Hills, CA 90212
Tel.: (310) 786-1600
Web Site: http://www.valencemediagroup.com
Year Founded: 2018
Holding Company; Entertainment Media
N.A.I.C.S.: 551112
Todd Boehly (Chm)
Asif Satchu (Co-CEO)
Modi Wiczyk (Co-CEO)

Subsidiaries:
Media Rights Capital II L.P. (1)
9665 Wilshire Blvd Ste 200, Beverly Hills, CA 90212
Tel.: (310) 786-1600
Web Site: http://www.mrcstudios.com
Film Production Services
N.A.I.C.S.: 512110
Asif Satchu (Co-CEO)
Brye Adler (Co-Pres)
Scott Tenley (COO)
James Glander (Exec VP-Physical Production)
Modi Wiczyk (Co-CEO)
D. J. Jacobs (CFO & Head-Bus Dev)
Jonathan Golfman (Co-Pres)
Peter Johnson (Co-Pres-Television)
Cindy Chen (Sr VP-Corp Bus & Legal Affairs)
Carol Dantuono (Sr VP-Post Production & Delivery)
Charlie Goldstein (Sr VP-Physical Production)
Melissa Reynolds Hunt (Sr VP-Fin)
Ken Makowski (Sr VP-Legal & Bus Affairs)
Pauline Micelli (Co-Pres-Bus & Legal Affairs)
Jennifer Watson (Co-Pres-Bus & Legal Affairs)
Peter Wentzel (Sr VP-Production Fin)

Prometheus Global Media LLC (1)
340 Madison Ave 6th Fl, New York, NY 10173
Tel.: (212) 493-4100
Web Site: http://www.prometheusgm.com
Holding Company; Publisher
N.A.I.C.S.: 551112
John Amato (CEO)

Group (Domestic):
Billboard (2)
340 Madison Ave 6th Fl, New York, NY 10173
Tel.: (315) 903-9260
Web Site: http://www.billboard.com
Magazine Publisher
N.A.I.C.S.: 513120
Lynne Segall (Publr & Exec VP)
Jay Penske (Chm & CEO)

Subsidiary (Domestic):
The Hollywood Reporter, LLC (2)
5700 Wilshire Blvd Ste 500, Los Angeles, CA 90036
Tel.: (323) 525-2000
Web Site: http://www.hollywoodreporter.com
Entertainment News Publisher
N.A.I.C.S.: 513120
Kelly Jones (Exec Dir-Production)
Lynne A. Segall (Sr VP)
Jon Frosch (Editor-Reviews)
Tom Seeley (Deputy Dir-Editorial-Digital Media)
Erika Cespedes (VP-Mktg)
Cathy Field (Dir-Bus Dev)
Christopher Hawkins (Dir-Art)
Elisabeth Deutschman (Sr VP-Television & Media)
Julian Holguin (Exec VP & Head-Brand Partnerships)
Kevin Kunis (Sr VP-Fin PGM)

Andrew Min *(Sr VP-Bus Dev & Licensing)*
Michele Singer *(Gen Counsel)*
Alison Smith-Pleiser *(Mng Dir-Intl)*
Kelsey Stefanson *(Deputy Dir-Design)*
Alexandra von Bargen *(VP-Luxury)*
Nekesa Mumbi Moody *(Dir-Editorial)*
Patricia Mays *(Exec Dir-News)*
Scott Feinberg *(Exec Editor-Awards)*
Jeanie Pyun *(Deputy Dir-Editorial)*
Tyler Coates *(Editor-Awards)*

dick clark productions, inc.   (1)
100 N Crescent, Beverly Hills, CA 90210
Tel.: (310) 255-4600
Web Site:
   http://www.dickclarkproductions.com
Television Programming, Media Licensing & Network Production Services
N.A.I.C.S.: 516210
Barry Adelman *(Exec VP-Television)*
Michael Mahan *(Vice Chm)*
Michael Kohn *(Gen Counsel & Exec VP-Bus Ops)*
Mark Rafalowski *(Exec VP-Intl Distr)*
Amy Thurlow *(Pres)*
Mark Bracco *(Exec VP-Programming & Dev)*
Ariel Elazar *(Exec VP-Brand Mktg & Digital Strategy)*
Amanda Powers *(COO)*

Subsidiary (Domestic):

dick clark restaurants, inc.   (2)
2900 Olympic Blvd, Santa Monica, CA 90404
Tel.: (310) 255-4600
Web Site: http://www.dickclark.com
Sales Range: $10-24.9 Million
Emp.: 20
Casual Dining Restaurants Owner & Operator
N.A.I.C.S.: 722511

VALENCE TECHNOLOGY, INC.
1807 W Braker Ln Ste 500, Austin, TX 78758
Tel.: (512) 527-2900   DE
Web Site:
   http://www.lithiumwerks.com
Year Founded: 1989
High Performance Cost Effective Battery Mfr
N.A.I.C.S.: 335910
Eric Lind *(Chief Comml Officer)*
Jason Park *(CFO)*
John Aittama *(COO)*
Arne Hovda Aas *(CIO)*
Yazid Saidi *(CTO)*
Eivind Aarnes Nilsen *(Chief Legal Officer)*
T. Joseph Fisher III *(Co-Founder & CEO)*

VALENT CAPITAL PARTNERS LLC
30 N LaSalle St Ste 2250, Chicago, IL 60602
Tel.: (312) 731-8630
Web Site:
   http://www.valentcapitalpartner.com
Rev.: $30,000,000
Privater Equity Firm
N.A.I.C.S.: 523999
Asim Aleem *(Mng Principal)*

Subsidiaries:

ISI Telemanagement Solutions, LLC   (1)
1051 Perimeter Dr Ste 200, Schaumburg, IL 60173
Tel.: (847) 592-3250
Web Site: http://www.isi-info.com
Automated Cost Recovery & Call Accounting Systems Mfr
N.A.I.C.S.: 541690
Dan Mueller *(VP-Product Dev)*
Mitchell Weiss *(Dir-Unified Comm Products)*
Mark McNeill *(VP-Enterprise & Healthcare UC Solutions)*
Asim Aleem *(Pres & CEO)*
Mark Risch *(CFO)*
Kathy Learnan *(Dir-Product Dev)*

Mike Mestemaker *(VP-Engrg)*
Susan Tylkowski *(VP-Customer Support Svcs)*
Darek Latawski *(VP-Mktg & Sls)*

VALENTI AUTO SALES, INC.
399 N Colony St Ste 5, Wallingford, CT 06492
Tel.: (203) 265-0991
Web Site: http://www.valchevy.com
Year Founded: 1954
Sales Range: $10-24.9 Million
Emp.: 50
New Car Dealers
N.A.I.C.S.: 441110
Donna Martin *(Sec)*
David F. Valenti *(Pres)*

VALENTI MOTORS, INC.
600 Straits Tpke, Watertown, CT 06795
Tel.: (860) 274-8846
Web Site: http://www.valentivw.com
Sales Range: $25-49.9 Million
Emp.: 90
New & Used Car Dealer
N.A.I.C.S.: 441110
Charles Sarafian *(Gen Mgr-Sls)*
Steve Pinkerton *(Bus Mgr)*

VALENTI TOYOTA
4 Langworthy Rd, Westerly, RI 02891
Tel.: (401) 322-7200
Web Site:
   http://www.valentitoyota.com
Year Founded: 1997
Sales Range: $10-24.9 Million
Emp.: 37
Car Whslr
N.A.I.C.S.: 441110
William G. Goodwin *(Gen Mgr)*
Robert Valenti *(Pres)*
Rocky Sposato *(Mgr-Sls)*

VALEO BEHAVIORAL HEALTH CARE
5401 SW 7th St, Topeka, KS 66606
Tel.: (785) 233-1730   KS
Web Site: http://www.valeotopeka.org
Year Founded: 1967
Sales Range: $10-24.9 Million
Emp.: 373
Behavioral Healthcare Services
N.A.I.C.S.: 623220
Richard Kline *(Treas)*
Patti Bossert *(Chm)*
Bill Cochran *(Vice Chm)*

VALER, INC.
2550 E Desert Inn Rd Ste 224, Las Vegas, NV 89121
Tel.: (602) 460-6520   NV
Year Founded: 2010
Investment Services
N.A.I.C.S.: 523999
Stephen A. Schramka *(Pres, CEO, CFO, Chief Acctg Officer, Sec & Treas)*

VALERA GLOBAL
3636 33rd St, Long Island City, NY 11101
Tel.: (718) 786-2222
Web Site:
   http://www.valeraglobal.com
Year Founded: 1987
Rev.: $28,100,000
Emp.: 87
Limousine Service
N.A.I.C.S.: 485320
Robert Mackasek *(CEO)*
Rod Barfield *(Exec VP)*
Naomi Glaser *(Sr VP)*
Dolores Battelli *(VP-Fin)*
David Eckstein *(Founder, Pres & Partner)*

VALERO CAPITAL PARTNERS LLC
70 Industrial Ave E, Lowell, MA 01852
Tel.: (978) 843-7677
Web Site:
   http://www.valerocapital.com
Leak Detection Equipment Mfr
N.A.I.C.S.: 339999
Jim Pelusi *(Mng Dir)*

Subsidiaries:

Vacuum Instrument Corp.   (1)
2101 9th Ave, Ronkonkoma, NY 11779
Tel.: (631) 737-0900
Web Site: http://www.vicleakdetection.com
Sales Range: $10-24.9 Million
Emp.: 75
Process Control
N.A.I.C.S.: 334513
Tom McNamee *(Dir-Standard Products & Customer Svc)*
Rick Yanez *(Dir-Product Mgmt)*

Division (Domestic):

VIC Leak Detection, Air Leak Testing Division   (2)
3203 Plainfield Rd, Dayton, OH 45432
Tel.: (937) 253-7377
Web Site: http://www.vicleakdetection.com
Sales Range: $10-24.9 Million
Emp.: 20
Process Control Instruments
N.A.I.C.S.: 334519
Chuck Wilkinson *(Dir-Mktg)*

VALESCO INDUSTRIES, INC
325 N St Paul St Ste 3200, Dallas, TX 75201
Tel.: (214) 880-8690
Web Site: http://www.valescoind.com
Year Founded: 1994
Privater Equity Firm
N.A.I.C.S.: 523999
Bud Moore *(Mng Partner)*
Jack Sadden *(Mng Partner)*
Angie Henson *(Partner)*
Heather Hubbard *(Partner)*
Patrick Floeck *(Principal)*
Pierce Edwards *(VP)*
Stephanie Drake *(Controller)*

Subsidiaries:

Blower Application Company, Inc.   (1)
N114W19125 Clinton Dr, Germantown, WI 53022
Tel.: (262) 255-5580
Sales Range: $1-9.9 Million
Emp.: 33
Commercial & Service Industry Machinery Mfr
N.A.I.C.S.: 333310

VALET PARKING SERVICE, LIMITED PARTNERSHIP
1335 S Flower St, Los Angeles, CA 90015-2907
Tel.: (213) 342-3388   CA
Web Site:
   http://www.valetparkingservice.com
Year Founded: 1946
Sales Range: $75-99.9 Million
Emp.: 400
Valet Parking
N.A.I.C.S.: 812930
Anthony Policella *(Co-Owner)*
Victor Morad *(Co-Owner)*

VALEXCONSULTING
132 Welsh Rd Ste 140, Horsham, PA 19044
Tel.: (215) 431-7679
Web Site:
   http://www.valexconsulting.com
Year Founded: 2001
Sales Range: $1-9.9 Million
Emp.: 20

Software Development Services
N.A.I.C.S.: 541511
Alex Zhitomirsky *(Principal)*

VALHALLA BUILDERS & DEVELOPERS INC.
6985 Via Del Oro Ste A5, San Jose, CA 95119
Tel.: (408) 225-5572
Sales Range: $10-24.9 Million
Emp.: 30
Provider of Construction Services
N.A.I.C.S.: 236210
Ray Tonkin *(Co-Pres)*
John Gallizoli *(Co-Pres)*

VALHALLA PARTNERS INC.
8000 Towers Crescent Dr Ste 1225, Vienna, VA 22182
Tel.: (703) 448-1400
Web Site:
   http://www.valhallapartners.com
Year Founded: 2002
Sales Range: $25-49.9 Million
Emp.: 16
Privater Equity Firm
N.A.I.C.S.: 523999
Arthur J. Marks *(Mng Gen Partner)*
Kiran Hebbar *(Gen Partner)*
Harry J. D'Andrea *(Mng Gen Partner)*

VALIANT INTEGRATED SERVICES LLC
205 Van Buren St Ste 310, Herndon, VA 20170
Tel.: (703) 462-7750   DE
Web Site:
   http://www.valiantintegrated.com
Year Founded: 2017
Logistics Consulting, Supply Chain Management & Other Business Operational Support Services
N.A.I.C.S.: 561499
Mike Pilon *(Pres)*
Dan Corbett *(CEO)*
John Hart *(Chief Growth Officer)*
Kent Smith *(Sr VP/Gen Mgr-Mission Support Vertical)*
Hector Alvarez *(Sr VP/Gen Mgr-Training & Readiness Vertical)*
Sarah Lynn *(Gen Counsel & Sec)*
Mike Devoto *(Exec VP-Strategic Programs)*
Kevin Sullivan *(CFO & Sr VP)*

Subsidiaries:

Omega Training Group, Inc.   (1)
8100 Wyoming Blvd Ste M4 #791, Albuquerque, NM 87113
Tel.: (877) 663-4244
Web Site: http://www.omegatraining.com
Defense Analysis, Training & Logistics Planning Services
N.A.I.C.S.: 611699

Valiant Global Defense Services Inc.   (1)
3940 Ruffin Rd, San Diego, CA 92123
Tel.: (858) 505-2489
Electrical Component Mfr
N.A.I.C.S.: 335999

VALIANT PRODUCTS CORP.
2727 W 5th Ave, Denver, CO 80204-4804
Tel.: (303) 892-1234   CO
Web Site:
   http://www.valiantproducts.com
Year Founded: 1961
Sales Range: $25-49.9 Million
Emp.: 160
Piece Goods & Notions, Hotel Supplies & Furniture
N.A.I.C.S.: 424310
Mark J. Norberg *(Pres & COO)*
Terry Sorensen *(Sr VP)*

VALIANT PRODUCTS CORP.   U.S. PRIVATE

Valiant Products Corp.—(Continued)
Subsidiaries:

Design Force Corporation (1)
2727 W 5th Ave, Denver, CO 80204-4804
Tel.: (303) 892-1234
Web Site: http://www.valiantproducts.com
Sales Range: $10-24.9 Million
Emp.: 75
Business Services; Interior Design for Hotels
N.A.I.C.S.: 541410
Bruce G. Davine (Pres)

VALIANT STEEL AND EQUIPMENT
6455 Old Peachtree Rd, Norcross, GA 30071
Tel.: (770) 417-1235
Web Site: http://www.valiantsteel.com
Sales Range: $10-24.9 Million
Emp.: 17
Iron & Steel (Ferrous) Pipe
N.A.I.C.S.: 423510

VALICOR, INC.
7400 Newman Blvd, Dexter, MI 48130
Tel.: (734) 426-9015   DE
Web Site: http://www.valicor.com
Year Founded: 1996
Emp.: 133
Non Hazardous Waste Management Service
N.A.I.C.S.: 562219
Tom Czartoski (Pres & CEO)

VALIDAR INC.
800 Maynard Ave S Ste 401, Seattle, WA 98134
Tel.: (206) 264-9151   WA
Web Site: http://www.validar.com
Year Founded: 2005
Sales Range: $1-9.9 Million
Emp.: 20
Lead Management Software Publisher
N.A.I.C.S.: 513210
Jeremy Norton (Mgr-Ops)
Duncan Harrod (CTO)
Kaarn Dempsey (Controller)

VALIDATEK INC.
1655 N Fort Myer Dr Ste 925, Arlington, VA 22209
Tel.: (703) 224-8162
Web Site: http://www.validatek.com
Year Founded: 2006
Sales Range: $1-9.9 Million
Emp.: 38
It Consulting
N.A.I.C.S.: 541690
Rahul Nemade (CEO)

VALIDIC, INC.
701 W Main St Ste 620, Durham, NC 27701
Web Site: https://validic.com
Year Founded: 2010
Digital Health & Remote Care Services
N.A.I.C.S.: 518210
Drew Schiller (CEO)

Subsidiaries:

Trapollo, LLC (1)
22897 Eaglewood Ct Ste 150, Sterling, VA 20166
Tel.: (866) 807-5047
Web Site: http://www.trapollo.com
Remote Health Monitoring Solutions
N.A.I.C.S.: 541690
Todd Leto (Founder & CEO)
John Aldridge (COO)

VALIDOR CAPITAL LLC
1900 Glades Rd Ste 500, Boca Raton, FL 33431
Tel.: (561) 962-2351
Web Site: http://www.validorcap.com
Holding Company
N.A.I.C.S.: 551112
Matthew C Kaufman (Chm & Mng Partner)
Matthew J Pearson (VP)
Steve Noe (Operating Partner)

Subsidiaries:

The Boehm Pressed Steel Co. (1)
5440 Wegman Dr, Valley City, OH 44280
Tel.: (330) 220-8000
Web Site: http://www.boehmstampings.com
Metal Stamping
N.A.I.C.S.: 332119
Nate Heckman (Gen Mgr)

The Marwin Company, Inc. (1)
107 McQueen St, West Columbia, SC 29172
Tel.: (803) 776-2396
Web Site: http://www.marwincompany.com
Rev.: $8,600,000
Emp.: 100
Fiscal Year-end: 12/31/2006
Specialty Door Products Mfr
N.A.I.C.S.: 321911
Andy Davis (CEO)

Subsidiary (Domestic):

Millwork 360 LLC (2)
12941 Memorial Hwy, Tampa, FL 33635
Tel.: (813) 854-3100
Web Site: http://www.millwork360.net
Clay Building Material & Refractories Mfr
N.A.I.C.S.: 327120
Mike Williams (Pres)

VALIMET INC.
431 Sperry Rd, Stockton, CA 95206
Tel.: (209) 982-4870
Web Site: http://www.valimet.com
Sales Range: $10-24.9 Million
Emp.: 35
Powder, Metal
N.A.I.C.S.: 331221
Kurt F. Leopold (Chm)
Valerie Waldon (Mgr-Sls)
George Campbell (Pres & COO)

VALIR HEALTH
700 Nw 7th St, Oklahoma City, OK 73102-1212
Tel.: (405) 609-3600
Web Site: http://www.valir.com
Year Founded: 2000
Rev.: $48,500,000
Emp.: 590
Health Care Srvices
N.A.I.C.S.: 623220
Laura Trammell (VP-Hospice Care)
Bill Turner (VP-HR)
Kitt Wakeley (Principal)
Jon Jiles (Chm & Principal)
Dirk O'Hara (Principal)

Subsidiaries:

Valir Rehabilitation Hospital of Okc, LLC (1)
700 NW 7th St, Oklahoma City, OK 73102
Tel.: (405) 236-3131
Web Site: http://www.valir.com
Sales Range: $1-9.9 Million
Emp.: 200
Outpatient Care Centers
N.A.I.C.S.: 621498
Tom Tucker (CEO)
Tim Moody (COO)
Marty Spake (CFO)
Bill Turner (VP-HR)
Laura Trammell (VP)
Amy Woolery (VP-Revenue Cycle)
Keith Ritchie (CTO)
Tonya Purvine (Chief Legal Officer)
Ginger Castleberry (VP-Risk & Compliance)

VALK MANUFACTURING COMPANY
66 E Main St, New Kingstown, PA 17072-0428
Tel.: (717) 766-0711   PA
Web Site: http://www.valkmfg.com
Year Founded: 1952
Sales Range: $75-99.9 Million
Emp.: 90
Mfr of Snow Plows & Replacement Cutting Edges
N.A.I.C.S.: 333120
Ted P. Valk (Pres & CEO)
Robert P. Lang (VP)
Linda Bassler (Controller)
William Lonnquist (Mgr-Warehouse & Transportation)

VALKRY CORPORATION & EXOTIC CARS SOUTH
1605 N Germantown Pkwy Ste 111-109, Cordova, TN 38016
Tel.: (901) 282-3550
Sales Range: $10-24.9 Million
Emp.: 46
Car Whslr
N.A.I.C.S.: 441110
Michael Brown (CEO)

VALKYRIE COMPANY INC.
60 Fremont St, Worcester, MA 01603
Tel.: (508) 756-3633
Rev.: $15,000,000
Emp.: 50
Personal Leather Goods
N.A.I.C.S.: 316990
James J. Devaney (Pres)
Marty Nathan (CFO)

VALLECITOS WATER DISTRICT
201 Vallecitos De Oro, San Marcos, CA 92069
Tel.: (760) 744-0460
Web Site: http://www.vwd.org
Year Founded: 1955
Sales Range: $10-24.9 Million
Emp.: 100
Water Supply & Sewage
N.A.I.C.S.: 221310
Dennis O. Lamb (Gen Mgr)
Darrell Gentry (VP)
Leonard Caudle (Asst Sec)
John Fusco (Mgr-Fin)

VALLERGAS DRIVE-IN MARKETS
2139 1st St, Napa, CA 94559
Tel.: (707) 253-2620
Web Site: http://www.vallergas.com
Rev.: $32,000,000
Emp.: 20
Grocery Retailer
N.A.I.C.S.: 445110
Ray Sercu (Pres)

VALLET FOOD SERVICE INC.
472 Badger Rd, Hazel Green, WI 53811-9787
Tel.: (563) 588-2346   IA
Year Founded: 1990
Sales Range: $75-99.9 Million
Emp.: 15
Producer & Retailer of Poultry & Poultry Products; Groceries; Fresh Fruits & Vegetables; Frozen Foods
N.A.I.C.S.: 424410
Ed White (Pres)
Cal Buss (Treas, Sec & VP)

VALLEY ACQUISITION CO. LLC
55 Sunset Dr, Basalt, CO 81621
Tel.: (970) 927-3146
Web Site: http://www.valleylumber.com
Rev.: $20,000,000
Emp.: 25
Lumber & Other Building Materials
N.A.I.C.S.: 423310

VALLEY AUTO WORLD INCORPORATED
3822 Sycamore Dairy Rd, Fayetteville, NC 28303
Tel.: (910) 864-0000
Web Site: http://www.valleyautoworld.com
Rev.: $27,200,000
Emp.: 55
Automobiles, New & Used
N.A.I.C.S.: 441110
Greg Dudak (Gen Mgr-Sls)
John W. Wyatt III (Pres)

VALLEY AUTOMOTIVE GROUP
7500 145th St W, Apple Valley, MN 55124
Tel.: (952) 432-9500
Web Site: http://www.valleycardealers.com
Sales Range: $10-24.9 Million
Emp.: 90
Sales of Motor Vehicles
N.A.I.C.S.: 811111
Bernie Wagnild (Owner)
Bob Vine (Controller)
Jim Paul (Owner)

VALLEY BAKERS COOP ASSOCIATION
W6470 Quality Dr, Greenville, WI 54942
Tel.: (920) 560-3200
Web Site: http://www.valleybakers.com
Sales Range: $25-49.9 Million
Emp.: 225
Flour; Bakers Ingredients & Supplies
N.A.I.C.S.: 424490
Mark Munroe (COO)

VALLEY BANK & TRUST
30 N 4th Ave, Brighton, CO 80601-1753
Tel.: (303) 659-5450   CO
Web Site: http://www.valleybankandtrust.com
Year Founded: 1971
Sales Range: $200-249.9 Million
Emp.: 115
Commercial Bank
N.A.I.C.S.: 522110
Doug Scherrer (Sr VP)
Donna Petrocco (Pres & CEO)
James O'Dell (Chm & Sec)
Brian Blehm (Pres-Reg Branch)
Russell C. Wray (Sr VP)
Todd Sadler (Pres-Mapleton & Danbury)

VALLEY CABINET INC.
845 Prosper St, De Pere, WI 54115
Tel.: (920) 336-3174
Web Site: http://www.valleycabinetinc.com
Year Founded: 1960
Custom Cabinetry; Cabinet Doors, Drawer Fronts & Wood Hoods Mfr
N.A.I.C.S.: 337110
Dean Stoller (Pres)

VALLEY CADILLAC OLDSMOBILE
2743 Franklin Rd S W, Roanoke, VA 24014
Tel.: (540) 344-9274
Web Site: http://www.valleycadillacolds.com
Sales Range: $10-24.9 Million
Emp.: 70
Automobiles, New & Used
N.A.I.C.S.: 441110
Karen Odell (Owner)

VALLEY CAPITAL CORPORATION

COMPANIES

10617 N Hayden Rd Ste 100, Scottsdale, AZ 85260-8200
Tel.: (480) 344-5000
Sales Range: $25-49.9 Million
Emp.: 7
Holding Company
N.A.I.C.S.: 523999
Charles Stroupe (Chm)
Andrew Browning (CFO)

Subsidiaries:

Tech Group Medical Products (1)
104 Scranton Blvd, Lake Bluff, IL 60044-1848
Tel.: (847) 615-7292
Mfr of Lab & Medical Products
N.A.I.C.S.: 459999

VALLEY CASTING, INC.
9462 Deerwood Ln N, Maple Grove, MN 55369
Tel.: (763) 425-1411
Web Site: http://www.valleycasting.com
Year Founded: 1931
Rev.: $2,500,000
Emp.: 25
Coin Banks, Slush Castings, Vinyl Reproductions, Replicas & Lapel Pins
N.A.I.C.S.: 339930
Darryl Knutson (Pres)
Benjamin Knutson (VP)

VALLEY CHEVROLET INC.
601 Kidder St, Wilkes Barre, PA 18702
Tel.: (570) 821-2781
Web Site: http://www.valleychevrolet.com
Sales Range: $25-49.9 Million
Emp.: 60
Automobiles, New & Used
N.A.I.C.S.: 441110
Blake Gagliardi (Mgr-Sls)
Jim Crane (Mgr-Fin)
Vince Ephault (Mgr-Parts)
Paul Karnafel (Dir-Svc)
Bernie Rentko (Mgr-Reconditioning Shop)
Frank Wallace (Mgr-Sls)
Jacqueline Mehelchick (Mgr-Mktg & Internet)
Rick Merrick (Mgr-Sls)
Susan Haase (Mgr-Customer Rels)

VALLEY CHRYSLER DODGE, INC.
2100 30th St, Boulder, CO 80301-1119
Tel.: (303) 442-1687
Web Site: http://www.valleydodge.com
Year Founded: 1997
Sales Range: $10-24.9 Million
Emp.: 55
New & Used Car Dealer
N.A.I.C.S.: 441110
William G. Grubich (Owner)
Sharon Adkins (Bus Mgr)

VALLEY CO-OP INC.
811 Mill St, Winfield, KS 67156
Tel.: (620) 221-4343
Web Site: http://www.vcoop.com
Rev.: $18,843,033
Emp.: 33
Grain Merchant Whslr
N.A.I.C.S.: 424510
Ron Kramer (Branch Mgr)
Donnie Roths (Branch Mgr-Kellogg)
Donna Fagg (Office Mgr)
Richard Kimbrel (Gen Mgr)

VALLEY CO-OP OIL MILL INC.
1901 N Express Way 77 Wilson Rd, Harlingen, TX 78550
Tel.: (956) 425-4545
Web Site: http://www.georestore.com
Year Founded: 1946
Sales Range: $10-24.9 Million
Emp.: 60
Provider of Farm Supplies
N.A.I.C.S.: 311224
Hollis G. Sullivan (Pres)
Aaron Pena (Asst Mgr-Sls)

VALLEY CO-OPS INC.
1833 S Lincoln Ave, Jerome, ID 83338-6138
Tel.: (208) 324-8000
Web Site: http://www.valleyco-ops.com
Year Founded: 1991
Sales Range: $10-24.9 Million
Emp.: 300
Petroleum Bulk Stations & Terminals
N.A.I.C.S.: 115210
Derick Brewer (Controller)
Dave Holton (Gen Mgr)

VALLEY COMMERCIAL CONTRACTORS
2237 Douglas Blvd Ste 100, Roseville, CA 95661
Tel.: (916) 781-8116
Web Site: http://www.valley.cc
Sales Range: $10-24.9 Million
Emp.: 10
Nonresidential Construction, Nec
N.A.I.C.S.: 236220
John Deweese (Founder & CEO)
Robin Rousselet (CFO)
Jeff DeWeese (Pres)

VALLEY CONSTRUCTION SUPPLY
234 Stewart Rd, Pacific, WA 98047
Tel.: (253) 863-6354
Web Site: http://www.valleyconstructionsupply.com
Rev.: $12,000,000
Emp.: 60
Building Materials, Interior
N.A.I.C.S.: 423310
Clifford Beatty (Pres)

VALLEY CONVERTING CO., INC.
405 Daniels St, Toronto, OH 43964
Tel.: (740) 537-2152
Web Site: http://www.valleyconverting.com
Sales Range: $10-24.9 Million
Emp.: 50
Building Paper, Laminated: Made From Purchased Material
N.A.I.C.S.: 322299
Michael D. Biasi (Pres)
Mark Seemiller (Mgr-Sls)

VALLEY COURIERS
646 N San Fernando Rd, Los Angeles, CA 90065
Tel.: (323) 225-8642
Sales Range: $10-24.9 Million
Emp.: 9
Delivery Service Vehicular
N.A.I.C.S.: 484110
Nasrollah Alamdari (Pres)

VALLEY DETROIT DIESEL ALLISON
425 S Hacienda Blvd, City of Industry, CA 91745-1123
Tel.: (626) 333-1243
Web Site: http://www.valleypowersystems.com
Year Founded: 1963
Sales Range: $125-149.9 Million
Emp.: 350
Wholesale Distributor of Diesel Engines & Parts

N.A.I.C.S.: 423830
Robert K. Humphryes (CFO)
Sam Hill (Pres)

VALLEY ELECTRIC COMPANY OF MOUNT VERNON, INC.
1100 Merrill Creek Pkwy, Everett, WA 98203-9037
Tel.: (425) 407-0832
Web Site: http://www.velectric.com
Year Founded: 1982
Sales Range: $100-124.9 Million
Emp.: 1,100
Electrical Work
N.A.I.C.S.: 238210
Patti L. Ward (Co-Pres)
Ernie Ward (Owner)
Robert D. Carrithers (CFO)
Andy Ward (Co-Pres & Gen Mgr)

VALLEY ELECTRIC SUPPLY CORP.
1361 N State Rd 67, Vincennes, IN 47591
Tel.: (812) 882-7860
Web Site: http://www.vesupply.com
Year Founded: 1959
Sales Range: $10-24.9 Million
Emp.: 40
Whslr of Electrical Supplies
N.A.I.C.S.: 423610
Richard J. Cannon (Pres)
Trae Spires (Mgr-Info Sys)

VALLEY ENERGY CORP.
523 S Keystone Ave, Sayre, PA 18840
Tel.: (570) 888-9664
Web Site: http://www.valley-energy.com
Sales Range: $1-9.9 Million
Emp.: 26
Natural Gas Distribution
N.A.I.C.S.: 221210
Robert J. Crocker (Pres & CEO)

VALLEY EXPRESS INC.
16553 37th St SE, Mapleton, ND 58059
Tel.: (701) 281-0475
Web Site: http://www.valleyexp.com
Sales Range: $1-9.9 Million
Emp.: 45
Truck Transportation Brokers
N.A.I.C.S.: 488510
Roger Nelson (VP)
Glenn Nelson (Treas)
Merle Jegtdeg (Pres)
Jeff Heidt (Office Mgr)

VALLEY FARMERS COOPERATIVE
920 N Congress Pkwy, Athens, TN 37303
Tel.: (423) 745-0443
Web Site: http://www.vfcoop.com
Sales Range: $10-24.9 Million
Emp.: 50
Farm Supplies
N.A.I.C.S.: 424910
Jeff Crisp (Treas)
Howard Hornsby (Pres)
John Walker (CEO)
Blan Dougherty (VP)
Jeff Howell (Sec)

VALLEY FASTENER GROUP LLC
1490 Mitchell Rd, Aurora, IL 60504
Tel.: (630) 299-8910
Web Site: http://www.valleyfastener.com
Sales Range: $10-24.9 Million
Emp.: 59
Mfr of Bolts, Nuts, Rivets & Washers
N.A.I.C.S.: 332722

Manny Desantis (Pres)

Subsidiaries:

Forgo Fasteners (1)
3302 Bloomingdale Ave, Melrose Park, IL 60160
Tel.: (708) 343-2496
Sales Range: $10-24.9 Million
Emp.: 15
Screw & Fastener Mfr
N.A.I.C.S.: 332722

Valley Fastener Group LLC - North Coast Rivet Division (1)
700 Sugar Ln, Elyria, OH 44035
Tel.: (440) 366-6829
Web Site: http://www.valleyfastener.com
Screw & Rivet Mfr
N.A.I.C.S.: 332722

VALLEY FIG GROWERS, INC.
2028 S 3rd St, Fresno, CA 93702
Tel.: (559) 237-3893
Web Site: http://www.valleyfig.com
Year Founded: 1959
Sales Range: $10-24.9 Million
Emp.: 180
Figs Producer
N.A.I.C.S.: 115114
Gary Jue (Pres)
Linda Cain (VP-Mktg & Retail Sls)
James Gargiulo (CFO)
Paul Mesple (Chm)
Richard DeBenedetto (Vice Chm)

VALLEY FIRST CREDIT UNION
PO Box 1411, Modesto, CA 95353-1411
Tel.: (209) 549-8500
Web Site: http://www.valleyfirstcu.org
Year Founded: 1956
Sales Range: $10-24.9 Million
Emp.: 166
Credit Union
N.A.I.C.S.: 522130
Dennis Barta (VP-Fin)
Paul Emanuels (VP-Lending)
James Kelly (VP-Admin)
Fred Cruz (Chm)
Hank Barrett (Pres & CEO)
Judy Jensen (Sec)
Gary Hall (Treas)
Ken Karn (Vice Chm)
Anita Morphew (VP-Mktg)

VALLEY FOOD SERVICES, LLC
1232 Vernon St, Kansas City, MO 64116
Tel.: (816) 387-9200
Year Founded: 2000
Sales Range: $10-24.9 Million
Emp.: 62
Grocery & Related Products Merchant Whslr
N.A.I.C.S.: 424490
Joe Johnston (Principal)

VALLEY FORD SALES INC.
910 S 1st St, Yakima, WA 98901
Tel.: (509) 453-3125
Web Site: http://www.drivevalley.com
Sales Range: $25-49.9 Million
Emp.: 55
Automobiles, New & Used
N.A.I.C.S.: 441110
Tom Sparling (Pres)

VALLEY FORD TRUCK SALES INCORPORATED
5715 Canal Rd, Cleveland, OH 44125
Tel.: (216) 524-2400
Web Site: http://www.valleyfordtruck.com
Rev.: $97,669,794
Emp.: 90
Trucks, Tractors & Trailers: New & Used

Valley Ford Truck Sales Incorporated—(Continued)
N.A.I.C.S.: 441110
Brian O'Donnell (Pres)

VALLEY FORGE FLAG COMPANY
875 Berkshire Blvd Ste 101, Wyomissing, PA 19610
Tel.: (610) 376-2400
Web Site: http://www.valleyforgeflag.com
Rev.: $38,813,000
Emp.: 200
Flags, Fabric
N.A.I.C.S.: 314999
Michael Liberman (Chm)

VALLEY FORGE INVESTMENT CORP.
120 S Warner Rd, King of Prussia, PA 19406
Tel.: (610) 687-2400
Rev.: $24,200,000
Emp.: 25
Management Investment, Open-End
N.A.I.C.S.: 525910
Richard W. Ireland (Chm)

VALLEY FREIGHTLINER INC.
277 Stewart Rd SW, Pacific, WA 98047
Tel.: (253) 863-7393
Web Site: http://www.valleyfreightliner.com
Sales Range: $75-99.9 Million
Emp.: 150
Sales of New & Used Trucks
N.A.I.C.S.: 441110
Allan Beardsley (Mgr-Parts)
Dan Speck (Branch Mgr)
Jonathan Callis (Mgr-Svc)
Larry J. Gordon (Owner, Pres & CEO)
Alex Bernasconi (Gen Mgr)
Kristen Hancock (Mgr-Parts-Columbus)

VALLEY FURNITURE SHOP, INC.
20 Stirling Rd, Watchung, NJ 07069
Tel.: (908) 756-7623
Web Site: http://www.valleyfurnitureshop.com
Year Founded: 1974
Sales Range: $10-24.9 Million
Emp.: 20
Furniture Retailer
N.A.I.C.S.: 449110
Joan Kipe (Pres)
Skip Kipe (Mgr-Adv)

VALLEY GLASS INC.
202 21 st, Ogden, UT 84401
Tel.: (801) 399-5625
Web Site: http://www.valleyglass.com
Sales Range: $10-24.9 Million
Emp.: 50
Manufacture & Distribute Glass Windows
N.A.I.C.S.: 444180
Marc Naylor (Owner & Pres)

VALLEY HEALTHCARE SYSTEMS, INC.
1300 National Dr Ste 140, Sacramento, CA 95834
Tel.: (916) 669-0508
Web Site: http://www.vhcsystems.com
Year Founded: 2002
Sales Range: $10-24.9 Million
Emp.: 130
Healthcare Employment Services
N.A.I.C.S.: 561311
Steven Swan (Pres & CEO)

VALLEY HONDA
4221 William Penn Hwy, Monroeville, PA 15146
Tel.: (412) 373-3000
Web Site: http://www.valleyhonda.net
Year Founded: 1918
Sales Range: $10-24.9 Million
Emp.: 62
Car Whslr
N.A.I.C.S.: 441110
Steve Werksman (Gen Mgr-Sls)

VALLEY HOPE ASSOCIATION
PO Box 510, Norton, KS 67654
Tel.: (785) 877-5111
Web Site: http://www.valleyhope.org
Year Founded: 1966
Sales Range: $25-49.9 Million
Emp.: 820
Alcohol Rehabilitation Services
N.A.I.C.S.: 621420
Dave Hill (Chm)
Pat George (Pres & CEO)

VALLEY HOSPICE, INC.
10686 State Route 150, Rayland, OH 43943
Tel.: (740) 859-5650
Web Site: http://www.valleyhospice.org
Year Founded: 1985
Sales Range: $10-24.9 Million
Emp.: 237
Individual & Family Healthcare Services
N.A.I.C.S.: 624190
Cynthia Bougher (CEO)

VALLEY HOSPITAL ASSOCIATION
950 E Bogard Rd Ste 218, Wasilla, AK 99654
Tel.: (907) 352-2863
Web Site: http://www.healthymatsu.org
Year Founded: 1948
Sales Range: $10-24.9 Million
Emp.: 9
Medical Devices
N.A.I.C.S.: 622110
Melissa Kemberling (Dir-Programs)
Robin Minard (Dir-Pub Affairs)
Elizabeth Ripley (Exec Dir)

VALLEY IMPLEMENT & MOTOR CO.
213 W 800 N, Preston, ID 83263
Tel.: (208) 852-0430
Web Site: http://www.valleyimplement.com
Sales Range: $10-24.9 Million
Emp.: 353
Farm & Garden Machinery
N.A.I.C.S.: 423820
Sid Titensor (Pres)

VALLEY IMPROVEMENT ASSOCIATION, INC.
386 W Rio Communities Blvd, Belen, NM 87002
Tel.: (505) 864-6654
Web Site: http://www.v-i-a.org
Year Founded: 1969
Sales Range: $1-9.9 Million
Emp.: 5
Neighborhood Development Services
N.A.I.C.S.: 813319
Antoinette Sedillo-Lopez (Vice Chm)
James H. Foley (Chm)
Paul A. Baca (Pres & CEO)

VALLEY INTERIOR SYSTEMS INC.
2203 Fowler St, Cincinnati, OH 45206
Tel.: (513) 961-0400
Web Site: http://www.visohio.com
Sales Range: $10-24.9 Million
Emp.: 540
Drywall
N.A.I.C.S.: 238310
John Strawser (COO)
Mike Strawser (CEO)
Jeff Hudepohl (Pres)
Jim Melaragno (VP & Branch Mgr)
Terry Gyetvai (Branch Mgr)
Marcus Taulbee (VP-Ops)
Gary Rudolf (CFO)

VALLEY ISLE PRODUCE, INC.
74 Hobron Ave, Kahului, HI 96732
Tel.: (808) 877-5055
Web Site: http://www.vipfoodservice.com
Year Founded: 1951
Sales Range: $125-149.9 Million
Emp.: 180
Packaged Frozen Goods; Fresh Fruits & Vegetables, Seafoods; General Line of Groceries; Fresh Meats, Paper Products & Sanitation Supplies Wholesale Distr
N.A.I.C.S.: 424420
Nelson Okumura (Pres)

VALLEY LIGHTING, LLC
601 U Hammonds Ferry Rd, Linthicum, MD 21090
Tel.: (410) 636-6010
Web Site: http://www.valleylighting.com
Year Founded: 1965
Sales Range: $10-24.9 Million
Emp.: 40
Commercial Lighting Fixtures & Related Products Distr
N.A.I.C.S.: 423610
Carl Rehrmann (VP)
Patrick Michaud (Mgr-Estimating Dept)
Steve Fouts (VP)
Thomas E. Jones Jr. (Pres)

VALLEY MANAGEMENT GROUP, INC.
3013 Enloe St, Hudson, WI 54016
Tel.: (715) 377-7575
Web Site: http://www.valleymanagementgroup.com
Year Founded: 2002
Sales Range: $25-49.9 Million
Emp.: 8
Global Sourcing & Supply Chain Services
N.A.I.C.S.: 488510
Jerry Gilbert (CEO)

VALLEY MANAGEMENT, INC.
18 Jewelers Park Dr No 100, Neenah, WI 54956-5902
Tel.: (920) 725-8969
Web Site: http://www.mcdonalds.com
Year Founded: 1976
Sales Range: $10-24.9 Million
Fast-Food Restaurant, Chain
N.A.I.C.S.: 722513
David Rause (Owner)

VALLEY MARKETS, INCORPORATED
1950 32nd Ave S Ste C, Grand Forks, ND 58201-6656
Tel.: (701) 746-0688
Web Site: http://www.gohugos.com
Sales Range: $100-124.9 Million
Emp.: 1,500
Supermarket
N.A.I.C.S.: 445110
Kristi Magnuson-Nelson (Pres)

Subsidiaries:
Hugo's Family Marketplace (1)
155 E 12th St, Grafton, ND 58237
Tel.: (701) 352-0770
Web Site: http://www.gohugos.com
Sales Range: $25-49.9 Million
Supermarket
N.A.I.C.S.: 445110
Kristi Magnuson-Nelson (Pres)

VALLEY MINING, INC.
4412 Pleasant Valley Rd SE, Uhrichsville, OH 44683
Tel.: (740) 922-3942
Sales Range: $10-24.9 Million
Emp.: 130
Bituminous Coal & Lignite Surface Mining Services
N.A.I.C.S.: 212114
Kathleen Hoffmann (Controller)
William C. Aubiel (Pres)

VALLEY MOUNTAIN REGIONAL CENTER INC.
702 N Aurora St, Stockton, CA 95202
Tel.: (209) 473-0951
Web Site: http://www.vmrc.net
Year Founded: 1974
Sales Range: $100-124.9 Million
Emp.: 276
Developmental Disabilities Services
N.A.I.C.S.: 622310
Melinda Gonser (Sec)
John Forrest (Treas)
Dennis Walker (VP)

VALLEY NETWORK SOLUTIONS, INC.
364 W Fallbrook Ave Ste 101, Fresno, CA 93711-5858
Tel.: (559) 650-2600
Web Site: http://www.vns.net
Year Founded: 1996
Sales Range: $1-9.9 Million
Emp.: 25
Information Technology Services for Business Networks
N.A.I.C.S.: 541512
Daniel Duffy (CEO & CIO)
Jake Klee (Mgr-Repair Svcs)
Tim Mann (Acct Exec)

VALLEY OIL CORPORATION
911 Richmond Ave, Staunton, VA 24401
Tel.: (540) 886-1150
Sales Range: $10-24.9 Million
Emp.: 50
Convenience Store
N.A.I.C.S.: 445131
James Ridenour Jr. (Treas)

VALLEY PACIFIC PETROLEUM SERVICES, INC.
152 Frank West Cir Ste 100, Stockton, CA 95206-4098
Tel.: (559) 732-8381
Web Site: http://www.vpps.net
Year Founded: 1947
Sales Range: $75-99.9 Million
Emp.: 200
Petroleum Products
N.A.I.C.S.: 457210
Dale Heinze (Pres-Retail Mktg)
Rob Taylor (Mgr-Retail Sls)

VALLEY PACKAGING INC.
206 Pegasus Ave, Northvale, NJ 07647
Tel.: (201) 784-8881
Sales Range: $10-24.9 Million
Emp.: 20
Paper Brokers
N.A.I.C.S.: 424130
Theodore J. Johansmeyer (Chm)

VALLEY PACKAGING INDUSTRIES, INC.

COMPANIES

110 N Kensington Dr, Appleton, WI 54915
Tel.: (920) 749-5840
Web Site: http://www.vpind.com
Rev.: $18,200,000
Emp.: 1,000
Packaging & Labeling Services
N.A.I.C.S.: 561910
Bob Russo (Pres)
John Hall (CFO)
Cindy Monette (Dir-HR)

VALLEY PALLET RECYCLERS INC.
522 El Camino Real S, Salinas, CA 93908
Tel.: (831) 422-3875
Web Site: http://www.valleypallet.com
Sales Range: $25-49.9 Million
Emp.: 400
Pallets, Wood
N.A.I.C.S.: 423310
Frank Shean (Pres)

VALLEY PAVING INC.
8800 13th Ave E, Shakopee, MN 55379
Tel.: (952) 445-8615
Web Site: http://www.valleypaving.com
Sales Range: $10-24.9 Million
Emp.: 105
Highway & Street Construction
N.A.I.C.S.: 237310
Richard Carron (Pres)
Carol Kadrlik (Office Mgr)

VALLEY PLATING WORKS
2707 N San Fernando Rd, Los Angeles, CA 90065
Tel.: (323) 223-1466
Web Site: http://www.valleyplating.com
Sales Range: $10-24.9 Million
Emp.: 100
Plating Of Metals Or Formed Products
N.A.I.C.S.: 332813
Francis Cullen (Pres)
John Cullen (VP)

VALLEY PONTIAC BUICK GMC, INC.
3104 Auburn Way N, Auburn, WA 98002-1808
Tel.: (253) 833-2420 WA
Web Site: http://www.valleybuickgmc.com
Year Founded: 1969
Sales Range: $100-124.9 Million
Emp.: 80
Retailer of New & Used Automobiles
N.A.I.C.S.: 441110
Ron Claudon (Gen Mgr)
Bill Russell (Mgr-Parts)
Brandan Wright (Mgr-Svc)
Craig Heyer (Gen Mgr-Sls)

VALLEY PRIDE PACK INC.
19081 Hwy 71, Norwalk, WI 54648
Tel.: (608) 823-7445
Rev.: $49,800,000
Emp.: 100
Meat Packing Plants
N.A.I.C.S.: 311611
Frederick Stewart (Pres)

VALLEY PRODUCTS CO.
384 E Brooks Rd, Memphis, TN 38109
Tel.: (901) 396-9646
Web Site: http://www.valproco.com
Rev.: $23,100,000
Emp.: 17
Soap: Granulated, Liquid, Cake, Flaked, Or Chip
N.A.I.C.S.: 325611

Kenneth J. Roberts (Pres)

VALLEY QUALITY HOMES INC.
1830 S 1st St, Yakima, WA 98903
Tel.: (509) 453-8937
Web Site: http://www.valleyqualityhomes.com
Year Founded: 1979
Sales Range: $10-24.9 Million
Emp.: 45
Mfr & Sales of Mobile Homes
N.A.I.C.S.: 459930
Arthur Berger (Pres)
Bruce Maley (Controller)
Tisha Busey (VP)
Robert Standfill (Treas & Sec)

VALLEY RECYCLING
20220 Plummer St, Chatsworth, CA 91311
Tel.: (818) 885-7318
Web Site: http://www.valleyrecyclingcenter.com
Sales Range: $1-9.9 Million
Emp.: 20
Recycling Services for Industries, Small Businesses & the General Public
N.A.I.C.S.: 541620
Sepand Samzadeh (CEO)

VALLEY RELOCATION & STORAGE
4020 Nelson Ave Ste 200, Concord, CA 94520
Tel.: (925) 682-3740
Web Site: http://www.valleyrelocation.com
Year Founded: 1983
Rev.: $26,649,554
Emp.: 75
Provider of Trucking Transportation & Logistic Services
N.A.I.C.S.: 484210
James Robson (Co-Pres)
Jack Griffin (Co-Pres)
Joe Rodgers (Mgr)
Stacy Graves (Gen Mgr)
Ann Bisely (Mgr-Accts)
Danny Garcia (Mgr-Ops)
Ralph Rojas (VP-Ops)
Matt MacPheators (Acct Mgr)
Scott Seppala (Acct Mgr)
Asal Bidokhti (Coord-Customer Svc)
Deanna Bridges (Coord-Logistics)

VALLEY REPUBLIC BANK
5000 California Ave Ste 110, Bakersfield, CA 93309
Tel.: (661) 371-2000
Web Site: http://www.valleyrepublicbank.com
Year Founded: 2009
Rev.: $23,238,000
Assets: $667,625,000
Liabilities: $611,198,000
Net Worth: $56,427,000
Earnings: $5,247,000
Fiscal Year-end: 12/31/17
Banking Services
N.A.I.C.S.: 522110
Stephen M. Annis (Chief Admin Officer & Exec VP)
Philip McLaughlin (Exec VP)
Jack Smith (Chief Credit Officer & Exec VP)
Michele Jasso (COO & Exec VP)
Garth A. Corrigan (CFO & Exec VP)
Geraud Smith (Pres & CEO)
Eugene J. Voiland (Chm)

VALLEY RIDGE INVESTMENT PARTNERS

340 Brushy Ridge Rd, New Canaan, CT 06840
Tel.: (347) 410-3531
Web Site: http://www.valleyridgeip.com
Year Founded: 2018
Holding Company
N.A.I.C.S.: 551112
John Sheffield (Founder & Mng Dir)
Mark Tedford (Founder & Mng Dir)

Subsidiaries:

National Power Corporation (1)
4541 Preslyn Dr, Raleigh, NC 27616
Tel.: (800) 790-1672
Web Site: http://www.natpow.com
Managed Power & Network Infrastructure Solutions
N.A.I.C.S.: 237130

VALLEY ROZ ORCHARDS INC.
10 E Mead Ave, Yakima, WA 98903
Tel.: (509) 457-4153
Sales Range: $25-49.9 Million
Emp.: 2,500
Apple Orchards
N.A.I.C.S.: 111331
Jason Betterton (Controller)

VALLEY RUBBER, LLC
3899 Hwy 31 N, Falkville, AL 35622
Tel.: (256) 784-5231 AL
Web Site: http://www.bigblackandugly.com
Sales Range: $10-24.9 Million
Emp.: 85
Wear-Resistant Rubber Industrial Products Mfr
N.A.I.C.S.: 326299
Cronan F. Connell (Pres & Gen Mgr)
Bob Cooper (Dir-Sls-Mining & Aggregate)
Deborah Moore (Exec Dir-Sls-OEM)
Damon Tumbleson (VP-Dev)
Mark T. Waters (VP-Ops & Fin)

VALLEY RURAL ELECTRIC COOPERATIVE, INC.
PO Box 477, Huntingdon, PA 16652
Tel.: (814) 643-2650
Web Site: http://www.valleyrec.com
Sales Range: $25-49.9 Million
Emp.: 65
Transmission, Electric Power
N.A.I.C.S.: 221121
Clair McCall (Treas)
James R. Stauffer (Chm)
Richard Bauer (Pres)

VALLEY STREAM LINCOLN MERCURY
676 W Merrick Rd, Valley Stream, NY 11580
Tel.: (516) 285-0505
Web Site: http://www.valleystreamsales.com
Rev.: $21,000,000
Emp.: 50
Owner & Operator of Car Dealerships
N.A.I.C.S.: 441110
Joe Vultaggio (VP & Gen Mgr)

VALLEY STRONG CREDIT UNION
11500 Bolthouse DR, Bakersfield, CA 93311
Tel.: (661) 833-7900 CA
Web Site: http://www.valleystrong.com
Credit Union
N.A.I.C.S.: 522130
Jim Hussey (VP-Wealth Mgmt)
Nick Ambrosini (Pres & CEO)

VALLEY SUPPLY & EQUIPMENT CO.

20332 Lighterburg Pike, Hagerstown, MD 21742
Tel.: (301) 733-7414
Web Site: http://www.valleysupplyequipment.com
Sales Range: $10-24.9 Million
Emp.: 23
General Construction Machinery & Equipment
N.A.I.C.S.: 423810
Howard J. Klein (Pres)
Adam Klein (Exec VP)

VALLEY TELEPHONE COOPERATIVE INC
480 S 6th St, Raymondville, TX 78580
Tel.: (956) 689-2484
Web Site: http://www.vtci.net
Sales Range: $10-24.9 Million
Emp.: 112
Local Telephone Communications
N.A.I.C.S.: 517121
Dave Osborn (Gen Mgr)
James Whitt (Supvr-Outside Plant Engrg)
Jacob Schmidt (Supvr-NOC & IT)

VALLEY TIRE CO., INC.
15 McKean Ave, Charleroi, PA 15022-1436
Tel.: (724) 489-4483 PA
Web Site: http://www.valleytireco.com
Year Founded: 1980
Sales Range: $25-49.9 Million
Emp.: 190
Auto & Home Supply Stores
N.A.I.C.S.: 441340
James F. Stankiewicz (Owner)

VALLEY TRUCK & TRACTOR CO.
1549 Colusa Hwy, Yuba City, CA 95993
Tel.: (530) 673-8283
Web Site: http://www.valleytruckandtractor.com
Sales Range: $10-24.9 Million
Emp.: 94
Agricultural Machinery & Equipment
N.A.I.C.S.: 423820
John Miller (Owner)

VALLEY TRUCK PARTS, INC.
1900 Chicago Dr, Wyoming, MI 49519
Tel.: (616) 241-5431 MI
Web Site: http://www.valleytruckparts.com
Year Founded: 1954
Sales Range: $10-24.9 Million
Emp.: 130
Motor Vehicle Supplies & Parts Mfr
N.A.I.C.S.: 423120
Jeff Powell (Dir-HR)
Dean Haverdink (CFO)
Dan Diltz (Mgr-Parts Counter)
Gary Troost (Gen Mgr)
Steve Burman (Dir-Bus Dev & Sls Mgmt)

Subsidiaries:

HME, Inc. (1)
1950 Byron Ctr Ave SW, Wyoming, MI 49519-1247
Tel.: (616) 534-1463
Web Site: http://www.hme.com
Sales Range: $10-24.9 Million
Emp.: 100
Motor Vehicles Mfr
N.A.I.C.S.: 336110

VALLEY TRUCKING CO., INC.
4550 Coffeeport Rd, Brownsville, TX 78521
Tel.: (956) 831-4511

VALLEY TRUCKING CO., INC. — U.S. PRIVATE

Valley Trucking Co., Inc.—(Continued)
Web Site:
http://www.valleytrucking.net
Sales Range: $10-24.9 Million
Emp.: 59
Trucking Except Local
N.A.I.C.S.: 484121
Colette Britt (Mgr-Ops)
Todd George (Sr VP)

VALLEY VIEW BANCSHARES, INC.
7500 W 95th St, Overland Park, KS 66212
Tel.: (913) 381-3311 KS
Web Site:
http://www.valleyviewbank.com
Year Founded: 1973
Sales Range: $125-149.9 Million
Emp.: 700
Bank Holding Company
N.A.I.C.S.: 551111
James S. Lewis (Pres & CEO)
Timothy J. Kelley (Pres/CEO-Valley View State Bank & Sec)
Kenneth W. Hollander (VP)
Tommy Wells (VP)
Wayne Forgey (VP)
Clay E. Coburn Jr. (VP)

Subsidiaries:

Bankers & Investors Co. (1)
1300 N 78th St Ste G3, Kansas City, KS 66112
Tel.: (913) 299-5008
Web Site: http://www.bankersinvestors.com
Sales Range: $1-9.9 Million
Emp.: 12
Investment Advisory, Securities Brokerage & Asset Management Services
N.A.I.C.S.: 523940
Jerrod Foresman (Pres & Chief Compliance Officer)

Security Bank of Kansas City (1)
701 Minnesota Ave, Kansas City, KS 66101
Tel.: (913) 281-3165
Web Site: http://www.securitybankkc.com
Sales Range: $25-49.9 Million
Emp.: 205
Commercial Banking
N.A.I.C.S.: 522110
James S. Lewis (Co-Pres & CEO)
Gregory R. Cox (COO & Exec VP)
Thomas J. Davies (Exec VP & Mgr-Retail Banking Network)
Cathy A. Keeling (Sr VP & Mgr-Retail Product Svcs)
Pete B. Gardner (Sr VP & Mgr-Trust)
Rhonda Dugan (Sr VP & Mgr-Loan Admin)
Sherry Stroud (SVP & Branch Mgr)
Steven C. Lynn (Chief Lending Officer & Exec VP)

Valley View Financial Group Trust Company (1)
5901 College Blvd Ste 100, Overland Park, KS 66211
Tel.: (913) 319-0350
Web Site: http://www.vvfgtrust.com
Trust & Investment Management Services
N.A.I.C.S.: 523991
James O'Sullivan (Pres)
David Yost (Exec VP & Mgr-Personal Trust)
Brad Beets (Officer-Trust & Sr VP)
Phil Heffley (VP-Bus Dev & Fin Plng)
Shellie Billau (Officer-Trust & VP)
Dana Blackmon (Officer-Trust & VP)
Lana Britz (Officer-Trust & VP)
Andrew Browne (Officer-Personal Trust & VP)
Kurt Clausing (Officer-Trust & VP)
Debbie Corcoran (Officer-Trust & VP)
Mark Drake (Officer-Trust & VP)
Allegra Gassman (Officer-Trust)
Patricia Grothoff (Officer-Trust & VP)
Carrie Jones (Officer-Trust & VP)

VALLEY VIEW HAVEN, INC.
4702 E Main St, Belleville, PA 17004
Tel.: (717) 935-2105 PA
Web Site: http://www.vvrconline.org
Year Founded: 1965
Sales Range: $10-24.9 Million
Emp.: 418
Lifecare Retirement Community Operator
N.A.I.C.S.: 623311
Kent Peachey (Exec Dir)

VALLEY VIEW HOSPITAL
1906 Blake Ave, Glenwood Springs, CO 81601
Tel.: (970) 945-6535 CO
Web Site: http://www.vvh.org
Year Founded: 1950
Sales Range: $150-199.9 Million
Emp.: 979
Health Care Srvices
N.A.I.C.S.: 622110
Lynn Kleager (Treas)
Steve Vanderhoof (Chm)
Gary Brewer (CEO)
Larry Dupper (CFO)
Stacey Gavrell (Chief Community Rels Officer)
Daniel Biggs (Chief HR Officer)
Sandra Hurley (Chief Nursing Officer)
Dick Escue (CIO)
Alan E. Saliman (CMO)
Bob Pazik (Exec Dir-Physician Practices)
John Bosco (Sec)

VALLEY VIEW PACKING
7547 Sawtelle Ave, Yuba City, CA 95991
Tel.: (408) 289-8300
Web Site:
http://www.valleyviewpacking.com
Sales Range: $10-24.9 Million
Emp.: 8
Producer of Prunes & Prune Juice Concentrates
N.A.I.C.S.: 311423

VALLEY VIEW TUBE, INC.
3450 Main St E, Fort Payne, AL 35968
Tel.: (256) 638-1015
Web Site:
http://www.valleyviewal.com
Year Founded: 2004
Sales Range: $10-24.9 Million
Emp.: 65
Iron & Steel Pipe Mfr
N.A.I.C.S.: 331210
Brent Wilborn (Pres)
Lee Ann Wilborn (VP)
Teresa Brooks (Acct Mgr)

VALLEY VISTA CARE CORPORATION
820 Elm St, Saint Maries, ID 83861
Tel.: (208) 245-4576 ID
Web Site: http://www.valleyvista.org
Year Founded: 2001
Sales Range: $10-24.9 Million
Emp.: 509
Community Care Services
N.A.I.C.S.: 624190
Kasey Borgman (Dir-Corp Compliance)
Heidi McGreal (Dir-HR)
Terri Capshaw (Dir-Fin)
Sandy Kennelly (CEO)

VALLEY WHOLESALE COMPANY INC.
1032 Idaho Ave, Burley, ID 83318
Tel.: (208) 678-8365 ID
Web Site: http://www.vwhlsl.com
Year Founded: 1942
Sales Range: $10-24.9 Million
Emp.: 400
Retail Toys Hobby Goods & Supplies
N.A.I.C.S.: 423920
Thomas King (Co-Owner)

VALLEY WIDE COOPERATIVE INC.
1833 S Lincoln Ave, Jerome, ID 83338
Tel.: (208) 324-8000 ID
Web Site:
http://www.valleywidecoop.com
Year Founded: 1940
Rev: $537,105,906
Assets: $276,063,813
Liabilities: $149,139,337
Net Worth: $126,924,476
Earnings: $10,553,794
Fiscal Year-end: 08/31/19
Petroleum Products & Fertilizers Mfr
N.A.I.C.S.: 424720
Dave Holtom (CEO)
Greg Mapes (COO-Retail & Energy)
Adam Clark (Chm)
Carl Pendleton (Vice Chm)
Richard Lloyd (VP-Agronomy-Valley Agronomics LLC)

VALLEY YOUTH HOUSE
829 Linden St, Allentown, PA 18101
Tel.: (610) 820-0166 PA
Web Site:
http://www.valleyyouthhouse.org
Year Founded: 1971
Sales Range: $25-49.9 Million
Emp.: 538
Child & Youth Counseling Services
N.A.I.C.S.: 624110
Sandra Molnar (VP-Clinical Svcs)
Tracey Smith (Vice Chm)
Allison Moore (VP-Southeast Independent Living Programs)
Christina J. Schoemaker (VP-Dev & Mktg)
Lisa Weingartner (VP-Northeast & Central Independent Living Programs)
Lorrie Reddy (Dir-Grp Home Svcs)
Paul C. Ziegenfus (Dir-Fin)
Terri L. Mento (Dir-HR)
Thomas R. Harrington (Pres & CEO)

VALLEY-HI TOYOTA SCION
14612 Vly Center Dr, Victorville, CA 92395-4205
Tel.: (760) 241-6484
Web Site:
http://www.valleyhitoyota.com
Year Founded: 1970
Sales Range: $25-49.9 Million
Emp.: 150
New Car Whslr
N.A.I.C.S.: 441110
Todd Stokes (Mgr)

VALLEYLIFE
1142 W Hatcher Rd, Phoenix, AZ 85021
Tel.: (602) 371-0806 AZ
Web Site: http://www.valleylifeaz.org
Year Founded: 1950
Sales Range: $10-24.9 Million
Emp.: 864
Disability Assistance Services
N.A.I.C.S.: 624120
Cletus Thiebeau (Pres & CEO)
Linda Miller (CFO)
Cindy Hallman (Co-Treas)
Clifford L. Mattice (Vice Chm)
Peter C. Connolly (Chm)
Steve McKamey (Sec)
Cindy Quenneville (Co-Treas)

VALLI INFORMATION SYSTEMS, INCORPORATED
1300 W 56th Ave Unit 14, Anchorage, AK 99518-1083
Tel.: (907) 563-7014 AK
Web Site:
http://www.alaskaarchives.com
Year Founded: 1993
Sales Range: $1-9.9 Million
Emp.: 7
Document Management & Shredding Services
N.A.I.C.S.: 561499
Robert Jenkins (Pres)

VALLI PRODUCE
450 E Golf Rd, Arlington Heights, IL 60005
Tel.: (847) 439-9700
Web Site:
http://www.valliproduce.com
Rev: $21,400,000
Emp.: 180
Supermarkets & Other Grocery Stores
N.A.I.C.S.: 445110
Frank Chilelli (Owner)
Fred Presta (Pres)
Lou Tenuta (Sec)

VALMARK INC.
160 Spring St W, Friday Harbor, WA 98250
Tel.: (360) 378-5228
Web Site: http://www.kings-market.com
Sales Range: $10-24.9 Million
Emp.: 70
Grocery Stores, Independent
N.A.I.C.S.: 445110
Wesley Corey (Gen Mgr)

VALOR EQUITY PARTNERS L.P.
875 N Michigan Ave Ste 3214, Chicago, IL 60611
Tel.: (312) 683-1900
Web Site: http://www.valorep.com
Sales Range: $25-49.9 Million
Emp.: 25
Privater Equity Firm
N.A.I.C.S.: 523999
Jonathan K. Shulkin (Co-Pres)
Timothy M. Watkins (Partner)
Antonio J. Gracias (CEO, Mng Partner & Chief Investment Officer)
Bradley Sheftel (Partner)
Bruce Johns (Controller)
Christopher Murphy (Partner)
David Heskett (Principal)
Jay Dave (Controller)
Juan Sabater (Co-Pres & Partner)
Constantine Saab (Mng Dir)

VALOR IT
14269 N 87th St Ste 203, Scottsdale, AZ 85260
Web Site: http://www.valorit.com
Sales Range: $1-9.9 Million
Emp.: 31
Business Management Consulting & Programming Services
N.A.I.C.S.: 541511
Simer S. Mayo (Founder)
Anthony Clark (Principal)
Donna Corcoran (Dir-Fin)
Joe Berardi (CEO)
Kathleen Jones (Dir-Bus Solutions)
Mike Lacrosse (CIO)
Mike Reardon (CTO)
Paul Perialas (CFO)
Ron Teagarden (COO)

VALOR LLC
1200 Alsop Ln, Owensboro, KY 42303
Tel.: (270) 683-2461
Web Site: http://www.valorllc.com
Sales Range: $10-24.9 Million
Emp.: 43
Petroleum Bulk Stations
N.A.I.C.S.: 424710
Gary Emmick (Chm, Pres & CEO)
Tencie Estes (Acct Mgr-Cardlock)

COMPANIES

VALORE VENTURES, INC.
9701 Wilshire Blvd 10th Floor, Beverly Hills, CA 90212
Tel.: (310) 651-3013　　CA
Web Site: http://www.valore-ventures.com
Privater Equity Firm
N.A.I.C.S.: 523999
Kenny De Angelis *(Owner & Principal)*
Blake Heafner *(Mgr-Asset & Dev)*

Subsidiaries:

McMurray Stern Inc.　　(1)
15511 Carmenita Rd, Santa Fe Springs, CA 90670
Tel.: (562) 623-3000
Web Site: http://www.mcmurraystern.com
Rev.: $3,700,000
Emp.: 50
Design & Build Services
N.A.I.C.S.: 238130
Linda Stern *(CEO)*
Matt Zirkle *(Gen Mgr)*
Shaun Ferguson *(Dir-Fin)*
John Fisher *(VP-Sls & Mktg)*

VALPAK DIRECT MARKETING SYSTEMS, INC.
805 Executive Ctr Dr W Ste 100, Saint Petersburg, FL 33702
Tel.: (727) 399-3000
Web Site: http://www.valpak.com
Year Founded: 1968
Direct Mail Advertising Services
N.A.I.C.S.: 541860
Rick McElwain *(Exec VP-Franchise)*
Matt Biasini *(CFO)*
Chris Cate *(COO)*
Janet Kolb *(VP-HR)*
Mike Davis *(Pres & CEO)*
Nancy Cook *(Sr VP-Franchise Dev)*
Jennifer Glen *(Sr VP-Natl Sls)*
Benjy Uhl *(VP-Product & Bus Dev)*

VALPO MEDIOS, INC.
PO Box 81026, Rancho Santa Margarita, CA 92688
Tel.: (949) 636-7800
Web Site: http://www.valpomedios.com
Year Founded: 2007
Sales Range: $1-9.9 Million
Emp.: 1
Media Buying Services
N.A.I.C.S.: 541830
Patty Homo *(Pres)*

VALS DISTRIBUTING COMPANY
6336 E Admiral Pl Ste 226, Tulsa, OK 74115
Tel.: (918) 835-9987
Web Site: http://www.valsdistributing.com
Sales Range: $10-24.9 Million
Emp.: 9
Meats, Fresh
N.A.I.C.S.: 424470
Ken Grabow *(Pres)*

VALSTONE PARTNERS, LLC
260 E Brown St Ste 250, Birmingham, MI 48009
Tel.: (248) 646-9200
Web Site: http://www.valstonepartners.com
Year Founded: 1998
Rev.: $400,000,000
Emp.: 25
Privater Equity Firm
N.A.I.C.S.: 523999
Eric R. Abel *(Co-Founder, Mng Dir & CFO)*
Glenn P. Murray *(Exec VP)*
Richard Huddleston *(VP)*
Hee-Jin Yi *(Chief Compliance Officer & VP)*
Michael Zuehlke *(Chief Compliance Officer & Dir-Acctg)*
Gerald C. Timmis III *(Sr Mng Dir)*
Larry E. Jennings Jr. *(Co-Founder & Sr Mng Dir)*

Subsidiaries:

ValStone Asset Management　　(1)
260 E Brown St Ste 250, Birmingham, MI 48009
Tel.: (248) 646-9200
Emp.: 20
Asset Management
N.A.I.C.S.: 523940
Gerald C. TimmisIII *(Co-Pres)*
Larry E. Jennings Jr. *(Co-Pres)*

VALTERRA PRODUCTS, INC.
15230 San Fernando Mission Blvd Ste 107, Mission Hills, CA 91345
Tel.: (818) 898-1671
Web Site: http://www.valterra.com
Rev.: $23,700,000
Emp.: 280
Metal Valve & Pipe Fitting Mfr
N.A.I.C.S.: 332919
George Grengs *(Pres)*
Tom Sowler *(Controller)*

VALU DISCOUNT, INCORPORATED
315 Whittington Pkwy, Louisville, KY 40222-4649
Tel.: (502) 327-8840　　KY
Web Site: http://www.valumarket.com
Year Founded: 1978
Sales Range: $200-249.9 Million
Emp.: 350
Operator of Supermarkets
N.A.I.C.S.: 445110
Gregory Neumann *(Pres)*
James Neumann *(VP)*

VALU HOME CENTERS INC.
Valu Plz Clinton Rossler St, Buffalo, NY 14206
Tel.: (716) 825-7377　　NY
Web Site: http://www.valuhomecenters.com
Year Founded: 1983
Sales Range: $50-74.9 Million
Emp.: 650
Provider Of Lumber & Other Building Materials
N.A.I.C.S.: 444110
Rick Arena *(VP)*
Bill Calos *(VP-Mdsg)*
Cheryl Crist *(VP-HR)*
Dan Diemert *(VP-Mdsg)*
Doug Wasiura *(VP-Mktg & Dev)*
Tony Kota *(Dir-IT)*
T. J. Gray *(VP-Ops)*

VALU.NET CORPORATION
11710 Plz America Dr Ste 2000, Reston, VA 20190
Tel.: (703) 689-0780　　DE
Web Site: http://www.valu.net
Year Founded: 1996
Sales Range: $10-24.9 Million
Emp.: 15
Business-to-Business Internet E-Commerce Solutions Including Software & Portal Products, Web & Catalog Hosting Facilities & Custom Systems Integration Services
N.A.I.C.S.: 449210
Jennifer Madaj *(Mgr-Warehouse & Customer Svc)*

VALUATION RESEARCH CORP.
330 E Kilbourn Ave Ste 1425, Milwaukee, WI 53202
Tel.: (414) 271-8662
Web Site: http://www.valuationresearch.com
Sales Range: $10-24.9 Million
Emp.: 90
Appraisers Except Real Estate
N.A.I.C.S.: 541990
Bryan Browning *(Mng Dir)*
John D. Czapla *(Mng Dir)*
Joseph J. Mickle *(Mng Dir)*
Peter L. Morrison *(Mng Dir)*
P. J. Patel *(Co-CEO)*
Justin E. Johnson *(Co-CEO)*
Steven E. Schuetz *(Mng Dir)*
Ronald Ewing *(Sr VP-Chicago)*
Ed Hamilton *(Sr VP-Princeton)*
Charles Sapnas *(Sr VP-Princeton)*
Michael Ardizzone *(VP)*
Heather Tullar *(Sr VP)*
Chris Mellen *(Mng Dir)*
Amir Alerasoul *(VP)*
Daniel Brunow *(Sr VP)*
John Bintz *(Mng Dir)*
Jim Budyak *(Sr VP)*
Kent Amarante *(VP)*
Paul Balynsky *(Sr VP)*
Paul Bourke *(Sr VP)*
Robert Barnett *(Sr VP)*
Adriana De La Mora *(VP)*
Ryan Werkheiser *(Sr VP-Real Estate)*
Joe Lee *(VP)*
James Pace *(VP)*
Bryson Miller *(Mng Dir-Dallas)*

VALUE BASED SOLUTIONS, LLC
1651 Crossings Pkwy Ste B & C, Westlake, OH 44145
Tel.: (216) 401-5004
Web Site: http://www.value-based-solutions.com
Sales Range: $1-9.9 Million
Emp.: 9
Business Management Consulting Services
N.A.I.C.S.: 541618
Jeff Moore *(Pres & CEO)*

VALUE DRUG COMPANY
1 Golf View Dr, Altoona, PA 16601
Tel.: (814) 944-9316
Web Site: http://www.valuedrugco.com
Year Founded: 1934
Sales Range: $400-449.9 Million
Emp.: 120
Drugs & Drug Proprietaries Distr
N.A.I.C.S.: 424210
Karla Moschella *(Mgr-Sls & Mktg)*
Francis X. Straub III *(Chm & Treas)*

VALUE EXCHANGE CORPORATION
3326 Aspen Grove Dr Ste 404, Franklin, TN 37067
Tel.: (615) 778-0909
Web Site: http://www.vxwebsite.com
Year Founded: 2007
Sales Range: $1-9.9 Million
Emp.: 15
Electronic Financial Payment Services
N.A.I.C.S.: 522320
Brian L. Cooper *(Pres & CEO)*
Damon Cummings *(COO & Exec VP)*
Lorrianne R. Curtis *(Sr VP & Mgr-Natl Accts)*
MaLinda Oden *(Sr VP & Mgr-Admin)*

VALUE IMPLEMENT
50971 10th St, Osseo, WI 54758
Tel.: (715) 831-8140
Web Site: http://www.valueimplement.com
Rev.: $18,400,000
Emp.: 90
Farm & Garden Machinery & Equipment Merchant Whslr
N.A.I.C.S.: 423820
Bob Salonek *(Pres)*

VALUE MUSIC CONCEPTS INC.
825 Franklin Ct SE Ste C, Marietta, GA 30067-8944
Tel.: (770) 919-2115　　GA
Year Founded: 1993
Sales Range: $50-74.9 Million
Emp.: 340
Record & Prerecorded Tape Stores
N.A.I.C.S.: 449210
Brian Smith *(VP-Opers)*
Debbie Barbeauld *(Mgr-Acctg)*

VALUE PARTNERS, LTD.
4514 Cole Ave Ste 740, Dallas, TX 75205
Tel.: (214) 522-2100
Web Site: http://www.valuepartners.com
Year Founded: 1989
Rev.: $13,100,000
Emp.: 370
Security Brokers & Dealers
N.A.I.C.S.: 523150

VALUE PAYMENT SYSTEMS, LLC
2207 Crestmoor Rd Ste 200, Nashville, TN 37215
Tel.: (615) 730-6367
Web Site: http://www.valuepaymentsystems.com
Year Founded: 2007
Sales Range: $25-49.9 Million
Emp.: 27
Electronic Financial Payment Services
N.A.I.C.S.: 522320
Jeff Gardner *(COO)*
Scott Slusser *(CMO)*
Jarred Finney *(VP-IT)*
Daniel Brown *(Dir-Mktg)*
Stephanie Greer *(Dir-Ops)*
Jeff Hosterman *(Dir-Relationship Dev)*
Joe Thomas *(Dir-Network Security)*
Todd Christensen *(Dir-Channel Mgmt)*
Suja Sebastian *(Dir-IT)*

VALUE RECOVERY GROUP, INC.
919 Old Henderson Rd, Columbus, OH 43220
Tel.: (614) 324-5959
Web Site: http://www.valuerecoverygroup.com
Year Founded: 1993
Sales Range: $1-9.9 Million
Emp.: 32
Receivables Management & Consulting Services to Government Agencies
N.A.I.C.S.: 541219
Ralph Griffith *(Pres & CEO)*
Jeffery J. Sniderman *(Gen Counsel & Sr VP)*
David Poe *(COO & Exec VP)*

Subsidiaries:

Scully Capital Services, Inc.　　(1)
1730 M St NW Ste 204, Washington, DC 20036-4534
Tel.: (202) 775-3434
Web Site: http://www.scullycapital.com
Emp.: 6
Financial Advisory Services
N.A.I.C.S.: 523940
Larry Scully *(Pres)*

VALUE VINYLS INC.
301 E. Trinity Blvd., Grand Prairie, TX 75050

VALUE VINYLS INC.   U.S. PRIVATE

Value Vinyls Inc.—(Continued)
Web Site: http://www.valuevinyls.com
Sales Range: $10-24.9 Million
Emp.: 11
Plastic Material Distr
N.A.I.C.S.: 424610
Randy Busch *(Pres)*

VALUE-TRONICS INTERNATIONAL, INC.
1675 Cambridge Dr, Elgin, IL 60123
Tel.: (847) 468-8258
Web Site: http://www.valuetronics.com
Year Founded: 1992
Sales Range: $10-24.9 Million
Emp.: 35
Refurbished Test Equipment Distr
N.A.I.C.S.: 423690
John Griffith *(Pres)*

VALUEACT CAPITAL MANAGEMENT, L.P.
1 Letterman Dr Bldg D 4th Fl, San Francisco, CA 94129
Tel.: (415) 362-3700
Web Site: http://www.valueact.com
Year Founded: 2000
Sales Range: $25-49.9 Million
Emp.: 27
Equity Investment & Portfolio Management
N.A.I.C.S.: 523999
Gregory Paul Spivy *(Partner)*
Alexander L. Baum *(Partner)*
Garrison Mason Morfit *(CEO & Chief Investment Officer)*
Brandon B. Boze *(Pres & Partner)*
Dylan G. Haggart *(Partner)*

Subsidiaries:

Seitel, Inc.   (1)
10811 S Westview Cir Dr Bldg C Ste 100, Houston, TX 77043
Tel.: (713) 881-8900
Web Site: http://www.seitel.com
Rev: $90,250,000
Assets: $364,048,000
Liabilities: $286,934,000
Net Worth: $77,114,000
Earnings: ($31,481,000)
Emp.: 82
Fiscal Year-end: 12/31/2017
Seismic Data & Related Geophysical Services
N.A.I.C.S.: 541360
Robert D. Monson *(Pres & CEO)*
Marcia H. Kendrick *(CFO & Exec VP)*
Ryan M. Birtwell *(Chm)*
Mark Sweeney *(VP-Mktg)*

Subsidiary (Non-US):

Olympic Seismic, Ltd.   (2)
407 2nd Street SW Suite 1900, Calgary, T2P 2Y3, AB, Canada   (100%)
Tel.: (403) 515-2800
Web Site: http://www.olysei.com
Sales Range: $25-49.9 Million
Emp.: 26
Seismic Data Creation & Licensing
N.A.I.C.S.: 213112

Subsidiary (Domestic):

Seitel Data, Ltd.   (2)
10811 S Westview Cir Dr Bldg C Ste 100, Houston, TX 77043-9300
Tel.: (713) 881-8900
Sales Range: $50-74.9 Million
Seismic Data Creation & Licensing Services
N.A.I.C.S.: 213112
Jana Stroud *(Mgr-HR)*

Subsidiary (Non-US):

Seitel Solutions Canada, Ltd.   (2)
5321 11th Street NE, Calgary, T2E 8N4, AB, Canada
Tel.: (403) 274-9100
Web Site: http://www.seitel-inc.com
Sales Range: $25-49.9 Million
Emp.: 20
Seismic & Geophysical Data
N.A.I.C.S.: 213112
Dragana Popovic *(Office Mgr)*

VALUEBANK TEXAS
3649 Leopard St, Corpus Christi, TX 78408
Tel.: (361) 888-4451
Web Site: http://www.valuebanktexas.com
Year Founded: 1967
Rev: $13,100,000
Emp.: 106
Banking Services
N.A.I.C.S.: 522110
R. Scott Heitkamp *(Pres & CEO)*
Harlan R. Heitkamp *(Chm)*
Seth Watts *(CFO & Exec VP)*

VALUED MERCHANT SERVICES
3544 E 17th St Ste 207, Idaho Falls, ID 83401
Tel.: (208) 243-0818
Web Site: http://www.valuedmerchants.com
Year Founded: 2006
Sales Range: $1-9.9 Million
Emp.: 160
Electronic Payment Processing
N.A.I.C.S.: 522320
Chris Del Grande *(Co-Founder & Pres)*
Sean Ruppel *(Co-Founder & CEO)*
Arlo Nelson *(Dir-Sls-Natl)*
Jarrid Barzee *(Dir-Sls-Natl)*

VALUEPETSUPPLIES.COM
167 Industrial Park Cir, Livingston, TN 38570
Tel.: (910) 338-4452
Web Site: http://www.valuepetsupplies.com
Year Founded: 2004
Sales Range: $1-9.9 Million
Emp.: 26
Pet Supplies
N.A.I.C.S.: 459910
Zachary Piech *(Co-Founder)*
Cheri Piech *(Co-Founder)*

VALVE CORPORATION
PO Box 1688, Bellevue, WA 98009
Tel.: (425) 889-9642
Web Site: http://www.valvesoftware.com
Year Founded: 1996
Sales Range: $25-49.9 Million
Emp.: 300
Entertainment Software & Technology Developer
N.A.I.C.S.: 513210
Scott Lynch *(COO)*

VALVERDE CONSTRUCTION INC.
10936 Shoemaker Ave, Santa Fe Springs, CA 90670
Tel.: (562) 906-1826
Web Site: http://www.valverdeconst.com
Year Founded: 1972
Sales Range: $10-24.9 Million
Emp.: 40
Water Main Construction
N.A.I.C.S.: 237110
Chris Valverde *(Project Mgr)*
Ahron Valverde *(Mgr-Equipment)*

VALVTECHNOLOGIES INC.
5904 Bingle Rd, Houston, TX 77092
Tel.: (713) 860-0400
Web Site: http://www.valv.com
Sales Range: $10-24.9 Million
Emp.: 80
Mfr of Industrial Valves
N.A.I.C.S.: 332911
Kevin Hunt *(Pres)*
Gary Gandolfi *(Dir-Global Distr & Svc)*
Edward Ferris *(VP-HR)*
Cliff Horsburgh *(Dir-Asia Pacific)*
Ron Anselmo *(VP-Key Accts)*

VAMAC INC.
4201 Jacque St, Richmond, VA 23230
Tel.: (804) 353-7811
Web Site: http://www.vamac.com
Sales Range: $25-49.9 Million
Emp.: 100
Plumbing & Hydronic Heating Supplies
N.A.I.C.S.: 423720
Norman Browning *(Mgr-Facility)*
Phil Haley *(Mgr)*
Kenneth Perry *(Chm)*
Rick Omohundro *(Dir-HR)*

VAN AIR, INC.
2950 Mechanic St, Lake City, PA 16423-2023
Tel.: (814) 774-2631
Web Site: http://www.vanairsystems.com
Year Founded: 1944
Sales Range: $50-74.9 Million
Emp.: 50
Compressed Air Drying & Treating Equipment Mfr
N.A.I.C.S.: 333912
James A. Currie Jr. *(Pres & CEO)*

Subsidiaries:

Van Air Systems Inc   (1)
2950 Mechanic St, Lake City, PA 16423
Tel.: (800) 840-9906
Compressed Air & Gas Treated Product Mfr
N.A.I.C.S.: 333912

VAN ANDEL & FLIKKEMA MOTOR SALES, INC.
3844 Plainfield Ave NE, Grand Rapids, MI 49525-2452
Tel.: (616) 363-9031
Web Site: http://www.vfcars.com
Year Founded: 1932
Sales Range: $10-24.9 Million
Emp.: 68
New Car Whslr
N.A.I.C.S.: 441110
Diana Yope *(VP & Gen Mgr)*
Ron Corson *(Mgr-Accts Payable)*
John C. Flikkema Sr. *(Pres)*

VAN ANDEL INSTITUTE
333 Bostwick Ave NE, Grand Rapids, MI 49503
Tel.: (616) 234-5000
Web Site: http://www.vai.org
Year Founded: 1996
Sales Range: $75-99.9 Million
Emp.: 1720
Biomedical Research Services
N.A.I.C.S.: 541715
Linda Zarzecki *(VP-HR)*
Jerry Callahan *(VP-Innovations & Collaborations)*
Timothy Myers *(CFO & VP)*
Brett Holleman *(Chief Dev Officer)*
Jana Hall *(COO)*

VAN AUKEN AKINS ARCHITECTS LLC
The Hanna Bldg 1422 Euclid Ave Ste 1010, Cleveland, OH 44115
Tel.: (216) 241-2220
Web Site: http://www.vaakins.com
Year Founded: 1992
Sales Range: $1-9.9 Million
Emp.: 24
Creates Architectural Drawings & Designs for Commercial & Residential Design
N.A.I.C.S.: 541310
Jill V. Akins *(Founder & Principal)*
Tom Kurtz *(Engr & Mgr-Project Construction)*
Milka Vranic *(Office Mgr)*

VAN AUSDALL & FARRAR INC.
6430 E 75th St, Indianapolis, IN 46250
Tel.: (317) 634-2913
Web Site: http://www.vanausdall.com
Year Founded: 1914
Sales Range: $25-49.9 Million
Emp.: 180
Provider of Technology-Based Solutions
N.A.I.C.S.: 423420
Laurie Parker *(Coord-Voice & Data Svcs)*
Chris McCalley *(Mgr-Sls)*
Nancy Brown *(Mgr-Site)*
Robert Purcell *(Mgr-Ops)*

VAN BEBBER & ASSOCIATES, INC.
132 Whitaker Rd, Lutz, FL 33549
Tel.: (813) 909-1819
Web Site: http://www.vanbebber.com
Year Founded: 1957
Sales Range: $1-9.9 Million
Emp.: 10
Construction & Real Estate Services
N.A.I.C.S.: 236220
Greg Van Bebber *(Pres)*
Bridget Begey *(Mgr-Ops)*

VAN BEURDEN INSURANCE SERVICES
1600 Draper St, Kingsburg, CA 93631
Tel.: (559) 897-2975
Web Site: http://www.vanbeurden.com
Sales Range: $10-24.9 Million
Emp.: 80
Insurance Agents, Nec
N.A.I.C.S.: 524210
William J. Van Beurden *(Pres)*
Chris Van Beurden *(COO)*
Diana Alvarez *(Mgr-Acct)*
Kathy Holman *(Mgr-HR)*
Mark Karlie *(VP-Employee Benefits)*
Peter Schwarz *(Dir-IS)*
Guy Teafatiller *(VP)*
Robin Hankins *(CFO)*
Brian Loven *(VP-Comml Insurance)*
Erik Van Beurden *(CEO)*

VAN BEUREN MANAGEMENT, INC.
330 S St, Morristown, NJ 07960
Tel.: (973) 540-0968
Rev: $60,800,000
Emp.: 1
Glassware, Novelty
N.A.I.C.S.: 561110
Kurt T. Borowsky *(Chm)*

VAN BLARCOM CLOSURES INC.
156 Sandford St, Brooklyn, NY 11205-3910
Tel.: (718) 855-3810
Web Site: http://www.vbcpkg.com
Year Founded: 1947
Sales Range: $25-49.9 Million
Emp.: 180
Mfr of Plastic Products
N.A.I.C.S.: 326199
Vincent Cadari *(Pres)*
Jerry Frey *(Mgr-Sls)*

Subsidiaries:

Johnson/V.B.C. Inc. (1)
163 Warren St, Paterson, NJ 07524-2439
Tel.: (973) 279-0890
Web Site: http://www.johnson-vbc.com
Sales Range: $10-24.9 Million
Emp.: 40
Mfr of Crowns & Closures
N.A.I.C.S.: 332119
James Johnson *(Gen Mgr)*

VBC-Bristol Inc. (1)
156 Sandford St 170, Brooklyn, NY 11205-3910
Tel.: (718) 855-3810
Web Site: http://www.vbc.com
Sales Range: $10-24.9 Million
Emp.: 1
Mfr of Plastic Products
N.A.I.C.S.: 326199

VBCJ, Inc. (1)
163 Warren St, Paterson, NJ 07524-2439
Tel.: (973) 279-0890
Web Site: http://www.johnson-vbc.com
Sales Range: $10-24.9 Million
Emp.: 15
Provider of Nonresidential Building Operator Services
N.A.I.C.S.: 531120
James Johnson *(Gen Mgr)*

VAN BORTEL AIRCRAFT INC.

4900 S Collins St, Arlington, TX 76018-1135
Tel.: (817) 557-5857   NY
Web Site: http://www.vanbortel.com
Year Founded: 1985
Sales Range: $10-24.9 Million
Emp.: 40
Transportation Equipment & Supplies
N.A.I.C.S.: 423860
Howard G. Van Bortel *(Pres)*
Gloria Hannon *(Controller)*

Subsidiaries:

Air Power Inc. (1)
4900 S Collins St, Arlington, TX 76018-1135
Tel.: (817) 557-5857
Web Site: http://www.factoryengines.com
Transportation Equipment & Supplies
N.A.I.C.S.: 423860
Howard G. Van Bortel *(Pres)*

Van Bortel Finance Corporation (1)
4912 S Collins, Arlington, TX 76018
Tel.: (817) 468-7788
Financial Management Services
N.A.I.C.S.: 523940

VAN BORTEL FORD

71 Marsh Rd, East Rochester, NY 14445
Tel.: (585) 586-4415
Web Site: http://www.vanbortelford.com
Year Founded: 2001
Sales Range: $50-74.9 Million
Emp.: 83
Automotive Part & Accessory Distr
N.A.I.C.S.: 441330
Bryan Zemaitis *(Bus Mgr)*
Guy Kalpin *(Mgr-Svc)*
Kitty Van Bortel *(Founder)*

VAN BORTEL SUBARU

6327 Route 96, Victor, NY 14564
Tel.: (585) 924-5230
Web Site: http://www.vanbortelsubaru.net
Year Founded: 1985
Sales Range: $10-24.9 Million
Emp.: 30
Car Whslr
N.A.I.C.S.: 441110
Mary C. Van Bortel *(Pres)*

VAN BUREN TRUCK SALES CORP.

2257 Jericho Tpke, New Hyde Park, NY 11040
Tel.: (516) 741-5060
Web Site: http://www.vanburenauto.com
Rev.: $49,297,274
Emp.: 60
Pickups, New & Used
N.A.I.C.S.: 441110
Richard V. Volpe *(VP)*
Eric Vila *(Mgr-Fin)*
Ken Williams *(Gen Mgr)*

VAN CAMPEN MOTORS, INC.

601 W 3rd St, Williamsport, PA 17701
Tel.: (570) 326-0567
Web Site: http://www.vancampenmotors.com
Sales Range: $25-49.9 Million
Emp.: 50
New Car Retailer
N.A.I.C.S.: 441110
George Wurster *(Gen Mgr)*
Celia Van Campen *(Sec)*

VAN CHEVROLET

8585 E Frank Lloyd Wright, Scottsdale, AZ 85260
Tel.: (480) 991-8300
Web Site: http://www.vanchevrolet.com
Rev.: $39,300,000
Emp.: 260
Car Dealer
N.A.I.C.S.: 441120
Chuck Mullins *(Gen Mgr)*
Smiley Elturk *(Dir-Used Car)*
Sheilah Keilman *(Mgr-HR)*
Richard Knase *(Dir-Internet)*
Matt Mylan *(Dir-Parts)*

VAN CLEEF ENGINEERING ASSOCIATES, INC.

32 Brower Ln, Hillsborough, NJ 08844
Tel.: (908) 359-8291   NJ
Web Site: http://www.vcea.org
Year Founded: 1971
Sales Range: $1-9.9 Million
Emp.: 110
Engineeering Services
N.A.I.C.S.: 541330
Neil Van Cleef *(Founder)*

Subsidiaries:

Van Cleef Engineering Associates LLC (1)
520 N New St, Bethlehem, PA 18018
Tel.: (610) 332-1772
Web Site: http://www.vcea.org
Sales Range: $1-9.9 Million
Emp.: 8
Engineering Consulting
N.A.I.C.S.: 541330
Mark Bahnick *(VP)*

VAN DALE INDUSTRIES INC.

180 Madison Ave FL 2, New York, NY 10016
Tel.: (212) 683-8181
Web Site: http://www.vandale.com
Sales Range: $10-24.9 Million
Emp.: 75
Mfr of Underwear
N.A.I.C.S.: 424350
Albert Ades *(Pres)*
Anna Maria Golia *(CFO)*
Naseema Hassan *(Coord-EDI)*

VAN DE POL ENTERPRISES, INC.

4895 S Airport Way, Stockton, CA 95206
Tel.: (209) 465-3421   CA
Web Site: http://www.vandepol.us
Year Founded: 1947
Rev.: $88,000,000
Emp.: 200
Holding Company; Fuel & Petroleum Products Dealer
N.A.I.C.S.: 551112
Ronald Van De Pol *(Pres)*
Tom Van De Pol *(Mktg Mgr-Van De Pol Petroleum)*
Scott MacEwan *(CFO)*
David Atwater *(Gen Mgr-Van De Pol Petroleum)*
Lee Atwater *(Founder & Chm)*

Subsidiaries:

Alliance Petroleum Corporation (1)
4895 S Airport Way, Stockton, CA 95206
Tel.: (209) 465-3421
Web Site: http://www.vandepol.us
Fuel & Petroleum Products Dealer
N.A.I.C.S.: 457210
Ronald Van De Pol *(Pres)*
Scott MacEwan *(CFO)*
David Atwater *(Gen Mgr)*
Jon Rosman *(VP-Branded Fuels)*
Curtis Thornhill *(VP-Comml Sls)*
Tom Van De Pol *(Mktg Mgr)*

VAN DIEST FAMILY, LLC

1434 220th St, Webster City, IA 50595
Tel.: (515) 832-2366   IA
Web Site: http://www.vdsc.com
Year Founded: 2006
Sales Range: $75-99.9 Million
Emp.: 500
Holding Company
N.A.I.C.S.: 551112
Robert Van Diest *(Pres)*

Subsidiaries:

Van Diest Investment Company (1)
1434 220th St, Webster City, IA 50595
Tel.: (515) 832-2366
Bank Holding Company
N.A.I.C.S.: 551111
Robert Van Diest *(Pres)*
Gregg Olson *(Treas)*

Subsidiary (Domestic):

First State Bank (2)
505 2nd St, Webster City, IA 50595
Tel.: (515) 832-2520
Web Site: http://www.fsbwc.com
Sales Range: $10-24.9 Million
Emp.: 109
Commericial Banking
N.A.I.C.S.: 522110
Sheila Johnson *(Coord-Club-Webster City)*
Dave Taylor *(Pres)*
Tiffany Lowe *(Mgr-Retail Svcs-Fort Dodge)*
Brandy Mayall *(Portfolio Mgr-Humboldt)*
Barb Anderson *(Dir-HR-Webster City)*
Eric Larson *(Portfolio Mgr-Webster City)*
Kim Peck *(Mgr-Mktg-Webster City)*
Alyssa Schwering *(Compliance Officer & Controller-Webster City)*
Emily Stockdale *(Mgr-Retail Svcs-Webster City)*

Van Diest Supply Company (1)
1434 220th St, Webster City, IA 50595
Tel.: (515) 832-2366
Web Site: http://www.vdsc.com
Agricultural Chemical Mfr
N.A.I.C.S.: 424910
Robert Van Diest *(Chm)*
John Van Diest *(VP)*
Lee Trask *(VP-Mfg)*
Karleen Carlson *(Mgr-IT)*
Mark Davis *(Coord-Mfg)*
Jody Klaver *(Controller)*
Tim Nilles *(Mgr-Inventory)*
Jake Van Diest *(Pres)*

VAN DRUNEN FORD

3233 183rd St, Homewood, IL 60430-2698
Tel.: (708) 798-1668
Web Site: http://www.vandrunenford.com
Sales Range: $25-49.9 Million
Emp.: 70
Car Whslr
N.A.I.C.S.: 441110
Marvin G. VanDrunen *(Pres)*

VAN DYK & COMPANY, INC.

12800 Long Beach Blvd, Terrace, NJ 08008
Tel.: (609) 492-1511   NJ
Web Site: http://www.vandykgroup.com
Year Founded: 1946
Sales Range: $10-24.9 Million
Emp.: 100
Insurance Agents
N.A.I.C.S.: 524210
Marlene Romanowski *(Mgr-Sls-Real Estates)*

VAN DYK BUSINESS SYSTEMS INC.

800 Trumbull Dr, Pittsburgh, PA 15205
Tel.: (412) 279-1400
Web Site: http://www.vandyk.net
Rev.: $15,251,368
Emp.: 60
Business Machines & Equipment
N.A.I.C.S.: 459999
David Kadyk *(VP-Svcs)*
Ronald G. Linaburg *(Pres & CEO)*

VAN DYKE DODGE INC.

28400 Van Dyke Ave, Warren, MI 48093
Tel.: (586) 573-4000   MI
Web Site: http://www.vandykedodge.com
Year Founded: 1978
Sales Range: $100-124.9 Million
Emp.: 1,100
Sales of New & Used Automobiles
N.A.I.C.S.: 441110
Bruce Williams *(Asst Mgr-Parts)*
Glenn Butterworth *(Mgr-Fleet)*
John Caldwell *(Gen Mgr)*
Mary Pittiglio-Hunley *(Bus Mgr)*
Tim Knaffla *(Mgr-Body Shop)*

VAN DYKE RANKIN & COMPANY INC.

211 S Austin St, Brenham, TX 77833
Tel.: (979) 836-5636
Web Site: http://www.vanranco.com
Year Founded: 1981
Sales Range: $10-24.9 Million
Emp.: 22
Provider of Insurance Services
N.A.I.C.S.: 524210
Robin Stephens *(Mgr)*
Eddie Van Dyke *(Pres)*
Jarvis Van Dyke *(VP)*
Kay Przyborski *(Mgr)*
Kathy Savell *(Acct Exec)*
Karen Herzog *(Acct Exec)*
Marilyn Schroeder *(Sec)*

VAN ECK ASSOCIATES CORP.

666 3rd Ave, New York, NY 10017
Tel.: (212) 687-5200
Web Site: http://www.vaneck.com
Year Founded: 1955
Rev.: $32,000,000,000
Emp.: 220
Mutual Funds & Investment Advice
N.A.I.C.S.: 523940
Jan F. van Eck *(Founder & CEO)*
Matthew Sigel *(Head-Digital Assets Res)*

Subsidiaries:

Market Vectors-Russia EFT (1)
335 Maddison 19th Fl, New York, NY 10017
Tel.: (212) 687-5200
Web Site: http://www.vaneck.com
Sales Range: $50-74.9 Million
Emp.: 100
Investment Fund
N.A.I.C.S.: 525910
Jan F. van Eck *(Pres, CEO & Treas)*

VAN ECK ASSOCIATES CORP.

Van Eck Associates Corp.—(Continued)

Unit (Domestic):

Market Vectors Commodity Trust (2)
335 Madison Ave, New York, NY 10017
Tel.: (212) 293-2000
Web Site: http://www.vaneck.com
Sales Range: $50-74.9 Million
Securities & Commodity Exchanges
N.A.I.C.S.: 523210

Market Vectors Redeemable Gold Trust (2)
335 Madison Ave, New York, NY 10017
Tel.: (212) 293-2000
Web Site: http://www.vaneck.com
Gold Sales
N.A.I.C.S.: 423940
Jan F. van Eck (Pres)
Joseph J. McBrien (Chief Legal Officer, Gen Counsel, Sr VP & Sec)

Market Vectors Redeemable Silver Trust (2)
335 Madison Ave, New York, NY 10017
Tel.: (212) 293-2000
Investment Services
N.A.I.C.S.: 523999

Van Eck Switzerland AG (1)
Churerstrasse 23, 8808, Pfaffikon, Switzerland
Tel.: (41) 55 417 8050
Investment Advisory Services
N.A.I.C.S.: 523940
Uwe E. Eberle (Mng Dir)

VAN EERDEN FOODSERVICE COMPANY
650 Ionia SW, Grand Rapids, MI 49503
Tel.: (616) 475-0900
Web Site: http://www.vaneerden.com
Sales Range: $150-199.9 Million
Emp.: 160
Food Service & Distribution Services
N.A.I.C.S.: 722310
Daniel Van Eerden (Pres)
Tracy Christian (Controller)
Adam Behen (Mgr-Sls)
Charlie Cook (VP)

VAN EERDEN TRUCKING COMPANY
10299 S Kent Dr, Byron Center, MI 49315
Tel.: (616) 877-0192   MI
Web Site: http://www.vetrucking.com
Year Founded: 1980
Sales Range: $25-49.9 Million
Emp.: 250
Trucking Transportation Services
N.A.I.C.S.: 484121
Daniel Van Eerden (Pres)
Roger Rottschafer (Gen Mgr)
Brad Vanderstel (Controller)

Subsidiaries:

Transportation Group (1)
10299 S Kent Dr, Byron Center, MI 49315
Tel.: (616) 877-0192
Sales Range: $25-49.9 Million
Emp.: 200
Trucking Except Local
N.A.I.C.S.: 484121
Daniel Van Eerden (Pres)
Brad Vanderstel (Controller)

VAN ENTERPRISES INC.
8500 Shawnee Mission Pkwy Ste 200, Shawnee Mission, KS 66202
Tel.: (913) 895-0200   MO
Sales Range: $100-124.9 Million
Emp.: 129
Owner & Operator of Auto Dealerships
N.A.I.C.S.: 441222
Cecil Van Tuyl (Chm & Pres)

VAN ERT ELECTRIC COMPANY INC
7019 Stewart Ave, Wausau, WI 54401-9339
Tel.: (715) 845-4308   WI
Web Site: http://www.vanert.com
Year Founded: 1964
Sales Range: $25-49.9 Million
Emp.: 350
Electrical Work
N.A.I.C.S.: 238210
Robert Van Ert (Pres)
Darrell Kurth (VP)
Jenni Cihlar (CFO)

VAN HOOSE CONSTRUCTION CO.
101 Ne 70th St, Oklahoma City, OK 73105-1206
Tel.: (405) 848-0415
Web Site: http://www.vhcon.com
Sales Range: $1-9.9 Million
Emp.: 25
Commercial & Office Building, New Construction
N.A.I.C.S.: 236220
Jeff Van Hoose (Pres)
Jeff Sanders (CEO)

VAN HORN AUTOMOTIVE GROUP, INC.
W5073 Co Rd, Plymouth, WI 53073
Tel.: (920) 892-6466
Web Site: http://www.vhcars.com
General Automotive Repair
N.A.I.C.S.: 811111
Ike Vorheis (Owner)

Subsidiaries:

Dick Brantmeier Ford Inc. (1)
3624 Kohler Meml Dr, Sheboygan, WI 53081
Tel.: (920) 458-6111
Web Site: http://www.dickbrantmeier.com
Sales Range: $10-24.9 Million
Emp.: 63
Automobiles, New & Used
N.A.I.C.S.: 441110
Richard J. Brantmeier (Pres)
Josua Mihm (Mgr-F&I)

VAN HORN BROS INC.
3700 Airport Rd, Waterford, MI 48329
Tel.: (248) 623-4830
Web Site: http://www.vanhornconcrete.com
Rev.: $14,556,937
Emp.: 30
Ready Mixed Concrete
N.A.I.C.S.: 327320
Richard B. Clark (Chm)

VAN HORN HYUNDAI OF FOND DU LAC INC.
N6652 Esterbrook Rd, Fond Du Lac, WI 54937
Tel.: (920) 924-0000
Web Site: http://www.fdlhyundai.com
Sales Range: $10-24.9 Million
Emp.: 50
New & Used Car Dealer
N.A.I.C.S.: 441110
Tom Burns (Gen Mgr)
Tim Goeckerman (Gen Mgr-Sls)
Josh Boersma (Mgr-Sls)
Paul Bathke (Mgr-Svc Dept)

VAN HORN METZ & CO. INC.
201 E Elm St, Conshohocken, PA 19428-0269
Tel.: (610) 828-4500   PA
Web Site: http://www.vanhornmetz.com
Year Founded: 1950
Sales Range: $10-24.9 Million
Emp.: 75
Chemicals & Allied Products

N.A.I.C.S.: 424690
Anthony Chrisafulli (Controller)
Morgan Smith (Chm)
Brian Boorman (Exec VP)
Laurie Barfield (Acct Mgr-Southeastern Territory)
Barrett C. Fisher III (Pres)

VAN KING & STORAGE INC.
13535 Larwin Cir, Santa Fe Springs, CA 90670
Tel.: (562) 921-0555
Web Site: http://www.kingrelocation.com
Year Founded: 1955
Sales Range: $10-24.9 Million
Emp.: 50
Moving Services
N.A.I.C.S.: 484210
Steve Komoroul (Pres)

VAN LAAN CONCRETE CONSTRUCTION, INC.
6875 Dutton Indus Dr, Dutton, MI 49316
Tel.: (616) 698-6397   MI
Web Site: http://www.vanlaan.com
Year Founded: 1962
Sales Range: $10-24.9 Million
Emp.: 85
Provider of Foundation & Footing Contracts
N.A.I.C.S.: 238110
Thomas Van Laan (Chm)
Scott Van Laan (Pres)

VAN LUMBER INC.
27 S Maple St, Bellingham, MA 02019
Tel.: (508) 966-4141   MA
Web Site: http://www.vanmillwork.com
Year Founded: 1952
Sales Range: $10-24.9 Million
Emp.: 35
Mfr of Wooden Doors
N.A.I.C.S.: 423310
Russ Clark (Controller)

VAN MANEN PETROLEUM GROUP
0-305 Lk Michigan Dr NW, Grand Rapids, MI 49534
Tel.: (616) 453-6344
Web Site: http://www.vanmanen.com
Year Founded: 1952
Sales Range: $50-74.9 Million
Emp.: 46
Provider of Petroleum Fuels
N.A.I.C.S.: 424720
Randy Van Manen (Pres)
Doug Van Hattum (CFO)
Dan Koetsier (Mgr-Accts)

Subsidiaries:

Fuel Management System (1)
0-305 Lk Michigan Dr, Grand Rapids, MI 49534-3355
Tel.: (616) 453-6344
Web Site: http://www.vanmanen.com
Sales Range: $10-24.9 Million
Emp.: 30
Provider of Fleet Fuel Management Systems
N.A.I.C.S.: 424720
Doug Van Hattum (CEO)

VAN METER INC.
240 33rd Ave 850 32nd Ave SW, Cedar Rapids, IA 52404-4606
Tel.: (319) 366-5301   IA
Web Site: http://www.vanmeterinc.com
Year Founded: 1928
Sales Range: $150-199.9 Million
Emp.: 250

U.S. PRIVATE

Electrical Apparatus & Equipment Sales
N.A.I.C.S.: 423610
Tom Durian (Controller)
Dave Klostermann (Mgr-Customized Solutions)
Nate Jensema (Controller)
Mike Gassmann (Chief Growth Officer)
Melanie Fisher Doyle (CFO)
Jeff Spadaro (VP-Automation)
Lura E. McBride (Pres & CEO)

Subsidiaries:

Werner Electric Supply Company (1)
7450 95th St, Cottage Grove, MN 55016
Tel.: (651) 458-3701
Web Site: http://www.wernermn.com
Provider of Electrical & Plumbing Equipment; Joint Venture of Werner Electric Supply Company & Van Meter Industrial Inc.
N.A.I.C.S.: 423610
Ben Granley (Pres)
John Farrell (VP-Mktg)
Bob Cunningham (Dir-Construction)

VAN NATTA MECHANICAL INC.
25 Whitney Rd, Mahwah, NJ 07430
Tel.: (201) 391-3700
Web Site: http://www.vannattamechanical.com
Rev.: $17,000,000
Emp.: 50
Plumbing Contractor
N.A.I.C.S.: 238220

VAN OWEN GROUP ACQUISITION COMPANY
3001 South Skyway, Irving, TX 75038
Tel.: (972) 659-1600
Rev.: $21,700,000
Conveyors & Conveying Equipment
N.A.I.C.S.: 333922
John Crossno (Owner)

VAN PELT CORPORATION
13700 Sherwood St, Detroit, MI 48212-2038
Tel.: (313) 365-6500   MI
Web Site: http://www.servicesteel.com
Year Founded: 1941
Sales Range: $75-99.9 Million
Emp.: 100
Steel Tubing Distr
N.A.I.C.S.: 423510
Van Pelt (Pres)

Subsidiaries:

Van Pelt - Service Steel Division (1)
13700 Sherwood St, Detroit, MI 48212-2038
Tel.: (313) 365-6500
Web Site: http://www.servicesteel.com
Steel Warehouse Service Center
N.A.I.C.S.: 423510

VAN PLYCON LINES INC.
280 Indian Head Rd, Kings Park, NY 11754
Tel.: (631) 269-7000
Web Site: http://www.plycongroup.com
Year Founded: 1982
Rev.: $16,278,325
Emp.: 300
Local Trucking with Storage
N.A.I.C.S.: 484110
Dean Pliaconis (Pres)
Christopher Pliaconis (VP)

Subsidiaries:

Nationwide Logistics Inc (1)
4240 W 190th St, Torrance, CA 90504
Tel.: (310) 419-5000
Rev.: $250,000
Emp.: 5

COMPANIES

Air Courier Services
N.A.I.C.S.: 492110

VAN RU CREDIT CORPORATION
1350 E Touhy Ave Ste 300E, Des Plaines, IL 60068
Tel.: (847) 824-2414 IL
Web Site: http://www.vanru.com
Year Founded: 1953
Sales Range: $100-124.9 Million
Emp.: 630
Adjustment & Collection Services
N.A.I.C.S.: 561440
Randy Smith *(CFO)*
Charlie Ficht *(Mgr-HR)*
Shelly Figard *(Supvr-FDSL)*
Albert Rubin *(Chm & CEO)*
Petrice Boursiquot *(Coord-AR)*
Michael Blue *(Mgr-Collection)*
Skip Spillone *(CFO & VP)*
Joe Santana *(Mgr)*
Brion Henes *(VP-IT)*

VAN SCHOUWEN ASSOCIATES, LLC
175 Dwight Rd Ste 201, Longmeadow, MA 01106
Tel.: (413) 567-8700
Web Site: http://www.vsamarketing.com
Year Founded: 1985
Sales Range: $10-24.9 Million
Emp.: 10
N.A.I.C.S.: 541810
Michelle van Schouwen *(Pres)*

VAN SON HOLLAND INK CORPORATION OF AMERICA
888 Veterans Memorial Hwy Ste 440, Hauppauge, NY 11788
Tel.: (631) 715-7000 DE
Web Site: http://www.vansonink.com
Year Founded: 1872
Sales Range: $25-49.9 Million
Emp.: 100
Printing Inks Importer Mfr & Distr
N.A.I.C.S.: 423840
Joe Bendowski *(CEO)*
Denise Marchese *(Acct Mgr-Natl Comml)*

VAN SYCKLE KIA INC.
729 Hogan Rd, Bangor, ME 04401
Tel.: (207) 947-4559
Web Site: http://www.vansycklekia.com
Sales Range: $10-24.9 Million
Emp.: 40
Car Dealership
N.A.I.C.S.: 441110
R. Peter Van Syckle *(Principal)*
Edward Viner *(Gen Mgr)*
J. J. Adams *(Gen Mgr-Sls)*
Ryan Macrae *(Mgr-Sls)*
Mike Kearns *(Mgr-Sls)*
Andrew Davis *(Mgr-Sls)*
Justin Hatch *(Mgr-Fin)*
Don Greenwood *(Mgr-Bus Dev Ctr)*

VAN VREEDE TV & APPLIANCE INCORPORATED
2450 W College Ave, Appleton, WI 54914
Tel.: (920) 730-4477
Web Site: http://www.vanvreedes.com
Sales Range: $25-49.9 Million
Emp.: 110
Household Appliance Stores
N.A.I.C.S.: 449210
Gary Brynjulsson *(VP)*
Rob Ernst *(Controller)*

VAN WAGNER COMMUNICATIONS, LLC
800 3rd Ave 28th Fl, New York, NY 10022
Tel.: (212) 699-8400
Web Site: http://www.vanwagner.com
Rev.: $11,500,000
Emp.: 250
Outdoor
N.A.I.C.S.: 541810
Richard Schaps *(CEO)*
John Massoni *(Pres-Western Div)*
Richard Silverton *(CEO-Van Wagner Asia Pacific)*
Liza Villafane *(VP-HR)*
Bob Becker *(Exec VP-VWSE Productions)*
Bruno Walmsley *(CFO)*
Chris Allphin *(Sr VP-Team & Venue Svcs)*
Hillary Thomas *(COO)*
Paul Kalil *(CEO-VWSE Productions)*
Robert Jordan *(Sr VP-Team & Venue Svcs)*
Steve Pretsfelder *(Gen Counsel & Exec VP)*

Subsidiaries:

American Blimp Corp. (1)
1900 NE 25th Ave Ste 5, Hillsboro, OR 97124
Tel.: (503) 693-1611
Web Site: http://www.americanblimp.com
Rev.: $4,383,000
Emp.: 15
Mfr of Helium-Filled Airships & Surveillance Equipment
N.A.I.C.S.: 336411
Jim Thiele *(Pres & CEO)*
Chris Wegener *(Mgr-Quality)*

Van Wagner Sports Group LLC (1)
800 3rd Ave 28th Fl, New York, NY 10022-7604
Tel.: (212) 699-8600
Emp.: 100
N.A.I.C.S.: 541810
Cliff Kaplan *(Pres)*
John Heagele *(COO)*
Kip Koslow *(Sr VP)*
Chris Pearlman *(VP-Media & Sls)*
Scott Epstein *(EVP-Sponsorship & Media Sls)*

VAN WALL EQUIPMENT INC.
22728 141 St Dr, Perry, IA 50220
Tel.: (515) 465-5681
Web Site: http://www.vanwall.com
Year Founded: 1977
Sales Range: $150-199.9 Million
Emp.: 300
Agricultural Machinery & Equipment
N.A.I.C.S.: 423820
Don Van Houweling *(CEO)*

VAN WERT COUNTY HOSPITAL
1250 S Washington St, Van Wert, OH 45891
Tel.: (419) 238-2390 OH
Web Site: http://www.vanwerthospital.org
Year Founded: 1905
Sales Range: $50-74.9 Million
Emp.: 347
Health Care Srvices
N.A.I.C.S.: 622110
Michael Holliday *(CFO)*
Joyce Pothast *(VP-Human & Environmental Svcs)*
Sheila Brokenshire *(VP-Nursing Svcs)*
Gary Clay *(Chm)*
Tim Jurozyk *(Vice Chm)*
James Pope *(Pres & CEO)*

VAN WYK INC.
1901 S 2nd Ave, Sheldon, IA 51201
Tel.: (712) 324-4687
Web Site: http://www.vanwyk.com
Rev.: $11,300,000
Emp.: 150
Trucking Except Local
N.A.I.C.S.: 484121
Arlan Van Wyk *(Chm)*
David Van Wyk *(Pres)*
Adam Vogel *(Mgr-Fleet)*

VAN ZEELAND OIL CO., INC.
4100 A W Prospect Ave, Appleton, WI 54914
Tel.: (920) 738-3520 WI
Web Site: http://www.vanzeelands.com
Year Founded: 1964
Sales Range: $10-24.9 Million
Emp.: 180
Gasoline Service Stations
N.A.I.C.S.: 457120
Todd Van Zeeland *(Pres)*
Gary Streich *(Controller)*

VAN ZYVERDEN INC.
8079 Van Zyverden Rd, Meridian, MS 39305
Tel.: (601) 679-8274
Web Site: http://www.vanzyverden.com
Sales Range: $25-49.9 Million
Emp.: 160
Flower & Field Bulbs
N.A.I.C.S.: 424910
Jacqueline Hogan *(CEO)*
Cherry Martin *(Dir-Mktg)*
Teresa Allbrook *(Mgr-Payroll & AP)*
Kerry Goodman *(Dir-Ops Support)*

VAN'S HONDA
2821 S Oneida St, Green Bay, WI 54304
Tel.: (920) 499-5483
Web Site: http://www.vans-honda.com
Car Whslr
N.A.I.C.S.: 441110
Bill Vander Perren *(Principal)*
Peter Moe *(Gen Mgr)*
John Norman *(Mgr-New Car)*
Dan Milkie *(Mgr-Used Car)*
Steve Lemke *(Asst Mgr-Used Car)*
Drew Vander Perren *(Dir-Used Vehicles)*
Clark Vander Perren *(Mgr-Internet)*
Peggy Whitcomb *(Office Mgr)*
Dawn Sawyer *(Bus Mgr)*
Nell Vander Perren *(Fin Dir)*
Randy Jenkins *(Bus Mgr)*
Jack Goedken *(Mgr-Svc Dept)*
Andrew Thor *(Mgr-Fixed Ops)*
Chris Siegel *(Mgr-Body Shop)*

VAN'S INC.
3730 W 131st St, Alsip, IL 60803-1519
Tel.: (708) 371-0372
Web Site: http://www.vansinc.com
Year Founded: 1960
Sales Range: $25-49.9 Million
Emp.: 300
Provider of Flowers & Florists Supplies
N.A.I.C.S.: 424930
Allen Tanouye *(Pres)*

Subsidiaries:

Van's of Michigan, Inc. (1)
1858 3 Mile Rd NW, Grand Rapids, MI 49544-1446
Tel.: (616) 785-9500
Web Site: http://www.kennicott.com
Sales Range: $10-24.9 Million
Emp.: 18
Provider Of Flowers & Florists Supplies
N.A.I.C.S.: 424930
Courtney Hill *(Gen Mgr)*

VAN'S LUMBER & CUSTOM BUILDERS
E176 County Rd S, Luxemburg, WI 54217
Tel.: (920) 866-2351
Web Site: http://www.vanslumber.com
Sales Range: $25-49.9 Million
Emp.: 50
New Construction, Single-Family Houses
N.A.I.C.S.: 236115
Craig VandenHouten *(Pres)*
Chris VandenHouten *(Coord-Job)*
Jean Willis *(Controller)*
Andy Strnad *(Coord-Job)*

VAN'S REALTY & CONSTRUCTION
2525 S Oneida St, Appleton, WI 54915
Tel.: (920) 734-1845
Web Site: http://www.vansconstruction.com
Year Founded: 1960
Sales Range: $10-24.9 Million
Emp.: 8
Commercial Buildings & House Construction
N.A.I.C.S.: 236117
Lance Haen *(VP)*
Jason A. Haen *(VP)*
Jerome Haen *(Pres)*

VAN-PAK INC.
255 Cadwell Dr, Springfield, MA 01104
Tel.: (413) 736-9168
Rev.: $40,000,000
Emp.: 297
Contract Haulers
N.A.I.C.S.: 484121
Neal Churchill *(Pres)*
John Peresky *(CFO)*

VAN-TROW TOYOTA
2015 Louisville Ave, Monroe, LA 71201
Tel.: (318) 387-2020
Web Site: http://www.vantrowtoyota.com
Year Founded: 1956
Sales Range: $25-49.9 Million
Emp.: 47
Car Whslr
N.A.I.C.S.: 441110
John Van Veckhoven *(Pres)*

VANASSE HANGEN BRUSTLIN, INC.
101 Walnut St, Watertown, MA 02472
Tel.: (617) 924-1770 MA
Web Site: http://www.vhb.com
Year Founded: 1979
Emp.: 1,600
Transportation, Land Development & Environmental Engineering, Design & Consulting Services
N.A.I.C.S.: 541990
Robert S. Brustlin *(Co-Founder & Chm)*
Michael J. Carragher *(Pres & CEO)*
William J. Roache *(Co-Founder)*
Dave Mulholland *(Reg Mgr-Southeast)*
David L. McIntyre *(Sr VP-Institutions)*
John B. Jackson *(CFO & Exec VP)*
Jonathan L. Feinstein *(Sr VP-Energy)*
Ken A. Schwartz *(Sr VP-Plng)*
Keri Kocur *(Chief People Officer & Sr VP)*
Khristopher M. Gregoire *(Chief Legal Officer, Gen Counsel & Sr VP)*
Matt Kennedy *(Mng Dir & Sr VP)*
Michael S. McArdle *(Chief Dev Officer & Sr VP)*
Nancy G. Barker *(Sr VP & Mgr-Federal Market)*

VANASSE HANGEN BRUSTLIN, INC.

Vanasse Hangen Brustlin, Inc.—(Continued)
Robert M. Dubinsky *(Sr VP-Corp Resources)*
Steve McElligott *(Sr VP)*
Terri Elkowitz *(Sr VP & Mgr-Northeast)*
Tom Jackmin *(Sr VP & Mgr-New England)*
Christian W. Crow Christian W. Crow *(Mgr-Aquatic Resources)*
Fabricio Ponce *(Mng Dir-VHB Atlanta)*
Subsidiaries:
CCR Environmental Inc. (1)
3772 Pleasantdale Rd Ste 150, Atlanta, GA 30340-3709
Tel.: (770) 458-7943
Web Site: http://www.ccrenvironmental.com
Environmental Consulting Services
N.A.I.C.S.: 541620
Christian Crow *(CEO)*

GMB Engineers & Planners Inc. (1)
225 E Robinson St Ste 300, Orlando, FL 32801
Tel.: (407) 898-5424
Web Site: http://www.gmb.cc
Emp.: 130
Traffic Engineering Services
N.A.I.C.S.: 541330
Dante Gabriel *(Pres)*
Jorge Tolosa *(Project Mgr)*
Rajashekar Pemmanaboina *(Project Mgr)*
Greg Moore *(Sr Project Mgr)*
David W. Mulholland *(Principal)*
Mansoor Khuwaja *(Principal)*
Simone Babb *(Dir-GIS)*
Christopher Cate *(Sr Project Mgr)*
Rodrikas Jones *(Supvr-Data Collection)*
Kathy Lee *(Sr Project Mgr)*
Kevin Redfield *(Mgr-Bus)*

VANCE BROTHERS INCORPORATED
5201 Brighton Ave, Kansas City, MO 64130
Tel.: (816) 923-4325
Web Site: http://www.vancebrothers.com
Sales Range: $25-49.9 Million
Emp.: 135
Asphalt & Asphaltic Paving Mixtures (Not From Refineries)
N.A.I.C.S.: 324121
Mike Mitchell *(Product Mgr-Dev)*

VANCE HOLDINGS INC.
950 Kingsland Ave, Saint Louis, MO 63130
Tel.: (314) 721-2888
Web Site: http://www.fsptbm.com
Rev.: $20,000,000
Emp.: 45
Filters, Industrial
N.A.I.C.S.: 423840
Angela O'Neil *(Mgr-HR)*

VANCE INDUSTRIES, INC.
5617 W Howard St, Niles, IL 60714-4011
Tel.: (847) 983-0960 DE
Web Site: http://www.vanceind.com
Year Founded: 1949
Sales Range: $75-99.9 Million
Emp.: 18
Stainless Steel Sinks, Brass Bar Sinks, Sink Frames, Tempered Glass Food Preparation Surfaces & Assorted Kitchen Accessories & Plastic & Wood Kitchen Products
N.A.I.C.S.: 327215
William M. Rapp *(CEO)*
Jacqueline Rapp *(Sec)*

VANCE PUBLISHING CORPORATION
400 Knightsbridge Pkwy, Lincolnshire, IL 60069
Tel.: (847) 634-2600 NY
Web Site: http://www.vancepublishing.com
Year Founded: 1937
Sales Range: $25-49.9 Million
Emp.: 150
Trade Journal Publisher
N.A.I.C.S.: 513120
William C. Vance *(Chm)*
Connie Dudziak *(Mgr-Adv Ops)*
Steve Reiss *(VP & Dir-Publ-Salon & Wood Interiors)*
Jenna Jordan *(Mgr-Natl Acct-Protein Grp-Lenexa)*

VANCE STREET CAPITAL LLC
11150 Santa Monica Blvd Ste 750, Los Angeles, CA 90025
Tel.: (310) 231-7100
Web Site: http://www.vancestreetcapital.com
Year Founded: 2007
Emp.: 12
Privater Equity Firm
N.A.I.C.S.: 523999
Richard R. Crowell *(Mng Partner)*
Richard K. Roeder *(Mng Partner)*
Brian D. Martin *(Mng Partner)*
John P. LeRosen *(Principal)*
Michael Janish *(Mng Partner)*
Nic Janneck *(Principal)*
Rustey Emmet *(Principal-Financial Ops)*
Steve Sandbo *(Principal)*
J. Mark King *(Operating Partner)*
Subsidiaries:
Eberle Design, Inc. (1)
3510 E Atlanta Ave, Phoenix, AZ 85040
Tel.: (480) 968-6407
Web Site: http://www.editraffic.com
Sales Range: $1-9.9 Million
Electronic Control Products Mfr
N.A.I.C.S.: 334419
Carl Proper *(Mgr-Mfg)*
Luis Silva *(VP-Ops)*
Bill Russell *(Pres & CEO)*
Joseph Dudich *(VP-Engrg)*

Excel Scientific, Inc. (1)
5550 Hess Rd, Phelan, CA 92371
Tel.: (760) 249-6371
Web Site: http://www.excelscientific.com
Sales Range: $1-9.9 Million
Emp.: 100
Professional Equipment & Supplies Merchant Whslr
N.A.I.C.S.: 423490
Julie Cameron *(CEO)*

Innovize, Inc. (1)
500 Oak Grove Pkwy, Saint Paul, MN 55127
Tel.: (651) 490-0000
Web Site: http://www.innovize.com
Sales Range: $1-9.9 Million
Emp.: 110
Commercial Screen Printing
N.A.I.C.S.: 323113
Julie Cameron *(Co-CEO)*
Dave Jessen *(VP-Sls & Mktg)*
Becky Bjorgum *(VP-HR)*
John Ledy *(Pres & Co-CEO)*
John Sopp *(VP-Mfg)*
Julie Beckman *(Dir-Sls Admin)*
Mark Rutkiewicz *(VP-Quality)*
Patrick Thielen *(CFO & CIO)*

Leading Edge Aviation Services Inc. (1)
5251 California Ave Ste 170, Irvine, CA 92617
Tel.: (714) 556-0576
Web Site: http://www.leadingedgecorp.com
Emp.: 10
Aircraft Maintenance Services
N.A.I.C.S.: 488190
Chris Harano *(Co-CEO)*
Daniel Zeddy *(Co-CFO)*
David Patterson *(Exec VP-Sls & Mktg)*
Rod Friese *(COO)*
Niall Cunningham *(Co-CEO)*
Eric Hersom *(Co-CFO)*

Subsidiary (Domestic):
Associated Painters, Inc. (2)
8924 W Electric Ave, Spokane, WA 99224
Tel.: (425) 710-9881
Web Site: http://www.associatedpaintersinc.com
Sales Range: $25-49.9 Million
Aircraft Refinishing Services
N.A.I.C.S.: 488190
Rod Friese *(Pres)*

Micronics, Inc. (1)
200 West Rd, Portsmouth, NH 03801
Tel.: (603) 433-1299
Web Site: http://www.micronicsinc.com
Sales Range: $25-49.9 Million
Industrial Filter Mfr
N.A.I.C.S.: 333248
Julie Pugh *(CFO)*
Subsidiary (Non-US):
Micronics Filtration Ltd. (2)
Sandbach Road Burslem, Stoke-on-Trent, ST6 2DR, United Kingdom
Tel.: (44) 1782 284 385
Web Site: http://www.micronicsinc.com
Industrial Filter Mfr
N.A.I.C.S.: 333248
David Phillips *(Mng Dir)*

Micronics Filtration Pty. Ltd. (2)
5 Mostyn Crescent, Bushland Beach, Townsville, 4818, QLD, Australia
Tel.: (61) 7 47880513
Industrial Filter Mfr
N.A.I.C.S.: 333248

Secure Communication Systems, Inc. (1)
1740 E Wilshire Ave, Santa Ana, CA 92705
Tel.: (714) 547-1174
Web Site: http://www.securecomm.com
Sales Range: $25-49.9 Million
Mfr of Computer Products
N.A.I.C.S.: 334220

Semicoa Corporation (1)
333 McCormick Ave, Costa Mesa, CA 92626
Tel.: (714) 979-1900
Web Site: http://www.semicoa.com
Semiconductor Mfr & Distr
N.A.I.C.S.: 334413

Smart Electronics & Assembly, Inc. (1)
2000 W Corporate Way, Anaheim, CA 92801
Tel.: (714) 991-6500
Web Site: http://www.smartelec.com
Electronic Components Mfr
N.A.I.C.S.: 334419
Dinesh Jain *(Mgr-Supply Chain)*
Patrick Huang *(Chief Admin Officer)*

Wytech Industries, Inc. (1)
960 E Hazelwood Ave, Rahway, NJ 07065
Tel.: (732) 396-3900
Web Site: http://www.wytech.com
Sales Range: $1-9.9 Million
Emp.: 60
Fabricated Wire Product Mfr
N.A.I.C.S.: 332618
Marcianna Pusillo *(Mgr-Customer Svc)*
Mike Casalino *(CEO)*
Subsidiary (Domestic):
Silvertip Associates, Inc. (2)
10800 Mankato St NE, Minneapolis, MN 55449
Tel.: (763) 717-0773
Web Site: http://www.silvertipgrinding.com
Metal Coating, Engraving & Allied Services to Manufacturers
N.A.I.C.S.: 332812
Dale Peterson *(Owner)*

VANCE THOMPSON VISION CLINIC PROF LLC
3101 W 57th St, Sioux Falls, SD 57108
Tel.: (605) 371-7057
Web Site: http://www.vancethompsonvision.com

U.S. PRIVATE

Freestanding Ambulatory Surgical & Emergency Centers
N.A.I.C.S.: 621493
Matt Jensen *(Mgr)*
Subsidiaries:
Nebraska Laser Eye Associates (1)
4909 S 118th St Ste 2, Omaha, NE 68137-2234
Tel.: (402) 397-2010
Web Site: http://www.nebraskaeye.com
Freestanding Ambulatory Surgical & Emergency Centers
N.A.I.C.S.: 621493
Heather Lee *(Mgr)*

VANCOREJONES COMMUNICATIONS INC.
906 Thomasville Rd, Tallahassee, FL 32303
Tel.: (850) 681-8530
Web Site: http://www.vancorejones.com
Sales Range: $1-9.9 Million
Emp.: 10
Public Relations Agencies
N.A.I.C.S.: 541820
Steven J. Vancore *(Pres)*
Andrew F. Jones *(Mng Partner)*

VANDE HEY BRANTMEIER ENTERPRISES, INC.
614 N Madison St, Chilton, WI 53014
Tel.: (920) 849-9331 WI
Web Site: http://www.vandebran.com
Rev.: $36,000,000
Emp.: 30
Holding Company; New & Used Car Dealerships
N.A.I.C.S.: 551112
David Brantmeier *(Owner)*
Dale Gebhart *(Mgr-Parts)*
Greg Schmitz *(Mgr-Parts)*
Jared Nelson *(Mgr-Svc)*
John Martin *(Gen Mgr)*
Justin Brantmeier *(Gen Mgr)*
Todd Klein *(Mgr-Fin)*
Subsidiaries:
Vande Hey Brantmeier Chevrolet-Buick-Pontiac-Oldsmobile, Inc. (1)
614 N Madison, Chilton, WI 53014 (100%)
Tel.: (920) 849-9301
Web Site: http://www.vandebran.com
Sales Range: $10-24.9 Million
Automobiles, New & Used
N.A.I.C.S.: 441110
Dave Brantmeier *(Pres)*

VANDER HAAG'S INC.
3809 4th Ave W, Spencer, IA 51301
Tel.: (712) 262-7000
Web Site: http://www.vanderhaags.com
Year Founded: 1939
Sales Range: $25-49.9 Million
Emp.: 300
Provider of Truck Parts & Accessories
N.A.I.C.S.: 423120
Dan Getting *(Controller)*
Dave Van Tol *(Gen Mgr)*
Shawn Andringa *(Asst Gen Mgr)*

VANDERBURGH & CO., INC.
286 Madison Ave Ste 402, New York, NY 10017
Tel.: (212) 947-5270
Web Site: http://www.vanderburghco.com
Rev.: $16,085,440
Emp.: 13
Industrial Machinery & Equipment
N.A.I.C.S.: 423830
Pedro M. Concha *(Pres)*
Kelly Murcia *(Coord-Exports)*

VANDERGRIFF CHEVROLET

1200 W Interstate 20, Arlington, TX 76017
Tel.: (817) 557-1200
Web Site:
http://www.vandergriffchevrolet.com
Year Founded: 1936
Sales Range: $100-124.9 Million
Emp.: 210
Retailer of New & Used Automobiles
N.A.I.C.S.: 441110
Rick Cantalini *(Partner & Gen Mgr)*
Cerise Garcia *(Controller)*

VANDERHEYDEN HALL, INC.
614 Cooper Hill Rd Route 355, Wynantskill, NY 12198
Tel.: (518) 283-6500
Web Site:
http://www.vanderheydenhall.org
Year Founded: 1956
Sales Range: $10-24.9 Million
Emp.: 276
Individual & Family Support Services
N.A.I.C.S.: 624190
Donald Hollendonner *(Dir-Facilities)*
Lori Eason *(CFO)*
Karen Carpenter Palumbo *(Pres & CEO)*
Cathy Yudzevich *(Dir-Mktg & Comm)*
Linda Madsen *(Sr Dir-HR)*
Kimberly Gibbs *(Controller)*
Mary Ellen Pace *(Dir-Health Svcs)*

VANDERHOUWEN & ASSOCIATES, INC.
6342 SW Macadam Ave, Portland, OR 97239
Tel.: (503) 299-6811
Web Site:
http://www.vanderhouwen.com
Year Founded: 1987
Sales Range: $10-24.9 Million
Emp.: 112
Employment Placement Agencies
N.A.I.C.S.: 561311
Kathy VanderHouwen *(CEO & Bus Mgr)*
Brad Fisch *(Acct Mgr)*
Cynthia VanderHouwen *(VP)*
Geoff Smith *(Acct Mgr)*
John Niemer *(Acct Mgr)*
Eric VanderHouwen *(Pres)*
Ben Newbill *(Acct Mgr)*
Brett Kadz *(Mgr-Recruiting)*
Brian Hathaway *(Gen Mgr)*
Mike Mitchell *(Acct Mgr)*
Reina Bluth *(Acct Mgr)*

VANDERLOOP EQUIPMENT, INC.
W2834 Dundas Rd, Brillion, WI 54110
Tel.: (920) 989-1517
Web Site: http://www.vanderloop.com
Rev.: $14,000,000
Emp.: 30
Farm & Garden Machinery & Equipment Merchant Whslr
N.A.I.C.S.: 423820
Scott Vanderloop *(Mgr)*
Donald Vanderloop *(Shop Mgr)*
Robb Vanderloop *(Gen Mgr)*

VANDERVERT CONSTRUCTION INC.
608 E Holland Ave, Spokane, WA 99218
Tel.: (509) 467-6654
Web Site:
http://www.vandervertconstruction.com
Year Founded: 1980
Sales Range: $75-99.9 Million
Emp.: 40
Nonresidential Construction Services
N.A.I.C.S.: 236220

Tim Stulc *(Owner)*

VANEE FOODS COMPANY INC.
5418 McDermott Dr, Berkeley, IL 60163-1201
Tel.: (708) 449-7300
Web Site:
htttp://www.vaneefoods.com
Year Founded: 1950
Sales Range: $10-24.9 Million
Emp.: 120
Canned Specialties
N.A.I.C.S.: 311422
Aloysius Van Eekeren *(Pres & Treas)*
Chuck Vanee *(Mgr-Sls)*
Robert Benson *(Dir-Res & Dev)*
Edie Hayden *(Mgr-Sls)*
Andy Homan *(Sls Mgr)*
Mike Vanee *(VP-Sls)*
Jay Willis *(Mgr-Sls)*
Terry Riha *(Mgr-Sls)*
Luke Vanee *(Sls Mgr)*

VANETTI INC.
12178 4th St, Rancho Cucamonga, CA 91730
Tel.: (909) 980-1679
Web Site:
http://www.bendettisuits.com
Sales Range: $10-24.9 Million
Emp.: 50
Mfr of Clothing
N.A.I.C.S.: 424350
Vic Jung-hua Chen *(CFO)*

VANGEO TECHNOLOGY GROUP, LLC
16573 N 92nd St Ste 101, Scottsdale, AZ 85260
Tel.: (800) 238-1774
Year Founded: 2024
Holding Company; Home Automation & Security Services
N.A.I.C.S.: 551112
Johnathan George *(CEO)*
Mike Vann *(COO)*
Mark Hockenberg *(CFO)*
Subsidiaries:
Homerun Electronics, Inc. (1)
3414 Fillmore Ridge Hts, Colorado Springs, CO 80907
Tel.: (719) 685-0660
Sales Range: $1-9.9 Million
Emp.: 10
Engineeering Services
N.A.I.C.S.: 541330
Lori Van *(VP)*

iWired, Inc. (1)
16573 N 92nd St Ste 101, Scottsdale, AZ 85260
Tel.: (480) 922-2500
Web Site: http://www.iwired.com
Sales Range: $1-9.9 Million
Emp.: 25
Electronic Services
N.A.I.C.S.: 238210

VANGUARD ATLANTIC LTD.
Moir Rd, Saranac Lake, NY 12983
Tel.: (518) 261-6608
Web Site:
http://www.vanguardatlantic.com
Year Founded: 1984
Sales Range: $25-49.9 Million
Emp.: 2
Management Investment, Open-End
N.A.I.C.S.: 525910
Ernest E. Lee Keet *(CEO & CIO)*

VANGUARD CAPITAL
12526 High Bluff Dr Ste 270, San Diego, CA 92130
Tel.: (858) 455-5070

Web Site:
http://www.vanguardcapital.com
Rev.: $12,000,000
Emp.: 5
Security Brokers
N.A.I.C.S.: 523150
Gregory Serras *(Pres)*
Chris Hanson *(Chief Compliance Officer)*

VANGUARD CLEANING SYSTEMS INC
920 Argonne Rd Ste 129, Spokane Valley, WA 99212
Tel.: (509) 922-1499
Web Site:
http://www.vanguardcleaning.com
Year Founded: 1984
Sales Range: $1-9.9 Million
Emp.: 10
Commercial Cleaning
N.A.I.C.S.: 561720

VANGUARD COMMUNICATIONS
2400 Broadway Ste 3, Denver, CO 80205
Tel.: (303) 382-2999
Web Site:
http://www.vanguardcommunications.net
Year Founded: 1994
Sales Range: $10-24.9 Million
Emp.: 12
Advertising Agencies
N.A.I.C.S.: 541810
Ron King *(CEO)*

VANGUARD DIRECT INC.
519 8th Ave Fl 23, New York, NY 10018
Tel.: (212) 736-0770
Web Site:
http://www.vanguarddirect.com
Rev.: $26,000,000
Emp.: 130
Communications & Business Forms
N.A.I.C.S.: 424120
Robert O'Connell *(Pres)*
Tim Murphy *(CFO & VP-Fin)*
Donald O'Connell *(Exec VP)*
Ralph Fucci *(COO & Sr VP)*

VANGUARD EMS, INC.
3725 SW Hocken Ave, Beaverton, OR 97005-0190
Tel.: (503) 644-4808
Web Site: http://www.vanguard-ems.com
Year Founded: 1988
Electronics Manufacturing Services
N.A.I.C.S.: 334412
Floyd Sutz *(Chm & CEO)*
Anh Vu *(Dir-Mfg)*
Joe Lariz *(Dir-IT)*
Jim Henderson *(Dir-Engrg)*

VANGUARD ENERGY PARTNERS, LLC
1 Commerce St, Branchburg, NJ 08876
Tel.: (908) 534-1302
Web Site:
http://www.vanguardenergypartners.com
Sales Range: $10-24.9 Million
Emp.: 35
Solar Power Equipment Installation Services
N.A.I.C.S.: 237130
Nelson Ferreira *(Chm)*
Alec Damon *(Project Mgr)*
Keith M. Helms *(CFO)*
Paul Zensky *(Owner)*

VANGUARD FIRE SYSTEMS, L.P.
2340 Patterson Industrial Dr, Pflugerville, TX 78660
Tel.: (512) 989-1600
Web Site: http://www.vgfire.com
Year Founded: 1998
Sales Range: $10-24.9 Million
Emp.: 45
Business Services
N.A.I.C.S.: 561990
Rance Richter *(Gen Partner)*
Cynthia Richter *(Gen Partner)*

VANGUARD FURNITURE CO. INC.
109 Simpson St, Conover, NC 28613
Tel.: (828) 328-5631
Web Site:
http://www.vanguardfurniture.com
Year Founded: 1969
Sales Range: $25-49.9 Million
Emp.: 500
Mfr of Household Furniture
N.A.I.C.S.: 337121
Birger Rasmussen *(Vice Chm)*
Laurie Hoover *(VP-Ops)*
Gary Dishman *(Mgr-Claims)*
Tammy Smith *(VP-HR)*
Andy Bray *(Pres)*
John Pigg *(VP-Sls)*

VANGUARD HEALTHCARE SERVICES LLC
Six Cadillac Dr Ste 310, Brentwood, TN 37027
Tel.: (615) 250-7100
Web Site:
http://www.vanguardhc.com
Year Founded: 1998
Emp.: 1,500
Nursing Care Facilities Operator
N.A.I.C.S.: 623110
William D. Orand *(CEO)*

VANGUARD HOLDINGS
239 Saint Nicholas Ave, South Plainfield, NJ 07080
Tel.: (908) 753-2770
Web Site:
http://www.vanguardholdings.com
Sales Range: $10-24.9 Million
Emp.: 30
Plating & Polishing
N.A.I.C.S.: 332813
Pete Costa *(Pres)*
Nick Stanford *(VP)*
Harry F. Sica Jr. *(CEO)*

VANGUARD LABEL, INC.
8800 NE Underground Dr Pillar 225E, Kansas City, MO 64161
Tel.: (816) 455-4000
Web Site:
http://www.vanguardlabel.com
Year Founded: 1996
Emp.: 60
Paper Tube & Label Mfr
N.A.I.C.S.: 322299
Mark Mathes *(Pres)*

VANGUARD MEDIA GROUP
4476 Manor Ridge Pl, Salt Lake City, UT 84124-2595
Tel.: (801) 531-0244
Year Founded: 1995
Rev.: $3,500,000
Emp.: 16
Media Advertising, Marketing & Public Relations
N.A.I.C.S.: 541840
Cindy Kindred *(Pres)*
John Kindred *(Mng Partner)*

VANGUARD MODULAR BUILDING SYSTEMS, LLC

VANGUARD MODULAR BUILDING SYSTEMS, LLC   U.S. PRIVATE

Vanguard Modular Building Systems, LLC—(Continued)
3 Great Valley Pkwy Ste 170,
Malvern, PA 19355
Tel.: (610) 240-8686
Web Site:
http://www.vanguardmodular.com
Year Founded: 1998
Sales Range: $25-49.9 Million
Emp.: 48
Modular Commmercial Building
N.A.I.C.S.: 444180
Paul Renze (Chm)
Mark Al-Soufi (Sr VP)
Barry DeSantis (CEO)
Peter Eberle (Sr VP)
Mark Meyers (VP-Mktg Svcs)

Subsidiaries:

Schiavi Leasing Corporation (1)
102 Industrial Dr, Oxford, ME 04270
Tel.: (207) 539-8211
Web Site:
http://www.schiavileasingcorp.com
Sales Range: $10-24.9 Million
Emp.: 8
Suppliers of Modular Space for Commercial & Educational Users in Northern New England
N.A.I.C.S.: 531190

VANGUARD PACKAGING
8800 NE Underground Dr Pillar Ste 255e, Kansas City, MO 64161
Tel.: (816) 455-4000
Web Site:
http://www.vanguardpkg.com
Year Founded: 1975
Sales Range: $10-24.9 Million
Emp.: 110
Corrugated & Solid Fiber Box Mfr
N.A.I.C.S.: 322211
Mark Mathes (CEO)
Jim Beard (Gen Mgr)
Ted Luczak (Designer-Structural)

VANGUARD PETROLEUM CORPORATION
1111 N Loop W Ste 1100, Houston, TX 77008-1773
Tel.: (713) 802-4242   TX
Year Founded: 1975
Sales Range: $300-349.9 Million
Emp.: 13
Producer & Distr of Wholesale Natural Gas & Liquified Petroleum
N.A.I.C.S.: 424720
Phillip Trotter (VP)
Thomas W. Garner (Pres)
John Kelly Jr. (Sec & VP)

VANGUARD PRINTING LLC
17 Hall Woods Rd, Ithaca, NY 14850
Tel.: (607) 272-1212
Web Site:
http://www.vanguardprintingllc.com
Sales Range: $10-24.9 Million
Emp.: 140
Commercial Printing
N.A.I.C.S.: 323111
Steve Rossi (Principal)

VANGUARD PRODUCTS GROUP, INC.
720 Brooker Creek Blvd Ste 223, Oldsmar, FL 34677
Tel.: (813) 855-9639
Web Site:
http://www.vanguardproductsgroup.com
Year Founded: 1999
Sales Range: $1-9.9 Million
Emp.: 75
Security System Services
N.A.I.C.S.: 561621
Christopher Kelsch (Pres & CEO)
Jack Figh (Dir-Product Mgmt)

Dennis Smith (Dir-Quality & Safety)
John O'Bryan (VP-Ops)
Carla Koah (Mgr-HR)
Bill Hamblin (Mgr-Ops)
Paul Williams (Mgr-Acct Svcs)
Lucas Swartwood (Mgr-Engrg)
Steve Wood (VP-Sls & Mktg)

VANGUARD PROPERTIES CO.
1150 NW Kerron St, Winlock, WA 98596
Tel.: (360) 785-3502
Sales Range: $10-24.9 Million
Emp.: 4
Window Glass, Clear & Colored
N.A.I.C.S.: 327211
Craig Barker (Chm)

VANGUARD TEMPORARIES INC.
110 E 40th St, New York, NY 10016
Tel.: (212) 682-6400
Web Site:
http://www.temporarypersonnel.com
Sales Range: $25-49.9 Million
Emp.: 50
Provider of Temporary Help Services
N.A.I.C.S.: 561320
John McGrath (Pres)
Charles Hattenbach (CEO)

VANGUARDCOMM
2 Disbrow Ct 3rd Fl, East Brunswick, NJ 08816
Tel.: (732) 246-0340   NJ
Web Site:
http://www.vanguardcomm.com
Year Founded: 1994
Sales Range: $10-24.9 Million
Emp.: 15
Advertising Agencies
N.A.I.C.S.: 541810
Esther Novak (Founder & CEO)
William F. Fox (COO & Mng Partner)
Lillian Ayala (VP & Acct Dir)
Joseph Ramirez (VP & Supvr-Acct)

Subsidiaries:

VanguardComm - Coral Gables (1)
1450 Madruga Ave, Coral Gables, FL 33146
Tel.: (305) 662-4466
Web Site: http://www.vanguardcomm.com
Advertising Agencies
N.A.I.C.S.: 541810

VANITY SHOP OF GRAND FORKS INC.
1001 25th St N, Fargo, ND 58102-3116
Tel.: (701) 237-3330
Web Site: http://www.vanity.com
Sales Range: $100-124.9 Million
Emp.: 1,400
Women's Wear Whslr
N.A.I.C.S.: 458110
Rhonda Ishaug (Mgr-Ops)
Scott Roller (COO)
Richard Weinstein (Pres)
Mary Miller (Dir-Mktg)

VANN YORK PONTIAC INC.
422 E Chester Dr, High Point, NC 27262
Tel.: (336) 841-6200
Web Site:
http://www.vannyorkauto.com
Rev.: $53,989,673
Emp.: 150
New & Used Car Dealers
N.A.I.C.S.: 441113
Gregory York (Pres)

VANN'S INCORPORATED
3623 Brooks St, Missoula, MT 59801-7359

Tel.: (406) 728-5099   MT
Web Site: http://www.vanns.com
Year Founded: 1961
Sales Range: $25-49.9 Million
Emp.: 150
Distribution of Radio Television & Electronic Equipments
N.A.I.C.S.: 449210
Paul Nisbet (CFO)

VANNER INSURANCE AGENCY
11 Pinchot Ct Ste 100, Amherst, NY 14228
Tel.: (716) 688-8888   NY
Web Site:
http://www.vannerinsurance.com
Year Founded: 1963
Sales Range: $75-99.9 Million
Emp.: 13
Insurance Agencies & Brokerages
N.A.I.C.S.: 524210
Ralph Vanner (Pres)
Deborah McMicking (Mgr-Ops)
William J. Quinn (VP)
Thomas Vanner (Pres & Dir-Sls)
Jennifer Colangelo (Mgr-Acct)
Kathy Bett (Acct Exec)
Kim Castiglione (Mgr-Acct)
Kim Stobnicki (Mgr-Personal Lines)
Robin Madej (Mgr-Acct)
Vicki Puglia (Mgr-Acct)
John Daughton (Partner & Dir-Mktg)
R. J. Vanner (Chm)
Jason Reid (Partner-Bond & Surety)
Craig Scarupa (CFO)

VANPIKE INC.
6336 Greenwich Dr Ste 100, San Diego, CA 92122
Tel.: (858) 597-4000   CA
Web Site: http://www.tristaff.com
Year Founded: 1971
Emp.: 200
Staffing & Consulting Services
N.A.I.C.S.: 561320
Gary van Eik (Co-Founder & CEO)
Rich Papike (Co-Founder & Pres)
Jill Martinelli (Dir-Technical Recruitment)
Alex Papike (VP)
Karen van Eik (Area Mgr)
Denise Ferraris (Dir-Staffing-San Diego)
Thomas Tanner (VP-Technical Staffing)
Laura Ebbinger (Dir-Recruiting-Renewable Energy Div)
Sherry Smiley (Dir-HR)
Jason van Eik (VP-Construction)
Chris Papike (VP-Media)
Jennifer Quinlan Smith (Dir-Construction & Bus Dev)
Kanani Masterson (Mng Dir-Tech & Exec Search)
Kelly Lucas (Dir-Acctg, Fin Recruitment, Exec Mgmt, HR & Healthcare Div)
Mike Wilson (Dir-Banking Div)

VANPORT MANUFACTURING, INC.
28590 SE Wally Rd, Boring, OR 97009-9451
Tel.: (503) 663-4466   OR
Web Site: http://www.vanport-intl.com
Year Founded: 1967
Sales Range: $75-99.9 Million
Emp.: 40
Provider of Manufacturing Services
N.A.I.C.S.: 321113
Jim Evertt (Sec)
Paul Owen (Pres)

Subsidiaries:

Vanport Canada, Co. (1)

1460 Main St, North Vancouver, V7J 1C8, BC, Canada
Tel.: (604) 985-0533
Web Site: http://www.vanport.ca
Emp.: 10
Lumber Whslr
N.A.I.C.S.: 423310
Don McGregor (Mgr)

VANPRO, INC.
345 Garfield St S, Cambridge, MN 55008-1375
Tel.: (763) 689-1559   MN
Web Site: http://www.vanpro-inc.com
Year Founded: 1977
Sales Range: $1-9.9 Million
Emp.: 11
Mfr of Specialized Products, Including Medical Devices & Hard Drives, for Medical, Defense & Communications Industries
N.A.I.C.S.: 332710
Robert Sholly (Plant Mgr)
Scott Clausen (Engr-Quality)

VANSON ENTERPRISES, INC.
1231 Kindel Ave, Winter Park, FL 32789
Tel.: (407) 647-2334   FL
Web Site: http://www.vanson.net
Year Founded: 1991
Sales Range: $1-9.9 Million
Emp.: 40
Industrial, Commercial & Residential Building Construction
N.A.I.C.S.: 236220
George Seay (VP)
Richard Loft (Project Mgr)
Rhonda Loft (Pres)

VANTAGE AGING
388 S Main St Ste 325, Akron, OH 44311
Tel.: (330) 253-4597   OH
Web Site:
http://www.vantageaging.org
Year Founded: 1975
Rev.: $11,948,740
Assets: $1,857,579
Liabilities: $822,757
Net Worth: $1,034,822
Earnings: $147,251
Emp.: 1,298
Fiscal Year-end: 09/30/14
Community Action Services
N.A.I.C.S.: 624190
Gizelle Jones (Clinical Director)

VANTAGE COMPANIES
2000 McKinney Ave Ste 600, Dallas, TX 75201
Tel.: (214) 559-9700   TX
Web Site:
http://www.vantagecompanies.com
Year Founded: 1959
Sales Range: $150-199.9 Million
Emp.: 60
Real Estate Services
N.A.I.C.S.: 531390
Frederick L. Albrecht (Pres)

Subsidiaries:

Weston Companies (1)
1755 Kirby Pkwy, Memphis, TN 38120
Tel.: (901) 682-9100
Sales Range: $25-49.9 Million
Emp.: 5
Provider of Real Estate Services
N.A.I.C.S.: 531120
Michael Caldwell (CEO)

VANTAGE CONTRACTORS, LLC
18212 E Petroleum Dr Ste 5A, Baton Rouge, LA 70809
Tel.: (225) 408-8885
Web Site: http://www.vantage-contractors.com
Year Founded: 2002

Construction, Maintenance & Disaster Recover Services
N.A.I.C.S.: 236220
Brad Roberts (Pres)
Subsidiaries:
Kelly's Industrial Services, Inc. (1)
2500 American Way Dr, Port Allen, LA 70767-6002
Tel.: (225) 749-6000
Web Site: http://www.kellysindustrialservices.com
Transportation Services
N.A.I.C.S.: 488999
Paul E. Kleinpeter (Founder & Mgr-Sls)
Kelly B. Kleinpeter (CFO)
Harry Comeaux (Mgr-Production)
Cliff Welch (Mgr-HR)
Lindsey K. Stelly (Mgr-Payroll)

VANTAGE CUSTOM CLASSICS, INC.
100 Vantage Dr, Avenel, NJ 07001-1080
Tel.: (732) 340-3000 NJ
Web Site: http://www.vantageapparel.com
Year Founded: 1977
Emp.: 500
Unisex Clothing Retailer
N.A.I.C.S.: 315250
Ira Neaman (Pres)
Eric Wukitsch (CFO & COO)

VANTAGE DELUXE WORLD TRAVEL
90 Canal St, Boston, MA 02114-2031
Tel.: (617) 878-6000
Web Site: http://www.vantagetravel.com
Sales Range: $25-49.9 Million
Emp.: 150
Travel Agency; Direct Marketing Services
N.A.I.C.S.: 561510
Linda Herlihy (VP-Air Contracting & Ops)
Eleonora Reitano (Coord-Flights)
Deirdre Dirkman (Dir-Air Svcs)
Christel Shea (Dir-Customer Svc)
Carol Pennini (Product Mgr)
Xuan Luo (Supvr-Costing)
Lorrie Wright (Sr Dir-Ops, Yield Mgmt & Product Plng-Worldwide)

VANTAGE ENERGY ACQUISITION CORP.
5221 N O Connor Blvd Fl 11, Irving, TX 75039
Tel.: (972) 432-1440 DE
Year Founded: 2017
Rev.: $9,777,780
Assets: $562,312,550
Liabilities: $557,312,547
Net Worth: $5,000,003
Earnings: $4,048,189
Emp.: 4
Fiscal Year-end: 12/31/18
Investment Services
N.A.I.C.S.: 523999
Roger J. Biemans (CEO)

VANTAGE HEALTH PLAN INC.
130 DeSiard St Ste 300, Monroe, LA 71201-7363
Tel.: (318) 361-0900
Web Site: http://www.vhpla.com
Rev.: $55,500,000
Emp.: 50
Medical Doctors Office
N.A.I.C.S.: 621491
P. G. Jones (Pres & CEO)
Mike Breard (Exec VP)

VANTAGE INVESTMENT CORP.
301 N Lake Ave Ste 140, Pasadena, CA 91101-5116
Tel.: (626) 683-8868
Sales Range: $10-24.9 Million
Emp.: 20
Miscellaneous Food Mfr
N.A.I.C.S.: 311999
Peggy Fan (Mgr-Pur)
Joshua Lee (VP)
Peggy Chang (Mgr)

VANTAGE MEDIA, LLC
2381 Rosecrans Ave Ste 400, El Segundo, CA 90245
Tel.: (310) 219-6200
Web Site: http://www.vantagemedia.com
Year Founded: 2002
Sales Range: $25-49.9 Million
Emp.: 50
Search Marketing & Online Lead Generation
N.A.I.C.S.: 541890
Steve Jillings (Chm)

VANTAGE PRESS, INC.
419 Park Ave S, New York, NY 10016
Tel.: (212) 736-1767
Year Founded: 1949
Sales Range: $50-74.9 Million
Emp.: 20
Book Publishers
N.A.I.C.S.: 513130
Martin Littlefield (Chm & Pres)

VANTAGE TRAILERS INC.
29335 Hwy 90, Katy, TX 77494
Tel.: (281) 391-2664
Web Site: http://www.vantagetrailers.com
Rev.: $18,000,000
Emp.: 28
Truck Trailers
N.A.I.C.S.: 336212
Pat Lemons (CEO)
Gene Shepherd (Pres)
Paul Stephan (Controller)

VANTAGE WEST CREDIT UNION
2480 N Arcadia Ave, Tucson, AZ 85712
Tel.: (520) 298-7882 AZ
Web Site: http://www.vwestcu.org
Year Founded: 1955
Sales Range: $50-74.9 Million
Emp.: 463
Financial Support Services
N.A.I.C.S.: 523999
Steven Mott (Sr VP-Tech)
R. D. Ramirez (Pres & CEO)
R. Almazan (Chief Lending Officer & Sr VP)
Scott B. Odom (CFO)
Tim Overton (VP-Bus Lending & Svcs)
Guillermo Caldelas (Dir-Mortgage Sls)
William Tong (Sr Mgr-Bus Relationship)
Eugene Santarelli (Vice Chm)
John Driskill (Sec)
Mitch S. Pisik (Chm)
Paul Melendez (Treas)
Danielle Bridges (VP-Consumer Lending)
Daniel Clemens (Chief Strategy Officer)
Brenda Gordon (VP)
Stefan Harris (VP-Tech)
Jamie Hernandez (VP & Reg Mgr-Sls)
Sandra Lueders (VP-HR & Dev)
Andrew Downin (VP-Mktg & Comm)

VANTAGEPOINT AI, LLC
5807 Old Pasco Rd, Zephyrhills, FL 33544
Tel.: (813) 973-0496
Web Site: http://www.tradertech.com
Year Founded: 1979
Sales Range: $1-9.9 Million
Emp.: 50
Trading Software Publisher
N.A.I.C.S.: 513210
Louis Mendelsohn (Founder & Principal)
Karen Grow (Mgr-Acctg)

VANTAGEPOINT CAPITAL PARTNERS
1111 Bayhill Dr Ste 220, San Bruno, CA 94066
Tel.: (650) 866-3100
Web Site: http://www.vpcp.com
Year Founded: 1996
Sales Range: $25-49.9 Million
Emp.: 55
Investment Services
N.A.I.C.S.: 523999
Alan E. Salzman (CEO & Mng Partner)
Harold Friedman (CFO)
David C. Fries (Mng Dir)
Jim Marver (Mng Dir)
Stephan Dolezalek (Mng Dir)
Lee Burrows (Mng Dir)
Thomas A. Bevilacqua (Mng Dir & Co-Head-IT Practice Grp)
Bill Harding (Mng Dir)
Neil Wolff (Mng Dir & Gen Counsel)
Patricia Splinter (Mng Dir & COO)
Richard Harroch (Mng Dir)
Terry Chen (Partner)
Stephen Gray (Partner)
Ramesh Venugopal (Partner)
Jon Quick (Principal)
Gene Gable (VP-Mktg)
Han Zhang (VP)
Karen Eliadis (CFO)

VANTAGEPOINT, INC.
80 Villa Rd, Greenville, SC 29615
Tel.: (864) 331-1240
Web Site: http://www.vantagep.com
Year Founded: 1993
Sales Range: $10-24.9 Million
Emp.: 19
Advertising Agencies
N.A.I.C.S.: 541810
David McQuaid (VP-Creative & Digital)
Tricia Cruver (CFO & VP)
Steve Woodington (Assoc Dir-Creative)
Nicole Viscome (Acct Exec)

VANTEM GLOBAL, INC.
860 Green Vly Rd Ste 200, Greensboro, NC 27408
Tel.: (229) 482-1200 DE
Web Site: https://vantem.com
Year Founded: 2010
Modular Construction Services
N.A.I.C.S.: 236117
Chris Anderson (CEO)
Subsidiaries:
Affinity Building Systems, LLC (1)
62 Murray Blvd, Lakeland, GA 31635-5855
Web Site: http://www.affinitybuildingsystems.com
Commercial & Institutional Building Construction
N.A.I.C.S.: 236220
Gary Davidson (Gen Mgr)
Wayne Morrison (CEO)
Charles Crews (COO)

VANTEON CORPORATION
250 Cross Keys Ofc Park, Fairport, NY 14450-3510
Tel.: (585) 419-9555
Web Site: http://www.vanteon.com
Rev.: $19,600,000
Emp.: 45
Computer Software Systems Analysis & Design
N.A.I.C.S.: 541512
David L. Wagner (Co-Owner, Pres & COO)
Brian Herrera (Mgr-QA)
Kyle Drerup (Engr-Hardware)
Joseph L. Burke (Co-Owner & CEO)
Aaron J. Roof (CTO)

VANZANDT CONTROLS, LLC
13409 W County Rd 132, Odessa, TX 79765
Tel.: (432) 242-8000 TX
Web Site: http://www.vanzandtcontrols.com
Year Founded: 2015
Valve Mfr
N.A.I.C.S.: 332912
Lance VanZandt (Owner)
Subsidiaries:
D.A. Criswell Sales Inc. (1)
700 Hwy 60, Canyon, TX 79015
Tel.: (806) 655-9367
Web Site: http://www.dacriswell.com
Automated Valves & Actuators Packaging & Distribution Services
N.A.I.C.S.: 423830

VAQUERIA TRES MONJITAS INC.
PO Box 366757, San Juan, PR 00936-6757
Tel.: (787) 754-1818 PR
Web Site: http://www.tresmonjitas.com
Year Founded: 1950
Sales Range: $25-49.9 Million
Emp.: 500
Mfr of Fluid Milk
N.A.I.C.S.: 311511
Juan Corraeh (Gen Mgr)
Subsidiaries:
Hato Rey Plastics Inc. (1)
215 Federico Costa, San Juan, PR 00918-1322
Tel.: (787) 754-1818
Sales Range: $10-24.9 Million
Emp.: 25
Mfr of Plastics Bottles
N.A.I.C.S.: 326160
Orlando Gonzalez (Controller)

VARAGE MOUNTAIN CO. INC.
6261 Variel Ave, Woodland Hills, CA 91367
Tel.: (818) 719-8623
Web Site: http://www.justsportsusa.com
Sales Range: $10-24.9 Million
Emp.: 20
Sports Apparel
N.A.I.C.S.: 458110

VARAGON CAPITAL CORPORATION
151 W 42nd St 53rd Fl, New York, NY 10036
Tel.: (212) 235-2600 MD
Web Site: https://www.varagon.com
Year Founded: 2019
Rev.: $38,229,000
Assets: $700,172,000
Liabilities: $296,495,000
Net Worth: $403,677,000
Earnings: $9,242,000
Fiscal Year-end: 12/31/22
Investment Management Service
N.A.I.C.S.: 523999

VARBROS CORPORATION

VARBROS CORPORATION — U.S. PRIVATE

Varbros Corporation—(Continued)
16025 Brookpark Rd, Cleveland, OH 44142
Tel.: (216) 267-5200
Web Site: http://www.varbroscorp.com
Year Founded: 1997
Sales Range: $10-24.9 Million
Emp.: 110
Metal Stamping Services
N.A.I.C.S.: 332119
David Gido (VP & Gen Mgr)

VARDATA LLC
135 Calkins Rd, Rochester, NY 14623
Tel.: (585) 321-1950
Web Site: http://www.vardata.com
Year Founded: 2004
Sales Range: $10-24.9 Million
Emp.: 20
Refurbished & Surplus Equipment for Voice, Data & Storage Networks
N.A.I.C.S.: 517121
Jeffrey Coke (Co-Founder & Pres)
Matthew Pease (VP-Engrg)
Mike McCabe (Co-Founder & VP)
Alissa Seidman (VP-Ops)

VARDE PARTNERS, INC.
350 N 5th St Ste 800, Minneapolis, MN 55401
Tel.: (952) 893-1554   DE
Web Site: https://www.varde.com
Year Founded: 1993
Private Equity & Investment Management Firm
N.A.I.C.S.: 523999
George G. Hicks (Co-Founder & Co-CEO)
Marcia L. Page (Co-CEO & Co-Chief Investment Officer)
Jeremy D. Hedberg (Co-Chief Investment Officer & Partner)
Rick Noel (Partner & Head-Specialty Fin-Global)
Andy Lenk (Partner)
Ilfryn Carstairs (Co-CIO & Partner)
Ali M. Haroon (Partner & Co-Head-Real Estate-Global)
David A. Marple (Gen Counsel)
Brendan Albee (COO)
Tim Mooney (Head-Global Real Estate)
Andrea Schilling (Head-HR-Global)
Jon McKeown (Head-Strategy, Risk & Analytics-Global)
Bradley P. Bauer (Deputy Chief Investment Officer)
Kirsten Voss (Sr Mng Dir)
Jon Fox (Partner & Head-Bus Dev & IR-Global)
Shannon Gallagher (Head-Bus Dev & IR-EMEA)
Elena Lieskovska (Partner)
Haseeb Malik (Partner)

Subsidiaries:

Embrace Group Limited (1)
Two Parklands Business Park Birmingham
Great Park, Rubery, Birmingham, B45 9PZ, W Midlands, United Kingdom
Tel.: (44) 844 980 3666
Web Site: http://www.embracegroup.co.uk
Emp.: 70
Holding Company; Health & Social Care Services
N.A.I.C.S.: 551112
Trish Lee (CEO)
David Manson (CFO)
Amanda Morgan-Taylor (Dir-Quality Dev)
Shane Gidman (Dir-IT)
Roger Poynton (Dir-Property)

Subsidiary (Domestic):

Embrace (UK) Limited (2)
Two Parklands Business Park Birmingham
Great Park, Rubery, Birmingham, B45 9PZ, W Midlands, United Kingdom
Tel.: (44) 844 980 3666
Web Site: http://www.embracegroup.co.uk
Health & Social Care Services
N.A.I.C.S.: 623110
Ted Smith (Chm)
Trish Lee (CEO)
Amanda Morgan-Taylor (Dir-Quality Dev)
Alison Whelan (Dir-Trng & Dev)
Roger Poynton (Dir-Property)

FirstCity Financial Corporation (1)
6400 Imperial Dr, Waco, TX 76712
Tel.: (254) 761-2800
Web Site: http://www.fcfc.com
Rev: $70,581,000
Assets: $244,637,000
Liabilities: $107,370,000
Net Worth: $137,267,000
Earnings: $19,048,000
Emp.: 286
Fiscal Year-end: 12/31/2012
Financial Services
N.A.I.C.S.: 523999
James C. Holmes (COO & Exec VP)
Mark B. Horrell (Pres & CEO)

Subsidiary (Domestic):

American Business Lending, Inc. (2)
1420 W Mockingbird Ln Ste 540, Dallas, TX 75247
Tel.: (214) 580-8660
Web Site: http://www.ablsba.com
Sales Range: $50-74.9 Million
Emp.: 12
Mortgage & Nonmortgage Loan Brokerage Services
N.A.I.C.S.: 522310
Jody Muse (Sr VP-Bus Dev)
David S. Green (Exec VP & Mgr-SBA Production)
George Taylor (Sr VP-Bus Dev)
Scott Keasel (VP-Bus Dev)
Terry Kemp (VP-Bus Dev-Atlanta)
David Doria (Sr VP-Bus Dev)
Charles D. Meyers (VP-Bus Dev-Salt Lake City)
Mark E. Jackson (Sr VP-Bus Dev-Atlanta)
Stephanie Ellingson (VP-Bus Dev-Greater Pittsburg)
Tricia Hoffman (VP-Bus Dev-Tampa)
Tim Meeks (VP-Servicing Dept)
William Woodard (VP & Mgr-Underwriting)
Charles P. Bell Jr. (Pres & CEO)

Trimont Real Estate Advisors LLC (1)
1 Alliance Center 3500 Lenox Rd Ste G1, Atlanta, GA 30326
Tel.: (404) 420-5600
Web Site: http://www.trimontrea.com
Asset Management Services
N.A.I.C.S.: 531210
Andrew Kroll (COO)
Steven Lauer (Chief Legal Officer)
Don Sather (Chief HR Officer)
Robert Brasfield (Mng Dir-Underwriting & Due Diligence)
Raquel Brown (Mng Dir-IT & Svcs)
Kimberly Carter (Mng Dir-Client Svcs)
John D'Amico (Sr Mng Dir-Client Svcs)
Michael Dillon (Mng Dir-Servicing)
Maxwell Ellerhost (Mng Dir-IT & Svcs)
Petra Fishert (Dir-Europe)
John Gass (Mng Dir-Bond Admin)
Lynette Hegeman (Dir-Mktg & Comm)
Mitchell Hunter (Chief Comml Officer-Global)
Eric Lind (Mng Dir-Asset Mgmt)
Scott Monroe (Mng Dir-Servicing)
Glen Peters (CFO)
Heather Alce (Mng Dir & Controller-Americas)
Bill Sexton (CEO)
Thomas Wise (Mng Dir-Client Svcs-Americas)
Jeff Stargardter (Mng Dir-Asset Mgmt-Americas)
Trey Smith (Mng Dir-Performing Asset Mgmt-Americas)
Amber Sefert (Mng Dir-Asset Mgmt-Americas)
Kevin Miller (Mng Dir-Underwriting & Advisory-Americas)
Jaymon Jones (Mng Dir-Asset Mgmt)
James Jones (Head-Bus Dev-Global)
Jeff Bolte (Mng Dir-Information Svcs)
Terri Magnani (Head-Investment Advisory-Global)

VARELA AUTO GROUP, LLC
1201 W US Hwy 84, Fairfield, TX 75840
Tel.: (903) 729-2171
Web Site: http://www.allstarford.com
Year Founded: 1994
Sales Range: $50-74.9 Million
Emp.: 100
New Car Dealers
N.A.I.C.S.: 441110
Fernando H. Varela (Pres & CEO)
Nicholas F. Varela (VP-Ops)

VARESE SARABANDE RECORDS, INC.
11846 Ventura Blvd Ste 130, Studio City, CA 91604-2620
Tel.: (818) 753-4143
Web Site: http://www.varesesarabande.com
Year Founded: 1978
Sales Range: $25-49.9 Million
Emp.: 10
Cinema Soundtracks & Music Recordings Reissues Distr
N.A.I.C.S.: 512290
Steve Knapp (Exec VP-Bus & Legal Affairs)

VARI CORPORATION
390 Old Reading Pike, Pottstown, PA 19464
Tel.: (610) 970-2800
Rev: $23,000,000
Emp.: 6
Mfr of Heating Equipment
N.A.I.C.S.: 333414
John J. Meade Jr. (Pres)

Subsidiaries:

BCS Managment Company (1)
390 Old Reading Pike, Pottstown, PA 19464
Tel.: (610) 970-2800
Emp.: 4
Mfr of Heating Equipment
N.A.I.C.S.: 333414
John J. Meade (Pres)

Subsidiary (Domestic):

EFM Sales Company (2)
302 S 4th St, Emmaus, PA 18049-3853
Tel.: (610) 965-9041
Web Site: http://www.efmheating.com
Sales Range: $10-24.9 Million
Emp.: 3
Mfr of Automatic Heating Equipment
N.A.I.C.S.: 333414

VARI TRONICS COMPANY, INC.
2745 Huntington Dr, Duarte, CA 91010-2302
Tel.: (626) 359-8321   CA
Year Founded: 1955
Sales Range: $75-99.9 Million
Emp.: 100
Telephone Apparatus Mfr
N.A.I.C.S.: 334210
E.C. Rothenberger (Pres)

VARIANT EQUITY ADVISORS, LLC
1880 Century Park E Ste 825, Los Angeles, CA 90067
Tel.: (310) 467-4700
Web Site: http://www.variantequity.com
Year Founded: 2017
Privater Equity Firm
N.A.I.C.S.: 523999
Farhaad Wadia (Mng Partner)
Ryan Kanaley (VP)

Subsidiaries:

Certegy Check Services, Inc. (1)
PO Box 30046, Tampa, FL 33630-3046
Tel.: (800) 237-3826
Web Site: http://www.certegy.com
Sales Range: $500-549.9 Million
Emp.: 2,000
Credit Card & Checking Accounts Enhancement Services
N.A.I.C.S.: 561499
William Cargan (VP & Controller)

Coach USA, Inc. (1)
160 S Route 17 N, Paramus, NJ 07652
Tel.: (201) 225-7500
Web Site: http://www.coachusa.com
Emp.: 4,500
Passenger Ground Transportation Services
N.A.I.C.S.: 561520
Linda Burtwistle (CEO)

Subsidiary (Domestic):

All West Coachlines, Inc. (2)
7701 Wilbur Way, Sacramento, CA 95828
Tel.: (916) 423-4000
Web Site: http://www.allwestcoachlines.com
Sales Range: $25-49.9 Million
Emp.: 50
Chartered Bus Transportation Services
N.A.I.C.S.: 485510
Carla Eisentrager (Dir-Fin)

RAZ Transportation Inc. (2)
11655 SW Pacific Hwy, Portland, OR 97223
Tel.: (503) 684-3322
Web Site: http://www.raztrans.com
Sales Range: $50-74.9 Million
Chartered Bus Transportation Services
N.A.I.C.S.: 485510

CompuCom Systems, Inc. (1)
8106 Calvin Hall Rd, Dallas, TX 29707
Tel.: (803) 228-7400
Web Site: http://www.compucom.com
Information Technology, Hardware, Software & Application Services
N.A.I.C.S.: 541519
Mike Zimmer (Sr VP-Sls)
Peter Inness (Sr VP-Delivery)
Sanjay S. Savla (Sr VP-Acct Mgmt)
Judith Burns (VP-Comml Fin, Analysis & Fin Plng)
Beth Forquer Ruch (Sr VP-HR)
Paul Gagnier (Gen Counsel & Sr VP)
Reem Gedeon (VP-Canada)
Mick Slattery (Pres)
Scott Ward (Chief Bus Officer)
Kevin Shank (CEO)

Subsidiary (Non-US):

CompuCom Canada Co. (2)
1830 Matheson Boulevard Unit 1, Mississauga, L4W 0B3, ON, Canada
Tel.: (289) 261-3000
Web Site: http://www.compucom.com
Information Technology, Hardware, Software & Application Services
N.A.I.C.S.: 541519

Division (Domestic):

CompuCom Systems, Inc. - Bellevue (2)
170 120th Ave NE Ste 203, Bellevue, WA 98005
Tel.: (425) 974-2000
Web Site: http://www.compucom.com
Computer Application & Software Development & Support Services
N.A.I.C.S.: 541519

VARIETY CARE
3000 N Grand Blvd, Oklahoma City, OK 73107
Tel.: (405) 632-6688   OK
Web Site: http://www.varietycare.org
Year Founded: 1980
Sales Range: $25-49.9 Million
Emp.: 299
Community Health Care Services
N.A.I.C.S.: 621498
Mariano Acuna (Pres)
Connie Baker (Sec)

COMPANIES

Amy Dunn *(Treas)*
Donald Nevard *(VP)*
Lou Carmichael *(CEO)*

VARIETY CHILD LEARNING CENTER
47 Humphrey Dr, Syosset, NY 11791
Tel.: (516) 921-7171   NY
Web Site: http://www.vclc.org
Year Founded: 1966
Sales Range: $10-24.9 Million
Emp.: 416
Disabled Child Assistance Services
N.A.I.C.S.: 624120
Ralph F. Palleschi *(Chm)*
Janice Friedman *(CEO)*
Joan Padron *(Dir-Family Svcs Program)*
Janet Slade *(Controller)*
Susan Ritz-Baumgarten *(Dir-HR)*
Andrea Rieger *(CFO)*
Alan J. Stearn *(Vice Chm)*
Donna Cantrell Gerzof *(Sec)*
Michael Rubin *(Treas)*
Judith S. Bloch *(Founder)*

VARIETY DISTRIBUTORS INC.
609 7th St, Harlan, IA 51537-1000
Tel.: (712) 755-2184
Web Site:
  http://www.varietydistributors.com
Year Founded: 1946
Sales Range: $25-49.9 Million
Emp.: 250
Piece Goods & Notions
N.A.I.C.S.: 424310
Don Lanz *(Gen Mgr)*
Gary Landolt *(Mgr-Sls)*
Marie Wiederin *(Dir-HR)*

VARIETY WHOLESALERS, INCORPORATED
218 S Garnett St, Henderson, NC 27536
Tel.: (252) 430-2600   DE
Web Site: http://www.vwstores.com
Year Founded: 1957
Sales Range: $150-199.9 Million
Emp.: 650
Discounted Products Distr
N.A.I.C.S.: 455219
Terry Ellenwood *(Dir-Transportation)*
Phil Pope *(Sr VP-Real Estate)*
A. J. Nepa *(Sr VP-GMM)*
Frances Winslow *(VP-HR)*
Lance Williams *(VP-Loss Prevention)*

VARILEASE TECHNOLOGY FINANCE GROUP INC.
8451 Boulder Ct Ste 200, Walled Lake, MI 48390
Tel.: (248) 366-5300
Web Site: http://www.varilease.com
Year Founded: 1987
Sales Range: $50-74.9 Million
General Equipment Lessor
N.A.I.C.S.: 532490
Robert W. VanHellemont *(CEO)*

VARIQ CORPORATION
2055 L Street NW Ste 650, Washington, DC 20036
Tel.: (202) 292-4236
Web Site: http://www.variq.com
Year Founded: 2003
Sales Range: $25-49.9 Million
Emp.: 250
Computer Software Whslr
N.A.I.C.S.: 423430
Ben Edson *(CEO)*
Tom Edson *(CFO & COO)*
Brian Edwards *(Dir-Bus Dev)*
Terry DiVittorio *(VP-Cyber Programs)*
Olin Green *(Sr VP-Svc Delivery)*

VARITE, INC.
12 S 1st St Ste 404, San Jose, CA 95113
Tel.: (408) 977-0700   CA
Web Site: http://www.varite.com
Year Founded: 2000
Sales Range: $10-24.9 Million
Emp.: 265
It Consulting
N.A.I.C.S.: 541511
Adarsh Katyal *(Pres & CEO)*

VARNELL-STRUCK & ASSOCIATES INC.
4470 Peachtree Lk Dr, Duluth, GA 30096
Tel.: (770) 242-0700
Sales Range: $125-149.9 Million
Emp.: 700
Provider of Sales & Services to Home Center & Hardware Industry
N.A.I.C.S.: 423220

VARNEY AGENCY, INC.
32 Oak St, Bangor, ME 04401-6515
Tel.: (207) 947-8637   ME
Web Site:
  http://www.varneyagency.com
Year Founded: 1982
Sales Range: $25-49.9 Million
Emp.: 55
Provider of Insurance Agent & Broker Services
N.A.I.C.S.: 524210
William Varney *(Pres)*
Dean Andrews *(Controller)*
Brandy Ellis *(Acct Mgr-Comml Insurance)*
Greg Palman *(Mgr-CL)*

VARNEY INC.
1701 Shenandoah Ave NW, Roanoke, VA 24017
Tel.: (540) 343-0155
Web Site: http://www.varney.biz
Sales Range: $25-49.9 Million
Emp.: 270
General Electrical Contractor
N.A.I.C.S.: 238210
Paul Bratton *(Pres)*

VAROUH OIL, INC.
970 Griswold Rd, Elyria, OH 44035
Tel.: (440) 324-5025
Web Site: http://www.varouhoil.com
Sales Range: $10-24.9 Million
Emp.: 15
Petroleum Product Whslr
N.A.I.C.S.: 424720
Ari Varouh *(Sr VP)*
Ron Varouh *(Pres)*

VARSITY CONTRACTORS, INC.
315 S 5th Ave, Pocatello, ID 83201
Tel.: (208) 232-8598   ID
Web Site: http://www.varsityfs.com
Year Founded: 1957
Sales Range: $50-74.9 Million
Emp.: 4,000
Building Maintenance Services
N.A.I.C.S.: 561720
Cathy Judge *(CFO)*
Eric Luke *(Pres & CEO)*

Subsidiaries:

Nuvek LLC   (1)
PO Box 1538, American Fork, UT 84003-6538
Tel.: (801) 770-0137
Web Site: http://www.nuvek.com
Information Technology Consulting Services
N.A.I.C.S.: 541512
Kirk Magleby *(CEO & Gen Mgr)*
Mike Barnes *(Dir-Tech Svcs)*
Dan Rigby *(Dir-Mktg & Sls)*
Jorge Merino *(Dir-Product Dev)*

VARSITY FORD LINCOLN MERCURY
1351 Earl Rudder Fwy S, College Station, TX 77845
Tel.: (979) 694-2022
Web Site: http://www.varsityflm.com
Sales Range: $50-74.9 Million
Emp.: 100
Automobiles, New & Used
N.A.I.C.S.: 441110
Anthony Y. Majors *(Pres)*

VARSITY LINCOLN-MERCURY INC.
49251 Grand River Ave, Novi, MI 48376
Tel.: (248) 305-5300
Web Site:
  http://www.varsityautos.com
Sales Range: $125-149.9 Million
Emp.: 155
Sell Automobiles, New & Used
N.A.I.C.S.: 441110
Jennifer McCloskey *(Mgr-Bus Dev)*

VARSITY MANAGEMENT COMPANY, LP
1925 Century Park E Ste 1300, Los Angeles, CA 90067
Tel.: (203) 580-4501
Web Site:
  http://www.varsityhealthcarepartners.com
Private Equity Investment Firm
N.A.I.C.S.: 523999
David Alpern *(Mng Partner)*
Kenton Rosenberry *(Partner)*

Subsidiaries:

Healthcare Billing Systems LLC   (1)
298 South Yonge St, Ormond Beach, FL 32174
Web Site: http://www.duvasawko.com
Revenue Cycle Management Services
N.A.I.C.S.: 518210
Charles D. Chuck *(Co-Founder & Chm)*
William Sawko *(Co-Founder & Chief Software Architect)*

Subsidiary (Domestic):

Martin Gottlieb & Associates, LLC   (2)
4131 Sunbeam Rd, Jacksonville, FL 32257
Tel.: (904) 346-3088
Web Site: http://www.gottlieb.com
Sales Range: $1-9.9 Million
Emp.: 120
Office Administrative Services
N.A.I.C.S.: 561110
Mike Drinkwater *(CEO)*

VARSITY TUTORS LLC
101 S Hanley Rd Ste 300, Saint Louis, MO 63105
Tel.: (314) 422-2007   MO
Web Site:
  http://www.varsitytutors.com
Year Founded: 2007
Test Preparation & Academic Tutorial Services
N.A.I.C.S.: 611710
Chuck Cohn *(Founder & CEO)*
Heidi Robinson *(Chief Product Officer)*
Ian Clarkson *(Pres & COO)*

Subsidiaries:

Veritas Prep, LLC   (1)
4500 Park Granada Ste 202, Calabasas, CA 91302
Tel.: (310) 456-8716
Web Site: http://www.veritasprep.com
Educational Support Services
N.A.I.C.S.: 611710
Jon Small *(VP-Sls)*
Chad Troutwine *(Founder)*

VASCULAR SPECIALISTS OF

VASSALLO INTERNATIONAL GROUP, INC.

CENTRAL FLORIDA, INC.
80 W Michigan St, Orlando, FL 32806
Tel.: (407) 648-4323   FL
Web Site:
  http://www.arteryandvein.com
Year Founded: 2001
Sales Range: $1-9.9 Million
Emp.: 30
Physicians Office Specializing In Vascular Work
N.A.I.C.S.: 621111
Charles S. Thompson *(Partner)*
Jon M. Wesley *(Partner)*
Adam B. Levitt *(Partner)*
Michael J. Muehlberger *(Partner)*

VASEY COMMERCIAL HEATING & AC
10830 Andrade Dr, Zionsville, IN 46077
Tel.: (317) 873-2512
Web Site: http://www.vasey.biz
Sales Range: $10-24.9 Million
Emp.: 63
Warm Air Heating & Air Conditioning Contractor
N.A.I.C.S.: 238220
David Sheffield *(CFO)*

VASHAW SCIENTIFIC INC.
11660 Alpharetta Hwy Ste 155, Norcross, GA 30076
Tel.: (770) 447-5632
Web Site: http://www.vashaw.com
Sales Range: $10-24.9 Million
Emp.: 10
Distr of Scientific Instruments
N.A.I.C.S.: 423490
Wayne F. Vashaw *(Pres)*

VASOACTIVE PHARMACEUTICALS, INC.
99 Rosewood Dr Ste 260, Danvers, MA 01923
Tel.: (978) 750-1991   DE
Web Site: http://www.vasoactive.us
Sales Range: Less than $1 Million
Emp.: 5
Pharmaceuticals Mfr
N.A.I.C.S.: 325412
Joseph Frattaroli *(CFO & CEO)*
Stephen G. Carter *(VP & Chief Scientific Officer)*
Elizabeth Russo *(Controller)*
Robert E. Anderson *(Chm)*

VASONA MANAGEMENT
18 E Main St, Los Gatos, CA 95030
Tel.: (408) 354-4200
Web Site:
  http://www.vasonamanagement.com
Rev.: $13,500,000
Emp.: 380
Office Administrative Services
N.A.I.C.S.: 561110
Terry Maas *(Pres)*
Killian Byrne *(VP & Mgr-Asset)*
Penny McMullen *(Reg Mgr-Property)*
Rita Canning *(Reg Mgr-On-Site)*
Ronald M. Heald *(Mgr-Community-CCRM & CPTED)*
Tim Daffeh *(Mgr-Community Property)*

VASS PIPE & STEEL CO. INC.
158 3rd St, Mineola, NY 11501
Tel.: (516) 741-8398
Web Site: http://www.vasspipe.com
Sales Range: $100-124.9 Million
Emp.: 20
Provider of Pipe & Tubing, Steel
N.A.I.C.S.: 423510
Sunil Jain *(Owner)*

VASSALLO INTERNATIONAL GROUP, INC.

VASSALLO INTERNATIONAL GROUP, INC.   U.S. PRIVATE

Vassallo International Group, Inc.—(Continued)
1000 Carr 506, Ponce, PR 00780
Tel.: (787) 848-1515
Web Site: http://www.vassallointernational.com
Year Founded: 1962
Sales Range: $10-24.9 Million
Emp.: 103
Plastic Pipe & Accessory Mfr & Distr
N.A.I.C.S.: 326122
Jose Valls *(VP-R&D)*

VATER'S OF OKLAHOMA CITY INC.
PO Box 54617, Oklahoma City, OK 73154
Tel.: (405) 524-2757
Web Site: http://www.vaternet.com
Sales Range: $10-24.9 Million
Emp.: 15
Office Furniture
N.A.I.C.S.: 449110
James Vater *(Pres)*

VAUGHAN & BUSHNELL MANUFACTURING COMPANY, INC.
11414 Maple Ave, Hebron, IL 60034
Tel.: (815) 648-2446
Web Site: http://www.vaughanmfg.com
Year Founded: 1869
Sales Range: $150-199.9 Million
Emp.: 550
Tool Mfr
N.A.I.C.S.: 332216
Robert Bachta *(Mgr-Mktg)*
Ron Miller *(VP-Fin)*
Charles Vaughan *(Pres & COO)*

Subsidiaries:

V & B Manufacturing Co. (1)
252 Law 408, Walnut Ridge, AR 72476
Tel.: (870) 886-3525
Web Site: http://www.vbmfg.com
Sales Range: $10-24.9 Million
Emp.: 35
Mfr Of Landscaping Tools.
N.A.I.C.S.: 332216
Howard A. Vaughan Jr. *(Chm & Pres)*

VAUGHAN & SONS, INC.
10800 Sentinel Dr, San Antonio, TX 78217-3816
Tel.: (210) 352-1300   TX
Web Site: http://www.alamo.doitbest.com
Year Founded: 1893
Sales Range: $100-124.9 Million
Emp.: 300
Mfr & Retailer of Lumber & Forest Products
N.A.I.C.S.: 423310
Bob Vaughan *(Exec VP)*

Subsidiaries:

Alamo Forest Products, Inc. (1)
10800 Sentinel Dr, San Antonio, TX 78217-3816   (100%)
Tel.: (210) 352-1333
Web Site: http://www.alamoforestproducts.com
Sales Range: $25-49.9 Million
Emp.: 8
Retailer of Lumber & Related Forest Products Mfr & Distr
N.A.I.C.S.: 423310
George C. Vaughan *(Owner)*

Alamo Lumber Company (1)
10800 Sentinel St, San Antonio, TX 78217-3816   (100%)
Tel.: (210) 352-1300
Web Site: http://www.alamo.doitbest.com
Sales Range: $25-49.9 Million
Emp.: 20
Retailer of Lumber Hardware & Building Product Distr
N.A.I.C.S.: 444140

Robert L. Vaughan *(Chm)*
Matt Mullin *(VP-Sls)*

Vaughan & Sons, Inc. Multi-Family Sales (1)
9301 Hwy 290 W Unit 105, Austin, TX 78736-7809   (100%)
Tel.: (512) 288-3000
Web Site: http://www.vs-austin.com
Sales Range: $25-49.9 Million
Emp.: 4
Distr of Lumber & Related Building Materials
N.A.I.C.S.: 423310

VAUGHAN FURNITURE COMPANY INC.
816 Glendale Rd, Galax, VA 24333
Tel.: (276) 236-6111   VA
Web Site: http://www.vaughanfurniture.com
Year Founded: 1923
Sales Range: $25-49.9 Million
Emp.: 600
Wood Household Furniture
N.A.I.C.S.: 423310
J. David Vaughan *(Pres)*
Taylor G. Vaughan *(Chm & Pres)*

Subsidiaries:

Big V Wholesale Co. Inc. (1)
816 Glendale Rd, Galax, VA 24333
Tel.: (276) 238-3229
Web Site: http://www.vaughanfurniture.com
Sales Range: Less than $1 Million
Emp.: 60
Maintenance Support & Engineering Services
N.A.I.C.S.: 423840

VAUGHAN INTERESTS INC.
529 E State Hwy 83, Weslaco, TX 78596
Tel.: (956) 968-0515   TX
Web Site: http://www.burtoncompanies.com
Year Founded: 1926
Automotive Supplies & Parts
N.A.I.C.S.: 423120
Scott Vaughan *(Pres)*

VAUGHAN-BASSETT FURNITURE COMPANY INC.
300 E Grayson St, Galax, VA 24333
Tel.: (276) 236-6161   VA
Web Site: http://www.vaughan-bassett.com
Year Founded: 1919
Sales Range: $125-149.9 Million
Emp.: 700
Wood Bedroom Furniture Mfr
N.A.I.C.S.: 337122
John D. Bassett III *(Chm)*

VAUGHN CHEVROLET
1311 Vaughn Dr, Ottumwa, IA 52501
Tel.: (641) 682-4574
Web Site: http://www.vaughnautomotive.com
Year Founded: 1987
Sales Range: $10-24.9 Million
Emp.: 58
Automobiles, New & Used
N.A.I.C.S.: 441110
Josh Benness *(Gen Mgr)*
Volle Beness *(Chm)*

VAUGHN INDUSTRIES, LLC.
1201 E Findlay St, Carey, OH 43316
Tel.: (419) 396-3900
Web Site: http://www.vaughnindustries.com
Sales Range: $75-99.9 Million
Emp.: 425
Electrical Wiring Services
N.A.I.C.S.: 238210
Timothy Vaughn *(CEO)*

VAUGHN WEDEEN KUHN
116 Central Ave Ste 300, Albuquerque, NM 87102
Tel.: (505) 243-4000
Web Site: http://www.vwk2.com
Year Founded: 1982
Sales Range: Less than $1 Million
Emp.: 15
Advetising Agency
N.A.I.C.S.: 541810
Steve Wedeen *(Principal)*
Richard Kuhn *(Mng Partner)*
Jodi Mari *(Mgr-Production)*
Chip Wyly *(Production Artist)*
Rudi Backart *(Sr Designer)*
Webb Johnson *(Acct Exec-Bus Dev)*
Stephanie McTee *(Designer)*
Nick Tauro Jr. *(Dir-Creative & Copywriter)*

VAUGHT, INC.
300 N Kanawha St Ste 201, Beckley, WV 25801
Tel.: (304) 929-6909
Web Site: http://www.vaughtinc.com
Year Founded: 2008
Sales Range: $1-9.9 Million
Emp.: 7
Health Care Consulting Services
N.A.I.C.S.: 621491
Christopher R. Vaught *(Pres & CEO)*

VAULT SPORTSWEAR, INC.
1407 Broadway Rm 1207, New York, NY 10018-3312
Tel.: (212) 391-5990
Web Site: http://www.vaultsportswear.com
Year Founded: 1998
Rev.: $12,600,000
Emp.: 9
Clothing & Accessories Merchant Whslrs
N.A.I.C.S.: 424350
Nouri Chaya *(VP)*
Sony Chaya *(Mgr-Mfg)*
Mousa Chaya *(CEO)*

VAULTED GOLD BULLION TRUST
c/o Bank of Montreal 3 Times Sq, New York, NY 10036
Tel.: (212) 885-4000   DE
Year Founded: 2013
Assets: $186,256,695
Liabilities: $203,470,539
Net Worth: ($17,213,844)
Earnings: ($36,948,499)
Fiscal Year-end: 10/31/18
Gold Bullion Trust Services
N.A.I.C.S.: 523991
Deland Kamanga *(Mng Dir & co-Head Global Structured Products)*
Vandra Goedvolk *(Asst Sec)*

VAVRINEK, TRINE, DAY AND CO., LLP
8270 Aspen St, Rancho Cucamonga, CA 91730
Tel.: (909) 466-4410
Web Site: http://www.vtdcpa.com
Sales Range: $10-24.9 Million
Emp.: 140
Certified Public Accountants
N.A.I.C.S.: 541211
Ron White *(Mng Partner)*

VAYAN MARKETING GROUP, LLC
7700 W Camino Real Ste 401, Boca Raton, FL 33433
Tel.: (561) 955-9660
Year Founded: 2000
Sales Range: $10-24.9 Million
Emp.: 12
Advetising Agency

N.A.I.C.S.: 541810
Laura Kall *(Chm)*
Warren Corpus *(VP-Bus Dev)*
Thomas Deters *(CEO)*
Curt Shaffer *(CFO)*
Jon Neveloff *(VP-Data Acq)*

VBRICK SYSTEMS INC.
12 Beaumont Rd, Wallingford, CT 06492
Tel.: (203) 303-0245
Web Site: http://www.vbrick.com
Security System Services
N.A.I.C.S.: 561621
Christian Rockwell *(Chief Mktg Officer)*
Jim Rich *(Chief Revenue Officer)*
Paul Sparta *(Chm & CEO)*

Subsidiaries:

Ramp Holdings Inc. (1)
27 Wormwood St, Boston, MA 02210
Tel.: (857) 202-3500
Web Site: http://www.ramp.com
Sales Range: $1-9.9 Million
Emp.: 40
SaaS Content Optimization Platform to Online Publishers
N.A.I.C.S.: 513210
Raymond Lau *(CTO)*
Bob Orlando *(CFO)*
Erik Herz *(VP-Bus Dev)*
Tom Racca *(Pres & CEO)*
Stephen Blankenship *(VP-Product & Ops)*
Neal Stanton *(Co-CEO & Chief Revenue Officer)*

VBS INC., MATERIAL HANDLING EQUIPMENT
5808 Midlothian Tpke, Richmond, VA 23225-6118
Tel.: (804) 232-7816   VA
Web Site: http://www.vbsmhe.com
Year Founded: 1928
Sales Range: $25-49.9 Million
Emp.: 135
Industrial Machinery & Equipment
N.A.I.C.S.: 423830
Claud D. Crosby *(Pres)*
Ginnie Lilley *(Coord-Svc)*
Melissa Moore *(Coord-Sls)*
Teresa Nixon *(Mgr-Sls Acct)*

VBT FINANCIAL CORPORATION
45 NE Loop 410 Ste 190, San Antonio, TX 78216
Tel.: (210) 408-5700   TX
Web Site: http://www.vantage.bank
Year Founded: 2018
Bank Holding Company
N.A.I.C.S.: 551111
Rafael G. Garza *(Vice Chm)*
Jeff Sinnott *(Pres & CEO)*

Subsidiaries:

Vantage Bank Texas (1)
45 NE Loop 410 Ste 190, San Antonio, TX 78216
Tel.: (210) 408-5700
Web Site: http://www.vantage.bank
Sales Range: $100-124.9 Million
Emp.: 457
Commericial Banking
N.A.I.C.S.: 522110
Rafael G. Garza *(Vice Chm & Mng Dir)*
Paul D. Thornton *(Reg Pres & Exec VP)*
Phil Lesh *(CFO & Exec VP)*
Jeff Sinnott *(Pres & CEO)*
Barry Bruce Conrad II *(Exec VP & Chief-Specialty Lending)*

VC3, INC.
1301 Gervais St Ste 1800, Columbia, SC 29201
Tel.: (803) 733-7333   DE
Web Site: http://www.vc3.com
Year Founded: 1994
Computer System Design Services

COMPANIES

N.A.I.C.S.: 541512
Sandy Reeser (CEO)
Ryan Vestby (Chief Growth Officer)
David Bridges (Pres)
Hunter Lindsay (Sr VP-Bus Dev)
Efrem Berman (Sr VP-Mktg)
Jill Menhart (Chief Admin Officer)
Russell Klein (CFO)
John Hey (Dir-Ops)

Subsidiaries:

Accent Computer Solutions, Inc. (1)
8438 Red Oak St, Rancho Cucamonga, CA 91730
Tel.: (909) 481-4368
Web Site: https://www.accentonit.com
Sales Range: $1-9.9 Million
Emp.: 57
Proactive Information Technology Management
N.A.I.C.S.: 541690
Corey Kaufman (Dir-Client Dev)
Marty Kaufman (Pres)
Derek Woolf (COO)
Peter O'Campo (CTO)

Subsidiary (Domestic):

Computer Gallery, Inc. (2)
73965 Hwy 111, Palm Desert, CA 92260-4007
Tel.: (760) 779-1001
Web Site: http://www.accentonit.com
Emp.: 25
Information Technology Services
N.A.I.C.S.: 541519
Joseph Popper (Founder & Pres)

Computer World, Inc. (1)
5614 Grand Ave, Duluth, MN 55807
Tel.: (218) 728-6000
Web Site: http://www.cwtechgroup.com
Computer & Office Machine Repair & Maintenance
N.A.I.C.S.: 811210
Bruce Beste (Gen Mgr)
David Manion (CEO)

FPA Technology Services Inc. (1)
16000 Ventura Blvd Ste 550, Encino, CA 91436
Tel.: (818) 501-3390
Web Site: http://www.fpainc.com
Sales Range: $1-9.9 Million
Emp.: 30
Computer & Office Machine Repair & Maintenance
N.A.I.C.S.: 811210
Dee Perez (Mgr-Support Svcs Grp)
Craig Pollack (Founder & CEO)

Go Concepts, Inc. (1)
777 Columbus Ave, Lebanon, OH 45036
Tel.: (513) 934-2800
Web Site: http://www.go-concepts.com
Sales Range: $1-9.9 Million
Emp.: 12
Computer System Design Services
N.A.I.C.S.: 541512
Dan Hollingshead (Sec)

VCAT, LLC
591 Camino de la Reina Ste 418, San Diego, CA 92108
Tel.: (619) 330-4000   UT
Web Site: http://www.vcat.com
Year Founded: 1992
Sales Range: $1-9.9 Million
Emp.: 38
Casino Marketing, Development & Technology
N.A.I.C.S.: 721120
Kelly Jacobs Speer (VP-Mktg & PR)
Greg Shay (CEO)
Kevin McIntosh (CFO & COO)
Donne Grable (VP-Gaming Ops)
Don Goldman (Exec VP-Internet Gaming)

VCG HOLDING CORP.
390 Union Blvd Ste 540, Lakewood, CO 80228
Tel.: (303) 934-2424   CO
Web Site: http://www.vcgh.com
Year Founded: 2002
Sales Range: $50-74.9 Million
Emp.: 868
Adult Night Club & Sports Bar Owner & Operator
N.A.I.C.S.: 713990
Troy H. Lowrie (Chm & CEO)
Michael L. Ocello (Pres & COO)

VCHECK GLOBAL LLC
5979 W 3rd St Ste 200, Los Angeles, CA 90036
Web Site: http://www.vcheckglobal.com
Year Founded: 2013
Sales Range: $1-9.9 Million
Emp.: 35
Business Management Services
N.A.I.C.S.: 541611
Michael Adams (Founder)
Adam Rudman (CEO)
Lyndee Fletcher (COO)
Seth Farbman (Co-Chm)
Shai Stern (Co-Chm)

VCM PRODUCTS, LLC
PO Box 6629, Freehold, NJ 07728
Tel.: (732) 677-3797
Web Site: http://www.vcmproducts.com
Year Founded: 2011
Sales Range: $1-9.9 Million
Pesticide Mfr
N.A.I.C.S.: 325320
Veronica Perlongo (Co-Owner)
Maria Curcio (Co-Owner)

VCOM
2540 Us Highway 130 Ste 101, Cranbury, NJ 08512-3500
Tel.: (609) 655-1200
Web Site: http://www.vcomm-eng.com
Year Founded: 1972
Sales Range: $10-24.9 Million
Emp.: 25
Engineering Consulting Service
N.A.I.C.S.: 541512
Dominic Villecco (Founder & Pres)

VCOM INTERNATIONAL MULTI-MEDIA CORPORATION
80 Little Falls Rd, Fairfield, NJ 07004
Tel.: (201) 229-9800
Web Site: http://www.vcomimc.com
Sales Range: $10-24.9 Million
Emp.: 45
Communication Equipment Mfr & Distr
N.A.I.C.S.: 423690
Martin Siegel (Chm)
Shelley Goldstein (Pres)
M. Picone (VP)
Randy Coles (CFO)

VCOM SOLUTIONS INC.
12657 Alcosta Blvd Ste 418, San Ramon, CA 94583
Tel.: (925) 244-1800
Web Site: http://www.vcomsolutions.com
Year Founded: 2002
Sales Range: $10-24.9 Million
Emp.: 32
Outsourced Telecom Expense & Inventory Management Services
N.A.I.C.S.: 561499
Gary Storm (Pres & CEO)
Sameer Hilal (COO)
Joe Condy (Co-Founder & Exec VP-Sls)
Ivy Lee (VP-Fin)
Jennifer Frey (VP-Customer Experience)
Adam Shawley (CIO)
Heather Faison (VP-Carrier Ops)
Brandon Hampton (Dir-Mobility Mgmt)
Bob Barnes (VP-Sls Ops)
Audrey Bold (VP-Mktg)

VCUSTOMER
4040 Lake Washington Blvd NE Ste 208, Kirkland, WA 98033-7874
Tel.: (206) 802-0200
Web Site: http://www.vcustomer.com
Year Founded: 1999
Sales Range: $25-49.9 Million
Emp.: 6,000
Contract Center & Technical Support Services
N.A.I.C.S.: 561499
Sanjay Kumar (Founder & CEO)
David Warren (VP-Sls)
Lori Inuzuka (VP-Intl Bus Unit)

VDART INC.
11180 State Bridge Rd Ste 402, Alpharetta, GA 30022
Tel.: (678) 685-8650
Web Site: http://www.vdartinc.com
Year Founded: 2007
Sales Range: $25-49.9 Million
Emp.: 239
It Consulting
N.A.I.C.S.: 541690
Sidd Ahmed (Pres & Grp CEO)
Tony Maley (CTO-VDart Digital)
Mohamed Irfan Peeran (Mng Dir-Mergers & Acq)
Oliver Sam (VP-People Strategy & Transformation)
Randy Jacques (Dir-Tech Partnerships & Alliances)

VDO-PH INTERNATIONAL, INC.
2700 E Sunset Rd Ste B-18, Las Vegas, NV 89120
Tel.: (702) 570-7700   NV
Web Site: http://www.vdo-ph.com
Year Founded: 2010
Emp.: 7
Telephony Appliance Mfr & Software Publisher
N.A.I.C.S.: 334220
Valeria Stringer (Pres & CFO)
Elizabeth Twitty (Sec)

VECAST, INC.
2 N Lake Ave Ste 870, Pasadena, CA 91101
Tel.: (626) 666-3909   DE
Web Site: http://www.vecast.com
Year Founded: 2003
Sales Range: $1-9.9 Million
Emp.: 32
Digital Cable Television Network Equipment & Devices Mfr & Sales
N.A.I.C.S.: 334220
George Wu (Chm, Pres, CEO, Interim CFO & Treas)
Lily Kuo (VP & Sec)
Jianhua Liu (CTO)

VECELLIO GROUP, INC.
101 Sansbury's Way, West Palm Beach, FL 33411
Tel.: (561) 793-2102
Web Site: http://www.vecelliogroup.com
Year Founded: 1938
Sales Range: $75-99.9 Million
Emp.: 1,200
Specialty Contractor
N.A.I.C.S.: 238990
Paula Burgess (VP-IT)
Robert Smith (Sr VP-Fin)
Christopher Vecellio (Co-Owner)
Kathryn Vecellio (Co-Owner)
Michael Vecellio (Co-Owner)
Leo A. Vecellio Jr. (Co-Owner & CEO)

Subsidiaries:

Vecellio & Grogan, Inc. (1)
2251 Robert C Byrd Dr, Beckley, WV 25801
Tel.: (304) 252-6575
Web Site: http://www.vecelliogrogan.com
Civil Engineering & Construction Services
N.A.I.C.S.: 237990

Subsidiary (Domestic):

Sharpe Brothers, Inc. (2)
204 Base Leg Rd, Greensboro, NC 27409
Tel.: (336) 235-2756
Web Site: http://www.sharpebrosvg.com
Sales Range: $25-49.9 Million
Emp.: 55
Highway, Street & Bridge Construction
N.A.I.C.S.: 237310
Ivan Clayton (VP & Gen Mgr)

VECNA TECHNOLOGIES, INC.
36 Cambridgepark Dr, Cambridge, MA 02140
Tel.: (617) 864-0636
Web Site: http://www.vecna.com
Year Founded: 1999
Sales Range: $50-74.9 Million
Emp.: 250
Healthcare-Related Research Services
N.A.I.C.S.: 541715
Deborah Theobald (Co-Founder)
Michael Bearman (VP-Gc-Vecna Robotics & Gen Mgr)
Daniel Theobald (Co-Founder/Chief Innovation Officer-Vecna Robotics)
Amanda Baldi (Dir-Mktg & Comm)
Al Ramsey (Dir-Product R&D)
Dwight Moore (CEO-VGo Brand)
Daniel Patt (CEO-Vecna Robotics)
Jeff Huerta (Sr VP-Sls-Vecna Robotics)
David Clear (Chief Revenue Officer-Vecna Robotics)
Denis Lussault (VP-Autonomy-Vecna Robotics)

VECTA INC.
1 World Trade Ctr Ste 8500, New York, NY 10007
Tel.: (212) 280-1000   MD
Web Site: https://vecta.com
SNNY—(OTCIQ)
Rev.: $2,145,005
Assets: $91,896,855
Liabilities: $75,579,444
Net Worth: $16,317,411
Earnings: ($202,722)
Emp.: 15
Fiscal Year-end: 12/31/22
Bank Holding Company
N.A.I.C.S.: 551111
Edward J. Lipkus III (CFO, Treas & VP)
John Leo (Chm, Pres & CEO)
Robert Brantl (Gen Counsel)

Subsidiaries:

Sunnyside Federal Savings & Loan Association of Irvington (1)
56 Main St, Irvington, NY 10533   (100%)
Tel.: (914) 591-8000
Web Site: http://www.sunnysidefederal.com
Rev.: $3,011,174
Emp.: 13
Fiscal Year-end: 12/31/2012
Federal Savings Institutions
N.A.I.C.S.: 522180
Timothy D. Sullivan (Pres & CEO)

VECTOR CAPITAL MANAGEMENT, L.P.
1 Market St Steuart Twr 23rd Fl, San Francisco, CA 94105
Tel.: (415) 293-5000   DE
Web Site: http://www.vectorcapital.com
Year Founded: 1997
Privater Equity Firm

VECTOR CAPITAL MANAGEMENT, L.P.

U.S. PRIVATE

Vector Capital Management, L.P.—(Continued)
N.A.I.C.S.: 523999
David Fishman *(Mng Dir)*
David A. Baylor *(Mng Dir & COO)*
Andy Fishman *(Mng Dir)*
Robert Amen *(Mng Dir)*
Alexander R. Slusky *(Mng Dir & Chief Investment Officer)*

Subsidiaries:

Alvaria, Inc. (1)
300 Apollo Dr, Chelmsford, MA 01824
Tel.: (978) 250-7900
Web Site: http://www.aspect.com
Sales Range: $25-49.9 Million
Emp.: 325
Call Center Software & Equipment Mfr
N.A.I.C.S.: 541511
Gwen Braygreen *(Sr VP-Aspect Customer Care)*
Michael Regan *(Sr VP-R&D)*
Spence Mallder *(CTO & Sr VP)*
Jim Freeze *(CMO & Sr VP)*
Guido de Koning *(Sr VP-Human Capital)*
Gary Barnet *(CTO & Exec VP)*
Gregg Clevenger *(CFO & Exec VP)*
Patrick Dennis *(Pres)*
Frank Ciccone *(Chief Revenue Officer)*
Jeff Cotten *(CEO)*
Colleen Sheley *(Sr VP-Global Mktg)*
Michael J. Provenzano III *(Exec VP-Fin)*

Branch (Non-US):

Aspect Software (2)
2 The Sq, Stockley Park, Uxbridge, UB11 1AD, Middlesex, United Kingdom (100%)
Tel.: (44) 2085891000
Web Site: http://www.aspect.com
Sales Range: $25-49.9 Million
Emp.: 140
Contact Center Products & Services
N.A.I.C.S.: 334418

Subsidiary (Non-US):

Aspect Software Asia Pacific Pte Ltd. (2)
7 Temasek Boulevard 08-02 Suntec Tower One, Singapore, 038987, Singapore (100%)
Tel.: (65) 6590 0388
Web Site: http://www.aspect.com
Sales Range: $10-24.9 Million
Emp.: 27
Software Development Services
N.A.I.C.S.: 541511
Arani Krishna *(Sr VP-Sls)*
Mike Bourke *(Sr VP-Product Mgmt)*
Gwen Braygreen *(Sr VP-Customer Care)*
Thomas L. Davies *(Sr VP-Cloud Ops)*
Guido De Koning *(Sr VP-Human Capital)*
Spencer C. Demetros *(Gen Counsel & Sr VP)*
Jim Haskin *(CIO & Sr VP)*
David Herzog *(Sr VP-Channels-Worldwide)*
Chris Koziol *(Pres & CEO)*
Spence Mallder *(CTO & Sr VP)*
Sherri Moyen *(CFO)*
Michael Regan *(Sr VP-R&D)*
Brad Scott *(Sr VP-Professional Svcs-Worldwide)*

Branch (Domestic):

Aspect Software, Inc. (2)
140 Baytech Dr, San Jose, CA 95134-2302
Tel.: (408) 325-2200
Web Site: http://www.aspect.com
Developer of Contact Center Products & Services Software
N.A.I.C.S.: 513210
James F. Mitchell *(Sr VP-Tech)*

Subsidiary (Domestic):

Noble Systems Corporation (2)
1200 Ashford Pkwy Ste 300, Atlanta, GA 30338
Tel.: (404) 851-1331
Web Site: http://www.noblesys.com
Sales Range: $10-24.9 Million
Emp.: 300
Communications IT Solutions
N.A.I.C.S.: 541519
Chris Hodges *(Sr VP-Sls & Mktg)*
Henry Danser *(VP-Sls-Western Reg)*
James K. Noble Jr. *(Pres)*

Subsidiary (Domestic):

ALI Solutions, Inc. (3)
1120 S Capital of Texas Hwy, Austin, TX 78746
Tel.: (512) 328-8215
Web Site: http://www.alisolutions.com
Sales Range: $1-9.9 Million
Emp.: 75
Contact Center Solutions
N.A.I.C.S.: 513210
Tom Miller *(CEO)*

Subsidiary (Non-US):

Noble Systems Australia PTY Limited (3)
Level 13 22 Market Street, Sydney, 2000, NSW, Australia
Tel.: (61) 2 8222 0500
Web Site: http://www.noblesystems.com
Information Technology Consulting Services
N.A.I.C.S.: 541512
Graham Estreich *(Dir-Natl Sls)*

Noble Systems France S.A.R.L. (3)
12 Avenue Des Saules, Oullins, 69600, Lyon, France
Tel.: (33) 4 72 68 80 46
Information Technology Consulting Services
N.A.I.C.S.: 541512

Noble Systems India Pvt. Ltd. (3)
Suite 507 BSI Business Park C-51 Sector 62, Bhikaji Cama Place, Noida, 201301, India
Tel.: (91) 11 6660 6500
Web Site: http://www.noblesystems.com
Emp.: 15
Information Technology Consulting Services
N.A.I.C.S.: 541512
Ashok Kumar *(Gen Mgr)*

Noble Systems Philippines Corporation (3)
Unit 2108 Raffles Corporate Center F Ortigas Jr Avenue Ortigas Center, Brgy San Antonio, Pasig, 1605, Philippines
Tel.: (63) 2 470 9282
Information Technology Consulting Services
N.A.I.C.S.: 541512
Oscar Jonnathan Perez *(Mng Dir)*

Noble Systems UK (3)
11 Commerce Way, Westinghouse Road, Manchester, M17 1HW, United Kingdom
Tel.: (44) 161 772 7100
Call Center IT Solutions
N.A.I.C.S.: 541519
Sian Ciabattoni *(Dir-Mktg)*
Colin Chave *(Gen Mgr)*

Subsidiary (Domestic):

Stratasoft, Inc. (3)
519 N Sam Houston Pkwy E Ste 550, Houston, TX 77060
Tel.: (832) 446-4499
Web Site: http://www.stratasoft.com
Call Center Software Developer
N.A.I.C.S.: 513210
Asim Saber *(CEO)*

Subsidiary (Domestic):

Voxeo Corporation (2)
189 S Orange Ave Ste 2050, Orlando, FL 32801-3263
Tel.: (831) 439-5130
Web Site: http://www.voxeo.com
Rev.: $75,000,000
Emp.: 75
Computer Integrated Systems Design
N.A.I.C.S.: 561110
David Herzog *(Sr VP & Gen Mgr)*
R.J. Auburn *(CTO)*

Subsidiary (Domestic):

Cheetah Digital, Inc. (1)
72 W. Adams St., 8th Floor, Chicago, IL 60603
Web Site: http://www.cheetahdigital.com
Emp.: 1,300
Marketing Services
N.A.I.C.S.: 541613
Michelle Curless *(Chief Customer Officer)*

Branch (Domestic):

Cheetah Digital (2)
72 W Adams St Fl 8, Chicago, IL 60603 (75%)
Tel.: (866) 499-1007
Web Site: http://www.cheetahdigital.com
Enterprise Cross-channel Marketing Technology Company
N.A.I.C.S.: 541910
Raymond Balingit *(Mgr-Software Engrg)*
Sameer Kazi *(CEO)*
Richard Jones *(CMO)*
Patrick Tripp *(Sr VP-Product Mktg)*

Subsidiary (Domestic):

Wayin, Inc. (2)
999 18th St Ste 1100S, Denver, CO 80202
Tel.: (303) 997-1722
Data Capture, Marketing Campaign Management & Digital Marketing
N.A.I.C.S.: 518210

ChyronHego Corporation (1)
5 Hub Dr, Melville, NY 11747
Tel.: (631) 845-2000
Web Site: http://www.chyronhego.com
Sales Range: $25-49.9 Million
Broadcast Graphics Hardware, Software & Associated Services
N.A.I.C.S.: 513210
Mary Sanders *(Dir-MIS)*
Karen Italo *(Mgr-Mktg)*
Johan Apel *(Chm)*
A. J. Steffenberg *(VP-Worldwide Customer Support)*
Neil Foster *(CFO & COO)*
Bill Apker *(Dir-Sls-West Reg)*
Brian Spiers *(Dir-Sls-Southern US & Canada)*
Jonathan Wong *(VP-Sls-Asia Pacific)*
Steve Papadakis *(Dir-Key Accts)*
Ariel Garcia *(Pres & CEO)*

Subsidiary (Non-US):

ChyronHego AB (2)
Tegeluddsvagen 3, 115 41, Stockholm, Sweden
Tel.: (46) 8 534 883 00
Web Site: http://chyronhego.com
Broadcast Graphics Hardware, Software & Associated Services
N.A.I.C.S.: 513210

ChyronHego Chile Limitada (2)
Santa Lucia 344 Oficina 41, Santiago, Chile
Tel.: (56) 99 886 4356
Web Site: http://chyronhego.com
Broadcast Graphics Hardware, Software & Associated Services
N.A.I.C.S.: 513210

ChyronHego Czech s.r.o. (2)
Purkynova 2855/97a, Brno, 612 00, Czech Republic
Tel.: (420) 731 963 534
Web Site: http://www.chyronhego.com
Broadcast Graphics Hardware, Software & Associated Services
N.A.I.C.S.: 513210

ChyronHego Danmark ApS (2)
Gribskowej, 22100, Copenhagen, Denmark
Tel.: (45) 4080 1432
Web Site: http://chyronhego.com
Broadcast Graphics Hardware, Software & Associated Services
N.A.I.C.S.: 513210

ChyronHego Finland Oy (2)
Uutiskatu 5 Suunnittelutalo, 00240, Helsinki, Finland
Tel.: (358) 400 630 261
Web Site: http://chyronhego.com
Emp.: 12
Broadcast Graphics Hardware, Software & Associated Services
N.A.I.C.S.: 513210
Timo Latanoja *(Gen Mgr)*

ChyronHego GmbH (2)
Borsigstrasse 11-13, 65205, Wiesbaden, Germany
Tel.: (49) 61221704480
Web Site: http://www.chyronhego.com
Emp.: 10
Broadcast Graphics Hardware, Software & Associated Services
N.A.I.C.S.: 513210

ChyronHego Norge A/S (2)
Sandakerveien 114a, 0484, Oslo, Norway
Tel.: (47) 2279 7030
Web Site: http://www.chyronhego.com

Broadcast Graphics Hardware, Software & Associated Services
N.A.I.C.S.: 513210

ChyronHego Slovakia s.r.o. (2)
Vajanskeho 43, 080 01, Presov, Slovakia
Tel.: (421) 692 003 451
Web Site: http://www.chyronhego.com
Broadcast Graphics Hardware, Software & Associated Services
N.A.I.C.S.: 513210

ChyronHego UK Ltd. (2)
Unit 1 Ironbridge House Windmill Place, Southall, London, UB2 4NJ, United Kingdom
Tel.: (44) 20 8867 9050
Web Site: http://www.chyronhego.com
Broadcast Graphics Hardware, Software & Associated Services
N.A.I.C.S.: 513210

Gerber Scientific LLC (1)
24 Industrial Park Rd W, Tolland, CT 06084
Tel.: (860) 870-2890
Web Site: http://www.gerberscientific.com
Sales Range: $300-349.9 Million
Produces Automated Manufacturing Systems for Sign Making, Specialty Graphics & Packaging, Apparel & Flexible Materials & Ophthalmic Lens Processing Industries
N.A.I.C.S.: 333248
Michael R. Elia *(Pres & CEO)*
Patricia L. Burmahl *(Sr VP-Global HR)*
John D. Henderson *(VP-Gerber Bus Sys)*
Donny Askin *(Sr VP)*
John Capasso *(CFO)*

Subsidiary (Non-US):

Gerber Scientific (Shanghai) Co., Ltd. (2)
99 Tian Zhou Road Building 16, Caohejing Hi-Tech Park, Shanghai, 200233, China
Tel.: (86) 2154450505
Web Site: http://www.gerbertechnology.com
Sales Range: $100-124.9 Million
Graphic Design Services
N.A.I.C.S.: 541430

Group (Domestic):

Gerber Scientific, Inc. - Gerber Scientific Products Group (2)
24 Industrial Park Rd W, Tolland, CT 06084
Tel.: (860) 644-1551
Web Site: http://www.gspinc.com
Digital Signage Mfr
N.A.I.C.S.: 339950
Robert J. McCann *(VP & Gen Mgr-Graphics Bus Unit)*
Jay Dorman *(Dir-Sls-Global)*

Gerber Scientific, Inc. - Gerber Technology Group (2)
24 Industrial Park Rd W, Tolland, CT 06084-2806
Tel.: (860) 871-8082
Web Site: http://www.gerbertechnology.com
Sales Range: $100-124.9 Million
Emp.: 1,100
Manufactures Systems for Product Design, Fabric Cutting & Materials Handling in Automotive, Apparel & Aerospace
N.A.I.C.S.: 333248
Patricia L. Burmahl *(Sr VP-HR)*
Karsten Newbury *(Sr VP)*
James Martin *(VP-Strategy Mgmt & Analysis)*
Joseph Gerber *(Founder)*
Bill Grindle *(CMO)*
Dom DiMascia *(CIO)*
Karen Gibbs *(CFO)*
Scott Schinlever *(Pres & CEO-Automation Solutions)*
Steven Gore *(Chief Growth Officer-Automation Solutions & Sr VP-Bus & Dev)*

Subsidiary (Non-US):

Gerber Scientific International Lda. (3)
Rua 28 de Janeiro 350, Edificio C Fraccao 3, 4400 335, Vila Nova de Gaia, Portugal
Tel.: (351) 226197878
Web Site: http://www.gerbertechnology.com
Sales Range: $100-124.9 Million
Emp.: 2
Automated Manufacturing Systems for Sign Making, Specialty Graphics & Packaging, Apparel & Flexible Materials & Ophthalmic Lens Processing Industries

COMPANIES

VECTOR CAPITAL MANAGEMENT, L.P.

N.A.I.C.S.: 333248
Francisco Aguiar *(Mgr-Sls)*

Division (Domestic):

Gerber Scientific, Inc. - Gerber Innovations Division
24 Industrial Park Rd W, Tolland, CT 06084
Tel.: (978) 694-0055
Web Site: http://www.gerberinnovations.com
Manufactures & Services Digital Equipment, Samplemakers, Lasers, Routers, Automatic Rule Benders & Water Jet Machines for Printing & Packaging Industries
N.A.I.C.S.: 333993
Steven Gore *(Pres)*

Subsidiary (Non-US):

Gerber Technology GmbH (3)
Carlzeissring 10, Ismaning, Munich, 85737, Germany
Tel.: (49) 894209980
Web Site: http://www.gerbertechnology.com
Sales Range: $100-124.9 Million
Emp.: 50
Automated Manufacturing Systems for Sign Making, Specialty Graphics & Packaging, Apparel & Flexible Materials & Ophthalmic Lens Processing Industries
N.A.I.C.S.: 333248
Regna Gerhat *(Mng Dir)*
Jeff An *(Dir-Pro Svcs-Product Lifecycle Mgmt-Shanghai)*

Gerber Technology Pty. Ltd. (3)
9 Hamley Road, Mount Kuring-Gai, 2080, NSW, Australia
Tel.: (61) 882763738
Web Site: http://www.gerbertechnology.com
Sales Range: $1-9.9 Million
Emp.: 1
Automated Manufacturing Systems for Sign Making, Specialty Graphics & Packaging, Apparel & Flexible Materials & Ophthalmic Lens Processing Industries
N.A.I.C.S.: 333248

Gerber Technology SA de CV (3)
Xola 613-202, Col Del Valle, 3100, Mexico, Mexico
Tel.: (52) 5591719020
Web Site: http://www.gerbertechnology.com
Sales Range: $10-24.9 Million
Emp.: 22
Automated Manufacturing Systems for Sign Making, Specialty Graphics & Packaging, Apparel & Flexible Materials & Ophthalmic Lens Processing Industries
N.A.I.C.S.: 333248
Jorge de Leon *(Mgr-Sls)*

Gerber Technology SARL (3)
45 Rue de Villeneuve Immeuble Panama Parc Tertiaire SILIC, 94573, Rungis, France
Tel.: (33) 169332100
Web Site: http://www.gerbertechnology.com
Sales Range: $100-124.9 Million
Emp.: 6
Automated Manufacturing Systems for Sign Making, Specialty Graphics & Packaging, Apparel & Flexible Materials & Ophthalmic Lens Processing Industries
N.A.I.C.S.: 333248
Dirk Moriau *(Reg Mgr)*

Gerber Technology, Ltd. (3)
302 Metroplex Business Park Broadway, Salford, Manchester, M50 2UE, United Kingdom
Tel.: (44) 1617722000
Web Site: http://www.gerbertechnology.com
Sales Range: $100-124.9 Million
Automated Manufacturing Systems for Sign Making, Specialty Graphics & Packaging, Apparel & Flexible Materials & Ophthalmic Lens Processing Industries
N.A.I.C.S.: 333248
Harry Davies *(Mgr-Sls)*

Virtek Vision International, Inc. (3)
785 Bridge St West Unit 8, Waterloo, N2V 2K1, ON, Canada
Tel.: (519) 746-7190
Web Site: https://virtekvision.com
Sales Range: $50-74.9 Million
Laser-Based Templating, Inspection, Marking & Engraving Services
N.A.I.C.S.: 332812
Katherine Campbell *(Controller)*

Host Analytics, Inc. (1)
555 Twin Dolphin Dr Ste 400, Redwood City, CA 94065
Tel.: (650) 249-7100
Web Site: http://www.marketing.hostanalytics.com
Sales Range: $25-49.9 Million
Emp.: 180
Performance Management Software Solutions
N.A.I.C.S.: 513210
Alison Holmlund *(Chief Customer Officer)*
Martin Cooke *(Sr VP-People)*
Bryan Katis *(Sr VP-Product Mgmt)*
Ben Plummer *(CMO)*
Dan Fletcher *(Interim CFO)*
Grant Halloran *(CEO)*
Melissa Dreuth *(Sr VP-People & Culture)*
Rowan Tonkin *(Sr VP-Mktg)*
Pier Barattolo *(Sr VP-Sls-North America)*

IPVALUE Management, Inc. (1)
2880 Lakeside Dr Ste 320, Santa Clara, CA 95054-1226
Tel.: (408) 869-4000
Web Site: https://www.ipvalue.com
Sales Range: $1-9.9 Million
Lessors of Nonfinancial Intangible Assets (except Copyrighted Works)
N.A.I.C.S.: 533110
Zahid Rahimtoola *(CFO)*
John Lindgren *(Pres & CEO)*

MarkLogic Corporation (1)
999 Skyway Rd Ste 200, San Carlos, CA 94070
Tel.: (650) 655-2300
Web Site: http://www.marklogic.com
Custom Computer Programming Services
N.A.I.C.S.: 541511
David Ponzini *(Sr VP-Corp Dev)*
Christopher Lindblad *(Founder)*
David Gorbet *(Sr VP-Engrg)*
Elisa Smith *(Gen Counsel & VP)*
Joe Pasqua *(Exec VP-Products)*
Jonathan Bakke *(Exec VP-Worldwide Field Ops)*
Michaline Todd *(CMO)*
Peter S. Norman *(CFO)*
Adrian Carr *(CEO)*
Robert A. Roepke Jr. *(VP-Fin)*

Mood Media Corporation (1)
2100 S IH 35 Ste 200, Austin, TX 78704
Tel.: (512) 380-8500
Web Site: http://us.moodmedia.com
Marketing & Advertising & Music Distr
N.A.I.C.S.: 512250
Stephen Duggan *(CFO, CIO & Exec VP)*
Paul Jankauskas *(Sr VP-Mood Content Platforms)*
Trey Courtney *(Chief Products & Partnership Officer-Global)*
Malcolm McRoberts *(CEO)*
Michael F. Zendan II *(Chief Admin Officer, Gen Counsel & Exec VP)*

Subsidiary (Non-US):

Mood Media A/S (2)
Alsikevej 14, 8920, Randers, Denmark
Tel.: (45) 86405622
Web Site: http://www.moodmedia.dk
In-Store Marketing Solutions
N.A.I.C.S.: 541613

Mood Media AB (2)
St Eriksgatan 113, SE-113 43, Stockholm, Sweden
Tel.: (46) 54 57 83 00
Web Site: http://www.moodmedia.se
In-Store Marketing Solutions
N.A.I.C.S.: 449210

Mood Media AS (2)
Kirkegt 8, 3211, Sandefjord, Norway
Tel.: (47) 94 48 10 00
Web Site: http://www.moodmedia.no
In-Store Marketing Solutions
N.A.I.C.S.: 541613

Mood Media Australia Pty Ltd (2)
Wharf 10 50-58 Pirrama Rd, Pyrmont, 2009, NSW, Australia
Tel.: (61) 285 14 8400
Web Site: http://www.moodmedia.com.au
In-Store Marketing Solutions
N.A.I.C.S.: 541613
Steve Hughes *(Mng Dir)*
Mark Larner *(Dir-Sls)*
Mohini Lata *(Fin Mgr)*
Stephen Lee *(Mgr-IT)*
Lindsay Corbett *(Sr Acct Mgr)*
Rhys Clayton *(Acct Mgr)*
Blake Carle *(Project Mgr)*

Mood Media Belgium NV (2)
Lange Lozanastraat 142, B-2018, Antwerp, Belgium
Tel.: (32) 15 744 100
Web Site: http://www.moodmedia.be
In-Store Marketing Solutions
N.A.I.C.S.: 541613

Mood Media Finland OY (2)
Ayritie 8 D Largo House, 01510, Vantaa, Finland
Tel.: (358) 10 666 2233
Web Site: http://www.moodmedia.fi
In-Store Marketing Solutions
N.A.I.C.S.: 541613

Mood Media GmbH (2)
Kristein 2, 4470, Enns, Austria
Tel.: (43) 49 40 69 44 060
Web Site: http://www.moodmedia.at
In-Store Marketing Solutions
N.A.I.C.S.: 541613

Mood Media GmbH (2)
Gasstrasse 18, 22761, Hamburg, Germany
Tel.: (49) 40 69 44 06 0
Web Site: http://www.moodmedia.de
In-Store Marketing Solutions
N.A.I.C.S.: 541613
Nicholas John Gilbert *(Exec Dir)*

Mood Media Group CZ, s.r.o. (2)
Lazarska 13/8 Building D, 120 00, Prague, 2, Czech Republic
Tel.: (420) 606 666 064
Web Site: http://moodmedia.cz
In-Store Marketing Solutions
N.A.I.C.S.: 541613

Mood Media Hungary Kft (2)
Hegyalja ut 7-13, 1016, Budapest, Hungary
Tel.: (36) 1 439 0979
Web Site: http://www.moodmedia.hu
In-Store Marketing Solutions
N.A.I.C.S.: 541613

Mood Media Ireland Limited (2)
Unit 1-2 19 The Rear Courtyard Castle St, Dalkey, Dublin, Ireland
Tel.: (353) 1 284 7244
Web Site: http://www.moodmedia.ie
In-Store Marketing Solutions
N.A.I.C.S.: 541613

Mood Media Japan Co., Ltd. (2)
CSS Building 1F 10-1 Nihonbashi Kodenmacho, Chuo-ku, Tokyo, 103-0001, Japan
Tel.: (81) 3 6661 6041
Web Site: http://www.moodmedia.jp
In-Store Marketing Solutions
N.A.I.C.S.: 541613

Mood Media Limited (2)
West House 46 High Street, Orpington, Kent, BR6 0JQ, United Kingdom
Tel.: (44) 800282717
Web Site: http://www.moodmedia.co.uk
In-Store Marketing Solutions
N.A.I.C.S.: 541613

Mood Media Netherlands B.V. (2)
Transistorstraat 22, 1322 CE, Almere, Netherlands
Tel.: (31) 36 7470700
Web Site: http://www.moodmedia.nl
In-Store Marketing Solutions
N.A.I.C.S.: 541613

Mood Media Polska Sp. z o.o. (2)
ul Targowa 24, 03-728, Warsaw, Poland
Tel.: (48) 22 518 01 50 51
Web Site: http://www.moodmedia.pl
In-Store Marketing Solutions
N.A.I.C.S.: 541613

Mood Media S.A. (2)
Pentelis Avenue 95C, Chalandri, 15243, Athens, Greece
Tel.: (30) 210 68 58 140
Web Site: http://www.moodmedia.gr
In-Store Marketing Solutions
N.A.I.C.S.: 541613

Mood Media S.A. (2)
C/La Volta 4 Planta Primera Local 7, Centre Comercial Parets, 08150, Barcelona, Spain
Tel.: (34) 93 568 92 28
Web Site: http://www.moodmedia.es
In-Store Marketing Solutions
N.A.I.C.S.: 541613

Mood Media SAS (2)
22 Quai Gallieni CS, 40044, Suresnes, Cedex, France
Tel.: (33) 1 30 79 50 00
Web Site: http://www.moodmedia.fr
In-Store Marketing Solutions
N.A.I.C.S.: 541613

Subsidiary (Domestic):

Muzak Holdings LLC (2)
3318 Lakemont Blvd, Fort Mill, SC 29708
Tel.: (803) 396-3000
Satellite Delivered & On-Premises Music Services & In-Store Audio Marketing
N.A.I.C.S.: 512290

Branch (Domestic):

Muzak LLC (3)
201 Hughes Ln, Saint Charles, MO 63301
Tel.: (636) 255-1010
Satellite Delivered & On-Premises Music Services & In-Store Audio Marketing
N.A.I.C.S.: 512290

Subsidiary (Domestic):

PlayNetwork, Inc. (2)
8727 148th Ave NE, Redmond, WA 98052
Tel.: (425) 497-8100
Web Site: http://www.playnetwork.com
Customized Audio, Music & Video Programming
N.A.I.C.S.: 334310
Leo Ku *(Mng Dir-APAC)*
Ross Honey *(CEO)*
Anthony Plesner *(CFO)*
Quentin Gallet *(CTO)*
Luke Ferro *(Exec VP)*
Marc Felsen *(CMO)*
Pam Schoenfeld *(Sr VP & Gen Counsel)*
Rick Gleave *(Mng Dir-EMEIA & ANZ)*

MoxiWorks, LLC (1)
1000 Second Avenue, Suite 1300, Seattle, WA 98104
Tel.: (206) 388-4789
Web Site: https://moxiworks.com
Real Estate Computer Software Company
N.A.I.C.S.: 513210
Bill Yaman *(Exec VP-Customer Experience)*
Jim Tarte *(CFO)*
York Baur *(CEO)*
Jim Crisera *(COO)*
Jim Crisera *(COO)*
Mark Carlson *(CTO)*
Ring Nishioka *(Chief People Officer)*

Subsidiary (Domestic):

Imprev, Inc. (2)
11400 SE 8th St Ste 450, Bellevue, WA 98004
Tel.: (855) 446-7738
Prepackaged Software
N.A.I.C.S.: 513210
Elise Mattson *(Dir-Creative Svcs)*

Riverbed Technology, Inc. (1)
680 Folsom St, San Francisco, CA 94107
Tel.: (415) 247-8800
Web Site: http://www.riverbed.com
Holding Company; Wide-Area Data Services Solutions
N.A.I.C.S.: 551112
Stephen R. Smoot *(Chief Customer Officer)*
Orlando Bravo *(Co-Founder & Mng Partner)*
Subbu Iyer *(CMO)*
Lori Spence *(Chief HR Officer)*
Andy Elder *(Chief Sls Officer)*
Mike Sargent *(Sr VP & Gen Mgr-SteelCentral)*
Rebecca Hazard *(Gen Counsel)*
Dan Smoot *(COO)*
Thoma Bravo *(Co-Founder & Mng Partner)*
Mogani Naidoo *(Dir-Client Svc)*
Bridget Johnson *(Exec Creative Dir)*
Kabelo Lehlongwane *(Dir-Strategy)*
Alpna J. Doshi *(Chief Digital Officer)*
Ian Halifax *(CFO)*
Shaun Bierweiler *(Sr VP-Pub Sector)*
Nader Barsoum *(Sls Dir-Channel-Australia & New Zealand)*
Nick Boyle *(VP-Sls-Asia Pacific & Japan)*
R. Carter Pate *(Chm)*

VECTOR CAPITAL MANAGEMENT, L.P.

U.S. PRIVATE

Vector Capital Management, L.P.—(Continued)

Subsidiary (Non-US):

Riverbed Technology (Beijing) Limited (2)
403-43 4/F One Indigo 20 Jiu Xian Qiao Road, Chaoyang District, Beijing, 100016, China
Tel.: (86) 10 5913 5900
Web Site: http://www.riverbed.com
Wide-Area Data Services (WDS) Solutions
N.A.I.C.S.: 518210

Branch (Domestic):

Riverbed Technology Shanghai (3)
Ste 09 47th Fl Hong Kong New World Tower, 300 Huaihai Zhong Road, Shanghai, 200021, China
Tel.: (86) 2151162829
Web Site: http://www.riverbed.com
Emp.: 6
Wide-Area Data Services (WDS) Solutions
N.A.I.C.S.: 518210
Jonathan Yu *(Dir-Sls)*

Subsidiary (Non-US):

Riverbed Technology AB (2)
Waterfront Building Klarabergsviadukten 63, Stockholm, 111 64, Sweden
Tel.: (46) 8 560 030 00
Emp.: 21
Wide-Area Data Services (WDS) Solutions
N.A.I.C.S.: 518210
Andy Elder *(Sr VP-Sls-EMEA)*

Riverbed Technology AG (2)
Europaallee 41, 8021, Zurich, Switzerland
Tel.: (41) 44 214 6150
Wide-Area Data Services (WDS) Solutions
N.A.I.C.S.: 518210
Giovanni Di Filippo *(VP-EMEA Channels & Sls)*
Michael Rudrich *(Reg VP-Germany, Austria & Switzerland)*

Riverbed Technology B.V. (2)
De Zuidtoren Taurusavenue 3 1st Floor, 2132 LS, Hoofddorp, Netherlands
Tel.: (31) 237115030
Sales Range: $100-124.9 Million
Data Solutions
N.A.I.C.S.: 513210

Riverbed Technology FZ-LLC (2)
Pfizer Building 1st Floor 102 AlFalak Street, Dubai Media City, Dubai, United Arab Emirates
Tel.: (971) 44482900
Web Site: http://www.riverbed.com
Network Software Development Services
N.A.I.C.S.: 541512
Salman Ali *(Mgr-Pre-Sls-Middle East & North Africa)*
Elie Dib *(VP-Middle East, Turkey & North Africa)*

Riverbed Technology GmbH (2)
Max-Planck-Strasse 8, 85609, Munich, Germany
Tel.: (49) 89 20304 4900
Web Site: http://www.riverbed.com
Sales Range: $10-24.9 Million
Emp.: 30
Wide-Area Data Services (WDS) Solutions
N.A.I.C.S.: 513210
Daniel Ringlstetter *(Sls Mgr-Austria & Germany)*
Michael Rudrich *(Reg VP-Germany, Austria & Switzerland)*

Riverbed Technology India Private Limited (2)
15/2 & 14/P7 Salarpuria & Sattva Group Block A 4th Floor, Kadubeesanahalli Varthur Hobli, Bengaluru, 560103, Karnataka, India
Tel.: (91) 80 4250 7781
Emp.: 5
Wide-Area Data Services (WDS) Solutions
N.A.I.C.S.: 518210
Nagendra Venkaswamy *(Mng Dir-India & South Asia)*

Riverbed Technology K.K. (2)
3F 303 Unosawa Tokyu Building 1-19-15 Ebisu, Shibuya-ku, Tokyo, 150-0013, Japan
Tel.: (81) 3 5423 6777
Web Site: http://www.riverbed.com

Emp.: 10
Wide-Area Data Services (WDS) Solutions
N.A.I.C.S.: 513210

Riverbed Technology Korea, Inc. (2)
KCC IT Tower 4th Floor 7-50 Galwol-dong, Yongsan-gu, Seoul, 140-800, Korea (South)
Tel.: (82) 2 6090 7120
Web Site: http://www.riverbed.com
Emp.: 30
Wide-Area Data Services (WDS) Solutions
N.A.I.C.S.: 518210
Jin Byun *(Mng Dir)*

Riverbed Technology LLC
7th Floor 746-749 Smolensky Passage 3 Smolenskaya Square, Moscow, 121099, Russia
Tel.: (7) 4956628081
Web Site: http://www.riverbed.com
Network Software Development Services
N.A.I.C.S.: 541512

Riverbed Technology Limited (2)
One Thames Valley House, Wokingham Road Level 2, Bracknell, RG42 1NG, Berks, United Kingdom
Tel.: (44) 1344 401900
Web Site: http://www.riverbed.com
Emp.: 50
IT Solutions
N.A.I.C.S.: 513210
Mark Hiley *(Dir-Sls-UK & Ireland)*
Giovanni Di Filippo *(VP-Channels Div-EMEA)*
Allan Paton *(Reg VP-UK & Ireland)*

Riverbed Technology Limited (2)
Level 8 Cambridge House Taikoo Place, 979 Kings Road Island East, Hong Kong, China (Hong Kong)
Tel.: (852) 37507880
Web Site: http://www.riverbed.com
Wide-Area Data Services (WDS) Solutions
N.A.I.C.S.: 518210

Riverbed Technology Ltd. (2)
36th Floor CRC Tower All Seasons Place 87/2 Wireless Road, Lumpini Pratumwan, Bangkok, 10330, Thailand
Tel.: (66) 26253009
Web Site: http://www.riverbed.com
Emp.: 2
Wide-Area Data Services (WDS) Solutions
N.A.I.C.S.: 518210
Vorkon Patra-Yanan *(Gen Mgr)*

Riverbed Technology Ltd. (2)
6 Hachoshlim St 1st Floor, Herzliya Pituach, 46722, Israel
Tel.: (972) 776935700
Network Optimization Solutions
N.A.I.C.S.: 541512

Riverbed Technology Pte Ltd. (2)
391A Orchard Road 14-01/02/08/09/10 Ngee Ann City Tower A, Singapore, 238873, Singapore
Tel.: (65) 65087400
Web Site: http://www.riverbed.com
Sales Range: $100-124.9 Million
Software Development Services
N.A.I.C.S.: 513210
Doris Tan *(Mgr-HR Ops-Asia Pacific & Japan)*
Bjorn Engelhardt *(Sr VP-Asia Pacific & Japan)*
Benny Lim *(VP-Association of Southeast Asian Nations)*
Aimy Yu *(Dir-HR & Employee Svcs-Asia Pacific & Japan)*
Sara Kao *(Dir-Program Mktg-Asia Pacific & Japan)*

Branch (Non-US):

Riverbed Technology Philippines (3)
18th Fl Philamlife Tower 8767 Paseo de Roxas, Makati, 1226W, Philippines
Tel.: (63) 28308697
Wide-Area Data Services (WDS) Solutions
N.A.I.C.S.: 518210
Jose Julio Lopez *(Sys Engr)*

Riverbed Technology Taiwan (3)
R2735 27F No 90 Songgao Road, Xinyi Dist, Taipei, 11073, Taiwan
Tel.: (886) 277430618
Web Site: http://www.riverbed.com
Wide-Area Data Services (WDS) Solutions

N.A.I.C.S.: 518210

Subsidiary (Non-US):

Riverbed Technology Pty Ltd. (2)
Level 29 123 Pitt Street, Sydney, 2000, NSW, Australia
Tel.: (61) 2 8415 6100
Web Site: http://www.riverbed.com
Emp.: 20
Wide-Area Data Services (WDS) Solutions
N.A.I.C.S.: 518210
Keith Buckley *(VP-Australia & New Zealand)*
Jean-Paul Baillon *(Reg Mgr-Sls-NSW)*
Charles de Jesus *(Dir-Channel Sls-Australia & New Zealand)*

Riverbed Technology S. de R.L. de C.V. (2)
Paseo de la Reforma 115 piso 4 c/Periferico, Del Miguel Hidalgo, Mexico, 11000, DF, Mexico
Tel.: (52) 55 8000 7285
Network Optimization Solutions
N.A.I.C.S.: 541512

Riverbed Technology S.r.l. (2)
Maciachini Center Mac4 Via Benigno Crespi 19 4th Floor, 20159, Milan, Italy
Tel.: (39) 02 00697176
Web Site: http://www.riverbed.com
Wide-Area Data Services (WDS) Solutions
N.A.I.C.S.: 518210
Vittorio Carosone *(Country Mgr & Dir-Sls)*

Riverbed Technology SL (2)
Paseo de la Castellana 135 Planta 7, Madrid, 28046, Spain
Tel.: (34) 912975479
Web Site: http://www.riverbed.com
Emp.: 5
Wide-Area Data Services (WDS) Solutions
N.A.I.C.S.: 518210
Miguel Angel Garcia *(Mng Dir)*

Riverbed Technology Sarl (2)
4 place de la Defense, 92974, Paris, Cedex, France
Tel.: (33) 158580150
Web Site: http://www.riverbed.com
Emp.: 15
Data Solutions & Processes
N.A.I.C.S.: 513210
Sebastien Weber *(VP-Worldwide Svc Providers-Strategy & Programs)*
Olivier Brot *(Dir-Enterprise Sls)*
Valerie Brisset *(Mgr-Distr Sls)*
Frederic Kunegel *(Dir-South EMEA Channels)*
Rejane Bouffaut Catelineau *(Reg Mgr-Mktg-Southern Europe)*

Riverbed Technology Sdn. Bhd. (2)
3.02D East Wing Menara BRDB, 285 Jalan Maarof Bukit, Kuala Lumpur, 59000, Malaysia
Tel.: (60) 3 2289 5017
Web Site: http://www.riverbed.com
Wide-Area Data Services (WDS) Solutions
N.A.I.C.S.: 518210
Andy Chiak Foo Tew *(Mgr-Technical Alliance/Enablement-Asia Pacfic & Japan)*

Riverbed Technology South Africa (Proprietary) Limited (2)
210 Amarand Avenue Waterklof Glen ext 2 Pegasus Building, Menlyn Maine, Pretoria, 0181, South Africa
Tel.: (27) 12 443 6551
Web Site: http://www.riverbed.com
Emp.: 25
Wide-Area Data Services (WDS) Solutions
N.A.I.C.S.: 518210
Wimpie Jansen Van Rensburg *(Dir-Bus Dev)*
Roma Smith *(Reg Dir-Africa)*

Riverbed Tecnologia De Informacao Ltda (2)
Rua Funchal 418 - 35 Andar, Vila Olimpia, Sao Paulo, 04551-060, SP, Brazil
Tel.: (55) 11 3521 7323
Web Site: http://www.riverbed.com
Emp.: 10
Computer Software Publisher
N.A.I.C.S.: 513210
Rosano Moraes *(Mng Dir)*

Roxio, Inc. (1)

455 El Camino Real, Santa Clara, CA 95050
Tel.: (408) 367-3100
Web Site: http://www.roxio.com
Sales Range: $100-124.9 Million
Consumer Digital Media Management Software Developer & Publisher
N.A.I.C.S.: 513210

Subsidiary (Non-US):

Roxio UK Ltd. (2)
Sunningvale House Caldecotte Bus Pk, Milton Keynes, MK7 8LF, Bucks, United Kingdom
Tel.: (44) 1908278100
Web Site: http://www.roxio.co.uk
Sales Range: $25-49.9 Million
Emp.: 8
Provider of Software
N.A.I.C.S.: 541519

Siqura B.V. (1)
Meridiaan 32, PO Box 415 2801 DD, 2801 DA, Gouda, Netherlands
Tel.: (31) 182592333
Web Site: http://www.siqura.com
Emp.: 55
Network Video Equipment Distr
N.A.I.C.S.: 423410
D. Verhagen *(Mgr-HR)*

Subsidiary (US):

TKH Security Solutions USA (2)
12920 Cloverleaf Ctr Dr, Germantown, MD 20874
Tel.: (301) 444-2200
Web Site: http://www.tkhsecurity-usa.com
Emp.: 17
Video Network Surveillance Equipment Mfr & Distr
N.A.I.C.S.: 334220
Ron Rogers *(Sls Mgr-Eastern Reg)*
Eldon Dehnert *(Sls Mgr-Western Reg)*
Steve Gorski *(Mng Dir)*
Luis Hernandez *(Sls Mgr-Mexico Reg)*
Andy Brunk *(Engr-Solutions)*
Yossman Infante *(Engr-Solutions)*
Amy Fleck *(Mgr-Sls & Mktg)*
Steve Moore *(Mgr-Engrg)*
Felix Chughtai *(Sr Engr-Staff)*

Sizmek Inc. (1)
500 W 5th St Ste 900, Austin, TX 78701
Tel.: (512) 469-5900
Web Site: http://www.sizmek.com
Holding Company; Digital Media Advertising Services
N.A.I.C.S.: 551112
Mike Caprio *(Chief Growth Officer)*
Rachel Walkden *(COO)*
Mark Grether *(CEO)*
Volker Hatz *(Chief Data Officer)*
David Rawden *(Interim CFO)*
Sarah Goodhart *(Interim Chief People Officer)*
Eric Duerr *(CMO)*
Neil Coleman *(Gen Mgr-Americas)*
Markus Plattner *(CTO)*
Phil Murrell *(Mgr-Australia & New Zealand)*
Patrick Bevilacqua *(Head-Customer Success-Global)*
Peter Hunter *(Gen Mgr-Asia Pacific)*
Paul Kent *(Comml Dir-APAC)*
Heidi Monro *(Sls Dir-NSW)*

Subsidiary (Domestic):

Sizmek Technologies, Inc. (2)
401 Park Ave S 5th Fl, New York, NY 10016
Tel.: (646) 202-1320
Web Site: http://www.sizmek.com
Interactive Advertisng Agency
N.A.I.C.S.: 541810
Danielle Rutkin *(Dir-Sls)*

Subsidiary (Non-US):

Sizmek Spain, S.L. (3)
Calle Marques de la Ensenada 16 Planta 2 Local 20, 28004, Madrid, Spain
Tel.: (34) 917458100
Web Site: http://www.sizmek.com
Advetising Agency
N.A.I.C.S.: 541870
David Gosen *(Gen Mgr)*

Sizmek Technologies GmbH (3)

Brandstwiete 1 Neuer Dovenhof, 20457, Hamburg, Germany
Tel.: (49) 40609448890
Web Site: http://www.sizmek.com
Advetising Agency
N.A.I.C.S.: 541870
David Gosen (Gen Mgr-EMEA)

Sizmek Technologies K.K. (3)
EBISU-WEST 5011-16-15, Ebisu-nishi
Shibuya-ku, Tokyo, Japan
Tel.: (81) 3 5457 2570
Web Site: http://www.sizmek.com
Digital Advertising & Campaign Management Solutions Provider
N.A.I.C.S.: 541890

Sizmek Technologies Ltd. (3)
34 Bow Street, London, WC2E 7AU, United Kingdom
Tel.: (44) 2036511300
Web Site: http://www.sizmek.com
Advetising Agency
N.A.I.C.S.: 541870
David Gosen (Gen Mgr)

Sizmek Technologies Ltd. (3)
7 Ha'Mada St, Herzliyya, 46513, Israel
Tel.: (972) 97760800
Web Site: http://www.sizmek.com
Digital Technology & Information Distribution Services
N.A.I.C.S.: 541870
David Gosen (Gen Mgr-EMEA)

Sizmek Technologies Pty. Ltd. (3)
Level 26 6 O'Connell Street, Sydney, 2000, NSW, Australia
Tel.: (61) 2 8243 0000
Web Site: http://www.sizmek.com
Digital Media Advertising Services
N.A.I.C.S.: 541870
Kees de Jong (Gen Mgr-APAC)

Trafficmaster Ltd (1)
Martell House, University Way, Cranfield, MK43 0TR, Bedfordshire, United Kingdom
Tel.: (44) 1234759000
Web Site: http://www.trafficmaster.co.uk
Sales Range: $50-74.9 Million
Satellite Navigation & Digital Traffic Information Products & Services
N.A.I.C.S.: 334511
Pat Gallagher (Dir-Vehicle Platform Bus)
Tony Eales (CEO)
Tony Eales (CEO)

Subsidiary (US):

Fleet Management Solutions, Inc. (2)
3426 Empresa Dr Ste 100, San Luis Obispo, CA 93401
Tel.: (805) 787-0508
Web Site: http://www.fmsgps.com
Sales Range: $25-49.9 Million
Emp.: 25
Mobile Asset Tracking & Management Solutions
N.A.I.C.S.: 517410

VECTOR CHOICE TECHNOLOGY SOLUTIONS, CORP.
2180 Satellite Blvd Ste 400, Duluth, GA 30097
Tel.: (678) 701-0210
Web Site: http://www.vectorchoice.com
Year Founded: 2008
Sales Range: $1-9.9 Million
Emp.: 13
Information Technology Development Services
N.A.I.C.S.: 541511
Will Nobles (CEO)
Jeremy Bello (Dir-Engrg)
Logan Nobles (Dir-Comm)
Tony Adger (Dir-Client Svcs)
Chelsea Vicknair (Mgr-Mktg)

Subsidiaries:

High Standards Technology, Inc. (1)
100 Glenborough Dr Ste 429A, Houston, TX 77060
Tel.: (281) 990-9422

Web Site: http://www.weredown.com
Rev.: $1,610,000
Emp.: 10
Data Processing, Hosting & Related Services
N.A.I.C.S.: 518210

VECTOR MEDIA GROUP INC.
99 Madison Ave 10th Fl, New York, NY 10016
Tel.: (212) 380-8227   NY
Web Site:
  http://www.vectormediagroup.com
Year Founded: 2003
Sales Range: $1-9.9 Million
Emp.: 12
Website Development Services
N.A.I.C.S.: 541511
Matt Weinberg (Co-Founder & Pres-Tech & Dev)
Lee Goldberg (Co-Founder & Pres-Mktg & Strategy)
Stuart Henry (Pres-Bus Dev)

VECTOR SPACE SYSTEMS
824 E 16th St, Tucson, AZ 85719
Tel.: (888) 346-7778
Web Site:
  http://www.vectorspacesystems.com
Year Founded: 2016
Micro Satellite Launches
N.A.I.C.S.: 517410
Jim Cantrell (Co-Founder & CEO)
John Garvey (Co-Founder & CTO)
Ken Sunshine (Co-Founder & CFO)
Eric Besnard (Co-Founder & VP-Engrg)
Robert Cleave (Chief Revenue Officer)

Subsidiaries:

Garvey Spacecraft Corporation (1)
389 Haines Ave, Long Beach, CA 90814
Tel.: (562) 498-2984
Web Site: http://www.garvspace.com
Aerospace Research & Development Services
N.A.I.C.S.: 927110
John M. Garvey (Founder & CEO)

VECTORA TRANSPORTATION
200 W Madison Ste 1820, Chicago, IL 60606
Tel.: (312) 646-7260
Web Site:
  http://www.vectoratransportation.com
Year Founded: 2007
Sales Range: $25-49.9 Million
Emp.: 14
Logistics & Transportation Services
N.A.I.C.S.: 541614
Jim OBrien (CFO)
Kirk Jordan (VP-Projects Ops)
Jim Walters (VP-Ops Terminals)

VECTORCSP, LLC
405 E Main St, Elizabeth City, NC 27909-4427
Tel.: (252) 338-2264
Web Site: http://www.vectorcsp.com
Year Founded: 2002
Sales Range: $10-24.9 Million
Emp.: 37
Aviation Logistics, Engineering & Technical Services
N.A.I.C.S.: 541614
Stan Walz (Pres & CEO)

VECTORUSA
3530 Voyager St, Torrance, CA 90503
Tel.: (310) 436-1000   CA
Web Site: http://www.vectorusa.com
Year Founded: 1988
Emp.: 450

Information Technology & Communication Specialization
N.A.I.C.S.: 238210
Dave Zukerman (Pres & CEO)
Robert Messinger (Exec VP-Sls & Ops)
Jeff Zukerman (Exec VP-Bus Dev)

VEDDER HOLSTERS LLC
1186 Camp Ave, Mount Dora, FL 32757
Tel.: (352) 729-6749
Web Site:
  http://www.vedderholsters.com
Year Founded: 2012
Sales Range: $1-9.9 Million
Emp.: 32
Gun Holsters & Accessory Mfr
N.A.I.C.S.: 332994
Mike Vedder (Co-Founder)
Brooke Vedder (Co-Founder)

VEDDER PRICE P.C.
222 N LaSalle St, Chicago, IL 60601-1003
Tel.: (312) 609-7500   IL
Web Site:
  http://www.vedderprice.com
Year Founded: 1952
Sales Range: $25-49.9 Million
Emp.: 500
Law firm
N.A.I.C.S.: 541110
Michael A. Nemeroff (Pres & CEO)
Katherine Miletich (Dir-Mktg & Bus Dev)
David Brookes (Partner-Global Transportation Fin Practice-London)

VEE-JAY CEMENT CONTRACTING CO., INC.
8053 Chivvis Dr, Saint Louis, MO 63123-2333
Tel.: (314) 351-3366
Web Site:
  http://www.veejaycement.com
Sales Range: $25-49.9 Million
Emp.: 150
Concrete Finishing Services
N.A.I.C.S.: 238140
Leonard Ehlmann (Controller)
Charles Vatale (VP)
Salvatore Vitale (Pres)

VEEGO PHARMA LLC
300, Franklin Square Dr., Somerset, NJ 08873
Tel.: (732) 554-1015
Pharmaceutical Preparations
N.A.I.C.S.: 325412

Subsidiaries:

Somerset Therapeutics Limited (1)
54/1 Budihal, Nelamangala, Bengaluru, 562123, Karnataka, India   (100%)
Tel.: (91) 8067086500
Web Site: https://somersetlimited.com
Rev.: $10,592,901
Assets: $19,518,274
Liabilities: $20,146,553
Net Worth: ($628,278)
Earnings: $15,645
Emp.: 351
Fiscal Year-end: 03/31/2019
Sterile Product Mfr & Whslr
N.A.I.C.S.: 325412
K. P. Murali (Exec Dir)
Jai Velusamy (COO & Chief Dev Officer)

VEENENDAALCAVE, INC.
1170 Peachtree St NE, Atlanta, GA 30309
Tel.: (404) 881-1811
Web Site: http://www.vcave.com
Year Founded: 1985
Sales Range: $1-9.9 Million
Emp.: 76
Interior Design Services

N.A.I.C.S.: 541410
Edward A. Cave (Founder)
Christine Veenendaal (Mng Principal)
Sarah Holliday (Dir-Design)
Lori Hancock (Sr Dir-Design)
Jeanette Meyers (Mng Dir)
Mark Schroeder (VP)
Carlos Pineda (VP)
Jodi Borges (VP)
Lindsay Murphy (VP)
Emily Knopp (Dir-Design)
Jackie Kassler (Sr Dir-Design)
Shannon Morris (Sr Dir-Design)

VEETHREE ELECTRONICS & MARINE LLC
2050 47th Ter E, Bradenton, FL 34203
Tel.: (941) 538-7775
Web Site:
  http://www.v3instruments.com
Year Founded: 1976
Sales Range: $1-9.9 Million
Emp.: 65
Mechanical & Electrical Instruments Mfr & Supplier
N.A.I.C.S.: 335999
Shekhar Tewatia (VP)
Steve Nelson (Product Mgr-Global)
Vishal Lalani (Pres)

VEEX, INC
2827 Lakeview Ct, Fremont, CA 94538
Tel.: (510) 651-0500   CA
Web Site: http://www.veexinc.com
DSL, Broadband & Cable TV Equipment Mfr
N.A.I.C.S.: 335999
Cyrille Morelle (CEO)
Terence Leong (Dir-Customer Care)
Tracy Lahti (Mgr-Acctg)

VEG-LAND SALES INC.
1518 E Valencia Dr, Fullerton, CA 92831
Tel.: (714) 871-6712
Web Site: http://www.veg-land.com
Sales Range: $25-49.9 Million
Emp.: 150
Bond Brokers
N.A.I.C.S.: 424410
Denise Folkins (CFO)
Jim Matiasevich (Pres)

Subsidiaries:

JBJ Distributing Inc. (1)
1518 E Valencia Dr, Fullerton, CA 92831
Tel.: (714) 992-4920
Web Site: http://www.veg-land.com
Sales Range: $10-24.9 Million
Emp.: 7
Fresh Fruits & Vegetables
N.A.I.C.S.: 424480
James Matiasevich (Pres)

Veg-Land Inc. (1)
1518 E Valencia Dr, Fullerton, CA 92831
Tel.: (714) 871-6712
Web Site: http://www.veg-land.com
Rev.: $3,100,000
Emp.: 25
Farm Product Warehousing & Storage
N.A.I.C.S.: 424410
James E. Matiasevich (Pres)

VEGALAB, INC.
636 US Hwy 1 Ste 110, North Palm Beach, FL 33408   NV
Year Founded: 1968
VEGL—(OTCBB)
Sales Range: $1-9.9 Million
Emp.: 90
Agricultural Products Mfr; All-Natural Fertilizers & Biopesticides
N.A.I.C.S.: 325311

Subsidiaries:

Vegalab LLC (1)
1201 N Orange St Ste 7233, Wilmington, DE 19801-1186

VEGALAB, INC.

Vegalab, Inc.—(Continued)
Tel.: (302) 298-0888
Web Site: http://www.vegalab.com
Organic Fertilizer Mfr
N.A.I.C.S.: 325311

VEGAS BRAZIL LLC
9550 S Eastern Ave Ste 253, Las Vegas, NV 89123
Tel.: (702) 883-3536
Web Site: https://vegasbrazil.com
Emp.: 100
Destination Management, Tours & Travel Accomodation
N.A.I.C.S.: 561520

VEGETABLE GROWERS SUPPLY CO. INC.
1360 Merrill St, Salinas, CA 93901-4432
Tel.: (831) 759-4600   CA
Web Site: http://www.veggrow.com
Year Founded: 1967
Sales Range: $10-24.9 Million
Emp.: 50
Nondurable Goods
N.A.I.C.S.: 424990
Lisa Erling *(Controller)*

VEGIWORKS, INC.
1910 Jerrold Ave, San Francisco, CA 94124
Tel.: (415) 643-8686
Web Site: http://www.vegiworks.com
Sales Range: $10-24.9 Million
Emp.: 65
Fruit & Vegetable Whslr
N.A.I.C.S.: 424480
Shing Ho *(Pres)*

VEHICLE MAINTENANCE PROGRAM, INC.
3595 N Dixie Hwy Bay 7, Boca Raton, FL 33431
Tel.: (561) 362-6080
Web Site: http://www.vmpparts.com
Sales Range: $10-24.9 Million
Emp.: 15
Aftermarket Automotive Parts & Accessories Distr
N.A.I.C.S.: 423140
Penny Brooks *(Pres)*
Sharyl Strachan *(Controller)*

VEHICLE TRACKING SOLUTIONS, LLC
10 E 5th St, Deer Park, NY 11729
Tel.: (631) 586-7400
Web Site: http://www.vehicletrackingsolutions.com
Year Founded: 2002
Sales Range: $1-9.9 Million
Emp.: 40
GPS Vehicle Tracking Solutions
N.A.I.C.S.: 334511
John Cuningham *(Principal)*
Allison Scalza *(Dir-Client Success-Commack)*

VEIT & COMPANY, INC.
14000 Veit Pl, Rogers, MN 55374
Tel.: (763) 428-2242
Web Site: http://www.veitusa.com
Year Founded: 1928
Sales Range: $10-24.9 Million
Emp.: 500
Specialty Contracting & Waste Management Services
N.A.I.C.S.: 562910
Vaughn Veit *(Pres & CEO)*

VELATEL GLOBAL COMMUNICATIONS, INC.
5950 La Place Ct Ste 160, Carlsbad, CA 92008
Tel.: (760) 230-8988   NV
Web Site: http://www.velatel.com
Year Founded: 2005
Sales Range: $1-9.9 Million
Emp.: 45
Holding Company; Wireless Telecommunications Carrier
N.A.I.C.S.: 551112
George Alvarez *(CEO)*
Colin Yong Lee Tay *(Pres)*
Carlos A. Trujillo *(CFO)*
Isidoro Gutierrez *(Chief Admin Officer)*
Kenneth Hobbs *(Gen Counsel & Sec)*
Subsidiaries:
China Motion Telecom (HK) Limited   (1)
Room 2604-08 26 F Harbour Center 25 Harbour Road, Wanchai, China (Hong Kong)
Tel.: (852) 3112 2333
Web Site: http://www.cmmobile.com.hk
Sales Range: $25-49.9 Million
Mobile Telecommunications Services
N.A.I.C.S.: 517810

VELCOR LEASING CORPORATION
2005 W Beltline Hwy Ste 200, Madison, WI 53713
Tel.: (608) 288-5700
Web Site: http://www.velcorleasingcorp.com
Year Founded: 1987
Sales Range: $75-99.9 Million
Emp.: 9
Vehicle Leasing & Fleet Management Services
N.A.I.C.S.: 532112
John O'Connor *(Pres)*
Laura Doyle *(Mgr-Reg Sls)*
Tiffany Lou *(Sr Acct Mgr)*

VELDKAMPS INC.
9501 W Colfax Ave, Lakewood, CO 80215-3920
Tel.: (303) 234-1732
Web Site: http://www.veldkampsflowers.com
Rev.: $13,800,000
Emp.: 15
Flowers, Fresh
N.A.I.C.S.: 459310
John Veldkamp *(Pres)*

VELICO MEDICAL
100 Cummings Ctr Ste 436H, Beverly, MA 01915
Tel.: (978) 232-8370
Web Site: http://www.velicomedical.com
Sales Range: $25-49.9 Million
Emp.: 10
Blood Enzyme Conversion Pharmaceuticals & Chemicals Mfr
N.A.I.C.S.: 325414
Ihab Rashad *(Project Coord)*

VELIR
212 Elm St Ste 401, Somerville, MA 02144
Tel.: (617) 491-6900
Web Site: http://www.velir.com
Year Founded: 2000
Sales Range: $1-9.9 Million
Emp.: 62
Web Design Services
N.A.I.C.S.: 541511
Mark Gregor *(Chm)*
Nicole Durand *(Dir-Production Sys)*
Andrea Gillespie *(Dir-HR)*
Barron Wernick *(Dir-Project Mgmt)*
Corey Caplette *(CTO)*
Daniel Delay *(Dir-Dev)*
Dave Valliere *(CEO)*
Edwina Nowicki *(Dir-Quality Assurance)*
George Bica *(Dir-IT)*
Kimiko Tanaka Vecchione *(Dir-Solutions Architecture)*
Mary Kate McArdle *(COO)*
Mike Dolan *(Chief Strategy Officer)*

VELLANO BROS., INC.
7 Hemlock St, Latham, NY 12110-2203
Tel.: (518) 785-5537   NY
Web Site: http://www.vellano.com
Year Founded: 1946
Sales Range: $10-24.9 Million
Emp.: 80
Metals Service Centers & Offices
N.A.I.C.S.: 423510
Joseph M. Vellano *(Pres & CEO)*
Steve Niedbalec *(CFO)*
Bill Latham *(VP-Mktg & Branch Mgr)*

VELOCITY COMMERCIAL CAPITAL, LLC
30699 Russell Ranch Rd Ste 295, Westlake Village, CA 91362
Tel.: (818) 532-3700   MD
Web Site: http://www.vcc-inc.com
Year Founded: 2004
Sales Range: $10-24.9 Million
Emp.: 20
Real Estate Mortgage Services
N.A.I.C.S.: 522310
Christopher D. Farrar *(Pres & CEO)*
Robert L. Weening *(Exec VP)*
Jeffrey T. Taylor *(Exec VP-Capital Markets)*
Louay Akel *(Chief Credit Officer)*
Hector M. Rodriguez *(Sr VP-Real Estate)*
Joy L. Schaefer *(Chm)*
Jack Jacob *(Exec VP)*
Mark Szczepaniak *(CFO)*

VELOCITY CREDIT UNION
610 E 11th St, Austin, TX 78701
Tel.: (512) 469-7000   TX
Web Site: http://www.velocitycu.com
Year Founded: 1947
Rev.: $36,810,795
Assets: $839,665,434
Liabilities: $32,779,301
Net Worth: $806,886,133
Earnings: $10,693,899
Fiscal Year-end: 12/31/18
Credit Union Operator
N.A.I.C.S.: 522130
John P. Chomout *(Treas & Sec)*
Debbie Mitchell *(Pres & CEO)*
James Chapman *(Chm)*
Kasha Bartholomew *(Vice Chm)*
Thomas Matthews *(Vice Chm)*

VELOCITY MERCHANT SERVICES
3051 Oak Grove Rd 2nd Fl, Downers Grove, IL 60515
Web Site: http://www.getvms.com
Year Founded: 1998
Sales Range: $1-9.9 Million
Emp.: 62
Merchant Services
N.A.I.C.S.: 522320
Dema Barakat *(Founder & Pres)*
Danoush Khairkhah *(CEO)*
Hafez Barakat *(VP)*

VELOCITY MERGER CORP.
520 Newport Ctr Dr 21st Fl, Newport Beach, CA 92660
Tel.: (949) 610-8067   Ky
Year Founded: 2021
Investment Services
N.A.I.C.S.: 523999

U.S. PRIVATE

Mitchell Caplan *(Chm & CEO)*
Rishi Reddy *(Pres)*
David Browne *(CFO)*
Josh Lane *(Sec)*

VELOCITY PORTFOLIO GROUP, INC.
1800 Rte 34 N Bldg 4 Ste 404A, Wall, NJ 07719
Tel.: (732) 556-9090   DE
Web Site: http://www.velocityrecoveries.com
Year Founded: 2004
Asset Management Services
N.A.I.C.S.: 522210
Jack C. Kleinert *(CEO)*
James J. Mastriani *(Pres & COO)*
Palma Fanetti *(Asst Controller)*
W. Peter Ragan Jr. *(VP)*
Subsidiaries:
VOM, LLC   (1)
1800 Rte 34 N Bldg 4 Ste 404A, Wall, NJ 07719
Tel.: (732) 556-9090
Web Site: http://www.velocityrecoveries.com
Property Investment Services
N.A.I.C.S.: 523999
John C. Kleinert *(Pres & CEO)*

VELOCITY PRINT SOLUTIONS
705 Corporations Park, Scotia, NY 12302
Tel.: (518) 370-1158
Web Site: http://www.velocitygaincontrol.com
Sales Range: $10-24.9 Million
Emp.: 183
Commercial Printing & Lithographic Services
N.A.I.C.S.: 323111
Jim Stiles *(CEO)*
Renee Martenn *(Pres)*
Subsidiaries:
Bajan Group, Inc.   (1)
950 New Loudon Rd Ste 280, Latham, NY 12110
Tel.: (518) 464-2884
Web Site: http://www.bajangroup.com
Stationery & Office Supplies Merchant Whslr
N.A.I.C.S.: 424120
Anthony Lombardo *(Pres)*

VELOCITY VEHICLE GROUP
2429 S Peck Rd, Whittier, CA 90601
Tel.: (800) 366-4621
Web Site: http://www.velocityvehiclegroup.com
Commercial Truck Dealerships
N.A.I.C.S.: 336120
James A. Barker *(Owner & Co-Pres)*
Deborah Cegielski *(Chief HR Officer)*
Subsidiaries:
Los Angeles Truck Centers LLC   (1)
2429 Peck Rd, Whittier, CA 90601
Tel.: (562) 695-0511
Web Site: http://www.lafreightliner.com
Rev.: $150,000,000
Emp.: 125
Trucks, Commercial
N.A.I.C.S.: 423110
Bradley Fauvre *(Co-Pres)*
Conan Barker *(Co-Pres)*

Subsidiary (Non-US):
First Industries Corporation   (2)
18688 96th Avenue, Surrey, V4N 3P9, BC, Canada
Tel.: (604) 265-6657
Web Site: http://www.firsttruck.ca
Sales Range: $25-49.9 Million
Emp.: 100
Truck Dealership
N.A.I.C.S.: 423110
Rod Graham *(Pres & CEO)*

COMPANIES VENADO OIL & GAS, LLC

Subsidiary (Domestic):

Premium Truck & Trailer Inc. (3)
1015 Great Street, Prince George, V2N
2K8, BC, Canada
Tel.: (250) 563-0696
Truck & Trailer Retailer
N.A.I.C.S.: 441110
Tom Coffey *(Pres & CEO)*

Subsidiary (Domestic):

Freightliner of Kelowna Ltd. (4)
1340 Stevens Rd #5, Kelowna, V1Z 1G2,
BC, Canada
Tel.: (250) 769-7255
Web Site: http://www.premiumtruck.ca
Sales Range: $10-24.9 Million
Emp.: 24
New & Used Truck Dealers
N.A.I.C.S.: 441110
Troy Thompson *(Mgr-Svc)*
Kelly Jones *(Mgr-Parts)*
Mark Jones *(Branch Mgr)*

Subsidiary (Domestic):

Star Bus Sales Inc. (3)
11313 170 Street Northwest, Edmonton,
T5M 3P5, AB, Canada
Tel.: (780) 413-8800
Bus Transportation Services
N.A.I.C.S.: 485410

Subsidiary (Domestic):

Neely Coble Company, Inc. (2)
319 Fesslers Ln, Nashville, TN 37210-2920
Tel.: (615) 244-8900
Web Site: http://www.neelycoble.com
Automobile Dealership
N.A.I.C.S.: 423110
Pam Kittrell *(Mgr-HR)*
Dudley Smith *(Mgr-Sls)*
Neely Coble III *(Pres)*

SVT Fleet, LLC (1)
429 S Peck Rd, Whittier, CA 90601
Tel.: (888) 804-3744
Web Site: https://www.svtfleetsolutions.com
Fleet Management & Logistics Services
N.A.I.C.S.: 541614

Subsidiary (Domestic):

Southern California Fleet Services,
Inc. (2)
2855 Sampson Ave, Corona, CA 92879-6126
Tel.: (702) 399-1747
Web Site: http://www.socalfleet.com
General Automotive Repair
N.A.I.C.S.: 811111

VELODYNE ACOUSTICS, INC.
345 Digital Dr, Morgan Hill, CA 95037
Tel.: (408) 465-2800
Web Site: http://www.velodyne.com
Year Founded: 1983
Sales Range: $10-24.9 Million
Emp.: 70
Mfr of Home Audio & Video Equipment
N.A.I.C.S.: 334310
David Hall *(Founder & CEO)*
Houshang Vala *(Controller)*
George Ross *(Gen Mgr)*
Pieter Kerstens *(VP-Engrg)*
Michael Jellen *(Pres & COO)*
Joseph B. Culkin *(Chm)*
Drew Hamer *(CFO)*

VELOSIO, LLC
5747 Perimeter Dr Ste 200, Columbus, OH 43017
Tel.: (888) 725-2555 DE
Web Site: http://www.velosio.com
Year Founded: 1984
Computer Software Solutions
N.A.I.C.S.: 513210
Bill Anderson *(CMO)*
Dan Petschke *(CFO)*
James Bowman *(Co-Chm)*
Liz Corey *(Chief HR Officer)*
Jeff Edwards *(Sr VP-Channels)*

Joe Longo *(Exec Chm)*
Robbie Morrison *(CTO)*
Dominic Cristelli *(Chief Sls Officer)*
Bob Knott *(CEO)*

Subsidiaries:

BroadPoint, Inc. (1)
7501 Wisconsin Ave Ste 720W, Bethesda, MD 20814
Tel.: (888) 920-2784
Customer Relationship Management & Enterprise Resource Planning Software Publisher
N.A.I.C.S.: 513210
Lee Raesly *(CEO)*

Subsidiary (Domestic):

BroadPoint Technologies, Inc. (2)
7501 Wisconsin Ave Ste 720w, Bethesda, MD 20814
Tel.: (301) 634-2400
Web Site: http://www.broadpoint.net
Rev.: $17,500,000
Emp.: 85
Computer Programming Services
N.A.I.C.S.: 541511
Lee Raesly *(CEO)*
Andy Gordon *(VP-Sls)*

Silverware, Inc. (1)
5644 E Thomas Rd, Phoenix, AZ 85018
Tel.: (480) 423-8324
Web Site: http://www.silverw.com
Sales Range: $1-9.9 Million
Emp.: 13
Custom Computer Programing
N.A.I.C.S.: 541512
Bob Silver *(Dir-Ops)*
Joe Cooperrider *(Mgr-IT)*
Reinhold Schmitz *(Mgr-Client Svcs)*
Bev Berger *(Office Mgr-Phoenix)*
Hub Gilbert *(Mng Dir-Seattle)*
Sara Silver *(Pres)*

Socius1 LLC (1)
7003 Post Rd, Dublin, OH 43016
Tel.: (614) 280-9880
Web Site: http://www.socius1.com
Software Publisher
N.A.I.C.S.: 513210
Terry Ginley *(Product Dir-Strategies & Mergers & Acq)*

Synergy Business Solutions Inc (1)
9725 SW Beaverton Hillsdale Hwy Ste 200, Beaverton, OR 97005
Tel.: (503) 601-4100
Computer Software Publisher
N.A.I.C.S.: 513210

VELOXION INC.
1 Industrial Dr, Pelham, NH 03076
Tel.: (603) 889-6871
Web Site: http://www.veloxion.com
Year Founded: 2006
Sales Range: $1-9.9 Million
Emp.: 2
Mfr of Electrical & Mechanical Parts & Assemblies
N.A.I.C.S.: 335999
Steve Robinson *(Pres)*

VELUR LAND INVESTMENTS, INC.
5990 N Sepulveda Blvd 610, Van Nuys, CA 91411
Tel.: (818) 786-0024
Web Site: http://www.velurii.com
Sales Range: $10-24.9 Million
Emp.: 22
Subdividers & Developers, Nec
N.A.I.C.S.: 237210
Lubor Hlavacek *(Pres)*

VELVET ICE CREAM COMPANY INC.
11324 Mt Vernon Rd, Utica, OH 43080
Tel.: (740) 892-3921
Web Site:
 http://www.velveticecream.com
Sales Range: $10-24.9 Million

Emp.: 175
Ice Cream, Bulk
N.A.I.C.S.: 311520
Joseph Dager *(Pres)*
Bob Bricking *(Dir-Ops)*
Ken Harold *(Plant Mgr)*
Jason Outland *(Reg Mgr-Sls)*
Melanie Pileski *(Mgr-Sls)*

VEN-TEL PLASTICS CORPORATION
11311 74th St N, Largo, FL 33773
Tel.: (727) 546-7470 FL
Web Site:
 http://www.ventelplastics.com
Year Founded: 1982
Sales Range: $10-24.9 Million
Emp.: 100
Plastic Injection Molding
N.A.I.C.S.: 326199
Edward F. Venner *(Pres & CEO)*
Les Sickler *(Mgr-Maintenance)*

VENABLE LLP
600 Massachusetts Ave NW, Washington, DC 20001
Tel.: (202) 344-4000
Web Site: https://www.venable.com
Year Founded: 1900
Sales Range: $300-349.9 Million
Emp.: 1,889
Law firm
N.A.I.C.S.: 541110
Todd Gustin *(Partner)*
Matthew D. Field *(Partner)*
Ari N. Rothman *(Partner)*
Craig A. Thompson *(Partner)*
Ellen Traupman Berge *(Partner)*
Lindsay B. Meyer *(Partner)*
Lisa Jose Fales *(Partner)*
Roger A. Colaizzi *(Partner)*
Joseph W. Creech *(Partner)*
Michael A. Signorelli *(Partner)*
Michael J. Bresnick *(Partner)*
Ari Schwartz *(Mng Dir-Cybersecurity Svcs)*
Claude E. Bailey *(Partner)*
Harry I. Atlas *(Partner)*
J. Douglas Baldridge *(Partner)*
Robert G. Ames *(Partner)*
Steven A. Adducci *(Partner)*
Linda J. Zirkelbach *(Partner)*
Kelly DeMarchis Bastide *(Partner)*
Joshua H. Raymond *(Partner)*
Jeremy A. Grant *(Mng Dir-Tech Bus Strategy)*
Lawrence H. Norton *(Partner)*
Andrew E. Bigart *(Partner)*
David L. Feinberg *(Partner)*
Allison D. Foley *(Partner)*
Rebecca Liebowitz *(Partner)*
David A. Mullon Jr. *(Partner)*
Tara Sugiyama Potashnik *(Partner)*
Vincent E. Verrocchio *(Partner)*
Kedrick Whitmore *(Partner)*
Thomas M. Boyd *(Partner)*
Jonathan L. Falkler *(Partner)*
Anthony James Pagano *(Partner)*
Janice M. Ryan *(Partner)*
Karen C. Hermann *(Partner)*
Charles J. Monterio Jr. *(Partner)*
Stuart P. Ingis *(Chm)*
Jamie M. Danker *(Sr Dir-Cybersecurity & Privacy Svcs)*
Ross B. Nodurft *(Sr Dir-Cybersecurity Svcs)*
Grant Schneider *(Sr Dir-Cybersecurity Svcs)*
Heather West *(Sr Dir-Cybersecurity & Privacy Svcs)*
Saminaz Akhter *(Partner)*
James D. Barnette *(Partner)*
Robert J. Bolger Jr. *(Partner)*
David M. Bonelli *(Partner)*
Jennifer J. Bruton *(Partner)*
James H. Burnley IV *(Partner)*

Timothy Carroll *(Partner)*
Wallace E. Christner *(Partner)*
Frank A. Ciatto *(Partner)*
Frank C. Cimino Jr. *(Partner)*
Arthur E. Cirulnick *(Partner)*
Emilio W. Cividanes *(Partner)*
Justin A. Coen *(Partner)*
George E. Constantine *(Partner)*
Alexei Cowett *(Partner)*
Ashley W. Craig *(Partner)*
Gregory A. Cross *(Partner)*
Andrew J. Currie *(Partner)*
Henry J. Daley *(Partner)*
Michael C. Davis *(Partner)*
Michael C. Davis *(Partner)*

Subsidiaries:

Fitzpatrick Cella Harper & Scinto (1)
1290 6th Ave of the Americas, New York, NY 10104
Tel.: (212) 218-2100
Law firm
N.A.I.C.S.: 541110

VENABLES, BELL & PARTNERS
201 Post St Ste 200, San Francisco, CA 94108
Tel.: (415) 288-3300
Web Site:
 http://www.venablesbell.com
Year Founded: 2001
Sales Range: $10-24.9 Million
Emp.: 130
Advetising Agency
N.A.I.C.S.: 541810
Paul Venables *(Founder & Chm)*
Eric Pfeifer *(Dir-Creative)*
Tom Scharpf *(Dir-Creative)*
Lee Einhorn *(Dir-Creative)*
Jeff Jan *(Dir-Comm Strategy)*
Will McGinness *(Partner & Exec Dir-Creative)*
Cris Logan *(Dir-Design)*
Justin Moore *(Dir-Creative)*
Alex Rice *(Assoc Dir-Creative)*
Allison Hayes *(Assoc Dir-Creative)*
Ariel Rosen *(Acct Mgr)*
Avery Oldfield *(Dir-Art)*
Brenda Pyles *(Acct Supvr)*
Brian Longtin *(Dir-Brain Strategy)*
Talya Fisher *(Sr Project Mgr)*
Kate Jeffers *(Pres)*

VENADO OIL & GAS, LLC
13301 Galleria Cir Ste 300, Austin, TX 78738
Tel.: (512) 518-2900
Web Site: http://www.vogllc.com
Year Founded: 2011
Crude Petroleum & Natural Gas Extraction
N.A.I.C.S.: 211120
Scott Garrick *(CEO)*

Subsidiaries:

Texas American Resources I, LLC (1)
201 W 5th St Ste 1300, Austin, TX 78701
Tel.: (512) 480-8700
Web Site: http://www.texasarc.com
Holding Company; Oil & Natural Gas Exploration & Production
N.A.I.C.S.: 551112
David E. Honeycutt *(Pres & CEO)*
Stephen P. Roberts *(COO)*
Thomas R. Hester *(CFO)*

Subsidiary (Domestic):

Texas American Resources Operating Company (2)
201 W 5th St Ste 1300, Austin, TX 78701
Tel.: (512) 480-8700
Web Site: http://www.texasarc.com
Emp.: 30
Oil & Gas Exploration & Production
N.A.I.C.S.: 211120

VENADO OIL & GAS, LLC

Venado Oil & Gas, LLC—(Continued)
David E. Honeycutt *(Founder, Pres & CEO)*
Jake Klein *(VP-Ops-South Texas)*
Keith Curtis *(VP-Drilling)*
Troy Gieselman *(VP-Land)*
Andy Lawther *(Mgr-Ops-Texas Panhandle)*
Chad Cluver *(Mgr-Reservoir)*
Cris Sherman *(Chief Acctg Officer)*
Lee Nix *(CFO)*

VENCAP TECHNOLOGIES, LLC
120 E Ogden Ave, Hinsdale, IL 60521
Tel.: (630) 789-3300
Holding Company
N.A.I.C.S.: 551112
Norman J. Beles *(Chm)*

Subsidiaries:

Allant Group, LLC (1)
2655 Warrenville Road Stte 200, Naperville, IL 60515
Tel.: (800) 367-7311
Web Site: http://www.allantgroup.com
Data Processing, Hosting & Related Services
N.A.I.C.S.: 518210
Gaurav Issar *(CEO)*
Tim Finnigan *(CMO)*
Marty Shepard *(Sr VP-Sls)*
Julie Schmidt *(Sr VP-Data Analytics)*
Tim Sullivan *(Sr VP-Client Solutions, Ops & Support)*
Paul Ernst *(Sr VP- Campaign Engagemnt)*
Mark Knapczyk *(CFO)*

VENCHURS PACKAGING, INC.
800 Liberty St, Adrian, MI 49221-3955
Tel.: (517) 263-8937
Web Site: http://www.venchurs.com
Year Founded: 1973
Sales Range: $75-99.9 Million
Emp.: 100
Provider of Packaging & Distribution Services
N.A.I.C.S.: 336390
Jeffrey Wyatt *(Pres)*

VENCOR INTERNATIONAL, INC.
6525 Gunpark Dr Ste 370-141, Boulder, CO 80301
Tel.: (303) 476-9998
Web Site: http://www.vencorintl.com
Sales Range: Less than $1 Million
Investment Services
N.A.I.C.S.: 523999
James Gaspard *(CEO)*

VEND FOOD SERVICES INC.
1120 Vend Dr, Watkinsville, GA 30677
Tel.: (706) 548-5238
Web Site: http://www.vendfoodservices.com
Year Founded: 1950
Sales Range: $10-24.9 Million
Vending Machine Operators
N.A.I.C.S.: 722330
James H. Roberts *(Gen Mgr)*
Tom Huges *(Gen Mgr)*
Dan Hart *(Owner & CEO)*

VEND MART INC.
1950 Williams St, San Leandro, CA 94577
Tel.: (510) 297-5132
Web Site: http://www.vendmart.com
Sales Range: $25-49.9 Million
Emp.: 27
Snack Foods
N.A.I.C.S.: 424450
Maninder Arora *(Pres)*

VENDETTI MOTORS INC.
411 W Central St, Franklin, MA 02038
Tel.: (508) 528-3450
Web Site: http://www.vendettimotors.com
Sales Range: $10-24.9 Million
Emp.: 30
Automobiles, New & Used
N.A.I.C.S.: 441110
Joe Vendetti *(Founder & Controller)*
Rob Webster *(Mgr-Comml Truck)*

VENDOMATIC INC.
1844 Brookfield Ct, Frederick, MD 21701
Tel.: (301) 696-0001
Web Site: http://www.vendomatic.com
Sales Range: $10-24.9 Million
Emp.: 75
Merchandising Machine Operators
N.A.I.C.S.: 445132
Barry John *(CEO)*
Don Joletz *(Pres)*
Tara Heon *(CFO)*

VENDORS EXCHANGE INTERNATIONAL, INC.
8700 Brookpark Rd, Cleveland, OH 44129
Tel.: (800) 321-2311
Web Site: http://www.veii.com
Year Founded: 1959
Vending Equipment Operator
N.A.I.C.S.: 445132
Matt Shene *(CEO)*

Subsidiaries:

American Vending Machines, Inc. (1)
5206 S 38th St, Saint Louis, MO 63116
Tel.: (314) 771-8363
Web Site: http://www.americanvendingmachines.com
Rev.: $1,300,000
Emp.: 15
Fiscal Year-end: 12/31/2010
Personal & Household Goods Repair & Maintenance
N.A.I.C.S.: 811490

VENDORS SUPPLY COMPANY INC.
201 Saluda River Rd, Columbia, SC 29210-7835
Tel.: (803) 772-6390
Web Site: http://www.vendorssupply.com
Year Founded: 1966
Sales Range: $10-24.9 Million
Emp.: 110
General Line Groceries
N.A.I.C.S.: 424410
Randy Sikes *(Pres)*

VENEER TECHNOLOGIES INC.
3337 W RailRd Blvd, Newport, NC 28570
Tel.: (252) 223-5600
Web Site: http://www.veneertech.com
Rev.: $10,000,000
Emp.: 135
Veneer Stock, Hardwood
N.A.I.C.S.: 321211
Christian Weygoldt *(Pres)*
Andy Shoptaugh *(Supvr-Safety & Maintenance)*

VENEGAS CONSTRUCTION CORP.
472 Dito Castro Ste 201, Ponce, PR 00716-4702
Tel.: (787) 848-4848
Web Site: http://www.venegasconstruction.com
Rev.: $10,788,505
Emp.: 120
Industrial Buildings; New Construction
N.A.I.C.S.: 236210
Emilio M. Venegas *(Pres)*
Carlos Pagam *(Controller)*

VENETIAN BLIND & FLOOR
2504 Bessonnet, Houston, TX 77005
Tel.: (713) 528-2404
Web Site: http://www.vbaf.com
Sales Range: $1-9.9 Million
Emp.: 20
Venetian Blinds
N.A.I.C.S.: 337920
Gary Touchton *(Mgr-Sls)*
Gwendolyn Redman *(Mgr-Showroom)*

VENEZIA DESIGN INC.
1988 L Arbolita Dr, Glendale, CA 91208
Tel.: (323) 965-9700
Year Founded: 1993
Sales Range: Less than $1 Million
Emp.: 2
Brand Development, Children's Market, Collateral, Consulting, Full Service, Graphic Design, Internet/Web Design, Logo & Package Design
N.A.I.C.S.: 541810
Jim Venezia *(Principal)*

VENEZIA HAULING INC.
86 Airport Rd, Pottstown, PA 19464
Tel.: (610) 495-5200
Web Site: http://www.veneziainc.com
Year Founded: 1977
Trucking, Frieght Hauling
N.A.I.C.S.: 484110
Frank Venezia *(Dir-Ops)*

VENGROFF WILLIAMS, INC.
2211 Fruitville Rd, Sarasota, FL 34237
Tel.: (941) 363-5200
Web Site: http://www.vwinc.com
Year Founded: 1963
Sales Range: $1-4.9 Billion
Emp.: 490
Collection Services
N.A.I.C.S.: 561440
Harvey Vengroff *(Founder & CEO)*
Robert Williams *(Chm)*
Joel Vengroff *(Co-Pres)*
Robert Sherman *(Co-Pres)*

VENICE FAMILY CLINIC
604 Rose Ave, Venice, CA 90291
Tel.: (312) 392-8630
Web Site: http://venicefamilyclinic.org
Year Founded: 1970
Medical Clinic
N.A.I.C.S.: 622110
Elizabeth Benson Forer *(CEO & Exec Dir)*

Subsidiaries:

South Bay Family Health Care (1)
23430 Hawthorne Blvd Ste 210, Torrance, CA 90505
Tel.: (310) 802-6177
Web Site: http://www.sbfhc.org
Sales Range: $10-24.9 Million
Individual & Family Health Care Services
N.A.I.C.S.: 621498
Janette Hicks *(Dir-Ops)*

VENICE GOLF ASSOCIATION, INC.
1801 Harbor Dr S, Venice, FL 34285
Tel.: (941) 488-3948
Web Site: http://www.lakevenicegolf.com
Year Founded: 1958
Sales Range: $1-9.9 Million
Emp.: 54
Golf Course & Country Club
N.A.I.C.S.: 713910
Michael Wheeler *(Pres)*
Rod Parry *(Gen Mgr)*

VENKEL LTD.
5900 Shepherd Mtn, Austin, TX 78730
Tel.: (512) 794-0081
Web Site: http://www.venkel.com
Sales Range: $25-49.9 Million
Emp.: 90
Surface-Mount Components Distr
N.A.I.C.S.: 423690
Anil Venkatrao *(CEO)*
Susan Chavez *(Mgr-Acct)*
Chris Gobbi *(Mgr-Acct)*
Julie McCauley *(Mgr-Acct)*
Jon Koonce *(Mgr-Acct)*
Blaise D'Mello *(Dir-Sls)*
Kathleen Fung *(Mgr-Acct)*
Pamela Shangreaux *(Sr Acct Mgr)*
Clarissa Aleman *(Mgr-Acct)*
Sarah Brewer *(Supvr-Acct)*
Jennifer Corzine *(Mgr-Acct)*
Thad Dameris *(Supvr-Acct)*

VENNERBECK, STERN, LEACH
49 Pearl St, Attleboro, MA 02703-3940
Tel.: (401) 333-1450
Rev.: $11,000,000
Emp.: 35
Mfr of Gold Filled & Rolled Gold Plate, Carat Gold & Silver Sheet Stock, Wire & Solders
N.A.I.C.S.: 331410

VENOM PRODUCTS, LLC
1289 Cormorant Ave, Detroit Lakes, MN 56501
Tel.: (218) 844-3283
Web Site: http://www.venomproducts.com
Automotive Aftermarket Clutch Products Mfr & Whslr
N.A.I.C.S.: 336350
Mark Schiffner *(Pres & Gen Mgr)*

VENQUEST CAPITAL PARTNERS LLC
3860 W Northwest Hwy # 205, Dallas, TX 75220-5183
Tel.: (214) 978-4640
Web Site: http://www.venquestcapital.com
Year Founded: 2000
Privater Equity Firm
N.A.I.C.S.: 523999
David E. Smartt *(Mng Partner)*
Paul L. Bureau III *(Mng Partner)*

Subsidiaries:

Alsay Incorporated (1)
6615 Gant Rd, Houston, TX 77066
Tel.: (281) 444-6960
Web Site: http://www.alsaywater.com
Sales Range: $25-49.9 Million
Emp.: 100
Pumps & Pumping Equipment Repair; Water Well Drilling & Servicing
N.A.I.C.S.: 237110
Joe Slavik *(Pres)*

VENRO PETROLEUM CORPORATION
45 Rockefeller Plz, New York, NY 10111-0100
Tel.: (212) 969-1722
Web Site: http://www.venro.com
Year Founded: 1987
Sales Range: $1-4.9 Billion
Emp.: 305
Petroleum Product Distr
N.A.I.C.S.: 424690
Rafael H. Rojas *(Pres & CEO)*
Tuo Ya *(Mgr)*

VENROCK ASSOCIATES
3340 Hillview Ave, Palo Alto, CA 94304

COMPANIES

Tel.: (650) 561-9580
Web Site: http://www.venrock.com
Emp.: 40
Venture Capital Investment Services
N.A.I.C.S.: 523999
Anthony B. Evnin *(Partner)*
Brian D. Ascher *(Partner)*
Steven D. Goldby *(Partner)*

Subsidiaries:

Venrock Associates (1)
530 5th Ave 22nd Fl, New York, NY 10036
Tel.: (212) 444-4100
Web Site: http://www.venrock.com
Emp.: 20
Venture Capital Investment Services
N.A.I.C.S.: 523999
David Pakman *(Partner)*

VENSURE EMPLOYER SERVICES, INC.
2600 W Geronimo Pl Ste 100, Chandler, AZ 85224
Web Site: https://www.vensure.com
Year Founded: 2004
Sales Range: $1-9.9 Million
Emp.: 1,000
Human Resource Consulting Services
N.A.I.C.S.: 541612
Alex Campos *(CEO)*

Subsidiaries:

Execupay, Inc. (1)
510 Portland Rd, San Antonio, TX 78216
Tel.: (210) 366-9511
Web Site: https://www.execupay.com
Sales Range: $1-9.9 Million
Emp.: 71
Payroll & Executive Business Services
N.A.I.C.S.: 541214
Gerald Stowers *(CEO)*
Logan Cashwell *(Dir-Info Svcs)*
Michelle Clark *(Controller)*
Tom Klingbeil *(VP)*
Rosa Robertson *(Mgr-Ops Compliance)*

Resource Management Inc. (1)
510 S 200 W, Salt Lake City, UT 84101
Tel.: (801) 355-0200
Web Site: http://www.rminc.com
Sales Range: $75-99.9 Million
Emp.: 45
Employee Leasing Services
N.A.I.C.S.: 561330

VENT-ALARM CORPORATION
Km 9 Hm 2 Rd 189, Gurabo, PR 00778
Tel.: (787) 737-5755
Web Site:
http://www.valcorsamcor.com
Sales Range: $10-24.9 Million
Emp.: 250
Security Control Equipment & Systems
N.A.I.C.S.: 335999
Jesus M. Sosa *(Founder & CEO)*
Fernando Sosa *(Pres)*

VENT-RITE VALVE CORPORATION
300 Pond St, Randolph, MA 02368
Tel.: (781) 986-2000
Web Site:
http://www.skidmorepump.com
Rev.: $10,000,000
Emp.: 100
Boiler & Boiler Shop Work
N.A.I.C.S.: 332410
Parker Wheat *(Pres)*

VENTA GLOBAL, INC.
2131 N Collins Ave 433-614, Arlington, TX 76011 **NV**
Year Founded: 2009
Sales Range: Less than $1 Million
Emp.: 4
Alternative Fuel Motor Vehicle Distr

N.A.I.C.S.: 423110
Dmitri Tisnoi *(Pres & CEO)*
Ray Colston *(CFO & Treas)*
Brenda Gray *(COO & Sec)*
Kyle Ford *(VP)*

VENTAMATIC LTD.
100 Washington Rd, Mineral Wells, TX 76068-0728
Tel.: (940) 325-7887 **TX**
Web Site: http://www.bvc.com
Year Founded: 1948
Sales Range: $75-99.9 Million
Emp.: 60
Mfr & Distributor of Fans & Household Ventilation Systems
N.A.I.C.S.: 333413
Terry Siegel *(Pres)*
Gary Sartor *(VP-Sls & Mktg)*
Steve Tarpley *(Mgr-Engrg)*
Cindy Denman *(Coord-Freight)*

VENTANA USA
6001 Enterprise Dr, Export, PA 15632
Tel.: (724) 325-3400
Web Site: http://www.ventana-usa.com
Sales Range: $10-24.9 Million
Emp.: 65
Windows, Plastics
N.A.I.C.S.: 326199
Tony Polley *(VP)*
Ann Paury *(Controller)*
Dave Zack *(Mgr-Supply Chain)*
Mike Pauly *(Mgr-Production)*

VENTECH INC.
1149 Ellsworth Dr, Pasadena, TX 77506-4858
Tel.: (713) 477-0201 **TX**
Web Site: http://www.ventech-eng.com
Year Founded: 1967
Sales Range: $25-49.9 Million
Emp.: 100
Engineeering Services
N.A.I.C.S.: 541330
Bill L. Stanley *(Pres)*
Paul Rawling *(Gen Mgr)*
Ian Anderson *(CEO)*
Joerg Matthiessen *(Chm)*

Subsidiaries:

Ventech Engineers Inc. (1)
1149 Ellsworth Dr 6th Fl, Pasadena, TX 77506-4858
Tel.: (713) 477-0201
Web Site: http://www.ventech.com
Sales Range: $25-49.9 Million
Providers of Heavy Construction Services
N.A.I.C.S.: 237990

Ventech Investment Co., Inc. (1)
1149 Ellsworth Dr 6th Fl, Pasadena, TX 77506-4858
Tel.: (713) 477-0201
Web Site: http://www.ventech.com
Sales Range: $1-9.9 Million
Emp.: 70
Real Estate Agents & Managers
N.A.I.C.S.: 541330

VENTECH SOLUTIONS INC.
8760 Orion Pl Ste 204, Columbus, OH 43240
Tel.: (614) 751-1167
Web Site:
http://www.ventechsolutions.com
Year Founded: 1996
Sales Range: $10-24.9 Million
Emp.: 185
Information Technology Consulting, System Integration & Software Development
N.A.I.C.S.: 541512
Dipanjan Nag *(Chief Investment Officer)*
Tonia Bleecher *(CEO)*
Kathrine Dass *(Chief Delivery Officer)*

VENTEON HOLDINGS, LLC.
3001 W Big Beaver Ste 220, Troy, MI 48084
Tel.: (248) 269-0000
Web Site: http://www.venteon.us.com
Sales Range: $10-24.9 Million
Emp.: 250
Consultant & Staffing Services
N.A.I.C.S.: 541612
Brad Smiles *(VP-Venteon Technical-Staffing Practice & Detroit Market)*
Ben Kohns *(Dir-Venteon Fin-Staffing Practice & Detroit Market)*
Bob Michalak *(VP-Venteon Fin-Search Practice & Detroit Market)*
Rachelle Winter *(Dir-HR)*
Karl Roehrig *(COO & Exec VP)*
Cedric Corera *(Pres & CEO)*

VENTRA SALEM, LLC
800 Pennsylvania Ave, Salem, OH 44460
Tel.: (330) 332-6300 **OH**
Year Founded: 1958
Sales Range: $75-99.9 Million
Emp.: 650
Custom Molded Plastics Mfr
N.A.I.C.S.: 326199
Tim Snow *(Mgr-Quality Assurance)*

VENTURA ASSOCIATES INTERNATIONAL LLC
60 E 42nd St Ste 650, New York, NY 10165
Tel.: (212) 302-8277
Web Site:
http://www.sweepspros.com
Year Founded: 1971
Sales Range: $1-9.9 Million
Emp.: 17
Sales Promotion
N.A.I.C.S.: 541810
Nigel Morgan *(CFO)*
Marla Altberg *(CEO)*
Al Wester *(Pres)*
Lisa Manhart *(CMO & Exec VP)*
Orlando Santiago *(Sr VP & Acct Dir)*

VENTURA COASTAL LLC
2325 Vista Del Mar Dr, Ventura, CA 93002
Tel.: (805) 653-7000 **CA**
Web Site:
http://www.venturacoastal.com
Year Founded: 1952
Sales Range: $10-24.9 Million
Emp.: 100
Citrus Products
N.A.I.C.S.: 311411
William Borgers *(Pres & CEO)*

VENTURA COUNTY CREDIT UNION
6026 Telephone Rd, Ventura, CA 93006-6920
Tel.: (805) 477-4000 **CA**
Web Site: http://www.vccuonline.net
Year Founded: 1950
Sales Range: $25-49.9 Million
Emp.: 188
Credit Union
N.A.I.C.S.: 522130
Joe Schroeder *(Pres & CEO)*
Clint Lovinger *(VP-Member Svcs)*
Gavin Bradley *(COO)*
Linda Rossi *(Chief Admin Officer)*
Linda Sim *(CFO)*
Anna Rader *(Mgr-Reg Ops)*
Broderick Crews *(Mgr-Ops)*
Ed Sahakian *(Dir-Business Svcs)*
Amy Ginnever *(Mgr-Branch)*
Anna Hovnanyan *(Mgr)*
Arturo Zaragoza *(Mgr-Branch)*
Cecilia Rivas *(Mgr-Acctg)*
Greg Bergan *(Mgr-Project)*
Roxy Ostrem *(Chm)*

VENTURE EXPRESS, INC.

VENTURCAP INVESTMENT GROUP V LLC
615 Reservoir Ave, Cranston, RI 02910
Tel.: (401) 781-8500
Web Site: http://www.jdbuyrider.com
Rev.: $10,576,162
Emp.: 20
Automobiles, New & Used
N.A.I.C.S.: 441110
Edward J. Wiggins *(Owner)*

VENTURE CONSTRUCTION COMPANY INC.
5660 Peachtree Industrial Blvd, Norcross, GA 30071-1412
Tel.: (770) 441-6555 **GA**
Web Site:
http://www.ventureconstruction.com
Year Founded: 1969
Sales Range: $25-49.9 Million
Emp.: 40
Nonresidential Construction
N.A.I.C.S.: 236220
E. Ray Morris *(Founder)*
L. F. Hollinsworth *(VP)*

VENTURE DEVELOPMENT CORP.
60 E Sir Francis Drake Blvd Ste 300, Mill Valley, CA 94939
Tel.: (415) 381-1600
Web Site:
http://www.venturecorporation.com
Rev.: $10,000,000
Emp.: 10
Land Subdividers & Developers, Commercial
N.A.I.C.S.: 237210
Robert J. Eves *(Pres)*

VENTURE ENGINEERING & CONSTRUCTION
100 Global View Dr Ste 600, Pittsburgh, PA 15086
Tel.: (412) 231-5890
Web Site:
http://www.ventureengr.com
Year Founded: 2007
Sales Range: $10-24.9 Million
Emp.: 66
Construction Engineering Services
N.A.I.C.S.: 541330
Dave Moniot *(Pres, CEO & Principal)*
Don Olmstead *(Principal & Exec VP)*
Kyle Snyder *(VP-Bus Dev)*
Daryl Jones *(Mgr-Electrical)*
John Mandarino *(Mgr-Construction)*
William Slatosky *(CTO)*
Alex Ussia *(Mgr-Instrumentation & Controls)*
Jeff Laskey *(Mgr-Projects)*
Robert Gambon *(Sr Project Mgr)*
Kevin O'Connor *(Project Mgr)*
Dennis Poskon *(VP-Las Vegas)*
Wayne Jacobs *(Mgr-Engrg)*
Patrick Vescovi *(Project Mgr)*

VENTURE EXPRESS, INC.
131 Industrial Blvd, La Vergne, TN 37086
Tel.: (615) 793-9500
Web Site:
http://www.ventureexpress.com
Year Founded: 1980
Sales Range: $25-49.9 Million
Emp.: 210
Trucking Services
N.A.I.C.S.: 484121

VENTURE EXPRESS, INC. U.S. PRIVATE

Venture Express, Inc.—(Continued)
Jimmy E. Allen (Pres)
Tim Oliver (Coord-Orientation)
Mern Maynord (Dir-Safety)

VENTURE FOR AMERICA
40 W 29th St Ste 301, New York, NY 10001
Tel.: (646) 736-6460 DE
Web Site: http://www.ventureforamerica.org
Year Founded: 2011
Sales Range: $1-9.9 Million
Emp.: 18
Business Support Services
N.A.I.C.S.: 561110
Andrew Yang (Founder & CEO)
Sy Jacobs (Chm)
Amy Nelson (VP-External Rels)

VENTURE INC OF BEAUFORT
22 Sams Point Rd, Beaufort, SC 29907
Tel.: (843) 521-8044
Web Site: http://www.graycoinc.com
Rev.: $10,000,000
Emp.: 15
Motor Vehicle Supplies & New Parts
N.A.I.C.S.: 423120
Herbert Gray (Pres)

VENTURE PIPE & SUPPLY
PO Box 749, Lindsay, OK 73052
Tel.: (405) 756-4807
Web Site: http://www.venturepipe.net
Year Founded: 1989
Sales Range: $10-24.9 Million
Emp.: 80
Plumbing & Heating Equipment Whslr
N.A.I.C.S.: 423720
Ernie Brooks (Pres)

VENTURE REALTY GROUP
1081 19th St Ste 203, Virginia Beach, VA 23451
Tel.: (757) 491-1990
Web Site: http://www.venturerealtygroup.com
Real Estate Development Services
N.A.I.C.S.: 531390
Donna MacMillan-Whitaker (Co-Founder & Mng Dir)
Bruce A. Berlin (Mng Partner)
Michael A. Culpepper (Mng Partner)
Elizabeth A. Matulenas (Partner-Fin & Acctg)
Steven D. Green (Partner-Gen Brokerage)
John L. Gibson III (Co-Founder & Mng Partner)

VENTURE SOLAR, LLC
327 Captain Lewis Rd, Southington, CT 06489
Web Site: http://www.venturesolar.com
Year Founded: 2015
Sales Range: $1-9.9 Million
Emp.: 500
Solar Panels Installation Services
N.A.I.C.S.: 221114
Alex Giles (Co-Founder)
Alex Yackery (Co-Founder)
Raymond Feliciano (Sr VP-Ops)
Maya Cohn (Mgr-Ops)
Cynthia Michaud (Mgr-HR)

VENTURE SOUTH DISTRIBUTORS
1640 Kimberly Rd, Twin Falls, ID 83301
Tel.: (208) 733-5705
Sales Range: $10-24.9 Million
Emp.: 30
Beer & Other Fermented Malt Liquors
N.A.I.C.S.: 424810

Mitch Watkins (Pres)

VENTUREDYNE, LTD.
600 College Ave, Pewaukee, WI 53072-3572
Tel.: (262) 691-9900 WI
Web Site: http://www.venturedyne.com
Year Founded: 1964
Sales Range: $100-124.9 Million
Emp.: 500
Industrial Machinery, Material Handling Equipment & Environmental Test Chamber Mfr
N.A.I.C.S.: 551112
Brian L. Nahey (Pres & CEO)
Marc Lenartz (Mgr-Tech Svcs & Ops)

Subsidiaries:

Advanced Detection Systems (1)
4740 W Electric Ave, Milwaukee, WI 53219-1626
Tel.: (414) 672-0553
Web Site: http://www.adsdetection.com
Sales Range: $25-49.9 Million
Emp.: 100
Industrial Bricks & Magnetic Products Mfr
N.A.I.C.S.: 334290
Matt Nagel (Controller)

Chisholm, Boyd & White Co. (1)
4101 W 126th St, Alsip, IL 60803-1901
Tel.: (708) 597-7550
Web Site: http://www.boydpress.com
Sales Range: $10-24.9 Million
Emp.: 25
Compaction Presses & Machinery for Refractories & Processing Industries
N.A.I.C.S.: 333517
Michael T. Gerardi (Gen Mgr)

Climet Instruments Co. (1)
1320 W Colton Ave, Redlands, CA 92374-2864
Tel.: (909) 793-2788
Web Site: http://www.climet.com
Sales Range: $10-24.9 Million
Emp.: 56
Electronic Pollution Monitoring Equipment & Meteorological Devices
N.A.I.C.S.: 333413
Randy Grater (Mgr)

Dings Dynamics Co. (1)
4740 W Electric Ave, Milwaukee, WI 53219-1626
Tel.: (414) 672-7830
Web Site: http://www.dingsco.com
Sales Range: $10-24.9 Million
Emp.: 100
Provider of Magnetic Motor Brakes
N.A.I.C.S.: 333413
Brian Nahey (Owner)

Dings Magnetic Co. (1)
4740 W Electric Ave, Milwaukee, WI 53219 (100%)
Tel.: (414) 672-7830
Web Site: http://www.dingsco.com
Sales Range: $10-24.9 Million
Emp.: 75
Magnetic Separation, Purification, Material Handling & Process Protection Equipment
N.A.I.C.S.: 333413
Gene Poker (Gen Mgr)

Scientific Dust Collectors (1)
4101 W 126th St, Alsip, IL 60803-1901
Tel.: (708) 597-7090
Web Site: http://www.scidustcollectors.com
Sales Range: $10-24.9 Million
Emp.: 30
Mfr of Dust Collecting Equipment
N.A.I.C.S.: 334519
Michael Gerardi (Gen Mgr)

Thermotron Industries (1)
291 Kollen Pk Dr, Holland, MI 49423
Tel.: (616) 392-1491
Web Site: http://www.thermotron.com
Sales Range: $50-74.9 Million
Emp.: 350
Environmental Test Chambers, Vibration Test Equipment, Failure Monitoring & Detection Equipment, Software & Peripherals
N.A.I.C.S.: 333998

Milt Bos (Engr-Mechanical)
Clint Peterson (Pres)

VENTUREFORTH, INC.
2323 Perimeter Park Dr Ste 100, Atlanta, GA 30341
Tel.: (770) 451-8045
Web Site: http://www.ventureforth.com
Year Founded: 1995
Rev.: $4,400,000
Emp.: 23
Software Publisher
N.A.I.C.S.: 513210
Maurice Edginton (CFO)

VENTURENET, INC.
1930 Pendleton Dr, Garland, TX 75041
Tel.: (214) 343-3550 TX
Web Site: http://www.vnetinc.com
Year Founded: 1990
Sales Range: $1-9.9 Million
Emp.: 15
Information Technology Outsourcing Services; Network & Telephony Support
N.A.I.C.S.: 541519
Jon Klaus (Pres)

VENTURI, INC.
2299 Traversefield Dr, Traverse City, MI 49686
Tel.: (231) 929-7732 MI
Web Site: http://www.venturi-inc.com
Year Founded: 1963
Sales Range: $10-24.9 Million
Emp.: 6
Fiscal Year-end: 12/31/15
Cigarette Filter Holders, 4-Week Stop-Smoking System, Disposable Toothbrushes, Safety Mats & Bath Accessories Mfr
N.A.I.C.S.: 423990
Tim Dutmers (Owner & Pres)
Adam Buchanan (Mgr-Multi-Channel Mktg)

VENTURITY FINANCIAL PARTNERS
14131 Midway Rd Ste 112, Addison, TX 75001
Tel.: (972) 692-0380
Web Site: http://www.venturity.net
Year Founded: 2001
Rev.: $2,500,000
Emp.: 40
Accounting Services
N.A.I.C.S.: 541219
Chris McKee (Founder & Mng Partner)
Deanna Walker (VP-Bus Dev)
Kristofer Russell (Dir-Bus Dev-Houston)

VENUE OF SCOTTSDALE
7117 E 3rd Ave, Scottsdale, AZ 85251-3821
Tel.: (480) 945-5150 AZ
Web Site: http://www.venueofscottsdale.com
Year Founded: 1997
Sales Range: $10-24.9 Million
Emp.: 60
Live Music Venue, Night Club & Restaurant
N.A.I.C.S.: 711110
Victor Perrillo (Pres)
Lauren Davis (Dir-Admin)

VENUS LABORATORIES INC.
11150 Hope St, Cypress, CA 90630
Tel.: (630) 595-1900
Web Site: http://www.ecos.com
Year Founded: 1967
Sales Range: $10-24.9 Million

Emp.: 130
Specialty Cleaning Chemical Mfr
N.A.I.C.S.: 325612
Kelly Vlahakis-Hanks (Pres & CEO)

Subsidiaries:

Earth Friendly Products (1)
11150 Hope St, Cypress, CA 90630
Web Site: http://www.ecos.com
Sales Range: $10-24.9 Million
Emp.: 100
Environmentally Safe Cleaning Product Mfr
N.A.I.C.S.: 325612

Venus Laboratories Inc. - Eastern Division (1)
15 Harold St, Westwood, NJ 07675
Tel.: (201) 666-6699
Chemical Products Mfr
N.A.I.C.S.: 325998

Venus Laboratories Inc. - South Eastern Division (1)
14810 NW 24th Ct, Opa Locka, FL 33054
Tel.: (305) 687-7300
Chemical Products Mfr
N.A.I.C.S.: 325998

Venus Laboratories Inc. - Western Division (1)
11150 Hope St, Cypress, CA 90630
Tel.: (714) 891-3100
Web Site: http://www.ecos.com
Emp.: 50
Chemical Products Mfr
N.A.I.C.S.: 325998
Ashley Gonzales (Office Dir)

VENUWORKS
4611 Mortensen Rd Ste 111, Ames, IA 50014
Tel.: (515) 232-5151
Web Site: http://www.venuworks.com
Rev.: $31,200,000
Emp.: 8
Convention & Show Services
N.A.I.C.S.: 531120
Steven Peters (Pres)
Tammy Koolbeck (Sr VP)
Tim Sullivan (CFO & VP)
Mike Cronin (Exec Dir-Sanford Center-Bemidji)
Joseph Romano (Exec VP)

VEOLIA WATER INDIANAPOLIS, LLC
1220 Waterway Blvd, Indianapolis, IN 46202-2157
Tel.: (317) 639-1501 IN
Year Founded: 1986
Sales Range: $200-249.9 Million
Emp.: 410
Water Utility Holding Company
N.A.I.C.S.: 221310
David L. Gadis (Pres, CEO & COO)

Subsidiaries:

Harbour Water Corporation (1)
1220 Waterway Blvd, Indianapolis, IN 46202-2157
Tel.: (317) 631-1431
Web Site: http://www.sd.com
Sales Range: $75-99.9 Million
Water Utility
N.A.I.C.S.: 221310

Zionsville Water Corporation (1)
101 W Washington St Ste 1400, Indianapolis, IN 46204
Tel.: (317) 639-1501
Web Site: http://www.veoliawaterna.com
Water Utility
N.A.I.C.S.: 221310

VER HOEF AUTOMOTIVE INC.
517 N Main Ave, Sioux Center, IA 51250
Tel.: (712) 722-0143
Web Site: http://www.verhoefautomotive.com
Sales Range: $10-24.9 Million
Emp.: 25

COMPANIES

New Car Dealers
N.A.I.C.S.: 441110
Kembe Hulstein (Co-Owner & Gen Mgr)

VERA WANG BRIDAL HOUSE LTD.
15 E 26th St 4th Fl, New York, NY 10010
Tel.: (212) 575-6400
Web Site: http://www.verawang.com
Rev.: $25,000,000
Emp.: 215
Bridal & Formal Gowns; Jewelry & Accessories
N.A.I.C.S.: 315250
Caroline Hegarty (Asst Mgr-Bridal Svcs)
Dawn West (Gen Mgr)
Erica Ann Arkin (Sr VP-Bridal)
Bill Mitchell (COO & Exec VP)

VERABANK, INC.
201 W Main St, Henderson, TX 75652-3106
Tel.: (903) 657-8521   TX
Web Site: http://www.verabank.com
Year Founded: 1991
Sales Range: $25-49.9 Million
Bank Holding Company
N.A.I.C.S.: 551111
Bradley H. Tidwell (Pres & CEO)

Subsidiaries:

VeraBank, N.A.   (1)
201 W Main St, Henderson, TX 75652-3106
Tel.: (903) 657-8521
Web Site: http://www.verabank.com
Sales Range: $25-49.9 Million
Commericial Banking
N.A.I.C.S.: 522110
Bradley H. Tidwell (Pres & CEO)
Ronald Nix (CTO & VP)

VERACEN FUNDS LP
Two Greenwich Office Park Ste 300, Greenwich, CT 06831
Tel.: (203) 485-7584
Web Site: http://www.veracen.com
Private Investment Firm
N.A.I.C.S.: 523999
Michael T. Kennedy (CEO)

Subsidiaries:

Turner Investments, Inc.   (1)
1000 Chesterbrook Boulevard 1st Fl, Berwyn, PA 19312
Tel.: (484) 329-2300
Web Site: http://www.turnerinvestments.com
Investment Advice & Services
N.A.I.C.S.: 523940
Robert E. Turner (Chm, CIO & Founder)
Mark D. Turner (Sr Portfolio Mgr)
Peter Niedland (Principal & Sr Portfolio Mgr)
Scott Swickard (Principal & Portfolio Mgr)
Stefania A. Perrucci (Head-Fixed Income-Global)
Michelle McKeown (Dir-Equity Trading & Principal)
Jason Schrothberger (Sr Portfolio Mgr)

VERACENTRA, INC.
690 Airpark Rd, Napa, CA 94558
Tel.: (707) 224-6161
Web Site: http://www.veracentra.com
Year Founded: 2006
Sales Range: $1-9.9 Million
Emp.: 40
Brand Marketing & Promotional Solutions
N.A.I.C.S.: 541613
Constance Hill (Founder & Pres)
David Resnick (VP-Tech Solutions)

VERACITY CONSULTING, INC.
8100 Newton St, Overland Park, KS 66204
Tel.: (913) 945-1912
Web Site: http://www.veracityit.com
Year Founded: 2006
Sales Range: $10-24.9 Million
Emp.: 100
Information Technology Development Services
N.A.I.C.S.: 541511
Chris Barr (VP-Federal Ops)
Rod Mack (Chief Delivery Officer)
Mike Gowan (VP-Comml Market)
Pat Shore (VP-Innovation)
Angela S. Hurt (CEO)

VERACITY ENGINEERING
955 L'enfant Plz SW Ste 700, Washington, DC 20024
Tel.: (202) 488-0975
Web Site: http://www.veracity-eng.com
Year Founded: 2001
Rev.: $6,700,000
Emp.: 35
Engineering & Programming Services
N.A.I.C.S.: 541330
Hai Tran (Founder & CEO)
Thomas Lamoureux (Chief Strategy Officer & Exec VP)

VERACITY MANAGEMENT GLOBAL, INC.
21819 Town Place Dr, Boca Raton, FL 33433
Tel.: (561) 998-8425   DE
Technology Consulting Services
N.A.I.C.S.: 541611
Peter B. Dauterman (CFO & Chief Acctg Officer)
Robert A. Shuey III (Chm & CEO)

VERACITY NETWORK INC.
745 North Dr Ste C, Melbourne, FL 32934
Tel.: (800) 864-8909
Web Site: http://www.veracitynetwork.us
Sales Range: $1-9.9 Million
Emp.: 6
Material Identification Technology Mfr
N.A.I.C.S.: 334516
Brian T. Mayo (Pres & CEO)

Subsidiaries:

XStream Systems, Inc.   (1)
10305 102nd Ter Ste 101, Sebastian, FL 32958
Tel.: (772) 646-6201
Web Site: http://www.xstreamsystems.net
Sales Range: Less than $1 Million
Medical Material Authentication & Detection Software & Hardware Products
N.A.I.C.S.: 339112

VERACITY NETWORKS
170 Election Dr Ste 200, Draper, UT 84020
Tel.: (435) 652-6207
Web Site: http://www.business.veracitynetworks.com
Sales Range: $25-49.9 Million
Emp.: 115
Telecommunication Servicesb
N.A.I.C.S.: 517810
Drew Peterson (CEO)
Scott Nelson (Pres & COO)
Chris Modesitta (CTO)
Darin J. Fielding (CFO)
Randy Christensen (VP-Sls & Mktg)
Mike Jasper (VP-Rels)

VERACITY SOLUTIONS, INC.
4038 Parkview Dr, Salt Lake City, UT 84124
Tel.: (801) 561-1074
Web Site: http://www.veracitysolutions.com
Sales Range: $1-9.9 Million
Emp.: 55
Software Consulting Services
N.A.I.C.S.: 541512
Galen Murdock (Co-Founder & Chm)
Michael Richards (Co-Founder & COO)
Scott Heffield (VP-Bus Dev)
Val Taylor (VP-Community)
Marva Sadler (Pres & CEO)

VERALYTIC INC.
PO Box 272358, Tampa, FL 33688
Tel.: (813) 908-8242
Web Site: http://www.veralytic.com
Sales Range: $1-9.9 Million
Emp.: 8
Life Insurance Research Services
N.A.I.C.S.: 541720
Barry D. Flagg (Founder & Pres)

VERANEX
5420 Wade Park Blvd Ste 204, Raleigh, NC 27607
Web Site: http://www.veranexsolutions.com
Medical Device Design & Engineering Services
N.A.I.C.S.: 339112
Tom Daulton (CEO)
Patrick Donnelly (Chm)
David W. Dockhorn (COO)

Subsidiaries:

Boston Healthcare Associates, Inc.   (1)
75 Federal St, Boston, MA 02110
Tel.: (617) 482-4004
Web Site: http://www.bostonhealthcare.com
Rev.: $3,100,000
Emp.: 30
Administrative Management & General Management Consulting Service
N.A.I.C.S.: 541611
Andrew J. Ferrara (CEO)
Charles Mathews (VP)
Betty Su (Mng Dir-Asia Pacific & VP)
Julia R. Ferrara (VP-Ops)
Timothy Sheflin (Exec Dir)

VERATEX, INC.
20362 Plummer St, Chatsworth, CA 91311
Tel.: (818) 994-6487
Web Site: http://www.veratex.com
Year Founded: 1992
Sales Range: $25-49.9 Million
Emp.: 255
Broadwoven Fabric Mill Services
N.A.I.C.S.: 313210
Avi Cohen (Pres)

VERDE ELECTRIC CORP.
100 Oak St, Mount Vernon, NY 10604
Tel.: (914) 664-7000
Web Site: http://www.verdeelectric.com
Sales Range: $10-24.9 Million
Emp.: 120
Electrical Wiring Services
N.A.I.C.S.: 238210
Maurice Wasserman (CFO)

VERDI CONSULTING INC
8400 W Park Dr 4th Fl, McLean, VA 22102
Tel.: (703) 584-7780
Web Site: http://www.verdiconsulting.net
Year Founded: 2002
Sales Range: $1-9.9 Million
Emp.: 35
Accounting & Financial Management
N.A.I.C.S.: 541211
Mariama Y. Levy (Founder)

VERDIGRIS VALLEY ELECTRIC COOPERATIVE
8901 E 146th St N, Collinsville, OK 74021
Tel.: (918) 371-2584
Web Site: http://www.vvec.com
Rev.: $30,629,405
Emp.: 410
Distribution, Electric Power
N.A.I.C.S.: 221122
Kenneth Easterling (Pres)
Alice Houston (Gen Mgr)
Clyde Willard (Dir-Fin)

VERENDRYE ELECTRIC CO-OPERATIVE
615 Hwy 52 W, Velva, ND 58790
Tel.: (701) 338-2855
Web Site: http://www.verendrye.com
Year Founded: 1939
Sales Range: $25-49.9 Million
Emp.: 63
Distribution, Electric Power
N.A.I.C.S.: 221122
Bruce Carlson (Gen Mgr)
Cindy Shattuck (Mgr-Credit)
Randy J. Hauck (Mgr-Member Svcs)
John P. Westby (Mgr-Engrg & Ops)
Jackie Schmaltz (Mgr-Billing)
Maxine Rognlien (Treas & Asst Sec)
Karen Hennessy (Vice Chm)
Tom Rafferty (Mgr-Community Rels & Comm)
Christel Laskowski (Bus Mgr)
Dan G. Kudrna (Supvr-Ops)
Tim R. Krumwiede (Supvr-Sys)
Blaine Bruner (Chm)
Sarah Kittleson (Accountant)
Kelly Finke (Vice Chm)
Steve Peterson (Sec)
Tom Pearson (Treas)

VERGANI & ASSOCIATES, LLC
800 3rd Ave Ste 2800, New York, NY 10022
Tel.: (212) 292-3797
Web Site: http://www.vandacapital.com
Privater Equity Firm
N.A.I.C.S.: 523999
Nicolo Vergani (Mng Partner)

Subsidiaries:

Cooney Brothers Inc   (1)
1850 Gravers Rd, Plymouth Meeting, PA 19462
Tel.: (610) 272-2100
Web Site: http://www.cooneybrothers.com
Rev.: $5,000,000
Emp.: 20
Plumbing & Heating Equipment & Supplies, Hydronics, Merchant Whslr
N.A.I.C.S.: 423720

Federal Steel Supply Inc.   (1)
747 Goddard Ave, Chesterfield, MO 63005
Tel.: (636) 537-2393
Web Site: http://www.fedsteel.com
Pipe & Tubing; Steel
N.A.I.C.S.: 423510
Vernon C. Smith (Co-Founder)
Brian J. Shinkle (Co-Founder)
Scott Harris (COO)
Joe Rumsey (Gen Mgr-Sls)
John Marino (Sr Mgr-Acct)
Mike Moore (Sr Mgr-Acct)
Bob Downey (Sr Mgr-Acct)
Paul Azerolo (Sr Mgr-Acct)

SinterMet LLC   (1)
North Park Dr West Hills Industrial Park, Kittanning, PA 16201
Tel.: (724) 548-7631
Web Site: http://www.sintermet.com
Tungsten Carbide Rolls Mfr
N.A.I.C.S.: 331529
Paul C. Fleiner (Pres & COO)
Tom Gallagher (Sr VP)
Bill Posey (Dir-Composite Roll Products)

VERGE PROMOTIONAL MARKETING

VERGE PROMOTIONAL MARKETING

Verge Promotional Marketing—(Continued)
233 5 Ave Rm 4b, New York, NY 10016-8733
Tel.: (646) 472-1830
Web Site:
  http://www.vergepromos.com
Year Founded: 2002
Rev.: $5,200,000
Emp.: 10
Sales Promotion Services
N.A.I.C.S.: 541820
Hayley Byer (VP)
Stephanie Cohen (Pres)
Francine Cyrus (Mgr-Ops)

VERGE180, LLC
20 Nassau St Ste 125, Princeton, NJ 08542
Tel.: (609) 924-3838
Sales Range: $10-24.9 Million
Emp.: 20
Advertising Services
N.A.I.C.S.: 541810
Alan Brooks (Pres & Chief Creative Officer)
Rocco Iacobellis (CEO)
Pam Weiss (Acct Mgr)
Howard Brooks (Controller)

VERHALEN INC.
500 Pilgrim Way, Green Bay, WI 54304-5264
Tel.: (920) 431-8900   WI
Web Site:
  http://www.verhaleninc.com
Year Founded: 1941
Sales Range: $300-349.9 Million
Emp.: 450
Commercial Interior Design & Building Materials
N.A.I.C.S.: 541410
John Calawerts (Pres)
Mike Calawerts (Owner & Pres)
Hector Serrano (Mgr-IT-Comml Construction)

VERHOFF MACHINE & WELDING, INC.
7300 County Rd 18 Rte 2, Continental, OH 45831
Tel.: (419) 596-3202
Web Site: http://www.verhoff.com
Year Founded: 1955
Sales Range: $1-9.9 Million
Emp.: 80
Machine Shop Operator
N.A.I.C.S.: 332710
Ed Verhoff (Pres)
Joe Verhoff (VP)

VERIATO, INC.
4440 PGA Blvd Ste 500, Palm Beach Gardens, FL 33410
Tel.: (772) 770-5670   DE
Web Site: http://www.veriato.com
Year Founded: 1998
Emp.: 200
Internet Monitoring Software, Surveillance & Security Log Monitoring Products & Services
N.A.I.C.S.: 541511
Larry Thompson (CEO)
David Green (Chief Security Officer)
Dominique Cultrera (VP-HR)

VERICHEM LABORATORIES INC.
90 Narragansett Ave, Providence, RI 02907
Tel.: (401) 461-0180
Web Site:
  http://www.verichemlabs.com
Sales Range: $10-24.9 Million
Emp.: 1
Chemical Products Mfr
N.A.I.C.S.: 325998

Anthony J. DiMonte (Pres)

VERICORR PACKAGING LLC
21000 Torrence Chapel Rd Ste 202-4, Cornelius, NC 28031-6848
Tel.: (229) 928-3598
Rev.: $11,000,000
Emp.: 23
Mfr of Corrugated & Solid Fiber Boxes
N.A.I.C.S.: 322211
Terri Lindley (Controller)

VERIDIAN CREDIT UNION
1827 Ansborough Ave, Waterloo, IA 50701
Tel.: (319) 236-5600
Web Site: http://www.veridiancu.org
Rev.: $86,434,772
Emp.: 400
Credit Union
N.A.I.C.S.: 522130
Paul Gengler (Sec)
Bob Kressig (Vice Chm)
Creston Van Wey (CFO)

VERIDIEN CORP.
1100 4th St N Ste 202D, Saint Petersburg, FL 33701-1790
Tel.: (727) 576-1600   DE
Web Site: http://www.veridien.com
Year Founded: 1991
Disinfectant & Antiseptic Products Mfr
N.A.I.C.S.: 325612
Sheldon C. Fenton (Pres & CEO)
Russell D. Van Zandt (Chm)
Rene A. Gareau (Vice Chm & Sec)

VERIFIER CAPITAL LLC
4171 W Hillsboro Blvd, Coconut Creek, FL 33073
Tel.: (561) 910-3980
Web Site:
  http://www.verifiercapital.com
Year Founded: 1995
Emp.: 6
Security & Alarm Industry Investment Services
N.A.I.C.S.: 523999
Addi Aloya (Pres)
Aaron Way (CFO)
Daniel M. Holtz (Chm)

VERIGENT, LLC.
149 Plantation Ridge Dr Ste 100, Mooresville, NC 28117
Tel.: (704) 658-9101
Web Site: http://www.verigent.com
Year Founded: 2003
Sales Range: $10-24.9 Million
Emp.: 32
Telecommunication & Information Technology Staffing Services
N.A.I.C.S.: 561311
Kevin Kiernan (Pres)

VERINON TECHNOLOGY SOLUTIONS LTD
3395 N Arlington Heights Rd, Arlington Heights, IL 60004
Tel.: (847) 577-5256
Web Site: http://www.verinon.com
Year Founded: 2002
Sales Range: $10-24.9 Million
Emp.: 550
Information Technology Consulting
N.A.I.C.S.: 541618
Tewabe Ayenew (Pres & CEO)
Michael Schinaman (VP-Bus Dev)

VERISSIMO GLOBAL, INC.
7904 Oregold Dr, New Port Richey, FL 34654
Tel.: (727) 856-1942
Web Site:
  http://www.verissimoglobal.com

Sales Range: $1-9.9 Million
Telecommunication Servicesb
N.A.I.C.S.: 517111
William J. Puopolo (Pres)

VERISTAR LLC
9501 W 144th Pl Ste 202, Orland Park, IL 60462
Tel.: (703) 717-5029
Web Site: http://www.veristar.tech
Year Founded: 2019
Legal Services; Forensics, Document Review & Legal Staffing
N.A.I.C.S.: 541199
Rick Avers (Founder & CEO)
Susan Najjar (VP-Mktg)
Ben Gardner (CFO)
Bob Saltzstein (Dir-Client Engagement)
Rick Kaminski (COO)

Subsidiaries:

Planet Data Solutions, Inc.   (1)
555 Taxter Rd Ste 150, Elmsford, NY 10523
Tel.: (914) 593-6900
Web Site: http://www.planetdata.com
Data Processing, Hosting & Related Services
N.A.I.C.S.: 518210
Howard Reissner (Co-Founder & CEO)
Anthony Dobson (VP-Client Svcs)
Dan Roose (VP-Ops)
David S. Cochran (COO)
Zoltan Horvath (Pres)

VERISTOR SYSTEMS, INC.
3308 Peachtree Industrial Blvd, Duluth, GA 30096
Tel.: (678) 990-1593
Web Site: http://www.veristor.com
Year Founded: 2001
Sales Range: $25-49.9 Million
Emp.: 65
Data Storage Products & Services
N.A.I.C.S.: 334112
Ashby A. Lincoln (CEO)
Steve Bishop (CTO)
James R. Glueckert (COO & Exec VP-Svcs & Support)
Murray Granger (Exec VP-Sls & Bus Dev)
Bob Necessary (CFO & Pres-VeriStor Capital)
Jay Waggoner (VP-Sls)
Michael Stolarczyk (VP-Cloud Managed Svcs)
Jessica Garrett (VP-Mktg)
John T. Kauffmann (VP-Cloud Ops)
Ferrol Macon (VP-Architecture & Product Strategy)
Jackie Groark (Chief Info Secuirty Officer & Dir-Security)

VERITAS CAPITAL FUND MANAGEMENT, LLC
9 W 57th St 32nd Fl, New York, NY 10019
Tel.: (212) 415-6700   DE
Web Site:
  http://www.veritascapital.com
Year Founded: 1992
Privater Equity Firm
N.A.I.C.S.: 523999
Hugh D. Evans (Mng Partner)
Jason Donner (CFO)
Daniel Sugar (Principal)
Christian Mittweg (Chief Legal Officer & Chief Compliance Officer)
Brian Gorczynski (Partner)
Benjamin Polk (Partner)
James Dimitri (Partner)
Aneal Krishnan (Principal)
Ashish Chandarana (Partner)
Mark Basile (Mng Dir-Credit)
Rick Cosgrove (VP)
Sumit Khatod (VP)

U.S. PRIVATE

Jay Longosz (VP)
Ted Shanahan (VP)
Ramzi M. Musallam (CEO & Mng Partner)

Subsidiaries:

Alion Science and Technology Corporation   (1)
1750 Tysons Blvd Ste 1300, McLean, VA 22102
Tel.: (703) 918-4480
Web Site: http://www.alionscience.com
Naval Architecture & Marine Engineering; Systems Analysis, Design & Engineering Services
N.A.I.C.S.: 541330
Terri Spoonhour (Sr VP & Grp Mgr)
Ali Zandi (CIO)
Kevin Cook (CFO & Exec VP)
Brian Fisher (Gen Counsel & Sr VP)
Steve Schorer (Chm & CEO)
Vince Stammetti (Sr VP)
Maliek Ferebee (Chief Human Capital Officer)
Alan Dietrich (Sr VP-ISR Grp & Gen Mgr-ISR Grp)
Todd Stirtzinger (Sr VP-Advanced Tech Grp)
Chris Bishop (Chief Growth Officer)
Doug Jankovich (VP-Bus Dev-Intelligence, Surveillance & Reconnaissance Grp)

Subsidiary (Domestic):

Macaulay-Brown, Inc.   (2)
4021 Executive Dr, Dayton, OH 45430
Tel.: (937) 426-3421
Web Site: http://www.macb.com
National Security & Intelligence Services
N.A.I.C.S.: 928110
Michael Zeiser (CFO & Sr VP)
Mike Ritter (Chief Security Officer & VP)
James Soos (Sr VP-Corp Strategy & Comm)
Mia Kerivan-O'Malley (Chief Admin Officer & Sr VP)
Vicki Summers (VP-Contracts & Procurement)
James Sawyer (VP & Co-CTO)
Robert Stafford (VP & Co-CTO)
Christopher T. Hill (VP-HR)
Sidney E. Fuchs (Pres & CEO)

Subsidiary (Domestic):

Commonwealth Technology, Inc.   (3)
5875 Barclay Dr, Alexandria, VA 22315
Tel.: (703) 719-6800
Web Site: http://www.cti1.net
Rev.: $8,855,000
Emp.: 55
Intelligence, Defense & Security Support Services
N.A.I.C.S.: 561499
Christopher D. Laux (Dir-Engrg)
James H. Sawyer (Sr Dir-Ops)
Scott D. Tilton (Dir-Mfg)

Enlighten IT Consulting Inc.   (3)
7467 Rdg Rd Ste 140, Hanover, MD 21076-3118
Tel.: (410) 850-7305
Web Site: http://www.eitcorp.com
Computer Related Services
N.A.I.C.S.: 541519
Duane Shugars (Sr VP & Gen Mgr)

Anthology Inc.   (1)
777 Yamato Rd Ste 400, Boca Raton, FL 33431-4498
Tel.: (561) 923-2500
Web Site: https://www.anthology.com
Computer System Design Services
N.A.I.C.S.: 541512
Jim Brigadier (Sr VP-Sls & Pro Svcs)
Emiliano Diez (VP-Cloud Ops & Svcs)

Subsidiary (Domestic):

iModules Software, Inc.   (2)
5101 College Blvd, Leawood, KS 66211
Tel.: (913) 888-0772
Web Site: http://www.imodules.com
Sales Range: $10-24.9 Million
Emp.: 85
Develops Web Based Software for Management of Online Communities

COMPANIES

VERITAS CAPITAL FUND MANAGEMENT, LLC

N.A.I.C.S.: 541512
Thomas R. Palmer *(Founder & Chm)*
Michael Novosel *(VP-Bus Dev)*
Troy Anderson *(CTO)*
Dan Frazier *(Sr VP-Sls)*
Jason Roberts *(Sr VP-Customer Success)*
Susan Scholes *(VP-Mktg)*
Craig Heldman *(Pres & CEO)*
Germaine Ward *(VP-Product Mgmt)*

Subsidiary (Domestic):

OrgSync, Inc. (3)
13140 Coit Rd Ste 405, Dallas, TX 75240
Tel.: (972) 907-0900
Web Site: http://www.orgsync.com
Sales Range: $1-9.9 Million
Emp.: 34
Software Development Services
N.A.I.C.S.: 541511
Alex Morales *(VP-Sls & Mktg)*
Cayce Stone *(Sr VP-Enterprise Sls)*
Don Fortenberry *(CFO)*
Eric Fortenberry *(Founder, Pres & CEO)*
Leanna Laskey McGrath *(VP-Customer Success)*
Michael Schwartz *(COO)*
Adam Cebulski *(Sr Dir-Res & Strategic Initiatives)*
J. D. Turner *(Dir-Technical Support)*
Brad Weltner *(Sr Dir-Bus Dev)*
Chris Boylan *(Sr Dir-Bus Dev)*
Matt Darner *(Sr Dir-Bus Dev)*
Kevin Wade *(Dir-Product)*

Cambium Learning Group, Inc. (1)
17855 N Dallas Pkwy Ste 400, Dallas, TX 75287
Tel.: (214) 932-9500
Web Site: http://www.cambiumlearning.com
Rev.: $158,184,000
Assets: $158,554,000
Liabilities: $172,846,000
Net Worth: ($14,292,000)
Earnings: $45,055,000
Emp.: 600
Fiscal Year-end: 12/31/2017
Educational Products & Services
N.A.I.C.S.: 611710
John Campbell *(CEO)*
Paul Fonte *(CTO)*
Barbara A. Benson *(CFO)*
David Shuster *(Pres-ExploreLearning)*
Patrick Marcotte *(Pres-Learning A-Z)*
Lisa Jabara-May *(Sr Dir-Mktg-Learning A-Z)*

Subsidiary (Domestic):

Cambium Education, Inc. (2)
17855 Dallas Pkwy Ste 400, Dallas, TX 75287
Tel.: (800) 547-6747
Web Site: http://www.cambiumlearning.com
Sales Range: $25-49.9 Million
Child Day Care Services
N.A.I.C.S.: 624410

Kurzweil/Intellitools, Inc. (2)
24 Prime Pkwy, Natick, MA 01760
Tel.: (781) 276-0600
Web Site: http://www.cambiumtech.com
Sales Range: $25-49.9 Million
Computer Software Development Services
N.A.I.C.S.: 541511

Rosetta Stone Inc. (2)
1621 N Kent St Ste 1200, Arlington, VA 22209
Tel.: (703) 387-5800
Web Site: http://www.rosettastone.com
Rev.: $182,702,000
Assets: $201,107,000
Liabilities: $217,299,000
Net Worth: ($16,192,000)
Earnings: $12,956,000
Emp.: 746
Fiscal Year-end: 12/31/2019
Language Learning Solutions Including Software, Online Services & Audio Practice Tools
N.A.I.C.S.: 513210
John Campbell *(Pres & CEO)*
Barbara Benson *(CFO)*

Subsidiary (Domestic):

Lexia Learning Systems, LLC (3)
200 Baker Ave, Concord, MA 01742
Tel.: (978) 405-6200
Technology Based Learning Solution Services
N.A.I.C.S.: 611691
Nicholas C. Gaehde *(Pres)*
Paul Griffin *(Head-Partnerships-Natl)*

Subsidiary (Non-US):

Rosetta Stone (UK) Ltd. (3)
4th Floor 85 Great Eastern Street, London, EC2A 3HY, United Kingdom
Tel.: (44) 2077492979
Web Site: http://www.rosettastone.co.uk
Emp.: 25
Language Learning Solutions Including Software, Online Services & Audio Practice Tools
N.A.I.C.S.: 513210

Subsidiary (Domestic):

VKidz, Inc. (2)
6300 NE 1st Ave Ste 203, Fort Lauderdale, FL 33334
Web Site: http://www.vkidz.com
Educational Products & Services
N.A.I.C.S.: 611710
John Edelson *(Founder)*

Voyager Learning Company (2)
17855 Dallas Pkwy Ste 400, Dallas, TX 75287-6857
Tel.: (214) 932-9500
Web Site: http://www.cambiumlearning.com
Sales Range: $25-49.9 Million
Educational Support Services
N.A.I.C.S.: 611710

Cubic Corporation (1)
9233 Balboa Ave, San Diego, CA 92123
Tel.: (858) 277-6780
Web Site: https://www.cubic.com
Rev.: $1,476,235,000
Assets: $2,324,221,000
Liabilities: $1,336,041,000
Net Worth: $988,180,000
Earnings: ($3,221,000)
Emp.: 6,100
Fiscal Year-end: 09/30/2020
Combat Simulation Training Products; Automatic Fare-Collection Systems Mfr for Public Transit
N.A.I.C.S.: 541519
Michael Knowles *(Pres-Mission & Performance Solutions Bus & Gen Mgr)*
Min Wei *(Chief Customer Officer & Sr VP)*
Stevan Slijepcevic *(Pres & CEO)*
Mac Curtis *(Chm)*
Peter Torrellas *(Pres-Transportation Sys & Sr VP)*
Paul Shew *(Pres-Defense & Sr VP)*
Travis Chester *(CFO & Sr VP)*
Deborah Cegielski *(Chief HR Officer, Chief Diversity Officer & Sr VP)*
Matt Luxton *(Gen Counsel & Sr VP)*

Subsidiary (Non-US):

CUBIC TRANSPORTATION SYSTEMS (ITMS) LIMITED (2)
Cavendish House Clearwater Park, Prince's Wharf, Stockton, TS17 6QY, United Kingdom
Tel.: (44) 1642636700
Web Site: http://www.cubic.com
Emp.: 200
Metal Container Mfr
N.A.I.C.S.: 332439
Chris Bax *(VP-Global ITS Strategy)*

Subsidiary (Domestic):

Consolidated Converting Co. (2)
879 E Rialto Ave, San Bernardino, CA 92408-1202 **(100%)**
Tel.: (562) 942-0524
Sales Range: $10-24.9 Million
Paper Products Conversion
N.A.I.C.S.: 322211

Subsidiary (Non-US):

Cubic (UK) Limited (2)
AFC House Honeycrock Lane, Salfords, RH1 5LA, Redhill, United Kingdom **(100%)**
Tel.: (44) 1737782200
Web Site: http://www.cubic.com
Holding Company
N.A.I.C.S.: 551112

Subsidiary (Domestic):

Cubic Defence UK Ltd (3)
Unit 3 Bridge Court River Lane, Wrecclesham, GU10 4QE, Surrey, United Kingdom
Tel.: (44) 1252725500
Web Site: http://www.cubic.com
Emp.: 30
Defense Systems Mfr
N.A.I.C.S.: 335999

Subsidiary (Non-US):

Cubic Transportation Systems (Deutschland) GmbH (3)
Alter Fischmarkt 11, 20457, Hamburg, Germany
Tel.: (49) 40 300863 690
Web Site: http://www.cubic-cts.de
Sales Range: $25-49.9 Million
Emp.: 40
Fare Collection Systems For Mass Transportation
N.A.I.C.S.: 334519
Stefan Jacobs *(Mng Dir)*

Subsidiary (Domestic):

Cubic Transportation Systems Limited (3)
AFC House Honeycrock Lane, Salfords, Redhill, RH1 5LA, Surrey, United Kingdom **(100%)**
Tel.: (44) 1737782200
Web Site: http://www.cts.cubic.com
Emp.: 500
Automatic Ticketing Machines Mfr & Revenue Collections for European Transport
N.A.I.C.S.: 334519
Roger Crow *(Mng Dir)*

Subsidiary (Non-US):

CTS - Nordic Aktiebolag (4)
S t Knuts vag 19 hus 7A, 211 57, Malmo, Sweden **(100%)**
Tel.: (46) 40942100
Fare Collection Systems For Mass Transportation
N.A.I.C.S.: 334519

Subsidiary (Domestic):

Cubic Advanced Learning Solutions, Inc. (2)
2001 W Oak Ridge Rd, Orlando, FL 32809
Tel.: (407) 514-1503
Web Site: http://www.atgsites.com
Online Education Services
N.A.I.C.S.: 611710
Tim Mullins *(Gen Mgr)*

Cubic Applications, Inc. (2)
4550 3rd Ave SE Ste B, Lacey, WA 98503-1033 **(100%)**
Tel.: (360) 493-6275
Web Site: http://www.cubic.com
Sales Range: $10-24.9 Million
Emp.: 40
Training Systems
N.A.I.C.S.: 541512

Cubic Cyber Solutions, Inc. (2)
205 Van Buren St Ste 310, Herndon, VA 20170 **(100%)**
Tel.: (703) 821-1516
Web Site: http://www.cubic.com
Sales Range: $10-24.9 Million
Emp.: 20
Security & Networking Services
N.A.I.C.S.: 334290

Cubic Data Systems, Inc. (2)
9333 Balboa Ave, San Diego, CA 92123-1515 **(90%)**
Tel.: (858) 277-6780
Web Site: http://www.cubic.com
Sales Range: $150-199.9 Million
Emp.: 500
Provider of Data Systems
N.A.I.C.S.: 333310

Subsidiary (Non-US):

Cubic Defence Australia Pty. Limited (2)
336 Bayswater Rd, Townsville, 4814, QLD, Australia
Tel.: (61) 747751881
Web Site: http://www.cubic.com
Emp.: 50
Industrial Machinery Mfr
N.A.I.C.S.: 333998
Taiga Aoki *(Mng Dir)*

Cubic Defence New Zealand Ltd. (2)
Wellesley St, PO Box 6008, 1141, Auckland, New Zealand **(100%)**
Tel.: (64) 93790360
Web Site: http://www.cdnz.co.nz
Sales Range: $25-49.9 Million
Emp.: 160
Mfr & Developer of Simulation System, Instrumentation & Control Equipment & Defense Training Instruments
N.A.I.C.S.: 334513

Subsidiary (Non-US):

Cubic Technologies Pte. Ltd. (3)
401 Commonwealth Dr 04-02-03, Hawpar Techno Center, Singapore, 149598, Singapore **(100%)**
Tel.: (65) 62589877
Web Site: http://www.cubic.com
Sales Range: $10-24.9 Million
Emp.: 80
Simulation System, Instrumentation & Control Equipment & Defense Training Instruments Mfr & Developer
N.A.I.C.S.: 334513
Thomas Scott *(Mng Dir)*

Cubic Technologies Singapore Pte. Ltd. (3)
401 Commonwealth Drive 04-02/03 Haw Par Technocentre, Singapore, 149598, Singapore
Tel.: (65) 65729440
Web Site: http://www.nitorprojects.com
Military Training Facility Design Services
N.A.I.C.S.: 541490

Subsidiary (Domestic):

Cubic Defense Applications, Inc. (2)
9333 Balboa Ave, San Diego, CA 92123-1515 **(100%)**
Tel.: (858) 277-6780
Web Site: http://www.cubic.com
Sales Range: $150-199.9 Million
Emp.: 500
Engineering, Research & Development of Military Systems
N.A.I.C.S.: 561499

Cubic Foreign Sales, Inc. (2)
9333 Balboa Ave, San Diego, CA 92123-1515 **(100%)**
Tel.: (858) 277-6780
Web Site: http://www.cubic.com
Sales Range: $125-149.9 Million
Emp.: 300
Distribution Services
N.A.I.C.S.: 333310

Cubic Global Tracking Solutions, Inc. (2)
1919 Gallows Rd Ste 900, Vienna, VA 22182
Tel.: (571) 722-1900
Web Site: http://www.cubic.com
Security System Services
N.A.I.C.S.: 561621

Cubic Land, Inc. (2)
9333 Balboa Ave, San Diego, CA 92123-1515 **(100%)**
Tel.: (858) 277-6780
Web Site: http://www.cubic.com
Sales Range: $100-124.9 Million
Real Estate Investment Services
N.A.I.C.S.: 531390

Cubic Microchip Development Corporation (2)
9333 Balboa Ave, San Diego, CA 92123-1515 **(100%)**
Tel.: (858) 277-6780
Sales Range: $100-124.9 Million
Emp.: 500
Developer of Microchips
N.A.I.C.S.: 333310

Cubic Simulation Systems, Inc. (2)
2001 W Oakridge Rd Ste 100, Orlando, FL 32809-3801
Tel.: (407) 859-7410
Web Site: http://www.cubic.com

4361

VERITAS CAPITAL FUND MANAGEMENT, LLC

Veritas Capital Fund Management, LLC—(Continued)
Sales Range: $25-49.9 Million
Emp.: 140
Computer-Controlled Simulators Distr
N.A.I.C.S.: 541330

Subsidiary (Non-US):

Cubic Transportation Systems (India) Pvt. Limited (2)
4th Floor Block C and D ILabs Technology Centre Plot No 18, Software Units Layout Sy No 64 Madhapur, Hyderabad, 500081, India
Tel.: (91) 4039605151
Web Site: http://www.cts.cubic.com
Sales Range: $25-49.9 Million
Emp.: 4
Computer Systems Design Mfr
N.A.I.C.S.: 541512
Kishan Kamojjhala *(Mng Dir)*

Subsidiary (Domestic):

Cubic Transportation Systems, Inc. (2)
5650 Kearny Mesa Rd, San Diego, CA 92111-5587 **(100%)**
Tel.: (858) 268-3100
Web Site: http://www.cubic.com
Sales Range: $250-299.9 Million
Emp.: 1,500
Fare Collection Systems For Mass Transportation
N.A.I.C.S.: 334519
Ab Jenkins *(Gen Counsel, Sec & VP)*
Matt Newsome *(Gen Mgr-Western Reg-North America)*
Tom Walker *(Mng Dir/Sr VP-Asia Pacific)*
Sushil Rajendran *(VP & Gen Mgr-Central Reg-Americas)*
Ian Woodroofe *(Sr VP-Strategy & Bus Dev)*
Laurent Eskenazi *(Interim Pres, Mng Dir-Europe, Middle East & Africa & Sr VP)*
Kay Maloney *(VP/Gen Mgr-East-North America)*
Theresa Yousey *(Sr VP-Projects & Delivery)*
Heather Yazdan *(VP-Fin Ops)*

Subsidiary (Non-US):

Cubic Transportation Systems (Australia) Pty. Limited (3)
Level 11/10 Eagle Street, Brisbane, 4000, QLD, Australia **(50%)**
Tel.: (61) 732321000
Web Site: http://www.cts.cubic.com
Sales Range: $10-24.9 Million
Emp.: 100
Automatic Fare Collection Systems
N.A.I.C.S.: 334519
Tom Walker *(Mng Dir & Sr VP)*

Cubic Transportation Systems Canada, Ltd. (3)
201 Drumlin Circle Unit 4, Concord, L4K 3E7, ON, Canada
Tel.: (905) 738-9505
Web Site: http://www.cubic.com
Industrial Machinery Mfr
N.A.I.C.S.: 333998

Division (Domestic):

Cubic Transportation Systems, Inc.-East (3)
462 7 Ave 14th Fl, New York, NY 10018 **(100%)**
Tel.: (212) 255-1810
Web Site: http://www.cubic.com
Sales Range: $10-24.9 Million
Emp.: 15
Fare Collection Systems For Mass Transportation
N.A.I.C.S.: 334519

Cubic Transportation Systems, Inc.-Manufacturing Center (3)
1308 S Washington St, Tullahoma, TN 37388-4333 **(100%)**
Tel.: (931) 455-8524
Web Site: http://www.cts.cubic.com
Sales Range: $25-49.9 Million
Emp.: 180
Mfr of Fare Collection Systems for Mass Transportation
N.A.I.C.S.: 334519

Subsidiary (Domestic):

Cubic Worldwide Technical Services, Inc. (2)
4285 Ponderosa Ave, San Diego, CA 92123 **(100%)**
Tel.: (858) 505-2489
Web Site: http://www.cubic.com
Sales Range: $1-9.9 Million
Emp.: 20
Provider of Technical & Management Support Services
N.A.I.C.S.: 811210

Subsidiary (Non-US):

Cubic de Mexico (2)
Prolongacion M Juarez 1089-9 Colonia Lindavista, Tijuana, 22129, Mexico
Tel.: (52) 6646215181
Sales Range: $1-4.9 Billion
Military Instrumentation, Training & Application Systems
N.A.I.C.S.: 561499

Subsidiary (Domestic):

DTECH LABS, Inc. (2)
21580 Beaumeade Cir Ste 230, Ashburn, VA 20147
Tel.: (703) 709-5805
Web Site: http://www.dtechlabs.com
Emp.: 30
Communications Systems Mfr
N.A.I.C.S.: 541330
Patrick Higdon *(COO)*

GATR Technologies Inc. (2)
330 Bob Heath Dr, Huntsville, AL 35806
Tel.: (256) 382-1334
Web Site: http://www.gatr.com
Developer & Marketer of Deployable, Inflatable SatCom Antennas & Systems for High-Bandwidth Communications in Remote Regions
N.A.I.C.S.: 517810
Paul Gierow *(Founder)*
Roark McDonald *(VP & Gen Mgr)*

Gridsmart Technologies, Inc. (2)
702 S Illinois Ave, Oak Ridge, TN 37830
Tel.: (865) 482-2112
Rev.: $1,000,000
Emp.: 11
Traffic & Energy Management Technology & Services
N.A.I.C.S.: 541690

INTIFIC, INC (2)
250 Josephine St Commercial Ofc, Peckville, PA 18452
Tel.: (570) 382-3164
Web Site: http://www.intific.com
Software Development Services
N.A.I.C.S.: 541511

MotionDSP, Inc. (2)
21580 Beaumeade Cir, Ashburn, VA 20147
Tel.: (650) 288-1164
Web Site: http://www.motiondsp.com
Custom Computer Programming Services
N.A.I.C.S.: 541511
Sean Varah *(Founder)*

NEK SERVICES, INC. (2)
2028 Aerotech Dr, Colorado Springs, CO 80916
Tel.: (719) 247-4300
Web Site: http://mss.cubic.com
Emp.: 30
Military Training Services
N.A.I.C.S.: 928110
Bo Todd *(Pres & Gen Mgr)*
Jeff Keers *(VP)*

Nuvotronics, Inc. (2)
2305 Presidential Dr, Durham, NC 27703
Tel.: (919) 296-5500
Electronic Components Mfr
N.A.I.C.S.: 334419
Noel Heiks *(Founder)*

PIXIA Corp. (2)
2350 Corporate Park Dr Ste 400, Herndon, VA 20171 **(100%)**
Tel.: (571) 203-9665
Web Site: http://www.pixia.com
Software Publisher
N.A.I.C.S.: 513210

Patrick Ernst *(Co-Founder & COO)*
Ian Heffernan *(VP-Tech)*
Rudi Ernst *(Co-Founder, CEO & CTO)*

TeraLogics LLC (2)
21580 Beaumeade Cr Ste 230, Ashburn, VA 20147
Tel.: (571) 258-5020
Web Site: http://www.teralogics.com
Emp.: 50
Software Engineering Services
N.A.I.C.S.: 541511
Mark Snellings *(Founder & Dir-Technical)*

URBAN INSIGHTS ASSOCIATES, INC. (2)
1225 S Clark St Ste 601, Arlington, VA 22202
Tel.: (914) 482-7621
Web Site: http://www.urban-insights.com
Transportation Consulting Services
N.A.I.C.S.: 488999

XIO Strategies, Inc. (2)
1919 Gallows Rd Ste 900, Vienna, VA 22182-3964
Tel.: (571) 722-1900
Business Consulting Services
N.A.I.C.S.: 541618

eAccess LLC (2)
4285 Ponderosa Ave M/S 2-1, San Diego, CA 92123
Tel.: (858) 565-4760
Web Site: http://www.eaccessid.com
Smartcard Mfr
N.A.I.C.S.: 334519

Dovel Technologies, Inc. (1)
7918 Jones Branch Dr Ste 600, McLean, VA 22102-3307
Tel.: (703) 288-5300
Web Site: http://www.doveltech.com
Software Development Services
N.A.I.C.S.: 513210
Elma Levy *(Co-Founder)*
Dov levy *(Co-Founder)*
Damon Griggs *(CEO)*
Amr Fahmi *(VP & Controller)*
Jon Hoehne *(VP-Quality Assurance)*
Sharon Palmeter *(VP-HR & Recruiting)*
Pablo Serritella *(VP-Bus Ops)*
Adam Welsh *(Sr VP-Market & Strategy Dev)*
Kimberly Zurliene *(VP-Health & Emerging Tech)*
Kelly Demaitre *(Chief HR Officer)*
Rod Fontecilla *(Chief Innovation Officer)*
Anthony Cristillo *(Sr VP-Health Info Sys-Medical Science & Computing)*
Sudhakar Kesavan *(Chm)*

Subsidiary (Domestic):

Ace Info Solutions, Inc. (2)
11490 Commerce Park Dr Ste 340, Reston, VA 20191
Tel.: (703) 391-2800
Web Site: http://www.aceinfosolutions.com
Information Technology Services
N.A.I.C.S.: 541512
Jay Challa *(Chm & CEO)*
Nar Koppula *(VP-Tech)*
Mike Cosgrave *(COO)*
Vinay Manne *(CTO)*
Alan Kaufax *(VP-Bus Dev)*

Frontgrade Colorado Springs LLC (1)
4350 Centennial Blvd, Colorado Springs, CO 80907-3701
Tel.: (719) 594-8000
Web Site: https://frontgrade.com
Supplier of Semicustom & Standard VLSI Circuits & Custom Circuit Card Assemblies
N.A.I.C.S.: 334413
Mike Elias *(Pres & CEO)*
Mitch Stevison *(Pres & CEO)*

Subsidiary (Domestic):

Aethercomm Inc. (2)
3205 Lionshead Ave, Carlsbad, CA 92010
Tel.: (760) 208-6002
Web Site: http://www.aethercomm.com
RF Amplifiers Mfr Services
N.A.I.C.S.: 334220
Terri Thornton *(VP)*
Court Shaw *(CFO)*
Richard Martinez *(CFO)*

Todd Thornton *(Pres & CEO)*
Leslie Caines *(Dir-HR)*
Freddie W. Chavez Jr. *(VP-Bus Dev)*

HMS Holdings Corp. (1)
5615 High Pt Dr, Irving, TX 75038
Tel.: (214) 453-3000
Web Site: http://www.hms.com
Rev.: $673,283,000
Assets: $1,329,677,000
Liabilities: $381,348,000
Net Worth: $948,329,000
Earnings: $70,149,000
Emp.: 3,170
Fiscal Year-end: 12/31/2020
Holding Company
N.A.I.C.S.: 551112
William C. Lucia *(Chm, Pres & CEO)*
Greg D. Aunan *(Chief Acctg Officer & Sr VP)*
Emmet O'Gara *(Pres-Population Health Mgmt-Grp)*
David Alexander *(Chief HR & Compliance Officer)*
Gary Call *(Chief Medical Officer)*

Subsidiary (Domestic):

Eliza Corporation (2)
75 Sylvan St, Danvers, MA 01923
Tel.: (978) 921-2700
Management Consulting Services
N.A.I.C.S.: 541611
John Puopolo *(Sr VP-Engrg)*

HMS Employer Solutions (2)
355 Quartermaster Ct, Jeffersonville, IN 47130
Tel.: (812) 285-8960
Web Site: http://www.hms.com
Human Resource Solutions
N.A.I.C.S.: 541612

Health Management Systems, Inc. (2)
401 Park Ave S, New York, NY 10016-8808 **(100%)**
Tel.: (212) 685-4545
Web Site: http://www.hms.com
Proprietary Information Management & Data Processing Services for Healthcare Industry
N.A.I.C.S.: 518210
William C. Lucia *(CEO)*

Subsidiary (Domestic):

Permedion Inc. (3)
350 Worthington Rd Ste H, Westerville, OH 43082
Tel.: (614) 895-9900
Sales Range: $1-9.9 Million
Administrative Management Consulting Services
N.A.I.C.S.: 541611
Thomas Schultz *(Gen Mgr & Pres)*
David Sand *(Chief Medical Officer)*
Dennis Gramlich *(VP)*
Seana Ferris *(Dir-Strategic Initiatives)*
Maureen Riley *(Dir-Clinical Review)*

Subsidiary (Domestic):

IntegriGuard, LLC (2)
2121 N 117 Ave Ste 200, Omaha, NE 68164
Tel.: (402) 498-2400
Web Site: http://www.integriguard.org
Administrative Management Consulting Services
N.A.I.C.S.: 541611

Reimbursement Services Group, Inc. (2)
360 Park Ave S 17th Fl, New York, NY 10010 **(100%)**
Tel.: (212) 857-5200
Web Site: http://www.reimburse-services.com
Sales Range: $75-99.9 Million
Medicare Reimbursement Services
N.A.I.C.S.: 518210

VitreosHealth, Inc. (2)
5151 Headquarters Dr Ste 220, Plano, TX 75024
Tel.: (972) 954-9992
Health Care Srvices
N.A.I.C.S.: 621999

Houghton Mifflin Harcourt Company (1)

COMPANIES

VERITAS CAPITAL FUND MANAGEMENT, LLC

125 High St, Boston, MA 02110
Tel.: (617) 351-5000
Web Site: https://www.hmhco.com
Rev.: $1,050,802,000
Assets: $1,974,280,000
Liabilities: $1,643,856,000
Net Worth: $330,424,000
Earnings: $213,578,000
Emp.: 2,300
Fiscal Year-end: 12/31/2021
Holding Company; Book Publisher
N.A.I.C.S.: 551112
William F. Bayers *(Gen Counsel, Sec & Sr VP)*
Bianca Olson *(Sr VP-Corp Affairs)*
Mike Evans *(Chief Revenue Officer)*
Jack Lynch *(Pres, CEO & Dir)*
Amy Metet *(CIO)*
Peter George *(CTO)*
Kristen Duffy Lavelle *(Exec VP-Global Ops & Customer Experience)*
Amy Dunkin *(Gen Mgr-Professional Svcs)*
Matthew Mugo Fields *(Gen Mgr-Supplemental & Intervention Solutions)*
Jim O'Neill *(Gen Mgr-Core Solutions)*
Andrew Goldman *(Exec VP-HMH Labs)*
Elizabeth Marengo *(Chief People Officer)*
Chris Minnich *(Pres)*
Joseph P. Abbott Jr. *(CFO & Exec VP)*

Subsidiary (Domestic):

Curiosityville, Inc. (2)
912 Western Run Rd, Cockeysville, MD 21030
Tel.: (410) 409-4995
Software Development Services
N.A.I.C.S.: 541511

HMH Publishers LLC (2)
222 Berkeley St, Boston, MA 02116-3764
Tel.: (617) 351-5000
Book Publishers
N.A.I.C.S.: 513130
Linda K. Zecher-Higgins *(Pres & CEO)*

Houghton Mifflin Company International, Inc. (2)
222 Berkeley St, Boston, MA 02116-3764
Tel.: (617) 351-3280
Books Publishing Services
N.A.I.C.S.: 513130

Houghton Mifflin Harcourt Publishing Company (2)
222 Berkeley St, Boston, MA 02116
Tel.: (617) 351-5000
Web Site: http://www.hmhco.com
Sales Range: $1-4.9 Billion
Emp.: 300
Book Publishers
N.A.I.C.S.: 513130
Chris Minnich *(Pres-NWEA Div)*

Subsidiary (Domestic):

Channel One LLC (3)
345 Seventh Ave 6th Fl, New York, NY 10001
Tel.: (212) 329-8377
Web Site: http://www.channelone.com
Emp.: 120
Television Broadcasting Services
N.A.I.C.S.: 516120

Choice Solutions, Inc. (3)
420 Lakeside Ave, Marlborough, MA 01752
Tel.: (508) 229-0044
Web Site: http://www.choicep20.com
Sales Range: $1-9.9 Million
Emp.: 25
End-to-End Global Enterprise IT Services & Solutions For Educational Entities
N.A.I.C.S.: 611710

Heinemann (3)
361 Hanover St, Portsmouth, NH 03801
Tel.: (603) 431-7894
Web Site: http://www.heinemann.com
Sales Range: $25-49.9 Million
Emp.: 70
Teacher Training Materials Publisher
N.A.I.C.S.: 513130

Division (Domestic):

Houghton Mifflin Harcourt International Publishers (3)
222 Berkeley St, Boston, MA 02116
Tel.: (617) 351-5000
Web Site: http://www.hmcl.com
Sales Range: $75-99.9 Million
Book Publishers; Educational Material & General Trade; Electronic Instructional Material
N.A.I.C.S.: 513130

Houghton Mifflin Harcourt Learning Technology (3)
222 Berkeley St, Boston, MA 02116
Tel.: (617) 351-5000
Web Site: http://www.hmhco.com
Sales Range: $75-99.9 Million
Education & Consumer Software
N.A.I.C.S.: 513210

Branch (Domestic):

Houghton Mifflin Harcourt Publishing Co. - Austin (3)
10801 Mopac Expwy Bldg 3, Austin, TX 78759
Tel.: (512) 343-8227
Sales Range: $75-99.9 Million
Educational Publishing
N.A.I.C.S.: 513130

Houghton Mifflin Harcourt Publishing Co. - Lewisville (3)
1175 N Stemmons Fwy, Lewisville, TX 75067
Tel.: (972) 459-6000
Web Site: http://www.hmhpub.com
Sales Range: $50-74.9 Million
Emp.: 150
Book Distributor
N.A.I.C.S.: 424920

Houghton Mifflin Harcourt Publishing Co. - Orlando (3)
9400 S Park Ctr Loop, Orlando, FL 32819
Tel.: (407) 345-2000
Web Site: http://www.hmhco.com
Educational Publisher
N.A.I.C.S.: 513130

Division (Domestic):

Houghton Mifflin Harcourt Trade & Reference Publishers (3)
125 High St, Boston, MA 02110
Tel.: (617) 351-5000
Web Site: http://www.hmco.com
Sales Range: $25-49.9 Million
Emp.: 300
Trade & Reference Books Publisher
N.A.I.C.S.: 513130
Linda K. Zecher-Higgins *(Pres & CEO)*

Branch (Domestic):

Houghton Mifflin Harcourt Trade & Reference Publishers (4)
3 Park Ave 18th Fl, New York, NY 10016
Tel.: (212) 420-5800
Emp.: 300
Book Publishing
N.A.I.C.S.: 513130
Ken Carpenter *(VP & Dir-Trade Paperbacks)*
Ellen Archer *(Pres)*
Adriana Rizzo *(VP-Mktg)*

Subsidiary (Domestic):

International Center for Leadership in Education, Inc. (3)
1587 Rte 146, Rexford, NY 12148
Tel.: (518) 399-2776
Web Site: http://www.leadered.com
Emp.: 30
Education Services
N.A.I.C.S.: 611710
Willard R. Daggett *(Founder)*
MaryEllen Elia *(Partner)*
Kyra Donovan *(Assoc Partner)*
Weston Kieschnick *(Assoc Partner)*
Joe Shannon *(Assoc Partner)*
Scott Traub *(Assoc Partner)*
Eric Sheninger *(Assoc Partner)*
Adam Drummond *(Dir-Professional Learning)*
Andrea Tottossy *(Dir-Professional Learning)*
Rachael Harshman *(Dir-Professional Learning)*
Monica Nicholas *(Dir-Professional Learning)*
Pamela Palmer *(Dir-Professional Learning)*
Linda Lucey *(Sr Dir-Content Dev-Intl Center)*
CeCe Mahre *(Dir-Professional Learning)*
Robert Peters *(Sr Dir-Professional Learning)*
Dennis Thompson *(Dir-Professional Learning)*
Penny Reinart *(Sr Dir-Product Mktg-HMH Svcs)*

Northwest Evaluation Association (3)
121 NW Everett St, Portland, OR 97209
Tel.: (503) 624-1951
Web Site: http://www.nwea.org
Sales Range: $100-124.9 Million
Emp.: 670
Child Educational Support Services
N.A.I.C.S.: 611710
Chris Minnich *(CEO)*
Matthew W. Chapman *(Pres)*
Jeff Strickler *(COO & Exec VP)*
Geri Cohen *(CFO & VP)*
Toni Jaffe *(VP-HR & Org Dev)*
Raymond Yeagley *(Chief Academic Officer & VP-Res)*
Mark Campillo *(CTO & VP-Product Engrg)*
Jan Larocca *(VP-Partner Svcs)*
Fred McDaniel *(VP-Product Mgmt & Publishing)*

Riverdeep, Inc. (3)
731 Market St Fl 6, San Francisco, CA 94103-2027
Tel.: (415) 659-2000
Web Site: http://www.riverdeep.net
Sales Range: $50-74.9 Million
Education & Training Software
N.A.I.C.S.: 513210

The Riverside Publishing Co. (3)
3800 Golf Rd Ste 100, Rolling Meadows, IL 60008
Tel.: (630) 467-7000
Web Site: http://www.riversidepublishing.com
Sales Range: $25-49.9 Million
Emp.: 100
Elementary & High School Text Books & Tests
N.A.I.C.S.: 513130

Subsidiary (Non-US):

Tribal Nova, Inc. (2)
4200 Boulevard St Laurent Suite 1203, Montreal, H2W 2R2, QC, Canada
Tel.: (514) 590-4234
Web Site: http://tribalnova.com
Educational Support Services
N.A.I.C.S.: 611710

Peraton Corp. (1)
12975 Worldgate Dr, Herndon, VA 20170-6008
Tel.: (703) 668-6000
Web Site: http://www.peraton.com
Information Technology Infrastructure Design & Management Services
N.A.I.C.S.: 541512
L. Roger Mason Jr. *(Pres-Space & Intelligence Sector)*
Stu Shea *(Chm, Pres & CEO)*
Alan Stewart *(CFO)*
Jim Winner *(Chief Legal Officer & Gen Counsel)*
Reginald Brothers *(CTO)*
Mike King *(Chief Growth Officer)*
Laurie Foglesong *(Chief HR Officer)*
Rob Gianneta *(CIO)*
Phil Mazzocco *(Chief Security Officer)*
Matt MacQueen *(Chief Comm Officer)*
Szu Yang *(VP-Contracts)*
Lori Ellis *(Chief Procurement Officer)*
Roger Mason *(Pres-Space, Intelligence & Cyber)*
Gus Bontzos *(Pres-Defense & Electric Warfare)*
John Coleman *(Pres-Citizen Security & Public Svcs)*
David Myers *(Pres-Comm)*
Alison Paris *(VP-Talent Acq)*
Brian Thompson *(VP/Gen Mgr-Intelligence Mission Solutions)*
William Manel *(Dir-Opportunity Strategy)*
Mark Kersh *(VP-Maritime Solutions)*
Amy Hopkins *(VP-Natl Security Space-Space & Intelligence & Gen Mgr-Natl Security Space-Space & Intelligence)*
John Svienty *(VP-Finance-Citizen Security & Pub Svcs)*
Frankie Velez *(VP/Gen Mgr-Cyber Intelligence Sys)*
Cathy Johnston *(VP-Mission Integration)*
Shaleeza Altaf *(VP & Deputy Gen Counsel)*

Subsidiary (Domestic):

Perspecta Inc. (2)
15052 Conference Ctr Dr, Chantilly, VA 20151 (14.5%)
Tel.: (571) 313-6000
Web Site: http://www.perspecta.com
Rev.: $4,504,000,000
Assets: $5,405,000,000
Liabilities: $4,048,000,000
Net Worth: $1,357,000,000
Earnings: ($676,000,000)
Emp.: 14,000
Fiscal Year-end: 03/31/2020
Holding Company; Information Technology Products & Services
N.A.I.C.S.: 551112
William G. Luebke *(Principal Acctg Officer, Sr VP & Controller)*
John P. Kavanaugh *(CFO & Sr VP)*
Barry Barlow *(Sr VP)*
Tammy M. Heller *(Chief HR Officer & Sr VP)*
James L. Gallagher *(Gen Counsel, Sec & Sr VP)*
Jeff Bohling *(Sr VP & Gen Mgr-Defense Grp)*
Ted Branch *(Sr VP & Gen Mgr-Navy & Marine Corps Bus Grp)*
Steve Heidt *(Sr VP & Program Mgr-NGEN)*
Mike Kirkland *(Sr VP-Offerings & Solution Dev)*
Bill Lovell *(Sr VP & Gen Mgr-Health Grp)*
Kent Matlick *(Sr VP & Gen Mgr-Intelligence Grp)*
Petros Mouchtaris *(Pres/Gen Mgr-Perspecta Labs)*
Kyle Spencer *(Sr VP-Delivery)*
Dave Tender *(VP-Security)*
Rocky Thurston *(Sr VP & Gen Mgr-Civilian, State & Local Grp)*
Orlando Figueredo *(VP-Bus Dev)*
Jennifer Swindell *(Sr VP & Gen Mgr-Risk Decision Grp)*

Subsidiary (Domestic):

DHPC Technologies, Inc. (3)
10 Woodbridge Ctr Dr Ste 650, Woodbridge, NJ 07095-1153
Tel.: (732) 791-5400
Web Site: http://www.dhpctech.com
Technical, Analytical Advice & Research Services
N.A.I.C.S.: 541690

Enterprise Services, LLC (3)
5400 Legacy Dr, Plano, TX 75024-3105
Tel.: (972) 605-6000
Web Site: http://h10134.www1.hp.com
Sales Range: $1-4.9 Billion
Information Technology Applications & Business Process Outsourcing Services
N.A.I.C.S.: 513210

Subsidiary (Non-US):

E Services Singapore Pte. Ltd. (4)
450 Alexandra Road, Singapore, 119960, Singapore
Tel.: (65) 6275 3888
Sales Range: $200-249.9 Million
Emp.: 500
Regional Managing Office; Information Technology Applications & Business Process Outsourcing Services
N.A.I.C.S.: 551114

Enterprise Services (Hong Kong) Limited (4)
14th Floor West Warwick House Taikoo Place, 979 King's Road, Hong Kong, China (Hong Kong)
Tel.: (852) 2953 7333
Web Site: http://h10134.www1.hp.com
Information Technology Applications & Business Process Outsourcing Services
N.A.I.C.S.: 513210

Group (Non-US):

Enterprise Services - Europe, Middle East & Africa (4)
88 Wood St, London, EC2V 7QT, United Kingdom
Tel.: (44) 52704567

VERITAS CAPITAL FUND MANAGEMENT, LLC

U.S. PRIVATE

Veritas Capital Fund Management, LLC—(Continued)
Sales Range: $1-4.9 Billion
Emp.: 16,000
Regional Managing Office; Information Technology Applications & Business Process Outsourcing Services
N.A.I.C.S.: 551114

Subsidiary (Domestic):

E.D.S. International Limited (5)
Cain Road Amen Corner, Bracknell, RG12 1HN, Berks, United Kingdom
Tel.: (44) 1256742000
Sales Range: $75-99.9 Million
Emp.: 90
Information Technology Applications & Business Process Outsourcing Services
N.A.I.C.S.: 513210

Subsidiary (Non-US):

Electronic Data Systems International B.V. (5)
Startbaan 16, 2909 LC, Capelle aan den IJssel, Netherlands
Tel.: (31) 887502211
Web Site: http://www.eds.nl
Rev.: $800,000,000
Emp.: 2,000
Information Technology Applications & Business Process Outsourcing Services
N.A.I.C.S.: 513210

Enterprise Services Belgium BVBA (5)
Mechelen Business Tower, Blarenberglaan 2, 2800, Mechelen, Belgium
Tel.: (32) 15783711
Web Site: http://www.hp.be
Sales Range: $300-349.9 Million
Emp.: 800
Information Technology Applications & Business Process Outsourcing Services
N.A.I.C.S.: 513210

Enterprise Services France SAS (5)
4 Avenue Pablo Picasso, 92000, Nanterre, Cedex, France
Tel.: (33) 147296000
Web Site: http://www.eds.fr
Sales Range: $300-349.9 Million
Emp.: 800
Information Technology Applications & Business Process Outsourcing Services
N.A.I.C.S.: 513210

Subsidiary (Domestic):

Enterprise Services Information Security UK Limited (5)
3200 Daresbury Park, Warrington, WA4 4BU, United Kingdom
Tel.: (44) 1925665500
Web Site: http://www.vistorm.com
Sales Range: $100-124.9 Million
Emp.: 220
Information Security Consulting Services
N.A.I.C.S.: 541690
Andrzej Kawalec (CTO)

Subsidiary (Non-US):

Enterprise Services Italia S.r.l. (5)
Via Gobetti 2b Cernusco sul Naviglio, 20063, Milan, Italy
Tel.: (39) 0299994111
Sales Range: $650-699.9 Million
Emp.: 3,300
Information Technology Applications & Business Process Outsourcing Services
N.A.I.C.S.: 513210

Enterprise Services Sverige AB (5)
Gustav III:s Blvd 36, 16985, Solna, Sweden
Tel.: (46) 86191000
Sales Range: $200-249.9 Million
Emp.: 600
Information Technology Applications & Business Process Outsourcing Services
N.A.I.C.S.: 513210

Subsidiary (Non-US):

Enterprise Services Japan, Ltd. (4)
4 Chome 2-12 Shibuya, Shibuya-ku, Tokyo, 150-0002, Japan
Tel.: (81) 3 3797 8811

Sales Range: $500-549.9 Million
Emp.: 1,000
Information Technology Applications & Business Process Outsourcing Services
N.A.I.C.S.: 513210

Unit (Domestic):

HPE Security - Data Security (4)
20400 Stevens Creek Blvd Ste 500, Cupertino, CA 95014
Tel.: (408) 886-3200
Web Site: http://www.voltage.com
Sales Range: $1-9.9 Million
Emp.: 70
Data Protection Data-centric Encryption, Tokenization & Key Management Solutions
N.A.I.C.S.: 513210

Subsidiary (Domestic):

NHIC, Corp. (4)
75 Sgt William Terry Dr, Hingham, MA 02043
Tel.: (317) 595-4371
Web Site: http://www.medicarenhic.com
Medicare Services
N.A.I.C.S.: 923130

SafeGuard Services LLC (4)
3450 Lakeside Dr 201, Miramar, FL 33027
Tel.: (954) 433-6423
Custom Computer Programming Services
N.A.I.C.S.: 541511

Wendover Financial Services Corporation (4)
1550 Liberty Ridge Ste 120, Wayne, PA 19087
Tel.: (610) 232-5000
Web Site: http://www1.hp.com
Rev.: $20,000,000
Emp.: 175
Auto Loans, Personal Loans, Home Equity Loans & Lines of Credit Services
N.A.I.C.S.: 522310
Susan O'Doherty (Pres)

Subsidiary (Domestic):

Knight Point Systems, LLC (3)
1775 Wiehle Ave Ste 101, Reston, VA 20190
Tel.: (703) 657-7050
Web Site: http://www.knightpoint.com
IT Strategy Consulting
N.A.I.C.S.: 541618
Douglas Duenkel (COO)

QWK Integrated Solutions, LLC (3)
890 Explorer Blvd NW, Huntsville, AL 35806
Tel.: (256) 922-6794
Web Site: http://www.qwkintegratedsolutions.com
Engineering Design Services
N.A.I.C.S.: 541330

Sequa Corporation (1)
200 Park Ave, New York, NY 10166
Tel.: (212) 986-5500
Web Site: http://www.sequa.com
Sales Range: $1-4.9 Billion
Emp.: 10,155
Aerospace Components, Metal Coatings & Aerospace Products Mfr
N.A.I.C.S.: 927110
Carlo Luzzatto (Exec VP)
Marc Werbach (VP-HR)

Subsidiary (Non-US):

Casco IMOS Italia S.p.a. (2)
Via Enrico Fermi 3 5, Alpignano Piedmont, Turin, 10091, Italy
Tel.: (39) 0119670301
Sales Range: $25-49.9 Million
Emp.: 80
Motor Vehicle Electronic Parts Mfr
N.A.I.C.S.: 336320
Roger Higgot (Mng Dir)

Subsidiary (Domestic):

Chromalloy Gas Turbine LLC (2)
3999 RCA Blvd, Palm Beach Gardens, FL 33410
Tel.: (561) 935-3571
Web Site: http://www.chromalloy.com
Emp.: 3,750
Aircraft Engines & Parts Mfr
N.A.I.C.S.: 336412

Subsidiary (Domestic):

Chromalloy Castings Tampa Corporation (3)
3401 Queen Palm Dr, Tampa, FL 33619-1349
Tel.: (813) 885-4781
Web Site: http://www.chromalloy.com
Sales Range: $50-74.9 Million
Emp.: 200
Nonferrous Metal Foundry Mfr
N.A.I.C.S.: 331529

Subsidiary (Non-US):

Chromalloy Gas Turbine Europa B.V. (3)
Sirusstraat 55, Tilburg, 5015 BT, Netherlands
Tel.: (31) 135328400
Web Site: http://www.chromalloy.com
Sales Range: $50-74.9 Million
Emp.: 150
Gas Turbine Mfr
N.A.I.C.S.: 333611
Enrigue Hernandez (Gen Mgr)

Chromalloy Gas Turbine France (3)
Zt Du Vert Galant Avenue Des Gros Chevaux, 95310, Saint-Ouen-l'Aumone, France
Tel.: (33) 134403636
Web Site: http://www.chromalloy.fr
Sales Range: $25-49.9 Million
Emp.: 100
Aircraft Engine Mfr
N.A.I.C.S.: 336412
Christophe Lecanu (Gen Mgr)

Division (Domestic):

Chromalloy Gas Turbine LLC (3)
303 Industrial Park, San Antonio, TX 78226
Tel.: (210) 331-2300
Web Site: http://www.chromalloy.com
Sales Range: $10-24.9 Million
Emp.: 19
Mfr & Repair of Turbine Airfoils & other Engine Components
N.A.I.C.S.: 811210

Chromalloy Gas Turbine LLC - Middletown (3)
105 Tower Dr, Middletown, NY 10940
Tel.: (845) 692-8912
Web Site: http://www.chromalloy.com
Sales Range: $50-74.9 Million
Emp.: 115
Aircraft Engines & Parts Mfr
N.A.I.C.S.: 336412

Subsidiary (Non-US):

Chromalloy Holland B.V. (3)
Sirius Straat 55, Tilburg, 5015 BT, Noord Brabant, Netherlands
Tel.: (31) 135328400
Web Site: http://www.chromalloy.com
Sales Range: $25-49.9 Million
Emp.: 200
Aircraft Engine Mfr
N.A.I.C.S.: 336412

Subsidiary (Domestic):

Chromalloy Power Services Corp. (3)
303 Industrial Park Kelly, San Antonio, TX 78226
Tel.: (210) 331-2400
Web Site: http://www.chromalloys.com
Sales Range: $25-49.9 Million
Emp.: 150
Aircraft Engine Repair
N.A.I.C.S.: 811310
Tom Lark (Gen Mgr)

Subsidiary (Non-US):

Chromalloy S.A. de C.V. (3)
Galaxia 91 Parque Industrial, Mexicali, 21210, BC, Mexico
Tel.: (52) 6865665333
Web Site: http://www.chromalloy.com
Sales Range: $50-74.9 Million
Emp.: 250
Aircraft Engine Parts Mfr
N.A.I.C.S.: 336412

Subsidiary (Domestic):

Chromalloy San Diego Corporation (3)
1071 Industrial Pl, El Cajon, CA 92020
Tel.: (619) 579-9876
Sales Range: $25-49.9 Million
Emp.: 150
Aircraft Engine Repair Services
N.A.I.C.S.: 811310

Subsidiary (Non-US):

Chromalloy Thailand Co. Ltd. (3)
25 Moo 5 Bungkhamproi, Lamlukka, Pathumthani, 12150, Thailand
Tel.: (66) 29850800
Web Site: http://www.chromalloy.com
Sales Range: $75-99.9 Million
Emp.: 500
Aircraft Engine Mfr
N.A.I.C.S.: 336412
Chan Kwai (Mng Dir)

Chromalloy United Kingdom Ltd. (3)
1 Linkmel Rd Eastwood, Nottingham, NG16 3RZ, United Kingdom
Tel.: (44) 1773763639
Web Site: http://www.chromalloy.com
Sales Range: $50-74.9 Million
Emp.: 300
Aircraft Engine Mfr
N.A.I.C.S.: 336412
Michael Foster (Mng Dir)

Syneos Health, Inc. (1)
1030 Sync St, Morrisville, NC 27560-5468
Tel.: (919) 876-9300
Web Site: https://www.syneoshealth.com
Rev.: $5,393,082,000
Assets: $8,199,218,000
Liabilities: $4,704,217,000
Net Worth: $3,495,001,000
Earnings: $266,497,000
Emp.: 28,768
Fiscal Year-end: 12/31/2022
Holding Company; Biopharmaceutical & Medical Device Mfr
N.A.I.C.S.: 551112
Colin Shannon (CEO)
Michelle Keefe (CEO)
Kristen Spensieri (Head-Corp Comm & Mktg-Global)
Baba Shetty (Pres-Tech & Data Solutions)
Jeanine O'Kane (Pres-Syneos Health Comm)
Hillary Bochniak (Chief HR Officer)
Larry A. Pickett Jr. (CIO)
Ben Rudnick (Chief Strategy Officer)
Michael J. Bonello (CFO)
Michael Brooks (COO)
Jim Momtazee (Mng Partner)
Costa Panagos (Co-CEO)
Max Ghez (Head-Clinical Bus Dev)
Larry A. Pickett Jr. (Chief Info & Digital Officer)
Margaret Alexander (Founder)

Subsidiary (Domestic):

INC Research, LLC (2)
3201 Beechleaf Ct Ste 600, Raleigh, NC 27604-1547
Tel.: (919) 876-9300
Web Site: http://www.incresearch.com
Pharmaceutical Research & Development Services
N.A.I.C.S.: 541715

Division (Domestic):

INC Research (3)
441 Vine St Ste 1200, Cincinnati, OH 45202
Tel.: (513) 381-5550
Web Site: http://www.incresearch.com
Sales Range: $400-449.9 Million
Data Processing of Biopharmaceutical Research
N.A.I.C.S.: 518210
Dana Magly (Mgr-Facilities)
Dan Schwartz (Mgr-IT)
David Schneider (Sr Dir-Medical)

Division (Non-US):

INC Research (3)
River View The Meadows Business Park, Station Approach Blackwater, Camberley, GU17 9AB, Surrey, United Kingdom

COMPANIES

Tel.: (44) 1276481000
Web Site: http://www.incresearch.com
Sales Range: $25-49.9 Million
Contract Biopharmaceutical Research & Development Services
N.A.I.C.S.: 541715
Rosie McKellar *(Sr Dir-Central Monitoring)*
Jane Winter *(Sr VP-Global Consulting Unit)*

INC Research (3)
Level 1 20 Atherton Road, Oakleigh, 3166, VIC, Australia
Tel.: (61) 395677600
Sales Range: $10-24.9 Million
Contract Biopharmaceutical Research & Development Services
N.A.I.C.S.: 541715

INC Research (3)
720 King St W, Toronto, M5V 2T3, ON, Canada
Tel.: (416) 963-9338
Web Site: http://www.incresearch.com
Sales Range: $10-24.9 Million
Early Phase Clinical Development Services
N.A.I.C.S.: 541715
Kerry Schoedel *(Dir-Scientific)*

INC Research - Global Clinical Development (3)
Einsteindreef 117-119, 2562 GB, Utrecht, Netherlands
Tel.: (31) 302584600
Web Site: http://www.incresearch.com
Sales Range: $25-49.9 Million
Contract Clinical Development Services
N.A.I.C.S.: 541715

INC Research - Munich (3)
Stefan-George-Ring 6, 81929, Munich, Germany
Tel.: (49) 899939130
Web Site: http://www.incresearch.com
Sales Range: $50-74.9 Million
Contract Biopharmaceutical Research & Development Services
N.A.I.C.S.: 541715

INC Research - Saronno (3)
Vicolo del Caldo 36, 21047, Saronno, VA, Italy
Tel.: (39) 029619921
Sales Range: $25-49.9 Million
Contract Biopharmaceutical Research & Development Services
N.A.I.C.S.: 541715

Subsidiary (Domestic):

Syneos Health, LLC (2)
1 Van de Graaff Dr, Burlington, MA 01803
Tel.: (781) 229-8877
Web Site: http://www.syneoshealth.com
Holding Company; Outsourced Clinical Biopharmaceutical Development & Commercialization Services
N.A.I.C.S.: 551112
John M. Dineen *(Chm)*

Subsidiary (Domestic):

Syneos Health US, Inc. (3)
1 Van de Graaff Dr, Burlington, MA 01803
Tel.: (781) 229-8877
Web Site: http://www.syneoshealth.com
Outsourced Clinical Biopharmaceutical Development & Commercialization Services
N.A.I.C.S.: 541618

Subsidiary (Domestic):

Syneos Health Clinical, LLC (4)
301 College Rd E, Princeton, NJ 08540
Tel.: (609) 951-0005
Web Site: http://www.syneoshealth.com
Holding Company; Clinical Research & Drug Development Services
N.A.I.C.S.: 551112

Branch (Domestic):

Syneos Health Clinical, LLC (5)
500 Atrium Dr, Somerset, NJ 08873
Tel.: (800) 416-0555
Web Site: http://www.syneoshealth.com
Clinical Trials Research
N.A.I.C.S.: 541715

Subsidiary (Domestic):

Syneos Health Consulting, Inc. (5)
1030 Sync St, Morrisville, NC 27560
Tel.: (919) 876-9300
Web Site: http://www.syneoshealth.com
Pharmaceutical & Biotechnology Management Consulting Services
N.A.I.C.S.: 541618

Subsidiary (Domestic):

Pharmaceutical Institute, LLC (6)
1030 Sync St, Morrisville, NC 27560
Tel.: (919) 876-9300
Web Site:
http://www.syneoshealthlearning.com
Training Solutions for Pharmaceutical & Biotech Industry
N.A.I.C.S.: 611430
Celeste Mosby *(VP-Solution Design & Business Dev)*
Yvonne Ash *(VP-Solution Design)*
Freddy Gozum *(Dir-Solutions Design)*
Marissa Liu-Glaister *(Dir-Learning Strategy)*

Subsidiary (Non-US):

Syneos Health IVH UK Limited (5)
Farnborough Business Park 1 Pinehurst Road, Farnborough, GU14 7BF, Hampshire, United Kingdom
Tel.: (44) 1276 713 000
Web Site: http://www.syneoshealth.com
Phase I-IV Clinical Trials; Data Management & Biostatistics; Regulatory Consulting & Marketing Services
N.A.I.C.S.: 541611

Subsidiary (Non-US):

Syneos Health Germany GmbH (6)
Triforum Haus C1, Frankfurter Strasse 233, 63263, Neu-Isenburg, Germany
Tel.: (49) 6102 8130
Web Site: http://www.syneoshealth.com
Phase I-IV Clinical Trials; Data Management & Biostatistics; Regulatory Consulting & Marketing Services
N.A.I.C.S.: 541611

Syneos Health Italy S.R.L. (6)
Via Gonzaga 7, 201123, Milan, Italy
Tel.: (39) 02 8905 3715
Web Site: http://www.syneoshealth.com
Phase I-IV Clinical Trials; Data Management & Biostatistics; Regulatory Consulting & Marketing Services
N.A.I.C.S.: 541611

Syneos Health Netherlands B.V. (6)
Oval Tower De Entree 99 197 14th floor, 1101 HE, Amsterdam, Netherlands
Tel.: (31) 20 3018 500
Web Site: http://www.syneoshealth.com
Phase I-IV Clinical Trials; Data Management & Biostatistics; Regulatory Consulting & Marketing Services
N.A.I.C.S.: 541611

Subsidiary (Domestic):

i3 Pharmaceutical Services, Inc. (5)
5430 Data Ct Ste 200, Ann Arbor, MI 48108
Tel.: (734) 887-0000
Web Site: http://www.syneoshealth.com
Regulatory Consulting, Clinical Research & Clinical Trial Management Services to Biological & Pharmaceutical Firms
N.A.I.C.S.: 541714

Subsidiary (Domestic):

Syneos Health Communications, Inc. (4)
500 Olde Worthington Rd, Westerville, OH 43082
Tel.: (614) 543-6650
Web Site: http://www.syneoshealth.com
Holding Company; Advertising Agencies
N.A.I.C.S.: 551112

Unit (Domestic):

Chamberlain Healthcare Public Relations (5)
200 Vesey St, New York, NY 10281
Tel.: (212) 884-0650
Web Site: http://www.chamberlainpr.com
Health Care, Public Relations
N.A.I.C.S.: 541820

Subsidiary (Domestic):

Gerbig, Snell/Weisheimer Advertising, LLC (5)
500 Olde Worthington Rd, Columbus, OH 43082
Tel.: (614) 848-4848
Web Site: http://www.gsw-w.com
Advetising Agency
N.A.I.C.S.: 541810
Dan Smith *(Gen Mgr)*
Amanda Joly *(Exec VP- Brand & Experience Strategy)*
Marc Lineveldt *(Exec VP)*
Jen Oleski *(Mng Dir & Exec VP)*
Wendy Rankin *(Sr VP & Dir-Agency Ops)*

Branch (Domestic):

Gerbig, Snell/Weisheimer Advertising, LLC - New York (6)
200 Vesey St 39th Fl, New York, NY 10281
Tel.: (646) 437-4800
Web Site: http://www.gsw-w.com
Advertising Services
N.A.I.C.S.: 541810
Nick Capanear *(Exec VP)*
Bryan Roman *(Sr VP-Creative Tech)*
Michael Austin *(Mng Dir-Creative & Tech)*

Subsidiary (Domestic):

Palio + Ignite, LLC (5)
450 W 15TH St Ste 600, New York, NY 10011-7082
Tel.: (518) 584-8924
Advetising Agency
N.A.I.C.S.: 541810

inVentiv Medical Communications, LLC (5)
1707 Market Pl Blvd Ste 350, Irving, TX 75063
Tel.: (972) 929-1900
Advetising Agency
N.A.I.C.S.: 541810

Subsidiary (Domestic):

Synteract Corp. (2)
5759 Fleet St Ste 100, Carlsbad, CA 92008
Tel.: (760) 268-8200
Web Site: http://www.synteracthcr.com
Sales Range: $25-49.9 Million
Emp.: 800
Human Clinical Drug Trials Services
N.A.I.C.S.: 621511
Matthew Smith *(Sr VP-Comml Ops-Global)*
Martine Dehlinger-Kremer *(VP-Pediatric Dev-Europe)*
Marlo Vasquez *(VP-Biometrics-Global)*
Heather Davis *(Exec Dir-Project Mgmt)*
Zia Haque *(Exec Dir-Clinical Data Mgmt)*
John Whitaker *(Exec Dir-Biostatistics)*
Steve Powell *(CEO)*
Frank Santoro *(Chief Medical Officer)*
Karl Deonanan *(CFO)*
Jack Shannon *(Chief Comml Officer)*
Lisa Dilworth *(VP-Rare & Orphan Diseases)*
Elisabeth Schrader *(Exec Dir-Program Strategy, Pediatrics & Rare Diseases)*
Mary Mattes *(Sr VP-Biometrics)*
Cheryl Murphy *(Sr VP-Clinical Dev)*
Charlotte Oehman *(Gen Counsel)*
Derek Ansel *(Dir-Rare & Orphan Disease Drug Dev)*
Hassan Aly *(Sr Dir-Medical)*

Subsidiary (Non-US):

SynteractHCR Benelux NV (3)
Newsroom Alfons Gossetlaan 30, Sint-Agatha-Berchem, 1702, Groot-Bijgaarden, Belgium
Tel.: (32) 2 4643 900
Web Site: http://www.synteract.com
Clinical Drug Development & Trials
N.A.I.C.S.: 541715
Griet Peeters *(Sr Mgr-Clinical Ops)*
Steve Powell *(CEO)*
Frank Santoro *(Chief Medical Officer)*
Jack Shannon *(Chief Comml Officer)*
Karl Deonanan *(CFO)*
Martina Kroner *(Sr VP-Corp Dev)*
Mary Mattes *(Sr VP-Biometrics)*
Cheryl Murphy *(Sr VP-Clinical Dev)*
Charlotte Oehman *(Gen Counsel)*

SynteractHCR Deutschland GmbH (3)
Albrechtstrasse 14, 80636, Munich, Germany
Tel.: (49) 89 12 66 80 0
Web Site: http://www.synteracthcr.com

VERITAS CAPITAL FUND MANAGEMENT, LLC

Clinical Drug Development & Trials
N.A.I.C.S.: 541715
Martina Kroener *(Mng Dir & VP-Europe)*

SynteractHCR Eastern Europe Forschungsgesellschaft m.b.H. (3)
Spiegelgasse 2/2/41, 1010, Vienna, Austria
Tel.: (43) 1 504 6591 0
Web Site: http://www.synteracthcr.com
Clinical Drug Development & Trials
N.A.I.C.S.: 541715

SynteractHCR France SAS (3)
16 rue Trezel, 92300, Levallois-Perret, France
Tel.: (33) 1 55 90 57 10
Web Site: http://www.synteracthcr.com
Clinical Drug Development & Trials
N.A.I.C.S.: 541715
Sebastien Duval *(VP-Bus Dev-Europe)*

SynteractHCR Iberica, SL (3)
Carrer del Princep jordi 21-23 Esc B Entresol 1 B, 08014, Barcelona, Spain
Tel.: (34) 93 226 69 64
Web Site: http://www.synteracthcr.com
Clinical Drug Development & Trials
N.A.I.C.S.: 541715
Steve Powell *(CEO)*
Charlotte Oehman *(Gen Counsel)*
Karl Deonanan *(CFO)*
Frank Santoro *(Chief Medical Officer)*
Jack Shannon *(Chief Comml Officer)*

SynteractHCR Limited (3)
Gemini House Bartholomew's Walk, Cambridgeshire Business Park Angel Drove, Ely, CB7 4EA, Cambs, United Kingdom
Tel.: (44) 1353 66 83 39
Web Site: http://www.synteracthcr.com
Emp.: 41
Clinical Drug Trials
N.A.I.C.S.: 541715
Jamie Pearson *(Reg Dir-EMEA)*
Linda Rawlings *(Exec Dir-Strategic Dev)*
Pascale Goujard-Paquette *(Sr Dir-Clinical Ops-Europe)*
Etienne Drouet *(VP-Strategic Dev)*

SynteractHCR S.r.l. (3)
Via Antonio Vivaldi 13, 00043, Ciampino, Rome, Italy
Tel.: (39) 06 79312131
Web Site: http://www.synteracthcr.com
Clinical Drug Development & Trials
N.A.I.C.S.: 541715
Massimo Ildebrando *(Dir-Project Mgmt & Office Mgr)*

SynteractHCR Sweden AB (3)
Ringvagen 100 9E, 11860, Stockholm, Sweden
Tel.: (46) 8 751 10 80
Web Site: http://www.synteracthcr.com
Clinical Drug Development & Trials
N.A.I.C.S.: 541715
Ilari Jauro *(Dir-Clinical Ops)*

The Wornick Company (1)
4700 Creek Rd, Cincinnati, OH 45242-8330
Tel.: (513) 552-7400
Web Site: http://www.wornick.com
Sales Range: $75-99.9 Million
Emp.: 550
Food Processing & Packaging
N.A.I.C.S.: 424420

Plant (Domestic):

The Wornick Company (2)
200 N First St, McAllen, TX 78501
Tel.: (956) 661-6600
Sales Range: $125-149.9 Million
Food Processing & Packaging
N.A.I.C.S.: 311423

Verscend Technologies, Inc. (1)
201 Jones Rd 4th Fl, Waltham, MA 02451
Tel.: (781) 693-3700
Web Site: http://www.verscend.com
Payment Accuracy Analytics & Insight Services
N.A.I.C.S.: 541219
Emad Rizk *(Pres & CEO)*

Subsidiary (Domestic):

Cotiviti Holdings, Inc. (2)
115 Perimeter Ctr Pl Ste 700, Atlanta, GA 30346 **(64.1%)**
Tel.: (770) 379-2800

VERITAS CAPITAL FUND MANAGEMENT, LLC

U.S. PRIVATE

Veritas Capital Fund Management, LLC—(Continued)
Web Site: http://www.cotiviti.com
Rev.: $678,661,000
Assets: $2,099,229,000
Liabilities: $997,761,000
Net Worth: $1,101,468,000
Earnings: $138,203,000
Emp.: 3,300
Fiscal Year-end: 12/31/2017
Holding Company; Payment Accuracy Analytics & Insight Services
N.A.I.C.S.: 551112
Richard Pozen *(Chief Medical Officer & Exec VP)*
Damien Creavin *(CIO)*
David Beaulieu *(COO)*
Michael Axt *(Sr VP-Solutions Dev, Mktg & Strategy)*
Jonathan Olefson *(Gen Counsel, Sec & Sr VP)*
Tad Kendall *(Sr VP-Go-to-Market & Sls)*
Tony Massanelli *(Pres-Connolly Div & Sr VP-Global Retail)*
Valerie Usilton *(Sr VP-Organizational Effectiveness)*
Jennifer W. DiBerardino *(VP-IR)*
Bradley A. Ferguson *(CFO & Sr VP)*
Nord E. Samuelson *(Chief Digital Officer & Sr VP)*
Mike Sick *(Exec VP-Cotiviti Healthcare)*
Steve Adegbite *(Chief Security Officer & Sr VP)*
Dorie Ramey *(Chief HR Officer)*

Subsidiary (Domestic):

Cotiviti Corporation (3)
The S Terraces 115 Perimeter Ctr Pl Ste 700, Atlanta, GA 30346
Tel.: (770) 379-2800
Web Site: http://www.cotiviti.com
Holding Company; Payment Accuracy Analytics & Insight Services
N.A.I.C.S.: 551112
Richard Pozen *(Chief Medical Officer & Exec VP)*
J. Douglas Williams *(CEO)*
David Beaulieu *(COO)*
Michael Axt *(Sr VP-Solutions Dev, Mktg & Strategy)*
Steve Senneff *(CFO)*
Tad Kendall *(Sr VP-Go-to-Market & Sls)*
Tony Massanelli *(Pres-Connolly Div & Sr VP-Retail-Global)*
Valerie Usilton *(Sr VP-Org Effectiveness)*
Mike Sick *(Exec VP-Healthcare Div)*
John Vitale *(Sr VP-HR)*
Steve Adegbite *(Chief Security Officer & Sr VP)*
Dorie Ramey *(Chief HR Officer)*

Subsidiary (Domestic):

Cotiviti, LLC (4)
1 Glenlake Pkwy Ste 1400, Atlanta, GA 30328
Tel.: (770) 379-2800
Web Site: http://www.cotiviti.com
Payment Accuracy Analytics & Insight Services
N.A.I.C.S.: 561499
Richard Pozen *(Chief Medical Officer & Exec VP)*
Damien Creavin *(CIO)*
Emad Rizk *(Pres & CEO)*
David Mason *(COO)*
Felix Morgan *(CFO)*
Chris Coloian *(Exec VP-Revenue & Growth)*
Joe Morrissey *(Exec VP-Client Engagement)*
Kerri Eskin *(Sr VP-HR)*
Peter Csapo *(Exec VP-Transformation)*

Division (Domestic):

Cotiviti, LLC - Healthcare Division (5)
The S Terraces 115 Perimeter Ctr Pl Ste 700, Atlanta, GA 30346
Tel.: (770) 379-2800
Web Site: http://www.cotiviti.com
Sales Range: $50-74.9 Million
Emp.: 200
Health Plan Payment Policy Management Services
N.A.I.C.S.: 561499
Richard Pozen *(Chief Medical Officer & Exec VP)*

Jon Grandstaff *(VP-Client Svcs)*
Mark A. Besh *(Exec VP-Bus Dev)*
Valerie Usilton *(Sr VP-Org Effectiveness)*
Mike Sick *(Exec VP & Gen Mgr)*

Wood Mackenzie Ltd. (1)
Exchange Place 2 5 Semple Street, Edinburgh, EH3 8BL, United Kingdom
Tel.: (44) 1312434400
Web Site: https://www.woodmac.com
Emp.: 280
Energy Industry Research & Consulting Services
N.A.I.C.S.: 519290
David Parkinson *(VP-Upstream Consulting)*
Alan Gelder *(VP-Refining, Chemicals & Oil Markets)*
Ann-Louise Hittle *(VP-Oils Res)*
Mark Cunningham *(VP-Grp Fin)*
Matthew Chadwick *(VP & Head-Petrochemicals-Global)*
Eilish Henson *(Sr VP-HR)*
Tom Ellacott *(Sr VP-Corp Res)*
Matt Overbeck *(Sr VP & Head-Power & Renewables)*
Louise Noble *(Sr VP & Head-Mktg-Global)*
Linda Doku *(Sr VP & Head-Metals & Mining)*
Valerie Purvis *(Sr VP & Head-Chemicals)*
Maria Cortez *(Sr Mgr-Res)*
Neal Anderson *(Pres)*
Anthony Damiano *(Head-Power & Renewables Res-Global)*
Quentin De Carvalho *(Head-Nylon & Polyamide)*
Daniel Finn-Foley *(Head-Energy Storage)*
Preston Cody *(Head-Analytics Solutions)*
Chris Grieve *(Exec VP-Strategy & Corp Dev)*
Joe Midgley *(Exec VP-Res)*
Mark Brinin *(CFO)*
Nick Gold *(Exec VP & Head-Sls-Global)*
Brett Blankenship *(Dir-Res)*
Greig Aitken *(Dir-M&A Res)*
Paul Gaster *(Dir-Flexible Pkg)*
Karen Padir *(Chief Product Officer)*
Martin Symmers *(Chief Infrastructure Officer)*
Joe Levesque *(Pres & CQO)*

Subsidiary (US):

Power Advocate, Inc. (2)
179 Lincoln St, Boston, MA 02111
Tel.: (857) 453-5800
Web Site: http://www.poweradvocate.com
Temporary Help Service
N.A.I.C.S.: 561320

VERITEQ CORPORATION
6560 W Rogers Cir Ste 19, Boca Raton, FL 33487
Tel.: (561) 846-7000
Medical Equipment Mfr
N.A.I.C.S.: 339112
Kenneth Shapiro *(CEO)*

Subsidiaries:

Brace Shop, LLC (1)
6560 W Rogers Cir Ste 19, Boca Raton, FL 33487
Tel.: (954) 574-9328
Web Site: http://www.braceshop.com
Sales Range: $1-9.9 Million
Emp.: 15
Online Orthopedic Extremity Braces & Rehabilitation Products Retailer
N.A.I.C.S.: 456199
Lynne Shapiro *(Co-CEO)*
Kenneth Shapiro *(Co-CEO & Dir-Medical)*

VERITY CREDIT UNION
11027 Meridian Ave N Ste 102, Seattle, WA 98133
Tel.: (206) 361-5346   WA
Web Site: http://www.veritycu.com
Year Founded: 1933
Sales Range: $25-49.9 Million
Emp.: 167
Credit Union
N.A.I.C.S.: 522130
John Zmolek *(CEO)*
Sherry Steckly *(COO & Sr VP)*
Greg Bruns *(CFO & VP)*

Sarah Slonksy *(Chief Lending Officer & VP-Lending Solutions)*
Jason Hirl *(CTO)*
Zachary S. Gose *(Chm)*
Benjamin Lundell *(Vice Chm)*
Heidi Cleveland *(Chief Mktg Officer)*
Justin Martin *(Co-COO)*
Tina Narron *(Co-Chief Lending Officer)*

VERKLER INC.
7240 Georgetown Rd, Indianapolis, IN 46268
Tel.: (317) 297-7054   IN
Web Site: http://www.verkler.com
Year Founded: 1935
Sales Range: $10-24.9 Million
Emp.: 15
General Contractors
N.A.I.C.S.: 236220
Fred Lusk *(CEO)*
Jim Lusk *(Pres)*

VERMEER CORPORATION
1210 Vermeer Rd E, Pella, IA 50219-7660
Tel.: (641) 628-3141   IA
Web Site: http://www.vermeer.com
Year Founded: 1948
Industrial Ditchers, Stump Cutters, Rock Cutters, Cable Plows, Tree Spades, Brush Chippers, Large Round Hay Balers & Rakes Mfr
N.A.I.C.S.: 333120
Jason M. Andringa *(Pres & CEO)*

Subsidiaries:

Vermeer MV Solutions, Inc (1)
2006 Perimeter Rd, Greenville, SC 29605
Tel.: (864) 277-5870
Web Site: https://www.vermeer.com
Emp.: 3,500
Horizontal Mining & Earth Drilling Equipment Mfr
N.A.I.C.S.: 333515

VERMEER EQUIPMENT OF TEXAS INC.
3025 State Hwy 161, Irving, TX 75062-2137
Tel.: (972) 255-3500   TX
Web Site: http://www.vermeertexas.com
Year Founded: 1978
Sales Range: $10-24.9 Million
Emp.: 150
Construction & Mining Machinery
N.A.I.C.S.: 423810
Maria Quinn *(Asst Controller)*

VERMEER GREAT PLAINS INC.
15505 S Hwy 169, Olathe, KS 66062
Tel.: (913) 782-3655
Web Site: http://www.vermeergreatplains.com
Rev.: $12,000,000
Emp.: 75
General Construction Machinery & Equipment
N.A.I.C.S.: 423810
Scott Ryle *(CEO)*

Subsidiaries:

Vermeer Great Plains Inc. (1)
19812 W Kellogg Dr, Goddard, KS 67052
Tel.: (316) 794-3500
Web Site: http://www.vermeergreatplains.com
Sales Range: $10-24.9 Million
Emp.: 8
General Construction Machinery & Equipment
N.A.I.C.S.: 423810

Vermeer Great Plains Inc. (1)
6260 W US Hwy 60, Brookline, MO 65619
Tel.: (417) 886-3500

Web Site: http://www.vermeer.com
Sales Range: $10-24.9 Million
Emp.: 9
General Construction Machinery & Equipment
N.A.I.C.S.: 423810
Art Swank *(Pres)*

Vermeer Great Plains Inc. (1)
20505 East Admiral St, Catoosa, OK 74015
Tel.: (918) 266-3300
Web Site: http://www.vermeergreatplains.com
Sales Range: $10-24.9 Million
Emp.: 5
General Construction Machinery & Equipment
N.A.I.C.S.: 423830
Charlie Mader *(Mgr-Parts)*
Vern Batley *(Mgr-Parts)*
Kevin Brooks *(Mgr-Svc)*
Ken Harvey *(Mgr-Parts)*
Scott Ryals *(Mgr-Ops)*
Mark Sonnenberg *(VP-Sls)*
Chad Jacobs *(Coord-Sls)*
John Corneliusen *(Mgr-Sls)*
Brian Kalinich *(Mgr-Svc)*
Aaron Swank *(Mgr-Parts)*

VERMEER MIDSOUTH INC
1200 Vermeer Cv, Cordova, TN 38018
Tel.: (901) 758-1928
Web Site: http://www.vermeermidsouth.com
Sales Range: $25-49.9 Million
Emp.: 25
Industrial Machinery & Equipment
N.A.I.C.S.: 423830
Tim Swindle *(Mgr-Credit)*
Charles Smith *(Mgr-Product Support-Memphis)*
Cody Williams *(Mgr-Product Support-Little Rock)*
Corey Vander Molen *(Mgr-Sls-Jackson)*
Forest Nabors *(Mgr-Sls-Memphis)*
Jess Johnson *(Mgr-Product Support-Shreveport)*
John Reeves *(Mgr-Product Support-Springdale)*
Jonathan Donahoe *(Mgr-Product Support-Jackson)*
Mark Ledbetter *(Mgr-Sls-Springdale)*

VERMEER MIDWEST, INC.
120 E Marten Dr, Goodfield, IL 61742
Tel.: (309) 467-3716
Web Site: http://www.vermeermidwest.com
Sales Range: $10-24.9 Million
Emp.: 31
General Construction Machinery & Equipment
N.A.I.C.S.: 423810
Steve Kool *(Pres)*
Matt Knapp *(Mgr-Fin-Vermeer Mid-West)*

VERMEER SALES & SERVICE OF COLORADO, INC.
5801 E 76th Ave, Commerce City, CO 80022
Tel.: (303) 286-1866
Web Site: http://www.vermeer.com
Year Founded: 1968
Sales Range: $10-24.9 Million
Emp.: 32
Whslr of Construction & Mining Machinery
N.A.I.C.S.: 423810
Jon L. Scott *(CEO)*

VERMEER SALES SOUTHWEST INC.
436 S Hamilton Ct, Gilbert, AZ 85233
Tel.: (480) 785-4800

Web Site:
http://www.vermeersouthwest.com
Rev.: $17,313,274
Emp.: 36
Distributing Construction & Mining Machinery
N.A.I.C.S.: 423810
Dale Siever (Mgr-Sls)
Larry Kayton (Mgr-IT & Fin)

VERMEER SOUTHEAST SALES & SERVICE, INC.
4401 Vineland Rd Ste A 14, Orlando, FL 32811
Tel.: (407) 648-1145
Web Site:
http://www.vermeersoutheast.com
Sales Range: $10-24.9 Million
Emp.: 100
Construction Equipment Sales & Services
N.A.I.C.S.: 423810
Jon Jeffcoat (CFO)
Kris Den Bestin (Pres & CEO)
Darrin Jensen (Mgr-Territory)

Subsidiaries:

Vermeer Sales & Service Inc. (1)
2950 Pinson Valley Pkwy, Birmingham, AL 35217
Tel.: (205) 841-9895
Web Site: http://www.vermeeralabama.com
Sales Range: $10-24.9 Million
Emp.: 25
Construction Equipment Sales & Services
N.A.I.C.S.: 423810

VERMEER-WISCONSIN INC.
3090 W County Rd B, West Salem, WI 54669
Tel.: (608) 786-1910
Web Site:
http://www.vermeerwisconsin.com
Sales Range: $10-24.9 Million
Emp.: 45
Industrial Machinery & Equipment
N.A.I.C.S.: 423830
Sam Grooms (Mgr-Svc-Butler)
Ben Brouws (Coord-Equipment & Svc Support-Butler)
Steve Fread (Mgr-Parts & Svc-West Salem)

VERMILION BANCSHARES CORPORATION
420 N Cushing Ave, Kaplan, LA 70548
Tel.: (337) 643-7900 LA
Web Site:
http://www.vermilionbank.com
Year Founded: 1986
Bank Holding Company
N.A.I.C.S.: 551111
James E. Benoit (Pres)

Subsidiaries:

Vermilion Bank & Trust Company (1)
420 N Cushing Ave, Kaplan, LA 70548
Tel.: (337) 643-7900
Web Site: http://www.vermilionbank.com
Commericial Banking
N.A.I.C.S.: 522110

VERMONT CLOCK COMPANY
239 Main St, Isle La Motte, VT 05463
Tel.: (802) 928-4190
Web Site:
http://www.vermontclock.com
Sales Range: Less than $1 Million
Emp.: 4
Reproduction Clock Mfr & Sales
N.A.I.C.S.: 334519
Jack McGuire (Owner)

VERMONT COUNTRY STORE, INC.
5650 Main St, Manchester Center, VT 05255-9711
Tel.: (802) 362-8460 VT
Web Site: http://www.vermontcountrystore.com
Year Founded: 1945
Sales Range: $450-499.9 Million
Emp.: 400
Mail-Order Services
N.A.I.C.S.: 455219
Lyman Orton (Chm)
Bill Shouldice (CEO)
Gloria Chandler (Coord-Ops Trng)
Jim Hall (Pres)

VERMONT ELECTRIC COOPERATIVE
42 Wescom Rd, Johnson, VT 05656-9579
Tel.: (802) 635-2331
Web Site:
http://www.vermontelectric.coop
Year Founded: 1938
Rev.: $76,640,149
Assets: $176,829,631
Liabilities: $101,295,365
Net Worth: $75,534,266
Earnings: $6,705,153
Emp.: 100
Fiscal Year-end: 12/31/18
Distribution of Electric Power
N.A.I.C.S.: 221122
Michael Bursell (CFO)
Peter Rossi (COO)
Vickie Brown (Interim CEO)
Rebecca Towne (CEO)

VERMONT ENERGY INVESTMENT CORPORATION
128 Lakeside Ave Ste 401, Burlington, VT 05401
Tel.: (802) 658-6060 VT
Web Site: http://www.veic.org
Year Founded: 1986
Sales Range: $75-99.9 Million
Emp.: 375
Energy Conservation Services
N.A.I.C.S.: 541690
David Barash (Dir-Bus Dev)
Erika Schramm (Dir-Admin Svcs)
Scott Comeau (CFO)
David Cawley (Dir-Efficiency Smart)
Christa Shute (Dir-Targeted Implementation)
Karen Glitman (Dir-Pub Affairs)
Patricia Sears (Dir-Comm)
Ted Trabue (Dir-DC Sustainable Energy Utility)
Beth Sachs (Founder)
Scott Johnstone (Exec Dir)
Jim Madej (CEO)
Richard Cowart (Pres)
Rebecca Foster (Dir-Efficiency Vermont)
Kerrick Johnson (Dir-Strategy & Corp Affairs)
Everett M. Woodel Jr. (Dir-Midwest)

VERMONT HISTORICAL SOCIETY
60 Washington St, Barre, VT 05641-4209
Tel.: (802) 479-8500 VT
Web Site:
http://www.vermonthistory.org
Year Founded: 1838
Sales Range: $1-9.9 Million
Emp.: 100
Museum & Historical Society
N.A.I.C.S.: 712110
John Grosvenor (Dir-Fin & Ops)
Dan Lord (Mgr-Facilities)
Richard J. Marek (Pres)
Dawn Schneiderman (Treas)

VERMONT HOUSING FINANCE AGENCY
164 Saint Paul St, Burlington, VT 05402-0408
Tel.: (802) 864-5743 VT
Web Site: http://www.vhfa.org
Year Founded: 1974
Sales Range: $25-49.9 Million
Emp.: 40
Housing Assistance Services
N.A.I.C.S.: 624229
Lisa Clark (Mgr-Fin & Ops)
Maura Collins (Dir-Policy & Admin)
Joseph A. Erdelyi (Mgr-Dev)
Tom Connors (CFO)

VERMONT LAND TRUST INC.
8 Bailey Ave, Montpelier, VT 05602
Tel.: (802) 223-5234
Web Site: http://www.vlt.org
Sales Range: $10-24.9 Million
Emp.: 47
Land Conservation
N.A.I.C.S.: 531190
Rick Provost (Dir-Fin)
Elise Annes (VP-Community Rels)
Nadine Berrini (Dir-Comm)
Donald Campbell (Dir-Southwest Reg)
Jon Osborne (Dir-GIS)
Carl Powden (Dir-Northeast Reg)
Teija Huttunen-Green (Dir-Ops & Tech)
Cara Montgomery (Reg Mgr-Stewardship)
Liz Thompson (Dir-Conservation Science)
Tracy Zschau (Dir-Conservation)
Shelly Weeks (Office Mgr)
Joan Weir (Dir-Southeast Reg)
Gil Livingston (Pres)
Julie Curtin (Dir-Legal Svcs)
Christa Kemp (Dir-Donor Rels)
Nick Richardson (VP-Enterprise & Fin)
Siobhan Smith (VP-Conservation & Stewardship)
Jon Ramsay (Dir-Farmland Access Program)
Pamela Burlingame (Reg Mgr-Stewardship)
Pieter van Loon (Dir-Forest Stewardship)

VERMONT MUTUAL INSURANCE CO., INC.
89 State St, Montpelier, VT 05601
Tel.: (802) 223-2341 VT
Web Site:
http://www.vermontmutual.com
Year Founded: 1828
Sales Range: $75-99.9 Million
Emp.: 300
Property & Casualty Insurance
N.A.I.C.S.: 524126
Brian Eagan (CFO, Treas & VP)
Richard Bland (Gen Counsel, Sec & VP)
Joanne M. Currier (VP-Info Tech)
David N. DeLuca (VP-Claims)
Daniel C. Bridge (Chm, Pres & CEO)
Shaun P. T. Farley (VP-Mktg)
Susan Chicoine (VP-HR)
Mark McDonnel (COO & Exec VP)
Terry Moore (VP-Underwriting)

Subsidiaries:

Northern Security Insurance Co. Inc. (1)
89 State St, Montpelier, VT 05602-2954
Tel.: (802) 223-2341
Web Site: http://www.vermontmutual.com
Sales Range: $1-9.9 Million
Emp.: 200
Insurance Agents, Brokers & Service
N.A.I.C.S.: 524126

Thomas J. Tierney (Pres)
Paula Clark (Sec)

VERMONT RAILWAY INC.
1 Railway Ln, Burlington, VT 05401
Tel.: (802) 658-2550
Web Site:
http://www.vermontrailway.com
Year Founded: 1964
Sales Range: $25-49.9 Million
Emp.: 150
Operator of Rail System Primarily Engaged in Freight Hauling
N.A.I.C.S.: 482111
Edward J. Fitzgerald (VP-Mktg)
Marianne Michaels (Controller)
Brent D. Brewer (Gen Mgr)

VERMONT SKI AREAS ASSOCIATION, INC.
26 State St, Montpelier, VT 05601
Tel.: (802) 223-2439
Web Site: http://www.skivermont.com
Year Founded: 1969
Sales Range: $10-24.9 Million
Emp.: 5
Trade Assocation
N.A.I.C.S.: 813910
Sarah Wojcik (Dir-Pub Affairs)
Kyle Lewis (Mgr-Mktg)
Hilary DelRoss (Dir-Mktg)

VERMONT STATE EMPLOYEES CREDIT UNION
1 Bailey Ave, Montpelier, VT 05602
Tel.: (802) 371-5162 VT
Web Site: http://www.vsecu.com
Year Founded: 1947
Sales Range: $25-49.9 Million
Credit Union Operator
N.A.I.C.S.: 522130
Terence Field (Officer-Fin & Sr VP)
Yvonne M. Garand (Officer-Mktg & Bus Dev & Sr VP)
Charles D. Karparis (Officer-Lending & Sr VP)
Rob Miller (CEO)
Kimberly B. Cheney (Chm)
Norman D. McElvany (Treas)
Andrew A. Stickney (Vice Chm)
Rick Hommel (Officer-Retal & Sr VP)

VERMONT SYMPHONY ORCHESTRA
2 Church St Ste 19, Burlington, VT 05401-4457
Tel.: (802) 864-5741
Web Site: http://www.vso.org
Sales Range: $10-24.9 Million
Emp.: 57
Symphony Orchestra
N.A.I.C.S.: 711130
Rebecca Stone (Dir-Mktg)
Grace Spain (Office Mgr)
Jose Daniel Flores-Caraballo (Dir-Chorus)

VERN EIDE MOTORCARS, INC.
5200 S Louis Ave, Sioux Falls, SD 57108
Tel.: (605) 362-9500
Web Site: http://www.verneide.com
Sales Range: $25-49.9 Million
Emp.: 700
Automobiles, New & Used
N.A.I.C.S.: 441110
Jim Lake (Gen Mgr)

Subsidiaries:

Sioux City Motorcars, LLC (1)
4625 Singing Hills Blvd, Sioux City, IA 51106
Tel.: (712) 274-6688
Web Site:
http://www.verneidehondasiouxcity.com

VERN EIDE MOTORCARS, INC.

Vern Eide Motorcars, Inc.—(Continued)
Sales Range: $10-24.9 Million
Emp.: 35
New & Used Car Dealers
N.A.I.C.S.: 441110

VERNAY LABORATORIES, INC.
120 E S College St, Yellow Springs, OH 45387
Tel.: (937) 767-7261   OH
Web Site: http://www.vernay.com
Year Founded: 1945
Sales Range: $25-49.9 Million
Emp.: 400
Precision Molded Rubber Parts Mfr
N.A.I.C.S.: 326291

Subsidiaries:

Vernay Brasil LTDA (1)
Calcadas das Paineiras 22 sala 04 Centro
Comercial Alphaville, Barueri, 06453-048, Sao Paulo, Brazil
Tel.: (55) 11 4191 0583
Medical Equipment Supplier
N.A.I.C.S.: 423450

Vernay Europa B.V. (1)
Kelvinstraat 6, Postbus 45, Oldenzaal, 7575 AS, Netherlands
Tel.: (31) 541 589999
Medical & Plastic Equipment Mfr
N.A.I.C.S.: 339112

Vernay Italia, s.r.l. (1)
Localita Rilate 21, 14100, Asti, Italy
Tel.: (39) 0141 413511
Web Site: http://www.vernay.com
Emp.: 100
Rubber Products Mfr
N.A.I.C.S.: 326299
Vanna Villata (Gen Mgr)

Vernay Laboratories, Inc (1)
Arex Bldg 6th Floor, Marunouchi 1-4-12, Naka-ku, Nagoya, 460-0002, Aichi, Japan
Tel.: (81) 52 857 1307
Web Site: http://www.vernay.jp
Sales Range: $10-24.9 Million
Emp.: 5
Fluid Control Valve Mfr
N.A.I.C.S.: 332912
Katsunor Goto (Country Mgr)

Vernay Manufacturing (Suzhou) Co., Ltd. (1)
No 99 Gangtian Road Gangtian Industrial Square Unit 20B, Suzhou, 215121, China
Tel.: (86) 51262623043
Fluid Control System Mfr
N.A.I.C.S.: 332912

Vernay Manufacturing, Inc. (1)
804 Greenbelt Pkwy, Griffin, GA 30223   (100%)
Tel.: (770) 228-6291
Web Site: http://www.vernay.com
Sales Range: $10-24.9 Million
Emp.: 100
Mfr of Precision Molded Rubber Parts
N.A.I.C.S.: 326299

VERNDALE PRODUCTS INC.
8445 Lyndon, Detroit, MI 48238
Tel.: (313) 834-4190
Web Site:
http://www.verndaleproducts.com
Year Founded: 1958
Dairy Products Mfr
N.A.I.C.S.: 311514
Dale Johnson (Pres)
Fred Kreger (Gen Mgr)
Barry Johnson (Mgr-Procurement)
Rich Perry (Plant Mgr)
Kyle Tannheimer (Sls Mgr)
Kathryn Parikh (Mgr-Quality Assurance)
LaMar Tannheimer (Traffic & Office Mgr)
Derek Townsend (Training Mgr)
Simon Jajjo (Mgr-Sanitation)

Bradley Schleicher (Mgr-Weaver Production)
Lina Gallego (Mgr-Quality Assurance)

VERNON DOWNS CASINO & HOTEL
4229 Stuhlman Rd, Vernon, NY 13476
Tel.: (315) 829-2201
Web Site:
http://www.vernondowns.com
Year Founded: 1953
Rev: $8,000,000
Emp.: 375
Casino, Hotel & Thoroughbred Horse Racing
N.A.I.C.S.: 721120
Scott Freeman (VP-Racing & Facilities Ops)

VERNON E. FAULCONER INC.
PO Box 7995, Tyler, TX 75701
Tel.: (903) 581-4382
Web Site: http://www.vefinc.com
Rev: $50,000,000
Emp.: 30
Crude Petroleum Production
N.A.I.C.S.: 211120
Vernon E. Faulconer (CEO)
Kelly Holbrook (Mgr-Tax)
Barbara Horton (Mgr-Payroll & Accts)
Steve Moses (Sr Mgr-Landman)

VERO BEACH MUSEUM OF ART, INC.
3001 Riverside Park Dr, Vero Beach, FL 32963
Tel.: (772) 231-0707   FL
Web Site:
http://www.verobeachmuseum.org
Year Founded: 1978
Sales Range: $1-9.9 Million
Emp.: 37
Art Museum
N.A.I.C.S.: 712110
Cari Weber (Dir-Fin)
Jo Anne Miller (Mgr-Museum Store)
Robyn P. Orzel (Dir-Dev)
J. Marshall Adams (Dir-Education)
Dane Roberts (Coord-Membership & Annual Giving)
Arthur Jewett (Dir-Facilities)
Sophie Bentham Wood (Dir-Mktg & Comm)
Shanti Sanchez (Mgr-School & Youth Programs)
Jim Liccione (Mgr-Studio)
Louis Collorec (Supvr-Security)
Jack Foley (Supvr-Security)
Bob Treloar (Supvr-Security)
Jaime Becerra (Dir-Security & Technical Svcs)
Sandra Rolf (Chm)
Brady Roberts (CEO)
Rose Ciampa (Sec)
Harvey J. Struthers Jr. (Treas)

VERONA OIL CO., INC.
PO Box 519, Roscoe, NY 12776-0519
Tel.: (607) 498-4141   NY
Year Founded: 1946
Sales Range: $25-49.9 Million
Emp.: 220
Grocery Stores; Petroleum Products
N.A.I.C.S.: 445131
F. Richard Verona (Pres)

VERONICA FOODS COMPANY
1991 Dennison St, Oakland, CA 94606
Tel.: (510) 535-6833   NY
Web Site: http://www.evoliveoil.com
Year Founded: 1924
Organic Olive Oil Producer & Whslr
N.A.I.C.S.: 424990

Michael Bradley (Pres)
Fred Johnson (Mgr-Ops & Quality Assurance)
Veronica Bradley (CEO)

VERONIS SUHLER STEVENSON PARTNERS LLC
390 Park Ave 13th Fl, New York, NY 10022-6022
Tel.: (212) 935-4990   DE
Web Site: http://www.vss.com
Year Founded: 1980
Sales Range: $25-49.9 Million
Emp.: 55
Investment Management Service
N.A.I.C.S.: 523940
Jeffrey Taylor Stevenson (Mng Partner)
David F. Bainbridge (Mng Dir)
Tanya Dessereau (Mgr-Mktg & Comm)
R. Trent Hickman (Mng Dir)
Jack Hartfelder (VP)
Randy Lehman (Dir-Tech)
Patrick N. W. Turner (Mng Dir)
Andrew Goscinski (CFO)
Jackie Jacobs (Chief Compliance Officer & Dir-Ops)
Brad Corbin (Principal)

Subsidiaries:

Access Intelligence, LLC (1)
4 Choke Cherry Rd 2nd Fl, Rockville, MD 20850
Tel.: (301) 354-2000
Web Site: http://www.accessintel.com
Sales Range: $50-74.9 Million
Periodicals, Publishing & Printing, Business to Business
N.A.I.C.S.: 513120
Donald Pazour (Pres & CEO)
Ed Pinedo (CFO & Exec VP)
Macy Fecto (Exec VP-HR & Admin)
Heather Farley (COO)
Jenn Heinold (Sr VP-Energy & Aerospace Events)
Jeffrey Hill (Editor-News-Satellite Grp)
Julie Blondeau Samuel (Dir-Satellite Online)
Steve Barber (VP-Fin Plng & Internal Audit)
Alison Johns (Sr VP-Digital Dev)
Michael Kraus (VP-Production, Digital Media & Design)
Mary Pinto Meyer (Dir-HR)
Rob Paciorek (CTO & Sr VP)
Gerald Stasko (VP & Controller)
Debra Richards (Mng Editor-Satellite Grp)

Subsidiary (Domestic):

Chemical Week Associates (2)
110 William St, New York, NY 10038   (100%)
Tel.: (212) 621-4900
Web Site: http://www.chemweek.com
Sales Range: $25-49.9 Million
Magazine Publishers Focusing on the Chemical Industry
N.A.I.C.S.: 513120
John Pearson (Pres)
Valeria Curzio (Mgr-Sls-Europe)

Films for the Humanities & Sciences, Inc. (1)
200 American Metro Blvd Ste 124, Hamilton, NJ 08619
Tel.: (609) 275-1400
Web Site: http://www.films.com
Educational Films
N.A.I.C.S.: 512110

VS&A Communications Partners III (1)
Park Ave Plaza 55 E 52nd St 33rd Fl, New York, NY 10055
Tel.: (212) 935-4990
Web Site: http://www.vss.com
Sales Range: $75-99.9 Million
Emp.: 50
Equity Fund
N.A.I.C.S.: 523940

Vault.com, Inc. (1)
79 Varick St, New York, NY 10013
Tel.: (212) 366-4212

Web Site: http://www.vault.com
Human Resources & Employment Information Directory Publisher
N.A.I.C.S.: 513130
Noverto Gonzalez (Asst Mgr-Product)

Veronis Suhler Stevenson International Ltd. (1)
8th Floor Buchanan House 3 St. James's Square, London, SW1Y 4JU, United Kingdom
Tel.: (44) 20 7484 1400
Privater Equity Firm
N.A.I.C.S.: 523999

VERRILL DANA LLP
1 Portland Sq, Portland, ME 04101-4054
Tel.: (207) 774-4000
Web Site: http://www.verrilldana.com
Year Founded: 1862
Emp.: 300
Law firm
N.A.I.C.S.: 541110
Charles P. Bacall (Partner)
Eric D. Altholz (Partner)
Scott D. Anderson (Mng Partner)
Lisa S. Boehm (Partner)
Kevin O'Connell (Partner)
Seth Coburn (Assoc Atty)
Kathryn Graber (Partner)
Tawny L. Alvarez (Partner)
Thomas O. Bean (Partner)
Phillip S. Bixby (Partner)
Robert C. Brooks (Partner)
Juliet T. Browne (Partner)
Anthony M. Calcagni (Partner)
Debra R. Cardinali (Partner)
James I. Cohen (Partner)
Kimberly S. Couch (Partner)
Douglas P. Currier (Partner)
Regina M. Flaherty (Partner)
Emily Chi Fogler (Partner)
Benjamin E. Ford (Partner)
Harold J. Friedman (Partner)
Gregory S. Fryer (Partner)
Martha C. Gaythwaite (Partner)
John P. Giffune (Partner)
Kenneth F. Ginder (Partner)
Keith E. Glidden (Chm)
Mark K. Googins (Partner)
Christopher M. Graham (Partner)
Karen K. Hartford (Partner)
James Durham (COO)
Roger A. Clement Jr. (Partner)
David L. Galgay Jr. (Partner)

Subsidiaries:

Rackemann, Sawyer & Brewster Professional Corporation (1)
160 Federal St, Boston, MA 02110-1700
Tel.: (617) 542-2300
Web Site: http://www.rackemann.com
Emp.: 43
Law firm
N.A.I.C.S.: 541110
Stuart T. Freeland (Atty)
Henry H. Thayer (Atty)
Alan B. Rubenstein (Atty)
Michael F. O'Connell (Atty)
Brian M. Hurley (Atty)
Thomas J. Corcoran (Exec Dir)
Mary Schulze (Mgr-HR)

VERSA COMPANIES
3943 Quebec Ave N, New Hope, MN 55427
Tel.: (763) 557-6737   MN
Web Site: http://www.versaco.com
Year Founded: 1983
Sales Range: $100-124.9 Million
Emp.: 235
Holding Company; Electronics Components Mfr & Distr
N.A.I.C.S.: 551112
John W. Moffat (CEO)
Scott Hamlet (Pres)

Subsidiaries:

Versa Electronics (1)

COMPANIES

3943 Quebec Ave N, Minneapolis, MN 55427
Tel.: (763) 557-6737
Web Site: http://www.versae.com
Sales Range: $25-49.9 Million
Emp.: 40
Electronics Components Mfr & Distr
N.A.I.C.S.: 334419

VERSA PRESS, INC.
1465 Spring Bay Rd, East Peoria, IL 61611-9788
Tel.: (309) 822-8272
Web Site: http://www.versapress.com
Year Founded: 1937
Sales Range: $10-24.9 Million
Emp.: 185
Book Printing Services
N.A.I.C.S.: 323117
Joseph F. Kennell *(Chm)*
Steven J. Kennell *(Pres)*

VERSA PRODUCTS COMPANY, INC.
22 Spring Vly Rd, Paramus, NJ 07652
Tel.: (201) 843-2400
Web Site: http://www.versa-valves.com
Sales Range: $1-9.9 Million
Emp.: 130
Control Valves, Fluid Power: Hydraulic & Pneumatic
N.A.I.C.S.: 332912
Gus Badia *(Controller)*
Bahram Nazmi *(Mgr-Engrg)*
Rich Cecilione *(Reg Mgr-Sls)*
Geoff Bekas *(Mgr-Tech Sls)*
Doug Harriman *(Reg Mgr-Sls)*
Stan Antonowich *(Mgr-Tech Sls)*
Jan Larsson *(Pres & CEO)*
Pat Ratchick *(Mgr-Customer Svc)*
Ron Morgner *(Mgr-Facilities)*
Gerry Gramegna *(Mgr-Sls & Mktg)*
Pete Shannon *(Mgr-Inside Sls)*
Koos Van Essen *(Mgr-Matls)*
Evert Ijsendoorn *(Mgr-Engrg)*
Aart Vos *(Mgr-Tech Sls)*
Toni Shostak *(Mgr-HR)*

VERSANT, INC.
11000 W Park Pl Ste A, Milwaukee, WI 53224
Tel.: (414) 410-0500   WI
Web Site: http://www.versantsolutions.com
Year Founded: 1972
Sales Range: $50-74.9 Million
Emp.: 35
Advetising Agency
N.A.I.C.S.: 541810
Will Ruch *(CEO)*

Subsidiaries:
Versant, Inc. - New York Office   (1)
48 Wall St Ste 1100, New York, NY 10005
Tel.: (212) 918-4755
Web Site: http://www.versantsolutions.com
Sales Range: $10-24.9 Million
Emp.: 5
Advetising Agency
N.A.I.C.S.: 541810

VERSARA LENDING LLC
711 3rd Ave 6th Fl, New York, NY 10017
Tel.: (855) 397-3392
Web Site: http://www.versaralending.com
Renting Services
N.A.I.C.S.: 522291
An Phan An Phan *(Sr VP)*

Subsidiaries:
Peerform, Inc.   (1)
369 Lexington Ave 2nd Fl, New York, NY 10017
Tel.: (646) 556-6633
Web Site: http://www.peerform.com
Software Publisher
N.A.I.C.S.: 513210
Ouriel Lemmel *(COO)*

VERSATECH AUTOMATION SERVICES, LLC
11349 FM 529 Rd, Houston, TX 77041
Tel.: (713) 939-6100   TX
Web Site: http://www.vtechas.com
Emp.: 600
Energy Industry Automation Systems Design, Engineering, Testing, Installation & Maintenance Services
N.A.I.C.S.: 541330
Mitchel Wiese *(VP-Sys & Mfg)*
Ted Brown *(Project Mgr)*
David R. Volz Jr. *(Pres)*

Subsidiaries:
VersaTech Automation Services, LLC - Harvey   (1)
1036 Destrehan Ave, Harvey, LA 70058-2517
Tel.: (504) 371-3000
Web Site: http://www.vtechas.com
Energy Industry Automation Systems Design, Engineering, Testing, Installation & Maintenance Services
N.A.I.C.S.: 541330
Marty Dworak *(VP-Global Svcs)*
Chan Dufrene *(Mgr-Health, Safety & Environment & Supvr-Field Svc)*
Kenny Himel *(Project Mgr)*
Kenneth Haas *(Dir-Special Projects)*

VERSATILE METALS INC.
Ste A 913 N Plum Grove Rd, Schaumburg, IL 60173-4752
Tel.: (847) 605-1177
Year Founded: 1976
Sales Range: $10-24.9 Million
Emp.: 4
Nonferrous Metals Scrap
N.A.I.C.S.: 423930
Terrence M. Brown *(Pres)*

VERSATILE PACKAGERS, INC.
933 Chad Ln Ste C, Tampa, FL 33619
Tel.: (813) 664-1171
Web Site: http://www.versatilepackagers.com
Year Founded: 1992
Sales Range: $1-9.9 Million
Emp.: 25
Packaging & Warehousing
N.A.I.C.S.: 561910
Bob Vande Weghe *(Pres)*
Rick Shave *(CEO)*

VERSATILE SYSTEMS INC.
2220 Boston St, Baltimore, MD 21231
Tel.: (717) 796-1936   BC
Web Site: http://www.versatile.com
Year Founded: 1955
Mobile Data Solutions
N.A.I.C.S.: 517112
Andrew Lynch *(Pres)*
Bertrand des Pallieres *(Chm)*
Vicki Turjan *(CFO)*
Rob Meyer *(Exec VP-Product & Mktg)*

Subsidiaries:
Versatile Europe Ltd.   (1)
Dukes Court Duke Street, Woking, GU21 5BH, Surrey, United Kingdom
Tel.: (44) 1483721515
Sales Range: $50-74.9 Million
Emp.: 6
Mobile Data Solutions
N.A.I.C.S.: 517112

Versatile Mobile Systems (Europe) Ltd.   (1)
3 Tannery Lane, Woking, GU23 7EF, Surrey, United Kingdom
Tel.: (44) 1483223789
Web Site: http://www.versatile.com
Sales Range: $25-49.9 Million
Emp.: 4
Software Development & Sales
N.A.I.C.S.: 449210

VERSE COMMUNICATIONS
13807 Ventura Blvd, Los Angeles, CA 91423
Tel.: (818) 981-3023
Web Site: http://www.verseinc.com
Sales Range: Less than $1 Million
Emp.: 5
Consumer Marketing, Crisis Communications, Media Relations, Media Training, Public Relations
N.A.I.C.S.: 541820
Jonathan Cutler *(Founder & CEO)*
Tracy Rubin *(Sr Acct Exec)*

VERSE INNOVATION PRIVATE LIMITED
11th Floor, Wing E, Helios Business Park Outer Ring Road, Kadubeesanahalli, Bengaluru, Karnataka, IN 560103
Tel.: (91) 8030231300
Web Site: https://www.verse.in
Year Founded: 2007
Emp.: 671
Software Publisher
N.A.I.C.S.: 513210
Virendra Gupta *(Founder)*

Subsidiaries:
Magzter Inc.   (1)
1 Rockefeller Plz 11th Fl, New York, NY 10020
Tel.: (646) 756-2524
Web Site: http://www.magzter.com
Software Publisher
N.A.I.C.S.: 513210
Josef Heinle *(Head-Sls-Europe)*

VERSO ADVERTISING, INC.
50 W 17th St 5th Fl, New York, NY 10011-5702
Tel.: (212) 292-2990
Web Site: http://www.versoadvertising.com
Year Founded: 1989
Sales Range: $75-99.9 Million
Emp.: 25
N.A.I.C.S.: 541810
Joelle Celestin *(VP & Art Dir)*
Denise Berthiaume *(Pres)*
Tom Thompson *(VP & Grp Dir)*
Michael Kazan *(Mng Dir & Exec VP)*
Jennifer Pasanen *(VP & Grp Dir)*
Wanda Candelario *(Office Mgr)*

VERST GROUP LOGISTICS, INC.
300 Shorland Dr, Walton, KY 41094
Tel.: (859) 485-1212
Web Site: http://www.verstgroup.com
Sales Range: $50-74.9 Million
Emp.: 400
General Warehousing, Storage & Transportation
N.A.I.C.S.: 493110
William G. Verst *(Chm)*
Robert Jackson *(COO)*
Willie Fox *(Dir-Bus Dev, Transportation & Warehousing)*
Steve Gadzinski *(Gen Mgr)*
Brian Bockrath *(VP-IT)*
Kyle Strenski *(Dir-Bus Dev & Pkg)*
Jeff Greelish *(Dir-HR)*
Jeff Antrobus *(Sr Dir-Bus Dev Warehousing & Logistics)*
Mike Hart *(VP-Risk Mgmt)*
Chris Cusick *(VP-Transportation)*

VERTEC BIOSOLVENTS, INC.

VERTEX DISTRIBUTION

1441 Branding Ave Ste 100, Downers Grove, IL 60515
Tel.: (630) 960-0600
Web Site: http://www.vertecbiosolvents.com
Sales Range: $1-9.9 Million
Emp.: 8
Petroleum Refinery Operating Services
N.A.I.C.S.: 324110
Skip Laubach *(Pres)*

VERTEK CORP
463 Mtn View Dr Ste 300, Colchester, VT 05446
Tel.: (802) 878-8822
Web Site: http://www.vertek.com
Year Founded: 1988
Sales Range: $10-24.9 Million
Emp.: 147
Business Process Outsourcing Services
N.A.I.C.S.: 561439
James M. McCormick *(CEO)*
Al Brisard *(VP-Mktg & Bus Dev)*
Brad Soutiere *(Pres & COO)*
Dan Kelly *(VP-Software Dev)*

VERTEK SOLUTIONS INC
101 Forrest Crossing Blvd Ste 107, Franklin, TN 37064
Tel.: (615) 467-6395
Web Site: http://www.vertexsolutionsinc.com
Year Founded: 2006
Sales Range: $1-9.9 Million
Emp.: 110
Employment Placement Agencies
N.A.I.C.S.: 561311
Brian Murphy *(Pres)*
Melissa May *(Mgr-Acct)*

VERTEX BODY SCIENCES INC.
6287-B Busch Blvd, Columbus, OH 43229
Tel.: (614) 568-7250
Web Site: http://www.vertexbsi.com
Year Founded: 2006
Sales Range: $10-24.9 Million
Emp.: 51
Food & Beverage Mfr
N.A.I.C.S.: 311930
Todd Williams *(Co-Founder & CEO)*
Melinda Inks *(Co-Founder & COO)*
Brittany Dorsey *(Co-Founder & Dir-Mktg)*
Scott Donnelly *(Mgr-External Financial)*
Jennifer Wilkinson *(Acct Mgr)*
Matt White *(Supvr-Customer Svc)*

VERTEX DISTRIBUTION
523 Pleasant St Bldg 10, Attleboro, MA 02703
Tel.: (508) 431-1120   RI
Web Site: http://www.vertexdistribution.com
Sales Range: $50-74.9 Million
Emp.: 18
High Carbon Steel Stainless Steel & Special Alloy Bolt Stud & Other Threaded Fastening Device Mfr
N.A.I.C.S.: 332722
Mark Klosek *(Exec VP)*
Kevin Kourtz *(Mgr-Ops)*
Richard Megliola *(Pres)*

Subsidiaries:
Stillwater Fasteners Inc.   (1)
25 Gurney Rd, East Freetown, MA 02717-1107
Tel.: (508) 763-8044
Web Site: http://www.stillwaterfasteners.com
Sales Range: $10-24.9 Million
Bolts, Nuts, Rivets & Washers
N.A.I.C.S.: 332722

VERTEX DISTRIBUTION U.S. PRIVATE

Vertex Distribution—(Continued)

Gary McLegt *(Gen Mgr)*

VERTEX ENGINEERING SERVICES, INC.
400 Libbey Pkwy, Weymouth, MA 02189
Tel.: (781) 952-6000   MA
Web Site: http://www.vertexeng.com
Sales Range: $10-24.9 Million
Emp.: 450
Environmental Consulting & Construction Services
N.A.I.C.S.: 541620
Jeffrey E. Picard *(Co-Founder & Pres-Environ Insurance Svcs)*
James B. O'Brien *(Co-Founder & Pres-Environ Svcs)*
William McConnell *(Co-Founder & Pres-Construction Svcs)*

VERTEX RESOURCE GROUP, INC.
2570 Fox Field Rd Ste 200, Saint Charles, IL 60174
Tel.: (630) 485-4401   IL
Web Site: http://www.vertexresourcegroup.com
Year Founded: 1992
Sales Range: $10-24.9 Million
Emp.: 693
Human Resource Consulting Services
N.A.I.C.S.: 541612
Jeff Kubas *(Pres)*

VERTEX WIRELESS LLC
500 Wegner Dr, Chicago, IL 60185
Web Site:
  http://www.vertexwireless.com
Wireless Headsets Distr
N.A.I.C.S.: 423690
John Wessel *(CEO)*
Brian Sipe *(Pres)*

Subsidiaries:

Conversa Solutions, LLC   (1)
300 Engelwood Dr Ste A, Orion, MI 48359
Tel.: (248) 276-1824
Web Site: http://www.conversasolutions.com
Software Integration, Application Development, Mobile Device Management & Homologation Support
N.A.I.C.S.: 513210
Robert L. Reed *(Pres)*

VERTICAL COMPUTER SYSTEMS, INC.
2100 N Greenville Ave Ste 201, Richardson, TX 75082
Tel.: (972) 437-5200   DE
Web Site: https://www.vcsy.com
Year Founded: 1992
VCSY—(OTCBB)
Sales Range: $1-9.9 Million
Emp.: 19
Software Publisher
N.A.I.C.S.: 513210
Richard S. Wade *(Pres & CEO)*
William K. Mills *(Sec)*
Laurent Tetard *(COO-SaaS)*
Luiz Valdetaro *(CTO)*
Len Chermack *(CEO)*
Harold Frazier Jr. *(Dir-Mobile Software Dev)*

Subsidiaries:

Now Solutions, Inc.   (1)
101 W Renner Rd Ste 300, Richardson, TX 75082
Tel.: (972) 479-9926
Web Site: http://www.nowsolutions.com
Human Resource Management Services
N.A.I.C.S.: 541612
Marianne Franklin *(Pres & CEO)*
Freddy Holder *(CFO)*
Laurent Tetard *(VP-Ops)*

VERTICAL MARKETING NETWORK LLC
15147 Woodlawn Ave, Tustin, CA 92780
Tel.: (714) 258-2400
Web Site:
  http://www.verticalmarketing.net
Year Founded: 1996
Sales Range: $10-24.9 Million
Emp.: 24
Advetising Agency
N.A.I.C.S.: 541810
Valerie Isozaki *(Acct Dir)*

VERTICAL SALES & MARKETING, INC.
3223 Crow Canyon Rd, San Ramon, CA 94583-4635
Tel.: (925) 901-0910
Sales Range: $10-24.9 Million
Emp.: 5
Frozen Specialty Food Mfr
N.A.I.C.S.: 311412
William Warnken *(COO)*

VERTICAL SEARCH WORKS INC.
1919 Gallows Rd Ste 1050, Vienna, VA 22182-3900
Tel.: (703) 761-3700   DE
Web Site:
  http://www.verticalsearchworks.com
Year Founded: 1980
Sales Range: Less than $1 Million
Emp.: 30
Search & Categorization Software Solutions Designer, Developer, Marketer, Implementer & Supporter
N.A.I.C.S.: 513210
Matthew G. Jones *(CFO)*
Keith Young *(Founder & Co-Chm)*
Colin Jeavons *(CEO)*
Mark MacDonald *(VP-Sls & Adv)*
Gerald Burnand *(CTO)*

VERTICAL VENTURES PARTNERS, INC.
3008 San Isidro St, Tampa, FL 33629
Tel.: (813) 247-4323
Web Site:
  http://www.airheadsusa.com
Sales Range: $1-9.9 Million
Children's Entertainment
N.A.I.C.S.: 713990
Stephen E. Johnston *(Pres)*

VERTICAL WEB MEDIA LLC
125 S Wacker Dr Ste 2900, Chicago, IL 60606
Tel.: (312) 362-9527   DE
Web Site:
  http://www.internetretailer.com
Year Founded: 2000
Sales Range: $10-24.9 Million
Emp.: 30
Periodical Publishers
N.A.I.C.S.: 513120
Cindy Wilkins *(Mgr-Midwest & Intl)*
Don Davis *(Editor-in-Chief)*
Judy Dellert *(Mgr-IR-Southeast)*
Nancy Bernardini *(Mgr-Northeast)*
Paul Demery *(Editor-B2BecNews)*
Sue Kroeger *(Mgr-Fin)*
Zak Stambor *(Mng Editor)*
Tom Duggan *(VP-Sls & Product Dev)*
Allison Enright *(Editor)*
Matt Holmes *(Mgr-Client Svcs & Webinar Program)*
Oliver Love *(Mgr-Sls-B2BecNews & B2BecommerceWorld.com)*
Stefany Zaroban *(Dir-Res)*
Winnie Lee *(Mgr-Customer Svcs & Ad Traffic)*
Mary Wagner *(Dir-Conference Program)*
Katie Evans *(Editor-Tech)*

Tracy Maple *(Mng Editor-Digital Content)*
Adam Campbell *(Mgr-Email)*

VERTICALRESPONSE, INC.
50 Beale St 10th Fl, San Francisco, CA 94105
Tel.: (415) 905-6880
Web Site:
  http://www.verticalresponse.com
Year Founded: 2001
Sales Range: $10-24.9 Million
Emp.: 105
Internet-Based Business Support Services
N.A.I.C.S.: 513210
David Shiba *(Gen Mgr)*
Rahul Dubey *(VP-Engrg)*

VERTIGLO
121 S Orange Ave Plaza Tower N Suite 1500, Orlando, FL 32801
Tel.: (866) 744-5665
Web Site: http://www.vertiglo.com
Year Founded: 1997
Sales Range: $10-24.9 Million
Emp.: 60
Developer of Custom Mobile Applications, Websites & Software
N.A.I.C.S.: 513210
Luke Roopra *(Co-Founder & Pres)*
Leanne Roopra *(Co-Founder)*

VERTILUX LTD.
7300 NW 35th Ter, Miami, FL 33122-1241
Tel.: (305) 591-1719   FL
Web Site: http://www.vertilux.com
Year Founded: 1983
Sales Range: $10-24.9 Million
Emp.: 70
Mfr Window Covering & Draperies
N.A.I.C.S.: 423220
Jose Garcia *(CEO)*
Bernardo Mendez *(Controller)*

VERTIVE, LLC
3721 Executive Center Dr Ste 100, Austin, TX 78731
Tel.: (512) 342-8378
Web Site: http://www.vertive.com
Year Founded: 2003
Sales Range: $1-9.9 Million
Search Engine Marketing & Affiliate Marketing Consulting
N.A.I.C.S.: 541613
Steve Schaffer *(Founder & CEO)*
Rohit Namjoshi *(VP-Tech)*
Howard Schaffer *(Gen Mgr)*
Josh Butts *(Dir-Engrg)*
Ryan Adams *(VP-Online Mktg & Customer Acquisition)*
Kate Sperber *(VP-Acct Partnerships)*
Michael Scheschuk *(VP-Mdsg & ECommerce Ops)*
Scott Griffin *(VP-Product)*

VERTRUE INC.
20 Glover Ave, Norwalk, CT 06850-1219
Tel.: (203) 324-7635   DE
Web Site: http://www.vertrue.com
Year Founded: 1989
Sales Range: $800-899.9 Million
Emp.: 2,500
Innovative Internet Discount Membership Programs Services
N.A.I.C.S.: 561499
Vincent DiBenedetto *(Exec VP-Health & Insurance Svcs)*
Vincent DiBenedetto *(Exec VP-Health & Insurance Svcs)*
George Thomas *(Gen Counsel)*

Subsidiaries:

Coverdell & Company, Inc.   (1)

8770 W Bryn Mawr Ave Ste 1000, Chicago, IL 60631-3515
Tel.: (773) 867-4400
Web Site: http://www.coverdell.com
Provider of Membership Program Services
N.A.I.C.S.: 524210
Vickie Mellon *(VP-Customer Svc)*
Vincent DiBenedetto *(Pres & CEO)*
Kathy Lannen *(Exec VP)*
Harry Amsden *(CFO)*
Jonty Yamisha *(CMO)*
Brian Branchick *(Controller & VP-Fin)*
David Putnam *(VP-Ops & IT)*

Division (Domestic):

Coverdell   (2)
8770 West Bryn Mawr Ste 1000, Chicago, IL 60631
Tel.: (773) 399-9000
Web Site: http://www.coverdell.com
Provider of Insurance Coverage Services
N.A.I.C.S.: 561499

Subsidiary (Non-US):

MemberWorks Canada Corporation   (2)
1801 McGill College Ave 8th Floor, Montreal, H3A 2N4, QC, Canada   (100%)
Tel.: (514) 847-7800
Web Site: http://www.memberworks.ca
Sales Range: $50-74.9 Million
Membership Program Services
N.A.I.C.S.: 561499

Neverblue Media Incorporated   (1)
Suite 201 1221 Broad Street, Victoria, V8W 2A4, BC, Canada
Tel.: (250) 386-5323
Web Site: http://www.globalwidemedia.com
Marketing Consulting Services
N.A.I.C.S.: 541613
Jennifer Carr *(VP-Fin & Acctg)*
Eric J. Gerritsen *(VP-Sls & Bus Dev)*
Bjorn Hougaard *(VP-Network Distr)*
Justyna Jakeman *(Dir-Compliance & Legal Affairs)*
Reed Pridy *(VP-Performance Media)*

VERUS BANK OF COMMERCE
3700 S College Ave Unit 102, Fort Collins, CO 80525
Tel.: (970) 204-1010
Web Site: http://www.verusboc.com
Year Founded: 2005
Sales Range: $10-24.9 Million
Emp.: 20
Banking & Financial Services
N.A.I.C.S.: 522110
Kathy Slavick *(COO)*
Todd Guymon *(Sr VP-Comml Lending)*

VERUS CONSULTING GROUP LLP
999 Vanderbilt Rd Ste 200, Naples, FL 34108
Web Site:
  http://www.verusconsulting.net
Year Founded: 2008
Sales Range: $1-9.9 Million
Emp.: 25
Financial Services Consulting
N.A.I.C.S.: 541618
Thomas D'Amato *(Sr VP-Bus Dev)*

VERVE, A CREDIT UNION
2900 Universal St, Oshkosh, WI 54904
Tel.: (920) 236-7040   WI
Web Site: http://www.verveacu.com
Year Founded: 1937
Sales Range: $10-24.9 Million
Emp.: 129
Credit Union Operator
N.A.I.C.S.: 522130
Kevin J. Ralofsky *(Pres & CEO)*
Mark Gross *(VP-Legal & Risk Mgmt)*
Audra Mead *(VP-HR & Admin)*
Eric Regner *(VP-IT)*
Robert Matz *(CFO & Exec VP)*

Subsidiaries:

South Central Bank, N.A. (1)
525 W Roosevelt Rd, Chicago, IL 60607
Tel.: (312) 491-7000
Web Site: http://www.banksouthcentral.com
Rev.: $10,258,000
Emp.: 45
State Trust Companies Accepting Deposits, Commercial
N.A.I.C.S.: 522110
Todd Grayson (CEO)
David Cohn (Sr VP)

VERVENT INC.
10182 Telesis Ct Ste 300, San Diego, CA 92121
Tel.: (858) 578-0010   DE
Web Site: https://www.vervent.com
Year Founded: 1988
Sales Range: $1-9.9 Million
Emp.: 11
Personal Credit Institutions
N.A.I.C.S.: 522291

Subsidiaries:

First Equity Card Corporation (1)
1120 Welsh Rd, North Wales, PA 19454
Tel.: (215) 631-1201
Rev.: $4,100,000
Emp.: 20
Commericial Banking
N.A.I.C.S.: 522110
Jeff Denton (CFO)
Tim Clarke (CEO)

VERY, INC.
PO Box 517, Menlo Park, CA 94026
Tel.: (650) 323-1101
Web Site: http://www.very-inc.com
Year Founded: 1997
Sales Range: Less than $1 Million
Emp.: 10
Collateral, Full Service, Print, Radio
N.A.I.C.S.: 541810
George Chadwick (Pres & Dir-Creative)

VESA HEALTH & TECHNOLOGY, INC.
427 E 9th St, San Antonio, TX 78215
Tel.: (210) 787-4469
Web Site: http://www.vesahealth.com
Year Founded: 2007
Sales Range: $10-24.9 Million
Emp.: 149
Human Resource Consulting Services
N.A.I.C.S.: 541612
Steve Gallegos (Pres & CEO)

VESCO MATERIAL HANDLING EQUIPMENT
355 Business Park Dr, Winston Salem, NC 27107
Tel.: (336) 397-5000
Web Site: http://www.actforklift.com
Year Founded: 1953
Sales Range: $10-24.9 Million
Emp.: 60
Materials Handling Machinery
N.A.I.C.S.: 423830
David Hair (Controller)
J. Williford (Pres)

VESCO OIL CORPORATION
16055 W 12 Mile Rd, Southfield, MI 48076-2909
Tel.: (248) 557-1600   MI
Web Site: http://www.vescooil.com
Year Founded: 1947
Sales Range: $100-124.9 Million
Emp.: 200
Mfr & Retailer of Petroleum Products
N.A.I.C.S.: 424720
Donald Epstein (CEO)
Lilly Epstein Stotland (Pres)
Marjory Winkelman Epstein (Chm)

VESEY STREET CAPITAL PARTNERS, L.L.C
412 W 15th St 2nd Fl, New York, NY 10011
Tel.: (646) 847-2474   DE
Web Site: https://www.vscpllc.com
Year Founded: 2014
Private Equity
N.A.I.C.S.: 523940

Subsidiaries:

Safecor Health, LLC (1)
317 New Boston St Ste 100, Woburn, MA 01801-6231
Web Site: http://www.safecorhealth.com
Packaging & Labeling Services
N.A.I.C.S.: 561910
Susan Blatti (Mgr-Quality Assurance)

VESPA GROUP, LLC
201 N Illinois St S Tower 16th Fl, Indianapolis, IN 46204
Tel.: (317) 360-5736
Web Site: http://www.vespa-group.com
Year Founded: 2014
Sales Range: $1-9.9 Million
Emp.: 59
Software Development Services
N.A.I.C.S.: 541511
Tony Vespa (Founder)

VESSCO LLC
601 S Broadway Ste X, Denver, CO 80209
Tel.: (303) 871-9944
Year Founded: 1983
Rev.: $20,000,000
Emp.: 23
Office Furniture Whslr
N.A.I.C.S.: 423210

VEST ADVERTISING
3007 Sprowl Rd, Louisville, KY 40299-3620
Tel.: (502) 267-5335
Web Site: http://www.vestadvertising.com
Year Founded: 1991
Sales Range: $25-49.9 Million
Emp.: 25
N.A.I.C.S.: 541810
Rita Vest (Pres)
Mitch Gregory (Dir-Creative)
Jake Stephenson (Dir-Art)

VESTA CORP.
11950 SW Garden Pl, Portland, OR 97223
Tel.: (503) 790-2500
Web Site: http://www.trustvesta.com
Year Founded: 1995
Sales Range: $25-49.9 Million
Emp.: 600
Provider of Fraud Prevention & Customer Service to the Telecommunications Industry
N.A.I.C.S.: 561499
Douglas M. Fieldhouse (Pres)
Chris Uriarte (Chief Payments & Strategy Officer)
Tom Byrnes (Chief Revenue Officer)
Jonathan Le (Chief Risk & Data Officer)
Eric Hopper (CTO)
Richard Hanlon (Sr VP-Intl)
Ashley Johnson (Dir-Compliance)
Michael T. Vollkommer (CFO)
Ron Hynes (CEO)
Tan Truong (CIO)
Laura Stepp (Chief People Officer)

VESTA EQUITY, LLC
6960 Professional Pkwy W, Sarasota, FL 34240
Tel.: (941) 388-0588
Web Site: http://www.vestaequity.com
Year Founded: 2008
Rev.: $90,000,000
Private Equity
N.A.I.C.S.: 523999
George W. Kruse (Mng Dir)
Adam Woodard (VP)
Ernie Pliscott (Mgr-Assets)

VESTA, INC.
9301 Annapolis Rd, Lanham, MD 20706
Tel.: (240) 296-6300   MD
Web Site: http://www.vesta.org
Year Founded: 1981
Sales Range: $10-24.9 Million
Emp.: 244
Behavioral Healthcare Services
N.A.I.C.S.: 621420
Jennifer Cooper (Mgr-Cafe)
Ruth Green (COO)
Stephen Freiman (Chm)
Jignesh Dalal (CEO)
Nicole Myrick (Mgr-Residential Program House)

VESTAL MANUFACTURING ENTERPRISES, INC.
176 Industrial Park Rd, Sweetwater, TN 37874
Tel.: (423) 337-6125   TN
Web Site: http://www.vestalmfg.com
Year Founded: 1946
Iron & Steel Fabricated Components & Municipal Castings Mfr & Distr
N.A.I.C.S.: 331511
Keith E. Shope (Pres & CEO)

VESTAR CAPITAL PARTNERS, LLC
520 Madison Ave 33rd Fl, New York, NY 10022
Tel.: (212) 351-1600   NY
Web Site: http://www.vestarcapital.com
Year Founded: 1988
Rev.: $11,000,000,000
Emp.: 55
Privateer Equity Firm
N.A.I.C.S.: 523999
Michelle D. Bergman (Chief Compliance Officer & Interim Gen Counsel)
James P. Kelley (Co-Founding Partner & Mng Dir)
Kenneth J. O'Keefe (Mng Dir, COO & Head-IR)
Daniel S. O'Connell (Co-Founder & CEO)
Norman W. Alpert (Co-Pres, Co-Founding Partner & Co-Head-Investments)
Kevin A. Mundt (Mng Dir)
Aaron J. Jenkins (Controller-Fund)
Arthur J. Nagle (Co-Founding Partner)
Brendan J. Spillane (Mng Dir & CFO)
Helen Lee (Mgr-IT & Facilities)
Chris A. Durbin (Mng Dir)
Robert L. Rosner (Co-Founding Partner)
Nikhil J. Bhat (Mng Dir & Co-Head-Investments)
Diya Talwar (Mng Dir-Consumer Team)
Roger C. Holstein (Mng Dir)
Mike Vaupen (Mng Dir)
Jake Olson (Mng Dir-Bus & Tech Svcs Team)
Angela Yun (Principal)
Wilson Orr (Principal-Healthcare Investments)
Ian Singleton (Principal)
Kimberly Lu (VP)
Alex Veronneau (VP)

Subsidiaries:

21st Century Oncology Holdings, Inc. (1)
2270 Colonial Blvd, Fort Myers, FL 33907
Tel.: (239) 931-7254
Web Site: http://www.21co.com
Rev.: $1,079,227,000
Assets: $1,128,244,000
Liabilities: $1,802,874,000
Net Worth: ($674,630,000)
Earnings: ($126,842,000)
Emp.: 3,930
Fiscal Year-end: 12/31/2015
Holding Company; Cancer Treatment Centers Operator
N.A.I.C.S.: 551112
William R. Spalding (Pres)
William R. Spalding (Pres)
Daniel E. Dosoretz (Founder)
Constantine A. Mantz (Chief Medical Officer)
Gary Delanois (Sr VP-Ops-United States)
Troy Guthrie (Dir-Clinical Res)
Ricardo Andisco (Dir-Projects)
Daniel H. Galmarini (CTO & Dir-Physics & Engrg)
Timothy D. Shafman (Sr VP & Dir-Natl Medical)
Matthew Anderson (Exec VP-Strategic Initiatives)
Doug Staut (Interim CFO)
Odette Bolano (Partner)

Subsidiary (Domestic):

21st Century Oncology, Inc. (2)
2270 Colonial Blvd, Fort Myers, FL 33907
Tel.: (239) 931-7333
Web Site: http://www.21stcenturyoncology.com
Radiation Therapy Services for Cancer Patients
N.A.I.C.S.: 621111
Daniel E. Dosoretz (Founder)
Joseph Biscardi (Chief Acctg Officer, Sr VP, Controller & Asst Treas)
Eduardo Fernandez (Sr VP-Medical Affairs & Dir-Medical-Radiation Oncologist)
Constantine A. Mantz (Chief Medical Officer)
Daniel H. Galmarini (CTO & Dir-Physics & Engrg)
Gary Delanois (Sr VP-United States Ops)
H. Hugo Myslicki (Sr VP-Corp Dev)
LeAnne M. Stewart (CFO)
Charlie Powell (COO)
Frank G. English IV (Treas & VP-Intl Fin)

OnCure Holdings, Inc. (2)
188 Inverness Dr W Ste 650, Englewood, CO 80112
Tel.: (303) 643-6500
Investment Management Service
N.A.I.C.S.: 523940

Subsidiary (Domestic):

Oncure Medical Corporation (3)
188 Inverness Dr W Ste 650, Englewood, CO 80112
Tel.: (303) 643-6500
Web Site: http://www.oncure.com
Emp.: 25
Health Care Srvices
N.A.I.C.S.: 621999
James D. Nadauld (Chm)
Bradford C. Burkett (CEO)
William Pegler (COO & Sr VP-Ops)
George A. Welton (CIO & Sr VP)
Timothy Peach (CFO & Treas)

American Roland Food Corp. (1)
71 W 23rd St, New York, NY 10010
Tel.: (212) 741-8290
Web Site: http://www.rolandfoods.com
Sales Range: $1-9.9 Million
Emp.: 100
Specialty Foods Distr
N.A.I.C.S.: 445298
James Wagner (CEO)
Tyler Hawes (COO)
Ted McCormick (CFO)

FL Selenia Luxco S.c.a. (1)
Via Santena 1 3, 10029, Villastellone, Italy
Tel.: (39) 0119613559
Sales Range: $550-599.9 Million
Lubricant Mfr
N.A.I.C.S.: 333310

Healthgrades Operating Company, Inc. (1)

VESTAR CAPITAL PARTNERS, LLC

Vestar Capital Partners, LLC—(Continued)

1801 California St Ste 800, Denver, CO 80202
Tel.: (303) 716-0041
Web Site: http://www.healthgrades.com
Sales Range: $50-74.9 Million
Medical Practice Management Services
N.A.I.C.S.: 621111
Norm Alpert (Chm)
Brad Bowman (Chief Medical Officer)
Rob Draughon (CEO)
Kate Hyatt (Chief People Officer)
Evan Marks (Chief Strategy Officer)
Keith Nyhouse (CMO)
C. J. Singh (CIO)
Rupen Patel (Chief Strategy Officer)
Scott Booker (CEO)

Subsidiary (Domestic):

Influence Health, Inc. (2)
3000 Riverchase Galleria Ste 1500, Birmingham, AL 35244
Tel.: (205) 982-5800
Web Site: http://www.influencehealth.com
Healthcare Connectivity Solutions
N.A.I.C.S.: 541511
Shaun L. Priest (Sr VP-Strategic Accts)
Dale Edwards (Exec VP-Sls)
Peter Kuhn (Pres & Chief Customer Officer)
Kyra Hagan (Sr VP-Mktg & Gen Mgr-Web Presence Solutions)
Tim Blackmon (Sr VP-Engrg)
Venkatesh Ravirala (Sr VP & Chief Analytics Officer)
Patti Mordecai (VP-HR)
Mike Oakman (VP-Clinical Delivery)
Eric Martin (Dir-Convert Implementation Svcs)
Ashley Thomas (Mgr-Product Mktg)
Scott Harvey (Mgr-Creative)
Brett Keenan (VP-Client Strategy)
Autumn Lunceford (Coord-Client-Directory Mgmt)
Hayley Gigous (Mgr-Campaign)
Stephan Cherak (Mgr-Campaign)
Sean Brasher (Dir-Tech)
John Brennan (Chm)
Joy Johnston (Dir-Client Engagement & Svc Delivery)
Chris Gilliam (Dir-QA & DevOps)
Suzanne Carlson (Partner-Strategic Mktg)
Jeffrey Allegrezza (Sr VP-Customer Care)
Michael Bermudez (VP-Architecture & Engrg)
Kyle Easterling (Engr-Software QA)
Nick Hogan (Mgr-Owned Media)
Boakai Mamey (Engr-Front End)
Jay Clark (Engr-DevOps)
Shawn Wideman (Dir-Creative)
Rupen Patel (CEO)
Dave Morgan (CFO)

Subsidiary (Domestic):

BrightWhistle, Inc. (3)
1440 Dutch Valley Pl NE Ste 1100, Atlanta, GA 30324
Tel.: (404) 919-7787
Web Site: http://www.brightwhistle.com
Digital Marketing Platform for Healthcare Industry
N.A.I.C.S.: 541519
Greg Foster (Co-Founder & CEO)

Third Wave Research Group, Ltd. (3)
305 S Main St, Verona, WI 53593
Tel.: (608) 848-9283
Sales Range: $10-24.9 Million
Commercial Nonphysical Research Services
N.A.I.C.S.: 541910

Lereta LLC (1)
1123 Park View Dr, Covina, CA 91724-3748
Web Site: http://www.lereta.com
Accounting Services
N.A.I.C.S.: 541219
John Walsh (Pres & CEO)
John Short (VP-Bus Dev)
Shannon McClaughry (VP-Customer Success)
Jim V. Micali (COO)
P. A. Larkins (Chm)

Nonni's Foods LLC (1)
3920 E Pine St, Tulsa, OK 74115
Tel.: (918) 560-4150
Web Site: http://www.nonnisfoods.com
Cookies & Cracker Mfr
N.A.I.C.S.: 311821
Michelle Talbot (Mgr-Corp Logistics & Supply Chain)

Nybron Flooring International Corporation (1)
Zurcherstrasse 170, CH 8645, Jona, Switzerland
Tel.: (41) 552206050
Web Site: http://www.nybron.com
Sales Range: $250-299.9 Million
Wood Flooring Mfr
N.A.I.C.S.: 321918

Subsidiary (Non-US):

AB Gustaf Kahr (2)
Dumderbergsgatan Laan 10, PO Box 805, Nybro, 38241, Sweden (100%)
Tel.: (46) 48146000
Web Site: http://www.kahrs.se
Sales Range: $75-99.9 Million
Wood Flooring Mfr
N.A.I.C.S.: 238330
Fredrik Alfredsson (Reg Mgr-Nordic)

Quest Analytics LLC (1)
4321 W College Ave Ste 300, Appleton, WI 54914
Tel.: (920) 739-4552
Web Site: http://www.questanalytics.com
Sales Range: $1-9.9 Million
Emp.: 12
Commercial Software Development & Consulting Services
N.A.I.C.S.: 513210
Roger C. Holstein (Chm)
David H. Hill (Co-Founder & CTO)
John P. Weis (Co-Founder & Pres)
Steven Levin (CEO)

Roland Foods, LLC (1)
71 W 23rd St, New York, NY 10010
Tel.: (212) 741-8290
Web Site: http://www.rolandfoods.com
Specialty Foods Importer & Supplier
N.A.I.C.S.: 311999
Tyler Hawes (Pres)
Ted McCormick (CFO)
Aimee Miralles (VP-People & Culture)
Keith Dougherty (CEO)

Subsidiary (Domestic):

Albert Uster Imports, Inc. (2)
9211 Gaither Rd, Gaithersburg, MD 20877
Tel.: (301) 258-7350
Web Site: http://secure.auifinefoods.com
Gourmet Food Company; Distinctive Pastry, Dessert, Savory & Beverage Offerings
N.A.I.C.S.: 424450
Andreas Galliker (VP-Bus Dev)
Walter von Rautenkranz (Reg Mgr-Sls)
Philipp Braun (Pres & CEO)

Sunrise Medical Inc. (1)
2842 N Business Park Ave, Fresno, CA 93727
Tel.: (303) 218-4600
Web Site: http://www.sunrisemedical.com
Sales Range: $500-549.9 Million
Homecare & Extended Health Care Products Mfr
N.A.I.C.S.: 339113
Pete Coburn (Pres-Comml Ops-US)
Thomas Babacan (Pres & CEO)
Johan E. K. (Chm)
Roxane Cromwell (Sr VP-Ops)

Subsidiary (Non-US):

Sunrise France S.A.S. (2)
13 Rue De La Painguetterie, 37390, Chanceaux, France
Tel.: (33) 247554400
Web Site: http://www.sunrisemedical.fr
Sales Range: $10-24.9 Million
Emp.: 30
Rehabilitation & Respiratory Products Distr
N.A.I.C.S.: 621399

Sunrise Medical AB (2)
Britta Sahlgrensgata 8A, SE-42131, Vastra Frolunda, Sweden
Tel.: (46) 317483700
Web Site: http://www.sunrisemedical.se
Sales Range: $10-24.9 Million
Emp.: 8
Rehabilitation Products Distr
N.A.I.C.S.: 621399
Orjan Strandin (Gen Mgr)
Orjam Strindem (Gen Mgr)

Sunrise Medical AG (2)
Luckhalde 14, Muri, 3074, Bern, Switzerland
Tel.: (41) 319583838
Web Site: http://www.sunrisemedical.ch
Sales Range: $10-24.9 Million
Emp.: 10
Rehabilitation Products Distr
N.A.I.C.S.: 623220
Bernd Humpert (Gen Mgr)

Sunrise Medical AS (2)
Delitorpo 3 Port B, 1540, Vestby, Norway
Tel.: (47) 66963800
Web Site: http://www.sunrisemedical.no
Sales Range: $10-24.9 Million
Emp.: 30
Rehabilitation & Respiratory Product Distr
N.A.I.C.S.: 621399
Johan Drodd (Mng Dir)

Sunrise Medical Benelus (2)
Groningenhaven 18 20, 3433 PE, Nieuwegein, Netherlands
Tel.: (31) 306082100
Web Site: http://www.sunrisemedical.nl
Sales Range: $10-24.9 Million
Emp.: 45
Rehabilitation Products, Communication Devices & Respiratory Products Distr
N.A.I.C.S.: 624310

Sunrise Medical Canada Inc. (2)
237 Romina Dr Unit 3, Concord, L4K 4V3, ON, Canada
Tel.: (905) 660-2459
Web Site: http://www.sunrisemedical.ca
Sales Range: $10-24.9 Million
Emp.: 45
Rehabilitation, Respiratory & Homecare Medical Products Distr
N.A.I.C.S.: 423450
Thomas Babacan (Pres)
Jim Barratt (Sr VP)
Roxane Cromwell (COO)
Thomas Hardt (Sr VP)
Larry Jackson (Pres)
Bernd Krebs (CTO)
Carol Liu (Sr VP)
Ignacio Paredes (Sr VP)
Adrian Platt (CFO)
Ben Stocks (Mng Dir)

Sunrise Medical GmbH (2)
Tel.: (49) 72539800
Web Site: https://www.sunrisemedical.de
Sales Range: $25-49.9 Million
Medical & Hospital Equipment Mfr
N.A.I.C.S.: 423450
Thomas Babacan (Pres & CEO)
Jim Barratt (Sr VP)
Thomas Hardt (Mng Dir & Sr VP)
Bernd Krebs (CTO)
Carol Liu (Sr VP-Corporate Development & Strategic Marketing)
Ignacio Paredes (Sr VP)
Adrian Platt (CFO)
Daniel Wade (Chief Sustainability Officer & Chief Procurement Officer)
Kai Schyktanz (Mng Dir)
Udo Loosen (Mng Dir)

Division (Domestic):

Sunrise Medical Inc. (2)
6899 Winchester Cir Ste 300, Boulder, CO 80301
Tel.: (303) 218-4500
Web Site: http://www.sunrisemedical.com
Sales Range: $150-199.9 Million
Wheelchairs & Accessories Mfr
N.A.I.C.S.: 339113
Kristyn Campbell (Sr Mgr-Mktg)

Sunrise Medical Long Term Care (2)
5001 Joerns Dr, Stevens Point, WI 54481-5040
Tel.: (800) 333-4000
Web Site: http://www.joerns.com
Sales Range: $50-74.9 Million
Hospital & Long Term Care Facilities Beds & Furnishings Mfr
N.A.I.C.S.: 423450

Subsidiary (Non-US):

Sunrise Medical Ltd. (2)
Thorns Road, Brierley Hill, DY5 2LD, West Midlands, United Kingdom
Tel.: (44) 8456056688
Web Site: http://www.sunrisemedical.co.uk
Sales Range: $50-74.9 Million
Homecare & Extended Care Product Mfr & Distr
N.A.I.C.S.: 326299
Jim Barratt (Sr VP-Comml Ops)

Division (Domestic):

Sunrise Medical Mobility Products (2)
2842 N Business Park Ave, Fresno, CA 93727-1328
Tel.: (559) 292-2171
Web Site: http://www.sunrisemedical.com
Sales Range: $50-74.9 Million
Wheelchairs & Wheelchair Accessories Mfr
N.A.I.C.S.: 339113
Kari Morris (Mgr-HR)

Subsidiary (Non-US):

Sunrise Medical Pty. Ltd. (2)
6 Healey Circuit, Huntingwood, 2148, NSW, Australia
Tel.: (61) 296786600
Web Site: http://www.sunrisemedical.com.au
Sales Range: $10-24.9 Million
Emp.: 25
Homecare, Rehabilitation & Respiratory Products Distr
N.A.I.C.S.: 623220

Sunrise Medical S.R.L. (2)
Via Riva 20, Montale, 29100, Piacenza, Italy
Tel.: (39) 0523573111
Web Site: http://www.sunrisemedical.it
Sales Range: $10-24.9 Million
Emp.: 18
Rehabilitation Products Distr
N.A.I.C.S.: 623220

Sunrise Spain (Uribarri) (2)
Poligono Bakiola 41, Arrankudiaga, 48498, Arene, Vizcaya, Spain
Tel.: (34) 902142434
Web Site: http://www.sunrisemedical.es
Sales Range: $25-49.9 Million
Wheelchairs, Crutches, Walkers, Commodes & Hoists Mfr
N.A.I.C.S.: 339113

The Woodstream Corporation (1)
29 E King St, Lancaster, PA 17602
Tel.: (717) 740-4600
Web Site: http://www.woodstream.com
Pest Control Equipment Mfr
N.A.I.C.S.: 339999
Probyn Forbes (Exec VP-Ops)
Craig Wirth (Pres-Pest & Animal Control Bus)
Steven Lorraine (Sr VP-Electronic Animal Containment & Wild Bird)
Kevin Hileman (Sr VP-Business Integration)
Joao Rodrigues (CEO)
Manuel Maza (CFO)
Melissa Oldfield (CIO)
Daniel Brown (Exec VP-Global Sales)
Paul McQuillian (Sr VP-R&D & Engrg)
Carla Phillips (Sr VP-HR)

Subsidiary (Domestic):

Dynamic Solutions Worldwide, LLC (2)
12247 W Fairview Ave, Milwaukee, WI 53226
Tel.: (877) 403-8727
Web Site: http://www.dynatrap.com
Insect Killer Product Mfr & Distr
N.A.I.C.S.: 325320

Subsidiary (Non-US):

Woodstream Europe Ltd. (2)
8 Lands End Way, Oakham, LE15 6RF, Rutland, United Kingdom
Tel.: (44) 1572722558
Web Site: http://www.rutland-electric-fencing.co.uk
Electric Security Fencing Mfr & Distr
N.A.I.C.S.: 561621

Wilton Re Holdings Ltd. (1)
187 Danbury Road, Wilton, CT 06897
Tel.: (203) 762-4400

COMPANIES
VETERANS ENTERPRISE TECHNOLOGY SOLUTIONS, INC.

Web Site: http://www.wiltonre.com
Sales Range: Less than $1 Million
Holding Company; Reinsurance Products & Services
N.A.I.C.S.: 551112
Ray Eckert *(CMO, Chief Sls Officer & Sr VP)*
Scott Sheefel *(VP-Pricing)*
David A. Van Der Beek *(Chief Underwriting Officer & VP)*
Perry H. Braun *(Chief Investment Officer & Sr VP)*
Michael E. Fleitz *(CFO & Sr VP)*
Mark R. Sarlitto *(Gen Counsel & Sr VP)*
Enrico J. Treglia *(COO & Sr VP)*
Andrew J. Wood *(CIO & Sr VP)*
Michael L. Greer *(Chief Pricing Officer & Sr VP)*
Cormac Treanor *(Head-Longevity Solutions)*
Chris Conrad Stroup *(Chm & CEO)*

Subsidiary (Domestic):

Allstate Life Insurance Company of New York (2)
878 Veteran's Memorial Hwy Ste 400, Hauppauge, NY 11788
Tel.: (631) 357-8920
Rev.: $573,635,000
Assets: $7,551,185,000
Liabilities: $6,425,084,000
Net Worth: $1,126,101,000
Earnings: $125,962,000
Fiscal Year-end: 12/31/2014
Direct Property & Casualty Insurance Carriers
N.A.I.C.S.: 524126
Mark A. Green *(Bd of Dirs, Executives)*

Texas Life Insurance Company (2)
900 Washington Ave, Waco, TX 76701 **(100%)**
Tel.: (254) 752-6521
Web Site: http://www.texaslife.com
Sales Range: $50-74.9 Million
Emp.: 100
Legal Reserve Life Insurance Services
N.A.I.C.S.: 524113
Doug Dixon *(Pres & CEO)*
Carroll Fadal *(Chief Sls Officer)*
Dennis Harms *(CFO & VP)*
Brad Kendrick *(CIO)*
Michael Khoury *(COO)*
Judy Sprague *(Officer-HR)*

Subsidiary (Non-US):

ivari Canada ULC (2)
200-5000 Yonge Street, Toronto, M2N 7E9, ON, Canada
Tel.: (416) 883-5000
Web Site: http://www.ivari.ca
Rev.: $1,204,318,642
Assets: $9,617,403,933
Liabilities: $8,709,674,715
Net Worth: $907,729,218
Earnings: $132,595,431
Fiscal Year-end: 12/31/2019
Holding Company; Insurance & Investment Products & Services
N.A.I.C.S.: 551112

Subsidiary (Domestic):

Transamerica Life Canada (3)
200-5000 Yonge Street, Toronto, M2N 7E9, ON, Canada **(100%)**
Tel.: (416) 883-5000
Web Site: https://www.ivari.ca
Life Insurance
N.A.I.C.S.: 524113

VESTAR/GRAY INVESTORS LLC
17622 Armstrong Ave, Irvine, CA 92614
Tel.: (949) 863-1171
Web Site: http://www.stjohnknits.com
Holding Company
N.A.I.C.S.: 551112
Bruce Fetter *(CEO)*

Subsidiaries:

St. John Knits International, Inc. (1)
17622 Armstrong Ave, Irvine, CA 92614-5726 **(92.94%)**
Tel.: (949) 863-1171
Web Site: http://www.stjohnknits.com
Sales Range: $350-399.9 Million
Emp.: 3,000
Women's Fashion Apparel Mfr
N.A.I.C.S.: 315120
Bernd E. Beetz *(Chm)*
Eran Cohen *(CEO)*

VESTED HEALTH LLC
PO Box 953, Charleston, WV 25323-0953
Tel.: (304) 347-3640
Web Site: http://www.vestedhealth.com
Year Founded: 2001
Sales Range: $1-9.9 Million
Emp.: 14
Consumer Directed Health Care Financing Services
N.A.I.C.S.: 524128
Carol Ball *(Mgr-Client Solutions)*
Melissa Adkins *(Supvr-Customer Svc)*
Sherry Parks *(CFO)*

VESTED METALS INTERNATIONAL, LLC
7000 US Hwy 1 N Ste 504, Saint Augustine, FL 32095
Tel.: (904) 495-7278
Web Site: http://www.vestedmetals.net
Year Founded: 2014
Sales Range: $1-9.9 Million
Emp.: 6
Metal Product Mfr & Distr
N.A.I.C.S.: 331491
Viv Helwig *(Founder, Owner & Pres)*

VESTIN GROUP, INC.
8880 W Sunset Rd Ste 200, Las Vegas, NV 89148
Tel.: (702) 227-0965 DE
Web Site: http://www.vestinmortgage.com
Year Founded: 1998
Holding Company; Real Estate Fund Management Services
N.A.I.C.S.: 551112

Subsidiaries:

Vestin Mortgage, LLC (1)
8880 W Sunset Rd Ste 200, Las Vegas, NV 89148
Tel.: (702) 227-0965
Web Site: http://www.vestinmortgage.com
Real Estate Fund Management Services
N.A.I.C.S.: 531390

Affiliate (Domestic):

Vestin Realty Mortgage I, Inc. (2)
8880 W Sunset Rd Ste 200, Las Vegas, NV 89148
Tel.: (702) 227-0965
Web Site: http://www.vestinrealtymortgage1.com
Real Estate Loan Investment Fund
N.A.I.C.S.: 525990

VESTIN REALTY MORTGAGE II, INC.
8880 W Sunset Rd Ste 200, Las Vegas, NV 89148
Tel.: (702) 227-0965 MD
VRTB—(OTCIQ)
Real Estate Loan Investment Fund
N.A.I.C.S.: 525990

VESTMARK, INC.
100 Quannapowitt Pkwy Ste 205, Wakefield, MA 01880
Tel.: (781) 224-3640 DE
Web Site: http://www.vestmark.com
Year Founded: 2001
Software Development Services
N.A.I.C.S.: 541511
Michael Blundin *(Pres & COO)*
Karl Roessner *(CEO)*
John Lunny *(CEO)*

VESTURE CORPORATION
120 E Pritchard St, Asheboro, NC 27203-4761
Tel.: (336) 629-3000 NC
Web Site: http://www.vesture.com
Sales Range: $50-74.9 Million
Emp.: 30
Mfr of Thermal Products
N.A.I.C.S.: 332999
Bonnie Thompson *(Mgr-Customer Svc)*
Brenda Delooze *(Mgr-Credit, Traffic & Procurement)*

VESTURE GROUP INC.
2220 N Screenland Dr, Burbank, CA 91505
Tel.: (818) 842-0200
Year Founded: 2007
Sales Range: $25-49.9 Million
Emp.: 42
Girls' Clothing Manufacturer
N.A.I.C.S.: 315250
Robert Galishoff *(Owner)*

VESTUS GROUP
26364 Carmel Rancho Ln Ste 200, Carmel, CA 93923
Tel.: (831) 656-1771
Web Site: http://www.vestusgroup.com
Retirement Planning Services
N.A.I.C.S.: 525110
Mark Williams *(Co-founder & Mng Partner)*

VET PHARM, INC.
392 15th St NE, Sioux Center, IA 51250
Tel.: (712) 722-3836
Web Site: http://www.animalhealthinternational.com
Year Founded: 1983
Sales Range: $25-49.9 Million
Emp.: 106
Pharmaceutical Preparation Mfr
N.A.I.C.S.: 325412
Chuck Vander Ploeg *(VP)*
Sherry Griffioen *(Controller)*
Orlan Huizenga *(Mgr-Sls)*

VETDEPOT.COM
543 Encinitas Blvd Ste 107, Encinitas, CA 92024
Tel.: (858) 357-8200
Web Site: http://www.vetdepot.com
Year Founded: 2005
Sales Range: $1-9.9 Million
Emp.: 15
Discount Pet Supplies & Medications
N.A.I.C.S.: 459910
Craig Gilmore *(CEO)*

VETERAN CONSTRUCTORS, INC.
8433 Enterprise Cir Ste 140, Lakewood Ranch, FL 34202
Tel.: (941) 893-6100
Web Site: http://www.veteranconstructors.com
Year Founded: 2009
Sales Range: $10-24.9 Million
Emp.: 20
Construction Services
N.A.I.C.S.: 237990
Andreas Knispel *(Pres & CEO)*

VETERAN CORPS OF AMERICA
10300 Eaton Pl Ste 340, Fairfax, VA 22030
Tel.: (703) 691-8387
Web Site: http://www.veterancorps.com
Year Founded: 2005
Sales Range: $10-24.9 Million
Emp.: 60
Government Contractor Supplying Detection, Explosives & Protection Equipment
N.A.I.C.S.: 921190
John R. Wheeler *(CFO & Sr VP)*
William G. Wheeler *(Pres & CEO)*

VETERAN INFRASTRUCTURE PRODUCTS LLC
9024 Opus Dr, Las Vegas, NV 89117-5736
Tel.: (702) 672-5759
Web Site: http://www.vipvetproducts.com
General Management Consulting Services
N.A.I.C.S.: 541611
Russell Rice *(Pres & CEO)*

Subsidiaries:

Knighthawk Protection, LLC (1)
15131 NE Caples Rd, Brush Prairie, WA 98606
Tel.: (360) 892-4885
Web Site: http://www.knighthawkprotection.com
Sales Range: $1-9.9 Million
Emp.: 56
Security Guard Services
N.A.I.C.S.: 561612
Lawrence Knight *(Pres)*

VETERAN LOGISTICS, INC.
3611 Dalbergia St, San Diego, CA 92113
Tel.: (619) 450-6880
Web Site: http://www.veteranlogistics.com
Sales Range: $10-24.9 Million
Emp.: 20
Industrial Supply Whslr
N.A.I.C.S.: 423840
Jeff Harrington *(Owner)*

VETERAN TICKETS FOUNDATION
3401 E Turquoise Ave, Phoenix, AZ 85028
Tel.: (888) 241-1550 AZ
Web Site: http://www.veteranticketsfoundation.org
Year Founded: 2008
Sales Range: $10-24.9 Million
Emp.: 8
Veteran Welfare Services
N.A.I.C.S.: 813410
Butch Hogan *(Co-Founder & CTO)*
Cindy Creed *(CFO & VP)*
Brandi Shannon *(Chief Community Officer)*
Al Maag *(CMO)*
Alan Dropkin *(Dir-Ticket Ops)*
Chris Blindheim *(Co-Founder & Treas)*
Dwayne D. Somers *(Co-Founder)*
Edward Rausch *(Co-Founder, Chm & COO)*
Mickey Focareto *(Sec)*
Jason Conviser *(Dir-Hero's Wish)*
Steven Weintraub *(Chief Strategy Officer)*
Michael A. Focareto III *(Co-Founder, CEO & Sec)*

VETERANS ENTERPRISE TECHNOLOGY SOLUTIONS, INC.
134 Commerce Dr, Clarksville, VA 23927
Tel.: (434) 374-2142
Web Site: http://www.vets-inc.com
Year Founded: 2005
Sales Range: $1-9.9 Million
Emp.: 30

VETERANS ENTERPRISE TECHNOLOGY SOLUTIONS, INC.   U.S. PRIVATE

Veterans Enterprise Technology Solutions, Inc.—(Continued)
IT Services for the Federal Government
N.A.I.C.S.: 921190
Jim Moody (Pres & CEO)

VETERANS HOME CARE LLC
11861 Westline Industrial Dr, Saint Louis, MO 63146
Tel.: (314) 514-2444
Web Site: http://www.veteranshomecare.com
Year Founded: 2003
Sales Range: $10-24.9 Million
Emp.: 96
Veterans' Benefits Assistance for At Home Personal Care
N.A.I.C.S.: 621610
Bonnie Laiderman (Founder)
Marcy Seeney (Dir-Mktg-Natl)
Howard Laiderman (Exec VP)
Donna Appel (VP-Sls & Mktg)

VETERANS INC.
69 Grove St, Worcester, MA 01605
Tel.: (508) 791-0956   MA
Web Site: http://www.veteransinc.org
Year Founded: 1990
Sales Range: $10-24.9 Million
Emp.: 130
Veterans Care Services
N.A.I.C.S.: 813410
Vincent J. Perrone (Pres)
Denis M. Leary (VP)
George M. Bourisk (Treas)
Roland W. Bercume (Sec)
Patrick J. Murphy (Chm)

VETERANS OF FOREIGN WARS OF THE UNITED STATES
406 W 34th St, Kansas City, MO 64111
Tel.: (816) 756-3390
Web Site: http://www.vfw.org
Year Founded: 1899
Sales Range: $75-99.9 Million
Emp.: 211
Veterans Care Services
N.A.I.C.S.: 813410
Richard Kolb (Dir-Pub)
William Bradshaw (Dir-Natl Veterans Svc)
James Lierz (Controller)
Randi K. Law (Mgr-Comm)

VETERANS OIL INC.
2070 Hwy 150, Bessemer, AL 35022
Tel.: (205) 424-4400
Web Site: http://www.veteransoilinc.com
Sales Range: $10-24.9 Million
Emp.: 40
Fuel Oil Dealers
N.A.I.C.S.: 457210
John H. Musgrove (Pres & Mgr-Sls)
Glenda Musgrove (CFO & VP)

VETERANS TRADING CO., LLC.
1755 Prospector Ave Ste 200, Park City, UT 84060-7486
Tel.: (435) 649-4566
Web Site: http://www.vtcusa.com
Year Founded: 2005
Sales Range: $10-24.9 Million
Emp.: 32
Semiconductor Device Whslr
N.A.I.C.S.: 423690
John Pierce (VP-Bus Dev)
Steve Culligan (VP-Sls)
Earl Huff (Dir-Quality)
Gregg Mynhier (Pres)

VETERINARIAN'S OUTLET INCORPORATED
975 Patrick St, Dublin, TX 76446
Tel.: (254) 445-3425
Web Site: http://www.vetoutletinc.com
Sales Range: $150-199.9 Million
Emp.: 20
Dairy Farm Equipment Distr
N.A.I.C.S.: 115210
Alfred Harper (Owner & Pres)

VETERINARY & POULTRY SUPPLY
120 S Greene Rd, Goshen, IN 46526
Tel.: (574) 534-2626
Web Site: http://www.vetpoultry.com
Sales Range: $10-24.9 Million
Emp.: 25
Provider of Animal Medicines
N.A.I.C.S.: 424210
Jim Bradford (Pres)

VETERINARY SERVICE INC.
4100 Bangs Ave, Modesto, CA 95356-8710
Tel.: (209) 545-5100   CA
Web Site: http://www.vsi.cc
Year Founded: 1960
Sales Range: $50-74.9 Million
Emp.: 120
Animal Health Supplies
N.A.I.C.S.: 423450
John Scheuber (Pres & CEO)

VETRI HOLDINGS LLC
1312 Spruce St, Philadelphia, PA 19107
Tel.: (215) 732-3478   PA
Holding Company; Restaurant & Charity Organization Operator
N.A.I.C.S.: 551112
Marc Vetri (CEO & Partner)
Jeff Michaud (Partner & Dir-Culinary)
Brad Spence (Partner & Dir-Culinary)

Subsidiaries:

Vetri Foundation for Children   (1)
211 N 13th st, Philadelphia, PA 19107
Tel.: (215) 600-2630
Web Site: http://www.vetrifoundation.org
Emp.: 14
Child Nutrition Educational & Grantmaking Foundation
N.A.I.C.S.: 813211
Genevieve Lynch (Mgr-Dev)
Jeff Benjamin (Founder)
Marlene L. Olshan (CEO)
Michael C. Forman (Chm)

Vetri Management Corporation   (1)
1312 Spruce St, Philadelphia, PA 19107-5885
Tel.: (215) 732-3478
Restaurant Management Services
N.A.I.C.S.: 561110
Marc Vetri (CEO)

Subsidiary (Domestic):

Vetri Restaurant Corp.   (2)
1312 Spruce St, Philadelphia, PA 19107
Tel.: (215) 732-3478
Web Site: http://www.vetriristorante.com
Sales Range: $1-9.9 Million
Restaurant Operators
N.A.I.C.S.: 722511
Marc Vetri (Founder, Grp CEO & Exec Chef)
Chuck Lisenbee (Gen Mgr)

VETS PLUS, INC.
102 3rd Ave E, Knapp, WI 54749
Tel.: (715) 665-2118   WI
Web Site: http://www.vets-plus.com
Year Founded: 1990
Mfg Prepared Feeds Whol Medical/Hospital Equipment
N.A.I.C.S.: 424910

Rajiv Behari Lall (Founder & CEO)
Steve Vale (VP-Sls & Mktg)
Dale R. Metz (Dir-Companion Animal Bus)
Karl Wayne (Dir-Bus Svcs & HR)
Killol Raval (Dir-Production Ops)
David Nelson (Pres)

Subsidiaries:

Merrick's Animal Health, LLC   (1)
654 Bridge St, Union Center, WI 53962
Tel.: (608) 462-8201
Web Site: http://www.merricks.com
Prepared Feeds & Baby Animal Nutrition Products
N.A.I.C.S.: 541715

VETSAMERICA BUSINESS CONSULTING, INC.
8300 Greensboro Dr Ste 800, McLean, VA 22102
Tel.: (571) 447-3651
Web Site: http://www.vetsamerica.us
Year Founded: 2002
Sales Range: $10-24.9 Million
Emp.: 51
Information Technology Consulting Services
N.A.I.C.S.: 541512
John E. Collins (CEO)
Akhil Handa (COO)
Jiying Spencer (CFO)

VETTA JEWELRY INC.
29 W 36th St Fl 9, New York, NY 10018
Tel.: (212) 564-8250
Web Site: http://www.springstreetdesign.com
Rev: $13,529,710
Emp.: 20
Costume Jewelry
N.A.I.C.S.: 339910
Rona Perlman (VP-Sls)
Amanda Scull (Coord-EDI)
Steven Balot (Controller)

VETTER EQUIPMENT COMPANY
610 14 Ave S, Denison, IA 51442
Tel.: (712) 263-4637   IA
Web Site: http://www.vetterequip.com
Year Founded: 1975
Sales Range: $75-99.9 Million
Emp.: 105
Provider of Farm Machinery
N.A.I.C.S.: 423820
Glen Vetter (Pres & Treas)

VETTER STONE COMPANY
23894 3rd Ave, Mankato, MN 56001
Tel.: (507) 345-4568
Web Site: http://www.vetterstone.com
Sales Range: $25-49.9 Million
Emp.: 120
Stone, Quarrying & Processing of Own Stone Products
N.A.I.C.S.: 327991
Howard J. Vetter (Chm)
Ron Vetter (Pres)
Brenda Klaus (Mgr-Estimating)
Lori Maday (Coord-Drafting)

VEVA COMMUNICATIONS
51 E St, Santa Rosa, CA 95404-4728
Tel.: (707) 542-6572   CA
Year Founded: 1951
Sales Range: Less than $1 Million
Emp.: 4
Advetising Agency
N.A.I.C.S.: 541810
Margo VanMidde (Partner & Media Dir)

VEXCEL HOLDINGS, INC.
12503 E Euclid Dr Ste 20, Centennial, CO 80111
Tel.: (425) 890-1863   DE
Holding Company
N.A.I.C.S.: 551112
Paul Steckler (Sr VP-Engrg & Ops)

Subsidiaries:

Keystone Aerial Surveys, Inc.   (1)
Ne Philadelphia Airport Grant Ave & Ashton Rd, Philadelphia, PA 19114
Tel.: (215) 677-3119
Web Site: http://www.keystoneaerialsurveys.com
Other Nonscheduled Air Transportation
N.A.I.C.S.: 481219
John Schmitt (Pres)
David Day (Exec VP)

VEYO, LLC
4875 Eastgate Mall Ste 200, San Diego, CA 92121
Web Site: http://www.veyo.com
Year Founded: 2015
Sales Range: $150-199.9 Million
Emp.: 512
Medical Transportation Services
N.A.I.C.S.: 485991
Josh Komenda (Pres)
Stanton Sipes (Exec VP-Bus Dev)
Michael Coleman (Exec VP-Bus Affairs)
Michael Singer (Exec VP-Tech)
David Gibson (VP-Ops)

VEZERS PRECISION INDUSTRIAL CO.
2526 Mankas Corner Rd, Fairfield, CA 94534
Tel.: (707) 435-8082
Web Site: http://www.vezerpic.com
Year Founded: 1985
Sales Range: $10-24.9 Million
Emp.: 50
Mechanical Engineers; Wholesaler of Industrial Machine Parts
N.A.I.C.S.: 423830
Frank Vezer (Pres)

VFP INC.
1701 Midland Rd, Salem, VA 24153
Tel.: (540) 977-0500
Web Site: http://www.vfpinc.com
Sales Range: $25-49.9 Million
Emp.: 250
Prefabricated Buildings, Wood
N.A.I.C.S.: 321992
Jerry Arnold (Pres)
Scott File (VP)
John Justice (CFO)

VHA CORP.
1550 Valley Vista Dr, Diamond Bar, CA 91765
Tel.: (626) 638-3700
Web Site: http://www.vhacorp.com
Year Founded: 2001
Sales Range: $300-349.9 Million
Emp.: 85
Wireless Telecommunication Services
N.A.I.C.S.: 517112
Vincent Huang (Pres)
Amy Malmquist (COO)
George Kwong (CFO)
Jay Marin (Sls Dir-West & Desert Mountain)
Cory Slipakoff (Sls Dir-South & South East)

VHC INC.
3090 Holmgren Way, Green Bay, WI 54304-5736
Tel.: (920) 336-7278   WI
Year Founded: 1985
Sales Range: $75-99.9 Million
Emp.: 3
Buildings Rentals

N.A.I.C.S.: 238210
Dave Van Den Heuvel (Pres)

Subsidiaries:

Best Built Inc. (1)
3100 Holmgren Way, Green Bay, WI 54304-5720
Tel.: (920) 337-6488
Web Site: http://www.bestbuilt.com
Sales Range: $10-24.9 Million
Construction Services
N.A.I.C.S.: 236115
Jim Boyea (Project Mgr)

Spirit Construction Services Inc. (1)
118 Coleman Blvd, Savannah, GA 31408-9565 **(100%)**
Tel.: (912) 748-8055
Web Site: http://www.spiritconstruction.com
Sales Range: $25-49.9 Million
Industrial Buildings & Warehouses
N.A.I.C.S.: 236210
Steve Van Den Heuvel (Owner)
Doug Barone (VP-Sls & Customer Rels)
Craig Kassner (Pres)

Spirit Fabs Inc. (1)
1255 Broadway St, Wrightstown, WI 54180 **(100%)**
Tel.: (920) 339-9607
Web Site: http://www.spiritfabs.com
Sales Range: $10-24.9 Million
Fabricated Structural Metal Mfr
N.A.I.C.S.: 332312
Dean McNeill (Pres)

VDH Electric Inc. (1)
3080 Holmgren Way, Green Bay, WI 54304-5736 **(100%)**
Tel.: (920) 336-8250
Electrical Work
N.A.I.C.S.: 238210
Ron Lentz (Pres)

Vos Electric Inc. (1)
3131 Market St, Green Bay, WI 54304-5611
Tel.: (920) 336-0781
Web Site: http://www.voselectric.com
Electrical Work
N.A.I.C.S.: 238210
Tim Van Den Heuvel (Pres)
William C. Bain (VP)
Butch Piontek (Sec)
Raymond Van Den Heuvel II (Treas)

VHMNETWORK LLLC

65 Broadway 7th Fl, New York, NY 10006
Tel.: (646) 723-4353
Web Site:
  http://www.vhmnetwork.com
Year Founded: 2007
Sales Range: $1-9.9 Million
Emp.: 8
Marketing Consulting
N.A.I.C.S.: 541613
Michael Derikrava (Pres)

VHS GROUP, LLC

19730 Ralston, Detroit, MI 48203
Tel.: (313) 366-0660
Sales Range: $10-24.9 Million
Emp.: 70
Medical Supply Chain Management Services
N.A.I.C.S.: 423450
Robert A. Schummer (Vice Chm & Pres)
Jeff Davis (COO-Commodity Integration)

VI MANUFACTURING INC.

164 Orchard St, Webster, NY 14580
Tel.: (585) 872-5650
Web Site: http://www.vimfg.com
Sales Range: $10-24.9 Million
Emp.: 65
Mfr of Dies
N.A.I.C.S.: 333514
Frank Chamberlain (Owner)
Tom Williams (VP & Dir-Ops)
Tina Cannioto (Office Mgr)
Paul Ozminkowsk (Co-Pres)

VIA CHRISTI HEALTH PARTNERS, INC.

8200 E Thorn, Wichita, KS 67226
Tel.: (316) 858-4900 KS
Web Site: http://www.viachristi.org
Year Founded: 1995
Administrative Office; Hospitals & Retirement & Senior Communities
N.A.I.C.S.: 621112

VIA CREDIT UNION

4505 S Adams St, Marion, IN 46953
Tel.: (765) 674-6631 IN
Web Site: http://www.viacu.org
Year Founded: 1936
Sales Range: $10-24.9 Million
Emp.: 88
Credit Union Operator
N.A.I.C.S.: 522130
Lori Fiene (CFO)

VIA FIELD

207 14th St N, Northwood, IA 50459-1233
Tel.: (641) 324-2753 IA
Web Site: http://www.viafield.com
Year Founded: 1923
Sales Range: $10-24.9 Million
Emp.: 35
Grain Whslr
N.A.I.C.S.: 424510
Kent Appler (Mgr)

VIA LUNA GROUP (VLG)

5717 Legacy Dr Ste 270, Plano, TX 75024
Tel.: (214) 299-8688
Web Site:
  http://www.wefightboredom.com
Year Founded: 2005
Sales Range: $1-9.9 Million
Emp.: 20
Interactive Multi-Channel Marketing Campaigns
N.A.I.C.S.: 541613
Brett Hersley (Founder)
Angela Shori (Dir-Creative)
Lee Parker (Principal-Client Svcs)
Pete Manias (Founder & Pres)
Shane Foster (Founder & CTO)
Corey Smith (CFO)
Don Abell (CMO)
Rafael Manias (Principal-Client Svcs)
Dan Naughton (Principal-Client Svcs)
Taylor Johnson (Principal-Client Svcs)
Rich Sangillo (Dir-Creative)
Jon Fullrich (Dir-Creative)
Lance Jones (Assoc Dir-Creative)

VIA MARKETING, INC.

2646 W Lincoln Hwy, Merrillville, IN 46410
Tel.: (219) 769-2299
Web Site:
  http://www.viamarketing.net
Year Founded: 1987
Sales Range: Less than $1 Million
Emp.: 5
Full Service
N.A.I.C.S.: 541810
Julie Olthoff (Owner)
Manni Nievera (Dir-Art)
Diane Chant (Mgr-Fin)

VIA METROPOLITAN TRANSIT

800 W Myrtle St, San Antonio, TX 78212
Tel.: (210) 362-2000
Web Site: http://www.viainfo.net
Year Founded: 1978
Sales Range: $10-24.9 Million
Emp.: 1,651
Provider of Transit Operations
N.A.I.C.S.: 485113
Terry Dudley (Mgr-Procurement)
Steve P. Allison (Vice Chm)
Linda Chavez-Thompson (Sec)
Rick Pych (Vice Chm)
Ryan Frazier (Mgr-Sls)
Tony Cade (VP-IT)
Brian D. Buchanan (VP-Bus & Rail SP&PD)
Shauna Walde (Controller)
Deepa Kumar (Mgr-Programming)
Jeffrey C. Arndt (Pres & CEO)
Tremell Brown (Deputy CEO & Chief Safety Officer)
Henry R. Munoz III (Chm)

VIA TRADING CORPORATION

2520 Industry Way, Lynwood, CA 90262
Tel.: (323) 214-8914
Web Site: http://www.viatrading.com
Year Founded: 2002
Rev.: $18,900,000
Emp.: 46
Business Services
N.A.I.C.S.: 561990
Jacques Stambouli (Founder)

VIACYTE, INC.

3550 General Atomics Ct, San Diego, CA 92121
Tel.: (858) 455-3708
Web Site: http://www.viacyte.com
Biotechnology Research & Development Services
N.A.I.C.S.: 541714
John West (Pres)
Allan Robins (Sr VP-Tech)
Anne Sandan (VP-Fin)
Daniel Pipeleers (Dir-Res)
Kevin Amour (VP & Chief Scientific Officer)
Paul Laikind (Pres & CEO)

VIALTA, INC.

48461 Fremont Blvd, Fremont, CA 94538
Tel.: (510) 870-3088
Web Site: http://www.vialta.com
Rev.: $12,700,000
Emp.: 38
Home Entertainment & Personal Communications Products Dev, Designer & Marketer
N.A.I.C.S.: 334310
Didier Pietri (CEO)
Fred S. L. Chan (Chm)
Yin-Wu Chan (Pres & COO)
Kenneth Tenaglia (VP-Mktg)
Jeff McHenry (VP-Sls)

VIAMERICAS CORPORATION

4641 Montgomery Ave Ste 400, Bethesda, MD 20814
Tel.: (301) 215-9294 DE
Web Site: http://www.viamericas.com
Year Founded: 1999
Sales Range: $1-9.9 Million
Emp.: 25
Money Transfer Services
N.A.I.C.S.: 525990
Joseph D. Argilagos (Co-Founder & Chm)
Luis R. Gonzalez (Treas)
Jaime Castaneda (Sec)
Paul S. Dwyer Jr. (Co-Founder & CEO)

VIANSA WINERY

25200 Arnold Dr, Sonoma, CA 95476
Tel.: (707) 935-4700
Web Site: http://www.viansa.com
Sales Range: $25-49.9 Million
Emp.: 250
Wine Mfr
N.A.I.C.S.: 312130
Kristen Hardy (Dir-Special Events)

VIANT MEDICAL, LLC

2 Hampshire St, Foxboro, MA 02035
Tel.: (480) 553-6400
Web Site:
  http://www.viantmedical.com
Year Founded: 2007
Engineered Custom Plastic Product Mfr
N.A.I.C.S.: 325211
Brian King (CEO)
Nino Gilarde (CFO)
Sean Crowley (COO)
Bill Flaherty (Chief Comml Officer)
Greg Kayata (Chief HR Officer)
Trish Albert (Corp VP & Gen Counsel)

Subsidiaries:

Viant Medical, Inc.-South
Plainfield (1)
6 Century Rd, South Plainfield, NJ 07080
Tel.: (908) 561-0717
Holding Company; Medical Devices & Components Designer, Mfr & Distr
N.A.I.C.S.: 551112
Brian King (CEO)

Unit (Domestic):

Vention Medical, Inc. - Grand Rapids (2)
620 Watson St SW, Grand Rapids, MI 49504
Tel.: (616) 643-5200
Web Site: http://www.ventionmedical.com
Sales Range: $25-49.9 Million
Medical Device Developer & Mfr
N.A.I.C.S.: 339112
Taylor Groll (Dir-Engrg)

Vention Medical, Inc. - Kerrville (2)
200 Holdsworth Dr, Kerrville, TX 78028
Tel.: (830) 896-6464
Web Site: http://www.ventionmedical.com
Sales Range: $10-24.9 Million
Medical Plastic Injection Molding Products Mfr
N.A.I.C.S.: 326199
Thomas Houdeshell (Pres)

Vention Medical, Inc. - West Haven (2)
68 Acton St, West Haven, CT 06516
Tel.: (203) 932-6406
Sales Range: $10-24.9 Million
Emp.: 25
Medical Device Mfr
N.A.I.C.S.: 339112
Gregory Georgelos (Mgr-Ops)

VIANT MEDICAL, LLC

2 Hampshire St, Foxboro, MA 02035
Tel.: (480) 553-6400 DE
Web Site: http://viantmedical.com
Year Founded: 2007
Medical Device Mfr
N.A.I.C.S.: 339112
Brian D. King (Pres & CEO)
Nino Gilarde (CFO)
Sean Crowley (COO)
Bill Flaherty (Chief Comml Officer)
Greg Kayata (Chief HR Officer)
Declan Smyth (Pres-Franchise)
Mark Allen (Pres-Orthoplastics)
Trish Albert (Corp VP & Gen Counsel)

Subsidiaries:

Coastal Life Technologies, Inc. (1)
7027 Fairgrounds Pkwy, San Antonio, TX 78238
Tel.: (210) 684-3454
Web Site: http://www.cltsa.com
Medical, Dental & Hospital Equipment Supplier & Whslr
N.A.I.C.S.: 423450
Paul Muller (Pres & CEO)
David Huff (COO)
J. Ian McDonald (Dir-RA/QA)

VIAS IMPORTS LTD.

875 6th Ave Ste 2200, New York, NY 10001

VIAS IMPORTS LTD.

Vias Imports Ltd.—(Continued)
Tel.: (212) 629-0200
Web Site: http://www.viaswine.com
Year Founded: 1983
Sales Range: $10-24.9 Million
Emp.: 30
Wine Mfr
N.A.I.C.S.: 312130
Luca Bigerna (Pres)
Tony Bernardini (Reg Mgr)
Luciano Brussolo (Reg Mgr-West)
Michael Burke (District Mgr)

VIATECH PUBLISHING SOLUTIONS

11935 N Stemmons Fwy, Dallas, TX 75234 — NY
Web Site: http://www.viatechpub.com
Year Founded: 1928
Sales Range: $25-49.9 Million
Emp.: 400
Advertising Aid Presentation Sales Manual Loose Leaf Binder Laser Printing & Fulfillment Mfr
N.A.I.C.S.: 323111
Michael Bertuch (Pres)
Tom Ginocchio (CFO)
Tom Bergenholtz (VP-Global Sls)
Ron Simmons (COO)

Subsidiaries:

ViaTech Publishing Solutions Limited (1)
Unit J3 & J4 Kingston Business Park, Kingston Bagpuize, Oxford, OX13 5FE, Oxfordshire, United Kingdom
Tel.: (44) 186 5822170
Web Site: http://www.viatech.com
Sales Range: $10-24.9 Million
Emp.: 15
Printing & Publishing Services
N.A.I.C.S.: 323111
Hajo Jansen (Dir-Europe)

VIBCO INC.

75 Stilson Rd, Wyoming, RI 02898
Tel.: (401) 539-2392 — NJ
Web Site: http://www.vibco.com
Year Founded: 1962
Sales Range: $50-74.9 Million
Emp.: 55
Industrial, Construction, Electric, Pneumatic & Hydraulic Vibrators, Vibratory Plate Compactors & Vibratory Single Drum Rollers Mfr
N.A.I.C.S.: 333120
Ted S. Wadensten (CEO)
Karl Wadensten (Pres)
John Goodwin (Plant Mgr)

Subsidiaries:

Vibco Vibration Products (1)
2215 Dunwin Drive, Mississauga, L5L 1X1, ON, Canada (100%)
Tel.: (905) 828-4191
Web Site: http://www.vibco.com
Sales Range: $25-49.9 Million
Emp.: 3
Sales & Service of Industrial Motors
N.A.I.C.S.: 561499

VIBE CREDIT UNION

44575 W 12 Mile Rd, Novi, MI 48377
Tel.: (248) 735-9500 — MI
Web Site: http://www.vibecreditunion.com
Year Founded: 1936
Sales Range: $10-24.9 Million
Emp.: 148
Credit Union
N.A.I.C.S.: 522130
Ronald Lang (CFO & Exec VP)

VIBRA HEALTHCARE, LLC

4600 Lena Dr, Mechanicsburg, PA 17055
Tel.: (717) 271-7158
Web Site: http://www.vibrahealthcare.com
Year Founded: 2004
Sales Range: $450-499.9 Million
Emp.: 9,000
Hospital Operator
N.A.I.C.S.: 622310
Brad Hollinger (Chm & CEO)
Clint Fegan (CFO)
Mike Thomas (Chief Admin Officer & Exec VP)
Douglas Yohe (Gen Counsel & Sr VP)
Robert Sutton (Exec VP-HR & Risk Mgmt)
Diane Pierce (Exec VP-Bus Dev)
Angelik Clover (Chief Compliance & HIPAA Officer)
Darla Perdue (Chief Clinical Officer)
Angelique Culver (Chief Compliance & HIPAA Officer)
Ann Gors (Pres-Div)
Edward Leary (Pres-Div)
Michael Long (Pres-Div)
Sean McCarthy (Pres-Div)

Subsidiaries:

Vibra Hospital of Charleston (1)
900 Bowman Rd Ste 102, Mount Pleasant, SC 29464
Tel.: (843) 881-4318
Sales Range: $1-9.9 Million
Emp.: 20
Specialty Hospitals
N.A.I.C.S.: 622310

VIBRA SCREW INC.

755 Union Blvd, Totowa, NJ 07512-2207
Tel.: (973) 256-7410 — NJ
Web Site: http://www.vibrascrew.com
Year Founded: 1955
Sales Range: $75-99.9 Million
Emp.: 100
Dry Materials Feeders, Bin Activators & Continuous Blenders Mfr
N.A.I.C.S.: 423830
Rich Wahl (Reg Mgr-Sls)
Eugene Wahl (Pres)
Joanne Young (Mgr-Pur)
Ellen Skibiak (Treas)

VIBRANT MEDIA

565 5th Ave 15th Fl, New York, NY 10017
Tel.: (646) 312-6100
Web Site: http://www.vibrantmedia.com
Sales Range: $10-24.9 Million
Emp.: 120
Advertising Specialties, E-Commerce, Interactive, Internet/Web Design, Web (Banner Ads, Pop-ups, etc.)
N.A.I.C.S.: 541810
Doug Stevenson (Co-Founder & CEO)
Craig Gooding (Co-Founder)
Julie R. Fenster (Gen Counsel)
James Piper (Sr VP-Sls & Ops)

Subsidiaries:

Vibrant Media (1)
75 Hawthorne St Ste 2000, San Francisco, CA 94105
Tel.: (415) 321-6060
Web Site: http://www.vibrantmedia.com
Emp.: 25
N.A.I.C.S.: 541810
James Piper (Sr VP-Sls & Gen Mgr-West Coast)

Vibrant Media France (1)
42 ave Montaigne, 75008, Paris, France
Tel.: (33) 1 7302 3236
Emp.: 5
N.A.I.C.S.: 541810
Martin Forbes (Sr VP)

Vibrant Media GmbH (1)
Neuer Wall 59, 20354, Hamburg, Germany
Tel.: (49) 40 380 819 0
Web Site: http://www.vibrantmedia.de
Emp.: 20
N.A.I.C.S.: 541810
Manfred Klaus (Mng Dir)
Florian Haller (Mng Dir)
Florian Hornstein (Mng Dir)
Christoph Von Reibnitz (Gen Mgr)

Vibrant Media Ltd. (1)
7th Floor, 140 Aldersgate Street, London, EC1A 4HY, United Kingdom
Tel.: (44) 207 239 0120
Web Site: http://www.vibrantmedia.co.uk
N.A.I.C.S.: 541810
Matt Boak (Dir-Sls & Strategic Partnerships)
Tom Pepper (Dir-Sls & Strategic Partnerships)
Sam Pattison (Head-Sls)

VIBRATION MOUNTINGS & CONTROLS, INC.

113 Main St, Bloomingdale, NJ 07403-0037
Tel.: (973) 838-1780 — NY
Web Site: http://www.thevmcgroup.com
Rev.: $16,000,000
Emp.: 100
Spring & Elastomer Mounts Mfr
N.A.I.C.S.: 326299
John J. Wilson (CEO)
John P. Giuliano (Pres)
Tom Steele (Exec VP)

Subsidiaries:

Cannon Fabrication, Inc. (1)
182 Granite St Ste 101, Corona, CA 92879
Tel.: (951) 278-1830
Web Site: http://www.canfab.com
Sales Range: $1-9.9 Million
Emp.: 61
Roofing/Siding Contractor
N.A.I.C.S.: 238390
Mary Prosser (Pres)
Steve Welch (Mgr-Engrg)

Dynamic Certification Laboratories (1)
1315 Greg St Ste 109, Sparks, NV 89431-6091
Tel.: (775) 358-5085
Web Site: http://www.shaketest.com
Commercial & Industrial Machinery & Equipment Repair & Maintenance
N.A.I.C.S.: 811310
Joseph L. La Brie (Mng Partner)
Kelly M. Laplace (Mgr-Quality & Project Engrg)
Traci Bartak (Coord-Project)

VIC BAILEY HONDA INC.

500 E Daniel Morgan Ave, Spartanburg, SC 29302
Tel.: (864) 585-5344
Web Site: http://www.vicbaileyhonda.com
Sales Range: $10-24.9 Million
Emp.: 45
Car Whslr
N.A.I.C.S.: 441110
Howell Foster Jr. (Owner)

VIC BAILEY-LINCOLN MERCURY

501 E Daniel Morgan Ave, Spartanburg, SC 29302
Tel.: (864) 585-3600
Web Site: http://www.vicbaileyauto.com
Sales Range: $25-49.9 Million
Emp.: 75
Automobiles, New & Used
N.A.I.C.S.: 441110
Vic Bailey Jr. (Pres)

VIC BOND SALES, INC.

1240 E Coldwater Rd, Flint, MI 48505
Tel.: (810) 787-5321 — MI

U.S. PRIVATE

Web Site: http://www.vicbondonline.com
Year Founded: 1972
Sales Range: $10-24.9 Million
Emp.: 40
Plumbing, Heating & Cabinetry Fixture Dealer
N.A.I.C.S.: 444110
Fred B. McAndrew (Pres)
Al Olmstead (Branch Mgr-Flint)

VIC CANEVER CHEVROLET CO.

3000 Owen Rd, Fenton, MI 48430
Tel.: (810) 519-5634
Web Site: http://www.viccaneverchevy.com
Year Founded: 1969
Sales Range: $50-74.9 Million
Emp.: 100
New Car Retailer
N.A.I.C.S.: 441110
Matt Stevens (Gen Mgr-Sls)
Matt McCormick (Mgr-Bus Dev)
Sarah Walters (Coord-Sls)
Mark Polbert (Mgr-Fin)

VICE SQUAD

1407 Main St Ste 904, Dallas, TX 75202
Tel.: (214) 682-1545
Sales Range: $10-24.9 Million
Emp.: 17
Strategic Planning/Research
N.A.I.C.S.: 541810
Mart Roberts (Co-Founder & VP)
David Marett (Co-Founder)

VICENTE CAPITAL PARTNERS, LLC

11726 San Vicente Blvd Ste 300, Los Angeles, CA 90049
Tel.: (310) 826-2255
Web Site: http://www.vicentecapital.com
Privater Equity Firm
N.A.I.C.S.: 523999
Jay Ferguson (Mng Partner)
Klaus Koch (Mng Partner)
Nicholas Memmo (Mng Partner)
David Casares (Partner)
Jason Beck (Principal)
Greg Arsenault (CFO)
Kimberly Magnin (Dir-Fin)

Subsidiaries:

MedBridge Healthcare, LLC (1)
430 Woodruff Rd Ste 450, Greenville, SC 29607
Tel.: (864) 527-5970
Web Site: http://www.medbridgehealthcare.com
Sleep Disorder Diagnosis & Treatment Services
N.A.I.C.S.: 621399
Ghentry Pace (CEO)
Klaus Koch (Chm)
David Leete (VP-Fin)
John Mathias (Chief Dev Officer)
Barbara Lebow (Gen Counsel & Sr VP-HR)
David Weiler (VP-IT)

Subsidiary (Domestic):

Sleep Services of America, Inc. (2)
890 Airport Park Rd Ste 119, Glen Burnie, MD 21061
Tel.: (410) 760-6990
Web Site: http://www.sleepservices.net
Sales Range: $25-49.9 Million
Emp.: 250
Sleep Diagnostic Services
N.A.I.C.S.: 621399
Andrew Brennan (Exec VP-Sls)
John Mathias (Pres)

VICEROY HOTEL MANAGEMENT, LLC

COMPANIES

1212 S Flower St Ste 100, Los Angeles, CA 90015
Tel.: (323) 930-3700   CA
Web Site:
  http://www.viceroyhotelgroup.com
Year Founded: 1990
Sales Range: $50-74.9 Million
Emp.: 1,000
Hotel Owner & Operator
N.A.I.C.S.: 721110
Michael R. Paneri *(Sr VP-Hotel Dev)*
Bill Walshe *(CEO)*
Diane Yost *(Dir-Sls & Mktg)*
Kristieq Goshow *(Sr VP-Comml)*
Mike Walsh *(Sr VP-Hotel Ops-Americas)*
Alex Novo *(Gen Mgr-Miami)*
Jeff Smith *(Sr VP-Fin)*
Sagar Desai *(VP-Acq & Dev)*
Yas Viceroy *(Reg VP & Gen Mgr)*
Mark Griffiths *(Mng Dir & VP-Yas Viceroy Abu Dhabi)*
Anton Bawab *(Reg VP)*
Graham Stuart *(Sr VP-Hotel Dev)*
Natasha Larkin *(VP-HR)*
Diego Fabian Heredia *(Gen Mgr-Viceroy L'Ermitage Beverly Hills)*

VICKERS ENGINEERING, INC.
3604 Glendora Rd, New Troy, MI 49119
Tel.: (269) 426-8545   MI
Web Site: http://www.vickerseng.com
Year Founded: 1970
Mfr Industrial Machinery
N.A.I.C.S.: 332710
Matt Tyler *(Pres & CEO)*
Scott Gourlay *(COO & VP)*
Matt Wermund *(VP-Ops)*
Scott Dawson *(CFO)*

Subsidiaries:

Metal Forming & Coining Corp.   (1)
1007 Illinois Ave, Maumee, OH 43537
Tel.: (419) 893-8748
Web Site: http://www.mfccorp.com
Machinery Metal Product Mfr
N.A.I.C.S.: 332999
Thomas M. Weinrich *(Pres)*
Paul Kessler *(VP)*
Tim Cripsey *(Pres)*

VICKIE MILAZZO INSTITUTE
5615 Kirby Dr Ste 425, Houston, TX 77005
Tel.: (713) 942-2200
Web Site: http://www.legalnurse.com
Year Founded: 1982
Sales Range: $1-9.9 Million
Emp.: 27
Management Consulting Services
N.A.I.C.S.: 541611
Vickie L. Milazzo *(Pres & CEO)*
Steve Nazarenus *(CFO)*
Brandy de Leon *(Mgr-Mktg)*
Evie Baron *(Dir-Sls Trng)*
Candy Wood *(Dir-Sls)*

VICKS LITHOGRAPH & PRINTING
5166 Commercial Dr, Yorkville, NY 13495
Tel.: (315) 736-9244
Web Site: http://www.vicks.biz
Sales Range: $10-24.9 Million
Emp.: 80
Books, Printing Only
N.A.I.C.S.: 323117
Leo McCoy *(CFO)*
Dwight E. Vicks Jr. *(Chm & Pres)*

VICKSBURG CHRYSLER DODGE JEEP RAM
13475 Portage Rd, Vicksburg, MI 49097
Tel.: (269) 649-2000
Web Site:
  http://www.vicksburgchryslerdodgejeepram.com
Car Dealer
N.A.I.C.S.: 441110
Angie Schiedel *(Dir-Internet & Mktg)*
Greg Chernoby *(Mgr-New Car)*
Ken Clark *(Mgr-Used Car)*
Todd Munson *(Asst Mgr-Used Car)*
Melanie Farrington *(Mgr-New & Used Vehicle Sls & Leasing)*
Christina Arebelo *(Office Mgr)*
Doug Kundtz *(Mgr-Svc)*

VICMARR AUDIO INC.
140 58th St Ste 5G, Brooklyn, NY 11220
Tel.: (718) 567-7754
Web Site: http://www.ttro.com
Sales Range: $10-24.9 Million
Emp.: 10
Household Appliance Stores & Electronics
N.A.I.C.S.: 423620
Shoshana Lapp *(Controller)*

VICON INDUSTRIES, INC.
135 Fell Ct, Hauppauge, NY 11788-4351
Tel.: (631) 952-2288   NY
Web Site: https://www.vicon-security.com
Year Founded: 1967
VCON—(OTCBB)
Sales Range: $25-49.9 Million
Emp.: 85
Video Security & Surveillance Systems Designer & Mfr
N.A.I.C.S.: 334290
Bret M. McGowan *(Sr VP-Sls & Mktg)*
Mark S. Provinsal *(Sr VP-Intl Sls)*
Saagar Govil *(Chm & CEO)*
Adam Seckinger *(Sls Mgr-North Carolina, South Carolina & Georgia)*
George Umansky *(Dir-Learning & Dev)*
Cindy B. Atkins *(Mgr-HR)*
Louis Rabenold *(Dir-Video Mgmt Software Products)*
Haim Shain *(Sr VP-Product Mgmt)*

Subsidiaries:

IQinVision, Inc.   (1)
33122 Valle Rd, San Juan Capistrano, CA 92675
Tel.: (949) 369-8100
Web Site: http://www.iqeye.com
Sales Range: $10-24.9 Million
Emp.: 65
Camera Mfr
N.A.I.C.S.: 333310

Vicon Industries Limited   (1)
Unit 4, Nelson industrial park, Hedge End Southampton, Fareham, SO30 2JH, Hamps, United Kingdom   (100%)
Tel.: (44) 1489 566300
Web Site: http://www.vicon-security.com
Sales Range: $10-24.9 Million
Emp.: 30
Video Security & Surveillance Systems Sales & Service
N.A.I.C.S.: 334220

Subsidiary (Non-US):

Vicon Deutschland GmbH   (2)
Kornstieg 3, D 24537, Neumunster, Germany
Tel.: (49) 4321 879 0
Web Site: http://www.vicon-security.de
Video Security & Surveillance Systems Sales & Service
N.A.I.C.S.: 334220
Christopher J. Wall *(Mng Dir)*

VICOR TECHNOLOGIES, INC.
2200 Corporate Blvd NW Ste 401, Boca Raton, FL 33431
Tel.: (561) 995-7313   DE
Web Site: http://www.vicortech.com
Year Founded: 2004
Sales Range: Less than $1 Million
Emp.: 16
Medical Diagnostic Technology Products Mfr
N.A.I.C.S.: 339112

VICTAULIC COMPANY
4901 Kesslersville Rd, Easton, PA 18040-6714
Tel.: (610) 559-3300   NJ
Web Site: http://www.victaulic.com
Year Founded: 1925
Sales Range: $1-4.9 Billion
Emp.: 2,500
Pipe Couplings, Fittings, Valves, Tools & Sprinkler Heads Mfr
N.A.I.C.S.: 332919
John F. Malloy *(Chm)*
Rick Bucher *(Pres & COO)*
Carolyn P. Stennett *(VP-HR)*

Subsidiaries:

Aquamine, LLC   (1)
247 A Vance Tank Rd, Bristol, TN 37620-5622   (100%)
Tel.: (423) 652-1576
Web Site: http://www.victaulic.com
Sales Range: $10-24.9 Million
Emp.: 10
Mfr of Impact Resistant Polyvinyl Chloride (PVC) Plastic Pipe & Fittings
N.A.I.C.S.: 332919

Gamma Foundries Ltd.   (1)
115 Newkirk Rd, Richmond Hill, L4C 3G4, ON, Canada
Tel.: (905) 884-9091
Web Site: http://www.gammafoundries.com
Sales Range: $25-49.9 Million
Emp.: 300
Nonferrous Metal Casting Distr
N.A.I.C.S.: 423510

Utility Coatings & Fabrication, LLC   (1)
5481 Bagley Park Rd, West Jordan, UT 84088
Tel.: (801) 280-1930
Web Site: http://www.utilitycoatings.com
Rev.: $5,256,000
Emp.: 24
Fabricated Structural Metal Mfr
N.A.I.C.S.: 332312
Jeff Dahle *(CEO)*
Ronald Dahle *(Project Mgr)*

Victaulic Company - Victaulic Construction Piping Services Division   (1)
1818 Vultee St, Allentown, PA 18103
Tel.: (610) 559-3488
Construction Piping Services
N.A.I.C.S.: 326122

Victaulic Fire Safety Company, LLC   (1)
4901 Kesslersville Rd, Easton, PA 18044-0031   (100%)
Tel.: (610) 559-3300
Sales Range: $25-49.9 Million
Emp.: 400
Fire Safety Products Mfr
N.A.I.C.S.: 332919
John F. Malloy *(Pres)*

Victaulic International   (1)
4901 Kesslersville Rd, Easton, PA 18040-6714   (100%)
Tel.: (610) 559-3300
Web Site: http://www.victaulic.com
Sales Range: $10-24.9 Million
Emp.: 50
Plumbing Supplies & Equipment
N.A.I.C.S.: 332919

Subsidiary (Non-US):

Victaulic Asia-Pacific   (2)
Ste 06 10 3A F A Mansion No 291 Fumin Rd, Shanghai, 200031, China   (100%)
Tel.: (86) 2161701222
Web Site: http://www.victaulic.com
Pipe Couplings, Fittings, Valves, Accessories & Tools Mfr
N.A.I.C.S.: 332919

K. C. Tan *(Gen Mgr)*

Victaulic Company of Canada Limited   (2)
123 Newkirk Rd, Richmond Hill, L4C 3G5, ON, Canada   (100%)
Tel.: (905) 884-7444
Web Site: http://www.victaulic.com
Mfr of Pipe Couplings; Fittings & Valves
N.A.I.C.S.: 332919

Victaulic Europe   (2)
Prijkelstraat 36, Nazareth, Belgium   (100%)
Tel.: (32) 93811500
Web Site: http://www.victaulic.com
Mfr of Pipe Fittings & Valves
N.A.I.C.S.: 332919

Victaulic Middle East   (2)
Al Munawala Street Jebel Ali Freezone - Southzone, PO Box 17683, Dubai, United Arab Emirates   (100%)
Tel.: (971) 48838870
Web Site: http://www.victaulic.com
Sales Range: $10-24.9 Million
Emp.: 30
Mfr of Pipe Couplings, Fittings, Valves, Accessories & Tools
N.A.I.C.S.: 332919
Mark Gilbert *(VP)*
Daniel Christian *(Chemical & Power Markets-EMEAI)*
Stephen Traynor *(Africa & India)*

Victaulic Tool Company   (1)
8023 Quarry Rd, Alburtis, PA 18011   (100%)
Tel.: (610) 559-3300
Web Site: http://www.victraulic.com
Sales Range: $10-24.9 Million
Emp.: 45
Pipe Preparation Tool Sales & Leasing; Mfr & Distributor of Grooved Piping Products including Couplings, Fittings, Valves & Accessories
N.A.I.C.S.: 332919
T. Warrelmann *(Mgr-Tool Sls)*
Tom Wernerstock *(Dir-Tool)*

VICTOR DISTRIBUTING COMPANY
11125 49th St N, Clearwater, FL 33762
Tel.: (727) 572-7276
Web Site: http://www.victordist.com
Rev.: $42,000,000
Emp.: 60
Warm Air Heating & Air-Conditioning Equipment & Supplies Merchant Whslr
N.A.I.C.S.: 423730
Ron Knish *(Dir-HR)*
Gerald Barnum *(Pres)*
Sylvia Howe *(Treas & Sec)*
Kevin Barnum *(VP)*
Barry Sanders *(Mgr-Pur)*

VICTOR GRAPHICS INC.
1211 Bernard Dr, Baltimore, MD 21223
Tel.: (410) 233-8300
Web Site:
  http://www.victorgraphics.com
Year Founded: 1983
Sales Range: $10-24.9 Million
Emp.: 75
Book Publishing & Printing Services
N.A.I.C.S.: 513130
Thomas H. Hicks *(Co-Owner, Chm & CEO)*
Dale Terzigni *(Treas)*

VICTOR MEDICAL CO.
50 Bunsen, Irvine, CA 92618
Tel.: (949) 788-0330
Web Site:
  http://www.victormedical.com
Sales Range: $10-24.9 Million
Emp.: 80
Veterinary Supplies
N.A.I.C.S.: 424210
Donald V. Louchios *(Pres)*

VICTOR SECURITIES

VICTOR SECURITIES

Victor Securities—(Continued)
285 Grand Ave, Englewood, NJ 07631
Tel.: (646) 820-8732
Web Site:
  http://www.victorsecurities.com
Year Founded: 2007
Sales Range: $1-9.9 Million
Emp.: 11
Security Brokerage Services
N.A.I.C.S.: 523150
Craig S. Aronoff (Dir-Bus Dev)
John T. A. Pawluk (CFO)
Scott Franzini (Dir-Trade Support & Client Svcs)

VICTOR TECHNOLOGY
175 E Crossrods Pkwy, Bolingbrook, IL 60440
Tel.: (630) 754-4400   PA
Web Site: http://www.victortech.com
Year Founded: 1981
Sales Range: $75-99.9 Million
Emp.: 30
Calculators Mfr & Distr
N.A.I.C.S.: 423420
Jordan Feiger (Pres)

VICTORIA ADVOCATE PUBLISHING COMPANY
311 E Constitution St, Victoria, TX 77901
Tel.: (361) 575-1451
Web Site: http://www.victx.com
Rev.: $15,588,251
Emp.: 131
Newspaper Publishers
N.A.I.C.S.: 513110
John M. Roberts (Owner & Pres)
Dan Easton (Co-Publr & VP-Interactive)

VICTORIA AIR CONDITIONING, LTD.
513 Profit Dr, Victoria, TX 77901
Tel.: (361) 578-5241
Web Site: http://www.victoriaair.com
Year Founded: 1973
Sales Range: $25-49.9 Million
Emp.: 175
Plumbing, Heating & Air-Conditioning Contracting Services
N.A.I.C.S.: 238220
Gay Heilker (Pres)
Benjamin F. Heilker (Sr VP)

VICTORIA NURSING & REHABILITATION CENTER, INC.
955 NW 3rd St, Miami, FL 33128
Tel.: (305) 548-4020   FL
Web Site:
  http://www.victorianursing.net
Year Founded: 1998
Sales Range: $25-49.9 Million
Emp.: 500
Skilled Nursing Care Facilities
N.A.I.C.S.: 623110
Ralph Stacey (Pres)
Mara Ferrer (Dir-Admissions)
Eugene Marini (COO)

VICTORIA THEATRE ASSOCIATION
138 N Main St, Dayton, OH 45402
Tel.: (937) 228-7591   OH
Web Site:
  http://www.victoriatheatre.com
Year Founded: 1976
Sales Range: $10-24.9 Million
Emp.: 193
Art Event Organizer
N.A.I.C.S.: 711110
Stephen M. Miller (Chm)
Martha Shaker (Sec)
Edgar M. Purvis Jr. (Treas)
Ty Sutton (Pres & CEO)

VICTORIAN PAPER COMPANY
15600 W 99th St, Lenexa, KS 66219
Tel.: (913) 438-3995
Web Site:
  http://victoriantradingco.com
Year Founded: 1987
Sales Range: $10-24.9 Million
Emp.: 60
Mail Order Sales of Paper Products
N.A.I.C.S.: 424120
Randy Rolston (Pres)
Melissa Rolston (Owner & Founder)

Subsidiaries:

Victorian Greetings (1)
15600 West 99th St, Shawnee Mission, KS 66219
Tel.: (913) 438-3995
Web Site: http://www.victoriantradingco.com
Fine Art Greeting Cards Mfr & Licensor
N.A.I.C.S.: 424120

Victorian Papers (1)
15600 W 99th St, Lenexa, KS 66219
Tel.: (913) 438-3995
Web Site: http://www.victoriantradingco.com
Business, Calling Cards & Corporate Greeting Cards Printer
N.A.I.C.S.: 424120

Victorian Trading Co. (1)
15600 W 99th St, Lenexa, KS 66219
Tel.: (913) 438-3995
Web Site: http://www.victoriantradingco.com
Mail Order & Internet Catalog Importer Gifts & Home Products Distr
N.A.I.C.S.: 424120
Randy Rolston (Founder & CEO)

VICTORY AUTOMOTIVE GROUP, INC.
46352 Michigan Ave, Canton, MI 48188
Tel.: (734) 495-3500   MI
Web Site:
  http://www.victoryautomotivegroup.com
Holding Company; New & Used Car Dealerships Owner & Operator
N.A.I.C.S.: 551112
Eric Cappo (CFO)
Megan Meinerding (Mktg Dir)
Katie Digsby (Corp Counsel)
Travis Zollner (Corp Counsel)

Subsidiaries:

Cappo Management II, Inc. (1)
1605 N Monroe St, Monroe, MI 48162
Tel.: (734) 242-2300
Web Site: http://www.victorymonroe.com
Sales Range: $10-24.9 Million
Emp.: 25
New & Used Car Dealer
N.A.I.C.S.: 441110
James Galofaro (Mgr-Internet Sls)

Cappo Management VI, Inc. (1)
315 W Ann Arbor Rd, Plymouth, MI 48170-2223
Tel.: (734) 453-3600
Web Site: http://www.victoryplymouth.com
Sales Range: $10-24.9 Million
New & Used Car Dealer
N.A.I.C.S.: 441110
Ken Litner (Gen Mgr)
Len Palmer (Sls Mgr & Bus Mgr)
Keith Friday (Gen Mgr-Sls)
Ed Burck (Mgr-Bus Dev)
Joe Goffney (Mgr-Fin)
Karl Messer (Mgr-Parts)
Harvey Walker (Mgr-Fin)

Cappo Management VII, Inc. (1)
6166 N Croatan Hwy, Kitty Hawk, NC 27949
Tel.: (252) 261-5900
Web Site: http://www.obxchevy.com
Sales Range: $10-24.9 Million
Emp.: 51
New & Used Car Dealer
N.A.I.C.S.: 441110
Marc Hellman (Gen Mgr)
Suanne Armstrong (Controller)

Ricardo Rojas (Mgr-Sls)
Tony Beakes (Mgr-Svc)
Kevin Russell (Mgr-Parts)

Cappo Management XVII, Inc. (1)
46352 Michigan Ave, Canton, MI 48188
Tel.: (734) 495-3535
Web Site:
  http://www.victorytoyotacanton.com
Sales Range: $10-24.9 Million
Emp.: 40
New & Used Car Dealer
N.A.I.C.S.: 441110
Jennifer Raft (Gen Mgr)
Brian Badrak (Gen Sls Mgr)
Brian Jones-Chance (Sls Mgr)
Holly Bolton (Mgr-BDC)

Cappo Management XXIII, Inc. (1)
3801 Soquel Dr, Soquel, CA 95073
Tel.: (831) 464-1500
Web Site:
  http://www.oceanhondasantacruz.com
Sales Range: $10-24.9 Million
Emp.: 90
New & Used Car Dealer
N.A.I.C.S.: 441110
Joe Enea (Mgr-Sls)
Kali Denicore (Mgr-Fin)
Chris Corder (Mgr-Parts)
Chris O'Connell (Mgr-Bus Dev)
Colin Fitzgerald (Gen Mgr)
Rick Heikens (Mgr-Svc)
Ernesto Ramirez (Dir-Detail)

Cappo Management, Inc. (1)
2774 N Main St, Crossville, TN 38555
Tel.: (931) 484-9746
Web Site:
  http://www.easttennesseedodge.com
Sales Range: $10-24.9 Million
Emp.: 40
New & Used Car Dealer
N.A.I.C.S.: 441110
Brandon Letner (Gen Mgr)
Rick Kilburn (Mgr-Bus Dev & Internet)
Erich Spence (Mgr-Sls)

Ocean Honda (1)
8442 US Hwy 19, Port Richey, FL 34668
Tel.: (727) 777-6531
Web Site:
  http://www.oceanhondaofportrichey.com
Sales Range: $10-24.9 Million
Emp.: 40
New & Used Car Dealer
N.A.I.C.S.: 441110
Brandon Maged (Mgr-Fin)
Patrick Sanders (Gen Mgr-Sls)
John Veltri (Mgr-Svc)
Eva Davney (Mgr-Cafe)
Curtis Tucker (Mgr-Fin)
Kenny Banaciski (Mgr-Internet/BDC)
Steven Davidson (Mgr-Sls)
Peter Gabriel (Mgr-Sls)
Pamela Key (Office Mgr)
Jeffrey E. Cappo (Owner)
Scott Harlib (Gen Mgr)
Jeanette Tamburri (Controller)

VICTORY COMMERCIAL MANAGEMENT, INC.
424 Madison Ave Ste 1002, New York, NY 10017
Tel.: (212) 922-2199   NV
Year Founded: 2017
Rev.: $8,191,130
Assets: $29,500,068
Liabilities: $267,022,575
Net Worth: ($237,522,507)
Earnings: ($9,619,713)
Emp.: 187
Fiscal Year-end: 12/31/19
Holding Company
N.A.I.C.S.: 551112
Alex Brown (Chm, Pres, CEO, Interim CFO, Interim Chief Acctg Officer & Treas)

VICTORY DEVELOPERS INC.
506 Manchester Expy B5, Columbus, GA 31904
Tel.: (706) 327-4774
Web Site: http://www.vrei.net
Rev.: $10,000,000

Emp.: 30
Real Estate Investment Services
N.A.I.C.S.: 523999
Kent Cost (Pres)

VICTORY FINANCIAL GROUP, INC.
PO Box 5902, Metairie, LA 70009
Tel.: (504) 837-2230   DE
Sales Range: $150-199.9 Million
Emp.: 3
Holding Company
N.A.I.C.S.: 524210
Louie Roussel (Pres)

VICTORY FOAM, INC.
3 Holland, Irvine, CA 92618
Tel.: (949) 474-0690
Web Site:
  http://www.victoryfoam.com
Year Founded: 1983
Sales Range: $10-24.9 Million
Emp.: 100
Industrial Supplies Whslr
N.A.I.C.S.: 423840
Angel Alvarado (Mgr-Matl)
Darrick Anderson (Dir-Specialty Products)

VICTORY FOOD SERVICE DISTRIBUTORS
515 Truxton St, Bronx, NY 10474
Tel.: (718) 378-1122
Web Site:
  http://www.victoryfoodservice.com
Sales Range: $10-24.9 Million
Emp.: 28
Provider of Grocery Services
N.A.I.C.S.: 424410
Mihail Tyras (Pres)
Don Carter (CFO)
Angela Valdes-Rasmussen (Mgr-Customer Svc)

VICTORY GROUND SUPPORT EQUIPMENT
8211 S Alameda St, Los Angeles, CA 90001
Tel.: (323) 581-7272
Web Site: http://www.victorygse.com
Sales Range: $1-9.9 Million
Emp.: 25
Ground Support Equipment Supplier
N.A.I.C.S.: 336999
Lloyd Weinstein (Pres)
Jamey Ekerling (VP)

VICTORY HOUSING, INC.
5430 Grosvenor Ln Ste 210, Bethesda, MD 20814
Tel.: (301) 493-6000
Web Site:
  http://www.victoryhousing.org
Rev.: $18,685,740
Emp.: 150
Housing Services
N.A.I.C.S.: 236115
Meg DeSchriver (Dir-Grace House)
Caryn Daniel (Office Mgr)
Jeffrey Blackwell (VP-Real Estate Dev)
Irene Dunn (VP-Assisted Living Ops)
John D. Spencer (Sr VP)
Elisabeth Orchard (Dir-Malta House)
Marcy Hunter (Dir-Marian Assisted Living)
Melissa Thomas (Dir-Byron House)
Timur Ryspekov (Sr Mgr-Asset)
Nellia Kaiyo (Dir-Raphael House)
Leila Finucane (Pres & CEO)

VICTORY LAYNE CHEVROLET
3980 Fowler St, Fort Myers, FL 33901
Tel.: (239) 603-7069

COMPANIES

Web Site:
http://www.victorylaynechevrolet.com
Sales Range: $25-49.9 Million
Emp.: 140
Car Dealership
N.A.I.C.S.: 441110
Jaime Layne *(Pres)*
Ed Ihoads *(Gen Mgr)*

VICTORY MEDIA INC.
429 Mill St, Coraopolis, PA 15108
Tel.: (412) 269-1663
Web Site:
http://www.victorymedia.com
Year Founded: 2001
Sales Range: $1-9.9 Million
Emp.: 50
Periodical Publishers
N.A.I.C.S.: 513120
Richard McCormack *(Founder & Pres)*
Chris Hale *(Founder, Chm & CEO)*
Scott Shaw *(Co-Founder & VP-Bus Dev)*
JoAnn Conner *(VP-Fin & HR)*
Jolene Jefferies *(VP-Trng & Dev)*
Daniel Nichols *(Chief Product Officer)*
Sean McAlister *(VP-Digital)*
Diane Katherine Mastramico *(Mgr-Project & QA)*
Ian Blyth *(Mgr-Digital Mktg)*
Mike Stevens *(COO)*

VICTORY MOTORS OF CRAIG
2705 W 1st St, Craig, CO 81625
Tel.: (970) 824-4424
Web Site:
http://www.victorymotors.com
Sales Range: $10-24.9 Million
Emp.: 36
Car & RV Dealership Owner & Operator
N.A.I.C.S.: 441110
Steve Maneotis *(Gen Mgr)*

VICTORY OF WEST VIRGINIA, INC.
PO Box 2648, Fairmont, WV 26555-2648
Tel.: (304) 363-4100   WV
Web Site: http://www.victorywv.com
Year Founded: 1997
Sales Range: $250-299.9 Million
Emp.: 100
Holding Company; Coal Mining Equipment Distr & Support Services
N.A.I.C.S.: 551112
Wayne H. Stanley *(Pres & CEO)*

Subsidiaries:

A.L. Lee Corp.   (1)
951 Lester Hwy, Glen White, WV 25849   (100%)
Tel.: (304) 934-5361
Web Site: http://www.alleecorp.com
Sales Range: $10-24.9 Million
Emp.: 70
Coal Mining Equipment Designer & Mfr
N.A.I.C.S.: 333131
Leonard Urtso *(Pres & CEO)*
Bruce Roehrig *(CFO)*
John Allen *(Mgr-IT)*
Deanna Richmond *(Mgr-Parts-Sls)*
Jeff Ramsey *(Mgr-Warehouse-IL)*
Samantha McBride *(Mgr-Documentation & CAD)*
Tom Acord *(Mgr-Electrical Engrg)*

Industrial Resources, Inc.   (1)
Industrial Rd, Fairmont, WV 26554 (100%)
Tel.: (304) 363-4100
Web Site: http://www.indres.com
Sales Range: $25-49.9 Million
Emp.: 40
Industrial Processing & Material Handling Equipment Designer Mfr
N.A.I.C.S.: 213113

Subsidiary (Domestic):

Industrial Contracting of Fairmont, Inc.   (2)
Industrial Rd, Fairmont, WV 26554 (100%)
Tel.: (304) 363-4100
Web Site: http://www.indres.com
Emp.: 25
Coal, Stone & Cement Processing & Material Handling Equipment Installation Contractor
N.A.I.C.S.: 238990
Phil Burnside *(Pres)*

McHal Corporation   (1)
2011 Pleasant Valley Rd, Fairmont, WV 26555   (100%)
Tel.: (304) 363-6900
Sales Range: $10-24.9 Million
Emp.: 40
Industrial Electrical Systems Installation Contractor
N.A.I.C.S.: 238990

West Virginia Electric Corp.   (1)
2011 Pleasant Valley Rd, Fairmont, WV 26554   (100%)
Tel.: (304) 363-6900
Web Site: http://www.wvelectric.com
Rev.: $8,300,000
Emp.: 15
Engineers & Installs Electrical Systems & Apparatus for All Segments of the Coal Industry
N.A.I.C.S.: 238210
Dennise Toothman *(Pres)*

Subsidiary (Domestic):

Salem Electric Company   (2)
633 7th St NW, Salem, OR 97304-0055   (100%)
Tel.: (503) 362-3601
Web Site: http://www.salemelectric.com
Sales Range: $25-49.9 Million
Emp.: 15
Installs Industrial Electrical Systems
N.A.I.C.S.: 238210
Lee Ann Godby *(Controller)*

VICTORY PACKAGING
800 Jct St, Plymouth, MI 48170-1200
Tel.: (734) 459-2000
Web Site:
http://www.victorypackaging.com
Year Founded: 1971
Sales Range: $75-99.9 Million
Emp.: 100
Provider of Warehousing & Distribution of Packaging Products
N.A.I.C.S.: 424130
Joe Schlicklin *(Engr-Pkg)*

VICTORY PARK CAPITAL ADVISORS, LLC
150 N Riverside Plz Ste 5200, Chicago, IL 60606
Tel.: (312) 701-1777   DE
Web Site:
http://www.victoryparkcapital.com
Year Founded: 2007
Investment Management & Private Equity Firm
N.A.I.C.S.: 523940
Richard Levy *(Co-Founder & CEO)*
Scott Zemnick *(Partner & Gen Counsel)*
Jeffrey Schneider *(Partner, COO & Chief Compliance Officer)*
Jason Brown *(Partner & Head-Los Angeles)*
Gordon Watson *(Partner)*
Anthony Barwacz *(Principal)*
Matthew Coad *(Principal)*
Andrew Murray *(Principal)*
Kelly Hitchman *(Office Mgr & Coord-HR)*
Connell Hasten *(Partner-Insurance Svcs)*
Joshua Platek *(Principal)*
Kevin Burke *(Partner)*
Olibia Stamatoglou *(CFO)*
Brendan Carroll *(Co-Founder & Sr Partner)*

Subsidiaries:

American Plastics, LLC   (1)
11840 Westline Industrial Dr Ste 200, Saint Louis, MO 63146
Tel.: (800) 325-1051
Web Site:
http://www.americanplasticsllc.com
Holding Company; Commercial Cleaning & Storage Products Mfr & Whslr
N.A.I.C.S.: 551112
Brian G. Nichols *(Chief Bus Officer & VP)*
Robert L. Guerra *(Pres & CEO)*

Subsidiary (Domestic):

Centrex Plastics, LLC   (2)
814 W Lima St, Findlay, OH 45840
Tel.: (419) 423-1213
Web Site: http://www.centrexplastics.com
Mfg Plastic Products
N.A.I.C.S.: 326199
Larry Ray *(Mgr-Production)*
Pamela Fennell *(Dir-HR)*
Eric Hummel *(Mgr-Tooling)*

Continental Commercial Products, LLC   (2)
11840 Westline Industrial Dr, Saint Louis, MO 63146
Tel.: (800) 325-1051
Commercial Cleaning & Storage Products Mfr
N.A.I.C.S.: 326199
Timothy C. Haeffner *(VP-Sls & Mktg)*
Michael B. Smith *(VP-Mfg Svcs)*

Cardenas Market, LLC   (1)
2501 E Guasti Rd, Ontario, CA 91761
Tel.: (909) 923-7426
Web Site:
https://www.cardenasmarkets.com
Fresh Product Store
N.A.I.C.S.: 445298
John Gomez *(CEO)*

The Fuller Brush Company, Inc.   (1)
1 Fuller Way, Great Bend, KS 67530
Tel.: (620) 792-1711
Web Site: http://www.fuller.com
Sales Range: $50-74.9 Million
Emp.: 250
Household Cleaning & Personal Care Products Mfr
N.A.I.C.S.: 325612

Division (Domestic):

Stanley Home Products   (2)
1340 Centre St Ste 212, Newton, MA 02459
Tel.: (413) 786-8455
Web Site: http://www.shponline.com
Sales Range: $25-49.9 Million
Emp.: 10
Home Products Mfr
N.A.I.C.S.: 424690

VICTORY PERSONNEL SERVICES, INC.
735 N Water St Ste 1411, Milwaukee, WI 53202
Tel.: (414) 271-0749
Web Site:
http://www.victorypersonnel.com
Year Founded: 1992
Sales Range: $25-49.9 Million
Emp.: 500
Professional, Administrative & Clerical Staffing Services
N.A.I.C.S.: 561311
Joe Tucker *(Pres & CEO)*

VICTORY RANCH
4330 Mecklinburg Dr, Bolivar, TN 38008
Tel.: (731) 659-2880
Web Site: http://www.victoryranch.org
Year Founded: 2002
Sales Range: $1-9.9 Million
Emp.: 102
Youth Camp Operator
N.A.I.C.S.: 721211
Chad Eoff *(Program Dir)*
Dennis Smith *(Chm)*

Garret Harrison *(Dir-Water Sports)*
Paul Warner *(Dir-Outdoor Adventure)*
Penny Russell *(Dir-Recreation)*
Chad Eoff *(Program Dir)*
Dennis Smith *(Chm)*
Garret Harrison *(Dir-Water Sports)*
Penny Russell *(Dir-Recreation)*
Rusty Hensley *(Treas & Sec)*
Zeb Russell *(Dir-Equestrian)*

VICTORY STEEL PRODUCTS CORP.
11166 Tesson Ferry Rd, Saint Louis, MO 63123
Tel.: (314) 849-7272
Web Site: http://www.vicsteel.com
Rev.: $11,000,000
Emp.: 18
Steel
N.A.I.C.S.: 423510
Jeffrey Stephens *(Gen Mgr)*
Verna Ramirez *(Mgr-Acctg)*

VICTORY TRANSPORTATION SYSTEMS, INC.
9009 N Loop E Ste 165, Houston, TX 77029-1299
Tel.: (713) 682-8900
Web Site:
http://www.victorytrucks.com
Year Founded: 2003
Rev.: $15,200,000
Emp.: 25
Freight Transportation Arrangement
N.A.I.C.S.: 488510
Brendan Neef *(Pres & CEO)*
Kelly Reed *(COO)*

VICTORY VAN CORP.
950 S Pickett St, Alexandria, VA 22304
Tel.: (703) 751-5200
Web Site: http://www.victoryvan.com
Sales Range: $10-24.9 Million
Emp.: 120
General Warehousing & Storage
N.A.I.C.S.: 493110
Chris Patton *(Pres)*

VICTORY WHITE METAL COMPANY, INC.
3027 E 55th St, Cleveland, OH 44127
Tel.: (216) 271-1400   OH
Web Site: http://www.vwmc.com
Year Founded: 1988
Sales Range: $10-24.9 Million
Emp.: 96
Mfr of Industrial Supplies
N.A.I.C.S.: 423830
Alex Stanwick *(Pres)*
Bill Clarke *(Mgr-Ops)*

VICTORY WORLDWIDE TRANSPORATION
1045 Cranbury S River Rd, Jamesburg, NJ 08831-3408
Tel.: (732) 719-0700
Web Site:
http://www.victoryworldwide.com
Sales Range: $10-24.9 Million
Emp.: 100
Household Goods Transport
N.A.I.C.S.: 484210
Henry Borchers *(Pres, CEO & CFO)*

VICTRA
1290-B E Arlington Blvd, Greenville, NC 27858
Tel.: (252) 317-0388
Web Site:
http://www.myawireless.com
Year Founded: 1996
Sales Range: $100-124.9 Million
Emp.: 4,500

Victra—(Continued)
Retailer of Verizon Wireless Products & Services
N.A.I.C.S.: 517112
Rich Balot *(Founder & Chm)*
Michael Moore *(Chief Customer Officer)*
George Sherman *(CEO)*

VICTUS, INC.
4918 SW 74th Ct, Miami, FL 33155
Tel.: (305) 663-2129
Web Site: http://www.victusinc.com
Sales Range: $1-9.9 Million
Emp.: 50
Medical Products Mfr & Distr
N.A.I.C.S.: 325412
Mariano Macias *(Co-Owner)*
Enrique Lopez *(Co-Owner)*
Melany Velasquez *(Product Mgr-Mktg)*

VIDA FLASH ACQUISITIONS
3550 Wilshire Ste 840, Los Angeles, CA 90010
Tel.: (310) 954-1575   Ky
Year Founded: 2021
Investment Services
N.A.I.C.S.: 523999
Frank Litvack *(CEO)*
R. Scott Huennekens *(Chm)*

VIDAROO CORPORATION
8 N Highland Ave, Winter Garden, FL 34787-2769
Tel.: (321) 293-3360   NV
Web Site: http://vidaroo.com
Sales Range: $1-9.9 Million
Emp.: 13
Online Video Broadcasting Services
N.A.I.C.S.: 516210
Thomas J. Moreland *(Chm, CEO, CFO, Treas & Sec)*

VIDCON ENTERPRISES, INC.
1910 W Main St, Battle Ground, WA 98604
Tel.: (360) 576-1991   WA
Year Founded: 1983
Convenience Store
N.A.I.C.S.: 445131
Kevin Schulz *(CEO)*

VIDEK, INC.
1387 Fairport Rd Bldg 1000 C, Fairport, NY 14450
Tel.: (585) 377-0377   NY
Web Site: http://www.videk.com
Year Founded: 1990
Mfr & Marketer of Vision Products for Printing & Manufacturing
N.A.I.C.S.: 333310
Tom Slechta *(Pres)*

VIDEO AND AUDIO CENTER
1426 Wilshire Blvd, Santa Monica, CA 90403
Tel.: (310) 451-6200
Web Site:
 http://www.videoandaudiocenter.com
Rev.: $13,847,304
Emp.: 80
Video Recorders, Players, Disc Players & Accessories
N.A.I.C.S.: 449210
Mayer Akhtarzad *(Principal)*
Joseph Akhtarzad *(Principal)*
Ervin Caprio *(Mgr-Mdse)*

VIDEO CORPORATION OF AMERICA
7 Veronica Ave, Somerset, NJ 08873-3447
Tel.: (732) 545-8000   NJ
Web Site: http://www.vca.com
Year Founded: 1972
Sales Range: $25-49.9 Million
Emp.: 115
Distribution of Electronic Parts & Equipment
N.A.I.C.S.: 449210
Albert J. Berlin *(CEO)*
Delores Berlin *(Controller)*
Holly Sova *(Dir-HR)*
Bob L. Antin *(Co-Founder, Chm, Pres & CEO)*

VIDEO GROUP DISTRIBUTORS
800 Belle Air Rd, Clearwater, FL 33756
Tel.: (727) 585-7737
Web Site: http://www.videogroup.com
Rev.: $10,600,000
Emp.: 23
Electronic Parts & Equipment Merchant Whslr
N.A.I.C.S.: 423690
Gene Gross *(Pres)*
Mary A. Gross *(CFO)*
Kelly Ellis *(Acct Exec)*

VIDEO GUIDANCE, INC.
8000 Norman Center Dr Ste 250, Bloomington, MN 55437
Tel.: (952) 831-7215   MN
Web Site:
 http://www.videoguidance.com
Year Founded: 1999
Sales Range: $10-24.9 Million
Emp.: 150
Video, Web, Streaming & Voice Conferencing Technology
N.A.I.C.S.: 334210
Michael J. Werch *(Founder & Pres)*
Brian Groff *(VP-Sls-North America)*
Dan Giesen *(VP-Global Svcs)*
Rachel Rice *(CFO)*
Paul Hanson *(Sr Acct Mgr)*
Clive Sawkins *(CEO)*
Sheila Mueller *(Mgr-User Adoption Svcs)*

VIDEO KING GAMING SYSTEMS, LLC
2717 N 118th Cir Ste 210, Omaha, NE 68164
Tel.: (402) 951-2970
Web Site:
 http://www.videokingnetwork.com
Sales Range: $50-74.9 Million
Emp.: 100
Electronic Gaming Device Mfr
N.A.I.C.S.: 339930
Tim Stuart *(Pres & CEO)*
Rusty Morin *(CFO)*
Carla Chance *(Dir-Mktg Comm)*
Dan Free *(CTO & VP)*
Brian Jenkins *(Dir-Mfg)*
Leslie Lombardi *(Controller)*
Sonya Huscroft *(Mgr-HR & Compliance)*
Brent Kizuik *(CTO & VP)*
Peggy Hansen *(Mgr-Bingo Hall Equipment)*
Cindy Martin *(Mgr-Customer Svc)*

Subsidiaries:

Video King Gaming & Entertainment Canada Limited   (1)
1146 Waverley St Unit 1, Winnipeg, R3T 0P4, MB, Canada
Tel.: (204) 452-0100
Electronic Gaming Equipment Distr
N.A.I.C.S.: 423690

Video King Gaming Systems, LLC - Bingo King Division   (1)
3402 SW 26th Ter Ste B4, Fort Lauderdale, FL 33312
Tel.: (954) 321-8300
Electronic Gaming Equipment Distr
N.A.I.C.S.: 423690

Video King Gaming Systems, LLC - Bingo Technology & Supply Division   (1)
9940 Currie Davis Dr Ste 122, Tampa, FL 33619
Tel.: (813) 628-4020
Electronic Gaming Equipment Distr
N.A.I.C.S.: 423690

Video King Gaming Systems, LLC - Manufacturing Division   (1)
7270 Pacific St, Omaha, NE 68114
Tel.: (402) 951-2970
Web Site: http://www.videokingnetwork.com
Emp.: 25
Electronic Gaming Equipment Mfr
N.A.I.C.S.: 335999
Lesley Lambardi *(Office Mgr)*

VIDEO MONITORING SERVICES OF AMERICA, LP
1500 Broadway 6th Fl, New York, NY 10036-6902
Tel.: (212) 736-2010   NY
Year Founded: 1996
Sales Range: $25-49.9 Million
Emp.: 250
Information Retrieval Services
N.A.I.C.S.: 517810
Laila Sayad *(CFO)*
Peter Wengryn *(CEO)*
Michael Giovia *(VP-Sls-News Div)*
Roy McInnis *(Sr VP-Sls-News Monitoring, Measurement & Analysis Div)*
Joseph J. Scotti *(Sr VP-Broadcast Media & Affiliate Rels)*

VIDEO NETWORKS, INC.
1577 Spring Hill Rd Ste 250, Vienna, VA 22182-2297
Tel.: (703) 637-8330
Web Site:
 http://www.videonetworksinc.com
Year Founded: 1999
Sales Range: $1-9.9 Million
Emp.: 8
Electronic Visual Security Systems Designer & Builder
N.A.I.C.S.: 561621
Brett Cosor *(CEO)*

VIDEO ONLY INC.
500 Strander Blvd, Seattle, WA 98188-2921
Tel.: (206) 444-1655   WA
Web Site: http://www.videoonly.com
Year Founded: 1983
Sales Range: $10-24.9 Million
Emp.: 117
Radio, Television & Electronic Stores
N.A.I.C.S.: 449210
Peter Edwards *(Pres)*
Jerry Prosio *(CFO)*
Dewey Sluk *(Mgr-Sls)*

VIDEO PROFESSOR INC.
26 W Dry Creek Cir Ste 715, Littleton, CO 80120-8065
Tel.: (303) 232-1244
Web Site:
 http://www.videoprofessor.com
Year Founded: 1987
Rev.: $50,000,000
Emp.: 200
Training Software Services
N.A.I.C.S.: 611420
John W. Scherer *(Owner)*
Joelle Clapham *(Project Mgr-Instructional Dev)*
Steven Snedker *(Coord-Telecom & Facilities)*

VIDEO SECURITY SPECIALISTS, INC.
632 N Victory Blvd, Burbank, CA 91502
Tel.: (818) 848-7305
Web Site:
 http://www.videosecurityspecialists.com
Rev.: $13,000,000
Emp.: 15
Electronic Parts & Equipment Merchant Whslr
N.A.I.C.S.: 423690
Art Artinjian *(Mgr-Ops)*
Brian Beltran *(Mgr)*
Greg Bier *(VP)*
Vic Korhonian *(Pres)*
Brian Meyer *(Mgr-Sls)*

VIDEOAMP, INC.
2229 S Carmelina Ave, Los Angeles, CA 90064
Tel.: (424) 272-7774
Web Site: http://www.videoamp.com
Year Founded: 2014
Sales Range: $10-24.9 Million
Emp.: 122
Advertising & Marketing Services
N.A.I.C.S.: 541810
Peter Liguori *(Exec Chm)*
Peter Bradbury *(Chief Comml & Growth Officer)*
Ross Mccray *(Founder & CEO)*
Michael Parkes *(Chief Revenue Officer)*
Marisa Peters *(Chief People Officer)*
Josh Nisenson *(Sr VP-Engrg)*
Jenny Wall *(CMO)*
Tony Fagan *(Pres-Tech & Strategy)*
Josh Hudgins *(Chief Product Officer)*
Paul Ross *(CFO)*
Hari Sankar *(Chief Data Officer)*

VIDEOLAND, INC.
6808 Hornwood Dr, Houston, TX 77074
Tel.: (713) 772-6200
Web Site:
 http://www.hometheaterstore.com
Year Founded: 1987
Rev.: $37,000,000
Emp.: 20
Consumer Electronics Retailer
N.A.I.C.S.: 449210
Mihir Mody *(CEO)*

VIDEOLOCITY INTERNATIONAL, INC.
1762-A Prospector Ave, Park City, UT 84060
Tel.: (435) 615-8838
Year Founded: 1985
Communication Equipment Mfr
N.A.I.C.S.: 334290
Dan Driscoll *(Chm)*

VIDEON CENTRAL, INC.
2171 Sandy Dr, State College, PA 16803
Tel.: (814) 235-1111
Web Site: http://www.videon-central.com
Year Founded: 1997
Sales Range: $10-24.9 Million
Emp.: 70
Digital Video System Mfr
N.A.I.C.S.: 334310
Todd A. Erdley *(CEO)*
Joan Potter *(Dir-HR)*
Paul Brown *(Pres & COO)*
Rob Bargo *(VP-Mfg)*
Robert J. Hicks *(CFO)*

VIDEOTAPE PRODUCTS INC.
1309 S Flower Ave, Burbank, CA 91502
Tel.: (818) 566-9898
Web Site: http://www.myvtp.com
Sales Range: $10-24.9 Million
Emp.: 35

COMPANIES

Video Cassettes; Accessories & Supplies
N.A.I.C.S.: 423990
Richard Marzec (Chm)
Barbara Susca (VP-Fin)
John Palazzola (Pres & CEO)

VIDEOTRONIX INC.
401 W Travelers Trl, Burnsville, MN 55337-2554
Tel.: (952) 894-5343
Web Site: http://www.vtisecurity.com
Sales Range: $10-24.9 Million
Emp.: 100
Integrator of Security Systems
N.A.I.C.S.: 561621
Thomas Asp (Pres & CEO)
Linda Larish (Controller)
Rick Allan (CTO)

VIDERITY INC.
1425 K St Suite 350, Washington, DC 20005
Tel.: (800) 690-9170
Web Site: http://www.viderity.com
Year Founded: 2007
Sales Range: $10-24.9 Million
Emp.: 30
Technology Design, Development & Management Services to Government Agencies & Commercial Businesses
N.A.I.C.S.: 541618
Rachel Everett (Founder & CEO)
Samantha Hodges (Project Mgr-IT)

VIDEX, INC.
1105 NE Cir Blvd, Corvallis, OR 97330
Tel.: (541) 758-0521
Web Site: http://www.videx.com
Year Founded: 1979
Sales Range: $10-24.9 Million
Emp.: 56
Data Collection & Access Control Products Designer & Mfr
N.A.I.C.S.: 334118
Paul Davis (Pres)

VIDI EMI, INC.
285 Washington Ave, San Leandro, CA 94571
Tel.: (510) 667-9999
Web Site: http://www.vidiemi.com
Year Founded: 2001
Sales Range: $1-9.9 Million
Emp.: 15
Email Marketing Software & Services
N.A.I.C.S.: 513210
John Ludgey (CEO)

VIDMAR HONDA
600 N Albany Ave, Pueblo, CO 81003-4123
Tel.: (719) 544-5844
Web Site: http://www.vidmarmotor.com
Sales Range: $25-49.9 Million
Emp.: 60
Car Whslr
N.A.I.C.S.: 441110
Derek Vidmar (Dir-Sls)
William Vidmar (Owner)

VIDYA BRANDS GROUP LLC
300 Knightsbridge Pkwy, Lincolnshire, IL 60069 DE
Web Site: https://www.vidyabrands.com
Emp.: 100
Packaging & Printing Services
N.A.I.C.S.: 561910
Anik Patel (Chm)
Kurt Hardy (CEO)

Subsidiaries:

Seaboard Folding Box Corp. (1)
100 Simplex Dr, Westminster, MA 01473
Tel.: (978) 342-8921
Web Site: http://www.seaboardfoldingbox.com
Sales Range: $10-24.9 Million
Emp.: 100
Folding Paperboard Boxes
N.A.I.C.S.: 322212
Sharon Drake (Mgr-HR)

Subsidiary (Domestic):

Pioneer Paper Corporation (2)
1 Madison St, East Rutherford, NJ 07073
Tel.: (201) 935-0123
Sales Range: $10-24.9 Million
Emp.: 80
Mfr of Blister Packaging & Paperboard Spools; Lithographic Printing
N.A.I.C.S.: 326199

VIE-DEL COMPANY
11903 S Chestnut Ave, Fresno, CA 93725
Tel.: (559) 834-2525
Sales Range: $10-24.9 Million
Emp.: 60
Fruit Juice Packaging Services
N.A.I.C.S.: 311421
Dianne S. Nury (Pres & CEO)

VIENNA SAUSAGE MFG. CO.
2501 N Damen Ave, Chicago, IL 60647-2101
Tel.: (773) 278-7800 IL
Web Site: http://www.viennabeef.com
Year Founded: 1893
Sales Range: $125-149.9 Million
Emp.: 300
Food Processor & Distr
N.A.I.C.S.: 424470
James W. Bodman (CEO)

Subsidiaries:

Bistro Soups, Ltd. (1)
2501 N Damen Ave, Chicago, IL 60647-2101
Tel.: (773) 278-7800
Web Site: http://www.viennabeef.com
Heat & Serve Soups & Chili Products without MSG
N.A.I.C.S.: 311422
Jim Bodman (CEO)

Chipico Pickles (1)
2501 N Damen Ave, Chicago, IL 60647-2101
Tel.: (773) 278-7800
Web Site: http://www.viennabeef.com
Sales Range: $50-74.9 Million
Processor & Distributor of Beef Products & Other Specialty Foods
N.A.I.C.S.: 311421

Pie Piper Products, Ltd. (1)
2501 N Damen Ave, Chicago, IL 60647-2101
Tel.: (773) 278-7800
Web Site: http://www.viennabeef.com
Sales Range: $10-24.9 Million
Emp.: 40
Baking of Deli Style Food Products
N.A.I.C.S.: 311421

VIENU CORPORATION
123 Town Sq Pl, Jersey City, NJ 07310-1756
Tel.: (201) 451-4000
Sales Range: $10-24.9 Million
Emp.: 100
Soft Drinks Mfr
N.A.I.C.S.: 312111
Diane Drey (Pres)
Rick May (Dir-Creative)

VIETNAM VETERANS OF AMERICA, INC.
8719 Colesville Rd Ste 100, Silver Spring, MD 20910
Tel.: (301) 585-4000 NY
Web Site: http://www.vva.org
Year Founded: 1978
Rev.: $23,918,438
Assets: $17,746,551
Liabilities: $4,614,789
Net Worth: $13,131,762
Earnings: $985,215
Emp.: 119
Fiscal Year-end: 02/28/18
Veteran Support Services
N.A.I.C.S.: 813410
John Rowan (Pres)
Marsha Four (VP)
Wayne Reynolds (Treas)
Bill Meeks Jr. (Sec)

VIETNAM VETERANS WORKSHOP INC.
17 Court St, Boston, MA 02108
Tel.: (617) 371-1800 MA
Web Site: http://www.nechv.org
Year Founded: 1988
Sales Range: $10-24.9 Million
Emp.: 161
Veterans Care Services
N.A.I.C.S.: 813410
C. Andrew McCawley (Pres & CEO)
Kevin A. Ward (CFO & Sr VP-Fin & Strategy)
Charlene F. Pontbriand (Sr VP-Advancement)
Victoria Bifano (VP-HR)
Kristine DiNardo (VP-Clinical Svcs)

VIEWMARKET INC.
2251 Vantage St Ste 300, Dallas, TX 75207
Tel.: (214) 558-1079
Web Site: http://www.viewmarket.com
Video Content Publisher
N.A.I.C.S.: 512110
Robert Bennett (Co-Founder & CEO)
Alexander Muse (Co-Founder & Chm)
Molly Cain (Co-Founder)
Peter Dirlis (Dir-Talent)

Subsidiaries:

CultureMap LLC (1)
2421 Tangley Ste 110, Houston, TX 77005
Tel.: (713) 581-8076
Web Site: http://www.culturemap.com
Internet News & Entertainment Publishing
N.A.I.C.S.: 513110
Chad Miller (Chief Revenue Officer)
Jessica Baldwin (Dir-Network Mktg)
Robert Bennett (CEO)

VIEWSONIC CORPORATION
10 Pointe Dr, Brea, CA 92821-7620
Tel.: (909) 444-8888 DE
Web Site: http://www.viewsonic.com
Year Founded: 1987
Sales Range: $1-4.9 Billion
Emp.: 100
Computer Displays, LCD & Plasma Television Sets, Wireless Networking Equipment, LCD Projectors & Handheld Computer Mfr
N.A.I.C.S.: 334118
Brian Igoe (VP-Sls & ViewSonic Americas)
Jeff Volpe (Pres-Americas)
Sung Yi (CFO)

Subsidiaries:

ViewSonic Australia Pty. Ltd. (1)
Unit 4 44 Dickson Avenue, Artarmon, 2064, NSW, Australia
Tel.: (61) 2 9906 6277
Web Site: http://www.viewsonic.com.au
Consumer Electronics Whslr
N.A.I.C.S.: 423620

ViewSonic China Limited (1)
9F No 950 Dalian Road, Yangpu District, Shanghai, 200092, China
Tel.: (86) 21 6501 9777
Consumer Electronics Whslr
N.A.I.C.S.: 423620
Rebecca Tsen (Gen Mgr)

ViewSonic Europe Ltd. (1)
ViewSonic House, Fleming Way, Crawley, RH10 2GA, W Sussex, United Kingdom (100%)
Tel.: (44) 293643900
Web Site: http://www.viewsonic.co.uk
Sales Range: $10-24.9 Million
Emp.: 80
Computer Peripheral Distr
N.A.I.C.S.: 423430

ViewSonic Hong Kong Ltd (1)
Unit 5-94 Yensheng Ctr 64 Hoiyuen Rd Kwuntong, Kwun Tong, Kowloon, China (Hong Kong)
Tel.: (852) 3690 1398
Web Site: http://www.hk.viewsonic.com
Consumer Electronics Whslr
N.A.I.C.S.: 423620

ViewSonic Singapore Pte Ltd (1)
10 Ubi Crescent 03-22 Ubi Techpark Lobby B, Singapore, 408564, Singapore
Tel.: (65) 62734018
Web Site: http://www.viewsonic.com.sg
Consumer Electronics Whslr
N.A.I.C.S.: 423620

ViewSonic Technology GmbH (1)
Herriotstrasse 1, 60528, Frankfurt, Germany
Tel.: (49) 69 677 33 233
Web Site: http://www.viewsoniceurope.com
Emp.: 5
Consumer Electronics Whslr
N.A.I.C.S.: 423620

VIEWTRADE SECURITIES INC.
525 Washington Blvd Fl 24, Jersey City, NJ 07310
Tel.: (201) 217-4422
Web Site: http://www.viewtrade.com
Rev.: $14,900,000
Emp.: 60
Stock Option Dealers & Financial Solutions
N.A.I.C.S.: 523150
Kenneth Chan (CIO)
James St. Clair (Pres)
Peter J. D'Agostino (Dir-Res)

VIFAH MANUFACTURING COMPANY
335 W 35th St 7th Fl, New York, NY 10001
Tel.: (212) 695-5330
Web Site: http://www.vifah.com
Year Founded: 2007
Sales Range: $1-9.9 Million
Emp.: 100
Outdoor Furniture
N.A.I.C.S.: 337126
Dao Huynh (CEO)

VIGEN CONSTRUCTION INC.
42247 180th St SW, East Grand Forks, MN 56721
Tel.: (218) 773-1159 MN
Web Site: http://www.vigenconstruction.com
Year Founded: 1968
Sales Range: $10-24.9 Million
Emp.: 125
Provider of Contracting Services
N.A.I.C.S.: 236220
Lyle Ross (Dir-Safety)

VIGET LABS LLC
400 S Maple Ave Ste 200, Falls Church, VA 22046
Tel.: (703) 891-0670
Web Site: http://www.viget.com
Year Founded: 1999
Sales Range: $1-9.9 Million
Emp.: 50
Website Developer & Internet Marketing
N.A.I.C.S.: 541519

Viget Labs LLC—(Continued)

Brian Williams (Co-Founder & CEO)
Andy Rankin (Co-Founder & Pres)
Wynne Williams (Co-Founder)
Amanda Ruehlen (Sr Project Mgr)
Cindy Caldwell (VP-Ops)
Josh Korr (Sr Project Mgr)
Kelly Kenny (Dir-Project Mgmt)
Patrick Reagan (Dir-Dev)
Becca James (Project Mgr)
Becky Tornes (Sr Project Mgr)
Elliott Munoz (Dir-Art)
Heather Muety (Sr Project Mgr)
Jackson Fox (Dir-User Experience)
Kevin Vigneault (Dir-Product Design)
Khanh Stenberg (Mgr-Events)
Sarah Schraer (Office Mgr)

VIGILANT DIVERSIFIED HOLDINGS, INC.
620 Newport Ctr Dr Ste 1100, Newport Beach, CA 92660-8011
Tel.: (949) 538-2700 NV
Year Founded: 2015
Assets: $928
Liabilities: $151,746
Net Worth: ($150,818)
Earnings: ($57,701)
Emp.: 2
Fiscal Year-end: 12/31/19
Holding Company
N.A.I.C.S.: 551112
Donald P. Hateley (Chm, CEO, CFO & Chief Acctg Officer)
Dennis C. Murchison (Sec & VP)

VIGILANT TECHNOLOGY, LLC
3290 W Big Beaver Rd Ste 310, Troy, MI 48084
Tel.: (248) 614-2500
Web Site: http://www.vigt.com
Year Founded: 2005
Sales Range: $1-9.9 Million
Emp.: 60
IT Specialist in Oracle Professional & Managed Services
N.A.I.C.S.: 519290
Srini Pillarisetty (Founder, Pres & CEO)
Sameera Buksh (VP-Strategic/Global Accts)

VIGILENT CORPORATION
701 El Cerrito Plz, El Cerrito, CA 94530-4022
Tel.: (510) 524-8480 DE
Web Site: http://www.vigilent.com
All Other Support Services
N.A.I.C.S.: 561990
Elisa Federspiel (Owner)
Mark Housley (CEO)

Subsidiaries:

SynapSense Corporation (1)
340 Palladio Pkwy Ste 530, Folsom, CA 95630
Tel.: (916) 294-0110
Web Site: http://www.synapsense.com
Software Development Services
N.A.I.C.S.: 541511
Bart Tichelman (CEO)
Raju Pandey (Co-Founder)
Christine M. Davis (CFO)
Phil London (Sr VP-Mktg & Technology)
Steve Chisholm (VP-World Wide Sls & Svcs)
Peter Van Deventer (Co-Founder)

VIGO IMPORTING COMPANY INC.
4701 W Comanche Ave, Tampa, FL 33614-5431
Tel.: (813) 884-3491 FL
Web Site: http://www.vigo-alessi.com
Year Founded: 1947
Sales Range: $10-24.9 Million
Emp.: 200
Italian Food Mfr
N.A.I.C.S.: 311999
Anthony Alessi (Pres)
Sam Ciccarello (CFO)

VIKCO INSURANCE SERVICES, INC.
12647 Alcosta Blvd Ste 4, San Ramon, CA 94583-4439
Tel.: (925) 743-9100
Rev.: $12,100,000
Emp.: 19
Fire, Marine & Casualty Insurance
N.A.I.C.S.: 524210
Brian Sedrick (CFO)

VIKING ALUMINUM PRODUCTS INC.
33-39 John St, New Britain, CT 06051-2748
Tel.: (860) 225-6478 CT
Year Founded: 1963
Sales Range: $10-24.9 Million
Emp.: 190
Metal Storm Doors & Windows & Vinyl Replacement Windows Mfr
N.A.I.C.S.: 332321
Fred Gross (Pres)

VIKING BUICK GMC
4646 Hwy 52 N, Rochester, MN 55901-0197
Tel.: (507) 288-1811
Web Site: http://www.vikingauto.com
Sales Range: $10-24.9 Million
Emp.: 65
Car Whslr
N.A.I.C.S.: 441110
Leslie Johnson (Dir-HR)
Chaun Favre (Gen Mgr)

VIKING COCA COLA BOTTLING CO
4610 Rusan St, Saint Cloud, MN 56303
Tel.: (320) 251-4602
Web Site: http://www.vikingcocacola.com
Rev.: $28,500,000
Emp.: 100
Carbonated Soft Drinks, Bottled & Canned
N.A.I.C.S.: 312111
Michael Faber (CEO)
John Van Heel (Mgr-Tech)

VIKING CONSTRUCTION INC.
2592 Shell Rd, Georgetown, TX 78628-9235
Tel.: (512) 930-5777 TX
Web Site: http://www.vciss.com
Year Founded: 1992
Sales Range: $10-24.9 Million
Emp.: 40
Surfacing And Paving
N.A.I.C.S.: 237310
Barry Dunn (Pres)
Brad Pearce (VP)
Dan Welsh (Mgr-Project Mktg)
Adele Wright (Controller)

VIKING DRILL & TOOL INC.
355 State St, Saint Paul, MN 55107
Tel.: (651) 227-8911
Web Site: http://www.vikingdrill.com
Sales Range: $25-49.9 Million
Emp.: 200
Drill Bits, Metalworking
N.A.I.C.S.: 333515
Denny Nyhus (Pres & CEO)
Mike Kuhl (Mgr-Accts)
Dave Swanson (Dir-Ops)
Kent Zachman (Reg Mgr-Sls)
Brent Harder (Reg Mgr-Sls)

VIKING ENGINEERING AND DEVELOPMENT INCORPORATED
5750 Main St NE, Minneapolis, MN 55432-5437
Tel.: (763) 571-2400 MN
Web Site: http://www.vikingeng.com
Year Founded: 1982
Rev.: $25,000,000
Emp.: 60
Woodworking Machinery
N.A.I.C.S.: 333243
Kristi Duffy (Controller)

Subsidiaries:

Viking Financial Services Inc. (1)
5750 Main St NE, Minneapolis, MN 55432-5437 (100%)
Tel.: (763) 571-2400
Rev.: $350,000
Emp.: 54
Equipment Rental & Leasing
N.A.I.C.S.: 532490

VIKING EQUIPMENT CO. KNOXVILLE
4600 Bobcat Ln, Knoxville, TN 37921
Tel.: (865) 588-8115
Web Site: http://www.bobcatofknoxville.com
Year Founded: 1977
Sales Range: $10-24.9 Million
Emp.: 50
Construction Equipment Sales & Rental
N.A.I.C.S.: 423830
Jennifer Parks (Pres)
Darrell Melton (VP)
Scott Corliss (Mgr-Rental)
Mike Borden (Controller)
Lynn Irwin (Mgr-Parts)
Isaac Collins (Mgr-Svc)
Danny Budd (Mgr-Yard)

VIKING FINANCIAL CORPORATION
4277 Dakota St, Alexandria, MN 56308
Tel.: (320) 762-0236 MN
Web Site: http://www.vikingsavings.com
Year Founded: 2007
Sales Range: $10-24.9 Million
Bank Holding Company
N.A.I.C.S.: 551111
John Minnerath (CEO)

Subsidiaries:

Viking Bank, N.A. (1)
4277 Dakota St, Alexandria, MN 56308
Tel.: (320) 762-0236
Web Site: http://www.vikingbankmn.com
Sales Range: $10-24.9 Million
Emp.: 34
Commercial Savings Bank
N.A.I.C.S.: 522110
Mark Grandgenett (Pres)
Doug Houska (CEO)
Shari Laven (COO)

VIKING INC.
166 Searsport Ave, Belfast, ME 04915
Tel.: (207) 338-3480
Web Site: http://www.vikinglumber.com
Sales Range: $25-49.9 Million
Emp.: 140
Lumber & Other Building Materials
N.A.I.C.S.: 423310
Maureen Flanagan (VP)
David C. Flanagan (Pres)

VIKING INDUSTRIES LLC
33505 Bainbridge Rd Ste 100, Solon, OH 44139
Tel.: (440) 349-1849
Sales Range: $1-4.9 Billion
Emp.: 1,140
Mfr of Solutions for Metal, Plastic & Rubber Based Products
N.A.I.C.S.: 326299
Jay Schabel (Pres)

VIKING PAPER CORP.
5148 Stickney Ave, Toledo, OH 43612
Tel.: (419) 729-4951
Web Site: http://www.packpros.net
Sales Range: $10-24.9 Million
Emp.: 36
Mfr of Corrugated Paper
N.A.I.C.S.: 322211
J. Anthony Mooter (Pres)
Robert Walker (VP & Controller)

VIKING PROCESSING CORPORATION
620 Clark Ave, Pittsburg, CA 94565
Tel.: (925) 427-2518
Web Site: http://www.vikingind.com
Sales Range: $10-24.9 Million
Emp.: 60
Metals Service Centers & Offices
N.A.I.C.S.: 423510

Subsidiaries:

Merit Ends Inc. (1)
620 Clark Ave, Pittsburg, CA 94565
Tel.: (925) 427-2500
Web Site: http://www.meritsteel.com
Sales Range: $10-24.9 Million
Sheet Metalwork
N.A.I.C.S.: 332322

VIKING RANGE, LLC
111 Front St, Greenwood, MS 38930
Tel.: (662) 455-1200 DE
Web Site: http://www.vikingrange.com
Year Founded: 1987
Kitchen Appliance Distr
N.A.I.C.S.: 423620
Selim A. Bassoul (CEO)

Subsidiaries:

The Gene Schick Company (1)
30826 Santana St, Hayward, CA 94544
Tel.: (510) 429-8200
Commercial Type & Home Appliances Stores
N.A.I.C.S.: 449210

VIKING VILLAGE INC.
150 Viking Dr, Reedsburg, WI 53959
Tel.: (608) 524-6108
Web Site: http://www.vikingvillagefoods.com
Sales Range: $25-49.9 Million
Emp.: 100
Specialty Merchandise & Grocery Stores
N.A.I.C.S.: 445110
Pam Coy (Owner & Gen Mgr-Ops)

VIKING YACHT COMPANY
Rte 9, New Gretna, NJ 08224
Tel.: (609) 296-6000 NJ
Web Site: http://www.vikingyachts.com
Year Founded: 1964
Sales Range: $150-199.9 Million
Emp.: 1,300
Yacht Mfr
N.A.I.C.S.: 336612
Patrick J. Healey (Pres & CEO)
Anthony Scola (Mgr-Sls-Intl)
Chris Landry (Dir-Comm)

Subsidiaries:

Atlantic Marine Electronics, Inc (1)
5724 Rte 9, New Gretna, NJ 08224
Tel.: (609) 296-8826
Web Site: http://www.atlantic-me.com

COMPANIES

Sales Range: $10-24.9 Million
Emp.: 30
Marine Engineering Services
N.A.I.C.S.: 541330
Augustus Buzby *(Mgr-Production)*
Todd Tally *(Gen Mgr)*

Palm Beach Towers (1)
2100 Ave B Ste 1, Riviera Beach, FL 33404
Tel.: (561) 493-2828
Web Site: http://www.pbtowers.com
Yacht Building Services
N.A.I.C.S.: 336612

The Viking Yacht Service Center (1)
1550 Ave C, Riviera Beach, FL 33404
Tel.: (561) 493-2800
Web Site:
 http://www.vikingservicecenter.com
Yacht Maintenance Services
N.A.I.C.S.: 811490
Rick Weiler *(Mgr-Svc)*
Steve Lewis *(Mgr-Quality Control)*

The Viking Yachting Center Inc (1)
5724 N Route 9, New Gretna, NJ 08224
Tel.: (609) 296-2388
Web Site:
 http://www.vikingyachtingcenter.com
Yacht Services
N.A.I.C.S.: 713930

VIKTOR BENES BAKERY, INC.
703 S Main St, Burbank, CA 91506
Tel.: (818) 841-9347
Web Site:
 http://www.viktorbenes.com
Year Founded: 1920
Sales Range: $10-24.9 Million
Emp.: 340
Baked Goods Mfr
N.A.I.C.S.: 311811
Roger Tergaolo *(VP)*
Ugo Mamolo *(Owner)*

VILA & SON LANDSCAPING CORP.
20451 SW 216th St, Miami, FL 33170
Tel.: (305) 255-9206
Web Site: http://www.vila-n-son.com
Sales Range: $10-24.9 Million
Emp.: 160
Landscape Services
N.A.I.C.S.: 561730
Juan Carlos Vila *(Founder, Pres & CEO)*

VILLA CONSTRUCTION OF CONNECTICUT, INC.
153 Broadway, Hawthorne, NY 10532
Tel.: (914) 747-3277
Web Site: http://www.villac.com
Sales Range: $10-24.9 Million
Emp.: 60
Concrete Finishing Services
N.A.I.C.S.: 238140
Frank Dellorso *(VP)*

VILLA ENTERPRISES MANAGEMENT LTD., INC.
25 Washington St, Morristown, NJ 07960
Tel.: (973) 285-4800   NJ
Web Site:
 http://www.villaenterprises.com
Year Founded: 1964
Sales Range: $100-124.9 Million
Emp.: 2,000
Limited & Full Service Restaurants
Owner & Operator
N.A.I.C.S.: 722513
Anthony Scotto *(CEO)*
Andrew Steinberg *(Sr VP-Bus Ops)*
Souhail Sara *(Dir-Ops)*
Connie Cafone *(Office Mgr)*
Peter Jurta *(Sr VP-Ops)*
Donald Mallo *(VP-HR)*
Steve Baliva *(Dir-Full Svc Ops)*

VILLA ESPERANZA SERVICES
2060 E Villa St, Pasadena, CA 91107
Tel.: (626) 449-2919   CA
Web Site:
 http://www.villaesperanzaservices.org
Year Founded: 1961
Sales Range: $10-24.9 Million
Emp.: 453
Developmental Disabilities Assistance Services
N.A.I.C.S.: 624190
Vicky Castillo *(CFO)*
Casey Gregg *(VP-Children & Youth Programs)*
Aaron Kitzman *(VP-Adult Programs)*
Gioia Pastre *(VP-Dev & Pub Rels)*
Michael Fedrick *(Sec)*
Wells Fargo *(Reg Mng Dir)*
Cynthia Kurtz *(Chm)*

VILLA LIGHTING SUPPLY CO. INC.
2929 Chouteau Ave, Saint Louis, MO 63103
Tel.: (314) 531-2600
Web Site: http://www.villalighting.com
Year Founded: 1971
Sales Range: $10-24.9 Million
Emp.: 60
Light Bulbs & Related Supplies
N.A.I.C.S.: 423610
John A. Villa *(Pres)*
Rick Moore *(CFO)*
Steve Barker *(VP-Sls)*

VILLA, INC.
1926 Arch St 3R, Philadelphia, PA 19103
Tel.: (215) 279-5688
Web Site: http://www.ruvilla.com
Sneaker Sales
N.A.I.C.S.: 424340
Jason Lutz *(CEO)*

VILLAGE AUTOMOTIVE GROUP
75 N Beacon St, Boston, MA 02134-1912
Tel.: (617) 560-1700
Web Site:
 http://www.villageautomotive.com
Sales Range: $50-74.9 Million
Emp.: 120
Owner & Operator of Car Dealership
N.A.I.C.S.: 441110
Raymond J. Ciccolo *(Founder & Pres)*
Chris Fousek *(Dir-e-Commerce)*
Alan Berkman *(Mgr-Sls)*
Mike Gaughran *(Gen Mgr-Sls)*
Randy Blue *(Mgr-Wholesale)*
William F. Cavanaugh Jr. *(Mgr-Fin)*

Subsidiaries:

Charles River Saab (1)
570 Arsenal St, Watertown, MA 02472
Tel.: (617) 923-9230
Web Site: http://www.crsaab.com
Sales Range: $25-49.9 Million
Emp.: 60
Owner & Operator of Car Dealership
N.A.I.C.S.: 441110
Ray Ciccoll *(Pres)*

VILLAGE BANCSHARES, INC.
3350 Bridge St NW, Saint Francis, MN 55070
Tel.: (763) 753-3007
Web Site:
 http://www.villagebankonline.com
Year Founded: 1995
Sales Range: $1-9.9 Million
Emp.: 50
Bank Holding Company
N.A.I.C.S.: 551111

Randy Diers *(Pres)*
Bill Rew *(CFO)*
Don Kveton *(Chm & CEO)*

Subsidiaries:

Village Bank (1)
9298 Central Ave NE, Minneapolis, MN 55434
Tel.: (763) 753-3007
Web Site: http://www.villagebankonline.com
Sales Range: $10-24.9 Million
Emp.: 20
Retail & Commercial Banking
N.A.I.C.S.: 522110
Don Kveton *(CEO)*
Dana Kinde *(Sr VP)*
Sara Mauch *(Sr VP-HR)*
Kim Anderson *(VP-Ops)*
Aleesha Webb *(Pres)*

VILLAGE CAR COMPANY
307 Hogan Rd, Bangor, ME 04401
Tel.: (207) 945-9401   ME
Web Site: http://www.quirkauto.com
Year Founded: 1986
Rev.: $93,321,399
Emp.: 350
New & Used Car Dealer
N.A.I.C.S.: 441110
John E. Quirk *(Pres)*
David Quirk *(Gen Mgr)*

Subsidiaries:

Village Subaru (1)
295 Hogan Rd, Bangor, ME 04401
Tel.: (207) 942-7364
Web Site: https://www.quirksubaru.com
Rev.: $84,036,768
Emp.: 250
New & Used Car Dealer
N.A.I.C.S.: 441110
John E. Quirk *(Pres)*

VILLAGE CHARTERS, INC.
8620 W 21st St N, Wichita, KS 67205
Tel.: (316) 721-4455   KS
Web Site: http://www.villagetours.net
Year Founded: 1980
Tour Operator
N.A.I.C.S.: 561520

Subsidiaries:

Village Tours, LLC (1)
7602 N Bryant Ave, Oklahoma City, OK 73121
Tel.: (405) 478-8687
Web Site: http://www.villagetours.net
Sales Range: $1-9.9 Million
Emp.: 30
Tour Operator
N.A.I.C.S.: 561520
Jeff Arensdorf *(Owner)*

Subsidiary (Domestic):

Arrow Coach Lines, Inc. (2)
2715 W 10th St, Little Rock, AR 72204
Tel.: (501) 663-6002
Web Site: http://www.arrowcoachlines.com
Charter Bus Industry
N.A.I.C.S.: 485510
Janie Lienhart *(Treas & Sec)*

VILLAGE FAMILY SERVICE CENTER
1201 25th St S, Fargo, ND 58103
Tel.: (701) 451-4900   ND
Web Site:
 http://www.thevillagefamily.org
Year Founded: 1891
Sales Range: $10-24.9 Million
Emp.: 316
Family Care Services
N.A.I.C.S.: 624190
Nicole Anderson *(CFO)*
Joni Medenwald *(Dir-Minnesota)*

VILLAGE FARM DAIRY
5131 Alexis Rd, Sylvania, OH 43560
Tel.: (419) 882-1871
Rev.: $20,000,000

VILLAGE INVESTMENTS

Emp.: 100
Convenience Store
N.A.I.C.S.: 445131
Sandy Esser *(Pres)*
Don Kowalski *(VP)*
Rich Dewey *(Mgr-Ops)*

VILLAGE FORD INC.
23535 Michigan Ave, Dearborn, MI 48124-1917
Tel.: (313) 565-3900   DE
Web Site: http://www.villageford.com
Year Founded: 1982
Sales Range: $125-149.9 Million
Emp.: 225
Sales of Automobiles
N.A.I.C.S.: 441110
James Seavitt *(Pres)*
Bob Wheat *(Gen Mgr)*
Dipak Shah *(Controller)*

VILLAGE GREEN COMMUNICATIONS, INC.
30833 Northwestern Hwy Ste 300, Farmington Hills, MI 48334-2583
Tel.: (248) 851-9600   MI
Web Site:
 http://www.villagegreen.com
Year Founded: 1984
Sales Range: $1-9.9 Million
Emp.: 1,000
Advertising Agencies, Advertising Specialties, Brand Development, Collateral, Communications, Corporate Identity, House Agencies, Internet/Web Design, Public Relations, Real Estate
N.A.I.C.S.: 541810
Diane Batayeh *(Pres)*
Jason Koehn *(CIO)*

VILLAGE GREEN MANAGEMENT COMPANY
30833 NW Hwy Ste 300, Farmington Hills, MI 48334
Tel.: (248) 851-9600   MI
Web Site:
 http://www.villagegreen.com
Year Founded: 1919
Emp.: 100
Apartment Building Property Manager & Multi-Family Housing Operative Builder
N.A.I.C.S.: 531311
Tom Haag *(Sr Dir-Facilities)*
David Ferszt *(Pres)*

VILLAGE HEALTH WORKS
45 W 36th St 8th Fl, New York, NY 10018
Tel.: (646) 398-1171
Web Site:
 https://www.villagehealthworks.org
Year Founded: 2007
Health Care Srvices
N.A.I.C.S.: 621610

VILLAGE HEARTH & HOME DISTRIBUTION, LLC
100 Zachary Rd, Manchester, NH 03109
Tel.: (603) 645-6060
Web Site:
 http://www.villagehearthandhome.com
Year Founded: 1972
Sales Range: $10-24.9 Million
Emp.: 20
Wood Burning Fireplaces & Stoves Distr
N.A.I.C.S.: 423220
Mike Mussog *(Pres)*

VILLAGE INVESTMENTS
2400 Main St Ste 201, Irvine, CA 92614

VILLAGE INVESTMENTS

Village Investments—(Continued)
Tel.: (949) 863-1500 CA
Web Site: http://www.village-investments.placestars.com
Rev.: $10,000,000
Emp.: 20
Real Estate Managers
N.A.I.C.S.: 531210
Philip H. McNamee (CEO)
Ryan Barker (VP-Acctg)
Steve Tomlin (Exec VP)

VILLAGE JEWELERS GROUP INC.
No 100 13636 Neutron Rd, Dallas, TX 75244-4410
Tel.: (972) 661-1100
Web Site: http://www.villagejewelers.com
Year Founded: 1980
Rev.: $11,800,000
Emp.: 25
Sales of Jewelry, Precious Stones & Precious Metals
N.A.I.C.S.: 458310
Phillip Samuels (Pres)

VILLAGE MARINA
107 Village Marina Rd, Lake Ozark, MO 65026
Tel.: (573) 365-1800
Web Site: http://www.villagemarina.com
Sales Range: $10-24.9 Million
Emp.: 35
Boat Dealers
N.A.I.C.S.: 441222
Mark Brick (VP)

VILLAGE MARKET, INC
2092 Village Ln, Hermann, MO 65041
Tel.: (573) 486-2916
Web Site: http://www.hermannsvillagemarket.com
Year Founded: 1996
Supermarkets & Other Grocery (except Convenience) Stores
N.A.I.C.S.: 445110
Tim Hubbard (Owner)

VILLAGE SHALOM, INC.
5500 W 123rd St, Overland Park, KS 66209
Tel.: (913) 317-2600 KS
Web Site: http://www.villageshalom.org
Year Founded: 1996
Sales Range: $10-24.9 Million
Emp.: 310
Continuing Care Retirement Community Operator
N.A.I.C.S.: 623311
Tami Middleton (Dir-HR)
Nicole Anthony (Fin Dir)
Tim McFarland (Dir-Facilities)
Eileen Miller (Dir-Resident Svcs)
Jill Craft (Dir-Assisted Living)
Lora Baugher (Dir-IT)
Michelle LaPointe (Dir-Philanthropy & Community Engagement)
Jill Allin (Dir-Sls & Mktg)
John Legrand (Dir-Dining Svcs)
Matt Lewis (Pres & CEO)
Paula Carpenter (Dir-Social Svcs)
Frank Lipsman (Chm)
Bruce Kershenbaum (Vice Chm)
David Spizman (Sec)
Bob Gershon (Treas)

VILLAGE VOICE MEDIA HOLDINGS, LLC
1201 E Jefferson St, Phoenix, AZ 85034
Tel.: (602) 271-0040 DE

Holding Company; Newspaper Publisher
N.A.I.C.S.: 551112
James Larkin (Chm, Pres & CEO)
Scott Tobias (COO)
Jed Brunst (CFO)
Gerard Goroski (CIO)

Subsidiaries:

Dallas Observer, LP (1)
2501 Oak Lawn Ave Ste 355, Dallas, TX 75219
Tel.: (214) 757-9000
Web Site: http://www.dallasobserver.com
Newspaper Publishers
N.A.I.C.S.: 513110
Patrick Williams (Mng Editor)
Tracie Louck (Dir-Art)
Pam Robinson (Mgr-Production)
Jennifer Robinson (Reg Dir-Mktg)
Carlos Garcia (Dir-Circulation)
Stuart Folb (Publr-Grp)
Joe Pappalardo (Editor-in-Chief)
Charlie Dondlinger (Dir-Ops)
Morgan Edwards (Coord-Digital Mktg)
Amy Ero (Dir-Adv)
Ricky Richards (Asst Mgr-Production)
Kelly Foster (Mgr-Bus)
Sara Means (Coord-Bus)
Taylor Pass (Mgr-Mktg)

Denver Westword, LLC (1)
969 Broadway, Denver, CO 80203
Tel.: (303) 296-7744
Web Site: http://www.westword.com
Emp.: 50
Newspaper Publishers
N.A.I.C.S.: 513110
Patricia Calhoun (Editor)
Teri Driskell (Dir-Adv)
Scott Tobias (Publr)
Dee Jones (Bus Mgr)
Curt Sanders (Dir-Circulation)
Michael Wilson (Production Mgr)
Taylor Wheeler (Mgr-Sls-Digital & Adv)
Patrick Eul (Asst Mgr-Production)
Jennifer Lynn Homan (Mgr-Mktg)
Danelle Trujillo (Sr Acct Exec-Multi-Media)

Miami New Times, LLC (1)
4500 Biscayne Blvd Ste 200, Miami, FL 33137
Tel.: (305) 576-8000
Web Site: http://www.miaminewtimes.com
Newspaper Publishers
N.A.I.C.S.: 513110
Adam Simon (Publr)
Russell A. Breiter (Gen Mgr)
Tim Elfrink (Mng Editor)
Miche Ratto (Dir-Art)
Don Farrell (Dir-Adv)
Mike Lugo (Mgr-Production)
Andrea Cruz (Dir-Art-Adv)
Jennifer Nealon (Dir-Mktg)
Jorge Sesin (Asst Mgr-Production)
Kristin Bjornsen (Asst Dir-Art)
Moses A. Betancourt (Mgr-Credit)
Nadine DeMarco (Mgr-Editorial Ops)
Richard Lynch (Dir-Circulation)
Ryan Garcia (Mgr-Online Support)
Kristin Ramos (Coord-Mktg)
Jeff Stewart (Mgr-Acctg)

New Times BPB, LLC (1)
16 NE 4th St Ste 200, Fort Lauderdale, FL 33301
Tel.: (954) 233-1600
Web Site: http://www.browardpalmbeach.com
Sales Range: $10-24.9 Million
Emp.: 75
Newspaper Publisher Services
N.A.I.C.S.: 513110
Russell A. Breiter (Gen Mgr-South Florida)
Andrea Cruz (Dir-Art & Adv)
Mike Lugo (Mgr-Production)
Moses Betancourt (Mgr-Credit)
Alexis Guillen (Dir-Sls-Digital)
Jeff Stewart (Mgr-Acctg)

OC Weekly, LP (1)
2975 Red Hill Ave Ste 150, Costa Mesa, CA 92626
Tel.: (714) 550-5900
Web Site: http://www.ocweekly.com
Emp.: 50
Newspaper Publishers

N.A.I.C.S.: 513110
Nick Schou (Editor-in-Chief)
Jennifer Besheer (Publr)
Daniel Werner (Mgr-Bus)
Pat Connell (Dir-Circulation)
Dustin Ames (Dir-Art)
Ashleigh Fleury (Mgr-Mktg)
Ryan Whipple (Dir-Sls)
Susan Belair (Sr VP-Sls)
Jed Brunst (CFO)
Gerard Goroski (CIO)
Joe Larkin (Sr VP-Sls Ops)
Curt Sanders (Mgr-Production-Natl)
Scott Spear (Sr VP-Corp Affairs)
Laura Weinrich (Mgr-Production-Natl)

Phoenix New Times, LLC (1)
1201 E Jefferson, Phoenix, AZ 85034-2300
Tel.: (602) 271-0040
Web Site: http://www.phoenixnewtimes.com
Newspaper Publishers
N.A.I.C.S.: 513110
Ellis Alvarez (Dir-Adv)
Kurtis Barton (Publr)
Eloy Vigil (Dir-Circulation)
Rick Barrs (Editor-in-Chief)
Matthew Bodkin (Mgr-Digital Product)
John Hunt (Asst Mgr-Production)
Zac McDonald (Mgr-Production)
Kristina Smith (Coord-Accts Payable)

Riverfront Times, LLC (1)
6358 Delmar Blvd Ste 200, Saint Louis, MO 63130
Tel.: (314) 754-5966
Web Site: http://www.riverfronttimes.com
Newspaper Publishers
N.A.I.C.S.: 513110
Brady Rehm (Dir-Adv)
Kevin G. Powers (Dir-Circulation)
Jeff Keller (Gen Mgr)
Jennifer Hawkins (Mgr-Acctg)
Nicole Starzyk (Acct Exec)
Robert Westerholt (Mgr-Production)
Rosalind Walters (Acct Exec)
Angie Rosenberg (Acct Exec)
Colin Bell (Dir-Sls)
Cory Nava (Acct Exec)
Kelly Glueck (Dir-Art)
Chris Keating (Publr)
Elizabeth Semko (Editor-Digital)

VILLAGE VOICE, LLC
36 Cooper Sq, New York, NY 10003-7118
Tel.: (212) 475-3300 DE
Web Site: http://www.villagevoice.com
Year Founded: 1955
Newspaper Publishers
N.A.I.C.S.: 513110
Rosemary Raposo Jorda (Sr Dir-Mktg & Product Dev)
Michael Pico (Gen Mgr)
Susan Eide (Dir-Adv)
Michael Moi (Dir-Circulation)
Robert Baker (Mgr-Layout)
Matt Barbey (Dir-Special Projects)
Renee Cuff (Coord-Mktg)
Nalini Edwin (Dir-Digital)
Meave Gallagher (Mng Editor)
Andrew Horton (Dir-Creative)
Shawn Moliatu (CFO)
Sherry Ann Pedro (Supvr-Acctg)
Christina Pettit (Dir-Mktg & Events)
Dennis Rakauckas (Mgr-Production)

VILLAGECARE
120 Broadway Ste 2840, New York, NY 10271
Tel.: (212) 337-5600 NY
Web Site: http://www.villagecare.org
Year Founded: 1995
Sales Range: $10-24.9 Million
Emp.: 112
Community Health Care Services
N.A.I.C.S.: 621498
Antoinette Cassetta (Exec VP-Managed Care)
Allison Silvers (Chief Strategy Officer)
Ricardo Santiago (CIO)
Matthew Lesieur (Dir-Pub Policy)
Rachel Amalfitano (CFO)
David H. Sidwell (Chm)

U.S. PRIVATE

VILLAWAY, INC.
8730 Sunset Blvd Ste 200, Los Angeles, CA 90069
Web Site: http://www.villaway.com
Year Founded: 2014
Sales Range: $1-9.9 Million
Emp.: 50
Software Development Services
N.A.I.C.S.: 541511
Joe Liebke (Founder & CEO)

VILLING & COMPANY, INC.
5909 Nimtz Pkwy, South Bend, IN 46628
Tel.: (574) 277-0215 IN
Web Site: http://www.villing.com
Year Founded: 1982
Sales Range: $125-149.9 Million
Emp.: 10
Brand Development, Public Relations, Sports Marketing
N.A.I.C.S.: 541810
Thomas A. Villing (Pres & CEO)
Ellen Imbur (Dir-Art)
Jeff Middaugh (Dir-Creative)
Adam Kizer (Dir-Interactive)

VIMCO INC.
300 Hansen Access Rd, King of Prussia, PA 19406
Tel.: (610) 768-0500
Web Site: http://www.vimcoinc.com
Sales Range: $10-24.9 Million
Emp.: 50
Concrete & Cinder Block
N.A.I.C.S.: 423810
Victor J. Maggitti (Pres)
David Gyuris (Mgr-Sls)
Gary Horner (Mgr-Production-Sls)

VIN DEVERS INC.
5570 Monroe St, Sylvania, OH 43560
Tel.: (419) 885-5111
Web Site: http://www.vindevers.com
Sales Range: $25-49.9 Million
Emp.: 110
New & Used Car Dealers
N.A.I.C.S.: 441110
Paul Devers (Pres)

VINART ENTERPRISES INC.
675 State Rd, Emmaus, PA 18049
Tel.: (610) 967-6500
Web Site: http://www.vinart.com
Sales Range: $50-74.9 Million
Emp.: 135
Sales of New & Used Automobiles
N.A.I.C.S.: 441110
Arthur W. Wright Jr. (Pres)

VINCE HAGAN COMPANY
330 Clay Rd, Mesquite, TX 75182
Tel.: (214) 330-4601
Web Site: http://www.vincehagan.com
Rev.: $14,000,000
Emp.: 200
Construction Machinery
N.A.I.C.S.: 333120
Carol Hagan (Pres)
Robert Shadot (CFO)

VINCE WHIBBS PONTIAC-GMC TRUCKS
5651 Pensacola Blvd, Pensacola, FL 32505
Tel.: (850) 433-7671
Web Site: http://www.vincewhibbs.com
Sales Range: $25-49.9 Million
Emp.: 90
Automobiles, New & Used
N.A.I.C.S.: 441110
Mark Whibbs (Partner & Gen Mgr)

COMPANIES

VINCENT & VINCENT COMPANIES, INC.
179 Country Rd Lower Level, Medford, NY 11763
Tel.: (631) 775-7915
Web Site:
http://www.vvcompanies.com
Year Founded: 1989
Sales Range: $1-9.9 Million
Emp.: 15
Business Support Services
N.A.I.C.S.: 561499
Marie Vincent *(Pres)*

Subsidiaries:

Vincent & Vincent Microsystems (1)
179 Country Rd Lowr Level, Medford, NY 11763
Tel.: (631) 775-7915
Web Site: http://www.vvcompanies.com
Sales Range: Less than $1 Million
Computer Related Consulting Services
N.A.I.C.S.: 541512
Nemahun Vincent *(Pres)*

VINCENT GIORDANO CORPORATION
2600 Washington Ave, Philadelphia, PA 19146
Tel.: (215) 467-6629
Web Site: http://www.vgiordano.com
Year Founded: 1969
Sales Range: $10-24.9 Million
Emp.: 85
Meat Product Production & Distribution Services
N.A.I.C.S.: 311612
Bruce Belack *(VP-Sls & Mktg)*
Guy Giordano *(Pres)*
John McVey *(VP-Ops)*
David Kottler *(Reg Mgr-Sls)*

VINCENT LIGHTING SYSTEMS CO.
6161 Cochran Rd Ste D, Solon, OH 44139
Tel.: (216) 475-7600
Web Site: http://www.vls.com
Year Founded: 1978
Sales Range: $10-24.9 Million
Emp.: 45
Supplier of Lighting Fixtures
N.A.I.C.S.: 423610
Paul Vincent *(Founder)*
Derek Hons *(Mgr-Production)*
Adam Hayward *(Gen Mgr-Erlanger)*
Tom Siko *(Pres)*
Walt Weber *(Sls Mgr-Natl)*
David Silvernail *(Mgr-Product & ECommerce)*

VINCENT PRINTING COMPANY INCORPORATED
1512 Sholar Ave, Chattanooga, TN 37406
Tel.: (423) 697-0808
Web Site:
http://www.vincentprinting.com
Rev.: $10,000,000
Emp.: 125
Screen Printing
N.A.I.C.S.: 323113
Charles F. Casey *(Chm)*
Gary Wouell *(VP)*
Dale Johnston *(Controller)*

VINCOMPASS CORP.
795 Folsom St 1st Fl, San Francisco, CA 94107
Tel.: (415) 817-9955 WY
Web Site:
http://www.vincompass.com
Year Founded: 2010
Assets: $13,952
Liabilities: $1,073,025
Net Worth: ($1,059,073)
Earnings: ($941,244)
Fiscal Year-end: 02/28/17
Wine Information & Sales
N.A.I.C.S.: 424820
Peter Lachapelle *(Founder, Pres, CEO, CFO, Treas & Sec)*

VINE HILL HARDWARE INC.
3503 Pacheco Blvd, Martinez, CA 94553
Tel.: (925) 228-6150
Web Site:
http://www.billsacehardware.com
Sales Range: $10-24.9 Million
Emp.: 110
Hardware Stores
N.A.I.C.S.: 444140
Wilma Hawkins *(Gen Mgr)*

VINE INTERNATIONAL
PO Box 52086, Knoxville, TN 37950
Tel.: (865) 471-6857 TN
Web Site:
http://www.vineinternational.org
Year Founded: 1993
Sales Range: $10-24.9 Million
Emp.: 2
Community Health Care Services
N.A.I.C.S.: 621498
Cindy McCutcheon *(Mgr-Distr)*
Dennis McCutcheon *(Mgr-Distr)*
Bruce White *(Mgr-Collection Center)*
Woody Woodson *(Founder & Pres)*

VINE RESOURCES INC.
5800 Granite Pkwy Ste 550, Plano, TX 75024
Tel.: (469) 606-0540 DE
Year Founded: 2016
Emp.: 84
Oil & Gas Field Development Solutions
N.A.I.C.S.: 333132
Eric D. Marsh *(Chm, Pres & CEO)*
Brian D. Dutton *(Chief Acctg Officer)*

VINE VILLAGE, INC.
4059 Old Sonoma Rd, Napa, CA 94559-9702
Tel.: (707) 255-4006 CA
Web Site: http://www.vinevillage.org
Year Founded: 1973
Sales Range: $1-9.9 Million
Emp.: 20
Developmental Disability Assistance Services
N.A.I.C.S.: 623210

VINELAND KOSHER POULTRY INC.
1050 S Mill Rd, Vineland, NJ 08360
Tel.: (856) 692-1871
Rev.: $15,070,895
Emp.: 200
Poultry Slaughtering & Processing
N.A.I.C.S.: 311615
Israel Leifer *(Pres)*

VINET HOLDINGS INC.
745 Fort St Mall Ste 1000, Honolulu, HI 96813
Tel.: (808) 546-7469
Web Site:
http://www.insurancefactors.com
Rev.: $13,100,000
Emp.: 20
Fire, Marine & Casualty Insurance
N.A.I.C.S.: 524126
Michel Vinet *(Pres & CEO)*

Subsidiaries:

Bonding Insurance Agency & Insurance Factors (1)
745 Fort St Ste 1000, Honolulu, HI 96813
Tel.: (808) 546-7469
Web Site: http://www.insurancefactors.com
Property & Casualty Insurance Agent
N.A.I.C.S.: 524210

VINEYARD BRANDS INC.
2000 Resource Dr, Birmingham, AL 35242-2995
Tel.: (205) 980-8802 CA
Web Site:
http://www.vineyardbrands.com
Year Founded: 1973
Sales Range: $10-24.9 Million
Emp.: 60
Distr of Wine & Distilled Beverage Services
N.A.I.C.S.: 424820
Allison Dallas *(Dir-Mktg)*
Pamela Thurber *(Asst Controller & Dir-Compliance)*
Lara Sailer Long *(VP & Dir-Brand Strategy)*
Greg Doody *(Pres & CEO)*

VINEYARD INDUSTRIES INC.
1460 Iris Dr SW, Conyers, GA 30094-5142
Tel.: (770) 483-6760
Sales Range: $10-24.9 Million
Fast Food Restaurants
N.A.I.C.S.: 722513
Bruce Vineyard *(Owner)*
David Miller *(Controller)*

VINEYARD VINES LLC
37 Brown House Rd, Stamford, CT 06902
Tel.: (203) 862-0793
Web Site:
http://www.vineyardvines.com
Year Founded: 1998
Sales Range: $10-24.9 Million
Emp.: 100
Clothing Designer & Mfr
N.A.I.C.S.: 315250
Shep Murray *(Owner)*
Ian Murray *(Owner)*
Nancy Gleason *(Controller)*
John Mehas *(CEO)*
John G. Mehas *(CEO)*

VINEYARDS DEVELOPMENT CORP.
75 Vineyards Blvd, Naples, FL 34119
Tel.: (239) 353-1551
Web Site:
http://www.vineyardsnaples.com
Sales Range: $50-74.9 Million
Emp.: 150
Builder & Developer
N.A.I.C.S.: 236115
Michael Saadeh *(Pres)*

VINEYARDS REALTY INC.
75 Vineyards Blvd 2nd Fl Ste 200, Naples, FL 34119
Tel.: (239) 353-1920
Web Site:
http://www.vineyardsnaples.com
Sales Range: $1-9.9 Million
Emp.: 20
Real Estate Broker
N.A.I.C.S.: 531210
Michael Procacci *(Owner)*

VINFEN CORPORATION
950 Cambridge St, Cambridge, MA 02141-1001
Tel.: (617) 441-1800 MA
Web Site: http://www.vinfen.org
Year Founded: 1977
Sales Range: $75-99.9 Million
Emp.: 1,400
Provider of Residential Care Services
N.A.I.C.S.: 623220
Bruce L. Bird *(Pres & CEO)*
Philip A. Mason *(Chm)*
Jana McClure *(VP-Connecticut)*
Jon Burt *(VP-IT)*
Kathy Krysiak *(VP-HR)*
Lurleen Gannon *(Gen Counsel & VP)*
Madeline Becker *(VP-Quality & Compliance)*
Richard Sullivan *(CFO)*

VINIFERA IMPORTS LTD.
205 13th Ave, Ronkonkoma, NY 11779
Tel.: (631) 467-5907
Web Site:
http://www.viniferaimports.com
Rev.: $36,600,000
Emp.: 10
Distr of Wine
N.A.I.C.S.: 424820
Judith Nocerino *(Pres)*
Dominic Nocerino *(Owner)*
Marco Turano *(Sr Acct Mgr)*

VINING OIL & GAS LLC
301 2nd Ave NW, Jamestown, ND 58401
Tel.: (701) 252-0890
Sales Range: $25-49.9 Million
Emp.: 35
Diesel Fuel
N.A.I.C.S.: 424720
Jo Ann Vining *(Owner)*

VINING-SPARKS IBG LP
775 Rdg Lk Blvd Fl 2, Memphis, TN 38120
Tel.: (901) 762-5800 TN
Web Site:
http://www.viningsparks.com
Year Founded: 1990
Sales Range: $50-74.9 Million
Emp.: 300
Provider of Security Broker Services
N.A.I.C.S.: 523150
James L. Vining *(Chm)*
Mark Ellen *(VP-Mktg)*
Randy Wade *(Exec VP & Dir-Sls)*
Mark A. Medford *(Pres & CEO)*

VINITECH, INC.
11710 Plaza America Ste 2000, Reston, VA 20190
Tel.: (703) 871-5353
Web Site: http://www.vinitech.com
Year Founded: 2003
Rev.: $4,100,000
Emp.: 6
Government Services
N.A.I.C.S.: 921190
Nick Grivas *(Founder & Pres)*
Alan Daniel *(VP)*

VINMAR INTERNATIONAL LIMITED
16800 Imperial Valley Dr Ste 499, Houston, TX 77060
Tel.: (281) 618-1300
Web Site: http://www.vinmar.com
Year Founded: 1978
Sales Range: $25-49.9 Million
Emp.: 100
Plastics Materials
N.A.I.C.S.: 424610
Hemant Goradia *(Pres)*
Andrew Fry *(CFO)*
Doug Friedman *(VP)*
Carlos Paez *(Exec VP)*

Subsidiaries:

Syncot Plastics, Inc. (1)
350 Eastwood Dr, Belmont, NC 28012
Tel.: (704) 967-0010
Web Site: http://www.syncot.com
Recyclable Material Merchant Whslr
N.A.I.C.S.: 423930
T. J. Moore *(Mgr)*

VINNYS GARDEN CENTER INC.

Vinnys Garden Center Inc.—(Continued)
1076 S Colony Rd, Wallingford, CT 06492
Tel.: (203) 265-9309
Year Founded: 1988
Sales Range: $10-24.9 Million
Emp.: 50
Sales of Potted & Garden Plants
N.A.I.C.S.: 459310
Vincent Gloria (Pres)

VINO VAULT, INC.
5800 W 3rd St, Los Angeles, CA 91311
Tel.: (866) 295-5700
Web Site: http://vinovaultwine.com
N.A.I.C.S.:
Jeff Anthony (CEO)

Subsidiaries:

La Cave Warehouse (1)
1931 Market Cent, Dallas, TX 75207-3399
Tel.: (214) 747-9463
Web Site: http://www.lacavewarehouse.com
Beer, Wine & Liquor Stores
N.A.I.C.S.: 445320

The Wine Locker, Inc. (1)
14819 Calvert St, Van Nuys, CA 91411-2708
Tel.: (818) 781-1600
Web Site: http://www.thewinelocker.net
Warehousing & Storage
N.A.I.C.S.: 493190

VINSON & ELKINS LLP
1001 Fannin St Ste 2500, Houston, TX 77002-6760
Tel.: (713) 758-2222
Web Site: http://www.velaw.com
Year Founded: 1917
Sales Range: $550-599.9 Million
Emp.: 1,001
Legal Advisory Services
N.A.I.C.S.: 541110
Douglas S. Bland (Partner)
Sean Becker (Partner)
Judith M. Blissard (Partner)
Alan Beck (Partner)
Steve R. Borgman (Partner)
Ryan K. Carney (Partner)
Bryan Loocke (Partner-Energy Transactions Practice)
Daniel Graham (Partner-Govt Contracts Practice)
Stephen Stout (Partner-Austin)
Shaun Rogers (Partner-Dallas)
Stephen Jacobson (Partner)
Julian Seiguer (Partner)
David Wall (Partner)
Mingda Zhao (Partner)
Dan Komarek (Partner-New York)
Jessica Mussallem (Partner-San Francisco)
Danny Tobey (Partner-Dallas)
Paul Dunbar (Partner-Private Equity-London)
Christopher C. Green (Partner-Capital Markets, Mergers & Acquisitions)
S. Gregory Cope (Partner-Washington)
Scott N. Wulfe (Mng Partner)
Michael Simons (Partner)
Fred Williams (Partner)
Todd Landis (Partner)
Eric Klein (Partner)
Paul Tobias (Partner-Austin)
Mark Kelly (Chm)
Milam Foster Newby (Partner-Mergers, Acquisitions & Venture Capital)
Keith Fullenweider (Head-Corp Dept)
Jennifer Chen (Partner-Intellectual Property Practice)
John Fuisz (Partner-Intellectual Property Practice)
Shaun Lascelles (Partner-Private Equity Practice Grp-London)
Jeff Eldredge (Head-Corp Dept)
Ian Frost (Partner-Fin-London)
Natan Leyva (Partner-Global Tax Practice-Washington)
Thomas Zentner (Partner)
Lande Spottswood (Partner)
Mark Brasher (Partner)
Michael Dry (Partner-Govt Investigations & White Collar Criminal Defense)
Jim Thompson (Head-Global Litigation)
Robert M. Schick (Partner)
Marisa Secco (Partner)
Darren Tucker (Partner)
Hill Wellford (Partner)
Lucy Jenkins (Partner-Leveraged Fin-London)
Damara Chambers (Partner-Washington)

VINSON PROCESS CONTROLS CO. LP
2747 Highpoint Oaks Dr, Lewisville, TX 75067
Tel.: (972) 459-8200
Web Site: http://www.vpcco.com
Year Founded: 1939
Sales Range: $10-24.9 Million
Emp.: 150
Provider of Oil & Gas Production, Processing, Transportation, Distribution & Refining
N.A.I.C.S.: 423830
Kimberly Crowdus (Controller)
Al Griggs (VP)

VINTAGE CAPITAL GROUP LLC
11611 San Vicente Blvd, Los Angeles, CA 90049
Tel.: (310) 979-9090
Web Site: http://www.vintagecapitalgroup.com
Year Founded: 2001
Sales Range: $25-49.9 Million
Emp.: 28
Privater Equity Firm
N.A.I.C.S.: 523999
Fred Sands (Pres & CEO)

VINTAGE CAPITAL MANAGEMENT LLC
4705 S Apopka Vineland Rd Ste 206, Orlando, FL 32819
Tel.: (407) 506-7085
Web Site: http://www.vintagecapitalmanagement.com
Year Founded: 1998
Privater Equity Firm
N.A.I.C.S.: 523999
Jeremy R. Nowak (Partner)
Brian Randall Kahn (Mng Partner & Mgr-Investment)

VINTAGE IT SERVICES
1210 W 5th St, Austin, TX 78703
Tel.: (512) 481-1117
Web Site: http://www.vintageits.com
Sales Range: $1-9.9 Million
Emp.: 20
Manages Networks
N.A.I.C.S.: 541618
Steve Hanes (VP)
Sheryl Hanes (Founder & CEO)

VINTAGE NURSERIES LLC
27920 McCombs Ave, Wasco, CA 93280
Tel.: (661) 758-4777
Web Site: http://www.vintagenurseries.com
Rev.: $15,000,000
Emp.: 100
Retail Nurseries & Garden Stores
N.A.I.C.S.: 444240
Melinda Richardson (VP-Production)
Brad Kroeker (Mgr-Quality Control)
Dustin Hooper (Dir-Sls)
Glendy Samano (Mgr-Inventory & Shipping)
Miguel Castillo (Mgr-Production & Field Ops)
Rick Burnes (Sr VP & Gen Mgr)
Wayne Andersen (VP-Fin)

Subsidiaries:

Vintage Nurseries (1)
27920 McCombs Ave, Wasco, CA 93280-0279
Tel.: (707) 542-5510
Web Site: http://www.vintagenurseries.com
Nursery Stock
N.A.I.C.S.: 444240

VINTAGE PARTS
120 Corporate Dr, Beaver Dam, WI 53916-3116
Tel.: (920) 887-8146
Web Site: http://www.vpartsinc.com
Year Founded: 1971
Sales Range: $75-99.9 Million
Emp.: 80
Service Parts Sales & Distr
N.A.I.C.S.: 423810

VINTAGE SENIOR MANAGEMENT INC.
23 Corporate Plz Ste 190, Newport Beach, CA 92660
Tel.: (949) 719-4080
Web Site: http://www.vintagesenior.com
Sales Range: $10-24.9 Million
Emp.: 100
Living Home
N.A.I.C.S.: 531390
Brian J. Flornes (CEO)

VINTNERS GLOBAL RESOURCE LLC
7050 S 216th St, Kent, WA 98032
Tel.: (509) 941-8002
Web Site: http://www.vintnersglobal.com
Year Founded: 2007
Sales Range: $1-9.9 Million
Emp.: 3
Glass Wine Bottles & Related Packaging
N.A.I.C.S.: 327213
Andy Brassington (Founder)

VINYLEX CORPORATION
2636 Byington Solway Rd, Knoxville, TN 37931
Tel.: (865) 690-2211
Web Site: http://www.vinylex.com
Year Founded: 1952
Sales Range: $25-49.9 Million
Emp.: 150
Mfr of Plastic Products
N.A.I.C.S.: 326121
Sam Reynolds (Pres)
William Gamble (Mgr-Quality)
Brenda Farmer (Project Mgr)
Mike Mitchell (Plant Mgr)

VIP CINEMA, LLC
101 Industrial Dr, New Albany, MS 38652-3016
Tel.: (662) 539-7017
Web Site: http://www.vipcinemaseating.com
Year Founded: 2008
Motion Picture Theater Seating Mfr
N.A.I.C.S.: 337127
Steve Simons (CEO)

VIP COMMUNICATIONS, INC.
45189 Research Pl ste 100, Ashburn, VA 20147
Tel.: (703) 708-1515
Web Site: http://www.joinvip.com
Year Founded: 1996
Sales Range: $10-24.9 Million
Emp.: 50
International Calling Services & Products
N.A.I.C.S.: 517111
Graham Milne (Founder & CEO)
Peter Rogers (COO)
Phillip Lewis (Sr Mgr-Engrg)

VIP INTERNATIONAL INC.
2590 Mercantile Dr Ste C, Rancho Cordova, CA 95742
Tel.: (916) 638-5802
Web Site: http://www.viphomeandgarden.com
Year Founded: 2005
Sales Range: $1-9.9 Million
Emp.: 15
Home Decor & Garden Items
N.A.I.C.S.: 449129
Kim Lecam (Pres)

VIP LOYALTY CORP.
123 N Post Oak Ln Ste 440, Houston, TX 77024
Tel.: (713) 621-2737
Web Site: http://www.vipmembers.com
Loyalty Program Software
N.A.I.C.S.: 513210
Robert Zayas (CEO)
Sean Connolly (Pres & CFO)
Alison Kratish (Sec)

VIP MORTGAGE, INC.
92 Piazza, Colleyville, TX 76034
Tel.: (817) 514-0110
Web Site: http://www.vipmtg.com
Year Founded: 2005
Sales Range: $1-9.9 Million
Emp.: 25
Mortgage Banker
N.A.I.C.S.: 522310
Clark Miller (Founder)
Brian Shatto (Founder)
Chuck Weaver (Founder)
Letty Huffman (Sr VP & Branch Mgr-Oro Valley)
Jay Barbour (Founder & Pres)
Jennifer Tulcan (Exec VP-Natl Sls)
John Suggs (VP-Process Mgmt)

VIP MOTOR CARS LTD.
4095 E Palm Canyon Dr, Palm Springs, CA 92264
Tel.: (760) 328-6525
Web Site: http://www.mbusa.com
Rev.: $35,300,000
Emp.: 50
Automobiles, New & Used
N.A.I.C.S.: 441110

VIP REALTY GROUP, INC.
13131 University Dr, Fort Myers, FL 33907
Tel.: (239) 489-1100
Web Site: http://www.viprealty.com
Year Founded: 1993
Sales Range: $1-9.9 Million
Emp.: 150
Real Estate Broker
N.A.I.C.S.: 531210
Charles Ashby (Pres)
Dave Michaud (Dir-Tech)
Linda Knowlton (Mgr-Mortgage Grp Svcs)
Robin Driskill (Mgr-Fort Myers Sls)
Jim Hall (Owner & Mng Partner)
Renae Henry (VP-Title Grp Svcs)

COMPANIES

VIRGINIA MIRROR COMPANY INCORPORATED

Harley Conrad *(Mgr-Sls-Naples)*
Janet Rizzo *(Dir-Relocation, Referrals, Customer Care-Special Project-Global)*

VIP SALES COMPANY, INC.
2395 American Ave, Hayward, CA 94545-1807
Tel.: (918) 252-5791 OK
Web Site: http://www.vipfoods.com
Year Founded: 1967
Sales Range: $75-99.9 Million
Emp.: 30
Frozen Vegetables, Fruits, Rice Entrees & Smoothies Mfr, Marketer & Distr
N.A.I.C.S.: 424420
Harry Bandelles *(CFO)*
Greg Costley *(Pres)*

VIP STAFFING, INC.
16500 San Pedro Ste 110, San Antonio, TX 78232
Tel.: (210) 340-2000
Web Site: http://www.vipstaffing.com
Sales Range: $25-49.9 Million
Emp.: 25
Temporary Help Service
N.A.I.C.S.: 561320
Michael Himoff *(Pres)*

VIP WIRELESS, INC.
1366 Ford Rd, Bensalem, PA 19020
Tel.: (215) 671-9700 PA
Web Site: http://www.vipwireless.com
Wireless Business Solutions Services
N.A.I.C.S.: 517112
Jack Huston *(CEO)*

Subsidiaries:

AWI, Inc. (1)
206 Terminal Dr, Plainview, NY 11803
Tel.: (516) 813-9500
Wireless & Mobile Workforce Solutions Services
N.A.I.C.S.: 517112

VIPDESK, INC.
324 N Fairfax St, Alexandria, VA 22314-2625
Tel.: (703) 299-4422 VA
Web Site: http://www.vipdesk.com
Year Founded: 1997
Sales Range: $10-24.9 Million
Emp.: 125
Online Concierge Services
N.A.I.C.S.: 541512
Mary Naylor *(CEO)*
Sally Hurley *(Chief Experience Officer-VIPdesk Connect)*
Dan Fontaine *(Sr VP-Tech)*
Jeff Kramp *(VP-Tech)*
Kristie McDonald *(VP-Fin)*
Maggie Piper-Presing *(Dir-Recruiting & Sys)*
Othmar Mueller Von Blumencron *(VP-Sls & Mktg)*
Valerie Burns *(Dir-Ops)*
Todd Hixson *(Dir-Workforce Mgmt-VIPdesk Connect)*

VIRAL STYLE LLC
601 N Ashley Dr Ste 500, Tampa, FL 33602
Web Site: http://www.viralstyle.com
Year Founded: 2014
Sales Range: $50-74.9 Million
Emp.: 35
Online Tracking System Services
N.A.I.C.S.: 517810
Thomas Bell *(Founder & CEO)*

VIRE TECHNOLOGIES, LLC
3051 Oak Grove Rd Ste 100, Downers Grove, IL 60515
Tel.: (630) 445-1101
Web Site: http://www.viretechnologies.com
Year Founded: 2007
Sales Range: $1-9.9 Million
Emp.: 17
Information Technology Consulting Services
N.A.I.C.S.: 541512
Faisal Mustafa *(Founder & CEO)*

VIRENT ENERGY SYSTEMS, INC
3571 Anderson St, Madison, WI 53704
Tel.: (608) 663-0228
Web Site: http://www.virent.com
Sales Range: $1-9.9 Million
Emp.: 99
Oil Refiners Mfr
N.A.I.C.S.: 541330
Lee Edwards *(CEO)*
Randy Cortright *(Founder & CTO)*
Jeff Moore *(COO)*
David Kettner *(VP-Legal Affairs)*
Andrew Held *(Sr Dir-Deployment & Engrg)*
Arpesh Mehta *(Dir-Black River Asset Mgmt)*

VIRGIN ISLAND WATER & POWER AUTHORITY
8189 Subbase, Saint Thomas, VI 00802
Tel.: (340) 774-3552
Year Founded: 1964
Rev.: $115,956,881
Emp.: 347
Electronic Services
N.A.I.C.S.: 221118
Hugo V. Hodge Jr. *(CEO)*

VIRGIN ORBIT HOLDINGS, INC.
4022 EAST CONANT STREET, LONG BEACH, CA 90808
Tel.: (562) 706-7108 Ky
N.A.I.C.S.: 334511

VIRGIN TRAINS USA INC.
161 NW 6 th St Ste 900, Miami, FL 33136
Tel.: (305) 521-4800 DE
Web Site: http://www.virgintrainsusa.com
Year Founded: 2013
Emp.: 322
Railway Transportation Services
N.A.I.C.S.: 482112
Wesley R. Edens *(Chm)*
Patrick Goddard *(Pres)*
Jeff Swiatek *(CFO)*
Michael Cegelis *(Exec VP-Infrastructure Dev)*
Chris Sariego *(COO)*
Ravneet Bhandari *(Chief Comml Officer)*
Gary L. Smith *(Chief Acctg Officer)*
Mike Salzman *(Chief Dev Officer)*
Myles Tobin *(Gen Counsel)*
Scott Sanders *(Exec VP-Dev & Construction)*
Adrian Share *(Exec VP-Rail Infrastructure)*
Olivier Picq *(Chief Transportation Officer)*
Tom Rutkowski *(Chief Mechanical Officer)*

VIRGINIA AIR DISTRIBUTORS INC.
2501 Waterford Lk Dr, Midlothian, VA 23112
Tel.: (804) 379-1610
Web Site: http://www.virginiaair.com
Rev.: $25,000,000
Emp.: 200
Warm Air Heating & Air Conditioning
N.A.I.C.S.: 423730
Kenneth Baker *(Pres & CEO)*

VIRGINIA BANK BANKSHARES, INC.
PO Box 3447, Danville, VA 24543-3447
Tel.: (434) 793-6411
Web Site: http://www.vabanktr.com
VABB—(OTCBB)
Bank Holding Company
N.A.I.C.S.: 551111
Roger C. Gillispie *(Pres & CEO)*
Harry T. Kolendrianos *(Chm)*

Subsidiaries:

Virginia Bank & Trust Co. (1)
336 Main St, Danville, VA 24541
Tel.: (434) 793-6411
Web Site: http://www.vabanktr.com
Sales Range: $1-9.9 Million
Emp.: 66
Banking Services
N.A.I.C.S.: 522110
Don Merricks *(Pres & CEO)*

VIRGINIA DARE EXTRACT CO., INC.
882 3rd Ave, Brooklyn, NY 11232
Tel.: (718) 788-1776 VA
Web Site: http://www.virginiadare.com
Year Founded: 1923
Sales Range: $100-124.9 Million
Emp.: 175
Mfr of Vanilla & other Flavoring Extracts for Food Products
N.A.I.C.S.: 311930
Howard Smith Jr. *(Pres)*

VIRGINIA ELECTRONIC COMPONENTS LLC
1155 5th St SW, Charlottesville, VA 22902
Tel.: (434) 296-4184
Web Site: http://www.vecsupply.com
Sales Range: $10-24.9 Million
Emp.: 27
Electronic Parts & Equipment, Nec
N.A.I.C.S.: 423690
Frank Stalzer *(Pres)*
Steve Vaughan *(Mgr-Lynchburg)*
Phil Moore *(Mgr-Mktg)*
Don Johnson *(Mgr-Charlottesville)*
Robert Kreider *(Mgr-Raleigh)*
Jim Gober *(Mgr-Morris Automation)*
Wayne Kelso *(Mgr-Birmingham)*

VIRGINIA FARM BUREAU MUTUAL INSURANCE COMPANY
12580 W Creek Pkwy, Richmond, VA 23238
Tel.: (804) 290-1000 VA
Web Site: http://www.vafb.com
Year Founded: 1950
Rev.: $149,831,717
Emp.: 541
Fire, Marine & Casualty Insurance
N.A.I.C.S.: 524126
Wayne F. Pryor *(Pres)*
Darlene Price Wells *(Exec VP & Gen Mgr)*
Scott E. Sink *(VP)*

Subsidiaries:

Virginia Farm Bureau Fire & Casualty Insurance Company (1)
12580 W Creek Pkwy, Richmond, VA 23238-1110
Tel.: (804) 290-1000
Web Site: http://www.vafb.com
Sales Range: Less than $1 Million
Emp.: 300
Insurance Agents, Brokers & Service
N.A.I.C.S.: 524210
Darlene Wells *(Exec VP & Gen Mgr)*

VIRGINIA HARDWOOD CO.
1000 W Foothill Blvd, Azusa, CA 91702
Tel.: (626) 815-0540
Web Site: http://www.virginiahardwood.com
Rev.: $11,200,000
Emp.: 40
Hardwood Distributor
N.A.I.C.S.: 423310
Gary Henzie *(Pres)*

VIRGINIA INDUSTRIAL PLSTCS INC.
2454 N East Side Hwy, Elkton, VA 22827
Tel.: (540) 298-1515
Web Site: http://www.vaplastic.com
Rev.: $1,968,000
Emp.: 12
All Other Plastics Product Mfr
N.A.I.C.S.: 326199
Brent Mercer *(Pres)*

VIRGINIA INDUSTRIES INC.
1022 Elm St, Rocky Hill, CT 06067-1809
Tel.: (860) 571-3602 CT
Web Site: http://www.hartfordtechnologies.com
Year Founded: 1982
Bearings, Balls, Rollers & Pins Supplier
N.A.I.C.S.: 332119
Robert M. Stanko *(Exec VP & Gen Mgr)*

VIRGINIA INTERNATIONAL TERMINALS INC.
601 World Trade Ctr, Norfolk, VA 23510
Tel.: (757) 440-7000 VA
Web Site: http://www.vit.org
Year Founded: 1972
Sales Range: $150-199.9 Million
Emp.: 330
Provider of Marine Cargo Handling Services
N.A.I.C.S.: 488320
John Jackson *(Dir-Customer Svc)*
Lynda Wilson *(Mgr-Sys Engrg)*
Kiym Ward *(Mgr-Customer Svc)*

VIRGINIA LEAGUE FOR PLANNED PARENTHOOD INC.
201 N Hamilton St, Richmond, VA 23221
Tel.: (804) 355-4358
Web Site: https://www.plannedparenthood.org
Year Founded: 1942
Health Care Srvices
N.A.I.C.S.: 621610

VIRGINIA MASON INSTITUTE
1100 9th Ave, Seattle, WA 98101-2756
Tel.: (206) 341-1600 WA
Web Site: http://www.virginiamasoninstitute.org
Year Founded: 2008
Sales Range: $1-9.9 Million
Health Care Educational Services
N.A.I.C.S.: 611710
Gary S. Kaplan *(Chm & CEO)*
Suzanne Anderson *(Exec VP & CIO & CFO)*
Andrew Jacobs *(Dir-Medical)*
Joyce Lammert *(Dir-Hospital Medica)*
Sarah Patterson *(Exec Dir)*
Kim Pittenger *(Dir-Quality & Innovation)*
Donna Smith *(Dir-Medical)*

VIRGINIA MIRROR COMPANY INCORPORATED

VIRGINIA MIRROR COMPANY INCORPORATED

Virginia Mirror Company Incorporated—(Continued)
300 Moss St S, Martinsville, VA 24112
Tel.: (276) 632-9816
Web Site: http://www.va-mirror.com
Year Founded: 1913
Rev.: $11,700,000
Emp.: 60
Mirror Mfr
N.A.I.C.S.: 327215
Christopher Beeler *(Chm, Pres & CEO)*

Subsidiaries:

Virginia Glass Products Corporation (1)
347 Old Sand Rd, Ridgeway, VA 24148
Tel.: (276) 956-3131
Web Site: http://www.va-glass.com
Sales Range: $10-24.9 Million
Glass Products Mfr
N.A.I.C.S.: 327211
W. Christopher Beeler Jr. *(Chm)*

VIRGINIA PELLA INC.
2207 Sta Rd, Richmond, VA 23234
Tel.: (804) 275-7809
Web Site: http://www.pellava.com
Rev.: $14,300,000
Emp.: 25
Doors & Windows
N.A.I.C.S.: 423310

VIRGINIA PORT AUTHORITY
600 World Trade Ctr, Norfolk, VA 23510
Tel.: (757) 683-8000 VA
Web Site:
 http://www.portofvirginia.com
Year Founded: 1952
Sales Range: $200-249.9 Million
Emp.: 135
Port Services for International Transportation & Maritime Commerce in Virginia that Operates & Markets Marine Terminal Facilities
N.A.I.C.S.: 926120
Russell J. Held *(VP-Economic Dev)*
Cathie J. France *(Chief Pub Affairs Officer)*
John F. Reinhart *(CEO & Exec Dir)*
James S. Bibbs *(Chief HR Officer)*
Joseph P. Ruddy *(Chief Innovations Officer)*
Tom D. Capozzi *(Chief Sls Officer)*
Holly Pearce *(Dir-Logistics-Intl)*
Lee Puckett *(VP & Gen Mgr)*
Brian Kobza *(Dir-Ocean Carrier Sls)*
Vann Rogerson *(Pres & CEO)*

VIRGINIA QUILTING INC.
100 Main St, La Crosse, VA 23950
Tel.: (434) 757-1809
Web Site:
 http://www.virginiaquilting.com
Year Founded: 1975
Sales Range: $50-74.9 Million
Emp.: 300
Bedding & Fabric Mfr & Distr
N.A.I.C.S.: 314120
Donna Adams *(Mgr)*
John W. McAden Sr. *(Pres)*

VIRGINIA SYMPHONY ORCHESTRA
150 Boush St Ste 201, Norfolk, VA 23510
Tel.: (757) 466-3060
Web Site:
 http://www.virginiasymphony.org
Year Founded: 1920
Sales Range: $10-24.9 Million
Emp.: 125
Symphony Orchestra
N.A.I.C.S.: 711130
Susan Goode *(Sec)*
Donna Hudgins *(Dir-PR)*

Patrick McDermott *(Chm)*
Carolyn Pittman *(Treas)*
Karen Philion *(Pres & CEO)*
Teresa Kraus *(CFO)*

VIRGINIA T'S INC.
2001 Anchor Ave, Petersburg, VA 23803
Tel.: (804) 862-2600
Web Site: http://www.virginiats.com
Rev.: $53,993,789
Emp.: 190
Men's Clothing
N.A.I.C.S.: 424350
Dale R. Call *(CEO)*
Michelle Hankins *(Asst Mgr-& Coord-Trng)*
Ann Riggs *(Mgr-Credit)*
Troy Brockwell *(VP-Sls)*

VIRGINIA TILE COMPANY
24404 Indoplex Cir, Farmington Hills, MI 48335
Tel.: (248) 476-7850
Web Site: http://www.virginiatile.com
Sales Range: $25-49.9 Million
Emp.: 120
Provider of Floor Coverings & Designs
N.A.I.C.S.: 423220
Bobby Braham *(CFO)*
Chad Treuthart *(VP-Residential Sls & Showrooms)*
Edmund Vaske *(COO)*
Sunil Palakodati *(CEO)*
Dana Kropke *(VP-Comml & Natl Acct Sls)*

VIRGINIA TRANSFORMER CORP.
220 Glade View Dr, Roanoke, VA 24012
Tel.: (540) 345-9892
Web Site:
 http://www.vatransformer.com
Year Founded: 1971
Sales Range: $10-24.9 Million
Emp.: 209
Specialty Transformers
N.A.I.C.S.: 335311
Prabhat K. Jain *(CEO)*
Steve Nelson *(CFO)*
Matt Gregg *(VP-Ops)*
Mudassar Mohsin *(Head-HR & IT & Mgr)*
Neeraj Baxi *(VP-Ops)*
Rakesh Rathi *(VP-Engrg & Matls)*
Anoop Nanda *(Pres)*

VIRGINIA TRUCK CENTER INC.
267 Lee Hwy, Roanoke, VA 24019
Tel.: (540) 777-7700
Web Site:
 http://www.virginiatruckcenter.com
Rev.: $39,500,000
Emp.: 100
Trucks, Tractors & Trailers: New & Used
N.A.I.C.S.: 441110
Frank T. Ellett *(Pres)*
Judy Parker *(Sec)*
John Votano *(Mgr-Svcs)*
Matt Taylor *(Mgr-Svcs)*
Matt Clark *(Supvr-Body Shop)*
Bret Ferguson *(Mgr-Parts)*
Troy Coffey *(Controller)*
Terrell Smith *(Dir-HR Safety & Risk)*
Robert Dye *(Mgr-Trailer Sls)*
Brian Carey *(Mgr-Body Shop)*
Terry Vandergrift *(Mgr-Body Shop)*
Ryan Brooks *(Mgr-Parts)*
Mike Dennis *(Mgr-Parts)*
Cliff Simmons *(Mgr-Parts)*

Richard Helms *(Mgr-Parts-Columbus)*
Bill Fuller *(Mgr-Sls)*
Clarence Davis *(Mgr-Svc)*

VIRGO CAPITAL
411 Brazos St 212, Austin, TX 78701
Tel.: (512) 291-6096
Web Site:
 http://www.virgocapital.com
Privater Equity Firm
N.A.I.C.S.: 523999
Hemanth Parasuram *(Mng Dir)*
Guhan Swaminathan *(Mng Dir)*
Nathaniel Robinson *(Partner)*
Arun Prakash *(Partner)*

Subsidiaries:

Accord Human Resources, Inc. (1)
210 Park Ave Ste 1200, Oklahoma City, OK 73102-5603
Tel.: (405) 232-9888
Sales Range: $400-449.9 Million
Emp.: 34
Employee Administration Solutions & Services
N.A.I.C.S.: 561330
Buton Goldfield *(Pres)*

VIRGO INVESTMENT GROUP LLC
1201 Howard Ave Ste 300, Burlingame, CA 94010
Tel.: (908) 897-0408 DE
Web Site: http://www.virgo-llc.com
Year Founded: 2009
Privater Equity Firm
N.A.I.C.S.: 523999
Jesse Watson *(Founder & CIO)*

VIRIDAX CORPORATION
270 NW 3rd Ct, Boca Raton, FL 33432-3720
Tel.: (561) 368-1427 FL
Web Site: http://www.viridax.com
Year Founded: 1998
Emp.: 2
Pharmaceuticals Product Mfr
N.A.I.C.S.: 325412
Richard C. Honour *(Chm, Pres & CEO)*

VIRIDIAN PARTNERS LLC
1805 Shea Center Dr Ste 250, Highlands Ranch, CO 80129
Tel.: (303) 271-9114 CO
Web Site:
 http://www.viridianpartners.com
Year Founded: 2003
Distressed Real Estate Investment, Remediation & Development Services
N.A.I.C.S.: 531390
Tate Goss *(Pres)*
William P. Lynott *(CEO)*
Steve Ganch *(Dir-Dev)*
Paul Schubert *(CFO)*
Erik Zitek *(Dir-Investments)*

VIROBAY, INC.
1360 Willow Rd Ste 100, Menlo Park, CA 94025
Tel.: (650) 833-5700 DE
Web Site: http://www.virobayinc.com
Year Founded: 2006
Sales Range: $1-9.9 Million
Emp.: 8
Pharmaceuticals Mfr
N.A.I.C.S.: 325412
Robert F. Booth *(CEO)*
Anantha R. Sudhakar *(VP-Chemistry, Mfg & Controls)*
Leslie J. Holsinger *(VP-Biology)*

VIRPIE INC.
1 Reservoir Ofc Park Ste 208 1449 Old Waterbury Rd, Southbury, CT 06488
Tel.: (203) 264-0999 CT

U.S. PRIVATE

Web Site: http://www.virpietech.com
Year Founded: 1997
Sales Range: $10-24.9 Million
Emp.: 25
IT & Outsourcing Staffing
N.A.I.C.S.: 561311
Srinivas Thammana *(Founder & CEO)*

Subsidiaries:

Virpie Tech (1)
1449 Old Waterbury Rd, Southbury, CT 06488 (100%)
Tel.: (203) 264-0999
Web Site: http://www.virpietech.com
Sales Range: $1-9.9 Million
Information & Technology Staffing
N.A.I.C.S.: 561311

VIRTELLIGENCE
6216 Baker Rd Ste 100, Minneapolis, MN 55346-1953
Tel.: (952) 746-9220
Web Site:
 http://www.virtelligence.com
Year Founded: 1998
Sales Range: $10-24.9 Million
Emp.: 120
Healthcare Information Technology Consulting Services
N.A.I.C.S.: 541512
Akhtar Chaudhri *(Founder & CEO)*
Martha Bolke *(Controller)*
Craig Carlson *(Reg VP)*
Casey Post *(Reg VP)*
John Cobb *(Reg VP)*
Nox Rupawalla *(Dir-Staffing Integration & Reporting)*
Kim Pederson *(VP-Automated Medical Records)*

VIRTEXCO CORPORATION
977 Norfolk Sq, Norfolk, VA 23502
Tel.: (757) 466-1114
Web Site: http://www.virtexco.com
Rev.: $45,000,000
Emp.: 200
General Contractors
N.A.I.C.S.: 236220
Robert H. Wells *(CEO)*
Donald Adams *(Pres)*
David S. Sterling *(VP)*

VIRTU INVESTMENTS
5973 Avenida Encinas Ste 220, Carlsbad, CA 92008-4478
Tel.: (760) 929-4700
Web Site:
 http://www.virtuinvestments.com
Emp.: 100
Offices of Real Estate Agents & Brokers
N.A.I.C.S.: 531210
David Carroll *(Mgr)*

VIRTUA SURGICAL GROUP
401 Route 73 N 50 Lake Ctr Dr Ste 400, Marlton, NJ 08053
Tel.: (856) 355-0620 NJ
Year Founded: 1984
Sales Range: $1-9.9 Million
Emp.: 23
Surgical Services
N.A.I.C.S.: 621493
Alfred Campanella *(Exec VP)*
Thomas Gordon *(CIO & Sr VP)*
Robert M. Segin *(CFO)*
Robert Michael DiRenzo *(COO & Exec VP)*
James P. Dwyer *(CMO & Exec VP)*

VIRTUAL ED LINK, INC.
87 Fairfield Rd, Fairfield, NJ 07004
Tel.: (973) 276-0555
Software Development Services
N.A.I.C.S.: 541511
John Bay *(Pres & Chief Bus Officer)*

COMPANIES

VIRTUAL FARM CREATIVE INC.
31 A Ridge Rd Ste 1, Phoenixville, PA 19460
Tel.: (610) 917-3131
Web Site: http://www.virtualfarm.com
Sales Range: $10-24.9 Million
Emp.: 22
Advetising Agency
N.A.I.C.S.: 541810
Todd Palmer (Pres, Dir-Creative, Writer & Designer)
Darren Price (Dir-Art)
Melissa Dyer (Designer)

VIRTUAL INSTRUMENTS, INC.
25 Metro Dr, San Jose, CA 95110
Tel.: (408) 579-4000
Web Site:
http://www.virtualinstruments.com
Sales Range: $25-49.9 Million
Emp.: 230
Information Technology Infrastructure Management Software Publisher
N.A.I.C.S.: 541511
George W. Harrington (Sr VP-Fin & Ops)
John Gentry (CTO)
Bo Barker (VP-Svcs)
Barry Cooks (Sr VP-Products, Engrg & Support)
Eileen Murphy (VP-Ops)
Mike Moore (CIO)
Ray Villeneuve (Pres)
Philippe Vincent (CEO)
Lisa Alger (Sr VP-Engrg)
Sheen Khoury (Exec VP-Sls-Worldwide)
Rick Haggart (Sr VP-Professional Svcs)
Peter Dayton (CFO)

Subsidiaries:

Xangati, Inc. (1)
10121 Miller Ave Ste 100, Cupertino, CA 95014
Tel.: (408) 252-0505
Web Site: http://www.xangati.com
Sales Range: $1-9.9 Million
Emp.: 16
Computer Integrated Systems Design, Nsk
N.A.I.C.S.: 541512
Jagan Jagannathan (Founder & CTO)
Atchison Frazer (VP-Mktg)
Steven M. Velardi (VP-Worldwide Sls)
Vasu Vasudevan (Founder & Chief Strategy Officer)

VIRTUAL SOURCING, LLC
1201 3rd Street Ste 100, Alexandria, LA 71301
Tel.: (318) 561-8330   NV
Web Site:
http://www.vpadvantage.com
Year Founded: 1999
Management Consulting Services
N.A.I.C.S.: 541611
Charlotte Wasmer (Pres)
Janis Barbin (Mgr-Client Svcs)
Michelle Bournstein (Mgr-Solution Specialist)
Kenneth J. Wasmer (VP)
Malllory Smith (Mgr-Fin & Ops)

Subsidiaries:

Custom Financial Solutions (1)
1201 Third St, Alexandria, LA 71301
Tel.: (318) 844-6353
Consumer Lending
N.A.I.C.S.: 522291
Charlotte Wasmer (Owner)

VIRTUAL TECH GURUS INC.
5050 Quorum Dr Ste 330, Dallas, TX 75254
Tel.: (214) 269-1314
Web Site:
http://www.virtualtechgurus.com

Year Founded: 2008
Sales Range: $10-24.9 Million
Emp.: 23
Information Technology Consulting Services
N.A.I.C.S.: 541512
Guru Moorthi (CEO)

VIRTUAL, INC
401 Edgewater Pl Ste 600, Wakefield, MA 01880
Tel.: (781) 224-1100
Web Site:
http://www.virtualmgmt.com
Sales Range: $10-24.9 Million
Emp.: 78
Association Business Operations Management Services
N.A.I.C.S.: 541611
Andy Freed (Pres & CEO)
Janice Carroll (VP-Client Svcs)
Ruth Cassidy (VP-Comm)
Ann Geary (Dir-HR)
Terry Lowney (COO & Sr VP)
Brant Picard (Dir-IT Infrastructure)
Christina Zagami (Dir-Fin Reporting)
Justin Wade (Dir-Bus Analytics)
Kathleen Gallagher (Sr VP-Strategic Initiatives)
Kristina Lantheaume (Controller-Client)
Deborah Leland (Sr Dir-Global Applications & Web Dev)
Valerie Moschella (Dir-Project Mgmt Office)
Kim Turner (Sr Dir-Client Svcs)
Bonnie J. Bystrek (Chief People Officer)
John Lessard (Dir-Client Svcs)
Alyssa Rhodes McArdle (Mgr-Events)
Jennifer Ashooh (Partner-People & Culture Bus)
Jaci Cochran (VP-Fin)
Mauro Lance (CFO)
Michelle Schneider (Dir-Client Fin & Reporting)
Jennifer Williams (VP-Ops)
Nick Deitmen (Sr Dir-Ops)

VIRTUAL-AGENT SERVICES
1920 N Thoreau Dr Ste 116, Schaumburg, IL 60173
Tel.: (847) 925-2340
Web Site: http://www.vagent.com
Year Founded: 1999
Rev.: $31,800,000
Emp.: 1,400
Scientific & Technical Consulting Services
N.A.I.C.S.: 541690
Robert Camastro (CEO)
Evan Blanco (Pres)

VIRTUE CAPITAL MANAGEMENT LLC
6 Cadillac Dr Ste 310, Brentwood, TN 37027
Web Site:
http://www.virtuecapitalmanagement.com
Year Founded: 2013
Sales Range: $1-9.9 Million
Emp.: 23
Financial Investment Services
N.A.I.C.S.: 523940
Matt Rettich (Founder & Partner)
Jeremy Rettich (Pres)
James Webb (VP)
Lars Anderson (Dir-Sls & Mktg)

VIRTUE GROUP
5755 N Point Pkwy Ste 85 86, Alpharetta, GA 30022
Tel.: (678) 578-4555
Web Site: http://www.virtuegroup.com
Year Founded: 2002

Sales Range: $10-24.9 Million
Emp.: 130
Software Services
N.A.I.C.S.: 449210
Raja Kalidindi (Founder & CEO)
Rob Newlan (Pres-Global)
Krystle Watler (Mng Dir-North America)
Simon Mogren (Exec Creative Dir-North America)

VIRTUMUNDO, INC.
11184 Antioch Rd Ste 412, Overland Park, KS 66210
Tel.: (913) 712-9615
Web Site: http://www.virtumundo.com
Year Founded: 1997
Sales Range: $1-9.9 Million
Emp.: 18
Advetising Agency
N.A.I.C.S.: 541850
Travis Tisa (CEO)

VIRTUOSO LTD.
505 Main St Ste 500, Fort Worth, TX 76102-3941
Tel.: (817) 870-0300   TX
Web Site: http://www.virtuoso.com
Year Founded: 1992
Sales Range: $100-124.9 Million
Emp.: 205
Travel Services
N.A.I.C.S.: 561510
Matthew D. Upchurch (CEO)
Misty Ewing (Dir-PR)
David Hansen (Exec VP-Ops & Fin)
Albert Herrera (Sr VP-Product Partnerships-Global)
David Kolner (Sr VP-Member Partnerships-Global)
Leonard E. Post (Chief Scientific Officer)

VIRTUS LLC
9800 Metcalf Ave Ste 500, Overland Park, KS 66206
Tel.: (816) 919-2323
Web Site:
http://www.virtusinsurance.com
Year Founded: 2013
Insurance Brokerage Services
N.A.I.C.S.: 524298
Andrew Gray (CEO)

Subsidiaries:

First Line Insurance Services, Inc. (1)
43 Inverness Dr E, Englewood, CO 80112
Tel.: (720) 875-0134
Web Site: http://www.firstlineins.com
Insurance Agencies & Brokerages
N.A.I.C.S.: 524210
Lynda Andrews (CEO)
Jaci Fischer (CFO)
Margaret Przygocki (Mgr)
Katherine Price (Exec VP)
Lora Smith (Mgr-Credit Union Div)

Kemmons Wilson Insurance Group, LLC (1)
8700 Trail Lake Dr W Ste 100, Memphis, TN 38125
Tel.: (901) 346-8808
Web Site: http://www.kwig.com
General Insurance Services
N.A.I.C.S.: 524210
Gene Douglass (Acct Exec)

VIRTUS PARTNERS LLC
1301 Fannin St Ste1700, Houston, TX 77002
Tel.: (713) 993-4300
Web Site: http://www.virtusllc.com
Year Founded: 2005
Emp.: 150
Alternative Asset Administrative & Middle Office Services
N.A.I.C.S.: 522320

Robert Tomicic (Founder)
Kelly Faykus (Mng Partner)
Mirna Herr (Partner)
Dean Fletcher (Chief Strategy Officer)
Dermot Caden (Head-Regulated Fund Admin Bus-Europe)
Jennifer Nolan (Sr Dir-Dublin)
Pradeep Rao (Mng Dir-Europe)

Subsidiaries:

Trade Settlement, Inc. (1)
27 W 24th St Ste 405, New York, NY 10010
Tel.: (212) 463-7801
Web Site: http://www.trade-settlement.com
Sales Range: $1-9.9 Million
Emp.: 15
Loan Settlement Services
N.A.I.C.S.: 522320
Jon Hoberman (VP)
Pat Loret de Mola (Founder & CEO)
John Brumfield (Mgr-Quality Assurance)
Simone Bullard (Mgr-Trng & Client Support)
Joylynn Jarvis (Asst VP)

VIRTUS REAL ESTATE CAPITAL
7004 Bee Cave Rd Bldg 3 Ste 300, Austin, TX 78746
Tel.: (512) 891-1222
Web Site: http://www.virtusre.com
Year Founded: 2003
Sales Range: $1-4.9 Billion
Emp.: 40
Real Estate Investment Services
N.A.I.C.S.: 523999
Terrell Gates (Founder & CEO)
Will Strong (CFO)
Robert Schweizer (Chief Investment Officer)
Kevin White (Dir-Acq-Alternative Multifamily)
Aaron D'Costa (Dir-Acq-Sr Living)
John Sweeny (Dir-Acq-Healthcare)
Nick Worontzoff (Dir-Capital Dev)
Jennifer Williams (Coord-Closing)
Dade Pham (Dir-Property Acctg)

VISAGE DERMATOLOGY & LASER CENTER, LLC
5253 Central Ave, Saint Petersburg, FL 33710
Tel.: (727) 388-6982
Web Site:
http://www.visagedermatology.com
Sales Range: $1-9.9 Million
Emp.: 20
Dermatologist Office
N.A.I.C.S.: 621111
Alexandra Kongsiri (Owner)

VISAGE MOBILE, INC.
500 Sansome St Ste 300, San Francisco, CA 94111
Tel.: (415) 200-2888
Web Site:
http://www.visagemobile.com
Sales Range: $1-9.9 Million
Emp.: 30
Wireless Technology
N.A.I.C.S.: 517112
Bzur Haun (CEO)
Mani Zarrehparvar (Pres)

VISAHQ.COM INC.
Embassy Row 2005 Massachusetts Ave NW, Washington, DC 20036
Tel.: (202) 558-2216
Web Site: http://www.visahq.com
Year Founded: 2002
Sales Range: $1-9.9 Million
Emp.: 14
Visa & Passport Application Services
N.A.I.C.S.: 721199
Oleg Naydonov (Pres)
Alexander Yaroshenko (CEO)
Stan Berteloot (VP-Growth-Global)

VISALIGN LLC

VISALIGN LLC

Visalign LLC—(Continued)
2002 Summit Blvd Ste 700, Atlanta, GA 30319-6416
Tel.: (610) 692-3290
Web Site: http://www.visalign.com
Rev.: $36,000,000
Emp.: 70
Computer Related Consulting Services
N.A.I.C.S.: 541512
Ronald Haantjes (VP)

VISIBLE CHANGES
1303 Campbell Rd, Houston, TX 77055
Tel.: (713) 984-8800 — TX
Web Site: http://www.visiblechanges.com
Year Founded: 1977
Sales Range: $150-199.9 Million
Emp.: 800
Beauty Salons
N.A.I.C.S.: 812112
John McCormack (Chm)
Maryanne McCormack (Founder & Pres)
Becky Poess (CFO, Treas & Controller)

VISIBLE SYSTEMS CORPORATION
63 Fountain St Ste 301B, Framingham, MA 01702
Tel.: (781) 778-0200
Web Site: http://www.visible.com
Sales Range: $10-24.9 Million
Emp.: 10
Mfr & Sales of Computer Software
N.A.I.C.S.: 513210
George G. Cagliuso (Founder, Chm & CEO)
Mike Cesino (Pres)
John Nash (VP-Mktg)

VISIBLE.NET, INC.
14953 NE 95th St, Redmond, WA 98052
Tel.: (425) 250-0969
Web Site: http://www.visible.net
E-Commerce Software & Internet Marketing
N.A.I.C.S.: 513210
Gilbert Walker (Chm)

VISIBLEGAINS, INC.
1666 Massachusetts Ave, Lexington, MA 02420
Tel.: (781) 350-3416
Web Site: http://www.postwire.com
Year Founded: 2010
Sales Range: $10-24.9 Million
Emp.: 10
Video Interaction Design & Management Analytics Software
N.A.I.C.S.: 513210
Cliff Pollan (Co-Founder, Pres & CEO)
Carrie Kuempel (Mgr-Mktg)

VISIBLETHREAD, LLC
1101 E 33rd St 3rd Fl Ste C300, Baltimore, MD 21218
Tel.: (443) 451-7005 — MD
Web Site: http://www.visiblethread.com
Year Founded: 2008
Sales Range: $10-24.9 Million
Document & Web Content Scanning & Risk Analysis Software Publisher
N.A.I.C.S.: 513210
Fergal McGovern (Co-Founder & CEO)
Jason O'Connell (Co-Founder & CTO)
John Nolan (Chief Comml Officer)

Subsidiaries:
VisibleThread Ltd. (1)
5-7 Westland Square Pearse Street, Dublin, 2, Ireland
Tel.: (353) 1 685 7730
Web Site: http://www.visiblethread.com
Emp.: 20
Software Whslr
N.A.I.C.S.: 423430

VISION ACE HARDWARE, LLC
1100 5th Ave S Ste 208, Naples, FL 34102
Tel.: (239) 435-0734
Web Site: http://www.visionacehardware.com
Year Founded: 1999
Sales Range: $25-49.9 Million
Emp.: 225
Hardware Stores
N.A.I.C.S.: 444140
Jim W. Ackroyd (CEO)

VISION AIRLINES INC.
2705 Airport Dr, Las Vegas, NV 89032
Tel.: (702) 647-7700
Web Site: http://www.visionairlines.com
Year Founded: 1994
Sales Range: $25-49.9 Million
Emp.: 200
Airline
N.A.I.C.S.: 481111
William Acor (Owner)
Jody Nolan (Gen Mgr)

VISION ATLANTA INC.
PO Box 867, Roswell, GA 30077
Tel.: (770) 971-0337 — GA
Year Founded: 2002
Sales Range: $1-9.9 Million
Christian Ministry Services
N.A.I.C.S.: 813110
Dave Pridemore (Exec Dir)

VISION AUTO, INC.
2746 Bernville Rd, Leesport, PA 19533
Tel.: (610) 777-6500
Web Site: http://vision-auto-group.ebizautos.com
Year Founded: 1997
Sales Range: $10-24.9 Million
Emp.: 55
Car Whslr
N.A.I.C.S.: 441110
R. Craig Rosenfeld (Pres)

VISION BANCSHARES, INC.
101 E Main St, Ada, OK 74820
Tel.: (580) 332-5132 — OK
Web Site: http://www.visionbankok.com
Sales Range: $10-24.9 Million
Emp.: 192
Bank Holding Company
N.A.I.C.S.: 551111
James R. Hamby (CEO)

Subsidiaries:
Vision Bank, N.A. (1)
101 E Main St, Ada, OK 74820
Tel.: (580) 332-5132
Web Site: http://www.visionbankok.com
Sales Range: $10-24.9 Million
Retail & Commercial Banking
N.A.I.C.S.: 522180
Steve Bagwell (Pres)

VISION BEVERAGE CORP.
1100 Independence Ave, Evansville, IN 47714-4549
Tel.: (812) 424-7978 — IN
Web Site: http://www.visionbev.com
Sales Range: $10-24.9 Million
Emp.: 220

Soft Drink Bottler & Whslr
N.A.I.C.S.: 312111
Nancy Hodge (Pres)
Derek Thompson (Controller)

VISION CAPITAL LP
One Bayshore Plz 700 Airport Rd Ste 370, Burlingame, CA 94010
Tel.: (650) 373-2720
Web Site: http://www.visioncap.com
Sales Range: $100-124.9 Million
Emp.: 15
Venture Capital
N.A.I.C.S.: 561499
Dag Syrrist (Gen Partner)
Linus Lundberg (Mng Dir)
William Wick (Mng Dir & CFO)

Subsidiaries:
Vision Capital - Geneva (1)
6 Rue De La Croix D, 1204, Geneva, Switzerland
Tel.: (41) 225446000
Web Site: http://www.visioncap.com
Sales Range: $50-74.9 Million
Emp.: 10
Investment Company
N.A.I.C.S.: 523999

VISION COUNCIL OF AMERICA
225 Reinekers Ln Ste 700, Alexandria, VA 22314
Tel.: (703) 548-4560 — VA
Web Site: http://www.thevisioncouncil.org
Year Founded: 2001
Sales Range: $10-24.9 Million
Emp.: 31
Trade Assocation
N.A.I.C.S.: 813910
Lisa Wright (Mgr-Database)
Brian Carroll (CFO & COO)
Sonjia Ford (Office Mgr)
Jessica Lutz (Mgr-Mktg & Comm)
Donna Jones (Sr Dir-HR)
Maureen Beddis (VP-Mktg & Comm)

VISION CREATIVE GROUP, INC.
16 Wing Dr, Cedar Knolls, NJ 07927-1694
Tel.: (973) 984-3454
Web Site: http://www.visioncreativegroup.com
Year Founded: 1987
Rev.: $12,000,000
Emp.: 45
Advetising Agency
N.A.I.C.S.: 541810
Andrew Bittman (Pres)
Christine Sainato (VP)
Sharon Petry (VP)
Kelly DiGiesi (Dir-Creative)
Michael Mazewski (Dir-Creative)

VISION ENGINEERING INC.
570 Danbury Rd, New Milford, CT 06776
Tel.: (860) 355-3776
Web Site: http://www.visioneng.com
Year Founded: 1958
Sales Range: $10-24.9 Million
Emp.: 45
Industrial Microscopes Mfr
N.A.I.C.S.: 333310
Robin J. Freeman (Founder)

Subsidiaries:
Vision Engineering Italia (1)
Via Cesare Cantu 9, 20092, Milan, Italy
Tel.: (39) 02 6129 3518
Vision Engineering Italia
N.A.I.C.S.: 423490

Vision Engineering Ltd. (1)
Send Road Send, Woking, GU23 7ER, United Kingdom

Tel.: (44) 1483248300
Web Site: http://www.visioneng.com
Emp.: 3
Industrial Microscopes Mfr
N.A.I.C.S.: 423490
Chris Milborrow (Mgr-Design)

VISION FINANCIAL MARKETS LLC
4 High Ridge Park Ste 100, Stamford, CT 06905-1325
Tel.: (212) 859-0200
Web Site: http://www.visionfinancialmarkets.com
Year Founded: 1988
Sales Range: $10-24.9 Million
Emp.: 120
Securities Trading Support Services & Securities Broker
N.A.I.C.S.: 523150
Robert M. Boshnack (Chm)
Eric Gaffin (CIO & CTO)
Steven Silver (CMO)
Michael Shaughnessy (COO)
Howard Rothman (Pres)
Scott Raymond (CFO)
John Felag (Chief Risk Officer)

VISION FS INC.
8348 Foxfire Dr, Orangevale, CA 95662
Tel.: (916) 726-1294
Sales Range: $10-24.9 Million
Emp.: 20
Denny's Franchise Owner & Operator
N.A.I.C.S.: 722511
Fara Mashhour (Owner & Pres)
Kelly Lyons (Office Mgr)

VISION GRAPHICS INC.
5610 Boeing Dr, Loveland, CO 80538
Tel.: (970) 613-0608
Web Site: http://www.visiongraphics-inc.com
Rev.: $12,000,000
Emp.: 80
Commercial Printing, Lithographic
N.A.I.C.S.: 323111
Mark Steputis (CEO)
Guy Timothy (Pres)

VISION GROUP HOLDINGS LLC
1555 Palm Beach Lakes Blvd Ste 200, West Palm Beach, FL 33401
Tel.: (561) 612-5150
Web Site: http://www.vgroupholdings.com
Laser Eye Surgery Services
N.A.I.C.S.: 621999
Ben Cook (CEO)
Carr Moody (CFO)
Ronald Antoniewicz (Sr VP-Human Capital & Professional Svcs)
John Geary (VP-Professional Dev)
Scott Kauffman (VP-Mktg)
Jonathan Simmons (VP-Sls)
Bill Tullo (VP-Clinical Svcs)
EJ Boschert (COO-Laser Eye Centers)
Ed Spear (VP-IT)
Thomas Piteo (VP-Real Estate & Procurement)
Linck Bascomb (VP-Managed Care & Group Sls)
Veronica Cardinale Ellinger (VP-Ops)
Avi Wallerstein (Dir-R&D)

Subsidiaries:
Whiting Clinic LASIK + Eye Care (1)
7415 Wayzata Blvd Ste 101, Minneapolis, MN 55426
Tel.: (952) 475-3787
Web Site: http://www.whitingclinic.com
Offices of All Other Miscellaneous Health Practitioners
N.A.I.C.S.: 621399

COMPANIES

VISION TECHNOLOGY CORP.

VISION INDUSTRIES CORP.
2230 E Artesia Blvd, Long Beach, CA 90805
Tel.: (310) 454-5658   FL
Web Site:
http://www.visionmotorcorp.com
Year Founded: 2004
Sales Range: Less than $1 Million
Emp.: 6
Electric Hybrid Vehicles Mfr
N.A.I.C.S.: 336110
Martin Schuermann *(Pres & CEO)*
Jerome Torresyap *(COO)*

VISION INTEGRATED GRAPHICS GROUP
8301 183rd St, Tinley Park, IL 60477
Tel.: (708) 429-2000
Web Site: http://www.visionps.com
Sales Range: $10-24.9 Million
Emp.: 120
Commercial Printing, Lithographic
N.A.I.C.S.: 323111
Doug Powell *(CEO)*
John Gagliano *(Exec VP-Client Svcs)*
Rick Goddard *(CTO)*

VISION INVESTMENTS, LLC
112 N 3918 E, Rigby, ID 83442-5275
Tel.: (208) 228-5834
Financial Investment Company
N.A.I.C.S.: 523999
Ryan Wolfensberger *(Owner)*
Subsidiaries:

Palm Beach Motoring Accessories, Inc.   (1)
7778 SW Ellipse Way, Stuart, FL 34997
Tel.: (772) 286-2701
Web Site:
http://www.palmbeachmotoring.net
Sales Range: $1-9.9 Million
Emp.: 11
Car Care Mail Order Sales
N.A.I.C.S.: 441330

VISION LAND CONSULTANTS, INC.
603 Park Point Dr Ste 100, Golden, CO 80401
Tel.: (303) 674-7355
Web Site:
http://www.bowmanconsulting.com
Year Founded: 1998
Sales Range: $1-9.9 Million
Emp.: 445
Civil Engineering & Construction Management Services
N.A.I.C.S.: 541330
Gary Bowman *(Pres)*

VISION MEDIA & MARKETING LLC
2310 Superior Ave E Ste 2501, Cleveland, OH 44114
Tel.: (440) 864-8774
Year Founded: 2008
Sales Range: Less than $1 Million
Emp.: 4
Advertising, Advertising Specialties, Branded Entertainment, Broadcast, Cable T.V., Commercial Photography, Graphic Design, Regional, T.V., Teen Market, Web (Banner Ads, Pop-ups, etc.)
N.A.I.C.S.: 541810
Don Gregory *(Owner)*
Alex Adzioski *(Acct Exec)*

VISION PLASTICS, INC.
26000 SW Pkwy Ctr, Wilsonville, OR 97070
Tel.: (503) 685-9000
Web Site:
http://www.visionplastics.com
Year Founded: 1988
Sales Range: $75-99.9 Million
Emp.: 130
Injection Molding Of Plastics
N.A.I.C.S.: 326199
Holly Sawyer *(Controller)*

VISION QUEST INDUSTRIES INCORPORATED
18011 Mitchell S, Irvine, CA 92614
Tel.: (949) 261-3020
Web Site:
http://www.vqorthocare.com
Year Founded: 1989
Sales Range: $25-49.9 Million
Orthopedic Supplies Mfr & Services
N.A.I.C.S.: 339113
James W. Knate *(CEO)*
Kevin Lunau *(COO)*

VISION RIDGE PARTNERS, LLC
1011 Walnut St Ste 200, Boulder, CO 80302
Tel.: (720) 616-6506   DE
Web Site: http://www.vision-ridge.com
Privater Equity Firm
N.A.I.C.S.: 523999
Reuben Munger *(Founder & Mng Partner)*
Justin Goerke *(Partner)*
Jonathan Levy *(Dir-Policy & Strategy)*
David R. Richardson *(Principal)*
Paul Luce *(Mng Dir)*
Subsidiaries:

Fjord1 ASA   (1)
Strandavegen 15, 6905, Floro, Norway
Tel.: (47) 57757000
Web Site: https://www.fjord1.no
Rev.: $264,169,222
Assets: $949,631,535
Liabilities: $712,243,396
Net Worth: $237,388,140
Earnings: $12,702,106
Emp.: 1,201
Fiscal Year-end: 12/31/2021
Tour Management Services
N.A.I.C.S.: 713990
Dagfinn Neteland *(CEO)*
Andre Hoyset *(COO)*
Anne-Mari Sundal Boe *(CFO)*
Nils Kristian Berge *(Project Dir)*
Vegard Saevik *(Chm)*
Subsidiary (Domestic):

Bolsones Verft AS   (2)
Fannestrandvegen 66, 6416, Molde, Norway
Tel.: (47) 71206400
Web Site: http://www.bolsonesverft.no
Shipyard Building Services
N.A.I.C.S.: 237990

NRG EV Services LLC   (1)
1000 N Post Oak Rd Ste 240, Houston, TX 77055
Tel.: (855) 509-5581
Web Site: http://www.nrgevgo.com
Electric Vehicle Charging Services Network Operator
N.A.I.C.S.: 221122
Arun Banskota *(Pres)*
Glen Stancil *(VP-Strategy & Products)*
Lance Boyce *(Dir-Fin)*
Terry O'Day *(VP-West Reg)*
Jeff Schoonover *(Dir-IT)*
David Davenport *(Dir-Ops)*
Brendan Jones *(Dir-East Reg)*
Jason Buckland *(Dir-Central Reg)*
Rob Barrossa *(Dir-Bus Dev)*
Paul Glenney *(Dir-New Products & Svcs)*
Cathy Zoi *(CEO)*
Jeff Ricketts *(VP-Engrg & Construction)*

Sun World International LLC   (1)
16350 Driver Rd, Bakersfield, CA 93308
Tel.: (661) 392-5000
Web Site: http://www.sun-world.com
Sales Range: $800-899.9 Million
Emp.: 905
Fruit & Vegetable Producer & Distr
N.A.I.C.S.: 111332

David Marguleas *(CEO)*
Juliana Escobar *(Dir-Export Sls)*
Jeff Jackson *(Exec VP-Bus Dev)*

VISION SECURITY LLC
508 W 800 N, Orem, UT 84057
Tel.: (801) 812-3474
Web Site:
http://www.visionhomesecurity.com
Year Founded: 2006
Sales Range: $25-49.9 Million
Emp.: 250
Security Alarm & Monitoring Services
N.A.I.C.S.: 561621
Robert Harris *(CEO)*

VISION SERVICE PLAN
3333 Quality Dr MS 163, Rancho Cordova, CA 95670
Tel.: (916) 858-7432
Web Site: http://www.vsp.com
Sales Range: $1-4.9 Billion
Eyecare Benefit Services
N.A.I.C.S.: 923120
Rob Lynch *(Interim CEO)*
Don Oakley *(Pres-VSP Optics)*
Kate Renwick-Espinosa *(Pres-VSP Vision Care)*
Bill Vaughan *(Pres-VSP Retail)*
Gordon W. Jennings *(Vice Chm)*
Matt Wickham *(Sec)*
Barbara Adachi *(Treas)*
Subsidiaries:

Eyeconic, Inc.   (1)
3333 Quality Dr, Rancho Cordova, CA 95670
Tel.: (855) 393-2664
Web Site: http://www.eyeconic.com
Optical Goods Distr
N.A.I.C.S.: 423460
Jim McGram *(CEO)*

Eyefinity, Inc.   (1)
10875 International Dr Ste 200, Rancho Cordova, CA 95670
Tel.: (916) 851-4531
Web Site: http://www.eyefinity.com
Online Eyecare Business Management Services
N.A.I.C.S.: 541618
Division (Domestic):

Officemate Software Solutions   (2)
15375 Barranca Pkwy, Irvine, CA 92618
Tel.: (949) 754-5000
Sales Range: $1-9.9 Million
Emp.: 25
Eyecare Custom Computer Programming Services
N.A.I.C.S.: 541511

Marchon Eyewear, Inc.   (1)
35 Hub Dr, Melville, NY 11747
Tel.: (631) 755-2020
Web Site: http://www.marchon.com
Sales Range: $500-549.9 Million
Emp.: 1,500
Eyewear & Sunwear Designer & Distr
N.A.I.C.S.: 423460
Al Berg *(Vice Chm)*
Larry Roth *(Pres)*
Tom O'Toole *(VP-Creative Svcs)*
Marty Fox *(COO)*
Claudio Gottardi *(CEO)*
Division (Domestic):

Altair Eyewear   (2)
10875 International Dr Ste 200, Rancho Cordova, CA 95670
Tel.: (916) 463-7500
Eyewear Products
N.A.I.C.S.: 456130
Steve Wright *(Pres)*
Subsidiary (Domestic):

Eye Designs, LLC   (2)
220 W 5th Ave, Collegeville, PA 19426
Tel.: (610) 409-1900
Optical Product Mfr
N.A.I.C.S.: 333310

Dave Oakill *(Dir-Digital Arts & CAD Graphics)*
Subsidiary (Non-US):

Marchon Germany GmbH   (2)
Kopernikusstrasse 15, Dachau, 85221, Germany
Tel.: (49) 813138350
Optical Product Mfr & Distr
N.A.I.C.S.: 456130

Marchon Hellas S.A.   (2)
160 Spanton Avenue, Pallini, 15351, Greece
Tel.: (30) 210 528 4400
Web Site: http://www.marchon.com
Optical Product Mfr & Distr
N.A.I.C.S.: 456130

Marchon Hispania, SL   (2)
Edifici Prima Muntadas Escalera A C/ Bergueda N 1 Mas Blau I, El Prat de Llobregat, 08820, Barcelona, Spain
Tel.: (34) 900 44 55 55
Eyewear Products Distr
N.A.I.C.S.: 423460

Marchon Italia S.r.l.   (2)
Viale Alpago 151 Loc Bastia, Puos d'Alpago, 32015, Belluno, Italy
Tel.: (39) 0437 476311
Web Site: http://www.marchon.com
Sales Range: $10-24.9 Million
Emp.: 50
Eyewear Distr
N.A.I.C.S.: 333310

Marchon Portugal Unipessoal LDA   (2)
Avenida D Joao II lote 1 12 02 Edificio Adamastor, Edificio B Piso 6, 1990-077, Lisbon, Portugal
Tel.: (351) 800 00110099
Optical Product Mfr & Distr
N.A.I.C.S.: 333310

Visionworks of America, Inc.   (1)
175 E Houston St, San Antonio, TX 78205
Tel.: (210) 340-3531
Web Site: http://www.visionworks.com
Sales Range: $400-449.9 Million
Emp.: 5,543
Optical Goods Retailer
N.A.I.C.S.: 456130
David L. Holmberg *(Chm & CEO)*

VISION SHARE
525 Avis Dr Ste 11, Ann Arbor, MI 48108
Tel.: (734) 887-2305   NC
Web Site: http://www.visionshare.org
Year Founded: 1998
Sales Range: $10-24.9 Million
Emp.: 11
Eye Tissue Distr
N.A.I.C.S.: 621991
Jennifer Mochinski *(Mgr-Ops)*
Philip Waitzman *(CEO)*

VISION TECHNOLOGIES, INC.
530 McCormick Dr Ste J, Glen Burnie, MD 21061
Tel.: (410) 424-2183
Web Site:
http://www.visiontechnologiesinc.net
Year Founded: 2000
Sales Range: $25-49.9 Million
Emp.: 300
Technical Services
N.A.I.C.S.: 541519
Kenny Redding *(Sr Acct Exec)*
Albert Saxon *(Sr VP-Mktg)*
Kevin Nolan *(Sr VP-Ops)*
S. Michael Quade *(CFO & Sr VP)*
Thomas Cuneo *(VP-Bus Dev)*
John Shetrone Jr. *(Pres & CEO)*

VISION TECHNOLOGY CORP.
2000 Schafer St Ste F, Bismarck, ND 58501
Tel.: (701) 222-3009
Web Site: http://www.vision-technology.com

4391

VISION TECHNOLOGY CORP.

Vision Technology Corp.—(Continued)
Sales Range: $1-9.9 Million
Emp.: 3
Custom Computer Programming Services
N.A.I.C.S.: 541511
Brad Kramer *(Gen Mgr)*

VISION WHEEL, INC.
3512 6th Ave SE, Decatur, AL 35603
Tel.: (256) 353-4957   **AL**
Web Site: http://www.visionwheel.com
Sales Range: $10-24.9 Million
Emp.: 40
Automotive Wheels Distr
N.A.I.C.S.: 423120
Roger G. Minor *(Pres)*

VISION Y COMPROMISO
2536 Edwards Ave, El Cerrito, CA 94530-1471
Tel.: (213) 613-0630   **CA**
Web Site: http://www.visionycompromiso.org
Year Founded: 2003
Sales Range: $1-9.9 Million
Emp.: 84
Workforce Development Services
N.A.I.C.S.: 561311
Nancy Marsh *(Dir-Fin)*
Hugo Ramirez *(Mgr-Program)*
Chely Romero *(Dir-Network)*
Mari Lopez *(Dir-Policy)*
Alma Esquivel *(Dir-Trng & Education)*
Maria Lemus *(Exec Dir)*
Cynthia Alvillar *(Chm)*
Barbara Ortega *(Treas)*
Mary-Anna Gonzales *(Sec)*

VISION33 INC.
6 Hughes Ste 220, Irvine, CA 92618
Tel.: (949) 420-3300
Web Site: http://www.vision33.com
Year Founded: 2004
Sales Range: $10-24.9 Million
Emp.: 80
SAP Business One Software Reseller, Including Training, Implementation & Customization
N.A.I.C.S.: 513210
Alex Rooney *(VP)*

VISIONAIRE PARTNERS
1117 Perimeter Ctr W Ste N311, Atlanta, GA 30338
Tel.: (404) 843-6965
Web Site: http://www.visionairepartners.com
Year Founded: 2008
Sales Range: $10-24.9 Million
Emp.: 24
Information Technology Staffing Consulting Services
N.A.I.C.S.: 561320
Todd Eichhorn *(Mng Partner)*
Pat Turner *(Mng Partner)*
Doug Henderson *(Mng Partner)*
Ray Stack *(Mng Partner)*

VISIONARY INTEGRATION PROFESSIONALS
80 Iron Point Cir Ste 100, Folsom, CA 95630
Tel.: (916) 985-9625
Web Site: http://www.vipconsulting.com
Year Founded: 1996
Rev.: $148,700,000
Emp.: 864
Computer Related Services
N.A.I.C.S.: 541519
Jonna A. Ward *(Founder, Chm & CEO)*
Patti Bennion *(CFO)*
Steve Carpenter *(Chief Admin Officer)*
Jeff Mullins *(COO)*
Terry Miller *(Sr Dir-Federal Bus Dev)*
Kelli Schnieder *(COO)*
Eric Martin *(VP-Federal Programs)*
Jill Peters *(Chief People Officer)*
Stacy Sakellariou *(CMO)*
Nishant Agrawal *(VP-Pub Sector)*
Mark Oliver *(Dir-Infor Practice)*

VISIONARY PRODUCTS, INC.
11814 S Election Rd Ste 200, Draper, UT 84020
Tel.: (801) 495-2310
Web Site: http://www.vpiengineering.com
Sales Range: $10-24.9 Million
Emp.: 58
Product Development & Engineering Services
N.A.I.C.S.: 541330
Kurt Jensen *(VP-Product Dev)*
Morgan Taylor *(Pres & CEO)*
Paul Hepworth *(CTO)*
Gary Olsen *(VP-Bus Dev)*
Jeremy Williams *(VP)*

VISIONARY SOLUTIONS, LLC
2553 Quality Ln, Knoxville, TN 37931
Tel.: (865) 482-8670
Web Site: http://www.vs-llc.com
Year Founded: 2000
Sales Range: $10-24.9 Million
Emp.: 41
Transportation of Radioactive Material, Hazardous Chemicals & Other High-Risk Cargo
N.A.I.C.S.: 562211
Cavanaugh Mims *(Pres)*
Dee Markelonis *(VP)*
George Taylor *(Gen Mgr-Tech Svcs)*
Jim Mowery *(Dir-Transportation)*

VISIONEERING INC.
31985 Groesbeck Hwy, Fraser, MI 48026
Tel.: (586) 293-1000
Web Site: http://www.vistool.com
Sales Range: $25-49.9 Million
Emp.: 110
Aerospace Tooling & Parts Mfr
N.A.I.C.S.: 336413
Jim Futterknecht *(CEO)*
Brad Hallett *(VP-Ops)*

VISIONIT
3031 W Grand Blvd Ste 600, Detroit, MI 48202
Tel.: (313) 664-5650
Web Site: http://www.visionit.com
Sales Range: $1-9.9 Million
Emp.: 1,000
Staffing Services
N.A.I.C.S.: 561330
David H. Segura *(CEO)*
Christine Rice *(Pres)*

VISIONSOFT INTERNATIONAL INC.
1842 Old Norcross Rd Ste 100, Lawrenceville, GA 30044
Tel.: (770) 682-2899
Web Site: http://www.vsiiusa.com
Year Founded: 1996
Sales Range: $10-24.9 Million
Emp.: 200
Computer Programming Services
N.A.I.C.S.: 541511
Antony Arputharaj *(Pres)*
Mahesh Bhat *(Engr-Software)*

VISIONSPRING
505 8th Ave Ste 12A-07, New York, NY 10018
Tel.: (212) 375-2599   **NY**
Web Site: http://www.visionspring.org
Year Founded: 2001
Sales Range: $1-9.9 Million
Emp.: 9
Visually Impaired People Care Services
N.A.I.C.S.: 623990
Nira Jethani *(VP-Fin & Admin-Global)*
Reade Fahs *(Co-Chm)*
Jordan Kassalow *(Founder & Co-Chm)*
Jorge Kreitz *(Dir-Central America)*
Chris Calvosa *(VP-Sls & Institutional Partnerships-Global)*
Ella Gudwin *(Founder)*
Anshu Taneja *(VP-Sls & Institutional Partnerships-Global)*

VISISTAT, INC.
2290 N 1st St Ste102, Campbell, CA 95008
Tel.: (408) 458-9981
Web Site: http://www.visistat.com
Year Founded: 2003
Sales Range: $1-9.9 Million
Emp.: 20
Marketing Software
N.A.I.C.S.: 513210
Stephen Oachs *(Pres)*

VISIT INDY, INC.
200 S Capitol Ave Ste 300, Indianapolis, IN 46225-1063
Tel.: (317) 262-3000   **IN**
Web Site: http://www.visitindy.com
Year Founded: 1932
Sales Range: $10-24.9 Million
Emp.: 67
Convention & Visitor Bureau Services
N.A.I.C.S.: 561591
Matthew B. Carter *(VP-Destination Dev & Exec Dir-Music Crossroads)*
Chris Gahl *(VP-Mktg & Comm)*
Daren Kingi *(Sr VP-Sls)*
James E. Wallis *(Exec VP)*
Janet Arnold *(VP-Partner Rels)*
Demi Barton *(Coord-Svcs)*
Elizabeth Huston *(Mgr-Sls)*
Joe Rivelli *(Mgr-Bus Dev)*
Leonard Hoops *(Pres & CEO)*
Dustin Arnheim *(Dir-Convention Sales)*
Diane J. Whitsitt *(Dir-Sls Admin)*
Janet L. Moritz *(Mgr-Production)*
Judy Thomas *(Dir-Convention Sales)*
Ryan Barth *(Mgr-Sls-Natl)*
Erin Morgan *(Mgr-Visual Comm)*

VISIT NAPA VALLEY
1001 2nd St Ste 330, Napa, CA 94559
Tel.: (707) 226-5813   **CA**
Web Site: http://www.visitnapavalley.com
Year Founded: 1990
Sales Range: $25-49.9 Million
Emp.: 20
Tour Operator
N.A.I.C.S.: 561510
Catherine Heywood *(Dir-Ops)*
Emily Hegarty *(Dir-Mktg)*
Teresa Savage *(VP-Sls)*
Stephen Corley *(Treas & Sec)*
Linsey Gallagher *(Pres & CEO)*
Stan Boyd *(Vice Chm)*
Lisa Poppen *(VP-Mktg & Comm)*

VISIT ORLANDO
6277 Sea Harbour Dr Ste 400, Orlando, FL 32821-8087
Tel.: (407) 363-5800
Web Site: http://www.visitorlando.com
Sales Range: $50-74.9 Million
Emp.: 173
Orlando Marketing & Promotion
N.A.I.C.S.: 561591
Danielle Courtenay *(CMO)*
Deborah Henrichs *(VP-Interactive & Print Support Svcs)*
Larry Henrichs *(CFO & COO)*
Karen Soto *(VP-HR)*
Sheryl Taylor *(VP-Member Bus Dev)*
Fred Shea *(Sr VP-Convention Sls & Svcs)*
Elaine Blazys *(Assoc VP-Travel Indus Sls)*
Jeff Braswell *(VP-Digital Strategy & Mktg)*
Stephanie Naegele *(VP-Sls Ops)*
Kristen Darby *(Sr VP-Membership & Support Svcs)*
Michael D. Waterman *(Chief Sls Officer)*
Casandra Matej *(CEO)*
Brian Comes *(Chm)*

VISITALK CAPITAL CORPORATION
9830 51st St Ste A128, Phoenix, AZ 85044
Tel.: (480) 759-9400   **AZ**
Web Site: http://visitalkcapital.com
Year Founded: 1999
Sales Range: $10-24.9 Million
Emp.: 2
Online Service Providers
N.A.I.C.S.: 541511
Stephen Best *(Gen Counsel & VP)*
Lanny Lang *(CFO)*

Subsidiaries:

House of Jane, Inc.   (1)
1 N 1st St Ste 654, Phoenix, AZ 85004
Tel.: (602) 688-9981
Web Site: https://www.hojinc.com
Emp.: 5
Grocery Product Distr
N.A.I.C.S.: 424490
Frederic J. Buonincontri *(Pres)*

VISITECH, INC.
2000 E 21st Ave, Denver, CO 80205
Tel.: (303) 752-3552
Web Site: http://www.visitechpr.com
Year Founded: 1998
Sales Range: Less than $1 Million
Emp.: 10
Public Relations Agency
N.A.I.C.S.: 541820
Lisa Wilson *(CEO)*

VISITING NURSE & HOSPICE OF FAIRFIELD COUNTY
761 Main Ave, Norwalk, CT 06851
Tel.: (203) 762-8958   **CT**
Web Site: http://www.visitingnurse.net
Year Founded: 1982
Sales Range: $10-24.9 Million
Emp.: 281
Elder Care Services
N.A.I.C.S.: 623312
Christine Pfeffer *(Dir-Hospice)*
Mary Ross *(Dir-Clinical)*
Christopher Cardone *(Dir-Fin)*

VISITING NURSE & HOSPICE OF VERMONT AND NEW HAMPSHIRE
66 Benning St Ste 6, West Lebanon, NH 03784-3407
Tel.: (603) 298-8399   **VT**
Web Site: http://www.vnhcare.org
Year Founded: 1907
Sales Range: $10-24.9 Million
Emp.: 279
Horse Association
N.A.I.C.S.: 813920
Johanna Beliveau *(CEO)*
Steve Whitman *(Vice Chm)*
Gary Mayo *(Chm)*

COMPANIES

VISITING NURSE ASSOCIATION OF SOMERSET HILLS INC.
200 Mount Airy Rd, Basking Ridge, NJ 07920
Tel.: (908) 766-0180
Web Site: http://www.visitingnurse.org
Year Founded: 1904
Rev.: $6,000,000
Emp.: 135
Women Healthcare Services
N.A.I.C.S.: 621610
Marie Sperber (Dir-Dev & Mktg)
Daniel E. Powell (Pres & CEO)

VISITING NURSE ASSOCIATION OF SOUTH CENTRAL CONNECTICUT
1 Long Wharf Dr Ste 501, New Haven, CT 06511
Tel.: (203) 777-5521 CT
Web Site: http://www.vnascc.org
Year Founded: 1904
Sales Range: $10-24.9 Million
Emp.: 222
Women Healthcare Services
N.A.I.C.S.: 621610
Carla Giugno (VP-Clinical Svcs)
Margaret T. Firla (VP-Ops)

VISITING NURSE ASSOCIATION OF STATEN ISLAND
400 Lake Ave, Staten Island, NY 10303
Tel.: (718) 816-3500
Web Site: http://www.vnasi.org
Year Founded: 1917
Rev.: $20,823,699
Emp.: 155
Women Healthcare Services
N.A.I.C.S.: 561990
Calvin C. Sprung (Pres & CEO)
William A. Bloom (CFO)
Audrey Penney (COO)
Lois Moses (VP-Quality Improvement)
David W. Lehr (Chm)

VISITING NURSE CORPORATION OF COLORADO, INC.
390 Grant St, Denver, CO 80203
Tel.: (303) 698-2121 CO
Web Site: http://www.vnacolorado.org
Year Founded: 1904
Sales Range: $10-24.9 Million
Emp.: 480
Horse Association
N.A.I.C.S.: 813920
Donna Walsh (CFO)
David Schrier (Dir-Hospice Medical)
Brenda Garrett (Dir-HR)
Christopher Lee (Pres & CEO)
Lora Daughtry (Dir-Nursing)
Jodie Deshmukh (Mgr-Dev)
Tara Fitzgerald (Mgr-Program)
Paul Tosetti (CFO)

VISITING NURSE SERVICE & HOSPICE OF SUFFOLK, INC.
505 Main St, Northport, NY 11768
Tel.: (631) 261-7200 NY
Web Site: http://www.visitingnurseservice.org
Year Founded: 1952
Sales Range: $10-24.9 Million
Emp.: 224
Nursing Care Services
N.A.I.C.S.: 623110
Scott Schafer (Dir-Info Svcs)
Linda Taylor (CEO)
Hillary Hoffman (Dir-Mktg Comm)
Steven Moller (CFO)

VISITING NURSE SERVICE AT ST. FRANCIS, INC.
4701 N Keystone Ave, Indianapolis, IN 46205
Tel.: (317) 722-8200 IN
Web Site: http://www.vnsi.org
Year Founded: 1983
Sales Range: $10-24.9 Million
Emp.: 209
Community Health Care Services
N.A.I.C.S.: 621498
Charles James (Treas)
Marlene Shapley (Sec)
Robert Brody (Chm)

VISITING NURSE SERVICE OF NEW YORK
107 E 70th St, New York, NY 10021-5006
Tel.: (212) 609-1500
Web Site: http://www.vnsny.org
Year Founded: 1893
Sales Range: $1-4.9 Billion
Emp.: 15,300
Home & Community-Based Health Care
N.A.I.C.S.: 621610
Michael Bernstein (Chief Admin Officer & Exec VP)
John P. Rafferty (Chm)
Lester Schindel (Exec VP)
Andria Castellanos (Exec VP)
Daniel Savitt (CFO & Exec VP)
David Rosales (Chief Strategy Officer & Exec VP)
Hany Abdelaal (Pres)
Kerry Parker (Chief Risk Officer, Gen Counsel & Exec VP)
Marki Flannery (Pres & CEO)

Subsidiaries:

Partners In Care Inc. (1)
1250 Broadway, New York, NY 10001
Tel.: (212) 609-7750
Web Site: http://www.partnersincareny.org
Health Care Srvices
N.A.I.C.S.: 621999
Anne Ehrenkranz (Vice Chm)
Jon E. Mattson (Chm)

Subsidiary (Domestic):

Partners In Care Maryland, Inc. (2)
8151c Ritchie Hwy, Pasadena, MD 21122
Tel.: (410) 544-4800
Web Site: http://www.partnersincare.org
Emp.: 20
Health Care Srvices
N.A.I.C.S.: 621999
Jim Brennan (Chm)
Rick Powell (Treas & VP)
Christine Beam (Asst Mgr-Boutique)
Lynn Bujanowski (Asst Mgr-Boutique)
Barb Cooke (Dir-Ops)
Tracey Dill (Asst Mgr-Boutique)
Kevin Engler (Partner-Ride & Mgr-Mobility)
Matt Jermann (Mgr-Mobility)
Ashley Johnson (Mgr-Member Care)
Mandy Arnold (Pres & CEO)

VNSNY CHOICE (1)
1250 Broadway 11th Fl, New York, NY 10001
Web Site: http://www.vnsnychoice.org
Health Care Srvices
N.A.I.C.S.: 621999
Romy Martinez (Coord-Medical Mgmt)
Diane Novy (Dir-Hospital & IPA Contracting)
Jay Dobkin (Dir-Medical)
Eli Camhi (Exec Dir-Select Health & Special Populations)
Marisol Vega Beecham (Mgr-Medical Mgmt)
May Schee (VP-Network Dev & Contracting)

Visiting Nurse Association of Central Jersey (1)
188 E Bergen Pl, Red Bank, NJ 07701-1014
Tel.: (732) 219-6620
Web Site: http://www.vnachc.org
Sales Range: $150-199.9 Million
Emp.: 1,000
Women Healthcare Services

N.A.I.C.S.: 561990
Brian T. Griffin (Chm)
Frank Vigilante (Sec)
Patrick McMenamin (Vice Chm)
John Chiappinelli (Asst Sec)
Steven Landers (Pres & CEO)
Vincent Zales (Vice Chm)
Ronald Klein (Treas)

VISITING NURSE SERVICES IN WESTCHESTER, INC.
360 Mamaroneck Ave, White Plains, NY 10605
Tel.: (914) 682-1480
Web Site: http://www.vns.org
Year Founded: 1901
Rev.: $12,000,000
Emp.: 125
Healtcare Services
N.A.I.C.S.: 621610
Suzanne Moses (Dir-Patient Svcs)
Deborah R. Gogliettino (Dir-HR)
Mary Gadomski (Dir-Bus Dev & Community Rels)
Joyce Infante (Dir-Dev)
Amy Ansehl (Chm)
Andrea McKay-Harris (Sec)
Nancy Rudolph (Treas)
Debra Swee (Vice Chm)

VISITING NURSE SERVICES OF NEWPORT AND BRISTOL COUNTIES
1184 E Main Rd, Portsmouth, RI 02871
Tel.: (401) 682-2100 RI
Web Site: http://www.vnsri.org
Year Founded: 1950
Sales Range: $10-24.9 Million
Emp.: 280
Nursing Care Services
N.A.I.C.S.: 623110
Candace Sharkey (CEO)
Therese Champion-Welford (Dir-Rehabilitation)
Aaron Pugatch (CFO)
Joan Silva (Dir-IT)
Matthew Burns (Dir-HR)
Jan Gordon (Dir-Mktg & Fund Dev)
Melanie McGinn (Dir-Hospice & Palliative Care)
Stephanie Mediate (Dir-Rehabilitation)
Susan Dugan (Dir-Quality)
Jill Ott (Dir-Reimburse & Authorization)
Rachel Carr (Dir-Homecare Nursing)
Stacey Carter (Pres)

VISIUM RESOURCES, INC.
541 S Orlando Ave, Maitland, FL 32751
Tel.: (321) 397-1016
Web Site: http://www.myvisium.com
Year Founded: 2002
Sales Range: $1-9.9 Million
Emp.: 60
Human Resources & Executive Search Consulting Services
N.A.I.C.S.: 541612
Bob Johns (Dir-Bus Dev)
Michael Forster (Owner)

VISIX, INC.
230 Scientific Dr Ste 800, Norcross, GA 30092
Tel.: (770) 446-1416
Web Site: http://www.visix.com
Year Founded: 1980
Sales Range: $1-9.9 Million
Emp.: 40
Communication Equipment Mfr
N.A.I.C.S.: 334290
Sean Matthews (Pres)

VISNIC HOMES, INC.
1684 E Gude Dr Ste 102, Rockville, MD 20850
Tel.: (301) 309-6470
Web Site: http://www.visnichomes.com
Year Founded: 2004
Sales Range: $10-24.9 Million
Emp.: 15
Housing Construction Services
N.A.I.C.S.: 236117
Kathleen R. McAleer (Controller)
Theodore Visnic (Owner)

VISP.NET
301 NE 6th St, Grants Pass, OR 97526
Tel.: (541) 955-6900
Web Site: http://www.visp.net
Year Founded: 1989
Sales Range: $1-9.9 Million
Emp.: 12
Internet Host Services
N.A.I.C.S.: 518210
Todd Grannis (Founder & CEO)
Nathan Miller (Pres & CTO)
Dave Thomas (Dir-Client Rels)

VISSERING CONSTRUCTION CO.
175 Benchmark Industrial Dr, Streator, IL 61364-9485
Tel.: (815) 673-5511
Web Site: http://www.vissering.com
Year Founded: 1986
Sales Range: $25-49.9 Million
Emp.: 200
Nonresidential Construction Services
N.A.I.C.S.: 236220
Al Slagel (Pres)

VISTA BANK
5840 W Northwest Hwy, Dallas, TX 75225
Tel.: (214) 416-8300 TX
Web Site: http://www.vistabank.com
Year Founded: 1912
Sales Range: $1-9.9 Million
Emp.: 21
Commericial Banking
N.A.I.C.S.: 522110
Kirk McLaughlin (Pres)
Cheryl Martin (VP)
Dana Marlar (Asst VP)
Jeff Rogers (Pres)
Kayla Altman (Dir-Mktg)
Kelly Wing (Pres)
Kyle Benson (Sr VP)
Matt Wilmeth (VP)
Mike Cary (Center Pres)
Randy Runquist (COO)
Stephanie Barton (Asst VP)
Toby Cecil (Asst VP)

VISTA CAPITAL LLC
80 Field Point Rd, Greenwich, CT 06830-6416
Tel.: (203) 622-6600 DE
Sales Range: $10-24.9 Million
Emp.: 6
Investment Company: Specializing on the Acquisition of Under Performing & Low Technology Manufacturing Consumer Companies
N.A.I.C.S.: 522292
Maurice J. Cunniffe (Chm & CEO)

VISTA CLINICAL DIAGNOSTICS, LLC
4290 S Hwy 27 Ste 201, Clermont, FL 34711
Tel.: (352) 536-9270 FL
Web Site: http://www.vista-clinical.com
Medical Laboratory & Clinical Diagnostic Services
N.A.I.C.S.: 621511

VISTA CLINICAL DIAGNOSTICS, LLC

U.S. PRIVATE

Vista Clinical Diagnostics, LLC—(Continued)
Davian Santana (Founder & Pres)

VISTA COLOR CORPORATION
1401 NW 78th Ave, Miami, FL 33126
Tel.: (305) 635-2000
Web Site: http://www.vistacolor.com
Year Founded: 1968
Sales Range: $50-74.9 Million
Emp.: 90
Provider of Offset Printing Services
N.A.I.C.S.: 323111
Henry Serrano (Pres)
Lola Hernandez (Coord-Production)
Israel Mendez (Owner)
Hernandez Maria (Mgr-Quality Sys)
Enrique Tefel (VP-Pur & Estimating)

VISTA CREDIT STRATEGIC LENDING CORP.
50 Hudson Yards Fl 77, New York, NY 10001
Tel.: (212) 804-9100   MD
Web Site: https://www.vistastrategiclending.com
Year Founded: 2022
Rev.: $780,000
Assets: $172,277,000
Liabilities: $97,600,000
Net Worth: $74,677,000
Earnings: ($1,515,000)
Fiscal Year-end: 12/31/23
Investment Management Service
N.A.I.C.S.: 523999
David Flannery (Pres)

VISTA DEL MAR CHILD AND FAMILY SERVICES
3200 Motor Ave, Los Angeles, CA 90034
Tel.: (310) 836-1223   CA
Web Site: http://www.vistadelmar.org
Year Founded: 1908
Sales Range: $25-49.9 Million
Emp.: 656
Behavioral Healthcare Services
N.A.I.C.S.: 623220
Susan Schmidt-Lackner (Dir-Medical)
Amy Jaffe (Sr VP-Intensive Intervention Programs)
Don McLellan (Exec VP-Bus & Fin)
Marla Kantor (Vice Chm)
Janis Black Warner (Sec)
Craig Prizant (VP-Dev & Mktg)
Leslie Askanas (VP-HR)
Nancy Tallerino (Pres & CEO)
Didi Watts (VP-Education)

VISTA DIRECT
21611 Ventura Blvd, Woodland Hills, CA 91364
Tel.: (818) 884-7600
Web Site: http://www.vistaauto.com
Sales Range: $125-149.9 Million
Emp.: 135
Automobiles, New & Used
N.A.I.C.S.: 441110
Carl Tasi (Controller)
John Schuken (Pres)

VISTA EQUITY PARTNERS, LLC
4 Embarcadero Ctr 20th Fl, San Francisco, CA 94111
Tel.: (415) 765-6500   DE
Web Site: http://www.vistaequitypartners.com
Year Founded: 2000
Rev.: $95,000,000,000
Privater Equity Firm
N.A.I.C.S.: 523999
Michael Fosnaugh (Sr Mng Dir-Private Equity)
James P. Hickey (Co-Head-Vista's Perennial Fund & Sr Mng Dir)
Marc Teillon (Sr Mng Dir-Private Equity-Foundation)
Ryan Atlas (Mng Dir-Private Equity-Foundation)
Burke F. Norton (Sr Mng Dir)
Justin Cho (Mng Dir-Private Equity-Endeavor)
Adrian Alonso (Mng Dir-Private Equity-Flagship-Chicago)
John Stalder (Mng Dir)
Rachel Arnold (Sr Mng Dir-Private Equity-Endeavor)
Bret Bolin (Mng Dir-Private Equity-Foundation)
Rene Yang Stewart (Sr Mng Dir-Private Equity-Endeavor)
William P. Bosworth (Mng Dir-Operating)
Kim Eaton (Mng Dir-Private Equity-Foundation)
Thomas Hogan (Mng Dir-Private Equity-Foundation)
Jamie Holden (Sr VP-Ops-Private Equity-Endeavor)
Doug Owens (Sr VP-Ops-Private Equity-Flagship)
Ben Benson (VP-Private Equity-Endeavor)
Stephen Foster (VP-Private Equity-Foundation)
Aaron Gupta (VP-Private Equity-Foundation)
Derek Klomhaus (VP-Private Equity-Foundation)
Sam Payton (VP-Flagship Fund)
Dan Sullivan (VP-Private Equity-Foundation)
Darko Dejanovic (Mng Dir-Private Equity-Foundation)
Fareed Adib (Mng Dir)
Maneet S. Saroya (Sr Mng Dir & Co-Head-Flagship Fund)
Nadeem Syed (Sr Mng Dir)
Nicolas Stahl (Sr VP)
Cheryl Leahy (Mng Dir-Capital & Partner Solutions)
Jessi Marshall (Mng Dir-Mktg)
Amy Mathews (Mng Dir & Head-Venture Capital Coverage-Vista Credit Partners)
Amy Mathews (Mng Dir & Head-Venture Capital Coverage-Vista Credit Partners)
Drew Tate (Mng Dir-Capital & Partner Solutions)
Steven White (Mng Dir-Private Equity-Flagship Fund)
Lauren Dillard (Sr Mng Dir & CFO)
David A. Breach (Pres & COO)
Lauren B. Dillard (Sr Mng Dir & CFO)
Maneet Saroya (Sr Mng Dir/Head-Flagship Fund)
Martin Taylor (Mng Dir & Pres-OneVista)
Robert F. Smith (Founder, Chm & CEO)
Betty Hung (Mng Dir)

Subsidiaries:

Accelya Holding World SL (1)
Avda Diagonal 567 3rd floor, 08029, Barcelona, Spain
Tel.: (34) 93 487 86 47
Web Site: http://w3.accelya.com
Information Technology Products And Services Provider
N.A.I.C.S.: 519290
John Johnston (Chm)
Jose Maria Hurtado (Acting CEO & CFO)
James Fernandez (Chief Comml Officer)
Eric Selvadurai (Exec VP-Accelya Managed Svcs)
Berry Van Veldhoven (Chief HR Officer)
Susan Boulton (Exec VP-Corp Mgmt & Planning)
Neela Bhattacherjee (Exec VP-Financial Solutions)
Brian Collins (Chief Technology Officer)
Jim Davidson (Chief Product Officer)
Tye Radcliffe (VP-Product Strategy)
Mario Segovia Sman (VP-Comml-Middle East)
Bryan Porter (Sr VP-Comml-Europe, Middle East & Africa)
Andrew Wilcock (Chief Revenue Officer)

Subsidiary (US):

Farelogix Inc. (2)
760 NW 107 Ave Ste 300, Miami, FL 33172
Tel.: (305) 552-6094
Web Site: http://www.farelogix.com
Airline Commerce Technology Software Developer
N.A.I.C.S.: 541511
Edna Wehby Lopez (Gen Counsel & Sr VP)
Theodorus Kruijssen (CFO & Treas)
Tim Reiz (CTO)
Susan Carter (Sr VP-Mktg)
John Stewart (Sr VP-Sls)
Jeff Mathew (Sr VP-Ops)
Manish Nagpal (VP-Global Sls Engrg)
Vitali Ruppel (VP-Product Dev, Architecture & Airline Solutions)
Nate Ranasinghe (VP-Offer Engines)
Michael Zumdieck (VP-Product Sls & Consultancy)

Acquia Inc. (1)
53 State St, Boston, MA 01803
Tel.: (781) 238-8600
Web Site: http://www.acquia.com
Sales Range: $25-49.9 Million
Emp.: 160
Software Developer
N.A.I.C.S.: 513210
Joe Wykes (VP-Global Channels)
Michael Cayer (Gen Counsel)
Christopher Stone (Chief Products Officer)
Heather Hartford (Chief People Officer)
Graham Sowden (Gen Mgr)
Tom Cochran (VP-Pub Sector)
Chris Andersen (CFO)
Stephen Reny (COO)
Mike Sullivan (CEO)
Matt Kaplan (Sr VP-Product)
Chris Doggett (Chief Revenue Officer)

Subsidiary (Non-US):

Acquia Australia (2)
Building 34 Suakin Drive, Mosman, 2088, NSW, Australia
Tel.: (61) 2 8815 8185
Software Developer
N.A.I.C.S.: 513210

Acquia UK (2)
John Eccles House Robert Robinson Avenue, Oxford, OX4 4GP, Oxon, United Kingdom
Tel.: (44) 1865 520 010
Software Developer
N.A.I.C.S.: 513210
Martyn Eley (Gen Mgr-EMEA)
Stephan Weiland (Dir-Sls-Germany, Austria & Switzerland)
Fredrik Blomqvist (Mgr-Sls-Nordics)

Subsidiary (Domestic):

AgilOne Inc. (2)
1091 N Shoreline Blvd, Mountain View, CA 94043
Tel.: (877) 769-3047
Web Site: http://www.agilone.com
Emp.: 100
Predictive Marketing Software Developer
N.A.I.C.S.: 513210
Omer Artun (CEO)
Saravanan Chettiar (VP-Fin)
Joe Mancini (Sr Dir-Product)
Ted Farrell (CTO)
Dan Moore (VP-Customer Success)
Gangadhar Konduri (Chief Product Officer)
Steve McDermott (VP-Sls)
Mike Weller (VP-Bus Dev)

Widen Enterprises Inc. (2)
6911 Mangrove Ln, Madison, WI 53713
Tel.: (608) 222-1296
Web Site: http://www.widen.com
Premedia & Web-Based Digital Asset Management Software Services
N.A.I.C.S.: 541512
Brian Becker (VP-Customer Dev)
Matthew Gonnering (CEO)
Jeffrey Abel (Mgr-Production & Scheduling)
Jacob Athey (Dir-Mktg)
Deanna Ballew (Dir-Product Mgmt)
Michael Kiesler (CFO)
Ben Dotte (Mgr-Software Dev)
Lanita Haag (Dir-Customer Support)
Nathan Holmes (Mktg Mgr)
Annette Jensen (Dir-Software Engrg)
Michael Orear (Mgr-Customer Experience)
Dustin Pence (Mgr-Customer Experience)
Rebecca Running (Mgr-Customer Experience)
Rome Wieser (Dir-Content Production)

ActiveOutdoors (1)
10182 Telesis Ct Ste 300, San Diego, CA 92121
Tel.: (858) 964-3800
Web Site: http://www.activeoutdoorsolutions.com
Technology & Marketing Solutions for State Recreation
N.A.I.C.S.: 541519

Advanced Computer Software Group Limited (1)
Ditton Park Riding Court Road Datchet, Slough, SL3 9LL, Berkshire, United Kingdom
Tel.: (44) 8451 606 162
Web Site: http://www.advcomputersoftware.com
Software & Information Technology Services
N.A.I.C.S.: 513210
Gordon Wilson (CEO)
Andrew Hicks (CFO)
Jon Wrennall (CTO)
Andy Williams (Head-Pro Svcs)
Shirley Wilson (Mgr-Scheduling)
Neil Barrett (Mgr-Community Product Support)
Dominic Barratt (Acct Mgr)
Phil Lea (Head-Security & Compliance)

Subsidiary (Domestic):

Advanced Business Solutions (2)
Munro House, Portsmouth Road, Cobham, KT11 1TF, Surrey, United Kingdom (100%)
Tel.: (44) 1932584000
Web Site: http://www.coasolutions.com
Sales Range: $25-49.9 Million
Business Software & Consultancy
N.A.I.C.S.: 449210
Paul Gibson (Dir-Fin)
Simon Fowler (Mng Dir-Comml)
Sally Brown (Dir-HR)
Nick Wilson (Mng Dir)

Advanced Health & Care (2)
210 Eureka Park Upper Pemberton, Ashford, TN25 4AZ, Kent, United Kingdom
Tel.: (44) 1233722700
Web Site: http://www.advancedcomputersoftware.com
Sales Range: $50-74.9 Million
Emp.: 200
Application Software Development Services
N.A.I.C.S.: 513210
Alex Yeates (Dir-Medical)
Emma Dew (Dir-Mktg)
George Thaw (Mng Dir)

Business Systems Holdings Group Plc (2)
BSG House 226-236 City Road, London, EC1V 2TT, United Kingdom
Tel.: (44) 2078808888
Web Site: http://www.advanced365.com
Sales Range: $25-49.9 Million
Information Technology Outsourcing Services
N.A.I.C.S.: 541512
Neil Cross (Mng Dir)

Healthy Software Ltd. (2)
Pacific House The Wyvern Business Park, Stanier Way, Derby, DE21 6BF, United Kingdom
Tel.: (44) 1332680022
Web Site: http://www.healthysoftware.co.uk
Medical Application Software Development Services
N.A.I.C.S.: 541511

StaffPlan Ltd. (2)
BSG House 226-236 City Rd, London, EC1V 2QY, United Kingdom

COMPANIES

Tel.: (44) 2087728773
Web Site: http://www.advancedcomputersoftware.com
Monitoring System Software Publishers
N.A.I.C.S.: 513210
Ian Horman *(Mgr-Bus Dev)*
Carrie Goodbourn *(Dir-Bus Dev)*
Jim Chase *(Mng Dir)*

Tikit Group plc (2)
12 Gough Square, London, EC4A 3DW, United Kingdom
Tel.: (44) 2074003737
Web Site: http://www.tikit.com
Software Development Services
N.A.I.C.S.: 541511
Simon Hill *(COO)*
Katherine Ainley *(CEO)*

Alegeus Technologies, LLC (1)
1601 Trapelo Rd, Waltham, MA 02451
Tel.: (781) 895-4900
Web Site: http://www.alegeus.com
Healthcare Benefit Administration & Payment Processing Services
N.A.I.C.S.: 524292
Roy S. Luria *(Gen Counsel & Sec)*
Anna Lyons *(Chief Talent Officer)*
John R. Defeo *(Chief Dev Officer & Chief Technology Operations Officer)*
Mark Waterstraat *(Chief Customer Officer)*
Melanie Hallenbeck *(Chief Growth Officer)*
Leif O'Leary *(CEO)*
Dan Brames *(Chief Payments Officer)*
Brian Colburn *(Chief Strategy Officer)*

Applause App Quality, Inc. (1)
100 Pennsylvania Ave Ste 500, Framingham, MA 01701
Tel.: (508) 861-7142
Web Site: http://www.applause.com
Software Testing Services
N.A.I.C.S.: 541511
Doron Reuveni *(Founder, Chm & CEO)*
Chris Malone *(CEO)*
Tom Bonos *(Chief Revenue Officer)*
Jan Wolter *(Gen Mgr-Applause Eu)*
Luke Damia *(Sr VP)*
Lisa Landa *(CMO)*
Rob Mason *(CTO)*
Kristin Simonini *(VP-Product)*
Mark Granot *(Gen Mgr-Applause Israel)*

Autotask Corporation (1)
26 Tech Valley Dr Ste 2, East Greenbush, NY 12061
Tel.: (518) 720-3500
Web Site: http://www.autotask.com
Sales Range: $10-24.9 Million
Business Software Developer
N.A.I.C.S.: 513210
Adam Stewart *(Sr VP-Engrg)*
Walt Mykins *(VP-Client Svcs)*

Subsidiary (Non-US):

Autotask (UK) Limited (2)
Ambassador House Paradise Road, Richmond, TW9 1SQ, Surrey, United Kingdom
Tel.: (44) 203 006 3147
Business Software Developer
N.A.I.C.S.: 513210

Subsidiary (Domestic):

Soonr, Inc. (2)
150 S Almaden Blvd Ste 1050, San Jose, CA 95113
Tel.: (408) 377-8500
Web Site: http://www.soonr.com
Emp.: 11
Information Technology Services
N.A.I.C.S.: 541512
Ahmet Tuncay *(CEO)*
Sam Liu *(VP-Mktg)*

Avalara, Inc. (1)
255 S King St Ste 1200, Seattle, WA 98104
Web Site: https://www.avalara.com
Rev.: $698,977,000
Assets: $2,698,531,000
Liabilities: $1,672,077,000
Net Worth: $1,026,454,000
Earnings: ($125,233,000)
Emp.: 4,465
Fiscal Year-end: 12/31/2021
Sales Tax Automation Software
N.A.I.C.S.: 513210
Scott M. McFarlane *(Founder & CEO)*
Tim Diekmann *(Sr VP & Chief Architect)*

Denis Gulsen *(Sr VP-Engineering)*
Meg Higgins *(Sr VP-Global Partners)*
Masa Karahashi *(Sr VP-Engineering)*
Marcus Larner *(Sr VP-Engineering)*
Milosh Nedic *(Sr VP-Finance & Accounting)*
Kevin Sellers *(CMO & Exec VP)*
Vsu Subramanian *(Sr VP-Engineering)*

Subsidiary (Non-US):

Avalara Technologies Pvt. Ltd. (2)
3rd Floor Pride Portal Shivaji Co-operative Housing Society, Bahiratwadi Shivajinagar, Pune, 411 016, India
Tel.: (91) 9175366744
Sales Tax Automation Software
N.A.I.C.S.: 513210
Sudhir Singh *(Mng Dir)*

Subsidiary (Domestic):

Compli, Inc. (2)
1650 Ramada Dr Ste 180, Paso Robles, CA 93446
Tel.: (805) 239-4502
Emp.: 100
Alcoholic Beverages Whslr & Distr
N.A.I.C.S.: 424820

Subsidiary (Non-US):

Impendulo Limited (2)
85 Gresham Street, London, EC2V 7NQ, United Kingdom
Tel.: (44) 2030087955
Web Site: http://www.impendulo.com
Insurance Services
N.A.I.C.S.: 524210
Chris James *(Mng Dir)*
Jayne-Ann Coombe *(Dir-Ops)*
Nick Manias *(Dir-Tech)*
Susannah James *(Office Mgr)*

Portway International Inc. (2)
Central Oakville Suite 2400, Oakville, L6J 7R4, ON, Canada
Tel.: (905) 997-8155
Web Site: http://www.portwayintl.com
Business Process Outsourcing
N.A.I.C.S.: 561422
Jonathan Robinson *(Co-Founder & CEO)*

Benchmark Digital Partners LLC (1)
5181 Natorp Blvd Ste 610, Mason, OH 45040
Tel.: (513) 774-1000
Web Site: https://benchmarkgensuite.com
Software Publisher
N.A.I.C.S.: 513210

Subsidiary (Domestic):

Anvl, Inc. (2)
11787 Lantern Rd Ste 202, Fishers, IN 46038
Web Site: https://anvl.com
Motor Vehicle Parts Mfr
N.A.I.C.S.: 336390

BigTime Software, Inc. (1)
1 S Wacker Ste 2920, Chicago, IL 60606
Tel.: (312) 346-3123
Web Site: http://www.bigtimesoftware.net
Software & Technology Development Services
N.A.I.C.S.: 513210
Brian Saunders *(Founder & CEO)*
Derek Slayton *(COO)*
Pete Smith *(VP-Sls)*

Subsidiary (Domestic):

Projector PSA, Inc. (2)
85 Merrimac St, Boston, MA 02114
Tel.: (617) 431-4111
Web Site: http://www.projectorpsa.com
Custom Computer Programming Services
N.A.I.C.S.: 541511
Jeff Richman *(Founder & VP-Engrg)*

Black Mountain Systems, LLC (1)
12526 High Bluff Dr Ste 160, San Diego, CA 92130
Tel.: (858) 866-8989
Web Site: http://www.blackmountainsystems.com
Sales Range: $1-9.9 Million
Emp.: 74
Financial Investment Advisory Services
N.A.I.C.S.: 523940

Kevin MacDonald *(CEO)*
Wayne Elpus *(CIO)*
Steve Miller *(Chm)*

CentralSquare Technologies, LLC (1)
1000 Business Ctr Dr, Lake Mary, FL 32746
Tel.: (800) 727-8088
Web Site: http://www.centralsquare.com
Software Publisher
N.A.I.C.S.: 513210
Tom Amburgey *(Sr VP & Gen Mgr-Pub Admin)*
Jatin Atre *(Chief Mktg Officer)*
Jeff Davison *(COO)*
John Pulling *(CTO)*
Chris Schwartz *(Chief Revenue Officer)*
Steve Seoane *(Exec VP & Gen Mgr-Pub Safety)*
Mandy Clark *(Chief HR Officer)*
Amir Siddiqi *(Chief Customer Officer)*

Subsidiary (Domestic):

Superion Public Sector, LLC (2)
1000 Business Center Dr, Lake Mary, FL 32746-5585
Web Site: http://www.superion.com
Software & Information Technology Solutions
N.A.I.C.S.: 513210

TriTech Software Systems Inc. (2)
9477 Watles Ste 100, San Diego, CA 92121
Tel.: (858) 799-7000
Web Site: http://www.tritech.com
Public Safety Software Developer
N.A.I.C.S.: 513210
Blake Clark *(CFO)*
Terri Jirak-Barry *(VP-Customer Svc)*
Tony Eales *(Pres & CEO)*
Scott MacDonald *(VP-Product Mgmt)*
Nasim Golzadeh *(VP-Ops)*
Joe Raposa *(VP & Gen Mgr)*
Phil Sisk *(VP-Perform)*
Brenda Stiehl *(VP-Fin)*
Steve Corgan *(VP-Engrg)*
Terri Barry *(VP-Customer Svc)*
Michael Zuercher *(Sr VP & Gen Mgr)*

Subsidiary (Domestic):

Emergitech, Inc. (3)
2545 Farmers Dr Ste 250, Columbus, OH 43235
Tel.: (614) 866-6712
Web Site: http://www.emergitech.com
Sales Range: $1-9.9 Million
Emp.: 42
Computer & Computer Peripheral Equipment & Software Merchant Whslr
N.A.I.C.S.: 423430
John Hablitzel *(COO)*
Mark Collins *(Pres)*
Chuck Brady *(Dir-Tech Product Support & Product Plng)*
Marti Litwiller *(Dir-Client Svcs)*

Law Enforcement Technology Group (3)
1951 Woodlane Dr, Woodbury, MN 55125
Tel.: (651) 578-2801
Web Site: http://www.letg.com
Custom Computer Programming Services
N.A.I.C.S.: 541511
Jeff Gottstein *(Owner)*

The Omega Group, Inc. (3)
5160 Carroll Canyon Rd Ste 100, San Diego, CA 92121
Tel.: (858) 450-2590
Web Site: http://www.theomegagroup.com
Computer & Software Developer
N.A.I.C.S.: 423430
Dean Daniels *(Project Mgr-GIS)*

Citrix Systems, Inc. (1)
851 W Cypress Creek Rd, Fort Lauderdale, FL 33309
Tel.: (954) 267-3000
Web Site: https://www.citrix.com
Rev.: $3,217,170,000
Assets: $6,975,517,000
Liabilities: $6,428,260,000
Net Worth: $547,257,000
Earnings: $307,499,000
Emp.: 9,700
Fiscal Year-end: 12/31/2021

VISTA EQUITY PARTNERS, LLC

Mfr & Reproducing Magnetic & Optical Media
N.A.I.C.S.: 334610
Tony Gomes *(Chief Legal Officer, Sec & Exec VP)*
Sridhar Mullapudi *(Exec VP-Product Mgmt)*
Hector Lima *(Exec VP-Customer Experience)*
Meerah Rajavel *(CIO)*
Thomas Berquis *(CFO)*
Tom Krause *(CEO)*
Andy Nallappan *(COO & CIO)*
Ric Chi *(VP-Corporate Strategy)*
Derek Baden *(Gen Mgr-NetScaler eCommerce)*
Jacus de Beer *(Gen Mgr-XenServer)*
Ali Ahmed *(Gen Mgr-TIBCO & Enterprise Applications)*
Kurt Heusner *(Gen Mgr-ShareFile)*

Subsidiary (Non-US):

Apere Enterprise Storage Solutions India Pvt. Ltd. (2)
14 3rd Floor Road No 2 Banjara Hills Huda Colony, Hyderabad, 500034, India
Tel.: (91) 9346255332
Software Publishing Services
N.A.I.C.S.: 513210

Subsidiary (Domestic):

App-DNA, Inc. (2)
20 N Martingale Rd Ste 110, Schaumburg, IL 60173
Tel.: (847) 230-0020
Emp.: 12
Software Publishing Services
N.A.I.C.S.: 513210

Subsidiary (Non-US):

Bytemobile European Development Center MEPE (2)
4 Kato - Ano Kastritsiou, Eparchiaki Odos, 26504, Patras, Greece
Tel.: (30) 2610935000
Software Publishing Services
N.A.I.C.S.: 513210

Subsidiary (Domestic):

Cedexis Inc. (2)
421 SW 6th Ave Ste 700, Portland, OR 97204
Web Site: http://www.cedexis.com
Software Development Services
N.A.I.C.S.: 541511

Citrix Online LLC (2)
7414 Hollister Ave, Goleta, CA 93117
Tel.: (805) 690-6400
Web Site: http://www.citrix.com
Sales Range: $100-124.9 Million
Emp.: 1,000
Remote Support & Access Technologies
N.A.I.C.S.: 517610
Brett Caine *(Pres)*

Subsidiary (Non-US):

Citrix Online AUS Pty Ltd. (3)
1 Julius Avenue Sydney, North Ryde, 2113, NSW, Australia
Tel.: (61) 1800451485
Web Site: http://www.citrixonline.com
Sales Range: $50-74.9 Million
Emp.: 250
Real-Time Application Software Publisher
N.A.I.C.S.: 513210

Subsidiary (Non-US):

Citrix R&D India Private Limited (2)
Prestige Dynasty Phase-2 Ground Floor 33/2 Ulsoor Road, Bengaluru, 560042, Karnataka, India
Tel.: (91) 806 120 2001
Web Site: https://www.citrix.com
Emp.: 1,500
Real-Time Application Software Publisher
N.A.I.C.S.: 513210

Citrix R&D Limited (2)
R&D Chalfont 2-3 Chalfont Park Chalfont St Peter, Gerrards Cross, SL9 0DZ, Buckinghamshire, United Kingdom
Tel.: (44) 1753276200
Software Development Services
N.A.I.C.S.: 541511

VISTA EQUITY PARTNERS, LLC

Vista Equity Partners, LLC—(Continued)

Citrix Sistemas de Argentina, S.R.L. (2)
Avenida Ingeniero Huergo 953 Piso 7, Buenos Aires, Argentina
Tel.: (54) 1145156300
Real-Time Application Software Publisher
N.A.I.C.S.: 513210

Citrix Sistemas do Brasil Ltda. (2)
Rua Professor Atilio Innocenti 165 - 13 andar, Itaim Bibi, Sao Paulo, 04538-000, Brazil
Tel.: (55) 113 702 7900
Web Site: https://www.citrix.com
Sales Range: $10-24.9 Million
Emp.: 40
Real-Time Application Software Publisher
N.A.I.C.S.: 513210

Citrix Systems Asia Pacific Pty Ltd. (2)
Level 23 100 Mount Street, North Sydney, 2060, NSW, Australia
Tel.: (61) 28 870 0800
Web Site: http://www.citrix.com
Emp.: 200
Real-Time Application Software Publisher
N.A.I.C.S.: 513210

Citrix Systems Belgium S.P.R.L. (2)
Stockholm Building Leonardo Da Vincilaan 19, 1831, Diegem, Belgium
Tel.: (32) 27882754
Software Services
N.A.I.C.S.: 541511

Citrix Systems Canada, Inc. (2)
125 Commerce Valley Drive West Suite 502, Markham, L3T 7W4, ON, Canada
Tel.: (289) 982-0905
Sales Range: $10-24.9 Million
Emp.: 20
Real-Time Application Software Publisher
N.A.I.C.S.: 513210

Citrix Systems Czech Republic SRO (2)
Na Pankraci 1724/129, 140 00, Prague, Czech Republic
Tel.: (420) 225992200
Software Publishing Services
N.A.I.C.S.: 513210

Citrix Systems Denmark ApS (2)
Kalkbraenderiloebskaj 4, Copenhagen, 2100, Denmark
Tel.: (45) 39193400
Sales Range: $10-24.9 Million
Emp.: 23
Real-Time Application Software Publisher
N.A.I.C.S.: 513210

Citrix Systems Finland Oy (2)
Keilaranta 16, 02150, Espoo, Finland
Tel.: (358) 925107341
Sales Range: $10-24.9 Million
Emp.: 7
Real-Time Application Software Publisher
N.A.I.C.S.: 513210

Citrix Systems France SARL (2)
Coeur Defense - Tour B Etage 31 100 Esplanade du General de Gaulle, La Defense, 92932, Paris, Cedex, France
Tel.: (33) 14 900 3300
Web Site: https://www.citrix.com
Emp.: 87
Real-Time Application Software Publisher
N.A.I.C.S.: 513210

Citrix Systems GmbH (2)
Mariahilferstrasse 123/3, Vienna, 1060, Austria
Tel.: (43) 159999223
Web Site: http://www.citrix.de
Emp.: 8
Real-Time Application Software Publisher
N.A.I.C.S.: 513210

Citrix Systems GmbH (2)
Erika-Mann-Str 67-69, 80636, Munich, Germany
Tel.: (49) 8944 456 4000
Web Site: https://www.citrix.com
Enterprise Mobility Management & Real-Time Application Software Publisher
N.A.I.C.S.: 513210

Citrix Systems Information Technology (Beijing) Ltd (2)
Unit 808-809 Level 8 Tower C Oriental Plaza No 1 East Chang An Street, Dong Cheng District, Beijing, 100738, China
Tel.: (86) 1065216500
Real-Time Application Software Publisher
N.A.I.C.S.: 513210

Citrix Systems International GmbH (2)
Rheinweg 9, 8200, Schaffhausen, Switzerland
Tel.: (41) 526357700
Sales Range: $25-49.9 Million
Emp.: 100
Holding Company
N.A.I.C.S.: 551112

Citrix Systems Netherlands, B.V. (2)
Spaces Zuidas 5th floor Barbara Strozzilaan 201, 1083 HN, Amsterdam, Netherlands
Tel.: (31) 20 301 3400
Web Site: https://www.citrix.com
Sales Range: $25-49.9 Million
Emp.: 40
Real-Time Application Software Publisher
N.A.I.C.S.: 513210

Citrix Systems Norway AS (2)
Nydalsveien 28, 0484, Oslo, Norway
Tel.: (47) 2 152 0150
Web Site: https://www.citrix.com
Real-Time Application Software Publisher
N.A.I.C.S.: 513210
Knut Alnaes (Mgr)

Citrix Systems Poland Sp. z o.o (2)
Sheraton Plaza Building 1st Floor Ul Prusa 2, Warsaw, 00-493, Poland
Tel.: (48) 226570171
Software Development Services
N.A.I.C.S.: 541511

Citrix Systems UK Limited (2)
Building 3 Chalfont Park, Chalfont St Peter, Gerrards Cross, SL9 0DZ, Buckinghamshire, United Kingdom
Tel.: (44) 175 327 6200
Web Site: https://www.citrix.com
Emp.: 300
Real-Time Application Software Publisher
N.A.I.C.S.: 513210

Subsidiary (Domestic):

Framehawk, Inc. (2)
177 Post St Ste 650, San Francisco, CA 94108
Tel.: (415) 371-9110
Software Publishing Services
N.A.I.C.S.: 513210

Grasshopper Group, LLC (2)
197 1st Ave Ste 200, Needham, MA 02494
Tel.: (617) 395-5700
Web Site: http://www.grasshopper.com
Emp.: 26
Online Virtual Phone Systems Management & Technical Support Services
N.A.I.C.S.: 517810
Siamak Taghaddoss (Co-Founder)
David Hauser (Co-Founder & CTO)

Subsidiary (Non-US):

Peninsula Finance LLC (2)
Studio 5-11, 5 Millbay Road, Plymouth, PL1 3LF, United Kingdom
Tel.: (44) 1752292568
Web Site: http://www.peninsulafinance.com
Financial Management Services
N.A.I.C.S.: 541611
Hugh Michelmore (Chm)
Daniel Palmer (CEO)
Robert Howard (Dir-Risk & Legal Svcs)
Suzanne Deacon (Acct Mgr)
Kelsey Stewart (Mgr-Case)
Matthew Cocking (Accountant)

Podio ApS (2)
Skelbaekgade 2 5th, 1717, Copenhagen, Denmark
Tel.: (45) 31147464
Software Development Services
N.A.I.C.S.: 541511

Ringcube Software Tech Pvt Ltd. (2)
304 Reliance Classic 3rd Floor, Banjara Hills, Hyderabad, 500034, India
Tel.: (91) 4023311125
Software Publishing Services
N.A.I.C.S.: 513210

Subsidiary (Domestic):

Sanbolic, Inc. (2)
309 Waverley Oaks Rd Ste 101, Waltham, MA 02452
Tel.: (617) 833-4242
Web Site: http://www.sanbolic.com
Software Publisher
N.A.I.C.S.: 513210

ShareFile LLC (2)
120 S West St, Raleigh, NC 27603
Tel.: (919) 745-6111
Web Site: http://www.citrix.com
Emp.: 100
File Sharing Software
N.A.I.C.S.: 334610

Solid Instance, Inc. (2)
5255 N Edgewood Dr Ste 300, Provo, UT 84604
Tel.: (801) 805-0300
Software Development Services
N.A.I.C.S.: 541511
Tyrone F. Pike (Co-Founder, Chm, Pres & CEO)
John Rafter (COO & VP-Ops)
Ron C. Steed (Co-Founder & Dir-Ops)
Donald Guarnieri (VP-Mktg)

Subsidiary (Non-US):

Todd Hsu Consultants, Inc. (2)
351 Northland Rd, Sault Sainte Marie, P6C 3N2, ON, Canada
Tel.: (514) 864-5999
Software Publishing Services
N.A.I.C.S.: 513210

Subsidiary (Domestic):

Unidesk Corporation (2)
313 Boston Post Rd W, Marlborough, MA 01752
Tel.: (508) 573-7800
Web Site: http://www.unidesk.com
Software Development Services
N.A.I.C.S.: 513210

Wrike, Inc. (2)
70 N 2nd St, San Jose, CA 95113
Tel.: (650) 318-3551
Web Site: https://www.wrike.com
Emp.: 70
Project Management Software Developer
N.A.I.C.S.: 513210
Andrew Filev (Founder & CEO)
Saranya Babu (Sr VP-Marketing)
Chad Bennett (Chief HR Officer)
Paul Fernandez (Sr Mgr-Corporate Communications)
Paul Fernandez (Sr Mgr-Corporate Communications)

Datto, Inc. (1)
101 Merritt 7 7th Fl, Norwalk, CT 06851
Tel.: (888) 294-6312
Web Site: http://www.dattobackup.com
Hardware-Based On-Site & Offsite Backup, Disaster Recovery & Business Continuity Services
N.A.I.C.S.: 562920
Austin McChord (Founder)
Michael Fass (Chief People Officer & Gen Counsel)
Timothy Weller (CEO)
Robert Petrocelli (CTO)
John F. Abbot (CFO)
Nathaniel Katz (Sr VP-Fin)

Subsidiary (Non-US):

Datto Europe Ltd. (2)
250 Longwater Avenue, Green Park, Reading, RG2 6GB, United Kingdom
Tel.: (44) 1184029609
Web Site: http://www.datto.com
Backup Data Recovery Systems
N.A.I.C.S.: 562920
Paul Ledger (Mgr-Ops)

Duck Creek Technologies, Inc. (1)
100 Summer St 8th Fl Ste 801, Boston, MA 02110
Tel.: (417) 777-6970
Web Site: https://www.duckcreek.com
Rev.: $302,917,000
Assets: $839,676,000
Liabilities: $107,271,000
Net Worth: $732,405,000
Earnings: ($8,332,000)

U.S. PRIVATE

Emp.: 1,883
Fiscal Year-end: 08/31/2022
Software Solution for Property & Casualty Insurance Industry Service
N.A.I.C.S.: 513210
Chris McCloskey (COO)
Michael A. Jackowski (CEO)
Rohit Bedi (Chief Revenue Officer)
Ben Dulieu (Chief Information Security Officer)
Jess Keeney (Chief Product Officer)
Shreyas Vasanthkumar (Mng Dir)
Julien Victor (Mng Dir)

Subsidiary (Domestic):

Outline Systems LLC (2)
2 Executive Dr Ste 230 A, Somerset, NJ 08873
Tel.: (732) 537-1234
Web Site: http://www.outlinesys.com
Sales Range: $10-24.9 Million
Emp.: 40
Computer Related Services
N.A.I.C.S.: 541512

EagleView Technologies, Inc. (1)
3700 Monte Villa Pkwy Ste 200, Bothell, WA 98021
Tel.: (855) 984-6590
Web Site: http://www.eagleview.com
Aerial Surveying & Data Analytics Services
N.A.I.C.S.: 541370
Chris Pershing (Founder & CTO)
Rishi Daga (Vice Chm)
Robert F. Smith (Chm)
Anthony Cross (VP-Product Strategy)
Jonathan Gadd (Dir-Strategic Programs)
Dave Schultz (Exec VP-Ops)
Frank Giuffrida (Exec VP & Chief Engr)
Jay Martin (Sr VP-Ops)
Kenneth Cook (Sr VP-EagleView OnSite Solutions)
Rich Spring (Chief Revenue Officer)
Ruby White (Sr VP-HR)
Chris Jurasek (CEO)

Subsidiary (Non-US):

Spookfish Limited (2)
10 Brodie-Hall Dr Technology Park, Bentley, 6102, WA, Australia
Tel.: (61) 8 6365 5626
Web Site: http://www.spookfish.com
Rev.: $10,467,073
Assets: $13,673,187
Liabilities: $2,262,506
Net Worth: $11,410,681
Earnings: ($8,454,171)
Emp.: 34
Fiscal Year-end: 12/31/2017
Investment Services
N.A.I.C.S.: 523999
Mike von Bertouch (Dir-Strategic Ops)
Simon Cope (CTO)
Guy Perkins (Dir-Strategic Sls)
Ian Magee (Co-Sec)
Jason Waller (CEO)

Ellucian Company L.P. (1)
2003 Edmund Halley Dr, Reston, VA 20191
Tel.: (703) 968-9000
Web Site: http://www.ellucian.com
Business Solution Software Developer
N.A.I.C.S.: 513210
Toby Williams (Chief Product Officer, Chief Strategy Officer & Sr VP)
Pete Sinisgalli (Chm)
Laura K. Ipsen (Pres & CEO)
Martin Banjo (Pres)
Harshan Bhangdia (CFO)
Greg Giangrande (Chief People Officer)
Melissa King (Chief Transformation Officer)
Susan Morrow (Chief Mktg Officer)
Martin Mrugal (COO)
Toby J. Williams (Chief Strategy Officer, Chief Product Officer & Sr VP)

Branch (Domestic):

Ellucian Company L.P. - Malvern (2)
4 Country View Rd, Malvern, PA 19355
Tel.: (610) 647-5930
Web Site: http://www.ellucian.com
Learning Software, Support & Consultation Systems
N.A.I.C.S.: 541512

Subsidiary (Domestic):

WriterAccess (2)

COMPANIES

VISTA EQUITY PARTNERS, LLC

205 Portland St Ste 500, Boston, MA 02114
Tel.: (617) 227-8800
Web Site: http://www.writeraccess.com
Sales Range: $1-9.9 Million
Emp.: 10
Document Preparation Services
N.A.I.C.S.: 561410

Finastra Group Holdings Limited (1)
1 Kingdom Street, Paddington, London, W2 6BL, United Kingdom
Tel.: (44) 2033205000
Web Site: http://www.misys.com
Sales Range: $1-4.9 Billion
Emp.: 400
Holding Company; Banking, Healthcare & Financial Services Software Publisher
N.A.I.C.S.: 551112
Bob Barthelmes *(Exec VP & Gen Mgr-Open Source Solutions)*
Graeme Beardsell *(Gen Mgr-Asia Pacific)*
Ellen M. Clarke *(CIO & Exec VP)*
Rick Bernard *(VP-Global Tech)*
Robin Crewe *(Head-Engrg & QA)*
Michel Daenen *(Dir-Sls-Capital Markets Bus-Middle East & Africa)*
Bret Bolin *(Chm)*
Ashish Dass *(Dir-Middle East, Africa & South Asia)*
Frank Brienzi *(Chief Sls Officer)*
Amanda Mesler *(COO)*
Boris Lipianen *(Head-Product Mgmt)*
Alan Somerville *(Head-Prof Svcs)*
Grace Van Til *(Head-Customer Support)*
Conor Colleary *(Head-Sls Ops)*
Tom Dawkins *(Chief of Staff & Dir-Corp Strategy)*
Scot Spear *(Dir-Sls-Middle East & Africa)*
Mourad Ayachi *(Head-Pro Svcs-Europe)*
Bob Kubala *(Mgr-Sls-Investment Mgmt-North America)*
Sebastien Roussotte *(Mng Dir-Investment Mgmt)*
Nicola Hamilton *(Sr Dir-Comm)*
Jim Fiesel *(Mng Dir-Capital Markets & Lending Sls-Americas)*
Sagive Greenspan *(Sr VP & Gen Mgr-Payments)*
Eli Rosner *(Chief Product & Tech Officer)*
Torsten Pull *(Gen Mgr-Corp Banking)*
Eric Duffaut *(Pres & Head-Field & Mktg-Global)*
Wissam Khoury *(Sr VP/Gen Mgr-Middle East, Africa & Asia Pacific)*
Benjamin Jun Tai *(Sr Mgr-PR-Asia Pacific)*
Caroline Duff *(Head-PR-Global)*
Mehjabeen Poonawala *(Head-Agile Center of Excellence & India)*
Lisa Fiondella *(Chief Data Officer)*
Patrick Kilhaney *(Head-Pub & Analyst Rels)*
Simon Paris *(CEO)*
Gary E. Bischoping Jr. *(CFO)*

Subsidiary (US):

Custom Credit Systems LP (2)
801 E Campbell Rd Ste 652, Richardson, TX 75081
Tel.: (972) 644-6270
Web Site: http://www.misys.com
Emp.: 25
Computer Software Development And Support Service
N.A.I.C.S.: 541511
Johanna Pugh *(VP-Sls)*
Kevin Taylor *(Dir-Product Support)*
Josh Marcy *(Dir-Dev)*

Subsidiary (Domestic):

DBS Financial Management PLC (2)
Independence House, Holly Bank Rd, Huddersfield, HD3 3HN, United Kingdom (100%)
Tel.: (44) 8700401983
Web Site: http://www.dbsfinancialmanagement.plc.uk
Sales Range: $25-49.9 Million
Provider of Financial Management Services
N.A.I.C.S.: 541611

Subsidiary (US):

Misys IQ LLC (2)
1180 6th Ave 4th Fl, New York, NY 10036-8401
Tel.: (212) 898-9500
Web Site: http://www.misys.com
Banking Software Development Services
N.A.I.C.S.: 541511

Subsidiary (Domestic):

Misys International Banking Systems Limited (2)
One Kingdom St, Paddington, London, W2 6BL, United Kingdom (100%)
Tel.: (44) 20 3320 5000
Web Site: http://www.misys.com
Sales Range: $50-74.9 Million
Emp.: 400
Supplier of Application Solutions & Services to International Finance Community
N.A.I.C.S.: 334610
Cristiana Grealy *(Mgr-Ops)*

Subsidiary (Non-US):

Misys International Banking Systems (CIS) Limited (3)
Sadovaya Samotechnaya 24/27, Moscow, 127051, Russia
Tel.: (7) 495 258 5030
Web Site: http://www.misys.com
Sales Range: $10-24.9 Million
Emp.: 1
Banking Software Development Services
N.A.I.C.S.: 541511
Theo Simons *(Reg Dir)*

Misys International Banking Systems GmbH (3)
Hedderich Strasse 36, Frankfurt am Main, 60594, Germany
Tel.: (49) 69 238527 505
Web Site: http://www.misys.com
Banking Software Development Services
N.A.I.C.S.: 541511
Joachim Vogel *(Mng Dir-Fin)*

Subsidiary (US):

Misys International Banking Systems Inc. (3)
285 Madison Ave 1st Fl, New York, NY 10017
Tel.: (212) 898-9500
Banking Software Development Services
N.A.I.C.S.: 541511
Tony Palmisano *(Mgr-SaaS Ops)*
Mark Sollecito *(Head-Summit SC & TCM America)*

Subsidiary (Domestic):

Misys International Banking Systems (Risk) LLC (4)
1180 Avenue of the Americas 5th Fl, New York, NY 10036 (100%)
Tel.: (212) 898-9500
Web Site: http://www.misys-ibs.com
Sales Range: $100-124.9 Million
Financial Risk Management Software Mfr
N.A.I.C.S.: 811210
Matheen Syed *(CEO)*

Unit (Domestic):

Misys Wholesale Banking Systems (4)
1180 6th Ave Fl 4, New York, NY 10036
Tel.: (212) 329-2700
Web Site: http://www.misys.com
Sales Range: $25-49.9 Million
Developer of Financial Software Solutions
N.A.I.C.S.: 541511

Subsidiary (Domestic):

Summit Systems, Inc. (4)
1180 Ave of the Americas 5th Fl, New York, NY 10036 (100%)
Tel.: (212) 896-3400
Sales Range: $75-99.9 Million
Provider of Capital Markets Trading Solutions
N.A.I.C.S.: 541511
Frank Weyns *(Mng Dir)*

Subsidiary (Non-US):

Misys International Banking Systems K.K (3)
Fukoku Seimei Building 5F 2-2-2 Uchisaiwaicho, Chiyoda-ku, Tokyo, 100-0011, Japan
Tel.: (81) 3 5512 71 91
Web Site: http://www.misys.com
Banking Software Development Services
N.A.I.C.S.: 541511
Shun Watanabe *(Country Mgr)*

Misys International Banking Systems Limited (3)
Suite 601 6/F Dah Sing Financial Centre 108 Gloucester Road, Wanchai, China (Hong Kong)
Tel.: (852) 2230 2300
Banking Software Development Services
N.A.I.C.S.: 541511

Misys International Banking Systems Limited (3)
Ground Floor Block K Eastpoint Business Park Clontarf, Dublin, Ireland
Tel.: (353) 16361500
Banking Software Development Services
N.A.I.C.S.: 541511

Misys International Banking Systems Mexico S.A. DE CV (3)
Torre Candela Sierra Candela 111-208 Lomas de Chapultepec, Seccion Miguel Hidalgo, Mexico, 11000, Mexico
Tel.: (52) 555 540 0184
Web Site: http://www.misys.com
Sales Range: $10-24.9 Million
Emp.: 25
Banking Software Development Services
N.A.I.C.S.: 541511
Mario Mirensky *(Gen Mgr)*

Misys International Banking Systems Pty Limited (3)
Suite 101 Level 10 Macquarie House 165-169 Macquarie Street, Sydney, 2000, NSW, Australia
Tel.: (61) 292168888
Banking Software Development Services
N.A.I.C.S.: 541511

Misys International Banking Systems SA (3)
63 Blvd Haussmann, 75008, Paris, France
Tel.: (33) 144782828
Sales Range: $10-24.9 Million
Banking Software Development Services
N.A.I.C.S.: 541511
Kader Oulae *(Gen Mgr)*

Subsidiary (Domestic):

Summit Systems SA (4)
42 Rue Washington Plaza, Paris, 75008, France
Tel.: (33) 144782828
Web Site: http://www.misys.com
Financial & Healthcare Software Development Services
N.A.I.C.S.: 541511

Subsidiary (Non-US):

Misys International Banking Systems SA (3)
Centre Descartes 287-289 route d'Arlon, Luxembourg, 1150, Luxembourg
Tel.: (352) 45 33 99 1
Sales Range: $10-24.9 Million
Emp.: 36
Banking Software Development Services
N.A.I.C.S.: 541511

Misys International Financial Systems (Pty) Limited (3)
JHI House Ground Floor 11 Cradock Avenue, Rosebank, 2196, Johannesburg, South Africa
Tel.: (27) 11 721 4200
Web Site: http://www.misys.com
Sales Range: $10-24.9 Million
Emp.: 15
Banking Software Development Services
N.A.I.C.S.: 541511
Simon Lester *(Office Mgr)*

Misys International Financial Systems Pte Limited (3)
2 Shenton Way 14-01 SGX Ctr 1, Singapore, 068804, Singapore
Tel.: (65) 64164096
Banking Software Development Services
N.A.I.C.S.: 541511

Misys International Financial Systems S.L. (3)
C/ Cardenal Marcelo Spinola 42 Edificio URBIS 3 dcha, 28016, Madrid, Spain
Tel.: (34) 91 766 98 66
Banking Software Development Services
N.A.I.C.S.: 541511

Misys International Systems Sdn Bhd (3)
level 33 Menaro Ilham Tower No 8 Jalan Binja, Kuala Lumpur, 50450, Malaysia
Tel.: (60) 321175010
Web Site: http://www.misys.com
Banking Software Development Services
N.A.I.C.S.: 541511

PT Misys International Financial Systems (3)
Indonesia Stock Exchange Building Tower 2 16th Floor Suite 1601 52-53, Jl Jend Sudirman Kav, Jakarta, 12190, Indonesia
Tel.: (62) 215152788
Financial & Healthcare Software Development Services
N.A.I.C.S.: 541511

Subsidiary (Non-US):

Misys Netherlands BV (2)
Orteliuslaan 850, 3528 BB, Utrecht, Netherlands
Tel.: (31) 308080060
Banking Software Development Services
N.A.I.C.S.: 541511

Misys Philippines Inc (2)
Zuellig Building 8nd Floor, Makati, 1226, Philippines
Tel.: (63) 2 479 9300
Financial & Healthcare Software Development Services
N.A.I.C.S.: 541511

Subsidiary (Domestic):

Misys Retail Banking Systems Ltd (2)
Key W, Windsor Rd, Slough, SL1 2DW, United Kingdom (100%)
Tel.: (44) 2088791188
Web Site: http://www.misys.com
Provider of Retail Banking Systems
N.A.I.C.S.: 334610

Misys Risk Management Systems Ltd (2)
1 St George's Rd, Wimbledon, London, SW19 4DR, United Kingdom (100%)
Tel.: (44) 20 8879 1188
Web Site: http://www.misys.com
Sales Range: $50-74.9 Million
Provider of Risk Management Systems
N.A.I.C.S.: 334610

Misys Services Limited (2)
One Kingdom Street, Paddington, London, W2 6BL, United Kingdom
Tel.: (44) 20 3320 5000
Web Site: http://www.misys.com
Sales Range: $50-74.9 Million
Emp.: 520
Banking Software Development Services
N.A.I.C.S.: 541511
Nadeem Syed *(CEO)*

Subsidiary (Non-US):

Misys Software Solutions (India) Private Limited (2)
Eagle Ridge Embassy Golf Links Business Park, Off Intermediate Ring Road, Bengaluru, 560071, India
Tel.: (91) 80 4040 4040
Web Site: http://www.misys.com
Banking Software Development Services
N.A.I.C.S.: 541511
Manoj Kumar *(Mng Dir)*

Gainsight, Inc. (1)
191 Castro St 2nd Fl, Mountain View, CA 94041
Tel.: (650) 532-8155
Web Site: http://www.gainsight.com
Software Development Services
N.A.I.C.S.: 541511
Dan Steinman *(Chief Customer Officer)*
Sreedhar Peddineni *(VP-Engrg)*
Jim Eberlin *(Founder & Pres)*
Irit Eizips *(Head-Solutions Consulting)*
Lisa DeVall *(Controller)*
Nikhil Mehta *(CEO)*

Granicus Inc. (1)

VISTA EQUITY PARTNERS, LLC

U.S. PRIVATE

Vista Equity Partners, LLC—(Continued)

600 Harrison St Ste 120, San Francisco, CA 94107
Tel.: (415) 357-3618
Web Site: http://www.granicus.com
Sales Range: $10-24.9 Million
Emp.: 450
Online Media Content Solutions
N.A.I.C.S.: 513210
Mark Hynes *(CEO)*
Scott Macfee *(COO)*
Bob Ainsbury *(Chief Product Officer)*
Eric Gibson *(CFO)*
Howard Langsam *(Exec VP-Sls)*
Lenny Maly *(Chief Information Security Officer)*
Suzanne Behrens *(CMO)*

Subsidiary (Domestic):

GovLoop, Inc. (2)
1152 15 St NW Ste 800, Washington, DC 20005
Tel.: (202) 407-7421
Web Site: http://www.govloop.com
Online Social Networking Services
N.A.I.C.S.: 516210
Doug Mashkuri *(VP-Bus Dev)*
Catherine Andrews *(Sr Dir-Editorial Svcs & Production)*
Megan Dotson *(Mgr-Events)*
Steve Ressler *(Founder & Pres)*

Greenway Medical Technologies, Inc. (1)
100 Greenway Blvd, Carrollton, GA 30117
Tel.: (770) 836-3100
Web Site: http://www.greenwaymedical.com
Rev.: $134,844,000
Assets: $126,129,000
Liabilities: $24,494,000
Net Worth: $101,635,000
Earnings: ($5,065,000)
Emp.: 810
Fiscal Year-end: 06/30/2013
Ambulator Healthcare Software
N.A.I.C.S.: 513210
Gregory H. Schulenburg *(COO & Exec VP)*
Sam Snider *(Gen Counsel)*
Mark Janiszewski *(Sr VP-Product Mgmt)*

Haiku Learning Systems, Inc. (1)
118 S Main St Ste 3, Goshen, IN 46526-0000
Tel.: (574) 538-2325
Web Site: http://www.haikulearning.com
Computer Related Services
N.A.I.C.S.: 541519
Allen Angell *(Founder & Pres-Los Angeles)*

Infoblox Inc. (1)
2390 Mission College Blvd Ste 501, Santa Clara, CA 95054
Tel.: (408) 986-4000
Web Site: https://www.infoblox.com
Rev.: $358,286,000
Assets: $449,103,000
Liabilities: $230,595,000
Net Worth: $218,508,000
Earnings: ($13,711,000)
Emp.: 804
Fiscal Year-end: 07/31/2016
Network Identity Appliances Developer
N.A.I.C.S.: 561621
Cricket Liu *(Chief Architect-DNS)*
Liza Burns *(VP-Bus Ops)*
Scott Harrell *(Pres & CEO)*
Ashley Kusowski *(Head-Corp Comm)*
Mukesh Gupta *(Chief Product Officer & Sr VP)*
Richard E. Belluzzo *(Chm)*
Mitch Breen *(Chief Revenue Officer)*
Padmini Kao *(Exec VP-Engineering)*
Brad Rinklin *(CMO & Exec VP)*
Wei Chen *(Chief Legal Officer & Exec VP-Government Affairs)*
Hoke Horne *(CFO & Exec VP)*
Anuradha Mayer *(Chief People Officer & Exec VP)*
Amy Farrow *(CIO & Sr VP)*

Integral Ad Science, Inc. (1)
95 Morton St Fl 8, New York, NY 10014
Tel.: (646) 278-4871
Web Site: http://integralads.com
Digital Marketing Services
N.A.I.C.S.: 541613
Micah Nessan *(Gen Counsel)*
Stephen Dolan *(Mng Dir-APAC)*
Yann Le Roux *(Mng Dir)*
Nick Morley *(Mng Dir-EMEA)*
James Diamond *(Mng Dir-Australia & New Zealand)*
Taro Fujinaka *(Mng Dir-Japan)*
Lisa Utzschneider *(CEO)*
Angela Barnett *(Dir-Corp Comm)*
Kevin McCurry *(Chief Strategy Officer)*
Chance Johnson *(Chief Revenue Officer)*
Adrian D'Souza *(Chief Customer Officer)*
Tom Sharma *(Chief Product Officer)*
Kent E. Wakeford *(Executives)*
Thomas V. Joseph *(CTO)*
Yannis Dosios *(Chief Comml Officer)*
Khurrum Malik *(CMO)*

Khoros, LLC (1)
7300 Ranch Rd 2222 Bldg 1, Austin, TX 78730-3204
Tel.: (512) 201-4090
Web Site: http://www.khoros.com
Customer Engagement Software Publisher
N.A.I.C.S.: 513210
Mike Betzer *(Chief Product Officer)*
Dan Doman *(Sr VP-Bus Dev)*
Doug Grigg *(Chief Sls Officer)*
Sam Monti *(CFO)*
Michael O'Donnell *(Chief HR Officer)*
Scott Sheperd *(Chief Legal Officer)*
Mike Graves *(CTO)*
Staci Satterwhite *(Chief Customer Officer)*
Sejal Amin *(Chief Product Tech Officer)*
Jason Perlewitz *(VP-Technical Ops)*
Tony Cetera *(Sr Dir-Info Security)*
Lindsay Sanchez *(CMO)*
Chris Tranquill *(CEO)*

Branch (Non-US):

Khoros International, LLC (2)
1st Floor Mid City Place, 71 High Holborn, London, WC1V 6DA, United Kingdom
Tel.: (44) 2036958750
Web Site: http://khoros.com
Software Publisher
N.A.I.C.S.: 513210

Khoros, LLC - Australia Office (2)
Christie Building Level 13 3 Spring St, Sydney, 2000, NSW, Australia
Tel.: (61) 2 8415 9877
Web Site: http://khoros.com
Software Publisher
N.A.I.C.S.: 513210

Khoros, LLC - France Office (2)
18 Boulevard Malesherbes, 75008, Paris, France
Tel.: (33) 15 527 3987
Web Site: http://khoros.com
Software Publisher
N.A.I.C.S.: 513210

Subsidiary (Domestic):

Klout, Inc. (2)
225 Bush St, San Francisco, CA 94104
Tel.: (415) 777-2001
User Engagement Software Publisher
N.A.I.C.S.: 513210

Spredfast, Inc. (2)
200 W Cesar Chavez Ste 600, Austin, TX 78701
Tel.: (512) 649-3289
Social Media Management, Social Relationship Platform, Strategy & Services
N.A.I.C.S.: 516210
Adriana Zolezzi *(Mktg Mgr-Product)*

Kibo Software, Inc. (1)
717 N Harwood St Ste 1900, Dallas, TX 75201
Tel.: (877) 350-3866
Web Site: https://kibocommerce.com
Commerce Software Publisher
N.A.I.C.S.: 513210
Ram Venkataraman *(CEO)*
Vinesh Vis *(Chief Revenue Officer)*
David Ricketts *(Head-Sls)*
Meagan White *(Head-Mktg)*

Branch (Domestic):

Kibo - Petaluma (2)
617 2nd St, Petaluma, CA 94952
Tel.: (707) 780-1600
Web Site: http://www.kibocommerce.com
Commerce Software Publisher
N.A.I.C.S.: 513210

Kibo - San Luis Obispo (2)
865 Aerovista Pl Ste 230, San Luis Obispo, CA 93401
Tel.: (877) 350-3866
Web Site: http://www.kibocommerce.com
E-Commerce Software Developer
N.A.I.C.S.: 513210

Subsidiary (Non-US):

Kibo Commerce Ltd. (2)
19-21 Newport St, Swindon, SN1 3DX, United Kingdom
Tel.: (44) 1793 461651
Web Site: http://kibocommerce.com
Commerce Software Publisher
N.A.I.C.S.: 513210

KnowBe4, Inc. (1)
33 N Garden Ave Ste 1200, Clearwater, FL 33755
Web Site: https://www.knowbe4.com
Rev.: $246,298,000
Assets: $537,678,000
Liabilities: $320,411,000
Net Worth: $217,267,000
Earnings: ($11,845,000)
Emp.: 1,366
Fiscal Year-end: 12/31/2021
Software Development Services
N.A.I.C.S.: 541511
Robert F. Reich *(CFO)*
Sjoerd Sjouwerman *(Founder, Chm & CEO)*
Lars Letonoff *(Pres & Chief Revenue Officer)*
Perry Carpenter *(Chief Evangelist & Strategy Officer)*
Kai Roer *(Chief Res Officer)*

LogicMonitor, Inc. (1)
820 State St Fl 5, Santa Barbara, CA 93101
Tel.: (805) 617-3884
Web Site: http://www.logicmonitor.com
Network, Server & Application Monitoring
N.A.I.C.S.: 513210
Kevin McGibben *(Chm)*
Steve Francis *(Founder)*
Brandon Holden *(COO)*
Tejaswi Redkar *(Chief Product Officer)*
Christina Kosmowski *(CEO)*
Carol Lee *(CFO)*
Will Corkery *(Chief Revenue Officer)*
Ryan Kam *(CMO)*
Nitin Navare *(CTO)*
Alyene Schneidewind *(Chief Performance Officer)*
Julie Solliday *(Chief Customer Officer)*
Yvonne Schroder *(Chief Legal Officer & Gen Counsel)*
Ryan Worobel *(CIO)*

MINDBODY, Inc. (1)
651 Tank Farm Rd, San Luis Obispo, CA 93401
Web Site: http://www.mindbodyonline.com
Business Management Health & Wellness Software Mfr
N.A.I.C.S.: 513210
Josh McCarter *(CEO)*
Richard L. Stollmeyer *(Founder & Chm)*
Josh Todd *(CMO)*
Sunil Rajasekar *(Pres & CTO)*
Michelle Berlin *(Sr VP-People & Culture)*
Marti Menacho *(Sr VP-IT)*
Kevin Teague *(Sr VP-Startegic Accts)*
Aaron Stead *(Chief Revenue Officer)*
Javad Ra'ed *(VP-Strategic Accts)*
Fritz Lanman *(CEO)*

Subsidiary (Domestic):

Booker Software, Inc. (2)
165 Broadway Ste 702, New York, NY 10006
Web Site: http://www.booker.com
Cloud-Based Business Marketing & Management Services
N.A.I.C.S.: 518210
Josh McCarter *(Co-Founder)*

Market Track, LLC (1)
233 S Wacker Dr Ste 2105, Chicago, IL 60606
Tel.: (312) 529-5102
Web Site: http://www.markettrack.com
Market Intelligence & Promotional Advertising Services
N.A.I.C.S.: 541890

Eric Pablo *(Exec VP-Ops)*
Kevin Harakal *(COO)*
Dennis Moore *(CEO)*
Regan Garrett *(CFO)*
Mark Detelich *(Chief Strategy Officer & Chief Solutions Officer)*
Alex Hase *(Chief Sls Officer)*
Ryne Misso *(Dir-Mktg)*

Mediaocean LLC (1)
45 W 18th St, New York, NY 10011
Tel.: (212) 633-8100
Web Site: http://www.mediaocean.com
Emp.: 800
Advertising Software Developer
N.A.I.C.S.: 541511
Bill Wise *(CEO)*
Robert Smith *(Chm)*
Michael Donovan *(Vice Chm)*
Nick Galassi *(CFO & COO)*
Manu Warikoo *(Chief Product Officer)*
Vedant Sampath *(CTO)*
Ramsey McGrory *(Chief Revenue Officer)*
Matt Field *(Pres-Tech)*
Allison Wallace *(Gen Counsel)*
Andy Jacobson *(Sr VP-Sls)*
Cordie Depascale *(Sr VP-Connect Partner Mgmt)*
Drew Kane *(Exec VP-Platforms Solutions & Demand-Global)*
Gordon H. Cohen *(Exec VP-Agency Sys-Global)*
Stephanie Dorman *(Chief People Officer-Global)*
Bradley A. Keywell *(Co-Founder)*

Subsidiary (Domestic):

ColSpace Corporation (2)
41 E 11th St 9th Fl, New York, NY 10003
Tel.: (212) 699-3797
Web Site: http://www.colspace.com
Sales Range: $1-9.9 Million
Emp.: 21
Internet Service Provider
N.A.I.C.S.: 517810
Matthew Greenhouse *(CEO)*

Branch (Domestic):

Mediaocean LLC - Los Angeles (2)
12100 Wilshire Blvd, Los Angeles, CA 90025
Tel.: (310) 571-0580
Web Site: http://www.mediaocean.com
Custom Computer Programming Services
N.A.I.C.S.: 541511

Naviga Inc. (1)
7900 International Dr Ste 800, Bloomington, MN 55425
Tel.: (651) 639-0662
Web Site: http://www.navigaglobal.com
Technology Solutions for News Industry
N.A.I.C.S.: 513210
Dan Paulus *(Chief Revenue Officer)*
Scott Roessler *(CEO)*
Leo Brunnick *(Chief Digital Officer)*

Subsidiary (Non-US):

Abacus Software Limited (2)
21 Southampton Row, London, WC1B 5HA, United Kingdom
Tel.: (44) 2077669810
Web Site: http://www.abacusemedia.com
Web Development Services
N.A.I.C.S.: 541511
Daniel Murphy *(Dir-Comml)*

Subsidiary (Domestic):

Atex Media Inc. (2)
1 Highwood Dr Ste 302, Tewksbury, MA 01876-1156
Tel.: (781) 275-2323
Web Site: http://www.atex.com
Sales Range: $10-24.9 Million
Emp.: 25
Computer Software Development
N.A.I.C.S.: 541511
Peter G. Marsh *(VP-Product Mktg)*
Malcolm McGrory *(Dir-Sls-Global)*
Scott M. Fagan *(Dir-Digital Sls)*
Anders Christiansen *(CEO)*
Nishant Fafalia *(CFO)*
Federico Marturano *(Mng Dir-Italy)*
Giulio Mola *(Mgr-Dev-Global)*
Hans Olsson *(Mgr-Global Product)*
Gian Camillo Vezzoli *(Dir-Mktg)*
Tom York *(Dir-Svc & Support)*

COMPANIES
VISTA EQUITY PARTNERS, LLC

DoApp, Inc. (2)
3908 Huntington Ln NW, Rochester, MN 55901-4127
Tel.: (612) 659-8443
Web Site: http://www.doapps.com
Consumer & Business Website Developer
N.A.I.C.S.: 541511
Joe Sriver *(Founder)*
Wade Beavers *(CEO)*

Subsidiary (Non-US):

Miles 33 Limited (2)
Miles House Easthampstead Road, Bracknell, RG12 1NJ, Berkshire, United Kingdom
Tel.: (44) 1344861133
Web Site: http://www.miles33.com
Sales Range: $25-49.9 Million
Emp.: 150
Enterprise Wide Publishing Systems
N.A.I.C.S.: 513210
Michael Moore *(CEO)*
Peter Meek *(Dir-Ops & Content Mgmt)*
John Skarin *(Dir-Dev & Bus Sys)*
David Farlow *(Dir-Fin)*
Albert de Bruijn *(VP-Mktg)*
Chris Habasinski *(Pres-Ops-US)*

Subsidiary (Non-US):

MILES 33 SERVICOS EM INFORMATICA LTDA (3)
Rua Porto Carrero n 60 - apto 502 - Bairro Gutierrez, Belo Horizonte, Minas Gerais, Brazil
Tel.: (55) 31 3516 5353
Software Development Services
N.A.I.C.S.: 541511
Fabio Coelho *(Country Mgr)*

Subsidiary (US):

Miles 33 (3)
3900 Lennane Dr Ste 100, Sacramento, CA 95834
Tel.: (916) 830-2400
Web Site: http://www.miles33.com
Sales Range: $25-49.9 Million
Computer Integrated Systems Design Services
N.A.I.C.S.: 541511

Miles 33 International Ltd (3)
40 Richards Ave, Norwalk, CT 06854
Tel.: (916) 844-2437
Software Development Services
N.A.I.C.S.: 541511
Chris Habasinski *(Pres)*

Subsidiary (Non-US):

Tera D.P. S.r.l. (3)
Viale Certosa 148, 20156, Milan, Italy
Tel.: (39) 02 38 09 87 1
Software Development Services
N.A.I.C.S.: 541511
Franz Rossi *(Country Mgr)*
Gian Luigi Cavallo *(CEO)*

Branch (Domestic):

NEWSCYCLE Solutions (2)
302 Knights Run Ave Ste 1150, Tampa, FL 33602
Tel.: (813) 221-1600
Sales Range: $10-24.9 Million
Emp.: 90
Software Publisher
N.A.I.C.S.: 513210
Anders Christiansen *(COO)*
Marcel Badowski *(VP-Project Svcs)*
Pat Stewart *(VP-Dev)*
Peter Ibsen *(VP-Strategy & Product Mgmt)*

Subsidiary (Non-US):

NEWSCYCLE Solutions A/S (2)
Visionsvej 55, Aalborg, 9000, Denmark
Tel.: (45) 96 31 42 00
Web Site: http://www.newscyclesolutions.com
Emp.: 40
Software Publisher
N.A.I.C.S.: 513210
Mette Kvistgaard *(Dir-HR & Ops-EMEA)*
Carsten Bedsted Pedersen *(VP-Svcs-EMEA)*

NEWSCYCLE Solutions AB (2)
Brovagen 5, 182 76, Stocksund, Sweden
Tel.: (46) 8 768 18 92

Software Publisher
N.A.I.C.S.: 513210

NEWSCYCLE Solutions AS (2)
Stigerveien 12, 3031, Drammen, Norway
Tel.: (47) 32 82 42 00
Software Publisher
N.A.I.C.S.: 513210

Subsidiary (Domestic):

NEWSCYCLE Solutions Americas, LLC (2)
350 S 400 W Ste 200, Lindon, UT 84042
Tel.: (801) 853-5000
Sales Range: $25-49.9 Million
Emp.: 40
Newspaper Publishing Software Mfr & Distr
N.A.I.C.S.: 513210
Lisa Speth *(Mgr-Mktg Comm)*
Trent Schoonmaker *(VP-Sls Ops)*

Zinio, LLC (2)
575 Lexington Ave, New York, NY 10022
Tel.: (415) 494-2700
Web Site: http://in.zinio.com
Digital Publisher
N.A.I.C.S.: 513199

Omnitracs, LLC (1)
10290 Campus Point Dr, San Diego, CA 92121
Tel.: (858) 587-1121
Web Site: http://www.omnitracs.com
Wireless Solutions & Services
N.A.I.C.S.: 517112
David Vice *(Chief Sls Officer)*
Jim Gardner *(VP-Mktg)*
Mansoor Bajowala *(VP-Pro Svcs)*
Mike Ham *(VP & Gen Mgr-Canada)*
Brad Taylor *(VP-Data & IOT Solutions)*
David H. Arnold *(Gen Counsel & VP)*
Kevin Haugh *(Gen Mgr)*
Kent Norton *(CTO)*
Greg Nelson *(Chief Comml Officer)*
Stacey Martin *(Chief HR Officer)*
John Hoffman *(CFO)*
Ashim Bose *(VP-Artificial Intelligence, Machine Learning & Data Engrg Org)*
Paul Kirkpatrick *(Chief Legal Officer)*
Pam Marion *(Chief Customer Officer)*

Subsidiary (Domestic):

Roadnet Technologies, Inc. (2)
849 Fairmount Ave Ste 500, Towson, MD 21286
Tel.: (410) 847-1900
Web Site: http://www.roadnet.com
Sales Range: $25-49.9 Million
Emp.: 130
Fleet Management & Logistics Software
N.A.I.C.S.: 513210
Malcolm Hooker *(Dir-HR)*
Kevin Haugh *(VP & Gen Mgr)*
Joseph Vastine *(Mgr-Intl Project)*

VisTracks, Inc. (2)
801 Warrenville Rd Ste 50, Lisle, IL 60532-4332
Tel.: (630) 596-5420
Web Site: http://www.vistracks.com
Information Technology Consulting Services
N.A.I.C.S.: 541512
Robert H. Holt *(Sr VP-Product Dev)*
Jim Williams *(Exec VP-Managed Svc Platforms)*
Abraham Levine *(COO)*
Stephen G. Eick *(Pres & CEO)*

Ping Identity Corporation (1)
1001 17th St, Denver, CO 80202
Tel.: (303) 468-2900
Web Site: http://www.pingidentity.com
Sales Range: $25-49.9 Million
Emp.: 300
Software Developer
N.A.I.C.S.: 513210
Patrick Harding *(CTO)*
David Packer *(Sr VP-Field Ops)*
Fawad Zakariya *(VP-Bus Dev)*
Jennifer Caracciolo *(VP-People Ops)*
Lauren Romer *(Gen Counsel & VP)*
Steve Shoaff *(Chief Product Officer)*
Raj Dani *(CFO)*
Aaron LaPoint *(Chief HR Officer)*
Bart Hammond *(VP-Customer Success)*
Kris Nagel *(COO)*
Ed Roberto *(Gen Mgr-Cloud Software)*
Kevin Sellers *(CMO-Global)*
Jason Kees *(Chief Info Security Officer)*
Andre Durand *(CEO)*

Subsidiary (Non-US):

Ping Identity Australia Pty. Ltd. (2)
Level 27 101 Collins Street, Melbourne, 3000, VIC, Australia
Tel.: (61) 3 9653 7349
Software Developer
N.A.I.C.S.: 513210

Branch (Non-US):

Ping Identity Corporation (2)
600-564 Beatty Street, Vancouver, V6B 2L3, BC, Canada
Tel.: (604) 697-7040
Software Development Services
N.A.I.C.S.: 513210

Subsidiary (Domestic):

UnboundID Corp. (2)
13809 Research Blvd Ste 500, Austin, TX 78750 (100%)
Tel.: (512) 600-7700
Web Site: http://www.unboundid.com
Emp.: 100
Customer Identity & Access Management Software Developer
N.A.I.C.S.: 541511
Steve Shoaff *(Chief Product Officer)*

PlanSource Benefits Administration, Inc. (1)
101 S Garland Ave, Orlando, FL 32801
Web Site: http://www.plansource.com
Emp.: 210
Human Resources Software
N.A.I.C.S.: 513210
Dayne Williams *(Chm)*
Anita Messal *(Pres & COO)*
Ryan Baldwin *(CTO)*
Phil Carollo *(Exec VP-Sls)*
Bill Wheeler *(Sr VP-Strategic Channels)*
Nancy Sansom *(Chief Comml Officer)*
Adam Hameed *(Chief Revenue Officer)*
Bradley Taylor *(Exec VP-Bus Dev)*
Michael Cooper *(CFO)*
Tom Signorello *(CEO)*
Ewan Auguste *(CMO)*

Subsidiary (Domestic):

Next Generation Enrollment, Inc. (2)
455 Pettis Ave, Ada, MI 49301
Web Site: http://www.nextgenerationenrollment.com
Employee Benefit Plan Administration
N.A.I.C.S.: 923130
Beth Steimel *(Acct Mgr)*

PowerSchool Group LLC (1)
150 Parkshore Dr, Folsom, CA 95630
Web Site: http://www.powerschool.com
Assessment Tools & Student Information Systems Solutions
N.A.I.C.S.: 611710
Rich Gay *(Chief Information Security Officer & VP-Dev)*
Maulik Datanwala *(COO)*
Alan Taylor *(Sr VP-Corp Dev & IR)*
Craig Greenseid *(Chief Revenue Officer)*
Rishi Rana *(Gen Mgr-Higher Education)*
Anthony Miller *(CMO)*
Darron Flagg *(Chief Compliance Officer & Chief Privacy Officer)*
Eric Shander *(CFO)*
Devendra Singh *(CTO)*

Subsidiary (Domestic):

PeopleAdmin, Inc. (2)
805 Las Cimas Pkwy Ste 400, Austin, TX 78746
Web Site: http://www.peopleadmin.com
Human Resource Software for Schools & Government Agencies
N.A.I.C.S.: 334610
Tony Montoya *(VP-Sls)*
Traci Gregorski *(Head-Mktg & Strategic Alliances)*

Solera Holdings, Inc. (1)
1500 Solana Blvd Bldg #6 Ste #6300 3rd Fl, Westlake, TX 76262
Tel.: (817) 961-2100
Web Site: http://www.solera.com
Holding Company; Risk & Asset Management, Software & Technology
N.A.I.C.S.: 551112

Renato C. Giger *(CFO)*
Jason M. Brady *(Chief Admin Officer, Gen Counsel & Sec)*
Darko Dejanovic *(CEO)*

Subsidiary (Non-US):

AUTOonline B.V. (2)
Huis ter Heideweg 30, 3705 LZ, Zeist, Netherlands
Tel.: (31) 306935667
Web Site: http://www.autoonline.net
Application Software Processing & Services
N.A.I.C.S.: 541511

AUTOonline Italia S.r.l. (2)
Stefano Fortini Via Giovanni Boccaccio 27, Milan, 20123, Italy
Tel.: (39) 0248517712
Web Site: http://www.autoonline.it
Application Software Processing & Services
N.A.I.C.S.: 541511
Stefano Fortini *(Gen Mgr)*

AUTOonline Magyaroszag Kft. (2)
Devai Utca 26-28, 1134, Budapest, Hungary
Tel.: (36) 17808874
Web Site: http://www.autoonline.hu
Application Software Processing & Services
N.A.I.C.S.: 541511
Tamas Nagy *(Mng Dir)*

AUTOonline Otomotiv Bilgi Islem Anonim Sirketi (2)
Maslak Mah Sumer Sok Ayazaga is Merkezi No 3, B Blok Kat 1, Istanbul, Turkiye
Tel.: (90) 8502006200
Web Site: http://www.autoonline.com.tr
Automobile Insurance Claims Processing Software & Services
N.A.I.C.S.: 513210

AUTOonline Sisteme Informatice SRL (2)
Ermil Pangratti 30A 1st Floor sector 1, Bucharest, 011884, Romania
Tel.: (40) 212114243
Web Site: http://www.autoonline.co.ro
Automobile Insurance Claims Processing Software & Services
N.A.I.C.S.: 513210

Audatex (UK) Limited (2)
The Forum Station Road, Theale, RG7 4RA, Reading, United Kingdom
Tel.: (44) 1189323535
Web Site: http://www.audatex.co.uk
Automobile Insurance Claims Processing & Estimating Software & Services
N.A.I.C.S.: 524298
Nicola Mascard *(Dir-Ops)*
Arek Kulczynski *(Dir-HR)*
Elliot Roberts *(Dir-Product Mgmt)*
Annette Chamberlain *(Head-Mktg)*
Stewart Myles *(Head-New Bus Dev & Crash Repair)*
Marc Mercer *(Dir-UK FP&A)*
David Shepherd *(Dir-Reg Managing)*

Audatex Australia Pty Ltd. (2)
Level 1 100 Cubitt Street, Cremorne, 3121, VIC, Australia
Tel.: (61) 300080880
Web Site: http://www.audatex.com.au
Insurance Claims Processing Software & Services
N.A.I.C.S.: 513210

Audatex Daten Internationale Datenentwicklungsgesellschaft mbH (2)
Bahnhofstr 18, Unterfohring, 85774, Munich, Germany
Tel.: (49) 3020969101
Web Site: http://www.audatex.de
Automobile Insurance Claims Processing Software Services
N.A.I.C.S.: 513210
Rainer Ruhe *(Gen Mgr)*

Audatex Espana S.A. (2)
Avenida de Bruselas 36, Alcobendas, 28108, Spain
Tel.: (34) 916572000
Web Site: http://www.solerainc.es
Automobile Insurance Claims Processing Software Services
N.A.I.C.S.: 513210
Victor Munoz *(Mgr-Key Acct)*

Audatex Information System (China) Co., Ltd. (2)

VISTA EQUITY PARTNERS, LLC

U.S. PRIVATE

Vista Equity Partners, LLC—(Continued)

Unit 909-911 Shui On Plaza 333 Huai Hai Zhong Road, Shanghai, 200120, China
Tel.: (86) 2150366665
Web Site: http://www.audatex.com.cn
Insurance Claims Processing Software & Services
N.A.I.C.S.: 513210
Evan Feng *(Dir-Acct Mgr)*

Audatex LTN S. de R.L. de C.V. (2)
Prolongacion Paseo de la Reforma No 600 Floor 3 Office 301, Col Pena Blanca Santa Fe Delegation, Mexico, 01210, Mexico
Tel.: (52) 5530033100
Web Site: http://www.audatex.com.mx
Automobile Information Software Services; Insurance Processing
N.A.I.C.S.: 513210

Audatex Network Services Netherlands B.V. (2)
Huis Ter Heideweg 30, 3705 LZ, Zeist, Netherlands
Tel.: (31) 306935603
Web Site: http://www.abz.nl
Automobile Insurance Claims Processing Software Provider
N.A.I.C.S.: 513210
Erik Meinders *(Mgr)*

Subsidiary (Domestic):

Audatex North America, Inc. (2)
7701 Las Colinas Ridge Ste 500, Irving, TX 75062
Tel.: (858) 946-1900
Web Site: http://www.audatex.us
Automobile Insurance Claims Processing & Estimating Software & Services
N.A.I.C.S.: 524298

Subsidiary (Non-US):

Audatex Canada, ULC (3)
1210 Sheppard Ave East Suite 204, North York, Toronto, M2K 1E3, ON, Canada
Web Site: https://www.audatex.ca
Automobile Insurance Claims Processing & Estimating Software Developer
N.A.I.C.S.: 524298
Atul Vohra *(Reg Mng Dir-Australia, Canada & India)*
Michel Caron *(VP-Sls, Dealer Fixed Operations, and Collision Repair Solutions)*
Roger Ryckewaert *(VP-Client Delivery & Professional Svcs)*

Subsidiary (Non-US):

Audatex Osterreich Ges.mbH (2)
Garnisongasse 1/1/21, 1090, Vienna, Austria
Tel.: (43) 135024100
Web Site: http://www.audatex.at
Insurance Claims Management Software Developer
N.A.I.C.S.: 513210

Audatex Polska Sp. z.o.o. (2)
Ul Marcelinska 90, Poznan, 60-324, Poland
Tel.: (48) 618862470
Web Site: http://www.audanet.pl
Autobody Repairs & Automobile Insurance Claims Processing Software
N.A.I.C.S.: 811198

Audatex Portugal Peritagens Informatizadas Derivadas de Acidentes, S.A. (2)
Edificio Infante Avenida D Joao II N 35 10 Piso, 1990-083, Lisbon, Portugal
Tel.: (351) 217232800
Web Site: http://www.solera.pt
Automobile Insurance Claims Processing Software Services
N.A.I.C.S.: 513210

Audatex Services SRL (2)
Str Ermil Pangratti nr 30A floor 1, sect 1, 011884, Bucharest, Romania
Tel.: (40) 213186525
Web Site: http://www.audanet.de
Automobile Insurance Claims Processing Software & Services
N.A.I.C.S.: 513210

Audatex Singapore Pte Ltd (2)
7 Temasek Boulevard Level 44 Suntec Tower One, Singapore, 038987, Singapore
Tel.: (65) 9181 4726
Web Site: http://audatex.com.sg
Automobile Insurance Claims Processing Software & Services
N.A.I.C.S.: 513210

Audatex Slovakia s.r.o. (2)
POLUS TOWER I 16 p Vajnorska 100/A, 831 04, Bratislava, Slovakia
Tel.: (421) 244630252
Web Site: http://www.audatex.sk
Automobile Insurance Claims Processing Software Provider
N.A.I.C.S.: 513210

Audatex Switzerland GmbH (2)
Elias-Canetti-Strasse 2, 8050, Zurich, Switzerland
Tel.: (41) 442788888
Web Site: http://www.audatex.ch
Automobile Insurance Claims Processing & Estimating Software Developer
N.A.I.C.S.: 524298
Marcel Schradt *(Mng Dir)*
Robert Hasler *(Head-Bus Delivery)*
Francesco Galvani *(Head-Sls)*
Steffen Lenz *(Head-IT)*

Audatex Systems Bilgi Teknolojileri Hizmetleri Limted Sirketi (2)
Maslak Mah Sumer Sok Ayazaga Tic Central, No.3 B Block Floor 1, Istanbul, Turkiye
Tel.: (90) 850 200 62 62
Web Site: http://www.cee.audatex.net
Insurance Claims Processing Software & Services
N.A.I.C.S.: 513210

Audatex Systems s.r.o. (2)
Zeletavska 1449/9, Prague 4, 140 00, Prague, Czech Republic
Tel.: (420) 272101777
Web Site: http://www.audatex.cz
Automobile Insurance Claims Processing Software Developer
N.A.I.C.S.: 513210

Subsidiary (Domestic):

Auto Point, Inc. (2)
10808 S River Front Pkwy Ste 500, South Jordan, UT 84095
Tel.: (877) 567-4349
Web Site: http://www.autopoint.com
Service Maintenance Repair; Automobile Dealership Management Software & Solutions
N.A.I.C.S.: 513210

DealerSocket, Inc. (2)
7301 State Hwy 161 Ste 400, Irving, TX 75039
Tel.: (949) 900-0300
Web Site: http://www.dealersocket.com
Sales Range: $25-49.9 Million
Emp.: 200
Automobile Dealership Management Software Developer & Publisher
N.A.I.C.S.: 513210
Jonathan Ord *(Co-Founder)*
Neha Patel *(VP & Head-Strategic Project Mgmt Office)*
Brad Perry *(Co-Founder & CTO-Dev)*
Reuben Muinos *(Dir-Bus Dev & Sls)*
Sam Rizek *(Dir-Bus Dev-Canada)*
Brandon Piersant *(Dir-Mktg)*
Nathan Usher *(Dir-Product Mgmt & Dev)*
Hunter Swift *(Dir-Sls Dev & Sls)*
Greg Reynolds *(CTO)*
Sejal Pietrzak *(Pres & CEO)*
Amber Skvarca *(VP-Customer Support)*
Brian Wagner *(VP-Ops)*
Bridget Townsend *(VP-Vendor Mgmt)*
Jared Kirkwood *(VP-Legal Affairs)*
Jennifer Lee *(VP-Customer Success)*
Jose Arcilla *(COO)*
Bryan Klann *(Chief Revenue Officer)*
Gary Ito *(CFO)*
Max Steckler *(Gen Mgr-DealerFire)*

Subsidiary (Domestic):

Auto/Mate, Inc. (3)
4 Airline Dr, Albany, NY 12205
Web Site: http://www.automate.com
Emp.: 180
Auto Dealership Management Software Developer & Publisher
N.A.I.C.S.: 513210
Mike Esposito *(Pres & CEO)*
Brian Davis *(Reg Sls Mgr-Mid-Atlantic Territory)*
Mike Siomacco *(District Mgr-East Coast)*

Autostar Solutions, Inc. (3)
1300 Summit Ave Ste 800, Fort Worth, TX 76102
Tel.: (817) 377-2995
Web Site: http://www.autostarsolutions.com
Sales Range: $1-9.9 Million
Emp.: 15
Computer Softwares Mfr
N.A.I.C.S.: 423430
Allen Dobbins *(Pres)*
Samuel Bohon *(Mgr-Mktg)*
Elbert Tilghman *(Gen Mgr)*
David Sertner *(Sr Mgr-Implementation)*
Jenny Lombardi *(Project Mgr)*
Antonio Rajan *(Chief Revenue Officer)*
David Finan *(Mgr-Tech Support)*
Robbie Hudson *(Mgr-IT)*
Steve Levine *(Chief Legal & Compliance Officer)*
Russ Asbury *(CFO)*

Finance Express, LLC (3)
30071 Tomas Ste 250, Rancho Santa Margarita, CA 92688
Tel.: (949) 635-5892
Web Site: http://www.financeexpress.com
Automobile Dealership Management System Software Developer & Publisher
N.A.I.C.S.: 513210
David Huber *(Founder, Pres & CEO)*

Subsidiary (Domestic):

Enservio, Inc. (2)
117 Kendrick St Ste 250, Needham, MA 02494
Tel.: (888) 567-7557
Web Site: http://www.enservio.com
Emp.: 400
Contents Software & Inventory Services; Claim Payment Solutions
N.A.I.C.S.: 541511
Jay Guden *(Sr VP-Ops)*
Robert Chase *(Mng Dir)*
Neil Murphy *(Chief Fin & Operating Officer)*
Joseph Bracken *(VP-Strategy & Bus Dev)*
Joel Makhluf *(VP-Mktg)*
Jen Walmsley *(VP-Ops)*
Chris Mills *(VP-Product)*

Explore Information Services, LLC (2)
2750 Blue Water Rd #200, Eagan, MN 55121
Tel.: (800) 531-9125
Web Site: http://www.exploredata.com
Data Solutions & Services
N.A.I.C.S.: 518210

GTS Services, LLC (2)
4211 SE International Way Ste A, Portland, OR 97222
Tel.: (800) 563-8555
Web Site: http://www.gtsservices.com
Glass Industry Software Products Publisher
N.A.I.C.S.: 513210
Stephen Branch *(Mgr-Bus Dev)*
Peter Keomanivanh *(Engr-Test Automation)*
Eddie Medina *(Acct Mgr)*
Linh Pham *(Engr-Sys)*
Sarah Salo *(Mgr-Bus Dev)*
Jeff VanSant *(Engr-Software)*

Subsidiary (Non-US):

HPI Limited (2)
Bond Court Wine Street, Leeds, LS1 5EZ, United Kingdom
Tel.: (44) 845 300 8905
Web Site: http://www.hpi.co.uk
Automobile Insurance Claims Processing Software & Services
N.A.I.C.S.: 518210

Hollander International Systems Limited (2)
Birch House 10 Bankhead Crossway South, Edinburgh, EH11 4EP, United Kingdom
Tel.: (44) 1315388538
Web Site: http://www.hollandereu.com
Automotive Recyclers System, Support & Service
N.A.I.C.S.: 423930
Dave Morgan *(Mgr-Interchange Product)*
Phil Peace *(Assoc Mng Dir)*

Chad Meyer *(Sr Dir-Product Mgmt)*
Mary Moberg *(Mktg Dir)*
Pravin Wilson *(Sr Dir-Software Engrg)*
Paul Cunningham *(Dir-Svc Delivery)*

Subsidiary (Domestic):

Identifix, Inc. (2)
2714 Patton Rd, Saint Paul, MN 55113
Tel.: (651) 633-8007
Web Site: http://www.identifix.com
Online Diagnostics, Factory Scheduled Maintenance & OEM Service & Repair
N.A.I.C.S.: 519290

Subsidiary (Non-US):

Informex S.A. (2)
Avenue Jules Bordet 168, 1140, Evere, Belgium
Tel.: (32) 27053500
Web Site: http://www.informex.be
Automobile Insurance Claims Processing Software & Services
N.A.I.C.S.: 513210
Olivier Staquet *(Gen Mgr)*
Hubert Bouhon *(Mgr-Tech Svcs)*
Jean-Francois Cherry *(Project Coordinator)*

Subsidiary (Domestic):

International Automotive Technicians' Network, Inc. (2)
640 W Lambert Rd, Brea, CA 92821
Tel.: (714) 257-1335
Web Site: http://www.iatn.net
Automotive Repair Professional Network
N.A.I.C.S.: 813910

Subsidiary (Non-US):

LLC Audatex Ukraine (2)
Kiev Svyatoshinsky district staLenin 1-B 4th Floor, Petropavlovskaya Borshchagovka, Kiev, 8130, Ukraine
Tel.: (380) 445865270
Web Site: http://www.audatex.ua
Automobile Insurance Claims Processing Software & Services
N.A.I.C.S.: 513210
Alexander Drobot *(Mng Dir)*

Subsidiary (Domestic):

LYNX Services, LLC (2)
6351 Bayshore Rd Ste 18, Fort Myers, FL 33917-3172
Tel.: (239) 479-6000
Web Site: http://www.lynxservices.com
Automotive Glass Insurance Claims Management Services
N.A.I.C.S.: 524298
John Wysseier *(Mng Dir)*
Brian Dvoroznak *(CFO-Solera Insurance Svcs)*
Bill O'Brien *(Bus Dir-Auto Physical Damage & FNOL)*
Paul Hoonjan *(Assoc VP-Customer Ops)*
Matt Olivo *(Dir-Call Center Ops-Fort Myers Florida)*
Paul McFarland *(Sr Dir-Supply Chain Mgmt & Auto Glass Claims Admin)*
Jignesh Modi *(Dir-IT)*
Lisa Langford *(Mgr-Product Dev & Integration-Auto Glass)*
Betsy Evanoff *(Project Mgr)*
Gary Bob Smith *(Acct Mgr-Strategic)*
Peter Masci *(Acct Mgr-Strategic)*
Barry Roberts *(Exec Acct Mgr & Mgr-ARG Alliance Glass Programs)*
Shireen Wedlock *(Mgr-Product Dev & Integration-First Notice Of Loss)*

License Monitor, Inc. (2)
169 S Main St #350, New City, NY 10956
Tel.: (800) 303-8063
Web Site: http://www.licensemonitor.net
Risk Management; Driver Data Management System
N.A.I.C.S.: 513210

Navex, Inc. (2)
5118 Park Ave Ste 106, Memphis, TN 38141
Tel.: (901) 363-9233
Web Site: http://www.navexinc.net
Automotive & Tire Markets Point of Sale Services
N.A.I.C.S.: 541512

VISTA EQUITY PARTNERS, LLC

Subsidiary (Non-US):

OOO Audatex (2)
Ul Argunovskaya 3 Bldg 1 3rd Floor, Moscow, 129075, Russia
Tel.: (7) 4994900770
Web Site: http://audatex.ru
Automobile Insurance Claims Processing Software & Services
N.A.I.C.S.: 513210

Subsidiary (Domestic):

See Progress, Inc. (2)
880 Technology Dr Ste A, Ann Arbor, MI 48108
Tel.: (877) 977-6473
Web Site: http://web.autowatch.com
Vehicle Repair Monitoring Services
N.A.I.C.S.: 513210

Subsidiary (Non-US):

Solera Italia s.r.l. (2)
Via Giovanni Boccaccio 27, Milan, 20123, Italy
Tel.: (39) 024983932
Web Site: http://www.soleraitalia.it
Automobile Information Software Services
N.A.I.C.S.: 513210

cap hpi Limited (2)
Capitol House Bond Court, Leeds, LS1 5EZ, W Yorkshire, United Kingdom
Tel.: (44) 113 222 2000
Web Site: http://www.cap-hpi.com
Vehicle Pricing, Technical Information & Services
N.A.I.C.S.: 513210

Subsidiary (Domestic):

eDriving, LLC (2)
211 Bayberry Dr Stes 1E & F, Cape May, NJ 08210
Tel.: (855) 999-9094
Web Site: http://www.edriving.com
Online Driving Services
N.A.I.C.S.: 458110
Jeff Grant (COO & Exec VP-eDriving Consumer)
Ross Green (CFO)
Ed Dubens (Founder & CEO)
Frank N. Chen (CTO & Sr VP-Engrg)
Gary Tsifrin (Chief Strategy Officer)
Heather Odom (VP-People Ops)
Chris Boyd (Sr VP-Product & Engrg)

Stats Perform (1)
203 N Lasalle St Ste 2200, Chicago, IL 60601
Tel.: (847) 583-2100
Sports Artificial Intelligence & Data Solutions
N.A.I.C.S.: 513210
Carl E. Mergele (CEO)
Steve Xeller (Chief Revenue Officer)
Reed Findlay (Mgr-Corp Comm)
Jason Markworth (VP-Sls-Americas)
Nancy Hensley (Chief Product & Mktg Officer)

Subsidiary (Non-US):

DAZN Group Limited (2)
Sussex House Plane Tree Crescent, Feltham, TW13 7HE, Mddx, United Kingdom (87.31%)
Tel.: (44) 2033720600
Web Site: http://www.performgroup.com
Sales Range: $300-349.9 Million
Emp.: 1,345
Holding Company
N.A.I.C.S.: 551112
Neil Colligan (COO)
James Rushton (CEO-Perform OTT)
Simon Denyer (Founder & CEO)
Stefano D'Anna (Mng Dir-Worldwide Sls & Brand Partnerships)
John Gleasure (Chief Comml Officer-New Ventures)
Ross MacEacharn (CEO-Perform Content)
Ben Warn (Mng Dir-Consumer Brands & Portals)
Florian Diederichsen (CTO)
Ben Wam (CEO-New Ventures)
Juan Delgado (CEO-Media)
Jacopo Tonoli (Chief Comml Officer)
Ashley Milton (CFO)
Kevin Mayer (Chm)

Subsidiary (US):

Goal.com North America, Inc. (3)
Park Ave S 470 11th Fl, New York, NY 10016
Tel.: (212) 500-0650
Web Site: http://www.goal.com
Internet Broadcasting Services
N.A.I.C.S.: 516210
Mike Slane (Mng Editor)

Subsidiary (Non-US):

Mangalore Sports Data India Private Limited (3)
North Block Soorya Infratech Park Melkar Cross Road, Mudipu, Mangalore, 574153, India
Tel.: (91) 824 4259894
Web Site: http://www.performgroup.com
Internet Broadcasting Services
N.A.I.C.S.: 516210
Rajesh D'Souza (Mgr-Ops)
Sowbhagya Shetty (Asst Mgr)

Perform Media Asia Pte Ltd (3)
137 Telok Ayer Street Ste 04-01, Singapore, 068602, Singapore
Tel.: (65) 64239585
Web Site: http://www.performgroup.com
Emp.: 20
Internet Broadcasting Services
N.A.I.C.S.: 516210
James Rushton (Gen Mgr)

Perform Media Deutschland GmbH (3)
Beta-Strasse 9A, 85774, Unterfohring, Germany
Tel.: (49) 89 200014 3290
Web Site: http://www.spox.com
Internet Broadcasting Services
N.A.I.C.S.: 516210
Florian Regelmann (Dir-Content)
Thomas Gaber (Head-Svcs)
Andreas Lehner (Head-Football)

Subsidiary (US):

Perform Media Inc (3)
470 Park Ave S, New York, NY 10016
Tel.: (646) 918-8256
Web Site: http://www.performgroup.com
Internet Broadcasting Services
N.A.I.C.S.: 516210

Subsidiary (Non-US):

Perform Media Japan KK (3)
6F Azabu KF Bldg 1-9-7 Azabujuban, Minato-ku, Tokyo, 106-0045, Japan
Tel.: (81) 3 4550 1894
Web Site: http://www.performgroup.com
Emp.: 10
Internet Broadcasting Services
N.A.I.C.S.: 516210
Yusuke Masuda (Sr Bus Mgr)

Perform Media Poland Zoo (3)
Aleja Wojciecha Korfantego 2 Pietro 4-D / Numer 448, 40-004, Katowice, Poland
Tel.: (48) 327 971 948
Web Site: http://www.performgroup.com
Internet Broadcasting Services
N.A.I.C.S.: 516210

Perform Media Services SRL (3)
Via Manuzio 7, 20124, Milan, Italy
Tel.: (39) 02 00638091
Web Site: http://www.performgroup.com
Internet Broadcasting Services
N.A.I.C.S.: 516210
Jacopo Tonoli (Chief Comml Officer)

Sportal GmbH (3)
Spaldingstrasse 64-68, 20097, Hamburg, Germany
Tel.: (49) 40 414004 0
Web Site: http://www.sportal.de
Internet Broadcasting Services
N.A.I.C.S.: 516210
Dirk Ifsen (Mng Dir)

Sportal New Zealand Pty Ltd (3)
Level 1 19 Graham Street, Auckland, New Zealand
Tel.: (64) 93779550
Web Site: http://www.performgroup.com
Internet Broadcasting Services
N.A.I.C.S.: 516210

James Rushton (Mng Dir)

mediasports Digital GmbH (3)
Gerhofstrasse 18, 20354, Hamburg, Germany
Tel.: (49) 40 348098 100
Web Site: http://www.mediasports.de
Internet Broadcasting Services
N.A.I.C.S.: 516210
Dirk Ifsen (Mng Dir)

Subsidiary (Domestic):

STATS LLC (2)
2775 Shermer Rd, Northbrook, IL 60062
Tel.: (847) 583-2100
Web Site: http://www.stats.com
Sales Range: $50-74.9 Million
Sports Data & Statistics
N.A.I.C.S.: 519290
Jodi Murphy (Acct Exec-Sls)
Greg Kirkorsky (Exec VP-Sls & Mktg)
Deborah Klein (Gen Counsel & Sr VP)
Ryan Paterson (Mng Dir)
Kirsten Porter (VP-Global Mktg)
Jordan Rosen (Sr VP-Corp Dev & Strategic Partnerships)
Robert L. Schur (COO)
Jayme Fuller (Sr VP-Partner Dev-Global)
Helen Sun (CTO)
Steve Xeller (Chief Revenue Officer)
Carl Mergele (CEO)
Jill Hansen (CFO)
Derk Osenberg (Dir-Sls)

Subsidiary (Domestic):

TVT Video Technologies, Inc. (3)
2056 NW Aloclek Dr Ste 313, Hillsboro, OR 97124
Tel.: (503) 466-1446
Web Site: http://www.stats.com
Emp.: 10
Video Technology & Engineering Solutions
N.A.I.C.S.: 513210
Justin W. Cole (Mgr-Ops)
Ken Rhodes (Co-Founder)
Mark W. Watson (Co-Founder)

TIBCO Software Inc. (1)
3307 Hillview Ave, Palo Alto, CA 94304
Tel.: (650) 846-1000
Web Site: http://www.tibco.com
Service-Oriented Architecture, Business Process Management & Business Optimization Software; Computer System Design, Integration & Installation Services
N.A.I.C.S.: 513210
William R. Hughes (Chief Admin Officer, Gen Counsel & Exec VP)
Matt Quinn (COO)
Vivek Rao (Sr VP-Pro Svcs-Global)
Michele Haddad (Sr VP-HR-Global)
Nelson Petracek (CTO)
Scott Roza (Pres & Head-Customer Ops)
Rani Johnson (CIO)

Subsidiary (Domestic):

Information Builders Inc. (2)
2 Penn Plz, New York, NY 10121-0101
Tel.: (212) 736-4433
Web Site: http://www.ibi.com
Sales Range: $300-349.9 Million
Emp.: 1,750
Computer Software Developer
N.A.I.C.S.: 541512
Gerald D. Cohen (Founder)
Michael Corcoran (CMO & Sr VP)
Harry Lerner (CFO & Sr VP)
David Sandel (Sr VP-Bus Intelligence Products Grp)
John G. Senor (Chief Dev Officer)
Monte Roy (Sr VP-North American Sls)
David Small (Sr VP-Intl)
Bill Macy (VP-Sls-Eastern Area)
Rich Hall (VP-Sls-Central Area)
Bob Gabriel (Sr VP-Pro Svcs)
Dave Upton (VP-Sls-Southern Area)
Dennis Bartels (VP-iWay Sls-Europe)
Gregory Dorman (Gen Mgr-iWay Software)
Tom Villani (VP-Bus Dev & Strategic Alliances)
Ron Iwersen (Sr VP-Systems & Comm)
Jeremy Ballanco (VP-iWare Software Sls)
Lyndsay Wise (Dir-Solution)
Frank J. Vella (CEO)
Brian Doheny (VP-Bus Dev-Global)
Bill Harmer (Sr VP-Europe, Middle East & Africa)

Subsidiary (Non-US):

Information Builders (Canada) Inc. (3)
150 York Street Suite 1000, Toronto, M5H 3S5, ON, Canada
Tel.: (416) 364-2760
Web Site: http://www.informationbuilders.com
Sales Range: $10-24.9 Million
Emp.: 60
Computer Services
N.A.I.C.S.: 541512

Branch (Domestic):

Information Builders (Canada) - Calgary (4)
150 6th Ave Southwest Ste 3000, Calgary, T2P 3Y7, AB, Canada
Tel.: (403) 538-5415
Computer Services
N.A.I.C.S.: 541512

Information Builders (Canada) - Vancouver (4)
1050 West Pender Street Suite 2110, Vancouver, V6E 3S7, BC, Canada
Tel.: (604) 688-2479
Web Site: http://www.informationbuilders.com
Computer Services
N.A.I.C.S.: 541512

Subsidiary (Non-US):

Information Builders (Deutschland) GmbH (3)
Mergenthaler Allee 35-37, Eschborn, 65760, Germany
Tel.: (49) 6196775760
Web Site: http://www.informationbuilders.de
Sales Range: $10-24.9 Million
Emp.: 18
Computer Services
N.A.I.C.S.: 541512
Dave Small (VP)

Information Builders Belgium (3)
Bldg Brand Withlocklaan 114, PO Box 6, 1200, Brussels, Belgium
Tel.: (32) 27430240
Web Site: http://www.informationbuilders.be
Sales Range: $10-24.9 Million
Emp.: 11
Computer Services
N.A.I.C.S.: 541512
Frans De Neve (Dir-IT)
Sylvain Pavlowski (Sr VP-Sls-Europe)

Information Builders France (3)
2 Rue Troyon, 92316, Sevres, Cedex, France
Tel.: (33) 145076600
Web Site: http://www.informationbuilders.fr
Sales Range: $10-24.9 Million
Emp.: 15
Computer Services
N.A.I.C.S.: 541512

Information Builders Mexico (3)
Paseo de la Reforma No 265 Piso 14, Col Cuauhtemoc, 06500, Mexico, DF, Mexico
Tel.: (52) 5552085620
Web Site: http://www.informationbuilders.com.mx
Computer Services
N.A.I.C.S.: 541512

Information Builders Netherlands (3)
Dr Willem Dreesweg 2, Amstelveen, 1185 VB, Netherlands
Tel.: (31) 204563333
Web Site: http://www.informationbuilders.nl
Sales Range: $10-24.9 Million
Emp.: 25
Computer Services
N.A.I.C.S.: 541512
Roland Kinket (Dir-Svcs)
Dennis Bartels (Dir-Sls)

Information Builders Portugal (3)
Centro de Escritorios das Laranjeiras Praca Nuno Rodrigues dos, Santo 7, Lisbon, 1600 171, Portugal
Tel.: (351) 217217400
Web Site: http://www.informationbuilders.pt
Sales Range: $10-24.9 Million
Emp.: 2
Computer Services

VISTA EQUITY PARTNERS, LLC

U.S. PRIVATE

Vista Equity Partners, LLC—(Continued)
N.A.I.C.S.: 541512
Antonio Mendes *(Mgr-Sls)*

Information Builders Pty., Ltd. (3)
20 Queen Street Level 6, Melbourne, 3000, VIC, Australia
Tel.: (61) 396317900
Web Site: http://www.informationbuilders.com.au
Sales Range: $10-24.9 Million
Emp.: 10
Software Solutions for Business Intelligence & Analytics
N.A.I.C.S.: 541512
Brian McLaughlin *(VP-Intl Ops)*

Information Builders Spain (3)
C/Joaquin Turina, Pozuelo de Alarcon, Madrid, 28224, Spain
Tel.: (34) 917102275
Web Site: http://www.informationbuilders.es
Sales Range: $10-24.9 Million
Emp.: 100
Computer Services
N.A.I.C.S.: 541512
John Manning *(Dir-Technical)*
Elena Llorente *(Dir-Fin)*

Information Builders Switzerland (3)
Loorenstrasse 9, CH 8305, Dietlikon, Switzerland
Tel.: (41) 18394949
Web Site: http://www.informationbuilders.ch
Computer Services
N.A.I.C.S.: 541512
Dieter Wolf *(Country Mgr)*

Information Builders UK (3)
Beaufort House Cricket Field Rd, Uxbridge, UB8 1QG, Middx, United Kingdom
Tel.: (44) 8456588484
Web Site: http://www.informationbuilders.co.uk
Sales Range: $10-24.9 Million
Emp.: 40
Computer Services
N.A.I.C.S.: 541512
Heidi Marron *(Office Mgr)*

Subsidiary (Domestic):

Jaspersoft Corporation (2)
350 Rhode Island St Ste 250, San Francisco, CA 94103
Tel.: (415) 348-2300
Web Site: http://www.jaspersoft.com
Business Intelligence Software Publisher, Whslr & Support Services
N.A.I.C.S.: 513210
Matthew Geise *(Sr Dir-Global Web & Community)*
Ann K. Freccero *(Dir-Mktg Ops)*

Subsidiary (Non-US):

Jaspersoft GmbH (3)
Balanstrasse 49, 60322, Munich, Germany
Tel.: (49) 89 48956 000
Web Site: http://www.jaspersoft.com
Business Intelligence Software Whslr & Support Services
N.A.I.C.S.: 423430
Peter Sander *(Mgr-Sls-DACH & Central Europe)*

Jaspersoft Limited (3)
The Grainstore The Digital Hub, Dublin, D08 TCV4, Ireland
Tel.: (353) 1 443 4700
Web Site: http://www.jaspersoft.com
Business Intelligence Software Whslr & Support Services
N.A.I.C.S.: 423430
Ernesto Ongaro *(Sr Mgr-Product Mktg)*

Jaspersoft Sarl (3)
25 rue Balzac, 75008, Paris, France
Tel.: (33) 1 4451 7094
Web Site: http://www.jaspersoft.com
Business Intelligence Software Whslr & Support Services
N.A.I.C.S.: 423430
Georges Carbonnel *(Reg Mgr-Sls)*

Subsidiary (Domestic):

Proginet LLC (2)
200 Garden City Plz Ste 220, Garden City, NY 11530
Tel.: (516) 535-3600
Web Site: http://www.proginet.com
Sales Range: $1-9.9 Million
Emp.: 37
Software Developer Enabling Secure Internet Exchange of Electronic Documents
N.A.I.C.S.: 513210
Tom Bauer *(CTO)*

TIBCO Loglogic LLC (2)
3303 Hillview Ave, Palo Alto, CA 94304
Tel.: (650) 846-1000
Web Site: http://www.tibco.com
Sales Range: $25-49.9 Million
Software Development Services
N.A.I.C.S.: 513210
Walt Banham *(Mgr-NAM/SAM Support)*

Subsidiary (Non-US):

TIBCO Software (Beijing) Co., Ltd. (2)
No 2 Haidian Dongsan Street Haidian District Suite 701-30 7/F, Beijing, 100080, China
Tel.: (86) 1065637955
Business Management Software
N.A.I.C.S.: 513210

TIBCO Software AB (2)
Farogatan 33 Kista Science Tower, 164 51, Kista, Sweden
Tel.: (46) 86197700
Web Site: http://www.tibco.com
Business Management Software
N.A.I.C.S.: 513210
Bengt Rogsater *(Dir-Nordic Reg)*

TIBCO Software Hong Kong Limited (2)
33 Hysan Ave Lee Garden One Room 3301, Causeway Bay, China (Hong Kong)
Tel.: (852) 22640835
Business Management Software
N.A.I.C.S.: 513210

Branch (Domestic):

TIBCO Software Inc. - Boston (2)
281 Summer St 3rd Fl, Boston, MA 02210
Tel.: (617) 859-6800
Web Site: http://spotfire.tibco.com
Computer Software Development & Applications
N.A.I.C.S.: 541511

Subsidiary (Domestic):

TIBCO Extended Results, Inc. (3)
1700 Westlake Ave N, Seattle, WA 98109-3012
Tel.: (206) 283-8802
Web Site: http://spotfire.tibco.com
Sales Range: $1-9.9 Million
Technology & Business Intelligence Services
N.A.I.C.S.: 513210
Aaron Meyers *(Mgr-Program)*
Tom Hurley *(VP-Engrg)*

Branch (Domestic):

TIBCO Software Inc. - Princeton (2)
707 State Rd Ste 212, Princeton, NJ 08540
Tel.: (609) 683-4002
Web Site: http://www.tibco.com
Emp.: 20
Inexact Data Matching Software Developer & Publisher
N.A.I.C.S.: 513210

Subsidiary (Non-US):

TIBCO Software Korea Ltd. (2)
158-24 Dongsung Bldg 3rd Fl Samseong-dong, Gangnam-gu, Seoul, 06169, Korea (South)
Tel.: (82) 25010610
Web Site: http://www.tibco.com
Sales Range: $10-24.9 Million
Emp.: 13
Business Management Software Development Services
N.A.I.C.S.: 513210
Jaeyoung Ju *(Country Mgr)*

TIBCO Software Limited (2)
110 Bishopsgate Floor 23, London, EC2N 4AY, United Kingdom
Tel.: (44) 203 817 8500
Web Site: http://www.tibco.com
Emp.: 70
Business Management Software
N.A.I.C.S.: 513210
Sakina Riviera *(Office Mgr)*

TIBCO Software N.V. (2)
Avenue Louise 65, PO Box 11, 1050, Brussels, Belgium
Tel.: (32) 25357813
Business Management Software
N.A.I.C.S.: 513210

TIBCO Software Portugal (2)
Quinta da Fonte Edifficio Dom Pedro 1, Paco D'Arcos, 2780-730, Lisbon, Portugal
Tel.: (351) 210001745
Business Management Software
N.A.I.C.S.: 513210

TIBCO Software SA de CV (2)
Av Presidente Masaryk No 111 Piso 1, Col Chapultepec Morales, Mexico, 11560, Mexico
Tel.: (52) 5591712002
Business Management Software
N.A.I.C.S.: 513210

TIBCO Software Singapore Pte Ltd. (2)
1 Raffles Quay North Tower 34-02A 34-03, Singapore, 048619, Singapore
Tel.: (65) 68363880
Web Site: http://www.tibco.com
Business Management Software
N.A.I.C.S.: 513210

TIBCO Yazilim Sanayi Ve Ticaret Limited Sirketi (2)
Buyukdere Cd No 173/A Kat 7 Levent Plaza, 34220, Istanbul, Turkiye
Tel.: (90) 212 386 3233
Business Management Software
N.A.I.C.S.: 513210

Telarix, Inc. (1)
1950 Old Gallows Rd 8th Fl, Vienna, VA 22182-2789
Tel.: (703) 564-9600
Web Site: http://www.telarix.com
Computer Software Services
N.A.I.C.S.: 513210
Marco Limena *(CEO)*
Rich Marano *(COO)*
Mike Salsbury *(Gen Counsel)*
Dan Dooley III *(Chief Revenue Officer)*

Subsidiary (Non-US):

Starhome Mach GmbH (2)
Seefeldstrasse 25, CH 8008, Zurich, Switzerland
Tel.: (41) 44 380 6777
Web Site: http://www.starhomemach.com
Sales Range: $200-249.9 Million
Cellular Roaming & Techology Services
N.A.I.C.S.: 517112
Shlomo Wolfman *(Co-Founder & COO)*
Tal Meirzon *(CEO)*
Meyrav Apirion *(VP-HR)*
Adi Sfadia *(CFO)*
Bruno Pagliuca *(COO)*
Neta Bloch *(Gen Counsel)*
Yishay Schwerd *(VP-R&D)*
Tamir Ron *(VP-Product & Strategy)*
Lena Wittbjer *(Chief Admin Officer)*
Guy Reiffer *(VP-Mktg & Partnerships)*
Ital Margalit *(VP-Sls)*

Subsidiary (Non-US):

Starhome Mach (3)
5 Heienhaff, 1736, Senningerberg, Luxembourg
Tel.: (352) 27 775 100
Web Site: http://www.starhomemach.com
Sales Range: $25-49.9 Million
Roaming Data Fraud Management Services
N.A.I.C.S.: 513210
Itai Margalit *(CEO)*
Maya Elkayam *(CFO)*
Neta Bloch *(Gen Counsel)*

Trgrp, Inc. (1)
2 Grand Central Tower 140 E 45th St 11th Fl, New York, NY 10017
Tel.: (212) 499-2680
Web Site: https://www.trgscreen.com
Sales Range: $1-9.9 Million
Emp.: 17
Management Consulting Services
N.A.I.C.S.: 541613
Leigh Walters *(CEO)*
Steve Matthews *(Chm)*

Tripleseat Software, LLC (1)
42 Davis Rd Ste 1, Acton, MA 01720
Tel.: (978) 841-9581
Web Site: http://www.tripleseat.com
Software Publisher
N.A.I.C.S.: 513210
Kevin Zink *(Co-Founder)*

Vista Equity Partners Management, LLC (1)
4 Embarcadero Ctr 20th Fl, San Francisco, CA 94111
Tel.: (415) 765-6500
Web Site: https://www.vistaequitypartners.com
Private Equity Investment Management Services
N.A.I.C.S.: 523940
Lauren Dillard *(CFO)*
David A. Breach *(Pres & COO)*
Lauren B. Dillard *(CFO)*
Robert F. Smith *(Founder, Chm & CEO)*

Subsidiary (Domestic):

EngageSmart, Inc. (2)
30 Braintree Hill Ofc Park Ste 101, Braintree, MA 02184 (65%)
Tel.: (781) 848-3733
Rev: $303,920,000
Assets: $886,497,000
Liabilities: $81,525,000
Net Worth: $804,972,000
Earnings: $20,593,000
Emp.: 971
Fiscal Year-end: 12/31/2022
Software Development Services
N.A.I.C.S.: 541511
Dan Freund *(Chief Sls Officer-Enterprise Solutions)*
Cassandra Hudson *(CFO)*
Jonathan Seltzer *(Pres)*
Alison Durant *(CMO)*
Frank Laura *(CTO)*
Patrick Donovan *(Chief Acctg Officer)*
Kevin O'Brien *(Pres)*
Robert P. Bennett *(Founder)*

Who's Calling, Inc. (1)
200 Quality Cir, College Station, TX 77845
Web Site: http://www.whoscalling.com
Sales Range: $50-74.9 Million
Consulting Services Designed to Optimize Sales, Marketing, Customer Support & Professional Development Efforts
N.A.I.C.S.: 541611

Xactly Corporation (1)
300 Park Ave Ste 1700, San Jose, CA 95110
Tel.: (408) 977-3132
Web Site: http://www.xactlycorp.com
Sales Range: $75-99.9 Million
Emp.: 450
On-Demand Sales Compensation Software & Services
N.A.I.C.S.: 513210
Chris Cabrera *(Founder & CEO)*
Bernard G. Kassar *(Chief Customer Officer)*
Ron W. Rasmussen *(CTO & Sr VP-Engrg)*
Nitin Mathur *(VP-Pro Svcs & Customer Support)*
Leanne Bernhardt *(VP-HR)*
Arnab Mishra *(Sr VP-Products)*
Anil Kona *(VP-Engrg)*
Dan King *(VP & Controller)*
Jamie Anderson *(Chief Revenue Officer)*
Soichiro Fukuma *(Country Mgr-Japan)*

VISTA FOOD EXCHANGE, INC.
101 Hunts Point Cooperative Market Bldg B, Bronx, NY 10474
Tel.: (718) 542-4401   NY
Web Site: http://www.vistafood.com
Year Founded: 1979
Sales Range: $100-124.9 Million
Emp.: 60
Provider of Cooperative Market Services
N.A.I.C.S.: 424440
Vincent Pacifico *(Founder & CEO)*
Phil Stephens *(VP)*
Alan Butterfass *(Controller)*

COMPANIES

VISTA FORD
21501 Ventura Blvd, Woodland Hills, CA 91364
Tel.: (818) 884-7600
Web Site: http://vistaford.net
Year Founded: 1974
Sales Range: $75-99.9 Million
Emp.: 190
New Car Whslr
N.A.I.C.S.: 441110
Jon Shuken *(CEO)*

VISTA GRANDE VILLA
2251 Springport Rd, Jackson, MI 49202
Tel.: (517) 513-6692 MI
Web Site: http://www.vistagrandevilla.com
Year Founded: 1970
Sales Range: $10-24.9 Million
Emp.: 25
Lifecare Retirement Community Operator
N.A.I.C.S.: 623311
Ellen Keatley *(Chm)*
Tom Keith *(Exec Dir)*

VISTA GROUP INC.
4561 Colorado Blvd, Los Angeles, CA 90039
Tel.: (818) 551-6789 CA
Web Site: http://www.vistagroupusa.com
Year Founded: 1972
Sales Range: $1-9.9 Million
Emp.: 10
Public Relations Agency
N.A.I.C.S.: 541820
Carol Schmiederer *(Mgr-Products Placement)*
Karl Dahlquist *(Dir-Ops)*
Eric E. Dahlquist Sr. *(Founder)*
Eric C. Dahlquist Jr. *(Dir-Client Svcs)*

VISTA IMAGING SERVICES, INC.
3941 Park Dr Ste 20-463, El Dorado Hills, CA 95762
Tel.: (415) 272-3925
Web Site: http://www.vistaimagingservices.com
Year Founded: 2004
Sales Range: $1-9.9 Million
Emp.: 10
X-Ray Imaging Services
N.A.I.C.S.: 621512
Kelly Hansen *(Mgr-Billing)*
Jeffrey Perry *(Owner)*
Sonya Linde *(Office Mgr)*

VISTA INTERNATIONAL TECHNOLOGIES, INC.
4835 Monaco St, Commerce City, CO 80022
Tel.: (303) 690-8300 DE
Web Site: http://www.vvit.us
Year Founded: 1996
Sales Range: Less than $1 Million
Emp.: 3
Materials Recovery Facilities
N.A.I.C.S.: 562920
Timothy D. Ruddy *(CEO)*

VISTA METALS INC.
1024 E Smithfield St, McKeesport, PA 15135
Tel.: (412) 751-4600 PA
Web Site: http://www.vistametalsinc.com
Year Founded: 1969
Sales Range: $10-24.9 Million
Emp.: 150
Mfr of Machine Tool Attachments & Accessories
N.A.I.C.S.: 333515

William Riley *(Pres)*
Brian Riley *(VP)*
Patricia Larue *(Controller)*
Jim Harchelroad *(Gen Mgr)*
Tom Manning *(Mgr-Sls)*

VISTA PAINT CORPORATION
2020 E Orangethorpe Ave, Fullerton, CA 92831
Tel.: (714) 680-3800
Web Site: http://www.vistapaint.com
Sales Range: $100-124.9 Million
Emp.: 500
Paints & Paint Additives
N.A.I.C.S.: 325510
Eddie R. Fischer *(Pres)*
Odis Freeman *(Reg Mgr)*

VISTA PRODUCTS INC.
18768 Barber Rd, Sarasota, FL 34240
Tel.: (941) 378-3844
Web Site: http://www.vistaproducts.com
Year Founded: 1980
Rev.: $24,000,000
Emp.: 400
Mfr of Vertical Blinds
N.A.I.C.S.: 337920
Mark Singer *(VP)*
Holly Noe *(Mgr-Accts-Natl)*

VISTA PROPPANTS AND LOGISTICS INC.
4413 Carey St, Fort Worth, TX 76119
Tel.: (817) 563-3500 DE
Web Site: http://www.vprop.com
Year Founded: 2017
Emp.: 558
Frac Sand Solution Provider
N.A.I.C.S.: 423840
Gary B. Humphreys *(Co-Chm & CEO)*
Martin W. Robertson *(Co-Chm, Pres & COO)*
Kristin W. Smith *(CFO)*

VISTA REAL ESTATE INC.
3801 Central Point Dr, Anchorage, AK 99503
Tel.: (907) 562-6464
Web Site: http://www.prudentialjackwhitevista.com
Sales Range: $10-24.9 Million
Emp.: 260
Real Estate Brokers & Agents
N.A.I.C.S.: 531210
Naomie Loueier *(Pres)*

VISTA STEEL COMPANY, INC.
6100 Botello Rd Ste A, Goleta, CA 93117
Tel.: (805) 964-4732
Rev.: $11,800,000
Emp.: 50
Wire Products
N.A.I.C.S.: 332312

VISTA SYSTEM, LLC
1800 N E Ave Unit 102, Sarasota, FL 34234
Tel.: (941) 365-4646 FL
Web Site: http://www.vistasystem.com
Year Founded: 2000
Sales Range: $10-24.9 Million
Emp.: 98
Signs & Display Mfr
N.A.I.C.S.: 339950
Alon Bar *(Gen Mgr)*

VISTA TECHNOLOGY SERVICES, INC.
7925 Jones Branch Dr Ste 2300, McLean, VA 22102

Tel.: (703) 561-4100
Web Site: http://www.vistatsi.com
Year Founded: 1983
Sales Range: $25-49.9 Million
Computer Maintenance Services
N.A.I.C.S.: 541512
David B. Baxa *(Chm)*
Hal McDonald *(VP)*
Rod Buck *(Pres & CEO)*
Carole Davis *(CFO)*
Hal McDonald *(VP)*
Cynthia Hawthorne *(Mgr-HR)*

VISTA WEST, INC.
6262 Patterson Pass Rd Ste C, Livermore, CA 94550-9576
Tel.: (925) 373-8400
Year Founded: 1985
Sales Range: $10-24.9 Million
Emp.: 65
Wholesalers of Electrical Appliances, Televisions & Radios
N.A.I.C.S.: 423620
James J. Hillman *(Pres & CEO)*

Subsidiaries:

Impact Merchandising Corp. (1)
3440 Silver Springs Ct, Lafayette, CA 94549-5250
Tel.: (925) 373-7900
Web Site: http://www.impact.com
Sales Range: $10-24.9 Million
Emp.: 62
Wholesalers of Electrical Appliances, Television & Radios
N.A.I.C.S.: 423620

VISTA WINDOW COMPANY, LLC
1701 Henn Pkwy, Warren, OH 44481
Tel.: (330) 259-4700
Web Site: http://www.vistawindowco.com
Year Founded: 2001
Rev.: $21,300,000
Emp.: 180
Specialty Trade Contractors
N.A.I.C.S.: 238990
Jim Collins *(COO)*

VISTAPAK INDUSTRIES INC.
1103 Thomas Ave, Leesburg, FL 34748
Tel.: (352) 315-9100
Web Site: http://www.vistapak.com
Rev.: $11,400,000
Emp.: 50
Industrial & Personal Service Paper Merchant Whslr
N.A.I.C.S.: 424130
Richard G. Martin *(Pres)*
Ken Parks *(Plant Mgr)*

VISTATECH ENTERPRISES LTD.
935 Broadway Fl 4, New York, NY 10010-6009
Tel.: (212) 254-9851 NY
Web Site: http://www.vistanyc.com
Year Founded: 1978
Sales Range: $10-24.9 Million
Emp.: 18
Distr of Electronic Equipment
N.A.I.C.S.: 423940
Morris L. Weiser *(Pres)*
Mickey Goldberg *(Dir-Sls & Mktg)*

VISTAUXX LTD.
Facility H 10630 Riggs Hill Rd, Jessup, MD 20794-9450
Tel.: (301) 498-8000
Web Site: http://www.vistauxx.com
Year Founded: 1968
Sales Range: $10-24.9 Million
Emp.: 50
Computer Integrated Systems Design, Internet & Network

N.A.I.C.S.: 541512
David Von Bisto *(CEO)*

VISTEX, INC.
2300 Barrington Rd Ste 550, Hoffman Estates, IL 60169
Tel.: (847) 490-0420
Web Site: http://www.vistex.com
Emp.: 50
Marketing Software & Solutions
N.A.I.C.S.: 541613
Sanjay Shah *(Founder)*

VISTRA COMMUNICATIONS
18315 N US Hwy 41, Lutz, FL 33549
Tel.: (813) 961-4700
Web Site: http://www.consultvistra.com
Year Founded: 2007
Sales Range: $1-9.9 Million
Emp.: 65
Marketing, Public Relations, Strategic Planning & Communications Consulting
N.A.I.C.S.: 541613
Brain A. Butler *(Founder, Pres & CEO)*
Matt Burnett *(Bus Mgr)*
Althea Paul *(Mgr-Corp Comm)*
Gregory Reyes *(VP-Federal Bus Growth)*
Steven Hendricks *(VP-Corp Comm)*
Zoe Gustafson *(CFO)*
Chris Butler *(Bus Mgr)*
Bart Scherschel *(COO)*

VISTRONIX, INC.
11091 Sunset Hills Rd Ste 700, Reston, VA 20190
Tel.: (703) 463-2059
Web Site: http://www.vistronix.com
Year Founded: 1990
Emp.: 450
Custom Computer Programming Services
N.A.I.C.S.: 541511
Kevin Wideman *(Pres)*
Ronald Jones *(Chief Strategy Officer)*
Paul Falkler *(Pres-Natl Intelligence Sector)*
Alan Stewart *(CFO)*
David Lee *(Pres-Intelligence & Digital Data)*

Subsidiaries:

ExaTech Solutions, Inc. (1)
2201 Cooperative Way Ste 600, Herndon, VA 20171
Tel.: (703) 788-6602
Web Site: http://www.exatechsolutions.com
Information Technology Consulting Services
N.A.I.C.S.: 541512
Roger Cook *(CFO)*
Don Goddard *(COO)*
Philip Peacock *(Pres & CEO)*

NetCentric Technology Inc. (1)
3349 Route 138 Bldg A, Wall, NJ 07719
Tel.: (732) 544-0888
Sales Range: $1-9.9 Million
Emp.: 17
Computer System Design Services
N.A.I.C.S.: 541512

VISUAL ACUMEN, INC.
432 Maple Hill Ave, Newington, CT 06111
Tel.: (860) 532-0427 FL
Web Site: http://www.visualacumen.com
Year Founded: 2013
Descriptive Data From Images Extracting Software
N.A.I.C.S.: 513210
Alex McKenna *(Pres, CEO, CFO, Treas & Sec)*

VISUAL AIDS ELECTRONICS CORP.

Visual Acumen, Inc.—(Continued)

VISUAL AIDS ELECTRONICS CORP.
Ste 100 12910 Clover Leaf Ctr Dr, Germantown, MD 20874-1182
Tel.: (301) 330-6900
Web Site: http://www.vaecorp.com
Year Founded: 1968
Rev.: $20,000,000
Emp.: 150
Wholesale & Rent of Audio-Visual Equipment
N.A.I.C.S.: 532289
David Martin (COO)
Dennis Alleman (Asst Controller)

VISUAL APEX, INC.
7950 NE Day Rd W Ste B, Bainbridge Island, WA 98110-1254
Tel.: (206) 780-8192
Web Site: http://www.visualapex.com
Year Founded: 2001
Sales Range: $10-24.9 Million
Emp.: 21
Online Electronic Retailer
N.A.I.C.S.: 449210
Charlie Moore (Pres)

VISUAL AWARENESS TECHNOLOGIES & CONSULTING, INC.
3611 W Swann Ave, Tampa, FL 33609
Tel.: (813) 207-5055
Web Site: http://www.vatcinc.com
Year Founded: 2003
Sales Range: $10-24.9 Million
Emp.: 140
Management Training Services
N.A.I.C.S.: 611430
Sara Moola (Pres)
Mike Vaughn (Co-Founder & COO)
Gary Bloomberg (Sr VP-Strategic Dev)
Donna Conceicao (CFO)
Kim Hardman (VP-Corp Svcs)
Natalie Bonner (VP-Contracts)
Frank Kuska (VP-Ops)
Thomas Miller (Mgr-Mktg)
Rita Maxwell (Dir-Fin & Acctg)
Jason Fulford (VP-Bids & Proposals)
Chad Ritchie (Dir-Intelligence Svcs)
Shands Pickett (VP-Applied Res & Tech)
Dennis Pannell (VP-Corp Strategy)

VISUAL COMMUNICATIONS COMPANY, INC.
12780 Danielson Ct Ste A, Poway, CA 92064
Tel.: (858) 386-5666
Web Site: http://www.vcclite.com
Year Founded: 1976
Sales Range: $1-9.9 Million
Emp.: 9
Electronic Components Mfr
N.A.I.C.S.: 334419
Andrew Zanelli (CEO)

VISUAL COMMUNICATIONS INC.
1 Stanley Dr Bridgewater Business Park, Aston, PA 19014
Tel.: (610) 859-7300
Web Site: http://www.vciexhibits.com
Year Founded: 1959
Sales Range: $10-24.9 Million
Emp.: 60
Exhibit Construction Services
N.A.I.C.S.: 561990
Thomas J. Barker (CEO)
Paul G. Barker (Owner)
Matthew Iacone (COO)
William J. Barker Jr. (Chm)

VISUAL CONCEPTS, LLC
1901 Holser Walk Ste 310, Oxnard, CA 93036-2633
Tel.: (805) 652-1347
Web Site: http://www.visualconcept.com
Year Founded: 1994
Sales Range: $1-9.9 Million
Emp.: 34
Custom Computer Programming Services
N.A.I.C.S.: 541511
Priscilla A. R. Becker (CEO)

VISUAL CONTROLS/CHAMP INC.
75 Cascade Blvd, Milford, CT 06460
Tel.: (203) 882-8222
Web Site: http://www.champdirectmail.com
Rev.: $10,400,000
Emp.: 89
Offset Printing
N.A.I.C.S.: 323111
Paul Featherston (Pres & CEO)
Mary Kokias (CFO)

VISUAL EDGE TECHNOLOGY, INC.
3874 Highland Pk, North Canton, OH 44720
Web Site: http://visualedgeit.com
Year Founded: 1986
Engineering & Imaging Custom Computer Programming Services
N.A.I.C.S.: 423420
Michael Brigner (Sr VP)
Austin Vanchieri (Chm & CEO)
Brian Frank (COO)
Michael Cozzens (Sr VP-Sls)
David Ramos (Chief Strategy Officer)

Subsidiaries:

Graphic Enterprises Inc. (1)
3874 Highland Park NW, Canton, OH 44720-4538
Tel.: (330) 494-9694
Web Site: http://www.geiworldwide.com
Sales Range: $10-24.9 Million
Emp.: 125
Copying & Printing Systems Distr
N.A.I.C.S.: 423420
Brian Frank (Pres)
Yvonne Curtis (Controller)
Ron Huff (CFO & VP-Fin)
John Sedlak (Mgr-IT)

Lexnet LLC (1)
108 Wind Haven Dr Ste A, Nicholasville, KY 40356
Tel.: (859) 266-1141
Web Site: http://www.lexnetinc.com
Rev.: $3,220,000
Emp.: 20
Consulting, Service & Training
N.A.I.C.S.: 541690
Craig Rouse (Owner)

Office Systems of Vermont, Inc. (1)
131 S Main St, Barre, VT 05641
Tel.: (802) 479-3311
Web Site: http://osvtech.com
Office Equipment Merchant Whslr
N.A.I.C.S.: 423420

Zeno Digital Solutions, LLC (1)
10688 Haddington Dr, Houston, TX 77043
Tel.: (713) 722-8778
Office Equipment Merchant Whslr
N.A.I.C.S.: 423420
Tom Frederick (Pres)

VISUAL EFFECTS SOCIETY
5805 Sepulveda Blvd Ste 620, Sherman Oaks, CA 91411
Tel.: (818) 981-7861
Web Site: http://www.visualeffectssociety.com
Year Founded: 1996
Sales Range: $1-9.9 Million
Emp.: 7

Professional Organizations
N.A.I.C.S.: 813920
Colleen Kelly (Office Mgr)
Nancy Ward (Dir-Program & Dev)
Jeff Casper (Mgr-Media & Graphics)
Brent Armstrong (Dir-Ops)
Bob Coleman (Treas)
Rita Cahill (Sec)
Mike Chambers (Chm)
Eric Roth (Exec Dir)

VISUAL GRAPHICS SYSTEMS, INC.
330 Washington Ave, Carlstadt, NJ 07072
Tel.: (201) 528-2700
Web Site: http://www.vgsonline.com
Year Founded: 2005
Sales Range: $1-9.9 Million
Emp.: 50
Signage & Visual Display Products Mfr
N.A.I.C.S.: 339950
Milton DiPietro (Chm)

Subsidiaries:

Posterloid Corporation (1)
48-62 36th St, Long Island City, NY 11101-1918
Tel.: (718) 433-2170
Web Site: http://www.posterloid.com
Mfr of Menuboards for Quick Service Restaurant Chains
N.A.I.C.S.: 339950

VISUAL IMAGE ADVERTISING
125 Park Ave Ste 200, Oklahoma City, OK 73102
Tel.: (405) 525-0055
Year Founded: 1989
Rev.: $25,000,000
Emp.: 25
Advertising, Collateral, Crisis Communications, Event Planning & Marketing, Investor Relations, Media Relations, Multimedia, Outdoor, Public Relations, Radio, T.V.
N.A.I.C.S.: 541810
Tim Berney (CEO)
Steve Sturges (Partner & Dir-Creative)
Deana Paulson (Office Mgr)
Jacquelyn LaMar (Dir-Mktg)
Chelsea Herring (Office Mgr)

VISUAL INNOVATIONS COMPANY INC
8500 Shoal Creek Blvd Bldg 1, Austin, TX 78757
Tel.: (512) 334-1100
Web Site: http://www.vis-innov.com
Sales Range: $10-24.9 Million
Emp.: 50
Audio-Visual Equipment & Supplies
N.A.I.C.S.: 459999
Brenda McCarley (Pres)
Llyod S. McCarley (Exec VP)

VISUAL LOGIC GROUP
402 E 4th St, Waterloo, IA 50703
Tel.: (319) 226-3022
Web Site: http://www.vlgux.com
Year Founded: 2002
Sales Range: $1-9.9 Million
Emp.: 9
It Consulting
N.A.I.C.S.: 541690
Andy Van Fleet (Partner)
Kurt Vander Wiel (Partner)

VISUAL PAK COMPANY
1909 S Waukegan Rd, Waukegan, IL 60085
Tel.: (847) 689-1000
Web Site: http://www.visualpak.com
Sales Range: $50-74.9 Million
Emp.: 700

U.S. PRIVATE

Packaging & Labeling Services
N.A.I.C.S.: 561910
Clayton Bolke (Pres)

VISUAL SOUND INC.
485 Park Way, Broomall, PA 19008
Tel.: (610) 544-8700
Web Site: http://www.visualsound.com
Sales Range: $25-49.9 Million
Emp.: 105
Audiovisual
N.A.I.C.S.: 449210
Joe Glennon (Mgr-Presentation Svcs)
Patricia Dolceamore (Mgr-Credit)
Ramon Aviles (Mgr-Sls Tech Applications Dev)
Daniel McKay (Mgr-Svc)
Michael Sansom (Acct Mgr)
Robert Woodruff (Mgr-Engrg)
Rob Wirth (Mgr-Ops)
Cynde Casar (Mgr-Acctg)

VISUAL TECHNOLOGIES CORP.
1620 Burnet Ave, Syracuse, NY 13206
Tel.: (315) 423-9741
Web Site: http://www.visualtec.com
Year Founded: 1980
Sales Range: $1-9.9 Million
Emp.: 18
Office Machinery & Equipment Rental & Leasing
N.A.I.C.S.: 532420
Andrew Reichel (Mgr)
David Foor (Pres)
Don Edds (Mgr)
Jim Blair (Mgr-Sls)
Jim Stanton (Mgr-Sls)

Subsidiaries:

Vtc Video Services (1)
1620 Burnet Ave, Syracuse, NY 13206
Tel.: (315) 423-2000
Web Site: http://www.visualtec.com
Services Allied To Motion Pictures
N.A.I.C.S.: 334610

VISUALMAX
630 9th Ave Ste 414, New York, NY 10036
Tel.: (212) 925-2938
Web Site: http://www.visualmax.com
Year Founded: 2001
Sales Range: $10-24.9 Million
Emp.: 15
N.A.I.C.S.: 541810
Steve McBride (Mng Partner)

VITA NONWOVENS, LLC
2215 Shore St, High Point, NC 27263
Tel.: (336) 431-7187
Web Site: http://www.vitausa.com
Emp.: 180
Nonwoven Fiber Materials Mfr
N.A.I.C.S.: 313230
Jason Johnson (COO)

Subsidiaries:

Vita Nonwovens (1)
9403 Avionics Dr, Fort Wayne, IN 46809
Tel.: (260) 747-0990
Web Site: http://www.vitanonwovens.com
Emp.: 100
Nonwoven Product Mfr
N.A.I.C.S.: 313230

VITA PLUS CORPORATION
PO Box 259126, Madison, WI 53725-9126
Tel.: (608) 256-1988
Web Site: http://www.vitaplus.com
Year Founded: 1948
Sales Range: $25-49.9 Million
Emp.: 345
Prepared Feeds

N.A.I.C.S.: 311119
Mark Miley (CFO)
Al Gunderson (VP-Sls & Mktg)
Marjorie Steve (Dir-Mktg)
Subsidiaries:

Dodgeville Agri-Service Inc. (1)
208 King St, Dodgeville, WI 53533-2102
Tel.: (608) 935-3371
Sales Range: $10-24.9 Million
Emp.: 12
Prepared Feeds
N.A.I.C.S.: 311119

Lake Mills Feed & Grain Inc. (1)
1219 S Main St, Lake Mills, WI
53551-1818 (100%)
Tel.: (920) 648-8388
Web Site: http://www.lakemills.com
Sales Range: $10-24.9 Million
Emp.: 14
Farm Supplies
N.A.I.C.S.: 424910

SF Transport Ltd. (1)
PO Box 277, Loyal, WI 84446
Tel.: (715) 255-8555
Web Site: http://www.vitaplus.com
Sales Range: $10-24.9 Million
Emp.: 50
Freight Transportation Services
N.A.I.C.S.: 484220
John Every (Gen Mgr)

Smith Feed Service Inc. (1)
213 E Mill St, Loyal, WI 54446-9441
Tel.: (715) 255-8252
Web Site: http://www.vitaplusfeed.com
Sales Range: $25-49.9 Million
Emp.: 90
Crop Preparation Services for Market
N.A.I.C.S.: 424910
Bob Tramburg (Pres)

VITA QUEST INTERNATIONAL INC.
8 Henderson Dr, West Caldwell, NJ 07006
Tel.: (973) 575-9200   DE
Web Site:
http://www.supplementmanufacturers.info
Year Founded: 1979
Sales Range: $100-124.9 Million
Emp.: 550
Mfr of Vitamin Preparations
N.A.I.C.S.: 325412
Keith Frankel (Owner & Pres)
David Ashley (Dir-Transportation)
Eileen Mangano (Dir-Pur)
Kelly Chippendale (Mgr-IT)
Nestor Giraldo (Mgr)

VITA-MIX CORPORATION
8615 Usher Rd, Cleveland, OH 44138-2199
Tel.: (440) 235-4840
Web Site: http://www.vitamix.com
Year Founded: 1921
Sales Range: $75-99.9 Million
Emp.: 1,000
Housewares Mail Order & Mfr
N.A.I.C.S.: 335220
Jodi Berg (Pres)
Daniel Cook (Coord-Shipping)
Christine Gresh (Coord-Comml-Intl)
Martina Oleksiak (Coord-Intl Sls)
Mike Campbell (Coord-Inventory)
Jack Gee (Mgr-Indus Design)
Holly Nanasy (Mgr-Shipping)

VITA-PAKT CITRUS PRODUCTS CO.
707 N Barranca Ave, Covina, CA 91723
Tel.: (626) 332-1101
Web Site: http://www.vita-pakt.com
Rev: $32,900,000
Emp.: 50
Fruit Juices: Fresh
N.A.I.C.S.: 311421

James R. Boyles (Chm & CEO)
Lloyd Shimizu (CFO)
Bryce Adolph (VP-Sls & Mktg)
Mark Reed (Pres & COO)

VITAKEM NUTRACEUTICAL, INC.
811 W Jericho Tpke, Smithtown, NY 11787
Tel.: (800) 233-2112
Web Site: http://www.vitakem.com
Year Founded: 2003
Sales Range: $10-24.9 Million
Vitamin Product Mfr
N.A.I.C.S.: 325412
Bret Hoyt Sr. (Founder, Pres & CEO)

VITAL CARE
761 Lafayette Ave, Cheboygan, MI 49721
Tel.: (231) 627-7157   MI
Web Site: http://www.hospiceltb.org
Year Founded: 1984
Sales Range: $10-24.9 Million
Health Care Srvices
N.A.I.C.S.: 622110
Kathy Erber (Chm)
Michael Nuorala (Treas & Sec)
Nancy C. Martin (Pres & CEO)
Susan Clark (CFO)

VITAL MARKETING GROUP LLC
1515 Broadway Fl 11, New York, NY 10036-8901
Tel.: (212) 995-9525   DE
Year Founded: 1997
Sales Range: Less than $1 Million
Emp.: 18
N.A.I.C.S.: 541810
Kwad Tufuoh (VP)
Garnet Morris (COO)
Joseph Anthony (Founder & CEO)

VITAL RECORDS INC.
563 New Ctr Rd, Flagtown, NJ 08821
Tel.: (908) 369-6900
Web Site:
http://www.vitalrecords.com
Sales Range: $10-24.9 Million
Emp.: 200
Data Storage Protection
N.A.I.C.S.: 493190
Ronald Riemann (Pres)
Andrew Rocco (CFO & VP)
Scott Meissner (Mgr-Tech Svcs)
Harry Triantis (Mgr-Ops)

VITAL VOICES GLOBAL PARTNERSHIP
1625 Massachusetts Ave NW Ste 300, Washington, DC 20036
Tel.: (202) 861-2625   DE
Web Site: http://www.vitalvoices.org
Year Founded: 1999
Sales Range: $10-24.9 Million
Emp.: 67
Civic & Social Organization
N.A.I.C.S.: 813410
Alvin Allgood (COO)
Hillary Rodham Clinton (Founder)
Kate James (Chm)
Geraldine Laybourne (Vice Chm)
Alyse Nelson (Pres & CEO)

VITALITY BOWLS ENTERPRISES, LLC
65 Oak Ct, Danville, CA 94526
Tel.: (925) 866-2224
Web Site:
http://www.vitalitybowls.com
Year Founded: 2011
Sales Range: $10-24.9 Million
Emp.: 721
Food & Beverage Product Distr
N.A.I.C.S.: 445298

Roy Gilad (Co-Founder & Co-Owner)
Tara Gilad (Co-Founder & Co-Owner)

VITALITY SENIOR LIVING MANAGEMENT, LLC
5500 Maryland Way Ste 320, 37027, Brentwood, TN
Tel.: (615) 538-3200   DE
Web Site:
https://www.vitalityseniorliving.com
Year Founded: 2016
Senior Care Facilities
N.A.I.C.S.: 623311
Sheila Flaschberger (VP-Ops)

VITALS
210 Clay Ave Ste 140, Lyndhurst, NJ 07071
Tel.: (201) 842-0760
Web Site: http://www.vitals.com
Sales Range: $1-9.9 Million
Emp.: 33
Health Care Providers
N.A.I.C.S.: 621610
Mitch Rothschild (Founder & Chm)
Larry West (CTO)
Tony Bellomo (COO)
Kyle Raffaniello (CEO)
Bryan Perler (Chief Fin & Admin Officer)

VITALWEAR, INC.
384 Oyster Point Blvd Ste 16, South San Francisco, CA 94080
Tel.: (650) 553-4100
Web Site: http://www.vitalwear.com
Year Founded: 2004
Sales Range: $10-24.9 Million
Emp.: 26
Form-Fitting Thermal Systems Mfr
N.A.I.C.S.: 334510
Dee Meisenbach (Dir-Outside Sls)

VITAMIN ANGEL ALLIANCE, INC.
111 W Micheltorena St Ste 300, Santa Barbara, CA 93101
Tel.: (805) 564-8400   CA
Web Site:
http://www.vitaminangels.org
Year Founded: 1998
Sales Range: $25-49.9 Million
Emp.: 28
Poor People Medical Assistance Services
N.A.I.C.S.: 813319
Kim Saam (Sr Mgr-Brand Mgmt & Comm)
Chris Hortinela (Mgr-Partnership Mktg)
Brittany McMeekin (Sr Mgr-Retail Partnerships)
Amy Steets (Sr Mgr-Program)

VITAMIN CLASSICS INC.
26135 Mureau Rd, Calabasas, CA 91302
Tel.: (818) 225-0375
Sales Range: $10-24.9 Million
Emp.: 10
Vitamin Mfr
N.A.I.C.S.: 325411
Gregory A. Rubin (CEO)
Melinda Rubin (Pres)
Subsidiaries:

Garcoa Inc. (1)
26135 Mureau Rd Ste 100, Calabasas, CA 91302-3184
Tel.: (818) 225-0375
Web Site: http://www.garcoa.com
Emp.: 30
Hair Preparations, Including Shampoos
N.A.I.C.S.: 325620
Gregory A. Rubin (CEO)
Melinda Rubin (Pres)

VITAMIN EXPRESS, INC.
1428 Irving St, San Francisco, CA 94122
Tel.: (415) 564-8160   CA
Web Site:
http://www.vitaminexpress.com
Year Founded: 1981
Sales Range: $1-9.9 Million
Emp.: 28
Food (Health) Supplement Stores
N.A.I.C.S.: 456191
Michael Levesque (Pres & CEO)
Teresa Manquen (Mgr-Admin)
Anna LeVesque (VP)

VITAMINSPICE
996 Old Eagle School Rd Ste 1102, Wayne, PA 19087
Tel.: (484) 367-7401   WY
Sales Range: Less than $1 Million
Vitamin-Enriched Gourmet Spices Devloper & Marketer
N.A.I.C.S.: 311942
Edward Bukstel (Pres, CEO & CFO)

VITEC, INC.
26901 Cannon Rd, Bedford, OH 4414
Tel.: (216) 464-4670   OH
Web Site: http://www.vitec-inc.com
Year Founded: 1987
Sales Range: $1-9.9 Million
Emp.: 28
Instruments & Related Products Mfr for Measuring, Displaying & Controlling Industrial Process Variables
N.A.I.C.S.: 334513

VITI, INC.
975 Fish Rd, Tiverton, RI 02878
Tel.: (401) 624-6181
Web Site: http://www.viti.com
Year Founded: 1985
Sales Range: $10-24.9 Million
Emp.: 75
Car Whslr
N.A.I.C.S.: 441110
James E. Gray (VP)
Michael J. Murphy (Pres)

VITIL SOLUTIONS
1777 Northgate Blvd Ste A1 & A2, Sarasota, FL 34234
Tel.: (941) 351-7600   FL
Web Site: http://www.vitil.com
Year Founded: 1977
Sales Range: $1-9.9 Million
Emp.: 30
IT Support Services
N.A.I.C.S.: 541519
Kathy Seiders (VP & Gen Mgr)

VITRO BIOPHARMA, INC.
4621 Technology Dr, Golden, CO 80403
Tel.: (303) 999-2130   NV
Web Site:
https://www.vitrobiopharma.com
Year Founded: 1986
VODG—(OTCQB)
Rev: $1,763,451
Assets: $8,343,534
Liabilities: $9,434,624
Net Worth: ($1,091,090)
Earnings: ($5,356,717)
Emp.: 10
Fiscal Year-end: 10/31/23
Stem Cell Researcher, Developer & Mfr
N.A.I.C.S.: 541715
John Evans (CFO)
Erik Van Horn (Dir-Quality Assurance)
Tiana A. Tonrey (COO)

VITTLES
141 Santa Rosa Ave, Sausalito, CA 94965

VITTLES

Vittles—(Continued)
Tel.: (415) 332-0840
Sales Range: Less than $1 Million
Emp.: 10
N.A.I.C.S.: 541810
Patricia A. Shea (Pres)
Tammy Deane (Partner & Dir-Creative)
Tammy Potter (Dir-Art)

VITUS MARINE LLC
113 W Northern Lights Blvd Ste 200, Anchorage, AK 99503
Tel.: (907) 278-6700
Web Site: http://www.vitus-energy.com
Emp.: 60
Marine Transportation Services
N.A.I.C.S.: 483113
Mark Smith (CEO)
Justin Charon (Pres)
Kevin O'Shea (Mgr-Safety & Environ)
Mike Poston (Dir-Sls)

Subsidiaries:

Great Circle Flight Services, LLC (1)
Ted Stevens Anchorage Intl Airport 6121 S Airpark Pl Ste 2, Anchorage, AK 99502
Tel.: (907) 245-1273
Web Site: http://www.greatcircleflight.com
Sales Range: $10-24.9 Million
Emp.: 7
Aviation Fixed Base Operator
N.A.I.C.S.: 488190
Cathy Porter (Mgr-Mktg)
Laura Charon (Gen Mgr)

VITUSA CORP.
1060 Main St Ste 203, River Edge, NJ 07661
Tel.: (201) 569-0800
Web Site: http://www.vitusa.com
Year Founded: 1957
Mfr, Marketer & Distr of Feedstuffs, Foodstuffs, Dairy Products & Wastewater Treatment Solutions
N.A.I.C.S.: 311119
Denny J. Herzberg (Pres)
Jack Forbes (CFO)
Rachelle Knopf (Mgr-Ops)

VITUSA PRODUCTS INC.
343 Snyder Ave, Berkeley Heights, NJ 07922-1520
Tel.: (908) 665-2900
Web Site: http://www.vitusaproducts.com
Year Founded: 1986
Sales Range: $10-24.9 Million
Emp.: 31
Provider of Chemicals & Allied Products
N.A.I.C.S.: 424690
David Grande (Pres & Treas)
Anthony Grande (Controller)
John Kovalcik (Mgr-IT)
Janeen Feliciano (Mgr-Customer Svc)

VIVA ENTERTAINMENT, LLC
164 Rollins Ave Ste 200, Rockville, MD 20852-4038
Tel.: (301) 670-9700 DE
Web Site: http://www.vivacreative.com
Convention & Trade Show Organizer
N.A.I.C.S.: 561920
Emily Greene (Pres)
Lorne Greene (CEO)
Asher Epstein (CFO)

VIVA PARTNERSHIP, INC.
3227 NE 2nd Ave, Miami, FL 33137
Tel.: (305) 576-0007
Web Site: http://www.vivamia.com
Year Founded: 1997
Sales Range: $25-49.9 Million
Emp.: 23

Advetising Agency
N.A.I.C.S.: 541810
Linda Lane Gonzalez (Pres & Co-CEO)
Jay Ben-Avner (Co-CEO & COO)
Debbie Richmond (Exec VP-Media & Res)

Subsidiaries:

Viva Media (1)
1100 NW Loop 410 Ste 420, San Antonio, TX 78229
Tel.: (210) 949-1710
Web Site: http://www.vivamia.com
N.A.I.C.S.: 541810
Deborah Richmond (Exec VP-Media & Res)
Linda Gonzalez (Pres)
Jay Ben-Avner (COO)

VIVA RAILINGS LLC
1454 Halsey Way, Carrollton, TX 75007
Tel.: (972) 353-8482
Web Site: http://www.vivarailings.com
Year Founded: 2005
Sales Range: $1-9.9 Million
Emp.: 65
Architectural Railings for Construction
N.A.I.C.S.: 423390
Mark Tinwala (VP)
Huzefa Tinwala (Pres)

VIVALDI CAPITAL MANAGEMENT, LLC
225 W Wacker Dr Ste #2100, Chicago, IL 60606
Tel.: (312) 248-8300 IL
Web Site: http://www.vivaldicap.com
Year Founded: 2011
Wealth Management Firm
N.A.I.C.S.: 523940
Michael Peck (Pres)
Michael Peck (Co-Chief Investment Officer-Vivaldi Holdings, LLC & Pres-Vivaldi Holdings, LLC)

Subsidiaries:

Cornerstone Wealth Management, LLC (1)
17140 Bernardo Center Dr 206, San Diego, CA 92128
Tel.: (858) 676-1000
Web Site: http://www.cornerstonewm.com
Portfolio Management
N.A.I.C.S.: 523940
Chris Mecham (Founder)
Alan Skrainka (Chief Investment Officer)

VIVALDI MUSIC ACADEMY, LLC
3914 Gramercy St Ste B, Houston, TX 77025
Tel.: (713) 858-9617 TX
Web Site: http://www.vivaldimusicademy.com
Year Founded: 2012
Sales Range: $1-9.9 Million
Emp.: 10
Educational Support Services
N.A.I.C.S.: 611710
Zeljko Pavlovic (Owner)

VIVAX PRO PAINTING
1050 Yuma St, Denver, CO 80204
Tel.: (720) 331-9735
Web Site: http://www.vivaxpropainting.com
Year Founded: 2004
Sales Range: $10-24.9 Million
Emp.: 27
Residential Painting Contractor
N.A.I.C.S.: 238320
Jeremiah Owen (Pres)
Randy Festog (Mgr-Field Mktg)
Zach Chambers (Mgr-Production)
Jessica Klein (Owner)

VIVENT HEALTH, INC.
820 N Plankinton Ave., Milwaukee, WI 53203
Tel.: (800) 359-9272
Web Site: https://viventhealth.org
Year Founded: 1985
Emp.: 100
Hospitals & Health Care
N.A.I.C.S.:

VIVEX BIOMEDICAL, INC.
3200 Windy Hill Rd Ste 1650W, Atlanta, GA 30339
Tel.: (770) 575-5185
Web Site: http://www.vivex.com
Year Founded: 2014
Biogenic Materials Mfr
N.A.I.C.S.: 541715
Timothy Ganey (Chief Scientific Officer)
Tracy S. Anderson (Founder)
Ricardo J. Nunez (Sec)
Barry Salzman (Vice Chm)
Lou Barnes (Pres & COO)
Reinaldo Pascual (Gen Counsel)

Subsidiaries:

University of Miami Tissue Bank (1)
1951 NW 7th Ave Ste 200, Miami, FL 33136
Tel.: (305) 243-6465
Web Site: http://www.umtb.med.miami.edu
Emp.: 25
Surgical Appliance & Supplies Mfr
N.A.I.C.S.: 339113
Christina Graquitena (Coord-Quality)

VIVIAL, INC.
3100 Research Blvd Ste 250, Dayton, OH 45420
Tel.: (937) 610-4100
Marketing Services
N.A.I.C.S.: 541810
Jim Continenza (Chm & CEO)

VIVID IMPACT CORPORATION
10116 Bunsen Way, Louisville, KY 40299
Tel.: (502) 491-8201
Web Site: http://vividimpact.com
Rev.: $9,672,700
Emp.: 92
Commercial Lithographic Printing
N.A.I.C.S.: 323111
Greg Buchheit (Chm)
Mike Ellis (VP-Client Solutions)

Subsidiaries:

Impressions Incorporated (1)
2500 Constant Comment Pl, Louisville, KY 40299
Tel.: (502) 266-6008
Web Site: http://www.impressionsinc.biz
Rev.: $4,200,000
Emp.: 30
Commercial Lithographic Printing
N.A.I.C.S.: 323111
Thomas L. Davidson (Pres)

VIVID INK INC.
8640 Airline Hwy, Baton Rouge, LA 70815
Tel.: (225) 751-7297
Web Site: http://www.vividink.com
Year Founded: 1999
Emp.: 15
Sign Mfr
N.A.I.C.S.: 339950
Erin Ourso (Gen Mgr)

VIVIDFRONT, LLC
1340 Sumner Ave, Cleveland, OH 44115
Tel.: (216) 373-8810
Web Site: http://www.vividfront.com
Year Founded: 2009
Sales Range: $1-9.9 Million
Emp.: 19

Digital Marketing Services
N.A.I.C.S.: 541810
Andrew Spott (CEO)

VIVO, INC.
7901 Stoneridge Dr Ste 440, Pleasanton, CA 94588
Tel.: (925) 271-6800
Web Site: http://www.vivoinc.com
Year Founded: 2006
Sales Range: $10-24.9 Million
Emp.: 9
IT Staffing & Consulting Services
N.A.I.C.S.: 519290
Marilyn Weinstein (Founder & CEO)

VIVOX, INC.
2-4 Mercer Rd, Natick, MA 01760
Tel.: (508) 650-3571 DE
Web Site: http://www.vivox.com
Year Founded: 2005
Voice Communications Integration Technologies & Software
N.A.I.C.S.: 541511
Dave Verratti (Pres)

Subsidiaries:

Droplets, Inc. (1)
555 Republic Ste 311, Plano, TX 75074
Tel.: (212) 691-0080
Web Site: http://www.droplets.com
Software Publisher
N.A.I.C.S.: 513210
David Berberian (COO)
Frank Rose (CTO)
Ingo B. Theuerkauf (CFO)

VIVRE, INC.
11 E 26th St 15th Fl, New York, NY 10010
Tel.: (212) 739-6205 DE
Year Founded: 1996
Sales Range: $10-24.9 Million
Emp.: 30
Direct Marketer of European Luxury Items
N.A.I.C.S.: 449129
Eva Jeanbart-Lorenzotti (Founder & CEO)

VIYYA TECHNOLOGIES, INC.
87 Fairfield Rd, Fairfield, NJ 07004
Tel.: (973) 276-0555
Web Site: http://www.viyya.com
Year Founded: 2005
Emp.: 10
Software Publisher
N.A.I.C.S.: 513210
John Bay (Pres & CEO)

VIZCONNECT, INC.
136 Dwight Rd, Longmeadow, MA 01106 NV
Web Site: http://www.myvizconnect.com
Year Founded: 2010
Sales Range: Less than $1 Million
Mobile Devices & Technologies for Targeted Marketing & Advertising
N.A.I.C.S.: 541519
Brian Dee (Sec)
Paul Cooleen (Pres & CEO)

VIZER GROUP, INC.
5609 W 6th Ave, Lakewood, CO 80214-2455
Tel.: (303) 439-0372
Web Site: http://www.vizergroup.com
Year Founded: 2001
Video Surveillance, Access Control & Intrusion Detection Services
N.A.I.C.S.: 561621

VIZERGY
4237 Salisbury Rd N Ste 200, Jacksonville, FL 32216
Tel.: (904) 389-1130

Web Site: http://www.vizergy.com
Year Founded: 1998
Sales Range: $1-9.9 Million
Emp.: 50
Internet Marketing Services for the Hospitality Industry
N.A.I.C.S.: 541810
Joseph R. Hyman *(Founder & CEO)*
Robert Arnold *(Pres & Principal)*
Mike Murray *(COO)*
Phil Faircloth *(Dir-Ops)*
Sean Taylor *(Dir-Creative)*
Jay Waite *(Dir-Client Experience)*
Pam Rothenberg *(Dir-Client Svcs)*
Julie Daniel *(VP-Client Mktg Svcs)*
Addams England *(COO)*

VIZIENT, INC.
290 E John Capenter Freeway, Irving, TX 75062
Tel.: (972) 830-0000
Web Site: http://www.vizientinc.com
Healthcare Industry Administrative Management Software Developer & Publisher
N.A.I.C.S.: 621610
David P. Blom *(Chm)*
Byron Jobe *(Pres & CEO)*
David F. Ertel *(CFO)*
Bharat Sundaram *(Pres & COO)*
Monica Davy *(Chief Culture, Diversity & Inclusion Officer)*
Patty Olsen *(Chief People Officer)*

Subsidiaries:

Healthcare Performance Partners (1)
1509 Hunt Club Blvd Ste 800, Gallatin, TN 37066
Tel.: (615) 206-0701
Web Site: http://www.hpp.bz
Emp.: 50
Health Care Consulting Services
N.A.I.C.S.: 541611
Marshall Leslie *(Pres & Mng Principal)*
W. Terry Howell *(Sr Principal)*
Dave Munch *(Sr Principal)*

Kaufman, Hall & Associates, LLC (1)
5202 Old Orchard Rd Ste N700, Skokie, IL 60077
Tel.: (847) 441-8780
Web Site: http://www.kaufmanhall.com
Emp.: 500
Consulting Services
N.A.I.C.S.: 541611
James Blake *(Mng Dir)*
David Cyganowski *(Mng Dir)*
Ryan Gish *(Mng Dir)*
Mark Grube *(Mng Dir)*
Kateh Guelich *(Mng Dir)*
Jody Hill-Mischel *(Mng Dir)*
Eric Jordahl *(Mng Dir)*
Kit Kamholz *(Mng Dir)*
Kenneth Kaufman *(Chm & Mng Dir)*
Andrew Majka *(Mng Dir)*
James Pizzo *(Mng Dir)*
Jason Sussman *(Mng Dir)*
Therese Wareham *(Mng Dir)*
Robert Zeller *(Mng Dir & Chief Revenue Officer)*
Anu Singh *(Mng Dir)*
Charles Kim *(Mng Dir)*
Patrick Allen *(Mng Dir)*
Todd Fitz *(Mng Dir)*
Paul Crnkovich *(Mng Dir)*
R. Wesley Champion *(CEO)*
Kristofer Blohm *(Sr VP)*
Sarah Dawkins *(Sr VP)*
Tim Drozd *(CFO)*
Therese A. Fitzpatrick *(Sr VP)*
Ryan Freel *(Sr VP)*
Kristopher Goetz *(Sr VP)*
Steve Hollis *(Sr VP)*
Nora Kelly *(Sr VP)*
Jeff Kilpatrick *(Sr VP)*
Kevin Livesay *(CIO)*
Dan Majka *(Mng Dir)*
Walter Morrissey *(Mng Dir)*
Laura Muma *(Gen Counsel)*
Kimberly Neese *(Sr VP)*
John Poziemski *(Sr VP)*
Robert W. Pryor *(Sr VP)*
Matt Robbins *(Sr VP)*
Jill Rupple *(Chief Talent Officer)*
Tim Shoger *(Sr VP)*
Patrick Smyth *(Sr VP)*
Robert Turner *(Sr VP)*
Rob York *(Sr VP)*
Robert Kunzler *(CMO)*
Dan Clarin *(Sr VP)*
David Cohen *(Sr VP)*
Andre Maksimow *(Mng Dir)*
Annie Melikian *(Mng Dir)*
Courtney Midanek *(Sr VP)*
Jason O'Riordan *(Sr VP)*
Dawn Samaris *(Sr VP)*
Glenn Wagner *(Sr VP)*
Jared Hodgson *(Exec VP-Customer Success)*
Kris Kildahl *(VP-HR)*
Javan Smith *(Exec VP-Product Dev)*
Mary Katherine White *(Exec VP-Pro Svcs)*
Jason Hahn *(Exec VP-Global Software Sls)*
James Bodan *(Exec VP-Strategy & Verticals)*
Kermit S. Randa *(CEO-Software)*
David Ratliff *(Sr VP)*
Gavin McDermott *(Sr VP)*
Gordy Sofyanos *(Sr VP)*
Lance Robinson *(Mng Dir)*
Lori Pilla *(Sr VP)*

Subsidiary (Domestic):

Axiom EPM (2)
10260 SW Greenburg Rd Ste 710, Portland, OR 97223
Tel.: (503) 977-0234
Web Site: https://www.axiomepm.com
Sales Range: $10-24.9 Million
Emp.: 75
Software Product Development Services
N.A.I.C.S.: 541511
Javan Smith *(VP-Dev)*
Jared Hodgson *(VP-Technical Svcs)*
Abe Cohen *(VP-Mktg)*
Ken Levey *(VP-Fin Institutions)*
Kris Kildahl *(VP-HR)*
Tony Ard *(VP-Higher Education)*
James Bodan *(Exec VP-Healthcare Software)*
Justin Lindsay *(Dir-Alliances)*
Tom McCarthy *(Dir-Solution Engrg)*
Paul Woeltje *(VP-Consulting Svcs & Implementation)*

Kreg Corporation (2)
2 Piedmont Ctr Ste 500, Atlanta, GA 30305
Tel.: (404) 261-5734
Web Site: https://www.kreg.com
Custom Computer Programming Services
N.A.I.C.S.: 541511
Brian Farber *(VP-Dev)*
Henry Lowendick *(VP-Info Sys)*
Kevin E. Wall *(VP-Sls)*
Shane H. Kreter *(VP-Ops)*
Greg Ferguson *(Co-Founder & Pres)*
John Bojarski *(Sr VP)*
Stephen Kreter *(Co-Founder & VP)*

Branch (Domestic):

Kreg Corporation - Connecticut Office (3)
101 Town Green Ste 100, Wilton, CT 06897
Tel.: (203) 762-2268
Web Site: https://www.kreg.com
Software Publisher
N.A.I.C.S.: 513210
Shane Kreter *(VP-Ops)*

Subsidiary (Domestic):

Ponder & Co. (2)
10 Cadillac Dr Ste 120, Brentwood, TN 37027
Tel.: (615) 613-0215
Web Site: https://www.ponderco.com
Financial & Strategic Advisory Services
N.A.I.C.S.: 541611
Cindy Pearcy *(Principal)*
Dave Johnson *(CFO)*
Julian Head *(CEO)*
Terry B. Shirey *(Pres & Mng Dir)*

Subsidiary (Domestic):

Knowledge Capital Group LLC (3)
7 Radcliffe St Ste 302, Charleston, SC 29403
Tel.: (843) 637-3920
Web Site: https://www.knowledgecapitalgroup.com
Management Consulting & Financial Advisory Services
N.A.I.C.S.: 541611
Cindy Pearcy *(Principal)*
Anthony Powell *(Mng Dir)*
Chrissie Hamilton *(Mgr)*

Provista, LLC (1)
250 E John Carpenter Fwy, Irving, TX 75062
Tel.: (972) 830-0000
Sales Range: $250-299.9 Million
Emp.: 3,300
Provider of Business Services
N.A.I.C.S.: 561499
Greg Cardenas *(Gen Counsel & Sr VP-Shared Svcs)*
Jim Cunniff *(Pres & CEO)*
Mitch Steiner *(Sr VP-Enterprise)*
Mitch Walters *(Sr VP-Ops)*

VIZION HEALTH LLC
10935 Winds Crossing Dr Ste 700, Charlotte, NC 28273
Tel.: (704) 626-2448   LA
Web Site: http://www.vizionhealth.com
Year Founded: 2016
Health Care Consulting Services
N.A.I.C.S.: 621999
Mark E. Schneider *(CEO)*
Aaron Kneas *(CFO)*
Stephen Chesney *(COO)*
Ann Miller *(Chief Dev Officer)*

Subsidiaries:

Brookhaven Hospital, Inc. (1)
201 S Garnett Rd, Tulsa, OK 74128
Tel.: (918) 438-4257
Web Site: http://www.brookhavenhospital.com
Sales Range: $1-9.9 Million
Emp.: 60
Psychiatric & Substance Abuse Hospitals
N.A.I.C.S.: 622210
Kenneth Pierce *(CFO)*
Ron Broughton *(Chief Clinical Officer)*
Thomas Brown *(CEO)*

Shoreline, Inc. (1)
1220 Gregory St, Taft, TX 78390
Tel.: (361) 528-3356
Web Site: http://www.shorelinetreatmentcenter.com
Drug Treatment Center
N.A.I.C.S.: 622210
Mark Jackson *(CEO)*
Deborah Jenkins *(Dir-HR)*
Gary L. Davis *(Dir-Clinical)*
Sherri L. Watson *(Dir-Nursing)*

VIZTEK, INC.
6491 Powers Ave, Jacksonville, FL 32217
Tel.: (904) 733-3656
Web Site: http://www.viztek.net
Rev.: $14,367,879
Emp.: 25
Digital Software & Hardware Imaging Solutions
N.A.I.C.S.: 423430
Josip Cermin *(Pres)*
Luis Moreno *(Mgr-Acct)*
Steve Deaton *(VP-Sls)*

VJ USINA CONTRACTING, INC.
4669 Ave A, Saint Augustine, FL 32095
Tel.: (904) 829-6727
Web Site: http://www.vjusina.com
Rev.: $24,300,000
Emp.: 100
Industrial Building Construction
N.A.I.C.S.: 236210
John W. Allen *(VP)*
Rick Crosby *(VP)*

VLADIMIR JONES
6 N Tejon St 4 Fl, Colorado Springs, CO 80903-1509
Tel.: (719) 473-0704   CO
Web Site: http://www.vladimirjones.com
Year Founded: 1970
Sales Range: $10-24.9 Million
Emp.: 80
Advetising Agency
N.A.I.C.S.: 541810
Joe Hodas *(Sr VP-Brand Comm)*
Joe Hodas *(Sr VP-Brand Comm)*
Nechie T. Hall *(Co-Pres & CEO)*
George Olson *(Chief Creative Officer)*
Diane Russelavage *(Dir-Special Projects)*
Phil Barber *(VP & Dir-Creative)*
Meredith Vaughan *(Co-Pres & Owner)*
Margot Pollock *(Sr Copywriter)*
Craig Rae *(Creative Dir)*
Trudy Rowe *(CFO)*
Christine Coe *(Copywriter)*
Ryan Johnson *(Creative Dir)*
Sally Miles *(Dir-Creative Svcs)*
Ann Van Orsdel *(VP-Bus Dev)*
Molly Matesich *(Sr Acct Exec)*

Subsidiaries:

Vladimir Jones (1)
5460 S Quebec St Ste 330, Greenwood Village, CO 80111-1927
Tel.: (303) 689-0704
Web Site: http://www.vladimirjones.com
Sales Range: $10-24.9 Million
Emp.: 10
N.A.I.C.S.: 541810
Nechie Hall *(Pres & CEO)*
Lisa Wiesner *(Acct Supvr)*
Cody Gore *(Dir-Acct Svc)*
Nick Bayne *(Exec Creative Dir)*

VLADMIR, LTD.
1648 Universal City Blvd, Universal City, TX 78148
Tel.: (210) 226-8100   TX
Web Site: http://www.globalthesource.com
Year Founded: 2002
Sales Range: $1-9.9 Million
Emp.: 16
Warm Air Heating & Air-Conditioning Equipment & Supplies Merchant Whslr
N.A.I.C.S.: 423730
Dickie Sirotiak *(Pres)*

Subsidiaries:

American Radionic Co. Inc. (1)
32 Hargrove Grade, Palm Coast, FL 32137
Tel.: (386) 445-6000
Web Site: http://www.amradcapacitors.com
Rev.: $14,700,000
Emp.: 30
Capacitors & Condensers
N.A.I.C.S.: 335999
Robert Stockman *(Pres)*

VLASIC INVESTMENTS LLC
S State Commons I 2723 S State St Ste 250, Ann Arbor, MI 48104
Tel.: (734) 930-6700   MI
Web Site: http://www.mavd.com
Year Founded: 1989
Computers & Accessories, Personal & Home Entertainment
N.A.I.C.S.: 423430
Rob Aldrich *(Pres)*
Mark Melchi *(VP-Planning & Design)*
Lorelei Smith *(Mgr-Acctg)*
Jeff Harshe *(VP & Asset Mgmt)*
Dan Kelly *(VP & CFO)*
Cindy Cole *(Mgr-Sr Property)*
Gerard Wald *(Mgr-Property Ops)*
Caroline Smith *(Mgr-Property)*

VLBF CORP.

VLBF CORP.   U.S. PRIVATE

VLBF Corp.—(Continued)
202 11th St SW Plz, Spencer, IA 51301-5814
Tel.: (712) 262-7773　IA
Year Founded: 1979
Sales Range: $10-24.9 Million
Emp.: 150
Provider of Dining Services
N.A.I.C.S.: 722513

VLC DISTRIBUTION COMPANY
16255 Port NW Dr Ste 150, Houston, TX 77041
Tel.: (713) 856-7254
Web Site:
　http://www.watchwholesalers.com
Year Founded: 1991
Sales Range: $25-49.9 Million
Emp.: 24
Watch Product Whslr
N.A.I.C.S.: 423940
John Urban (Pres)

VLG ADVERTISING
5717 Legacy Dr Ste 270, Plano, TX 75024
Tel.: (214) 299-8688
Web Site:
　http://www.wefightboredom.com
Sales Range: $1-9.9 Million
Emp.: 50
Advertising Agency Services
N.A.I.C.S.: 541810
Brett Hersley (Co-Founder)
Pete Manias (Co-Founder & Pres)
Shane Foster (Founder & CTO)
Taylor Johnson (Principal)
Lance Jones (Assoc Dir-Creative)
Corey Smith (CFO)
Don Abell (CMO & Exec Dir-Creative)
Jon Fullrich (Dir-Creative)
Rich Sangillo (Dir-Creative)
Angela Shori (Dir-Creative)
Lee Parker (Principal-Client Svcs)
Pete Manis (Pres)

VLINK INCORPORATED
701 John Fitch Blvd, South Windsor, CT 06074
Tel.: (860) 247-1400
Web Site: http://www.vlinkinfo.com
Year Founded: 1999
Sales Range: $1-9.9 Million
Emp.: 55
Software Development & IT Staffing Solutions
N.A.I.C.S.: 513210
Sharad Patney (Sr VP-Sls & Ops)

VLP HOLDING CO. INC.
4100 Gardner Ave, Kansas City, MO 64120-1832
Tel.: (816) 241-9290　MO
Web Site: http://www.vlpco.com
Year Founded: 1978
Sales Range: $10-24.9 Million
Emp.: 110
Construction & Mining Machinery
N.A.I.C.S.: 423810
James W. Foreman (Chm)
David A. Leavitt (CEO & VP)
Subsidiaries:
Rex Spencer Equipment Company Inc.　(1)
323 N Mullen Rd, Belton, MO 64012-2136
Tel.: (816) 331-6078
Web Site: http://www.rexspencer.com
Sales Range: $10-24.9 Million
Emp.: 11
Construction & Mining Machinery
N.A.I.C.S.: 423810
Bill Schoenfelder (Gen Mgr)
Jack Conard (Mgr-Parts)
Joe Drummond (Mgr-Svc)

The Victor L. Phillips Company Inc.　(1)
4100 Gardner Ave, Kansas City, MO 64120-1832
Tel.: (816) 241-9290
Web Site: http://www.vlpco.com
Sales Range: $10-24.9 Million
Emp.: 52
Construction & Mining Machinery
N.A.I.C.S.: 423810
James W. Foreman (Chm)
David A. Leavitt (CFO & VP)

VLS IT CONSULTING
University Plz Office Complex 260 Chapman Rd Ste 104A, Newark, DE 19702
Tel.: (302) 368-5656
Web Site:
　http://www.vlsitconsulting.com
Year Founded: 2002
Sales Range: $1-9.9 Million
Emp.: 63
It Consulting
N.A.I.C.S.: 541690
Vibert Sahadatalli (Pres)

VMD SYSTEMS INTEGRATORS, INC.
8245 Boone Blvd Ste 200, Vienna, VA 22182
Tel.: (703) 288-3100
Web Site:
　http://www.vmdsystems.com
Year Founded: 2002
Rev.: $9,100,000
Emp.: 100
Computer System Design Services
N.A.I.C.S.: 541512
Michael Brokaw (Dir-Consulting Svcs)
Vivek Malhotra (Pres)
Deepti Malhotra (CEO)

VMG PARTNERS, LLC
39 Mesa St Ste 310, San Francisco, CA 94129
Tel.: (415) 632-4200　DE
Web Site:
　http://www.vmgpartners.com
Year Founded: 2005
Privater Equity Firm
N.A.I.C.S.: 523999
David G. Baram (Partner)
Kara Cissell-Roell (Mng Dir)
Michael L. Mauze (Mng Dir)
Robin Tsai (Mng Dir)
Wayne K. Wu (Mng Dir)
Jarom Fawson (Principal)
Cassie Burr (Partner-Talent)
Brianna Rizzo (Partner-Talent)
Subsidiaries:
Velocity Snack Brands　(1)
5510 Lincoln Blvd, Playa Vista, CA 90094
Tel.: (866) 217-9327
Snack Products
N.A.I.C.S.: 311919
Amit Pandhi (CEO)

Subsidiary (Domestic):
Popchips, Inc.　(2)
5510 Lincoln Blvd, Playa Vista, CA 90094
Tel.: (415) 391-2211
Web Site: http://www.popchips.com
Chips Mfr & Distr
N.A.I.C.S.: 311919
Patrick Turpin (Co-Founder & Pres)
Keith Belling (Co-Founder & Co-Chm)

VMI, INC.
211 Weddell Dr, Sunnyvale, CA 94089
Tel.: (408) 745-1700
Web Site: http://www.vmivideo.com
Sales Range: $10-24.9 Million
Emp.: 35
Video Equipment, Electronic
N.A.I.C.S.: 459999

Jacquilene Dorsa (Pres)

VMS ALARMS
60 Jefferson Park Rd, Warwick, RI 02888
Web Site: http://www.vmsalarms.com
Year Founded: 2003
Sales Range: $10-24.9 Million
Emp.: 196
Alarm System Mfr
N.A.I.C.S.: 334290

VMS BIOMARKETING
501 Pennsylvania Pky Ste 100, Indianapolis, IN 46280
Tel.: (317) 805-6600
Web Site:
　http://www.vmsbiomarketing.com
Year Founded: 1995
Emp.: 70
Medical Education Services
N.A.I.C.S.: 923120
Abigail E. Mallon (Sr VP-Innovation & Strategy)
Shelagh Anne Fraser (Dir-Medical)
Wendy L. McGrath (VP-Client Svcs)
Kristin Sherman (CFO)
Brion Brandes (Sr VP-Bus Dev)
Bradley Garrett (VP-Customer Experience Center)
Andrea Heslin Smiley (Pres & CEO)
Jennifer Wilson (CFO)
Thomas D. Fagan Jr. (COO)

VNA & HOSPICE OF THE SOUTHWEST REGION, INC.
7 Albert Cree Dr, Rutland, VT 05701
Tel.: (802) 775-0568　VT
Web Site:
　http://www.vermontvisitingnurses.org
Year Founded: 1946
Healtcare Services
N.A.I.C.S.: 623110
Ronald J. Cioffi (CEO)
Jamie Belchak (Mgr-Rehab Svcs)
Subsidiaries:
Manchester Health Services　(1)
5468 Main St, Manchester Center, VT 05255-9481
Tel.: (802) 362-2126
Nursing & Hospice Care Services
N.A.I.C.S.: 621610

VNA HOSPICE & PALLIATIVE CARE OF SOUTHERN CALIFORNIA
150 W 1st St, Claremont, CA 91711-4750
Tel.: (909) 624-3574　CA
Web Site: http://www.vnasocal.org
Year Founded: 1952
Sales Range: $25-49.9 Million
Emp.: 370
Hospice & Palliative Care Services
N.A.I.C.S.: 623110
Marsha Fox (Pres & CEO)
Timothy Dauwalder (Dir-Medical)
Valerie Hogman (Dir-HR)
Greg Dahlquist (Dir-Medical)
Cindy Cameron (CFO)

VNA OF RHODE ISLAND
475 Kilvert St, Warwick, RI 02886
Tel.: (401) 574-4900　RI
Web Site: http://www.vnari.org
Year Founded: 1984
Sales Range: $10-24.9 Million
Emp.: 121
Women Healthcare Services
N.A.I.C.S.: 621610
Thomas Peckham (CFO)
Colleen Rose (Mgr-Quality)

VNOMICS CORP.
175 Sullys Trl Ste 203, Pittsford, NY 14534
Tel.: (585) 377-9700
Web Site:
　http://www.vnomicscorp.com
Year Founded: 2008
Sales Range: $25-49.9 Million
Computer Technology Development Services
N.A.I.C.S.: 541511
David Chauncey (Pres)
Edward McCarthy (VP-Ops)
Lloyd Palum (CTO)
Alan Farnsworth (CEO)

VNS CORPORATION
325 Commerce Loop, Vidalia, GA 30474
Tel.: (912) 537-8964
Web Site: http://www.vnscorp.com
Year Founded: 1947
Rev.: $61,100,000
Emp.: 320
Building Material Supplier
N.A.I.C.S.: 444180
Bob Dixon (CIO)
Shane Belcher (Sr VP & VP-Ops)
Loyd Mobley (Exec VP & Dir-Pur & Corp Dev)
Brian Fabacher (CFO & Treas)
Gary R. Campbell (Pres & COO)
Hugh Peterson Jr. (Chm & CEO)

VNS HOMECARE INC.
14 Woodruff Ave, Narragansett, RI 02882
Tel.: (401) 782-0500　RI
Year Founded: 1967
Sales Range: $10-24.9 Million
Emp.: 181
Community Health Care Services
N.A.I.C.S.: 621498
Jason Marshall (Chm)
Linda Butcher (Sec)
Karen Hockhousen (Dir-Education)
Susan Jameson (Dir-Bus Dev)
Jeffery Bandola (Dir-Medical)

VOBILE GROUP LIMITED
2880 Lakeside Dr Ste 360, Santa Clara, CA 95054
Tel.: (408) 217-5000　Ky
Web Site:
　http://www.vobilegroup.com
Year Founded: 2005
Rev.: $15,225,000
Assets: $50,836,000
Liabilities: $7,003,000
Net Worth: $43,833,000
Earnings: ($2,502,000)
Emp.: 71
Fiscal Year-end: 12/31/18
Software Development Services
N.A.I.C.S.: 541511
Bernard Yangbin Wang (Chm & CEO)
Michael Paul Witte (Exec VP-Bus Dev & Sls)
Timothy John Erwin (Sr VP-Sls & Customer Rels)
Benjamin Russell Smith (Sr VP-Bus Dev)
Vincent Sai Hong Ho (Sec & Controller-Fin)
Adam Goldstein (Sr VP-Bus Dev)
Masaaki Matsuzawa (Pres-Strategy & Investments & Exec Dir)

VOCATIONAL DEVELOPMENT CENTER
612 S Main St, Council Bluffs, IA 51503
Tel.: (712) 328-2638　IA
Web Site: http://www.vodec.org
Year Founded: 1968
Sales Range: $10-24.9 Million
Emp.: 771

COMPANIES

Disability Assistance Services
N.A.I.C.S.: 624120
Steve Hodapp (CEO)
Joe Bosco (Dir-HR)
Jeremy Dunkirk (Dir-Production)
Terry Howell (CFO)

VOCATIONAL GUIDANCE SERVICES
2239 E 55th St, Cleveland, OH 44103
Tel.: (216) 431-7800 OH
Web Site: http://www.vgsjob.org
Year Founded: 1890
Sales Range: $10-24.9 Million
Emp.: 975
Vocational Rehabilitation Services
N.A.I.C.S.: 624310
Frank H. Porter (Chm)
James C. Hudak (Sr VP-Ops)
Julius M. Singleton (Vice Chm)
Betty J. Goodman II (CFO & Treas)
Stephen F. Kirk (Vice Chm)
Stephen F. Kirk (Vice Chm)

VOCATIONAL INDEPENDENCE PROGRAM INC
5069 Van Slyke Rd, Flint, MI 48507
Tel.: (810) 238-3671 MI
Web Site: http://www.viprogram.org
Year Founded: 1968
Sales Range: $1-9.9 Million
Emp.: 173
Developmental Disability Assistance Services
N.A.I.C.S.: 624120
Vicki McMahon (Dir-Ops)
Max Galanter (Exec Dir)
Jerry Ragsdale (First VP)
Joe Kendall (Pres)
Lori McLean (Sec)
Terry Pfaff (Treas)
Shawn Bryson (Supvr-Clinical)
Lisa Lindell (Supvr-Program)

VOCELLI PIZZA
1005 S Bee St, Pittsburgh, PA 15220
Tel.: (412) 919-2100
Web Site: http://www.vocellipizza.com
Year Founded: 1988
Sales Range: $10-24.9 Million
Emp.: 42
Franchise Pizzerias
N.A.I.C.S.: 722513
Varol Ablak (Founder)
Harry Ablak (Chm)
Seckin Ablak (VP-Franchises)

VOCON DESIGN, INC.
3142 Prospect Ave, Cleveland, OH 44115
Tel.: (216) 588-0800 OH
Web Site: http://www.vocon.com
Year Founded: 1987
Sales Range: $10-24.9 Million
Emp.: 70
Architectural & Interior Design Services
N.A.I.C.S.: 541410
Frank Mercuri (CFO)
Lance Amato (Principal)

VOGEL BROS BUILDING CO. INC.
2701 Packers Ave, Madison, WI 53704-7541
Tel.: (608) 241-5454 WI
Web Site: http://www.vogelbldg.com
Year Founded: 1969
Sales Range: $25-49.9 Million
Emp.: 125
General Contractors-Nonresidential Construction
N.A.I.C.S.: 236220

David L. Vogel (Chm)
Ross A. Rehfeldt (VP-Ops-Wisconsin)
Peter C. Vogel (Pres & CEO)
Eric Ballweg (CFO & Treas)
Rojeane Anderson (Sec)
Darren Vogel (VP-Operation-Florida)

VOGEL DISPOSAL SERVICE INC.
121 Brickyard Rd, Mars, PA 16046
Tel.: (724) 625-1511
Web Site: http://www.vogeldisposal.com
Sales Range: $10-24.9 Million
Emp.: 80
Garbage: Collecting, Destroying & Processing
N.A.I.C.S.: 562111
Judy Gschnell (Sec)
Doug Vogel (Vp)
Edward L. Vogel Sr. (Pres)

VOGEL PAINT, INC.
1110 Albany Pl SE, Orange City, IA 51041-1982
Tel.: (712) 737-8880 IA
Web Site: http://www.diamondvogel.com
Year Founded: 1971
Sales Range: $1-9.9 Million
Emp.: 850
Paint & Coating Mfr
N.A.I.C.S.: 325510
Drew F. Vogel (Pres & CEO)
Nate Baas (Mgr-HR)

VOGEL SEED & FERTILIZER, INC.
1891 Spring Vly Rd, Jackson, WI 53037
Tel.: (262) 677-2273
Web Site: http://www.springvalleyusa.com
Sales Range: $25-49.9 Million
Emp.: 50
Fertilizer Mfr
N.A.I.C.S.: 325314
Bill Vogal (CEO)
Randy Vogal (Pres)
Chuck Paulson (Mgr-Sls)
Kathy Widmann (Office Mgr)
Diane Malchom (Mgr-Credit)
John Steelman (CFO)
Joyce Vogel (Treas)

VOGLER MOTOR COMPANY, INC.
1170 E Main St, Carbondale, IL 62901
Tel.: (618) 457-8135 IL
Web Site: http://www.voglerford.com
Year Founded: 1923
Sales Range: $1-9.9 Million
Emp.: 103
Retail Sales of New & Used Automobiles, Pickups & Vans; Retail & Wholesale Parts
N.A.I.C.S.: 441110
Dennis Rathjen (Pres & Gen Mgr)
Bryan Black (Treas, Sec & Mgr-Parts)
Dave Basler (Mgr-Parts)
Tim Hirsch (Mgr-Sls)
Jeanette Glenn (Mgr-Fin)

VOGUE TYRE & RUBBER CO., INC.
1101 Feehanville Dr, Mount Prospect, IL 60056-6008
Tel.: (847) 297-1900 IL
Web Site: http://www.voguetyre.com
Year Founded: 1914
Sales Range: $25-49.9 Million
Emp.: 200
Provider of Motor Vehicle Supplies
N.A.I.C.S.: 423130

Greg Hatchcock (Pres)
Kevin Goyak (VP)
Jerry Vestweber (VP-Fin)
David Long (Mgr-Sls-Key Accts-Natl)

VOICE 1 DIRECT LTD.
4110 Kostoryz Rd, Corpus Christi, TX 78415
Tel.: (503) 997-7677
Web Site: http://www.voice1direct.com
Year Founded: 2003
Wireless Network Services
N.A.I.C.S.: 517112
Bob Pritchard (Chm)
Rob Coghill (CEO & CFO)
John Falting (Sec)
John Ogden (Dir-Technical)

VOICE OF PROPHECY, INC.
255 E 6th St, Loveland, CO 80539-0999
Tel.: (805) 955-7611
Web Site: http://www.voiceofprophecy.com
Year Founded: 1929
Broadcaster & Bible Study Courses
N.A.I.C.S.: 516120
Victor Pires (Treas & Gen Mgr)

VOICE-TECH, INC.
551 N Cattlemen Rd Ste 300, Sarasota, FL 34232
Tel.: (941) 556-0150 FL
Web Site: http://www.voicetechinc.com
Year Founded: 1993
Sales Range: $1-9.9 Million
Emp.: 27
Telephone Apparatus Mfr
N.A.I.C.S.: 334210
Tim Garofalo (Owner)

VOICEINTEROP, INC.
8000 N Federal Hwy Ste 100, Boca Raton, FL 33487
Tel.: (561) 939-3300 FL
Web Site: http://www.voiceinterop.com
Year Founded: 2007
Rev.: $87,254
Assets: $4,136
Liabilities: $195,226
Net Worth: ($191,090)
Earnings: ($104,547)
Emp.: 1
Fiscal Year-end: 09/30/19
Software Development Services
N.A.I.C.S.: 541511
Larry Reid (Founder, Pres, CEO, CFO, Chief Acctg Officer & Sec)
James Concannon (Dir-Sls & Mktg)
John Boteler (Dir-Software Support & Engrg)

VOICES FOR INDEPENDENCE
1107 Payne Ave, Erie, PA 16503
Tel.: (814) 874-0064 PA
Web Site: http://www.vficil.org
Year Founded: 1993
Sales Range: $1-9.9 Million
Emp.: 39
Disabled People Assistance Services
N.A.I.C.S.: 624120
Heidi Dukich (Dir-Quality Assurance)
Nancy Lawrence (Dir-Personal Attendant Care Svcs)
Tiffany Frey (Dir-Activities)
Doug McClintock (Dir-Fin)
Shona Eakin (Exec Dir)
Shari Holmstrom (Coord-File)
Joe Buckley (Coord-Nursing Home Transition)
Bridget Gasiewski (Coord-Attendant Case File)

Emily Crofoot (Coord-Nursing Home Transition)
Lanisha Chimenti (Coord-Nursing Home Transition)
Rick Hoffman (Dir-Home Modification, Housing & Advocacy)

VOIGHT ENTERPRISES, INC.
37485 Schoolcraft Rd, Livonia, MI 48150
Tel.: (734) 464-8500
Web Site: http://www.bowldetroit.com
Sales Range: $10-24.9 Million
Emp.: 20
Bowling Centers
N.A.I.C.S.: 713950

VOIGT-ABERNATHY COMPANY, INC.
7550 Commerce Cir, Trussville, AL 35173-2897
Tel.: (205) 655-0434 AL
Web Site: http://www.voigtab.com
Year Founded: 1964
Rev.: $1,600,000
Emp.: 10
Industrial Machinery & Equipment Merchant Whslr
N.A.I.C.S.: 423830
William Voigt (Pres & Sec)

Subsidiaries:

Pnucor LLC (1)
10525 A Granite St PO Box 7209, Charlotte, NC 28273
Tel.: (704) 588-3333
Web Site: http://www.pnucor.com
Emp.: 8
Pumps, Filtration Equipment & Process Engineered Systems Marketer
N.A.I.C.S.: 423830
Stacy McConaghy (Engr-Applications)
Brenda Welty (Mgr-Shipping)

VOIPLINK CORPORATION
5611 Palmer Way Ste F, Carlsbad, CA 92010
Tel.: (760) 918-9116
Web Site: http://www.voiplink.com
Year Founded: 2006
Sales Range: $1-9.9 Million
Emp.: 10
Law firm
N.A.I.C.S.: 541110
Larry West (CEO)

VOISARD MANUFACTURING INC.
60 Scott St, Shiloh, OH 44878
Tel.: (419) 896-3191
Web Site: http://www.voisard.com
Sales Range: $10-24.9 Million
Emp.: 100
Metal Stamping Mfr
N.A.I.C.S.: 332119
Sharon Emmer (Mgr-HR)
Bob Forsythe (Mgr-Pur)

VOISIN CONSULTING, INC.
222 Third St Ste 3121, Cambridge, MA 02142
Tel.: (617) 492-1537
Web Site: http://www.voisinconsulting.com
Emp.: 100
Healthcare Product Development Consulting Services
N.A.I.C.S.: 541690
Emmanuelle M. Voisin (Founder & CEO)
Anne Dupraz-Poiseau (Exec VP)
Tacye Connolly (Exec VP)
Daniel Muscionico (Head-Ops-Global)
Carole Jones (Dir-Market Access)

Subsidiaries:

B&H Consulting Services, Inc. (1)

VOISIN CONSULTING, INC.

Voisin Consulting, Inc.—(Continued)
50 Division St Ste 206, Somerville, NJ 08876
Tel.: (908) 704-1691
Web Site: http://www.bhconsultingservices.com
Sales Range: $1-9.9 Million
Emp.: 18
Regulatory Consulting Services for Healthcare Industry
N.A.I.C.S.: 541690
Helen M. Ribbans (Founder & Pres)
Stephanie M. Pierson (CEO)
Abhijit Pangu (Assoc Dir)

VOIT REAL ESTATE SERVICES, INC.

101 Shipyard Way Ste M, Newport Beach, CA 92663
Tel.: (949) 644-8648
Web Site: http://www.voitco.com
Year Founded: 1971
Sales Range: $25-49.9 Million
Emp.: 220
Real Estate & Brokerage Services
N.A.I.C.S.: 531210
Vance McNeilly (COO)
Kipp Gstettenbauer (Sr VP)
Ryan King (VP)
Eric Hinkelman (CEO)
Jessamyn Wilkinson (Dir-Mktg)
Liz Hurley (Sr VP-Irvine)
Tony Archer (Sr VP)
Arthur Bleier (Sr VP)
Jonathan Boland (Sr VP)
Michael Boomer (VP)
Mike Bouma (Sr VP)
Bob Brady (VP)
Ian Britton (Mng Dir)

Subsidiaries:

Voit Commercial Brokerage LP (1)
101 Shipyard Way Ste M, Newport Beach, CA 92663
Tel.: (949) 644-8648
Web Site: http://www.voitco.com
Commercial Real Estate Brokerage Services
N.A.I.C.S.: 531210

VOLATILE ANALYSIS CORPORATION

29750 US Hwy 431, Grant, AL 35747-9330
Tel.: (256) 486-3531 DE
Web Site: http://www.volatileanalysis.com
Year Founded: 2007
Biotechnology Research & Development
N.A.I.C.S.: 541714
Russell Bazemore (Chief Res Officer)
Katherine Malmay-Bazemore (Pres & CEO)
Chris Christenson (Chief Analytical Officer)
Jeremy Cummings (VP-Sls & Mktg)
Mitchell White (VP-Project Implementation)

Subsidiaries:

Microanalytics (1)
2011A Lamar Dr, Round Rock, TX 78664
Tel.: (512) 218-9873
Web Site: http://www.volatileanalysis.com
Emp.: 4
Multidimensional Gas Chromatographs Mfr & Whslr
N.A.I.C.S.: 333310
Roger Bleiler (VP-Sls)

VOLCANO COMMUNICATIONS CO.

20000 State Hwy 88, Pine Grove, CA 95665
Tel.: (209) 296-7502
Web Site: http://www.volcanocommunications.com
Year Founded: 1903
Sales Range: $10-24.9 Million
Emp.: 115
Telecommunication Servicesb
N.A.I.C.S.: 517121
Sharon J. Lundgren (Pres)

VOLITION CAPITAL LLC

177 Huntington Ave 16th Fl, Boston, MA 02115
Tel.: (617) 830-2100
Web Site: http://www.volitioncapital.com
Privater Equity Firm
N.A.I.C.S.: 523999
Sean Cantwell (Mng Partner)
Raul J. Fernandez (Mng Partner)
Larry Cheng (Mng Partner)

VOLK CORPORATION

23936 Industrial Park Dr, Farmington Hills, MI 48335
Tel.: (248) 477-6700
Web Site: http://www.volkcorp.com
Rev.: $12,256,862
Emp.: 51
Marking Devices
N.A.I.C.S.: 424120
John Fox (VP)
Scott Szumanski (Mgr-Pur)

VOLK ENTERPRISES, INC.

1335 Ridgeland Pkwy, Alpharetta, GA 30004
Tel.: (770) 663-5400
Web Site: http://www.volkenterprises.com
Rev.: $73,000,000
Emp.: 10
Kitchenware, Plastics
N.A.I.C.S.: 326199
Burt Hewitt (Reg Mgr-Sls)
Daniel J. Volk (VP)
Tony Volk Jr (Pres)

Subsidiaries:

Safety Today Inc. (1)
3287 Southwest Blvd, Grove City, OH 43123
Tel.: (614) 409-7200
Web Site: http://www.safetytoday.com
Sales Range: $50-74.9 Million
Emp.: 25
Safety Equipment & Supplies
N.A.I.C.S.: 423830

Volk Europe Ltd (1)
2 William House Old Saint Michaels Rayne Road, Braintree, CM7 2QU, Essex, United Kingdom
Tel.: (44) 1376 331584
Industrial Machinery & Equipment Distr
N.A.I.C.S.: 423830

VOLKERT, INC.

11 N Water St Ste 18290, Mobile, AL 36602
Tel.: (251) 342-1070 AL
Web Site: http://www.volkert.com
Year Founded: 1925
Sales Range: $25-49.9 Million
Emp.: 1,000
Engineeering Services
N.A.I.C.S.: 541330
Perry Hand (Chm)
Dennis C. Morrison (Sr VP-Mid-Atlantic)
David A. Allsbrook (CEO)
Jerry Stump (CEO-Strategic Succession Plan)
Mike Harper (Sr VP-Gulf Field)
Randall Redmond (Sr VP-Texas)
Thomas Hand (Chief Mktg Officer)
Michael Deas (Dir-Comm & PR)
Dan Houston (Chief Admin Officer)
Mike Sampson (CFO)
Leon Barkan (Sr VP-Program Mgmt)
Bill Moyers (Sr VP-Carolinas)
Bob Polk (Sr VP-Central)
Bo Sanchez (Sr VP-Florida)
David Webber (Sr VP-Gulf Design)
David Young (Sr VP-West Central)

Subsidiaries:

Bolt Underwater Services, Inc. (1)
7930 62nd St N, Pinellas Park, FL 33781-2208
Tel.: (727) 546-4198
Web Site: http://www.boltunderwater.com
Professional, Scientific & Technical Services
N.A.I.C.S.: 541990
Mollie Griswold (Pres)

Kennedy Engineering & Associates Group, LLC. (1)
6300 Powers Ferry Rd NW, Atlanta, GA 30339
Tel.: (678) 904-8591
Web Site: http://www.keagroup.com
Rev.: $1,700,000
Emp.: 10
Industrial Machinery & Equipment Merchant Whslr
N.A.I.C.S.: 423830
Lori Kennedy (Pres)

Volkert Environmental, Inc. (1)
3809 Moffett Rd, Mobile, AL 36618
Tel.: (251) 342-1070
Web Site: http://www.volkert.com
Environmental Consulting Services
N.A.I.C.S.: 541620
Brett Gaar (VP)
Jason Goffinet (Project Mgr)

Volkert, Inc. (1)
5028 Wisconsin Ave NW Ste 403, Washington, DC 20016-4118 (100%)
Tel.: (202) 237-6269
Web Site: http://www.volkert.com
Sales Range: $10-24.9 Million
Emp.: 25
Engineering & Architectural Services
N.A.I.C.S.: 541330
Dennis C. Morrison (COO & Sr VP-Mid-Atlantic)

Volkert, Inc. (1)
2 20th St N Ste 300, Birmingham, AL 35203
Tel.: (205) 214-5500
Web Site: http://www.volkert.com
Sales Range: $25-49.9 Million
Emp.: 15
Engineering & Architectural Services
N.A.I.C.S.: 541330
Alicia Rudolph (VP)
Kirk Mills (VP)

Volkert, Inc. (1)
1428 Chestnut St Ste 1200, Chattanooga, TN 37402-4457 (100%)
Tel.: (423) 842-3335
Web Site: http://www.volkert.com
Sales Range: $25-49.9 Million
Emp.: 40
Engineeering Services
N.A.I.C.S.: 541330
Christopher Davis (Project Mgr)
David Young (VP)
Jeremy Sims (Project Mgr)

Volkert, Inc. (1)
5400 Shawnee Rd Ste 301, Alexandria, VA 22312-2300 (100%)
Tel.: (703) 642-8100
Web Site: http://www.volkert.com
Sales Range: $10-24.9 Million
Emp.: 25
Engineering & Architectural Services
N.A.I.C.S.: 541330
Dennis C. Morrison (Sr VP & COO-Mid Atlantic Reg)

Volkert, Inc. - Georgia (1)
400 Perimeter Ctr Ter Ste 900, Atlanta, GA 30346 (100%)
Tel.: (770) 919-9520
Web Site: http://www.volkert.com
Engineering & Architectural Services
N.A.I.C.S.: 541330

Volkert, Inc. - Tampa (1)
1408 N Westshore Blvd Ste 600, Tampa, FL 33607
Tel.: (813) 875-1365
Web Site: http://www.volkert.com
Engineering, Architectural & Bridge Inspection Services
N.A.I.C.S.: 541330
Nancy Pelzer (Office Mgr)
Nicole Harris (Project Mgr)

VOLKMANN RAILROAD BUILDERS

N 60 W 14625 Kaul Ave, Menomonee Falls, WI 53051
Tel.: (262) 252-3377
Web Site: http://www.volkmannrr.com
Sales Range: $10-24.9 Million
Emp.: 45
Railroad & Railway Roadbed Construction
N.A.I.C.S.: 236210
Rick Volkmann (Pres)
Edward Webb (VP)

VOLKSWAGEN OF ALAMO HEIGHTS

1402 NE Loop 410, San Antonio, TX 78209
Tel.: (210) 828-1201
Web Site: http://www.volkswagenofalamoheights.com
Year Founded: 2012
Sales Range: $10-24.9 Million
Emp.: 55
Car Whslr
N.A.I.C.S.: 441110
Frank Grese (Pres)
Earl Hesterberg (CEO)
Michael Handwerger (Gen Mgr)

VOLKSWAGEN OF OLD SAYBROOK

319 Middlesex Tpke, Old Saybrook, CT 06475
Tel.: (860) 388-3400
Web Site: http://www.valentivwofoldsaybrook.com
Year Founded: 2001
Sales Range: $10-24.9 Million
Emp.: 50
Car Whslr
N.A.I.C.S.: 441110
Robert Valenti (VP)

VOLKSWAGEN SANTA MONICA, INC.

2440 Santa Monica Blvd, Santa Monica, CA 90404
Tel.: (310) 829-1888
Web Site: http://www.volkswagensantamonica.com
Sales Range: $125-149.9 Million
Emp.: 120
Automobiles, New & Used
N.A.I.C.S.: 441110
Michael Sullivan (Pres)
Jan Wagner (Controller)
Melvante Williams (Mgr-Internet Sls)

VOLLAND ELECTRIC EQUIPMENT

75 Innsbruck Dr, Buffalo, NY 14227
Tel.: (716) 656-9900
Web Site: http://www.volland.com
Rev.: $17,000,000
Emp.: 75
Distr Of Electric Motors
N.A.I.C.S.: 423610
Chris Graham (Pres)
Ron Graham (CEO)

VOLLERS, INC.

3311 US Hwy 22, Somerville, NJ 08876-3433
Tel.: (908) 725-1026
Year Founded: 1969
Sales Range: $25-49.9 Million
Emp.: 250
Provider of Excavation Services

COMPANIES

N.A.I.C.S.: 238910
Thomas Vollers (CEO)
John Amato (Mgr-AP)
Rob Vollers (Chm)
Carol Weisneck (Mgr-HR)
Chris Vollers (VP-Sls)
John Fitzsimmons (CFO)
Bob Albanese (Exec VP-Corp Dev)
Brendan Murray (Pres)

Subsidiaries:

Rob-Tom Inc. (1)
3311 US Hwy 22, Somerville, NJ 08876-3433
Tel.: (908) 725-1026
Web Site: http://www.vollers.com
Sales Range: $10-24.9 Million
Emp.: 4
Operators Of Nonresidential Buildings
N.A.I.C.S.: 531120

Vollers Excavating & Construction Inc. (1)
3311 US Hwy 22, Somerville, NJ 08876-3433 (100%)
Tel.: (908) 725-1026
Sales Range: $25-49.9 Million
Emp.: 200
Provider of Excavation Svcs.
N.A.I.C.S.: 238910
Joe Erwin (Mgr-Surveying)

VOLM BAG COMPANY, INC.
1804 Edison St, Antigo, WI 54409-2438
Tel.: (715) 627-4826 WI
Web Site: http://www.volmbag.com
Year Founded: 1941
Sales Range: $10-24.9 Million
Emp.: 84
Providers of Industrial & Personal Service Paper
N.A.I.C.S.: 424130
Jim Ferk (Controller)

VOLMAR CONSTRUCTION INC.
4400 2nd Ave, Brooklyn, NY 11232
Tel.: (718) 832-2444
Web Site: http://www.volmar.com
Sales Range: $50-74.9 Million
Emp.: 40
Nonresidential Construction
N.A.I.C.S.: 236220
Joseph Mosca (Mgr-Quality Control)
Hemant Shah (Project Mgr)
Sam Nortey (Project Mgr)
Prasad Sulikunte (Controller)
Geily Severino (Project Coord)
Krishna Dwaraganahalli (Project Mgr)

VOLT ATHLETICS, INC.
701 N 36th St Ste 450, Seattle, WA 98103
Tel.: (206) 701-6432
Web Site:
 http://www.voltathletics.com
Year Founded: 2011
Sales Range: $1-9.9 Million
Emp.: 25
Fitness Training Services
N.A.I.C.S.: 812990
Dan Giuliani (Co-Founder & CEO)
Trevor Watkins (Co-Founder & COO)
Brian McNaboe (CTO)

VOLTAIR CONSULTING ENGINEERS, INC.
220 W 7th Ave Ste 210, Tampa, FL 33602
Tel.: (813) 867-4899
Web Site:
 http://www.voltairengineers.com
Engineering Consulting Services
N.A.I.C.S.: 541330
Larry Stoff (Dir-Mechanical Engrg)
John Jennings (Sr Project Mgr-Info & Tech Sys)

VOLTAIX LLC
3121 Rt 22 E Ste 200, Branchburg, NJ 08876
Tel.: (908) 231-9060 NJ
Web Site: http://www.voltaix.com
Year Founded: 1986
Sales Range: $25-49.9 Million
Emp.: 185
Specialty Chemicals Mfr
N.A.I.C.S.: 325998
Ann Marie Hansen (VP-Fin & Admin)
Gregory T. Muhr (Dir-Global Sls & Mktg)
Mark A. Wilkinson (Exec VP-Ops & Tech)
Michael Pikulin (Sr VP)
Matthew D. Stephens (CTO & Exec VP-Sls & Mktg)
Paul C. Burlingame (Pres & CEO)
Rick Hallett (CFO)

VOLTARI CORPORATION
767 5th Ave Ste 4700, New York, NY 10153
Tel.: (212) 388-5500 DE
Year Founded: 2013
Mobile Data Solutions
N.A.I.C.S.: 551112
Kenneth A. Goldman (CEO)

Subsidiaries:

Motricity, Inc. (1)
601 W 26th St Ste 415, New York, NY 10001
Tel.: (646) 957-6200
Web Site: http://www.motricity.com
Rev.: $90,042,000
Assets: $81,517,000
Liabilities: $62,667,000
Net Worth: $18,850,000
Earnings: ($34,242,000)
Emp.: 152
Fiscal Year-end: 12/31/2012
Mobile Information & Entertainment Content Software & Services
N.A.I.C.S.: 513210

VOLUME 9 INC
1660 S Albion St Ste 800, Denver, CO 80222
Tel.: (303) 955-5228
Web Site: http://www.v9co
Year Founded: 2006
Sales Range: $1-9.9 Million
Emp.: 33
Online Marketing Consulting Services
N.A.I.C.S.: 541613
Chuck Aikens (CEO)
Dave Young (Dir-Tech)
Natalie Henley (Pres)
Mark Kutowy (Dir-Bus Dev)

VOLUME CHEVROLET BUICK
909 Veterans Pkwy, Barnesville, GA 30204
Tel.: (770) 358-0246
Web Site:
 http://www.volumechevrolet.com
Sales Range: $10-24.9 Million
Emp.: 19
Car Dealership Owner & Operator
N.A.I.C.S.: 441110
Jason Connell (Owner & Gen Mgr)
Buddy Beck (Mgr-Fin)
Todd Stone (Mgr-Sls)
Tiffany Bruce (Mgr-Svc)

VOLUME DISTRIBUTORS INC.
4199 Bandini Blvd, Vernon, CA 90023-4608
Tel.: (323) 981-1400 CA
Web Site:
 http://www.volumebrandsint.com
Year Founded: 1982
Sales Range: $25-49.9 Million
Emp.: 150
Supplier of Nondurable Goods
N.A.I.C.S.: 424990

Perry Rahban (Chm)
Maria Tovar (Mgr-Warehouse)

VOLUME PUBLIC RELATIONS
6212 S Fiddlers Green Cir Ste 400N, Greenwood Village, CO 80129
Tel.: (720) 529-4850
Web Site: http://www.volumepr.com
Year Founded: 2001
Sales Range: Less than $1 Million
Emp.: 7
Public Relations
N.A.I.C.S.: 541820
Elizabeth Edwards (Founder, Pres & CEO)

VOLUMETRIC BUILDING COMPANIES
6128 Ridge Ave, Philadelphia, PA 19128
Tel.: (215) 259-7509
Web Site: http://www.vbc.co
Year Founded: 2009
Sales Range: $1-9.9 Million
Emp.: 10
Real Estate Development Services
N.A.I.C.S.: 237210
Vaughan Buckley (Founder & CEO)
Robert Schmalbach (VP-Construction)
Michael Pesarchik (Gen Mgr)

VOLUNTARY PURCHASING GROUPS, INC.
230 N Fm 87, Bonham, TX 75418
Tel.: (903) 583-5501 TX
Web Site: http://www.fertilome.com
Year Founded: 1950
Sales Range: $25-49.9 Million
Emp.: 100
Wholesalers of Farm Supplies
N.A.I.C.S.: 424910
Marsha Dobson (Project Coord-Mktg)

Subsidiaries:

Ferti-Lome Distributors Inc. (1)
230 N Fm 87, Bonham, TX 75418
Tel.: (903) 583-5501
Web Site: http://www.fertilome.com
Sales Range: $10-24.9 Million
Emp.: 3
Lessors of Real Property
N.A.I.C.S.: 531190
Steve Money (Pres)

VOLUNTEER CORPORATE CREDIT UNION
2460 Atrium Way, Nashville, TN 37214
Tel.: (615) 232-7900 TN
Web Site: http://www.volcorp.org
Year Founded: 1981
Sales Range: $10-24.9 Million
Emp.: 53
Credit Union Operator
N.A.I.C.S.: 522130
Phillip Cochran (Chief Investment Officer & VP)
Jeffrey W. Merry (CFO & Sr VP)
Karla Knisley (COO & Sr VP)

VOLUNTEER ENERGY COOPERATIVE, INC.
18359 Hwy 58 N, Decatur, TN 37322-0277
Tel.: (423) 334-1020 TN
Web Site: http://www.vec.org
Year Founded: 1935
Sales Range: $25-49.9 Million
Emp.: 163
Providers of Electrical Services
N.A.I.C.S.: 221122
Rody Blevins (Pres & CEO)
Laney Colvard (Chm)
Larry Storie (Vice Chm)

VOLVO OF EDISON

VOLUNTEER FEDERAL SAVINGS BANK
108 Main St, Madisonville, TN 37354
Tel.: (423) 442-4545
Web Site: http://www.volfed.com
Year Founded: 1973
Sales Range: $10-24.9 Million
Emp.: 60
Banking Services
N.A.I.C.S.: 522180
Larry Hicks (Pres)

VOLUNTEERS FOR ECONOMIC GROWTH ALLIANCE
1726 M St NW Ste 800, Washington, DC 20036
Tel.: (202) 223-7012 DC
Web Site:
 http://www.vegaalliance.org
Year Founded: 2003
Sales Range: $25-49.9 Million
Emp.: 15
Economic Development Services
N.A.I.C.S.: 541720
Long Tien Nguyen (Mng Dir-Fin & Admin)
David Simpson (Mng Dir-Programs & Compliance)
John D. Pompay (Treas)
Thomas J. Miller (Vice Chm)
Jennifer Brinkerhoff (Sec)
Angela Canterbury (Mng Dir-Comm & Advocacy)

VOLUNTEERS FOR INTER-AMERICAN DEVELOPMENT ASSISTANCE
1519 63rd St, Emeryville, CA 94608
Tel.: (510) 655-8432 CA
Web Site: http://www.vidausa.org
Year Founded: 1991
Sales Range: $10-24.9 Million
Emp.: 2
Project Development Services
N.A.I.C.S.: 561990
Antonio Valla (Sec)
Adam See (Exec Dir)
Haydee Rodriguez-Pastor (Chm)
Ben Pellegrino (Treas)

VOLUSION, INC.
8911 N Capital of Texas Hwy Ste 1200, Austin, TX 78759
Web Site: http://www.volusion.com
Year Founded: 1999
Sales Range: $1-9.9 Million
Emp.: 150
E-Commerce Software
N.A.I.C.S.: 513210
Clay Olivier (CEO)
Kevin Sproles (Chm)
Jason Wallis (VP-Architecture)
Randon Kelly (VP-Fin)

VOLVO FINANCE NORTH AMERICA INC.
9009 Carothers Pkwy, Franklin, TN 37067-1634
Tel.: (201) 358-6600 NJ
Year Founded: 1999
Sales Range: $150-199.9 Million
Emp.: 100
Automobile Finance Leasing
N.A.I.C.S.: 522299

VOLVO OF EDISON
842 Route 1 N, Edison, NJ 08817
Tel.: (732) 248-0500
Web Site:
 http://www.volvoofedison.com
Sales Range: $10-24.9 Million
Emp.: 40
Car Whslr
N.A.I.C.S.: 441110
David Long (Pres)

Volvo of Edison—(Continued)

VOLVO OF FORT WASHINGTON
115 Bethlehem Pike, Fort Washington, PA 19034
Tel.: (215) 653-7300
Web Site: http://www.volvofw.com
Sales Range: $10-24.9 Million
Emp.: 45
Car Whslr
N.A.I.C.S.: 441110
Chip Ott (Pres)

VOLVO OF LISLE
4375 Lincoln Ave, Lisle, IL 60532
Tel.: (630) 852-6000
Web Site: http://www.volvooflisle.com
Year Founded: 1962
Sales Range: $125-149.9 Million
Emp.: 300
New & Used Car Dealer
N.A.I.C.S.: 441110
Horst Korallus (Pres)
Guenther Korallus (Sec & VP)
Jeff Carr (Gen Mgr)
Thomas Taylor (Controller)

VOLVO OF THE TRIAD
701 Peters Creek Pkwy, Winston Salem, NC 27103
Tel.: (336) 723-4111
Web Site:
 http://www.volvoofthetriad.com
Sales Range: $25-49.9 Million
Emp.: 64
Car Whslr
N.A.I.C.S.: 441110
Robert Satter (Owner)

VOLVO SALES & SERVICE CENTER
4375 Lincoln Ave, Lisle, IL 60532
Tel.: (630) 852-6000
Web Site:
 http://www.thevolvosuperstore.com
Rev.: $240,000,000
Emp.: 300
Automobiles, New & Used
N.A.I.C.S.: 441110
Horst Korallus (Pres)
Ghunter Carollis (Co-Owner & Vice Chm)

VOMELA SPECIALTY COMPANY
845 Minnehaha Ave E, Saint Paul, MN 55106
Tel.: (651) 228-2200
Web Site: http://www.vomela.com
Year Founded: 1947
Sales Range: $200-249.9 Million
Emp.: 925
Poster & Decal Printing Mfr
N.A.I.C.S.: 323111
Thomas Auth (Chm)

Subsidiaries:
B2B Media (1)
34 Ellwood Ct Ste C, Greenville, SC 29607
Tel.: (864) 627-1992
Web Site: http://www.b2bmedia.com
Sales Range: $10-24.9 Million
Emp.: 20
Brand Development
N.A.I.C.S.: 541870
Chuck Driskell (Pres & CEO)
Laura Hortis (CFO)
Robert Chapman (Chm)

C2 IMAGING, LLC (1)
274 E Fillmore Ave, Saint Paul, MN 55107
Tel.: (646) 557-6300
Web Site: http://www.c2imagingllc.com
Media Graphics Solutions
N.A.I.C.S.: 541810

Branch (Domestic):
C2 IMAGING, LLC - Gaithersburg (2)
220 Perry Pkwy, Gaithersburg, MD 20877
Tel.: (240) 224-7890
Web Site: http://www.vomela.com
Emp.: 16
Digital Printing & Advertising Related Services
N.A.I.C.S.: 541810
Ryan Bush (VP)

C2 IMAGING, LLC-Chicago (2)
329 W 18th Ste 508, Chicago, IL 60616
Tel.: (312) 235-3800
Web Site: http://www.c2imaging.com
Media Business Solutions
N.A.I.C.S.: 541810

C2 IMAGING, LLC-Englewood (2)
1400 W Dartmouth Ave, Englewood, CO 80110
Tel.: (720) 941-5900
Media Business Solutions
N.A.I.C.S.: 541810

C2 IMAGING, LLC-Houston (2)
6650 Roxburgh Dr Ste 180, Houston, TX 77041
Tel.: (713) 956-3400
Web Site: http://www.c2spark.com
Sales Range: $25-49.9 Million
Emp.: 16
Media Business Solutions
N.A.I.C.S.: 541810
Mary Anna Bond (Gen Mgr)

C2 IMAGING, LLC-New York (2)
423 W 55th St Fl 6, New York, NY 10019
Tel.: (646) 557-6300
Web Site: http://www.c2media.com
Rev.: $100,000,000
Emp.: 150
Color Printing: Gravure
N.A.I.C.S.: 323111

Subsidiary (Domestic):
Superior Imaging Group, Inc. (2)
8041 S 228th stSte107, Kent, WA 98032
Tel.: (253) 872-7200
Web Site: http://www.superiorimaging.com
Sales Range: $25-49.9 Million
Emp.: 25
Screen Printing & Digital Design Services
N.A.I.C.S.: 323113
Peter Ouzman (Gen Mgr)

FUSION Imaging, Inc. (1)
601 Boro St, Kaysville, UT 84037
Tel.: (801) 546-4567
Web Site: http://www.fusionimaging.com
Sales Range: $10-24.9 Million
Emp.: 75
Commercial Flexographic Printing & Graphic Design Services
N.A.I.C.S.: 323111
Joseph Covington (Dir-Organizational Dev)
Kim Griesemer (Owner)
Wayne Boydstun (COO)

Pratt Corporation (1)
3035 N Shadeland Ave, Indianapolis, IN 46226
Tel.: (317) 924-3201
Web Site: http://www.prattcorp.com
Sales Range: $50-74.9 Million
Emp.: 200
Store Decor & Point-of-Purchase Printing Services
N.A.I.C.S.: 323113
Tom Pratt (VP-Sls & Mktg)

Visualz (1)
845 Minnehaha Ave East, St. Paul, MN 55106
Tel.: (507) 455-9076
Web Site: https://getvisualz.com
Online Education Services
N.A.I.C.S.: 611430
Joyce Mattson (Gen Mgr)

VON HOUSEN'S MOTORS
1810 Howe Ave, Sacramento, CA 95825-1026
Tel.: (916) 924-8000
Web Site: http://www.vonhousen.com
Year Founded: 1957

Sales Range: $75-99.9 Million
Emp.: 250
Holding Company; New & Used Car Dealerships Owner & Operator
N.A.I.C.S.: 551112
George A. Grinzewitsch Jr. (Owner & CEO)

Subsidiaries:
Von Housen's Sacramento, Inc. (1)
1810 Howe Ave, Sacramento, CA 95825
Tel.: (916) 924-8000
Web Site: http://www.mbsacramento.com
New & Used Car Dealer
N.A.I.C.S.: 441110
Jason Bryner (Gen Sls Mgr)
Joann Cordero (Mgr-Bus Dev)
Mike Moreno (Mgr-Svc)

VON MAUR INC.
6565 Brady St, Davenport, IA 52806-2052
Tel.: (563) 388-2200
Web Site: http://www.vonmaur.com
Year Founded: 1872
Sales Range: $400-449.9 Million
Emp.: 5,000
Departmental Store Operator
N.A.I.C.S.: 455110
Charles R. von Maur (Co-Chm)
Richard B. von Maur (Co-Chm)
James D. von Maur (Pres)
Shannon Keene (Mgr-Recruiting)
Robert Larson (CFO)
Joy Place (VP-Mdsg)
Melody Westendorf (COO)
James Partin (Dir-Loss Prevention)

VON SCHRADER COMPANY
1600 Jct Ave, Racine, WI 53403-2568
Tel.: (262) 634-1956
Web Site:
 http://www.vonschrader.com
Year Founded: 1935
Sales Range: $75-99.9 Million
Emp.: 50
Portable Carpet Shampoo Machines, Upholstery Cleaning Equipment, Wall & Ceiling Cleaning Equipment & Accessories, Detergents & Chemicals Mfr
N.A.I.C.S.: 423850
Herb Meyer (VP-Ops)
Jeff Ranch (CFO)
Trudy Schatzman (Mgr-Customer Svc)

VON TOBEL CORPORATION
256 S Washington St, Valparaiso, IN 46383
Tel.: (219) 462-6184
Web Site: http://www.vontobels.com
Sales Range: $25-49.9 Million
Emp.: 150
Lumber & Other Building Materials
N.A.I.C.S.: 423510
Ken Pylipow (Pres)
Cheryl Gazdich (Controller)
Charles Nathan (Mgr-IT)

VONLANE, LLC
6310 Lemmon Ave Ste 125, Dallas, TX 75209
Tel.: (214) 612-7234
Web Site: http://www.vonlane.com
Year Founded: 2013
Sales Range: $10-24.9 Million
Emp.: 103
Travel Agency Services
N.A.I.C.S.: 561510
Alex Danza (Founder & CEO)

VOODOO BBQ & GRILL
40306 Hwy 42 Ste 202 D, Prairieville, LA 70769
Tel.: (225) 926-8780

Web Site:
 http://www.voodoobbqandgrill.com
Year Founded: 2002
Sales Range: $1-9.9 Million
Emp.: 13
Casual Dining Restaurants
N.A.I.C.S.: 722511
Dino Arvanetes (COO)
Stephen Gill (Mgr-Construction & Maintenance)
Tony Avila (Owner)

VORA VENTURES LLC
10290 Alliance Rd, Blue Ash, OH 45242
Tel.: (513) 792-5100
Web Site:
 https://www.voraventures.com
Private Investment Company
N.A.I.C.S.: 523999
Mahendra Vora (Exec Chm)
Mike Jones (Exec VP-Fin)
Kevin Dooley (Chief Strategy Officer & Exec VP)

Subsidiaries:
Ascendum Solutions LLC (1)
10290 Alliance Rd, Blue Ash, OH 45242
Tel.: (513) 792-5100
Web Site: http://www.ascendum.com
Information Technology Solutions
N.A.I.C.S.: 541519
Mahendra Vora (Chm)
Kris Nair (Pres & CEO)
Mark Olszewski (Exec VP-Global Solutions Delivery)
Uday Kumar (VP-Sls)
Mike Jones (Exec VP-Fin)
Heather Schwab (Asst VP-HR)

Subsidiary (Domestic):
Sourcebits Digital LLC (2)
995 Market St, San Francisco, CA 94103
Tel.: (415) 985-8580
Web Site: http://www.sourcebits.com
Mobile Application Developer
N.A.I.C.S.: 513210
Kris Nair (Pres & CEO)

AssureCare, LLC (1)
250 W Ct St Ste 450E, Cincinnati, OH 45202
Tel.: (513) 618-2150
Web Site: https://assurecare.com
Healthcare Software Developer
N.A.I.C.S.: 513210
Yousuf Ahmad (Pres & CEO)
Mayur Yermaneni (Exec VP-Innovation & Growth)

Subsidiary (Domestic):
Cureatr, Inc. (2)
17 W 20th St 3rd.fl, New York, NY 10011
Tel.: (212) 203-3927
Web Site: http://www.cureatr.com
Software Publisher
N.A.I.C.S.: 513210
Alex Khomenko (CTO)
Greg Leone (VP-Sls)
Aman Bhasin (VP-Bus Dev & Strategy)
Jonathan Sherman (Chief Product Officer)

Subsidiary (Domestic):
SinfoniaRx, Inc. (3)
100 N Stone Ave Ste 109, Tucson, AZ 85701
Tel.: (520) 499-3388
Web Site: http://sinfoniarx.com
Healtcare Services
N.A.I.C.S.: 621999
Sandra Leal (Exec VP-Health Plan & Payer Bus Unit)
Rose T. Martin (Sr VP-Ops)
Ann Wild (Chief Clinical Officer)
Ian Hubbell (Dir-Acct Mgmt)
Ashley Coleman (VP-Pharmacy Ops)
Jennifer Parker (Mktg Mgr)
Todd A. Plesco (Chief Information Security Officer)
Dave Schlewitt (VP-Enterprise Infrastructure Engrg)

Vora Technology Park LLC (1)

101 Knightsbridge Dr, Hamilton, OH 45011
Tel.: (513) 895-8000
Web Site: http://www.voratechpark.com
Emp.: 10
Commercial Technology Park & Data Center; Office Leasing
N.A.I.C.S.: 531120
Cheryl Vitek *(Mgr-Bus)*
Mahendra B. Vora *(Co-Founder & CEO)*
Tom Koffel *(Mgr-Facility)*

VORDERMAN MOTOR WERKS INC.
5811 Cross Creek Blvd, Fort Wayne, IN 46818
Tel.: (260) 213-4181
Web Site:
    http://www.vordermanvw.com
Sales Range: $10-24.9 Million
Emp.: 42
New Car Dealers
N.A.I.C.S.: 441110
Reg Vorderman *(Pres)*
Lori Miller *(Mgr-Sls)*
Naomi Shaw *(Mgr-Fin & Insurance)*
Chad Probst *(Dir-Parts & Svc)*

VORTEQ COIL FINISHERS, LLC
930 Armour Rd, Oconomowoc, WI 53066
Tel.: (262) 567-1112   DE
Web Site: http://www.vorteqcoil.com
Year Founded: 1982
Sales Range: $10-24.9 Million
Emp.: 100
Steel & Aluminum Product Coil Coating & Related Services
N.A.I.C.S.: 332812
Jim Dockey *(CEO)*
Jim Boyle *(COO)*
Rick Walters *(Dir-Operating Svcs)*
Sunny Flynn *(Dir-Mktg)*

Subsidiaries:

Vorteq Allentown, LLC   (1)
2233 26th St SW, Allentown, PA 18103
Tel.: (610) 797-5200
Steel & Aluminum Product Coil Coating & Related Services
N.A.I.C.S.: 332812
Don Hagenauer *(VP-Sls)*

Vorteq Jackson, LLC   (1)
200 Conalco Dr, Jackson, TN 38301
Tel.: (731) 422-3605
Steel & Aluminum Product Coil Coating & Related Services
N.A.I.C.S.: 332812
Matt Dournaux *(Mgr-Customer Svc)*

Vorteq Valencia, LLC   (1)
125 McFann Rd, Valencia, PA 16059
Tel.: (724) 898-1511
Steel & Aluminum Product Coil Coating & Related Services
N.A.I.C.S.: 332812
Jim Barr *(Gen Mgr-Ops)*

Vorteq Woodstock, LLC   (1)
15920 Nelson Rd, Woodstock, IL 60098
Tel.: (815) 338-6410
Steel & Aluminum Product Coil Coating & Related Services
N.A.I.C.S.: 332812

Zegers, Inc.   (1)
16727 Chicago Ave, Lansing, IL 60438-1111
Tel.: (708) 474-7700
Web Site: http://www.zegers-inc.com
Fabricated Structural Metal Mfr
N.A.I.C.S.: 332312
Bill Zegers *(Pres)*
Nancy Mitros *(Pres)*

VORTEX COMPANY, LLC
18150 Imperial Valley Dr, Houston, TX 77060
Tel.: (713) 750-9081
Web Site:
    https://vortexcompanies.com
Year Founded: 2017
Water, Sewer & Iindustrial Infrastructure Services
N.A.I.C.S.: 237110
Michael Vellano *(Founder, Pres & CEO)*
Quin Breland *(Mng Dir-Vortex Europe)*
Andrew Gonnella *(Pres-Production Division)*
Matthew Samford *(CFO)*
Wesley Kingery *(Pres-Services Division)*
Ryan Graham *(Sr VP-Sls)*
Ram Vela *(CIO)*
Matt Timberlake *(Chief Admin Officer)*
Jaclyn Herrera *(CMO & Head-DE&I)*

Subsidiaries:

Applied Felts, Inc.   (1)
450 College Dr, Martinsville, VA 24112
Tel.: (276) 656-1904
Web Site: http://www.appliedfelts.com
Rev.: $5,000,000
Emp.: 70
Fabricated Pipe & Pipe Fitting Mfr
N.A.I.C.S.: 332996
Alex Johnson *(Pres)*
Charles Mattox *(Gen Mgr)*

Planned & Engineered Construction, Inc.   (1)
3400 Centennial Dr, Helena, MT 59601
Tel.: (406) 447-5030
Web Site: http://www.pechelena.com
Sales Range: $1-9.9 Million
Emp.: 12
Water & Sewer Line & Related Structures Construction
N.A.I.C.S.: 237110
Chris Peccia *(Pres)*
Christy Austin *(Treas)*
Don Harriott *(Sec)*
Justin Noble *(Supvr-Wet Out)*
Nikki Peters *(Office Mgr)*
Mike Vetsch *(Project Engr)*
Robert Peccia *(VP)*

Ted Berry Company LLC   (1)
521 Federal Rd, Livermore, ME 04253
Tel.: (207) 897-3348
Web Site:
    https://www.tedberrycompany.com
Sewage Treatment Facilities
N.A.I.C.S.: 221320

VORTEX ENTERPRISES INCORPORATED
25 W Official Rd, Addison, IL 60101
Tel.: (630) 458-8600
Web Site:
    http://www.vortexchicago.com
Rev.: $17,200,000
Emp.: 60
Floor Coverings
N.A.I.C.S.: 423220
Del Church *(Pres)*

VORTEX INDUSTRIES INC.
20 Odyssey, Irvine, CA 92618-3144
Tel.: (714) 434-8000
Web Site:
    http://www.vortexdoors.com
Year Founded: 1937
Sales Range: $25-49.9 Million
Emp.: 350
Commercial & Industrial Door & Window Repair
N.A.I.C.S.: 811490
Mike Kattan *(Pres)*
Randy Moore *(Dir-IS)*
Stacey Muto *(Dir-Mktg)*

VORTEX MARINE CONSTRUCTION
1 Maritime Way, Oakland, CA 94509
Tel.: (510) 261-2400
Web Site: http://www.vortex-sfb.com
Rev.: $16,000,000
Emp.: 15
Marine Construction
N.A.I.C.S.: 236210
Blaise Fettig *(Co-Founder)*
Matt Fettig *(Co-Founder)*

Subsidiaries:

Deep Ocean Engineering Inc.   (1)
1431 Doolittle Dr, San Leandro, CA 94577
Tel.: (510) 562-9300
Web Site: http://www.deepocean.com
Rev.: $1,663,000
Emp.: 25
Submersible Marine Robot Manned Or Unmanned Mfr
N.A.I.C.S.: 336611

VORTEX RECYCLING
61 Riverpark Dr, New Castle, PA 16101
Tel.: (724) 657-0333
Web Site:
    http://www.vortexrecycling.com
Year Founded: 2002
Sales Range: $1-9.9 Million
Emp.: 8
Materials Recovery Facilities
N.A.I.C.S.: 562920
Donald Kleine *(Owner)*
Stephanie Weymer *(Office Mgr)*
John Greer *(Mgr-Sls)*

VORYS, SATER, SEYMOUR & PEASE LLP
52 E Gay St, Columbus, OH 43215
Tel.: (614) 464-6400   OH
Web Site: http://www.vorys.com
Year Founded: 1909
Sales Range: $150-199.9 Million
Emp.: 501
Legal Advisory Services
N.A.I.C.S.: 541110
Russell M. Gertmenian *(Mng Partner)*
John Kuhl *(Partner)*
Christine Poth *(Partner)*
Jonathan Ishee *(Partner)*
Elizabeth Weinewuth *(Partner)*
Angela Gibson *(Partner)*
Paul Kerlin *(Partner)*
Natalie McLaughlin *(Partner)*
Martha Motley *(Partner)*
Benjamin Shepler *(Partner)*
Michael Ball *(Partner)*
John Furniss III *(Partner)*

VOS WINDOW & DOOR INC.
7600 Wedd St, Overland Park, KS 66204
Tel.: (913) 962-8880
Web Site:
    http://www.voswindows.com
Sales Range: $10-24.9 Million
Emp.: 3
Lumber, Plywood & Millwork
N.A.I.C.S.: 423310
James R. Vosburgh Sr. *(Pres)*

VOSGES HAUT-CHOCOLAT, LTD.
2950 N Oakley Ave, Chicago, IL 60618
Tel.: (773) 388-5560
Web Site:
    http://www.vosgeschocolate.com
Sales Range: $1-9.9 Million
Emp.: 60
Chocolate Mfr & Distr
N.A.I.C.S.: 311351
Ron Tremaroli *(Mgr-Production)*
Natalia Rusecka *(Asst Mgr)*
Elliot Schulz *(Coord-Sls)*
David Crosby *(Dir-Sls)*

VOSS CHEVROLET, INC.
100 Loop Rd, Centerville, OH 45459
Tel.: (937) 433-9640
Year Founded: 1972
Sales Range: $50-74.9 Million
Emp.: 190
Car Whslr
N.A.I.C.S.: 441110
Gregory Stout *(CFO)*
John E. Voss *(Pres)*

VOSS ELECTRIC COMPANY
1601 Cushman Dr, Lincoln, NE 68512
Tel.: (402) 328-2281
Web Site:
    http://www.vosslighting.com
Sales Range: $25-49.9 Million
Emp.: 150
Electrical Apparatus & Equipment
N.A.I.C.S.: 423610
Michael Voss *(Chm-Board)*
Bill Cooley *(VP-Mktg)*
Steve Sanderson *(Exec VP-Ops)*

VOSS EQUIPMENT INCORPORATED
15241 Commercial Ave, Harvey, IL 60426
Tel.: (708) 596-7000
Web Site:
    http://www.vossequipment.com
Sales Range: $10-24.9 Million
Emp.: 80
Industrial Machinery & Equipment
N.A.I.C.S.: 423830
Tom Mateja *(Controller)*
Peter W. Voss Sr. *(CEO)*

VOTACALL, INC.
185 Devonshire St Ste 700, Boston, MA 02110
Web Site: http://www.votacall.com
Year Founded: 2005
Business Communications Solutions
N.A.I.C.S.: 517810
Edward Lennon *(Pres & CEO)*

VOTIGO, INC.
251 Lafayette Circle Suite 330, Lafayette, CA 94549
Tel.: (800) 519-1850
Web Site: http://www.votigo.com
Year Founded: 2006
Sales Range: $1-9.9 Million
Emp.: 42
Social Media Marketing & Promotions
N.A.I.C.S.: 541613
Michael La Rotonda *(Co-Founder & Co-CEO)*
James Risner *(Co-Founder & Co-CEO)*
Priyanka Luthra *(Dir-Interactive Design & Dev)*
Maninder Singh *(CTO)*

Subsidiaries:

Votigo Software Private Limited   (1)
8-2-332/8/A Aditya House 1st Floor Rd #3 Banjara Hills, 500034, Hyderabad, India   (100%)
Tel.: (91) 40 3058 6673
Web Site: http://www.votigo.com
Social Media & Marketing Developer
N.A.I.C.S.: 513210
Maninder Singh *(Sr VP-Tech)*

VOTO MANUFACTURERS SALES CO. INC.
500 N 3rd St, Steubenville, OH 43952
Tel.: (740) 282-3621
Web Site: http://www.votosales.com
Sales Range: $10-24.9 Million
Emp.: 42
Industrial Supplies
N.A.I.C.S.: 423840
Janie K. Mayle *(Pres)*
Richard Smith *(Gen Mgr-Sls)*
David C. Mayer *(VP & Mgr-Sls)*

VOUK TRANSPORTATION INC.
701 Judi Dr, Little Rock, AR 72117-2913

VOUK TRANSPORTATION INC. U.S. PRIVATE

Vouk Transportation Inc.—(Continued)
Tel.: (501) 945-4541 AR
Year Founded: 1979
Sales Range: $25-49.9 Million
Emp.: 20
Freight Transportation Arrangement
N.A.I.C.S.: 488510
Pat Koch (Controller)
Chris Blakeley (Pres)

VOX COMMUNICATIONS GROUP LLC
70 Walnut St, Wellesley, MA 02481
Tel.: (781) 239-8018 DE
Web Site: http://www.voxcommunications.com
Year Founded: 2005
Holding Company; Radio Station Owner & Operator
N.A.I.C.S.: 551112
Bruce Danziger (CEO & Partner)
Ken Barlow (COO & Partner)
Keith Thomas (CFO & Partner)
Kevin LeRoux (Partner & Reg VP)
Race Ashlyn (VP & Mgr-Market-VA-Harrisonburg)

Subsidiaries:
Vox Communications - Western Massachusetts (1)
211 Jason St, Pittsfield, MA 01201 (100%)
Tel.: (413) 499-3333
Web Site: http://www.live959.com
Sales Range: $10-24.9 Million
Emp.: 16
Radio Stations
N.A.I.C.S.: 516110
Peter Barry (VP-Sls)
Victoria Spencer (Mgr-Sls)

WSIG 96.9FM (1)
639 N Main St, Mount Crawford, VA 22841 (100%)
Tel.: (540) 432-1063
Web Site: http://www.969wsig.com
Sales Range: $10-24.9 Million
Emp.: 20
Radio Stations
N.A.I.C.S.: 516110
Molly Miller (Dir-Brdcst Production)
Scott Richards (Gen Mgr)

WWUS 104.1FM (1)
30336 Overseas Hwy, Big Pine Key, FL 33043 (100%)
Tel.: (305) 872-9100
Web Site: http://www.us1radio.com
Sales Range: $10-24.9 Million
Emp.: 20
Radio Stations
N.A.I.C.S.: 516110
Erika Bowman (Mgr-Ops)

VOX NETWORK SOLUTIONS
8000 Marina Blvd Ste 130, Brisbane, CA 94005
Tel.: (650) 989-1000
Web Site: http://www.voxns.com
Year Founded: 2006
Sales Range: $10-24.9 Million
Emp.: 52
Voice, Data & IP Telephony Services
N.A.I.C.S.: 517112
Scott Landis (Pres & CEO)
Ron Kingsford (VP-Sls & Mktg)
Garrett Gilkison (VP-Cloud & Consulting)
Nick Kolintzas (CTO & VP-Engrg)
Craig Schneider (VP-Ops)
Phoebe Gavin (Exec Dir-Learning & Dev)

VOXITAS
1030 Hastings St, Traverse City, MI 49686
Tel.: (877) 277-4297
Web Site: http://www.voxitas.com
Year Founded: 2002
Rev: $3,300,000
Emp.: 50

Wired Telecommunications Carriers
N.A.I.C.S.: 517111
Jason Ulm (VP-Sls & Mktg)

VOXWARE, INC.
300 American Metro Blvd Ste 155, Hamilton, NJ 08619
Tel.: (609) 514-4100 DE
Web Site: http://www.voxware.com
Sales Range: $10-24.9 Million
Emp.: 56
Speech Recognition Systems for Data Entry by Voice
N.A.I.C.S.: 541512
Keith Phillips (Pres & CEO)

VOXX ACCESSORIES CORP.
3502 Woodview Trace, Indianapolis, IN 46268
Tel.: (317) 218-7300
Year Founded: 2007
Consumer Electronics Mfr & Distr
N.A.I.C.S.: 423620
Frank Rebel (VP-Sls)
Derek Jensen (Mgr-Product Mktg)

VOYAGE-AIR GUITAR, INC.
6752 Preston Ave Ste E, Livermore, CA 94551
Tel.: (800) 371-6478
Web Site: http://www.voyageairguitar.com
Sales Range: $1-9.9 Million
Guitar Mfr
N.A.I.C.S.: 339992
Jeff Cohen (CEO)

VOYAGER CAPITAL, LLC
719 2nd Ave Ste 1400, Seattle, WA 98104
Tel.: (206) 438-1800
Web Site: http://www.voyagercapital.com
Year Founded: 1997
Emp.: 25
Private Investment Firm
N.A.I.C.S.: 523999
Erik Benson (Partner)
Geoff Entress (Partner)
Diane Fraiman (Partner)
Tom Huseby (Mng Dir)
Tom Kippola (Partner-Venture)
Bill McAleer (Mng Dir)
Chrismon Nofsinger (Partner-Venture)
Jennifer Harris (CFO)
Bruce R. Chizen (Partner-Venture)

Subsidiaries:
Zettics, Inc. (1)
5 Lyberty Way, Westford, MA 01886
Tel.: (978) 254-5329
Data Analytic Services
N.A.I.C.S.: 518210
Sterling Wilson (Pres & CEO)
Asa Kalavade (CTO & Sr VP)
Tal Kedar (CFO)
John Gillespie (Sr VP-Sls)
Ian Herbert-Jones (Sr VP)
Joe Levy (VP-Customer Strategy & Mktg)
Andrew Gibbs (VP-Product Mgmt)
Prasasth Palnati (VP-Engrg)
Stephen Douglas (VP-Tech)
John Thomas (Dir-Res)
Adam Guy (VP-Monetization)

Subsidiary (Domestic):
Velocent Systems, Inc. (2)
1250 E Diehl Rd, Naperville, IL 60563
Tel.: (630) 799-3800
Web Site: http://www.velocent.com
Emp.: 15
Data Processing Services
N.A.I.C.S.: 423430
Ian Herbert Jones (CEO)
Stephen Douglas (CTO)
Tom Smith (COO)
Jagadeesh Dantuluri (VP-Mktg)

Randy Johnson (VP-Engrg)
Eric Hong (Co-Founder)
Philip Stevens (Sr VP-Sls)
Larry Border (Dir-Fin)

VOYAGER INC.
2500 Ada Dr, Elkhart, IN 46514
Tel.: (574) 264-9504
Web Site: http://www.voyagerinc.net
Year Founded: 1975
Sales Range: $10-24.9 Million
Emp.: 75
Manufacture Metal Chair Frames
N.A.I.C.S.: 337215
Tom Williams (Pres)
Jerry Rummel (CFO)
R. Stephen Bennett (CEO)

VOYAGER INTERESTS, LLC
1334 Brittmoore Rd Ste 2611, Houston, TX 77043
Tel.: (713) 986-9222 TX
Web Site: https://www.voyagerinterests.com
Privater Equity Firm
N.A.I.C.S.: 523999
Robert Trainer (Partner)

Subsidiaries:
Aegion Coating Services, LLC (1)
10655 Jefferson Chemical Rd, Conroe, TX 77301
Tel.: (936) 539-3294
Web Site: http://www.aegion.com
Infrastructure & Pipeline Protection Product & Services
N.A.I.C.S.: 811310
Bryan Kirchmer (Pres)

VOYAGER SPACE HOLDINGS, INC.
1225 17th St Ste 1100, Denver, CO 80202
Tel.: (303) 500-6985 DE
Web Site: http://voyagerspaceholdings.com
First Space Focused Holding Company
N.A.I.C.S.: 551112
Matthew Kuta (Pres & COO)
Dylan Taylor (Chm & CEO)
Thomas Ayres (Chief Legal Officer)
Jeffrey Manber (Pres-Intl & Space Stations)
Clay Mowry (Chief Revenue Officer)

Subsidiaries:
Space Micro Inc. (1)
15378 Ave of Science, San Diego, CA 92128-3451
Tel.: (858) 332-0700
Web Site: http://www.spacemicro.com
Government Services
N.A.I.C.S.: 334413
David J. Strobel (Co-Founder, Chm & CEO)
David R. Czajkowski (Pres & COO)
Michael Dowd (VP-Bus Dev)
Patricia Ellison (VP-HR & Admin)
Michael Jacox (VP-Engrg)
Bert Vermeire (CTO)

Zin Technologies Inc. (1)
6745 Engle Rd Airport Executive Park, Cleveland, OH 44130
Tel.: (440) 625-2200
Web Site: http://www.zin-tech.com
Rev: $16,495,650
Emp.: 150
Engineering Laboratory
N.A.I.C.S.: 541715
Daryl Z. Laisure (CEO)
Gary W. Mynchenberg (VP-Fin & Admin)
Carlos Grodsinsky (Pres)

VOZZCOM, INC.
11768 W Sample Rd, Coral Springs, FL 33065
Tel.: (954) 753-8600 FL
Web Site: http://www.vozzcom.net
Year Founded: 2000

Sales Range: $10-24.9 Million
Emp.: 215
Field Services for Cable Operators
N.A.I.C.S.: 238210
David E. Vozzola (COO)
Doreen Vozzola (Pres)

VP HOLDINGS CORPORATION
2514 Hatchery Rd, Madison, WI 53713
Tel.: (608) 256-1988
Web Site: http://www.vitaplus.com
Sales Range: $50-74.9 Million
Emp.: 327
Feed Premixes
N.A.I.C.S.: 311119
Robert S. Tramburg (Pres)

VP SUPPLY CORP.
3445 Winton Pl, Rochester, NY 14623-2950
Tel.: (585) 272-0110
Web Site: http://www.vpsupply.com
Year Founded: 1990
Sales Range: $10-24.9 Million
Emp.: 100
Provider of Plumbing Fixtures, Equipment & Supplies
N.A.I.C.S.: 423720
Gary Curwin (Pres)
Gary Perkins (VP)
Hadar Kamal (Dir-Residential Sls)
Chip Wallace (Mgr-Warehouse)

VPI SYSTEMS
300 Atrium Dr Ste 400, Somerset, NJ 08873-4160
Tel.: (732) 332-0233
Web Site: http://www.vpisystems.com
Sales Range: $10-24.9 Million
Emp.: 100
Computer Software Development
N.A.I.C.S.: 541511
Tito Sharma (Pres & CEO)
Matthew Rosner (CFO)
Sudhir Kumar (VP-Tech & Svcs)

Subsidiaries:
VPI Systems (1)
943 Holmdel Rd, Holmdel, NJ 07733
Tel.: (732) 332-0233
Web Site: http://www.vpisystems.com
Sales Range: $10-24.9 Million
Emp.: 27
Computer Software Development
N.A.I.C.S.: 541511
Tito Sharma (CEO)

VPIphotonics GmbH (1)
Carnotstr 6, 10587, Berlin, Germany
Tel.: (49) 30 398058 0
Web Site: http://www.vpiphotonics.com
Emp.: 40
Information Technology Consulting Services
N.A.I.C.S.: 541512
Andre Richter (Mng Dir)

VPP GROUP, LLC.
19081 Hwy 71 E, Norwalk, WI 54648
Tel.: (608) 823-7445
Web Site: http://www.vppbeef.com
Year Founded: 1967
Sales Range: $50-74.9 Million
Emp.: 21
Processed Beef Mfr
N.A.I.C.S.: 311611
Montana Stewart (Mgr-Procurement)
Steve Turriff (Dir-Production & Mktg)
Fredrick R. Stewart (Owner)

VPSI INC.
1220 Rankin Dr, Troy, MI 48083
Tel.: (248) 597-3500
Web Site: http://www.vpsiinc.com
Sales Range: $25-49.9 Million
Emp.: 150
Commuter Transportation & Mobility Management Programs

N.A.I.C.S.: 485410
Michelle Grassa (CFO)

VR HOLDINGS, INC.
1825 Ponce de Leon Blvd Ste 56,
Coral Gables, FL 33134
Tel.: (305) 602-1010   DE
Web Site:
http://www.vrholdingsinc.com
Year Founded: 1998
Investment Services
N.A.I.C.S.: 523999
Lamar Neville (Treas & Sec)
Matthew A. Lapides (Chm, Pres, CEO, CFO & Asst Sec)

VR LABORATORIES, LLC
3301 Bonita Beach Rd Ste 315, Bonita Springs, FL 34134
Tel.: (239) 597-9878
Web Site: http://www.vr-laboratories.com
Sales Range: $10-24.9 Million
Emp.: 10
Botanical Pharmaceuticals, Medicinal Foods & Botanical Based Consumer Products Mfr
N.A.I.C.S.: 325412
John Saltamartine (COO)
Kay F. Gow (Chief Admin Officer)
Tom Hall (Dir-Sls & Mktg)
Reginald Steele (Dir)
Robert Haynes (Sr VP-Product Introduction & Licensing)

VRATSINAS CONSTRUCTION COMPANY, INC.
216 Louisiana St, Little Rock, AR 72201
Tel.: (501) 376-0017   AZ
Web Site: http://www.vccusa.com
Year Founded: 1987
Sales Range: $25-49.9 Million
Emp.: 154
Provider of Nonresidential Construction Services
N.A.I.C.S.: 236220
Gus M. Vratsinas (Chm)

VRDT CORPORATION
12223 Highland Ave Ste 106-542, Rancho Cucamonga, CA 91739
Tel.: (949) 633-3467   DE
Web Site:
http://www.verdantautomotive.com
Emp.: 18
Electric Automotive Technology
N.A.I.C.S.: 336320
Stephen C. Aust (Pres)
Michael Sheikh (CFO)

VRH CONSTRUCTION CORP.
320 Grand Ave, Englewood, NJ 07631
Tel.: (201) 871-4422
Web Site: http://www.vrhcorp.com
Rev.: $39,512,999
Emp.: 80
Industrial Buildings & Warehouses
N.A.I.C.S.: 236220
Frank Hurley (CFO)
Kenneth Frisina (Superintendent)
Maurice Curran (VP)
Rob Carr (Superintendent)
Rich Gilmartin (Project Mgr)
Carrie Wilson (Mgr-Payroll)
Jeff Konen (COO)

VSA, INC.
6929 Seward Ave, Lincoln, NE 68507
Tel.: (402) 467-3668
Web Site: http://www.vsa1.com
Year Founded: 1976
Sales Range: $10-24.9 Million
Emp.: 25
Video & Audio Equipment Distr

N.A.I.C.S.: 423410
Jay Ostermeyer (Mgr-Pur)
Brice Schuldt (Acct Mgr-Natl)
Alan Dayton (Owner)
Mark Simmons (Program Mgr)
Valerie Schlitt (Founder, Owner & CEO)
Maureen Tucker (Dir-Program Mgmt)
Ken Peffer (VP-Bus Dev)

VSC FIRE & SECURITY, INC.
10343B Kings Acres Rd, Ashland, VA 23005-8121
Tel.: (804) 459-2220   VA
Web Site: http://www.vscfs.com
Year Founded: 1958
Sales Range: $150-199.9 Million
Emp.: 900
Sprinkler Systems, Fire Detection, Alarms & Security Systems Installation & Inspection
N.A.I.C.S.: 561621
Fritz Mehler (CFO)
Michael P. Martin (COO)
Michael F. Meehan (Pres)
Emory O. Hall Jr. (Sr VP-Low Voltage Divisions)

VSI NEARSHORE OUTSOURCING
199 E Flagler St Suite 276, Miami, FL 33131
Tel.: (866) 285-0673
Web Site: http://www.vsiteam.com
Year Founded: 2004
Sales Range: $1-9.9 Million
Emp.: 219
Outsourced Services Including Software Development & Mortgage Processing Support
N.A.I.C.S.: 522310
Esteban Reyes (Mng Partner, Founder & CEO)
Juan Carlos Perdomo (Dir-Bus Dev)

VSOFT CORPORATION
6455 E Johns Crossing Ste 450, Duluth, GA 30097
Tel.: (770) 840-0097
Web Site: http://www.vsoftcorp.com
Year Founded: 1996
Sales Range: $10-24.9 Million
Emp.: 300
Financial Technology Services
N.A.I.C.S.: 513210
Puneet Malhotra (Sr VP-Sls & Bus Dev)
Murthy Veeraghanta (Co-Founder, Chm & CEO)
Shekar Viswanathan (Co-Founder & Pres)
Terrence Faurote (Sr VP-Ops)
Don Walton (VP-Bus Dev)

VSPEED CAPITAL, LLC
4204 Midpark Ln, Plano, TX 75074-1626
Tel.: (214) 453-5600   TX
Web Site:
http://www.vspeedcapital.com
Privater Equity Firm
N.A.I.C.S.: 523999
Brian Alton (Mng Partner)
Brendon Mills (Mng Partner)

Subsidiaries:

Kosse Partners I, LLC   (1)
2100 10th St Ste 300, Plano, TX 75074
Tel.: (214) 453-5600
Web Site: http://www.fortsol.com
Communications Equipment Repair & Maintenance Services
N.A.I.C.S.: 811210
Brendon Mills (Pres & CEO)
Brian Alton (CFO)
Josh Orender (COO)
John Somerville (CIO)

Grant Davis (VP-Strategic Acct Dev)
David Deas (Sr VP-Bus Dev)
Dan Walsh (VP-Program Mgmt)
Joe Uhr (VP-Ops-Repair Svcs)

VSSCO INCORPORATED
412 N Shelton, Colorado Springs, CO 80909
Tel.: (719) 591-9700
Web Site:
http://www.rockymountaincycleplaza.com
Rev.: $10,000,000
Emp.: 60
Retailer of Motorcycles
N.A.I.C.S.: 441227
Vernon H. Clark (Pres)

VST CONSULTING, INC.
200 Middlesex-Essex Ste 209, Iselin, NJ 08830
Tel.: (732) 404-0025
Web Site:
http://www.vstconsulting.com
Sales Range: $1-9.9 Million
Emp.: 45
Information Technology Consulting Services
N.A.I.C.S.: 541512
Suresh Chatakondu (VP)

VT INC.
8500 Shawnee Mission Pkwy Ste 200, Merriam, KS 66202-2960
Tel.: (913) 432-6400   MO
Web Site: http://www.vt-group.com
Year Founded: 1973
Sales Range: $1-4.9 Billion
Emp.: 7,000
Holding Company; Operator of Automobile Dealerships
N.A.I.C.S.: 441110
Kristin Gawlik (CFO)

VT INDUSTRIES, INC.
1000 Industrial Park, Holstein, IA 51025-8084
Tel.: (712) 368-4381   DE
Web Site:
http://www.vtindustries.com
Year Founded: 1956
Rev.: $180,000,000
Emp.: 1,000
Laminate Countertops & Architectural Wood Doors Mfr
N.A.I.C.S.: 337110
Tom Hoffert (Mgr-Tech Dev)

Subsidiaries:

Eggers Industries Inc.   (1)
One Eggers Dr, Two Rivers, WI 54241-2612
Tel.: (920) 793-1351
Web Site: http://www.eggersindustries.com
Wood Products & Millwork Services
N.A.I.C.S.: 321911

V-T West Inc.   (1)
16222 Phoebe Ave, La Mirada, CA 90638
Tel.: (712) 368-4381
Sales Range: $10-24.9 Million
Emp.: 50
Wood Partitions & Fixtures
N.A.I.C.S.: 337110

VTI of Georgia, Inc.   (1)
1351 Redmond Cir NW, Rome, GA 30165
Tel.: (706) 235-5586
Emp.: 20
Wood Door Mfr
N.A.I.C.S.: 321911
Wayne Paulk (Gen Mgr)

VTI of Iowa, Inc.   (1)
525 N 16th St, Sac City, IA 50583
Tel.: (712) 662-4177
Web Site: http://www.vtindustries.com
Emp.: 100
Wood Door Mfr
N.A.I.C.S.: 321911
Gary Hendry (Gen Mgr)

VTI of Texas Inc.   (1)
6201 Mumford Rd, Bryan, TX 77807
Tel.: (979) 778-8677
Web Site: http://www.vtindustries.com
Sales Range: $10-24.9 Million
Emp.: 58
Wood Partitions & Fixtures
N.A.I.C.S.: 337110

VTC ENTERPRISES
2445 A St, Santa Maria, CA 93455
Tel.: (805) 928-5000   CA
Web Site: http://www.vtc-sm.org
Year Founded: 1962
Sales Range: $10-24.9 Million
Emp.: 430
Disability Assistance Services
N.A.I.C.S.: 624120
Jason Telander (CEO)
Cole Kinney (Sec)
Kathy Fargen (Pres)
Emilie Koff-Martin (VP)

VTECH ADVANCED AMERICAN TELEPHONES
9590 Southwest Gemini Dr Ste 120, Beaverton, OR 97008
Tel.: (503) 643-8981
Web Site:
http://www.vtechphones.com
Year Founded: 1976
Sales Range: $350-399.9 Million
Emp.: 100
Communication Telephone Equipment
N.A.I.C.S.: 423690
Tom Bacon (Exec Dir-Mktg Communications)

VTEL PRODUCTS CORPORATION
12741 Research Blvd Ste 400, Austin, TX 78759
Tel.: (512) 535-1948   TX
Web Site: http://www.vtel.com
Year Founded: 1985
PC based Videoconferencing & Conferencing Equipment Mfr
N.A.I.C.S.: 334290
Richard Ford (CEO)

VTG CORP.
3581 Larch Ln, Jackson, MO 63755
Tel.: (573) 243-1433   MO
Holding Company
N.A.I.C.S.: 551112
Vincent T. Gorguze (Chm)

Subsidiaries:

Major Custom Cable Inc.   (1)
281 Lotus Dr, Jackson, MO 63755
Tel.: (573) 204-1008
Web Site:
http://www.majorcustomcable.com
Sales Range: $25-49.9 Million
Emp.: 225
Coaxial Cable Mfr
N.A.I.C.S.: 517112

VUCOVICH INC.
4288 S Bagley Ave, Fresno, CA 93725
Tel.: (559) 486-8020
Web Site:
http://www.fresnoequipment.com
Rev.: $18,200,000
Emp.: 45
Agricultural Machinery & Equipment
N.A.I.C.S.: 423820
Steve Vucovich (Owner & Pres)

VULCAN ELECTRIC COMPANY
28 Endfield St, Porter, ME 04068-3502
Tel.: (207) 625-3231
Web Site:
http://www.vulcanelectric.com
Year Founded: 1927
Sales Range: $125-149.9 Million
Emp.: 140

VULCAN ELECTRIC COMPANY

Vulcan Electric Company—(Continued)
Electric Heating Units, Thermostats & Controls Mfr
N.A.I.C.S.: 333994
James Marsh (Mgr-Info Sys)
Fred Conroy (VP-Sls)

Subsidiaries:

Vulcan Flex Circuit Corpoation (1)
6 George Ave, Londonderry, NH 03053-2016
Tel.: (603) 883-1500
Printed & Etched Circuit Board Mfr
N.A.I.C.S.: 334412
AnnMarie Reczko (VP-HR)

VULCAN INC.
505 5th Ave S Ste 900, Seattle, WA 98104
Tel.: (206) 342-2000
Web Site: http://www.vulcan.com
Year Founded: 1986
Sales Range: $25-49.9 Million
Emp.: 100
Investment Holding Company
N.A.I.C.S.: 551112
Ada M. Healey (VP-Real Estate Dev)
Barbara Bennett (Pres & COO)
Dave Stewart (Gen Counsel & Exec VP)
Anthony Banbury (Chief Philanthropy Officer)
Chris Orndorff (Chief Investment Officer)
Bill Hilf (CEO)
Tim Mulligan (Chief HR Officer)

Subsidiaries:

Vulcan Capital (1)
505 5th Ave S Ste 900, Seattle, WA 98104
Tel.: (206) 342-2000
Web Site: http://www.capital.vulcan.com
Sales Range: $50-74.9 Million
Emp.: 50
Equity Investment Firm
N.A.I.C.S.: 523999
Abhishek Agrawal (Mng Dir & Head-Growth Equity)
Ben Kolpa (Mng Dir-Fixed Income)

Subsidiary (Domestic):

Vulcan Sports & Entertainment LLC (2)
505 5th Ave S Ste 900, Seattle, WA 98104
Tel.: (206) 342-2000
Web Site: http://www.vulcan
Holding Company
N.A.I.C.S.: 551112

Holding (Domestic):

Portland Trail Blazers (3)
1 Center Ct Ste 200, Portland, OR 97227-2103
Tel.: (503) 234-9291
Web Site: http://www.trailblazers.com
Sales Range: $75-99.9 Million
National Basketball Team
N.A.I.C.S.: 711211
Dick Vardanega (VP-Digital Entertainment)
Lori Spencer (Dir-Internal Ticketing)
Neil Olshey (Pres-Basketball Ops)
Sara Dettenmaier (Dir-Premium Svcs)
Chase Sbicca (Mgr-Loyalty Programs)
Tyler Howell (VP-Ticket Sls & Svc)
Vince Ircandia (Sr VP-Bus Ops)
Anthony Jones-Deberry (VP-Premium Seating)
Ben Lauritsen (Sr VP-Legal & Corp Affairs)
Collin Romer (Dir-Basketball Comm)
Jim Taylor (VP-Basketball Comm)
Christa Thoeresz (VP-Social Responsibility)

Seattle Seahawks (3)
12 Seahawks Way, Renton, WA 98056
Tel.: (425) 203-8000
Web Site: http://www.seahawks.com
Sales Range: $100-124.9 Million
Professional Football Franchise
N.A.I.C.S.: 711211
Peter McLoughlin (Pres)
Chuck Arnold (COO)
Rick Ninomiya (Dir-Security)
Dave Pearson (Sr VP-Comm & Brdcst)
Cindy Kelley (Sr VP-HR & Admin)
Rick Crawford (Dir-Production Svcs & Game Presentation)
Mike Flood (VP-Community Outreach)
Lane Gammel (VP-Football Comm)
Amy Sprangers (VP-Corp Partnerships & Suites)
Sarita Carter (Mng Dir-HR)
Suzanne Lavender (Dir-Comm & Community Rels)
Brad Campbell (Dir-Video)
Rich Gonzales (Mgr-Comm)
Sandy Gregory (Mng Dir-Community Outreach)
Maurice Kelly (VP-Player Engagement)
Erik Kennedy (Dir-Equipment)
Brian O'Connell (Dir-Brdcst)
Kenton Olson (Dir-Digital Media & Emerging Media)
John Weaver (Dir-Creative)
John Wright (Dir-Fields & Conversion)
Eric Engberg (Mng Dir-Suite Sls)
Sam Ramsden (Dir-Player Health & Performance)
John Schneider (Gen Mgr)
Chip Suttles (VP-Tech)
Peter Fonfara (Mng Dir-Fin)
Jeff Richards (VP-Mktg)
John Pleas (Mng Dir-Sls & Corp Partnerships)
Gina Martinez Todd (Dir-Sls)
Lisa Young (Dir-Partnership Activation)
Luke Grothkopp (Dir-Sls)
Chris Lawrence (Dir-Ticket Sls & Svcs)
Erin Johnson (Mgr-Box Office)
Vikki Knopf (Mgr-Mdse)
Sean Vanos (Dir-Facility Ops)
Sterling Monroe (Officer-Info Security & Dir-IT)
Ping Chen (Mgr-Fin Reporting)
Becca Rollins (Dir-Hospitality & Events)
Matt Thomas (VP-Football Admin)
Jeff Dunn (VP-Bus Strategy & Analytics)
Kris Richard (Coord-Defensive)
Matt Berry (Dir-College Scouting)
Kelly Creeden (Mng Dir & Head-Coach Initiatives & Seahawks Special Projects)
Jeff Garza (Dir-Bus Comm)
Doug Orwiler (Dir-Retail Ops)
Rob Porteus (Sr Dir-Video Ops)
Mark Tamar (Mng Dir-Fan Dev & Game Presentation)
Sherri Thompson (Dir-Sea Gals)
Lisa Bregman (Dir-Mktg)
Becca Stout (Mng Dir-Community Engagement & Hospitality)
Bert Kolde (Vice Chm)
Ed Goines (Gen Counsel & Sr VP-Govt Affairs)
Karen Spencer (CFO)

Vulcan Productions Inc. (1)
505 5th Ave S Ste 900, Seattle, WA 98104-3821
Tel.: (206) 342-2000
Web Site: http://www.vulcanproductions.com
Sales Range: $25-49.9 Million
Independent Film Production
N.A.I.C.S.: 512110
Jody Allen Patton (Pres)
Jody Allen Patton (Pres)

Vulcan Real Estate (1)
505 5th Ave S Ste 900, Seattle, WA 98104
Tel.: (206) 342-2000
Web Site: http://www.vulcanrealestate.com
Sales Range: $75-99.9 Million
Real Estate Developer & Manager
N.A.I.C.S.: 531390
Ada M. Healey (VP-Real Estate)
Robert S. Arron (Sr Dir-Real Estate Mktg & Leasing)
Sharon Eschbach Coleman (Dir-Real Estate Dev)
Maria C. Mackey Gunn (Dir-Real Estate)
Steve Van Til (Dir-Real Estate Portfolio Mgmt)
Lori Mason Curran (Dir-Real Estate Investment Strategy)
Scott Matthews (Sr Dir-Acq)

VULCAN INTERNATIONAL CORPORATION
103 Foulk Rd Ste 202, Wilmington, DE 19803
Tel.: (302) 656-1950 DE
Web Site: http://www.vulcorp.com
Year Founded: 1909
Sales Range: $10-24.9 Million
Emp.: 68
Rubber & Foam Products Mfr
N.A.I.C.S.: 326299

Subsidiaries:

Vulcan Corporation (1)
1151 College St, Clarksville, TN 37040-3324 (100%)
Tel.: (931) 645-6431
Web Site: http://www.vulcorp.com
Sales Range: $10-24.9 Million
Emp.: 35
Fabricated Rubber Products
N.A.I.C.S.: 326299
Henry Robinson (Mgr-Pur)
Willis Kean (Mgr-Sls)
Dennis Anderson (Dir-Maintenance)
Mark Britton (Mgr-Quality Control)

Vulcan Property Management Co. (1)
30 Garfield Pl Ste 1040, Cincinnati, OH 45202-4357
Tel.: (513) 621-2850
Web Site: http://www.vulcorp.com
Real Estate Management & Development
N.A.I.C.S.: 531390
Benjamin Gettler (Chm & Pres)

VULCAN INVESTMENT PARTNERS, LLC
175 SW 7th St Ste 1107, Miami, FL 33130
Tel.: (305) 507-8442 DE
Web Site: http://www.vulcanfunds.com
Year Founded: 2011
Sales Range: $25-49.9 Million
Emp.: 10
Real Estate Investment & Leasing
N.A.I.C.S.: 523999
Inaki Negrete (Partner & CEO)
Mario Alonso (Partner & Chief Admin Officer)
Juan Ramon Zaragoza (Partner & COO)
Emilio Braun Burillo (Partner & Chief Media Officer)

VULCAN PAINTERS INC.
2400 Woodward Rd, Bessemer, AL 35021
Tel.: (205) 428-0556
Web Site: http://www.vulcan-group.com
Rev.: $13,991,180
Emp.: 42
Metal Plating Services
N.A.I.C.S.: 332812
David R. Boyd (Pres)
John Dempsey (Pres)
Les Wain (Project Mgr)

VULCAN SPRING & MFG. CO.
501 Schoolhouse Rd, Telford, PA 18969
Tel.: (215) 721-1721 PA
Web Site: http://www.vulcanspring.com
Spring Mfr & Whslr
N.A.I.C.S.: 332613
Alexander Rankin (Pres)

VULCAN STEEL STRUCTURES, INC.
500 Vulcan Pkwy, Adel, GA 31620
Tel.: (229) 896-7903
Web Site: http://www.vulcansteel.com
Sales Range: $25-49.9 Million
Emp.: 110
Prefabricated Metal Buildings Construction
N.A.I.C.S.: 332311

U.S. PRIVATE

Steve Browning (Pres)
Brian Browning (Exec VP)
Jefferey Spradley (Exec VP)

VULCAN TIRE & AUTOMOTIVE, INC.
3214 Edwards Lk Pkwy, Birmingham, AL 35235
Tel.: (205) 661-2970
Web Site: http://www.vulcantireandauto.com
Year Founded: 1975
Tire Dealer & Automotive Service Center
N.A.I.C.S.: 441340
Richard Estes (Co-Owner)
Chris Cutshall (Co-Owner)

VULCAN, INC.
410 E Berry Ave, Foley, AL 36535-2833
Tel.: (251) 943-7000 AL
Web Site: http://www.vulcaninc.com
Year Founded: 1935
Sales Range: $100-124.9 Million
Emp.: 200
Traffic Control Signs Mfr
N.A.I.C.S.: 332119
Cater Lee (Founder)
Thomas Lee (Pres & CEO)

Subsidiaries:

Vulcan, Inc. - Vulcan Aluminum Division (1)
400 E Berry Ave, Foley, AL 36535
Tel.: (251) 943-2645
Aluminum Sheet Mfr
N.A.I.C.S.: 331315
Mark Strobel (Mgr-Quality)

Vulcan, Inc. - Vulcan Technology Center Division (1)
414 E Berry Ave, Foley, AL 36535
Tel.: (251) 943-7477
Sign Mfr
N.A.I.C.S.: 339950

VULCANFORMS INC.
20 N Ave, Burlington, MA 01803
Tel.: (781) 472-0160
Web Site: https://www.vulcanforms.com
Sales Range: $1-9.9 Million
Precision Machining, Automation & Assembly Services
N.A.I.C.S.: 333248
A. John Hart (Co-Founder)
Philip Garton (CFO)
Martin Feldmann (Co-Founder, Pres & CEO)

Subsidiaries:

Arwood Machine Corporation (1)
95 Parker St Ste 4, Newburyport, MA 01950-4033
Tel.: (978) 463-3777
Web Site: http://www.arwoodmachine.com
Machine Shops
N.A.I.C.S.: 332710
Daniel Sedler (VP-Sls)

VVV CORPORATION
2400 Wisconsin Ave, Downers Grove, IL 60515
Tel.: (630) 543-7998
Web Site: http://www.vvvcorporation.com
Sales Range: $25-49.9 Million
Emp.: 200
Repairing Fire Damage, Single-Family Houses
N.A.I.C.S.: 236118

VYOPTA INCORPORATED
4515 Seton Ctr Pkwy Ste 330, Austin, TX 78759
Tel.: (512) 891-4200
Web Site: http://www.vyopta.com

COMPANIES

Sales Range: $1-9.9 Million
Emp.: 23
Software Development Services
N.A.I.C.S.: 541511
Alfredo Ramirez *(Pres & CEO)*
Rick Leung *(CTO & VP-Dev)*
Andrew Chen *(Co-Founder, Gen Counsel & VP-Ops)*
Al Burns *(VP-Fin)*
Ivan Montoya *(VP-Mktg & Bus Dev)*
Bret Hern *(VP-Customer Success)*
Ruston Vickers *(VP-Engrg)*
Brett Panter *(CFO)*
Subo Guha *(VP-Product & Strategy)*
Joe Lohmeier *(VP-Sls)*

VYRIAN, INC.
4660 Sweetwater Blvd Ste 200, Sugar Land, TX 77036
Tel.: (866) 874-0598 NV
Web Site: http://www.vyrian.com
Year Founded: 2002
Electronic Components Distr
N.A.I.C.S.: 423690
Sath Sivasothy *(CEO)*
Tony Sivasothy *(Treas)*

VYSTAR CREDIT UNION
76 S Laura St, Jacksonville, FL 32202
Tel.: (904) 777-6000 FL
Web Site: http://www.vystarcu.org
Year Founded: 1952
Rev.: $471,395,000
Assets: $9,117,137,000
Liabilities: $8,325,200,000
Net Worth: $791,937,000
Earnings: $58,987,000
Fiscal Year-end: 12/31/19
Credit Union
N.A.I.C.S.: 522130
John H. Turpish *(CFO & Exec VP)*
Jenny Vipperman *(Chief Lending Officer)*
Brian E. Wolfburg *(Pres & CEO)*
Ryan McIntyre *(Chief Strategy Officer)*
Sandy Baker *(VP-Comm & PR)*
Don Halleck *(VP-Adv & Promos)*
Chad Meadows *(COO & Exec VP)*
Dana Karzan *(CMO)*
Lance Davies *(Chief Risk Officer & Gen Counsel)*
Joel Swanson *(Chief Member Experience Officer)*
Lisa Cochran *(CIO)*
Matt Brockelman *(VP-Govt Affairs)*
Kawanza Humphrey *(Chief HR Officer)*

Subsidiaries:

121 Financial Credit Union (1)
9700 Touchton Rd, Jacksonville, FL 32246
Tel.: (904) 723-6300
Web Site: http://www.121fcu.org
Sales Range: $10-24.9 Million
Emp.: 163
Credit Union
N.A.I.C.S.: 522130
David Marovich *(Pres & CEO)*

W & O CONSTRUCTION CO., INC.
150 Construction Dr, Livingston, TN 38570
Tel.: (931) 403-1000
Web Site: http://www.wocc.com
Sales Range: $10-24.9 Million
Emp.: 125
Sewer Construction Services
N.A.I.C.S.: 237110
Brenda Sullivan *(VP)*

W BAR E INVESTMENTS CORP.
1600 Union Meeting Rd, Blue Bell, PA 19422
Tel.: (215) 542-8000
Rev.: $55,400,000
Emp.: 5
Plastics Working Machinery
N.A.I.C.S.: 333248
David Borthwick *(Chm)*

W CAPITAL MANAGEMENT LLC
400 Park Ave, New York, NY 10022
Tel.: (212) 561-5240
Web Site: http://www.wcapgroup.com
Year Founded: 2001
Commodity Contracts Dealing
N.A.I.C.S.: 523160
David S. Wachter *(Founder & Mng Dir)*
Robert Migliorino *(Founder & Mng Dir)*
Alison Killilea *(Mng Dir)*
Todd Miller *(Mng Dir)*
Katie Stitch *(Mng Dir)*
Blake Heston *(Mng Dir)*
Stephen N. Wertheimer *(Founder & Mng Dir)*
Simon Harris *(Principal)*
John Lambrech *(CFO & Chief Compliance Officer)*
Kathy Glass *(Chief Admin Officer)*

W FLYING PLASTICS, INC.
487 Vanhorn Dr, Glenville, WV 26351
Tel.: (304) 462-5779
Web Site: http://www.flyingwplastics.com
Year Founded: 1984
Sales Range: $10-24.9 Million
Emp.: 121
Pipe Fitting Mfr
N.A.I.C.S.: 326122
Wes Smith *(Plant Mgr)*
Frank Montgomery *(Mgr-Maintenance & Gen Mgr)*
Fred Lowther *(Mgr-Shipping)*
Nick Dent *(Mgr-Safety)*
Jim Harper *(Mgr-Polyethylene Production)*

W INC.
1215 Hightower Trl Ste B100, Atlanta, GA 30350
Tel.: (770) 993-7204 GA
Web Site: http://www.wincorporated.com
Year Founded: 1971
Rev.: $2,000,000
Emp.: 2
Fiscal Year-end: 12/31/04
Advetising Agency
N.A.I.C.S.: 541810
Libby Whelan *(Pres-Mktg & Adv Comm Firm)*
Jerry Andrews *(Sr Dir-Art)*

W W CAPITAL CORPORATION
235 Welch Ave Unit A-4, Berthoud, CO 80513
Tel.: (970) 532-2506 NV
Sales Range: $10-24.9 Million
Emp.: 110
Livestock Equipment Mfr
N.A.I.C.S.: 333111
Michael A. Dick *(CFO)*
Harold Gleason *(Pres & CEO)*

Subsidiaries:

Eagle Enterprises Inc. (1)
175 Windle Comm Rd, Livingston, TN 38570
Tel.: (931) 823-7332
Rev.: $2,793,469
Emp.: 10
Barn, Silo, Poultry, Dairy & Livestock Machinery
N.A.I.C.S.: 333111
Eddie Burnette *(Plant Mgr)*

WW Manufacturing Co. Inc. (1)
8832 Hwy 54, Thomas, OK 73669
Tel.: (580) 661-3720
Web Site: http://www.wwmanufacturing.com
Rev.: $8,398,501
Emp.: 80
Cattle Feeding, Handling & Watering Equipment
N.A.I.C.S.: 423820
Chuck Vogt *(Plant Mgr)*

W W T, INC.
1951 Old Cuthbert Rd Ste 206, Cherry Hill, NJ 08034
Tel.: (856) 795-4500 NJ
Web Site: http://www.voipnetworks.com
Year Founded: 1984
Cloud-Based Telecommunications Services
N.A.I.C.S.: 517121
Chuck Reagan *(Pres & CEO)*
Richard Butler *(CFO)*
Mark Mowad *(COO & Exec VP)*
John R. Collins *(CTO)*
Robert Handel *(Chief Revenue Officer)*
John Carr *(Sr VP-Cloud Svcs)*
Cliff Karpo *(VP-Ops)*
Brice A. Bogar *(Dir-Sls Engrg)*
Larry Libassi *(Mgr-Customer Svc)*

W&H PACIFIC INC.
12100 NE 195 St Ste 300, Bothell, WA 98011
Tel.: (425) 951-4800 WA
Web Site: http://www.whpacific.com
Year Founded: 1988
Sales Range: $25-49.9 Million
Emp.: 450
Provider of Engineering Services
N.A.I.C.S.: 541330
Rob Macomber *(Pres)*

W&L SALES CO., INC.
4050 Indus Rd, Harrisburg, PA 17110-2947
Tel.: (717) 441-7991 DE
Web Site: http://www.wlsales.com
Year Founded: 1945
Sales Range: $50-74.9 Million
Emp.: 100
Distr of Beer & Ale Products
N.A.I.C.S.: 424810
Stephen M. Symons *(Chm & CEO)*
Aran N. Dym *(Controller)*
David Rose *(Pres & Gen Mgr)*
John Geib *(Mgr-Ops)*
Horace Howells *(Gen Counsel & VP)*
Peggy Nye *(Mgr-Brand)*
Andrew Rose *(Mgr-Brand)*
Jesse Jorich *(Mgr-Sls)*
Keith Brandt *(Mgr-Sls)*
Kim Weigel *(Mgr-Sls)*
Peggy Bargo *(Mgr-Sls)*

Subsidiaries:

W&L Sales (1)
4050 Industrial Rd, Harrisburg, PA 17110-2947
Tel.: (717) 441-7991
Web Site: http://www.wlsales.com
Sales Range: $25-49.9 Million
Emp.: 110
Operators Of Nonresidential Buildings
N.A.I.C.S.: 531120
Aaro Dym *(Controller)*

W&W STEEL COMPANY INC.
1730 W Reno Ave, Oklahoma City, OK 73106-3216
Tel.: (405) 235-3621 OK
Web Site: http://www.wwsteel.com
Year Founded: 1945
Sales Range: $75-99.9 Million
Emp.: 1,100
Fabricators Of Structural Metal
N.A.I.C.S.: 332312
Rick Cooper *(Pres)*
Pat Hare *(CFO)*

Subsidiaries:

Afco Steel (1)
1423 E 6th St, Little Rock, AR 72202
Tel.: (501) 340-6233
Web Site: http://www.afcosteel.com
Emp.: 1,000
Steel Mfrs
N.A.I.C.S.: 332111
Michael Noernberg *(VP-Engrg & Quality)*
Grady Harvell *(COO)*
Kevin Reynolds *(Sr VP-Sls & Estimating)*
Bert Cooper *(Pres & CEO)*
Gary Johnson *(Sr VP-Contracts)*

W&W WHOLESALE INCORPORATED
2323 Avenida Costa Este Ste 500, San Diego, CA 92154
Tel.: (619) 710-4220
Rev.: $12,255,575
Emp.: 26
Children's Clothing
N.A.I.C.S.: 458110

W-DIAMOND GROUP CORPORATION
125 Park Ave 7th Fl, New York, NY 10017
Tel.: (212) 826-6510
Web Site: http://www.hmxgroup.com
Holding Company
N.A.I.C.S.: 551112
Doug Williams *(CEO)*

W-L MOLDING COMPANY
8212 Shaver Rd, Portage, MI 49024
Tel.: (269) 327-3075
Web Site: http://www.wlmolding.com
Sales Range: $10-24.9 Million
Emp.: 54
Injected Molded Plastic Products Mfr
N.A.I.C.S.: 326199
Nigam Tripathi *(Owner)*
Connie MacDonald *(Bus Mgr)*
Steve Klosterman *(Mgr-Process)*
Cathy Hale *(Mgr-Pur)*
Kim Mitchell *(Mgr-Quality)*
Nail Arakkal *(Mgr-Engrg)*

W. ATLEE BURPEE & CO.
300 Park Ave, Warminster, PA 18974-4808
Tel.: (215) 674-4900 PA
Web Site: http://www.burpee.com
Year Founded: 1876
Sales Range: $100-124.9 Million
Emp.: 240
Mail Order Seed Bulbs Nursery Stock & General Merchandise Services
N.A.I.C.S.: 111422
Don Zeidler *(Dir-Direct Mktg)*
Chris Romas *(Pres)*
George Ball Jr. *(Chm & CEO)*

W. CAPRA CONSULTING GROUP, INC.
221 N Lasalle Ste 1325, Chicago, IL 60601
Tel.: (312) 873-3300
Web Site: http://www.wcapra.com
Scientific & Technical Consulting Services
N.A.I.C.S.: 541690
Lesley Saitta *(Partner)*
Lisa Biggs *(Partner)*
Martin Wolf *(Program Mgr)*
Kevin Saum *(Sr VP-Global Sls)*

Subsidiaries:

Impact 21 Group LLC (1)
2700 Old Rosebud Rd Ste 240, Lexington, KY 40509-8625
Tel.: (859) 219-3040
Web Site: http://www.impact21group.com

W. CAPRA CONSULTING GROUP, INC.

W. Capra Consulting Group, Inc.—(Continued)
Process, Physical Distribution & Logistics Consulting Services
N.A.I.C.S.: 541614
Gabe Olives (VP-Emerging Technologies)
Rob Gallo (Chief Strategy Officer)
Scott Burchfield (COO)

W. E. BLAIN & SONS, INC.
98 Pearce Rd, Mount Olive, MS 39119
Tel.: (601) 797-4551
Web Site: http://www.blain-co.com
Year Founded: 1954
Sales Range: $25-49.9 Million
Emp.: 200
Highway & Street Construction Services
N.A.I.C.S.: 237310
Bill Blain (Pres)

W. GAMBY & CO.
494 8th Ave Rm 1500, New York, NY 10001-2542
Tel.: (212) 354-4040   NY
Year Founded: 1949
Sales Range: $150-199.9 Million
Emp.: 10
Textile Importing & Converting
N.A.I.C.S.: 424310
Michael Scherer (Pres & CFO)
Peter Kaye (Exec VP)

W. GOHMAN CONSTRUCTION CO.
815 Co Rd 75 E, Saint Joseph, MN 56374
Tel.: (320) 363-7781
Web Site: http://www.wgohman.com
Year Founded: 1950
Sales Range: $10-24.9 Million
Emp.: 28
Commercial & Institutional Building Construction Services
N.A.I.C.S.: 236220
Michael Gohman (Pres)

W. H. CRESS COMPANY, INC.
9966 SW Katherine St, Tigard, OR 97223
Tel.: (503) 620-1664
Web Site: http://www.whcress.com
Sales Range: $10-24.9 Million
Emp.: 20
Lumber, Plywood, Millwork & Wood Panel Whslr
N.A.I.C.S.: 423310
Scott Cress (Owner & Pres)
Kelly Cress (Project Mgr)
Bob Krauss (Project Mgr)

W. J. MOUNTFORD CO.
170 Commerce Way, South Windsor, CT 06074-1151
Tel.: (860) 291-9448
Web Site: http://www.wjmountford.com
Sales Range: $25-49.9 Million
Emp.: 70
Commerical & Institutional Building Construction
N.A.I.C.S.: 236220
Scott Mountford (Pres)
Leola Lamothe (Sec)

W. J. O'NEIL COMPANY
34525 Glendale St, Livonia, MI 48150
Tel.: (734) 458-2300
Web Site: http://www.wjo.com
Year Founded: 1983
Sales Range: $50-74.9 Million
Emp.: 250
Plumbing Services
N.A.I.C.S.: 238220
Bob Larson (Controller)

W. JOE SHAW INCORPORATED
4101 W Pinecrest Dr, Marshall, TX 75670
Tel.: (903) 935-1811
Web Site: http://www.gosafe.com
Sales Range: $10-24.9 Million
Emp.: 150
Distr of Safety Equipment & Supplies
N.A.I.C.S.: 423990
W. Joe Shaw (Chm)
Burk Shaw (Pres)
Scott Springfield (VP-Ops)

W. LEE FLOWERS & COMPANY INC.
127 E W Lee Flowers Rd, Scranton, SC 29591
Tel.: (843) 389-2731   SC
Web Site: http://www.igaguy.com
Year Founded: 1977
Sales Range: $25-49.9 Million
Emp.: 300
Provider of Grocery Services
N.A.I.C.S.: 531120
Henry Johnson (Pres)

Subsidiaries:
Aynor Foods Inc.   (1)
715 S Main St, Aynor, SC 29511-3121   (100%)
Tel.: (843) 358-3761
Web Site: http://www.rgastore.com
Sales Range: $10-24.9 Million
Emp.: 35
Provider of Grocery Services
N.A.I.C.S.: 445110
Richard Gore (Mgr)

Eutawville IGA   (1)
225 Branchdale Hwy, Eutawville, SC 29048
Tel.: (803) 492-7515
Sales Range: $10-24.9 Million
Emp.: 37
Provider of Grocery Services
N.A.I.C.S.: 445131
Ruffin Baird (Mng Dir)

Floco Foods Inc.   (1)
Hwy 52 N, Scranton, SC 29591
Tel.: (843) 389-2731
Web Site: http://www.igaguy.com
Sales Range: $25-49.9 Million
Emp.: 250
Provider of Grocery Services
N.A.I.C.S.: 445110

Subsidiary (Domestic):
Haddens IGA   (2)
200A S Main St, Wrens, GA 30833
Tel.: (706) 547-3091
Web Site: http://www.iga.com
Rev: $14,300,000
Emp.: 30
Grocery Retailer
N.A.I.C.S.: 445110
Dave Bennett (Sr VP-Procurement & Private Brands)

W. OLIVER TRIPP COMPANY, INC.
6 Brooks Dr, Braintree, MA 02184-3839
Tel.: (781) 848-1230   MA
Web Site: http://www.tripp.com
Year Founded: 1946
Sales Range: $25-49.9 Million
Emp.: 25
Graphics Art Suppliers
N.A.I.C.S.: 424990
Gerry L. Tripp (Pres & CEO)
Michael B. Tripp (Exec VP & Mgr-Roller Div)

W. R. MEADOWS, INC.
300 Industrial Dr, Hampshire, IL 60140
Tel.: (847) 214-2100   DE
Web Site: http://www.wrmeadows.com
Year Founded: 1926
Sales Range: $75-99.9 Million
Emp.: 800
Construction Products & Systems Designer, Mfr & Marketer
N.A.I.C.S.: 325998
H. G. Meadows (Chm)
Ruth A. Meadows (Treas & Sec)
W. R. Meadows (Exec VP)
James F. Dwyer (CEO)
Matthew L. Price (Pres)
Merrie Meadows Derderian (Exec VP-PR & Community Rels)
Ann Meadows Dwyer (Exec VP)
David Carey (VP-Plant Ops)
Glenn Tench (VP-Sls)
Mark Vogel (Dir-Sls-Intl)
Rick Waters (CFO)
Isaac Sorensen (Sls Mgr)

Subsidiaries:
Blue Ridge Fiberboard, Inc.   (1)
250 Celotex Dr, Danville, VA 24541   (100%)
Tel.: (434) 797-1321
Web Site: http://www.blueridgefiberboard.com
Fibreboard Mfr
N.A.I.C.S.: 321219
Jim Pieczynski (Gen Mgr)

Plant (Domestic):
Blue Ridge Fiberboard, Inc. - Lisbon Falls   (2)
743 Lisbon St, Lisbon Falls, ME 04252-1811
Tel.: (207) 353-4311
Web Site: http://www.blueridgefiberboard.com
Sales Range: $50-74.9 Million
Emp.: 120
Fibreboard Mfr
N.A.I.C.S.: 321219

W. ROGERS COMPANY
649 Bizzell Dr, Lexington, KY 40510
Tel.: (859) 231-6290
Web Site: http://www.wrogers.com
Year Founded: 1970
Sales Range: $100-124.9 Million
Emp.: 150
Water Treatment & Waste Water Treatment Plant Construction
N.A.I.C.S.: 237110
Warren P. Rogers (Pres)
Tom McConathy (VP & Project Mgr)
W. Boyd Rogers (VP)

W. S. KEEL LUMBER CO., INC.
345 Fleitas Ave, Pass Christian, MS 39571
Tel.: (228) 452-4353
Sales Range: $10-24.9 Million
Emp.: 87
Home Improvement Distr
N.A.I.C.S.: 444110
Leonard J. Keel (Pres)
Rodney P. Keel (Treas, Sec & VP)

W. SCHILLER & CO., INC.
9240 Manchester Rd, Saint Louis, MO 63144
Tel.: (314) 968-3650   MO
Web Site: http://www.schillers.com
Year Founded: 1967
Sales Range: $25-49.9 Million
Emp.: 79
Photographic Equipment & Supplies
N.A.I.C.S.: 423410
William Schiller (CEO)
Andrew Miller (Gen Mgr)
Dave Lepper (Engr-Sys)

W. SILVER RECYCLING, INC.
1720 Magoffin Ave, El Paso, TX 79901
Tel.: (915) 532-5643   TX
Web Site: http://www.wsilverrecycling.com
Rev.: $10,700,000
Emp.: 53
Industrial Materials Recovery & Recycling Services
N.A.I.C.S.: 562920
Bernard Fenenbock (Pres)

Subsidiaries:
El Paso Iron & Metal I, Ltd.   (1)
1535 E San Antonio Ave, El Paso, TX 79901
Tel.: (915) 532-6981
Web Site: http://www.epironmetal.com
Scrap Metal Recycling Services
N.A.I.C.S.: 562920
Ricardo Marin (Gen Mgr)
Mike Hernandez (Mgr-HR)

W. Silver Recycling of New Mexico, Inc.   (1)
1800 1st St NW, Albuquerque, NM 87102-1577
Tel.: (505) 244-1508
Web Site: http://www.wsilverrecycling.com
Industrial Materials Recovery & Recycling Services
N.A.I.C.S.: 562920
Patrick Merrick (Dir-Ferrous Sls)

W. Silver Recycling, Inc. - Donna Facility   (1)
520 W US Business Hwy 83, Donna, TX 78537-9486
Tel.: (956) 461-5944
Web Site: http://www.wsilverrecycling.com
Industrial Materials Recovery & Recycling Services
N.A.I.C.S.: 562920
Juan Delgado (Mgr)

W. SOULE & COMPANY
7125 Sprinkle Rd, Portage, MI 49002
Tel.: (269) 324-7001
Web Site: http://www.wsoule.com
Sales Range: $25-49.9 Million
Emp.: 100
Mechanical Contractor
N.A.I.C.S.: 238220
Jerry Ruoff (Project Mgr)
Jason Carter (Mgr-Ops)
Ned Hawkins (Dir-QA & QC)
Tim Clow (Project Mgr)

W.A. BAUM COMPANY, INC.
620 Oak St, Copiague, NY 11726-3217
Tel.: (631) 226-3940   NY
Web Site: http://www.wabaum.com
Year Founded: 1916
Sales Range: $50-74.9 Million
Emp.: 80
Mfr of Blood Pressure Instruments
N.A.I.C.S.: 339112
James M. Baum (VP-Sls & Mktg)
W. A. Baum Jr. (Chm)
W. A. Baum III (Treas & Sec)

W.A. KLINGER, LLC.
2015 E 7th St, Sioux City, IA 51102
Tel.: (712) 277-3900
Web Site: http://www.waklinger.com
Year Founded: 1919
Sales Range: $250-299.9 Million
Emp.: 600
Industrial Building Construction Services
N.A.I.C.S.: 236210
Dave Larson (Pres)
Steve Koza (Sr VP)
Matt Thompson (VP)
Lonnie Ehlers (Project Mgr)
Chad Willer (Asst Project Mgr)
Ryan Bolinger (Project Mgr)
Nick Mathistad (Project Mgr)

W.A. ROOSEVELT COMPANY
2727 Commerce St, La Crosse, WI 54603-1760

Tel.: (608) 781-2000 WI
Web Site:
http://www.waroosevelt.com
Year Founded: 1868
Sales Range: $400-449.9 Million
Emp.: 650
Distr of Plumbing, Heating, Electrical, Air Conditioning & Refrigeration Supplies & Equipment
N.A.I.C.S.: 423720
Todd Eber *(Pres)*
John Gearman *(Mgr-Electrical & Automation)*
Phil Baumel *(Mgr-Plumbing)*
Greg Servais *(Mgr-HVAC/R)*
Chad Veitenheimer *(Mgr-Utility)*
Malcolm Macdonald *(Mgr-Waterworks & Metering)*
Rick Anderson *(Mgr-Comm)*

W.A. SHEETS & SONS, INC.
1336 Polk St, Fort Wayne, IN 46808
Tel.: (260) 424-5332
Web Site: http://www.washeets.com
Year Founded: 1936
Sales Range: $10-24.9 Million
Emp.: 65
Commercial & Institutional Building Construction Services
N.A.I.C.S.: 236220
Philip J. Sheets Jr. *(Owner & Pres)*

W.A. THOMAS CO.
25940 Northline Rd, Taylor, MI 48180-4413
Tel.: (734) 955-6500
Web Site: http://www.wathomas.com
Sales Range: $10-24.9 Million
Emp.: 66
Screw Machine Products
N.A.I.C.S.: 332721
Mark Nelms *(Pres)*

W.A. WILSON & SONS, INC.
6 Industrial Park Dr, Wheeling, WV 26003
Tel.: (304) 232-2200
Web Site:
http://www.wawilsonglass.com
Year Founded: 1841
Sales Range: $10-24.9 Million
Glass Mfr & Distr
N.A.I.C.S.: 327211
Robert H. Hartong *(Pres)*
John Roth *(Project Mgr-Glass)*
Steve Perilstein *(Exec VP)*
Carole Cain *(VP-Ops)*
Michael Winesburg *(CFO)*
Gretchen Dahl *(Asst Mgr-Credit)*
Rob Talaini *(Dir-Glass Sls)*
Bernie Kessler *(VP-Architectural Aluminum)*
Terri Nejus *(VP-Mgmt Information Systems)*
Rick Meredith *(Production Mgr)*
Rich Magers *(Mgr-Logistics)*
Brian Beck *(Mgr-Metal Sls)*

W.B. HOPKE CO.
5421 Vine St, Alexandria, VA 22310
Tel.: (703) 971-0404
Web Site: http://www.wbhopke.com
Year Founded: 1956
Sales Range: $10-24.9 Million
Emp.: 125
Sewer Line & Related Structure Construction Services
N.A.I.C.S.: 237110
Mike Hopke *(Owner & Pres)*

W.B. HUNT CO., INC.
100 Main St, Melrose, MA 02176-6104
Tel.: (781) 662-8822
Web Site:
http://www.huntsphotoandvideo.com
Year Founded: 1965
Sales Range: $10-24.9 Million
Emp.: 80
Distr of Camera & Photographic Supplies & Accessories
N.A.I.C.S.: 449210
Richard Yagjan *(COO)*
Ian Simon *(CFO)*
Michael Mitchell *(Dir-Retail Ops)*

W.B. MASON COMPANY
59 Ctr St, Brockton, MA 02303
Tel.: (508) 586-3434 MA
Web Site: http://www.wbmason.com
Year Founded: 1898
Sales Range: $250-299.9 Million
Emp.: 1,000
Office Furniture & Supplies & Printing Supplies Whslr
N.A.I.C.S.: 449110
John Greene *(Exec VP)*
Thomas Golden *(Sr VP)*
Steven Greene *(Chm)*
Peter Manning *(Branch Mgr)*
Dean Orr *(VP-Mktg)*
Laura McNeil *(Dir-Pur)*
Pasty Celancy *(CFO)*
Joanne Stratton *(Controller)*
Leo J. Meehan III *(Pres & CEO)*

W.B. MCCARTNEY OIL COMPANY
Hwy 8 W, Jena, LA 71342
Tel.: (318) 992-8223
Web Site:
http://www.mccartneyoil.com
Sales Range: $10-24.9 Million
Emp.: 40
Fuel Oil & Tires
N.A.I.C.S.: 811111
W. B. McCartney *(Owner)*
Darrel W. McCartney *(VP)*
Joe D. McCartney *(VP)*

W.B. MCCLOUD & COMPANY, INC.
1635 N Lancaster Rd, South Elgin, IL 60177
Tel.: (877) 284-6333
Web Site:
http://www.mccloudservices.com
Year Founded: 1904
Sales Range: $10-24.9 Million
Emp.: 20
Exterminating & Fumigating
N.A.I.C.S.: 561710
Chris McCloud *(Pres)*

W.C. & A.N. MILLER COMPANIES
4315 50th St Northwest, Washington, DC 20016
Tel.: (202) 895-2700
Web Site: http://www.wcanmiller.com
Sales Range: $10-24.9 Million
Emp.: 25
Speculative Builder, Single-Family Houses
N.A.I.C.S.: 236115

W.C. BRADLEY CO.
1017 Front Ave, Columbus, GA 31901-5260
Tel.: (706) 571-6056 GA
Web Site: http://www.wcbradley.com
Year Founded: 1885
Sales Range: $150-199.9 Million
Emp.: 2,500
Gas & Electric Outdoor Barbecue Grill Mfr
N.A.I.C.S.: 335220
Marc R. Olivie *(Pres & CEO)*
John T. Turner *(Chm)*
John H. Irby *(Vice Chm)*
Pace M. Halter *(Pres/CEO-Real Estate)*
Christine M. Robins *(Pres & CEO-Char-Broil)*
Donald R. Freeman *(Sr VP)*
James G. Hillenbrand *(CFO & Exec VP)*
Mark Werner *(Pres & COO-Lamplight)*
Steve Smits *(Pres & COO-Zebco Brands)*
John H. Irby *(Vice Chm)*
D. Abbott Turner II *(Chm)*

Subsidiaries:

Bradley Direct Services (1)
PO Box 1240, Columbus, GA 31902-1240 (100%)
Web Site: http://www.grilllovers.com
Direct Mail Merchandiser
N.A.I.C.S.: 541613

Char-Broil, LLC (1)
1017 Front Ave, Columbus, GA 31902-1240
Tel.: (706) 571-7000
Web Site: http://www.charbroil.com
Outdoor Grilling Product Mfr & Distr
N.A.I.C.S.: 335220
Kembrough Williams *(Asst Mgr-Supply Chain Logistics)*
Jim Jollay *(Engr-Regulatory)*
Chasitie Branch *(Mgr-Consumer Rels)*
Keith Williams *(Mgr-Direct)*
Brad Gillespie *(Product Dir-New Dev)*
Alex Gafford *(VP & Dir-R&D)*
Christine M. Robins *(Pres & CEO)*

Developers Investors, Inc. (1)
1001 Front Ave, Columbus, GA 31901-5260 (100%)
Tel.: (706) 571-6059
Web Site:
http://www.wcbradleyrealestate.com
Sales Range: $25-49.9 Million
Emp.: 16
Real Estate Development
N.A.I.C.S.: 525990
Pace Halter *(Pres)*

Lamplight Farms Incorporated (1)
W140 N 4900 Lilly Rd, Menomonee Falls, WI 53051-7035
Tel.: (262) 781-9590
Web Site: http://www.tikibrand.com
Candle & Torches Mfr
N.A.I.C.S.: 339999

W.C. Bradley Farms Inc. (1)
PO Box 140, Columbus, GA 31902-0140
Tel.: (706) 571-6040
Web Site:
http://www.wcbradleyrealestate.com
Sales Range: $10-24.9 Million
Emp.: 100
Holding Company; Various Industries
N.A.I.C.S.: 551112

Zebco (1)
6101 E Apache St, Tulsa, OK 74115-3370
Tel.: (918) 836-5581
Web Site: http://www.zebco.com
Sales Range: $10-24.9 Million
Emp.: 100
Fishing Tackle & Electric Trolling Motors Mfr
N.A.I.C.S.: 459110

W.C. ENGLISH INCORPORATED
615 Church St, Lynchburg, VA 24504
Tel.: (434) 845-0301
Web Site:
http://www.englishconst.com
Sales Range: $75-99.9 Million
Emp.: 42
Highway Construction, Elevated
N.A.I.C.S.: 237310
John Jordan *(VP)*
Gary Colly *(Controller)*
A. Douglas Dalton Jr. *(Pres)*

Subsidiaries:

English Construction Co. Inc. (1)
615 Church St, Lynchburg, VA 24504
Tel.: (434) 845-0301
Web Site: http://www.englishconst.com
Sales Range: $25-49.9 Million
Provider of Highway & Street Construction Services
N.A.I.C.S.: 237310
Douglas Dalton *(Pres)*
Gary Collie *(CFO)*

Lee Construction Co. (1)
PO Box 7667, Charlotte, NC 28241-7667
Tel.: (704) 588-5272
Web Site: http://www.leecarolinas.com
Sales Range: $25-49.9 Million
Heavy Construction
N.A.I.C.S.: 237310
Ronald Shaw *(Pres)*

W.C. HELLER & CO.
201 Wabash Ave, Montpelier, OH 43543
Tel.: (419) 485-3176
Web Site: http://www.wcheller.com
Year Founded: 1891
Sales Range: $50-74.9 Million
Emp.: 10
Library Furniture & Equipment for Schools, Colleges, Public Libraries & Institutions; Cabinets & Store Equipment for Hardware, Paint & Seed Stores
N.A.I.C.S.: 337127
Robert L. Heller *(Pres)*
Andrew M. Heller *(VP-Production & Plant Mgr)*
Patricia A. Heller *(Treas)*
Robert L. Heller II *(VP-Sls)*

W.C. MCQUAIDE INC.
153 Macridge Ave, Johnstown, PA 15904
Tel.: (814) 269-6000
Web Site: http://www.mcquaide.com
Rev.: $26,645,643
Emp.: 155
Contract Haulers
N.A.I.C.S.: 484121
Stan R. McQuaide *(Pres)*
William F. McQuaide *(Chm)*

W.D. HOARD & SONS COMPANY INC.
28 Milwaukee Ave W, Fort Atkinson, WI 53538-2018
Tel.: (920) 563-5551 WI
Web Site: http://www.hoards.com
Year Founded: 1972
Sales Range: $10-24.9 Million
Emp.: 100
Periodicals
N.A.I.C.S.: 513120
Brian V. Knox *(Pres)*

W.D. MATHEWS INC.
196 Belwood Rd SE, Calhoun, GA 30701
Tel.: (706) 625-1108
Sales Range: $25-49.9 Million
Emp.: 20
Wholesale Distributor & Retailer of Carpets
N.A.I.C.S.: 423220
William D. Mathews *(Pres)*
Robert Parlo *(VP)*
Becky Mathews *(Treas & Sec)*

W.D. MATTHEWS MACHINERY CO.
901 Center St, Auburn, ME 04210-6456
Tel.: (207) 784-9311 ME
Web Site:
http://www.wdmatthews.com
Year Founded: 1935
Sales Range: $25-49.9 Million
Emp.: 140
Industrial Machinery & Equipment
N.A.I.C.S.: 423830
Scott B. Plummer *(Pres)*
Ron Cloutier *(CEO)*

W.D. MATTHEWS MACHINERY CO.

W.D. Matthews Machinery Co.—(Continued)
Devon Day (Mgr-Sls)
Alan Hill (Mgr-Svcs)
Michael Stevens (Mgr-IT)

W.E JOHNSON EQUIPMENT COMPANY
7801 NW 52nd St, Doral, FL 33166
Tel.: (305) 882-7000
Web Site: http://www.wejohnson-fl.com
Year Founded: 1958
Rev.: $18,000,000
Emp.: 35
Whslr of Industrial Supplies
N.A.I.C.S.: 423840
Gary A. Work (Pres)
Paul Grubb (CFO & Controller)

W.E. AUBUCHON CO., INC.
95 Aubuchon Dr, Westminster, MA 01473-1470
Tel.: (978) 874-0521   MA
Web Site: http://www.aubuchon.com
Year Founded: 1908
Sales Range: $500-549.9 Million
Emp.: 1,100
Hardware Stores
N.A.I.C.S.: 444140
Marcus M. Moran (CEO)
Gregory J. Moran (VP-Real Estate)
Michael Mattson (Dir-Adv & PR)
Danny Aubuchon (COO)
Jeff Aubuchon (Dir-Fin)
Ken Moore (VP-Sls & Mktg)
William E. Aubuchon III (Chm & CEO)

W.E. BEDDING CORPORATION
15300 Valley View Ave, La Mirada, CA 90638
Tel.: (562) 865-6007
Web Site: http://www.orthomattress.com
Year Founded: 1957
Sales Range: $125-149.9 Million
Emp.: 200
Retail Bedding
N.A.I.C.S.: 449219
Ken Karmen (Pres)

W.E. IMHOFF & CO. INC.
1106 Smith Rd, Austin, TX 78721
Tel.: (512) 385-4574
Web Site: http://www.intertechflooring.com
Year Founded: 1988
Sales Range: $10-24.9 Million
Emp.: 75
Flooring Products, Installation & Maintenance Services
N.A.I.C.S.: 238330
Terry Bessire (VP-Sls)
Mark Jones (VP-Ops)
Willard E. Imhoff III (Pres & CEO)

W.E. SALMON INC.
514 Broad St, Rome, GA 30161-3010
Tel.: (706) 234-4547
Rev.: $24,032,538
Emp.: 11
Grocery Stores, Independent
N.A.I.C.S.: 445110

W.G. TOMKO, INC.
2559 State Rte 88, Finleyville, PA 15332
Tel.: (724) 348-2000   PA
Web Site: http://www.wgtomko.com
Year Founded: 1970
Sales Range: $25-49.9 Million
Emp.: 400
Plumbing, Heating & Air-Conditioning Services
N.A.I.C.S.: 238220

Sharee A. Waskowiak (Owner, CFO, Treas & Sec)
Jack Barry (VP-Estimating & Sls)
Dan White (COO)
Joseph Jarosz (Controller-Admin)
Debbie Fitzpatrick (Coord-Trucking)
Justin Krall (Dir-Field Ops)
Tim Frew (Dir-Heavy & Civial)
Gloria J. Simko (Dir-Operational Admin)
Cary Earnest (Dir-Safety)
Ron Miller (Mgr-CADD & Coordination)
John Mondock (Mgr-Fabrication & Oil & Gas)
Jeff Folco (Dir-Ops)
Dave Porupski (Mgr-Sheet Metal Fabrication)
Mike Mohnacs (Mgr-Washington & Baltimore)
Chad Wissinger (VP-Risk Mgmt)
Leonard Tsupros (Pres)
William G. Tomko III (Owner, Pres & CEO)

W.G. YATES & SONS CONSTRUCTION COMPANY
1 Gully Ave, Philadelphia, MS 39350
Tel.: (601) 656-5411   MS
Web Site: https://www.wgyates.com
Year Founded: 1964
Sales Range: Less than $1 Million
Emp.: 7,000
Commercial & Institutional Building Construction
N.A.I.C.S.: 236220
William G. Yates III (Pres & CEO)

Subsidiaries:

Blaine Construction Corporation (1)
6510 Deane Hill Dr, Knoxville, TN 37919
Tel.: (865) 693-8900
Web Site: http://www.blaineconstruction.com
Sales Range: $25-49.9 Million
Emp.: 40
Commercial & Industrial General Contracting, Construction Management & Pre-Engineered Metal Building Services
N.A.I.C.S.: 236220
Gary Bennett (Pres)

JESCO, Inc. (1)
2020 McCullough Blvd, Tupelo, MS 38801
Tel.: (662) 842-3240
Web Site: http://www.jescoinc.net
Sales Range: $150-199.9 Million
Emp.: 800
Commercial & Industrial Construction
N.A.I.C.S.: 236220
Jerry Maxcy (Pres)
Sid McMillan (VP-Bus Dev)

Superior Asphalt Inc. (1)
6000 I-55 S, Jackson, MS 39272-9779
Tel.: (601) 372-1400
Web Site: http://www.superasphalt.com
Sales Range: $10-24.9 Million
Emp.: 250
Asphalt Paving Mixtures & Blocks
N.A.I.C.S.: 324121
Butch Morgan (Controller)
William G. Yates Jr. (Chm)

WG Yates & Sons Construction Company - Heavy Division (1)
5990 I 55 S, Jackson, MS 39272-9779
Tel.: (601) 372-1400
Web Site: http://www.wgyates.com
Sales Range: $25-49.9 Million
Emp.: 300
Construction Services
N.A.I.C.S.: 236220

WG Yates & Sons Construction Company, Biloxi (1)
115 Main St, Biloxi, MS 39530-3108
Tel.: (228) 374-6011
Web Site: http://www.yatescompanies.com
Commercial & Industrial Construction
N.A.I.C.S.: 236220
Dan Green (Office Mgr)
William G. Yates Jr. (Chm)

WG Yates & Sons Construction Company, Destin (1)
4014 Tomas Dr W St 110, Destin, FL 32541-1662
Tel.: (850) 650-1616
Web Site: http://www.wga.net
Sales Range: $25-49.9 Million
Emp.: 8
Commercial & Industrial Construction
N.A.I.C.S.: 236220
Mike Lovrekovic (Gen Mgr)

WG Yates & Sons Construction Company, Jackson (1)
781 Larson St, Jackson, MS 39202
Tel.: (601) 352-7396
Web Site: http://www.yates.com
Sales Range: $900-999.9 Million
Emp.: 7,000
Commercial & Industrial Construction
N.A.I.C.S.: 236118
Ted Dearman (Sr VP)

WG Yates & Sons Construction Company, Memphis (1)
5050 Poplar Ave Ste 634, Memphis, TN 38157-0634
Tel.: (901) 761-0010
Web Site: http://www.wgyates.com
Sales Range: $25-49.9 Million
Emp.: 20
Commercial & Industrial Construction
N.A.I.C.S.: 236220

WG Yates & Sons Construction Company, Mobile (1)
115 Main St, Biloxi, MS 39530-4314
Tel.: (251) 478-7585
Web Site: http://www.wgyates.com
Sales Range: $25-49.9 Million
Emp.: 12
Commercial & Industrial Construction
N.A.I.C.S.: 236220
Chet Nadolski (VP)

W.H. BRESHEARS, INC.
720 B St, Modesto, CA 95354
Tel.: (209) 522-7291
Web Site: http://www.whbreshears.com
Year Founded: 1938
Sales Range: $75-99.9 Million
Emp.: 60
Petroleum Product Whslr
N.A.I.C.S.: 424710
Holley Coppetti (CEO)
Mike Foren (Mgr-Ops)

W.H. EMMART & SON INC.
305 Brick Kiln Rd, Winchester, VA 22601-5402
Tel.: (540) 662-8445   VA
Year Founded: 1985
Sales Range: $100-124.9 Million
Emp.: 120
Provider of Petroleum Bulk Station Services
N.A.I.C.S.: 424710
Timothy Emmart (Pres)
James Emmart (VP)
Hal Duff (Gen Mgr)

W.H. KOCH CO., INC.
PO Box 737, Chillicothe, MO 64601
Tel.: (660) 707-0906
Web Site: http://www.yourpiggywiggly.com
Rev.: $12,100,000
Emp.: 31
Grocery Stores, Chain
N.A.I.C.S.: 445110
Bill Koch (Pres & Treas)

W.H. MAZE COMPANY
100 Church St, Peru, IL 61354
Tel.: (815) 223-8290   IL
Web Site: http://www.mazenails.com
Year Founded: 1848
Sales Range: $75-99.9 Million
Emp.: 150
Mfr of Specialty Nails
N.A.I.C.S.: 332618

Roelif M. Loveland (Pres)

Subsidiaries:

Independent Nail Company (1)
30 Mozzone Blvd, Taunton, MA 02780-3751
Tel.: (508) 880-7202
Web Site: http://www.mazenails.com
Sales Range: $10-24.9 Million
Emp.: 20
Mfrof Nails
N.A.I.C.S.: 332618

Maze Lumber (1)
1100 Water St, Peru, IL 61354-3654
Tel.: (815) 223-1742
Web Site: http://www.mazelumber.com
Sales Range: $10-24.9 Million
Emp.: 22
Retail Lumber Suppliers
N.A.I.C.S.: 332618
Pete M. Loveland (Gen Mgr-Sls)
Jennifer Smith (Office Mgr)

Sales Stretcher Enterprises (SSE) (1)
4920 E Plank 103rd Rd, Peru, IL 61354-9356
Tel.: (815) 223-9681
Sales Range: $10-24.9 Million
Emp.: 25
Packaging Services
N.A.I.C.S.: 324122

W.H. MCADAMS COMPANY
1211 E Levee St, Dallas, TX 75207
Tel.: (214) 748-6417
Year Founded: 1952
Sales Range: $25-49.9 Million
Emp.: 8
Manufacturers Representative of Warm Air Heating Equipment & Supplies
N.A.I.C.S.: 336320
William H. Mcadams (Owner)
Gerald Mcadams (Pres)

W.H.P.M., INC.
5358 Irwindale Ave, Irwindale, CA 91706
Tel.: (626) 443-8480
Web Site: http://www.whpm.com
Year Founded: 1993
Medical Diagnostic Products Developer, Mfr & Whslr
N.A.I.C.S.: 339112
John Wan (Founder & Pres)

Subsidiaries:

Express Diagnostics Int'l, Inc. (1)
PO Box 310, Blue Earth, MN 56013
Tel.: (507) 526-3951
Web Site: http://www.drugcheck.com
Sales Range: $10-24.9 Million
Emp.: 91
Drug Testing Product Mfr
N.A.I.C.S.: 334519
Rich Strasser (COO)

W.I. CLARK COMPANY
30 Barnes Indus Park Rd S, Wallingford, CT 06492
Tel.: (203) 265-6781
Web Site: http://www.wiclark.com
Sales Range: $10-24.9 Million
Emp.: 87
General Construction Machinery & Equipment
N.A.I.C.S.: 423810
Judy Dunn (Controller)
Gary Cox (Mgr-Svc)

W.J. BRADLEY MORTGAGE CAPITAL, LLC.
6465 Greenwood Plz Blvd Ste 500, Centennial, CO 80111
Tel.: (303) 825-5670
Web Site: http://www.wjbradley.com
Year Founded: 2002
Sales Range: $200-249.9 Million
Emp.: 1,300

COMPANIES

Real Estate Credit Services
N.A.I.C.S.: 522292
William J. Bradley *(Founder & CEO)*
Danya Sawyer *(Sr VP-Mortgage Ops)*
Mark Simon *(VP-Sls-Emery-Newport Beach)*
John Sadler *(CIO)*

W.J. DEUTSCH & SONS LTD.
201 Tresser Blvd Ste 500, Stamford, CT 06901-3435
Tel.: (203) 965-4100   NY
Web Site:
http://www.deutschfamily.com
Year Founded: 1981
Wine Importer & Distr
N.A.I.C.S.: 424820
Peter Deutsch *(CEO)*

W.J. HAGERTY & SONS, LTD., INC.
3801 Linden Ave, South Bend, IN 46619-1844
Tel.: (574) 288-4991
Web Site: http://www.hagertyusa.com
Year Founded: 1895
Sales Range: $1-9.9 Million
Emp.: 40
Precious Metal Care Products, Jewelry Cleaners, Silver Storage Bags & Kits Mfr
N.A.I.C.S.: 325612
Debra Hagerty *(Pres)*
Dominic Gilbert *(Acct Mgr)*

Subsidiaries:

W.J. Hagerty & Sons Canada Ltd.   (1)
151-14800 Yonge Street, PO Box 28532, Aurora, L4G 1N3, ON, Canada   **(100%)**
Tel.: (416) 255-9599
Web Site: https://wjhagerty.ca
Jewelry
N.A.I.C.S.: 339910

W.L. BUTLER CONSTRUCTION INC.
204 Franklin St, Redwood City, CA 94063
Tel.: (650) 361-1270
Web Site: http://www.wlbutler.com
Rev.: $123,023,704
Emp.: 150
Commercial & Office Building, New Construction
N.A.I.C.S.: 236220
William L. Butler *(CEO)*
Daniel Warren *(VP)*
Brett Crail *(VP-Construction)*
Gina Henson *(CFO)*
David A. Nevens Jr. *(COO)*

W.L. GORE & ASSOCIATES, INC.
555 Papermill Rd, Newark, DE 19711
Tel.: (302) 738-4880   DE
Web Site: https://www.gore.com
Year Founded: 1958
Emp.: 13,000
Special Wiring & Cable, Waterproof Breathable Membranes & Industrial Sealants & Filters Mfr
N.A.I.C.S.: 335921
Bret Snyder *(Chm & CEO)*
Sherry L. Buck *(CFO)*
Paula Owurowa *(Project Mgr)*

Subsidiaries:

Carmeda AB   (1)
Drottning Kristinas Esplanad 4, 170 67, Solna, Sweden   **(100%)**
Tel.: (46) 850551200
Web Site: www.carmeda.se
Bioactive Surfaces & Biocompatible Materials Mfr, Developer & Marketer
N.A.I.C.S.: 541714

Gore Industrial Products Trade (Shanghai) Co., LTD   (1)
43rd Floor Zhongxin Building No 1468 Nanjing West Road, Jing'an District, Shanghai, 200040, China
Tel.: (86) 2151728299
Industrial Product Whslr
N.A.I.C.S.: 423840

W. L. Gore & Associates (Australia) Pty, Ltd.   (1)
Suite 1 13a Narabang Way, Belrose, 2085, NSW, Australia
Tel.: (61) 294736800
Plastics Product Mfr
N.A.I.C.S.: 326199

W. L. Gore & Associates (Korea), Ltd.   (1)
17F AIA Tower 16 Tongil-ro 2-gil, Jung-gu, Seoul, 04511, Korea (South)
Tel.: (82) 23933411
Cable Assembly Mfr
N.A.I.C.S.: 335931

W. L. Gore & Associates (Pacific) Pte Ltd.   (1)
150 Beach Road 17-08 Gateway West, Singapore, 189720, Singapore
Tel.: (65) 67332882
Electrical Equipment Whslr
N.A.I.C.S.: 423610

Branch (Non-US):

W. L. Gore & Associates (Pacific) Pte.Ltd. - India Branch   (2)
703 A-Wing 215 Atrium Andheri-Kurla Road, Andheri East, Mumbai, 400093, India
Tel.: (91) 2267687000
Fabricated Metal Products Mfr
N.A.I.C.S.: 332999

W. L. Gore & Associates (South Africa) (Proprietary) Ltd.   (1)
150 Craig Rd, Anderbolt, 1459, Boksburg, South Africa
Tel.: (27) 11 894 2248
Filtering Materials & Supplies Mfr
N.A.I.C.S.: 423840

W. L. Gore & Associates (UK) Ltd.   (1)
Simpson Parkway Kirkton Campus, West Lothian, Livingston, EH54 7BH, United Kingdom
Tel.: (44) 1506460123
Wire Equipment Mfr
N.A.I.C.S.: 335921

W. L. Gore & Associates Canada, Inc.   (1)
5401 Eglinton Avenue W Unit 202, Etobicoke, Toronto, M9C 5K6, ON, Canada
Tel.: (416) 789-3416
Hospital Equipment Whslr
N.A.I.C.S.: 423450

W. L. Gore & Associates Hong Kong, Ltd.   (1)
Unit 1101-09 & 16-18 Level 11 Tower 1 Kowloon Commerce Centre, No 51 Kwai Cheong Road Kwai Chung, Kowloon, China (Hong Kong)
Tel.: (852) 26229622
Hospital & Medical Equipment Supplier
N.A.I.C.S.: 423450

W. L. Gore & Associates Scandinavia AB   (1)
Neongatan 9B, 431 53, Molndal, Sweden
Tel.: (46) 317067800
Aircraft Equipment Mfr & Whslr
N.A.I.C.S.: 336413

W. L. Gore & Associates Technologies (Shenzhen) Co., LTD   (1)
C1 Shenfubao Science & Technology Industrial Park 1 Huanghuai Road, Futian Free Trade Zone, Shenzhen, 518038, China
Tel.: (86) 755 83 59 82 62
Electronic Product Whslr
N.A.I.C.S.: 423690

W. L. Gore & Associates de Mexico, S. de R.L. de C.V.   (1)
1500 Avenida Homero Suite 102, Colonia Polanco, 11560, Mexico, Miguel Hidalgo, Mexico

Tel.: (52) 8182881281
Cable Products Mfr
N.A.I.C.S.: 335921

W. L. Gore & Associates do Brasil Ltda.   (1)
Edificio Bolsa de Imoveis de Sao Paulo Av das Nacoes Unidas 11-541, Brooklin Paulista, 04578-000, Sao Paulo, 04578-000, Brazil
Tel.: (55) 1155027800
Web Site: https://www.gore.com.br
Industrial Equipment Distr
N.A.I.C.S.: 423850

W. L. Gore & Associates, Co., Ltd.   (1)
W Building 1-8-15 Konan, Minato-ku, Tokyo, 108-0075, Japan
Tel.: (81) 367462600
Electronic Components Mfr
N.A.I.C.S.: 334419

W. L. Gore & Associates, Polska Sp.z.o.o.   (1)
ul Migdalowa 4, 02-796, Warsaw, Poland
Tel.: (48) 226451537
Plastics Product Mfr
N.A.I.C.S.: 326199

W. L. Gore & Associati S.r.l.   (1)
Via Enrico Fermi 2/4, 37135, Verona, Italy
Tel.: (39) 0456209111
Web Site: https://www.gore.it
Aircraft Equipment Mfr & Whslr
N.A.I.C.S.: 336413

W. L. Gore & Associes S.A.R.L.   (1)
8 place des vins de France, 75012, Paris, France
Tel.: (33) 156956565
Web Site: https://www.gore.fr
Medical Equipment Distr
N.A.I.C.S.: 423450

W. L. Gore y Asociados, S.L.   (1)
C/ Ciutat de Granada 178, 08018, Barcelona, Spain
Tel.: (34) 934806900
Medical Equipment Whslr
N.A.I.C.S.: 423450

W.L. HALSEY GROCERY COMPANY, INC.
401 Lanier Rd, Madison, AL 35758
Tel.: (256) 772-9691
Web Site:
http://www.halseyfoodservice.com
Rev.: $33,300,000
Emp.: 106
Groceries
N.A.I.C.S.: 424410
Cecilia Halsey *(Pres & CEO)*

W.L. MCCORMACK & CO. INC.
16101 SW 72nd Ave, Portland, OR 97224
Tel.: (503) 624-2090   OR
Web Site: http://www.perlo.biz
Year Founded: 1979
Sales Range: $25-49.9 Million
Emp.: 70
Provider of Construction Services
N.A.I.C.S.: 236220
Jeff Perala *(Co-Pres)*
Gayland Looney *(Co-Pres)*

Subsidiaries:

Perlo McCormack Pacific   (1)
7190 SW Sandburg St, Tigard, OR 97223-8080
Tel.: (503) 624-2090
Web Site:
http://www.perlomcmormackpacific.com
Rev.: $50,000,000
Emp.: 30
Industrial Buildings & Warehouses
N.A.I.C.S.: 236210
William McCormack *(CEO)*

W.L. MILLER CO. INC.
750 E County Rd 1220, Hamilton, IL 62341
Tel.: (217) 847-3316

W.M. GRACE DEVELOPMENT COMPANY

Web Site: http://www.wlmillerco.com
Sales Range: $10-24.9 Million
Emp.: 85
General Contractor; Highway & Street Construction
N.A.I.C.S.: 237310

W.L. PETREY WHOLESALE COMPANY, INC.
PO Box 68, Luverne, AL 36049
Tel.: (334) 230-5674
Web Site: http://www.petrey.com
Rev.: $196,700,000
Emp.: 60
Grocery Distr
N.A.I.C.S.: 424410
James W. Jackson Sr. *(Chm)*

W.M. AUTOMOTIVE WAREHOUSE INC.
208 Penland St, Fort Worth, TX 76111-4623
Tel.: (817) 834-5550   TX
Web Site:
http://www.wmautomotive.com
Year Founded: 1976
Sales Range: $25-49.9 Million
Emp.: 180
Motor Vehicle Supplies & New Parts
N.A.I.C.S.: 423120
Wilson M. McMillion *(Chm & CEO)*

W.M. BARR & COMPANY, INC.
2105 Channel Ave, Memphis, TN 38113
Tel.: (901) 775-0100   TN
Web Site: http://www.wmbarr.com
Year Founded: 1946
Sales Range: $150-199.9 Million
Emp.: 350
Specialty Cleaning, Polishing Agents & Paint Mfr
N.A.I.C.S.: 325612
Richard Loomis *(Pres & CEO)*
Jill Lusk *(Mgr)*

W.M. CRAMER LUMBER CO. INC.
3486 Tex's Fish Camp Rd, Connelly Springs, NC 28612-7635
Tel.: (828) 397-7481   NC
Web Site:
http://www.cramerlumber.com
Year Founded: 1969
Sales Range: $10-24.9 Million
Emp.: 76
Lumber Mill
N.A.I.C.S.: 423310
Wemdell M. Cramer *(Founder & Pres)*

W.M. GRACE DEVELOPMENT COMPANY
6925 E Indian School Rd, Scottsdale, AZ 85251
Tel.: (602) 956-8254   AZ
Web Site:
http://www.wmgraceco.com
Year Founded: 1966
Sales Range: $25-49.9 Million
Emp.: 25
Real Estate Developers
N.A.I.C.S.: 531210
Howard T. Grace *(Pres & CEO)*
Jim Stamatis *(Sr VP)*
Valerie Dana *(Mgr-Real Estate Asset)*
Mike Pearlstein *(VP)*
Thomas Grace *(VP)*
John Dorsett *(Mgr-Construction & Architect)*
Bill Strathman *(Controller)*
Jim Kaiser *(VP-Property Mgmt)*
Melissa Lenz *(Mgr-Property)*
Jody Harwood *(Sr VP-Hospitality)*
Steve Carver *(VP-Hospitality)*

W.M. Grace Development Company—(Continued)

Christine Hebets (Sls Mgr-Reservations)
Patricia Ellenburg (CFO)

Subsidiaries:

Prescott Resort & Convention Center L.P. (1)
1500 Hwy 69, Prescott, AZ 86301
Tel.: (928) 776-1666
Web Site: http://www.prescottresort.com
Sales Range: $10-24.9 Million
Motel, Franchised
N.A.I.C.S.: 721120

W.M. JORDAN COMPANY INC.
11010 Jefferson Ave, Newport News, VA 23601
Tel.: (757) 596-6341
Web Site: http://www.wmjordan.com
Year Founded: 1957
Sales Range: $25-49.9 Million
Emp.: 332
Contracting & Construction Services
N.A.I.C.S.: 236220
James C. Burnett (CFO)
John J. Angle (Sr VP-Ops)
Jennifer Johnson (Mktg Mgr)
Ken Taylor (Exec VP)
Raynald Morris (CIO)
Tom Shelton (Treas)
John R. Lawson II (Chm)
Ronald J. Lauster Jr. (Pres)

Subsidiaries:

W.M. Jordan Company (1)
708 Bainbridge St, Richmond, VA 23224-2320 (100%)
Tel.: (804) 233-6921
Web Site: http://www.wmjordan.com
Sales Range: $10-24.9 Million
Emp.: 285
Provider Of Contracting And Construction Services
N.A.I.C.S.: 236220

W.M. SCHLOSSER CO. INC.
2400 51st Pl, Hyattsville, MD 20781-1303
Tel.: (301) 773-1300
Web Site: http://www.wmschlosser.com
Year Founded: 1962
Sales Range: $25-49.9 Million
Emp.: 200
Construction Services
N.A.I.C.S.: 236220
Andrew Schlosser (Pres)
Christopher Chapman (Mgr-QC)
Dave Voliziani (Mgr-Safety)

W.M. SPRINKMAN CORP.
4234 Courtney St, Franksville, WI 53126
Tel.: (262) 835-2390
Web Site: http://www.sprinkman.com
Sales Range: $10-24.9 Million
Emp.: 100
Food Industry Machinery
N.A.I.C.S.: 423830
Dale Metcoff (Controller)
Brian Sprinkman (Pres)
Graham Broadhurst (Dir-Brewing Ops)
A. J. Naber (Dir-Engrg)
Brian Armstrong (Mgr-Accts-Natl)
James Dieck (Engr-Design-Waukesha)
Nathan Vander Pas (Engr-Process-Waukesha)

W.M. TINDER INCORPORATED
7930 Notes Dr, Manassas, VA 20109
Tel.: (703) 368-9544
Web Site: http://www.tinderwholesale.com
Rev.: $13,000,000
Emp.: 54
Lumber, Plywood & Millwork
N.A.I.C.S.: 423310

W.N. VAN ALSTINE & SONS INC.
18 New Cortland St, Cohoes, NY 12047
Tel.: (518) 237-1613
Web Site: http://www.vanalstineinc.com
Sales Range: $10-24.9 Million
Emp.: 50
Packaging Materials
N.A.I.C.S.: 424990
Nicholas Van Alstine (Pres)
Ed Wickted (Controller)
Joan Godzik (Mgr-Corp Credit)

W.O. BLACKSTONE & COMPANY, INC.
1841 Shop Rd, Columbia, SC 29201
Tel.: (803) 252-8222
Web Site: http://www.woblackstone.com
Year Founded: 1937
Sales Range: $10-24.9 Million
Emp.: 100
Plumbing & HVAC Systems
N.A.I.C.S.: 238220
Lewis M. Caswell (Pres)
Beverly Austin (Office Mgr & Mgr-HR)

W.O. GRUBB STEEL ERECTION INC.
5120 Jefferson Davis Hwy, Richmond, VA 23234
Tel.: (804) 271-9471 VA
Web Site: http://www.wogrubb.com
Year Founded: 1965
Sales Range: $25-49.9 Million
Emp.: 315
Provider of Structural Steel Erection
N.A.I.C.S.: 532412
William O. Grubb (Pres)
Chuck Cooke (Mgr-Corp Safety)

W.P. & R.S. MARS COMPANY
4319 W 1st St, Duluth, MN 55807
Tel.: (218) 628-0303 MN
Web Site: http://www.marssupply.com
Year Founded: 1942
Sales Range: $10-24.9 Million
Emp.: 150
Provider of Industrial Supplies
N.A.I.C.S.: 423840
Ron De Grio (Acct Mgr)
Robert S. Mars Jr. (Chm)

W.P. LAW INC.
303 Riverchase Way, Lexington, SC 29072
Tel.: (803) 461-0599
Web Site: http://www.wplawinc.com
Year Founded: 1970
Sales Range: $10-24.9 Million
Emp.: 70
Supplier of Fluid Handling Equipment
N.A.I.C.S.: 423820
Terry Brady (Pres)
Brian M. Fields (Exec VP)

W.R. COBB COMPANY
800 Waterman Ave, East Providence, RI 02914
Tel.: (401) 467-7400 RI
Web Site: http://www.wrcobb.com
Year Founded: 1877
Sales Range: $75-99.9 Million
Emp.: 100
Jeweler Findings, Master Alloy, Casting Grain, Wire & Flat Stock Mfr
N.A.I.C.S.: 339910
Roderick H. Lichtenfels (CEO)

Subsidiaries:

Cobb Hong Kong (1)
Unit 1206 Peninsula Square 18 Sung On Street, Hunghom, Kowloon, China (Hong Kong)
Tel.: (852) 2337 2060
Sales Range: $10-24.9 Million
Emp.: 5
Jewelry Whslr
N.A.I.C.S.: 423940
Ralph Quackenbush (Mng Dir)

W.R. HESS COMPANY
3030 NW Expy Ste 1500, Oklahoma City, OK 73112
Tel.: (405) 948-8818
Web Site: http://www.factor.com
Year Founded: 1979
Sales Range: $50-74.9 Million
Emp.: 50
Holding Company
N.A.I.C.S.: 551112
Jerry Hess (Owner, Pres & CEO)
Tom Hess (Owner)
Jason Berkel (VP-Customer Support)
Frankie Shannon (VP-Pro Svcs & Bus Consulting)

Subsidiaries:

Factor (1)
3030 NW Expy # 1500, Oklahoma City, OK 73112
Tel.: (405) 948-8819
Web Site: http://www.factor.com
Developer of Petroleum Marketing & Business Management Software
N.A.I.C.S.: 513210

W.R. HUFF ASSET MANAGEMENT CO., INC.
412 Mt Kemble Ave, Morristown, NJ 07901
Tel.: (973) 984-1233
Sales Range: $25-49.9 Million
Emp.: 50
Provider of Equity Investment Services
N.A.I.C.S.: 523940
William Robert Huff (Pres, Chief Investment Officer & Principal)
Donna B. Charlton (Founder)
Peter Bentz (Mgr-HR)
Bryan E. Bloom (Gen Counsel & Portfolio Mgr)

W.R. STARKEY MORTGAGE LLP
5055 W Park Blvd Ste 300, Plano, TX 75093
Tel.: (972) 599-5210
Web Site: http://www.wrstarkey.com
Rev.: $11,500,000
Emp.: 400
Mortgage Services
N.A.I.C.S.: 522310
Jim Clapp (CFO)
Sherry Colley (Chief Credit Officer & Exec VP)
Sean A. Malone (Asst VP & Mgr-Post Closing)

W.R. VERNON PRODUCE CO., INC.
1035 N Cherry St, Winston Salem, NC 27115
Tel.: (336) 725-9741 NC
Web Site: http://www.vernonproduce.com
Year Founded: 1974
Sales Range: $450-499.9 Million
Emp.: 100
Sales of Fresh Fruits & Vegetables
N.A.I.C.S.: 424480
Pete Vernon (COO & VP)
William R. Doss (CFO & VP)

W.S. ADAMSON & ASSOCIATES, INC.
175 West 200 South Ste 3003 First Commerce Ctr, Salt Lake City, UT 84101
Tel.: (801) 532-5322 UT
Year Founded: 1950
Sales Range: Less than $1 Million
Emp.: 2
Public Relations
N.A.I.C.S.: 541820
Bruce D. Whitehead (Pres & Owner)
Lynne Winsor (Mgr-Admin, Corp Sec & Treas)

W.S. BADGER COMPANY, INC
768 Rte 10, Gilsum, NH 03448
Tel.: (603) 357-2958
Web Site: http://www.badgerbalm.com
Sales Range: $1-9.9 Million
Emp.: 36
Cosmetics Mfr
N.A.I.C.S.: 333998
Bill Whyte (CEO)

W.S. BELLOWS CONSTRUCTION CORPORATION
1906 Afton St, Houston, TX 77055-2209
Tel.: (713) 680-2132 TX
Web Site: http://www.wsbellows.com
Year Founded: 1996
Sales Range: $25-49.9 Million
Emp.: 310
Provider of Nonresidential Construction Services
N.A.I.C.S.: 236220
Charlie Kubin (VP)
Paul Oliver (VP)
David Morris (VP)
Russell Jones (VP)
Laura Bellows (Pres)
Tommy Lee (VP-Safety)
Ray Mancias (VP-Safety)
Tony Mansoorian (COO)
Mark A. Wallace (Pres & CEO)

W.S. CUMBY, INC.
938 Lincoln Ave, Springfield, PA 19064
Tel.: (610) 328-5353
Web Site: http://www.cumby.com
Year Founded: 1981
Rev.: $46,738,458
Emp.: 50
Building Construction Services
N.A.I.C.S.: 236118
Michael O'Brien (VP-Bus Dev)
Craig Irvine (VP-Ops)
Erik Fay (VP)
William S. Cumby Jr. (Pres)

W.S. DARLEY & CO., INC.
325 Spring Lake Dr, Itasca, IL 60143-1019
Tel.: (708) 345-8050
Web Site: http://www.darley.com
Year Founded: 1976
Sales Range: $10-24.9 Million
Emp.: 170
Provider of Pumps & Pumping Equipment
N.A.I.C.S.: 333914
Nick Dafta (CFO)
Paul Darley (Pres)

W.S. EMERSON CO., INC.
15 Acme Rd, Brewer, ME 04412
Tel.: (207) 989-3410
Web Site: http://www.wsemerson.com
Sales Range: $10-24.9 Million
Emp.: 60
Men's & Boy's Furnishings
N.A.I.C.S.: 315250

John A. Vickery (Pres)
Russel M. Vickery (VP)

W.S. NEWELL, INC.
10480 Hwy 80 E, Montgomery, AL 36117
Tel.: (334) 215-8000
Web Site: http://www.wsnewell.com
Sales Range: $25-49.9 Million
Emp.: 250
Excavation & Grading, Building Construction
N.A.I.C.S.: 238910
Sam Newell (VP)
David Rhodes (Controller)

W.S. NIELSEN CO., INC.
8270 Industrial Pl, Alpharetta, GA 30004
Tel.: (770) 475-7321
Web Site: http://www.wsnielsen.com
Rev.: $10,000,000
Emp.: 35
Glass Construction Materials
N.A.I.C.S.: 423390
Michael J. Nielsen (Pres)
David Freise (Mgr-Construction)
Rick Strickland (Project Mgr)

W.S. REICHENBACH & SON INC.
406 Minor St, Emmaus, PA 18049
Tel.: (610) 434-7234
Web Site: http://www.reichenbachs.com
Rev.: $15,964,182
Emp.: 8
Fuel Oil Dealers
N.A.I.C.S.: 457210
Bill Reichenbach (Office Mgr)

W.S. TOWNSEND COMPANY
106 E Oliver Dr, Marshall, MI 49068
Tel.: (269) 781-5131 MI
Web Site: http://www.thekitchenshops.com
Year Founded: 1962
Sales Range: $10-24.9 Million
Emp.: 135
Millwork & Lumber
N.A.I.C.S.: 444110
Steve Townsend (Pres)
Jack W. Townsend (CEO)

W.S. TRIMBLE CO., INC.
2200 Atchley St, Knoxville, TN 37920-1704
Tel.: (865) 573-1911 TN
Web Site: http://www.wmstrimble.com
Year Founded: 1933
Sales Range: $10-24.9 Million
Emp.: 100
Mfr of Metal Doors & Frames, Finish Hardware, Folding Partitions, Overhead Doors, Wood Doors & Building Specialties
N.A.I.C.S.: 423310
William S. Trimble Jr. (Pres)

W.S. VOGEL AGENCY, INC.
290 W Mt Pleasant Ave Ste 3100, Livingston, NJ 07039
Tel.: (973) 992-7171 DE
Web Site: http://www.katznassau.com
Year Founded: 1970
Sales Range: $1-9.9 Million
Emp.: 10
Life Insurance
N.A.I.C.S.: 524113
Lynda M. Baccoli (Pres)
Nick Manzi (Mgr-Underwriting)
Eloisa Tumin (Controller & Mgr-Acctg-Commissions)

W.T. CHEN & CO., INC.
5 Mount Royal Ave, Marlborough, MA 01752
Tel.: (508) 357-8888
Web Site: http://www.wtchen.com
Sales Range: $10-24.9 Million
Emp.: 14
Computer Facilities Management
N.A.I.C.S.: 541513
Wayne Chen (Pres & CEO)

W.T. COX SUBSCRIPTIONS, INC.
201 Village Rd, Shallotte, NC 28470
Tel.: (910) 754-3145
Web Site: http://www.wtcox.com
Year Founded: 1974
Sales Range: $10-24.9 Million
Emp.: 48
Magazine & Newspaper Subscription Fulfillment Services
N.A.I.C.S.: 561499
Michael Cox (Pres & CEO)

W.W. ADCOCK INC.
2611 Philmont Ave, Huntingdon Valley, PA 19006
Tel.: (215) 947-3800
Web Site: http://www.wwadcock.com
Sales Range: $10-24.9 Million
Emp.: 100
Provider of Swimming Pools
N.A.I.C.S.: 423910
Steve McIntyre (Controller)

W.W. GAY MECHANICAL CONTRACTOR, INC.
524 Stockton St, Jacksonville, FL 32204-2535
Tel.: (904) 474-5600 FL
Web Site: http://www.wwgmc.com
Year Founded: 1962
Sales Range: $150-199.9 Million
Emp.: 780
Plumbing, Heating, Air Conditioning & Industrial Contracting Services
N.A.I.C.S.: 238220
David D. Boree (Chm & COO)
William W. Gay (Founder & CEO)

W.W. LEISURE, INC.
5847 San Felipe St, Houston, TX 77057-3076
Tel.: (713) 266-7300
Web Site: http://www.whg.com
Year Founded: 1998
Sales Range: $25-49.9 Million
Emp.: 810
Operators of Hotels & Motels
N.A.I.C.S.: 721110
Mues Mangalji (Pres)
Mohamed Thouseek (VP & Dir-Ops)

Subsidiaries:
W.W. Lodging, Inc. (1)
1825 Gillespie Way Ste 101, El Cajon, CA 92020
Tel.: (619) 258-6565
Sales Range: $10-24.9 Million
Emp.: 50
Operators of Hotels & Motels
N.A.I.C.S.: 721110

W.W. NORTON & COMPANY, INC.
500 5th Ave, New York, NY 10110-0002
Tel.: (212) 354-5500 NY
Web Site: http://books.wwnorton.com
Year Founded: 1923
Sales Range: $100-124.9 Million
Emp.: 300
Books Publisher & Whslr
N.A.I.C.S.: 513130
Julia A. Reidhead (Pres)
Damon Williams (Office Mgr)

Subsidiaries:
Liveright Publishing Corp. (1)
500 5th Ave, New York, NY 10110-0002
Tel.: (212) 354-5500
Web Site: http://www.liveright.com
Publishing
N.A.I.C.S.: 513130

National Book Company Inc. (1)
800 Keystone Industrial Park, Dunmore, PA 18512
Tel.: (570) 346-2020
Web Site: http://www.norton.com
Sales Range: $25-49.9 Million
Emp.: 200
Book Distributor
N.A.I.C.S.: 493190
Ray Worrell (Gen Mgr)

W. W. Norton & Company Ltd. (1)
15 Carlisle Street, London, W1D 3BS, United Kingdom
Tel.: (44) 20 7323 1579
Web Site: http://www.wwnorton.co.uk
Emp.: 12
Book Publishers
N.A.I.C.S.: 513130
Edward Crutchley (Mng Dir)

W.W. Norton & Company, Inc. - Countryman Press Division (1)
43 Lincoln Corners Way, Woodstock, VT 05091
Tel.: (802) 457-4826
Web Site: http://www.countrymanpress.com
Sales Range: $10-24.9 Million
Emp.: 5
Book Publishers
N.A.I.C.S.: 513130
Kermit Hummel (Dir-Editorial)

W.W. TIRE SERVICE, INC.
PO Box 22, Bryant, SD 57221-0022
Tel.: (605) 628-2501
Web Site: http://www.wwtireservice.com
Sales Range: $25-49.9 Million
Emp.: 105
Home Supply Whslr
N.A.I.C.S.: 441330
Wayne Weelborg (Pres)
Shaine Weelborg (Principal)

W.W. TRANSPORT, INC.
701 E Mount Pleasant St W, West Burlington, IA 52655
Tel.: (319) 754-1944 IA
Web Site: http://www.wwtransportinc.com
Year Founded: 1991
General & Specialized Freight Trucking Services
N.A.I.C.S.: 484121
Jeff Walters (Co-Founder & Pres)
Terri Russell (Controller-Fin)
Colin Wagenbach (Co-Founder & VP)
Kyle Weuve (CFO)
Clay Crews (Gen Mgr)
Tyler Huggins (Dir-Safety, Claims & Compliance)
Robert Mariniello (Dir-Bus Dev)

W.W. WALLWORK, INC.
900 35th St N, Fargo, ND 58102-3089
Tel.: (701) 476-7000 ND
Web Site: http://www.wallworktrucks.com
Year Founded: 1921
Sales Range: $10-24.9 Million
Emp.: 500
Whslr & Retailer of Cars, Trucks & Parts; Truck Trailers Service & Repairs; Finance Leasing
N.A.I.C.S.: 441110
Cim Drewicke (CFO)
Curry Quenette (Exec VP)
William W. Wallwork III (CEO)

Subsidiaries:
Valley Imports, Inc. (1)
402 40th St S, Fargo, ND 58103 (100%)
Tel.: (701) 277-1777
Web Site: http://www.valleyimportsnd.com
Import Automobile Franchise (Mercedes Benz, Porshe, Audi & VW)
N.A.I.C.S.: 441110
William Wallwork (Pres)
Jeff Richmond (Gen Mgr)

Wallwork Financial Corp. (1)
401 38th St SW, Fargo, ND 58103 (100%)
Tel.: (701) 476-7000
Web Site: http://www.wallworkfinancial.com
Emp.: 15
Leasing of Heavy Duty Truck & Trailer Distr
N.A.I.C.S.: 441110
Steve Lausch (Gen Mgr)
Kelly Geiger (Mng Dir)
Bradon R. Marshall (Sls Dir-Natl)

W3I, LLC
1900 Medical Arts Ave S, Sartell, MN 56377
Tel.: (320) 257-7550
Web Site: http://www.w3i.com
Sales Range: $25-49.9 Million
Emp.: 90
Application Software & Marketing Solutions
N.A.I.C.S.: 541613
Andy Johnson (CEO)
Ryan Weber (Sr VP-Product Dev)
Joe Bergstrom (VP-Acct Dev)

WABASH CENTER INC.
2000 Greenbush St, Lafayette, IN 47904
Tel.: (765) 423-5531 IN
Web Site: http://www.wabashcenter.com
Year Founded: 1953
Sales Range: $10-24.9 Million
Emp.: 679
Disability Assistance Services
N.A.I.C.S.: 624120
Richard Rhoad (Exec Dir)
Linda Bowman (Sec)

WABASH ELECTRIC SUPPLY INC.
1400 S Wabash St, Wabash, IN 46992
Tel.: (260) 563-4146 IN
Web Site: http://www.wabashelectric.com
Year Founded: 1960
Sales Range: $25-49.9 Million
Emp.: 200
Designer & Wholesale Distributorships of Commercial & Residentail Lighting
N.A.I.C.S.: 423610
Cathy Minne (Mgr-Showroom)
Jeremy Frick (Branch Mgr)
Mark Webb (Engr-Support)
Rick White (VP-Sls)

WABASH MEMORIAL HOSPITAL ASSOCIATION
501 N Water St, Decatur, IL 62525
Tel.: (217) 429-5246 IL
Web Site: http://www.wabashcannonball.org
Year Founded: 1884
Sales Range: $10-24.9 Million
Emp.: 18
Health Care Srvices
N.A.I.C.S.: 813920
Randy Thaxton (Chm)

WABASH PLASTICS INC.
1300 Burch Dr, Evansville, IN 47725
Tel.: (812) 867-2447
Web Site: http://www.wabashplastics.com
Rev.: $16,600,000
Emp.: 225
Plastics Product Mfr
N.A.I.C.S.: 326199

WABASH PLASTICS INC.

Wabash Plastics Inc.—(Continued)
John H. Schroeder (Chm & CEO)
Richard Schroeder (Principal)
Jon Edwards (Mgr-Production)
Chad Cissna (Mgr-Engrg)
Joe Barker (VP & Plant Mgr)
Patricia Simpson (Coord-FPA)
Tom Stallings (Supvr-Support Svcs)

WABASH STEEL COMPANY, LLC
450 E 96th St Ste 100, Indianapolis, IN 46240
Tel.: (317) 818-1622 IN
Web Site: http://www.wabashsteel.biz
Year Founded: 2006
Steel Fabrication
N.A.I.C.S.: 332312
Mark Osborn (Plant Mgr)

WABASH VALLEY SERVICE CO.
909 N Court St, Grayville, IL 62844
Tel.: (618) 375-2311
Web Site:
   http://www.wabashvalleyfs.com
Rev.: $64,066,727
Emp.: 200
Farm Supplies
N.A.I.C.S.: 424910
Todd Neibel (Gen Mgr)

WACHTELL LIPTON ROSEN & KATZ
51 W 52nd St, New York, NY 10019-6150
Tel.: (212) 403-1000
Web Site: http://www.wlrk.com
Year Founded: 1965
Sales Range: $600-649.9 Million
Emp.: 501
Legal Advisory Services
N.A.I.C.S.: 541110
Edward D. Herlihy (Co-Chm)
Herbert M. Wachtell (Partner-Litigation)
Martin Lipton (Partner)
Andrew J. Nussbaum (Partner)
Marc Wolinsky (Partner-Litigation)
Jeffrey M. Wintner (Partner-Litigation)
David B. Anders (Partner-Litigation)
Ian Boczko (Partner-Litigation)
Andrew R. Brownstein (Partner)
Karessa L. Cain (Partner)
Joshua R. Cammaker (Partner)
Wayne M. Carlin (Partner)
Scott K. Charles (Partner-Restructuring & Fin)
Ronald C. Chen (Partner)
Steven A. Cohen (Partner)
Nicholas G. Demmo (Partner)
Damian G. Didden (Partner)
Stephen R. DiPrima (Partner)
Adam O. Emmerich (Partner)
Joshua A. Feltman (Partner)
George T. Conway III (Partner)

WACHTER MANAGEMENT COMPANY INC.
16001 W 99th St, Shawnee Mission, KS 66219
Tel.: (913) 541-2500
Web Site: http://www.wachter.com
Sales Range: $200-249.9 Million
Emp.: 1,040
General Electrical Contractor
N.A.I.C.S.: 561110
Brad Botteron (Pres)

WACKERLI AUTO CENTER
1363 N Holmes Ave, Idaho Falls, ID 83401
Tel.: (208) 522-6060
Web Site: http://www.gowackerli.com
Sales Range: $50-74.9 Million

Emp.: 22
New & Used Car Dealers
N.A.I.C.S.: 441110
Steve Wackerli (Co-Owner, Pres & CEO)
Peggy Kennard (Office Mgr)
Paul Wareing (Principal, Gen Mgr & Co-Owner)
Carol Hodges (Mgr-Fin)
Shasta Howard (Bus Mgr)
Dalena Wareing (Mgr-HR)

WACO ASSOCIATES INC.
2546 General Armistead Ave, Norristown, PA 19403
Tel.: (610) 630-4800
Web Site: http://www.wacofilters.com
Year Founded: 1964
Sales Range: $25-49.9 Million
Emp.: 74
Filters, Industrial
N.A.I.C.S.: 423840
Jeff Rose (Pres & CEO)
Bob Cherry (CFO)
Judy Undercuffler (VP-Ops)
Linda Moyer (VP-Natl Accts)

Subsidiaries:

Waco Associates Inc. - San Diego Office (1)
7466 101 Ste C Carroll Rd, San Diego, CA 92121
Tel.: (858) 271-8111
Web Site: http://www.waco.com
Filters, Furnaces & Air Conditioning Equipment Mfr
N.A.I.C.S.: 333413

WACO OIL & GAS CO., INC.
1595 US Hwy 33 E, Glenville, WV 26351
Tel.: (304) 462-5741 WV
Year Founded: 1975
Sales Range: $10-24.9 Million
Crude Petroleum Mfr
N.A.I.C.S.: 211120
Kenneth L. Greenlief (VP)

WACO, INC.
5450 Lewis Rd, Sandston, VA 23150-1922
Tel.: (804) 222-8440 VA
Web Site: http://www.wacoinc.net
Year Founded: 1963
Sales Range: $50-74.9 Million
Emp.: 300
Industrial Piping Contractor
N.A.I.C.S.: 238220
Larry E. Battaile (VP-Valley Ops)
Harry Judy (VP-Demolition Div)
Rex H. Luzar (VP)
Louis W. Walker (VP-Piedmont Ops)
Tom Carswell (Treas & Sec)
Keith Matheson (VP-Tidewater Ops)
Ron Rost (VP-Mechanical Svcs)

WACONIA DODGE INC.
905 Strong Dr, Waconia, MN 55387-1198
Tel.: (952) 442-2010
Web Site:
   http://www.waconiadodgechrysler jeep.com
Sales Range: $10-24.9 Million
Emp.: 30
Car Whslr
N.A.I.C.S.: 441110
Heidi Strong (Gen Mgr)

WACONIA FARM SUPPLY
801 S Hwy 284, Waconia, MN 55387-4578
Tel.: (952) 442-2126
Web Site:
   http://www.waconiafarm.com
Year Founded: 1946
Sales Range: $10-24.9 Million

Emp.: 65
Farm Feed & Garden Supplies
N.A.I.C.S.: 424910
Geoff Lemke (Mgr-Credit)

WADDINGTON-RICHMAN, INC.
849 Route 40, Woodstown, NJ 08098
Tel.: (856) 769-0356
Sales Range: $25-49.9 Million
Ice Cream Mfr; Dairy Products Distr; Restaurant Owner & Operator
N.A.I.C.S.: 424430

WADE INC.
1505 Hwy 82 W, Greenwood, MS 38930
Tel.: (662) 453-6312
Web Site:
   http://www.wadeincorporated.com
Year Founded: 1909
Rev.: $16,700,000
Emp.: 150
Farm & Garden Machinery & Equipment Sales, Service & Distr
N.A.I.C.S.: 423820
William P. Litton (Pres)

Subsidiaries:

Wade Inc. (1)
645 N Gaines Hwy, Cleveland, MS 38730
Tel.: (662) 843-5321
Web Site: http://www.wadeincorporated.com
Sales Range: $25-49.9 Million
Emp.: 35
Farm & Garden Machinery & Equipment Sales, Service & Distr
N.A.I.C.S.: 423820

WADE MANUFACTURING COMPANY
US Hwy 74 E, Wadesboro, NC 28170
Tel.: (704) 694-2131
Rev.: $22,600,000
Emp.: 225
Cotton Broad Woven Goods
N.A.I.C.S.: 313210
Bernard M. Hodges (Pres)
Roger Fisher (Plant Mgr)

WADE PAPER CORPORATION
1141 Lake Cook Rd Ste H, Deerfield, IL 60015
Tel.: (847) 940-9777
Web Site: http://www.wadepaper.com
Rev.: $80,000,000
Emp.: 13
Printing Paper
N.A.I.C.S.: 424110
Kevin P. Wade (Founder & Pres)
Douglas Major (CFO)

WADE-CARY ENTERPRISES INC.
1029 Hammond St, Rocky Mount, NC 27803
Tel.: (252) 977-3221
Web Site:
   http://www.gardnerfoods.com
Sales Range: $10-24.9 Million
Emp.: 7
Fast-Food Restaurant, Chain
N.A.I.C.S.: 722513
Jay Gardner (Pres)
Gerry Gardner (CEO)

WADE-TRIM GROUP INC.
25251 Northline Rd, Taylor, MI 48180-4596
Tel.: (734) 947-9700 MI
Web Site: http://www.wadetrim.com
Year Founded: 1979
Sales Range: $25-49.9 Million
Emp.: 375
Provider of Engineering Consulting Services
N.A.I.C.S.: 541330

Kevin Roberts (Dir-IT)
David Anthony (Sr Project Mgr)
Christopher Haney (VP)
Andrew McCune (Pres & CEO)
David Dipietro (COO)
Ralph Picano (CFO)
Tim Orourke (CTO)
Tom Brzezinski (Chief Bus Dev Officer)

Subsidiaries:

Wade-Trim Associates Inc. (1)
25251 Northline Rd, Taylor, MI 48180-4596
Tel.: (734) 947-9700
Web Site: http://www.wade-trim.com
Sales Range: $25-49.9 Million
Emp.: 140
Provider of Engineering Services
N.A.I.C.S.: 541330
Linda Junod (Office Mgr)

Wade-Trim Inc. (1)
1 Tampa City Ctr 201 N Franklin St Ste 1350, Tampa, FL 33602 (100%)
Tel.: (813) 882-4373
Web Site: http://www.wadetrim.com
Sales Range: $1-9.9 Million
Emp.: 30
Engineeering Services
N.A.I.C.S.: 541330
Thomas Brzezinski (Chief Bus Dev Officer)
Thomas Wilson (Sr Project Mgr-Water Resources Market Segment)
John Pacifici (Sr Project Mgr-Water Resources Market Segment)
David DiPietro (COO)
Andrew McCune (Pres & CEO)
Tim O'Rourke (CTO)
Ralph Picano (CFO)

Wade-Trim Inc. (Michigan) (1)
3933 Monitor Rd, Bay City, MI 48706-9292
Tel.: (989) 686-3100
Web Site: http://www.wadetrim.com
Sales Range: $10-24.9 Million
Emp.: 60
Provider of Engineering Services
N.A.I.C.S.: 541330
Erich Smith (Office Mgr)

WADES FOODS, INC.
510 Roanoke St, Christiansburg, VA 24073
Tel.: (540) 382-4995
Web Site: http://www.wades-foods.com
Year Founded: 1925
Rev.: $11,186,233
Emp.: 85
Grocery Store Operator
N.A.I.C.S.: 445110
Lowell E. Wade (Pres)
Greg Wade (Dir-Adv)

WADHAMS ENTERPRISES INC.
369 Bostwick Rd, Phelps, NY 14532-9309
Tel.: (315) 789-8871 NY
Web Site: http://www.wadhams.com
Year Founded: 1950
Rev.: $35,000,000
Emp.: 500
Provider of Trucking Services
N.A.I.C.S.: 484110
Rick Wadhams (Treas, VP & Co-Owner)
Steve Wadhams (Co-Owner & Pres)
William Skinner (Controller)
Mark Stevenson (Mgr-ETW)

Subsidiaries:

ARG Trucking Corp (1)
369 Bostwick Rd, Phelps, NY 14532-9309
Tel.: (315) 789-8871
Web Site: http://www.wadhams.com
Sales Range: $25-49.9 Million
Provider of Trucking Services
N.A.I.C.S.: 484110
Steve Wadhams (Pres)

Earl T. Wadhams Inc. (1)

COMPANIES

369 Bostwick Rd, Phelps, NY
14532-9309 **(100%)**
Tel.: (315) 789-8871
Web Site: http://www.wadhams.com
Sales Range: $25-49.9 Million
Trucking Service
N.A.I.C.S.: 484110
Rick Wadhams (Pres)

Rist Transport Ltd. (1)
369 Bostwick Rd, Phelps, NY 14532-9309
Tel.: (315) 789-8871
Web Site: http://www.wadhams.com
Sales Range: $10-24.9 Million
Emp.: 60
Provider of Trucking Services
N.A.I.C.S.: 484110

Subsidiary (Domestic):

AMA Transportation Company,
Inc. (2)
28 Plank St, Billerica, MA 01821
Tel.: (978) 667-9133
Web Site: http://www.amatrans.com
Rev.: $2,416,000
Emp.: 16
General Freight Trucking Services
N.A.I.C.S.: 484121
Joseph Cappello (Mgr)

WADLEY-DONOVAN GROUP
101 Fieldcrest Ave, Edison, NJ 08837
Tel.: (732) 790-1300
Web Site: http://www.wadley-donovan.com
Sales Range: $1-9.9 Million
Emp.: 11
Administrative Management & General Management Consulting Service
N.A.I.C.S.: 541611
Dennis Donovan (Owner)
John Gutshaw (Founder)

Subsidiaries:

Wadley-Donovan GrowthTech
LLC (1)
150 Morris Ave Ste 203, Springfield, NJ
07081-1315
Tel.: (973) 379-7700
Web Site: http://www.wdgtech.com
Economic Development Advisor
N.A.I.C.S.: 523940
William A. Fredrick (Pres)

Wadley-Donovan-Gutshaw Consulting, LLC (1)
981 US Hwy 22 W Ste 100, Bridgewater,
NJ 08807
Tel.: (908) 864-5580
Web Site: http://www.wdgconsulting.com
Management Consulting Services
N.A.I.C.S.: 541611
Dennis J. Donovan (Principal)
K. John Gutshaw (Principal)
Katie S. Burdorf (Principal)

WADMAN CORPORATION
2920 S 925 W, Ogden, UT 84401-3800
Tel.: (801) 621-4185
Web Site: http://www.wadman.com
Year Founded: 1951
Sales Range: $75-99.9 Million
Emp.: 100
Nonresidential Construction Services
N.A.I.C.S.: 236220
Keith Buswell (VP-Bus Dev)
Dave Hogan (Pres)
Spencer Bradley (VP-Bus Dev)

WADSWORTH ATHENEUM MUSEUM OF ART
600 Main St, Hartford, CT 06106
Tel.: (860) 278-2670 CT
Web Site:
   http://www.thewadsworth.org
Year Founded: 1842
Sales Range: $1-9.9 Million
Emp.: 93
Art Museum
N.A.I.C.S.: 712110

Cindy J. Martinez (CFO)
Christine Engel (Chief HR Officer)
Amanda Young (Dir-Comm & Mktg)
Henry R. Martin (Pres)
Hy J. Schwartz (Sec & VP)

WADSWORTH OIL CO. OF CLANTON INC.
2201 Holiday Inn Dr, Clanton, AL
35046-6209
Tel.: (205) 755-4545
Year Founded: 1977
Sales Range: $10-24.9 Million
Emp.: 80
Gasoline Service Stations
N.A.I.C.S.: 457120
James D. Wadsworth (Pres)
Terry Carroll (Controller)

WAFFLE HOUSE, INCORPORATED
5986 Financial Dr, Norcross, GA
30071
Tel.: (770) 729-5700 GA
Web Site:
   http://www.wafflehouse.com
Year Founded: 1955
Sales Range: $75-99.9 Million
Emp.: 6,000
Short-Order Restaurants
N.A.I.C.S.: 722511
Will Mizell (VP)
Jon Waller (Gen Counsel)
Joe W. Rogers Jr. (Chm)

WAFRA INVESTMENT ADVISORY GROUP, INC.
345 Pk Ave 41st Fl, New York, NY
10154-0101
Tel.: (212) 515-7600
Web Site: http://www.wafra.com
Year Founded: 1985
Sales Range: $50-74.9 Million
Emp.: 70
Investment Manager
N.A.I.C.S.: 523940
Anthony G. Barbuto (CFO)
Mohamad W. Khouja (Chm & CEO)
Fawaz Al-Mubaraki (Chief Investment Officer & Exec VP-Alternative Investments)
Vincent Campagna (Chief Operating & Compliance Officer & Exec VP)
Paul Steinberger (Dir-Alternative Investment)
Peter Petrillo (Exec VP-Direct Equity)
Paul Mackin (Exec VP-Private Asset Mgmt)
Frank P. Lively (Exec VP-Real Estate)
P. Christopher Leary (Exec VP-Securities)
Russell J. Valdez (Mng Dir)
Jeanine MacFadyen (Sr VP & Controller)
Adel A. Alderbas (VP)
Edward Tsai (VP)
John K. Ames (VP)

Subsidiaries:

Wafra Partners LLC (1)
345 Park Ave 41st Fl, New York, NY 10154-0101
Tel.: (212) 515-7600
Web Site: http://www.wafrapartners.com
Sales Range: $25-49.9 Million
Emp.: 10
Private Equity Investor
N.A.I.C.S.: 523940
Peter Petrillo (Sr Mng Dir)
Michael D. Goodman (Mng Dir)
Eric Norfleet (Mng Dir)
Ryan T. Wierck (Mng Dir)
Rudy Karsan (CEO)
Ali Behbehani (Asst VP)
Alex Blair (Asst VP)

Jeffrey P. Gerson (Mng Dir)
Sam Green (Asst VP)
Andrew Thompson (Mng Dir)

Holding (Domestic):

Mitchell Gold & Bob Williams (2)
135 One Comfortable Pl, Taylorsville, NC
28681-6106
Tel.: (828) 492-4179
Web Site: http://www.mgbwhome.com
Sales Range: $100-124.9 Million
Upholstered Household Furniture & Design Mfr
N.A.I.C.S.: 337121
Mitchell Gold (Co-Founder & Chm)
Bob Williams (Co-Founder & Pres-Design)

Vulcan Engineering Co. (2)
1 Vulcan Dr Helena Industrial Pk, Helena,
AL 35080
Tel.: (205) 663-0732
Web Site: http://www.vulcangroup.com
Sales Range: $50-74.9 Million
Foundry Engineering, Manufacturing & Installation Services
N.A.I.C.S.: 333994
Chris Cooper (VP-Sls & Mktg)

WAFRA, INC.
345 Park Ave Fl 41, New York, NY
10154
Tel.: (212) 759-3700
Web Site: http://www.wafra.com
Year Founded: 1988
Sales Range: $1-9.9 Million
Emp.: 65
Investment Advice
N.A.I.C.S.: 523940
Anthony Barbuto (CFO)

WAGERS INC.
412 S 8th St, Boise, ID 83702-7105
Tel.: (208) 342-5505 ID
Web Site: http://www.idahospud.com
Year Founded: 1901
Candy Mfr & Whslr
N.A.I.C.S.: 424450
David Wagers (Owner & Pres)

WAGGENER EDSTROM
225 108th Ave NE Ste 600, Bellevue,
WA 98004-5737
Tel.: (425) 638-7000
Web Site:
   http://www.waggeneredstrom.com
Year Founded: 1983
Sales Range: $75-99.9 Million
Emp.: 766
Public Relations Agency
N.A.I.C.S.: 541820
Melissa Waggener Zorkin (Co-Founder, Pres & CEO)
Tiffany Cook (Exec VP-Consumer-North America)
Emily Benning (Dir-Social & Digital Strategies)
Matt Haynes (Exec VP-Integrated Svcs)
Kass Sells (Pres-North America)
Alan VanderMolen (Pres-Intl)
Corey Kalbfleisch (CFO)
Dawn Beauparlant (Chief Client Officer)
Kate Richmond (Chief Talent Officer)
Jennifer Granston Foster (COO-Global)
Katie Huang Shin (Exec VP-Client Dev)
Aaron Petras (Partner-Strategy & VP-Agency-Global)
Stephanie Marchesi (Pres-Health Sector & Eastern)
Seema Bhende (Sr VP-Social Innovation)
Marcus Sorour (VP-UK & Gen Mgr)

Subsidiaries:

Maloney & Fox (1)
89 5th Ave 4th Fl, New York, NY 10003

WAGIC INC

Tel.: (212) 243-2000
Sales Range: $10-24.9 Million
Emp.: 25
Public Relations Agency
N.A.I.C.S.: 541820

Waggener Edstrom (1)
Ste 200N 124 Mount Auburn St, Cambridge, MA 02138-5787
Tel.: (617) 576-5785
Emp.: 17
Public Relations Agency
N.A.I.C.S.: 541820

Waggener Edstrom (1)
750 3rd Ave 31th Fl, New York, NY 10017
Tel.: (212) 551-4800
Emp.: 25
Public Relations Agency
N.A.I.C.S.: 541820
John Baird (VP-Brand Strategy & Mktg)

Waggener Edstrom (1)
106 E 6th St Ste 750, Austin, TX 78701
Tel.: (512) 527-7000
Web Site: http://www.waggeneredstrom.com
Emp.: 25
Public Relations Agency
N.A.I.C.S.: 541820
Melissa Waggener Zorkin (Founder & CEO-Global)

Waggener Edstrom (1)
3 Centerpointe Dr Ste 300, Lake Oswego,
OR 97035
Tel.: (503) 443-7000
Emp.: 300
Public Relations Agency
N.A.I.C.S.: 541820
Rachel MacGillivray (Mgr-Acct)

Waggener Edstrom (1)
575 Market St, San Francisco, CA 94105
Tel.: (415) 547-7000
Web Site: http://www.waggeneredstrom.com
Emp.: 20
Public Relations Agency
N.A.I.C.S.: 541820
Melissa Waggener Zorkin (Founder & CEO-Global)

Waggener Edstrom (1)
Apartment 20-1801-2 SOHO No 8
Dongdaqiao Rd, Chaoyang District, Beijing,
China
Tel.: (86) 10 5900 1278
Web Site: http://www.waggeneredstrom.com
Emp.: 35
Advetising Agency
N.A.I.C.S.: 541810
Antoine Calendrier (VP)
Shefali Srinivas (Dir-Healthcare-Asia Pacific)
Christopher Millward (Gen Mgr)
Henry Wood (Head-Studio D-Asia Pacific)

Waggener Edstrom (1)
24/F SUP Tower 75-83 Kings Rd, HKSAR,
North Point, China (Hong Kong)
Tel.: (852) 2578 2823
Web Site: http://www.waggeneredstrom.com
Emp.: 50
Advetising Agency
N.A.I.C.S.: 541810
Cathleen Witter (Head-Healthcare Practice)
Penny Stevens (Pres)
Chris Marcolefas (CFO)
Debra Rosenthal (VP-Customer Svc)
Kris Davis (VP-Customer Svc)
Antoine Calendrier (Gen Mgr-China)
Emma Richards (Gen Mgr)

Waggener Edstrom (1)
3 Pickering St, #02-50 Mankin Row, China
Square Central, Singapore, 048660, Singapore
Tel.: (65) 6303 8466
Advetising Agency
N.A.I.C.S.: 541810
Matthew Lackie (Sr VP-Asia Pacific)
Carolyn Camoens (VP-Southeast Asia)

Waggener Edstrom GmbH (1)
Sandstrasse 33, 80335, Munich, Germany
Tel.: (49) 89 628175 0
Web Site: http://www.waggeneredstrom.com
Emp.: 12
Advetising Agency
N.A.I.C.S.: 541810

WAGIC INC

WAGIC INC

WAGIC Inc—(Continued)
16780 Lark Ave, Los Gatos, CA 95032
Tel.: (408) 399-5002
Web Site: http://www.wagic.com
Year Founded: 1985
Sales Range: $10-24.9 Million
Emp.: 25
Product Development & Logistics Services
N.A.I.C.S.: 541614
Ronald Johnson *(Pres)*
Kelly Kasper *(Dir-Corp Affairs)*
Tammy Cheney *(Dir-Acctg)*

WAGMAN COMPANIES, INC.
3290 N Susquehanna Trl, York, PA 17406
Tel.: (717) 764-8521
Web Site: http://www.wagman.com
Year Founded: 1982
Sales Range: $10-24.9 Million
Emp.: 385
Holding Company; Construction Services
N.A.I.C.S.: 551114
Rich Wagman *(Pres)*
Don Posey *(VP-Geotechnical Construction Svcs)*
Bill McCrudden *(Sr VP-HR)*
Wanda Turner *(Treas & Mgr)*

Subsidiaries:

G.A. & F.C. Wagman, Inc. (1)
3290 N Susquehanna Trl, York, PA 17406
Tel.: (717) 764-8521
Web Site: http://www.wagman.com
Sales Range: $10-24.9 Million
Emp.: 80
Bridge, Tunnel & Elevated Highway
N.A.I.C.S.: 237310
Greg Andricos *(Pres & COO)*

Subsidiary (Domestic):

Key Construction Inc. (2)
741 W 2nd St N, Wichita, KS 67203
Tel.: (316) 263-9515
Web Site: http://www.keyconstruction.com
Commercial & Office Building, New Construction
N.A.I.C.S.: 236220
David E. Wells *(Co-Founder & Pres)*
Ken Wells *(Co-Founder)*
Steven Hopper *(Project Mgr-Accts Div-Natl)*
Jennifer Evans *(CFO)*

Wagman Construction, Inc. (1)
3290 Susquehanna Trl N, York, PA 17406
Tel.: (717) 767-8289
Web Site: http://www.wagman.com
Sales Range: $1-9.9 Million
Emp.: 30
Construction of Industrial Buildings & Warehouses
N.A.I.C.S.: 236220
Michael Konieczka *(Pres & COO)*
Mike Glezer *(CEO)*
Mark Morrow *(Dir-Ops)*
James Weber *(Dir-Preconstruction)*

WAGNER & BROWN, LTD.
300 N Marienfeld St Ste 500, Midland, TX 79701-4334
Tel.: (432) 682-7936
Web Site: http://www.wbltd.com
Year Founded: 1962
Crude Petroleum & Natural Gas Production
N.A.I.C.S.: 324110
Lawrence Rhodes *(Controller)*
Gary Douglas *(Pres & Gen Counsel)*
Michelle Brown *(Mgr-Tax)*

WAGNER CADILLAC CO., LP.
4100 S Broadway Ave, Tyler, TX 75701-8719
Tel.: (903) 561-1212
Web Site: http://www.wagnercadillac.com
Sales Range: $10-24.9 Million
Emp.: 70
Car Whslr
N.A.I.C.S.: 441110
Scott Jordan *(Owner)*

WAGNER ENTERPRISES
1719 N 8th St, Paducah, KY 42001
Tel.: (270) 443-5361
Web Site: http://www.wagnerenterprises.com
Sales Range: $25-49.9 Million
Emp.: 60
Warehousing & Storage
N.A.I.C.S.: 493110
Bob Wagner *(Pres)*

WAGNER EQUIPMENT CO.
18000 Smith Rd, Aurora, CO 80011
Tel.: (303) 739-3000
Web Site: http://www.wagnerequipment.com
Year Founded: 1976
Rev.: $388,000,000
Emp.: 1,100
Retailer of Construction & Mining Machinery
N.A.I.C.S.: 423810
Joseph Wagner *(Chm)*
Vicki Sayre *(Mgr-Fin Svcs)*
Pat Dodd *(Mgr-Bus Solution)*
Steve Givigliano *(Acct Mgr)*
Eric Floodeen *(Bus Mgr-Rental Unit)*
Matt Connell *(Controller)*
Chris Cahal *(Gen Mgr)*
Larry Ragan *(Mgr-Mining Bus)*
Alex Roise *(Sr Mgr-Credit)*

WAGNER INDUSTRIES, INC.
1201 E 12th Ave, Kansas City, MO 64116
Tel.: (816) 421-3520
Web Site: http://www.wagnerlogistics.com
Year Founded: 1946
Sales Range: $100-124.9 Million
Emp.: 285
Integrated Logistics, Freight Transportation, Warehousing, Order Fulfillment & Packaging Services
N.A.I.C.S.: 488510
Kevin Service *(CFO)*
Mike Moon *(VP-HR)*
Alexis Consuegra *(Dir-Indus Engrg)*
Brian R. Smith *(CEO)*
Justin Eck *(Dir-Ops)*
Michelle Frazier *(Dir-Project Mgmt)*
Eric Orr *(Dir-Transportation)*
Joe Johnson *(VP-IT)*
Shawn Closser *(VP-Sls & Mktg)*
John E. Wagner Jr. *(Chief Customer Officer)*

WAGNER MOTORS
760 Boston Tpke, Shrewsbury, MA 01545-3202
Tel.: (508) 581-5600
Web Site: http://www.wagnermotors.com
Year Founded: 1964
Sales Range: $25-49.9 Million
Emp.: 90
New Car Dealers
N.A.I.C.S.: 441110
Brad Macomber *(Gen Mgr)*

WAGNER OIL CO. INC.
709 S Superior St, Antigo, WI 54409
Tel.: (715) 623-5386
Web Site: http://www.wagner-oil.com
Year Founded: 1948
Sales Range: $10-24.9 Million
Emp.: 55
Petroleum Bulk Stations & Terminals
N.A.I.C.S.: 424710
Bob Kapitz *(CFO)*

WAGNER POOLS
750 Wordin Ave, Darien, CT 06820
Tel.: (203) 335-3960
Web Site: http://www.wagnerswimmingpools.com
Year Founded: 1919
Sales Range: $75-99.9 Million
Emp.: 110
Construction & Retailer of Swimming Pools, Landscaping & Lighting
N.A.I.C.S.: 238990
Pedro Miguel *(Mgr-Warehouse)*
J.G. Gedney Jr. *(Pres)*

WAGNER REALTY
3639 Cortez Rd W Ste 200, Bradenton, FL 34210
Tel.: (941) 727-2800
Web Site: http://www.wagnerrealty.com
Year Founded: 1939
Sales Range: $25-49.9 Million
Emp.: 200
Real Estate Broker
N.A.I.C.S.: 531210
David Eckel *(Owner & Pres)*
Polly Gaar *(VP)*
Ron Cornette *(Dir-Mktg & Trng)*

WAGNER'S LLC
366 N Broadway, Jericho, NY 11753
Tel.: (516) 933-6580
Web Site: http://www.wagners.com
Year Founded: 1957
Sales Range: $25-49.9 Million
Emp.: 210
Wild Bird & Pet Food
N.A.I.C.S.: 424910
Harry Tyre *(Pres)*

Subsidiaries:

Shafer Seed Company, Inc. (1)
109 S Fourth St, Oakes, ND 58474-1603
Tel.: (701) 742-2144
Web Site: http://www.shaferseed.com
Sales Range: $10-24.9 Million
Emp.: 15
Bird Feed Product Mfr & Distr
N.A.I.C.S.: 311119

Wagner's LLC (1)
16 E 4th St, Flagler, CO 80815
Tel.: (719) 765-4402
Sales Range: $10-24.9 Million
Emp.: 35
Wild Bird & Pet Food
N.A.I.C.S.: 424910
Pat Edwards *(Gen Mgr)*

WAGSTAFF INC.
3910 N Flora Rd, Spokane, WA 99216
Tel.: (509) 922-1404
Web Site: http://www.wagstaff.com
Year Founded: 1946
Sales Range: $150-199.9 Million
Emp.: 350
Develops, Engineers, Designs & Manufactures Molds, Casting Machines, Automated Systems & Ancillary Equipment for Aluminum Producers
N.A.I.C.S.: 333248
Ken Parkes *(Pres)*
Mike Anderson *(VP-Res & Product Dev)*
Mike Wagstaff *(CEO-Northern Kentucky Ops)*
Mike Megaard *(Sec)*
Gary Grealy *(Mgr-Technical Svc)*
Kevin Person *(CEO)*
John Blackburn *(Project Mgr)*
Jack White *(Mgr-Applications-Engrg)*
Olivier Gabis *(Mgr-Eastern USA & Canada)*
Tyler Robbins *(CFO)*
Ryan Faulkner *(Engr-Mechanical)*

U.S. PRIVATE

WAGUESPACK OIL CO. INC.
1818 Hwy 3185, Thibodaux, LA 70301
Tel.: (985) 447-3668
Web Site: http://www.wagoil.com
Sales Range: $10-24.9 Million
Emp.: 10
Petroleum Brokers
N.A.I.C.S.: 424720
Monica Aleman *(Office Mgr)*

WAHL CLIPPER CORPORATION
2900 Locust St, Sterling, IL 61081-0578
Tel.: (815) 625-6525
Web Site: http://www.wahlclipper.com
Year Founded: 1919
Sales Range: $350-399.9 Million
Emp.: 2,000
Hair Clippers, Beard & Mustache Trimmers, Cordless Soldering Irons, Shavers & Massagers Mfr
N.A.I.C.S.: 339999
Gregory S. Wahl *(Pres)*
Bill Dempsey *(HR Dir)*
Steven Yde *(VP-Div)*
Patricia J. Schmeda *(CIO-Global)*

WAHL REFRACTORY SOLUTIONS, LLC
767 S State Rte 19, Fremont, OH 43420
Tel.: (419) 334-2658
Web Site: http://www.wahlref.com
Sales Range: $10-24.9 Million
Emp.: 60
Clay Refractories
N.A.I.C.S.: 327120
Steve Cherico *(Pres)*

WAIANAE DISTRICT COMPREHENSIVE HEALTH & HOSPITAL BOARD, INCORPORATED
86-260 Farr Hwy, Waianae, HI 96792
Tel.: (808) 697-3300
Web Site: http://www.wcchc.com
Year Founded: 1972
Sales Range: $50-74.9 Million
Emp.: 610
Health Care Services Organization
N.A.I.C.S.: 813920
Richard P. Bettini *(Pres & CEO)*
Stephen P. Bradley *(Dir-Medical)*
Vija M. Sehgal *(Assoc Dir-Medical)*
Robert Thomas Bonham *(Dir-Emergent Care)*

WAIKEM, GEORGE FORD, INC.
4321 Lincoln Way E, Massillon, OH 44646
Tel.: (330) 478-1801
Web Site: http://www.georgewaikemford.com
Sales Range: $50-74.9 Million
Emp.: 80
Car Whslr
N.A.I.C.S.: 441110
David Waikem *(Owner)*
Chip Waikem *(Pres)*

WAITE SPECIALTY MACHINE, INC.
1356 Tennant Way, Longview, WA 98632
Tel.: (360) 577-0777
Web Site: http://www.waitespecialty.com
Year Founded: 1961
Rev.: $20,400,000
Emp.: 70
Fabrication Services
N.A.I.C.S.: 238390
Steve Waite *(Pres & Project Mgr)*

COMPANIES

WAITEX INTERNATIONAL CO. LTD
135 W 36th St, New York, NY 10018
Tel.: (212) 967-8100
Web Site: http://www.waitex.com
Emp.: 300
General Warehousing & Storage
N.A.I.C.S.: 493110
Howard Li (Chm & CEO)

WAITTCORP LLC
1125 S 103rd St Ste 425, Omaha, NE 68124
Tel.: (402) 697-8000
Web Site: http://www.waittcompany.com
Sales Range: $25-49.9 Million
Emp.: 8
Holding Company Investment Services
N.A.I.C.S.: 551112

WAKAZURU ENTERPRISES INC.
19705 Viking Ave NE, Poulsbo, WA 98370-8351
Tel.: (360) 697-4445
Web Site: http://www.poulsborv.com
Year Founded: 1986
Rev.: $10,000,000
Emp.: 275
Recreational Vehicle Sales
N.A.I.C.S.: 441210
Ken Wakazuru (Owner & Pres)
Rick Wakazuru (Sec)

WAKE COUNTY MEDICAL SOCIETY
2500 Blue Ridge Rd Ste 330, Raleigh, NC 27607
Tel.: (919) 792-3623
Web Site: http://www.wakedocs.org
Year Founded: 2000
Sales Range: $10-24.9 Million
Emp.: 101
Health Care Srvices
N.A.I.C.S.: 622110
Paul Harrison (Exec Dir)
Susan L. Davis (Exec Dir)
Pam Carpenter (Mgr-Membership & Program Mgr-Project Access)
Andrew Wu (Pres)
Robert Munt (Treas & Dir-Fin)

WAKE COUNTY SMARTSTART, INC.
4901 Waters Edge Dr Ste 101, Raleigh, NC 27606
Tel.: (919) 851-9550
Web Site: http://www.wakesmartstart.org
Year Founded: 1993
Child Day Care Services
N.A.I.C.S.: 624410
Gary Carr (Dir-Fin)
Phyllis Barbour (Dir-Community Rels)
Pamela Dowdy (Exec Dir)
Melinda Schlesinger (Mgr-Evaluation)
Angie Welsh (Chm)
Barbara Morales Burke (Vice Chm)
Anna Troutman (Dir-Programs)
Debi Bartholomew (Mgr-Pre-Kindergarten)
Carol Orji (Mgr-Early Childhood Initiatives)
Liz Hamner (Sec)

WAKE STONE CORPORATION
6821 Hwy 64 E, Knightdale, NC 27545
Tel.: (919) 266-1100
Web Site: http://www.wakestonecorp.com
Year Founded: 1970
Sales Range: $25-49.9 Million
Emp.: 135

Mfr of Crushed Stone & Broken Granite
N.A.I.C.S.: 212313
Pete Mangum (Controller)
Roland Massey (Dir-Safety & Health)
Seth Miedema (Dir-Construction Engrg)
Sam Bratton (Pres)
Bill Crook (VP-Ops)
Holt Browning (VP-Construction)
Steve Petty (Office Mgr)
Thomas B. Oxholm (VP-Fin & Admin)
Jared Miedema (Dir-Mine Engrg & IT)
John Bratton Jr. (Chm)

WAKE SUPPLY CO. INC.
658 Maywood Ave A, Raleigh, NC 27603
Tel.: (919) 828-0965
Web Site: http://www.wakesupply.com
Rev.: $11,037,557
Emp.: 11
Roofing, Siding & Insulation & Windows
N.A.I.C.S.: 423330
J. C. Downing (Owner)
Stephen Trent (COO)

WAKEFIELD MUNICIPAL GAS LIGHT DEPARTMENT
9 Albion St, Wakefield, MA 01880
Tel.: (781) 246-6363
Web Site: http://www.wmgld.com
Sales Range: $10-24.9 Million
Emp.: 40
Distribution of Electric Power
N.A.I.C.S.: 221122
Eugene J. Sullivan (Asst Mgr)
Peter D. Dion (Gen Mgr)
Frank White (Mgr-Bus Div)

WAKEFERN FOOD CORPORATION
5000 Riverside Dr, Keasbey, NJ 08832
Tel.: (908) 527-3300
Web Site: http://www2.wakefern.com
Year Founded: 1948
Sales Range: $5-14.9 Billion
Emp.: 70,000
Largest Retailer-Owned Grocery & Non-Food Cooperative
N.A.I.C.S.: 424410
Joseph Sheridan (Pres & COO)
Cheryl Williams (CIO & VP-CISD Div)
Ann Burke (VP-HR)
Bill Mayo (Sr VP-Logistics & Tech)
Chris Lane (Exec VP)
Jeff Reagan (Sr VP-Retail Mktg)
Karen Meleta (VP-Consumer & Corp Comm)
Thomas S. Cummiskey (VP-Bus Dev & Real Estate)
Dan Tarnopol (VP-Real Estate, Site Dev & Member Svcs)
Erik Keptner (Sr VP-Mktg)
Bryant Harris (Chief Mdsg Officer)
Steve Henig (Chief Customer Officer)
Laura Kind (VP-Brand Strategy)
Ranjana Choudhry (VP-Adv & Social Media)
Nazesh Cattelona (Dir-Diversity & Inclusion)
Nicole Gasaway (Chief HR Officer)
Kevin McDonnell (Pres-Price Rite Marketplace)
Erik Keptner (Sr VP-Mktg)

Subsidiaries:

National Transport Services Co. (1)
600 York St, Elizabeth, NJ 07207
Tel.: (908) 527-3300
Web Site: http://www.wakefern.com

Sales Range: $100-124.9 Million
Emp.: 1,000
Distribution of Groceries
N.A.I.C.S.: 484121

ShopRite Beverages, Inc. (1)
5000 Riverside Dr, Keasbey, NJ 08832
Tel.: (908) 527-3300
Web Site: http://www.wakefern.com
Sales Range: $350-399.9 Million
Emp.: 2,500
Wholesale Groceries
N.A.I.C.S.: 424410

ShopRite Supermarkets, Inc. (1)
244 Raritan Ctr Pkwy, Edison, NJ 08837
Tel.: (908) 527-3300
Web Site: http://www.wakefern.com
Sales Range: $25-49.9 Million
Emp.: 100
Supermarket
N.A.I.C.S.: 445110
Joseph Colalillo (Pres)

ShopRite Supermarkets, Inc. (1)
176 N Main St, Florida, NY 10921-1021
Tel.: (845) 651-4411
Sales Range: $25-49.9 Million
Emp.: 150
Supermarket Chain Operator
N.A.I.C.S.: 445110
Mike Dybas (Mgr-Mdse)
Brett Wing (Pres)

WAKEFIELD & ASSOCIATES, LLC
3033 S Parker Rd Ste 1010, Aurora, CO 80701
Tel.: (800) 221-5431
Web Site: https://www.wakeassoc.com
Year Founded: 1946
Financial Services
N.A.I.C.S.: 561440
Chuck Koch (CIO)
Matt Laws (Pres & CEO)
Chuck Koch (CIO)

Subsidiaries:

Choice Recovery, Inc. (1)
1550 Old Henderson Rd Ste S100, Columbus, OH 43220-3662
Web Site: http://www.choicerecovery.com
Collection Agencies
N.A.I.C.S.: 561440
Chad Silverstein (Pres)

WAKEFIELD DISTRIBUTION SYSTEMS
4 First Ave, Peabody, MA 01923
Tel.: (978) 777-5630
Web Site: http://www.wakefielddistribution.com
Year Founded: 1959
Rev.: $21,709,589
Emp.: 175
Local Trucking with Storage
N.A.I.C.S.: 484110
John M. Lucey (Pres)

WAKEFIELDS INC.
1212 Quintard Ave, Anniston, AL 36201
Tel.: (256) 237-9521
Web Site: http://www.wakefields.com
Sales Range: $50-74.9 Million
Emp.: 75
Family Clothing Stores
N.A.I.C.S.: 458110
Bill Wakefield (Pres)
Mike Dowd (Mgr-IT)

WAKEFLY
1800 W Park Dr Ste 100, Westborough, MA 01581
Tel.: (508) 616-2042
Web Site: http://www.wakefly.com
Year Founded: 2002
Sales Range: $1-9.9 Million
Emp.: 24
Online Marketing Services

N.A.I.C.S.: 541810
Dean Dorazio (CEO)
Justin Perry (Dir-Client Svcs)
Tim Hawkins (Creative Dir)

WAKEMED
3000 New Bern Ave, Raleigh, NC 27610
Tel.: (919) 350-8000
Web Site: http://www.wakemed.org
Year Founded: 1965
Sales Range: $900-999.9 Million
Emp.: 9,351
Health Care Srvices
N.A.I.C.S.: 622110
John Piatkowski (Sr VP-Physician Svcs)
Rebecca E. Andrews (VP-Health Info & Utilization Mgmt)
Donald R. Gintzig (Pres & CEO)

WAL-BON OF OHIO, INC.
PO Box 508, Belpre, OH 45714
Tel.: (740) 423-6351
Sales Range: $25-49.9 Million
Emp.: 250
Bakery Products Mfr
N.A.I.C.S.: 311812
William D. Waldeck (Chm & CEO)
Neil Hinton (Mgr)

WALBON AND COMPANY INC.
4230 Pine Bend Trl, Rosemount, MN 55068
Tel.: (651) 437-2011
Web Site: http://www.walbon.com
Sales Range: $10-24.9 Million
Emp.: 120
Provider of Transportation Services
N.A.I.C.S.: 484121
Darby Walbon (Pres)

WALBRIDGE ALDINGER LLC
777 Woodward Ave Ste 300, Detroit, MI 48226
Tel.: (313) 963-8000
Web Site: https://www.walbridge.com
Year Founded: 1916
Sales Range: $200-249.9 Million
Emp.: 1,500
Commercial & Institutional Building Construction
N.A.I.C.S.: 236220
Michael R. Haller (Pres)
Terry Merritt (Sr VP)
Richard Marshall (VP & Reg Mgr)
John Rakolta Jr. (Chm)
Mary Layton (Mgr-Bus Dev)
Genevieve O'Hara (Mgr-Bus Dev)
Mark McClelland (VP-New Bus Dev)
Dave Robson (VP-New Bus Dev-Detroit)

WALBROOK MILL & LUMBER CO. INC.
2630-48 W N Ave, Baltimore, MD 21216
Tel.: (410) 462-2200
Web Site: http://www.walbrooklumber.com
Year Founded: 1942
Sales Range: $10-24.9 Million
Emp.: 89
Lumber, Plywood & Millwork Whslr
N.A.I.C.S.: 423310
Elliot Zulver (Pres)

WALDEN ENERGY, LLC.
111 W 5th St Ste 1000, Tulsa, OK 74103-4264
Tel.: (918) 488-8663
Web Site: http://www.waldenenergy.com
Year Founded: 2003
Sales Range: $10-24.9 Million
Emp.: 6

WALDEN ENERGY, LLC.

U.S. PRIVATE

Walden Energy, LLC.—(Continued)
Natural & Electricity Provider
N.A.I.C.S.: 211120
Walden J. Tamara (Pres)
Larry David (VP)

WALDEN SAVINGS BANKS
CrossRds Corporate Park 15 Scott's Corners Dr, Montgomery, NY 12549
Tel.: (845) 457-7700 NY
Web Site: http://www.waldensavingsbank.com
Year Founded: 1872
Sales Range: $10-24.9 Million
Emp.: 100
Provider of Banking Services
N.A.I.C.S.: 522180
Gloria Kozlowski (Asst VP)
Lois E. Bartholomew (Asst Treas)
Lisa Gariolo (VP)

WALDEN SECURITY COMPANY
694 Manufacturers Rd, Chattanooga, TN 37405
Tel.: (423) 267-6724
Web Site: http://www.waldensecurity.com
Sales Range: $75-99.9 Million
Emp.: 3,000
Security Guard Services
N.A.I.C.S.: 561613
Michael S. Walden (Pres)
Amy S. Walden (Chm & CEO)
Curtis Casey (CFO & Sr VP)
Lauren S. Tudor (Exec VP-Sls & Mktg/Learning & Dev)
Dick Wong (VP-Federal Svcs)
Jeremy Flemmons (Mgr-Bus Dev-Chattanooga & Alabama Markets)
Adrian Peters (Mgr-Bus Dev-South Carolina)

WALDEN VENTURE CAPITAL
750 Battery St Ste 700, San Francisco, CA 94111
Tel.: (415) 391-7225
Web Site: http://www.waldenvc.com
Year Founded: 1974
Emp.: 50
Digital Media, Internet Commerce & Technology-Enabled Services Venture Capital Investment Firm
N.A.I.C.S.: 523999
Art Berliner (Mng Dir)
Larry Marcus (Mng Dir)
Matt Miller (Mng Dir)
George Sarlo (Partner)
Robert Raynard (CFO)
Bill McDonagh (Partner)
Drew Marcus (Partner)

WALDO BROS. COMPANY
202 Southampton St, Boston, MA 02118-2716
Tel.: (617) 445-3000
Web Site: http://www.waldobros.com
Year Founded: 1869
Sales Range: $25-49.9 Million
Emp.: 40
Marketing of a General Line of Building Materials
N.A.I.C.S.: 444180
Patti Loveday (Controller)
Brenda Colgan (Pres)
Mike Dacey (Mgr-Sls)

Subsidiaries:
Waldo Bros. Company (1)
1390 John Fitch Blvd, South Windsor, CT 06074-1017
Tel.: (860) 289-9500
Web Site: http://www.waldo.com
Sales Range: $10-24.9 Million
Emp.: 10
Marketing of a General Line of Building Materials
N.A.I.C.S.: 423320

WALDORF FORD INC.
2440 Crain Hwy, Waldorf, MD 20601
Tel.: (301) 843-2400
Web Site: http://www.waldorfford.com
Sales Range: $50-74.9 Million
Emp.: 145
Car Dealership Owner & Operator
N.A.I.C.S.: 441110
Adam Rinaldi (Mgr-New Sls)
Jim Cantor (Mgr-Used Sls)
Jason Moore (Mgr-Used Sls)
Faruq Demesme (Mgr-Fin)
Sam Reed (Mgr-Used Car Inventory)
Jelani Samuel-Hall (Mgr-Fin)
Phil Thomas (Dir-Fin)
Marsha Johns (Mgr-Fin)
Troy Price (Mgr-Fin)
Reggie Rainey (Mgr-Fin)
Kaitlyn Campbell (Mgr-Internet)
Jim Burd (Mgr-Parts)

WALDRON & COMPANY
101 Stewart St Ste 1200, Seattle, WA 98101
Tel.: (206) 441-4144 WA
Web Site: http://www.waldronhr.com
Year Founded: 1981
Sales Range: $1-9.9 Million
Emp.: 38
Human Resource Consulting Services
N.A.I.C.S.: 541612
Kevin Osborne (VP-Client Svcs)
Yvonne Pommerville (Mng Dir-Phoenix)
Mike Humphries (CEO)
Kim Bohr (Pres & COO)

WALDROP CONSTRUCTION CO. INC.
3208 4th St, Brownwood, TX 76801-6506
Tel.: (325) 646-2529
Web Site: http://www.waldropconstruction.com
Year Founded: 1946
Sales Range: $25-49.9 Million
Emp.: 85
Commercial & Institutional Building Construction Services
N.A.I.C.S.: 236220
Paul Waldrop Jr. (Pres)

WALKER & ASSOCIATES, INC.
7129 Old Hwy 52 N, Welcome, NC 27374
Tel.: (336) 731-6391 NC
Web Site: http://www.walkerfirst.com
Year Founded: 1970
Sales Range: $75-99.9 Million
Emp.: 130
Distr of Telephone & Telecommunications Products
N.A.I.C.S.: 423690
Doug Leckie (CFO & VP-Corp Dev)
Jane Brightwell (VP-Federal & Intl-RBOC Sls)
Tom Kane (VP-Comml Sls)
Lisa Smiley (Dir-Enterprise)
Hal Sveum (VP-Ops)
Chrystie Walker Brown (Chm & CEO)
Mark Walker (Pres)
Trey Hall (VP-Mktg & Tech)

WALKER & ASSOCIATES, INC.
5100 Poplar Ave Ste 2812, Memphis, TN 38137
Tel.: (901) 522-1100 TN
Web Site: http://www.walker-assoc.com
Year Founded: 1965
Sales Range: Less than $1 Million
Emp.: 12
Advetising Agency
N.A.I.C.S.: 541810
Ceil T. Walker-Norris (CEO)
Deborah Harrison (Mgr-Bus Dev)
Andy Windham (COO)
Jeff White (Sr Dir-Art)
Glen Childs (Dir-Pub Rels)
Ceil Walker Norris (CEO)

WALKER & COMPANY, INC.
931 N Pennsylvania Ave, Winter Park, FL 32789
Tel.: (407) 645-0500
Web Site: http://www.walkercc.com
Year Founded: 1974
Sales Range: $1-9.9 Million
Emp.: 50
Construction Services
N.A.I.C.S.: 236220
Joe Fisher (VP)
Alan Fredrickson (VP)
Tristan Walker (Founder & CEO)
R. Lance Walker Jr. (Pres)

WALKER & LABERGE COMPANY INCORPORATED
7613 Sewells Point Rd, Norfolk, VA 23513
Tel.: (757) 587-8701
Web Site: http://www.walkerlaberge.com
Sales Range: $10-24.9 Million
Emp.: 85
Glass & Glazing Work
N.A.I.C.S.: 238150

WALKER & ZANGER, INC.
8901 Bradley Ave, Sun Valley, CA 91352
Tel.: (818) 256-1500 NY
Web Site: http://www.walkerzanger.com
Year Founded: 1952
Sales Range: $100-124.9 Million
Emp.: 300
Marble, Granite, Soapstone, Limestone, Slate, Onyx, Quartzite, Agglomerates & Ceramic Tile Distr
N.A.I.C.S.: 423320
Leon Zanger (Founder & CEO)
Jonathan A. Zanger (Pres)

Subsidiaries:
Excellence in Stone, Inc. (1)
1654 NW 108th Ave, Miami, FL 33172 (33%)
Tel.: (305) 716-2827
Sales Range: $10-24.9 Million
Emp.: 20
Installer of Tile & Stone Products
N.A.I.C.S.: 238340

Walker & Zanger Stoneworks (1)
6850 Lyons Technology Cir, Coconut Creek, FL 33073-3634
Tel.: (954) 418-6000
Web Site: http://www.walkerzanger.com
Sales Range: $25-49.9 Million
Emp.: 20
Marble, Granite, Slate, Limestone, Ceramic Tile & Related Building Materials Contractor
N.A.I.C.S.: 238140

Walker & Zanger, Inc - Mount Vernon (1)
36 Midland Ave, Port Chester, NY 10573 (100%)
Tel.: (914) 934-4600
Web Site: http://www.walkerzanger.com
Sales Range: $25-49.9 Million
Emp.: 35
Stone Tiles & Slabs
N.A.I.C.S.: 423320
Jonathan A. Zanger (Pres)
Pat Petrocelli (CFO)
Behrad Karbassi (Mgr-Pur)
Jared Becker (Mgr-Mktg)

WALKER ADVERTISING, INC.
1010 S Cabrillo Ave, San Pedro, CA 90731-4067
Tel.: (310) 519-4050 CA
Web Site: http://www.walkeradvertising.com
Year Founded: 1984
Rev.: $11,500,000
Emp.: 45
N.A.I.C.S.: 541810
Mary Ann Walker (Founder & CEO)
Nereida Casarez (VP-Media)
Mary Lou Potter (Sr Acct Exec)
Connie Romo (Mgr-Customer Svc)

WALKER AUTO GROUP, INC.
8457 Springboro Pike, Miamisburg, OH 45342
Tel.: (937) 433-4950
Web Site: http://www.walkerautogroup.com
Year Founded: 1980
Sales Range: $25-49.9 Million
Emp.: 95
Car Whslr
N.A.I.C.S.: 441110
Kevin Newton (Gen Mgr)
John Walker (Owner)

WALKER AUTOMOTIVE
1616 MacArthur Dr, Alexandria, LA 71301
Tel.: (318) 445-6421
Web Site: http://www.walkerautomotive.com
Sales Range: $25-49.9 Million
Emp.: 300
New & Used Car Dealers Service & Parts
N.A.I.C.S.: 441110
Foster Walker III (Owner)

WALKER AUTOMOTIVE SUPPLY INC.
705 E Six Forks Rd, Raleigh, NC 27609
Tel.: (919) 833-8955
Web Site: http://www.walkerautostores.com
Sales Range: $10-24.9 Million
Emp.: 50
Automotive Supplies & Parts
N.A.I.C.S.: 423120
Dan Walker (Pres)
Lee Walker (Dir-Pur)
Harry G. Walker Jr. (Chm)

WALKER COMPONENT GROUP INC.
1795 E 66th Ave, Denver, CO 80229
Tel.: (303) 292-5537 CO
Web Site: http://www.walkercomponent.com
Year Founded: 1975
Sales Range: $25-49.9 Million
Emp.: 125
Electronic Parts & Equipment
N.A.I.C.S.: 423690
Craig J. Walker (Pres)

WALKER CONCRETE COMPANY INC.
220 Corporate Center Dr Ste D, Stockbridge, GA 30281
Tel.: (770) 506-7125
Web Site: http://www.walkerconcrete.com
Sales Range: $10-24.9 Million
Emp.: 95
Provider of Ready-Mixed Concrete Services
N.A.I.C.S.: 327320
Joe Dixon (Pres)
Danny Lowe (Plant Mgr)
Mark Orler (Gen Mgr-Sls)
Chad Burg (Plant Mgr)

WALKER CONTRACTING GROUP INC.
3074 Horseshoe Dr N, Naples, FL 34104
Tel.: (239) 263-7500
Web Site:
http://www.walkercontractinggroup.com
Year Founded: 2001
Sales Range: $10-24.9 Million
Emp.: 50
Poured Concrete Foundation & Structure Contractor
N.A.I.C.S.: 238110
Michael K. Walker *(Founder & Pres)*
William Golden *(VP)*
Beth Mixter *(Exec VP-Fin)*
Jason Swanson *(Dir-Ops)*
Will North *(Mgr-Construction)*
Steve Bauer *(Sr Project Mgr)*

WALKER COUNTY HOSPITAL CORPORATION
110 Memorial Hospital Dr, Huntsville, TX 77340-4362
Tel.: (936) 291-3411
Web Site:
http://www.huntsvillememorial.com
Year Founded: 2005
Sales Range: $75-99.9 Million
Emp.: 740
Health Care Srvices
N.A.I.C.S.: 622110
Sheila Ard *(Chief Nursing Officer)*
Guy Gros *(CFO)*
Shannon Brown *(CEO)*

WALKER DESIGN GROUP, INC.
1810 W Kennedy Blvd, Tampa, FL 33606
Tel.: (813) 875-3322
Web Site:
http://www.walkerbrands.com
Year Founded: 1992
Sales Range: $1-9.9 Million
Emp.: 8
Graphic Design & Branding Services
N.A.I.C.S.: 541430
Nancy Walker *(Pres)*

WALKER ENGINEERING, INC.
1505 W Walnut Hill Ln, Irving, TX 75038
Tel.: (817) 540-7777
Web Site: http://www.walkertx.com
Sales Range: $250-299.9 Million
Emp.: 900
Electrical Contractor
N.A.I.C.S.: 238210
Brent Walker *(VP-Houston Div)*

WALKER FORD CO., INC.
17556 US 19 N, Clearwater, FL 33764
Tel.: (727) 535-3673
Web Site: http://www.walkerford.com
Year Founded: 1957
Sales Range: $50-74.9 Million
Emp.: 120
Car Dealership
N.A.I.C.S.: 441110
Ivey Thigpen *(Gen Mgr-Sls)*
Bill Gordon *(Mgr-Sls & Leasing)*
Kevin Jewel *(Mgr-New Car Internet Sls)*
Bill Merkel *(Mgr-Pre-Owned Sls)*
Vince Romano *(Mgr-Svc)*
Tracy Affrunti *(Mgr-Sls & Leasing)*
George Parker *(Mgr-Pre-Owned Sls)*
Russ Caron *(Mgr-Parts)*
Denise Newman *(Mgr-Accessories)*
Dave Weaver *(Mgr-Collision Center)*
Mickey Alperstein *(Mgr-Fin)*
Brett Hughes *(Mgr-Fin)*
Harry Rumberger *(Mgr-Fin)*
Randy Mason *(Mgr-Inventory)*
Jason Gillespie *(Mgr-Pre-Owned Internet)*
Jay Wright *(Mgr-Pre-Owned Internet)*
Gregg Ledbetter *(Mgr-Sls & Leasing)*
Don Dithmer Sr. *(Mgr-Comml Sls)*

WALKER FORGE INC.
222 E Erie St Ste 300, Milwaukee, WI 53202
Tel.: (262) 554-2929
Web Site:
http://www.walkerforge.com
Year Founded: 1950
Sales Range: $10-24.9 Million
Emp.: 10
Mfr of Iron & Steel Forgings
N.A.I.C.S.: 332111
Robert Swanson *(CFO)*
Mike Gray *(VP-Sls & Mktg)*

WALKER FURNITURE CO.
301 S Martin Luther King Blvd, Las Vegas, NV 89106-4310
Tel.: (702) 384-9300
Web Site:
http://www.walkerfurniture.com
Sales Range: $200-249.9 Million
Emp.: 400
Furniture Retailer
N.A.I.C.S.: 449110
Larry Alterwitz *(Chm)*
Patti Gerace *(VP-Mktg)*
Cathy Daniell *(VP-Sls)*
Lee Goodman *(CEO)*
Mike Cohen *(Pres)*

WALKER INFORMATION INC.
301 Pennsylvania Pkwy, Indianapolis, IN 46280
Tel.: (317) 843-3939
Web Site: http://www.walkerinfo.com
Year Founded: 1939
Sales Range: $25-49.9 Million
Emp.: 150
Market Research Services
N.A.I.C.S.: 541910
Steven F. Walker *(Chm, CEO & Principal)*
Phillip A. Bounsall *(Pres)*
Jennifer Batley *(Sr VP)*
Sean Clayton *(Sr VP-Consulting Svc & Mgr-Strategic Acct)*
Patrick Gibbons *(Sr VP)*
Allison Grayson *(VP)*
Noah Grayson *(Sr VP)*
Brian Kovacs *(CIO & Sr VP)*
Sonya McAllister *(Sr VP & Mgr-Consulting Svcs Strategic Acct)*
Randy Shoemaker *(COO & Exec VP)*

WALKER MOTOR CO.
11800 Santa Monica Blvd, Los Angeles, CA 90025
Tel.: (310) 820-2631
Web Site: http://www.buerge.com
Rev.: $102,154,568
Emp.: 200
Automobiles, New & Used
N.A.I.C.S.: 441110
Jim Buerge *(Gen Mgr)*

WALKER OLDSMOBILE COMPANY, INC.
PO Box 12250, Alexandria, LA 71301
Tel.: (318) 445-6421
Web Site:
http://www.walkerautomotive.com
Year Founded: 1919
Sales Range: $75-99.9 Million
Emp.: 300
New Car Dealers
N.A.I.C.S.: 441110
Foster Walker *(Owner)*

WALKER PARKING CONSUL-
TANTS & ENGINEERS, INC.
505 Davis Rd, Elgin, IL 60123-1303
Tel.: (847) 697-2640
Web Site:
http://www.walkerparking.com
Year Founded: 1965
Sales Range: $25-49.9 Million
Emp.: 202
Construction Engineering & Consulting Services
N.A.I.C.S.: 541330
Judy Williamson *(Office Mgr)*
John Bushman *(Pres & CEO)*
Don Monahan *(Pres)*
Mary Smith *(Sr VP)*
Bushman John *(Chm)*
Robert Stanley *(VP-Denver)*
Scott Froemming *(Principal)*
Steffen Turoff *(Principal & Dir-Plng & Policy Studies-Pacific Reg)*
Brad Navarro *(Principal)*

WALKER PRODUCTS INC.
14291 Commerce Dr, Garden Grove, CA 92843
Tel.: (714) 554-5151
Web Site:
http://www.walkerproducts.com
Rev.: $12,400,000
Emp.: 40
Carburetors
N.A.I.C.S.: 336310
Michael Weaver *(Pres)*
Grant Kitching *(VP & Gen Mgr)*

WALKER SANDS, INC.
121 N Jefferson St, Chicago, IL 60661
Tel.: (312) 267-0066
Web Site:
http://www.walkersands.com
Year Founded: 2001
Sales Range: $1-9.9 Million
Emp.: 35
Advertising & Marketing Services
N.A.I.C.S.: 541890
Mike Santoro *(CEO)*
Ken Gaebler *(Founder & Principal)*
John Fairley *(VP-Digital Svcs)*
Daniel Laloggia *(Mgr-Digital Strategy)*
Dave Parro *(Acct Dir)*
Andrew Cross *(Sr VP-PR)*
Will Kruisbrink *(Acct Dir)*
Robert Chilver *(VP)*
Sarah Brandon *(Acct Exec)*
John Everette *(Acct Exec)*
Rachel Gulden *(Acct Exec)*
Kaitlin Mansour *(Acct Exec)*
Jennifer Mulligan *(Acct Exec)*
Payal Shukla *(Acct Exec)*
Ellen Hanson *(COO)*
Courtney Beasley *(Mgr-Mktg)*
Will Barthel *(VP-Bus Dev)*
Allison Ward *(VP)*
Erin Jordan *(VP)*
Payal Pathak *(VP-PR)*
Ann Hagner *(VP)*
Dion Manly *(VP-Ops)*
Sandeep Goswami *(VP-Engrg & Tech)*
Kellie Sink *(VP-PR)*
Hailey Melamut *(VP-PR)*
Cheryl Gale *(Exec VP-PR)*

Subsidiaries:

Komarketing Associates LLC (1)
374 Congress St, Ste 507, Boston, MA 02210
Tel.: (781) 209-1989
Web Site:
http://www.komarketingassociates.com
Professional, Scientific & Technical Services
N.A.I.C.S.: 541990
Casie Gillette *(Dir-Online Mktg)*

March Communications, Inc. (1)
560 Harrison Ave Ste 408, Boston, MA 02118
Tel.: (312) 577-5557
Web Site: http://www.marchpr.com
Advertising Services
N.A.I.C.S.: 541810
Kelby Troutman *(VP)*
Cheryl Gale *(Pres)*

WALKER-SCHORK INTERNATIONAL INC.
1055 S 7th St, Rochelle, IL 61068
Tel.: (815) 562-3119
Web Site: http://www.wsint.com
Sales Range: $10-24.9 Million
Emp.: 30
Retailer of Farm & Garden Machinery, Parts & Supplies
N.A.I.C.S.: 423820
Lee Prunty *(Pres)*

WALKERS FURNITURE INC.
2611 N Woodruss Rd 3808 N Bldg 22, Spokane Valley, WA 99216
Tel.: (509) 535-1995
Web Site:
http://www.walkersfurniture.com
Year Founded: 1980
Sales Range: $10-24.9 Million
Emp.: 100
Operates Furniture Stores
N.A.I.C.S.: 449110
Mark M. Walker *(Pres)*
Dan Taylor *(Mgr-Store)*
Dana Hopkins *(Mgr-Distr Center)*

WALKERTEK INTERACTIVE MARKETING, INC.
219 Changebridge Rd, Montville, NJ 07045
Tel.: (973) 227-6003
Web Site: http://www.walkertek.com
Sales Range: $1-9.9 Million
Emp.: 5
Interactive Marketing Services
N.A.I.C.S.: 541613
Mike Walker *(Co-Owner)*
Steve Walker *(Co-Owner)*

WALL COLMONOY CORPORATION
101 W Girard, Madison Heights, MI 48071
Tel.: (248) 585-6400
Web Site:
http://www.wallcolmonoy.com
Year Founded: 1938
Sales Range: $100-124.9 Million
Emp.: 300
Hard Surfacing Alloy Mfr
N.A.I.C.S.: 332811
Nathan Stroud *(Dir-Comml-Europe)*
Robert Davies *(Gen Mgr-Europe)*
Ed Mohrbach *(VP-Fin & Ops)*
Jim Lockbaum *(Mgr-Bus Dev)*
Nicholas Clark *(Pres)*

Subsidiaries:

Wall Colmonoy Corporation - Aerobraze Engineered Technologies Division (1)
4700 SE 59th, Oklahoma City, OK 73135
Tel.: (405) 672-1361
Web Site: http://www.wallcolmonoy.com
Emp.: 50
Material Engineering Component Mfr
N.A.I.C.S.: 333248
Brian Martin *(Dir-Bus Dev)*

Wall Colmonoy Corporation - Wall Colmonoy Technologies Division (1)
Rue des Aulnettes, PO Box 216, 95106, Argenteuil, France
Tel.: (33) 130259860
Web Site: http://www.wallcolmonoy.fr
Surface Engineering Component Mfr
N.A.I.C.S.: 332999
Frank Norgren *(Mng Dir)*

Wall Colmonoy Limited (1)
Alloy Industrial Estate Pontardawe, Swansea, SA8 4HL, United Kingdom

WALL COLMONOY CORPORATION

Wall Colmonoy Corporation—(Continued)
Tel.: (44) 1792 862287
Web Site: http://www.wallcolmonoy.com
Emp.: 205
Engineering Component Mfr
N.A.I.C.S.: 332999
Robert Davies (Mng Dir-Europe)

WALL DRUG STORE INC.
510 Main St, Wall, SD 57790
Tel.: (605) 279-2175
Web Site: http://www.walldrug.com
Rev.: $11,708,561
Emp.: 240
Souvenirs
N.A.I.C.S.: 459420
Rick Hustead (Chm)
Ted Hustead (Pres)

WALL FAMILY ENTERPRISE, INC.
4810 Forest Run Rd, Madison, WI 53704-7336
Tel.: (608) 241-1201   WI
Web Site:
  http://www.wallfamilyenterprise.com
Year Founded: 1905
Sales Range: $200-249.9 Million
Emp.: 700
Holding Company
N.A.I.C.S.: 551112
Robert E. Conway (Chm)
Sean Ryan (CEO)

Subsidiaries:

DEMCO, Inc.   (1)
4810 Forest Run Rd, Madison, WI 53704-7336
Tel.: (608) 241-1201
Web Site: http://www.demco.com
Sales Range: $150-199.9 Million
Emp.: 175
Library & School Furniture, Equipment & Supplies Distr
N.A.I.C.S.: 424120
Sue Sippola (Dir-HR)
Nedra Sadorf (Pres)

Subsidiary (Non-US):

DEMCO Europe Limited   (2)
Grange House 2 Geddings Road, Hoddesdon, EN11 0NT, Herts, United Kingdom   (100%)
Tel.: (44) 1992454500
Web Site: http://www.demcoeurope.eu
Sales Range: $25-49.9 Million
Emp.: 100
Holding Company; Library & School Furniture, Equipment & Supplies Mfr & Distr
N.A.I.C.S.: 551112
David Southern (Mng Dir)

Subsidiary (Domestic):

Don Gresswell Ltd.   (3)
Grange House 2 Geddings Road, Hoddesdon, EN11 0NT, Herts, United Kingdom   (100%)
Tel.: (44) 1992454512
Web Site: http://www.gresswell.co.uk
Sales Range: $50-74.9 Million
Emp.: 60
Library Furniture, Equipment & Supplies Distr
N.A.I.C.S.: 424120
Will Hink (Mng Dir)

Subsidiary (Domestic):

Highsmith, LLC   (2)
401 S Wright Rd, Janesville, WI 53546-8729
Tel.: (920) 563-9571
Web Site: http://www.highsmith.com
Sales Range: $50-74.9 Million
Library & School Furniture, Equipment & Supplies Distr; Educational Materials Developer & Publisher
N.A.I.C.S.: 424120

Hatch, Inc.   (1)
301 N Main St Ste 101, Winston Salem, NC 27101
Tel.: (336) 744-7280

Web Site:
  http://www.hatchearlychildhood.com
Sales Range: $10-24.9 Million
Emp.: 120
Early Childhood Educational Materials Developer & Publisher
N.A.I.C.S.: 513199
Shea Crews (Mgr-Pur)
Nathan Frye (VP-Sls)
Steve Shaw (Sr VP-Sls, Svc & Mktg)
Marian Soare (Dir-Tech)
John Yazumbek (VP-Fin & Admin)

WALL LENK CORPORATION
1950 Dr Martin Luther King Jr Blvd, Kinston, NC 28501-1802
Tel.: (252) 527-4186   PA
Web Site: http://www.wlenk.com
Year Founded: 1864
Sales Range: $1-9.9 Million
Emp.: 40
Electric Soldering Irons, Pencils & Guns, Butane Torches, Solder & Decorative Stencils Mfr
N.A.I.C.S.: 333992
Kathy Cauley (Mgr-Pur)
Mike Gillikin (Mgr-Sls-Natl)

WALL STREET ACCESS CORP.
100 Wall St, New York, NY 10005
Tel.: (212) 232-5602
Web Site: http://www.wsaccess.com
Year Founded: 1981
Brokers, Security & Other Financial Services
N.A.I.C.S.: 523150
Denis P. Kelleher (Founder & Chm)
Thomas Burnett (Vice Chm & Dir-Res)
Sean M. Kelleher (Pres)
William Lavin (Sr VP-Ops)
Arthur L. Goetchius (CEO)
Colleen Kelleher Sorrentino (Mng Dir-Asset Mgmt)
Greg Viscovich (Chief Compliance Officer)
Dana A. Pascucci (Mng Dir-Institutional Sls & Trading)
Christopher DeMeo (Co-CEO, Partner & CIO)
Russell O'Brien (Co-CEO & Partner)

Subsidiaries:

Vandham Securities Corp.   (1)
1 Maynard Dr Ste 2201, Park Ridge, NJ 07656
Tel.: (201) 782-3300
Web Site: http://www.vandham.com
Investment Banking & Securities Dealing
N.A.I.C.S.: 523150
Frank Catrini (Pres)

WALL STREET ACQUISITIONS CORP.
4440 S Piedras Dr Ste 136, San Antonio, TX 78228
Tel.: (973) 277-4239   DE
Year Founded: 2016
Assets: $18,671
Liabilities: $231,028
Net Worth: ($212,357)
Earnings: ($19,899)
Fiscal Year-end: 12/31/21
Investment Services
N.A.I.C.S.: 523999
Franklin Ogele (CFO, Sec & VP)
Jimmy Ramirez (Pres & CEO)

WALL STREET COMMUNICATIONS
1299 E 4500 S, Salt Lake City, UT 84117
Tel.: (801) 266-0077
Web Site: http://www.wallstcom.com
Year Founded: 1996
Sales Range: $10-24.9 Million
Emp.: 25

Local Marketing, Media Buying Services, Public Relations, Web (Banner Ads, Pop-ups, etc.)
N.A.I.C.S.: 541820
Christopher Lesieutre (Founder & Pres)
Pat Brown (Dir-Admin)

WALL STREET NETWORK SOLUTIONS
140 Littleton Rd Ste 310, Parsippany, NJ 07054
Tel.: (973) 585-7543
Web Site: http://www.wsnsllc.com
Year Founded: 2008
Sales Range: $1-9.9 Million
Emp.: 10
Network Integration Services
N.A.I.C.S.: 541512
Michael J. Fritzlo (CEO)
Chris Marino (Head-Sls)

WALL STREET SYSTEMS INC.
1345 Avenue of the Americas 49th Fl, New York, NY 10105
Tel.: (212) 809-7200
Web Site:
  http://www.wallstreetsystems.com
Sales Range: $10-24.9 Million
Emp.: 250
Computer Software Development
N.A.I.C.S.: 541511
Bing Sun (Engr-Software)
Mark Tirschwell (CTO)

WALL SYSTEMS, INC.
4395 Corporate Sq, Naples, FL 34104
Tel.: (239) 643-1921
Web Site: http://www.walls-swfl.com
Year Founded: 1986
Sales Range: $10-24.9 Million
Emp.: 20
Drywall & Insulation Contractors
N.A.I.C.S.: 238310

WALL TIMBER PRODUCTS INC.
1825 Effingham Hwy, Sylvania, GA 30467
Tel.: (912) 863-5108
Web Site: http://www.walltimber.com
Sales Range: $10-24.9 Million
Emp.: 140
Wood Products Sales
N.A.I.C.S.: 423990
Britt Wall (Pres)
Amy Lawson (Mgr)

WALL WORKS USA INC.
1981 Moreland Pkwy Bldg 5, Annapolis, MD 21401
Tel.: (410) 295-9911
Web Site:
  http://www.wallworksusa.com
Sales Range: $10-24.9 Million
Emp.: 42
Ceramic Tile Installation Services
N.A.I.C.S.: 238990
Stephen Hodgins (Pres)
Roberto S. Lopez (Project Coord)

WALL-TECH, INC.
7025 Raywood Rd, Madison, WI 53713
Tel.: (608) 257-1595
Web Site: http://www.walltechinc.com
Rev.: $19,700,000
Emp.: 216
Specialty Trade Contractors
N.A.I.C.S.: 238990
Conrad Doering (Pres)
Pete Braun (VP)
Alice Doering (VP)
Timothy Stadelman (Treas & Sec)

U.S. PRIVATE

WALLACE & COOK FOOD SALES, INC.
Hunts Point Cooperative Market Bldg E20, Bronx, NY 10474
Tel.: (718) 617-7600   NY
Year Founded: 1988
Sales Range: $10-24.9 Million
Emp.: 6
Producer of Meats & Meat Products
N.A.I.C.S.: 424470
Ted Cook (Pres)
Yvonne Gonzales (Office Mgr)

WALLACE AUTOMOTIVE MANAGEMENT CORPORATION, INC.
3555 SE Federal Hwy, Stuart, FL 34997
Tel.: (772) 286-3555   FL
Web Site:
  http://www.wallaceautogroup.com
Sales Range: $75-99.9 Million
Emp.: 300
Holding Company; New & Used Car Dealerships Owner & Operator
N.A.I.C.S.: 551112
William L. Wallace (Owner & Pres)
D. Lee Smith (Pres)

Subsidiaries:

Wallace Chevrolet, LLC   (1)
3575 SE Federal Hwy, Stuart, FL 34997
Tel.: (772) 287-3232
Web Site: http://www.wallacechevrolet.com
Sales Range: $10-24.9 Million
Emp.: 60
New & Used Car Dealer
N.A.I.C.S.: 441110
Mark Adams (Gen Mgr)

Wallace Chrysler Jeep, LLC   (1)
2755 SE Federal Hwy, Stuart, FL 34994
Web Site: http://www.wallacecjd.com
Sales Range: $25-49.9 Million
Emp.: 60
New Car Dealership
N.A.I.C.S.: 441110

WALLACE CASCADE TRANSPORT, INC.
9290 E Hwy 140, Planada, CA 95365
Tel.: (209) 382-0131
Sales Range: $10-24.9 Million
Emp.: 1
Transportation & Moving Services
N.A.I.C.S.: 484121
Bud Wallace (Pres)

WALLACE FORGE COMPANY INC.
3700 Georgetown Rd NE, Canton, OH 44704
Tel.: (330) 488-1205
Web Site:
  http://www.wallaceforge.com
Year Founded: 1942
Sales Range: $10-24.9 Million
Emp.: 65
Iron & Steel Forging Services
N.A.I.C.S.: 332111
Dean L. Wallace (Pres)

WALLACE HARDWARE COMPANY, INC.
5050 S Davy Crockett Pkwy, Morristown, TN 37813-3903
Tel.: (423) 586-5650   TN
Web Site:
  http://www.wallacehardware.com
Year Founded: 1936
Sales Range: $100-124.9 Million
Emp.: 340
Hardware
N.A.I.C.S.: 423710
Bill Trusler (CFO & Exec VP)
Richard Snowden (Sr VP-Mktg)

COMPANIES

Walker's Supply Company Inc. (1)
1526 W. Andrew Johnson Hwy, Morristown, TN 37814 (100%)
Tel.: (423) 586-4721
Sales Range: $10-24.9 Million
Emp.: 50
Plumbing Fixtures, Equipment & Supplies Sales
N.A.I.C.S.: 423720

WALLACE OIL COMPANY INC
5370 Oakdale Rd SE, Smyrna, GA 30082-5218
Tel.: (404) 799-6508   GA
Web Site: http://www.wallaceoil.net
Year Founded: 1950
Sales Range: $10-24.9 Million
Emp.: 18
Sales of Petroleum Products
N.A.I.C.S.: 424720
James C. Wallace (Pres)

WALLACE PACKAGING, LLC.
820 E 47th St Ste B6, Tucson, AZ 85713-5074
Tel.: (520) 322-0213
Web Site: http://www.wallacepack.com
Year Founded: 2000
Sales Range: $10-24.9 Million
Emp.: 17
Metal Tank Mfr
N.A.I.C.S.: 332431
Paul Tomeh (Pres)
Manu Jain (Mgr-Sls)

WALLACE ROBERTS & TODD LLC
1700 Market St 28th Fl, Philadelphia, PA 19103
Tel.: (215) 732-5215
Web Site: http://www.wrtdesign.com
Year Founded: 1963
Sales Range: $25-49.9 Million
Emp.: 100
Architectural Services
N.A.I.C.S.: 541310
Joe Healy (Mng Principal)
Ignacio Bunster-Ossa (Principal)
Jim Stickley (Principal)

WALLACH SURGICAL DEVICES, INC.
75 Corporate Dr, Trumbull, CT 06611
Tel.: (203) 799-2000   CT
Web Site: http://www.wallachsurgical.com
Year Founded: 1980
Sales Range: $25-49.9 Million
Emp.: 50
Cryosurgical Instruments, Colposcopes, Operating Microscopes, Electrosurgical Instruments & Disposables Mfr for Gynecology
N.A.I.C.S.: 339112
Edward Carroll (Dir-Sls)

WALLDESIGN INC.
2350 SE Bristle St, Newport Beach, CA 92660
Tel.: (949) 251-9959
Web Site: http://www.walldesigninc.com
Sales Range: $10-24.9 Million
Emp.: 350
Plaster & Drywall Work
N.A.I.C.S.: 238310
Mike Bello (Owner)
Marilyn Tintorer (Controller)
Steve Huntington (Pres)

WALLE CORPORATION
200 Hembree Park Dr Ste H, Roswell, GA 30076
Tel.: (770) 667-3973   LA
Web Site: http://www.walle.com
Year Founded: 1872
Sales Range: $150-199.9 Million
Emp.: 500
Provider of Lithograph & Flexographic Printing for Consumer Package Label Mfr
N.A.I.C.S.: 323111
Robert Pokowitz (CFO)
Deshone Farley (Office Mgr)

Subsidiaries:
Walle Corporation - Flexographic Division (1)
1 Walle Dr, Winchester, KY 40391
Tel.: (859) 745-2819
Labeling Services
N.A.I.C.S.: 561910

Walle Corporation - Lithographic Division (1)
600 Elmwood Park Blvd, Harahan, LA 70123
Tel.: (504) 734-8000
Web Site: http://www.walle.com
Emp.: 130
Labeling Services
N.A.I.C.S.: 561910
Jo Hunley (Mgr-HR)

WALLEYE CAPITAL, LLC
315 Park Ave S, 18th Fl., New York, NY 10010
Web Site: https://www.walleyecapital.com
Year Founded: 2005
Financial Services
N.A.I.C.S.: 523999

WALLICK AND VOLK INC.
222 E 18th St, Cheyenne, WY 82001
Tel.: (307) 634-5941
Web Site: http://www.wvmb.com
Year Founded: 1932
Sales Range: $100-124.9 Million
Emp.: 350
Mortgage Banker
N.A.I.C.S.: 522310
Michael Groff (CEO)
Jim Volk (Chm)
Robert Moore (Sr VP-IT)
Joanne Demorest (Sr VP-Reg Production)
Nikki Groff (Chief Mktg & Dev Officer)
Sara Moore (COO)
Nicholas Morgan (Sr VP-Reg Production)
Brian P. Rogerson (Pres)

WALLINGFORD AUTO COMPANY
1122 Old N Colony Rd, Wallingford, CT 06492
Tel.: (203) 269-8741
Web Site: http://www.wallingfordbuickgmc.com
Rev: $25,800,792
Emp.: 45
Automobiles, New & Used
N.A.I.C.S.: 441110
Christopher Backer (Owner)

WALLINGFORD COFFEE MILLS INC.
11401 Rockfield Ct, Cincinnati, OH 45241
Tel.: (513) 771-3131   OH
Web Site: http://www.wallingfordcoffee.com
Year Founded: 1909
Sales Range: $10-24.9 Million
Emp.: 53
Distr of Coffee & Related Products
N.A.I.C.S.: 311920
Gary Davis (VP-Ops)

WALLIS COMPANIES, INC.
106 E Washington St, Cuba, MO 65453
Tel.: (573) 885-2277
Web Site: http://www.wallisco.com
Rev.: $43,100,000
Emp.: 1,000
Convenience Store
N.A.I.C.S.: 457120
Lynn Wallis (Pres)
Rachel Mehl (Mgr-Specialized Category)

Subsidiaries:
Wallis Energy Co. Inc. (1)
106 E Washington St, Cuba, MO 65453 (100%)
Tel.: (573) 885-2277
Web Site: http://www.wallisco.com
Rev.: $12,600,000
Petroleum Bulk Stations
N.A.I.C.S.: 423850

Wallis Oil Co. Inc. (1)
106 E Washington St, Cuba, MO 65453-1827
Tel.: (573) 885-2277
Web Site: http://www.wallisco.com
Sales Range: $50-74.9 Million
Provider of Gasoline Service Stations
N.A.I.C.S.: 457120
Lynn Wallis (Pres & CEO)

WALLIS STATE BANK INC.
6510 Railroad St, Wallis, TX 77485
Tel.: (979) 478-6151
Web Site: http://www.wallisbank.com
Year Founded: 1906
Rev.: $12,845,000
Emp.: 35
State Commercial Banks
N.A.I.C.S.: 522110
Musa A. Dakri (Chm)
Asif M. Dakri (CEO)

WALLKILL VALLEY BANCORP INC.
23 Wallkill Avenue, Wallkill, NY 12589
Tel.: (845) 895-2051
Web Site: https://www.wallkill.com
Year Founded: 2017
Savings & Loan Holding Company
N.A.I.C.S.: 551111

Subsidiaries:
Wallkill Valley Federal Savings & Loan Association (1)
23 Wallkill Ave, Wallkill, NY 12589
Tel.: (845) 895-2051
Web Site: http://www.wallkill.com
Savings Institutions
N.A.I.C.S.: 522180
Michael J. Horodyski (Pres & CEO)

WALLNER TOOLING/EXPAC INC.
9160 Hyssop Dr, Rancho Cucamonga, CA 91730-6100
Tel.: (909) 481-8800
Web Site: http://www.expac.com
Rev.: $13,157,898
Emp.: 55
Machine Tools, Metal Forming Type
N.A.I.C.S.: 333517
Mike Wallner (CEO)
Paul Wallner (COO)

WALLOWA COUNTY GRAIN GROWERS
911 S River St, Enterprise, OR 97828
Tel.: (541) 426-3116
Sales Range: $10-24.9 Million
Emp.: 40
Grains
N.A.I.C.S.: 424510
Steve Wilcox (Gen Mgr)

WALLPAPERS-TO-GO, INC.
7342 San Pedro Ave, San Antonio, TX 78216-6224
Tel.: (830) 693-1056   TX
Web Site: http://www.wallpaperstogo.com
Year Founded: 1977
Sales Range: $100-124.9 Million
Emp.: 80
Wallpaper Sales
N.A.I.C.S.: 444120
Harold Otto (Pres)
Debra Newman (Mgr-Mktg)

WALLWORK CURRY MCKENNA
10 City Sq 5th Fl, Charlestown, MA 02129
Tel.: (617) 266-8200   MA
Web Site: http://www.wcm-partners.com
Year Founded: 1993
Sales Range: $25-49.9 Million
Emp.: 30
Advetising Agency
N.A.I.C.S.: 541810
Jack Wallwork (CEO & Dir-Creative)
Joe Delaney (Dir-Production)
James Rowean (Mgr-Acct Svc)
Alison Costello (Sr VP & Dir-Client Svc)

WALLY FINDLAY GALLERIES INTERNATIONAL INC
165 Worth Ave, Palm Beach, FL 33480-4406
Tel.: (561) 655-2090   DE
Web Site: http://www.wallyfindlay.com
Year Founded: 1870
Sales Range: $100-124.9 Million
Emp.: 35
Retail Original Oil Paintings
N.A.I.C.S.: 459920
James R. Borynack (Chm & CEO)
Juan M. Pretel (Dir-Gallery)

Subsidiaries:
Wally Findlay Galleries, Inc. (1)
165 Worth Ave, Palm Beach, FL 33480 (100%)
Tel.: (561) 655-2090
Web Site: http://www.wallyfindlay.com
Sales Range: $10-24.9 Million
Emp.: 12
Retail Original Oil Paintings
N.A.I.C.S.: 459920
Juan Preteo (VP)

Wally Findlay Galleries, Inc. (1)
124 E 57th St, New York, NY 10022-1006
Tel.: (212) 421-5390
Web Site: http://www.wallyfindlay.com
Sales Range: $10-24.9 Million
Emp.: 10
Retail Original Oil Paintings
N.A.I.C.S.: 459920
Frederick S. Clark (Dir-Gallery)
Stephanie B. Clark (Dir-Gallery)

WALLY MCCARTHY'S CADILLAC
2325 N Prior Ave, Saint Paul, MN 55113
Tel.: (651) 636-6060
Web Site: http://www.mccarthyauto.com
Year Founded: 1991
Sales Range: $25-49.9 Million
Emp.: 80
New Car Retailer
N.A.I.C.S.: 441110

WALMAN OPTICAL COMPANY
801 12th Ave N, Minneapolis, MN 55411-4230
Tel.: (612) 520-6000   MN
Web Site: http://www.walman.com
Year Founded: 1915
Sales Range: $150-199.9 Million
Emp.: 750

WALMAN OPTICAL COMPANY

Walman Optical Company—(Continued)
Eyeglasses & Contact Lenses Mfr
N.A.I.C.S.: 339115
Martin L. Bassett (Pres & CEO)
Charles Pillsbury (Treas & VP)
Teresa Ranallo (Controller)

Subsidiaries:

ADO Buying Group (1)
200 South St, Tracy, MN 56175
Tel.: (507) 629-3361
Web Site: http://www.adobuying.com
Optical Goods Reseller
N.A.I.C.S.: 456130
Jobe Sellers (VP & Gen Mgr)

The Walman Instrument Group (1)
230 S Eva St, Saint Paul, MN 55107
Tel.: (612) 520-6031
Web Site:
 http://www.walmaninstruments.com
Sales Range: $10-24.9 Million
Emp.: 30
Ophthalmic Instrument Distr
N.A.I.C.S.: 423460
Jon Dymit (Gen Mgr)

Walman Optical Company - Imagewear Division (1)
801 12th Ave N, Minneapolis, MN 55411
Tel.: (800) 414-7656
Web Site: http://www.imagewear.com
Eyewear Distr
N.A.I.C.S.: 423460

X-Cel Contacts (1)
2775 Premiere Pkwy Ste 600, Duluth, GA 30097
Tel.: (770) 622-9235
Web Site: http://www.xcelcontacts.com
Emp.: 200
Contact Lens Mfr
N.A.I.C.S.: 339115
Robert Chambers (Mgr)
Allison Penn (Mgr-Sls)
Felipe Arroyave (Acct Mgr-Intl)

WALNUT CREEK ASSOCIATES
1707 N Main St, Walnut Creek, CA 94596
Tel.: (925) 934-0530
Web Site:
 http://www.walnutcreekhonda.com
Sales Range: $25-49.9 Million
Emp.: 91
Car Dealership Owner & Operator
N.A.I.C.S.: 441110
David Robb (Owner)

WALNUT INVESTMENT CORP.
1620 S Maple Ave, Montebello, CA 90640
Tel.: (323) 721-9011
Web Site: http://www.a-m-s.com
Year Founded: 1969
Sales Range: $50-74.9 Million
Emp.: 588
Construction Product Mfr
N.A.I.C.S.: 423310
Bettie Donate (Mgr-Trng & Sls)
Curtis Leach (Mgr-Inventory Control)
Todd Tremper (Branch Mgr)
John Magana (Gen Mgr-Mexico)
Keri Mowrey (Branch Mgr-Acoustical Matl Svcs)
Mark Foley (Mgr-Bridgeport)
Carlos Hernandez (Mgr-Bridgeport)
Joe King (Mgr-Bridgeport)
Sandra Ortiz (Mgr-Bridgeport)
Jeremiah Regalado (Mgr-Bridgeport)
Richard Sasseen (Mgr-Bridgeport)
Pablo Amezcua (Mgr-Ops)
Arturo Felix (Mgr-Ops)
David Guerrero (Mgr-Ops)
Enrique Hernandez (Mgr-Ops)

WALNUT STREET THEATRE CORPORATION
825 Walnut St, Philadelphia, PA 19107
Tel.: (215) 574-3550   DE
Web Site:
 http://www.walnutstreettheatre.org
Year Founded: 1969
Sales Range: $10-24.9 Million
Emp.: 443
Theater Operator
N.A.I.C.S.: 711110
Richard A. Mitchell (Chm)
David S. Blum (Vice Chm)
Robert L. B. Harman (Treas)
Francis J. Mirabello (Vice Chm)
Scott Rankin (Vice Chm)
Ramona Gwynn (Vice Chm & Sec)

WALPOLE COOPERATIVE BANK
982 Main St, Walpole, MA 02081
Tel.: (508) 668-1080
Web Site:
 http://www.walpolecoop.com
Sales Range: $25-49.9 Million
Emp.: 35
Cooperative Bank
N.A.I.C.S.: 522180
Philip W. Prescott (COO, Treas & Exec VP)
Joseph V. Scholl (Pres & CEO)
Paul M. Chaggaris (Sr VP)
Michael P. Gookin (Officer-Comml Loan & VP)
Joanne Flaherty Mailhot (VP)
Gail Criasia (Asst VP & Officer-Ops)
Donna M. Leary (Officer-Mktg, Retail & Security & Sr VP-HR)
Tracy L. Murphy (VP-Credit-Admin)

WALPOLE INC.
269 NW 9th St, Okeechobee, FL 34972-2115
Tel.: (863) 763-5593
Web Site: http://www.walpoleinc.com
Year Founded: 1952
Sales Range: $25-49.9 Million
Emp.: 400
Contract Haulers
N.A.I.C.S.: 484121
John Cincotta (VP-Terminal Ops)
Keith Walpole (Owner)
Edwin E. Walpole III (Owner & Pres)

Subsidiaries:

Walpole Leasing Company (1)
4201 N Williams Rd, Tampa, FL 33610   (100%)
Tel.: (813) 623-1702
Web Site: http://www.walpoleinc.com
Sales Range: $10-24.9 Million
Emp.: 15
Truck Transportation Services
N.A.I.C.S.: 484121
Ed Walpole (VP)
John Sincotta (Gen Mgr)
Joseph Ford (Controller)

WALPOLE WOODWORKERS, INC.
767 East St, Walpole, MA 02081
Tel.: (508) 668-2800   MA
Web Site:
 http://www.walpolewoodworkers.com
Year Founded: 1933
Sales Range: $100-124.9 Million
Emp.: 250
Wood Products Including Fences, Furniture & Prefabricated Buildings
N.A.I.C.S.: 321999
Louis A. Maglio (CEO)
Sid Tildsley (VP-Ops)
Sue Donahue (Dir-Mktg)

WALRUS
18 E 17th St Fl 3, New York, NY 10003
Tel.: (212) 645-2646
Web Site: http://www.walrusnyc.com
Year Founded: 2005
Rev.: $15,000,000
Emp.: 12
N.A.I.C.S.: 541810
Deacon Webster (Owner & Chief Creative Officer)
Frances Webster (Owner)
Mary O'Keefe (Dir-Art)
Paula Beer Levine (Mng Dir)
Valerie Hope (Dir-Integrated Production & Creative Svcs)

WALSER AUTOMOTIVE GROUP, LLC
4401 American Blvd W, Bloomington, MN 55437
Tel.: (612) 294-0220   MN
Web Site: http://www.walser.com
Year Founded: 1956
Sales Range: $300-349.9 Million
Emp.: 1,000
Holding Company; New & Used Car Dealerships Owner & Operator
N.A.I.C.S.: 551112
Paul Walser (CEO)
Andrew Walser (Pres)

Subsidiaries:

Walser Burnsville M, LLC (1)
14720 Buck Hill Rd, Burnsville, MN 55306-4984
Tel.: (952) 388-2244
Web Site: http://www.walser-mazda.com
Emp.: 68
New & Used Car Dealer
N.A.I.C.S.: 441110
Bret Juedes (Pres)

Walser Burnsville Motors, LLC (1)
14750 Buck Hill Rd, Burnsville, MN 55306
Tel.: (612) 395-4999
Web Site: http://www.walsernissan.com
Emp.: 58
New & Used Car Dealer
N.A.I.C.S.: 441110
Robert Walser (Chm)

Walser H., LLC (1)
14800 Buck Hill Rd, Burnsville, MN 55306
Tel.: (952) 388-2231
Web Site: http://www.walserhonda.com
New & Used Car Dealer
N.A.I.C.S.: 441110
Bruce Kittilstved (Gen Mgr)

Walser HY., LLC (1)
8100 Lakeland Ave N, Brooklyn Park, MN 55445
Tel.: (651) 705-0151
Web Site: http://www.walserhyundai.com
New & Used Car Dealer
N.A.I.C.S.: 441110
Mark Fisch (Gen Mgr)

WALSH & ALBERT COMPANY, LTD.
19300 Oil Center Blvd, Houston, TX 77073
Tel.: (281) 449-2787
Web Site:
 http://www.walshalbert.com
Year Founded: 1982
Sales Range: $10-24.9 Million
Emp.: 200
Fabrication Services
N.A.I.C.S.: 238390
Pete Walsh (Pres)
Larry Vines (Mgr-Production)

WALSH & ASSOCIATES, INC.
1400 Macklind Ave, Saint Louis, MO 63110
Tel.: (314) 781-2520
Web Site: http://www.walsh-assoc.com
Year Founded: 1968
Sales Range: $50-74.9 Million
Emp.: 50
Whslr of Industrial Chemicals
N.A.I.C.S.: 424690

Ellen W. Murphy (Pres & CEO)
Brian T. Walsh (Controller)
Steve Bihun (Dir-Pur)
Marcelo Zocchi (Acct Mgr-Great Lakes)
Dan Butler (Acct Mgr-West)
Jim Kron (Coord-Environmental, Health, Safety & Responsible Distr)
Jonathan Faith (Acct Mgr-Southeast Reg)

WALSH & WATTS INC.
500 W 7th St Ste 1007, Fort Worth, TX 76102
Tel.: (817) 335-5417
Rev.: $32,100,000
Emp.: 85
Crude Petroleum Production
N.A.I.C.S.: 211120
Howard Walsh Jr. (Pres)

WALSH ADVERTISING INC.
3823 Beech Ave, Baltimore, MD 21211-2223
Tel.: (410) 235-3035
Year Founded: 1988
Sales Range: Less than $1 Million
Emp.: 1
Education, Media Buying Services, Newspaper, Newspapers & Magazines, Recruitment, Trade & Consumer Magazines
N.A.I.C.S.: 541830
Nancy Walsh (Pres)

WALSH BROTHERS INC.
210 Commercial St, Boston, MA 02109
Tel.: (617) 878-4800   MA
Web Site:
 http://www.walshbrothers.com
Year Founded: 1901
Sales Range: $150-199.9 Million
Emp.: 112
Providers of Commercial & Office Building, New Construction Contracts
N.A.I.C.S.: 236220
Richard C. Walsh (Pres & CEO)
Ed Bullock (Mgr-Safety)
Darlene Conners (Mgr-HR)
John H. Greenip (Chief Strategy Officer)

WALSH CONSTRUCTION CO.
2905 SW 1st Ave, Portland, OR 97201
Tel.: (503) 222-4375
Web Site:
 http://www.walshconstructionco.com
Sales Range: $150-199.9 Million
Emp.: 220
Multi-Family Dwellings, New Construction
N.A.I.C.S.: 236116
John Weid (CFO & VP)
Mike Steffen (VP & Gen Mgr)
Matt Leeding (Pres)
Ross Cornelius (Mgr-Client Svc)
Ryan Wilde (VP & Gen Mgr)
Helen Smith (Dir-HR)
Matt Godt (Mgr-Bus Dev-Oregon)

WALSH COUNTY MUTUAL INSURANCE COMPANY
429 2nd St, Minto, ND 58261
Tel.: (701) 248-3231
Web Site:
 https://www.walshcountymutual.com
Property Insurance Services
N.A.I.C.S.: 524126

Subsidiaries:

Griggs Nelson Mutual Insurance Co. (1)
112 S Main St, McVille, ND 58254-4208
Tel.: (701) 322-5118

Web Site: http://www.griggsnelson.com
Insurance Agencies & Brokerages
N.A.I.C.S.: 524210
Audrey Reinhart (Mgr)

WALSH DUFFIELD COMPANIES, INC.
801 Main St, Buffalo, NY 14203-1215
Tel.: (716) 853-3820 NY
Web Site: http://walshduffield.com
Year Founded: 1860
Insurance Agents
N.A.I.C.S.: 524210
John N. Walsh (Chm)
Lisa M. Petronio (VP-Retirement Plan Solutions)
Barney Walsh (Exec VP)
Mark Garvelli (VP-Personal Lines Div)
Michael K. Walsh (Sec & Exec VP)
Sean P. Keenan (Pres & COO)
Edward F. Walsh Jr. (CEO)

WALSH HONDA
2056 Eisenhower Pkwy, Macon, GA 31206-3168
Tel.: (478) 788-4510
Web Site:
  http://www.walshhonda.com
Year Founded: 1969
Sales Range: $10-24.9 Million
Emp.: 44
Car Whslr
N.A.I.C.S.: 441110
Mac Angley (Mgr-IT)
Jack Woods (Mgr-Svc)
Vickie Brewer (Office Mgr)
Kevin Parrish (Mgr-Sls)
David Komaee (Gen Mgr)

WALSH INVESTMENT COMPANY INC.
12000 NE 8th St Ste 204, Bellevue, WA 98005
Tel.: (425) 455-1313
Sales Range: $10-24.9 Million
Emp.: 1
Investment Services
N.A.I.C.S.: 523999
Charles E. Walsh (Pres)

WALSH PARTS & SERVICE
1222 Hannah Ave, Forest Park, IL 60130-2448
Tel.: (708) 771-2480
Year Founded: 1907
Sales Range: Less than $1 Million
Emp.: 9
Punch Presses Mfr
N.A.I.C.S.: 333517
David Paulinski (Pres)

WALSH SHEPPARD
111 W 9th Ave, Anchorage, AK 99501
Tel.: (907) 338-3567
Web Site:
  http://www.walshsheppard.com
Sales Range: $10-24.9 Million
Emp.: 15
Services Related to Advertising
N.A.I.C.S.: 541810
Pat Walsh (CEO)
Jack Sheppard (Pres & COO)
Kirsten Sheppard (CFO)
Christy Cresap (Mgr-Acctg)
Jen Derks (Dir-Art)
Karen Miovas (Acct Mgr)
Jesse Kreger (Acct Mgr)

WALSH TIMBER COMPANY LLC
500 Oosta Rd, Zwolle, LA 71486
Tel.: (318) 645-6122
Web Site:
  http://www.walshtimbercompany.com

Year Founded: 1985
Sales Range: $10-24.9 Million
Emp.: 80
Whslr of Wood Products
N.A.I.C.S.: 423990
Nancy Sannin (Co-CFO)
Garrett Walsh (CEO)
David Cupp (Pres)
Katie Bell (Co-CFO)

WALSH TRUCKING CO. LTD
1650 NW Sundial Rd, Troutdale, OR 97060
Tel.: (503) 667-1912
Web Site:
  http://www.walshtruckingco.com
Rev.: $28,249,261
Emp.: 180
Trucking Service
N.A.I.C.S.: 484121
Cal Clarke (CFO)

WALSWORTH PUBLISHING COMPANY, INC.
306 N Kansas Ave, Marceline, MO 64658-2105
Tel.: (660) 376-3543 MO
Web Site:
  http://www.walsworthprinting.com
Year Founded: 1937
Sales Range: $75-99.9 Million
Emp.: 1,400
Books & Yearbooks Mfr
N.A.I.C.S.: 513199
Joe Cupp (Exec VP-Sls-Intl)
Mark Hatfield (Exec VP-Mfg Ops)
Gary O'Toole (Gen Mgr-Print Facilities-Marceline)
Jeff Vogel (CFO)
Jim Mead (COO)
Edward Kennedy (VP-HR)
Dan Dority (Plant Mgr)
Jim Worthington (VP-Sls & Mktg)
Don O. Walsworth Sr. (CEO)
Don Walsworth Jr. (Pres)

Subsidiaries:

IPC Print Services, Inc. (1)
2180 Maiden Ln, Saint Joseph, MI 49085-2432 (100%)
Tel.: (269) 983-7105
Web Site: http://www.ipcprintservices.com
Sales Range: $25-49.9 Million
Emp.: 100
Printing Services
N.A.I.C.S.: 323111
Richard Butterworth (CFO)

Lyke Corporation (1)
656 S Douglas St, Ripon, WI 54971
Tel.: (920) 748-3136
Web Site: http://www.riponprinters.com
Catalogs, Directories, Manuals & Soft-Cover Educational Products Printing
N.A.I.C.S.: 323111
Jeffrey Spence (VP-Ops)
Tim Lyke (Publr-Ripon Commonwealth Press)
Jeff Hopp (VP-Sls & Mktg)
Julie Newhouse (Pres)
Andy Luke (CFO)

Branch (Domestic):

Ripon Printers - Milwaukee (2)
16000 W Rogers Dr, New Berlin, WI 53151-0160
Tel.: (262) 784-9500
Web Site: http://www.riponprinters.com
Emp.: 160
Commercial Printing Mfr
N.A.I.C.S.: 323111

Walsworth Publishing Company, Inc. - Marceline Printing and Bindery Facility (1)
803 S Missouri Ave, Marceline, MO 64658
Web Site: http://www.walsworth.com
Printing & Binding Services
N.A.I.C.S.: 323117

Walsworth Publishing Company, Inc. - Saint Joseph Printing and Bindery Facility (1)
2180 Maiden Ln, Saint Joseph, MI 49085
Tel.: (800) 369-2646
Sales Range: $25-49.9 Million
Emp.: 220
Printing & Binding Services
N.A.I.C.S.: 323117
Mike Wells (Gen Mgr)

WALT & COMPANY COMMUNICATIONS INC.
2105 S Bascom Ave Ste 240, Campbell, CA 95008
Tel.: (408) 369-7200
Web Site: http://www.walt.com
Year Founded: 1991
Sales Range: $1-9.9 Million
Emp.: 18
Public Relations Agency
N.A.I.C.S.: 541820
Robert Walt (Founder & CEO)
Jeannie Gustlin (VP-HR)
Merritt Woodward (Sr VP)
Cyndi Babasa (Sr VP)

WALT MASSEY AUTOMOTIVE, INC.
49 W Frontage Rd, Lucedale, MS 39452-6612
Tel.: (601) 947-3001
Web Site:
  http://www.waltmassey.com
New Car Dealers
N.A.I.C.S.: 441110
Walt Massey (Owner)

Subsidiaries:

Mack Grubbs Motors Inc. (1)
1480 Hwy 98 E, Columbia, MS 39429
Tel.: (601) 736-2565
Web Site: http://www.buygrubbsgm.com
Sales Range: $10-24.9 Million
Emp.: 31
New & Used Car Dealers
N.A.I.C.S.: 441110
Gary Mack Grubbs (Pres)

WALT SWEENEY
5400 Glenway Ave, Cincinnati, OH 45238
Tel.: (513) 922-4500
Web Site:
  http://www.waltsweeney.com
Year Founded: 1971
Sales Range: $75-99.9 Million
Emp.: 150
New Car Retailer
N.A.I.C.S.: 441110
Walt Sweeney (Owner)
Tim Sweeney (Owner & Gen Mgr)
Mark Campbell (Mgr-New Vehicle)
Keith Maines (Mgr-Used Vehicle)
Brandi Armes (Mgr-Bus Dev & Digital Mktg)
Rebecca Shackelford (Controller)
John Treglia (Mgr-Bus)
Megan Volkerding (Mgr-Bus)
Jeff Gross (Mgr-Collision Center)
Bob Luchsinger (Mgr-Fleet)
Bobby Cain (Mgr-Parts-Columbus)
Mike Struble (Mgr-Special Fin)
Judy Mitchell (Mgr-Svc Customer Rels)
Billy Blount (Mgr-Svc-Columbus)
Vonnetta Dorsey (Office Mgr)

WALTECH INC.
15 Old Flanders Rd 2nd Fl, Westborough, MA 01581
Tel.: (508) 460-7007
Web Site: http://www.waltechinc.com
Sales Range: $10-24.9 Million
Emp.: 40
Custom Computer Programming Services

N.A.I.C.S.: 541511
Harsh Walia (Pres)

WALTER DORWIN TEAGUE ASSOCIATES INC.
110 Union St Ste 500, Seattle, WA 98101-2163
Tel.: (206) 838-4200
Web Site: http://www.teague.com
Rev.: $17,550,000
Emp.: 130
Design, Commercial & Industrial
N.A.I.C.S.: 541420
Ken Dowd (VP)
John Barratt (Pres & CEO)
Dan Mock (Controller)

WALTER E. NELSON CO.
5937 North Cutter Cir, Portland, OR 97217
Tel.: (503) 285-3037
Web Site:
  http://www.walterenelson.com
Sales Range: $10-24.9 Million
Emp.: 53
Janitors' Supplies
N.A.I.C.S.: 423850
Tim Walters (Gen Mgr)
Marla Seaborg (Acct Mgr-Outside Sls)
Joe Stingle (Acct Mgr)
Janet Lennon (Acct Mgr-Outside Sls)

WALTER E. SMITHE FURNITURE INC.
1251 W Thorndale Ave, Itasca, IL 60143-1149
Tel.: (630) 285-8000
Web Site: http://www.smithe.com
Year Founded: 1982
Sales Range: $25-49.9 Million
Emp.: 400
Sales of Furniture
N.A.I.C.S.: 337212
Audrey Canavino (Mgr-Store)
Bob Wiles (Gen Mgr)
Cheryl Maiorano (Sr Dir-Design)
Machiko Penny (Mgr-Mdsg)
Mariann Curran (Gen-Mgr-Multi-Store)
Michele Ramirez (Gen Mgr)
Talea Bloom (Sr Mgr)
Terry Cortes (Asst Controller)
Patricia Calesini (Dir-Visual Display)
Walter E. Smithe III (Pres)

WALTER F. CAMERON ADVERTISING INC.
350 Motor Pkwy Ste 410, Hauppauge, NY 11788-5125
Tel.: (631) 232-3033 NY
Web Site:
  http://www.cameronadv.com
Year Founded: 1977
Sales Range: $50-74.9 Million
Emp.: 50
Advertising Agencies
N.A.I.C.S.: 541810
Mark Preiser (Owner)
Andrew Kline (VP)
Joseph J. Cameron III (Owner)

WALTER G. LEGGE COMPANY, INC.
444 Central Ave, Peekskill, NY 10566-0591
Tel.: (914) 737-5040 NY
Web Site:
  http://www.leggesystems.com
Year Founded: 1928
Sales Range: $10-24.9 Million
Emp.: 15
Nonslip Floor Polishes & Cleaners, Germicides & Anti-Static Products & Systems Mfr & Sales
N.A.I.C.S.: 325612
Elizabeth Bauer (Pres)

WALTER J. MUELLER INC.

WALTER J. MUELLER INC.

Walter J. Mueller Inc.—(Continued)
3711 Chester Ave, Cleveland, OH 44114
Tel.: (216) 432-0088
Web Site: http://www.dealertire.com
Rev.: $65,600,000
Emp.: 400
Automobile Tires & Tubes
N.A.I.C.S.: 423130
Scott Mueller (CEO)

WALTER LAGESTEE, INC.
330 W Taft Dr, South Holland, IL 60473-2026
Tel.: (708) 596-3166
Web Site: http://www.waltsfoods.com
Year Founded: 1937
Sales Range: $50-74.9 Million
Emp.: 650
Distr of Groceries
N.A.I.C.S.: 445110
John Lagestee (Pres)
Robert Lagestee (CFO)
Jose Mendez (Dir-HR)

WALTER LYONS & ASSOCIATES
1 Oakland St PO Box 35, Amesbury, MA 01913-3013
Tel.: (978) 388-2032   MA
Year Founded: 1965
Rev.: $500,000
Emp.: 4
Fiscal Year-end: 12/31/04
N.A.I.C.S.: 541810
Walter H. Israel (Pres & Treas)
J. Israel (VP & Dir-Mktg)

Subsidiaries:

Walter Lyons & Associates (1)
7 Charles Rd, Swampscott, MA 01907-1619
Tel.: (978) 388-2032
N.A.I.C.S.: 541810
Walter H. Israel (Pres & COO)
Lisa J. Israel (Art Dir)

WALTER P MOORE AND ASSOCIATES, INC.
1301 McKinney Ste 1100, Houston, TX 77010
Tel.: (713) 630-7300
Web Site:
  http://www.walterpmoore.com
Year Founded: 1931
Sales Range: $10-24.9 Million
Emp.: 300
Engineeering Services
N.A.I.C.S.: 541330
Jim Jacobi (CIO)
Tom Magnusson (Chief Admin Officer)
Rick Craft (Mgr-Mktg)
Dilip Choudhuri (CEO)
Dennis Wittry (Sr Principal)
Rick Miles (Principal)
Brian Lozano (Dir-Parking Svcs Grp)
Hakim Bouadi (Principal-Diagnostics)
Blair Hanuschak (Dir-Northeast)
Lee Slade (Chm & Exec Dir-Structures)
Matt Feagins (Dir-Design)
Aaron White (Dir-Digital Practice)
Dirk Kestner (Dir-Sustainable Design)
Edwin Friedrichs (Exec Dir)
Gabriel Jimenez (Exec Dir)
Karin Dwight (Gen Counsel)
Scott Gauthier (Mgr-Application Dev)
Ceri Warnie (Principal)
Manoj Adwaney (Principal)
Thomas Duncan (Dir-Traffic Engrg Svcs)
Ryan Seckinger (Mng Dir-Washington)
Kevin Anderson (Principal)
Trevor Acorn (Principal)
Lee Anne Dixon (Dir-Ops-Infrastructure Grp)
Dan Orlich (Principal)
Michelle Perry (Chief HR Officer & Principal)
Chris Harper (Principal)
Rachel Calafell (Principal)
Jeff Thompson (Principal)
Kathleen Irwin (Mgr-Corp Comm)
Jennifer Peek (Exec Dir-Infrastructure)
Christopher Pinto (Principal/Mng Dir-Diagnostics Grp-New York)
Gustav Fagerstrom (Principal)
Karim Zulfiqar (Mng Dir-Structural Engrg Grp)

Subsidiaries:

Walter P Moore & Associates, Inc. (1)
1201 Peachtree St NE 400 Colony Sq Ste 1600, Atlanta, GA 30361
Tel.: (404) 898-9620
Web Site: http://www.walterpmoore.com
Sales Range: $1-9.9 Million
Emp.: 34
Engineering Services
N.A.I.C.S.: 541330
Doug Robinson (Principal)
Jeff Nixon (Principal)
Mark Larsen (Sr Principal)
Ben Cheplak (Principal & Mgr-Structural Design)
Brent Bandy (Principal)
Kelly Roberts (Principal)
Sunil Puri (Principal)
Tim Santi (Principal)

Walter P Moore & Associates, Inc. (1)
1100 Walnut St Ste 1825, Kansas City, MO 64106
Tel.: (816) 701-2100
Web Site: http://www.walterpmoore.com
Sales Range: $1-9.9 Million
Emp.: 40
Engineeering Services
N.A.I.C.S.: 541330
David T. Ford (Principal)
Shruti Sharma (Principal)
Greg Rhodes (Principal)
Dan Brown (Principal)

WALTER WOOD SUPPLY CO.
4509 Rossville Blvd, Chattanooga, TN 37407
Tel.: (423) 867-1033
Web Site:
  http://www.walterwood.com
Rev.: $21,696,169
Emp.: 98
Industrial Supplies
N.A.I.C.S.: 423840
David Henry (Pres)

WALTER'S WHOLESALE ELECTRIC COMPANY INC.
2825 Temple Ave, Signal Hill, CA 90755
Tel.: (562) 988-3100
Web Site:
  http://www.walterswholesale.com
Year Founded: 1953
Sales Range: $25-49.9 Million
Emp.: 350
Suppliers of Electrical Apparatus & Equipment
N.A.I.C.S.: 541690
John L. Walter (Owner)
Roland Wood (CFO & Controller)
Jay Melfi (VP-Pur & Logistics)
Steve Valcourt (Pres)
Bill Durkee (Chm)

WALTERS & WOLF
41450 Boscell Rd, Fremont, CA 94538
Tel.: (510) 490-1115   CA
Web Site:
  http://www.waltersandwolf.com
Year Founded: 1977
Sales Range: $200-249.9 Million
Emp.: 500
Glass & Glazing Contractors
N.A.I.C.S.: 238150
Rick Calhoun (Pres)

Subsidiaries:

Walters & Wolf Construction Specialties, Inc. (1)
889 N Colorado St, Gilbert, AZ 85233
Tel.: (480) 705-6810
Web Site: http://www.waltersandwolf.com
Sales Range: $50-74.9 Million
Emp.: 200
Design, Manufacturing, Installation of Glass, Aluminum & Stone Window Wall Systems, Storefront & Entrance Systems, Metal Panel Systems, Ornamental Metals, Skylights, Sunscreens, Louvers, Handrails
N.A.I.C.S.: 238150

Walters & Wolf Curtain Wall, LLC (1)
4725 116th St SW, Mukilteo, WA 98275
Tel.: (425) 290-7700
Web Site: http://www.waltersandwolf.com
Design, Manufacturing, Installation of Glass, Aluminum & Stone Window Wall Systems, Storefront & Entrance Systems, Metal Panel Systems, Ornamental Metals, Skylights, Sunscreens, Louvers, Handrails
N.A.I.C.S.: 238150

Walters & Wolf Interiors (1)
41450 Boscell Rd, Fremont, CA 94538-3103   (100%)
Tel.: (510) 490-1115
Sales Range: $100-124.9 Million
Emp.: 125
Building Cladding Services
N.A.I.C.S.: 238150
Randy Wolf (Owner)

Walters & Wolf Precast (1)
41777 Boyce Rd, Fremont, CA 94538
Tel.: (510) 226-9800
Web Site: http://www.waltersandwolf.com
Sales Range: $25-49.9 Million
Emp.: 70
Mfr & Installer of Architectural Precast Concrete
N.A.I.C.S.: 327390
Randy A. Wolf (Pres)
Ed Knowles (VP-Sls)

WALTERS GROUP
2030 E Flamingo Rd Ste 290, Las Vegas, NV 89119-5163
Tel.: (702) 450-8100
Web Site: http://www.waltersgolf.com
Sales Range: $10-24.9 Million
Emp.: 20
Real Estate Managers
N.A.I.C.S.: 531210
William T. Walters (Founder & CEO)

WALTERS-MORGAN CONSTRUCTION
2616 Tuttle Creek Blvd, Manhattan, KS 66502-4479
Tel.: (785) 539-7513
Web Site:
  http://www.waltersmorgan.com
Year Founded: 1988
Sales Range: $25-49.9 Million
Emp.: 80
Civil Engineering Services
N.A.I.C.S.: 237310
Scott Mueller (Pres)

WALTHALL OIL COMPANY
2510 Allen Rd, Macon, GA 31216
Tel.: (478) 781-1234
Web Site: http://www.walthall-oil.com
Sales Range: $75-99.9 Million
Emp.: 200
Petroleum Products
N.A.I.C.S.: 424720
Shawn Heacox (VP-Atlanta Div)
Matt Rhodes (Pres)
Rod Coston (VP-Fin)
Malcolm Walthall (VP-Information Sys)
Wesley Walthall (VP-Sls)
Frank Walthall III (CEO)

WALTKOCH LTD.
315 W Ponce De Leon Ave Ste 500, Decatur, GA 30030
Tel.: (404) 378-3666
Web Site: http://www.waltkoch.com
Sales Range: $10-24.9 Million
Emp.: 10
Frozen Fish, Meat & Poultry
N.A.I.C.S.: 424420

WALTON & CO. INC.
1800 Industrial Hwy, York, PA 17402
Tel.: (717) 755-9030
Web Site: http://www.waltonco.com
Sales Range: $25-49.9 Million
Emp.: 200
Plumbing Contractor
N.A.I.C.S.: 238220
John E. Kinsley (Chm)
Andy Volovar (CFO & Treas)
Bill Vervaeke (Mgr-Building Svcs)

WALTON BEVERAGE CO.
1350 Pacific Pl, Ferndale, WA 98248
Tel.: (360) 380-1660   WA
Web Site:
  http://www.waltonbeverage.com
Year Founded: 1959
Sales Range: $10-24.9 Million
Emp.: 100
Soft Drink Bottler & Distr
N.A.I.C.S.: 312111
John Walton (Pres)
Aaron Cheney (Mgr-Route)
Les Blouin (Mgr-Large Format Sls)
Jim Callaghan (Dir-Bus Strategy)

WALTON ELECTRIC MEMBERSHIP CORP.
842 Hwy 78 N W, Monroe, GA 30655
Tel.: (770) 267-2505
Web Site: http://www.waltonemc.com
Rev.: $136,573,619
Emp.: 220
Electric Power Distribution
N.A.I.C.S.: 221122
Ronnie Lee (Pres & CEO)
Russell DeLong (Sr VP-Corp Svcs)
Ron Marshall (Sr VP-Engrg & Ops)
Keith Taylor (Acct Exec)
Scott Walker (Acct Exec)
Allen Powers (Dir-Natural Gas Ops)
Brad Adcock (Dir-Safety & Trng)
Robert Rentfrow (Sr VP)
Marsha Shumate (Sr VP)

WALTON INDUSTRIES, INC.
1220 E North Ave, Fresno, CA 93725
Tel.: (559) 495-4004   CA
Web Site:
  http://www.generalcoatings.net
Year Founded: 1987
Sales Range: $1-9.9 Million
Emp.: 17
Urethane & Other Foam Product (except Polystyrene) Mfr
N.A.I.C.S.: 326150
Eric Montie (Gen Mgr)
Josh Amezola (Mgr-Sls-SE & Midwest)
Will Lorenz (VP-Sls)

Subsidiaries:

Contractors Coating Supply Inc. (1)
1220 E North Ave, Fresno, CA 93725
Tel.: (559) 495-4004
Web Site:
  http://www.contractorscoatingsupply.com
Roofing & Coating Supplier
N.A.I.C.S.: 423330
Jerry Carmona (Mgr-Warehouse)

COMPANIES

WALTON SIGNAGE CORPORATION
3419 E Commerce St, San Antonio, TX 78220
Tel.: (210) 886-0644 TX
Web Site: http://www.waltonsignage.com
Year Founded: 1980
Sales Range: $25-49.9 Million
Emp.: 101
Sign Mfr
N.A.I.C.S.: 339950
Gary Walton (Pres & CEO)
Sue Johnson (VP-HR)

WALTON STREET CAPITAL, LLC
900 N Michigan Ave Ste 1900, Chicago, IL 60611
Tel.: (312) 915-2800 DE
Web Site: http://www.waltonst.com
Year Founded: 1997
Sales Range: $10-24.9 Million
Emp.: 100
Private Equity Real Estate Investment Firm
N.A.I.C.S.: 531390
Neil G. Bluhm (Mng Principal)
Jeffrey S. Quicksilver (Mng Principal)
Ira J. Schulman (Mng Principal)
Matthew A. Brody (Principal)
Raphael Dawson (Principal & Sr Mgr-Asset)

Subsidiaries:

Amfac Hawaii LLC (1)
94-200 Paioa Pl, Waipahu, HI 96797-5011
Tel.: (808) 543-8900
Sales Range: $350-399.9 Million
Property Investment & Participation in Agricultural Activities
N.A.I.C.S.: 237210

Athletic Club At One Cleveland (1)
1650 W 82nd St Ste 1100, Minneapolis, MN 55431-1475
Tel.: (216) 621-0770
Rev.: $1,300,000
Emp.: 30
Physical Fitness Clubs With Training Equipment
N.A.I.C.S.: 713940

KLC Land Company (1)
700 Bishop St Ste 1920, Honolulu, HI 96813-4124
Tel.: (808) 543-8900
Rev.: $1,800,000
Irrigation Systems
N.A.I.C.S.: 221310

Waikele Golf Club Inc. (1)
94-200 Paioa Pl, Waipahu, HI 96797-5011
Tel.: (808) 676-9000
Web Site: http://www.golfwaikele.com
Sales Range: $1-9.9 Million
Emp.: 90
Golf Club
N.A.I.C.S.: 713910

WALTON'S INC.
3639 N Comotara St, Wichita, KS 67226
Tel.: (316) 262-0651
Web Site: http://www.waltonsinc.com
Year Founded: 1986
Meat Processing Equipment Distr
N.A.I.C.S.: 423830
Don Walton (Owner)
Brett Walton (Founder, Pres, Pres & CEO)
Brett Walton (Pres)

WALZ HARMAN HUFFMAN COMPANIES
5615 Huffman Dr, Kechi, KS 67067
Tel.: (316) 744-2081
Web Site: http://www.whhconst.com
Rev.: $27,459,375
Emp.: 3
Commercial & Office Building Construction
N.A.I.C.S.: 236220
Gregory L. Harman (Pres)

Subsidiaries:

Sub-Contractors Inc (1)
5615 Huffman Dr, Kechi, KS 67067
Tel.: (316) 744-0479
Web Site: http://www.whhconst.com
Sales Range: $10-24.9 Million
Masonry & Other Stonework
N.A.I.C.S.: 238140

WALZ TETRICK ADVERTISING
6299 Nall Ave Ste 300, Mission, KS 66202-3547
Tel.: (913) 789-8778
Web Site: http://www.wtads.com
Year Founded: 1967
Rev.: $10,000,000
Emp.: 20
N.A.I.C.S.: 541810
Beverly Bellinger (VP & Dir-Creative)
Shannon Jeffries (Acct Supvr)
Charles M. Tetrick (Pres & CEO)
Lesley Hause (Mgr-Adv)
Amanda Coleman (Dir-Art)
Eric M. Lykins (Controller)
Siobhan McLaughlin Lesley (Dir-Client Svcs)
Melba Morris (Sr Media Buyer)
Heather Winker (Acct Supvr)
Blair Overesch (Dir-Media)
Mike Campbell (Dir-Client Partnerships)
Kelli Oestreich (Sr Dir-Art)
Jennifer Hade (Dir-Project Mgmt)
Anne Fundakowski (Sr Acct Mgr)

WALZCRAFT INDUSTRIES INC.
2600 Hemstock St, La Crosse, WI 54602
Tel.: (608) 781-6355
Web Site: http://www.walzcraft.com
Rev.: $26,200,000
Emp.: 400
Wood Kitchen Cabinet & Countertop Mfr
N.A.I.C.S.: 337110
Marc Rothering (Controller)
Richard Walz (Pres)
Ron Schlegel (VP)

WAMBERG GENOMIC ADVISORS, INC.
4330 La Jolla Village Dr Ste 230, San Diego, CA 92122
Web Site: http://www.wamberggenomic.com
Health Care Consulting Services
N.A.I.C.S.: 541618
Greig Woodring (Chm)
Tom Wamberg (CEO)
Darren Rowe (Chief Innovation Officer)
Chad Stoerp (CFO)
Mickie Henshall (CMO)
Irene Guterman (VP-Cancer Svcs)
David Stertzer (Mng Dir)
Lynnette Bates (Sr VP-Bus Dev)
Nick Bellanca (Exec VP-Group Benefits)
Tammy Kwok-Johnson (VP-Client Success)
Darrell Smith (Reg Dir-Sls)
Kathryn Aguirre (Mgr-Client Success)
Kerry Connor (Reg Dir-Sls)
Jennifer Todd (VP-Digital Ops)

WAMEGO BANCSHARES, INC.
806 W 5th St, Wamego, KS 66547
Tel.: (785) 456-2221 KS
Web Site: http://www.bankflinthills.com
Year Founded: 1978
Sales Range: $10-24.9 Million
Bank Holding Company
N.A.I.C.S.: 551111
Charles White (Chm)
Lance L. White (Pres & CEO)

Subsidiaries:

Bank of the Flint Hills (1)
806 W 5th St, Wamego, KS 66547
Tel.: (785) 456-2221
Web Site: http://www.bankflinthills.com
Sales Range: $10-24.9 Million
Emp.: 76
Commericial Banking
N.A.I.C.S.: 522110
Lance L. White (Pres & CEO)
Dennis Hadley (Sr VP)

WAMEGO SAND COMPANY, INC.
701 S 4th St, Manhattan, KS 66502
Tel.: (785) 776-8811 KS
Web Site: http://www.4mcm.com
Year Founded: 1927
Sales Range: $10-24.9 Million
Emp.: 100
Ready-Mixed Concrete Mfr & Aggregate Mining
N.A.I.C.S.: 327320

WAMPLER REALTY, INC.
64 Wendover Rd, Daleville, VA 24083
Tel.: (540) 992-2500
Web Site: http://www.wamplerrealty.com
Year Founded: 1974
Sales Range: $10-24.9 Million
Emp.: 2
Real Estate Services
N.A.I.C.S.: 531210
Todd Wampler (Principal-Broker)

WAMPLERS FARM SAUSAGE CO. INC.
781 Hwy 70 W, Lenoir City, TN 37771
Tel.: (865) 986-2056
Web Site: http://www.wamplersfarm.com
Rev.: $20,400,000
Emp.: 160
Sausage Mfr
N.A.I.C.S.: 311611
Ruthann Wampler (VP)

WAND PARTNERS INC.
260 Crandon Blvd Ste 32 Ste 75, Key Biscayne, FL 33149
Tel.: (212) 909-2620 NY
Web Site: http://www.wandpartners.com
Year Founded: 1985
Investment Company & Active Private Equity Investor With a Significant Focus on the Financial Services Industry
N.A.I.C.S.: 561499
John S. Struck (Mng Dir)
Bruce W. Schnitzer (Chm & Mng Dir)

WAND, INC.
2170 S Parker Rd Ste 295, Denver, CO 80231
Tel.: (303) 623-1200
Web Site: http://www.wandinc.com
Sales Range: $25-49.9 Million
Emp.: 50
Structured Multi Lingual Vocabularies Developer to Power Search & Classification Internet Applications; Internet Taxonomy Structures Developer
N.A.I.C.S.: 519290
Ross Leher (Founder, Chm & CEO)
Jeff Burinda (CTO)
Richard Avery (Sr VP-Corp Dev)

WANDERLUST
297 River St, Troy, NY 12180
Tel.: (518) 272-2500
Web Site: http://www.createwanderlust.com
Year Founded: 1985
Rev.: $22,000,000
Emp.: 12
N.A.I.C.S.: 541810
Mark Shipley (Pres & Chief Strategic Officer)
Sara Tack (Exec VP-Image & Identity)
Patrick Reilly (Exec VP-Plng & Res)

WANGARD PARTNERS, INC.
1200 N Mayfair Rd Ste 310, Milwaukee, WI 53226
Tel.: (262) 717-0700
Web Site: http://www.wangard.com
Year Founded: 1995
Sales Range: $10-24.9 Million
Emp.: 15
Commercial Real Estate Broker
N.A.I.C.S.: 531210
Stewart M. Wangard (Chm & CEO)
Kim Guerrero (Sr Mgr-Property)
Wayne Wiertzema (Pres)
Chad Venne (Exec VP-Property Mgmt)
Dorothy Snow (Dir-Mktg)
Peter Ginn (Sr VP-Indus Investments)
Alex Brackman (Mgr-Property)
Jeremy Hillenbrand (VP-Capital Markets)
Beth Schumacher (CFO)
Jon de Fiebre (Project Mgr-Construction)
Shawn Becker (Coord-Tenant Svcs)
Landon Wirth (Dir-Mortgage Financing)
Matt Moroney (COO & Gen Counsel)

WANNEMACHER ENTERPRISES INC.
400 E Hanthorn Rd, Lima, OH 45804
Tel.: (419) 225-9060
Web Site: http://www.wannti.com
Sales Range: $25-49.9 Million
Emp.: 120
Local Trucking without Storage
N.A.I.C.S.: 484110
Greg Wannemacher (Pres)
Beth Nickles (VP-Admin)
Randy Fetter (VP)

WANNEMACHER JENSEN ARCHITECTS INC.
180 Mirror Lake Dr, Saint Petersburg, FL 33701
Tel.: (727) 822-5566
Web Site: http://www.wjarc.com
Year Founded: 1992
Sales Range: $1-9.9 Million
Emp.: 9
Architectural Services
N.A.I.C.S.: 541310
Lisa Wannemacher (Pres & Partner)
Jason Jensen (Partner)

Subsidiaries:

Hoffmann Architects, Inc. (1)
2321 Whitney Ave, Hamden, CT 06518
Tel.: (203) 239-6660
Web Site: http://www.hoffarch.com
Rev.: $5,656,500
Emp.: 23
Architectural Services
N.A.I.C.S.: 541310
Avi A. Kamrat (CFO & Dir-Admin)
John J. Hoffmann (Pres)
Robert Delagrange (Mgr-Bus Dev)
Stephanie Hughes-White (Mgr-Mktg)
Kara Shypula (Sr Project Coord)
Cindy Lattanzio (Mgr-HR)
Daniel L. Bishop (Sr Project Coord)
Maureen J. Dobbins (Dir-Bus Dev)
Kevin T. Edwards (Mgr-Bus Dev)
Alison B. Hoffmann (Mgr-Comm)

Wannemacher Jensen Architects Inc.—(Continued)
Juan Kuriyama *(VP & Dir-Architecture)*
Marian S. McFarland *(Sec)*
Russell M. Sanders *(Exec VP)*
Lauren Mulrooney *(Mgr-Bus Dev-Manhattan)*
Tai Mahmuti *(Sr Project Coord)*
David Obrizzo *(Coord-CAD & IT)*
Rachel Mesite *(Sr Coord-Fin)*
Mary MacIlvain *(Coord-Mktg)*

WANNER ENGINEERING INC.
1204 Chestnut Ave, Minneapolis, MN 55403
Tel.: (612) 332-5681
Web Site: http://www.wannereng.com
Rev.: $14,500,000
Emp.: 150
Injection Molding Of Plastics
N.A.I.C.S.: 333914
Joseph Grewe *(Pres)*
Christine Kargel *(Coord-Receiving)*
John Rekuski *(Mgr-Customer Svc)*
Tom West *(Reg Mgr-Sls)*

Subsidiaries:

Wanner International Ltd. (1)
Grange Court Grange Road, Farnham, GU10 1DW, Surrey, United Kingdom
Tel.: (44) 1252 781234
Injection Molding Of Plastics
N.A.I.C.S.: 326199

Wanner Pumps Ltd. (1)
Flat A 21 F Chatham Commercial Building 399 Chatham Road, North Hunghom, Kowloon, China (Hong Kong)
Tel.: (852) 3428 6534
Web Site: http://www.wannerpumps.com
Emp.: 1
Industrial Pumps Whslr
N.A.I.C.S.: 423830
Joseph Loo *(Mgr-Sls)*

WANOBA GROUP INC.
1815 W 213th St Ste 235, Torrance, CA 90501-2825
Tel.: (310) 782-1900 CA
Year Founded: 1997
Sales Range: $1-9.9 Million
Emp.: 7
Investment & Consulting
N.A.I.C.S.: 445110
Yoshiya Watanabe *(Pres)*

Subsidiaries:

Daikichi Corporation (1)
1815 W 213th St Ste 235, Torrance, CA 90501-2825
Tel.: (310) 618-8700
Take-Out Sushi Chain
N.A.I.C.S.: 445250

Mitsuwa Corporation (1)
1815 W 213 St Ste 235, Torrance, CA 90501-2825
Tel.: (310) 782-6800
Grocery Stores
N.A.I.C.S.: 445110
Yoshiya Watanabe *(Pres & CEO)*

WANTAGH AUTO SALES INC.
3614 Sunrise Hwy, Wantagh, NY 11793
Tel.: (516) 785-1700
Year Founded: 1954
Sales Range: $25-49.9 Million
Emp.: 50
Car Whslr
N.A.I.C.S.: 441110
Robert B. Green *(Pres)*

WANTMAN GROUP, INC.
2035 Vista Pkwy, West Palm Beach, FL 33411
Tel.: (561) 687-2220 FL
Web Site:
   http://www.wantmangroup.com
Year Founded: 1972
Emp.: 600

Engineeering Services
N.A.I.C.S.: 541330
Lon Ogden *(Sr Project Mgr)*
Danielle Dux *(Coord-Mktg)*
Jennifer Morton *(Mgr-Land Dev)*
Adam Schildmeier *(Project Mgr-Civil Engrg & Plng)*
Tom Sullivan *(Mgr-Municipal)*
Brian Flynn *(Sr Project Mgr)*
Jason Mihalovits *(Project Mgr)*
Brett Oldford *(Dir-Municipal Engrg)*
Steve Graham *(Project Mgr)*
Anthony Alfred *(Sr Project Mgr)*
Coriann Salas *(Sr Engr-Structural)*
Julie Vers *(Sr Engr-Structural)*
Mario Echagarrua *(COO)*
Chris Stermer *(Mgr-Utility Coordination)*
Karla Bloom *(Project Mgr)*
Jonathan Gilbert *(Sr Project Mgr)*
Chris Presnell *(Mgr-North Florida)*
Cheryl Callender *(Sr Project Mgr-Land Design Svcs Div)*
Jeffrey Kistner *(Sr Project Mgr)*
Michael LeComte *(Sr Project Engr)*
Barbara Stiles *(Mgr-Bus Dev)*
Richard Hasko *(Engr-Field)*
Alan Boaz *(Sr Coord-Utility)*
Christen Hutton *(Sr Project Mgr)*
Julie Tom *(Project Engr)*
Kevin Randolph *(Project Mgr)*
Erik Salgado *(Sr Project Engr-Transportation)*
Raymond Valido *(Project Mgr-Roadway-Miami)*
Slivia M. Fernandez *(Project Mgr-Roadway-Miami)*
David Wantwan *(CEO)*

Subsidiaries:

BIG RED DOG, Inc. (1)
2021 E 5th St Ste 200, Austin, TX 78702
Tel.: (512) 669-5560
Web Site: http://www.bigreddog.com
Engineering Consulting
N.A.I.C.S.: 541330
Brad Lingvai *(Pres)*
Will Schnier *(CEO)*
Shannon Boyd *(VP)*
Douglas Barrilleaux *(Pres)*
Stephen Glenn *(Engr-Mechanical)*
Victor Duspiva *(Project Mgr-Comml Civil)*
Rachel John *(Project Engr-Traffic Engrg)*
Joel Blok *(Mgr-Construction)*
Forrest Bratton *(Project Mgr-Structural Engrg)*
Arnaud Thibonnier *(Dir-Structural Engrg Svcs)*
Amy Garza *(Coord-Pub Infrastructure Proposal & Bus Dev)*
Erica Valenzuela *(Project Coord-Comml Project Sector)*

WANXIANG AMERICA CAPITAL, LLC
123 N Wacker Dr Ste 820, Chicago, IL 60606
Tel.: (312) 525-8500 DE
Web Site:
   http://www.genevaglencapital.com
Year Founded: 2008
Emp.: 5
Privater Equity Firm
N.A.I.C.S.: 523999
Jeff Gonyo *(Mng Dir)*
Adam Schecter *(Mng Dir)*
Tom Wuellner *(Principal)*

Subsidiaries:

Dianne's Fine Desserts, Inc. (1)
4 Graf Rd, Newburyport, MA 01950-4015
Tel.: (978) 462-3248
Web Site:
   http://www.diannesfinedesserts.com
Sales Range: $25-49.9 Million
Emp.: 100
Fresh Baked & Frozen Desserts Mfr & Distr
N.A.I.C.S.: 311812

Tom Lundquist *(CFO)*
Susan Sweeney *(Dir-HR)*
Dan Scales *(Pres)*
Mike Knowles *(CEO)*
Peter Franggos *(Controller)*

WAPSIE VALLEY CREAMERY, INC.
PO Box 391, Independence, IA 50644-0391
Tel.: (319) 334-7193
Sales Range: $50-74.9 Million
Emp.: 55
Cheese Mfr
N.A.I.C.S.: 311513
Mark Nielsen *(CEO)*
Randy Schafer *(Controller)*

WAR MEMORIAL HOSPITAL
500 Osborn Blvd, Sault Sainte Marie, MI 49783
Tel.: (906) 635-4460 MI
Web Site:
   http://www.warmemorialhospital.org
Year Founded: 1985
Sales Range: $75-99.9 Million
Emp.: 1,016
Health Care Services
N.A.I.C.S.: 622110
Jim Haglund *(VP-Rehabilitation)*
David Jahn *(Pres & CEO)*
Kevin Kalchik *(CFO)*
Marla Bunker *(VP-Nursing & Ops)*

WARBURG PINCUS LLC
450 Lexington Ave, New York, NY 10017-3147
Tel.: (212) 878-0600 NY
Web Site:
   http://www.warburgpincus.com
Year Founded: 1966
Privater Equity Firm
N.A.I.C.S.: 523999
Charles R. Kaye *(Co-CEO)*
Joseph P. Landy *(Co-CEO)*
Peter R. Kagan *(Mng Dir)*
Mark Colodny *(Mng Dir-Exec Mgmt, Healthcare, Tech, Media & Telecommunications)*
Alex Berzofsky *(Mng Dir & Co-Head-China)*
Jeffrey Goldfaden *(Mng Dir)*
Steven G. Glenn *(CFO & Mng Dir)*
Timothy F. Geithner *(Pres)*
Cary Davis *(Mng Dir)*
Parag Gupta *(Mng Dir)*
Angel Pu Shum *(Principal)*

Subsidiaries:

AA PLC (1)
Fanum House Basing View, Basingstoke, RG21 4EA, Hampshire, United Kingdom
Tel.: (44) 3705042000
Web Site: https://www.theaacorporate.com
Rev.: $1,305,042,000
Assets: $2,511,714,000
Liabilities: $4,585,353,600
Net Worth: $(2,073,639,600)
Earnings: $114,109,200
Emp.: 7,536
Fiscal Year-end: 01/31/2020
Roadside Assistance Services
N.A.I.C.S.: 561990
Edmund King *(Pres)*
Rick Haythornthwaite *(Chm)*
Jakob Pfaudler *(CEO)*
Thomas Mackay *(CFO)*
Louise Benford *(Co-Chief People Officer)*

Subsidiary (Domestic):

Drivetech (UK) Limited (2)
Fanum House Basing View, Basingstoke, RG21 4EA, Hampshire, United Kingdom
Tel.: (44) 1256610907
Web Site: http://www.drivetech.co.uk
Driver Training Services
N.A.I.C.S.: 611692
Charlie Norman *(Mng Dir)*
Ian Dudley *(Dir-IT)*

Sarah Homer *(Head-Fin)*
Colin Paterson *(Head-Mktg)*
Tanya Hills *(Head-Bus Ops)*

Accelya Solutions India Limited (1)
801 Tower-A Embassy 247 Park LBS Marg, Vikhroli, Mumbai, MH 400 083, India
Tel.: (91) 2268538888
Web Site: https://w3.accelya.com
Rev.: $51,357,961
Assets: $48,457,923
Liabilities: $12,600,765
Net Worth: $35,857,158
Earnings: $10,399,621
Emp.: 1,247
Fiscal Year-end: 06/30/2022
Software Solutions to the Airline & Travel Inducstry
N.A.I.C.S.: 541511
Jose Maria Hurtado *(CFO)*
Jim Davidson *(Pres & Chief Strategy Officer)*
Ninad Umranikar *(Sec)*

Aion SA/NV (1)
Rue de la Loi 34, 1040, Brussels, Belgium
Tel.: (32) 22207211
Web Site: http://www.aion.be
Banking Services
N.A.I.C.S.: 522110

Brady Industries Inc. (1)
7055 Lindell Rd, Las Vegas, NV 89118
Tel.: (702) 876-3990
Web Site: http://www.bradyindustries.com
Sales Range: $50-74.9 Million
Emp.: 420
Sanitation Preparations
N.A.I.C.S.: 424690
Eric Brady *(CFO)*
Travis Brady *(Pres)*
Michelle Harrison *(Dir-Mktg)*
Ryan Banks *(Corp VP-Sls & Mktg)*

Subsidiary (Domestic):

Envoy Solutions LLC (2)
2101 Claire Ct, Glenview, IL 60025
Tel.: (800) 508-5830
Web Site: http://www.envoysolutions.com
Janitorial Supply, Packaging Solutions & Specialty Products Distr
N.A.I.C.S.: 423850
Mark Fisher *(CEO)*

Subsidiary (Domestic):

Delta Packaging & Supply, LLC (3)
500 Gulf South Dr, Flowood, MS 39232
Tel.: (601) 354-8986
Web Site: http://www.deltapackaging.net
Rev.: $4,140,000
Emp.: 5
Industrial & Personal Service Paper Merchant Whslr
N.A.I.C.S.: 424130
Johnie Weems *(Pres & CEO)*

GPMI Company (3)
1051 N Fiesta Blvd, Gilbert, AZ 85233
Tel.: (480) 503-0006
Web Site: http://www.gpmicompany.com
Sales Range: $1-9.9 Million
Emp.: 100
Home Care & Automotive Products Mfr
N.A.I.C.S.: 423220
Chuck Tornabene *(COO)*
Leslie Bendor *(Dir-Mktg)*

H.T. Berry Co. Inc. (3)
50 N St, Canton, MA 02021
Tel.: (781) 828-6000
Web Site: http://www.htberry.com
Sales Range: $10-24.9 Million
Emp.: 50
Wholesale Distributor of Food Service, Janitorial/Sanitary & Industrial Packaging Products
N.A.I.C.S.: 424130
Chris Nolan *(Pres)*
James Berry *(VP)*

Sunbelt Packaging, LLC (3)
7826 Park Place Rd, York, SC 29745
Tel.: (803) 684-2286
Web Site:
   http://www.sunbeltpackagingllc.com
Packaging Materials Mfr & Distr
N.A.I.C.S.: 423990
Jade Boling *(COO)*

COMPANIES — WARBURG PINCUS LLC

Superior Supply Co., Inc. (3)
1331 Wisconsin Ave, Sheboygan, WI 53081
Tel.: (920) 457-4481
Web Site: http://www.northwoodstm.com
Sales Range: $1-9.9 Million
Emp.: 50
Chemical & Allied Products Merchant Whslr
N.A.I.C.S.: 424690
Tim Junior *(Office Mgr)*
Terry Schaller *(Pres)*

Swish White River Ltd. (3)
1118 Route 14, Hartford, VT 05047
Tel.: (800) 639-7226
Web Site: http://www.swishusa.com
Janitorial Equipment Distr & Mfr
N.A.I.C.S.: 561720
Anthony W. Ambler *(Pres)*
Peter Crouse *(CEO)*

United Packaging Supply Co. (3)
102 Wharton Rd, Bristol, PA 19007
Tel.: (215) 633-0700
Web Site: http://www.unitedpkg.com
Sales Range: $1-9.9 Million
Emp.: 40
Packaging & Shipping Supplies Distr
N.A.I.C.S.: 424990
Scott Paul *(Mgr-Distr Center)*
Jeff Seidel *(Pres & CEO)*

Subsidiary (Domestic):

FPC Holdings, Inc. (2)
6630 Amberton Dr, Elkridge, MD 21075
Tel.: (410) 579-1000
Web Site: http://www.fpcsolutions.com
Motor Vehicle & Engine Parts Mfr
N.A.I.C.S.: 336310
Richard W. Roe *(Pres)*

Subsidiary (Domestic):

FPC Distribution, Inc. (3)
6630 Amberton Dr Ste A, Elkridge, MD 21075-6246
Tel.: (410) 579-1000
Web Site: http://www.fpcdistribution.com
Industrial & Personal Service Paper Merchant Whslr
N.A.I.C.S.: 424130
Richard Roe *(Pres)*

Subsidiary (Domestic):

Gorm, Inc. (2)
150 S Hudson Ave, Ontario, CA 91761
Tel.: (909) 292-1400
Web Site: http://www.gorminc.com
Sales Range: $1-9.9 Million
Emp.: 20
Service Establishment Equipment & Supply Whslr
N.A.I.C.S.: 423850
Ron Johnson *(VP-Sls)*

Idaho Package Company (2)
2140 Heyrend Way, Idaho Falls, ID 83402
Tel.: (208) 529-0891
Web Site: http://www.idahopackage.com
Sales Range: $10-24.9 Million
Emp.: 30
Packaging Solutions Services
N.A.I.C.S.: 424990
Conn Hix *(Pres & CEO)*

PFS Sales Company (2)
4701 Beryl Rd, Raleigh, NC 27606
Tel.: (919) 829-1116
Web Site: http://www.pfssales.com
Sales Range: $1-9.9 Million
Emp.: 26
Industrial & Personal Service Paper Whslr
N.A.I.C.S.: 424130

YPV Distribution, Inc. (2)
160 Scott St, Elk Grove Village, IL 60007-1211
Tel.: (847) 718-1100
Web Site: http://www.ypvdist.com
Industrial & Personal Service Paper Merchant Whslr
N.A.I.C.S.: 424130
John Bouzas *(Pres)*

CYREN Ltd. (1)
10 Ha-Menofim St 5th Floor, Herzliyya, 4672561, Israel
Tel.: (972) 98636888
Web Site: http://www.cyren.com
Rev.: $31,187,000
Assets: $46,128,000
Liabilities: $32,300,000
Net Worth: $13,828,000
Earnings: ($23,039,000)
Emp.: 200
Fiscal Year-end: 12/31/2021
Cloud Internet Security Software
N.A.I.C.S.: 513210
Jeffrey R. Dauer *(CFO & Chief Acctg Officer)*
James A. Hamilton *(Chm)*
Lior Kohavi *(Chief Strategy Officer & Exec VP-Advanced Solutions)*
Michael Tamir *(VP-Global Support Svcs)*
Boris Bogod *(VP-Cloud Ops-Global)*
Brett Michael Jackson *(CEO)*
Richard Ford *(CTO)*
Bruce Johnson *(VP-Sls-North America)*

Chisholm Energy Holdings, LLC (1)
801 Cherry St Ste 1200 Unit 20, Fort Worth, TX 76102
Tel.: (817) 953-6063
Web Site: http://www.chisholmenergy.com
Investment Holding Company; Oil & Gas Extraction
N.A.I.C.S.: 551112
Mark Whitley *(Founder & CEO)*
Aaron Gaydosik *(CFO)*
Scott Herstein *(VP-Bus Dev)*

Civitas Learning, Inc. (1)
100 Congress, Austin, TX 78701
Tel.: (512) 692-7175
Web Site: http://www.civitaslearning.com
Online Education Services
N.A.I.C.S.: 513210
Charles Thornburgh *(Co-Founder & Chief Strategy & Innovation Officer)*
Mark Milliron *(Co-Founder & Chief Learning Officer)*
Eric Grunden *(Chief Customer Officer)*
Chris Hester *(CEO)*

Consolidated Precision Products Corp. (1)
4200 W Valley Blvd, Pomona, CA 91769
Tel.: (909) 595-2252
Web Site: http://www.cfi-pac.com
Sales Range: $75-99.9 Million
Aluminum, Steel & Magnesium Mfr
N.A.I.C.S.: 331524

Plant (Domestic):

Consolidated Precision Products Corp. - Bloomington (2)
8701 Harriet Ave S, Minneapolis, MN 55420-2729
Tel.: (952) 881-1000
Web Site: http://www.cppcorp.com
Sales Range: $50-74.9 Million
Nonferrous Castings Primarily for the Aerospace Market
N.A.I.C.S.: 331524

Consolidated Precision Products Corp. - Cudahy (2)
8333 Wilcox Ave, Cudahy, CA 90201-5919
Tel.: (323) 773-2363
Web Site: http://www.ccpcorp.com
Sales Range: $25-49.9 Million
Emp.: 128
Mfr of Aluminum Castings
N.A.I.C.S.: 331524

Consolidated Precision Products Corp. - Pomona (2)
4200 W Valley Blvd, Pomona, CA 91769
Tel.: (909) 595-2252
Web Site: http://www.cfi-pac.com
Sales Range: $25-49.9 Million
Emp.: 155
Aluminum Foundries
N.A.I.C.S.: 331524

Consolidated Precision Products Corp. - Rancho Cucamounga (2)
11000 Jersey Blvd, Rancho Cucamonga, CA 91730-5103
Tel.: (909) 987-4721
Web Site: http://www.cppcorp.com
Sales Range: $25-49.9 Million
Emp.: 140
Mfr of Steel & Ferrous Investment Castings
N.A.I.C.S.: 331512

Subsidiary (Domestic):

Pacific Cast Technologies, Inc. (2)
150 Queen Ave SW, Albany, OR 97322
Tel.: (541) 926-7711
Web Site: http://www.paccast.com
Sales Range: $50-74.9 Million
Emp.: 400
Cast Titanium Part & Aerospace Component Mfr
N.A.I.C.S.: 331529

Selmet, Inc. (2)
PO Box 689, Albany, OR 97321-0231
Tel.: (541) 926-7731
Web Site: http://www.selmetinc.com
Sales Range: $10-24.9 Million
Emp.: 250
Provider of Foundry Services
N.A.I.C.S.: 331529
Dick Humphrey *(VP-Tech)*
Derek Schweitzer *(VP-Sls)*
Art Hill *(VP-Engrg)*

Subsidiary (Domestic):

Onamac Industries Inc. (3)
11504 Airport Rd Bldg G, Everett, WA 98204
Tel.: (425) 743-6676
Web Site: http://www.onamac.com
Sales Range: $75-99.9 Million
Precision Machinery Parts Mfr
N.A.I.C.S.: 333248
Jim Loveall *(Chm)*
Mike Thorburn *(Pres)*
Rick Skorka *(Supvr-CNC Mill)*
Steve Ulvestad *(Dir-Mfg & Production Control)*

DKSH (Shanghai) Co., Ltd. (1)
3/F Tomson Commercial Building 710 Dong Fang Road, Pudong, Shanghai, 200122, China
Tel.: (86) 2158300518
Web Site: http://www.dksh.com
Commercial Sourcing, Marketing, Logistics & Distribution Support Services
N.A.I.C.S.: 425120
Annie Bai *(Dir-HR)*
Alfred Chen *(Mgr-Bus Dev & Pharmaceutical Industry)*
Christian Haueter *(Gen Mgr-Hospital & Tech)*
William Li *(Gen Mgr-Gear Machinery & Tech)*

Duravant LLC (1)
3500 Lacey Rd Ste 290, Downers Grove, IL 60515
Tel.: (630) 635-3910
Web Site: http://www.duravant.com
Holding Company; Industrial Engineered Equipment Mfr
N.A.I.C.S.: 551112
Michael J. Kachmer *(Pres & CEO)*
Craig Reuther *(CFO)*
Eleni Yianas *(VP-Mktg)*
David Parker *(VP-HR)*
Vivek Joshi *(VP-Ops)*
Kurt Huelsman *(Sr VP-Corp Dev)*
Rich Proszowski *(Chief Digital Officer)*
Georg Waldmueller *(Sr VP-Bus Dev)*

Subsidiary (Domestic):

Arpac LLC (2)
9555 W Irving Park Dr, Schiller Park, IL 60176
Tel.: (847) 678-9034
Web Site: http://www.arpac.com
Packaging Machinery Mfr
N.A.I.C.S.: 333993
Rick Allegretti *(Pres)*
Gary Ehmka *(VP-Sls & Mktg)*

Cloud Packaging Solutions LLC (2)
424 Howard Ave, Des Plaines, IL 60018-1910
Tel.: (847) 390-9410
Web Site: http://www.cloudeg.com
Contract Packaging Services & Container Mfr; Packaging Machinery Developer & Mfr
N.A.I.C.S.: 561910
Donn D. Hartman *(VP-Equipment & Engrg Svcs)*
Michael Werner *(Gen Mgr)*

FMH Conveyors LLC (2)
410 Horizon Dr Ste 200, Suwanee, GA 30024
Tel.: (678) 745-3720
Web Site: http://www.fmhconveyors.com
Conveyor & Conveying Equipment Mfr
N.A.I.C.S.: 333922
Mark Hogan *(VP-Ops)*
Kurt Huelsman *(Sr VP & Gen Mgr)*
Ashley Jones *(Sr Coord-Mktg & Sls)*

Plant (Domestic):

FMH Conveyors, LLC - Jonesboro Operations (3)
107 Flint St, Jonesboro, AR 72401
Tel.: (870) 935-0970
Web Site: http://www.fmhconveyors.com
Emp.: 100
Conveyor & Conveying Equipment Mfr
N.A.I.C.S.: 333922
Garland Martin *(VP-Sls & Mktg)*

Subsidiary (Domestic):

Hamer-Fischbein LLC (2)
14650 28th Ave North, Plymouth, MN 55447
Tel.: (763) 231-0100
Web Site: http://www.hamerinc.com
Packaging Machinery Mfr
N.A.I.C.S.: 333993
Dan Brown *(Pres)*

Division (Domestic):

Hamer-Fischbein LLC - Fischbein Division (3)
151 Walker Rd, Statesville, NC 28625
Tel.: (704) 871-1159
Web Site: http://www.fischbein.com
Sales Range: $25-49.9 Million
Packaging Machinery & Material Handling Equipment Mfr
N.A.I.C.S.: 333993
Lee Thompson *(VP-Sls & Mktg)*
Allan Sutherland *(Sr VP-Ops-Statesville)*

Subsidiary (Non-US):

Fischbein Deutschland GmbH (4)
Lohestrasse 63, 53773, Hennef, Germany
Tel.: (49) 224 2873 1622
Emp.: 2
Packaging Machinery & Material Handling Equipment Mfr
N.A.I.C.S.: 333993
Vincent Valentine *(Gen Mgr)*

Fischbein Packaging (S) Pte Ltd. (4)
No 37 Lorong 23 Geylang, 02-03 Yu Li Indus Bldg, Singapore, 388371, Singapore
Tel.: (65) 67450246
Web Site: http://www.fischbein.com
Sales Range: $10-24.9 Million
Emp.: 4
Packaging Machinery & Material Handling Equipment Mfr
N.A.I.C.S.: 333993
Ricky Tan *(Reg Mgr)*

Fischbein S.A. (4)
Paepsem Business Park Boulevard Paepsem 8, 1070, Brussels, Belgium
Tel.: (32) 25551170
Web Site: http://www.fischbein.com
Sales Range: $10-24.9 Million
Packaging Machinery & Material Handling Equipment Mfr
N.A.I.C.S.: 333993
Rene Bontemps *(VP & Gen Mgr-Eastern Hemisphere Bus Unit)*
Eddy Palstermans *(Mgr-Ops)*
Ostilio Bonacini *(Mgr-Fin & Admin)*
Benedicte Van Kan *(Mgr-Pur & Logistics)*

Fischbein-Saxon, Ltd. (4)
Alexandra Business Centre 274 Alma Road, Enfield, EN3 7RS, Middlesex, United Kingdom
Tel.: (44) 8443722877
Web Site: http://www.fischbein.com
Emp.: 20
Packaging Machinery & Material Handling Equipment Mfr
N.A.I.C.S.: 333993
Yvan Mannekens *(Dir-Sls)*
Barry Cox *(Mgr-Sls & Svc)*

Subsidiary (Domestic):

Key Technology, Inc. (2)
150 Avery St, Walla Walla, WA 99362
Tel.: (509) 529-2161
Web Site: http://www.key.net

WARBURG PINCUS LLC

Warburg Pincus LLC—(Continued)
Sales Range: $125-149.9 Million
Process Automation Systems Designer, Mfr, Retailer & Servicer
N.A.I.C.S.: 333310
John J. Ehren *(Pres & CEO)*
Louis C. Vintro *(Sr VP-Bus Dev & Global Ops)*
Jeff Nielsen *(Sls Mgr-Southeast & South Central)*
Daniel Leighty *(VP-Sls-Global)*

Subsidiary (Non-US):

Key Technology Australia Pty. Ltd. (3)
Unit 6 7-11 Rodeo Drive, Dandenong South, 3175, VIC, Australia
Tel.: (61) 387108200
Web Site: http://www.key.net
Food Processing Automation System Mfr
N.A.I.C.S.: 333241

Key Technology B.V. (3)
Beijerdstraat 10, 4112 NE, Beusichem, Netherlands
Tel.: (31) 345509900
Mfr, Designer & Retailer of Processing Automation Systems
N.A.I.C.S.: 333241
Daniel Leighty *(Mng Dir)*

Subsidiary (Domestic):

Marlen International, Inc. (2)
4780 NW 41st St Ste 100, Riverside, MO 64150
Tel.: (913) 888-3333
Web Site: http://www.marlen.com
Food Processing Equipment Mfr
N.A.I.C.S.: 333241
Doug Vogelsmeier *(Mgr-Product)*
Pete Johnson *(Product Mgr-Carruthers)*
John Fields *(Reg Sls Mgr)*
Jan Erik Kuhlmann *(Sr VP-Global Sls & Mktg)*
Bill Williams *(Mgr-Product-Carruthers Brand Food Processing Equipment)*
Matt White *(Reg Sls Mgr-Northeast)*
Bob Campbell *(Pres)*

National Presort, LP (2)
3901 La Reunion Pkwy, Dallas, TX 75212
Tel.: (214) 634-2288
Web Site: http://www.npisorters.com
Sales Range: $1-9.9 Million
Emp.: 70
Automated Sortation Solutions Services
N.A.I.C.S.: 541512
Catherine Daboub *(Treas)*
Dwayne Machacek *(Mgr-Mfg Engrg)*
Meinhard Nattermann *(Mgr-Engrg Program)*
Brent Daboub *(Pres)*

Ohlson Packaging, Inc. (2)
490 Constitution Dr, Taunton, MA 02780
Tel.: (508) 977-0004
Web Site: http://www.ohlsonpack.com
Packaging Machinery Mfr
N.A.I.C.S.: 333993
Timothy Griffin *(Mgr-Mktg)*

PPM Technologies, Inc. (2)
500 E Illinois St, Newberg, OR 97132-2307
Tel.: (503) 538-3141
Web Site: http://www.ppmtech.com
Sales Range: $10-24.9 Million
Emp.: 120
Technologies & Solutions for Food Processing & Packaging
N.A.I.C.S.: 423830
Robert Pedersen *(Pres)*

Subsidiary (Non-US):

PPM TECHNOLOGIES EMEA Ltd. (3)
Axis 40 Oxford Road, Stokenchurch, HP14 3SX, Buckinghamshire, United Kingdom
Tel.: (44) 1494682800
Conveyor Equipment Mfr
N.A.I.C.S.: 333922

PPM TECHNOLOGIES INDIA Ltd. (3)
3rd Floor Madhupala Towers Greenlands Ameerpat, Hyderabad, 500016, India
Tel.: (91) 4066627735
Conveyor Equipment Mfr
N.A.I.C.S.: 333922

Division (Non-US):

Rosenqvists Food Technologies (3)
Grinfelstadsvagen 360, Gards Kopinge, SE 291 97, Kristianstad, Sweden
Tel.: (46) 44204400
Web Site: http://foodtechnologies.rosenqvists.com
Sales Range: $10-24.9 Million
Emp.: 25
Food Processing Equipment Mfr
N.A.I.C.S.: 333241

Subsidiary (Domestic):

Woodside Electronics Corporation (2)
1311 Bluegrass Pl, Woodland, CA 95776
Tel.: (530) 666-9190
Web Site: http://www.wecotek.com
Electronic Sorting Services
N.A.I.C.S.: 115114
Eric Horner *(VP)*
Don Douglas *(Pres)*

Endurance Energy Ltd. (1)
Suite 800 215 9th Avenue SW, Calgary, T2P 1K3, AB, Canada
Tel.: (587) 230-2767
Holding Company; Natural Gas Exploration & Extraction
N.A.I.C.S.: 551112
Steven R. VanSickle *(Pres & CEO)*
David Summers *(COO)*
David Cymbalisty *(VP-Drilling & Completions)*
Tom Park *(VP-Mktg & Corp Plng)*
David Pyke *(VP-Land & Contracts)*

Experity, Inc. (1)
877 Velocity Dr Machesney Park, Rockford, IL 61115
Tel.: (877) 697-4696
Healthcare Solutions
N.A.I.C.S.: 621610
Benjamin Barlow *(Chief Medical Officer)*
David Stern *(CEO)*
Callan Young *(Sr VP-Mktg)*
Matt Blosl *(Chief Revenue Officer)*
Tim Dybvig *(Sr VP-Patient Engagement)*
Melissa Rohwedder *(Mktg Dir-Creative)*
Brian Berning *(CFO)*

Subsidiary (Domestic):

DocuTAP Inc. (2)
101 S Phillips Ave Ste 300, Sioux Falls, SD 57104
Tel.: (605) 336-6962
Web Site: http://www.docutap.com
Sales Range: $1-9.9 Million
Emp.: 250
Software Development Services
N.A.I.C.S.: 541511
Eric McDonald *(Founder & CEO)*
Amanda Tiede *(Sr Dir-Software Engrg & Client Priorities)*
Patrice Pash *(Dir-Consulting Svcs)*
Christina Boyd *(VP-Client Solutions)*
Darin Vander Well *(Dir-Product Mktg)*
Dusty Schroeder *(VP-Mktg)*
Eric Pederson *(Dir-Software Engrg-Corp Priorities)*
Tammy Mallow *(Dir-Contracting & Credentialing)*
Matt Blosl *(Chief Revenue Officer)*
Monte Sandler *(Exec VP-Revenue Cycle Mgmt)*
Adam Steinberg *(Sr VP-Acct Mgmt)*
Robert Rueckl *(CFO)*
Jared Lisenby *(Sr VP-Sls)*
Ron Curtis *(Sr VP-Product)*
Mike Noble *(Sr VP-RCM Ops)*
David Sommers *(CTO)*
Kerri Tietgen *(Exec VP-People & Culture)*
Ben Tischler *(Sr VP-RCM Sls & Solutions)*

Subsidiary (Domestic):

Practice Velocity, LLC (3)
1673 Belvidere Rd, Belvidere, IL 61008
Tel.: (815) 544-7480
Web Site: http://www.practicevelocity.com
Medical Software Development Services
N.A.I.C.S.: 541512
Jaimie Kowalski *(VP-Mktg)*
Joshua Porter *(VP-Bus Dev)*

Fetch Insurance Services, LLC (1)
3805 W Chester Pike Ste 240, Newtown Square, PA 19073
Tel.: (855) 332-1550
Web Site: http://www.gopetplan.com
Pet Health Insurance Providers
N.A.I.C.S.: 812910
John Giannuzzi *(Chm)*
Paul Guyardo *(CEO)*

FlexXray LLC (1)
3751 New York Ave Ste 130, Arlington, TX 76014-4404
Tel.: (817) 453-3539
Web Site: http://www.flexxray.com
Food Inspection & Recovery Services
N.A.I.C.S.: 561499
Kevin Fritzmeyer *(CEO)*
Chris Keith *(VP-Sls & Customer Svc)*

Gabriel Brothers Inc. (1)
55 Scott Ave, Morgantown, WV 26508
Tel.: (304) 292-6965
Web Site: http://www.mygabes.com
Family Clothing & Accessories Retailer
N.A.I.C.S.: 458110
Jason T. Mazzola *(CEO)*
Rachel P. Cook *(VP-Mktg)*

Subsidiary (Domestic):

Old Time Pottery Inc. (2)
480 River Rock Blvd, Murfreesboro, TN 37128
Tel.: (615) 890-6060
Web Site: http://www.oldtimepottery.com
Sales Range: $125-149.9 Million
Emp.: 230
Home Decor & Housewares Retailer
N.A.I.C.S.: 459999
Scott Peterson *(Pres & CEO)*
Bill Hauck *(VP-Msdg)*
Eric Polk *(Mgr-Store)*
Nancy Stockwell *(Dir-Mktg & Adv)*
Reba Beasley *(Dir-Store Ops)*

Housatonic Publications Inc. (1)
65 Bank St, New Milford, CT 06776-2701
Tel.: (860) 354-2261
Web Site: http://www.ctcentral.com
Rev: $2,300,000
Emp.: 50
Newspaper Publishers
N.A.I.C.S.: 513110

Infoniqa Holding GmbH (1)
Bahnhofstrasse 100, CH-8001, Zurich, Switzerland
Tel.: (41) 445627172
Software Solutions & Services
N.A.I.C.S.: 513210
Leon Vergnes *(Mng Dir)*

Integra Telecom Holdings, Inc. (1)
1201 NE Lloyd Blvd Ste 500, Portland, OR 97232-1259
Tel.: (503) 748-1000
Web Site: http://www.integratelecom.com
Facilities-Based, Integrated Communication Services
N.A.I.C.S.: 517810
Robert E. Guth *(Vice Chm)*
Matt Smith *(VP-Sls-Bus Svcs)*
Jesse Selnick *(CFO)*
Ken Smith *(Exec VP-Sls)*
Karen Clauson *(Gen Counsel, Sec & Sr VP)*
Tom Weaver *(VP-Indirect Channel)*
Michael Sharpe *(COO)*
Felicity O'Herron *(Sr VP-HR)*
Martha Tate *(VP-Sls-Wholesale & Government Education)*
Craig Pierce *(VP-Sls-Enterprise, Indirect & Small Bus)*
Paul Sunu *(Chm)*
Marc Willency *(CEO)*

Subsidiary (Domestic):

Integra Telecom, Inc. (2)
4690 Colorado St SE, Minneapolis, MN 55372
Tel.: (952) 226-7000
Web Site: http://www.integratelecom.com
Telephone Equipment Services
N.A.I.C.S.: 517111
Robert E. Guth *(Vice Chm)*
Dan Wigger *(Sr VP-Minnesota & North Dakota)*
Jesse Selnick *(CFO)*

U.S. PRIVATE

Marc Willency *(CEO)*
Karen Clauson *(Gen Counsel & Sr VP)*
Jason Koenders *(CTO & Sr VP)*
Michael Sharpe *(Exec VP-Ops)*

Subsidiary (Domestic):

Integra Telecom of North Dakota, Inc. (3)
4749 Amber Valley Pkwy Ste A, Fargo, ND 58104
Tel.: (701) 365-4500
Sales Range: $10-24.9 Million
Emp.: 30
Wired Telecommunications Carriers
N.A.I.C.S.: 517111

Integra Telecom of Oregon Inc. (3)
1201 N E Lloyd Blvd Ste 500, Portland, OR 97232
Tel.: (503) 453-8000
Web Site: http://www.ogitel.com
Sales Range: $100-124.9 Million
Telephone Communication Services
N.A.I.C.S.: 551112
Matt Fahey *(Sr VP-Fin)*

Integra Telecom of Washington, Inc. (3)
20435 72nd Ave S Ste 150, Kent, WA 98032
Tel.: (253) 867-1000
Telecommunications Consultant
N.A.I.C.S.: 541690

United Communications, Inc. (3)
389 SW Scalehouse Ct Ste 100, Bend, OR 97702
Tel.: (541) 388-8711
Web Site: http://www.uci.net
Long Distance Telephone Communications Services
N.A.I.C.S.: 517121

Subsidiary (Domestic):

ProTel Inc. (2)
1336 South 1100 East, Salt Lake City, UT 84105
Tel.: (801) 485-1107
Web Site: http://www.protelnetworks.com
Emp.: 20
Communication Service
N.A.I.C.S.: 334210
David Glissmeyer *(Founder)*

K2 Insurance Services, LLC (1)
12651 High Bluff Dr Ste 250, San Diego, CA 92130
Tel.: (858) 866-8966
Web Site: http://www.k2ins.com
Insurance & Underwriting Services
N.A.I.C.S.: 524298
Pat Kilkenny *(Chm)*
Robert J. Kimmel *(CEO)*
Matt LuBien *(COO)*
Nate Hunter *(CFO)*
Rebecka Kilkenny *(CIO)*
Mark Smith *(Pres)*

Subsidiary (Domestic):

Aegis Security Insurance Co. (2)
2407 Park Dr Ste 200 PO Box 3153, Harrisburg, PA 17110-3153
Tel.: (717) 657-9671
Web Site: http://www.aegisfirst.com
Sales Range: $50-74.9 Million
Emp.: 97
Fire, Marine & Casualty Insurance
N.A.I.C.S.: 524126
Trevor Hash *(Sr VP-Surety)*
William Wollyung *(Pres)*

Subsidiary (Domestic):

JMT Property Corp. (3)
2407 Park Dr Ste 200, Harrisburg, PA 17110-9303 (100%)
Tel.: (717) 657-9671
Sales Range: $25-49.9 Million
Emp.: 3
Local Passenger Transportation
N.A.I.C.S.: 485999
Martin Lane *(CEO)*

Subsidiary (Domestic):

Mid-America Risk Managers, LLC (2)

COMPANIES — WARBURG PINCUS LLC

5036 S 136th St Ste 2, Omaha, NE 68137-1680
Tel.: (402) 894-2666
Web Site: https://www.marm.net
Insurance Agencies & Brokerages
N.A.I.C.S.: 524210
Brett Hyde (Pres)

Kestra Financial, Inc. (1)
5707 SW Pkwy Bldg 2 Ste 400, Austin, TX 78735
Tel.: (512) 697-6000
Web Site: http://www.kestrafinancial.com
Holding Company; Securities Brokerage, Dealing & Investment Advisory Services
N.A.I.C.S.: 551112
James Poer (CEO)
Daniel Schwamb (Exec VP-Bus Dev)
John Amore (Exec VP-Wealth Mgmt)
Kris Chester (COO & Exec VP)
Joel Bennett (CFO)
Stephen Langlois (Pres)
Elena Stebakov (VP-Product & Platform Mgmt)
Chris MacLaughlin (CMO & Exec VP)

Subsidiary (Domestic):

Arden Trust Company (2)
2751 Centerville Rd Ste 400, Wilmington, DE 19808
Tel.: (302) 246-5400
Web Site: http://www.ardentrust.com
Trust Services
N.A.I.C.S.: 523991
Theresa De Leon (Natl Dir-Sls)
Doug Sherry (Pres)

Bluespring Wealth Partners LLC (2)
5707 SW Pkwy Ste 2-400, Austin, TX 78735-6221
Tel.: (737) 443-2110
Web Site: https://www.bluespringwealth.com
Wealth Management Firm
N.A.I.C.S.: 523999
Stuart Silverman (Chm)
Alan Brum (VP-Internal Bus Dev)
David Canter (Pres)

Subsidiary (Domestic):

Tatro Capital LLC (3)
104 Richmond Ave, Nicholasville, KY 40356-1110
Web Site: http://www.tatrocapital.com
Intermediation
N.A.I.C.S.: 523910

Vector Wealth Management (3)
43 Main St SE Ste 236, Minneapolis, MN 55414-1048
Tel.: (612) 378-7560
Web Site: http://www.vectorwealth.com
Investment Advisory Services
N.A.I.C.S.: 523940
Jason Ranallo (Dir-Portfolio Mgmt Grp)
Thomas G. Fee (Mng Partner)

WealthPartners, LLP (3)
220 Trace Colony Park Dr, Ridgeland, MS 39157
Tel.: (601) 414-4455
Web Site: http://www.wealthpartnersnfp.com
Investment Advice
N.A.I.C.S.: 523940
Jeff Turnipseed (Pres)
Steven C. Massey (Dir-Retirement Plan Svcs)
John Hill (CEO)
Steve Massey (Dir)

Welty Capital Management, LLC (3)
3650 Mt Diablo Blvd Ste 103, Lafayette, CA 94549-3768
Tel.: (925) 283-4960
Web Site: http://www.weltycapital.com
Portfolio Management
N.A.I.C.S.: 523940
Richard Welty (Owner)

Subsidiary (Domestic):

H. Beck, Inc. (2)
2440 Research Blvd Ste 500, Rockville, MD 20850
Tel.: (301) 944-5900
Web Site: http://www.hbeckinc.com
Security Brokerage & Investment Advisory Services
N.A.I.C.S.: 523150
Michelle Barry (Pres)
Rob Costello (COO)

Kestra Investment Services, LLC (2)
5707 SW Pkwy Bldg 2 Ste 400, Austin, TX 78735
Tel.: (512) 697-6000
Web Site: http://www.kestrafinancial.com
Securities Brokerage & Dealing Services
N.A.I.C.S.: 523150
Kelly Yin (VP & Controller)

Mariner Finance, LLC (1)
8211 Town Ctr Dr, Baltimore, MD 21236
Web Site: http://www.marinerfinance.com
Consumer Lending & Credit Intermediation
N.A.I.C.S.: 522291
Joshua C. Johnson (CEO)
Scott Frankle (Sr Exec VP)
Bob Burns (Sr VP-Branch Ops)
Laird Oskin (Sr VP-Acq)
James Schneider (COO)
Mark Keidel (CFO)

Subsidiary (Domestic):

Personal Finance Company, LLC (2)
8211 Town Center Dr, Nottingham, MD 21236 (100%)
Web Site: http://www.personalfinancecompany.com
Personal Loan & Other Financial Services
N.A.I.C.S.: 522291

Mercator Solutions FZE (1)
Dubai Silicon Oasis, Dubai, United Arab Emirates
Tel.: (971) 4 501 3700
Web Site: http://www.mercator.com
IT Services
N.A.I.C.S.: 513210
David Tibble (Chm)
Corma Whelan (CEO)
Raj Bhavnani (CFO)
Eric Selvadurai (COO)

Subsidiary (US):

Revenue Management Systems Inc. (2)
2003 Western Ave Ste 700, Seattle, WA 98121
Tel.: (206) 209-5400
Web Site: http://ww1.revenuemanagement.com
Business Consulting Services
N.A.I.C.S.: 541611
Scott Schade (CTO)
Dan Whelan (CEO)
Eric Nordling (COO)
David Kern (VP-Global Sls)
Martin Kaduc (VP-Sls & Support-Americas)
Adrian Flores (VP-EMEA)
Andrew Millar (VP-Sls & Support-Asia Pacific)
Sean Moriarty (VP-Dev)

Oona Holdings Pte. Ltd. (1)
30 Raffles Place #23-01 Oxley, Singapore, 048622, Singapore
Tel.: (65) 63207500
Web Site: https://www.oona-insurance.co
Holding Company
N.A.I.C.S.: 551112

Subsidiary (Domestic):

Oona Insurance Pte Ltd (2)
30 Raffles Place #23-01 Oxley, Singapore, 048622, Singapore
Tel.: (65) 63207500
Insurance Services
N.A.I.C.S.: 524210

Parksons Packaging Ltd. (1)
701/702 Indiabulls Finance Centre Tower 1 7th Floor, Senapati Bapat Marg Elphinstone Road, Mumbai, 400 013, India
Tel.: (91) 2266667200
Web Site: http://www.parksonspackaging.com
Folding Cartons Mfr
N.A.I.C.S.: 322212

Subsidiary (Domestic):

M.K. PrintPack (P) Ltd. (2)
201 2nd Floor Crystal Paradise Veera Desai Road Andheri W, Village Ambivali, Mumbai, India
Tel.: (91) 2226302728
Web Site: http://www.mkprintpack.com
Packaging Products Mfr
N.A.I.C.S.: 322299
Anil Kumar (Mng Dir)
Sanjeev Kumar (Mng Dir-Technical)
Vipin Kalra (Dir-Ops)

Pregis LLC (1)
1650 Lk Cook Rd Ste 400, Deerfield, IL 60015
Tel.: (847) 597-2200
Web Site: http://www.pregis.com
Protective Packaging Products Mfr & Distr
N.A.I.C.S.: 326112
Kevin J. Baudhuin (Pres & CEO)

Subsidiary (Domestic):

Sharp Packaging Systems, LLC (2)
N59 W22387 Silver Spring Dr, Sussex, WI 53089
Tel.: (262) 246-8815
Poly Bags & Packaging Equipment Mfr
N.A.I.C.S.: 326111
Raymond McDowell (VP-Mfr)

Qualifacts Systems, Inc. (1)
315 Deaderick St Ste 2300, Nashville, TN 37238
Tel.: (615) 386-6755
Web Site: http://www.qualifacts.com
Computer System Design Services
N.A.I.C.S.: 541512
David Klements (Pres)
Robert Patton (Sr Dir-Ops)
Jeremy Landa (CFO)
Tom Keen (CTO)
Todd Charest (Chief Product Officer)
Michelle Endres (Sr Dir-HR)
Brandi Sanders (Sr Dir-Client Svcs)
Josh Schoeller (CEO)
Andrew Park (Mng Dir)

Quantum Health, LLC (1)
7450 Huntington Park Dr Ste 100, Columbus, OH 43235-5617
Tel.: (614) 846-4318
Web Site: http://www.quantum-health.com
Sales Range: $1-9.9 Million
Emp.: 330
Develops & Operates Healthcare Management Programs
N.A.I.C.S.: 923130
Kara J. Trott (Founder)
Randy Gebhardt (Chief Innovation Officer)
Sandy Freer (VP-Bus Partner Rels)
Elliott R. Tobias (VP-HR)
Shannon Skaggs (Pres)
Clanton Lynch (VP-Sls-Southwest)
Dana Andrews (Chief Medical Officer)
Debra A. Gold (Sr VP-Strategy)
Scott Doolittle (CFO)
Mike Formica (Exec VP-Sls)
Tony Callander (VP-HR)
Diane Bernard (VP-Mktg)
Jenny Corotis Barnes (VP-Legal)
Bill Lahrmann (Sr VP-Client Engagement)
John Hallock (Chief Comm Officer)
Zane Burke (CEO)

Reorg Research, Inc. (1)
11 E 26th St 12th Fl, New York, NY 10010
Tel.: (212) 588-8890
Web Site: http://www.reorg.com
Sales Range: $25-49.9 Million
Emp.: 200
Investment Services
N.A.I.C.S.: 523999
Kent Collier (Founder & CEO)
Rich Jones (CTO)
Steve Vigliotti (CFO)
Lynda Logan (Chief Revenue Officer)
Emily Ruda (VP-Fin & People Ops)
Jeff Winter (CMO)

Sotera Health LLC (1)
9100 S Hills Blvd Ste 300, Broadview Heights, OH 44147
Tel.: (440) 262-1410
Web Site: http://soterahealth.com
Holding Company; Contract Sterilization & Ionization Supply Chain Management, Laboratory Testing & Consulting Services
N.A.I.C.S.: 551112
Mike Smith (CIO)
Philip MacNabb (Pres-Sterigenics)
Jeff Nelson (Pres-Nelson Labs)
Kevin Brooks (Pres-Nordion)
Kristin Gibbs (CMO)
Matthew J. Klaben (Sr VP & Gen Counsel)
Kevin Theriault (Sr VP-Ops)
Kurt Roth (Sr VP-Corp Dev & Strategy)
Michael B. Petras Jr. (CEO)

Subsidiary (Non-US):

Nordion Inc. (2)
447 March Road, Ottawa, K2K 1X8, ON, Canada
Tel.: (613) 592-2790
Web Site: http://www.nordion.com
Sales Range: $200-249.9 Million
Drug Development & Disease Management Products Distr
N.A.I.C.S.: 541715
Leslee Tape (VP-HR)
Riaz Bandali (Pres)
Don Lim (VP)

Branch (Domestic):

Sterigenics International LLC - Shared Services Center (2)
2015 Spring Rd Ste 650, Oak Brook, IL 60523
Tel.: (630) 928-1700
Web Site: http://www.sterigenics.com
Office Administrative & Information Technology Services
N.A.I.C.S.: 561110

Subsidiary (Domestic):

Sterigenics U.S., LLC (2)
3 Pkwy N Ctr Ste 100N, Deerfield, IL 60019
Tel.: (847) 607-6060
Web Site: http://www.sterigenics.com
Contract Sterilization & Ionization Supply Chain Management, Laboratory Testing & Consulting Services
N.A.I.C.S.: 541990
Michael J. Mulhern (Chm)

StorHub Management Pte Ltd (1)
615 Toa Payoh Lorong 4, Singapore, 319516, Singapore
Tel.: (65) 63372000
Web Site: https://www.storhub.com
Real Estate
N.A.I.C.S.: 531390

Subsidiary (Non-US):

Storage Plus Corp. (2)
BC Plaza 2-3-10 Kudanminami, Chiyoda-ku, Tokyo, 102-0074, Japan
Tel.: (81) 332375101
Web Site: https://www.storageplus.co.jp
Storage & Warehousing Services
N.A.I.C.S.: 493190

Sweeping Corporation of America, Inc. (1)
4141 Rockside Rd Ste 100, Cleveland, OH 44131
Tel.: (216) 777-2750
Web Site: http://www.sweepingcorp.com
Emp.: 1,200
Industrial Sweeping Services
N.A.I.C.S.: 561730
Christopher Valerian (Pres & CEO)
Michael Latanza (Exec VP-Strategy & Dev)
Matt Spencer (COO & Exec VP)
Dan Nauert (CFO-Interim)
Paula Malone (Chief HR Officer)
Doug Saunders (CIO)
Erin Quinn (Gen Counsel & VP)
Joe Frola (Exec VP)
Robert Bartee (Sr VP-EHS)
Keith Cordesman (Pres-East Area)
Michael Siragusa (VP-Sls)

Subsidiary (Domestic):

A-1 Striping Inc. (2)
3855 E 10 Mile Rd, Warren, MI 48091
Tel.: (586) 755-4440
Rev.: $1,548,000
Emp.: 12
Poured Concrete Foundation & Structure Contractors
N.A.I.C.S.: 238110
Jerry Patalon (Owner)

Accusweep Services, Inc. (2)
2645 Commerce Dr, Columbia, SC 29205
Tel.: (803) 798-4391
Web Site: http://www.accusweep.com
Sales Range: $1-9.9 Million
Emp.: 50
Landscape Architectural Services

WARBURG PINCUS LLC   U.S. PRIVATE

Warburg Pincus LLC—(Continued)
N.A.I.C.S.: 541320
David McCaskil *(Owner)*

Bills Sweeping Service, Inc. (2)
715 W Fletcher Ave, Orange, CA 92865
Tel.: (714) 637-3180
Web Site: http://www.streetsweeper.com
Sales Range: $1-9.9 Million
Emp.: 20
Highway And Street Construction
N.A.I.C.S.: 237310
Deanna Carter *(Sec)*

Buckeye Sweeping, Inc. (2)
1071 Eastwood Ave, Akron, OH 44305
Tel.: (330) 798-9200
Web Site: http://www.buckeyesweeping.com
Sales Range: $1-9.9 Million
Emp.: 13
Sanitary Services, Nec
N.A.I.C.S.: 561730
Marnie Maze *(Mgr)*

Central Valley Sweeping, Inc. (2)
PO Box 6787, Visalia, CA 93290-6787
Tel.: (559) 739-7532
Road Transportation Support
N.A.I.C.S.: 488490

CleanStreet Inc. (2)
1937 W 169th St, Gardena, CA 90247
Tel.: (310) 538-5888
Web Site: http://www.cleanstreet.com
Specialty Trade Contractors
N.A.I.C.S.: 238990
Chase Harris *(Dir-Fleet Maintenance)*
Jere Costello *(Founder)*

Contract Sweepers & Equipment Company (2)
561 Short St, Columbus, OH 43215
Tel.: (614) 221-7441
Web Site: http://www.sweepers.com
Sales Range: $10-24.9 Million
Emp.: 100
Sanitary Services, Nec
N.A.I.C.S.: 561730
Bill Miller *(CFO)*
Mark Borden *(Area Mgr)*
Mark Dusseau *(Area Mgr)*
Kenny Crabtree *(Mgr-Parts)*

DMC Sweeping, LLC (2)
222 S Bollinger St, Visalia, CA 93291
Tel.: (559) 625-4636
Web Site: http://www.dmcsweeping.com
Rev.: $1,656,000
Emp.: 9
All Other Miscellaneous Waste Management Services
N.A.I.C.S.: 562998
Joann Bawks *(Co-Founder)*
Christy Bawks *(VP)*

Major Clean, Inc. (2)
500 Scholtz Rd, Charlotte, NC 28217-2139
Tel.: (704) 201-5532
Web Site: http://www.majorcleaninc.com
Foundation, Structure & Building Exterior Contractors
N.A.I.C.S.: 238190
Scott Major *(Founder)*

Sunset Property Services, Inc. (2)
16251 Construction Cir W, Irvine, CA 92606
Tel.: (949) 551-5151
Sales Range: $1-9.9 Million
Emp.: 80
Landscaping Services
N.A.I.C.S.: 561730
John D. Howhannesian *(Pres)*

Sweeping South, Inc. (2)
1930 Varner St, Summerville, SC 29483-8040
Tel.: (843) 821-2192
Web Site: http://www.sweepingsouth.com
Street & Parking Lot Sweeping Services
N.A.I.C.S.: 561210

USA Services Of Florida, Inc. (2)
448 Spring Hammock Ct, Longwood, FL 32750
Tel.: (407) 339-1800
Web Site: http://www.sweepingcorp.com
Landscaping Services
N.A.I.C.S.: 561730

Terra Energy Partners LLC (1)
4828 Loop Central Dr Ste 900, Houston, TX 77081
Tel.: (281) 936-0355
Web Site: http://www.terraep.com
Oil & Gas Exploration & Production
N.A.I.C.S.: 211120
Michael S. Land *(CEO)*

TriMark USA LLC (1)
505 Collins St, South Attleboro, MA 02703
Tel.: (508) 399-2400
Web Site: http://www.trimarkusa.com
Emp.: 1,500
Commercial Cooking & Food Service Equipment Mfr
N.A.I.C.S.: 423440
Jerry Hyman *(CEO)*
Kim Gill Rimsza *(Pres-TriMark Gill Mktg)*
Joe Thibert *(Pres-TriMark United East)*
Marty Monnat *(Pres-TriMark Strategic)*
Tom Wienclaw *(Pres-TriMark SS Kemp)*

Subsidiary (Domestic):

Adams-Burch, LLC (2)
1901 Stanford Ct, Landover, MD 20785
Tel.: (301) 276-2000
Web Site: http://www.adams-burch.com
Restaurant Equipment & Supplies Whslr
N.A.I.C.S.: 423440
Daniel M. Blaylock *(Owner)*
Kevin McClamroch *(VP)*
Jeff Brodsky *(Sls Mgr)*
Rick Gallagher *(VP)*
Tom McMahon *(Sls Mgr)*

Hockenbergs Equipment & Supply Co., Inc. (2)
14063 Cornhusker Rd, Omaha, NE 68138
Tel.: (402) 339-8900
Web Site: http://www.hockenbergs.com
Foodservice Equipment & Supplies Distr
N.A.I.C.S.: 423440

R.W. Smith & Co. (2)
10101 Old Grove Rd, San Diego, CA 92131
Tel.: (858) 530-1800
Web Site: http://www.rwsmithco.com
Emp.: 500
Restaurant Equipment & Supplies Distr
N.A.I.C.S.: 423440
Allan Keck *(Pres)*
Danielle Fontenot *(Mgr-Bus Dev-Dallas Territory)*
Michael Smith *(Mgr-Bus Dev-Los Angeles Territory)*
Cristina O. *(Mgr-Bus Dev-San Francisco Territory)*
Sarah R. *(Mgr-Bus Dev-Los Angeles Territory)*
Colleen G. *(Mgr-Bus Dev-San Diego Territory)*
Anthony H. *(Sr Acct Mgr-Natl Accts)*

S.S. Kemp & Co., LLC (2)
4567 Willow Pkwy, Cleveland, OH 44125
Tel.: (216) 271-7700
Web Site: http://www.trimarkusa.com
Emp.: 200
Food Service Equipment & Supplies Dealer & Designer
N.A.I.C.S.: 423440
Tom Wienclaw *(Pres)*
Steve Fishman *(Exec VP)*

Branch (Domestic):

Trimark SS Kemp (3)
590 Vista Park Dr, Pittsburgh, PA 15205
Tel.: (412) 787-3250
Web Site: http://www.trimarkusa.com
Food Service Equipment & Supplies Distr
N.A.I.C.S.: 423440
Tony Pappis *(Gen Mgr)*
Carl Fazio *(Mgr-Bus Dev)*

Subsidiary (Domestic):

Strategic Equipment & Supply Corp. (2)
1461 S Belt Line Rd Ste 100, Coppell, TX 75019
Tel.: (469) 240-7200
Emp.: 400
Foodservice Equipment & Supplies Distr
N.A.I.C.S.: 423850
Marty Monnat *(Pres)*
Karen McCain *(CFO)*

TriMark Marlinn Inc. (2)
6100 W 73rd St, Bedford Park, IL 60638
Tel.: (708) 496-1700
Web Site: http://www.trimarkusa.com
Restaurant Equipment & Supplies Distr
N.A.I.C.S.: 423440
Mike Siegel *(Pres)*
Paul Meek *(Controller)*

TriMark Raygal Inc (2)
210 Commerce, Irvine, CA 92602
Tel.: (949) 474-1000
Web Site: http://www.trimarkusa.com
Emp.: 180
Commercial Kitchen Designer & Commercial Equipment Installation Services
N.A.I.C.S.: 238990

TriMark RobertClark (2)
2801 Mcgaw Ave, Irvine, CA 92614
Tel.: (949) 753-7171
Web Site: http://www.trimarkusa.com
Restaurant Equipments Design, Custom Engineering & Installation Services
N.A.I.C.S.: 541330
Robert Heimstra *(Pres)*

Trident Energy Management Limited (1)
129 Wilton Road, London, SW1V 1JZ, United Kingdom
Tel.: (44) 20 3879 9171
Web Site: http://www.trident-energy.com
Oil & Gas Exploration & Production Services
N.A.I.C.S.: 213112
Jean-Michel Jacoulot *(CEO)*
Eric Descourtieux *(CFO)*
Francois Raux *(COO)*
Oliver Byrne *(Gen Counsel)*

Joint Venture (Non-US):

Hess Equatorial Guinea Inc. (2)
Triton House Calle Acasio, Mane, Malabo, 90726, Equatorial Guinea
Tel.: (240) 24090728
Oil & Gas Exploration Services
N.A.I.C.S.: 213111

VistaPharm, Inc. (1)
630 Central Ave, New Providence, NJ 07974
Tel.: (205) 981-1387
Web Site: http://www.vistapharm.com
Generic Pharmaceutical Mfr
N.A.I.C.S.: 325412

Vivtera Global Business LLP (1)
Sector 43 Road, Gurgaon, 122011, Haryana, India
Tel.: (91) 9654860164
Financial Services
N.A.I.C.S.: 523999
Harpreet Duggal *(Mng Partner)*

Subsidiary (US):

Arise Virtual Solutions, Inc. (2)
3450 Lakeside Dr Ste 620, Miramar, FL 33027
Tel.: (954) 392-2600
Web Site: http://www.arise.com
Home-Based Virtual Contact Center Services
N.A.I.C.S.: 561499
Doug Vinson *(CMO)*

WebPT, Inc. (1)
625 S 5th St Building A, Phoenix, AZ 85004
Tel.: (866) 221-1870
Web Site: http://www.webpt.com
Cloud-Based Electronic Medical Records Systems
N.A.I.C.S.: 513210
Heidi Jannenga *(Co-Founder & Chief Clinical Officer)*
Brad Jannenga *(Co-Founder)*
Kim Hamby *(Mgr-Sls Dev)*
Shawn McKee *(VP-Mktg)*
Nita Chen *(CFO)*
Ashley Chaffin Glover *(CEO)*

Subsidiary (Domestic):

Clinicient, Inc. (2)
111 SW 5th Ave Ste 700, Portland, OR 97204
Tel.: (503) 525-0275
Web Site: http://www.clinicient.com
Rev.: $3,500,000
Emp.: 32

Custom Computer Programming Services
N.A.I.C.S.: 541511
Stephen Molen *(VP-Sls)*
Rick Jung *(Pres)*
Steven Sipowicz *(CFO)*
Jim Neumann *(VP-Mktg)*
Janet Lanham *(VP-Svc Delivery)*
Jeremy Cader *(VP-Product, IT & Engrg)*
Saundra Pennington *(VP-People & Process)*
Sturdy McKee *(Sr Dir-Client Executives)*
Doug Schumann *(VP-Customer Success)*

Zenith Energy, L.P. (1)
3900 Essex Ln Ste 700, Houston, TX 77027
Tel.: (713) 395-6200
Web Site: http://www.zenithterminals.com
Oil & Petroleum Terminals Storage
N.A.I.C.S.: 424710
Jeffrey Armstrong *(CEO)*
Jay Reynolds *(Chief Commi Officer)*
Carlos Ruiz *(CFO)*
Rich Reynolds *(COO)*

Subsidiary (Domestic):

Zenith Energy Logistics Partners LP (2)
3900 Essex Ln Ste 700, Houston, TX 77027
Tel.: (713) 395-6200
Web Site: http://www.zenithterminals.com
Sales Range: $100-124.9 Million
Crude Oil & Petroleum Products Terminalling, Storage, Throughput & Transloading
N.A.I.C.S.: 424710
John S. Blanchard *(Pres)*
Dennis Courtney *(VP-Bus Dev)*

Subsidiary (Domestic):

Arc Logistics LLC (3)
6255 W County Road 110 S, French Lick, IN 47432
Tel.: (812) 936-7701
Emp.: 2
Transportation Services
N.A.I.C.S.: 488999
Aristeo Canales *(Owner)*

Arc Terminals Holdings LLC (3)
3000 Research Forest Dr Ste 250, Spring, TX 77381
Tel.: (281) 292-3008
Emp.: 15
Holding Company
N.A.I.C.S.: 551114
John Blanchard *(Pres)*

Arc Terminals Joliet Holdings LLC (3)
1035 W Laraway Rd, Joliet, IL 60436
Tel.: (815) 726-2016
Holding Company
N.A.I.C.S.: 551112

WARCO CONSTRUCTION INC.
3910 Stuart Andrews Blvd, Charlotte, NC 28217
Tel.: (704) 521-5200
Web Site:
http://www.warcoconstruction.com
Year Founded: 1985
Sales Range: $10-24.9 Million
Emp.: 130
Fireproofing & Interior Construction Services
N.A.I.C.S.: 238990
Donald Dobbins *(Superintendent-Field)*
Jim Tolman *(VP)*
Sherri Rader *(Mgr-Acctg)*
Andrew Brooks *(Project Mgr)*
Mark Tompkins *(Project Mgr)*
Michael Thomas *(Project Mgr)*
Randy McFalls *(Project Mgr)*
Hans Warren Jr. *(Pres)*

WARD CORPORATION
642 Growth Ave, Fort Wayne, IN 46808
Tel.: (260) 426-8700
Web Site: http://www.wardcorp.com
Year Founded: 1964

Sales Range: $10-24.9 Million
Emp.: 225
Aluminum Foundries
N.A.I.C.S.: 331524
Vern D. Ward *(Co-Founder & CEO)*
Marion Ward *(Co-Founder & Pres)*
Sky Heiney *(Controller)*
Tim Atkins *(VP-Sls)*
Don Ward *(VP)*
Kimberley Almeida *(Mgr-HR)*

WARD DAVIS ASSOCIATES INC.
2623 Manhattan Beach Blvd, Redondo Beach, CA 90278
Tel.: (310) 643-6977
Web Site: http://www.warddavis.com
Rev.: $14,795,647
Emp.: 27
Electronic Parts & Equipment
N.A.I.C.S.: 423690
William C. Breyer *(Pres)*

WARD IMPLEMENT COMPANY
525 Main St, Beech Grove, KY 42322
Tel.: (270) 273-3572
Web Site:
  http://www.wardimplementco.com
Sales Range: $10-24.9 Million
Emp.: 23
Farm Implements
N.A.I.C.S.: 423820
Herman Ward *(Pres)*
Timothy Ward *(VP)*

WARD INTERNATIONAL TRUCKS INC.
2101 Perimeter Rd, Mobile, AL 36615
Tel.: (251) 433-5616
Web Site:
  http://www.wardintltrucks.com
Year Founded: 1985
Sales Range: $25-49.9 Million
Emp.: 65
Dealer of New & Used Trucks, Tractors & Trailers
N.A.I.C.S.: 441110
William A. Ward *(Pres)*
Chip Wright *(VP-Ops)*
Lynn Waite *(Acct Mgr-Lease)*
Chip Maier *(Controller)*

WARD MECHANICAL EQUIPMENT INC.
210 Marketridge Dr, Ridgeland, MS 39157
Tel.: (601) 956-3002
Web Site: http://www.wardmech.com
Rev.: $12,000,000
Emp.: 40
Warm Air Heating & Air Conditioning
N.A.I.C.S.: 423730
Devere McLennan *(Pres)*
Blair Johnson *(VP)*

WARD MUSCATELL AUTOMOTIVE GROUP
1313 30th Ave S, Moorhead, MN 56560
Tel.: (218) 477-7000
Web Site: http://www.muscatell.com
Rev.: $41,500,000
Emp.: 68
New & Used Car Dealers
N.A.I.C.S.: 441110
Ward Muscatell *(Pres)*

WARD PETROLEUM CORPORATION
502 S Fillmore St, Enid, OK 73702
Tel.: (580) 234-3229   OK
Web Site:
  http://www.wardpetroleum.com
Year Founded: 1971
Sales Range: $10-24.9 Million
Emp.: 59

Operates Oil & Gas Properties
N.A.I.C.S.: 221210
L. O. Ward *(Chm)*
William C. Ward *(Pres & CEO)*
Richard R. Tozzi *(CFO & Exec VP)*
Gilbert C. Tompson *(VP-Land)*

WARD TIMBER LTD
1101 Hwy 59 S, Linden, TX 75563
Tel.: (903) 756-7700
Web Site: http://www.wardtimber.com
Rev.: $32,000,000
Emp.: 75
Timber Product Mfr
N.A.I.C.S.: 423990
Linda Price *(Coord-Safety)*
Jim Moore *(Supvr-Procurement)*

WARD TRUCKING CORP.
1436 Ward Trucking Dr, Altoona, PA 16602
Tel.: (814) 944-0803   PA
Web Site:
  http://www.wardtrucking.com
Year Founded: 1931
Sales Range: $125-149.9 Million
Emp.: 1,057
General Commodities Transportation
N.A.I.C.S.: 484121
Michael P. Ward *(Exec VP)*
Bill T. Ward *(Pres)*
Mike Johnson *(Mgr-Territory Sls)*
Ed Slater *(Mgr-Ops)*
Ed R. Gaudio *(Mgr-Territory-Sls-Philadelphia)*
Greg Hrebinko *(Mgr-Territory-Sls-Pittsburgh)*
John Strenkowski *(Mgr-Territory-Sls-Pittsburgh)*

WARD WILLISTON OIL COMPANY
36700 Woodward Ave Ste 101, Bloomfield Hills, MI 48304
Tel.: (248) 594-6622
Web Site:
  http://www.wardwilliston.com
Year Founded: 1952
Sales Range: $50-74.9 Million
Oil & Gas Exploration
N.A.I.C.S.: 213112
Rodney Conway *(Sr VP)*

WARD/KRAFT, INC.
2401 Cooper St, Fort Scott, KS 66701
Tel.: (620) 223-5500   KS
Web Site: http://www.wardkraft.com
Year Founded: 1972
Sales Range: $150-199.9 Million
Emp.: 500
Business Forms & Label Mfr
N.A.I.C.S.: 323111
Roger Kraft *(Owner & CEO)*
Amy Clark *(Office Mgr-Ward/Kraft Ohio Sls)*
Gina Holt *(Pres-Natl Sls & Mktg)*
Phil Quick *(Pres-Mfg)*

Subsidiaries:

Ward/Kraft, Inc. - KANSAS Plant   (1)
2401 Cooper St, Fort Scott, KS 66701
Tel.: (620) 223-5500
Commercial Printing Services
N.A.I.C.S.: 323111

WARDENS OFFICE INC.
1415 J St, Modesto, CA 95354
Tel.: (209) 529-6321
Web Site:
  http://www.wardensopc.com
Sales Range: $10-24.9 Million
Emp.: 35
Office Supplies & Office Furniture
N.A.I.C.S.: 424120

Patrick Warden *(Chm)*
Joe Cunningham *(Pres-Furniture)*
Jerry Warden *(Owner)*

WARDS COVE PACKING COMPANY
303 NE Northlake Way, Seattle, WA 98105
Tel.: (206) 323-3200
Web Site: http://www.wardscove.com
Sales Range: $10-24.9 Million
Emp.: 50
Open-End Investment Funds
N.A.I.C.S.: 525910
Alec W. Brindle *(Chm)*

WARE INDUSTRIES
400 Metuchen Rd, South Plainfield, NJ 07080
Tel.: (908) 757-9000
Web Site:
  http://www.marinoware.com
Sales Range: $25-49.9 Million
Emp.: 392
Building Construction Material
N.A.I.C.S.: 236210
Chip Garner *(CEO)*
Michael Fenbert *(VP-Sls)*
Gerry Compton *(VP-Sls)*

Subsidiaries:

Marino/WARE   (1)
400 Metuchen Rd, South Plainfield, NJ 07080
Tel.: (908) 757-9000
Web Site: http://www.marinoware.com
Sales Range: $25-49.9 Million
Emp.: 100
Metal Framing Systems
N.A.I.C.S.: 236210
Chip Gardner *(Pres)*

WARE MALCOMB
10 Edelman, Irvine, CA 92618
Tel.: (949) 660-9128
Web Site:
  http://www.waremalcomb.com
Year Founded: 1972
Sales Range: $1-9.9 Million
Emp.: 450
Architectural Services
N.A.I.C.S.: 541310
Chris Strawn *(Principal)*
Tom Jansen *(Principal-Civil Engrg)*
Nelson Tello *(Project Mgr)*
Tobin Sloane *(CFO)*
Maureen Bissonnette *(Dir-Mktg)*
Ken Wink *(Exec VP)*
Jay Todisco *(Exec VP)*
Lawrence R. Armstrong *(CEO)*
Jinger Tapia *(Dir-Design)*
Moses Gonzales *(Dir-IT)*
Lon Stephenson *(Dir-Ops)*
Ted Heisler *(VP-Interior Architecture & Design)*
Tom Myers *(Reg VP)*
John Thomas *(Sr Designer)*
Debra Bryant *(Dir-Branding)*
Leslie Espiritu *(Dir-HR)*
Ilyes Nouizi *(Dir-Resource Svcs)*
Michael Petersen *(Principal-Architecture)*
Matt Brady *(Reg VP)*
Ruth Brajevich *(CMO)*
Kevin Evernham *(Principal-Phoenix)*
Cameron Trefry *(Principal-Chicago)*
Frank Di Roma *(Principal-Toronto)*
Jan Davis *(Dir-Comml Architecture)*
Alan Lambert *(Dir-Seattle)*
Cindy Kang *(Dir-Interior Architecture & Design-Seattle)*
Matt Chaiken *(Principal)*
Tiffany English *(Principal)*
Jim Terry *(Principal-Comml Architecture-Pleasanton)*
Radwan Madani *(Principal-Los Angeles)*

Michael Bennett *(Principal-New Jersey)*
Gary Drew *(VP-Pleasanton, San Francisco & Seattle)*
Lucas Corsbie *(Reg Mgr-Engrg)*
Lucas Corbie *(Dir-Civil Engrg)*
Kimberly Huffman *(Reg Dir-Ops)*
Nathan Dean *(Dir-Ops-San Diego)*
David Newson *(Mgr-Engrg-Toronto)*
Catherine Quintero *(Dir-Interior Architecture-Denver)*
Heather Groff *(Dir-Interior Architecture & Design-New York)*
Trevor Wells *(Mgr-Studio-Science & Tech)*
Cynthia Milota *(Dir-Workplace Strategy-Oak Brook)*
Joseph Stryker *(Dir-Architecture-Atlanta)*
Erica Godun *(Dir-Reg Ops-Northeast)*
Sergio Valentini *(Dir-Architecture-Los Angeles)*
Adam Segalla *(Mgr-Studio-Architecture-Seattle)*
Cory Adams *(Dir-Architecture)*

Subsidiaries:

Jansen Strawn Consulting Engineers, Inc.   (1)
45 W 2nd Ave, Denver, CO 80223-1431
Tel.: (303) 561-3333
Web Site: http://www.jansenstrawn.com
Emp.: 40
Engineeering Services
N.A.I.C.S.: 541330
Tom Jansen *(Pres)*

WARE OIL & SUPPLY COMPANY INC.
2715 S Byron Butler Pkwy, Perry, FL 32348-6309
Tel.: (850) 584-6666   FL
Year Founded: 1975
Sales Range: $200-249.9 Million
Emp.: 125
Provider of Petroleum Products
N.A.I.C.S.: 424720
Don Everett Jr. *(VP)*

WAREHEIM INSURANCE CONSULTANTS, INC.
8486 Seminole Blvd, Seminole, FL 33772
Tel.: (727) 397-3200
Web Site:
  http://www.wareheiminsurance.com
Sales Range: $1-9.9 Million
Emp.: 5
Insurance Agents
N.A.I.C.S.: 524210
Jim Wareheim *(Pres & CEO)*

WAREHOUSE DIRECT, INC
2001 S Mount Prospect Rd, Des Plaines, IL 60018   DE
Web Site:
  http://www.warehousedirect.com
N.A.I.C.S.: 459410
John Moyer *(Pres)*

WAREHOUSE EQUIPMENT & SUPPLY CO.
116 W Park Dr, Birmingham, AL 35211
Tel.: (205) 942-1900
Web Site:
  http://www.warehouseequipment.com
Year Founded: 1958
Rev.: $20,739,953
Emp.: 16
Material Handling Machinery Distr
N.A.I.C.S.: 423830
Hearal Guess *(Owner)*

WAREHOUSE HOME FURNISHINGS DISTRIBUTOR, INC.

WAREHOUSE HOME FURNISHINGS DISTRIBUTOR, INC.   U.S. PRIVATE

Warehouse Home Furnishings Distributor, Inc.—(Continued)
1851 Telfair St, Dublin, GA 31021
Tel.: (478) 275-3150　　GA
Web Site:
　http://www.farmershomefurniture.com
Year Founded: 1949
Furniture Retailers
N.A.I.C.S.: 449110
Clint Hall *(VP-Store Ops)*
Robbie Cook *(Exec Dir-Adv & Mktg)*
Claudia Peavy *(Exec Dir-HR)*

WAREHOUSE MARKET INC.
6207 S Peoria Ave, Tulsa, OK 74170
Tel.: (918) 749-6621
Web Site:
　http://www.warehousemarket.com
Sales Range: $125-149.9 Million
Emp.: 263
Grocery Retailer
N.A.I.C.S.: 445110
Sharon Harlan *(Office Mgr)*
Christian Cox *(Gen Counsel)*

WAREHOUSE SERVICES INC.
58 S Burty Rd, Piedmont, SC 29673
Tel.: (864) 422-9955
Web Site: http://www.wsionline.com
Sales Range: $25-49.9 Million
Emp.: 42
Provider of General Warehousing & Logistics Services
N.A.I.C.S.: 493110
Margaret Jill Cox *(CEO)*
Jeff Denning *(CFO)*
Kelli Rohlman *(Dir-Quality Assurance)*
Tim Steele *(Dir-Indus Rels)*

Subsidiaries:

Sky Transportation Services　　(1)
1001 Eastside Rd, El Paso, TX 79915
Tel.: (915) 778-8844
Web Site: http://www.sky-transportation.com
Sales Range: $1-9.9 Million
Emp.: 45
Trucking Except Local
N.A.I.C.S.: 484121
Albert M. Luna *(Pres)*
Ricardo De La Rosa *(VP & Gen Mgr)*
Manny Roman *(Dir-Safety)*
Jason Nesbitt *(VP-Ops)*

WAREHOUSE SOLUTIONS INC.
12562 Hwy 67, Lakeside, CA 92040
Tel.: (619) 873-4410
Web Site:
　http://www.warehousesolutions.com
Sales Range: $1-9.9 Million
Emp.: 22
Industrial Storage & Material Handling Equipment Distr
N.A.I.C.S.: 423830
Alex Molina *(Mgr-Sls)*
Mark Wallace *(Pres)*

WARFEL CONSTRUCTION CO.
1110 Enterprise Rd, East Petersburg, PA 17520
Tel.: (717) 299-4500
Web Site: http://www.warfelcc.com
Year Founded: 1911
Sales Range: $25-49.9 Million
Emp.: 135
Commercial & Institutional Building Construction Services
N.A.I.C.S.: 236220
Matthew Hartzler *(Pres)*
Kristi Reed *(Controller)*
Ralph Simpson Jr. *(CEO)*
Rupert Taylor III *(CFO & Exec VP)*

WARHAFTIG & LITTMAN ADV/SALES PROMOTION/PR
24 Clonover Rd, West Orange, NJ 07052-4304
Tel.: (973) 731-7963　　DE
Year Founded: 1983
Sales Range: Less than $1 Million
Emp.: 2
N.A.I.C.S.: 541810
Annette Littman *(Pres)*

WARI INC.
1717 Pennsylvania Ave NW, Washington, DC 20006
Tel.: (202) 559-9196　　NV
Year Founded: 2014
Liabilities: $94,887
Earnings: ($119,485)
Shell Company
N.A.I.C.S.: 525990
Amadou Diop *(Pres & CFO)*

WARING OIL COMPANY, LLC
431 Port Terminal Cir, Vicksburg, MS 39183
Tel.: (601) 636-1065
Web Site: http://www.waringoil.com
Sales Range: $150-199.9 Million
Emp.: 450
Supplier of Wholesale Fuels, Lubricants & Greases
N.A.I.C.S.: 424720

WARKO ROOFING COMPANY INC.
18 Morgan Dr, Reading, PA 19608
Tel.: (610) 796-4545　　PA
Web Site:
　http://www.thewarkogroup.com
Year Founded: 1952
Sales Range: $25-49.9 Million
Emp.: 200
Provider of Roofing Construction & Services
N.A.I.C.S.: 238220
Robert J. Warkoczewski *(Pres & CEO)*

WARMEL CORP.
636 N Eckhoff St, Orange, CA 92868
Tel.: (714) 937-5266
Web Site: http://www.warmel.com
Rev.: $20,100,000
Emp.: 10
Fast-Food Restaurant, Chain
N.A.I.C.S.: 722513
William Brownstein *(VP)*
Mark Brownstein *(VP)*
Peter Horner *(VP)*
Bryan Carmack *(VP)*
Laura Williams *(Office Mgr)*

WARMINSTER FIBERGLASS, LLC
3630 Central Pkwy SW, Decatur, AL 35603
Tel.: (215) 953-1260　　AL
Year Founded: 2020
Plastics Product Mfr
N.A.I.C.S.: 326199
Ty Batchelor *(Pres)*

Subsidiaries:

W.F.C. Company, Inc.　　(1)
725 County Line Rd, Southampton, PA 18966
Tel.: (215) 953-1260
Web Site:
　http://www.warminsterfiberglass.com
Rev.: $6,000,000
Emp.: 60
All Other Plastics Product Mfr
N.A.I.C.S.: 326199
Carl Schmidt *(Treas)*
John Roley *(Pres)*
Branch (Domestic):

Warminster Fiberglass Co.　　(2)
1428 Elberta St, Jacksonville, TX 75766
Tel.: (903) 586-7666
Web Site:
　http://www.warminsterfiberglass.com
Mineral Wool Mfr
N.A.I.C.S.: 327993
John Roley *(Pres)*

WARMLYYOURS.COM INC.
590 Telser Rd Unit B, Lake Zurich, IL 60047
Tel.: (847) 540-7775　　IL
Web Site:
　http://www.warmlyyours.com
Year Founded: 1998
Sales Range: $25-49.9 Million
Emp.: 20
Online Retailer of Home Heating Products & Services
N.A.I.C.S.: 423730
Julia Stalfort *(Founder & COO)*
Elodie Pasek *(Dir-Bus Dev-North America)*
Julia Billen *(Pres)*

WARNER CANDY COMPANY
1240 Don Haskins Dr Ste B, El Paso, TX 79936-7887
Tel.: (847) 928-7200　　IL
Year Founded: 1927
Sales Range: $10-24.9 Million
Emp.: 100
Wholesale Distributor of Candy, Salted & Roasted Nuts & Novelties
N.A.I.C.S.: 424450
Mike Halverson *(Pres)*

WARNER COMMUNICATIONS CORP.
1340 Baur Blvd, Saint Louis, MO 63132
Tel.: (314) 993-7070　　MO
Web Site:
　http://www.warnercomm.com
Year Founded: 1962
Sales Range: $1-9.9 Million
Emp.: 40
Radio, Television, And Electronic Stores
N.A.I.C.S.: 449210
Leslie Zucker *(VP)*
Steve Guller *(Pres)*

WARNER CONNECT, INC.
452 Northco Dr NE Ste 100, Fridley, MN 55432-3310
Tel.: (612) 454-1100　　MN
Web Site:
　http://www.warnerconnect.com
Year Founded: 2001
IT Consulting, Managed Services, Voice & Data Connectivity, Productivity Software & Web Services
N.A.I.C.S.: 541512
Henry Warner *(CEO)*
Scott Muggli *(Owner)*

WARNER FERTILIZER COMPANY
1405 Hwy 2227, Somerset, KY 42503
Tel.: (606) 679-8484
Web Site: http://www.warnerfc.com
Sales Range: $10-24.9 Million
Emp.: 25
Fertilizer Sales
N.A.I.C.S.: 325314
C. Richard Warner *(Pres & CEO)*
Paulette M. Large *(Controller)*
Gary Rowe *(Mgr-Credit)*
Gerald Edens *(Plant Mgr)*

WARNER MANUFACTURING COMPANY
13435 Industrial Park Blvd, Minneapolis, MN 55441
Tel.: (763) 559-4740
Web Site: http://www.warnertool.com
Rev.: $22,900,000
Emp.: 44
Hand & Edge Tools
N.A.I.C.S.: 332216
Craig Warner *(Pres)*

WARNER PACIFIC INSURANCE SERVICES, INC.
32110 Agoura Rd, Westlake Village, CA 91361
Tel.: (818) 225-0101
Web Site:
　http://www.warnerpacific.com
Year Founded: 1982
Sales Range: $1-9.9 Million
Emp.: 100
Insurance Agencies & Brokerages
N.A.I.C.S.: 524210
David Nelson *(Co-CEO)*
John Nelson *(Co-CEO)*
Jeff Papenfus *(Sr VP-Sls-California)*
Debbie Vaillancourt *(Sr VP-Ops)*
Clare Resnick *(CFO)*
John Kurath *(VP-Sls-Colorado)*
Mike Ashamalla *(VP-IT Ops)*
Memo Rodriguez *(VP-Application Dev)*
John Nelson Sr. *(Pres)*

Subsidiaries:

BeneUSA LLC　　(1)
1851 Lk Dr W Ste 350, Chanhassen, MN 55317
Tel.: (952) 361-0600
Web Site: http://www.beneusa.com
Insurance Agencies & Brokerages
N.A.I.C.S.: 524210
Timothy Swenson *(Gen Mgr)*

WARNER PRESS, INC.
2902 Enterprise Dr, Anderson, IN 46013
Tel.: (765) 644-7721
Web Site:
　http://www.warnerpress.org
Year Founded: 1881
Religious Materials Publisher
N.A.I.C.S.: 513130
C. Eric King *(Pres)*
Michael Meadows *(Mgr-Mktg & Comm)*

WARNER ROBINS SUPPLY CO. INC.
2756 Watson Blvd, Warner Robins, GA 31093-2948
Tel.: (478) 953-4100　　GA
Web Site: http://www.wrsupply.com
Year Founded: 1947
Sales Range: $25-49.9 Million
Emp.: 230
Provider of Lumber & Other Building Materials
N.A.I.C.S.: 423310
Chris Baroni *(Gen Mgr)*

WARNER VINEYARDS
706 S Kalamazoo St, Paw Paw, MI 49079-1558
Tel.: (269) 657-3165　　MI
Web Site:
　http://www.warnerwines.com
Year Founded: 1938
Sales Range: $1-9.9 Million
Emp.: 10
Wines, Champagnes & Non-Alcoholic Sparkling Juices Mfr
N.A.I.C.S.: 312130
Patrick K. Warner *(Owner)*
James Warner *(Pres)*

WARNER'S STELLIAN CO., INC.
550 Atwater Cir, Saint Paul, MN 55103-4401
Tel.: (651) 222-0011

COMPANIES

WARNERS
Web Site:
http://www.warnersstellian.com
Rev.: $28,154,911
Emp.: 900
Electric Household Appliances
N.A.I.C.S.: 449210
Carla Warner (Dir-Sls & VP)
Jeff Warner (Pres)
Bill Warner (Dir-Mdsg & Customer Svc)

WARNERS MOTOR EXPRESS INC.
W Country Club Rd, Red Lion, PA 17356
Tel.: (717) 244-4537   PA
Web Site:
http://www.warnersmoving.com
Year Founded: 1982
Sales Range: $10-24.9 Million
Emp.: 30
Provider of Household Goods Transport
N.A.I.C.S.: 493190
Donald H. Warner (Pres)

WAROQUIER COAL INC.
3056 Washington Ave, Clearfield, PA 16830
Tel.: (814) 765-5681
Sales Range: $10-24.9 Million
Emp.: 75
Coal
N.A.I.C.S.: 423520
Joseph L. Waroquier Jr. (Pres)

WARP TECHNOLOGIES INC.
PO Box 500, Holly Springs, NC 27540-0500
Tel.: (919) 552-2311
Year Founded: 1988
Sales Range: $10-24.9 Million
Emp.: 150
Noncellulosic Organic Fiber Mfr
N.A.I.C.S.: 325220
Marek Alapin (Principal)

WARRANTY CORPORATION AMERICA
22660 Executive Dr Ste 122, Sterling, VA 20166-9535
Tel.: (800) 243-8830
Year Founded: 1985
Sales Range: $25-49.9 Million
Emp.: 200
Provider of Warranty Insurance Services
N.A.I.C.S.: 524128
Doug Toutor (Pres)

Subsidiaries:

Planet Metrix   (1)
3110 Crossing Park, Norcross, GA 30071
Tel.: (770) 416-9222
Web Site: http://www.waca.com
Rev.: $190,000
Emp.: 3
Telecommunications Consultant
N.A.I.C.S.: 541690

WARREN ALLOY VALVE FITTING LP
7200 Mykawa Rd, Houston, TX 77033
Tel.: (713) 672-9416
Web Site:
http://www.warrenalloy.com
Rev.: $15,000,000
Emp.: 200
Valves & Fittings
N.A.I.C.S.: 423830
Adam D. Finn (Pres)

WARREN AVERETT, LLC
2500 Acton Rd, Birmingham, AL 35243
Tel.: (205) 979-4100   AL
Web Site:
http://www.warrenaverett.com
Emp.: 800
Accounting, Tax & Consulting Services
N.A.I.C.S.: 541211
Paul M. Perry (Sr Mgr-Consulting)
Dana Schmidt (Dir-Pro Dev)
Douglas B. Schauer (Partner)
Lisa K. Billings (Partner)
F. William Aderholt (Partner-Tax Div)
April A. Harry (CFO)
Jeffrey J. Burleson (Partner)
Dawn Barranco (Principal)
Allison Deskin (Principal-Tax Div)
Kelly Cochran (Dir-HR)
Marlene M. McCain (Partner)
Nancy F. Clevenger (Principal-Tax Div)
Ann Cotton (Firm Administrator)
Chris Morow (CIO)
Scott Bradbary (Chief Talent Officer)
Mary F. Elliiott (COO)
Thomas E. Sisson (Chief Growth Officer)
Todd Decker (CMO & Head-Bus Dev)
Laura Watkins (Mgr-Mktg-Personal Svcs & HR Solutions)
Mary Elliott (CEO)
Colleen Aldridge (Mgr-Consulting Div)
Barbara Blackerby (Principal-Estate & Trust Tax Div)
Jimmy Musso (Sr Mgr-Audit Div)

WARREN COUNTY WATER DISTRICT
523 US Highway 31-W Bypass, Bowling Green, KY 42101
Tel.: (270) 842-0052
Web Site:
http://www.warrenwater.com
Year Founded: 1974
Sales Range: $10-24.9 Million
Emp.: 58
Water Supply & Irrigation Systems Services
N.A.I.C.S.: 221310
John Dix (Gen Mgr)
Ryan Leisey (Mgr-Engrg & Construction)
Jeff Peeples (Mgr-Fin & Admin)
Tim Minnicks (Mgr-Construction)
Regina Coffee (Supvr-Billing & Customer Svc)
Robin Thomas (Coord-Ops & Customer Svc)
Mirna Casas (Coord-Customer Svc)
Henry Honaker (Chm)

WARREN DISTRIBUTING CO.
2 Laurel Dr, Flanders, NJ 07836
Tel.: (973) 927-2727
Web Site: http://www.warrenbeer.com
Year Founded: 1975
Sales Range: $150-199.9 Million
Emp.: 633
Distr of Beer & Other Fermented Malt Liquors
N.A.I.C.S.: 424810
Frank Banco (CEO)
Frank Banko III (Pres)

WARREN DISTRIBUTING INC.
8737 Dice Rd, Santa Fe Springs, CA 90670
Tel.: (562) 789-3360
Web Site: http://www.warrendist.com
Sales Range: $25-49.9 Million
Emp.: 55
Automotive Supplies & Parts
N.A.I.C.S.: 423120
Dave Erlenbach (VP-IT)
Jim Takakuwa (Gen Mgr-Las Vegas)
Alma Talton (Controller)
Brian Weiss (Pres)
Eric Katnic (Controller)
Gary Jacobson (Mgr-Pur)
Pat Winters (VP-IT)

WARREN DISTRIBUTION, INC.
727 S 13th St, Omaha, NE 68102-3204
Tel.: (402) 341-9397   NE
Web Site: http://www.wd-wpp.com
Year Founded: 1922
Sales Range: $150-199.9 Million
Emp.: 600
Mfr, Marketer & Distributor of Industry Oils & Greases, Anti-Freeze & Automotive Accessories
N.A.I.C.S.: 324191
Robert Schlott (Chm & CEO)
Richard Jacobson (VP)
Jim Douglas (Sr VP-Ops)

Subsidiaries:

Pace Transportation   (1)
2849 River Rd, Council Bluffs, IA 51501   (100%)
Tel.: (402) 341-9397
Sales Range: $10-24.9 Million
Emp.: 70
Provider of Automotive Services
N.A.I.C.S.: 493120

WARREN ELECTRIC SUPPLY INC.
281 Dix Ave, Queensbury, NY 12804
Tel.: (518) 793-0274
Web Site:
http://www.warrenelectricsupply.com
Sales Range: $10-24.9 Million
Emp.: 20
Wire & Cable
N.A.I.C.S.: 423610
Brain Olejarski (Gen Mgr)

WARREN EQUITY PARTNERS, LLC
1030 2nd St S Ste 201, Jacksonville Beach, FL 32250
Tel.: (904) 746-7027
Web Site:
http://www.warrenequity.com
Year Founded: 2015
Privater Equity Firm
N.A.I.C.S.: 551112
Henrik Dahlback (Partner & COO)
Steven Wacaster (Mng Partner)
Scott Bruckmann (Partner)
Michael Zhang (VP)
Michael Ouyang (VP)

Subsidiaries:

ADB Companies, Inc.   (1)
21 Progress Pkwy, Union, MO 63084
Tel.: (314) 426-5200
Web Site: http://www.adbcompanies.com
Utility Engineering & Construction Services
N.A.I.C.S.: 237990
Chad Johnson (CEO)
Rusty Keeley (CEO)
Andrew Trautman (Controller)
John Naccarato (Sr VP-Bus Dev)
Anthony Sumner (Sr VP-OSP West)
Jeremy Bryan (Sr VP-OSP East)
Dennis Mooney (Sr VP)
Raymond J. Boehm (Sr VP-Risk Mgmt)
DeLayne Black (VP-Fleet Mgmt)
Bianca Strickland (Dir-HR)

Subsidiary (Domestic):

Mercury Communications, Inc.   (2)
18777 US Hwy 66, Pacific, MO 63069
Tel.: (636) 717-2700
Web Site:
http://www.mercurycommunications.com
Wireless Telecommunication Line Construction Services
N.A.I.C.S.: 237130
Jeffery Fischer (Pres)

PrimeTech Communications Inc.   (2)
4505 Mulhauser Rd, West Chester, OH 45011
Tel.: (513) 942-6000
Web Site: http://www.primetechusa.com
Electrical Contractor
N.A.I.C.S.: 238210
Dave Schmuelling (Project Mgr)
Brad Shoemaker (CEO)

ZeroDay Technology Solutions, Inc.   (2)
2675 Scott Ave Ste A, Saint Louis, MO 63103
Tel.: (314) 684-4350
Web Site: http://www.zero-day.com
Information Technology Support Services
N.A.I.C.S.: 541990
Mike Rupinski (Pres)

Magneto & Diesel Injector Service, Inc.   (1)
7902 FM 1960 Bypass W, Houston, TX 77338
Tel.: (713) 928-5686
Web Site: http://www.mddistributors.com
Diesel Engine Parts & Components Distr
N.A.I.C.S.: 423830
Trey Ingram (CEO)

Magnolia River Services, Inc.   (1)
408 Bank St, Decatur, AL 35601
Tel.: (256) 773-9420
Web Site: http://www.magnolia-river.com
Rev.: $3,474,200
Emp.: 34
Engineeering Services
N.A.I.C.S.: 541330
Ronnie Hoff (Founder)
Hayden Strickland (VP-Sys Engrg & GIS)
Heath McCleskey (Pres)
Samir Jain (CEO)
Ronald S. Hoff Jr. (COO & Exec VP)

Subsidiary (Domestic):

Heath & Associates Inc.   (2)
108 W Warren St Ste 300, Shelby, NC 28150-5396
Tel.: (704) 487-8516
Web Site: http://www.heathweb.com
Engineeering Services
N.A.I.C.S.: 541330
Eric Scott Heath (CEO)

Meridian Waste Acquisitions, LLC   (1)
1010 Vlg Park Ln Ste 103, Greensboro, GA 30642
Tel.: (770) 691-6350
Solid Waste Collection, Disposal & Recycling Services
N.A.I.C.S.: 562998
Wally Hall (CEO)

Mobotrex, Inc.   (1)
109 W 55th St, Davenport, IA 52806
Tel.: (563) 323-0009
Web Site: http://www.mobotrex.com
Traffic Solutions
N.A.I.C.S.: 488490
Tom Wells (Mgr-Svc)

New Urban Forestry, LLC   (1)
1010 Winterville Rd, Athens, GA 30605
Tel.: (706) 389-0398
Web Site: http://www.newurbanforestry.com
Landscaping Services
N.A.I.C.S.: 561730
John Ritzler (Owner)

SSP Innovations, LLC   (1)
6766 S Revere Pkwy Ste 100, Centennial, CO 80112
Tel.: (720) 279-9894
Web Site: http://www.sspinnovations.com
Custom Software Development & Consulting Services
N.A.I.C.S.: 541613
Skye Perry (CEO)
Aaron Patterson (Pres)
Brett Maxam (CFO)
Adam Tonkin (CTO)
Darrell Rhodes (Exec VP)
Keith Freeman (Dir-Mktg)

Superior Industrial Maintenance Company, LLC   (1)
4801 Stough Rd, Concord, NC 28027
Tel.: (704) 795-0001
Web Site: http://www.gosuperior.net
Highway, Street & Bridge Construction
N.A.I.C.S.: 237310

WARREN EQUITY PARTNERS, LLC

Warren Equity Partners, LLC—(Continued)
Fred Bishop (Pres & COO)

WARREN FABRICATING CORPORATION
3240 Mahoning Ave NW, Warren, OH 44483
Tel.: (330) 847-0596
Web Site: http://www.warfab.com
Sales Range: $25-49.9 Million
Emp.: 90
Fabricated Structural Metal
N.A.I.C.S.: 332312
Eric Rebhan (CEO)
Regina Mitchell (Pres)

Subsidiaries:

Warren Fabricating Corporation - Hubbard Facility (1)
7845 Chestnut-Ridge Rd, Hubbard, OH 44425-9702
Tel.: (330) 534-5017
Fabricated Machine Mfr
N.A.I.C.S.: 332999

Warren Fabricating Corporation - Niles (1)
907 S Main St, Niles, OH 44446
Tel.: (330) 544-4101
Web Site: http://www.warfab.com
Sales Range: $10-24.9 Million
Emp.: 20
Fabricated Structural Metal Mfr
N.A.I.C.S.: 332312

WARREN HENRY AUTOMOBILES INC.
20800 NW 2nd Ave, Miami, FL 33169
Tel.: (305) 654-3900
Web Site: http://www.warrenhenryauto.com
Sales Range: $300-349.9 Million
Emp.: 280
New & Used Car Dealerships
N.A.I.C.S.: 441110
Warren Henry Zinn (Owner, Pres & CEO)

Subsidiaries:

Keys Auto Center (1)
1618 N Roosevelt Bd, Key West, FL 33040
Tel.: (305) 294-5126
Web Site: https://www.keysautocenter.com
Car Dealership &
N.A.I.C.S.: 441110
Lee Holt (Gen Mgr)

Subsidiary (Domestic):

Niles Sales & Service, Inc. (2)
3500 N Roosevelt Blvd, Key West, FL 33040
Tel.: (305) 294-1003
Web Site: http://www.nilesgm.com
Sales Range: $10-24.9 Million
Emp.: 50
New Car Dealers
N.A.I.C.S.: 441110
Roberta Chango (Controller)
Stephen Bender (Mgr-Sls)
Victor Ovidiyenko (Mgr-Sls)
Steve Hungate (Mgr-Sls & Internet)
Bob Ouellet (Dir-Svc)
John Griffin (Mgr-Parts)
Tony Lazarus (Mgr-Fin)
Roger Morgan (Mgr-Svc)

WARREN INDUSTRIES INC.
3100 Mount Pleasant St, Racine, WI 53404
Tel.: (262) 639-7800
Web Site: http://www.wrind.com
Rev.: $38,800,000
Emp.: 250
Packaging & Labeling Services
N.A.I.C.S.: 561910
David Namowicz (Pres)
Phil Paul (Controller)
Thomas Nemotz (CFO)

WARREN LUMBER & MILLWORK
256 Belvidere Ave, Washington, NJ 07882-3091
Tel.: (908) 835-4200
Year Founded: 1971
Sales Range: $25-49.9 Million
Emp.: 150
Provider of Lumber & Other Building Materials
N.A.I.C.S.: 423310

WARREN MARKETING, INC.
17 Oakview Dr, Cape Elizabeth, ME 04107
Tel.: (207) 831-2457
Year Founded: 1979
Sales Range: $10-24.9 Million
Emp.: 1
N.A.I.C.S.: 541810
Mel Warren (Owner)

WARREN MIDTOWN MOTORS INC.
1995 Market St, Warren, PA 16365
Tel.: (814) 723-5400
Web Site: http://www.midtownmotors.com
Sales Range: $10-24.9 Million
Emp.: 43
Car Whslr
N.A.I.C.S.: 441110
Charles Johnson (Pres)

WARREN MOTORS, INC.
4530 Brentwood Ave, Jacksonville, FL 32206
Tel.: (904) 356-8491 FL
Web Site: http://www.warrenmotorsinc.com
Year Founded: 1955
Sales Range: $1-9.9 Million
Emp.: 20
Car Dealership
N.A.I.C.S.: 441110
Sherry Nye (VP)

WARREN OIL COMPANY INC.
2340 US Hwy 301 N, Dunn, NC 28334-6165
Tel.: (910) 892-6456 NC
Web Site: http://www.warrenoil.com
Year Founded: 1975
Sales Range: $10-24.9 Million
Emp.: 125
Provider of Petroleum Products
N.A.I.C.S.: 424720
Harold Lambert (Plant Mgr)

WARREN PAVING INC.
562 Elks Lake Rd, Hattiesburg, MS 39401
Tel.: (601) 544-7811
Web Site: http://www.warrenpaving.com
Rev.: $18,108,715
Emp.: 150
Highway & Street Paving Contractor
N.A.I.C.S.: 237310
Lawrence Warren (CEO)
Bobby Sullivan (VP)
Steven Warren (Pres)

WARREN POWER & MACHINERY, INC.
10325 Younger Rd, Midland, TX 79706
Tel.: (806) 745-4495 TX
Web Site: http://www.warrencat.com
Year Founded: 1971
General Construction Machinery & Equipment
N.A.I.C.S.: 423820
Richard D. Folger (CEO)

WARREN PROPERTIES, INC.
140 N Escondido Blvd, Escondido, CA 92025
Tel.: (760) 480-6211 DE
Web Site: http://www.warrenproperties.com
Year Founded: 1945
Sales Range: $200-249.9 Million
Emp.: 700
Property Management Services
N.A.I.C.S.: 531110
Frank Raymond Warren (Pres)
Bruce Warren (Sr VP)
Debbie Gaylord (Mgr-Payroll)
Janice Wells (CFO)
Mark Riesenberg (Dir-Tax)

WARREN RESOURCES, INC.
2 Lincoln Ctr 5420 LBJ Freeway Ste 600, Dallas, TX 75240
Tel.: (214) 393-9688 MD
Web Site: http://www.warrenresources.com
Sales Range: $75-99.9 Million
Emp.: 58
Onshore Natural Gas & Oil Reserves
N.A.I.C.S.: 211120
Ellis G. Vickers (Sr VP-Land Mgmt & Regulatory Affairs)
Robert Michael Dowell (VP & Gen Mgr)
James A. Watt (Pres & CEO)
Greg Fox (Sr VP-Ops & Reservoir Engrg)
Frank T. Smith Jr. (CFO & Sr VP)

Subsidiaries:

Warren Energy Services, LLC (1)
1114 Avenue of The Americas, New York, NY 10036
Tel.: (212) 697-9660
Emp.: 10
Oil & Gas Exploration Services
N.A.I.C.S.: 213112

Warren Resources of California, Inc. (1)
301 E Ocean Blvd Ste 1010, Long Beach, CA 90802
Tel.: (562) 590-0909
Oil & Gas Production Services
N.A.I.C.S.: 211130

WARREN RURAL ELECTRIC COOPERATIVE CORP.
951 Fairview Ave, Bowling Green, KY 42101-4937
Tel.: (270) 842-6541 KY
Web Site: http://www.wrecc.com
Year Founded: 1938
Sales Range: $25-49.9 Million
Emp.: 370
Provider of Electric Services
N.A.I.C.S.: 221122
Rick Carroll (Dir-Mktg)
Wendy Meador (Supvr-Customer Svc)
Andrew Lindsey (Engr)
Patty Kantosky (VP-Member & Customer Svcs)

WARREN STEEL PRODUCTS INC.
2201 Loveland Ave, Erie, PA 16506
Tel.: (814) 838-8681
Web Site: http://www.thewarrencompany.com
Sales Range: $25-49.9 Million
Emp.: 100
Metals Service Centers & Offices
N.A.I.C.S.: 423510
Robert Warren (Pres)

WARREN TIRE SERVICE CENTER, INC.
4 Highland Ave Ste 3, Queensbury, NY 12804
Tel.: (518) 792-0316 NY

Web Site: http://www.warrentiresvc.com
Sales Range: $10-24.9 Million
Emp.: 12
General Automotive Repair Shops
Owner & Operator
N.A.I.C.S.: 811111
Robert Kellogg (Pres)

WARREN WOOD INC.
515 Division St N, Rice, MN 56367-8774
Tel.: (320) 393-4444
Year Founded: 1982
Sales Range: $10-24.9 Million
Emp.: 34
Wood Products Mfr
N.A.I.C.S.: 321912
Gary Piotrowski (Pres)

WARREN'S AIR CONDITIONING & HEATING SERVICE, INC.
9000 Ramsey St, Linden, NC 28356-8922
Tel.: (910) 488-1632
Web Site: http://www.warrensac.com
Sales Range: $10-24.9 Million
Emp.: 75
Air Conditioning System Installation Services
N.A.I.C.S.: 238220
Robert Warren (Owner)

WARREN'S WOOD WORKS, INC.
8708 Brooks Dr, Easton, MD 21601
Tel.: (410) 820-8984
Web Site: http://www.warrenswoodworks.com
Year Founded: 1983
Sales Range: $10-24.9 Million
Emp.: 40
Millwork Services
N.A.I.C.S.: 321918
Warren Clem (Pres)
Irvin Stiles (Gen Mgr)

WARRENDER ENTERPRISE INC.
43360 N US Hwy 41 Unit H, Zion, IL 60099
Web Site: http://www.liftedmade.com
Santizer Mfr
N.A.I.C.S.: 456120
Nicholas S. Warrender (CEO)

WARRENTON OIL CO.
2299 S Spoede Ln, Warrenton, MO 63383
Tel.: (636) 456-3346
Web Site: http://www.fastlane-cstore.com
Sales Range: $100-124.9 Million
Emp.: 315
Convenience Store
N.A.I.C.S.: 445131
Wayne Baker (Pres)

Subsidiaries:

Thoele Inc. (1)
1703 N 4th St, Saint Charles, MO 63301
Tel.: (636) 724-1617
Rev.: $22,900,000
Emp.: 10
Fuel Oil Dealers
N.A.I.C.S.: 457210
Lindakbianchi Bianchi (VP)
Linda Thoele (Pres)

WARRIOR INSURANCE NETWORK, INC
6640 S Cicero Ave, Bedford Park, IL 60638
Tel.: (866) 400-8600
Web Site: https://www.warriorinsurancenetwork.com

Year Founded: 2020
Insurance Agencies
N.A.I.C.S.: 524210
James P. Hallberg (Pres & CEO)

Subsidiaries:

West Virginia National Auto Insurance Co., Inc. (1)
330 Scott Ave 2, Morgantown, WV 26508
Tel.: (304) 296-0507
Web Site: http://www.wvnational.com
Sales Range: $1-9.9 Million
Emp.: 15
Direct Property & Casualty Insurance Carriers
N.A.I.C.S.: 524126
David Remmells (CFO)

WARRIOR TRACTOR & EQUIPMENT COMPANY INC.
6801 McFarland Blvd W, Northport, AL 35476-3421
Tel.: (205) 339-0300   AL
Web Site:
    http://www.warriortractor.com
Year Founded: 1967
Sales Range: $10-24.9 Million
Emp.: 60
Distr of Industrial Machinery & Equipment
N.A.I.C.S.: 423830
Gene Ray Taylor (Pres)
Fred Tanner (Mgr-Credit)

WARSCHAWSKI
1501 Sulgrave Ave Ste 350, Baltimore, MD 21209
Tel.: (410) 367-2700
Web Site:
    http://www.warschawski.com
Year Founded: 1996
Emp.: 17
Full Service Branding, Marketing, Public Relations, Advertising & Interactive Agency
N.A.I.C.S.: 541820
David Warschawski (CEO)
Shana Harris (COO)
Michele Tomlinson (VP)
Mark Ludwig (Dir-Design Dev)
Lauren Scheib (Dir-Design)
Ben Plum (Dir-Design Dev)
Sam Ruchlewicz (Dir-Digital Strategy & Data Analytics)
Steve Battista (VP-Brand Mktg)
John Margaritis (VP-Comm & Issues Mgmt-New York)

Subsidiaries:

Warschawski (1)
86 Sanborn Ave, West Roxbury, MA 02132
Tel.: (617) 553-8020
Public Relations Agency
N.A.I.C.S.: 541820

WARSHAUER ELECTRIC SUPPLY COMPANY
800 Shrewsbury Ave, Tinton Falls, NJ 07724
Tel.: (732) 741-6400
Web Site: http://www.warshauer.com
Rev.: $23,300,000
Emp.: 54
Electrical Supplies
N.A.I.C.S.: 423610
James Warshauer (Pres)
Gene Fay (VP-Energy Solutions)
Sarah Barton (Coord-Mktg)
Terri Vandeweghe (Mgr-Credit & Collection)
Bruce Pilger (VP-Bus Dev)
Jim Dunn (Exec VP-Sls & Mktg)
Michael Sparandera (Coord-Mobile Rental)
Joe Vanore (VP-Fin)
David Thalhammer (Dir-Pur)

Kennie Marie Blanck (Exec VP-Sls & Mktg)
John Pardenek (VP-Tech Sls)
George Kattak (Controller)

WARWICK CONSTRUCTION, INC.
365 FM 1959, Houston, TX 77034
Tel.: (832) 448-7000
Web Site:
    http://www.warwickconstruction.com
Sales Range: $25-49.9 Million
Emp.: 75
Nonresidential Construction Services
N.A.I.C.S.: 236220
Melissa Davis (Office Mgr)
Richard Nielsen (Superintendent-Construction)
Brad Downs (VP-Construction)

WARWICK PLUMBING AND HEATING CORPORATION
11048 Warwick Blvd, Newport News, VA 23601-3229
Tel.: (757) 599-6111   VA
Web Site: http://www.wphcorp.com
Year Founded: 1983
Sales Range: $10-24.9 Million
Emp.: 100
Plumbing Heating & Air-Conditioning Services
N.A.I.C.S.: 238220
G. Royden Goodson (Pres)

WASATCH ADVANTAGE GROUP, LLC
595 S Riverwoods Pkwy, Ste 400, Logan, UT 84321
Tel.: (435) 755-2000
Web Site:
    https://www.wasatchgroup.com
Emp.: 1,700
Investment Services
N.A.I.C.S.: 523999
Dell Loy Hansen (Founder & CEO)

Subsidiaries:

Biomerics, LLC (1)
6030 W Harold Gatty Dr, Salt Lake City, UT 84116
Tel.: (801) 355-2705
Web Site: https://www.biomerics.com
Emp.: 120
Polymer Solution Mfr
N.A.I.C.S.: 326199
Travis Sessions (Founder, Pres & CEO)
Jeff Clark (VP-Mfg)

Subsidiary (Domestic):

Access Point Technologies, LLC (2)
12560 Fletcher Ln Ste 300, Rogers, MN 55374
Tel.: (763) 428-0010
Web Site: http://www.accesspointtech.com
Surgical & Medical Instrument Mfr
N.A.I.C.S.: 339112
Steven Berhow (CEO)

Joint Venture (Domestic):

Catheter Research, Inc. (2)
5610 W 82nd St, Indianapolis, IN 46278
Tel.: (317) 872-0074
Web Site: http://www.catheterresearch.com
Emp.: 116
Medical Device Mfr
N.A.I.C.S.: 339112
Mike Andrus (VP-Sls & Mktg)
Gary T. Cerasale (Mgr-Extrusion & Ops)
Brian Bading (Engr-Mfg)
Christine Cook (COO)
Andy Beard (Engr-Mfg)

Subsidiary (Domestic):

Precision Concepts Group LLC (2)
2701 Boulder Park Ct, Winston Salem, NC 27101
Tel.: (336) 761-8572
Web Site: http://www.precisionconcepts.com

Sales Range: $25-49.9 Million
Emp.: 35
Metal Stamping & Insert Molding Mfr
N.A.I.C.S.: 332119
Vincent Marino (Owner & Pres)
Vincent Christopher (VP-Ops-North Carolina)

Wasatch Property Management, Inc. (1)
595 S Riverwoods Pkwy Ste 400, Logan, UT 84321-6845
Tel.: (435) 755-2000
Web Site: https://www.wasatchgroup.com
Sales Range: $1-9.9 Million
Emp.: 600
Real Estate Brokerage Services
N.A.I.C.S.: 531210
Cody Knowles (Controller)
Dell Loy Hansen (Owner & CEO)

Subsidiary (Domestic):

MarketStar Corporation (2)
2475 Washington Blvd, Ogden, UT 84401
Tel.: (801) 393-1155
Web Site: http://www.marketstar.com
Sales Range: $125-149.9 Million
Emp.: 2,600
Sales & Marketing Solutions
N.A.I.C.S.: 541613
Vaughn Aust (Exec VP-Mktg & Product)
Keith Titus (Pres & CEO)
Justin Nalder (Sr VP-Client Svcs & Corp Ops)
Heather Barnes (VP-Client Svcs & Partner Channel)
Paul Grant (Chief Revenue Officer)
Michelle Gunter (Sr VP-Client Svcs)
Todd Handy (VP-Client Svcs & Digital Media)
Sam Newey (VP-Bus Dev)
Joel Rackham (VP-Bus Dev)
Michael Ray (VP-Bus Dev)
Paul Stout (VP-Client Svcs & Partner Channel)
Bryan Summerhays (VP-Client Svcs & Direct)
Ben Kaufmann (CFO)

WASATCH SOFTWARE, INC.
5242 S College Dr Ste 200, Murray, UT 84123
Tel.: (801) 983-3671
Web Site:
    http://www.wasatchsoftware.com
Year Founded: 2002
Sales Range: $1-9.9 Million
Emp.: 25
Software Publisher
N.A.I.C.S.: 513210
Spencer E. Ferguson (Pres)

WASCHKE FAMILY GM CENTER
2300 Hwy 53, International Falls, MN 56649-4012
Tel.: (218) 741-6000
Web Site:
    http://www.waschkegm.com
Sales Range: $10-24.9 Million
Emp.: 74
New Car Whslr
N.A.I.C.S.: 441110
Ken Waschke (Exec VP)
Kerry Waschke (Owner)

WASCO INC.
1138 2nd Ave N, Nashville, TN 37208
Tel.: (615) 244-9090
Web Site: http://www.wasco-inc.com
Year Founded: 1966
Sales Range: $25-49.9 Million
Emp.: 250
Provider of Masonry & Other Stonework
N.A.I.C.S.: 238140
Brad Procter (Chm)
Jason Kinnard (VP)
Ken Moore (CFO)

Mike Kincaid (CFO)
Shawn Gallant (VP)
William A. Sneed Jr. (Pres & CEO)

WASH DEPOT HOLDINGS, INC.
14 Summer St Ste 302, Malden, MA 02148-3994
Tel.: (781) 324-2000   DE
Web Site:
    http://www.cleancarfeeling.com
Year Founded: 1995
Holding Company; Car Cleaning Services
N.A.I.C.S.: 811192
Greg Anderson (Pres & CEO)

WASHBURN CENTER FOR CHILDREN
1100 Glenwood Ave, Minneapolis, MN 55405
Tel.: (612) 871-1454   MN
Web Site: http://www.washburn.org
Year Founded: 1883
Sales Range: $10-24.9 Million
Emp.: 155
Child Care Services
N.A.I.C.S.: 624110
Tom Steinmetz (CEO & COO)
Arlene Schatz (Dir-Clinical)
Kate Hudak (Dir-HR)
Lance First (Treas)
Frank Bennett (Pres)
Linda Ortner (Chief Advancement Officer)
Cadwallader C. Washburn (Co-Founder)

WASHCO BANCSHARES, INC.
625 Veterans Dr, Mineral Point, MO 63660
Tel.: (573) 438-5421   MO
Web Site: http://www.unicobank.com
Year Founded: 1984
Sales Range: $10-24.9 Million
Emp.: 100
Bank Holding Company
N.A.I.C.S.: 551111
Leon Brinkley (Chm & CEO)
Jonnathan Mays (Pres)

Subsidiaries:

Unico Bank (1)
625 Veterans Dr, Mineral Point, MO 63660
Tel.: (573) 438-5421
Web Site: http://www.unicobank.com
Sales Range: $10-24.9 Million
State Commercial Banks
N.A.I.C.S.: 522110
Wilma Lou Wideman (Asst VP)
Paula Glore (Controller)

Branch (Domestic):

Unico Bank - Paragould, Kingshighway (2)
506 W Kings Hwy, Paragould, AR 72450
Tel.: (870) 236-1700
Web Site: http://www.unicobank.com
Sales Range: $75-99.9 Million
Emp.: 14
Retail & Commercial Banking
N.A.I.C.S.: 522110
Jonathan Mays (Pres)

WASHING EQUIPMENT OF TEXAS
4121 McKinney Falls Pkwy, Austin, TX 78744
Tel.: (512) 389-2822
Web Site: http://www.wet-texas.com
Rev.: $13,100,000
Emp.: 25
Carwash Equipment & Supplies
N.A.I.C.S.: 423850
Tom Lye (Co-Founder)
Charles Allen (Co-Founder)
Gary Dial (Mgr-Houston Branch)

WASHING SYSTEMS, LLC.

Washing Systems, LLC.—(Continued)

WASHING SYSTEMS, LLC.
167 Commerce Dr, Loveland, OH 45140
Tel.: (513) 870-4830
Web Site: http://www.washingsystems.com
Year Founded: 1989
Sales Range: $10-24.9 Million
Emp.: 43
Chemical Product & Preparation Mfr
N.A.I.C.S.: 325998
Terry Shoreman (Pres)
Steve Freeman (Gen Mgr-Canadian Ops)
Craig Nikrant (CEO)
Bobby Fisher (Vice Chm)
Steve Donly (Chm)

WASHINGTON AIR REPS INC.
3290 146th Pl SE Ste A, Bellevue, WA 98007
Tel.: (425) 562-1150
Web Site: http://www.airreps.com
Rev.: $13,138,177
Emp.: 25
Air Conditioning Equipment
N.A.I.C.S.: 423730
Mike Hawkins (Pres & CEO)
Matt Adkins (Acct Exec)
Bob Guerin (VP)
Ken Horsfall (VP-Engrg)

WASHINGTON ALDER, LLC
13421 Farm to Market Rd, Mount Vernon, WA 98273
Tel.: (360) 428-8583 **WA**
Web Site: http://www.washington-alder.com
Year Founded: 1998
Sales Range: $50-74.9 Million
Emp.: 90
Sawmill & Hardwood Lumber Whslr
N.A.I.C.S.: 321113
Richard Tinney (Pres)
Paula Norman (CFO)

WASHINGTON ATHLETIC CLUB
1325 6th Ave, Seattle, WA 98101
Tel.: (206) 622-7900
Web Site: http://www.wac.net
Rev.: $21,213,000
Emp.: 330
Membership Sports & Recreation Clubs
N.A.I.C.S.: 713940
Paul Lowber (CFO)
Wayne Milner (VP)
Michelle Pinson (VP-Membership & Mktg)
Chuck Nelson (Pres & CEO)
Amanda Brynn (Dir-Member Svcs)
Robert Laurneti (VP-Club Programs)

WASHINGTON CAPITAL MANAGEMENT, INC.
1200 6th Ave Ste 700, Seattle, WA 98101
Tel.: (206) 382-0825 **WA**
Web Site: http://www.wcmadvisors.com
Year Founded: 1977
Investment Advisory Services
N.A.I.C.S.: 523940
Michael Russell (Chm)
Michael Cheung (VP & Principal)
Russell J. Smith (Controller)
Cory Carlson (Pres, CEO & Chief Investment Officer)

Subsidiaries:

Great Point Investors, LLC (1)
2 Ctr Plz Ste 410, Boston, MA 02108-1926
Tel.: (617) 526-8800
Investment Advisory Firm

N.A.I.C.S.: 523150
Gary Schwandt (Principal)

WASHINGTON CARE CENTER
2821 S Walden St, Seattle, WA 98144
Tel.: (206) 725-2800 **WA**
Web Site: http://www.wacenter.com
Year Founded: 2004
Sales Range: $10-24.9 Million
Emp.: 249
Elder Care Services
N.A.I.C.S.: 623312
Ruben Santiago (Dir-Environmental)
Sharon Nienow (Dir-Health Info Svcs)

WASHINGTON CEDAR & SUPPLY CO.
1400 W Main St, Auburn, WA 98001
Tel.: (253) 833-6766
Web Site: http://www.washingtoncedar.com
Rev.: $20,000,000
Emp.: 85
Roofing Siding & Insulation Material Merchant Whslr
N.A.I.C.S.: 423330
Bob Karney (Gen Mgr)
Mytra Humphrey (Asst Mgr)

WASHINGTON CORPORATIONS
101 International Way, Missoula, MT 59808-1549
Tel.: (406) 523-1300 **MT**
Web Site: http://www.washingtoncompanies.com
Year Founded: 1957
Transportation Equipment Services
N.A.I.C.S.: 551112
Dennis R. Washington (Founder & Chm)

Subsidiaries:

Aviation Partners, Inc. (1)
PO Box 81107, Seattle, WA 98108-1107
Tel.: (206) 762-1171
Web Site: http://www.aviationpartners.com
Sales Range: $1-9.9 Million
Emp.: 20
Aircraft Part Mfr
N.A.I.C.S.: 336413
Joe Clark (Co-Founder)
Gary Dunn (Pres)
Dennis R. Washington (Co-Founder)
Robert MacKenzie (Dir-Sls)

Envirocon, Inc. (1)
101 International Way, Missoula, MT 59808 (100%)
Tel.: (406) 523-1150
Web Site: http://www.envirocon.com
Sales Range: $25-49.9 Million
Emp.: 350
Environmental Remediation Services
N.A.I.C.S.: 541620
Kris Kok (Sr VP-Project Delivery)
John D'Antuono (Dir-Contracts)
Harry Foreman (COO & Sr VP)
Pete Joy (Sr VP-Technical Svcs & Bus Dev)
Kelly King (Sr VP-HR)
Mark Fallon (Pres & CEO)
Brandon Parker (CFO)
Jeff Thompson (Sr VP-Environment, Health & Safety)

Branch (Domestic):

Envirocon, Inc. (2)
3330 NW Yeon Ave Ste 240, Portland, OR 97210 (100%)
Tel.: (503) 285-6164
Web Site: http://www.envirocon.com
Sales Range: $25-49.9 Million
Emp.: 20
Environmental Remediation Services
N.A.I.C.S.: 541620
David Jacobs (VP-Demolition & Remediation Svcs)

Envirocon, Inc. (2)

1687 Eureka Rd Ste 200, Roseville, CA 95661 (100%)
Tel.: (916) 787-4044
Web Site: http://www.envirocon.com
Sales Range: $25-49.9 Million
Emp.: 25
Environmental Remediation Services
N.A.I.C.S.: 541620

Envirocon, Inc. (2)
457 Campbell St, Valparaiso, IN 46385 (100%)
Tel.: (219) 548-0042
Web Site: http://www.envirocon.com
Sales Range: $25-49.9 Million
Emp.: 20
Environmental Remediation Services
N.A.I.C.S.: 541620

Envirocon, Inc. (2)
2163 Windridge, Omaha, NE 68152 (100%)
Tel.: (402) 451-7171
Web Site: http://www.envirocon.com
Environmental Remediation Services
N.A.I.C.S.: 541620

Envirocon, Inc. (2)
651 Corporate Cir Ste 114, Golden, CO 80401 (100%)
Tel.: (303) 215-0187
Web Site: http://www.envirocon.com
Sales Range: $25-49.9 Million
Emp.: 50
Environmental Remediation Services
N.A.I.C.S.: 541620
Steve Schurman (Mgr-Bus Dev)
Jeff Woltemath (Dir-Nuclear Svcs)
Bud Stevens (Mgr-Demolition)
Dan Allen (Supvr-Health & Safety)
Peter Holmyard (Mgr-Health & Safety)

Envirocon, Inc. (2)
1400 E Ocean Blvd Ste 2411, Long Beach, CA 90802 (100%)
Tel.: (979) 412-2191
Web Site: http://www.envirocon.com
Sales Range: $25-49.9 Million
Emp.: 20
Environmental Remediation Services
N.A.I.C.S.: 541620
Jeff Rankin (Mgr-Bus Dev)

Envirocon, Inc. (2)
3919 Laurel Oaks Cir, Murrysville, PA 15668 (100%)
Tel.: (724) 325-1629
Web Site: http://www.envirocon.com
Sales Range: $25-49.9 Million
Emp.: 4
Environmental Remediation Services
N.A.I.C.S.: 541620

Modern Machinery Co. (1)
101 International Dr, Missoula, MT 59808-1549 (100%)
Tel.: (406) 523-1100
Web Site: http://www.modernmachinery.com
Sales Range: $50-74.9 Million
Emp.: 30
Heavy Equipment Sales, Service, Parts & Leasing
N.A.I.C.S.: 423810
Bill Granoall (CFO)

Montana Rail Link, Inc. (1)
101 International Dr, Missoula, MT 59808-1549
Tel.: (406) 523-1500
Web Site: http://www.montanarail.com
Sales Range: $50-74.9 Million
Emp.: 950
Line-Haul Railroad Operating Services
N.A.I.C.S.: 482111
Jacquie Duhame (Dir-Claims)
Van Blakely (Chief Procurement & Real Estate Officer)
Mark Krause (Controller)
Jean Laber (Dir-Gen Acctg)
Bill Cornish (Dir-Track Maintenance)
Joe Gentri (Mgr-Real Estate Admin)
Jim Lewis (CIO, CMO & Chief Sls Officer)
Mike Rahl (Dir-Structures)
Jody Verity (Dir-HR)
Stacey Posey (Pres)
Joe Racicot (Chief Admin Officer & Gen Counsel)
Mark Smith (Chief Safety Officer)

U.S. PRIVATE

Ross Lane (Chief Comm Officer)
Rourk Price (Chief Mechanical Officer)
Scott Hendrickson (Chief Transportation Officer)

Unit (Domestic):

Montana Rail Link, Inc. (2)
Livingston
704 E Gallatin St, Livingston, MT 59047
Tel.: (406) 222-4200
Support Activities for Rail Transportation
N.A.I.C.S.: 488210

Montana Resources (1)
600 Shields Ave, Butte, MT 59701 (100%)
Tel.: (406) 496-3200
Web Site: http://www.montanaresources.com
Sales Range: $75-99.9 Million
Emp.: 365
Open Pit Copper & Molybdenum Mining
N.A.I.C.S.: 212220
Dennis R. Washington (Owner)
Mike McGivern (VP-HR)

Southern Railway of British Columbia Limited (SRY) (1)
2102 River Drive, New Westminster, V3M 6S3, BC, Canada (100%)
Tel.: (604) 521-1966
Web Site: http://www.sryraillink.com
Sales Range: $10-24.9 Million
Emp.: 120
Freight Railway Transportation Services
N.A.I.C.S.: 482111
Gerald Linden (Pres)

Subsidiary (Domestic):

Southern Railway of Vancouver Island Limited (2)
7 Port Way, Nanaimo, V9R 5L3, BC, Canada
Tel.: (250) 754-9222
Rail Transportation Services
N.A.I.C.S.: 488210
Derek Ollman (Pres)

Washington Development (1)
101 International Way, Missoula, MT 59808 (100%)
Tel.: (406) 523-1315
Web Site: http://www.washdev.com
Commercial, Residential & Industrial Real Estate
N.A.I.C.S.: 531390

Washington Marine Group (1)
10 Pemberton Ave, North Vancouver, V7P 2R1, BC, Canada (100%)
Tel.: (604) 988-3111
Web Site: http://www.seaspan.com
Sales Range: $100-124.9 Million
Emp.: 1,000
International Shipping & Freight Operations
N.A.I.C.S.: 483111
Kevin N. Irvine (Pres-Marine Div & Exec VP)
Nancy L. McKenzie (CFO)
Jonathan Whitworth (CEO)

Subsidiary (Domestic):

Marine Petrobulk Ltd. (2)
10 Pemberton Ave, North Vancouver, V7P 2R1, BC, Canada
Tel.: (604) 987-4415
Web Site: http://www.marinepetrobulk.com
Emp.: 6
Bunker Fuel Distr
N.A.I.C.S.: 424720
Tony Brewsteer (Mgr)

Seaspan Ferries Corporation (2)
7700 Hopcott Road, Delta, V4G 1B6, BC, Canada
Tel.: (604) 940-7245
Web Site: http://www.seaspan.com
Emp.: 150
Deep Sea Freight Transportation Services
N.A.I.C.S.: 483111

Vancouver Drydock Company Ltd. (2)
203 East Esplanade, North Vancouver, V7L 1A1, BC, Canada
Tel.: (778) 729-0288
Web Site: https://drydockprojects.com
Ship Repairing Services

COMPANIES

N.A.I.C.S.: 336611
Paul Hebson *(VP & Gen Mgr)*

Vancouver Shipyards Co. Ltd. (2)
2 Pemberton Avenue, North Vancouver,
V7P 2R2, BC, Canada
Tel.: (604) 988-6361
Web Site: http://www.seaspan.com
Emp.: 200
Ship Repairing Services
N.A.I.C.S.: 336611
Tony Matergio *(VP & Gen Mgr)*

Victoria Shipyards Co. Ltd. (2)
825 Admirals Road, Victoria, V9A 2P1, BC,
Canada
Tel.: (250) 380-1602
Ship Repairing Services
N.A.I.C.S.: 336611

WASHINGTON COUNTY CHAMBER OF COMMERCE
375 Southpointe Blvd Ste 240, Canonsburg, PA 15317
Tel.: (724) 338-8884   PA
Web Site:
 http://www.washcochamber.com
Year Founded: 1881
Rev.: $1,052,759
Assets: $206,554
Liabilities: $7,965
Net Worth: $198,589
Earnings: $28,676
Emp.: 8
Fiscal Year-end: 12/31/14
Business Community Development Services
N.A.I.C.S.: 813910
Dana M. Bucci *(Dir-Fin & Tourism Admin)*
Jeff M. Kotula *(Pres)*
Mary J. Stollar *(Specialist-Economic Dev)*
Dana M. Bucci *(Dir-Tourism & Admin & Dir-Fin & Tourism Admin)*
Jeff M. Kotula *(Pres)*
Mary J. Stollar *(Sr VP/Specialist-Economic Dev)*
Brook Ward *(Sec)*
Stacey Brodak *(Co-Chm)*
Tara M. Gleason *(Dir-Mktg & Member Rels)*
Terry Wiltrout *(Vice Chm)*
Gerald Cathell *(Chm)*
Laural Ziemba *(Vice Chm)*
Matt Thiel *(Treas)*
Brook Ward *(Sec)*

WASHINGTON EARLY LEARNING FUND
1111 3rd Ave Ste 210, Seattle, WA 98101
Tel.: (206) 621-5555   WA
Web Site:
 http://www.thrivebyfivewa.org
Year Founded: 2006
Sales Range: $10-24.9 Million
Emp.: 23
Educational Support Services
N.A.I.C.S.: 611710
Carmen Loh *(Dir-Fin & Admin)*
Molly O'Connor *(Dir-Comm & External Affairs)*
Holly Wyrwich *(Program Mgr)*
Dan Torres *(Dir-Community Momentum)*
Beverly Jacobson *(Sec)*
Dan Kranzler *(Treas)*
Don Stark *(VP)*
Kevin Washington *(Chm)*
Ruth Kagi *(VP)*
Sam Whiting *(Pres & CEO)*
Arigin Sakda *(Coord-Data & IT)*
Danielle Friedman *(Mgr-Policy)*
Doug Coleman *(Mgr-Fin)*
Eiledon McClellan *(Project Coord)*
Karen Hoffman *(Officer-Foundation & Corp Rels)*
Kelly Smith *(Program Officer)*
Leah Hausman *(Dir-Fund Dev)*
Liv Woodstrom *(Mgr-Community Partnerships)*
Liz Clagett *(Coord-Coalition Dev-VISTA)*
Melanie Krevitz *(Sr Mgr-Home Visiting)*
Monika Sanchez *(Sr Mgr-Res & Evaluation)*
Priti Mody-Pan *(Dir-Grants & Program Innovation)*
Rupal Shah *(Mgr-Grants)*

WASHINGTON EDUCATIONAL TELECOMMUNICATIONS ASSOCIATION
3939 Campbell Ave, Arlington, VA 22206
Tel.: (703) 998-2600
Web Site: http://www.weta.org
Sales Range: $50-74.9 Million
Emp.: 194
Television & Radio Broadcasting Stations
N.A.I.C.S.: 516120
Sharon Percy Rockefeller *(Pres & CEO)*
Dalton Delan *(Chief Programming Officer & Exec VP)*
Timothy C. Coughlin *(Chm)*
Ann Dibble Jordan *(Vice Chm & Sec)*
James C. Bond *(CFO & Sr VP)*

WASHINGTON ELECTRIC CO. INC.
32 W 39th St Ste 900, New York, NY 10018
Tel.: (212) 997-9882
Web Site: http://www.washcomp.com
Sales Range: $10-24.9 Million
Emp.: 25
Computers, Peripherals & Software
N.A.I.C.S.: 423430
Jeffrey Singer *(Pres)*

WASHINGTON ELECTRIC CO-OPERATIVE, INC.
40 Church St, East Montpelier, VT 05651
Tel.: (802) 223-5245   VT
Web Site:
 http://www.washingtonelectric.coop
Year Founded: 1939
Rev.: $17,956,947
Assets: $64,588,093
Liabilities: $40,770,805
Net Worth: $23,817,288
Earnings: $744,207
Emp.: 41
Fiscal Year-end: 12/31/18
Electric Power Distr
N.A.I.C.S.: 221122
Patricia H. Richards *(Gen Mgr)*
Dan Weston *(Dir-Engrg & Ops)*
Cheryl Willette *(Fin Dir)*
Linda Nelson *(Asst Dir-Fin)*
Bill Powell *(Dir-Products & Svcs)*
Barry Bernstein *(Pres)*
Donald Douglas *(Treas)*
Anne Reed *(Sec)*
Roger Fox *(VP)*
Susan Golden *(Supvr-Member Svcs)*

WASHINGTON ELECTRIC MEMBERSHIP CORPORATION
258 N Harris St, Sandersville, GA 31082
Tel.: (478) 552-2577
Web Site:
 http://www.washingtonemc.com
Rev.: $24,634,598
Emp.: 80
Distribution of Electric Power
N.A.I.C.S.: 221122
Mark Riner *(VP-Ops & Engrg)*
Wendy Sellers *(Pres & CEO)*

WASHINGTON EQUITY PARTNERS L.L.C.
8200 Greensboro Drive, Suite 900, McLean, VA 22102
Tel.: (202) 839-3410
Web Site: http://www.w-equity.com
Privater Equity Firm
N.A.I.C.S.: 523999
Robert Knibb *(Partner)*
Jesse Liu *(Partner)*
B. Hagen Saville *(Partner)*

Subsidiaries:

Accu-Tube Corp.   (1)
3211 W Bear Creek Drive, Englewood, CO 80110
Tel.: (303) 761-2258
Web Site: http://www.accutube.com
Iron & Steel Pipe & Tube Manufacturing from Purchased Steel
N.A.I.C.S.: 331210

Subsidiary (Domestic):

Mercury Tube Products LLC   (2)
3211 W Bear Creek Dr, Englewood, CO 80110-3210
Tel.: (303) 761-1835
Web Site: http://www.mercurytubular.com
Iron & Steel Mills
N.A.I.C.S.: 331110
Dennis Sims *(Mgr-Engrg)*

WASHINGTON FOOTBALL, INC.
21300 Redskin Park Dr, Ashburn, VA 20147
Tel.: (703) 726-7411   MD
Web Site: http://www.redskins.com
Year Founded: 1932
Sales Range: $125-149.9 Million
Emp.: 750
Professional Football Franchise
N.A.I.C.S.: 711211
Dennis Greene *(Pres-Bus Ops)*
Daniel M. Snyder *(Owner)*
Mitch Gershman *(CMO)*
Mike Bracken *(Dir-Video)*
Scot McCloughan *(Gen Mgr)*
Scott Campbell *(Dir-College Scouting)*
Tony Wyllie *(Sr VP-Comm)*
Doug Williams *(Sr VP-Player Personnel)*
Julie Donaldson *(Sr VP-Media)*
Jason Wright *(Pres)*
Zaheer Benjamin *(VP-Bus Intelligence & Analytics)*
Barbara Roberts *(Dir-Wellness & Clinical Svcs)*

WASHINGTON HOME CENTER INC.
61 SE Ryan Rd, Shelton, WA 98584
Tel.: (360) 748-6667
Web Site: http://www.washhome.com
Sales Range: $10-24.9 Million
Emp.: 70
Mobile Home Dealers
N.A.I.C.S.: 459930
Rod Richards *(Pres)*

WASHINGTON LIFTRUCK INC.
700 S Chicago St, Seattle, WA 98108-4321
Tel.: (206) 762-2040   WA
Web Site:
 http://www.washingtonlift.com
Year Founded: 1984
Sales Range: $10-24.9 Million
Emp.: 35
Provider of Industrial Machinery & Equipment
N.A.I.C.S.: 423830
Jeff Darlin *(VP)*

WASHINGTON MUSIC SALES CENTER

WASHINGTON METROPOLITAN AREA TRANSIT AUTHORITY
600 5th St NW, Washington, DC 20001-2610
Tel.: (202) 637-7000   DC
Web Site: http://www.wmata.com
Year Founded: 1976
Sales Range: $1-4.9 Billion
Emp.: 10,000
Mass Transit Services
N.A.I.C.S.: 485119
James Dougherty *(Chief Safety Officer)*
Daniel Smith *(Deputy Chief Procurement Officer)*
Brian Dwyer *(COO)*
Randy Clarke *(Gen Mgr)*
Mike Haas *(Sr VP)*

WASHINGTON MILLS COMPANY INC.
20 N Main St, North Grafton, MA 01536-1558
Tel.: (508) 839-6511
Web Site:
 http://www.washingtonmills.com
Year Founded: 1972
Sales Range: $25-49.9 Million
Emp.: 500
Abrasive Products, Electro Minerals, Electro-Fused Materials Mfr
N.A.I.C.S.: 327910
Peter H. Williams *(Pres)*

Subsidiaries:

Washington Mills Ceramics
Corporation   (1)
165 King St, Sun Prairie, WI 53590
Tel.: (608) 837-5155
Web Site:
 http://www.washingtonmillsceramics.com
Abrasive Product Mfr
N.A.I.C.S.: 327910

Washington Mills Company Inc.   (1)
13230 Prairie Inds Pkwy, Hennepin, IL 61327-9737
Tel.: (815) 925-7302
Web Site: http://www.washingtonmills.com
Sales Range: $25-49.9 Million
Emp.: 68
Mfr Silicon Carbide
N.A.I.C.S.: 327910
Armond Ladage *(Plant Mgr)*

Washington Mills Electro Minerals
Corporation   (1)
1801 Buffalo Ave, Niagara Falls, NY 14303-1528
Tel.: (716) 278-6600
Web Site: http://www.washingtonmills.com
Sales Range: $10-24.9 Million
Emp.: 110
Mfr of Abrasive Products
N.A.I.C.S.: 327910
Don McLeod *(Gen Mgr)*

Washington Mills Tonawanda,
Inc.   (1)
1000 E Niagara St, Tonawanda, NY 14150
Tel.: (800) 828-1666
Abrasive Product Mfr
N.A.I.C.S.: 327910

WASHINGTON MUSIC SALES CENTER
11151 Veirs Mill Rd, Wheaton, MD 20902
Tel.: (301) 946-8808
Web Site:
 http://www.chucklevins.com
Sales Range: $25-49.9 Million
Emp.: 100
Drums & Related Percussion Instruments
N.A.I.C.S.: 459140
Alan Levin *(Pres)*
David Fox *(CFO)*

WASHINGTON NATIONALS, L.P.

Washington Music Sales Center—(Continued)

WASHINGTON NATIONALS, L.P.
1500 S Capitol St SE, Washington, DC 20003-1507
Tel.: (202) 675-6287 DE
Web Site: http://www.nationals.com
Sales Range: $75-99.9 Million
Emp.: 200
Professional Baseball Club
N.A.I.C.S.: 711211
Lori Creasy *(CFO)*
Bob Miller *(VP & Asst Gen Mgr)*
Zach Galkin *(Mgr-Corp Partnerships)*
Fredrick D. Schaufeld *(Partner)*
Fred Schaufeld *(Partner)*

WASHINGTON ORNAMENTAL IRON WORKS
17926 S Broadway St, Gardena, CA 90248
Tel.: (310) 327-8660
Web Site: http://washingtoniron.com
Sales Range: $10-24.9 Million
Emp.: 250
Architectural Metalwork
N.A.I.C.S.: 332323
Louis Welsh *(Chm)*
Chris Powell *(CFO)*
Pat Semoore *(Office Mgr)*

WASHINGTON PRIME GROUP INC.
Tel.: (614) 621-9000 IN
Web Site: https://wpgus.com
Year Founded: 2014
WPG—(NYSE)
Rev.: $524,418,000
Assets: $4,105,347,000
Liabilities: $3,504,149,000
Net Worth: $601,198,000
Earnings: ($219,786,000)
Emp.: 717
Fiscal Year-end: 12/31/20
Real Estate Investment Trust; Commercial Real Estate Investment, Development & Property Management Services
N.A.I.C.S.: 525990
Christopher Conlon *(CEO)*
Amanda Bailey *(Chief HR Officer & Sr VP)*
Jeff Brown *(Sr VP-Accounting)*
Mark Delcher *(CIO & Sr VP)*
Greg Fleser *(Sr VP-Property Mgmt)*
Steve Gerber *(Sr VP & Head-Property Mgmt)*
Amy Jonas *(Sr VP-Leasing)*
Matt Jurkowitz *(Sr VP-Investments)*
David Keane *(Chief Investment Officer & Exec VP)*
Scottie Lee *(Sr VP-Finance)*
Joshua Lindimore *(Exec VP & Head-Leasing)*
Maria Manley-Dutton *(Chief Legal Officer & Exec VP)*
Kurt Palmer *(Sr VP-Specialty Leasing & Sponsorships)*
Courtney Smith *(Sr VP-Investment & Asset Mgmt)*
Erich Stehle *(Sr VP-Construction)*
John Swagerty *(Sr VP-Mixed-Use Dev)*
Christa Vesy *(CFO & Exec VP)*

Subsidiaries:

Arbor Walk Mall, LLC (1)
10515 N Mo Pac Expy, Austin, TX 78759
Tel.: (512) 338-4755
Web Site: http://www.shopsatarborwalk.com
Nonresidential Building Leasing Services
N.A.I.C.S.: 531120

Arboretum Mall, LLC (1)
10000 Research Blvd, Austin, TX 78759
Tel.: (512) 338-4755
Web Site: http://www.thearboretum.com
Nonresidential Building Leasing Services
N.A.I.C.S.: 531120

BRE/Pearlridge, LLC (1)
98-1005 Moanalua Rd, Aiea, HI 96701
Tel.: (808) 488-0981
Web Site: http://www.pearlridgeonline.com
Shopping Mall Operator
N.A.I.C.S.: 531120
David Cianelli *(Gen Mgr)*
Diana Su-Niimi *(Mktg Dir)*

Bowie Mall Company, LLC (1)
15606 Emerald Way, Bowie, MD 20716
Tel.: (301) 860-1818
Web Site: http://www.wpg.com
Nonresidential Building Leasing Services
N.A.I.C.S.: 531120

Boynton Beach Mall, LLC (1)
801 N Congress Ave, Boynton Beach, FL 33426-3315
Tel.: (561) 736-7900
Web Site: http://www.boyntonbeachmall.com
Nonresidential Building Leasing Services
N.A.I.C.S.: 531120

Brunswick Square Mall, LLC (1)
755 State Route 18, East Brunswick, NJ 08816
Tel.: (732) 238-3601
Web Site: http://www.shopbrunswicksquare.com
Nonresidential Building Leasing Services
N.A.I.C.S.: 531120

Charlottesville Fashion Square, LLC (1)
1600 Rio Rd E, Charlottesville, VA 22901
Tel.: (434) 973-9332
Web Site: http://www.charlottesvillefashion.com
Nonresidential Building Leasing Services
N.A.I.C.S.: 531120

Chautauqua Mall, LLC (1)
318 E Fairmount Ave, Lakewood, NY 14750
Tel.: (716) 763-9355
Web Site: http://www.chautauquamall.com
Nonresidential Building Leasing Services
N.A.I.C.S.: 531120
Julie Bihler *(Gen Mgr)*
Sharon Bennett *(Mktg Dir)*

Chesapeake Mall, LLC (1)
4200 Portsmouth Blvd Ofc, Chesapeake, VA 23321
Tel.: (757) 488-9639
Web Site: http://www.simon.com
Nonresidential Building Leasing Services
N.A.I.C.S.: 531120

Clay Terrace Partners, LLC (1)
14390 Clay Terrace Blvd, Carmel, IN 46032
Tel.: (317) 818-0725
Web Site: http://www.simon.com
Nonresidential Building Leasing Services
N.A.I.C.S.: 531120

Edison Mall, LLC (1)
4125 Cleveland Ave, Fort Myers, FL 33901
Tel.: (239) 939-5464
Web Site: http://www.shopedisonmall.com
Nonresidential Building Leasing Services
N.A.I.C.S.: 531120

Forest Mall, LLC (1)
835 W Johnson St, Fond Du Lac, WI 54935
Tel.: (920) 922-5863
Web Site: http://www.forestmall.com
Nonresidential Building Leasing Services
N.A.I.C.S.: 531120

Gulf View Square, LLC (1)
9409 Us Hwy 19, Port Richey, FL 34668
Tel.: (727) 848-3858
Web Site: http://shopgulfviewsquare.com
Lessors of Nonresidential Buildings
N.A.I.C.S.: 531120

Highland Lakes Center, LLC (1)
4240 Lakeland Highlands Rd, Lakeland, FL 33813
Tel.: (863) 646-8699
Web Site: http://www.opishighlandslakecenter.com
Nonresidential Building Leasing Services
N.A.I.C.S.: 531120

Knoxville Center, LLC (1)
3001 Knoxville Ctr Dr, Knoxville, TN 37924
Tel.: (865) 544-1500
Web Site: http://www.easttowneknoxville.com
Nonresidential Building Leasing Services
N.A.I.C.S.: 531120

Lakeline Plaza, LLC (1)
11066 Pecan Park Blvd, Cedar Park, TX 78613
Tel.: (512) 930-8038
Web Site: http://www.shoplakelineplaza.com
Nonresidential Building Leasing Services
N.A.I.C.S.: 531120

Lincolnwood Town Center, LLC (1)
3333 W Touhy Ave, Lincolnwood, IL 60712
Tel.: (847) 674-1219
Web Site: http://www.lincolnwoodtowncenter.com
Nonresidential Building Leasing Services
N.A.I.C.S.: 531120
Peter Abraham *(Gen Mgr)*
Elizabeth Bobak *(Dir-Mktg)*

Lindale Mall, LLC (1)
4444 1st Ave NE, Cedar Rapids, IA 52402
Tel.: (319) 393-9393
Web Site: http://www.lindalemall.com
Emp.: 7
Nonresidential Building Leasing Services
N.A.I.C.S.: 531120

Mall at Jefferson Valley, LLC (1)
650 Lee Blvd, Yorktown Heights, NY 10598
Tel.: (914) 245-4688
Web Site: http://www.jeffersonvalleymall.com
Nonresidential Building Leasing Services
N.A.I.C.S.: 531120
Alexa O'Rourke *(Gen Mgr)*
Heather Novak *(Dir-Mktg)*

Mall at Johnson City REIT, LLC (1)
2011 N Roan St, Johnson City, TN 37601
Tel.: (423) 282-5312
Web Site: http://www.mallatjohnsoncity.com
Shopping Mall Operator
N.A.I.C.S.: 531120
Tembra Aldridge *(Dir-Trng & Dev)*
Ashley Grindstaff *(Gen Mgr)*
Sheila Reed *(Mktg Dir)*

Mall at Longview, LLC (1)
3500 McCann Rd, Longview, TX 75605
Tel.: (903) 753-4453
Web Site: http://www.washingtonprime.com
Nonresidential Building Leasing Services
N.A.I.C.S.: 531120

Mall at Valle Vista, LLC (1)
2020 S Expressway 83, Harlingen, TX 78552
Tel.: (956) 425-8392
Web Site: http://www.vallevistamall.com
Nonresidential Building Leasing Services
N.A.I.C.S.: 531120

Marketplace at Concord Mills, LLC (1)
8111 Concord Mills Blvd, Concord, NC 28027-6462
Tel.: (704) 979-3000
Nonresidential Building Leasing Services
N.A.I.C.S.: 531120

Markland Mall, LLC (1)
1114 17th St, Kokomo, IN 46902
Tel.: (765) 454-6940
Web Site: http://www.marklandmall.com
Nonresidential Building Leasing Services
N.A.I.C.S.: 531120

Markland Plaza, LLC (1)
1400 S Reed Rd, Kokomo, IN 46902
Tel.: (765) 454-6940
Nonresidential Building Leasing Services
N.A.I.C.S.: 531120

Melbourne Square, LLC (1)
1700 W New Haven Ave, Melbourne, FL 32904
Tel.: (321) 727-8062
Web Site: http://www.melbournesquare.com
Nonresidential Building Leasing Services
N.A.I.C.S.: 531120

Muncie Mall, LLC (1)
3501 N Granville Ave, Muncie, IN 47303
Tel.: (765) 282-1276

Web Site: http://www.munciemall.com
Nonresidential Building Leasing Services
N.A.I.C.S.: 531120

Northlake Mall, LLC (1)
4800 Briarcliff Rd NE, Atlanta, GA 30345
Tel.: (770) 938-3565
Web Site: http://northlakemall.com
Emp.: 5
Nonresidential Building Leasing Services
N.A.I.C.S.: 531120

Oak Court Mall, LLC (1)
4465 Poplar Ave, Memphis, TN 38117
Tel.: (901) 681-0642
Web Site: http://www.oakcourtmall.com
Nonresidential Building Leasing Services
N.A.I.C.S.: 531120

Orange Park Mall, LLC (1)
1910 Wells Rd, Orange Park, FL 32073
Tel.: (904) 269-9413
Web Site: http://www.washingtonprime.com
Nonresidential Building Leasing Services
N.A.I.C.S.: 531120
Randy Bowman *(Gen Mgr)*
Chelsea Commodari *(Mktg Dir)*

PFP Columbus, LLC (1)
1500 Polaris Pkwy, Columbus, OH 43240
Tel.: (614) 456-0120
Web Site: http://www.polarisfashionplace.com
Shopping Mall Property Management Services
N.A.I.C.S.: 531312

Paddock Mall, LLC (1)
3100 SW College Rd, Ocala, FL 34474
Tel.: (352) 237-1223
Web Site: http://paddockmall.com
Sales Range: $1-9.9 Million
Emp.: 30
Lessors of Nonresidential Buildings
N.A.I.C.S.: 531120
Ashley Wheeler-Gerds *(Gen Mgr)*
Katie Hunnicutt *(Dir-Mktg)*

Palms Crossing Town Center, LLC (1)
3300 Expressway 83 Ware Rd, McAllen, TX 78501
Tel.: (956) 687-2668
Shoe Whslr
N.A.I.C.S.: 424340

Plaza at Northwood, LLC (1)
117 Main St, Oolitic, IN 47451
Tel.: (812) 279-9733
Nonresidential Building Leasing Services
N.A.I.C.S.: 531120

Polaris Fashion Place REIT, LLC (1)
1500 Polaris Pkwy, Columbus, OH 43240
Tel.: (614) 456-0120
Web Site: http://www.polarisfashionplace.com
Shopping Mall Operator
N.A.I.C.S.: 531120
Mary Dimitrijeska *(Dir-Mktg)*
Tamra Bower *(Gen Mgr)*

Port Charlotte Mall, LLC (1)
1441 Tamiami Trl, Port Charlotte, FL 33948
Tel.: (941) 624-4447
Web Site: http://portcharlottetowncenter.com
Nonresidential Building Leasing Services
N.A.I.C.S.: 531120

Richmond Town Square Mall, LLC (1)
691 Richmond Rd, Richmond Heights, OH 44143
Tel.: (440) 683-1083
Web Site: http://www.richmondtownsquare.com
Nonresidential Building Leasing Services
N.A.I.C.S.: 531120

River Oaks Center, LLC (1)
96 River Oaks Ctr Dr, Calumet City, IL 60409-5551
Tel.: (708) 868-5574
Web Site: http://www.shopriveroakscenter.com
Nonresidential Building Leasing Services
N.A.I.C.S.: 531120

Rockaway Town Court, LLC (1)
343 Mount Hope Ave, Rockaway, NJ 07866
Tel.: (317) 986-8500

COMPANIES

Web Site: http://www.simon.com
Nonresidential Building Leasing Services
N.A.I.C.S.: 531120

Rolling Oaks Mall, LLC (1)
6909 N Loop 1604 E, San Antonio, TX 78247
Tel.: (210) 651-5601
Web Site: http://www.rollingoaksmall.com
Nonresidential Building Leasing Services
N.A.I.C.S.: 531120

SM Mesa Mall, LLC (1)
2424 Old US Hwy 6 & 50, Grand Junction, CO 81505
Tel.: (970) 242-0009
Web Site: http://www.simon.com
Nonresidential Building Leasing Services
N.A.I.C.S.: 531120

SM Rushmore Mall, LLC (1)
2200 N Maple Ave, Rapid City, SD 57701
Tel.: (605) 348-3378
Web Site: http://www.rushmoremall.com
Nonresidential Building Leasing Services
N.A.I.C.S.: 531120

SM Southern Hills Mall, LLC (1)
4400 Sergeant Rd, Sioux City, IA 51106
Tel.: (712) 274-0109
Web Site: http://www.southernhillsmall.com
Nonresidential Building Leasing Services
N.A.I.C.S.: 531120

SPG Anderson Mall, LLC (1)
3131 N Main St, Anderson, SC 29621
Tel.: (864) 226-7088
Web Site: http://www.simon.com
Nonresidential Building Leasing Services
N.A.I.C.S.: 531120

Seminole Towne Center Limited Partnership (1)
200 Towne Center Cir, Sanford, FL 32771
Tel.: (407) 323-1843
Web Site: http://www.seminoletownecenter.com
Nonresidential Building Leasing Services
N.A.I.C.S.: 531120

Shops at Northeast Mall, LLC (1)
1101 Melbourne Rd, Hurst, TX 76053
Tel.: (817) 589-9603
Web Site: http://www.shopsatnortheastmall.com
Nonresidential Building Leasing Services
N.A.I.C.S.: 531120

Southern Park Mall, LLC (1)
7401 Market St, Youngstown, OH 44512
Tel.: (330) 758-4511
Web Site: http://www.southernparkmall.com
Nonresidential Building Leasing Services
N.A.I.C.S.: 531120
Brian Gabbert *(Gen Mgr)*
Christina Cleary *(Mktg Dir)*

St. Charles Towne Plaza, LLC (1)
11110 Mall Cir, Waldorf, MD 20603
Tel.: (317) 986-8500
Web Site: http://www.stcharlestowneplaza.com
Nonresidential Building Leasing Services
N.A.I.C.S.: 531120

Sunland Park Mall, LLC (1)
750 Sunland Park Dr, El Paso, TX 79912-6709
Tel.: (915) 833-5596
Web Site: http://www.sunlandparkmall.com
Nonresidential Building Leasing Services
N.A.I.C.S.: 531120

Town Center at Aurora, LLC (1)
14200 E Alameda Ave, Aurora, CO 80012
Tel.: (303) 344-9764
Web Site: http://www.towncenterataurora.com
Nonresidential Building Leasing Services
N.A.I.C.S.: 531120

Towne West Square, LLC (1)
4600 W Kellogg Dr, Wichita, KS 67209
Tel.: (316) 945-1236
Web Site: http://www.townewestsquare.com
Nonresidential Building Leasing Services
N.A.I.C.S.: 531120

University Park Mall CC, LLC (1)
6501 N Grape Rd, Mishawaka, IN 46545-1008
Tel.: (574) 271-5531
Nonresidential Building Leasing Services
N.A.I.C.S.: 531120

Village Park Plaza, LLC (1)
200 E Greyhound Pass, Carmel, IN 46033
Tel.: (317) 818-0725
Nonresidential Building Leasing Services
N.A.I.C.S.: 531120

Virginia Center Commons, LLC (1)
10101 Brook Rd, Glen Allen, VA 23059
Tel.: (804) 266-9002
Web Site: http://www.shopvirginiacentercommons.com
Nonresidential Building Leasing Services
N.A.I.C.S.: 531120

WPG Wolf Ranch, LLC (1)
1015 W University Ave, Georgetown, TX 78628
Tel.: (512) 930-8008
Web Site: http://www.wolfranchtowncenter.com
Nonresidential Building Leasing Services
N.A.I.C.S.: 531120

Washington Prime Group, L.P. (1)
180 E Broad St, Columbus, OH 43215
Tel.: (614) 621-9000
Rev.: $524,417,999
Assets: $4,105,346,999
Liabilities: $3,504,148,999
Net Worth: $601,197,999
Earnings: ($261,887,000)
Fiscal Year-end: 12/31/2020
Real Estate Investment Trust
N.A.I.C.S.: 525990
Louis G. Conforti *(CEO)*

Washington Prime Properties LLC (1)
180 E Broad St Ste 20, Columbus, OH 43215
Tel.: (614) 621-9000
Sales Range: $75-99.9 Million
Emp.: 250
Real Estate Manangement Services
N.A.I.C.S.: 531320
Michael P. Glimcher *(Pres)*

Washington Prime Property Limited Partnership (1)
180 E Broad St 21st Fl, Columbus, OH 43215-4206
Tel.: (614) 621-9000
Real Estate Investment Trust Services
N.A.I.C.S.: 531120
George A. Schmidt *(Chief Investment Officer & Exec VP)*
Thomas J. Drought Jr. *(Exec VP-Leasing)*

Subsidiary (Domestic):

Leawood TCP, LLC (2)
5000 W 119th St, Leawood, KS 66209
Tel.: (913) 498-1111
Web Site: http://www.towncenterplaza.com
Emp.: 8
Commercial Retail Property Management & Leasing Services
N.A.I.C.S.: 531312

Morgantown Mall Associates, LP (2)
9500 Mall Rd, Morgantown, WV 26501
Tel.: (304) 983-6200
Web Site: http://www.morgantownmall.com
Emp.: 25
Shopping Mall Property Management Services
N.A.I.C.S.: 531312

OKC Classen Curve, LLC (2)
5825 NW Grand Blvd, Oklahoma City, OK 73118
Tel.: (405) 902-2505
Web Site: http://www.classencurve.com
Shopping Mall Operator
N.A.I.C.S.: 531120
Shannon Barghols *(Dir-Mktg)*
Shane McWhorter *(Gen Mgr)*

WPG WestShore, LLC (2)
250 WestShore Plz, Tampa, FL 33609
Tel.: (813) 286-0790
Web Site: http://www.westshoreplaza.com
Shopping Mall Operator
N.A.I.C.S.: 531312
Larry Scollo *(Gen Mgr)*
Jamie Zimbleman *(Mktg Dir)*

West Ridge Mall, LLC (1)
1801 SW Wanamaker Rd, Topeka, KS 66604
Tel.: (785) 272-5119
Web Site: http://www.washingtonprimegroup.com
Nonresidential Building Leasing Services
N.A.I.C.S.: 531120

West Town Corners, LLC (1)
280 S State Rd 434, Altamonte Springs, FL 32714
Tel.: (407) 737-2866
Web Site: http://westtowncorners.com
Nonresidential Building Leasing Services
N.A.I.C.S.: 531120

Westminster Mall, LLC (1)
1025 Westminster Mall, Westminster, CA 92683
Tel.: (714) 898-2558
Web Site: http://www.westminstermall.com
Nonresidential Building Leasing Services
N.A.I.C.S.: 531120
Valerie Flores *(Gen Mgr)*
Patrice Conover *(Dir-Mktg)*

White Oaks Plaza, LLC (1)
2900 Veterans Pkwy, Springfield, IL 62704
Tel.: (217) 787-0110
Web Site: http://www.simon.com
Nonresidential Building Leasing Services
N.A.I.C.S.: 531120

WASHINGTON PRODUCTS INC.
1875 Harsh Ave SE, Massillon, OH 44646
Tel.: (330) 837-5101
Web Site: http://www.wpimass.com
Year Founded: 1972
Sales Range: Less than $1 Million
Emp.: 5
Point of Purchase Displays Mfr & Designer; Lightshields Painter for the Automotive Industry; Built-in Kitchen Hardware
N.A.I.C.S.: 332119
John Boring *(Pres)*

WASHINGTON REGIONAL TRANSPLANT COMMUNITY
7619 Little River Tpke Ste 900, Annandale, VA 22003
Tel.: (703) 641-0100   DC
Web Site: http://www.beadonor.org
Year Founded: 1989
Sales Range: $10-24.9 Million
Emp.: 107
Organ Transplantation Services
N.A.I.C.S.: 621991
Sylvie Muldoon *(CFO)*
Cindy Speas *(Dir-Community Affairs)*
Kenny Boyd *(Dir-Hospital Svcs)*
Jerry K. Harris *(Mgr-Tissue Svcs)*
Barbara Gordon *(Mgr-Quality Sys)*

WASHINGTON ST. TAMMANY ELECTRIC COOPERATIVE INC.
950 Pearl St, Franklinton, LA 70438
Tel.: (985) 839-3562   LA
Web Site: http://www.wste.coop
Year Founded: 1938
Sales Range: $75-99.9 Million
Electric Power Distr Cooperative
N.A.I.C.S.: 813990
Bryan Jones *(Mgr-Engrg)*
Walter Sylvest *(Mgr-Fin)*
Mike Stafford *(Mgr-Ops)*
Coylean Schloegel *(Mgr-Mktg & Media Rels)*
Charles Hill *(CEO & Gen Mgr)*
Kim Tynes *(Supvr-Acctg)*
Chad Angelo *(Mgr-Safety & Loss Control)*
Verdie Mae Knight *(Supvr-Billing)*

WASHINGTON STATE HOSPITAL ASSOCIATION

WASHTENAW COUNTY ROAD COMMISSION

300 Elliott Ave W Ste 300, Seattle, WA 98119
Tel.: (206) 281-7211   WA
Web Site: http://www.wsha.org
Year Founded: 1987
Sales Range: $10-24.9 Million
Emp.: 64
Health Care Srvices
N.A.I.C.S.: 813910
Mary Kay Clunies Ross *(VP-Comm & Pub Affairs)*
Andrew Busz *(Dir-Policy-Fin)*
Nhi Eklund *(Accountant)*
Toni Fox-Corwin *(Dir-Ops & Event Mgmt)*

WASHINGTON SUBURBAN SANITARY COMMISSION
14501 Sweitzer Ln, Laurel, MD 20707
Tel.: (301) 206-4001
Web Site: http://www.wsscwater.com
Year Founded: 1918
Sales Range: $700-749.9 Million
Emp.: 1,623
Water Supply Services
N.A.I.C.S.: 221310
Maxene Bardwell *(Dir-Internal Audit)*
Towanda R. Livingston *(Dir-Office of Supplier Diversity & Inclusion)*
Christopher Lawson *(Vice Chm)*
Sheila R. Finlayson *(Sec)*
David E. Malone *(Chief Procurement Officer)*
Todd Allen *(Dir-HR)*
Carla A. Reid *(CEO & Gen Mgr)*
Monica Johnson *(Deputy Gen Mgr-Strategic Partners)*
Joe Mantua *(Deputy Gen Mgr-Ops)*
Thomas J. Street *(Deputy Gen Mgr-Admin)*
Karyn Riley *(Dir-Intergovernmental Rels Office)*
Bryan Samuels *(Dir-WS SC Stat)*
Joe Beach *(CFO)*
Vennard Wright *(CIO)*

WASHINGTON-SAINT TAMMANY ELECTRIC COOPERATIVE INC.
950 Pearl St, Franklinton, LA 70438-1736
Tel.: (985) 839-3562
Web Site: http://www.wste.coop
Year Founded: 1938
Sales Range: $75-99.9 Million
Emp.: 114
Provider of Electric Services
N.A.I.C.S.: 221122
Francis Cefalu *(Pres)*
Leon Hickman *(Treas)*
Walter Sylvest *(Mgr-Fin)*
Mike Stafford *(Mgr-Ops)*
Bryan Jones *(Mgr-Engrg)*
Kim Tynes *(Mgr-Fin & Admin)*
Coylean Schloegel *(Mgr-Mktg)*
Chad Angelo *(Mgr-Safety & Loss Control)*
Verdie Mae Knight *(Supvr-Billing)*

WASHINGTONIAN LIMOUSINE COACH CORP.
1984 Amherst Sta, Silver Spring, MD 20915
Tel.: (301) 593-5840
Web Site: http://www.washingtoniancoach.com
Sales Range: $10-24.9 Million
Emp.: 15
Limousine Rental, With Driver
N.A.I.C.S.: 485320
L. Rogers Hardy *(Pres)*

WASHTENAW COUNTY ROAD COMMISSION

WASHTENAW COUNTY ROAD COMMISSION

U.S. PRIVATE

Washtenaw County Road Commission—(Continued)

555 N Zeeb Rd, Ann Arbor, MI 48103
Tel.: (734) 761-1500
Web Site: http://www.wcroads.org
Rev.: $15,700,000
Emp.: 131
General Contractor, Highway & Street Construction
N.A.I.C.S.: 237310
Roy D. Townsend *(Mng Dir-Admin)*
Sheryl Soderholm Siddall *(Dir-Engrg & Engr-County Highway)*
Kelly Jones *(Project Mgr)*
Barbara Fuller *(Vice Chm)*
Douglas Fuller *(Chm)*
Dan Ackerman *(Dir-Fin)*
Katherine Doyle *(Mgr-IT)*
Jim Harmon *(Dir-Ops)*
Alicia Held *(Coord-Admin)*
Nicole Peterson *(Mgr-HR)*
Gary Streight *(Project Mgr)*

WASHWORLD, INC.

2222 American Blvd, De Pere, WI 54112
Tel.: (920) 338-9278
Web Site: http://www.washworldinc.com
Year Founded: 1998
Car Wash Systems Mfr
N.A.I.C.S.: 423850
Jeff Martin *(Dir-Ops)*

Subsidiaries:

O'Hanrahan Consultants, Inc. (1)
6414 125th Ave N, Largo, FL 33773
Tel.: (727) 531-3375
Web Site: http://www.gallowaychemical.com
Car Wash Equipment Sales, Installation, Service & Chemicals Mfr
N.A.I.C.S.: 423850
Andy Mcgill *(Mgr)*
Edward J. O'Hanrahan Jr. *(Pres)*

WASP INC.

20631 State Hwy 55, Glenwood, MN 56334
Tel.: (320) 634-5126
Web Site: http://www.waspinc.com
Rev.: $24,200,000
Emp.: 400
Aircraft Support Products
N.A.I.C.S.: 333924
Geanne Kramer *(CFO)*
Dane Anderson *(Pres)*
DeWayne Nelson *(VP)*

WASSCO

12778 Brookprinter Pl, Poway, CA 92064
Tel.: (858) 679-0444
Web Site: http://www.wassco.com
Sales Range: $10-24.9 Million
Emp.: 45
Distr of Production Soldering Material & Supplies
N.A.I.C.S.: 423610
Paul Wess *(Pres)*

WASSER FILTRATION INC.

1215 Fee Ana Street, Anaheim, CA 92807
Tel.: (714) 525-0630
Web Site: http://www.pacpress.com
Rev.: $14,000,000
Emp.: 70
Filtration Products Mfr
N.A.I.C.S.: 333998
Sean Duvy *(Pres)*

WASSERMAN MEDIA GROUP, LLC

500 Park Ave Ste 650, New York, NY 10022
Tel.: (212) 704-0488
Web Site: https://www.teamwass.com
Sales Range: $1-9.9 Million
Emp.: 20
Management Consulting Services
N.A.I.C.S.: 541613
Stephanie Rudnick *(VP-Mktg & Comm)*
Marisela Rodriguez *(VP-Brand Creation & Licensing)*
Casey Wasserman *(Chm & CEO)*
Todd Palmerton *(VP-Event Creation & Mgmt)*
Jason Ranne *(COO & Exec VP-Talent)*
Joe Rosenberg *(Sr VP-Ops)*

Subsidiaries:

Brillstein Entertainment Partners, LLC (1)
9150 Wilshire Blvd Ste 350, Beverly Hills, CA 90212
Tel.: (310) 275-6135
Web Site: http://www.bepmedia.com
Sales Range: $50-74.9 Million
Emp.: 100
Television Film Production
N.A.I.C.S.: 512110
John Liebman *(Co-CEO)*

CSM Sport & Entertainment LLP (1)
3rd Floor 62 Buckingham Gate, London, SW1E 6AJ, United Kingdom
Tel.: (44) 2075935200
Web Site: http://www.csm.com
Sports & Entertainment Marketing & Public Relations Agency
N.A.I.C.S.: 541820
Sebastian Coe *(Chm)*
Edward Leask *(Deputy Chm)*
Jim Glover *(Deputy Chm)*
Zak Brown *(CEO)*
Roopesh Prashar *(CFO)*
Tim Bampton *(CMO)*
David Sim *(Head-Football & Brdcst)*
Sarah Crampton *(Head-Mktg)*
Gareth Bowhill *(Dir-Strategy & Corp Dev)*
Magnus Leask *(Dir-IT & Infrastructure-Global)*
Charlotte Macartney *(Dir-HR)*
Ashlee Huffman *(Gen Mgr-Motorsport Practice-North America)*
Gary Brosnan *(Exec Creative Dir)*
Matt Godbout *(Sr VP-Client Partnerships-Indianapolis)*
Jennifer Magley *(Sr Mgr-Brand Partnerships-Indianapolis)*

Subsidiary (Domestic):

CSM Events Limited (2)
3rd Floor 62 Buckingham Gate, London, SW1E 6AJ, United Kingdom
Tel.: (44) 207 593 5200
Web Site: http://www.csm.com
Event Management Services
N.A.I.C.S.: 711310
Jonathan Castleman *(Mng Dir-Brands-EMEA & APAC)*

Subsidiary (Domestic):

Fast Track Sailing Limited (3)
3rd Floor 62 Buckingham Gate, London, SW1E 6AJ, United Kingdom
Tel.: (44) 207 593 5200
Web Site: http://www.csm.com
Sports Marketing Consultancy Services
N.A.I.C.S.: 541613

Subsidiary (US):

CSM Production (2)
6427 Saddle Creek Ct, Harrisburg, NC 28075
Tel.: (704) 455-8888
Web Site: http://www.gojhe.com
Entertainment Promotion Services
N.A.I.C.S.: 711310
Lisa Ward *(CFO)*
Matthew Davis *(VP-Ops)*
Ryan Baxter *(COO)*
Jay Howard *(Founder & Pres)*
Jeff Gajewski *(VP-Bus Dev)*

Subsidiary (Domestic):

Essentially Sports Marketing Limited (2)
3rd Floor 62 Buckingham Gate, London, SW1E 6AJ, United Kingdom
Tel.: (44) 20 7820 7000
Web Site: http://www.essentiallygroup.com
Sports Marketing Management
N.A.I.C.S.: 541810
Bart Campbell *(CEO)*
Charles Adams *(Controller-Fin)*
Kevin Vandrau *(Dir)*
Sarah Dawson *(Dir-Client Svcs)*

Subsidiary (Non-US):

CSM Sport & Entertainment New Zealand Limited (3)
Level 2 2 Heather Street, PO Box 9169, Newmarket, Auckland, New Zealand
Tel.: (64) 9921 4250
Web Site: http://www.essentiallygroup.com
Athlete Management Consulting Services
N.A.I.C.S.: 541618

Group (Domestic):

ICON (2)
Heather Court 6 Maidstone Road, Sidcup, DA14 5HS, Kent, United Kingdom
Tel.: (44) 2083024921
Web Site: http://www.icon-world.com
Marketing & Design Agency
N.A.I.C.S.: 541613
John Francis *(Chm)*

Subsidiary (Domestic):

Curb Media Limited (3)
7A Hanson Street, London, W1W 6TE, United Kingdom
Tel.: (44) 2076312021
Web Site: http://www.curbmedia.com
Advetising Agency
N.A.I.C.S.: 541810
Anthony Ganjou Sr. *(Founder & CEO)*
Anthony Sinclair Ganjou Jr. *(Mktg Dir)*

Branch (Non-US):

ICON Brazil (3)
Rua Rodrigo Silva Numero 26 / 22o e 23o Andar, Centro, Rio de Janeiro, Brazil
Tel.: (55) 2124606800
Sign Board Distr
N.A.I.C.S.: 423440

ICON Dubai (3)
PO Box 12256, Dubai, United Arab Emirates
Tel.: (971) 43403881
Sign Board Distr
N.A.I.C.S.: 423440

Branch (US):

ICON North America (3)
18th Fl 112 W 34th St, New York, NY 10120
Tel.: (646) 750-2955
Sign Board Distr
N.A.I.C.S.: 423440
Luke Jarman *(Pres)*

Branch (Non-US):

ICON Oman (3)
108 1/F Maktabi Building, PO Box 1982, Al Khuwair, Muscat, 111, Oman
Tel.: (968) 24391996
Sign Board Distr
N.A.I.C.S.: 423440

Division (Domestic):

ICON Overlay and Fitout (3)
Unit 9 Fosters Business Park Old School Road, Hook, RG27 9NY, Hampshire, United Kingdom
Tel.: (44) 1256764994
Sign Board Distr
N.A.I.C.S.: 423440

Branch (Non-US):

ICON Qatar (3)
5/F 5 Aljazeera Street, Bin Mahmoud, Doha, Qatar
Tel.: (974) 44499001
Sign Board Distr
N.A.I.C.S.: 423440

ICON Russia (3)
11/4 Michurinskiy Prospect, Moscow, 119192, Russia
Tel.: (7) 9250080307
Sign Board Distr
N.A.I.C.S.: 423440

WASSERSTEIN & CO., LP

1185 Avenue of the Americas 39th Fl, New York, NY 10036
Tel.: (212) 702-5602 DE
Web Site: http://www.wasserco.com
Year Founded: 2001
Private Equity & Credit Investment Firm
N.A.I.C.S.: 523999
Ellis B. Jones *(Chm)*
Rajay Bagaria *(Pres & Chief Investment Officer)*
Joseph Dutton *(CFO & Chief Compliance Officer)*
Andrew McLellan *(Mng Dir)*
Randall J. Weisenburger *(Founder)*

WASSERSTROM COMPANY

477 S Frnt St, Columbus, OH 43215-5625
Tel.: (614) 228-6525 OH
Web Site: http://www.wasserstrom.com
Year Founded: 1902
Sales Range: $10-24.9 Million
Emp.: 250
Provider of Office Furniture & Restaurant Equipment
N.A.I.C.S.: 423850
Rodney Wasserstrom *(Pres & CEO)*
Robert Stone *(Exec VP)*
Ursula Vermillion *(Exec VP)*
Shelly Myers *(Exec VP-HR)*
Alan Wasserstrom *(Treas)*
Phil Smith *(CIO & VP)*
Lori Shepherd *(VP & Controller)*

WASTE PRO USA, INC.

2101 W State Rd 434 Ste 305, Longwood, FL 32779-5053
Tel.: (407) 869-8800 FL
Web Site: http://www.wasteprousa.com
Sales Range: $400-449.9 Million
Emp.: 2,500
Holding Company; Waste Collection, Disposal & Recycling Services
N.A.I.C.S.: 551112
Fred V. Wood *(VP-Central Mississippi)*
John J. Jennings *(Founder, Chm & CEO)*
Ron Pecora *(Chief Mktg Officer)*
Leigh Thomas *(Dir-Acctg)*
Sean Jennings *(Pres)*
Cort Sabina *(CFO)*
Sharon Tolopka *(Chief Acctg Officer)*
Brian Wintjen *(VP-North Florida)*
Stormy Lewis *(Mgr-Jackson)*
Russell Mackie *(VP-Bus Dev-Southeast Florida)*
Keith Banasiak *(COO & Sr VP)*

Subsidiaries:

Delta Sanitation, LLC (1)
4205 Beasley Rd, Gautier, MS 39553
Tel.: (228) 818-5393
Web Site: http://www.wasteprousa.com
Waste Collection, Disposal & Recycling Services
N.A.I.C.S.: 562111
John Jennings *(Pres)*

Waste Pro of Georgia, Inc. (1)
3512 Oakcliff Rd, Doraville, GA 30340-3003
Tel.: (770) 777-1447
Web Site: http://www.wasteprousa.com
Emp.: 60
Waste Collection, Disposal & Recycling Services
N.A.I.C.S.: 562111
Fred V. Wood *(Pres)*

WASTE RECYCLING INC.

COMPANIES

824 N Decatur St, Montgomery, AL 36104
Tel.: (334) 262-1070
Rev.: $15,000,000
Emp.: 115
Provider of Recycling Services
N.A.I.C.S.: 423930
Robert J. Armstrong (Pres)
Mal Sport (Comptroller)

WASTREN ADVANTAGE, INC.
1862 Shyville Rd Ste 212, Piketon, OH 45661
Tel.: (740) 289-9761   ID
Web Site: http://www.wastrenadvantage.com
Year Founded: 2006
Sales Range: $10-24.9 Million
Emp.: 100
Environmental Management, Technical Consulting & Field Services
N.A.I.C.S.: 813312
Steve Moore (Pres & CEO)
James Gardner (Exec VP)
Doug Collins (Dir-PMO)
Keith Tucker (VP-Bus Dev)
Glenn Henderson (COO)
Rick Penpek (Office Mgr-Bus)

Subsidiaries:

Geo-Tech Polymers, LLC   (1)
300 Westdale Ave, Westerville, OH 43082
Tel.: (614) 797-2300
Web Site: http://www.geo-tech.com
Sales Range: $1-9.9 Million
Emp.: 12
Plastics Material & Resin Mfr
N.A.I.C.S.: 325211
Sanjay Dutta (CEO)

Wastren Advantage, Inc.   (1)
1231 N 23rd Str Ste 206, Grand Junction, CO 81501
Tel.: (970) 254-1283
Web Site: http://www.wastrenadvantage.com
Environmental Management & Field Services
N.A.I.C.S.: 541620
James W. Gardner (COO & Gen Mgr)

WATAIR INC.
21900 Burbank Blvd 3rd Fl, Woodland Hills, CA 91367
Tel.: (310) 728-6306   WA
Web Site: http://www.watair.com
Year Founded: 2000
Sales Range: Less than $1 Million
Water Generator Mfr
N.A.I.C.S.: 335312

WATANABE FLORAL, INC.
1607 Hart St, Honolulu, HI 96817
Tel.: (808) 832-9360
Web Site: http://www.watanabefloral.com
Year Founded: 1945
Rev.: $11,228,352
Emp.: 125
Floral Whslr
N.A.I.C.S.: 424930
Russell Watanabe (Pres)

WATAUGA GROUP LLC
1600 N Orange Ave Ste 13, Orlando, FL 32804
Tel.: (407) 234-8539   FL
Web Site: http://www.wataugagroup.com
Sales Range: $10-24.9 Million
Emp.: 7
Advetising Agency
N.A.I.C.S.: 541810
Leslie Osborne (Partner & Dir-Media)
Neil Romaine (Partner & Dir-Strategic Mktg)

WATAUGA MEDICAL CENTER

PO Box 2600, Boone, NC 28607-2600
Tel.: (828) 262-4100   NC
Web Site: http://www.apprhs.org
Year Founded: 1932
Sales Range: $75-99.9 Million
Emp.: 1,500
Health Care Center
N.A.I.C.S.: 622110
Herman A. Godwin (Sr VP & Dir-Medical)
Mary Etta Long (Sr VP-Medical Staff)

WATCH LA JEANS
1138 Wall St, Los Angeles, CA 90015
Tel.: (213) 747-1838
Web Site: http://www.watchla.com
Sales Range: $10-24.9 Million
Emp.: 40
Women's, Misses' & Juniors' Jeans
N.A.I.C.S.: 315250
Pierre Mitri (Pres)
Sam Pierre (VP)

WATER & POWER COMMUNITY CREDIT UNION
1053 W Sunset Blvd, Los Angeles, CA 90012-2134
Tel.: (213) 580-1600   CA
Web Site: http://www.wpcu.org
Year Founded: 1936
Sales Range: $10-24.9 Million
Emp.: 108
Credit Union
N.A.I.C.S.: 522130
Mike Tufegdzich (VP-Sls & Lending)
Craig Luna (Co-Chm)
Gladys Berry (Sec)
Louie Ferrar (Asst Sec)
Michele Wilson (Treas)
Bill Younger (Co-Chm)
Felipe Castaneda (CFO)
Barry Roach (Pres & CEO)

WATER ASSET MANAGEMENT, LLC
509 Madison Ave Ste 804, New York, NY 10022
Tel.: (212) 754-5132
Web Site: http://www.waterinv.com
Sales Range: $25-49.9 Million
Emp.: 10
Alternative Investment Management Services
N.A.I.C.S.: 523999
Marc Robert (COO)
Joseph Kirincich (CFO)

Subsidiaries:

SouthWest Water Company   (1)
1 Wilshire Bldg 624 S Grand Ave Ste 2900, Los Angeles, CA 90017
Tel.: (213) 929-1800
Web Site: http://www.southwestwater.com
Sales Range: $200-249.9 Million
Holding Company; Owner of Water & Wastewater Management Operations
N.A.I.C.S.: 221310
Anton C. Garnier (Pres & CEO)
Michael O. Quinn (Mng Dir-West Utilities)

Subsidiary (Domestic):

SWWC Utilities, Inc.,   (2)
9511 Ranch Rd 620 N, Austin, TX 78726-2908
Tel.: (512) 335-7580
Web Site: http://www.swwc.com
Water & Wastewater Utility Services
N.A.I.C.S.: 221310

Suburban Water Systems   (2)
1325 N Grand Ave Ste 100, Covina, CA 91724-3603
Tel.: (626) 543-2640
Web Site: https://www.swwc.com
Sales Range: $50-74.9 Million
Water Utility Services
N.A.I.C.S.: 221310

Windermere Utility Company   (2)
2700 Pecan St W Ste 430, Pflugerville, TX 78660
Tel.: (713) 405-1717
Web Site: http://www.swwc.com
Water Management Operations
N.A.I.C.S.: 221310

WATER ENVIRONMENT FEDERATION
601 Wythe St, Alexandria, VA 22314-1994
Tel.: (703) 684-2400   VA
Web Site: http://www.wef.org
Year Founded: 1928
Sales Range: $10-24.9 Million
Emp.: 103
Educational Support Services
N.A.I.C.S.: 611710
Pamela Henry (Sr Dir-Conference Ops & Exhibitions)
Jeff Eger (Exec Dir)
Eileen O'Neill (Exec Dir)
Zhen He (Editor-In-Chief-Water Environ Res)

WATER GAS & LIGHT COMMISSION
401 Pine Ave, Albany, GA 31701
Tel.: (229) 883-8330
Web Site: http://www.albanyutil.org
Sales Range: $100-124.9 Million
Emp.: 275
Combination Utilities Water & Light
N.A.I.C.S.: 221118
Dorothy Hubbart (Chm)

WATER GREMLIN COMPANY
1610 Whitaker St, White Bear Lake, MN 55110
Tel.: (651) 429-7761
Web Site: http://www.watergremlin.com
Rev.: $20,300,000
Emp.: 180
Sporting & Athletic Goods
N.A.I.C.S.: 339920
Robert Neil (Pres)
Mike Garin (VP-Ops)
Steve Mende (VP-Sls & Mktg)
Laure Peot (Dir-HR)
Christophe Chandler (Mgr-R&D)
Scott Schulz (VP-Fin)

WATER HEATERS ONLY INCORPORATED
970 E Main St Ste 200, Grass Valley, CA 95945
Tel.: (650) 349-3747
Web Site: http://www.waterheatersonly.com
Rev.: $23,100,000
Emp.: 20
Household Appliance Stores
N.A.I.C.S.: 449210
John P. McGee (Pres)
Yana Carpenter (Dir-Sls & Mktg)

WATER PRODUCTS COMPANY OF ILLINOIS, INC.
3255 E New York St, Aurora, IL 60504
Tel.: (630) 898-6100
Web Site: http://www.waterproductscompany.com
Sales Range: $10-24.9 Million
Emp.: 30
Water Supply
N.A.I.C.S.: 423720
William C. Witzel (CEO)

WATER REMEDIATION TECHNOLOGY LLC
901 W 116th Ave Ste 400, Westminster, CO 80234

WATER STREET HEALTHCARE PARTNERS, LLC

Tel.: (303) 424-5355   CO
Web Site: http://www.wrtnet.com
Year Founded: 2000
Waste Treatment Services
N.A.I.C.S.: 221310
Michael Dimitriou (Pres)
Ron Dollar (VP-Sls & Mktg)

Subsidiaries:

Loprest Water Treatment Company   (1)
901 W 116th Ave Ste 400, Westminster, CO 80234
Tel.: (303) 424-5355
Web Site: http://www.loprest.com
Other Commercial & Service Industry Machinery Mfr
N.A.I.C.S.: 333310
Randy Richey (Pres)

WATER RESOURCES INTERNATIONAL, INC.
2800 E Chambers St, Phoenix, AZ 85040
Tel.: (602) 268-2580   AZ
Web Site: http://www.wrintl.com
Sales Range: $10-24.9 Million
Emp.: 50
Water Purification Equipment & Bottled Water
N.A.I.C.S.: 333310
Lowell E. Foletta (CEO)

WATER SERVICES OF AMERICA, INC.
2018 S 1st St, Milwaukee, WI 53207-6408
Tel.: (414) 481-4120   WI
Web Site: http://www.wsaes.com
Year Founded: 1971
Sales Range: $100-124.9 Million
Emp.: 200
Automatic Tube Cleaning Systems For Condensers, Heat Exchangers & Backflush Valves Mfr
N.A.I.C.S.: 333310
Kaveh Someah (Pres & CEO)

WATER STANDARD MANAGEMENT
4265 San Felipe Ste 620, Houston, TX 77027
Tel.: (713) 400-4777
Web Site: http://www.waterstandard.com
Water Supply & Irrigation Systems
N.A.I.C.S.: 221310
Kirk Wagner (Pres)
Lisa Henthorne (CTO & Sr VP)

Subsidiaries:

Monarch Separators Inc.   (1)
5410 Trafalgar Dr, Houston, TX 77045-6034
Tel.: (713) 433-7441
Web Site: http://www.monarchseparators.com
Plastic Mfr
N.A.I.C.S.: 326111
Karl Wagner (Owner)

WATER STREET BREWERY
1101 N Water St, Milwaukee, WI 53202
Tel.: (414) 272-1195
Web Site: http://www.waterstreetbrewery.com
Sales Range: $10-24.9 Million
Emp.: 100
Brewery Mfr
N.A.I.C.S.: 312120
Tina Lawler (Dir-Mktg)

WATER STREET HEALTHCARE PARTNERS, LLC
444 W Lake St Ste 1800, Chicago, IL 60606-1220
Tel.: (312) 506-2900   DE
Web Site: http://www.waterstreet.com

WATER STREET HEALTHCARE PARTNERS, LLC

U.S. PRIVATE

Water Street Healthcare Partners, LLC—(Continued)
Year Founded: 2005
Healthcare Industry Private Equity Firm
N.A.I.C.S.: 523999
Steven D. Cosler (Partner-Operating)
Tim Dugan (Mng Partner)
James G. Connelly III (Partner)
Patrick J. Griffin (Executives)
Jeff Holway (CFO & Chief Admin Officer)
Alan Heller (Operating Partner)
Kevin Swan (Partner)
Katie Hayes (Controller)
Katie Ossman (Principal)
Nicklaus Daley (VP)
Jim Lang (CEO)
Michael S. Zappala (VP)
Caroline Kenter Larew (VP)
Deepak Batheja (CIO)
Max Mishkin (Partner)
Ryan Pavlik (VP-Debt Capital Markets)
Curtis M. Selquist (Operating Partner)
Scott T. Garrett (Sr Partner-Operating & Operating Partner)

Subsidiaries:

Access MediQuip, LLC (1)
255 Primera Blvd Ste 230, Lake Mary, FL 32746
Tel.: (407) 268-8447
Web Site: http://www.accessmediquip.com
Sales Range: $75-99.9 Million
Outsourced Implantable Device Management Solutions
N.A.I.C.S.: 339910
Jonathan Buffa (Interim Pres & Interim Chief Growth Officer)
Jorge Amaro (COO)

BREG, Inc. (1)
2885 Loker Ave E, Carlsbad, CA 92010
Tel.: (760) 795-5440
Web Site: http://www.breg.com
Sales Range: $50-74.9 Million
Emp.: 1,200
Orthopedic, Reconstructive & Postoperative Product Mfr
N.A.I.C.S.: 339112
Brad Lee (Pres & CEO)
Geoff Siegel (VP-Innovation)
Carol Emerson (VP-Quality Assurance & Regulatory Affairs)
Joanne Woolfall (VP-HR)
Steve Paul (VP-Sls & Comml Ops)
Benjamin Hutson (VP-Ops)
Stuart F. Simpson (Chm)
Jonathon Singer (CFO)

Subsidiary (Domestic):

Omni Motion, Inc. (2)
2888 Loker Ave E Ste 208, Carlsbad, CA 92010
Tel.: (760) 242-6452
Web Site: http://www.breg.com
Orthopedic Rehabilitation Equipment Mfr
N.A.I.C.S.: 339112
Deanna Berman (VP)
J. J. Anderson (Mgr-San Francisco Bay Area)

Definitive Media Corp. (1)
2000 Centregreen Way Ste 300, Cary, NC 27513
Tel.: (866) 392-4788
Web Site: http://www.threadresearch.com
Technology & Service Provider
N.A.I.C.S.: 541990
John Reites (CEO)

Subsidiary (Domestic):

inVibe Labs, LLC (2)
2900 Bristol D201, Costa Mesa, CA 92626
Tel.: (949) 438-4836
Web Site: http://www.invibe.co
Pharmaceutical Product Mfr & Distr
N.A.I.C.S.: 325412
Fabio Gratton (Co-Founder & CEO)
Jeremy Franz (Co-Founder & CTO)
Stephanie Huminski (Assoc Dir-Research)
Sunny Shah (Head-Strategy)
Adam Kleger (Head-Client Solutions)

EVERSANA (1)
190 N Milwaukee St, Milwaukee, WI 53202
Tel.: (414) 299-4900
Web Site: http://www.eversana.com
Pharmaceutical Mfr & Dist
N.A.I.C.S.: 456110
Scott A. Snyder (Chief Digital Officer)
Jim Lang (CEO)
Greg Skalicky (Chief Revenue Officer)
Kelly Baker (CFO)
Mark MacNaughton (CIO)
Eric Bishea (Pres-Mktg & Market Access)
James Lang (Founder & CEO)

Eversana Life Science Services, LLC (1)
190 N Milwaukee St, Milwaukee, WI 53202
Tel.: (414) 299-4900
Web Site: http://www.eversana.com
Pharmaceuticals Mfr
N.A.I.C.S.: 325412
Jim Lang (CEO)

Subsidiary (Domestic):

Alamo Pharma Services, Inc. (2)
77 N Broad St, Doylestown, PA 18901
Tel.: (215) 489-9500
Web Site: http://www.alamopharmaservices.com
Pharmaceutical Product Whslr
N.A.I.C.S.: 424210
Amanda DaSilva (Project Mgr)
Amy Peek (Dir-Employee Rels & Recruiting)
Joelle Novak (Project Mgr)
Kevin Horak (Dir-HR)
Melissa Hayes (Project Mgr)
Peter Marchesini (Pres)
Denise Fullowan (Exec Dir-Trng & Dev)
Leora Haas (Mgr-Employee Engagement & Retention)
Susan Pike (Mgr-Talent Acq)

HVH Precision Analytics LLC (2)
1255 Drummers Ln Ste 100, Wayne, PA 19087
Web Site: http://www.hvhprecision.com
Information Technology Support Services
N.A.I.C.S.: 541512
Steve Costalas (CEO)
Pierantonio Russo (Sr VP-Medical Affairs)
Jennifer Furniss (Sr Dir-Fin)
Oodaye Shukla (Chief Data & Analytics Officer)

Triplefin LLC (2)
11333 Cornell Pk Dr, Cincinnati, OH 45242
Tel.: (513) 794-9870
Web Site: http://www.triplefin.com
Order to Cash Solutions to Healthcare & Pharmaceutical Companies
N.A.I.C.S.: 541613

HealthPlan Holdings, Inc. (1)
PO Box 30208, Tampa, FL 33630-3208
Tel.: (813) 289-1000
Web Site: http://www.healthplanholdings.com
Sales Range: $1-4.9 Billion
Emp.: 2,450
Holding Company; Health Insurance & Employee Benefits Business Outsourcing & Data Processing Services
N.A.I.C.S.: 551112
Jeffery W. Bak (Pres & CEO)
Anne Marie Faria (CMO, Chief Sls Officer & Exec VP)
Gregory C. Fisher (Sr VP & Controller)
Stephen Saft (CFO & Chief Admin Officer)
Blake Lasky (Sr VP-Client Mgmt)
Ronald L. Walters (Sr VP-Ops)

Subsidiary (Domestic):

American Benefit Plan Administrators, Inc. (2)
1325 N Grand Ave, Covina, CA 91724-4044
Tel.: (626) 732-2100
Web Site: http://www.abpa.com
Sales Range: $150-199.9 Million
Employee Benefit Plan Administration Services
N.A.I.C.S.: 524292
Daniel P. Maier (COO)
Tammy Peltzer (VP-Fin Acctg & Payroll Auditing Svcs)
Kathie Pittman (VP-Claims & Customer Svc)
Patricia Kuchenreuther (Dir-Internal Audit & Regulatory Compliance)

Annette M. English (Sr VP-Culinary Health Fund)
Teresa Warren (Sr VP-Southeast Reg)
Chiemi J. Watanabe (VP)

Subsidiary (Domestic):

Tedro & Associates, Inc. (3)
333 Pierce Rd Ste 410, Itasca, IL 60143
Tel.: (630) 960-3322
Sales Range: $50-74.9 Million
Emp.: 20
Employee Benefit Plan Administration Services
N.A.I.C.S.: 524292

Medical Guradian, LLC (1)
1818 Market St Suite 1200, Philadelphia, PA 19103
Tel.: (800) 313-1191
Web Site: http://www.medicalguardian.com
Sales Range: $1-9.9 Million
Emp.: 67
Home Medical Alert Systems to Seniors
N.A.I.C.S.: 621610
Geoff Gross (CEO)
Brian Simmermon (CIO)

Subsidiary (Domestic):

MobileHelp, LLC (2)
3701 FAU Blvd Ste 300, Boca Raton, FL 33431
Tel.: (561) 347-6255
Web Site: http://www.mobilehelpnow.com
Sales Range: $1-9.9 Million
Mobile Medical Alert System
N.A.I.C.S.: 624230
Robert S. Flippo (CEO)
Dennis V. Boyle (Pres & COO)
Jean Robichaud (CTO)
Joel Richardson (CFO)
Jeffrey E. Hilton (Chief Mktg Officer)
Chris Otto (Sr VP-Healthcare Div)
Ellen deClaire (VP-HR)
Kurt Stelzer (Dir-Dealer Sls)

Safeguard Medical, LLC (1)
44 W Lk St Ste 1800, Chicago, IL 60606
Tel.: (312) 506-2900
Web Site: http://www.safeguardmedical.com
Healthcare Products Mfr & Emergency Response Services
N.A.I.C.S.: 456199
Adam Johnson (CEO)
Mark Lait (Pres-Intl Product Sls)

Subsidiary (Domestic):

H&H Medical Corporation (2)
328 McLaws Cir, Williamsburg, VA 23185
Tel.: (252) 203-7002
Web Site: http://www.gohandh.com
Surgical Appliance & Supplies Mfr
N.A.I.C.S.: 339113
Brooke Spotswood (Sec)
Paul Harder (Pres)

Water-Jel Technologies, LLC (2)
50 Broad St, Carlstadt, NJ 07072
Tel.: (201) 507-8300
Web Site: http://www.waterjel.com
First Aid Supplies Distr
N.A.I.C.S.: 424210
James Hartnett (Pres & CEO)
Jim Geraghty (VP-Global Supply Chain)
John McAndris (CFO & VP)
Paul Slot (VP-Indus, EMS & Special Markets)
Robin Latchney (Mgr-Customer Svc)
Janet Ryan (Mgr-Regulatory Affairs)
Edward Bellerose (Reg Sls Mgr-Western)
Mark Lait (Mng Dir-WaterJel Intl)

WATER WORKS & SANITARY SEWER

22 Bibb St 116 Coosa St, Montgomery, AL 36104
Tel.: (334) 206-1600
Web Site: http://www.mwwssb.com
Rev.: $48,849,326
Emp.: 253
Water Utility
N.A.I.C.S.: 221310
Thomas Morgan (Gen Mgr)

WATERBORNE ENVIRONMENTAL INC.

897B Harrison St SE, Leesburg, VA 20175
Tel.: (703) 777-0005
Web Site: http://www.waterborne-env.com
Year Founded: 1993
Sales Range: $1-9.9 Million
Emp.: 59
Environmental Consulting Services
N.A.I.C.S.: 541620
Patrick W. Holden (CEO)

WATERBURY COMPANIES, INC.

64 Ave of Industry, Waterbury, CT 06705
Tel.: (203) 597-1812 DE
Web Site: http://www.watco.com
Year Founded: 1812
Sales Range: $75-99.9 Million
Emp.: 120
Custom Molded Plastic Products Mfr
N.A.I.C.S.: 325120
Carl Contalini (Pres)
Paul Hebert (Mgr-Natl Retail Sls)

WATERBURY HOSPITAL

64 Robbins St, Waterbury, CT 06708 CT
Tel.: (203) 573-6000
Web Site: http://www.waterburyhospital.org
Year Founded: 1951
Sales Range: $200-249.9 Million
Emp.: 2,000
Health Care Srvices
N.A.I.C.S.: 622110
Michael J. Cemeno (CIO)
Thomas M. Burke (VP-Ops)
Edward Romero (CFO)
Diane M. Woolley (VP-HR)
Sandra A. Iadarola (Chief Nursing Officer)
Peter Adamo (Pres & CEO)

WATERFALL ASSET MANAGEMENT LLC

1140 Avenue of Americas 7th Fl, New York, NY 10036
Tel.: (212) 257-4600
Web Site: http://www.waterfallam.com
Year Founded: 2005
Rev.: $6,300,000,000
Emp.: 120
Asset Management Services
N.A.I.C.S.: 523940
Jack Jay Ross (Co-Founder & Mng Partner)
Brian Breakstone (CFO)
Kenneth Nick (Gen Counsel)
Crager Boardman (COO)
Ronen Rub (CTO)
Leo Wong (Partner)
Keerthi Raghavan (Partner)
Patrick Lo (Partner & Co-Chief Investment Officer)
Brian Rebello (Partner & Co-Chief Investment Officer)

Subsidiaries:

Mortgage Assets Management LLC (1)
1875 Connecticut Ave NW Ste 405, Washington, DC 20009
Tel.: (202) 750-4497
Web Site: http://www.mamassets.com
Privater Equity Firm
N.A.I.C.S.: 523999
Patrick Journy (CFO)

Ready Capital Corporation (1)
1251 Ave of the Americas 50th Fl, New York, NY 10020
Tel.: (212) 257-4600
Web Site: https://www.readycapital.com
Rev.: $806,992,000

Assets: $9,534,031,000
Liabilities: $8,253,433,000
Net Worth: $1,280,598,000
Earnings: $150,241,000
Emp.: 787
Fiscal Year-end: 12/31/2021
Real Estate Investment Trust
N.A.I.C.S.: 525990
Jack Jay Ross (Pres)
Thomas Edward Capasse (Chm, CEO & Chief Investment Officer)
Gary T. Taylor (COO)
Andrew Ahlborn (CFO)
John Moshier (Pres-Small Bus Lending)
Adam Zausmer (Chief Credit Officer)
Lisa Cappelletti (Exec Dir)
John DePasquale (VP)
David A. Cohen (Mng Dir & Chief Production Officer)
Jordan Goforth (Exec Dir-Natl Bridge Originations)
Alex Gursky (VP-Natl Bridge Originations)
Michel Gilbert (Exec Dir-Strategic Partnerships)
Mike Kim (Exec Dir-Southern California Loan Originations)
Sonny Ko (Exec Dir-Pacific Northwest Loan Originations)
Seth Hejny (Officer-Bus Dev & VP)
Dan Gaylord (VP & Dir)
Russell Grigg (VP & Exec Dir)
Christopher Grimes (Treas)
Jessica Lang (Controller)
Justin Levy (Pres-Small Bus Lending)
Travis Reichling (Head-Capital Markets)
Dominick D. Scali (Mng Dir, Chief Credit Officer & Head-Bridge Lending)

Subsidiary (Domestic):

Anworth Mortgage Asset Corporation (2)
1299 Ocean Ave 2nd Fl, Santa Monica, CA 90401
Tel.: (310) 255-4493
Web Site: http://www.anworth.com
Rev.: $83,085,000
Assets: $2,384,490,000
Liabilities: $1,975,451,000
Net Worth: $409,039,000
Earnings: ($103,693,000)
Fiscal Year-end: 12/31/2020
Real Estate Investment Trust
N.A.I.C.S.: 525990
Heather U. Baines (Exec VP)
John T. Hillman (VP & Dir-IR)
Brett I. Roth (Sr VP & Portfolio Mgr)
Bistra Pashamova (Sr VP & Portfolio Mgr)
Bistra Pashamova (Sr VP & Portfolio Mgr)

Broadmark Realty Capital Inc. (2)
1420 5th Ave Ste 2000, Seattle, WA 98101
Tel.: (206) 971-0800
Web Site: https://www.broadmark.com
Rev.: $108,877,000
Assets: $1,051,507,000
Liabilities: $123,454,000
Net Worth: $928,053,000
Earnings: ($116,391,000)
Emp.: 63
Fiscal Year-end: 12/31/2022
Mortgage Lending Services
N.A.I.C.S.: 522310

Subsidiary (Domestic):

Broadmark Private REIT Management, LLC (3)
1420 5th Ave Ste 2000, Seattle, WA 98101
Tel.: (206) 623-1200
Web Site: http://broadmarkprivatecapital.com
Mortgage Loan Broker Services
N.A.I.C.S.: 522310

Trinity Merger Corp. (3)
1420 5 Ave Ste 2000, Seattle, WA 98101
Tel.: (808) 529-0909
Investment Services
N.A.I.C.S.: 523999

Subsidiary (Domestic):

GMFS LLC (2)
7389 Florida Blvd Ste 200A, Baton Rouge, LA 70806
Tel.: (225) 214-5000
Web Site: http://www.gmfslending.com
Emp.: 243
Mortgage Lending Services
N.A.I.C.S.: 522310
Tee Brown (Pres & CEO)

Owens Realty Mortgage, Inc. (2)
2221 Olympic Blvd, Walnut Creek, CA 94595
Tel.: (925) 935-3840
Web Site: http://www.owensmortgage.com
Rev.: $16,797,021
Assets: $209,070,040
Liabilities: $17,711,258
Net Worth: $191,358,782
Earnings: $6,889,531
Emp.: 2
Fiscal Year-end: 12/31/2018
Real Estate Investment Services
N.A.I.C.S.: 525990
William C. Owens (Chm & CEO)
Bryan H. Draper (CFO, Treas & Sec)

Subsidiary (Domestic):

Zalanta Resort at the Village, LLC (3)
4125 Lake Tahoe Blvd Ste G, South Lake Tahoe, CA 96150
Tel.: (530) 600-3780
Web Site: http://www.zalanta.com
Resort Management Services
N.A.I.C.S.: 721120
Mike Dunn (Mgr-Sls)

WATERFIELD TECHNOLOGIES, INC.

110 S Hartford Ave, Ste 2502, Tulsa, OK 74120
Tel.: (918) 858-6400   OK
Web Site: http://www.waterfieldtechnologies.com
Voice & Mobile Technologies Consulting & Contact Center Services
N.A.I.C.S.: 541690
Mark Osen (COO)
Steve Kezirian (Pres & CEO)
Evan Jones (Chief Customer Officer)
Vladimir Babiuc (VP-Fin & Acctg)
Cynthia Stryker (Head-Mktg & Dir)
Michael Fisher (Chief Product Officer)

Subsidiaries:

Blueworx (1)
1 W 3rd St Ste 1115, Tulsa, OK 74103
Tel.: (918) 858-3942
Web Site: http://www.blueworx.com
Voice Response & Recognition Software Platform Developer
N.A.I.C.S.: 541511
John Marino (Pres & CEO)

Chrysalis Software, Inc. (1)
126 Clock Twr Pl Ste 215, Carmel, CA 93923
Tel.: (831) 761-1307
Web Site: http://www.chrysalis.net
Sales Range: $1-9.9 Million
Contact Center Software Consulting Services
N.A.I.C.S.: 541690
John Marino (Pres & CEO)
Steve Hoffman (VP-Sls)

Dice Communications, Inc. (1)
3000 Farnam St, Ste 1B, Omaha, NE 68131
Tel.: (402) 597-2923
Web Site: http://www.dicecommunications.com
Telecommunications Resellers
N.A.I.C.S.: 517121
Tina Dice (Pres)

PDT Communications, Ltd. (1)
8330 Amberleigh Way, Dublin, OH 43017
Tel.: (301) 515-0450
Telecommunications Resellers
N.A.I.C.S.: 517121

WATERFILTERS.NET LLC.

560 22nd St, Zumbrota, MN 55992
Tel.: (612) 605-6910
Web Site: http://www.WaterFilters.net
Year Founded: 2002
Sales Range: $10-24.9 Million
Emp.: 25
Water Dstr
N.A.I.C.S.: 325412
Jamin Arvig (CEO)

WATERFORD GROUP, LLC

914 Hartford Tpke, Waterford, CT 06385-0715
Tel.: (860) 442-4559
Web Site: http://www.waterfordgroup.net
Year Founded: 1986
Sales Range: $25-49.9 Million
Emp.: 60
Casino Hotel Development, Hospitality & Gaming Management Services
N.A.I.C.S.: 721120
Len Wolman (Chm & CEO)
Alan Angel (CFO)
Lisa Beers (VP-PR)
Judy Moran (VP-HR)

Subsidiaries:

Waterford Gaming, LLC (1)
914 Hartford Tpke, Waterford, CT 06385-0715   (100%)
Tel.: (860) 442-4559
Web Site: http://www.waterfordgroup.net
Sales Range: $25-49.9 Million
Emp.: 1
Holding Company
N.A.I.C.S.: 551112
Len Wolman (Chm & CEO)
Mark Wolman (Principal & Dir)
Alan Angel (CFO)
Del J. Lauria (Sec)

Joint Venture (Domestic):

Trading Cove Associates (2)
914 Hartford Tpke, Waterford, CT 06385-0715
Tel.: (860) 442-1202
Web Site: http://www.waterfordhotelgroup.com
Sales Range: $75-99.9 Million
Emp.: 1
Casino Investment & Development Company; Owned 50% by Waterford Gaming, LLC & 50% by Kerzner International Limited
N.A.I.C.S.: 523999
Len Wolman (Mng Partner)
Alan Angel (CFO)

Subsidiary (Domestic):

Waterford Gaming Finance Corp. (2)
PO Box 715, Waterford, CT 06385-0715   (100%)
Tel.: (860) 442-4559
Web Site: http://www.waterfordgroup.net
Assets: $100
Emp.: 2
Equity Investment Company
N.A.I.C.S.: 523999

Waterford Hotel Group, Inc. (1)
914 Hartford Tpke, Waterford, CT 06385-4229
Tel.: (860) 442-4559
Web Site: http://www.waterfordhotelgroup.com
Sales Range: $10-24.9 Million
Emp.: 50
Hotel & Convention Property Development & Management Services
N.A.I.C.S.: 721110
Wendy Russell (Dir-Sls)
Gary Azigne (VP-Dev)
Alan Angel (CFO)
Karen Bachofner (VP-Sls & Revenue Mgmt)
John DelGrosso (VP-Construction, Engrg & Technical Svcs)
Michael Heaton (Pres)
Judith Moran (VP-HR)
Mark Wolman (Principal)
Dave Mattesen (Gen Mgr)
Duane Schroder (VP-Ops)

Subsidiary (Domestic):

Waterton Associates LLC (2)
30 S Wacker Dr Ste 3600, Chicago, IL 60606
Tel.: (312) 948-4500
Web Site: http://www.watertonassociates.com
Residential Real Estate Investment, Development & Property Management Services
N.A.I.C.S.: 531390
David R. Schwartz (Co-Founder & CEO)
Peter V. Vilim (Co-Founder & Vice Chm)
Douglas G. Denyer (CFO)
Lela Cirjakovic (Exec VP-Ops)
Scott Ferguson (VP-Reg Ops)
Adrienne Smith (Sr VP-Residential Acctg)
Alisha Kalous (Chief HR Officer)
Edward Kruse (Sr VP & Portfolio Mgr)
Matthew Masinter (Sr VP-Acquisitions)
Michelle C. Wells (Exec VP-IR)
Philip J. Lukowski (Exec VP & Portfolio Mgr)
Rick Hurd (Chief Investment Officer)
Cynthia Bock (Sr VP-Hospitality)
Dennis Langley (Exec VP-Hospitality)
Doug Pearce (Sr VP-Tech)
Erin Ankin (Chief Compliance Officer & Gen Counsel)
John Daley (Sr VP-Design & Construction)
Patricia Feller (Sr VP-Corp Fin)
Philip Martin (Sr VP-Market Res)
Rob Sanchez (Sr VP-Asset Mgmt)
Steve Carlson (Sr VP-Debt Capital Markets)

Subsidiary (Domestic):

Ultima Hospitality, LLC (3)
30 S Wacker Dr Ste 3600, Chicago, IL 60606
Tel.: (312) 948-4500
Web Site: http://www.ultimahospitality.com
Hotel Real Estate Investment, Development & Property Management Services
N.A.I.C.S.: 531390
Nir Liebling (Chief Investment Officer)

Wolman Construction (1)
914 Hartford Tpke, Waterford, CT 06385-0535   (100%)
Tel.: (860) 447-0201
Web Site: http://www.waterfordgroup.com
Sales Range: $10-24.9 Million
Custom Residential & Commercial Building Construction
N.A.I.C.S.: 236220

WATERFORD SPEED BOWL

Rte 85 1080 Hartford Rd, Waterford, CT 06385
Tel.: (860) 442-1585
Web Site: http://www.speedbowl.com
Rev.: $10,600,000
Emp.: 3
Stock Car Racing
N.A.I.C.S.: 711219
Terry Eames (Owner & Dir-Track Ops)
Mark Caise (Dir-Business Dev)
Scott Tapley (Race Dir)
Deb Gilot (Mgr-Box Office)
Carl Field (Mgr-Customer Svc)
Brian Darling (Mgr-Outside Mktg & PR)
Valerie Longo (Office Mgr)

WATERFRONT RESCUE MISSION

380 W Herman St, Pensacola, FL 32505
Tel.: (850) 478-4027   FL
Web Site: http://www.waterfrontmission.org
Year Founded: 1949
Sales Range: $10-24.9 Million
Christian Ministry Services
N.A.I.C.S.: 813110
Bob Rogers (VP-Ministry)
Danny Pipkins (Sr VP-Ops)
Chris Kelly (Sec)
Ken Bell (Vice Chm)
Pete Jones (Chm)
Charles Welk (Treas)
Devin Simmons (Pres)
Angie Ishee (Sr VP-PR & Dev)
Marsha Clark (VP-Fin)

WATERKEEPER ALLIANCE INC.

WATERKEEPER ALLIANCE INC.

Waterkeeper Alliance Inc.—(Continued)
17 Battery Pl Ste 1329, New York, NY 10004
Tel.: (212) 747-0622   NY
Web Site: http://www.waterkeeper.org
Year Founded: 1999
Sales Range: $10-24.9 Million
Waste Water Clean Services
N.A.I.C.S.: 924110
Peter Cleary (Dir-Comm & Mktg)
Rachel Cook (Dir-Ops)
Donna Lisenby (Mgr-Clean and Safe Energy Campaign)
Marc Yaggi (Exec Dir)
Robert F. Kennedy (Founder & Pres-Emeritus)
Gloria Reuben (Pres)

WATERMAN BROADCASTING CORP.
3719 Central Ave, Fort Myers, FL 33901
Tel.: (239) 939-2020
Web Site: http://www.water.net
Sales Range: $25-49.9 Million
Emp.: 200
Television Broadcasting Station
N.A.I.C.S.: 516120
Lara Kunkler (Pres-Montclair Comm & ABC7)
Bob Beville (Dir-Sls)
Darrel Adams (Exec Dir-News)
Dan Billings (Dir-Engrg)
Amy Court (Mgr-Sls-Interactive)
Bob Hannon (Dir-Production)
Matt Koenigs (Mgr-Online Adv)
Todd Ofenbeck (Dir-Photojournalism)
Steve Pontius (Exec VP & Gen Mgr)
Gerry Poppe (Dir-Fin)
Harris Segel (Dir-Res)
Edith B. Waterman (Pres)

Subsidiaries:

WZVN TV ABC 7   (1)
3719 Central Ave, Fort Myers, FL 33901
Tel.: (239) 939-2020
Web Site: http://www.abc-7.com
Sales Range: $10-24.9 Million
Emp.: 230
Television Broadcasting Station
N.A.I.C.S.: 516120
Lara Kunkler (Owner)
Bob Hannon (Dir-Production)
Bill Beard (Mgr-Sls)
Bob Beville (Gen Mgr-Sls)
Brian Colleran (Dir-Sports)
Deborah Abbott (Dir-Programming)
Rich Crum (Acct Exec)
Alain Fernandez (Acct Exec)
Ann Marie Fox (Acct Exec)
Carolyn Green (Acct Exec)
Laurel Lofton (Acct Exec)
Mary Rine (Acct Exec)
Cassandra Vitella (Mgr-HR)

WATERMARK DONUT COMPANY
370 Dorchester Ave, South Boston, MA 02127
Tel.: (617) 464-4001
Web Site: http://www.watermarkdonutcompany.com
Rev.: $25,000,000
Emp.: 450
Coffee Shop
N.A.I.C.S.: 722513
Shawn Solomon (Pres)

WATERMARK ENVIRONMENTAL, INC.
175 Cabot St, Lowell, MA 01854
Tel.: (978) 452-9696
Web Site: http://www.watermarkenv.com
Year Founded: 2001
Sales Range: $10-24.9 Million
Emp.: 45

Engineeering Services
N.A.I.C.S.: 541330
Joseph G. Spangenberger (VP & Branch Mgr)
John J. Haley (Pres)
Michele Calvani (Sec)

WATERMARK GROUP, INC.
4271 Gate Crest, San Antonio, TX 78217
Tel.: (210) 599-0400   NV
Web Site: https://thewatermarkgroup.com
Year Founded: 2009
WNSS—(OTCBB)
Emp.: 1
Holding Company
N.A.I.C.S.: 551112
Mark Mendez (COO)
Brad Elmhorst (VP-Operations & Marketing)
Simon Esparza (Dir-Business Development)
Heather Ramirez (Project Mgr)
Jason Williams (Acct Exec)
Terrie Reagan (Acct Exec)

WATERMARKE HOMES LLC
1535 S D St Ste 200, San Bernardino, CA 92408
Tel.: (909) 381-6007
Web Site: http://www.watermarke-homes.com
Sales Range: $75-99.9 Million
Emp.: 130
Single-Family Housing Construction
N.A.I.C.S.: 236115
John Pavelak (Principal)
Wanda Robinson (Controller)

WATERMILL EXPRESS LLC
1309 E Jasmine Sta, McAllen, TX 78501
Tel.: (956) 686-2482
Web Site: http://www.watermillexpress.com
Rev.: $13,438,717
Emp.: 25
Beverage Stores
N.A.I.C.S.: 445298

Subsidiaries:

Watermill Express   (1)
177 W Jessup St, Brighton, CO 80601   (100%)
Tel.: (303) 659-1573
Web Site: http://www.watermillexpress.com
Sales Range: $10-24.9 Million
Automatic Vending Machines
N.A.I.C.S.: 333310
Jennifer Baker (Dir-HR)

WATERPURE INTERNATIONAL, INC.
525 Plymouth Rd Ste 310, Plymouth Meeting, PA 19462
Tel.: (267) 231-3720   FL
Web Site: http://www.waterpureinternational.com
Year Founded: 2005
Sales Range: Less than $1 Million
Emp.: 10
Atmospheric Water Generators Marketer & Mfr
N.A.I.C.S.: 335312
Robert F. Orr (CFO)

WATERS INC.
129 E 6th St, Junction City, KS 66441
Tel.: (785) 238-3114
Web Site: http://www.waterstruevalue.com
Rev.: $15,104,538
Emp.: 45
Hardware Stores

N.A.I.C.S.: 532289
Jim Waters (Pres)

WATERS TRUCK & TRACTOR INC.
96 E Plymouth Rd, Columbus, MS 39701
Tel.: (662) 328-1575
Web Site: http://www.waterstruck.com
Sales Range: $100-124.9 Million
Emp.: 100
Trucks, Tractors & Trailers: New & Used
N.A.I.C.S.: 441110
Mike Waters (Pres)

WATERSIDE BUILDERS INC.
790 Harbour Dr, Naples, FL 34103
Tel.: (239) 430-3883
Web Site: http://www.watersidebuildersinc.com
Sales Range: $1-9.9 Million
Emp.: 5
Residential Construction
N.A.I.C.S.: 236115
Mike Assaad (Owner)
Scott Tackett (Project Mgr)

WATERSTONE MORTGAGE CORP.
N25 W23255 Paul Rd, Pewaukee, WI 53072
Tel.: (262) 691-9300   WI
Web Site: http://www.waterstonemortgage.com
Year Founded: 2000
Emp.: 700
Mortgage Loan Brokers
N.A.I.C.S.: 522310
Eric Egenhoefer (Founder)
Jacquelyn Krecklow (Mgr-Ops)
Jeff McGuiness (Pres & CEO)
Brian Richard Kludt (Mgr-Bridgeport)
Julie Ann Zielinski (Mgr-Sls)
Lisa Fenske (Sr VP-Mktg & Comm)
Eric Putt (Mgr-Producing-Central Florida)
Dustin Owen (Mgr-Florida)
Kerry Wirth (COO)
Dan Spaulding (VP-Retail Production-Midwest)
Ericka Smith (VP-Mktg)
Kevin Allen (Sr VP)
Rocky Rockwell (Sls Mgr-California)
Eric Debelack (Mgr-Southeast Wisconsin)
Stephanie Ziebell (Gen Counsel & Sr VP)
Chris Fleming (Sr VP-Natl Sls)

WATERSTREET COMPANY
215 S Complex Dr, Kalispell, MT 59901
Tel.: (801) 984-5554
Web Site: http://www.waterstreetcompany.com
Sales Range: $10-24.9 Million
Emp.: 37
Management Services
N.A.I.C.S.: 561110
Gregg Barrett (Pres)

WATERSTREET, LTD.
300 Block N Water St, Corpus Christi, TX 78401
Tel.: (361) 881-9448   TX
Web Site: http://www.waterstmarketcc.com
Year Founded: 1983
Seafood Restaurants
N.A.I.C.S.: 722511
Bradley Lomax (Founder & Owner)

WATERTOWN COOPERATIVE

U.S. PRIVATE

ELEVATOR ASSOCIATION
811 Burlington Northern Dr, Watertown, SD 57201
Tel.: (605) 886-3039
Web Site: http://www.watertowncoop.com
Sales Range: $25-49.9 Million
Emp.: 31
Grain Elevators
N.A.I.C.S.: 424510
Jerry Tordoff (Office Mgr)

WATERTOWN SAVINGS BANK
111 Clinton St, Watertown, NY 13601
Tel.: (315) 788-7100   NY
Web Site: http://www.watertownsavingsbank.com
Year Founded: 1894
Emp.: 120
Banking Services
N.A.I.C.S.: 522110
Scott M. Pooler (CIO & VP)
Mark S. Bellinger (COO & Exec VP)
Darlene A. Jobson (CFO & VP)
Terri J. Erdner (VP-Branch Admin)
Heather A. Makuch (VP-Deposit Ops)
Diana Hadlock (Sec)
Meredith Fox (Officer-Bus Dev)
John Morgia (Mktg Dir)

WATERTOWN SAVINGS BANK INC.
60 Main St, Watertown, MA 02472-4413
Tel.: (617) 928-9000
Web Site: http://www.watertownsavings.com
Year Founded: 1870
Sales Range: $50-74.9 Million
Emp.: 150
Savings Institutions
N.A.I.C.S.: 522180
Randall A. Buck (Sr VP)
Matthew DesMeules (VP-Loan Servicing & Loan Compliance)

WATERVILLE VALLEY SKI RESORT, INC.
1 Ski Area Rd, Waterville Valley, NH 03215
Tel.: (603) 236-8311   DE
Web Site: http://www.waterville.com
Sales Range: $25-49.9 Million
Emp.: 200
Skiing & Snowboarding Resort
N.A.I.C.S.: 713920
Conrad Oldenburg (Mgr-Grp Sls)
Lisa Keating (Mgr-Season Pass Sls & Ticket Office)
Tim Smith (Pres)

WATHNE IMPORTS LTD.
42 W 39th St Fl 12, New York, NY 10018-2084
Tel.: (212) 757-3001
Rev.: $11,500,000
Emp.: 146
Patent Owners & Lessors
N.A.I.C.S.: 533110
Berglot Wathne (Pres)

WATKINS ASSOCIATED INDUSTRIES INC.
1958 Monroe Dr NE, Atlanta, GA 30324-4844
Tel.: (404) 872-3841   GA
Web Site: http://www.watkins.com
Year Founded: 1932
Sales Range: $1-4.9 Billion
Emp.: 10,000
Diversified Holding Company
N.A.I.C.S.: 551112
Eric Wahlen (Pres)

Subsidiaries:

Land Span Inc.   (1)
1120 West Griffin Rd, Lakeland, FL 33805

Tel.: (863) 688-1102
Web Site: http://www.landspan.com
Common Carrier Long Distance Trucking
N.A.I.C.S.: 484121
Scott Bruneau (Coord-Maintenance)
Chesson Turbeville (Mgr-Customer Svc-West Coast)
Pete Yachmetz (Mgr-Security)
Eric Templin (VP-Safety & Security)

Lexington Manufacturing Inc. (1)
1330 115th Ave NW, Minneapolis, MN 55448-3133
Tel.: (763) 754-9055
Web Site: http://www.lexingtonmfg.com
Rev.: $20,993,883
Emp.: 125
Window, Door & Structural Millwork Component Parts Mfr & Distr
N.A.I.C.S.: 321999
Robert Dimke (Pres)
John Dimke (VP-Ops)
Steve McKoskey (COO)
Steve Giebler (Controller)
Mike Dillion (Pres)

Sunco Carriers, Inc. (1)
1025 N Chestnut Rd, Lakeland, FL 33805
Tel.: (800) 237-8288
Web Site: http://www.suncocarriers.com
Logistics Consulting Servies
N.A.I.C.S.: 541614
Barbara Adamson (Mgr-IT)
Eric Templin (Dir-Safety)
Monica Holley (Mgr-Logistics)
Dave Richardson (Dir-IT)
Dennis Carroll (Dir-Fleet Managers)

Watkins Associated Developers (1)
1958 Monroe Dr NE, Atlanta, GA 30324-4844
Tel.: (404) 872-3841
Web Site: http://www.watkinsretailgroup.com
Sales Range: $10-24.9 Million
Emp.: 11
Non-Residential Property Operator
N.A.I.C.S.: 531120
Rachel Jaustice (Mgr-HR)
Lee Freeman (VP)
Neal Freeman (Exec VP-Dev)

WATKINS AUTOMOTIVE GROUP
269 W Main St, Forest City, NC 28043
Tel.: (828) 245-0128
Web Site: http://www.watkinsauto.com
Sales Range: $25-49.9 Million
Emp.: 250
Automobiles & Other Motor Vehicles Whslr
N.A.I.C.S.: 423110
Tim Ridenhour (Pres)

WATKINS CONSTRUCTION CO., INC.
3229 S 15th St, Corsicana, TX 75110
Tel.: (903) 874-6587
Web Site: http://www.watkinsconstruction.com
Year Founded: 1957
Sales Range: $25-49.9 Million
Emp.: 500
Pipeline Construction & Maintenance, Utility Construction, Earth Work, Mining Reclamation, Specialized Transportation & Crane & Rigging Services
N.A.I.C.S.: 237110
Jerry Watkins (Pres)
Scott Watkins (VP)
Kimmy Gorden (Controller)

WATKINS INCORPORATED
150 Liberty St, Winona, MN 55987-3707
Tel.: (507) 457-3300   MA
Web Site: http://www.watkinsonline.com
Year Founded: 1868
Sales Range: $25-49.9 Million
Emp.: 350
Mfr & Retailer of Extracts, Spices, Health/Beauty Aids, Insecticides, Medicines & Food Specialties
N.A.I.C.S.: 311942
Irwin Jacobs (Owner)
James R. Yenish (VP-Ops)
J. R. Rigely (Pres & CMO)

WATKINS INSURANCE GROUP INC.
3834 Spicewood Springs Ste 100, Austin, TX 78759
Tel.: (512) 452-8877
Web Site: http://www.watkinsinsurancegroup.com
Sales Range: $10-24.9 Million
Emp.: 100
Insurance Agents, Brokers & Service
N.A.I.C.S.: 524210
Patrick Watkins (Pres)
Sheila Noxon (Dir-Ops)
Brent Howel (VP & Acct Exec-Employee & Grp Benefits)
Chris Scott (VP-Fin)
Greg Meserole (VP)
Scott McGuire (VP)

WATONWAN FARM SERVICE CO. INC.
823 1st Ave S, Saint James, MN 56081-0026
Tel.: (507) 375-3355   MN
Web Site: http://www.wfsag.com
Year Founded: 1937
Sales Range: $25-49.9 Million
Emp.: 220
Farm Goods & Services
N.A.I.C.S.: 444240
Dawn Abel (Dir-HR)
Randy Cole (VP-Energy)
Craig Kilian (VP-Grain)
Mike Minnehan (VP-Ops)
Charlie Johnson (Chm)
Todd Ludwig (CEO)
Merlyn Kruger (VP-Feed)
Cathy Smith (CFO)
Jo Ann Gumto (Dir-Mktg Comm)
Jason Smith (Vice Chm)
Trent Frederickson (Treas & Sec)

WATSEKA FORD-LINCOLN MERCURY, INC.
101 Bell Rd, Watseka, IL 60970
Tel.: (815) 432-2418
Web Site: http://www.watsekaford.com
Sales Range: $10-24.9 Million
Emp.: 40
Car Whslr
N.A.I.C.S.: 441110
John Bell (Gen Mgr)
David Bell (Owner & Pres)

WATSEKA INTERSTATE, LLC
815 S 2nd St, Watseka, IL 60970
Tel.: (815) 432-6524
Sales Range: $10-24.9 Million
Emp.: 15
Grain Elevator & Fertilizer Distr
N.A.I.C.S.: 424510
Greg Oberting (Pres)
Harry Gillette Jr. (Mgr-Agronomy & Fertilizer)

WATSON & CHALIN HOLDING CORP.
725 E University Dr, McKinney, TX 75069-2325
Tel.: (972) 547-6020
Web Site: http://www.watsonsuspensions.com
Rev.: $31,000,000
Emp.: 110
Motor Vehicle Parts & Accessories
N.A.I.C.S.: 336390
Donald R. Watson (Pres)
Tom Chalin (VP)
Richard Dissinger (Controller)
Subsidiaries:

Watson & Chalin Manufacturing, Inc. (1)
725 E University Dr, McKinney, TX 75069-2325
Tel.: (972) 547-6020
Web Site: http://www.watsonsuspensions.com
Motor Vehicle Parts & Accessories
N.A.I.C.S.: 336390

WATSON CHEVROLET, INC.
625 W Auto Mall Dr, Tucson, AZ 85705-6010
Tel.: (520) 292-1500
Web Site: http://www.watsonchevrolet.com
Sales Range: $50-74.9 Million
Emp.: 200
Car Whslr
N.A.I.C.S.: 441110
Joe Watson (Gen Mgr)

WATSON CLINIC LLP
1600 Lakeland Hills Blvd, Lakeland, FL 33805
Tel.: (863) 680-7000
Web Site: http://www.watsonclinic.com
Year Founded: 1985
Sales Range: $250-299.9 Million
Emp.: 1,300
Specialty Medical Clinics
N.A.I.C.S.: 622310
Louis S. Saco (Mng Partner)
Stanley Piotrowski (Chief Admin Officer)
Richard J. Cardosi (Mng Dir)
Joffre R. Rivera (Mng Dir)
Lijian Wang (Mng Dir)
John R. Ellington Jr. (Interim Mng Partner)

WATSON FURNITURE GROUP, INC.
26246 Twelve Trees Ln NW, Poulsbo, WA 98370
Tel.: (360) 394-1300
Web Site: http://www.watsonfurniture.com
Rev.: $31,000,000
Emp.: 150
Wood Office Furniture Mfr
N.A.I.C.S.: 337211
Clif McKenzie (CEO)
Steve Hayes (VP-Sls)
Dale Anderson (Acct Mgr)

WATSON GRAVEL, INC.
2728 Hamilton Cleves Rd, Hamilton, OH 45013
Tel.: (513) 863-0070
Web Site: http://www.watsongravel.com
Year Founded: 1969
Sales Range: $10-24.9 Million
Emp.: 90
Gravel Mining
N.A.I.C.S.: 212321
Ronald E. Watson (Pres)
Brian Bottoms (Mgr-Ops)
Labreeska Stanifer (Mgr-HR)

WATSON GROUP FINANCIAL CORPORATION
6501 Highland Rd, Waterford, MI 48327-1655
Tel.: (248) 666-2700   MI
Web Site: http://www.watsongrp.com
Year Founded: 1991
Sales Range: $25-49.9 Million
Emp.: 20
Provider of Mortgage Banking Services
N.A.I.C.S.: 522292
Brian A. Seibert (Pres)
Jeff McGee (VP)

WATSON HEGNER CORPORATION
160 Gibson Ct, Dallas, NC 28034
Tel.: (704) 922-9660
Web Site: http://www.watsonhegner.com
Sales Range: $1-9.9 Million
Emp.: 8
Whslr of Industrial Machinery & Equipment
N.A.I.C.S.: 423830
Randy Pennington (Pres)
Mark Skinner (VP)
John Wolf (Mgr-SC)
Eminey Y. Pennington (VP & Controller)
Todd Hebert (Mgr-VA & NC)
Dan Adler (Mgr-Svc Technician)

WATSON INDUSTRIES, INC.
616 Hite Rd, Harwick, PA 15049-8945
Tel.: (724) 275-1000
Web Site: http://www.watsonstandard.com
Year Founded: 1944
Sales Range: $10-24.9 Million
Emp.: 60
Solid State Gyroscopes & Sensing Systems
N.A.I.C.S.: 334519
James Lore (Pres)
H. Knox Watson III (Chm)
Subsidiaries:

Watson-Standard Company (1)
616 Hite Rd, Harwick, PA 15049-8945
Tel.: (724) 275-1000
Web Site: http://www.watsonstandard.com
Paints, Varnishes, Enamels, Industrial Finishes & Lithograph Coatings, Protective Coatings, Vinyl Plastic Coatings Mfr
N.A.I.C.S.: 325510
James Lore (Vice Chm)
Henry Knox Watson III (Chm)
Henry K. Watson IV (Pres)

WATSON MORTGAGE CORP.
6206-1 Atlantic Blvd, Jacksonville, FL 32211
Tel.: (904) 645-7111
Web Site: http://www.watsonmortgagecorp.com
Sales Range: $100-124.9 Million
Emp.: 50
Mortgage Bankers & Loan Correspondents
N.A.I.C.S.: 522310
Ginger Frye (Controller)
Bill Watson III (Pres)

WATSON REALTY CORP.
1410 Palm Coast Pkwy NW, Palm Coast, FL 32137
Tel.: (386) 246-9222
Web Site: http://www.watsonrealtycorp.com
Year Founded: 1997
Sales Range: Less than $1 Million
Emp.: 8
Real Estate Agents & Managers
N.A.I.C.S.: 531210
Ed Forman (Pres)
Tina Arant (VP)
Jeffrey Fagan (VP-Orlando)
Ryan Ford (VP)
Carlotta W. Landschoot (Exec VP)
Wendell D. Davis (Exec VP)
Amanda Feagle (VP)
William A. Watson Jr. (Chm)

Watson Realty Corp.—(Continued)

WATSON TRUCK & SUPPLY, INC.
1501 N Grimes St, Hobbs, NM 88240-3719
Tel.: (575) 397-2411
Web Site:
http://www.watsonhopper.com
Sales Range: $125-149.9 Million
Emp.: 283
Automobile & Truck Dealerships
N.A.I.C.S.: 441110
Charley R. Smith *(Chrm & CEO)*
Finn Smith *(Pres)*

WATSONVILLE HOSPITAL CORPORATION
75 Nielson St, Watsonville, CA 95076
Tel.: (831) 724-4741
Web Site:
http://www.watsonvillehospital.com
Year Founded: 1895
Health Care Srvices
N.A.I.C.S.: 622110
Jeri Gilbert *(Dir-HR)*

WATT COMPANIES, INC.
2716 Ocean Park Blvd Ste 3040, Santa Monica, CA 90405
Tel.: (310) 314-2430
Web Site:
http://www.wattcompanies.com
Year Founded: 1948
Sales Range: $50-74.9 Million
Emp.: 75
Commercial Real Estate Owner, Developer & Manager
N.A.I.C.S.: 531390
Jennifer Hall-Awni *(Chief Admin Officer)*
Mark Humphreys *(VP-Litigation & Risk Mgmt)*
Nadine Watt *(CEO)*
J. Scott Watt *(Chm)*
Ryoko Takata *(Exec VP)*
Brian Burdzinski *(CFO)*
Paul Timm *(COO)*
Jamie Bergantz *(Dir-Leasing)*
Adam Siegman *(Mng Dir)*
Dave Johnson *(VP-Engrg)*
Michael Von Quilich *(VP-Ops)*
Jennifer McElyea *(Mng Dir)*
Brett Trebil *(VP-Ops)*
John Devereux *(Pres)*

Subsidiaries:

Watt Communities (1)
2716 Ocean Park Blvd Ste 3040, Santa Monica, CA 90405
Tel.: (310) 314-2430
Web Site: http://www.wattcompanies.com
Sales Range: $25-49.9 Million
Emp.: 50
Residential Housing Property Redeveloper & Manager
N.A.I.C.S.: 236118
Howard Press *(Pres)*
Brian Burdzinski *(VP-Fin & Acctg)*
Christopher Chase *(Gen Counsel)*
Jennifer Hall-Awni *(Chief Admin Officer)*
Mark Humphreys *(VP-Litigation & Risk Mgmt)*
Allison Lynch *(VP-Asset Mgmt)*
Jim Maginn *(Mng Partner)*
Kathleen Magner *(Mgr-Sls & Mktg)*
Steven Pritulsky *(Pres & CEO-Arizona)*
Paul Timm *(COO)*
Courtney Trujillo *(Sr Mgr-Asset)*

Watt Properties & Leasing (1)
2716 Ocean Park Blvd Ste 2025, Santa Monica, CA 90405
Tel.: (310) 314-2430
Web Site: http://www.wattcompanies.com
Emp.: 65
Commercial, Industrial & Residential Property Owner & Manager
N.A.I.C.S.: 531312

Allison Lynch *(VP-Asset Mgmt)*
Kathy McKay *(VP-Leasing)*
Max Frank *(VP-Dev Svcs)*

Watt Realty Advisors (1)
2716 Ocean Park Blvd Ste 2025, Santa Monica, CA 90405
Tel.: (310) 314-2430
Web Site: http://www.wattcompanies.com
Emp.: 65
Commercial Property Acquisition, Disposition & Asset Management Services
N.A.I.C.S.: 531390
Allison Lynch *(Gen Mgr)*

Watt Retail Development (1)
2716 Ocean Park Blvd Ste 2025, Santa Monica, CA 90405
Tel.: (310) 314-2430
Web Site: http://www.wattcompany.com
Sales Range: $25-49.9 Million
Emp.: 60
Commercial Retail Shopping Center Developer
N.A.I.C.S.: 236220

WATT FUEL CELL CORP.
402 E Main St Ste 800, Mount Pleasant, PA 15666
Tel.: (724) 547-9170
Web Site: http://www.wattfuelcell.com
Year Founded: 2013
Solid Oxide Fuel Cell Components & Systems Mfr
N.A.I.C.S.: 334413
Caine Finnerty *(Pres & CEO)*
Paul DeWald *(Co-Founder & VP-Engrg)*
Rich Romer *(VP-Bus Dev)*
Bob Berger *(Dir-Sls)*
Owen Taylor *(Co-Pres)*
Sarah DeWald *(Co-Founder, Sec & Dir-Fin & Ops)*
Wenhua Huang *(Co-Founder & Dir-Fuel Cells)*

Subsidiaries:

Pittsburgh Electric Engines, Inc. (1)
Mount Pleasant Glass Centre 402 E Main St Ste 800, Mount Pleasant, PA 15666
Tel.: (724) 547-9170
Web Site: http://www.pghengine.com
Emp.: 15
Solid Oxide Fuel Cell Components Mfr
N.A.I.C.S.: 335999
Owen S. Taylor *(Pres)*

WATT PUBLISHING COMPANY
303 North Main Street Ste 500, Rockford, IL 61101
Tel.: (815) 996-5400
Web Site: http://www.wattnet.com
Year Founded: 1917
Sales Range: $75-99.9 Million
Emp.: 65
Magazine Publisher
N.A.I.C.S.: 513120
Gregory A. Watt *(Pres & COO)*
Dingding Li *(Mgr-Intl Sls)*
Frans Willem van Beemen *(Mgr-Intl Sls)*
Ginny Stadel *(Mgr-Northeast & ClassifiedÂ Sls)*
Jeff Miller *(Dir-Custom Media-Global Agribusiness)*
Karen Blandford-Anderson *(Mgr-Sls)*
Mary Harris *(Mgr-Agri-Food Sls)*
Michael van den Dries *(Mgr-Intl Sls)*
Steve Akins *(VP & Publr)*
Tineke van Spanje *(Mgr-Intl Sls)*

WATTS COPY SYSTEMS INC.
2860 Stanton St, Springfield, IL 62703
Tel.: (217) 529-6697
Web Site: http://www.wattscopy.com
Year Founded: 1982
Sales Range: $10-24.9 Million
Emp.: 140
Copiers & Business Machines

N.A.I.C.S.: 423690
Carol Watts *(Pres)*

WATTS EQUIPMENT CO., INC.
17547 Comconex Rd, Manteca, CA 95336
Tel.: (209) 825-1700
Web Site:
http://www.wattsequipment.com
Year Founded: 1967
Sales Range: $10-24.9 Million
Emp.: 40
Industrial Equipment Whsr
N.A.I.C.S.: 423830
Cheryl Koenig *(Controller)*
Shirley Perreira *(VP & Gen Mgr)*
Kelly Dolan *(Mgr-Sls)*
Jose Ortega *(Mgr-Aftermarket)*
Everett Cardenas *(Mgr-Svc)*
Brock Watts *(Owner)*

WATTS PETROLEUM CORPORATION
1505 Rutherford St, Lynchburg, VA 24501
Tel.: (434) 846-6509
Web Site:
http://www.wattspetroleum.com
Sales Range: $10-24.9 Million
Emp.: 35
Petroleum Bulk Stations
N.A.I.C.S.: 424710
Randall Watts *(Treas & VP)*
Michael Ion *(Mgr-Propane)*
John A. Watts Jr. *(Pres)*

WATTS TRUCKING SERVICE, INC.
525 17th St, Rock Island, IL 61201-8131
Tel.: (309) 788-7700
Year Founded: 1948
Sales Range: $10-24.9 Million
Emp.: 300
Refuse Transportation Systems & Services
N.A.I.C.S.: 562111
James L. Watts *(Pres)*

Subsidiaries:

A-1 Disposal Service, Inc. (1)
5415 Downs Blvd SW, Cedar Rapids, IA 52404-4323
Tel.: (319) 364-1566
Web Site: http://www.wattstrucking.com
Sales Range: $10-24.9 Million
Emp.: 30
Trucking Service
N.A.I.C.S.: 562111
Bill Coleman *(Gen Mgr)*

Blackhawk Waste Disposal Co., Inc. (1)
811 Dearborn Ave, Waterloo, IA 50703-5450
Tel.: (319) 232-4150
Web Site: http://www.blackhawkwaste.com
Rev.: $1,000,000
Emp.: 30
Local Trucking without Storage
N.A.I.C.S.: 562111
Blane Denhan *(Gen Mgr)*

Central Waste Systems, Inc (1)
4303 S 79th Cir, Omaha, NE 68127-1848
Tel.: (402) 331-4300
Sales Range: $10-24.9 Million
Emp.: 35
Trucking Service
N.A.I.C.S.: 562111

County Waste Systems, Inc. (1)
438 4th St, Coal Valley, IL 61240-9741
Tel.: (309) 799-5501
Rev.: $2,000,000
Emp.: 20
Refuse System
N.A.I.C.S.: 562211

Delta Waste Systems, Inc. (1)
2510 Lester St, Harvey, LA 70058-3563
Tel.: (504) 367-4811

Sales Range: $10-24.9 Million
Emp.: 5
Local Trucking without Storage
N.A.I.C.S.: 562211

Gulf Waste Systems, Inc. (1)
5100 Airline Hwy, Baton Rouge, LA 70805-1705 (100%)
Tel.: (225) 357-4959
Rev.: $2,700,000
Emp.: 20
Refuse System
N.A.I.C.S.: 562211

Hawkeye Waste Systems, Inc. (1)
PO Box 1090, Iowa City, IA 52244 (100%)
Tel.: (319) 351-5932
Sales Range: Less than $1 Million
Emp.: 15
Local Trucking without Storage
N.A.I.C.S.: 562111
Chris Dohrer *(Gen Mgr)*

L & M Waste Systems, Inc. (1)
5111 59th Ave W, Muscatine, IA 52761-6032 (100%)
Tel.: (563) 263-5474
Sales Range: $10-24.9 Million
Emp.: 13
Waste Disposal Services
N.A.I.C.S.: 562111
Jim Watts *(Gen Mgr)*

Tri-Star Waste Systems, Inc. (1)
701 41st Ave N, Nashville, TN 37209-2419
Tel.: (615) 340-0850
Web Site: http://www.tristar.com
Sales Range: $10-24.9 Million
Emp.: 100
Waste Management
N.A.I.C.S.: 562211

Watts Freight Systems, Inc. (1)
525 17th St, Rock Island, IL 61201-8131
Tel.: (309) 788-7700
Sales Range: $1-9.9 Million
Emp.: 50
Trucking & Freight Transportation Services
N.A.I.C.S.: 484121

WATUMULL BROTHERS LTD. INC.
307 Lewers St Ste 600, Honolulu, HI 96815-2357
Tel.: (808) 971-8800
Year Founded: 1915
Sales Range: $75-99.9 Million
Emp.: 100
Men's, Boy's & Women's Clothing
N.A.I.C.S.: 424350
Gulab Watumull *(Treas & Sec)*
Jaidev Watumull *(VP)*

Subsidiaries:

American T-Shirt Co (1)
1217 N King St, Honolulu, HI 96817-4576
Tel.: (808) 842-4466
Web Site: http://www.americant-shirt.com
Sales Range: $10-24.9 Million
Emp.: 30
Mens & Boys Clothing
N.A.I.C.S.: 424350
Jojo Watumull *(Pres)*

WAUD CAPITAL PARTNERS LLC
300 N LaSalle St Ste 4900, Chicago, IL 60654
Tel.: (312) 676-8400
Web Site:
http://www.waudcapital.com
Year Founded: 1993
Emp.: 100
Privater Equity Firm
N.A.I.C.S.: 523999
Mark D. Flower *(CFO & Chief Compliance Officer)*
Christopher J. Graber *(Partner-Healthcare Svcs)*
Matthew W. Clary *(Partner)*
David O. Neighbours *(Partner-Healthcare Svcs)*
Jennifer Sammis *(Dir-Fin)*
Reeve Byron Waud *(Mng Partner)*

COMPANIES

Justin C. DuPere (Partner)
Andrew Rueff (Operating Partner)
Timothy J. Cremieux (Principal)
Matthew Albers (Partner-Capital Markets)

Subsidiaries:

Dimensional Management Corp. (1)
1030 St Georges Ave Ste 102, Avenel, NJ 07001
Tel.: (732) 750-0707
Sales Range: $1-9.9 Million
Emp.: 58
Dentistry Services
N.A.I.C.S.: 621210
Melvin Feiler (Pres)

Health & Safety Institute Inc. (1)
1450 Westec Dr, Eugene, OR 97402
Tel.: (800) 447-3177
Web Site: http://www.hsi.com
Environmental, Health & Safety Services
N.A.I.C.S.: 922190
Mark Streifel (Exec Gen Mgr-Industrial Skills Solutions)
Rory Seidens (VP-HR)
Jose Arcilla (COO)
Chad Birckelbaw (CEO)
Steve Babick (CFO)
Tom Benson (Chief Revenue Officer)
Frank Powers (CTO)

Subsidiary (Domestic):

Comprehensive Loss Management, Inc. (2)
1450 Westec Dr, Eugene, OR 97402
Tel.: (763) 551-1022
Web Site: http://www.clmi-training.com
Management Consulting Services
N.A.I.C.S.: 541618
Dave Zimmerman (Acct Exec)
Janelle Holte (Acct Exec)
Ken Hopper (Acct Exec)
Randy Archer (Acct Exec)

EJ4, LLC (2)
4 CityPlace Dr Ste 450, Saint Louis, MO 63141
Tel.: (314) 878-6700
Web Site: http://www.ej4.com
Sales Range: $1-9.9 Million
Emp.: 36
Online Learning Services
N.A.I.C.S.: 513199
Ryan Eudy (CEO)
Tom Lynch (CTO)
Kathy Irish (Dir-Ops)
Paul Russell (Founder)
Chris Scherting (Mktg Dir)

Subsidiary (Non-US):

EMS Safety Services Inc. (2)
Tel.: (800) 215-9555
Web Site: http://www.emssafety.com
All Other Schools & Instruction
N.A.I.C.S.: 611699

Subsidiary (Domestic):

Martech Media (2)
611 Main St, Washburn, ND 58577
Tel.: (701) 462-3525
Web Site: http://www.martechmedia.com
Rev.: $1,099,000
Emp.: 7
Custom Computer Programming Services
N.A.I.C.S.: 541511
Mark Streifel (Exec Dir)

The Rowing Team, LLC (2)
9702 Gayton Rd Ste 226, Richmond, VA 23238-4907
Web Site: http://www.blueoceanbrain.com
Software Publisher
N.A.I.C.S.: 513210
Laura Howard (Founder & VP-Bus Dev)

Vivid Learning Systems, Inc. (2)
5728 Bedford St, Pasco, WA 99301
Web Site: http://www.vividlearningsystems.com
Custom Computer Programming Services
N.A.I.C.S.: 541511
Matthew J. Hammer (Pres)

Integrated Practice Solutions, Inc. (1)
9265 Sky Pk Ct Ste 200, San Diego, CA 92123
Tel.: (844) 307-4901
Web Site: http://www.chirotouch.com
Healthcare Practice Management Software Solutions
N.A.I.C.S.: 621399
Robert Moberg (Pres)

Regional Toxicology Services, LLC (1)
2617 E L St, Tacoma, WA 98421
Tel.: (253) 552-1551
Web Site: http://www.sterlingreflabs.com
Sales Range: $10-24.9 Million
Medical Laboratories
N.A.I.C.S.: 621511
Daniel Baker (Principal)
David Lowenberg (Chm)
Sue Sommer (Pres)

TeamSnap, Inc. (1)
2040 14th St, Boulder, CO 80302
Web Site: http://www.teamsnap.com
Emp.: 200
Sports Team Management Software Developer
N.A.I.C.S.: 541511
Andrew Berkowitz (Chief Creative Officer)
Keith McDonald (Chief Growth Officer)
Shane Emmons (CTO)
Sarah Berg (Dir-Mktg Comm)
Woody Hartman (Pres)
Alex Underwood (Gen Mgr-Adv & Commerce)
Peter Frintzilas (CEO)
Andrew Rueff (Chm)
Joyce Bell (CFO)
Michael Fox (VP-Product & Design)

Subsidiary (Domestic):

Korrio, Inc. (2)
1941 1st Ave S, Seattle, WA 98134
Tel.: (206) 333-2400
Web Site: http://www.korrio.com
Sport Automation Software Development Services
N.A.I.C.S.: 541511
Steve Goldman (Founder & CEO)

WAUKESHA FOUNDRY INC.

1300 Lincoln Ave, Waukesha, WI 53186
Tel.: (262) 542-0741   WI
Web Site:
http://www.waukeshafoundry.com
Year Founded: 1912
Sales Range: $100-124.9 Million
Emp.: 250
Stainless Steel, High Alloy Steel, Brass & Aluminum Castings Mfr
N.A.I.C.S.: 331513
Todd Kurtz (Mgr-Market Segment)

WAUKESHA METAL PRODUCTS

N53 W24635 S Corporate Cir, Sussex, WI 53089-0328
Tel.: (262) 820-9000
Web Site:
http://www.waukeshametal.com
Year Founded: 1997
Sales Range: $10-24.9 Million
Emp.: 100
Metalforming Mfr
N.A.I.C.S.: 332119
Michael Steger (Pres & COO)

WAUKESHA STATE BANK

151 E St Paul Ave, Waukesha, WI 53187-0648
Tel.: (262) 549-8500
Web Site:
http://www.waukeshabank.com
Sales Range: $50-74.9 Million
Emp.: 280
State Commercial Banks
N.A.I.C.S.: 522110
Ann Pascavis (CFO)
Jeffrey Lightfoot (Officer-Comml Banking & VP)
James Riley (Sr VP & Mgr-Comml Real Estate Lending)
Don L. Taylor (VP)
Tony Laszewski (Sr VP & Mgr-Comml Lending)
Natalie Walters (Asst VP & Officer-Comml Banking)
Lisa Persohn (VP & Mgr-Acct & Bus Ops)
Doug Schnier (Officer-Comml Banking & VP)
Brian Cayon (Chief Investment Officer & VP)
Bob Meidenbauer (Officer-Comml Real Estate & VP)
Michele Young (VP-Prairie Fin Grp)
Stephen Zimmel (VP-Prairie Fin Grp)
Nancy Schoenberg (VP-Prairie Fin Grp)
Trisha Dahl (Mgr-Mukwonago)
Linda Yeikowski (Mgr-Mortgage Sls)
Heather Pfalz (VP/Mgr-Sussex)
Keith Shepard (Asst VP/Mgr-East Main Street)
Trevor Arnold (Asst VP)
Erika Nowak (VP & Controller)
DeAnne Price (Mgr-Payroll Svcs)
Kyle Kees (VP)
David Rosenwald (VP)

Subsidiaries:

Waukesha State Bank - Wealth Management (1)
1227 Corporate Center Dr, Oconomowoc, WI 53066
Tel.: (262) 522-7400
Web Site: http://www.waukeshabank.com
Sales Range: $50-74.9 Million
Emp.: 20
Wealth Management Services
N.A.I.C.S.: 523940

WAUKON YAMAHA, INC.

208 Hwy 9, Waukon, IA 52172
Tel.: (563) 568-3471
Web Site:
http://www.waukonharley.com
Sales Range: $10-24.9 Million
Emp.: 39
Motorcycle Dealers
N.A.I.C.S.: 441227
Irvin Fosaaen Jr. (Pres)

WAUSAU COATED PRODUCTS INC.

825 S 77th Ave, Wausau, WI 54401-9327
Tel.: (715) 848-2741   WI
Web Site:
http://www.wausaucoated.com
Year Founded: 1981
Sales Range: $25-49.9 Million
Emp.: 180
Distr of Coated & Laminated Paper
N.A.I.C.S.: 322220
Matt Reif (Coord-Mktg)
Kevin Thiel (Mgr-Engrg & Maintenance)
Beth Lyon (Mgr-Transportation)
Bill Schein (CFO)
Lori Ann Manteufel (Mgr-Inside Sls)
Gina Paoli Roemke (Product Mgr-Mktg)

WAUSAU HOMES, INC.

10805 Bus Hwy 51, Rothschild, WI 54474
Tel.: (715) 359-7272   WI
Web Site:
http://www.wausauhomes.com
Year Founded: 1960
Sales Range: $150-199.9 Million
Emp.: 70
Pre-Fabricated Homes
N.A.I.C.S.: 321992
Len Kats (Mgr-Bus Dev)
Blake Zurawski (Project Coord)

Subsidiaries:

Sterling Building Systems, Inc. (1)
10805 Business Hwy 51, Rothschild, WI 54474   (100%)
Tel.: (715) 359-7272
Sales Range: $25-49.9 Million
Emp.: 90
Pre-Fabricated Homes
N.A.I.C.S.: 321992

WAUSAU SUPPLY COMPANY

4704 Bayberry St, Schofield, WI 54476-6097
Tel.: (715) 359-2524   WI
Web Site:
http://www.wausausupply.com
Year Founded: 1947
Sales Range: $200-249.9 Million
Emp.: 400
Whslr of Building Supplies, Roofing, Siding & Insulation
N.A.I.C.S.: 423330
Ronald L. Klimisch (Pres)
Joe Jordan (Sec & VP)
Tom Thornton (Treas & VP)
Kurt Cheyka (Gen Mgr)

WAUSAU TILE, INC.

9001 Business Hwy 51, Rothschild, WI 54474
Tel.: (715) 359-3121   WI
Web Site: http://www.wausautile.com
Year Founded: 1953
Sales Range: $25-49.9 Million
Emp.: 300
Concrete Products
N.A.I.C.S.: 423220
Edward Creske (Founder & CEO)
William Creske (Chm)
Yvonne Smith (Mgr-Mktg)
John Knauf (Controller)

Subsidiaries:

Imperial Industries Inc. (1)
505 W Industrial Park Ave, Rothschild, WI 54474-7917
Tel.: (715) 359-0200
Web Site: http://www.imperialind.com
Sales Range: $10-24.9 Million
Emp.: 130
Industrial Filos Mfr
N.A.I.C.S.: 332420
Russell Putnam (Gen Mgr)

WAUSEON MACHINE AND MANUFACTURING, INC.

995 Enterprise Ave, Wauseon, OH 43567
Tel.: (419) 337-0940   OH
Web Site:
http://www.wauseonmachine.com
Year Founded: 1983
Rev.: $11,000,000
Emp.: 200
Automotive Related Machinery
N.A.I.C.S.: 333248
Luis Sanchez (Engr-Sls)
Luis Sanchez (Engr-Sls)

Subsidiaries:

Mcalister Design, Inc. (1)
510 Pickett St, Greenville, SC 29609
Tel.: (864) 232-8325
Web Site: http://www.mcalisterdesign.com
Sales Range: $1-9.9 Million
Emp.: 13
Custom Computer Programming Services
N.A.I.C.S.: 541511
Troy McAlister (Founder & Pres)
Ron Fuller (Gen Mgr-Ops)
Clay Jester (VP)
Judy Brooks (Office Mgr)
Rick Reames (Mgr-Sls-South Carolina)
Chris Palmer (Supvr-Mfg)
Scott Legg (Mgr-Sls-Georgia)

WAV, INC.

2380 A Cross Dr, Aurora, IL 60502
Tel.: (630) 818-1000

WAV, INC.

WAV, Inc.—(Continued)

Web Site: http://www.wavonline.com
Year Founded: 1991
Sales Range: $25-49.9 Million
Emp.: 35
Distr of Wireless LAN & Data Collection Products
N.A.I.C.S.: 423430
Norm Dumbroff *(CEO)*
Cary Cooper *(Mgr-Acct)*
Dave Hempe *(Mgr-Acct)*
Nick Schraufnagel *(Mgr-IT & Sr Engr-Sys)*
Zach Hubeck *(VP-Sls & Mktg)*
Ashley Bilobran *(Mgr-Mktg)*
Chad Cuda *(Mgr-Ops)*
Francisco Mendez *(Mgr-Support Svcs & Sr Engr-Sys)*
Robert Nelson *(COO)*
Mark Billets *(Sr Engr-Sys)*
Ashley Guziec *(Coord-Mktg)*

WAVE 3 COMMUNICATIONS INC.

15 N Main St, Sapulpa, OK 74066-3901
Tel.: (918) 877-9200
Rev.: $13,300,000
Emp.: 50
Telephone Communications
N.A.I.C.S.: 517121
Linden Wood *(Pres & CEO)*
Mark Stephens *(VP)*

WAVE DISPERSION TECHNOLOGIES, INC.

269 Sheffield St Ste 5D, Mountainside, NJ 07092-2318
Tel.: (908) 233-7503
Web Site:
http://www.whisprwave.com
Year Founded: 1995
Sales Range: $1-9.9 Million
Emp.: 10
Erosion Control Floating Polyethylene Breakwaters for Marine, Waterfronts & Dams
N.A.I.C.S.: 237110
Dennis G. Smith *(Founder & CEO)*
Jonathan B. Smith *(COO)*

WAVE FORM SYSTEMS INC.

20475 SW Avery Ct, Tualatin, OR 97062
Tel.: (503) 626-2100
Web Site:
http://www.waveformsys.com
Year Founded: 1986
Rev.: $9,900,000
Emp.: 33
Healtcare Services
N.A.I.C.S.: 423450
Charles R. Watkins Jr. *(Pres)*
Karen Wiersma *(Dir-Admin & Mgr-Office & HR)*

WAVE SOFTWARE, LLC

300 S Orange Ave Ste 900, Orlando, FL 32801
Tel.: (407) 325-5006
Web Site:
http://www.discoverthewave.com
Year Founded: 2005
Sales Range: $1-9.9 Million
Emp.: 18
Software Development Services
N.A.I.C.S.: 541511
Robert E. Childress *(Founder & Pres)*

WAVE TECHNOLOGY SOLUTIONS GROUP

320 Goddard Ste 100, Irvine, CA 92618
Tel.: (949) 341-9300

Web Site:
http://www.waveimaging.com
Year Founded: 1992
Content Management, Business Process Outsourcing & Managed Services & Solutions
N.A.I.C.S.: 513210
Howard Miyakawa *(Engr-Software)*
Fred Woitt *(Dir-Sls Ops)*
Adam Torab *(Pres)*
Amir Afzali *(VP)*

Subsidiaries:

Metronome, Inc. (1)
320 Goddard Ste 100, Irvine, CA 92618
Tel.: (714) 429-0031
Web Site: http://www.metronome.net
Sales Range: $10-24.9 Million
Emp.: 32
Technology Solutions
N.A.I.C.S.: 541618

WAVEGARD, INC.

4938 Hampden Ln Ste 423, Bethesda, MD 20814
Tel.: (888) 928-3835
Web Site: http://www.wavegard.com
Sales Range: $1-9.9 Million
IT Security Consulting, Communications Infrastructure Engineering & Training Services
N.A.I.C.S.: 541690
Richard Dreger *(Pres)*

WAVEGUIDE, INC.

10 N Southwood Dr, Nashua, NH 03063
Tel.: (978) 670-0000
Web Site:
http://www.waveguidefiber.com
Year Founded: 1998
Rev.: $6,500,000
Emp.: 60
Electrical Contractor
N.A.I.C.S.: 238210
Peter C. Farrell *(Chm)*
James R. Carmichael *(Pres)*
Jacqueline Hayes *(Treas)*
Branden Allen *(Project Mgr)*
Mark Abate *(Dir-Fin)*
Julie Nguyen *(Asst Controller)*

WAVELAND INVESTMENTS, LLC

900 N Michigan Ave Ste 1100, Chicago, IL 60611
Tel.: (312) 506-6450
Web Site: http://www.wavelandinvestments.com
Year Founded: 2000
Privater Equity Firm
N.A.I.C.S.: 523999
Dennis Zaslavsky *(Founder & Partner)*
Meghan P. Otis *(Partner)*

Subsidiaries:

Always For Me, LLC (1)
740 Veterans Memorial Hwy Ste 303, Hauppauge, NY 11788
Tel.: (631) 237-4881
Web Site: http://www.alwaysforme.com
Rev.: $10,000,000
Emp.: 15
Women's Plus Size Clothing Retailer
N.A.I.C.S.: 458110
Greg Barone *(CEO)*
David Pfeifer *(Pres)*
Jeanne Grasso *(Mgr-Mktg)*

WAVEPOINT 3PL EXPEDITE LLC

5501 Route 89, North East, PA 16428
Tel.: (814) 347-1300
Web Site:
http://www.wavepoint3pl.com
Logistic Services
N.A.I.C.S.: 541614

Kirk Hill *(Pres)*

Subsidiaries:

Alcor Corp. (1)
2100 Pittsburgh Ave, Erie, PA 16502
Tel.: (814) 453-6911
Web Site: http://www.alcorcoldstorage.com
Refrigerated Warehousing & Storage
N.A.I.C.S.: 493120
James Alberico *(Pres)*

Robert's Trucking (1)
5501 Route 89, North East, PA 16428-5054
Tel.: (814) 347-1300
Web Site: http://www.robertstrucking.com
Specialized Freight Trucking; Long-Distance
N.A.I.C.S.: 484230
William Roberts *(Pres)*

WAVERLY HEIGHTS LTD.

1400 Waverly Rd, Gladwyne, PA 19035
Tel.: (610) 645-8600   PA
Web Site:
http://www.waverlyheightsltd.org
Year Founded: 1982
Sales Range: $25-49.9 Million
Emp.: 395
Elder Care Services
N.A.I.C.S.: 624120
Meredith Feher *(VP-Health Care Svcs)*
Thomas P. Garvin *(Pres & CEO)*
Robert L. Supper *(CFO & VP)*
Janet Thompson *(VP-Mktg)*
Kathleen Jungclaus *(VP-HR)*
Marc Heil *(VP-Building Svcs)*
Jackie Donnelly *(Dir-Nursing)*
James Heffren *(Dir-Dining Svcs)*
Tom Lynch *(Mgr-Maintenance)*

WAVERLY LUMBER & MANUFACTURING

12443 San Jose Blvd, Jacksonville, FL 32257
Tel.: (904) 262-2531
Rev.: $12,916,432
Emp.: 3
Rough, Dressed & Finished Lumber
N.A.I.C.S.: 423310
Sam Pratt Jr. *(Pres)*

WAVERLY PARTNERS INC.

175 Strafford Ave Ste 1, Wayne, PA 19087
Tel.: (610) 687-7867
Web Site:
http://www.waverlypartners.com
Rev.: $10,200,000
Emp.: 2
Metal Stamping
N.A.I.C.S.: 332119
Patrick Burke *(Co-Founder)*
Debbie Galbraith *(Mng Dir & Principal)*

Subsidiaries:

Berkshire Manufactured Products, Inc. (1)
116 Parker St, Newburyport, MA 01950
Tel.: (978) 462-8161
Web Site: http://www.whitcraftgroup.com
Aircraft Engine Parts Mfr
N.A.I.C.S.: 334511

WAVESPLITTER TECHNOLOGIES, INC.

2080 Rancho Higuera Ct, Fremont, CA 94539-7309
Tel.: (510) 651-7800
Web Site:
http://www.wavesplitter.com
Sales Range: $10-24.9 Million
Emp.: 170
Fiber Optics Communications Equipment
N.A.I.C.S.: 334210

Sheau Sheng Chen *(Founder, Chm & CEO)*

WAVETABLE LABS LLC

440 North Wells St Ste 720, Chicago, IL 60654
Tel.: (312) 447-6100
Web Site: http://www.wavetable.com
Digital Business Services
N.A.I.C.S.: 561499
Matt Moog *(CEO)*
Corey Haines *(CTO)*

WAVETECH GLOBAL, INC.

609 Willow Ave, Hoboken, NJ 07030
Tel.: (201) 280-9850   DE
Web Site:
http://www.wavetechglobal.com
Energy Optimization & Lifecycle Management Products & Services
N.A.I.C.S.: 561990
Keith Barksdale *(Chm & CEO)*

Subsidiaries:

Power Analytics Corporation (1)
2621 Spring Forest Rd Ste 101, Raleigh, NC 27616
Tel.: (919) 848-8625
Web Site: http://www.poweranalytics.com
Electric Power Grid Planning & Operation Software Developer & Publisher
N.A.I.C.S.: 513210
Kevin Meagher *(Pres & CEO)*

Re-Tron Technologies (1)
620 Gotham Pkwy, Carlstadt, NJ 07072
Tel.: (201) 969-3456
Web Site: http://www.re-tron.com
Battery Installation, Maintenenance & Testing Services
N.A.I.C.S.: 238990
Chris Schaffroth *(VP-Ops)*

WAVICLE DATA SOLUTIONS LLC

564 W Randolph St Ste 600, Chicago, IL 60661
Tel.: (630) 756-2632
Web Site:
http://www.wavicledata.com
Year Founded: 2013
Sales Range: $10-24.9 Million
Emp.: 171
Software Development Services
N.A.I.C.S.: 541511
Naveen Venkatapathi *(Mng Partner)*
Niyaz Kamookagath *(Mng Partner)*
Anita Lee *(Specialist-HR)*
Jackie Sikich *(Acct Exec)*
Tom Palenik *(Dir-Bus Dev & Ops)*
Sue Pittacora *(Chief Strategy Officer)*

WAVSYS LLC

101 Broadway Ste 406, Brooklyn, NY 11249
Tel.: (347) 292-8797
Web Site: http://www.wavsys.com
Year Founded: 2007
Sales Range: $10-24.9 Million
Emp.: 575
Network Engineering for Wireless Telecommunications
N.A.I.C.S.: 517810
Sean Yazbeck *(Pres)*
Josh Mangerson *(COO)*

WAWA, INC.

Red Roof 260 W Baltimore Pike, Media, PA 19063-5620
Tel.: (610) 358-8000   NJ
Web Site: https://www.wawa.com
Year Founded: 1902
Sales Range: $10-24.9 Million
Emp.: 42,000
Convenience Retailer
N.A.I.C.S.: 445131
Stephanie Capaccio *(Dir-Benefits & Risk Mgmt)*

COMPANIES

Christopher T. Gheysens *(Pres & CEO)*
Cathy Pulos *(Chief People Officer & VP)*

WAWONA FROZEN FOODS INC.
100 W Alluvial Ave, Clovis, CA 93611
Tel.: (559) 299-2901
Web Site: http://www.wawona.com
Rev.: $43,883,028
Emp.: 1,100
Fruits, Quick Frozen & Cold Pack (Frozen)
N.A.I.C.S.: 311411
Julie Olsen *(CFO)*
Enrique Herrera *(Mgr-Refrigeration)*
Hortencia Calderon *(Mgr-Safety Trng)*
Christine Boyland *(Controller)*
Chris Linhares *(Dir-HR)*
Larry Narbaitz *(Dir-Ops)*
William S. Smittcamp *(Owner & Pres)*

WAX WORKS INC.
325 E 3rd St, Owensboro, KY 42303
Tel.: (270) 926-0008
Web Site:
  http://www.waxworksonline.com
Rev.: $55,091,226
Emp.: 100
Whslr & Distributor of Entertainment Products
N.A.I.C.S.: 423990
Terry Woodward *(Pres)*
Barb Birgy *(Dir-Pur & Vendor Rels)*
Misty Coffman *(Mgr-Adv)*
Andrew Goetz *(Dir-Video)*

WAXMAN INDUSTRIES, INC.
24460 Aurora Rd, Bedford, OH 44146-1728
Tel.: (440) 439-1830 DE
Web Site:
  http://www.waxmanind.com
Year Founded: 1934
Sales Range: $50-74.9 Million
Emp.: 440
Holding Company; Plumbing & Floorcare Products Mfr, Marketer & Whslr
N.A.I.C.S.: 551112
Melvin Waxman *(Co-Chm)*
Armond Waxman *(Co-Chm)*
Laurence S. Waxman *(Pres & CEO)*
Patrick Ferrante *(VP-Ops)*

Subsidiaries:

TWI International, Inc. **(1)**
No 10 7th Rd Taichung Industrial Park, 407, Taichung, Taiwan **(100%)**
Tel.: (886) 423593307
Web Site: http://www.twindustries.com
Sales Range: $10-24.9 Million
Emp.: 40
Wholesale Distributor of Plumbing & Heating Supplies
N.A.I.C.S.: 423720

Subsidiary (Non-US):

CWI International China, Ltd. **(2)**
Dan King Vlg Fumin County, Guanlan Town, Shenzhen, 518110, Bao An District, China **(100%)**
Tel.: (86) 75528010919
Web Site: http://www.cwi.com.cn
Mfr & Packager of Floor-Protective Hardware & Other Products
N.A.I.C.S.: 332510

Subsidiary (Domestic):

TWI International Taiwan, Inc. **(2)**
No 10 7th Rd Taichung Industrial Pk, 407, Taichung, Taiwan **(100%)**
Tel.: (886) 423593307
Web Site: http://www.twi.com.tw
Assembly, Packaging & Distribution of Packaged Plumbing & Electrical Products
N.A.I.C.S.: 423720

Waxman Consumer Products Group Inc. **(1)**
24455 Aurora Rd, Bedford, OH 44146-1727
Tel.: (440) 439-1830
Web Site: http://www.waxmancpg.com
Sales Range: $25-49.9 Million
Emp.: 100
Plumbing & Floorcare Products Marketer & Whslr
N.A.I.C.S.: 423720
Melvin Waxman *(Co-Chm)*

WAY HOLDING LTD
5308 Ashbrook Dr, Houston, TX 77081
Tel.: (713) 666-3541
Rev.: $18,600,000
Emp.: 19
Investor
N.A.I.C.S.: 523999
Peter Way *(Partner)*

WAY MEDIA INC.
PO Box 64500, Colorado Springs, CO 80962
Tel.: (719) 533-0300 FL
Year Founded: 1985
Sales Range: $10-24.9 Million
Emp.: 118
Radio Station Operator
N.A.I.C.S.: 516110
Billy J. O'Neal *(Sr Dir-Dev)*
Ralph Rhodes *(Sr VP)*
Felice Augsburg *(Sec)*
Joe Battaglia *(Chm)*
John Scaggs *(Pres & CEO)*
Neal Joseph *(Vice Chm)*
Robert Augsburg *(Founder)*
Faron Dice *(VP)*
Lloyd Parker *(COO)*
Mike Russell *(Dir-Ops-WAYI FM-Louisville)*
Paul Van Sickle *(Dir-Ops-WAY FM-Portland)*
Aaron Traylor *(Dir-Ops-WAYM FM-Nashville)*
Dan Raymond *(Dir-Ops-KXWA FM-Denver)*

WAYBILL USA INC.
4720 Bowling Green Rd, Franklin, KY 42134-7621
Tel.: (270) 586-8201 DE
Year Founded: 2017
Holding Company; Inner-Grooved Metal Tube Mfr
N.A.I.C.S.: 551112
David Lilley *(CEO)*

Subsidiaries:

Luvata Franklin, Inc. **(1)**
4720 Bowling Green Rd, Franklin, KY 42134-7621
Tel.: (270) 586-8201
Web Site: http://www.luvata.com
Stainless Steel Mfr
N.A.I.C.S.: 331420

WAYFIELD FOODS INC.
5145 Wellcome All Rd, Atlanta, GA 30349
Tel.: (404) 559-3200
Web Site:
  http://www.wayfieldfoods.com
Year Founded: 1982
Rev.: $48,600,000
Emp.: 500
Operator of Grocery Stores
N.A.I.C.S.: 445110
Ron B. Edenfield *(Co-Founder & Pres)*
Valincea Robinson *(Mgr-Customer Svc)*
Rhunell Walker *(Coord-Sea Food)*

Subsidiaries:

Super Low Foods **(1)**
2532 Bouldercrest Rd, Atlanta, GA 30316
Tel.: (404) 243-7441
Web Site: http://www.wayfieldfoods.com
Sales Range: $25-49.9 Million
Emp.: 201
Sales of Groceries
N.A.I.C.S.: 445110
Latavius Thomas *(Mgr-Store)*

Wayfield Foods, Inc. **(1)**
1970 Candler Rd, Decatur, GA 30022
Tel.: (404) 284-0191
Web Site: http://www.wayfieldfoods.com
Sales of Groceries
N.A.I.C.S.: 445110
Cindi Edenfield *(Controller)*

Wayfield Foods, Inc. **(1)**
1901 Metropolitan Pkwy, Atlanta, GA 30315
Tel.: (404) 768-5830
Web Site: http://www.wayfieldfoods.com
Sales Range: $10-24.9 Million
Emp.: 30
Sales of Groceries
N.A.I.C.S.: 445110

WAYNE ACTION GROUP FOR ECONOMIC SOLVENCY, INC.
601 Royall Ave, Goldsboro, NC 27534
Tel.: (919) 734-1178 NC
Web Site: http://www.wagesnc.org
Year Founded: 1966
Sales Range: $10-24.9 Million
Emp.: 250
Community Action Services
N.A.I.C.S.: 813319
Marlee Ray *(Exec Dir)*
Patricia Beier *(Dir-Children & Families)*
Isabelle Doss *(Dir-Older Adult Svcs)*
Brenda Ipock *(Mgr-Ops)*

WAYNE ASPHALT & CONSTRUCTION CO.
6600 Ardmore Ave, Fort Wayne, IN 46809-9703
Tel.: (260) 747-7531
Web Site:
  http://www.wayneasphalt.com
Sales Range: $10-24.9 Million
Emp.: 43
Highway & Street Construction Services
N.A.I.C.S.: 237310
Rick Walters *(Dir-Safety)*

WAYNE AUTOMATIC FIRE SPRINKLERS, INC.
222 Capitol Ct, Ocoee, FL 34761
Tel.: (407) 656-3030
Web Site: http://www.waynefire.com
Year Founded: 1978
Sales Range: $25-49.9 Million
Emp.: 350
Fire Sprinkler System Installation
N.A.I.C.S.: 238220
Wayne H. Gey *(Founder & CEO)*
Clark Gey *(Pres)*
Scott Holland *(Dir-Fire Protection Svcs)*

WAYNE COUNTY BANK
216 S High St Hwy 64 W, Waynesboro, TN 38485
Tel.: (931) 722-5438
Web Site:
  http://www.waynecountybank.com
Year Founded: 1914
Sales Range: $1-9.9 Million
Emp.: 83
Provider of Banking Services
N.A.I.C.S.: 524126
Sibyl Haggard *(Exec VP)*
Deadra Keaton *(Chief Credit Officer)*

WAYNE COUNTY HOSPITAL, INC.
166 Hospital St, Monticello, KY 42633
Tel.: (606) 348-9343 KY
Web Site:
  http://www.waynehospital.org
Year Founded: 1972
Sales Range: $10-24.9 Million
Emp.: 204
Health Care Srvices
N.A.I.C.S.: 622110
Lora Elam *(Chief Nursing Officer)*
Katherine Tucker *(Dir-Nutrition Svcs)*
Sandra Anderson *(Dir-Pharmacy)*
Mollie Dick *(Dir-HR)*
Anne Sawyer *(CFO)*
Anita Hopper *(Sec)*
Gordon Crowley *(Treas)*
Joe Murrell *(CEO)*
Kelly Elmore *(Dir-Mktg & PR)*
Larry Bates *(Chm)*

WAYNE CROUSE INC.
3370 Stafford St, Pittsburgh, PA 15204
Tel.: (412) 771-5176
Web Site:
  http://www.waynecrouse.com
Sales Range: $25-49.9 Million
Emp.: 30
Waste Water & Sewage Treatment Plant Construction
N.A.I.C.S.: 238220
William P. Lugaila *(Owner)*
Thomas V. Manz *(VP-Fin)*
David A. DeSalle *(VP-Estimating)*
Edwin L. Walters *(VP-Project Mgmt)*

WAYNE DAVIS CONCRETE CO.
10 Wayne Davis Dr, Tallapoosa, GA 30176
Tel.: (770) 574-2326
Web Site:
  http://www.waynedavisconcrete.com
Sales Range: $10-24.9 Million
Emp.: 200
Ready Mixed Concrete
N.A.I.C.S.: 327320
Chris Davis *(Pres)*
Richard Davis *(Treas & Sec)*

WAYNE INDUSTRIES INC.
1105 N Market St Ste 1300, Wilmington, DE 19801
Tel.: (302) 478-6160
Rev.: $13,199,426
Emp.: 5
Bindings, Textile
N.A.I.C.S.: 313220

Subsidiaries:

Franklin Braid Manufacturing Co. **(1)**
620 Davis St, Emporia, VA 23847
Tel.: (434) 634-4142
Web Site: http://www.franklinbraid.com
Sales Range: $1-9.9 Million
Braided Cords & Ropes Mfr
N.A.I.C.S.: 314994

WAYNE J. GRIFFIN ELECTRIC INC.
116 Hopping Brook Rd, Holliston, MA 01746-1455
Tel.: (508) 429-8830 MA
Web Site:
  http://www.waynejgriffinelectric.com
Year Founded: 1978
Rev.: $45,211,057
Emp.: 750
Electrical Contractor
N.A.I.C.S.: 238210
Marc McNair *(Mgr-Raleigh Reg)*
Micah Blum *(Project Mgr)*
Mike Boike *(Project Mgr)*
Tim Cortis *(Mgr-Info Sys)*
Gary Mosca *(Mgr-Svcs Div)*
Al Sordillo *(Project Mgr)*
Patricia Walls *(Mgr-AP)*
John Nadworny *(Mgr-Pre-Fab)*

WAYNE J. GRIFFIN ELECTRIC INC.

Wayne J. Griffin Electric Inc.—(Continued)
Thomas Hughes (Mgr-Contracts)
Jon Buchanan (Supvr-Electrical Job)
Cheryl Kewley (Office Mgr)
Rui Reis (Project Mgr)

Subsidiaries:

Wayne J. Griffin Electric Inc. (1)
296 Cahaba Valley Pkwy, Pelham, AL
35124-1145 **(100%)**
Tel.: (205) 733-8848
Web Site:
http://www.waynejgriffinelectric.com
Sales Range: $25-49.9 Million
Emp.: 60
Electrical Contractor
N.A.I.C.S.: 238210
Calvin Mize (Reg Mgr)

Wayne J. Griffin Electric Inc. (1)
2501 Blue Ridge Rd Ste G-100, Raleigh,
NC 27607
Tel.: (919) 782-0720
Web Site:
http://www.waynejgriffinelectric.com
Sales Range: $25-49.9 Million
Emp.: 125
Electrical Contractor
N.A.I.C.S.: 238210
Mark McNair (Mgr-Reg)

WAYNE LEES GROCERY & MARKET

1317 Telephone Rd, Pascagoula, MS
39567
Tel.: (228) 762-4101
Web Site:
http://www.wayneleesgrocery.com
Sales Range: $50-74.9 Million
Emp.: 150
Independent Supermarket
N.A.I.C.S.: 445110
Perry Lee (Pres)
Tracy Cooper (Office Mgr)

WAYNE MAPLES PLUMBING & HEATING

317 W Cedar St, Eureka, CA 95501
Tel.: (707) 445-2500
Web Site:
http://www.maplesplumb.com
Sales Range: $10-24.9 Million
Emp.: 130
Provider of Plumbing Contracts
N.A.I.C.S.: 238220
Rodney Maples (Pres, CEO & Co-Owner)
Dale Maples (Owner & Sec)

WAYNE NURSING & REHABILITATION CENTER, INC.

6999 Route 152, Wayne, WV 25570
Tel.: (304) 697-7007
Web Site: http://www.amfmwv.com
Year Founded: 1982
Nursing Care Facility
N.A.I.C.S.: 623110
Cindy Cooper (Exec Dir)

WAYNE PERRY, INC.

8281 Commonwealth Ave, Buena
Park, CA 90621-2537
Tel.: (714) 826-0352
Web Site: http://www.wpinc.com
Year Founded: 1969
Sales Range: $25-49.9 Million
Emp.: 200
Provider of Special Trade Contracting
Services
N.A.I.C.S.: 238990
Elisabeth Ortega (Coord-Groundwater Program)
William Cline (Project Coord & Coord-Permit)
Vince Santangelo (Project Mgr)
Tom Ritchie (VP-Engrg, Health & Safety)

WAYNE PIGMENT CORP.

7350 S 6th St, Oak Creek, WI 53154
Tel.: (414) 225-2400
Web Site:
http://www.waynepigment.com
Rev.: $11,932,750
Emp.: 35
Developer of Inorganic Pigments
N.A.I.C.S.: 325130

WAYNE THOMAS CHEVROLET, INC.

1400 E Dixie Dr, Asheboro, NC
27203
Tel.: (336) 625-2107
Web Site:
http://www.waynethomaschevrolet.com
Sales Range: $10-24.9 Million
Emp.: 35
Car Whslr
N.A.I.C.S.: 441110
Jerry Norman (Owner & Mgr)
Dwight Saunders (Gen Mgr)

WAYNE TRANSPORTS INC.

14345 Conley Ave, Rosemount, MN
55068
Tel.: (651) 437-6422
Web Site:
http://www.waynetransports.com
Rev.: $35,585,615
Emp.: 32
Trucking Except Local
N.A.I.C.S.: 484121
Ann Rotty (Asst Dir-Safety)
Brad Guggisberg (VP-Sls & Mktg)
Carl Vedders (Owner)

WAYNE WILES FLOOR COVERINGS, INC.

16430 S Tamiami Trl, Fort Myers, FL
33908
Tel.: (239) 482-7600
Web Site:
http://www.waynewiles.com
Year Founded: 1985
Sales Range: $10-24.9 Million
Emp.: 35
Floor Covering Stores
N.A.I.C.S.: 449121
Wayne T. Wiles (Founder)
Mark Wiles (Pres)

WAYNE WIRE CLOTH PRODUCTS, INC.

200 E Dresden St, Kalkaska, MI
49646
Tel.: (231) 258-9187
Web Site: http://www.waynewire.com
Year Founded: 1943
Sales Range: $100-124.9 Million
Emp.: 200
Mfr of Industrial Filters & Strainers
Screw Machine Products & Stampings
N.A.I.C.S.: 332618
Michael W. Brown (Pres)
Valerie McInerney (Mgr-HR)
David Brown (Co-Pres)
Steve Brown (Co-Pres)
Steve Waugh (COO)

Subsidiaries:

Wayne Wire Air Bag Components,
Inc. - Juarez Facility (1)
Juarez-Ave Libre Comercio 2164 Parque
Ind Las Americas Cd, 32596, Ciudad
Juarez, Mexico
Tel.: (52) 656 683 5354
Fabricated Metal Products Mfr
N.A.I.C.S.: 332999

Wayne Wire Cloth Products Hillman
Division (1)
221 Garfield St, Hillman, MI 49746 **(100%)**
Tel.: (989) 742-4591

Web Site: http://www.waynewire.com
Sales Range: $10-24.9 Million
Emp.: 50
Mfr of Hardware Cloth, Woven Wire & Metal
Stampings; Welding Repairs
N.A.I.C.S.: 333998
Alice Thomson (Gen Mgr)

WAYNE-SANDERSON FARMS

4110 Continental Dr, Oakwood, GA
30566
Web Site:
https://www.waynesanderson
farms.com
Year Founded: 2022
Emp.: 26,000
Poultry Product Distr
N.A.I.C.S.: 424440
J. Clint Rivers (Pres & CEO)
Kevin McDaniel (COO)
T. J. Wolfe (CFO & Treas)
Pamela Roach (Chief HR Officer)
Jeremy Kilburn (Chief Legal Officer & Chief Compliance Officer)

WAYNES MOBILE HOME SALES INC.

Hwy 301 S, Glennville, GA 30427
Tel.: (912) 654-3461
Rev.: $13,809,425
Emp.: 30
Mobile Home Dealers
N.A.I.C.S.: 459930
Wayne Durrence (Pres)

WAYNES TIRE INC.

302 W Betteravia Rd, Santa Maria,
CA 93455
Tel.: (805) 928-2661
Web Site: http://www.waynestire.com
Sales Range: $10-24.9 Million
Emp.: 20
Automotive Tires
N.A.I.C.S.: 441340
Mark Davis (Mgr)

WAYNESBORO CONSTRUCTION CO. INC.

215 W 5th St, Waynesboro, PA
17268
Tel.: (717) 762-1151
Web Site:
http://www.waynesboroconstruction.com
Sales Range: $100-124.9 Million
Emp.: 100
Commercial & Office Building, New
Construction
N.A.I.C.S.: 236220
Robert W. Brown (Chm)
Greg Brown (Pres)
Herb Sandifer (Exec VP)

WAYNESBORO NURSERIES, INC.

2597 Lyndhurst Rd, Waynesboro, VA
22980
Tel.: (540) 946-3800
Web Site:
http://www.waynesboronurseries.com
Year Founded: 1932
Sales Range: $1-9.9 Million
Emp.: 60
Whslr of Nursery Stock, Garden Supplies & Landscape Services
N.A.I.C.S.: 111421
Ed Quillen (Pres)
Kirk Quillen (VP & Mgr-Wholesale Sls)
Tim Quillen (Treas, Sec & Mgr-Landscape)
David Quillen (VP-Production)
Noirin Quillen (VP-Production)

U.S. PRIVATE

WAYPOINT CAPITAL PARTNERS

555 Theodore Fremd Ave Ste C-207,
Rye, NY 10580
Tel.: (914) 417-6960
Web Site:
https://www.waypointcapitalpartners.com
Holding Company
N.A.I.C.S.: 551112
John Henry Moulton (Partner)

Subsidiaries:

Greenshades Software, Inc. (1)
7020 AC Skinner Pkwy Ste 100, Jacksonville, FL 32256
Tel.: (904) 807-0160
Web Site: http://www.greenshades.com
Software Publisher
N.A.I.C.S.: 513210
David Rosas (Co-Founder & CEO)

WAYPOINT GLOBAL LLC

8345 Clearvista Pl Ste 350, Indianapolis, IN 46256
Tel.: (844) 827-8254
Web Site:
http://www.waypointglobal.com
Year Founded: 1987
Supply Chain Management Solutions
N.A.I.C.S.: 541614
H. Dave Chambliss (Pres & CEO)
Howard Clark (COO & Exec VP)

WAYPOINT SOLUTIONS GROUP, LLC.

9311 Monroe Rd Ste A, Charlotte, NC
28270
Tel.: (704) 246-1717
Web Site: http://www.waypointsg.com
Sales Range: $1-9.9 Million
Emp.: 14
Information Technology Consulting
Services
N.A.I.C.S.: 541512
Dan Wilson (Co-Founder)
David Ellis (Co-Founder)

WAYSIDE CHRISTIAN MISSION

432 E Jefferson St, Louisville, KY
40202
Tel.: (502) 584-3711
Web Site:
http://www.waysidechristianmission.org
Year Founded: 1957
Sales Range: $10-24.9 Million
Emp.: 49
Community Food Services
N.A.I.C.S.: 624210
Nina Moseley (COO)

WAYSIDE FURNITURE INC.

1367 Canton Rd, Akron, OH 44312
Tel.: (330) 733-6221
Web Site: http://www.wayside-furniture.com
Rev.: $24,521,985
Emp.: 100
Sales of Furniture
N.A.I.C.S.: 449110
Brian Regenos (Mgr-Store)
Richard Valerio (Coord-Visual)
Shelly Murray (Office Mgr)
John Ferrato Jr. (Owner)

WAYSIDE YOUTH & FAMILY SUPPORT NETWORK

1 Frederick Abbott Way, Framingham, MA 01701
Tel.: (508) 879-9800
Web Site:
http://www.waysideyouth.org
Year Founded: 1977
Sales Range: $10-24.9 Million
Emp.: 508
Family Support Services

N.A.I.C.S.: 624190
Eric L. Masi *(Pres & CEO)*
Andrea Salzman *(VP-Community Svcs)*
Elizabeth Reid *(VP)*
Marisa Rowe *(Dir-Dev & Comm)*
David Simmons *(VP-Fin)*

WAYZATA INVESTMENT PARTNERS LLC
701 E Lake St Ste 300, Wayzata, MN 55391
Tel.: (952) 345-0700   DE
Web Site:
  http://www.wayzatainvestment
  partners.com
Year Founded: 2004
Sales Range: $25-49.9 Million
Emp.: 41
Privater Equity Firm
N.A.I.C.S.: 523999
Patrick J. Halloran *(Mng Partner)*
John E. Foley *(Partner)*
Joseph M. Deignan *(Partner)*
Mary I. Burns *(Partner)*
Blake M. Carlson *(Partner)*
John D. McEvoy *(Partner)*

Subsidiaries:

Propex Operating Company, LLC   (1)
4019 Industry Dr, Chattanooga, TN 37416
Tel.: (423) 855-1466
Web Site: http://www.propexglobal.com
Sales Range: $700-749.9 Million
Mfr of Engineered Geosynthetics & Reinforcement Fibers for Construction of Major Infrastructure Projects
N.A.I.C.S.: 325220
Michael K. Gorey *(Pres & CEO)*
Randal D. Powell *(COO)*

Subsidiary (Domestic):

Propex Geosolutions Corporation   (2)
6025 Lee Hwy Ste 425, Chattanooga, TN 37421
Tel.: (423) 899-0444
Web Site: http://www.propexllc.com
Sales Range: $25-49.9 Million
Erosion Control Construction Fabrics Mfr
N.A.I.C.S.: 313230

Super Service Holdings, LLC   (1)
6000 Clay Ave SW, Grand Rapids, MI 49503
Tel.: (800) 669-8658
Web Site: http://www.superservicellc.com
Sales Range: $300-349.9 Million
Holding Company; Trucking Services
N.A.I.C.S.: 551112
Larry Carrier *(CFO)*
Daniel Strong *(Pres & CEO)*

Subsidiary (Domestic):

Super Service, LLC   (2)
6000 Clay Ave SW, Grand Rapids, MI 49548-5785
Tel.: (616) 530-8558
Web Site: http://www.superservicellc.com
Freight Trucking Services
N.A.I.C.S.: 484121
Larry Carrier *(CFO)*
Daniel Strong *(Pres & CEO)*
Vaughn Yow *(VP-Ops)*
Eric Pell *(Dir-IT)*
Steve Maat *(Dir-HR)*

Branch (Domestic):

Super Service, LLC - Kentucky Office   (3)
250 Super Service Dr, Somerset, KY 42501-6146
Tel.: (606) 679-1141
Web Site: http://www.superservicellc.com
Freight Trucking Services
N.A.I.C.S.: 484121
Chuck Creekmore *(Dir-Safety-Kentucky Div)*
Jay Thomas *(Dir-Safety-Natl)*

WAYZATA MARINE, INC.
3324 Northshore Dr, Wayzata, MN 55391
Tel.: (952) 471-7000   MN
Web Site:
  http://www.wayzatamarine.com
Year Founded: 1967
Sales Range: $10-24.9 Million
Emp.: 20
Boat Dealers
N.A.I.C.S.: 441222
David Briggs *(Pres)*

WAYZATA NISSAN
15906 Wayzata Blvd, Wayzata, MN 55391-1477
Tel.: (952) 475-3939
Web Site:
  http://www.wayzatanissan.com
Sales Range: $25-49.9 Million
Emp.: 61
Car Whslr
N.A.I.C.S.: 441110
Mark Saliterman *(Owner)*
Arnold Thoms *(Mgr-Sls)*
Ellie Swenson *(Gen Mgr)*

WAZANA BROTHERS INTERNATIONAL INC.
8201 Woodley Ste 201 Ave Vean Nuys, Chatsworth, CA 91406
Tel.: (818) 407-7500
Sales Range: $100-124.9 Million
Emp.: 900
Facsimile Equipment
N.A.I.C.S.: 333248
Avi Wazana *(CEO)*
Yoel Wazana *(Pres)*

WB COMMUNITY HEALTH
300 Jefferson Blvd Ste 205, Warwick, RI 02888
Tel.: (401) 499-4291   RI
Web Site:
  http://www.wbcommunityhealth.org
Year Founded: 1997
Sales Range: $100-124.9 Million
Emp.: 1
Health Insurance Services
N.A.I.C.S.: 524114
Alan Lord *(Exec Dir)*
Maryanne Crawford *(Treas)*
Robert Ross *(Pres)*
John Ritchotte *(VP)*

WB GUIMARIN & COMPANY INC.
1124 Bluff Indus Blvd, Columbia, SC 29201
Tel.: (803) 256-0515
Web Site:
  http://www.wbguimarin.com
Sales Range: $10-24.9 Million
Emp.: 100
Mechanical Contractor
N.A.I.C.S.: 238220
C. Carroll Heyward *(Pres)*
Scott Davis *(Mgr-Svc Ops)*
Jeff Tober *(VP-Svc)*
Brad Gunnells *(Dir-Safety)*
Richard Byrd *(Project Mgr)*
Bob Privette *(CFO)*
Sidney Heyward Rex *(Exec VP & Project Mgr)*
Chris Bigalke *(Mgr-Bus)*
Bryan Bochette *(Mgr-Ops)*
Chad Cothran *(Mgr-Ops)*
Trey Foster *(Mgr-Sheet Metal Shop)*
James Simpson *(Mgr-Small Projects)*
Whit Gulledge *(Project Mgr)*

WB PROMOTIONS, INC.
16107 Kensington Dr Ste 172, Sugar Land, TX 77479
Web Site:
  http://www.wbpromotion.com
Sales Range: $1-9.9 Million
Emp.: 43
Online Marketing Services
N.A.I.C.S.: 458110
Azim Maknojia *(Owner)*
Jisan Makanojiya *(Owner)*
Zishan Momin *(Owner & Mgr-Ops)*

WBH INDUSTRIES INC
3016 Ave E E, Arlington, TX 76011-5212
Tel.: (817) 649-5700   TX
Year Founded: 1955
Sales Range: $10-24.9 Million
Emp.: 20
Retailer of Hardware & Millwork
N.A.I.C.S.: 423310
Richard Page *(Pres)*
Linda Beckham *(Project Mgr)*

WBK 1, INC.
1530 W Lewis Ave, Phoenix, AZ 85007
Tel.: (480) 788-5368   DE
Year Founded: 2014
Investment Services
N.A.I.C.S.: 523999
Toan Thanh Tran *(Chm, Pres, CEO & Sec)*

WBM ENTERPRISES INC.
3275 Brown St, Boise, ID 83714
Tel.: (208) 345-2951
Web Site: http://www.wbmclean.com
Year Founded: 1962
Sales Range: $25-49.9 Million
Emp.: 220
Building Maintenance Services
N.A.I.C.S.: 561720
Bret Vaterlaus *(Pres)*

Subsidiaries:

Western Building Maintenance   (1)
3275 Brown St, Boise, ID 83714
Tel.: (208) 345-2951
Web Site: http://www.wbmclean.com
Building Maintenance Services
N.A.I.C.S.: 561720

WC DESIGNS
18025 Sky Park Cir Ste H, Irvine, CA 92614-0500
Tel.: (714) 634-2002
Sales Range: $10-24.9 Million
Emp.: 40
Mfr of Table Linens
N.A.I.C.S.: 423220
Patrick J. McCullagh *(Pres)*

WC HOLDING, INC.
1101 King St Ste 550, Alexandria, VA 22314
Tel.: (703) 739-0084
Year Founded: 2007
Sales Range: $50-74.9 Million
Emp.: 400
Holding Company
N.A.I.C.S.: 551112
Russel T. Wright *(Co-Founder)*
Darrell L. Crapps *(Co-Founder)*

WC TINGLE COMPANY
2615 NE Hagen Rd, Lees Summit, MO 64064
Tel.: (816) 472-4801
Web Site: http://www.wctingle.com
Rev.: $19,200,000
Emp.: 78
Floor Coverings
N.A.I.C.S.: 423220
Danny Welsh *(COO)*
Tyler Barr *(VP-Mktg)*
W. L. Moxley Jr. *(Pres)*

WCA HOSPITAL
207 Foote Ave, Jamestown, NY 14701
Tel.: (716) 487-0141
Web Site: http://www.wcahospital.org
Rev.: $42,700,000
Emp.: 1,000
Ambulance Service
N.A.I.C.S.: 621910
Daniel Johnson *(Dir-Svcs)*
William Geary *(Treas & Sec)*
Karl Sisson *(VP-Membership)*

Subsidiaries:

Allied Orthopedic Appliances, Inc.   (1)
512 W Third St, Jamestown, NY 14701
Tel.: (716) 664-5092
Sales Range: $10-24.9 Million
Emp.: 10
Medical Apparatus & Supplies
N.A.I.C.S.: 456199

WCA Services Corp.   (1)
28 Maple St, Jamestown, NY 14701
Tel.: (716) 664-7353
Web Site: http://www.wcaservices.com
Rev.: $4,737,760
Emp.: 120
Ambulance Service
N.A.I.C.S.: 621910

Woman's Christian Association   (1)
207 Foote Ave, Jamestown, NY 14701
Tel.: (716) 487-0141
Web Site: http://www.wcahospital.org
Emp.: 1,200
General Medical & Surgical Hospitals
N.A.I.C.S.: 622110
Betsy Wright *(Pres & CEO)*

WCC CABLE, INC.
4809 Ewell Rd, Fredericksburg, VA 22408
Tel.: (540) 898-9315
Web Site: http://www.wcccable.com
Year Founded: 1991
Sales Range: $10-24.9 Million
Emp.: 100
Construction Engineering Services
N.A.I.C.S.: 237310
Warn Kubra *(VP)*

WCIT ARCHITECTURE, INC.
725 Kapiolani Blvd Ste C400, Honolulu, HI 96813
Tel.: (808) 592-2345   HI
Web Site: http://www.wcitarch.com
Year Founded: 2000
Sales Range: $10-24.9 Million
Emp.: 31
Architectural Services
N.A.I.C.S.: 541310
Daniel Kanekuni *(Sr VP)*
Lawrence Cunha *(Sr VP)*
Mark H. Higa *(Sr VP)*

WCM INDUSTRIES INC.
2121 Waynoka Rd, Colorado Springs, CO 80915
Tel.: (719) 574-0600
Web Site: http://www.wcmind.com
Sales Range: $10-24.9 Million
Emp.: 100
Faucets & Spigots, Metal & Plastic
N.A.I.C.S.: 332913
Steve Woodford *(Pres)*
Kevin Fink *(VP)*

WCS CONTRACTORS, LTD.
7271 Bagby Ave, Hewitt, TX 76643
Tel.: (254) 666-9000
Web Site:
  http://www.wcscontractors.com
Year Founded: 1959
Sales Range: $10-24.9 Million
Emp.: 120
Drywall & Insulation Contractor Services
N.A.I.C.S.: 238310
Leon Wilson *(Pres & CEO)*
Bob McGowan *(VP & Mgr-Ops)*
Nathan Stehling *(Mgr-Field Ops)*
Ivan Wilson *(Project Mgr)*

WCS CONTRACTORS, LTD.

WCS Contractors, Ltd.—(Continued)

Angela Baze *(Office Mgr & Comptroller)*
Stephanie Eads *(Mgr-HR)*
Essex Wilson *(Project Mgr)*

WCS LENDING, LLC
951 Yamado Rd Ste 150, Boca Raton, FL 33431
Tel.: (561) 241-5200
Web Site: http://www.wcslending.com
Year Founded: 2001
Sales Range: $10-24.9 Million
Emp.: 250
Mortgage Banker
N.A.I.C.S.: 522310
Carlos Cepeda *(Co-Founder & Co-CEO)*
Eric Wallberg *(Co-Founder & Co-CEO)*
Avi Mizrahi *(VP-Mortgage Ops)*
Michael Alexander *(VP-Mortgage Sls)*

WCS, INC.
1515 N Academy Blvd Ste 400, Colorado Springs, CO 80909
Tel.: (719) 573-8557
Holding Company; Restaurant Franchise Owner & Operator
N.A.I.C.S.: 551112
Richard W. Holland *(Pres & CEO)*
Thomas J. Reinhard *(CFO)*

Subsidiaries:

Northern GC, LLC (1)
1515 N Academy Ste 400, Colorado Springs, CO 80909
Tel.: (719) 573-8557
Buffet Restaurant Operator
N.A.I.C.S.: 722514
Richard W. Holland *(Pres & CEO)*

Wendy's of Colorado Springs, Inc. (1)
1515 N Academy Blvd Ste 400, Colorado Springs, CO 80909
Tel.: (719) 573-8557
Fast-Food Restaurant Franchise Operator
N.A.I.C.S.: 722513
Thomas J. Reinhard *(CFO)*

WCS-333 SOUTH STREET, INC.
333 South St Ste 290, Shrewsbury, MA 01545
Tel.: (508) 856-1507
Year Founded: 2010
Sales Range: $10-24.9 Million
Real Estate Management Services
N.A.I.C.S.: 531390
Sandra Flynn *(Treas)*
Nancy Vasil *(Pres)*

WD HALL EXPLORATION COMPANY
1869 E Seltice Way Ste 363, Post Falls, ID 83854
Tel.: (208) 651-6374
Year Founded: 2010
Metal Mining Services
N.A.I.C.S.: 212290
William Hall *(Pres, CEO & CFO)*
Brett Wyatt *(Treas & Sec)*

WDD INC
9845 S 142 St, Omaha, NE 68138
Tel.: (402) 331-9225
Year Founded: 1967
Sales Range: $25-49.9 Million
Emp.: 100
Distr & Retailer of Windows
N.A.I.C.S.: 423310
Gregg Boulay *(Pres)*
Stephen Noel *(VP)*
Alan Weedin *(Treas)*

WDF/FIVE STAR HOLDING CORPORATION
101-32 101st St, Ozone Park, NY 11416-2616
Tel.: (718) 641-5000
Web Site: http://www.fivestarelectric.net
Sales Range: $25-49.9 Million
Plumbing, Mechanical & Electrical Contracting Services
N.A.I.C.S.: 238210
Stephen H. Kornfeld *(CEO)*

Subsidiaries:

Five Star Electric Corp. (1)
101-32 101st St, Ozone Park, NY 11416
Tel.: (718) 641-5000
Web Site: http://www.fivestarelectric.net
Sales Range: $25-49.9 Million
Emp.: 150
Electrical Contracting Services
N.A.I.C.S.: 238210
Gary Segal *(Pres)*

WDF Inc. (1)
30 N Macquesten Pkwy, Mount Vernon, NY 10550-1841
Tel.: (914) 776-8000
Web Site: http://www.wdfinc.net
Plumbing & Mechanical Contracting Services
N.A.I.C.S.: 238220
Lawrence Roman *(CEO)*

WDIT, INCORPORATED
335 N Liberty St, Centreville, MD 21617
Tel.: (443) 262-9290
Web Site: http://www.corsicatech.com
Computer System Design Services
N.A.I.C.S.: 541512
Dale Walls *(Pres)*
Jody Walls *(CFO)*

Subsidiaries:

EDTS, LLC (1)
933 Broad St Ste 301, Augusta, GA 30901
Tel.: (706) 722-6604
Web Site: http://www.edtsolutions.com
Sales Range: $1-9.9 Million
Emp.: 26
Computer Integrated Systems Design & Security Systems Services
N.A.I.C.S.: 541512
Charles Johnson *(Founder & CEO)*
Will McGee *(COO)*
Donna Davis *(Office Mgr)*
Craig Tarkenton *(CTO)*
Lynn Mays *(Dir-Comm Tech)*
Doug Rankin *(Mgr-Automation Svcs)*
Stephen Luster *(Mgr-Smart Desk)*
Shannon Person *(Mgr-Support Sls)*
Emily Logan *(Mgr-Client Svcs)*
Pradeep Satyaprakash *(Acct Exec)*
Jonathan Bolt *(Acct Exec)*
Jeff Cox *(Acct Exec)*
Peter Franklin *(Acct Exec)*
Gerry Owen *(CFO)*
Danielle Chaney *(Controller)*
Judy Boyle Chun *(Chief Admin Officer)*

WE CARE FOOD STORES INC.
1209 S Heaton St, Knox, IN 46534
Tel.: (574) 772-4184
Sales Range: $10-24.9 Million
Emp.: 65
Grocery Stores, Chain
N.A.I.C.S.: 445110
Randall Weiss *(Pres)*

WE SELL CELLULAR, INC.
20 Nancy St Unit B, West Babylon, NY 11704
Tel.: (516) 334-6400
Web Site: http://www.wesellcell.com
Year Founded: 2003
Rev: $22,400,000
Emp.: 16
Electronic Parts & Equipment Merchant Whslr
N.A.I.C.S.: 423690

Brian Tepfer *(Founder & CEO)*
Scott Tepfer *(Pres)*
Dan Coyne *(Mgr-ECommerce)*
Kathy Koziol *(COO)*

WE TRANSPORT, INC.
75 Commercial St, Plainview, NY 11803
Tel.: (516) 349-8200
Web Site: http://www.wetransport.com
Year Founded: 1960
Emp.: 1,300
Bus Transportation Services
N.A.I.C.S.: 485410
Jerome B. Marksohn *(VP)*
Cynthia Reed *(Chief Acctg Officer)*
Helena Marksohn *(Corp Sec)*
Bret Savit *(Controller)*
Carmen Tomeo *(CEO)*
Bart Marksohn *(Pres)*

WEA MIDSTATE
711 N Keys Rd, Yakima, WA 98901
Tel.: (509) 452-6559
Web Site: http://www.wea-midstate.org
Year Founded: 1956
Emp.: 100
Public Education Promoter
N.A.I.C.S.: 611710

WEAKLEY COUNTY MUNICIPAL ELECTRIC SYSTEM
11181 Hwy 22, Martin, TN 38237
Tel.: (731) 587-9521
Web Site: http://www.weakleycountychamber.com
Sales Range: $25-49.9 Million
Emp.: 70
Distribution, Electric Power
N.A.I.C.S.: 221122
Faron L. Collins *(Gen Mgr)*
Thomas Brewer *(Mgr-Acctg)*

WEALTHCLASSES, LLC
1931 San Miguel Dr Ste 200, Walnut Creek, CA 94596
Tel.: (925) 395-4983
Web Site: http://www.wealthclasses.com
Year Founded: 2007
Sales Range: $1-9.9 Million
Emp.: 30
Educational Support Services
N.A.I.C.S.: 611710
Maria G. Lepe *(Office Mgr)*

WEALTHENGINE.COM
4330 E West Hwy Ste 950, Bethesda, MD 20814-4581
Tel.: (301) 215-5980
Web Site: http://www.wealthengine.com
Year Founded: 1991
Sales Range: $10-24.9 Million
Emp.: 125
Management Consulting Services
N.A.I.C.S.: 541618
Tony Glowacki *(Pres)*
Robert Hines *(Chief Revenue Officer)*
Bobby Yazdani *(Chm)*
Dennis Ainge *(Interim CEO)*

WEALTHFRONT CORPORATION
261 Hamilton Ave, Palo Alto, CA 94301
Tel.: (650) 325-2717
Web Site: http://www.wealthfront.com
Online Investment, Wealth Management & Financial Advisory Data Services
N.A.I.C.S.: 522320

Burton Gordon Malkiel *(Chief Investment Officer)*
Alan Imberman *(CFO)*
David Fortunato *(CEO)*

WEALTHPIRE INC
3435 Ocean Park Blvd Ste 107-334, Santa Monica, CA 90405
Tel.: (310) 882-6440
Web Site: http://www.wealthpire.com
Year Founded: 2006
Sales Range: $1-9.9 Million
Emp.: 10
Investment Newsletters
N.A.I.C.S.: 513120
Manny Backus *(Founder)*

WEAR FIRST SPORTSWEAR INC.
42 W 39th St 13th Fl, New York, NY 10018-3895
Tel.: (212) 869-8686
Web Site: http://www.wearfirst.com
Sales Range: $10-24.9 Million
Emp.: 30
Men's & Boy's Clothing
N.A.I.C.S.: 424350
Jonathan Lee *(Chm & CEO)*

WEARBEST SIL-TEX MILLS LTD.
325 Midland Ave, Garfield, NJ 07026
Tel.: (973) 340-8844
Web Site: http://www.wearbest.com
Sales Range: $10-24.9 Million
Emp.: 100
Broadwoven Fabric Mills
N.A.I.C.S.: 313210
Irwin Gasner *(Pres & CEO)*
Melissa Battah *(Dir-Contract)*
Ari Gasner *(Exec VP)*
Richard Isaacson *(CFO)*

WEATHERBY CONSTRUCTION CORP.
139 N Iowa Ave, Atlantic City, NJ 08401
Tel.: (609) 487-8555
Sales Range: $25-49.9 Million
Emp.: 45
Provider of Commercial & Office Building Construction
N.A.I.C.S.: 236220
Marilyn Weatherby *(Pres)*

WEATHERBY, INC.
1605 Commerce Way, Paso Robles, CA 93446
Tel.: (805) 227-2600
Web Site: http://www.weatherby.com
Year Founded: 1945
Sales Range: $25-49.9 Million
Emp.: 35
Rifles, Shotguns, Scopes & Ammunition Mfr
N.A.I.C.S.: 332994
Mike Schwiebert *(VP-Mktg)*

WEATHERCHEM CORP
2222 Highland Rd, Twinsburg, OH 44087
Tel.: (330) 425-4206
Web Site: http://www.weatherchem.com
Sales Range: $10-24.9 Million
Emp.: 130
Mfr of Injection Molded Finished Plastics Products
N.A.I.C.S.: 326199
David Beveridge *(Controller)*

WEATHERSHIELD MFG. INC.
1 Weather Shield Plz, Medford, WI 54451
Tel.: (715) 748-6555

Web Site:
http://www.weathershield.com
Rev.: $252,900,000
Emp.: 200
Holding Company
N.A.I.C.S.: 321911

Subsidiaries:

SNE Enterprises, Inc. (1)
880 Southview Dr, Mosinee, WI 54455-8290
Tel.: (715) 693-7000
Sales Range: $100-124.9 Million
Mfr of Wooden & Vinyl Windows, Doors
N.A.I.C.S.: 321911

Schield Family Brands (1)
880 Southview Dr, Mosinee, WI 54455
Tel.: (715) 693-7000
Sales Range: $25-49.9 Million
Mfr of Steel & Fiberglass Entry & Patio Doors; Wood & Wood Clad Windows
N.A.I.C.S.: 321918
Jill Dassow *(Mgr-Benefits)*

Weather Shield Manufacturing, Inc. (1)
1 Weathershield Plz, Medford, WI 54451-2206
Tel.: (715) 748-2100
Web Site: http://www.weathershield.com
Sales Range: $300-349.9 Million
Mfr of Doors & Windows
N.A.I.C.S.: 321911
Chris Schield *(VP-Mktg)*

WEATHERTEC CORPORATION
5645 E Clinton Ave, Fresno, CA 93727-1308
Tel.: (559) 291-5555
Web Site: http://www.weathertec.com
Year Founded: 1970
Sales Range: $50-74.9 Million
Emp.: 50
Mfr of Irrigation Equipment
N.A.I.C.S.: 332919
Ben Merlo *(Controller)*

WEATHERTECH DISTRIBUTING CO. INC
501 28th St, Irondale, AL 35210
Tel.: (205) 956-5400
Web Site: http://www.weathertech.net
Sales Range: $25-49.9 Million
Emp.: 65
Warm Air Heating & Air Conditioning
N.A.I.C.S.: 423730
Doral Atkins *(CEO)*
Lantis Hollis *(VP-Sls & Mktg)*

WEATHERVANE SEAFOOD COMPANY
31 Badgers Is W, Kittery, ME 03904
Tel.: (207) 439-0335
Web Site:
http://www.weathervaneseafoods.com
Sales Range: $25-49.9 Million
Emp.: 70
Seafood Restaurants Owner & Operator
N.A.I.C.S.: 722511
Terry Gagner *(Owner & Pres)*
Jeremy Gagner *(VP-Site Dev)*

WEAVE CORPORATION
433 Hackensack Ave Fl 4, Hackensack, NJ 07601
Tel.: (201) 646-1500
Rev.: $14,100,000
Emp.: 15
Weave Fabrics
N.A.I.C.S.: 313210
Roger L. Berkley *(Pres)*
Jeff Harbst *(VP)*
Janet Drew *(VP-Admin)*
Pat Snoke *(VP-Mfg)*

WEAVER & HOLIHAN, INC.
148 W State St Ste 102, Kennett Square, PA 19348
Tel.: (610) 925-5888
Web Site:
http://www.weaverholihan.com
Year Founded: 2001
Strategic Marketing Research & Consulting Services
N.A.I.C.S.: 541910
Mary Jo Newtown *(Founder & Sr Partner)*
Russ Holihan *(Sr Partner)*

WEAVER & TIDWELL, L.L.P.
2821 W 7th St Ste 700, Fort Worth, TX 76107
Tel.: (817) 332-7905
Web Site: http://www.weaver.com
Year Founded: 1950
Accounting, Tax & Consulting Services
N.A.I.C.S.: 541211
Kerry D. Caves *(COO)*
David Rook *(COO-Assurance & Advisory Svcs)*
Robert Henry *(Partner-Central Texas Tax & Strategic Bus Svcs)*
Greg Bailes *(Partner-Tech Bus Svcs)*
Shelby Lackey *(Partner)*
Cory Bunyard *(Partner-Tax Svcs)*
Sarah Roberts *(Partner-Assurance Svcs)*
Jon Roberts *(Partner-Tax Svcs)*
Reema Parappilly *(Partner-IT Advisory Svcs)*
Aracely Rios *(Partner-Assurance Svcs)*
Cindy Carradine *(Mng Dir-Forensics & Litigation Svcs)*
Frank McElroy *(Partner & Gen Counsel)*
Todd Potas *(Dir-Energy Compliance Svcs)*
John J. Mackel III *(CEO & Mng Partner)*

WEAVER COOKE CONSTRUCTION, LLC
8401 Key Blvd, Greensboro, NC 27409
Tel.: (336) 378-7900
Web Site:
http://www.weavercooke.com
Year Founded: 1939
Sales Range: $50-74.9 Million
Emp.: 100
Provider of Contracting & Construction Services
N.A.I.C.S.: 236116
Doug George *(Exec VP)*
Linda Wall *(VP)*
Dan Estes *(Pres)*

WEAVER ENTERPRISES LTD.
10216 W Civil Defense Rd, Brimfield, IL 61517
Tel.: (309) 691-7021
Rev.: $20,000,000
Emp.: 600
Family Restaurant Chain
N.A.I.C.S.: 722511
Jerry Weaver *(Pres)*
Terry Moffit *(Dir-Ops)*

WEAVER MARKETS INC.
2610 N Reading Rd, Adamstown, PA 17517
Tel.: (717) 484-4302
Web Site:
http://www.weavermarkets.com
Year Founded: 1962
Rev.: $30,000,000
Emp.: 279
Owner & Operator of Grocery Stores
N.A.I.C.S.: 445110
Mable Weaver *(Pres)*
Mike Weaver *(Owner & Store Mgr)*
Gene Weaver *(Gen Mgr)*

WEAVER NUT COMPANY INC.
1925 W Main St, Ephrata, PA 17522
Tel.: (717) 738-3781
Web Site: http://www.weavernut.com
Sales Range: $10-24.9 Million
Emp.: 25
Salted & Roasted Nuts
N.A.I.C.S.: 424450
Vincent Weaver *(Gen Mgr)*

WEAVER POPCORN COMPANY, INC.
9850 W Point Dr Ste 100, Indianapolis, IN 46250
Tel.: (765) 934-2101
Web Site: http://www.popweaver.com
Year Founded: 1928
Sales Range: $100-124.9 Million
Emp.: 250
Popcorn Producer & Processor
N.A.I.C.S.: 424450
Doug Dent *(Mktg Svcs Dir)*
Randy Herring *(Mgr-Pur)*
Ryan Brodkorb *(Mgr-Production)*
Tiffany Mangona *(Coord-Quality Assurance)*
Mike Verslype *(Plant Mgr)*
Rodney King Jr. *(Mgr-Shipping & Logistics)*

WEAVER PRECAST INC.
824 E Main St, Ephrata, PA 17522
Tel.: (717) 733-6565
Web Site:
http://www.weaverprecast.com
Sales Range: $10-24.9 Million
Emp.: 35
Bricklaying
N.A.I.C.S.: 238140
Gary L. Weaver *(Pres)*

WEAVER PUBLICATIONS INC.
900 S Broadway Ste 300, Denver, CO 80209
Tel.: (303) 458-1211
Rev.: $11,000,000
Emp.: 60
Magazines: Publishing & Printing
N.A.I.C.S.: 513120
Peter J. Koclanes *(Pres & CEO)*
Tara Zucker *(Dir-Mktg)*

WEAVER SALES OF SAUK CITY INC.
808 Industry Rd, Sauk City, WI 53583
Tel.: (608) 643-2734
Web Site:
http://www.weaverautoparts.com
Sales Range: $10-24.9 Million
Emp.: 30
Automotive Supplies & Parts
N.A.I.C.S.: 423120
Mark A. Weaver *(Pres)*

WEAVERTOWN TRANSPORT LEASING, INC.
2 Dorrington Rd, Carnegie, PA 15106
Tel.: (724) 746-4850
Web Site:
http://www.weavertown.com
Year Founded: 1981
Sales Range: $25-49.9 Million
Emp.: 180
Petroleum Haulage Local Distr
N.A.I.C.S.: 484220
Donald E. Fuchs *(Founder & Owner)*
Dawn Fuchs-Heiser *(Pres)*
Rosemary Vulcano *(Dir-Corp HR)*

Subsidiaries:

WEG Engineering (1)
2 Dorington Rd, Carnegie, PA 15106
Tel.: (724) 746-4850
Sales Range: $10-24.9 Million
Emp.: 15
Provider of Environmental Engineering, Consulting, Investigation, Remediation, Planning, Reporting & Management Services
N.A.I.C.S.: 541690

WEB & SONS INC.
1010 1/2 Thompson Blvd, Sedalia, MO 65301-2243
Tel.: (660) 826-8600
Web Site:
http://www.websonsinc.com
Year Founded: 1952
Sales Range: $25-49.9 Million
Emp.: 55
Commercial Real Estate Services
N.A.I.C.S.: 445110
Tom Munson *(Pres)*
Mike Bolin *(VP)*

WEB ADVANCED
49 Discovery Ste 150, Irvine, CA 92618
Tel.: (949) 453-1805
Web Site:
http://www.webadvanced.com
Year Founded: 2000
Rev.: $2,000,000
Emp.: 20
IT Services
N.A.I.C.S.: 541511
Victor Liu *(Co-Founder & CEO)*
Adam Bonner *(Co-Founder & CTO)*
Andrew McLendon *(Chief Creative Officer)*
Halle Nguyen *(Dir-Ops)*

WEB CONSTRUCTION CO.
2201 Eastland Dr Ste 4, Bloomington, IL 61704
Tel.: (309) 663-5301
Web Site:
http://www.bradyhomes.com
Sales Range: $10-24.9 Million
Emp.: 8
New Construction, Single-Family Houses
N.A.I.C.S.: 236115
Ed Brady *(Pres)*

WEB FX INC.
6871 Laurelton Ave, Garden Grove, CA 92845-1418
Tel.: (714) 896-8004
Web Site: http://www.webfx.com
Data Processing, Hosting & Related Services
N.A.I.C.S.: 518210
Shawn Youngquist *(CEO)*

Subsidiaries:

Nutshell, Inc. (1)
229 Depot St, Ann Arbor, MI 48104
Tel.: (717) 385-7090
Web Site: http://www.nutshell.com
Software Publisher
N.A.I.C.S.: 513210
Lindsay Snider *(Partner)*

WEB INDUSTRIES INC.
377 Simarano Dr Ste 220, Marlborough, MA 01752
Tel.: (508) 898-2988
Web Site:
http://www.webindustries.com
Year Founded: 1969
Rev.: $27,821,190
Emp.: 350
Converting Services for Flexible Materials
N.A.I.C.S.: 322220
Carl Rubin *(CFO)*
Mark Pihl *(Chm)*

WEB INDUSTRIES INC.

Web Industries Inc.—(Continued)
Kevin Young *(VP-Corp Dev)*
Andrew O'Connor *(VP-Quality)*
John S. Madej *(CEO)*
Subsidiaries:

Web Industries (1)
20 Louisa Viens Dr, Dayville, CT 06241
Tel.: (860) 779-3403
Web Site: http://www.webindustries.com
Rev.: $8,930,897
Emp.: 50
Medical Diagnostics, Micro-Fluidics, Solar & Data Communications Applications
N.A.I.C.S.: 621511
Donald Romine *(CEO & Dir-Mgmt)*
Mark Pihl *(Pres, COO & Dir-Mgmt)*
Kevin Young *(VP-Corp Dev & Dir-Mgmt)*
Carl Ted Lind *(Chm)*
John MacInnes *(CFO)*

Web Industries Inc. (1)
510 Jealouse Way, Cedar Hill, TX 75104
Tel.: (972) 291-0932
Web Site: http://www.webindustries.com
Sales Range: $1-9.9 Million
Emp.: 31
Paper, Coated Or Laminated For Packaging
N.A.I.C.S.: 322220

Web Industries, Inc. (1)
410 Horizon Dr, Suwanee, GA 30024-7268
Tel.: (678) 804-3020
Web Site: http://www.webindustries.com
Sales Range: $1-9.9 Million
Emp.: 100
Composites Formatting & Contract Mfr Services
N.A.I.C.S.: 333515
Donald Romine *(CEO)*
Jason Surman *(VP-Sls)*

WEB PRINTING CONTROLS COMPANY INCORPORATED
23872 N Kelsey Rd, Barrington, IL 60010
Tel.: (847) 382-7970
Web Site: http://www.wpcteam.com
Rev.: $19,300,000
Emp.: 65
Printing Trades Machinery
N.A.I.C.S.: 333248
Dean Fetherling *(Chm, Pres & CEO)*
David Funni *(Engr-Software)*

WEB RIVER GROUP, INC.
5911 Benjamin Center Dr, Tampa, FL 33634
Tel.: (813) 769-2451
Web Site:
 http://www.4wheelonline.com
Year Founded: 2001
Sales Range: $25-49.9 Million
Emp.: 28
Automobile Parts Distr
N.A.I.C.S.: 441330
Ryan Heath *(Pres)*

WEB SHOP MANAGER
3760 Convoy St Ste 340, San Diego, CA 92111
Tel.: (619) 278-0872
Web Site:
 http://www.webshopmanager.com
Sales Range: $1-9.9 Million
Emp.: 15
Ecommerce Solutions
N.A.I.C.S.: 541890
Dana Nevins *(Founder & CEO)*
Paulette Palladino *(Dir-Ops)*
Mike Brodsky *(Dir-Engrg)*
Dale Payton-Engle *(CFO & COO)*

WEB-DON INC.
1400 Ameron Dr, Charlotte, NC 28206
Tel.: (704) 375-0250
Web Site: http://www.web-don.com
Year Founded: 1972
Sales Range: $10-24.9 Million
Emp.: 100
Plastics Materials
N.A.I.C.S.: 424610

WEB-HED TECHNOLOGIES, INC.
1617 E Commerce St Ste 4104, San Antonio, TX 78205
Tel.: (210) 354-1661
Web Site:
 http://www.webheadtech.com
Year Founded: 1994
Sales Range: $1-9.9 Million
Emp.: 35
Hardware & Software Services
N.A.I.C.S.: 449210
Janie M. Gonzalez *(CEO)*

WEB2CARZ.COM LTD
PO Box 805, Highland Park, IL 60035
Web Site: http://www.web2carz.com
Year Founded: 2006
Sales Range: $1-9.9 Million
Emp.: 5
Online Auto Magazine
N.A.I.C.S.: 513120
Alex Bravy *(Co-Founder)*

WEBB & SONS CONSTRUCTION CO. INC
815 S White St, Athens, TN 37303
Tel.: (423) 745-1774
Sales Range: $10-24.9 Million
Emp.: 30
Commercial Industrial Building Services
N.A.I.C.S.: 236220

WEBB AND PARTNERS, INC.
4110 Old Pineville Rd, Charlotte, NC 28217
Tel.: (704) 945-0374
Web Site:
 http://www.webbandpartners.com
Sales Range: $10-24.9 Million
Emp.: 9
Commercial Real Estate Development & Management Services
N.A.I.C.S.: 236220
Sherwood L. Webb *(Pres)*

WEBB CHEVROLET, INC.
9440 S Cicero Ave, Oak Lawn, IL 60453-2520
Tel.: (708) 423-9440
Web Site:
 http://www.webbchevroletoaklawn.com
Sales Range: $10-24.9 Million
Emp.: 50
Car Whslr
N.A.I.C.S.: 441110
J. Michael Webb *(Owner)*
John Damore *(Gen Mgr-Sls)*
Kelly Webb *(Owner)*

WEBB CONCRETE COMPANY INC.
64 Hunnicutt St, Heflin, AL 36264-1161
Tel.: (256) 463-2195
Web Site:
 http://www.webbconcrete.com
Rev.: $15,677,633
Emp.: 75
Ready Mixed Concrete
N.A.I.C.S.: 327320
Phillip M. Webb *(Pres)*

WEBB FORD, INC.
9809 Indianapolis Blvd, Highland, IN 46322-2622
Tel.: (219) 924-3400
Web Site: http://www.webbford.com
Sales Range: $75-99.9 Million
Emp.: 400
New Car Whslr
N.A.I.C.S.: 441110
Terri Smith *(Mgr-Telecom)*

WEBB FURNITURE ENTERPRISES INC.
602 E Stuart Dr, Galax, VA 24333
Tel.: (276) 236-2984
Web Site: http://www.webbfurn.com
Year Founded: 1924
Sales Range: $1-9.9 Million
Emp.: 140
Wood Household Furniture
N.A.I.C.S.: 337122
John Baffett *(Chm)*

WEBB PR
455 Sherman Ste 250, Denver, CO 80203
Tel.: (303) 796-8888
Web Site:
 http://www.webbstrategic.com
Sales Range: $25-49.9 Million
Emp.: 10
Advertising Agencies
N.A.I.C.S.: 541810
Peter Webb *(CEO)*
Ginny Williams *(Principal)*
Sheryl East *(Mgr-Admin)*

WEBB WHEEL PRODUCTS INC.
2310 Indus Dr SW, Cullman, AL 35055-6331
Tel.: (256) 739-6660
Web Site: http://www.webbwheel.com
Year Founded: 1988
Sales Range: $25-49.9 Million
Emp.: 500
Provider of Motor Vehicle Parts & Accessories
N.A.I.C.S.: 336390
Mark Foster *(Mgr-OES Sls-Western Reg)*

WEBB-MASON INC.
10830 Gilroy Rd, Hunt Valley, MD 21031
Tel.: (410) 785-1111
Web Site:
 http://www.webbmason.com
Sales Range: $75-99.9 Million
Emp.: 250
Commercial Printing, Lithographic
N.A.I.C.S.: 323111
Warner P. Mason *(Chm & CEO)*
Douglas D. Traxler *(Exec VP-Sls & Mktg)*
Ernie Vaile *(COO & Exec VP)*
Scott Bradway *(Sr VP-Sls-Southeast)*
Enam Noor *(Mng Dir)*
Kip Webb *(Co-Founder & Exec VP)*
Tony Abunassar *(Pres-Interactive & COO-Comml)*
Amer Mallah *(CIO & CTO-Interactive Solutions Div)*
Jennifer Moag Black *(Sr Exec VP-Ops)*
David Rich *(Chm/CEO-Interactive Solutions Div)*
Michelle Bengermino *(VP-Product Dev)*
Kevin Perzan *(VP-Distr Ops)*
Steve Benshoof *(VP-Sls)*
Lynn Brewton *(VP-Supplier Rels)*
Jeff Wright *(VP-Sls)*
Richard Barbato Jr. *(CFO)*

WEBB-STILES COMPANY
675 Liverpool Dr, Valley City, OH 44280
Tel.: (330) 225-7761
Web Site: http://www.webb-stiles.com
Year Founded: 1956
Sales Range: $10-24.9 Million
Emp.: 90
Designer, Mfr & Installer of Engineered Conveyor Systems
N.A.I.C.S.: 333922

WEBBER METAL PRODUCTS INC.
PO Box 10, Cascade, IA 52033-0010
Tel.: (563) 852-7122
Web Site:
 http://www.webbermetals.com
Year Founded: 1973
Sales Range: $10-24.9 Million
Emp.: 175
Provider of Metal Stampings
N.A.I.C.S.: 332119
Kathy Hoffman *(Controller)*
Dave Webber *(Mgr-Quality Control)*
Steve Webber *(Pres)*

WEBBER OIL COMPANY
700 Main St, Bangor, ME 04401
Tel.: (207) 942-5501
Web Site:
 http://www.weberenergy.com
Sales Range: $200-249.9 Million
Emp.: 95
Petroleum Products
N.A.I.C.S.: 424720
Lisa Hartman *(Controller)*
Sandy Adams *(Mgr)*

WEBBMASON, INC.
10830 Gilroy Rd, Hunt Valley, MD 21031
Tel.: (410) 785-1111
Web Site:
 http://www.webbmason.com
Advertising & Marketing Services
N.A.I.C.S.: 541870
Donald Carver *(Product Mgr)*

WEBCO GENERAL PARTNERSHIP
24600 Millstream Dr 3300, Aldie, VA 20105
Tel.: (703) 653-1400
Web Site: http://www.webcogp.com
Rev.: $30,200,000
Emp.: 75
Bond Brokers
N.A.I.C.S.: 424410
Joe Olding *(Pres-Commissary)*
Roy Thomas *(Chm & CEO)*
Sam Barnum *(Sr Mgr-Bus Dev)*
Walter Buckert *(Dir-Govt & Indus Affairs)*
Kellee Turner *(Dir-Customer Svc)*
Timothy Ivey *(VP-Fin)*
Glenn Greene *(Mgr-Perishable-Eastern Reg)*
Kent Blue *(Mgr-Sls)*
Joe Giacco *(VP-Mktg)*
Sandy Kraft *(Acct Exec)*
Rick Thomas *(Pres-Ops)*
John Catlett *(VP-Exchange Ops)*

WEBCOR PACKAGING CORPORATION
5081 Exchange Dr, Flint, MI 48507
Tel.: (810) 230-8680
Web Site: http://www.comwebinc.com
Year Founded: 1969
Sales Range: $10-24.9 Million
Emp.: 100
Corrugated Boxes
N.A.I.C.S.: 322211
Robert T. Sibilsky *(Co-Owner & Pres)*
Scott Konieczny *(Controller)*
Jeffery S. Dingman *(Plant Mgr)*
Mark A. Blackburn *(Plant Mgr)*
Arthur C. Hutchinson *(Plant Mgr)*
Joel B. Liggett *(Dir-Sls)*
William H. Martin III *(Chm)*

WEBCRAFTERS INC.

2211 Fordem Ave, Madison, WI 53704-4611
Tel.: (608) 244-3561
Web Site: http://www.webcrafters-inc.com
Year Founded: 1921
Sales Range: $50-74.9 Million
Emp.: 560
Provider of Book Printing Services
N.A.I.C.S.: 323117
John J. Frautschi (Chm)
Jack Gardner (Pres)
Bob Malinowski (CEO)

WEBER & JUDD PHARMACY
1814 15th St NW Ste 1, Rochester, MN 55901-0734
Tel.: (507) 289-1666
Web Site: http://www.weberjudd.com
Sales Range: $10-24.9 Million
Emp.: 90
Pharmaceutical Product Whslr
N.A.I.C.S.: 424210
Lowell Janssen (Mgr)
Steve Muellen (Mgr)
Irv Nehring (CFO)
Kitty Tesmer (Mgr)

WEBER BASIN WATER CONSERVANCY DISTRICT
2837 E Hwy 193, Layton, UT 84040-8406
Tel.: (801) 771-1677
Web Site: http://www.weberbasin.com
Rev.: $18,816,712
Emp.: 80
Agricultural Consulting Services
N.A.I.C.S.: 115112
Tage I. Flint (CEO & Gen Mgr)
Jeff Connor (Plant Mgr)
Mark D. Anderson (Asst Gen Mgr & Chief Engr)
Michael Midgley (Supvr-Electrical)
Scott Paxman (Asst Gen Mgr)

WEBER CARPET INC.
11400 Rogers Rd, Lenexa, KS 66215
Tel.: (913) 469-5430
Web Site: http://www.webercarpet.com
Rev.: $21,558,410
Emp.: 180
Floor Coverings
N.A.I.C.S.: 423220
Mark Weber (Owner)
Joe Weber (VP)
Dave Sinclair (COO)

WEBER DISTRIBUTION WAREHOUSES, LLC
13530 Rosecrans Ave, Santa Fe Springs, CA 90670-5023
Tel.: (562) 802-8802
Web Site: http://www.weberdistribution.com
Year Founded: 1924
Sales Range: $25-49.9 Million
Emp.: 500
Warehousing Facilities Operator & Local Freight Transportation Services
N.A.I.C.S.: 484110
Nicholas N. Weber (Chm & CEO)

WEBER DISTRIBUTION, LLC
15500 Phoebe Ave, La Mirada, CA 90638
Tel.: (714) 739-0357
Web Site: http://www.weberdistribution.com
Rev.: $7,000,000
Emp.: 70
General Freight Trucking, Long-Distance, Truckload
N.A.I.C.S.: 484121

Tom Pickett (CFO)
William Wells (Mgr-Distr Center)
Subsidiaries:
Pacific Coast Warehouse Co (1)
5125 Schaefer Ave, Chino, CA 91710
Tel.: (909) 590-1743
Web Site: http://www.pcwc.com
Rev.: $6,616,200
Emp.: 66
General Warehousing & Storage
N.A.I.C.S.: 493110
David Boras (CFO)
Jim Marcoly (Pres)

WEBER ENTERPRISES INC.
840 Conger St, Eugene, OR 97402
Tel.: (541) 687-8445
Web Site: http://weberenterprises.com
Year Founded: 1968
Sales Range: $25-49.9 Million
Emp.: 400
Franchise Owner of Mexican Restaurants
N.A.I.C.S.: 722511
Devawn Peterson (Mgr-HR)

WEBER ENVIRONMENTAL SERVICE, INC.
5935 State Rd 542 W, Winter Haven, FL 33880
Tel.: (863) 551-1820
Web Site: http://www.weberes.com
Year Founded: 1995
Sales Range: $1-9.9 Million
Emp.: 100
Landscaping Services
N.A.I.C.S.: 561730
Donna Weber (VP)
Ken Weber (Owner)

WEBER GRANITE CITY CHEVROLET COMPANY
3499 Progress Pkwy, Granite City, IL 62040
Tel.: (618) 451-7913
Web Site: http://www.webergranitecitychevy.com
Rev.: $14,800,000
Emp.: 48
New Car Dealers
N.A.I.C.S.: 441110
Jeff Kohler (Gen Mgr)

WEBER MANUFACTURING & SUPPLIES, INC.
3430 Technology Dr, Nokomis, FL 34275
Tel.: (941) 488-5185
Web Site: http://www.webermfg.com
Sales Range: $1-9.9 Million
Emp.: 30
Precision Product Mfr
N.A.I.C.S.: 332721
Pam Prost (CEO)
Pat Smith (VP-Production)
Sam Prost (Pres)
Rick Hatfield (Mgr-Quality Assurance)

WEBER MARINE INCORPORATED
10148 Louisiana Hwy 44, Convent, LA 70723
Tel.: (225) 562-3547
Web Site: http://www.webermarine.com
Sales Range: $10-24.9 Million
Emp.: 110
Marine Construction
N.A.I.C.S.: 236210
Douglas Weber (Pres)
Donald Hawthorne (Mgr-Shop)

WEBER PACKAGING SOLUTIONS, INC.
711 W Algonquin Rd, Arlington Heights, IL 60005-4415
Tel.: (847) 364-8500
Web Site: http://www.weberpackaging.com
Year Founded: 1932
Sales Range: $100-124.9 Million
Emp.: 700
Labeling & Coding Equipment & Pressure Sensitive Labels Mfr
N.A.I.C.S.: 333248
Joseph Weber Jr. (Chm)
Subsidiaries:
Weber Etiket ve Etiketleme Sistemleri San ve Tic Ltd. Sti. (1)
Akbaci Ismertezi 208, TR 80670, Istanbul, Turkiye (100%)
Tel.: (90) 2122859400
Sales Range: $10-24.9 Million
Emp.: 20
Mfr of Labeling & Coding Equipment & Pressure Sensitive Labels
N.A.I.C.S.: 339940

Weber Etiketten BV (1)
Steurstraat 19, 1317 NZ, Almere, Netherlands (100%)
Tel.: (31) 365345254
Web Site: http://www.webermarking.nl
Sales Range: $10-24.9 Million
Emp.: 20
Mfr & Sales of Labeling & Coding Equipment & Pressure Sensitive Labels
N.A.I.C.S.: 339940

Weber Labelling & Coding Ltd. (1)
Kilcannon Industrial Est, Old Dublin Rd, Wexford, Enniscorthy, Ireland (100%)
Tel.: (353) 5433778
Web Site: http://www.webermarking.com
Sales Range: $10-24.9 Million
Emp.: 11
Sales of Labeling & Coding Equipment & Pressure Sensitive Labels
N.A.I.C.S.: 339940

Weber Marking Systems (Thailand) Ltd. (1)
39/73 Samutsakom Industrial Estate Moo 2 Rama 2 Road, Bang Ka-Jao Muang, Samut Sakhon, 74000, Thailand
Tel.: (66) 34490639
Web Site: http://www.weber.co.th
Mfr of Labeling & Coding Equipment & Pressure Sensitive Labels
N.A.I.C.S.: 561910

Weber Marking Systems Canada Ltd. (1)
6180 Danville Road, Mississauga, L5T 2H7, ON, Canada (100%)
Tel.: (905) 564-6881
Web Site: http://www.webermarking.ca
Sales Range: $10-24.9 Million
Emp.: 30
Marking Supplies, Labels, Labeling Machines, Hand Stampers, Stencils & Duplicating Ink Mfr
N.A.I.C.S.: 339940
Michael Brown (VP & Gen Mgr)

Weber Marking Systems GmbH (1)
Maarweg 33, 53619, Rheinbreitbach, Germany (100%)
Tel.: (49) 222477080
Web Site: http://www.weber-marking.com
Sales Range: $25-49.9 Million
Emp.: 320
Mfr of Labeling & Coding Equipment & Pressure Sensitive Labels
N.A.I.C.S.: 339940

Weber Marking Systems Ltd. (1)
MacMerry Industrial Estate MacMerry, Tranent, EH33 1HD, E Lothian, United Kingdom (100%)
Tel.: (44) 1827 611111
Mfr of Marking Sytems
N.A.I.C.S.: 339940

Weber Marking Systems NV/SA (1)
Interleuvenlaan 23, PO Box 2, 3001, Heverlee, Belgium (100%)
Tel.: (32) 16387950
Web Site: http://www.webermarking.be
Sales Range: $10-24.9 Million
Emp.: 10

Sales of Labeling & Coding Equipment & Pressure Sensitive Label Mfr
N.A.I.C.S.: 339940
Ulof Ruthe (Mng Dir)
Mireille Peters (Office Mgr)

WEBER PAPER CO.
4300 Chavenelle Rd, Dubuque, IA 52002
Tel.: (563) 588-4611
Web Site: http://www.weberpaper.com
Sales Range: $10-24.9 Million
Emp.: 30
Cups, Disposable Plastic & Paper Mfr
N.A.I.C.S.: 424130
Jim Weber (Pres & CEO)

WEBER SCREWDRIVING SYSTEMS INC.
1401 Front St, Yorktown Heights, NY 10598
Tel.: (914) 962-5775
Web Site: http://www.weberusa.com
Sales Range: $10-24.9 Million
Emp.: 23
Power-Driven Handtools
N.A.I.C.S.: 333991
Tom Rougeux (Dir-Natl Sls-Charlotte)
Harold Johnson (Mgr-Inside Sls)
Tom Ash (Mgr-Product-OEM)

WEBER-KNAPP COMPANY
441 Chandler St, Jamestown, NY 14701-3803
Tel.: (716) 484-9135
Web Site: http://www.weberknapp.com
Emp.: 100
Hinge & Office Furniture Fitting Mfr
N.A.I.C.S.: 332510
Wayne Rishell (CFO)
Rhonda Johnson (Pres)

WEBEYECARE
176 N Pine St, Bristol, PA 19007
Tel.: (888) 536-7480
Web Site: http://www.webeyecare.com
Year Founded: 2009
Sales Range: $1-9.9 Million
Emp.: 10
Online Retailer of Contact Lenses
N.A.I.C.S.: 423460
Peter Batushansky (Pres)

WEBGILITY INC.
201 Mission St Ste 1500, San Francisco, CA 94105
Tel.: (415) 666-2621
Web Site: http://www.webgility.com
Year Founded: 2007
Sales Range: $25-49.9 Million
Emp.: 75
Ecommerce Integration Software
N.A.I.C.S.: 513210
Parag Mamnani (Founder & CEO)
Manoj Chhablani (Dir-Ops)
Ghanshyam Bagora (Sr Mgr-Technical Product)
Brajkishor Shacywar (Sr Mgr-Technical)
Allegra Mitchell (Mgr-Customer Success)
Brenda Le (Sr Mgr-Mktg)
Christina Del Villar (Dir-Mktg)
Rob McGrorty (Dir-Ops & Product-San Francisco)
Gaurav Singh (Mgr-Technical Support)
Khushbu Jagwani (Product Mgr)
Rohit Maheshwari (Product Mgr)
Michael Mansour (VP-Sls)
Kinnar Vora (VP-Engrg)

WEBGILITY INC.

Webgility Inc.—(Continued)
Melanie Kalemba *(Sr VP-Partnerships & Bus Dev)*
Billy Leung *(Sr VP-Product)*

WEBHOUSE, INC.
2365 Milburn Ave Bldg 2, Baldwin, NY 11510
Tel.: (516) 764-6300 NY
Web Site: http://www.webhse.com
Year Founded: 1997
Sales Range: $10-24.9 Million
Emp.: 31
IT Consulting Services & Support
N.A.I.C.S.: 541519
Daniel Kerning *(Pres & CEO)*
Steve Webber *(Bus Mgr-Mktg)*

WEBIMAX
2 Aquarium Loop Dr Ste 140, Camden, NJ 08103
Tel.: (856) 840-8301
Web Site: http://www.webimax.com
Year Founded: 2008
Sales Range: $10-24.9 Million
Emp.: 150
Online Marketing
N.A.I.C.S.: 541613
Kenneth C. Wisnefski *(Founder & CEO)*
Kevin O'Brien *(COO & Principal)*
Sean O'Donnell *(VP-Tech)*

Subsidiaries:

WebiMax (1)
World Trade Center Edificio Sur 2 Planta, 8039, Barcelona, Spain
Tel.: (34) 931816948
Online Marketing
N.A.I.C.S.: 541613

WebiMax (1)
1 Northumberland Ave, Trafalgar Square, London, United Kingdom
Tel.: (44) 2078725470
Web Site: http://www.webimax.com
Online Marketing
N.A.I.C.S.: 541613

WebiMax (1)
Level 1 488 Botany Road Suite 10, Alexandria, 2015, NSW, Australia
Tel.: (61) 291912785
Web Site: http://www.webimax.com.au
Online Marketing
N.A.I.C.S.: 541613
David Touri *(Mng Dir)*

WebiMax (1)
100 King Street West 56th Floor, Toronto, ON, Canada
Tel.: (416) 800-1052
Online Marketing
N.A.I.C.S.: 541613

WEBISTIX, INC.
1180 Lincoln Ave Ste 6, Holbrook, NY 11741
Tel.: (631) 472-1400
Web Site: http://www.webistix.com
Sales Range: $1-9.9 Million
Computer Software
N.A.I.C.S.: 513210
David Salav *(Pres)*
Vinny DiSpigno *(CEO)*

WEBIT SERVICES, INC.
1815 W Diehl Rd Ste 200, Naperville, IL 60563
Tel.: (630) 870-1088
Web Site: http://www.webitservices.com
Year Founded: 1996
Sales Range: $1-9.9 Million
Emp.: 11
Information Technology Services
N.A.I.C.S.: 541512
Eric Rieger *(Founder & Pres)*

WEBJET MARKETING NORTH AMERICA LLC
215 N Howard Ave Ste 202, Tampa, FL 33606
Tel.: (813) 381-5383
Web Site: http://www.webjet.com
Sales Range: $1-9.9 Million
Emp.: 20
Online Travel Services
N.A.I.C.S.: 561599
Mathias Friess *(CEO)*
Jessica Sokolowski *(Head-Acctg)*

WEBMARKETING123
1485 Park Ave Ste 103, Emeryville, CA 94608
Web Site:
http://www.webmarketing123.com
Year Founded: 2004
Sales Range: $1-9.9 Million
Emp.: 31
Advetising Agency
N.A.I.C.S.: 541810
Paul Taylor *(Founder & CEO)*

WEBOLUTIONS, INC.
6160 S Syracuse Way Ste 120, Greenwood Village, CO 80111
Tel.: (303) 300-2640
Web Site:
http://www.webolutions.com
Year Founded: 1994
Sales Range: $1-9.9 Million
Emp.: 13
Website Development & Internet Marketing
N.A.I.C.S.: 541519
John Vachalek *(CEO)*
Kristin Dye *(Mgr-Ops)*

WEBPAGEFX INC.
453 Lincoln St 1st Fl, Harrisburg, PA 17013
Tel.: (717) 609-0360
Web Site: http://www.webpagefx.com
Year Founded: 2006
Sales Range: $1-9.9 Million
Emp.: 26
Advetising Agency
N.A.I.C.S.: 541810
William Craig *(Pres)*
Karie Shearer *(COO & Exec VP)*

WEBRUNNERS, INC.
1000 Town Center Ste 1150, Southfield, MI 48075
Tel.: (248) 358-1002 MI
Web Site: http://www.w3r.com
Year Founded: 1995
Sales Range: $25-49.9 Million
Emp.: 300
Technology Consulting Services
N.A.I.C.S.: 541690
Eric A. Hardy *(Pres & CEO)*
Keith Echols *(Exec VP)*
Patrick Tomina *(CFO)*
JoAnn Mackie *(Sr Dir-Bus Dev)*
Dave Reich *(VP-Delivery & Strategy Dev)*
Stacey Sieber *(Mgr-HR)*
Bashar Hannosh *(VP-New Market Dev)*

WEBSCOPE
99 W Hawthorne Ave Ste 420, Valley Stream, NY 11580
Tel.: (516) 561-3935 NY
Web Site: http://www.webscope.com
Year Founded: 1992
Sales Range: $10-24.9 Million
Emp.: 6
Advertising Agencies
N.A.I.C.S.: 541810
David Staschover *(Pres)*
Ed Rochelle *(Sls Mgr)*

WEBSITE MAGAZINE INCORPORATED
999 E Touhy Ave, Des Plaines, IL 60018
Tel.: (773) 628-2779
Web Site:
http://www.websitemagazine.com
Year Founded: 2007
Sales Range: $10-24.9 Million
Emp.: 10
Magazine & Website Publisher
N.A.I.C.S.: 513120
Peter Prestipino *(Editor-in-Chief)*
Allison Howden *(Assoc Editor)*
Shannon Rickson *(Designer-Graphic)*
Troy Pickett *(Mgr-Bus Dev & Sls)*
Maureen Alley *(Mng Editor)*

WEBSITE PIPELINE, INC.
555 N Pleasantburg Dr Ste 214, Greenville, SC 29607
Tel.: (864) 272-4000
Web Site:
http://www.websitepipeline.com
Sales Range: $1-9.9 Million
Emp.: 20
Computer Graphics Services
N.A.I.C.S.: 541512
Brian Seidel *(Pres & CEO)*
Eric Ward *(Co-Founder & CTO)*
Gary Lamb *(Project Mgr)*
Chris Bradley *(Dir-Dev)*

WEBSITEBIZ, INC.
1713 Cleveland Ave, Charlotte, NC 28203
Tel.: (704) 338-1794
Web Site: http://www.websitebiz.com
Year Founded: 1997
Rev.: $4,000,000
Emp.: 15
Advertising & Marketing Services
N.A.I.C.S.: 541810
Eric Dudley *(Founder & CEO)*
Kyle Bumgardner *(VP)*
Michele Dudley *(Controller)*
Dave McDaniel *(Exec VP)*
Chad Lasure *(Acct Dir)*
Paul Yoder *(Sr VP)*

WEBSTARTS
235 W Brandon Blvd Ste 252, Brandon, FL 33511
Tel.: (813) 600-6585
Web Site: http://www.webstarts.com
Sales Range: $10-24.9 Million
Website Hosting Services
N.A.I.C.S.: 541519
Adam Barger *(Founder)*

WEBSTER AT RYE
795 Washington Rd, Rye, NH 03870
Tel.: (603) 964-8144 NH
Web Site:
http://www.websteratrye.com
Year Founded: 1977
Sales Range: $1-9.9 Million
Emp.: 145
Nursing Care Services
N.A.I.C.S.: 623110
Melissa Bird *(Dir-Social Svcs)*
Moe Desrochers *(Dir-Environmental Svcs)*
Todd Fernald *(Dir-HR)*
Thomas W. Argue *(Co-CEO)*
Rebecca Helm *(Chm)*
Mark Sykas *(Vice Chm)*
Randolph Holt *(Treas)*
David Timmerman *(Sec)*
Angel Blais *(Office Mgr)*
Jennifer Peloquin *(Co-CEO)*

WEBSTER CHRYSLER JEEP, INC.
2111 Empire Blvd, Webster, NY 14580

Tel.: (585) 671-1010
Year Founded: 1991
Sales Range: $25-49.9 Million
Emp.: 43
Car Whslr
N.A.I.C.S.: 441110
Randolph Henderson Jr. *(Pres)*

WEBSTER EQUITY PARTNERS, LLC
1000 Winter St Ctr Entrance, Waltham, MA 02451
Tel.: (781) 419-1515 DE
Web Site:
http://www.webstercapital.com
Year Founded: 2003
Privater Equity Firm
N.A.I.C.S.: 523999
Donald Steiner *(Founding Partner)*
David Malm *(Mng Partner)*
Mark Greene *(CFO & VP)*
Mehran Ahmed *(Mng Dir)*
John Garbarino *(Partner)*
Daniel Schultz *(VP-Bus Dev)*
Doug Williams *(Partner & COO)*

Subsidiaries:

Bay Area Addiction Research & Treatment, Inc. (1)
1145 Market St, San Francisco, CA 94103
Tel.: (415) 552-7914
Web Site: http://www.baartprograms.com
Sales Range: $1-9.9 Million
Drug Treatment & Rehabilitation Services
N.A.I.C.S.: 621420
Evan Kletter *(CFO)*

BayMark Health Services, Inc. (1)
1720 Lakepointe Dr Ste 117, Lewisville, TX 75057
Tel.: (214) 379-3300
Web Site: http://www.baymark.com
Health Care Srvices
N.A.I.C.S.: 621999
David K. White *(CEO)*
Jason Kletter *(Pres)*
Frank Baumann *(Exec VP & COO)*
Jason Carmichael *(Chief Compliance Officer & Chief Clinical Officer)*
Peter R. Coleman *(Dir-Natl Medical)*
Gavin Scruggs *(Sr VP-Dev)*
Sheldon Glass *(Dir-Natl Medical)*
Philip Isherwood *(Dir-Natl Medical)*
Robin A. Johnson *(Sr VP-Mktg & Bus Dev)*
Michelle Kletter *(VP-Primary Care & Behavioral Health)*

Subsidiary (Domestic):

AppleGate Recovery, LLC (2)
1605 Benton Rd Ste D, Bossier City, LA 71111
Tel.: (888) 488-5337
Web Site: https://applegaterecovery.com
Health Care Srvices
N.A.I.C.S.: 621999

Subsidiary (Domestic):

Fritz Clinic, LLC (3)
120 Oxmoor Blvd Ste 170, Birmingham, AL 35209-5952
Tel.: (205) 877-8585
Web Site: http://www.fritzclinic.com
Freestanding Ambulatory Surgical & Emergency Centers
N.A.I.C.S.: 621493
Victoria Fritz *(Office Mgr)*

Subsidiary (Domestic):

Choices of Louisiana, Inc. (2)
2116 N Bolton Ave, Alexandria, LA 71303
Tel.: (985) 565-3777
Web Site:
http://www.choicesoflouisiana.com
Other Social Advocacy Organizations
N.A.I.C.S.: 813319

San Antonio Recovery Services (2)
4710 Callaghan Rd, San Antonio, TX 78228-2654
Tel.: (210) 279-1701
Web Site:
http://www.sanantoniorecovery.com
Repossession Services

COMPANIES

N.A.I.C.S.: 561491
Gary Allen (Pres)

SpecialCare Hospital Management Corporation (2)
1551 Wall St Ste 210 St, Saint Charles, MO 63303
Tel.: (314) 770-2212
Web Site: http://www.specialcarecorp.com
Health Care Srvices
N.A.I.C.S.: 621498
Anthony J. Torrente (Pres & CEO)
Albert Satcher (Chief Compliance Officer)
Robin Denicola (VP-Ops)

Belmar Pharmacy (1)
12860 W Cedar Dr Ste 210, Lakewood, CO 80228-1971
Tel.: (202) 777-3502
Web Site: http://www.belmarpharmacy.com
Pharmacies & Drug Stores
N.A.I.C.S.: 456110
Charles Hakala (Owner)

Bristol Hospice, LLC (1)
206 N 2100 W Ste 202, Salt Lake City, UT 84116
Tel.: (916) 782-5511
Web Site: http://www.bristolhospice.com
Nursing Care Facilities
N.A.I.C.S.: 623110
Erin Starr (Exec Dir)
Hyrum Kirton (CEO)

Subsidiary (Domestic):

Companion Management Group, LLC (2)
3200 Park Pl Ave, Costa Mesa, CA 92626
Tel.: (626) 247-2277
Web Site: http://www.companionhealthgroup.com
Nursing Care Facilities
N.A.I.C.S.: 623110
Mike Uranga (CEO)

Cardiovascular Associates of America, LLC (1)
610 Sycamore St, Ste 220, Celebration, FL 34747
Tel.: (833) 728-2872
Web Site: https://cvausa.com
Hospitals & Health Care
N.A.I.C.S.: 621111

Subsidiary (Domestic):

Daytona Heart Group Holdings, P.A. (2)
630 W Plymouth Ave, Deland, FL 32720-3260
Tel.: (386) 734-3654
Web Site: http://www.daytonaheart.com
Offices of Physicians (except Mental Health Specialists)
N.A.I.C.S.: 621111
Kim Brennan (Office Mgr)

Heart & Vascular Center of Arizona, PLLC (2)
1331 N 7th St Ste 375, Phoenix, AZ 85006
Tel.: (602) 307-0070
Web Site: http://www.heartcenteraz.com
Sales Range: $1-9.9 Million
Emp.: 30
Ambulatory Health Care Services
N.A.I.C.S.: 621999
Nathan Laufer (Founder & Dir-Medical)

Cirrus Medical Staffing, Inc. (1)
309 E Morehead St Ste 200, Charlotte, NC 28202
Tel.: (704) 887-3900
Web Site: http://www.cirrusmedicalstaffing.com
Medical Staffing Services
N.A.I.C.S.: 561311
Andrea Zveibil (Pres & COO)
Jane Perez (CFO)
Melissa Nicholson (Mgr-Client Svcs)
Joseph Carlino (Dir-Staffing Ops)

Dominion Fertility (1)
4040 N Fairfax Dr Ste 600, Arlington, VA 22203
Tel.: (703) 920-3890
Web Site: http://www.dominionfertility.com
Treatment for Fertility Related Concerns
N.A.I.C.S.: 621999
Jen Burton (Office Mgr)

Dover Saddlery, Inc. (1)
525 Great Rd, Littleton, MA 01460
Tel.: (978) 952-8062
Web Site: http://www.doversaddlery.com
Equestrian Products Retailer
N.A.I.C.S.: 459110
Brad Wolansky (CEO)

FULLBEAUTY Brands, Inc. (1)
1 New York Plz, New York, NY 10004
Tel.: (212) 613-9500
Web Site: http://www.fbbrands.com
Men & Women Plus-sized Clothing Mfr
N.A.I.C.S.: 458110
Flo Kamil Dessen (Sr VP & Gen Mgr-Fullbeauty.com)
David Reinke (Sr VP & Gen Mgr)
Emilie Arel (CEO)

Subsidiary (Domestic):

FULLBEAUTY Brands, L.P. (2)
2300 Southeastern Ave, Indianapolis, IN 46201
Tel.: (317) 266-3300
Web Site: http://www.fbbrands.com
Women's & Men's Special-Size Apparel Retailer
N.A.I.C.S.: 458110

OSP Group Management Services, L.P. (2)
2300 Southeastern Ave, Indianapolis, IN 46201
Tel.: (317) 266-3300
Mail Ordering Shopping Services
N.A.I.C.S.: 523940

Fullbeauty.com (1)
1 New York Plz, New York, NY 10004
Web Site: http://www.fullbeauty.com
Online Apparel Retailer
N.A.I.C.S.: 458110

MJC Acquisition, LLC (1)
4031 Merchant Rd, Fort Wayne, IN 46818
Tel.: (260) 424-3511
Web Site: http://www.matildajaneclothing.com
Women's, Children's & Infants' Clothing & Accessories Retailer
N.A.I.C.S.: 424350
Allison Flatjord (CMO & Chief Mdsg Officer)

Orbis Clinical, LLC (1)
100 Unicorn Park Dr 2nd Fl, Woburn, MA 01801
Tel.: (781) 569-0607
Web Site: http://www.orbisclinical.com
Emp.: 15
Drug Safety Consulting Services
N.A.I.C.S.: 813319
Jessica Leveille (Mgr-Delivery Svcs)

Subsidiary (Domestic):

Talentmine LLC (2)
4208 6 Forks Rd Ste 1000, Raleigh, NC 27609-5738
Tel.: (919) 838-1700
Web Site: http://www.talentmine.net
Human Resource Consulting Services
N.A.I.C.S.: 541612

PharmaLogic Holdings Corp. (1)
1 S Ocean Blvd Ste #206, Boca Raton, FL 33432
Tel.: (561) 416-0085
Web Site: http://www.pharmalogic.info
Pharmaceutical Preparation Mfr
N.A.I.C.S.: 424210
Glen Palmer (VP-Ops)
Steven Chilinski (Pres & CEO)
Frank Edwards (CFO)
Richard Van Sant (Dir-Regulatory Affairs & Quality Assurance)
Don Widener (Mgr-Sls-Central US & WV)
Christine Brown (Mgr-Pharmacy-Syracuse)
Tim Summers (Mgr-Pharmacy-Albany)
Laurie Stallings (Mgr-Pharmacy-Pennsylvania)
Steve Green (Mgr-Pharmacy-West Virginia)
Rich Sucese (Mgr-Pharmacy-Vermont)
Kevin Hart (Mgr-Pharmacy-Maine)
Dana Suttle (Mgr-Pharmacy-Michigan)
James Cordonier (Mgr-Pharmacy-Wyoming)
Terry Scheidel (Mgr-Pharmacy-Montana)

Subsidiary (Domestic):

Mid-America Isotopes, Inc. (2)
706 E Liberty Ln, Ashland, MO 65010
Tel.: (573) 657-1776
Web Site: http://www.mid-americaisotopes.com
Sales Range: $1-9.9 Million
Emp.: 20
Radiopharmacy with Nuclear Medicine, Technologist Services, Pharamceuticals, Equipment & Drug Analysis for Health Related Businesses
N.A.I.C.S.: 423450
William C. McHugh (Pres & Mgr-Pharmacy)
Brian McVey (Dir-Technologist Svcs)
Scott C. Brower (Treas & Sec)
B. J. Tuck (Office Mgr)
W. Brent McHugh (VP)
Jon Woodward (VP)

PharmaLogics Recruiting LLC (1)
2 Heritage Dr Ste 401, Quincy, MA 02171
Tel.: (781) 848-5500
Web Site: http://www.pharmalogicsrecruiting.com
Pharmaceutical Staffing Services
N.A.I.C.S.: 561311
Megan Driscoll (Founder & CEO)
Megan Lanham (Partner & Head-Global Bus Dev)
Adam Kaner (Partner & Head-Recruitment)

WEBSTER FIVE CENTS SAVINGS BANK
10 A St, Auburn, MA 01501-2102
Tel.: (508) 943-9401
Web Site: http://www.web5.com
Sales Range: $10-24.9 Million
Emp.: 166
Banking Services
N.A.I.C.S.: 522180
Joseph D. Radovanic (Sr VP-Retail Admin)
Donald F. Doyle (Exec VP)
Theodore Parkman (Sr VP)
Terry Flynn (Sr VP & Dir-HR)
Russ Dye (Sr VP-Bus Banking & Officer-Lending)
Pawel Powaza (Mgr-Shrewsbury)
Loreta Sulejman (Mgr-Worcester)
Alex Cruz (Officer-Bus Lending)
Ann Kane (VP-Comml Lending)
Brian Westerlind (CFO, Treas & Sr VP)
Jane Cullen (VP-Bus Svcs)
Louis Corapi (VP-Bus Banking)
Richard T. Leahy (Pres & CEO)
Keith Kirkland (VP-Bus Lending)
Robert Kelley Jr. (VP & Officer-Bus Loan)

WEBSTER HOUSE
135 Webster St, Manchester, NH 03104
Tel.: (603) 622-8013 NH
Web Site: http://www.websterhousenh.org
Year Founded: 1884
Rev.: $1,421,065
Assets: $6,422,314
Liabilities: $24,835
Net Worth: $6,397,479
Earnings: $335,387
Emp.: 32
Fiscal Year-end: 12/31/14
Housing & Support Services
N.A.I.C.S.: 623110
Debbie Landwehr (Pres)
Ed Ithier (Pres)
Ed Ithier (Pres)
Sherry Nannis (VP)
Michelle O'Malley (CEO)
Blair Stairs (Exec Dir-Ops)
Ashley Campbell (Sec)
Lesley Patti (Treas)

WEBSTER PACKAGING CORP.
715 S Riverside Ave, Loveland, OH 45140
Tel.: (513) 683-5666
Web Site: http://www.akers-pkg.com
Sales Range: $25-49.9 Million

WEBWORKS ALLIANCE

Emp.: 14
Boxes, Solid Fiber: Made From Purchased Materials
N.A.I.C.S.: 322211
Dennis Phillips (Pres)
Fred Peticone (Controller)

WEBSTER TRUCKING CORPORATION
20 A St, Burlington, MA 01803
Tel.: (781) 229-6380
Web Site: http://www.webstercompany.com
Rev.: $15,000,000
Emp.: 18
Private Business Trucking
N.A.I.C.S.: 484121
Thomas A. Di Silva (Pres)
James Di Silva (CEO)

WEBTIVITY DESIGN SOLUTIONS
4654 E State Rd 64, Bradenton, FL 34208
Tel.: (941) 753-7574 FL
Web Site: http://www.webtivitydesigns.com
Year Founded: 1999
Sales Range: $1-9.9 Million
Emp.: 5
Internet Marketing Services
N.A.I.C.S.: 541613
Terry Thompson (Pres & CEO)

WEBTRENDS INC.
111 SW 5th Ave Ste 3200, Portland, OR 97204
Tel.: (503) 294-7025
Web Site: http://www.webtrends.com
Sales Range: $25-49.9 Million
Emp.: 400
Web Analytics Software
N.A.I.C.S.: 513210
Mike Laber (CEO)
Darbi Michel (Dir-Mktg & Legal Brand Mktg)
Frans Poldervaart (Mgr-Web Analytics)
Nick Sharp (VP & Gen Mgr-EMEA & APAC)
Jeff Porter (VP-Client Svcs)
Jim Goings (VP-Tech & Security Ops)
Jonathan Creasy (VP & Gen Mgr-EMEA)

Subsidiaries:

Webtrends Australasia (1)
Level 27 Rialto South Tower 525 Collins Street, Melbourne, 3000, VIC, Australia
Tel.: (61) 3 9935 2939
Web Site: http://www.webtrends.com
Emp.: 5
Web Analytics Software
N.A.I.C.S.: 513210

Webtrends EMEA (1)
Mallard Court Market Square, Staines-upon-Thames, TW18 4RH, Middlesex, United Kingdom
Tel.: (44) 1784 415 700
Web Analytics Software
N.A.I.C.S.: 513210
Nick Sharp (VP & Gen Mgr)

Webtrends Nordic (1)
Axel Johanssons gata 4-6, 754 51, Uppsala, Sweden
Tel.: (46) 18 16 90 90
Web Analytics Software
N.A.I.C.S.: 513210

WEBWORKS ALLIANCE
95 Caterson Ter, Hartsdale, NY 10530
Tel.: (914) 390-0060
Web Site: http://www.webworksalliance.net
Year Founded: 2003
Sales Range: $50-74.9 Million

WEBWORKS ALLIANCE

Webworks Alliance—(Continued)
Emp.: 17
Advertising Agencies
N.A.I.C.S.: 541810
Jon Parets (Partner)

WEBYES LLC
400 Continental Blvd # 11, El Segundo, CA 90245
Tel.: (310) 426-2871
Year Founded: 2006
Sales Range: $10-24.9 Million
Emp.: 10
Management Services
N.A.I.C.S.: 541611
George Meldrum (Acct Mgr)

WECHCO, INC.
1000 Herrontown Rd N, Princeton, NJ 08540
Tel.: (609) 921-0501   NY
Year Founded: 1982
Sales Range: $25-49.9 Million
Emp.: 150
Holding Company; Specialty Chemicals Mfr
N.A.I.C.S.: 551112
Gerry Enroth (Dir-Sls-Mktg)

Subsidiaries:

Penetone Corporation   (1)
700 Gotham Pkwy #2, Carlstadt, NJ 07072
Tel.: (201) 567-3000
Mfr & Sales of Industrial Chemicals
N.A.I.C.S.: 325612
Joyce Seccia (Controller)

Subsidiary (Non-US):

West Penetone, Inc.   (2)
10900 Rue Secant, Anjou, H1J 1S5, QC, Canada
Tel.: (514) 355-4660
Emp.: 30
Specialty Chemicals, Degreasers, Agricultural Sanitizers, Disinfectants, Specialty Oils & Greases Mfr
N.A.I.C.S.: 325612
Craig Phares (Chm & Pres)

Petron Corporation
16800 Glendale Dr, New Berlin, WI 53151   (1)
Tel.: (262) 797-4680
Web Site: http://www.petroncorp.com
Specialty Lubricants & Grease Mfr
N.A.I.C.S.: 324191
Roger Wichner (Controller)
Todd Allison (Sls Mgr-North America-Eastern Div)
Kiran Batchu (Mgr-Prod)
Jim Bittner (Dir-Ops)
Francisco Cerrillo (Sls Mgr-Latin America)
Matt McClellan (Engr-Sls & Svc)
John McHale (Pres)
Armando Munoz (Engr-Sls & Svc)
Elisa Pieroni (VP-Quality & Tech)
Dinesh Ramachandran (Mgr-Sls & Svc)
Chandra Sekar (Sls Mgr-India, Middle East & Asia)
David Smith (Supvr-Production)
Daniel Song (Mgr-China)
Chuck Strait (Supvr-Svc & Training)

WECHTER FELDMAN WEALTH MANAGEMENT, INC.
1719 Rte 10 E Ste 224, Parsippany, NJ 07054-4507
Tel.: (973) 605-1448
Web Site:
   http://www.wechterfeldman.com
Year Founded: 1984
Sales Range: $1-9.9 Million
Emp.: 11
Investment Management Service
N.A.I.C.S.: 523999
David M. Feldman (Pres & Sr Mgr-Wealth)
Melissa Weisz (VP)
Michael L. Green (Mgr-Wealth)

WECKWORTH ELECTRIC

COMPANY, INC.
389 Governor Dr Ste 104, El Dorado Hills, CA 95762
Tel.: (916) 939-6636
Sales Range: $25-49.9 Million
Emp.: 65
Electrical Wiring Services
N.A.I.C.S.: 238210
Jason Weckworth (Owner)
Kristen Weckworth (Owner)

WECO TRADING INC.
21 N Skokie Hwy Ste 101, Lake Bluff, IL 60044-1777
Tel.: (847) 615-1020   DE
Rev.: $12,900,000
Emp.: 5
Ferrous Metal Scrap & Waste
N.A.I.C.S.: 423930
W.T. Roth (CEO)

WEDBUSH CAPITAL PARTNERS
1000 Wilshire Blvd, Los Angeles, CA 90030-0014
Tel.: (213) 688-8000   CA
Web Site: http://www.wedbush.com
Year Founded: 1955
Emp.: 100
Securities Brokerage Services
N.A.I.C.S.: 523150
Edward W. Wedbush (Founder & CEO)
Gary L. Wedbush (Head-Capital Markets & Exec VP)
Benjamin J. Davey (Mng Dir & Head-Equity Capital Markets)
Christopher Hagar (Mng Dir & Dir-Consumer Investment Banking)
Richard M. Jablonski (Exec VP & Head-Treasury)
Sheri Kaiserman (Mng Dir & Head-Advanced Securities Div)
Mark G. Madden (Sr VP-Strategy & Bus Dev)
Robert E. Paset (Sr VP-Correspondent Svcs Div)
James R. Richards (Exec VP & Head-Wealth Mgmt)
Robert W. Woods (Sr VP & Office Mgr)

Subsidiaries:

Lime Brokerage, LLC   (1)
377 Broadway Fl 11, New York, NY 10013
Tel.: (212) 219-6000
Sales Range: $25-49.9 Million
Emp.: 35
Investment Services
N.A.I.C.S.: 523150
Antonio Manuel Abad (CTO)
Farid Naib (CEO)

Wedbush Bank   (1)
1000 Wilshire Blvd Ste 1150, Los Angeles, CA 90017
Tel.: (866) 933-2874
Web Site: http://www.wedbushbank.com
Commercial Banking Services
N.A.I.C.S.: 522110

Wedbush Capital Partners, L.P.   (1)
1000 Wilshire Blvd Ste 830, Los Angeles, CA 90017
Tel.: (213) 688-8018
Web Site: http://www.wedbushcapital.com
Investment Management Service
N.A.I.C.S.: 523940
Daniel Simon (CFO & Chief Compliance Officer)
Eric Wedbush (Mng Dir)
Geoff Bland (Mng Dir)
Kevin Tom (VP)
Peter Shoemaker (Mng Dir)

Subsidiary (Domestic):

Criterion Brock, Inc.   (2)
4500 SE Criterion Ct, Milwaukie, OR 97222
Tel.: (503) 654-0206
Web Site: http://www.criterionbrock.com

Flooring Contractors
N.A.I.C.S.: 238330
Grant Ebright (COO)
Kerri Silver (Pres)
Cathi Brock (CEO)
Jim Voss (CFO)

Reyn Spooner, Inc.   (2)
534 Finney Ct, Gardena, CA 90248
Web Site: http://www.reynspooner.com
Sales Range: $1-9.9 Million
Emp.: 100
Mens Clothing Retailer Distr
N.A.I.C.S.: 458110
Lei Rowan (Mgr-Website)

Wedbush Leasing, Inc.   (1)
1000 Wilshire Blvd 9th Fl, Los Angeles, CA 90017-2457
Tel.: (213) 688-8000
Web Site: http://www.wedbushinc.com
Sales Range: $25-49.9 Million
Emp.: 300
Provider of Equipment Rental & Leasing Services
N.A.I.C.S.: 532490

Wedbush Securities, Inc.   (1)
1000 Wilshire Blvd, Los Angeles, CA 90017
Tel.: (213) 688-8000
Web Site: http://www.wedbush.com
Securities Brokerage Services
N.A.I.C.S.: 523150
Gary L. Wedbush (Co-Pres)
Richard H. Osgood III (Founder)
Craig A. Pirtle (Sr VP & Head-Bus Dev & Expansion Markets)
Jim Richards (Dir-Ops-Wealth Mgmt)
Moshe Katri (Mng Dir)
Christopher Svezia (Sr VP)
Richard M. Jablonski (Co-Pres)
Robert Fitzsimmons (Exec VP-Fixed Income, Futures, Prime Brokerage & Stock Loan)
Danny Nadalalicea (CIO)
Daniel Ives (Mng Dir-Equity Res-Tech Grp-New York)
Jesse Bigelow (Dir-Res)
Christopher Mone (Exec VP & Head-Wealth Mgmt)
Andrea Epinger (Sr VP & Head-Change Mgmt & Process Improvement)
Andrew Druch (Chief Admin Officer, Gen Counsel & Exec VP)
Michael McMaster (Chief Compliance Officer & Sr VP)
David C. Smith (Mng Dir-Investments)
Andrew Hutcheson (Branch Mgr)
Thomas J. Schatzman (Mng Dir & Head-Institutional Consulting)
Jay C. McCanless III (Sr VP)

WEDCO INC.
450 Tolano St, Reno, NV 89512
Tel.: (775) 329-1131
Web Site: http://www.wedcoinc.com
Rev.: $10,411,329
Emp.: 27
Power Transmission Equipment, Electric
N.A.I.C.S.: 423610
Richard Elmore (CEO)
Pat McNerney (Mgr-Sls)
Rich Stoltz (VP)

WEDDLE BROS. CONSTRUCTION CO., INC.
1201 W 3rd St, Bloomington, IN 47402-5018
Tel.: (812) 339-9500   IN
Web Site:
   http://www.weddlebros.com
Year Founded: 1947
Sales Range: $10-24.9 Million
Emp.: 180
Provider of Nonresidential Construction Services
N.A.I.C.S.: 236220
Lee E. Carmichael (Pres & CEO)
Steven T. Hunt (CFO)
Mike Hemmerling (VP-Weddle Bros. Building Group, LLC)
Kelly Abel (VP-Pre-Construction Svcs-Weddle Bros. Building Group, LLC)

U.S. PRIVATE

Brad Boring (Project Mgr)
Steve Mishler (Sr Project Mgr)
Scott Lentz (Project Mgr)
Blake Rowe (Project Mgr)

WEDEKIND MOTORS, INC.
1595 State St, Schenectady, NY 12304
Tel.: (518) 374-4167
Web Site:
   http://www.wedekindcars.com
Year Founded: 1921
Sales Range: $10-24.9 Million
Emp.: 35
Auto Operator & Services
N.A.I.C.S.: 441110
Micheal Thompson (Co-Owner & VP)
David Elmendorf (Co-Owner & Pres)
Arthur Marotta (Mgr-Sls)
Kevin Berger (Mgr-Fin)

WEDGCOR INC.
6800 E Hampden Ave, Denver, CO 80224
Tel.: (303) 759-3200
Web Site: http://www.wedgcor.com
Year Founded: 1965
Sales Range: $10-24.9 Million
Emp.: 275
Mfr of Steel Building Systems & Prefabricated Metal
N.A.I.C.S.: 332311
Amy Wirth (Pres)

WEDGE COMMUNITY CO-OP INC.
2105 Lyndale Ave S, Minneapolis, MN 55405
Tel.: (612) 871-3993
Web Site: http://www.wedge.coop
Rev.: $20,601,852
Emp.: 250
Grocery Stores, Independent
N.A.I.C.S.: 445110
Kristi Pluimer (Project Mgr)

WEDGE GROUP INC.
1415 Louisiana St Ste 3000, Houston, TX 77002-7360
Tel.: (713) 739-6500   TX
Web Site:
   http://www.wedgegroup.com
Year Founded: 1970
Investment Services
N.A.I.C.S.: 237120
Fares I. Fares (Founder)

WEE BURN COUNTRY CLUB
410 Hollow Tree Ridge Rd, Darien, CT 06820
Tel.: (203) 655-1477   CT
Web Site: http://www.weeburn.org
Year Founded: 1945
Sales Range: $10-24.9 Million
Emp.: 278
Country Club
N.A.I.C.S.: 713910
Warren S. Burdock (Gen Mgr & Asst Sec)
Sharon McGrath (Controller)
Timothy Szemplinski (Mgr-Clubhouse)
Frank Ross (Mgr-Ops)

WEED INVESTMENT GROUP, INC.
10 S 1st St, Cheyenne Wells, CO 80810
Tel.: (719) 767-5652
Web Site:
   http://www.yourfriendlybank.com
Year Founded: 1944
Bank Holding Company
N.A.I.C.S.: 551111
Brett Legg (Pres-Eastern Colorado Bank)

COMPANIES

Subsidiaries:

The Eastern Colorado Bank (1)
10 S 1st St, Cheyenne Wells, CO 80810
Tel.: (719) 767-5652
Web Site: http://www.yourfriendlybank.com
Retail & Commercial Banking
N.A.I.C.S.: 522110
Brett Legg (Pres)
Sheila Brase (Asst VP)

WEEDHIRE INTERNATIONAL, INC.

2075 91st St Unit 2, North Bergen, NJ 07047
Tel.: (877) 766-3050   DE
Web Site: http://www.anythingit.com
Year Founded: 1992
Sales Range: $1-9.9 Million
Emp.: 18
Computer Products Recycling Services
N.A.I.C.S.: 423930
David Bernstein (Co-Founder, Pres & CEO)
Vlad Stelmak (Co-Founder & COO)
Paul Brundage (Sr VP-Sls)

WEEKENDS ONLY

349 Marshall Ave 3rd Fl, Saint Louis, MO 63119-1862
Tel.: (314) 447-1500
Web Site:
  http://www.weekendsonly.com
Sales Range: $25-49.9 Million
Emp.: 350
Furniture Whslr
N.A.I.C.S.: 449110
Laura Hannick (Principal)
Michelle Reckelhoff (VP-HR)
Tom E. Phillips Jr. (Pres)

WEEKES FOREST PRODUCTS INC.

2600 Como Ave, Saint Paul, MN 55108-1217
Tel.: (651) 644-9807   MN
Web Site:
  http://www.weekesforest.com
Year Founded: 1978
Sales Range: $10-24.9 Million
Emp.: 70
Provider of Lumber Plywood & Millwork
N.A.I.C.S.: 423310
Bob Fabian (Gen Mgr)
Bob Hanson (Mgr-Trng & Mktg)
Dave Bolgren (Mgr-Saint Paul)
Larry Hansen (Mgr-MILWAUKEE Div)
Gary Schulz (VP-Fin)
Tom LeVere (Pres)
Thomas Le Vere (Co-Pres)

WEEKI WACHEE SPRINGS STATE PARK

6131 Commercial Way, Spring Hill, FL 34606-1121
Tel.: (352) 592-5656   FL
Web Site:
  http://www.weekiwachee.com
Year Founded: 1946
Natural Spring & Theme Park
N.A.I.C.S.: 712190
John Athanason (Mgr-PR)

WEEKS MEDICAL CENTER

173 Middle St, Lancaster, NH 03584
Tel.: (603) 788-4911   NH
Web Site:
  http://www.weeksmedical.org
Year Founded: 1948
Sales Range: $25-49.9 Million
Emp.: 427
Health Care Srvices
N.A.I.C.S.: 622110
Celeste Pitts (CFO)

WEEKS ROBINSON PROPERTIES

3350 Riverwood Pkwy Ste 700, Atlanta, GA 30339
Tel.: (404) 815-2000
Web Site:
  http://www.weeksrobinson.com
Year Founded: 2008
Sales Range: $25-49.9 Million
Emp.: 15
Commercial Real Estate Development, Investment & Management
N.A.I.C.S.: 237210
Ray Weeks (Chm & Partner)
Forrest Robinson (CEO & Partner)
Kit Baker (Partner)

WEGMANS FOOD MARKETS, INC.

1500 Brooks Ave, Rochester, NY 14603-0844
Tel.: (585) 328-2550   NY
Web Site: https://www.wegmans.com
Year Founded: 1916
Sales Range: $1-4.9 Billion
Emp.: 53,000
Supermarkets & Other Grocery Retailers (except Convenience Retailers)
N.A.I.C.S.: 445110
Dave Corsi (VP-Produce & Floral)
Nicole Wegman (Pres-Brand)
Becky Sonricker (Mgr-Store)
Danny R. Wegman (Chm)

WEGO CHEMICAL & MINERAL CORPORATION

239 Great Neck Rd, Great Neck, NY 11021-3301
Tel.: (516) 487-3510   NY
Web Site: http://www.wegochem.com
Year Founded: 1982
Sales Range: $200-249.9 Million
Emp.: 38
Mfr & Distribution of Chemicals & Allied Products
N.A.I.C.S.: 424690
Bert Eshaghpour (Pres)
Vincent Gamboli (Gen Mgr)
Cuthbert Frederick (Mgr)
Barry Okun (CFO)

WEHCO MEDIA, INC.

115 E Capitol Ave, Little Rock, AR 72201-3819
Tel.: (501) 378-3400   AR
Web Site: http://www.wehco.com
Year Founded: 1973
Sales Range: $75-99.9 Million
Emp.: 100
Holding Company; Operator of Newspapers, Radio, TV & Cable Systems
N.A.I.C.S.: 513110
Nat Lea (Pres & CEO)
Janet Wilson (Supvr-PR & HR & AP)
Ninette Morse (Mgr-Ops)
Susan Linker (Mgr-Tele Mktg & Sls)
Terri Leifeste (Pres-Palmer Newspaper)
Jay Horton (Pres-Digital)

Subsidiaries:

California Democrat (1)
319 S High St, California, MO 65018
Tel.: (573) 796-2135
Web Site:
  http://www.californiademocrat.com
Emp.: 10
Newspaper Publishers
N.A.I.C.S.: 513110
Denise McMillen (Dir-Adv)

Camden News Publishing Company (1)
121 E Capitol Ave, Little Rock, AR 72201-3819
Tel.: (501) 378-3400
Web Site: http://www.camdenarknews.com
Sales Range: $25-49.9 Million
Newspapers
N.A.I.C.S.: 513110
Walter E. Hussman Jr. (Pres & CEO)
Lynn Hamilton (VP-Product)
Charles Van Deventer (CFO)
Scott Stein (Dir-Adv)

Subsidiary (Domestic):

Arkansas Democrat-Gazette, Inc. (2)
121 E Capital Ave, Little Rock, AR 72201
Tel.: (501) 378-3400
Web Site: http://www.arkansasonline.com
Emp.: 200
Newspaper Publishing Services
N.A.I.C.S.: 516210
Lynn Hamilton (Pres & Gen Mgr)
Larry Graham (VP-Circulation)
Scott Stine (VP-Adv & Mktg)

Banner News Publishing Co. Inc. (2)
134 S Washington St, Magnolia, AR 71753
Tel.: (870) 234-5130
Web Site:
  http://www.magnoliabannernews.com
Sales Range: $25-49.9 Million
Emp.: 10
Publishing Newspapers
N.A.I.C.S.: 513110
Walter E. Hussman Jr. (Pres)
Sue Silliam (Gen Mgr)

Cam-Tel Co. Inc. (2)
113 Madison Ave, Camden, AR 71701
Tel.: (870) 836-8111
Web Site: http://www.camdencabletv.com
Rev.: $1,200,000
Emp.: 13
Internet Cable & Digital Service
N.A.I.C.S.: 516210

Chattanooga Publishing Co. Inc. (2)
400 E 11th St, Chattanooga, TN 37403-4203
Tel.: (423) 756-6900
Web Site: http://www.timesfreepress.com
Newspapers
N.A.I.C.S.: 513110
Russell Lively (Controller)

Subsidiary (Domestic):

Chattanooga Times Free Press Company (3)
400 E 11th St, Chattanooga, TN 37403-4203
Tel.: (423) 756-6900
Web Site: http://www.timesfreepress.com
Sales Range: $50-74.9 Million
Newspapers
N.A.I.C.S.: 513110
Stephen Hargis (Editor-Sports)

Subsidiary (Domestic):

East Arkansas Video Inc. (2)
521 N Washington, Forrest City, AR 72335
Tel.: (870) 633-8932
Web Site:
  http://www.eastarkansasvideo.com
Rev.: $590,000
Emp.: 35
Cable & Other Pay Television Services
N.A.I.C.S.: 516210

Hope Community TV Inc. (2)
506 S Walnut St, Hope, AR 71801-5355
Tel.: (870) 777-4684
Web Site: http://www.hopecabletv.com
Rev.: $390,000
Emp.: 5
Cable & Other Pay Television Services
N.A.I.C.S.: 516210

Longview Cable Television Inc. (2)
711 N High St, Longview, TX 75601
Tel.: (501) 378-3400
Web Site: http://www.longviewcabletv.com
Rev.: $3,100,000
Emp.: 35
Cable & Other Pay Television Services
N.A.I.C.S.: 516210

News-Times Publishing Company Inc. (2)
111 North Madison, El Dorado, AR 71730
Tel.: (870) 862-6611
Web Site: http://www.eldoradonews.com
Rev.: $3,600,000
Emp.: 75
Publishing Newspapers
N.A.I.C.S.: 513110
Walter E. Hussman Jr. (Chm & Pres)

Pine Bluff Cable Television Inc. (2)
715 Poplar Ave, Pine Bluff, AR 71601-3819
Tel.: (870) 536-0350
Web Site: http://www.pinebluffcabletv.com
Rev.: $1,900,000
Emp.: 30
Cable & Other Pay Television Services
N.A.I.C.S.: 516210

Resort Television Cable Company Incorporated (2)
410 Airport Rd Ste H, Hot Springs, AR 71913
Tel.: (501) 624-5781
Web Site: http://www.resortstvcable.com
Rev.: $2,300,000
Emp.: 75
Cable & Other Pay Television Services
N.A.I.C.S.: 516210

Sentinel-Record Inc. (2)
300 Spring St, Hot Springs, AR 71902
Tel.: (501) 623-7711
Web Site: http://www.hotsr.com
Newspapers
N.A.I.C.S.: 513110

Tahlequah Cable Television Inc. (2)
110 E Keetoowah, Tahlequah, OK 74464
Web Site: http://www.tahlequahcabletv.com
Cable & Other Pay Television Services
N.A.I.C.S.: 516210
Walter E. Hussman Jr. (Pres)
Joseph Knight (Gen Mgr)
Shirley Little (Office Mgr)

Texarkana Newspaper Inc. (2)
315 Pine St, Texarkana, TX 75501
Tel.: (903) 794-0091
Web Site: http://www.texarkanagazette.com
Publishing Newspapers
N.A.I.C.S.: 513110
Kirk Blair (Gen Mgr)

United Wehco Inc. (2)
115 E Capital Scotts St, Little Rock, AR 72201
Tel.: (501) 378-3529
Web Site: http://www.wehco.com
Sales Range: $25-49.9 Million
Emp.: 10
Newspaper Publishers
N.A.I.C.S.: 513110
Charlotte Dial (VP-Admin)
Nat Lea (Pres & CEO)
Philip S. Anderson (Sec)
Lori Haight (VP-Mktg)
J. P. Morbeck (Pres)
Charles C. Van Deventer (VP-Admin)
Robert Young (VP-Mktg)

Vicksburg Video Inc. (2)
900 Hwy 61 N, Vicksburg, MS 39183
Tel.: (601) 636-1351
Web Site: http://www.vicksburgvideo.com
Sales Range: $25-49.9 Million
Emp.: 20
Cable & Other Pay Television Services
N.A.I.C.S.: 516210

Wehco Video Inc. (2)
115 E Capitol Ave Fl 2, Little Rock, AR 72201-3819
Tel.: (501) 378-3400
Web Site: http://www.wehco.com
Sales Range: $25-49.9 Million
Emp.: 50
Cable & Other Pay Television Services
N.A.I.C.S.: 516210

White County Video Inc. (2)
1927 W Beebe Capps Expwy, Searcy, AR 72143-5012
Tel.: (501) 268-4117
Web Site: http://www.whitecountycable.com
Sales Range: $1-9.9 Million
Emp.: 17
Cable & Other Pay Television Services
N.A.I.C.S.: 516210

White County Video Inc. (2)
115 W Capitol Ave, Little Rock, AR 72201-5731
Tel.: (501) 378-3529
Rev.: $1,800,000
Emp.: 25

WEHCO MEDIA, INC.

Wehco Media, Inc.—(Continued)
Cable & Other Pay Television Services
N.A.I.C.S.: 516210

Y95 Radio Station Inc. (2)
612 Fairview Rd, Camden, AR 71701
Tel.: (870) 836-9567
Web Site: http://www.y95online.com
Rev.: $160,000
Emp.: 8
Radio Broadcasting Stations
N.A.I.C.S.: 516110
Helen Aregood *(Gen Mgr)*

El Dorado News-Times (1)
111 N Madison Ave, El Dorado, AR 71730
Tel.: (870) 862-6611
Web Site: http://www.eldoradonews.com
Sales Range: $10-24.9 Million
Emp.: 14
Newspaper Publishers
N.A.I.C.S.: 513110
Lauren Martin *(Editor-Weekend)*
Janice McIntyre *(Editor-City)*
Caitlan Butler *(Mng Editor-Wehco)*
Rita Haldeman *(Gen Mgr)*

Hot Springs On the Go! (1)
300 Spring St, Hot Springs, AR 71902
Tel.: (501) 623-7711
Web Site: http://www.hotsr.com
Magazine Publisher
N.A.I.C.S.: 513120
Walter Hussman *(Publr)*

Northwest Arkansas Newspapers LLC (1)
212 N East Ave, Fayetteville, AR 72701-5225
Tel.: (479) 684-5504
Web Site: http://www.nwaonline.com
Newspaper Publishers
N.A.I.C.S.: 513110
Sandy Thompson *(Dir-Fin)*
Rusty Turner *(Publr & Editor)*
Cathy Wiles *(Mgr-Sls-Classified)*
Hector Cueva *(Dir-Circulation)*
Broderick Daniels *(Dir-HR)*
Todd A. Nelson *(Pres)*
Kiesha Doss *(Mgr-Digital Sls Operation)*
Eric Gilreath *(Dir-IT)*
David Hancock *(Mgr-Creative Svcs)*
Katie Horner *(Office Mgr)*
Kaye Hunton *(Mgr-Retail Sls)*
Lisa Thompson *(Mng Editor)*

Subsidiary (Domestic):

Benton County Daily Record (2)
304 SW 16th St Ste 14, Bentonville, AR 72712
Tel.: (479) 271-3700
Web Site: http://www.nwaonline.com
Newspaper Publishers
N.A.I.C.S.: 513110
Melinda Lenda *(Mgr-HR)*

La Prensa Libre (2)
2560 N Lowell Rd, Springdale, AR 72765
Tel.: (479) 872-5163
Web Site: http://www.laprensawa.com
Newspaper Publishers
N.A.I.C.S.: 513110

Rogers Morning News (2)
313 S 2nd St, Rogers, AR 72756
Tel.: (479) 636-4411
Newspaper Publishers
N.A.I.C.S.: 513110

Springdale Morning News (2)
2560 N Lowell Rd, Springdale, AR 72764
Tel.: (479) 872-5000
Newspaper Publishers
N.A.I.C.S.: 513110

The Free Weekly (2)
212 NE Ave, Fayetteville, AR 72701
Tel.: (479) 442-1700
Web Site: http://www.freeweekly.com
Newspaper Publishers
N.A.I.C.S.: 513110

The Siloam Springs Herald Leader (2)
101 N Mount Olive St, Siloam Springs, AR 72761
Tel.: (479) 524-5144
Web Site: http://www.mwaonline.com

Sales Range: $25-49.9 Million
Emp.: 10
Newspaper Publishers
N.A.I.C.S.: 513110
Kent Marts *(Publr & Editor)*
Graham Thomas *(Editor-Sports)*

The Weekly Vista (2)
313 Town Ctr W, Bella Vista, AR 72714
Tel.: (479) 855-3724
Web Site: http://www.bvnw.nwaonline.com
Emp.: 8
Newspaper Publishers
N.A.I.C.S.: 513110
Kent Marts *(Editor)*

Washington County Enterprise-Leader (2)
128 Southwinds Ste 1, Farmington, AR 72744
Tel.: (479) 267-6502
Newspaper Publishers
N.A.I.C.S.: 513110

Westside Eagle Observer (2)
123 Main St SE, Gravette, AR 72736
Tel.: (479) 787-5300
Web Site: http://www.eagleobserver.com
Newspaper Publishers
N.A.I.C.S.: 513110

Noticias Libres Sureste de Tennessee (1)
400 E 11th St, Chattanooga, TN 37401
Tel.: (423) 756-6900
Newspaper Publishers
N.A.I.C.S.: 513110

Texarkana Gazette (1)
315 Pine St, Texarkana, TX 75501
Tel.: (903) 794-3311
Web Site: http://www.texarkanagazette.com
Newspaper Publishers
N.A.I.C.S.: 513110
Les Minor *(Mng Editor)*
Kirk Blair *(Dir-Mktg)*
Bobby Perry *(Mgr-Circulation)*
Maurice H. King *(Publr)*

The Lake Today (1)
101 Crossings W Ste 203, Lake Ozark, MO 65049
Tel.: (573) 365-2827
Web Site: http://www.thelaketoday.com
Emp.: 4
Newspaper Publishers
N.A.I.C.S.: 513110
Samantha Edmondson *(Editor)*
Jane Haslag *(Mgr-Adv)*
Walter E. Hussman *(Publr)*
Mike Johns *(Dir-Circulation)*
Gary Editor *(Editor)*

WEHCO Newspapers, Inc. (1)
115 E Capitol Ave, Little Rock, AR 72201-3819
Tel.: (501) 378-3400
Web Site: http://www.wehcomedia.com
Emp.: 50
Newspaper Publishers
N.A.I.C.S.: 513110
Mark Lane *(Pres)*

WEHR CONSTRUCTORS, INC.
2517 Plantside Dr, Louisville, KY 40299-2529
Tel.: (502) 491-9250   KY
Web Site: http://www.wehrconstructors.com
Year Founded: 1946
Sales Range: $50-74.9 Million
Emp.: 280
General Contractor Commercial & Industrial Buildings
N.A.I.C.S.: 541618
Dale R. Berry *(CEO)*
Nick Fears *(Principal-Bus Dev)*
Kelly Holcomb *(Principal-Ops-Western Kentucky)*
Edward M. Berry *(COO)*
Shawn Woosley *(CFO)*

WEHR FORD OF MOUNTAIN GROVE INC.
11311 US Bus Hwy 60, Mountain Grove, MO 65711-0783

Tel.: (417) 926-3192
Web Site: http://www.wehrautos.com
Year Founded: 1997
Sales Range: $10-24.9 Million
Emp.: 100
New Car Whslr
N.A.I.C.S.: 441110
Kelly Akers *(Principal)*
Jay Loveland *(Gen Mgr)*
Jim Wehr *(Pres)*

WEIBEL, INC.
1 Winemaster Way, Lodi, CA 95240-0860
Tel.: (209) 365-9463   CA
Web Site: http://www.weibel.com
Year Founded: 1945
Sales Range: $75-99.9 Million
Emp.: 30
Producer of Wine & Champagne
N.A.I.C.S.: 312130
Fred E. Weibel Jr. *(Pres & CEO)*

WEICHERT CO.
1625 Route 10 E, Morris Plains, NJ 07950-2905
Tel.: (973) 605-1619   NJ
Web Site: http://www.weichert.com
Year Founded: 1969
Sales Range: $450-499.9 Million
Emp.: 1,500
Real Estate Services
N.A.I.C.S.: 531210
Aram Minnetian *(COO)*
Barry Taylor *(Mgr-Great Falls)*
Mark Ackermann *(Pres-Capital)*
Denise Smith *(Pres-Real Estate Svcs)*
Carlo Siracusa *(Pres-Residential Brokerage)*
James M. Weichert Jr. *(Founder & Vice Chm)*

Subsidiaries:

Mortgage Access Corp. (1)
225 Littleton Rd, Morris Plains, NJ 07950
Tel.: (973) 605-1515
Web Site: http://www.weichertfs.com
Rev.: $22,200,000
Emp.: 300
Mortgage Banker
N.A.I.C.S.: 522292
Tim McLaughlin *(COO)*
Bob Groody *(Pres)*

Weichert Real Estate Affiliates, Inc. (1)
225 Littleton Rd, Morris Plains, NJ 07950
Tel.: (877) 533-9007
Web Site: http://www.weichertfranchise.com
Real Estate Management Services
N.A.I.C.S.: 531390
Debra Chandler-Protass *(Dir-Reg)*
Bill Scavone *(Pres & COO)*
Denise Smith *(Pres-Weichert Affiliated Svcs Grp)*

Weichert Workforce Mobility Inc. (1)
1625 Rte 10, Morris Plains, NJ 07950-2905
Tel.: (973) 397-3500
Web Site: http://www.weichertworkforcemobility.com
Sales Range: $75-99.9 Million
Emp.: 400
Corporate Relocation Consultants
N.A.I.C.S.: 541614
Jim Schneider *(Exec VP-Bus Dev)*
Ellie Sullivan *(Dir-Mktg & Consulting)*
John Bartoloni *(VP-Client Svcs)*
Kelly Reiss *(Reg VP)*
Mike Cahill *(VP-Bus Dev)*
Don Smith *(Sr VP-Bus Dev-North America)*
Lisa Rodriguez *(VP-Midwest)*
Vicki Lander *(Exec VP)*
Avrom Goldberg *(Mng Dir/VP-Asia Pacific)*
Lawrence Mahmarian *(Sr VP-Global Ops)*

Subsidiary (Domestic):

Franconia Real Estate Services, Inc. (2)
12531 Clipper Dr, Woodbridge, VA 22192
Tel.: (703) 924-2300

U.S. PRIVATE

Web Site: http://www.rmxtracker.com
Relocation Management Services
N.A.I.C.S.: 531390
Tim Bonette *(VP-Govt Svcs)*
Peggy Pastore *(CFO-Govt)*

Branch (Domestic):

Weichert Workforce Mobility Inc. - Boston (2)
120 Longwater Dr Ste 206, Norwell, MA 02061
Tel.: (781) 871-4500
Web Site: http://www.weichertworkforcemobility.com
Relocation & Assignment Management Services
N.A.I.C.S.: 561990

WEIDENHAMMER SYSTEMS CORPORATION
935 Berkshire Blvd, Wyomissing, PA 19610
Tel.: (610) 378-1149
Web Site: http://www.hammer.net
Year Founded: 1978
Sales Range: $10-24.9 Million
Emp.: 200
Prepackaged Software Developer
N.A.I.C.S.: 513210
John P. Weidenhammer *(CEO)*
Frank W. Heins *(Exec VP)*
Kevin A. Hargreaves *(VP-Bus Dev)*
Jane M. Lewis *(VP-Education Solutions Div)*
Kevin Gorski *(Dir-Cloud Svcs)*
Mark Werner *(Mgr-Svc Delivery)*
Chuck Zwicker *(COO)*
James Cox *(CFO)*
Dave Christy *(VP-Digital Solutions Div)*
Aaron Sheehan *(Dir-Commerce-Digital Solutions Div)*
Anthony Cartolaro *(VP-Digital Platforms)*
Curtis Johnson III *(VP-Creative Svcs)*

WEIDNER INVESTMENT SERVICES
9757 NE Juanita Dr No 300, Kirkland, WA 98034
Tel.: (425) 821-3844
Web Site: http://www.weidner.com
Year Founded: 1977
Sales Range: $75-99.9 Million
Emp.: 40
Commercial & Industrial Building Operation
N.A.I.C.S.: 531120
Dean Weidner *(Pres)*
Ben Katon *(VP-Fin & Acq)*

WEIFIELD GROUP CONTRACTING, LLC
146 Yuma St, Denver, CO 80223
Tel.: (303) 428-2011
Web Site: http://www.weifieldcontracting.com
Year Founded: 2002
Sales Range: $25-49.9 Million
Emp.: 150
Cutting Edge Electrical Construction Services
N.A.I.C.S.: 238210
Karla Nugent *(Chief Bus Dev Officer)*
Jim Dent *(Dir-Preconstruction)*
Mike Osborne *(VP-Construction)*
Pete Farreny *(COO)*
Seth Anderson *(CEO)*
Mike Megara *(Controller)*
Doug Angerman *(Mgr-Prefabrication)*
Lauren Worth *(Mgr-HR)*
Chad Bowman *(Project Mgr-Svc)*
James Selecky *(Chief Special Projects Officer)*
Sam Gluck *(Mgr-Svc-Columbus)*

Shannon Palobmi (Coord-Preconstruction)
Chris A. Cerveny (Sr VP)
Don Fitzmartin (Pres & CEO)

WEIGEL BROADCASTING CO.
26 N Halsted St, Chicago, IL 60661
Tel.: (312) 705-2600
Web Site: http://www.wciu.com
Sales Range: $10-24.9 Million
Emp.: 100
Television Broadcasting Station
N.A.I.C.S.: 516120
John R. Hendricks (Exec VP-Sls)
Rick O'Dell (Dir-Program-Me-TV FM)

WEIGEL'S STORES INC.
3100 Weigel Ln, Powell, TN 37849-4256
Tel.: (865) 938-2042 TN
Web Site: http://www.weigels.com
Year Founded: 1938
Sales Range: $125-149.9 Million
Emp.: 350
Provider of Grocery Store Services
N.A.I.C.S.: 445131
Bill Weigel (Chm)

WEIL CADILLAC
1050 S Milwaukee Ave, Libertyville, IL 60048
Tel.: (847) 362-4100
Web Site:
    http://www.weilcadillac.com
Sales Range: $50-74.9 Million
Emp.: 70
New Car Retailer
N.A.I.C.S.: 441110
Dominic Florio (Gen Mgr)

WEIL CERAMICS & GLASS INC.
1 Lladro Dr, Moonachie, NJ 07074-1019
Tel.: (201) 807-1177
Web Site: http://www.lladro.com
Year Founded: 1977
Sales Range: $25-49.9 Million
Emp.: 200
Porcelain Giftware Distr
N.A.I.C.S.: 424990

Subsidiaries:

Lladro USA Inc. (1)
12 E 49 St Fl 11, New York, NY 10017 (100%)
Tel.: (201) 807-1177
Web Site: http://www.lladro.com
Sales Range: $10-24.9 Million
Emp.: 81
Porcelain Giftware Distr
N.A.I.C.S.: 424990
Sandra Jordan (CEO-Americas)

WEIL, GOTSHAL & MANGES LLP
767 5th Ave, New York, NY 10153
Tel.: (212) 310-8000
Web Site: http://www.weil.com
Year Founded: 1931
Sales Range: $1-4.9 Billion
Legal Advisory Services
N.A.I.C.S.: 541110
Joseph S. Allerhand (Co-Partner)
Michael J. Aiello (Chm-Corp Dev)
Joshua S. Amsel (Co-Partner)
Morgan Bale (Partner)
Jennifer A. Bensch (Partner-New York)
Robert S. Berezin (Partner-New York)
Ronit J. Berkovich (Partner-New York)
Jon-Paul A. Bernard (Partner-New York)
Kimberly S. Blanchard (Partner-New York)
W. Michael Bond (Partner-New York)
Todd Lang (Partner-New York)
John Quattrocchi (Partner-Dallas)
Damian P. Ridealgh (Partner-New York)
Ray C. Schrock (Partner-New York)
Sachin Kohli (Partner-Mergers & Acq)
Faiza Rahman (Partner-Capital Markets)
Stephanie Srulowitz (Partner-Private Funds)
Paul Genender (Partner)
Craig W. Adas (Partner-Silicon Valley)
Frank R. Adams (Partner-New York)
Karen N. Ballack (Partner-Silicon Valley)
Christopher Machera (Partner-Private Equity Practice)
Barry Wolf (Partner)
Douglas Warner (Head-Global Private Equity Practice)
Sarah Downie (Partner-Exec Compensation & Benefits Practice)
Paul Wessel (Chm-Tax Dept & Head-Exec Compensation & Benefits Practice)
Brian Gingold (Partner-Global Private Equity Practice)
Matthew Stewart (Partner-Private Equity Practice-Global)
Dana C. O'Brien (Assoc)
Joseph Pari (Chm-Global Tax Dept/Partner-Washington & New York)
Richard Frye (Partner-Dallas)
Jeffery Malonson (Partner-Private Equity Practice-Houston)
Rodney Moore (Partner-Private Equity Practice & Head-Oil & Gas Practice)

WEILER CORPORATION
1 Weiler Dr, Cresco, PA 18326
Tel.: (570) 595-7495 DE
Web Site: http://www.weilercorp.com
Year Founded: 1944
Sales Range: $25-49.9 Million
Emp.: 400
Mfr of Brooms & Brushes
N.A.I.C.S.: 339994
Christopher Weiler (Pres & CEO)
Bill Dwyre (Mng Dir)
Brian Seelig (VP-Global Ops)
Ray Burke (CFO)

Subsidiaries:

Anderson Products, Inc. (1)
1 Weiler Dr, Cresco, PA 18326
Tel.: (508) 755-6100
Web Site: http://www.andersonproducts.com
Sales Range: $10-24.9 Million
Emp.: 50
Industrial Power Brushes, Maintenance & Paint Brushes, Non-Woven Abrasives, Anderlex Non-Woven Abrasives, Maintenance Brushes
N.A.I.C.S.: 339994

WEILER WELDING COMPANY INC.
2400 Sandridge Dr, Dayton, OH 45439-1849
Tel.: (513) 874-9353
Web Site:
    http://www.weilerwelding.com
Sales Range: $10-24.9 Million
Emp.: 80
Compressed Gases; Welding & Safety Supplies; Internet Service
N.A.I.C.S.: 424690
Herbert Weiler (VP-Ops)
Linda Chiovaro (VP-Admin)
Nancy Lush (Sec)

WEILL CORNELL MEDICINE
1300 York Ave, New York, NY 10065
Tel.: (212) 746-5454
Web Site: https://weill.cornell.edu
Educational Support Services
N.A.I.C.S.: 611710

WEIMAR CONSTRUCTION COMPANY, INC.
101A Estus Dr, Savannah, GA 31404
Tel.: (912) 443-0757
Sales Range: $10-24.9 Million
Emp.: 6
Commercial & Institutional Building Construction Services
N.A.I.C.S.: 236220
Charles F. Weimar (CEO)

WEIMER BEARING & TRANSMISSION
W13131 Mequon Rd, Germantown, WI 53022
Tel.: (262) 781-1992
Web Site:
    http://www.weimerbearing.com
Rev.: $10,000,000
Emp.: 35
Power Transmission Equipment & Apparatus
N.A.I.C.S.: 423840
Robert Holowitz (CFO)
Frank Stangl (Pres)
Christopher Wagner (VP-Ops)

WEINBERG CAPITAL GROUP, INC.
5005 Rockside Rd Ste 1140, Cleveland, OH 44131
Tel.: (216) 503-8303 OH
Web Site:
    http://www.weinbergcap.com
Privater Equity Firm
N.A.I.C.S.: 523999
Ronald E. Weinberg (Principal)
John E. Herman (Principal)
Ronald E. Weinberg Jr. (Mng Dir & Principal)

Subsidiaries:

Carl's Patio, Inc. (1)
6598 N Federal Hwy, Boca Raton, FL 33487
Tel.: (561) 998-5575
Web Site: http://www.carls-patio.com
Sales Range: $10-24.9 Million
Outdoor Furniture Retailer
N.A.I.C.S.: 449110
Paul D. Otiwchits (Pres)
Scott Spainhour (Mgr)

Channel Products, Inc. (1)
30700 Solon Industrial Pkwy, Solon, OH 44139 (100%)
Tel.: (440) 423-0113
Web Site: http://www.channelproducts.com
Sales Range: $25-49.9 Million
Emp.: 150
Control Filter & Transducer Mfr
N.A.I.C.S.: 334512
Teresa Lindsey (Pres & COO)
James Becker (Chief Tech & Innovation Officer)
Suzanne French (Chief Mfg & Sourcing Officer)
Steve Marrero (Chief Comml Officer)
Roxana Stoicea (CFO)

H-D Advanced Manufacturing Company (1)
2418 Greens Rd, Houston, TX 77032
Tel.: (346) 219-0320
Web Site: http://www.h-dam.com
Holding Company
N.A.I.C.S.: 551112
Dale B. Mikus (CFO & Sr VP)
Michael Vincent (Pres & CEO)
Tom Hicks (Chm)

Holding (Domestic):

Firstmark Corp. (2)
2200 Georgetowne Dr Ste 300, Sewickley, PA 15143
Tel.: (724) 759-2850
Web Site: http://www.firstmarkcorp.com
Mfr of Components & Sub-Assemblies for Aerospace & Defense Applications
N.A.I.C.S.: 334511
William H. Coogan Jr. (CEO)

Subsidiary (Domestic):

Aircraft Belts, Inc. (3)
1176 Telecom Dr, Creedmoor, NC 27522-8294
Tel.: (919) 956-4395
Web Site: http://www.aircraftbelts.com
Sales Range: $1-9.9 Million
Emp.: 21
Aircraft Safety Restraints Mfr
N.A.I.C.S.: 336413
Rick O'Quinn (Sls Mgr)

Centroid, Inc. (3)
111 E Ames Ct, Plainview, NY 11803
Tel.: (516) 349-0070
Web Site: http://www.centroidinc.com
Sales Range: $1-9.9 Million
Emp.: 24
Electronic Components Mfr
N.A.I.C.S.: 334419
Matt Isley (Pres)

Firstmark Aerospace Corporation (3)
1176 Telecom Dr, Creedmoor, NC 27522-8294
Tel.: (919) 956-4200
Web Site:
    http://www.firstmarkaerospace.com
Precision Electronic, Electromagnetic & Mechanical Components & Systems Mfr
N.A.I.C.S.: 334419
Derek Ashcroft (Program Mgr)
David Devine (Exec VP)

Twin Commander Aircraft LLC (3)
1176 Telecom Dr, Creedmoor, NC 27522-8294
Tel.: (919) 956-4300
Web Site:
    http://www.twincommander.com
Aircraft Original Equipment Parts Mfr & Repair Services
N.A.I.C.S.: 336413
Allen Goad (Pres)

Holding (Domestic):

Overton Chicago Gear Inc. (2)
530 S Westgate Dr, Addison, IL 60101-4525
Tel.: (630) 543-9570
Web Site: http://www.oc-gear.com
Engineering Components & Industrial Gear Products Mfr
N.A.I.C.S.: 333612
Louis Ertel (CEO)
Kevin Walsh (VP-Ops)
Don Brown (CEO)

Sungear, Inc. (2)
8535-G Arjons Dr, San Diego, CA 92126
Tel.: (858) 549-3166
Web Site: http://www.sungearinc.com
Emp.: 50
Aerospace Gear Mfr
N.A.I.C.S.: 336413
John Gizicki (Founder)
James Wilson (Dir-Mfg)
Paul M. Scott (Dir-Quality Assurance)

Salt River Aviation, LLC (1)
175 S Hamilton Pl Ste 112, Gilbert, AZ 85233
Tel.: (480) 558-1455
Web Site: http://www.saltriveraviation.com
Other Nonscheduled Air Transportation
N.A.I.C.S.: 481219
Greg Crill (CEO)

WEINBRENNER SHOE COMPANY, INC.
108 S Polk St, Merrill, WI 54452-2348
Tel.: (715) 536-5521 WI
Web Site:
    http://www.weinbrennerusa.com
Year Founded: 1892
Sales Range: $150-199.9 Million
Emp.: 350
Uniform, Work, Safety, Outdoor Boots & Shoes Mfr & Supplier
N.A.I.C.S.: 316210
Pat Miner (Pres)

WEINGARTZ SUPPLY CO. INC.　　　　　　　　　　　　　　　　　　　　　　　　　　　　　U.S. PRIVATE

Weingartz Supply Co, Inc.—(Continued)

WEINGARTZ SUPPLY CO. INC.
46061 Van Dyke Ave, Utica, MI 48317
Tel.: (586) 731-7240　　MI
Web Site: http://www.weingartz.com
Year Founded: 1945
Sales Range: $10-24.9 Million
Emp.: 50
Provider of Lawn & Garden Equipment
N.A.I.C.S.: 444230
Dan Weingartz (Pres)

WEINGEROFF ENTERPRISES, INC.
1 Weingeroff Blvd, Cranston, RI 02910
Tel.: (401) 467-2200
Sales Range: $10-24.9 Million
Emp.: 100
Metal Picture Frames & Costume Jewelry Mfr & Sales
N.A.I.C.S.: 332999
Sara Lloyd (CFO)
Skip Weingeroff (Exec VP)
Jane Westell (Mgr-Import Pur)

WEINRICH ADVERTISING & COMMUNICATIONS, INC.
915 Clifton Ave Ste 2, Clifton, NJ 07013-2725
Tel.: (973) 473-6643　　NJ
Year Founded: 1968
Sales Range: Less than $1 Million
Emp.: 9
Advetising Agency
N.A.I.C.S.: 541810
Lori W. Fabisiak (Pres)
Lisa Lessner (Creative Dir)

WEINSTEIN BEVERAGE CO. INC.
410 E Peters S, Wenatchee, WA 98801-1531
Tel.: (509) 662-9631　　WA
Year Founded: 1941
Sales Range: $10-24.9 Million
Emp.: 110
Groceries & Related Products
N.A.I.C.S.: 424490
Joseph Weinstein (Pres)
Steve Gerstmann (CEO)

WEINSTEIN MINKOFF INVESTMENTS
6169 McKee Rd, Madison, WI 53719
Tel.: (608) 271-1234
Rev.: $11,400,000
Emp.: 220
Commercial & Industrial Building Operation
N.A.I.C.S.: 531120
Dan Weinsiein (Pres)

WEINSTEIN OTTERMAN & ASSOCIATES
56 W 22nd St Rm 700, New York, NY 10010-7286
Tel.: (212) 505-5650
Year Founded: 1978
Rev.: $16,500,000
Emp.: 30
Fiscal Year-end: 02/01/02
N.A.I.C.S.: 541810
Ileen Otterman (Chm, Pres & Dir-Creative)
Marleen Gura (CFO & Exec VP)
Martin Solar (VP-Special Markets)

WEINSTEIN SUPPLY CORPORATION
3155 Terwood Rd, Willow Grove, PA 19090-0911
Tel.: (215) 659-0672　　PA
Web Site: http://www.weinsteinsupply.com
Year Founded: 1922
Sales Range: $25-49.9 Million
Emp.: 30
Plumbing Fixtures, Equipment, Supplies & Sales
N.A.I.C.S.: 423720
Alex Lochetto (Mgr-Sls)
Kevin Ireson (Mgr-Branch)
Ed Boone (Mgr-Sls)
Bill Ticcllo (Mgr-Sls)

WEINSTOCK BROTHERS CORP.
140 E Mineola Ave, Valley Stream, NY 11580
Tel.: (516) 568-2171
Web Site: http://www.weinstockbros.com
Sales Range: $10-24.9 Million
Emp.: 19
Mfr of Fasteners, Nuts, Bolts & Screws
N.A.I.C.S.: 423840

WEINTRAUB ADVERTISING
7745 Carondelet Ave Ste 308, Saint Louis, MO 63105-3315
Tel.: (314) 721-5050
Web Site: http://www.weintraubadv.com
Year Founded: 1953
Sales Range: $25-49.9 Million
Emp.: 40
N.A.I.C.S.: 541810
Lawrence Weintraub (Chm)
Robert Weintraub (Pres & Dir-Creative)
Dwight Stamp (Sr Dir-Art)
Dawn Walter (Acct Exec)
Betsy Bartholomew (Dir-Media)
Kristin Stine (Graphic Designer)
Blair Mindak (Acct Exec)

WEINTRAUB CONSTRUCTION CO. INC.
20900 NE 30th Ave Ste 318, Hialeah, FL 33180
Tel.: (305) 557-9398　　FL
Year Founded: 1978
Sales Range: $25-49.9 Million
Emp.: 18
General Contracting in South Florida Condo Community
N.A.I.C.S.: 236116
Avi Weintraub (Pres)

WEINTRAUB TOBIN CHEDIAK COLEMAN GRODIN LAW CORPORATION
400 Capitol Mall 11th Fl, Sacramento, CA 95814-4434
Tel.: (916) 558-6003
Web Site: http://www.weintraub.com
Year Founded: 1852
Emp.: 29
Law firm
N.A.I.C.S.: 541110
C. Kevin Kelso (Atty)
Kenneth J. Sylva (Atty)
Dale C. Campbell (Atty)
Michael A. Kvarme (Atty)
Louis A. Gonzalez Jr. (Atty)

Subsidiaries:

Salem & Green Corp.　　(1)
3604 Fair Oaks Blvd Ste 200, Sacramento, CA 95864-7256
Tel.: (916) 480-9453
Web Site: http://www.salemgreen.com
Law firm
N.A.I.C.S.: 541110

WEIR BROS. INC.
10721 Luna Rd, Dallas, TX 75220
Tel.: (972) 556-9696
Web Site: http://www.weirbrosinc.com
Sales Range: $25-49.9 Million
Emp.: 50
Excavation Work
N.A.I.C.S.: 238910
Lee Weir (Pres)
Amber Allen (Dir-HR)
James Shelton (Project Mgr)

WEIR CHEVROLET, INC.
1507 S Main St, Red Bud, IL 62278
Tel.: (618) 282-2353
Year Founded: 1967
Sales Range: $10-24.9 Million
Emp.: 100
New Car Whslr
N.A.I.C.S.: 441110
Norman L. Roy (Pres)

WEIR SPM
7601 Wyatt Dr, Fort Worth, TX 76108-2530
Tel.: (817) 246-2461　　TX
Web Site: http://www.weiroilandgas.com
Year Founded: 1958
Sales Range: $25-49.9 Million
Emp.: 500
Industrial Machinery Services
N.A.I.C.S.: 333998
Grant Kelly (Supvr-Ops)

WEIR'S FURNITURE VILLAGE
4800 Spring Vly Rd, Farmers Branch, TX 75244
Tel.: (214) 522-3780
Web Site: http://www.weirsfurniture.com
Year Founded: 1948
Sales Range: $25-49.9 Million
Emp.: 120
Furniture Whslr
N.A.I.C.S.: 449110
Mark Moore (Pres)

WEIRTON MEDICAL CENTER
601 Colliers Way, Weirton, WV 26062
Tel.: (304) 797-6000　　WI
Web Site: http://www.weirtonmedical.com
Year Founded: 1949
Sales Range: $75-99.9 Million
Emp.: 1,147
Community Health Care Services
N.A.I.C.S.: 621498
Joseph P. Endrich (CEO)
Kelly McCoy (Mgr-Mktg)

WEIS BUILDERS INC.
7645 Lyndale Ave Ste 300, Minneapolis, MN 55423-6009
Tel.: (612) 243-5000　　MN
Web Site: http://www.weisbuilders.com
Year Founded: 1960
Sales Range: $25-49.9 Million
Emp.: 150
Provider of Construction Services
N.A.I.C.S.: 236117
Cassie Warner (CFO & Sr VP)
Micheal Biskupski (Controller-Ops)
Tony Rand (Superintendent-Construction)
Brett Christofferson (VP-Bus Dev)

WEISER REALITY ADVISORS LLC
135 W 50th St 13th Fl, New York, NY 10020
Tel.: (212) 812-7000　　NY
Web Site: http://www.weiserrealty.com
Year Founded: 1999
Sales Range: $10-24.9 Million
Emp.: 200
Real Estate Consulting Service
N.A.I.C.S.: 541618
Douglas Phillips (Mng Dir)

WEISER SECURITY SERVICES INC.
1900 Canal St Fl 2, New Orleans, LA 70112
Tel.: (504) 949-7558
Web Site: http://www.weisersecurity.com
Year Founded: 1970
Sales Range: $25-49.9 Million
Emp.: 5,000
Security Guard Services
N.A.I.C.S.: 561612
Chuck Remington (Reg VP)
Mike Burke (Reg VP)
Lisa George (VP)
Irma Parone (Reg VP)
John Elzner (VP)
Carol Schmitz (VP-Sls)

WEISLER & ASSOCIATES INC.
10235 W Little York Rd Ste 159, Houston, TX 77040
Tel.: (713) 849-3799
Web Site: http://www.weisler.com
Sales Range: $10-24.9 Million
Emp.: 9
Electronic Parts & Equipment Whslr
N.A.I.C.S.: 423690
Thomas Barnett (Pres)

WEISMAN HOME OUTLETS
21801 Merrick Blvd, Springfield Gardens, NY 11413
Tel.: (718) 723-4000
Web Site: http://www.weismahomeoutlets.com
Sales Range: $10-24.9 Million
Emp.: 55
Kitchen Cabinets & General Hardware Sales
N.A.I.C.S.: 423310
Skip Abrams (Pres)

WEISNER STEEL PRODUCTS INC.
77 Moraga Way Ste F, Orinda, CA 94563
Tel.: (925) 254-6800
Web Site: http://www.weisnersteel.com
Year Founded: 1970
Sales Range: $10-24.9 Million
Emp.: 20
Importer & Wholesaler of Steel Products
N.A.I.C.S.: 423510
Ivor J. Silver (Pres)
Mark Silver (VP)
Craig Sundstrom (Controller)

WEISS CONSTRUCTION
3649 Chipman Rd, Easton, PA 18045
Tel.: (610) 253-9807
Web Site: http://www.weissconstruction.com
Sales Range: $10-24.9 Million
Emp.: 8
Nonresidential Construction Services
N.A.I.C.S.: 236220
Paul D. Weiss (Pres)

WEISS CONSTRUCTION COMPANY LLC
400 Renaissance Center Ste 2170, Detroit, MI 48243
Tel.: (313) 567-4500
Web Site: http://www.weiss-construction.com
Year Founded: 1969
Sales Range: $25-49.9 Million
Emp.: 30

Industrial Construction & Mechanical Contracting Services
N.A.I.C.S.: 236210
Christopher Fitch (Gen Mgr)
Chuck Gold (Project Mgr)
Leticia Perez (Mgr-HR)
Gregg Penn (Project Mgr)

WEISS GROUP, LLC
15430 Endeavour Dr, Jupiter, FL 33478
Tel.: (561) 627-3300   FL
Web Site: http://www.weissinc.com
Year Founded: 1971
Sales Range: $125-149.9 Million
Emp.: 100
Holding Company; Financial Investment Research & Ratings Newsletter Publisher
N.A.I.C.S.: 551112
Martin D. Weiss (Founder, Chm & Editor-Money & Markets)
Jeff Rano (Controller)
Thomas J. Clarke Jr. (CEO)

Subsidiaries:

Weiss Research, Inc.   (1)
15430 Endeavour Dr, Jupiter, FL 33478
Tel.: (561) 627-3300
Web Site: http://www.weissinc.com
Sales Range: $10-24.9 Million
Emp.: 85
Financial Investment Research & Analysis Newsletter Publisher
N.A.I.C.S.: 513120
Martin D. Weiss (Pres)

WEISS SHEET METAL COMPANY
1715 W 135th St, Gardena, CA 90249-2507
Tel.: (310) 354-2700   CA
Web Site: http://www.metcoe.com
Year Founded: 1943
Sales Range: $10-24.9 Million
Roofing, Sheet Metal Work & Custom Skylights Services
N.A.I.C.S.: 238160
Andre Sarai (Pres)

Subsidiaries:

Global Architectural Panels   (1)
1715 W 135th St, Gardena, CA 90249-2507
Tel.: (310) 354-2641
Web Site: http://www.metcoe.com
Sales Range: $10-24.9 Million
Emp.: 100
Metal Panel Mfr
N.A.I.C.S.: 332311

Metcoe Skylight Specialties   (1)
PO Box 1605, Gardena, CA 90249-0605
Tel.: (310) 354-0030
Web Site: http://www.metcoe.com
N.A.I.C.S.: 238390
Jim Wilkinson (Controller)

WEJ-IT FASTENING SYSTEMS
10541 E Ute St, Tulsa, OK 74116-1522
Tel.: (918) 743-1030
Web Site: http://www.wejit.com
Year Founded: 1952
Sales Range: $75-99.9 Million
Emp.: 100
Concrete Masonry Anchors Mfr
N.A.I.C.S.: 332722

WEL COMPANIES INC.
PO Box 5610, De Pere, WI 54115-5610
Tel.: (920) 339-0110   WI
Web Site: http://www.welcompanies.com
Year Founded: 1975
Sales Range: $100-124.9 Million
Emp.: 750
Provider of Non-Local Trucking Services
N.A.I.C.S.: 484230
Bruce Tielens (Pres & CEO)
Greg Bredael (CFO)
Jason Townsend (Coord-Freight)
Colleen Burg (Coord-HR)
Jason Johnson (Dir-Sls & Accts-Natl)

WELBERT PINKUS
450 Lexington Ave, New York, NY 10017
Tel.: (212) 878-0600
Web Site: http://www.warburgpincus.com
Rev.: $42,900,000
Emp.: 450
Book Publishers
N.A.I.C.S.: 513130
Lionel Pincis (Pres)

WELBRO BUILDING CORPORATION
2301 Maitland Ctr Pwy Ste 250, Maitland, FL 32751
Tel.: (407) 475-0800
Web Site: http://www.welbro.com
Year Founded: 1979
Sales Range: $100-124.9 Million
Emp.: 100
Construction Services
N.A.I.C.S.: 236220
Bruce Holmes (Pres)
Ken Wuenschell (Exec VP)
John Sfeir (VP)
Steve Melco (Mgr-Ops)
Brian Pak (Dir-Special Svcs)

WELBY GARDENS, CO.
2761 E 74th Ave, Denver, CO 80229
Tel.: (303) 288-3398
Web Site: http://www.hardyboyplant.com
Year Founded: 1948
Sales Range: $10-24.9 Million
Emp.: 200
Floriculture Production Services
N.A.I.C.S.: 111422
Al Gerace (CEO)

WELCH EQUIPMENT COMPANY INC.
5025 Nome St, Denver, CO 80239-2725
Tel.: (303) 393-8181
Web Site: http://www.welchequipment.com
Sales Range: $25-49.9 Million
Emp.: 100
Materials Handling Machinery
N.A.I.C.S.: 423830
Stephen Rice (Pres)
Steve Koscik (Controller)
Joe Stone (VP-Sls)

WELCH PACKAGING GROUP, INC.
1130 Herman St., Elkhart, IN 46516
Tel.: (574) 295-2460   IN
Web Site: http://www.welchpkg.com
Year Founded: 1985
Sales Range: $50-74.9 Million
Emp.: 1,000
Mfr of Corrugated & Solid Fiber Boxes
N.A.I.C.S.: 322211
M. Scott Welch (Founder, Pres & CEO)
Julian Golan (Mgr-Ops)

Subsidiaries:

American Corrugated Products, Inc.   (1)
4700 Alkire Rd, Columbus, OH 43228
Tel.: (614) 870-2000
Web Site: http://www.americancorrugated.com
Emp.: 200
Corrugated & Solid Fiber Box Mfr
N.A.I.C.S.: 322211
Donald Youell (Pres)

Barger Packaging-IN   (1)
2901 Oakland Ave, Elkhart, IN 46517
Tel.: (574) 389-1860
Web Site: http://www.bargerpkg.com
Sales Range: $25-49.9 Million
Emp.: 65
Medical & Pharmaceutical Sterile & Non-Sterile Packaging Mfr
N.A.I.C.S.: 322211

CRK, LLC   (1)
501 Richardson Dr, Lancaster, PA 17603
Tel.: (717) 207-0545
Web Site: http://www.ipsinnovations.com
Rev.: $6,624,000
Emp.: 8
Industrial & Personal Service Paper Merchant Whslr
N.A.I.C.S.: 424130
Chuck Kelley (Pres)

Heritage Packaging, LLC   (1)
2350 5th St, Lincoln, IL 62656
Tel.: (217) 735-4406
Web Site: http://www.hpackaging.com
Corrugated & Solid Fiber Box Mfr
N.A.I.C.S.: 322211
Greg Basford (Pres)
Steve Douglass (Owner)

Pax Corrugated Products, Inc.   (1)
1899 Kingsview Dr, Lebanon, OH 45036
Tel.: (513) 932-9855
Web Site: http://www.paxbox.com
Sales Range: $1-9.9 Million
Emp.: 38
Corrugated & Solid Fiber Box Mfr
N.A.I.C.S.: 322211
James Cory (Pres)
Tim Schenck (Controller)

Pierce Box & Paper Corp.   (1)
4133 Newburg Rd, Belvidere, IL 61008
Tel.: (815) 547-1505
Web Site: http://www.piercebox.com
Rev.: $6,666,666
Emp.: 20
All Other Converted Paper Product Mfr
N.A.I.C.S.: 322299
John Menzies (Pres)

Welch Packaging   (1)
1130 Herman St, Elkhart, IN 46516   (100%)
Tel.: (574) 295-2460
Web Site: http://www.welchpkg.com
Sales Range: $25-49.9 Million
Emp.: 70
Corrugated Packaging Mfr
N.A.I.C.S.: 322211

WELCOME DAIRY INC.
H4489 Maple Rd, Colby, WI 54421
Tel.: (715) 223-2874
Web Site: http://www.welcomedairy.com
Sales Range: $10-24.9 Million
Emp.: 70
Processed Cheese Mfr
N.A.I.C.S.: 311513
Dustin Stark (Mgr-Quality Assurance)
Jo Anne Leonhard (Mgr-Pur & Transportation)

Subsidiaries:

North Star Processing, LLC   (1)
725 Aspen Dr, Litchfield, MN 55355
Tel.: (320) 693-7211
Web Site: http://www.nsp-llc.com
Sales Range: $1-9.9 Million
Emp.: 34
Pharmaceutical Preparation Mfr
N.A.I.C.S.: 325412
Peter Duddleston (Principal)

WELCOME FUNDS, INC.
6001 Broken Sound Pkwy Ste 320, Boca Raton, FL 33487
Tel.: (561) 862-0244
Web Site: http://www.welcomefunds.com
Sales Range: $75-99.9 Million
Emp.: 16
Life Settlement Broker
N.A.I.C.S.: 524128
John M. Welcom (Founder, Pres & CEO)
Daniel Ohman (COO & VP)

WELCOME MARKET, INC.
2931 Faber St, Union City, CA 94587-1215
Tel.: (510) 487-8899
Web Site: http://www.99ranch.com
Sales Range: $25-49.9 Million
Emp.: 30
Independent Supermarket
N.A.I.C.S.: 445110
Avery M. Lim (Project Mgr-Construction)
Henry Sun (Mgr)
Jiangguo Yang (Mgr)
Teddy Chow (Mgr-Mktg)
Vivian L. Yeh (Coord-SAP)

WELCOME TRAVELERS FURNITURE CO.
405 Sentress Blvd, Daytona Beach, FL 32114
Tel.: (386) 255-8532
Web Site: http://www.haynesbrosfurniture.com
Year Founded: 1942
Sales Range: $10-24.9 Million
Emp.: 100
Furniture Retailer
N.A.I.C.S.: 449110
Arlington D. Haynes (Owner)
Tom Haynes (Owner)
David Haynes (Gen Mgr)

WELCOMM, INC.
7975 Raytheon Rd Ste 340, San Diego, CA 92111-1622
Tel.: (858) 279-2100
Web Site: http://www.welcomm.com
Year Founded: 1985
Sales Range: $10-24.9 Million
Emp.: 12
N.A.I.C.S.: 541810
Gregory W. Evans (CEO)
Michael W. Gerow (Dir-PR)
Kathy Naraghi (CFO)
Mat Naraghi (Pres)
Marsha Lisak (Sr Acct Exec)
Lisa W. de Garrido (Acct Exec)
Brad Buckingham (Mgr-Web Svcs)
Sandy LaFlair (Admin Asst)
Jayme Pontious (Acct Mgr)

WELD COUNTY GARAGE INC.
2699 47th Ave 80634, Greeley, CO 80634
Tel.: (970) 352-1313
Web Site: http://www.weldcountygarage.com
Sales Range: $75-99.9 Million
Emp.: 180
New & Used Automobiles
N.A.I.C.S.: 441110
Warren Yoder (Pres)
Jim Baca (Controller)
David Slone (Gen Mgr-Sls-Used Car)

WELD POWER SERVICE COMPANY, INC.
14 Technology Dr, Auburn, MA 01501
Tel.: (508) 832-3550
Web Site: http://www.weldpower.com
Year Founded: 1961
Sales Range: $1-9.9 Million
Emp.: 23
Electrical Equipment Sales & Maintenance Services
N.A.I.C.S.: 423610

WELD POWER SERVICE COMPANY, INC. U.S. PRIVATE

Weld Power Service Company, Inc.—(Continued)
Timothy Geary (Pres)
John Reilly (Mgr-Svc)
Jim Chianese (VP-Ops)

WELDED CONSTRUCTION LP
26933 Eckel Rd, Perrysburg, OH 43551
Tel.: (419) 874-3548
Web Site: http://www.welded.com
Sales Range: $10-24.9 Million
Emp.: 20
Oil & Gas Pipeline Construction
N.A.I.C.S.: 237120
Diane Ingmire (Mgr-Admin)
Don Thorn (VP-Bus Dev)

WELDED RING PRODUCTS CO., INC.
2180 W 114th St, Cleveland, OH 44102-3516
Tel.: (216) 961-3800   OH
Web Site: http://www.weldedring.com
Year Founded: 1982
Sales Range: $25-49.9 Million
Emp.: 100
Aircraft Engines & Engine Parts
N.A.I.C.S.: 336412
James C. Janosek (Pres)
Gary Horvath (VP-Sls & Mktg)
Tom Carlin (VP-Mfg)

WELDED TUBES INC.
135 Penniman Rd, Orwell, OH 44076
Tel.: (440) 437-5144
Web Site: http://www.weldedtubes.com
Sales Range: $10-24.9 Million
Emp.: 100
Welded Steel Tube Mfr
N.A.I.C.S.: 331210
Jeff Thibodeau (Supvr)

WELDING ENGINEERING SUPPLY CO.
940 N Martin Luther King Dr, Prichard, AL 36610
Tel.: (251) 457-8681
Web Site: http://www.wescoweld.com
Rev.: $16,984,651
Emp.: 65
Welding Machinery & Equipment
N.A.I.C.S.: 423830
Ronald C. Pierce (Pres & CEO)

WELDING OUTLETS, INC.
1341 Hill Rd, Houston, TX 77039
Tel.: (281) 590-0190
Web Site: http://www.woihouston.com
Year Founded: 1999
Sales Range: $10-24.9 Million
Emp.: 82
Iron & Steel Pipe & Tube Mfr
N.A.I.C.S.: 331210
Sheryl Michalak (Pres)
Gabriel Dominguez (Engr-Product)
Enrique Arjona (Mgr-Quality Assurance)
Lisa Evans (Mgr-Pur)

WELDING TECHNOLOGY CORPORATION
24775 Crestview Ct, Farmington Hills, MI 48335
Tel.: (248) 477-3900
Web Site: http://www.weltronic.com
Sales Range: $10-24.9 Million
Emp.: 150
Resistance Welding Technology Services
N.A.I.C.S.: 335314
Daniel Thibodeau (Exec VP)
John Vogeli (VP-Tech)
Rae Martin (Mgr-HR)

Brian Johnston (Mgr-Engrg)
Heather Nelson (Mgr-Customer Svc)
Dave Desautel (Mgr-Production Control)

Subsidiaries:
WTC   (1)
24775 Crestview Ct, Farmington Hills, MI 48335-1507
Tel.: (248) 477-3900
Web Site: http://www.weldtechcorp.com
Sales Range: $10-24.9 Million
Emp.: 100
Resistance Welding Controls
N.A.I.C.S.: 333992

Welding Technology Corporation   (1)
24775 Crestview Ct, Farmington Hills, MI 48335-1507
Tel.: (248) 477-3900
Web Site: http://www.weldtechcorp.com
Provider of Resistance Welding Technology
N.A.I.C.S.: 333992
Miriam Kmetzo (Chief Customer Officer & VP Global Quality)

WELDON ASPHALT CORP.
141 Central Ave, Westfield, NJ 07090
Tel.: (908) 233-4444
Web Site: http://www.weldonmat.com
Sales Range: $10-24.9 Million
Emp.: 100
Asphalt Paving Mixtures & Blocks
N.A.I.C.S.: 324121
Richard T. Weldon (Pres)

WELDON MECHANICAL CORPORATION
3428 W Pioneer Pkwy, Arlington, TX 76013
Tel.: (817) 460-1111   TX
Web Site: http://www.weldon-contractors.com
Sales Range: $10-24.9 Million
Emp.: 120
Mechanical, Plumbing, Piping & Service Contractor
N.A.I.C.S.: 238220
J. Phillip Weldon (Founder & Pres)
Travis Miller (Controller)

WELDON PARTS INC.
711 W California Ave, Oklahoma City, OK 73102
Tel.: (405) 272-0417
Web Site: http://www.weldonparts.com
Year Founded: 1972
Sales Range: $10-24.9 Million
Emp.: 100
Truck Parts & Accessories
N.A.I.C.S.: 423120
David C. Settles (Pres)
Dean Clinton (Mgr-Sls)
David Rider (Mgr-IT)

WELDON SOLUTIONS
425 E Berlin Rd, York, PA 17408
Tel.: (717) 846-4000   PA
Web Site: http://www.weldonsolutions.com
Year Founded: 1971
Sales Range: $10-24.9 Million
Emp.: 33
Mfr of CNC Cylindrical Grinders
N.A.I.C.S.: 333517
George C. Sipe (Pres)
Denny L. Rowe (Dir-Sls & Mktg)
Travis Gentzler (Co-Pres)
Charles C. Gales (Mgr-Automation Sls)
John Bennett (Mgr-Engrg)

WELDON, WILLIAMS & LICK, INC.
711 N A St, Fort Smith, AR 72901-2121
Tel.: (479) 783-4113   AR

Web Site: http://www.wwlinc.com
Year Founded: 1898
Sales Range: $150-199.9 Million
Emp.: 350
Provider of Specialty Printing Services
N.A.I.C.S.: 323111
Tracey Geren (Pres)

Subsidiaries:
Just Arrive, LLC   (1)
PO Box 168, Fort Smith, AR 72902
Tel.: (800) 621-5245
Web Site: http://www.justarrive.com
Emp.: 2
Ticket Reservation Services
N.A.I.C.S.: 561599
Travis Porter (Gen Mgr)

WELDOTRON 2000, INC.
300 Bryant Ln, Woodbury, TN 37190-1630
Tel.: (615) 893-7577   TN
Web Site: http://www.weldotron.com
Year Founded: 1998
Shrink-Wrap Equipment & Replacement Parts Mfr
N.A.I.C.S.: 326150
David Olsen (Pres)

WELDSTAR COMPANY
1750 Mitchell Rd, Aurora, IL 60504
Tel.: (630) 859-3100
Web Site: http://www.weldstar.com
Rev.: $20,549,982
Emp.: 32
Welding Machinery & Equipment
N.A.I.C.S.: 423830
Chet Deking (VP-Ops & Gen Mgr)
Dan Regnier (Mgr-Sls)

WELDY-LAMONT ASSOCIATES INC.
1040 W Northwest Hwy, Mount Prospect, IL 60056
Tel.: (847) 398-4510
Web Site: http://www.weldy-lamont.com
Rev.: $48,000,000
Emp.: 18
Electrical Apparatus & Equipment
N.A.I.C.S.: 423610
Patrick Hennelly (Pres)
William Heberer (VP)
Joe Bolsinger (VP-Sls)

WELESKI TRANSFER INC.
140 W 4th Ave, Tarentum, PA 15084
Tel.: (724) 224-3330
Web Site: http://www.weleski.com
Rev.: $10,248,334
Emp.: 100
Household Goods Transport
N.A.I.C.S.: 484210
Gary Weleski (Pres)
F. Lynn Thompson (VP-Fin)
Mike Chick (Gen Mgr)

WELFL CONSTRUCTION CORPORATION
800 W 23rd St, Yankton, SD 57078-1207
Tel.: (605) 665-3258
Web Site: http://www.welfl.com
Year Founded: 1984
Sales Range: $10-24.9 Million
Emp.: 40
Nonresidential Construction Services
N.A.I.C.S.: 236220
Kevin Schulz (Owner)

WELK MUSIC GROUP INC.
11400 W Olympic Blvd Ste 1450, Los Angeles, CA 90064
Tel.: (310) 829-9355   CA
Sales Range: $1-9.9 Million
Emp.: 30

Music Publishing & Production Services
N.A.I.C.S.: 512230
Kevin Welk (Pres)
Lucy Sabini (VP-Media & Artist Rels)

Subsidiaries:
Easy Sound Recording Co.   (1)
11400 W Olympic Blvd Ste 760, Los Angeles, CA 90064
Tel.: (310) 829-9355
Emp.: 5
Record Production
N.A.I.C.S.: 512250
Stephen Brower (Gen Mgr)

WELL SPRING RETIREMENT COMMUNITY
4100 Well Spring Dr, Greensboro, NC 27410
Tel.: (336) 545-5400   NC
Web Site: http://www.well-spring.org
Year Founded: 1987
Sales Range: $10-24.9 Million
Emp.: 506
Lifecare Retirement Community Operator
N.A.I.C.S.: 623311
Misti Byler (Dir-Health Svcs)
Carol Owens (Dir-HR)
Stephen Fleming (Pres & CEO)
Leslie Daisy (Dir-Retirement Relocation)
George Galvin (Dir-Dining Svcs)
K. Alan Tutterow (CFO & Exec Dir)
Andrew Warren (Dir-Facility Ops & Resident Svcs)
Andrea Hunn (Mgr-Quality Assurance)
Chip Cromartie (VP-Home & Community Based Svcs)
Leslie Conway (VP-Mktg)
Jerry Hayes (VP-Construction Svcs)
Don Gwynn (Controller)
Marilyn Matier (Dir-Environmental Svcs)
Philip Johnson (Dir-Facility Svcs)
Alison Munroe-Lyles (Dir-Nursing)
Garrett Saake (Dir-Programs & Wellness)
Barbara Adams (Dir-Resident & Community Rels)
Jeremy Lane (Dir-Security Transportation)

WELL-PICT INC.
209 Riverside Rd, Watsonville, CA 95076
Tel.: (831) 722-3871   CA
Web Site: http://www.wellpict.com
Year Founded: 1972
Sales Range: $50-74.9 Million
Emp.: 100
Fresh Fruits & Vegetables
N.A.I.C.S.: 424480
Dan Crowley (Mgr-Sls)

WELLBORN CABINET, INC.
38669 Hwy 77 S, Ashland, AL 36251
Tel.: (256) 354-7151   AL
Web Site: http://www.wellborn.com
Year Founded: 1961
Sales Range: $200-249.9 Million
Emp.: 1,400
Wood Kitchen Cabinet Mfr
N.A.I.C.S.: 337110
Paul D. Wellborn (Pres & CEO)
Jeff Uhrin (CFO & CIO)
Lisa Mahon (Dir-HR)

Subsidiaries:
Cabinetry by Karman   (1)
6000 Stratler St, Salt Lake City, UT 84107-3304
Tel.: (801) 268-3581
Web Site: http://www.cabinetrybykarman.com

Sales Range: $25-49.9 Million
Emp.: 250
Mfr of Wood Kitchen Cabinets
N.A.I.C.S.: 337110
Adam Kinne *(Gen Mgr)*
Jeff Welch *(Asst Mgr-Production)*

Wellborn Holdings Inc. (1)
215 Diller Ave, New Holland, PA 17557
Tel.: (717) 351-1700
Web Site: http://www.rutt.net
Sales Range: $10-24.9 Million
Emp.: 100
Mfr of Custom Kitchen Cabinets, Custom Bath Vanities & Office, Den & Bar Furniture
N.A.I.C.S.: 337110
David Roos *(CEO)*

WELLEN CAPITAL, LLC
600 W Jackson Blvd, Chicago, IL 60661
Web Site: http://www.wellen.com
Year Founded: 2012
Sales Range: $10-24.9 Million
Emp.: 25
Financial Services
N.A.I.C.S.: 541611
Heidi Fisher *(Mgr-Customer Svc & Collection)*
Ed Job *(CEO)*
Ryan Miller *(VP-Data Analytics)*
Steve O'Connor *(Chief Revenue Officer)*
Brent Wagstaff *(Ops Mgr)*

WELLENS & CO., INC.
PO Box 24627, Minneapolis, MN 55424-0627
Tel.: (952) 925-4600   MN
Web Site: http://wellenscompany.com
Year Founded: 1959
Sales Range: $75-99.9 Million
Emp.: 5
Producer & Distributor of Animal Feed Ingredients
N.A.I.C.S.: 424910
Leroy Wellens *(Pres, CEO & CFO)*
Matthew Wellens *(Owner)*
Martha Wellens *(Treas & Sec)*

WELLER AUTO PARTS INC.
2019 Chicago Dr, Grand Rapids, MI 49509-9585
Tel.: (616) 241-2110   MI
Web Site: http://www.partsbyweller.com
Year Founded: 1935
Sales Range: $25-49.9 Million
Emp.: 220
Provider of Motor Vehicle Supplies & New Parts
N.A.I.C.S.: 423120
Harry R. Weller *(Pres)*

WELLESLEY COUNTRY CLUB
300 Wellesley Ave, Wellesley, MA 02481
Tel.: (781) 235-7333   MA
Web Site: http://www.wellesleycc.com
Year Founded: 1910
Sales Range: $10-24.9 Million
Country Club Operator
N.A.I.C.S.: 713910
David McNaughton *(Dir-Tennis)*
Jeffrey Phillips *(Head-Golf Professional & Dir-Golf)*
W. Chris Gustus *(CFO & COO)*
Martin Ryan *(Gen Mgr)*
Heather Rich *(Dir-Comm)*
Kathy Aylward *(Asst Controller)*
Pam Towle *(Dir-Catering)*
Ricardo Bertelli *(Dir-Ops)*
Tyler Wehr *(Mgr-Bar)*
Andrew Swett *(Dir-Fitness)*
William Sansone *(Dir-Golf Course Ops)*
Mark Thomas *(Dir-Pool)*
Bryan Wade *(Mgr-Svc)*
Judi Rizoli *(Coord-Function)*
Jeff Philips *(Head-Golf Professional)*
Frank Cartaglia *(Mgr-Outside)*

WELLEX CORPORATION
551 Brown Rd, Fremont, CA 94539
Tel.: (510) 743-1800
Web Site: http://www.wellex.com
Sales Range: $50-74.9 Million
Emp.: 200
Printed Circuit Boards
N.A.I.C.S.: 334412
Pablo Wei *(Dir-Quality Assurance)*
Susan Huang *(Mgr-Acctg)*
Emerieta Bautista *(Supvr-Quality Assurance)*

WELLFLEET FLEA MARKET
51 State Highway Route 6, Wellfleet, MA 02667
Tel.: (508) 349-7176
Web Site: http://www.wellfleetfleamarket.com
All Other Business Support Services
N.A.I.C.S.: 561499

WELLFOUNT CORP
5751 W 73rd St, Indianapolis, IN 46278-1741
Tel.: (317) 524-1515
Web Site: http://www.wellfount.com
Year Founded: 2006
Sales Range: $1-9.9 Million
Emp.: 70
Institutional Pharmacy that Serves Nursing, Assisted Living & Mental Health Facilities
N.A.I.C.S.: 456110
Paul Leamon *(Pres & CEO)*

WELLINGTON DIAGNOSTIC SERVICES
111 Wellington Pl, Cincinnati, OH 45219
Tel.: (513) 721-7226
Web Site: http://www.wdcmri.com
Sales Range: $1-9.9 Million
Emp.: 18
Management Consulting Services
N.A.I.C.S.: 541611
James Armitage *(Principal)*

WELLINGTON EQUESTRIAN PARTNERS, LLC
14440 Pierson Rd, Wellington, FL 33414
Tel.: (561) 459-6800   FL
Holding Company; Equestrian Real Estate Investment, Development & Management Services
N.A.I.C.S.: 551112
Mark J. Bellissimo *(Mng Partner)*

Subsidiaries:

International Polo Club Palm Beach (1)
3667 120th Ave S, Wellington, FL 33414
Tel.: (561) 204-5687
Web Site: http://ipc.coth.com
Sales Range: $10-24.9 Million
Emp.: 100
Polo Sports Facility & Club Operator
N.A.I.C.S.: 711310
Ray Mooney *(Dir-Facilities)*
Maria Feola *(Mgr-Box Office)*
Susan Eckels *(Dir-Retail)*
Nelson Tamargo *(Mgr-Food & Beverage)*
Farish Ensenat *(Mgr-Special Events)*
Jimmy Newman *(Dir-Polo Ops)*
Rick Landry *(Dir-Croquet)*
Michael Stone *(Pres)*

WELLINGTON EQUESTRIAN REALTY, LLC
13501 S Shore Blvd, Wellington, FL 33414
Tel.: (561) 818-4299   FL
Web Site: http://www.wellingtonequestrianrealty.com
Year Founded: 2010
Luxury Home & Farm Real Estate Agency
N.A.I.C.S.: 531210
Christopher J. Desino *(Co-Owner)*
Rob Desino *(Co-Owner)*
Matthew T. Varney *(Mgr)*

WELLINGTON HAMRICK, INC.
415 W College Ave, Boiling Springs, NC 28017
Tel.: (704) 434-6551
Web Site: http://www.wellingtonhamrick.com
Readymix Concrete Mfr
N.A.I.C.S.: 327320
Katherine Hoyle *(Pres)*

Subsidiaries:

Wellington Hamrick, Inc. - Shelby (1)
1111 Airport Road, Shelby, NC 28150
Tel.: (704) 487-6552
Web Site: http://www.wellingtonhamrick.com
Emp.: 10
Readymix Concrete Mfr
N.A.I.C.S.: 327320
Kitty Hoyle *(Pres)*

WELLINGTON MANAGEMENT COMPANY, LLP
280 Congress St, Boston, MA 02210
Tel.: (617) 951-5000
Web Site: http://www.wellington.com
Year Founded: 1979
Sales Range: $200-249.9 Million
Emp.: 1,100
Provider of Investment Advice
N.A.I.C.S.: 523940
Phillip H. Perelmuter *(Dir-Investment Res)*
Jean Hynes *(CEO)*

Subsidiaries:

Wellington Global Investment Management Ltd (1)
17 F Two International Finance Centre 8 Finance Street, Hong Kong, China (Hong Kong)
Tel.: (852) 2846 6000
Investment Management Service
N.A.I.C.S.: 523940
Ray Helfer *(Mng Dir)*

Wellington International Management Company Pte Ltd (1)
8 Marina Boulevard 03-01 Tower 1 Marina Bay Financial Centre, Singapore, 018981, Singapore
Tel.: (65) 6534 5115
Investment Management Service
N.A.I.C.S.: 523940

Wellington Management International Ltd (1)
80 Victoria Street, London, SW1E 5JL, United Kingdom
Tel.: (44) 20 7126 6000
Web Site: http://www.wellington.com
Investment Management Service
N.A.I.C.S.: 523940
Mark Jordy *(Mng Dir)*

Wellington Trust Co. (1)
75 State St, Boston, MA 02109-1814
Tel.: (617) 951-5000
Web Site: http://www.welligton.com
Sales Range: $125-149.9 Million
Investment Company
N.A.I.C.S.: 531120

WELLINGTON SHIELDS & CO., LLC
140 Broadway, New York, NY 10005
Tel.: (212) 320-3000   NY
Web Site: http://www.wellingtonshields.com
Year Founded: 2009
Emp.: 75
Investment Advisory, Securities Brokerage & Dealing Services
N.A.I.C.S.: 523150
David V. Shields *(CEO)*
Georges C. Boyer *(Sr VP & Sr Portfolio Mgr)*
Alexander Cripps *(Co-Chief Investment Officer & Sr Portfolio Mgr)*
Dimitri Kuriloff *(Sr VP & Coord-Res)*
Edward K. March *(COO & Principal-Municipal & Options)*
Mark Pankoff *(Exec VP & Portfolio Mgr-New York)*
Steve Portas *(Chief Compliance Officer)*
Alan M. Silverman *(Sr VP)*
Mark P. Sperry *(Sr VP & Sr Portfolio Mgr)*
B. K. Stafford *(Sr VP & Sr Portfolio Mgr)*
W. Jameson McFadden *(Pres & Sr Portfolio Mgr)*
Paul I. Gulden Jr. *(Co-Chief Investment Officer)*

WELLINGTON STATE BANK
1000 8th St, Wellington, TX 79095
Tel.: (806) 447-2551   TX
Web Site: http://www.wellingtonsb.com
Year Founded: 1906
Commercial Banking
N.A.I.C.S.: 522110
Richard Sims *(Pres & CEO)*
Bret Holloway *(Sr VP)*

WELLINGTON TECHNOLOGIES, INC.
802 Sharon Dr, Westlake, OH 44145
Tel.: (440) 238-4377   OH
Web Site: http://www.wtimaintains.com
Year Founded: 1996
Sales Range: $10-24.9 Million
Emp.: 26
Computer Server Maintenance
N.A.I.C.S.: 811210
Denise Trezbucowski *(Coord-Ops)*
Jerry F. Taylor Jr. *(Gen Mgr)*

WELLIVER MCGUIRE INC.
250 N Genefee Rd, Montour Falls, NY 14865
Tel.: (607) 535-5400   NY
Web Site: http://www.wellivermcguire.com
Year Founded: 1898
Sales Range: $25-49.9 Million
Emp.: 200
Nonresidential Construction
N.A.I.C.S.: 236220
Scott A. Welliver *(Chm & CEO)*
Tammy Goll *(CFO)*
Margaret Petrillose *(Mgr-Project Admin)*
Andrew Cove *(VP-Estimating)*
Luke Brown *(Project Mgr)*
Stephen Campbell *(Pres)*
Anne Welliver-Hartsing *(VP-Fin)*

WELLKEEPER INC
1208 San Pedro Dr NE, Albuquerque, NM 87110
Tel.: (505) 232-6908
Web Site: http://www.wellkeeper.com
Year Founded: 2001
Sales Range: $1-9.9 Million
Emp.: 20
Fiscal Year-end: 12/31/14
Oil & Gas Field Machinery & Equipment Mfr
N.A.I.C.S.: 333132

WELLMARK BLUE CROSS & BLUE SHIELD

WELLMARK BLUE CROSS & BLUE SHIELD

Wellmark Blue Cross & Blue Shield—(Continued)
1331 Grand Ave Sta 5W623, Des Moines, IA 50309
Tel.: (515) 376-4500
Web Site: http://www.wellmark.com
Year Founded: 1939
Sales Range: $10-24.9 Million
Emp.: 2,013
Direct Health & Medical Insurance Services
N.A.I.C.S.: 524114
Cory Harris *(Gen Counsel & Sr VP)*

WELLNESS CORPORATE SOLUTIONS, LLC
7617 Arlington Rd, Bethesda, MD 20814
Tel.: (301) 229-7555
Web Site:
http://www.wellnesscorporatesolutions.com
Year Founded: 2004
Sales Range: $1-9.9 Million
Emp.: 80
Business Management Consulting Services
N.A.I.C.S.: 541611
Fiona Gathright *(Pres & CEO)*
Juliet Rodman *(Co-Founder & Chief Wellness Officer)*
Emily Kolakowski *(COO)*
Doreen Moreira *(Dir-Medical)*
Erin Budd DeHaven *(Dir-Program Mgmt)*
Jared Rice *(VP-Tech)*
Matt Walnock *(Chief Info Security Officer)*
Melissa Fowler *(VP-Sls & Mktg)*
Nancy Lesch *(Dir-Strategy & Engagement)*

WELLNESS MATRIX GROUP, INC.
17011 Beach Blvd 9th Fl, Huntington Beach, CA 62647
Tel.: (310) 990-0336
Software Development Services
N.A.I.C.S.: 541511

WELLNESS NETWORKS INC
2751 E Jefferson Ave, Detroit, MI 48207
Tel.: (313) 446-9800 MI
Year Founded: 1983
Individual/Family Services
N.A.I.C.S.: 624190

WELLNESS POINTE
PO Box 3647, Longview, TX 75606
Tel.: (903) 758-2610 TX
Web Site:
http://www.wellnesspointe.org
Year Founded: 1997
Sales Range: $10-24.9 Million
Emp.: 248
Family Health Care Services
N.A.I.C.S.: 621498
Hollis Hill *(Sr Dir-Social Svcs)*
Hope Echols *(Dir-HR)*
Talia Peterson *(CFO)*
Chad T. Jones *(CEO)*
Annette Okpeki *(Chief Medical Officer)*

WELLONS INC.
2525 W Fire Stone Ln, Vancouver, WA 98660
Tel.: (503) 625-6131 OR
Web Site: http://www.wellons.com
Year Founded: 1972
Sales Range: $25-49.9 Million
Emp.: 200
Fabricated Plate Work (Boiler Shop)-Manufacturer
N.A.I.C.S.: 423740

Martin Nye *(Pres)*
Ken Kensley *(VP-Ops)*
Iqbal Diwan *(Engr-Controls)*
Jim Ashley *(Engr-Controls)*
Kenneth Kinsley *(VP-Ops)*
Scott Carlson *(Mgr-Matl Control)*
Tim Funk *(Engr-Mechanical)*
Jurgen Daub *(Chief Engr)*
Jim Turner *(Mgr-Field Projects)*

WELLPARTNER, INC.
7216 SW Durham Rd Ste 200, Portland, OR 97224
Tel.: (503) 718-5700
Web Site: http://www.wellpartner.net
Year Founded: 2001
Sales Range: $50-74.9 Million
Emp.: 135
Mail Order Pharmacy
N.A.I.C.S.: 325412
Larry D. Cartier *(VP-Pharmacy Ops)*
James P. Bradley *(Chm)*
James R. Love *(Pres & CEO)*
Ken Bodmer *(CFO & Exec VP-Fin & Admin)*
Tom Hagan *(Exec VP-Client Tech)*
Michael Majerik *(Exec VP-Sls & Mktg)*
Sharon Royer *(Sr Dir-Market Intelligence)*

WELLS & TATE ELECTRIC COMPANY INC.
160 Wells Rd, Meridianville, AL 35759
Tel.: (256) 828-0761
Web Site:
http://www.wellsandtate.com
Rev.: $10,000,000
Emp.: 75
Electrical Contractor
N.A.I.C.S.: 238210
Greg McCormick *(VP)*
Phillip McCormick *(VP)*
Britton M. McCormick *(Pres)*
Robert McCormick *(Treas & Sec)*

WELLS COMMUNICATIONS, INC.
3460 4th St, Boulder, CO 80304
Tel.: (303) 417-0696
Web Site:
http://www.wellscommunications.net
Sales Range: Less than $1 Million
Emp.: 5
Advertising Agencies
N.A.I.C.S.: 541810
Michele Wells *(Pres)*

WELLS CONCRETE PRODUCTS COMPANY INC.
835 Hwy 109 NE, Wells, MN 56097
Tel.: (507) 553-3138 MN
Web Site:
http://www.wellsconcrete.com
Year Founded: 1957
Sales Range: $25-49.9 Million
Emp.: 200
Concrete Products Mfr
N.A.I.C.S.: 327390
Spencer Kubat *(VP-Sls & Mktg Wells)*
Gregg Jacobson *(Sr VP-New Product Dev Wells)*
Dan Juntunen *(Pres & CEO-Albany)*
Ryan Stroschein *(CFO-Albany)*

Subsidiaries:

The Spancrete Group, Inc. (1)
N16 W23415 Stoneridge Dr, Waukesha, WI 53188-1154
Tel.: (414) 290-9000
Web Site: http://www.spancrete.com
Sales Range: $125-149.9 Million
Emp.: 620
Holding Company; Concrete Products Mfr
N.A.I.C.S.: 551112

John Schnell *(VP-Precast Ops-North)*
Jeff Winters *(Exec VP)*
George Wolfe *(Mgr-New Bus Dev-Newnan)*
Edward Lee *(Mgr-New Bus Dev-Newnan)*

Subsidiary (Domestic):

Spancrete Inc. (2)
N16 W23415 Stone Rdg Dr, Waukesha, WI 53188-1154
Tel.: (414) 290-9000
Web Site: http://www.spancrete.com
Sales Range: $10-24.9 Million
Emp.: 75
Concrete Products
N.A.I.C.S.: 327390
John H. Nagy *(Pres & CEO)*

Spancrete Machinery Corp. (2)
N16 W23415 Stoneridge Dr, Waukesha, WI 53188-1154
Tel.: (414) 290-9000
Web Site: http://www.spancrete.com
Sales Range: $10-24.9 Million
Emp.: 80
Construction Machinery
N.A.I.C.S.: 333120
John H. Nagy *(Chm & CEO)*
Nicholas Passint *(Gen Mgr)*

Spancrete of Illinois Inc. (2)
N16 W23415 Stone Rdg Dr, Waukesha, WI 53188-1154
Tel.: (414) 290-9000
Web Site: http://www.spancrete.com
Sales Range: $10-24.9 Million
Emp.: 70
Concrete Products
N.A.I.C.S.: 327390
John H. Nagy *(Chm & CEO)*

WBC Corp. (2)
N 16 W 23415 Stone Ridge Dr, Waukesha, WI 53188-1154 (100%)
Tel.: (414) 290-9000
Sales Range: $10-24.9 Million
Emp.: 15
Local Trucking
N.A.I.C.S.: 484220

WELLS ENTERPRISES, INC.
1 Blue Bunny Dr SW, Le Mars, IA 51031
Tel.: (712) 546-4000 IA
Web Site: http://www.wellsdairy.com
Year Founded: 1913
Sales Range: $1-4.9 Billion
Emp.: 2,500
Ice Cream Novelty Products
N.A.I.C.S.: 311520
Michael C. Wells *(Pres & CEO)*
Liam Killeen *(Pres)*
Erick Opsahl *(Gen Counsel & Sr VP-Legal Affairs)*
Jeremy Pinkerman *(CFO & Exec VP)*

Subsidiaries:

FieldBrook Foods Corporation (1)
1 Ice Cream Dr, Dunkirk, NY 14048-6318
Tel.: (716) 366-5400
Web Site: http://www.fieldbrookfoods.com
Sales Range: $150-199.9 Million
Emp.: 350
Ice Cream Product Mfr
N.A.I.C.S.: 311520
Norma Pulci *(Treas & Sec)*
Ron Odebralski *(Controller)*
Robin Galloway *(CEO)*

WELLS FARGO BANK
835 E Levee St, Brownsville, TX 78520
Tel.: (956) 548-6281
Web Site: http://www.wellsfargo.com
Year Founded: 1910
Sales Range: $1-9.9 Million
Emp.: 13
Commericial Banking
N.A.I.C.S.: 522110

WELLS GROUP LLC
460 W Main St, West Liberty, KY 41472
Tel.: (606) 743-3485

U.S. PRIVATE

Sales Range: $10-24.9 Million
Emp.: 20
Ready Mixed Concrete
N.A.I.C.S.: 327320
Joe S. Wells *(Pres)*

WELLS LAND DEVELOPMENT, INC.
12885 62nd St N Ste 300, Largo, FL 33773
Tel.: (727) 535-8241 FL
Web Site: http://www.wellsld.com
Year Founded: 1984
Sales Range: $1-9.9 Million
Emp.: 14
Excavation, Utilities & Paving Contractor
N.A.I.C.S.: 238110
Roger H. Wells *(Pres)*

WELLS MANUFACTURING LLC
8444 Rayson Rd, Houston, TX 77080
Tel.: (713) 690-4204
Web Site: http://www.wells-mfg.net
Year Founded: 2002
Sales Range: $1-9.9 Million
Emp.: 9
Machine Tools Mfr
N.A.I.C.S.: 333517
Patsy Wells *(CEO)*
James T. Wells *(COO)*

WELLS REAL ESTATE FUNDS, INC.
5445 Triangle Pkwy Ste 320, Peachtree Corners, GA 30092
Tel.: (770) 243-4600
Web Site: http://www.wellsref.com
Year Founded: 1984
Sales Range: $550-599.9 Million
Emp.: 300
Real Estate Investment Trust
N.A.I.C.S.: 525990
Leo Wells *(Owner)*

WELLS RURAL ELECTRIC COMPANY
1451 Humboldt Ave, Wells, NV 89835
Tel.: (775) 752-3328 NV
Web Site: http://www.wrec.coop
Year Founded: 1958
Electronic Services
N.A.I.C.S.: 221122
Clay Fitch *(CEO)*
Scott Egbert *(Pres)*
Gerald Anderson *(VP)*
Jonathan Dahl *(Treas & Sec)*

WELLS-KEOWN & ASSOCIATES INC.
301 Plauche St Ste A, Harahan, LA 70123
Tel.: (504) 733-0301 LA
Web Site:
http://www.wkaliahning.com
Rev.: $12,000,000
Emp.: 12
Lighting Fixtures
N.A.I.C.S.: 423610
Tom Keown *(Pres & Principal)*
Melody E. Heggins *(Engr-Applications)*
Chuck Nicholson *(Partner)*

WELLSPAN HEALTH
45 Monument Rd, York, PA 17403
Tel.: (717) 851-4275 PA
Web Site: http://www.wellspan.org
Emp.: 12,500
Health Care Services Organization
N.A.I.C.S.: 813910
Robert J. Longo *(Sr VP)*
Sandra Bennis *(VP-Home Care Svcs)*
Barbara Yarrish *(Sr VP-Post Acute Svcs)*

COMPANIES

Jason Trout *(Chief Dev Officer & VP-Philanthropy)*
Maria Royce *(Chief Strategy Officer & Sr VP-Strategy & Market Dev)*
Roxanna L. Gapstur *(Pres & CEO)*
Megan Lecas *(Sr VP-Svc Lines)*
Thomas McGann *(Exec VP-Clinical Practice)*

Subsidiaries:

The Good Samaritan Health Services Foundation of Lebanon, Pennsylvania (1)
4th & Walnut Sts, Lebanon, PA 17042
Tel.: (717) 270-7500
Web Site: http://www.gshleb.org
Health Care Services Organization
N.A.I.C.S.: 813910
Robert J. Longo *(Pres & CEO)*

WELLSPRING CANCER CENTER PLC

6600 66th St N, Pinellas Park, FL 33781
Tel.: (727) 343-0600
Web Site:
http://www.wellspringoncology.org
Sales Range: $10-24.9 Million
Emp.: 30
Oncology Services
N.A.I.C.S.: 622310
Lan Pratt *(Exec Dir)*
Janet Starr *(Bus Mgr & Mgr-Billing)*

WELLSPRING CAPITAL MANAGEMENT LLC

390 Park Ave 5th Fl, New York, NY 10022
Tel.: (212) 318-9800   DE
Web Site:
http://www.wellspringcapital.com
Year Founded: 1995
Privater Equity Firm
N.A.I.C.S.: 523999
Greg S. Feldman *(Founder, Chm & Partner)*
Alexander E. Carles *(Mng Partner)*
William L. Ramsey *(Operating Partner)*
John E. Morningstar *(Mng Partner)*
William F. Dawson Jr. *(CEO & Partner)*
Matthew G Harrison *(Mng Partner)*
Seth R. Pearson *(Partner)*
Paul D. Kaminski *(CFO)*
Alexander G. Bues *(Head-Bus Dev)*
Sarah A. Mudho *(Chief Complaince Officer & Gen Counsel)*
Marlene L. Reinhard *(Chief Admin Officer)*
Anthony M. Rivelli *(Controller)*
Michael B. Schwartzman *(VP)*
Naishadh Lalwani *(Partner)*
Jeffrey A. Gould *(Head-Mktg & IR)*

Subsidiaries:

Center for Diagnostic Imaging, Inc. (1)
5775 Wayzata Blvd Ste 400, Saint Louis Park, MN 55416
Tel.: (952) 543-6500
Web Site: http://www.cdiradiology.com
Sales Range: $100-124.9 Million
Emp.: 200
Diagnostic & Therapeutic Radiology Services
N.A.I.C.S.: 621498
Patrick Bakker *(VP & Controller)*
Jessica Larson *(VP-HR)*
Mark Arnold *(COO)*
Linda Bagley *(Sr VP/Gen Mgr-Central)*
Christopher Crancer *(Dir-Legislative)*
Matt Malloy *(VP-Mktg & Corp Comm)*
Ryan Raschke *(CFO)*
Anh Le Kremer *(Chief Compliance Officer & Gen Counsel)*
Glenn Galloway *(CIO)*
Anh Le Kremer *(Chief Admin Officer)*
Kimberly J. Commins-Tzoumakas *(CEO)*

Hoffmaster Group, Inc. (1)
2920 N Main St, Oshkosh, WI 54901
Web Site: http://www.hoffmaster.com
Disposable Tableware & Food Service Products Mfr
N.A.I.C.S.: 322219
Mike Marquardt *(VP-Pur)*
Frank Piotter *(Mgr-Shift)*
Tim Allen *(VP-Mfg)*
Wendy Nehring *(Supvr-Payroll)*
Paul Zuehlke *(Mgr-Art & Mktg Svcs)*
Timm Kaminski *(Dir-logistics-Food Svc Div & Mgr-Corp Transportation & Logistics)*
Craig Cappel *(CEO)*
Bree Gaber *(Mktg Comm Mgr)*

Division (Domestic):

Creative Converting (2)
255 Spring St, Clintonville, WI 54929
Tel.: (715) 823-3104
Web Site:
http://www.creativeconverting.com
Decorative Disposable Paper Plate & Napkin Mfr
N.A.I.C.S.: 322219
William Mullenix *(Pres)*
Daniel Buboltz *(Dir-Corp Customer Svc)*

Subsidiary (Domestic):

Paterson Pacific Parchment Co. (2)
625 Greg St, Sparks, NV 89431
Tel.: (775) 353-3000
Web Site: http://www.patersonpaper.com
Converted Paper Product Mfr
N.A.I.C.S.: 322299
Steven Page *(CFO)*
Joseph Buckley *(Pres)*

JW Aluminum Co. (1)
435 Old Mount Holly Rd, Goose Creek, SC 29445
Tel.: (843) 572-1100
Web Site: http://www.wellspringcapital.com
Sales Range: $75-99.9 Million
Specialty Flat Rolled Aluminum Products Mfr
N.A.I.C.S.: 331315
Philip Cavatoni *(CFO)*

Subsidiary (Domestic):

JW Aluminum Co. (2)
6100 S Broadway, Saint Louis, MO 63111-2597
Tel.: (314) 481-7000
Web Site: http://www.jwaluminum.com
Aluminum Foil Mfr
N.A.I.C.S.: 331315
Chester Roush *(Chief Strategy Officer)*
Lee McCarter *(CEO)*
Philip Cavatoni *(CFO)*
Ryan Roush *(Chief Comml Officer)*
Stan Brant *(COO)*

Paragon Films, Inc. (1)
3500 W Tacoma, Broken Arrow, OK 74012-1164
Tel.: (918) 250-3456
Web Site: http://www.paragonfilms.com
Stretch Films Mfr
N.A.I.C.S.: 326112
Scott King *(Plant Mgr)*
Keith Lay *(VP-Sls & Mktg)*
Darin Tang *(CEO)*
Mike Hildreth *(Dir-Analytics & Trng)*
Mike Fritts *(CFO)*
Rolly Cochlin *(COO)*

Pentec Health, Inc. (1)
50 Applied Bank Blvd, Glen Mills, PA 19342
Tel.: (610) 494-8700
Web Site: http://www.pentechealth.com
Sales Range: $25-49.9 Million
Emp.: 176
Women Healthcare Services
N.A.I.C.S.: 621610
Joseph Cosgrove *(Chm, Pres & CEO)*
Michael Abens *(Exec VP-Specialty Infusion Svcs & Gen Mgr)*
Barbara Knightly *(VP-Pharmacy)*
Tim Leffler *(CIO)*
Robert Provonche *(Exec VP-Sls & Mktg)*
Art Rea *(CFO)*
Charlie Wilson *(VP-HR)*
Karen McHenry *(Sr VP-Nursing Svcs)*
Kevin Mohler *(VP-Operational Excellence)*
Matthew L. Deans *(Chief Strategy Officer & Exec VP-Renal Div)*

Qualitor, Inc. (1)
24800 Denso Dr Ste 255, Southfield, MI 48033-7449
Tel.: (248) 204-8600
Web Site: http://www.qualitorinc.com
Automotive Products Mfr & Distr
N.A.I.C.S.: 336390
Gary Cohen *(CEO)*

Subsidiary (Domestic):

International Brake Industries, Inc. (2)
1840 Mccullough, Lima, OH 45801
Tel.: (419) 227-4421
Web Site: http://www.ibilima.com
Emp.: 28
Disk & Drum Brake Hardware
N.A.I.C.S.: 336340
Tony Sroufe *(Mktg Mgr)*
Teresa Holden *(VP & Controller)*
Andy Mayfield *(Chief Comml Officer)*
Gary Cohen *(Pres)*

Pylon Manufacturing Corporation (2)
1341 W Hillsboro Blvd Ste 400, Deerfield Beach, FL 33441
Tel.: (954) 428-7373
Web Site: http://www.pylonhq.com
Emp.: 27
Auto Parts & Accessories Mfr
N.A.I.C.S.: 336320
Michael Fretwell *(Pres)*
Harry Piedra *(CIO)*

Rohrer Corporation (1)
717 Seville Rd, Wadsworth, OH 44281-1077
Tel.: (330) 335-1541
Web Site: http://www.rohrer.com
Custom Skin & Blister Card Packaging Paper Spool Die-cut Paperboard Mfr
N.A.I.C.S.: 326199
David Rohrer *(Founder)*
Tim Swanson *(CEO)*
Jeremy Selin *(Mktg Mgr)*
Scott Sumser *(Sr VP-Sls & Mktg)*

Subsidiary (Domestic):

Jay Packaging Group, Inc. (2)
100 Warwick Industrial Dr, Warwick, RI 02886-2417
Tel.: (401) 739-7200
Web Site: http://www.jaypack.com
Label Printing & Specialty Packaging
N.A.I.C.S.: 323111
Richard E. Kelly *(CEO)*
Fernando Lemos *(Exec VP-Fin & Admin)*
Mark McCutcheon *(Mgr-Converting & Facilities)*

Plant (Domestic):

Rohrer Corp. - Buford Plant (2)
1800 Enterprise Dr, Buford, GA 30518
Tel.: (770) 945-1050
Web Site: http://www.rohrer.com
Sales Range: $25-49.9 Million
Emp.: 130
Skin & Blister Packaging
N.A.I.C.S.: 424130
Barry Dewitt *(Mgr-Pur)*
Bill Waters *(Gen Mgr)*

Rohrer Corp. - Huntley Plant (2)
13701 George Bush Ct, Huntley, IL 60142
Tel.: (847) 961-5920
Web Site: http://www.rohrercorporation.com
Sales Range: $25-49.9 Million
Emp.: 43
Producer of Customer Skin & Blister Carded Packaging
N.A.I.C.S.: 326199
Rob van Gilse *(Grp VP-Sls & Mktg)*

Unit (Domestic):

Rohrer Corp. - Printing Services (2)
159 W 1st Ave, Mesa, AZ 85210-1311
Tel.: (480) 964-2951
Web Site: http://www.rohrer.com
Sales Range: $1-9.9 Million
Emp.: 80
Commercial Printing Services
N.A.I.C.S.: 323111

Plant (Domestic):

Rohrer Corporation of Pennsylvania (2)
5 Industrial Park Rd, Lewistown, PA 17044-9342
Tel.: (717) 242-3308
Web Site: http://www.rohrer.com
Emp.: 50
Thermoformed Plastic Packaging Products Mfr
N.A.I.C.S.: 326199
Barry Feathers *(Mgr-Plant)*

Subsidiary (Domestic):

Transparent Container Co., Inc. (2)
325 S Lombard Rd, Addison, IL 60101
Tel.: (708) 449-8520
Web Site:
http://www.transparentcontainer.com
Sales Range: $25-49.9 Million
Emp.: 200
Provider of Plastic Products
N.A.I.C.S.: 326199

Subsidiary (Domestic):

Richardson & Edwards Printing, Inc. (3)
1110 W National Ave, Addison, IL 60101
Tel.: (630) 543-1818
Web Site: http://www.richanded.com
Sales Range: $1-9.9 Million
Emp.: 40
Paperboard Folding Carton & Other Retail Packaging Printing Services
N.A.I.C.S.: 323111

Plant (Non-US):

Transparent Container Co., Inc. - Mexico Facility (3)
Blvd Las Torres 916 Parque Industrial Cd Obregon, Ciudad Obregon, 85065, Sonora, Mexico
Tel.: (52) 888 449 8520
Paperboard Container Mfr
N.A.I.C.S.: 322219

Plant (Domestic):

Transparent Container Co., Inc. - Paperboard Facility (3)
1110 National Ave, Addison, IL 60101
Tel.: (630) 543-1818
Paperboard Container Mfr
N.A.I.C.S.: 322219

Steele Solutions, Inc. (1)
9909 S 57th St, Franklin, WI 53132
Tel.: (414) 367-5099
Web Site: http://www.steelesolutions.com
Designs & Manufactures Support Structures for Warehouse & Distribution Spaces
N.A.I.C.S.: 332312
Kevin O'Neill *(CEO)*
Mike Thelen *(Chm)*
Terry Young *(VP-Engrg)*

Subsidiary (Domestic):

Tiffin Metal Products Co. (2)
450 Wall St, Tiffin, OH 44883
Tel.: (419) 447-8414
Web Site: http://www.tiffinmetal.com
Rev.: $19,990,772
Emp.: 80
Bill Boards & Security Locks Mfr
N.A.I.C.S.: 332510
Timothy A. Demith *(CFO)*
Richard M. Wyka *(VP-Mfg)*
Ronald J. Myers *(VP-Sls & Mktg)*
Willard P. Heddles *(Chm & CEO)*

SupplyOne, Inc. (1)
11 Campus Blvd Ste 150, Newtown Square, PA 19073
Tel.: (484) 582-5005
Web Site: http://www.supplyone.com
Packaging Products Mfr
N.A.I.C.S.: 322211
William T. Leith *(Founder, Pres & CEO)*

Subsidiary (Domestic):

Bacon & Graham, Inc. (2)
34 E 25th St, Paterson, NJ 07514
Tel.: (973) 684-1488
Web Site: http://www.baconandgraham.com
Sales Range: $1-9.9 Million
Emp.: 35
Whol Indstl/Svc Paper Whol Svc Estblshmt Equip Whol Chemicals/Products
N.A.I.C.S.: 424130

WELLSPRING CAPITAL MANAGEMENT LLC

U.S. PRIVATE

Wellspring Capital Management LLC—(Continued)
Craig Bacon (Pres)

Omni Packaging Corporation (2)
12322 E 55th St, Tulsa, OK 74146
Tel.: (918) 461-1700
Web Site: http://www.omnipackaging.com
Packaging Material Distr
N.A.I.C.S.: 424990

SupplyOne Cleveland, Inc. (2)
26801 B Fargo Ave, Cleveland, OH 44146
Tel.: (216) 514-7000
Packaging Products Mfr
N.A.I.C.S.: 322211

SupplyOne Tucson, Inc. (2)
6874 S Palo Verde, Tucson, AZ 85756
Tel.: (520) 573-7080
Packaging Products Mfr
N.A.I.C.S.: 322211
Mark S. McArthur (Pres-Southwest Reg)

Plant (Domestic):

SupplyOne Tucson, Inc. - Albuquerque Plant (3)
8330 Jefferson NE, Albuquerque, NM 87113
Tel.: (505) 821-7225
Packaging Products Mfr
N.A.I.C.S.: 322211

Subsidiary (Domestic):

SupplyOne Weyers Cave, Inc. (2)
90 Packaging Dr, Weyers Cave, VA 24486
Tel.: (540) 234-9292
Packaging Products Mfr
N.A.I.C.S.: 322211
Tracy Stallard (Acct Mgr)

Plant (Domestic):

SupplyOne Weyers Cave, Inc. - Chesapeake Plant (3)
3813 Cook Blvd, Chesapeake, VA 23323
Tel.: (757) 485-3570
Corrugated Packaging Product Mfr
N.A.I.C.S.: 322211

Subsidiary (Domestic):

SupplyOne Wisconsin, LLC (2)
W209 N17450 Industrial Dr, Jackson, WI 53037
Tel.: (262) 677-8655
Corrugated Packaging Product Mfr
N.A.I.C.S.: 322211
Linnea Koenigs (Mgr-HR)

Plant (Domestic):

SupplyOne, Inc. - Dallas Plant (2)
1608 Plantation Rd, Dallas, TX 75235
Tel.: (214) 637-0160
Corrugated Packaging Product Mfr
N.A.I.C.S.: 322211

ThermaSys, Corp. (1)
2776 Gunter Park Dr E Ste RS, Montgomery, AL 36109-1016
Tel.: (334) 244-9240
Web Site: http://www.thermasys.com
Sales Range: $25-49.9 Million
Mfr Heat Exchange Products for Automotive Industry
N.A.I.C.S.: 333414
Joe Scheurer (Dir-Ops)
Gail Wells (Mgr-HR)

WELLSPRING WORLDWIDE, LLC

350 N Lasalle St 12th Fl, Chicago, IL 60654-3973
Tel.: (312) 643-5100
Web Site:
 http://www.wellspringworldwide.com
Custom Computer Programming Services
N.A.I.C.S.: 541511
Sandi Lowe (Chief Experience Officer)
Sean Downs (CEO)

Subsidiaries:

Sopheon Plc (1)
Dorna House One Guildford Road, West End, London, GU24 9PW, Surrey, United Kingdom
Tel.: (44) 1276919560
Web Site: https://www.sopheon.com
Rev.: $29,996,000
Assets: $48,278,000
Liabilities: $18,123,000
Net Worth: $30,155,000
Earnings: $1,496,000
Emp.: 165
Fiscal Year-end: 12/31/2020
Information Management Software
N.A.I.C.S.: 513210
Barry K. Mence (Chm)
Andrew L. Michuda (CEO)
Arif Karimjee (CFO, Fin Dir & Sec)
Pieter Leijten (VP-Europe)
Steve Alexander (VP-Global Consulting)
Greg Coticchia (Pres)
Heather MacIntosh (CMO)
Mike Bauer (Chief Product Officer)
John Beischer (Sr VP)
Mark Meakins (VP)
Charles Charles (VP)
Peter Loerincs (VP)

Subsidiary (Non-US):

Sopheon NV (2)
Kantoorgebouw Officia 1 De Boelelaan 7, 1083 HJ, Amsterdam, Netherlands
Tel.: (31) 203013900
Software Services
N.A.I.C.S.: 327910

Subsidiary (Non-US):

Sopheon GmbH (3)
Lise-Meitner-Str 10, 64293, Darmstadt, Germany
Tel.: (49) 6151860420
Software Services
N.A.I.C.S.: 541511

Subsidiary (Domestic):

Sopheon UK Ltd. (3)
Dorna House One Guildford Road, West End, London, GU24 9PW, Surrey, United Kingdom
Tel.: (44) 1276919560
Software Services
N.A.I.C.S.: 541511

WELLSTAR HEALTH SYSTEM, INC.

805 Sandy Plains Rd, Marietta, GA 30066
Tel.: (770) 792-7600
Web Site: http://www.wellstar.org
Sales Range: $1-4.9 Billion
Emp.: 11,347
Healthcare; Physicians, Hospitals, Hospice, Home Care Programs, Senior Living, Urgent Care Facilities
N.A.I.C.S.: 622110
Candice L. Saunders (Pres & CEO)
Dan Woods (Sr VP)
John A. Brennan (Chief Clinical Integration Officer & Exec VP)
Barry Mangel (Chief Cardiology Officer)
Jeffrey Tharp (Chief Medicine Div Officer)
Avril Beckford (Chief Pediatrics Officer)
Hank Capps (Chief Info & Digital Officer & Exec VP)

Subsidiaries:

WellStar Atlanta Medical Center South (1)
1170 Cleveland Ave, East Point, GA 30344
Tel.: (404) 466-1170
Web Site: http://www.wellstar.org
Hospital Operator
N.A.I.C.S.: 622110
Jane Hamilton (Dir-Surgical Svcs)

WellStar Atlanta Medical Center, Inc. (1)
303 Pkwy Dr NE, Atlanta, GA 30312
Tel.: (404) 265-4000
Web Site: http://www.wellstar.org
Hospital Operator
N.A.I.C.S.: 622110

Subsidiary (Domestic):

Peachtree Surgical & Bariatric, PC (2)
285 Blvd NE Ste 120, Atlanta, GA 30312-4205
Tel.: (404) 881-8020
Web Site: http://www.wellstar.org
Health Care Srvices
N.A.I.C.S.: 621999

WellStar Medical Group Neurosurgery (2)
285 Blvd NE Ste 415, Atlanta, GA 30307
Tel.: (404) 265-4400
Web Site: http://www.wellstar.org
Neurological Hospital
N.A.I.C.S.: 622310

WellStar Medical Group Rheumatology (2)
285 Blvd NE Ste 625, Atlanta, GA 30312
Tel.: (404) 265-3330
Web Site: http://www.wellstar.org
Health Care Srvices
N.A.I.C.S.: 621999

Wellstar Medical Group Interventional Neurology (2)
285 Blvd NE Ste 415, Atlanta, GA 30307
Tel.: (404) 265-5545
Web Site: http://www.wellstar.org
Neurological Services
N.A.I.C.S.: 621111

WellStar North Fulton Hospital, Inc. (1)
3000 Hospital Blvd, Roswell, GA 30076
Tel.: (770) 751-2500
Web Site: http://www.wellstar.org
Hospital Operator
N.A.I.C.S.: 622110
Debbie Keel (CEO)

Subsidiary (Domestic):

Endoscopy Consultants, LLC (2)
5669 Peachtree Dunwoody Rd 290, Atlanta, GA 30342
Tel.: (678) 399-2050
Web Site:
 http://www.endoscopyconsultantsllc.com
Health Care Srvices
N.A.I.C.S.: 621999

Roswell Georgia Surgery Center, L.L.C. (2)
1285 Hembree Rd Ste 200-C, Roswell, GA 30076
Tel.: (770) 772-5520
Web Site: http://www.roswell-sc.com
Medical Devices
N.A.I.C.S.: 622110
Steven Waronker (Dir-Medical)
Stephanie Carver (Office Mgr-Bus)
Susan West (Mgr-Operating Room)

Wellstar North Fulton Hospital (2)
3000 Hospital Blvd, Roswell, GA 30076-4915
Tel.: (770) 751-2500
Web Site: http://www.wellstar.org
Health Care Srvices
N.A.I.C.S.: 621999

Subsidiary (Domestic):

Wellstar Medical Group Cardiovascular Medicine (2)
4500 Hospital Blvd Ste 230, Roswell, GA 30076
Tel.: (770) 410-4520
Web Site: http://www.wellstar.org
Health Care Srvices
N.A.I.C.S.: 621999
Debbie Todd (Office Mgr)

Wellstar Medical Group Northside ENT (3)
1360 Upper Hembree Rd Ste 201, Roswell, GA 30076-1171
Tel.: (770) 475-3361
Web Site: http://www.wellstar.org
Specialty Clinical Services
N.A.I.C.S.: 622310
Paula Chambers (Office Mgr)

WellStar Spalding Regional Hospital, Inc. (1)
601 S 8th St, Griffin, GA 30224
Tel.: (770) 228-2721
Web Site: http://www.wellstar.org
News Syndicates
N.A.I.C.S.: 516210
Wadra McCullough (Chief Nursing Officer)

WellStar Sylvan Grove Hospital, Inc. (1)
1050 McDonough Rd, Jackson, GA 30233
Tel.: (770) 775-7861
Web Site: http://www.wellstar.org
Hospital Operator
N.A.I.C.S.: 622110
Lisa Johnson (Chief Nursing Officer & VP)

Wellstar Medical Group Family Medicine (1)
14205 Highway 92 Ste 105, Woodstock, GA 30188-7138
Tel.: (678) 293-7854
Web Site: http://www.wellstar.org
Emp.: 5
Health Care Srvices
N.A.I.C.S.: 621999
Jennifer Atkins (Mgr)

WELLTEK CORPORATION

87 Ave De Diego, San Juan, PR 00927
Tel.: (787) 756-5222
Rev.: $21,300,000
Emp.: 84
Diet Foods
N.A.I.C.S.: 424490
Barbara Wellman (Pres)

WELLTEK INCORPORATED

1030 N Orange Ave Ste 300, Orlando, FL 32801
Tel.: (407) 704-8950
Sales Range: $1-9.9 Million
Emp.: 20
Pharmacy Operator
N.A.I.C.S.: 456110
Mark Szporka (CFO)
Randy Lubinsky (CEO)
Vladimir Kravchenko (Pres)
Peter Sidorenko (Sr VP)

WELLTOK, INC.

1515 Arapahoe St Tower 3 Ste 700, Denver, CO 80202
Web Site: http://www.welltok.com
Social Health Management Services
N.A.I.C.S.: 923120
Jeff Margolis (Chm)
James Sullivan (Chief Admin Officer & Sr VP)
Maneesh Goyal (Sr VP-Corp Dev)
Rob Scavo (Pres & Co-COO)
Khaled Nasr (Co-COO)
Chaz Hinkle (Chief People Officer & Sr VP)
Chris Power (CFO & Sr VP)
Bob Fabbio (CEO)

Subsidiaries:

Predilytics, Inc. (1)
1 New England Executive Park Ste 104, Burlington, MA 01803-5005
Tel.: (781) 202-9160
Web Site: http://www.predilytics.com
Data Processing, Hosting & Related Services
N.A.I.C.S.: 518210
William Panak (VP-Analytics Dev)
Sashi Desikan (Sr VP-Solution Engrg & Tech)
Chris Coloian (Pres)
Hariharan Sundram (Chief Medical Officer)
Phil Fiero (Sr VP-Analytic Solutions)
Carla Galisin (VP-Client Rels)
Kevin Smith (VP-Sls)
April Gill (VP-Client Rels)

Silverlink Communications, LLC (1)
67 S Bedford St Ste 300E 1 Burlington Bus Ctr, Burlington, MA 01803
Tel.: (781) 425-5700

Web Site: http://www.silverlink.com
Rev.: $2,200,000
Emp.: 20
Healthcare Communications & Services
N.A.I.C.S.: 517810
Stan Nowak (Pres)
Paul G. Fitzgerald (CFO & Treas)
Jim Wolf (Sr VP-Sls)
Paulo Matos (Chief Product Officer)

WELOCALIZE, INC.
241 E 4th St Ste 207, Frederick, MD 21701-3612
Tel.: (301) 668-0330   DE
Web Site: http://www.welocalize.com
Year Founded: 1997
Sales Range: $10-24.9 Million
Emp.: 102
Multilingual Software, Product Localization & Translation Services
N.A.I.C.S.: 541930
Smith E. Yewell (Co-Founder & CEO)
Julia Yewell (Co-Founder & VP-Fin)
Chris Grebisz (Chief Innovation Officer)
Jeff Ash (CFO)
Erin Wynn (Chief Customer Officer)
Ashwin Bhatia (Chief Svcs Officer)

Subsidiaries:

Global Language Solutions, LLC   (1)
19800 MacArthur Blvd Ste 200, Irvine, CA 92612
Tel.: (949) 798-1400
Sales Range: $1-9.9 Million
Emp.: 28
Translation & Interpretation Services
N.A.I.C.S.: 541930
Olga Smirnova (CEO)
Inna Kassatkina (Pres)
Dylan Jackson (Dir-Bus Dev)
Joyce Logrono (Mgr-HR)

Welocalize GmbH   (1)
Nell-Breuning-Allee 10, Saarbrucken, 66115, Germany
Tel.: (49) 681992940
Web Site: http://www.welocalize.de
Sales Range: $10-24.9 Million
Emp.: 25
Multilingual Software, Product Localization & Translation Services
N.A.I.C.S.: 541930
Christian Krumb (Mng Dir)

Welocalize Ireland   (1)
Hibernia House Cherrywood Business Park, Loughlinstown, Dublin, 18, Ireland
Tel.: (353) 12187700
Web Site: http://www.welocalize.com
Emp.: 50
Multilingual Software, Product Localization & Translation Services
N.A.I.C.S.: 541930
Eugene McGinty (Mng Dir)

WELSCH HEATING & COOLING CO.
2175 Welsch Industrial Ct, Saint Louis, MO 63146-4220
Tel.: (314) 872-8070
Web Site: http://welsch-heatcool.com
Year Founded: 1895
Sales Range: $10-24.9 Million
Emp.: 75
Air Conditioning System Installation Services
N.A.I.C.S.: 238220
George Welsch (CEO)

WELSCO INC.
9006 Crystal Hill Rd, North Little Rock, AR 72113-6693
Tel.: (501) 771-1204   AR
Web Site: http://www.welsco.com
Year Founded: 1941
Sales Range: $75-99.9 Million
Emp.: 105
Mfr & Vendor of Industrial Gases & Welding Supplies
N.A.I.C.S.: 423840

Angela Harrison (Chm & CEO)
Aline Daniels (VP-HR)
Charles Ross (VP-Pur)
Rhonnie Goyne (VP-Safety & Compliance)
Chris Layton (VP-Sls-Eastern Div)
Stacey Shellnut (Mgr-Credit)
Adam Kohler (Pres-Sls)

WELSH COMPANIES LLC
4350 Baker Rd 400, Minnetonka, MN 55343
Tel.: (952) 897-7700
Web Site: http://www.welshco.com
Sales Range: $50-74.9 Million
Emp.: 276
Real Estate Managers
N.A.I.C.S.: 531210
Dennis J. Doyle (CEO)
Jean Kane (CEO-Welsh & Colliers Intl-Minneapolis)
Scott T. Frederiksen (CEO)
John Johannson (Sr VP-Retail Team)
Mike Schraad (Pres-Construction)
William M. Wardwell (Exec VP & Mng Dir-Brokerage)

Subsidiaries:

Genesis Architecture LLC   (1)
4350 Baker Rd Ste 400, Minnetonka, MN 55343
Tel.: (952) 897-7874
Web Site: http://www.welshco.com
Rev.: $1,049,000
Emp.: 15
Architectural Services
N.A.I.C.S.: 541310
Lynn D. Sloat (Sr VP)

Welsh Construction LLC   (1)
4350 Baker Rd Ste 400, Minnetonka, MN 55343
Tel.: (952) 897-7860
Web Site: http://www.welshco.com
Emp.: 200
Warehouse Construction
N.A.I.C.S.: 236220
Mike Schraad (Pres)
Steve Anderson (Sr Project Mgr-Melbourne)
Jason McMillen (Dir-Project Mgmt)
Allen Overturf (CFO)

WELSH PROPERTY TRUST, INC.
4350 Baker Rd Ste 400, Minnetonka, MN 55343
Tel.: (952) 897-7700   MD
Web Site: http://www.welshco.com
Sales Range: $50-74.9 Million
Emp.: 250
Real Estate Investment Services
N.A.I.C.S.: 525990
Dennis J. Doyle (Chm)
Jean Kane (Pres & COO)
Scott T. Frederiksen (CEO)

WELSH, CARSON, ANDERSON & STOWE
599 Lexington Ave Ste 1800, New York, NY 10022
Tel.: (212) 893-9500
Web Site: http://www.wcas.com
Year Founded: 1979
Privater Equity Firm
N.A.I.C.S.: 523999
Bruce Kirkpatrick Anderson (Co-Founder & Gen Partner)
Jonathan M. Rather (Gen Partner)
Patrick J. Welsh (Co-founder & Gen Partner)
D. Scott Mackesy (Mng Partner)
Thomas A. Scully (Gen Partner)
Fran Higgins (Dir-IR)
Eric J. Lee (Gen Partner-Tech)
Anthony J. de Nicola (Pres & Mng Partner)
Russell L. Carson (Co-Founder & Gen Partner)

Christopher W. Solomon (Dir-Capital Markets)
Tracy L. Bahl (Operating Partner)
Michael E. Donovan (Gen Partner)
Edward P. Sobol (Gen Partner-Healthcare)
Brian T. Regan (Gen Partner)
Ting Gu (VP)
Christian Heim (Principal)
Alex Kerr (VP)
Sidney Ouyang (Principal)
Daniel Pang (VP)
Emily Victor-Smith (VP-IR)
Christopher Hooper (Gen Partner-San Francisco)
Ian MacLeod (Operating Partner)
Caroline Dechert (VP)
Gregory Lau (Gen Partner)
H. Lee Cooper (Operating Partner)
Andrew Hausman (Operating Partner-Tech Grp)
Ryan Harper (Gen Partner)
Kevin Gordon (VP)
James H. Hinton (Operating Partner)
Sean M. Traynor (Gen Partner)

Subsidiaries:

Absorb Software Inc.   (1)
685 Centre St S Ste 2500, Calgary, T2G 1S5, AB, Canada
Tel.: (403) 717-1971
Web Site: http://www.absorblms.com
E-Learning & Professional Development
N.A.I.C.S.: 513210
Mike Owens (Founder & CEO)

Subsidiary (US):

ePath Learning, Inc.   (2)
300 State St Ste 400, New London, CT 06320
Tel.: (860) 444-6989
Web Site: http://www.epathlearning.com
Sales Range: $1-9.9 Million
Emp.: 24
Professional Training
N.A.I.C.S.: 611430
Dudley Molina (Founder, Pres & CEO)
Steve Morse (VP-Client Svcs)
Carol Wojtkun (VP-Pro Svcs)

Abzena plc   (1)
Babraham Research Campus, Babraham, Cambridge, CB22 3AT, United Kingdom
Tel.: (44) 1223 496 190
Web Site: http://www.abzena.com
Pharmaceuticals Mfr
N.A.I.C.S.: 325412
Matthew Baker (Chief Scientific Officer)
Donna Hackett (VP-Intellectual Property, Comml & Legal Affairs)
Thomas P. Castellano (CFO)
John Manzello (Pres-US)
Sven Lee (Chief Bus Officer-US)
Kimball Hall (COO)
Jim Kennamer (Sr VP & Head-Site-North Carolina)
Matt Stober (CEO)

Subsidiary (US):

The Chemistry Research Solution LLC   (2)
360 George Patterson Blvd Ste 180, Bristol, PA 19007-3628
Tel.: (215) 788-3603
Web Site: http://www.tcrs.us
Emp.: 35
Produces & Analyzes Antibody Drug Conjugates
N.A.I.C.S.: 541715
Naresh Jain (Mng Dir)
John Burt (Pres & CEO)

Avetta, LLC   (1)
3300 Triumph Blvd Ste 800, Lehi, UT
Tel.: (800) 506-7427
Web Site: http://www.avetta.com
Software Publisher
N.A.I.C.S.: 513210
Jeff Kristick (Chief Revenue Officer)
Aaron Wattam (Chief HR Officer)
Raj Amin (CFO & Exec VP)
Taylor Allis (Chief Product & Marketing Officer)
Christopher Lewis (CTO)
Arshad Matin (Pres & CEO)

Concentra Inc.   (1)
5080 Spectrum Dr Ste 1200W, Addison, TX 75001-6484
Tel.: (972) 364-8000
Web Site: https://www.concentra.com
Holding Company; Healthcare Services
N.A.I.C.S.: 551112
Giovanni Gallara (Chief Clinical Svcs Officer & Exec VP)
Dani Kendall (Sr VP-Human Resources)
Michael Kosuth (COO-East Reg & Sr VP)
Tom Devasia (Chief Innovation Officer)
Mike Rhine (Exec VP)

Subsidiary (Domestic):

Concentra Akron, LLC   (2)
1450 Firestone Pkwy, Akron, OH 44301
Tel.: (330) 724-3345
Web Site: https://www.concentra.com
Emp.: 25
Insurance & Healthcare Services
N.A.I.C.S.: 524114

Concentra Health Services, Inc.   (2)
5080 Spectrum Dr W Tower Ste 400, Addison, TX 75001
Tel.: (972) 364-8000
Insurance Carrier
N.A.I.C.S.: 524114
Pedro Marzocca (Dir-Reimbursement Primary Care)
Mary Turner (Assoc Gen Counsel)

Concentra Occupational Health Research Institute   (2)
5080 Spectrum Dr Ste 1200 W Tower, Addison, TX 75001
Tel.: (512) 467-7232
Web Site: https://www.cohri.net
Medical Education & Research Services
N.A.I.C.S.: 541720

Concentra Operating Corporation   (2)
5080 Spectrum Dr Ste 1200 W, Addison, TX 75001-6484
Tel.: (972) 364-8000
Web Site: https://www.concentra.com
Emp.: 500
Occupational, Auto & Group Healthcare Cost Containment, Case Management & Workers Compensation Services
N.A.I.C.S.: 621399
Keith Newton (Pres & CEO)
John Anderson (Chief Medical Officer & Sr VP)
John deLorimier (CMO, Chief Sls Officer & Exec VP)
Greg Gilbert (Sr VP-Reimbursement & Govt Affairs)
Jim Talalai (CIO & Sr VP)
Su Zan Nelson (CFO)
Jon Conser (Sr VP-Sls)
Matthew DiCanio (Sr VP-Strategy & Corp Dev)
Dani Kendall (Sr VP-HR)
Giovanni Gallara (Sr VP & Dir-Natl Therapy)
Michael Kosuth (Sr VP-Ops-East Reg)
Doug McAndrew (Sr VP-Ops-West Reg)

Subsidiary (Domestic):

Concentra Medical Center   (3)
3580 Atlanta Ave, Hapeville, GA 30354-1706
Tel.: (404) 768-3351
Web Site: http://www.concentra.com
Emp.: 30
Occupational Medicine & Health Care Services
N.A.I.C.S.: 621111

Subsidiary (Domestic):

Concentra Solutions, Inc.   (2)
500 Sugar Mill Rd Bldg A Ste 130, Sandy Springs, GA 30350
Web Site: https://www.concentrasolutions.com
Marketing Consulting Services
N.A.I.C.S.: 541618
Rica Askew (VP-Sales-Marketing)
Kim Christmas (VP-HR)

U.S. HealthWorks Medical Group, Prof. Corp.   (2)
28035 Ave Stanford W, Valencia, CA 91355
Tel.: (661) 678-2300
Web Site: http://www.ussouthworks.com

WELSH, CARSON, ANDERSON & STOWE

Welsh, Carson, Anderson & Stowe—(Continued)

Occupational Medicine & Urgent Care Services
N.A.I.C.S.: 621999
Don Bopp *(Reg Dir-Sls)*

Consumer Safety Technology, LLC (1)
11035 Aurora Ave, Des Moines, IA 50325
Tel.: (515) 331-7643
Web Site: http://www.intoxalock.com
Motor Vehicle Ignition Interlock Device Developer, Mfr & Whslr
N.A.I.C.S.: 336320
Kimberly Williams *(CEO)*
Brad Fralick *(Dir-Govt Rels)*

Green Street Advisors Inc. (1)
660 Newport Center Dr Ste 800, Newport Beach, CA 92660
Tel.: (949) 640-8780
Web Site: http://www.greenst.com
Sales Range: $10-24.9 Million
Emp.: 100
Investment Advice
N.A.I.C.S.: 523940
Mike Kirby *(Founder & Dir-Res)*
Robyn Francis *(Mgr-Compliance)*
Jon A. Fosheim *(Co-Founder)*

Nester Consulting LLC (1)
8400 Braddock Way, Columbia, MD 21046-1264
Tel.: (443) 535-1599
Web Site: http://www.governmentcio.com
Management Consulting Services
N.A.I.C.S.: 541618
William Giandoni *(Sr VP)*

Paycom Software, Inc. (1)
7501 W Memorial Rd, Oklahoma City, OK 73142
Tel.: (405) 722-6900
Web Site: https://www.paycom.com
Rev.: $1,693,674,000
Assets: $4,197,539,000
Liabilities: $2,894,503,000
Net Worth: $1,303,036,000
Earnings: $340,788,000
Emp.: 7,308
Fiscal Year-end: 12/31/2023
Internet Payroll & Human Resources Software
N.A.I.C.S.: 513210
Jason D. Clark *(Chief Admin Officer)*
Brad Smith *(CIO)*
James Samford *(Head-IR)*
Chad Richison *(Founder, Chm, Pres & CEO)*

TrueCommerce, Inc. (1)
210 W Kensinger Dr St 100, Cranberry Township, PA 16066
Tel.: (724) 940-5520
Web Site: http://www.truecommerce.com
Rev.: $4,800,000
Emp.: 70
Software Publisher
N.A.I.C.S.: 513210
John Fay *(CEO)*
Yegor Kuznetsov *(Dir-Mktg Comm)*
Lacey Ford *(CMO)*

Subsidiary (Domestic):

Dicentral Corp. (2)
17625 El Camino Real Ste 200, Houston, TX 77058
Tel.: (281) 480-1121
Web Site: http://secure1.dicentral.com
Sales Range: $1-9.9 Million
Emp.: 85
Software Publisher
N.A.I.C.S.: 513210
Thuy Mai *(Pres & CEO)*
Chuck Adams *(Exec VP-Delivery & Pro Svcs)*
Trung Pham *(CTO)*
David Swanlaw *(Dir-Customer Success)*
Jeff Fiesinger *(CFO)*
George Hall *(Exec VP-HR)*

United Vision Logistics Holding Corp. (1)
4021 Ambassador Caffery Pkwy Ste 200 Bldg A, Lafayette, LA 70503
Tel.: (337) 291-6700
Web Site: http://www.uvlogistics.com
Sales Range: $75-99.9 Million
Emp.: 400
Trucking Service
N.A.I.C.S.: 484121
Rusty Guilbeau *(COO)*
Kurt Antkiewicz *(Sr VP-Sls & Mktg)*

Unit (Domestic):

United Vision Logistics Mexico (2)
14709 Atlanta Dr, Laredo, TX 78045
Tel.: (956) 724-2598
Web Site: http://www.uvlogistics.com
Sales Range: $10-24.9 Million
Emp.: 20
Trucking Service
N.A.I.C.S.: 484121
Gerardo Garza *(Gen Mgr)*

WELTRONICS CORP.
1414 Fair Oaks Ave Ste 7, South Pasadena, CA 91030
Tel.: (626) 799-6396
Web Site: http://www.amchome.com
Sales Range: $10-24.9 Million
Emp.: 7
Electrical Entertainment Equipment
N.A.I.C.S.: 423620
Amcli Lin *(Chm)*
Reed Leonard *(Engr-Software)*

WELTY BUILDING COMPANY, LTD.
3421 Ridgewood Rd Ste 200, Fairlawn, OH 44333
Tel.: (330) 867-2400   OH
Web Site: http://www.thinkwelty.com
Year Founded: 1945
Sales Range: $1-9.9 Million
Emp.: 60
Industrial Bldg Cnstn Nonresidential Cnstn
N.A.I.C.S.: 236210
Donzell Taylor *(Pres & CEO)*
Ed Paparone *(Grp Pres-Cleveland)*
Adam Chafe *(CMO & Chief Sls Officer)*
John Castilla *(Pres-Houston)*
Brad Ewing *(Pres-Energy)*
John Hartman *(Pres-Columbus)*
Bill Paolillo *(Pres-Infrastructure)*

Subsidiaries:

Brae Burn Construction, Co. (1)
6655 Rookin St, Houston, TX 77074
Tel.: (713) 777-0063
Web Site: http://www.braeburnconstruction.com
Sales Range: $1-9.9 Million
Emp.: 30
Nonresidential Construction
N.A.I.C.S.: 236220
Donna Gerould *(Mgr)*
Eddie Heikkila *(Exec VP)*
David Vu *(Project Mgr)*

WEMBLY ENTERPRISES LLC
931 Briarwoods Rd, Franklin Lakes, NJ 07417
Web Site: http://www.wemblyenterprises.com
Privater Equity Firm
N.A.I.C.S.: 523999
Sunil Kumar *(Chm & Mng Principal)*
Jay Kumar *(Principal)*
Pia Kumar *(Principal)*
Monica Kumar *(CFO & Principal)*
Jonathan McEuen *(Principal)*

Subsidiaries:

Bradford Industries, Inc. (1)
75 Rogers Rd, Lowell, MA 01852
Tel.: (978) 459-4100
Web Site: http://www.bradfordind.com
High Technology Coated Fabrics Mfr
N.A.I.C.S.: 313320
Robert Pliskin *(VP-Technical Dev & Sls)*
Stephen Olsen *(Pres)*
Jay Kumar *(CEO)*
Larry Vincent *(VP-Ops & Supply Chain)*
Ivy Muchuma *(Mgr-Reporting & Engr-Environmental)*
Charlie Lojek *(Supvr-Maintenance)*

Subsidiary (Domestic):

Shawsheen Rubber Co., Inc. (2)
220 Andover St, Andover, MA 01810
Tel.: (978) 475-1710
Web Site: http://www.shawsheencc.com
Sales Range: $10-24.9 Million
Emp.: 50
Coated & Laminated Paper Mfr
N.A.I.C.S.: 322220
Denis J. Kelley *(Mgr-Ophthalmic Products)*

Mayfield Plastics, Inc. (1)
68 Providence Road, Sutton, MA 01590
Tel.: (508) 865-8150
Web Site: http://www.mayfieldplastics.com
Rev.: $4,333,333
Emp.: 35
All Other Plastics Product Mfr
N.A.I.C.S.: 326199

Nylon Corporation of America (1)
333 Sundial Ave, Manchester, NH 03103-7230
Tel.: (603) 627-5150
Web Site: http://www.nycoa.net
Sales Range: $25-49.9 Million
Emp.: 100
Nylon Resins Mfr
N.A.I.C.S.: 325211
Jay Bigarro *(Pres)*

Universal Plastics Corp. (1)
75 Whiting Farms Rd, Holyoke, MA 01040
Tel.: (413) 592-4791
Web Site: http://www.universalplastics.com
Plastics Product Mfr
N.A.I.C.S.: 326199
Pia Sareen Kumar *(Owner & Pres)*

Subsidiary (Domestic):

Premium Plastic Solutions LLC (2)
59 Bay Hill Dr, Latrobe, PA 15650
Tel.: (724) 424-7000
Web Site: http://www.universalplastics.com
Plastics Product Mfr
N.A.I.C.S.: 333511

Sajar Plastics, LLC (2)
15285 S State Ave, Middlefield, OH 44062
Tel.: (440) 632-5203
Web Site: http://www.sajarplastics.com
Injection Molding Plastic Component Mfr
N.A.I.C.S.: 326199

WEMMERS CONSULTING GROUP INC.
4955 Olde Towne Way Ste 300, Marietta, GA 30068
Tel.: (770) 565-8727   GA
Year Founded: 1978
Sales Range: $10-24.9 Million
Emp.: 5
Advetising Agency
N.A.I.C.S.: 541810
F. Richard Wemmers *(Sr Partner)*
Steve Sisk *(Art Dir)*
Marcelle Lewis *(Acct Exec)*
Lani Wemmers *(Sec)*

WEMS INC.
4650 W Rosecrans Ave, Hawthorne, CA 90250
Tel.: (310) 644-0251
Web Site: http://www.wems.com
Rev.: $12,000,000
Emp.: 90
Blowers & Fans
N.A.I.C.S.: 333413
Gary Fleming *(Mgr-IT)*

WEN-ALABAMA INC
154 Creekside Ln, Winchester, VA 22602-2447
Tel.: (540) 662-8910
Rev.: $13,600,000
Emp.: 12
Fast-Food Restaurant, Chain
N.A.I.C.S.: 722513
Rick Lynch *(Pres & Controller)*

WENATCHEE PETROLEUM CO

601 N Wenatchee Ave Bldg E, Wenatchee, WA 98801
Tel.: (509) 662-4423
Web Site: http://www.wenpetco.com
Sales Range: $25-49.9 Million
Emp.: 30
Gasoline
N.A.I.C.S.: 424720
Robert Ogan *(Owner & Pres)*

WENCO, INC.
1807 Dalton Dr, New Carlisle, OH 45344-2305
Tel.: (937) 849-6002   OH
Web Site:
  http://www.wencoconstruction.com
Year Founded: 1983
Sales Range: $10-24.9 Million
Emp.: 86
Full Service Design-Build Commercial Contractor
N.A.I.C.S.: 236220
Dean McGillivray *(VP-New Construction)*
Suzanne Winters *(Owner & Pres)*
Nelson Wenrinck *(Founder & CEO)*
Terry Gladman *(VP)*

WENDCO CORP.
220 W Garden St Ste 500, Pensacola, FL 32502
Tel.: (850) 433-5425
Web Site: http://www.wendco.com
Sales Range: $10-24.9 Million
Emp.: 1,400
Fast-Food Restaurant Owner & Operator
N.A.I.C.S.: 722513
Rick Watson *(Controller)*

WENDCO OF PUERTO RICO INC.
PO Box 11662, San Juan, PR 00922-1662
Tel.: (787) 792-2001   PR
Year Founded: 1979
Sales Range: $50-74.9 Million
Emp.: 1,000
Provider of Public Dining Facilities
N.A.I.C.S.: 722513
Jorge Colon-Gerena *(Pres)*

WENDELL FOSTER'S CAMPUS FOR DEVELOPMENTAL DISABILITIES
815 Triplett St, Owensboro, KY 42303-1668
Tel.: (270) 683-4517   KY
Web Site: http://www.wfcampus.org
Year Founded: 1948
Sales Range: $10-24.9 Million
Emp.: 377
Developmental Disability Assistance Services
N.A.I.C.S.: 624120
Maggie Price *(VP-Dev & Community Education)*
Clay Ford *(Chm)*
Eric Scharf *(CEO)*

WENDLE MOTORS INC.
9000 N Division St, Spokane, WA 99218
Tel.: (509) 484-4800
Web Site: http://www.wendle.com
Rev.: $94,385,777
Emp.: 250
New & Used Automobiles
N.A.I.C.S.: 441110
Bill Camarda *(Mgr-Sls)*
Scott Christensen *(Mgr-Sls)*
Sean Gallagher *(Mgr-Sls)*
Ammon Cordova *(Mgr-Bus)*
Ron Kaiser *(Mgr-Bus)*
Kevin Parker *(Mgr-Bus)*
Andy Keys *(Mgr-Gen Sls)*

Nate Harvey *(Mgr-Sls)*
Emory Pirtle *(Mgr-Sls)*
Craig Goodman *(Mgr-Sls-BDC & Internet)*

WENDT PRODUCTIONS, INC.
17301 Solie Rd, Odessa, FL 33556
Tel.: (813) 920-5000
Web Site: http://www.wendtproductions.com
Year Founded: 1986
Sales Range: $10-24.9 Million
Emp.: 9
Advertising Specialties, Marketing & Consumer Rewards
N.A.I.C.S.: 541890
Alan Wendt *(Exec VP)*
Susan Wendt *(Pres)*
Ryan Wendt *(VP)*
William Wendt *(Mgr-Global Procurement Sls)*

WENDT, INC.
105 Park Dr S, Great Falls, MT 59401
Tel.: (406) 454-8500   MT
Web Site: http://www.thewendtagency.com
Year Founded: 1929
Sales Range: $10-24.9 Million
Emp.: 12
Advetising Agency
N.A.I.C.S.: 541810
Lorie Hager *(CFO)*
Carmen Moore *(Dir-Production)*
Carol Kruger *(Sr VP)*
Brenda Peterson *(Pres & CEO)*
Johna Wilcox *(Mgr-Acct)*
Kara Mayernik-Smith *(Dir-Creative)*
Jennifer Fritz *(VP-Client Svcs)*

WENDY WEIHE STORLIE, INC.
4032 Shoreline Dr, Spring Park, MN 55384
Tel.: (952) 541-9001
Sales Range: $50-74.9 Million
Emp.: 8
Edible Fat & Oil Mfr
N.A.I.C.S.: 311225
Ted Storlie *(COO)*
Wendy W. Storlie *(Pres & CEO)*

WENDY'S BOWLING GREEN INC.
2501 Crossings Blvd, Bowling Green, KY 42104
Tel.: (270) 782-6124
Rev.: $33,432,449
Emp.: 1,300
Fast-Food Restaurant, Chain
N.A.I.C.S.: 722513
Larie Vernon *(Dir-HR)*

WENDY'S OF MISSOURI INC.
1855 S Ingram Mill Rd Ste 100, Springfield, MO 65804
Tel.: (417) 887-7677
Web Site: http://www.wendysofmissouri.com
Sales Range: $10-24.9 Million
Emp.: 30
Fast Food Restaurants
N.A.I.C.S.: 722513
Michael Hamra *(Pres)*

WENDY'S OF MONTANA INC.
2906 2nd Ave N Fl 2, Billings, MT 59101
Tel.: (406) 252-5125
Web Site: http://www.wendys.com
Rev.: $22,100,000
Emp.: 20
Fast-Food Restaurant, Chain
N.A.I.C.S.: 722513

WENDY'S RESTAURANTS OF ROCHESTER, INC.
20 N Union St, Rochester, NY 14607
Tel.: (585) 262-3630
Web Site: http://www.wenroch.com
Year Founded: 1976
Sales Range: $10-24.9 Million
Emp.: 35
Fast-Food Restaurant, Chain
N.A.I.C.S.: 722513
Richard C. Fox *(Pres)*

WENGER CORPORATION
555 Park Dr, Owatonna, MN 55060
Tel.: (507) 455-4100   MN
Web Site: http://www.wengercorp.com
Year Founded: 1946
Sales Range: $150-199.9 Million
Emp.: 500
Mfr of Music Chairs, Music Stands, Lighting & Sound Systems, Standard & Custom Stages, Risers & Acoustical Shells
N.A.I.C.S.: 337215
Chris Simpson *(Pres & CEO)*
Subsidiaries:
JR Clancy, Inc.   (1)
7041 Interstate Island Rd, Syracuse, NY 13209
Tel.: (315) 451-3440
Web Site: http://www.jrclancy.com
Sales Range: $10-24.9 Million
Emp.: 50
Stage Rigging Equipment Mfr
N.A.I.C.S.: 238990
Mike Murphy *(Pres)*

Secoa, Inc.   (1)
8650 109th Ave N, Champlin, MN 55316
Tel.: (763) 506-8800
Web Site: http://www.secoa.com
Sales Range: $1-9.9 Million
Emp.: 60
Special Trade Contractors, Nec, Nsk
N.A.I.C.S.: 238990

WENGER OIL INC.
2701 N Anderson Rd, Newton, KS 67114
Tel.: (316) 283-8795
Sales Range: $10-24.9 Million
Emp.: 23
Petroleum Bulk Stations
N.A.I.C.S.: 424710
Barry Power *(Gen Mgr)*

WENGER'S FEED MILL INC.
101 W Harrisburg Ave, Rheems, PA 17570
Tel.: (717) 367-1195   PA
Web Site: http://www.wengerfeeds.com
Year Founded: 1944
Sales Range: $25-49.9 Million
Emp.: 400
Mfr of Prepared Feeds
N.A.I.C.S.: 311119
F. Barry Shaw *(Chm)*
James L. Adams *(CEO & CMO)*
Geoffrey C. Finch *(Pres & COO)*
Jeffrey Murphy *(COO-Poultry Div)*

WENGERS FARM MACHINERY INC.
831 S College St, Myerstown, PA 17067
Tel.: (717) 866-2130
Web Site: http://www.wengers.com
Sales Range: $10-24.9 Million
Emp.: 60
Agricultural Machinery & Equipment
N.A.I.C.S.: 423820
Glenn Wenger *(Pres & CEO)*
Rose Walmer *(Chief Personnel Officer & Sec)*
Terry Wolfe *(CIO)*

WENSCO MICHIGAN CORPORATION
5760 Safety Dr NE, Belmont, MI 49306
Tel.: (616) 785-3333   MI
Web Site: http://www.wensco.com
Year Founded: 1937
Rev.: $16,000,000
Emp.: 100
Neon Signs
N.A.I.C.S.: 423440
Judy Nelson *(Pres & CEO)*

WENSTROM COMMUNICATIONS, INC.
2431 Estancia Blvd Bldg C, Clearwater, FL 33761
Tel.: (727) 791-1188
Web Site: http://www.wenstrom.net
Year Founded: 1991
Sales Range: $10-24.9 Million
Emp.: 8
Advertising & Marketing Services
N.A.I.C.S.: 541810
Steve Wenstrom *(Pres)*
Cheryl Wenstrom *(Founder & CEO)*
Lisa M. Ennis *(VP & Dir-Media)*

WENTE VINEYARDS
5565 Tesla Rd, Livermore, CA 94550-9149
Tel.: (925) 456-2300   CA
Web Site: http://www.wentevineyards.com
Year Founded: 1883
Sales Range: $25-49.9 Million
Emp.: 150
Mfr of Wines, Brandy & Spirits
N.A.I.C.S.: 312130
Carolyn Wente *(Pres)*
Larry Di Pietro *(VP-Natl Sls)*
Eric Wente *(Chm)*
Philip Wente *(Vice Chm)*

WENTWORTH FINANCIAL PARTNERS, LLC
18 Corporate Woods Blvd 4th Fl, Albany, NY 12211
Tel.: (855) 757-5433   DE
Web Site: http://wentworthfp.com
Professional & Financial Services
N.A.I.C.S.: 541611
Jerome Clement *(Pres & CEO)*
Robert Bush *(VP)*
Doug Keenholts *(VP & Dir-Ops)*
Jeremy Ward *(Dir-Bus Dev)*

WENTWORTH GALLERY HOLDINGS INC.
1118 NW 159th Dr, Miami, FL 33169
Tel.: (305) 624-0715
Web Site: http://www.wentworthgallery.com
Rev.: $16,000,000
Emp.: 50
Art Dealers
N.A.I.C.S.: 459920
Michael O'Mahoney *(Owner)*
Christian O'Mahoney *(Pres)*

WENTWORTH HOLDINGS
930 Main St, Acton, MA 01720
Tel.: (978) 263-7000
Sales Range: $10-24.9 Million
Emp.: 125
Residential & Commercial Architectural Design Services
N.A.I.C.S.: 321992
Tom Trudeau *(Owner & CEO)*

WENTWORTH MANAGEMENT SERVICES LLC
200 Vesey St 24th Fl, New York, NY 10280
Tel.: (212) 388-6200   NY
Holding Company
N.A.I.C.S.: 551112
Ryan Morfin *(CEO)*
Robert Jansen *(COO)*
Subsidiaries:
World Equity Group, Inc.   (1)
425 N. Martingale Rd Ste 1220, Schaumburg, IL 60173
Tel.: (847) 342-1700
Web Site: http://www.worldequitygroup.com
Rev.: $10,000,000
Emp.: 22
Investment Banking & Securities Dealing
N.A.I.C.S.: 523150
Patrick Power *(Mng Dir-Investment Banking)*
Mark Lischynsky *(COO)*
Steve Crothers *(VP-Sls & Mktg)*
William D. Webb Jr. *(Chief Compliance Officer)*

WENTWORTH TIRE SERVICE INC.
11130 S Corliss Ave, Chicago, IL 60628
Tel.: (773) 821-4802
Web Site: http://www.wentworthtire.com
Rev.: $16,010,713
Emp.: 35
Tire Recapping
N.A.I.C.S.: 811198
Ken Jager *(Owner)*

WENTZ GROUP INC.
555 Twin Dolphin Dr Ste 160, San Carlos, CA 94070
Tel.: (650) 592-3950
Web Site: http://lewentzco.com
Year Founded: 1975
Rev.: $15,000,000
Emp.: 15
Provider of Management, Construction & Engineering Services: Renovation & Repair
N.A.I.C.S.: 236220
Brad Wentz *(Pres)*
Craig Kinsman *(Project Mgr)*

WENZEL METAL SPINNING INC.
701 W Water St, Fremont, IN 46737
Tel.: (260) 495-9898
Web Site: http://www.wenzelmetalspinning.com
Sales Range: $10-24.9 Million
Emp.: 80
Spinning Metal for Trade Sheet Metal Forming
N.A.I.C.S.: 332119
Mathew Tubergen *(Pres)*

WERHANE ENTERPRISES LTD.
509 E Main St, Lena, IL 61048
Tel.: (815) 369-4574
Web Site: http://www.werhane.com
Sales Range: $10-24.9 Million
Emp.: 70
Distr of Milk
N.A.I.C.S.: 424430
James D. Werhane *(Pres)*

WERMERS CORPORATION
5120 Shoreham Pl Ste 150, San Diego, CA 92122
Tel.: (858) 535-1475
Year Founded: 1964
Sales Range: $10-24.9 Million
Emp.: 130
Residential Construction Services
N.A.I.C.S.: 236118
Thomas Wermers *(Pres)*

WERNER CONSTRUCTION INC.

WERNER CONSTRUCTION INC.

U.S. PRIVATE

Werner Construction Inc.—(Continued)
129 E 2nd St, Hastings, NE 68901
Tel.: (402) 463-4545   NE
Web Site: http://www.wernercos.com
Year Founded: 1955
Sales Range: $100-124.9 Million
Emp.: 220
Highway & Street Construction
N.A.I.C.S.: 237310
David Werner *(Owner & VP)*
Jim McKee *(Controller)*
David Werner *(VP)*
Philip Werner Jr. *(Pres)*

WERNER ELECTRIC SUPPLY COMPANY
4800 W Prospect Ave, Appleton, WI 54914
Tel.: (920) 815-4050   WI
Web Site:
http://www.wernerelectric.com
Year Founded: 1948
Distr of Electrical & Electronic Materials
N.A.I.C.S.: 423610
Craig Wiedemeier *(COO)*
Bill Kocha *(VP-Acctg & Fin Plng & Analysis)*

Subsidiaries:

Werner Electric Supply Company   (1)
7450 95th St, Cottage Grove, MN 55016
Tel.: (651) 458-3701
Web Site: http://www.wernermn.com
Provider of Electrical & Plumbing Equipment; Joint Venture of Werner Electric Supply Company & Van Meter Industrial Inc.
N.A.I.C.S.: 423610
Ben Granley *(Pres)*
John Farrell *(VP-Mktg)*
Bob Cunningham *(Dir-Construction)*

WERRES CORPORATION
807 E South St, Frederick, MD 21701-5753
Tel.: (301) 620-4000   DE
Web Site: http://www.werres.com
Year Founded: 1984
Sales Range: $10-24.9 Million
Emp.: 120
Mfr of Industrial Machinery & Equipment
N.A.I.C.S.: 423830
Cathy Hood *(Mgr-Svc)*
Keith Burlingame *(Pres)*

WERTHAN
448 Chestnut St, Nashville, TN 37203
Tel.: (615) 242-4919
Web Site: http://www.werthan.net
Year Founded: 2002
Sales Range: $1-9.9 Million
Emp.: 33
Natural Stone & Tile Distr
N.A.I.C.S.: 423320
Jeremy Werthan *(Pres)*
Jason Donoho *(Mgr-Sls)*
Beth Nagy *(Dir-Sls)*

WERTS WELDING & TANK SERVICE
400 N Old Saint Louis Rd, Wood River, IL 62095
Tel.: (618) 254-6967
Web Site:
http://www.wertswelding.com
Sales Range: $10-24.9 Million
Emp.: 60
Industrial Machinery & Equipment
N.A.I.C.S.: 423830
Dwight Werts *(Pres & CEO)*
Bruce Cornelius *(Mgr-Parts)*
Randy Brenneise *(Dir-Svcs)*

WERTZ YORK CAPITAL MANAGEMENT GROUP LLC
5502 N Nebraska Ave, Tampa, FL 33604
Tel.: (813) 238-4800
Web Site: http://www.wertzyork.com
Year Founded: 2000
Rev.: $322,000,000
Emp.: 5
Investment Banking & Advisory Services
N.A.I.C.S.: 523150
M. Brent Wertz *(Principal)*
Jeffrey Kern *(VP-Bus Dev)*

WES FINCH AUTO PLAZA INC.
410 West St, Grinnell, IA 50112
Tel.: (641) 236-3181
Web Site: http://www.wesfinch.com
Sales Range: $10-24.9 Million
Emp.: 35
Automobiles, New & Used
N.A.I.C.S.: 441110
Jeff E. Finch *(Pres)*
Lee McFee *(Controller)*

WES-GARDE COMPONENTS GROUP INC.
190 Elliott St E, Hartford, CT 06114
Tel.: (860) 527-7705
Web Site: http://www.wesgarde.com
Sales Range: $50-74.9 Million
Emp.: 30
Electronic Parts & Equipment
N.A.I.C.S.: 423690
Robert C. Sorenson *(Pres)*
Jjhon Gallary *(Controller)*

WES-TECH AUTOMATION SOLUTIONS
720 Dartmouth Ln, Buffalo Grove, IL 60089
Tel.: (847) 541-5070
Web Site: http://www.wes-tech.com
Year Founded: 1976
Sales Range: $10-24.9 Million
Emp.: 75
Assembly Machines
N.A.I.C.S.: 333519
Greg Ernst *(Dir-Matls)*
John Anderson *(Engr-Controls)*
Vern Ambrus *(Supvr-Site)*
Richard Decker *(Engr-Controls)*

WESCO FOUNTAINS, INC.
3440 Technology Dr, North Venice, FL 34275
Tel.: (941) 484-8224   FL
Web Site:
http://www.wescofountains.com
Year Founded: 1984
Sales Range: $1-9.9 Million
Emp.: 35
Fountain Mfr
N.A.I.C.S.: 332323
Janis Coquillard *(Pres)*
John Phillips *(Mgr-Sls)*
Melissa Cline *(Dir-Fin)*

WESCO GAS & WELDING SUPPLY INC.
940 N Martin Luther King Dr, Prichard, AL 36610
Tel.: (251) 457-8681
Web Site: http://www.wescoweld.com
Rev.: $12,200,000
Emp.: 106
Industrial Machinery & Equipment Merchant Whslr
N.A.I.C.S.: 423830
Jenny McCall *(Pres)*

WESCO GROUP, INC.
21601 66th Ave W, Mountlake Terrace, WA 98043-2101
Tel.: (206) 363-0747
Web Site: http://www.wescobpe.com
Sales Range: $10-24.9 Million
Emp.: 200
Collision Equipment, Automotive Paint & Accessories Supplier
N.A.I.C.S.: 441330
Lloyd White *(Pres)*
Roger Howe *(VP-Bus Affairs)*
John Lindsey *(VP)*
Karen Bostron *(Treas & Sec)*

Subsidiaries:

Leading Edge Auto Refinishes, Inc.   (1)
1444 W 10th Pl, Tempe, AZ 85281
Tel.: (480) 966-8819
Web Site: http://www.leadingedge-az.com
Sales Range: $1-9.9 Million
Emp.: 40
Auto Paint Supplies & Auto Paint Equipment Distr
N.A.I.C.S.: 423120
David Brannon *(Mgr-Ops)*
Mike Priest *(Gen Mgr)*

WESCOM CREDIT UNION
123 S Marengo Ave, Pasadena, CA 91101-2428
Tel.: (626) 535-1000   CA
Web Site: http://www.wescom.org
Year Founded: 1934
Sales Range: $125-149.9 Million
Emp.: 819
Credit Union
N.A.I.C.S.: 522130
Darren Williams *(Pres & CEO)*
Cindy Law *(VP-Fin)*
Karen Fall *(VP-Member Svcs)*
Tim Dolan *(Sr VP-Fin Svcs)*
Jane P. Wood *(COO & Exec VP)*
Javier Morales *(Vice Chm)*
Daniel Kraus *(Sec)*
Noel Ross *(Chm)*
Ron Fischer *(Treas)*
Jonathon Bauman *(VP-Real Estate & Default Mgmt)*
Jeanne Brown *(VP-Risk Mgmt)*
Mark Dilbeck *(Vice Chm)*
Linnie Gooch *(VP-IT Ops)*
Ralph Guerra *(VP-Insurance Svcs)*
David Gumpert-Hersh *(VP-Credit Risk Mgmt)*
Connie Knox *(VP-Investment Svcs)*
Susan McCready *(Sr VP-Member Svcs)*
Deena Otto *(Sr VP-Admin)*
Keith Pipes *(Exec VP-Lending & Fin Svcs)*
Kevin Sarber *(Sr VP-Tech & Delivery)*
Colleen Savage *(VP-Payment Sys)*
Charles Thomas *(Sr VP-Lending)*
Adriana Welch *(VP-Consumer Lending)*
Stephanie Winkler *(VP-HR)*
Liz Wood *(Sec)*
Irving Yu *(CFO & Sr VP)*

WESCOSVILLE AUTO SALES, INC.
4576 Hamilton Blvd, Allentown, PA 18103
Tel.: (610) 395-3745
Sales Range: $25-49.9 Million
Emp.: 40
Car Whslr
N.A.I.C.S.: 441110
Robert R. Becker *(Pres)*

WESCOTT FINANCIAL ADVISORY GROUP LLC
30 S 17th St, Philadelphia, PA 19103-4196
Tel.: (215) 979-1600
Web Site: http://www.wescott.com
Sales Range: $1-9.9 Million
Emp.: 20
Financial Advisory Services
N.A.I.C.S.: 523940
Grant Rawdin *(Founder & CEO)*
Lydia P. Sheckels *(Chief Investment Officer)*
David B. Lafferty *(Partner)*
Scott A. Michalek *(Partner)*
Karen McIntyre *(Mng Dir)*
Matthew T. Regan *(COO)*
Matthew J. Sgro *(Chief Compliance Officer & Dir-Fin)*

WESFAM RESTAURANTS INC.
206 Gates Ave SE PO Box 18157, Huntsville, AL 35801
Tel.: (256) 533-0211
Web Site: http://www.wesfam.com
Rev.: $44,700,000
Emp.: 1,300
Limited-Service Restaurants
N.A.I.C.S.: 722513
Tristenne W. Robin *(VP)*
Jean Wessel Templeton *(CEO)*
Rich Wyckoff *(Pres)*

WESLEY ALLEN INC.
1001 E 60th St, Los Angeles, CA 90001
Tel.: (323) 231-4275
Web Site:
http://www.wesleyallen.com
Sales Range: $10-24.9 Million
Emp.: 150
Metal Household Furniture
N.A.I.C.S.: 337126
Victor Sawan *(Pres & CEO)*
Earlene Marbury *(Office Mgr)*
Nasri Aboussouan *(Pres)*

WESLEY B. LASHER INVESTMENT CORP.
8575 Laguna Grove Dr, Elk Grove, CA 95757
Tel.: (916) 290-8500   CA
Web Site: http://www.lasherauto.com
Year Founded: 1955
Rev.: $100,000,000
Emp.: 120
New & Used Car Dealer
N.A.I.C.S.: 441110
Mark Lasher *(Pres & CEO)*
Scott Lasher *(CFO & Sec)*

Subsidiaries:

Wes Lasher Inc.   (1)
8585 Laguna Grove Dr, Elk Grove, CA 95757   (100%)
Tel.: (916) 392-1400
Web Site: http://www.lasherautogroup.com
Sales Range: $25-49.9 Million
Emp.: 75
New & Used Car Dealers
N.A.I.C.S.: 441110
Mark Lasher *(Co-Owner)*
Scott Lasher *(Co-Owner)*
Sarah Self *(Office Mgr)*

WESLEY COMMUNITY SERVICES
2091 Radcliff Dr, Cincinnati, OH 45204
Tel.: (513) 661-2777   OH
Web Site: http://www.wesleycs.org
Year Founded: 1997
Sales Range: $1-9.9 Million
Emp.: 182
Elder Care Services
N.A.I.C.S.: 624120
Michael Hodges *(Dir-Transportation & Nutrition)*
Barb Macke *(Mgr-HR)*
Ericka Dansby *(Exec Dir)*
Lewis E. Bunton *(Sec)*
Thomas A. Kaylor *(Chm)*
Robert Schilling *(Pres)*
David Warren *(Treas)*

WESLEY DAY & COMPANY, INC.

COMPANIES

1441 29th St Ste 111, West Des Moines, IA 50266-1309
Tel.: (515) 224-9330   IA
Web Site: http://www.wesleyday.com
Year Founded: 1949
Rev.: $8,000,000
Emp.: 10
Fiscal Year-end: 12/31/04
N.A.I.C.S.: 541810
David A. Sanderson *(Pres & Acct Exec)*
Wil Steinhart *(Treas & Exec VP)*
Debbie Werner *(Yellow Pages Acct Exec)*
Dale Roberson *(Acct Exec)*

WESLEY GARDENS
3 Upton Park, Rochester, NY 14607
Tel.: (585) 241-2100   NY
Web Site: http://www.wesleygardens.com
Year Founded: 1991
Sales Range: $10-24.9 Million
Emp.: 474
Elder Care Services
N.A.I.C.S.: 623312
Jamie Clark *(Dir-Rehabilitation Svcs)*
Rich Mileo *(CFO)*
Tamra Sarubbi *(Asst Sec)*

WESLEY SPECTRUM SERVICES
221 Penn Ave, Pittsburgh, PA 15221
Tel.: (412) 342-2300   PA
Web Site: http://www.wesleyspectrum.org
Year Founded: 1965
Sales Range: $25-49.9 Million
Emp.: 971
Child & Family Care Services
N.A.I.C.S.: 624190
Shanicka L. Kennedy *(Sec)*
Kevin Oakley *(Chm)*
Diane Hallett *(Vice Chm)*

WESSCO INTERNATIONAL LTD.
11400 Olympic Blvd Ste 450, Los Angeles, CA 90064
Tel.: (310) 477-4272
Web Site: http://www.wessco.net
Rev.: $34,000,000
Emp.: 34
Supplier of Customized Amenities & Accessories for Travel Industry
N.A.I.C.S.: 325620
Sharon Conway Deherder *(Exec VP-Sls & Mktg)*
Anita Gittelson *(Exec VP-Product Dev & Branding)*
Robert Bregman Jr. *(Pres & CEO)*
Tyler Shepodd *(VP-Fin & Admin)*

WESSELN CONSTRUCTION CO., INC.
292 N Wilshire Ave No 103, Anaheim, CA 92801
Tel.: (714) 772-0888
Rev.: $23,595,452
Emp.: 320
Construction of Single-Family Houses
N.A.I.C.S.: 236115
Henry B. Wesseln *(Pres)*

WESSELS COMPANY
101 Tank St, Greenwood, IN 46143
Tel.: (317) 888-9800
Web Site: http://www.wesselscompany.com
Year Founded: 1908
Sales Range: $10-24.9 Million
Emp.: 250
Mfr & Marketer of ASME & Non-ASME Pressure Vessels & Related Products
N.A.I.C.S.: 332420

Jim Fuller *(Pres)*
Guy Kirk *(VP)*

WESSELS OIL CO., INC.
421 Railroad Ave, Palmer, IA 50571
Tel.: (712) 359-7712
Web Site: http://www.wesselsoil.com
Sales Range: $10-24.9 Million
Emp.: 15
Petroleum Bulk Stations
N.A.I.C.S.: 424710
Ronald Wessels *(CEO)*

WESSIN TRANSPORT INC.
7550 24th Ave S Ste 140 Lewis Rd, Golden Valley, MN 55427
Tel.: (763) 746-4050
Sales Range: $10-24.9 Million
Emp.: 3
Courier Service
N.A.I.C.S.: 492110
Tom Miles *(Sec & VP-HR)*

WESSON, INC.
165 Railroad Hill St, Waterbury, CT 06708
Tel.: (203) 757-7950
Web Site: http://www.wessonenergy.com
Sales Range: $25-49.9 Million
Emp.: 55
Heating & Air Conditioning Services
N.A.I.C.S.: 423730
Robert W. Wesson *(CEO)*

WEST ADVERTISING
1410 Park Ave, Alameda, CA 94501
Tel.: (510) 865-9378   CA
Web Site: http://www.westadvertising.com
Year Founded: 1988
Sales Range: $10-24.9 Million
Emp.: 12
N.A.I.C.S.: 541810
Peter Halberstadt *(Pres)*

WEST ALABAMA BANK & TRUST
509 1st Ave W, Reform, AL 35481
Tel.: (205) 375-6261
Web Site: http://www.wabt.com
Year Founded: 1944
Sales Range: $10-24.9 Million
Emp.: 134
Provider of Banking Services
N.A.I.C.S.: 522110
William R. Finney *(Pres & CEO)*
Andrew C. Wade *(Chm)*
Nancy Turner *(CFO)*
Marshal Puckett *(CTO)*

WEST AMERICAN RUBBER CO., LLC
1337 W Braden Ct, Orange, CA 92868
Tel.: (714) 532-3355
Web Site: http://www.warco.com
Sales Range: $25-49.9 Million
Emp.: 390
Sheets, Hard Rubber
N.A.I.C.S.: 326299
Dorothy David *(Mgr-HR)*

WEST AMERICAN RUBBER CO., LLC
1337 W Braden Ct, Orange, CA 92868
Tel.: (714) 532-3355
Web Site: http://www.warco.com
Industrial Supplies Merchant Whslr
N.A.I.C.S.: 423840
Timothy Hemstreet *(Pres & CEO)*

WEST ASSET MANAGEMENT
2221 New Market Pkwy Ste 118, Marietta, GA 30067

Tel.: (678) 498-9800
Web Site: http://www.westassetmanagement.com
Sales Range: $10-24.9 Million
Emp.: 300
Adjustment & Collection Services
N.A.I.C.S.: 561440
Eugene Lynch *(Mgr-Agency)*
Shabar Bass *(Dir-Ops)*
T. R. Brown *(VP-Investment Analysis)*

WEST BAY RESIDENTIAL SERVICES, INC.
158 Knight St, Warwick, RI 02886
Tel.: (401) 738-9300   RI
Web Site: http://www.westbayri.org
Year Founded: 1981
Sales Range: $10-24.9 Million
Emp.: 383
Community Development & Residential Services
N.A.I.C.S.: 925120
Gloria Perry Quinn *(Exec Dir)*
Victoria Zanghi-Brown *(Dir-HR)*
Sherri Sarault *(Dir-Trng & Dev)*
Penelope Merris *(Dir-Day Supports & Employment)*
Kenneth Beaton *(Pres)*

WEST BEND MUTUAL INSURANCE COMPANY INC.
1900 S 18th Ave, West Bend, WI 53095
Tel.: (262) 334-5571   WI
Web Site: http://www.thesilverlining.com
Year Founded: 1894
Sales Range: $900-999.9 Million
Emp.: 1,050
Property-Casualty Insurance Services
N.A.I.C.S.: 524126
Kevin Steiner *(Pres & CEO)*
David Ertmer *(Sr VP-Claims)*
Gary Alexander *(VP-NSI Bonds)*
Rick Fox *(Chief Actuary Officer, Chief Risk Officer & Sr VP)*
Rob Jacques *(Sr VP-Comml Lines)*
Gary Klein *(VP-NSI)*
Jim Schwalen *(Sr VP-Personal Lines & Mktg)*
Kelly Tighe *(Sr VP-Sls)*
Chris Zwygart *(Chief Legal Officer & VP)*
Deb Cahoon *(Asst VP-HR)*
Mike DeLaney *(Asst VP-Argent Loss Control)*
Heather Dunn *(CFO & Sr VP)*
Jason Moore *(Asst VP-IT)*
John Reyzer *(VP-NSI Fin)*
David Nettum *(Asst VP-Argent Claims)*
Mike Kapfer *(Asst VP-NSI Underwriting)*
Murali Natarajan *(CIO & Sr VP)*
Mike Faley *(Sr VP-HR & Admin)*
Derek L. Tyus *(Chief Investment Officer & VP)*

WEST BOND INC.
1551 Harris Ct, Anaheim, CA 92806
Tel.: (714) 978-1551
Web Site: http://www.westbond.com
Year Founded: 1966
Sales Range: $10-24.9 Million
Emp.: 45
Mfr & Designer of Wire Bonding & Die Attach Machines, Wire Pull & Shear Test Equipment, Ultrasonic Components & Accessories for the Microelectronics Packaging Industry
N.A.I.C.S.: 333998
Phyllis Eppig *(Controller)*

WEST BROTHERS TRANSFER & STORAGE
224 N Hover Rd, Durham, NC 27703
Tel.: (919) 878-8411
Web Site: http://www.brownintegratedlogistics.com
Sales Range: $25-49.9 Million
Emp.: 100
Local Trucking with Storage
N.A.I.C.S.: 493110
Billy Wright *(Mgr-Bus Dev)*
Michael Flanagan *(Pres)*
Doug Ostanek *(Exec VP-Sls & Mktg)*

WEST CAROLINA FREIGHTLINER
3682 Curleys Fish Camp Rd, Connelly Springs, NC 28612
Tel.: (828) 322-8620
Web Site: http://www.westcarolinafreightliner.com
Sales Range: $25-49.9 Million
Emp.: 53
Trucks, Tractors & Trailers Whslr
N.A.I.C.S.: 441110
Kenneth Maynard *(Pres)*
Karen La Fevers *(Bus Mgr)*
Tommy Carter *(Mgr-Svcs)*

WEST CARROLLTON PARCHMENT & CONVERTING, INC.
400 E Dixie Dr, West Carrollton, OH 45449
Tel.: (937) 859-3621   OH
Web Site: http://www.wcpconv.com
Emp.: 75
Packaging Paper Products Mfr & Distr
N.A.I.C.S.: 322220
Cameron Lonergan *(CEO)*

WEST CENTRAL AGRICULTURAL SERVICE INC.
220 1st St SW PO Box 368, Ulen, MN 56585
Tel.: (218) 596-8821
Web Site: http://www.westcentralag.com
Sales Range: $25-49.9 Million
Emp.: 42
Grain & Field Beans Storage
N.A.I.C.S.: 424510
Dave Stumbo *(Treas)*
Jesse McCollum *(Gen Mgr)*

WEST CENTRAL ELECTRIC COOPERATIVE
7867 S Hwy 13, Higginsville, MO 64037
Tel.: (660) 584-2131
Web Site: http://www.westcentralelectric.com
Sales Range: $10-24.9 Million
Emp.: 45
Distribution, Electric Power
N.A.I.C.S.: 221120
Brent Schlotzhauer *(Branch Mgr)*
Sandy Starke *(Office Mgr)*
Heather Hoflander *(Specialist-Member Svcs & Comm)*
Mike Gray *(Gen Mgr)*
Kim Lewis *(Sec)*
Stan Rhodes *(Asst Sec)*
Densil Allen *(Pres)*
Dale Jarman *(Treas)*
Clark Bredehoeft *(VP)*

WEST CENTRAL FS, INC.
1445 Monmouth Blvd, Galesburg, IL 61401
Tel.: (309) 343-1600   IL
Web Site: http://www.westcentralfs.com
Year Founded: 1926
Sales Range: $25-49.9 Million
Emp.: 125
Agricultural Services
N.A.I.C.S.: 424510

WEST CENTRAL FS, INC.

West Central FS, Inc.—(Continued)

Mike DeSutter *(Pres)*

WEST CENTRAL KANSAS ASSOCIATION, INC.
200 S Main St, Russell, KS 67665
Tel.: (785) 483-3131
Web Site:
http://www.russellhospital.org
Year Founded: 1997
Sales Range: $10-24.9 Million
Emp.: 213
Health Care Srvices
N.A.I.C.S.: 622110
Shelley Boden *(CEO)*
Joy Bretz *(CFO)*

WEST CENTRAL MISSOURI COMMUNITY ACTION AGENCY
106 W 4th St, Appleton City, MO 64724
Tel.: (660) 476-2185
Web Site: http://www.wcmcaa.org
Sales Range: $25-49.9 Million
Emp.: 486
Community Action Services
N.A.I.C.S.: 624190
Mary Lou Schussler *(Dir-HR)*
Willene A. Engel *(Vice Chm)*
Patricia L. Jacobs *(Sec)*
Fred R. Bunch *(Chm)*
Linda Schreck *(Dir-Early Childhood Education)*
Lee Ann Gatzemeyer *(Dir-Employment & Trng & Health Svcs)*
Kenney Hutchison *(Dir-IT)*
Gina Ensor *(Dir-Strategic Dev & Comm)*
Chris Richardon-McQueen *(Dir-Multi-Family Housing & Energy Conservation)*
Deborah Vickers *(Mgr-Grant Research & Dev)*
Chris Thompson *(Pres & CEO)*

WEST CHESTER HOLDINGS, INC.
100 Corridor Park Dr, Monroe, OH 45050
Tel.: (513) 705-2100
Web Site: http://www.west-chester.net
Sales Range: $75-99.9 Million
Emp.: 100
Safety Equipment & Supplies
N.A.I.C.S.: 423990
David Hershey *(CEO)*
Tim Fogarty *(Pres & CFO)*
Kyle Packer *(Controller)*
Ryan Lee *(Mgr-Retail Program)*
Greg Plunkett *(Mgr-Customer Mktg)*

WEST COAST CAPITAL LLC
15233 Ventura Blvd Ste 306, Sherman Oaks, CA 91403
Tel.: (818) 501-2666 CA
Web Site:
http://www.westcoastcapital.com
Year Founded: 1995
Emp.: 2,500
Private Investment Firm
N.A.I.C.S.: 523999
Lorne A. Goldberg *(Founder, Owner & Principal)*

Subsidiaries:

Stix Holdings, LLC (1)
3600 American Blvd W, Minneapolis, MN 55431-1079
Tel.: (952) 890-5128
Holding Company
N.A.I.C.S.: 551112

Holding (Domestic):

Pick Up Stix (2)
1330 Calle Avanzado, San Clemente, CA 92673
Tel.: (949) 366-8747
Web Site: http://www.pickupstix.com
Fast Casual Chinese Restaurant Chain
N.A.I.C.S.: 722511
Rick Vasconez *(Mgr-IT)*
Dana Alexander *(Mgr-HR & Trng)*

WEST COAST COMPUTER EXCHANGE
2751 Mercantile Dr Ste 100, Rancho Cordova, CA 95742
Tel.: (916) 635-9340
Web Site: http://www.wex-it.com
Year Founded: 1977
Sales Range: $10-24.9 Million
Emp.: 15
Computer Peripheral Equipment
N.A.I.C.S.: 423430
James Vu *(Mgr-Tech)*
Bill Lindberg *(COO)*

WEST COAST CUSTOMS, INC.
181 Via Trevizio, Corona, CA 92879
Tel.: (951) 284-0680
Web Site:
http://www.westcoastcustoms.com
Sales Range: $1-9.9 Million
Emp.: 35
Automotive Custom Mfr, Repair & Sales
N.A.I.C.S.: 811198
Ryan Friedlinghaus *(Founder)*

WEST COAST FLOORING CENTER
2105 Industrial Ct, Vista, CA 92081
Tel.: (760) 736-4222
Web Site:
http://www.westcoastflooring.com
Sales Range: $10-24.9 Million
Emp.: 75
Floor Covering Stores
N.A.I.C.S.: 449121
Edward Kruger *(Pres)*

WEST COAST FOUNDRY, INC.
2450 E 53rd St, Huntington Park, CA 90255
Tel.: (323) 583-1421 WY
Web Site:
http://www.westcoaststainless.com
Year Founded: 2003
Sales Range: $1-9.9 Million
Emp.: 100
Silverware & Holloware Mfr
N.A.I.C.S.: 339910
Michael Bargani *(Owner)*

WEST COAST LEATHER
363 Grant Ave, San Francisco, CA 94108
Tel.: (415) 362-8300
Web Site:
http://www.westcoastleather.com
Sales Range: $10-24.9 Million
Emp.: 10
Leather Garments Sales
N.A.I.C.S.: 458110
Joe Ane *(Gen Mgr)*

WEST COAST MATERIALS, INC.
7312 Orangethorpe Ave, Buena Park, CA 90621-3313
Tel.: (714) 522-0282
Web Site: http://www.wcsg.com
Sales Range: $10-24.9 Million
Emp.: 100
Brick, Stone & Related Construction Material Merchant Whslr
N.A.I.C.S.: 423320
Dan Reyneveld *(CEO)*

Subsidiaries:

Valley Building Materials (1)
23271 Cherry Ave, Lake Forest, CA 92630
Tel.: (949) 598-0256
Web Site:
http://www.valleybuildingmaterials.com
Sales Range: $10-24.9 Million
Emp.: 30
Brick, Slate & Stone Construction Product Whslr
N.A.I.C.S.: 423320
Steve Harris *(Mgr)*

WEST COAST MILLS INC.
887 NW State Ave, Chehalis, WA 98532
Tel.: (360) 748-3351
Rev.: $11,700,000
Emp.: 2
Manufacture & Distribute Millwork
N.A.I.C.S.: 423310
Richard Jones *(Pres)*

WEST COAST PAPER COMPANY
6703 S 234th St Ste 120, Kent, WA 98032
Tel.: (253) 850-3560
Web Site: http://www.wcpc.com
Rev.: $172,900,000
Emp.: 425
Stationery & Office Supplies Merchant Whslr
N.A.I.C.S.: 424120
Teresa Russell *(Chm)*
Tom Groves *(CEO)*
Amy Swanson *(CFO)*

WEST COAST PRIME MEATS LLC
340 Cliffwood Park St, Brea, CA 92821
Tel.: (714) 255-8560
Web Site: http://www.westcoastprime meats.com
Year Founded: 1952
Sales Range: $25-49.9 Million
Emp.: 170
Meat & Meat Products
N.A.I.C.S.: 424470
Terry Hanks *(Partner)*
Jay Henderson *(Partner)*
Bill Hustedt *(Mng Partner)*
Eddie Juarez *(Partner)*
Dave Wicker *(Partner)*
Craig Nickoloff *(Partner)*
Grace Nelson *(Mgr-Credit)*

WEST COAST REALTY TRUST, INC.
650 Howe Ave Ste 730, Sacramento, CA 95825
Tel.: (916) 925-9278 MD
Year Founded: 2012
Real Estate Investment Services
N.A.I.C.S.: 525990
Jeffrey B. Berger *(Chm, Pres & CEO)*
David A. Rane *(CFO & Chief Acctg Officer)*
Richard P. Bernstein *(Vice Chm)*
Christine M. Hock *(Treas)*
Sonia Sworak *(Sec)*

WEST COAST SALES & ASSOCIATES LLC
15255 Dewey Crest Ln, Anacortes, WA 98221
Tel.: (360) 202-4876 WA
Web Site:
http://www.westcoastsales.com
Manufacturers Representative in the Boating Industry
N.A.I.C.S.: 561499
Mark Steiner *(Mng Partner)*
Mark Richards *(Area Sls Mgr)*

Subsidiaries:

Richards Marine Marketing, Inc. (1)
PO Box 67, Heisson, WA 98622-0067

U.S. PRIVATE

Tel.: (360) 687-6194
Web Site: http://www.richardsmarine.com
Transportation Equipment & Supplies Merchant Whslr
N.A.I.C.S.: 423860

WEST COAST SHUTTERS & SUNBURST, INC.
128 19th St S, Saint Petersburg, FL 33712
Tel.: (727) 894-0044
Web Site:
http://www.westcoastshutters.com
Sales Range: $1-9.9 Million
Emp.: 10
Wood Shutters & Custom Moldings Mfr
N.A.I.C.S.: 321911
Joseph Fecera *(Pres)*

WEST COAST VINYL, INC.
4023 S Orchard St, Tacoma, WA 98466
Tel.: (253) 565-4920
Web Site:
http://www.westcoastvinyl.com
Year Founded: 1971
Sales Range: $10-24.9 Million
Emp.: 106
Plastics Product Mfr
N.A.I.C.S.: 326199
Jamie Keirstead *(Pres)*
Drew Field *(Mgr-Phone Room)*
Steve Keirstead *(VP)*
Cherie Keirstead *(Sec)*

WEST COAST WIRE ROPE & RIGGING, INC.
2900 N W 29th Ave, Portland, OR 97210
Tel.: (503) 228-9353
Web Site: http://www.wcwr.com
Rev.: $17,325,000
Emp.: 33
Rope, Wire (Not Insulated)
N.A.I.C.S.: 423510
Karen Newton *(Pres)*
Dale Hansen *(CFO)*
Brian Cameron *(Mgr-Acctg & HR)*

WEST CONSTRUCTION COMPANY
6120 A St, Anchorage, AK 99518
Tel.: (907) 561-9811
Sales Range: $10-24.9 Million
Emp.: 10
Bridge Construction & Docks
N.A.I.C.S.: 237310
Bradley West *(Pres)*
George Tipner *(VP)*
Patty Howell *(Controller)*

WEST COUNTY HEALTH CENTERS, INC.
14045 Mill St, Guerneville, CA 95446
Tel.: (707) 869-5977 CA
Web Site: http://www.wchealth.org
Year Founded: 1973
Sales Range: $10-24.9 Million
Emp.: 171
Health Care Srvices
N.A.I.C.S.: 622110
Phyllis Early *(Dir-HR)*
Michelle Davey *(Dir-Medical-Human Immunodeficiency Virus)*
John Kornfeld *(Pres)*
Mary Felton *(Sec)*
Dwight Cary *(Treas)*
Debra Johnson *(VP)*

WEST CREEK FINANCIAL, INC.
PO Box 5518, Glen Allen, VA 23058-5518
Web Site:
http://www.westcreekfin.com

COMPANIES — WEST KENTUCKY RURAL ELECTRIC COOPERATIVE CORP., INC.

Year Founded: 2014
Sales Range: $75-99.9 Million
Emp.: 158
Financial Investment Services
N.A.I.C.S.: 523999
Rob Finnegan *(Co-Founder & CEO)*
Boomer Muth *(Co-Founder & Pres)*
Rajesh Rao *(CFO & Chief Risk Officer)*
Gene Burke *(Chief Revenue Officer)*
Jim Kresge *(CTO)*

WEST DERMATOLOGY MED MANAGEMENT, INC.
200 Station Way Ste E, Arroyo Grande, CA 93420
Tel.: (805) 249-1183
Web Site:
  http://www.westdermatology.com
Offices of Physicians (except Mental Health Specialists)
N.A.I.C.S.: 621111
Gregory Westek *(Pres)*

Subsidiaries:

Dermatology & Laser-Del Mar Inc. (1)
12865 Pointe Del Mar Way Ste 160, Del Mar, CA 92014-3860
Tel.: (858) 350-7546
Web Site: http://www.dermdelmar.com
Offices of Physicians (except Mental Health Specialists)
N.A.I.C.S.: 621111
Lita Doody *(Office Mgr)*

WEST EDGE PARTNERS, LLC
2219 Main St Unit 494, Santa Monica, CA 90405
Tel.: (949) 307-2409   DE
Web Site:
  https://www.westedgepartners.com
Privater Equity Firm
N.A.I.C.S.: 523999
Ted C. Nark *(Chm)*
Cole Kirby *(Partner)*

Subsidiaries:

Dakotaland Autoglass Inc. (1)
313 N Main, Aberdeen, SD 57401-3433
Tel.: (605) 785-3660
Web Site:
  http://www.dakotalandautoglass.com
Rev.: $18,900,000
Emp.: 175
Automobile Glass
N.A.I.C.S.: 423120
Daryl Anderson *(Founder)*
Stan Biondi *(CEO)*

WEST END ADVERTISING
12464 Natural Bridge Rd, Bridgeton, MO 63044
Tel.: (314) 209-7200   MO
Web Site: http://www.2dive.com
Year Founded: 1960
Sales Range: $10-24.9 Million
Emp.: 75
Retail, Travel & Tourism
N.A.I.C.S.: 541810
Douglas C. Goergens *(Pres & CEO)*

WEST END DIVING & SALVAGE, INC.
12464 Natural Bridge Rd, Bridgeton, MO 63044
Tel.: (314) 731-5003
Web Site: http://www.2dive.com
Year Founded: 1960
Sales Range: $50-74.9 Million
Emp.: 36
Scuba Equipment, Sales & Instruction; Resort Operator; Salvage Operations
N.A.I.C.S.: 423910
Douglas Goergens *(CIO & Dir-Mktg)*
Catherine Goergens *(Treas, Exec VP & Dir-Promo)*

WEST END FINANCIAL CORP.
155 E Cloverland Dr, Ironwood, MI 49938
Tel.: (906) 932-7646
Rev.: $2,408,000
Emp.: 15
Rubber & Plastics Footwear Mfr
N.A.I.C.S.: 316210
Donald Armata *(Mgr)*

Subsidiaries:

Gogebic Range Bank (1)
155 E Cloverland Dr, Ironwood, MI 49938   (100%)
Tel.: (906) 932-7646
Web Site:
  http://www.gogebicrangebank.com
Banking Services
N.A.I.C.S.: 522110
Neil J. Beckman *(Pres, CEO & Officer-Comml Loan-Ironwood)*
Marcy Elsemore *(Officer-Mortgage Loan & Comml Loan & VP-Bessemer)*
Cherie LaMarche *(Officer-Mortgage Loan & Asst VP-Ironwood)*
Amy Livingston *(Officer-Loan & Branch Mgr-Ewen)*
Dennis Jilek *(Officer-Mortgage Loan-Ewen)*
Erica Hanson *(Officer-Consumer Loan-Ironwood)*
Carl Ahlskog *(Officer-Consumer Loan-Bergland)*
Linda Pieschel *(Officer-Compliance)*

WEST END HOLDINGS LLC
302 Hillwood Blvd, Nashville, TN 37205
Tel.: (615) 294-9940
Web Site:
  http://www.westendholdings.com
Privater Equity Firm
N.A.I.C.S.: 523999
Lyle Beasley *(Mng Partner)*

Subsidiaries:

American Hometown Publishing, Inc. (1)
302 Hillwood Blvd, Nashville, TN 37205
Tel.: (615) 294-9940
Web Site:
  http://www.americanhometownpublishing.com
Holding Company; Newspaper Publisher
N.A.I.C.S.: 551112
Brad Dennison *(Pres & CEO)*
Clarissa Williams *(COO)*
Gregory McNutt *(CFO)*

Unit (Domestic):

Osceola News-Gazette (2)
108 Church St, Kissimmee, FL 34741
Tel.: (407) 846-7600
Web Site: http://www.aroundosceola.com
Newspaper Publishers
N.A.I.C.S.: 513110
Tom Overton *(Publr)*
Brian McBride *(Editor)*
Angelique Priore *(Production Mgr)*

WEST FLORIDA BANK CORPORATION
29750 US Hwy 19 N, Clearwater, FL 33761
Tel.: (727) 451-2020   FL
Web Site:
  http://www.flagshipbank.com
Year Founded: 2019
Bank Holding Company
N.A.I.C.S.: 551111
Paul J. Wikle *(Chm)*
Robert B. McGivney *(Vice Chm & CEO)*
Kenneth E. Bailey *(CFO & Sr VP)*

Subsidiaries:

Flagship Bank (1)
29750 US Hwy 19 N, Clearwater, FL 33761
Tel.: (727) 451-2020
Web Site: http://www.flagshipbank.com
Sales Range: $1-9.9 Million
Emp.: 37
Commericial Banking
N.A.I.C.S.: 522110
Melanie Wetzel *(VP-Loan Ops)*
Dave Gilby *(VP & Branch Mgr)*
Pam Bremen *(VP-Ops)*
Lee Weatherford *(VP)*
James Cusick *(Asst VP)*
Martine E. Moore *(Asst VP-Loan Ops)*
Patricia Wallenhurst *(Asst VP & Asst Branch Mgr)*
Kenneth E. Bailey *(CFO & Sr VP)*
James P. Nelson *(Pres, COO & Sr Lending Officer)*

WEST FLORIDA ELECTRICAL COOPERATIVE ASSOCIATION
5282 Peanut Rd, Graceville, FL 32440
Tel.: (850) 263-3231
Web Site:
  http://www.westflorida.coop
Sales Range: $25-49.9 Million
Emp.: 25
Distribution, Electric Power
N.A.I.C.S.: 221122
William Rimes *(CEO)*

WEST GATE HOME SALES INC
4431 NW 13th St, Gainesville, FL 32609
Tel.: (352) 373-5428
Sales Range: Less than $1 Million
Emp.: 6
Mobile Home Dealers
N.A.I.C.S.: 459930
Wayne Friers *(Pres)*
Mike Reese *(Mgr)*

WEST GERMAN MOTOR IMPORTS, INCORPORATED
525 N Bethllehem Pike, Ambler, PA 19002
Tel.: (215) 643-3322
Web Site:
  http://www.westgermanmotors.com
Sales Range: $50-74.9 Million
Emp.: 50
Car Whslr
N.A.I.C.S.: 441110
Mario P. Cesarini *(Pres)*

WEST GROUP MANAGEMENT LLC
1600 Anderson Rd, McLean, VA 22102
Tel.: (703) 356-2400
Web Site: http://www.west-group.com
Sales Range: $200-249.9 Million
Emp.: 7
Commercial & Industrial Building Operation
N.A.I.C.S.: 531120
Gerald T. Halpin *(Founder, Chm, Pres & CEO)*
John D.T. Gerber *(Exec VP)*
William B. Rucker *(Sr VP-Leasing)*
Tasso N. Flocos *(Sr VP)*
Eric Maggio *(CFO)*

WEST HERR AUTOMOTIVE GROUP, INC.
3552 Southwestern Blvd, Orchard Park, NY 14127
Tel.: (716) 312-4082   NY
Web Site: http://www.westherr.com
Year Founded: 1950
Sales Range: $1-9.9 Million
Emp.: 35
Car Dealer
N.A.I.C.S.: 441110
Scott Bieler *(Pres & CEO)*
Brad Hafner *(Chm)*
Stan Kicinski *(CFO)*
Cathie Hassler *(Supvr-Payroll)*
Craig Przyklek *(Controller)*
Desiree Sanchez *(Mgr-Accounts Recievable)*
John Wabick *(VP)*
Paul Balbierz *(Dir-Acctg)*
Ray Ammerman *(Mgr-Customer Satisfaction)*
Bradley Gelber *(Mgr-Digital Media & Content Marketing)*

Subsidiaries:

Doan Dodge Chrysler Jeep RAM Fiat (1)
4477 Rdg Rd W, Rochester, NY 14626
Tel.: (585) 537-4199
Web Site:
  https://www.westherrcdjrfrochester.com
Emp.: 102
New Car Dealers
N.A.I.C.S.: 441110
Brandon Thompson *(Gen Mgr)*
Christopher Spade *(Branch Svcs Mgr)*

Le Brun Toyota (1)
1002 State Route 5 And 20, Geneva, NY 14456
Tel.: (315) 781-1410
Web Site: http://www.lebruntoyota.com
Sales Range: $1-9.9 Million
Emp.: 20
New Car Dealers
N.A.I.C.S.: 441110
Steven Brun *(Principal)*

Transitowne Hyundai LLC (1)
5485 Transit Rd, Clarence, NY 14221
Tel.: (716) 634-3000
Web Site: http://www.transitowne.com
New & Used Car Dealers
N.A.I.C.S.: 441110
James Hillery *(Owner)*

Subsidiary (Domestic):

Mazda of West Ridge (2)
4692 Rdg Rd W, Spencerport, NY 14559
Tel.: (585) 352-5995
Web Site:
  http://www.mazdaofwestridge.com
New Car Dealers
N.A.I.C.S.: 441110
Marcy Edmiston *(Owner & Pres)*
Greg Muscato *(Mgr-Sls)*
Jesus Vega *(Mgr-Svc)*
Sean Cole *(Mgr-Parts)*

West Herr Toyota of Rochester (1)
4374 W Rdg Rd, Rochester, NY 14626
Tel.: (585) 225-6600
Web Site:
  http://www.vanderstynetoyota.com
Automotive Repair & Maintenance
N.A.I.C.S.: 811198
Anne Schutz *(Office Mgr)*

WEST HERR CHEVROLET OF HAMBURG
5025 Southwestern Blvd, Hamburg, NY 14075
Tel.: (716) 649-7800
Web Site:
  http://www.hamburgchevrolet.com
Year Founded: 1991
Sales Range: $10-24.9 Million
Emp.: 60
Car Whslr
N.A.I.C.S.: 441110
Scott Bieler *(Pres)*
Dean Lucas *(Gen Mgr)*

WEST KENTUCKY RURAL ELECTRIC COOPERATIVE CORP., INC.
1218 W Broadway St, Mayfield, KY 42066-0589
Tel.: (270) 247-1321   KY
Web Site: http://www.wkrecc.com
Year Founded: 1938
Sales Range: $25-49.9 Million
Emp.: 86
Electricity Distr Services
N.A.I.C.S.: 221122

WEST KENTUCKY RURAL ELECTRIC COOPERATIVE CORP., INC.   U.S. PRIVATE

West Kentucky Rural Electric Cooperative Corp., Inc.—(Continued)
David Smart (Pres & CEO)
Ron Mays (Pres-Fin)
Jack Clifford (Mgr-Acctg)

WEST KNOX UTILITY DISTRICT
2328 Lovell Rd, Knoxville, TN 37950
Tel.: (865) 690-2521
Web Site: http://www.wkud.com
Sales Range: $10-24.9 Million
Emp.: 55
Water Supply & Irrigation System Maintenance Services
N.A.I.C.S.: 221310
Drexel Heidel (Gen Mgr)
Doug Alderman (Superintendent)

WEST LAKE FOOD CORPORATION
2430 Cape Cod Way, Santa Ana, CA 92703-3540
Tel.: (714) 973-2286
Web Site: http://www.tayho.com
Sales Range: $10-24.9 Million
Emp.: 75
Processed Meat Mfr & Distr
N.A.I.C.S.: 311611
Jayce Yenson (CEO)

WEST LOUISIANA HEALTH SERVICES INC
600 S Pine St, Deridder, LA 70634
Tel.: (337) 462-7409   LA
Web Site: http://www.beauregard.org
Year Founded: 1946
Sales Range: $25-49.9 Million
Emp.: 477
Health Care Srvices
N.A.I.C.S.: 622110
Darrell Kingham (VP-Fin)

WEST MAUI CONSTRUCTION, INC.
305 E Wakea Ave Ste 100, Kahului, HI 96732
Tel.: (808) 757-7001
Construction Services
N.A.I.C.S.: 236220

WEST MEDIA GROUP, INC.
5856 Route 981, Latrobe, PA 15650
Tel.: (724) 532-3300
Web Site: http://www.westmediagroup.com
Sales Range: Less than $1 Million
Emp.: 5
Advetising Agency
N.A.I.C.S.: 541810
Debbie Coulson (Office Mgr)

WEST MICHIGAN OFFICE INTERIORS INC.
300 E 40th St, Holland, MI 49423
Tel.: (616) 396-7303
Web Site: http://www.wmoi.com
Year Founded: 1982
Sales Range: $50-74.9 Million
Emp.: 50
Retailer, Wholesaler & Remanufacturer of Office Furniture
N.A.I.C.S.: 449110
Thomas J. Schaap (Co-Owner)
Chuck Schaap (Co-Founder)
Peter Wagenmaker (CFO)
David Miedema (Controller)
Ken Weenum (Mgr-Ops)

WEST MILTON STATE BANK
940 High St, West Milton, PA 17886
Tel.: (570) 568-6851
Web Site: http://www.westmiltonstatebank.com
Sales Range: $10-24.9 Million
Emp.: 55
Provider of Financial Services
N.A.I.C.S.: 522110
Belinda M. Diefenbach (VP)
Dennis E. Keefer (VP)
David G. Myers (VP)
Trisha K. Shearer (VP & Dir-Mktg & HR)
Debbie Shief (Officer-Community Banking)
Michael Loeh (Mgr-West Milton)
Sarah Maneval (Mgr-Beaver Springs)
Wyatt Troxell (Mgr-Mifflinburg)

WEST MONROE PARTNERS, LLC
311 W Monroe St 14th Fl, Chicago, IL 60606
Tel.: (312) 602-4000   DE
Web Site: http://www.westmonroepartners.com
Year Founded: 2002
Corporate Consulting Services
N.A.I.C.S.: 541611
Kevin McCarty (Chm & CEO)
Doug Armstrong (Co-COO)
Gil Mermelstein (Co-COO)
Casey Foss (Chief Comml Officer)
Daniel Ferris (Principal)
Mazen Ghalayini (Mng Partner)

Subsidiaries:
Carbon Five Inc.   (1)
585 Howard St 2nd Fl, San Francisco, CA 94105
Tel.: (415) 546-0500
Web Site: http://www.carbonfive.com
Computer Software Product Development Services
N.A.I.C.S.: 513210
Michael Wynholds (CEO & Partner)
Don Thompson (COO)
Erik Ingenito (Partner)
David Hendee (Partner & Dir-Design)
Christian Nelsen (Partner & Dir-Engrg)
Courtney Hemphill (Partner)
Ruth C. White (Dir-Diversity, Equity & Inclusion)

Invoyent, LLC   (1)
222 West Adams St, Chicago, IL 60606   (100%)
Tel.: (312) 235-6962
Web Site: http://www.invoyent.com
Emp.: 200
Healthcare Advisory & Planning, IT & Delivery Management & Quality & Testing Solutions
N.A.I.C.S.: 541690

Pace Harmon, LLC   (1)
1650 Tysons Blvd Ste 200, McLean, VA 22102
Tel.: (703) 637-4700
Web Site: http://www.paceharmon.com
Management Consulting Services
N.A.I.C.S.: 541611
Steve Martin (Exec Mng Dir)
David Rutchik (Exec Mng Dir)
Andrew Alpert (Mng Dir)
Andy Sealock (Mng Dir)
Steve Keegan (Dir)
Steven Kirz (Mng Dir)
Marc Tanowitz (Mng Dir)
Craig Wright (Mng Dir)
Christopher Stacy (Dir)
Lisa Kloster (CFO)
David Borowski (Dir)
Adam Cummins (Dir)
Nick Wray (Dir)
Melanie Prestridge (Dir)
Shehzad Amin (Dir)
Michael McKinney (Dir)
David Clifford (Dir)
John Eagleson (Dir)
Gordon Wong (Dir)
Rahul Singh (Mng Dir)
John DiCarlo (Mng Dir)

Verys, LLC   (1)
1251 E Dyer Rd Ste 210, Santa Ana, CA 92705
Tel.: (949) 751-6085
Web Site: http://www.verys.com

Software Development Services
N.A.I.C.S.: 541511
Chris Antonius (Co-Founder & CEO)
Mike Zerkel (Co-Founder)

WEST MOTOR COMPANY INC.
296 N State St, Preston, ID 83263
Tel.: (208) 852-1337
Web Site: http://www.westmotorco.com
Sales Range: $10-24.9 Million
Emp.: 40
Automobiles, New & Used
N.A.I.C.S.: 441110
Douglas Porter (Pres)

WEST MUSIC CO.
1212 5th St, Coralville, IA 52241
Tel.: (319) 351-2000
Web Site: http://www.westmusic.com
Year Founded: 1942
Sales Range: $10-24.9 Million
Emp.: 150
Distr of Musical Instruments & Print Music to Educational Institutions
N.A.I.C.S.: 459140
Glenda O'Neil (Supvr-Accts Payable)
Robin Walenta (VP & Dir-HR)

WEST OAHU AGGREGATE CO., INC.
Lualualei Naval Rd, Waianae, HI 96792
Tel.: (808) 847-7780
Web Site: http://www.woahawaii.com
Year Founded: 1993
Sales Range: $1-9.9 Million
Emp.: 100
Waste Collection & Recycling Services
N.A.I.C.S.: 562111
Trudy Harris (Pres)
Joaquin Silva (VP)
Georgette Silva (Sec & Treas)

WEST OIL COMPANY INCORPORATED
431 Bankhead Hwy, Winfield, AL 35594
Tel.: (205) 487-4397
Rev.: $23,118,369
Emp.: 17
Petroleum Products
N.A.I.C.S.: 424720
Harold West (Pres)

WEST OREGON ELECTRIC COOPERATIVE, INC.
652 Rose Ave, Vernonia, OR 97064
Tel.: (503) 429-3021   OR
Web Site: http://www.westoregon.org
Year Founded: 1944
Sales Range: $10-24.9 Million
Emp.: 28
Electric Power Transmission Services
N.A.I.C.S.: 221121
Robert Vannatta (Pres)
Rosemary Lohrke (Treas & Sec)
Jim Buxton (VP)

WEST PAK AVOCADO, INC.
38655 Sky Canyon Dr, Murrieta, CA 92563
Tel.: (951) 296-5757   CA
Web Site: http://www.westpakavocado.com
Year Founded: 1982
Sales Range: $25-49.9 Million
Emp.: 70
Crop Preparation Services for Market
N.A.I.C.S.: 115114
Galen Newhouse (VP & Dir-Field)
Randy Shoup (Pres)
Kevin Bollinger (Controller)

Robert Salaski (Mgr-Buyer)
Scott Ross (Mgr-Sls-East)
Doug Meyer (Sr VP-Sls & Mktg)

WEST PARTNERS LLC
5796 Armada Dr Ste 300, Carlsbad, CA 92008-4694
Tel.: (760) 602-5827
Web Site: http://www.westpartners.com
Holding Company
N.A.I.C.S.: 551112
Kurt Wickham (Partner)

Subsidiaries:
Asset Development Group, Inc.   (1)
8050 N Port Washington Rd, Milwaukee, WI 53217
Tel.: (414) 352-9310
Web Site: http://www.homesourceone.net
Real Estate Lessor
N.A.I.C.S.: 531190
Jim Reitzner (Pres)

WEST PHILADELPHIA COMMUNITY MENTAL HEALTH CONSORTIUM, INC.
3751 Island Ave 3rd Fl, Philadelphia, PA 19153-3237
Tel.: (215) 596-8100   PA
Web Site: http://www.consortium-inc.org
Year Founded: 1967
Sales Range: $10-24.9 Million
Emp.: 360
Behavioral Healthcare Services
N.A.I.C.S.: 623220
Kathleen Kline (Chief Medical Officer)
Laverne Pearsall (Dir-Talent & Stakeholders Support Dept)
Patricia Brooker (VP-Ops)
Charles Patterson (Dir-Addiction Svcs)
Dawn Curry (Dir-Behavioral Health Svcs)
Lana Watkins (Dir-Mktg)
Douglas Carpenter (Sec)
Joseph Ruane (Vice Chm)
John F. White Jr. (Pres & CEO)

WEST PHYSICS CONSULTING LLC
3825 Paces Walk SE Ste 250, Atlanta, GA 30339
Tel.: (770) 435-9186
Web Site: http://www.westphysics.com
Year Founded: 2002
Sales Range: $1-9.9 Million
Health Services
N.A.I.C.S.: 621511
W. Geoffrey West (Pres & Chief Medical Officer)

WEST PLAINS IMPLEMENT CO., INC.
Hwy 10, Beach, ND 58621
Tel.: (701) 872-4154   ND
Web Site: http://www.westplains.com
Year Founded: 1967
Sales Range: $25-49.9 Million
Emp.: 80
Retail of Agricultural Farm Machinery
N.A.I.C.S.: 423820
Les Olson (Owner)

WEST PLAINS LLC
14210 Hillsdale Cir, Omaha, NE 68137
Web Site: http://www.westplainsllc.com
Sales Range: $650-699.9 Million
Emp.: 50
Farm Product Raw Material Merchant Distr
N.A.I.C.S.: 424590

COMPANIES

Darin Hanson *(VP-Bus Dev)*

WEST POINT MARKET INC.
1711 W Market St, Akron, OH 44313
Tel.: (330) 864-2151   OH
Web Site:
http://www.westpointmarket.com
Year Founded: 1936
Sales Range: $10-24.9 Million
Emp.: 150
Provider of Independent Supermarket
N.A.I.C.S.: 445110

WEST POINT PRODUCTS LLC.
250 W Wylie Ave, Washington, PA 15301
Tel.: (304) 547-1360
Web Site:
http://www.westpointproducts.com
Rev.: $21,500,000
Emp.: 300
Photographic Film, Paper, Plate & Chemical Mfr
N.A.I.C.S.: 325992
Thomas J. Day Jr. *(CEO)*

WEST QUALITY FOOD SERVICE INC.
220 N 16th Ave, Laurel, MS 39440
Tel.: (601) 649-2522
Web Site: http://www.westquality.com
Year Founded: 1967
Sales Range: $50-74.9 Million
Emp.: 25
Fast-Food Restaurant, Chain
N.A.I.C.S.: 722513
William West *(Sr VP)*
David Childress *(VP-Fin Admin)*
Alton Ishee *(VP-Ops Support)*
Hillary Black *(Dir-HR & Trng-South)*
Janet Phillips *(Acctg Dir)*

WEST RIVER ELECTRIC ASSOCIATION
Interstate 90 Exit 109, Wall, SD 57790
Tel.: (605) 279-2135
Web Site: http://www.westriver.com
Sales Range: $10-24.9 Million
Emp.: 49
Distribution, Electric Power
N.A.I.C.S.: 221122
Veronica Kusser *(Mgr-Member Svcs)*
Dick Johnson *(CEO)*
Mike Letcher *(Mgr-Ops)*

WEST RIVER TELECOM COOP
101 Main St W, Hazen, ND 58545
Tel.: (701) 748-2211
Web Site: http://www.westriv.com
Sales Range: $10-24.9 Million
Emp.: 85
Local Telephone Communications
N.A.I.C.S.: 517121
Troy Schilling *(CEO)*

WEST ROOFING SYSTEMS, INC.
121 Commerce Dr, LaGrange, OH 44050
Tel.: (440) 355-9929   OH
Web Site:
http://www.westroofingsystems.com
Year Founded: 1979
Sales Range: $10-24.9 Million
Roofing Contractors
N.A.I.C.S.: 238160
Ray Chavalia *(VP-Production-South)*
Aubrey Barto *(Mktg Mgr)*
Jeff Johnson *(VP-Production-North)*
Jack L. Moore Jr. *(Pres & CEO)*

WEST SHORE WINDOW & DOOR, INC.
5024 Simpson Ferry Rd, Mechanicsburg, PA 17050-3625
Tel.: (717) 697-4033
Web Site:
http://www.westshorewindow.com
Siding Contractors
N.A.I.C.S.: 238170
B. J. Werzyn *(Owner)*
Subsidiaries:
America's Window, LLC   (1)
9414 Highway 62, Charlestown, IN 47111
Tel.: (859) 721-0740
Web Site:
http://www.americaswindowusa.com
Sales Range: $10-24.9 Million
Window Replacement; Vinyl Siding, Bath Liners, Patio Rooms, Gutter Products Mfr
N.A.I.C.S.: 321911
Brittney Darnell *(Mgr-HR)*

Quality Advantage Home Products, Inc.   (1)
610 N Armistead Ave, Hampton, VA 23669
Tel.: (757) 728-3755
Web Site: http://www.qualityadvantage.com
Rev.: $2,000,000
Emp.: 20
New Single-Family Housing Construction, except Operative Builders
N.A.I.C.S.: 236115
John Campbell *(Pres)*

WEST SIDE FOODS INC.
355 Food Ctr Dr E Bldg, Bronx, NY 10474
Tel.: (718) 842-8500
Web Site:
http://www.westsidefoodsinc.com
Rev.: $94,400,000
Emp.: 240
Bond Brokers
N.A.I.C.S.: 424410
Thomas Ryan *(Pres)*
Linda Gonzalez *(Office Mgr)*
Seymour Adelson *(CFO)*

WEST SIDE GARAGE INC.
822 Broadway St, Berlin, WI 54923
Tel.: (920) 361-5100
Web Site:
http://www.westsidegarage.com
Sales Range: $10-24.9 Million
Emp.: 40
Automobiles, New & Used
N.A.I.C.S.: 441110
Jeff Maldwin *(Owner & Gen Mgr)*
Todd Giese *(Comptroller)*
Bob Hogan *(Dir-Svc)*
Ozzie Hoffman *(Bus Mgr)*
James Grant *(Mgr-Sls)*

WEST SIDE HAMMER ELECTRIC
1325 Clay St, Bethlehem, PA 18018
Tel.: (610) 868-3535
Web Site:
http://www.westsidehammer.com
Sales Range: $10-24.9 Million
Emp.: 79
General Electrical Contractor
N.A.I.C.S.: 238210
Luke R. Cunningham *(Pres)*
Meghan McMahon *(Project Coord)*
Ralph Ebner *(Project Mgr)*

WEST SIDE TRACTOR SALES CO.
1400 W Ogden Ave, Naperville, IL 60563
Tel.: (630) 355-7150
Web Site:
http://www.westsidetractorsales.net
Rev.: $52,878,392
Emp.: 90
General Construction Machinery & Equipment
N.A.I.C.S.: 423810
Steve Benck *(Pres)*
Dee Bernacki *(Coord-Sls)*
Alan Walker *(Mgr-Parts)*
Tim Sorn *(Mgr-Parts)*
Jennifer Snow *(Mgr-HR)*
Mary Wright *(Mgr-Credit)*
Tom Stern *(Mgr-Sls)*

WEST SIDE UNLIMITED CORPORATION
4201 16th Ave SW, Cedar Rapids, IA 52404-1207
Tel.: (319) 390-4466   IA
Web Site:
http://www.westsidetransport.com
Year Founded: 1968
Sales Range: $150-199.9 Million
Emp.: 525
Holding Company; Freight Trucking & Grain Salvage, Storage & Distr
N.A.I.C.S.: 551112
Donald Vogt *(Pres & CEO)*
Subsidiaries:
West Side Grain Sales Corp.   (1)
207 Commercial St, Shellsburg, IA 52332
Tel.: (319) 436-2251
Web Site: http://www.shellsburgelevator.com
Sales Range: $50-74.9 Million
Emp.: 5
Grain & Field Bean Storage & Distribution Services
N.A.I.C.S.: 424510
Donald Vogt *(Chm & CEO)*

West Side Salvage, Inc.   (1)
7251 32nd Ave, Atkins, IA 52206   (100%)
Tel.: (319) 446-7600
Web Site: http://www.westsideunlimited.com
Sales Range: $10-24.9 Million
Emp.: 23
Grain Salvage & Other Support Services
N.A.I.C.S.: 561990
Donald Vogt *(Chm & CEO)*
Gene Schwers *(Pres)*
Patrick Brecht *(Dir-Maintenance)*
Ken Langham *(Dir-Ops)*
Jon Vogt *(Mgr-Special Projects)*

West Side Transport, Inc.   (1)
4201 16th Ave SW, Cedar Rapids, IA 52404-1207
Tel.: (319) 390-4466
Web Site: http://www.westsidetransport.com
Sales Range: $25-49.9 Million
Emp.: 400
Trucking Transportation
N.A.I.C.S.: 484121
Donald Vogt *(Pres & CEO)*
Sue Smith *(Dir-Driver Svcs)*
Tim Whitney *(Coord-Orientation)*
Kim Varo *(Dir-Ops)*

WEST SUBURBAN CURRENCY EXCHANGES
1400 E Touhy Ave Ste 100, Des Plaines, IL 60018
Tel.: (847) 299-3100
Web Site: http://www.wsce.com
Year Founded: 1942
Sales Range: $25-49.9 Million
Check Cashing Agencies
N.A.I.C.S.: 522390
Ryan Beilman *(VP-Dev & Compliance Officer)*

WEST TENNESSEE ORNAMENTAL DOOR CO., INC.
1800 Transport Ave, Memphis, TN 38116
Tel.: (901) 346-0662
Web Site: http://www.wtndoor.com
Year Founded: 1993
Sales Range: $1-9.9 Million
Emp.: 15
Door Mfr
N.A.I.C.S.: 321911
James Hoffa *(Pres)*

WEST TEXAS INSURANCE EXCHANGE, INC.
1000 Maple Ave, Odessa, TX 79761
Tel.: (432) 333-4106
Web Site: http://www.wtie.net
Year Founded: 1962
Rev.: $11,000,000
Emp.: 10
Insurance Agents
N.A.I.C.S.: 524210
Bill F. Rea *(Founder & CEO)*
Jeff Rea *(Pres)*
Klata Hernandez *(Mgr-Mktg)*

WEST VALLEY CONSTRUCTION COMPANY INC.
580 E McGlincey Ln, Campbell, CA 95008-4907
Tel.: (408) 371-5510   CA
Web Site:
http://www.westvalleyconstruction.com
Year Founded: 1958
Sales Range: $25-49.9 Million
Emp.: 280
Provider of Water, Sewer & Utility Line Services
N.A.I.C.S.: 237110
Mike Kelly *(Pres)*

WEST VALLEY NURSING HOMES, INC.
3801 Summitview Ave, Yakima, WA 98902
Tel.: (509) 965-5260   WA
Web Site:
http://www.livingcarecenters.com
Year Founded: 1958
Sales Range: $10-24.9 Million
Emp.: 266
Elder Care Services
N.A.I.C.S.: 623312
Katie Jacoby *(Dir-Nursing Svcs)*
Jennifer Vimont *(Dir-Activity)*
Michelle Cruz *(Dir-Assisted Living)*
Cal Groenenberg *(Exec Dir)*

WEST VIRGINIA ELECTRIC SUPPLY CO
250 12th St W, Huntington, WV 25704
Tel.: (304) 525-0361
Web Site: http://www.wvesco.com
Sales Range: $10-24.9 Million
Emp.: 100
Electrical Supplies
N.A.I.C.S.: 423610
Matt Colker *(Pres)*
Lee Colker *(VP)*
Sandra Colker *(CFO)*

WEST VIRGINIA PAINT LLC
1051 Paulison Ave, Clifton, NJ 07011
Tel.: (973) 772-6565
Web Site: http://www.wvapaint.com
Rev.: $12,000,000
Emp.: 51
Industrial Painting
N.A.I.C.S.: 238320
Victoria Luzzi *(Controller)*
David Cushman *(Gen Mgr)*

WEST VIRGINIA PAVING INC
219 S Elks Rd, Parsons, WV 26287
Tel.: (304) 478-2400
Web Site: http://www.wv-paving.com
Rev.: $14,020,846
Emp.: 75
General Contractor, Highway & Street Construction
N.A.I.C.S.: 212312
John Ladden *(Gen Mgr)*

WEST VIRGINIA RADIO CORPORATION
1251 Earl L Core Rd, Morgantown, WV 26505
Tel.: (304) 296-0029
Web Site: http://www.wvaq.com
Sales Range: $10-24.9 Million
Emp.: 200

WEST VIRGINIA RADIO CORPORATION

West Virginia Radio Corporation—(Continued)
Radio Stations
N.A.I.C.S.: 516110
Dale B. Miller *(Pres & CEO)*
Kevin Nicholas *(Acct Exec)*
John Halford *(Mgr-Market-Clarksburg)*

WEST VIRGINIA-OHIO MOTOR SALES
142 River Rd, Wheeling, WV 26003
Tel.: (304) 232-7517
Sales Range: $10-24.9 Million
Emp.: 28
Sales of New & Used Trailers For Trucks
N.A.I.C.S.: 423110
Thomas Mendenhall *(Pres & Principal)*

WEST YOST ASSOCIATES, INC.
2020 Research Park Dr Ste 100, Davis, CA 95618
Tel.: (530) 756-5905
Web Site: http://www.westyost.com
Year Founded: 1990
Sales Range: $1-9.9 Million
Emp.: 102
Civil Engineering Services
N.A.I.C.S.: 541330
Charles Duncan *(Pres & COO)*
Dianne Lee *(VP-Mktg)*

Subsidiaries:
West Yost Associates, Inc.-Pleasanton (1)
7041 Koll Center, Pleasanton, CA 94566
Tel.: (925) 426-2580
Web Site: http://www.westyost.com
Emp.: 12
Civil Engineering
N.A.I.C.S.: 237990

West Yost Associates, Inc.-Roseville (1)
2281 Lava Ridge Ct Ste 100, Roseville, CA 95661
Tel.: (916) 789-1090
Civil Engineering & Construction Management Services
N.A.I.C.S.: 237990
Frank Helmick *(VP)*

WEST-ATANTIC PARTNERS LLC
264 Arlington Ave, Kensington, CA 94707
Tel.: (510) 647-8328
Web Site: http://www.west-atlanticpartners.com
Privater Equity Firm
N.A.I.C.S.: 523999
Eric Leach *(Mng Partner)*

WEST-FAIR ELECTRIC CONTRACTORS INC.
200 Brady Ave, Hawthorne, NY 10532
Tel.: (914) 769-8050
Web Site: http://www.west-fair.com
Rev.: $28,000,000
Emp.: 100
General Electrical Contractor
N.A.I.C.S.: 238210

WEST-REEVES INC.
402 Cantrell St, Waxahachie, TX 75165
Tel.: (972) 938-9623
Web Site: http://www.cabinetspecialists.com
Sales Range: $50-74.9 Million
Emp.: 200
Wood Kitchen Cabinets
N.A.I.C.S.: 337110
Richard West *(Partner)*
Robert Reeves *(Co-Owner)*

WESTAIR GAS & EQUIPMENT LP.
4258 S Treadaway Blvd, Abilene, TX 79602
Tel.: (325) 670-0444
Year Founded: 1996
Rev.: $24,000,000
Emp.: 55
Industrial Machinery & Equipment Merchant Whslr
N.A.I.C.S.: 423830
Ken Morrison *(Partner)*
Ken Shira *(CFO & VP)*
Joe Smith *(Partner)*
Ken Shira *(VP)*

WESTAK, INC.
1116 Elko Dr, Sunnyvale, CA 94089-2211
Tel.: (408) 734-8686
Web Site: http://www.westak.com
Year Founded: 1972
Sales Range: $10-24.9 Million
Emp.: 115
Mfr of Printed Circuit Boards
N.A.I.C.S.: 423690
Louise Crisham *(CEO)*
Chung Namgung *(COO)*
Debby Hall *(Mgr-Sls & Mktg)*
Dicie Hinaga *(CFO)*
Andrew Takle *(Dir-Ops-Intl)*
Jay Latin *(VP-Sls)*

Subsidiaries:
Qualitek (1)
1272 Forgewood Ave, Sunnyvale, CA 94089-2211
Tel.: (408) 734-8686
Web Site: http://www.westak.com
Sales Range: $10-24.9 Million
Mfr of Printed Circuit Boards
N.A.I.C.S.: 334412
Louise Crisham *(CEO)*

Westak International Sales Inc. (1)
1225 Elko Dr, Sunnyvale, CA 94089-2211
Tel.: (408) 734-8686
Web Site: http://www.westak.com
Sales Range: $10-24.9 Million
Emp.: 100
Provider of Electronic Parts & Equipment
N.A.I.C.S.: 423690
Debby Hall *(Mgr-Sls & Mktg)*
Jackie Carothers *(Mgr-Debby Hall Sls & Mktg)*

Westak of Oregon Inc. (1)
3941 24th Ave, Forest Grove, OR 97116-2208 (100%)
Tel.: (503) 359-3593
Web Site: http://www.westak.com
Printed Circuit Board Mfr
N.A.I.C.S.: 334412
Phil Henry *(Mgr)*

WESTAR CONTRACT KITCHEN & BATH CORP.
9025 S Kyrene Rd, Tempe, AZ 85284
Tel.: (602) 271-0100
Web Site: http://www.westar-sw.com
Sales Range: $25-49.9 Million
Emp.: 70
Electrical Appliances, Major
N.A.I.C.S.: 423620
John Edily *(Branch Mgr)*

WESTAR DISTRIBUTION, LLC.
8700 Robert Fulton Dr Ste B, Columbia, MD 21046
Tel.: (301) 490-0010
Web Site: http://www.westardistribution.com
Year Founded: 1986
Sales Range: $10-24.9 Million
Emp.: 30
Motor Vehicle Parts Whslr
N.A.I.C.S.: 423120
Hardeep Singh Chadha *(Pres & CEO)*
Chetan Singh Chadha *(COO & Gen Mgr)*
Manish Kedia *(Controller)*
Kevin Krul *(Mgr-Catalog)*

WESTAR NUTRITION CORP.
350 Paularino Ave, Costa Mesa, CA 92626
Tel.: (949) 645-6100
Web Site: http://www.vivalife.com
Medicinals & Botanicals Mfr
N.A.I.C.S.: 325411
David Fan *(Pres & CEO)*
Cheryl Cartwright *(VP-Regulatory & Bus Affairs)*
Jose Ramos *(Dir-Production)*

Subsidiaries:
Viva Life Science Corp (1)
350 Paularino Ave, Costa Mesa, CA 92626
Tel.: (949) 645-6100
Web Site: http://www.vivalife.com
Sales Range: $10-24.9 Million
Nutritional Supply
N.A.I.C.S.: 541613
David Fan *(Pres & CEO)*
Cheryl Cartwright *(VP-Regulatory & Bus Affairs)*
Joe Ramos *(Dir-Production)*

WESTAR ROOFING CORPORATION
2516 Squadron Ct, Virginia Beach, VA 23453-3155
Tel.: (757) 368-4199
Web Site: http://www.westarroofing.com
Sales Range: $10-24.9 Million
Emp.: 100
Roofing Installation Services
N.A.I.C.S.: 238390
Jim Donovan *(Pres)*
Tim Whited *(CEO)*

WESTBAY AUTO PARTS INC.
2610 SE Mile Hill Dr, Port Orchard, WA 98366
Tel.: (360) 876-8008
Web Site: http://www.westbayautoparts.com
Sales Range: $10-24.9 Million
Emp.: 120
Automotive Parts
N.A.I.C.S.: 441330
Ken Price *(Pres)*
James Civilla *(Treas)*

WESTBORN CHRYSLER JEEP, INC.
23300 Michigan Ave, Dearborn, MI 48124
Tel.: (313) 562-3200
Web Site: http://www.westbornchryslerjeep.net
Year Founded: 1981
Sales Range: $10-24.9 Million
Emp.: 70
New & Used Car Dealer
N.A.I.C.S.: 441110
Douglas Moore *(Pres)*

WESTBOUND COMMUNICATIONS, INC.
625 The City Dr Ste 360, Orange, CA 92868
Tel.: (714) 663-8188
Web Site: http://www.westboundcommunications.com
Sales Range: $10-24.9 Million
Emp.: 5
Government/Political/Public Affairs, Local Marketing, New Technologies, Public Relations, Strategic Planning/Research
N.A.I.C.S.: 541810

Scott Smith *(Pres & CEO)*
Carrie Gilbreth *(Sr VP & Gen Mgr)*
Rick Miltenberger *(Sr VP)*
Angela Meluski *(Acct Exec)*
Phiphi Tran *(Sr Acct Exec)*
Robert Chevez *(Acct Supvr)*
Jenny Corsey *(Sr Acct Exec)*
Gina DePinto *(Acct Dir-Orange County & Long Beach)*

WESTBRIDGE RESEARCH GROUP
1260 Avenida Chelsea, Vista, CA 92081
Tel.: (760) 599-8855
Web Site: http://westbridge.com
Year Founded: 1982
Sales Range: $1-9.9 Million
Emp.: 21
Biological Product Mfr & Whslr
N.A.I.C.S.: 325414
Christine Koenemann *(Pres & CEO)*
Larry Parker *(VP & Dir-R&D)*
Richard Forsyth *(CFO, Gen Counsel & Sec)*

WESTBROOK MANUFACTURING INC.
600 N Irwin St, Dayton, OH 45403
Tel.: (937) 254-2004
Web Site: http://www.westbrookohio.com
Sales Range: $10-24.9 Million
Emp.: 175
Diversified Manufacturing & Other Job Shop Work
N.A.I.C.S.: 332710
Robert F. Mays *(Chm & Treas)*
David W. Lillich *(VP-Sls & Mktg)*
Douglas F. Mays *(Pres)*
John C. White *(VP-Ops)*
Mark R. Schmitt *(VP-Tech Svcs)*
Gary Cushman *(Mgr-Mfg)*
Debbie Dove *(Mgr-Control)*
Bradley R. Kirkpatrick *(Mgr-Dev)*
Tim O'Donnell *(Dir-Quality)*
Keith G. Larsen *(Controller)*

WESTBROOK REAL ESTATE PARTNERS, LLC
645 Madison Ave 18th Fl, New York, NY 10022
Tel.: (212) 849-8800
Web Site: http://www.westbrookpartners.com
Year Founded: 1994
Sales Range: $10-24.9 Million
Emp.: 16
Real Estate Investment Firm
N.A.I.C.S.: 525990
William H. Walton III *(Mng Principal)*

Subsidiaries:
Courtyard by Marriott - San Diego Old Town (1)
2435 Jefferson St, San Diego, CA 92110
Tel.: (619) 260-8500
Web Site: http://www.marriott.com
Emp.: 50
Hotel
N.A.I.C.S.: 721110
Steve Bascor *(Gen Mgr)*
Katee Maola *(Gen Mgr)*

SP East Highlands Ranch (1)
28909 Baseline St, Highland, CA 92346
Tel.: (909) 864-8918
Rev.: $480,000
Emp.: 2
Subdividers & Developers
N.A.I.C.S.: 237210

WESTBROOK TECHNOLOGIES, INC.
22 Summit Pl, Branford, CT 06405
Tel.: (203) 483-6666
Web Site: http://www.westbrooktech.com
Year Founded: 1990
Sales Range: $10-24.9 Million

Emp.: 70
Software Applications Developer
N.A.I.C.S.: 541513
Paul Remington (CFO)

WESTBURNE SUPPLY, INC.
4111 W Clarendon Ave, Phoenix, AZ 85019
Tel.: (602) 278-8547
Web Site: http://www.ferguson.com
Sales Range: $10-24.9 Million
Emp.: 60
Sales of Plumbing Fittings & Supplies
N.A.I.C.S.: 423740
Douglas P. Strup (Sr VP-Branch Ops)
Paul E. Kennedy (VP)
Thomas J. Strup (VP)
Keith D. VanderVennet (Sr VP-Canada)
Steven F. Grosslight (Sr VP-Southwest Region)
Terry E. Hall (Gen Counsel & VP)
John L. Wilcox (Dir-Strategic Plng)

WESTBURY JEEP CHRYSLER DODGE, INC.
111 Bond St, Westbury, NY 11590
Tel.: (516) 333-2666
Web Site:
http://www.westburyjeep.com
Sales Range: $100-124.9 Million
Emp.: 67
Automobiles, New & Used
N.A.I.C.S.: 441110
Joel Sporn (Pres & Co-Owner)
Randy Sporn (Co-Owner & VP)
Keith Donnelly (Gen Mgr)

WESTBY CO-OP CREDIT UNION
501 N Main St, Westby, WI 54667
Tel.: (608) 634-3118
Web Site:
http://www.wccucreditunion.coop
Year Founded: 1939
Sales Range: $10-24.9 Million
Credit Union Services
N.A.I.C.S.: 522130
Kevin Hauser (Pres & CEO)
John Rudie (CFO)
Monte Torgerson (Vice Chm)
Ronald Larson (Chm)

WESTCHESTER ACADEMIC LIBRARY DIRECTORS ORGANIZATION
118 N Bedford Rd Ste 201, Mount Kisco, NY 10549
Tel.: (914) 930-7682 NY
Web Site: http://www.waldolib.org
Year Founded: 1992
Sales Range: $25-49.9 Million
Library
N.A.I.C.S.: 519210
Robert Karen (Dir-Procurement Svcs)
Celine Karabinos (Mgr-Accts)
Joanne Montgomery (Dir-Member Svcs)
Lucye Boland (Mgr-Subscription Fulfillment)
Rick Palladino (Treas)

WESTCHESTER COUNTRY CLUB INC.
99 Biltmore Ave, Rye, NY 10580
Tel.: (914) 967-6000
Web Site:
http://www.westchestercountryclub.net
Year Founded: 1929
Sales Range: $10-24.9 Million
Emp.: 400
Country Club
N.A.I.C.S.: 713910
Robert James (Exec Dir)

WESTCHESTER GAS COMPANY
Ste 300 6007 Financial Plz, Shreveport, LA 71129-2662
Tel.: (903) 687-3264 TX
Rev.: $21,000,000
Emp.: 25
Crude Petroleum Production
N.A.I.C.S.: 211120

WESTCHESTER INSTITUTE FOR HUMAN DEVELOPMENT
20 Hospital Oval W, Valhalla, NY 10595
Tel.: (914) 493-8150 NY
Web Site: http://www.wihd.org
Year Founded: 2004
Sales Range: $10-24.9 Million
Emp.: 271
Disability Assistance Services
N.A.I.C.S.: 624120
David O'Hara (COO)
Marianne Ventrice (VP-Fin & Admin)
David M. C. Stern (Treas)
Pamela Thornton (Vice Chm)
William H. Bave (Chm)
William H. Frishman (Sec)
Susan Fox (CEO)
Jenean Castillo (Dir-Leadership Education in Neurodevelopmental & related Disabili)
Karen Edwards (Dir-University Center for Developmental Disabilities)

WESTCHESTER PUBLISHING SERVICES, LLC
4 Old Newtown Rd, Danbury, CT 06810
Tel.: (203) 658-6581
Web Site:
http://www.westchesterpublishingservices.com
Year Founded: 1969
Book Publishing
N.A.I.C.S.: 513130
Tyler M. Carey (Chief Revenue Officer)
Dennis J. Pistone (Founder)
Paul J. Crecca (Pres & CEO)
Terry Colosimo (VP-Editorial Svcs)
Michael Jon Jensen (Dir-Tech)
Tim Davies (Interim Dir-UK)
Nicole Tomassi (Mgr-Mktg & Conference)
Kevin J. Gray (Mng Dir)
Deb Taylor (COO)
Christober Masilamani (Mng Dir)
Scott Keeney (Dir-Production & Customer Svc)
Celeste Bilyard (Dir-Journal Svcs)
Mercy Thomas (Dir-Ops-India)

Subsidiaries:

Kinetic Publishing Services, LLC (1)
202 N Thornton Ave Ste 2, Madison, WI 53703
Tel.: (608) 251-6944
Web Site: http://www.kineticpub.com
Information Services
N.A.I.C.S.: 519290
John Ferguson (Owner)

WESTCLIFF UNIVERSITY
16715 Von Karman Ave #100, Irvine, CA 92606
Tel.: (888) 491-8686
Web Site: http://www.westcliff.edu
Educational Institution
N.A.I.C.S.: 611310
Anthony Lee (Pres)

WESTCO CLOSET CORPORATION
16 Saw Mill River Rd, Hawthorne, NY 10532
Tel.: (914) 592-1001 NY

Web Site:
http://www.californiaclosets.com
Year Founded: 1978
Closet Organizers, Installation & Designer
N.A.I.C.S.: 238990
Brian Berger (CFO)
Robert J. Westenberg (Pres & VP)
Bill Barton (Pres & CEO)

WESTCO INC.
400 22nd Ave NW, Miami, OK 74354
Tel.: (918) 540-2464
Web Site:
http://www.westcohomefurnishings.com
Rev.: $13,064,959
Emp.: 30
Furniture
N.A.I.C.S.: 449210
Rudy Schultz (Pres)

WESTCO IRON WORKS, INC.
5828 S Naylor Rd, Livermore, CA 94551
Tel.: (408) 436-0711
Web Site:
http://www.westcoironworks.com
Year Founded: 2005
Sales Range: $10-24.9 Million
Emp.: 135
Hand & Edge Tool Mfr
N.A.I.C.S.: 332216
Brad Thompson (CFO)
Mark Schermesser (Pres)
Scott Hofstede (VP)
John Wenger (VP)

WESTCOAST LANDSCAPE & LAWNS, INC.
3880 76th Ave N Unit C, Pinellas Park, FL 33781
Tel.: (727) 585-0697
Web Site:
http://www.westcoastlawns.com
Sales Range: $1-9.9 Million
Emp.: 200
Landscaping Services
N.A.I.C.S.: 561730
Ken Dobler (Acct Mgr)

WESTCOAST STRUCTURAL CONCRETE & MASONRY, INC.
17061 Alico Commerce Ct Ste 102, Fort Myers, FL 33967
Tel.: (239) 590-6408 FL
Web Site:
http://www.westcoaststructural.com
Year Founded: 1998
Sales Range: $1-9.9 Million
Emp.: 40
Poured Concrete Foundation & Masonry Contractor
N.A.I.C.S.: 238110
Jimmy Rodgers (Pres)
Stuart Hoyer (VP & Project Manager)

WESTCODE INC.
233 Wilmington-West Chester Pike Ste 105, Chadds Ford, PA 19317
Tel.: (610) 738-1200 PA
Web Site:
http://www.westcodeuk.com
Year Founded: 1971
Sales Range: $75-99.9 Million
Emp.: 20
Pneumatic & Electro Pneumatic Railway Braking Equipment Mfr
N.A.I.C.S.: 336510
Edward J. Widdowson (CEO)
Deborah Kingsley (VP-Fin)

Subsidiaries:

Westcode Inc. - Binghamton Plant (1)
2226 Airport Rd, Binghamton, NY 13905

Tel.: (607) 766-9881
Web Site: http://www.westcodeus.com
Emp.: 21
Rail Air Conditioning Supplier
N.A.I.C.S.: 221330
Keith Serkl (Gen Mgr)

WESTCONSIN CREDIT UNION
3333 Schneider Ave, Menomonie, WI 54751
Tel.: (715) 235-3403 WI
Web Site:
http://www.westconsincu.org
Year Founded: 1939
Sales Range: $50-74.9 Million
Emp.: 370
Credit Union Operator
N.A.I.C.S.: 522130
Mike Tomasek (CIO)
Jim Wookey (COO)
Jay Fahl (CMO)
Jerilyn Kinderman (CFO)
Mark Willer (Chief Lending Officer)
Lora Benrud (CEO)
Gerald Wolf (Vice Chm)
Rita Lunderville (Treas)
Dave Maves (Chm)
Lynn Brantner (Sec)

WESTCOR CONSTRUCTION
5620 Stephanie St, Las Vegas, NV 89122-0200
Tel.: (702) 433-1414
Sales Range: $25-49.9 Million
Emp.: 238
Carpentry Services
N.A.I.C.S.: 238350
David Canonico (Coord-Customer Care)
Michael Coronado (Pres)
Lori Olivas (Dir-HR)

WESTECH CAPITAL CORP.
8226 Bee Caves Rd, Austin, TX 78746
Tel.: (512) 306-8222
Year Founded: 1994
Financial Investment Services
N.A.I.C.S.: 523999
James Fellus (CEO)

WESTECH FRAMING LLC.
1824 Woodmoor Dr Ste 201, Monument, CO 80132-9097
Tel.: (719) 534-9253
Web Site:
http://www.westechconstruction.com
Sales Range: $10-24.9 Million
Emp.: 7
Carpentry Services
N.A.I.C.S.: 238350
Robert Jasinski (Owner)

WESTECH INTERNATIONAL, INC.
2500 Louisiana Blvd NE, Albuquerque, NM 87110
Tel.: (505) 888-6666
Web Site: http://www.westech-intl.com
Year Founded: 1995
Sales Range: $10-24.9 Million
Emp.: 250
Engineering, Information Management, Anaysis, Testing, Evaluation, Training, Technical & Administrative Support Services
N.A.I.C.S.: 541330
Betty Chao (Pres & CEO)
Joe Bonin (Dir-Bus Dev & Ops)
Susan Marquez (Dir-HR)

WESTED
730 Harrison St Fl 5, San Francisco, CA 94107-1260
Tel.: (415) 565-3000
Web Site: http://www.wested.org

Wested—(Continued)

Year Founded: 1966
Sales Range: $10-24.9 Million
Emp.: 600
Educational Research & Development Agency
N.A.I.C.S.: 541715
Glen H. Harvey (CEO)
Danny S. Torres (Sr Mgr-Publ & Dissemination)
Richard Wenn (Dir-Digital Dev)
Aida Walqui (Dir-Teacher Pro Dev)
Paul Koehler (Dir-Policy Center)
Steve Schneider (Sr Dir-Program-Science, Tech, Engrg, & Mathematics)
Gregory Austin (Dir-Human Health Dev)
Sylvie Hale (Dir-Program Dev, Strategic Plng & Innovation Studies)
Nancy M. Riddle (CFO)
Catherine M. Walcott (Chief Dev Officer)
Max McConkey (Chief Policy & Comm Officer)
Jonathan Mills (Dir-Facilities)
Mike J. Neuenfeldt (Dir-Fin & Contracts)
Steve W. Mitchell (Dir-HR)
Nikola N. Filby (Dir-Innovation Studies)
Ginger Tulley (Dir-Media Rels)
Yvonne Gemmell Keene (Dir-Tech & Svcs)

WESTEK ARCHITECTURAL WOODWORKING INC.
97 Servistar Indus Way, Westfield, MA 01085-5601
Tel.: (413) 562-6363
Year Founded: 1990
Sales Range: $10-24.9 Million
Emp.: 16
Architectural Woodwork Mfr
N.A.I.C.S.: 321918
Bruce Scheible (Pres)
James Kotowicz (Treas)

WESTEK ELECTRONICS INC.
314 Westridge Dr, Watsonville, CA 95076-4170
Tel.: (831) 740-6300
Web Site: http://www.westek.com
Rev.: $20,109,935
Emp.: 50
Intercommunication Systems, Electric
N.A.I.C.S.: 334290

WESTEL, INC.
12015 Park Thirty Five Cir, Austin, TX 78753
Tel.: (512) 480-5500   TX
Web Site: http://www.westel.net
Year Founded: 1981
Sales Range: $10-24.9 Million
Emp.: 45
Provider of Telephone Communication Services
N.A.I.C.S.: 517121
Tommy Garner (Pres)
Crystal Zwernemann (Product Mgr)

WESTERBEKE CORPORATION
Myles Standish Indus Pk 150 John Hancock Rd, Taunton, MA 02780
Tel.: (508) 823-7677   DE
Web Site:
   http://www.westerbeke.com
Year Founded: 1937
Sales Range: $10-24.9 Million
Emp.: 70
Mfr of Marine Diesel Engines, Diesel & Gasoline Generators, Marine Air Conditioning with Land Based Generator
N.A.I.C.S.: 335312

Gregory Haidemenos (Pres & CEO)
Thomas Sutherland (Dir-Sls & Mktg)
John H. Westerbeke Jr. (Chm)

WESTERCHIL CONSTRUCTION CO.
1833 Sterkx Rd, Alexandria, LA 71301
Tel.: (318) 442-3392
Web Site: http://www.calex.com
Rev.: $21,400,000
Emp.: 100
Commercial & Office Building, New Construction
N.A.I.C.S.: 236220
Charles R. Westerchil Jr. (Pres)

WESTERMEYER INDUSTRIES, INC.
1441 State Rte 100, Bluffs, IL 62621
Tel.: (217) 754-3277
Web Site:
   http://www.westermeyerind.com
Year Founded: 2001
Rev.: $7,400,000
Emp.: 54
Engineeering Services
N.A.I.C.S.: 541330
Gary Westermeyer (VP)

WESTERN & SOUTHERN FINANCIAL GROUP, INC.
400 Broadway, Cincinnati, OH 45202-3341
Tel.: (513) 362-2296   OH
Web Site:
   http://www.westernsouthern.com
Year Founded: 1888
Rev.: $5,333,846,000
Assets: $58,427,654,000
Liabilities: $47,543,701,000
Net Worth: $10,883,953,000
Earnings: $764,545,000
Fiscal Year-end: 12/31/19
Holding Company; Life Insurance Products & Services, Investment Advisory & Securities Brokerage Services
N.A.I.C.S.: 551112
James J. Vance (Co-Chief Investment Officer & Sr VP)
James N. Clark (Co-CFO & Sec)
Bradley J. Hunkler (Co-CFO & Sr VP)
Jonathan D. Niemeyer (Chief Admin Officer, Gen Counsel & Sr VP)
Nicholas P. Sargen (Sr VP)
David Todd Henderson (Chief Risk Officer & Sr VP)
Keith T. Clark (VP & Dir-Medical)
Phillip E. King (Sr VP & Auditor)
Bruce W. Maisel (Chief Compliance Officer & VP)
Karen A. Chamberlain (CIO & Sr VP)
Lisa B. Fangman (Sr VP-Insurance Ops)
Brendan M. White (Co-Chief Investment Officer & Sr VP)
Daniel W. Harris (Chief Actuary & Sr VP)
Jill T. McGruder (CMO & Sr VP)
Linda M. Lake (Sr VP-HR)
Wade M. Fugate (VP & Controller)
Edward J. Babbitt (VP-Govt Rels)
Kevin L. Howard (VP & Deputy Gen Counsel)
Todd A. Lee (VP-Mktg & Digital Center-Excellence)
David E. Nevers (VP-PR & Corp Comm)
John Finn Barrett (Chm, Pres & CEO)
Stephen G. Hussey Jr. (Sr VP-Compensation & Benefits)

Subsidiaries:

Columbus Life Insurance Co.   (1)
400 E 4th St, Cincinnati, OH 45202-3302   (100%)
Tel.: (513) 361-6700
Web Site: http://www.columbuslife.com
Sales Range: $250-299.9 Million
Emp.: 2,000
Life Insurance
N.A.I.C.S.: 524113
J. J. Miller (Pres & CEO)
Jim Koth (VP-Mid South)
Matt Canterbury (VP-Sls-East)

Eagle Realty Group, LLC   (1)
421 E 4th St, Cincinnati, OH 45202   (100%)
Tel.: (513) 361-7700
Web Site: http://www.realtygroup.com
Sales Range: $50-74.9 Million
Emp.: 100
Full Real Estate Asset Management Company
N.A.I.C.S.: 524113
Mario San Marco (Pres)
Edward Grout (CFO)

Fort Washington Investment Advisors, Inc.   (1)
303 Broadway St Ste 1200, Cincinnati, OH 45202-4203   (100%)
Tel.: (513) 361-7600
Web Site: http://www.fortwashington.com
Sales Range: $50-74.9 Million
Emp.: 75
Investment Advisory Company Service
N.A.I.C.S.: 523940
Michele Hawkins (Mng Dir & Chief Compliance Officer)
Joe Don Cole (VP-Bus Dev)
Ken J. Ryan (VP & Dir-Institutional Relationship Mgmt)
Roger M. Lanham (Co-Chief Investment Officer & Sr VP)
Jeffrey D. Meek (Co-CFO & VP)
Barry D. Pavlo (VP-Bus Dev)
Michael E. Rudnicki (Asst VP & Sr Mgr-Relationship)
Eric J. Walzer (VP-Investment Ops)
Brendan M. White (Co-Chief Investment Officer & Sr VP)
Margaret Smith Bell (Mng Dir-Bus Dev)
Stephen A. Baker (Mng Dir & Head-Private Equity)
Martin W. Flesher (Mng Dir-Bus Dev & Relationship Mgmt)
Gerald J. Ulland (Co-CFO & Mng Dir-Private Client Grp)
James E. Wilhelm (Mng Dir & Head-Private Equity)
Timothy J. Policinski (Mng Dir & Sr Portfolio Mgr)
Scott D. Weston (Mng Dir & Sr Portfolio Mgr)
M. Robert Maeder (Mng Dir & Deputy Head-Private Equity)
Julia Ossipov (Mng Dir)
Maribeth Sembach Rahe (Pres & CEO)

Gerber Life Insurance Company   (1)
1311 Mamaroneck Ave, White Plains, NY 10605-5223
Tel.: (800) 704-2180
Web Site: http://www.gerberlife.com
Life & Health Insurance Carrier
N.A.I.C.S.: 524113
David Fier (Sr VP)

IFS Financial Services, Inc.   (1)
303 Broadway Ste 1100, Cincinnati, OH 45202
Tel.: (513) 362-8000
Web Site:
   http://www.westernsouthernlife.com
Direct Marketing of Financial Products
N.A.I.C.S.: 523150

Subsidiary (Domestic):

Touchstone Securities, Inc.   (2)
303 Broadway Ste 1100, Cincinnati, OH 45202
Tel.: (800) 638-8194
Web Site: http://www.touchstonefunds.com
Sales Range: $75-99.9 Million
Emp.: 100
Insurance
N.A.I.C.S.: 524128
Steve Graziana (Pres)

Integrity Life Insurance Company   (1)
PO Box 5720, Cincinnati, OH 45201-5720   (100%)
Tel.: (513) 362-8000
Web Site:
   http://www.integritycompanies.com
Sales Range: $900-999.9 Million
Emp.: 225
Life Insurance & Annuities Products & Services
N.A.I.C.S.: 524113

Subsidiary (Domestic):

National Integrity Life Insurance Company   (2)
15 Matthews St Ste 200, Goshen, NY 10924-1995   (100%)
Tel.: (502) 582-7900
Web Site:
   http://www.integritycompanies.com
Sales Range: $50-74.9 Million
Emp.: 15
Long-Term Asset Accumulation & Retirement Savings
N.A.I.C.S.: 523150

The Lafayette Life Insurance Company   (1)
1905 Teal Rd, Lafayette, IN 47905
Tel.: (765) 477-7411
Web Site: http://www.llic.com
Sales Range: $50-74.9 Million
Emp.: 165
Fire Insurance Services
N.A.I.C.S.: 524113

The Western & Southern Life Insurance Company   (1)
400 Broadway St, Cincinnati, OH 45202-3312   (100%)
Tel.: (513) 629-1800
Web Site:
   http://www.westernsouthernlife.com
Sales Range: $250-299.9 Million
Emp.: 2,000
Health Insurance Services
N.A.I.C.S.: 523150
John Finn Barrett (Chm, Pres & CEO)
Daniel Amodeo (Mgr-Fort Lauderdale)

WESTERN AGCREDIT
10980 S Jordan Gateway, South Jordan, UT 84095
Tel.: (801) 571-9200
Web Site:
   http://www.westernagcredit.com
Rev.: $19,457,625
Emp.: 50
Federal Land Banks
N.A.I.C.S.: 522299
Matthew Y. Jarrett (CFO & Sr VP)
Ross Baadsgaard (Mgr-Southern Reg)

WESTERN BAGEL BAKING CORP.
7814 Sepulveda Blvd, Van Nuys, CA 91405-1020
Tel.: (818) 786-5847
Web Site:
   http://www.westernbagel.com
Year Founded: 1946
Sales Range: $25-49.9 Million
Emp.: 300
Sales of Bread, Cake & Related Products
N.A.I.C.S.: 311812
Steven Ustin (Pres)
Jeff Ustin (VP-Production)
Greg Linzner (Mgr-Sls & Mktg)
David Beltran (Controller)

WESTERN BANCORPORATION, INC.
201 N Central Ave, Duluth, MN 55807
Tel.: (218) 723-5100   MN
Year Founded: 1991
Multi-Bank Holding Company
N.A.I.C.S.: 551111
Stephen Lewis (Pres)

COMPANIES

Subsidiaries:

Western National Bank (1)
201 N Central Ave, Duluth, MN 55807
Tel.: (218) 723-5100
Web Site: http://www.wbduluth.com
Sales Range: $1-9.9 Million
Emp.: 28
Commericial Banking
N.A.I.C.S.: 522110
Bill Lewis (Sr VP-Bus Banking)

Western National Bank (1)
210 2nd St NW, Cass Lake, MN 56633
Tel.: (218) 335-4131
Web Site: http://www.wbcasslake.com
Sales Range: $1-9.9 Million
Commericial Banking
N.A.I.C.S.: 522110

WESTERN BANCSHARES OF CLOVIS, INC.
901 Pile St, Clovis, NM 88101-5908
Tel.: (575) 769-1975   NM
Web Site: http://www.wbclovis.com
Bank Holding Company
N.A.I.C.S.: 551111
Connie T. Connolly (Pres)

Subsidiaries:

Western Bank of Clovis (1)
901 Pile St, Clovis, NM 88101
Tel.: (505) 769-1975
Sales Range: $1-9.9 Million
Emp.: 21
Commericial Banking
N.A.I.C.S.: 522110

WESTERN BEEF, INC.
47 05 Metropolitan Ave, Ridgewood, NY 11385-1046
Tel.: (718) 366-1444   DE
Web Site:
  http://www.westernbeef.com
Year Founded: 1985
Sales Range: $400-449.9 Million
Emp.: 2,000
Full-Service Retail Supermarkets & Food Outlet Stores Owner & Operator
N.A.I.C.S.: 445110
Frank Castellana (Co-Owner)
Rocky Rodriquez (Exec VP-Plng)
Peter Castellana Jr. (Pres-Florida Div)

Subsidiaries:

Awesome Transportation, Inc. (1)
4705 Metropolitan Avenue, Ridgewood, NY 11385-1046 (100%)
Tel.: (718) 417-3770
Web Site: http://www.westernbeef.com
Sales Range: $10-24.9 Million
Emp.: 50
Local Trucking without Storage
N.A.I.C.S.: 484110
Al D'Auria (Gen Mgr)

WESTERN BEVERAGE COMPANY
1075 Owen Loop S, Eugene, OR 97402
Web Site:
  http://www.abwholesaler.com
Beer Distr
N.A.I.C.S.: 424810
Jim Marion (Branch Mgr)

WESTERN BEVERAGE INC
301 E Wyatt Earp Blvd, Dodge City, KS 67801
Tel.: (620) 227-7641
Rev.: $6,300,000
Emp.: 42
Beer & Ale Merchant Whslr
N.A.I.C.S.: 424810
Joe Bogner (Pres)

WESTERN BEVERAGES INC.
4837 W Ave, San Antonio, TX 78213
Tel.: (210) 341-7171
Rev.: $11,800,000
Emp.: 8
Liquor Stores
N.A.I.C.S.: 445320

WESTERN BLUE PRINT COMPANY LLC
1220 W Cambridge Cir Dr, Kansas City, KS 66103-1314
Tel.: (816) 300-6600
Web Site: http://www.westblue.com
Year Founded: 1908
Sales Range: $10-24.9 Million
Emp.: 116
Commercial Printing, Lithographic
N.A.I.C.S.: 323111
Matt West (Dir-Digital Svc)

WESTERN BRANCH DIESEL INCORPORATED
3504 Shipwright St, Portsmouth, VA 23703-2428
Tel.: (757) 673-7000   VA
Web Site:
  http://www.westernbranchdiesel.com
Year Founded: 1946
Sales Range: $50-74.9 Million
Emp.: 300
Distr of Diesel Engines & Transmissions
N.A.I.C.S.: 423830
Keith Butler (Treas)
Herbert A. Haneman Jr. (Pres)

WESTERN BUILDING CENTER OF KALISPELL
1745 3rd Ave E, Kalispell, MT 59901
Tel.: (406) 257-7231   MT
Web Site:
  http://www.westernbuildingcenter.com
Year Founded: 1956
Sales Range: $50-74.9 Million
Emp.: 175
Building Material Retailer
N.A.I.C.S.: 326199
Dave Ottun (VP)
Eric Martin (VP)
Don Kocubinski (VP)
Randy Kjos (VP)
Doug Shanks (Pres)

WESTERN BUS SALES INC.
30355 SE Hwy 212, Boring, OR 97009
Tel.: (503) 905-0002
Web Site:
  http://www.westernbus.com
Sales Range: $25-49.9 Million
Emp.: 30
Dealer Of Busses
N.A.I.C.S.: 423110
Marlan Rohlena (Co-Owner)
Colby Blagg (Dir-Parts & Svc)
Mollie Blagg (Pres)
Jim Pederson (Mgr-Warranty)
Ty Anderson (Controller)

WESTERN CAPITAL CORPORATION
1750 W Front St Ste 150, Boise, ID 83702
Tel.: (208) 332-0700   ID
Web Site: http://www.northwest-bank.com
Year Founded: 2007
Bank Holding Company
N.A.I.C.S.: 551111
Steven D. Wasson (Vice Chm)

Subsidiaries:

Northwest Bank (1)
1750 W Front St Ste 150, Boise, ID 83702
Tel.: (208) 332-0700
Web Site: http://www.northwest-bank.com
Sales Range: $10-24.9 Million
Emp.: 51
Commericial Banking
N.A.I.C.S.: 522110
Kay Harwood (VP & Mgr-Comml Real Estate Relationship)
Jeffery D. Gow (Chm)
William K. Ilett (Chm)
Jeff Banks (VP & Mgr-Comml Banking)
Ben Chaney (VP-Treasury Mgmt)
Scott Gibson (Pres-Market)

WESTERN CAROLINA COMMUNITY ACTION, INC.
220 King Creek Blvd, Hendersonville, NC 28792
Tel.: (828) 693-1711   NC
Web Site: http://www.wcca.net
Year Founded: 1966
Sales Range: $10-24.9 Million
Emp.: 180
Community Action Services
N.A.I.C.S.: 624190
Betty Depina (Dir-Children's Svcs)
Debbie Haight (Dir-CSBG)
Sheryl Fortune (Dir-Housing)
David White (CEO)
Elizabeth Whitten (CFO)

WESTERN CAROLINA FORKLIFT INC.
6392 Burnt Poplar Rd, Greensboro, NC 27409
Tel.: (336) 668-0959
Web Site: http://www.wcforklift.com
Year Founded: 1976
Sales Range: $1-9.9 Million
Emp.: 42
Lift Trucks & Parts
N.A.I.C.S.: 423830
David Hayes (Owner & CEO)
David Woods (Controller)
Aleta Hayes (Vice Chm)

WESTERN CARPET & LINOLEUM CO.
202 Wythe Ave, Brooklyn, NY 11211
Tel.: (718) 782-0333
Web Site:
  http://www.westerncarpet.com
Rev.: $17,800,000
Emp.: 40
Floor Coverings
N.A.I.C.S.: 423220
Marvin Jacoby (Controller)
Jeff Henick (Chm)
Alan Henick (Pres)

WESTERN CARRIERS INC.
5 Westec Dr, Auburn, MA 01501
Tel.: (508) 756-4181
Web Site:
  http://www.westerncarriers.com
Rev.: $31,420,013
Emp.: 300
General Warehousing
N.A.I.C.S.: 493110
Gerard H. Cohen (Pres)

WESTERN CATHOLIC UNION
510 Maine St, Quincy, IL 62301
Tel.: (217) 223-9721   IL
Web Site: http://www.wculife.org
Year Founded: 1877
Sales Range: $10-24.9 Million
Emp.: 21
Fraternal Life Insurance Services
N.A.I.C.S.: 524113
Robert J. Ley (Dir-Sls)
Roger W. Player (Chm)
Steven L. Looten (VP-Fraternal)
Kent D. Stegeman (CFO, Treas & Sec)

WESTERN COLORADO COMMUNITY FOUNDATION
225 N 5th St Ste 505, Grand Junction, CO 81501
Tel.: (970) 243-3767   CO
Web Site: http://www.wc-cf.org
Year Founded: 1996
Sales Range: $10-24.9 Million
Emp.: 8
Grantmaking Services
N.A.I.C.S.: 813211
Cecile Aday (Mgr-Scholarship Program)
Tedi Gillespie (Dir-Grants & Community Outreach)
Anne Wenzel (Pres & Exec Dir)
Doug Shawcroft (Dir-Fin & Admin)

WESTERN COMMERCE BANK
127 S Canyon St, Carlsbad, NM 88220
Tel.: (575) 887-6687
Web Site: http://www.wcb.net
Sales Range: $10-24.9 Million
Emp.: 138
Commercial Bank
N.A.I.C.S.: 522110
Don Kidd (Chm & CEO)
Twilla Thomason (VP)

WESTERN COMMUNICATIONS INC.

WESTERN COMMUNICATIONS INC.
1777 SW Chandler Ave, Bend, OR 97702
Tel.: (541) 382-1811   OR
Web Site:
  http://www.bendbulletin.com
Year Founded: 1903
Newspaper Publisher & Specialty Publications
N.A.I.C.S.: 513110
Amy Husted (Mgr-Circulation Office)
Ray Mierjeski (Mgr-Pre-Press)

Subsidiaries:

Curry Coastal Pilot (1)
507 Chetco Ave, Brookings, OR 97415
Tel.: (541) 469-3123
Web Site: http://www.currypilot.com
Sales Range: $10-24.9 Million
Emp.: 25
Newspapers
N.A.I.C.S.: 513110
David Jeffcoat (Reg Mgr-Circulation)
Robin Fornoff (Editor-in-Chief)
Kim Fowler (Publr)

La Grande Observer (1)
1406 5th St, La Grande, OR 97850
Tel.: (541) 963-3161
Web Site: http://www.lagrandeobserver.com
Sales Range: $10-24.9 Million
Emp.: 40
Newspapers
N.A.I.C.S.: 513110
Frank Everidge (Gen Mgr & Mgr-Ops)

Redmond Spokesman (1)
226 NW 6th St, Redmond, OR 97756
Tel.: (541) 548-2184
Web Site:
  http://www.redmondspokesmanonline.com
Rev.: $1,485,000
Emp.: 11
Newspaper Publishers
N.A.I.C.S.: 513110
Deanne Bain (Sec)
Steve Hawes (Publr)

The Baker City Herald (1)
1915 First St, Baker City, OR 97814
Tel.: (541) 523-3673
Web Site: http://www.bakercityherald.com
Sales Range: $10-24.9 Million
Emp.: 25
Newspapers
N.A.I.C.S.: 513110
Kari Borgen (Publr)

The Bulletin (1)
1777 SW Chandler Ave, Bend, OR 97702
Tel.: (541) 382-1811
Web Site: http://www.bendbulletin.com

WESTERN COMMUNICATIONS INC.

U.S. PRIVATE

Western Communications Inc.—(Continued)
Sales Range: $25-49.9 Million
Emp.: 200
Newspapers
N.A.I.C.S.: 513110
Bill Bigelow *(Editor-Sports)*
Richard Coe *(Editor-Editorial Page)*
Dean Guernsey *(Editor-Photo)*
Jody Lawrence-Turner *(Editor-Features)*
Julie Johnson *(Editor-City)*
Dena DeRose *(Dir-Adv)*

The Del Norte Triplicate (1)
312 H St PO Box 277, Crescent City, CA 95531
Tel.: (707) 464-2141
Web Site: http://www.triplicate.com
Newspaper Publishers
N.A.I.C.S.: 513110
Matthew C. Durkee *(Mng Editor)*
Michael Zogg *(Editor-Sports)*
David Jeffcoat *(Dir-Circulation)*
Elizabeth Carter *(District Mgr)*
David DeLonge *(Production Mgr)*

The Union Democrat (1)
84 South Washington St, Sonora, CA 95370
Tel.: (209) 532-7151
Web Site: http://www.uniondemocrat.com
Sales Range: $10-24.9 Million
Emp.: 70
Newspapers
N.A.I.C.S.: 513110
Peggy Pietrowicz *(Mgr-Adv)*
Sharon Sharp *(Mgr-Circulation)*

WESTERN CONSOLIDATED COOPERATIVES INC.
101 Rand St, Holloway, MN 56249-1107
Tel.: (320) 394-2171 MN
Web Site: http://www.west-con.com
Year Founded: 1983
Sales Range: $100-124.9 Million
Emp.: 70
Producer Of Grain & Field Beans
N.A.I.C.S.: 424510
Dean Isaacson *(Gen Mgr)*
Craig Wilkening *(Pres)*
Sheila Hoffman *(Mgr-IT)*

WESTERN CONSTRUCTION GROUP
1637 N Warson Rd, Saint Louis, MO 63132-1027
Tel.: (314) 427-6733
Web Site: http://www.westerngroup.com
Year Founded: 1915
Sales Range: $10-24.9 Million
Emp.: 30
Holding Company
N.A.I.C.S.: 238990
Rod O'Bannon *(Branch Mgr)*
Dennis C. Ahrenhoersterbaeumer *(Dir-Bus Dev)*
Aaron Toney *(Mgr-Anaheim-CA)*
Jennifer Ballengee *(Gen Counsel & Sec)*
John Burger *(Mgr-Ridgefield)*
Michael R. Bishop *(VP)*
Michael P. Mercier *(VP-Ops-Omaha)*
Paul Gillstrom *(Chief Fin & Strategic Growth Officer)*
Tom Brooks *(VP-Ops & Bus Dev)*
Mary Faris *(Sr Dir-HR & Talent Dev)*
Ken Black *(Sr Dir-Enterprise Risk Mgmt)*
Benjamin M. Bishop Jr. *(CEO)*

Subsidiaries:

Brisk Waterproofing Company (1)
720 Grand Ave, Ridgefield, NJ 07657
Tel.: (201) 945-0210
Waterproofing Contractor
N.A.I.C.S.: 238390
Kevin Chorba *(Branch Mgr)*

Great Plains Roofing & Sheet Metal (1)
2820 Roe Ln, Kansas City, KS 66103

Tel.: (913) 677-4679
Roofing Contractors
N.A.I.C.S.: 238160

Harry S. Peterson Company (1)
2658 W Van Buren St, Chicago, IL 60612
Tel.: (630) 458-5206
Concrete Contractor
N.A.I.C.S.: 238110

Michigan Ornamental Metals (1)
1033 Slocum Ave, Ridgefield, NJ 07657
Tel.: (201) 945-4930
Web Site: http://www.michiganornamental.com
Metal Ornamentation Mfr
N.A.I.C.S.: 332323

North Texas Waterproofing & Restoration Co. (1)
2414 E Hwy 80, Mesquite, TX 75149
Tel.: (972) 289-7000
Sales Range: $1-9.9 Million
Emp.: 6
Waterproofing & Restoration Services
N.A.I.C.S.: 238390
Rick Troutte *(Gen Mgr)*

Peoria Roofing and Restoration Company (1)
307 Troth St, Peoria, IL 61603-3505
Tel.: (309) 676-2374
Roofing Contractors
N.A.I.C.S.: 238160
Mike Coyle *(Gen Mgr)*

Western Restoration & Waterproofing Co. (1)
11534 Gondola St, Cincinnati, OH 45241
Tel.: (513) 772-9544
Waterproofing & Restoration Services
N.A.I.C.S.: 238390

Western Roofing & Insulation Co. (1)
1947 Gravois Ave, Saint Louis, MO 63104
Tel.: (314) 773-8813
Web Site: http://www.westernconstructiongroup.com
Emp.: 25
Roofing Contractors
N.A.I.C.S.: 238160
Bob Diehl *(Branch Mgr)*

Western Waterproofing Company Inc. (1)
1947 Gravois Ave, Saint Louis, MO 63104
Tel.: (314) 773-8813
Web Site: http://www.westerngroup.com
Sales Range: $10-24.9 Million
Specialty Trade Contractors
N.A.I.C.S.: 238990
Jim Reckman *(Gen Mgr)*

WESTERN CONSTRUCTION SERVICES, INC.
2300 E 3rd Loop Ste 110, Vancouver, WA 98661
Tel.: (360) 699-5317
Web Site: http://www.westernconstruction.com
Sales Range: $10-24.9 Million
Emp.: 50
Commercial & Institutional Building Construction
N.A.I.C.S.: 236220
Kenneth Andrews *(Pres)*
Gene Kunze *(Superintendent)*

WESTERN CONTRACT FURNISHERS OF SACRAMENTO INC.
11455 Folsom Blvd, Rancho Cordova, CA 95742-6207
Tel.: (916) 638-3338 CA
Web Site: http://www.westerncontract.com
Year Founded: 1957
Sales Range: $10-24.9 Million
Emp.: 30
Home & Business Furnishings
N.A.I.C.S.: 449110
Bill Yee *(Pres)*

WESTERN COOPERATIVE COMPANY
724 W 3rd St, Alliance, NE 69301
Tel.: (308) 762-3112
Web Site: http://www.westco.coop
Sales Range: $10-24.9 Million
Emp.: 80
Fertilizers & Agricultural Chemicals
N.A.I.C.S.: 424910
David Briggs *(Gen Mgr)*
Dawn Butcher *(Mgr-HR)*
Deb Hoffman *(Mgr-Credit)*

Subsidiaries:

Jirdon Agri Chemicals, Inc. (1)
70927 Hwy 26, Morrill, NE 69358
Tel.: (308) 247-2126
Web Site: http://www.jirdon.com
Sales Range: $10-24.9 Million
Emp.: 50
Fertilizer, Chemicals, Seed, Livestock, Lawn & Garden Products
N.A.I.C.S.: 424910

Slafter Oil Co (1)
PO Box 950, Scottsbluff, NE 69363-0950
Tel.: (308) 635-2814
Automobile Lubricant Distr
N.A.I.C.S.: 424690

WESTERN COOPERATIVE CREDIT UNION
1300 Bison Dr, Williston, ND 58802-2237
Tel.: (701) 572-4000 ND
Web Site: http://www.wccu.org
Year Founded: 1937
Sales Range: $10-24.9 Million
Emp.: 115
Credit Union Operator
N.A.I.C.S.: 522130
Justin Maddison *(CFO)*
Melanie Stillwell *(Pres & CEO)*

WESTERN COOPERATIVE ELECTRIC ASSOCIATION, INC.
635 S 13th St, Wa Keeney, KS 67672
Tel.: (785) 743-5561 KS
Web Site: http://www.westerncoop.com
Year Founded: 1945
Sales Range: $125-149.9 Million
Emp.: 50
Distr of Electric Power
N.A.I.C.S.: 221122
Larry J. Evans *(Pres)*
Donald L. Schultz *(VP)*
Craig Crossland *(Chm)*

WESTERN CREATIVE, INC.
26135 Plymouth Rd, Redford, MI 48239
Tel.: (800) 500-4210 MI
Web Site: http://www.westerncreative.com
Year Founded: 1996
Rev: $7,000,000
Emp.: 16
Fiscal Year-end: 12/31/06
Advetising Agency
N.A.I.C.S.: 541810
Mark Young *(Chm)*
Sally Young *(Pres)*
Robb Taylor *(Chief Creative Officer)*
Lisa Spencer *(Acct Mgr)*
Noelle Pressotto *(Coord-Production)*
Jeff Peterman *(Dir-Media)*
Angelica Pietrasik *(Art Dir-Print)*
Rob Cozad *(Graphic Designer)*
Corrine Watson *(Acct Mgr)*

WESTERN DAKOTA INSURERS INC.
816 5th St, Rapid City, SD 57701
Tel.: (605) 342-3130

Web Site: http://www.westerndakotainsurors.com
Sales Range: $10-24.9 Million
Emp.: 30
Fire, Marine & Casualty Insurance
N.A.I.C.S.: 524126
Gary Larson *(Pres)*

WESTERN DIESEL SERVICES, INC.
1100 Research Blvd, Saint Louis, MO 63132
Tel.: (314) 868-8620 DE
Web Site: http://www.ckpower.com
Year Founded: 1976
Engines & Parts Distr & Mfr
N.A.I.C.S.: 423830
John R. Costello *(Owner & CEO)*
Paul Ostby *(Pres)*

WESTERN DOVETAIL, INC.
1155 Nimitz Ave Bldg 118, Vallejo, CA 94592
Tel.: (707) 556-3683 CA
Web Site: http://www.westerndovetail.com
Year Founded: 1993
Sales Range: $1-9.9 Million
Emp.: 20
Drawer & Custom Cabinetry Mfr
N.A.I.C.S.: 337122
Maxfield Hunter *(Pres & CEO)*

WESTERN ELECTRICAL SALES INC.
521 Glide Ave Unit A, West Sacramento, CA 95691
Tel.: (916) 372-1001
Web Site: http://www.wesisales.com
Sales Range: $10-24.9 Million
Emp.: 7
Wire & Cable
N.A.I.C.S.: 423610
Joseph Lascola *(Pres)*

WESTERN ELECTRICITY CO-ORDINATING COUNCIL
155 N 400 W Ste 200, Salt Lake City, UT 84103
Tel.: (801) 582-0353 UT
Web Site: http://www.wecc.biz
Year Founded: 1994
Sales Range: $50-74.9 Million
Emp.: 271
Electric Industry Association
N.A.I.C.S.: 813910
Michael Moon *(VP-Entity Oversight)*
Melanie M. Frye *(Pres & CEO)*
David Godfrey *(Chief Admin Officer & VP)*
Steve Goodwill *(Gen Counsel, Sec & VP)*
Jillian Lessner *(CFO & VP)*
Gary Leidich *(Chm)*
Kris Hafner *(Vice Chm)*

WESTERN ELITE INCORPORATED SERVICES
103 S 2nd St, Roslyn, WA 98941
Tel.: (509) 649-2211
Web Site: http://www.inlandnetworks.com
Rev: $12,500,000
Emp.: 85
Holding Company; Telecommunications Resellers
N.A.I.C.S.: 551112
Nathan R. Weis *(VP)*
Douglas Weis *(Pres)*
Gregory A. Maras *(Sec)*
James K. Brooks *(Treas)*

Subsidiaries:

Inland Networks (1)
103 S 2nd St, Roslyn, WA 98941 (100%)
Tel.: (509) 649-2211

Web Site: http://www.inlandnetworks.com
Telecommunication Servicesb
N.A.I.C.S.: 517121
Nathan R. Weis (VP)

WESTERN ENGINEERING CO. INC.
1149 Hwy 44, Harlan, IA 51537-4905
Tel.: (402) 445-4500   IA
Web Site:
   http://www.westernengineering.biz
Year Founded: 1986
Sales Range: $25-49.9 Million
Emp.: 300
Provider of Highway & Street Construction Services
N.A.I.C.S.: 237310
Marlon Thompson (Controller)
Gary Lemons (Pres)
Larry Peters (Mgr-Risk & HR)

WESTERN EQUIPMENT DISTRIBUTORS, INC.
20224 80th Ave S, Kent, WA 98032
Tel.: (253) 872-8858
Web Site: http://www.western-equip.com
Sales Range: $10-24.9 Million
Emp.: 32
Garden Machinery & Equipment
N.A.I.C.S.: 423820
Paul Veach (Mgr-RLC & Siteworks Sls)
Dick Bergeron (Mgr-Comml Equipment Sls)
Jeff Zicha (Mgr-Irrigation Sls & Svc)
Scott McDonald (Mgr-Svc & Repair)

WESTERN EQUIPMENT LLC
404 Frisco Ave, Clinton, OK 73601
Tel.: (580) 323-0030
Web Site: http://www.west-equip.com
Year Founded: 1916
Emp.: 300
Farm & Garden Machinery & Equipment Distr
N.A.I.C.S.: 423820
Colby Flaming (Mgr-Store)

Subsidiaries:
Ray Lee Equipment Company   (1)
910 N Date St, Plainview, TX 79072
Tel.: (806) 293-2538
Web Site: http://www.rlec.com
Agricultural Equipment Distr
N.A.I.C.S.: 423820
Ray Lee (Gen Mgr)
Kirk Lewis (Mgr-Parts)

WESTERN EXPRESS HOLDINGS, INC.
7135 Centennial Pl, Nashville, TN 37209
Tel.: (615) 259-9920
Web Site:
   http://www.westernexp.com
Year Founded: 1991
Sales Range: $300-349.9 Million
Emp.: 400
Holding Company
N.A.I.C.S.: 484121
Richard L. Prickett Jr. (CFO, Treas, Exec VP & Asst Sec)

Subsidiaries:
Western Express, Inc.   (1)
7135 Centennial Pl, Nashville, TN 37209
Tel.: (615) 259-9920
Web Site: http://www.westernexp.com
Sales Range: $25-49.9 Million
Emp.: 150
Truckload Carrier Services
N.A.I.C.S.: 484121
Paul Wieck (Pres)

WESTERN EXTRUSIONS
1735 Sandy Lk Rd, Carrollton, TX 75006-3612
Tel.: (972) 245-7515   TX
Web Site:
   http://www.westernextrusions.com
Year Founded: 1979
Sales Range: $150-199.9 Million
Emp.: 800
Mfr of Aluminum Extruded Products
N.A.I.C.S.: 331318
Charles McEvoy (Exec VP)
Pat Lenburg (VP)
A.P. McEvoy Jr. (Pres)

WESTERN FAMILY HOLDING CO., INC.
3445 N Williams, Portland, OR 97227
Tel.: (503) 639-6300   OR
Web Site:
   http://www.westernfamily.com
Year Founded: 1963
Grocery Distr
N.A.I.C.S.: 424410
Steve Hauke (VP-Sls)

Subsidiaries:
Mckenzie Buying Company   (1)
6700 SW Sandburg St, Tigard, OR 97223-8008
Tel.: (503) 639-6300
Web Site:
   http://www.westernfamilyfoods.com
Emp.: 70
Nondurable Goods
N.A.I.C.S.: 424990
Ronald S. King (Pres)
Pete Craven (CFO & Sr VP)

Western Family Foods Inc.   (1)
6700 SW Sandburg St, Tigard, OR 97223-8008
Tel.: (503) 639-6300
Web Site: http://www.westernfamily.com
Emp.: 70
Private Label Groceries
N.A.I.C.S.: 424410
Ronald S. King (Pres)
Steve Hauke (VP-Sls-Mktg)
Pete Craven (CFO & Sr VP)

WESTERN FARMERS ELECTRIC COOPERATIVE, INC.
701 NE 7th St, Anadarko, OK 73005
Tel.: (405) 247-3351
Web Site: http://www.wfec.com
Year Founded: 1941
Sales Range: $250-299.9 Million
Emp.: 355
Electric Power Generation & Services
N.A.I.C.S.: 221118
Gary R. Roulet (CEO)
Jane Lafferty (CFO & VP)
Brian Hobbs (VP-Legal & Corp Svcs)
Mark Faulkenberry (Sr Mgr-Member Svcs)
Ron Cunningham (VP-Power Delivery)
Charles Hickey (Pres)
Mike Lebeda (VP)

Subsidiaries:
WFEC Railroad Co., Inc.   (1)
Hwy 70 E 4 Mi W, Fort Towson, OK 74735
Tel.: (580) 873-2201
Web Site: http://www.wfec.com
Sales Range: Less than $1 Million
Emp.: 80
Railroads, Line-Haul Operating, Nsk
N.A.I.C.S.: 482111

WESTERN FOREST PRODUCTS INC.
2192 Division St, Bellingham, WA 98226
Tel.: (360) 733-5474
Web Site:
   http://www.westernforestprod.com
Sales Range: $10-24.9 Million
Emp.: 45
Lumber: Rough, Dressed & Finished
N.A.I.C.S.: 423310

Terry Dawn (Pres)

WESTERN FORMS INC.
6200 Equitable Rd, Kansas City, MO 64120
Tel.: (816) 241-0477
Web Site:
   http://www.westernforms.com
Rev.: $13,600,000
Emp.: 300
Sheet Metalwork
N.A.I.C.S.: 332322
Richard Johnson (Mgr-Mktg & Bus Dev)
Matt Nimmo (Supvr-Mfg)
Jim Aylward (Reg Mgr)
Kevin Bohne (VP-Mfg & Ops)
Mike Carlson (Reg Mgr-Sls)
Sarisa Grindstaff (Mgr-Customer Svc)

WESTERN FRATERNAL LIFE ASSOCIATION
1900 1st Ave NE, Cedar Rapids, IA 52402
Tel.: (319) 363-2653
Web Site: http://www.wflains.org
Rev.: $19,600,000
Emp.: 35
Life Insurance
N.A.I.C.S.: 524113
Craig Van Dyke (Pres)
Donald Nieland (Sec & VP-IT)
Ann Day (VP)
Jack Minder (Treas & VP)
Duane Jirik (Chm)
Daniel Anderegg (Mgr-Sls & Mktg)

WESTERN FUNDING INC.
3915 E Patrick Ln, Las Vegas, NV 89120
Tel.: (702) 434-1990
Web Site:
   http://www.westernfundinginc.com
Year Founded: 1962
Rev.: $13,900,000
Emp.: 50
Specialized Automobile Financing Services
N.A.I.C.S.: 522291
LaVida Mize (Dir-Collateral Custody)
Bret Pangborn (Mgr-Natl Credit & VP)
Jim Murray (Pres)

WESTERN GENERAL INSURANCE CO., INC.
5230 Las Virgenes Rd Ste 100, Calabasas, CA 91302
Tel.: (818) 880-9070
Web Site:
   http://www.westerngeneral.com
Year Founded: 1971
Sales Range: $50-74.9 Million
Emp.: 210
Mechanical Breakdown Protection for Automobile Manufacturers & Retailers
N.A.I.C.S.: 524298
Robert M Ehrlich (Chm, Pres & CEO)
John Albanese (CFO)
Dan Mallut (Gen Counsel & Exec VP)

Subsidiaries:
All Motorists Insurance Agency Inc.   (1)
5230 Lost Virginges Rd Ste 100, Calabasas, CA 91302
Tel.: (818) 880-9070
Web Site: http://www.westerngeneral.com
Rev.: $18,557,328
Emp.: 130
Insurance Agents, Brokers & Service
N.A.I.C.S.: 524210
Robert M Ehrlich (Pres)
Bob Early (CEO)

WESTERN GRADE, LLC
1350 N Penrod, Show Low, AZ 85901

Tel.: (928) 532-8361
Web Site:
   http://www.westerncos.com
Year Founded: 2001
Sales Range: $1-9.9 Million
Residential Remodeler
N.A.I.C.S.: 236118
Trent Gillespie (Founder & Owner)

WESTERN HOME COMMUNITIES INC.
420 E 11th St, Cedar Falls, IA 50613
Tel.: (319) 277-2141
Web Site:
   http://www.westernhomecommunities.org
Rev.: $14,200,000
Emp.: 300
Homes for the Elderly
N.A.I.C.S.: 623312
Jerry Harris (COO)
Kris Hanson (CEO)
Kelly Meir (CFO)
Tim Boettger (Dir-Spiritual Care)

WESTERN ILLINOIS BANCSHARES, INC.
200 E Broadway, Monmouth, IL 61462
Tel.: (309) 734-2265   IL
Web Site:
   http://www.westernilbancshare.com
Year Founded: 2005
Sales Range: $10-24.9 Million
Bank Holding Company
N.A.I.C.S.: 551111
Christopher J. Gavin (Sec & Treas)
Raymond E. Defenbaugh (VP)
Augustin S. Hart III (Pres)

Subsidiaries:
Midwest Bank   (1)
200 E Broadway, Monmouth, IL 61462-1871
Tel.: (309) 734-2265
Web Site: http://www.mbwi.com
Sales Range: $10-24.9 Million
Commericial Banking
N.A.I.C.S.: 522110
Christopher J. Gavin (Pres & CEO)
Amanda Campbell (CFO & VP)
Aaron Jensen (COO & VP)
Matt Gillen (Chief Credit Officer & Sr VP)
Terri Hippen (VP-Mktg & HR)

WESTERN INDUSTRIAL CERAMICS
10725 SW Tualatin Sherwood Rd, Tualatin, OR 97062
Tel.: (503) 692-3770
Web Site: http://www.wicinc.com
Sales Range: $25-49.9 Million
Emp.: 50
Ceramic Fiber
N.A.I.C.S.: 327999
Jim Huston (Founder)
Bill Largent (Mgr-Sls)
Glen Buchanan (Pres)
Mike Hopkins (Mgr-Fabrication)
Kevin Keeler (Mgr-Sls)
Lois Sullivan (Office Mgr-Los Angeles)
Sam Sullivan (Mgr-Shop-Los Angeles)

WESTERN INDUSTRIES CORPORATION
4249 SW 29th St, Oklahoma City, OK 73119
Tel.: (405) 419-3100
Web Site: http://www.wicpack.com
Sales Range: $10-24.9 Million
Emp.: 113
Packaging Product Mfr & Distr
N.A.I.C.S.: 326150
Jim Robertson (CEO)
Claudia Robertson (Chief Specialist Officer)

WESTERN INDUSTRIES CORPORATION — U.S. PRIVATE

Western Industries Corporation—(Continued)
Louis Morelli (COO)
Thomas Wang (Gen Partner-Asia)
Chris Bruehl (CFO)

Subsidiaries:

WICPACK Malaysia Sdn Bhd (1)
112 Jalan Tampoi Kawasan Perindustrian Tampoi, 81200, Johor Bahru, Johor, Malaysia
Tel.: (60) 12 200 8287
Inventory Planning Services
N.A.I.C.S.: 541614

WICPACK Singapore Pte Ltd (1)
10 Changi South Lane 01-03 OSSIA Building, Singapore, 486162, Singapore
Tel.: (65) 6861 7101
Inventory Planning Services
N.A.I.C.S.: 541614
Ryan Lim (Mgr-Acct)

Western Industries Corp. (1)
4616 W Howard Ln Bldg 7 Ste 750, Austin, TX 78728
Tel.: (512) 832-1197
Web Site: http://www.wicokc.com
Sales Range: $25-49.9 Million
Emp.: 60
Corrugated & Solid Fiber Box Mfr
N.A.I.C.S.: 322211
Wayne Goolsby (Pres)
Don Peterson (Gen Mgr)

Western Industries Corporation, Corrugated Division (1)
4249 SW 29th St, Oklahoma City, OK 73119
Tel.: (405) 419-3100
Web Site: http://www.wicokc.com
Sales Range: $10-24.9 Million
Emp.: 40
Mfr of Custom Corrugated Shipping Containers & Boxes
N.A.I.C.S.: 326150

WESTERN INDUSTRIES, INC.
W156 N9073 Pilgrim Rd, Menomonee Falls, WI 53051-2269
Tel.: (920) 261-0660   WI
Web Site: http://www.westernind.com
Year Founded: 1944
Sales Range: $350-399.9 Million
Emp.: 1,100
Engineered Products Mfr
N.A.I.C.S.: 332313
Michael L. Mosner (VP-Sls & Mktg)
Robert Davis (Dir-HR)
Bob Schneider (CFO)

Subsidiaries:

Anaheim Manufacturing Company (1)
2680 Orbiter St, Brea, CA 92821-6265 **(100%)**
Tel.: (714) 524-7770
Web Site: http://www.anaheimmfg.com
Sales Range: $10-24.9 Million
Emp.: 100
Residential & Commercial Food Waste Disposal Mfr
N.A.I.C.S.: 335220
Trevor Wainwright (Dir-Ops)

Chilton Products (1)
300 Breed St, Chilton, WI 53014 **(100%)**
Tel.: (920) 849-2381
Sales Range: $10-24.9 Million
Emp.: 59
Contract Metal & Plastic Components, Sub-Systems or Complete Products for OEM Markets
N.A.I.C.S.: 332420

Gerett Products (1)
W156 N9073 Pilgrim Rd, Menomonee Falls, WI 53051-2269 **(100%)**
Tel.: (262) 251-7860
Contract Manufacturer of Metal Products
N.A.I.C.S.: 332313

Western Industries, Inc. (1)
1141 S 10th St, Watertown, WI 53094-6740 **(100%)**
Tel.: (920) 261-0660
Web Site: http://www.westernind.com
Sales Range: $25-49.9 Million
Emp.: 240
Contract Manufacturing of Metal Products
N.A.I.C.S.: 332312

Western Industries, Inc. - Plastic Products Group (1)
7727 First Ave Strother Field, Winfield, KS 67156 **(100%)**
Tel.: (620) 221-9464
Web Site: http://www.westernind.com
Sales Range: $25-49.9 Million
Emp.: 350
Contract Manufacturing & Blow Molding of Plastics
N.A.I.C.S.: 326199
Joe Messina (Pres)

WESTERN INTEGRATED TECHNOLOGIES, INC.
7651 S 190th St, Kent, WA 98032
Tel.: (425) 747-0927   WA
Web Site: http://www.westernintegrated.com
Year Founded: 1969
Sales Range: $10-24.9 Million
Emp.: 150
Distr of Mobile & Industrial Hydraulic & Mechanical Products
N.A.I.C.S.: 423630
Steve Schwasnick (VP)
Bill Hill (Pres)
Michelle Kenney (Mgr-HR)
Tim O'Hara (VP-Fin & Ops)

WESTERN IOWA COOPERATIVE
3330 Moville Blacktop, Hornick, IA 51026
Tel.: (712) 874-3211
Web Site: http://www.westerniowacoop.com
Sales Range: $50-74.9 Million
Emp.: 110
Provider of Grains
N.A.I.C.S.: 424510
Daniel Dix (Gen Mgr)

WESTERN LUMBER CO.
2240 Tower E Ste 200, Medford, OR 97504-7026
Tel.: (541) 779-5121
Web Site: http://www.westernlumber.com
Year Founded: 1986
Sales Range: $10-24.9 Million
Emp.: 11
Provider of Lumber, Plywood & Millwork
N.A.I.C.S.: 423310
Bob Crews (Mgr-Sls)

WESTERN MATERIALS INC.
1202 S 1st St, Yakima, WA 98901
Tel.: (509) 575-3000
Web Site: http://www.westernmaterials.com
Rev.: $22,000,000
Emp.: 40
Lumber & Other Building Materials
N.A.I.C.S.: 423310
William B. Douglas (Co-Pres)
Stan Martinkuss (Co-Pres & CEO)

WESTERN MILLING, LLC
31120 Nutmeg Rd, Goshen, CA 93227
Tel.: (559) 302-1000
Web Site: http://www.westernmilling.com
Year Founded: 1935
Nursery & Garden Centers
N.A.I.C.S.: 444240
Mark Labounty (COO & Gen Counsel)

Subsidiaries:

Western Foods LLC (1)
440 N Pioneer Ave Ste 200, Woodland, CA 95776
Tel.: (530) 601-5991
Web Site: http://www.westernfoodsco.com
Rice Flours & Grain Milling, Blending & Packaging
N.A.I.C.S.: 111199

Subsidiary (Domestic):

American Sunny Foods, Inc. (2)
2404 Stagecoach Rd, Stockton, CA 95215-7932
Tel.: (209) 943-0143
Sales Range: $1-9.9 Million
Emp.: 16
Flour Milling Services
N.A.I.C.S.: 311211

WESTERN MIXERS INC.
2910 N San Fernando Rd, Los Angeles, CA 90065-1322
Tel.: (323) 344-5270
Web Site: http://westernmixers.com
Year Founded: 1966
Sales Range: $10-24.9 Million
Emp.: 20
Provider of Fresh Fruits, Vegetables & Nuts
N.A.I.C.S.: 424480
Dave Bolstad (Pres)

WESTERN MORTGAGE & REALTY CO.
3825 W Ct St Ste 2, Pasco, WA 99301
Tel.: (509) 545-4545
Sales Range: $50-74.9 Million
Emp.: 220
Property Operator Real Estate & Investment Agents
N.A.I.C.S.: 531120
Tim Tippett (Sec & VP)
Frank Tigs (Pres)

WESTERN MOTOR COMPANY INC.
409 E Fulton St, Garden City, KS 67846
Tel.: (620) 275-4291
Web Site: http://www.shopwesternmotor.com
Rev.: $33,243,069
Emp.: 48
Automobiles, New & Used
N.A.I.C.S.: 441110
Troy Nanninga (Principal)

WESTERN MUTUAL INSURANCE GROUP
27489 Agoura Rd Ste 200, Agoura Hills, CA 91301
Tel.: (818) 879-2142
Web Site: http://www.westernmutual.com
Rev.: $18,000,000
Emp.: 40
Homeowners, Fire & Casualty Insurance Services
N.A.I.C.S.: 524126
Brent Scheib (Project Mgr)
Daniel Greulich (Sr VP)
John Shen (Mgr-Direct Sls)

WESTERN NATIONAL GROUP
8 Executive Cir, Irvine, CA 92614
Tel.: (949) 862-6200
Web Site: http://www.wng.com
Rev.: $95,000,000
Emp.: 800
Apartment Management
N.A.I.C.S.: 236117
Michael K. Hayde (CEO)
Jeffrey R. Scott (CFO)

Rex F. Delong (Pres-Western Natl Realty Advisors)
Jerry LaPointe (VP-Acq)
Daniel Reynolds (Exec Mng Dir)

WESTERN NATIONAL MUTUAL INSURANCE CO.
4700 W 77th St, Edina, MN 55435
Tel.: (952) 835-5350
Web Site: http://www.wnins.com
Sales Range: $200-249.9 Million
Emp.: 350
Property Damage Insurance
N.A.I.C.S.: 524126
Stuart Henderson (Pres & CEO)
Mara Bain (Chief Experience Officer & Asst VP)

Subsidiaries:

Pioneer Specialty Insurance Company (1)
5350 W 78th St, Edina, MN 55436
Tel.: (952) 835-5350
Web Site: http://www.pioneerspecialty.com
Business Insurance Services
N.A.I.C.S.: 524210

Titan Property & Casualty Insurance Company (1)
10310 Orland Pkwy, Orland Park, IL 60467
Tel.: (815) 464-8141
Web Site: http://www.titanbusinessins.com
Insurance Services
N.A.I.C.S.: 524126

WESTERN NEVADA SUPPLY CO.
950 S Rock Blvd, Sparks, NV 89431
Tel.: (775) 359-5800
Web Site: http://www.goblueteam.com
Sales Range: $75-99.9 Million
Emp.: 400
Plumbing Fittings & Supplies
N.A.I.C.S.: 423720
Laurie Baxter (CFO)
Jeanna Mitchell (Dir-IT)
Ted Reviglio (VP)

WESTERN NEW YORK CLINICAL INFORMATION EXCHANGE, INC.
2568 Walden Ave Ste 107, Buffalo, NY 14225
Tel.: (716) 206-0993   NY
Web Site: http://www.wnyhealthelink.com
Year Founded: 2006
Sales Range: $10-24.9 Million
Emp.: 48
Health Information Exchange Services
N.A.I.C.S.: 518210
Stephen Allen (Dir-Ops)
Daniel E. Porreca (Exec Dir)
Drew McNichol (Dir-Tech)
Jacqueline Welsch (Controller)
Art Wingerter (Vice Chm)
David Scamurra (Chm)

WESTERN NEW YORK PUBLIC BROADCASTING ASSOCIATION
PO Box 1263, Buffalo, NY 14240-1263
Tel.: (716) 845-7000   NY
Web Site: http://www.wned.org
Year Founded: 1955
Rev.: $13,019,504
Assets: $41,353,229
Liabilities: $6,197,101
Net Worth: $35,156,128
Earnings: $200,650
Emp.: 136
Fiscal Year-end: 06/30/19
Broadcasting Industry Association
N.A.I.C.S.: 813910

COMPANIES

WESTERN PLAINS ENERGY, LLC.

Sylvia Bennett *(Chief Dev Officer & Sr VP)*
Nancy Hammond *(COO & Exec VP)*
Donald K. Boswell *(Pres & CEO)*
Carlton Brock Jr. *(Treas)*

WESTERN NEWSPAPERS, INC.
8303 E Hwy 69, Yuma, AZ 85314
Tel.: (928) 783-3311
Web Site: http://www.westernnews.com
Year Founded: 1978
Sales Range: $25-49.9 Million
Emp.: 320
Newspaper Publishers
N.A.I.C.S.: 513110
Donald Soldwedel *(Chm)*
Joseph Edward Soldwedel *(Pres & CEO)*
Blake Dewitt *(Sr VP)*
Kit Atwell *(Exec VP)*
Richard Haddad *(VP-Fin)*
Rebecca Munger *(VP-Fin)*
Debbie White-Hoel *(Publr)*

Subsidiaries:

Havasu Newspapers Inc. (1)
2225 W Acoma Blvd, Lake Havasu City, AZ 86403
Tel.: (928) 453-4237
Web Site: http://www.havasunews.com
Sales Range: $10-24.9 Million
Emp.: 40
Newspaper Publishers
N.A.I.C.S.: 513110

Kingman Daily Miner (1)
3015 Stockton Hill Rd, Kingman, AZ 86401 (100%)
Tel.: (928) 753-6397
Web Site: http://www.kdminer.com
Sales Range: $10-24.9 Million
Emp.: 40
Publisher of Newspapers
N.A.I.C.S.: 513110
Joe Soldwedel *(Pres)*

Prescott Newspapers Inc. (1)
1958 Palmer Center Cir, Prescott, AZ 86301 (100%)
Tel.: (928) 445-3333
Sales Range: $25-49.9 Million
Emp.: 180
Publisher of Newspapers
N.A.I.C.S.: 513110
Mark Lewis *(Editor-Relief)*

Verde Valley Newspapers Inc. (1)
116 S Main St, Cottonwood, AZ 86326
Tel.: (928) 634-2241
Web Site: http://www.verdevalleynews.com
Sales Range: $10-24.9 Million
Emp.: 30
Publisher of Newspapers
N.A.I.C.S.: 513110

Williams GC Newspapers Inc. (1)
118 S 3rd St, Williams, AZ 86046
Tel.: (928) 635-4426
Web Site: http://www.williamsnews.com
Sales Range: $10-24.9 Million
Emp.: 9
Newspaper Publishers
N.A.I.C.S.: 513110
Loretta Yerian *(Mng Editor)*
Madeline Keith *(Publr)*

WESTERN NORTH CAROLINA COMMUNITY HEALTH SERVICES, INC.
257 Biltmore Ave, Asheville, NC 28801
Tel.: (828) 285-0622   NC
Web Site: http://www.wncchs.org
Sales Range: $10-24.9 Million
Emp.: 192
Community Health Care Services
N.A.I.C.S.: 621498
Minnie Jones *(Vice Chm)*
Curtis B. Venable *(Chm)*

Thomas Vanblaricom *(Treas)*
Carlos Gomez *(Exec Dir)*
Polly Ross *(Dir-Medical)*

WESTERN OFFICE INTERIORS INC.
500 Citadel Ave Ste 250, Los Angeles, CA 90040
Tel.: (323) 721-8833
Web Site: http://www.westernoffice.com
Year Founded: 1988
Sales Range: $10-24.9 Million
Emp.: 30
Contract Office Furniture
N.A.I.C.S.: 423210
Yvonne Ramirez *(Project Coord)*
Janet Moore *(Project Mgr)*
Kevin Lyngholm *(Project Mgr)*
Esther Chan *(Coord-Mktg)*

WESTERN OIL INC.
3553 Rider Trl S, Earth City, MO 63045
Tel.: (314) 738-9900
Web Site: http://www.western-oil.com
Rev.: $22,400,000
Emp.: 200
Gasoline Stations
N.A.I.C.S.: 457120
Grant Eble *(VP)*
Vicki Eble *(Treas & Sec)*
George Eble Jr. *(Pres)*

WESTERN OILFIELDS SUPPLY CO.
3404 State Rd, Bakersfield, CA 93308
Tel.: (661) 399-9124
Web Site: http://www.powerprime.com
Rev.: $22,100,000
Emp.: 200
Water Distribution Or Supply Systems For Irrigation
N.A.I.C.S.: 532490
John W. Lake *(Pres)*
Robert Lake *(CFO)*

WESTERN OUTDOORS PUBLICATIONS
PO Box 73370, San Clemente, CA 92673
Web Site: http://www.wonews.com
Rev.: $10,000,000
Emp.: 33
Publisher of Newspapers
N.A.I.C.S.: 513110
Bill Jaenicke *(Dir-Circulation)*
Chuck Buhagiar *(Dir-Sls & Mktg)*

WESTERN OVERSEAS CORPORATION
10731 Walker St Ste B, Cypress, CA 90630-4757
Tel.: (562) 985-0616
Web Site: http://www.westernoverseas.com
Sales Range: $10-24.9 Million
Emp.: 80
Customhouse Brokers
N.A.I.C.S.: 488510
Carlo De Aatougia *(VP)*
Michael Dugan *(Pres)*
Doreen Bonnici *(VP-Ocean Ops)*
Anthony Castrovillo *(VP-Air Ops)*

WESTERN PACIFIC BUILDING MATERIALS
2805 NW 31st Ave, Portland, OR 97210
Tel.: (503) 224-9142
Web Site: http://www.wpbm.net
Sales Range: $200-249.9 Million
Emp.: 320
Building Materials

N.A.I.C.S.: 423310
Robert Harrison *(Co-Owner)*
Tom Rosenthol *(Controller)*
Aaron Prettyman *(Mgr)*
Hank Muschenheim *(Mgr-Bend Branch)*
Jereme Hall *(Mgr-IT)*

WESTERN PACIFIC DISTRIBUTORS
1739 Saber St, Hayward, CA 94545
Tel.: (510) 732-0100
Web Site: http://www.teamwpd.com
Sales Range: $10-24.9 Million
Emp.: 15
Ice Making Machines
N.A.I.C.S.: 423440
John E. Palm *(Pres & CEO)*
Vince Palm *(COO & Controller)*

WESTERN PACIFIC ROOFING CORPORATION
2229 E Avenue Q, Palmdale, CA 93550-4140
Tel.: (661) 273-1336   CA
Web Site: http://www.westpacroof.com
Year Founded: 1949
Sales Range: $75-99.9 Million
Emp.: 75
Installation & Repair of Roofing Systems
N.A.I.C.S.: 238160
Johnny Zamrzla *(Pres)*

WESTERN PACIFIC STORAGE SYSTEMS INC.
300 E Arrow Hwy, San Dimas, CA 91773-3339
Tel.: (909) 451-0303   CA
Web Site: http://www.wpss.com
Sales Range: $10-24.9 Million
Emp.: 200
Mfr of Steel Shelving & Shelving Related Products
N.A.I.C.S.: 337126
Tom Rogers *(Pres)*
Soheir Hakim *(Controller)*

WESTERN PARTITIONS, INC.
8300 SW Hunziker St, Tigard, OR 97223
Tel.: (503) 620-1600
Web Site: http://www.westernpartitions.com
Year Founded: 1972
Sales Range: $50-74.9 Million
Emp.: 50
Contracting Services for Drywall, Metal Studs, Acoustic Ceilings, Wall Panels, Fireproofing, Firestopping & Stucco
N.A.I.C.S.: 238310
Michael A. Roach *(Co-Founder)*
Victor Roach *(Pres)*
Michell Baer *(CFO)*
Pam Roach *(Co-Founder)*
Angela Roach *(Exec VP)*
Ryan Wilson *(VP-Field Ops-Portland)*
Nate Hillestad *(VP-Ops-Nevada)*
Devin Deller *(VP-Ops-Oregan)*
Shawn Coates *(VP-Sls & Estimating)*
Steve Litchtenberg *(VP-Specialty Ops)*

WESTERN PETROLEUM CO., INC.
2517 Grand Ave, Glenwood Springs, CO 81601-4125
Tel.: (970) 945-6214   CO
Web Site: http://www.westernpetroleumco.com
Year Founded: 1962
Sales Range: $10-24.9 Million
Emp.: 20

Provider of Petroleum Bulk Station & Terminal Services
N.A.I.C.S.: 424710
Mike S. Fattor *(Pres)*
Mike Lucero *(Mgr)*

WESTERN PIEDMONT COUNCIL OF GOVERNMENTS
1880 2nd Ave NW, Hickory, NC 28601
Tel.: (828) 322-9191   NC
Web Site: http://www.wpcog.org
Year Founded: 1968
Sales Range: $10-24.9 Million
Emp.: 63
Community Development Services
N.A.I.C.S.: 624190
H. Dewitt Blackwell *(Exec Dir)*
Sherry Long *(Dir-Community Dev)*
John Marshall *(Dir-Plng)*
Wendy Johnson *(Dir-Workforce Dev)*
April Lail *(Mgr-Workforce Dev-Fin)*
George B. Holleman *(Co-Chm)*
Larry Yoder *(Sec)*
Robert L. Smyre *(Chm)*

WESTERN PIEDMONT SYMPHONY
243 3rd Ave NE Ste 1-N, Hickory, NC 28601
Tel.: (828) 324-8603
Web Site: http://www.wpsymphony.org
Emp.: 125
Symphony Orchestra
N.A.I.C.S.: 711130
John Gordon Ross *(Dir-Music & Conductor)*
Paulette Miller *(Dir-Mktg)*
Ingrid Keller *(Exec Dir)*
Dan Green *(Pres)*

WESTERN PIONEER INC.
4601 Shilshole Ave NW, Seattle, WA 98107
Tel.: (206) 789-1930
Web Site: http://www.westernpioneer.com
Sales Range: $10-24.9 Million
Emp.: 60
Grocery Stores
N.A.I.C.S.: 445110
Larry Soriano *(Pres)*
Sean Santo *(Asst Controller)*

WESTERN PLAINS ENERGY, LLC.
3022 County Rd 18, Oakley, KS 67748
Tel.: (785) 672-8810
Web Site: https://www.wpellc.com
Year Founded: 2001
Sales Range: $10-24.9 Million
Emp.: 37
Ethyl Alcohol Mfr
N.A.I.C.S.: 325193
Benedict C. Dickman *(Sec)*
Jeff Torluemke *(Pres)*
Dave Mann *(Mgr)*
Brian Baalman *(Mgr)*
Scott Foote *(Mgr)*
Rick Billinger *(Mgr)*
Steve Sershen *(Mgr)*
Derek Peine *(CEO)*
Dusty Zerr *(CFO)*
Rick Holaday *(Plant Mgr)*
Greg Doll *(Mgr-Commodities)*
Jeff Brittenham *(Mgr-Information Technology)*
Joni Wilson *(Mgr-Distillers Sls & Commodities)*
Aaron Betz *(Mgr-EHS)*
Miranda Ashmore *(Mgr-Human Resources)*
Tawny Shaw *(Mgr-Lab)*

WESTERN PLAINS ENERGY, LLC.

Western Plains Energy, LLC.—(Continued)
Josh Brown *(Production Mgr)*
Cody Holzmeister *(Mgr-Materials)*
Joe Renner *(Mgr-Materials)*

WESTERN PORTS TRANS-PORTATION, INC.
9369 8th Ave S, Seattle, WA 98108
Tel.: (206) 762-2600
Web Site:
http://www.westernports.com
Sales Range: $10-24.9 Million
Emp.: 21
Intermodal Cargo Drayage
N.A.I.C.S.: 484220
Steven D. Tyner *(Owner)*
Sheri Stewart *(VP)*
Kent Christopher *(Pres)*

WESTERN POWER SPORTS INCORPORATED
601 E Gowen Rd, Boise, ID 83716
Tel.: (208) 376-8400
Web Site: http://www.wps-inc.com
Sales Range: $25-49.9 Million
Emp.: 450
Motor Vehicle Supplies & New Parts
N.A.I.C.S.: 423120
Craig Shoemaker *(Pres)*
Pete Treadwell *(Mgr-Sls & Mktg)*
Randy Lawrence *(CFO)*
Alex Baylon *(Mgr-Sls-Southwest Reg)*
Dale Spangler *(Dir-Mktg)*
Krys Brown *(Product Dir-V-Twin)*

WESTERN PRINTING MACHINERY CO.
9229 Ivanhoe Ave, Schiller Park, IL 60176
Tel.: (847) 678-1740
Web Site: http://www.wpm.com
Sales Range: $10-24.9 Million
Emp.: 54
Printing Trades Machinery
N.A.I.C.S.: 333248
Tim Kapolnek *(Dir-Mfg)*
Paul Kapolnek *(Pres & CEO)*
Kelvin O'Meara *(CFO)*

WESTERN PRODUCTS
7777 N 73rd St, Milwaukee, WI 53223-4021
Tel.: (414) 354-2310 WI
Web Site:
http://www.westernplows.com
Year Founded: 1995
Sales Range: $25-49.9 Million
Emp.: 500
Mfr of Spare Parts for Trucks
N.A.I.C.S.: 333120
Linda Evans *(VP-HR)*
Joe DeWall *(Mgr-Sls-Plainfield)*

WESTERN PULP PRODUCTS CO.
5025 SW Hout St, Corvallis, OR 97333
Tel.: (541) 757-1251
Web Site:
http://www.westernpulp.com
Sales Range: $10-24.9 Million
Emp.: 50
Pressed Fiber & Molded Pulp Products
N.A.I.C.S.: 322299
Rick Hurley *(Pres)*

WESTERN REGIONAL OFF-TRACK BETTING CORPORATION
700 Ellicott St, Batavia, NY 14020-3744
Tel.: (585) 343-1423 NY
Web Site: http://www.batavia-downs.com
Year Founded: 1973
Sales Range: $150-199.9 Million
Emp.: 514
Pari-Mutual Off-Track Wagering
N.A.I.C.S.: 237110
Timothy McCarthy *(Gen Counsel)*
James Haas *(Mgr-Mutuels & Comm)*
Patrick Murphy *(Exec VP)*
Henry F. Wojtaszek *(Pres & Gen Counsel)*
Scott P. Kiedrowski *(VP-Ops)*
Michael P. Nolan *(COO)*

WESTERN RESERVE AREA AGENCY ON AGING
925 Euclid Ave Ste 600, Cleveland, OH 44115-1405
Tel.: (216) 621-0303
Web Site: http://www.psa10a.org
Year Founded: 1974
Sales Range: $10-24.9 Million
Emp.: 200
Provider of Individual & Family Services
N.A.I.C.S.: 624120
John Pallotta *(Mgr-Care)*
Karen Abercrombie *(Mgr-Case)*
Dell Whitaker *(COO)*
Bernice Brown-Finch *(Supvr-Ops)*
Rebekah Dickson *(Mgr-RN Case)*
Stephanie Manning *(Coord-Dev)*
Douglas Beach *(CEO)*

WESTERN RESERVE FARM COOPERATIVE
14961 S State Ave, Middlefield, OH 44062
Tel.: (440) 632-0271 OH
Web Site: http://www.wrfc.org
Year Founded: 1934
Sales Range: $25-49.9 Million
Emp.: 150
Farm Supply Sales
N.A.I.C.S.: 424910
Michael Eastlake *(Gen Mgr)*
Bill Bullock *(Controller)*
Robert Gerlosky *(Supvr-Warehouse)*
Kendra Mohney *(Coord-Safety)*

WESTERN RESERVE LAND CONSERVANCY
3850 Chagrin River Rd, Moreland Hills, OH 44022-1131
Tel.: (440) 528-4150 OH
Web Site:
http://www.wrlandconservancy.org
Year Founded: 1987
Sales Range: $10-24.9 Million
Emp.: 42
Land Conservation Services
N.A.I.C.S.: 813312
Rich Cochran *(Pres & CEO)*
Dennis Bower *(CFO & CIO)*
Jim Rokakis *(VP)*
Nancy G. Rubin *(Treas)*
Mitchell Schneider *(Vice Chm)*
Elizabeth Juliano *(Chm)*
Scott Mueller *(Vice Chm)*
Michael Shaughnessy *(Vice Chm)*
Bob Owen *(Gen Counsel)*
Emily Bacha *(Dir-Comm & Mktg)*
Joy Mulinex *(Dir-Govt Rels)*
Kate Pilacky *(Assoc Dir-Firelands Field)*
Kendrick Chittock *(Project Mgr)*
Pete McDonald *(Dir-Land Stewardship)*
Robin Darden Thomas *(Dir-Land Bank Program)*
Stella Dilik *(Chief Dev Officer)*
Andy McDowell *(VP-Western Field Ops)*
Brett Rodstrom *(VP-Eastern Field Ops)*
Matt Zone *(Sr VP)*

WESTERN RESERVE MUTUAL CASUALTY CO., INC.
1685 Cleveland Rd, Wooster, OH 44691-2335
Tel.: (330) 262-9060
Web Site: http://www.wrg-ins.com
Year Founded: 1937
Sales Range: $150-199.9 Million
Emp.: 275
Fire, Marine & Casualty Insurance
N.A.I.C.S.: 524126
Kevin W. Day *(Pres & CEO)*

WESTERN RESERVE RESTAURANT MANAGEMENT
20 N Union St, Rochester, NY 14607
Tel.: (585) 262-3630
Web Site: http://www.wenroch.com
Sales Range: $10-24.9 Million
Emp.: 200
Provider of Fast-Food Restaurant Services
N.A.I.C.S.: 722513
Richard C. Fox *(Pres)*

WESTERN RESTAURANTS INC.
10000 Shelbyville Rd, Louisville, KY 40223
Tel.: (502) 245-6623
Rev.: $15,200,000
Emp.: 15
Fast-Food Restaurant, Chain
N.A.I.C.S.: 722513
James A. Patterson *(Pres)*
Janice Morgan *(Controller)*

WESTERN RIM PROPERTY SERVICES
3130 Stag Rd, Dallas, TX 75241
Tel.: (214) 290-9000
Web Site:
http://www.villasofserrento.com
Sales Range: $50-74.9 Million
Emp.: 6
Apartment Building Operator
N.A.I.C.S.: 531110
Jane Rogers *(Mgr-HR)*
DeAnn Witt *(Dir-Community-Multi Family Housing)*
Stacey Spies *(Coord-Lifestyle)*
Lori Bush *(Exec VP)*

WESTERN ROTO ENGRAVERS INC.
533 Banner Ave, Greensboro, NC 27401
Tel.: (336) 275-9821
Web Site: http://www.wrecolor.com
Rev.: $13,500,000
Emp.: 46
Engraving Copper Pipes
N.A.I.C.S.: 323111
Brent MacKay *(Pres & CEO)*
Charlie Bell *(Reg Mgr-Sls)*
Dan Comerford *(VP-Ops)*
Don MacKay *(Plant Mgr)*
Kathleen Harrelson *(CFO)*
Greg MacKay *(Acct Exec)*

WESTERN SADDLERY & SPORTING GOODS
7038 Commerce Cir, Pleasanton, CA 94588
Tel.: (925) 460-0373
Web Site:
http://www.westernsaddlery.com
Sales Range: $10-24.9 Million
Emp.: 10
Saddlery & Equestrian Equipment
N.A.I.C.S.: 459110
Frank Wipfli *(VP)*
Ed Whitley *(Pres)*

WESTERN SECURITY SUR-PLUS INSURANCE BROKERS, INC.
4965 Preston Park Blvd #650, Plano, TX 75093
Tel.: (626) 584-0110 CA
Web Site: http://www.wssib.com
Year Founded: 1981
Emp.: 100
Insurance Agents, Brokers, And Service, N
N.A.I.C.S.: 524210
Andrea L. Zenner *(Reg VP)*
Judy Hall *(VP & Mgr)*
Kyle Stevens *(Pres & CEO)*
Mark L. Kaufmann *(COO)*

Subsidiaries:

Klein & Costa Insurance
Services .... (1)
200 Sandpointe Ave Ste 310, Santa Ana, CA 92707-5746
Tel.: (714) 918-0914
Web Site: http://www.kleincosta.com
Insurance Agencies & Brokerages
N.A.I.C.S.: 524210

WESTERN SHAMROCK CORPORATION
801 S Abe St, San Angelo, TX 76903
Tel.: (325) 653-6814
Web Site:
http://www.westernshamrock.com
Rev.: $33,500,000
Emp.: 30
Personal Finance Licensed Loans
N.A.I.C.S.: 522291
Scott Wisniewski *(Pres & CEO)*
James Hudgins *(VP)*

WESTERN SPECIALTY CONTRACTORS
1637 North Warson Rd, Saint Louis, MO 63132
Tel.: (314) 427-1637
Web Site:
http://www.westernspecialtycontractors.com
Year Founded: 1915
Masonry, Concrete, Waterproofing & Facades Restoration
N.A.I.C.S.: 238140
Paul Gillstrom *(CFO & Chief Strategy Officer)*

WESTERN STAR TRANSPORTATION
1065 E Walnut St, Carson, CA 90746-1346
Tel.: (714) 854-1307
Web Site:
http://www.westernstartransportation.com
Rev.: $10,000,000
Emp.: 15
Trucking Company
N.A.I.C.S.: 484121
Lee Cadwallader *(Co-Pres)*
Warren Cadwallader *(Co-Pres)*
Teresa Scott *(Asst Mgr-Safety)*

WESTERN STATE AGENCY, INC.
110 4th St SE, Devils Lake, ND 58301
Tel.: (701) 662-4936
Web Site:
http://www.westernbanks.com
Rev.: $10,500,000
Emp.: 35
Bank Holding Company
N.A.I.C.S.: 551111
Brett Johnston *(Pres)*

Subsidiaries:

Western Finance & Lease,
Inc.1990 .... (1)
503 Highway 2 W, Devils Lake, ND 58301
Tel.: (701) 662-4538

Web Site:
http://www.westernequipmentfinance.com
Rev.: $15,000,000
Emp.: 32
Financing: Automobiles, Furniture, Etc., Not A Deposit Bank
N.A.I.C.S.: 522291
Brian Houkom (CEO)
Todd Heilman (CFO)

Western Financial, Inc. (1)
100 2nd Ave NW, Mandan, ND 58554
Tel.: (701) 667-7266
Web Site: http://www.wowbanking.com
Rev.: $290,000
Emp.: 2
Automobile Finance Leasing
N.A.I.C.S.: 522220

Western Insurance (1)
110 4th St SE, Devils Lake, ND 58301
Tel.: (701) 662-5027
Rev.: $130,000
Emp.: 3
Insurance Agents, Brokers & Service
N.A.I.C.S.: 524210
Brian Houkom (CEO)
Darwin Robinson (Mgr-HR)

Western State Bank (1)
110 4th St S, Devils Lake, ND 58301
Tel.: (701) 662-4936
Web Site: http://www.westernbanks.com
Rev.: $28,693,000
Emp.: 40
Full Service Bank
N.A.I.C.S.: 522110
Matthew Oachs (Officer-Bus Banking & Asst VP)
Greg Kolton (Exec VP & Dir-Bus Dev & Sls Trng)
Chad Cota (Officer-Bus Banking & Asst VP)
Dan Jacobson (Pres-Mktg-West Fargo)
Jill Mattson (Officer-Cash Mgmt)
Kale Stromme (Officer-Ag Banking)
Ryan Rued (Officer-Bus Banking & VP)

WESTERN STATES BANCORPORATION
3430 E Grand Ave, Laramie, WY 82070
Tel.: (307) 721-9100 WY
Web Site: http://www.wsb.bank
Year Founded: 2007
Bank Holding Company
N.A.I.C.S.: 551111
Gary E. Crum (Pres & CEO)

Subsidiaries:

Western States Bank (1)
3430 E Grand Ave, Laramie, WY 82070
Tel.: (307) 721-9100
Web Site: http://www.wsb.bank
Emp.: 20
Commericial Banking
N.A.I.C.S.: 522110
Tom Michelena (Sr VP)

WESTERN STATES ENVELOPE & LABEL
4480 N 132nd St, Butler, WI 53007-2099
Tel.: (262) 781-5540 WI
Web Site:
http://www.westernstatesenvelope.com
Year Founded: 1908
Sales Range: $150-199.9 Million
Emp.: 600
Envelope & Label Mfr
N.A.I.C.S.: 322220
George F. Moss (Founder)
Steve Bayerlein (CEO)

Subsidiaries:

Vision Envelope, Inc. (1)
2451 Executive St, Charlotte, NC 28208
Tel.: (704) 392-9090
Web Site: http://www.visionenvelope.com
Rev.: $4,500,000
Emp.: 16
Other Commercial Printing
N.A.I.C.S.: 323111

Mark Zerona (Pres)
Susan Zerona (CEO)
Titus Thorn (Mgr-Production)

Western States Envelope & Label - Kentucky Division (1)
1347 Jamike Ln, Erlanger, KY 41018-3115
Tel.: (859) 283-1300
Web Site: http://www.wsel.com
Sales Range: $25-49.9 Million
Emp.: 78
Envelope & Label Mfr
N.A.I.C.S.: 322220
Bob Thode (Plant Mgr)

Western States Envelope & Label - Label Division (1)
861 Progress Way, Sun Prairie, WI 53590
Tel.: (608) 834-5656
Web Site: http://www.wsel.com
Emp.: 150
Label Mfr
N.A.I.C.S.: 322220
Tim Bresser (Plant Mgr)

Western States Envelope & Label - Minnesota Division (1)
980 Berwood Ave E Ste 400, Vadnais Heights, MN 55110-5110
Tel.: (651) 773-8723
Web Site: http://www.wsel.com
Emp.: 100
Envelope & Label Mfr
N.A.I.C.S.: 322220
George Moff (Pres)

Western States Envelope & Label - Ohio Division (1)
6859 Commodore Dr, Walbridge, OH 43465-9765
Tel.: (419) 666-7480
Envelope & Label Mfr
N.A.I.C.S.: 322220

WESTERN STATES MACHINERY CORPORATION
650 Lighthouse Ave, Pacific Grove, CA 93950-2672
Tel.: (831) 655-2100 CA
Web Site: http://www.wsm-corp.com
Year Founded: 1983
Sales Range: $10-24.9 Million
Emp.: 11
Mfr of Industrial Machinery & Equipment
N.A.I.C.S.: 423830
John Chaffin (Pres)

WESTERN STATES PETROLEUM INC.
450 S 15th Ave, Phoenix, AZ 85007-3327
Tel.: (602) 252-4011 AZ
Web Site:
http://www.westernstatespetroleum.com
Year Founded: 1975
Sales Range: $50-74.9 Million
Emp.: 21
Producer & Retailer of Petroleum & Farm Supplies; Operator of Gas Service Stations
N.A.I.C.S.: 424710
Roselinda Apodaca (Mgr-Credit)
Steve Tolboe (VP-Sls & Mgr-Retail Sls)
Todd Branton (Mgr-Safety & Driver)
Alex Noriega (Mgr-Warehouse)
Sharon Mexicotte (Mgr-Acctg)
David Kec (Mgr-C-Store)
Jerri McGuire (Plant Mgr-Parker)

WESTERN STATES WHOLESALE INC.
1420 S Bon View Ave, Ontario, CA 91761
Tel.: (909) 947-0028
Web Site: http://www.wswcorp.com
Rev.: $23,500,000
Emp.: 80
Concrete Block & Brick

N.A.I.C.S.: 327331
Cindy Jones (Coord-HR Safety)

WESTERN SUPER MARKETS INC.
2614 19th St S, Birmingham, AL 35209-1914
Tel.: (205) 879-3471
Web Site:
http://www.westernsupermarket.com
Year Founded: 1987
Sales Range: $50-74.9 Million
Emp.: 675
Provider of Grocery Store Services
N.A.I.C.S.: 445110
Ken Hebbard (Pres & CFO)
Darwin Metcals (VP)

WESTERN SUPREME INC.
865 Produce Ctr, Los Angeles, CA 90021
Tel.: (213) 627-3861
Rev.: $16,300,000
Emp.: 5
Chicken Slaughtering & Processing
N.A.I.C.S.: 311615
Teresa Malagon (Controller)
Frank Fogarty (Pres)

WESTERN SWITCHES & CONTROLS
750 Challenger St, Brea, CA 92821
Tel.: (747) 482-4100
Web Site:
http://www.westernswitches.com
Year Founded: 1976
Sales Range: $10-24.9 Million
Emp.: 230
Motor Controls, Starters & Relays: Electric
N.A.I.C.S.: 423610
Leo Alonzo (CEO)
Claudio Moreno (Mgr-Sls)
Frank Martinez (VP)
Sergio Villalobos (Engr-Application)

WESTERN TECHNOLOGY SERVICES INTERNATIONAL, INC.
415 1st St, Mills, WY 82644
Tel.: (307) 235-1591
Web Site: http://www.wstch.com
Year Founded: 1992
Sales Range: $25-49.9 Million
Emp.: 335
Mfr of Fabricated Structural Metal
N.A.I.C.S.: 332312
Steve Shellenberger (Pres & CEO)
Johnny Greer (Mgr-Matls)
Linda Akers (Mgr-HR)
Rich Peters (Mgr-Sls-North America)

Subsidiaries:

Wotco, Inc. (1)
415 1st St, Mills, WY 82644 (100%)
Tel.: (307) 235-1591
Web Site: http://www.wstch.com
Sales Range: $25-49.9 Million
Emp.: 180
Mfr of Fabricated Structural Metal
N.A.I.C.S.: 332312
Steve Shellenberger (Pres)

WESTERN TEL-COM INC.
4273 Blue Star Hwy, Holland, MI 49423
Tel.: (616) 393-0138
Web Site: http://www.westerntel-com.com
Sales Range: $10-24.9 Million
Emp.: 40
Provider of Telephone & Telephone Equipment Installation Services
N.A.I.C.S.: 238210
Jason Onstott (VP)
Kurt Friedreichsen (Pres)

WESTERN TILE & MARBLE CONTRACTORS, INC.
1880 136th Pl NE, Bellevue, WA 98005
Tel.: (425) 643-1380
Web Site: http://www.westerntile.com
Sales Range: $1-9.9 Million
Emp.: 350
Terrazzo, Tile, Marble & Mosaic Work
N.A.I.C.S.: 238340
Jim Arnold (CFO)
Todd Junker (Pres)

WESTERN TIMBER PRODUCTS INC.
610 W Hubbard St Ste 203, Coeur D'Alene, ID 83814-2288
Tel.: (208) 253-4605 ID
Web Site:
http://www.westerntimber.com
Year Founded: 1983
Sales Range: $10-24.9 Million
Emp.: 130
Producer of Lumber, Plywood & Millwork
N.A.I.C.S.: 423310
Dan Seid (Pres)

WESTERN TIRE CENTERS INC.
3545 S Richey Blvd, Tucson, AZ 85713
Tel.: (520) 748-1700
Web Site: http://www.westerntire.com
Sales Range: $25-49.9 Million
Emp.: 180
Automotive Tires
N.A.I.C.S.: 441340
John G. Furrier (Pres)
Sean Furrier (Founder)

WESTERN TOOL SUPPLY CORPORATION
2315 25th St SE, Salem, OR 97302
Tel.: (503) 588-8222
Web Site:
http://www.westerntool.com
Year Founded: 1982
Sales Range: $25-49.9 Million
Emp.: 150
Power Tools & Accessories Mfr
N.A.I.C.S.: 423710
Kevin D. Kiker (Pres)
Rick Ikeda (VP)
Brad Garvin (Mgr-Pur)

WESTERN TRAILER CO.
251 W Gowen Rd, Boise, ID 83716
Tel.: (208) 344-2539
Web Site:
http://www.westerntrailer.com
Sales Range: $25-49.9 Million
Emp.: 300
Semitrailers for Truck Tractors
N.A.I.C.S.: 336212
Jerry M. Whitehead (Pres)
Kay Panter (Mgr-Mfg)
Todd Swanstrom (Mgr-Engrg)
Dave Babcock (Mgr-Sls & Fin)

WESTERN TRUCK EXCHANGE
159 E Manchester Ave, Los Angeles, CA 90003
Tel.: (323) 750-1277
Web Site: http://www.usedtrucks.net
Rev.: $11,764,875
Emp.: 20
Trucks, Tractors & Trailers: New & Used
N.A.I.C.S.: 441110
Dan Holtzman (Gen Mgr)

WESTERN UNITED LIFE ASSURANCE COMPANY
929 W Sprague Ave, Spokane, WA 99210

WESTERN UNITED LIFE ASSURANCE COMPANY

Western United Life Assurance Company—(Continued)
Tel.: (509) 835-2500
Web Site: http://www.wula.com
Rev.: $80,000,000
Emp.: 45
Direct Life Insurance Carriers
N.A.I.C.S.: 524113
Dale Whitney (Pres)

WESTERN UNITED STATES AGRICULTURAL TRADE ASSOCIATION
4601 NE 77th Ave Ste 240, Vancouver, WA 98662
Tel.: (360) 693-3373
Web Site: http://www.wusata.org
Year Founded: 1980
Sales Range: $10-24.9 Million
Emp.: 23
Agricultural Trade Association
N.A.I.C.S.: 813910
Tricia Walker (Mgr-Branded Program)
Andy Anderson (Exec Dir)
Janet Kenefsky (Dir-Mktg-Intl)
Brendia Baxter (Accountant)

WESTERN WELL PRODUCTION SERVICES LTD.
2213 State Hwy 79 S, Wichita Falls, TX 76310
Tel.: (940) 723-2550
Web Site: http://www.westernwellproductionservices.com
Drilling Oil & Gas Wells
N.A.I.C.S.: 213111
Trace Moran (Mgr-Well Svc & Fishing Tool)
Johnny Wise (Supvr-Well Svc Rig)
Cody Hicks (Mgr-Roustabout)
Rusty Blanton (Mgr-Ops)
Mike Mason (Office Mgr)

WESTERN WELL TOOL INC.
9758 Whithorn Dr, Houston, TX 77095
Tel.: (281) 345-8019
Web Site: http://www.wwtco.com
Rev.: $11,312,737
Emp.: 30
Oil Field Machinery & Equipment
N.A.I.C.S.: 333132
Rudolph Ernst Krueger (Pres)

WESTERN WYOMING BEVERAGES INC.
100 Reliance Rd, Rock Springs, WY 82901
Tel.: (307) 362-6356
Web Site: http://www.westernwyomingbeverages.com
Year Founded: 1969
Sales Range: $10-24.9 Million
Emp.: 35
Whslr of Beer & Soft Drinks
N.A.I.C.S.: 424490
Robert M. Spicer (Pres)
Marcie Valentine (Controller)
Fritz Valentine (Mgr-Sls)

WESTERN-CULLEN-HAYES INC.
2700 W 36th Pl, Chicago, IL 60632
Tel.: (773) 254-9600
Web Site: http://www.wch.com
Rev.: $15,000,000
Emp.: 90
Railroad Signaling Devices, Electric
N.A.I.C.S.: 334290
Barbara Gulick (VP-Fin)
Ronald L. McDaniel (Pres)

WESTERNTECHSYSTEMS INC.
410 Freeport Pkwy Ste 100, Coppell, TX 75019
Tel.: (469) 718-0004
Web Site: http://www.westerntechsystems.com
Year Founded: 2009
Sales Range: $125-149.9 Million
Emp.: 150
Information Technology Services
N.A.I.C.S.: 541512
Jamil Ashour (Founder & CEO)
Rajesh Padole (CTO)
Alazar Neway (VP-Global Sls)
Garry Myers (COO)

WESTFALIA TECHNOLOGIES, INC.
3655 Sandhurst Dr, York, PA 17406
Tel.: (717) 764-1115
Web Site: http://www.westfaliausa.com
Sales Range: $10-24.9 Million
Emp.: 150
Conveyor & Conveying Equipment Mfr
N.A.I.C.S.: 333922
Daniel Labell (Pres)
Jody Leav (Mgr-Svc)
John Hinchey (VP-Sls)
Juergen Conrad (Dir-Sls & Svc)
Martin Herskowitz (Engr-Controls)
Daniel Hill (Mgr-Controls Software)
John Garrity (Mgr-Production)
Kevin Wood (Gen Mgr)

WESTFALL ROOFING
5413 W Sligh Ave, Tampa, FL 33634
Tel.: (813) 264-5690
Web Site: http://www.westfallroofing.com
Year Founded: 1989
Sales Range: $1-9.9 Million
Roofing Contractors
N.A.I.C.S.: 238160
Kirk Westfall (Owner & Pres)
Ryan Westfall (VP-Sls & Dir-Mktg)
Maria Westfall (Office Mgr)

WESTFALL-O'DELL GMC INC.
3915 NE Randolph Rd, Kansas City, MO 64161
Tel.: (816) 455-7262
Web Site: http://www.westfallgmc.com
Rev.: $56,829,362
Emp.: 77
New & Used Car Dealers
N.A.I.C.S.: 441110
David Wood (Controller)

WESTFIELD ELECTROPLATING COMPANY
68 N Elm St, Westfield, MA 01085
Tel.: (413) 568-3716
Web Site: http://www.westfieldplating.com
Year Founded: 1946
Sales Range: $10-24.9 Million
Emp.: 135
Electroplating, Polishing & Coloring Services
N.A.I.C.S.: 332813
Peter Sienkiewicz (VP-Ops)
Wayne Dolby (Mgr-Sls)
Lynn Poulin (Controller)
Mike Stolpinski (Pres)
Lynn Poulin (Controller)

WESTFIELD STEEL INC.
530 State Rd 32 W, Westfield, IN 46074-9349
Tel.: (317) 896-5587
Web Site: http://www.westfieldsteel.com
Year Founded: 1977
Sales Range: $25-49.9 Million
Emp.: 160
Supplier of Metals Service Centers & Offices
N.A.I.C.S.: 423510
Jon Deakyne (Mgr-Sls)
Ronald Santana (Project Mgr-Ops Tech Applications Support)

Subsidiaries:

Remington Steel, Inc. (1)
1120 S Burnett Rd, Springfield, OH 45505
Tel.: (937) 322-2414
Web Site: http://www.remingtonsteel.com
Metal Cutting Machinery Mfr & Distr
N.A.I.C.S.: 423510
Harry Osborne (VP-Ops)

WESTGATE MANAGEMENT CO. INC.
133 Franklin Corner Rd, Lawrenceville, NJ 08648
Tel.: (609) 895-8890
Sales Range: $10-24.9 Million
Emp.: 7
Multi-Family Dwelling Construction
N.A.I.C.S.: 236116
Michael Feit (Pres)
Shirley Senior (VP)

WESTGATE, INC.
1355 Beaulieu Rd, Port Allen, LA 70767-5871
Tel.: (225) 749-2635
Web Site: http://www.westgatellc.com
Year Founded: 1974
Sales Range: $200-249.9 Million
Emp.: 350
Provider of Industrial Maintenance & Construction Services
N.A.I.C.S.: 238210
John C. Thigpen (Pres & COO)
Tim Thigpen (Gen Mgr)
Kevin Venable (Mgr-Construction)
Dwain Bickham (Estimating Mgr)

WESTHAB
8 Bashford St, Yonkers, NY 10701
Tel.: (914) 345-2800
Web Site: http://www.westhab.org
Year Founded: 1981
Sales Range: $10-24.9 Million
Emp.: 364
Community Housing Services
N.A.I.C.S.: 624229
Jim Coughlin (Sr VP-Svcs)
Ken Belfer (Sr VP-Housing)
Patricia Vitelli (VP-Fin)
Jefferson C. Boyce (Sec)
Jesse Krasnow (Chm)
Richard Nightingale (Pres & CEO)
William R. Frey (Treas)

WESTHAM TRADE COMPANY LIMITED
3620 NW 114th Ave, Miami, FL 33172
Tel.: (305) 597-0230
Web Site: http://www.wtrade.com
Year Founded: 1984
Sales Range: $25-49.9 Million
Emp.: 15
Sales of Computers, Peripherals & Software
N.A.I.C.S.: 423430
Francisco Celedom Jr. (VP)
Francisco Celedom Sr. (Pres)

WESTIN AUTOMOTIVE PRODUCTS, INC.
320 W Covina Blvd, San Dimas, CA 91773
Tel.: (626) 960-6762
Web Site: http://www.westinautomotive.com
Year Founded: 1977
Automobile Parts Mfr

N.A.I.C.S.: 423120
Deborah Quiroz (VP-Fin & Admin)
Bob West (Exec VP)
Jeff White (Project Manager)
Kurt Miller (Mgr-Mktg)
Michael Stickney (Mgr-National Sls)

WESTIN CONSTRUCTION COMPANY INC.
10828 Mesbitt, Bloomington, MN 55437
Tel.: (952) 946-1519
Web Site: http://www.westinconstruction.com
Year Founded: 1994
Sales Range: $10-24.9 Million
Emp.: 20
Provider of Nonresidential Construction Services
N.A.I.C.S.: 236220
John Arbogaft (Pres)

WESTIN FOODS, INC.
11808 W Center Rd, Omaha, NE 68144-4397
Tel.: (402) 691-8800
Web Site: http://www.westinfoods.com
Year Founded: 1971
Sales Range: $200-249.9 Million
Emp.: 250
Food Products Distr
N.A.I.C.S.: 424490
Scott Carlson (Owner & CEO)
Brad Poppen (Pres & COO)

Subsidiaries:

Ott Food Products (1)
705 W Fairview, Carthage, MO 64836-3724
Tel.: (417) 358-2585
Web Site: http://www.ottfoods.com
Sales Range: $25-49.9 Million
Emp.: 18
Salad Dressings & Barbecue Sauces Mfr
N.A.I.C.S.: 311941

WESTINGHOUSE LIGHTING CORPORATION
12401 McNulty Rd, Philadelphia, PA 19154-1004
Tel.: (215) 671-2000
Web Site: http://www.westinghouselighting.com
Year Founded: 1946
Sales Range: $75-99.9 Million
Emp.: 450
Decorative Electrical & Lighting Products, Door Chimes & Wall Plates Mfr, Distributor & Marketer
N.A.I.C.S.: 335131
Stanley Angelo (Chm)
Raymond Angelo (Pres-Westinghouse Lighting & Owner)
Carl Thon (VP-Ops)

WESTLAKE ASSOCIATES INC.
1200 W Lake Ave N Ste 310, Seattle, WA 98109
Tel.: (206) 505-9400
Web Site: http://www.westlakeassociates.com
Year Founded: 1975
Sales Range: $10-24.9 Million
Emp.: 3
Real Estate Agency Services
N.A.I.C.S.: 531110
Richard L. Kemp (Pres & Principal)
Matt Little (Partner)

WESTLAKE AUDIO INC.
2696 Lavery Court Ste 18, Newbury Park, CA 91320
Tel.: (805) 499-3686
Web Site: http://www.westlakeaudio.com
Sales Range: $10-24.9 Million
Emp.: 15

COMPANIES

WESTLAKE DEVELOPMENT CO., INC.
520 S El Camino Real Ste 700, San Mateo, CA 94402-1722
Tel.: (650) 579-1010
Web Site: http://www.westlakecompany.com
Year Founded: 1972
Sales Range: $50-74.9 Million
Emp.: 230
Operators Of Nonresidential Buildings
N.A.I.C.S.: 531120
Will Chang (CEO)

WESTLAKE PLASTICS COMPANY
490 Lenni Rd, Lenni, PA 19052
Tel.: (610) 459-1000 PA
Web Site: http://www.westlakeplastics.com
Year Founded: 1952
Sales Range: $10-24.9 Million
Emp.: 150
Mfr of Plastic Products
N.A.I.C.S.: 326121
James Fagan (Reg Mgr-Market Dev)
Lisa Carr (Mgr-Customer Svc)

WESTLANDS WATER DISTRICT INC.
3130 N Fresno St, Fresno, CA 93703-1126
Tel.: (559) 224-1523 CA
Web Site: http://www.westlandswater.org
Year Founded: 1952
Sales Range: $50-74.9 Million
Emp.: 105
Water Supply & Irrigation Systems
N.A.I.C.S.: 221310
Thomas W. Birmingham (Gen Mgr)
Philip Williams (Gen Counsel)
Daniel Errotabere (VP)
Don Peracchi (Pres)
Dan Pope (COO)

WESTLEX INC.
12000 Old Katy Rd, Houston, TX 77079
Tel.: (281) 558-3030
Web Site: http://www.westsidelexus.com
Sales Range: $150-199.9 Million
Emp.: 151
Automobiles, New & Used
N.A.I.C.S.: 441110
Brett Aldridge (Pres)
Ronnie Brush (Mgr-Collision Center)
Gerald Chomer (Dir-Fin)
Gary Cohen (Mgr-New Car Sls)
Tracy Harbes (Asst Mgr-Parts)
Bob Niedzielski (Mgr-New Car Sls)
Paul Rockett (Mgr-Fin Svcs)
Robert Parnell (Dir-Parts & Svc)
Dale McMullen (Gen Mgr)
Kevin Jacobson (Mgr-Fin Svcs)
Michael Lorch (Mgr-Svc Dept)
Hans Schackmann (Mgr-Svc Drive)
Ross Zuerner (Mgr-Parts Dept)
Ty Stanberry (Mgr-Pre-Owned Sls)

WESTLIE MOTOR COMPANY
500 S Broadway, Minot, ND 58701-4451
Tel.: (701) 852-1354 ND
Web Site: http://www.westliemotors.com
Year Founded: 1947
Sales Range: $25-49.9 Million
Emp.: 150
Retailer of New & Used Automobiles, Pickups & Vans; Rental Car Service; Truck Leasing; Automotive Supplies & Parts; Automotive Repair Shops
N.A.I.C.S.: 441110
Darek Zaun (CFO)
Steve Blasing (Principal)
Curt Helgeson (Mgr-Gen Sls)
Mike Werre (Mgr-Center)
Pat Miller (Mgr-Truck Center-Minot)
Georgene Kary (Mgr-Bus & F&I)
Shelly Adams (Mgr-Mktg, PR & Internet)
Jerry Jobczynski (Mgr-Svcs)
Stacy Frank (Dir-Fin & Mgr-Comml Fleet)
Verla Walter (Mgr-Bus & F&I)
Scott Jensen (Mgr-Parts-Columbus)
Jason Henke (Mgr-Sls)
Bob Opperude (Mgr-Sls)

WESTLUND WARREN BUICK-GMC TRUCK
927 N 128th St, Seattle, WA 98133-7515
Tel.: (206) 361-2150
Rev.: $25,000,000
Emp.: 50
Automobiles, New & Used
N.A.I.C.S.: 441110
Mark Westlund (Pres)

WESTMARK INDUSTRIES INC.
6701 McEwan Rd, Lake Oswego, OR 97035
Tel.: (503) 620-0945
Web Site: http://www.westmarkind.com
Rev.: $13,600,000
Emp.: 93
Labels (Unprinted), Gummed; Made From Purchased Materials
N.A.I.C.S.: 322220
Michael J. Offer (Pres)
Sean Berg (Mgr-Engrg)

WESTMARK PRODUCTS, INC.
11721 Steele St S, Tacoma, WA 98444
Tel.: (253) 531-3470
Web Site: http://www.westmarkproducts.com
Rev.: $40,800,000
Emp.: 200
Wood Kitchen Cabinet & Countertop Mfr
N.A.I.C.S.: 337110
Gary M. Lean (Treas & Sec)
Laurie St. George (Coord-Scheduling)
Lewis Cooper (Mgr-Production)
Jesse Perbix (Pres)

WESTMINSTER CAPITAL INC.
17383 Sunset Blvd Ste A400 Pacific, Palisades, CA 90272
Tel.: (310) 278-1930 DE
Year Founded: 1959
Sales Range: $10-24.9 Million
Emp.: 5
Diversified Holding Company
N.A.I.C.S.: 522299
Greggory Belzberg (CEO)

Subsidiaries:

Matrix Visual Solutions, Inc. (1)
1748 W Business Ctr Dr, Orange, CA 92867-7901 (68%)
Tel.: (949) 756-5500
Web Site: http://www.matrixvisual.com
Sales Range: $10-24.9 Million
Emp.: 10
Rents & Sells A Wide Range of Audio-Visual Equipment & Provides Related Presentation Services
N.A.I.C.S.: 459999
Victoria Acton (Owner)

One Source Industries, LLC (1)
185 Technology Dr, Irvine, CA 92618 (80%)
Tel.: (949) 784-7700
Web Site: http://www.osicreative.com
Point of Purchase Display & Packaging
N.A.I.C.S.: 424130
John Kellogg (Pres & CEO)

Subsidiary (Domestic):

New Dimensions Research Corp. (2)
260 Spagnoli Rd, Melville, NY 11747-1747
Tel.: (631) 694-1356
Plastics Product Mfr
N.A.I.C.S.: 326199

WESTMINSTER HOLDING
622 Cabin Hill Dr, Greensburg, PA 15601-1657
Tel.: (412) 856-1739
Web Site: http://www.ghplus.com
Rev.: $40,000,000
Emp.: 200
Provider of Commercial Printing & Newspaper Publishing Services
N.A.I.C.S.: 513110

WESTMINSTER LIVESTOCK AUCTION LLC
1117 New Windsor Rd, Westminster, MD 21790
Tel.: (410) 848-9820
Year Founded: 1936
Sales Range: $10-24.9 Million
Emp.: 30
Livestock Auctioning Services
N.A.I.C.S.: 424520
James Hoark (Owner)

WESTMINSTER PRESBYTERIAN RETIREMENT COMMUNITY, INC.
12191 Clipper Dr, Lake Ridge, VA 22192
Tel.: (703) 643-9711 VA
Year Founded: 1993
Sales Range: $10-24.9 Million
Emp.: 372
Retirement Community Care Services
N.A.I.C.S.: 623311
Yoram Tanay (CFO)
Lynn O'Connor (Pres)
Monique Eliezer (VP-Sls, Mktg & Strategy)
Susan Hadeka (Dir-Nursing)
Kimberly Andreadis (Dir-Mktg)

WESTMINSTER VILLAGE NORTH
11050 Presbyterian Dr Near 63rd Sunnyside Rd, Indianapolis, IN 46236
Tel.: (317) 823-6841 IN
Web Site: http://www.westminstervillagenorth.com
Year Founded: 1972
Sales Range: $10-24.9 Million
Emp.: 446
Community Housing Services
N.A.I.C.S.: 624229
Shelley Rauch (Exec Dir)
Donna Trisler (Dir-HR)
Jamie Polston (Mgr-Environmental Svcs)
Wilda Duncan (Dir-Campus Environment)
Melissa Wyatt (Mgr-Resident Acct)
Jami Blanton (Mgr-Nursing)
Kim Arter (Mgr-Acctg)
Chuck Gaskins (Dir-Fin Ops)
Rhonda Garcia (Dir-Nursing Svc)
Laura Roman (Dir-Mktg & PR)
Brandon Deluhery (Dir-Plant Ops)
Tracy Pope (Mgr-Health Center Admissions)
Yarnell Sherrell (Mgr-Social Svcs)

WESTMINSTER VILLAGE, INC.
12000 N 90th St, Scottsdale, AZ 85260
Tel.: (480) 451-2000
Web Site: http://www.wmvaz.com
Year Founded: 1982
Sales Range: $10-24.9 Million
Emp.: 175
Property Management Services
N.A.I.C.S.: 531110
Leslie Morrison (Dir-Mktg)

WESTMORELAND CASEMANAGEMENT AND SUPPORTS, INC.
770 E Pittsburgh St, Greensburg, PA 15601
Tel.: (724) 837-1808 PA
Web Site: http://www.wcsi.org
Year Founded: 1994
Sales Range: $10-24.9 Million
Emp.: 261
Intellectual Disability Assistance Services
N.A.I.C.S.: 623210
Kathy Wohlgemuth (Pres)
Kathie M. Tanyer (VP)
Michele Bononi (Treas)
Monica Ritenour (Sec)
Lynnette Emerick (CEO)

WESTMORELAND COAL COMPANY
9540 S Maroon Cir Ste 300, Englewood, CO 80112
Tel.: (303) 922-6463 DE
Web Site: http://www.westmoreland.com
Year Founded: 1854
WLB—(NASDAQ)
Rev.: $1,384,568,000
Assets: $1,389,099,000
Liabilities: $2,132,547,000
Net Worth: ($743,448,000)
Earnings: ($71,340,000)
Emp.: 2,950
Fiscal Year-end: 12/31/17
Holding Company; Coal Surface Mining & Whslr; Coal-Fired Power Plant Owner & Operator
N.A.I.C.S.: 551112
Lorna Souther (Corp Mgr-HR)
Richard C. Stone (VP-Power Devel)
Edward J. Demeter (Pres-Westmoreland Coal Sls Co)
Joseph Earl Micheletti (COO)
Robert C. Scharp (Chm)

Subsidiaries:

Buckingham Coal Company, LLC (1)
21525 St Rte 13, Glouster, OH 45732
Tel.: (740) 767-2907
Sales Range: $10-24.9 Million
Coal Mining
N.A.I.C.S.: 212114

Dakota Westmoreland Corporation (1)
6204 13th St SW, Beulah, ND 58523 (100%)
Tel.: (701) 873-4333
Web Site: http://www.westmoreland.com
Coal Surface Mining
N.A.I.C.S.: 212114

Prairie Mines & Royalty ULC (1)
1600 Oxford Tower 10235 - 101 Street, Edmonton, T5J 3G1, AB, Canada
Tel.: (780) 420-5810
Web Site: http://www.westmoreland.com
Emp.: 40
Coal Mining Services
N.A.I.C.S.: 213113

Texas Westmoreland Coal Company (1)
4336 FM 39 S, Jewett, TX 75846-0915 (100%)
Tel.: (903) 626-5485

WESTMORELAND COAL COMPANY U.S. PRIVATE

Westmoreland Coal Company—(Continued)
Web Site: http://www.westmoreland.com
Sales Range: $125-149.9 Million
Emp.: 50
Coal Surface Mining
N.A.I.C.S.: 212114
Joseph E. Micheletti (Pres)

WCC Holding B.V. (1)
Strawinskylaan 3127, 1077 ZX, Amsterdam, Netherlands
Tel.: (31) 885609950
Coal Mining Services
N.A.I.C.S.: 213113

Western Energy Company (1)
138 Rosebud Ln, Colstrip, MT 59323-0099 (100%)
Tel.: (406) 748-5100
Web Site: http://www.westmoreland.com
Emp.: 380
Coal Surface Mining
N.A.I.C.S.: 212114

Westmoreland Canada Holdings Inc. (1)
1100 10123 99 St, Edmonton, T5J 3H1, AB, Canada
Tel.: (780) 420-5810
Coal Mining Services
N.A.I.C.S.: 213113

Westmoreland Energy LLC (1)
290 Power Pl, Weldon, NC 27870 (100%)
Tel.: (252) 536-3201
Holding Company; Coal-Fired Power Plants Operator
N.A.I.C.S.: 551112

Subsidiary (Domestic):

Westmoreland Partners (2)
290 Power Pl, Weldon, NC 27870
Tel.: (252) 536-3201
Web Site: http://www.westmoreland.com
Coal-Fired Power Plants Operator
N.A.I.C.S.: 221112

Westmoreland Kemmerer, Inc. (1)
6520 Elkol County Rd 304, Kemmerer, WY 83101
Tel.: (307) 828-2200
Web Site: http://www.westmoreland.com
Sales Range: $125-149.9 Million
Emp.: 300
Bituminous Coal Mining Services
N.A.I.C.S.: 212114

Westmoreland Resources GP, LLC (1)
41 S High St Ste 3450, Columbus, OH 43215 (100%)
Tel.: (614) 643-0314
Holding Company; Coal Mining
N.A.I.C.S.: 551112
Scott Henry (Chief Acctg Officer & Controller)

Westmoreland Resources, Inc. (1)
100 Sarpy Creek Rd, Hardin, MT 59034-0449
Tel.: (406) 342-5241
Web Site: http://www.westmoreland.com
Sales Range: $10-24.9 Million
Emp.: 10
Coal Surface Mining
N.A.I.C.S.: 212114

Subsidiary (Domestic):

Absaloka Coal, LLC (2)
100 Sarpy Creek Rd, Hardin, MT 59034
Tel.: (406) 342-4502
Web Site: http://www.westmoreland.com
Coal Mine Operator
N.A.I.C.S.: 212115

Westmoreland Savage Corporation (1)
33804 County Rd 107, Savage, MT 59270 (100%)
Tel.: (406) 798-3651
Web Site: http://www.westmoreland.com
Emp.: 13
Coal Surface Mining
N.A.I.C.S.: 212114
Jody Mann (Pres)

WESTMORELAND COUNTY HOUSING AUTHORITY
154 S Greengate, Greensburg, PA 15601
Tel.: (724) 832-7248
Web Site: http://www.wchaonline.com
Year Founded: 1941
Rev.: $21,878,424
Emp.: 130
Housing Authority Operator
N.A.I.C.S.: 531390
Michael Washowich (Exec Dir)
Mark Swetz (Comptroller)
Lynn Wackenhuth (Dir-Hope in Life Program)
Claudia Guldenschuh (Sec)
Erik Spiegel (Dir-A & E Svcs)
Andi McKee (Sec-Weatherization)
Gloria Page (Project Mgr)
James Dzurica (Accountant)
Jim Rectenwald (Accountant)
Katie Clawson (Dir-Weatherization)
Rachel Fritz (Accountant)

WESTNY BUILDING PRODUCTS CO.
2580 Walden Ave, Buffalo, NY 14225
Tel.: (716) 681-2000
Emp.: 85
Windows & Doors Distr
N.A.I.C.S.: 444180
Bert Kriegh (Owner & CEO)

Subsidiaries:

Duratherm Window Corporation (1)
720 Main St, Vassalboro, ME 04989
Tel.: (207) 872-5558
Web Site: http://www.durathermwindow.com
Emp.: 70
Window & Door Manufacturing
N.A.I.C.S.: 339999
Timothy Downing (Pres)

Reilly Windows & Doors (1)
901 Burman Blvd Bldg 701, Calverton, NY 11933 (100%)
Tel.: (631) 208-0710
Web Site: http://www.reillywd.com
Emp.: 180
Wood Windows & Doors Mfr
N.A.I.C.S.: 321911
Stephen Johnson (Project Mgr)
Michael Reilly (Pres)

WESTON & SAMPSON, INC.
5 Centennial Dr, Peabody, MA 01960
Tel.: (978) 532-1900
Web Site: http://www.westonandsampson.com
Sales Range: $25-49.9 Million
Emp.: 400
Engineeering Services
N.A.I.C.S.: 541330
Michael J. Scipione (Pres & CEO)
Robert Goober (Dir-Mktg)
Chris Perkins (VP & Mgr-Portsmouth)

WESTON PONTIAC BUICK GMC INC.
22555 SE Stark St, Gresham, OR 97030-2678
Tel.: (503) 665-2166   OR
Web Site: http://www.westonpontiac.com
Year Founded: 1975
Sales Range: $25-49.9 Million
Emp.: 100
New & Used Car Dealers
N.A.I.C.S.: 441110
James M. Weston (Pres)

WESTON PRESIDIO CAPITAL
John Hancock Tower 200 Clarendon St 50th Fl, Boston, MA 02116
Tel.: (617) 988-2500
Web Site: http://www.westonpresidio.com
Year Founded: 1991
Private Equity & Venture Capital Firm
N.A.I.C.S.: 523999
Michael F. Cronin (Mng Partner-Boston)
Michael P. Lazarus (Mng Partner-San Francisco)
Michael W. Rubel (Principal)

WESTOVER CORPORATION
6580 Federal Blvd, Denver, CO 80221
Tel.: (303) 429-3600
Web Site: http://www.westover-usa.com
Year Founded: 1987
Sales Range: $10-24.9 Million
Emp.: 50
Temperature Controls; Building Automation & Security Systems
N.A.I.C.S.: 423830
Larry N. Brand (Pres)
Joe Bogetich (CEO)
Edwin McKenney (VP-Tech Svcs & VP)
Edwin McKenney (VP)
Larry Brand (Pres)
Jay Chapman (Branch Mgr)

WESTPORT CORPORATION
331 Changebridge Rd, Pine Brook, NJ 07058
Tel.: (973) 575-0110   NJ
Web Site: http://www.mundiwestport.com
Year Founded: 1969
Sales Range: $125-149.9 Million
Emp.: 100
Retailer of Leather Goods, Luggage & Belting
N.A.I.C.S.: 424990
Richard Florin (Chm)
Kevin Ross (Pres)
Paul Berchman (Exec VP)

WESTPORT CORPORATION
22800 Indian Creek Dr Ste C, Sterling, VA 20166-6713
Tel.: (703) 404-1900
Web Site: http://www.westportcorporation.com
Sales Range: $10-24.9 Million
Emp.: 40
Construction Services
N.A.I.C.S.: 236220
Stephen V. Mullaney (Pres)

WESTRIAN GROUP, INC.
7200 S Alton Way Ste C100, Centennial, CO 80112
Tel.: (303) 740-9393
Rev.: $18,329,152
Emp.: 180
Survey & Engineering Services
N.A.I.C.S.: 541370
Rocky L. Carns (Sr VP & COO)
Michael S. Brake (VP)
Mike A. Bramlett (VP)
Aaron Clutter (VP)

WESTROCK COMPANY, INC.
3700 S Shackleford Rd, Little Rock, AR 72204-7106
Tel.: (501) 228-0330   AR
Web Site: http://www.westrockusa.com
Year Founded: 1981
Construction & Mining Machinery Parts & Services
N.A.I.C.S.: 423810
Drake Teague (Pres)

WESTRUX INTERNATIONAL
1555 Valley View Ave, Santa Fe Springs, CA 90670
Tel.: (562) 404-1020
Web Site: http://www.westrux.com
Year Founded: 2009
Sales Range: $50-74.9 Million
Emp.: 205
New Car Whslr
N.A.I.C.S.: 441110
Julene Fallen (Dir-Ops)

WESTSHORE CAPITAL PARTNERS LLC
Rivergate Twr Ste 1175, Tampa, FL 33602
Tel.: (813) 223-3600
Web Site: http://www.westshorecapitalpartners.com
Sales Range: $1-9.9 Million
Emp.: 3
Privater Equity Firm
N.A.I.C.S.: 523999
David J. Malizia (Mng Partner)
Andrew Krusen (Principal)
Earl W. Powell (Principal)
Michael J. Sullivan (VP)

Subsidiaries:

American Paper Optics, LLC (1)
2995 Appling Rd Ste 106, Bartlett, TN 38133
Tel.: (901) 381-1515
Web Site: http://www.3dglassesonline.com
Sales Range: $10-24.9 Million
Converted Paper Product Mfr
N.A.I.C.S.: 322299
John Jerit (Founder)

Subsidiary (Domestic):

Jaco Bryant Printing LLC (2)
4783 Hickory Hill Rd, Memphis, TN 38141
Tel.: (901) 546-9600
Sales Range: $10-24.9 Million
Emp.: 26
Commercial Lithographic Printing Services
N.A.I.C.S.: 323111

WESTSIDE COMMUNITY MENTAL HEALTH CENTER
1189 Oak St, San Francisco, CA 94117
Tel.: (415) 431-9000   CA
Web Site: http://www.westside-health.org
Year Founded: 1967
Sales Range: $10-24.9 Million
Emp.: 157
Mental Health Services
N.A.I.C.S.: 621420
Mary Ann Jones (CEO)
Donna Rowe (Sec)
Marcellus Ducreay (VP)

WESTSIDE EQUIPMENT CO.
18 Fink Rd, Crows Landing, CA 95313
Tel.: (209) 856-4700   CA
Web Site: http://www.westsideequipment.com
Year Founded: 1986
Sales Range: $10-24.9 Million
Emp.: 50
Tomato Harvesting Machinery Mfr & Distr
N.A.I.C.S.: 333111
Dan Rodrick (Owner & CEO)

Subsidiaries:

California Tomato Machinery (1)
2500 Industrial Ave, Madera, CA 93637
Tel.: (559) 577-1800
Web Site: http://www.tomatoharvester.com
Emp.: 15
Farm Harvesting Machinery Mfr
N.A.I.C.S.: 333111

WESTSIDE FAMILY HEALTHCARE
1802 W 4th St, Wilmington, DE 19805
Tel.: (302) 655-5822   DE

COMPANIES

WESTWOOD PROFESSIONAL SERVICES, INC.

Web Site:
http://www.westsidehealth.org
Year Founded: 1988
Sales Range: $10-24.9 Million
Emp.: 252
Health Care Srvices
N.A.I.C.S.: 622110
Thomas Stephens *(Chief Medical Officer)*
Teresa Cheek *(Chief Legal & HR Officer)*
Michelle Adams *(Dir-Quality Improvement & Risk Mgmt)*
Lolita A. Lopez *(Pres & CEO)*
Donna M. Goodman *(CFO, COO & VP)*
David R. Lewis *(Treas)*
Thomas A. Sweeney *(Chm)*
Beryl Barmore *(Sec)*
Christopher L. Fraser *(Dir-Ops)*
John Hundley *(Dir-Site Ops)*
Lisa Goss *(Dir-Dental Ops)*
Kelleanne Smith *(Mgr-Healthcare Coordination)*

WESTSIDE HABILITATION CENTER, INC.
PO Box 7917, Alexandria, LA 71306-0917
Tel.: (318) 445-1551
Web Site:
http://www.westsidehabcenter.com
Sales Range: $10-24.9 Million
Emp.: 615
Developmental Disability Assistance Services
N.A.I.C.S.: 624120
Billy Debevec *(Sec)*
Nancy Allen *(VP)*
Rodney D. Kendrick Jr. *(Pres)*

WESTSTAR BANK HOLDING COMPANY, INC.
500 N Mesa, El Paso, TX 79901
Tel.: (915) 532-1000
Web Site:
http://www.weststarbank.com
Year Founded: 2008
Bank Holding Company
N.A.I.C.S.: 551111
L. Frederick Francis *(Chm)*
Yolanda Garcia *(Chief Customer Svcs Officer & Exec VP)*

Subsidiaries:

WestStar Bank (1)
500 N Mesa St, El Paso, TX 79901-1200
Tel.: (915) 532-1000
Web Site: http://www.weststarbank.com
Sales Range: $10-24.9 Million
Emp.: 160
Commericial Banking
N.A.I.C.S.: 522110
L. Frederick Francis *(Chm)*
Burt Blacksmer *(Exec VP-Lending)*
Debi Dyar *(Mgr-Accts Payable)*
Edward Escudero *(Vice Chm)*
Veronica Watts *(VP)*
Sandra Payan *(Asst VP & Branch Mgr)*

WESTSTAR DISTRIBUTING LTD.
5957 W Vandal Rd, Boise, ID 83709-3200
Tel.: (208) 362-1111
Rev.: $15,000,000
Emp.: 10
Variety Stores
N.A.I.C.S.: 424990
Cary Goldstein *(Pres)*

WESTVIEW CAPITAL PARTNERS, L.P.
125 High St Ste 2612, Boston, MA 02110
Tel.: (617) 261-2050   DE
Web Site: http://www.wvcapital.com

Year Founded: 2004
Rev.: $200,000,000
Privater Equity Firm
N.A.I.C.S.: 523999
Carlo A. von Schroeter *(Mng Partner)*
John H. Turner *(Gen Partner)*
Richard J. Williams *(Mng Partner)*
Matthew T. Carroll *(Gen Partner)*
Jonathan E. Hunnicutt *(Gen Partner)*
Cheryl Czyrklis-Coleman *(Office Mgr)*
Kevin M. Daury *(CFO & Chief Compliance Officer)*

Subsidiaries:

Abacus Group, LLC (1)
655 3rd Ave, New York, NY 10017
Tel.: (866) 888-1943
Web Site: http://www.abacusgroupllc.com
IT Solutions & Services; Enterprise Technology Platform Designer
N.A.I.C.S.: 518210
Chris Grandi *(CEO)*
Viktor Tadijanovic *(Chief Strategy Officer)*
Jonathan Bohrer *(CFO)*
Paul Ponzeka *(CTO)*
Mike Herman *(Mng Dir-Client Support)*
Darrell Tucker *(Mng Dir-Sls & Bus Dev)*
Brian Sigmond *(Mng Dir-Sls & Bus Dev)*
Chris Steele *(Mng Dir-Software Svcs)*
Adam Wayne *(Mng Dir-HR)*
Tom Cole *(Mng Dir-Europe)*
Jacob Cane *(Mng Dir)*
Dave Cava *(Mng Dir)*

Subsidiary (Domestic):

Proactive Technologies, LLC (2)
370 Lexington Ave, New York, NY 10016
Tel.: (212) 710-9670
Web Site: http://www.proactivetech.net
Information Technology Services
N.A.I.C.S.: 541512

AccountabilIT, LLC (1)
8660 E Hartford Ste 110, Scottsdale, AZ 85255
Tel.: (866) 407-0803
Web Site: http://www.accountabilit.com
Information Technology Services
N.A.I.C.S.: 518210
Chuck Vermillion *(Founder & CEO)*
Michael Tobin *(CFO)*
Jim Hertle *(COO)*
Paul Zalewski *(CTO)*
Jackie Shipley *(Chief People Officer)*
Brian Lamberger *(Chief Revenue Officer)*
Clayton Mach *(Dir-Ops)*

Subsidiary (Domestic):

ClearPointe, Inc. (2)
7 Ofc Park Dr Ste 200, Little Rock, AR 72211
Tel.: (501) 225-1155
Web Site: http://www.clearpointe.com
Computer Facilities Management Services
N.A.I.C.S.: 541513
Bob Longo *(Exec VP-Bus Dev)*
Danielle Collie *(Acct Mgr)*

Enterprise Technology Services LLC (2)
730 N 52nd St Ste 100, Phoenix, AZ 85008
Tel.: (602) 426-8600
Web Site: http://www.etechservices.com
Sales Range: $10-24.9 Million
Emp.: 30
Provider of Computer Integrated Systems Design Services
N.A.I.C.S.: 541512
James D. Siragusa *(Pres & CEO)*
Renee Mullender *(Mgr-Ops)*

Advanced Technology Services, Inc. (1)
8201 N University, Peoria, IL 61615-1887
Tel.: (309) 693-4000
Web Site: http://www.advancedtech.com
Sales Range: $125-149.9 Million
Emp.: 2,000
Outsourced Production Equipment Maintenance & Managed IT Solution Services
N.A.I.C.S.: 811310
Jeffrey A. Owens *(CEO)*
Robert Currier *(VP-Sls)*
William M. Lutz *(Pres & COO)*

James Hefti *(VP-HR & Intl Ops)*
Jeff Kosiorek *(VP-Mktg)*
Jason Montgomery *(CFO)*

BODY CENTRAL CORP. (1)
6225 Powers Ave, Jacksonville, FL 32217
Tel.: (904) 737-0811
Sales Range: $250-299.9 Million
Emp.: 3,901
Holding Company; Women's Clothing & Accessory Stores
N.A.I.C.S.: 551112
Timothy J. Benson *(Sec & Sr VP-Fin)*
Ben Rosenfeld *(Pres & CEO)*

Subsidiary (Domestic):

Body Central Stores, Inc. (2)
6225 Powers Ave, Jacksonville, FL 32217
Tel.: (904) 737-0811
Women Apparel & Accessory Store Operator
N.A.I.C.S.: 458110

Body Shop of America, Inc. (2)
6225 Powers Ave, Jacksonville, FL 32217-2215
Tel.: (904) 737-0811
Women's Clothing Retailer
N.A.I.C.S.: 458110

Bell & Howell, LLC (1)
3791 S Alston Ave, Durham, NC 27713
Tel.: (800) 961-7282
Web Site: http://www.bowebellhowell.net
Document Finishing Products, Precision Cutting Systems & Document Management Software Mfr
N.A.I.C.S.: 333248
Ramesh Ratan *(Vice Chm)*
Arthur Bergens *(CFO)*
Larry Blue *(COO)*

Branch (Non-US):

Bell & Howell - Canada (2)
30 Mural St Unit 6&7, Richmond Hill, L4B 1B5, ON, Canada (100%)
Tel.: (416) 746-2200
Web Site: http://www.bellhowell.net
Sales Range: $25-49.9 Million
Emp.: 40
Visual Communications, Mail Handling & Microimagery
N.A.I.C.S.: 333248

Branch (Domestic):

Bell & Howell, LLC - Wheeling Office (2)
3791 S Alston Ave, Durham, NC 27713
Tel.: (847) 675-7600
Web Site: http://www.bellhowell.net
Sales Range: $25-49.9 Million
Emp.: 150
Solutions & Services for Paper-Based & Digital Messaging
N.A.I.C.S.: 333248

Collaborative Solutions, LLC (1)
11190 Sunrise Vly Dr Ste 110, Reston, VA 20191-0000
Web Site:
http://www.collaborativesolutions.com
Custom Computer Programming Services
N.A.I.C.S.: 541511
Carroll Ross *(CEO)*
Steve Csuka *(COO)*

Prime Electric, Inc. (1)
3460 161st Ave SE, Bellevue, WA 98008
Tel.: (425) 747-5200
Web Site: https://www.primeelectric.com
Rev.: $7,500,000
Emp.: 71
Electrical Contractor
N.A.I.C.S.: 238210
Eric Reichanadter *(Pres & Principal)*

WESTWARD360, INC.
1464 W Webster Ave, 60614, Chicago, IL
Tel.: (800) 901-5431   IL
Web Site:
http://www.westward360.com
Year Founded: 2006
Property Management & Real Estate Services
N.A.I.C.S.: 531210

Brent Straitiff *(CEO)*
Nathan Brown *(Chief Investment Officer)*
Brawley Reishman *(CTO)*
David Westveer *(CFO)*
Travis Taylor *(COO)*
Patrick Gill *(CMO)*
Ian Duni *(Chief Sls Officer)*

WESTWATER CONSTRUCTION, INC.
5583 Marquesas Cir, Sarasota, FL 34233
Tel.: (941) 366-9936   FL
Web Site:
http://www.westwaterconstruction.com
Year Founded: 1992
Sales Range: $50-74.9 Million
Emp.: 25
Single Family Home Construction
N.A.I.C.S.: 236115
Mark S. Miller *(CEO)*
Emma Joels *(Exec VP)*
Lee W. VanDegrift *(COO)*

WESTWAYS STAFFING SERVICES INC.
500 City Pkwy W Ste 130, Orange, CA 92868
Tel.: (714) 712-4150
Web Site:
http://www.westwaysstaffing.com
Rev.: $17,938,458
Emp.: 50
Nurse Staffing Services
N.A.I.C.S.: 561311
Harold Sterling *(Pres & CEO)*
Scott Gearhart *(Branch Mgr)*
Khristine Matias *(Supvr-Staffing)*

WESTWIND INC.
5588 Airport Rd, Anderson, SC 29626
Tel.: (864) 226-9644   FL
Web Site:
http://www.westwindinc.com
Year Founded: 1954
Sales Range: $10-24.9 Million
Emp.: 20
Operator of Fast-Food Restaurant Chain
N.A.I.C.S.: 722513
Loretta Bridwell *(Mgr-HR)*
Thomas Roose Jr. *(CEO)*

WESTWOOD CONTRACTORS INC.
951 W 7th St, Fort Worth, TX 76102-5335
Tel.: (817) 877-3800   TX
Web Site:
http://www.westwoodcontractors.com
Year Founded: 1983
Sales Range: $50-74.9 Million
Emp.: 35
Nonresidential Construction
N.A.I.C.S.: 236220
Robert D. Benda *(Chm)*
Mike McBride *(Pres & COO)*
Andy Bohon *(VP)*
Stefan Figley *(CEO)*

WESTWOOD PROFESSIONAL SERVICES, INC.
12701 Whitewater Dr Ste 300, Minnetonka, MN 55343
Tel.: (952) 937-5150
Web Site:
http://www.westwoodps.com
Year Founded: 1972
Surveying & Engineering Services
N.A.I.C.S.: 541330
Paul Greenhagen *(Pres & CEO)*
Bryan P. Powell *(COO)*
Aaron Tippie *(Chief Strategy Officer)*
Kevin Larabee *(VP-HR)*

WESTWOOD PROFESSIONAL SERVICES, INC.

U.S. PRIVATE

Westwood Professional Services, Inc.—(Continued)
Dan Beckmann *(Sr VP-Power Div)*
Mallory Lindgren *(Sr VP-Market Dev)*
Rob Copouls *(Sr VP-Land Div)*
Randall P. Pogue *(VP-Southern Land)*
Jenn Bradbury *(CFO)*
Subsidiaries:
Site Consultants Inc. (1)
6909 E Greenway Pkwy Ste 250, Scottsdale, AZ 85254
Tel.: (480) 747-6558
Web Site: http://www.siteconsultants.net
Rev.: $2,484,000
Emp.: 12
Engineeering Services
N.A.I.C.S.: 541330
Gary Stocker *(Pres)*
Michael Caylor *(VP)*

WESTWOOD UNITED SUPER INC.
4701 Mission Rd, Shawnee Mission, KS 66205
Tel.: (913) 262-2270
Web Site:
http://www.westwoodhomesforsale-ks.com
Sales Range: $25-49.9 Million
Emp.: 150
Owner of Grocery Store
N.A.I.C.S.: 445110

WET PLANET BEVERAGE CO.
100 Hollister Rd Unit 1, Teterboro, NJ 07608-1139
Tel.: (585) 381-3560 NY
Web Site: http://www.joltenergy.com
Year Founded: 1985
Sales Range: $75-99.9 Million
Emp.: 20
Soft Drinks Mfr & Distr
N.A.I.C.S.: 424490
C. J. Rapp *(Founder)*

WETHERILL ASSOCIATES INC.
155 S Limerick Rd Bldg 200 Ste 2200, Limerick, PA 19468
Tel.: (484) 875-6600 DE
Web Site: http://www.waiglobal.com
Year Founded: 1978
Sales Range: $50-74.9 Million
Emp.: 650
Distr of Motor Vehicle Supplies & New Parts
N.A.I.C.S.: 423120
Sherry Packer *(Supvr-Customer Svc)*
Galina Konovalova *(Dir-Fin)*
Subsidiaries:
Renard Manufacturing Co. Inc. (1)
1101 Enterprise Dr, Royersford, PA 19468-4201
Tel.: (305) 592-1500
Sales Range: $25-49.9 Million
Emp.: 340
Mfr of Semiconductors
N.A.I.C.S.: 334413

WAI Europe b.v. (1)
Klappolder 225, 2665 MR, Bleiswijk, Netherlands
Tel.: (31) 10 524 1980
Web Site: http://www.waiglobal.com
Emp.: 25
Automobile Parts Mfr
N.A.I.C.S.: 336390
J. Stembach *(Gen Mgr)*

WAI Global (1)
3300 Corporate Way, Miramar, FL 33025
Tel.: (407) 298-4563
Web Site: http://www.waiglobal.com
Sales Range: $25-49.9 Million
Mfr & Marketer of Automotive Voltage Regulators, Supplies & Parts
N.A.I.C.S.: 336320

Ryan Moul *(CEO)*
Jordan Siegel *(CFO & COO)*
Jeff Sween *(Co-Chm)*
Doug Moul *(Co-Chm)*

Wetherill Associates Inc. - Montreal Division (1)
4723 Boul Couture, Montreal, H1R 3H7, QC, Canada
Tel.: (514) 324-7922
Emp.: 12
Automobile Parts Mfr
N.A.I.C.S.: 336390
Tony Di Lalla *(Mgr)*

Wetherill Associates Inc. - Toronto Division (1)
535 Millway Avenue Unit 1, Vaughan, L4K 3V4, ON, Canada
Tel.: (416) 740-9200
Emp.: 20
Automobile Parts Mfr
N.A.I.C.S.: 336390

Wetherill Associates Inc. - WAIglobal Shanghai Division (1)
Building No 36 215 De Bao Rd Wai Gao Qiao Free Trade Zone, Pudong, Shanghai, 200131, China
Tel.: (86) 21 50482700
Web Site: http://www.waiglobal.com.cn
Automobile Parts Mfr
N.A.I.C.S.: 336390

WETHERINGTON TRACTOR SERVICE, INC.
1901 Industrial Park Dr, Plant City, FL 33566
Tel.: (813) 752-4510 FL
Web Site:
http://www.wetheringtontractorservice.com
Year Founded: 1985
Sales Range: $1-9.9 Million
Emp.: 60
Underground Utility & Excavation Contractor
N.A.I.C.S.: 238990
Jeff Hughes *(VP)*
Kimball W. Wetherington *(Pres)*
Rich Bolesta *(Sr Project Mgr)*

WETTERMAN INC.
3030 S Hwy 94, Saint Charles, MO 63303
Tel.: (636) 441-0100
Rev.: $21,184,760
Emp.: 90
Home Center Operator
N.A.I.C.S.: 444110
Brenda Wetter Ward *(Pres)*

WETTSTEIN INVESTMENTS INC.
215 3rd St N, La Crosse, WI 54601
Tel.: (608) 784-6868
Web Site: http://www.wettsteins.com
Sales Range: $150-199.9 Million
Emp.: 5
Household Appliance Stores
N.A.I.C.S.: 449210
Dan Wettstein *(Pres)*
Subsidiaries:
Wettstein & Sons, Inc. (1)
215 3rd St N, La Crosse, WI 54601
Tel.: (608) 784-6868
Web Site: http://www.wettstein.com
Sales Range: $25-49.9 Million
Household Appliance Stores
N.A.I.C.S.: 449210
Dan Wettstein *(Owner)*

WEVER PETROLEUM INC.
100 S Hudson St, Mechanicville, NY 12118
Tel.: (518) 664-7331
Web Site:
http://www.weverpetroleum.com
Year Founded: 1928
Sales Range: $10-24.9 Million

Emp.: 16
Fuel Oil Dealers
N.A.I.C.S.: 457210
Ellen K. Alonzo *(Sec)*
Michael Alonzo *(VP)*
Joseph Alonzo Jr. *(Pres)*

WEXCO INCORPORATED
3490 Board Rd, York, PA 17406
Tel.: (717) 764-8581
Web Site: http://www.foxpool.com
Year Founded: 1958
Sales Range: $10-24.9 Million
Emp.: 4
Mfr of Extruded Finished Plastics Products
N.A.I.C.S.: 326199
Subsidiaries:
Fox Pool Corporation (1)
3490 Board Rd, York, PA 17402
Tel.: (717) 764-8581
Web Site: http://www.foxpool.com
Sales Range: $10-24.9 Million
Vinyl Liner Swimming Pools Mfr & Distr
N.A.I.C.S.: 339920

Quaker Plastic Corporation (1)
250 Route 61 S, Schuylkill Haven, PA 17972-9708
Tel.: (717) 285-4571
Web Site: http://www.quakerplastic.com
Extruded Finished Plastics Products
N.A.I.C.S.: 326199

Wexco Incorporated FSC (1)
3500 Board Rd, York, PA 17406
Tel.: (717) 764-8581
Web Site: http://www.wexcoinc.com
Sales Range: Less than $1 Million
Management Services
N.A.I.C.S.: 541611

WEXFORD CAPITAL LIMITED PARTNERSHIP
Wexford Plz 411 W Putnam Ave, Greenwich, CT 06830-6275
Tel.: (203) 862-7300 DE
Web Site: http://www.wexford.com
Year Founded: 1994
Rev.: $3,300,000,000
Investment Advisor & Private Equity Firm
N.A.I.C.S.: 523999
Arthur Harris Amron *(Partner & Gen Counsel)*
Paul M. Jacobi *(Partner)*
Joseph Michael Jacobs *(Pres)*
Charles E. Davidson *(Chm & Chief Investment Officer)*
Mark D. Zand *(Partner)*
Kenneth A. Rubin *(Partner)*
Dante Domenichelli *(Partner & COO)*
Philip Braunstein *(Partner)*
Marc McCarthy *(Partner)*
Aaron Meyer *(Partner)*
James L. Rubin *(Partner)*
John C. Sites Jr. *(Partner)*
Subsidiaries:
Drew Shoe Corporation (1)
252 Quarry Rd, Lancaster, OH 43130
Tel.: (740) 653-4271
Web Site: http://www.drewshoes.com
Sales Range: $10-24.9 Million
Emp.: 55
Men's & Women's Orthopedic Shoes Mfr
N.A.I.C.S.: 316210
Bob D'Amore *(Controller)*

Mammoth Energy Partners LP (1)
4727 Gaillardia Pkwy Ste 200, Oklahoma City, OK 73134
Tel.: (405) 265-4600
Sales Range: $125-149.9 Million
Emp.: 914
Oil & Gas Exploration
N.A.I.C.S.: 211120
Marc T. McCarthy *(Chm)*
Mark Layton *(CFO)*
Phil Lancaster *(Pres)*

Subsidiary (Domestic):
Mammoth Energy Services, Inc. (2)
14201 Caliber Dr Ste 300, Oklahoma City, OK 73134
Tel.: (405) 608-6007
Web Site: https://www.mammothenergy.com
Rev.: $362,086,000
Assets: $724,678,000
Liabilities: $262,062,000
Net Worth: $462,616,000
Earnings: ($619,000)
Emp.: 1,037
Fiscal Year-end: 12/31/2022
Oil Exploration & Development Services
N.A.I.C.S.: 211120
Arthur Harris Amron *(Chm)*
Arty Straehla *(CEO)*
Mark Layton *(CFO)*

The Elk Horn Coal Company LLC (1)
544 S Lk Dr, Prestonsburg, KY 41653-1299
Tel.: (606) 886-2330
Web Site: http://www.elkcoal.com
Coal Mining Reserve Leasing Services
N.A.I.C.S.: 531190
James Newman *(Pres)*

WEXFORD HEALTH SOURCES INC.
501 Holiday Dr Foster Plz 4, Pittsburgh, PA 15220
Tel.: (412) 937-8590 FL
Web Site:
http://www.wexfordhealth.com
Year Founded: 1992
Sales Range: $25-49.9 Million
Emp.: 650
Health Care Srvices
N.A.I.C.S.: 541611
Anna Vozar *(Mgr-Staffing & Recruitment)*
Maryanne Hollerich *(Mgr-Pur)*
Mark Blewett *(Dir-HR)*
Daniel L. Conn *(CEO)*
Elaine J. Gedman *(Chief Admin Officer & Exec VP)*
John M. Froehlich *(CFO & Sr VP-Fin)*

WEXNER COMPANIES INC.
418 S Grove Park Rd, Memphis, TN 38117-3518
Tel.: (901) 763-3925
Web Site:
http://www.josephstores.com
Sales Range: $10-24.9 Million
Emp.: 30
Women's Apparel
N.A.I.C.S.: 458210
Alfred B. Wexner *(Founder & Pres)*

WEXNER HERITAGE VILLAGE
1151 College Ave, Columbus, OH 43209
Tel.: (614) 559-5590 OH
Web Site: http://www.whv.org
Year Founded: 1969
Sales Range: $10-24.9 Million
Emp.: 410
Elder Care Services
N.A.I.C.S.: 624120
Chris Christian *(Sr VP-Real Estate)*
Tom McDermott *(CFO)*
David T. Rosen *(Pres & CEO)*
Mark Yale *(Treas)*
Geri Ellman *(Asst Sec)*

WEYAND & SON INC.
2801 West Hillsborough, Tampa, FL 33610
Tel.: (813) 234-2151
Web Site:
http://www.weyandfood.com
Sales Range: $10-24.9 Million
Emp.: 122
Fruits & Vegetables Whslr
N.A.I.C.S.: 424480
Rick Weyand *(Co-Owner)*
Larry Weyand *(Co-Owner)*

Kitty McPhillips *(Co-Owner)*
Mary Anne Lyle *(Co-Owner)*
Jeff Hawkins *(VP-Admin & Sls)*

WEYAND FOOD DISTRIBUTORS, INC.
2707 E Wilder Ave, Tampa, FL 33610
Tel.: (813) 236-5923
Web Site:
  http://www.weyandfood.com
Year Founded: 1977
Sales Range: $10-24.9 Million
Emp.: 50
Fruit & Vegetable Whslr
N.A.I.C.S.: 424480
Rick Weyand *(Co-Owner)*
Larry Weyand *(Co-Owner)*
Kitty McPhillips *(Co-Owner)*
Mary Anne Lyle *(Co-Owner)*
Jeff Hawkins *(VP-Admin)*

WEYAUWEGA STAR DAIRY INC.
113 W Wisconsin St, Weyauwega, WI 54983
Tel.: (920) 867-2870
Web Site:
  http://www.wegastardairy.com
Sales Range: $10-24.9 Million
Emp.: 30
Natural Cheese
N.A.I.C.S.: 311513
James Knaus *(Pres)*

WEYBRIDGE, LLC
4530 Hamann Pkwy, Willoughby, OH 44094
Tel.: (440) 951-5500   OH
Sheet Metal Mfr
N.A.I.C.S.: 332322
Ryan Thomas *(Pres)*

Subsidiaries:

Mika Metal Fabricating, Co.   (1)
4530 Hamann Pkwy, Willoughby, OH 44094
Tel.: (440) 951-5500
Web Site: http://www.metalfabricatorsinc.net
Sales Range: $1-9.9 Million
Emp.: 30
Sheet Metal Work Mfg
N.A.I.C.S.: 332322
Scott Shelfer *(Chm)*

WEYMOUTH AUTO MALL
25 Main St, Weymouth, MA 02188
Tel.: (781) 335-4400
Year Founded: 1959
Sales Range: $10-24.9 Million
Emp.: 45
Car Whslr
N.A.I.C.S.: 441110
Rick Smith *(Pres)*
Aaron Smith *(VP)*

WF AUTOMOTIVE OF COLUMBUS, LLC
3900 W Broad St, Columbus, OH 43228
Tel.: (614) 275-0500   DE
Web Site:
  http://www.markwahlbergchevy.com
New & Used Car Dealer
N.A.I.C.S.: 441110
Mark Wahlberg *(Co-Owner)*
Jay Feldman *(Co-Owner)*

WF HOLDINGS INC.
3 E Spit Brook Rd, Nashua, NH 03060
Tel.: (603) 888-5443
Web Site: http://www.worthenind.com
Rev.: $42,000,000
Emp.: 200
Adhesives
N.A.I.C.S.: 325520
David S. Worthen *(Pres)*

WFD CONSULTING, INC.
Ste 2 55 Chapel St, Waltham, MA 02452
Tel.: (617) 673-3100   MA
Web Site: http://www.wfd.com
Year Founded: 1983
Sales Range: $50-74.9 Million
Emp.: 25
Corporate Consulting Strategy Services, Flexibility & Work Redesign, Work Force Commitment, Womens Retention & Advancement, Dependent Care Supports
N.A.I.C.S.: 624190
Peter Linkow *(Pres)*
Debbie Phillips *(Pres)*

WFKR INC.
404 E Highland Blvd, Austin, TX 78752
Tel.: (512) 451-1711
Rev.: $15,400,000
Emp.: 400
Cabaret
N.A.I.C.S.: 722410
Pat Seibert *(Office Mgr)*

WFN STRATEGIES
21495 Ridgetop Cir Ste 201, Sterling, VA 20166
Tel.: (703) 444-2527
Web Site:
  http://www.wfnstrategies.com
Year Founded: 2001
Sales Range: $10-24.9 Million
Emp.: 9
Business Consulting Services & Printing
N.A.I.C.S.: 541690
Richard Hoffman *(Mgr-Cable Installation)*
Heather Case *(Project Mgr)*
Kristian Nielsen *(Bus Mgr)*
Kevin Summers *(Mgr-Creative Content)*

WG BLOCK CO.
1414 Mississippi Blvd, Bettendorf, IA 52722
Tel.: (563) 823-2080   IA
Year Founded: 1936
Sales Range: $25-49.9 Million
Emp.: 160
Central-Mixed Concrete
N.A.I.C.S.: 327320
Christopher A. Rayburn *(Chm, Pres & CEO)*

Subsidiaries:

Acme Materials Company   (1)
2544 Pettibone Ave, Muscatine, IA 52761
Tel.: (563) 263-1105
Web Site: http://www.acmematerialsco.co
Sales Range: $25-49.9 Million
Emp.: 7
Construction Sand & Gravel, Readymix Concrete & Drycrete
N.A.I.C.S.: 212321

Scott County Ready Mix Inc.   (1)
113 E Lincoln Rd, Eldridge, IA 52748
Tel.: (563) 823-2080
Sales Range: Less than $1 Million
Emp.: 27
Central-Mixed Concrete
N.A.I.C.S.: 327320

WG STROHWIG TOOL & DIE INC.
3285 Industrial Rd, Richfield, WI 53076
Tel.: (262) 628-4477
Web Site: http://www.strohwig.com
Sales Range: $10-24.9 Million
Emp.: 144
Forms (Molds), For Foundry & Plastics Working Machinery
N.A.I.C.S.: 333511

Wolfgang Strohwig *(Founder & Pres)*
Mike Hagen *(Plant Mgr)*
Dan Glass *(Dir-Sls)*

WG VALENZUELA DRYWALL INC.
4085 N Hwy Dr, Tucson, AZ 85705
Tel.: (520) 887-5652
Sales Range: $10-24.9 Million
Emp.: 100
Drywall
N.A.I.C.S.: 238310
Kim Dillavou *(Pres)*

WG WHITE & COMPANY
2119 US Hwy 601 N, Mocksville, NC 27028
Tel.: (336) 492-2111
Web Site: http://www.wgwhite.com
Rev.: $12,312,614
Emp.: 18
Groceries
N.A.I.C.S.: 424410
Robin White *(Owner)*

WG&R FURNITURE CO., INC.
900 Challenger Dr, Green Bay, WI 54311-8329
Tel.: (920) 469-4880   WI
Web Site:
  http://www.wgrfurniture.com
Year Founded: 1946
Sales Range: $25-49.9 Million
Emp.: 225
Furniture Retailer
N.A.I.C.S.: 449110
James Greene *(Pres)*
Clifford Hook *(Mgr-Store)*
Greg Wolf *(Mgr-Sls)*
Melissa Bachmann *(Mgr-Sls)*

WGBH EDUCATIONAL FOUNDATION
1 Guest St, Boston, MA 02135
Tel.: (617) 300-2000
Web Site: http://www.wgbh.org
Sales Range: $25-49.9 Million
Emp.: 700
Television Film Production
N.A.I.C.S.: 512110
Ann Marie Fudge *(Chm)*
Lynn Bay Dayton *(Vice Chm)*
William A. Lowell *(Bd of Dirs & Vice Chm)*
Terry Fitzpatrick *(VP-Children's Education & Media)*
John Bredar *(VP-Natl Programming)*
Amy Abrams *(Pres-Abrams Foundation)*
Cathy E. Minehan *(Vice Chm)*
Susan Goldberg *(Pres & CEO)*
Shane Miner *(COO)*
Debra Adams Simmons *(Sr Dir-Editorial Projects)*
Tina Cassid *(CMO)*
Liz Cheng *(Gen Mgr-Television)*
Ann Dexter *(VP-Human Resources)*
Pam Johnston *(Gen Mgr-News)*
Evie Kintzer *(VP-Strategy & Business Development)*
James Levy *(CFO & Treas)*
Yemisi Oloruntola-Coates *(Chief Inclusion Officer, Chief Equity Officer & VP)*
Ed Wilson *(Chief Dev Officer)*

WHALEN FURNITURE MANUFACTURING
1578 Airwing Rd, San Diego, CA 92154
Tel.: (619) 423-9948
Web Site:
  http://www.whalenfurniture.com
Sales Range: $25-49.9 Million
Emp.: 100
Wood Household Furniture

N.A.I.C.S.: 337122
Kenneth J. Whalen *(Owner)*
Alba Wylie *(VP-Fin)*
Al Schwerin *(Pres)*
Jesse Quinones *(Project Mgr-Ops)*

WHALLEY COMPUTER ASSOCIATES INC.
1 Whalley Way, Southwick, MA 01077
Tel.: (413) 569-4200   MA
Web Site: http://www.wca.com
Year Founded: 1981
Sales Range: $25-49.9 Million
Emp.: 150
Retail of Computers, Peripherals & Software
N.A.I.C.S.: 423430
John Whalley *(Founder)*
Cindy Wells *(Dir-Corp Dev)*
Kevin Learned *(Dir-Svcs)*
Steve Cross *(Dir-Sls)*
Paul Whalley *(VP)*

WHALLEY GLASS CO., INC.
72 Chapel St, Derby, CT 06418
Tel.: (203) 735-4665   CT
Web Site:
  http://www.curvedglassdist.com
Year Founded: 1945
Sales Range: $10-24.9 Million
Emp.: 129
Distr of Glass Products & Services
N.A.I.C.S.: 811122
Mark Vece *(Pres)*

WHAM! ADVERTISING
2103 Fairways Lane, Roseville, MN 55113
Tel.: (651) 639-1947
Web Site:
  http://www.whamadvertising.com
Emp.: 5
Advetising Agency
N.A.I.C.S.: 541810
Ron Strauss *(Co-Owner & Art Dir)*
Roxanna Strauss *(Co-Owner, CEO & Project Dir)*

WHAM-O, INC.
5903 Christie Ave, Emeryville, CA 94608
Tel.: (510) 653-8847   CA
Web Site: http://www.wham-o.com
Year Founded: 1948
Sales Range: $50-74.9 Million
Emp.: 45
Toy Mfr
N.A.I.C.S.: 339930
Jane Lock *(Dir-HR)*

WHANAU INTERESTS LLC.
405 Colorado St. Ste 1600, Austin, TX 78701
Tel.: (512) 745-5250   DE
Web Site:
  https://www.haveliinvestments.com
Year Founded: 2021
Holding Company
N.A.I.C.S.: 551112

Subsidiaries:

Haveli Investment Management LLC   (1)
405 Colorado St., Ste 1600, Austin, TX 78701
Tel.: (512) 987-7314
Private Equity
N.A.I.C.S.: 523999
Brian N. Sheth *(Founder)*
Ian Loring *(Chm & Sr Mng Dir)*

Holding (Domestic):

ZeroFox Holdings, Inc.   (2)
1834 S Charles St, Baltimore, MD 21230
Web Site: https://www.zerofox.com
Rev.: $233,300,000

WHANAU INTERESTS LLC.

Whanau Interests LLC.—(Continued)
Assets: $464,837,000
Liabilities: $319,568,000
Net Worth: $145,269,000
Earnings: ($356,558,000)
Emp.: 914
Fiscal Year-end: 01/31/2024
Holding Company; Cyber Security & Reputation Management Services
N.A.I.C.S.: 551112

Subsidiary (Domestic):

LookingGlass Cyber Solutions, LLC (3)
10740 Parkridge Blvd Ste 200, Reston, VA 20191
Tel.: (703) 351-1000
Web Site: https://www.lgscout.com
Threat Intelligence Software Developer
N.A.I.C.S.: 513210
Allan Thomson *(CTO)*
Pete Agresta *(Chief Revenue Officer)*
Stewart Curley *(CFO)*
Doug Dangremond *(Sr VP-Threat Intelligence Svcs)*
Jeremy Haas *(Chief Security Officer)*
Dave Horn *(Sr VP-Engrg)*
Lee Mariano *(VP-HR)*
Joy Nemitz *(CMO)*
Eric Olson *(Sr VP-Product Mgmt)*
Michael Taxay *(Gen Counsel & Chief Risk Officer)*
Gilman Louie *(Executives)*
Don Gilberg *(Pres & COO)*
Bryan Ware *(CEO)*

ZeroFox, Inc. (3)
1834 S Charles St, Baltimore, MD 21230
Web Site: https://www.zerofox.com
Security Software Publisher
N.A.I.C.S.: 513210
James C. Foster *(Co-Founder, Chm & CEO)*
John R. Prestridge III *(CMO)*
Kevin T. Reardon *(COO)*
Michael Price *(CTO)*
Scott O'Rourke *(Chief Revenue Officer)*

Subsidiary (Domestic):

Identity Theft Guard Solutions, Inc. (4)
Lincoln Center One 10300 SW Greenburg Rd Ste 570, Portland, OR 97223
Tel.: (503) 726-4500
Web Site: https://www.idx.us
Identity Theft Recovery & Prevention Products & Services
N.A.I.C.S.: 561611
Heidi Nelson *(Mgr-HR)*
Chuck Thomas *(Controller)*
Paul O'Mara *(Sr VP-Sls & Pro Svcs)*
Andrew Migliore *(Dir-Software Engrg)*
Heather Noonan *(Sr Project Mgr)*
Christine Arevalo *(VP-Healthcare Fraud Solutions)*
Kimberly Holmes *(Sr VP)*
Thomas F. Kelly *(Pres & CEO)*

WHARTON COUNTY ELECTRIC COOPERATIVE, INC.
1815 E Jackson St, El Campo, TX 77437
Tel.: (979) 543-6271 TX
Web Site: http://www.wcecnet.net
Year Founded: 1938
Sales Range: $10-24.9 Million
Emp.: 44
Electric Power Industry Association
N.A.I.C.S.: 813910
Gary Raybon *(Gen Mgr)*
Wesley Lange *(Mgr-Engrg & Ops)*
Kenneth Christensen *(VP)*
Leroy Kaspar *(Pres)*
Peggy Glaze *(Treas & Sec)*

WHARTON HARDWARE & SUPPLY
7724 Crescent Blvd, Pennsauken, NJ 08110
Tel.: (856) 662-6935
Web Site: http://www.whartonhardware.com
Rev.: $10,700,000
Emp.: 300
Hardware
N.A.I.C.S.: 423710
Aldo Magistrelli *(Chm)*

WHARTON-SMITH, INC.
750 Monroe Rd, Sanford, FL 32771
Tel.: (407) 321-8410 FL
Web Site: http://www.whartonsmith.com
Year Founded: 1984
Sales Range: $200-249.9 Million
Emp.: 480
Waste Water & Sewage Treatment Plant Construction
N.A.I.C.S.: 237110
George E. Smith *(Chm)*
Ron Davoli *(Pres & CEO)*
Darin Crafton *(Exec VP-Comml)*
Thomas Iarossi *(Mgr-Area-Comml)*
Tom Murphy *(Dir-Ops-Comml-Sanford)*
Bret Estridge *(Mgr-Comml-Charlotte)*
Tim Smith *(Exec VP-Charlotte)*
Pat Hewitt *(Exec VP-Orlando)*
David Hayes *(Exec VP-Comml)*
Devon Lewis *(VP-Entertainment-Intl)*
John Lyons *(VP-Comml Preconstruction Svcs)*
Todd O'Donnell *(Dir-Bus Dev-Water/Wastewater)*

WHAT ON EARTH
5581 Hudson Industrial Pkwy, Hudson, OH 44236
Tel.: (330) 650-5000
Web Site: http://www.whatonearthcatalog.com
Sales Range: $25-49.9 Million
Emp.: 90
Catalog & Mail Order Houses
N.A.I.C.S.: 513199
Jared S. Florian *(Owner)*
Ken Harris *(Pres)*

WHATABURGER OF MESQUITE INC.
3200 N Town E Blvd, Mesquite, TX 75150
Tel.: (972) 270-3400
Web Site: http://www.womtx.com
Year Founded: 1969
Sales Range: $25-49.9 Million
Emp.: 700
Franchise Owner of Fast-Food Restaurants
N.A.I.C.S.: 722513
Bob Potter *(CFO & VP)*
Joyce Heiman *(Treas & Sec)*
Randell Kirk *(VP)*
John L. Heiman Sr. *(Chm)*
John L. Heiman Jr. *(Pres)*

WHATABURGER, INC.
300 Concord Plz Dr, San Antonio, TX 78216-6903
Tel.: (210) 476-6000 TX
Web Site: http://www.whataburger.com
Year Founded: 1950
Sales Range: $1-4.9 Billion
Emp.: 12,000
Fast Food Restaurants Owner & Operator
N.A.I.C.S.: 722513
Michael McLellan *(Exec VP)*
Preston Atkinson *(CEO)*
Pam Cox *(VP-Comm-Whatabrands)*
Rich Scheffler *(VP-Mktg & Innovation)*
Dino Del Nano *(COO)*
Leonard Mazzocco *(VP-Bus Ops)*

WHATCOM EDUCATIONAL CREDIT UNION
600 E Holly St, Bellingham, WA 98225
Tel.: (360) 676-1168 WA
Web Site: http://www.wecu.com
Year Founded: 1936
Sales Range: $50-74.9 Million
Emp.: 353
Credit Union
N.A.I.C.S.: 522130
Kathleen Gavin *(Sr VP)*
Jennifer Kutcher *(Pres & CEO)*
Robert Langei *(COO & Exec VP)*
Brandon Hahnel *(VP-Fin)*
Barbara Krigbaum *(VP-Trng & Dev)*
Bolor Smith *(VP-Risk Mgmt)*
Colin Naylor *(CIO & VP)*
Jeff Dykstra *(Chief Lending Officer & Exec VP)*
Matt Berendsen *(VP-Real Estate)*
Cindy Klein *(Chief HR Officer)*
Janet McGary *(VP-Ops)*
Kent Bouma *(VP-Business Svcs)*
Lisa Langei *(VP-Mktg & Compliance)*

WHATLEY OIL & AUTO PARTS COMPANY INC.
720 Blakely St, Cuthbert, GA 39840
Tel.: (229) 732-3392
Web Site: http://www.whatleyoil.com
Year Founded: 1955
Sales Range: $10-24.9 Million
Emp.: 50
Provider of Petroleum & Auto Parts
N.A.I.C.S.: 424710
Steven Whatley *(Pres)*
Ted Bridges *(Gen Mgr)*

WHAYNE SUPPLY COMPANY
1400 Cecil Ave, Louisville, KY 40211
Tel.: (502) 774-4441
Web Site: http://www.whayne.com
Sales Range: $200-249.9 Million
Emp.: 1,200
General Construction Machinery & Equipment
N.A.I.C.S.: 423810
Tom Bentley *(Mgr-Central Dispatch)*
Ron Boutelle *(Supvr-Used & Rental Svc)*
Mike Craft *(Reg Mgr-Sls)*
Edwin Downer *(Gen Mgr-Tech Div)*
Michael French *(Mgr-Rental & Used)*
Scott Hodoval *(Mgr-Parts)*
David Hovekamp *(VP & Branch Mgr-Ops)*
Bernie Jackson *(Mgr-Parts Ops)*
Frances King *(Coord-Svcs)*
Frank Lewis *(VP-Product Support)*
Kathy Little *(Coord-HR)*
Harold Tincher *(Mgr-Continuous Improvement Solutions)*
Gene Westfall *(Asst Mgr-Inventory Control)*
Joe Yonce *(Mgr-Products)*
David Fuson *(Acct Mgr)*
Wayne Seelye *(Mgr-Info Svcs)*
Judith O'Bryan *(Mgr-Trng)*
Allen Edelen *(Mgr-Used Parts)*
Bentley Floyd *(Product Mgr-Support)*
Paul Cave *(Reg Mgr-Sls)*
Rick Palmisano *(Area Mgr-Rental)*
Tracy Knapp *(Bus Mgr-Comml)*
Tara Dahl *(Coord-Comm)*
Lynn Wilcoxson *(Mgr-Facility Svcs)*

WHC, INC.
300 Industrial Ter, Broussard, LA 70518
Tel.: (337) 837-8765
Web Site: http://www.whc-inc.com
Sales Range: $10-24.9 Million
Emp.: 70
Sewer Construction Services
N.A.I.C.S.: 237110

George Crain *(Pres)*
Shannon Broussard *(Mgr-EH&S)*

WHEATLAND ELECTRIC COOPERATIVE
101 Main St, Scott City, KS 67871
Tel.: (620) 872-5885
Web Site: http://www.weci.net
Sales Range: $50-74.9 Million
Emp.: 130
Distribution, Electric Power
N.A.I.C.S.: 221122
Ron Davis *(Pres)*
Bruce Mueller *(Gen Mgr & CEO)*
Lynn Freese *(Dir-Member Svcs)*

WHEATLAND SEED INC.
1780 N Hwy 38, Brigham City, UT 84302
Tel.: (435) 734-9191
Web Site: http://www.centralmilling.com
Sales Range: $10-24.9 Million
Emp.: 15
Broker Services
N.A.I.C.S.: 541990
Kent Perry *(Owner)*
Bob Payne *(Mgr-Acctg)*
Lynn Perry *(Pres & CEO)*

WHEATLEY & TIMMONS
737 N Michigan Ave 22 Fl, Chicago, IL 60611-6750
Tel.: (312) 755-6200
Sales Range: $10-24.9 Million
Emp.: 17
N.A.I.C.S.: 541810
Bob Wheatley *(CEO)*
Rich Timmons *(Pres)*
Kerri Erb *(Sr VP & Dir-Media Svcs)*
Krista S. Cortese *(Assoc Dir-Media Svcs)*
Mary Clare Middleton *(VP & Dir-Consumer Brands)*

WHEATON FRANCISCAN HEALTHCARE
400 W River Woods Pkwy, Glendale, WI 53212
Tel.: (414) 465-3000
Web Site: http://www.mywheaton.org
Sales Range: $1-4.9 Billion
Emp.: 17,143
Medical Health Network
N.A.I.C.S.: 622110
Andrew Hillig *(VP-Ops Excellence)*
Susan Boland *(COO & Sr VP)*
Kenneth R. Buser *(Pres-South Market)*
Debra K. Standridge *(Pres-North Market)*
Ibzan Monteagudo *(Dir-Language Access Svcs)*
Coreen Dicus-Johnson *(Pres-Central Market)*
Jess Owens *(Mgr-Comm & PR)*

WHEATON FRANCISCAN SERVICES INC.
26 W 171 Roosevelt Rd, Wheaton, IL 60187-6078
Tel.: (630) 462-9271 IL
Web Site: http://www.wheatonfranciscan.org
Year Founded: 1983
Sales Range: $75-99.9 Million
Emp.: 1,024
Hospital Services
N.A.I.C.S.: 541611

Subsidiaries:

Marianjoy Rehabilitation Hospital (1)
26 W 171 Roosevelt Rd, Wheaton, IL 60187
Tel.: (630) 909-8000
Web Site: http://www.marianjoy.org

Sales Range: $25-49.9 Million
Emp.: 800
Rehabilitation Hospital
N.A.I.C.S.: 622310
Kathleen C. Yosko (Pres & CEO)
Michael Hedderman (CFO & VP-Fin)
Jeffrey Oken (VP-Medical Affairs)
Noel Rao (Dir-Medical Residency Program)
Denise LeBloch (Dir-Mktg)
Teresa Chapman (VP-HR)
Brandi Moore (Dir-Nursing Svcs & Clinical Support)

Rush Oak Park Hospital (1)
520 S Maple Ave, Oak Park, IL 60304-1097
Tel.: (708) 383-9300
Web Site: http://www.roph.org
General Medical & Surgical Hospital Services
N.A.I.C.S.: 622110
Bruce M. Elegant (Pres & CEO)
Michael R. Silver (CIO & VP-Medical Affairs)
Melissa Coverdale (VP-Fin)
Karen M. Mayer (VP-Patient Care Svcs)

WHEATON PARK DISTRICT
102 E Wesley St, Wheaton, IL 60187
Tel.: (630) 665-4710
Web Site: http://www.wheatonparkdistrict.com
Sales Range: $25-49.9 Million
Emp.: 500
Recreational Services
N.A.I.C.S.: 713990
Michael Benard (Exec Dir)
Diane Hirshberg (Dir-HR)
Mary Beth Cleary (Dir-Athletics Programs & Leagues)
Bradley Keene (Dir-Athletic)
Kristina Nemetz (Superintendent-Mktg & Special Events)
Deborah Seymour (Superintendent-Horticulture, Turf & Natural Resources)
Brian Whitkanack (Mgr-Restaurant & Banquet Ops)
Jason Hospes (Mgr-Athletic)
Bruce Stoller (Dir-Golf)
Danielle Salerno (Dir-Banquets, Catering & Sls)
Linda Dolan (Mgr-Mary Lubko Center)
Michelle Podkowa (Mgr-Museum)
Sue Wahlgren (Dir-Zoo)
Terra Johnson (Mgr-Program)
Vicki Beyer (Mgr-Community Center)
Wendy Russell (Mgr-Aquatic & Safety)

WHEATON VAN LINES, INC.
8010 Castleton Rd, Indianapolis, IN 46250-2005
Tel.: (317) 849-7900　　　IN
Web Site: http://www.wheatonworldwide.com
Year Founded: 1945
Sales Range: $100-124.9 Million
Emp.: 200
Relocation Services
N.A.I.C.S.: 484210
Mark Kirschner (CEO)
Fred McBroom (VP-Agency Dev)
Jerrod Carter (CIO)
John Weissert (VP-Rev Acctg & Claims)
A. J. Schneider (Exec VP)
Mike Harvey (Dir-Agency Recruiting)
Stephen F. Burns (Chm)
Subsidiaries:

Bekins Van Lines, LLC (1)
8010 Castleton Rd, Indianapolis, IN 46250
Tel.: (317) 558-0728
Web Site: http://www.bekins.com
Relocation Services
N.A.I.C.S.: 484210
Nicole Munoz (Mgr-Mktg Comm)
Mark Kirschner (CEO)
Ron Borkowski (VP-Ops)

Jerrod Carter (CIO)
Fred McBroom (VP-Agency Dev)
A. J. Schneider (Exec VP)
John Weissert (VP-Revenue Acctg & Claims)
Tim Wiley (VP-Military)
Chris Banguis (VP-Sls)

Clark & Reid Company, Inc. (1)
17 Bridge St, Watertown, MA 02472
Tel.: (978) 670-1100
Web Site: http://www.clarkreid.com
Sales Range: $10-24.9 Million
Emp.: 20
Moving Services
N.A.I.C.S.: 484121
Michael Gilmartin Sr. (Pres)

Crown Moving & Storage Inc. (1)
8040 Castleton Rd, Indianapolis, IN 46250-2005　　　(100%)
Tel.: (317) 842-8111
Web Site: http://www.crownmovingstorage.com
Sales Range: $10-24.9 Million
Emp.: 62
Mover of Used Household Goods
N.A.I.C.S.: 484210
Stephen F. Burns (Chm)
Dave Witzerman (Pres)

La Habra Relocations, Inc. (1)
2895 E Miraloma Ave, Anaheim, CA 92806
Tel.: (714) 627-5440
Web Site: http://www.lahabrarelocations.com
Packaging & Crating Services
N.A.I.C.S.: 488991

Road Runner Moving & Storage Inc. (1)
12425 Chimney Rock Rd, Houston, TX 77035　　　(100%)
Tel.: (713) 270-1616
Web Site: http://www.roadrunner-moving.com
Sales Range: $10-24.9 Million
Emp.: 25
Mover of Used Household Goods
N.A.I.C.S.: 484220

WHEATON-DUMONT COOP ELEVATOR INC.
1115 Broadway, Wheaton, MN 56296-1307
Tel.: (320) 563-8152　　　MN
Web Site: http://www.wdcoop.com
Year Founded: 1905
Sales Range: $75-99.9 Million
Emp.: 35
Provider Of Agricultural Services
N.A.I.C.S.: 424510
Philip Deal (Gen Mgr)
Mark Suek (Controller)

WHEATON-OAKS SPORT CENTER, INC.
1000 West Prairie Ave, Wheaton, IL 60187
Tel.: (630) 690-0887　　　IL
Web Site: http://www.wheatonsportcenter.com
Year Founded: 1978
Sales Range: $1-9.9 Million
Emp.: 110
Fitness & Recreational Sports Center
N.A.I.C.S.: 713940
Ann Impola (Dir-Reception)
Becky Sandberg (Mgr-Property)
Subsidiaries:

HealthTrack Sports & Wellness, LLC (1)
875 Roosevelt Rd, Glen Ellyn, IL 60137-6168
Tel.: (630) 942-9600
Web Site: http://www.htsw.net
Fitness & Wellness Facility
N.A.I.C.S.: 713940
Cris Castillo (Gen Mgr)
Jill Feitl (Mgr-Web Site Dev & Internet Mktg)
Sue Kamphuis (Dir-Sls & Mktg)
Peggy Hayley (Dir-Programs)

WHECO CORP.
2989 Kingsgate Way, Richland, WA 99354
Tel.: (509) 544-0933　　　WA
Web Site: http://www.wheco.com
Year Founded: 1979
Sales Range: $1-9.9 Million
Emp.: 40
Construction Machinery Mfr
N.A.I.C.S.: 333120
David Wood (Pres)
Karl Reitmayer (Mgr-Santa Fe Springs)
Jeff Williams (VP)
Michael Saranovich (Mgr-Parts & Safety-Richland)
Tom Hofbauer (CFO)
Scott Suemori (COO & VP)

WHEEL CHAIR HOME, INC.
3333 Elmwood Ave, Kenmore, NY 14217
Tel.: (716) 874-1566　　　NY
Web Site: http://www.schofieldcare.org
Year Founded: 1915
Sales Range: $10-24.9 Million
Emp.: 368
Elder Care Services
N.A.I.C.S.: 624120
Marie Trainor (Dir-Fin)
Edward Gray (Pres)

WHEELCHAIR ADL SOLUTIONS CORPORATION
1324 N Liberty Lake Rd 169, Liberty Lake, WA 99019
Tel.: (509) 995-5250　　　NV
Web Site: http://www.wheelchairadlsolutions.com
Year Founded: 2010
Sales Range: Less than $1 Million
Wheelchair Accessories Mfr & Distr
N.A.I.C.S.: 339112
Matthew Allen (Pres, Treas & Sec)

WHEELER BROTHERS GRAIN CO.
PO Box 29, Watonga, OK 73772-0029
Tel.: (580) 623-7223　　　OK
Web Site: http://www.wheelerbrothers.com
Year Founded: 1991
Sales Range: $100-124.9 Million
Emp.: 20
Grain Storage & Railroad Operation
N.A.I.C.S.: 112112
Cinda Lafferty (Chm)
Mike Mahoney (Pres & CEO)
Richard Cowan (Treas, Sec & Controller)
Austin Lafferty (VP)
Subsidiaries:

AT&L Railroad (1)
505 W Main, Watonga, OK 73772-0029　　　(100%)
Tel.: (580) 623-7229
Web Site: http://www.wheelerbrothers.com
Sales Range: $10-24.9 Million
Emp.: 4
Short Line Railroad
N.A.I.C.S.: 482111
Danny Williams (Gen Mgr)
Mike Mahoney (Pres)

Wheeler Bros. Grain Co. (1)
420 Santa Fe St, Alva, OK 73717
Tel.: (580) 327-0141
Web Site: http://www.wheelarbrothers.com
Sales Range: $10-24.9 Million
Emp.: 7
Grain & Kindred Products
N.A.I.C.S.: 424510
Dot Tyree (Sec)

WHEELER CLINIC, INC.
91 Northwest Dr, Plainville, CT 06062
Tel.: (860) 793-3500　　　CT
http://www.wheelerclinic.org
Year Founded: 1968
Sales Range: $75-99.9 Million
Emp.: 1,071
Community Care Services
N.A.I.C.S.: 624190
Stewart Joslin (CFO)
Sabrina Trocchi (Chief Strategy Officer)
Patricia Speicher Werbner (VP-HR)
John R. Sponauer (VP-Comm)
Elisabeth Cannata (VP-Community-Based Family Svcs & Practice Innovation)
Sharon M. Hasbani (VP-Medical Svcs)
Susan Walkama (Pres)
Todd M. Raymond (VP-Facilities)
Kimberly M. Nelson (VP-Outpatient & Community Svcs)

WHEELER MACHINERY CO.
4901 W 2100 S, Salt Lake City, UT 84120
Tel.: (801) 974-0511
Web Site: http://www.wheelercat.com
Rev.: $230,000,000
Emp.: 500
Industrial Tractors
N.A.I.C.S.: 423810
Robert Campbell (Pres)
Chuck Rardin (Mgr-Credit)
Jonathan Campbell (VP-Sls & Rental)
Bret Calder (Mgr-Site)
Craig Banyard (Mgr-Product Support Sls)
Colby Bryant (Mgr-Rental)
Andrea Young (Mgr-Mktg)
Dan Brown (Mgr-Network)
Jon Jessop (Supvr-Warehouse)
Steve Semadeni (Mgr-Svc)
Jeff Ipsen (CFO)
Lori Barrow (Coord-IT Help Desk)
Ken Lloyd (Mgr-Crushing Sys)
Greg Roth (Mgr-e-Business)
Cody Rhoades (Mgr-Rental Ops)
Bryan Campbell (VP-Product Support)

WHEELER MATERIAL HANDLING
9839 S Tryon St, Charlotte, NC 28273-6505
Tel.: (704) 588-6930　　　NC
Web Site: http://www.yalecarolinas.com
Year Founded: 1988
Sales Range: $25-49.9 Million
Emp.: 198
Provider of Industrial Machinery & Equipment
N.A.I.C.S.: 423830
Gray Wheeler (Pres)

WHEELER'S CORPORATION
15 Old Airport Rd, Rome, GA 30165
Tel.: (706) 413-0137
Web Site: http://www.wheelers.com
Year Founded: 1949
Sales Range: $50-74.9 Million
Emp.: 900
Lumber, Plywood & Millwork Services
N.A.I.C.S.: 423310
Jim Langston (Mgr-Design)
Michael Bryan (Plant Mgr)
Subsidiaries:

Manis Lumber Company (1)
100 Elizabeth St NW, Rome, GA 30165-2424
Tel.: (706) 378-3485
Sales Range: $10-24.9 Million
Emp.: 20
Provider of Lumber, Plywood & Millwork

WHEELER'S CORPORATION

U.S. PRIVATE

Wheeler's Corporation—(Continued)
N.A.I.C.S.: 423310

Wheeler's-Newnan (1)
547 Hwy 29 S, Newnan, GA 30263-5292
Tel.: (770) 254-1000
Sales Range: $10-24.9 Million
Emp.: 25
Provider of Lumber, Plywood & Millwork
N.A.I.C.S.: 423310

Wheeler's-Rome (1)
2 Riverside Industrial Park NE, Rome, GA 30161-7301
Tel.: (706) 378-3485
Sales Range: $10-24.9 Million
Emp.: 100
Provider of Lumber, Plywood & Millwork
N.A.I.C.S.: 423310

WHEELFIRE INC
2501 NW 34th Pl #30, Pompano Beach, FL 33069
Web Site: http://www.wheelfire.com
Year Founded: 2007
Sales Range: $1-9.9 Million
Emp.: 20
Discount Retailer of Automobile Wheels, Rims & Tires
N.A.I.C.S.: 441340
Jeffrey A. Benet (Pres)

WHEELING HOSPITAL, INC.
1 Medical Park, Wheeling, WV 26003
Tel.: (304) 243-3000 WV
Web Site:
  http://www.wheelinghospital.org
Year Founded: 1850
Emp.: 275
Hospital Operator
N.A.I.C.S.: 622110
Gregg Warren (VP-Mktg & PR)
Ron Violi (CEO)

Subsidiaries:

Harrison Community Hospital, Inc. (1)
951 E Market St, Cadiz, OH 43907
Tel.: (740) 942-4631
Web Site:
  http://www.harrisoncommunity.com
Emp.: 220
Hospital Operator
N.A.I.C.S.: 622110
John DeBlasis (Acting Mgr)

WHEELOCK STREET CAPITAL L.L.C.
660 Steamboat Rd 3rd Fl, Greenwich, CT 06830
Tel.: (203) 413-7700
Web Site: http://www.wheelockst.com
Year Founded: 2008
Sales Range: $25-49.9 Million
Emp.: 18
Real Estate Investment Services
N.A.I.C.S.: 523999
Merrick R. Kleeman (Partner)
Jonathan H. Paul (Mng Partner)
Patrick W. Campbell (Principal)
Jeffrey S. Laliberte (Mng Dir & Head-Acquisition)
James B. Eberhart (Principal)
Lawrence D. Settanni (CFO & Principal)
Al Hatfield (Dir-Asset Mgmt)
Daniel B. Green (Principal)
Timothy R. Hodes (Principal)
Claude T. Chandonnet (Principal & Dir-Retail)
Hunter Jones (VP)
Elizabeth Devito (VP-Fin)

Subsidiaries:

Boot Ranch Circle LLC (1)
1447 Boot Ranch Cir, Fredericksburg, TX 78624
Tel.: (830) 997-6200
Web Site: http://www.bootranch.com

Sales Range: $1-9.9 Million
Performing Arts Companies
N.A.I.C.S.: 711190
Hal Sutton (Owner)
Leigh Lacy (Dir-Member Svcs)
Sean Gioffre (Dir-Real Estate Sls & Mktg)

WHEELWRIGHT LUMBER CO.
3127 Midland Dr, Ogden, UT 84401-3399
Tel.: (801) 627-0850
Sales Range: $10-24.9 Million
Emp.: 50
Lumber & Building Material Whslr
N.A.I.C.S.: 444110
Paul Wheelwright (Owner & Pres)
Brandan Taylor (Mgr-Retail Store)

WHELAN & ASSOCIATES INC.
3720 W 74th St, Chicago, IL 60629
Tel.: (773) 581-1261
Sales Range: $10-24.9 Million
Emp.: 7
Trucking Except Local
N.A.I.C.S.: 484121
John Whelan (Pres & CEO)

WHELAN SECURITY CO., INC.
1699 S Hanley Rd Ste 100, Saint Louis, MO 63144-2900
Tel.: (314) 644-1974 MO
Web Site:
  http://www.whelansecurity.com
Year Founded: 1949
Sales Range: $75-99.9 Million
Emp.: 1,400
Provider of Security Services
N.A.I.C.S.: 561612
Patrick A. Twardowski (Chm)
Prentice Robertson (COO)
Guy Stiebing (Sr VP-Sls & Mktg)
Greg Twardowski (Pres & CEO)

WHELEN ENGINEERING COMPANY, INC.
51 Winthrop Rd, Chester, CT 06412
Tel.: (860) 526-9504
Web Site: http://www.whelen.com
Rev.: $44,400,000
Emp.: 1,000
Automotive Lighting Fixtures
N.A.I.C.S.: 336320
Geoff Marsh (Pres & CEO)
George Whelen (Exec VP)

Subsidiaries:

Whelen Aerospace Technologies LLC (1)
210 Airport D E, Sebastian, FL 32958
Tel.: (800) 859-4757
Web Site: http://flywat.com
Aircraft Landing Lighting & Aviation Safety Services
N.A.I.C.S.: 488119
Tyler Wheeler (CEO)

WHER-RENA BOAT SALES INC.
18919 W Catawba Ave, Cornelius, NC 28031
Tel.: (704) 892-0161
Web Site: http://www.wher-rena.com
Rev.: $10,000,000
Emp.: 10
Inboard Boats
N.A.I.C.S.: 441222
Jeffery M. Junker (Pres)

WHEREOWARE LLC
505 Huntmar Park Dr Ste 200, Herndon, VA 20170
Tel.: (703) 821-7448
Web Site:
  http://www.whereoware.com
Sales Range: $1-9.9 Million
Emp.: 40
Online Strategy, Design, Development & Marketing Solutions

N.A.I.C.S.: 541890
Bill Haskitt (Partner-Client Mktg)
Jim Rothey (CTO & Partner)
Joe Harris (Partner-Dev)
Teya Tuccio-Flick (VP-Mktg)
Caitlin Kelly (Sr Acct Mgr)
Deysi Lopez (Mgr-Fin & Office Mgr)
Aaron Lemley (Sr Mgr-Mktg)
Elizabeth Zelman (Mgr-Mktg)
Jared Ruppert (Mgr-Mktg)
Jay Beutler (Dir-Bus Dev)
Kelly King (Acct Mgr)
Lisa Fanoni (Project Mgr)
Lizz Donnelly (Mgr-Mktg)
Nora Liberti (Mgr-Mktg)
Scott Brinser (CFO & Controller)
Teddy Pekalski (Mgr-Sls)

WHETSTONE CHOCOLATES, INC.
1 Dolphin Dr, Saint Augustine, FL 32080
Tel.: (904) 825-1700
Web Site:
  http://www.whetstonechocolate.com
Sales Range: $1-9.9 Million
Chocolate Mfr & Retailer
N.A.I.C.S.: 311351
Virginia Whetstone (Pres)

WHETSTONE COMPANY
101 Chestnut St Ste 110, Gaithersburg, MD 20877
Tel.: (301) 948-2924
Web Site:
  http://www.whetstonecompany.com
Year Founded: 1978
Sales Range: $10-24.9 Million
Emp.: 18
Real Estate Agents & Managers
N.A.I.C.S.: 531110

WHIBCO, INC.
87 Commerce St E, Bridgeton, NJ 08302-2601
Tel.: (856) 455-9200 NJ
Web Site: http://www.whibco.com
Year Founded: 1841
Sales Range: $1-9.9 Million
Emp.: 65
Whslr of Industrial Sands & Foundry Products & Commercial Sand & Gravel
N.A.I.C.S.: 212322
William Simcox (Controller)
Wade Sjogren (Pres)
Richard Bertonazzi (Dir-HR)
Walter R. Sjogren Jr. (Exec VP)

Subsidiaries:

Whibco, Inc. - Port Elizabeth Plant (1)
377 Port Cumberland Rd, Port Elizabeth, NJ 08348
Tel.: (856) 825-5200
Sand & Gravel Mining Services
N.A.I.C.S.: 212321

WHICH WICH, INC.
1310 Elm St Ste 180LL, Dallas, TX 75202
Tel.: (214) 747-9424
Web Site: http://www.whichwich.com
Sales Range: $50-74.9 Million
Emp.: 1,820
Food Products Mfr & Distr
N.A.I.C.S.: 311999
Jeff Sinelli (Founder, CEO & Chief Vibe Officer)
Jeff Vickers (VP-Dev)
Cherry Hearn (Pres)

WHIDBEY TELECOM
14888 SR 525, Langley, WA 98260
Tel.: (360) 321-1122
Web Site: http://www.whidbeytel.com

Sales Range: $10-24.9 Million
Emp.: 110
Local Telephone Communications
N.A.I.C.S.: 517121
George Henny (CEO)

WHIP INDUSTRIES INC.
3010 S Main St, Fort Worth, TX 76110
Tel.: (817) 289-1404
Web Site:
  http://www.whipindustries.com
Year Founded: 1990
Sales Range: $10-24.9 Million
Emp.: 99
Fabricated Metal Products Mfr
N.A.I.C.S.: 332999
Gary McGee (Pres)

WHIP-MIX CORPORATION
361 Farmington Ave, Louisville, KY 40209
Tel.: (502) 637-1451
Web Site: http://www.whipmix.com
Rev.: $22,190,710
Emp.: 180
Compounds, Dental
N.A.I.C.S.: 339114
James Robinson (Mgr-Institutional Sls)
Margaret Overmeer (Dir-Customer Rels)
Flemming Poulsen (Dir-Sls-Global)
Jim Myers (Pres)
Rick Brown (VP-Ops-Louisville & Ft. Collins)
Bernie Jaroslow (Mgr-Laboratory Product)
Bryan Murphy (Mgr-Sls-North American)
Craig Pickett (Mgr-Technical Support)
Peter Kazunas (Sls Mgr-Intl)

WHIPPOORWILL ASSOCIATES, INC.
11 Martine Ave 11th Fl, White Plains, NY 10606
Tel.: (914) 683-1002 NY
Year Founded: 1991
Sales Range: $1-9.9 Million
Emp.: 13
Private Investment Firm
N.A.I.C.S.: 523999
Brant Loucks (Dir-Ops)

Subsidiaries:

Commercial Furniture Group, Inc. (1)
810 W Highway 25 70, Newport, TN 37821-8044
Tel.: (423) 623-0031
Web Site:
  http://www.commercialfurnituregroup.com
Sales Range: $50-74.9 Million
Institutional & Office Furniture Mfr
N.A.I.C.S.: 337127
Larry Pace (Mgr-Bus Admin & Resource)
Tracy Laden (Mgr-Treasury & Credit)

Division (Domestic):

Commercial Furniture Group, Inc. - Falcon Products Division (2)
810 W Hwy 25/70, Newport, TN 37821-8044
Tel.: (423) 623-0031
Web Site: http://www.falconproducts.com
Sales Range: $75-99.9 Million
Commercial Furnishings Mfr
N.A.I.C.S.: 337127

Subsidiary (Non-US):

Falcon de Juarez, S.A. de C.V. (3)
Cerrada 5681 Parque Industrial Gema II, C D Juarez, Ciudad Juarez, 32650, Chihuahua, Mexico
Tel.: (52) 6566200668

COMPANIES

Sales Range: $25-49.9 Million
Commercial Furnishings Mfr
N.A.I.C.S.: 337211

Unit (Domestic):

Falcon-Belmont (3)
22 Falcon Dr, Belmont, MS 38827-9752
Tel.: (662) 454-3451
Sales Range: $25-49.9 Million
Metal Chairs Mfr
N.A.I.C.S.: 337126

Falcon-Lewisville (3)
PO Box 70, Lewisville, AR 71845-0070
Tel.: (870) 921-5721
Sales Range: $25-49.9 Million
Commercial Furnishings Mfr
N.A.I.C.S.: 921110

Subsidiary (Domestic):

Howe Furniture Corporation (2)
10650 Gateway Blvd, Saint Louis, MO 63132
Tel.: (423) 586-7000
Web Site: http://www.howefurniture.com
Sales Range: $10-24.9 Million
Emp.: 12
Folding & Non-Folding Tables; Flip Top Tables; Computer Support Furniture; Training, Conference & Hospitality Tables
N.A.I.C.S.: 337214

Subsidiary (Non-US):

Howe A/S (3)
Filosofgangen 18, 5000, Odense, Denmark
Tel.: (45) 63416400
Web Site: http://www.howe.com
Sales Range: $10-24.9 Million
Furniture Mfr
N.A.I.C.S.: 337127
Lars Bruntse *(Mgr-Mktg)*
Henrik Olsson *(Mgr-Supply Chain)*
Lars Prumb *(Mgr-Mktg & Sls)*
Michael Jacobsen *(Pres & CEO)*

Division (Domestic):

Phonet & Johnson (2)
810 W Highway 25 70, Newport, TN 37821-8044
Tel.: (423) 586-7000
Folding & Non-Folding Tables, Corporate Dining Tables, Occassional Tables & Healthcare Tables
N.A.I.C.S.: 337127
Larry Pace *(Gen Mgr)*

Subsidiary (Domestic):

Shelby Williams Industries, Inc. (2)
810 W Hwy 25 70, Newport, TN 37821-8044
Tel.: (423) 586-7000
Web Site: http://www.shelbywilliams.com
Hotel & Restaurant Upholstered & Wood Office Furniture Mfr; Upholstery Fabrics Mfr & Importer
N.A.I.C.S.: 337127

Subsidiary (Domestic):

Sellers & Josephson (3)
86 Rte 4 E, Englewood, NJ 07631
Tel.: (201) 567-1353
Vinylized Wall Coverings Mfr
N.A.I.C.S.: 322220

WHIRLEY INDUSTRIES, INC.
618 4th Ave, Warren, PA 16365-0988
Tel.: (814) 723-7600 PA
Web Site: http://www.whirleydrinkworks.com
Year Founded: 1960
Mfr of Plastic Mugs
N.A.I.C.S.: 326199
Robert D. Sokolski *(CEO)*

WHIRLWIND BUILDING SYSTEM
8234 Hansen Rd, Houston, TX 77075
Tel.: (713) 946-7140
Web Site: http://www.whirlwindsteel.com
Rev.: $80,000,000
Emp.: 359

Buildings, Portable: Prefabricated Metal
N.A.I.C.S.: 332311
Norma Hernandez *(Mgr-HR)*

WHIRLWIND STEEL
8234 Hansen Rd, Houston, TX 77234
Tel.: (713) 946-7140
Web Site: http://www.whirlwindsteel.com
Sales Range: $100-124.9 Million
Emp.: 417
Metal Building & Components Mfr
N.A.I.C.S.: 332311
Steve Wright *(Mgr-Engrg)*

WHISKEY ACQUISITION, INC.
15321 NW 60th Ave Ste 109, Miami Lakes, FL 33014
Tel.: (941) 347-7380 NV
Year Founded: 2015
Investment Services
N.A.I.C.S.: 523999
Miguel Dotres *(Pres)*
John Brown *(Treas & Sec)*

WHISTLE SPORTS INC.
79 Madison Ave 8th FL, New York, NY 10016
Tel.: (646) 661-5786
Web Site: http://www.teamwhistle.com
Year Founded: 2007
Sales Range: $25-49.9 Million
Emp.: 70
Sports Broadcasting Services
N.A.I.C.S.: 516120
John West *(Founder & CEO)*

WHIT-MART INC.
56 Wentworth St, Charleston, SC 29401
Tel.: (843) 720-5010
Sales Range: $25-49.9 Million
Emp.: 5
Retailer of Family Restaurants
N.A.I.C.S.: 722511
Michael Wiser *(CFO)*

WHITACRE ENGINEERING CO. INC.
4645 Rebar Ave NE, Canton, OH 44705
Tel.: (330) 455-8505
Web Site: http://www.whitacreengineering.com
Sales Range: $10-24.9 Million
Emp.: 30
Engineeering Services
N.A.I.C.S.: 332322
Keith D. Le Page *(Pres)*
Todd LePage *(VP)*

WHITACRE GREER COMPANY
1400 S Mahoning Ave, Alliance, OH 44601
Tel.: (330) 823-1610
Web Site: http://www.wgpaver.com
Year Founded: 1916
Sales Range: $10-24.9 Million
Emp.: 80
Brick & Structural Clay Tile Mfr
N.A.I.C.S.: 327120
J. J. Whitacre *(Pres)*

WHITACRE LOGISTICS, LLC.
12602 S Dixie Hwy, Portage, OH 43451
Tel.: (419) 686-0055
Web Site: http://www.whitacrelogistics.com
Year Founded: 2008
Sales Range: $10-24.9 Million
Emp.: 135
Logistics & Transportation Services
N.A.I.C.S.: 541614

Gary Whitacre *(CEO)*
Dan Whitacre *(Dir-Safety)*
Ken Whitacre *(Mgr-Compliance)*
John Willard *(Controller)*
Aaron Owens *(Mgr-Terminal)*

WHITAKER BANK CORPORATION OF KENTUCKY
2001 Pleasant Rdg Dr, Lexington, KY 40509
Tel.: (859) 543-4000 KY
Web Site: http://www.whitakerbank.com
Year Founded: 1991
Sales Range: $75-99.9 Million
Emp.: 351
Bank Holding Company
N.A.I.C.S.: 551111
Jack E. Whitaker *(Chm & CEO)*
Elmer Keith Whitaker *(Pres)*
Frank L. Wilford *(Sec)*

Subsidiaries:

Peoples Bank & Trust Company of Madison County (1)
419 Chestnut St, Berea, KY 40403-1510
Tel.: (859) 986-6860
Web Site: http://www.whitakerbank.com
Sales Range: $10-24.9 Million
Emp.: 74
Commericial Banking
N.A.I.C.S.: 522110
Melinda Carter *(Head-Mktg)*

Whitaker Bank, Inc. (1)
2001 Pleasant Rdg Dr, Lexington, KY 40509
Tel.: (859) 543-4000
Web Site: http://www.whitakerbank.com
Sales Range: $50-74.9 Million
Emp.: 277
Commericial Banking
N.A.I.C.S.: 522110
Elmer Keith Whitaker *(Pres & CEO)*
Jack E. Whitaker *(Chm)*
Rick Lautzenhiser *(Dir-Mktg & Sls)*
Brad Thomas *(VP-Investments)*
Brian Smith *(Asst VP-Mktg)*
Sean Alcorn *(Asst VP-HR)*

WHITAKER BUICK JEEP EAGLE CO.
131 19th St SW, Forest Lake, MN 55025-1348
Tel.: (651) 464-5612
Web Site: http://www.whitakerauto.com
Sales Range: $25-49.9 Million
Emp.: 70
New Car Retailer
N.A.I.C.S.: 441110
Steve Whitaker *(Pres)*
Jim Bush *(Mgr-Used Vehicle)*
Bob Flinn *(Mgr-Fin)*

WHITAKER CONSTRUCTION COMPANY
44 S 1050 W, Brigham City, UT 84302
Tel.: (435) 723-2921
Web Site: http://www.whitcon.com
Sales Range: $100-124.9 Million
Emp.: 210
Provider of Oil & Gas Pipeline Construction
N.A.I.C.S.: 237120
Robert Whitaker *(Chm)*

WHITAKER OIL COMPANY
1557 Marietta Rd NW, Atlanta, GA 30318-3652
Tel.: (404) 605-8385 GA
Web Site: http://www.whitakeroil.com
Year Founded: 1971
Sales Range: $10-24.9 Million
Emp.: 47
Distr of Chemicals & Allied Products
N.A.I.C.S.: 424690

WHITE & CASE LLP

Victoria Whitaker *(CFO)*
Dan Boyle *(VP-Sls)*
Camon Worsham *(Plant Mgr)*
Debbie Schulties *(Office Mgr)*
Rodney Fambrough *(Plant Mgr)*

WHITCOM PARTNERS, INC.
45th Fl 712 5th Ave, New York, NY 10019
Tel.: (212) 582-2300
Year Founded: 1969
Sales Range: $50-74.9 Million
Emp.: 5
Holding Services for Publishing Industry
N.A.I.C.S.: 551112
Edward L. Barlow *(Sr Partner)*
Edward Cohen *(CFO)*
Robert S. Blank Jr. *(Sr Partner)*

WHITCORP FINANCIAL COMPANY
104 S 2nd St, Leoti, KS 67861
Tel.: (620) 375-2229
Year Founded: 1961
Bank Holding Company
N.A.I.C.S.: 551111
Barth E. Whitham *(VP)*
Stewart A. Whitham *(VP)*
Clay G. Whitham *(Pres)*
Jeffrey G. Whitham *(VP)*
Jennifer E. Jensik *(VP)*
Janis R. Whitham *(VP)*

Subsidiaries:

Frontier Bank (1)
200 S Main St, Lamar, CO 81052
Tel.: (719) 336-4351
Web Site: http://www.frontierbankco.com
Emp.: 35
Commericial Banking
N.A.I.C.S.: 522110
Clay Whitham *(CEO)*
Jon D. Hanavan *(Sr VP)*
Karen Clarke *(VP)*
Kelli Hess *(Asst VP-Mortgage Loan Dept)*
Ron Sicklebower *(Mgr-IT)*

WHITE & CASE LLP
1221 Ave of the Americas, New York, NY 10020-1095
Tel.: (212) 819-8200 NY
Web Site: https://www.whitecase.com
Year Founded: 1901
Sales Range: Less than $1 Million
Emp.: 2,600
Law firm
N.A.I.C.S.: 541110
Noah A. Brumfield *(Partner)*
Richard J. Burke *(Partner)*
Kim Marie Boylan *(Partner)*
Linda E. Carlisle *(Partner)*
Donna M. Attanasio *(Partner)*
Troy Alexander *(Partner)*
Joseph Angland *(Partner)*
Douglas Baumstein *(Partner)*
Eric Berg *(Partner & Head-Asia Pacific)*
David Bilkis *(Partner)*
Oliver Brahmst *(Partner)*
Joseph Brazil *(Partner)*
Ronald Brody *(Partner)*
Paul Carberry *(Partner)*
Adam Chernichaw *(Partner)*
John Chung *(Partner)*
Daniel Fridman *(Partner)*
Michael Garcia *(Partner)*
Christopher Utting *(Partner)*
Kevin Petrasic *(Partner-Washington)*
Arlene Hahn *(Partner-Global Intellectual Property Practice)*
Fernando Aenlle-Rocha *(Partner-Los Angels)*
Borries Ahrens *(Partner-Hamburg)*
Timo Airisto *(Partner-Helsinki)*
Meltem Akol *(Co-Partner)*
Dana Foster *(Partner)*

WHITE & CASE LLP

White & Case LLP—(Continued)
Claire DeLelle (Partner)
Jason Tomita (Partner-San Francisco)
Raymond Azar (Partner-Global Project Fin Practice)
Heather Burke (Partner)
Michael Deyong (Partner-Global Mergers & Acq Practice)
Binoy Dharia (Partner-Global Banking Practice)
Steven Gee (Partner-Global Tax Practice)
Brody K. Greenwald (Partner-Global Intl Arbitration Practice-Washington)
Kim Haviv (Partner-Comml Litigation Grp)
Eric Lancaster (Partner-Global Intellectual Property Practice-Silicon Valley)
Thomas MacWright (Partner)
Damien Nyer (Partner-Global Intl Arbitration Practice)
Jane E. Rueger (Partner)
Andrew Weisberg (Partner-Global Capital Markets Practice)
Kristen M. Young (Partner-Global Intl Arbitration Practice-Washington)
Muriel Alhadeff (Partner-Global Mergers & Acq Practice-Brussels)
Paul Brumpton (Partner-Global Intl Arbitration Practice-London)
Katja Butler (Partner)
Amanda Cowell (Partner-Global Comml Litigation Practice-London)
Ben Davies (Partner)
Joanna Dimmock (Partner-White Collar Practice)
Leonardo Graffi (Global Mergers & Acq Practice-Milan)
Justus Herrlinger (Partner-Global Antitrust Practice-Hamburg)
Gareth Hodder (Partner-Global Project Fin Practice)
Gregoire Karila (Partner-Global Capital Markets Practice-Paris)
Jan Linda (Partner-Global Banking Practice-Prague)
Jarlath McGurran (Partner-Global Mergers & Acq Practice-London)
Kirsten Odynski (Partner-Intl Arbitration Practice)
Luke Robottom (Partner-Construction & Engrg Grp)
Hendrik Rohricht (Partner-Global Mergers & Acq Practice-Frankfurt)
Michal Subocz (Partner-Global Comml Litigation Practice-Warsaw)
Yoko Takagi (Partner-Global Mergers & Acq Practice-Madrid)
Melody Chan (Partner-Dispute Resolution Practice)
Seiji Matsuzoe (Partner-Global Banking Practice-Tokyo)
Jan Parik (Partner-Local-Global Tax Practice)
Dov Gottlieb (Partner)
Colin Diamond (Partner-Capital Markets Practice-Global)
Max Bonnell (Partner-Arbitration Practice-Intl)
Paul Friedland (Head-Arbitration Practice-Intl)
Jack Pace (Partner)
James Cuclis (Partner-Houston)
Christopher Richardson (Partner)
Charlie Ofner (Partner)
Saul Daniel (Partner-Houston)
Jason Webber (Partner & Co-Head-Oil & Gas Indus Grp-Global)
Philip Stopford (Co-Head-Oil & Gas Indus Grp-Global)
Saam Golshani (Partner-Paris)
Alexis Hojabr (Partner-Paris)
Guillaume Vitrich (Partner-Paris)
John Reiss (Partner & Head-Merger & Acq Practice-Global)
Denise Diallo (Partner)
Oliver Brettle (Partner)

WHITE & PARTNERS
8603 Westwood Crr Dr 4th Fl, Herndon, VA 22182-4607
Tel.: (703) 793-3000 VA
Web Site:
http://www.whiteandpartners.com
Year Founded: 1966
Rev.: $51,500,000
Emp.: 50
Advertising Agencies, Food Service, Full Service, High Technology, Information Technology, Leisure, Public Relations, Retail, Travel & Tourism
N.A.I.C.S.: 541810
Matthew C. White (Chm & CEO)
Kipp Monroe (Creative Dir)
Jose Banzon (Exec VP)
Matt Walker (Creative Dir)
Alicia Gehring (VP-Media)
Kerry Beutel (COO)

WHITE & WILLIAMS LLP
1650 Market St Ste 1800, Philadelphia, PA 19103
Tel.: (215) 864-7000 PA
Web Site:
http://www.whiteandwilliams.com
Year Founded: 1870
Rev.: $35,500,000
Emp.: 525
Law firm
N.A.I.C.S.: 541110
Jerrold Anders (Partner-Litigation)
Christopher DiMuro (Partner)
James F. Coffey (Partner)
Meredith A. Bieber (Partner)
Brian Tetro (Partner)
Debra Weinrich (Partner)
Eric Hermanson (Partner)

WHITE + WARREN
80 W 40th St Fl 3, New York, NY 10018-2701
Tel.: (212) 398-3295
Web Site:
http://www.whiteandwarren.com
Year Founded: 1996
Sales Range: $10-24.9 Million
Emp.: 20
Women's, Children's & Infants' Clothing & Accessories Merchant Whslr
N.A.I.C.S.: 424350
Susan White (Co-Founder & Pres)
Barbara Benenson (VP)
Diana Jankovsky (Acct Exec-Sls)
Lauren Soloway Feld (Mgr-E-Commerce)

WHITE ARROW SERVICE STATIONS
2125 Walden Ave, Buffalo, NY 14225
Tel.: (716) 684-5411
Web Site:
http://www.jimstruckplaza.com
Rev.: $15,400,000
Emp.: 30
Petroleum Products
N.A.I.C.S.: 424720

WHITE BEAR LAKE SUPERSTORE
3900 Hwy 61 N, White Bear Lake, MN 55110-4634
Tel.: (651) 426-5441
Web Site:
http://www.whitebearlakesuperstore.com
Sales Range: $25-49.9 Million
Emp.: 120
Car Whslr
N.A.I.C.S.: 441110

Charles Gatrell (Mgr-Sls-New Car)
Lee Gatrell (VP & Gen Mgr)
Steve Rubin (Controller)
Paul Rubin (Pres)
Brooke Waldo (Mgr-Fin)
Molly Sievert (Mgr-Fin)
Kevin Shafer (Dir-Fin)
Mike Thunstrom (Mgr-Parts)
Mike Thunstrum (Dir-Parts & Svc)

WHITE CASTLE SYSTEM, INC.
555 W Goodale St, Columbus, OH 43215-1158
Tel.: (614) 228-5781 DE
Web Site: http://www.whitecastle.com
Year Founded: 1921
Sales Range: $550-599.9 Million
Emp.: 12,000
Fast Food Hamburger & Frozen Grocery Hamburger & Cheeseburger Producer & Sales
N.A.I.C.S.: 722513

Subsidiaries:

PSB Co. (1)
555 W Goodale St, Columbus, OH 43215-1158 (100%)
Tel.: (614) 228-5781
Sales Range: $25-49.9 Million
Emp.: 250
Mfr of Steel, Lawn Spreaders, Powder Painting, No Guess Lawn Spreader Markers, Job Shop Orders
N.A.I.C.S.: 722513

White Castle Distributing, Inc. (1)
555 W Goodale St, Columbus, OH 43215 (100%)
Tel.: (614) 228-5781
Web Site: http://www.whitecastle.com
Sales Range: $10-24.9 Million
Emp.: 74
Frozen Food Products
N.A.I.C.S.: 424420
Robert A. Camp (VP & Gen Mgr)

White Castle System, Inc.-Evendel (1)
3126 Exon Ave, Cincinnati, OH 45241-2548 (100%)
Tel.: (513) 563-2290
Web Site: http://www.whitecastle.com
Sales Range: $25-49.9 Million
Emp.: 40
Bakery Services
N.A.I.C.S.: 311812

WHITE CLOUD GRAIN COMPANY INC.
1803 Oregon St, Hiawatha, KS 66434-0276
Tel.: (785) 742-3000 KS
Year Founded: 1961
Sales Range: $10-24.9 Million
Emp.: 36
Supplier of Grain & Fertilizer
N.A.I.C.S.: 424510
Warren L. Beavers (Pres)
Ron Dodge (Mgr-Production)

WHITE CONSTRUCTION COMPANY INC.
US Hwy 19, Chiefland, FL 32626
Tel.: (352) 493-1444 FL
Year Founded: 1945
Sales Range: $50-74.9 Million
Emp.: 500
Highway & Street Construction
N.A.I.C.S.: 237310
Dominic Padilla (VP-Relationship Dev)

Subsidiaries:

The Rancher Inc. (1)
4821 Northwest Sixth St, Gainesville, FL 32609-1785
Tel.: (352) 376-4595
Web Site: http://www.therancher.com

Sales Range: $10-24.9 Million
Emp.: 8
Miscellaneous Apparel & Accessory Store
N.A.I.C.S.: 458110

WHITE CONTRUCTION, INC.
2524 Gateway Rd, Carlsbad, CA 92009
Tel.: (760) 931-1130
Web Site:
http://www.whiteconstructioninc.com
Year Founded: 1983
Sales Range: $10-24.9 Million
Emp.: 18
Building Construction Services
N.A.I.C.S.: 236220
Steve White (CEO)
Debbe Damron (VP)
Travis Shain (Pres)
Pamela Workman (Controller)

WHITE COUNTY FORD-CHRYSLER
1337 Il Hwy 1, Carmi, IL 62821
Tel.: (618) 382-4611
Web Site:
http://www.whitecountyford.net
Year Founded: 1931
Sales Range: $10-24.9 Million
Emp.: 20
Automobiles, New & Used
N.A.I.C.S.: 441110
Anthony Huffer (Gen Mgr)

WHITE CREEK WIND PROJECT
1131 Dot Rd, Roosevelt, WA 99356
Tel.: (509) 896-5246
Web Site:
http://www.whitecreekwind.com
Sales Range: $10-24.9 Million
Emp.: 10
Electrical Wiring Services
N.A.I.C.S.: 238210
Kim Chapman (Office Mgr)

WHITE DEER MANAGEMENT LLC
700 Louisiana Ste 4770, Houston, TX 77002
Tel.: (713) 581-6900 DE
Web Site:
http://www.whitedeerenergy.com
Year Founded: 2008
Emp.: 13
Privater Equity Firm
N.A.I.C.S.: 523999
Thomas J. Edelman (Mng Partner)
Joseph S. Compofelice (Operating Partner)
Ben A. Guill (Mng Partner)
Joseph R. Edwards (Partner)
Amanda N. Coussens (Co-CFO)
Whitney Toombs Voute (Dir-IR)
Erin E. Rathke (Co-CFO)
Meghan C. Leggett (VP)
Varun S. Babbili (VP)
James K. Meneely III (Partner)

Subsidiaries:

Flogistix, LP (1)
204 N Robinson Ave Ste 2200, Oklahoma City, OK 73102
Tel.: (405) 536-0000
Web Site: http://www.flogistix.com
Sales Range: $10-24.9 Million
Petroleum & Natural Gas Well Compression Equipment Mfr & Whslr
N.A.I.C.S.: 333132
Denis Baker (VP-Environment, Health, Safety & Sustainability)
Mims Talton (Pres & CEO)
Jim Merrill (CFO)
Drake Andarakes (VP-Sls & Mktg)
Charles Crenshaw (VP-Field Svc)

Legacy Measurement Solutions, Inc. (1)

16415 Addison Rd Ste 800, Addison, TX 75001
Tel.: (214) 295-9550
Web Site:
    http://www.legacymeasurement.com
Sales Range: $1-9.9 Million
Emp.: 450
Oil & Gas Measuring Equipment Mfr
N.A.I.C.S.: 333132
Mark B. Newman *(CFO)*
Joseph S. Compofelice *(Chm & CEO)*
G. Gene Gradick Jr. *(COO)*

Unicat Catalyst Technologies, Inc. (1)
1600 E Hwy 6 Ste 320, Alvin, TX 77511-2560
Tel.: (281) 331-2231
Web Site: http://www.unicatcatalyst.com
Printing Ink Mfr
N.A.I.C.S.: 325910
Mani Erfan *(Pres)*

WHITE DIGITAL MEDIA
5901 Priestly Dr, Carlsbad, CA 92008
Tel.: (760) 827-7800
Year Founded: 2007
Rev.: $15,000,000
Emp.: 132
N.A.I.C.S.:
Glen White *(Founder & Pres)*
Mark Blakely *(Dir-Global Sls)*
Brian Smith *(CEO)*
Nathan P. Weber *(CFO)*

WHITE ELECTRICAL CONSTRUCTION CO.
1730 Chattahoochee Ave NW, Atlanta, GA 30318-2112
Tel.: (404) 351-5740   GA
Web Site: http://www.white-electrical.com
Year Founded: 1910
Sales Range: $50-74.9 Million
Emp.: 500
Electrical Construction & Maintenance Services
N.A.I.C.S.: 238210
Chad Krompak *(Dir-Bus Dev)*
Jerry Brittendall *(Mng Dir-Bus Dev)*
Nicholas Maddox *(Pres)*

WHITE FLOWER FARM, INC.
30 Irene St, Torrington, CT 06790-6657
Tel.: (860) 496-9624   CT
Web Site:
    http://www.whiteflowerfarm.com
Year Founded: 1950
Retailer & Catalog Sales of Perennials, Shrubs & Bulbs
N.A.I.C.S.: 444240
Cheryl Dunbar *(Mgr-Nursery Inventory & Mdsg)*
Ray Hinman *(Coord-Product Dev)*
Barbara Pierson *(Mgr-Nursery)*

WHITE GLOVE PLACEMENT INC.
630 Flushing Ave, Brooklyn, NY 11206
Tel.: (718) 387-8163
Web Site:
    http://www.whiteglovecare.com
Sales Range: $25-49.9 Million
Emp.: 500
Nursing Placement Agency
N.A.I.C.S.: 561311
Meir Lefkowitz *(Pres)*

WHITE GOLD COTTON MARKETING, LLC.
5555 Business Park S Ste 210, Bakersfield, CA 93309
Tel.: (661) 636-0280
Web Site: http://www.wgacotton.com
Sales Range: $10-24.9 Million
Emp.: 7
Cotton Farming Services
N.A.I.C.S.: 111920
Mark Costa *(CEO)*
Keith Jenkin *(Exec VP)*
David Weaver *(Mgr-Grower Rels)*
Yuleen Gifford *(VP-Traffic)*

WHITE GOOD & CO. ADVERTISING
226 N Arch St Ste 1, Lancaster, PA 17603
Tel.: (717) 396-0200
Web Site: http://www.whitegood.com
Year Founded: 1981
Sales Range: $10-24.9 Million
Emp.: 9
N.A.I.C.S.: 541810
Sherry H. Qualls *(Pres & CEO)*
N. Scott Qualls *(Principal-Adv)*
Rose Lantz *(CFO & Dir-HR)*
Jeanne Duvall *(Office Mgr)*
Jonathan Soucy *(Acct Dir)*
Danielle Floyd *(Account Exec-PR)*
Kelly Seipe *(Acct Exec)*
Amanda Eden *(Acct Mgr-PR)*

WHITE HORSE VILLAGE
535 Gradyville Rd, Newtown Square, PA 19073
Tel.: (610) 558-5000   PA
Web Site:
    http://www.whitehorsevillage.org
Year Founded: 1989
Sales Range: $25-49.9 Million
Emp.: 437
Continuing Care Retirement Community Operator
N.A.I.C.S.: 623311
Dorothy L. Mallon *(VP-Mktg)*
Mary Kathryn S. Burke *(Pres & CEO)*
Robert J. Higgins *(VP-Porperty)*
Anna May Grzeczkowski *(VP-Healthcare)*
Jennifer K. Schilpp *(VP-Fin)*

WHITE HOUSE CUSTOM COLOUR, INC.
2840 Lone Oak Pkwy, Eagan, MN 55121
Tel.: (651) 646-8263
Web Site: http://www.whcc.com
Year Founded: 1978
Rev.: $11,000,000
Emp.: 74
Printing Services for Professional Photographers
N.A.I.C.S.: 323111
Mike Hanline *(Co-Owner & CEO)*
Nick Palleon *(Engr-Network)*
Patrick Skallerud *(Mgr-Supply Chain)*
Tyler Yotter *(Mgr-Press Dept)*

WHITE HOUSE HISTORICAL ASSOCIATION
740 Jackson Pl NW, Washington, DC 20506
Tel.: (202) 737-8292
Web Site:
    http://www.whitehousehistory.org
Year Founded: 1961
Sales Range: $10-24.9 Million
Emp.: 100
Gifts & Educational Materials Related to the White House
N.A.I.C.S.: 513130
John F. W. Rogers *(Treas)*
Frederick J. Ryan Jr. *(Chm)*

WHITE KNIGHT BROADCASTING, INC.
700 Saint John St Ste 301, Lafayette, LA 70501
Tel.: (337) 237-9965   DE
Web Site:
    http://www.whiteknightbroadcasting.com
Holding Company; Television Broadcasting Stations Owner & Operator
N.A.I.C.S.: 551112
Sheldon H. Galloway *(VP)*
Jaime Quebedeaux *(Program Dir)*

WHITE KNIGHT LIMOUSINE INC.
7238 S Hwy 163, Columbia, MO 65203-8910
Tel.: (573) 875-2936
Web Site:
    http://www.gowhiteknight.com
Ambulance Service
N.A.I.C.S.: 621910
Ted Littell *(Pres)*

WHITE LOTUS HOME
431 Raritan Ave, Highland Park, NJ 08904
Tel.: (732) 828-2111
Web Site:
    http://www.whitelotushome.com
Year Founded: 1981
Emp.: 15
Chemical-Free Mattress & Furniture Mfr
N.A.I.C.S.: 337122
Marlon Pando *(Pres & Owner)*

WHITE MOUNTAIN IMAGING INC.
1617 Battle St, Concord, NH 03303-7319
Tel.: (603) 648-2124
Year Founded: 1981
Medical Equipment & Supplies
N.A.I.C.S.: 423450
Thomas Whitman *(CFO)*
Carrie Martin *(Coord-Digital Sls)*

WHITE OAK CORPORATION
7 W Main St, Plainville, CT 06062-1903
Tel.: (860) 747-1627   CT
Year Founded: 1969
Sales Range: $25-49.9 Million
Emp.: 180
Highway & Street Construction Services
N.A.I.C.S.: 237310
Roger L. Toffolon *(Pres & Treas)*

WHITE OAK GLOBAL ADVISORS, LLC
88 Kearny St 4th Fl, San Francisco, CA 94108
Tel.: (415) 644-4100
Web Site: http://www.whiteoaksf.com
Year Founded: 2007
Emp.: 70
Investment Services
N.A.I.C.S.: 523999
Andre A. Hakkak *(Co-Founder & CEO)*
Barbara J. S. McKee *(Co-Founder & Mng Partner)*
John H. Fitzpatrick *(Chm & Partner)*
Diane C. Altieri *(Dir-Ops)*
Dave Ray *(Gen Counsel & Chief Compliance Officer)*
Eric A. Snyder *(Chief Acctg Officer & Head-Fin)*
David C. Quon *(Mng Dir)*
Kenneth Wendler *(Chief Credit Officer & Partner)*
Stephen M. Metivier *(Mng Dir-White Oak Asset Finance, GP)*
Darius Mozaffarian *(Co-Pres)*
David Hackett *(Co-Pres)*
John Felix *(Head-Originations)*
Tom Finnigan *(Head-Underwriting)*
Susan George *(Head-Asset Mgmt)*
Subsidiaries:

Finacity Corporation (1)
281 Tresser Blvd 2 Stamford Plz 11th Fl, Stamford, CT 06901
Tel.: (203) 428-3500
Web Site: http://www.finacity.com
Secondary Market Financing
N.A.I.C.S.: 522299
Jeremy Blatt *(Mng Dir-Deal Structuring & Execution)*
Darren Davies *(Mng Dir-Originations)*
Adrian Katz *(Pres)*
Michael Rodgers *(COO & Exec VP)*
Jeffrey Gulbin *(CFO)*

WHITE OAK MILLS INC.
419 W High St, Elizabethtown, PA 17022-0419
Tel.: (717) 367-1525   PA
Web Site:
    http://www.whiteoakmills.com
Year Founded: 1976
Sales Range: $10-24.9 Million
Emp.: 69
Animal Feed
N.A.I.C.S.: 311119
Jenifer Hampshire *(Mgr-Sls & Mktg)*
Mark C. Wagner *(Pres)*
Mat Mountain *(Supvr-Maintenance)*

WHITE PLAINS HONDA
344 Central Ave, White Plains, NY 10606
Tel.: (914) 428-0880
Web Site:
    http://www.whiteplainshonda.com
Rev.: $18,800,000
Emp.: 12
New & Used Automobiles
N.A.I.C.S.: 441110
Cory Singer *(Owner)*
Walter Trusdell *(Mgr-Internet)*

WHITE RIVER AREA AGENCY ON AGING INC
3998 Harrison St, Batesville, AR 72503
Tel.: (870) 612-3000   AR
Web Site: http://www.wraaa.com
Year Founded: 1979
Sales Range: $10-24.9 Million
Emp.: 750
Senior Living Services
N.A.I.C.S.: 623311
Leigh Ann Chronister *(Dir-HR)*

WHITE RIVER HARDWOODS-WOODWORKS, INC.
1197 Happy Hollow Rd, Fayetteville, AR 72701
Tel.: (479) 442-6986
Web Site: http://www.whiteriver.com
Year Founded: 1979
Sales Range: $10-24.9 Million
Emp.: 50
Mfr of Traditional & Decorative Hardwood Millwork
N.A.I.C.S.: 321999
Richard Enrique *(Dir-Mktg)*
Bruce Johnson *(Founder)*
Gerry Wood *(VP-Cabinet Sls)*

WHITE RIVER VALLEY ELECTRIC COOP
2449 State Hwy 76 E, Branson, MO 65616
Tel.: (417) 335-9335
Web Site: http://www.whiteriver.org
Rev.: $36,819,983
Emp.: 150
Electronic Services
N.A.I.C.S.: 221118
Christopher L. Hamon *(CEO)*
Jeff Pardeck *(Mgr-Svcs)*
Rick Burkhart *(Mgr-Ops)*

WHITE ROCK PRODUCTS CORP.
14107 20th Ave Ste 403, Whitestone, NY 11357-3055
Tel.: (718) 746-3400   NY

WHITE ROCK PRODUCTS CORP.

U.S. PRIVATE

White Rock Products Corp.—(Continued)
Web Site:
http://www.whiterockbeverages.com
Year Founded: 1871
Sales Range: $75-99.9 Million
Emp.: 16
Mfr of Sparkling/Spring Water, Carbonated/Natural Teas & Flavored Beverages
N.A.I.C.S.: 424490
Lawrence Bodkin *(Pres)*

WHITE SHIELD, INC.
320 N 20th Ave, Pasco, WA 99301
Tel.: (509) 547-0100   **WA**
Web Site: http://www.whiteshield.com
Year Founded: 1978
Sales Range: $1-9.9 Million
Emp.: 62
Engineering Services Surveying Services
N.A.I.C.S.: 541620
Stuart W. Fricke *(Pres)*
Dale Schwartzenhauer *(Controller)*

WHITE SMILE GLOBAL, INC.
927 Lincoln Rd Ste 200, Miami, FL 33139-2618   **NV**
Web Site:
http://www.whitesmileglobal.com
Year Founded: 2008
Oral Health & Teeth Whitening Products Mfr
N.A.I.C.S.: 339114
Omar John Ahmadzai *(Pres, CEO, CFO, Treas & Sec)*
Martin S. Giniger *(Chief Scientific Officer & Dir-Scientific Res)*

WHITE WOLF CAPITAL LLC
501 Brickell Key Dr Ste 104, Miami, FL 33131
Tel.: (305) 605-8888
Web Site:
http://www.whitewolfcapital.com
Year Founded: 2011
Privater Equity Firm
N.A.I.C.S.: 523999
Corry Doyle *(Mng Dir & Head-Portfolio Ops)*
Elie Azar *(Founder, CEO & Chief Investment Officer)*
Blake Conner *(Mng Dir)*
Andres Gutierrez *(Mng Dir)*
Richard Leggio II *(Mng Dir)*

Subsidiaries:

Astro-Tek Industries Inc.   (1)
1198 N Kraemer Blvd, Anaheim, CA 92806-1916
Tel.: (714) 238-0022
Web Site: http://www.astro-tek.com
Personal & Household Goods Repair & Maintenance
N.A.I.C.S.: 811490

CSI IT, LLC   (1)
3421 Bannerman Rd Ste 200, Tallahassee, FL 32312
Tel.: (850) 205-2111
Web Site: http://www.csifl.com
Technology Consulting & Recruiting Services
N.A.I.C.S.: 541690

Subsidiary (Domestic):

JDC Group, LLC   (2)
980 Hammond Dr Ste 1250, Atlanta, GA 30328
Tel.: (404) 601-3210
Web Site: http://www.jdc-group.com
Sales Range: $10-24.9 Million
Emp.: 75
Human Resource Consulting Services
N.A.I.C.S.: 541612
Rhett Bingham *(Dir-Bus Dev)*
Greg Beyer *(Pres)*

Bill Flemming *(VP-Strategy & Solutions)*
Andrew Maher *(Sr Dir-Sls)*
Steve Tatum *(Dir-Tech, Recruiting & Inside Sls)*

Technical Resource Group, Inc.   (2)
5910 N Central Expwy Ste 780, Dallas, TX 75206
Tel.: (214) 245-8040
Web Site: http://www.dreamjob.com
IT Staffing & Consulting
N.A.I.C.S.: 541611
Ellerson Castille *(VP-ERP Services)*
Scott Clary *(CEO & Dir-Staffing Svcs)*
Kevin Morley *(Mgr-Tech Solutions & Mgr-Plano Office)*
Melissa Shook *(Mgr-VMS Staffing)*
Jason Tompkins *(Sr Mgr-Bus Dev)*

Consolidated Machine & Tool Holdings, LLC   (1)
601 Brickell Key Dr Ste 700, Miami, FL 33131
Tel.: (888) 317-9990
Web Site: http://www.cmth.com
Holding Company; Precision Turned Products Mfr
N.A.I.C.S.: 551112
Sean Lafferty *(CFO)*

Subsidiary (Domestic):

Delva Tool & Machine Corp.   (2)
1911 Rowland St, Cinnaminson, NJ 08077
Tel.: (856) 786-8700
Web Site: http://www.delvatool.com
Rev.: $7,682,000
Emp.: 46
Miscellaneous Fabricated Metal Product Mfr
N.A.I.C.S.: 332999
Stephen Voellinger *(Pres)*

DCCM, LLC   (1)
1800 Post Oak Blvd Ste 450, Houston, TX 77056
Tel.: (713) 874-9162
Web Site: https://www.dccm.com
Design, Consulting & Program & Construction Management Services
N.A.I.C.S.: 541618
James F. Thompson *(Chm & CEO)*
Jack Miller *(Pres)*

Subsidiary (Domestic):

Chastain-Skillman, Inc.   (2)
4705 Old Highway 37, Lakeland, FL 33813
Tel.: (863) 646-1402
Web Site: http://www.chastainskillman.com
Rev.: $7,064,500
Emp.: 70
Engineeering Services
N.A.I.C.S.: 541330
Keith S. Dodds *(Controller)*
James Chastain *(Principal)*
Jay Chastain *(Pres & CEO)*

Matthews Design Group, LLC   (2)
7 Waldo St, Saint Augustine, FL 32084
Tel.: (904) 826-1334
Web Site: http://www.matthewsdesign.net
Rev.: $1,100,000
Emp.: 15
Engineering Services
N.A.I.C.S.: 541330
Rob Matthews III *(Pres)*
Christina Griggs DeStephens *(Project Engr)*
Keri Matthews *(CEO)*

RQAW Corp.   (2)
4755 Kingsway Dr Ste 400, Indianapolis, IN 46205
Tel.: (317) 255-6060
Web Site: http://www.rqaw.com
Rev.: $7,000,000
Emp.: 70
Architectural Services
N.A.I.C.S.: 541310
Joseph M. Mrak *(Sr VP)*
Richard T. O'Connor *(Pres)*
Kevin Jasinski *(Dir-Major Projects & Sr Project Mgr)*
Randall Brooks *(Dir-Bridge Svcs)*
Lisa Casler *(Dir-Roadway Svcs)*
Joe Dabkowski *(Dir-Environmental Svcs)*
Eric Wathen *(Sr Dir-Ops & Fin)*

Fall Machine Company, LLC.   (1)
10 Willand Dr, Somersworth, NH 03878
Tel.: (603) 750-7100
Web Site: http://www.fallmachine.com

Cutting Tool & Machine Tool Accessory Mfr
N.A.I.C.S.: 333515

Pacific Power & Systems, Inc.   (1)
312 Railroad Ave Ste 206, Danville, CA 94526
Tel.: (925) 794-0005
Web Site: http://pacificpowersystem.com
Electrical & Specialty Services Contractor
N.A.I.C.S.: 238210
Wally Budgell *(Pres & CEO)*

Subsidiary (Domestic):

Adkins Electric, Inc.   (2)
10477 New Kings Rd, Jacksonville, FL 32219
Tel.: (904) 765-1622
Web Site: http://www.adkinselectric.com
Electrical Contractor
N.A.I.C.S.: 238210
Jim Holman *(VP)*

Putnam Mechanical, LLC   (1)
131 Crosslake Park Dr Ste 202, Mooresville, NC 28117-3503
Tel.: (704) 799-3665
Web Site:
http://www.putnammechanical.com
Electrical Contractor
N.A.I.C.S.: 238210
Renee Fortin *(Owner)*

WHITE'S ELECTRONICS
1011 Pleasant Valley Rd, Sweet Home, OR 97386-1034
Tel.: (541) 367-6121
Web Site:
http://www.whiteselectronics.com
Year Founded: 1950
Sales Range: $50-74.9 Million
Electronic Metal Detector & Equipment Mfr
N.A.I.C.S.: 334511
Melissa Wise *(Mgr-Mktg)*

Subsidiaries:

White's Electronics (UK) Ltd   (1)
35J Harbour Road, Inverness, IV1 1UA, United Kingdom
Tel.: (44) 1463 223456
Web Site: http://www.whites.co.uk
Metal Detector Mfr
N.A.I.C.S.: 334519

White's of Long Island, Inc.   (1)
240 Route 112, Patchogue, NY 11772
Tel.: (631) 447-7196
Web Site:
http://www.whitesoflongisland.com
Metal Detector Mfr
N.A.I.C.S.: 334519

WHITE'S INTERNATIONAL TRUCKS
1700 Hwy 301 S, Wilson, NC 27893
Tel.: (252) 291-0131   **NC**
Web Site:
http://www.whitestractor.com
Year Founded: 1922
Sales Range: $25-49.9 Million
Emp.: 186
Truck & Tractor Dealer
N.A.I.C.S.: 459999
D. Steve White *(CEO-Wilson)*
Edwin Ellis *(Gen Mgr)*
Michael V. Bullock *(Mgr-Goldsboro Branch)*
Sandra Pridgen *(Treas, Sec & Office Mgr-Wilson)*
Larry Davis *(Mgr-Body Shop-Wilson)*
William Carter Herring White *(Pres-Wilson)*

Subsidiaries:

White's International Trucks   (1)
7045 Albert Pick Rd, Greensboro, NC 27409-9654
Tel.: (336) 668-0491
Web Site: http://www.whitestractor.com
Rev.: $350,000
Emp.: 50
Automobiles & Other Motor Vehicle Distr

N.A.I.C.S.: 441110
Steve D. White *(CEO)*
Steven Kappus *(Dir-Parts-West Div)*
A. J. Cornman *(Mgr-Svc)*
Edwin Ellis *(Gen Mgr)*
Dell Medlin *(Mgr-Parts)*
Sandra Pridgen *(Treas, Sec & Office Mgr)*

WHITE'S MOUNTAIN MOTORS
2400 E Yellowstone Hwy, Casper, WY 82609
Tel.: (307) 237-2438
Web Site: http://www.whitesmountain chevy.com
Year Founded: 1998
Sales Range: $10-24.9 Million
Emp.: 52
Car Whslr
N.A.I.C.S.: 441110
Brad Follensbee *(Owner & Gen Mgr)*
Ron Bush *(Mgr-Svc)*

WHITE'S RESIDENTIAL & FAMILY SERVICES, INC.
5233 S 50 E, Wabash, IN 46992
Tel.: (260) 563-1158
Web Site: http://www.whiteskids.org
Year Founded: 1850
Emp.: 250
Foster Care, Adoption & Residential Treatment Services
N.A.I.C.S.: 624110
Dee Gibson *(CEO)*
Ron Evans *(Pres & CEO)*
Jacqueline Agee *(Co-Treas)*
Damon Seacott *(Sec)*
Kelly Stouffer *(Chm)*
Brandt Downing *(Co-Treas)*

Subsidiaries:

White's Residential & Family Services of Northwest Indiana   (1)
12501 N State Rd 49, Wheatfield, IN 46392
Tel.: (219) 956-3125
Web Site: http://www.whiteskids.org
Mental Health Treatment Services
N.A.I.C.S.: 623220

WHITE'S SITE DEVELOPMENT, INC.
4000 Nyah White Cove, Sanford, FL 32771
Tel.: (407) 302-1549
Web Site: http://www.whites-site.com
Sales Range: $10-24.9 Million
Emp.: 100
Civil Engineering Services
N.A.I.C.S.: 237310
Robert Wright *(Principal)*

WHITE-TUCKER COMPANY
13895 W Fair E Dr, Houston, TX 77041
Tel.: (281) 664-7444
Web Site: http://www.whitetucker.com
Rev.: $15,000,000
Emp.: 25
Filters, Industrial
N.A.I.C.S.: 424720
Lydia Cowey *(Pres)*

WHITE/THOMPSON, LLC
1808 Patterson St, Nashville, TN 37203
Tel.: (615) 321-1033   **TN**
Web Site:
http://www.whitethompson.com
Year Founded: 1983
Sales Range: $100-124.9 Million
Emp.: 13
Advertising Agencies, Automotive, Consulting, Consumer Marketing, Full Service, Health Care, Logo & Package Design, Strategic Planning/Research
N.A.I.C.S.: 541810

Sherri Jones (Sr VP & Dir-Client Svcs)
Evette White (CEO)
Stacy Gardner (Dir-Media)
Bryan Morse (Dir-Creative)
Nikki Butler (Dir-Art)
David Dasenbrock (Sr VP & Dir-Media)
Michael H. Thompson Jr. (Pres)

WHITEBIRCH ENTERPRISES, INC.
9252 Breezy Point Dr, Pequot Lakes, MN 56472
Tel.: (218) 562-4204   MN
Web Site: http://whitebirchresort.com
Sales Range: $10-24.9 Million
Emp.: 400
Holding Company; Resort Developer, Owner & Operator
N.A.I.C.S.: 551112
Robert Spizzo (Owner & CEO)
Joyce Bzoskie (Pres)

Subsidiaries:

Breezy Point International, Inc.   (1)
9252 Breezy Point Dr, Breezy Point, MN 56472
Tel.: (218) 562-7811
Web Site: http://www.breezypointresort.com
Land Subdividers & Developers
N.A.I.C.S.: 237210
Robert B. Spizzo (CEO)

Unit (Domestic):

Deacon's Lodge Golf Course   (2)
9348 Arnold Palmer Dr, Breezy Point, MN 56472
Tel.: (218) 562-6262
Web Site: http://www.breezypointresort.com
Sales Range: $10-24.9 Million
Emp.: 40
Golf Course Operator
N.A.I.C.S.: 713910

Whitebirch, Inc.
9252 Breezy Point Dr, Pequot Lakes, MN 56472
Tel.: (218) 562-4204
Web Site: http://www.whitebirchresort.com
Sales Range: $10-24.9 Million
Emp.: 150
Resort Hotel
N.A.I.C.S.: 721110
Robert Spizzo (CEO)

WHITEBOARD LABS LLC
3100 Richmond Ave Ste 550, Houston, TX 77098
Tel.: (713) 333-9944   TX
Emp.: 100
Application Software Development Services
N.A.I.C.S.: 541511

WHITEBOX ADVISORS, LLC
3033 Excelsior Blvd # 300, Minneapolis, MN 55416
Tel.: (612) 253-6025
Web Site: http://www.whiteboxadvisors.com
Year Founded: 1999
Sales Range: $10-24.9 Million
Emp.: 84
Investment Advisory & Management Services
N.A.I.C.S.: 523940
Andrew Redleas (Principal)

Subsidiaries:

Nalpropion Pharmaceuticals, Inc.   (1)
3344 N Torrey Pines Ct Ste 200, La Jolla, CA 92037
Tel.: (858) 875-8600
Web Site: http://www.nalpropion.com
Pharmaceuticals Mfr
N.A.I.C.S.: 325412
John Sedor (Chm & CEO)
Kenneth R. Pina (Exec VP)
Angus Smith (Exec VP)

Salma Jutt (Chief Comml Officer & Sr VP)
Amy Fox (VP-HR)
Amy Halseth (VP-Clinical Dev)
Kris Hanson (VP-Legal & Compliance)

WHITECLIFF CAPITAL PARTNERS, INC.
7400 Metro Blvd Ste 309, Edina, MN 55439
Tel.: (612) 373-2000
Web Site: http://www.whitecliff
Privater Equity Firm
N.A.I.C.S.: 523999
William Brown (Founder & Principal)

WHITECO INDUSTRIES INC.
1000 E 80th Pl Ste 700 N, Merrillville, IN 46410
Tel.: (219) 769-6601   IN
Year Founded: 1952
Sales Range: $75-99.9 Million
Emp.: 1,000
Outdoor Advertising Services
N.A.I.C.S.: 541850
John Peterman (Pres)
Ed Furgerson (Controller)

WHITED FORD TRUCK CENTER
207 Perry Rd, Bangor, ME 04401
Tel.: (207) 947-3673
Web Site: http://www.whitedford.com
Sales Range: $25-49.9 Million
Emp.: 80
Retailer of Trucks
N.A.I.C.S.: 423110
Pete Webb (Gen Mgr)
Mark Campbell (Mgr-Comml Accts)

WHITEFAB INC.
724 Avenue W, Birmingham, AL 35214
Tel.: (205) 791-2011
Web Site: http://www.whitefab.com
Rev.: $10,000,000
Emp.: 35
Plate, Steel
N.A.I.C.S.: 331110
Charles Wood (Pres)

WHITEFISH CREDIT UNION
300 Baker Ave, Whitefish, MT 59937-0037
Tel.: (406) 862-3525   MT
Web Site: http://www.whitefishcu.com
Year Founded: 1934
Sales Range: $25-49.9 Million
Emp.: 135
Credit Union
N.A.I.C.S.: 522130
Mike Blubaugh (CFO & Sr VP)
Paul Iversen (Sr VP-Consumer Lending)
Jim Kenyon (CEO)
Zoe Gustafson (Sr VP-Ops)
Char Rygg (Treas & Sec)
Lyle Phillips (Chm)
Tom Cullen (Vice Chm)
Steven Moss (Chief Credit Officer)
Jennifer Archer (VP-Credit Admin)
Allison Deaver (VP-HR)
Brett Merkel (VP & Controller)
Barb Pearson (VP)
Colleen Murphy (Sr VP-Ops)
Stephen W. Haugen (CIO & Sr VP)

WHITEGLOVE HOUSE CALL HEALTH, INC.
1601 S Mopac Expy Ste 450, Austin, TX 78746
Tel.: (512) 329-9223   TX
Web Site: http://www.whiteglove.com
Year Founded: 2006
Sales Range: $1-9.9 Million
Emp.: 77
Medical Care Services

N.A.I.C.S.: 621399
Michael Grabert (VP-Software Dev & IT)

WHITEHALL PRODUCTS, INC.
4514 S Church Ave, Tampa, FL 33611
Tel.: (813) 247-2500   FL
Web Site: http://www.whitehall-products.com
Year Founded: 1992
Sales Range: $25-49.9 Million
Emp.: 12
Can Liners, Paper, Gloves, Specialty Bags, Molded Products, Plastic Cutlery, Soap, Chemicals & Specialty Packaging Wholesale Distr
N.A.I.C.S.: 425120
Joseph S. Justin (CEO)
Mike Russo (Pres)
Mark Justin (VP)

WHITEHEAD OIL CO., INC.
2537 Randolph St, Lincoln, NE 68510-3041
Tel.: (402) 435-3509   NE
Web Site: http://www.u-stop.com
Year Founded: 1959
Emp.: 125
Petroleum Bulk Stations & Terminals
N.A.I.C.S.: 457120
Todd Burgason (Controller)

Subsidiaries:

Whitehead Oil Co., Inc.   (1)
2537 Randolph St, Lincoln, NE 68510
Tel.: (402) 467-4344
Web Site: http://www.u-stop.com
Sales Range: $25-49.9 Million
Emp.: 18
Grocery Stores
N.A.I.C.S.: 445131

WHITEMAN CHEVROLET, INC.
79-89 Dix Ave, Glens Falls, NY 12801
Tel.: (518) 792-2196
Web Site: http://www.whitemanchevrolet.com
Year Founded: 1956
Sales Range: $10-24.9 Million
Emp.: 53
Car Whslr
N.A.I.C.S.: 441110
Amy W. Brown (Exec VP)

WHITEMYER ADVERTISING, INC.
254 E 4th St, Zoar, OH 44697
Tel.: (330) 874-2432   OH
Web Site: http://www.whitemyer.com
Year Founded: 1971
Sales Range: $25-49.9 Million
Emp.: 14
Full Service
N.A.I.C.S.: 541810
Lisa Geers (VP-Media & Res)
Tom Simmelink (Pres)
Tim Whitemyer (Exec VP)

Subsidiaries:

Zoar Interactive   (1)
254 E 4th St, Zoar, OH 44697
Tel.: (330) 874-0813
Sales Range: $10-24.9 Million
N.A.I.C.S.: 541810
Tim Whitemeyer (Pres)
Lisa Geers (VP & Gen Mgr)

WHITEOAK GROUP
23 S Harrison St, Easton, MD 21601
Tel.: (410) 690-3511
Web Site: http://www.whiteoak-group.com
Year Founded: 2007
Sales Range: $1-9.9 Million
Emp.: 19

Engineeering Services
N.A.I.C.S.: 541330
Daryl D. Dixon (Founder & CEO)
Doug Keeton (COO)

WHITEPAGES.COM INC.
1301 5th Ave Ste 1600, Seattle, WA 98101
Tel.: (206) 973-5100
Web Site: http://www.whitepagesinc.com
Sales Range: $10-24.9 Million
Emp.: 100
Online Directory Services
N.A.I.C.S.: 513140
Alex Algard (Founder & Chm)
Suki Hayre (VP-Fin & Admin)
Jason Eglit (CFO)
Kelly Schmitt (Chief Privacy Officer & Gen Counsel)
Geoffrey Arone (Exec VP-Product Dev)
Rob Eleveld (CEO)
Leigh McMillan (VP-Consumer Mktg)
Heather Glenn Wade (VP-Engrg)

WHITERIVER CONSTRUCTION, INC.
5805 Wagon Wheel Ln, Lakeside, AZ 85929-5131
Tel.: (928) 537-2920   AZ
Web Site: http://www.whiteriverconstruction.com
Year Founded: 1994
Sales Range: $10-24.9 Million
Emp.: 25
Public Works Construction
N.A.I.C.S.: 236220
Jason Carter (VP)

WHITES FARM SUPPLY INC.
4154 State Rte 31, Canastota, NY 13032
Tel.: (315) 697-2214
Web Site: http://www.whitesfarmsupply.com
Sales Range: $10-24.9 Million
Emp.: 66
Distribute Farm Equipment & Supplies
N.A.I.C.S.: 459999
Dale White (Pres, CEO & VP)
Arthur White (VP)

WHITES KINGCO INC.
858 E Hwy 54, Kingman, KS 67068
Tel.: (620) 532-3851
Sales Range: $25-49.9 Million
Emp.: 60
Grocery Stores
N.A.I.C.S.: 445110
Joe Patrick White (Pres)

WHITES LUMBER INC.
231 N Rutland St, Watertown, NY 13601
Tel.: (315) 788-6200
Web Site: http://www.whiteslumber.com
Rev.: $16,000,000
Emp.: 55
Home Center Operator
N.A.I.C.S.: 444110
Roger White (Co-Pres)
Brad White (Co-Pres)

WHITES TIRE SERVICE OF WILSON
701 Hines St S, Wilson, NC 27893
Tel.: (252) 237-5426
Web Site: http://www.whitestireservice.net
Rev.: $13,271,071
Emp.: 137
Automotive Tire Sales & Retreading
N.A.I.C.S.: 441340

Whites Tire Service of Wilson—(Continued)
Sandra White (Office Mgr)
Bobby White (VP)
James E. White Sr. (Chm & CEO)

WHITESBURG ARH HOSPITAL
240 Hospital Rd, Whitesburg, KY 41858-7627
Tel.: (606) 633-3500
Web Site: http://www.arh.org
Sales Range: $25-49.9 Million
Emp.: 4
Pharmaceutical Product Whslr
N.A.I.C.S.: 424210
Dena Sparkman (CEO)

WHITESELL CONSTRUCTION INC.
1 Underwood Ct Ste 2, Delran, NJ 08075
Tel.: (856) 764-2600
Web Site: http://www.whitesellco.com
Sales Range: $10-24.9 Million
Emp.: 80
Industrial Buildings & Warehouses
N.A.I.C.S.: 236220
Thomas R. Whitesell (Chm)
Loraine Tiberi (Controller)
Thomas J. Heitzman (Pres)

WHITESELL CORPORATION
2703 E Avalon Ave, Muscle Shoals, AL 35662
Tel.: (256) 248-8500   AL
Web Site:
  http://www.whitesellgroup.com
Year Founded: 1971
Sales Range: $100-124.9 Million
Emp.: 600
Metal Fasteners, Fastening Systems & Cold-Formed Steel Products Mfr
N.A.I.C.S.: 332722
Neil L. Whitesell (Chm & CEO)
Judy Frazier (Mgr-HR)

Subsidiaries:

Whitesell International
Corporation   (1)
5331 Dixie Hwy, Waterford, MI 48329
Tel.: (313) 299-8500
Web Site: http://www.fabristeel.com
Holding Company; Cold-Rolled Steel & Steel Fastener Products Mfr
N.A.I.C.S.: 551112
Neil L. Whitesell (Chm & CEO)

Division (Domestic):

FabriSteel Products   (2)
22100 Trolley Industrial Dr, Taylor, MI 48180-1872   (100%)
Tel.: (313) 299-1178
Web Site: http://www.fabristeel.com
Sales Range: $75-99.9 Million
Emp.: 150
Steel Fasteners & Fastener Installation Equipment Mfr
N.A.I.C.S.: 332722

Plant (Domestic):

Profile Steel & Wire   (3)
22100 Trolley Industrial Dr, Taylor, MI 48180-1872
Tel.: (313) 299-7880
Sales Range: $25-49.9 Million
Emp.: 50
Cold-Rolled Steel Products Mfr
N.A.I.C.S.: 331221

Whitesell Wire Form Unit   (1)
915 E Tyler St, Washington, IA 52353-0486
Tel.: (319) 653-2168
Sales Range: $10-24.9 Million
Emp.: 100
Fabricated Rod & Wire Products Mfr
N.A.I.C.S.: 332618
Kelly Slack (Gen Mgr)

WHITESPACE CREATIVE
24 N High St Ste 200, Akron, OH 44308
Tel.: (330) 762-9320
Web Site: http://www.whitespace-creative.com
Year Founded: 1994
Rev.: $2,500,000
Emp.: 30
Fiscal Year-end: 12/31/05
N.A.I.C.S.: 541810
Keeven White (Founder)
Greg Kiskadden (VP)
Jennifer Snider (Assoc Dir-Creative & Copywriter)

WHITESPACE DESIGN GROUP, INC.
243 Furnace St, Akron, OH 44304
Tel.: (330) 762-9320
Web Site: http://www.whitespace-creative.com
Year Founded: 1995
Emp.: 40
Advertising Agency & Marketing Services
N.A.I.C.S.: 541810
Greg Kiskadden (Exec VP)
Keeven White (Pres & CEO)
Jen Snider (VP-Talent Dev)
Sharon Griffiths (Art Dir & Project Mgr)
Susan Breen (Assoc Dir-Creative)
Sean Mooney (Assoc Dir-Interactive Dev)
Bob Zajac (Exec VP)

WHITESPEED
29672 Zuma Bay Way, Malibu, CA 90265
Tel.: (310) 869-9979
Web Site:
  http://www.whitespeed.com
Sales Range: $10-24.9 Million
Emp.: 12
N.A.I.C.S.: 541810
Susan White (Founder & CEO)

WHITESTONE COMMUNICATIONS, INC.
51 E 42nd St 11th Fl, New York, NY 10017
Tel.: (212) 672-0077
Web Site:
  http://www.whitestonecommunications.com
Sales Range: $10-24.9 Million
Investment & Advisory Services
N.A.I.C.S.: 523999
Baran Rosen (Pres)
Edward H. Fitzelle (Mng Dir)
Ronald A. Hoxter (Mng Dir)
Susan Isserman (Mng Dir)

WHITEWATER EXPRESS, INC.
1549 Clairmont Rd, Decatur, GA 30033
Tel.: (404) 325-5295
Web Site:
  http://www.whitewaterexpress.com
Rev.: $2,000,000
Emp.: 60
All Other Amusement & Recreation Industries
N.A.I.C.S.: 713990
Dan Gilbert (Pres)

Subsidiaries:

Jerry's Express Carwash   (1)
8301 N Beach St, Keller, TX 76244-4975
Tel.: (817) 431-3220
Web Site:
  http://www.jerrysexpresscarwash.com
Car Washes
N.A.I.C.S.: 811192
Jeremy Cox (Mgr)

WHITEWATER HOLDING COMPANY, LLC
16412 N Eldridge, Tomball, TX 77377
Tel.: (346) 367-2500
Web Site:
  http://www.whitewatercw.com
Car Wash Services
N.A.I.C.S.: 811192
Steve Mathis (CEO)
Clayton Clar (Pres & COO)
Ronnie Corbin (Pres-Dev)

Subsidiaries:

Rev Car Wash, LLC   (1)
5005 Lyndon B Johnson Freeway 840, Dallas, TX 75244
Tel.: (281) 858-8383
Web Site: http://www.revcarwash.com
Car Washes
N.A.I.C.S.: 811192
Brett Sheldon (CEO)

WHITEWATER OUTDOORS INCORPORATED
W 4228 Church Rd, Hingham, WI 53031
Tel.: (920) 564-2674
Web Site:
  http://www.robinsonoutdoors.com
Sales Range: $10-24.9 Million
Emp.: 10
Men's & Boy's Clothing
N.A.I.C.S.: 424350
Scott Schultz (Pres)

WHITEWATER WHIRLPOOL BATHS SYSTEMS
195 S Geneva Rd, Lindon, UT 84042
Tel.: (801) 785-3554
Sales Range: $10-24.9 Million
Emp.: 50
Whirlpool Baths
N.A.I.C.S.: 459999
Kirk Williamson (Pres)

WHITEWOOD INDUSTRIES, INC.
100 Liberty Dr, Thomasville, NC 27360
Tel.: (336) 472-0303
Web Site: http://www.whitewood.net
Year Founded: 1982
Sales Range: $50-74.9 Million
Emp.: 170
Wood Household Furniture Mfr
N.A.I.C.S.: 337122
Jorge Mata (Pres)
Robert Lamar (VP)
Dolly Cormer (Controller)

WHITFIELD FOODS, INC.
1101 N Court St, Montgomery, AL 36104
Tel.: (334) 263-2541   AL
Web Site:
  http://www.whitfieldfoods.com
Year Founded: 1906
Sales Range: $100-124.9 Million
Emp.: 150
Juice, Syrup & Sauce Mfr & Distr
N.A.I.C.S.: 311999
Les Massey (Pres & CEO)
Joe Friday (VP-Ops)

WHITFIELD TIMBER INC.
PO Box 674, Wewahitchka, FL 32465
Tel.: (850) 639-5556
Sales Range: $25-49.9 Million
Emp.: 38
Pulpwood Contractors Engaged In Cutting
N.A.I.C.S.: 113310
Theodore L. Whitfield (Pres)

WHITING DOOR MANUFACTURING CORP.
113 Cedar St, Akron, NY 14001
Tel.: (716) 542-5427
Web Site:
  http://www.whitingdoor.com
Rev.: $25,500,000
Emp.: 300
Lessors Nonresidential Buildings
N.A.I.C.S.: 531120
Bob Finnigan (Mgr)
Donald Whiting (Pres)
Ray Hackett (Mgr-Sls)
Michael Whiting (VP)
Joe Dry (Product Mgr)

WHITING MANUFACTURING CO., INC.
6975 Dixie Hwy, Fairfield, OH 45014-5431
Tel.: (513) 874-8750
Rev.: $30,000,000
Emp.: 400
Mfr of Comforters, Draperies, Bed Pillows, Bed Ruffles & Pillow Shams
N.A.I.C.S.: 314120
Jerry Momper (VP-Natl Sls)
Terry Edgington (Traffic Mgr)

WHITLAM GROUP, INC.
24800 Sherwood Ave, Center Line, MI 48015
Tel.: (586) 757-5100   MI
Web Site: http://www.whitlam.com
Year Founded: 1957
Emp.: 120
Flexographic Printing, Labeling & Packaging Solutions
N.A.I.C.S.: 323111
Richard J. Shaieb (CEO)
Payman Mahjoory (Pres)
Jay Terranella (Sls Dir)
Jim Dobiesz (Product Mgr-Plng & Mgr-Engr Pre-Press)
Marie Shaieb (Mgr-HR)
Michelle Shaieb (Mktg Mgr)
Don Clifford (CFO)

WHITLEY MANUFACTURING COMPANY, INC.
201 W 1st St, South Whitley, IN 46787
Tel.: (260) 723-5131
Web Site: http://www.whitleyman.com
Year Founded: 1945
Sales Range: $10-24.9 Million
Emp.: 150
Commercial & Institutional Building Construction Services
N.A.I.C.S.: 236220
Simon Dragan (Pres)
Mike Ransbottom (VP-Ops)
Bob Jones (VP-Fin)
Drew Welborn (VP)

WHITLEY PENN LLP
640 Taylor St Ste 2200, Fort Worth, TX 76102
Tel.: (817) 259-9100   TX
Web Site:
  http://www.whitleypenn.com
Year Founded: 1983
Sales Range: $50-74.9 Million
Emp.: 200
Accounting & Auditing Services
N.A.I.C.S.: 541211
Leslie Wilks (Sr Mgr-Audit)
Jeff Edwards (Partner-Audit)
Thomas Stewart (Partner-Forensic, Litigation & Valuation)
Terry Cosand (Partner-Audit)
Christy Cates (Partner-Tax)
Daniel A. Boarder (Partner-Transaction Advisory Svcs)
Elizabeth Pettijohn (Partner)
Dan Manley (Dir-State & Local Tax)
Leslie Haines (Sr Mgr-Tax)
Brian Mitchell (Partner-Tax-Intl)
Mary Gauss (Sr Mgr-Tax)

Anne Slattery *(Sr Mgr-Risk Advisory Svcs)*
Beth Engelhardt *(Partner-Tax)*
Chris Grasher *(Partner-Tax)*
Christopher Breaux *(Partner-Audit)*
Griff Babb *(Partner-Audit)*
Lydia Cook *(Partner-Tax)*
Mark DeSimone *(Partner-Tax)*
Mel Henkes *(Partner-Tax)*
Michael Bodwell *(Partner-Audit)*
Toby Cotton *(Partner-Tax)*
Dallas Packer *(Dir-State & Local Tax)*
Cole Elliott *(Mgr-Tax)*
Josh Livingston *(Mgr-Tax)*
Jim Martin *(Mgr-Audit)*
Paul Morris *(Mgr-Audit)*
Mike Nabors *(Partner-Audit)*
Larry Nichols *(Partner-Audit)*
Brendan O'Connor *(Mgr-Tax)*
John Wagner *(Partner-Tax)*
Keleigh Wentworth *(Mgr-Tax)*
Greg LeBlanc *(Sr Mgr-Tax)*
Trey Cook *(Sr Mgr-Tax)*
JoAnne Midwikis *(Partner-Tax)*
Tom Granger *(Partner-Tax)*
Gary Scarborough *(Partner-Tax)*
Justin Blok *(Mng Dir)*
Walter Bratic *(Mng Dir)*
Carmen Eggleston *(Mng Dir)*
Carre Hanner *(Principal-Tax)*
Elizabeth Iles *(Principal-Tax)*
Melinda Jones *(Principal-Tax)*
James F. Reeves *(COO)*
Clint Crane *(Partner)*
Camron Harris *(Partner)*
Brett Murphy *(Partner)*
Justin Roberts *(Partner)*
Robert Metz *(Partner)*
Ashley Kimery *(Partner-Tax)*
Nick Wells *(Partner-Audit)*
Brandi Fletcher *(Partner-Tax)*
Mark Duffy *(Partner-Tax)*
Kyle Willey *(Partner-Audit)*

Subsidiaries:

Fisher Herbst & Kemble, PC (1)
9501 Console Dr Ste 200, San Antonio, TX 78229
Tel.: (210) 614-2284
Web Site: http://www.fhkcpa.com
Sales Range: $1-9.9 Million
Emp.: 23
Accounting/Auditing/Bookkeeping
N.A.I.C.S.: 541219

WHITLOCK HOLDING COMPANY
Warren Pl 2 Ste 1250, Tulsa, OK 74136
Tel.: (918) 478-7096
Sales Range: $10-24.9 Million
Emp.: 300
Fruit & Vegetable Canning Services
N.A.I.C.S.: 311421
Ted Smith *(VP-HR)*
David Moller *(VP-Bus Dev)*

WHITMAN CASTINGS, INC.
40 Raynor Ave, Whitman, MA 02382
Tel.: (781) 447-4417
Web Site: http://www.whitmancastings.com
Sales Range: $25-49.9 Million
Emp.: 25
Ductile & Gray Iron Castings Mfr
N.A.I.C.S.: 331511
Brian Ladner *(Pres)*

WHITMAN-WALKER CLINIC, INC.
1701 14th St NW, Washington, DC 20009
Tel.: (202) 745-7000   DC
Web Site: http://www.whitman-walker.org
Year Founded: 1978
Sales Range: $10-24.9 Million
Emp.: 168
Primary Health Care Services
N.A.I.C.S.: 622110
Raymond C. Martins *(Sr Dir-Clinical Education & Trng)*
Naseema Shafi *(Deputy Exec Dir)*
Daniel Bruner *(Sr Dir-Policy)*
Chris Holleman *(CFO)*
Mark Edward *(Treas)*
Winifred Quinn *(Sec)*
Don Blanchon *(Exec Dir)*
Harry Fox *(Chm)*
Sandy James *(Vice Chm)*
Abby Paige Fenton *(Chief External Affairs Officer)*
Abbie Gibbs *(Chief Dev Officer)*

WHITMOR, INC.
8680 Swinnea Rd Ste 103, Southaven, MS 38671
Tel.: (662) 393-1489   DE
Web Site: http://www.whitmor.com
Year Founded: 1961
Sales Range: $150-199.9 Million
Emp.: 210
Home Organization, Storage, Laundry & Garment Care Products Designer, Mfr & Distr
N.A.I.C.S.: 332618
Peter Felsenthal *(CEO)*
James M. Felsenthal *(Sr VP-Ops)*
Sandy A. Felsenthal *(Pres)*
James Young *(Sr VP-Ops)*
Scott W. Felsenthal *(Exec VP)*
Donna Macri *(CFO)*

WHITMOR/WIRENETICS
27737 Ave Hopkins, Valencia, CA 91355
Tel.: (661) 257-2400
Web Site: http://www.wireandcable.com
Year Founded: 1959
Sales Range: $1-9.9 Million
Emp.: 100
Custom Cable Mfr & Distr
N.A.I.C.S.: 332618
Michael Weiss *(Pres)*
Mark Lee *(VP-Sls)*
Jeff Seibert *(VP-Mfg)*
Dwight Van Lake *(Dir-Mktg)*
Stella Reaza *(Mgr-Quality Assurance)*

WHITNEY & CO., LLC
130 Main St, New Canaan, CT 06840
Tel.: (203) 716-6100
Web Site: http://www.whitney.com
Year Founded: 1946
Rev.: $10,000,000
Emp.: 18
Private Equity Firm & Investment Services
N.A.I.C.S.: 523150

WHITNEY BLAKE CO., INC.
20 Indus Dr, Bellows Falls, VT 05101-3122
Tel.: (802) 463-9558   VT
Web Site: http://www.whitneyblake.com
Year Founded: 1985
Sales Range: $50-74.9 Million
Emp.: 75
Mfr of Rubber & Plastic Insulated Retractile Cords & Communications Cables
N.A.I.C.S.: 335931
Sheldon Scott *(Pres)*
Hardy Merrill *(VP-Fin & Admin)*

WHITNEY INSURANCE AGENCY, INC.
721 W KingsMill Ave, Pampa, TX 79065
Tel.: (806) 662-5995   TX
Web Site: http://www.whitneyins.com
Insurance Agents
N.A.I.C.S.: 524210
Donald R. Whitney *(Principal)*

WHITNEY M. YOUNG, JR. HEALTH CENTER
920 Lark Dr, Albany, NY 12207
Tel.: (518) 465-4771   NY
Web Site: http://www.wmyhealth.org
Year Founded: 1974
Sales Range: $10-24.9 Million
Emp.: 245
Health Care Srvcs
N.A.I.C.S.: 622110
Maureen Yee *(Dir-Dev)*
Mary Connolly *(CFO)*
Gail Waring *(Chm)*
Carol Hausamann *(Treas)*
Janice Prichett *(Chief Behavior Health Officer)*
David Skory *(Assoc Dir-Medical-Women's Health & Clinical Quality)*
Theodore Zeltner *(Chief Medical Officer)*
Michael McGuire *(CIO)*
Jill Broderick *(Coord-HIV Care)*
Amanda Duff *(Dir-Community Based Programs)*
Gina Picarillo *(Dir-Nursing)*
Marlowe Cochran *(Sec)*
Antoine Harrison *(Vice Chm)*
Maureen Krone *(Officer-Corp Compliance & Asst VP-Total Quality Mgmt)*

WHITNEY PARTNERS INC.
747 3rd Ave, New York, NY 10017
Tel.: (212) 508-3500
Web Site: http://www.whitneypartners.net
Year Founded: 1992
Sales Range: $1-9.9 Million
Emp.: 12
Provider of Employment Agency Services
N.A.I.C.S.: 541612
Gary Goldstein *(Pres)*

WHITNEY'S VALUE FORD
620 Schouweiler Trats Rd E, Elma, WA 98541
Tel.: (360) 482-2241
Web Site: http://www.valueford.com
Sales Range: $10-24.9 Million
Emp.: 15
Automobiles, New & Used
N.A.I.C.S.: 441110
Kevin Pinson *(Owner)*
Sharon Daniels *(Comptroller)*

WHITSON - MORGAN MOTOR COMPANY
1300 S Rogers St, Clarksville, AR 72830
Tel.: (479) 754-3020
Web Site: http://www.whitsonmorgan.com
Sales Range: $10-24.9 Million
Emp.: 45
Car Whslr
N.A.I.C.S.: 441110
Michael Dickerson *(Owner)*
Julie Dickerson *(Principal)*
Patrick Haberer *(Gen Mgr)*

WHITSONS FOOD SERVICE CORP.
1800 Motor Pkwy, Islandia, NY 11749-5216
Tel.: (631) 424-2700
Web Site: http://www.whitsons.com
Year Founded: 1979
Contract Food Services
N.A.I.C.S.: 722310
Robert E. Whitcomb *(Co-Founder & Chief Innovation Officer-Prepared Meals)*
Douglas Whitcomb *(Pres & Chief Product Officer)*
Beth Bunster *(CFO)*
Paul Whitcomb *(Pres & CEO)*
John Whitcomb *(Chief Innovation Officer-Contract Mgmt)*
Michael Whitcomb *(VP-Customer Rels)*
William Whitcom *(Dir-Fleet Svcs)*
Kellyann Friend *(COO-Contract Management)*
S. Chris Fautas *(Sr VP-Ops)*
John Gersbeck *(Sr VP)*
Craig Whitcomb *(VP-Regional)*
John Prunier *(Mgr-District)*
Rick Emery *(Mgr-District)*
Joseph Armenti *(Mgr-District)*
Scott Berry *(Mgr-District)*
Christine Kunnmann *(Mgr-District)*
Mark Kirn *(Mgr-District)*
Corinne P. Kevorkian *(Sr VP-Admin & Gen Counsel)*
Karen Scott *(VP-Fin)*
Lou Sollicito *(VP-HR)*
Michael Marinaro *(Dir-Pur)*
Erin Norton *(Dir-Recruiting)*
Karen Dittrich *(Dir-Mktg)*
Brenna Schettino *(Dir-Workplace Safety)*
Karen Gersbeck *(Bus Partner-HR-New England Region)*
Ozzie Orsillo *(Sr VP)*
David DeScenza *(VP-Regional-Bus Dev)*
Jeanine Walshon *(Dir-Bus Dev)*
Bill Whitcomb Jr. *(Auditor)*

WHITTENBERG CONSTRUCTION CO.
4774 Allmond Ave, Louisville, KY 40209-1405
Tel.: (502) 361-8891   KY
Web Site: http://www.wccbuild.com
Year Founded: 1924
Sales Range: $25-49.9 Million
Emp.: 100
Provider of Contracting Services
N.A.I.C.S.: 236220
Pat Noonan *(Pres)*
Andrew Mays *(Exec VP)*
Jack Mull *(VP)*
Stephen Roth *(Mgr-Safety)*

WHITTIER TRUST COMPANY
1600 Huntington Dr, South Pasadena, CA 91030
Tel.: (626) 441-5111   CA
Web Site: http://www.whittiertrust.com
Emp.: 80
Investment & Wealth Management Services
N.A.I.C.S.: 523940
Michael J. Casey *(Chm)*
Steven A. Anderson *(Mng Dir & Gen Counsel)*
Rebecca M. Duguid *(Sr VP)*
Greg E. Custer *(Exec VP & Mgr-Admin-South Pasadena)*
Kathleen A. Briley *(Sr VP)*
Lisa K. Edwards *(Sr VP)*
Caleb Silsby *(Sr Portfolio Mgr)*
Liam J. McGuinness *(CFO)*
Robert W. Renken *(Sr VP & Deputy Gen Counsel)*
Sandip A. Bhagat *(Chief Investment Officer)*
Eric B. Derrington *(Sr VP & Sr Portfolio Mgr)*
Bryce Coats *(VP & Portfolio Mgr)*
Peter J. Zarifes *(Mng Dir & Dir-Wealth Mgmt)*
Tom J. Doud *(Sr VP)*

WHITTIER TRUST COMPANY

Whittier Trust Company—(Continued)
Brian H. Flynn (Sr VP-Bus Dev)
Pegine E. Grayson (Sr VP-Philanthropic Svcs)
Sean C. Kraus (Sr VP & Portfolio Mgr)
Julie Lytle Nesbit (Exec VP & Exec Dir-Philanthropic Svcs)
Carl P. Pierleoni (Chief Compliance Officer, Chief Risk Officer & Sr VP)
Gus Sanchez (Sr VP-HR)
Teague Sanders (Sr VP & Portfolio Mgr)
Andre B. van Niekerk (Sr VP-Bus Dev)
Charles Adams III (Sr VP-Real Estate)
Thomas J. Frank Jr. (Exec VP & Reg Mgr-Northern California)
David G. Covell Jr. (Sr VP)

Subsidiaries:

The Whittier Trust Company of Nevada, Inc. (1)
100 W Liberty St Ste 890, Reno, NV 89501
Tel.: (775) 886-5400
Web Site: http://www.whittier.com
Rev.: $5,500,000,000
Emp.: 100
Investment & Wealth Management Services
N.A.I.C.S.: 523940
Michael J. Casey (Chm & CEO)
William E. Ramsey (Pres & Mng Dir)
Harold J. Depoali (Sr VP & Mgr-Client Advisor)
Deborah L. Wetzel (Exec VP & Mgr-Client Advisor)
Dean R. Byrne (Sr VP & Sr Portfolio Mgr)
Robert L. Levy (Sr VP & Sr Portfolio Mgr)
Marie R. Dawson (VP & Client Advisor)
Daylene G. Hendricks (VP & Client Advisor)
Ronald R. Zideck (VP-Bus Dev)

WHITTIER WOOD PRODUCTS CO.

3787 W 1st Ave, Eugene, OR 97402
Tel.: (541) 687-0213
Web Site: http://www.whittierwood.com
Sales Range: $25-49.9 Million
Emp.: 500
Unassembled Or Unfinished Furniture, Household: Wood
N.A.I.C.S.: 337122
Scott Whittier (Pres)
Leigh Raaen (Mgr-Customer Svc)

WHITTLESEY & HADLEY, P.C.

280 Trumbull St 24th Fl, Hartford, CT 06103-3509
Tel.: (860) 522-3111 CT
Web Site: http://www.wadvising.com
Year Founded: 1961
Accounting, Auditing, Tax Preparation & Consulting Services
N.A.I.C.S.: 541211
Andrew G. Andrews (Mng Partner)
Robert S. Pelletier (Partner-Hartford)
Mario L. Solari (Partner-Holyoke, Hamden & Hartford)
Stephen A. Toross (Partner-Hartford)
Nicholas Yanouzas (Partner-Hartford & Hamden)
Lisa Wills (Partner)

Subsidiaries:

Whittlesey & Hadley, P.C. - Hamden Office (1)
2319 Whitney Ave Ste 2A, Hamden, CT 06518
Tel.: (203) 397-2525
Web Site: http://www.whcpa.com
Sales Range: $1-9.9 Million
Accounting, Auditing, Tax Preparation & Consulting Services
N.A.I.C.S.: 541211
Roger J. Sciascia (Partner & Head-Hamden Office)
Vincenzo Fini (Partner-Acctg & Auditing)

Michael J. Pyne (Partner-Tax)
Kevin F. LaChapelle (Partner-Acctg & Auditing)
Julia Agvent (Mktg Dir)

Whittlesey & Hadley, P.C. - Holyoke Office (1)
14 Bobala Rd, Holyoke, MA 01040-9402
Tel.: (413) 536-3970
Web Site: http://www.whcpa.com
Emp.: 20
Accounting, Tax Preparation & Consulting Services
N.A.I.C.S.: 541211
Betty Jane Bourdon (Partner)
Mary-Anne S. Stearns (Partner)
Thomas A. Terry (Partner)

WHOLE EARTH PROVISION COMPANY

1010 W 11th St, Austin, TX 78703
Tel.: (512) 476-4811
Web Site: http://www.wholeearthprovision.com
Year Founded: 1970
Sales Range: $250-299.9 Million
Emp.: 160
Retailer of Travel & Camping Sports Apparel
N.A.I.C.S.: 458110
Walter Wakefield (VP)
Linda Jones (Treas)
Joe Jones (VP)
Jack B. Jones Jr. (Pres)

WHOLE LIFE, INC

28 Haughton Rd, Bozrah, CT 06334
Tel.: (860) 886-6900 CT
Web Site: http://www.wholelifeinc.org
Year Founded: 1987
Sales Range: $10-24.9 Million
Emp.: 341
Developmentally Disabled People Housing Services
N.A.I.C.S.: 623210
Erich Audretsch (Pres)
Jack Malone (Sec)
Maria Delgreco (Dir-Fin)
Sheila Cordock (Exec Dir)

WHOLE WHEAT CREATIVE

1006 W Nineth St, Houston, TX 77007
Tel.: (713) 993-9339
Web Site: http://www.wholewheatcreative.com
Year Founded: 1996
Sales Range: $10-24.9 Million
Emp.: 12
Advertising Agencies
N.A.I.C.S.: 541810
Lee Wheat (Pres)

WHOLESALE BUILDERS SUPPLY INC.

200 1st St, Carnegie, PA 15106
Tel.: (412) 279-8260
Web Site: http://www.wbsinc.org
Sales Range: $10-24.9 Million
Emp.: 60
Building Materials, Interior
N.A.I.C.S.: 423310
Eric Johnson (Mgr-Ops)
Lynne Bateson (Mgr-Credit)

WHOLESALE CARRIER SERVICES, INC.

12350 NW 39th St, Coral Springs, FL 33065-2418
Tel.: (954) 227-1700
Web Site: http://www.wcs.com
Year Founded: 1994
Sales Range: $10-24.9 Million
Emp.: 25
Commercial Telecom Networks Services
N.A.I.C.S.: 517111
Chris S. Barton (Pres & CEO)

WHOLESALE ELECTRIC SUPPLY CO. INC.

803 S Robison Rd, Texarkana, TX 75501
Tel.: (903) 794-3404 TX
Web Site: http://www.netwes.com
Year Founded: 1947
Emp.: 100
Electrical Equipment Distr
N.A.I.C.S.: 423610

WHOLESALE ELECTRIC SUPPLY HOUSTON LP

4040 Gulf Freeway, Houston, TX 77004
Tel.: (713) 748-6100
Web Site: http://www.wholesaleelectric.com
Sales Range: $125-149.9 Million
Emp.: 400
Electronic Parts & Equipment
N.A.I.C.S.: 423690
Richard Timme (VP-Comml Sls)
Pam McKellop (CFO & VP)

WHOLESALE ELECTRONIC SUPPLY, INC.

1225 Round Table Dr, Dallas, TX 75247-3503
Tel.: (214) 969-9400 TX
Year Founded: 1950
Sales Range: $10-24.9 Million
Emp.: 50
Wholesale Distributor of Television Sets; Video Cassette Recorders & Accessories; Radios; Communication Equipment For Education & Duplicating Fields
N.A.I.C.S.: 423620
John N. Leedom Jr. (Partner)

WHOLESALE EQUIPMENT BROKERS

22 Perchwood Dr, Fredericksburg, VA 22405
Tel.: (540) 657-5855
Web Site: http://www.webequipment.com
Year Founded: 1981
Sales Range: $10-24.9 Million
Emp.: 5
Sales of New & Webconditioned Construction Equipment
N.A.I.C.S.: 333120
Allen C. Erkert (Gen Mgr & CEO)
Mary Ann Paszkiewicz (Controller)

WHOLESALE EQUIPMENT OF FRESNO

3183 S Golden State Blvd, Fresno, CA 93725
Tel.: (559) 268-6285
Web Site: http://www.wholesaleequipment.net
Sales Range: $10-24.9 Million
Emp.: 40
Industrial Truck Rental & Sales
N.A.I.C.S.: 532490
Gerry Hudson (Owner)
Daniel Selph (Branch Mgr)
Carlos Hernandez (Branch Mgr)
Darren Eskew (Gen Mgr)

WHOLESALE HEATING & COOLING SUPPLY COMPANY

5620 S 85th Cir, Omaha, NE 68127
Tel.: (402) 331-7272 NE
Web Site: http://www.wholesaleheating.com
Year Founded: 1960
Sales Range: $1-9.9 Million
Emp.: 12
Heating, Air-Conditioning & Sheet Metal Products Whslr
N.A.I.C.S.: 423730

U.S. PRIVATE

Greg Morrison (VP-Pur)
John Dietrich (Pres)
Jim Olbertz (Mgr-Warehouse)
Mike Wordekemper (Controller & VP-Sls)

WHOLESALE INDUSTRIAL ELECTRONICS, INC.

4451 Leeds Pl W, North Charleston, SC 29405
Tel.: (843) 722-2634
Web Site: http://www.wieinc.com
Year Founded: 1948
Sales Range: $10-24.9 Million
Emp.: 70
Wholesale Distr of Radio Parts & Accessories
N.A.I.C.S.: 423690
Gerald Sonenshine (Owner & Pres)
Kenneth Sonenshine (VP)
Kristina Sota (Mgr-Accts Payable)

WHOLESALE OUTLET INC.

25 N White Horse Pke, Waterford Works, NJ 08089
Tel.: (856) 719-9200
Web Site: http://www.outletcars.com
Rev.: $12,000,000
Emp.: 6
Used Cars
N.A.I.C.S.: 441120
Patrick Long (Comptroller)
Rebecca Eby (Office Mgr)

WHOLESALE PETROLEUM INC.

1734 E Parrish Ave, Owensboro, KY 42303-0908
Tel.: (270) 685-3500 KY
Year Founded: 1978
Sales Range: $25-49.9 Million
Emp.: 140
Whole Sale & Retail of Petroleum Products
N.A.I.C.S.: 424710
Charles L. Clark (Pres)
Lynn Northern (CFO)

WHOLESALE PLUMBING SUPPLY CO.

2080 Exch Dr, Saint Charles, MO 63303
Tel.: (636) 255-9900
Web Site: http://www.wpsco.com
Sales Range: $10-24.9 Million
Emp.: 45
Plumbing & Hydronic Heating Supplies
N.A.I.C.S.: 423720
Gerald R. D'Angelo (Pres)
Tom Ditchfield (VP)

WHOLESALE PUMP & SUPPLY INC.

1284 N Market St, Shreveport, LA 71107
Tel.: (318) 221-4275
Web Site: http://www.wpspump.com
Sales Range: $10-24.9 Million
Emp.: 15
Sales of Industrial Machinery & Equipment
N.A.I.C.S.: 423830
Charles R. Laborde (Pres)
Rick Floyd (Gen Mgr-Shreveport)
Ralph E. Reed (Mgr-Jennings)
Jody LaBorde (Mgr-Vidor)
J. Peyton Laborde (CFO)
Mathew Harris (Mgr-Tyler)

WHOLESALE SUPPLY GROUP INC.

885 Keith St NW, Cleveland, TN 37320-4080
Tel.: (423) 479-5997 TN

Web Site: http://www.wsginc.com
Year Founded: 1945
Sales Range: $25-49.9 Million
Emp.: 220
Provider of Electrical Equipment
N.A.I.C.S.: 423610
Lloyd Rogers *(Pres)*
Larry Brackett *(VP-Ops)*
Gary Millaway *(VP)*

WHOLESALE TIRE INC.
Armory Rd, Clarksburg, WV 26301
Tel.: (304) 624-8465
Web Site: http://www.wholesaletire-auto.com
Rev.: $11,900,000
Emp.: 70
Tire & Tube Merchant Whslr
N.A.I.C.S.: 423130
Ron Campbell *(Mgr-Retail)*

WHOLESALE TOOL CO., INC.
12155 Stephens Rd, Warren, MI 48089
Tel.: (586) 754-9270
Web Site: http://www.wttool.com
Year Founded: 1960
Sales Range: $10-24.9 Million
Emp.: 45
Industrial Machinery & Equipment
N.A.I.C.S.: 423830
Mark Dowdy *(Pres)*
Chuck Loewen *(CFO & Controller)*

WHOLESOME HOLDINGS GROUP, LLC
8240 Preston Rd Ste 320, Plano, TX 75024-2373
Tel.: (214) 937-4750 DE
Web Site: http://www.wholesomefarms.com
Year Founded: 2006
Privater Equity Firm
N.A.I.C.S.: 523999
Terence O'Brien *(Chm & CEO)*
Mike Roggero *(Exec VP-Bus Dev)*
Mike Kurilecz *(CFO)*

WHP GLOBAL
230 Park Ave, New York, NY 10169
Tel.: (646) 518-8402
Web Site: http://www.whp-global.com
Marketing & Advertising; Management Platform
N.A.I.C.S.: 523940
Yehuda Shmidma *(Chm & CEO)*
Effy Zinkin *(COO & Gen Counsel)*
Scott Brook *(Mng Dir-Corp Dev)*

Subsidiaries:

Express, Inc. (1)
1 Express Dr, Columbus, OH 43230
Tel.: (614) 474-4001
Web Site: https://www.express.com
Rev.: $1,854,357,000
Assets: $1,289,740,000
Liabilities: $1,195,973,000
Net Worth: $93,767,000
Earnings: ($208,539,000)
Emp.: 10,000
Fiscal Year-end: 02/03/2024
Clothing Stores Owner & Operator
N.A.I.C.S.: 458110
Mylle Bell Harvey Mangum *(Chm)*
Stewart F. Glendinning *(CEO)*
Sara Tervo *(CMO & Exec VP)*
Brian Atwood *(Creative Dir-Footwear)*

Subsidiary (Domestic):

Bonobos, Inc. (2)
45 W 25th St 5th Fl, New York, NY 10010
Web Site: http://www.bonobos.com
Men's Apparel & Accessories Retailer & Whslr
N.A.I.C.S.: 424350
Brian A. Spaly *(Executives)*

Express Fashion Operations, LLC (2)

40820 Winchester Rd 1830, Temecula, CA 92591
Tel.: (951) 296-5688
Sales Range: $25-49.9 Million
Emp.: 20
Apparel & Accessory Retailer
N.A.I.C.S.: 458110
Tracy Wyarra *(Gen Mgr)*

Express Topco LLC (2)
1 Express Dr, Columbus, OH 43230-1496
Tel.: (614) 474-4001
Apparel & Accessory Retailer
N.A.I.C.S.: 458110

Takmor LLC (1)
1411 Broadway Fl 20, New York, NY 10018
Tel.: (845) 928-9470
Web Site: http://anneklein.com
Womens Clothing & Accessories
N.A.I.C.S.: 458110

Toys "R" Us, Inc. (1)
1 Geoffrey Way, Wayne, NJ 07470
Tel.: (973) 617-3500
Web Site: http://www.trukidsbrands.com
Holding Company; Toys, Games & Children's Clothing Retailer
N.A.I.C.S.: 551112

Subsidiary (Domestic):

Geoffrey, LLC (2)
1 Geoffrey Way, Wayne, NJ 07470
Tel.: (973) 617-3500
Web Site: http://www.tru.com
Sales Range: $10-24.9 Million
Emp.: 1
Trademark Licensing Services
N.A.I.C.S.: 533110
Gerald L. Storch *(CEO)*

Toys "R" Us International, LLC (2)
1 Geoffrey Way, Wayne, NJ 07470
Tel.: (973) 617-3500
Web Site: http://www.toysrus.com
Sales Range: $100-124.9 Million
Emp.: 55
Holding Company; Toys, Games & Children's Clothing Retailer
N.A.I.C.S.: 551112
Larry Gardner *(VP-Ops & Franchise)*

Subsidiary (Non-US):

Toys "R" Us Japan, Ltd. (3)
Muza Kawasaki Central Tower 25F/26F 1310 Omiya-cho, Saiwai-ku, Kawasaki, 212-8566, Kanagawa, Japan
Tel.: (81) 359578825
Web Site: http://www.toysrus.co.jp
Toys, Children's Products, Furniture & Clothing, School Supplies & Sporting Goods Retailer
N.A.I.C.S.: 459120
Monika Merz *(Pres & CEO)*
Zenichiro Ishibashi *(CFO & Exec VP)*
Yumiki Abe *(Auditor)*
Takashi Hasegawa *(Auditor)*

Subsidiary (Domestic):

Toysrus.com (Japan), Ltd. (4)
Muza Kawasaki Central Tower 25F/26F 1310 Omiya-cho, Saiwai-ku, Kawasaki, 212-8566, Kanagawa, Japan
Tel.: (81) 445499072
Web Site: http://www.toysrus.co.jp
Sales Range: $50-74.9 Million
Emp.: 6,500
Toys, Children's Products, Furniture & Clothing, School Supplies & Sporting Goods Online Distr
N.A.I.C.S.: 459120
Monika Merz *(CEO & Pres)*

Subsidiary (Non-US):

Toys "R" Us Portugal, Limitada (3)
Estrada Nacional 9, 2645 543, Alcabideche, Portugal
Tel.: (351) 214602020
Web Site: http://www.toysrus.pt
Sales Range: $25-49.9 Million
Emp.: 8
Toy Retailer
N.A.I.C.S.: 459120
Maria Aeracau *(Mng Dir)*

WHYY INC.
150 N 6th St, Philadelphia, PA 19106-1521
Tel.: (215) 351-1200 DE
Web Site: http://www.whyy.org
Year Founded: 1954
Sales Range: $25-49.9 Million
Emp.: 200
Radio & Television Broadcasting Stations
N.A.I.C.S.: 516110
Kyra G. McGrath *(COO & Exec VP)*
William J. Weber *(CTO & VP)*
Lewis Frederick Sutherland *(Chm)*
William J. Marrazzo *(Pres & CEO)*
Roseann Oleyn *(VP-Institutional Advancement)*
Barbara C. Bisgaier *(Sec)*
John F. Salveson *(Vice Chm)*
Larry Weiss *(Treas)*
A. William Dana *(CFO & Exec VP)*
Arthur Ellis *(VP-Comm & Member Rels)*
Kevin Yoshioka *(VP-Data Analytics & Plng)*

WI HARPER GROUP
50 California St Ste 2580, San Francisco, CA 94111
Tel.: (415) 397-6200
Web Site: http://www.wiharper.com
Rev.: $400,000,000
Emp.: 50
Privater Equity Firm
N.A.I.C.S.: 523999
Peter Liu *(Chm)*
Francis W. Chen *(Vice Chm)*
Paul Chau *(Mng Dir)*

WI-SKY INFLIGHT, INC.
5 Concourse Pkwy Ste 3000, Atlanta, GA 30328
Tel.: (404) 539-9954
Web Site: http://www.wi-skyinflight.com
Sales Range: $75-99.9 Million
Communication Product Mfr
N.A.I.C.S.: 334220
Grant Sharp *(CEO)*
Michael Leabman *(CTO)*
Steve Snyder *(VP-Radio Ops)*
Jerry Ballington *(VP-Aircraft Ops)*

WICHITA KENWORTH INC.
5115 N Broadway St, Wichita, KS 67219
Tel.: (316) 838-0867
Web Site: http://www.wichitakenworth.com
Rev.: $30,264,786
Emp.: 97
Trucks, Commercial
N.A.I.C.S.: 423110
Cliff Adams *(Pres)*
Jack Evans *(Controller)*
Galen Esslinger *(Mgr-Sls)*

WICHMAN CONSTRUCTION
5029 W Grace St, Tampa, FL 33607
Tel.: (813) 282-1179
Web Site: http://www.wichmanconstruction.com
Year Founded: 1997
Sales Range: $25-49.9 Million
Emp.: 10
Commercial Construction
N.A.I.C.S.: 236220
Mike Wichman *(Founder & Pres)*
Brenda Schultz *(Controller)*
Roger Borthwick *(Project Mgr)*

WICK BUILDINGS, LLC
405 Walter Rd, Mazomanie, WI 53560-9202
Tel.: (855) 438-9425

Web Site: http://www.wickbuildings.com
Year Founded: 1954
Custom Building Mfr
N.A.I.C.S.: 321991
Jeff Farquhar *(CFO)*
Allan Breidenbach *(Pres)*

WICK NEWS CORPORATION
333 W Wilcox Dr Ste 302, Sierra Vista, AZ 85635-1756
Tel.: (520) 458-0200 AZ
Web Site: http://www.wickcommunication.com
Sales Range: $250-299.9 Million
Emp.: 500
Newspaper Publishers
N.A.I.C.S.: 513110
Deborah A. Marple *(Mgr-Tech)*

Subsidiaries:

Wick Communications Co., Inc. (1)
333 W Wilcox Dr Ste 302, Sierra Vista, AZ 85635-1756
Tel.: (520) 458-0200
Web Site: http://www.wickcommunications.com
Sales Range: $10-24.9 Million
Emp.: 8
Publisher of Newspapers
N.A.I.C.S.: 513110
Steve Phillips *(Chm)*
Francis Wick *(Pres & CEO)*
Cindy Hefley *(Dir-Adv Digital)*
Clay Lambert *(Dir-Editorial)*
Deborah A. Marple *(Dir-Admin Svcs)*
Mike Rand *(CFO)*

WICKENBURG COMMUNITY HOSPITAL
520 Rose Ln, Wickenburg, AZ 85390
Tel.: (928) 684-5421 AZ
Web Site: http://www.wickhosp.com
Year Founded: 1946
Sales Range: $1-9.9 Million
Community Health Care Services
N.A.I.C.S.: 621498
Peter Stachowicz *(Dir-Ambulatory Svcs)*
Richard Wedig *(Dir-Clinic & Surgical Svcs)*
Kate Pina *(Dir-HR)*
Michael McKay *(Dir-Info Svcs)*
Jim Tavary *(CEO)*
Richard Abbuhl *(Sec)*
Uwe Gross *(Pres)*
Gary Turner *(Treas)*

WICKERS SPORTSWEAR INC.
340 Veterans Memorial Hwy, Commack, NY 11725
Tel.: (631) 543-1700
Web Site: http://www.wickers.com
Sales Range: $10-24.9 Million
Emp.: 10
Men's & Boys' Underwear
N.A.I.C.S.: 315250
Anthony Mazzenga *(CEO)*
Marianne D'Erario *(Treas)*

WICKLAND OIL CORPORATION
8950 Cal Center Dr Ste 125, Sacramento, CA 95826-3262
Tel.: (916) 978-2400 CA
Year Founded: 1960
Sales Range: $75-99.9 Million
Emp.: 8
Holding Company: Wholesale Petroleum Products
N.A.I.C.S.: 424720
Roy Wickland *(Owner)*
John Wickland *(CFO)*
John A. Wickland III *(Chm)*

Subsidiaries:

Wickland Oil Co., Inc. (1)
3600 American River Dr Ste 145, Sacramento, CA 95864-5997 (100%)
Tel.: (916) 978-2400

WICKLAND OIL CORPORATION

Wickland Oil Corporation—(Continued)
Sales Range: $25-49.9 Million
Emp.: 3
Wholesale Petroleum Products & Petrol Terminals
N.A.I.C.S.: 424720
John W. Reho (CFO)

Wickland Properties (1)
3610 American River Dr Ste 140, Sacramento, CA 95864-5919 (100%)
Tel.: (916) 978-2400
Sales Range: $25-49.9 Million
Emp.: 3
Real Estate Acquisition, Management, Operation & Development
N.A.I.C.S.: 551112

WICKSTROM CHEVROLET
555 E Irving Park Rd, Roselle, IL 60172-2301
Tel.: (630) 529-7070
Web Site:
http://www.wickstromchevrolet.com
Sales Range: $10-24.9 Million
Emp.: 40
New Car Whslr
N.A.I.C.S.: 441110
Jarred Wickstrom (Principal)

WICKSTROM FORD LINCOLN MERCURY
600 W NW Hwy, Barrington, IL 60010
Tel.: (847) 381-8850
Web Site:
http://www.wickstromford.com
Sales Range: $25-49.9 Million
Emp.: 120
Automobiles, New & Used
N.A.I.C.S.: 441110
Colin Wickstrom (Pres)

WICO METAL PRODUCTS CO., INC.
23500 Sherwood Ave, Warren, MI 48091-2025
Tel.: (586) 755-9600 MI
Web Site: http://www.wicometal.com
Year Founded: 1995
Sales Range: $10-24.9 Million
Emp.: 500
Supplier of Automotive Stampings
N.A.I.C.S.: 336370
Richard A. Brodie (Owner)
Mike Piatt (Controller)

WIDENET CONSULTING GROUP
11400 SE 6th St Ste 130, Bellevue, WA 98004
Tel.: (425) 643-0366
Web Site: http://www.widenet-consulting.com
Year Founded: 2009
Sales Range: $10-24.9 Million
Emp.: 95
Technology Consulting & Recruitment Services
N.A.I.C.S.: 541690
Kory Avaiusini (Co-Founder & CEO)
David Tang (Co-Founder & Pres)
Chris Zimney (VP-Pro Svcs)

WIDGIX, LLC
4888 Pearl E Cir Ste 100 W, Boulder, CO 80301
Tel.: (720) 496-2990
Web Site:
http://www.surveygizmo.com
Year Founded: 2006
Sales Range: $1-9.9 Million
Emp.: 58
Software Publisher
N.A.I.C.S.: 513210
Scott McDaniel (Co-Founder)
Christian Vanek (Co-Founder)

Marybeth Alexander (Mgr-Customer Support)
Christina Bell (Mgr-Pro Svcs)
Aleta Hubbell (Coord-Mktg)
Joshua Robitaille (Mgr-Client Svcs)
Bill Flagg (Chm)
David Roberts (CEO)
Rich Park (Sr VP-Sls)
Jove Oakley (CFO)
Chris Benham (CMO)
Ryan Tamminga (VP- Customer Success)
Mary Beth Addison (Sr VP-Sls)

WIDMER INTERIORS INC.
8415 N Allen Rd, Peoria, IL 61615
Tel.: (309) 693-9300
Web Site:
http://www.widmerinteriors.com
Sales Range: $10-24.9 Million
Emp.: 40
Office Furniture
N.A.I.C.S.: 423210
Christy Egart (Mgr-Sls & Acct)
Frank M. Gutwein (Pres)
Winston J. Stoller (CEO)

WIEDEN + KENNEDY, INC.
224 NW 13th Ave, Portland, OR 97209-2953
Tel.: (503) 937-7000 OR
Web Site: http://www.wk.com
Year Founded: 1982
Sales Range: $150-199.9 Million
Emp.: 327
Advetising Agency
N.A.I.C.S.: 541810
Ryan O'Rourke (Dir-Creative)
Alberto Ponte (Dir-Creative)
Jeff Williams (Dir-Art)
Claudia Valderrama (CFO)
Aaron Allen (Dir-Creative)
Karl Lieberman (Dir-Creative)
Joe Staples (Exec Dir-Creative)
Lee Gunther (Mgr-PR-UK)
Karrelle Dixon (Mng Dir)
Mike Davidson (Dir-Production)
Matt Hunnicutt (Dir-Production)
Patty Brebner (Head-Content Studio)
Neal Arthur (CEO-Global)

Subsidiaries:

Wieden + Kennedy (1)
Floor 5th No1035 ChangLe Road, Shanghai, 200031, China
Tel.: (86) 21 5158 3900
Web Site: http://www.wk.com
Sales Range: $25-49.9 Million
Emp.: 100
Advetising Agency
N.A.I.C.S.: 541810

Wieden + Kennedy - Amsterdam (1)
Herengracht 258, 1016 BV, Amsterdam, Netherlands
Tel.: (31) 20 712 6500
Web Site: http://www.wk.com
Sales Range: $25-49.9 Million
Emp.: 150
Marketing, Electronic Arts & Advertising
N.A.I.C.S.: 541810

Wieden + Kennedy India (1)
B-10 DDA Complex, Sheikh Sarai Phase 1, New Delhi, 11017, India
Tel.: (91) 11 4600 95 95
Sales Range: $25-49.9 Million
Emp.: 60
Advetising Agency
N.A.I.C.S.: 541810
Anirban Roy (Head-Strategic Plng-Delhi & Mumbai)
Ayesha Ghosh (Pres)
Santosh Padhi (Chief Creative Officer)

Wieden + Kennedy Japan (1)
7-5-6 Roppongi, Minato-ku, Tokyo, 106-0032, Japan
Tel.: (81) 3 5771 2900
Web Site: http://www.wk.com
Rev.: $60,000,000

Emp.: 35
Advetising Agency
N.A.I.C.S.: 541810
John C. Jay (Partner & Creative Dir)

Wieden + Kennedy UK Limited (1)
16 Hanbury Street, London, E1 6QR, United Kingdom
Tel.: (44) 207 194 7000
Web Site: http://www.wklondon.com
Sales Range: $10-24.9 Million
Emp.: 50
Advetising Agency
N.A.I.C.S.: 541810
Tony Davidson (Exec Dir-Creative & Partner-Global)
Neil Christie (Partner & Mng Dir)
Rob Steiner (Dir-Ops & Head-Production)
Paul Colman (Chief Strategy Officer)
Helen Andrews (Mng Dir)

Wieden + Kennedy-New York (1)
150 Varick St Fl 7, New York, NY 10013-1218
Tel.: (917) 661-5200
Web Site: http://www.wk.com
Rev.: $178,300,000
Emp.: 105
Advetising Agency
N.A.I.C.S.: 541810
Derek Barnes (Dir-Creative)
Barbara Biancalana (Grp Acct Dir)
Sean McLaughlin (Dir-Creative)
Lana Shahmoradian (Dir-Art)
Brian Yessain (Dir-Creative)

WIEGAND CUSTOM WATCH, LLC
7245 B Industrial Park Blvd, Mentor, OH 44060
Tel.: (440) 951-1296
Web Site:
http://www.wiegandwatches.net
Sales Range: $1-9.9 Million
Watch Mfr
N.A.I.C.S.: 339910
Chris Wiegand (Pres)

WIEGERS CAPITAL PARTNERS
1600 Broadway Ste 1030, Denver, CO 80202
Tel.: (303) 399-4492
Web Site: http://www.wiegersco.com
Year Founded: 1998
Emp.: 100
Investment Management Service
N.A.I.C.S.: 523940
E. Alexander Wiegers (Founder & Mng Partner)

Subsidiaries:

Hart Energy Publishing LP (1)
1616 S Voss Rd Ste 1000, Houston, TX 77057
Tel.: (713) 260-6400
Web Site: http://www.hartenergy.com
Sales Range: $25-49.9 Million
Magazine Newsletter Directory & Online Source Services
N.A.I.C.S.: 513199
Richard A. Eichler (Chm)
Jennifer Presley (Exec Editor-E&P Magazine)
Greg Salerno (VP-Corp Comm)
Mark E. Chiles (Chief Digital Officer & Sr VP-Digital)
Chris Arndt (CFO)
Reinold Tagle (Sr VP-Data Svcs)
Russell Laas (Sr VP-Media E&P & Conferences)
Shelley Lamb (Sr VP)
John Hartig (CEO)

Subsidiary (Domestic):

Gotham Image Works Inc. (2)
4710 Bellaire Blvd Ste 300, Bellaire, TX 77401-4505
Tel.: (713) 662-3636
Web Site:
http://www.gothamimageworks.com
Motion Picture & Video Production
N.A.I.C.S.: 512110
David Skalsky (Owner)

WIEGMANN ASSOCIATES INC.
750 Fountain Lakes Blvd, Saint Charles, MO 63301-4353
Tel.: (636) 940-1056
Web Site:
http://www.wiegmannassoc.com
Sales Range: $25-49.9 Million
Emp.: 100
Plumbing Services
N.A.I.C.S.: 238220
Gerry Wiegmann (CEO)
Tim Hummel (Engr-HVAC Svc Sls)
Brian Smith (Project Mgr)

WIELAND DESIGNS INC.
901 E Madison St, Goshen, IN 46528
Tel.: (574) 533-2168 IN
Web Site:
http://www.wielanddesigns.com
Year Founded: 1976
Sales Range: $10-24.9 Million
Emp.: 350
Supplier of Office Furniture
N.A.I.C.S.: 336360
Clifford Wieland (Founder)
Bruce Wolfe (CFO)
Kip Wieland (Exec VP)

WIELAND SALES INC.
430 Midland Rd, Bay City, MI 48706
Tel.: (989) 662-4455
Web Site:
http://www.wielandtrucks.com
Sales Range: $25-49.9 Million
Emp.: 40
Sales of New & Used Trucks, Tractors & Trailers
N.A.I.C.S.: 441110
Kirk Wieland (Pres)
Mike Wieland (Controller)

WIENER CROWLEY & ST JOHN
135 Fort Lee Rd, Leonia, NJ 07605
Tel.: (201) 944-5559
Web Site: http://www.wcslumber.com
Sales Range: $10-24.9 Million
Emp.: 20
Distr of Lumber: Rough, Dressed & Finished
N.A.I.C.S.: 423310
Bill Thompson (Mgr-Sls)
Dennis J. Crowley (Co-Pres)
James St. John (Co-Pres)

WIER & ASSOCIATES, INC.
701 Highlander Blvd Ste 300, Arlington, TX 76015
Tel.: (817) 467-7700 TX
Web Site:
http://www.wierassociates.com
Year Founded: 1978
Sales Range: $1-9.9 Million
Emp.: 32
Civil Engineering & Surveying
N.A.I.C.S.: 541330
Carlo Silvestri (Pres)
John Wier (Founder & Principal)
Ulys Lane III (Principal & Exec VP)

WIESE INDUSTRIES
1501 5th St, Perry, IA 50220
Tel.: (515) 465-9854
Web Site: http://www.wiesecorp.com
Sales Range: $25-49.9 Million
Emp.: 50
Farm Machinery & Equipment
N.A.I.C.S.: 333111
Steve Pierce (Gen Mgr)
David Pitt (Pres)
Deanna Smith (Controller)

WIESE TOYOTA
10265 N US Hwy 31, Taylorsville, IN 47280
Tel.: (812) 526-2100

COMPANIES

Web Site:
http://www.easywithwiese.com
Sales Range: $25-49.9 Million
Emp.: 60
Car Whslr
N.A.I.C.S.: 441110
Angie Ogle *(Office Mgr)*

WIESE USA, INC.
1435 Woodson Rd, Saint Louis, MO 63132
Tel.: (314) 997-4444 MO
Web Site: http://www.wieseusa.com
Year Founded: 1944
Rev.: $110,000,000
Emp.: 600
Materials Handling Machinery
N.A.I.C.S.: 423830
Harold E. Wiese *(Pres & CEO)*
Kevin Reed *(Mgr-Storage Products)*

WIESER CONCRETE PRODUCTS INC.
W 3716 US Hwy 10, Maiden Rock, WI 54750
Tel.: (715) 647-2311
Web Site:
http://www.wieserconcrete.com
Sales Range: $10-24.9 Million
Emp.: 120
Concrete Products
N.A.I.C.S.: 327390
Andrew Wieser *(Pres)*
Mark Wieser *(Exec VP & Gen Mgr-Wieser Environ Engrg)*
Denise Pelzel *(Dir-HR)*
Tom Gruber *(Plant Mgr)*

WIESNER PUBLISHING, LLC
5970 Greenwood Plaza Blvd # 1, Greenwood Village, CO 80111-4703
Tel.: (303) 397-7600
Web Site:
http://www.wiesnerpublishing.com
Sales Range: $25-49.9 Million
Emp.: 135
Publisher of Magazines
N.A.I.C.S.: 513120
E. Patrick Wiesner *(Pres)*
Dan Wiesner *(CEO)*
Betsy Kominsky *(VP & Grp Publr)*
John Rich *(CFO)*
John Wiesner *(VP-IT)*

Subsidiaries:

Senior Market Advisor (1)
7009 S Potomac St Ste 200, Centennial, CO 80112
Tel.: (303) 397-7600
Web Site:
http://www.seniormarketadvisor.com
Sales Range: $25-49.9 Million
Emp.: 80
Business Magazine
N.A.I.C.S.: 513120

WIESNER, INC.
230 I Hwy 45, Huntsville, TX 77320
Tel.: (936) 291-7500
Web Site:
http://www.wiesnerhuntsville.com
Year Founded: 1993
Sales Range: $10-24.9 Million
Emp.: 80
New Car Whslr
N.A.I.C.S.: 441110
Clint McLaren *(Gen Mgr)*
John Wiesner *(Chm & CEO)*
Don Edd Wiesner *(VP)*

WIGDAHL ELECTRIC CO.
625 Pratt Blvd Ste 2, Elk Grove Village, IL 60007-5100
Tel.: (847) 439-8200
Web Site: http://wigdahlelectric.com
Sales Range: $10-24.9 Million
Emp.: 90

Electrical Wiring Services
N.A.I.C.S.: 238210
Donna Wigdahl *(Sec)*

WIGGINS AIRWAYS INC.
1 Garside Way, Manchester, NH 03103
Tel.: (603) 629-9191
Web Site: http://www.wiggins-air.com
Sales Range: $10-24.9 Million
Emp.: 163
Self-Propelled Aircraft, Fixed Base Operation
N.A.I.C.S.: 441227
Jim Thomforde *(Pres)*
Maureen Dwyer *(Asst Treas)*
Steve Lemire *(Dir-Pur)*

WIGINTON CORP.
699 Aero Ln, Sanford, FL 32771-6699
Tel.: (407) 585-3200 FL
Web Site: http://www.wiginton.net
Year Founded: 1967
Sales Range: $25-49.9 Million
Emp.: 310
Fire Protection Contractors
N.A.I.C.S.: 238220
Joe E. Wiginton *(Chm)*
Don Wiginton *(Pres)*
Allan Wiginton *(Exec VP)*

WIGWAM MILLS, INC.
3402 Crocker Ave, Sheboygan, WI 53081-6402
Tel.: (920) 457-5551 WI
Web Site: http://www.wigwam.com
Year Founded: 1905
Sales Range: $100-124.9 Million
Emp.: 250
Sports & Athletic Socks; Knit Headwear
N.A.I.C.S.: 315120
Jill Skarda *(Dir-HR)*
Jared Oviatt *(VP-Sls)*
Thomas M. Wheeler *(Pres & CEO)*

WIKIMEDIA FOUNDATION INC.
149 New Montgomery St Fl 3, San Francisco, CA 94105-3740
Tel.: (415) 839-6885
Web Site:
http://www.wikimediafoundation.org
Sales Range: $50-74.9 Million
Emp.: 50
Free Educational Content Collection & Development Services
N.A.I.C.S.: 513199
Sue Gardner *(Exec Dir)*
Domas Mituzas *(Engr-Data & Performance)*
Maria Sefidari *(Chm)*
Toby Hegrin *(Dir-Analytics)*
Rob Lanphier *(Dir-Architecture)*
Tomasz Finc *(Dir-Discovery)*
Lisa Seitz Gruwell *(Chief Advancement Officer)*
James Forrester *(Sr Product Mgr)*
Kenan Wang *(Mgr-Mobile Product)*
Asaf Bartov *(Officer-Program-Emerging Wikimedia Communities)*
Daniel D. Foy *(Partner & Mgr-Technical-Mobile Partnerships)*
Megan Hernandez *(Dir-Online Fundraising)*
Jonathan Curiel *(Sr Mgr-Dev Comm)*
Caitlin Virtue *(Dir-Dev)*
Pats Pena *(Dir-Fundraising Ops)*
Luis Villa *(Sr Dir-Community Engagement)*
Heather Walls *(Chief Creative Officer)*
Tony Le *(Controller)*
Lynette Logan *(Dir-Admin)*
Doreen Dunican *(Mgr-Travel)*
Joady Lohr *(Chief Talent & Culture Officer)*

Boryana Dineva *(VP-HR)*
Terence Gilbey *(COO)*
Dario Taraborelli *(Head-Res)*
Deborah Tankersley *(Product Mgr)*
Josh Minor *(Product Mgr)*
Katherine Maher *(Exec Dir)*
Marc Brent *(Dir-Endowment)*
Michelle Paulson *(Dir-Legal)*
Moiz Syed *(Mgr-Design)*
Nirzar Pangarkar *(Mgr-Design)*
Sarah R. Rodlund *(Sr Project Coord-Product & Tech)*
Yana Welinder *(Dir-Legal)*
Natalia Tymkiv *(Acting Chm)*
Christophe Henner *(Vice Chm)*
Victoria Coleman *(CTO)*
Marti Johnson *(Officer-Individual Grants Program)*
Jaime Villagomez *(CFO)*
Toby Negrin *(Chief Product Officer)*
Eileen Hershenov *(Gen Counsel)*
Tony Sebro *(Deputy Gen Counsel)*
Kui Kinyanjui *(VP-Comm)*
Robyn Arville *(Chief Talent & Culture Officer)*
Maryana Iskander *(CEO)*

WIKOFF COLOR CORPORATION
1886 Merritt Rd, Fort Mill, SC 29715-7707
Tel.: (803) 548-2210
Web Site: http://www.wikoff.com
Year Founded: 1956
Sales Range: $25-49.9 Million
Emp.: 500
Mfr of Printing Inks
N.A.I.C.S.: 325910
Philip L. Lambert *(Pres & CEO)*
Ben Price *(Mgr-Mktg)*
Buck Rorie *(Treas & VP-Fin)*
Daryl Collins *(VP-Reg Ops & Mktg)*
Daniel Cavalcanti *(Mgr-Latin America & Caribbean)*

WIKREATE
145 Vallejo St Ste 6, San Francisco, CA 94111
Tel.: (415) 362-0440
Web Site: http://www.wikreate.com
Year Founded: 2008
Sales Range: Less than $1 Million
Emp.: 8
Advetising Agency
N.A.I.C.S.: 541810
Ezequiel Trivino *(CEO)*
Elena Castanon *(Founder & COO)*

WILBER DUCK CHEVROLET BUICK, INC.
116 Broad St, Oneida, NY 13421
Tel.: (315) 280-6052
Web Site: http://www.wilberduck.com
Rev.: $50,000,000
Emp.: 29
New Car Dealers
N.A.I.C.S.: 441110
Frank Duck *(VP & Co-Owner)*

WILBRECHT LEDCO, INC.
1400 Energy Park Dr Ste 20, Saint Paul, MN 55108
Tel.: (651) 659-0919
Web Site:
http://www.wilbrechtledco.com
Sales Range: $10-24.9 Million
Emp.: 6
Electro-Mechanical Component Mfr
N.A.I.C.S.: 334419
Jon K. Wilbrecht *(Pres)*
Laurie Wilbrecht *(Product Mgr)*

WILBUR-DUCK CHEVROLET & BUICK
116 Broad St, Oneida, NY 13421
Tel.: (315) 363-4600

Web Site: http://www.wilberduck.com
Rev.: $50,000,000
Emp.: 20
Retailer of New & Used Automobiles
N.A.I.C.S.: 441110
Craig Wilbur *(Gen Mgr)*

WILBUR-ELLIS COMPANY
345 California St 27th Fl, San Francisco, CA 94104-2644
Tel.: (415) 772-4000 CA
Web Site: https://www.wilburellis.com
Year Founded: 1921
Emp.: 4,400
Farm Supplies Merchant Wholesalers
N.A.I.C.S.: 424910
Anne Cleary *(VP-HR)*
Michael Hunter *(CFO)*
John Buckley *(Pres & CEO)*
Tim Nestler *(Gen Counsel, Sec & VP)*
Dan Wiley *(CIO)*
Amie Thesingh *(VP-Corp Bus Dev)*
Jeanne Forbis *(VP-Corp Comm)*

Subsidiaries:

Connell Bros. Co. Ltd. (1)
345 California St 27th Fl, San Francisco, CA 94104
Tel.: (415) 772-4000
Web Site: http://www.connellbrothers.com
Sales Range: $10-24.9 Million
Emp.: 70
Industrial Chemical Distr
N.A.I.C.S.: 424690
Azita Owlia *(Pres)*
Brian Scutt *(COO)*

Nachurs Alpine Solutions, LLC (1)
421 Leader St, Marion, OH 43302
Tel.: (740) 382-5701
Web Site: https://www.nachurs-alpine.com
Fertilizer Mfr
N.A.I.C.S.: 325314
John Grega *(Sec & VP-Admin & Fin)*
Angela Kloha *(VP-Mktg)*
Greg Bame *(Dir-Technical Svcs)*
Karen Carter *(Controller)*

Seed House, Inc. (1)
87194 494th Ave, Oneill, NE 68763-5385
Tel.: (402) 336-1250
Web Site: http://www.theseedhouse.com
Nursery, Garden Center & Farm Supply Stores
N.A.I.C.S.: 444240

Wilbur-Ellis Company (1)
4160 10 Mile Rd NW, Sparta, MI 49345-9717
Tel.: (616) 887-8333
Web Site: http://www.wilburellis.com
Sales Range: $25-49.9 Million
Emp.: 40
Agricultural Chemical Products Distr
N.A.I.C.S.: 424910

Wilbur-Ellis Company - Wilbur-Ellis Agribusiness Division (1)
3300 S Parker Rd Ste 500, Aurora, CO 80014
Tel.: (720) 306-6340
Web Site: http://www.ag.wilburellis.com
Crop Protection Services
N.A.I.C.S.: 115112

Wilbur-Ellis Nutrition, LLC (1)
2001 SE Columbia River Dr Ste 200, Vancouver, WA 98661
Tel.: (360) 892-2677
Web Site: http://www.wilbur-ellisfeed.com
Animal Feed Mfr
N.A.I.C.S.: 311119
Jon Hus *(Mng Dir-Feed Asia)*
Matt Fanta *(Pres)*

Subsidiary (Domestic):

Ameri-Pac, Inc. (2)
751 S 4th St, Saint Joseph, MO 64501
Tel.: (816) 233-4530
Web Site:
https://www.wilburellisnutrition.com
Animal Feed Mfr
N.A.I.C.S.: 311119

WILBUR-ELLIS COMPANY

Wilbur-Ellis Company—(Continued)
Marcia Colescott *(VP-Ops)*

Rangen, Inc. (2)
115 13th Ave S, Buhl, ID 83316
Tel.: (208) 543-6421
Web Site: http://www.rangen.com
Prepared Foods; Aquaculturis Foods; Dairy & Animal Feed; Bulk Dry Beans
N.A.I.C.S.: 311119
Christopher Rangen *(Pres)*
J. Dee May *(Sec)*

Division (Domestic):

Rangen Aquaculture Research (3)
2928 S 1175 E B, Hagerman, ID 83332-5841
Tel.: (208) 837-6191
Web Site: http://www.rangen.com
Sales Range: $10-24.9 Million
Emp.: 2
Commercial Physical Research
N.A.I.C.S.: 112511

Rangen, Inc. - Aquaculture Division (3)
115-13th Ave, Buhl, ID 83316
Web Site: http://www.rangen.com
Aquaculture Feed Mfr
N.A.I.C.S.: 311119

Rangen, Inc. - Commodities Division (3)
115 13th Ave S, Buhl, ID 83316-0706
Tel.: (208) 543-6421
Agricultural Product Services
N.A.I.C.S.: 926140

Rangen, Inc. - Rangen Logistics Division (3)
115-13th Ave, Buhl, ID 83316
Tel.: (208) 543-2458
Logistics Management Consulting Services
N.A.I.C.S.: 541614

WILBURN OIL CO., INC.
619 Crossover Rd, Tupelo, MS 38802
Tel.: (662) 842-4772
Rev.: $24,000,000
Emp.: 20
Petroleum Bulk Stations
N.A.I.C.S.: 424710
Jerry Wilburn *(Pres)*
Margret Wilburn *(VP)*

WILCAS CORP.
3200 Dickerson Pike, Nashville, TN 37207-2906
Tel.: (615) 255-1665
Web Site: http://wilcascorp.com
Fabricated Wire Product Mfr
N.A.I.C.S.: 332618
Mark Patel *(Pres)*
Minal Patel *(Owner)*
Drupal Patel *(Dir-Ops)*

Subsidiaries:

Marcole Enterprises LLC (1)
1108 Oakdale St, Manchester, TN 37355-2207 (100%)
Tel.: (931) 723-4442
Web Site: http://www.marcole-ent.com
Sales Range: $1-9.9 Million
Emp.: 87
Electrical Wire Harnesses Mfr
N.A.I.C.S.: 334419

WILCO ENTERPRISES INC.
3790 N US Hwy 441, Ocala, FL 34475
Tel.: (352) 629-8157
Web Site: http://www.suncoastinsulators.com
Year Founded: 1977
Sales Range: $10-24.9 Million
Emp.: 60
Insulation, Buildings
N.A.I.C.S.: 238310
Patsy J. Bowen *(Pres & CEO)*

WILCO FARMERS INC.
200 Industrial Way NE, Mount Angel, OR 97362-9576
Tel.: (503) 845-6122 OR
Web Site: http://www.wilco.coop
Year Founded: 1967
Rev.: $64,327,698
Emp.: 325
Gasoline Service Stations
N.A.I.C.S.: 457120
Douglas Hoffman *(Pres, CEO & Treas)*

WILCO MACHINE & FAB, INC.
1326 S Broadway St, Marlow, OK 73055
Tel.: (580) 658-6993 OK
Web Site: http://www.wilcofab.com
Year Founded: 1990
Sales Range: $75-99.9 Million
Emp.: 440
Machine Shops
N.A.I.C.S.: 332710
Larry Wortham *(VP-Sls)*
Brad Boles *(Pres)*

WILCOM, INC.
RR 3 73 Daniel Webster Hwy, Belmont, NH 03220
Tel.: (603) 524-2622 NH
Web Site: http://www.wilcominc.com
Year Founded: 1967
Sales Range: $10-24.9 Million
Emp.: 25
Mfr of Telecommunication Test Equipment
N.A.I.C.S.: 334513
Dennis McCarthy *(Pres)*
John Helenek *(CFO & VP)*
Andy Leclerc *(Controller & Mgr-IS)*
Gloria Robichaud *(Supvr-Documentation Control)*

WILCOX AUTOMOTIVE
533 19th St SW, Forest Lake, MN 55025-1354
Tel.: (651) 464-1400
Web Site: http://www.wilcoxautomotive.com
Sales Range: $25-49.9 Million
Emp.: 40
New Car Whslr
N.A.I.C.S.: 441110
Randy Wilcox *(Owner)*
Mathew Wilcox *(VP)*

WILCOX BANCSHARES, INC.
523 NW 1st Ave, Grand Rapids, MN 55744
Tel.: (218) 326-9414 MN
Web Site: http://www.grsb.com
Year Founded: 1980
Sales Range: $10-24.9 Million
Emp.: 50
Bank Holding Company
N.A.I.C.S.: 551111
Noah W. Wilcox *(Pres & CEO)*
Steven M. Wilcox *(Vice Chm)*
Edward M. Zabinski *(Sr VP)*
Shelly D. Steere *(COO & Sr VP)*

Subsidiaries:

Grand Rapids State Bank (1)
523 NW 1st Ave, Grand Rapids, MN 55744
Tel.: (218) 326-9414
Web Site: http://www.grsb.com
Sales Range: $10-24.9 Million
Emp.: 25
Commericial Banking
N.A.I.C.S.: 522110
Steven M. Wilcox *(Vice Chm)*
Noah W. Wilcox *(Pres & CEO)*
Shelly D. Steere *(CFO, COO & Exec VP)*
Jeffrey Lee *(Chief Credit Officer & Sr VP-Lending)*
Lynn Acheson *(VP-Ops)*
Julie Birkey *(VP-Mktg)*
Nate Lloyd *(VP-Bus Banking)*
Kristi Poling *(Project Mgr-Mktg)*

Jill Mattson *(Mgr-HR)*
Andy Dehon *(Dir-IT)*
Jared Pink *(VP-Bus Banking)*

Minnesota Lakes Bank (1)
710 Babcock Blvd E, Delano, MN 55328
Tel.: (763) 972-3385
Web Site: http://www.mnlakesbank.com
Sales Range: $1-9.9 Million
Emp.: 15
Commericial Banking
N.A.I.C.S.: 522110
Noah Wynter Wilcox *(Chm & CEO)*
David Krause *(Pres)*
Josh Gehlen *(Sr VP-Lending)*

WILCOX FARMS INC.
40400 Harts Lake Vly Rd, Roy, WA 98580-9182
Tel.: (360) 458-7774 WA
Web Site: http://www.wilcoxfarms.com
Year Founded: 1909
Sales Range: $100-124.9 Million
Emp.: 230
Fluid Milk, Shelled & Liquid Eggs & Breeding Program
N.A.I.C.S.: 311511
Natalya Washburn *(Controller)*

WILCOXSON BUICK CADILLAC GMC TRUCK INC.
902 N Santa Fe Ave, Pueblo, CO 81003-4146
Tel.: (719) 544-4423
Web Site: http://www.wilcoxsonauto.com
Year Founded: 1967
Sales Range: $10-24.9 Million
Emp.: 45
Car Whslr
N.A.I.C.S.: 441110
William Wilcoxson *(Owner)*

WILD ADVENTURES, INC.
3766 Old Clyattville Rd, Valdosta, GA 31601
Tel.: (229) 219-7080
Web Site: http://www.wildadventures.com
Sales Range: $25-49.9 Million
Emp.: 600
Provider of Amusement Rides, Shows, Animal Safaris, Concerts
N.A.I.C.S.: 713110
Chris Wallace *(Mgr-Facilities)*

WILD BUILDING CONTRACTORS INC.
5524 W Andrew Johnson Hwy, Morristown, TN 37814
Tel.: (423) 581-5639
Web Site: http://www.wildbuilding.com
Sales Range: $10-24.9 Million
Emp.: 40
Commercial & Office Buildings, Renovation & Repair
N.A.I.C.S.: 236220
David A. Wild *(Pres)*
Tim C. Wild *(Treas & Sec)*

WILD CRAZE INC.
17 State St 22nd Fl, New York, NY 10004 NV
Year Founded: 2003
Sales Range: Less than $1 Million
Emp.: 1
Marketing Services
N.A.I.C.S.: 541890
Justin Jarman *(Chm, Pres, CEO, Sec & Treas)*

WILD CREATIONS
1560 Pine Island Rd Unit C, Myrtle Beach, SC 29577
Tel.: (843) 448-8880

Web Site: http://www.wildcreations.com
Year Founded: 2004
Sales Range: $1-9.9 Million
Emp.: 24
Aquarium Dealers & Pet Shops
N.A.I.C.S.: 459910
Janet Noto *(Mgr-Acct)*

WILD GOOSE CANNING TECHNOLOGIES INC.
1750 55th St, Boulder, CO 80301
Tel.: (720) 406-7442
Web Site: http://www.wgcanning.com
Mfr of Canning Systems for Brewing Industry
N.A.I.C.S.: 333310
Alexis Foreman *(Co-Founder & COO)*

Subsidiaries:

Meheen Manufacturing, Inc. (1)
325 N Oregon Ave, Pasco, WA 99301
Tel.: (509) 547-7029
Web Site: http://www.meheen.com
Carbonated Beverage Bottling Machine Mfr
N.A.I.C.S.: 333993
Chris Fergen *(CEO)*

WILD PLANET FOODS, INC.
1585 Heartwood Dr Ste F, McKinleyville, CA 95519
Tel.: (707) 839-3270 DE
Web Site: http://www.wildplanetfoods.com
Rev.: $18,600,000
Emp.: 15
Packaged Frozen Food Merchant Whslr
N.A.I.C.S.: 424420
William Carvalho *(Pres)*
Terry Hunt *(CEO)*
William J. McCarthy *(VP-Ops)*
Brandon Vinum *(Mgr-Shipping)*

WILD RICE ELECTRIC COOPERATIVE INC.
502 N Main St, Mahnomen, MN 56557
Tel.: (218) 935-2517 MN
Web Site: http://www.wildriceelectric.com
Year Founded: 1939
Sales Range: $25-49.9 Million
Emp.: 46
Electric Power Distr
N.A.I.C.S.: 221122
Russ Okeson *(Vice Chm)*
Mark Habedank *(Sec)*
Jeff Nornes *(Chm)*
Lary Sollie *(Treas)*
Steven Haaven *(CEO)*

WILD ROSE CASINO & RESORT
777 Wild Rose Dr, Clinton, IA 52732
Tel.: (563) 243-9000 IA
Web Site: http://www.wildroseresorts.com
Year Founded: 1993
Sales Range: $25-49.9 Million
Emp.: 400
Casino & Resort Services
N.A.I.C.S.: 721120
Tim Bollman *(Gen Mgr)*
Kathy Trevino *(Mgr-Hospitality)*
Peggi Johnson *(Mgr-Mktg)*
Tammy Kadlec *(Mgr-HR)*
Steve Cody *(Gen Mgr)*
Tom Timmons *(Pres & COO)*

WILD SALES, LLC.
17401 Tiller Ct Ste A, Westfield, IN 46074-8967
Tel.: (317) 848-8800
Rev.: $100,000,000
Emp.: 5

COMPANIES

Sporting & Recreational Goods & Supplies Merchant Whslr
N.A.I.C.S.: 423910

WILD THINGS SNACKS, LLC
5221 Ballard Ave NW, Seattle, WA 98107
Web Site: http://www.skinnydipped.com
Year Founded: 2013
Sales Range: $10-24.9 Million
Emp.: 21
Chocolate Product Mfr
N.A.I.C.S.: 311351
Valerie Griffith (Co-Founder)
Breezy Griffith (Co-Founder)
Lizzie Resta (Co-Founder)
Chrissy Haller (Co-Founder)

WILD WINGS INC.
2101 S Hwy 61, Lake City, MN 55041
Tel.: (651) 345-5355
Web Site: http://www.wildwings.com
Rev.: $20,000,000
Emp.: 70
Mail-Order Houses
N.A.I.C.S.: 513199
Randy Eggenberger (CEO)

WILDCAT DISCOVERY TECHNOLOGIES INC.
6985 Flanders Dr, San Diego, CA 92121
Tel.: (858) 550-1980
Web Site: http://www.wildcatdiscovery.com
Primary Battery Mfr
N.A.I.C.S.: 335910
Laura Marion (CFO)

WILDER ARCHITECTURE, INC.
1517 E 7th Ave Ste C, Tampa, FL 33605-3716
Tel.: (813) 242-6677
Web Site: http://www.wilderarchitecture.com
Year Founded: 2003
Sales Range: $10-24.9 Million
Emp.: 8
Architectural Services
N.A.I.C.S.: 541310
Larry Wilder (Pres & Partner)
Eric Rice (Partner, VP & Sec)
John Thompson (Partner, VP & Treas)
Dee Covington (Coord-Admin & Mktg)
Sonya Hudson (Coord-Mktg & Admin)

WILDER CORPORATION
2536 Country Side Blvd Ste 250, Clearwater, FL 33763
Tel.: (727) 799-2111 DE
Web Site: http://www.rvresorts.com
Sales Range: $125-149.9 Million
Emp.: 300
Mobile Home Site Operators
N.A.I.C.S.: 531190
Maurice Wilder (Pres)
Mary Carotenuto (VP)

WILDER DEEM, INC.
417 Park Ave Ste 3 E, New York, NY 10022-4401
Tel.: (212) 223-4766 DE
Year Founded: 1973
Sales Range: $50-74.9 Million
Emp.: 35
Mfr of Steel Castings
N.A.I.C.S.: 541611
Duane Wilder (Chm, Pres & Treas)

WILDERNESS LOG HOMES INC.
N5821 County Rd S, Plymouth, WI 53073
Tel.: (920) 893-8416
Rev.: $18,000,000
Emp.: 50
Prefabricated Wood Cabins
N.A.I.C.S.: 321992
Jerry Kuhl (Pres)

WILDERNESS SOCIETY
1615 M St NW, Washington, DC 20036
Tel.: (202) 833-2300 DC
Web Site: http://www.wilderness.org
Year Founded: 1935
Sales Range: $25-49.9 Million
Emp.: 181
Wilderness Protection Services
N.A.I.C.S.: 813312
Jamie Williams (Pres)
Jerry Arthur (Mgr-Facilities)
Lois Epstein (Dir-Arctic Program)
Ame Hellman (VP-Philanthropy)
Rachel Howell (Gen Counsel)
Thomas Tepper (VP-Fin & Admin)
Melyssa Watson (VP)
Kitty Thomas (VP)
Chase Huntley (Dir-Renewable Energy)
Jennifer Dickson (Dir-Comm)

WILDERNEST LOGISTICS SOLUTIONS INCORPORATED
3500 N Windsor Dr Unit 400, Aurora, CO 80011-8120
Tel.: (720) 988-2618
Web Site: http://www.wildernestlogistics.com
Rev.: $15,500,000
Emp.: 42
Freight Forwarding
N.A.I.C.S.: 488510
Tom Eagney (Owner)

WILDFIRE LLC
709 N Main St, Winston Salem, NC 27101
Tel.: (336) 777-3473
Web Site: http://www.wildfireideas.com
Year Founded: 2004
Sales Range: $10-24.9 Million
Emp.: 35
Advetising Agency
N.A.I.C.S.: 541810
Brad Bennett (Owner)
Mike Grice (Principal & Creative Officer)

WILDFLOWER INTERNATIONAL, LTD.
1500 S Saint Francis Dr, Santa Fe, NM 87505
Tel.: (505) 466-9111
Web Site: http://www.wildflowerintl.com
Year Founded: 1991
Sales Range: $10-24.9 Million
Emp.: 50
Computer Hardware & Software Reseller
N.A.I.C.S.: 423430
Kimberly DeCastro (Pres & CEO)
Jim Montoya (Mgr-Sls-Natl)
Mark Armijo (Acct Exec-Health Care)

WILDISH LAND COMPANY
3600 Wildish Ln, Eugene, OR 97408-4616
Tel.: (541) 485-1700 OR
Web Site: http://www.wildish.com
Year Founded: 1935
Sales Range: $25-49.9 Million
Emp.: 200
Highway & Street Construction
N.A.I.C.S.: 237310
James A. Wildish (Pres & CEO)

Subsidiaries:

McKenzie Properties Inc. (1)
3600 Wildish Ln, Eugene, OR 97408-4616
Tel.: (541) 485-1700
Sales Range: $10-24.9 Million
Emp.: 2
Subdivider & Developer
N.A.I.C.S.: 237210

Wildish Building Co. (1)
3600 Wildish Ln, Eugene, OR 97408-5003
Tel.: (541) 683-7732
Construction Engineering Services
N.A.I.C.S.: 541330

Wildish Building Material Co., Inc. (1)
3600 Wildish Ln, Eugene, OR 97408-4616
Tel.: (541) 485-1700
Web Site: http://www.wildish.com
Sales Range: $10-24.9 Million
Emp.: 20
Brick, Stone & Related Material
N.A.I.C.S.: 237990
Steven J. Wildish (VP & Gen Counsel)

Wildish Construction Co., Inc. (1)
3600 Wildish Ln, Eugene, OR 97408-4616
Tel.: (541) 485-1700
Web Site: http://www.wildish.com
Sales Range: $10-24.9 Million
Emp.: 30
Highway & Street Construction
N.A.I.C.S.: 531120
Michael C. Wildish (VP)

Wildish Equipment Co. (1)
3600 Wildish Ln, Eugene, OR 97408-4616 (100%)
Tel.: (541) 485-1700
Web Site: http://www.wildish.com
Sales Range: $50-74.9 Million
Heavy Construction Equipment Rental
N.A.I.C.S.: 531120
Wait Westmoreland (Mgr-Equipment)

Wildish Paving Co., Inc. (1)
3600 Wildish Ln, Eugene, OR 97408-4616 (100%)
Tel.: (541) 485-1700
Web Site: http://www.wildish.com
Sales Range: $10-24.9 Million
Emp.: 40
Heavy Construction
N.A.I.C.S.: 237310
Harold South (Controller)

Wildish Sand & Gravel Co. (1)
3600 Wildish Ln, Eugene, OR 97408
Tel.: (541) 683-7715
Web Site: http://www.wildish.com
Emp.: 150
Readymix Concrete Mfr
N.A.I.C.S.: 327320
Jim Wildish (Pres)
Karl Walrod (Mgr)
Jesse Bluhm (Project Mgr-Bus Dev)

Wildish Standard Paving Co., Inc. (1)
3600 Wildish Ln, Eugene, OR 97408-4616
Tel.: (541) 485-1700
Web Site: http://www.wildish.com
Sales Range: $50-74.9 Million
Highway & Street Construction
N.A.I.C.S.: 237310
Tom Deines (Mgr-Project Proposal)
Red Gilliland (Project Mgr)
Jim Wildish (Pres & CEO)
Randy Hledik (Dir-Gen Svcs)
Harold Foutz (Controller)
Walt Westmoreland (Mgr-Equipment)

Branch (Domestic):

Wildish Standard Paving (2)
2710 N E 78th St, Vancouver, WA 98665
Tel.: (360) 573-8929
Sales Range: $25-49.9 Million
Emp.: 30
Bridge Construction
N.A.I.C.S.: 237310
Eric Holland (Project Mgr)

Willamette Crushing Co., Inc. (1)
3600 Wildish Ln, Eugene, OR 97404
Tel.: (541) 485-1700

Web Site: http://www.wildish.com
Sales Range: $10-24.9 Million
Emp.: 10
Highway & Street Construction
N.A.I.C.S.: 237310
Jim Wildish (Pres & CEO)

WILDMAN BUSINESS GROUP INC.
800 S Buffalo St, Warsaw, IN 46580
Web Site: http://www.wildmanbg.com
Service Establishment Equipment & Supplies Merchant Whslr
N.A.I.C.S.: 423850
Josh Wildman (CEO)

Subsidiaries:

West Michigan Uniform (1)
407 W 17th St, Holland, MI 49423-3499
Web Site: http://www.wmuniform.com
Other Clothing Stores
N.A.I.C.S.: 458110
Ken Van Tuinen (Owner)

WILDROSE MINING, INC.
1013 S Cedar Ave, Fullerton, CA 92833
Tel.: (714) 441-2096 DE
Year Founded: 2009
Mineral Mining Services
N.A.I.C.S.: 212290
Robin Hansen (Pres, CEO, CFO, Treas & Sec)

WILEN MEDIA
5 Wellwood Ave, Farmingdale, NY 11735
Tel.: (631) 439-5000
Web Site: http://www.wilengroup.com
Year Founded: 1981
Rev.: $30,200,000
Emp.: 100
Public Relations Agencies
N.A.I.C.S.: 541820
Richard Wilen (CEO)
Leslee Marin (VP-Fin)
Darrin Wilen (Pres)
Corey Wilen (VP)

WILEN NEW YORK
45 Melville Park Rd, Melville, NY 11747
Tel.: (631) 439-5000 DE
Web Site: http://www.wilennewyork.com
Year Founded: 1981
Sales Range: $75-99.9 Million
Cable T.V., Direct Marketing, Print
N.A.I.C.S.: 541613
Darrin Wilen (Pres)
Paul Caravello (Mng Dir & Exec VP)
Allison Rekus (VP-Client Experience)
Rich Meschi (VP)
Corey Wilen (Exec VP)
Wayne Schombs (Dir-Creative)
Victoria Gennaro (VP-Sls & Natl Accts)
Nicole Carini (Assoc Dir-Client Data Strategies)
Rob Masi (VP-Tech)
Gregg Gantwarg (Mgr-Mktg)

Subsidiaries:

Wilen Press (1)
3333 SW 15th St, Deerfield Beach, FL 33442
Tel.: (954) 246-5000
Web Site: http://www.wilendirect.com
Emp.: 200
N.A.I.C.S.: 541810
Kevin Wilen (Exec VP)
Peter Bryk (VP-Ops)

WILEY METAL FABRICATING, INC.
4589 N Wabash Rd, Marion, IN 46952
Tel.: (765) 671-7865

WILEY METAL FABRICATING, INC.

U.S. PRIVATE

Wiley Metal Fabricating, Inc.—(Continued)
Web Site: http://www.wileymetal.com
Year Founded: 1982
Sales Range: $10-24.9 Million
Emp.: 150
Mfr of Metal Products
N.A.I.C.S.: 332322
Edward Wiley *(Co-Owner & Pres)*
Robert Wiley *(VP & Co-Owner)*

WILEY REIN LLP
1776 K St NW, Washington, DC 20006
Tel.: (202) 719-7000
Web Site: http://www.wileyrein.com
Year Founded: 1983
Sales Range: $200-249.9 Million
Emp.: 501
Legal Advisory Services
N.A.I.C.S.: 541110
Rand L. Allen *(Partner)*
Gregory M. Williams *(Partner)*
Richard E. Wiley *(Co-Founder)*
Bert W. Rein *(Partner)*
Peter D. Shields *(Mng Partner)*
Kevin P. Anderson *(Partner)*
Thomas W. Antonucci *(Partner)*
Jan Witold Baran *(Partner)*
Robert D. Benton *(Partner)*
Richard J. Bodorff *(Partner)*
Mary E. Borja *(Partner)*
Rachel A. Alexander *(Partner)*
Dorthula H. Powell-Woodson *(Partner)*
Andrew G. Woodson *(Partner)*
Martha E. Marrapese *(Partner)*
Stephen J. Claeys *(Partner-Renowned International Trade Practice)*
Richard Sofield *(Partner-Security Practice-Natl)*
Peter Hyun *(Partner-White Collar Defense & Govt Investigations Practice)*
Stephanie Bell *(Partner)*
Matthew Gardner *(Partner)*
Ari Meltzer *(Partner)*
Karen Toto *(Partner)*
Feinstein Feinstein *(Partner)*
Scott Wilkens *(Partner-Telecom, Media & Tech Practice)*
Richard O'Keeffe Jr. *(Partner)*

Subsidiaries:

McBee Strategic Consulting, LLC (1)
455 Massachusetts Ave NW, Washington, DC 20001
Tel.: (202) 234-1224
Web Site: http://www.mcbeestrategic.com
Emp.: 50
Professional, Scientific & Technical Services
N.A.I.C.S.: 541990
Jessica Rihani *(COO)*
Ted Anderson *(Exec VP)*
Julie Bertoson *(VP)*
Eric Bovim *(Mng Dir)*
Robert Chamberlin *(Mng Dir)*
Charles Cooper *(Exec VP)*
Kathleen Frangione *(Exec VP)*
Rob Hobart *(Mng Dir-Govt Capital)*
Bruce Holmes *(VP)*
Ryan Hubbard *(Dir-Ops)*
Megan Humphreys *(VP)*
Chelsea Koski *(VP)*
Jim Lemanski *(Dir-Fin)*
Jeff Markey *(Mng Dir)*
Elizabeth Northrup *(Exec VP)*
John Procter *(Exec VP)*
Mike Sheehy *(Exec VP)*
Sam Whitehorn *(Mng Dir)*
Clare Adams *(Mgr)*
Will Dempster *(VP)*
Erin Neal *(Exec VP)*
Kim Olson Dorgan *(Mng Dir)*
Greg Garcia *(Exec VP)*
Mark Duffy *(Mgr-Comm Practice)*
Langston Emerson *(Exec VP)*
Garth Moore *(VP-Digital)*
Robert Marcus *(Exec VP)*
Savannah Bailey *(Mgr)*
Andrew Deerin *(VP-Creative)*

Noe Garcia *(Exec VP)*
Iman Ghanizada *(Dir-IT)*
Martin Gold *(Sr Dir-Bus Dev & Mktg)*

WILEY SANDERS TRUCK LINES INC.
100 Sanders Rd, Troy, AL 36081
Tel.: (334) 566-5184
Web Site: http://www.wileysanders.com
Year Founded: 1972
Sales Range: $75-99.9 Million
Emp.: 600
Provider of Trucking Services
N.A.I.C.S.: 484121
Frankie Farris *(VP-Sls)*
Frankie Sarris *(VP-Sales)*
Wiley C. Sanders Jr. *(Chm)*

WILFRED MACDONALD INC.
19 Central Blvd, South Hackensack, NJ 07606
Tel.: (201) 931-1720
Web Site: http://www.wilfredmacdonald.com
Sales Range: $25-49.9 Million
Emp.: 40
Lawn & Garden Machinery & Equipment
N.A.I.C.S.: 423820
Michael Pelrine *(Pres)*

WILHEIT PACKAGING LLC
1527 May Dr, Gainesville, GA 30507
Tel.: (770) 532-4421
Web Site: http://www.wilheit.com
Rev.: $40,000,000
Emp.: 50
Distributes Packaging Materials
N.A.I.C.S.: 424990
Philip A. Wilheit *(Pres & CEO)*
David Chester *(VP)*
Kelly Hewell *(Mgr-Accts Payable)*

WILHITE CRANE SERVICE, INC.
1304 State Rd 209, Clovis, NM 88101
Tel.: (505) 763-1216   NM
Web Site: http://www.wilhitelimited.com
Year Founded: 2004
Crane Services
N.A.I.C.S.: 333923
Jarod Wilhite *(VP)*

WILIAN HOLDING CO., INC.
1800 NE Broadway Ave, Des Moines, IA 50313-2644
Tel.: (515) 266-1141   IA
Web Site: http://www.efco-usa.com
Year Founded: 1985
Sales Range: $100-124.9 Million
Emp.: 1,000
Mfr of Steel Forms
N.A.I.C.S.: 423510
A. L. Jennings *(CEO)*

Subsidiaries:

Construction Products Inc. (1)
1625 NE Broadway Ave, Des Moines, IA 50313-2644
Tel.: (515) 266-1141
Web Site: http://www.efcoforms.com
Sales Range: $10-24.9 Million
Emp.: 300
Special Dies, Tools, Jigs & Fixtures
N.A.I.C.S.: 333511
Sara Stafford *(Mgr-Payroll)*
Tom Hamilton *(Dir-HR)*

EFCO Corp. (1)
1800 NE Broadway Ave, Des Moines, IA 50313-2644
Tel.: (515) 266-1141
Web Site: http://www.efco-usa.com
Sales Range: $25-49.9 Million
Emp.: 300
Mfr of Steel Forms

N.A.I.C.S.: 423510
Cathy Howell *(Mgr-Mktg)*
Brent Stanford *(Mgr-Ops)*

EFCO Malaysia SDN. BHD. (1)
Lot 38 & 39 Persiaran Sabak Bernam Hicom Industrial Estate Section 26, 40400, Shah Alam, Selangor Darul Ehsan, Malaysia
Tel.: (60) 3 5191 0928
Web Site: http://www.efcoforms.com
Emp.: 70
Building Materials Whslr
N.A.I.C.S.: 444180
Ken Thon *(Mgr-District)*

WILK SHIRT CORP.
1412 Broadway Rm 2300, New York, NY 10018-9240
Tel.: (212) 564-4300
Year Founded: 1956
Rev.: $28,163,100
Emp.: 34
Retail of Men's & Boys' Clothing
N.A.I.C.S.: 424350

WILKENS MANUFACTURING INC
1480 Hwy 183, Stockton, KS 67669
Tel.: (785) 425-7070
Web Site: http://www.wilkensusa.com
Year Founded: 1973
Sales Range: $10-24.9 Million
Emp.: 90
Walking Floor Trailers
N.A.I.C.S.: 333111
Art Wilkens *(Founder & Pres)*

WILKERSON FUEL CO., INC.
534 Pendleton St, Rock Hill, SC 29730
Tel.: (803) 324-4080   SC
Year Founded: 1980
Rev.: $32,655,878
Emp.: 10
Independent Convenience Store
N.A.I.C.S.: 445131
Frank Wilkerson *(Chm)*

WILKES BASHFORD COMPANY
375 Sutter St Ste 320, San Francisco, CA 94108
Tel.: (415) 986-4380
Web Site: http://www.wilkessport.com
Rev.: $13,600,000
Emp.: 40
Men's & Women's Clothing Stores
N.A.I.C.S.: 458110
Tyler Mitchell *(Co-Owner)*
Antonello Pagliuca *(Mgr-Alteration)*

WILKES COMMUNICATIONS
1400 River St, Wilkesboro, NC 28697
Tel.: (336) 973-3103
Telecommunication Network Services
N.A.I.C.S.: 517112
Eric Cramer *(Pres & CEO)*

WILKINS BUICK, INC. & WILKINS SUBARU, LLC.
6913 Ritchie Hwy, Glen Burnie, MD 21061-2313
Tel.: (410) 768-1700
Year Founded: 1946
Sales Range: $10-24.9 Million
Emp.: 70
Car Whslr
N.A.I.C.S.: 441110
Bruce Catterton *(Gen Mgr)*
Jeremy Wilkins *(Mgr-Ops)*
Maury Wilkins *(Pres)*
Jeff Hutson *(Mgr-Svc)*

WILKINS MEDIA COMPANY
8010 Roswell Rd Ste 120, Atlanta, GA 30350-7014
Tel.: (770) 804-1818   GA

Year Founded: 1965
Rev.: $56,000,000
Emp.: 25
Media Buying Agency
N.A.I.C.S.: 541830
Bill Wilkins *(Chm & CEO)*
Lisa Weaver *(Pres)*
Kris Hall *(Sr VP-Mktg)*
Dana Burleson *(Sr VP & Dir-Res-NY)*
Vince Hohman *(Mgr-Production)*
Andrea Messimer Henley *(Dir-Client Partnerships)*

Subsidiaries:

Outdoor First, Inc. (1)
W 175 N11117 Stonewood Dr Ste 206, Germantown, WI 53022-6506
Tel.: (262) 253-4900
Web Site: http://www.outdoorfirst.com
Sales Range: $10-24.9 Million
Emp.: 20
Media Buying Services
N.A.I.C.S.: 541830
Melissa Ward *(Pres)*

Wilkins Media Company (1)
2728 Kettering Dr, Saint Charles, MO 63303-5486
Tel.: (636) 939-1022
Media & Public Relations
N.A.I.C.S.: 541810
Vince Hohman *(Mgr-Production Svcs)*

Wilkins Media Company (1)
Graybar Building 420 Lexington Ave Ste 1734, New York, NY 10017
Tel.: (646) 398-5375
N.A.I.C.S.: 541810

WILKINS-ROGERS, INC.
27 Frederick Rd, Ellicott City, MD 21043-4759
Tel.: (410) 465-5800   PA
Web Site: http://www.wrmills.com
Year Founded: 1913
Sales Range: $25-49.9 Million
Emp.: 155
Family Flours; Bakery Flours; Corn Meal; Prepared Baking Mixes; Bread & Cake Mixes
N.A.I.C.S.: 445291
Aaron D. Black *(Dir-Ops)*
Nora L. Adams *(Dir-Food Safety)*

Subsidiaries:

Spanglers Flour Mills of Mt. Joy (1)
19 N 12 Market St, Mount Joy, PA 17552   (100%)
Tel.: (717) 653-1403
Sales Range: $10-24.9 Million
Emp.: 15
Flour Mills
N.A.I.C.S.: 311211
Erin Black *(Dir-Ops)*

Washington Quality Foods (1)
PO Box 308, Ellicott City, MD 21041-0308
Tel.: (410) 465-5800
Sales Range: $10-24.9 Million
Emp.: 59
Grain-Based Products Mfr
N.A.I.C.S.: 115114
Steve Friesner *(Mgr-Comml Sls)*

WILKINSBERG-PENN JOINT WATER AUTHORITY
2200 Robinson Blvd, Pittsburgh, PA 15221-1193
Tel.: (412) 243-6200
Web Site: http://www.wpjwa.com
Sales Range: $10-24.9 Million
Emp.: 87
Water Supply
N.A.I.C.S.: 221310
Doug Komandt *(Controller)*

WILKINSON & ASSOCIATES REAL ESTATE
8824-B Bellhaven Blvd, Charlotte, NC 28214
Tel.: (704) 248-8657

Web Site:
http://www.wilkinsonandassociates.com
Real Estate Services
N.A.I.C.S.: 531210
Scott Wilkinson (Pres & CEO)

Subsidiaries:

Atlantic Realty Professionals, Inc. (1)
2C Merchants Row, Bald Head Island, NC 28461
Tel.: (910) 457-6463
Web Site:
http://www.baldheadislandrealestatesales.com
Real Estate Agents & Brokers
N.A.I.C.S.: 531210
David Berne (Principal)

WILKINSON COUNTY INDUSTRIAL DEVELOPMENT AUTHORITY
PO Box 516, Woodville, MS 39669
Tel.: (601) 888-4381   MS
Year Founded: 1993
Sales Range: $10-24.9 Million
Industrial Development Services
N.A.I.C.S.: 813910
Thomas C. Tolliver Jr. (Pres)

WILKINSON REAL ESTATE ADVISORS INC
2100 Riveredge Pkwy Ste 825, Atlanta, GA 30328
Tel.: (770) 952-4200
Web Site:
http://www.wilkinsonrea.com
Sales Range: $25-49.9 Million
Emp.: 200
Real Estate Agents & Managers
N.A.I.C.S.: 561110
Debbie Millwood (Pres & COO)
Wanda Siniard (Exec VP)

Subsidiaries:

Wilkinson Construction Inc (1)
2100 Riveredge Pkwy Ste 825, Atlanta, GA 30328
Tel.: (770) 952-4200
Web Site: http://www.wilkinsonrea.com
Rev.: $23,924,817
Emp.: 160
Remodeling, Multi-Family Dwellings
N.A.I.C.S.: 236118
Jay Wicklund (Pres & COO)

WILKINSON SUPPLY COMPANY
3300 Bush St, Raleigh, NC 27609
Tel.: (919) 834-0395
Web Site:
http://www.wilkinsonsupplyco.com
Year Founded: 1965
Emp.: 100
Plumbing, Kitchen Appliances, Showroom & Supplies
N.A.I.C.S.: 423720
Bob Van Sant (Project Mgr)
Stuart Ferrell (Ops Mgr)
Ken Wertz (Pres)
David Soto (Branch Mgr-Sls)
Janet Ferrell (Mgr-Credit)

WILKS BROTHERS LLC
17010 Interstate 20, Cisco, TX 76437-6471
Tel.: (817) 850-3650
Web Site:
http://www.wilksbrothers.com
Privater Equity Firm
N.A.I.C.S.: 523999
Ian M. Shaw (VP-Acctg & Fin)
Sergei Krylov (Partner-Investment & CFO)
Stephen Ferguson (VP-Tax)

Subsidiaries:

Dawson Geophysical Company (1)
508 W Wall Ste 800, Midland, TX 79701   (73.5%)
Tel.: (432) 684-3000
Web Site: https://dawson3d.gcs-web.com
Rev: $37,480,000
Assets: $60,541,000
Liabilities: $19,432,000
Net Worth: $41,109,000
Earnings: ($20,451,000)
Emp.: 226
Fiscal Year-end: 12/31/2022
Holding Company; Onshore Seismic Data Acquisition & Analysis Services
N.A.I.C.S.: 551112
Matthew D. Wilks (Chm)
Ian M. Shaw (CFO)
Ray L. Mays (COO & Exec VP)
Philip Lathram (VP-IT)
David Nobles (Gen Counsel & VP)
Tom Phillips (VP-Applied Geophysical Technologies)
Matthew D. Wilks (Chm)
Anthony Clark (Pres & CEO)

Subsidiary (Domestic):

Dawson Operating Company (2)
508 W Wall Ste 800, Midland, TX 79701
Tel.: (432) 684-3000
Web Site: http://www.dawson3d.com
Onshore Seismic Data Acquisition & Analysis Services
N.A.I.C.S.: 213112

Subsidiary (Non-US):

Dawson Seismic Services ULC (3)
7015 8 Street NE, Calgary, T2E 8A2, AB, Canada
Tel.: (403) 776-3490
Onshore Seismic Data Acquisition & Analysis Services
N.A.I.C.S.: 213112
Jason Nelson (Gen Mgr)

Subsidiary (Non-US):

Eagle Canada, Inc. (2)
6806 Railway Street SE, Calgary, T2H 3A8, AB, Canada
Tel.: (403) 263-7770
Web Site: http://www.eaglecanada.ca
Land Subdivision & Data Acquisition Services
N.A.I.C.S.: 237210
Terry Jackson (Pres)

Subsidiary (Domestic):

Exploration Surveys, Inc. (2)
101 E Park Blvd Ste 955, Plano, TX 75074
Tel.: (972) 881-1099
Web Site: http://www.dawson3d.com
Geophysical Surveying & Mapping Services
N.A.I.C.S.: 541360

Tidelands Geophysical Co., Inc. (2)
306 W Wall St, Midland, TX 79701
Tel.: (432) 687-6700
Scientific Consulting Services
N.A.I.C.S.: 541690

WILKS MASONRY CORPORATION
1430 Markum Ranch Rd, Fort Worth, TX 76126
Tel.: (682) 587-8150
Web Site:
http://www.wilksmasonry.com
Rev.: $42,014,431
Emp.: 400
Masonry & Other Stonework
N.A.I.C.S.: 238140
Matt Wilks (Exec VP)
Kyle Wilks (Exec VP)

WILL & BAUMER
1009 Veterans Dr, Lewisburg, TN 37091
Tel.: (315) 451-1000   DE
Web Site: http://www.willbaumer.com
Year Founded: 1855
Sales Range: $100-124.9 Million
Emp.: 50
Mfr of Religious Candles & Accessories
N.A.I.C.S.: 339999
Marshall Ciccone (Exec VP-Fin)

WILLAMETTE BEVERAGE COMPANY
8676 McVey Hwy, Eugene, OR 97403
Tel.: (541) 687-0251
Web Site:
http://www.bigfootbeverages.com
Rev.: $47,463,101
Emp.: 110
Soft Drinks Distribution
N.A.I.C.S.: 523999

WILLAMETTE MANAGEMENT ASSOCIATES
8600 W Bryn Mawr Ave, Chicago, IL 60631
Tel.: (773) 399-4300
Web Site: http://www.willamette.com
Sales Range: $25-49.9 Million
Emp.: 50
Appraisers, Except Real Estate
N.A.I.C.S.: 541618
Robert P. Schweihs (Mng Dir)
Robert F. Reilly (Mng Dir)
Timothy J. Meinhart (Mng Dir)
Curtis R. Kimball (Mng Dir)
James G. Rabe (Mng Dir)
Charles A. Wilhoite (Mng Dir)

WILLAMETTE VIEW, INC.
12705 SE River Rd, Portland, OR 97222
Tel.: (503) 654-6581   OR
Web Site:
http://www.willametteview.org
Year Founded: 1955
Sales Range: $10-24.9 Million
Emp.: 442
Continuing Care Retirement Community Operator
N.A.I.C.S.: 623311
Brian Thompson (CFO)
Craig Van Valkenburg (CEO)
Mark Hollis (Dir-Sls)

WILLARD ASPHALT PAVING, INC.
PO Box1183, Lebanon, MO 65536
Tel.: (417) 532-7107
Web Site: http://willardasphalt.com
Sales Range: $10-24.9 Million
Emp.: 10
Highway & Street Construction Services
N.A.I.C.S.: 237310
Lisa Scott (Mgr)

WILLARD OIL COMPANY INC.
2024 Howard St, Spartanburg, SC 29303
Tel.: (864) 583-9307
Sales Range: $10-24.9 Million
Emp.: 25
Petroleum Bulk Stations
N.A.I.C.S.: 424710
Ben S. Willard (Pres)
William Willard (VP)

WILLCREST PARTNERS
100 Spear St Ste 1500, San Francisco, CA 94105
Tel.: (415) 816-0086
Web Site: http://www.willcrest.com
Privater Equity Firm
N.A.I.C.S.: 523999
Benjamin A. Krick (Partner)
Bret Forster (Partner)

Subsidiaries:

Pearce Services, LLC (1)
1222 Vine St Ste 301, Paso Robles, CA 93446
Tel.: (805) 467-2528
Web Site: http://www.pearce-services.com
Power & Communication Line & Related Structures Construction & Repair Services
N.A.I.C.S.: 237130
Bret Forster (CEO)
Ben Krick (Pres)

Subsidiary (Domestic):

EF&I Services Corp. (2)
109 Falkenburg Rd, Tampa, FL 33619
Tel.: (813) 654-6411
Web Site: http://www.eficorp.com
Communication Network Services
N.A.I.C.S.: 238210
O'Neal Sutton Sr. (Pres & CEO)

MaxGen Energy Services Corp. (2)
1690 Scenic Ave, Costa Mesa, CA 92626
Tel.: (844) 629-4364
Web Site: http://www.maxgenservices.com
Sales Range: $10-24.9 Million
Alternative Energy Service Provider
N.A.I.C.S.: 237130
Robert Forster (VP-Client Svcs)
Mark McLanahan (CEO)
Michael Eyman (VP-Bus Dev)
Billy Wang (Sr VP)

Division (Domestic):

Pearce Renewables LLC (2)
1222 Vine St, Ste 301, Paso Robles, CA 93462
Tel.: (805) 467-2528
Web Site: https://www.pearce-renewables.com
IT Consulting Services
N.A.I.C.S.: 513210

Subsidiary (Domestic):

Natron Resources, Inc. (3)
954 Bayview Ave, Oakland, CA 94610-4066
Tel.: (510) 868-0701
Web Site: http://www.natronresources.com
Engineeering Services
N.A.I.C.S.: 541330
Jeff Ansley (Pres)

WILLE BROS CO.
15800 S Lamon, Oak Forest, IL 60452
Tel.: (708) 535-4101
Web Site:
http://www.willebrothers.com
Rev.: $14,600,000
Emp.: 55
Millwork & Lumber
N.A.I.C.S.: 444110
Mark Feret (Mgr)
Rich Shadle (VP-Technical Sls)

WILLE ELECTRIC SUPPLY CO.
101 S 7th St, Modesto, CA 95353
Tel.: (209) 527-6800
Web Site:
http://www.willeelectric.com
Rev.: $16,253,404
Emp.: 30
Electrical Apparatus & Equipment
N.A.I.C.S.: 423610
Lawrence Robinson III (CEO)

WILLERT HOME PRODUCTS, INC.
4044 Park Ave, Saint Louis, MO 63110-2320
Tel.: (314) 772-2822   MO
Web Site: http://www.willert.com
Year Founded: 1952
Sales Range: $100-124.9 Million
Emp.: 300
Mfr of Household Insecticides & Deodorants
N.A.I.C.S.: 325320
Brian Warner (CFO)
Derek Winters (VP-Sls)
Bill Linde (Controller)

WILLERT HOME PRODUCTS, INC.   U.S. PRIVATE

Willert Home Products, Inc.—(Continued)
Subsidiaries:
Willert Home Products (Shanghai) Co., Ltd. (1)
No 338 Haohai Road Xinbang Industrial Park, Xinbang Town Songjiang-Qu, Shanghai, 201606, China
Tel.: (86) 2157893082
Home Care Product Mfr
N.A.I.C.S.: 325620

WILLETT HOFMANN & ASSOC INC.
809 E 2nd St, Dixon, IL 61021
Tel.: (815) 284-3381
Web Site: http://www.willetthofmann.com
Year Founded: 1935
Rev.: $6,794,000
Emp.: 43
Engineeering Services
N.A.I.C.S.: 541330
Ronald J. Steenken (Pres)
Brian Converse (VP)
Curt A. Bender (VP)
G. Matthew Hansen (VP)
Subsidiaries:
Wendler Engineering Service Inc. (1)
698 Timber Creek Rd, Dixon, IL 61021
Tel.: (815) 288-2261
Web Site: http://www.wendlerengineering.com
Rev.: $2,844,000
Emp.: 18
Engineeering Services
N.A.I.C.S.: 541330
Dick Baumann (Pres)

WILLEY MOTORS INC.
2215 S 500 W, Bountiful, UT 84010
Tel.: (801) 295-4477
Web Site: http://www.willeyhonda.com
Sales Range: $10-24.9 Million
Emp.: 50
New & Used Car Dealers
N.A.I.C.S.: 441110
Kay Grover (Office Mgr)
Duff Willey (Owner & Pres)

WILLIAM A. HARRISON INC.
1501 W Park Dr Ste 9, Little Rock, AR 72204
Tel.: (501) 661-0621
Web Site: http://www.harrisontranearkansas.com
Rev.: $10,000,000
Emp.: 60
Air Conditioning Repair
N.A.I.C.S.: 811412
William A. Harrison (Owner)

WILLIAM A. HAZEL INC.
4305 Hazel Park Ct, Chantilly, VA 20151-2925
Tel.: (703) 378-8300   VA
Web Site: http://www.wahazel.com
Year Founded: 1963
Sales Range: $10-24.9 Million
Emp.: 2,100
Total Site Development
N.A.I.C.S.: 237110
William A. Hazel (Founder & Chm)
Dave Speed (VP-Engrg)
David L. Hazel (COO)
Jay B. Keyser (CEO)

WILLIAM A. RANDOLPH, INC.
820 Lakeside Dr Ste 3, Gurnee, IL 60031-9165
Tel.: (847) 856-0123   IL
Web Site: http://www.warandolph.com
Year Founded: 1959
Sales Range: $50-74.9 Million
Emp.: 40
General Contractors, Builders & Construction Managers
N.A.I.C.S.: 236220
Anthony Riccardi (Pres & Principal)
Edward A. Smith (Controller)
Eric P. Handley (VP-Construction)

WILLIAM A. STRAUB INC.
8282 Forsyth Blvd, Saint Louis, MO 63105
Tel.: (314) 725-2121
Web Site: http://www.straubs.com
Sales Range: $10-24.9 Million
Emp.: 250
Grocery Stores, Chain
N.A.I.C.S.: 445110
Tripp Drive (VP)
Jack W. Straub Jr. (Co-Owner & Pres)

WILLIAM B. COLEMAN CO., INC.
4001 Earhart Blvd Ste 1100, New Orleans, LA 70125
Tel.: (504) 822-1000
Web Site: http://www.wbcinc.net
Sales Range: $10-24.9 Million
Emp.: 100
Women's & Children's Clothing
N.A.I.C.S.: 424350
Frank Howes (Controller)

WILLIAM B. MEYER INC.
255 Long Beach Blvd, Stratford, CT 06615
Tel.: (203) 375-5801   CT
Web Site: http://www.wmbmeyer.com
Year Founded: 1915
Sales Range: $25-49.9 Million
Emp.: 750
Transporation & Distribution Logistics
N.A.I.C.S.: 484210
Tom Gillon (Chm)
Chuck Mattes (Exec VP)
Ted Kennedy (VP-Sls)
Mike Racette (CEO)
Tom Gillon Jr. (Pres)

WILLIAM B. MORSE LUMBER CO.
340 Main St W, Rochester, NY 14608
Tel.: (585) 328-1400
Web Site: http://www.morselbr.com
Sales Range: $10-24.9 Million
Emp.: 75
Lumber, Plywood & Millwork
N.A.I.C.S.: 423310
William B. Morse III (Pres)

WILLIAM BLAIR & COMPANY LLC
150 N Riverside Plz, Chicago, IL 60606-5312
Tel.: (312) 236-1600   DE
Web Site: http://www.williamblair.com
Year Founded: 1935
Sales Range: $25-49.9 Billion
Emp.: 1,100
Investment Services
N.A.I.C.S.: 523999
John R. Ettelson (Chm)
Brent W. Gledhill (Pres & CEO)
John C. Moore (Vice Chm-Equities)
Kelly Martin (Head-Fixed Income & Leveraged Fin)
Ryan DeVore (Head-Private Client Advisors)
Beth Satterfield (COO)
Christina Bresani (Mng Dir & Head-Fin Svcs Investment Banking)
Amber Kennelly (Chief HR Officer)
Stephanie Braming (Head-Investment Mgmt-Global)
Alex Rolfe (Head-Institutional Distr-Australia & New Zealand)
Jason R. Stefanelli (Dir-Canada)
Daniel T. Mena (Mng Dir & Head-Fixed Income Sls-New York)
Daniel Furham (VP-San Francisco)
Blake Pontius (Dir-Sustainable Investing)
Paul M. Hindsley (Partner & Mng Dir)
Robert Duwa (Head-Distr-North America)
Thomas Ross (Head-Distr-Europe)
Matt Zimmer (Mng Dir & head-Svcs & Indus Investment Banking Grp)
Bram Hall (Mng Dir)
Anu Sharma (Head-Europe Investment Banking)
Rainer Hepberger (Mng Dir)
Marcelo Assalin (Head-Emerging Markets Debt)
Brett L. Paschke (Vice Chm-Investment Banking & Partner)
Scott McLaughlin (Head-Equities)
Matthew Flynn (Mng Dir)
Mike Custar (Head-Private Capital Advisory)
Michael Trimberger (CFO)

WILLIAM BLAIR INVESTMENT MANAGEMENT LLC
150 N Riverside Plz, Chicago, IL 60606
Tel.: (312) 236-1600
Web Site: http://www.williamblair.com
Investment Services
N.A.I.C.S.: 523940
Stephanie Braming (Head-Global)
Vesta Marks (Portfolio Mgr-Fixed Income)
Ruta Ziverte (Head-Fixed Income-US)
Subsidiaries:
Investment Counselors of Maryland, LLC (1)
300 E Lombard St Ste 810, Baltimore, MD 21202   (100%)
Tel.: (410) 539-3838
Web Site: http://www.icomd.com
Sales Range: $50-74.9 Million
Emp.: 20
Financial Investment Advice Services
N.A.I.C.S.: 523940
Gary J. Merwitz (Principal-Consumer Discretionary & Staples)
Joshua S. Overholt (Principal-Tech)
Deborah Parks (Chief Compliance Officer)
Greg J. Czarnecki (Head-Client Svc & Mktg)
Matthew E. Fleming (Principal-Energy, Producer Durables & Utilities)
Craig A. Miller (Principal & Head-Trading)
William V. Heaphy IV (Mng Principal & Portfolio Mgr)

WILLIAM BROJACK LUMBER COMPANY
RR 1 Box 482, Olyphant, PA 18447-9801
Tel.: (570) 586-2281
Year Founded: 1946
Sales Range: $75-99.9 Million
Emp.: 35
Provider of Wood Milling Services
N.A.I.C.S.: 423310
David Brojack (Gen Mgr)
Jan Kuha (Gen Counsel)

WILLIAM BRONNER & SON CONTRACTORS INC.
393 List St, Frankenmuth, MI 48734
Tel.: (989) 652-3229
Web Site: http://www.bronnerconstruction.com
Sales Range: $10-24.9 Million
Emp.: 5
Commercial & Office Building, New Construction
N.A.I.C.S.: 236220
Anne Bronner (VP)
Matthew Bronner (Pres)

WILLIAM C. HUFF COMPANIES
4227 Progress Ave, Naples, FL 34104
Tel.: (239) 263-8081
Web Site: http://www.wchuffmoving.com
Year Founded: 1908
Sales Range: $1-9.9 Million
Emp.: 16
Moving & Storage
N.A.I.C.S.: 484110
Jim Henderson (Owner & Pres)

WILLIAM C. SMITH & COMPANY
1100 New Jersey Ave SE Ste 1000, Washington, DC 20003-3302
Tel.: (202) 371-1250
Web Site: http://www.williamcsmith.com
Year Founded: 1968
Sales Range: $50-74.9 Million
Emp.: 100
Real Estate Managers
N.A.I.C.S.: 531120
Matthew Ritz (VP)
Lawrence L. Brooks (Mgr-Property)
Stuart Washington (Mgr-Property)
Brad Fennell (Sr VP)
Raj Rathor (Mgr-Resident)

WILLIAM CHARLES, LTD.
1401 N 2nd St, Rockford, IL 61107
Tel.: (815) 963-7400   IL
Web Site: http://www.williamcharles.com
Year Founded: 1982
Sales Range: $50-74.9 Million
Emp.: 350
Highway & Street Construction Services
N.A.I.C.S.: 237310
Nathan Howard (Pres)
David Pomilia (CIO)
Heather Lambdin (Controller)
Subsidiaries:
Environmental Contractors of Illinois Inc. (1)
5290 Nimtz Rd, Loves Park, IL 61111-3932   (100%)
Tel.: (815) 654-4700
Web Site: http://www.eci-il.com
Sales Range: $10-24.9 Million
Emp.: 15
Construction Facilities Support Services
N.A.I.C.S.: 561210
Ben Holmstrom (Gen Mgr)
Rockford Truck Sales Inc. (1)
4301 N Bell School Rd, Loves Park, IL 61111-5623
Tel.: (815) 639-2000
Web Site: http://www.rockfordtrucksales.com
Sales Range: $25-49.9 Million
Emp.: 68
Sales of Trucking Related Products
N.A.I.C.S.: 423110
W.C. Equipment Company Inc. (1)
5290 Nimtz Rd, Loves Park, IL 61111-3932
Tel.: (815) 654-4700
Sales Range: $10-24.9 Million
Emp.: 3
Provider of Truck Rental & Leasing Services
N.A.I.C.S.: 532120
WC Investment Company (1)
4920 Forest Hills Rd, Loves Park, IL 61111-5936
Tel.: (815) 654-4711
Sales Range: $10-24.9 Million
Emp.: 20
Provider of Subdivider & Development Services
N.A.I.C.S.: 237210
William Charles Ltd (1)
5290 Nimtz Rd, Loves Park, IL 61111-3932

Tel.: (815) 654-4700
Web Site:
   http://www.williamcharlesconstruction.com
Sales Range: $10-24.9 Million
Emp.: 30
Producer of Wheat Products
N.A.I.C.S.: 111140

William Charles Real Estate Co (1)
8966 E State St, Rockford, IL 61108
Tel.: (815) 963-7463
Web Site:
   http://www.williamcharlesrealestate.com
Emp.: 7
Real Estate Development Services
N.A.I.C.S.: 531390
Charles F. Thompson *(Pres)*
Erik W. Lindberg *(VP)*
Linda Cooper *(Mgr-Comml Sls & Asset)*
Julie Grace *(Controller)*

William Charles West Inc (1)
5920 W Clearwater Ave Ste 201, Kennewick, WA 99336
Tel.: (509) 783-9031
General Construction Services
N.A.I.C.S.: 237990

Winnebago Fleet Service, Inc. (1)
954 River Ln, Loves Park, IL 61111-2725
Tel.: (815) 633-1978
Sales Range: $10-24.9 Million
Emp.: 6
Mfr of Tires & Tubes
N.A.I.C.S.: 423130

Winnebago Reclamation Service Inc. (1)
8403 Lindenwood Rd, Rockford, IL 61109-5239
Tel.: (815) 874-4806
Web Site: http://www.winnebagolandfill.com
Sales Range: $10-24.9 Million
Emp.: 10
Provider of Refuse Systems Services
N.A.I.C.S.: 562212

WILLIAM E. WALTER INC.
1917 Howard Ave, Flint, MI 48503
Tel.: (810) 232-7459
Web Site:
   http://www.williamewalter.com
Sales Range: $25-49.9 Million
Emp.: 40
Mechanical Contractor
N.A.I.C.S.: 238220
John Walter *(Pres)*

WILLIAM F. HURST CO., INC.
2121 SW Blvd, Wichita, KS 67213
Tel.: (316) 942-7474
Web Site: http://www.wmhurst.com
Sales Range: $10-24.9 Million
Emp.: 30
Aircraft & Space Vehicle Supplies & Parts
N.A.I.C.S.: 423860
John Mullen *(Pres)*

WILLIAM F. MEYER COMPANY
1855 East New York St, Aurora, IL 60504
Tel.: (630) 851-4441
Web Site: http://www.wmfmeyer.com
Sales Range: $25-49.9 Million
Emp.: 100
Paints
N.A.I.C.S.: 424950
William J. Meyer *(Pres)*
Tom Kieso *(CEO)*

WILLIAM FENTON INC.
591 Monadnock Hwy, Swanzey, NH 03446
Tel.: (603) 352-2155
Web Site:
   http://www.toyotakeene.com
Rev.: $12,000,000
Emp.: 150
Car Dealership
N.A.I.C.S.: 441110
William Fenton *(Owner)*

WILLIAM GEORGE PRODUCE CO., INC.
1002 Mize Ave, Lufkin, TX 75904
Tel.: (936) 634-7738   TX
Web Site:
   http://www.williamgeorgeinc.com
Year Founded: 1965
Sales Range: $25-49.9 Million
Emp.: 90
Food Distr
N.A.I.C.S.: 424410
Randy George *(Pres & CEO)*
Jeffery George *(VP)*
Frank George Jr. *(Treas & Sec)*

WILLIAM H. LEAHY ASSOCIATES INC.
2350 Ravine Way Ste 200, Glenview, IL 60025
Tel.: (847) 498-0240
Web Site: http://www.ecarbotrol.com
Sales Range: $10-24.9 Million
Emp.: 24
Groceries
N.A.I.C.S.: 531120
Timothy J. Leahy *(Chm)*
Greg Lojkutz *(Vice Chm)*

WILLIAM HARRIS INVESTORS, INC.
191 N Wacker Dr Ste 1500, Chicago, IL 60606
Tel.: (312) 621-0590
Web Site: http://www.whicapital.com
Year Founded: 1976
Sales Range: $25-49.9 Million
Emp.: 55
Investment Advisory & Asset Management Services
N.A.I.C.S.: 523940
Marc Bassewitz *(Chief Compliance Officer, Gen Counsel & VP)*
Duane Dibble *(Dir-Portfolio Admin & IT)*
Subsidiaries:

Veridiam, Inc. (1)
1717 N Cuyamaca St, El Cajon, CA 92020-1110
Tel.: (619) 448-1000
Web Site: http://www.veridiam.com
Sales Range: $25-49.9 Million
Tubular Metal Component Mfr
N.A.I.C.S.: 331210
Rich Hockman *(Dir-Sls)*

WILLIAM J. SCHULTZ INC.
500 W Trammell Ave, Fort Worth, TX 76140
Tel.: (817) 293-1864
Sales Range: $10-24.9 Million
Emp.: 200
Water Main Construction
N.A.I.C.S.: 237110

WILLIAM KAVANAGH FURNITURE CO.
443 State St, Springfield, MA 01105
Tel.: (413) 733-6641   MA
Year Founded: 1951
Sales Range: $10-24.9 Million
Emp.: 38
Retailer of Furniture
N.A.I.C.S.: 449110
John D. Nelen *(CEO)*
Tim Nelen *(Pres)*

WILLIAM L. MARTIN JR.
1100 Fatherland St, Nashville, TN 37206
Tel.: (615) 228-6403
Rev.: $12,717,267
Emp.: 8
Grocery Stores
N.A.I.C.S.: 445110
William L. Martin Jr. *(Owner)*

WILLIAM M. BIRD & COMPANY, INC.
PO Box 20040, Charleston, SC 29413
Tel.: (843) 554-3040   SC
Web Site: http://www.wmbird.com
Year Founded: 1865
Sales Range: $100-124.9 Million
Emp.: 300
Floor Coverings Hardwood Floors Carpets & Vinyl Flooring Distr
N.A.I.C.S.: 423220
D. Maybank Hagood *(CEO)*
Subsidiaries:

Design Distributing Inc. (1)
900 Aviation Pkwy Ste 150, Morrisville, NC 27560
Tel.: (919) 313-0204
Web Site: http://www.wmbird.com
Sales Range: $25-49.9 Million
Emp.: 75
Floor Coverings, Hardwood Floors, Carpets & Vinyl Flooring Mfr
N.A.I.C.S.: 423220

WILLIAM M. BLOOMFIELD INC.
170 Barnard Ave, San Jose, CA 95125
Tel.: (408) 998-2995
Rev.: $12,000,000
Emp.: 30
Furniture Retailer
N.A.I.C.S.: 449110

WILLIAM MACKLOWE COMPANY LLC
950 3rd Ave, New York, NY 10022
Tel.: (212) 554-5900   NY
Web Site: https://macklowe.com
Year Founded: 2010
Real Estate Investment & Development
N.A.I.C.S.: 531390
William Macklowe *(Chm, Pres & CEO)*

WILLIAM MASTERS INC.
401 Olympia Dr, Bloomington, IL 61704
Tel.: (309) 662-8481
Web Site:
   http://www.wmmastersinc.com
Rev.: $13,198,267
Emp.: 100
General Electrical; Heating; & Plumbing Contractor
N.A.I.C.S.: 238210
William R. Masters *(Pres)*

WILLIAM MORRIS ENDEAVOR ENTERTAINMENT, LLC
9601 Wilshire Blvd, Beverly Hills, CA 90210
Tel.: (310) 285-9000   DE
Web Site:
   http://www.wmeagency.com
Year Founded: 2009
Holding Company; Talent Agency & Entertainment Services
N.A.I.C.S.: 551112
Subsidiaries:

Endeavor Streaming, LLC (1)
1600 Old Country Rd, Plainview, NY 11803
Tel.: (516) 622-8300
Web Site: http://www.neulion.com
Internet Television Broadcasting Services
N.A.I.C.S.: 516120
Michael Her *(Exec VP-Tech & R&D)*
Fred Santarpia *(Pres)*
Matthew Starker *(Chief Bus Officer)*
Fern Pucheu *(CMO)*
Goncalo Luiz *(CTO)*
Peter Bellamy *(Chief Comml Officer)*
Michael Her *(Exec VP-Tech Res & Dev)*
Joao Valverde Ramos *(Sr VP & Head-Ops)*
Charles Mellilo *(Sr VP-Global Client Svcs)*

Subsidiary (Non-US):

MainConcept GmbH (2)
Elisabethstrasse 1, 52062, Aachen, Germany
Tel.: (49) 241401080
Web Site: http://www.mainconcept.com
Software Solutions Services
N.A.I.C.S.: 541511
Tim Alavathil *(Mng Dir)*
Nicholas Wilson *(Mng Dir)*

MainConcept Japan, Inc. (2)
Building 2 Nippo Shin-Osaka 1-8-33 Nishimiyahara, Yodogaw- ku, Osaka, 532 0004, Japan
Tel.: (81) 648077177
Web Site: http://www.mainconcept.com
Software Solutions Services
N.A.I.C.S.: 541511

Subsidiary (Domestic):

MainConcept LLC (2)
9444 Waples St Ste 210, San Diego, CA 92121
Tel.: (858) 882-0666
Web Site: http://www.mainconcept.com
Software Development Services
N.A.I.C.S.: 541511

One Sixty Over Ninety, Inc. (2)
510 Walnut St 19th Fl, Philadelphia, PA 19106
Tel.: (215) 732-3200
Web Site: http://www.160over90.com
Marketing & Advertising Services
N.A.I.C.S.: 541611
Shannon Slusher *(Founder & Exec Chm)*

IMG Worldwide, Inc. (1)
200 5th Ave 7th Fl, New York, NY 10010
Tel.: (212) 489-8300
Web Site: http://www.img.com
Sales Range: $1-4.9 Billion
Media & Public Relations Agency
N.A.I.C.S.: 541830
Catherine Bennett *(Sr VP & Mng Dir-Fashion Events)*

Subsidiary (Domestic):

Fusion Marketing (2)
6404 International Pkwy Ste 2250, Plano, TX 75093
Tel.: (678) 405-7654
Web Site: http://thisisfusion.com
Corporate & Incentive Travel Services
N.A.I.C.S.: 561520
Julie McCulloch *(Acct Dir-Performance Solutions)*
Bill Decker *(CEO)*
Caron Arnold *(Creative Dir)*
Gina Monroe *(Sr Dir-HR)*
Greg Litwicki *(Chief Creative Officer)*
Heather Heign *(Sr Mgr-Program Support)*
Pat Olds *(Assoc Dir-Creative)*
Samantha Dulle *(Acct Coord)*
Ben Loos *(Dir-Dev & Digital Experiences)*
Caroline O'keefe *(Acct Coord)*
Cam Phillips *(Mgr-Production)*
Dina Phillipi *(Dir-Technical Program Mgmt)*
Eric Schneider *(Acct Mgr)*
Jason Hackett *(Dir-Art)*
Jennifer Wubker *(Acct Dir)*
Jessen Wabeke *(Creative Dir)*
John Nolan *(Controller)*
Lisa Lawless *(Sr Mgr-Production)*
Lori Ryan *(Dir-Strategic Account & Experiential Mktg)*
Kyle Zimmerman *(Mgr-Production)*
Mike Beck *(Dir-Production)*
Nick Bommarito *(Assoc Dir-Creative)*
Lindsey Jaeger *(Acct Dir)*
Meghan Martz *(Acct Svcs Dir-Mktg)*
Michael Bischoff *(Dir-Art)*
Matthew Maddox *(Assoc Dir-Creative)*
Brad Harris *(VP-Tech)*
Nikki Spoto *(Acct Coord)*
Mike Cox *(CFO)*
Theresa Blomker *(Acct Exec)*
Rich Wells *(Dir-IT)*
Scott Gaterman *(VP-Mktg-Acct Svcs)*
Shanna Welsh *(Acct Exec)*
Zach Hollowood *(Sr Dir-Art)*
Samantha Porter *(Assoc Mgr-Production)*

WILLIAM MORRIS ENDEAVOR ENTERTAINMENT, LLC

U.S. PRIVATE

William Morris Endeavor Entertainment, LLC—(Continued)
Tyler Schario (Dir-Strategy & Insights)
Vanessa Tutka (Dir-Art)
Grant Stiff (VP-Bus Dev)
Katey Hindes (Dir-Art)
Melanie Flanagan (Sr Acct Exec)
Stephen Dennis (VP-Bus Dev)
Alexa Churchwell (Sr Dir-Association Mgmt)
Rebecca Freeman-Hoff (Acct Dir)
Raleigh Moore (Acct Coord-Performance Solutions)
Heather Baumbach (Sr Project Mgr-Planning & Costing)
Nicole Kramer (Acct Dir)
Megan May (Project Mgr-Digital)
Sarah Bradley (Acct Exec)
Maggie Halliday (Acct Coord)
Ashley Davis (Mgr-Field)
Adam Flach (Acct Exec)
Cara Baldwin (Acct Coord)
Olivia Scalise (Acct Coord)
Jennifer Leans (Sr Mgr-Association)
Caroline Scott (Assoc Mgr)
Kelsey Settle (Coord-Field)
Anne Marie Connelly (Acct Coord)
Megan Tillery (Dir-Production)
Nicole Guanlao (Acct Exec)
Hannah Nichols (Acct Exec)
Darlene Clark (Sr VP-Sls)
Janel Mcneal (Coord-Accts Payable)

Division (Domestic):

IMG College (2)
540 N Trade St, Winston Salem, NC 27101
Tel.: (336) 831-0700
Web Site: http://www.imgcollege.com
Sales Range: $75-99.9 Million
Emp.: 700
Collegiate Sports Marketing Agency
N.A.I.C.S.: 541830
Scott MacKenzie (VP-Bus Dev & Partnership Mgmt)
Rick Barakat (VP-Sls Strategy & Ops)
Tracy White (VP-Southeast Reg)
Jim Connelly (Sr VP-Special Projects)
Mark Dyer (Sr VP)
Tom Fletcher (VP-West Reg)
Andrew Giangola (VP-Strategic Comm)
Cameron Scholvin (VP-Midwest Reg)
Rex Hough (VP-Bus Dev & Partnership Mgmt)
Andrew Judelson (Sr VP-Natl, Reg & Digital Sls & Mktg)
Joe Potter (Sr VP-Ops)
Joe Weatherly (CFO & VP)
Dan Barrett (VP-Bus Ventures)
John Hite (VP-Stadium Seating)
Tim Pernetti (Pres-Multimedia)
Franklin Yancey (VP-Stadium Seating)

Branch (Non-US):

IMG Toronto (2)
175 Bloor Street East Ste 1001 South Tower, Toronto, M4W 3R8, ON, Canada
Tel.: (416) 960-5312
Web Site: http://www.img.com
Sales Range: $10-24.9 Million
Emp.: 40
Advertising & Media Services
N.A.I.C.S.: 541810
Nadean Jackson (Office Mgr)

Subsidiary (Domestic):

IMG Universe LLC (2)
1370 Ave of the Americas 16th Fl, New York, NY 10019
Tel.: (212) 373-4986
Web Site: http://press.missuniverse.com
Producer of the Miss Universe, Miss USA & Miss Teen USA Pageants
N.A.I.C.S.: 711320
Jackie Shahinian (Dir-Public Rels)

Subsidiary (Domestic):

Miss Universe, L.P. (3)
1370 Avenue of the Americas 16th Fl, New York, NY 10019 (100%)
Tel.: (212) 373-4999
Web Site: http://www.missuniverse.com
Producer of the Miss Universe, Miss USA & Miss Teen USA Pageants
N.A.I.C.S.: 711320

Branch (Non-US):

IMG Worldwide - Asia-Pacific Headquarters (2)
18/F East Exchange Tower 38 Leighton Rd, Causeway Bay, China (Hong Kong)
Tel.: (852) 2894 0288
Sales Range: $10-24.9 Million
Emp.: 30
Media Agency
N.A.I.C.S.: 541810
Chris Guinness (Sr VP & Head-Asia Pacific)

Branch (Non-US):

IMG Mumbai (3)
608 1-B/2 Western Express Highway Service Road, Bandra East, Mumbai, 400 51, India
Tel.: (91) 22 6145 5900
Web Site: http://www.img.com
Emp.: 30
Advertising & Media Services
N.A.I.C.S.: 541810
Ashu Jindal (COO)

Branch (Non-US):

IMG Worldwide - EMEA Headquarters (2)
Building 6 566 Chiswick High Road, Chiswick, London, W4 5HR, United Kingdom
Tel.: (44) 20 8233 5300
Web Site: http://www.img.com
Sales Range: $50-74.9 Million
Emp.: 400
Advertising & Media Services
N.A.I.C.S.: 541810
Sally Wharmby (Mgr-Facilities)
Kathleen Brookbanks (Mng Dir)
Barbara Cipolla (CMO)

Branch (Non-US):

IMG Barcelona (3)
VIA Augusta 200 4th Floor, 08021, Barcelona, Spain
Tel.: (34) 93 200 34 55
Web Site: http://www.img.com
Emp.: 20
Advertising & Media Services
N.A.I.C.S.: 541810
Fernando Soler (Mng Dir)

IMG Hungary (3)
Andrassy ut 98, 1062, Budapest, Hungary
Tel.: (36) 1 312 2406
Web Site: http://www.img.com
Advertising & Media Services
N.A.I.C.S.: 541810

IMG Middle East - Dubai (3)
Building 5 Suite 121 Gold and Diamond Park, PO Box 282339, Sheikh Zayed Rd, Dubai, United Arab Emirates
Tel.: (971) 4 408 8388
Web Site: http://www.img.com
Sales Range: $25-49.9 Million
Emp.: 10
Advertising & Media Services
N.A.I.C.S.: 541810
Greg Sproule (Mng Dir-Middle East & North Africa)

Branch (Domestic):

IMG Worldwide, Inc. - Cleveland (2)
IMG Ctr 1360 E 9th St Ste 100, Cleveland, OH 44114
Tel.: (216) 522-1200
Web Site: http://www.imgworld.com
Holding Company; Media & Public Relations Agencies
N.A.I.C.S.: 551112

WME IMG, LLC (1)
9601 Wilshire Blvd, Beverly Hills, CA 90210
Tel.: (310) 285-9000
Web Site: http://www.endeavorco.com
Talent Agency & Entertainment Services
N.A.I.C.S.: 711410
Ariel Z. Emanuel (CEO)
Mark S. Shapiro (Pres)

William Morris Agency, LLC (1)
9601 Wilshire Blvd, Beverly Hills, CA 90210
Tel.: (310) 285-9000
Web Site: http://www.wma.com
Talent Agency
N.A.I.C.S.: 711410
Patrick Whitesell (Co-CEO)
Ariel Z. Emanuel (Co-CEO)
David Wirtschafter (Partner & Agent)
Lance Klein (Partner & Co-Head-Non-Scripted Television)

Branch (Domestic):

William Morris Agency, LLC - New York Office (2)
11 Madison Ave 18th Fl, New York, NY 10010
Tel.: (212) 586-5100
Web Site: http://www.wma.com
Talent Agency
N.A.I.C.S.: 711410
Jennifer Walsh (Exec VP & Co-Head-Literary Dept-Worldwide)

WILLIAM MORRIS HOME FASHIONS
1811 Crestwood Blvd, Birmingham, AL 35210
Tel.: (205) 956-1994
Web Site: http://www.lazboy.com
Sales Range: $10-24.9 Million
Emp.: 95
Furniture Retailer
N.A.I.C.S.: 449110
William Morris (Pres)
Connie Jones (Office Mgr)

WILLIAM MUELLER & SONS INC.
831 Park Ave, Hamburg, MN 55339
Tel.: (952) 467-2720
Web Site: http://www.wmmueller.com
Sales Range: $10-24.9 Million
Emp.: 80
Provider of Resurfacing Contracts
N.A.I.C.S.: 237310
Brad Droege (Pres)
Mori Willemsen (VP)
Tim Mueller (Sec)

WILLIAM NEWTON HOSPITAL
1300 E 5th Ave, Winfield, KS 67156
Tel.: (620) 221-2300   KS
Web Site: http://www.wnmh.org
Year Founded: 1927
Sales Range: $25-49.9 Million
Emp.: 357
Health Care Srvices
N.A.I.C.S.: 622110
Ben Quinton (CEO)

WILLIAM NOBBE & CO., INC.
6469 State Rte 3, Waterloo, IL 62298
Tel.: (618) 939-6717
Web Site: http://www.wmnobbe.com
Sales Range: $10-24.9 Million
Emp.: 56
Farm Implements, Lawn & Garden
N.A.I.C.S.: 423820
Tom Nobbe (Gen Mgr)

WILLIAM O'NEIL & CO., INC.
12655 Beatrice St, Los Angeles, CA 90066
Tel.: (310) 448-6800   CA
Web Site: http://www.williamoneil.com
Sales Range: $450-499.9 Million
Emp.: 450
Security Brokers, Financial Newspaper Publisher, Data Service & Technical Printing
N.A.I.C.S.: 523150
William J. O'Neil (Founder)
Gregory Jannetta (COO)
Vida Bruozis (Mng Dir-Institutional Svcs)
Richard Crehan (Mng Dir-Institutional Svcs)
Peter Doerr (Mng Dir-Institutional Sls)
David Gerber (Mng Dir-Institutional Sls)
Matthew Koob (Mng Dir-Institutional Sls)
Rob Windsor (Mng Dir-Institutional Sls)

Subsidiaries:

O'Neil Data Systems, Inc. (1)
12655 Beatrice St, Los Angeles, CA 90066
Tel.: (310) 448-6400
Web Site: http://www.oneildata.com
Rev.: $12,000,000
Emp.: 150
Data Processing & Technical Printing Services
N.A.I.C.S.: 323111
William J. O'Neil (Chm & Pres)

O'Neil Securities, Incorporated (1)
12655 Beatrice St Ste 2B, Los Angeles, CA 90066
Tel.: (310) 881-3939
Web Site: http://www.oneilsecurities.com
Investment Management & Brokerage Services
N.A.I.C.S.: 523150
Michael P. McCauley (CEO)
Kevin Carroll (Mng Dir & Head-Sls Trading)
Jack Strack (Mng Dir-Equity Sls-New York)
Mike Chrisman (Mng Dir-Equity Sls-San Francisco)

WILLIAM P. HEARNE INC.
28410 S Crown Rd, Fruitland, MD 21826
Tel.: (410) 742-1552   MD
Web Site: http://www.leafygreens.org
Year Founded: 1981
Sales Range: $25-49.9 Million
Emp.: 12
Produce
N.A.I.C.S.: 424910
Tam Haney (Mgr)

WILLIAM PENN ASSOCIATION
709 Brighton Rd, Pittsburgh, PA 15233
Tel.: (412) 231-2979   PA
Web Site: http://www.williampennlife.org
Year Founded: 1886
Sales Range: $50-74.9 Million
Emp.: 33
Civic & Social Organization
N.A.I.C.S.: 813410
Robert G. Bisceglia (Dir-Natl Sls)
William J. Bero (Vice Chm)
George S. Charles (Pres)

WILLIAM PITT SOTHEBY'S INTERNATIONAL REALTY
170 Washington Blvd Ste 10, Stamford, CT 06902
Tel.: (877) 772-5081
Web Site: http://www.williampitt.com
Lessors of Other Real Estate Property
N.A.I.C.S.: 531190
Kristine Newell (Sr VP)

Subsidiaries:

Julia B. Fee Sotheby's International Realty (1)
28 Chase Rd, Scarsdale, NY 10583
Tel.: (914) 725-3305
Web Site: http://www.williampitt.com
Real Estate Services
N.A.I.C.S.: 531210
Jim Whittemore (VP & Mgr)

WILLIAM R. BEACH GENERAL CONTRACTOR, INC.
17431 Jefferson Davis Hwy, Ruther Glen, VA 22546
Tel.: (804) 448-8777
Year Founded: 1975
Sales Range: $10-24.9 Million
Emp.: 10
Housing Construction Services
N.A.I.C.S.: 236117
William R. Beach (Pres)

WILLIAM R. NASH INC.
12981 NW 113th Ct, Miami, FL 33178

Tel.: (305) 885-8155
Web Site: http://www.wrnash.com
Year Founded: 1965
Sales Range: $25-49.9 Million
Emp.: 300
Plumbing Contractor
N.A.I.C.S.: 238220
Benjamin P. Nash *(Chm & COO)*
Russell P. Nash *(Pres & CEO)*
William R. Nash Jr. *(COO)*

WILLIAM RYAN HOMES, INC.
945 N Plum Grove Rd, Schaumburg, IL 60173
Tel.: (847) 995-8700
Web Site: http://www.williamryanhomes.com
Year Founded: 1992
Sales Range: $1-9.9 Million
Emp.: 50
New Home Construction
N.A.I.C.S.: 236115
William J. Ryan *(CEO)*
Jeff Meyer *(Mgr-Production)*

WILLIAM S. HEIN & CO., INC.
2350 N Forest Rd, Getzville, NY 14068
Tel.: (716) 882-2600
Web Site: http://www.wshein.com
Year Founded: 1961
Sales Range: $25-49.9 Million
Emp.: 120
Book Publishing
N.A.I.C.S.: 513130
Daniel P. Rosati *(Sr VP)*
David DeBalski *(Controller)*
William S. Hein *(Chm)*
Dale Missert *(Mgr-Accts Svcs & Royalties)*
Shane Marmion *(Pres)*
William Shannon Hein *(Exec VP)*
James Moore *(Dir-Production & Facilities)*
Kyle Daving *(Mgr-IT)*
Michael Marmion *(Mgr-Metro Self Storage Center)*
Christopher Czopp *(Mgr-Heinonline Production)*
Justin Fronczak *(Mgr-Imaging & Microform)*
Noah Short *(Coord-Imaging)*
Katie Aquilina *(Coord-Heinonline)*
Timothy Hooge *(Dir-Mktg)*
Steven Roses *(Dir-Sls)*
Shannon Sabo *(Dir-Mktg)*

WILLIAM STEINEN MANUFACTURING CO.
29 E Halsey Rd, Parsippany, NJ 07054
Tel.: (973) 887-6400
Web Site: http://www.steinen.com
Sales Range: $25-49.9 Million
Emp.: 100
Valves & Pipe Fittings
N.A.I.C.S.: 332911
William F. Steinen *(Founder & Chm)*

WILLIAM T. SPAEDER CO., INC.
1602 E 18th St, Erie, PA 16510
Tel.: (814) 456-7014
Web Site: http://www.wmtspaeder.com
Year Founded: 1919
Sales Range: $10-24.9 Million
Emp.: 115
Mechanical Contractor
N.A.I.C.S.: 332999
Terry Spaeder *(Pres)*
Kathleen Peyton *(Exec VP)*
Mary Kay Rever *(Sec)*

WILLIAM W. MEYER & SONS INC.
1700 Franklin Blvd, Libertyville, IL 60048
Tel.: (847) 918-0111
Web Site: http://www.wmwmeyer.com
Sales Range: $10-24.9 Million
Emp.: 87
Bulk Handling Conveyor Systems
N.A.I.C.S.: 333922
Greg Buric *(Pres)*

WILLIAMS & CONNOLLY, LLP
725 12th St NW, Washington, DC 20005
Tel.: (202) 434-5000
Web Site: http://www.wc.com
Year Founded: 1967
Sales Range: $300-349.9 Million
Emp.: 260
Law firm
N.A.I.C.S.: 541110
Joseph M. Terry *(Partner)*
David D. Aufhauser *(Partner)*
Emmet T. Flood *(Partner)*
Jessamyn S. Berniker *(Partner)*
Nicholas J. Boyle *(Partner)*
Paul K. Dueffert *(Partner)*
Craig D. Singer *(Partner)*
Deneen C. Howell *(Partner)*
Dan F. Katz *(Partner)*
Edward J. Bennett *(Partner)*
Heidi K. Hubbard *(Partner)*
Kannon K. Shanmugam *(Partner)*
Dane H. Butswinkas *(Chm & Partner)*
Edward C. Barnidge *(Partner)*
Jonathan M. Landy *(Partner)*
Robert A. Van Kirk *(Partner)*
Thomas G. Hentoff *(Partner)*
Tobin J. Romero *(Partner)*
Tom H. L. Selby *(Partner)*
Sarah F. Teich *(Partner)*
Katherine Trefz *(Partner)*
Liam Montgomery *(Partner)*
Christopher Mandernach *(Partner)*
Colette Connor *(Partner)*
Steven Cady *(Partner)*
F. Lane Heard III *(Partner)*

WILLIAMS & ROWE CO., INC.
5215 Hwy Ave, Jacksonville, FL 32254
Tel.: (904) 387-2333
Web Site: http://www.williamsrowe.com
Sales Range: $25-49.9 Million
Emp.: 50
Commercial & Office Buildings, Renovation & Repair
N.A.I.C.S.: 236220
John R. Williams Sr. *(Pres)*

WILLIAMS AUTO GROUP INC.
220 Spring St, Sayre, PA 18840
Tel.: (570) 888-2135
Web Site: http://www.williamsautogroup.com
Sales Range: $10-24.9 Million
Emp.: 42
New & Used Automobiles
N.A.I.C.S.: 441110
Emily Osborn *(Dir-Mktg & Internet)*
Kevin Horn *(Gen Mgr)*
Tony Robbins *(Mgr-Ford Lincoln Sls)*
Tom Turner *(Mgr-Used Car)*
Donald Stuckey *(Mgr-Nissan & Kia Sls)*
Anne Maloney *(Mgr-Svc-Honda)*
Andy Liguori *(Mgr-Svc-Toyota)*

WILLIAMS BROTHERS CONSTRUCTION INC.
1200 E Kelly Ave, Peoria, IL 61616
Tel.: (309) 688-0416
Web Site: http://www.wbci.us
Rev.: $12,000,000
Emp.: 75
Commercial & Institutional Building Construction
N.A.I.C.S.: 236220
Joseph S. Heck *(VP)*
David M. Williams *(Pres)*
Joseph P. Williams *(VP-Field Ops)*

WILLIAMS BROTHERS TRUCKING
US Hwy 341, Hazlehurst, GA 31539
Tel.: (912) 375-7777
Web Site: http://www.wbtus.com
Rev.: $12,900,000
Emp.: 110
Trucking Except Local
N.A.I.C.S.: 484121
Roger L. Williams *(Pres)*
Shirley Maley *(Treas)*
Celena Phillips *(Mgr-Safety & Orientation)*

WILLIAMS COMPANY INC.
2301 Silver Star Rd, Orlando, FL 32804
Tel.: (407) 295-2530
Web Site: http://www.williamsco.com
Year Founded: 1920
Sales Range: $75-99.9 Million
Emp.: 80
Contract Construction Services
N.A.I.C.S.: 236210
Brad Kubin *(COO)*
R. Ed McWhorter *(Dir-Bus Dev)*
Bob Lipscomb *(CEO)*
Taylor Huddleston *(Pres)*
Roger Whitty *(CFO)*
Matt Olberding *(VP-Ops)*

WILLIAMS DISTRIBUTING INC.
658 Richmond NW, Grand Rapids, MI 49504
Tel.: (616) 456-1613
Web Site: http://www.wmsdist.com
Year Founded: 1968
Kitchen, Bath & HVAC Products Retail
N.A.I.C.S.: 459999
Jim Williams *(Owner & CEO)*
Mike Koster *(VP)*

Subsidiaries:

Williams Distributing - Motors & Drives (1)
840 Motor Dr, Howell, MI 48843
Tel.: (517) 546-9661
Web Site: http://www.motors.wmsdist.com
Sales Range: $25-49.9 Million
Emp.: 9
Electric Motors, Heating & Air Conditioning Equipment Retail
N.A.I.C.S.: 423610
Don Faulkner *(VP-Motors & Drives)*
Todd Priestley *(Mgr-Customer Svc)*

WILLIAMS ENTERPRISES OF GEORGIA, INC.
1285 Hawthorne Ave SE, Smyrna, GA 30080-2133
Tel.: (770) 436-1596
Year Founded: 1967
Sales Range: $50-74.9 Million
Emp.: 380
Provider of Structural Steel Erection Services
N.A.I.C.S.: 238120
Frank E. Williams Jr. *(Chm)*
Sharan Brian *(Controller)*
Phillip Torchio III *(Pres)*

Subsidiaries:

Atlanta Steel Erectors, Inc. (1)
1285 Hawthorne Ave SE, Smyrna, GA 30080-2133 (100%)
Tel.: (770) 436-1596
Web Site: http://www.williamenterprises.com
Sales Range: $10-24.9 Million
Emp.: 14

Provider of Structural Steel Erection Services
N.A.I.C.S.: 238120
Frank Williams III *(Pres)*

Chattanooga Boiler & Tank Co., Inc. (1)
1011 E Main St, Chattanooga, TN 37408-1526
Tel.: (423) 266-7118
Web Site: http://www.cbtank.com
Sales Range: $10-24.9 Million
Emp.: 50
Provider of Structural Steel Erection Services
N.A.I.C.S.: 238120

Industrial Fabricators Inc. (1)
2408 Vance Ave, Chattanooga, TN 37404-3813
Tel.: (423) 698-1917
Sales Range: $10-24.9 Million
Emp.: 40
Provider of Fabricated Structural Metal Services
N.A.I.C.S.: 493110
Tim Davis *(Project Mgr)*

Williams Erection Company Inc. (1)
1285 Hawthorne Ave SE, Smyrna, GA 30080-2133
Tel.: (770) 436-1596
Web Site: http://www.williamserection.com
Rev.: $300,000
Emp.: 156
Provider of Structural Steel Erection Services
N.A.I.C.S.: 238120
Steve Schell *(Controller)*

WILLIAMS FINANCIAL GROUP, INC.
CityPlace Twr 2711 N Haskell Ave Ste 2900, Dallas, TX 75204
Tel.: (972) 661-8700
Web Site: http://www.williams-financial.com
Year Founded: 1988
Sales Range: $75-99.9 Million
Emp.: 230
Financial Advisory, Brokerage & Wealth Management Services
N.A.I.C.S.: 523940
Wilson Williams *(Founder, Chm & CEO)*
David Williams *(Pres)*
Claude Connelly *(COO)*
Greg Beltzer *(Sr VP-IT)*
L. Dan Fry *(VP)*
Ed Kern *(CFO)*
Fred N. Knopf *(Gen Counsel)*
Robert Schlangen *(Chief Compliance Officer)*
Theresa Fanning *(Sr VP-Field Svcs)*
Tom Kowalczyk *(Sr VP-Advisory Svcs)*

WILLIAMS FOODS INC.
615 N Church St, Rocky Mount, NC 27804
Tel.: (252) 977-3939
Web Site: http://www.williamsfoodsinc.com
Sales Range: $10-24.9 Million
Emp.: 25
Groceries, General Line
N.A.I.C.S.: 424410
Robert Gurganis *(Controller)*
Bill Williams *(Pres & CEO)*

WILLIAMS FORM ENGINEERING CORP.
8165 Graphic Dr NE, Belmont, MI 49306-9448
Tel.: (616) 866-0815
Web Site: http://www.williamsform.com
Sales Range: $10-24.9 Million
Emp.: 125
Concrete & Cinder Building Products
N.A.I.C.S.: 333248

WILLIAMS FORM ENGINEERING CORP.   U.S. PRIVATE

Williams Form Engineering Corp.—(Continued)
Rob Overbeek *(VP-Ops)*
Steve Kamp *(Mgr-Sls-Eastern United States)*
Ronald Townsend *(Pres)*
Ronald R. Williams Sr. *(Chm)*

WILLIAMS GROUP INTERNATIONAL, INC.
2076 W Park Pl, Stone Mountain, GA 30087-3530
Tel.: (770) 879-4000   GA
Year Founded: 1996
Sales Range: $300-349.9 Million
Emp.: 211
Specialized Industrial Services
N.A.I.C.S.: 238990
Larry Blount *(VP-Fin)*

WILLIAMS GROUP LLC
8447 US Hwy 60 W, Mountain View, MO 65548
Tel.: (816) 290-5567
Web Site: http://www.williams-groupllc.com
Sales Range: $10-24.9 Million
Emp.: 50
Holding Company
N.A.I.C.S.: 551112
Michael Williams *(Owner)*

Subsidiaries:

St. Maries River Railroad Company   (1)
318 N 10th St, Saint Maries, ID 83861   **(100%)**
Tel.: (208) 245-4531
Web Site: http://www.stmariesriverrr.com
Sales Range: $1-9.9 Million
Emp.: 8
Railroad
N.A.I.C.S.: 482112
Jodie Jackson *(Supvr-Ops & Office)*
Bill Barnholt Jr. *(Gen Mgr)*

WILLIAMS GUN SIGHT COMPANY, INC.
7389 Lapeer Rd, Davison, MI 48423-2533
Tel.: (810) 653-2131
Web Site: http://www.williamsgunsight.com
Year Founded: 1926
Sales Range: $50-74.9 Million
Emp.: 51
Gun Sights & Accessories; Gun Cleaning Equipment, Scope Mounts
N.A.I.C.S.: 333310
Thomas Wright *(Pres)*
Elisea Singson *(VP)*
Jody Provost *(Controller)*

WILLIAMS INDUSTRIES, INC.
8624 JD Reading Dr, Manassas, VA 20109
Tel.: (703) 335-7800   VA
Web Site: http://www.wmsi.com
Year Founded: 1960
Sales Range: $50-74.9 Million
Emp.: 333
Holding Company; Construction Services
N.A.I.C.S.: 551112

Subsidiaries:

Insurance Risk Management Group, Inc.   (1)
PO Box 1770, Manassas, VA 20108
Tel.: (703) 560-5196
Web Site: http://www.wmsi.com
Sales Range: $75-99.9 Million
Insurance Management Services
N.A.I.C.S.: 524210

Piedmont Metal Products, Inc.   (1)
915 Orange St, Bedford, VA 24523   **(80%)**
Tel.: (540) 586-0674
Sales Range: $50-74.9 Million
Emp.: 40
Fabricates Light Weight Steel for Industrial & Ornamental Use
N.A.I.C.S.: 332312

S.I.P. Inc. of Delaware   (1)
2204 Chestnut St, Gadsden, AL 35904
Tel.: (256) 546-5858
Web Site: http://www.wmsi.com
Sales Range: $100-124.9 Million
Insurance Services
N.A.I.C.S.: 332312

WII Realty Management   (1)
PO Box 1770, Manassas, VA 20108
Tel.: (703) 560-5196
Real Estate Management Services
N.A.I.C.S.: 531210

Williams Bridge Co.   (1)
8624 JD Reading Dr, Manassas, VA 20109   **(100%)**
Tel.: (703) 335-7800
Web Site: http://www.williamsbridge.com
Sales Range: $50-74.9 Million
Emp.: 60
Steel Fabrication
N.A.I.C.S.: 332312

Williams Equipment Corporation   (1)
PO Box 1770, Manassas, VA 20108   **(100%)**
Tel.: (703) 335-7800
Sales Range: $10-24.9 Million
Emp.: 50
Construction Equipment Leasing
N.A.I.C.S.: 532412
Art Williams *(CEO)*

Williams Steel Erection Co., Inc.   (1)
8624 JD Reading Dr, Manassas, VA 20109   **(100%)**
Tel.: (703) 335-7850
Metal Erection & Installation Services
N.A.I.C.S.: 238190

WILLIAMS INLAND DISTRIBUTORS LLC
1505 N Bradley, Spokane, WA 99212
Tel.: (509) 568-1260
Sales Range: $10-24.9 Million
Emp.: 85
Ice Cream
N.A.I.C.S.: 424430
Roger Williams *(Pres)*

WILLIAMS INTERNATIONAL
2000 Centerpoint Pkwy, Pontiac, MI 48341
Tel.: (248) 624-5200   MI
Web Site: http://www.williams-int.com
Year Founded: 1955
Gas Turbine Engines Mfr
N.A.I.C.S.: 336412
John Sordyl *(Dir-Government Bus Dev)*
Dylan Tribbey *(Mgr-Comml Bus Dev)*
Gregg G. Williams *(Chm, Pres & CEO)*

WILLIAMS INVESTMENT COMPANY
1203 W 4th St Ste 11, Adel, GA 31620
Tel.: (229) 896-4511
Sales Range: $10-24.9 Million
Emp.: 20
Hotel
N.A.I.C.S.: 721110
James Michael Williams *(Pres)*
Rick Williams *(VP)*

WILLIAMS LUMBER INC.
6760 Route 9 N, Rhinebeck, NY 12572
Tel.: (845) 876-7011
Web Site: http://www.williamslumber.com
Year Founded: 1946
Sales Range: $25-49.9 Million
Emp.: 180
Home Center Operator
N.A.I.C.S.: 444110
Kim Williams *(VP-Inventory)*
Kelly Williams *(VP-Sls)*
Sandy Williams *(Pres)*

WILLIAMS MECHANICAL CORPORATION
156 Hwy 601 S, Lugoff, SC 29078
Tel.: (803) 438-3587
Web Site: http://www.williamsmechanical.com
Rev.: $28,844,742
Emp.: 50
Plumbing Contractor
N.A.I.C.S.: 238220
Carl E. Williams *(CEO)*

WILLIAMS METALS AND WELDING ALLOYS, INC.
125 Strafford Ave Ste 108, Wayne, PA 19087
Tel.: (610) 225-0105
Web Site: http://www.wmwa.net
Sales Range: $50-74.9 Million
Emp.: 61
Metal Products Processing & Distribution Service
N.A.I.C.S.: 423510
Mark Azzaro *(VP)*
Donna Wise *(Gen Mgr-Concord)*
David Christian *(Mgr-Shipping-Mansfield)*
Forrest Mabry *(Mgr-Ops-Birmingham)*
Dick Barnett *(Gen Mgr-Birmingham)*
Trent Heyman *(Gen Mgr)*
Joe Wallace *(Mgr-Sls-Welding)*
Billy Huffman *(Mgr-Warehouse)*

WILLIAMS MULLEN
Williams Mullen Ctr 200 S 10th St Ste 1600, Richmond, VA 23219
Tel.: (804) 420-6000
Web Site: http://www.williamsmullen.com
Year Founded: 1909
Sales Range: $100-124.9 Million
Emp.: 501
Legal Advisory Services
N.A.I.C.S.: 541110
Farhad Aghdami *(Partner)*
David D. Addison *(Co-Partner)*
D. Earl Baggett *(Partner)*
William D. Bayliss *(Co-Partner)*
William J. Benos *(Co-Partner)*
Gregory R. Bishop *(Atty)*
Judy Lin Bristow *(Partner)*
Turner A. Broughton *(Co-Partner)*
Lynn K. Brugh *(Partner)*
David F. Paulson *(Mng Partner-Carolina & VP)*
Matthew M. Cobb *(Partner)*
David M. Saravitz *(Partner)*
Cinnamon A. Baker *(Dir-Talent Mgmt)*
Mike Sajovec *(Partner)*
Wyatt Booth *(Partner-Real Estate Practice)*
Allison T. Domson *(Vice Chm)*
Craig L. Rascoe *(COO & VP)*
Danny W. Jackson *(Exec Dir)*
J. Conrad Garcia *(Partner & VP)*
Anthony H. Anikeeff *(Partner)*
George H. Bowles *(Partner)*
Phil Conner *(Partner-Environment & Natural Resources Practice)*
Michael Maloney *(Partner-Govt Contracts Practice)*
Brad Nowak *(Partner-Corp, Energy, Public & Private Partnerships)*
Robert E. Korroch *(VP)*
Kristin P. Richardson *(Chief Mktg Officer)*
Christine N. Piersall *(Atty)*
Rebecca E. Ivey *(Partner-Health Care)*
Jamie Baskerville Martin *(Chm-Health Care Section)*
Joel Johnson *(Partner-Health Care Section)*
Sean M. Sullivan *(Partner--Raleigh)*
Ethan Ware *(Chm-Environment)*
Ralph L. Axselle Jr. *(Co-Partner)*
Wyatt S. Beazley IV *(Gen Counsel & Atty)*
Paul S. Bliley Jr. *(Partner)*

WILLIAMS OIL COMPANY INC.
207 York Ave N, Towanda, PA 18848
Tel.: (570) 265-6673   PA
Web Site: http://www.williamsoil.com
Year Founded: 1983
Sales Range: $50-74.9 Million
Emp.: 125
Retailers of Petroleum Products
N.A.I.C.S.: 424720
Randy B. Williams *(Pres)*
Larry Huber *(CFO)*

Subsidiaries:

Dandy Mini Marts Inc.   (1)
101 N Main St, Athens, PA 18810
Tel.: (570) 888-4344
Web Site: http://www.dandyminimarts.com
Grocery Stores
N.A.I.C.S.: 445131

Williams Lubricants Inc.   (1)
York Ave N, Towanda, PA 18848
Tel.: (570) 265-6673
Web Site: http://www.williamsoil.net
Sales Range: $10-24.9 Million
Emp.: 25
Petroleum Products
N.A.I.C.S.: 424720
Jim Barnes *(Mgr-Sls)*

WILLIAMS PATENT CRUSHER & PULVERIZER CO., INC.
2701 N Broadway, Saint Louis, MO 63102-1509
Tel.: (314) 621-3348   MO
Web Site: http://www.williamscrusher.com
Year Founded: 1886
Sales Range: $75-99.9 Million
Emp.: 100
Crushing & Grinding Machinery Mfr
N.A.I.C.S.: 333131
Dijana Taylor *(Mgr-Supply Chain)*
Robert E. Williams Jr. *(CEO)*

WILLIAMS STEEL COMPANY INC.
315 Lk St, Jackson, TN 38301-5842
Tel.: (731) 423-4900   TN
Web Site: http://www.williams-steel-co.com
Year Founded: 1963
Sales Range: $10-24.9 Million
Emp.: 85
Supplier of Structural Metal
N.A.I.C.S.: 332312
Charles Campbell *(Pres & CEO)*

WILLIAMS SUPPLY INC.
210 7th St SW, Roanoke, VA 24001
Tel.: (540) 343-9333   VA
Web Site: http://www.williams-supply.com
Year Founded: 1960
Sales Range: $10-24.9 Million
Emp.: 95
Supplier of Electrical Equipment
N.A.I.C.S.: 423610
Tom Moody *(Pres)*
Joe Wunder *(VP-Sls)*
Keith Beheler *(VP-Technical Sls)*
Jeff Jackson *(Sr Mgr-Fluid Power & Instrumentation)*

WILLIAMS TANK LINES
1477 Tillie Lewis Dr, Stockton, CA 95206
Tel.: (209) 944-5613

Web Site:
http://www.williamstanklines.com
Sales Range: $10-24.9 Million
Emp.: 400
Liquid Petroleum Transport
N.A.I.C.S.: 484230
Michael I. Williams *(Pres)*
David Ray *(Dir-Safety & HR)*
Daniel McDonnell *(Owner)*
Mark Lill *(Gen Mgr)*

WILLIAMS TRACTOR INC.
2501 N Shiloh Dr, Fayetteville, AR 72702
Tel.: (479) 442-8284
Web Site:
http://www.williamstractor.com
Rev.: $29,807,175
Emp.: 40
Agricultural Machinery & Equipment
N.A.I.C.S.: 423820
Doug Williams *(Pres)*

WILLIAMS VOLKSWAGEN INC.
2845 E Saginaw St, Lansing, MI 48912
Tel.: (517) 484-1341
Web Site:
http://www.williamsautoworld.com
Year Founded: 1971
Sales Range: $25-49.9 Million
Emp.: 50
New & Used Automobiles
N.A.I.C.S.: 441110
Jim Barnes *(Controller)*
David Williams *(Pres)*

WILLIAMS WEALTH MANAGEMENT GROUP, INC.
3639 Cortez Rd W Ste 225, Bradenton, FL 34210
Tel.: (941) 756-4500
Web Site:
http://www.williamswealth360.com
Year Founded: 2007
Sales Range: $1-9.9 Million
Emp.: 3
Wealth Management, Investment Advisory & Financial Planning Services
N.A.I.C.S.: 523940
Derek R. Williams *(Pres)*
Beth A. Deyo *(VP)*

WILLIAMS WHITTLE ASSOCIATES, INC.
711 Princess St, Alexandria, VA 22314-2221
Tel.: (703) 836-9222   DC
Web Site:
http://www.williamswhittle.com
Year Founded: 1967
Sales Range: $50-74.9 Million
Emp.: 28
N.A.I.C.S.: 541810
Robert L. Whittle *(Pres & CEO)*
Martha Wilcox *(Exec VP)*
Rich Park *(Dir-Creative)*
Wendy Weaver *(Dir-Media)*
Frank Merecicky *(Mgmt Supvr-Bus Devel)*
Rainee Dove *(Controller)*
Howard Bomstein *(CMO)*
Mike Leimbach *(Assoc Dir-Creative)*
Joanne Williams *(Mgr-Studio)*
Glenn Gimmell *(Sr Art Dir)*
Caitlin McCarthy *(Acct Dir)*

Subsidiaries:

Time & Space   (1)
711 Princess St, Alexandria, VA 22314
Tel.: (703) 836-9222
Web Site: http://www.williamswhittle.com
Sales Range: $10-24.9 Million
Emp.: 6
N.A.I.C.S.: 541810

Wendy C. Weaver *(Media Dir)*
Rob Whittle *(Pres & CEO)*
Martha Wilcox *(Exec VP)*
Rich Park *(Dir-Creative)*

WILLIAMS, INC.
3816 Tongass Ave, Ketchikan, AK 99901-5641
Tel.: (907) 225-1279   AK
Web Site:
http://www.akaandproud.com
Year Founded: 1985
Sales Range: $25-49.9 Million
Emp.: 200
Provider of Grocery Store Services
N.A.I.C.S.: 445110
Ben Williams *(CEO)*

Subsidiaries:

A&P Markets   (1)
3816 Tongass Ave, Ketchikan, AK 99901
Tel.: (907) 225-1279
Web Site: http://www.akandproud.com
Sales Range: $10-24.9 Million
Emp.: 15
Grocery Store Operator
N.A.I.C.S.: 445110

WILLIAMS/CRAWFORD & ASSOCIATES
415 N 5th St PO Box 789, Fort Smith, AR 72902
Tel.: (479) 782-5230
Web Site: http://www.williams-crawford.com
Year Founded: 1982
Rev.: $20,000,000
Emp.: 21
Advetising Agency
N.A.I.C.S.: 541810
Fred O. Williams *(Owner)*
Kevin Crawford *(COO & Exec VP)*
Branden Sharp *(Dir-Creative)*
Denise Williams *(Exec VP & Media Dir)*
Brock Girard *(Dir-Art)*
Brent McCord *(Acct Exec)*
Jenny Thompson *(Media Buyer)*
Laura McKinnon *(Media Buyer)*
Janice Faulkenberry *(Acctg Supvr)*
Amanda Coffman *(Traffic Mgr)*
Chip Paris *(Dir-Client Svcs)*
Rham Cunningham *(Mgr-Traffic)*

WILLIAMS/GERARD PRODUCTIONS INC.
420 N Wabash Ave Ste 500, Chicago, IL 60611-5626
Tel.: (312) 467-5560   IL
Web Site: http://www.wgp.com
Year Founded: 1976
Sales Range: $10-24.9 Million
Emp.: 120
Provider of Video Production Services
N.A.I.C.S.: 512110
Paul Hurder *(CFO)*
Steve Dennison *(VP-Tech)*
Fides Paiso *(Sr Dir-Art)*
John Passi *(VP-Production)*
Dean Watson *(Dir-Tech)*

WILLIAMSBURG ENTERPRISES LTD.
3 Riverway Ste 1100, Houston, TX 77056
Tel.: (713) 804-1030   TX
Web Site:
http://www.williamsburgent.com
Year Founded: 2009
Sales Range: $25-49.9 Million
Emp.: 10
Real Estate Investment Services
N.A.I.C.S.: 531210
Khaled Salem *(CEO)*
Jason Ford *(Pres & COO)*

Hank Youk *(CFO)*
Spencer Harkness *(VP-Dev)*
Ash Thakore *(VP-IR)*

WILLIAMSBURG LANDING, INC.
5700 Williamsburg Landing Dr, Wiliamsburg, VA 23185
Tel.: (757) 565-6505   VA
Web Site:
http://www.williamsburglanding.com
Year Founded: 1982
Sales Range: $25-49.9 Million
Emp.: 447
Elder Care Services
N.A.I.C.S.: 624120
Brandy Day *(Chief Talent Officer)*
Chester Tellis *(CFO & VP-Fin)*
Virginia McLaughlin *(Chm)*
Greg Storer *(Pres & CEO)*

WILLIAMSBURG POTTERY FACTORY
Rte 60 W, Lightfoot, VA 23090
Tel.: (757) 564-3326
Web Site:
http://www.williamsburgpottery.com
Rev.: $28,086,833
Emp.: 250
Housewares
N.A.I.C.S.: 449129
Kimberley A. Maloney *(Pres)*
Peter Kao *(Exec VP)*

WILLIAMSON COUNTY EQUIPMENT CO., INC.
1006 Carlos G Parker Blvd SW, Taylor, TX 76574-4511
Tel.: (512) 352-6381
Web Site:
http://www.wmcoequip.com
Year Founded: 1985
Sales Range: $10-24.9 Million
Emp.: 19
Farm & Garden Machinery & Equipment Whslr
N.A.I.C.S.: 423820
Jeff Rinderknecht *(Gen Mgr)*
Rick Thornton *(Mgr-Sls)*
Ricky Rinderknecht *(Mgr-Parts)*
Mike Rinderknecht *(Mgr-Svc)*

WILLIAMSON DACAR ASSOCIATES INC.
15500 Lightwave Dr, Clearwater, FL 33760
Tel.: (727) 725-0951
Web Site:
http://www.williamsondacar.com
Year Founded: 1994
Sales Range: $1-9.9 Million
Emp.: 12
Architectural & Engineering Services
N.A.I.C.S.: 541310
Theodore J. Williamson *(Co-Founder & Partner)*
David Dacar *(Co-Founder & Partner)*

WILLIAMSON MOTOR CO., INC
3323 E Nettleton Ave, Jonesboro, AR 72401
Tel.: (870) 972-1970
Web Site:
http://www.williamsonmotorcompany.com
Sales Range: $10-24.9 Million
Emp.: 20
New & Used Automobiles
N.A.I.C.S.: 441110
George Williamson *(Pres)*

WILLIE WASHER MANUFACTURING CO.
2101 Greenleaf Ave, Elk Grove Village, IL 60007
Tel.: (847) 956-1344
Web Site:
http://www.williewasher.com
Sales Range: $10-24.9 Million
Emp.: 100
Washers, Metal
N.A.I.C.S.: 332722
William L. Neumann *(Founder & Pres)*

WILLIS & SMITH CAPITAL, LLC
7700 Windrose, 3rd Fl, Plano, TX 75024
Tel.: (469) 209-5108
Web Site: https://www.willis-smithcap.com
Private Equity
N.A.I.C.S.: 523999
Eric M. Willis *(Co-Founder & Mng Partner)*

Subsidiaries:

Performance Stamping Co., Inc.   (1)
20 Lk Marian Rd, Carpentersville, IL 60110
Tel.: (847) 426-2233
Web Site:
http://www.performancestamping.com
Iron & Steel Forging
N.A.I.C.S.: 332111
Scott Spencer *(Owner & CEO)*

WILLIS A. SMITH CONSTRUCTION, INC.
5001 Lakewood Ranch Blvd N, Sarasota, FL 34240
Tel.: (941) 366-3116   FL
Web Site: http://www.willissmith.com
Year Founded: 1972
Sales Range: $50-74.9 Million
Emp.: 53
Commercial & Industrial Building Construction
N.A.I.C.S.: 236220
F. John Lacivita *(VP)*
David E. Sessions *(Pres & CEO)*
Kim French *(VP-Clients)*

WILLIS ALLEN REAL ESTATE COMPANY
1131 Wall St, La Jolla, CA 92037
Tel.: (858) 459-4033   CA
Web Site: http://www.willisallen.com
Year Founded: 1914
Sales Range: $10-24.9 Million
Emp.: 10
Real Estate Brokers & Agents
N.A.I.C.S.: 531210
Andrew E. Nelson *(Owner, Pres & CEO)*
Bud Clark *(Exec VP)*
Cecil Shuffler *(Mgr-Point Loma)*
Andrew E. Nelson *(Owner & Pres)*
Ashley McEvers *(Dir-Relocation)*
Peyton Cabano *(Dir-Mktg)*
Jane Granados *(COO)*

WILLIS CASE HARWOOD MARKETING COMMUNICATIONS INC.
3411 Office Park Dr, Dayton, OH 45439-2285
Tel.: (937) 299-7394   OH
Year Founded: 1918
Sales Range: $10-24.9 Million
Emp.: 8
Advetising Agency
N.A.I.C.S.: 541810
Dean H. Pingrey *(Owner, Chm & Chief Creative Officer)*
Sandra Link *(CFO & Media Dir)*
Deborah A. Sibert *(Pres)*

WILLIS GROUP LLC
1400 Post Oak Blvd Ste 200, Houston, TX 77056-3008

WILLIS GROUP LLC

Willis Group LLC—(Continued)
Tel.: (713) 547-4500
Web Site:
http://www.willisgroupus.com
Year Founded: 2006
Rev.: $4,000,000
Emp.: 286
Business Management Services
N.A.I.C.S.: 561499
Matt Eckert (Exec VP-Bus Dev)

Subsidiaries:

Genuent, LLC (1)
1400 Post Oak Blvd Ste 200, Houston, TX 77056
Tel.: (713) 547-4444
Web Site: http://www.genuent.com
Information Technology Services
N.A.I.C.S.: 541512
MacKeever Tedford (Mng Dir-West)
Kip Wright (Pres & CEO)
Julie Olson (Mng Dir-Talent Path)
John Hurst (Mng Dir-East)
John McCarthy (CFO)

Subsidiary (Domestic):

Genuent USA, LLC (2)
15 Constitution Dr Ste 2b, Bedford, NH 03110
Tel.: (603) 472-3705
Sales Range: $25-49.9 Million
Emp.: 110
Provider of Custom Computer Programming Services
N.A.I.C.S.: 541511

WILLIS OIL CO. INC.
1403 N Expy Ste B, Griffin, GA 30223-9015
Tel.: (770) 227-5724
Web Site: http://www.willisoil.com
Year Founded: 1932
Sales Range: $10-24.9 Million
Emp.: 60
Provider of Petroleum Products
N.A.I.C.S.: 424720
Jimmy Cain (Pres)
Don Seeton (Controller)

WILLIS PERMIAN MOVERS, INC.
2415 Catalina Dr, Odessa, TX 79763
Tel.: (432) 580-7802
Web Site:
http://www.willispermianmovers.com
Used Household & Office Goods Moving
N.A.I.C.S.: 484210
John Willis (Pres)

Subsidiaries:

Texas Moving Company Inc. (1)
908 North Bowser Road, Richardson, TX 75081
Tel.: (972) 234-6371
Web Site: http://www.texasmoving.com
Used Household & Office Goods Moving
N.A.I.C.S.: 484210
Bill R. Andis (Exec VP)
Bobby Quillen (VP)
David Grubbs (VP)
Richard D. Dumais (Founder & Chm)
Steven M. Dumais (Pres)

WILLIS STEIN & PARTNERS, LLC
1 N Wacker Dr Ste 4800, Chicago, IL 60606
Tel.: (312) 422-2400
Web Site: http://www.willisstein.com
Year Founded: 1995
Sales Range: $25-49.9 Million
Emp.: 13
Privater Equity Firm
N.A.I.C.S.: 523999
Avy H. Stein (Mng Partner)
David T. Mills (CFO)

Christopher F. Larson (Partner)
Christopher G. Boehm (CFO-Education Corp-America)

Subsidiaries:

Velocitel Inc. (1)
1033 Skokie Blvd Ste 320, Northbrook, IL 60062
Tel.: (224) 757-0001
Web Site: http://www.velocitel.com
Sales Range: $10-24.9 Million
Outsourced Services to Wireless Telecommunication Companies
N.A.I.C.S.: 517810
James Estes (Chm)
John Meyer (VP & Dir-RF Engrg Svcs)
William Panek (VP-Engrg)
Ken Czosnowski (Sr VP-Bus Dev & Sls)
Kevin G. Hostetler (CEO)
Todd A. Coke (CFO)
Jon Marcusse (Mgr-Sls-Brdcst-Natl)
Sabrina C. Newson (VP-Sls & Mktg)
Kevin Hostetler (CEO)

Subsidiary (Domestic):

Velocitel Management Services (2)
200 N Gleb Rd Ste 1000, Arlington, VA 22203
Tel.: (703) 276-1100
Administrative Management
N.A.I.C.S.: 561110
Douglas Hall (Pres)

WILLISTON FINANCIAL GROUP, LLC
12909 SW 68th Pkwy, Portland, OR 97223
Tel.: (503) 387-3636
Web Site:
http://www.willistonfinancial.com
Sales Range: $10-24.9 Million
Title Insurance Services
N.A.I.C.S.: 524127
Mark Adams (CIO & Exec VP)
Justin Tucker (CMO)
Lance Melber (Pres-west)
Gorkem Kuterdem (CTO-west)
Steven A. Ozonian (Pres & CEO)

Subsidiaries:

MyHome, a Williston Financial Group Company, LLC (1)
500 Technology Dr, Irvine, CA 92618
Tel.: (833) 451-5718
Web Site: https://myhome.com
Online Transaction Services
N.A.I.C.S.: 518210
Marty Frame (Pres)

Subsidiary (Domestic):

LoyaltyExpress Inc. (2)
53 Commerce Way, Woburn, MA 01801
Tel.: (781) 938-1175
Web Site: http://www.loyaltyexpress.com
Sales Range: $1-9.9 Million
Emp.: 25
Marketing Programs for Mortgage Lenders & Brokers
N.A.I.C.S.: 541613
Jeffrey Doyle (CEO)
Eric Packer (COO)
Kelly Doyle (Sr VP-Corp Rels)
Robert Goulart (CTO)

WFG National Title Insurance Company (1)
700 N Brand Blvd Ste 1100, Glendale, CA 91203
Tel.: (818) 476-4000
Web Site:
http://www.california.wfgnationaltitle.com
Emp.: 60
Title Insurance & Escrow Services
N.A.I.C.S.: 524127
A. Kirchen (Sr VP)
Michael T. Gallaher (CFO)
Donald O'Neill (COO & Exec VP)
Patrick F. Stone (Founder & Chm)
Joseph V. McCabe Jr. (Gen Counsel, Sec & Exec VP)

WILLKIE FARR & GALLAGHER LLP

787 7th Ave, New York, NY 10019-6099
Tel.: (212) 728-8000
Web Site: http://www.willkie.com
Year Founded: 1888
Sales Range: $500-549.9 Million
Emp.: 1,001
Legal Advisory Services
N.A.I.C.S.: 541110
Adrienne L. Atkinson (Partner)
Mitchell J. Auslander (Partner)
Gregory B. Astrachan (Partner)
Marc Abrams (Partner)
Rajab S. Abbassi (Partner)
Joseph T. Baio (Partner)
Barry P. Barbash (Partner)
Serge Benchetrit (Partner)
David K. Boston (Partner)
P. Georgia Bullitt (Partner)
Leah Campbell (Partner)
Thomas M. Cerabino (Co-Chm)
Steven J. Gartner (Co-Chm)
James R. Burns (Partner)
Verena Etzel (Partner-Natl)
Michael Niebruegge (Partner)
William Stellmach (Partner)
Amelia A. Cottrell (Partner-Litigation Dept)
Scott Miller (Partner)
Alexandra Bigot (Partner)
Anthony Carbone (Partner)
Elizabeth Bower (Partner)
Eugene L. Chang (Partner)
Jeffrey D. Clark (Partner)
Michael E. Brandt (Partner)
Peter Burrell (Mng Partner)
Sameer Advani (Partner)
Stephen Arbuthnot (Atty-Discovery)
Nathalie Duguay (Partner-Paris)
Jacques-Philippe Gunther (Mng Partner-Paris)
Lior Ohayon (Partner-Asset Mgmt)
Denis A. Fallon (Partner-Houston)
Michael De VoePiazza (Partner & Head-Energy Practice)
Justin Browder (Partner-Washington)
Anne Choe (Partner-Washington)
Ashley Young (Partner-Debt Fin)
Gavin Gordon (Partner-Private Equity)
David Arnold (Partner-Private Equity)
Jane Scobie (Partner-Tax)

WILLMAR POULTRY COMPANY INC.
3735 W 1st Ave, Willmar, MN 56201-9712
Tel.: (320) 235-8850
Web Site:
http://www.willmarpoultry.com
Year Founded: 1951
Sales Range: $75-99.9 Million
Emp.: 1,000
Provider of Poultry Products
N.A.I.C.S.: 112330
Theodore Huisinga (Co-Founder, Chm & CEO)
Ray Norling (Co-Founder & Pres)

WILLO PRODUCTS COMPANY INC.
714 Willo Industrial Dr SE, Decatur, AL 35601
Tel.: (256) 353-7161
Web Site:
http://www.willoproducts.com
Sales Range: $10-24.9 Million
Emp.: 80
Structural Steel Erection
N.A.I.C.S.: 334290
Lynn D. Ozier (Pres)
Jack Ozier (VP)
Dave Wood (Treas & Sec)

WILLOUGHBY INC.

600 Pickwick St S, Savannah, TN 38372
Tel.: (731) 925-3221
Web Site:
http://www.willoughbyoil.com
Sales Range: $50-74.9 Million
Emp.: 35
Petroleum Products
N.A.I.C.S.: 424720
David Willoughby (Pres)
Lee Willoughby (VP)

WILLOUGHBY'S INC.
298 5th Ave, New York, NY 10001
Tel.: (212) 564-1600
Web Site:
http://www.willoughbys.com
Year Founded: 1898
Sales Range: $50-74.9 Million
Emp.: 20
Cameras, Binoculars, Camera Accessories, Audio Equipment & Home & Business Computers Retailer
N.A.I.C.S.: 541512
Silvio Cohen (VP-Admin & Controller)

WILLOW BEND MORTGAGE COMPANY
5800 W Plano Pkwy Ste 105, Plano, TX 75093
Tel.: (972) 818-1666
Web Site: http://www.wbm.com
Year Founded: 1993
Sales Range: $10-24.9 Million
Emp.: 97
Financial Services
N.A.I.C.S.: 522310
Craig Schrank (Exec VP)
Bill Shaddock (Founder & Pres)
Mike Wolfe (Exec VP)
Tracy L. Kell (Sr VP)
Natalie Alexander (CFO)
Steve Ward (CFO)
William Shaddock Jr. (VP)

WILLOW MARKETING
3590 N Meridian Ste 200, Indianapolis, IN 46208
Tel.: (317) 257-5225
Web Site:
http://www.willowmarketing.com
Year Founded: 1992
Rev.: $2,200,000
Emp.: 17
Marketing Research Service
N.A.I.C.S.: 541910
Brad Gillum (Co-Owner)
Lauren Fiedler (Acct Mgr)
Zach Thomas (Dir-Art)
Mark Manuszak (Dir-Art)
Anne Holden (Sr Acct Mgr)
Dylan Stone (Acct Mgr)
Maggie Hendrickson (Sr Mgr-Project & Events)
Kim Jones (Co-Owner, Partner & Sr VP)
Eric Gray (Creative Dir)

WILLOW VALLEY ASSOCIATES INC.
100 Willow Valley Lakes Dr, Willow Street, PA 17584-9450
Tel.: (717) 464-2741
Web Site:
http://www.willowvalley.com
Year Founded: 1966
Sales Range: $25-49.9 Million
Emp.: 350
Provider of Food & Hospitality Services
N.A.I.C.S.: 623312
Marlin H. Thomas (Chm)
Sheryl A. Holzbauer (Treas & Asst Sec)
Steve P. Phenegar (Controller)

James T. Nagle (Dir-Real Estate Dev)
Joseph R. Lucia (CFO)
Diane Poillon (Pres & COO)

WILLOW VALLEY COMMUNITIES
100 Willow Valley Lakes Dr, Willow Street, PA 17584
Tel.: (717) 464-2741 PA
Web Site:
http://www.willowvalleycommunities.org
Year Founded: 1982
Sales Range: $75-99.9 Million
Emp.: 1,616
Continuing Care Retirement Community Operator
N.A.I.C.S.: 623311
Sharon A. Habanec (VP-Culinary Svcs)
Kendall K. Hunsicker (VP-Healthcare Svcs)
James M. Tracy (Dir-Property Mgmt & Svcs)
David W. Haverstick (COO)
John G. Swanson (CEO)
Marlin H. Thomas (Chm)
Dennis W. Griest (CFO)
Kim Daly Nobbs (CMO)
James W. Hostetter (Pres)
Jill E. Gilbert (Treas)
Joseph F. McDonald (Asst Sec)
Jane R. Barley (Sec)
Leslie W. Brant (VP)

WILMAC BUSINESS EQUIPMENT CO, INC.
73 State St, Rochester, NY 14614
Tel.: (585) 454-1160 NY
Web Site: http://www.wilmacco.com
Year Founded: 1988
Sales Range: $1-9.9 Million
Emp.: 50
Office Equipment Merchant Whslr
N.A.I.C.S.: 423420
Stephen McDonnell (VP)

WILMER CUTLER PICKERING HALE & DORR LLP
1875 Pennsylvania Ave NW, Washington, DC 20006
Tel.: (202) 663-6000
Web Site: http://www.wilmerhale.com
Year Founded: 2004
Sales Range: $1-4.9 Billion
Emp.: 1,001
Legal Advisory Services
N.A.I.C.S.: 541110
Charlene Barshefsky (Sr Partner-Intl)
Paul M. Architzel (Co-Partner)
Thomas E. Anderson (Co-Partner)
Bruce M. Berman (Partner & Gen Counsel)
Jason D. Kipnis (Co-Partner)
Marian Freed (Chief Admin Officer)
Peggy L. Giunta (Chief Legal Personnel & Dev Officer & Chief Practice Mgmt Officer)
Robert J. Dunne (Chief HR Officer)
Christopher E. Babbitt (Partner)
Dan M. Berkovitz (Partner)
David W. Bowker (Partner)
Christopher Lupo (CFO)

WILMES CHEVROLET BUICK, INC.
2215 E Broadway, Altus, OK 73521
Tel.: (580) 482-4866
Web Site:
http://www.wilmeschevrolet.net
Sales Range: $10-24.9 Million
Emp.: 44
Car Whslr
N.A.I.C.S.: 441110
Tim R. Wilmes (Pres)

WILMES FORD-LINCOLN, INC.
108 N Veterans Dr, Altus, OK 73521
Tel.: (866) 263-5153 OK
Web Site: http://www.wilmesford.com
Car Dealer
N.A.I.C.S.: 441110

WILMES SUPERSTORE, INC.
108 N Veterans Dr, Altus, OK 73521
Tel.: (580) 482-0617
Web Site:
http://www.wilmessuperstore.com
Sales Range: $10-24.9 Million
Emp.: 48
Car Whslr
N.A.I.C.S.: 441110
Jeff Wilmes (Pres)

WILMINGTON COUNTRY CLUB
4825 Kennett Pike, Wilmington, DE 19807
Tel.: (302) 655-6171 DE
Web Site:
http://www.wilmingtoncc.com
Year Founded: 1901
Sales Range: $10-24.9 Million
Emp.: 296
Country Club Operator
N.A.I.C.S.: 713910
Ed McQuillin (Dir-Rackets)
Philip Iannelli (Gen Mgr)
Sherman Tribbitt (Dir-Food & Beverage)

WILMINGTON HEALTH ASSOCIATES, PA.
1202 Medical Ctr Dr, Wilmington, NC 28401-7394
Tel.: (910) 341-3300
Web Site:
http://www.wilmingtonhealth.com
Freestanding Ambulatory Surgical & Emergency Centers
N.A.I.C.S.: 621493
Melanie Frank (Mgr)

Subsidiaries:

Penslow Medical Center (1)
206 N Dyson St, Holly Ridge, NC 28445
Tel.: (910) 329-7591
Web Site:
http://www.penslowmedicalcenter.com
Health Care Srvices
N.A.I.C.S.: 622110
Cheryl Hines (Office Mgr)
Mary Piner (Chm)
Kathy Sandlin (Treas)
Jennifer Bartz (Vice Chm)

WILMINGTON PRODUCTS-USA INC.
49 Bryant Ave, Roslyn, NY 11576
Tel.: (516) 484-6996
Web Site:
http://www.thenorthwest.com
Sales Range: $10-24.9 Million
Emp.: 130
Blanketings, Manmade Fiber
N.A.I.C.S.: 313210
Ross Auerbach (Pres)

WILMORE ELECTRONICS COMPANY
Old Hwy 86 & 70 A, Hillsborough, NC 27278
Tel.: (919) 732-9351
Web Site:
http://www.wilmoreelectronics.com
Rev.: $10,000,000
Emp.: 48
Power Switching Equipment
N.A.I.C.S.: 335313
E. T. Moore (Pres)

WILMORITE INC.
1265 Scottsville Rd, Rochester, NY 14624
Tel.: (585) 464-9400
Web Site:
http://www.eastviewmall.com
Rev.: $100,000,000
Emp.: 75
Shopping Center
N.A.I.C.S.: 541618
Thomas C. Wilmott (Pres)
Gerald Battoglia (Mgr-Construction & Coord-Tenant)
William Dumont (Mgr-Help Desk)

WILO USA LLC
9550 W Higgins Rd #300, Rosemont, IL 60656
Tel.: (888) 945-6872 DE
Web Site: http://www.wilo-usa.com
Year Founded: 2010
Water Pumps Mfr
N.A.I.C.S.: 333914
Tim Ruppert (Pres & Mng Dir)
Mohammed Siddiqi (Dir-Engrg)

Subsidiaries:

Weil Pump Co. Inc. (1)
W 57 N 14363 Doerr Way, Cedarburg, WI 53012
Tel.: (262) 377-1399
Web Site: http://www.weilpump.com
Pump Equipment Mfr
N.A.I.C.S.: 333914
Bill Kanetzke (Sls Mgr)

WILSEY BENNETT COMPANY
235 Kansas St Ste 200, San Francisco, CA 94103-5162
Tel.: (415) 255-7666 CA
Year Founded: 1950
Sales Range: $50-74.9 Million
Emp.: 10
Real Estate Development & Investment
N.A.I.C.S.: 484121
Dale Carrigan (Sec)

Subsidiaries:

Wilsey Bennett Real Estate Division (1)
235 Kansas Ste 200, San Francisco, CA 94103
Tel.: (415) 255-7666
Real Estate Development & Investment
N.A.I.C.S.: 424210
Michael Wilsey (CEO)

WILSHIRE ASSOCIATES, INC.
1299 Ocean Ave Ste 700, Santa Monica, CA 90401
Tel.: (310) 451-3051
Web Site: http://www.wilshire.com
Year Founded: 1972
Emp.: 200
Financial Risk Analytics Services
N.A.I.C.S.: 561499
Dennis A. Tito (Chm & CEO)
John C. Hindman (Pres)
Leah Emkin (Mng Dir-Funds Mgmt-Global Client Svcs Grp)
Mark E. Brubaker (Mng Dir-Wilshire Consulting)
Jason A. Schwarz (COO)
Daniel Ingram (VP-Responsible Investment Res & Consulting-Wilshire Consulting)
Bradley Baker (Mng Dir-Wilshire Consulting)
Rose Dean (Mng Dir-Wilshire Consulting)
Ali Kazemi (Mng Dir-Wilshire Consulting)
Ned McGuire (Mng Dir-Wilshire Consulting)
Karyn L. Williams (Mng Partner)
Jim Gentleman (Mng Dir-Wilshire Funds Mgmt-Chicago)
Suehyun Kim (VP & Portfolio Mgr-Wilshire Funds Mgmt)
Benkai E. H. Bouey (Chief Compliance Officer)
Joshua M. Emanuel (Mng Dir & Chief Investment Officer)
Reena S. Lalji (Gen Counsel)
William Van Eesteren (Mng Dir-Wilshire Private Markets)
Lawrence Davanzo (Founder-Pension Consulting Bus & Pres-Mutual Fund Complexes)

Subsidiaries:

Wilshire Associates Europe B.V. (1)
World Trade Center Tower H 25th Floor, Zuidplein 204, Amsterdam, 1077 XV, Netherlands
Tel.: (31) 20 305 7530
Web Site: http://www.wilshire.com
Emp.: 10
Financial Risk Analytics Services
N.A.I.C.S.: 561499

Wilshire Australia Pty Limited (1)
Suite 3 Level 10 470 Collins Street, Melbourne, 3000, VIC, Australia
Tel.: (61) 3 9678 0300
Financial Risk Analytics Services
N.A.I.C.S.: 561499

WILSHIRE CONNECTION, LLC
624 S Grand Ave Ste 2500, Los Angeles, CA 90017
Tel.: (213) 213-8636 DE
Web Site: http://www.wilcon.com
Year Founded: 1998
Rev.: $5,500,000
Emp.: 3
Telecommunications Resellers
N.A.I.C.S.: 517121
Eric Bender (Pres)

WILSHIRE ENTERPRISES, INC.
100 Eagle Rock Ave Ste 100, East Hanover, NJ 07936-3149
Tel.: (973) 585-7770 DE
Web Site:
http://www.wilshireenterprises.com
Year Founded: 1951
Residential Property Investment & Management Services
N.A.I.C.S.: 531390
Sherry Izak (CEO)

WILSON & COMPANY, INC.
1227 E Broadway St Ste 101, Oviedo, FL 32765
Tel.: (407) 365-0906
Web Site:
http://www.wilsoncompany.net
Year Founded: 1994
Sales Range: $10-24.9 Million
Commercial Construction
N.A.I.C.S.: 236220
Parks Wilson (Pres & CEO)
Ameila Wilson (CFO)

WILSON & COMPANY, INC.
4900 Lang Ave NE, Albuquerque, NM 87109
Tel.: (505) 348-4000
Web Site: http://www.wilsonco.com
Year Founded: 1932
Sales Range: $10-24.9 Million
Emp.: 425
Engineering, Architecture, Surveying, Mapping, Environmental & Planning Services
N.A.I.C.S.: 541330
James A. Brady (Pres & CEO)
James E. Ross (CFO & Sr VP)
Daniel Aguirre (Sr VP)
Ryan Branfort (Sr VP)
Kenneth Hancock (Chm & Sr VP)
Troy Eisenbraun (Sr VP)
Glen Selover (Engr-Civil)
Christopher Perea (Assoc VP)
Derek Meier (Assoc VP)

WILSON & COMPANY, INC.

U.S. PRIVATE

Wilson & Company, Inc.—(Continued)
Michael W. King (Sr VP & Mgr-Transportation Div)
Savina Garcia (Mgr-Transportation Ops-New Mexico)
Stefany Barone (Chief Mktg Officer)
Rebecca Timmer (Mgr-Bus Dev-Arizona)
Paul Fensterer (VP-Federal Program)

WILSON & MUIR BANCORP INC
107 N 3rd St, Bardstown, KY 40004
Tel.: (502) 348-5996
Web Site:
http://www.wilsonmuirbank.com
Sales Range: $25-49.9 Million
Emp.: 30
State Commercial Banks
N.A.I.C.S.: 522110
Betty Bandy (VP)
Brad Hamilton (COO)
Brian Bates (Sr VP)
Charles L. Wathen (Sr VP)
Lawrence W. Fox (VP)
Davis L. Huston (Sr VP)
Sharron J. Mathews (VP)
Darin Logsdon (VP)
Frank B. Wilson (Pres, CEO & Sec)
Mary Ellen Robison (VP)
Jenean Anderson (VP)
Vinet Herovic (Officer-Loan)
Jeff Blair (VP & Branch Mgr)
Ryan Bratcher (VP & Branch Mgr)
Mike Wilbourn (CFO)
Chris Mayo (Officer-Loan)
Ellen Zutterman (Officer-Loan)

Subsidiaries:

Wilson & Muir Bancorp Inc - Mortgage Division (1)
130 St Matthews Ave, Louisville, KY 40207
Tel.: (502) 454-5400
Mortgage Insurance Services
N.A.I.C.S.: 524126

Wilson & Muir Bank & Trust Co (1)
107 N 3rd St, Bardstown, KY 40004
Tel.: (502) 348-5996
Web Site: http://www.wilsonmuirbank.com
Rev.: $4,900,000
Emp.: 32
State Commercial Banks
N.A.I.C.S.: 522110
Frank B. Wilson (Pres & CEO)
Mike Wilbourn (CFO & Sr VP)
Brad Hamilton (COO)

Wilson & Muir Bank & Trust Company (1)
118 S Main St, Leitchfield, KY 42754
Tel.: (270) 259-4001
Web Site: http://www.wilsonmuirbank.com
Sales Range: $25-49.9 Million
Emp.: 17
State Commercial Banks
N.A.I.C.S.: 522110
Ryan Bratcher (VP)

WILSON 5 SERVICE CO. INC.
6 Page St, Kittery, ME 03904
Tel.: (207) 439-2361
Web Site: http://www.wilsonfive.com
Sales Range: $10-24.9 Million
Emp.: 150
Property Maintenance Services
N.A.I.C.S.: 238990
James E. Wilson (Pres)
Edward K. Wilson (VP)

WILSON ASSOCIATES
3811 Turtle Creek Blvd Ste 1600, Dallas, TX 75219
Tel.: (214) 521-6753
Web Site:
http://www.wilsonassociates.com
Year Founded: 1971
Sales Range: $25-49.9 Million
Emp.: 310

Resort & Hotel Construction
N.A.I.C.S.: 236220
Cheryl Neumann (Co-Pres)
Beth Campbell (CEO-Los Angeles)
Ashley Bickerstaff (VP-Bus Dev-Real Estate)

WILSON AUTO GROUP
2212 S Duff Ave, Ames, IA 50010-8017
Tel.: (515) 232-4081
Web Site:
http://www.wilsonautogroup.com
Year Founded: 1982
Sales Range: $10-24.9 Million
Emp.: 38
Car Whslr
N.A.I.C.S.: 441110
Danny Wilson (Owner)

WILSON AUTO GROUP, INC.
4200 Lakeland Dr, Flowood, MS 39232
Tel.: (601) 914-4200
Web Site:
http://www.wilsonautogroup.com
Year Founded: 1988
Sales Range: $10-24.9 Million
Emp.: 65
Car Whslr
N.A.I.C.S.: 441110
Doug Wilson (Owner & Pres)

WILSON BAKER INC.
25056 Shortly Rd, Georgetown, DE 19947
Tel.: (302) 856-2895
Web Site:
http://www.bakerpetroleumde.com
Sales Range: $10-24.9 Million
Emp.: 150
Operator of Convenience Stores
N.A.I.C.S.: 445131
W. Wayne Baker (Pres)
Alan Baker (VP)

WILSON BATES APPLIANCE STORES
1710 Kimberly Rd, Twin Falls, ID 83301
Tel.: (208) 733-6146
Web Site:
http://www.wilsonbates.com
Sales Range: $10-24.9 Million
Emp.: 65
Furniture Retailer
N.A.I.C.S.: 449110
Rick White (Pres)
Todd White (VP)

WILSON COMPANY
16301 Addison Rd, Addison, TX 75001
Tel.: (972) 931-8666
Web Site: http://www.wilson-company.com
Sales Range: $10-24.9 Million
Emp.: 100
Hydraulic Systems Equipment & Supplies
N.A.I.C.S.: 423830
Richard A. Bills (Pres)
Gary Kruger (Controller)

WILSON CONSTRUCTION CO., INC.
1190 NW 3rd Ave, Canby, OR 97013-3441
Tel.: (503) 263-6882 OR
Web Site:
http://www.wilsonconst.com
Year Founded: 1956
Sales Range: $25-49.9 Million
Emp.: 250
Contractor of Water, Sewer & Utility Lines

N.A.I.C.S.: 237130
Donald Wilson (Pres)
Debbie Greene (Controller)
Scott Carr (Mgr-Fleet)

Subsidiaries:

Wilson Utility Equipment Co. (1)
1190 NW 3rd Ave, Canby, OR 97013-3441
Tel.: (503) 263-6882
Sales Range: $10-24.9 Million
Emp.: 30
Provider of Repair Services
N.A.I.C.S.: 811210
Donald Wilson (Pres)

WILSON CONSTRUCTION COMPANY INC.
345 Highlandia Dr, Baton Rouge, LA 70810-1457
Tel.: (225) 926-3000 LA
Year Founded: 1976
Sales Range: $10-24.9 Million
Emp.: 60
Provider of Commercial Construction Services
N.A.I.C.S.: 236220
Mark A. Wilson (Pres)
Joyce Davis (Controller)
Jim A. Wilson (VP)
Kurt Wilson (VP)

WILSON COUNTY AUTOMOTIVE DEALER GROUP
9030 S Hartman Dr, Lebanon, TN 37090
Tel.: (615) 444-9642
Web Site:
http://www.wilsoncountyautomotive.com
Sales Range: $100-124.9 Million
Emp.: 130
New & Used Automobile Dealer
N.A.I.C.S.: 441110
W. P. Bone (Owner)
Randy Jackson (Dir-Automotive Svc)

Subsidiaries:

Premier Dodge-Chrysler-Jeep (1)
1700 W Main St, Lebanon, TN 37087
Tel.: (615) 444-5777
Web Site:
http://www.wilsoncountyautomotive.com
New & Used Automobile Dealer
N.A.I.C.S.: 441110
Steve Gregory (Gen Mgr)

WILSON DANIELS WHOLESALE LLC
19 W 24th St 7th Fl, New York, NY 10010
Tel.: (844) 939-9463
Web Site:
http://www.wilsondanielswholesale.com
Wine & Distilled Alcoholic Beverage Merchant Whslr
N.A.I.C.S.: 424820
Benjy Kirschner (VP-Sls)
Kevin Murphy (VP-Ops)
Alexandra Schrecengost (Asst VP-PR)
Rocco Lombardo (Pres)
William Davis (Dir-Education)

Subsidiaries:

Futo Wines (1)
1575 Oakville Grade, Oakville, CA 94562
Tel.: (707) 944-9333
Web Site: http://www.futo-wines.com
Wineries
N.A.I.C.S.: 312130
Joshua Lowell (Gen Mgr)

Galaxy Wine Company LLC (1)
2755 NW 31st Ave, Portland, OR 97210-7210
Tel.: (503) 248-9493
Web Site:
http://www.galaxywinecompany.com

Wine & Distilled Alcoholic Beverage Merchant Whslr
N.A.I.C.S.: 424820
Bob Liner (Co-Owner)

WILSON ELECTRIC SERVICES CORP.
600 E Gilbert Dr, Tempe, AZ 85281
Tel.: (480) 505-6500
Web Site:
http://www.wilsonelectric.net
Rev.: $89,691,939
Emp.: 800
Electrical Contractor
N.A.I.C.S.: 238210
Wes McClure (Pres)
Todd Klimas (VP)
Mark Holohan (Mgr-Solar Div)

WILSON ELSER MOSKOWITZ EDELMAN & DICKER
150 E 42nd St, New York, NY 10017-5612
Tel.: (212) 490-3000
Web Site: http://www.wemed.com
Year Founded: 1962
Sales Range: $75-99.9 Million
Emp.: 1,000
Provider of Legal Services
N.A.I.C.S.: 541110
Mitchell S. Milby (Partner)
John Jay Bove (Partner)
Bradley Pryba (Partner)
Wilson Elser (Partner-Chicago)
Daniel J. McMahon (Chm)
Mark Vespole (Partner-New Jersey)
Joanna Crosby (Partner-New Jersey)
Katherine Tammaro (Partner-New Jersey)
Kathleen Williams (Partner-New Jersey)

WILSON EQUIPMENT COMPANY INC.
2180 Old Frankfort Pke, Lexington, KY 40510
Tel.: (859) 254-6443
Web Site:
http://www.wilsonequipment.com
Sales Range: $10-24.9 Million
Emp.: 40
Construction & Mining Machinery
N.A.I.C.S.: 423810
Will Rodes (Gen Mgr)

WILSON FERTILIZER & GRAIN INC.
1827 E Lucas St, Rochester, IN 46975
Tel.: (574) 223-3175
Sales Range: $10-24.9 Million
Emp.: 14
Distr Grains
N.A.I.C.S.: 424510
Jeff Zent (Pres)

WILSON GROUP LTD.
1444 Oak Lawn Ste 545, Dallas, TX 75207
Tel.: (972) 488-4100
Web Site: http://www.wilsonoi.com
Rev.: $61,303,728
Emp.: 100
Office & Public Building Furniture
N.A.I.C.S.: 423210
Pithou Nuth (CFO)

WILSON HUMAN CAPITAL GROUP, LLC
400 N Ashley Dr Ste 3000, Tampa, FL 33602
Tel.: (813) 600-4303
Web Site: http://www.wilsonhcg.com
Year Founded: 2002
Sales Range: $1-9.9 Million
Emp.: 100
Recruitment Services
N.A.I.C.S.: 561312

John Wilson *(Founder & CEO)*
Cynthia Cancio *(VP-Engagement)*
Kim Pope *(Exec VP-Client Solution)*
Andy Zahn *(CFO)*
Jennifer Locklear *(Chief People & Culture Officer)*
Geoff Dubiski *(Exec VP-Global HR & Consulting)*
Jana Smyth *(VP-Client Strategy)*
Jerry Wright *(Exec VP-Global Talent Solutions)*
Jesper Bendtsen *(Exec VP-Global Strategy)*
Marisol Hughes *(Gen Counsel & VP-Global Affairs)*
Jonathan Edwards *(VP-Executive Search)*

WILSON INDUSTRIAL SALES CO.
201 S Wilson St, Brook, IN 47922
Tel.: (219) 275-7333
Web Site:
http://www.wilsonindustrial.com
Year Founded: 1988
Sales Range: $10-24.9 Million
Emp.: 25
Fertilizer & Fertilizer Materials
N.A.I.C.S.: 424910
Thomas Wilson *(Founder, Treas & Sec)*
Steve Wilson *(Pres)*

WILSON IRON WORKS INC.
208 S Lodge St, Wilson, NC 27894
Tel.: (252) 291-4465
Web Site:
http://www.easternhydraulic.com
Sales Range: $10-24.9 Million
Emp.: 60
Hydraulic Systems Equipment & Supplies
N.A.I.C.S.: 423830
Ken Dollar *(CEO)*

Subsidiaries:

Wilson Iron Works Inc. (1)
208 Lodge St S, Wilson, NC 27893
Tel.: (252) 291-6314
Web Site: http://www.wilsonironworks.com
Sales Range: $10-24.9 Million
Hydraulic Systems Equipment & Supplies
N.A.I.C.S.: 425120
Dugg Beyman *(CEO)*

WILSON LOGISTICS, INC.
3769 E Evergreen St, Springfield, MO 65803
Tel.: (888) 586-0331
Web Site:
http://www.wilsonlogistics.com
Trucking Service
N.A.I.C.S.: 484122
Lane Williams *(Dir-Recruiting & Retention)*

Subsidiaries:

Market Logistics Services, Ltd. (1)
575 Madison Ave, Elizabeth, NJ 07201-1559
Tel.: (908) 361-4988
Logistics Consulting Servies
N.A.I.C.S.: 541614

WILSON LUMBER COMPANY INC.
4818 Meridian St N, Huntsville, AL 35811-1139
Tel.: (256) 852-7411
Web Site:
http://www.wilsonlumber.net
Year Founded: 1949
Sales Range: $25-49.9 Million
Emp.: 165
Supplier of Lumber & Building Materials
N.A.I.C.S.: 423310

Russ Wilson *(Office Mgr)*

WILSON MARINE CORPORATION
6095 Grand River Rd, Brighton, MI 48114
Tel.: (517) 546-3774 MI
Web Site:
http://www.wilsonboats.com
Year Founded: 1949
Sales Range: $10-24.9 Million
Emp.: 50
Retailer of Boats & Marine Supplies
N.A.I.C.S.: 441222
Ronald Wilson *(Pres)*
Randy Wilson *(VP & Mgr-Store)*
Debbie Schroeder *(Controller)*
Marge Wilson *(VP)*
Randy Wilson *(Mgr-Store)*

WILSON MOTOR COMPANY
328 N Main St, Logan, UT 84321-3997
Tel.: (435) 752-7355
Web Site:
http://www.wilsonmotor.com
Year Founded: 1943
Sales Range: $10-24.9 Million
Emp.: 50
Car Whslr
N.A.I.C.S.: 441110
Larry Speth *(Mgr-Parts & Svc)*
Nate Wilson *(Mgr-Sls)*
Chris Wilson *(Pres)*

WILSON OIL, INC.
95 Panel Way, Longview, WA 98632-1035
Tel.: (360) 575-9222 WA
Web Site:
http://www.wilcoxandflegel.com
Year Founded: 1971
Emp.: 170
Fuel, Oil & Lubricant Distr
N.A.I.C.S.: 424720
Steven C. Wilcox *(Pres)*
Brian Chace *(Sls Mgr-Retail Fuels)*

WILSON PERKINS ALLEN OPINION RESEARCH (WPA)
324 Second St SE, Washington, DC 20003
Tel.: (202) 470-6300
Web Site: http://www.wpaintel.com
Year Founded: 1998
Sales Range: $1-9.9 Million
Emp.: 20
Various Research Services & Campaigns
N.A.I.C.S.: 541910
Bryon Allen *(Partner & COO)*

WILSON PLYWOOD & DOOR, INC.
833 Shepherd Dr, Garland, TX 75042
Tel.: (972) 494-3545 TX
Web Site:
http://www.wilsonplywood.com
Year Founded: 1948
Sales Range: $10-24.9 Million
Emp.: 101
Lumber; Plywood & Millwork
N.A.I.C.S.: 423810
James M. Preddy *(Pres)*
Mike Godfrey *(CFO)*

WILSON SONSINI GOODRICH & ROSATI
650 Page Mill Rd, Palo Alto, CA 94304-1050
Tel.: (650) 493-9300
Web Site: http://www.wsgr.com
Year Founded: 1961
Sales Range: $500-549.9 Million
Emp.: 1,001
Legal Advisory Services

N.A.I.C.S.: 541110
John E. Aguirre *(Partner & Atty)*
Suzanne Y. Bell *(Partner & Atty)*
Mark B. Baudler *(Partner & Atty)*
Larry Sonsini *(Chm)*
Jeffrey D. Saper *(Vice Chm)*
Boris Feldman *(Partner)*
Barry M. Kaplan *(Partner & Atty-Seattle)*
Jamillia Ferris *(Partner)*
Doug Clark *(Mng Partner)*
Eileen Marshall *(Partner)*
Keith Eggleton *(Partner)*
Michael Ringler *(Partner)*
Susan Creighton *(Partner)*
Tony Jeffries *(Partner)*
Vern Norviel *(Partner)*
John Wehrli *(Partner-San Diego)*
Salil Gandhi *(Partner-New York)*
David Strong *(Partner)*
Katharine A. Martin *(Partner & Partner)*

WILSON STRUCTURAL CONSULTANTS, INC.
6731 Professional Pkwy W Ste 103, Sarasota, FL 34240
Tel.: (941) 907-4789
Web Site:
http://www.wilsonstructural.com
Sales Range: $1-9.9 Million
Emp.: 10
Engineeering Services
N.A.I.C.S.: 541330
Richard Wilson *(Owner)*
Ricardo Marques *(Mgr-CAD)*

WILSON TOOL INTERNATIONAL INC.
12912 Farnham Ave, White Bear Lake, MN 55110
Tel.: (651) 286-6000
Web Site: http://www.wilsontool.com
Rev.: $22,100,000
Emp.: 450
Mfr of Punches, Forming & Stamping
N.A.I.C.S.: 333514
Paul Johnson *(Pres-Corp Dev)*
Klaus Neumann *(VP-Sls-Europe)*

Subsidiaries:

The Wilson Company S. de R.L. de C.V. (1)
BLVD Diaz Ordaz no 140 piso 20 Col Santa Maria, 64650, Monterrey, Nuevo Leon, Mexico
Tel.: (52) 8007412510
Industrial Machinery Whslr
N.A.I.C.S.: 423830

Wilson Tool Argentina, S.R.L. (1)
Dardo Rocha 1294, Martinez, Buenos Aires, Argentina
Tel.: (54) 11 4792 0056
Industrial Machinery Whslr
N.A.I.C.S.: 423830

Wilson Tool Canada Inc. (1)
120 Van Kirk Drive, Brampton, L7A 1B1, ON, Canada
Tel.: (800) 268-4180
Web Site: http://www.wilsontoolcanada.com
Press Brake Mfr
N.A.I.C.S.: 333517
Frank Rajk *(VP)*

Wilson Tool International A/S (1)
Ejby Industrivej 40, 2600, Glostrup, Denmark
Tel.: (45) 44 53 16 99
Industrial Machinery Whslr
N.A.I.C.S.: 423830
Colin Well *(Gen Mgr)*

WILSON TRAILER COMPANY INC.
4400 S Lewis Blvd, Sioux City, IA 51106-9518
Tel.: (712) 252-6500 IA

Web Site:
http://www.wilsontrailer.com
Year Founded: 1897
Sales Range: $25-49.9 Million
Emp.: 700
Mfr of Truck Trailers
N.A.I.C.S.: 336212
Rick Davis *(Branch Mgr)*
Scott Lamb *(Mgr-Svc)*
Perry Hegstrom *(Branch Mgr)*
Lynn Shelton *(Branch Mgr)*
Tony Sheldon *(Mgr-Parts)*
Shawn Barnes *(Mgr-Svc-Dodge City)*
Ray Ridgway *(Branch Mgr)*
Tracy Howard *(Mgr-Bridgeport)*
Tom Osborne *(Mgr-Parts-Columbus)*
Ronnie Burnside *(Mgr-Svc-Columbus)*

WILSON TRUCKING CORPORATION
137 Wilson Blvd, Fishersville, VA 22939
Tel.: (540) 949-3200 VA
Web Site:
http://www.wilsontrucking.com
Year Founded: 1874
Sales Range: $75-99.9 Million
Emp.: 1,560
Provider of Trucking Services
N.A.I.C.S.: 484121
Charles L. Wilson *(Chm & CEO)*
D. B. Collier *(VP-Sls & Mktg)*
L. A. Combs *(Dir-Info Sys)*
T. G. Wilson *(Vice Chm)*
A. L. Branch *(Dir-Loss Prevention)*
G. A. Megibben *(Reg Dir-Sls & Ops)*
S. D. Gast *(CFO & Exec VP)*

WILSON WAY TIRE COMPANY INC.
221 N Wilson Way, Stockton, CA 95205
Tel.: (209) 465-0281
Web Site:
http://www.wilsonwaytire.com
Sales Range: $10-24.9 Million
Emp.: 40
Automotive Tires
N.A.I.C.S.: 441340
Anthony Mattioli Jr. *(Pres)*

WILSON-DAVIS & COMPANY
236 S Main St, Salt Lake City, UT 84101
Tel.: (801) 532-1313
Web Site: http://www.wdco.com
Year Founded: 1968
Sales Range: $10-24.9 Million
Emp.: 50
Security Brokers
N.A.I.C.S.: 523150
Paul N. Davis *(Pres)*

WILSON-FINLEY COMPANY
5901 Chapel Hill Rd, Raleigh, NC 27607
Tel.: (919) 851-3261
Web Site:
http://www.wilsonfinley.com
Year Founded: 1955
Sales Range: $10-24.9 Million
Emp.: 100
Distr of General Construction Machinery & Equipment
N.A.I.C.S.: 423810
Mark Wilson *(VP)*
Doug Wilson *(Pres)*
Charlotte Davis *(Controller)*

WILSON-MCSHANE CORP.
3001 Metro Dr Ste 500, Bloomington, MN 55425-1799
Tel.: (952) 854-0795
Web Site: http://www.wilson-mcshane.com
Year Founded: 1969

Wilson-Mcshane Corp.—(Continued)

Sales Range: $75-99.9 Million
Emp.: 132
Trust, Fiduciary & Custody Activity Services
N.A.I.C.S.: 523991
Matt Winkel (Pres)
Karen Holt (VP)

WILSONVILLE THRIFTWAY
8255 SW Wilsonville Rd, Wilsonville, OR 97070
Tel.: (503) 682-9053
Web Site: http://www.thriftwaystores.com
Sales Range: $10-24.9 Million
Emp.: 110
Grocery Stores
N.A.I.C.S.: 445110

WILSQUARE CAPITAL LLC
3 City Place Dr Ste 1090, Saint Louis, MO 63141
Tel.: (314) 925-7650   DE
Web Site: http://www.wilsquare.com
Year Founded: 2015
Privater Equity Firm
N.A.I.C.S.: 523999
Jeff DePlanty (Operating Partner & Exec VP)
William L. Willhite (Mng Partner)
James G. Wilmsen (Partner)
Kathy Kristof-Chapman (Chief Compliance Officer & Controller)
Jack Randazzo (Mng Dir)
Andrew Scharf (Dir)
John Curry (Dir)
Heather Lewis (VP-Bus Dev)

Subsidiaries:
Automotive Color & Supply, LLC   (1)
1902 S Calhoun St, Fort Wayne, IN 46802
Tel.: (260) 456-1237
Sales Range: $10-24.9 Million
Emp.: 25
Automobile Painting Products
N.A.I.C.S.: 424950

Outerbox LLC   (1)
Kasier Hall 323 S Main St 3rd Fl, Akron, OH 44308
Tel.: (234) 542-6503
Web Site: http://www.outerboxdesign.com
Sales Range: $1-9.9 Million
Emp.: 25
Web Design & Search Engine Optimization Services
N.A.I.C.S.: 541511
Justin Smith (CEO)
Nick Nolan (COO & Partner)
Jason Dutt (Pres)

Subsidiary (Domestic):
Trinity Insight, LLC   (2)
32 N Front St, Philadelphia, PA 19106
Web Site: http://www.trinityinsight.com
Sales Range: $1-9.9 Million
Emp.: 19
Software Development Services
N.A.I.C.S.: 541511
Craig Smith (CEO)
Nate Ende (Chief Innovation Officer)
Jeremy Weis (Dir-UX Programs)
Bill Rowland (Dir-SEO)
Kyle Kuster (Dir-Engrg)

TekBrands LLC   (1)
8843 S 137th Cir, Omaha, NE 68138
Tel.: (855) 541-0064
Web Site: https://tekbrandsllc.com
Quilting & Crafting Products Dsigner & Marketer
N.A.I.C.S.: 315120

Subsidiary (Domestic):
AccuQuilt, LLC   (2)
8843 S 137th Cir, Omaha, NE 68138
Tel.: (402) 934-1110
Web Site: https://www.accuquilt.com
Quilting Products Whslr
N.A.I.C.S.: 459130

Subsidiary (Domestic):
June Tailor, Inc.   (3)
2861 Highway 175, Richfield, WI 53076
Tel.: (262) 644-5288
Sales Range: $1-9.9 Million
Emp.: 60
Mfr Industries, Nec, Nsk
N.A.I.C.S.: 339999

Versare Solutions, LLC   (1)
3236 NE California St, Minneapolis, MN 55418
Tel.: (612) 782-5260
Web Site: http://www.versare.com
Sales Range: $1-9.9 Million
Emp.: 22
Institutional Furniture Mfr
N.A.I.C.S.: 337127
Brian Olsem (Pres & CEO)

Subsidiary (Domestic):
Screenflex Portable Partition, LLC   (2)
585 Capital Dr, Lake Zurich, IL 60047
Tel.: (847) 726-2900
Web Site: http://www.screenflex.com
Rev.: $8,605,000
Emp.: 50
Showcase, Partition, Shelving & Locker Mfr
N.A.I.C.S.: 337215
John Maas (Pres)

WILTSHIRE & GRANNIS LLP
1919 M St NW 8th Fl, Washington, DC 20036-3537
Tel.: (202) 730-1300
Web Site: http://www.wiltshiregrannis.com
Year Founded: 1998
Emp.: 27
Law Firm
N.A.I.C.S.: 541110
Mark D. Davis (Atty)
Kent D. Bressie (Atty)
Madeleine V. Findley (Atty)
Thomas G. Connolly (Atty)
Charley Kimmett (Partner)
Pat O'Donnell (Partner)
Walter E. Anderson (Co-Partner)
Jennifer Bagg (Co-Partner)
Adrienne Fowler (Atty)
Steven Fredley (Co-Partner)
Shiva Goel (Atty)
S. Roberts Carter III (Atty)

WIMBERLY ALLISON TONG & GOO INC.
700 Bishop St Ste 800, Honolulu, HI 96813-4124
Tel.: (949) 574-8500   HI
Web Site: http://www.watg.com
Year Founded: 1945
Sales Range: $10-24.9 Million
Emp.: 300
Provider of Architectural Services
N.A.I.C.S.: 541310
Jennifer Ploszaj (Chief Mktg Officer)
David D. Moore (Chm, Pres & CEO)

WIMCO CORP.
2533 W 5th St, Washington, NC 27889
Tel.: (252) 946-5175
Web Site: http://www.wimcocorp.com
Sales Range: $25-49.9 Million
Emp.: 50
Commercial & Building Construction Services
N.A.I.C.S.: 236220
Kevin Rawls (Pres)
Jeryl Rawls (CEO)

WIMMER BROTHERS REALTY INC.
5300 S 108th St Ste 1, Hales Corners, WI 53130
Tel.: (414) 529-3900

Web Site: http://www.wimmercommunities.com
Year Founded: 1985
Sales Range: $50-74.9 Million
Emp.: 54
Real Estate Agents & Managers
N.A.I.C.S.: 531210
Mark J. Wimmer (Pres)
John J. Wimmer (VP)
Heather Gerbensky (Mgr-Property)
Jamie Kemke (Mgr-Property)
Lynn Reynolds (Dir-Sls & Mktg)

Subsidiaries:
Suburban Developments Inc.   (1)
5300 S 108th St, Hales Corners, WI 53130-1368   (100%)
Tel.: (414) 529-3900
Web Site: http://www.wimmercommunities.com
Rev.: $410,000
Emp.: 20
Subdividers & Developers
N.A.I.C.S.: 237210

WIMMER SOLUTIONS
1341 N Northlake Way, Seattle, WA 98103
Tel.: (206) 324-4594
Web Site: http://www.wimmersolutions.com
Year Founded: 2002
Rev.: $22,000,000
Emp.: 260
Computer Related Services
N.A.I.C.S.: 541512
Matt Sauri (CEO)
David Robson (Dir-Fin)
Mark Wilson (VP-Sls & Mktg)

WIMSATT BUILDING MATERIALS CORPORATION
36340 Van Born Rd, Wayne, MI 48184-2071
Tel.: (734) 722-3460   MI
Web Site: http://www.wimsattdirect.com
Year Founded: 1936
Sales Range: $25-49.9 Million
Emp.: 140
Provider of Roofing Siding & Insulation Services
N.A.I.C.S.: 423330
Linda Martin (Controller)
Debra Hensley (Mgr-Accts Payable)
Dave Karras (Mgr-Mktg)
Mike Helferich (Branch Mgr)

WIN CHEVROLET, INC.
2201 E 223rd St, Carson, CA 90810-1614
Tel.: (310) 830-5100   CA
Web Site: http://www.winchevrolet.com
Year Founded: 1951
Sales Range: $100-124.9 Million
Emp.: 110
Car Dealership Owner & Operator
N.A.I.C.S.: 441110
Danny Hernandez (Dir-BDC)
Rey Gonzalez (Mgr-Sls)
Vince Nguyen (Mgr-Mktg)
Jerry Pepin (Mgr-Internet)

WIN ENERGY REMC
3981 S US Hwy 41, Vincennes, IN 47591
Tel.: (812) 882-5140
Web Site: http://www.winenergyremc.com
Year Founded: 1997
Sales Range: $25-49.9 Million
Emp.: 50
Electric Power Distr
N.A.I.C.S.: 221122
Harley Drake (Vice Chm)
Marion Jochim (Treas)

WIN SCHULER FOODS
27777 Franklin Rd Ste 1520, Southfield, MI 48034-8261
Tel.: (248) 262-3450   MI
Year Founded: 1993
Sales Range: $75-99.9 Million
Emp.: 11
Snack Foods, Frozen Soups, Sauces, Salad Dressings & Cheese Spreads Mfr
N.A.I.C.S.: 311412
Robert P. Nunez (Pres)
Thomas Bitterman (Gen Mgr)

WIN WIN, INC.
6748 Patterson Ave SE, Caledonia, MI 49316
Tel.: (866) 369-6178
Web Site: https://aslmhc.com
Emp.: 100
Warehouse Equipment Mfr; Storage & Warehousing Services
N.A.I.C.S.: 333922

Subsidiaries:
Binghamton Material Handling, Inc.   (1)
295 Court St Ste 2, Binghamton, NY 13904
Tel.: (607) 723-3456
Web Site: http://www.bmhinc.com
Sales Range: $1-9.9 Million
Emp.: 15
Building Material Dealers
N.A.I.C.S.: 444180
John Foley (Pres)
Jeff Lubs (Controller)

WIN, LLC
4955 Bullis Farm Rd, Eau Claire, WI 54701
Tel.: (715) 874-6300
Web Site: https://wintechnology.com
Year Founded: 1997
Rev.: $6,060,000
Emp.: 6
Radio, Television & Other Electronics Stores
N.A.I.C.S.: 449210
Matthew Yach (Sr Dir-Network Engrg & Ops)
Scott Hoffmann (CEO)
Kristina M. Bourget (VP)

Subsidiaries:
Digicorp, Inc.   (1)
2322 W Clybourn St, Milwaukee, WI 53233
Tel.: (414) 343-1080
Web Site: http://www.digicorp-inc.com
Sales Range: $1-9.9 Million
Emp.: 29
Telephone Communication, Except Radio
N.A.I.C.S.: 517121
Milton Kuyers (CEO)
Dean Wyco (Engr-Voice)

WIN-CON ENTERPRISES INC.
483 NW End Ave, New Braunfels, TX 78130
Tel.: (830) 643-9030
Web Site: http://www.win-con.com
Sales Range: $25-49.9 Million
Emp.: 180
Commercial & Office Building, New Construction
N.A.I.C.S.: 236220
Stanley Ruyle (Pres)
James Lynn Perkins (VP)
Robert Summerville (Project Mgr)

WIN-HOLT EQUIPMENT GROUP
20 Crossways Park N Ste 205, Woodbury, NY 11797
Tel.: (516) 222-0335   NY
Web Site: http://www.winholt.com
Year Founded: 1946
Food Service Equipment
N.A.I.C.S.: 333241

Jonathan J. Holtz (Chm)
Dominick Scarfogliano (Pres & CEO)
Kevin Yates (VP-Sls)
Anthony Smiles (Engr-Mechanical & Sls)
Alex Piscitelli (Dir-Matls)

WIN-SUM SKI CORPORATION
6677 Holiday Vly Rd, Ellicottville, NY 14731
Tel.: (716) 699-2345
Web Site: http://www.holidayvalley.com
Rev.: $17,918,555
Emp.: 140
Resort Hotel
N.A.I.C.S.: 721110
Dennis Eshbaugh (Pres & Gen Mgr)
David Trathen (VP-Fin)
John Northrup (VP)

WINBCO TANK COMPANY
1200 E Main St, Ottumwa, IA 52501
Tel.: (641) 683-1855
Web Site: http://www.winbco.com
Rev.: $32,000,000
Emp.: 99
Tanks, Standard or Custom Fabricated: Metal Plate
N.A.I.C.S.: 332420
John A. Travlos (Pres)
Kermit Knott (Mgr-Ops)

WINBRO GROUP LTD.
70 Conn St, Woburn, MA 01801
Tel.: (781) 933-5300
Sales Range: $10-24.9 Million
Emp.: 5
Cleaning & Polishing Preparations
N.A.I.C.S.: 325612
Winfield Perry (Pres)

WINBROOK INC.
15 Alexander Rd, Billerica, MA 01821
Tel.: (978) 964-1900
Web Site: http://www.winbrook.com
Rev.: $7,977,300
Emp.: 45
Stationery & Office Supplies Merchant Whslr
N.A.I.C.S.: 424120
Charles Lattanzio (Treas)
Scott Lattanzio (Pres)
Subsidiaries:

Brandmark Creative Inc. (1)
35 Technology Park Dr, East Falmouth, MA 02536
Tel.: (508) 444-6165
Web Site:
http://www.brandmarkcreative.com
Printing
N.A.I.C.S.: 323120
Mike Dubie (Pres)

WINCHESTER CAPITAL INVESTMENT MANAGEMENT CORPORATION
445 Orange St, New Haven, CT 06511
Tel.: (203) 787-5029   CT
Web Site: http://www.winchestercapital.com
Year Founded: 1986
Sales Range: $10-24.9 Million
Investment Banking, Advisory & Asset Management Services
N.A.I.C.S.: 523150
Ceasar N. Anquillare (Chm & CEO)
Michael Vincent (Exec Dir)
Gillian Nixon (Comptroller)
Richard Tavelli (Dir-Strategy)
Pippa Smith (Dir-Corp Comm)
Subsidiaries:

Winchester Capital Partners, LLC (1)
445 Orange St, New Haven, CT 06511
Tel.: (203) 787-5029
Web Site: http://www.winchestercapital.com
Privater Equity Firm
N.A.I.C.S.: 523999
Ceasar N. Anquillare (Chm & CEO)
David Bowen (Mng Dir)

WINCHESTER EQUIPMENT CO.
121 Indian Hollow Rd, Winchester, VA 22603
Tel.: (540) 667-2244
Web Site: http://www.winchesterequipment.com
Sales Range: $10-24.9 Million
Emp.: 70
Industrial Machinery & Equipment
N.A.I.C.S.: 423830
Douglas C. Rinker (Chm, Pres & Treas)
Janna Cather (Sec & Coord-Sls)
Robert Sutphin (Mgr-AG Sls)
Tommy Price (Mgr-Sls-Lawn & Garden)

WINCHESTER OPTICAL COMPANY
1935 Lake St, Elmira, NY 14901
Tel.: (607) 734-4251
Web Site: http://www.winoptical.com
Sales Range: $10-24.9 Million
Emp.: 100
Frames, Lenses & Parts, Eyeglass & Spectacle
N.A.I.C.S.: 339115
Brian Lynch (VP)

WINCHESTER SAVINGS BANK
661 Main St, Winchester, MA 01890
Tel.: (781) 729-2130
Web Site:
http://www.winchestersavings.com
Sales Range: $10-24.9 Million
Emp.: 88
State Savings Banks, Not Federally Chartered
N.A.I.C.S.: 522180
Sharon Gearty (Dir-HR)

WINCHESTER WOODWORKING CORP.
351 Victory Rd, Winchester, VA 22602
Tel.: (540) 667-1700
Year Founded: 1987
Sales Range: $10-24.9 Million
Emp.: 63
Provider of Millwork Services
N.A.I.C.S.: 321918
John M. Hamilton (Mgr-Sls)
Paulette Dennis (Controller)
Nancy Streiff (Mgr-HR)
Jan Adler (Sr Project Mgr)
James R. Hamilton (CEO)
Robert Hamilton (Mgr-Info Sys)
Richard S. Bern (Owner, VP & Mgr-Ops)
James Hamilton Jr. (Mgr-Mktg)

WINCO FOODS, INC.
650 N Armstrong Pl, Boise, ID 83704-0825
Tel.: (208) 377-0110   ID
Web Site: https://www.wincofoods.com
Year Founded: 1967
Sales Range: $1-4.9 Billion
Emp.: 22,000
Supermarkets & Other Grocery Retailers (except Convenience Retailers)
N.A.I.C.S.: 445110
Gary R. Piva (CFO & Exec VP)
Del Ririe (VP & Controller)
Michael Read (VP-Pub & Legal Affairs)
Rich Charrier (COO & Exec VP)
Wayne Duncan (Dir-Transportation)
David Van Etten (VP-Engrg)
Grant Haag (Pres)
Subsidiaries:

WinCo Foods (1)
4575 Comml St SE, Salem, OR 97302
Tel.: (503) 362-1029
Grocery Stores
N.A.I.C.S.: 445110
Chad Stewart (Mgr)
Tanith Wilson (Mgr-Apprentice)
Brett Mason (Mgr-Produce)
Roxie Booze (Mgr-Variety)
Don Johnson (Mgr-Warehouse)

WINCO GENERATORS
225 S Cordova Ave, Le Center, MN 56057-1805
Tel.: (507) 357-6821   MN
Web Site: http://www.wincogen.com
Year Founded: 1996
Sales Range: $250-299.9 Million
Emp.: 70
Holding Company
N.A.I.C.S.: 551112
Ralph Call (Pres & CEO)
Subsidiaries:

WINCO Inc (1)
225 S Cordova Ave, Le Center, MN 56057-1805
Tel.: (507) 357-6821   (100%)
Web Site: http://www.wincogen.com
Sales Range: $10-24.9 Million
Mfr of Generators Systems
N.A.I.C.S.: 335312
Kush Shrestha (Engr-Mechanical)

Winpower Inc. (1)
225 S Cordova Ave, Le Center, MN 56057   (100%)
Tel.: (507) 357-6700
Web Site: http://www.wincogen.com
Sales Range: $25-49.9 Million
Emp.: 60
Backup Generator Mfr
N.A.I.C.S.: 423610
Ralph Call (CEO)

WINCO, INC.
5516 SW 1st Ln, Ocala, FL 34474
Tel.: (352) 854-2929   FL
Web Site: http://www.wincomfg.com
Year Founded: 1954
Sales Range: $10-24.9 Million
Emp.: 83
Mfr of Medical Furniture, Including Exam Tables, Stools, Privacy Screens & Ring Binder Carts
N.A.I.C.S.: 332999
Jim Ankoviak (Pres)
Mark Campbell Winmill (Exec VP)

WINCOVE PRIVATE HOLDINGS, LP
220 E 42nd St 29th Fl, New York, NY 10017
Tel.: (212) 360-1904
Web Site: http://www.wincove.com
Year Founded: 2008
Holding Company
N.A.I.C.S.: 551112
Michael McGovern (Partner)
John Lenahan (Partner)
Subsidiaries:

Bluff Manufacturing, Inc. (1)
1400 Everman Pkwy Ste 156, Fort Worth, TX 76140
Tel.: (817) 293-3018
Web Site:
http://www.bluffmanufacturing.com
Sales Range: $1-9.9 Million
Emp.: 38
Prefabricated Metal Building & Component Mfr
N.A.I.C.S.: 332311
Andrea Curreri (Pres)
Chad Albert (Mgr-Engrg)
Lane Moss (VP-Ops)
Amy Hamilton (VP-Mktg)
Bruce Parker (Dir-Fin & Acctg)
Harry Davidson (Mgr-Bus Dev)
Russell Smith (Mgr-Sls Support)
Silvia Enriques (Controller)
Tony Otto (Mgr-IT)

WIND & SEA RESTAURANTS INC.
34699 Golden Lantern St, Dana Point, CA 92629
Tel.: (949) 496-6500
Web Site: http://www.windandsearestaurants.com
Rev.: $12,000,000
Emp.: 150
Restaurant Service
N.A.I.C.S.: 722511
Robert C. Mardian Jr. (Pres)

WIND COMPOSITE SERVICE GROUP, LLC
5151 World Huston Pkwy, Houston, TX 77032
Tel.: (281) 227-5130   TX
Web Site: http://www.windcomservices.com
Year Founded: 2006
Wind Blade Services
N.A.I.C.S.: 221115
Gary Kanaby (Gen Mgr)

WIND POINT ADVISORS LLC
676 N Michigan Ave Ste 3700, Chicago, IL 60611
Tel.: (312) 255-4800   DE
Web Site: http://www.wppartners.com
Year Founded: 1983
Privater Equity Firm
N.A.I.C.S.: 523999
Rich Kracum (Co-Founder)
Paul Peterson (Mng Dir)
Robert Cummings (Co-Founder)
Nathan Brown (Mng Dir)
Alex Washington (Mng Dir)
Konrad Salaber (Mng Dir)
David Stott (Mng Dir)
Kristen L. Trotta (CFO)
Ron Liberman (Head-IR)
Trish Gilbert (Chief Talent Officer)
Niel Olsen (Controller)
Subsidiaries:

American Trailer Rental Group (1)
13121 Walton Verona Rd, Walton, KY 41094
Tel.: (859) 485-4188
Web Site: http://americantrg.com
Storage & Cartage Rental Services
N.A.I.C.S.: 532120
Garrett Vilven (VP-Container Ops)
Jonathan Brooks (CEO)

Subsidiary (Domestic):

Advantage Trailer Company (2)
931 Metro Media Pl, Dallas, TX 75247
Tel.: (214) 637-4506
Web Site: http://advantagerents.com
Tire & Tube Merchant Whslr
N.A.I.C.S.: 423130
Richard Vilven (Pres)

Ascensus Specialties LLC (1)
2821 Northup Way Suite 275, Bellevue, WA 98004
Tel.: (425) 448-1679
Web Site:
http://www.ascensusspecialties.com
Pharmaceutical Drug Mfr
N.A.I.C.S.: 325412
Mike Huff (CEO)
Ephraim S. Honig (Chief Science & Innovation Officer)

WIND POINT ADVISORS LLC

Wind Point Advisors LLC—(Continued)

Subsidiary (Domestic):

Strem Chemicals, Inc. (2)
7 Mulliken Way, Newburyport, MA 01950
Tel.: (978) 462-3191
Web Site: http://www.strem.com
Rev.: $9,150,000
Emp.: 25
All Other Miscellaneous Chemical Product & Preparation Mfr
N.A.I.C.S.: 325998
Michael Strem *(Founder & Pres)*

Central Moloney Inc. (1)
2400 W 6th Ave, Pine Bluff, AR 71601-3862
Tel.: (855) 417-6893
Web Site: http://www.centralmoloneyinc.com
Provider of Power Services
N.A.I.C.S.: 335311
Patrick Colclasure *(VP)*
Kent Gossage *(Sr VP)*
Chris Hart *(Pres & CEO)*
Emily Griffin *(Components Sales Manager)*
Akasha Claremboux *(Components Inside Sales Coordinator)*
Reid Stewart *(Reg Sls Mgr)*
Hunter Neal *(Reg Sls Mgr)*
Leesa Kappler *(Reg Sls Mgr)*
Miachelle Cantrell *(Order Specialist)*

Clock Spring Company, Inc. (1)
621 Lockhaven Dr, Houston, TX 77073
Tel.: (281) 590-8491
Web Site: http://www.clockspring.com
Composite & Permanent Pipeline Repair, Pipeline Integrity, Onshore & Offshore Pipeline Repair & Plant & Refinery Repairs
N.A.I.C.S.: 331210
Matt Boucher *(CEO)*
Andrew Patrick *(VP-Strategic Opportunities)*
Emily Robertson *(CFO)*
Vikki Dun *(CMO)*
Harry Gray *(Pres-AVT)*

Subsidiary (Domestic):

Advanced Valve Technologies, LLC (2)
800 Busse Road, Elk Grove Village, IL 60007
Tel.: (847) 364-3700
Web Site: http://www.cs-nri.com
Apping, Line Stopping, Valve Insertion Equipment & Insertion Valves Mfr
N.A.I.C.S.: 332911
Beverly Harrison *(Mgr-Pur)*

Envera Systems LLC (1)
7280 W Palmetto Park Rd Ste 306, Boca Raton, FL 33433
Tel.: (561) 910-5826
Web Site: http://www.enverasystems.com
Sales Range: $1-9.9 Million
Emp.: 75
Security Systems & Services
N.A.I.C.S.: 561621
Addi Aloya *(CEO)*
Tom Swain *(Dir-Sls)*
Aaron Wray *(CFO)*
Nathan Charette *(Sr VP-Ops)*
Paul Goodner *(VP-Tech)*
Greg Barrett *(Dir-Customer Care)*
Nathan Varn *(Dir-Sls & Bus Dev)*

FoodScience Corporation (1)
929 Harvest Ln, Williston, VT 05452
Tel.: (802) 878-5508
Web Site: http://www.foodsciencecorp.com
Sales Range: $50-74.9 Million
Emp.: 200
Human & Animal Nutritional Food Supplements
N.A.I.C.S.: 424210
Melinda Elmadjian *(Mgr-Natl Sls)*
Linny Curtis *(Coord-Label)*
Dom Orlandi *(Pres)*
Donna McGonagle *(Supvr-QC)*
Sharon Rossi *(CEO)*
Tammy Johnson *(VP-Human Supplements)*
David Buley *(VP-Mfg & Supply Chain)*

Freshedge, LLC (1)
4501 Massachusetts Avenue, Indianapolis, IN 46218
Tel.: (317) 981-3599
Web Site: https://www.freshedgefoods.com
Food & Beverages Services
N.A.I.C.S.: 424480

Greg Corsaro *(Pres & COO)*
Steve Grinstead *(CEO)*

Subsidiary (Domestic):

Greenberg Fruit Company (2)
9705 I St, Omaha, NE 68127
Tel.: (402) 339-6900
Web Site: http://www.greenbergfruit.com
Sales Range: $1-9.9 Million
Emp.: 50
Fresh Fruits And Vegetables
N.A.I.C.S.: 424480

IF&P Foods LLC (2)
4501 Massachusetts Ave, Indianapolis, IN 46218
Tel.: (317) 546-2425
Web Site: https://indyfruit.com
Holding Company
N.A.I.C.S.: 551112
Greg Corsaro *(CEO)*

Subsidiary (Domestic):

Get Fresh Produce LLC (3)
1441 Brewster Creek Blvd, Bartlett, IL 60103
Tel.: (630) 665-9665
Web Site: http://www.getfreshproduce.com
Fresh Fruit & Vegetable Merchant Whslr
N.A.I.C.S.: 424480

Piazza Produce Inc. (3)
5941 W 82nd St, Indianapolis, IN 46268-6268
Tel.: (317) 872-0101
Web Site: http://www.piazzaproduce.com
Fresh Fruit & Vegetable Merchant Whslr
N.A.I.C.S.: 424480
Nick Miceli *(Dir-Ops)*

Subsidiary (Domestic):

Sirna & Sons, Inc. (2)
7176 State Rte 88, Ravenna, OH 44266-9189
Tel.: (330) 298-2222
Web Site: http://www.sirnaandsonsproduce.com
Fresh Fruit & Vegetable Merchant Whslr
N.A.I.C.S.: 424480
Tom Sirna *(Pres)*
Allie Sirna *(Coord-Bus Solutions)*

Testa Produce Inc (2)
1501 S Blue Island Ave, Chicago, IL 60608
Tel.: (312) 226-3237
Web Site: http://www.testaproduce.com
Rev.: $7,500,000
Emp.: 31
Fruit & Vegetable Markets
N.A.I.C.S.: 445230
John Adamo *(Dir-Sls)*
Chuxk Leuze *(Acct Mgr)*
Barbara Donaldson Daly *(Mgr-Facility & Quality Assurance)*
Peter Testa *(Pres)*

Gaytan Foods (1)
15430 Proctor Ave, City of Industry, CA 91745
Tel.: (626) 330-4553
Web Site: http://www.gaytanfoods.com
Processed Meat Mfr
N.A.I.C.S.: 311612
Ignacio Huerta *(Dir-Ops)*

Gehl Foods, LLC (1)
N116 W15970 Main St, Germantown, WI 53022
Tel.: (262) 251-8572
Web Site: http://www.gehls.com
Miscellaneous Food Mfr
N.A.I.C.S.: 311999
Lyle Roecker *(Project Mgr)*
Tom Roetz *(Mgr-Pur)*

Subsidiary (Domestic):

California Natural Products, Inc. (2)
1250 E Lathrop Rd, Lathrop, CA 95330
Tel.: (209) 858-2525
Web Site: http://www.cnp.com
Specialty Rice & Soy-based Ingredients, Dried & Dehydrated Food Mfr
N.A.I.C.S.: 311423

Handgards Inc. (1)
901 Hawkins, El Paso, TX 79915-1202
Tel.: (915) 779-6606

Web Site: http://www.handgards.com
Sales Range: $100-124.9 Million
Emp.: 250
Mfr & Distributor of Disposable Plastic Products, Including Gloves, Aprons, Bags, Bibs, Table Coverings & Shoe Covers
N.A.I.C.S.: 326199
Bob McLellan *(Pres)*
Tom Lore *(Controller)*
Jesus Licon *(CFO)*
Joe Kubicek *(CEO)*
John Lewchenko *(Exec VP-Sls & Mktg)*

Knape & Vogt Manufacturing Company (1)
2700 Oak Industrial Dr NE, Grand Rapids, MI 49505-3408
Tel.: (616) 459-3311
Web Site: http://www.knapeandvogt.com
Sales Range: $150-199.9 Million
Mfr of Shelving Hardware, Drawer Slides & Storage Products
N.A.I.C.S.: 337215
Dan Pickett *(VP-Distr Sls)*
Peter Martin *(Pres & CEO)*
Gordon Kirsch *(VP-Ops)*
Jack Master *(VP-Bus Products)*
Rick McQuigg *(CFO & VP)*
Steve Beckwith *(Sr Mgr-Mktg Svcs)*
Derek Timm *(Mgr-Tech Svcs-Ergonomic Products)*
Miles Mullins *(Product Mgr-Kitchen & Bath Products)*
Andy Marzolf *(VP-HR)*
Gary Ottenjan *(VP-OEM Sls)*
Peter Ross *(VP-Mktg & Product Dev)*
Mike Trottman *(VP-Retail Sls)*

Nelson Global Products, Inc. (1)
1560 Williams Dr, Stoughton, WI 53589
Tel.: (608) 719-1800
Web Site: http://www.nelsonglobalproducts.com
Sales Range: $450-499.9 Million
Emp.: 2,800
Automotive Aftermarket Products Mfr
N.A.I.C.S.: 336390
Kris Radhakrishnan *(CFO)*
Joseph Freeman *(VP-HR)*
Santosh Joshi *(Gen Mgr-Bus Dev)*

Subsidiary (Domestic):

Bradley Services, Inc. (2)
7232 W Wheeler Rd, Mapleton, IL 61547
Tel.: (309) 263-8914
Automotive Exhaust Metal Tube & Pipe Mfr
N.A.I.C.S.: 332996

Cambridge Metals & Plastics, Inc. (2)
500 Cleveland St S, Cambridge, MN 55008
Tel.: (763) 689-4800
Web Site: http://www.cmp-wwm.com
Fabricated Sheet Metal Pipe & Tube Mfr
N.A.I.C.S.: 332996

Interlaken Technology Corporation (2)
8175 Century Blvd, Chaska, MN 55318
Tel.: (952) 856-4210
Web Site: http://www.interlaken.com
Sales Range: $25-49.9 Million
Emp.: 20
Hydroforming & Testing Equipment Mfr
N.A.I.C.S.: 332996
Lois Walters *(Controller)*
Jim Higgins *(VP-Sls & Mktg)*

Plant (Domestic):

Nelson Global Products, Inc. - Arcadia Manufacturing Facility (2)
1450 E Wilson Ave, Arcadia, WI 54612
Tel.: (608) 323-3369
Web Site: http://www.nelsonglobalproducts.com
Automotive Exhaust Tube & Pipe Mfr
N.A.I.C.S.: 332996

Nelson Global Products, Inc. - Black River Falls Manufacturing Facility (2)
915 Red Iron Rd, Black River Falls, WI 54615
Tel.: (715) 284-3700
Automobile Parts Mfr
N.A.I.C.S.: 336390

Nelson Global Products, Inc. - Fort Wayne Manufacturing Facility (2)
3405 Engle Rd, Fort Wayne, IN 46809
Tel.: (260) 478-2363
Sales Range: $100-124.9 Million
Automotive Exhaust Tube & Pipe Mfr
N.A.I.C.S.: 332996
Jason Wright *(Plant Mgr)*

Nelson Global Products, Inc. - Viroqua Manufacturing Facility (2)
1202 Nelson Pkwy, Viroqua, WI 54665
Tel.: (608) 637-2181
Sales Range: $50-74.9 Million
Fabricated Tube & Pipe Product Mfr
N.A.I.C.S.: 332996

Subsidiary (Domestic):

Peoria Tube Forming Corp. (2)
1331 Spring Bay Rd, East Peoria, IL 61611-1937
Tel.: (309) 822-0274
Metal Tube & Pipe Mfr
N.A.I.C.S.: 332996

Tru-Flex, LLC (2)
2391 S State Road 263, West Lebanon, IN 47991
Tel.: (765) 893-4403
Web Site: http://www.tru-flex.com
Sales Range: $1-9.9 Million
Emp.: 100
Flexible Exhaust Products Mfr
N.A.I.C.S.: 332999
Gregg Notestine *(Pres & CEO)*

Water Works Fabrication, LLC (2)
500 S Cleveland St, Cambridge, MN 55008
Tel.: (763) 689-4800
Web Site: http://www.hydroformers.com
Sales Range: $10-24.9 Million
Emp.: 250
Advanced Metal Forming Solutions
N.A.I.C.S.: 332710
James Shear *(Pres & CEO)*

Neptune Research, LLC (1)
3875 Fiscal Ct #100, Riviera Beach, FL 33404
Tel.: (561) 683-6992
Web Site: http://www.neptuneresearch.com
Hardware Mfr; Custom Engineered Composite Repair (ECR) Systems
N.A.I.C.S.: 332510
Brian Kirkpatrick *(CFO)*
Davie Peguero *(Engr-Mechanical)*
Erblina Vokshi *(Engr-Civil)*
Jordan Griffith *(COO)*

Nonni's Foods LLC (1)
1901 S Meyers Rd, Oakbrook Terrace, IL 60181
Tel.: (630) 705-0031
Web Site: http://www.nonnisfoods.com
Sales Range: $10-24.9 Million
Biscotti Mfr & Marketer
N.A.I.C.S.: 311821
David L. Bere *(Chm)*
Brian Hansberry *(CEO)*

Pacifica Foods LLC (1)
13415 Estelle St, Corona, CA 92879
Tel.: (951) 371-3123
Web Site: http://www.pacificafoods.net
Refrigerated, Frozen & Shelf Stable Dressings, Sauces (Pasteurized & Ambient Fill), Soups, Fresh Salsas & Dips
N.A.I.C.S.: 311941

Palmex Alimentos SA de CV (1)
Francisco I Madero Ste 145, El Lechugal, 66376, Santa Catarina, Mexico
Tel.: (52) 8281513150
Web Site: https://www.palmex.com
Snack Food Mfr
N.A.I.C.S.: 311919
Jose Luis Prado *(Chm & CEO)*

Subsidiary (US):

Evans Food Group Ltd. (2)
4118 S Halsted St, Chicago, IL 60609
Tel.: (773) 254-7400
Web Site: https://www.benestarbrands.com
Snack Food Mfr
N.A.I.C.S.: 311919

Subsidiary (Domestic):

Turkey Creek Pork Skins, LLC (3)
4118 S Halsted St, Chicago, IL 60609
Tel.: (773) 254-7400

COMPANIES

Snack Food Mfr
N.A.I.C.S.: 311919

Pavion Corp. (1)
4151 Lafayette Ctr Dr Ste 700, Chantilly, VA 20151
Tel.: (703) 631-3377
Web Site: http://www.ctsi-usa.com
Local Area Network Systems Integrator
N.A.I.C.S.: 541512
Joe Oliveri (Pres & CEO)

Subsidiary (Domestic):

AFA Protective Systems, Inc. (2)
155 Michael Dr, Syosset, NY 11791-5319
Tel.: (516) 496-2322
Web Site: http://www.afap.com
Rev.: $77,741,824
Assets: $34,031,000
Liabilities: $24,825,234
Net Worth: $9,205,766
Earnings: $1,101,433
Emp.: 400
Fiscal Year-end: 12/31/2018
Security & Fire Systems Installation & Customization Services
N.A.I.C.S.: 561621
Robert Kleinman (CEO)
Richard D. Kleinman (Pres & COO)
Joseph H. Goren (CFO, Treas & VP)
Mark A. LaBua (CIO & VP)
Stephen P. Hyle (VP & Dir-Natl Accts)
Jared D. Kleinman (VP)
Michael J. Slattery (VP-Branch Ops)

Subsidiary (Domestic):

AFA Massachusetts, Inc. (3)
200 High St 5th Fl, Boston, MA 02110-3036 (100%)
Tel.: (617) 772-5900
Web Site: http://www.afap.com
Sales Range: $10-24.9 Million
Emp.: 35
Security & Fire Systems Installation & Customization Services
N.A.I.C.S.: 561621

Branch (Domestic):

AFA Protective Systems, Inc. - Altamonte Springs, Florida (3)
217 Altamonte Commerce Blvd Ste 1234, Altamonte Springs, FL 32714
Tel.: (407) 812-9200
Web Site: http://www.afap.com
Sales Range: $10-24.9 Million
Emp.: 13
Security & Fire Systems Installation & Customization Services
N.A.I.C.S.: 561621
Kevin Richards (Branch Mgr)

Division (Domestic):

AFA Protective Systems, Inc. - National Accounts Division (3)
150 Wood Rd Ste 301, Braintree, MA 02184
Tel.: (781) 848-6200
Web Site: http://www.afap.com
National Business Security Monitoring Services
N.A.I.C.S.: 561621
Stephen P. Hyle (VP & Dir-Ops-Natl Accts)

Branch (Domestic):

AFA Protective Systems, Inc. - Northern New Jersey (3)
961 Joyce Kilmer Ave, North Brunswick, NJ 08902-1851
Tel.: (732) 846-4000
Web Site: http://www.afap.com
Fire & Burglary Protection Services
N.A.I.C.S.: 561621

Subsidiary (Domestic):

AFA Southeast, Inc. (3)
805 Franklin Ct SE Ste C, Marietta, GA 30067-8942 (100%)
Tel.: (770) 794-9000
Web Site: http://www.afap.com
Sales Range: $10-24.9 Million
Emp.: 50
Security & Fire Systems Installation & Customization Services
N.A.I.C.S.: 561621

Mark Giglio (Gen Mgr)

Subsidiary (Domestic):

Firecom, Inc. (2)
39-27 59th St, Woodside, NY 11377
Tel.: (718) 899-6100
Web Site: http://www.firecominc.com
Fire Alarm Apparatus Mfr
N.A.I.C.S.: 334290
Howard Kogen (COO)
Antoine Sayour (Exec VP)
Sal Fedele (VP-Ops)
Tom Spudis (VP-Technical Svcs)

Subsidiary (Domestic):

Casey Fire Systems, Inc. (3)
39-27 59th St, Woodside, NY 11377
Tel.: (212) 564-3960
Web Site: http://www.caseysystems.com
Alarm Systems Mfr & Design
N.A.I.C.S.: 334290

Subsidiary (Domestic):

Netronix Integration, Inc. (2)
1450 Koll Cir, San Jose, CA 95112
Tel.: (408) 573-1444
Web Site: http://www.netronixint.com
Electrical Contractor
N.A.I.C.S.: 238210
Craig Jarrett (Pres)
Steve Piechota (Partner)

Subsidiary (Domestic):

Premier Security Solutions Corp (2)
270 Harbor Blvd, Belmont, CA 94002
Tel.: (650) 595-3836
Web Site: http://www.premiersecuritysolutions.com
Rev.: $1,200,000
Emp.: 15
Security Systems Services, except Locksmiths
N.A.I.C.S.: 561621
Larry Pott (Co-Founder)
Paul Frankos (Co-Founder)
Scott Reno (Pres)

RFI Electronics, Inc. (2)
25977 S W Cannyon Creek Rd Ste E, Wilsonville, OR 97070-9678
Tel.: (503) 682-9900
Web Site: http://www.rcss.us
Security System Services
N.A.I.C.S.: 561621
Gina S. Reece (Sec)
Dean Reece (Pres)

RFI Enterprises, Inc. (2)
360 Turtle Creek Ct, San Jose, CA 95125
Tel.: (408) 298-5400
Web Site: http://www.rfi.com
Sales Range: $25-49.9 Million
Emp.: 100
Safety & Security Specialization
N.A.I.C.S.: 238210
Brad J. Wilson (Pres & COO)
Michelle Brooks (CFO)
Brian Lund (Sr VP)
Dee Ann Harn (CEO)

Subsidiary (Domestic):

Reeces Fantasies Inc. (3)
360 Turtle Creek Ct, San Jose, CA 95125
Tel.: (408) 298-5400
Web Site: http://www.rfi.com
Communications Specialization
N.A.I.C.S.: 238210
Lawrence Reece (Founder & Pres)

Subsidiary (Domestic):

Short Circuit Electronics, Inc. (2)
4201 NE Port Dr, Lees Summit, MO 64064
Tel.: (816) 878-6700
Web Site: http://www.shortcircuitinc.com
Sales Range: $1-9.9 Million
Emp.: 20
Electrical Contractor
N.A.I.C.S.: 238210
Daniel Israel (VP)

Star Asset Security, LLC (2)
1411 Edgewater Dr Ste 203, Orlando, FL 32804
Tel.: (977) 801-1616
Web Site: http://www.securethinking.com

Electrical Apparatus & Equipment, Wiring Supplies & Related Equipment Merchant Whslr
N.A.I.C.S.: 423610
Roger Hirschy (Exec VP)

Structure Works, Inc. (2)
43 Mill St, Dover Plains, NY 12522
Tel.: (845) 877-1460
Web Site: http://www.structureworksinc.com
New Housing Operative Builders
N.A.I.C.S.: 236117
James Muncey (Pres)
Michelle Buonaiuto (Mgr-Acctg & Fin)
Fred Conover Jr. (Project Mgr)

Systems Electronics, Inc. (2)
4432 K Held Rd, Knightdale, NC 27545
Tel.: (919) 266-9908
Web Site: http://www.systemselectronics.com
Commercial & Institutional Building Construction
N.A.I.C.S.: 236220
Mike Strickland (Pres)

Quantix SCS, Inc. (1)
24 Waterway Ave Ste 450, Woodlands, TX 77380
Tel.: (800) 542-8058
Web Site: https://quantixscs.com
Bulk Transportation & Supply Chain Services
N.A.I.C.S.: 488510
Steven B. Hochhauser (Chm)
Christopher A. Black (CFO)
Daniel D. Jaworski (Chief Comml Officer & Sr VP)
Chris Ball (CEO)
Alex Buck (Grp Pres-Supply Chain)
Julie Block (Chief People Officer)
Blake Osman Deitrich (Gen Counsel)
David Perry (Pres-Liquid Chemicals)

Subsidiary (Domestic):

Bwp Transport, Inc. (2)
1289 S Range Rd, Saint Clair, MI 48079
Tel.: (810) 329-5809
Web Site: http://www.bwpt.net
Sales Range: $1-9.9 Million
Emp.: 28
Local Trucking Operator
N.A.I.C.S.: 484110

First Choice Logistics Inc. (2)
12550 S Stony Is Ave, Chicago, IL 60633
Tel.: (708) 210-3160
Web Site: http://www.firstchoicelogistics.com
Specialized Freight Trucking; Long-Distance
N.A.I.C.S.: 484230
Tim Vanderbent (Mgr)
Luke Jousma (VP)

RailWorks Corp. (1)
5 Penn Plz Fl 15, New York, NY 10001
Tel.: (212) 502-7900
Web Site: http://www.railworks.com
Rail Systems Products & Services; Highway & Bridge Support Structures
N.A.I.C.S.: 238210
Ben D'Alessandro (Pres-RailWorks Transit)
John August (Exec VP)
Gene Cellini (Sr VP-Tax)
Veronica A. Lubatkin (CFO & Exec VP)
Harry Z. Glantz (VP-HR)
Edward Kennedy (VP)
James R. Hansen (VP-Freight Rail Infrastructure)
Edgar Butsch (Mgr-Corp Equipment)
Robert Cummings (VP-Info Sys & Tech)
Kirk Johnson (Chief HR Officer & VP)
Benjamin D. Levy (Gen Counsel, Sec & Exec VP)
Greg Muldoon (Chm)
John Young (Exec VP)
Kevin Riddett (Pres & CEO)

Subsidiary (Domestic):

H&H Engineering Construction (2)
212 Industrial Dr, Stockton, CA 95206-3905
Tel.: (209) 983-0708
Web Site: https://www.hheng.com
Rev.: $10,100,000
Emp.: 80
Railroad & Railway Roadbed Construction
N.A.I.C.S.: 236210
Robert L. Hallanger (Pres)
Doug Reynolds (Treas & Exec VP)
Lou Castaneda (VP-Contraction & Ops)

WIND POINT ADVISORS LLC

HSQ Technology Inc (2)
26227 Research Rd, Hayward, CA 94545-3725
Tel.: (510) 259-1334
Web Site: http://www.hsq.com
Data Acquisition & Communication System Mfr
N.A.I.C.S.: 334210
Harold Spence (Pres)
James Wilkinson (CTO & VP)
Tom Johnson (Dir-Mktg)
Asha Singh (Controller)

L.K. Comstock & Company, Inc. (2)
5 Penn Plz, New York, NY 10001
Tel.: (212) 502-7900
Sales Range: $25-49.9 Million
Emp.: 25
Track & Transit System Construction Services
N.A.I.C.S.: 238210
Ben D'Alessandro (Pres-NY Transit)

Subsidiary (Non-US):

PNR Railworks Inc (2)
2595 Deacon Street, PO Box 2280, Abbotsford, V2T 4X2, BC, Canada
Tel.: (604) 850-9166
Web Site: http://www.pnrrailworks.com
Railroad Construction Services
N.A.I.C.S.: 237990
John Brohm (Exec VP)
Richard Carney (Exec VP)

Division (Domestic):

PNR Railworks Inc - Signals & Communications Division (3)
65 Massey Rd, Guelph, N1H 7M6, ON, Canada
Tel.: (519) 837-2018
Web Site: http://www.pnrrailworks.com
Railway Signal & Communication Services
N.A.I.C.S.: 237990
Todd Galliford (Mgr-Div)

Subsidiary (Domestic):

RailWorks Signals & Communications, Inc. (2)
9250 Baymeadows Rd Ste 250, Jacksonville, FL 32256-1813
Tel.: (904) 296-5055
Web Site: http://www.railworks.com
Sales Range: $25-49.9 Million
Emp.: 5
Railway Communication Services
N.A.I.C.S.: 517810
Tim Orlandi (VP & Gen Mgr)

RailWorks Track Systems, Inc. (2)
8485 W 210th St, Lakeville, MN 55044
Tel.: (952) 469-4907
Web Site: http://www.railworks.com
Railroad Construction Services
N.A.I.C.S.: 237990

RailWorks Transit, Inc. (2)
83 Central Ave, Farmingdale, NY 11735
Tel.: (631) 752-4110
Mechanical Engineering Services
N.A.I.C.S.: 541330
Mike Esposito (VP)
Gary Guild (VP)
Christopher Spira (Mgr-Aconex)
Thomas Hennessy (Mgr-Fin & Track Ops)

St George Logistics Corp. (1)
2001 Butterfield Rd Ste 1010, Downers Grove, IL 60515
Tel.: (630) 581-0519
Logistics, Warehousing & Distribution Centers
N.A.I.C.S.: 493110

Subsidiary (Domestic):

Channel Distribution Corporation (2)
950 Supreme Dr, Bensenville, IL 60106-0106
Tel.: (630) 875-3000
Web Site: http://www.channeldc.com
Warehouse & Distribution Center
N.A.I.C.S.: 493110

Freight Force, Inc. (2)
14445 Alondra Blvd, La Mirada, CA 90638
Tel.: (714) 995-9300
Web Site: http://www.freightforce.com

WIND POINT ADVISORS LLC

U.S. PRIVATE

Wind Point Advisors LLC—(Continued)
Transportation, Trucking & Railroad Services
N.A.I.C.S.: 484110
Chris Coppersmith (CEO)
Mark H. Schenewer (Dir-Ops)
Jessie OBryan (Controller)
Sue Beattie (Dir-Admin)
Carlton Henderson (Mgr-IT)

Stir Foods, LLC (1)
1581 N Main St, Orange, CA 92867
Tel.: (714) 637-6050
Web Site: http://www.stirfoods.com
Specialty Canning Services
N.A.I.C.S.: 311422
Monte Loiacono (Partner)
Bill Happy (VP-Culinary Ops)
Milton Liu (CEO)
Pablo Gallo Llorente (CFO)

Subsidiary (Domestic):

Lancaster Fine Foods, Inc. (2)
501 Richardson Dr Ste 300, Lancaster, PA 17603
Tel.: (717) 397-9578
Web Site:
http://www.lancasterfinefoods.com
Sales Range: $1-9.9 Million
Emp.: 48
Fruit & Vegetable Canning Services
N.A.I.C.S.: 311421
Matthew Hunt (Dir-Product Dev)
Kevin Kumher (Mgr)
Mike Thompson (CEO)

Vanlaw Food Products, Inc. (2)
2325 Moore Ave, Fullerton, CA 92833
Tel.: (714) 578-3123
Web Site: http://www.vanlaw.com
Prepared Sauces Mfr
N.A.I.C.S.: 311941
Mary Steinbeck (Dir-Sls)

Taylor-Wharton International LLC (1)
4718 Old Gettysburg Rd Ste 300, Mechanicsburg, PA 17055
Tel.: (717) 763-5060
Web Site: http://www.taylor-wharton.com
Sales Range: $25-49.9 Million
Gas Containment Products Mfr
N.A.I.C.S.: 332439
Jim Hoppel (CFO)

Subsidiary (Domestic):

American Welding & Tank Co. (2)
4718 Old Gettysburg Rd Ste 300, Mechanicsburg, PA 17055
Tel.: (717) 763-5080
Sales Range: $25-49.9 Million
Industrial & Commercial Natural Gas Container Mfr
N.A.I.C.S.: 332439
Jim Alderman (Dir-Bus Dev)
Dean Redd (Dir-Sls)

Sherwood Valve LLC (2)
2200 N Main St, Washington, PA 15301-6150
Tel.: (724) 225-8000
Web Site: http://www.sherwoodvalve.com
Sales Range: $25-49.9 Million
Air Conditioning, Refrigeration & Natural Gas Valve Mfr
N.A.I.C.S.: 332911
Darryl Pamplin (Mgr-Natl Sls-LPG)

Plant (Domestic):

Sherwood Valve (3)
2200 N Main St, Washington, PA 15301-6181
Tel.: (716) 283-1010
Web Site: http://www.sherwoodvalve.com
Sales Range: $50-74.9 Million
Air Conditioning, Refrigeration & Natural Gas Valve Mfr
N.A.I.C.S.: 332911

Sherwood Valve LLC - Valley View Facility (3)
7900 Hub Pkwy, Valley View, OH 44125
Tel.: (216) 264-5023
Precision Valve Mfr
N.A.I.C.S.: 332911

Subsidiary (Non-US):

Taylor-Wharton Australia Pty. Ltd. (2)
Unit 1 882 Leslie Dr, Albury, 2640, NSW, Australia
Tel.: (61) 260402533
Web Site: http://www.taylorwharton.com
Sales Range: $10-24.9 Million
Emp.: 3
Natural Gas Container Mfr
N.A.I.C.S.: 332439
Bill Smits (Gen Mgr)

Subsidiary (Domestic):

Taylor-Wharton Cryogenics, LLC (2)
4075 Hamilton Blvd, Theodore, AL 36582
Tel.: (251) 443-8680
Cryogenic Tank Mfr
N.A.I.C.S.: 332420
Luke Bradshaw (Dir-Mktg & Sls)

Subsidiary (Non-US):

Taylor-Wharton (Beijing) Cryogenic Equipment Co.,Ltd. (3)
East End of Ping An Street Xianghe Economic Development Zone, Xianghe City, Langfang, Hebei, China
Tel.: (86) 316 8219770
Emp.: 100
Cryogenic Tank Mfr
N.A.I.C.S.: 332420
Fang Ying (Gen Mgr)

Taylor-Wharton Germany GmbH (3)
Mildstedter Landstr 1, 25866, Mildstedt, Germany
Tel.: (49) 48 41 9 85 0
Web Site: http://www.taylorwharton.com
Sales Range: $10-24.9 Million
Emp.: 8
Cryogenic Tank Mfr
N.A.I.C.S.: 332420
Nils Wittig (Mgr-Sls)

Taylor-Wharton Slovakia S.R.O. (3)
Vstupny Areal U S Steel, 04454, Kosice, Slovakia
Tel.: (421) 55 727 71 24
Web Site: http://www.taylorwharton.com
Sales Range: $10-24.9 Million
Emp.: 100
Cryogenic Liquid Storage & Gas Cylinder Mfr
N.A.I.C.S.: 332420
Alexander Soltis (Gen Mgr)
Viktor Sabo (Mgr-Sls)
Tatiana Tomasova (Mgr-Customer Svc)

The Vertex Companies, Inc. (1)
400 Libbey Pkwy, Weymouth, MA 02189
Tel.: (781) 952-6000
Web Site: http://www.vertexeng.com
Sales Range: $25-49.9 Million
Emp.: 190
Engineeering Services
N.A.I.C.S.: 541330
William J. McConnell (Co-Founder & CEO)
James B. O'Brien (Co-Founder & Chm)
Jeffrey E. Picard (Co-Founder, Pres & COO)

Subsidiary (Domestic):

Fulcrum LLC (2)
7373 E Doubletree Ranch Rd Ste B-150 & B-215, Scottsdale, AZ 85258
Tel.: (602) 759-7884
Web Site: http://fulcrumcompany.com
Building Construction Services
N.A.I.C.S.: 236220
Hugh C. Coyle (CEO & Mgr)
Stephen W. Wright (COO)
Kevin L. Hanson (CFO)
Yvonne Pommerville (Chief People Officer)
Raymond I. Harrower (Mgr-Mktg & Bus Dev)

Lockwood Kessler & Bartlett, Inc. (2)
1 Aerial Way, Syosset, NY 11791
Tel.: (516) 938-0600
Web Site: http://www.lkbinc.com
Engineeering Services
N.A.I.C.S.: 541330
Steven Hanuszek (Exec VP & VP-Construction Admin)
Andre Haddad (Pres & CEO)
Paul Lappano (VP-Environmental Svcs)
Wayne Culver (Dir-Structural Engrg)
Brian Ednie (VP-Engrg)
John Gerlach (Dir-Environmental Svcs)
Theresa Heneveld (Dir-Environmental En-grg)
Debra Marino (Dir-Fin & Admin)
Bart Marino (Chief Engr-Civil)
Robert Gizzi (VP-Enrg Svcs)
Charles Laut (Dir-Information Technologies & Sr Engr-Network & Security)
Babar Zia (Mgr-Electrical & Mechanical En-grg)

Holding (Domestic):

Xpera, Inc. (2)
10911 Technology Pl, San Diego, CA 92127
Tel.: (858) 284-4712
Web Site: http://www.xperagroup.com
Construction Management Services
N.A.I.C.S.: 236220
John Kyrklund (Dir-Quality Assurance)
Ted Bumgardner (Founder & Chm)
Steve Grimes (Pres)
Brian L. Hill (Dir-Mktg & Tech)
Alan Nevin (Dir-Economic & Market Res)
Ron Whitehead (Dir-Corp Svcs)

Tropicale Foods, LLC (1)
1237 W State St, Ontario, CA 91762
Tel.: (800) 586-1677
Web Site: http://www.heladosmexico.com
Ice Cream Mfr
N.A.I.C.S.: 311520
Jose Luis Prado Becerra (Chm)
Steven Schiller (CEO)

Subsidiary (Domestic):

PLM Operations, LLC (2)
2068 Lapham Dr, Modesto, CA 95351
Tel.: (209) 523-7413
Web Site: http://www.michoacana.com
Ice Cream & Frozen Dessert Mfr
N.A.I.C.S.: 311520
Ignacio Gutierrez (Pres)
Patricia Gutierrez (VP)

US Nonwovens Corp. (1)
100 Emjay Blvd, Brentwood, NY 11717
Tel.: (631) 952-0100
Web Site: http://www.usnonwovens.com
Polyesters
N.A.I.C.S.: 325612
Shervin Zade (CEO)

Subsidiary (Domestic):

Multi-Pack - Chicago (2)
1804 W Central Rd, Mount Prospect, IL 60056
Tel.: (847) 635-6772
Contract Consumer Water Soluble Product Packaging Services
N.A.I.C.S.: 561910

Vision Ease, LP (1)
7000 Sunwood Dr NW, Ramsey, MN 55303
Tel.: (320) 251-8140
Web Site: https://www.visionease.com
Hard Resin Plastic, Polycarbonate & Glass Eyewear Lenses Mfr
N.A.I.C.S.: 333310
Jose Orozco Rodriguez (Sr Engr)
Joe Richards (Engr-Environmental, Health & Safety)
Craig Swiecichowski (Mgr-R&D Film & Laminate Tech)
Jennifer Barker (Sr Program Mgr)

Voyant Beauty (1)
6710 River Rd, Hodgkins, IL 60525
Tel.: (708) 482-8881
Web Site: http://voyantbeauty.com
Cosmetic Preparations
N.A.I.C.S.: 325620
David Eveslage (Mgr-Plng & Customer Care)
Shelly Knack (Mgr-Pur)
John Colllins (Mgr-Quality Assurance)
Don Jenkins (Mgr-Compounding)
Victoria Filippini (Dir-HR)

Zone Mechanical, Inc. (1)
12539 S Holiday Dr, Alsip, IL 60803
Tel.: (708) 388-1370
Web Site: http://www.zonemechanical.com
Rev.: $3,500,000
Emp.: 31
Site Preparation Contractor
N.A.I.C.S.: 238910
Steven B. Hochhauser (Chm)
Frank Petrosino (Co-Founder & CEO)

Subsidiary (Domestic):

EEC Acquisition LLC (2)
370 Wabasha St N, Saint Paul, MN 55102
Tel.: (800) 822-2303
Web Site:
http://www.smartcaresolutions.com
Kitchen Equipment Advertising & Maintenance
N.A.I.C.S.: 541870
Gyner Ozgul (Pres & COO)

Subsidiary (Domestic):

Almcoe Refrigeration Co. (3)
4050 Cresthill Rd, Dallas, TX 75227-4008
Tel.: (214) 381-2113
Web Site: http://www.almcoe.com
Sales Range: $10-24.9 Million
Emp.: 73
Plumbing Services
N.A.I.C.S.: 238220
Bill Almquist (Pres & CEO)

Espresso Partners Inc. (3)
5155 E River Rd Ste 411, Minneapolis, MN 55421
Tel.: (763) 533-4350
Web Site: http://www.espressopartners.com
Snack & Nonalcoholic Beverage Bars
N.A.I.C.S.: 722515
Jason Weimer (Mgr)

Richard Meek Air Conditioning, Inc. (3)
1430 380 Byp, Graham, TX 76450-2324
Tel.: (806) 622-3986
Web Site: http://www.richardmeekac.com
Heating, Ventilation & Air Conditioning Services
N.A.I.C.S.: 238220

WIND RIVER HOLDINGS, L.P.

555 Croton Rd Ste 200, King of Prussia, PA 19406-3171
Tel.: (610) 962-3770
Web Site:
http://www.windriverholdings.com
Gears, Power Transmission, Except Auto
N.A.I.C.S.: 423840
Robert H. Strouse (Pres)
Russell Ball (CEO)
David Proctor (Sr VP)

Subsidiaries:

Goddard Systems, Inc. (1)
1016 W 9th Ave Ste 210, King of Prussia, PA 19406
Tel.: (610) 265-8510
Web Site: http://www.goddardschool.com
Sales Range: $25-49.9 Million
Emp.: 80
Early Childhood Learning Centers
N.A.I.C.S.: 624410
Heidi Torgerson (Controller-Acctg)
Robert Scopinich (CFO)
Paul Koulogeorge (VP-Mktg, Adv & PR)
Renee Benedict (VP-IT)
Dennis R. Maple (Chm & CEO)
Christina Estrada (VP-HR)
Matt Zaia (Chief Dev Officer & Sr VP)

Samson Rope Technologies (1)
2090 Thornton St, Ferndale, WA 98248-9314
Tel.: (360) 384-4669
Web Site: http://www.samsonrope.com
Sales Range: $25-49.9 Million
Emp.: 250
Rope Mfr
N.A.I.C.S.: 314994
Charlotte Wells (Mgr-Mktg)
Kevin Stack (Project Mgr-Facility)
Janet Silva (Controller)
Paul Murphy (Dir-Pur & Supply Chain)

WIND RIVER PETROLEUM

2046 E Murray Rd Ste 200, Salt Lake City, UT 84117
Tel.: (801) 272-9229
Web Site: http://www.topstop.net
Year Founded: 1988
Sales Range: $25-49.9 Million
Emp.: 150

Owner & Operator of Convenience Stores
N.A.I.C.S.: 445131
J. Craig Larson (Pres)
Jan Keysaw (Controller)
Michael Mix (Mgr-Store)

WIND-UP ENTERTAINMENT, INC.
79 Madison Ave Fl 7, New York, NY 10016-8731
Tel.: (212) 251-9665
Web Site:
    http://www.winduprecords.com
Year Founded: 1995
Sales Range: $10-24.9 Million
Emp.: 60
Provider of Recording Services
N.A.I.C.S.: 512240
Alan Meltzer (Chm)

Subsidiaries:

Wind-up Records (1)
79 Madison Ave, New York, NY 10016 (100%)
Tel.: (212) 895-3100
Web Site: http://www.winduprecords.com
Music Company
N.A.I.C.S.: 512230
Chelsea Junker (Dir-Publ)
Drew Hauser (Sr VP-Promo)
Alison Shepard (VP-D2C Mktg)
Alan Galbraith (Gen Mgr)
Shawn Cohen (Mgr-A&R)
Christopher Graham (VP-Digital Strategy & Sls)
Michelle Lukianovich (Sr Dir-Art)
Shannon Weil-Maehr (Mgr-Production & YouTube Ops)
Kenneth Golden Jr. (Mgr-Licensing & Catalog Admin)

WINDBER HOSPITAL INC
600 Somerset Ave, Windber, PA 15963
Tel.: (814) 467-3000 PA
Web Site: http://www.windbercare.org
Year Founded: 1973
Sales Range: $50-74.9 Million
Emp.: 584
Health Care Srvices
N.A.I.C.S.: 622110
Richard Sukenik (CFO & VP-Fin)

WINDEMULLER ELECTRIC INC.
1176 Electric Ave, Wayland, MI 49348-0466
Tel.: (616) 877-8770 MI
Web Site: http://www.windemuller.us
Year Founded: 1954
Sales Range: $100-124.9 Million
Emp.: 180
Provider of Electrical Contracting & Information Technology Services
N.A.I.C.S.: 238210
Darrell Holwerda (Mgr-Mktg)
David Beemer (Pres)
Jim Rose (VP)
Steve Alles (Treas, Sec & Controller)
James Foster (Sr Mgr-Automation)

WINDEMULLER TECHNICAL SERVICES, INC.
1611 Northgate Blvd, Sarasota, FL 34234
Tel.: (941) 355-8822 FL
Web Site:
    http://www.windemuller.com
Sales Range: $1-9.9 Million
Emp.: 75
Electrical Work
N.A.I.C.S.: 238210
Mike Cantalamessa (VP & Mgr-Svc)
Nancy Windemuller-Sedlar (Co-Owner & Pres)
John Sedlar (Co-Owner & VP)
John Barber (VP)

WINDERMERE REAL ESTATE SERVICES COMPANY
1151 Fairview Ave N Ste 105, Seattle, WA 98109
Tel.: (206) 527-3801 WA
Web Site:
    http://www.windermere.com
Year Founded: 1972
Sales Range: $10-24.9 Million
Emp.: 50
Provider of Residential & Commercial Real Estate Services
N.A.I.C.S.: 561110
Michael Fanning (Sr VP-Client Svcs)
Geoff P. Wood (CEO)
John Jacobi (Founder)
Noelle Bortfeld (Chief Mktg Officer)
Tara Scholl (Pres-Svcs-Northern California & Nevada)
Brooks Burton (COO)
Mark Oster (CFO)
Mike Teather (Sr VP-Client Svcs)
O. B. Jacobi (Pres)

Subsidiaries:

William L. Lyon & Associates, Inc. (1)
3640 American River Dr, Sacramento, CA 95864-5901
Tel.: (916) 483-4450
Web Site: http://www.golyon.com
Sales Range: $10-24.9 Million
Emp.: 120
Real Estate Services
N.A.I.C.S.: 531210
Jim Waters (VP)
Scott Palmer (Mgr-Sls-Downtown)
Cathy Harrington (Dir-Mktg)
Pat Shea (Pres & COO)
Michael Levedahl (CFO)
Sara Baty (Controller)
David Wilson (CTO)
Heidi Nigel (Dir-Office Support Svcs)
Herb Cross (Dir-Property Mgmt)
Rosie Carvajal (Mgr-HR)
Janet Hubbard (Dir-Relocation)
Cheryle Ackerman Griffin (Mgr-Roseville)

WINDES, INC.
111 W Ocean Blvd 22nd Fl, Long Beach, CA 90802
Tel.: (562) 435-1191 CA
Web Site: http://www.windes.com
Year Founded: 1926
Emp.: 140
Certified Public Accountants
N.A.I.C.S.: 541211
John L. Di Carlo (Mng Partner)
Therese Cheevers (Sr Mgr)
Guy Nicio (Partner-Tax & Acctg Svcs Practice)
J. Lyle Scheppele (Partner & Chm-Audit & Assurance Svcs)
Lance G. Adams (Partner-Audit & Assurance Svcs)
Michael J. Barloewen (Partner-Audit & Assurance Svcs)

Subsidiaries:

Smith, Linden & Basso, LLP (1)
5120 Birch St Ste 200, Newport Beach, CA 92660-2101
Tel.: (949) 752-0660
Web Site: http://www.slb-cpa.com
Accounting Services
N.A.I.C.S.: 541219
Allen L. Basso (Co-Partner)
Scott H. Harada (Co-Partner)
Gordon E. Michie (Co-Partner)

WINDGATE ACQUISITION LTD.
105 W Main St Ste 2B PO Box 10250, Bozeman, MT 59719 DE
Year Founded: 2010
Sales Range: $25-49.9 Million
Emp.: 5
Real Estate Investment Services; Hotels
N.A.I.C.S.: 531390

Michael B. Elliott (Pres & CEO)
Mark A. Jones (COO)
Ryan W. Springer (Exec VP & Dir-Ops & Mgmt)
Timothy P. Reid (Exec VP & Dir-Acq)
Cameron J. Holt (Exec VP & Dir-Dev)

WINDHAM & MCDONALD CONSTRUCTION., INC.
1245 Big Orange Rd, Cordova, TN 38018
Tel.: (901) 755-7718
Year Founded: 1996
Rev.: $10,400,000
Emp.: 20
New Multifamily Housing Construction
N.A.I.C.S.: 236116
Kelly McDonald (Treas)
Doug L. Windham (Pres)

WINDHAM INJURY MANAGEMENT GROUP, INC.
500 N Commercial St Ste 301, Manchester, NH 03101
Tel.: (603) 626-5789
Web Site:
    http://www.windhamgroup.com
Year Founded: 1989
Rev.: $15,500,000
Emp.: 15
Provider of Managed Care, Medical Case Management & Ergonomic Services
N.A.I.C.S.: 524126
Sebastian Grasso (Pres)
David D. Heffner (Chief Sls Officer)

WINDISH RV CENTER INC.
11225 W 6th Ave, Lakewood, CO 80215
Tel.: (303) 274-9009
Web Site: http://www.windishrv.com
Rev.: $16,551,120
Emp.: 60
Automobiles & Other Motor Vehicle Service
N.A.I.C.S.: 441210
Carolyn Windish Irwin (Owner & Pres)

WINDJAMMER CAPITAL INVESTORS, LLC
840 Newport Ctr Dr Ste 650, Newport Beach, CA 92660
Tel.: (949) 721-9944 DE
Web Site:
    http://www.windjammercapital.com
Year Founded: 1990
Privater Equity Firm
N.A.I.C.S.: 523999
Robert Bartholomew (Founder & Mng Principal)
Jeffery J. Dunnigan (CFO & Chief Compliance Officer)
Connie Choung (Portfolio Mgr)
Costa Littas (Co-Founder & Mng Principal)
Jeff Miehe (Mng Principal)
Matthew Anderson (Mng Dir)
Michael Bartholomew (Dir-Mktg)
Shannon Moffett (Controller)
Brandon Edlefsen (Dir-Operating)
Kerry Muse (Dir-Bus Dev)
Gregory J. Bondick (Mng Principal)
John Donahue (Mng Dir-Bus Dev)
Craig S. Majernik (Mng Dir)
Ryan Pertz (Mng Dir)
Robert Quandt (Mng Dir)

Subsidiaries:

Compex Legal Services Inc. (1)
325 Maple Ave, Torrance, CA 90503
Tel.: (310) 782-1801
Web Site: http://www.cpxlegal.com
Microfilm Recording & Developing Legal Services
N.A.I.C.S.: 541611

Anthony Bazurto (Chief Comml Officer)
Humilidad Pasimio (VP & Controller)
Nitin Mehta (Chm)
Paul Boroditsch (CEO)
Lauren Brown (Exec Dir-Mktg & Partnerships)
Sujata Bajaj (CTO)

Engineered Controls International LLC (1)
100 Rego Dr, Elon, NC 27244-9159
Tel.: (336) 449-7707
Web Site: http://www.regoproducts.com
Sales Range: $75-99.9 Million
Emp.: 330
Valves & Controls for LP Gas & Fluids; Cryogenic Valves & Regulator Mfr
N.A.I.C.S.: 332911
Loryn Payne (Controller)

Division (Domestic):

Engineered Controls International LLC - RegO Cryo-Flow Products Division (2)
3181 Lear Dr, Burlington, NC 27215-8817
Tel.: (336) 226-3244
Pressure Valve Mfr
N.A.I.C.S.: 332911

Subsidiary (Non-US):

RegO S. DE R.L. DE C.V. (2)
Ave Apolo 504 Parque Industrial Kalos Del Poniente, Santa Catarina, 66370, Nuevo Leon, Mexico
Tel.: (52) 81 8032 5250
Industrial Valve & Regulator Mfr
N.A.I.C.S.: 334413

Rego Europe GmbH (2)
Industriestrasse 9, 35075, Gladenbach, Germany
Tel.: (49) 6462 9147 10
Web Site: http://www.rego-europe.de
Sales Range: $10-24.9 Million
Emp.: 15
Pressure Valve Mfr
N.A.I.C.S.: 332911
Freddy Deyk (Mgr-Ops)
Jutta Nold (Asst Sec-Fin)

Heritage Food Service Group, Inc. (1)
5130 Executive Blvd, Fort Wayne, IN 46808-1149
Tel.: (800) 458-5593
Web Site: http://www.heritageparts.com
Kitchen Equipment Distr
N.A.I.C.S.: 423440
John McDonough (Pres & CEO)
Roger Jorgensen (Sr Vp & CFO)
Tom Szafranski (Exec VP-Comml Bus Dev)
Mike Sajdak (CIO & Sr VP)
Larry Colestock (COO)

Hermetic Solutions Group, LLC (1)
8 Neshaminy Interplex Ste 221, Trevose, PA 19053
Tel.: (732) 722-8780
Web Site: http://hermeticsolutions.com
Hermetic Packaging, Components & Services
N.A.I.C.S.: 561910
Chris Andrews (VP-Intl Sls)
Keith Barclay (Pres & CEO)

Subsidiary (Domestic):

Cristek Interconnects, Inc. (2)
5395 E Hunter Ave, Anaheim, CA 92807-2054
Web Site: http://www.cristek.com
Electronic Connector Mfr
N.A.I.C.S.: 334417
Cristi Cristich (Founder & Pres)

Hi-Rel Group, LLC (2)
16 Plains Rd, Essex, CT 06426
Tel.: (860) 767-9031
Web Site: http://www.hirelgroup.com
Holding Company; Microelectronic Packaging Industry Metal Components Mfr
N.A.I.C.S.: 551112
Richard L. Ferraid (Chm)
Mike Kelley (CFO)
Bill Hubbard (Pres)

Subsidiary (Non-US):

Hi-Rel Alloys Ltd. (3)

WINDJAMMER CAPITAL INVESTORS, LLC

Windjammer Capital Investors, LLC—(Continued)
6934 Kinsmen Ct, Niagara Falls, L2H 0Y5, ON, Canada
Tel.: (289) 296-4078
Microelectronic Packaging Industry Metal Components Mfr
N.A.I.C.S.: 332999

Hi-Rel Lids Ltd. (3)
Fuller Road, Harleston, Norfolk, IP20 9EA, United Kingdom
Tel.: (44) 1379 853 944
Microelectronic Packaging Industry Metal Components Mfr
N.A.I.C.S.: 332999

Subsidiary (Domestic):

Hi-Rel Products, LLC (3)
16 Plains Rd, Essex, CT 06426
Tel.: (860) 767-9031
Web Site: http://hirelgroup.com
Microelectronic Packaging Industry Metal Components Mfr
N.A.I.C.S.: 332999
Scott Jenkins *(Pres)*

Mission Critical Electronics, LLC (1)
1580 Sunflower Ave Ste 100, Costa Mesa, CA 92626
Tel.: (714) 751-0488
Web Site: http://www.mission-critical-electronics.com
Power Conversion, Battery Charging & Battery Products Mfr
N.A.I.C.S.: 335910
Justin Purkey *(VP-Admin & Integration)*
Mark Kroh *(Pres-Network & Indus Power)*
Dale Tompkins *(Pres-Vehicle Power Segment)*
Kevin Moschetti *(CEO)*
Wolfgang Hombrecher *(CFO)*
John Hoeft *(VP-Ops & IT)*
Mitul Chandrani *(VP-Mktg)*

Subsidiary (Domestic):

Purkey's Fleet Electric, Inc. (2)
823 S Lincoln St, Lowell, AR 72745
Tel.: (479) 419-4800
Web Site: https://purkeys.net
Electrical Apparatus & Equipment, Wiring Supplies & Related Equipment Merchant Whslr
N.A.I.C.S.: 423610
Justin Purkey *(CEO)*

Subsidiary (Non-US):

Xantrex Technology, Inc. (2)
3700 Gilmore Way, Burnaby, V5A 4B5, BC, Canada
Tel.: (604) 422-8595
Web Site: http://www.xantrex.com
Sales Range: $200-249.9 Million
Electronic Components Mfr
N.A.I.C.S.: 334419
Richard Gaudet *(VP & Gen Mgr)*

Pasternack Enterprises, Inc. (1)
17802 Fitch, Irvine, CA 92614
Tel.: (949) 261-1920
Web Site: http://www.pasternack.com
Sales Range: $1-9.9 Million
Emp.: 50
Radio Frequency Microwave & Fiber Optic Component Whslr
N.A.I.C.S.: 423690
Terry G. Jarnigan *(CEO)*

Protective Industries, Inc. (1)
2150 Elmwood Ave, Buffalo, NY 14207
Tel.: (716) 876-9855
Sales Range: $10-24.9 Million
Emp.: 318
Industrial & Commercial Protective Caps, Plugs & Nettings Mfr; Circulating Fluid Temperature Control Systems Mfr
N.A.I.C.S.: 326199
Jim Ray *(VP-Ops)*

Division (Domestic):

Caplugs (2)
2150 Elmwood Ave, Buffalo, NY 14207-1910
Tel.: (716) 876-9855
Web Site: http://www.caplugs.com
Industrial & Commercial Protective Caps, Plugs & Nettings Mfr
N.A.I.C.S.: 326199
Jim Ray *(VP-Ops)*

Subsidiary (Domestic):

Shercon, Inc. (3)
6262 Katella Ave, Cypress, CA 90630
Tel.: (714) 548-3999
Web Site: http://www.shercon.com
Sales Range: $10-24.9 Million
Emp.: 60
Rubber & Masking Products Mfr
N.A.I.C.S.: 326299

Division (Domestic):

Mokon (2)
2150 Elmwood Ave, Buffalo, NY 14207-1910
Tel.: (716) 876-9951
Web Site: http://www.mokon.com
Circulating Fluid Temperature Control Systems Mfr
N.A.I.C.S.: 334513
Robert Kennery *(VP-Sls & Mktg)*

Rowmark LLC (1)
5409 Hamlet Dr, Findlay, OH 45840
Tel.: (419) 425-8974
Web Site: http://www.rowmarkllc.com
Engravable Plastic Sheet Mfr
N.A.I.C.S.: 326130
Phil Noakes *(Dir-Sls-North America)*
Beth Kroetz *(VP-HR)*
Jen Schoenberger *(Mgr-Exec Comm)*
Eric Short *(VP-Ops)*
Dennis Demuth *(Supvr-Customer Svc)*
Jessica Heldman-Beck *(Mgr-Mktg)*
Bobbi Payne *(Supvr-Customer Svc)*
Jim Ellward *(CEO)*

The Hilsinger Company Parent, LLC (1)
33 W Bacon St, Plainville, MA 02762
Web Site: http://www.hilcovision.com
Optical Accessories, Small Parts & Tools Mfr & Distr
N.A.I.C.S.: 339115
Ross Brownlee *(CEO)*

Subsidiary (Non-US):

Hilco Europe (2)
Brunt Acres Road Industrial Estate, Hawes, DL8 3UZ, North Yorkshire, United Kingdom
Tel.: (44) 1969 667 688
Optical Product Distr
N.A.I.C.S.: 423450

Subsidiary (Domestic):

M&S Technologies, Inc. (2)
5715 West Howard St, Niles, IL 60714
Tel.: (847) 763-0500
Web Site: http://www.mstech-eyes.com
Rev: $2,586,886
Emp.: 12
Household Appliance Stores
N.A.I.C.S.: 449210
Kevin Butler *(Dir-Tech & Product Dev)*
Joseph Marino *(Owner & Pres)*

Optego Vision USA Inc. (2)
4646 S Overland Dr, Tucson, AZ 85714
Tel.: (520) 321-1262
Web Site: http://www.eyecareandcure.com
Ophthalmic Goods Mfr
N.A.I.C.S.: 339115
Johan Van Dalen *(Founder & CEO)*

VRC Companies, LLC (1)
5384 Poplar Ave, Memphis, TN 38119
Tel.: (910) 310-2005
Web Site: https://vitalrecordscontrol.com
Information Management (IM) Solutions
N.A.I.C.S.: 519290
Dan McFarland *(COO)*
Danny Palo *(CEO)*

Subsidiary (Domestic):

2-20 Records Management, LLC (2)
374 Starke Rd, Carlstadt, NJ 07072
Tel.: (908) 203-4634
Web Site: http://www.2-20rm.com
Information Records Storage & Management Services
N.A.I.C.S.: 519290
Doug Mann *(CEO)*
Christopher Marquart *(CFO)*

Patrick McKillop *(Exec VP-Sls)*
Allison M. Doyle *(Exec VP-HR & Admin)*
Walter L. Caudill *(Sr VP-Ops)*

Subsidiary (Domestic):

IWC Media Services (3)
4401 21st St, Long Island City, NY 11101
Tel.: (718) 721-7101
Web Site: http://www.2-20rm.com
Sales Range: $1-9.9 Million
Emp.: 18
Media Storage, Preservation & Digitization Services
N.A.I.C.S.: 493190
Joe Fernandez *(Pres)*
Charlie Quinones *(VP-Sls & Mktg)*
Sam Verga *(Dir-Ops)*
Jonah Flateman *(Dir-Customer Svc)*

WINDMILL INTERNATIONAL, INC.
12 Murphy Dr Ste 200, Nashua, NH 03062
Tel.: (603) 888-5502
Web Site: http://www.windmill-intl.com
Year Founded: 1988
Sales Range: $25-49.9 Million
Emp.: 100
Provider of Program Management Support Services
N.A.I.C.S.: 541330
Steve Chimelski *(VP-Pro & Engrg Svcs)*
Jay Davison *(VP-Specialty Products)*
Richard Manganello *(Founder)*
Carl D'Alessandro *(Pres & CEO)*

WINDOW AND DOOR FACTORY INC.
530 Francisco Blvd W, San Rafael, CA 94901
Tel.: (415) 453-2500
Web Site: http://www.bayareawindowfactory.com
Year Founded: 1994
Sales Range: $10-24.9 Million
Emp.: 23
Sash, Wood Or Metal
N.A.I.C.S.: 444110
John Hoyer *(CEO)*

WINDOW MART, INC.
5760 Albert Pike Rd, Royal, AR 71968
Tel.: (501) 760-4730
Web Site: http://www.windowmart.com
Year Founded: 1996
Sales Range: $10-24.9 Million
Emp.: 125
Plastics Product Mfr
N.A.I.C.S.: 326199
Mike Allbritton *(Pres)*
Robert Tankersley *(VP)*

WINDOW PROS
3200 S Congress Ave Ste 102, Boynton Beach, FL 33426
Tel.: (561) 736-1353
Rev.: $19,800,000
Emp.: 50
Door & Window Products
N.A.I.C.S.: 444110
Michael Mason *(Pres)*
Sarah Ireland *(Asst Mgr)*

WINDOW TECHNOLOGY, INC.
201 N Industrial Dr, Mohett, MO 65708
Tel.: (417) 235-7821
Web Site: http://www.wintechinc.com
Year Founded: 1991
Sales Range: $10-24.9 Million
Emp.: 100
Metal Window & Door Mfr
N.A.I.C.S.: 332321

Robert E. Berger *(Pres)*
Adam Verstraete *(Sr Mgr-Sls)*
Stephen McColloch *(Grp Product Mgr-Comml Window Products)*
Carrie Utter *(Mgr-Customer Svc)*
Neal Messer *(Engr-Sls)*

WINDOW TO THE WORLD COMMUNICATIONS, INC.
5400 N St Louis Ave, Chicago, IL 60625-4623
Tel.: (773) 583-5000
Web Site: http://www.wttw.com
Year Founded: 1995
Sales Range: $25-49.9 Million
Emp.: 230
Broadcasting & Publishing
N.A.I.C.S.: 516120
Paul Ansell *(Mgr-Sls)*
Dan Soles *(Chief Television Content Officer & Sr VP)*
Anne Gleason *(Sr VP-Mktg & Interactive Media)*
David C. Blowers *(Chm)*
Sandra Cordova Micek *(Pres & CEO)*
George Preston *(VP & Gen Mgr)*

Subsidiaries:

98.7 FM (1)
5400 N St Louis Ave, Chicago, IL 60625-4623 (100%)
Tel.: (773) 583-5000
Sales Range: $25-49.9 Million
Emp.: 210
Radio Stations
N.A.I.C.S.: 516120

Network Chicago (1)
737 N Michigan Ave Ste 1900, Chicago, IL 60611-5421
Tel.: (312) 787-1979
Web Site: http://www.thechicagonetwork.org
Sales Range: $25-49.9 Million
Emp.: 190
Television Station Services
N.A.I.C.S.: 516120

WWCI Inc (1)
5400 N Saint Louis Ave, Chicago, IL 60625-4698
Tel.: (773) 583-5000
Web Site: http://www.wttw.com
Sales Range: $25-49.9 Million
Emp.: 198
Weekly Newspaper
N.A.I.C.S.: 516120

WINDOW WORLD INC.
118 Shaver St, North Wilkesboro, NC 28659
Tel.: (336) 667-2100
Web Site: http://www.windowworld.com
Year Founded: 1997
Sales Range: $25-49.9 Million
Emp.: 8
Single-Family Windows Installation Services
N.A.I.C.S.: 423220
Tammy Whitworth *(Chm & CEO)*
Steven Kamody *(Pres)*
Beth Vannoy *(Chief Legal Officer)*
Duffy Sweeney *(Sr VP-IT & Digital Ops)*
Fred Bauer *(Corp Counsel)*

Subsidiaries:

Window World of Upstate (1)
2161 Ridge Rd, Greenville, SC 29607
Tel.: (864) 236-0411
Web Site: http://www.windowworldupstate.com
Rev.: $340,000
Emp.: 3
Single-Family Home Remodeling, Additions & Repairs
N.A.I.C.S.: 236118
Theron Campbell *(Mgr-Installation Svc)*

WINDOW WORLD OF BATON ROUGE, LLC

COMPANIES

8405 Airline Hwy, Baton Rouge, LA 70815
Tel.: (225) 706-2100
Web Site: http://www.windowworld-btr.com
Year Founded: 1995
Sales Range: $25-49.9 Million
Emp.: 111
Supplier of Vinyl Replacement Windows & Doors
N.A.I.C.S.: 321911
Jim Roland (CEO)

WINDOWIZARDS INC.
Rte 13 PA Tpke, Bristol, PA 19007
Tel.: (215) 945-3200 PA
Web Site: http://www.windowizards.com
Year Founded: 1972
Sales Range: $10-24.9 Million
Emp.: 82
Provider of Building Material Services
N.A.I.C.S.: 444110
Meagan Brown (Sec & VP-Legal)

WINDOWRAMA ENTERPRISES INC.
71 Heartland Blvd, Edgewood, NY 11717-8330
Tel.: (631) 667-2555
Web Site: http://www.windowrama.com
Year Founded: 1977
Sales Range: $25-49.9 Million
Emp.: 200
Provider of Lumber, Other Building Materials, Wood & Vinyl Doors & Windows
N.A.I.C.S.: 444110
Marc Axinn (CEO)

WINDOWS AND WALLS UNLIMITED, INC.
375 County Rd 39, Southampton, NY 11968
Tel.: (631) 287-1515 DE
Web Site: http://www.wwunlimited.com
Year Founded: 1985
Sales Range: $1-9.9 Million
Emp.: 5
Draperies, Blinds, Shutters, Slipcovers & Bed Ensembles Designer & Installer
N.A.I.C.S.: 321911
Linda Nuszen (Chm & Pres)
Paul Nuszen (Treas & Sec)

WINDRIDGE IMPLEMENTS LLC
2073 State Hwy 9, Decorah, IA 52101
Tel.: (563) 382-3613
Web Site: http://www.windridgeimplement.com
Sales Range: $10-24.9 Million
Emp.: 40
Farm Equipment & Supplies
N.A.I.C.S.: 459999
Eric Nordschow (Chm)
Jeanne Pecinovsky (Controller)

WINDSAIL CAPITAL GROUP, LLC
133 Federal St Ste 702, Boston, MA 02110
Tel.: (617) 423-6066
Web Site: https://www.windsailcapital.com
Privater Equity Firm
N.A.I.C.S.: 523940
Jane E. Silfen (Mng Dir)
Ian Bowles (Co-Founder & Mng Dir)
Michael Rand (Co-Founder & Mng Dir)

WINDSOR AUTOMOTIVE INC.
85 Rte 17, Wood Ridge, NJ 07075
Tel.: (201) 939-9400
Web Site: http://www.eastcoasttoyota.com
Sales Range: $25-49.9 Million
Emp.: 35
New & Used Automobiles
N.A.I.C.S.: 441110
Jeffrey Brown (Gen Mgr)

WINDSOR ENERGY RESOURCES, INC.
14301 Caliber Dr Ste 300, Oklahoma City, OK 73134
Tel.: (405) 463-6900 DE
Web Site: http://www.windsorenergy.com
Rev.: $9,130,000
Emp.: 45
Oil & Gas Exploration
N.A.I.C.S.: 211120
Steven E. West (CEO)
Travis D. Stice (Pres & COO)
Mike Liddell (Chm)

WINDSOR FASHIONS, INC.
9603 John St, Santa Fe Springs, CA 90670
Tel.: (323) 282-9000 CA
Web Site: http://www.windsorstore.com
Year Founded: 1959
Sales Range: $200-249.9 Million
Emp.: 500
Ladies Ready-To-Wear Shoes, Apparel & Accessories
N.A.I.C.S.: 458110
Leon Zekaria (Pres)
Ike Zekaria (VP)
Steven Brodkin (Mgr-Acctg)
Bob Slatter (VP-Ops)
Mironda Jones (VP-Stores)

WINDSOR FROZEN FOODS CO.
PO Box 767, Toluca, IL 61369
Tel.: (815) 452-2361
Sales Range: $25-49.9 Million
Emp.: 265
Frozen Specialty Food Mfr
N.A.I.C.S.: 311412
Stan Smith (Mgr-Quality Assurance)
Rick Alden (Dir-Demand Plng & Logistics)
Paula Nixon (Mgr-Hiring)
Bruce Schroeder (Mgr-Mfg)
Frank Stoeger (Plant Mgr)
Angela Mekley (Mgr-Fin)
Joan Perona (Dir-Res)
George Young (Dir-HR)
Tim Arndt (Mgr-Pur)

WINDSOR HEALTH AND REHAB CENTER
809 W Benton, Windsor, CT 65360
Tel.: (660) 647-3102
Web Site: http://www.windsorhealthcarecenter.com
Nursing & Rehabilitation Facility
N.A.I.C.S.: 623110

WINDSOR MILL COMPANY
7950 Redwood Dr Ste 4, Cotati, CA 94931
Tel.: (707) 655-9669
Web Site: http://www.windsormill.com
Year Founded: 1972
Sales Range: $10-24.9 Million
Emp.: 100
Unfinished & Prefinished Wood Moldings
N.A.I.C.S.: 321918
Raymond Flynn (Founder)
Doug Shear (CFO)

John A. Hankins (VP-Mfg)
Craig A. Flynn (VP-Sls-Mktg)
Kevin Platte (VP-Mfg)
Alicia Wood (Exec Acct Mgr)

WINDSOR OFFICE PRODUCTS INC.
33 Fairfield Pl, Caldwell, NJ 07006
Tel.: (973) 227-5050
Web Site: http://www.windsorws.com
Rev.: $20,517,935
Emp.: 30
Office Furniture
N.A.I.C.S.: 423210
Tom Buraszeski (Pres)
Rick White (Controller)

WINDSOR PROPERTIES INC.
3125 Windsor Blvd, Vero Beach, FL 32963
Tel.: (772) 388-5050
Web Site: http://www.windsorflorida.com
Rev.: $10,000,000
Emp.: 100
Land Subdividers & Developers, Residential
N.A.I.C.S.: 237210
W. Galen Weston (Founder)

WINDSOR SHADE TOBACCO COMPANY, INC.
80 King Spring Rd, Windsor Locks, CT 06096-1137
Tel.: (860) 627-6122 CT
Year Founded: 1937
Sales Range: $50-74.9 Million
Emp.: 15
Tobacco Warehousing & Storage
N.A.I.C.S.: 813910
Jean-Marc Bade (Mgr)

WINDSOR-MOUNT JOY MUTUAL INSURANCE CO.
21 W Main St, Ephrata, PA 17522
Tel.: (717) 733-8648
Web Site: http://www.windsor1844.com
Year Founded: 1844
Sales Range: $10-24.9 Million
Emp.: 23
Direct Property & Casualty Insurance Carrier Services
N.A.I.C.S.: 524126
Deborah Bartholomew (Principal)

WINDSTREAM TECHNOLOGIES, INC.
819 Buckeye St, North Vernon, IN 47265
Tel.: (812) 953-1481 VG
Web Site: http://www.windstream-inc.com
Sales Range: $1-9.9 Million
Emp.: 47
Wind Energy Solutions Developer
N.A.I.C.S.: 221118
Daniel Bates (Chm & CEO)
Travis Campbell (COO)
Daniel C. Harris (Exec VP-Sls-Global)
William K. Thorpe (CFO)
Wanda Ferguson (Sec)
Claudio Chami (Sr VP-Sls-Latin America)

WINDWARD BUILDERS INC.
27845 N Irma Lee Cir Ste 102, Lake Forest, IL 60045
Tel.: (847) 281-8300
Web Site: http://www.windwardbuilders.com
Rev.: $10,110,723
Emp.: 3
Single-Family Housing Construction
N.A.I.C.S.: 236115
Ross Friedman (Pres)

WINDWAY CAPITAL CORP.

WINDWARD CAPITAL PARTNERS LP
712 5th Ave 21st Fl, New York, NY 10019
Tel.: (212) 382-6500
Year Founded: 1994
Sales Range: $250-299.9 Million
Emp.: 2,100
Investor
N.A.I.C.S.: 523999

Subsidiaries:

HCC Industries International (1)
49 53 Hazelwood Rd, Northampton, NN1 1LG, United Kingdom (100%)
Tel.: (44) 604233101
Web Site: http://www.hccindustries.com
Engineering Support Services
N.A.I.C.S.: 541330

WINDWARD ROOFING & CONSTRUCTION, INC.
919 S Sacramento, Chicago, IL 60612-3912
Tel.: (773) 638-6580
Web Site: http://www.windwardroofing.com
Sales Range: $10-24.9 Million
Emp.: 80
Roofing Installation Services
N.A.I.C.S.: 238390
Randall B. Kuhn (Pres)

WINDWAY CAPITAL CORP.
630 Riverfront Dr Ste 200, Sheboygan, WI 53081-4629
Tel.: (920) 457-8600 DE
Web Site: http://www.windway.com
Year Founded: 1988
Sales Range: $50-74.9 Million
Emp.: 20
Holding Company; Fabricated Stainless Steel Food Service Products; Marine Industry Products, Sails & Accessories for Sailboats
N.A.I.C.S.: 332215
Terry J. Kohler (Pres)
Mary Kohler (Dir-PR)
Barbara Quasius (CFO)

Subsidiaries:

North Cutting Systems, LLC (1)
20 Barnes Court Building G, Vaughan, L4K 4L4, ON, Canada
Tel.: (905) 761-8400
Web Site: http://www.northcuttingsystems.com
Industrial Textile Cutting Services
N.A.I.C.S.: 561499

North Sails Collection USA (1)
317 Chester Ave, Annapolis, MD 21403
Tel.: (410) 269-5662
Web Site: http://www.northsails.com
Apparel Distr
N.A.I.C.S.: 458110

North Sails Direct (1)
23 Glendale St, Salem, MA 01970
Tel.: (888) 424-7328
Web Site: http://www.northsailsdirect.com
Boat Accessory Whslr
N.A.I.C.S.: 423860

North Sails Group, LLC (1)
125 Old Gate Ln, Milford, CT 06460
Tel.: (203) 877-7621
Web Site: http://www.northsails.com
Sailing Product Whslr
N.A.I.C.S.: 423910
Jay Mueller (Mgr-Svc)

North Thin Ply Technology, SARL (1)
Closel 3, 1020, Renens, Switzerland
Tel.: (41) 21 811 08 88
Web Site: http://www.thinplytechnology.com
Thin Ply Composite Mfr
N.A.I.C.S.: 325220

WINDWAY CAPITAL CORP.

U.S. PRIVATE

Windway Capital Corp.—(Continued)

Southern Spars Ltd (1)
15 Jomac Place Rosebank Road, Rosebank, Auckland, 1026, New Zealand
Tel.: (64) 9 845 7200
Web Site: http://www.southernspars.com
Emp.: 200
Carbon Spar Mfr
N.A.I.C.S.: 339999
Mark Hauser *(Mng Dir)*
Jarred Wallace *(Mgr-Design)*
Stefano Scarpa *(Dir-Svc-STP-Palma de Mallorca)*
James Austin *(Gen Mgr-Future Fibres)*

Subsidiary (Non-US):

RSB Rigging Solutions S.L. (2)
STP Boatyard Edificio Global Espigon Exterior S/N Local n 8 Oficina 24, Muelle Viejo, 07012, Palma de Mallorca, Baleares, Spain
Tel.: (34) 971 495 931
Web Site: http://www.rsb-rigging.com
Rigging Services
N.A.I.C.S.: 561499
Steve Branagh *(Mng Dir)*
Russ Brown *(Gen Mgr)*
Andy Hartridge *(Project Mgr)*
Mark Timmins *(Project Mgr)*

Southern Spars Europe A/S (2)
Bergensvej 6, 6230, Rodekro, Denmark
Tel.: (45) 7462 0060
Carbon Spar Mfr
N.A.I.C.S.: 339999
Rene Villefrance *(Mgr-Sls)*
Lars Netterstrom *(Gen Mgr-Europe)*

Southern Spars International (PVT) Ltd (2)
Biyagama Export Processing Zone, Colombo, Sri Lanka
Tel.: (94) 64 9 845 7200
Carbon Spar Mfr
N.A.I.C.S.: 339999
Percy Karunaweera *(Mgr)*

Plant (Non-US):

Southern Spars Ltd - Cape Town Facility (2)
22 Bolt Avenue Montague Gardens, Milnerton, Cape Town, 7435, South Africa
Tel.: (27) 21 555 3470
Carbon Spar Mfr
N.A.I.C.S.: 339999
Peter Shaw *(Gen Mgr)*
Richard Stubbs *(Mgr-Sls)*
Trent Justice *(Project Mgr)*

Plant (US):

Southern Spars Ltd - Rig Pro Rhode Island Facility (2)
Ste 2 14 Regatta Way, Portsmouth, RI 02871
Tel.: (401) 683-6966
Carbon Spar Mfr
N.A.I.C.S.: 339999
Scott Vogel *(Gen Mgr)*
Tony Reaper *(Mgr-Sls)*
Ike Bowen *(Mgr-Svc)*
Richie Boyd *(Mgr-Design)*
George Reekie *(Mgr-R&D)*

WINDY CITY DISTRIBUTION
30w315 Calumet Ave, Warrenville, IL 60555
Tel.: (630) 836-9503
Web Site:
http://www.windycitydistribution.com
Year Founded: 1999
Rev.: $5,900,000
Emp.: 16
Beer Distr
N.A.I.C.S.: 424810
Ray Daniels *(Dir-Cicerone Certification Program)*
Letty Ebel *(VP)*
Kimberly Ebel *(Pres)*

WINDY CITY ELECTRIC COMPANY
7225 W Touhy Ave, Chicago, IL 60631
Tel.: (773) 774-0201
Web Site:
http://www.windycityelectric.com
Rev.: $12,700,000
Emp.: 6
Electrical Contractor
N.A.I.C.S.: 238210
Susan Thies *(Mgr)*
Nancy McMahon *(Pres)*

WINDY CITY EQUIPMENT SERVICE, INC.
278 S Hamilton Pl, Gilbert, AZ 85233
Web Site:
http://www.windycityequip.com
Year Founded: 2003
Sales Range: $1-9.9 Million
Emp.: 36
Refrigeration Equipment Maintenance Services
N.A.I.C.S.: 811310
Joel Zolin *(Owner)*
Josh Zolin *(CEO)*

WINDY CITY FIELDHOUSE
2367 W Logan Blvd, Chicago, IL 60647
Tel.: (773) 486-7300
Web Site: http://www.wcfevents.com
Year Founded: 1995
Rev.: $5,400,000
Emp.: 216
Amusement & Recreation Services
N.A.I.C.S.: 713940
Bob Beaubien *(Co-Founder & Exec VP)*
Murrel Karsh *(Co-Founder & Pres)*
Jimmy Dahm *(Mgr-Event Ops)*

WINDY CITY LIMOUSINE
9377 W Grand Ave, Franklin Park, IL 60131
Tel.: (847) 916-9300
Web Site:
http://www.windycitylimos.com
Year Founded: 2006
Sales Range: $10-24.9 Million
Emp.: 373
Limousine & Bus Transportation
N.A.I.C.S.: 485320
George Jacobs *(Co-Founder)*
Sal Milazzo *(Co-Founder)*

WINDY CITY NOVELTIES, INC.
300 Lakeview Pkwy, Vernon Hills, IL 60061
Web Site:
https://www.windycitynovelties.com
Party & Seasonal Decorations Wholesalers
N.A.I.C.S.: 423920

Subsidiaries:

U.S. Toy Co., Inc. (1)
13201 Arrington Rd, Grandview, MO 64030-2886
Tel.: (816) 761-5900
Web Site: http://www.ustoy.com
Sales Range: $10-24.9 Million
Emp.: 130
Carnival, Party & Seasonal Decorations, Novelty Toys, Stuffed Animals & Balloons Whslr
N.A.I.C.S.: 423490
Jonathan Freiden *(Pres & Co-CEO)*
Seth Freiden *(Co-CEO)*

WINDY CITY PROMOTIONS, LLC
2400 E Main St Ste 331, Saint Charles, IL 60174
Web Site: http://www.luxeyard.com
Online Home Furnishings Retailer
N.A.I.C.S.: 449129

WINE & SPIRITS WHOLESALERS OF AMERICA, INC.
805 15th St NW Ste 430, Washington, DC 20005
Tel.: (202) 371-9792
Web Site: http://www.wswa.org
Year Founded: 1943
Sales Range: $10-24.9 Million
Emp.: 22
Trade Assocation
N.A.I.C.S.: 813910
Craig Wolf *(Pres & CEO)*
Jake Hegemen *(VP-Legal & Regulatory Affairs)*
Becca Britt *(Coord-Tech & Support, Meetings & Conventions)*
Ali Prolago *(Mgr-Govt Affairs)*
Bob Wiggans *(Sr Dir-Membership)*
Joanne Moak *(Sr VP & Gen Counsel)*
Jeff Solsby *(VP-Comm & Membership)*
Sam Block *(VP-Fin & Admin)*
Catherine McDaniel *(VP-Govt Affairs)*
Dawson Hobbs *(Sr VP-Govt Affairs)*
Kari Langerman *(Dir-Expositions & Meetings)*
Reid Teschner *(VP-Legal & Regulatory Affairs)*

WINECOMMUNE LLC
7305 Edgewater Dr Ste D, Oakland, CA 94621
Tel.: (510) 632-5300
Web Site:
http://www.winecommune.com
Year Founded: 1999
Sales Range: $10-24.9 Million
Emp.: 40
Online Wine Seller
N.A.I.C.S.: 424820
Shaun Bishop *(Co-Founder & Pres)*
Natlie Trembley *(Dir-Mktg)*

WINEDIRECT, INC.
450 Green Island Rd, American Canyon, CA 94503
Tel.: (707) 603-4000
Web Site: http://www.winedirect.com
Year Founded: 2002
Wine Online Marketplace Services
N.A.I.C.S.: 561499
Joe Waechter *(Pres & CEO)*
Jim Agger *(VP-Mktg & Bus Dev)*
John Gilmer *(CFO)*

Subsidiaries:

Elypsis, Inc. (1)
1886 El Centro Ave, Napa, CA 94558
Tel.: (707) 257-8912
Sales Range: $10-24.9 Million
Emp.: 11
Software Products Mfr & Consulting Services
N.A.I.C.S.: 513210

WINEGAR'S SUPERMARKETS INC.
1080 W 300 N, Clearfield, UT 84015
Tel.: (801) 298-5407
Web Site: http://www.winegars.com
Year Founded: 1917
Sales Range: $10-24.9 Million
Emp.: 235
Grocery Stores
N.A.I.C.S.: 445110
Cheryl Jones *(Office Mgr)*

WINEGARD COMPANY
3000 Kirkwood St, Burlington, IA 52601-2000
Tel.: (319) 754-0600
Web Site: http://www.winegard.com
Year Founded: 1954
Sales Range: $50-74.9 Million
Emp.: 300
Mfr of Television Reception Products
N.A.I.C.S.: 334220
Randy Winegard *(CEO)*
Jude Bliss *(Mgr-Mktg Svcs)*
Jim Riffel *(Dir-Satellite Bus Grp)*
Keith Larson *(Dir-Sls & Mktg)*
Grant Whipple *(Pres & COO)*
Ed Spicer *(CFO)*
Erik Guldager *(Mgr-Sls-Natl)*
Tom Faludy *(Interim Gen Mgr-Consumer Products Bus)*
Jason Helling *(Product Mgr-Mobile Satellite)*
Jennifer Hernandez *(Mgr-RV OEM Bus Dev-Elkhart)*
Lance Beck *(Dir-Product Dev-Internet of Things)*
Marvin Metzler *(Sr Dir-Bus Dev-Mobile Div)*
James Witty *(Dir-Bus Dev-RV OEM Div)*
Chris Panelli *(Acct Mgr-RV OEM)*
Steven Zonker *(Acct Mgr-RV OEM)*
Shelby DeWulf *(Dir-Corp Mktg)*

WINEGARDNER & HAMMONS, INC.
4243 Hunt Rd, Cincinnati, OH 45242
Tel.: (513) 891-1066
Web Site: http://www.whihotels.com
Year Founded: 1959
Sales Range: $10-24.9 Million
Emp.: 80
Hotels Owner & Management Services
N.A.I.C.S.: 721110
J. Erik Kamfjord *(Chm & CEO)*
Kent Bruggeman *(Exec VP)*
Terry Dammeyer *(Sr VP-Construction)*
Mike Conway *(Pres)*
Debbie McAtee *(VP-Mgmt Info Sys & DP)*
Brian Perkins *(Sr VP)*

WINERY EXCHANGE INC.
500 Redwood Blvd Ste 200, Novato, CA 94947
Tel.: (415) 382-6754
Web Site:
http://www.wineryexchange.com
Sales Range: $50-74.9 Million
Emp.: 61
Wine Producer & Bottler
N.A.I.C.S.: 312130
Abbott Wolfe *(Sr VP-Sls)*
Marc Kibbey *(VP-Sls-Beer)*
Michael Manning *(Mgr-Sls-Beer-South)*
John Derringer *(Mgr-Sls-Beer-Central Reg)*
Kevin Meehan *(Mgr-Sls-Wine Sls-Southeast)*
Tom Roberts *(Dir-Sls-UK)*

WINFIELD MOTOR CO., INC.
1901 Main St, Winfield, KS 67156
Tel.: (620) 221-2840
Web Site:
http://www.winfieldmotor.com
Rev.: $14,000,000
Emp.: 25
New & Used Automobiles
N.A.I.C.S.: 441110
Larry Raber *(Pres)*
Jack Karl *(Mgr-Fin)*

WINFIELD PUBLISHING CO.
201 E 9th Ave, Winfield, KS 67156
Tel.: (620) 221-1050
Web Site:
http://www.winfieldcourier.com
Sales Range: $10-24.9 Million
Emp.: 30
Newspaper Publishers
N.A.I.C.S.: 513110
Dvid Allen *(Pres)*

Subsidiaries:

The Arkansas City Traveler (1)

200 E 5th Ave, Arkansas City, KS 67005
Tel.: (620) 442-4200
Web Site: http://www.arkcity.net
Sales Range: $10-24.9 Million
Newspaper Publishers
N.A.I.C.S.: 513110
Susie Kincaid *(Bus Mgr)*
Joey Sprinkle *(Editor-Sports)*
Marilyn Coury *(Mgr-Circulation)*
Arty Hicks *(Dir-Adv)*
Terri Snow *(Mgr-Classified)*

Winfield Daily Courier (1)
201 E 9th St, Winfield, KS 67156
Tel.: (620) 221-1100
Web Site: http://www.winfieldcourier.com
Sales Range: $10-24.9 Million
Newspaper Publishers
N.A.I.C.S.: 513110
Marsha Wesseler *(Publr)*

WINFIELD UNITED, LLC
4001 Lexington Ave N, Arden Hills, MN 55126
Tel.: (855) 494-6343   MN
Web Site:
http://www.winfieldunited.com
Year Founded: 1998
Crop Nutrients;Herbicides, Insecticides & Fungicides Mfr
N.A.I.C.S.: 325320
Cory Collins *(Ops Mgr-Lab)*

Subsidiaries:

GreenPoint AG, LLC (1)
3350 Players Club Pkwy, Memphis, TN 38125
Tel.: (901) 758-1341
Web Site: http://www.greenpointag.com
Retail Farm Supply Stores
N.A.I.C.S.: 424910
Tim Witcher *(Pres & CEO)*

Subsidiary (Domestic):

Tipton Farmers Cooperative (2)
2060 Hwy 51 S, Covington, TN 38019
Tel.: (901) 476-8692
Farm Supplies
N.A.I.C.S.: 424910
Joey Caldwell *(Treas)*

WING AVIATION, LLC
Houston Hobby Airport 8410 Larson, Houston, TX 77061
Tel.: (713) 645-9464
Web Site:
http://www.wingaviation.com
Year Founded: 1992
Air Passenger Carrier
N.A.I.C.S.: 481219
Brian Wing *(Pres)*
Jeffrey Reid *(CEO)*

WING INFLATABLES, INC.
1220 5th St, Arcata, CA 95521
Tel.: (707) 826-2887   CA
Web Site: http://www.wing.com
Year Founded: 1993
Sales Range: $1-9.9 Million
Emp.: 90
Inflatable Tubes & Accessories for Inflatable Boats Mfr
N.A.I.C.S.: 326299
Mark French *(CFO)*

Subsidiaries:

Mustang Survival Corp. (1)
7525 Lowland Drive, Burnaby, V5J 5L1, BC, Canada
Tel.: (604) 270-8631
Web Site: http://www.mustangsurvival.com
Floatation & Personal Protection Equipment Designer, Mfr & Whslr
N.A.I.C.S.: 339920
Vanessa Fors *(Mgr-Category)*

Subsidiary (US):

Mustang Survival, Inc. (2)
1215 Old Fairhaven Pkwy Ste C, Bellingham, WA 98225
Tel.: (360) 676-1782
Web Site: http://www.mustangsurvival.com
Sales Range: $1-9.9 Million
Floatation & Personal Protection Equipment Mfr & Whslr
N.A.I.C.S.: 339113
Sean McCarthy *(VP)*

Subsidiary (Domestic):

Mustang Survival Mfg, Inc. (3)
190 Mustang Way, Spencer, WV 25276
Tel.: (304) 927-1111
Web Site: http://www.mustangsurvival.com
Floatation & Personal Protection Equipment Mfr
N.A.I.C.S.: 339113
P. J. Wilson *(Coord-HR)*

WINGATE & ASSOCIATES REALTY, INC.
3380 Tampa Rd, Palm Harbor, FL 34684
Tel.: (727) 786-7368
Web Site:
http://www.wingaterealtors.com
Sales Range: $10-24.9 Million
Emp.: 20
Real Estate Broker
N.A.I.C.S.: 531210
Kathleen Wingate *(Pres)*
Michael Warnstedt *(VP)*
Eric Ramquist *(Mgr-Maintenance)*

WINGATE PARTNERS, LLP
750 N Saint Paul St Ste 1200, Dallas, TX 75201-3249
Tel.: (214) 720-1313
Web Site:
http://www.wingatepartners.com
Year Founded: 1987
Sales Range: $500-549.9 Million
Privater Equity Firm
N.A.I.C.S.: 523999
Jason H. Reed *(Principal)*
Jay I. Applebaum *(Principal)*
James A. Johnson *(Principal)*
Michael B. Decker *(Partner)*

Subsidiaries:

Binswanger Enterprises, LLC (1)
965 Rdg Lk Blvd Ste 305, Memphis, TN 38120
Tel.: (877) 456-3612
Web Site: http://www.binswangerglass.com
Automotive Glass Replacement Services; Architectural Glass Designer & Installer
N.A.I.C.S.: 811122
Jill Read *(Mgr-Key Acct Dev)*

National Print Group, Inc. (1)
2464 Amnicola Hwy, Chattanooga, TN 37406
Tel.: (423) 622-2254
Web Site: http://www.tnpg.com
Sales Range: $75-99.9 Million
Digital, Screen, Lithograph, Out-of-Home & Large Format Point-of-Purchase Printing Services
N.A.I.C.S.: 323111
Dale Rutherford *(Dir-IT Infrastructure)*

Subsidiary (Domestic):

National Print Group-Digital & Screen (2)
1601 S Holtzclaw Ave, Chattanooga, TN 37404
Tel.: (423) 698-2108
Web Site: http://www.tnpg.com
Sales Range: $25-49.9 Million
Digital & Screen Printing Services
N.A.I.C.S.: 323111

Sunrise Oilfield Supply, Inc. (1)
105 S Broadway Ste 610, Wichita, KS 67202-4221
Tel.: (316) 263-6060
Web Site: http://www.sunriseoilfield.com
Oil Field Equipment Mfr
N.A.I.C.S.: 333132
Mike Reed *(Pres & CEO)*
Ryan Quattlebaum *(CFO)*

WINGED KEEL GROUP, LLC
1430 Broadway Fl 21, New York, NY 10018
Tel.: (212) 527-8000   NY
Web Site: http://www.wingedkeel.com
Year Founded: 1991
Sales Range: $1-9.9 Million
Emp.: 45
Insurance Agencies & Brokerages
N.A.I.C.S.: 524210
Mark J. Richard *(Principal)*
Campbell Gerrish *(Pres)*
Brady C. Knight *(Principal)*
Eric Naison-Phillips *(Principal)*

Subsidiaries:

Knight Planning Corp. (1)
2001 Kirby Dr, Houston, TX 77019-6042
Tel.: (713) 942-8820
Web Site: http://www.knightplanning.com
Insurance Agencies & Brokerages
N.A.I.C.S.: 524210
Brady Knight *(Pres)*

Nease Lagana Eden & Culley, Inc. (1)
2100 River Edge Pky 200, Atlanta, GA 30328
Tel.: (770) 956-1800
Web Site: http://www.nlec.com
Rev.: $3,700,000
Emp.: 33
Insurance Agencies & Brokerages
N.A.I.C.S.: 524210
Lawton M. Nease *(Pres)*
Dale Culler *(Dir-Acctg)*
Janet Prescher *(Mgr-Ops)*
Peter Fleming *(VP-Bus Dev)*
John Endriss *(Dir-Advanced Markets)*
Linda Hughes *(Dir-Underwriting)*

The Madison Group, Inc. (1)
5299 DTC Blvd Ste 1100, Greenwood Village, CO 80111
Tel.: (978) 263-6877
Web Site: http://www.themadisongroup.com
Sales Range: $1-9.9 Million
Emp.: 23
Insurance Agencies & Brokerages
N.A.I.C.S.: 524210
Jonathan Goddard *(Pres)*
Mark Richards *(CEO & Pres-Sole Shareholder)*

WINGED MEDIA LLC
12121 Wilshire Blvd Ste 504, Los Angeles, CA 92673
Tel.: (310) 979-9100
Web Site:
http://www.wingedmedia.com
Sales Range: $1-9.9 Million
Domain Name Registration, Hosting & Parking Services
N.A.I.C.S.: 518210
Troy Rushton *(CEO)*
Andrew Chinn *(CTO)*
Kayolan Avroniev *(Mgr-Software Dev)*

WINGER CONTRACTING CO.
918 Hayne St, Ottumwa, IA 52501
Tel.: (641) 682-3407
Web Site:
http://www.wingermechanical.com
Sales Range: $10-24.9 Million
Emp.: 180
Mechanical Contractor
N.A.I.C.S.: 238220
Tom Keck *(Pres)*

WINGFOOT ENTERPRISES INC.
1600 W Sam Houston Pkwy N, Houston, TX 77043
Tel.: (713) 722-0220
Web Site:
http://www.allegiancestaffing.com
Sales Range: $10-24.9 Million
Emp.: 13
Temporary Help Service
N.A.I.C.S.: 561320
Thomas Landry *(Pres)*

WINGMAN MEDIA
4061 Glencoe Ave # A, Marina Del Rey, CA 90292-5607
Tel.: (310) 302-9400
Web Site:
http://www.wingmanmedia.com
Rev.: $30,000,000
Emp.: 30
N.A.I.C.S.: 541810
Luz Ongkiko *(Dir-Fin)*
Brian Diedrick *(Dir-Interactive Mktg)*
Stephanie Kendrick-O'Curran *(Grp Acct Dir)*
Meredith Marcus *(Dir-Media)*
Rich Kagan *(Owner)*
Steve Dubane *(Pres)*

WINGRA STONE COMPANY
2975 Kapec Rd, Madison, WI 53719
Tel.: (608) 271-5555
Web Site:
http://www.wingrastone.com
Year Founded: 1928
Ready-Mixed Concrete Products & Services
N.A.I.C.S.: 327320
Robert F. Shea *(Pres)*
Andy Balch *(Mgr-Sls-Wingra Redi-Mix)*
Steven C. Shea *(VP)*
Douglas C. Block *(Controller)*
Nick Carpenter *(Mgr-Acctg)*
Amber Femrite *(Supvr-Dispatch)*
Charlie Stark *(Supvr-Crushing)*
Gary Nechvatal *(Mgr-Maintenance)*

WINGS FINANCIAL ADVISORS, LLC
14985 Glazier Ave, Apple Valley, MN 55124-7440
Web Site:
http://www.wingsfinancial.com
Credit Union
N.A.I.C.S.: 522130
Frank Weidner *(Pres & CEO)*

WINGSPAN TECHNOLOGY, INC.
460 Norristown Rd Ste 200, Blue Bell, PA 19422
Tel.: (610) 941-6500
Web Site: http://www.wingspan.com
Sales Range: $1-9.9 Million
Emp.: 50
IT Consulting Services
N.A.I.C.S.: 541512
Troy Deck *(Founder & CEO)*
Rose Volpe *(Dir-Admin)*
Kathie Clark *(VP-Product Mgmt)*

WINGSWEPT
800 Benson Rd, Garner, NC 27529
Tel.: (919) 779-0954
Web Site: http://www.wingswept.com
Year Founded: 1995
Sales Range: $1-9.9 Million
Emp.: 25
IT Consulting Services
N.A.I.C.S.: 519290
Jay Strickland *(Founder & Pres)*
Jason Middendorf *(Dir-Special Projects-VM)*
Nicole Botti *(Acct Mgr-Inside Sls)*
Carrie Scott *(Coord-HR & Mgr- HR)*

WINICK & GALLAHER, PC
35 S Washington St, Suite 300, Naperville, IL 60540
Tel.: (630) 548-5800
Web Site:
http://www.winickgallaher.com
Law firm
N.A.I.C.S.: 541110
Kevin M. Gallaher *(Principal)*

Winick & Gallaher, PC—(Continued)

Subsidiaries:

Poznak Law Firm Ltd. (1)
2001 Midwest Rd Ste 206, Oak Brook, IL 60523-4392
Tel.: (630) 573-9300
Web Site: http://www.poznaklaw.com
Law firm
N.A.I.C.S.: 541110

WINK, INCORPORATED
126 N 3rd St #100, Minneapolis, MN 55401
Tel.: (612) 455-2642
Web Site: http://www.wink-mpls.com
Year Founded: 2000
Sales Range: Less than $1 Million
Emp.: 5
N.A.I.C.S.: 541810
Richard Boynton (Partner & Designer)
Scott Thares (Owner & Designer)

WINKEL DISTRIBUTING COMPANY
2200 S Redhill Dr, Richfield, UT 84701
Tel.: (435) 896-6368
Sales Range: $10-24.9 Million
Emp.: 32
Beer & Other Fermented Malt Liquors
N.A.I.C.S.: 424810
Lisa Robinson (Office Mgr)
Kody Winkel (Pres)

WINKING LIZARD INC.
25380 Miles Rd, Bedford Heights, OH 44146
Tel.: (216) 831-0505
Web Site:
  http://www.winkinglizard.com
Year Founded: 1983
Sales Range: $10-24.9 Million
Emp.: 900
Tavern (Drinking Places)
N.A.I.C.S.: 722410
John Lane (Controller)
Dave Costantini (VP-Acctg)

WINKLER INCORPORATED
535 E Medcalf St, Dale, IN 47523-9384
Tel.: (812) 937-4421   IN
Web Site: http://www.winklerinc.com
Year Founded: 1911
Sales Range: $50-74.9 Million
Emp.: 500
Provider of Wholesale Grocery Services
N.A.I.C.S.: 424410
Jay Guth (Dir-IT)
Pat Schickinger (Dir-Adv)
Josh Winkler (Dir-Sls)
Daryl Lovell (Asst Dir-IT)
Kermit Greulich (Dir-Procurement)
Phil Fischer (Dir-Warehousing)
Rick Irvine (Coord-Meat)
Tom Winkler (Pres)

WINKLER TREGER & ASSOCIATES LLC
2600 McCormick Dr Ste 110, Clearwater, FL 33759
Tel.: (727) 442-4900
Web Site:
  http://www.winklertreger.com
Sales Range: $1-9.9 Million
Insurance Adjusters
N.A.I.C.S.: 524291
Jeff Winkler (CEO)
Dale Treger (Chief Claims Officer)
Steve Backman (COO)

Barbara Slawiak (Mgr-Support Svcs)
Abbie Boudreau (Dir-Ops)
Dale Hammond (Chm)
Tim Journy (CFO)

WINKLEVOSS BITCOIN TRUST
30 W 24th St 4th Fl, New York, NY 10010
Tel.: (646) 751-4444   NY
Year Founded: 2013
Investment Services
N.A.I.C.S.: 523999
Cameron Winklevoss (CEO)
Tyler Winklevoss (CFO)

WINLAND ELECTRONICS, INC.
1950 Excel Dr, Mankato, MN 56001
Tel.: (800) 635-4269   MN
Web Site: http://www.winland.com
Year Founded: 1972
Sales Range: $1-9.9 Million
Custom Electronic Controls Mfr
N.A.I.C.S.: 334513
Brian D. Lawrence (Pres & CFO)
Thomas Braziel (Co-Chm)
Matthew D. Houk (Co-Chm)

WINMILL SOFTWARE COMPANY
420 Lexington Ave Ste 444, New York, NY 10170
Tel.: (212) 850-0400
Web Site: http://www.winmill.com
Year Founded: 1994
Sales Range: $10-24.9 Million
Emp.: 100
Online Services Technology Consultants
N.A.I.C.S.: 541512
Joseph Strazza (Co-Founder, Chm & CEO)
Kevin Kilgore (Pres)
Erika Paredes (Project Mgr-Quality Assurance)
David Warshowsky (Project Mgr)
David Stone (Acct Mgr)

WINN DESIGN, LLC
100 W Jefferson St Ste 202, Falls Church, VA 22046-3400
Tel.: (703) 876-9696
Web Site: http://www.winndesign.net
Year Founded: 2002
Sales Range: $1-9.9 Million
Emp.: 6
Home Remodeler
N.A.I.C.S.: 236118
Michael S. Winn (Founder & CEO)

WINN MANAGEMENT CORPORATION
6 Faneuil Hall Market Pl, Boston, MA 02109
Tel.: (617) 742-4500
Web Site: http://www.winnco.com
Rev.: $13,600,000
Emp.: 3,000
Real Estate Managers
N.A.I.C.S.: 531210
William Wollinger (Pres & COO-Residential)
Lawrence Curtis (Pres-Winn Dev & Mng Partner)

WINN TECHNOLOGY GROUP, INC.
523 Palm Harbor Blvd, Palm Harbor, FL 34683
Tel.: (727) 789-0006   FL
Web Site: http://www.winntech.net
Year Founded: 1990
Sales Range: $1-9.9 Million
Emp.: 100
Integrated Marketing Solutions
N.A.I.C.S.: 541613

Geoffrey C. Swallow (Pres & CEO)
Anne F. Swallow (Co-Founder, CFO & Exec VP)
James M. Hannagan (Exec VP-Bus Dev)
Nancy M. Burkhart (VP-Client Svcs & Ops)
Beth Vavoularis (Sr Dir-Fin & HR)
Derrick Anderson (Dir-IT)
Alan Feldman (Mgr-Bus Dev)

WINNAN CORP.
831 Laca St, Dayton, NV 89403
Tel.: (925) 420-4700   NV
Year Founded: 2016
Emp.: 1
Video Production Services
N.A.I.C.S.: 512110
Dmitrii Klevchick (Pres, Treas & Sec)

WINNEMUCCA FARMS INC.
1 Potato Pl, Winnemucca, NV 89445-3693
Tel.: (775) 623-2900   NV
Year Founded: 1971
Sales Range: $25-49.9 Million
Emp.: 180
Provider of Farm Products
N.A.I.C.S.: 311423
Tim Topliff (Gen Mgr)

WINNER AUTOMOTIVE GROUP, INC.
520 East Walnut St, Wilmington, DE 19801
Tel.: (302) 656-1237   DE
Web Site: http://www.winnerauto.com
Year Founded: 1976
Sales Range: $200-249.9 Million
Emp.: 600
Automobile Dealership
N.A.I.C.S.: 441110
Bob Barcoski (CFO)
Joseph Ferrara (Mgr-Svc & Parts)
Wendell Woods (Mgr-Body Shop)
Frank Fitzwater (Gen Mgr-Sls)
Ed Heinemann (Dir-Collision Center)
Jenn Riley (Dir-HR)
Rich Harrisson (Dir-Ops)
Thomas Mihok (Gen Mgr-Audi Wilmington)
Sean Johnson (Gen Mgr-Porsche-Delaware)
Adrian Wilson (Gen Mgr-Sls-Winner Ford Hyundai)
Brian Ferrell (Gen Mgr-Winner Auto World)
Michael Hynansky (Pres)

WINNER AUTOWORLD
1801 Ogletown Rd, Newark, DE 19711
Tel.: (302) 292-8200
Web Site:
  http://www.winnerautoworld.com
Year Founded: 1966
Sales Range: $10-24.9 Million
Emp.: 60
Car Whslr
N.A.I.C.S.: 441110
Michael Hynansky (Pres)

WINNER CHEVROLET INC.
1624 S Canyon Way, Colfax, CA 95713
Tel.: (530) 346-2247
Web Site:
  http://www.winnerchevy.com
Sales Range: $10-24.9 Million
Emp.: 44
New & Used Automobiles
N.A.I.C.S.: 441110
David C. Gard (Pres)
Keith Brown (Mgr-Parts)

WINNER COMMUNICATIONS, INC.
90 John St Ste 310, New York, NY 10038
Tel.: (212) 206-0111   NY
Web Site:
  http://www.winnercommunications.com
Year Founded: 1972
Sales Range: $50-74.9 Million
Emp.: 25
Media Buying Services
N.A.I.C.S.: 541810
Martin P. Feinberg (Pres)

WINNER DOVER AUTOCENTER
591 S Dupont Hwy, Dover, DE 19901
Tel.: (302) 734-0445
Web Site: http://www.winnerauto.com
Year Founded: 1981
Sales Range: $10-24.9 Million
Emp.: 93
Car Whslr
N.A.I.C.S.: 441110
Michael Hynansky (Pres)

WINNER GROUP INCORPORATED
911 N Tatnall St, Wilmington, DE 19801
Tel.: (302) 661-4500
Web Site: http://www.winnerauto.com
Rev.: $20,400,000
Emp.: 30
Commercial & Industrial Building Operation
N.A.I.C.S.: 531120
John Hynansky (Chm & CEO)
Michael Hynansky (Pres)

WINNER INTERNATIONAL, LLC
32 W State St, Sharon, PA 16146
Tel.: (724) 981-1152
Web Site: http://www.winner-intl.com
Year Founded: 1986
Rev.: $13,000,000
Emp.: 80
Car Safety Devices Mfr
N.A.I.C.S.: 332510
Karen Winner-Hale (COO)
Jerry Trontel (Pres)

WINNESHIEK COOPERATIVE ASSOCIATION
801 Commerce Dr, Decorah, IA 52101
Tel.: (563) 382-8927
Web Site: http://www.winncoop.com
Year Founded: 1917
Sales Range: $10-24.9 Million
Emp.: 10
Animal Feed Mfr
N.A.I.C.S.: 424910
Douglas VanSloten (Gen Mgr)
Gerald Reicks (Sec & Treas)
Randy Hanson (Pres)
Kelvin Rue (VP-Ridgeway)
Brian Aberg (Dir-Mahel)
Mark Sollien (Dir-Burr Oak)
Paul Hunter (Dir-Deccorah)
Steve Kuboushek (Dir-Ridgeway)
John Wiedman (Dir-Cresco)

WINNING MOVES GAMES, INC.
75 Sylvan St Ste C-104, Danvers, MA 01923
Tel.: (978) 777-7464
Web Site: http://www.winningmoves.com
Year Founded: 1995
Sales Range: $1-9.9 Million
Emp.: 14
Mfr & Marketer of Games
N.A.I.C.S.: 339930

WINNING STRATEGIES PUBLIC RELATIONS
550 Broad St Ste 910, Newark, NJ 07102-4517
Tel.: (973) 799-0200
Web Site: http://www.winningstrat.net
Year Founded: 1997
Sales Range: $1-9.9 Million
Emp.: 30
Government/Political/Public Affairs, Public Relations
N.A.I.C.S.: 541820
Jim McQueeny (Chm & CEO)
Adam Dvorin (Dir-Media)
Andy Gabron (VP-Strategic Accts)
Peter J. McDonough (Partner)

Subsidiaries:

Princeton Public Affairs Group, Inc. (1)
160 W State St, Trenton, NJ 08608-1102
Tel.: (609) 396-8838
Web Site: http://www.ppag.com
Emp.: 20
Public Relations
N.A.I.C.S.: 541820
Dale J. Florio (Founder)
Bradley Brewster (Exec Dir)
Sonia Delgado (Dir-Client Svcs-Healthcare)
Lorna D. O'Hara (Dir-Political Dev)

Winning Strategies Washington (1)
409 7th St NW Ste 450, Washington, DC 20004
Tel.: (202) 589-0800
Web Site: http://www.wswdc.com
Emp.: 10
Public Relations
N.A.I.C.S.: 541820
Michael Merola (Partner)
Robert Zucker (Partner)
Laura Lay (Principal & Dir-Grants)
Carl Chidlow (Principal)
Chelsey Penrod Hickman (Principal & Dir-Ops)
Charla Penn McManus (Principal)
Molly McDonnell (Principal)
Mike McMenamin (Principal)

WINNRESIDENTIAL LIMITED PARTNERSHIP
6 Faneuil Hall Marketplace, Boston, MA 02109
Tel.: (617) 742-4500
Year Founded: 2001
Sales Range: $25-49.9 Million
Emp.: 1,000
Land Subdividing Services
N.A.I.C.S.: 237210
William P. Wollinger (Pres)
Cynthia Tanner (CFO)
Nicole Salmieri (Dir-Mktg)
Michelle Moriello (Dir-Digital Mktg)
Julie Fawcett (Dir-Compliance)
Charlene Love (Dir-Corp Mktg & Bus Dev)

WINNSBORO PETROLEUM CO. INC.
401 S Congress St Drawer 449, Winnsboro, SC 29180
Tel.: (803) 635-4668 SC
Year Founded: 1946
Sales Range: $25-49.9 Million
Emp.: 200
Wholesale of Petroleum
N.A.I.C.S.: 424710
William McMaster (Pres & CEO)
Harper Shull (CFO)

WINONA HEATING & VENT CO.
374 E 2nd St, Winona, MN 55987
Tel.: (507) 452-2064
Web Site: http://www.whvr.com
Sales Range: $10-24.9 Million
Emp.: 130
Ventilation & Duct Work Contractor
N.A.I.C.S.: 238220

Michael M. Gostomski (Pres & CEO)

WINROCK ENTERPRISES, INC.
1501 N University Ave Ste 360, Little Rock, AR 72207
Tel.: (501) 663-5340 AR
Year Founded: 1955
Sales Range: Less than $1 Million
Emp.: 4
Provider of Land Development Services
N.A.I.C.S.: 237210
Meda Hargrove (Office Mgr)
Russell B. McDonough Jr. (Chm, Pres & CEO)

WINSFORD II CORPORATION
1933 E Locust St, Ontario, CA 91761
Tel.: (310) 277-5666 CA
Year Founded: 1980
Sales Range: $10-24.9 Million
Emp.: 210
Fabricated Metal Products Mfr
N.A.I.C.S.: 332999
John W. Sweetland (Pres & COO)

Subsidiaries:

Forbes Industries, Inc. (1)
1933 E Locust St, Ontario, CA 91761-7608
Tel.: (800) 832-5427
Web Site: http://www.forbesindustries.com
Restaurant & Service Supply Mfr
N.A.I.C.S.: 337127
Timothy Sweetland (Founder & Sr VP)

Subsidiary (Non-US):

Forbes Industries Asia Pte. Ltd. (2)
100 Beach Road 28-05 Shaw Tower, Singapore, 189702, Singapore
Tel.: (65) 6295 2262
Web Site: http://www.forbes-asia.com.sg
Hotel & Restaurant Service Equipment Distr
N.A.I.C.S.: 423440
Michael Koo (Mng Dir)

The Winsford Corporation (1)
650 Ford St, Colorado Springs, CO 80915
Tel.: (719) 434-5948
Web Site: http://www.harloff.com
Emp.: 55
Medical Carts & Storage Cabinets Mfr
N.A.I.C.S.: 332999
John Sweetland (Pres)
Steve Streight (VP-Sls)
Darren Wheeler (Mgr-Mfg)

WINSLOW BMW
5845 N Nevada Ave, Colorado Springs, CO 80918
Tel.: (719) 473-1373
Web Site: http://www.winslowbmw.com
Year Founded: 1961
Rev.: $13,800,000
Emp.: 55
Automobile Dealers
N.A.I.C.S.: 441120
Jim Carlson (Mgr-Fin)
Mike Evelyn (Asst Mgr-Svc)
Steve Simmons (Mgr-Sls)

WINSLOW TECHNOLOGY GROUP, LLC
75 Arlington St Ste 500, Boston, MA 02116
Tel.: (857) 241-3815
Web Site: http://www.winslowtechgroup.com
Year Founded: 2003
Sales Range: $1-9.9 Million
Emp.: 10
Healthcare Staffing & Workforce Procurement Services
N.A.I.C.S.: 541612
Scott A. Winslow (Pres)
Rick Gouin (CTO)
Michael Tibaudo (Dir-Sls)
Brian K. Vienneau (Dir-Engrg)

Christopher M. Newton (Sr Acct Exec)
Coby A. Lieblein (Acct Exec)
James S. Harrell (VP-Sys Engrg)
Jon D. Klippert (Acct Exec)
Mark L. Wingrove (Acct Exec)
Michael C. Sheeran (Dir-Pro Svcs & Sr Acct Exec)

WINSLOWS INC.
123 W Superior St Ste 301, Duluth, MN 55802
Tel.: (218) 722-1557
Web Site: http://www.specialthoughts.com
Rev.: $10,722,592
Emp.: 4
Gift Shop
N.A.I.C.S.: 459420

WINSOME TRADING INC.
16111 Woodinville Redmond Rd NE, Woodinville, WA 98072-9046
Tel.: (425) 483-8888
Web Site: http://www.winsomewood.com
Rev.: $27,500,000
Emp.: 50
Homefurnishings
N.A.I.C.S.: 423220
Somchai Chaipatanapong (Pres)
Papp Sinteppadon (Engr-Logistics)

WINSOUTH CREDIT UNION
110 S 26th St, Gadsden, AL 35904
Tel.: (256) 543-7302 AL
Web Site: http://www.winsouthcu.com
Year Founded: 1951
Sales Range: $10-24.9 Million
Emp.: 151
Credit Union Operator
N.A.I.C.S.: 522130
David Eubanks (Pres & CEO)
Rick O'Neal (VP-Lending & Collections)
Joan Smith (COO & VP)
Kelly Whisenant (Comptroller)

WINSPER INC.
115 Broad St 5th Fl, Boston, MA 02110
Tel.: (617) 695-2900
Web Site: http://www.winsperinc.com
Year Founded: 2002
Sales Range: $25-49.9 Million
Emp.: 12
Advetising Agency
N.A.I.C.S.: 541810
Jeff Winsper (Pres)
Gillian Lynch (Mng Dir & VP)

WINSTANLEY PARTNERS
114 Main St, Lenox, MA 01240-2353
Tel.: (413) 637-9887 MA
Web Site: http://www.winstanley.com
Year Founded: 1986
Rev.: $25,000,000
Emp.: 25
N.A.I.C.S.: 541810
Nathan B. Winstanley (Founder & Pres)
Ralph Frisina (VP & Dir-Creative)
Michael Coakley (VP-Acct Svcs)
Jaclyn Stevenson (Dir-PR)
Ron Thompson (COO)
Patrick Consolati (CFO & Mgr-Software Product)
Vanessa Leikvoll (Coord-Event)

WINSTEAD PC
5400 Renaissance Tower 1201 Elm St Ste 5400, Dallas, TX 75270-2103
Tel.: (214) 745-5400 TX
Web Site: http://www.winstead.com
Year Founded: 1973
Sales Range: $25-49.9 Million

Emp.: 587
Law firm
N.A.I.C.S.: 541110
Glen Pryor (CFO)
Patty Stewart (Dir-HR)
Shannon Tipton (Mgr-PR)
Howard L. Mudrick (Exec Dir)
Teresa Schneider (Chief Recruiting Officer)
David Dawson (Chm & CEO)
Allen Fuqua (CMO)
Chris Di Masi (CTO)
Todd Arritola (Chief Bus Dev Officer)

WINSTON & STRAWN LLP
35 W Wacker Dr, Chicago, IL 60601
Tel.: (312) 558-5600
Web Site: http://www.winston.com
Year Founded: 1853
Sales Range: $700-749.9 Million
Emp.: 870
Law firm
N.A.I.C.S.: 541110
Thomas M. Dunham (Partner-Washington & Atty)
Gerald L. Shargel (Partner-New York)
Michael Elkin (Vice Chm & Mng Partner-New York)
Seth C. Farber (Chm-White Collar, Regulatory Defense & Investigations Practice)
Paul Christian Goulet (Partner-Washington)
Craig S. Vogelsang (Partner-Houston)
John Keville (Mng Partner-Houston)
Chris A. Ferazzi (Partner-Houston)
Eva Davis (Mng Partner-External Affairs)
Kobi Kennedy Brinson (Partner-Charlotte)
Sheryl A. Falk (Partner-Houston)
Dustin J. Edwards (Partner-Houston)
Tom Fitzgerald (Chm)
Dominick DeChiara (Chief Strategic Officer)
Matthew C. Bate (Partner-London & New York & Atty)
Shibeer Ahmed (Partner & Head-Banking & Islamic Fin-Dubai)
Robin Feiner (Partner-New York)
Deepak Reddy (Partner-Transportation Fin Practice-New York)
Natalie Arbaugh (Partner)
Tom Walsh (Partner)
Danielle Williams (Partner-Charlotte)
Taj Clayton (Partner)
Richard Frye (Partner)
Thomas Melsheimer (Mng Partner-Dallas)
Geoffrey Harper (Partner)
Michael Bittner (Partner)
Chad Walker (Partner)
Kathi Vidal (Mng Partner-Silicon Valley)
Andrew Grossman (Partner-Los Angeles)
Ben Bruton (Partner-Dubai)
Esha Bandyopadhyay (Partner-Intellectual Property Practice-Silicon Valley)
Nimalka Wickramasekera (Partner-Intellectual Property Practice-Los Angeles)
Anne M. Heathcock (Mng Dir)
David Cunningham (CIO)
David McDonald (CFO)
Melissa Ertek (Chief Dev Officer)
Susan Manch (Chief Talent Officer)
David Rogers (Mng Partner)
Eric Meiring (Partner-Antitrust & Competition Practice-Washington)
Richard E. Ginsberg (Partner & Chm-Tech & Emerging Companies Practice)
Katrina Eash (Partner)

WINSTON & STRAWN LLP

Winston & Strawn LLP—(Continued)
Rex Mann (Partner)
Justin Reinus (Partner)
Christopher Monahan (Partner-Washington)
Jonathan Birenbaum (Mng Partner-New York)
James T. Bentley (Partner-New York)
David Stauber (Partner-New York)
Jeffrey R. Shuman (Partner)
Linda Coberly (Mng Partner)
Scott Delaney (Partner-Dallas)
Bryan Goolsby (Mng Partner-Dallas)
Rodney Moore (Partner)
Sam Peca (Partner)
Peter Crowther (Mng Partner-Intl Affairs)
Cardelle Spangler (Mng Partner-Internal Affairs)

WINSTON ADVERTISING
122 E 42nd St, New York, NY 10168
Tel.: (212) 682-1063
Year Founded: 1984
Sales Range: Less than $1 Million
Emp.: 10
Magazines, Print, Radio, Real Estate, Recruitment
N.A.I.C.S.: 541810
Sy Kaye (Chm)
Bruce Papkin (Pres)
Jesse Ulezalka (CFO)

WINSTON COUNTY MEDICAL FOUNDATION
17550 E Main St, Louisville, MS 39339
Tel.: (662) 773-6211 MS
Web Site:
  http://www.winstonmedical.org
Year Founded: 1994
Sales Range: $10-24.9 Million
Emp.: 265
Health Care Srvices
N.A.I.C.S.: 622110
Robert Higginbotham (Dir-Radiology)

WINSTON ELECTRIC
108 East 82nd St, Lubbock, TX 79404
Tel.: (806) 745-7720
Rev: $12,617,799
Emp.: 150
Electrical Work
N.A.I.C.S.: 238210

WINSTON HARTON HOLDINGS, LLC
c/o AWH Partners 1040 Ave of the Americas 9th Fl, New York, NY 10018
Tel.: (212) 459-2940 DE
Web Site: http://www.whhllc.com
Emp.: 3
Holding Company; Commercial Real Estate Investment & Management
N.A.I.C.S.: 551112
Russell Flicker (Co-Founder & Mng Partner)
Jonathan Rosenfeld (Co-Founder & Mng Partner)
Philip Haspel (VP)

Subsidiaries:

AWH Partners, LLC (1)
1040 Ave of the Americas 9th Fl, 10018, NY (50%)
Tel.: (212) 459-2940
Web Site: http://www.awhpartners.com
Commercial Real Estate Investment, Development & Management Services
N.A.I.C.S.: 531390
Russell Flicker (Co-Founder & Mng Partner)
Jonathan Rosenfeld (Co-Founder & Mng Partner)
Chad E. Cooley (Co-Founder & Mng Partner)

Laura Hansen Barlowe (Exec VP-Ops)
Daniel Benda (VP-Dev & Construction)
Timothy Osiecki (Pres-AWH Dev)

Holding (Domestic):

Spire Hospitality, LLC (2)
111 S Pfingsten Rd Ste 425, Deerfield, IL 60015
Tel.: (847) 498-6650
Web Site: http://www.spirehotels.com
Hotel Operator
N.A.I.C.S.: 721110
William DeForrest (Pres)
Debra W. Stinson (VP-HR)
Greg Horeth (COO)
Tim Foley (VP-Ops)
Ginny Morrison (VP-Sls & Mktg)
Chris Russell (CEO)
Dawna Comeaux (Sr VP)
Hadrian Fishel (VP-Revenue Mgmt)
David Altshuler (VP-Acctg)
Barbara Doucet (VP-HR)

Topnotch Resort & Spa (2)
4000 Mtn Rd, Stowe, VT 05672
Tel.: (802) 253-8585
Web Site: http://www.topnotchresort.com
Ski Lodge & Resort
N.A.I.C.S.: 721199
Ryan Krukar (Gen Mgr)

WINSTON INDUSTRIES, LLC
2345 Carton Dr, Louisville, KY 40299
Tel.: (502) 495-5400
Web Site: http://www.winstonind.com
Year Founded: 1969
Emp.: 172
Mfr of Commercial Cooking & Foodwarming Equipment
N.A.I.C.S.: 333310
David B. Shelton (Pres & CEO)
Thomas C. Ford (Mgr-Distr)
Tina Thompson (Controller)

WINSTON PRINTING COMPANY
8095 North Point Blvd, Winston Salem, NC 27106
Tel.: (336) 759-0051
Web Site:
  http://www.winstonpackaging.com
Sales Range: $10-24.9 Million
Emp.: 53
Commercial Printing, Lithographic; Packaging Components For Consumer Products
N.A.I.C.S.: 323111
Susan Gordon (Mgr-Mktg Svcs)
Joe Whitman (Mgr-Legacy Bus Grp)

WINSTON RESOURCES, LLC
122 E 42nd St, New York, NY 10168-3620
Tel.: (212) 557-5000 DE
Web Site:
  http://www.winstonresources.com
Year Founded: 1967
Sales Range: $50-74.9 Million
Emp.: 120
Employment Services Permanent Temporary Recruitment Advertising
N.A.I.C.S.: 561320
Jesse Ulezalka (CFO)
Todd Kayne (Co-Pres)
Eric Kugler (Sr VP)
Sy Kaye (Chm)

WINSTON-JAMES DEVELOPMENT, INC.
933 Beville Rd Ste 103-F, South Daytona, FL 32119
Tel.: (386) 760-2555
Web Site: http://www.winston-james.com
Sales Range: $1-9.9 Million
Property Development & Management Services
N.A.I.C.S.: 236115

Winston Schwartz (Pres)
Jamie Adley (VP)

WINSTON-SALEM INDUSTRIES FOR THE BLIND, INC.
7730 North Point Dr, Winston Salem, NC 27106
Tel.: (336) 759-0551
Web Site: http://www.wsifb.com
Emp.: 250
Employment, Training & Services for Visually Impaired
N.A.I.C.S.: 624310
David Horton (Pres & CEO)
Karen Carey (Asst Treas)
Dan Boucher (Co-Chm)
Heather Robinson (Co-Chm)
Carver Rudolph (Sec)
Shirley Shouse (Asst Sec)
Ann Johnston (Vice Chm)
Danny Kelly (COO)
Silas Martin (VP-Base Svc Centers & IT)
Sam George (CFO)
David Hampton (VP-HR)
Seth Anderson (Dir-Mktg & Comm)
Vasudha Rangapathy (Dir-IT & ECommerce)
Ken Edwards (VP-Integrated Supply & Logistics)

Subsidiaries:

The Arkansas Lighthouse For The Blind (1)
6818 Murray St, Little Rock, AR 72209
Tel.: (501) 562-2222
Web Site:
  http://www.arkansaslighthouse.org
Sales Range: $1-9.9 Million
Emp.: 60
Job Training & Employment Services
N.A.I.C.S.: 624310
Daniel Novielli (COO)
John McAtee (CFO)
Margaret Ruffin (Supvr-Production)
Shawn Sims (Supvr-Production)

WINSUPPLY INC.
3110 Kettering Blvd, Dayton, OH 45439-1924
Tel.: (937) 294-5331 DE
Web Site:
  http://www.winwholesale.com
Year Founded: 1956
Sales Range: $1-4.9 Billion
Emp.: 5,200
Holding Company; Industrial & Agricultural Product Wholesale Distr
N.A.I.C.S.: 551112
Richard W. Schwartz (Chm)
Jack W. Johnston (Pres & CEO)
Jeffrey Dana (CTO)
Ward Allen (VP-Fin)
Monte Salsman (COO)
Steven B. Edwards (Dir-Corp Comm)
James R. McCann (VP-Sourcing Svcs, Supply Chain & Logistics)
Matt Newcomer (Dir-Talent Acq & Succession Plng)

Subsidiaries:

M. Cooper Winsupply (1)
8605 Spring Lake Dr, Mokena, IL 60448
Tel.: (708) 444-1600
Web Site: http://www.mcoopersupply.com
Sales Range: $1-9.9 Million
Emp.: 50
Plumbing & Cabinet Products Distr
N.A.I.C.S.: 423720
Rob Johnson (Pres)

Noland Company (1)
3110 Kettering Blvd, Dayton, OH 45439
Tel.: (757) 928-9000
Web Site: http://www.noland.com
Sales Range: $400-449.9 Million
Emp.: 1,000
Plumbing, Air Conditioning, Electrical & Industrial Supplies Distr

U.S. PRIVATE

N.A.I.C.S.: 423720
Subsidiary (Domestic):

Noland Properties, Inc. (2)
3110 Kettering Blvd, Dayton, OH 45429
Tel.: (757) 247-8200
Web Site: http://www.noland.com
Sales Range: $25-49.9 Million
Emp.: 11
N.A.I.C.S.: 444180

Security Plumbing & Heating Supply Co. (1)
196 Maple Ave, Selkirk, NY 12158
Tel.: (518) 767-2226
Web Site: http://www.secsupply.com
Plumbing, Heating & Air Conditioning Products Distr
N.A.I.C.S.: 423720
Tom Nachbar (Pres-Schenectady)
Kim Willey (Pres-Albany)
James Canning (Pres-Kingston)
Pete Knapik (Pres-Johnstown)
Larry Wildey (Pres-Glens Falls)
Roberta Caputo (Mgr-Showroom-Glens Falls)
Dan Shandor (Pres-North Adams)
Ken Mortensen Jr. (Dir-Special Markets-Albany)

West Coast Winsupply Co. (1)
2720 N 36th St, Tampa, FL 33605
Tel.: (813) 247-7202
Web Site:
  http://www.westcoastwinsupply.com
Sales Range: $10-24.9 Million
Emp.: 32
Fire Sprinkler Systems Mfr
N.A.I.C.S.: 423720
Doris Cimino (Office Mgr)
Sal Cimino (Pres)

Wyatt Irrigation Co. (1)
747 Yolanda Ave, Santa Rosa, CA 95404
Tel.: (707) 578-3747
Web Site: http://www.wyattsupply.com
Sales Range: $10-24.9 Million
Irrigation Supplies Distr
N.A.I.C.S.: 423820
Scott Leytem (Pres)

WINSUPPLY, INC.
3110 Kettering Blvd, Dayton, OH 45439
Tel.: (937) 294-5331 DE
Web Site:
  http://www.winsupplyinc.com
Year Founded: 1956
Commercial Construction & Industrial Supplies & Equipment Distr
N.A.I.C.S.: 236220
Rob Ferguson (Pres-Winsupply Local Company Grp)
Rick Schwartz (Chm)
John McKenzie (Pres)
Monte Salsman (Pres-Winsupply Acq Grp)
Jeff Dice (Pres-Equity Grp)
Greg Holbrock (VP-Fin Integration & M&A)
Eric Roush (VP-Supply Chain)
Robert DiTommaso (Pres-Support Svcs Grp)
Adam Marshall (Dir-Comm)
Kamna Gupta (VP-Shared Svcs)

Subsidiaries:

APCO, Inc. (1)
5511 Enterprise Dr, Lansing, MI 48910
Tel.: (517) 882-2455
Web Site: http://www.apcoinc.com
Warm Air Heating Equipment & Supplies
N.A.I.C.S.: 423730
Mike Nussdorfer (Pres)

ASAP Industrial Supply, Inc. (1)
10927 Jasmine St, Fontana, CA 92337-6966
Tel.: (909) 429-4749
Web Site: http://www.asapis.com
Plumbing & Heating Equipment & Supplies Merchant Whslr
N.A.I.C.S.: 423720
Keith Travis (Mgr-Warehouse)

COMPANIES

Allegheny Pipe & Supply Co (1)
Lewis Ave Groveton, Coraopolis, PA 15108
Tel.: (412) 264-7100
Web Site: http://www.alleghenypipe.com
Rev.: $7,900,000
Emp.: 28
Metal Service Centers & Other Metal Merchant Whslr
N.A.I.C.S.: 423510
Tom Morse (VP)
Jim Morse (Pres)

Atlantic Coastal Supply, Inc (1)
4539 Us Hwy 13 S, Greenville, NC 27834
Tel.: (252) 321-0556
Web Site: http://www.acsparts.net
Plumbing & Heating Equipment & Supplies, Hydronics, Merchant Whslr
N.A.I.C.S.: 423720
John Meeks (Pres)

Discount Drainage Supplies, LLC (1)
4675 Westerville Rd, Columbus, OH 43231-6040
Tel.: (614) 882-3402
Web Site: http://www.discountdrainage.com
Other Building Material Dealers
N.A.I.C.S.: 444180
Matt Huebner (CEO)

Electrical Sales Inc. (1)
2300 La Mirada Dr, Vista, CA 92081
Tel.: (760) 598-1510
Web Site:
  http://estore.electricalsalesinc.com
Electrical Apparatus & Equipment Distr
N.A.I.C.S.: 423610
David Leon (Mgr-Warehouse/Counter)
Kevin Musbach (Mgr-Pur)
Shannon Hart (Supvr-Acctg)
Ryan Sullivan (Pres)
Kandyce Toth (Mgr-Ops)
Danny Alvarado (Mgr-Inside Sls)
Heather Altmaier (Sr Mgr-Project)
Lily Steffen (Supvr-Shipping/Receiving)

H2O Supply Inc. (1)
2535 B E Hwy 121 Ste 140, Lewisville, TX 75056
Tel.: (972) 242-2289
Web Site: http://www.h2osupply.net
Rev.: $5,964,000
Emp.: 12
Plumbing & Heating Equipment & Supplies, Hydronics, Merchant Whslr
N.A.I.C.S.: 423720

Hydrologic Distribution Company (1)
6365 53rd St N, Pinellas Park, FL 33781
Tel.: (727) 608-1800
Web Site: https://www.hydrodc.com
Plumbing Product Distr
N.A.I.C.S.: 423720
Chris Lynch (Pres)

Industrial Equipment & Parts Inc. (1)
13705 26th Ave N Ste 106, Plymouth, MN 55441
Tel.: (763) 249-1899
Web Site: http://www.ieppumps.com
Industrial Equipment Distr
N.A.I.C.S.: 333996

Keidel Supply Company Inc. (1)
1150 Tennessee Ave, Cincinnati, OH 45229
Tel.: (513) 351-1600
Web Site: http://www.keidel.com
Sales Range: $10-24.9 Million
Emp.: 70
Plumbing & Hydronic Heating Supplies
N.A.I.C.S.: 423720
Mike Barton (Pres)

MB Family Holdings, Inc. (1)
1620 NE 8th Rd, Ocala, FL 34470
Tel.: (352) 629-8191
Web Site: http://www.winsupplyinc.com
Plumbing Fittings & Supplies
N.A.I.C.S.: 423720

MPS Enterprises, Inc. (1)
531 John Wiley Rd, Justin, TX 76247
Tel.: (575) 397-6400
Web Site: https://milfordonline.com
Rev.: $1,500,000
Emp.: 18
Fabricated Pipe & Pipe Fitting Mfr
N.A.I.C.S.: 332996
Cody Tippy (VP)
Daniel Harris (Mgr-Ops)
Felix Hettler (Comptroller)

Jeremy Hohn (Mgr-Sls)
Scott Brown (Pres)
Jason Willis (VP)
Shawn Beard (CEO)
Joe Pomykal (CFO)
Mark Tufts (VP)
Chase Brown (COO)

MSI Supply, Inc. (1)
1357 Sheffield Blvd, Houston, TX 77015
Tel.: (713) 733-5500
Pipes, Valves, Fittings, Gaskets & Fasteners Distr
N.A.I.C.S.: 332919

May Supply Company (1)
1775 Erickson Ave, Harrisonburg, VA 22801-8555
Tel.: (540) 433-2611
Web Site: http://www.maysupply.com
Whslr & Retailer of Plumbing Supplies & Water Systems
N.A.I.C.S.: 423720

Rosen Supply Company Inc. (1)
2920 S Chandler St, Tacoma, WA 98409
Tel.: (253) 627-3176
Web Site: http://www.rosenplumbing.com
Plumbing Fittings & Supplies
N.A.I.C.S.: 423720
Harvey D. Rosen (Pres)
Barbara Patterson (Office Mgr)

Tacoma Electric Supply Inc. (1)
1311 S Tacoma Way, Tacoma, WA 98409-8230
Tel.: (253) 475-0540
Web Site: http://www.tacomaelectric.com
Emp.: 100
Electrical Apparatus & Equipment Whslr
N.A.I.C.S.: 423610
Charlie Silva (Branch Mgr)

Thomas Pipe & Supply Co. (1)
1429 S 7th St, Phoenix, AZ 85034-4503
Tel.: (602) 254-0410
Web Site: http://www.thomaspipe.net
Industrial Supplies Merchant Whslr
N.A.I.C.S.: 423840
Don Helmlinger (Pres)

WINTEC INDUSTRIES INC.
675 Sycamore Dr, Milpitas, CA 95035
Tel.: (408) 856-0500
Web Site: http://www.wintecind.com
Year Founded: 1988
Sales Range: $25-49.9 Million
Emp.: 150
Computer Peripheral Equipment Mfr
N.A.I.C.S.: 334112
David Jeng (Chief Strategy Officer)
Michael Geraghty (VP-OEM Sls)
Frank Patchel (CFO)
Bhaskar Bhatt (CTO)
Sanjay Bonde (CEO)
Kelley Corten (VP-Corp Mktg)
Sue Jeng (Founder, Pres & COO)
Brad Rawlings (VP-SCM Pre-Sls & Client Delivery)

WINTER CHEVROLET HONDA
3750 Century Ct Ste 3850, Pittsburg, CA 94565-7121
Tel.: (925) 439-8222
Web Site:
  http://www.winterchevrolet.com
Year Founded: 1957
Sales Range: $25-49.9 Million
Emp.: 90
Car Whslr
N.A.I.C.S.: 441110
Rose Winter (Pres)

WINTER CONSTRUCTION COMPANY
191 Peachtree St NE Ste 2100, Atlanta, GA 30303
Tel.: (404) 588-3300
Web Site: http://www.winter-construction.com
Sales Range: $50-74.9 Million
Emp.: 500
Commercial Construction

N.A.I.C.S.: 236220
Timothy Thomas (VP-Safety)
Ralph Mumme (CFO & Exec VP)
Brent Reid (CEO)
Margaret Rauber (VP-Ops)
Alan Brossoie (Dir-Preconstruction)
Matt Loveless (Mgr-Winter SPACES)
David Epps (Dir-Construction Tech)
Troy Dunnam (Superintendent)
Heather Tuskowski (Dir-Ops)
Andy Brown (Dir-Ops)

WINTER HAVEN DODGE-CHRYSLER-JEEP INC.
299 Cypress Gardens Blvd, Winter Haven, FL 33880
Tel.: (863) 299-1243
Web Site: http://www.dcjofwh.com
Sales Range: $25-49.9 Million
Emp.: 82
New Car Dealers
N.A.I.C.S.: 441110
Mike Mahalak (VP)
Ralph Mahalak (Pres)
Myra Brssinger (Mgr)

WINTER HILL BANK
342 Broadway, Somerville, MA 02145
Tel.: (617) 666-8600
Web Site:
  http://www.winterhillbank.com
Year Founded: 1906
Sales Range: $10-24.9 Million
Emp.: 85
Federal Savings & Loan Associations
N.A.I.C.S.: 522180
Sandra L. McGoldrick (Pres & CEO)
Pauline D'aurora (Sr VP)
Denise Ingala (VP-Admin)
Kevin J. Gatlin (Chief Lending Officer)
Rich Brenner (VP-Comml Lending)
Richard Erickson (VP)
Steve Nigro (Branch Mgr)

WINTER LIVESTOCK INC.
11802 W Owen K Garriott Rd, Enid, OK 73703
Tel.: (580) 796-2150
Web Site:
  http://www.winterlivestock.com
Year Founded: 1936
Sales Range: $10-24.9 Million
Emp.: 130
Auctioning Livestock
N.A.I.C.S.: 424520
Mark Winter (Pres)
Raymond Winter (VP)

WINTER PROPERTIES INC.
1330 Spring St NW, Atlanta, GA 30309-2810
Tel.: (404) 588-3300
Sales Range: $125-149.9 Million
Emp.: 500
Civil Engineering Services
N.A.I.C.S.: 237310
Ralph Mumy (CFO)
Brent Reid (CEO)
Rick Singer (Pres)

WINTER SPORTS, INC.
3889 Big Mountain Rd, Whitefish, MT 59937
Tel.: (406) 862-2900   MT
Web Site:
  http://www.skiwhitefish.com
Year Founded: 1947
Sales Range: $1-9.9 Million
Emp.: 200
Ski & Summer Resort Owner & Operator
N.A.I.C.S.: 721110
Christina Polumbus (Mgr-PR)

WINTRONICS INC.

Subsidiaries:

Whitefish Mountain Resort (1)
3840 Big Mountain Rd, Whitefish, MT 59937-8642
Tel.: (406) 862-2900
Web Site: http://www.skiwhitefish.com
Resort Operating Services
N.A.I.C.S.: 713990
Riley Polumbus (Mgr-PR)

WINTER, KLOMAN, MOTER & REPP, S.C.
235 N Executive Dr Ste 160, Brookfield, WI 53122
Tel.: (262) 797-9050
Web Site: http://www.wkmr.com
Sales Range: $10-24.9 Million
Emp.: 49
Accounting Services, Except Auditing
N.A.I.C.S.: 541219
Dan Gotter (Pres)
Lawrence Gebhard (Mgr)
Lynn Braden (Mgr)
Amanda McNutt (Supvr)

WINTERBERRY GROUP, LLC
60 Broad St 38th Fl, New York, NY 10004
Tel.: (212) 842-6000
Web Site:
  http://www.winterberrygroup.com
Year Founded: 1988
Sales Range: $1-9.9 Million
Emp.: 18
Marketing, Advertising & Media Consulting Services
N.A.I.C.S.: 541613
Bruce A. Biegel (Sr Mng Partner)
Jonathan C. Margulies (Mng Dir)
Charles Ping (Mng Dir)
Brittany Meeks (Dir-Engagement)

WINTERS BROS WASTE SYSTEMS OF LONG ISLAND LLC
120 Nancy St, West Babylon, NY 11704
Tel.: (631) 491-4923   NY
Web Site:
  http://www.wintersbros.com
Year Founded: 1968
Solid Waste Collection
N.A.I.C.S.: 562111
Kevin T. Nolan (COO)

WINTHROP FINANCIAL ASSOCIATES LP
7 Bulfinch Pl 500, Boston, MA 02114
Tel.: (617) 570-4600
Web Site:
  http://www.winthropreit.com
Year Founded: 1975
Sales Range: $25-49.9 Million
Emp.: 50
Real Estate Investors, Except Property Operators
N.A.I.C.S.: 523999
John Garelli (CFO)
Michael L. Ashner (CEO)

Subsidiaries:

First Winthrop Corporation (1)
7 Bulsinch Pl Ste 500, Boston, MA 02114
Tel.: (617) 570-4600
Web Site: http://www.winthropcapital.com
Real Estate Investors, Except Property Operators
N.A.I.C.S.: 531210
Michael Aschner (CEO)
Mark D. John (Dir-IT)
Dayna Cassesso (Asst VP)
Tracey Martensen (Dir-HR)

WINTRONICS INC.
191 Pitt St, Sharon, PA 16146
Tel.: (724) 981-5770

WINTRONICS INC.

U.S. PRIVATE

Wintronics Inc.—(Continued)
Web Site:
http://www.wintronicsinc.com
Rev.: $10,000,000
Emp.: 50
Assembles Printed Circuit Boards
N.A.I.C.S.: 334412
Doug McKenzie *(Mgr-Pur)*
Steve Quillen *(Dir-Ops)*

WINZELER GEAR
7355 W Wilson Ave, Harwood Heights, IL 60706-4707
Tel.: (708) 867-7971
Web Site:
http://www.winzelergear.com
Year Founded: 1940
Sales Range: $50-74.9 Million
Emp.: 35
Mfr of Molded Polymer Gears
N.A.I.C.S.: 326199
John H. Winzeler Jr. *(Owner)*

WINZELER STAMPING CO.
129 W Wabash St, Montpelier, OH 43543
Tel.: (419) 485-3147
Web Site:
http://www.winzelerstamping.com
Sales Range: $25-49.9 Million
Emp.: 150
Clamps & Couplings, Hose
N.A.I.C.S.: 332510
Richard Conrad *(CFO, COO & VP)*
Michael Winzeler *(Pres & CEO)*
Ned Hugg *(Controller)*

WIPAIRE INC.
1700 Henry Ave, South Saint Paul, MN 55075
Tel.: (651) 451-1205
Web Site: http://www.wipaire.com
Year Founded: 1960
Sales Range: $10-24.9 Million
Emp.: 180
Aircraft Float Products Mfr
N.A.I.C.S.: 336413
Robert Wiplinger *(Chm & CEO)*
Rod Edlund *(Asst Dir-Maintenance)*
Dale Fehrenbach *(Mgr-Turbine Aircraft Sls)*
Grant Wallace *(Mgr-Tech Support & Parts Sls)*
Bill Pike *(Gen Mgr-Leesburg)*
Paul Wells *(VP-Aircraft Svcs)*
Curt Sneddeker *(Project Mgr)*
Jason Erickson *(Dir-Maintenance)*
Larry Brickey *(Project Mgr)*
Ted Delgado *(Asst Dir-Maintenance)*
Tom Carlson *(Sls Mgr-Svcs & Components)*

WIPLIANCE, LLC
2020 124th Ave NE Ste C-105, Bellevue, WA 98005
Tel.: (425) 702-8600
Web Site: https://wipliance.com
Year Founded: 2006
Emp.: 100
Audio, Video, Lighting Control & Security Services
N.A.I.C.S.: 334310
Lee Travis *(Owner)*
Subsidiaries:
Huppin's Hi-Fi, Photo & Video Inc. (1)
8016 N Division, Spokane, WA 99208
Tel.: (509) 893-5588
Web Site: https://huppins.com
Sales Range: $10-24.9 Million
Emp.: 85
Provider of Consumer Electonics
N.A.I.C.S.: 449210
Murray Huppin *(Pres)*

WIRE PRODUCTS COMPANY INC.
14601 Industrial Pkwy, Cleveland, OH 44135
Tel.: (216) 267-0777
Web Site: http://www.wire-products.com
Sales Range: $10-24.9 Million
Emp.: 150
Mechanical Springs, Precision
N.A.I.C.S.: 332613
E. Scot Kennedy *(Chm)*
Dale Veleznik *(CEO)*

WIRE SHOP INC.
6155 US Hwy 341 S, Fort Valley, GA 31030
Tel.: (478) 825-2132
Web Site:
http://www.thewireshopinc.com
Year Founded: 1991
Sales Range: $10-24.9 Million
Emp.: 95
Electrical Wiring Harnesses & Battery Cables
N.A.I.C.S.: 423610
Austin Davis *(VP-Ops)*

WIRE STONE, LLC
920 20th St, Sacramento, CA 95811
Tel.: (916) 446-6550
Web Site: http://www.wirestone.com
Year Founded: 1999
Sales Range: $25-49.9 Million
Emp.: 175
Advertising Services
N.A.I.C.S.: 541810
Dan Lynch *(CEO)*
Tony Schlangen *(COO, Mng Dir-Boise & VP)*
Gary Robinett *(Sr VP & Dir-Fin)*
Jon Baker *(Sr VP-Tech-West Reg)*
Ti Bensen *(Sr VP & Mng Dir-Fort Collins)*
Fabio Matsui *(CTO)*
Lianne Morgan *(Mng Dir-Seattle & VP)*
Greg Rattenborg *(Chief Creative Officer)*
Jason Michaels *(Mng Dir & VP)*
Drew Rayman *(CMO)*
Subsidiaries:
Tenthwave Digital, LLC (1)
31 W 27th St 12th Fl, New York, NY 10001
Tel.: (212) 933-9221
Web Site: http://www.tenthwave.com
Business Marketing Agency
N.A.I.C.S.: 541613
Rob Kaplan *(Partner-Program Dev)*
Drew Rayman *(Partner)*
Steve Caputo *(Partner)*

Wirestone (1)
101 Remington St, Fort Collins, CO 80524
Tel.: (970) 493-3181
Web Site: http://www.wirestone.com
Sales Range: $25-49.9 Million
Emp.: 40
N.A.I.C.S.: 541810
Ti Benson *(Mng Dir)*
Jamie Arbizo *(Project Mgr)*
Mike Higgins *(Mgr-Tech Svcs)*

Wirestone (1)
312 S Cedros Ave Ste 340, Solana Beach, CA 92075
Tel.: (858) 509-1125
Web Site: http://www.wirestone.com
Sales Range: $10-24.9 Million
Emp.: 8
N.A.I.C.S.: 541810

Wirestone (1)
913 W River St Ste 200, Boise, ID 83702
Tel.: (208) 343-2868
Web Site: http://www.wirestone.com
Emp.: 50
N.A.I.C.S.: 541810
Dan Lynch *(Pres)*

Wirestone (1)
920 20th St 2nd Fl, Sacramento, CA 95811
Tel.: (916) 446-6550
Web Site: http://www.wirestone.com
Sales Range: $10-24.9 Million
Emp.: 15
N.A.I.C.S.: 541810
Dan Lynch *(Pres)*
Ti Bensen *(Mng Dir)*

Wirestone (1)
2153 Williams St, Palo Alto, CA 94306
Tel.: (408) 439-7582
Web Site: http://www.wirestone.com
N.A.I.C.S.: 541810

Wirestone, LLC (1)
225 W Illinois Ste 400, Chicago, IL 60654
Tel.: (312) 222-0733
Web Site: http://www.wirestone.com
Sales Range: $10-24.9 Million
Emp.: 30
N.A.I.C.S.: 541810
Ti Bensen *(Mng Dir)*
Brent Van Horne *(Assoc Dir-Creative)*
Fabio Matsui *(CTO)*
Neil Michel *(Chief Strategy Officer)*
Greg Rattenborg *(Chief Creative Officer)*
Gary Robinett *(Sr VP & Dir-Fin)*
Jon Baker *(Mng Dir & Sr VP-California)*
Lianne Morgan *(Mng Dir & Sr VP-Seattle)*
Tony Schlangen *(Mng Dir, COO & Sr VP-Boise)*

WIRE WELD USA INC.
8 Short St, Lockport, NY 14094
Tel.: (716) 439-8771
Web Site: http://www.wireweld.com
Rev.: $10,000,000
Emp.: 20
Wire Shelving Mfr
N.A.I.C.S.: 337126
Rich King *(Owner)*

WIRED REAL ESTATE GROUP INC.
2110 Gateway Oaks 150 N, Sacramento, CA 95833
Tel.: (916) 572-9606
Web Site: http://www.wiredre.com
Sales Range: $10-24.9 Million
Emp.: 10
Data Center Broker
N.A.I.C.S.: 518210
Everett Thompson *(Founder & CEO)*
Doug Newcomb *(CTO)*
Grant Morgove *(Mgr-Natl Acct)*
Kelly Tenuta *(Dir-Mktg)*
Subsidiaries:
Applied Computer Research, Inc. (1)
16841 N 31st Ave Ste 101, Phoenix, AZ 85080
Tel.: (623) 937-4700
Web Site:
http://www.itmarketintelligence.com
Sales Range: $10-24.9 Million
Emp.: 25
Technical Publishing Services
N.A.I.C.S.: 513199
Alan Howard *(Pres)*

WIREDRIVE
5340 Alla Rd Ste 109, Los Angeles, CA 90066
Tel.: (310) 823-8238
Web Site: http://www.wiredrive.com
Year Founded: 1999
Rev.: $2,900,000
Emp.: 22
Software Services
N.A.I.C.S.: 541511
Farah Fima *(Acct Mgr)*
Ruth Schiller *(VP-On-Air Promo)*

WIREDTREE
412 S Wells St Ste 2011, Chicago, IL 60607
Tel.: (312) 447-0510
Web Site: http://www.wiredtree.com
Year Founded: 2006
Sales Range: $1-9.9 Million

Emp.: 21
Web Hosting & Internet Service Providers
N.A.I.C.S.: 517810
Zac Cogswell *(Pres)*
Devon Rutherford *(Dir-Sls)*

WIREGRASS CONSTRUCTION COMPANY
8974 N US Hwy 231, Ariton, AL 36311
Tel.: (334) 762-2397
Web Site:
http://www.wiregrassconstruction.com
Sales Range: $25-49.9 Million
Emp.: 175
Highway & Street Paving Contractor
N.A.I.C.S.: 237310
John L. Harper *(Pres)*

WIREGRASS ELECTRIC CO-OPERATIVE
509 N State Hwy 167, Hartford, AL 36344
Tel.: (334) 588-2223
Web Site: http://www.wiregrass.coop
Sales Range: $10-24.9 Million
Emp.: 45
Distribution, Electric Power
N.A.I.C.S.: 221122
Brad Kimbro *(COO)*
Danny Ealum *(Sr Engr)*
Larry Galloway *(Mgr-Svc Dept)*
Les Moreland *(CEO)*
Lisa Lenoir *(Controller)*
Deanna Albritton *(Coord-Member Svcs)*
Jason Thrash *(Dir-Engrg & Ops)*
Robbie Daniels *(Mgr-Corp Svcs)*
Jessie Ingram *(Mgr-Energy Svcs)*
Stevie Sauls *(Mgr-Field Svcs)*
Kay Sullivan *(Mgr-Member Accts)*
Rhonda Webb *(Mgr-Member Svcs)*
Joey Brown *(Mgr-Ops)*

WIREGRASS ELECTRIC CO-OPERATIVE, INC.
509 N State Hwy 167, Hartford, AL 36344
Tel.: (334) 588-2223
Web Site: http://www.wiregrass.coop
Year Founded: 1939
Sales Range: $25-49.9 Million
Emp.: 63
Electric Power Distr
N.A.I.C.S.: 221122
Leslie Moreland *(CEO)*
Danny Ealum *(Sr Engr)*
Brad Kimbro *(COO)*
Debra E. Baxley *(Sec)*
Danny McNeil *(Pres)*
John A. Clark Jr. *(VP)*

WIRELESS COMMUNICATIONS INC.
105 E N St Ste 100, Greenville, SC 29601
Tel.: (864) 631-2392
Web Site: http://www.thewcinc.com
Year Founded: 2008
Sales Range: $10-24.9 Million
Emp.: 150
Wireless Retailer
N.A.I.C.S.: 334220
Krish V. Patel *(Pres)*

WIRELESS COMMUNICATIONS INC.
4800 Reagan Dr, Charlotte, NC 28206
Tel.: (704) 597-5220
Web Site: http://www.wirelessnc.com
Rev.: $10,000,000
Emp.: 40

COMPANIES

Provider of Radio & Telephone Communication Services
N.A.I.C.S.: 517112
Leo Dagostin (Owner & Pres)
Charles M. Buie (Owner & Sr VP)

WIRELESS ELECTRONICS, INC.
2905 Southampton Rd, Philadelphia, PA 19154
Tel.: (215) 698-6850 DE
Communication Equipment Repair & Maintenance
N.A.I.C.S.: 811210

WIRELESS EMPORIUM, INC.
1410 Batavia St, Orange, CA 92867
Tel.: (714) 278-1930
Web Site:
  http://www.wirelessemporium.com
Year Founded: 2001
Sales Range: $10-24.9 Million
Emp.: 15
Cell Phone Accessory Retailer
N.A.I.C.S.: 459999
Ruben Leon (Mgr-Ops)
Edwin Choi (Dir-Mktg)

WIRELESS ENVIRONMENT, LLC
32333 Aurora Rd Ste 100, Solon, OH 44139
Tel.: (877) 298-9082
Web Site: http://wirelessenv.com
Year Founded: 2007
Sales Range: $1-9.9 Million
Emp.: 8
Develops & Sells Motion-Sensing Battery-Powered LED Lights
N.A.I.C.S.: 335139
Michael Recker (CTO)
David Levine (Pres)

WIRELESS TOYZ LLC
29155 Northwestern Hwy, Southfield, MI 48034-1011
Tel.: (248) 426-8200
Web Site:
  http://www.wirelesstoyz.com
Year Founded: 1995
Telecommunicatons Equipment Retailer
N.A.I.C.S.: 517112
Joe Barbat (Chm & CEO)

WIRELESS VENTURES LLC
4996 Indiana Ave, Winston Salem, NC 27016
Tel.: (260) 484-0466
Web Site:
  http://www.amerizonwireless.com
Rev.: $22,147,174
Emp.: 100
Radiotelephone Communication
N.A.I.C.S.: 517112
Dean Cayton (VP)

Subsidiaries:

Scadata Scientific, LLC (1)
1818 Research Dr, Fort Wayne, IN 46808
Tel.: (260) 373-0100
Web Site: http://www.scadata.net
Sales Range: $1-9.9 Million
Emp.: 8
Radiotelephone Communication
N.A.I.C.S.: 517112
Kevin L. Stock (Pres)

WIRELESS WORLD
3793 S Main St, Marion, NY 14505
Tel.: (315) 926-4147 NY
Web Site: http://ewirelessworld.com
Year Founded: 2003
Sales Range: $1-9.9 Million
Emp.: 49
Telecommunications Resellers
N.A.I.C.S.: 517121

Daniel Gardner (Chm & Pres)
Rob Crowder (CEO)
Timothy Smith (CFO & Controller)

WIRELESSUSA, INC.
148 Weldon Pkwy, Maryland Heights, MO 63043
Tel.: (314) 615-3100
Web Site:
  http://www.wirelessusa.com
Year Founded: 1962
Sales Range: $10-24.9 Million
Emp.: 90
Electronic Equipment Sales & Distr
N.A.I.C.S.: 423690
Robert Taylor (Pres)
Terry Schieler (VP-Sls)
Dave Hoelscher (VP-Svcs)
Mark Schoenfeld (CFO)

WIREVIBE
125 E John Carpenter Ste 190, Irving, TX 75062
Web Site: http://www.wirevibe.com
Year Founded: 2006
Sales Range: $1-9.9 Million
Emp.: 18
It Consulting
N.A.I.C.S.: 541690
Terrence Shaw (Partner)
Lincoln Fellingham (CTO)

WIREWAY/HUSKY CORPORATION
6146 Denver Industrial Park Cir, Denver, NC 28037
Tel.: (704) 483-1900
Web Site:
  http://www.wirewayhusky.com
Sales Range: $10-24.9 Million
Emp.: 240
Wire Partition Products Mfr
N.A.I.C.S.: 332618
Ron Young (Pres & CEO)
Aime Ritchotte (Project Mgr)
Franklin Quito (Engr-Applications)
Stella Duggins (Mgr-Matls)
Steve Cockerham (Reg Mgr-Sls)
Susan Meyers (CFO)
Vickie Lawrence (Mgr-Pur)

WIRTHS LUMBER CO., INC.
2471 Doc Ridgeway Dr, Macks Creek, MO 65786-6722
Tel.: (573) 363-5349
Year Founded: 1969
Sales Range: $10-24.9 Million
Emp.: 6
Lumber Distr
N.A.I.C.S.: 423310
Kenneth Wirths (Pres)
Kelly Wirth (VP)
Michael K. Wirths (Sec)

WIRTZ CORPORATION
680 N Lake Shore Dr, Chicago, IL 60611
Tel.: (312) 943-7000 DE
Year Founded: 1926
Sales Range: $1-4.9 Billion
Emp.: 3,000
Investment Holding Company
N.A.I.C.S.: 551112
W. Rockwell Wirtz (Chm, Pres & CEO)
Linda Boskelly (Controller)
Nadine Heidrich (CFO & VP)

Subsidiaries:

Benefit Services Group, Inc. (1)
680 Lake Shore Dr Ste 2050, Chicago, IL 60611
Tel.: (800) 619-6306
Web Site: http://www.bsgi401k.com
General Insurance Services
N.A.I.C.S.: 524210

Pete Pugal (Chief Admin Officer & Sr VP)
Carol Noble (VP-HR & Admin)

Chicago Blackhawk Hockey Team, Inc. (1)
1901 W Madison St, Chicago, IL 60612
Tel.: (312) 455-7000
Web Site: http://www.nhl.com
Sales Range: $75-99.9 Million
Emp.: 150
Professional Hockey Team
N.A.I.C.S.: 711211
W. Rockwell Wirtz (Chm)
Kelly Bednarchuk Smith (Sr Mgr-Client Svcs)
Steve Waight (VP-Corp Sponsorships)
James K. Bare (Exec Dir-Ticket Ops)
Stan Bowman (Sr VP & Gen Mgr)
Sara Bailey (Dir-Corp Sponsorship)
Al MacIsaac (Sr VP-Hockey Ops)
Dan Rozenblat (Sr Dir-Ticket Sls & Svc)
Jay Blunk (Exec VP)
John F. McDonough (Pres & CEO)
Marie Sutera (VP-HR)
T. J. Skattum (VP-Fin)
Michael Dorsch (Dir-Fin)
Adam Rogowin (VP-Comm)
Adam Kempenaar (VP-Digital Content)
Julie Lovins (Dir-Svc & Retention)
Steve DiLenardi (Dir-Grp Sls)
Chris Werner (VP-Ticket Ops & Customer Rels)
Norm MacIver (Asst Gen Mgr)
Pierre Gauthier (Dir-Player Personnel)
Troy Parchman (Mgr-Equipment)
John Sandberg (Dir-Creative)
Mark Bernard (Gen Mgr-Minor League Affiliations & Dir-Hockey Admin)
Ron Anderson (Dir-Player Recruitment)
Annie Camins (Sr Dir-Fun Dev)
Laura Clawson (Dir-Mdsg)
Mats Hallin (Dir-European Scouting)
Kyleen Howe (Mgr-HR)
Barry Smith (Dir-Player Evaluation)
Ryan Stewart (Dir-Pro Scouting)

First Security Bancorp, Inc. (1)
7315 W Grand Ave, Elmwood Park, IL 60707
Tel.: (708) 453-3131
Web Site: http://www.fstsb.com
Bank Holding Company
N.A.I.C.S.: 551111
W. Rockwell Wirtz (Chm, Pres & CEO)

Subsidiary (Domestic):

First Security Trust & Savings Bank (2)
7315 W Grand Ave, Elmwood Park, IL 60707
Tel.: (708) 453-3131
Web Site: http://www.fstsb.com
Sales Range: $1-9.9 Million
Emp.: 50
Commericial Banking
N.A.I.C.S.: 522110
Drew A. Dammeier (Exec VP)
Thomas L. Nelson (Chief Lending Officer)
Thomas J. Schnell (Sr VP-Ops)

Wirtz Insurance Agency, Inc. (1)
680 N Lake Shore Dr, Chicago, IL 60611
Tel.: (312) 943-7000
Web Site: http://www.wirtzinsurance.com
Insurance & Brokerage Services
N.A.I.C.S.: 524210

Wirtz Realty Corporation (1)
680 N Lake Shore Dr Ste 1900, Chicago, IL 60611 (100%)
Tel.: (312) 943-7000
Web Site: http://www.wirtzresidential.com
Sales Range: $10-24.9 Million
Emp.: 70
Residential Housing Rental Services
N.A.I.C.S.: 531110
Rock Well (Pres)

WIRTZ MANUFACTURING COMPANY INC.
1105 24th St, Port Huron, MI 48060
Tel.: (810) 987-4700 MI
Web Site: http://www.wirtzusa.com
Year Founded: 1932
Sales Range: $10-24.9 Million
Emp.: 126

Industrial Equipment Mfr
N.A.I.C.S.: 333248
Joel Arundel (Mgr-Sls)
Amol Jambhekar (Asst Project Mgr)

WIS-PAK, INC.
860 W St, Watertown, WI 53094-3517
Tel.: (920) 262-6300 WI
Web Site: http://www.wis-pak.com
Year Founded: 1969
Sales Range: $1-9.9 Million
Emp.: 500
Soft Drinks Mfr & Distr
N.A.I.C.S.: 312111
Barbara Parish (Pres)

WISCNET
740 Regent St Ste 203, Madison, WI 53715
Tel.: (608) 442-6761 WI
Web Site: http://www.wiscnet.net
Year Founded: 1990
Sales Range: $1-9.9 Million
Emp.: 14
Research & Education Networking Services
N.A.I.C.S.: 541512
Ross Wilson (Chm)
Tom Lange (Treas)
Vicki Lyons (Vice Chm)
Joshua Klingbeil (Sec)

WISCO INDUSTRIES INC.
736 Janesville St, Oregon, WI 53575
Tel.: (608) 835-3106
Web Site: http://www.wiscoind.com
Sales Range: $25-49.9 Million
Emp.: 120
Stamping Metal For The Trade
N.A.I.C.S.: 332119
Elving J. Kjellstrom (Chm)
Mike O'Malley (Controller)
Bob Hartung (Dir-IT)
David Walsh (Superintendent)
Tina Kjerstad (Product Mgr-Line Mktg)
Tom Michel (Chief Engr-Mfg)
Mary Laube (Mgr-HR)
Sandy Harried (Mgr-Production)
Teri Moe (Asst Controller)

WISCO PRODUCTS, INC.
109 Commercial St, Dayton, OH 45402-2211
Tel.: (937) 228-2101 OH
Web Site:
  http://www.wiscoproducts.com
Year Founded: 1936
Sales Range: $50-74.9 Million
Emp.: 25
Mfr of Fuel Caps, Adapters, Strainers, Stampings & Metal Assemblies
N.A.I.C.S.: 332119
Mark Paxson (Pres)
D. J. Maier (VP-Mfg)
Kyle Paxson (Mgr-Ops)

WISCONSIN ALUMINUM FOUNDRY COMPANY, INC.
838 S 16th St, Manitowoc, WI 54220
Tel.: (920) 682-8286
Web Site: http://www.wafco.com
Rev.: $73,700,000
Emp.: 400
Nonferrous Foundries
N.A.I.C.S.: 331529
Kory Brockman (VP-Fin)
Phillip Jacobs (Pres & CEO)
Milton Schwartz (Chm)
Don Noworatzkey (Mgr-Quality Control)

WISCONSIN ALUMNI RESEARCH FOUNDATION

WISCONSIN ALUMNI RESEARCH FOUNDATION

Wisconsin Alumni Research Foundation—(Continued)
614 Walnut St 13th Fl, Madison, WI 53726
Tel.: (608) 263-2500 WI
Web Site: http://www.warf.org
Year Founded: 1925
Sales Range: $300-349.9 Million
Emp.: 130
Science Research Services
N.A.I.C.S.: 541715
Maureen Miner (Dir-HR)
Carrie Thome (Dir-Investments)
Leigh Cagan (Chief Tech Commercialization Officer)
Travis Tangen (Mgr-Education & Outreach)
Peter P. Tong (Chm)
Erik Iverson (Mng Dir)
John Gransee (CFO)
Steve Mixtacki (CFO & COO)
James G. Berbee (Vice Chm)

WISCONSIN AVIATION INC.
1741 River Dr, Watertown, WI 53094
Tel.: (920) 261-4567
Web Site: http://www.wisconsinaviation.com
Year Founded: 1981
Sales Range: $10-24.9 Million
Emp.: 40
Provider of Aviation Services Including Charter, Flight Training, Aircraft Rental, Aircraft Sales, Maintenance, Avionics & Line Services
N.A.I.C.S.: 488119
Krys Brown (Dir-HR)
Mary Gasper (Mgr-FBO-Airport)
Tyler Bellmore (Supvr-Ops)

WISCONSIN BOX COMPANY
929 Town Line Rd, Wausau, WI 54403
Tel.: (715) 842-2248
Web Site: http://www.wisconsinbox.com
Sales Range: $10-24.9 Million
Emp.: 75
Manufacture Rectangular Boxes & Crates, Wire Bound & Wood
N.A.I.C.S.: 321920
W. Jeff Davis (Pres)
Michael Shipway (Controller)

WISCONSIN BREWING COMPANY LLC
1079 American Way, Verona, WI 53593
Tel.: (608) 848-1079
Web Site: http://www.wbcll.com
Brewery
N.A.I.C.S.: 312120
Carl Nolen (Pres & CEO)

Subsidiaries:

Lake Louie Brewing LLC (1)
7556 Pine Rd, Arena, WI 53503-9236
Tel.: (608) 753-2675
Web Site: http://www.lakelouie.com
Beer, Wine & Liquor Stores
N.A.I.C.S.: 445320
Tom Porter (Owner)

WISCONSIN BUILT INC.
400 Interpane Ln, Deerfield, WI 53531
Tel.: (608) 764-8661
Web Site: http://www.wisconsin-built.com
Sales Range: $10-24.9 Million
Emp.: 200
Cabinets, Lockers & Shelving
N.A.I.C.S.: 337212
Dan Peterson (Pres)
Mike Wild (Controller)

WISCONSIN CHEESE GROUP INC.
105 3rd St, Monroe, WI 53566-1879
Tel.: (608) 325-2012 WI
Web Site: http://www.wisconsincheesegroup.com
Year Founded: 1986
Sales Range: $10-24.9 Million
Emp.: 100
Provider of Dairy Products
N.A.I.C.S.: 424430
Bill Hoesly (Mgr-New Products)
Michelle Riese (Dir-Quality Assurance)

WISCONSIN CHEESE INC.
2050 N 15 Ave, Melrose Park, IL 60160
Tel.: (708) 681-1470
Web Site: http://www.wisconcorp.com
Rev.: $21,929,000
Emp.: 70
Cheese; Natural & Processed
N.A.I.C.S.: 561110
Rene Caputo (Pres)

WISCONSIN DISTRIBUTORS L.P.
900 Progress Way, Sun Prairie, WI 53590
Tel.: (608) 834-2337
Web Site: http://www.wdbud.com
Sales Range: $25-49.9 Million
Emp.: 140
Distr of Beer
N.A.I.C.S.: 424810
Pierre McCormick (Pres)

WISCONSIN EARLY CHILDHOOD ASSOCIATION
744 Williamson St Ste 200, Madison, WI 53703
Tel.: (608) 240-9880 WI
Web Site: http://www.wisconsinearlychildhood.org
Year Founded: 1979
Sales Range: $10-24.9 Million
Emp.: 80
Child Care Services
N.A.I.C.S.: 624110
Cindy Poole (Program Dir)
Jeanette Paulson (Dir-Workforce Initiatives)
Caroline Oldershaw (Dir-Mktg & Dev)
Andrea Murray (Dir-Trng & Conference)
Autumn Gehri (Dir-TEACH & Pro Dev Program)
Candace Duerst (Mgr-Fin)
Luke Chirhart (Sec)
Sue Schimke (Pres)
Ruth Schmidt (Exec Dir)

WISCONSIN EDUCATIONAL COMMUNICATIONS BOARD
3319 W Beltline Hwy, Madison, WI 53713-2834
Tel.: (608) 264-9600
Web Site: http://www.ecb.org
Year Founded: 1971
Sales Range: $10-24.9 Million
Emp.: 45
Provider of Radio & TV Broadcasting Services
N.A.I.C.S.: 516110
Gene Purcell (Exec Dir)
Peter Ives (Mgr-Svcs)

WISCONSIN HEALTH FUND
6200 W Bluemound Rd, Milwaukee, WI 53213-4145
Tel.: (414) 771-5600 WI
Web Site: http://www.whfund.org
Year Founded: 1952
Sales Range: $25-49.9 Million
Emp.: 101
Health Care Srvices
N.A.I.C.S.: 622110
Michael S. Lovely (Exec Dir)

WISCONSIN HOMES INC.
425 W McMillan St, Marshfield, WI 54449
Tel.: (715) 384-2161
Web Site: http://www.wisconsinhomesinc.com
Rev.: $26,400,000
Emp.: 150
Prefabricated Wood Building Mfr
N.A.I.C.S.: 321992
Mark Frey (Chm)
Paul Frey (Pres)
Joseph Martell (Treas & Sec)
Shannon Nienast (VP & Gen Mgr)

WISCONSIN HUMANE SOCIETY
4500 W Wisconsin Ave, Milwaukee, WI 53208
Tel.: (414) 264-6257 WI
Web Site: http://www.wihumane.org
Year Founded: 1879
Sales Range: $1-9.9 Million
Emp.: 173
Animal Protection Services
N.A.I.C.S.: 813312
Tony Enea (Vice Chm)
Robert Davis (Treas)
David Hecker (Sec)
Anne Reed (Pres & CEO)
Mike Wamser (CFO & VP-Fin)
Matt Witte (COO & VP-Ops)
Jenny Mueller (VP-Dev)
Angela Speed (VP-Comm)
Jill Kline (VP-Community Impact Programs)
John P. Matter (Chm)

Subsidiaries:

Kenosha County Humane Society (1)
7811 60th Ave, Kenosha, WI 53142
Tel.: (262) 694-4047
Web Site: http://www.safeharborhumanesociety.org
Sales Range: $1-9.9 Million
Emp.: 25
Humane Society Services
N.A.I.C.S.: 813312
William Bohlman (VP)
Amanda Angove (Exec Dir)
Marc Skurski (Pres)
Jennifer Somerlott (Sec)

WISCONSIN LIFT TRUCK CORP.
3125 Intertech Dr, Brookfield, WI 53045-5113
Tel.: (262) 781-8010 WI
Web Site: http://www.wisconsinlift.com
Year Founded: 1962
Sales Range: $100-124.9 Million
Emp.: 475
Material Handling Services
N.A.I.C.S.: 423830
Jerry Weidmann (Pres)
Otto J. Wolter (Founder & CEO)

Subsidiaries:

Witco Systems Inc (1)
3125 Intertech Dr, Brookfield, WI 53045-5113
Tel.: (414) 615-2000
Sales Range: $10-24.9 Million
Emp.: 40
Materials Handling Services
N.A.I.C.S.: 423830
Elmer Grichtmeier (VP & Gen Mgr)
Tim Wilson (Mgr-Parts)

U.S. PRIVATE

WISCONSIN MANAGEMENT COMPANY
2040 S Park St, Madison, WI 53713
Tel.: (608) 258-2080
Web Site: http://www.wimci.com
Sales Range: $24-49.9 Million
Emp.: 200
Real Estate Managers
N.A.I.C.S.: 531210
Russ Endres (CEO)

WISCONSIN METAL PRODUCTS CO.
1807 DeKoven Ave, Racine, WI 53403
Tel.: (262) 633-6301
Web Site: http://www.wmpco.com
Rev.: $12,800,000
Emp.: 30
Metal Stamping
N.A.I.C.S.: 332119
John J. Janes Jr. (Pres & Treas)
Lee Mutchie (Engr-Maintenance)
Robert Stillman (Gen Mgr)

WISCONSIN MUTUAL INSURANCE CO.
8201 Excelsior Dr, Madison, WI 53717-1907
Tel.: (608) 836-4663
Web Site: http://www.wiins.com
Year Founded: 1903
Sales Range: $50-74.9 Million
Emp.: 65
Property Damage Insurance & Auto
N.A.I.C.S.: 524126
Daniel A. Keyes (Pres)
Eric Bower (Mgr-Acctg)

WISCONSIN PACKING CO. INC. DELAWARE
PO Box 913, Butler, WI 53007
Tel.: (262) 781-2400
Sales Range: $10-24.9 Million
Emp.: 350
Meat Product Production Services
N.A.I.C.S.: 311612
George F. Lang (Exec VP)
Robert Segel (VP)
Nick Marquz (CIO)
Justin N. Segel (Pres)

WISCONSIN PHARMACAL COMPANY, LLC
1 Pharmacal Way, Jackson, WI 53037-9583
Tel.: (262) 677-4121 WI
Web Site: http://www.pharmacalway.com
Year Founded: 1896
Sales Range: $10-24.9 Million
Emp.: 60
Insect Repellent, Insect Bite Lotion, Water Purification Tablets, Fishing Chemicals, Hand Cleaner, Sunscreen Products, First Aid Kits & Camp & Travel Accessories Mfr & Marketer
N.A.I.C.S.: 325320
John Wundrock (Owner)
Jeff Potts (CFO)
Andy Wundrock (VP-Sls & Mktg)

Subsidiaries:

Lake Consumer Products, Inc. (1)
1 Pharmacal Way, Jackson, WI 53037
Tel.: (262) 677-7179
Web Site: http://www.lakeconsumer.com
Sales Range: $10-24.9 Million
Emp.: 22
Pharmaceuticals
N.A.I.C.S.: 325412

WISCONSIN PHYSICIANS SERVICE INSURANCE CORPORATION
1717 W Broadway, Madison, WI 53708-8190
Tel.: (608) 221-4711 WI

Web Site: http://www.wpshealth.com
Year Founded: 1977
Sales Range: $700-749.9 Million
Emp.: 4,000
Health Insurance
N.A.I.C.S.: 524114
Scott Kowalski *(COO & Exec VP-Health Insurance)*
Chris Cashell *(Sr VP-Bus Unit Svcs)*
Jay Martinson *(COO)*
Maria Brasda *(VP-Acct Svcs)*
Thomas Nelson *(CFO)*

Subsidiaries:

Arise Health Plan (1)
PO Box 11625, Green Bay, WI 54307-1625
Web Site:
http://www.wecareforwisconsin.com
Health Insurance Services
N.A.I.C.S.: 524114
Michael Ostrov *(Chief Medical Officer)*
Scott Kowalski *(Exec VP)*

The EPIC Life Insurance Co. (1)
1765 W Broadway, Madison, WI 53713-1500 (100%)
Tel.: (608) 223-2100
Web Site: http://www.epiclife.com
Sales Range: $25-49.9 Million
Emp.: 12
Life Insurance
N.A.I.C.S.: 524113
Rich Robinson *(Reg Dir-Sls)*

WPS Community Bank (1)
5900 Gisholt Dr, Madison, WI 53713
Tel.: (608) 224-5500
Web Site: http://www.bankwps.com
Commercial Banking Services
N.A.I.C.S.: 522110

WISCONSIN PIPE TRADES HEALTH FUND
11270 W Park Pl Ste 950, Milwaukee, WI 53224
Tel.: (414) 577-3700 WI
Year Founded: 1952
Sales Range: $10-24.9 Million
Health Fund Provider
N.A.I.C.S.: 525120
Kevin La mere *(Treas & Sec)*
Ed Tonn Jr. *(Chm)*

WISCONSIN REINSURANCE CORP.
2810 City View Dr, Madison, WI 53718
Tel.: (608) 242-4500
Web Site:
http://www.thewrcgroup.com
Sales Range: $10-24.9 Million
Emp.: 63
Reciprocal Interinsurance Exchanges: Fire, Marine, Casualty
N.A.I.C.S.: 524113
Terry Wendorff *(Pres & CEO)*
Chuck Scadden *(Mgr-Re-Insurance)*
Michele Weber *(Mgr-Acctg)*
Rick Franz *(VP-IT)*
Todd Lentz *(Sr VP-Treas & Re-Insurance)*
Peg Mickelson *(VP-Admin)*

WISCONSIN RIVER CO-OP
540 S Main St, Adams, WI 53910-9701
Tel.: (608) 339-3394
Web Site: http://www.wrc.coop
Sales Range: $25-49.9 Million
Emp.: 120
Refined Fuels, Agronomy, Feed & Grain Retailer
N.A.I.C.S.: 457210
Timothy Diemert *(CEO)*
Pam Dahlke *(Controller)*
Karmen Bernacchi *(Mgr-Mktg Comm)*
Gerry Fanta *(Mgr-Agronomy Fin-Mauston)*

WISCONSIN STEEL & TUBE CORPORATION
1555 N Mayfair Rd, Milwaukee, WI 53226
Tel.: (414) 453-4441
Web Site: http://www.wisteeltube.com
Rev.: $40,000,000
Emp.: 50
Metal Service Centers & Other Metal Merchant Whslr
N.A.I.C.S.: 423510
Joseph Teich *(Pres)*

WISCONSIN TECHNICOLOR LLC
W237n2889 Woodgate Rd Ste A, Pewaukee, WI 53072
Tel.: (262) 523-3900
Rev.: $10,800,000
Emp.: 85
Color Printing Services
N.A.I.C.S.: 323120

WISCONSIN THERMOSET MOLDING, INC.
900 E Vienna Ave, Milwaukee, WI 53212
Tel.: (414) 964-5200
Web Site:
http://www.withermoset.com
Year Founded: 1997
Sales Range: $10-24.9 Million
Emp.: 80
Plastics Product Mfr
N.A.I.C.S.: 326199
Boyd C. Miller *(Pres & Owner)*
Andy Stroh *(VP-Sls)*
Noah Brushel *(VP-Engrg)*

Subsidiaries:

Cornerstone Composites Inc. (1)
900 E Vienna Street, Milwaukee, WI 53212
Tel.: (414) 964-5200
Web Site: http://www.rosepolymer.com
Plastic Mfr
N.A.I.C.S.: 326199
Boyd Miller *(Pres)*

WISCONSIN VISION ASSOCIATES INC.
139 W Chestnut St, Burlington, WI 53105-1202
Tel.: (262) 763-0100 WI
Web Site: http://www.wisvis.com
Year Founded: 1982
Sales Range: $10-24.9 Million
Emp.: 30
Distr of Ophthalmic Goods & Services
N.A.I.C.S.: 423460
Robert Fait *(Pres)*
Christopher Fait *(VP & Mgr-Sls-Natl)*

WISDOM HOMES OF AMERICA, INC.
500 N Northeast Loop 323, Tyler, TX 75708 NV
Year Founded: 2003
WOFA—(OTCBB)
Sales Range: Less than $1 Million
Emp.: 8
Manufactured Home Retail Centers Owner & Operator
N.A.I.C.S.: 459930

WISDOM INFOTECH
18650 W Corporate Dr Ste 120, Brookfield, WI 53045
Tel.: (262) 792-0200
Web Site:
http://www.wisdominfotech.com
Year Founded: 2000
Sales Range: $10-24.9 Million
Emp.: 8,200
Custom Software Solutions & Services

N.A.I.C.S.: 541511
Suresh Thankavel *(Pres & CEO)*

WISDOMTOOLS, LLC
501 N Morton St Ste 206, Bloomington, IN 47404
Tel.: (812) 856-4202 IN
Web Site:
http://www.wisdomtools.com
Year Founded: 1999
Sales Range: $1-9.9 Million
Emp.: 37
Educational Software
N.A.I.C.S.: 513210
Tom Myers *(VP-Bus Dev & Military Rels)*
Sonny Kirkley *(Chm & CEO)*
Jamie Kirkley *(Chief Learning Officer)*
Kelly Clark *(Project Mgr)*

WISE ALLOYS LLC
4805 2nd St, Muscle Shoals, AL 35661
Tel.: (410) 636-6500
Web Site: http://www.wisealloys.com
Sales Range: $300-349.9 Million
Emp.: 1,250
Aluminum Sheet, Plate & Foil
N.A.I.C.S.: 331315
Phil Tays *(Exec VP)*
Richard B. Evans *(Chm)*

WISE AUTOMOTIVE, INC.
671 Orange Dr, Vacaville, CA 95687
Tel.: (707) 392-2729 CA
Web Site:
http://www.wiseautogroup.com
Car Dealer Services
N.A.I.C.S.: 441110
Michael Maldonado *(Dir-HR)*

Subsidiaries:

Harley Davidson of Victorville, Inc. (1)
14522 Valley Center Dr, Victorville, CA 92395
Tel.: (760) 951-1119
Web Site: http://www.victorvillehd.com
Sales Range: $1-9.9 Million
Emp.: 20
Ret Motorcycles Repair Services
N.A.I.C.S.: 441227
Cary Fischer *(Pres)*

Shasta Hardey-Davidson, Inc. (1)
1268 Twin View Blvd, Redding, CA 96003
Tel.: (530) 684-1916
Web Site: https://www.shastahd.com
Sales Range: $1-9.9 Million
Emp.: 12
Ret Motorcycles Repair Services
N.A.I.C.S.: 441227

WISE BUSINESS FORMS INCORPORATED
555 McFarland 400 Dr, Alpharetta, GA 30004
Tel.: (770) 442-1060 PA
Web Site: http://www.wbf.com
Year Founded: 1969
Sales Range: $25-49.9 Million
Emp.: 500
Business Form Mfr
N.A.I.C.S.: 323111
Marc Picardo *(Dir-IT)*
Jeffrey L. Prettyman *(Exec VP & Dir-Mktg)*
Mark Wells *(Controller)*
Randy Albertson *(Mgr-Sls-Midwest)*
Roger Lindsey *(Mgr-Sls-Northeast)*
Bob Saunders *(VP-Sls)*
H. T. Smith *(Gen Mgr-Alpharetta)*
Jon Wright *(Mgr-Sls-Southeast)*
Lisa Parks *(Mgr-Sls-South)*
Vince Hanhold *(Mgr-Sls-Mid-Atlantic)*

Subsidiaries:

Wise Business (1)

33 McAlister Farm Rd, Portland, ME 04103
Tel.: (207) 775-2216
Sales Range: $10-24.9 Million
Emp.: 125
Printer & Retailer of Business Forms & Envelopes
N.A.I.C.S.: 323111
Mark Jackman *(Gen Mgr)*

Wise Business Forms Incorporated - Commercial Printing Plant (1)
33 McAlister Farm Rd, Portland, ME 04103
Tel.: (207) 774-6560
Web Site: http://www.wbf.com
Digital Printing Services
N.A.I.C.S.: 323111
Mark Jackman *(Gen Mgr)*

Wise Business Forms Incorporated - Indiana Plant (1)
4301 Merchant Rd, Fort Wayne, IN 46818
Tel.: (260) 489-1561
Web Site: http://www.wbf.com
Digital Printing Services
N.A.I.C.S.: 323111
Chris Kumfer *(Mgr-Customer Svc)*
Sally Spurr *(Gen Mgr)*

Wise Business Forms Incorporated - Pennsylvania Plant (1)
150 Kriess Rd, Butler, PA 16001
Tel.: (724) 789-9700
Digital Printing Services
N.A.I.C.S.: 323111
H. T. Smith *(Gen Mgr)*
Rob Vinroe *(Mgr-Customer Svc)*
Sally Spurr *(Gen Mgr)*

Wise Business Forms Incorporated - South Carolina Plant (1)
118 Hurricane Creek Rd, Piedmont, SC 29673-8468
Tel.: (864) 845-5100
Digital Printing Services
N.A.I.C.S.: 323111

WISE COMPONENTS INC.
79 Harbor View Ave, Stamford, CT 06902
Tel.: (203) 325-2191
Web Site:
http://www.wisecomponents.com
Sales Range: $10-24.9 Million
Emp.: 30
Communications Equipment
N.A.I.C.S.: 423690
Scott Blaustein *(Pres)*
John Gallicano *(VP & Product Mgr)*
John Conti *(COO & VP)*
Mike Visci *(Mgr-Outside Sale)*

WISE EL SANTO COMPANY INC.
11000 Linpage Pl, Saint Louis, MO 63132-1012
Tel.: (314) 428-3100 MO
Web Site:
http://www.wiseelsanto.com
Year Founded: 1947
Sales Range: $25-49.9 Million
Emp.: 169
Industrial Supplies & Equipment Whslr
N.A.I.C.S.: 423840
Rudolph L. Wise *(Pres)*
Ed Nations *(VP)*

Subsidiaries:

Reis Environmental Inc. (1)
11022 Linpage Pl, Saint Louis, MO 63132-1012
Tel.: (314) 426-5600
Web Site: http://www.reisenv.com
Sales Range: $25-49.9 Million
Emp.: 40
Environmental Removal Supplies & Equipment Whslr
N.A.I.C.S.: 423840

Subsidiary (Domestic):

Oha Instruments Inc (2)
11022 Linpage Pl, Saint Louis, MO 63132
Tel.: (314) 426-5600

Wise El Santo Company Inc.—(Continued)

Safety Product Distr
N.A.I.C.S.: 423830

WISE ELECTRIC COOPERATIVE, INC.
1900 N Trinity St, Decatur, TX 76234
Tel.: (940) 627-2167
Web Site: http://www.wiseec.com
Year Founded: 1938
Sales Range: $10-24.9 Million
Emp.: 80
Distr of Electric Power
N.A.I.C.S.: 221122
Kelly Myers (Asst Gen Mgr)
Betsy Freeman (Supvr-Customer Svc)
Chris Walsh (Mgr-Engrg & Warehouse)
Scott White (Supvr-Dispatch-AMR)

WISE FORKLIFT INC.
107 Commercial Ln, Dothan, AL 36303
Tel.: (334) 794-8468
Web Site: http://www.wiseforklift.com
Year Founded: 1985
Sales Range: $10-24.9 Million
Emp.: 15
Industrial Machinery & Equipment Merchant Whslr
N.A.I.C.S.: 423830
Gary Smith (Mgr)

WISE GAS, INC.
1126 Hammondville Rd, Pompano Beach, FL 33069
Tel.: (954) 636-4291
Web Site: http://www.wisegasinc.com
Year Founded: 2008
Sales Range: $1-9.9 Million
Emp.: 4
Compressed Natural Gas Distr
N.A.I.C.S.: 221210
Christine Greene (Pres & CEO)
Scott Nobles (Mgr-Technical & Mechanical Svcs)

WISE OIL & FUEL INCORPORATED
503 Washington St, Cambridge, MD 21613-2715
Tel.: (410) 228-4131
Web Site: http://www.aeroenergy.com
Sales Range: $10-24.9 Million
Emp.: 38
Petroleum Bulk Stations
N.A.I.C.S.: 424710
William L. Wise III (Pres)

WISE RECYCLING LLC
555 Wise Rd, Clayton, NC 27520
Tel.: (410) 636-6501
Web Site: http://www.wiserecycling.com
Year Founded: 1998
Sales Range: $25-49.9 Million
Emp.: 123
Recycling Services
N.A.I.C.S.: 562920

WISEMAN GROUP INTERIOR DESIGN INC.
301 Pennsylvania Ave, San Francisco, CA 94107-2950
Tel.: (415) 282-2880
Web Site: http://www.wisemangroup.com
Rev.: $20,000,000
Emp.: 27
Provider of Interior Design Services
N.A.I.C.S.: 541410
Paul Vincent Wiseman (Founder & Pres)

WISENBAKER BUILDER SERVICES LTD.
1703 Westfield Loop Rd, Houston, TX 77073
Tel.: (281) 233-4000
Web Site: http://www.wisenbaker.com
Year Founded: 1972
Sales Range: $75-99.9 Million
Emp.: 250
Floor Coverings
N.A.I.C.S.: 423220
John Wisenbaker (Founder & CEO)
Joe Chiavone (CFO)

WISER CAPITAL LLC
2020 Alameda Padre Serra Sue 220, Santa Barbara, CA 93103
Tel.: (805) 899-3400
Web Site: http://www.wisercapital.com
Emp.: 9
Investment Services
N.A.I.C.S.: 523999
Michael R. McGuire (Chm)
Stephen Honikman (Pres)
Nathan Homan (Mng Partner)
Megan Birney (Dir-Strategic Affairs)

WISEWAY MOTOR FREIGHT INC.
1450 Swasey Rd, Hudson, WI 54016-9285
Tel.: (715) 381-2952
Web Site: http://www.wiseway.com
Rev.: $29,000,000
Emp.: 200
Trucking Except Local
N.A.I.C.S.: 484121
Jeff Wines (Pres)
Marcus Cary (VP-Sls & Mktg)

WISEWAY SUPPLY INC.
8301 Dixie Hwy, Florence, KY 41042
Tel.: (859) 371-2211
Web Site: http://www.wisewaysupply.com
Sales Range: $10-24.9 Million
Emp.: 60
Plumbing Lighting & Electrical Fittings & Supplies
N.A.I.C.S.: 423720
John S. Cain (Pres)
Robert Sizelove (Mgr-Electrical Div)

Subsidiaries:

Stearns Plumbing Inc (1)
2550 N State Highway 7, North Vernon, IN 47265
Tel.: (812) 346-4413
Web Site: http://www.stearnssupplycenter.com
Rev.: $4,000,000
Emp.: 25
Plumbing & Heating Equipment & Supplies, Hydronics, Merchant Whslr
N.A.I.C.S.: 423720

WISHNATZKI, INC.
100 Stearns St, Plant City, FL 33563
Tel.: (813) 752-5111
Web Site: http://www.wishfarms.com
Sales Range: $10-24.9 Million
Emp.: 250
Strawberry Grower, Producer & Distr
N.A.I.C.S.: 111333
Gary Wishnatzki (Pres)

WISHON & CARTER BUILDERS
1412 W Main St, Yadkinville, NC 27055
Tel.: (336) 679-2031
Web Site: http://www.wishoncarter.com
Year Founded: 1971
Rev.: $40,000,000
Emp.: 55

Commercial & Institutional Building Construction
N.A.I.C.S.: 236220
Dorothy Carter (Sec)
Mark Colbert (Project Mgr)
Ted Baity (Project Mgr)

WISS, JANNEY, ELSTNER ASSOCIATES, INC.
330 Pfingsten Rd, Northbrook, IL 60062-2003
Tel.: (847) 272-7400
Web Site: http://www.wje.com
Year Founded: 1989
Rev.: $38,000,000
Emp.: 400
Provider of Engineering Services
N.A.I.C.S.: 541330
William J. Nugent (Pres & CEO)
Ed Gerns (Principal)
Thomas B. Brady (Principal & Dir-Corp Ops & Admin-West Reg)
Wade Garlin (Assoc Principal)
David Green (Principal)
Martina Driscoll (Principal)
Travis Green (Assoc Principal)
Dan Lemieux (Dir-Intl Ops, Architecture & Science)
Bruce McMahon (Principal)
Jonathan Lewis (Principal)

WISSLER MOTORS, INC.
1205 W Main St, Mount Joy, PA 17552
Tel.: (717) 653-2091
Web Site: http://www.wisslers.com
Year Founded: 1969
Sales Range: $10-24.9 Million
Emp.: 65
Car Whslr
N.A.I.C.S.: 441110
Devin Wissler (VP & Gen Mgr)

WIT GROUP INC.
13 St Andrews Ct Ste 201, Brunswick, GA 31520
Tel.: (912) 554-0095
Rev.: $12,000,000
Emp.: 200
Franchise Owner of Fast-Food Restaurants
N.A.I.C.S.: 722513
David Bland (Pres)
Michael Cudd (Sec & VP)

WITCH EQUIPMENT COMPANY, INC.
1901 E Loop 820 S, Fort Worth, TX 76112-7802
Tel.: (817) 429-4824
Web Site: http://www.witchequipment.net
Sales Range: $10-24.9 Million
Emp.: 20
Construction & Mining Machinery Whslr
N.A.I.C.S.: 423810
Jimmy Creecy (Mgr-Parts)
Clyde Mollins (Mgr-Svc)
Kevin Knuckley (Mgr-Sls)

WITH CLARITY INC.
38W 48th St, New York, NY 10036
Web Site: http://www.withclarity.com
Year Founded: 2013
Sales Range: $10-24.9 Million
Emp.: 50
Jewelry Product Retailer
N.A.I.C.S.: 458310
Anubh Shah (Co-Founder)
Slisha Kankariya (Co-Founder & CMO)

WITHAM AUTO CENTERS, INC.
2033 Laporte Rd, Waterloo, IA 50702-2759
Tel.: (319) 234-4200
Web Site: http://www.withamauto.com
Sales Range: $10-24.9 Million
Emp.: 100
Car Whslr
N.A.I.C.S.: 441110
Tim Godfrey (VP)
Jason Witham (Pres)

WITHERS BROADCASTING COMPANY OF WEST VIRGINIA
1 Sleepy Hollow, Mount Vernon, IL 62864
Tel.: (618) 997-8123
Web Site: http://www.mywithersradio.com
Holding Company; Radio & Television Broadcasting Stations Owner & Operator
N.A.I.C.S.: 551112
Dana R. Withers (Pres)

Subsidiaries:

Withers Broadcasting Company of Illinois, LLC (1)
3501 Broadway St, Mount Vernon, IL 62864
Tel.: (618) 242-3500
Web Site: http://www.wmix94.com
Sales Range: $1-9.9 Million
Emp.: 8
Radio Broadcasting Stations
N.A.I.C.S.: 516110
Jolie Birchfield (Mgr-Sls)
Chad Baker (Dir-News)
Chris Hugo (Dir-Sports)

WITHERS WORLDWIDE
11431 NW 107th St Ste1, Miami, FL 33178
Tel.: (305) 477-0030
Web Site: https://www.witherstrans.com
Sales Range: $10-24.9 Million
Emp.: 35
Provider of Moving & Storage & Trucking Services
N.A.I.C.S.: 484220

WITHLACOOCHEE RIVER ELECTRIC COOPERATIVE, INC.
14651 21st St, Dade City, FL 33523-2920
Tel.: (352) 567-5133
Web Site: http://www.wrec.net
Year Founded: 1941
Sales Range: $75-99.9 Million
Emp.: 430
Electronic Services
N.A.I.C.S.: 221121
Billy E. Brown (Exec VP & Gen Mgr)
Linda Mann (Controller)
Carol Molnar (Coord-District Svcs)
David Lambert (Mgr-Member Rels)
Derek Rowell (Supvr-Call Center)
Patrick Durden (Superintendent-Sys Reliability)
Alan F. Hengesbach (Treas & Sec)
Terrence E. Schrader (Pres)

WITHNELL MOTOR COMPANY
2650 Commercial St SE, Salem, OR 97302
Tel.: (503) 364-0184
Web Site: http://www.withnellauto.com
Rev.: $50,700,000
Emp.: 140
Automobiles, New & Used
N.A.I.C.S.: 441110
Richard Withnell (CEO)
David Withnell (Pres)

WITHUMSMITH+BROWN PC

5 Vaughn Dr, Princeton, NJ 08540
Tel.: (609) 520-1188
Web Site: http://www.withum.com
Year Founded: 1974
Sales Range: $75-99.9 Million
Emp.: 388
Accounting, Tax & Consulting Services
N.A.I.C.S.: 541211
Leonard H. Smith *(Partner)*
Thomas J. Hoberman *(Partner & Dir-Litigation Svcs)*
Charles Bramley *(Partner)*
Eric Stephen *(Partner)*
Carleen J. Gaskin *(Partner)*
Sheri Wronko *(Partner)*
Michael D. Yarrow *(Partner)*
Bill Hagaman *(CEO & Mng Partner)*
Dawn Darnell *(Sr Mgr-Boston)*
Adrienne Anderson *(Partner)*
Ray Bastin *(Partner)*
Leanne F. Miliotes *(Principal-Orlando)*
Erik Halluska *(Partner)*

Subsidiaries:

McGuigan Tombs & Co. (1)
2399 Hwy 34 Bldg D2, Manasquan, NJ 08736
Web Site: http://www.mcguiganco.com
Accounting Services
N.A.I.C.S.: 541211
Walter Tombs *(Partner)*

WITMER PUBLIC SAFETY GROUP, INC.
104 Independence Way, Coatesville, PA 19320
Tel.: (610) 857-8070
Web Site: http://www.thefirestore.com
Sales Range: $10-24.9 Million
Emp.: 75
Metal Stamping Services
N.A.I.C.S.: 336370
Jim Witmer *(Chm & CEO)*
Elizabeth McShea *(Mgr-Embroidery)*

WITS BASIN PRECIOUS MINERALS, INC.
80 S Eigth St Ste 900 IDS Ctr, Minneapolis, MN 55402
Tel.: (612) 349-5277 MN
Web Site: http://www.witsbasin.com
Year Founded: 1992
Sales Range: $25-49.9 Million
Emp.: 3
Gold & Precious Metal Minerals Exploration & Development
N.A.I.C.S.: 212220
Stephen D. King *(CEO)*
Clyde L. Smith *(Pres)*
Mark D. Dacko *(CFO, Sec & Controller)*

WITT BUILDING MATERIAL COMPANY
1242 E Weisgarber Rd, Knoxville, TN 37909
Tel.: (865) 588-5331
Web Site: http://www.wittbuilding.com
Rev.: $10,000,000
Emp.: 50
Lumber: Rough, Dressed & Finished
N.A.I.C.S.: 423310
W. Robert Witt *(Pres)*

WITT LINCOLN
588 Camino Del Rio N, San Diego, CA 92108
Tel.: (619) 358-5000
Web Site: http://www.wittlincoln.com
Sales Range: $50-74.9 Million
Emp.: 95
New & Used Car Dealers
N.A.I.C.S.: 441110
Ed Witt *(Pres & CEO)*
Todd Witt *(Mgr-Sls)*
Scott Witt *(Dir-Svc)*

WITT, KIEFFER, HADELMAN, LLOYD & FORD CO. INC.
2015 Spring Rd Ste 510, Oak Brook, IL 60523
Tel.: (630) 990-1370
Web Site: http://www.wittkieffer.com
Sales Range: $25-49.9 Million
Emp.: 150
Executive Placement
N.A.I.C.S.: 541612
Dennis M. Barden *(Sr VP)*
Alexander H. Sandy *(VP)*
Kathleen M. Gillespie *(VP)*
Paul Bohne *(Mng Partner-Boston)*
Andrew P. Chastain *(Pres & CEO)*
Amy Backus *(Dir-Athletic)*
John Morris *(Dir-Athletic)*
Jena E. Abernathy *(Mng Partner & Chm-Bd Svcs)*
Werner Boel *(Sr Partner)*
Tiffany Morris *(Chief HR Officer)*
Morten Nielsen *(Mng Partner-Life Sciences Practice-Global)*
Jennifer Chase *(Mng Dir-Life Sciences Practice-Boston)*
Hillary Ross *(Sr Partner)*
C. J. Bolster *(Mng Dir-Global)*
Inga Walter *(Mng Dir-Life Sciences, Healthcare & Higher Education Practices)*
Natalie Derry *(Mng Partner-Intl)*

WITTE BROTHERS EXCHANGE INC.
575 Witte Industrial Ct, Troy, MO 63379
Tel.: (314) 219-4200
Web Site: http://www.wittebros.com
Sales Range: $25-49.9 Million
Emp.: 200
Trucking Service
N.A.I.C.S.: 484121
Brent B. Witte *(Pres)*
Chuck Harris *(Dir-Maintenance)*

WITTENBERG WEINER CONSULTING, LLC
3837 Northdale Blvd Ste 368, Tampa, FL 33624
Tel.: (813) 639-8658
Web Site: http://www.ww-consult.com
Year Founded: 2004
Sales Range: $1-9.9 Million
Emp.: 65
Management Consulting Services
N.A.I.C.S.: 541611
Lauren G. Weiner *(Founder & Pres)*
Donna S. Huneycutt *(Exec VP)*
Joe Osborne *(Dir-Defense Practice)*

WITTIGS OFFICE INTERIORS LTD.
2013 Broadway St, San Antonio, TX 78215
Tel.: (210) 270-0100
Web Site: http://www.wittigs.com
Sales Range: $10-24.9 Million
Emp.: 50
Office Furniture
N.A.I.C.S.: 423210
Mark Wittig *(Owner & Pres)*

WITTS FOODS INC.
214 N Hwy 141, Crivitz, WI 54114
Tel.: (715) 854-2115
Web Site: http://www.wittspigglywiggly.com
Sales Range: $10-24.9 Million
Emp.: 100
Independent Supermarket
N.A.I.C.S.: 445320
Nicholas Witt *(Owner)*
John Witt *(Co-Owner)*

WIXON INDUSTRIES INC.
1390 E Bolivar Ave, Saint Francis, WI 53235-4506
Tel.: (414) 769-3000 WI
Web Site: http://www.wixon.com
Year Founded: 1980
Sales Range: $25-49.9 Million
Emp.: 215
Food Preparations
N.A.I.C.S.: 311942
A. Peter Gottsacker *(CEO)*
Peter Caputa *(COO)*
Patrick McGarry *(CFO)*

WIZARD SOFTWARE SOLUTIONS INCORPORATED
4147 N Ravenswood Ste 400, Chicago, IL 60613
Tel.: (773) 832-0200
Web Site: http://www.facilitywizard.com
Year Founded: 1996
Sales Range: $1-9.9 Million
Emp.: 24
Software Publisher
N.A.I.C.S.: 513210
Dave Johnson *(Pres)*
Mark Sorich *(VP-Sls & Mktg)*
Scott Karch *(Dir-IT)*

WIZEHIVE, INC.
555 E North Ln Ste 5030A, Conshohocken, PA 19428
Web Site: http://www.wizehive.com
Year Founded: 2008
Sales Range: $1-9.9 Million
Emp.: 50
Application Software Development Services
N.A.I.C.S.: 541511
Mike Levinson *(Founder & Chm)*
Carl Guarino *(CEO)*
Kristen Knouft *(CMO)*
Steve Reid *(VP-Sls)*
Kendra Muscella *(VP-Client Svcs)*

WJ PARTNERS, LLC
100 Dunbar St Ste 202, Spartanburg, SC 29306
Tel.: (864) 594-5709 DE
Web Site: http://www.wjpartners.com
Year Founded: 2008
Privater Equity Firm
N.A.I.C.S.: 523999
Benjamin Wall *(Mng Partner)*
Jaime Wall *(Mng Dir)*
Rhett McCraw *(VP)*

Subsidiaries:

Power Utility Products Company (1)
8710 Air Park W Dr Ste 100, Charlotte, NC 28214
Tel.: (704) 741-5138
Web Site: http://www.pupco.com
Rev.: $7,000,000
Emp.: 16
Electrical Apparatus & Equipment, Wiring Supplies & Related Equipment Merchant Whslr
N.A.I.C.S.: 423610
Ralph Turnege *(Pres)*

Subsidiary (Domestic):

NAPAC, Inc. (2)
229 Southbridge St, Worcester, MA 01608
Tel.: (508) 363-4411
Web Site: http://www.napacinc.com
Rev.: $8,000,000
Emp.: 15
Plumbing & Heating Equipment & Supplies, Hydronics, Merchant Whslr
N.A.I.C.S.: 423720
Norman Romano *(Pres)*
Patricia A. Melick *(Mgr-Acctg)*
Charlie W. Roche *(VP-Sls)*
Brian Wilbur *(VP & Gen Mgr)*
Dave Keddy *(Mgr-Warehouse & Logistics)*

WJW ASSOCIATES, LTD.
6417 Deere Rd, Syracuse, NY 13206
Tel.: (315) 432-9282
Web Site: http://www.wjwltd.com
Rev.: $12,700,000
Emp.: 70
Trucking Service
N.A.I.C.S.: 484110
Robet K. Fresh *(Pres)*

WJW ENTERPRISES SAN DIEGO INC.
1240 Simpson Way, Escondido, CA 92029
Tel.: (760) 746-4800
Web Site: http://www.takeabreakservice.com
Year Founded: 1973
Rev.: $22,000,000
Emp.: 10
Food Vending Machines
N.A.I.C.S.: 445132

WJYY
NH Media Ct 4 Church St, Concord, NH 03106
Tel.: (603) 230-9000
Web Site: http://www.wjyy.com
Radio Stations
N.A.I.C.S.: 516110

WKO INVESTMENTS INC.
1203 NW Jefferson Ct, Blue Springs, MO 64015
Tel.: (816) 224-5705
Sales Range: $25-49.9 Million
Emp.: 1,100
Holding Company
N.A.I.C.S.: 551112
William Wrisinger *(CEO)*
Gary Koepke *(COO)*
Lori Moon *(Dir-HR)*

WLMD
1715 Kibby Rd, Merced, CA 95341
Tel.: (209) 723-9120
Web Site: http://www.wlmd.com
Rev.: $24,000,000
Emp.: 130
Commercial Fluorescent Lighting Fixtures
N.A.I.C.S.: 332322
Jerry Yon *(Controller)*

WLOFM, CORP.
1109 N Ohio Ave, Live Oak, FL 32060
Tel.: (386) 362-1112
Sales Range: $10-24.9 Million
Emp.: 50
Car Whslr
N.A.I.C.S.: 441110
Sabrina Cherry *(Principal)*
Walter Bryan *(CEO)*

WLP ENERGY SERVICES, LLC
2851 State Hwy 214, Denver City, TX 79323
Tel.: (806) 592-3113
Sales Range: $10-24.9 Million
Emp.: 120
Oil Field Services
N.A.I.C.S.: 213112
Wayne Harper *(Mng Partner)*

WLS STAMPING & FABRICATING CO.
3292 E 80th St, Cleveland, OH 44104
Tel.: (216) 271-5100
Web Site: http://www.wlsstamping.com
Sales Range: $25-49.9 Million
Emp.: 100
Metal Stamping Services
N.A.I.C.S.: 332119

WLS STAMPING & FABRICATING CO.

WLS Stamping & Fabricating Co.—(Continued)
Daniel C. Cronin (Chm)
Craig Kotnik (VP-Engrg)
Keith DeVaul (VP-Quality Assurance)
Sue Nash (Controller-Fin)

WLX, LLC
1401 Iron St, Kansas City, MO 64116
Tel.: (816) 746-2800
Web Site: http://www.wlxtrans.com
Year Founded: 2004
Rev.: $24,200,000
Emp.: 128
Logistics & Transportation
N.A.I.C.S.: 541614
Michael Murrell (VP-Ops)

WM OHS INC.
5095 Peoria St, Denver, CO 80239
Tel.: (303) 371-6550 CO
Web Site: http://www.wmohs.com
Year Founded: 1972
Sales Range: $50-74.9 Million
Emp.: 100
Mfr of Wood Cabinets
N.A.I.C.S.: 337110
Bob Cilli (Pres)
Lee Puckett (Mgr-HR)
Rick Casey (VP-Ops)

WM PARTNERS LP
1815 Griffin Rd Ste 404, Fort Lauderdale, FL 33004
Tel.: (754) 260-6500
Web Site: http://www.wmplp.com
Year Founded: 2015
Privater Equity Firm
N.A.I.C.S.: 523999
Jose Minski (Co-Founder)

Subsidiaries:

Allergy Research Group LLC (1)
2300 South Main St S, Salt Lake City, UT 84115
Tel.: (510) 263-2000
Web Site:
  http://www.allergyresearchgroup.com
Nutritional Services
N.A.I.C.S.: 722310
Tim Gerke (Pres)

WM T. BURNETT & CO.
1500 Bush St, Baltimore, MD 21230-1928
Tel.: (410) 837-3000 MD
Web Site: http://www.wmtburnett.com
Year Founded: 1898
Sales Range: $25-49.9 Million
Emp.: 550
Mfr of Foam & Nonwovens
N.A.I.C.S.: 326150

Subsidiaries:

STX, LLC (1)
1500 Bush St, Baltimore, MD 21230-1928 (100%)
Tel.: (410) 837-2022
Web Site: http://www.stx.com
Sales Range: $10-24.9 Million
Emp.: 40
Sporting & Athletic Goods
N.A.I.C.S.: 339920
Jessica Bieber (Mgr-Category Brand-Women's Lacrosse)
Nate Cundy (Asst Mgr-Mktg-Digital Comm)
Caitlin Walker (Assoc Mgr-Field Hockey Product)
Spencer Stevens (Product Mgr-Men's Lacrosse Dept)

Wm T. Burnett & Co. - Foam Division (1)
2112 Montevideo Rd, Jessup, MD 20794
Tel.: (410) 799-1788
Web Site: http://www.wtbfoam.com
Polystyrene Foam Product Mfr
N.A.I.C.S.: 326140

Wm T. Burnett & Co. - Nonwovens Division (1)
2550 W Front St, Statesville, NC 28677
Tel.: (704) 872-2477
Web Site: http://www.williamtburnett.com
Nonwoven Fabric Mfr
N.A.I.C.S.: 313230

WM. BLANCHARD CO.
199 Mountain Ave, Springfield, NJ 07081-1755
Tel.: (973) 376-9100 NJ
Web Site:
  http://www.wmblanchard.com
Year Founded: 1860
Sales Range: $75-99.9 Million
Emp.: 90
Hospital & Office Building Construction
N.A.I.C.S.: 236220
Jeff Kinder (Mgr-IT)
Pat Cochran (Dir-Safety)
Mike Nervine (Project Mgr)
Carl MacDonald (Project Mgr)

WM. F. MCDONOUGH PLUMBING, INC.
6468 Parkland Dr, Sarasota, FL 34243
Tel.: (941) 753-6436 FL
Web Site:
  http://www.mcdonoughplumbing.com
Year Founded: 1946
Sales Range: $1-9.9 Million
Emp.: 65
Plumbing, Heating & Air-Conditioning Contractors
N.A.I.C.S.: 238220
Donald McDonough (Owner & Pres)

Subsidiaries:

McDonough Contracting Services (1)
6468 Parkland Dr, Sarasota, FL 34243
Tel.: (941) 753-6436
Plumbing Contracting
N.A.I.C.S.: 238220

McDonough Fire Service (1)
6468 Parkland Dr, Sarasota, FL 34243
Tel.: (941) 753-6436
Web Site:
  http://www.mcdonoughplumbing.com
Emp.: 60
Fire Repression Systems Installation
N.A.I.C.S.: 922160
Donald McDonough (Pres)

McDonough Plumbing Service (1)
6468 Parkland Dr, Sarasota, FL 34243
Tel.: (941) 753-6436
Plumbing Services
N.A.I.C.S.: 238220

WM. K. WALTHERS, INC.
5601 W Florist Ave, Milwaukee, WI 53218
Tel.: (414) 527-0770
Web Site: http://www.walthers.com
Rev.: $12,300,000
Emp.: 130
Toy & Hobby Goods & Supplies Merchant Whslr
N.A.I.C.S.: 423920
Philip J. Walthers (Pres)
Stacey Naffah (VP-Mktg)
Patricia Ayer (Mgr-Fin)

WMCR CO. LLC
1035 W Washington Ave, Alpena, MI 49707
Tel.: (989) 356-3048 MI
Year Founded: 1992
Sales Range: $10-24.9 Million
Emp.: 8
Holding Company; Franchise Fast Food Restaurants Owner & Operator
N.A.I.C.S.: 551112
Tim Fitzpatrick (Pres)
Doug Horne (CFO)

WMI LIQUIDATING TRUST
800 Fifth Ave Ste 4100, Seattle, WA 98104
Tel.: (206) 922-2956 DE
Year Founded: 2012
Holding Company
N.A.I.C.S.: 551112
John Maciel (CFO & Exec VP)
Charles Edward Smith (Gen Counsel, Sec & Exec VP)
Doreen Logan (Treas, Exec VP & Controller)

WMS SALES INC.
9580 County Rd, Clarence Center, NY 14032
Tel.: (716) 741-9575
Web Site: http://www.wmssales.com
Year Founded: 1959
Sales Range: $10-24.9 Million
Emp.: 15
Plumbing & Hydronic Heating Supplies
N.A.I.C.S.: 423720
Randy Schaefer (Pres)
Paul Schaefer (CEO)
Shelly DiGiacomo (Gen Mgr)
Bryan Schaefer (VP)
Bill Sestak (VP-Sls)

WNC CORPORATION
180 N Stetson Ave, Chicago, IL 60601-6710
Tel.: (312) 819-1825
Year Founded: 1986
Rev.: $16,700,000
Emp.: 477
Holding Company
N.A.I.C.S.: 541611

Subsidiaries:

Universal Manufacturing Company (1)
5450 Deramus Ave, Kansas City, MO 64120-1202
Tel.: (816) 231-2771
Web Site: http://www.umcprint.com
Mfr of Paper-Based Small Games of Chance; Manufacturer of Jar Tickets, Pull Tabs, Punch Boards, Tip Boards & Match Packs
N.A.I.C.S.: 323111
Delbert Coleman (Owner & Chm)

WNC PALLET & FOREST PRODUCTS CO.
1414 Smokey Park Hwy, Candler, NC 28715
Tel.: (828) 667-5426
Sales Range: $10-24.9 Million
Emp.: 80
Wood Products Mfr
N.A.I.C.S.: 321920
Jennie Matthews (Office Mgr)

WNC REAL ESTATE
707 N Green St, Morganton, NC 28655
Tel.: (828) 544-5290 NC
Web Site:
  http://www.wncrealestateinc.com
Year Founded: 2007
Rev.: $4,061,002
Fiscal Year-end: 06/30/14
Real Estate Management Services
N.A.I.C.S.: 531390
Graham Keever (Pres & Treas)
Sheryl Aikman (Sec & VP)

WNDRCO HOLDINGS, LLC
9355 Wilshire Blvd Ste 400, Beverly Hills, CA 90210
Tel.: (424) 363-3066 DE
Web Site: http://www.wndrco.com
Year Founded: 2016
Holding Company
N.A.I.C.S.: 551112

U.S. PRIVATE

Andrew Chang (Gen Partner & Gen Counsel)

Subsidiaries:

WC SACD One, Inc. (1)
15 Network Dr, Burlington, MA 01803
Tel.: (617) 818-1887
Vehicle Company
N.A.I.C.S.: 523940

Subsidiary (Domestic):

Intersections Inc. (2)
2553 Dulles View Dr 4th Fl, Herndon, VA 20171
Tel.: (703) 488-6100
Web Site: http://www.auracompany.com
Identity Management Solutions
N.A.I.C.S.: 518210
Stephen Ruggieri (VP-Partner Solutions)

Subsidiary (Domestic):

American Background Services, Inc. (3)
629 Cedar Creek Grade Ste C, Winchester, VA 22601
Tel.: (540) 665-8056
Web Site:
  http://www.americanbackground.com
Sales Range: $100-124.9 Million
Background Screening
N.A.I.C.S.: 561611

Captira Analytical, LLC (3)
3 E Comm Sq 11 Pruyn St, Albany, NY 12207
Tel.: (518) 312-4163
Web Site: http://www.captira.com
Sales Range: $10-24.9 Million
Emp.: 20
Software & Automated Service Solutions for Bail Bond Industry
N.A.I.C.S.: 513210
Steven Alan Sjoblad (Chm & CEO)

Intersections Insurance Services Inc. (3)
315 W University Dr, Arlington Heights, IL 60004-1811
Tel.: (847) 797-8500
Web Site:
  http://www.intersectionsinsurance.com
Insurance Brokerage Services
N.A.I.C.S.: 524210

Net Enforcers, Inc. (3)
2633 E Indian School Rd Ste 270, Phoenix, AZ 85016
Tel.: (270) 721-5491
Web Site: http://www.netenforcers.com
Sales Range: $10-24.9 Million
Emp.: 25
Brand Protection Services
N.A.I.C.S.: 541519

i4c Innovations Inc. (3)
3800 Concorde Pkwy Ste 400, Chantilly, VA 20151
Tel.: (703) 961-6596
Web Site: http://www.voyce.com
Animal Production Services
N.A.I.C.S.: 112990

WNET
825 8th Ave, New York, NY 10019
Tel.: (212) 560-2000
Web Site: http://www.wnet.org
Sales Range: $125-149.9 Million
Emp.: 550
Television Broadcasting Services
N.A.I.C.S.: 516120
Neal B. Shapiro (Pres & CEO)
Stephen Segaller (VP-Programming)
Charlene Shapiro (VP-HR)
Roslyn Davis (VP-Media & Broadcast Ops & Gen Mgr-Thirteen)
Daniel Greenberg (Chief Digital Officer)
Robert Feinberg (Gen Counsel, Sec & VP)
Caroline C. Croen (CFO, Treas & VP)
John Servidio (VP-Subsidiary Stations & Gen Mgr-NJTV)
Carole Wacey (VP-Education)

COMPANIES

Diane Masciale *(VP & Gen Mgr-WLIW)*
Cheryl Milstein *(Vice Chm)*
Eugenia Harvey *(Chief Diversity, Equity & Inclusion Officer)*
Edgar Wachenheim III *(Chm)*

Subsidiaries:

Long Island Educational TV Council, Inc. (1)
WLIW 21 1 Channel 21 Dr, Plainview, NY 11803
Tel.: (516) 367-2100
Web Site: http://www.wliw.org
Sales Range: $10-24.9 Million
Emp.: 60
Operator of Television Broadcasting Stations
N.A.I.C.S.: 811210

WNR INC.
5740 Big River Dr, The Colony, TX 75056
Tel.: (972) 741-9770
Web Site: http://www.wnrinc.net
Year Founded: 2005
Sales Range: $1-9.9 Million
Emp.: 19
Roofer & Roofing Material Distribution
N.A.I.C.S.: 238160
Kimberly May *(Pres)*

WOBURN FOREIGN MOTORS INC.
394 Washington St, Woburn, MA 01801
Tel.: (781) 933-1100
Web Site: http://www.wobfm.com
Rev.: $107,994,497
Emp.: 108
New & Used Automobiles
N.A.I.C.S.: 441110
George T Albrecht *(Pres)*
Martin Phillips *(Mgr-Internet Sls & Coord-Mktg & Media)*
Jack Motzi *(Mgr-Used Car)*

WODA GROUP INC.
229 Huber Village Blvd Ste 100, Westerville, OH 43081
Tel.: (614) 396-3200
Web Site: http://www.wodagroup.com
Year Founded: 1990
Sales Range: $10-24.9 Million
Emp.: 20
Developers, General Contractors & Property Management
N.A.I.C.S.: 236116
Jeffrey J. Woda *(Founder & Principal)*
Aaron Buehrer *(Project Mgr)*
Garrett LeDonne *(VP-Fin)*
Bryan Ridge *(Controller)*
David Cooper Jr. *(Principal)*

WODA MANAGEMENT & REAL ESTATE, LLC.
229 Huber Village Blvd Ste 100, Westerville, OH 43081
Tel.: (614) 396-3200
Sales Range: $75-99.9 Million
Emp.: 20
Residential Construction Services
N.A.I.C.S.: 236118
Jodelle Carder *(Sr VP-Ops)*
Jeffery J. Woda *(Founder)*

WOEBER MUSTARD MANUFACTURING COMPANY
1966 Commerce Cir, Springfield, OH 45501-0388
Tel.: (937) 323-6281
Web Site: http://www.woebermustard.com
Year Founded: 1905
Sales Range: $10-24.9 Million
Emp.: 128
Mustard Recipe Mfr

N.A.I.C.S.: 311941
Ray Woeber *(Pres & CEO)*
Dick Woeber *(VP-Comml & Private Label Sls)*
Rick Schmidt *(VP-Natl Sls Retail, Food Svc & Distr Sls)*
Bob Sharp *(Mgr-Logistics)*
Judy Finnegan *(Mgr-HR)*
Randy Weyant *(Dir-Quality Control)*
Christopher Woeber *(Mgr-Ops)*
Kevin Nugent *(Dir-Supply Chain)*
Dale Ulrich *(Supvr-Maintenance)*
Nate Golden *(Dir-Pur)*

WOERNER HOLDINGS INC.
Phillips Point E Twr 777 S Flagler Dr Ste 1100, West Palm Beach, FL 33401
Tel.: (561) 835-3747   FL
Year Founded: 1998
Sales Range: $25-49.9 Million
Emp.: 350
Produces & Distributes Ornamental Nursery Products
N.A.I.C.S.: 111422
Kathy Miller *(Pres)*
Chris Gryskiewicz *(CFO)*

Subsidiaries:

Woerner South Inc. (1)
275 SW 3rd Ave, South Bay, FL 33493
Tel.: (561) 835-3747
Rev.: $14,379,735
Emp.: 20
Ornamental Nursery Products
N.A.I.C.S.: 111422

Woerner Turf Group Inc. (1)
275 Sw 3rd Ave, South Bay, FL 33493-2221
Tel.: (561) 835-3747
Rev.: $13,750,325
Emp.: 1
Ornamental Nursery Products
N.A.I.C.S.: 111422

WOHLSEN CONSTRUCTION COMPANY
548 Steel Way, Lancaster, PA 17604-7066
Tel.: (717) 299-2500   PA
Web Site: http://www.wohlsenconstruction.com
Year Founded: 1890
Sales Range: $125-149.9 Million
Emp.: 375
Nonresidential Construction Services
N.A.I.C.S.: 236220
J. Gary Langmuir *(Pres & CEO)*
R. Edward Gordon *(CFO & Exec VP)*
Michael B. Funck *(Sr VP)*
Kenneth D. Noreen *(Sr VP)*
Jeff Sturla *(VP-Bus Dev)*
Gerald J. Clinton *(Superintendent)*
Nicole L. Geary *(Project Engr-Dev-Oakwood Hills)*
Kevin Ream *(Mgr-Mechanical, Electrical & Plumbing Preconstruction)*
Mike Pluta *(Sr Project Mgr-Wilbur Chocolate Building Redevelopment)*
John K. Ball *(COO & Exec VP)*
Michael B. Berardi *(Sr VP)*
David B. Brodie *(Sr VP)*
Gregory Gutierrez *(Sr VP)*
Mauro Rubbo *(Reg VP-Connecticut Ops & North Jersey Ops)*

WOHLT CHEESE CORPORATION
1005 Orville Dr, New London, WI 54961
Tel.: (920) 982-9000
Web Site: http://www.wohltcheese.com
Sales Range: $10-24.9 Million
Emp.: 50
Processed Cheese
N.A.I.C.S.: 311513

Marilyn Taylor *(Pres)*

WOJAN WINDOW & DOOR CORPORATION
217 Stover Rd, Charlevoix, MI 49720
Tel.: (231) 547-2931   MI
Web Site: http://www.wojan.com
Year Founded: 1952
Sales Range: $10-24.9 Million
Emp.: 150
Mfr of Commercial Windows & Doors
N.A.I.C.S.: 332321
Dennis Wojan *(Pres)*
Alice Pletz-Miller *(Mgr-Acctg)*

WOJCIK BUILDERS, INC.
7579 First Pl, Oakwood Village, OH 44146
Tel.: (440) 786-1776   OH
Web Site: http://www.wojcikbuilders.com
Year Founded: 1983
Sales Range: $1-9.9 Million
Emp.: 24
Building Contractors
N.A.I.C.S.: 236220
Nick Childs *(Owner & Pres)*
Jamie Childs *(VP)*
Doug Rich *(Project Mgr)*
Tim Skala *(Project Mgr)*

WOL DIRECT
925 Oak St, Scranton, PA 18515-0999
Tel.: (570) 342-7701
Web Site: http://www.pennfoster.edu
Year Founded: 1890
Rev.: $18,000,000
Emp.: 35
N.A.I.C.S.: 541810
Mary Ann Riccardella *(Sr Media Buyer)*
Kathy McIlwee *(Dir-Mktg)*
Staurt Udell *(CEO)*
Michelle Dempsey *(Internet Media Planner)*
Raymond J. McNulty *(Sr VP-Intl Center)*

WOLBERG ELECTRICAL SUPPLY CO. INC
35 Industrial Pk Rd, Albany, NY 12206-0309
Tel.: (518) 489-8451
Web Site: http://www.wolberg.com
Sales Range: $10-24.9 Million
Emp.: 75
Electrical Supplies
N.A.I.C.S.: 423610
Paul Trawinski *(Gen Mgr)*
Jay Bindell *(Pres)*
Richard Keeler *(Dir-Mgmt Info Sys)*

WOLCOTT ARCHITECTURE INTERIORS
3859 Cardiff Ave, Culver City, CA 90232
Tel.: (310) 204-2290
Web Site: http://www.wolcottai.com
Year Founded: 1975
Sales Range: $1-9.9 Million
Emp.: 50
Architectural & Interior Design Services
N.A.I.C.S.: 541410
A. J. Wilder *(Pres)*
Amanda Kaleps *(Principal)*
Scott Johnson *(Principal-Design)*

WOLCOTT BANCORP
105 N Range St, Wolcott, IN 47995
Tel.: (219) 279-2185   IN
Web Site: http://www.bankofwolcott.com
Year Founded: 1983
Bank Holding Company

WOLF RIVER BANCORP, INC.

N.A.I.C.S.: 551111
Kevin M. Bender *(Pres)*

Subsidiaries:

Bank of Wolcott (1)
105 N Range St, Wolcott, IN 47995
Tel.: (219) 279-2185
Web Site: http://www.bankofwolcott.com
Commercial Banking
N.A.I.C.S.: 522110
Kevin M. Bender *(Pres)*

WOLD ARCHITECTS, INC.
332 Minnesota St Ste W2000, Saint Paul, MN 55101
Tel.: (651) 227-7773   MN
Web Site: http://www.woldae.com
Year Founded: 1968
Architectural Services
N.A.I.C.S.: 541310
Paul Aplikowski *(Partner)*
Sal Bagley *(Architect)*
Matt Bickel *(Partner)*

WOLDE FLOORING, LLC
8751 Hwy 72 West, Madison, AL 35758
Tel.: (256) 325-8453
Web Site: http://www.woldeflooring.com
Sales Range: $1-9.9 Million
Emp.: 15
Floor Covering Specialists
N.A.I.C.S.: 449121
Terry Wolde *(CEO, Co-Owner & Mgr-Wholesale Sls)*
Leon Wink *(Co-Owner & Mgr-Ops & Projects)*

WOLF MANUFACTURING COMPANY
1801 W Waco Dr, Waco, TX 76707
Tel.: (254) 753-7301   TX
Web Site: http://www.worldsbesttravelpillows.com
Emp.: 200
Blanket & Travel Pillows Mfr & Whslr
N.A.I.C.S.: 313210
Abby Silver *(Pres)*

WOLF MOTOR COMPANY INC.
600 W 2nd St, Jordan, MN 55352
Tel.: (952) 492-2340
Web Site: http://www.wolfmotorcompany.com
Sales Range: $10-24.9 Million
Emp.: 54
New Car Whslr
N.A.I.C.S.: 441110
Tim Rajewsky *(Gen Mgr-Sls)*
Char Wolf *(VP)*

WOLF RIVER BANCORP, INC.
309 E Main St, Hortonville, WI 54944-9451
Tel.: (920) 779-7000   WI
Web Site: http://www.wolfriverbank.com
Year Founded: 2003
Sales Range: $1-9.9 Million
Bank Holding Company
N.A.I.C.S.: 551111
Joseph Peikert *(Pres & CEO)*
Miranda Schultz *(CFO)*

Subsidiaries:

Wolf River Community Bank (1)
309 E Main St, Hortonville, WI 54944
Tel.: (920) 779-7000
Web Site: http://www.wolfriverbank.com
Sales Range: $1-9.9 Million
Emp.: 39
Commericial Banking
N.A.I.C.S.: 522110
Joseph Peikert *(Pres & CEO)*
William Kedinger *(VP-Lending)*
Janice A. Young *(VP-Admin)*
Karen Duch *(VP-Lending)*

WOLF RIVER BANCORP, INC.   U.S. PRIVATE

Wolf River Bancorp, Inc.—(Continued)
Jason Bloxham (*Chief Lending Officer & Exec VP*)
Robbie Miller (*VP-Acctg & Ops*)
Chelsea Hanson (*VP-Compliance*)
Jeff Myster (*VP-Retail Banking*)
Miranda Schultz (*CFO*)

WOLFBONE MARKETING
3455 Peachtree Rd NE Ste 600, Atlanta, GA 30326
Tel.: (404) 995-4620
Year Founded: 2004
Sales Range: Less than $1 Million
Emp.: 6
N.A.I.C.S.: 541810
Chuck Wolf (*CEO*)
Jerry Carbone (*Pres & Partner*)
Amanda Swain (*Acct Mgr*)
Jessica Lambert (*Dir-Creative*)

WOLFE & TRAVIS ELECTRIC COMPANY, INC.
2001 Gladstone Ave, Nashville, TN 37211-2009
Tel.: (615) 244-6800
Web Site: http://www.wolfeandtraviselectric.com
Sales Range: $25-49.9 Million
Emp.: 140
Electrical Wiring Services
N.A.I.C.S.: 238210
Tracy Potts (*Principal*)

WOLFE DYE & BLEACH WORKS INC.
25 Rdg Rd, Shoemakersville, PA 19555
Tel.: (610) 562-7639
Sales Range: $10-24.9 Million
Emp.: 46
Dyeing: Raw Stock, Yarn & Narrow Fabrics
N.A.I.C.S.: 313310
Andrew Wolfe (*Pres*)
Mark Wolfe (*Sec*)

WOLFE ENGINEERING INC.
3040 N 1st St, San Jose, CA 95134
Tel.: (408) 232-2600
Web Site: http://www.e-wolfe.com
Sales Range: $75-99.9 Million
Emp.: 140
Fabricated Pipe & Fittings
N.A.I.C.S.: 332996
Rita Wolfe (*VP*)
Ken Kostlan (*Engr-Mfg & Mgr-Facility*)
Brad Durrett (*Mgr-Production*)
Marco Anton Cua (*Engr-Mechanical Design*)
Carlos Prado (*Engr-Mfg*)
Tom Bissett (*COO & Dir-Engrg*)
Brad Ventres (*Dir-Matls*)
John Wolfe (*Pres & CEO*)

WOLFE INDUSTRIES, INC.
14420 Marquardt Ave, Santa Fe Springs, CA 90670-5119
Tel.: (562) 921-2202
Web Site: http://www.wolfeindustries.net
Metal Crown, Closure & Metal Stamping
N.A.I.C.S.: 332119
Charles Wolfe (*Owner*)

WOLFE/DOYLE ADVERTISING
36 W 34th St 5th Fl, New York, NY 10001
Tel.: (212) 244-9050
Web Site: http://www.wolfedoyle.com
Sales Range: Less than $1 Million
Emp.: 10
Advetising Agency

N.A.I.C.S.: 541810
Daniel Wolfe (*Pres*)

WOLFENSON ELECTRIC, INC.
7902 Cowart, Houston, TX 77029-4106
Tel.: (713) 676-1201
Web Site: http://www.wolfenson.com
Year Founded: 1959
Rev: $14,765,795
Emp.: 300
Electrical Contracting Services
N.A.I.C.S.: 238210
Amando Gonzalez (*VP*)
Rocky Revia (*CEO*)

Subsidiaries:
Civil Mechanical Inc. (1)
430 W Plantation Dr, Clute, TX 77531
Tel.: (979) 265-0655
Web Site: http://www.wolfenson.com
Industrial Buildings, New Construction
N.A.I.C.S.: 236210

WOLFF BROTHERS SUPPLY, INC.
6078 Wolff Rd, Medina, OH 44256-9487
Tel.: (330) 725-3451   OH
Web Site: http://www.wolfbros.com
Year Founded: 1950
Sales Range: $25-49.9 Million
Emp.: 255
Sales of Electrical Apparatus & Equipment
N.A.I.C.S.: 423610
Howard Wolff (*Pres*)
Jeff Wolff (*Controller-Fin*)
George Wolff (*VP*)

WOLFF SHOE COMPANY INC.
1705 Larkin Williams Rd, Fenton, MO 63026-2024
Tel.: (636) 343-7770   MO
Web Site: http://www.wolffshoe.com
Year Founded: 1918
Sales Range: $10-24.9 Million
Emp.: 124
Provider of Footwear
N.A.I.C.S.: 424340
William Wolff (*Chm*)

WOLFF URBAN MANAGEMENT, INC.
11828 La Grange Ave Ste 200, Los Angeles, CA 90025-5212
Tel.: (310) 477-3593   CA
Web Site: http://www.wolffurban.com
Year Founded: 1971
Commercial Real Estate Investment, Development & Management Services
N.A.I.C.S.: 531312
Lewis N, Wolff (*Chm & CEO*)
Michael Mao (*Dir-Acctg & Controller*)

Subsidiaries:
Wolff Urban Development, LLC (1)
11828 La Grange Ave Ste 200, Los Angeles, CA 90025
Tel.: (310) 477-3593
Web Site: http://www.wolffurban.com
Sales Range: $25-49.9 Million
Emp.: 33
Commercial Real Estate Investment & Development Services
N.A.I.C.S.: 531390
Lewis N. Wolff (*Chm & CEO*)
Keith M. Wolff (*Pres*)
Sharyl Gabriel (*CFO & COO*)
Ross H. Walker (*Partner*)
Adam Keller (*Partner*)
Timothy Groff (*Sr VP-Ops*)
David Cornish (*Pres-Hotel Ops*)
Guy S. Wolff (*VP-Property Mgmt*)
Simone Kaltgrad (*VP-Tech*)

WOLFINGTON BODY COMPANY, INC.
30 N Pottstown Pke, Exton, PA 19341
Tel.: (610) 458-8501   PA
Web Site: http://www.wolfington.com
Year Founded: 1876
Sales Range: $100-124.9 Million
Emp.: 100
Distr of School & Commercial Buses, Ambulances & Funeral Cars & Limousines
N.A.I.C.S.: 441227
Richard I. Wolfington (*Pres*)
Dane Colestock (*VP & Dir-Facilities*)
Frank K. Dutcher III (*Sr VP*)

WOLFKILL FEED & FERTILIZER CORPORATION
217 E Stretch St, Monroe, WA 98272
Tel.: (360) 794-7065   WA
Year Founded: 1938
Sales Range: $10-24.9 Million
Emp.: 36
Mfr of Fertilizers
N.A.I.C.S.: 325314
Mary Wolfkill (*Pres*)

WOLFRAM RESEARCH INC.
100 Trade Centre Dr, Champaign, IL 61820
Tel.: (217) 398-0700
Web Site: http://www.wolfram.com
Year Founded: 1987
Sales Range: $10-24.9 Million
Emp.: 500
Computer Software Development
N.A.I.C.S.: 541511
Stephen Wolfram (*Founder & CEO*)

Subsidiaries:
Wolfram Alpha LLC (1)
100 Trade Ctr Dr, Champaign, IL 61820
Tel.: (217) 398-0700
Web Site: http://www.wolframalpha.com
Computer Software
N.A.I.C.S.: 513210
Stephen Wolfram (*Founder & CEO*)

WOLFSON CASING CORP.
700 S Fulton Ave, Mount Vernon, NY 10550
Tel.: (914) 668-9000
Web Site: http://www.wolfsoncasing.com
Sales Range: $25-49.9 Million
Emp.: 87
Sausage Casings Mfr
N.A.I.C.S.: 424490
Stephen Bardfield (*COO*)

Subsidiaries:
Casing Associates LLC (1)
1120 Close Ave, Bronx, NY 10472
Tel.: (718) 842-7151
Sales Range: $10-24.9 Million
Emp.: 30
Other Grocery & Related Products Merchant Whslr
N.A.I.C.S.: 424490

WOLFTRAP FOUNDATION FOR THE PERFORMING ARTS
1645 Trap Rd, Vienna, VA 22182
Tel.: (703) 255-1900
Web Site: http://www.wolftrap.org
Year Founded: 1966
Sales Range: $10-24.9 Million
Emp.: 80
Theater Building Owner & Operator
N.A.I.C.S.: 711320
Christopher J. Eckert (*Sr Dir-Ops*)
Kim Pensinger Witman (*Sr Dir-Opera*)
Beth Brummel (*VP-External Affairs*)

Hillary D. Baltimore (*Vice Chm & Sec*)
Melania Trump (*Co-Chm*)
Daniel A. D'Aniello (*Co-Chm*)

WOLGAST CORPORATION
1494 N Graham Rd, Freeland, MI 48623-8832
Tel.: (989) 790-9120   MI
Web Site: http://www.wolgastcorporation.com
Year Founded: 1947
Sales Range: $50-74.9 Million
Emp.: 95
Provider of Construction Services
N.A.I.C.S.: 236220
Brian Stadler (*Pres*)
Steve Salyers (*VP-Construction Mgmt*)
James C. Lehman (*Project Mgr-Design & Build-Gen Construction*)
Rich Ramsey (*Dir-Educational Facilities*)
Marc Rummler (*Dir-HR*)
Steve Seibert (*VP-Contract Mgmt*)

WOLTCOM, INC.
650 San Benito St Ste 230, Hollister, CA 95023
Tel.: (831) 638-4900
Web Site: http://www.woltcom.com
Year Founded: 1966
Sales Range: $10-24.9 Million
Emp.: 130
Communications Equipment Installer
N.A.I.C.S.: 238210
Mona Wolters (*Pres*)
Kimberly Morgan (*Exec VP*)
Steve Johnson (*Mgr-WOLTCOM*)

Subsidiaries:
Woltcom, Inc. - Eastern Division (1)
19641 Parthenia Ste 202, Northridge, CA 91324
Tel.: (818) 993-8066
Installer of Communications Equipment
N.A.I.C.S.: 423840

WOLTER GROUP LLC
3125 Intertech Dr, Brookfield, WI 53045
Tel.: (262) 781-8010   WI
Web Site: http://www.woltergroupllc.com
Year Founded: 2011
Industrial Machinery & Equipment Whslr
N.A.I.C.S.: 423830
Otto J. Wolter (*Founder & CEO*)
Steve Kletzien (*CFO*)
Jerry Weidmann (*Pres*)
Martin Park (*COO*)
Kristin Lelewicz (*CMO*)
Julie Williams (*CIO*)
Kim Wachs (*Chief HR Officer*)

Subsidiaries:
A D Lift Truck (1)
5434 Natural Bridge Ave, Saint Louis, MO 63120
Tel.: (314) 389-1700
Web Site: http://www.adlifttruck.com
Rev: $9,516,000
Emp.: 52
Consumer Electronics & Appliances Rental
N.A.I.C.S.: 532210
Rudy Dodorico (*Pres & CEO*)
Gus Dodorico (*VP*)

Bohnert International, Inc. (1)
1010 S 9th St, Louisville, KY 40203
Tel.: (502) 584-3391
Industrial Machinery & Equipment Merchant Whslr
N.A.I.C.S.: 423830

WOLVERINE BUILDING GROUP

4045 Barden St SE, Grand Rapids, MI 49512-5447
Tel.: (616) 949-3360 MI
Web Site: http://www.wolvgroup.com
Year Founded: 1939
Builder of Industrial Buildings
N.A.I.C.S.: 236220
Curt Mulder *(Co-Pres)*
Aaron Jonker *(Co-Pres)*
Mike Houseman *(Pres-North America Div)*
Bill Pursifull *(VP)*
Troy Redman *(VP)*
Jamerson M. Ries *(VP)*
Klm McLaughlin *(VP-Mktg & Community Engagement)*
Dick VnaderZyden *(Chm-Bus & Fin)*
Kurtis Fritz *(Dir-Construction)*

WOLVERINE CAPITAL PARTNERS LLC
39400 Woodward Ste 210, Bloomfield Hills, MI 48304
Tel.: (248) 220-2200 MI
Web Site:
http://www.wolverinecapital.com
Year Founded: 2005
Miscellaneous Financial Investment Services
N.A.I.C.S.: 523999
J. Michael Davis *(Pres & CEO)*

Subsidiaries:

Burkland Inc. (1)
6520 S State Rd, Goodrich, MI 48438-8710
Tel.: (810) 636-2233
Web Site: http://www.burklandinc.com
Sales Range: $25-49.9 Million
Emp.: 90
Automotive Stamping Mfr
N.A.I.C.S.: 336370
Wayne Morey *(VP)*

Vital Plastics, Inc. (1)
680 Vandeberg St, Baldwin, WI 54002
Tel.: (715) 684-5300
Web Site: http://www.vitalplastics.com
Sales Range: $10-24.9 Million
Emp.: 300
Plastic Pipe Fitting Mfr
N.A.I.C.S.: 326122
Terry Townsend *(Pres)*
Scott Glor *(Mgr-Bus Dev)*
Jamie Larson *(Mgr-Ops)*
Cindy Erickson *(Mgr-HR)*

WOLVERINE COIL SPRING CO.
818 Front Ave NW, Grand Rapids, MI 49504-4422
Tel.: (616) 459-3504
Web Site:
http://www.wolverinecoilspring.com
Year Founded: 1946
Sales Range: $10-24.9 Million
Emp.: 70
Spring, Stamping, Clip, Wire Form & Assembly Mfr
N.A.I.C.S.: 332510
Jay R. Dunwell *(Pres)*
Jim Bennett *(Mgr-Sls)*

WOLVERINE FIRE PROTECTION CO.
G 8067 N Dort Hwy, Mount Morris, MI 48458
Tel.: (810) 686-4630
Web Site:
http://www.wolverinefp.com
Sales Range: $25-49.9 Million
Emp.: 50
Provider of Fire Sprinkler System Installation
N.A.I.C.S.: 238220
Jim Bier *(Mgr-Construction Svcs)*
Yolanda Troxell *(Dir-Bus Dev)*
Mark Measel *(Project Mgr)*

WOLVERINE HARDWOODS INC.
2810 113th Ave, Allegan, MI 49010-7004
Tel.: (269) 686-7004 MI
Web Site: http://www.wolverinehardwoods.com
Year Founded: 1995
Sales Range: $1-9.9 Million
Emp.: 25
Hardwood Products
N.A.I.C.S.: 423310
Javan Mallery *(Founder & Pres)*
Mike Mallery *(VP & Buyer-Lumber Sls)*

WOLVERINE MUTUAL INSURANCE COMPANY
One Wolverine Way, Dowagiac, MI 49047
Tel.: (269) 782-3451
Web Site:
http://www.wolverinemutual.com
Year Founded: 1917
Sales Range: $25-49.9 Million
Emp.: 50
Direct Property & Casualty Insurance Carrier Services
N.A.I.C.S.: 524126
James Laing *(Pres)*
Becky Grabemeyer *(Controller)*

WOLVERINE PACKING CO.
2535 Rivard St, Detroit, MI 48207-2621
Tel.: (313) 259-7500 MI
Web Site:
http://www.wolverinepacking.com
Sales Range: $100-124.9 Million
Emp.: 145
Packer & Distributor of Meat
N.A.I.C.S.: 311611
Roger Bonahoom *(Owner)*
Brian Bartis *(Controller)*
Jim Bonahoom Jr. *(Pres & Treas)*

WOLVERINE PIPE LINE COMPANY
8075 Creekside Dr Ste 210, Portage, MI 49024
Tel.: (269) 323-2491 DE
Web Site:
http://www.wolverinepipeline.com
Year Founded: 1952
Refined Petroleum Products Pipeline Operator
N.A.I.C.S.: 486910
Allan Sawyer *(Pres)*

WOLVERINE POWER SUPPLY COOPERATIVE INC.
10125 W Watergate Rd, Cadillac, MI 49601-8458
Tel.: (231) 775-5700 MI
Web Site:
http://www.wolverinepowercooperative.com
Year Founded: 1948
Sales Range: $25-49.9 Million
Emp.: 100
Provider of Electric Services
N.A.I.C.S.: 221118
Daniel H. DeCoeur *(VP-Ops)*
Craig S. Borton *(VP-HR)*
Kimberly B. Molitor *(VP-External Affairs)*
Eric D. Baker *(Pres & CEO)*
Dawn Y. Coon *(VP-Admin)*
Janet L. Kass *(CFO)*
Brian L. Warner *(VP-Environmental Strategy)*

WOLVERINE SUPPLY INC.
5099 E Blue Lupine Dr, Wasilla, AK 99654
Tel.: (907) 373-6572
Web Site: http://www.wsiak.com
Sales Range: $10-24.9 Million
Emp.: 50
Construction Services
N.A.I.C.S.: 423310
Mark Van Buskirk *(Gen Mgr)*
Tod Blohm *(Sr Project Mgr)*
Marc Van Buskirk *(Gen Mgr)*
Luke Van Buskirk *(Supvr-Project)*
Rome Gilman *(Supvr-Project)*

WOLVERINE TRUCK SALES INC.
3550 Wyoming St, Dearborn, MI 48120
Tel.: (313) 849-0800
Web Site:
http://www.wolverinefordsales.dealerconnection.com
Sales Range: $10-24.9 Million
Emp.: 70
Retailer of New & Used Commercial Trucks
N.A.I.C.S.: 441110
Lynn Terry *(Pres)*
Shiela Dracka *(Treas & Sec)*
Steve Coulter *(Gen Mgr)*

WOMACK ELECTRIC & SUPPLY CO.
518 Newton St, Danville, VA 24541
Tel.: (434) 793-5134
Web Site:
http://www.womackelectric.com
Rev: $20,000,000
Emp.: 8
Electrical Apparatus & Equipment
N.A.I.C.S.: 423610
Todd Woodlief *(Mgr-Sls)*
Al Stewart *(Area Mgr)*
John Campbell *(Mgr-Acct-Outside)*

WOMACK PUBLISHING COMPANY, INC.
30 N Main St, Chatham, VA 24531
Tel.: (434) 432-1654 VA
Web Site:
http://www.womackpublishing.com
Year Founded: 1960
Newspaper, Directory & Specialty Publication Publisher
N.A.I.C.S.: 513110
Charles A. Womack *(Reg Gen Mgr)*
Chad Harrison *(Pres)*
Randy Velvin *(Reg Gen Mgr)*
Richard I. Ingram *(VP & Gen Mgr)*

Subsidiaries:

Creative Loafing-Charlotte (1)
100 NC Music Factory Blvd Ste c-2, Charlotte, NC 28206
Tel.: (704) 522-8334
Web Site: http://www.clclt.com
Sales Range: $10-24.9 Million
Emp.: 50
Newspaper Publishers
N.A.I.C.S.: 513110
Kimberly Lawson *(Editor)*
Melissa Oyler *(Dir-Creative)*
Candice Andrews *(Acct Exec)*
Sarah Stark *(Acct Exec)*
Pat Moran *(Coord-Adv)*
Ryan Pitkin *(Editor-News)*
Dana Vindigni *(Designer-Graphic)*
Charles Womack *(Publr)*

WOMAN'S LIFE INSURANCE SOCIETY
1338 Military St, Port Huron, MI 48061-5020
Tel.: (810) 985-5191
Web Site: http://www.womanslife.org
Year Founded: 1892
Sales Range: $10-24.9 Million
Emp.: 69
Fraternal Life Insurance Organization
N.A.I.C.S.: 524113

Janice Ulseth Whipple *(Chm)*
Christopher Martin *(Pres)*
Karen Deschaine *(Dir-Mktg)*

WOMANWISE LLC
505 Highway 169 N Ste 175, Minneapolis, MN 55441-6443
Tel.: (952) 797-5000 MN
Web Site:
http://www.womanwise.com
Year Founded: 1984
Sales Range: $10-24.9 Million
Emp.: 20
N.A.I.C.S.: 541820
Dori Molitor *(CEO)*
Kim Rudrud *(VP-Womens Insight & Brand Leadership)*
Sherry Gray *(Creative Dir)*

WOMBLE CARLYLE SANDRIDGE & RICE, LLP
One W 4th St, Winston Salem, NC 27101
Tel.: (336) 721-3600 NC
Web Site: http://www.wcsr.com
Year Founded: 1876
Sales Range: $250-299.9 Million
Emp.: 1,001
Legal Advisory Services
N.A.I.C.S.: 541110
Mary Craven Adams *(Partner)*
Patrick M. Allen *(Partner)*
Janice C. Baldwin *(Partner)*
Keith W. Vaughan *(Partner)*
William R. Whitehurst *(Partner)*
Hails Foster *(CFO)*
Bradley Bragg *(CIO)*
Randal S. Baringer *(Partner)*
Jimmy H. Barnhill *(Partner)*
Geoffrey K. Beach *(Partner)*
Anthony H. Brett *(Partner)*
David P. Broughton *(Partner)*
Scott Anderson *(Partner)*
Sudhir Shenoy *(Partner)*
Jennifer Collins *(Partner)*
Bradley Wood *(Partner)*
Raymond Bennett *(Partner)*
Eric Glidewell *(Partner)*
Julia Kreyskop *(Partner)*
Todd Conley *(Partner)*
Thomas Horan *(Partner)*
Robert Gaumont *(Partner)*
Candace Gill *(Dir-Client Svcs)*
Rhett Weiss *(Mng Dir-Strategic Initiatives Grp)*
Jason Watson *(Partner)*
Tryn Stimart *(Partner)*
Dana Severance *(Partner)*
Amanda Ray *(Partner)*
Jennifer Ammirati *(Partner)*
Alex Park *(Partner-Washington)*
Marty Stern *(Partner-Washington)*
John Cuddihy *(Partner-Washington)*
Les Jacobs *(Partner-Washington)*
Jessica Dickerson *(Atty)*
Victoria Bruno *(Atty)*
Ari Katz *(Chief Recruiting Officer)*
Bill Turner *(Chief Strategy Officer)*
Terry Wiley *(Exec Dir)*
Anna Mills *(Atty)*
Gary Nunes *(Mng Partner-North Virginia)*
Dan Mackesey *(Partner-Real Estate)*
Chip Sturm *(Atty-Baltimore)*
Joshua Davis *(Atty-Atlanta)*
Chris Iavarone *(Partner)*
Patrick Buckler *(Atty)*
Joseph Bach *(Partner)*
Jenny Matthews McKellar *(Atty-Raleigh)*
Jonathon Townsend *(Atty)*
Flynt Strean *(Partner-Charlotte)*
Joe Tirone *(Partner-Burgeoning Energy Practice)*
Reid C. Adams Jr. *(Partner)*
H. Grady Barnhill Jr. *(Partner)*

WOMBLE COMPANY INC.

Womble Company Inc.—(Continued)

WOMBLE COMPANY INC.
12821 Industrial Rd, Houston, TX 77015
Tel.: (713) 635-8300
Web Site: http://www.wombleco.com
Sales Range: $10-24.9 Million
Emp.: 400
Painting, Coating & Hot Dipping
N.A.I.C.S.: 332812
Alice F. Womble *(Owner)*
Nick Stefanakos *(Controller)*

Subsidiaries:

Labarge Coating, LLC (1)
PO Box 2005, Channelview, TX 77530
Tel.: (713) 636-8700
Web Site: http://www.labargecoating.com
Metal Heat Treating
N.A.I.C.S.: 332811
Suzy Pawlow *(VP-Ops)*

WOMEN FOR WOMEN INTERNATIONAL
2000 M St NW Ste 200, Washington, DC 20036
Tel.: (202) 737-7705
Web Site:
  http://www.womenforwomen.org
Year Founded: 1993
Sales Range: $25-49.9 Million
Emp.: 122
Woman Welfare Services
N.A.I.C.S.: 813311
Afshan Khan *(Pres)*
Colleen Zakrewsky *(VP-Mktg, Dev & Comm)*
Jennifer L. Windsor *(CEO)*
Brita Fernandez Schmidt *(Exec Dir)*
Zainab Salbi *(Founder)*
Julianna Lindsey *(VP-Programs)*
Laurie Adams *(Co-CEO)*
Mandana Hendessi *(Founder)*

WOMEN HELPING WOMEN
215 E 9th St 7th Fl, Cincinnati, OH 45202
Tel.: (513) 977-5541
Web Site:
  http://www.womenhelpingwomen.org
Year Founded: 1976
Rev.: $1,027,968
Assets: $507,269
Liabilities: $61,720
Net Worth: $445,549
Earnings: $102,741
Emp.: 40
Fiscal Year-end: 12/31/14
Woman Welfare Services
N.A.I.C.S.: 813410
Jenny Neyer Berg *(Treas)*
Melanie Garner *(First VP)*
Susan B. Baggott *(Pres)*

WOMEN IN BUSINESS/FABRIQUE
47 Flying Point Rd, Stony Creek, CT 06405
Web Site: http://www.wibbags.com
Year Founded: 1978
Sales Range: $25-49.9 Million
Emp.: 20
Designer & Mfr of Business Cases for Technology Products Including Notebooks, Tablets, Projectors, Computer Accessories & Mobile Phones
N.A.I.C.S.: 541490
Francine Farkas Sears *(Founder, CEO & Pres)*

WOMEN'S HEALTH CONNECTICUT, INC.
19 Woodland St Ste 31, Hartford, CT 06105
Tel.: (860) 728-1212
Web Site:
  http://www.womenshealthct.com
Year Founded: 2000
Sales Range: $10-24.9 Million
Emp.: 85
Women's Healthcare
N.A.I.C.S.: 621111
Nancy Bernstein *(Pres & CEO)*
Michael Pascetta *(CFO & Sr VP)*
Paula Greenberg *(Sr VP-Clinical Ops & Programs)*
Richard S. Ruben *(Chm)*
Matthew L. Saidel *(Chief Medical Officer)*

WOMEN'S HOUSING & ECONOMIC DEVELOPMENT CORPORATION
50 E 168th St, Bronx, NY 10452
Tel.: (718) 839-1100
Web Site: http://www.whedco.org
Year Founded: 1991
Sales Range: $10-24.9 Million
Emp.: 319
Community Development Services
N.A.I.C.S.: 624190
Davon Russell *(Exec VP)*
Katie Aylwin *(Sr Dir-Education & Youth Dev)*
Rebecca Kramnick *(Gen Counsel & VP)*
Nicole Lavan *(Dir-Res, Policy & Evaluation)*
Meredith Leverich *(Dir-Strategic Initiatives)*
Nancy Biberman *(Founder & Pres)*
Sara Kay *(Sec)*
Analisa Torres *(Chm)*

WOMEN'S INTERNATIONAL PHARMACY
2 Marsh Ct, Madison, WI 53718
Tel.: (608) 221-7800
Web Site:
  http://www.womensinternational.com
Year Founded: 1985
Rev.: $16,900,000
Emp.: 160
Hormone Therapy Developer
N.A.I.C.S.: 456110
Wallace L. Simons *(Founder & Pres)*

WOMENS CAMPAIGN INTERNATIONAL
3701 Chestnut St 6th Fl, Philadelphia, PA 19104
Tel.: (215) 387-2601
Web Site:
  http://www.womenscampaigninternational.org
Year Founded: 1998
Sales Range: $1-9.9 Million
Emp.: 7
Woman Welfare Services
N.A.I.C.S.: 813410
Marjorie Margolies *(Pres)*
Nina Ahmad *(Vice Chm)*
Edie Hunt *(Chm)*
Hetherington Smith *(Treas)*

WON-DOOR CORPORATION
1865 S 3480 W, Salt Lake City, UT 84104
Tel.: (801) 973-7500
Web Site: http://www.wondoor.com
Rev.: $13,000,000
Emp.: 160
Partition Mfr
N.A.I.C.S.: 332323
J. D. Porter *(CFO)*
Ted Decker *(Mgr-Sls-Natl)*
Mike Carter *(Dir-Strategic Accts)*
Dave Larsen *(Dir-Sls-Intl)*

WONDER BANCORP, INC.
7526 Hancock Dr, Wonder Lake, IL 60097
Tel.: (815) 728-8000
Web Site:
  http://www.thestatebankgroup.com
Year Founded: 1986
Sales Range: $1-9.9 Million
Emp.: 49
Bank Holding Company
N.A.I.C.S.: 551111
Maliea Penuela *(CFO)*
Michelle Toll *(Chief Risk Officer & Sr VP)*

Subsidiaries:

State Bank (1)
7526 Hancock Dr, Wonder Lake, IL 60097
Tel.: (815) 728-8000
Web Site:
  http://www.thestatebankgroup.com
Commericial Banking
N.A.I.C.S.: 522110
Maliea Penuela *(CFO)*
Michelle Toll *(Pres & CEO)*
Dave Weber *(Sr VP-Loans)*
Suzanne Conrad *(Ops Officer)*

WONDER GROUP, INC.
4 World Trade Ctr, 150 Greenwich St 57th Fl, New York, NY 10007
Tel.: (424) 320-0944
Web Site: https://www.wonder.com
Food Delivery Application Developer
N.A.I.C.S.: 513210
Kelley E. Morrell *(CFO)*
Marc Lore *(Founder & CEO)*

Subsidiaries:

Blue Apron Holdings, Inc. (1)
28 Liberty St 28th Fl, New York, NY 10005
Tel.: (347) 719-4312
Web Site: https://www.blueapron.com
Rev.: $458,467,000
Assets: $171,142,000
Liabilities: $137,421,000
Net Worth: $33,721,000
Earnings: ($109,733,000)
Emp.: 1,549
Fiscal Year-end: 12/31/2022
Food Service
N.A.I.C.S.: 624210
Linda Findley Kozlowski *(Pres & CEO)*

WONDER ICE CREAM CO.
1065 Martin Ave, Santa Clara, CA 95050
Tel.: (510) 818-9102
Web Site: http://www.wonderic.com
Rev.: $16,128,334
Emp.: 10
Ice Cream, Bulk
N.A.I.C.S.: 311520

WONDER INTERNATIONAL EDUCATION & INVESTMENT GROUP CORPORATION
8040 E Morgan Trl Ste 18, Scottsdale, AZ 85258
Tel.: (480) 966-2020
Web Site: http://www.wondedu.com
Year Founded: 2008
Sales Range: $10-24.9 Million
Emp.: 209
Holding Company; Vocational Training Schools Owner & Operator
N.A.I.C.S.: 551112
WenMing Xie *(CFO)*
Shiding Hu *(Dir-Supervising)*
Keith Wong *(CEO)*

WONDERWARE, INC.
2224 Pawtucket Ave, East Providence, RI 02914
Tel.: (401) 431-0700
Web Site: http://www.corebt.com
Sales Range: $10-24.9 Million
Emp.: 125
Solutions Integrator for Revenue, Network & Document Management

N.A.I.C.S.: 561410
Peter Whealton *(Chm)*
Bryan T. Durkin *(COO & Exec VP)*
William Farrow *(Exec VP-Information Technology)*
Connie Nicolosi *(Dir-Mktg)*

Subsidiaries:

eGov Strategies LLC (1)
233 S McCrea St Ste 600, Indianapolis, IN 46225-1068
Web Site: http://www.egovstrategies.com
Software Publisher
N.A.I.C.S.: 513210
Ira Maher *(Dir-Sls & Mktg)*

WONTON FOOD INC.
220 222 Moore St, Brooklyn, NY 11206
Tel.: (718) 628-6868
Web Site:
  http://www.wontonfood.com
Sales Range: $10-24.9 Million
Emp.: 200
Chinese Food Manufacturing Company
N.A.I.C.S.: 311999
Ching Sun Wong *(Chm & Pres)*
Derrick Wong *(VP-Sls & Mktg)*
Cheuk Chan *(Mgr-Logistic)*
Danny Zeng *(VP-Sls)*
David Tong *(Mgr-Pur)*
Lawrence Leung *(Gen Mgr-Admin)*
Megan Tong *(Asst Mgr)*
Wei Lik Chan *(Mgr-HR)*

WOOD AND HUSTON BANCORPORATION
27 E N St, Marshall, MO 65340
Tel.: (660) 886-6825
Web Site:
  http://www.woodhuston.com
Sales Range: $25-49.9 Million
Emp.: 100
State Commercial Banks
N.A.I.C.S.: 522110
John P. Huston *(Chm)*

Subsidiaries:

Wood and Huston Bank (1)
27 E N St, Marshall, MO 65340
Tel.: (660) 886-6825
Web Site: http://www.woodhuston.com
Rev.: $28,058,000
Emp.: 200
State Commercial Banks
N.A.I.C.S.: 522110
Mark Thompson *(CFO & Exec VP)*
Nick Huston *(Chm)*
Kay Maclaughlin *(Branch Mgr)*

WOOD COUNTY HOSPITAL
950 W Wooster St, Bowling Green, OH 43402
Tel.: (419) 354-8900
Web Site:
  http://www.woodcountyhospital.org
Year Founded: 1951
Sales Range: $75-99.9 Million
Emp.: 767
Health Care Srvices
N.A.I.C.S.: 622110
Carole Matthews *(VP-Patient Svcs)*
Todd Leopold *(Dir-Pharmacy)*

WOOD GUTMANN & BOGART INSURANCE BROKERS
15901 Red Hill Ave Ste 100, Tustin, CA 92780
Tel.: (714) 505-7000
Web Site: http://www.wgbib.com
Year Founded: 1984
Sales Range: $10-24.9 Million
Emp.: 96
Insurance Brokerage Services
N.A.I.C.S.: 524210
Ralph Molyneux *(Dir-Environmental Svcs)*

COMPANIES

Dena Wood-Manke (Mgr-Claims)
Amanda Vanderlip (Acct Mgr)
Erik Johansson (Pres)

WOOD LANE RESIDENTIAL SERVICES, INC.
545 Pearl St, Bowling Green, OH 43402
Tel.: (419) 353-9577 OH
Web Site:
http://www.woodlaneresidential.org
Year Founded: 1978
Sales Range: $10-24.9 Million
Emp.: 388
Developmental Disability Assistance Services
N.A.I.C.S.: 623210
Diane Daniels (Mgr-HR)
Tonia Peterson (CFO)
Sheri Damron (Dir-Support Svcs)
Debbie Leibig (Program Dir)
Greg Bair (CEO)

WOOD MOTOR COMPANY INC.
600 Hwy 62-65 Bypass N, Harrison, AR 72601
Tel.: (870) 741-8211
Year Founded: 1971
Sales Range: $10-24.9 Million
Emp.: 40
Car Whslr
N.A.I.C.S.: 441110
John W. Wood (Pres)

WOOD PARTNERS, L.L.C.
3715 Northside Pkwy NW Ste 4-600, Atlanta, GA 30327
Tel.: (404) 965-9965
Web Site:
http://www.woodpartners.com
Year Founded: 1998
Wood Residential Services
N.A.I.C.S.: 237210
Joseph Keough (Chm & CEO)
Lynne Churillo (Sr VP-Ops)
Ryan L. Dearborn (Chm)
Sean Reynolds (COO & Gen Counsel)
Kim Small (Sr VP-Central Reg)
Goldie Bartlett (VP-South)
Patrick Trask (Pres)
Michael Nagy (VP-Dev-Portland)
Greg Cavanaugh (VP-Dev)
Carol Jones (Sr VP-East Reg)
Jillian Kral (Sr VP-Ops Support)
Matt Trammell (CFO)
Kelly Keech (Sr VP-Ops)
Josh Lloyd (Exec VP-Ops)

Subsidiaries:

Wood Partners, L.L.C. - Orlando (1)
636 W Yale St, Orlando, FL 32804
Tel.: (407) 926-3701
Web Site: http://www.woodpartners.com
Land Subdivision
N.A.I.C.S.: 237210

WOOD PETROLEUM CO., INC.
943 E Hwy 76, Branson, MO 65616
Tel.: (417) 334-7016 MO
Year Founded: 1974
Sales Range: $10-24.9 Million
Emp.: 100
Wholesale Petroleum Products
N.A.I.C.S.: 424710
Karen Ballard (CFO)

WOOD PRO INC.
6 Elm St, Auburn, MA 01501
Tel.: (508) 832-3291
Web Site:
http://www.woodproinc.com
Rev.: $14,500,000
Emp.: 11
Floor Coverings
N.A.I.C.S.: 423220
Brian Salatiello (Branch Mgr)
Fred Timberlin (Branch Mgr)
Jonah Dupont (Branch Mgr)
Scott Melfi (Branch Mgr)
Tony Figuerido (Mgr-Auburn)
Christopher Daoust (CFO)
Steve Diggins (Dir-Trng & Mgr-Salem)
Michael Benvenuti (Mgr-Ops)
Peter Nolan (Mgr-Outside Sls)
Anthony Benvenuti (Pres & CEO)

WOOD TRADE INTERNATIONAL LLC
12700 SW Hall Blvd Ste E, Sisters, OR 97759
Tel.: (541) 549-0500 OR
Web Site:
http://www.woodtradeinternational.com
Year Founded: 2004
Lumber Retailer & Distr
N.A.I.C.S.: 423310
Heather Persons (Mgr-Office)
Mike Persons (CEO & Pres)
Colby Ashbaugh (Mgr-Shipping/Warehouse)
Sara Persons (Mgr-Accounting/Logistics)
Tony Pistilli (Mgr-Domestic/International Sales)

WOOD'N PALLETS, INC.
130 16th St, Windom, MN 56101-1237
Tel.: (507) 831-1132
Year Founded: 1982
Sales Range: $10-24.9 Million
Emp.: 16
Wood Container & Pallet Mfr
N.A.I.C.S.: 321920
Bob Lindeman (Pres)

WOOD-MIZER PRODUCTS INC.
8180 W Tenth St, Indianapolis, IN 46214-2430
Tel.: (317) 271-1542 IN
Web Site: http://www.woodmizer.com
Year Founded: 1972
Sales Range: $25-49.9 Million
Emp.: 650
Mfr of Woodworking Machinery.
N.A.I.C.S.: 333243
Richard Vivers (CEO)

WOOD-MODE INCORPORATED
1 2nd St, Kreamer, PA 17833
Tel.: (570) 374-2711
Web Site: http://www.woodmode.com
Sales Range: $150-199.9 Million
Emp.: 1,100
Wood Kitchen Cabinets
N.A.I.C.S.: 337110
Jeff Wolfe (Dir-Mktg)
Cathie Langton (Asst Mgr-Credit)
Keith Roush (Project Mgr-IS)
Michael Moyer (Mgr-Tech Svcs)
Mike Morningstar (Reg Mgr-Sls)
Stephen Rhoads (Mgr-Cost Product)
John Troxell (Dir-Design)

WOODALL CONSTRUCTION CO. INC.
1332 Cahill Dr, Lexington, KY 40504
Tel.: (859) 233-2909
Web Site:
http://www.woodallconst.com
Sales Range: $10-24.9 Million
Emp.: 50
Excavation Work
N.A.I.C.S.: 238910

Jerry Woodall (Pres)
Scott Woodall (Pres)
John Cranfill (Controller)
Gary Caudill (Project Mgr)

WOODARD & CURRAN INC.
41 Hutchins Dr, Portland, ME 04102
Tel.: (207) 774-2112
Web Site:
http://www.woodardcurran.com
Year Founded: 1979
Rev.: $28,500,000
Emp.: 1,000
Engineeering Services
N.A.I.C.S.: 541330
Douglas McKeown (Chm & CEO)
Brent Bridges (Sr Mgr-Client-Govt & Institutional)
Tom Schwartz (Sr Project Mgr)
David Remick (CFO)
Kenneth Danila (Dir-Info Svcs)
Brendan McLaughlin (Sr Mgr-Client)
Eric Carlson (Dir-Innovations & New Svcs)
Jennifer Andrews (Dir-Mktg)
Kevin Bethke (Sr Project Mgr)
Lisa Campe (Sr Project Mgr-Corrective Action)
Shannon Eyler (Dir-Health & Safety)
Dave Dedian (Sr Mgr-Area-Ops & Mgmt)
Kathleen Welter (VP)
Phyllis Brunner (Pres-Consulting)

Subsidiaries:

RMC Water & Environment (1)
2175 N California Blvd Ste 315, Walnut Creek, CA 94596-7122 (100%)
Tel.: (925) 627-4100
Web Site: http://www.rmcwater.com
Emp.: 120
Complex Water Related Solutions
N.A.I.C.S.: 488390
Randy Raines (Sr Project Mgr)
Alyson Watson (Pres)
Lyndel Melton (Sr Engr-Water Resources)

WOODARD TECHNOLOGY & INVESTMENTS LLC
4937 S 78th E Ave, Tulsa, OK 74145
Tel.: (918) 270-7000
Rev.: $30,649,846
Emp.: 25
Holding Company
N.A.I.C.S.: 523999
Daryl J. Woodard (CEO)
Rodney Kramer (CFO)

Subsidiaries:

SageNet LLC (1)
10205 E 61st St, Tulsa, OK 74133
Tel.: (918) 270-7000
Web Site: http://www.sagenet.com
Managed Network Services
N.A.I.C.S.: 541512
Daryl J. Woodard (CEO)
Dale Higganbotham (VP-Sls)
Rodney Kramer (CFO)
Brad Wise (Pres)
Jim Norton (Sr VP-Ops & Engrg)
Rosemary Blum (CMO)
Marilyn Gholson (Exec VP-Project Mgmt Office)
Craig Talbot (Sr VP-Enterprise Sls)
Christy Ptak (VP-HR)
Bill Morris (Exec VP-Sls & Svc Delivery)
Tom Watson (CIO & Exec VP-Ops)
Andrew Ruiz de Gamboa (Gen Counsel & Sec)
Paul Truitt (CTO & Chief Security Officer)

Subsidiary (Domestic):

Convergent Media Systems, LLC (2)
190 Bluegrass Vly Pkwy, Alpharetta, GA 30005
Tel.: (770) 369-9000
Web Site: http://www.convergent.com
Sales Range: $150-199.9 Million
Emp.: 400

WOODEN SOLDIER LTD.

Satellite Communications Networks for Corporations
N.A.I.C.S.: 516210
Trevor S. Davies (Sr VP-Engrg)
Kristopher Konrath (Dir-Mktg Comm)
John Campbell (Pres)

Spacenet, Inc. (2)
1750 Old Meadow Rd, McLean, VA 22102-4327 (100%)
Tel.: (703) 848-1000
Web Site: http://www.spacenet.com
Sales Range: $75-99.9 Million
Managed Network Services
N.A.I.C.S.: 541512
Mike Mazza (VP)
Michael Barthlow (Gen Mgr-North America)

WOODBOLT DISTRIBUTION, LLC
3891 S Traditions Dr, Bryan, TX 77807
Tel.: (800) 870-2070
Web Site: http://www.cellucor.com
Year Founded: 2002
Holding Company: Nutritional & Weight Loss Products
N.A.I.C.S.: 551112
Manish Patel (CFO)

Subsidiaries:

Cellucor (1)
715 N Main St, Bryan, TX 77840 (100%)
Tel.: (800) 870-2070
Web Site: http://www.cellucor.com
Dietary Supplements for Fitness & Bodybuilding
N.A.I.C.S.: 456191
Erin Weaver (Mgr-Acct)
Devin Strong (Mgr-Market Dev)

Scivation Inc. (1)
300 W Morgan Str, Durham, NC 27701
Tel.: (866) 996-3489
Web Site: http://www.officialxtend.com
Nutritional Supplements Mfr
N.A.I.C.S.: 456191
Mike McCandless (CEO)

WOODBURY AUTO WHOLESALER ENTERPRISE LLC
605 Albany Ave, Amityville, NY 11701
Tel.: (631) 789-2500
Web Site:
http://www.partsauthority.com
Rev.: $27,300,000
Emp.: 175
Automotive Supplies & Parts
N.A.I.C.S.: 493110
Charles Jacabacci (VP)

WOODCRAFT SUPPLY, LLC
1177 Rosemar Rd, Parkersburg, WV 26105
Tel.: (304) 422-5412 DE
Web Site: http://www.woodcraft.com
Year Founded: 1928
Woodworking Tools & Accessories Retailer
N.A.I.C.S.: 444140
Jack Bigger (Pres & CEO)
Ryan Knost (CIO)
Andrew Bondi (VP-Retail & Franchise Ops)
Amanda Harris Silvus (CFO)

WOODEN SHIPS OF HOBOKEN
231 W 39th St Ste 711, New York, NY 10018
Tel.: (212) 221-3660
Web Site: http://www.wooden-ships.com
Year Founded: 1992
Rev.: $15,000,000
Emp.: 300
Clothing Mfr & Retailer
N.A.I.C.S.: 424310
Paola Buendia (Pres)
Mark Donovan (Co-Owner)

WOODEN SOLDIER LTD.
Hwy 16302, Intervale, NH 03845
Tel.: (603) 356-5643

WOODEN SOLDIER LTD.   U.S. PRIVATE

Wooden Soldier Ltd.—(Continued)

Web Site:
http://woodensoldierltd.com
Rev.: $19,238,690
Emp.: 73
Gift Items; Mail Order
N.A.I.C.S.: 459420
David G. Mennella (Pres)
Yvonne P. Menella (VP)

WOODFIELD GROUP INC.
2760 Spectrum Dr, Elgin, IL 60124
Tel.: (847) 426-5357
Sales Range: $25-49.9 Million
Emp.: 100
Mfr of Computer Equipment
N.A.I.C.S.: 423430
Tom Lesniak (Pres & CEO)
Jeff Ramsey (VP)
Tina Walsh (Dir HR)

WOODFIELD INC.
3161 Hwy 376 S, Camden, AR 71701
Tel.: (870) 231-6020
Web Site:
http://www.woodfieldinc.com
Rev.: $21,000,000
Emp.: 140
Freight Trucking Services
N.A.I.C.S.: 484121
Kathy Starr (Owner & Sec)
Kathryn Gober (Mgr-Fleet)

WOODFIN HEATING INC.
1823 N Hamilton St, Richmond, VA 23230
Tel.: (804) 730-5000   VA
Web Site: http://www.askwoodfin.com
Year Founded: 1977
Fuel Oil Dealers
N.A.I.C.S.: 424720
Jack Woodfin (CEO & Pres)
Dave Kibiloski (Treas)
Justin R. Andress (Pres)
Kevin W. Walsh (VP)
Jen Loving (CFO)
A. Penn Staples (Gen Mgr-Petroleum Products)
Travis D. Riddle (Gen Mgr-Mechanical Svcs)
Robbie Lee (Sls Mgr-Mechanical Svcs)
H.O. Harcum (Dir-Retails Ops)

WOODFORD PLYWOOD INC.
1504 S Mock Rd, Albany, GA 31705-4124
Tel.: (229) 883-4900   GA
Web Site:
http://www.woodfordplywood.com
Year Founded: 1975
Sales Range: $10-24.9 Million
Emp.: 86
Provider of Lumber, Plywood & Millwork
N.A.I.C.S.: 423310
Karen Iler (Owner)
Stevie Williams (Mgr-Sls)

WOODFOREST FINANCIAL GROUP, INC.
1330 Lake Robbins Dr Ste 100, The Woodlands, TX 77380
Tel.: (832) 375-2000
Web Site: http://www.woodforest.com
Sales Range: $150-199.9 Million
Emp.: 1,200
Bank Holding Company
N.A.I.C.S.: 522110
Michael Richmond (Vice Chm & CFO)
Robert E. Marling Jr. (Chm & CEO)

Subsidiaries:

Woodforest National Bank   (1)
3101 W Davis St, Conroe, TX 77304

Tel.: (936) 538-1405
Web Site: http://www.woodforest.com
Rev.: $74,667,000
Emp.: 50
National Commercial Banks
N.A.I.C.S.: 522110
Michael Richmond (Vice Chm & CFO)
Julie V. Mayrant (Pres-Retail)
Cathleen Nash (Pres & CEO)
Brenda Wendt (Mgr-Gulf Coast)
Scott Jones (Mgr-Relationship)
Julie Dargani (Mgr-Middle Market Relationship)
Willy Gomez (Pres-Comml Banking-Florida)
Derrick Ragland (Pres-Comml Banking)
Andrew Rabuck (Sr VP-South Carolina)
Marcia Yearwood (Sr VP & Mgr-Illinois & Indiana)
Ann Healy (VP & Mgr-Ohio)
Matthew Clatworthy (Sr VP-North Carolina)
Stuart Forsyth (Exec VP & Mgr-Middle Market Relationship-Tampa)
Kimberlee Peveto (Mgr-Pennsylvania & New York)
Cecilia Castelo (VP-Retail Banking)

WOODGRAIN, INC.
300 NW 16th St, Fruitland, ID 83619-0566
Tel.: (208) 452-3801   ID
Web Site: http://www.woodgrain.com
Year Founded: 1959
Sales Range: $400-449.9 Million
Emp.: 1,500
Millwork, Molding, Window & Door Parts
N.A.I.C.S.: 321918
Reed Dame (Chm)
Kelly Dame (Pres & CEO)
Mike Ball (VP-Millwork Ops)
Dave Lindsey (VP-Prefinish Ops)
Dan Puckett (VP-Intl Millwork Ops)

Subsidiaries:

Huttig Building Products, Inc.   (1)
555 Maryville University Dr Ste 400, Saint Louis, MO 63141
Tel.: (314) 216-2600
Web Site: http://www.huttig.com
Rev.: $937,800,000
Assets: $309,800,000
Liabilities: $216,700,000
Net Worth: $93,100,000
Earnings: $48,500,000
Emp.: 1,100
Fiscal Year-end: 12/31/2021
Millwork, Building Materials & Wood Products Whslr For Use in New Residential Construction & Home Improvement Remodeling & Repair Work
N.A.I.C.S.: 321918
Robert Furio (COO & Exec VP)
Delbert H. Tanner (Chm)
Jon P. Vrabely (Pres & CEO)
Brian D. Robinson (CIO & Sr VP)

Subsidiary (Domestic):

BenBilt Building Systems LP   (2)
123 BenBilt Place, Greensburg, PA 15601
Tel.: (724) 879-8800
Web Site: http://www.benbilt.com
Emp.: 110
Wholesale Distr of Therma-Tru Doors
N.A.I.C.S.: 332321

Huttig Texas Limited Partnership   (2)
2115 Valley View Ln, Dallas, TX 75234-8934
Tel.: (972) 620-2200
Web Site: http://www.huttig.com
Sales Range: $25-49.9 Million
Emp.: 130
Building Materials Whslr
N.A.I.C.S.: 444180

Huttig, Inc.   (2)
555 Maryville University Dr, Saint Louis, MO 63141
Tel.: (314) 216-2600
Building Materials Distr
N.A.I.C.S.: 444180
Robert Furio (Exec VP-Grip Div)
David A. Fishbein (Exec VP-Grip)

Monarch Windows & Doors Inc   (1)
1608 Frank Akers Rd, Anniston, AL 36207
Tel.: (256) 831-7000
Web Site: http://www.monarchwindows.com
Building Materials Whslr
N.A.I.C.S.: 423390
Joe Webster (Gen Mgr & Mgr-Natl Sls)
Ricardo Amaral (Mgr-Production)
Renee Zipp (Mgr-Matls)
Bob Ager (Mgr-Product)
Richard Bousack (Mgr-Sls-Alabama)
Fred Bousack (Mgr-Sls-Alabama)
Randy Lamotte (Mgr-Sls-Arkansas, Illinois, Missouri & Western Tennessee)
Bruce Deppa (Mgr-Sls-Georgia)
Ed Hannold (Mgr-Sls-Indiana)
Scott Hibner (Mgr-Sls-Southeast Texas)
Fred Lyle (Mgr-Sls-Kentucky)
Nelson Melvin (Mgr-Sls-North & South Carolina)
Tom Peden (Mgr-Sls-Louisiana & Southern Mississippi)
Jim Rowland (Mgr-Sls-Central Texas)
John Rowland (Mgr-Sls-West Texas & Oklahoma Panhandle)
Inside Sales (Mgr-Sls-Virginia)

Windsor Windows & Doors Co   (1)
900 S 19th St, West Des Moines, IA 50265
Web Site: http://www.windsorwindows.com
Emp.: 350
Wood Window & Door Mfr
N.A.I.C.S.: 321911
Cathy Leonard (Mgr-Mktg Comm)

Woodgrain Distribution, Inc.   (1)
6280 Best Friend Rd Ste 400, Norcross, GA 30071
Tel.: (770) 729-7965
Wood Window & Door Distr
N.A.I.C.S.: 423310
Todd Dame (Dir-Supply Chain & Pricing)

Woodgrain Doors   (1)
1201 W Karcher Rd, Nampa, ID 83687
Tel.: (208) 467-5221
Web Site: http://www.woodgraindoors.com
Emp.: 330
Door Mfr & Distr
N.A.I.C.S.: 321911
Kelly Dame (Pres & CEO)
Greg Easton (CFO)
Steve Atkinson (Controller)
John Jurcek (VP & Gen Mgr-Door Div)

Woodgrain Millwork, Inc. - Nature's Division   (1)
1948 N Main St, Prineville, OR 97754
Tel.: (888) 746-3001
Web Site:
http://www.naturesbywoodgrain.com
Pet Product Mfr
N.A.I.C.S.: 339999
Brian Michaels (Mgr-Sls)

WOODHAVEN LEARNING CENTER
1405 Hathman Pl, Columbia, MO 65201
Tel.: (573) 875-6181   MO
Web Site:
http://www.woodhaventeam.org
Year Founded: 1964
Sales Range: $10-24.9 Million
Emp.: 406
Intellectual & Developmental Disability Assistance Services
N.A.I.C.S.: 623210
Robert Palmer (Dir-Health Svcs)
Stacy Brown (Dir-Programs)
Cindy Bush (COO)
Sarah Read (VP)
Ed Scavone (Pres)
Jerome Rader (Treas)
Brad Miller (Sec)
C. Mark Palmer (CEO)

WOODHAVEN LUMBER & MILLWORK
200 James St, Lakewood, NJ 08701
Tel.: (732) 901-0030
Web Site:
http://www.woodhavenlumber.com
Sales Range: $25-49.9 Million
Emp.: 230

Millwork & Lumber
N.A.I.C.S.: 444110
James T. Robinson (Treas)
Alan Robinson (Owner)
Paul Glinn (Mgr-Sls)

WOODHOUSE CHRYSLER DODGE JEEP RAM
2101 E 6th St, Sioux City, IA 51101
Tel.: (712) 277-3221
Web Site:
http://www.woodhousechrysler
dodgejeepram.com
Sales Range: $10-24.9 Million
Emp.: 950
Car Dealership Owner & Operator
N.A.I.C.S.: 441110
Lance Pittack (Co-Owner)
Becky Pittack (Co-Owner)
Dominic Marasco (Mgr-Sls)
Jason Larrabee (Mgr-Fin)
Lee Bobier (Mgr-Sls)
Marcus Sanchez (Mgr-Parts)
Rick Sweitzer (Mgr-Fin)
Ryan Trotter (Mgr-Sls)

WOODINGS INDUSTRIAL CORPORATION
218 Clay Ave EXT, Mars, PA 16046
Tel.: (724) 625-3170
Web Site: http://woodings.com
Sales Range: $25-49.9 Million
Emp.: 80
Drilling Machine Tools (Metal Cutting)
N.A.I.C.S.: 333517
Robert T. Woodings (Pres & CEO)
Don Howell (VP-Ops)
Al Colucci (Gen Mgr-Engrg)

Subsidiaries:

Munroe, Inc.   (1)
1820 N Franklin St, Pittsburgh, PA 15233-2222
Tel.: (412) 231-0600
Web Site: http://www.munroeinc.com
Sales Range: $100-124.9 Million
Mfr & Wholesale Distributor of Boiler Components, Pressure Vessels, Heat Exchangers & Chemical Plant Construction Equipment
N.A.I.C.S.: 332410

Superior Machine Company of South Carolina, Inc.   (1)
692 N Cashua Dr, Florence, SC 29502
Tel.: (843) 468-9200
Web Site: http://www.smco.net
Sales Range: $100-124.9 Million
Emp.: 240
Heavy Industrial Machinery Manufacturing & Repair
N.A.I.C.S.: 332313
Kent Carraway (Pres)
Vaughn William (Mgr-Sls)
John L. Ham Jr. (Pres)

Division (Domestic):

Superior Machine Company Division   (2)
169 Machine Shop Rd, Marion, NC 28752-1169
Tel.: (828) 652-6141
Web Site: http://www.smco.net
Sales Range: $10-24.9 Million
Emp.: 55
Rock Crusher Repair Facility; Machine Shop; Fabrication & Repair of Steel Mill Equipment
N.A.I.C.S.: 332710
James Odom (CEO)

WOODINVILLE LUMBER, INC.
15900 Woodinville Redmond Rd NE, Woodinville, WA 98072-4541
Tel.: (425) 488-1818   MN
Year Founded: 1970
Sales Range: $50-74.9 Million
Emp.: 350
Mfr of Lumber Plywood & Millwork
N.A.I.C.S.: 423310
Michelle Halderman (Controller)

COMPANIES

WOODLAND AVIATION INC.
25170 Aviation Ave, Davis, CA 95616
Tel.: (530) 662-9631
Web Site:
http://www.woodlandaviation.com
Year Founded: 1963
Sales Range: $350-399.9 Million
Emp.: 60
Aircraft Sales & Service
N.A.I.C.S.: 488119
Gary Pelfrey (VP-Woodland Aviation)
Terry Clark (Controller)

WOODLAND FOODS INC.
3751 Sunset Ave, Waukegan, IL 60087
Tel.: (847) 625-8600
Web Site:
http://www.woodlandfoods.com
Year Founded: 1989
Sales Range: $10-24.9 Million
Emp.: 70
Frozen Specialty Food Mfr
N.A.I.C.S.: 311412
Mike Brundidge (Exec VP)
Aram Karapetian (COO)
Mary Schabel (Dir-HR)
Janice Lagergren (Project Mgr)
Deanine Rexford (Mgr-Trade Show)
Ray Janson (CFO & Treas)
David Moore (Pres & CEO)
Robert Linder (VP-Sls & Mktg)
Paul Nagy (VP-Supply Chain)

WOODLAND FOREST PRODUCTS INC.
1272 Helmo Ave N, Oakdale, MN 55128
Tel.: (651) 714-8100
Web Site:
http://www.woodlandforestproducts.com
Rev.: $17,400,000
Emp.: 7
Lumber, Plywood & Millwork
N.A.I.C.S.: 423310
Dan Jacobson (Pres)

WOODLAND MOTORS CORP.
1680 E Main St, Woodland, CA 95776
Tel.: (530) 662-3255   CA
Web Site:
http://www.woodlandmotors.com
Year Founded: 1987
Rev.: $34,169,353
Emp.: 20
Car Dealership Owner & Operator
N.A.I.C.S.: 441110
Scott Banderbeek (Owner & Pres)
Jose Hernandez (Dir-Fin)
Susan Kite (Controller)

WOODLAND PARK ZOOLOGICAL SOCIETY
5500 Phinney Ave N, Seattle, WA 98103
Tel.: (206) 548-2500   WA
Web Site: http://www.zoo.org
Year Founded: 1965
Sales Range: $25-49.9 Million
Emp.: 577
Zoo Conservation Services
N.A.I.C.S.: 712130
Jim Bennett (Dir-Mktg & Corp Rels)
Valerie Krueger (Dir-Fin)
Becky Barker (VP-Interim-Education)
Bruce W. Bohmke (COO)
Dana Keeler (VP-HR)
Darin Collins (Dir-Animal Health)
Fred W. Koontz (VP-Field Conservation)
Jeff Leppo (Chm)
Jill Walker (Treas)
Margaret Wetherald (Sec)
Matt Rosauer (Vice Chm)

Alejandro Grajal (Pres & CEO)
Lauri Hennessey (VP-Comm & Pub Affairs)
Wei Ying Wong (VP-Education)
David C. Wu (Chief Advancement Officer)
Serae Kim (VP-People & Culture)

WOODLAND PARTNERS LLC
24 Walpole Pk S, Walpole, MA 02081
Tel.: (508) 660-9300
Web Site: http://www.woodland-partners.com
Rev.: $43,280,000
Emp.: 30
Bond Brokers
N.A.I.C.S.: 424410
Kenneth D. Chipman (Pres)
Ashley Aucoin (Controller)

WOODLANDS OPERATING COMPANY LP
24 Waterway Ave Ste 1100, Woodlands, TX 77380
Tel.: (281) 719-6100
Web Site:
http://www.thewoodlands.com
Rev.: $79,500,000
Emp.: 130
Subdividers & Developers
N.A.I.C.S.: 237210
Dan Leverett (VP-Comml)
Susan Vreeland (Mgr-Mktg)
Tim Welbes (Co-Pres)
Alex Sutton (Co-Pres)

Subsidiaries:

Corporate Housing   (1)
2201 Timberloch Pl, The Woodlands, TX 77380
Tel.: (281) 719-6222
Sales Range: $10-24.9 Million
Emp.: 3
Apartment Building Operator
N.A.I.C.S.: 531110

Woodland Resort Conference Centre   (1)
2301 N Millbend, The Woodlands, TX 77380
Tel.: (281) 367-1100
Web Site: http://www.woodlandsresort.com
Payroll Accounting Service
N.A.I.C.S.: 541214
Greg Parson (Gen Mgr)

WOODLANDS RELIGIOUS COMMUNITY INC.
4242 Interfaith Way, The Woodlands, TX 77381
Tel.: (281) 367-1230   TX
Web Site:
http://www.woodlandsinterfaith.org
Year Founded: 1974
Sales Range: $10-24.9 Million
Social Service Agency
N.A.I.C.S.: 813410
Mario M. Coll (Chm)
Debra Sukin (Chm)

WOODLAWN CONSTRUCTION COMPANY
11006 Cobbs Rd, Glen Allen, VA 23059
Tel.: (804) 798-3214
Web Site:
http://www.woodlawnconstruction.com
Sales Range: $25-49.9 Million
Emp.: 75
Underground Utilities Contracting Services
N.A.I.C.S.: 237110
Anita Mellard (Treas & Sec)

WOODLAWN PARTNERS, INC.
321 N Clark St Ste 2800, Chicago, IL 60654

Tel.: (773) 255-9085
Web Site:
http://www.woodlawnpartners.com
Privater Equity Firm
N.A.I.C.S.: 523999
Greg Bregstone (Partner)
Evan Gobdel (Partner)

Subsidiaries:

Pacific Aviation Corporation   (1)
201 Continental Blvd Ste 130, El Segundo, CA 90245
Tel.: (310) 322-6290
Web Site: http://www.pacificaviation.com
Other Airport Operation Distr
N.A.I.C.S.: 488119
Phil Shah (Co-Founder)
Victor Mena (Co-Founder)

WOODLEYS FINE FURNITURE INC.
320 S Sunset St, Longmont, CO 80501
Tel.: (303) 651-3701
Web Site: http://www.woodleys.com
Sales Range: $25-49.9 Million
Emp.: 200
Furniture Retailer
N.A.I.C.S.: 449110
Brandy Hayes (Gen Mgr)
Paulette Ogden (Mgr-Sls-Longmont)
Tim O'Connell (Mgr-Store)

WOODLOCH PINES INC.
731 Welcome Lake Rd, Lackawaxen, PA 18435
Tel.: (570) 685-8000
Web Site: http://www.woodloch.com
Sales Range: $25-49.9 Million
Emp.: 600
Resort Hotel Operator
N.A.I.C.S.: 721110
John Pillar (Dir-Golf)
Lauretta Sullivan (Mgr-Dining Room)
John S. Kiesendahl (Pres & CEO)

WOODMAN CONSTRUCTION INC.
3 Lake Blvd Dr Ste 201, Bellevue, WA 98005
Tel.: (425) 454-3621
Web Site:
http://www.woodmanconstruction.com
Rev.: $30,000,000
Emp.: 35
Shopping Center Construction
N.A.I.C.S.: 236220
Peter Woodman (Pres)

WOODMAN'S FOOD MARKET INC.
2631 Liberty Ln, Janesville, WI 53545-0741
Tel.: (608) 754-3373   WI
Web Site: http://www.woodmansfood.com
Year Founded: 1920
Sales Range: $300-349.9 Million
Emp.: 2,500
Retail Grocery Stores
N.A.I.C.S.: 445110
Phillip Woodman (Pres)
Donna Roosch (Controller)
John Adams (VP)

WOODMEN OF THE WORLD LIFE INSURANCE SOCIETY, INC.
1700 Farnam St, Omaha, NE 68102-2075
Tel.: (402) 342-1890   NE
Web Site: http://www.woodmen.org
Year Founded: 1890
Sales Range: $500-549.9 Million
Emp.: 1,950
Fire Insurance Services

N.A.I.C.S.: 524113
Blake Warneke (Dir-Product Devel)
Annette Devine (VP-Acctg Svcs)
Karla J. Gochenour (VP-HR)

WOODMONT COUNTRY CLUB
1201 Rockville Pike, Rockville, MD 20852
Tel.: (301) 424-7200   DC
Web Site:
http://www.woodmontcc.com
Year Founded: 1913
Sales Range: $10-24.9 Million
Emp.: 373
Country Club
N.A.I.C.S.: 713910
John M. Bille (Dir-Admin)
Michael Sheppard (Dir-Fin)
David Dorn (Dir-Golf)
Bruce Lipka (Dir-Tennis)
Brian Pizzimenti (CEO & Gen Mgr)

WOODMONT REAL ESTATE SERVICES LTD.
1050 Ralston Ave, Belmont, CA 94002
Tel.: (650) 592-3960
Web Site: http://www.wres.com
Year Founded: 1963
Sales Range: $50-74.9 Million
Emp.: 300
Real Estate Services & Property Management
N.A.I.C.S.: 525110
Ronald V. Granville (CEO)
Claudia Blakeslee (CFO)
Caroline Anzur (VP-Mktg & Education)
Scott Pritchett (Pres-Comml Ops)
Jeff Bosshard (Pres-Multifamily Ops)
Melody La Rue (VP-Sacramento)

Subsidiaries:

Woodmont Real Estate Services Ltd. - Commercial Division   (1)
2001 Winward Way Ste 100, San Mateo, CA 94404
Tel.: (650) 592-3960
Real Estate Manangement Services
N.A.I.C.S.: 531390

Woodmont Realty Advisors Inc.   (1)
1050 Ralston Ave, Belmont, CA 94002-2243
Tel.: (650) 592-3960
Web Site: http://www.wres.com
Sales Range: $25-49.9 Million
Emp.: 50
Real Estate Services
N.A.I.C.S.: 525110
Ronald V. Granville (CEO)
Claudia Blakeslee (CFO)
Jeffrey S. Bosshard (Co-Pres)
Scott M. Pritchett (Co-Pres)
Brigitte Spinale (VP-HR)
Caroline Anzur (VP-Mktg & Education)
Kirk Ohlendorf (VP-Building & Facilities Svcs)

WOODPECKER TRUCK & EQUIPMENT INCORPORATED
40275 Clark Ln, Pendleton, OR 97801
Tel.: (541) 276-5515
Web Site:
http://www.woodpeckertruck.com
Sales Range: $25-49.9 Million
Emp.: 70
Commercial Trucks
N.A.I.C.S.: 423110
E. M. Clark (Pres)
Mike Florence (Mgr-Auto Body Shop)

WOODROW WILSON CONSTRUCTION COMPANY, INC.
345 Highlandia Dr, Baton Rouge, LA 70810
Tel.: (225) 926-3000
Web Site: http://www.wwcci.com
Rev.: $109,700,000

Woodrow Wilson Construction Company, Inc.—(Continued)
Emp.: 110
Non-Residential Construction & Industrial Building Construction
N.A.I.C.S.: 236220
Jim Alan Wilson (VP)
Mark A. Wilson (Pres & CEO)
Joyce B. Davis (Controller)
Wesley Gifford (Project Mgr)
Gregg Rome (Project Mgr)
Jason Catlin (Project Mgr)
Bret Hosch (Asst Project Mgr)
W. Kurt Wilson Sr. (VP)
W. Kurt Wilson Jr. (Project Mgr)

WOODRUFF & SONS INC.
6450 - 31st St E, Bradenton, FL 34203
Tel.: (941) 756-1871
Web Site:
    http://www.woodruffandsons.com
Year Founded: 1946
Sales Range: $10-24.9 Million
Emp.: 133
Sewer Line & Road Construction
N.A.I.C.S.: 237110
Bruce Woodruff (VP)
Donald Woodruff (Pres)
Linda Wakeman (Treas & Sec)
Jerry Konieczny (Dir-Field Ops)
Dennis Holt (Dir-Estimating Ops)
Paul Bakker (Dir-Fin Ops)
Todd Bell (VP-Indiana)
Mike Edinger (Asst Sec-Indiana)

WOODRUFF CONSTRUCTION LLC
1890 Kountry Ln, Fort Dodge, IA 50501
Tel.: (515) 576-1118
Web Site:
    http://www.woodruffcompanies.com
Sales Range: $25-49.9 Million
Emp.: 60
Commercial & Office Building, New Construction
N.A.I.C.S.: 236220
Don Woodruff (Pres)
Dave O'Brien (Pres-West)

WOODRUFF ELECTRIC COOPERATIVE CORPORATION
3190 N Washington St, Forrest City, AR 72335-9578
Tel.: (870) 633-2262   AR
Web Site:
    http://www.woodruffelectric.com
Year Founded: 1937
Sales Range: $25-49.9 Million
Emp.: 83
Distr of Electric Power
N.A.I.C.S.: 221122
Byron J. Ponder (Vice Chm)
Michael Swan (Pres & CEO)
Joe Whittenton (Chm)

WOODRUFF ENERGY
73 Water St, Bridgeton, NJ 08302
Tel.: (856) 455-1111
Web Site:
    http://www.woodruffenergy.com
Rev.: $28,671,957
Emp.: 54
Fuel Oil Dealers
N.A.I.C.S.: 457210
Robert A. Woodruff (Pres)
Robert Muffley (Mgr-Sls)
Daniel C. Dilks (Plant Mgr)

WOODRUFF SWEITZER
501 Fay St, Columbia, MO 65201
Tel.: (573) 875-7917
Web Site:
    http://www.woodruffsweitzer.com
Year Founded: 1992
Sales Range: $10-24.9 Million
Advertising Agencies
N.A.I.C.S.: 541613
Shelley Thompson (COO)

Subsidiaries:

Woodruff Sweitzer Canada Inc.   (1)
200 630 - 8th Avenue SW, Calgary, T2P 1G6, AB, Canada
Tel.: (403) 930-4900
Web Site: https://www.simplyws.com
N.A.I.C.S.: 541810

WOODRUFF-SAWYER & CO.
50 California St 12th Fl, San Francisco, CA 94111
Tel.: (415) 391-2141
Web Site: http://www.wsandco.com
Rev.: $25,000,000
Emp.: 200
Provider of Insurance Services
N.A.I.C.S.: 524210
Andy Barrengos (CEO)
Steve Sawyer (Exec VP)
Priya Cherian Huskins Jr. (Partner & Sr VP)
Mary Sklarski (Chief Strategic Dev Officer)
Zac Overbay (COO)
Casey Soares (Sr VP & Specialist-Property)
Jared Pelissier (Partner & Sr VP)
Michelle Droz (Sr VP-Benefits)
Kim Armanasco (Sr VP-Insurance Ops)
Andrea Buchanan (Dir-HR)
Bret Lawrence (Sr VP-Construction)
Carolyn Polikoff (Sr VP)
Jennifer Walsh (Sr VP)
Susan Miner (Sr VP-Corp & Exec Protection)
Melissa Schellinkhout (VP & Dir-Northwest Practice)
Stephen Glazier (VP)
Jeanna Madlener (VP-Property & Casualty Practice-Oregon)
Andy Blasher (Acct Exec-Southern California)
Drew Johnston (VP-Aviation)
Josh Pasek (Asst VP-Property & Casualty Practice-South)
Tim Matthews (VP-Risk Control)
Dan Burke (VP)
Brian Cushard (Sr VP-Property & Casualty)
Jen Scales (VP/Acct Exec-Employee Benefits Practice)
Matthew Parsons (VP/Acct Exec-Construction Practice)
Luke Parsons (VP-Private Equity & Transactional Risk Grp)
Evan Hessel (VP)
Mike Reph (VP)
Walter Winter (VP-Seattle)
Jeff Colby (VP)
Norman Allen (Chief Revenue Officer)
Sean Coady (Sr VP)
Dan Schaller (Sr VP)
Jeff Friesen (Sr VP-Property & Casualty)
Ronan Eggleston (Sr VP-Mgmt Liability)
Teresa Milano (VP-Mgmt Liability-Boston)

WOODS ROGERS PLC
Dominion Twr 10 S Jefferson St Ste 1400, Roanoke, VA 24011
Tel.: (540) 983-7600   VA
Web Site:
    http://www.woodsrogers.com
Year Founded: 1893
Law firm
N.A.I.C.S.: 541110
Paula Hess (Dir-HR)
Charles Helvey (Dir-IT)
Susan Caldwell (Mktg Dir)
Dawn Montgomery (Mgr-Payroll & Benefits)
Jane Baugh (Dir-Library Svcs)
Victor O. Cardwell (Chm & Principal)
Agnis C. Chakravorty (Principal)
J. Alden English (Principal)
Joshua F. P. Long (Principal)
Christopher Stevens (Principal)
James W. Jennings Jr. (Principal)
Alton L. Knighton Jr. (Principal)
Heman A. Marshall III (Principal)
Daniel C. Summerlin III (Pres & CEO)
Eric J. Sorenson Jr. (Principal)

WOODS SUPER MARKET INC.
703 E College St, Bolivar, MO 65613-2630
Tel.: (417) 326-7603   MO
Web Site:
    http://www.woodssupermarket.com
Year Founded: 1956
Sales Range: $50-74.9 Million
Emp.: 350
Grocery Sales
N.A.I.C.S.: 445110
Donald C. Woods Jr. (Pres)

WOODS WITT DEALY & SONS, INC.
110 W 40th St Ste 1902, New York, NY 10018
Tel.: (212) 768-1259
Web Site:
    http://www.woodswittdealy.com
Sales Range: Less than $1 Million
Emp.: 10
N.A.I.C.S.: 541810
Phyllis Dealy (Partner & Dir-Acct Svcs)
Harry Woods (Partner & Dir-Creative)
Gill Witt (Partner & Dir-Creative)
Daniel Gearity (Dir-Art)
Eric Altbush (Dir-Art)

WOODSAGE HOLDINGS, LLC
7400 Airport Hwy, Holland, OH 43528
Tel.: (419) 866-8000   OH
Web Site: http://www.woodsage.com
Sales Range: $25-49.9 Million
Emp.: 50
Holding Company
N.A.I.C.S.: 551112
Dan Brown (CEO)

Subsidiaries:

Woodsage Industries   (1)
7400 Airport Hwy, Holland, OH 43528
Tel.: (419) 866-8000
Web Site: http://www.woodsage.com
Sales Range: $10-24.9 Million
Emp.: 85
Metal Tube & Bar Cutting & Fabricating Services
N.A.I.C.S.: 331210
Daniel Brown (CEO)

WOODSBORO BANK
5 N Main St, Woodsboro, MD 21798
Tel.: (301) 898-4000
Web Site:
    http://www.woodsborobank.com
Year Founded: 1899
Sales Range: $1-9.9 Million
Emp.: 62
Commericial Banking
N.A.I.C.S.: 522110
Janet I. McCurdy (Sec)
Thomas R. Rozynek (Vice Chm)
M. Natalie McSherry (Chm)
Stephen K. Heine (Pres & CEO)
Robin L. McConaughey (COO & Sr VP)
Kimberly A. Arnold (Chief Credit Officer & Sr VP)
Patricia D. Muldoon (CFO & Sr VP)
Bethany S. Lord (VP & Mgr-HR)
Linda S. Warehime (VP & Mgr-Residential & Consumer Lending)
Shelane Francisco (VP & Mgr-Downtown)
Thomas Ramsay (VP)
Yvonne Reeder (VP)
Debbie Dart (Asst Mgr-Deposit Ops)

WOODSIDE CAPITAL PARTNERS
25 Mall Rd, Burlington, MA 01803
Tel.: (781) 272-1501
Web Site:
    http://www.woodsidemanagement.com
Privater Equity Firm
N.A.I.C.S.: 523999
Scott M. Schooley (Pres)

Subsidiaries:

Hamilton Specialty Bar Corp.   (1)
319 Sherman Ave N, Hamilton, L8N 3R5, ON, Canada
Tel.: (905) 312-8650
Web Site: http://www.hsbsteel.com
Sales Range: $75-99.9 Million
Emp.: 450
Specialty Steel Bar Products Mfr
N.A.I.C.S.: 331110
Scott Zimmerman (Acct Mgr)

WOODSIDE HOTELS & RESORTS
1100 Alma St Ste 106, Menlo Park, CA 94025
Tel.: (650) 830-8888
Web Site:
    http://www.woodsidehotels.com
Owner & Operator of Hotels
N.A.I.C.S.: 721110

Subsidiaries:

Lafayette Park Hotel Corp.   (1)
1100 Alma St Ste 106, Menlo Park, CA 94025
Tel.: (650) 330-8888
Web Site: http://www.lafayetteparkhotel.com
Rev.: $16,800,000
Emp.: 8
Owner & Operator of Hotels
N.A.I.C.S.: 721110

WOODSMAN KITCHENS & FLOORS
11732 Beach Blvd, Jacksonville, FL 32246
Tel.: (904) 641-8336
Web Site: http://www.woodsman.biz
Sales Range: $125-149.9 Million
Emp.: 130
Kitchen Cabinets
N.A.I.C.S.: 423310
Richard S. Woods (Founder)

WOODSON EQUITY LLC
935 W. Chestnut St, Ste 307, Chicago, IL 60642
Tel.: (312) 448-6607
Web Site:
    https://www.woodsonequity.com
Private Equity
N.A.I.C.S.: 523940

Subsidiaries:

First Source Electronics, LLC   (1)
6650 Business Pkwy, Elkridge, MD 21075-6349
Tel.: (410) 379-1310
Web Site: http://www.fsellc.com
Control Panels, Electro-mechanical Assemblies & Cable Assemblies Mfr
N.A.I.C.S.: 335931

WOODSONS CASH STORE INC.
2221 Jacksboro Pike Ste A 15, La Follette, TN 37766
Tel.: (423) 562-1234

COMPANIES

Web Site:
http://www.woodsonsmall.com
Rev.: $10,728,394
Emp.: 60
Independent Supermarket
N.A.I.C.S.: 445110
Becky Aiken (Gen Mgr)

WOODSTOCK WIRE WORKS INC.
19 N Western Ave, Carpentersville, IL 60110-1730
Tel.: (815) 338-6501
Sales Range: $10-24.9 Million
Emp.: 398
Lamp Frames, Wire
N.A.I.C.S.: 332618

WOODSVILLE GUARANTY SAVINGS BANK
63 Central St, Woodsville, NH 03785
Tel.: (603) 747-2735   NH
Web Site:
http://www.theguarantybank.com
Year Founded: 1889
Sales Range: $250-299.9 Million
Emp.: 115
Federal Savings Institutions
N.A.I.C.S.: 522180
James E. Graham (Pres & CEO)
Wendy S. Hazlett (COO & VP)
Walter O. Young (Chm)
Robert Miller (VP-Info Sys)
Frank Stiegler (VP)
Anthony L. Brainerd (Asst VP)
Janine B. Carver (Officer-Mktg)
Shannon C. McKee (VP & Officer-Admin Branch)
A. Frank Stiegler (VP)
Linda R. Livengood (Asst VP-Retail Svcs)
Jeneil C. McAllister (VP)
Pamela S. Kinder (Asst VP & Mgr-Core Banking)
Rhonda L. Caswell (VP & Officer-Retail & HR)
Richard Manzi (Mgr-Market)
Daniel X. Stannard Jr. (VP & Officer-Lending)

WOODTRUST FINANCIAL CORPORATION
181 2nd St S, Wisconsin Rapids, WI 54494
Tel.: (715) 423-7600
Web Site: http://www.woodtrust.com
Year Founded: 1969
Sales Range: $10-24.9 Million
Emp.: 70
Bank: National Trust Companies
N.A.I.C.S.: 522110
Chad D. Kane (Pres & COO)

Subsidiaries:

WoodTrust Bank, N.A.   (1)
181 2nd St S, Wisconsin Rapids, WI 54494
Tel.: (715) 423-7600
Web Site: http://www.woodtrust.com
Sales Range: $50-74.9 Million
Emp.: 80
Commericial Banking
N.A.I.C.S.: 522110
Steven C. Bell (Chm & CEO)

WOODVINE GROUP, LLC
131 Airline Dr Ste 202, Metairie, LA 70001
Tel.: (504) 830-5400   LA
Web Site:
http://www.woodvinegroup.com
Sales Range: $25-49.9 Million
Emp.: 4
Holding Company
N.A.I.C.S.: 551112
Ned Diefenthal (Pres)
Jackie Snelling (Controller)

Subsidiaries:

Anvil Attatchments, LLC   (1)
261 Hwy 19, Slaughter, LA 70777
Tel.: (225) 654-8223
Web Site: http://www.anvilattachments.com
Sales Range: $1-9.9 Million
Emp.: 45
Mfr Construction Supplies
N.A.I.C.S.: 333120

Louisiana Chemical Equipment Co., LLC   (1)
7911 Wrenwood Blvd Ste A, Baton Rouge, LA 70809-1775
Tel.: (225) 923-3602
Web Site: http://www.lcec.com
Sales Range: $10-24.9 Million
Emp.: 20
Industrial Machinery & Equipment
N.A.I.C.S.: 423830
Stephen Rotenberg (Pres)
Dennis Vaughn (VP-Sls-Louisiana)
Raul Cantu (Exec VP-Intl Plant & Compressor Sls)
Richard Hildebrand (VP-Ops-Texas)
Steve Nelson (Gen Mgr)
Steve O'Brien (Exec VP-Intl Sls-Louisiana)
Georgia Edwards (Controller & Office Mgr)

WOODWARD ASSET CAPITAL LLC
29623 Northwestern Hwy, Southfield, MI 48034
Web Site:
http://www.woodwardassetcapital.com
Year Founded: 2007
Sales Range: $1-9.9 Million
Emp.: 7
Bank & Mortgage Software
N.A.I.C.S.: 513210
Rodney Carey (CEO)
Ronald Jasgur (Pres)

WOODWARD COMMUNICATIONS, INC.
801 Bluff St, Dubuque, IA 52001
Tel.: (563) 588-5687
Web Site: http://www.wcinet.com
Sales Range: $25-49.9 Million
Emp.: 400
Newspaper Publishers
N.A.I.C.S.: 513110
Steve Larson (CFO, Treas & Dir-Corp Svcs)
Andy Bradley (Dir-IT)
Becky Wiegel (Dir-HR)
Bob Woodward III (Sec)

Subsidiaries:

Providence Business News Inc.   (1)
300 Richmond St, Providence, RI 02903
Tel.: (401) 273-2201
Web Site: http://www.pbn.com
Rev.: $5,220,000
Emp.: 30
Newspaper Publishers
N.A.I.C.S.: 513110

WOODWARD DESIGN+BUILD
1000 S Jefferson Davis Pkwy, New Orleans, LA 70125
Tel.: (504) 822-6443
Web Site:
http://www.woodwarddesignbuild.com
Sales Range: $250-299.9 Million
Emp.: 292
Construction Services
N.A.I.C.S.: 236210
Paul Flower (CEO)
Bill Hoffman (Sr VP-Corp Plng & Dev)
Terry McCubbin (CFO)
Jerry Arnold (Dir-Safety)
Nancy Scherer (Mgr-HR)
Gary Middleton (Mgr-Woodward Millwork Grp)
Jeff Cherry (VP-Ops Support)
Lane Louque (VP & Mgr-Bus Unit)
Sean Tynan (CFO)

WOODWARD INDUSTRIES, INC.
233 Fillmore Ave, Tonawanda, NY 14150
Tel.: (716) 692-2242   NY
Web Site: http://woodwardind.com
Year Founded: 1953
Sales Range: $1-9.9 Million
Emp.: 16
Mfg C&C Prototype Foundry Patterns Blow Molds
N.A.I.C.S.: 332999
Clayton Woodward (Owner, Pres & CEO)

WOODWARD LANDSCAPE SUPPLY, INC.
661 Schuylkill Rd, Phoenixville, PA 19460
Tel.: (610) 983-9810
Web Site:
http://www.woodwardlandscapesupply.com
Year Founded: 1994
Landscaping Services
N.A.I.C.S.: 561730
Barbara Babcock (Treas)

WOODWARD YOUTH CORPORATION
1251 334th St, Woodward, IA 50276
Tel.: (515) 438-3481   IA
Web Site:
http://www.wwacademy.com
Year Founded: 1995
Sales Range: $10-24.9 Million
Child & Youth Care Services
N.A.I.C.S.: 623220
Guthrey Fritz (Dir-Admissions)
Trent Fleshner (Dir-Grp Living)
Mark Moses (Mgr-Trng)
Marcia Dodds (Dir-HR)

WOODWAY COUNTRY CLUB, INC.
540 Hoyt St, Darien, CT 06820
Tel.: (203) 322-1661   CT
Web Site: http://www.woodway.org
Year Founded: 1916
Sales Range: $10-24.9 Million
Country Club Operator
N.A.I.C.S.: 713910
John R. Considine (Pres)
Glenn W. Crafford (Treas)

WOODWING USA, INC.
19 Clifford St 8th Fl, Detroit, MI 48226
Tel.: (313) 962-0542
Web Site: http://www.woodwing.com
Multichannel Publishing & Digital Asset Management Software Publisher
N.A.I.C.S.: 513210
Ross Paterson (CEO)

WOODWORKS UNLIMITED
287 Shady Glen Dr, Coraopolis, PA 15108
Tel.: (724) 457-1331
Sales Range: $10-24.9 Million
Emp.: 7
Industrial & Personal Service Paper
N.A.I.C.S.: 424130

WOODWORTH CHEVROLET-CADILLAC-BUICK
339 N Main St 345, Andover, MA 01810
Tel.: (978) 475-6200   MA
Web Site:
http://www.woodworthmotors.com
Year Founded: 1939
Sales Range: $25-49.9 Million
Emp.: 85
Sales of New & Used Automobiles
N.A.I.C.S.: 441110

William P. Deluca Jr. (Pres)

WOODY SANDER FORD INC.
235 W Mitchell Ave, Cincinnati, OH 45232
Tel.: (513) 541-5586   OH
Web Site:
http://www.woodysanderford.com
Year Founded: 1962
Sales Range: $10-24.9 Million
Emp.: 60
Sales of New & Used Automobiles
N.A.I.C.S.: 441110
William Sander (Pres)
Len Wilkin (Mgr-Svc)
Michael Kaiser (Mgr-Fleet)
Ed Crawford (Gen Mgr)

WOODY'S ENTERPRISES LTD.
580 W Wickenburg Way, Wickenburg, AZ 85390-2266
Tel.: (928) 684-7868   AZ
Year Founded: 1971
Sales Range: $25-49.9 Million
Emp.: 300
Gasoline Station Operator
N.A.I.C.S.: 457120
Jack D. Lowe (Pres)

WOODYARD & ASSOCIATES, LLC
12995 S Cleveland Ave Ste 219, Fort Myers, FL 33907
Tel.: (239) 425-6000
Web Site: http://wa-cr.com
Sales Range: $1-9.9 Million
Emp.: 12
Real Estate Broker
N.A.I.C.S.: 531210
Tom Woodyard (Pres)

WOOFOUND, INC.
54 Earls Rd, Middle River, MD 21220
Tel.: (410) 967-9666
Web Site: http://www.traitify.com
Custom Computer Programming Services
N.A.I.C.S.: 541511
Hal Ashman (Exec Dir)

WOOL AND TUSK LTD.
420 W 23rd St, New York, NY 10011-2172
Tel.: (646) 207-4351
Web Site:
http://www.woolandtusk.com
Year Founded: 2012
Services Related to Advertising
N.A.I.C.S.: 541890
Robert Kaplan (CEO)

WOOL WHOLESALE PLUMBING SUPPLY, INC.
4340 SW 74th Ave, Miami, FL 33155
Tel.: (305) 266-7111
Web Site: http://www.woolsupply.com
Rev.: $14,700,000
Emp.: 32
Plumbing & Hydronic Heating Supplies
N.A.I.C.S.: 423720
Randy S. Wool (Pres & CEO)

WOOLDRIDGE CONSTRUCTION CO., INC.
395 Taylor Blvd Ste 120, Pleasant Hill, CA 94523
Tel.: (925) 680-7979   CA
Year Founded: 1972
Sales Range: $10-24.9 Million
Emp.: 125
Subdividers & Developers
N.A.I.C.S.: 237210
Robert Lewis (CFO)
Robert E. Wooldridge Jr. (Pres)

WOOLDRIDGE CONSTRUCTION CO., INC.

Wooldridge Construction Co., Inc.—(Continued)

Subsidiaries:

Hershey's Mill Golf Club Inc. (1)
401 Chandler Dr, West Chester, PA 19380-6951
Tel.: (610) 431-1600
Sales Range: $10-24.9 Million
Emp.: 40
Membership Sports & Recreation Clubs
N.A.I.C.S.: 713910

Hershey's Mill Restaurant Service Inc. (1)
401 Chandler Dr, West Chester, PA 19380-5838
Tel.: (610) 692-6592
Web Site:
http://www.hersheysmillgolfclub.com
Sales Range: $10-24.9 Million
Emp.: 50
Eating Place
N.A.I.C.S.: 722511
Teresa Redcay (Gen.Mgr)

Wooldridge Construction Co., Inc. (1)
1389 E Boot Rd, West Chester, PA 19380-5988
Tel.: (610) 436-8900
Sales Range: $10-24.9 Million
Emp.: 6
Subdividers & Developers
N.A.I.C.S.: 237210

Wooldridge Construction of Pennsylvania Inc. (1)
401 Chandler Dr, West Chester, PA 19380
Tel.: (610) 436-8900
Sales Range: $10-24.9 Million
Emp.: 100
Single-Family Housing Construction
N.A.I.C.S.: 236115

WOOLF DISTRIBUTING COMPANY INC.

8550 Ridgefield Rd, Crystal Lake, IL 60012
Tel.: (815) 477-9680
Web Site:
http://www.woolfdistributing.net
Sales Range: $50-74.9 Million
Emp.: 45
Distributing Building Material
N.A.I.C.S.: 423330
S. Craig Steagall (Owner & Pres)

WOOLPERT INC.

4454 Idea Ctr Blvd, Dayton, OH 45430
Tel.: (937) 461-5660
Web Site: http://www.woolpert.com
Year Founded: 1911
Engineeering Services
N.A.I.C.S.: 541330
Jeff Lovin (Sr VP & Dir-Market)
Mike Timko (Project Mgr-Facilities Market)
Jon Wiley (Mgr-Transportation Project)
Judi DeWilde Craig (Program Dir-Roads & Bridges Market)
Kirk McClurkin (COO & Sr VP)
Keith Zecchini (CTO)
Tom Mochty (Sr VP)
Scott Cattran (Pres & CEO)
Prateek Sharma (Project Mgr-Aviation Geospatial)
Suzette Stoler (VP)
Bryan Dickerson (VP & Dir-Ops & Infrastructure)

Subsidiaries:

CivilTech Engineering, Inc. (1)
11821 Telge Rd, Cypress, TX 77429
Tel.: (281) 304-0200
Web Site: http://www.civiltecheng.com
Rev.: $3,160,000
Emp.: 20
Engineeering Services
N.A.I.C.S.: 541330

Melvin G. Spinks (Pres & CEO)
Darrell L. Kaderka (VP)
Erin G. Ward (CFO)

Geomatics Data Solutions, LLC (1)
5920 NE Ray Cir Ste 210, Hillsboro, OR 97124
Tel.: (760) 536-6852
Web Site:
http://www.geomaticsdatasolutions.com
Surveying & Mapping Services
N.A.I.C.S.: 541370

Optimal GEO Inc. (1)
118 W Market St, Athens, AL 35611
Tel.: (256) 882-7788
Web Site: http://www.optimalgeo.com
Engineeering Services
N.A.I.C.S.: 541330
Colum Caldwell (Pres & CEO)
Mark Brooks (COO)

WOOLPERT LLP

4454 Idea Centre Blvd, Dayton, OH 45430-1500
Tel.: (937) 461-5660   OH
Web Site: http://www.woolpert.com
Year Founded: 1911
Sales Range: $150-199.9 Million
Emp.: 737
Planning, GIS, Environmental Services, Engineering Services, Architecture, Landscape Architecture
N.A.I.C.S.: 541330
Greg Shuttleworth (Dir-Aviation Project-Blue Ash)
Mike Avellano (VP)
Rich Simpkins (Project Mgr)
Christopher Snyder (Project Dir)
Scott Cattran (Pres & CEO)
Michael Solar (Engr-Structural)
Mark Zara (Engr-Transportation)
Jen Davis (Coord-Proposal)
Carla Fischer (Project Mgr-Aviation Design)
Ryan Thomas (Program Dir-Energy Market)
Mike Battles (Sr VP & Dir-Energy Market)
Danielle Meggyesy (Project Mgr-Energy Market)

WOOLRICH, INC.

2 Mill St, Woolrich, PA 17779
Tel.: (570) 769-6464   PA
Web Site: http://www.woolrich.com
Year Founded: 1830
Sales Range: $500-549.9 Million
Emp.: 150
Wool & Blended Fabrics, Blankets, Outdoor Apparel & Home Furnishing Product Licensing, Mfr, Whslr & Retailer
N.A.I.C.S.: 313210
Rick Osbourne (VP-Mill Ops)
Bob Spagnoletti (VP-Fin)
Nick Brayton (Pres)

Subsidiaries:

John Rich & Sons (1)
300 Delaware Ave, Wilmington, DE 19801-1671
Tel.: (302) 421-7361
Web Site: http://www.woolrich.com
Wool & Blends Cloth Work & Sport Garments Down Filled Garments Ski Wear Blankets Upholstery Wall Paneling Fabric
N.A.I.C.S.: 551112

Woolcan, Inc. (1)
1880 32nd Ave, Lachine, H8T 3J7, QC, Canada (100%)
Tel.: (514) 631-2272
Web Site: http://www.woolcan.com
Sales Range: $10-24.9 Million
Emp.: 21
Mfr of Mens & Womens Sportswear & Outerwear, Upholstery & Panel Fabrics, Blankets
N.A.I.C.S.: 313210
Jennifer Pahh (Pres & CEO)

Woolrich, Inc. - Store Division (1)
2 Mill St, Woolrich, PA 17779
Tel.: (570) 769-6464
Web Site: http://www.woolrich.com
Outdoor Apparel & Home Furnishing Stores Operator
N.A.I.C.S.: 455219
Nicholas Brayton (Pres & CEO)

WOOLWINE FORD LINCOLN, INC.

3080 Hwy 49, Collins, MS 39428
Tel.: (888) 723-6270
Web Site: http://woolwineford.com
Car Whslr
N.A.I.C.S.: 441110

WOOSTER PRODUCTS, INC.

1000 Spruce St, Wooster, OH 44691
Tel.: (330) 264-2844
Web Site: http://www.wooster-products.com
Year Founded: 1921
Sales Range: $10-24.9 Million
Emp.: 80
Ornamental & Architectural Metal Work Mfr
N.A.I.C.S.: 332323
Tim Brennan (Mgr-Sls-East & Intl)
Don Wiles (Mgr-Mktg)
Chuck Hess (Mgr-Sls-West & South)
Mike Sees (Mgr-Sys, Bar Coding & Traffic)

WOOTTON TRANSPORTATION SERVICES

1400 E Geer St Ste 6, Durham, NC 27704
Tel.: (919) 956-5726
Web Site:
http://www.woottontransportation.com
Year Founded: 1991
Sales Range: $10-24.9 Million
Emp.: 1,500
Transportation Agents & Brokers
N.A.I.C.S.: 488510
Linda Stence (Controller)

WORCESTER CENTER FOR PERFORMING ARTS

2 S Bridge St, Worcester, MA 01608
Tel.: (508) 471-1760
Year Founded: 2002
Sales Range: $10-24.9 Million
Emp.: 235
Theater
N.A.I.C.S.: 711110
Maurice Boisvert (Chm)
Kallin Johnson (Sec)
David Greenfield (Treas)
Richard Lavey (Vice Chm)
Troy Siebels (Pres & CEO)

WORCESTER COMMUNITY ACTION COUNCIL, INC.

484 Main St 2nd Fl, Worcester, MA 01608
Tel.: (508) 754-1176   MA
Web Site: http://www.wcac.net
Year Founded: 1965
Sales Range: $10-24.9 Million
Emp.: 504
Economic Development & Assistance Services
N.A.I.C.S.: 928120
Anne O'Brien (Dir-Plng)
Ellen Ganley (Dir-Dev)
Kerry Brennan (Dir-Ops & HR)
Mary Knittle (Dir-Energy Resources)

WORCESTER COUNTY FOOD BANK

474 Boston Tpke, Shrewsbury, MA 01545
Tel.: (508) 842-3663   MA

Web Site: http://www.foodbank.org
Year Founded: 1989
Sales Range: $10-24.9 Million
Emp.: 18
Food Service
N.A.I.C.S.: 624210
Jean G. McMurray (Exec Dir)
Naomi R. LeBlanc (Dir-Dev)
George M. Mange (Mgr-Warehouse)
Liz Sheehan Castro (Dir-Advocacy)
Bryanne Wainford (Dir-Ops)

WORCESTER REGIONAL TRANSIT AUTHORITY

287 Grove St, Worcester, MA 01605
Tel.: (508) 791-2389
Web Site: http://www.therta.com
Year Founded: 1974
Rev.: $24,046,094
Emp.: 220
Local & Suburban Transit
N.A.I.C.S.: 485119
Stephen O'Neil (Chief Admin. Officer)

WORD & BROWN, INSURANCE ADMINISTRATORS, INC.

721 S Parker St Ste 300, Orange, CA 92868
Tel.: (714) 835-6752   CA
Web Site:
http://www.wordandbrown.com
Year Founded: 1977
Sales Range: $25-49.9 Million
Emp.: 350
Insurance Brokerage & Benefit Administration Services
N.A.I.C.S.: 524210
Jessica Word (Pres-Word & Brown Gen Agency)
John M. Word III (Co-Founder)
Edward J. Brown Jr. (Co-Founder)
Jim W. Bennett Jr. (Reg VP)

Subsidiaries:

California Choice Benefit Administrators, Inc. (1)
721 S Parker St Ste 200, Orange, CA 92868
Tel.: (714) 542-4200
Web Site: http://www.calchoice.com
Rev.: $15,000,000
Emp.: 300
Third Party Administrator for Health Insurance
N.A.I.C.S.: 524298
Ron Goldstein (Pres & CEO)
Brenda Scott (Sr VP)

WORD OF GOD FELLOWSHIP INC.

3901 HWY 121, Bedford, TX 76021
Tel.: (817) 571-1229
Web Site: http://www.daystar.com
Rev.: $15,096,843
Emp.: 300
Television Broadcasting Station
N.A.I.C.S.: 516120
Marcus Lamb (Pres)

WORD OF MOUTH FINE CATERING

919 W 12th St, Austin, TX 78703-4117
Tel.: (512) 472-9500
Web Site:
http://www.wordofmouthcatering.com
Caterers
N.A.I.C.S.: 722320

WORD SYSTEMS, INC.

9045 River Rd Ste 125, Indianapolis, IN 46240
Tel.: (317) 544-0499
Web Site: http://www.wsystems.com
Year Founded: 1977
Commuication System Services
N.A.I.C.S.: 517810
Jim Halsmer (Pres)

COMPANIES / WORKHOUSE PUBLICITY

Subsidiaries:

Joloha Enterprises, Inc. (1)
2737 Gilchrist Rd, Akron, OH 44305
Tel.: (330) 253-2000
Web Site: http://www.rros.com
Office Equipment Merchant Whslr
N.A.I.C.S.: 423420

WORDEN BROTHERS, INC.
Five Oaks Ofc Park 4905 Pine Cone Dr, Durham, NC 27707
Tel.: (919) 408-0542
Web Site: http://www.worden.com
Sales Range: $10-24.9 Million
Emp.: 80
Free Stock Market Software, Databases, Investing Advice & Seminars
N.A.I.C.S.: 541512
Michael Thompson (Dir-Bus & Client Rels)

WORDEN COMPANY
199 E 17th St, Holland, MI 49423
Tel.: (616) 392-1848
Web Site:
 http://www.wordencompany.com
Rev.: $20,000,000
Emp.: 150
Library Furniture
N.A.I.C.S.: 337127
Bill Hendrick (Owner)

WORDEN MARTIN INC.
1404 N Dunlap Ave, Savoy, IL 61874
Tel.: (217) 352-7901   DE
Web Site:
 http://www.wordenmartin.com
Year Founded: 1948
Sales Range: $75-99.9 Million
Emp.: 225
New & Used Car Dealers
N.A.I.C.S.: 441110
Mark Pelafos (COO & Controller)
Charles Shapland (Pres & CEO)
Drew Danalewich (Mgr-Sls)

WORK SERVICES CORPORATION
1343 Hatton Rd, Wichita Falls, TX 76302-3007
Tel.: (940) 766-3207   TX
Web Site:
 http://www.workservicescorp.com
Year Founded: 1954
Sales Range: $25-49.9 Million
Emp.: 650
Disability Assistance Services
N.A.I.C.S.: 624120
Gary L. Cardwell (Vice Chm)
David TooGood (Pres & CEO)

WORK TRAINING CENTER, INC
2255 Fair St, Chico, CA 95928
Tel.: (530) 343-7994   CA
Web Site: http://www.wtcinc.org
Year Founded: 1960
Sales Range: $10-24.9 Million
Emp.: 376
Disability Assistance Services
N.A.I.C.S.: 624120
Andrea Moriarty (Dir-Community Svcs)
Brett Barker (Dir-Admin Svcs)
Don Krysakowski (Exec Dir)
Jose Bravo (Pres)
Laura Carter (CFO)

WORK, INC.
25 Beach St, Dorchester, MA 02122
Tel.: (617) 691-1500   MA
Web Site: http://www.workinc.org
Year Founded: 1970
Sales Range: $10-24.9 Million
Emp.: 939
Disability Assistance Services

N.A.I.C.S.: 624120
James Cassetta (Pres & CEO)
Sharon Smith (COO & Sr VP)
Philip J. Carver (Asst Treas)
Dave Anderson (CFO & Treas)
James R. Flanagan (Chm)
Phil Dould (Vice Chm)
Al Fava (VP-Comml Svcs)

WORKCARE, INC.
300 S Harbor Blvd Ste 600, Anaheim, CA 92805
Tel.: (714) 978-7488
Web Site: http://www.workcare.com
Year Founded: 1997
Sales Range: $1-9.9 Million
Emp.: 85
Other Management Consulting Services
N.A.I.C.S.: 541618
Peter P. Greaney (Chm & Chief Medical Officer)
John Paul M. Longphre (Sr VP)
William Nixon (Pres & CEO)
Jonathan M. Szenics (Assoc Dir-Medical)
Dennis W. Stephens (Assoc Dir-Medical)
Patrick D. OCallahan (Assoc Dir-Medical)
Rajy S. Abulhosn (Assoc Dir-Medical)
Maria Henderson (COO & Chief Innovation Officer)
Barry Fager (CFO)
Allison Khosroshahin (VP-HR)
Alyson Smith Lebow (Dir-Ops-Incident Intervention Program)
Jeffrey Jacobs (VP)
Anthony Harris (VP)

Subsidiaries:

Hpm Corp. (1)
2625 W Entiat Ave, Kennewick, WA 99336
Tel.: (509) 737-8939
Web Site: http://www.hpmcorporation.com
Sales Range: $1-9.9 Million
Emp.: 37
Management Consulting Services
N.A.I.C.S.: 541611
Cleveland Mooers (Pres & Founder)

WORKCOMPEDI, INC.
4250 Veterans Memorial Hwy Ste 301e, Holbrook, NY 11741
Tel.: (800) 297-6909
Web Site:
 http://www.workcompedi.com
Year Founded: 2007
Sales Range: $1-9.9 Million
Emp.: 15
Clearinghouse for The Work Comp, Auto & Personal Injury Markets
N.A.I.C.S.: 522320
Marc Menendez (Pres & CEO)
Jen Jones-Novara (Dir-Ops & Support)
Amy Chiarelli (Controller)
Brendan Friar (Sr VP)

WORKER BEES, INC.
500 Aurora Ave N Ste 105, Seattle, WA 98109
Tel.: (206) 930-3417
Web Site:
 http://www.workerbees.com
Year Founded: 1992
Sales Range: $10-24.9 Million
Emp.: 1
Advertising Services
N.A.I.C.S.: 541810
Larry Asher (Dir-Creative)

WORKERS UNITED
22 S 22nd St, Philadelphia, PA 19103
Tel.: (646) 448-6414
Web Site:
 https://www.workersunited.org

Year Founded: 2009
Labor Organization Services
N.A.I.C.S.: 813930

WORKERS' COMPENSATION RATING & INSPECTION BUREAU OF MASSACHUSETTS
101 Arch St, Boston, MA 02110
Tel.: (617) 439-9030   MA
Web Site: http://www.wcribma.org
Year Founded: 1915
Sales Range: $10-24.9 Million
Emp.: 60
Insurer Association
N.A.I.C.S.: 813910
Daniel Judson (Pres)

WORKERS' CREDIT UNION
815 Main St, Fitchburg, MA 01420-0900
Tel.: (800) 221-4020   MA
Web Site: http://www.wcu.com
Year Founded: 1914
Credit Union
N.A.I.C.S.: 522130
Douglas J. Petersen (Pres & CEO)
Marina M. Raher (Chm)
Mary Heafy (Vice Chm)

Subsidiaries:

The Braley & Wellington Insurance Agency Corporation (1)
44 Park Ave, Worcester, MA 01609
Tel.: (508) 754-7255
Web Site:
 http://www.braleywellingtongroup.com
Insurance Services
N.A.I.C.S.: 524298
Faith E. Canario (VP & Partner)
Joe Gatchell (Mgr-Claims)
John W. Braley III (VP & Partner)
Parker Wellington Jr. (Pres & CEO)

WORKFORCE INVESTMENT BOARD OF HERKIMER, MADISON & ONEIDA COUNTIES
209 Elizabeth St, Utica, NY 13501
Tel.: (315) 798-6462   NY
Web Site: http://www.working-solutions.org
Year Founded: 1982
Sales Range: $1-9.9 Million
Emp.: 100
Human Resource Consulting Services
N.A.I.C.S.: 541612
Alice J. Savino (Exec Dir)
Wilber Allen (Chm)
Mike Choquette (Vice Chm)
Barbara Schram (Sec)
Amy Turner (Treas)

WORKFORCE INVESTMENT BOARD OF THE SOUTHWEST REGION, INC.
105 Range Line Rd Lower Level E, Joplin, MO 64801
Tel.: (417) 206-1717   MO
Web Site:
 http://www.workforcezone.net
Year Founded: 2001
Sales Range: $10-24.9 Million
Emp.: 8
Employment Placement Services
N.A.I.C.S.: 561311
Jasen Jones (Exec Dir)
Bob Shryock (Mgr-Fiscal)
Sherri Rhuems (Mgr-Ops)

WORKFORCE OUTSOURCE SERVICES, INC.
475 Riverside Dr Ste 1350, New York, NY 10115
Tel.: (212) 870-2260   NY
Web Site: http://www.wforce.org
Year Founded: 2005

Sales Range: $10-24.9 Million
Emp.: 199
Workforce Development Services
N.A.I.C.S.: 561311
David Rast (Mgr-Client Svc)
Addie Rimmer (Dir-Student Learning)
Daniella Olibrice (Mgr-University & Community External Affairs)
Anthony Amato (Dir-Academic Ops)
Jessica Miller (Asst Dir-Academics)
Arthur M. Langer (Founder & Chm)
Beatrice Leon (Exec Dir-External Rels)
Danny Black (Mgr-Client Svc)
Jim Minta (Program Mgr & Mgr-Client Svc)
Russ Yorks (Dir-Veterans Programs)

WORKFORCE SOLUTIONS CAMERON
851 Old Alice Rd, Brownsville, TX 78521
Tel.: (956) 548-6700   TX
Web Site: http://www.wfscameron.org
Year Founded: 1983
Sales Range: $10-24.9 Million
Emp.: 15
Employment Placement Services
N.A.I.C.S.: 561311
Pat Stanley Hobbs (Exec Dir)
Gabriela Sanchez (Mgr-Fin)

WORKFORCE SOLUTIONS CAPITAL AREA WORKFORCE BOARD
6505 Airport Blvd Ste 101 A, Austin, TX 78752
Tel.: (512) 454-9675   TX
Web Site:
 http://www.wfscapitalarea.com
Year Founded: 1984
Sales Range: $25-49.9 Million
Emp.: 37
Workforce Development Services
N.A.I.C.S.: 561311
Alan Miller (Exec Dir)
Jerry Neef (CFO)
Angela Benavides (CIO)
Adrian Neely (Chm)
Michelle Adamolekun (Treas & Sec)

WORKFORCE SOLUTIONS FOR SOUTH TEXAS
1701 E Hillside Rd, Laredo, TX 78044-1757
Tel.: (956) 722-3973   TX
Web Site:
 http://www.southtexasworkforce.org
Year Founded: 1997
Sales Range: $10-24.9 Million
Emp.: 16
Employment Placement Services
N.A.I.C.S.: 561311
Bertha Gomez (Accountant)
Kelly Elizondo (Mgr-Contract)
Rogelio Trevino (Exec Dir)

WORKGROUP TECHNOLOGY PARTNERS
207 Larrabee Rd, Westbrook, ME 04092
Tel.: (207) 856-5300
Web Site: http://www.wgtech.com
Year Founded: 1995
Emp.: 100
IT Consulting Services
N.A.I.C.S.: 541512
Jack Eaton (Founder & CEO)
Wayne Krauth (CTO)
Rob Herman (Mgr-Integration)

WORKHOUSE PUBLICITY
1 Little W 12th St, New York, NY 10014
Tel.: (212) 645-8006

4563

WORKHOUSE PUBLICITY

WORKHOUSE Publicity—(Continued)
Web Site:
http://www.workhousepr.net
Year Founded: 1999
Sales Range: $1-9.9 Million
Emp.: 22
Publicity, Marketing, Advertising, Design & Special Events
N.A.I.C.S.: 541810
Adam Nelson (CEO)
Devon Mack (COO)

WORKING CLASS, INC.
168 Duane St, New York, NY 10013
Tel.: (212) 941-1199
Sales Range: Less than $1 Million
Emp.: 5
N.A.I.C.S.: 541810
Charlie Metcalf (Founder & Dir-Creative)

WORKING MEDIA GROUP
21 W 38th St, New York, NY 10018
Tel.: (212) 251-0021
Web Site:
http://www.workingmediagroup.com
Year Founded: 2005
Sales Range: $25-49.9 Million
Emp.: 14
Fiscal Year-end: 12/31/14
Advertising Agencies
N.A.I.C.S.: 541810
Kerry P. Tracy (Co-Founder & CEO)
Martin D. Avallone (Co-Founder, Chm & Pres)

WORKLYN PARTNERS
101 Ave of Americas 9th Fl, New York, NY 10013
Web Site:
http://www.worklynpartners.com
Year Founded: 2020
Venture Capital & Private Equity
N.A.I.C.S.: 523999
Zack Miller (Co-Founder & Partner)

Subsidiaries:

Softwink, Inc. (1)
4651 Salisbury Rd Ste 185, Jacksonville, FL 32256-0935
Tel.: (904) 296-9100
Web Site: http://www.quadrantsec.com
Computer Related Services
N.A.I.C.S.: 541519
Ian Bush (Pres & CEO)
Champ Clark (CTO)

WORKMAN COMMERCIAL CONSTRUCTION SERVICES, LTD.
2211 S I Hwy 35 Ste 401, Austin, TX 78741
Tel.: (512) 326-9293
Web Site:
http://www.workmancommercial.com
Year Founded: 1971
Sales Range: $25-49.9 Million
Emp.: 40
Nonresidential Construction
N.A.I.C.S.: 236220
Kyle D. Workman (Pres & CEO)
Paula W. Workman (CFO)

WORKMENS CIRCLE INC.
247 W 37th St Fl 5, New York, NY 10018
Tel.: (212) 889-6800
Web Site: http://www.circle.org
Rev.: $25,800,000
Emp.: 35
Fraternal Life Insurance Organization
N.A.I.C.S.: 524113
Robert Kaplan (Pres)
Madelon Braun (Pres)
Tony Lopez (Dir-Engrg)

WORKNET PINELLAS INC.
2312 Gulf-to Bay Blvd, Clearwater, FL 33755
Tel.: (727) 524-4344
Web Site:
http://www.worknetpinellas.org
Sales Range: $10-24.9 Million
Employment Services
N.A.I.C.S.: 561311
Ed Peachey (Pres & CEO)
Kristin Dailey (Dir-Economic Dev Svcs)
Don Shepherd (Dir-Special Projects)

WORKPLACE IMPACT
9325 Progress Pkwy, Mentor, OH 44060-1855
Tel.: (440) 639-9100 DE
Web Site:
http://www.workplaceimpact.com
Year Founded: 1988
Sales Range: $10-24.9 Million
Emp.: 60
Sales Promotion
N.A.I.C.S.: 541810
Shelly Sekki (Pres)
Terry Goins (Exec VP-Sls)

WORKPLACE INSTALL NETWORK, INC.
10102 Whitesel Rd, Ashland, VA 23005
Tel.: (804) 412-2127
Web Site:
https://workplaceinstallnetwork.com
Year Founded: 1995
Transportation, Logistics, Supply Chain & Storage
N.A.I.C.S.: 485999
Kent Ford (Pres & CEO)

Subsidiaries:

Office Interiors of Virginia, Inc. (1)
10168 Cedar Ridge Dr, Ashland, VA 23005
Tel.: (804) 550-0003
Web Site: http://www.oi-va.com
Sales Range: $1-9.9 Million
Emp.: 28
Home Furnishing Distr
N.A.I.C.S.: 423220

WORKPLACE SOLUTIONS INC.
317 Village Rd Ste 103, Virginia Beach, VA 23454
Tel.: (757) 563-2845
Web Site:
http://www.yourofficedesign.com
Year Founded: 1999
Sales Range: $1-9.9 Million
Emp.: 6
Contract Furniture Dealer
N.A.I.C.S.: 423210
Maryann Woods (Pres)

WORKPLACE SOLUTIONS, LLC
30800 Telegraph Rd Ste 2985, Bingham Farms, MI 48025-4524
Tel.: (248) 430-2500
Web Site:
http://www.myworkplacesolutions.com
Sales Range: $50-74.9 Million
Emp.: 250
Office Furniture
N.A.I.C.S.: 423210
Joesph Eatman Jr. (CEO)

WORKS24 CORPORATION
3508 French Park Dr, Edmond, OK 73034
Tel.: (800) 460-4653
Web Site: http://www.works24.com
Year Founded: 1994
Digital Marketing Services
N.A.I.C.S.: 334610

Brian W. Robinson (VP-Sls & Mktg)
Rick Wilson (Exec VP-Sls)

WORKSCAPES INC.
1173 N Orange Ave, Orlando, FL 32804
Tel.: (407) 599-6770 FL
Web Site:
http://www.workscapes.com
Year Founded: 1998
Sales Range: $10-24.9 Million
Emp.: 50
Equipment & Related Product Distr
N.A.I.C.S.: 449110
Elizabeth Dvorak (Owner & CEO)
Richard Dvorak (Pres)
Christie Hill (Exec VP-Sls & Mktg)

Subsidiaries:

Workscapes Inc. (1)
9302 Florida Palm Dr, Tampa, FL 33169
Tel.: (813) 463-9261
Web Site: http://www.workscapes.com
Sales Range: $10-24.9 Million
Emp.: 15
Office Furniture Dealer
N.A.I.C.S.: 423210
Mo Tawfik (Pres-Market)
Richard Dvorak (Pres)
Christie Hill (Exec VP-Sls & Mktg)

WORKSIGHTED
275 Hoover Blvd, Holland, MI 49423
Tel.: (616) 546-2691
Web Site:
http://www.worksighted.com
Year Founded: 2000
Sales Range: $1-9.9 Million
Emp.: 71
Information Technology Consulting Services
N.A.I.C.S.: 541512
Mat Nguyen (Pres)
Mike Harris (CEO)

WORKSMART
100 Meredith Dr Ste 200, Durham, NC 27713
Tel.: (919) 484-1010
Web Site: http://www.worksmart.com
Year Founded: 2000
Rev.: $3,200,000
Emp.: 25
Information Technology Services & Solutions
N.A.I.C.S.: 519290
Ronald Unger (Founder & CEO)
Ricky Ayers (CFO)
Clay Harris (Pres & COO)

WORKSPACE DEVELOPMENT LLC
5601 6th Ave S, Seattle, WA 98108-2522
Tel.: (206) 768-8000
Web Site:
http://www.bankandoffice.com
Year Founded: 1934
Sales Range: $25-49.9 Million
Emp.: 100
Commercial Interior Design Services
N.A.I.C.S.: 423210
Jeff Ros (Pres)

WORKSQUARED INC.
4633 Patterson E Ste A, Grand Rapids, MI 49512
Tel.: (616) 774-9122
Web Site:
http://www.worksquared.com
Year Founded: 1959
Sales Range: $25-49.9 Million
Emp.: 65
Distr Of Furniture
N.A.I.C.S.: 423210

Dan Rosema (Pres)
Janet Barnes (Acct Mgr)
Barbara Church (Acct Mgr)

WORKWAY, INC.
601 S Glenoaks Blvd Ste 211, Burbank, CA 91502
Tel.: (818) 333-1766
Web Site: http://www.workway.com
Year Founded: 2005
Sales Range: $25-49.9 Million
Emp.: 500
Staffing Services
N.A.I.C.S.: 561311
Rachel Franchi (Mgr-Recruiting)

Subsidiaries:

eWork Healthcare (1)
100 Spear St Ste 740, San Francisco, CA 94103-2113
Tel.: (415) 546-4800
Sales Range: $10-24.9 Million
Emp.: 60
Healthcare Staffing Support Services
N.A.I.C.S.: 561311

WORKWELL TECHNOLOGIES, INC.
2796 Loker Ave W Ste 111, Carlsbad, CA 92010-6618
Tel.: (760) 707-5530
Web Site:
http://www.processingpoint.com
Office Equipment Merchant Whslr
N.A.I.C.S.: 423420
Chad Buckmaster (Pres)

WORKWISE, LLC
N 80 W 12878 Fond Du Lac Ave, Menomonee Falls, WI 53051
Tel.: (262) 345-3600 WI
Web Site:
http://www.workwisellc.com
Year Founded: 2001
Sales Range: $1-9.9 Million
Emp.: 80
RB-ERP Mfg System Software Solutions
N.A.I.C.S.: 513210
Wayne T. Wedell (Pres & CEO)

Subsidiaries:

OnContact Software Corp. (1)
N80 W12878 Fond du Lac Ave, Menomonee Falls, WI 53051
Tel.: (262) 345-3600
Web Site: http://www.oncontact.com
Rev.: $5,000,000
Emp.: 40
CRM Solutions for Mid-Market Companies
N.A.I.C.S.: 513210
George Kofman (Chm)
Jon Zimmerman (Gen Mgr)
Wayne Wedell (Pres)

WORLD AEROSPACE CORPORATION
8625 Monticello Ln N, Maple Grove, MN 55369-4548
Tel.: (763) 424-8999 MN
Web Site:
http://www.worldaerospace.com
Year Founded: 1946
Sales Range: $50-74.9 Million
Emp.: 20
Provider of Parts & Components for Jet Engines & Aircraft
N.A.I.C.S.: 336413
Isaac E. Phelps (Chm, Pres & CEO)
Todd Shopp (Mgr-Quality Assurance)

WORLD AFFAIRS COUNCIL OF PHILADELPHIA
1 S Broad St Ste 2M, Philadelphia, PA 19107
Tel.: (215) 561-4700 PA
Web Site: http://www.wacphila.org
Year Founded: 1948

Sales Range: $1-9.9 Million
Emp.: 15
Social Advocacy Services
N.A.I.C.S.: 813319
Mitchell Abrams *(Fin Dir)*
Hayley Boyle *(Dir-Dev & Membership)*
Denise Bala *(Dir-Public Programs)*
Raza Bokhari *(Vice Chm)*
Joseph V. Del Raso *(Treas)*
William F. MacDonald *(Sec)*
Craig Snyder *(Pres & CEO)*

WORLD CLASS DRIVING
125 Maple Ave, Chester, NJ 07930
Web Site:
    http://www.worldclassdriving.com
Year Founded: 2007
Sales Range: $1-9.9 Million
Emp.: 15
Guided Road & Track Tours
N.A.I.C.S.: 561520
Aaron Fessler *(Co-Founder & CEO)*
Tom Mizzone *(Co-Founder & CFO)*
Rob Messmer *(VP-Sls)*

WORLD CLASS FLOWERS
1601 Duerer St, Egg Harbor City, NJ 08215
Tel.: (609) 965-4200
Web Site:
    http://www.worldclassflowers.com
Sales Range: $25-49.9 Million
Emp.: 245
Provider of Flowers & Florist Services
N.A.I.C.S.: 424930
Robert Gravitz *(Pres)*
Bobby Pauls *(Mgr-Shipping)*

WORLD CLASS INDUSTRIES INC.
925 N 15th Ave, Hiawatha, IA 52233
Tel.: (319) 378-1766
Web Site:
    http://www.worldclassind.com
Sales Range: $10-24.9 Million
Emp.: 22
Iron & Steel (Ferrous) Products
N.A.I.C.S.: 423510
Sandy Kaloutek *(VP)*
Jack Boser *(Mgr-Site)*
Jenny Gundacker *(Controller)*
Brent R. Cobb *(CEO)*

WORLD COUNCIL OF CREDIT UNIONS, INC.
5710 Mineral Point Rd, Madison, WI 53705-4493
Tel.: (608) 395-2000   WI
Web Site: http://www.woccu.org
Year Founded: 1970
Sales Range: $25-49.9 Million
Emp.: 75
Credit Union Operator
N.A.I.C.S.: 522130
Brian Branch *(Pres & CEO)*
Paul Treinen *(COO)*
Brian McCrory *(Chm)*
Steve Stapp *(Vice Chm)*
Diana Dykstra *(Treas)*

WORLD ELECTRONICS SALES & SERVICE
3000 Kutztown Rd, Reading, PA 19605
Tel.: (610) 939-9800
Web Site: http://www.world-electronics.com
Sales Range: $25-49.9 Million
Emp.: 120
Printed Circuit Boards
N.A.I.C.S.: 334412
Ryan Gardecki *(Mgr-IT)*

WORLD EMBLEM INTERNATIONAL, INC.
1500 NE 131 St, Miami, FL 33161
Tel.: (305) 899-9006
Web Site: http://www.weicatalog.com
Year Founded: 1993
Rev.: $18,800,000
Emp.: 200
Miscellaneous Textile Product Mills
N.A.I.C.S.: 314999
Erin Gallagher *(Dir-Mktg & Mgr-Bus Dev)*
Randy Carr *(Pres & CEO)*
Barbara Azcuy *(Dir-Client Svcs)*
Clarence Foster *(Chief People Officer)*
James Kozel *(VP-Ops)*
Manuel Figueroa *(VP-Res & Dev)*
Nicolas Restrepo *(VP-Sls)*
Tony Morando *(Reg VP-Sls)*

WORLD EMERGENCY RELIEF
425 W Allen Ave Ste 111, San Dimas, CA 91773
Tel.: (909) 593-7140   CA
Web Site:
    http://www.worldemergencyrelief.org
Year Founded: 1985
Sales Range: $10-24.9 Million
Hunger Relief Services
N.A.I.C.S.: 624210
Kristy Scott *(CEO)*
Lawrence E. Cutting *(Sec)*
Gary Becks *(Chm)*
Mark Duzik *(CFO)*

WORLD ENERGY ALTERNATIVES, LLC
225 Franklin St Ste 1460, Boston, MA 02110
Tel.: (617) 889-7300
Web Site: http://www.worldenergy.net
Year Founded: 1998
Biodiesel Mfr & Whslr
N.A.I.C.S.: 325199
Ignacio J. Diaz Bobillo *(Mng Dir-Bus Dev-Intl)*
Gene Gebolys *(Founder, Pres & CEO)*
Michael Laznik *(CFO & COO)*
Susan Purdue *(VP-Mfg)*
Brendan Marusa *(VP-Logistics & Ops)*
Greg Hopkins *(Mng Dir-Engrg & Tech Svcs)*

WORLD ENTERPRISES
53 W Angelo Ave, Salt Lake City, UT 84115   UT
Web Site: http://www.coin-opgames.com
Year Founded: 1977
Sales Range: $25-49.9 Million
Emp.: 50
Game Machines, Coin-Operated
N.A.I.C.S.: 423990
Carson Jenkins *(Pres)*

WORLD FINANCIAL NETWORK CREDIT CARD MASTER TRUST
3100 Easton Sq P 3108, Columbus, OH 43219
Tel.: (614) 729-5044   DE
Credit Card Processing Services
N.A.I.C.S.: 522320
Michael Blackham *(Treas)*

WORLD FINER FOODS, INC.
300 Broadacres Dr, Bloomfield, NJ 07003-3153
Tel.: (973) 338-0300   NY
Web Site: http://www.worldfiner.com
Year Founded: 1990
Sales Range: $75-99.9 Million
Emp.: 82
Specialty Foods Sales, Marketing & Distribution; Food Importer

N.A.I.C.S.: 424490
John H. Affel *(Dir-Mktg)*
Todd Newstadt *(VP-Mktg)*
William Flynn *(CFO)*
Susan Guerin *(Pres & CEO)*

Subsidiaries:

InterNatural Foods LLC.   (1)
1455 Broad St 4th Fl, Bloomfield, NJ 07003
Tel.: (973) 338-1499
Web Site: http://www.internaturalfoods.com
Food Products Mfr
N.A.I.C.S.: 311999

Liberty Richter   (1)
1455 Broad St 4th Fl, Bloomfield, NJ 07003
Tel.: (973) 338-0300
Web Site: http://www.libertyrichter.com
Sales Range: $25-49.9 Million
Emp.: 70
Natural & Specialty Gourmet Food Distr
N.A.I.C.S.: 424490

WORLD FORD PENSACOLA
6397 Pensacola Blvd, Pensacola, FL 32505
Tel.: (850) 476-9050
Web Site:
    http://www.worldfordpensacola.com
Year Founded: 1969
Sales Range: $25-49.9 Million
Emp.: 145
New Car Dealers
N.A.I.C.S.: 441110
Jason McDonald *(Mgr-Sls)*

WORLD GOLF FOUNDATION
1 World Golf Pl, Saint Augustine, FL 32092
Tel.: (904) 940-4000   FL
Web Site:
    http://www.worldgolffoundation.org
Year Founded: 1989
Sales Range: $25-49.9 Million
Emp.: 137
Golf Promotion Services
N.A.I.C.S.: 711310
Steve Mona *(CEO)*
Jay Monahan *(Chm)*

WORLD HOLDINGS INC.
100 N Arlington Ave Ste 340, Reno, NV 89501
Tel.: (775) 323-1066
Rev.: $11,900,000
Emp.: 125
Subdividers & Developers
N.A.I.C.S.: 237210

Subsidiaries:

Plaza Resort Club Inc.   (1)
121 W St, Reno, NV 89501
Tel.: (775) 786-2200
Web Site: http://www.plazaresortclub.com
Sales Range: $1-9.9 Million
Emp.: 35
Subdividers & Developers, Nec
N.A.I.C.S.: 237210

RJB Development Co. Inc.   (1)
100 N Arlington Ave Ste 340, Reno, NV 89501
Tel.: (775) 323-1066
Rev.: $8,900,000
Emp.: 40
Subdividers & Developers, Nec
N.A.I.C.S.: 237210

RJB Management Co.   (1)
100 N Arlington Ave Ste 340, Reno, NV 89501
Tel.: (775) 323-1066
Rev.: $110,000
Emp.: 45
Real Estate Managers
N.A.I.C.S.: 531210

WORLD HOPE INTERNATIONAL
1330 Braddock Pl Ste 301, Alexandria, VA 22314

Tel.: (703) 594-8527   IN
Web Site: http://www.worldhope.org
Year Founded: 1996
Sales Range: $10-24.9 Million
Emp.: 43
Christian Ministry Services
N.A.I.C.S.: 813110
Gayle Rietmulder *(CFO & VP-Fin)*
Keith Norris *(Dir-Water & Sanitation)*
Alison Padget *(VP-Programs)*

WORLD INSURANCE ASSOCIATES LLC
100 Wood Ave S 4th Fl, Iselin, NJ 08830
Tel.: (732) 380-0900
Web Site:
    https://www.worldinsurance.com
Year Founded: 2011
Emp.: 200
Insurance Agencies & Brokerages Services
N.A.I.C.S.: 524210
Jeff Kroeger *(Exec VP & Head-Comml Lines)*
Rich Eknoian *(Co-Founder, CEO & Partner)*
Frank Costa *(Chief Growth Officer)*
Phil Nisbet *(Co-Founder)*
Greg Kroeger *(Exec VP & Co-Head-Transportation Unit)*
Ed Wagins *(Founder & Co-Head-Transportation Unit)*
Jeffrey Deldin *(Exec VP & Head-Surety Bonds Unit & New England Reg)*
Kimberly Briggs *(Deputy Gen Counsel)*
Michael Mann *(Chief Placement Officer)*
Joe Klein *(Exec VP-Natl Accts Practice)*
Tom Fitzgerald *(Pres-World Retail)*
Jeff Kroeger *(Exec VP & Head-Comml lines)*

Subsidiaries:

Calhoun Agency, Inc.   (1)
19 Tanner St, Haddonfield, NJ 08033
Tel.: (856) 428-8090
Web Site: http://www.calhounagency.com
Insurance Agencies & Brokerages
N.A.I.C.S.: 524210
Pete LaMaina *(VP)*

Cohen Partners, LLC   (1)
500 5th Ave Ste 2210, New York, NY 10110
Tel.: (212) 661-0465
Web Site: http://www.cpinsurance.com
Sales Range: $1-9.9 Million
Emp.: 10
Insurance Agencies & Brokerages
N.A.I.C.S.: 524210
Barry Cohen *(Pres)*
Karl Janssen *(Acct Exec)*
Renuka Khanna *(Controller)*
Sonia Smith *(Acct Exec)*
Daniel Cohen *(Acct Exec)*

Dunhour Agency, Inc.   (1)
44 Tanner St, Haddonfield, NJ 08033
Web Site: https://www.worldinsurance.com
Insurance Related Activities
N.A.I.C.S.: 524298

Durfee-Buffinton Insurance Agency Inc.   (1)
377 2nd St, Fall River, MA 02722
Tel.: (508) 679-6486
Web Site:
    http://www.durfeebuffintoninsurance.com
Insurance Related Activities
N.A.I.C.S.: 524298
Gloria Correia *(Office Mgr)*

Exchange Underwriters, Incorporated   (1)
2111 N Franklin Dr Ste 100, Washington, PA 15301
Tel.: (724) 745-1600
Web Site:
    https://www.exchangeunderwriters.com

WORLD INSURANCE ASSOCIATES LLC

World Insurance Associates LLC—(Continued)
Insurance Agents
N.A.I.C.S.: 524210
James Andy (VP-Bus Dev)
Debbie Crawford (Mgr-Policy & Procedure)
Diane Merrick (Mgr-Comml Lines)
John Dowling (VP-Comml Accounts)
Steve Sculli (VP)
Donna Spina (VP-Sls)
Bill Cunningham (COO)
Gilda Chen (Controller)
Donna Lynch (VP-Mktg)
Cindy Spalla (Mgr-Personal Lines)
Robert Heinle (VP-Sls)
Edward Powell (VP-Sls)
Marni M. Barnhart (Mgr-Mktg)
Kara Dantry (Acct Mgr-Comml Lines)
Karen Frame (Acct Mgr-Comml Lines)
Debbie Sim (Acct Mgr-Comml Lines)
Kate Thompson (Acct Mgr-Comml Lines)
Kimberly Wietasch (Acct Mgr-Comml Lines)
Brenda Bellotti (Acct Mgr-Personal Lines)
Cindy Slade (Acct Mgr-Personal Lines)
Jenny Zatawski (Acct Mgr-Personal Lines)
Sunny Schreckengost (Acct Mgr-Personal Lines)

Fairways Insurance Services, Inc. (1)
Monroe Bldg Ste 210 101 Route 130 S,
Cinnaminson, NJ 08077
Tel.: (856) 786-9100
Web Site: http://www.fairwaysinsurance.com
Insurance Related Activities
N.A.I.C.S.: 524298
Patrick Dever (VP-Sls)

Foy Insurance Group, Inc. (1)
64 Portsmouth Ave, Exeter, NH 03833
Tel.: (603) 772-4781
Web Site: http://www.foyinsurance.com
Sales Range: $1-9.9 Million
Emp.: 25
Insurance Agents, Brokers, And Service, N
N.A.I.C.S.: 524210
Barbara Harris (Mgr-Salem)
Crystal Moretti (Acct Mgr-Dover)
Daniel C. Mariotti (VP-Dover)
Denise Stark (Mgr-Tilton)
Dennis Purnell (Sr Acct Exec)
Heidi SanSouci (Asst Mgr-Manchester)
Jeff Foy (COO, Principal & Mgr-Manchester Office)
Michael W. Sawyer (Mgr-Sls & Mktg-Scardorough)
Mike Calzone (Mgr-Milford)
Peter Camello (Mgr-Nashua)
Sompong Healey (Mgr-Customer Svc-Dover)
Linda Hamel (Supvr-Acctg)
Mike Foy (Pres)

HTK/Hunt Traina Kennard Insurance Agency, Inc. (1)
656 Shrewsbury Ave Ste 200, Tinton Falls, NJ 07724
Tel.: (732) 747-6400
Web Site: http://www.worldins.net
Sales Range: $1-9.9 Million
Emp.: 150
Commercial & Personal Insurance Related Activities
N.A.I.C.S.: 524298
Glenn M. Kennard (Partner)
Kevin Stiesi (Mgr-Comml Lines)
W. Richard Hunt (Partner)

Hadley & Lyden, Inc. (1)
1960 Howell Branch Rd, Winter Park, FL 32792
Tel.: (407) 679-8181
Web Site: http://www.hadley-lyden.com
Insurance Agents, Brokers, And Service, N
N.A.I.C.S.: 524210
James P. Lyden (CEO)
Scott A. Lyden (Pres)
Brad Allen (VP)
Patrick Dejong (VP)
Martin S. Weckerle (Treas)

Livingston Insurance Agency, Inc. (1)
301 S Livingston Ave, Livingston, NJ 07039
Tel.: (973) 994-9898
Web Site: http://www.livingstonagency.com
Sales Range: $1-9.9 Million
Emp.: 15
Insurance Agent/Broker

N.A.I.C.S.: 524210
Edward Sperling (Dir)
Mitchell Bisgeier (COO & Principal)
Robert Peason (CFO & Principal)

Pensionmark Retirement Group LLC (1)
24 E Cota St, Santa Barbara, CA 93101
Tel.: (805) 456-6260
Web Site: http://www.pensionmark.com
Sales Range: $1-9.9 Million
Emp.: 50
Investment Consulting
N.A.I.C.S.: 523940
Troy Hammond (Pres & CEO)
Devyn Duex (VP-Client Rels)
Ronnie Cox (Dir-Investments & Tech)
Taylor Stone (Branch Mgr-Rels)
Melinda Thomas (Mng Dir)
Michael Woods (Mng Dir)
David Heroux (Mng Dir-Westlake)
Michelle Florence (Mgr-Ops)

Sapoznik Insurance & Associates, Inc. (1)
1100 NE 163 St, North Miami Beach, FL 33162
Tel.: (954) 760-4774
Web Site: http://www.sapoznik.com
Sales Range: $1-9.9 Million
Emp.: 40
Insurance Agencies & Brokerages
N.A.I.C.S.: 524210
Rachel Sapoznik (Pres & CEO)
Michelle Masferrer (Dir-HR)
Beatriz Lucki (Dir-Mktg)
Kenneth Nahman (CFO)

TW Group, Inc. (1)
850 N Cass Ave, Westmont, IL 60559
Tel.: (630) 737-0300
Web Site: http://www.twgroupinc.com
Commericial Banking
N.A.I.C.S.: 522110
Ken Zahn (Mgr-Personal Lines)

WORLD JOINT CORP.
535 8th Ave Ste 801, New York, NY 10018
Tel.: (212) 972-3200   NY
Web Site: http://www.iace-usa.com
Year Founded: 1970
Sales Range: $25-49.9 Million
Emp.: 150
Travel Agencies
N.A.I.C.S.: 513130
Keiko Ishida (Pres)

WORLD LUNG FOUNDATION
61 Broadway Ste 2800, New York, NY 10006
Tel.: (212) 542-8870   NY
Web Site:
  http://www.worldlungfoundation.org
Year Founded: 2004
Sales Range: $50-74.9 Million
Emp.: 20
Health Care Srvices
N.A.I.C.S.: 622110
Jennifer S. Klopp (Dir-Dev)
Sandra Mullin (Sr VP-Policy & Comm)
Joanna Thomas (VP-Ops)
Andrew S. Rendeiro (Vice Chm-Ops)
Eric Rosenbaum (Sec)
Jose Luis Castro (Pres & CEO)
Louis James De-Viel Castel (Chm)
Marc Sznajderman (Vice Chm-Programs)
Scott Halstead (Treas)

WORLD MEDICAL RELIEF, INC.
11745 Rosa Parks Blvd, Detroit, MI 48206
Tel.: (313) 866-5333   MI
Web Site:
  http://www.worldmedicalrelief.org
Year Founded: 1953
Sales Range: $10-24.9 Million
Emp.: 16
Medical Equipment Supply Services

N.A.I.C.S.: 456199
Crystal Staffney (Dir-Dev & Community Affairs)
Raymond Gibson (Dir-Pharmacy)
Cheryl Newton (Fin Dir)
Carolyn Racklyeft (Dir-Local Programs)

WORLD MICRO, INC.
205 Hembree Park Dr Ste 105, Roswell, GA 30076
Tel.: (770) 698-1900
Web Site: http://www.worldmicro.com
Year Founded: 1994
Rev.: $17,400,000
Emp.: 50
Electronic Parts & Equipment
N.A.I.C.S.: 423690
Chris Ellsworth (Co-Founder & VP-Ops)
Dan Ellsworth (Co-Founder & Pres-World Micro & CEO-MIT Distr)
Bettina Clark (Dir-Supplier Dev)

Subsidiaries:
McDonald Industries, Inc. (1)
4275 Kellway Cir Ste 160, Addison, TX 75001
Tel.: (972) 733-3322
Web Site: http://www.mitfind.com
Sales Range: $10-24.9 Million
Emp.: 100
Electronic Parts & Equipment Merchant Whslr
N.A.I.C.S.: 423690
Dan Ellsworth (CEO)

WORLD MONUMENTS FUND, INC.
350 5th Ave Ste 2412, New York, NY 10118-2494
Tel.: (646) 424-9594   NY
Web Site: http://www.wmf.org
Year Founded: 1965
Sales Range: Less than $1 Million
Emp.: 37
Historical Site Preservation Services
N.A.I.C.S.: 712120
Lisa Ackerman (COO & Exec VP)
Christopher Jeannopoulos (CFO)
David B. Ford (Treas)
John J. Kerr (Vice Chm & Sec)
Lorna B. Goodman (Chm)
Ashley Tierney (Dir-Dev)
Jeff Allen (Dir-Program)
Sharon Breland (Dir-Special Events)
Johnette Pride (Office Mgr)
Tara Morris (VP-External Affairs)
Benedicte De Montlaur (CEO)

WORLD OF BEER FRANCHISING, INC.
10910 Sheldon Rd, Tampa, FL 33626
Tel.: (813) 926-9300
Web Site: http://www.wobusa.com
Year Founded: 2007
Emp.: 30
Bar & Restaurant Owner & Franchisor
N.A.I.C.S.: 722410
Scott D. Zepp (Co-Founder)
Matthew L. LaFon (Co-Founder & Co-Owner)
James R. Pollard (Co-Owner & Chief Dev Officer)
Paul E. Avery (Pres & CEO)
Donald R. Everts (VP-Dev-Intl)
Dave Reid (COO)
Kevin MacCormack (CFO)
James Buell (VP-Mktg)

WORLD OF FORD SALES INC.
6129 Richmond Hwy, Alexandria, VA 22303
Tel.: (703) 660-9000
Web Site:
  http://www.ourismanva.com

U.S. PRIVATE

Sales Range: $50-74.9 Million
Emp.: 120
Automobiles, New & Used
N.A.I.C.S.: 441110
Mandell J. Ourisman (Chm)
Chuck Jackowski (Dir-Svcs)
Lou A. King (Gen Mgr)
Bob Haggart (CEO)
Mike Walton (Mgr-Parts)

WORLD OF GOOD TASTES, INC.
8109 Fruitridge Rd, Sacramento, CA 95820
Tel.: (916) 386-1515
Web Site: http://www.labou.com
Sales Range: $25-49.9 Million
Emp.: 50
Cafe
N.A.I.C.S.: 722511
Sandie Fredericks (Mgr)
Annie Ngo (Owner & Pres)

WORLD OIL CORP.
9302 Garfield Ave, South Gate, CA 90280-3805
Tel.: (562) 928-0100   CA
Web Site:
  http://www.tidelandsoilandgas.com
Year Founded: 1948
Sales Range: $200-249.9 Million
Emp.: 410
Provider of Petroleum Refining & Marketing
N.A.I.C.S.: 457120
Steven F. Roth (Exec VP)
Toshiko Chan (Sec)
Chris Mahoney (CFO)

WORLD PAC PAPER, LLC
1821 Summit Rd Ste 317, Cincinnati, OH 45237
Tel.: (513) 779-9595
Web Site:
  http://www.worldpacpaper.com
Year Founded: 2004
Sales Range: $25-49.9 Million
Emp.: 23
Printing & Packaging Papers Distr
N.A.I.C.S.: 423840
Richard A. Baptiste (Pres & COO)
Toni M. Robinson-Smith (VP-Admin)
John P. Clifford (Mgr)
Edgar L. Smith Jr. (Chm & CEO)

WORLD POINT TERMINALS, INC.
8235 Forsyth Blvd Ste 400, Saint Louis, MO 63105
Tel.: (314) 889-9660   DE
Holding Company; Petroleum Terminals Operator
N.A.I.C.S.: 551112
Jonathan Q. Affleck (CFO & VP)

Subsidiaries:
World Point Terminals, LP (1)
8235 Forsyth Blvd Ste 400, Saint Louis, MO 63105   (73.6%)
Tel.: (314) 889-9660
Web Site: http://www.worldpointlp.com
Rev.: $99,624,000
Assets: $205,085,000
Liabilities: $13,071,000
Net Worth: $192,014,000
Earnings: $36,429,000
Emp.: 161
Fiscal Year-end: 12/31/2016
Petroleum Storage Terminals Operator
N.A.I.C.S.: 424710
Jonathan Q. Affleck (CFO & VP)
Kenneth E. Fenton (Pres & COO)
Paul Anthony Novelly II (Chm & CEO)

WORLD PRODUCTS INC.
19654 8th St E, Sonoma, CA 95476
Tel.: (707) 996-5201   MN

COMPANIES

Web Site:
http://www.worldproducts.com
Year Founded: 1970
Sales Range: $10-24.9 Million
Emp.: 45
Provider of Electronic Parts & Equipment
N.A.I.C.S.: 423690
Mark Beynon *(Pres)*
Bob Stone *(Chm & CEO)*

WORLD PUBLICATIONS INC.
100 Laurel St, East Bridgewater, MA 02333
Tel.: (508) 880-5555
Web Site: http://www.wrldpub.com
Year Founded: 1985
Rev.: $26,936,105
Emp.: 5
Whslr of Books
N.A.I.C.S.: 424920
Jeffrey Press *(Owner)*

WORLD REALTY & DEVELOPMENT, LTD.
327A Watertown St, Newton, MA 02458
Tel.: (617) 969-4154
Year Founded: 1987
Sales Range: $10-24.9 Million
Emp.: 5
Portfolio Management Services
N.A.I.C.S.: 523940
Mark D. Coppola *(Pres)*

WORLD RESOURCES COMPANY
1600 Anderson Rd Ste 200, McLean, VA 22102-1609
Tel.: (703) 734-9800   VA
Web Site:
http://www.worldresourcescompany.com
Year Founded: 1976
Sales Range: $75-99.9 Million
Emp.: 100
Provider of Refuse Services
N.A.I.C.S.: 331221
Peter T. Halpin *(CEO)*

WORLD SHIP SUPPLY TEXAS INCORPORATED
1485 E Sam Houston Pkwy Ste 100, Pasadena, TX 77503
Tel.: (713) 222-6005
Web Site: http://wrist.com
Sales Range: $25-49.9 Million
Emp.: 100
Food & Supplies Delivery to Ships
N.A.I.C.S.: 424410
Jubi Hillery *(Pres)*
John Anton *(Mgr-Sls)*

WORLD SHIPPING, INC.
1340 Depot St Ste 200, Rocky River, OH 44116-1741
Tel.: (440) 356-7676   OH
Web Site:
http://www.worldshipping.com
Year Founded: 1962
Sales Range: $100-124.9 Million
Emp.: 200
International Shipping & Container Services
N.A.I.C.S.: 484121
Frederick M. Hunger *(Pres & CEO)*
John E. Hunger *(CFO & Treas)*
Maureen H. Cosentino *(Dir-Org Dev)*
David N. Messer *(Pres-World Distribution Services LLC)*

Subsidiaries:

Container Port Group   (1)
1340 Depot St 2nd Fl, Cleveland, OH 44116-1741
Tel.: (440) 333-1330

Web Site: http://www.containerport.com
Sales Range: $10-24.9 Million
Emp.: 60
Marine Container Repair & Storage; Inland Transportation; Trucking
N.A.I.C.S.: 484121
Glenn A. Fehribach *(CFO)*
Michael Smith *(Pres)*
Robert L. Leef *(Sr VP-Intermodal Ops)*
Jim Sledd *(Sr VP-Comml)*

WORLD SURVEILLANCE GROUP INC.
State Rd 405 Bldg M6-306A Rm 1400, Kennedy Space Center, FL 32815
Tel.: (321) 452-3545   DE
Web Site: http://www.wsgi.com
Sales Range: $1-9.9 Million
Emp.: 7
Lighter-Than-Air (LTA) Unmanned Aerial Vehicles Mfr; Security & Wireless Communications
N.A.I.C.S.: 336414
Glenn D. Estrella *(Pres & CEO)*
W. Jeffrey Sawyers *(CFO & Treas)*

WORLD TESTING INC.
72 E Hill St, Mount Juliet, TN 37122
Tel.: (615) 754-4147
Web Site:
http://www.worldtesting.com
Year Founded: 1979
Sales Range: $1-9.9 Million
Emp.: 40
Business Services
N.A.I.C.S.: 561990
Vernon O'Neal Jr. *(Co-Owner & CEO)*
Scott Bradley *(Mgr-Quality)*
Robert O'Neal Sr. *(Co-Owner)*
Jeff Wright *(Mgr-Millington Field Office)*

WORLD TRAVEL HOLDINGS, INC.
10 Harbor Park Dr, Port Washington, NY 11050
Tel.: (516) 621-7666
Web Site:
http://www.worldtravelholdings.com
Year Founded: 2005
Holding Company; Cruise & Travel Agencies
N.A.I.C.S.: 551112
Bradley Tolkin *(Co-Chm & Co-CEO)*
Jeff Tolkin *(Co-Chm & Co-CEO)*
Jamie Cash *(Sr VP-Tech)*
Don Graff *(CFO)*
Jeffrey Sherota *(Sr VP-House Brands)*
Debbie Fiorino *(Sr VP)*
Angie Ranck *(Mgr-Corp Comm)*
David Crooks *(Sr VP-Product & Ops)*
Jennifer Gasser *(Sr VP-Partner Brands-Wilmington)*
Loren Kennedy *(VP-HR-Wilmington)*

Subsidiaries:

CruiseOne and Cruises Inc.   (1)
1201 W Cypress Creek Rd Ste 100, Fort Lauderdale, FL 33309
Tel.: (954) 958-3700
Web Site: http://www.cruiseone.com
Sales Range: $150-199.9 Million
Emp.: 90
Travel Arrangement Services
N.A.I.C.S.: 561599
Brad Tolkin *(Co-CEO)*
Jeff Tolkin *(Co-CEO)*
Debbie Fiorino *(Sr VP)*
Rosemarie Reed *(VP-Mktg)*

World Travel Holdings   (1)
100 Sylvan Rd Ste 600, Woburn, MA 01801-1852   (100%)
Tel.: (617) 424-7990
Web Site:
http://www.worldtravelholdings.com
Sales Range: $50-74.9 Million
Emp.: 900
Cruise & Travel Agencies
N.A.I.C.S.: 561510
Don Graff *(CFO)*
Jamie Cash *(Sr VP-Tech)*
Jeff Sherota *(Sr VP-House Brands)*
David Crooks *(Sr VP-Product & Ops)*
Jeff Smith *(Sr VP-Customer Care & Luxury Travel Holdings)*
James Cole *(Mng Dir-Cruise Div)*
Jeff Tolkin *(Co-Chm & Co-CEO)*
Angie Ranck *(Mgr-Corp Comm)*

Subsidiary (Domestic):

CruisesOnly Inc.   (2)
100 Fordham Rd, Wilmington, MA 01887   (100%)
Tel.: (407) 898-5353
Web Site: http://www.cruisesonly.com
Sales Range: $25-49.9 Million
Emp.: 200
Cruise Travel Agency
N.A.I.C.S.: 561510

WORLD TRAVEL PARTNERS ORLANDO
Ste 460 4901 Vineland Rd, Orlando, FL 32811-7368
Tel.: (407) 839-0027   FL
Year Founded: 1989
Sales Range: $10-24.9 Million
Emp.: 200
Travel Agency
N.A.I.C.S.: 561510

WORLD VARIETY PRODUCE, INC.
5325 S Soto St, Vernon, CA 90058
Tel.: (323) 588-0151
Web Site: http://www.melissas.com
Year Founded: 1984
Specialty Food Product Importer & Distr
N.A.I.C.S.: 424480
Joe Hernandez *(Pres & CEO)*

WORLD VISION INC.
PO Box 9716, Federal Way, WA 98063
Tel.: (253) 815-1000   CA
Web Site: http://www.worldvision.org
Year Founded: 1950
Sales Range: $1-4.9 Billion
Emp.: 1,321
Child Welfare Services
N.A.I.C.S.: 624110
Larry Probus *(CFO & Sr VP-Strategic Solutions)*
Chris Glynn *(Sr VP-Transformational Engagement)*
Gary Duim *(Treas & Sec)*
Richard E. Stearns *(Pres)*
Christine Talbot *(Sr VP-HR)*
Edgar Sandoval *(COO)*
Kent Hill *(Sr VP-Programs-Intl)*
Grant Bayldon *(CEO-New Zealand)*
Peter McClure *(Chm-New Zealand)*
Douglas J. Treff *(Chief Admin Officer)*

WORLD WATER WORKS, INC.
4000 SW 113th St, Oklahoma City, OK 73173
Tel.: (405) 943-9000
Web Site:
http://www.worldwaterworks.com
Year Founded: 1998
Sales Range: $10-24.9 Million
Emp.: 85
Waste Water Treatment Services
N.A.I.C.S.: 221310
Mark Fosshage *(Pres)*
Greg Parks *(VP-Tech)*
Scott Poe *(VP-Customs)*
John Schnecker *(Dir-Sls & Mktg)*

WORLD WEB PARTNERS, INC.

WORLD WIDE TECHNOLOGY HOLDING CO., LLC

2001 Hollywood Blvd Ste 305, Hollywood, FL 33020
Tel.: (954) 306-6373
Web Site:
http://www.worldwebpartners.com
Year Founded: 2008
Sales Range: $10-24.9 Million
Emp.: 22
Marketing Consulting Services
N.A.I.C.S.: 541613
Anthony Rolon *(Pres)*
Desmond Yeekee *(CFO)*

WORLD WIDE FITTINGS, INC.
600 Corporate Woods Pkwy, Vernon Hills, IL 60061
Tel.: (847) 588-2200
Web Site:
http://www.worldwidefittings.com
Sales Range: $75-99.9 Million
Emp.: 300
Metal Valve & Pipe Fitting Mfr
N.A.I.C.S.: 332919
Michael Casey *(Sr VP)*
Patrick O'Connor *(VP-Sls-North America)*

WORLD WIDE PARTS & ACCESSORIES CORPORATION
37137 Hickory St, Newark, CA 94560-5522
Tel.: (510) 742-8900   DE
Web Site: http://www.worldpac.com
Year Founded: 1994
Sales Range: $500-549.9 Million
Emp.: 1,850
Sale of Motor Vehicle Supplies
N.A.I.C.S.: 423120
Tadd Baker *(Dir-Sls-Southern California, Arizona & Nevada)*
Pat Burns *(Dir-Sls-Northwest)*
Frank Cresci *(Dir-Field Sls-Natl)*
Roy Geddie *(Sr Dir-Sls-Northern California & Colorado)*
Darius Kondaki *(VP-Sls-East)*
Chuck Hoekzema *(Dir-Sls-Texas, Oklahoma, Kansas, Missouri & Minnesota)*
Jeff Puccini *(Dir-Mktg)*
Mario Recchia *(VP-Bus Dev)*
Peter Manchee *(Dir-Sls-South-East)*
Susan Grass *(VP-Customer First & Credit)*
Buddy Crowley *(VP-Sls-California)*

WORLD WIDE SECURITY GROUP
990 Stewart Ave Ste 520, Garden City, NY 11530
Web Site:
http://www.worldwidesecurity.nyc
Year Founded: 1979
Emp.: 70
Security System Services
N.A.I.C.S.: 561621
Kenneth F. Mara *(Pres & CEO)*
Joe Ingegno *(Owner & Sr VP)*
Lou Martorello *(VP-Sls)*
Dave Young *(VP-Visions Monitoring Svcs)*
Patricia Mara *(VP)*

WORLD WIDE SIRES, LTD.
5545 Avda De Los Robles, Visalia, CA 93291
Tel.: (559) 622-2222
Web Site: http://www.wwsires.com
Sales Range: $10-24.9 Million
Emp.: 28
Cattle Genetics Services
N.A.I.C.S.: 115210
Jennifer Fernandes Hanf *(Dir-Info Sys)*

WORLD WIDE TECHNOLOGY HOLDING CO., LLC

WORLD WIDE TECHNOLOGY HOLDING CO., LLC

U.S. PRIVATE

World Wide Technology Holding Co., LLC—(Continued)
1 World Wide Way, Maryland Heights, MO 63146
Tel.: (314) 569-7000   DE
Web Site: http://www.wwt.com
Year Founded: 1990
Sales Range: $5-14.9 Billion
Emp.: 6,000
Holding Company; Information Technology Products Whslr & Consultancy Services
N.A.I.C.S.: 551112
David Lloyd Steward *(Co-Founder & Chm)*
Joseph G. Koenig *(Pres-WWT)*
Thomas W. Strunk *(CFO)*
Mike P. Taylor *(CTO)*
Erika Schenk *(Gen Counsel & VP-Compliance)*
Kevin Randall *(Dir-Client-Federal Sys Integrators)*

Subsidiaries:

Telcobuy.com LLC   (1)
60 Weldon Pkwy, Maryland Heights, MO 63043   **(100%)**
Web Site: http://www.telcobuy.com
Sales Range: $800-899.9 Million
Telecommunications Industry Information Technology, Supply Chain & Data Center Products Whslr & Support Services
N.A.I.C.S.: 423690
David Lloyd Steward *(Co-Founder & Chm)*
James Patrick Kavanaugh *(Co-Founder & CEO)*
Kraig Ecker *(Sr VP-Sls)*

World Wide Technology, LLC   (1)
1 World Wide Way, Maryland Heights, MO 63146
Tel.: (314) 569-7000
Web Site: https://www.wwt.com
Emp.: 10,000
Other Scientific & Technical Consulting Services
N.A.I.C.S.: 541690
David Lloyd Steward *(Co-Founder & Chm)*
James Patrick Kavanaugh *(Co-Founder & CEO)*
Joseph G. Koenig *(Pres)*
Steven J. Pelch *(COO)*
Robert Ferrell *(VP-Strategy-Federal & Pub Sector)*
Thomas W. Strunk *(CFO)*
Mike P. Taylor *(CTO)*
Erika Schenk *(Gen Counsel & VP-Compliance)*
Robert M. Olwig *(VP-Corp Bus Dev)*
Sara Goellner *(VP-Exec Initiatives)*
Matt S. Horner *(Sr VP-Sls-Global Enterprise)*
Bryan Thomas *(Sr VP-Sls-Pub Sector)*
Bob Olsavsky *(VP-Innovation)*
Chester T. Gloyd *(VP-Ops)*
Jeree Hanavec *(VP-Global Ops)*
Mark Franke *(VP-Supply Chain Svcs-Global)*
Mark S. Donnel *(VP-Fin)*
Tim P. Loughman *(VP-Sls Ops)*
Tom Gain *(VP-Pro Svcs)*
Brian Kane *(Dir-Client)*
Rebecca Morrison *(Sr Mgr-PR)*

Subsidiary (Non-US):

WWT APJ-Singapore Pte. Ltd.   (2)
10 Marina Bay Boulevard 14-03 Tower 2, Singapore, 018983, Singapore
Tel.: (65) 3138 9494
Web Site: http://www.wwt.com
Commercial & Civil Information Technology Products Whslr & Consultancy Services
N.A.I.C.S.: 541690
Nilesh Mistry *(Grp VP & Head-Asia Pacific & Japan)*
Eric Helfer *(Head-Sls-Asia Pacific & Japan)*
Huey Ong *(Head-Engrg-Asia Pacific & Japan)*
Chris Canale *(Head-Bus Dev-Asia Pacific)*

WWT Brasil Comercio e Servicos Ltda.   (2)
1701 Avenida Carlos Grimaldi, 13091-908, Campinas, SP, Brazil

Tel.: (55) 19 3343 4700
Commercial & Civil Information Technology Products Whslr & Consultancy Services
N.A.I.C.S.: 541690

WWT EMEA UK Ltd.   (2)
25 Canada Square 37th Floor, London, E14 5LQ, United Kingdom
Tel.: (44) 207 151 0871
Web Site: http://www.wwt.com
Commercial & Civil Information Technology Products Whslr & Consultancy Services
N.A.I.C.S.: 541690
Ben Boswell *(Area VP-Europe & Dir-UK & Ireland)*
Dave Locke *(CTO-Field-EMEA)*
Paul Allen *(Mng Dir-Global Fin Svcs-EMEA)*
Dave Langhorn *(Dir-Global Enterprises-EMEA)*
Nilay Patel *(Dir-Mgmt Consulting, Architecture & Engrg-EMEA)*
Stacey Kingshott *(Dir-HR-Global)*

Branch (Non-US):

World Wide Technology - Hong Kong Sales Office   (2)
Suite 1901 19/F Cheung Kong Center, Central, China (Hong Kong)
Tel.: (852) 5819 5842
Web Site: http://www.wwt.com
Commercial & Civil Information Technology Products Whslr
N.A.I.C.S.: 423430

Subsidiary (Domestic):

World Wide Technology Asynchrony Labs, LLC   (2)
900 Spruce St Ste 700, Saint Louis, MO 63102
Tel.: (314) 678-2200
Web Site: http://www.asynchrony.com
IT Consulting Firm
N.A.I.C.S.: 541990
Bob Elfanbaum *(Co-Founder & Gen Mgr)*
Nate McKie *(Co-Founder & CTO)*
Steve Elfanbaum *(Co-Founder & VP)*
Jim Rubin *(COO)*
Dave Elfanbaum *(Co-Founder & VP-Mktg)*

WORLD WIDE WEB FOUNDATION
1110 Vermont Ave NW Ste 500, Washington, DC 20005
Tel.: (202) 595-2892   DE
Web Site: http://www.webfoundation.org
Year Founded: 2008
Sales Range: $1-9.9 Million
Emp.: 13
Internet Research Services
N.A.I.C.S.: 519290
Lauran Potter *(Mgr-Comm)*
Andreas Pawelke *(Mgr-Open Data Labs)*
Sabine Majewski *(Dir-Fin & Ops)*
Arthur Glenn Maail *(Mgr-Res-Open Data Lab-Jakarta)*
Tim Berners-Lee *(Co-Founder)*
Rosemary Leith *(Co-Founder)*
Hania Farhan *(Program Mgr-Web Index)*
Adrian Lovett *(Pres & CEO)*
Afsaneh Beschloss *(Chm)*

WORLD WIRELESS COMMUNICATIONS INC
5670 GREENWOOD PLAZA BLVD, SUITE 340, ENGLEWOOD, CO 80111
Tel.: (801) 575-6600   NV
N.A.I.C.S.: 485310

WORLD WOODS CORPORATION
17590 Ponce De Leon Blvd, Brooksville, FL 34614
Tel.: (352) 796-5500
Web Site: http://www.worldwoods.com
Sales Range: $10-24.9 Million

Emp.: 100
Golf Club & Resort
N.A.I.C.S.: 713910
Yukihisa Inoue *(Pres)*
Scott Wyckoff *(Head-Golf)*
Susan Burkel *(Mgr-Golf Villa Reservations)*

WORLD'S FINEST CHOCOLATE, INC.
4801 S Lawndale Ave, Chicago, IL 60632-3065
Tel.: (773) 847-4600   DE
Web Site: http://www.worldsfinestchocolate.com
Year Founded: 1938
Sales Range: $200-249.9 Million
Emp.: 700
Mfr of Chocolate & Cocoa Products
N.A.I.C.S.: 311351
Michael Broz *(CFO)*
Al Gomez *(Controller)*
Edmond F. Opler III *(Owner)*

Subsidiaries:

World's Finest Chocolate Canada Company   (1)
157 Cockburn, Campbellford, K0L 1L0, ON, Canada   **(100%)**
Tel.: (705) 653-3590
Web Site: http://www.worldsfinest.ca
Sales Range: $10-24.9 Million
Emp.: 25
Cocoa & Chocolate Product Mfr
N.A.I.C.S.: 311352
Milton Newman *(Mgr-Sls)*

WORLD-WIDE HOLDINGS CORP.
950 3 Ave 18th Fl, New York, NY 10022
Tel.: (212) 486-2000
Sales Range: $10-24.9 Million
Emp.: 25
Land Subdividers & Developers, Commercial
N.A.I.C.S.: 531110
Victor Elmaleh *(Chm)*
Jim Stanton *(Pres)*
Jodi Gerstman *(CFO)*
Neal Cohen *(Dir-Construction)*
Patricia Farrell *(Mgr-HR)*

Subsidiaries:

WW Venture Corp.   (1)
950 3rd Ave, New York, NY 10022
Tel.: (212) 486-2000
Investment Holding Companies, Except Banks
N.A.I.C.S.: 551112
Victor Elmaleh *(Chm)*

WORLDATA INFOCENTER, INC.
3000 N Military Trl, Boca Raton, FL 33431-6321
Tel.: (561) 393-8200   NY
Web Site: http://www.worldata.com
Year Founded: 1975
Sales Range: $1-9.9 Million
Emp.: 110
Direct Mail Advertising Services
N.A.I.C.S.: 541860
Jay Schwedelson *(Pres & CEO)*
Helene Schwedelson *(CFO)*

WORLDCELL, INC.
6110 Executive Blvd Ste 470, Rockville, MD 20852-3927
Tel.: (301) 822-4030   MD
Web Site: http://www.devicecloudnetwork.com
Year Founded: 1996
Sales Range: $10-24.9 Million
Emp.: 20
Wireless Telecommunication Services

N.A.I.C.S.: 517112
Blake Swensrud *(Chm)*
Elvar Thorkelsson *(VP & Gen Mgr)*
Richard Beckley *(Sr VP-Bus Dev)*

WORLDCENTRIC.ORG
2121 Staunton Ct, Palo Alto, CA 94306
Tel.: (650) 283-3797
Web Site: http://www.worldcentric.org
Year Founded: 2004
Sales Range: $10-24.9 Million
Emp.: 20
Compostable Food Service Containers
N.A.I.C.S.: 322219
Aseem Das *(Founder & Exec Dir)*

WORLDCOM EXCHANGE, INC.
43 Northwestern Dr, Salem, NH 03079
Tel.: (603) 893-0900
Web Site: http://www.wei.com
Sales Range: $10-24.9 Million
Emp.: 30
Computer Integrated Systems Design Services
N.A.I.C.S.: 541512
Belisario A. Rosas *(Owner & Pres)*

WORLDDOC, INC.
231 S 3rd St Ste 100, Las Vegas, NV 89101
Tel.: (702) 821-0818
Web Site: http://www.socialwellth.com
Year Founded: 2000
Sales Range: $25-49.9 Million
Emp.: 24
Consumer Care Management Systems to Health Plans, Third Party Administrators & Employers
N.A.I.C.S.: 513210
David Vinson *(CEO)*
Ramesh Srinivasan *(CMO)*
Michael Morris *(Sr VP-Ops)*
Ric Colgan *(CTO & VP)*
Michael Effner *(Chief Info Security Officer)*

WORLDGATE COMMUNICATIONS, INC.
3800 Horizon Blvd Ste 103, Trevose, PA 19053
Tel.: (215) 354-5100   DE
Web Site: http://www.wgate.com
Year Founded: 1995
Sales Range: $10-24.9 Million
Emp.: 49
Personal Video Telephony Mfr
N.A.I.C.S.: 334210
Robert Stevanovski *(Chm)*
Allan M. Van Buhler *(Chief Admin Officer & Sr VP-Sls, Mktg & Bus Dev)*
Edward L. Cummings *(CFO & Chief Acctg Officer)*

WORLDLINK, INC.
3880 Parkwood Blvd Ste 204, Frisco, TX 75034
Tel.: (972) 671-3434   DE
Web Site: http://www.worldlink-us.com
Year Founded: 1996
Sales Range: $10-24.9 Million
Emp.: 110
IT & Consulting Services
N.A.I.C.S.: 519290
Theresa Linson *(VP-Tech Innovation)*
Ed Silva *(VP-Data & Analytics)*
Jason Skinner *(VP-Cloud Solutions)*
Maria Wiemann *(Gen Counsel & VP)*
Matt Yoon *(Pres-Asia Pacific)*

WORLDMEDIA INTERACTIVE
3401 N Miami Ave Ste 239, Miami, FL 33127

Tel.: (305) 572-0404
Web Site: http://www.worldmedia.net
Year Founded: 1999
Sales Range: $10-24.9 Million
Emp.: 45
Interactive Advertising & Marketing
N.A.I.C.S.: 541890
Paul R. Pellerin *(Pres & CEO)*
Andrew Stewart *(Exec VP)*
Stephan Bechtoldt *(Dir-Interactive Art)*
Caroline Villada *(Sr Partner-Client)*
Tatiana Romero *(Sr Partner-Client)*
Katherine Cajiao *(Dir-Client Svcs)*

WORLDNET, INC. OF NEVADA
281 369 E 900 S, Salt Lake City, UT 84111
Tel.: (801) 323-2395   NV
Year Founded: 1986
Assets: $196
Liabilities: $337,585
Net Worth: ($337,389)
Earnings: ($32,462)
Fiscal Year-end: 12/31/18
Investment Services
N.A.I.C.S.: 523999
Brett D. Mayer *(Pres, CFO, Chief Acctg Officer, Treas & Sec)*

WORLDONE, INC.
200 Park Ave S Ste 1301, New York, NY 10003
Tel.: (212) 358-0800   NC
Web Site: http://www.sermo.com
Year Founded: 2010
Emp.: 35
Holding Company; Healthcare Industry Data Services
N.A.I.C.S.: 551112
Peter Kirk *(CEO)*
Gerard Smith *(CFO)*
Richard Hall *(COO)*
Jim Fredrick Schneider *(Exec VP)*
Corinne Dulles *(VP-Bus Dev)*
Stefanie Malka *(Exec VP)*

Subsidiaries:

Sermo, Inc.   (1)
215 1st St, Cambridge, MA 02142
Tel.: (617) 497-1110
Web Site: http://www.sermo.com
Sales Range: $1-9.9 Million
Online Physician Data Services
N.A.I.C.S.: 518210
Mark Antonacci *(Exec VP & Head-Sls-Global)*
Oren Hallale *(Sr VP & Head-Comml Ops-Global)*
Peter Kirk *(CEO)*
Gerard Smith *(CFO)*
Giles Stanley *(Gen Counsel)*

WORLDQUANT, LLC
1700 E Putnam Ave 3rd Fl, Old Greenwich, CT 06870
Tel.: (203) 344-6050
Web Site: https://www.worldquant.com
Year Founded: 2007
Investment Management Service
N.A.I.C.S.: 523940
Igor Tulchinsky *(Founder, Chm & CEO)*
David Rushkin *(CTO)*
Jonathan Marom *(CFO)*
Jeffrey Blomberg *(Chief Admin Officer & Gen Counsel)*
Paul Griffin *(Co-Chief Investment Officer)*
Nitish Maini *(Chief Strategy Officer)*
Jordana Upton *(Head-Human Resources)*
Andreas Kreuz *(Deputy Chief Investment Officer)*
Istvan Maricza *(Chief Research Talent Officer)*
Peter Norley *(COO)*

WORLDSTAGE, INC.
259 W 30th St 12th Fl, New York, NY 10001
Tel.: (212) 582-2345
Web Site: http://www.worldstage.com
Year Founded: 2007
Audio-Visual Equipment & Supply Rental
N.A.I.C.S.: 532289
Josh Weisberg *(Pres & COO)*
Stanley Jacobs *(Controller)*
Paul Clements *(Dir-Special Projects)*
Micheal DeRosa *(Mgr-Audio Rental)*
Anita Martino *(Mgr-HR)*
Rodney Miller *(CFO-Tustin)*

WORLDTECH COMPUTERS INC.
16161 Ventura Blvd # 683, Encino, CA 91436
Tel.: (818) 990-1659
Sales Range: $10-24.9 Million
Emp.: 130
Office Supplies
N.A.I.C.S.: 424120
John Gordon Jones *(Pres)*

WORLDWAYS, INC.
8100 E Maplewood Ave Ste 110, Greenwood Village, CO 80111
Tel.: (303) 779-3004
Sales Range: $1-9.9 Million
Emp.: 18
Advetising Agency
N.A.I.C.S.: 541810
Maureen Cronin *(Founder & Principal)*

WORLDWIDE CONSTRUCTION EQUIPMENT INC.
79 Manor Cir, Bristol, PA 19007
Tel.: (215) 788-0734
Web Site: http://www.wwcequip.com
Sales Range: $10-24.9 Million
Emp.: 9
Construction & Mining Machinery Whslr
N.A.I.C.S.: 423810
Nick Lombardi *(VP)*
Bob Tressler II *(Pres)*

WORLDWIDE DIAMOND CO.
607 S Hill St Ste 811, Los Angeles, CA 90014
Tel.: (213) 622-2191
Web Site: http://www.wwdiamond.com
Sales Range: $10-24.9 Million
Emp.: 4
Jewelry & Precious Stones
N.A.I.C.S.: 423940
Robert Winer *(Pres)*

WORLDWIDE DISTRIBUTORS
8211 S 194th St, Seattle, WA 98032
Tel.: (253) 872-8746
Web Site: http://www.wdi-wdi.com
Year Founded: 1955
Sales Range: $10-24.9 Million
Emp.: 50
Non-Durable Goods Whslr
N.A.I.C.S.: 424990
Deb Hammond *(VP)*
Rachel Weddle *(Coord-Trade Show)*

WORLDWIDE EQUIPMENT, INC.
107 WE Drive, Prestonsburg, KY 41653
Tel.: (800) 394-8447
Web Site: http://www.teamworldwide.com
Emp.: 900
Commercial Truck Leasing & Rentals, Sales & Services
N.A.I.C.S.: 423110

Terry Dotson *(Pres & CEO)*
Scott Blevins *(COO)*
Robert Gomez *(Exec VP-Sls)*
Steven Chan *(Dir-Pur)*
Lee Dotson *(CMO)*

Subsidiaries:

Volunteer Volvo and GMC Inc.   (1)
6614 Wilbanks Rd, Knoxville, TN 37912
Tel.: (865) 688-4300
Web Site: http://www.thetruckpeople.com
Rev.: $26,400,000
Emp.: 85
Trucks, Tractors & Trailers: New & Used
N.A.I.C.S.: 441110
Terry L. Dotson *(Pres)*

Worldwide Equipment, Inc. - Lexington Division   (1)
945 Nandino Dr, Lexington, KY 40511
Tel.: (859) 281-5152
Web Site: http://www.teamworldwide.com
Truck Rental & Leasing Services
N.A.I.C.S.: 532120

WORLDWIDE ERC
4401 Wilson Blvd Ste 510, Arlington, VA 22203
Tel.: (703) 842-3400   IL
Web Site: http://www.worldwideerc.org
Year Founded: 1964
Sales Range: $10-24.9 Million
Emp.: 40
Business Associations
N.A.I.C.S.: 813910
David Stephenson *(Dir-IT)*
Heidi Hume *(Sr Mgr-Mktg & Comm)*
Christine Wilson *(VP-Res & Education)*
Lynn Shotwell *(Pres & CEO)*
Ed Hannibal *(Chm)*

WORLDWIDE FOOD PRODUCTS INC.
14707 94th Ave, Jamaica, NY 11435-4513
Tel.: (718) 658-4000   NY
Web Site: http://www.geishaseafood.com
Year Founded: 1989
Sales Range: $25-49.9 Million
Emp.: 25
Mfr of Seafood Products
N.A.I.C.S.: 424460
Lloyd Glazer *(Mgr-Sls)*

WORLDWIDE GOLF ENTERPRISES, INC.
1430 S Village Way Ste T, Santa Ana, CA 92705-4715
Tel.: (714) 543-8284   CA
Web Site: http://www.worldwidegolfshops.com
Year Founded: 1993
Sales Range: $25-49.9 Million
Emp.: 125
Retailer of Golf Club & Accessory Golf Shop Franchiser
N.A.I.C.S.: 423910
Christine Vo *(Controller)*
Al Morris *(Pres)*
John Kopacz *(VP)*
Rick Powell *(VP-Pur)*

Subsidiaries:

Golfers Warehouse Inc.   (1)
75 Brainard Rd, Hartford, CT 06114
Tel.: (860) 522-6829
Web Site: http://www.worldwidegolfshops.com
Sales Range: $10-24.9 Million
Emp.: 50
Golf Goods & Equipment
N.A.I.C.S.: 459110

Van's Pro Shop   (1)
801 S Power Ste 115, Mesa, AZ 85206
Tel.: (480) 985-0601

Sales Range: $10-24.9 Million
Emp.: 8
Sporting Goods & Bicycle Shops
N.A.I.C.S.: 459110
Rick Levy *(VP)*

WORLDWIDE GROUND TRANSPORTATION SOLUTIONS INC.
651 Aldo Ave, Santa Clara, CA 95054
Tel.: (408) 727-0000
Web Site: http://www.elpaseolimo.com
Year Founded: 1987
Sales Range: $10-24.9 Million
Emp.: 100
Limousine Service
N.A.I.C.S.: 485320
Cyrus B. Monsef *(Dir-Ops)*
James Brown *(CEO)*

WORLDWIDE INVENTORY NETWORK
5100 San Francisco Ave, Saint Louis, MO 63115
Tel.: (314) 385-3006   MO
Web Site: http://www.winwarehouse.org
Year Founded: 1991
Sales Range: $25-49.9 Million
Emp.: 9
Donation Distr
N.A.I.C.S.: 813219
Kathy Reznikov *(Treas)*

WORLDWIDE JET CHARTER, INC.
22601 N 17th Ave Ste 220, Phoenix, AZ 85027
Tel.: (602) 726-9993
Web Site: http://www.worldwidejet.com
Year Founded: 2012
Sales Range: $1-9.9 Million
Emp.: 200
Aircraft Charter Services
N.A.I.C.S.: 481212
Andrew S. Kaufman *(Pres & CEO)*
Carlos Avila *(VP-Ops)*
Ronald Schiffman *(Dir-Retail Sls)*
John Gaines *(Dir-Maintenance)*
Noel Fournier *(VP-Bus Dev)*

WORLDWIDE LOGISTICS LIMITED
80 Rte 4 E Ste 410, Paramus, NJ 07652
Tel.: (201) 556-0909
Web Site: http://www.worldwidelogistics.com
Rev.: $10,000,000
Emp.: 4
Freight Transportation Arrangement
N.A.I.C.S.: 488510
Joseph P. Monaghan *(Pres)*

WORLDWIDE LOGISTICS, INC.
729 1st Ave SW, Hickory, NC 28602
Web Site: http://www.worldwidelogisticsinc.com
Sales Range: $10-24.9 Million
Emp.: 50
Trucking Service
N.A.I.C.S.: 484121
Richard Eanes *(Chm)*

Subsidiaries:

Warren Trucking Company Inc.   (1)
443 Old Sand Rd, Ridgeway, VA 24148
Tel.: (276) 956-3181
Web Site: http://www.warrentruck.com
Furniture Transportation Services
N.A.I.C.S.: 484121
Richard Eanes *(Pres)*
Ronnie Reeves *(Dir-Safety)*

WORLDWIDE MACHINERY INC.
U.S. PRIVATE

Worldwide Machinery Inc.—(Continued)

WORLDWIDE MACHINERY INC.
16031 E Freeway, Channelview, TX 77530-4313
Tel.: (281) 452-5800
Web Site: http://www.worldwidemachinery.com
Year Founded: 1978
Sales Range: $10-24.9 Million
Emp.: 75
Rental of Heavy Construction Equipment
N.A.I.C.S.: 532412
Adam Greenberg (Sr VP)
Evan Greenberg (Sr VP-Intl Ops)
David Sinclair (Pres)

WORLDWIDE OILFIELD MACHINE, INC.
11809 Canemont St, Houston, TX 77035
Tel.: (713) 729-9200
Web Site: http://www.womusa.com
Sales Range: $10-24.9 Million
Emp.: 500
Oil Field Machinery & Equipment
N.A.I.C.S.: 333132
Monica Vickous (Mgr-Inside Sls Parts)
Steve Barker (Engr-Subsea)

WORLDWIDE POWER PRODUCTS, LLC
5901 Thomas Rd, Houston, TX 77041
Tel.: (281) 201-4056
Web Site: http://www.wpowerproducts.com
Year Founded: 2008
Sales Range: $10-24.9 Million
Emp.: 15
Power Generation Equipment Rental Services
N.A.I.C.S.: 532490
Will Perry (Pres)
Mark Lum (Exec VP)
Dave Vennie (VP-Sls & Engrg)
John Conine (Dir-Sls)
Charles Matthews (CFO)
Greg O'Brien (Co-CFO)

WORLDWIDE SUPPLY
1 Park Dr, Franklin, NJ 07416
Tel.: (973) 823-6400
Web Site: http://www.worldwidesupply.net
Sales Range: $25-49.9 Million
Emp.: 50
Telecommunication Equipment Distr
N.A.I.C.S.: 423690
Jay VanOrden (CEO)
James P. Smith (COO)
Dennis Perugino (Dir-Fin-Worldwide Supply)
Shawn Grennan (Dir-Sls-Natl)
John Herman (Dir-Ops-Worldwide Supply)
Owen Grohman (Dir-NetGuard Svcs)
Allison Kraut (Dir-Mktg)
Francisco Rodriguez (CTO)

WORLDWIDE TECHSERVICES, INC
836 N St, Tewksbury, MA 01876-1253
Tel.: (978) 848-9149
Web Site: http://www.wwts.com
Year Founded: 2000
Sales Range: $75-99.9 Million
Emp.: 2,000
Information Technology Services
N.A.I.C.S.: 541513
Dov Horowitz (Pres & CEO)
Karen Moriarty (Mgr-HR)

Donald Crim (Mgr-Global IT Infrastructure)
Maureen Dellisola (Project Mgr)
Jim Leith (Sr Dir)
Nancy Latorre (CFO)
Donna Martin (COO)
Tim Hipskind (Sr VP)
Tye Kuhlman (Sr VP)
Lloyd Nolan (Sr VP)
Andy Wayne (Sr VP)
Fred Gillis (VP)
John Macrae (VP)
Wes Odenburg (VP)

WORLDWIDE TERMINALS FERNANDINA, LLC
501 N 3rd St, Fernandina, FL 32034
Tel.: (910) 395-4777
Web Site: https://www.worldwideterminals.com
Warehouse & Logistics Opeartion
N.A.I.C.S.: 493190

Subsidiaries:

Nassau Terminals LLC (1)
501 N 3rd St, Fernandina Beach, FL 32034
Tel.: (904) 261-5027
Multi-Purpose Terminal
N.A.I.C.S.: 488320

WORLDWIDE TRAVEL STAFFING, LIMITED
2829 Sheridan Dr, Tonawanda, NY 14150
Tel.: (716) 821-9001
Web Site: http://www.worldwidetravelstaffing.com
Year Founded: 1993
Sales Range: $75-99.9 Million
Emp.: 170
Domestic & International Placement of Healthcare Professionals
N.A.I.C.S.: 561311
Leo Blatz (CEO)
Laurie Dolega (Pres)
Joseph B. Giaimo (COO)

WORLDWIDE WHOLESALE FLOOR COVERINGS
1055 US Hwy 1, Edison, NJ 08837
Tel.: (732) 906-1400
Web Site: http://www.worldwidewholesale.com
Rev.: $18,653,603
Emp.: 100
Carpets
N.A.I.C.S.: 449121
Alan Braunstein (Pres)
Freddy Botello (Mgr)
Kathy Corveleyn (Mgr-Payroll & HR)
Suzette Stoddard (Mgr-Show Room)
Alex Vaynstein (Mgr-Store)

WORLY PLUMBING SUPPLY INC.
400 Greenlawn Ave, Columbus, OH 43223
Tel.: (614) 445-1000
Web Site: http://www.worly.com
Rev.: $20,000,000
Emp.: 50
Plumbing & Hydronic Heating Supplies
N.A.I.C.S.: 423720
Jay Worly (Pres & COO)
Judy Tompkins (Controller)
Amy Riffle (Mgr-Credit)

WORTH & CO., INC.
6263 Kellers Church Rd, Pipersville, PA 18947
Tel.: (267) 362-1100
Web Site: http://www.worthandcompany.com
Sales Range: $300-349.9 Million

Emp.: 600
Mechanical Contractor
N.A.I.C.S.: 238220
Stephen Worth (Pres & CEO)

Subsidiaries:

Landmark Service Co, LLC (1)
5 Highland Ave, Bethlehem, PA 18017
Tel.: (610) 264-5152
Energy Efficiency Services
N.A.I.C.S.: 561499

WORTH HIGGINS & ASSOCIATES INC.
8770 Park Central Dr, Richmond, VA 23227
Tel.: (804) 264-2304
Web Site: http://www.worthhiggins.com
Year Founded: 1999
Printing Services
N.A.I.C.S.: 323111
Brian Losch (VP-Sls)

WORTH INVESTMENT GROUP, LLC
3634 McCain Rd Ste 8, Jackson, MI 49203
Tel.: (517) 750-9900
Web Site: http://www.worth-investments.com
Holding Company
N.A.I.C.S.: 551112
M. Eric Boorom (CEO)

Subsidiaries:

The Shane Group, LLC (1)
263 Industrial Dr, Hillsdale, MI 49242-1075
Tel.: (517) 439-4316
Web Site: http://www.shanegroup.com
Sales Range: $75-99.9 Million
Emp.: 165
Holding Company
N.A.I.C.S.: 551112
Sue Caulkins (Controller)

Subsidiary (Domestic):

American Copper & Brass, LLC (2)
170 E South St, Hillsdale, MI 49242
Tel.: (517) 439-9368
Web Site: http://www.acandb.com
Copper Tubing, Valves & Brass Fittings Distr
N.A.I.C.S.: 423720
Michael Meadows (CEO)
Don Gaier (Pres)

Biological Mediation Systems, LLC (2)
2625 Redwing Rd Ste 110, Fort Collins, CO 80526-6314
Tel.: (970) 221-5949
Web Site: http://www.biologicalmediation.com
Sales Range: $25-49.9 Million
Emp.: 10
Prefabricated Restrooms, Concession Buildings, Park Entry Stations & Utility Buildings Mfr
N.A.I.C.S.: 321992
Glenn Rachak (Pres)

Qualite Sports Lighting, LLC (2)
250 Industrial Dr, Hillsdale, MI 49242
Tel.: (517) 439-1581
Web Site: http://www.qualite.com
Sales Range: $25-49.9 Million
Emp.: 20
Designer & Installer of Lighting Systems
N.A.I.C.S.: 335139
Rusty Belman (Mgr-Pur & Production)
Troy Tyler (Dir-Design & Quotations)
Paula Frantz (Mgr-Quotations)
Rodney Sullivan (Head-Engrg)
Patrick Kinney (Mgr-Sls-Southeast)

Recreation Creations, LLC (2)
215 W Mechanic St, Hillsdale, MI 49242
Tel.: (517) 439-1591
Web Site: http://www.rec-creations.com
Sales Range: $10-24.9 Million
Emp.: 10

Playground Equipment & Park Amenities Mfr
N.A.I.C.S.: 339920
Curt Shaneour (Pres)

WORTHGROUP MASTERBUILDERS, INC.
9400 Gateway Dr Ste B, Reno, NV 89521-8993
Tel.: (775) 852-3977
Web Site: http://www.worthgroup.com
Year Founded: 1999
Sales Range: $25-49.9 Million
Emp.: 50
Provider of Construction Services
N.A.I.C.S.: 236115

WORTHINGTON DEALERSHIP GROUP
2950 N Bellflower Blvd, Long Beach, CA 90815
Tel.: (760) 431-1222
Web Site: http://www.calworthington.com
Rev.: $85,700,000
Emp.: 120
New & Used Automobiles
N.A.I.C.S.: 441110
David Karalis (Gen Mgr)

WORTHINGTON ENERGY, INC.
295 Hwy 50 Ste 25, Stateline, NV 89449
Tel.: (775) 588-5390
Year Founded: 2004
Oil & Gas Exploration Services
N.A.I.C.S.: 213112

WORTHINGTON JEWELERS
692 High St, Worthington, OH 43085
Tel.: (614) 430-8800
Web Site: http://www.worthingtonjewelers.com
Year Founded: 2000
Sales Range: $1-9.9 Million
Emp.: 22
Fashion Jewelry Distr
N.A.I.C.S.: 423940
Bob Capace (Pres)

WORTHPOINT CORPORATION
5 Piedmont Ctr NE Ste 435, Atlanta, GA 30305
Tel.: (404) 996-1470
Web Site: http://www.worthpoint.com
Year Founded: 2007
Sales Range: $1-9.9 Million
Emp.: 14
Online Marketing Research Services
N.A.I.C.S.: 541910
William Seippel (Founder & CEO)
William N. McAtee (CFO)
Scott Thomas (VP-Mktg)

WOUND CARE ADVANTAGE
304 W Sierra Madre Blvd, Sierra Madre, CA 91024
Tel.: (626) 355-7611
Web Site: http://www.woundcareadvantage.com
Year Founded: 2002
Sales Range: $1-9.9 Million
Emp.: 30
Develops & Manages Wound Care & Hyperbaric Medicine Programs for Hospitals & Medical Centers
N.A.I.C.S.: 622110
Michael Comer (Founder, Chm & CEO)
Karen Redmond (Pres)
Morgan Craven (VP-HR)
Rylan Smith (CFO)
Nancy Zeller (Pres)
Christina Le (VP-Clinician Dev)
Craig Johns (VP-Bus Dev)
Lynn McLeod (VP-Program Implementation)

Melissa Bailey *(VP-Corp Ops)*
Nick Keezer *(CTO)*
Randall B. Brooker *(Pres-Center Ops)*

WOVEN DIGITAL, INC.
10381 Jefferson Blvd, Culver City, CA 90232
Tel.: (424) 238-2039　　CA
Web Site: http://www.woven.com
Emp.: 135
Digital Media Publisher & Online Advertising Services
N.A.I.C.S.: 541870
Michael Laur *(COO)*
Scott Grimes *(Founder)*
Colin Digiaro *(Chm)*
Jarret Myer *(Gen Mgr-Publ)*
Matthew P. Polesetsky *(Gen Counsel)*
Benjamin Blank *(CEO)*
Eileen Carty *(Chief Revenue Officer)*
Kyle Arbaugh *(Sr VP-Sls & Brand Partnerships)*
Julie Butler *(Sr VP-Revenue Ops)*
Jerry Thompson *(VP-Tech)*

Subsidiaries:

Dime Magazine Publishing Co., Inc.　　(1)
291 Broadway Ste 1204, New York, NY 10007
Tel.: (212) 629-5066
Web Site: http://www.dimemag.com
Sales Range: $1-9.9 Million
Emp.: 5
Sports Magazine Publishers
N.A.I.C.S.: 513120
Josh Gotthelf *(Exec VP-Mktg)*
Chris Mottram *(Mng Dir)*
Spencer Lund *(Mng Editor)*

WOVEN LEGENDS INC.
2400 Market St Market Pl Design Ctr Ste 401, Philadelphia, PA 19103
Tel.: (215) 849-8344
Web Site: http://www.wovenlegends.com
Sales Range: $10-24.9 Million
Emp.: 50
Carpets
N.A.I.C.S.: 423220
N. C. Jevremovic *(CEO)*

WOW LOGISTICS COMPANY
3040 W Wisconsin Ave, Appleton, WI 54914
Tel.: (920) 734-9924
Web Site: http://www.wowlogistics.com
Year Founded: 1977
Sales Range: $10-24.9 Million
Emp.: 170
Rent Out Warehouse Space; General Warehousing
N.A.I.C.S.: 493110
Harold E. Schiferl *(Co-Owner)*
Donald Utschig *(Co-Owner)*
Peter Upton-Rowley *(Dir-Trade Fin)*

WOW MEDIA PRODUCTS, INC.
1261 Broadway Ste 604, New York, NY 10001
Tel.: (516) 528-3686
Web Site: http://www.purewow.com
Year Founded: 2010
Sales Range: $10-24.9 Million
Emp.: 70
Online Women's Lifestyle Media Publisher
N.A.I.C.S.: 513199
Ryan Harwood *(CEO)*

WOZNIAK INDUSTRIES, INC.
2 Mid America Plz Ste 700, Oakbrook Terrace, IL 60181-4717
Tel.: (630) 954-3400　　IL
Web Site: http://www.wozniakindustries.com
Year Founded: 1985
Sales Range: $150-199.9 Million
Emp.: 630
Metal Stampings; Injection Molding of Plastics; Iron & Steel Forgings
N.A.I.C.S.: 332119
Alexis Stadt *(VP-Admin)*
Michael Wozniak *(Pres & CEO)*
Michael Powers *(CFO)*

Subsidiaries:

Commercial Forged Products　　(1)
5757 W 65th St, Bedford Park, IL 60638-5503　　(100%)
Tel.: (708) 458-1220
Web Site: http://www.commercialforged.com
Sales Range: $10-24.9 Million
Emp.: 100
Absorbed Forging Services
N.A.I.C.S.: 332111
Herbert Little *(Gen Mgr)*
Sandra Wozniak *(Chm)*

GMP Metal Products　　(1)
3883 Delor St, Saint Louis, MO 63116-3327　　(100%)
Tel.: (314) 481-0300
Web Site: http://www.gmpmetal.com
Sales Range: $25-49.9 Million
Emp.: 200
Metal Products Mfr
N.A.I.C.S.: 332119
Michael Wosnick *(Pres & CEO)*
Michael Powers *(CFO)*
Sandra Wozniak *(Chm)*

WP BEVERAGES, LLC
6176 Pepsi Way, Windsor, WI 53598-9649
Tel.: (608) 846-1200　　WI
Year Founded: 1982
Sales Range: $25-49.9 Million
Emp.: 225
Provider of Groceries & Related Products
N.A.I.C.S.: 424490
Kitty Newton *(Dir-Adv & PR)*
Barb Parish *(Pres)*
Laurie Ogletree *(Supvr-Acctg)*
George Liegel *(VP)*
Keith Goldsmith *(Mgr-Ops Support)*
Neal Burkle *(Dir-IT)*

WPC III, INC.
221 Circle Dr, Maitland, FL 32751
Tel.: (407) 644-8923
Web Site: http://www.wpc.com
Sales Range: $150-199.9 Million
Emp.: 80
Multifamily Housing & Commercial Construction
N.A.I.C.S.: 236117
Tracy Forrest *(Chm & CEO)*
Jeff Forrest *(Pres)*
Chuck Reynolds *(VP-Pre-Construction & Estimating)*
Kevin Corrado *(COO)*

WPCS INTERNATIONAL - SUISUN CITY, INC.
521 Railroad Ave, Suisun City, CA 94585-4244
Tel.: (707) 398-3421　　CA
Web Site: http://www.wpcs-suisuncity.com
Year Founded: 1993
Wireless Device & Related Product Whslr
N.A.I.C.S.: 423690
Brandon Ripley *(Project Mgr)*

WPENGINE, INC.
504 Lavaca St Ste 1000, Austin, TX 78701
Tel.: (512) 273-3906
Web Site: http://wpengine.com
Data Processing, Hosting & Related Services
N.A.I.C.S.: 518210
Heather J. Brunner *(Chm & CEO)*
Annette Alexander *(Chief People Officer)*
David Brolsma *(CFO)*
Lisa Box *(Sr VP-Corp Dev)*
Ramadass Prabhakar *(Sr VP-Global Engrg)*
Jason Teichman *(COO)*
Sachin Puri *(CMO & Sr VP)*

Subsidiaries:

Fancy Chap, Inc.　　(1)
1111 N 13th St Ste 208, Omaha, NE 68102
Tel.: (402) 235-6105
Web Site: http://www.getflywheel.com
Cloud Hosting Services Platform Developer
N.A.I.C.S.: 541511
Rick Knudtson *(Co-Founder & CMO)*
Dusty Davidson *(Co-Founder & CEO)*
Tony Noecker *(Co-Founder & CTO)*
Karen Borchert *(COO)*
Dan White *(Head-Support)*
Jamie Clare Bell *(Head-Mktg)*
Michael Struthers *(Head-People Ops)*
Amanda Kohler *(Dir-Product)*
Kaitlin Grohmann *(Head-Customer Success)*

WPH AIRPORT ASSOCIATES
617 Dingens St, Buffalo, NY 14206
Tel.: (716) 893-6551
Web Site: http://www.harthotels.com
Rev.: $18,500,000
Emp.: 200
Hotel
N.A.I.C.S.: 721110
William P. Hart *(Chm)*
David P. Hart *(Pres & CEO)*
Allen Incorvaia *(VP-Ops)*

Subsidiaries:

Hart Hotels, Inc.　　(1)
617 Dingens St, Buffalo, NY 14206
Tel.: (716) 893-6551
Web Site: http://www.harthotels.com
Sales Range: $10-24.9 Million
Emp.: 900
Provider of Hotel Services
N.A.I.C.S.: 541611
David P. Hart *(Pres & CEO)*

WPM INC.
8127 Indus Park Dr, Grand Blanc, MI 48439
Tel.: (810) 606-1400
Web Site: http://www.wpmexc.com
Rev.: $15,936,248
Emp.: 100
Excavation Work
N.A.I.C.S.: 238910
Chris Leoni *(Project Mgr)*
William H. Leoni Jr. *(Pres)*

WPS INDUSTRIES INC.
228 Industrial St, West Monroe, LA 71292
Tel.: (318) 255-6665
Web Site: http://www.wpsindustries.com
Rev.: $12,786,673
Emp.: 70
Pneumatic Tube Conveyor Systems Mfr
N.A.I.C.S.: 333922
Mike Clark *(Chm & Owner)*
Tony Clark *(Pres)*

WPS, INC.
525 W Allen Ave Ste 9, San Dimas, CA 91773
Tel.: (909) 599-9415　　NV
Year Founded: 2008
Sales Range: Less than $1 Million
Emp.: 1
Fastener Mfr
N.A.I.C.S.: 339993

Guillermo Pina *(Pres, CEO, CFO, Chief Acctg Officer, Treas & Sec)*
Patricia Pina *(Owner)*

WR HAMBRECHT & CO. LLC
Pier 1 Bay 3, San Francisco, CA 94133
Tel.: (415) 551-8600
Web Site: http://www.wrhambrecht.com
Year Founded: 1998
Sales Range: $10-24.9 Million
Emp.: 32
Investment Banking & Securities Broking
N.A.I.C.S.: 523150
Elizabeth Betsy Hambrecht *(Partner)*
William R. Hambrecht *(Chm)*

WR RESTAURANTS MANAGEMENT LLC
3211 W Sencord Dr, Sioux Falls, SD 57107
Tel.: (605) 965-1400
Web Site: http://www.wrrestaurants.com
Sales Range: $25-49.9 Million
Emp.: 1,500
Operator of Eating Places
N.A.I.C.S.: 722511
Paul Van Bockern *(Co-Founder, Pres & CEO)*
Terry Van De Walle *(Dir-HR Dev & Trng)*

WR VERMILLION CO., INC.
1207 S Scenic Ave, Springfield, MO 65802
Tel.: (417) 862-3785
Web Site: http://www.vermillion-flooring.com
Sales Range: $10-24.9 Million
Emp.: 140
Novelties, Wood Fiber
N.A.I.C.S.: 321999
Art Thomas *(Pres)*
John Thomas *(Vp)*

WRA
4260 W Linebaugh Ave, Tampa, FL 33624
Tel.: (813) 265-3130
Web Site: http://www.wraengineering.com
Year Founded: 1997
Sales Range: $1-9.9 Million
Emp.: 28
Engineeering Services
N.A.I.C.S.: 541330
Mark D. Farrell *(Principal)*
Peter G. Hubbell *(Principal)*
Clint Cuffle *(VP & Partner)*
Joe Cimino *(VP & Partner)*

WRAGG & CASAS PUBLIC RELATIONS, INC.
1000 Brickell Ave Ste 400, Miami, FL 33131
Tel.: (305) 372-1234
Web Site: http://www.wraggcasas.com
Year Founded: 1991
Sales Range: $10-24.9 Million
Emp.: 17
Public Relations Agency
N.A.I.C.S.: 541820
Otis O. Wragg *(Principal)*
Ray Casas *(Principal)*
Joanna Wragg *(Principal)*
Jeanmarie Ferrara *(Exec VP)*
Jeanne Becker *(Sr VP)*
Alexandra Curbelo *(Acct Coord)*
Elysa Delcorto *(Acct Exec)*

WRAGG & CASAS PUBLIC RELATIONS, INC.

Subsidiaries:

Wragg & Casas Public Relations, Inc. (1)
27499 Riverview Ctr Blvd Ste 115, Bonita Springs, FL 34134
Tel.: (239) 444-1724
Web Site: http://www.wraggcasas.com
Emp.: 3
N.A.I.C.S.: 541820

Wragg & Casas Public Relations, Inc. (1)
121 S Orange Ave Ste 1500, Orlando, FL 32801
Tel.: (407) 244-3685
Web Site: http://www.wraggcasas.com
Emp.: 2
N.A.I.C.S.: 541820

WRAP & SEND SERVICES, LLC
8005 Plainfield Rd Ste 20, Cincinnati, OH 45236
Tel.: (513) 791-2022
Web Site: http://www.wrapandsend.com
Rev.: $17,500,000
Emp.: 100
Gift Wrapping Services
N.A.I.C.S.: 812990
Denise Dehan *(VP)*

WRAY FORD INC.
2851 Benton Rd, Bossier City, LA 71111
Tel.: (318) 686-7300
Web Site: http://www.wrayford.com
Sales Range: $50-74.9 Million
Emp.: 102
New & Used Car Dealers
N.A.I.C.S.: 441110
Rachel Wheeler *(Controller)*
George D. Wray III *(Owner)*

WRAY MAZDA VOLKSWAGEN
655 Broad River Rd, Columbia, SC 29210-7971
Tel.: (803) 988-1000
Year Founded: 1998
Sales Range: $10-24.9 Million
Emp.: 87
Car Whslr
N.A.I.C.S.: 441110

WRAY WARD MARKETING COMMUNICATIONS
900 Baxter St, Charlotte, NC 28204
Tel.: (704) 332-9071
Web Site: http://www.wrayward.com
Year Founded: 1977
Sales Range: $50-74.9 Million
Emp.: 60
Advertising Agencies
N.A.I.C.S.: 541810
Jennifer O. Appleby *(Pres & Chief Creative Officer)*
Sue Tatge *(VP & Dir-Media)*
Judy Allison *(VP & Controller)*
John Roberts *(VP & Exec Dir-Creative)*
Kent Panther *(VP & Dir-Bus Dev)*
Rusty Williams *(Dir-Studio)*
Bill Baker *(Dir-Measurement)*
Scott Ellmaker *(Dir-Copy)*
Patricia Propst *(VP & Dir-Fin & Ops)*
John Mader *(VP & Dir-Connections)*
Leslie Gillock *(VP & Dir-Insights)*
Rob Horton *(VP & Dir-Client Engagement)*
Vivian Mize *(VP & Dir-Creative)*
Wendy Storey *(Dir-Search)*
Courtney Reese *(Acct Coord-PR & Content)*
Laureston Hawley *(Acct Mgr-PR & Content)*
Ilana Wiles *(Assoc Dir-Media)*
Christy Marion *(Acct Mgr-PR & Content)*
Billie Meacham *(Coord-Media)*
Sarah Headley *(Acct Coord-PR & Content)*
Becca Scott *(Project Coord-Mgmt)*
Teena Ray *(Dir-Corp Svcs)*
Morgan Rodden *(Controller)*

WRAY'S INC.
5605 Summitview Ave, Yakima, WA 98908-3039
Tel.: (509) 966-1808
Web Site: http://www.wraysfoods.com
Year Founded: 1955
Sales Range: $25-49.9 Million
Emp.: 170
Grocery Store Operator
N.A.I.C.S.: 445110
Christopher Brown *(CEO)*
Karen Brown *(Sec)*

WRB ENTERPRISES, INC.
1414 Swann Ave Ste 201, Tampa, FL 33606-2533
Tel.: (813) 251-3737
Web Site: http://www.wrbenterprises.com
Year Founded: 1969
Sales Range: $50-74.9 Million
Emp.: 220
Operators Of Nonresidential Buildings
N.A.I.C.S.: 531120
Edward H. Parry *(CFO)*
G. Robert Blanchard Jr. *(Chm & CEO)*

Subsidiaries:

Blanchard Investments, Inc. (1)
3151 Charleston Hwy, West Columbia, SC 29172-2723
Tel.: (803) 791-7100
Web Site: http://www.blanchardmachinery.com
Construction & Mining Machinery Sales
N.A.I.C.S.: 423810

WREN CORPORATION
PO Box 130280, Roseville, MN 55113-0003
Tel.: (651) 636-8900
Web Site: http://www.lakevillemotor.com
Year Founded: 1985
Sales Range: $100-124.9 Million
Emp.: 300
Holding Company
N.A.I.C.S.: 551112
Karen Vanney *(VP-Fin)*
Roger Wilsey *(CEO)*

Subsidiaries:

Lakeville Motor Express Inc. (1)
500 W County Rd D, New Brighton, MN 55112
Tel.: (651) 636-8900
Web Site: http://www.lakevillemotor.com
Sales Range: $10-24.9 Million
Emp.: 100
Trucking Except Local
N.A.I.C.S.: 484122

WRENN CONSTRUCTION
72 Bruce Rd, Manchester, NH 03087
Tel.: (603) 893-2556
Web Site: http://www.wrenn.com
Year Founded: 1984
Sales Range: Less than $1 Million
Emp.: 10
Construction Services
N.A.I.C.S.: 236220
Sylvester M. Wrenn *(Pres)*
Paul W. Kent *(VP)*

WRG SERVICES, INC.
38585 Apollo Pkwy, Willoughby, OH 44094
Tel.: (440) 942-8650
Year Founded: 1980
Sales Range: $10-24.9 Million
Emp.: 50
ATM Repair Services
N.A.I.C.S.: 811310
James N. Penza *(Pres)*
Michael J. Stevenson *(CEO)*

WRH REALTY SERVICES, INC.
415 1st Ave N, Saint Petersburg, FL 33701
Tel.: (727) 892-3000
Web Site: http://www.wrhrealty.com
Year Founded: 1998
Sales Range: $25-49.9 Million
Emp.: 435
Multifamily Property Manager
N.A.I.C.S.: 531311
Mark Rutledge *(Pres & CEO)*
Clive Bamford *(Dir-Construction Svcs)*
Dan Buschlen *(Controller)*
Edward McCluskey *(Dir-Maintenance Accts)*
Gina Lee *(Mgr-Property Mgmt Ops)*
Cynthia A. Haines *(COO & Sr VP)*
Jay Meder *(CFO & Exec VP)*
John G. Withers *(Sr VP)*

WRIGHT & FILIPPIS INC.
2845 Crooks Rd, Rochester Hills, MI 48309
Tel.: (248) 853-1888
Web Site: http://www.firsttoserve.com
Sales Range: $25-49.9 Million
Emp.: 650
Prosthetic Appliances
N.A.I.C.S.: 339113
Anthony J. Filippis *(Founder, Chm & CEO)*
Pam Lupo *(Dir-Orthotics)*
John F. Wright *(VP-Bus Dev)*
Robert DeWolf Jr. *(Pres)*

WRIGHT & MCGILL CO.
4245 E 46th Ave, Denver, CO 80216
Tel.: (303) 321-1481
Web Site: http://www.eagleclaw.com
Year Founded: 1925
Sales Range: $75-99.9 Million
Emp.: 275
Fishhooks Mfr; Supplier of Rods, Reels, Terminal Tackle; Baits & Scents Mfr
N.A.I.C.S.: 339920
William Miller *(Sec)*
John Jilling *(Pres)*
Don Schaible *(Pres)*
Joe Bartell *(VP-Engrg)*
Cory Steele *(Controller)*
Mike Jackson *(VP-Sls)*
Linda M. Martin *(Mgr-Adv)*
Chris Russell *(Dir-Mktg)*
Matt Gray *(Product Mgr)*

WRIGHT & MORRISSEY, INC.
PO Box 421, Burlington, VT 05402
Tel.: (802) 863-4541
Web Site: http://www.wmorrissey.com
Year Founded: 1934
Sales Range: $10-24.9 Million
Emp.: 60
Civil Engineering Services
N.A.I.C.S.: 237310
Daniel B. Morrissey *(Pres)*

WRIGHT & PERCY INSURANCE AGENCY INC.
4041 Essen Ln Ste 400, Baton Rouge, LA 70809
Tel.: (225) 336-3200
Web Site: http://www.bxsi.com
Year Founded: 1800
Sales Range: $10-24.9 Million
Emp.: 160
Insurance Agents, Brokers & Service
N.A.I.C.S.: 524210
Charlotte Wright *(Mgr-HR)*
Kerry Drake *(Pres & CEO)*
Christine Roux *(Acct Mgr)*

WRIGHT AUTOMOTIVE GROUP
11015 Perry Hwy, Wexford, PA 15090
Tel.: (724) 935-4646
Web Site: http://www.wrightcars.com
Year Founded: 1926
Sales Range: $10-24.9 Million
Emp.: 70
Car Whslr
N.A.I.C.S.: 441110
Ken Wright *(Owner)*
Benjamin Holt *(Dir-Fin)*
Robert Turzillo *(Mgr-Sls)*

WRIGHT BROTHERS BUILDING CO.
779 E State St PO Box 637, Eagle, ID 83616-5942
Tel.: (208) 939-0377
Web Site: http://www.wbtbc.com
Year Founded: 1997
Sales Range: $10-24.9 Million
Emp.: 50
Construction Management & General Contracting Services
N.A.I.C.S.: 236220
Rob Fraser *(Project Mgr)*
Robert Grubb *(Project Mgr)*
Terry Hayden *(Treas)*
Joe Rausch *(VP)*
Robert A. Wright *(Pres)*

WRIGHT BUSINESS FORMS, INC.
18440 NE San Rafael, Portland, OR 97230-7009
Tel.: (503) 661-2525
Web Site: http://www.wrightbg.com
Year Founded: 1970
Sales Range: $25-49.9 Million
Emp.: 300
Manifold Business Forms Mfr
N.A.I.C.S.: 323111
James T. Wright *(Founder, Chm & CEO)*
Brian Cicerchi *(VP-Fin)*
Debbie Aker *(VP & Gen Mgr-Wright Imaging)*
Dan Adkison *(Pres & COO)*

Subsidiaries:

Wright Business Forms, Inc. - Chino Facility (1)
13602 12th St Ste A, Chino, CA 91710
Tel.: (909) 614-6700
Web Site: http://www.wrightbg.com
Emp.: 50
Commercial Printing Services
N.A.I.C.S.: 323111
Jeff Trump *(VP)*

Wright Business Forms, Inc. - Kent Facility (1)
7015 S 212th St, Kent, WA 98032
Tel.: (800) 523-2741
Commercial Printing Services
N.A.I.C.S.: 323111

Wright Imaging Solutions (1)
13107 NE Airport Way, Portland, OR 97230-1036
Tel.: (503) 445-3250
Web Site: http://www.wrightimg.com
Sales Range: $10-24.9 Million
Emp.: 25
Commercial Printing
N.A.I.C.S.: 323111
Debbie Aker *(Gen Mgr)*

COMPANIES

WRIGHT CONSTRUCTION GROUP, INC.
5811 Youngquist Rd, Fort Myers, FL 33912
Tel.: (239) 481-5000
Web Site: http://www.wrightg.com
Year Founded: 1946
Sales Range: $1-9.9 Million
Emp.: 45
Construction Services
N.A.I.C.S.: 236220
Fred Edman *(Pres)*
Andy Powell *(VP)*
Scott Loiacano *(Project Mgr)*
Chris Campbell *(Dir-Project Dev)*

WRIGHT DISTRIBUTING CO., INC.
10095 US 290, Manor, TX 78653
Tel.: (512) 321-4411
Web Site: http://www.wrightdist.com
Sales Range: $25-49.9 Million
Emp.: 1,000
Beer & Other Fermented Malt Liquors
N.A.I.C.S.: 424810
Jane Wright *(Pres)*
Jill McCann *(Controller)*
Sandy Kibby *(VP)*
Tom Clayton *(Gen Mgr)*

WRIGHT DO IT CENTER
208 S Williams St, Murphysboro, IL 62966
Tel.: (618) 687-1702
Web Site: http://www.wrightdoit.com
Year Founded: 1964
Sales Range: $50-74.9 Million
Emp.: 80
Other Building Material Retailer
N.A.I.C.S.: 444180
Dennis McIntyre *(Mgr)*

WRIGHT ENERGY PARTNERS, LLC
1600 E Grand Blvd Ste 330, Detroit, MI 48211   MI
Web Site: http://www.wrightled.com
Year Founded: 2015
Sales Range: $1-9.9 Million
Emp.: 15
Energy Efficiency Inspection Services
N.A.I.C.S.: 541350
Clark Covert *(Owner)*

WRIGHT ENGINEERED PLASTICS, INC.
3225 Regional Pkwy, Santa Rosa, CA 95403
Tel.: (707) 575-1218
Web Site: http://www.wepmolding.com
Sales Range: $10-24.9 Million
Emp.: 40
Provider of Plastics Hardware & Building Products
N.A.I.C.S.: 326199
Barbara Roberts *(Pres & CEO)*
Mike Nellis *(COO & Exec VP)*
Karrie Bertsch *(Dir-Engrg)*
Peter O'Brien *(Dir-Product Dev)*
Kevin McKinney *(Mgr-Tool Dev)*
Dale Lawler *(Mgr-Tooling)*

WRIGHT GRAPHICS INC.
12327 Santa Monica Blvd Ste 101, Los Angeles, CA 90025-2552
Tel.: (818) 882-4172
Rev: $15,000,000
Emp.: 80
Promotional Printing Lithographic
N.A.I.C.S.: 323111
Daniel Wright *(Pres)*
Marge Samuelson *(CFO)*

WRIGHT MANAGEMENT COMPANY, LLC
81 Enterprise Dr, Debord, KY 41214
Tel.: (606) 298-2300   KY
Web Site: http://www.boothenergy.zohosites.com
Coal Mining Assets Management Services
N.A.I.C.S.: 561110
James H. Booth *(Pres & CEO)*

Subsidiaries:

Cambrian Coal Corporation   (1)
620 Ohio St, Elkhorn City, KY 41522
Tel.: (606) 754-9580
Coal Mining
N.A.I.C.S.: 212114
James H. Booth *(Pres & CEO)*

WRIGHT PLASTIC PRODUCTS CO., LLC
201 Condensery Rd, Sheridan, MI 48884
Tel.: (989) 291-3211
Web Site: http://www.wrightplasticproducts.com
Sales Range: $100-124.9 Million
Emp.: 150
Mfr of Molded Plastic Products
N.A.I.C.S.: 326199
Robert Luce *(Pres)*
John Christenson *(Dir-Admin)*

WRIGHT RUNSTAD & COMPANY
1201 3rd Ave Ste 2700, Seattle, WA 98101
Tel.: (206) 447-9000
Web Site: http://www.wrightrunstad.com
Sales Range: $25-49.9 Million
Emp.: 75
Property Managers
N.A.I.C.S.: 237210
Walt R. Ingram *(CFO & Exec VP)*
H. Jon Runstad *(Founder, Chm & CEO)*
Gregory K. Johnson *(Pres)*

WRIGHT TOOL COMPANY, INC.
1 Wright Dr, Barberton, OH 44203
Tel.: (330) 848-0600
Web Site: http://www.wrighttool.com
Year Founded: 1927
Sales Range: $10-24.9 Million
Emp.: 160
Hand & Edge Tool Mfr
N.A.I.C.S.: 332216
Tom Futey *(CFO & VP)*
Richard B. Wright *(Chm)*

WRIGHT TOTAL INDOOR COMFORT, INC.
1315 Ford St, Colorado Springs, CO 80915
Tel.: (719) 694-3653
Web Site: http://www.thewrightguys.com
Year Founded: 1937
Emp.: 25
Plumbing, Heating & Air-Conditioning Contractors
N.A.I.C.S.: 238220
Shawn Gayle *(Dir-Ops)*

WRIGHT TRAVEL AGENCY INC.
2505 21st Ave S Ste 500, Nashville, TN 37212-5652
Tel.: (615) 783-1111   TN
Web Site: http://www.wrighttravel.net
Year Founded: 1981
Sales Range: $100-124.9 Million
Emp.: 50
Travel Agencies
N.A.I.C.S.: 561510

Pamela J. Wright *(Pres & CEO)*

WRIGHT TREE SERVICE INC.
5930 Grand Ave, West Des Moines, IA 50266
Tel.: (515) 277-6291   IA
Web Site: http://www.wrighttree.com
Year Founded: 1933
Ornamental Shrub & Tree Services; Tree Trimming Services
N.A.I.C.S.: 561730
Scott Packard *(Chm & CEO)*
Will Nutter *(COO & Sr VP)*
Terry McGonegle *(CFO & Sr VP)*

WRIGHT VALLEY OIL INC.
514 W Ave, Alamosa, CO 81101
Tel.: (719) 589-2322
Sales Range: $10-24.9 Million
Emp.: 35
Petroleum Bulk Stations
N.A.I.C.S.: 424710

WRIGHT WISNER DISTRIBUTING CORP.
3165 Brighton Henrietta Town Line Rd, Rochester, NY 14623-2751
Tel.: (585) 427-2880
Web Site: http://www.wrightbev.com
Year Founded: 1953
Sales Range: $100-124.9 Million
Emp.: 350
Beer & Ale Products Distr
N.A.I.C.S.: 424810
Brian Lambert *(CFO & Treas)*
Dan Bresnahan *(Dir-Sls)*
Woody Marsh *(Dir-Ops)*

Subsidiaries:

B.E. Wright, Inc.   (1)
Mound Rd Route 414, Waterloo, NY 13165   (100%)
Tel.: (315) 539-5091
Sales Range: $25-49.9 Million
Emp.: 75
Distr of Soda, Beer, Ale & Other Beverages
N.A.I.C.S.: 424810

C.H. Wright, Inc.   (1)
3 Wright Ave, Le Roy, NY 14482
Tel.: (585) 502-0502
Sales Range: $10-24.9 Million
Emp.: 80
Beer & Ale Distr
N.A.I.C.S.: 424810
Dean Kendall *(Gen Mgr)*
Nick Palmiero *(Gen Mgr)*

WRIGHT'S FOODLANE INC.
3623 W Main St, Norman, OK 73072
Tel.: (405) 360-6870
Web Site: http://www.wrightsfamilymarket.com
Sales Range: $10-24.9 Million
Emp.: 120
Independent Supermarket
N.A.I.C.S.: 445110
Tom Wilson *(Mgr)*
Larry Wright *(Pres)*

WRIGHT'S FOODLINER INC.
2862 Willamette St # B, Eugene, OR 97405-3240
Tel.: (541) 345-0566   OR
Web Site: http://www.marketofchoice.com
Year Founded: 1978
Sales Range: $50-74.9 Million
Emp.: 500
Provider of Grocery Services
N.A.I.C.S.: 445110
Richard L. Wright *(Pres & CEO)*

WRIGHT'S MEDIA, LLC
2407 Timberloch Pl Ste B, The Woodlands, TX 77380
Tel.: (281) 419-5725

WRIGHTWAY CREATIVE GROUP

Web Site: http://www.wrightsmedia.com
Sales Range: $1-9.9 Million
Emp.: 40
Business Information Solutions
N.A.I.C.S.: 513199
Richard Wright *(Pres)*
Scott Barnes *(CFO)*

WRIGHT-HENNEPIN COOPERATIVE ELECTRIC ASSOCIATION
6800 Electric Dr, Rockford, MN 55373-0330
Tel.: (763) 477-3000   MN
Web Site: http://www.whe.org
Year Founded: 1937
Sales Range: $75-99.9 Million
Emp.: 122
Electricity Distr
N.A.I.C.S.: 221122
Dale Jans *(Treas & Sec)*
Chris Lantto *(Chm)*
Dale Jans Buffalo *(Treas & Sec)*

WRIGHT-K TECHNOLOGY, INC.
2025 E Genesee Ave, Saginaw, MI 48601-2425
Tel.: (989) 752-3103   MI
Web Site: http://www.wright-k.com
Year Founded: 1982
Sales Range: $1-9.9 Million
Emp.: 40
Mfr of Special Machinery
N.A.I.C.S.: 333517
John P. Sivey *(Pres & CEO)*
Connie M. Kostrzewa *(Chm)*
Clive Moore *(Mgr-Quality)*
Jerry Vermeesch *(Mgr-Parts)*
Jim Nicoson *(Mgr-Engrg)*

WRIGHT-RYAN CONSTRUCTION INC.
10 Danforth St, Portland, ME 04101
Tel.: (207) 773-3625
Web Site: http://www.wright-ryan.com
Sales Range: $25-49.9 Million
Emp.: 70
Commercial & Office Building, New Construction
N.A.I.C.S.: 236220
Suzanne Benoit *(Dir-HR)*
Cordelia Pitman *(Dir-Preconstruction Svcs)*
Kevin Griffeth *(Dir-Safety & Mgr-Ops)*
Jeff Heseltine *(Gen Mgr-Field Ops)*
John Ryan *(Pres)*

WRIGHTIMC, LLC
660 N Central Expy Ste 450, Plano, TX 75074
Tel.: (972) 215-7167
Web Site: http://www.wrightimc.com
Year Founded: 2008
Sales Range: $1-9.9 Million
Emp.: 35
Interactive Marketing Services
N.A.I.C.S.: 541810
Clint Spaulding *(VP)*
John Confer *(Principal)*
Minh Nguyen *(VP)*
Tim Wagner *(VP)*
Tim Wright *(CFO)*
Tony Wright *(Founder & CEO)*
Brad Cook *(Dir-Creative)*
Hien Khuu *(Dir-Dev)*

WRIGHTWAY CREATIVE GROUP
28 W 44th St Ste 1600, New York, NY 10036
Tel.: (212) 866-9209
Year Founded: 1999
Rev: $10,000,000
Emp.: 4
N.A.I.C.S.: 541810
Homer Wright *(Pres)*

WRISCO INDUSTRIES INC.

Wrightway Creative Group—(Continued)

WRISCO INDUSTRIES INC.
355 Hiatt Dr Ste B, Palm Beach Gardens, FL 33418-7106
Tel.: (561) 626-5700 DE
Web Site: http://www.wrisco.com
Year Founded: 1982
Sales Range: $50-74.9 Million
Emp.: 70
Distr of Pre-Finished Aluminum & Steel Products; Components For Window Coverings; Components For Awnings; Insulated & Non Insulated Patio Enclosures, Carports & Screen Rooms
N.A.I.C.S.: 423510
A. James Monastra (Pres)
Paul Sullivan (Controller)
Garry Fiske (Mgr-Pur)
Amy Williams (Asst Controller)

Subsidiaries:

Wrisco Industries Inc. - Atlanta Division (1)
1116 Fleetwood Dr, Atlanta, GA 30316
Tel.: (404) 622-1066
Web Site: http://www.wrisco.com
Aluminum Sheet Mfr
N.A.I.C.S.: 331315

Wrisco Industries Inc. - Chicago Division (1)
6075 W 115th St, Alsip, IL 60803
Tel.: (708) 385-7000
Aluminum Sheet Mfr
N.A.I.C.S.: 331315

Wrisco Industries Inc. - Dallas Division (1)
12102 Corporate Dr, Dallas, TX 75228
Tel.: (972) 270-8848
Aluminum Sheet Mfr
N.A.I.C.S.: 331315

Wrisco Industries Inc. - Edison Division (1)
21 Executive Ave, Edison, NJ 08817
Tel.: (732) 287-8500
Aluminum Sheet Mfr
N.A.I.C.S.: 331315

WRL ADVERTISING, INC.
4470 Dressler Rd NW, Canton, OH 44718-2716
Tel.: (330) 493-8866 OH
Web Site: http://www.wrladv.com
Year Founded: 1954
Sales Range: $25-49.9 Million
Emp.: 23
N.A.I.C.S.: 541810
C. Todd Locke (Pres)
C. Thomas Locke (VP)
Bob Isenberg (VP-Creative Svcs)
Thomas Budinsky (Sr Dir-Art)
Betty Williams (Office Mgr)
Norio Saneshige (Sr Dir-Art)
James Hill (Dir-Multimedia)
David Jensen (Dir-Art)
Dan Kelly (Dir-Motion Graphics)
Dennis Warner (Dir-Internet)
Teresa Fedorchak (Sr Acct Mgr)
Todd Dummermuth (Dir-Art)
Rick Worrell (Gen Sls Mgr)
Jeff LeBeau (Dir-New Bus)
Dave Fenn (Sr Acct Exec)
Christina Morello (Dir-PR)

WROUGHT WASHER MFG., INC.
2100 S Bay St, Milwaukee, WI 53207-1208
Tel.: (414) 744-0771 WI
Web Site:
    http://www.wroughtwasher.com
Year Founded: 1887
Sales Range: $75-99.9 Million
Emp.: 125
Mfr of Washers & Stampings
N.A.I.C.S.: 332119

Diane Banach (Mgr-Customer Svc)
Larry Gaynor (Mgr-Sls)

WRS GROUP LTD.
5045 Franklin Ave, Waco, TX 76710
Tel.: (254) 776-6461
Web Site: http://www.wrsgroup.com
Sales Range: $10-24.9 Million
Emp.: 145
Mfr & Distributor of Education Aids
N.A.I.C.S.: 339999
Scott Salmans (CEO)
Cathi Davis (VP-Sls & Mktg)
Michael Bankhead (VP-Plant Ops)
Brian Bellamy (VP-Plant Ops)

WRT WORLD ENTERPRISES INC.
11300 NW 131st St, Medley, FL 33178
Tel.: (305) 884-3700
Web Site: http://www.wrtworld.com
Sales Range: $10-24.9 Million
Emp.: 37
Toy & Hobby Goods & Supplies Merchant Whslr
N.A.I.C.S.: 423920
Maria Wright (Treas, Sec & VP)
Ronald Wright (Chm)
Fred Wright (Pres)

WRZ BANKSHARES, INC.
100 4th Ave SE, Plainview, MN 55964
Tel.: (507) 534-3137 MN
Web Site:
    http://www.peoplesstatebank.com
Year Founded: 1989
Bank Holding Company
N.A.I.C.S.: 551111
Richard Zabel (Pres & CEO)

Subsidiaries:

Peoples State Bank of Plainview (1)
100 4th Ave Se, Plainview, MN 55964
Tel.: (507) 534-3137
Web Site: http://www.peoplesstatebank.com
Rev.: $8,436,000
Emp.: 18
Commericial Banking
N.A.I.C.S.: 522110
Diane Speedling (COO)
Jennifer Pazour (Coord-IS)
Dick Zabel (Owner)

WSF INDUSTRIES, INC.
7 Hackett Dr, Tonawanda, NY 14150-3711
Tel.: (716) 692-4930 NY
Web Site: http://www.wsf-inc.com
Year Founded: 1941
Sales Range: $10-24.9 Million
Emp.: 25
Processing Equipment, Autoclaves, Bonders, Cappers, Canners, Curers, Couplers, Vacuums, Cookers & Loaders
N.A.I.C.S.: 333248
Gary R. Fornasiero (Pres)
Lana Antonov (Controller)
Tom Ivancic (Engr-Automation)
John L. Hettrick Jr. (Chm & CEO)

WSG PARTNERS, LLC
1415 Rte 70 E Ste 500, Cherry Hill, NJ 08034
Tel.: (856) 429-0005
Web Site:
    http://www.wsgpartners.com
Year Founded: 2003
Privater Equity Firm
N.A.I.C.S.: 551112
William Green (Mng Partner)

WSI INTERNATIONAL, LLC
1709 W Baltic Pl, Englewood, CO 80110

Tel.: (303) 985-0885 CO
Web Site: http://www.wsi-llc.com
Water Treatment Plant Construction Services
N.A.I.C.S.: 237110
John Poe Tyler (Pres)

WSM INDUSTRIES INC.
1601 S Sheridan St, Wichita, KS 67213
Tel.: (316) 942-9412
Web Site: http://www.wsm-industries.com
Rev.: $19,976,353
Emp.: 75
Furnace Mfr
N.A.I.C.S.: 423730
John Griffitt (Partner)
Jim Harshfield (Mgr-Ops)

Subsidiaries:

Wichita Sheet Metal Supply Co., Inc. (1)
1601 S Sheridan St, Wichita, KS 67213
Tel.: (316) 942-9412
Web Site: http://www.wichita.com
Sales Range: $10-24.9 Million
Emp.: 50
Furnaces, Warm Air
N.A.I.C.S.: 423730

WSMC INC.
US Route 1, Falmouth, ME 04105
Tel.: (207) 781-4020
Web Site: http://www.morong.com
Sales Range: $10-24.9 Million
Emp.: 3
Automobiles, New & Used
N.A.I.C.S.: 441110
Horace William Sowles (Pres)
Anne Cote (Mgr-Sls)
Peter Sowles (VP & Mgr)

Subsidiaries:

Morong Brunswick (1)
314 Bath Rd, Brunswick, ME 04011
Tel.: (207) 725-4323
Web Site: http://www.morong.net
Sales Range: $10-24.9 Million
Emp.: 12
Automobile Services & Sale
N.A.I.C.S.: 441110
Horace William Sowles (Pres)
Matt Brown (Mgr-Sls)

WSOS COMMUNITY ACTION COMMISSION, INC.
109 S Front St, Fremont, OH 43420
Tel.: (419) 334-8911 OH
Web Site: http://www.wsos.org
Year Founded: 1965
Sales Range: $25-49.9 Million
Emp.: 487
Financial Assistance Services
N.A.I.C.S.: 541611
Paul Harrison (Vice Chm)
Chris Galvin (Chm)
Adrienne Fausey (Dir-HR)
Cheryl Denny (Dir-Plng & Dev)
Deb Martin (Dir-Community Dev)
Dave Kipplen (CFO)
Jacquie Wells (Dir-Family Dev)
Kerry Adkins (Dir-Admin & IT)
Terry Jacobs (Dir-Housing & Energy)

WSRP, LLC
155 N 400 W Ste 400, Salt Lake City, UT 84103
Tel.: (801) 328-2011
Web Site: http://www.wsrp.com
Offices of Certified Public Accountants
N.A.I.C.S.: 541211
Steven Racker (Partner)

WTA TOUR, INC.
100 2nd Ave S Ste 1100-S, Saint Petersburg, FL 33701

Tel.: (727) 895-5000 NY
Web Site: http://www.wtatennis.com
Year Founded: 1994
Sales Range: $50-74.9 Million
Emp.: 63
Tennis Association
N.A.I.C.S.: 711211
Joan Pennello (Sr VP-Ops)
Micky Lawler (Pres)
Laurence Applebaum (Exec VP)
Matthew Cenedella (COO)
Pam Valentine (Dir-HR)
Ashley Keber (VP)
Bob Campbell (Dir-Security)
Steve Simon (Chm & CEO)

WTECH
1568 Spring Hill Rd Ste 401, McLean, VA 22102
Tel.: (703) 847-4748
Web Site: http://www.wtechusa.com
Year Founded: 2003
Sales Range: $50-74.9 Million
Emp.: 39
Value Added Reseller Specializing in Incentive Sales Marketing & Consulting
N.A.I.C.S.: 541613
Michelle Samad (Pres)

WTWH MEDIA, LLC
1111 Superior Ave 26th Fl, Cleveland, OH 44114
Tel.: (888) 543-2447 DE
Web Site: http://www.wtwhmedia.com
Year Founded: 2006
Business-To-Business Marketer & Publisher
N.A.I.C.S.: 425120
Marshall Matheson (Exec VP)
Mike Emich (Founder & Publr)
Scott McCafferty (Mng Dir)
Mary Gannon (Sr Editor-Design World)
Virginia Goulding (Dir-Digital Mktg)
Lisa Rosen (Mgr-Webinar)
Jennifer Kolasky (Mgr-Event)
Jim Powers (Mgr-Key Acct)
Michael Caruso (VP-EE Bus Dev)
Michael Ference (VP-Bus Dev)
David Geltman (VP-Bus Dev)
Dan Kara (VP-Robotics)
Garrett Cona (Mgr-Reg Sls)

Subsidiaries:

The Robot Report (1)
3463 State St Ste 602, Santa Barbara, CA 93105
Tel.: (805) 895-4141
Web Site: http://www.therobotreport.com
Computer System Design Services
N.A.I.C.S.: 541512
Frank Tobe (Founder)
Paul Heney (VP & Dir-Editorial)
Dan Kara (VP-Robotics & Intelligent Sys)

WU BA SUPERIOR PRODUCTS HOLDING GROUP, INC.
2850 W Horizon Rdg Pkwy Ste 200, Henderson, NV 89052
Tel.: (702) 430-4610
Year Founded: 2010
Software Development Services
N.A.I.C.S.: 541511
Manfred Ruf (Chm, Pres, CEO & CFO)

WUEST'S INC.
9318 Fm 725, McQueeney, TX 78123
Tel.: (830) 379-3442 TX
Year Founded: 1938
Sales Range: $1-9.9 Million
Emp.: 116
Holding Company; Wholesale Grocery Retail Stores Owner & Operator
N.A.I.C.S.: 551112

Robert William Wuest *(Pres)*
Harvey Wuest *(VP)*
Phill Wuest *(Dir-Ops)*
Subsidiaries:

Wuest's of San Marcos (1)
9318 Fm 725, McQueeney, TX 78123
Tel.: (830) 379-3442
Wholesale Grocery Retail Store Operator
N.A.I.C.S.: 455211
Robert William Wuest *(Pres)*
Teresa Schneider *(Dir-HR)*

WULCO INC.
6899 Steger Dr, Cincinnati, OH 45307
Tel.: (513) 761-6899
Web Site: http://www.wulco.com
Rev.: $13,000,000
Emp.: 120
Industrial Supplies
N.A.I.C.S.: 423840
Reck Wulfeck *(Pres & CEO)*

Subsidiaries:

Jet Machine & Manufacturing (1)
6899 Steger Dr, Cincinnati, OH 45237
Tel.: (513) 679-2600
Web Site: http://www.jet-machine.com
Sales Range: $10-24.9 Million
Emp.: 94
Machining, Fabricating & Assembly Services
N.A.I.C.S.: 332710
Rick Wulfeck *(Pres & CEO)*

Rocket Supply (1)
6899 Steger Dr, Cincinnati, OH 45237
Tel.: (513) 679-2626
Web Site: http://www.rocket-supply.com
Sales Range: $25-49.9 Million
Emp.: 30
Industrial Product Distr
N.A.I.C.S.: 423840
Gary Wulfeck *(Owner)*
Steve Ruwe *(Office Mgr)*

WUNDERKIND, LLC
1 World Trade Ctr Fl 74, New York, NY 10007
Tel.: (212) 292-3162
Web Site: http://www.wunderkind.co
Year Founded: 2010
Sales Range: $10-24.9 Million
Software Development Services
N.A.I.C.S.: 541511
Brenda C. Freeman *(Chief Brand Officer)*
Ryan Urban *(Founder)*
Bill Ingram *(CEO)*
Stephen Collins *(Chm)*

Subsidiaries:

SmarterHQ, Inc. (1)
9102 N Meridian St Ste 415, Indianapolis, IN 46260
Tel.: (800) 913-9559
Web Site: http://www.smarterhq.com
Sales Range: $1-9.9 Million
Digital Marketing Services
N.A.I.C.S.: 541613
Michael Osborne *(Pres & CEO)*
Dean Abbott *(Founder)*
Barry Clark *(Sr VP-Sls & Mktg)*
Jason Fordham *(VP-Solutions)*
Matt Tyner *(VP-Fin & Ops)*

WUNDERLICH-MALEC ENGINEERING, INC.
6101 Blue Cir Dr, Eden Prairie, MN 55343
Tel.: (952) 933-3222
Web Site: http://www.wmeng.com
Year Founded: 1982
Rev.: $42,100,000
Emp.: 170
Engineeering Services
N.A.I.C.S.: 541330
Neal K. Wunderlich *(Pres)*
Antony Jones *(Dir-IT)*
Walter Malec *(VP)*

WURZEL BUILDERS, LTD.
630 Ralph Ablanedo Dr B 1, Austin, TX 78748
Tel.: (512) 282-9488
Web Site: http://www.wurzelbuilders.com
Sales Range: $10-24.9 Million
Emp.: 8
Commercial & Institutional Building Construction Services
N.A.I.C.S.: 236220
Barry Wurzel *(Pres)*

WW ENERGY, INC.
400 Sandstone Ave, Farmington, NM 87401
Tel.: (505) 326-1322
Year Founded: 2006
Sales Range: $1-9.9 Million
Emp.: 30
Support Activities for Oil & Gas Operations
N.A.I.C.S.: 213112
Olin Glover *(Pres)*

WW GROUP INC.
28555 Orchard Lake Rd, Farmington Hills, MI 48333
Tel.: (248) 553-8555
Web Site: http://www.8883florine.com
Sales Range: $75-99.9 Million
Emp.: 110
Diet Center without Medical Staff
N.A.I.C.S.: 812191
Florine Mark *(Pres & CEO)*
Sheryl Fellows *(Dir-Corp Comm)*

WW JOHNSON MEAT COMPANY
2001 E 24th St, Minneapolis, MN 55404
Tel.: (612) 746-0600
Web Site: http://www.wwjmeat.com
Year Founded: 1946
Sales Range: $10-24.9 Million
Emp.: 70
Beef Product Production Services
N.A.I.C.S.: 311612
Cory Plys *(Dir-Sls)*
Michael Ferraro *(Reg Mgr-Sls)*
George Venti *(Reg Mgr-Sls)*
Nick Faraclas *(Reg Mgr-Sls)*
Dean Hiracheta *(Mgr-Bus Dev)*
Brad Pawek *(Reg Mgr-Sls)*
Steve Thibault *(Reg Mgr-Sls)*

WXXA-TV
341 Northern Blvd, Albany, NY 12204
Tel.: (518) 436-4822
Web Site: http://www.news10.com
Emp.: 120
Television Broadcasting Station
N.A.I.C.S.: 516120
Christa Burke *(Mgr-HR)*

WXXI PUBLIC BROADCASTING COUNCIL
280 State St, Rochester, NY 14603-3021
Tel.: (585) 258-0200 NY
Web Site: http://www.wxxi.org
Year Founded: 1958
Sales Range: $10-24.9 Million
Emp.: 122
Television & Radio Broadcasting Services
N.A.I.C.S.: 334220
Cynthia Reddeck-LiDestri *(Chm)*
David Still *(Treas)*
Mark Cleary *(Sec)*
Norm Silverstein *(Pres)*
Robert A. Healy *(Vice Chm)*
Susan Rogers *(Exec VP & Gen Mgr)*

WYANDOT INC.
135 Wyandot Ave, Marion, OH 43302-1538
Tel.: (740) 383-4031 OH
Web Site: http://www.wyandotsnacks.com
Year Founded: 1936
Corn & Potato Based Snack Foods for Food Service & Retail Sales
N.A.I.C.S.: 311919
Robert Shaw *(Mgr-Info Svcs)*
Kelly McGowan *(Mgr-HR & Employee Rels)*
Robert J. Sarlls *(Bd of Dirs, Pres & CEO)*

WYANDOTTE TRIBAL CORPORATION
15 Turtle Dr, Wyandotte, OK 74370
Tel.: (918) 678-3030
Holding Company
N.A.I.C.S.: 551112
Kelly Carpino *(CEO)*
Scott Hoerner *(Dir-HR)*
Jan Woody *(Controller)*

Subsidiaries:

Bearskin Services (1)
15 Turtle Dr Ste 4, Wyandotte, OK 74370-2143
Tel.: (918) 678-3030
Web Site: http://www.bearskinservices.com
Information Technology Services
N.A.I.C.S.: 541519
Billy Friend *(Pres)*

Wyandotte NetTel (1)
15 Turtle Dr, Wyandotte, OK 74370
Tel.: (918) 678-3030
Sales Range: $10-24.9 Million
Emp.: 31
Telecommunications & Information Services
N.A.I.C.S.: 517810

Wyandotte Tribal Petroleum, Inc. (1)
15 Turtle Dr, Wyandotte, OK 74370
Tel.: (918) 678-3030
Web Site: http://www.wyandotte-corp.com
Sales Range: $1-9.9 Million
Emp.: 25
Petroleum Product Mfr
N.A.I.C.S.: 424720
Kelly Carpino *(CEO)*

WYATT INCORPORATED
4545 Campbells Run Rd, Pittsburgh, PA 15205-1313
Tel.: (412) 787-5800 PA
Web Site: http://www.wyattinc.com
Year Founded: 1970
Sales Range: $50-74.9 Million
Emp.: 350
Plastering, Drywall & Insulation
N.A.I.C.S.: 238310
Frederick T. Episcopo *(Pres)*
Richard B. Wyatt Jr. *(Owner & Chm)*

WYATT MANAGEMENT, INC.
1400 Woodloch Forest Dr 3rd Fl Ste 9, The Woodlands, TX 77380
Tel.: (281) 825-2960 MN
Web Site: http://www.wyattmngt.com
Year Founded: 1998
Sales Range: Less than $1 Million
Emp.: 8
General Contracting Services
N.A.I.C.S.: 236220
Tim Wyatt *(Pres)*

WYATT SEAL INC.
324 Piney Woods Rd, Columbia, SC 29212
Tel.: (803) 749-1212
Web Site: http://www.wyattseal.com
Year Founded: 1972
Sales Range: $10-24.9 Million
Emp.: 37
Industrial Seal
N.A.I.C.S.: 423840

Douglas Wyatt *(Pres)*
Janice Barnette *(Gen Mgr)*
Hank McMillan *(Exec VP)*
Subsidiaries:

Florida Seal & Rubber, LLC (1)
417 Hobbs St, Tampa, FL 33619
Tel.: (813) 681-5502
Web Site: http://www.flaseal.com
Sales Range: $1-9.9 Million
Emp.: 16
Industrial Product Distr
N.A.I.C.S.: 423840
Brittany Khorramian *(Gen Mgr-Tampa)*

WYATT-JOHNSON BUICK, PONTIAC, GMC TRUCK, INC.
2600 Wilma Rudolph Blvd, Clarksville, TN 37040
Tel.: (931) 647-5651 TN
Web Site: http://www.wyattjohnson.com
Rev.: $45,000,000
Emp.: 138
New & Used Automobiles
N.A.I.C.S.: 441110
S. M. Johnson *(Pres)*

WYBLE ADVERTISING
529 Buck St, Millville, NJ 08332
Tel.: (856) 825-3403
Year Founded: 1953
Sales Range: Less than $1 Million
Emp.: 3
Advetising Agency
N.A.I.C.S.: 541810
Arnold Eldridge *(Sr Art Dir)*
Henry Wyble Jr. *(Pres)*

WYCKOFF FARMS, INCORPORATED
160602 W Evans Rd, Grandview, WA 98930
Tel.: (509) 882-3934 WA
Web Site: http://www.wyckoff-farms.com
Year Founded: 1950
Berry Farming, Processing & Whslr
N.A.I.C.S.: 111334
David Wyckoff *(Chm & CEO)*
Courtney Wyckoff *(Pres)*

Subsidiaries:

Milne Fruits Products, Inc. (1)
804 Bennett Ave, Prosser, WA 99350
Tel.: (509) 786-2611
Web Site: http://www.milnefruit.com
Fruit Juices, Fruit Purees, Blends, Premixes & Ingredients Mfr & Processor
N.A.I.C.S.: 311411
Michael Sorenson *(Pres & Gen Mgr)*
Steve Nugent *(Dir-Frozen Fruit, Dried & Export Sls)*

Joint Venture (Domestic):

Dohler-Milne Aseptics LLC (2)
804 Bennett Ave, Prosser, WA 99350
Tel.: (509) 786-2240
Web Site: http://www.doehler-milne.com
Fruit Juice Blending & Compounding; Owned by Wyckoff Farms, Incorporated & by Dohler GmbH
N.A.I.C.S.: 311411
David Wyckoff *(Mng Partner)*

Subsidiary (Domestic):

Valley Processing, Inc. (2)
108 Blaine Ave, Sunnyside, WA 98944
Tel.: (509) 837-8084
Web Site: http://www.valleyprocessing.com
Sales Range: $1-9.9 Million
Emp.: 34
Fruit & Vegetable Canning
N.A.I.C.S.: 311421
Mary A. Glazner *(Owner)*

WYCKOFF HEIGHTS MEDICAL CENTER

WYCKOFF HEIGHTS MEDICAL CENTER — U.S. PRIVATE

Wyckoff Heights Medical Center—(Continued)
374 Stanhope St, Brooklyn, NY 11237
Tel.: (718) 963-7272 — NY
Web Site: http://www.wyckoffhospital.org
Year Founded: 1889
Sales Range: $250-299.9 Million
Emp.: 2,208
Health Care Srvices
N.A.I.C.S.: 622110
Ramon J. Rodriguez (Pres & CEO)
Jebashini Jesurasa (CIO & VP-IT)
Margaret Cornelius (VP-HR)
Gustavo Del Toro (Chief Medical Officer & Exec VP)
Kenneth E. Freiberg (VP-Medical Education)
Thelca Hinds (VP-Medical Education)

WYFFEL'S HYBRIDS, INC.
13344 US Hwy 6, Geneseo, IL 61254
Tel.: (309) 944-8334
Web Site: http://www.wyffels.com
Sales Range: $50-74.9 Million
Emp.: 110
Hybrid Seed Corn Developer & Marketer
N.A.I.C.S.: 111150
Robert Wyffel (Co-Owner)
Brian Humphries (Bus Mgr-Eastern)
John Wyffels (Pres)
William Wyffel Jr. (Co-Owner)

WYK SORBENTS, LLC
11721 Lackland Rd, Saint Louis, MO 63146
Tel.: (314) 426-3336
Web Site: http://www.wyksorbents.com
Absorbent Products Mfr
N.A.I.C.S.: 423850
Carol Dunn (Mng Partner)

WYKSTRA OIL CO., INC.
917 E Allegan St, Martin, MI 49070
Tel.: (269) 672-5049
Sales Range: $10-24.9 Million
Emp.: 60
Convenience Store Operator
N.A.I.C.S.: 445131
Ron VanDenBerg (Pres)
Dianne Bonner (Office Mgr)
Harold Wykstra (VP)

WYLACO SUPPLY COMPANY, INC.
315 Vallejo St, Denver, CO 80223
Tel.: (303) 778-8201
Web Site: http://www.wylaco.com
Sales Range: $10-24.9 Million
Emp.: 35
Industrial Machinery & Equipment
N.A.I.C.S.: 423830
Terry Carpenter (Pres)
Todd Madigan (Mgr-Pur)
Pam Casey (Office Mgr)

WYLAND WORLDWIDE LLC
6 Mason, Irvine, CA 92618
Tel.: (949) 643-7070
Web Site: http://www.wyland.com
Sales Range: $10-24.9 Million
Emp.: 40
Art Gallery & Distr
N.A.I.C.S.: 459920
R. Wyland (Pres & CEO)
Darlene Wyland (VP)
Christy Nguyen (Mgr-Mktg)

Subsidiaries:

Wyland Enterprises Hawaii LLC (1)
66-150 Kam Hwy, Haleiwa, HI 96712
Tel.: (808) 637-7498
Web Site: http://www.wyland.com
Emp.: 5

Art Dealers
N.A.I.C.S.: 459920
Jean Riehl (Gen Mgr)

Wyland Studios Inc. (1)
5 Columbia, Aliso Viejo, CA 92656
Tel.: (949) 643-7070
Web Site: http://www.wyland.com
Sales Range: $10-24.9 Million
Emp.: 15
Art Goods
N.A.I.C.S.: 424990

WYLIE MANUFACTURING COMPANY
702 E 40th St, Lubbock, TX 79404
Tel.: (806) 763-1335
Web Site: http://www.wyliesprayers.com
Year Founded: 1930
Tractors, Sprayers & Other Farm Equipment Whslr
N.A.I.C.S.: 423820
Mike Abbott (CFO)

Subsidiaries:

Wylie Implement & Spray Center-Amarillo (1)
14200 I 40 E, Amarillo, TX 79118
Tel.: (806) 335-2861
Web Site: http://www.wylieimplement.com
Sales Range: $10-24.9 Million
Emp.: 33
Tractors & Agricultural Equipment, Parts & Service
N.A.I.C.S.: 423820
Scott Wylie (Pres)
Max Pearson (Mgr)

WYLIE MUSSER CHEVROLET CADILLAC
1212 W Moore Ave, Terrell, TX 75160-3007
Tel.: (972) 524-2663
Web Site: http://www.mussermotors.com
Year Founded: 1962
Sales Range: $10-24.9 Million
Emp.: 40
New Car Whslr
N.A.I.C.S.: 441110
Gabe Musser (Gen Mgr)

WYMAN, GREEN & BLALOCK REAL ESTATE, INC.
1101 6th Ave W Ste 101, Bradenton, FL 34205
Tel.: (941) 748-9776
Web Site: http://www.blalockrealestate.com
Year Founded: 1908
Sales Range: $1-9.9 Million
Emp.: 3
Real Estate Broker
N.A.I.C.S.: 531210
William M. Blalock (Pres)
Shana Maguire (Office Mgr)
Dan S. Blalock Jr. (VP)

WYNDALL'S ENTERPRISES INC.
2920 Sairview Dr, Owensboro, KY 42303-2206
Tel.: (270) 684-9493 — KY
Year Founded: 1937
Sales Range: $25-49.9 Million
Emp.: 370
Grocery Services
N.A.I.C.S.: 722513
Ted Belcher (Pres & CEO)

WYNDHAM GROUP INC.
2207 Concord Pike Ste 696, Wilmington, DE 19803
Tel.: (704) 905-9750
Web Site: http://www.wyndhamgroup.net
Year Founded: 2008

Sales Range: $1-9.9 Million
Emp.: 15
It Consulting
N.A.I.C.S.: 541690
Adam James (Co-Founder)
Roger Kerr (Co-Founder & Mng Principal)

WYNDHAM JADE LLC
6100 W Plano Pkwy Ste 3500, Plano, TX 75093-8215
Tel.: (972) 349-7300
Web Site: https://www.wyndhamjade.com
Year Founded: 1983
Emp.: 150
Incentive & Meeting Services; Convention Housing & Registration; Travel Management Services
N.A.I.C.S.: 561510
Sue Trizila (Pres & CEO)
Mike Bates (CFO)
Tom Levine (CIO)
Bill Lemmon (Dir-Accts-Natl)
Bryan A. Scott (Pres-Convention)

WYNGATE INTERNATIONAL, INC.
2000 E Oakland Park Blvd, Oakland Park, FL 33306
Web Site: http://www.gotoprospects.com
Year Founded: 2006
Sales Range: $1-9.9 Million
Emp.: 35
Sales Leads Generation
N.A.I.C.S.: 541618

WYNIT, INC.
5801 E Taft Rd, North Syracuse, NY 13212
Tel.: (315) 437-7617 — NY
Web Site: http://www.wynit.com
Year Founded: 1987
Holding Company; Consumer & Commercial Electronics & Equipment Distr & Contract Logistics Services
N.A.I.C.S.: 551112
Geoffrey Lewis (Founder & CEO)
Pete Richichi (COO)
Derek Noce (Dir-Bus Dev Retail)
Jon Stanton (Exec Dir-Sls)
Mark Ferrante (Exec Dir-Sls)

Subsidiaries:

WYNIT Distribution, LLC (1)
5801 E Taft Rd, North Syracuse, NY 13212
Tel.: (315) 437-7617
Web Site: http://www.wynit.com
Consumer & Commercial Electronics & Equipment Distr & Contract Logistics Services
N.A.I.C.S.: 423620
Pete Richichi (COO)
Brian Caruana (VP-Sls)
Mark Ferrante (Exec Dir-Sls)
Vern Meyer (Mgr-Accts-Northeast Natl)
Derek Noce (Dir-Bus Dev Retail)
Jon Stanton (Exec Dir-Sls)

Subsidiary (Domestic):

Navarre Distribution Services, Inc. (2)
9700 W 76th St Ste 116, Eden Prairie, MN 55344
Tel.: (763) 535-8333
Web Site: http://www.navarre.com
Consumer Electronics & Software Distr
N.A.I.C.S.: 423620
Ward Thomas (Exec VP)

WYNN O. JONES & ASSOCIATES
754 Alderson St, Schofield, WI 54476
Tel.: (715) 359-5196
Web Site: http://www.wynnjones.com
Year Founded: 1975
Sales Range: $10-24.9 Million

Emp.: 30
Provider of Home/Office Interiors Finishing, Furnishing & Remodeling
N.A.I.C.S.: 238990
Wynn O. Jones (Chm, Pres & CEO)
Carol Niehaus (CFO)
Shane Kole (Dir-Engrg Svs)
Shane Schlueter (Project Mgr)

WYNN PROPERTIES, INC.
9220 Bonita Beach Rd Ste 200, Bonita Springs, FL 34135
Tel.: (239) 947-4848
Web Site: http://www.wynn-properties.com
Year Founded: 1938
Sales Range: $1-9.9 Million
Emp.: 10
Real Estate Broker
N.A.I.C.S.: 531210
Jeff D. Wynn (Pres)
Barbara Buckingham (Mgr-Acctg)
Tiffany Wheeler (Coord-Mktg)

WYNN STARR FLAVORS INC.
225 Rte 303 N St 109, Congers, NY 10920
Tel.: (201) 934-7800
Web Site: http://www.wynnstarr.com
Sales Range: $10-24.9 Million
Emp.: 25
Mfr & Selling Flavoring Extracts & Syrups
N.A.I.C.S.: 311930
Steven B. Zavagli (Chm)
Roland Abate (VP-Flavor Div)
Mike Buononato (VP-Savory Div)
Tara Criscola (Mgr)
Barbara Doyle (Office Mgr)
Dale Eskin (Exec VP)
Peter Farkas (Production Mgr)
Barry Friedson (VP-Mfg)
Mark Laslo (VP-Quality Assurance)
Joann Rakestraw (Mgr-Pur)

WYNNCHURCH CAPITAL, L.P.
6250 N River Rd Ste 10-100, Rosemont, IL 60018
Tel.: (847) 604-6100 — DE
Web Site: http://www.wynnchurch.com
Year Founded: 1999
Privater Equity Firm
N.A.I.C.S.: 523999
John A. Hatherly (Mng Partner)
Frank G. Hayes (Mng Partner)
Christopher P. O'Brien (Mng Partner)
Duncan S. Bourne (Mng Dir)
Neel K. Mayenkar (Partner)
Roy E. Sroka (Partner, CFO & Chief Compliance Officer)
Stephen M. Welborn (Mng Dir)
Brian R. Crumbaugh (Partner)
Michael A. Teplitsky (Partner)
Erin L. Murphy (Partner)
Greg B. Gleason (Mng Partner)
Scott S. Fitch (Partner)
Paul Ciolino (Partner)
Ramsay McLearie (VP)
Carl R. Howe (Principal)
Ursula Djurickovic (Controller)
Scott Farrell (Operating Partner)
Aron Beach (Mng Dir)

Subsidiaries:

America II Group, LLC (1)
2600 118th Ave N, Saint Petersburg, FL 33716
Tel.: (727) 573-0900
Web Site: http://www.americaii.com
Electronic Components Distr
N.A.I.C.S.: 334419
Michael Galinski (CEO & Founder)
Gary Jenkins (CFO)

Subsidiary (Domestic):

Advanced MP Technology Inc. (2)

COMPANIES — WYNNCHURCH CAPITAL, L.P.

1010 Calle Sombra, San Clemente, CA 92673
Tel.: (949) 492-3113
Web Site: http://www.advancedmp.com
Electronic Component Distribution & Inventory Management
N.A.I.C.S.: 334419
Homey Shorooghi *(Pres & CEO)*
Kamran Malek *(Global VP-Mktg)*

Burtek Enterprises, Inc. (1)
50325 Patricia St, Chesterfield, MI 48051
Tel.: (586) 421-8000
Web Site: http://www.burtekenterprises.com
Design, Production, Testing & Integration of Complex Systems & Applications for Mobile Military Ground Vehicles, Radar Platforms & Other Defense Systems
N.A.I.C.S.: 541519
Jeff Daniel *(Pres & CEO)*

Subsidiary (Domestic):

Votaw Precision Technologies, Inc. (2)
13153 Lakeland Rd, Santa Fe Springs, CA 90670
Tel.: (562) 944-0661
Web Site: http://www.votaw.com
Precision Components, Fixtures & Tools Designer & Mfr
N.A.I.C.S.: 333514
Art Montes *(Mgr-Program)*
Art Talavera *(Mgr-Mfg)*
Scott Merrell *(Mgr-Quality Assurance)*
Scott Wallace *(Pres)*
Mike Carlson *(Mgr-Program)*
Daniel Telles *(Mgr-Program)*
Mike Petriccione *(Dir-Sls & Mktg)*
L. Wood Bullock *(Controller)*

Critical Process Systems Group, Inc. (1)
11789 W Executive Dr, Boise, ID 83713
Tel.: (802) 448-5860
Web Site: http://www.cpsgrp.com
Custom Bio Pharm Equipment Design Services
N.A.I.C.S.: 541990
Dmitry Shashkov *(CEO)*

Subsidiary (Domestic):

Nuance Systems, LLC (2)
7233 SW Kable Ln Ste 500, Portland, OR 97224-7183
Tel.: (503) 620-9922
Web Site: http://www.nsi-mfg.com
Electrical Apparatus & Equipment, Wiring Supplies & Related Equipment Merchant Whslr
N.A.I.C.S.: 423610
Kyle Kimmberle *(Pres)*
Bill Kimmerle *(CEO)*

Drew Foam Companies, Inc. (1)
1093 Hwy 278 E, Monticello, AR 71655
Tel.: (870) 367-6245
Web Site: http://www.drewfoam.com
Sales Range: $10-24.9 Million
Emp.: 275
Plastics Foam Products Mfr
N.A.I.C.S.: 326150
Susan McClendon *(Controller)*
Mike Ragland *(Mgr-Ops)*
Barbara Hayden *(Mgr-HR)*
Bill Givens *(CEO)*

Subsidiary (Domestic):

Huntington Foam, LLC (2)
125 Caliber Ridge Dr Ste 200, Greer, SC 29651
Tel.: (864) 530-0080
Web Site: http://www.hunt-sol.com
Packaging Solutions & Energy Management Components Mfr
N.A.I.C.S.: 326112
Benjamin Raygoza *(VP-Ops)*

Subsidiary (Domestic):

Radva Corporation (3)
604 17th St, Radford, VA 24141-1506
Tel.: (410) 451-8343
Web Site: http://www.radva.com
Styrofoam Packaging; Polystyrene Foam Product Mfr
N.A.I.C.S.: 326140

Texas Foam, Inc. (3)
1278 Highway 71 W, Bastrop, TX 78602
Tel.: (512) 581-7500
Plastics Foam Products
N.A.I.C.S.: 326150

Eastern Metal Supply Inc. (1)
3600 23rd Ave S, Lake Worth, FL 33461
Tel.: (561) 533-6061
Web Site: https://www.easternmetal.com
Sales Range: $25-49.9 Million
Emp.: 300
Aluminum Bars, Rods, Ingots, Sheets, Pipes, Plates & Other Related Items
N.A.I.C.S.: 423510
Susan Walsh *(Pres)*
Greg Weekes *(Founder & Pres)*
Michael Harvard *(Mgr-Warehouse)*
Craig Lightle *(Gen Mgr)*
Isabel Linares *(Mgr-Support Sys)*
Kevin Parkes *(Controller)*
Clifford Ponce *(Mgr-Sys Dev)*
Mike Swedick *(CEO)*
Chris O'Brien *(Mng Partner)*
Paul Ciolino *(Partner)*
Greg Gleason *(Mng Partner)*
Carl Howe *(Principal)*

Subsidiary (Domestic):

Eastern Metal Supply Texas Inc. (2)
9400 Telge Rd, Houston, TX 77095
Tel.: (281) 656-2296
Web Site: http://www.easternmetal.com
Sales Range: $10-24.9 Million
Emp.: 40
Metals Service Centers & Offices
N.A.I.C.S.: 423510
Susan Walsh *(Founder)*

Fabco Automotive Corporation (1)
151 Lawrence Dr, Livermore, CA 94551-5126
Tel.: (925) 454-9500
Web Site: http://www.fabcoautomotive.com
Sales Range: $25-49.9 Million
Automotive Parts Mfr & Supplier
N.A.I.C.S.: 336390
Al Sunderland *(Pres)*
Mark Reitz *(VP-Engrg)*

Subsidiary (Domestic):

R. Cushman & Associates, Inc. (2)
32840 W 8 Mile Rd 12623 Newburgh, Livonia, MI 48150
Tel.: (248) 477-9900
Web Site: http://www.rcushman.com
Drive Train & Power Transmission Design & Production
N.A.I.C.S.: 336350
Kevin Krause *(Mgr-Quality)*

FloWorks International LLC (1)
3750 Highway 225, Pasadena, TX 77503
Tel.: (713) 672-2222
Web Site: http://www.gofloworks.com
Valve Mfr
N.A.I.C.S.: 332996
Scott Jackson *(Pres & CEO)*

Subsidiary (Domestic):

Genesis Systems, Inc. (2)
1501 10th St, Plano, TX 75074
Tel.: (972) 578-5105
Web Site: http://www.callgenesis.com
Rev: $2,100,000
Emp.: 12
Industrial Supplies Merchant Whslr
N.A.I.C.S.: 423840
Tom L. Blanc *(Pres)*
Andy Tepera *(Project Mgr & Engr-Sls Tech)*

SemiTorr Group, Inc. (2)
10655 SW Manhasset Dr, Tualatin, OR 97062
Tel.: (877) 318-9275
Web Site: http://www.semitorrinc.com
Industrial & Commercial Products Sls & Distr
N.A.I.C.S.: 423840
Kevin Waddell *(Pres & CEO)*

Subsidiary (Domestic):

McKenna Engineering & Equipment Co., Inc. (3)
13720 Cimarron Ave, Gardena, CA 90249
Tel.: (310) 763-7929
Web Site: http://www.mckennaengineering.com
Sales Range: $10-24.9 Million
Emp.: 40
Pumps & Pumping Equipment
N.A.I.C.S.: 423830
Collin Boettcher *(Engr-Project Applications)*
Michael Stadler *(CFO & VP)*
Ed McKenna *(CEO)*

Tru-Flow LLC (3)
6252 W 91st Ave, Westminster, CO 80031-2920
Tel.: (877) 409-8590
Web Site: http://www.tru-flow.com
Research & Development in Biotechnology
N.A.I.C.S.: 541714
Paul Trunzo *(Pres)*

Subsidiary (Domestic):

netMercury, Inc. (2)
13438 Floyd Cir, Dallas, TX 75243
Tel.: (972) 783-1501
Web Site: http://www.netmercury.net
Sales Range: $10-24.9 Million
Emp.: 21
Industrial Equipment & Supplies Distr
N.A.I.C.S.: 423830
Terry Hollingshead *(Pres & CEO)*
Greg Shepard *(VP & Gen Mgr-Arizona)*

Branch (Domestic):

netMercury, Inc. - Austin (3)
3912 Gattis School Rd Ste 103, Round Rock, TX 78664
Tel.: (512) 989-0600
Web Site: http://www.netmercury.net
Industrial Equipment & Supplies Distr
N.A.I.C.S.: 423830

netMercury, Inc. - Fremont (3)
47000 Warm Springs Blvd Ste 1 #503, Fremont, CA 94539
Tel.: (510) 249-9299
Web Site: http://www.netmercury.net
Industrial Equipment & Supplies Distr
N.A.I.C.S.: 423830
Sara Parsoneault *(Controller)*

Highway Technologies, Inc. (1)
6811 Dixie Dr, Houston, TX 77087 (100%)
Tel.: (713) 845-1800
Traffic Safety, Control Services & Equipment Mfr for the Road Repair, Construction & Maintenance Industry
N.A.I.C.S.: 532490
Angela Hill *(Dir-HR)*

Industrial Service Solutions LLC (1)
875 N Michigan Ave Ste 4020, Chicago, IL 60611
Tel.: (312) 573-6420
Industrial Equipment Services
N.A.I.C.S.: 811310
Jim Rogers *(Chm & CEO)*
Jim Richard *(Partner)*
Jeff Musser *(Partner)*
Doug Staab *(Partner)*
Wade Stockstill *(CEO)*
Joshua Chambers *(Partner)*
Mike Thompson *(Partner & CFO)*
Jim Young *(Exec VP & Partner)*

Subsidiary (Domestic):

Midwest Valve Parts Supply Company, Inc. (2)
11711 Chillicothe Rd, Chesterland, OH 44026
Tel.: (440) 729-0008
Web Site: http://www.midwestvalveparts.com
Sales Range: $1-9.9 Million
Emp.: 15
Replacement Valve & Actuator Parts Mfr
N.A.I.C.S.: 423830
Lucius Clark *(Pres)*

PTI Industries, Inc (2)
2 Peerless Way, Enfield, CT 06082
Tel.: (860) 698-9266
Web Site: https://ptiindustries.com
Sales Range: $1-9.9 Million
Emp.: 120
Non-Destructive Testing Services
N.A.I.C.S.: 541380
Dawn Stokes *(Mgr-Quality Assurance)*
Wesley Gordon *(Mgr-Acctg & HR)*
Stephen Woicik *(CFO)*
Harley Dulude Jr. *(Pres)*

Servo South, Inc. (2)
515 Plato Lee Rd, Shelby, NC 28150-9418
Tel.: (704) 434-4770
Web Site: http://www.servosouth.com
Consumer Electronics Repair & Maintenance
N.A.I.C.S.: 811210
Barry Beaver *(Pres)*

Northstar Aerospace, Inc. (1)
6006 W 73rd St, Bedford Park, IL 60638
Tel.: (708) 728-2000
Web Site: http://www.nsaero.com
Sales Range: $200-249.9 Million
Emp.: 750
Aerospace Industries Products Mfr
N.A.I.C.S.: 336413
William Corley *(Dir-HR)*
David G. Anderson *(Gen Counsel)*
Jim Smith *(Dir-SHEA & Facilities)*
David McConnaughey *(Pres & CEO)*
Robert L. Burkhardt *(CFO)*
Scott Crego *(Dir-IT)*
John Giudici *(VP-Continuous Improvement)*
Mike Annen *(VP-Bus Dev)*
Brian Cheek *(Interim VP/Gen Mgr-Chicago Ops)*
Alan Darmon *(Interim VP/Gen Mgr-Milton Ops)*
Gary Clinton *(VP & Gen Mgr-Phoenix Ops)*
Matt Seguin *(Gen Mgr-Windsor Ops)*

Plant (Domestic):

Northstar Aerospace - Chicago (2)
6006 W 73rd St, Bedford Park, IL 60638-6106 (100%)
Tel.: (708) 728-2000
Web Site: http://www.nsaero.com
Sales Range: $50-74.9 Million
Aerospace Industries Products Mfr
N.A.I.C.S.: 336413
Brian Cheek *(Interim VP/Gen Mgr)*

Plant (Non-US):

Northstar Aerospace - Milton (2)
180 Market Dr, Milton, L9T 3H5, ON, Canada (100%)
Tel.: (905) 875-4000
Web Site: http://www.nsaero.com
Sales Range: $50-74.9 Million
Aerospace Products Mfr
N.A.I.C.S.: 336413
Krista Bunn *(Mgr-HR)*
Alan Darmon *(Interim VP/Gen Mgr)*

Plant (Domestic):

Northstar Aerospace - Phoenix (2)
401 S 36th St, Phoenix, AZ 85034-2812 (100%)
Tel.: (602) 275-4406
Web Site: http://www.dvelco.com
Sales Range: $50-74.9 Million
Precision Machined Aerospace Products, Assemblies & Fabrications Mfr
N.A.I.C.S.: 336413
Kimberly Clark *(Mgr-Sls & Acct)*
Gary Clinton *(VP & Gen Mgr)*

Plant (Non-US):

Northstar Aerospace - Windsor (2)
204 East Pike Creek Road, PO Box 100, Tecumseh, N8N 2L9, ON, Canada (100%)
Tel.: (519) 979-9400
Web Site: http://www.northstaraerospace.com
Sales Range: $25-49.9 Million
Mfr of Gears & Drives for Aerospace Industry
N.A.I.C.S.: 336413
Matt Seguin *(Gen Mgr)*

Pennsylvania Machine Works, LLC (1)
201 Bethel Ave, Aston, PA 19014
Tel.: (610) 497-3300
Web Site: http://www.pennusa.com
Rev: $23,500,000
Emp.: 200
Iron & Steel Forgings
N.A.I.C.S.: 332111
Ronald C. Lafferty *(Chm)*
Michael M. Seaman *(Acct Supvr)*
Ray Derrickson *(Mgr-Production)*
Brian Fabian *(Plant Mgr)*
Susan Watras *(Mgr-HR)*
Joe Pro *(Pres)*

WYNNCHURCH CAPITAL, L.P.

Wynnchurch Capital, L.P.—(Continued)

Subsidiary (Domestic):

Western Forge & Flange Co. (2)
687 County Rd 2201, Cleveland, TX 77327
Tel.: (281) 727-7000
Web Site: http://www.western-forge.com
Sales Range: $10-24.9 Million
Emp.: 72
Iron & Steel Forgings
N.A.I.C.S.: 332111
Walter Pierce (CEO)
Carol Buonfiglio (Controller-Acctg)
James Smith (VP-Sls)
Parwinder Gill (Dir-Quality Assurance)

Premier Forge Group, LLC (1)
250 E Lafayette St, Portland, IN 47371-0905
Tel.: (260) 726-8121
Web Site: http://www.premierforge.com
Sales Range: $125-149.9 Million
Emp.: 270
Mfr of Forgings
N.A.I.C.S.: 332112
Steve Barcus (Pres)
Bill Kerfin (CEO)

Subsidiary (Domestic):

California Amforge Corp. (2)
750 N Vernon Ave, Azusa, CA 91702-2231
Tel.: (630) 990-4600
Web Site: http://www.cal-amforge.com
Sales Range: $10-24.9 Million
Emp.: 4
Iron & Steel Forgings
N.A.I.C.S.: 332111
Lee H. Edwards (Sr Dir-Bus Dev & Matls)
Micheal J. Wright (VP-Engrg)
Marie T. Turacek (VP-Fin)
Donald R. Ansell (VP-Mfg)
Simone Sutherland (VP-Quality)
Susan T. Congalton (Chm & CEO)
Kenneth R. Klein (VP-Mktg & Sls)
Paula J. Gutierrez (Mgr-HR)

Reagent Chemical & Research Inc. (1)
115 US Hwy 202, Ringoes, NJ 08551-1908
Tel.: (908) 284-2800
Web Site: https://www.reagentchemical.com
Sales Range: $25-49.9 Million
Emp.: 400
Mfr of Industrial Inorganic Chemicals
N.A.I.C.S.: 325180

Subsidiary (Domestic):

Cali'Co Hardwoods Inc. (2)
3580 Westwind Blvd, Santa Rosa, CA 95403-8239
Tel.: (707) 546-4045
Web Site: http://www.calicohardwoods.com
Sales Range: $10-24.9 Million
Emp.: 17
Hardwood Dimension & Flooring Mfr
N.A.I.C.S.: 321999
Daniel Kynoch (Gen Mgr)

PROSYS Innovative Packaging Equipment Inc. (2)
422 E Fountain Rd, Webb City, MO 64870
Tel.: (417) 673-5551
Web Site: http://www.prosysfill.com
Emp.: 30
Packaging Services
N.A.I.C.S.: 561910
Buster Van Fleet (Mgr-Customer Svc)

White Flyer Targets, LLC (2)
1300 Post Oak Blvd Ste 680, Houston, TX 77056
Tel.: (713) 626-1843
Web Site: http://www.whiteflyer.com
Emp.: 15
Sporting & Athletic Goods Mfr
N.A.I.C.S.: 339920
Phil Murray (Mgr-Natl Sls)

Stampede Meat, Inc. (1)
7351 S 78th Ave, Bridgeview, IL 60455
Tel.: (800) 353-0933
Web Site: http://www.stampedemeat.com
Beef & Pork Product Production Services
N.A.I.C.S.: 311612
Dennis Gruber (VP-Tech Innovation & Culinary Dev)
Blake Miller (VP-Food Safety & Quality Assurance)
Brock Furlong (Pres & CEO)
Vito Giustino (CFO)
Raymond McKiernan (Sr VP-Sls & Mktg)
Mary Hrycyk (Dir-Sls)
Jim Scott (COO)
Christina Hackney (Dir-HR)
Alicia Talavera (Sr Mgr-Sls & Mktg)
Krys Harbut (VP-Production)
John Cokowski (VP-Logistics)

Texas Hydraulics, Inc. (1)
3410 Range Rd, Temple, TX 76504
Tel.: (254) 778-4701
Web Site: http://www.texashydraulics.com
Hydraulic Components Mfr
N.A.I.C.S.: 333995
Patrick Taylor (CEO)
Naimesh Dave (Exec VP-Sls & Bus Dev)
William Jones (Exec VP & Gen Mgr)

Subsidiary (Domestic):

The Oilgear Company (2)
1424 International Dr, Traverse City, MI 49686
Tel.: (231) 929-1660
Web Site: http://www.oilgear.com
Hydraulic Systems & Components, Flow Measurement Equipment, Petrochemical & Oilfield Equipment Mfr
N.A.I.C.S.: 332912

Subsidiary (Non-US):

Oilgear Towler GmbH (3)
Im Gotthelf 8, 65795, Hattersheim, Germany
Tel.: (49) 61453770
Mechanical & Hydraulic Power Transmission Machinery & Industrial Controls Mfr
N.A.I.C.S.: 333996

Oilgear Towler Ltd. (3)
37 Burley Road, Leeds, LS3 1JT, West Yorkshire, United Kingdom
Tel.: (44) 1133947300
Mechanical & Hydraulic Power Transmission Machinery & Industrial Controls Mfr
N.A.I.C.S.: 333996

Oilgear Towler S.A. (3)
Entidad Zicunaga 62 Apartado 104, Hernani, 20120, Gipuzkoa, Spain
Tel.: (34) 943552700
Mechanical & Hydraulic Power Transmission Machinery & Industrial Controls Mfr
N.A.I.C.S.: 333996

Oilgear Towler S.r.l. (3)
Via Artigianale 23, Montirone, 25010, Brescia, Italy
Tel.: (39) 0302677557
Mechanical & Hydraulic Power Transmission Machinery & Industrial Controls Retailer
N.A.I.C.S.: 423830

Oilgear Towler SAS (3)
5 Allee des Freres Montgolfier, 77183, Croissy-Beaubourg, Croissy, France
Tel.: (33) 164627200
Mechanical & Hydraulic Power Transmission Machinery & Industrial Controls Mfr
N.A.I.C.S.: 333996

Plant (Domestic):

The Oilgear Company - Fremont (3)
905 S Downing St, Fremont, NE 68025-6206
Tel.: (402) 727-9700
Web Site: http://www.oilgear.com
Hydraulic Pumps & Valves Mfr
N.A.I.C.S.: 333612

Trimlite LLC (1)
901 SW 39th St, Renton, WA 98057
Tel.: (425) 251-8685
Web Site: http://www.trimlite.com
Sales Range: $1-9.9 Million
Emp.: 50
Pressed & Blown Glass & Glassware Mfr
N.A.I.C.S.: 327212

Subsidiary (Domestic):

Builders Hardware, Inc. (2)
5615 E Powhatan Ave, Tampa, FL 33610
Tel.: (813) 971-4700
Web Site: http://www.buildershardwareflorida.com
Sales Range: $1-9.9 Million
Emp.: 49
Lumber, Plywood, Millwork & Wood Panel Merchant Whslr
N.A.I.C.S.: 423310
Milt Brown (Mgr-Ops)
Emily Cook (Controller)
Mike Mathis (Mgr-Door Shop)
Alex Suero (Mgr-Pur)
Joshua Troop (Mgr-Pur)

Francis-Schulze, Co. (2)
3880 Rangeline Rd, Russia, OH 45363
Tel.: (937) 295-3941
Web Site: http://www.francisschulze.com
Sales Range: $1-9.9 Million
Emp.: 45
Whol Lumber/Plywood/Millwork Mfg Metal Doors/Sash/Trim
N.A.I.C.S.: 423310
Ralph Schulze (Pres)

U.S. Manufacturing Corporation (1)
28201 Van Dyke Ave, Warren, MI 48093-2713
Tel.: (586) 467-1600
Web Site: http://www.usmfg.com
Sales Range: $150-199.9 Million
Emp.: 240
Supplier of Automotive Products, Machined Castings & Forgings, Metal Extrusions & Welding Mfr
N.A.I.C.S.: 336390
Jack Falcon (Pres & CEO)
Adel Khanfar (VP-Product Dev)
Mark Theisen (VP-Sls & Mktg)
Spencer Harris (Dir-HR)
Thomas Neill (Dir-Ops)
Donald E. Ross (Dir-Quality)
Dennis Bucholtz (Dir-Engrg-Extrusion)
Garrett Baitinger (Dir-Program Mgmt)
Jeff Cwiek (Dir-Pur)
Jerry Krizinski (VP-HR)
Mike Moriarty (CFO)

Subsidiary (Non-US):

USM de MEXICO, S. de R.L. de C.V. (2)
A V Ingenieros 1200 Parque Industrial Fipasi, Carretera Silao-Irapuato, Silao, 36100, Guanajuato, Mexico
Tel.: (52) 4727910050
Axle Bearing Mfr
N.A.I.C.S.: 336350

Vista-Pro Automotive, LLC (1)
2 Lakeview Pl 15 Century Blvd Ste 600, Nashville, TN 37214 (100%)
Tel.: (615) 622-2300
Web Site: http://www.vistaproauto.com
Aftermarket Motor Vehicle Parts Designer, Mfr & Distr; Used Remanufactured Motor Vehicle Parts Distr
N.A.I.C.S.: 336390
Steve Scharnhorst (Pres & CEO)
Joe Rich (Dir-Distr & Logistics)
Mike Maupin (VP-Ops)

WYNNE BUILDING CORPORATION
12804 SW 122nd Ave, Miami, FL 33186-6203
Tel.: (305) 235-3175 FL
Year Founded: 1983
Sales Range: $25-49.9 Million
Emp.: 240
Land Development Services
N.A.I.C.S.: 531190
Cesar Saavedra (Dir-Ops)
Tony DiClemente (Mgr-Sls)

WYNNE RESIDENTIAL CORPORATE HOUSING
2214 Westwood Ave, Richmond, VA 23230
Tel.: (804) 359-8534
Year Founded: 1986
Sales Range: $10-24.9 Million
Emp.: 25
Relocation Services
N.A.I.C.S.: 561990
J. Michael Henderson (Pres)
Jack Grace (Controller)

WYNNE TRANSPORT SERVICE INC.
2222 N 11th St, Omaha, NE 68110-2524
Tel.: (402) 342-4001 NE
Web Site: http://www.wynnetr.com
Year Founded: 1956
Sales Range: $25-49.9 Million
Emp.: 200
Trucking Service
N.A.I.C.S.: 484121
Bob Wynne (Pres)
Denzil Gage (Dir-Personnel)

WYNNS SALES & SERVICE INC.
3147 Park Ave, Paducah, KY 42001-4004
Tel.: (270) 443-1728
Web Site: http://www.chipwynn.com
Sales Range: $10-24.9 Million
Emp.: 10
New & Used Car Dealers
N.A.I.C.S.: 441110
Chip Wynn (Pres)
Barry Doherty (Gen Mgr)
A. O. Wynn Sr. (Chm)

WYOMING BANK & TRUST
5827 Yellowstone Rd, Cheyenne, WY 82009
Tel.: (307) 632-7733 WY
Web Site: http://www.wyomingbank.com
Year Founded: 1919
Sales Range: $25-49.9 Million
Emp.: 25
Banking Services
N.A.I.C.S.: 522110
Dennis Wallace (Chm)
Jeff Wallace (CEO)
Judy Lane (Sr VP-Real Estate)
Kathy Hartwig (VP-Trust Admin)
Kevin Kisicki (VP-Loan Risk Mgmt)
Linda Butcher (Sr VP-Ops)
Tom Bass (Pres)
Dershie Barber (Officer-Trust & VP)
Nancy Bliss (VP-Loan Ops)
Rana Slavik (Officer-Compliance)
Ryan Whitehead (VP-Credit Admin)
Susie Havner (VP-Ops)
Toby Hytrek (VP-Lending)

WYOMING BUSINESS COUNCIL
214 W 15th St, Cheyenne, WY 82002
Tel.: (307) 777-2800
Web Site: http://www.wyomingbusiness.org
Year Founded: 1998
Sales Range: $25-49.9 Million
Emp.: 60
Economic Development
N.A.I.C.S.: 925120
Shawn Reese (Pres)
Kim Porter (Dir-Community Initiatives)
Chava Case (Mgr-HR)
Ron Gullberg (Dir-Bus Dev)
Mark Gordon (Chm)
Sarah Fitz-Gerald (Chief Strategy Officer)
Amy Grenfell (COO)

Subsidiaries:

Wyoming Business Council - Agribusiness Division (1)
214 W 15th St, Cheyenne, WY 82002-0240
Tel.: (307) 777-2807
Web Site: http://www.wyomingbusiness.org
Agricultural Services
N.A.I.C.S.: 541690
Cindy Garretson-Weibel (Dir-Agribusiness)

WYOMING COMMUNITY FOUNDATION

COMPANIES

1472 N 5th St Ste 201, Laramie, WY 82072
Tel.: (307) 721-8300   WY
Web Site: http://www.wycf.org
Year Founded: 1989
Sales Range: $10-24.9 Million
Emp.: 13
Grantmaking Services
N.A.I.C.S.: 813211
Craig R. Showalter *(Pres & CEO)*
Samin Dadelahi *(COO)*
Misty Gehle *(CFO)*
Susan Day *(Office Mgr)*
Vickery Fales Hall *(Dir-Donor Rels)*
Kathy Tomassi *(Treas)*
Connie Brezik *(Sec)*
Alison Ochs Gee *(Chm)*
Cynthia Chace Gray *(Vice Chm)*

WYOMING MACHINERY COMPANY
5300 W Old Yellowstone Hwy, Casper, WY 82604-1954
Tel.: (307) 472-1000   WY
Web Site:
   http://www.wyomingcat.com
Year Founded: 1969
Sales Range: $125-149.9 Million
Emp.: 820
Mfr of General Construction Machinery & Equipment
N.A.I.C.S.: 423810
Richard Wheeler *(COO & Exec VP)*
Mike Walker *(Mgr-HR)*

WYOMING MEDICAL CENTER
1233 E 2nd St, Casper, WY 82601
Tel.: (307) 577-7201   WY
Web Site:
   http://www.wyomingmedicalcenter.org
Year Founded: 1986
Sales Range: $200-249.9 Million
Emp.: 1,602
Health Care Srvices
N.A.I.C.S.: 622110
Carol Solie *(Chief Medical Officer)*
Yvonne Wigington *(CFO & Sr VP)*
Bill Huppert *(Sec)*
John Masterson *(Chm)*
Michele Chulick *(Pres & CEO)*
Edith Selby *(Vice Chm)*

WYOMING VALLEY MOTORS
126 Narrows Rd, Larksville, PA 18651
Tel.: (570) 288-7411
Web Site:
   http://www.wyomingvalleymotors.com
Sales Range: $100-124.9 Million
Emp.: 150
Automobiles, New & Used
N.A.I.C.S.: 441110
Steve Ubaldini *(Gen Mgr)*
Charlie McFadden *(Mgr-Sls)*

WYSE
668 Euclid Ave, Cleveland, OH 44114
Tel.: (216) 696-2424   OH
Year Founded: 1951
Rev.: $144,000,000
Emp.: 100
Advetising Agency
N.A.I.C.S.: 541810
Michael C. Marino *(CEO)*
Maggie Weitzel *(CFO)*
Susanne Brockman *(Dir-Media)*
Julie Telesz *(VP & Dir-Acct Mgmt)*
Linda Bremkamp *(VP-Strategic Plng)*
Subsidiaries:

North Coast Behavioral Research Group   (1)
668 Euclid Ave, Cleveland, OH 44114
Tel.: (216) 861-5780

N.A.I.C.S.: 541810
Michael C. Marino *(Pres & CEO)*

WYTEC INTERNATIONAL, INC.
19206 Huebner Rd Ste 202, San Antonio, TX 78258
Tel.: (210) 233-8980   NV
Web Site: https://www.wytecintl.com
Year Founded: 2011
Rev.: $255,634
Assets: $1,221,268
Liabilities: $2,097,393
Net Worth: ($876,125)
Earnings: ($3,311,013)
Emp.: 5
Fiscal Year-end: 12/31/23
Wireless Telecommunication Services
N.A.I.C.S.: 517112
Robert Sanchez *(Interim CTO)*
William H. Gray *(Chm & CEO)*
Erica Perez *(Sec)*

WYVERN RESTAURANTS INC.
575 W College Ave 201, Santa Rosa, CA 95401
Tel.: (707) 545-7447
Web Site: http://www.rtwyvern.com
Sales Range: $10-24.9 Million
Emp.: 25
Pizzeria Chain
N.A.I.C.S.: 722513
James Michael Carney *(Pres)*

WZ FRANCHISE CORP.
900 Circle 75 Pky Ste 930, Atlanta, GA 30339
Tel.: (404) 875-5045
Web Site: http://www.wingzone.com
Year Founded: 1999
Sales Range: $1-9.9 Million
Emp.: 14
Limited-Service Restaurants
N.A.I.C.S.: 722513
Matthew A. Friedman *(Co-Founder & CEO)*
Adam J. Scott *(Co-Founder & CFO)*
Jeff Daughenbaugh *(Dir-New Store Openings & Construction)*
Hair Parra *(VP-Intl Dev)*

X CORP.
1355 Market St Ste 900, San Francisco, CA 94103
Tel.: (415) 222-9670   NV
Web Site: https://x.com
Year Founded: 2023
Emp.: 2,300
Offices of Other Holding Companies
N.A.I.C.S.: 551112

X STUDIOS INC.
2700 Westhall Ln Ste 225, Maitland, FL 32751
Tel.: (321) 281-1708
Web Site: http://www.xstudios.agency
Sales Range: $1-9.9 Million
Advertising Agency; Web Design & Development
N.A.I.C.S.: 541810
Timothy Santor *(Pres)*

X! PROMOS
15375 Barranca Pkwy Ste A 104, Irvine, CA 92618
Tel.: (949) 450-8190   CA
Web Site: http://www.xpromos1.com
Year Founded: 1989
Sales Range: $1-9.9 Million
Emp.: 5
Sales Promotion
N.A.I.C.S.: 541810
Shari Nomady *(Pres)*
Yvette Brown *(Owner)*

X-CEL OPTICAL CO.
806 S Benton Dr, Sauk Rapids, MN 56379
Tel.: (320) 251-8404
Web Site: http://www.x-celoptical.com
Sales Range: $25-49.9 Million
Emp.: 140
Optical Lenses
N.A.I.C.S.: 327212
Joseph E. Doescher *(Pres & CEO)*
Wayne Gottwalt *(VP-Fin)*
Leon Fischer *(VP-Engrg)*
Connie Achman *(VP-Sls-Mktg)*
Dave Gohman *(Mgr-Customer Svc)*

X-L CABLE CORPORATION
910 Valley Ave NW Ste 105, Tacoma, WA 98371
Tel.: (253) 770-7200
Web Site: http://www.xlcable.com
Rev.: $18,358,230
Emp.: 200
Communications Specialization
N.A.I.C.S.: 516210
D. Chris Alexander *(Pres & CEO)*

X-L PLASTICS INC.
220 Clifton Blvd, Clifton, NJ 07011
Tel.: (973) 777-1888
Web Site: http://www.x-lplastics.com
Year Founded: 1985
Sales Range: $10-24.9 Million
Emp.: 100
Polyethylene Film & Bags Mfr & Distr
N.A.I.C.S.: 326111
Melvin Fishman *(Pres)*

X-RAY INC. OF RHODE ISLAND
14 Woodruff Ave Unit 1a, Warwick, RI 02886
Tel.: (401) 732-4300
Web Site: http://www.xrin.com
Sales Range: $10-24.9 Million
Emp.: 60
Medical Equipment & Supplies
N.A.I.C.S.: 423450
Richard Ernst *(Pres)*
Michael E. Butcher *(VP-Ops)*

X-RAY INDUSTRIES INC.
1961 Thunderbird St, Troy, MI 48084
Tel.: (248) 362-2242   MI
Web Site:
   http://www.xrayindustries.com
Year Founded: 1941
Sales Range: $25-49.9 Million
Emp.: 75
Industrial Product Inspection Services
N.A.I.C.S.: 541380
Scott W. Thams *(Pres)*
Subsidiaries:

Arcadia Aerospace Industries LLC   (1)
27256 Mooney Ave Bldg 110, Punta Gorda, FL 33982
Tel.: (941) 205-5700
Web Site: http://www.arcadiaaerospace.com
Emp.: 26
Aerospace Structure Inspection Services
N.A.I.C.S.: 541380
Byron Vines *(Dir-Nondestructive Inspection Ops)*
Charles Bushman *(Pres & CEO)*

MobileX   (1)
1961 Thunderbird, Troy, MI 48083
Tel.: (877) 974-4638
Web Site: http://www.mobilex.us
X-Ray Equipment Inspection Services
N.A.I.C.S.: 541380

PPI Aerospace Acquisition LLC   (1)
23514 Groesbeck Hwy, Warren, MI 48089
Tel.: (586) 772-7736
Web Site: http://www.ppiaerospace.com
Sales Range: $10-24.9 Million
Emp.: 50
Industrial Coating, Plating & Panting Services

XAEL CHARTERS INC.

N.A.I.C.S.: 332813
Larry Carlson *(Dir-Ops)*

Test Equipment Distributors, LLC   (1)
1370 Piedmont, Troy, MI 48083
Tel.: (248) 524-1900
Web Site: http://www.tedndt.com
Sales Range: $10-24.9 Million
Emp.: 22
Testing Equipment Distr
N.A.I.C.S.: 423690
Mike Hamel *(Pres)*

X-R-I Testing   (1)
1961 Thunderbird Ln, Troy, MI 48084
Tel.: (248) 362-5050
Web Site: http://www.xritesting.com
Emp.: 30
Equipment Testing & Inspection Services
N.A.I.C.S.: 541380
Robert Broaddus *(Pres)*

X-TREME INVESTMENTS, INC.
1401 W Fort St No 311082, Detroit, MI 48231
Tel.: (248) 773-1601   NV
Year Founded: 2013
Investment Services
N.A.I.C.S.: 523999
Anthony Passmore *(Chm, Pres, CEO, CFO, Principal Acctg Officer & Sec)*

X2NSAT, INC.
1310 Redwood Way Ste C, Petaluma, CA 94954
Tel.: (707) 664-5119
Web Site: http://www.occsat.com
Year Founded: 1996
Wireless Network & Communication Solutions
N.A.I.C.S.: 517112
Garrett C. Hill *(CEO)*
Richard Doherty *(CFO)*
Karen Siembieda *(Dir-Program Mgmt)*
Jena Blazer *(Dir-Sls & Mktg)*
Dave Starkey *(Engr)*

X8E, INC
1110 North Ave T, Lubbock, TX 79415
Tel.: (806) 939-0033
Web Site: http://www.x8e.us
Civil Engineering, Surveying & Environmental Services
N.A.I.C.S.: 541330

XA, THE EXPERIENTIAL AGENCY, INC.
875 N Michigan Ave Ste 2626, Chicago, IL 60611
Tel.: (312) 397-9100
Web Site:
   http://www.experientialagency.com
Sales Range: $1-9.9 Million
Emp.: 80
Event Marketing
N.A.I.C.S.: 541890
Joseph W. Wagner *(CEO)*
Amanda Puck *(Exec VP-PR)*

XACTWARE INC.
1100 West Traverse Pkwy, Lehi, UT 84043
Tel.: (801) 226-2251
Web Site: http://www.xactware.com
Year Founded: 1981
Sales Range: $10-24.9 Million
Emp.: 750
Provider of Computer Software Development Services
N.A.I.C.S.: 541511
Gina Millard *(Mgr-Bus Dev-Europe)*
Vernon Davenport *(Dir-Ops-Europe)*

XAEL CHARTERS INC.
4475 SW 8th St, Miami, FL 33134
Tel.: (305) 643-2200
Web Site: http://www.xaeltocuba.com
Sales Range: $1-9.9 Million
Charter Flights
N.A.I.C.S.: 481111
Xiomara Almaguer-Levy *(Pres)*

XAMAX INDUSTRIES, INC.

Xael Charters Inc.—(Continued)

XAMAX INDUSTRIES, INC.
63 Silvermine Rd, Seymour, CT 06483
Tel.: (203) 888-7200
Web Site: http://www.xamax.com
Year Founded: 1949
Rev.: $20,000,000
Emp.: 50
Insulation Products Mfr & Distr
N.A.I.C.S.: 423330
Jim Yuan *(Sr VP-Sls)*
Martin Weinberg *(Pres)*
Anna Durham *(COO)*
Bob Markowski *(VP-Sls & New Product Dev-FRP & Electrical)*
Margaret Pederson *(Vice Chm & CEO-Strategy, Mktg & Digital)*
Paul Oei *(VP-Ops)*

XANDROS INC.
149 Madison Ave, New York, NY 10016
Tel.: (212) 213-8083
Year Founded: 2001
Sales Range: $25-49.9 Million
Emp.: 150
Developer of Server & Desktop Cross-Platform Systems Management Tools
N.A.I.C.S.: 541512
Ming Poon *(COO & Sr VP-Product Dev)*
Pascal Lauria *(VP-Sls-EMEA)*
Larry Kettler *(VP-Bus Dev)*
Brian Lesser *(CEO)*
Mark Serhan *(Comml Dir)*
Philip Coetzee *(Assoc Dir-Product Mgmt)*
Archana Ganesh *(Assoc Dir-Asia Pacific)*
Conor McKeown *(Sr Acct Dir)*
Taylor Seymour *(Acct Dir)*

XANGO, LLC
3300 N Ashton Blvd Ste 100, Lehi, UT 84043
Tel.: (801) 816-8000
Web Site: http://www.xango.com
Sales Range: $550-599.9 Million
Emp.: 450
Nutritional Supplement Mfr & Direct Seller
N.A.I.C.S.: 325411
Aaron Garrity *(Co-Founder, Chm & CEO)*
Beverly Hollister *(Sr VP)*
Gordon Morton *(Co-Founder)*
Joe Morton *(Co-Founder & Pres-Americas & Australia)*
Kent Wood *(Co-Founder & Pres-Europe, CIS & South Africa)*
Bryan Davis *(Co-Founder)*
Leslie A. Gallacher *(Pres)*
Ryan Palmer *(Pres & CEO)*

Subsidiaries:
XanGo Goodness (1)
2889 Ashton Blvd, Lehi, UT 84043
Tel.: (801) 816-8000
Web Site: http://www.xangogoodness.org
Sales Range: $25-49.9 Million
Charitable Services
N.A.I.C.S.: 813211

XANTRION, INC.
651 20th St, Oakland, CA 94612
Tel.: (510) 272-4701   CA
Web Site: http://www.xantrion.com
Year Founded: 2000
Sales Range: $1-9.9 Million
Emp.: 45
Information Technology Services
N.A.I.C.S.: 518210

Anne Bisagno *(Co-Founder & Pres)*
Tom Snyder *(Co-Founder, CFO & COO)*
Nick Hensley *(Mgr-Ops)*

XAP CORPORATION
600 Corporate Pointe Ste 220, Culver City, CA 90230
Tel.: (310) 842-9800
Web Site: http://www.xap.com
Year Founded: 1996
Rev.: $7,000,000
Emp.: 60
Online College Admission Preparation Services
N.A.I.C.S.: 541511
George Yang *(Head-Client Svcs)*

Subsidiaries:
Bridges Transitions Inc. (1)
Ste 205 1726 Dolphin Ave, Kelowna, V1Y 9R9, BC, Canada
Tel.: (250) 869-4200
Web Site: http://www.bridges.com
Sales Range: $10-24.9 Million
Emp.: 25
Education Planning Software
N.A.I.C.S.: 513210
Terry M. Holland *(Chm)*
Douglas J. Manning *(Pres)*
Micheal Thompson *(Pres & CFO)*

XAVIER CREATIVE HOUSE LLC
PO Box 457, Jamison, PA 18929
Tel.: (215) 583-2323
Web Site: http://www.xaviercreative.com
Year Founded: 2013
Sales Range: $1-9.9 Million
Emp.: 6
Advertising & Marketing Services
N.A.I.C.S.: 541890
Sunny White *(Founder & CEO)*
Heather Hunt *(VP-Brand Strategy & Plng)*
Jenna Devries *(Creative Dir)*
Leah Knotts *(Project Mgr)*

XBYTE TECHNOLOGIES, INC.
4614 19th St Ct E, Bradenton, FL 34203
Tel.: (941) 358-9770
Web Site: http://www.xbyte.com
Year Founded: 2001
Sales Range: $1-9.9 Million
Emp.: 37
Computer Equipment Distr
N.A.I.C.S.: 423430
Thomas Santilli *(Founder & Chm)*
Stephen Jaynes *(Vice Chm)*
Andrew Ripley *(Mgr-Sls)*
Ryan Brown *(CEO)*

XCCENT INC.
5240 257th St, Wyoming, MN 55092
Tel.: (715) 294-2236
Web Site: http://www.xccent.biz
Sales Range: $25-49.9 Million
Emp.: 100
Plastic Coating Services
N.A.I.C.S.: 332812
John Mathiesen *(CEO)*
Marlys Dunne *(CFO)*

XCEL FINANCIAL LLC
345 W 600 S, Heber City, UT 84032-2282
Tel.: (435) 657-0154
Web Site: http://www.xcelfinancialutah.com
Home Loan, Insurance & Investment Options
N.A.I.C.S.: 522390
Eddie Garcia *(Mgr-Lending)*

Subsidiaries:
Berrett Mortgage Services (1)
1670 Bonanza Dr Ste 205, Park City, UT 84060-7239
Tel.: (435) 649-3497
Mortgage Loans
N.A.I.C.S.: 522310

XCEL MANAGEMENT, INC.
7361 Calhoun Pl Ste 600, Rockville, MD 20855
Tel.: (301) 340-3800
Web Site: http://www.xcelhr.com
Year Founded: 1994
Sales Range: $250-299.9 Million
Emp.: 100
Help Supply Services
N.A.I.C.S.: 561320
Mike Todd *(Gen Counsel)*
Chuck Ehrig *(CFO & VP)*
Ted Winglass *(Pres)*

XCEL MECHANICAL SYSTEMS, INC.
1710 W 130th St, Gardena, CA 90249
Tel.: (310) 660-0090
Web Site: http://www.xcelmech.com
Year Founded: 1988
Sales Range: $10-24.9 Million
Emp.: 125
Heating & Airconditioning Contractor
N.A.I.C.S.: 238220
Kevin Michel *(Pres)*

XCEL SOLUTIONS, CORP.
254 Rte 34 Ste 3 Oakdale Plz, Matawan, NJ 07747
Tel.: (732) 765-9235
Web Site: http://www.xcelcorp.com
Year Founded: 2003
Sales Range: $1-9.9 Million
Emp.: 100
IT Services & Solutions
N.A.I.C.S.: 519290
Jit Kumar *(Pres)*
Gary Albertson *(Sr Mgr-Bus Dev)*
Paola Gavino *(Acct Mgr)*
Tia Augustine *(Owner)*

XCELERATE MEDIA
61 W Bridge St, Dublin, OH 43017
Tel.: (614) 336-9722
Web Site: http://www.xceleratemedia.com
Year Founded: 1999
Sales Range: $1-9.9 Million
Emp.: 52
E-Learning & Online Coursework
N.A.I.C.S.: 611430
Bob Mahaffey *(Pres & CEO)*

XCELIGENT, INC.
4231 S Hocker Dr, Independence, MO 64055
Tel.: (816) 303-2805   MO
Web Site: http://www.xceligent.com
Year Founded: 1999
Sales Range: $10-24.9 Million
Emp.: 55
Computer System Design Services
N.A.I.C.S.: 541512
Monique Ebel *(Dir-Res)*
Matt Nelson *(Dir-Analytics-Res & Analytics-Los Angeles)*
Steve Golin *(VP-Strategic Vertical Markets)*
Soozi Jones Walker *(Pres-Comml Alliance-Las Vegas)*
David Verwer *(Reg VP-Sls)*
Erin Curry *(Chief People Officer)*
Bill Evans *(CIO)*
Andrew Jenkins *(Exec VP)*

XCEND GROUP, INC.
732 W Grand River Ave, Brighton, MI 48116
Tel.: (810) 494-7144   MI
Web Site: http://www.xcendgroup.com
Year Founded: 2004
Sales Range: $1-9.9 Million
Emp.: 16
Computer System Design Services
N.A.I.C.S.: 541512
Michael Brummel *(VP-Application Dev)*
Ron Schoenherr *(Pres & CEO)*
Bill Johnson *(CFO)*

XCEO, INC.
2880 Lakeside Dr, Santa Clara, CA 95054
Tel.: (408) 855-0000   CA
Web Site: http://www.xceo.net
Emp.: 8
Professional Mentoring & Leadership Development Training & Consulting Services
N.A.I.C.S.: 611430
Michelle Ronco *(CMO)*
Mike Dobmeier *(CTO)*
Curtis J. Crawford *(Pres & CEO)*

XCHANGE GROUP LLC
200 Business Park Dr Ste 303, Armonk, NY 10504
Tel.: (914) 437-7359
Web Site: http://www.xbllc.com
Year Founded: 2010
Insurance & Reinsurance Agency
N.A.I.C.S.: 524298
Peter Mcguire *(Pres & CEO)*
James Denison *(Chief Underwriting Officer & Exec VP)*
Ned Browne *(CMO & Exec VP)*
Kenneth Zieden-Weber *(COO, CFO & Exec VP)*

XCHANGE SOFTWARE
10 Austin Ave 2nd Fl, Iselin, NJ 08830
Tel.: (732) 444-6666
Web Site: http://www.xchangesoft.com
Year Founded: 2007
Sales Range: $1-9.9 Million
Emp.: 60
Instructor-Led & Online Training in Software Development
N.A.I.C.S.: 611420
Prabhaka Reddy *(Pres)*

XCONOMY, INC.
2 International Pl Ste 2610, Boston, MA 02110-4104
Tel.: (857) 504-6725
Web Site: http://www.xconomy.com
News Publishing Services
N.A.I.C.S.: 513120
Rebecca Zacks *(Co-Founder, COO & Exec Editor)*
William A. Ghormley *(Sr VP-Bus Dev)*
Robert Buderi *(Co-Founder & Chm)*
Richard Freierman *(Bus Mgr)*
Walter Kupiec *(Exec VP-Bus Dev)*

XCOR AEROSPACE, INC.
1314 Flight Line, Mojave, CA 93501
Tel.: (661) 824-4714
Web Site: http://www.xcor.com
Year Founded: 1999
Sales Range: $10-24.9 Million
Emp.: 80
Reusable Rocket Powered Vehicles & Systems Developer
N.A.I.C.S.: 336413
Jeff Greason *(Founder & Partner)*
Geoffrey Nunn *(VP-Ops & Programs)*
Michael Valant *(CTO & VP-Engrg)*
John H. Gibson II *(Chm, Pres & CEO)*

COMPANIES

XDUCE CORP.
510 Thornall St Ste 210, Edison, NJ 08837
Tel.: (732) 465-9100
Web Site: http://www.xduce.com
Year Founded: 2006
Sales Range: $1-9.9 Million
Emp.: 30
It Consulting
N.A.I.C.S.: 541690
Vaibhavi Kulkarni (VP-Staffing)

XEBEC CORPORATION
5612 Brighton Ter, Kansas City, MO 64130-4530
Tel.: (816) 444-9700   MO
Web Site: http://www.ditmco.com
Year Founded: 1948
Holding Company
N.A.I.C.S.: 334515
F. L. Thompson (Chm, Pres & CEO)
Sharon Kever (Sec)

XEI SCIENTIFIC, INC.
1755 E Byshore Rd Ste 17, Redwood City, CA 94063
Tel.: (650) 369-0133
Web Site: http://www.evactron.com
Year Founded: 1991
Analytical Laboratory Instrument Mfr
N.A.I.C.S.: 334516
Mike Muniz (Office Mgr)
Ronald A. Vane (Founder & Pres)
Barbara Armbruster (Dir-Mktg)

XENIA MANUFACTURING INC.
1507 Church St, Xenia, IL 62899
Tel.: (618) 678-2218
Web Site:
   http://www.xmiharness.com
Sales Range: $10-24.9 Million
Emp.: 240
Harness Wiring Sets, Internal Combustion Engines
N.A.I.C.S.: 336320
Paul A. Knapp (Pres)
Rick Forth (Sec)
Steve McCarthy (CFO & Controller)
Ed Knapp (Gen Mgr)

XENOPHON STRATEGIES
1120 G St NW 450, Washington, DC 20005
Tel.: (202) 289-4001
Web Site:
   http://www.xenophonstrategies.com
Year Founded: 2000
Emp.: 25
Public Relations, Public Affairs, Crisis Communications, Government Affairs, Advertising & Advocacy
N.A.I.C.S.: 541820
David A. Fuscus (Pres & CEO)
Mark Hazlin (Sr VP)
Jennifer June Lay (VP)
Bob Brady (Mng Dir)
Michael Green (Mng Dir)

XENOSOFT TECHNOLOGIES
2701 Dallas Pkwy Ste 550, Dallas, TX 75093
Tel.: (972) 755-1800   CA
Web Site: http://www.xtglobal.com
Year Founded: 1998
Sales Range: $10-24.9 Million
Emp.: 87
Software Technology & Consulting Services Primarily on Oracle Applications
N.A.I.C.S.: 541690
Ramarao Mullapudi (Founder & CEO)

XENSPIRE, INC.
11 Apex Dr Ste 300, Marlborough, MA 01752
Tel.: (234) 568-7990   DE
Web Site: https://xenspire.com
IT Consulting & Services
N.A.I.C.S.: 541690
Ram Konduru (Founder & CEO)

Subsidiaries:

Laboratory Staffing Inc.   (1)
5841 Cedar Rd Ste #118, Saint Louis Park, MN 55416
Tel.: (952) 525-2019
Web Site: http://www.labstaff.com
Employment Placement Agencies
N.A.I.C.S.: 561311

XENTURY CITY DEVELOPMENT COMPANY, L.C.
7575 Dr Phillips Blvd Ste 260, Orlando, FL 32819
Tel.: (407) 363-7883
Web Site: http://www.xenturycity.com
Sales Range: $1-9.9 Million
Land Subdivision
N.A.I.C.S.: 237210
Dimitri Toumazos (CFO)
James Thomas (Pres)

XETEX INC.
9405 Holly St NW, Minneapolis, MN 55433
Tel.: (612) 724-3101
Web Site: http://www.xetexinc.com
Year Founded: 1985
Sales Range: $10-24.9 Million
Emp.: 44
Outdoor Air Ventilation Equipment
N.A.I.C.S.: 333415
Keith Hoehenstein (Owner)
Dean Doble (Dir-Engrg)

XF ENTERPRISES INC.
Tel.: (806) 367-5810
Web Site: https://www.xfent.com
Sales Range: $25-49.9 Million
Emp.: 250
Veterinary Pharmaceutical Preparations
N.A.I.C.S.: 325412
Paul Dominguez (CFO)
Hollis Klett (Pres)
Wes Klett (COO)

XFACT, INC.
120 Water St Ste 214, North Andover, MA 01845
Tel.: (978) 686-3180
Web Site: http://www.xfact.com
Year Founded: 2000
Sales Range: $1-9.9 Million
Emp.: 20
Public Sector Management Services
N.A.I.C.S.: 541820
Amit Banerji (Founder & Pres)

XFS GLOBAL LLC
7701 France Ave S Ste 240, Minneapolis, MN 55435 - 5298
Tel.: (910) 320-4728
Web Site: https://www.xfactorsg.com
Year Founded: 2023
Integrated Semi-Permanent Engineered Fabric Shelter Systems
N.A.I.C.S.: 332999

Subsidiaries:

Bondcote Performance Textiles, LLC   (1)
509 Burgiss Ave, Pulaski, VA 24301-5305
Tel.: (540) 980-2640
Web Site: http://www.bondcote.com
Sales Range: $10-24.9 Million
Provider of Coated Fabrics
N.A.I.C.S.: 313320
David Harrison (Mgr-Roofing Technical)
Donnie Kemp (Plant Mgr)
Sherry Fisher (Mgr-Technical & Mktg)
Paul Riggins (Assoc Mgr-Military & Customer Svc)
Eric Brown (Mgr-Sls-Natl)
Morgan Leonard (Mgr-Product)

Creative Tent International, Inc.   (1)
451 Mirror Ct Ste 101, Henderson, NV 89011
Tel.: (725) 259-4808
Web Site: https://www.creativetent.us
Sales Range: $25-49.9 Million
Emp.: 90
Tent Design & Installation Services
N.A.I.C.S.: 541490
Carol Fontius (Pres)
Robert Stafford (Dir-Creative)

XG SCIENCES, INC.
3101 Grand Oak Dr, Lansing, MI 48911
Tel.: (517) 703-1110
Web Site: http://www.xgsciences.com
Year Founded: 2006
Rev.: $782,692
Assets: $7,353,576
Liabilities: $15,036,113
Net Worth: ($7,682,537)
Earnings: ($7,101,748)
Emp.: 24
Fiscal Year-end: 12/31/20
Graphene Nanoplatelet Mfr
N.A.I.C.S.: 335991
Arnold A. Allemang (Chm)
Hiroyuki Fukushima (Dir-Technical)
Lawrence T. Drzal (Founder)
Robert M. Blinstrub (Pres & CEO)
Jacqueline M. Lemke (CFO)
Leroy Magwood (CTO)
Andrew J. Boechler (Chief Comml Officer)
Robert Budlong (Mgr-Sls & Customer Support)

XHALE, INC.
3630 SW 47th Ave Ste 100, Gainesville, FL 32608
Tel.: (352) 371-8488
Web Site: http://www.xhale.com
Sales Range: $1-9.9 Million
Emp.: 20
Medical Device Mfr
N.A.I.C.S.: 339112
Richard R. Allen (CEO)
Richard J. Melker (CTO)
Donn Dennis (Chief Scientific Officer)
Hank Wohltjen (VP-Engrg)
Douglas M. Crumb (Pres & COO)
John Moscarillo (VP-Comml Ops)
Mark Tanner (VP-Info Architecture)

XIDAX, LLC
145 W 7200 S Ste A, Midvale, UT 84047
Web Site: http://www.xidax.com
Year Founded: 2014
Sales Range: $10-24.9 Million
Emp.: 48
Custom Computer Retailer
N.A.I.C.S.: 449210
Sean McPharlin (Dir-HR)

XIPHIAS ENTERPRISES INC.
830 W Main St, Hyannis, MA 02601
Tel.: (508) 778-7878
Web Site:
   http://www.hyannishonda.com
Year Founded: 1969
Sales Range: $10-24.9 Million
Emp.: 100
Automobiles, New & Used
N.A.I.C.S.: 441110
Robert Goodwin (Owner)

XIUM CORPORATION
106 E Old Settlers Blvd, Round Rock, TX 78664
Tel.: (512) 218-4100
Web Site: http://www.goxium.com

Sales Range: $10-24.9 Million
Emp.: 25
Wireless Antenna Technologies
N.A.I.C.S.: 334310

XL FIRE PROTECTION CO.
3022 N Hesperian Pkwy, Santa Ana, CA 92706
Tel.: (714) 554-6132
Web Site:
   http://www.xlfireprotection.com
Sales Range: $10-24.9 Million
Emp.: 50
Fire Sprinkler System Installation
N.A.I.C.S.: 238220
Brian Callahan (Pres)
Sunny Schwartv (VP-Fin)

XL, INC.
7900 Westpark Dr Ste T-307, McLean, VA 22102
Tel.: (703) 848-0400
Web Site: http://www.xla.com
Year Founded: 1989
Rev.: $7,300,000
Emp.: 110
Business Consulting Services
N.A.I.C.S.: 541690
Douglas Kollme (CFO & Exec VP)
Nelson McClung (COO & Sr VP)
Patty Todaro Bolin (Sr VP-Bus Dev & Capture)
Cynthia Andrews (Sr VP-Bus Ops)
Lloyd M. Mustin II (CEO)

XLA, INC.
8614 Westwood Center Dr Ste 700, Vienna, VA 22182
Tel.: (703) 848-0400
Web Site: http://www.xla.com
Project Management, Engineering & Technical Consulting Services
N.A.I.C.S.: 541611
Gary Slack (Pres & CEO)
Cynthia Andrews (Sr VP-Bus Ops)
Nelson McClung (COO & Sr VP)

XM INTERNATIONAL INC.
433 Hackensack Ave Fl L, Hackensack, NJ 07601-6332
Tel.: (201) 849-5277
Web Site: http://www.wexcell.com
Year Founded: 1991
Sales Range: $25-49.9 Million
Emp.: 250
Building Materials Distr
N.A.I.C.S.: 423390
Jane Dong (Founder & Pres)

XML FINANCIAL GROUP
1 Preserve Pkwy Ste 120, Rockville, MD 20852
Tel.: (301) 770-5234
Web Site: http://www.xmlfg.com
Year Founded: 2004
Sales Range: $1-9.9 Million
Emp.: 20
Wealth Management Services
N.A.I.C.S.: 523940
Brett Shane Bernstein (Co-Founder & Mng Partner)
Robert D. Kantor (Co-Founder, Chief Compliance Officer & Mng Partner)
Jason Elliot Klopman (Partner)
Susan A. Harpe (Dir-Ops)

XO HOLDINGS, INC.
13865 Sunrise Valley Dr, Herndon, VA 20171
Tel.: (703) 547-2000   DE
Web Site: http://www.xo.com
Year Founded: 1994
Sales Range: $1-4.9 Billion
Emp.: 3,654
Holding Company; Telecommunications Services

XO HOLDINGS, INC.

XO Holdings, Inc.—(Continued)
N.A.I.C.S.: 551112
Carl Celian Icahn *(Chm)*
Maureen Schasser *(VP-HR)*

Subsidiaries:

XO Communications, LLC (1)
13865 Sunrise Valley Dr, Herndon, VA 20171
Tel.: (703) 547-2000
Web Site: http://www.xo.com
Sales Range: $200-249.9 Million
Telecommunications Services for Business & Telecom Carriers
N.A.I.C.S.: 517810
Deborah Accinelli *(Acct Exec-Enterprise-Southeast)*

Subsidiary (Domestic):

XO Colorado, LLC (2)
1660 Lincoln St Ste 2600, Denver, CO 80264
Tel.: (303) 839-8351
Web Site: http://www.xo.com
Telecommunications Resellers
N.A.I.C.S.: 517121

XO Utah Inc. (2)
7050 Union Park Ave Ste 400, Midvale, UT 84047
Tel.: (801) 983-1600
Web Site: http://www.xo.com
Sales Range: $25-49.9 Million
Emp.: 3,000
Provider of Telephone Communication Services
N.A.I.C.S.: 517121
Simone Wu *(Gen Counsel, Sec & Exec VP-Legal & Admin)*
Michael Toplisek *(Exec VP-Advanced Solutions)*

XOJET, INC.
2000 Sierra Point Pkwy, Brisbane, CA 94005
Tel.: (650) 676-4700
Web Site: http://www.xojet.com
Year Founded: 2006
Sales Range: $125-149.9 Million
Emp.: 140
Global Business Aviation Services
N.A.I.C.S.: 481211
Dave Colbert *(Sr VP-Flight Ops & Dir-Maintenance)*
Mark S. Long *(CFO)*
Gregg Slow *(Exec VP-Sls & Client Svcs)*
Shari Jones *(CMO)*
Jerry Joondeph *(Gen Counsel)*
James Henderson *(Chief Bus Officer)*
Daniel Ramirez *(Dir-Safety)*
Kriste Hauswirth *(VP-Scheduling)*
Rebecca Kodesh *(VP-Scheduling)*
Matthew Rehm *(Sr VP-Revenue Mgmt)*
William E. McGlashan Jr. *(Chm)*

XONEX INC.
20 E Commons Blvd, New Castle, DE 19720
Tel.: (302) 323-6181
Web Site: http://www.xonex.com
Rev.: $29,852,224
Emp.: 163
Trucking Except Local
N.A.I.C.S.: 484121
Bill Humphrey *(Pres)*

Subsidiaries:

George B. Holman & Co. Inc. (1)
435 Main St, Hackensack, NJ 07601
Tel.: (201) 487-3900
Web Site: http://www.xonex.com
Rev.: $22,972,010
Emp.: 50
Household Goods Transport
N.A.I.C.S.: 484210

XOXIDE, INC.
2885 Jupiter Park Dr Ste 1200, Jupiter, FL 33458
Tel.: (561) 282-6001
Web Site: http://www.xoxide.com
Year Founded: 2000
Sales Range: $10-24.9 Million
Emp.: 32
Online Electronic Component & Parts Retailer
N.A.I.C.S.: 459999

XPANSIV DATA SYSTEMS INC.
50 California Street, 15th Floor, San Francisco, CA 94111
Tel.: (415) 915-5124
Web Site: https://xpansiv.com
Year Founded: 2016
Software Publisher
N.A.I.C.S.: 513210
John Melby *(Pres & COO)*

Subsidiaries:

Evolution Markets, LLC (1)
10 Bank St, White Plains, NY 10606
Tel.: (914) 323-0200
Web Site: http://www.evomarkets.com
Commodity Contracts Brokerage
N.A.I.C.S.: 523160
Andrew Ertel *(Pres & CEO)*

XPERIA SOLUTIONS APPAREL SOFTWARE
22 S 2nd St, Emmaus, PA 18049
Tel.: (610) 967-5821
Web Site: http://www.xperiasolutions.com
Year Founded: 1984
Sales Range: $1-9.9 Million
Emp.: 18
Software Solutions, Applications & Services
N.A.I.C.S.: 513210
Gene Bonett *(Pres)*
Gina Bauer *(VP)*

XPERTTECH INC.
400 W Cummings Park Ste 2850, Woburn, MA 01801
Tel.: (781) 281-0856
Web Site: http://www.xperttech.com
Year Founded: 2002
Sales Range: $1-9.9 Million
Emp.: 155
Computer Software Whslr
N.A.I.C.S.: 423430
Venkat Janapareddy *(CEO)*

XPLANE CORP.
411 SW 6th Ave, Portland, OR 97204
Tel.: (503) 548-4343
Web Site: http://www.xplane.com
Year Founded: 1993
Graphic Design Consulting Services
N.A.I.C.S.: 541430
Aric Wood *(CEO)*

XPLOSION INCORPORATED
Ste 3882 304 S Jones Blvd, Las Vegas, NV 89107
Tel.: (702) 583-3283 NV
Web Site: http://www.xplosionincorporated.com
Year Founded: 2015
Assets: $3,383,175
Liabilities: $324,692
Net Worth: $3,058,483
Earnings: $243,395
Fiscal Year-end: 10/31/19
Electronic Product Distr
N.A.I.C.S.: 423690
Eugenio Gregorio *(Pres, CEO, CFO, Treas & Sec)*

XPONENTIAL, INC.
6400 Atlantic Blvd Ste 190, Norcross, GA 30071
Tel.: (678) 720-0660 DE
Year Founded: 1994
Sales Range: $10-24.9 Million
Emp.: 154
Holding Company; Pawn Stores Owner & Operator
N.A.I.C.S.: 551112
Robert W. Schleizer *(CFO, Exec VP & Exec VP)*
Jeffrey Alan Cummer *(Chm & CEO)*

XPR LLC
217 N Main St Ste 200, Santa Ana, CA 92701
Tel.: (714) 881-2310
Sales Range: $10-24.9 Million
Emp.: 12
Business-To-Business, Consumer Marketing, Crisis Communications, Planning & Consultation
N.A.I.C.S.: 541810

XPT GROUP LLC
28 Liberty St 6th Fl, New York, NY 10005
Tel.: (646) 927-2755 DE
Web Site: http://xptspecialty.com
Specialty Insurance Services
N.A.I.C.S.: 524298
Betty Sikora *(Exec VP-Reg)*
Landon Parnell *(Exec VP-Grp)*
Kyle Stevens *(Exec VP-Grp)*
Mark Smith *(Pres)*
Glen Pomeroy *(Exec VP-Personal Lines)*

Subsidiaries:

Cal Inspection Bureau, Inc. (1)
19528 Ventura Blvd 347, Tarzana, CA 91356
Tel.: (818) 346-2422
Web Site: http://www.calinspect.com
Sales Range: $1-9.9 Million
Emp.: 10
Insurance Agent/Broker
N.A.I.C.S.: 524298
Emil Moskowitz *(Pres & Founder)*

LP Risk, Inc. (1)
17361 Vlg Green Dr, Houston, TX 77040
Tel.: (713) 939-8585
Web Site: http://lp-risk.com
Insurance Services
N.A.I.C.S.: 524210
Landon Parnell *(Pres)*

Subsidiary (Domestic):

Houston Surplus Lines, Inc. (2)
14090 SW Fwy #400, Sugar Land, TX 77478
Tel.: (281) 491-3311
Web Site: http://www.houstonsurplus.com
Insurance Brokerage Services
N.A.I.C.S.: 524210

S&H Underwriters, Inc. (1)
3030 US Route 2, East Montpelier, VT 05651-9760
Tel.: (802) 229-5660
Web Site: http://www.sh-underwriters.com
Insurance Agencies & Brokerages
N.A.I.C.S.: 524210

Sierra Specialty Insurance Services, Inc. (1)
234 Clovis Ave, Clovis, CA 93612
Tel.: (559) 256-6900
Web Site: http://www.sierraspecialty.com
Insurance Agencies & Brokerages
N.A.I.C.S.: 524210
Kathy Schroeder *(Exec VP-Grp)*
Mark Schroeder *(Sr VP)*
Lizette Felde *(VP)*
Esmeralda Mendez *(Mgr-P&C Underwriter)*

W.E. Love & Associates Inc. (1)
2040 S Church St, Burlington, NC 27215-5391
Tel.: (336) 226-1191
Web Site: http://www.welove.com
Sales Range: $25-49.9 Million
Insurance Agents, Brokers & Service
N.A.I.C.S.: 524210

U.S. PRIVATE

XS INTERNATIONAL, INC.
1005 Alderman Dr Ste 212, Alpharetta, GA 30005
Tel.: (770) 740-0040
Web Site: http://www.xsnet.com
Year Founded: 1990
Sales Range: $1-9.9 Million
Emp.: 15
IT Oriented Service Provider
N.A.I.C.S.: 518210
Todd Bone *(CEO)*

XSE GROUP INC.
35 Philmack Dr, Middletown, CT 06457-1526
Tel.: (860) 632-7329 CT
Web Site: http://www.xsegroup.com
Year Founded: 1984
Sales Range: $10-24.9 Million
Emp.: 120
Provider of Stationery & Office Supplies
N.A.I.C.S.: 424120
Gerald Crean *(Pres)*
Jeff Johnson *(CEO)*

XSELL RESOURCES, INC.
660 American Ave Ste 103, King of Prussia, PA 19406-4032
Tel.: (215) 706-4500
Web Site: http://www.xsellresources.com
Year Founded: 2002
Sales Range: $1-9.9 Million
Emp.: 15
Information Technology Professional Recruiter
N.A.I.C.S.: 561311
Christine Price *(VP-Sls)*

XSOLIS, INC.
4031 Aspen Grove Dr Ste 500, Franklin, TN 37067
Tel.: (855) 371-0867
Web Site: http://www.xsolis.com
Year Founded: 2013
Heathcare Technolgy Services
N.A.I.C.S.: 621999
Rachel Vincion *(Chief Finance Officer)*
Tim Kostner *(Chief Revenue Officer)*
Chris Bayham *(COO)*
Joan Butters *(Founder & CEO)*
Heather Bassett *(Chief Medical Officer)*
Brent Teveit *(Chief Data Science Officer)*
Mallika Edwards *(Chief Product Officer)*
Zach Evans *(CTO)*

XSTATIC PUBLIC RELATIONS
1 Broadway Ste 311, Denver, CO 80203
Tel.: (303) 928-7144
Web Site: http://www.xstaticpr.com
Sales Range: Less than $1 Million
Emp.: 10
Advetising Agency
N.A.I.C.S.: 541810
J.D. McCartney *(Co-Founder & CEO)*
Stacey Sepp *(Co-Founder & COO)*

XSTELOS HOLDINGS, INC.
630 5th Ave Ste 2260, New York, NY 10020
Tel.: (212) 729-4962 DE
Sales Range: $25-49.9 Million
Emp.: 2
Holding Company; Pharmaceutical Mfr
N.A.I.C.S.: 551112
Jonathan M. Couchman *(Chm, Pres, CEO & CFO)*

COMPANIES

Subsidiaries:

Bradley Lifting Corporation (1)
1030 Elm St, York, PA 17403-2597
Tel.: (717) 848-3121
Web Site: http://www.bradleylift.com
Emp.: 45
Lifting Equipment Mfr
N.A.I.C.S.: 333998
Tom Thole (Pres)

Xtek Europe s.r.o. (1)
Domazlicka 180a, 318 00, Plzen, Czech Republic
Tel.: (420) 377331377
Web Site: http://www.xtek.com
Sales Range: $10-24.9 Million
Emp.: 15
Crane Wheel Assembly Mfr
N.A.I.C.S.: 333519
Roman Stichenwirth (Mng Dir)

XTIVA FINANCIAL SYSTEMS, INC.
28 W 44th St Ste 815, New York, NY 10036
Tel.: (212) 228-6200   CA
Web Site: http://www.xtiva.com
Year Founded: 1998
Sales Range: $1-9.9 Million
Emp.: 44
Software Developer
N.A.I.C.S.: 513210
Thomas J. Moysak (CEO)
George Kuzma (Controller)
William Lieberman (Mgr-Comm)
Glen Schreitmueller (VP-Svcs Strategy & Ops)
Pegeen Channell (VP-Pro Svcs)
Roy Austin (Dir-Enterprise Projects)
Robert Kenig (VP-Technical Ops, Engrg & Support)
Michael Richardson (CIO-Miami)
Jeff Marsden (Chief Product & Strategy Officer)
Rick Scearbo (COO)

XTREME COMMUNICATIONS, INC.

Subsidiaries:

CPEX Pharmaceuticals, Inc. (1)
1105 N Market St Ste 1300, Wilmington, DE 19801
Tel.: (603) 658-6100
Web Site: http://www.cpexpharmaceuticals.com
Sales Range: $10-24.9 Million
Pharmaceuticals Product Mfr
N.A.I.C.S.: 325412

XTC PRODUCTS, INC.
136 Jimmo Dr Ste 4, Colchester, VT 05446
Tel.: (802) 891-6645   NY
Web Site: http://www.peacetoys.com
Year Founded: 1982
Toys, Soft Fabric Globes, Map Related Products & Organic Cotton Garments Sales & Distr
N.A.I.C.S.: 423920

XTEK, INC.
11451 Reading Rd, Cincinnati, OH 45241-2246
Tel.: (513) 733-7800   OH
Web Site: http://www.xtek.com
Year Founded: 1909
Sales Range: $100-124.9 Million
Emp.: 200
Hardened Steel Machine Mfr
N.A.I.C.S.: 333613
Jim Raible (VP-Sls & Mktg)
John W. Mayhan (VP-Engrg)
Jennifer G. King (VP-Admin)
Tom Mulhern (Gen Mgr-Avon Engrg)
Frank Petrek (Grp VP)
Chris Hainrihar (VP-Mfg)
A. J. Schreiver (VP-Acctg & Fin)

24023 NE Shea Ln Ste 215, Troutdale, OR 97060
Tel.: (503) 618-8816
Web Site: http://www.xtremecabling.com
Year Founded: 2001
Sales Range: $10-24.9 Million
Emp.: 15
Electrical Contractor
N.A.I.C.S.: 238210
Mark Jacobs (Pres)
Carl Rickert (VP)
Bill Mildfelt (VP)

XTREME CONSULTING GROUP, INC.
3500 Carillon Pt, Kirkland, WA 98033
Tel.: (425) 861-9460
Web Site: http://www.xtremeconsulting.com
Year Founded: 2005
Sales Range: $10-24.9 Million
Emp.: 185
Business & Tech Solutions
N.A.I.C.S.: 541611
Greg Rankich (CEO)
Tony Richardson (Co-Founder & CTO)
Doug Snider (COO)
Jacob Peterson (Sr Dir-Talent Acq & Retention)
Randall Hopkins (Sr Dir-Talent Solutions)
Brett Hoover (Dir-Consulting Svcs)
Dale Johns (Chief Delivery Officer)
Evelyn Bohan (Mng Dir)
Jay Wendt (Mgr-Bus Dev)
Jeff Hanson (Dir-Project Mgmt)
Lori Whitten (Mng Dir)
Martin Dey (Dir-IT Architecture)
Shawn Plowman (Mng Dir)
Shea Putnam (Mng Dir)
Frank Smith (Mng Dir)
Gaith Kadir (Mng Dir-Dubai)

XTREME GREEN ELECTRIC VEHICLES INC.
3010 E Alexander Rd Ste 1002, North Las Vegas, NV 89030
Tel.: (702) 870-0700   NV
Web Site: http://www.xgpinc.com
Year Founded: 2005
Sales Range: Less than $1 Million
Eco-Friendly Electric Powered Personal Mobility Vehicles Mfr
N.A.I.C.S.: 336991
Byron S. Georgiou (Chm & CEO)

XTREME HEALTHCARE CORPORATION
4636 Mission Gorge Pl Ste 103-C, San Diego, CA 92120
Tel.: (619) 822-2674   DE
Web Site: http://www.xtremecareambulance.com
Sales Range: Less than $1 Million
Emp.: 40
Ambulance & Emergency Medical Services
N.A.I.C.S.: 621999
Souheil Jawad (Pres, Treas & Sec)
Alohi Rieger (Office Mgr)

XTREME LASHES, LLC
24127 W Hardy Rd Ste C, Spring, TX 77373
Tel.: (281) 907-0689   TX
Web Site: http://www.xtremelashes.com
Sales Range: $1-9.9 Million
Emp.: 70
Eyelash Extension Retailer
N.A.I.C.S.: 456120

Joumana Mousselli (Founder & Pres)
Natalie Miller (Acct Mgr)
Laura Jones (Project Mgr)

XTREME MANUFACTURING, LLC
1415 W Bonanza Rd, Las Vegas, NV 89106
Tel.: (702) 636-2969   NV
Web Site: http://www.xmfg.com
Year Founded: 2003
Telescopic Material Handling Equipment Designer, Mfr & Distr
N.A.I.C.S.: 333924
Lee F. Kramer (Pres)
Robby Hagan (Sr VP-Sls)
Richard Hoffelmeyer (VP-Engrg)
Brandon Main (VP-Cube Div)
Amelia Pearce (Dir-Mktg-Global)
Danny Soto (Mgr-Parts)
Don Schulz (VP-Sls)
Mike Henderly (Gen Mgr)
Steve Watts (VP-Strategic Partnerships)

Subsidiaries:

Snorkel International Holdings, LLC (1)
2009 Roseport Rd, Elwood, KS 66024   (51%)
Tel.: (785) 989-3000
Web Site: https://www.snorkellifts.com
Emp.: 200
Holding Company; Aerial Work Platforms Mfr & Whslr
N.A.I.C.S.: 551112
Don F. Ahern (Owner)
Matthew Elvin (CEO)

Subsidiary (Non-US):

Snorkel Europe Limited (2)
Vigo Centre Birtley Road, Washington, NE38 9DA, Tyne & Wear, United Kingdom
Tel.: (44) 8451550057
Web Site: https://www.snorkellifts.com
Aerial Work Platforms Mfr & Whslr
N.A.I.C.S.: 333923
Amelia Pearce (Mktg Dir-Global)
Mick Wright (Dir-Sls-Middle East)
Matthew Elvin (CEO)

Subsidiary (Non-US):

Ahern Australia Pty. Ltd. (3)
8-10 McIlwraith Street, Wetherill Park, 2164, NSW, Australia
Tel.: (61) 29 609 8500
Web Site: https://www.ahernaustralia.com.au
Aerial Work Platforms Mfr & Whslr
N.A.I.C.S.: 333923
Bruce MacLean (Gen Mgr-Asia Pacific)
Glenn Martin (Mng Dir)

Subsidiary (Non-US):

Snorkel New Zealand Limited (4)
36 Bruce Rd, Horowhenua, Levin, 5510, New Zealand
Tel.: (64) 80 076 6753
Web Site: https://www.snorkellifts.com
Aerial Work Platforms Whslr
N.A.I.C.S.: 423830
Rob Theunissen (Pres)
Simon Mulhane (Mgr-Svc-Natl)
Jonathan Tulitt (Mng Dir)

Subsidiary (US):

Snorkel International, LLC (3)
2009 Roseport Rd, Elwood, KS 66024
Tel.: (785) 989-3000
Web Site: http://www.snorkellifts.com
Aerial Work Platforms Mfr & Whslr
N.A.I.C.S.: 333923
Don Ahern (Owner)
Matthew Elvin (CEO)

Subsidiary (Non-US):

Snorkel Japan Co., Ltd. (3)
3F Yamamoto Building 3-15-2 Shibaura, Minato-ku, Tokyo, 108-0023, Japan
Tel.: (81) 3 5765 6841
Web Site: http://www.snorkeljp.com

XYLO TECHNOLOGIES, INC.

Emp.: 1,200
Aerial Work Platforms Whslr
N.A.I.C.S.: 423830

XTTRIUM LABORATORIES INC.
1200 E Business Ctr Dr Ste 400, Mount Prospect, IL 60056
Tel.: (773) 268-5800
Web Site: http://www.xttrium.com
Rev.: $10,117,323
Emp.: 68
Surgical Appliances & Supplies
N.A.I.C.S.: 325412
Vijay Verma (CFO)
Lori Miller (Supvr-QA & RA)
David Maldonado (Dir-Ops)
Joe Scalise (Dir-Regulatory Affairs & Quality Assurance)

XY - THE PERSISTENT COMPANY
1405 30th St, San Diego, CA 92154
Web Site: http://xy.company
Year Founded: 2012
Sales Range: $10-24.9 Million
Emp.: 75
Software Development Services
N.A.I.C.S.: 541511
Arie Trouw (Co-Founder)
Markus Levin (Co-Founder & Head-Ops)

XYBERNAUT CORPORATION
5175 Parkstone Dr Ste 130, Chantilly, VA 20151-3832
Tel.: (703) 480-0480   DE
Web Site: http://www.xybernaut.com
Year Founded: 1990
Sales Range: $1-9.9 Million
Emp.: 91
Mfr of Mobile Computer Systems & Equipment
N.A.I.C.S.: 334210
Michael Binko (VP-Corp Devel)
Ed Maddox (Pres)
Nancy Hogan (VP-Fin & Admin)

XYBION CORPORATION
201 Littleton Rd, Morris Plains, NJ 07950
Tel.: (973) 538-5111   DE
Web Site: http://www.xybion.com
Year Founded: 1975
Sales Range: $1-9.9 Million
Emp.: 40
Software & Information Technology Services for Life Sciences Industry
N.A.I.C.S.: 513210
Pradip K. Banerjee (Chm & CEO)
Steve Porfano (CFO)
Carlos Frade (VP-Pre-Clinical R&D Solutions)
David Chiaramonte (VP-Consulting Svcs)
Kamal Biswas (Pres & COO)

Subsidiaries:

Vital Path, Inc. (1)
Two Greenwood Sq 3331 St Rd Ste 300, Bensalem, PA 19020
Tel.: (215) 638-9700
Content Integration & Business Process Management Solutions
N.A.I.C.S.: 541519
Pradip Banerjee (CEO)

XYLO TECHNOLOGIES, INC.
2434 Superior Dr NW Ste 105, Rochester, MN 55901
Tel.: (507) 289-9956   MN
Web Site: http://www.xylotechnologies.com
Year Founded: 2000
Sales Range: $10-24.9 Million
Emp.: 60
IT Services & Solutions
N.A.I.C.S.: 519290

XYLO TECHNOLOGIES, INC.

Xylo Technologies, Inc.—(Continued)
Dharani Ramamoorthy *(Pres)*
Santhi Arunachalam *(Mgr-Ops)*

XYMID LLC
200 Lake Drive Ste A, Newark, DE 19702
Web Site: http://www.xymidllc.com
Year Founded: 1998
Rev.: $25,000,000
Emp.: 31
Mfr of Cloth
N.A.I.C.S.: 314910

XYONICZ CORPORATION
6754 Martin St, Rome, NY 13440-7119
Tel.: (315) 334-4214
Web Site: http://www.xyonicz.com
Year Founded: 1994
Sales Range: Less than $1 Million
Emp.: 5
Mfr of Material Handling Equipment for the Newspaper Industry & Soft-metal Melting Industry
N.A.I.C.S.: 332811
Edward Zionc *(Pres & CEO)*

XYPRO TECHNOLOGY CORPORATION
4100 Guardian St Ste 100, Simi Valley, CA 93063
Tel.: (805) 583-2874   CA
Web Site: http://www.xypro.com
Year Founded: 1983
Sales Range: $10-24.9 Million
Data Management Software & Technical Consulting Services
N.A.I.C.S.: 541511
Lisa Partridge *(Pres & CEO)*
Andrew Price *(VP-Tech)*
Richard Nissenbaum *(CFO)*
Ellen Gershev *(Dir-Engrg)*
Ken Scudder *(Sr Dir-Bus Dev & Strategic Alliances)*
Robert Massa *(Mgr-Support)*
Jorge Alonzo *(Mgr-Software Dev)*

XZERES CORP.
9025 SW Hillman Ct Ste 3126, Wilsonville, OR 97070
Tel.: (503) 388-7350   NV
Web Site: http://www.xzeres.com
Rev.: $4,410,204
Assets: $7,136,517
Liabilities: $18,345,743
Net Worth: ($11,209,226)
Earnings: ($10,738,444)
Emp.: 42
Fiscal Year-end: 02/28/15
Wind Turbine Systems & Equipment Mfr
N.A.I.C.S.: 333611
Frank Greco *(Pres)*
John M. McCoury *(VP-Engrg)*
David J. Hofflich *(CEO)*

Y&S HANDBAG CO. INC.
3351 Tremley Pt Rd, Linden, NJ 07036
Tel.: (908) 862-3880
Web Site: http://www.yandshandbags.com
Sales Range: $10-24.9 Million
Emp.: 20
Retailer of Women's Accessories & Specialty Stores
N.A.I.C.S.: 458110
Pinny Rand *(Pres)*

Y-W ELECTRIC ASSOCIATION INC
250 Main Ave, Akron, CO 80720
Tel.: (970) 345-2291   CO
Web Site: http://www.ywelectric.coop
Year Founded: 1945
Sales Range: $10-24.9 Million
Emp.: 50
Distr of Electric Power
N.A.I.C.S.: 221122
Marjie Hottinger *(Mgr-HR)*
Samantha Gebauer *(Mgr-Payroll)*
Terence J. Hall Jr. *(Gen Mgr)*

Y. HATA & CO. LTD.
285 Sand Island Access Rd, Honolulu, HI 96819-2227
Tel.: (808) 447-4100
Web Site: http://www.yhata.com
Year Founded: 1922
Sales Range: $10-24.9 Million
Emp.: 111
Grocery Sales
N.A.I.C.S.: 424410
Russell Hata *(Chm & CEO)*

YAAKOV SERLE ADVERTISING
147-25 70th Ave, Flushing, NY 11367
Tel.: (718) 263-2483
Year Founded: 1986
Sales Range: Less than $1 Million
Emp.: 3
Advetising Agency
N.A.I.C.S.: 541810
Yaakov Serle *(Pres)*

YABOO, INC.
70 W Madison St Ste 1400, Chicago, IL 60602
Tel.: (312) 214-6116   NV
Year Founded: 2008
Sales Range: Less than $1 Million
Emp.: 33
Restaurant Owner & Operator
N.A.I.C.S.: 722511
Baoguo Jiang *(Chm & CEO)*
Zhanming Gao *(Sec)*
Zhongming Wang *(VP)*

YADAV ENTERPRISES, INC.
3550 Mowry Ave, Fremont, CA 94538
Tel.: (510) 792-3393
Web Site: http://www.jbxmanagement.com
Restaurant Operators
N.A.I.C.S.: 722511
Ani Yadav *(CEO)*

Subsidiaries:

Taco Cabana, Inc. (1)
3923 Lemmon Ave, Dallas, TX 75219
Tel.: (214) 522-3770
Web Site: http://www.tacocabana.com
Fast Food Restaurant Operator
N.A.I.C.S.: 722513

Subsidiary (Domestic):

T.C. Management, Inc. (2)
8918 Tesoro Dr Ste 200, San Antonio, TX 78217
Tel.: (210) 804-0990
Web Site: http://www.tacocabana.com
Rev.: $5,800,000
Emp.: 100
Management Consulting Services
N.A.I.C.S.: 541611
Dan Equordino *(Pres)*

YAFFE GROUP
26100 American Dr Ste 401, Southfield, MI 48034
Tel.: (248) 262-1700   MI
Web Site: http://www.yaffe.com
Year Founded: 1959
Rev.: $40,000,000
Emp.: 40
Fiscal Year-end: 12/31/03
N.A.I.C.S.: 541810
Fred Yaffe *(Chm)*
Michael Morin *(Exec VP)*
John Cassidy *(Pres & CEO)*
Michael McClure *(Sr VP-Digital Comm)*
Karen Jameson *(Print Production Mgr)*
Sheila Smith *(Office Mgr & Exec Asst)*
Todd Gentzel *(Chief Strategy Officer)*
Diane Pittman *(Dir-Creative)*
Buffy O'Connor *(Dir-Media)*
Mark Simon *(Chief Creative Officer)*

Subsidiaries:

Barrelhouse Creative (1)
26913 Northwestern Hwy Ste 500, Southfield, MI 48034
Tel.: (248) 262-1700
Web Site: http://www.yaffe.com
Emp.: 5
N.A.I.C.S.: 541810
Mike McClure *(VP & Dir-Creative, Mng Dir-Barrelhouse Creative)*

Yaffe Direct (1)
26100 American Dr 4th Fl Ste 401, Southfield, MI 48034
Tel.: (248) 262-1700
Web Site: http://www.yaffe.com
Sales Range: $25-49.9 Million
Emp.: 25
N.A.I.C.S.: 541810
Michael Morin *(Exec VP & Dir-Client Svcs)*
Fred Yaffe *(Chm & CEO)*
John Cassidy *(CFO & Exec VP)*
Brad Deutser *(Pres)*
Todd Gentzel *(Chief Strategy Officer)*
Buffy O'Connor *(Dir-Media)*

Yaffe/Deutser (1)
1330 Post Oak Blvd Ste 1350, Houston, TX 77056
Tel.: (713) 212-0700
Web Site: http://www.yaffedeutser.com
Sales Range: $10-24.9 Million
Emp.: 8
N.A.I.C.S.: 541810
Brad Deutser *(Pres)*
Todd Gentzel *(Mng Dir)*
Diana Lovelace *(Bus Mgr & Mgr-Production)*
Diane Pittman *(Dir-Creative)*
Catherine Campbell *(Acct Exec)*
Kate Duncan *(Acct Exec)*
Stacy Christian *(Acct Dir)*
Treasure Hance *(Office Mgr)*

YAFFE IRON & METAL COMPANY INC.
1200 S G St, Muskogee, OK 74402
Tel.: (918) 687-7543   OK
Web Site: http://www.yaffeco.net
Year Founded: 1954
Sales Range: $50-74.9 Million
Emp.: 411
Scrap Metal Recycling
N.A.I.C.S.: 423930
Sharla McKeefe *(Controller)*
Kenny Williams *(Mgr-Yard)*

Subsidiaries:

Ball Pipe & Supply Inc. (1)
701 E Hardesty Rd, Shawnee, OK 74801
Tel.: (405) 275-5006
Web Site: http://www.yaffeco.net
Sales Range: $10-24.9 Million
Emp.: 40
Scrap Metal Recycling
N.A.I.C.S.: 423930
James Pine *(VP)*

Missouri Metal Recycling Inc. (1)
PO Box 231, Webb City, MO 64870
Tel.: (417) 673-3232
Web Site: http://www.yaffeco.net
Sales Range: $10-24.9 Million
Emp.: 25
Scrap Metal Recycling
N.A.I.C.S.: 423930
Johnny Boyd *(Pres)*

Ponca Iron & Metal Inc. (1)
200 E Oakland Ave, Ponca City, OK 74601   (100%)
Tel.: (580) 765-8420
Web Site: http://www.yaffeco.net
Sales Range: $10-24.9 Million
Emp.: 20
Scrap Metal Recycling
N.A.I.C.S.: 423930
Rogers Iron & Metal Corp. (1)
721 N Arkansas St, Rogers, AR 72756-6613   (100%)
Tel.: (479) 636-2666
Sales Range: $10-24.9 Million
Emp.: 25
Scrap Metal Recycling
N.A.I.C.S.: 423510

Siloam Springs Metal Recycling Inc. (1)
1004 E Main St, Siloam Springs, AR 72761
Tel.: (479) 524-3611
Sales Range: $10-24.9 Million
Emp.: 12
Scrap Metal Recycling
N.A.I.C.S.: 562920
Stacy Warder *(Mgr)*

YAHSGS LLC
PO Box 667, Richland, WA 99352
Tel.: (509) 375-5359   WA
Web Site: http://www.yahsgs.com
Sales Range: $1-9.9 Million
Emp.: 33
Scientific & Technical Consulting Services
N.A.I.C.S.: 541690
Katherine Yuracko *(CEO)*
Bill Hewitt *(Pres)*

YAKIMA BAIT CO.
1000 Bailey Ave, Granger, WA 98932
Tel.: (509) 854-1311
Web Site: http://www.yakimabait.com
Year Founded: 1934
Sales Range: $50-74.9 Million
Emp.: 120
Mfr of Fishing Tackle
N.A.I.C.S.: 339920
Mark Masterson *(Gen Mgr)*
Karen Weissburg *(Controller)*

YAKIMA COOPERATIVE ASSOCIATION
501 S Front St, Yakima, WA 98901-3260
Tel.: (509) 457-5380
Web Site: http://www.yakimacoop.com
Sales Range: $10-24.9 Million
Emp.: 15
Petroleum Bulk Stations
N.A.I.C.S.: 424710
Kevin Skolrud *(Gen Mgr)*

YAKIMA FEDERAL SAVINGS & LOAN ASSOCIATION
118 E Yakima Ave, Yakima, WA 98901
Tel.: (509) 248-2634
Web Site: http://www.yakimafed.com
Year Founded: 1905
Sales Range: $25-49.9 Million
Emp.: 135
Savings & Loan Services
N.A.I.C.S.: 522180
Pete Bansmer *(Chm)*
Richard Strain *(Vice Chm)*
Colton Meek *(Sec & Sr VP)*
Michael Gilmore *(Pres & CEO)*
Dan Gaulke *(Sr VP & Mgr-Auditing)*
Leanne Antonio *(Exec VP-Savings Admin)*
Gary Pero *(Treas & Sr VP)*
Carolyn Dresker *(Sr VP-HR)*
John Fries *(VP & Mgr-Acctg)*

YAKIMA VALLEY MEMORIAL HOSPITAL
2811 Tieton Dr, Yakima, WA 98902
Tel.: (509) 575-8000   WA
Web Site: http://www.yakimamemorial.org
Year Founded: 1950
Sales Range: $350-399.9 Million

Emp.: 2,819
Health Care Srvices
N.A.I.C.S.: 622110
James Berg (Chm)
Scott Wagner (Vice Chm)
William Feldmann (Treas & Sec)

YALE ELECTRIC SUPPLY CO.
312 N 8th St, Lebanon, PA 17046
Tel.: (717) 273-4514
Web Site: http://www.yaleelectric.net
Sales Range: $10-24.9 Million
Emp.: 200
Electrical Supplies
N.A.I.C.S.: 423610
G. David Thomas (CEO)
Robert Ludwig (Branch Mgr)

YALE EQUIPMENT & SERVICES INC.
W 136 N 4901 Campbell Dr, Menomonee Falls, WI 53051
Tel.: (262) 783-7510
Web Site: http://www.yesfleet.com
Sales Range: $10-24.9 Million
Emp.: 100
Trucks, Tractors & Trailers: New & Used
N.A.I.C.S.: 441110
Clifford Anglewicz (CEO)
Darrin Sullivan (VP)
Tracy Clark (Pres)

YALE KENTUCKIANA INC.
4092 McCollum Ct, Louisville, KY 40218
Tel.: (502) 451-8300
Web Site: http://www.yalekentuckiana.com
Sales Range: $10-24.9 Million
Emp.: 52
Materials Handling Machinery
N.A.I.C.S.: 423830
Barry Paul (Pres)
Chris Windler (COO)

YALE UNIVERSITY PRESS
302 Temple St, New Haven, CT 06511-8909
Tel.: (203) 432-0960   CT
Web Site: http://www.yalepress.yale.edu
Year Founded: 1908
Sales Range: $50-74.9 Million
Emp.: 120
Publisher of Books
N.A.I.C.S.: 611310
John D. Rollins (Dir-Fin)
Katherine Boller (Assoc Editor-Art & Architecture)
Ariana Parenti (Coord-Online Mktg)

YAMADA GROUP USA LTD.
2150 N Nimitz Hwy, Honolulu, HI 96819
Tel.: (808) 847-4113
Web Site: http://www.yamadagroup.com
Sales Range: $10-24.9 Million
Emp.: 10
Holding Company; Land Subdividers & Developers, Commercial
N.A.I.C.S.: 237210
Brent Suezaki (VP)

Subsidiaries:

Hy-Pac Self Storage   (1)
2150 N Nimitz Hwy, Honolulu, HI 96819
Tel.: (808) 847-5302
Web Site: http://www.hypac.net
Rev.: $340,000
Emp.: 5
General Warehousing & Storage Facilities
N.A.I.C.S.: 493110
Hideo Yamada (Pres)

Kobe Japanese Steak House LLC   (1)
69-838 Hwy 111, Rancho Mirage, CA 92270
Tel.: (760) 324-1717
Web Site: http://www.koberanchomirage.com
Japanese Restaurant
N.A.I.C.S.: 722511
Hy Aisenstat (Co-Founder)
Rod Gardiner (Co-Founder)

YAMAHA SUZUKI OF TEXAS
633 NE Loop 820, Hurst, TX 76053
Tel.: (817) 285-9999
Web Site: http://www.ntxhouseofcycles.com
Sales Range: $10-24.9 Million
Emp.: 35
Motorcycle Dealers
N.A.I.C.S.: 441227
C. B. Standridge (Gen Mgr)

YAMAMOTO MOSS AND MACKENZIE MARKETING
252 First Ave N, Minneapolis, MN 55401
Tel.: (612) 375-0180
Web Site: http://www.yamamoto-moss.com
Year Founded: 1979
Sales Range: $10-24.9 Million
Emp.: 35
Brand Development & Integration
N.A.I.C.S.: 541810
Shelly Regan (Pres)
Jodi Beaupre (Dir-Ops)
Stacey Davies (CFO)
Darryl Kluskowski (Chief Creative Officer)

YAMHILL COMMUNITY CARE ORGANIZATION
807 NE 3rd St, McMinnville, OR 97128
Tel.: (503) 488-2800   OR
Web Site: http://www.yamhillcco.org
Year Founded: 2012
Sales Range: $50-74.9 Million
Community Care Services
N.A.I.C.S.: 624190
Dennis Gray (Treas & Sec)
Lori Van Zanten (Co-Chm)
Rebecca Eichhorn (Co-Chm)

YAMHILL COUNTY MUSHROOMS, INC.
7246 Lilac Hill Rd, Yamhill, OR 97148
Tel.: (503) 662-4131
Sales Range: $10-24.9 Million
Emp.: 4
Vegetable Farming Services
N.A.I.C.S.: 111419
Robert W. Darm (Pres & Sec)

YAMPA VALLEY ELECTRIC ASSOCIATION
2211 Elk River Rd, Steamboat Springs, CO 80487
Tel.: (970) 879-1160
Web Site: http://www.yvea.com
Rev.: $59,569,286
Assets: $120,728,228
Liabilities: $42,165,734
Net Worth: $78,562,494
Earnings: $4,877,820
Emp.: 75
Fiscal Year-end: 12/31/18
Electronic Services
N.A.I.C.S.: 221118

YAMPA VALLEY MEDICAL CENTER
1024 Central Park Dr, Steamboat Springs, CO 80487
Tel.: (970) 879-1322   CO
Web Site: http://www.yvmc.org
Year Founded: 1946
Sales Range: $75-99.9 Million
Emp.: 450
Health Care Srvices
N.A.I.C.S.: 622110
Karen McRight (Sr Dir-Bus Dev & Mktg)
Marie Timlin (Chief Nursing Officer)
Soniya Fidler (Sr Dir-HR)
Frank May (CEO)
Rich Lowe (Treas)
Bryan Roach (CFO)
Ken Lindsey (Chief Medical Officer)
Mark Clark (CIO)
Dave Garner (COO)
Liz Finegan (Exec Dir-Healthcare Foundation)
Mike Nelson (Sr Dir-Physician Svcs)
Kelly Classen (Sr Dir-Revenue Cycle)

YAMRON JEWELERS
5555 Tamiami Trl N Ste 11, Naples, FL 34108
Tel.: (239) 592-7707
Web Site: http://www.yamron.com
Year Founded: 1987
Sales Range: $1-9.9 Million
Emp.: 20
Jewelry Stores
N.A.I.C.S.: 458310
Harold Yamron (Founder)
Jacob Tuchman (Partner, VP-Sls & Dir-Watch Div)
Satacy Lederer (Gen Mgr)

YANCEY BROS. CO.
330 Lee Industrial Blvd, Austell, GA 30168
Tel.: (770) 941-2300   GA
Web Site: http://www.yanceybros.com
Year Founded: 1914
Sales Range: $150-199.9 Million
Emp.: 2,000
Earthmoving, Mining & Construction Machinery Dealer & Rental Services; Engine Mfr
N.A.I.C.S.: 441227
James E. Stephenson (CEO)
Bud Wilfore (VP)
Greg DeWalt (Mgr-Corp Mktg)
Mark Kincer (VP-Product Support-Machine Div)
Kim Parker (Mgr-Corp Credit)
Jim Larson (Mgr-Corp Tier 4)
Stan Lassiter (VP-Redistribution)
Rick Ream (VP-HR)
Mike Sisco (Mgr-Used Parts)
Trey Googe (Pres & COO)
Eric Arnold (VP-Power Sys Div)
Marshall Ford (CFO & VP)
Jim Radcliffe (Mgr-Corp Adv & Promotion)
David Solakian (Mgr-Technical Svcs)
Jennifer Teal (Mgr-Inventory Control)
Ty Berrian (Mgr-Warranty)
Chris Burns (VP-Machine Div Sls)
Tim McCauley (VP-Machine Div Product Support)
Goodloe H. Yancey III (Chm)

Subsidiaries:

All Star International Trucks Inc.   (1)
2703 Carpenter Rd S, Tifton, GA 31793
Tel.: (229) 386-5834
Sales Range: $10-24.9 Million
Emp.: 15
Commercial Truck Dealership
N.A.I.C.S.: 532120

Yancey Bus Sales & Service, LLC   (1)
259 Lee Industrial Blvd I-20 W & 6 Flags Pkwy, Austell, GA 30168
Tel.: (770) 941-2424
Web Site: http://www.yanceybus.com
Bus Whslr
N.A.I.C.S.: 423110
Eric Arnold (VP & Gen Mgr)
Jay McDuffie (Mgr-Sls-School Bus)
Roger Carter (Mgr-Parts)
Don DuLong (Mgr-Parts Ops)

Yancey Engineered Solutions   (1)
96 Ethridge Mill Park, Griffin, GA 30224
Tel.: (770) 233-4397
Web Site: http://www.yanceyengineeredsolutions.com
Emp.: 60
Electrical Engineering Services
N.A.I.C.S.: 541330

Yancey Power Systems, Inc.   (1)
1604 S Slappey Blvd, Albany, GA 31702-2632
Tel.: (229) 435-6262
Web Site: http://www.yanceypower.com
Generator Whslr
N.A.I.C.S.: 423610
Christian Lammers (Engr-Project)

YANG ENTERPRISES, INC.
1420 Alafaya Trl Ste 200, Oviedo, FL 32765
Tel.: (407) 365-7374
Web Site: http://www.yangenterprises.com
Rev.: $19,600,000
Emp.: 250
Custom Computer Programming Services
N.A.I.C.S.: 541511
Li-Woan Yang (Pres & CEO)

YANG MING MARINE TRANSPORT CORPORATION
1085 Raymond Blvd Fl 9, Newark, NJ 07102
Tel.: (201) 222-8899   DE
Web Site: http://www.yml.com.tw
Year Founded: 1974
Emp.: 350
Freight Transportation Arrangement
N.A.I.C.S.: 488510
Danny Lau (Sr VP)
Peter Klaver (Head-HR)
Wen-Jin Lee (Pres & CEO)

YANKEE ALLIANCE
138 River Rd, Andover, MA 01810
Tel.: (978) 470-2000   MA
Web Site: http://www.yankeealliance.com
Year Founded: 1988
Sales Range: $10-24.9 Million
Supply Chain Management Services
N.A.I.C.S.: 541614
James W. Oliver (Pres & CEO)
Cathy Spinney (COO)
Anne Marie Martineau (CFO)

YANKEE ENVIRONMENTAL SERVICES, LLC
29 Esquire Rd, Billerica, MA 01862
Tel.: (978) 663-6506   DE
Environmental Remediation Services
N.A.I.C.S.: 562910
Albie Cail (Ops Mgr)

YANKEE GREYHOUND RACING INC.
New Zealand Rd, Seabrook, NH 03874
Tel.: (603) 474-3065
Web Site: http://www.seabrookgreyhoundpark.com
Sales Range: $25-49.9 Million
Emp.: 50
Dog Racing
N.A.I.C.S.: 711219
Robert E. Davidson (Controller)

YANKEE PUBLISHING INC.
1121 Main St, Dublin, NH 03444
Tel.: (603) 563-8111   NH
Web Site: http://www.ypi.com
Year Founded: 1935
Sales Range: $50-74.9 Million
Emp.: 85
Publisher of Magazines & Periodicals
N.A.I.C.S.: 513120

YANKEE PUBLISHING INC.

U.S. PRIVATE

Yankee Publishing Inc.—(Continued)

Mel Allen *(Editor)*

Subsidiaries:

McLean Communications (1)
150 Dow St, Manchester, NH 03101
Tel.: (603) 624-1442
Web Site:
 http://www.mcleancommunications.com
Media Publisher
N.A.I.C.S.: 513120
Melanie Hitchcock *(Editor)*
Jeff Feingold *(Editor)*

YANKEE RETAIL COMPANY LLC
841 Route 32 Ste 12, Norwich, CT 06254
Tel.: (860) 642-7790
Web Site:
 http://www.yankeeretail.com
Year Founded: 2000
Sales Range: $10-24.9 Million
Emp.: 40
Online Retailer of Luxury Branded Home Products
N.A.I.C.S.: 459999
Justin Potts *(CEO)*
Matthew Trant *(Mgr-Mktg)*

YANKEE SPIRITS INC.
376 Main St, Sturbridge, MA 01566-1057
Tel.: (508) 347-2231 MA
Web Site:
 http://www.yankeespirits.com
Year Founded: 1988
Sales Range: $25-49.9 Million
Emp.: 115
Owner of Liquor Stores
N.A.I.C.S.: 445320
Joe Santos *(Mgr-Store)*
Morris Karraz *(Mgr-Store)*
Ray Roy *(Mgr-Store)*

YANKEE TELECOM INC.
600 S Stark Hwy, Weare, NH 03281
Tel.: (603) 529-9941
Web Site: http://www.mygsc.com
Sales Range: $10-24.9 Million
Emp.: 90
Local Telephone Communications
N.A.I.C.S.: 517121
William Stafford *(COO)*
Susan Rand King *(Pres)*
Steven Schilling *(Controller)*

YANKTON MEDIA, INC.
319 Walnut, Yankton, SD 57078
Tel.: (605) 665-7811
Web Site: http://www.yankton.net
Sales Range: $10-24.9 Million
Emp.: 25
Newspaper Publishers
N.A.I.C.S.: 513110
Kathy Pritchard *(Mgr-Composing)*
Kelly Hertz *(Editor)*
Micki Schievelbein *(Dir-Adv)*
Tonya Schild *(Bus Mgr)*

Subsidiaries:

Yankton Daily Press & Dakotan (1)
319 Walnut St, Yankton, SD 57078
Tel.: (605) 665-7811
Web Site: http://www.yankton.net
Sales Range: $10-24.9 Million
Newspaper Publishers
N.A.I.C.S.: 513110
Micki Schievelbein *(Dir-Adv)*
Beth Rye *(Dir-New Media)*
Kathy Larson *(Mgr-Composing)*

Unit (Domestic):

The Broadcaster (2)
201 W Cherry St, Vermillion, SD 57069-1109
Tel.: (605) 624-4429
Web Site: http://www.broadcasteronline.com

Sales Range: $1-9.9 Million
Classified Advertising Print Publisher
N.A.I.C.S.: 513199

YANTIS COMPANY
3611 Paesanos Pkwy Ste 300, San Antonio, TX 78231
Tel.: (210) 655-3780 TX
Web Site:
 http://www.yantiscompany.com
Year Founded: 1975
Sales Range: $10-24.9 Million
Emp.: 220
Heavy Highway & Utility Construction; Land Development
N.A.I.C.S.: 525990
John M. Yantis *(Founder)*
J. Mike Yantis *(Chm)*
Todd Compton *(Dir-Bus Dev)*
Paul Sparks *(CFO)*
Arnold Briones *(COO)*
Matt Yantis *(Pres)*
Grant Robinson *(Mgr-Austin)*
Mike Yantis Jr. *(CEO)*

YAO YANG ENTERPRISE LLC
4281 Katella Ave Ste 222, Los Alamitos, CA 90720
Tel.: (714) 826-9022
Rev.: $30,656,443
Emp.: 10
Brokers, Shipping
N.A.I.C.S.: 488510
Peter M. Chang *(Pres)*

YAPPA WORLD INCORPORATED
4201 Via Marina Unit D402, Marina Del Rey, CA 90292
Tel.: (424) 288-9022 DE
Web Site: http://www.yappaapp.com
Year Founded: 2015
Emp.: 2
Audio & Video Software Commenting Services
N.A.I.C.S.: 541511
Jennifer Dyer *(Pres & CEO)*
Kiaran Sim *(COO)*

YARDE METALS INC.
45 Newell St, Southington, CT 06489
Tel.: (860) 406-6061 CT
Web Site: http://www.yarde.com
Year Founded: 1976
Sales Range: $25-49.9 Million
Emp.: 600
Provider of Metals Services
N.A.I.C.S.: 423510
Jack Nicklis *(Controller)*
Mathew Smith *(Pres & COO)*
Robert Paradis *(Mgr-Credit)*
Susan Butler *(Controller)*

YARDI SYSTEMS, INC.
430 S Fairview Ave, Santa Barbara, CA 93117
Tel.: (805) 699-2040
Web Site: http://www.yardi.com
Year Founded: 1984
Sales Range: $150-199.9 Million
Emp.: 5,000
Asset & Property Management Software Development
N.A.I.C.S.: 513210
Anant Yardi *(Founder & Pres)*
Terri Dowen *(Sr VP-Sls)*
John Pendergast *(Sr VP-Client Svcs)*
Robert Teel *(Sr VP-Global Solutions)*
Fritz Schindelbeck *(Sr VP-Ancillary Svcs)*
Ray Elliot *(VP)*

Subsidiaries:

Peak Insurance Advisors, LLC (1)
17738 Preston Rd, Dallas, TX 75252
Tel.: (800) 566-1186

Web Site:
 http://www.multifamilyinsurancegroup.com
Property Insurance Services
N.A.I.C.S.: 524126

Pierce Eislen, Inc. (1)
9200 E Pima Ctr Pkwy Ste 150, Scottsdale, AZ 85258
Tel.: (480) 663-1149
Web Site: http://www.pi-ei.com
Sales Range: $10-24.9 Million
Emp.: 50
Online Property Services
N.A.I.C.S.: 519290
Ron Brock Sr. *(Pres & CEO)*
Ron Brock Jr. *(VP & Dir-Sls)*

Proliphix, Inc. (1)
234 Littleton Rd Ste 2C, Westford, MA 01886
Tel.: (978) 692-3375
Web Site: http://www.proliphix.com
Rev.: $1,500,000
Emp.: 15
Facility Thermostat Maintenance
N.A.I.C.S.: 561210

SiteStuff, Inc. (1)
12401 Research Blvd Bldg 1 Ste 250, Austin, TX 78759
Tel.: (512) 514-7800
Web Site: http://www.sitestuff.com
Procurement Software Solution Services
N.A.I.C.S.: 541511
Emily Shelton *(Mgr-Client Relationship)*

Yardi Canada Ltd. (1)
516 Wellman Crescent, Saskatoon, S7T 0J1, SK, Canada
Tel.: (306) 955-1855
Web Site: https://www.point2homes.com
Software Development Services
N.A.I.C.S.: 541511

Yardi Singapore Pte Ltd (1)
17-06 Samsung HUB 3 Church Street, Singapore, 049483, Singapore
Tel.: (65) 6369 9713
Software Development Services
N.A.I.C.S.: 541511

Yardi Software India Pvt Ltd (1)
2nd Floor Sigma House Off Senapati Bapat Road, Pune, 411 016, India
Tel.: (91) 20 6723 9000
Software Development Services
N.A.I.C.S.: 541511
Avinash Shivani *(Sr Project Mgr)*

Yardi Sydney Ltd (1)
Suite 3 Level 23 25 Bligh Street, Sydney, 2000, NSW, Australia
Tel.: (61) 2 8227 2200
Software Development Services
N.A.I.C.S.: 541511

Yardi Systems (HK) Ltd. (1)
20th Floor 199 Des Voeux Road, Central, China (Hong Kong)
Tel.: (852) 2851 6638
Web Site: http://www.yardi.com
Emp.: 10
Software Development Services
N.A.I.C.S.: 541511

Yardi Systems BV (1)
Dreeftoren Haaksbergweg 57, 1101 BR, Amsterdam, Netherlands
Tel.: (31) 20 565 0050
Web Site: http://www.yardi.com
Emp.: 28
Software Development Services
N.A.I.C.S.: 541511
Ronald Wevers *(Gen Mgr)*

Yardi Systems GmbH (1)
7 Prinzenallee, Dusseldorf, 40549, Germany
Tel.: (49) 211 523 91 466
Software Development Services
N.A.I.C.S.: 541511

Yardi Systems Ltd (1)
Avebury House 201-249 Avebury Boulevard, Milton Keynes, MK9 1AX, United Kingdom
Tel.: (44) 1908 308400
Web Site: http://www.yardi.com
Emp.: 40
Software Development Services
N.A.I.C.S.: 541511

John Bennett *(CEO)*

YARDS BREWING COMPANY
901 N Delaware Ave, Philadelphia, PA 19123
Tel.: (215) 634-2600
Web Site:
 http://www.yardsbrewing.com
Year Founded: 1988
Sales Range: $10-24.9 Million
Emp.: 20
Beer Mfr
N.A.I.C.S.: 312120
Trevor Prichett *(COO)*
Frank Winslow *(Dir-Quality Control)*
Rick Anstotz *(Mgr-Sls)*
Tim Roberts *(Head-Brewer & Mgr-Production)*
Steve Welsh *(Mgr-Pkg)*
Tim Sieck *(Mgr-Warehouse)*
Zack Artz *(Mgr-Private Events)*

YAREMA DIE & ENGINEERING CO.
300 Minnesota Dr, Troy, MI 48083
Tel.: (248) 585-2830
Web Site: http://www.yarema.com
Sales Range: $25-49.9 Million
Emp.: 150
Automotive Stampings
N.A.I.C.S.: 336370
Les Fisher *(Pres)*
Mladen Antoski *(Project Mgr)*
Mark Burgess *(Supvr-Stamping)*
Donald Sawyers *(Mgr-Quality Assurance)*
Bob Trombley *(Mgr-Fin)*

YARNALL WAREHOUSE, INC.
1590 NE Ave, Sarasota, FL 34237
Tel.: (941) 365-3060 FL
Web Site: http://www.yarnall.com
Year Founded: 1913
Sales Range: $1-9.9 Million
Emp.: 60
Long Distance & Local Trucking With Storage & Record Management
N.A.I.C.S.: 484121
Stephanie Reed *(Coord-Sls)*
Jay Vandroff *(Pres)*
Tammy McAdams *(Mgr-Facilities)*

YARRUM MARKETING, INC.
5761 Ferry Rd, Wakeman, OH 44889
Tel.: (419) 929-0130 OH
Year Founded: 1985
Sales Range: Less than $1 Million
Emp.: 2
Media Buying Services, Retail
N.A.I.C.S.: 541810
Chuck Murray *(Pres)*
Rachel Drozdowski *(Dir-Art-Graphic Design)*

YASH TECHNOLOGIES, INC.
841 Ave of the Cities, East Moline, IL 61244
Tel.: (309) 755-0433
Web Site: http://www.yash.com
Year Founded: 1996
Sales Range: $10-24.9 Million
Emp.: 200
Provider of IT Consulting Services
N.A.I.C.S.: 541512
Ryan Hodge *(Dir-Info Mgmt Practice-North America)*

YASUTOMO & CO.
490 Eccles Ave, South San Francisco, CA 94080-1901
Tel.: (650) 737-8888 CA
Web Site: http://www.yasutomo.com
Year Founded: 1954
Rev.: $9,275,000
Emp.: 22

Stationery Supplies, Art Material, Paper Products & Writing Instruments Whslr
N.A.I.C.S.: 424990
Daniel H. Egusa *(Owner, Pres & CEO)*
Glen Egusa *(COO)*

YATES BUICK GMC
13845 W Test Dr, Goodyear, AZ 85338
Tel.: (623) 932-1818
Web Site: http://www.yatesbuickgmc.com
Year Founded: 1984
Sales Range: $10-24.9 Million
Emp.: 80
Car Whslr
N.A.I.C.S.: 441110
Michael A. Yates *(Pres)*
Tony McCarty *(Mgr-Comml & Fleet)*
Brent Nogowski *(Mgr-Sls)*

YATES BUICK PONTIAC GMC, INC.
215 US Hwy 79 S, Henderson, TX 75654-3605
Tel.: (903) 657-8999
Web Site: http://www.yatesbuick.com
Sales Range: $10-24.9 Million
Emp.: 32
Car Whslr
N.A.I.C.S.: 441110
Hollis Yates *(Pres)*

YATES-AMERICAN MACHINE COMPANY
2880 Kennedy Dr, Beloit, WI 53511-3933
Tel.: (608) 364-0333
Web Site: http://www.yatesamerican.com
Year Founded: 1883
Sales Range: $1-9.9 Million
Emp.: 20
Woodworking Machinery Cutterheads & Knives
N.A.I.C.S.: 333243
Darrell Borghi *(Pres)*
Merri Boos *(Office Mgr)*

YAVAPAI COMMUNITY HOSPITAL ASSOCIATION
1003 Willow Creek Rd, Prescott, AZ 86301
Tel.: (928) 445-2700
Web Site: http://www.yrmc.org
Year Founded: 1942
Sales Range: $200-249.9 Million
Emp.: 2,058
Health Care Srvices
N.A.I.C.S.: 622110
Jane Bristol *(Co-Treas)*
Paula Kneisl *(Chm)*
Mike Beatty *(Co-Treas)*
Steve Sischka *(Vice Chm)*

YAZOO VALLEY ELECTRIC POWER ASSOCIATION
2255 Gordon Ave, Yazoo City, MS 39194
Tel.: (662) 746-4251
Web Site: http://www.yazoovalley.com
Rev.: $11,500,000
Emp.: 55
Electric Power Distr
N.A.I.C.S.: 813910
Wilkons Crawford *(CFO)*

YEAGER ENTERPRISES CORP.
7100 Vlg Dr, Buena Park, CA 90621
Tel.: (714) 994-2040
Web Site: http://www.pacificabrasive.com
Sales Range: $25-49.9 Million
Emp.: 100
Abrasive Belt Manufacturing
N.A.I.C.S.: 327910
David M. Yeager *(Pres)*

YEAGER SUPPLY, INC.
1440 N 6th St, Reading, PA 19601
Tel.: (610) 376-8037
Web Site: http://www.yeagersupplyinc.com
Year Founded: 1967
Rev.: $18,000,000
Emp.: 100
Supplier of Pipes, Valves & Fittings
N.A.I.C.S.: 423840
Richard Keough *(Controller)*
James Gingrich *(Mgr-Sls)*
Randy McNulty *(Engr-Sls)*
Leslie Giardiello *(VP)*

YEAR ONE INC.
1001 Cherry Dr Ste 1, Braselton, GA 30517
Tel.: (706) 658-2140
Web Site: http://www.yearone.com
Year Founded: 1981
Catalog & Mail-Order Houses
N.A.I.C.S.: 423120
Kevin L. King *(Pres & Sec)*
Len Athanaslades *(CEO)*
Teresa Wellwood *(CFO)*

YEARGIN POTTER SHACKELFORD CONSTRUCTION, INC.
121 Edinburgh Ct, Greenville, SC 29607
Tel.: (864) 232-1491
Web Site: http://www.ypsconst.com
Year Founded: 1919
Sales Range: $25-49.9 Million
Emp.: 40
Contracting & Construction Services
N.A.I.C.S.: 236220
Kirk T. Carter *(VP-Ops)*
Bruce Smith *(VP-Preconstruction)*
R. Lynn Yeargin *(Pres)*

YELED V'YALDA EARLY CHILDHOOD CENTER INC.
1312 38th St, Brooklyn, NY 11218
Tel.: (718) 686-3700
Web Site: http://www.yeled.org
Year Founded: 1991
Sales Range: $75-99.9 Million
Emp.: 1,837
Child & Family Care Services
N.A.I.C.S.: 624190
Solomon Igel *(Founder & CEO)*
Rebecca Gutman *(CFO)*
Chaim Szanzer *(Dir-Special Svcs)*
Samuel Feferkorn *(Dir-IT)*
Gitty Lichtenstein *(Dir-HR)*
Jacob Ungar *(Chm)*
Hersh Moskovitz *(Sec)*
Aryeh Ringel *(Treas)*

YELLIN/MCCARRON, INC.
326 A St Ste 2C, Boston, MA 02210-1722
Tel.: (617) 426-9211
Web Site: http://www.yellinmccarron.com
Year Founded: 1978
Rev.: $10,000,000
Emp.: 6
Media Buying Services
N.A.I.C.S.: 541830
Patricia E. Mccarron *(Pres)*

YELLOW CAB COMPANY OF TAMPA, INC.
4413 N Hesperides St, Tampa, FL 33614
Tel.: (813) 253-8871
Web Site: http://www.yellowcaboftampa.com
Year Founded: 1952
Sales Range: $1-9.9 Million
Emp.: 40
Taxi Service
N.A.I.C.S.: 485310
Darryl K. Minardi *(Pres)*

YELLOW THUNDER CORPORATION
W7810 Hwy 21 E, Wautoma, WI 54982
Tel.: (920) 787-3331
Web Site: http://www.mssupply.com
Sales Range: $75-99.9 Million
Emp.: 100
Plumbing & Hydronic Heating Supplies
N.A.I.C.S.: 423720
Steve Norlin *(CEO)*

YELLOW WOOD PARTNERS LLC
255 State St 7th Fl, Boston, MA 02109
Tel.: (617) 500-6340
Web Site: http://www.yellowwoodpartners.com
Year Founded: 2009
Privater Equity Firm
N.A.I.C.S.: 523999
Dana L. Schmaltz *(Founder & Partner)*
Mike Fink *(Partner-Operating)*
Gerry Butler *(Partner-Operating)*
Tad Yanagi *(Partner)*
Eric Millar *(Partner-Operating)*
Kevin McCafferty *(Principal)*
Rich Howard *(Partner-Operating)*
Joe Atencio *(Partner)*
Tracy Pizzi *(CFO)*
Mario Soussou *(Partner-Operating)*
Jennifer Roach Pacini *(VP)*
Andrew Nguyen *(VP)*
Scott Kirk *(Operating Partner)*

Subsidiaries:

Parfums de Coeur Ltd. (1)
6 High Ridge Park, Stamford, CT 06905
Tel.: (203) 655-8807
Web Site: http://www.pdcbeauty.com
Beauty, Cosmetics, Hair Care, Fragrance, Wellness & Bath & Body Products Mfr & Distr
N.A.I.C.S.: 325620
Alex Tosolini *(CEO)*

Subsidiary (Domestic):

ME Bath Experience Inc. (2)
750 E St Fl 10, Stamford, CT 06902
Tel.: (310) 338-1490
Web Site: http://www.mebath.com
Other Home Furnishings Stores
N.A.I.C.S.: 449129

Subsidiary (Non-US):

Original Additions (Beauty Products) Ltd. (2)
Ventura House Bullsbrook Road, Hayes, UB4 0UJ, Middlesex, United Kingdom
Tel.: (44) 20 8573 9907
Web Site: http://www.originaladditions.com
Cosmetic Product Whslr
N.A.I.C.S.: 424210
Simon Zussman *(Mng Dir)*

Paris Presents, Inc. (1)
3800 Swanson Ct, Gurnee, IL 60031-1216
Tel.: (847) 263-5500
Web Site: http://www.parispresents.com
Cosmetic Accessories & Beauty Related Items Importer & Whslr
N.A.I.C.S.: 424990
Patrick O'Brien *(Vice Chm)*
Bill George *(CEO)*
Dana Schmaltz *(Chm)*

Scholl's Wellness Co. (1)
27070 Miles Rd Ste A, Solon, OH 44139
Web Site: http://www.drscholls.com
Surgical Appliance & Supplies Mfr
N.A.I.C.S.: 339113
Craig Stevenson *(CEO)*

pH Beauty Labs, Inc. (1)
1964 Westwood Blvd Ste 300, Los Angeles, CA 90025-8425
Tel.: (310) 446-9300
Web Site: http://www.freemanbeauty.com
Hair & Skin Beauty Products Mfr
N.A.I.C.S.: 325199
Mark Freeman *(Pres)*

YELLOWHAMMER, LLC.
44 W 28th St Fl 4, New York, NY 10001
Tel.: (646) 490-9841
Web Site: http://www.yhmg.com
Year Founded: 2009
Sales Range: $10-24.9 Million
Emp.: 27
Advertising Services
N.A.I.C.S.: 541810
Joseph Hirsch *(CEO)*
Hagan Major *(Chief Strategy Officer)*
Jared Christopherson *(CIO)*
Sam Appelbaum *(Sr VP-Bus Dev)*

YELLOWHOUSE MACHINERY CO.
11500 E Interstate 40, Amarillo, TX 79118
Tel.: (806) 335-1681
Web Site: http://www.yellowhousemachinery.com
Sales Range: $10-24.9 Million
Emp.: 80
Construction & Mining Machinery
N.A.I.C.S.: 423810
John Kritser *(Pres)*
Robbie Hance *(Branch Mgr)*

YELLOWSTONE COMMUNICATIONS
401 S Main St, Livingston, MT 59047
Tel.: (406) 222-2000
Web Site: http://www.yellowstonecommunications.com
Holding Company; Newspaper Publishing, Office Supply Stores & Commercial Printing Services
N.A.I.C.S.: 551112
Scott Squillace *(Controller)*

Subsidiaries:

Yellowstone Newspapers (1)
401 S Main St, Livingston, MT 59047
Tel.: (406) 222-2000
Web Site: http://www.yellowstonecommunications.com
Newspaper Publishing
N.A.I.C.S.: 513110
John Sullivan *(Pres)*

Unit (Domestic):

Lewistown News-Argus (2)
521 W Main St, Lewistown, MT 59457
Tel.: (406) 535-3401
Web Site: http://www.lewistownnews.com
Emp.: 20
Newspaper Publishing
N.A.I.C.S.: 513110
Jacques Rutten *(Publr)*

Livingston Enterprise (2)
401 S Main St, Livingston, MT 59047
Tel.: (406) 222-2000
Web Site: http://www.livingstonenterprise.com
Emp.: 40
Newspaper Publishers
N.A.I.C.S.: 513110
Justin Post *(Mng Editor)*
Jim Durfey *(Mgr-Adv)*
Amelia Murphy *(Mgr-Adv)*

Miles City Star (2)
818 Main St, Miles City, MT 59301
Tel.: (406) 234-0450
Web Site: http://www.milescitystar.com

YELLOWSTONE COMMUNICATIONS

Yellowstone Communications—(Continued)
Emp.: 40
Newspaper Publishers
N.A.I.C.S.: 513110
Jeff Virag *(Mgr-Circulation)*
Denise Hartse *(Editor-Community)*
Dan Killoy *(Publr)*
Dan Hance *(Office Mgr-Supply)*
Margo Kelsey *(Mgr-Comml Printing)*

Subsidiary (Domestic):

Star Printing & Supply Co., Inc. (2)
818 Main St, Miles City, MT 59301
Tel.: (406) 232-0450
Web Site:
  http://www.yellowstonecommunications.com
Sales Range: $1-9.9 Million
Office Supplies & Printing Services
N.A.I.C.S.: 459410

Unit (Domestic):

The Laurel Outlook (2)
415 E Main St, Laurel, MT 59044
Tel.: (406) 628-4412
Web Site: http://www.laureloutlook.com
Emp.: 14
Newspaper Publishing
N.A.I.C.S.: 513110
Jennifer Ries *(Mng Editor)*

YELLOWSTONE ENERGY LP
1087 W River St Ste 200, Boise, ID 83702
Tel.: (208) 344-3570
Rev.: $11,600,000
Emp.: 8
Generation, Electric Power
N.A.I.C.S.: 221118
Shannon Morgam *(Office Mgr)*

YELLOWSTONE PLASTICS, INC.
3725 W 65th S, Idaho Falls, ID 83402
Tel.: (208) 542-1200
Year Founded: 1998
Sales Range: $10-24.9 Million
Emp.: 91
Paper Bag & Plastic Bad Mfr & Distr
N.A.I.C.S.: 423990
Alan Mueller *(Owner)*

YELLOWWOOD ACRES INC
911 N Studebaker Rd, Long Beach, CA 90815
Tel.: (562) 257-5100   IN
Web Site: http://www.rhf.org
Year Founded: 1983
Sales Range: $10-24.9 Million
Emp.: 332
Nursing Care & Housing Assistance Services
N.A.I.C.S.: 623110
Peter Oscar Peabody *(VP-Healthcare Ops)*
Stuart J. Hartman *(VP-Housing Ops)*
Robert R. Amberg *(Gen Counsel & Sr VP)*
Laverne Joseph *(Pres & CEO)*
Anders Plett *(VP-Bus Acquisition & Dev)*
Frank Rossello Jr. *(CFO & VP-Fin)*

YENKIN-MAJESTIC PAINT CORPORATION
1920 Leonard Ave, Columbus, OH 43219-2514
Tel.: (614) 253-8511   OH
Web Site: http://www.yenkin-majestic.com
Year Founded: 1920
Sales Range: $125-149.9 Million
Emp.: 250
Paints, Resins, Varnishes & Enamels Mfr
N.A.I.C.S.: 325510

Bernard K. Yenkin *(Chm)*
John Gerhold *(Dir-Pur)*
Mark Hollinger *(VP-Ops)*
Richard Olson *(VP-Polymers Grp)*
Jonathan M. Petuchowski *(Pres)*
Kathy Streng *(VP)*
Andrew O. Smith *(Pres & CEO)*

YENNI CAPITAL, INC.
1271 Ave of the Americas Ste 4300, New York, NY 10020
Tel.: (212) 843-1828
Web Site:
  http://www.yennicapital.com
Investment Brokerage
N.A.I.C.S.: 523999
Musa Yenni *(Founder & Pres)*

Subsidiaries:

Steven Feller P.E., PL (1)
500 NE 3rd Ave, Fort Lauderdale, FL 33301
Tel.: (954) 467-1402
Web Site: http://www.fellerpe.com
Sales Range: $1-9.9 Million
Emp.: 67
Engineeering Services
N.A.I.C.S.: 541330
Steven Feller *(Founder & Pres)*
Tony Averbuch *(VP)*
Bob Raynor *(Head-Electrical Dept)*
Jack Nedlin *(Head-HVAC & Mechanical Dept)*
Michael Torrey *(Head-Plumbing & Fire Protection Dept)*

YENTER COMPANIES INC.
20300 W Hwy 72, Arvada, CO 80007
Tel.: (303) 279-4458
Web Site: http://www.yenter.com
Sales Range: $25-49.9 Million
Emp.: 60
Specializes in Drilling, Blasting, Design & Construction of Rock & Soil Stabilization Systems, Retaining Walls, Bridge & Tunnel Rehabilitation & Improvement
N.A.I.C.S.: 238910
Bill Roberts *(COO)*
Robin Parkhill *(Controller)*

YEO & YEO, P.C.
5300 Bay Rd Ste 100, Saginaw, MI 48604
Tel.: (989) 793-9830
Web Site: http://www.yeoandyeo.com
Year Founded: 1923
Sales Range: $25-49.9 Million
Emp.: 200
Accounting & Tax Services
N.A.I.C.S.: 541211
Peter J. Bender *(Principal)*
Steven P. Witt *(Principal)*
David R. Youngstrom *(Principal)*
Brian R. Dixon *(Principal)*
Amy R. Buben *(Principal)*
Danielle A. Cary *(Principal)*
Michael A. Georges *(Principal)*
Suzanne R. Lozano *(Principal)*
Michael Oliphant *(Principal)*
Alan D. Panter *(Principal)*
Jamie L. Rivette *(Principal)*
Jacob R. Sopczynski *(Principal)*
Tara Stensrud *(Principal)*

Subsidiaries:

Yeo & Yeo Computer Consulting, LLC (1)
3023 Davenport Ave, Saginaw, MI 48602
Tel.: (989) 797-4075
Web Site: http://www.yeoandyeo-consulting.com
Sales Range: $1-9.9 Million
Emp.: 50
Commercial Computer Consulting Services
N.A.I.C.S.: 541519
Jeff McCulloch *(Co-Pres)*
Thomas E. Hollerback *(CEO)*
Joe Smith *(Sr Engr-Sys)*

Marshall Bilodeau *(Mgr-Svc)*
Jessica Estabrook *(Office Mgr)*
Mark Kunitzer *(Asst Mgr-Sys)*

YEOMANS DISTRIBUTING COMPANY
1503 W Altorfer Dr, Peoria, IL 61615
Tel.: (309) 691-3282
Web Site:
  http://www.yeomansdist.com
Sales Range: $10-24.9 Million
Emp.: 14
Distribute Warm Air Heating Equipment & Supplies
N.A.I.C.S.: 423730
Albert E. Cioni *(Pres)*
Brad Johnson *(VP)*

YEPREMYAN LAW FIRM INC.
13949 Ventura Blvd Ste 230, Sherman Oaks, CA 91423
Tel.: (818) 574-5544
Web Site: http://www.vylawfirm.com
Year Founded: 1998
Sales Range: $1-9.9 Million
Emp.: 14
Law firm
N.A.I.C.S.: 541110
Vahan Yepremyan *(Founder & Mng Partner)*
Diego Mora *(Mgr-Case)*
Romela Davityan *(Mgr-Case & Specialist-Litigation)*

YERBA BUENA ENGINEERING & CONSTRUCTION
1340 Egbert Ave, San Francisco, CA 94124
Tel.: (415) 822-4400
Web Site: http://www.yerba-buena.net
Year Founded: 2002
Rev.: $14,600,000
Emp.: 35
Engineeering Services
N.A.I.C.S.: 541330
Miguel Galarza *(Pres)*

YES INC.
1216 Thomasboro Rd SW, Carolina Shores, NC 28467-2267
Tel.: (910) 057-9371
Web Site: http://www.yes-one.com
Residential Property Managers
N.A.I.C.S.: 531311
Jeter Young *(Owner)*

YES& HOLDINGS, LLC
1700 Diagonal Rd Ste 450, Alexandria, VA 22314
Tel.: (703) 823-1600
Web Site:
  http://www.yesandagency.com
Year Founded: 1985
Sales Range: $10-24.9 Million
Emp.: 68
Digital Marketing Services
N.A.I.C.S.: 541810
Robert W. Sprague *(Pres & CEO)*
Mike Smith *(Sr VP-PR)*
Jeb Brown *(Chm)*
Edith M. Bullard *(Sr VP-Mktg)*
Max Entman *(VP-Acct Svcs)*

Subsidiaries:

EFX Media (1)
2300 S 9th St Ste 136, Arlington, VA 22204
Tel.: (703) 486-2303
Web Site: http://www.efxmedia.com
Emp.: 20
Media Buying Services
N.A.I.C.S.: 541830
Jim Franco *(Pres & CEO)*
Bruce Dixon *(CTO & VP)*
Joseph Gross *(COO)*
Dave Kristiansen *(Editor)*
Kevin Schmitt *(Dir-Interactive Svcs)*
Marc Magram *(Editor)*

Robin Evans *(VP-Bus Dev)*
Tracy Fitzpatrick *(Office Mgr)*
Victor Van Rees *(VP-Federal Sls & Mktg)*

YESCO ELECTRICAL SUPPLY, INC.
648 Marshall St, Youngstown, OH 44502
Tel.: (330) 747-8593
Web Site: http://www.yeselectric.com
Year Founded: 1987
Sales Range: $10-24.9 Million
Emp.: 60
Electrical Apparatus & Equipment Whslr
N.A.I.C.S.: 423610
Dom LaRocca *(Product Mgr-Tech)*

YESWAY, INC.
2301 Eagle Pkwy Ste 100, Fort Worth, TX 76177
Tel.: (682) 428-2400   DE
Web Site: http://www.yesway.com
Year Founded: 2021
Emp.: 4,090
Convenience Store Operator
N.A.I.C.S.: 445131
Thomas N. Trkla *(Founder, Chm, Pres & CEO)*
Ericka L. Ayles *(CFO & Treas)*
Kurt M. Zernich *(Gen Counsel & Sec)*

YET2.COM, INC.
199 Wells Ave Ste 102, Newton, MA 02459
Tel.: (617) 244-4149   DE
Web Site: http://www.yet2.com
Year Founded: 1999
Sales Range: $1-9.9 Million
Emp.: 20
Online Technology Purchasing, Selling, Licensing & Information Services
N.A.I.C.S.: 561499
Ben du Pont *(Co-Founder & Pres)*
Tim Bernstein *(CEO)*
Hideyuki Fujii *(Mng Dir & VP-Asia)*
Phillip B. Stern *(Co-Founder)*
Bob Miller *(VP)*

YETI COOLERS LLC
3411 Hidalgo St, Austin, TX 78702-4923
Tel.: (512) 394-9384
Web Site: http://www.yeticoolers.com
Year Founded: 2006
Sales Range: $1-9.9 Million
Emp.: 11
Extra Insulated Coolers Mfr
N.A.I.C.S.: 326199
Ryan Seiders *(Founder)*
David Bullock *(CFO)*
Will Morgan *(Dir-Sls)*
Todd Adams *(Mgr-Inside Sls & Accts Receivable)*
Corey Maynard *(VP-Mktg)*
Roy J. Seiders *(Chm)*

YETTER MANUFACTURING CO., INC.
109 S McDonough St, Colchester, IL 62326
Tel.: (309) 776-4111   IL
Web Site: http://www.yetterco.com
Year Founded: 1930
Sales Range: $75-99.9 Million
Emp.: 150
Farm Equipment Mfr
N.A.I.C.S.: 333111
Bernard Whalen *(Pres)*
Susan Wherley *(Mgr-Adv)*
Kristoffer Griffith *(Mgr-Pur)*

Subsidiaries:

AMCO Manufacturing, Inc. (1)
800 S Industrial Pkwy, Yazoo City, MS 39194

Tel.: (662) 746-4464
Web Site: http://www.amcomfg.com
Sales Range: $10-24.9 Million
Emp.: 35
Farm Machinery & Equipment Mfr
N.A.I.C.S.: 333111

YEW BIO-PHARM GROUP, INC.
9460 Telstar Ave Ste 6, El Monte, CA 91731
Tel.: (626) 401-9588   NV
YEWB—(OTCBB)
Rev: $27,307,687
Assets: $58,446,662
Liabilities: $12,964,094
Net Worth: $45,482,568
Earnings: $1,464,882
Emp.: 35
Fiscal Year-end: 12/31/20
Yew Tree Grower; Medicinal Mfr
N.A.I.C.S.: 325411

Subsidiaries:

Harbin Yew Science and Technology
Development Co., Ltd. (1)
Floor 5 Area B No 18 Hengshan Road, Xiangfang District, Harbin, Heilongjiang, China
Tel.: (86) 45182292379
Pharmaceuticals Product Mfr
N.A.I.C.S.: 325411
Zhiguo Wang *(Chm & CEO)*
Guifang Qi *(Treas)*
Xuehai Wu *(Deputy Gen Mgr)*

YF INTERNATIONAL
180 Park Rd, Burlingame, CA 94010
Tel.: (650) 342-6560
Sales Range: $10-24.9 Million
Emp.: 5
Waste Paper Exports
N.A.I.C.S.: 424610
Ralph Ho *(Pres)*

YGOMI LLC
701 DeMers Ave 3rd Fl, Grand Forks, ND 58201
Tel.: (701) 335-2367
Web Site: http://www.ygomi.com
Holding Company; Software Development
N.A.I.C.S.: 551112
T. Russell Shields *(Chm)*
Yuka Gomi *(Pres)*
Paul Barnard *(CTO)*
Brian Haan *(Chief Security Officer)*
Errol Scialom *(CFO)*

Subsidiaries:

ArrayComm, Inc. (1)
1110 W Lake Cook Rd Ste 350, Buffalo Grove, IL 60089
Tel.: (224) 676-2619
Web Site: http://www.arraycomm.com
Sales Range: $10-24.9 Million
Emp.: 40
Software Development & Custom Computer Programing
N.A.I.C.S.: 513210
Paul Barnard *(Pres)*
Xin Huang *(VP-Bus Dev)*

Connexis LLC (1)
1 2nd St N Ste 214, Fargo, ND 58102
Tel.: (701) 335-2369
Web Site: http://www.connexis.com
Vehicle Communications & Services
N.A.I.C.S.: 517810
Kenji Ikeura *(Pres)*

YICK FUNG FUR LTD.
150 W 30th St 20 Fl, New York, NY 10001
Tel.: (212) 645-6565
Sales Range: $10-24.9 Million
Emp.: 5
Sales of Leather Goods & Furs
N.A.I.C.S.: 424350
Kam Lam *(Pres)*

YIELDSTREET, INC.
300 Park Ave 15th Fl, New York, NY 10022
Web Site: http://www.yieldstreet.com
Year Founded: 2015
Sales Range: $10-24.9 Million
Emp.: 66
Investment Management Service
N.A.I.C.S.: 523999
Lea Stendahl *(CMO)*
Milind Mehere *(Co-Founder)*
Michael Weisz *(Co-Founder & CEO)*
Lindsey Fielding *(VP-Growth & IR)*
Nicole Keller *(Chief People Officer)*
Hrishi Dixit *(CTO)*
Timothy Schott *(CFO)*
Rick Winslow *(Chief Product Officer)*
Ted Yarbrough *(Chief Investment Officer)*

YINGST HOMES INC.
4712 Smith St, Harrisburg, PA 17109
Tel.: (717) 599-5344
Web Site:
http://www.yingsthomes.com
Year Founded: 1975
Sales Range: $10-24.9 Million
Emp.: 32
Speculative Builder, Single-Family Houses
N.A.I.C.S.: 236115
Randy Swank *(Mgr-Custom Home)*

YIYI MOTORS INC.
PO Box 352, Bayamon, PR 00960-0352
Tel.: (787) 785-4295
Web Site: http://www.yiyimotors.com
Rev: $45,000,000
Emp.: 30
Automobiles, New & Used
N.A.I.C.S.: 441110
Kevin Perez *(Pres)*

YM INTERNATIONAL INC.
165 Valley Dr, Brisbane, CA 94005-1340
Tel.: (415) 467-3888
Sales Range: $10-24.9 Million
Emp.: 50
Retail Contractor
N.A.I.C.S.: 458110
Mei Zhang *(Pres)*

YMC AVIATION INC.
9800 Premier Pkwy, Miramar, FL 33025
Tel.: (954) 364-0085   FL
Web Site:
http://www.unitedaerospace.com
Year Founded: 1996
Sales Range: $10-24.9 Million
Emp.: 37
Distr of Aircraft Equipment & Supplies
N.A.I.C.S.: 423860
John P. Yurgealitis *(Pres)*
Manuel Martinez *(CFO & VP-Admin & Fin)*

Subsidiaries:

United Aerospace Corp. (1)
9800 Premier Pkwy, Miramar, FL 33025-3211
Tel.: (954) 364-0085
Sales Range: $10-24.9 Million
Emp.: 32
Aircraft Equipment Distr
N.A.I.C.S.: 423860

YMF MEDIA LLC
395 Hudson St 7th Fl, New York, NY 10014
Tel.: (212) 447-1000   DE
Holding Company; Radio Stations Owner & Operator
N.A.I.C.S.: 551112

William Cooper *(CFO)*
Irene Lee *(Controller)*

Subsidiaries:

YMF Media Mississippi LLC (1)
731 S Pear Orchard Rd Ste 27, Ridgeland, MS 39157
Tel.: (601) 957-1300
Sales Range: $10-24.9 Million
Emp.: 60
Radio Broadcasting Stations
N.A.I.C.S.: 516110
Kevin Webb *(Mgr)*
Lene Branson *(Bus Mgr)*

YMF Media New York LLC (1)
395 Hudson St 7th Fl, New York, NY 10014
Tel.: (212) 447-1000
Radio Broadcasting Stations
N.A.I.C.S.: 516110
Skip Dillard *(Program Dir & Ops Mgr)*
Doug James *(Dir-Sls)*
Koren Vaughan *(Dir-Sls & Mktg-Interactive)*
Sherise Wright *(Dir-Promos)*
Victoria D. Fleary *(Dir-Interactive)*

YMF Media South Carolina LLC (1)
1900 Pineview Dr, Columbia, SC 29209
Tel.: (803) 695-8600
Web Site: http://www.innercitysc.com
Radio Broadcasting Stations
N.A.I.C.S.: 516110

Unit (Domestic):

WARQ-FM (2)
1900 Pineview Rd, Columbia, SC 29209-5079
Tel.: (803) 695-8600
Web Site: http://www.warq.com
Radio Broadcasting Stations
N.A.I.C.S.: 516110
Greg Titt *(Program Dir)*
Brendan Croghan *(Dir-Music)*
Mike Hartel *(VP & Gen Mgr)*

WWDM-FM (2)
1900 Pineview Rd, Columbia, SC 29209-5079
Tel.: (803) 695-8600
Web Site: http://www.thebigdm.com
Emp.: 75
Radio Broadcasting Stations
N.A.I.C.S.: 516110
Chris Connors *(Dir-Program)*

YMH TORRANCE INC.
1495 Hawkeye Dr, Hiawatha, IA 52233
Tel.: (319) 247-6039
Web Site:
http://www.ymhtorrance.com
Sales Range: $10-24.9 Million
Emp.: 70
Construction Equipment Repair
N.A.I.C.S.: 238210
Steve Gallagher *(Pres)*
Paul Cherry *(Controller)*

YMT VACATIONS
100 N Sepulveda Blvd Ste 1700, El Segundo, CA 90245
Tel.: (310) 649-3820   CA
Web Site:
http://www.ymtvacations.com
Year Founded: 1967
Sales Range: $10-24.9 Million
Emp.: 100
Travel Agency
N.A.I.C.S.: 561510
William Price *(Pres)*
Oliver Milton *(Gen Mgr-Mktg)*
Melanie Mueller *(VP-Detroit)*

YODER & SONS INC.
312 E Hwy 78 PO Box 235, Wayland, IA 52654
Tel.: (319) 256-6195   IA
Year Founded: 1967
Sales Range: $10-24.9 Million
Emp.: 25
Whslr of Feed
N.A.I.C.S.: 424910

YODER INDUSTRIES INC.
2520 Needmore Rd, Dayton, OH 45414
Tel.: (937) 278-5769
Web Site:
http://www.yoderindustries.com
Sales Range: $25-49.9 Million
Emp.: 200
Nonferrous Die-Castings Except Aluminum
N.A.I.C.S.: 331523
Tim Stewart *(Pres & CEO)*
Rick Harden *(Controller)*

YODER OIL COMPANY INC.
1221 N Mappanee St, Elkhart, IN 46514-1230
Tel.: (574) 264-2107   IN
Web Site: http://www.yoderoil.com
Year Founded: 1937
Sales Range: $75-99.9 Million
Emp.: 35
Distr of Petroleum; Operator of Convenience Stores & Carwash
N.A.I.C.S.: 424710
Kent Yoder *(CEO)*
Brett Yoder *(Pres)*
Marie Hunter *(Controller)*

YOGA WORKS, INC.
5780 Uplander Way, Culver City, CA 90230
Tel.: (310) 664-6470   CA
Web Site: http://www.yogaworks.com
Year Founded: 1987
Yoga & Pilates Schools Operator
N.A.I.C.S.: 611699
Maya Magennis *(Pres)*

YOGURTLAND FRANCHISING, INC.
17801 Cartwright Rd, Irvine, CA 92614
Tel.: (949) 265-8000
Web Site: http://www.yogurt-land.com
Year Founded: 2006
Sales Range: $100-124.9 Million
Emp.: 320
Retail Store Operator
N.A.I.C.S.: 445110
Phillip Chang *(Founder & CEO)*
John Wayne Carlson *(VP-Dev)*
Chad Bailey *(Sr Dir-Mktg)*

YOHAY BAKING COMPANY, INC.
146 Albany Ave, Lindenhurst, NY 11757
Tel.: (631) 225-0300
Web Site: http://www.yohay.com
Sales Range: Less than $1 Million
Emp.: 40
Bakery Products
N.A.I.C.S.: 311812
Mike Solomon *(Pres)*

YOKE'S WASHINGTON FOODS INC.
3426 S University Rd, Spokane, WA 99206-5855
Tel.: (509) 921-2292   WA
Web Site:
http://www.yokesfoods.com
Year Founded: 1946
Sales Range: $250-299.9 Million
Emp.: 970
Suppliers of Grocery Services
N.A.I.C.S.: 445110
John Bole *(CEO)*

YOLA INC.
201 Mission St Ste 2250, San Francisco, CA 94105
Tel.: (415) 227-0250
Web Site: http://www.yola.com
Sales Range: $1-9.9 Million

YOLA INC.

Yola Inc.—(Continued)
Emp.: 20
Software Publisher & Website Developer
N.A.I.C.S.: 513210
Trevor Harries-Jones (CEO)
Brent Viljoen (CTO)
David Saxton (VP-Bus Dev & Mktg)
Monique Viljoen-Platts (VP-Customer Svc)
Lisa Retief (VP-Engrg)
Jason Taney Young (Chm)

YONKERS CONTRACTING COMPANY INC.
969 Midland Ave, Yonkers, NY 10704-1027
Tel.: (914) 965-1500 NY
Web Site: http://www.yonkerscontracting.com
Year Founded: 1946
Contracting Services
N.A.I.C.S.: 237310
Carl E. Petrillo (Founder)
Michael Ryan (Pres & CEO)
Mike Keller (CFO)
William Jordan (VP-Construction)
Joseph Sagaria (VP)
Paul Hubert (VP)
John Chrysogelos (VP)

YONKERS MOTORS CORP.
870 Nepperhan Ave, Yonkers, NY 10703
Tel.: (914) 963-7001
Web Site: http://www.yonkershonda.com
Sales Range: $25-49.9 Million
Emp.: 30
Automobiles, New & Used
N.A.I.C.S.: 441110
Joy Libert-Gelb (Co-Pres)
Gay Steinberge (Co-Pres)
Robert Steinberge (VP)
Bob Feinberg (Gen Mgr)

YOR HEALTH
2802 Kelvin Ave Ste 150, Irvine, CA 92614
Tel.: (949) 681-6090
Web Site: http://www.yorhealth.com
Year Founded: 2006
Sales Range: $25-49.9 Million
Emp.: 26
Nutritional Supplements
N.A.I.C.S.: 456191
Dave Enders (Pres)

YORK AUTO GROUP
1885 Whiteford Rd, York, PA 17402
Tel.: (717) 755-2961
Web Site: http://www.toyotaofyork.com
Sales Range: $125-149.9 Million
Emp.: 200
Sales of New & Used Automobiles
N.A.I.C.S.: 441110
Jim O'Polka (Owner)
Derek Helwig (Mgr-Sls)
Jeffrey Dorsey (Mgr-Collision Center)

YORK BARBELL COMPANY, INC.
3300 Board Rd, York, PA 17406
Tel.: (717) 767-6481 PA
Web Site: http://www.yorkbarbell.com
Year Founded: 1932
Sales Range: $50-74.9 Million
Emp.: 19
Mfr of Food Supplements; Physical Fitness Equipment; Gray Iron Castings
N.A.I.C.S.: 339920

YORK BRIDGE CONCEPTS
2420 Brunello Trace, Lutz, FL 33558
Tel.: (813) 933-1304
Web Site: http://www.ybc.com
Year Founded: 1985
Sales Range: $500-549.9 Million
Emp.: 30
Provider of Bridge Contruction Services
N.A.I.C.S.: 236210
Lee Preiser (Controller)
Bill Voigt (Project Mgr)
Brian Kennedy (Mgr-Construction)

YORK BUILDING PRODUCTS CO., INC.
950 Smile Way, York, PA 17404
Tel.: (717) 848-2831 PA
Web Site: http://www.yorkbuilding.com
Year Founded: 1948
Sales Range: $25-49.9 Million
Emp.: 150
Building Blocks Mfr; Quarrying & Asphalt Processing
N.A.I.C.S.: 327331
David Stewart (Pres)
Dan Longenderfer (Mgr-Mktg)

YORK CAPITAL MANAGEMENT GLOBAL ADVISORS, LLC
767 5th Ave 17th Fl, New York, NY 10153
Tel.: (212) 300-1311 NY
Web Site: http://www.yorkcapital.com
Year Founded: 1991
Emp.: 200
Investment Advisory, Private Equity & Portfolio Management Services
N.A.I.C.S.: 523940
Tracy Poulter Hart (Sr VP & Dir-HR)
Seth Pearson (Mng Dir)

Subsidiaries:
Healthcare Linen Services Group (1)
255 38th Ave Ste M St, Charles, IL 60174
Tel.: (888) 873-4740
Web Site: https://healthcarelinensg.com
Textile Mfr
N.A.I.C.S.: 313310
Dan Darr (VP)
Joe LaPorta (Pres & CEO)

Subsidiary (Domestic):
Linen King, LLC (2)
1521 W 36th Pl, Tulsa, OK 74107
Web Site: http://www.thelinenking.com
Linen Supply
N.A.I.C.S.: 812331

Reino Linen Services Inc. (2)
119 South Main St, Gibsonburg, OH 43431
Tel.: (419) 637-2151
Web Site: http://www.reinolinen.com
Drycleaning & Laundry Services, except Coin-Operated
N.A.I.C.S.: 812320
Leonard Reino (Chm)
Judy Reino (CEO)
Kevin Bock (CFO & Controller)

Superior Health Linens, LLC. (2)
1160 Pierson Dr Ste 104, Batavia, IL 60510
Tel.: (630) 593-5091
Web Site: http://www.superiorhealthlinens.com
Sales Range: $1-9.9 Million
Emp.: 70
Textile Product Mill Services
N.A.I.C.S.: 314999
Jennie Swartz (Dir-Customer Svc)
Greg Schermerhorn (COO)
Paul Czajka (CFO)

Titan Home Improvement Inc. (1)
3081 SW 30th Ave, Fort Lauderdale, FL 33312
Tel.: (602) 999-0308
Web Site: http://www.titanhomeimprovement.com
Home Improvement Services
N.A.I.C.S.: 236118

Mel Feinberg (Chm)
Daniel Gluck (CEO)

Subsidiary (Domestic):
MaxHome, LLC (2)
819 Central Ave Ste 200, Jefferson, LA 70121
Tel.: (504) 934-4789
Web Site: http://www.maxhomenow.com
Sales Range: $1-9.9 Million
Emp.: 50
Home Improvement Services
N.A.I.C.S.: 236118
Larry Closs (CEO)

Paradise Home Improvement LLC (2)
3651 Ctr Cir, Fort Mill, SC 29715
Tel.: (864) 849-0167
Web Site: http://www.paradisehomeimprove.com
Residential Remodeler
N.A.I.C.S.: 236118
Larry Libelle (Mgr)
Jeffery Becker (Gen Mgr)

YORK CHRYSLER DODGE JEEP INC.
1765 Hwy 231 S, Crawfordsville, IN 47933
Tel.: (765) 362-1600
Web Site: http://www.yorkchryslerdodgejeep.com
Sales Range: $10-24.9 Million
Emp.: 23
Car Whslr
N.A.I.C.S.: 441110
Robert York (Treas & Sec)

YORK CORRUGATING CO.
1524 Monroe St, York, PA 17404
Tel.: (717) 845-3512
Web Site: http://www.ycprecision.com
Sales Range: $25-49.9 Million
Emp.: 60
Plumbing & Hydronic Heating Supplies
N.A.I.C.S.: 423720
Dave Heck (CFO)

YORK COUNTY COMMUNITY ACTION CORPORATION
6 Spruce St, Sanford, ME 04073
Tel.: (207) 324-5762 ME
Web Site: http://www.yccac.org
Year Founded: 1965
Sales Range: $10-24.9 Million
Emp.: 290
Community Action Services
N.A.I.C.S.: 624190
Diane Laurendeau (CFO)
Barbara Crider (Exec Dir)
Donna Finneran (VP)
Joan Nass (Sec)
Don Burns (Treas)
Claudette Dupee (Pres)
Bob Currie (Dir-Transportation)
Andrew Lederer (Mgr-Ops)
Terrence McCarthy (CIO)

YORK ELECTRIC COOPERATIVE INC.
1385 E Alexander Love Hwy, York, SC 29745
Tel.: (803) 684-4247
Web Site: http://www.yorkelectric.net
Year Founded: 1941
Sales Range: $25-49.9 Million
Emp.: 90
Distr of Electric Power
N.A.I.C.S.: 221122
R. Marcus Howie (VP-Community Dev)
Mary T. Rogers (Dir-Billing & CIS Admin)
J. Craig Spencer (Dir-Engrg)
Paul Basha (Pres & CEO)

Joel Stevens (Mgr-Fin)
Joyce Baker (Coord-Mktg & PR)
Paulette Warmoth (Dir-Member Svcs)
Patty Moss (Mgr-HR)
Jim Salmon (Mgr-Info Svcs)
Richard B. Sadler (Treas & Sec)
E. Jack Cornwell (Chm)
Max T. Settlemyre (Vice Chm)

YORK GRAPHIC SERVICES CO.
3650 W Market St, York, PA 17404
Tel.: (717) 505-9701
Web Site: http://www.theygsgroup.com
Sales Range: $10-24.9 Million
Emp.: 140
Commercial Flexographic Printing, Publishing & Marketing
N.A.I.C.S.: 323111
James M. Kell (Owner & CEO)
Brad Altman (Pres)
Tom Grentz (CFO)
Erica Montgomery (Exec VP)
Brian Hershey (Acct Mgr)
Christine Tracy (Sr Project Mgr)
Erik Woodland (Mgr-IT)
Kelly Matthias (Mgr-Production)
Matt Roy (Mgr-Web Dev)
Rachel Rohrbaugh (Acct Mgr)

YORK HOLDINGS, INC.
700 N Lincoln Ave, York, NE 68467
Tel.: (402) 362-4411 NE
Web Site: http://www.yorkstatebank.com
Year Founded: 2014
Sales Range: $1-9.9 Million
Emp.: 34
Bank Holding Company
N.A.I.C.S.: 551111
Clarkson D. Lauritzen (Pres)
Bruce R. Lauritzen (Chm)

Subsidiaries:
York State Bank (1)
700 N Lincoln Ave, York, NE 68467
Tel.: (402) 362-4411
Web Site: http://www.yorkstatebank.com
Sales Range: $1-9.9 Million
Commericial Banking
N.A.I.C.S.: 522110
Mark Way (CFO)

YORK HOSPITAL
15 Hospital Dr, York, ME 03909
Tel.: (207) 363-4321 ME
Web Site: http://www.yorkhospital.com
Year Founded: 1904
Sales Range: $150-199.9 Million
Emp.: 1,275
Health Care Srvices
N.A.I.C.S.: 622110
Jody Marriyl (Dir-Mktg)

YORK MANAGEMENT SERVICES, INC.
154 Tices Ln, East Brunswick, NJ 08816
Tel.: (732) 296-6600
Web Site: http://www.yorkms.com
Sales Range: $10-24.9 Million
Emp.: 10
Privater Equity Firm
N.A.I.C.S.: 523999
William F. Taggart (Founder & Principal)

Subsidiaries:
Northern Reflections Ltd. (1)
21 Four Seasons Place 2nd Fl, Toronto, M9B 6J8, ON, Canada (100%)
Web Site: http://www.northernreflections.com
Sales Range: $25-49.9 Million
Women's Casual Clothing Retailer
N.A.I.C.S.: 458110

Lalonnie Biggar *(Pres)*
Hanspal Jando *(CFO)*

Regal Gifts Corporation (1)
130 Bell Farm Road Units 2 & 3, Barrie,
L4M 6J4, ON, Canada
Tel.: (705) 721-5454
E-Commerce, Catalogue & Direct Marketing
Services
N.A.I.C.S.: 459420

YORK PROPERTIES, INC. OF RALEIGH
1900 Cameron St, Raleigh, NC 27605
Tel.: (919) 821-1350   NC
Web Site:
   http://www.yorkproperties.com
Year Founded: 1954
Sales Range: $10-24.9 Million
Emp.: 100
Provider of Real Estate Property
Management Services
N.A.I.C.S.: 237210
G. Smedes York *(Chm)*
Peter Pace *(VP-Comml Sls-Leasing)*
Amy Rogers *(Mgr-Property)*
Heather Toler *(Mgr-Corp Support)*
Susan Collier *(Mgr-Property)*
Jack Forbes *(Mgr-Property)*
Karen Ruoff Brown *(Sr VP-Property Mgmt)*
Kathy Decker *(Assoc Mgr)*
Lyle Wilkinson *(Mgr-Property & Dir-Construction)*
Steven Jackson *(Dir-Maintenance)*
Julie Paul *(Mgr-Bus Dev)*

YORK RIVER ELECTRIC, INC.
108 Production Dr, Yorktown, VA 23693-4024
Tel.: (757) 369-3673
Web Site:
   http://www.yorkriverelectric.com
Sales Range: $25-49.9 Million
Emp.: 85
Electrical Wiring Services
N.A.I.C.S.: 238210

YORK SOLUTIONS, LLC.
1 Westbrook Corporate Ctr Ste 910, Westchester, IL 60154
Tel.: (708) 531-8363
Web Site:
   http://www.yorksolutions.net
Year Founded: 1989
Sales Range: $10-24.9 Million
Emp.: 129
Information Technology Consulting Services
N.A.I.C.S.: 541512
Jim Hanselman *(Sr Dir-Consulting Svcs)*
Tom Parker *(VP-Bus Dev)*
Bill Carr *(CEO)*

YORK STREET CAPITAL PARTNERS
364 Main St Ste 200, Bedminster, NJ 07921
Tel.: (908) 658-4700
Web Site:
   http://www.yorkstreetcapital.com
Sales Range: $25-49.9 Million
Emp.: 7
Privater Equity Firm
N.A.I.C.S.: 523999
Robert Golding *(Co-Founder, Owner & Mng Partner)*
Christopher Layden *(Mng Partner)*

YORKS OF HOULTON, INC.
US Route 1, Houlton, ME 04730
Tel.: (207) 532-6534
Web Site:
   http://www.yorksofhoulton.com
Rev.: $14,400,000
Emp.: 75
New Car Dealers
N.A.I.C.S.: 441110
Jerry York *(Co-Owner & Gen Mgr)*
Dale Ivey *(Mgr-Parts Dept)*
Galen Howe *(Mgr-Used Cars)*
Dick York *(Co-Owner & Mgr-Sls)*
Roger Graham *(Mgr-Bodyshop)*

YORKSHIRE FOOD SALES CORP.
2000 Plz Ave, New Hyde Park, NY 11040
Tel.: (516) 328-1500
Web Site: http://www.nysnacks.com
Sales Range: $10-24.9 Million
Emp.: 100
Potato Chips
N.A.I.C.S.: 424450
Anthony Gerbino *(Pres)*
Bob Salzano *(Mgr-IT)*
Mike Trietsch *(Gen Mgr-Logistics)*

YORKTEL, INC.
81 Corbett Way, Eatontown, NJ 07074
Tel.: (732) 413-6000
Web Site: http://www.yorktel.com
Year Founded: 1985
Sales Range: $25-49.9 Million
Emp.: 350
Video Conferencing, Unified Communications, Media & Streaming Services & Cloud Services
N.A.I.C.S.: 512110
York Wang *(Founder & Chm)*
Ronald J. Gaboury *(CEO)*
Ken Scaturro *(Chief Revenue Officer)*
Bin Guan *(CTO)*
Greg Douglas *(Exec VP-Sls & Mktg)*
Joe-E Hu *(CIO)*
Judi Pulig *(CFO & Exec VP-Corp Svcs)*
Karen Paglia *(Exec VP-Bus Mgmt)*
Mark Maxey *(Exec VP-Media Svcs)*
Aaron Wentzel *(VP-Bus Dev-Asia Pacific)*
Vishal Brown *(Sr VP-Consultancy)*
Mike Brandofino *(COO)*

Subsidiaries:

Yorktel (1)
3 Hazelwood Lime Tree Way Chineham Park, Basingstoke, RG24 8WZ, Hampshire, United Kingdom   **(100%)**
Tel.: (44) 1256 372700
Web Site: http://www.yorktel.com
Video Conferencing, System Integrator & Cloud Services
N.A.I.C.S.: 512110

Yorktel France SAS (1)
53 Avenue Hoche, 75008, Paris, France
Tel.: (33) 5 82 88 14 80
Visual Communication Services
N.A.I.C.S.: 541410
Simon Murphy *(Mgr)*

Yorktel, Inc. (1)
33 Upton Dr, Wilmington, MA 01887
Tel.: (978) 658-5150
Web Site: http://www.yorktel.com
Sales Range: $100-124.9 Million
Emp.: 125
Video Conferencing, Unified Communications, Cloud Services & Media Services
N.A.I.C.S.: 334310
York Wang *(Founder & Chm)*
Ron Gaboury *(CEO)*
Bin Guan *(CTO)*
Joe-E Hu *(CIO)*
Judi Pulig *(CFO & Exec VP-Corp Svcs)*
Karen Paglia *(Exec VP-Bus Mgmt)*
Mark Maxey *(Exec VP-Media Svcs)*
Joseph M. Arena *(Sr VP-Advanced Svcs)*
Peter McLain *(Sr VP-Healthcare)*
John Vitale *(Sr VP-Product Mgmt)*
Vishal Brown *(Sr VP)*
Frankie Escribano *(Exec VP-Ops)*
Jeremy Short *(Sr VP-Microsoft Solutions)*
Kelly Harman *(Sr VP-Mktg)*

Yorktel, Inc. (1)
81 Corbett Way, Eatontown, NJ 07724   **(100%)**
Tel.: (732) 413-6000
Web Site: http://www.yorktel.com
Video Conferencing & Digital Signage Services
N.A.I.C.S.: 512110

Yorktel, Inc. (1)
4140 Sheridan Dr Suite 4, Williamsville, NY 14221   **(100%)**
Tel.: (716) 810-9550
Web Site: http://www.yorktel.com
Video Conferencing Services
N.A.I.C.S.: 512110

Yorktel, Inc. (1)
342 Victory Dr, Herndon, VA 20170   **(100%)**
Tel.: (571) 612-8991
Web Site: http://www.yorktel.com
Video Conferencing, Cloud Services & Media Services
N.A.I.C.S.: 512110

YORKTOWN FINANCIAL HOLDINGS, INC.
2222 S Utica Pl Ste 350, Tulsa, OK 74114
Tel.: (918) 491-7000   OK
Web Site:
   http://www.yorktownbank.com
Year Founded: 2012
Emp.: 19
Bank Holding Company
N.A.I.C.S.: 551111
Steve H. Austin *(Pres & CEO)*
Elena C. Forsyth *(CFO)*

Subsidiaries:

Yorktown Bank (1)
2222 S Utica Pl Ste 350, Tulsa, OK 74114
Tel.: (918) 491-7000
Web Site: http://www.yorktownbank.com
Sales Range: $1-9.9 Million
Emp.: 20
Commericial Banking
N.A.I.C.S.: 522110
Steve H. Austin *(CEO)*
Elena C. Forsyth *(CFO & Exec VP)*
Abba J. Williams *(VP-Admin)*

YORKTOWN SYSTEMS GROUP, INC.
2905 Westcorp Blvd Suite 116, Huntsville, AL 35805
Tel.: (877) 406-0262
Web Site: http://www.ysginc.com
Year Founded: 2008
Sales Range: $10-24.9 Million
Emp.: 122
Support Services, Training, Financial Management, IT & Program Support to Military & Government Personnel
N.A.I.C.S.: 921190
Bryan Dyer *(Pres & CEO)*
C. Nick Fuller *(VP-Trng & Education Solutions)*
Dave Dolph *(VP-Fin & Mgmt Svcs)*
Steve Flanagan *(Mgr-TRAC Program)*

YORKVILLE ADVISORS, LLC
1012 Springfield Ave, Mountainside, NJ 07092
Tel.: (201) 985-8300   DE
Web Site:
   http://www.yorkvilleadvisors.com
Year Founded: 2001
Alternative Investment Management Services
N.A.I.C.S.: 523940
Mark Angelo *(Partner)*
Steven S. Goldstein *(Chief Compliance Officer)*
Troy J. Rillo *(Sr Mng Dir)*
Matthew Beckman *(Partner)*
Gerald Eicke *(Partner)*
David Gonzalez *(Partner & Gen Counsel)*
Michael Rosselli *(Mng Dir)*
Saad Gilani *(VP)*

YOSEMITE FOUNDATION
101 Montgomery St Ste 1700, San Francisco, CA 94104
Tel.: (415) 434-1782   CA
Web Site:
   http://www.yosemiteconservancy.org
Year Founded: 1988
Sales Range: $10-24.9 Million
Emp.: 69
Park Preservation Services
N.A.I.C.S.: 712190
Jerry Edelbrock *(CFO & VP)*
Kit Thomas *(Controller)*
Kim Coull *(Dir-Dev)*
Edin Draper-Beard *(Mgr-Exec Affairs)*
Philip L. Pillsbury Jr. *(Chm)*

YOSEMITE MANAGEMENT GROUP LLC
PO Box 650, Mariposa, CA 95318
Tel.: (209) 379-2817
Web Site:
   http://www.yosemiteresorts.us
Rev.: $17,354,129
Emp.: 100
Hotel
N.A.I.C.S.: 721110
Gerald Fisher *(Pres & Owner)*

YOU & MR JONES INC.
54 W 40 St, New York, NY 10018
Tel.: (347) 683-1859
Web Site: http://youandmrjones.com
Year Founded: 2015
User & Machine Generated Content, Programmatic Media Buying, Creative, Brand & Content Strategy & Social Media Marketing
N.A.I.C.S.: 541613
David Jones *(Founder)*
Sarah Davies *(Partner)*
Emma Cookson *(Partner)*
Julie Hardy *(Partner)*

Subsidiaries:

Inside Ideas Group Ltd. (1)
151 Rosebery Avenue, London, EC1R 4AB, United Kingdom
Tel.: (44) 203 142 3500
Web Site: http://www.insideideas.agency
Holding Company; Advertising, Media Representation & Marketing Services
N.A.I.C.S.: 551112
Simon Hedley Martin *(CEO)*
Simon David Weaver *(CFO)*
Sharon Whale *(CEO-Oliver Grp UK)*
Robert Green *(Dir-Bus Dev)*

Subsidiary (Domestic):

Adjust Your Set Limited (2)
151 Rosebery Avenue, London, EC1R 4AB, United Kingdom
Tel.: (44) 20 7580 5933
Web Site: http://www.adjustyourset.com
Emp.: 600
Advetising Agency
N.A.I.C.S.: 541810
Chris Gorell Barnes *(Founder & CEO)*
Will Barnett *(Exec Creative Dir)*
Anna-Louise Gladwell *(Mng Dir)*

Aylesworth Fleming Limited (2)
Holland House St Paul's Place, Bournemouth, BH8 8GG, United Kingdom
Tel.: (44) 1202 295723
Web Site: http://www.afagency.co.uk
Sales Range: $10-24.9 Million
Emp.: 120
Advetising Agency
N.A.I.C.S.: 541810
Carolyn Jackson Potter *(Mng Dir)*

Dare Digital Limited (2)
151 Rosebery Avenue, London, EC1R 4AB, United Kingdom
Tel.: (44) 20 3142 3500

YOU & MR JONES INC.

You & Mr Jones Inc.—(Continued)
Web Site: http://www.thisisdare.com
Advetising Agency
N.A.I.C.S.: 541810

Oliver Marketing Limited (2)
151 Rosebery Avenue, London, EC1R 4AB,
United Kingdom
Tel.: (44) 203 142 3500
Web Site: http://www.oliver.agency
Media Representative Services
N.A.I.C.S.: 541840
Simon Martin *(Founder & Grp CEO)*
Sharon Whale *(CEO)*
Robert Green *(Mng Partner-New Bus)*
Matthew Baldwin *(Mng Dir)*
Mark Bell *(Chief Experience Officer)*
Brian Cooper *(Chief Creative Officer)*
Leo Harrison *(Mng Dir)*
Rachel Hatton *(Chief Strategy Officer)*
Michael Olaye *(CTO)*
David Russell *(Mng Dir)*
Milan Semelak *(Chief Disruption Officer)*
Jeffrey Gorder *(Chief Growth Officer-North America)*

YOU FIT, INC.
4171 W Hillsboro Blvd Ste 12, Coconut Creek, FL 33073
Tel.: (954) 642-5200
Web Site:
  http://www.youfithealthclubs.com
Sales Range: $1-9.9 Million
Emp.: 60
Health Club
N.A.I.C.S.: 713940
Rick Berks *(Founder & Pres)*

YOUNAN PROPERTIES, INC.
5959 Topanga Canyon Blvd, Woodland Hills, CA 91367-3611
Tel.: (818) 703-9600   CA
Web Site:
  http://www.younanproperties.com
Year Founded: 2002
Sales Range: $150-199.9 Million
Emp.: 120
Real Estate Investment & Management
N.A.I.C.S.: 525990
Zaya S. Younan *(Chm & CEO)*
Denise Davis *(VP-Comm & IR)*
John R. Cook *(Reg VP-Leasing & Ops)*
Sarah Sadat *(VP-Acctg & Fin)*
Tony Avila *(VP-Acq)*
Wallace Smith *(VP-Facilities & Engrg)*
Joy DeBacker *(Reg VP-Leasing & Ops)*
Terry L. Smolich *(VP-HR)*

YOUNG & ASSOCIATES
3102 W End Ave, Ste 175, Nashville, TN 37203
Tel.: (775) 285-6585
Web Site: https://youngonline.com
Year Founded: 1997
Emp.: 367
Property Damage Consulting Firm
N.A.I.C.S.: 541618
Ray Young *(Founder)*

Subsidiaries:

Guardian Group, Inc. (1)
2350 W 205th St, Torrance, CA 90501
Tel.: (310) 320-0120
Web Site: http://www.guardiangroup.com
Sales Range: $1-9.9 Million
Emp.: 15
Management Consulting Services
N.A.I.C.S.: 541618
Michael W. Saba *(VP)*
Wick Hutchison *(VP)*
Mark Hopkins *(Reg Mgr)*
Mark Stein *(Mgr-Texas)*
Todd M. Bauer *(Exec VP)*

Inline Consulting, LLC (1)
402 Bell Ct, Woodstock, GA 30188-1659
Tel.: (303) 256-6920
Web Site: http://www.in-lineconsulting.net

Administrative Management & General Management Consulting Services
N.A.I.C.S.: 541611
Mark Lively *(Co-Founder)*
Matt Watson *(Co-Founder & Pres)*

YOUNG & ASSOCIATES
3102 W End Ave. Ste 175, Nashville, TN 37203
Tel.: (888) 614-1372
Web Site: https://www.yagroup.com
Business Consulting Services
N.A.I.C.S.: 541618

Subsidiaries:

Bloomberg Consulting, Inc. (1)
105 Bay Bridge Dr, Gulf Breeze, FL 32561-4470
Tel.: (850) 932-8509
Web Site:
  http://www.bloombergconsulting.com
Technology & Management Consulting Services
N.A.I.C.S.: 541511
Chris Bloomberg *(Pres & Engr-Pro)*
David DeLonga *(Engr-Pro)*
J. Marcus Hollis *(Engr-Biomechanical & Pro)*
Chris J. Medwell *(Engr-Pro)*

YOUNG & ASSOCIATES INC.
2847 W State St, Bristol, TN 37620
Tel.: (423) 968-1743
Sales Range: $10-24.9 Million
Emp.: 10
Franchise Owner of Family Restaurants
N.A.I.C.S.: 722511
Donna Layton *(Asst Controller)*
Kristen Modean *(Acct Mgr-Comml)*
Caroline Routley *(Acct Mgr-Personal)*

YOUNG & BEASLEY INCORPORATED
153 W 900 S, Salt Lake City, UT 84101
Tel.: (801) 328-2038
Sales Range: $10-24.9 Million
Emp.: 30
Electric Household Appliances
N.A.I.C.S.: 449210

YOUNG & CHAMPAGNE ELECTRICAL SALES INC.
7500 Intervale St, Detroit, MI 48238
Tel.: (313) 491-6500
Web Site: http://www.ycesales.com
Electrical/Electronic Mfr
N.A.I.C.S.: 335999
Michael Young *(Pres-Outside Sls)*
Dan LeBlanc *(VP-Outside Sls)*
Troy Olsen *(Principal)*
Jill Siarto *(Principal-Inside Sls)*
Fred Williams *(Mgr-Warehouse)*

Subsidiaries:

Young & Champagne Company (1)
7500 Intervale St, Detroit, MI 48238
Tel.: (313) 491-6500
Web Site: http://www.ycesales.com
Electrical Apparatus & Equipment, Wiring Supplies & Related Equipment Merchant Whslr
N.A.I.C.S.: 423610

YOUNG & LARAMORE
407 N Fulton St, Indianapolis, IN 46202
Tel.: (317) 264-8000   IN
Web Site: http://www.yandl.com
Year Founded: 1983
Sales Range: $25-49.9 Million
Emp.: 60
Advertising Agencies
N.A.I.C.S.: 541810
Paul J. Knapp *(CEO)*
Tom Denari *(Pres & Chief Strategy Officer)*
Carolyn Hadlock *(Exec Dir-Creative)*

Bryan Judkins *(Dir-Creative)*
Brad Bobenmoyer *(VP-Mktg & New Bus Inquiries)*
Kyle Klinger *(Sr Dir-Art)*

Subsidiaries:

Perkins Nichols Media (1)
6330 E 75th St Ste 144, Indianapolis, IN 46250-2021
Tel.: (317) 585-0000
Sales Range: $1-9.9 Million
Emp.: 4
Media Buying Services
N.A.I.C.S.: 541830

YOUNG & MCQUEEN GRADING COMPANY, INC.
25 Crest View Rd, Burnsville, NC 28714
Tel.: (828) 682-7714
Web Site:
  http://www.youngmcqueen.com
Year Founded: 1986
Sales Range: $10-24.9 Million
Emp.: 100
Excavation Services
N.A.I.C.S.: 238910
Earl Tipton *(VP)*

YOUNG ADULT INSTITUTE, INC.
460 W 34th St, New York, NY 10001-2382
Tel.: (212) 273-6100   NY
Web Site: http://www.yai.org
Year Founded: 1957
Sales Range: $150-199.9 Million
Emp.: 3,429
Disability Assistance Services
N.A.I.C.S.: 624120
Roberta G. Koenigsberg *(Chief Compliance Officer)*
Stephen E. Freeman *(CEO)*
Sanjay Dutt *(CFO)*
Karen Wegmann *(Chief Bus Officer)*
Matthew Sturiale *(Exec VP-Empowerment & Svcs)*

YOUNG AMERICA'S FOUNDATION
11480 Commerce Park Dr Ste 600, Reston, VA 20191-1556
Tel.: (703) 318-9608   TN
Web Site: http://www.yaf.org
Year Founded: 1969
Rev.: $24,155,455
Assets: $74,757,386
Liabilities: $4,743,260
Net Worth: $70,014,126
Earnings: $527,197
Emp.: 56
Fiscal Year-end: 12/31/18
Social Advocacy Organization
N.A.I.C.S.: 813319
Jason Barbour *(Dir-Dev)*
Cheri Cerame *(Dir-IT)*
Darla Anzalone *(Dir-Comm)*
Ron Robinson *(Pres)*
Ronald Pearson *(VP)*
Frank Donatelli *(Treas & Sec)*
Scott Walker *(CEO)*
Victor Bernson *(Gen Counsel & VP)*
Andrew Coffin *(VP & Dir-Reagan Ranch)*

YOUNG AUTOMOTIVE GROUP
645 N Main St, Layton, UT 84041-2230
Tel.: (801) 544-1234
Year Founded: 1989
Sales Range: $10-24.9 Million
Emp.: 50
Car Whslr
N.A.I.C.S.: 441110
Spencer W. Young *(Pres)*
Seldon O. Young *(VP)*

Mike Capron *(Gen Mgr)*
Larry Daubs *(Principal)*
L. S. McCullough *(Owner)*
Justin Messick *(Principal)*

YOUNG AUTOMOTIVE GROUP, INC.
5737 S Pennsylvania Ave, Lansing, MI 48911
Tel.: (517) 393-5700   MI
Web Site:
  http://www.kiaoflansing.com
Emp.: 33
New & Used Car Dealer
N.A.I.C.S.: 441110
Anthony M. Young *(Owner)*
Greg Miller *(Gen Sls Mgr)*

Subsidiaries:

Berger Motor Sales Incorporated (1)
3669 S State Rd, Ionia, MI 48846
Tel.: (616) 527-4800
Web Site: http://www.youngioniagm.com
Sales Range: $1-9.9 Million
New & Used Car Dealer
N.A.I.C.S.: 441110
Eric Ridenour *(Gen Mgr)*
Bob Hayden *(Sls Mgr)*
Armando Orta *(Fin Mgr)*

YOUNG CHEVROLET COMPANY
645 N Main St, Layton, UT 84041
Tel.: (801) 544-1234
Web Site: http://www.youngchev.com
Sales Range: $25-49.9 Million
Emp.: 200
Automobiles, New & Used
N.A.I.C.S.: 441110
Seldon Young *(Chm)*
Spencer Young *(Owner & Principal)*
Ray Seely *(CFO)*

YOUNG COMPANY CREATIVE MARKETING COMMUNICATIONS, INC.
361 Forest Ave Ste 105, Laguna Beach, CA 92651
Tel.: (949) 376-8404   CA
Web Site:
  http://www.youngcompany.com
Year Founded: 1949
Sales Range: $1-9.9 Million
Emp.: 10
Fiscal Year-end: 12/31/14
Advetising Agency
N.A.I.C.S.: 541810
Barton Young *(CEO & Dir-Creative)*
Michael Mittelstaedt *(Assoc Dir-Creative)*
Lori Robinson *(Mgr-Media)*
John Dillon *(VP-PR)*

YOUNG CORPORATION
3231 Utah Ave S, Seattle, WA 98134
Tel.: (206) 624-1071
Web Site: http://www.youngcorp.com
Year Founded: 1902
Sales Range: $10-24.9 Million
Emp.: 145
Conveyors & Conveying Equipment
N.A.I.C.S.: 331513
Robert H. Lindberg *(Pres)*
Mark Lindberg *(Pres)*

YOUNG DAN TIPTON LLC
875 E Jefferson St, Tipton, IN 46072
Tel.: (765) 675-7491
Web Site:
  http://www.danyounggm.com
Sales Range: $25-49.9 Million
Emp.: 48
Automobiles, New & Used
N.A.I.C.S.: 441110
Richard Brown *(Owner & Pres)*
Charles Wiet *(Mgr)*

COMPANIES

YOUNG ELECTRIC SIGN COMPANY
1605 S Gramercy Rd, Salt Lake City, UT 84104
Tel.: (801) 487-8481   UT
Web Site: http://www.yesco.com
Year Founded: 1920
Sales Range: $350-399.9 Million
Emp.: 1,250
Neon & Electric Sign Sign Rental Installation & Maintenance Mfr
N.A.I.C.S.: 339950
Michael T. Young *(Pres)*
Paul Young *(Exec VP)*
Ben F. Jones *(Sr VP-Engrg)*
Ryan Young *(Mgr-Sls-Outdoor Media)*
Thomas Young Jr. *(Chm)*

Subsidiaries:

Young Electric Sign Co. - Boise   (1)
416 E 41st St, Boise, ID 83714
Tel.: (208) 345-2982
Web Site: http://www.yesco.com
Sales Range: $10-24.9 Million
Emp.: 50
Mfr of Signs not Made in Custom Sign Painting Shops; Sign Installation & Maintenance; Signs, Except Electric
N.A.I.C.S.: 339950

Young Electric Sign Co. - Denver   (1)
1220 E 53rd Ave Ste 300, Denver, CO 80239
Tel.: (303) 375-9933
Web Site: http://www.yesco.com
Sales Range: $10-24.9 Million
Emp.: 78
Sign Mfr
N.A.I.C.S.: 339950
Rick Bellefeuille *(Gen Mgr & Mgr-Sls)*

Young Electric Sign Co. - Las Vegas   (1)
5119 Cameron St, Las Vegas, NV 89118-1512
Tel.: (702) 876-8080
Web Site: http://www.yesco.com
Sales Range: $50-74.9 Million
Emp.: 450
Sign Mfr
N.A.I.C.S.: 339950

Young Electric Sign Co. - Phoenix   (1)
6725 W Chicago St, Chandler, AZ 85226
Tel.: (480) 449-3726
Web Site: http://www.yesco.com
Sales Range: $10-24.9 Million
Emp.: 80
Mfr of Signs not Made in Custom Sign Painting Shops
N.A.I.C.S.: 541850
Jake Winkleplech *(Mgr-Sls)*
Paul Gullo *(Gen Mgr)*

Young Electric Sign Co. - Reno   (1)
775 E Glendale Ave, Sparks, NV 89431-6408
Tel.: (775) 359-3131
Web Site: http://www.yesco.com
Sales Range: $10-24.9 Million
Emp.: 100
Mfr of Electric Signs
N.A.I.C.S.: 339950
Bill Buttrum *(VP-Sls)*

Young Electric Sign Co. - Salt Lake City   (1)
1605 S Gramercy Rd, Salt Lake City, UT 84104
Tel.: (801) 487-8481
Web Site: http://www.yesco.com
Sales Range: $25-49.9 Million
Emp.: 200
Mfr of Sign Boards
N.A.I.C.S.: 339950
Jeffrey S. Young *(Gen Mgr)*

YOUNG LIVING ESSENTIAL OILS, LC
1538 W Sandalwood Dr, Lehi, UT 84043
Tel.: (801) 418-8900   UT
Web Site: http://www.youngliving.com
Essential Oil Mfr
N.A.I.C.S.: 325998
Mary Young *(Founder & CEO)*
Jared S. Turner *(COO)*
Michael Green *(CIO)*
Carlos Ortega *(Mgr-Colombia)*
Mark R. Bartlett *(Exec VP-Science & Dev)*
Steve Carlile *(Chief Mktg & Digital Officer)*
Ben Riley *(Pres)*

Subsidiaries:

Oxyfresh Worldwide, Inc.   (1)
1875 N Lakewood Dr 3rd Fl, Coeur D'Alene, ID 83814
Tel.: (208) 292-1200
Web Site: http://www.oxyfresh.com
Personal & Home Care, Dental Products, Nutrition Supplements & Pet Products Mfr & Whslr
N.A.I.C.S.: 424210
Melissa Gulbranson *(VP-Mktg)*

YOUNG MARINES OF THE MARINE CORPS LEAGUE
PO Box 70735, Washington, DC 20024-0735
Tel.: (202) 521-9030   DC
Web Site: http://www.youngmarines.com
Year Founded: 1981
Sales Range: $50-74.9 Million
Emp.: 10
Youth Care Services
N.A.I.C.S.: 624110
Michael Kessler *(CEO)*

YOUNG SUPPLY CO.
52000 Sierra Dr, Chesterfield, MI 48047-1307
Tel.: (586) 421-2400   MI
Web Site: http://www.youngsupply.com
Year Founded: 1935
Sales Range: $125-149.9 Million
Emp.: 156
Refrigeration, Air Conditioning, Heating & Food Service Equipment & Parts Whslr
N.A.I.C.S.: 423740
David K. Cornett *(VP-Fin)*
Ronald L. VanderMeulen *(VP-Branch Ops)*
Colette Helm *(Controller)*
John Grillo *(Mgr-Store-Chesterfield Twp)*

YOUNG TRUCK SALES INC.
4970 Southway St SW, Canton, OH 44706
Tel.: (330) 477-6271   OH
Web Site: http://www.youngtrucks.com
Year Founded: 1954
Sales Range: $10-24.9 Million
Emp.: 63
Sales of New & Used Trucks, Tractors & Trailers
N.A.I.C.S.: 441110
Rita Burchett *(Bus Mgr)*
Bob Smith *(Mgr-Svc)*
Dave Androw *(Dir-Parts)*
Larry Clay *(Mgr-Svcs)*
Chip Tucci *(Mgr-Parts-Columbus)*
Scott Baker *(Mgr-Sls)*
Bob Young Sr. *(Mgr-Used Truck)*

YOUNG'S FURNITURE COMPANY
1 Diamond St, Portland, ME 04101
Tel.: (207) 775-3747   ME
Web Site: http://www.youngsfurniture.com
Sales Range: $10-24.9 Million
Emp.: 10
Operates Furniture Stores
N.A.I.C.S.: 449110
Stephen Young *(Pres)*
Jonathan Young *(VP)*

YOUNG'S HOLDINGS, INC.
14402 Franklin Ave, Tustin, CA 92780
Tel.: (714) 368-4615   DE
Web Site: http://www.youngsmarket.com
Sales Range: $1-4.9 Billion
Emp.: 2,400
Holding Company; Alcoholic Beverage Distr
N.A.I.C.S.: 551112
Vernon O. Underwood *(Chm)*
Christopher Underwood *(CEO)*
Dan Ewer *(Exec VP-Corp Wine)*

Subsidiaries:

Young's Market Company, LLC   (1)
14402 Franklin Ave, Tustin, CA 92780   (100%)
Tel.: (714) 368-4615
Web Site: http://www.youngsmarket.com
Alcoholic Beverage Distr
N.A.I.C.S.: 424820
Vernon O. Underwood *(Chm)*
Christopher Underwood *(CEO)*

Subsidiary (Domestic):

K&L Beverage Company, LLC   (2)
3215 Lind Ave SW, Renton, WA 98057   (80%)
Tel.: (206) 808-6000
Sales Range: $25-49.9 Million
Emp.: 200
Wine & Distilled Spirits Distr
N.A.I.C.S.: 424820

Unit (Domestic):

Young's Market - Hawaii   (2)
94-501 Kau St, Waipahu, HI 96797-4236
Tel.: (808) 676-6111
Sales Range: $25-49.9 Million
Emp.: 160
Wines & Distilled Spirits Whslr
N.A.I.C.S.: 424820

Subsidiary (Domestic):

Young's Market Company of Arizona, LLC   (2)
200 S 49th Ave, Phoenix, AZ 85043-3805
Tel.: (602) 442-6622
Alcoholic Beverage Distr
N.A.I.C.S.: 424820

Young's Market Company of Oregon, LLC   (2)
6840 N Cutter Cir, Portland, OR 97217   (100%)
Tel.: (503) 289-9600
Web Site: http://www.coldist.com
Emp.: 200
Wine & Distilled Spirits Distr
N.A.I.C.S.: 424820
Daniel Ewer *(Pres-Youngs Market)*
Jay Nelson *(Pres-Brokerage)*
Andy Lytle *(Exec VP)*

Young's Market Company of Washington, LLC   (2)
20301 59th Pl S, Kent, WA 98032   (100%)
Tel.: (425) 251-9300
Web Site: http://www.coldist.com
Wine & Spirits
N.A.I.C.S.: 424820
Chris Underwood *(CEO)*

YOUNG'S NURSERIES INC.
211 Danbury Rd, Wilton, CT 06897
Tel.: (203) 762-5511
Web Site: http://www.youngsnurseries.com
Year Founded: 1930
Sales Range: $1-9.9 Million
Emp.: 55
Landscape Contractors
N.A.I.C.S.: 561730
R. Thomas Daily *(Treas, VP & Controller)*
Scott Deniston *(Pres)*
David L. Gindek *(Sec & VP)*

YOUNG'S RV CENTERS, INC.
1450 Dickinson St, Fremont, OH 43420
Tel.: (419) 334-2648
Web Site: http://www.youngsmfghousing.com
Rev.: $10,000,000
Emp.: 12
Recreational Vehicle Dealers
N.A.I.C.S.: 441210
David Young *(Pres)*

YOUNG'S TRUCK CENTER INC.
3880 Jeff Adams Dr, Charlotte, NC 28206
Tel.: (704) 597-0551
Web Site: http://www.advtrks.com
Year Founded: 1995
Truck Dealership
N.A.I.C.S.: 423110
Terry Young *(Pres & CEO)*

YOUNGBERG INDUSTRIES, INC.
6863 Indy Dr, Belvidere, IL 61008
Tel.: (815) 544-2177
Web Site: http://www.youngbergindustries.com
Year Founded: 1944
Sales Range: $10-24.9 Million
Fabricated Plate Mfr & Distr
N.A.I.C.S.: 332313
Thomas Larson *(Chm)*
Michael White *(Engr-Processing)*

YOUNGBLOOD OIL CO. INC.
420 N Pine St, Hendersonville, NC 28792
Tel.: (828) 693-6219
Sales Range: $10-24.9 Million
Emp.: 5
Fuel Oil Dealers
N.A.I.C.S.: 457210
David Parris *(Pres)*

YOUNGER BROTHERS GROUP INC.
8525 N 75th Ave, Peoria, AZ 85345
Tel.: (623) 979-1111   AZ
Web Site: http://www.ybcco.com
Year Founded: 1987
Rev.: $12,300,000
Emp.: 1,300
Holding Company
N.A.I.C.S.: 238130
James A. Younger III *(Pres)*
Barbara Margolies *(CEO)*

Subsidiaries:

Liberty Lumber Company   (1)
8525 N 75th Ave, Peoria, AZ 85345
Tel.: (623) 487-3311
Building Materials Whslr
N.A.I.C.S.: 444180
Don Pruitt *(Gen Mgr)*
Janie Woodard *(Office Mgr)*

XO Windows, LLC   (1)
601 N 44th Ave Ste 102, Phoenix, AZ 85043
Tel.: (602) 499-4556
Web Site: http://www.xowindows.com
Door & Window Whslr
N.A.I.C.S.: 444180
Mike Siebert *(Mgr-Sls)*
Robin Knox *(Office Mgr)*
Scott McGill *(Partner & VP-Sls)*

YB Vehicle Services   (1)
8525 N 75th Ave, Peoria, AZ 85345
Tel.: (623) 487-3114
Web Site: http://www.ybcco.com
Emp.: 600

YOUNGER BROTHERS GROUP INC. U.S. PRIVATE

Younger Brothers Group Inc.—(Continued)
Motor Vehicle Maintenance Services
N.A.I.C.S.: 811198
Scott Pirgge (Gen Mgr)

Younger Brothers Builders Express Liberty LLC (1)
3910 E Weir Ave, Phoenix, AZ 85040
Tel.: (602) 264-0100
Building Materials Whslr
N.A.I.C.S.: 444180

Younger Brothers Components Inc. (1)
8525 N 75th Ave, Peoria, AZ 85345
Tel.: (623) 412-7979
Web Site: http://www.ybcco.com
Rev.: $10,809,639
Emp.: 60
Structural Wood Members
N.A.I.C.S.: 321215

Younger Brothers Construction Company (1)
8525 N 75th Ave, Peoria, AZ 85345
Tel.: (623) 979-1111
Web Site: http://www.ybcco.com
Carpentry Work
N.A.I.C.S.: 321215
James A. Younger III (Pres)

Younger Brothers Door & Trim, LLC (1)
3910 E Wier Ave, Phoenix, AZ 85040
Tel.: (602) 304-1000
Building Materials Whslr
N.A.I.C.S.: 444180
Jennifer Hayes (Office Mgr)

Younger Brothers Exterminating (1)
8525 N 75th Ave, Peoria, AZ 85345
Tel.: (623) 487-3147
Pest Control Services
N.A.I.C.S.: 561710
Jenifer Salcido (Gen Mgr)

YOUNGER MFG. CO.
2925 California St, Torrance, CA 90503-3914
Tel.: (310) 783-1533   CA
Web Site:
  http://www.youngeroptics.com
Year Founded: 1955
Sales Range: $150-199.9 Million
Emp.: 700
Eyeglass Lenses & Optical Products Mfr
N.A.I.C.S.: 339115
David Rips (Founder, Pres & CEO)
Robert Lee (Dir-Sls & Mktg)
Tom Balch (Mng Dir)

Subsidiaries:

Younger Optics Europe S.r.o. (1)
Obchodni 110, Pruhonice, 251 70, Cestlice, Czech Republic
Tel.: (420) 234 097 222
Web Site: http://www.youngeroptics.eu
Optical Lens Mfr
N.A.I.C.S.: 333310

YOUNGER MOTOR CARS INC.
1945 Dual Hwy, Hagerstown, MD 21740
Tel.: (301) 733-2300
Web Site:
  http://www.youngercars.com
Sales Range: $25-49.9 Million
Emp.: 250
Automobiles, New & Used
N.A.I.C.S.: 441110
Eric Eichelberger (Mgr-Fin Svcs)

YOUNGSTEDT INC.
4711 Shady Oak Rd, Hopkins, MN 55343
Tel.: (952) 933-4305
Web Site:
  http://www.youngstedts.com
Sales Range: $10-24.9 Million
Emp.: 120
Automotive Tires

N.A.I.C.S.: 441340
Larry D. Youngstedt (Chm)
Steve Yougstedt (CEO)
Craig Stoesz (Pres)

YOUNGWORLD STORES GROUP INC.
15 W 34th St, New York, NY 10001
Tel.: (212) 594-2340   NY
Web Site:
  http://www.youngworld.com
Year Founded: 1994
Sales Range: $50-74.9 Million
Emp.: 600
Retailer of Children's & Infant's Wear
N.A.I.C.S.: 458110

Subsidiaries:

Youngworld Inc. (1)
362 5th Ave, New York, NY 10001
Tel.: (215) 548-7020
Rev.: $9,600,000
Emp.: 30
Childrens & Infants Wear Stores
N.A.I.C.S.: 531120

YOUNT, HYDE & BARBOUR PC
50 S Cameron St, Winchester, VA 22601
Tel.: (540) 662-3417
Web Site: http://www.yhbcpa.com
Year Founded: 1947
Accounting & Financial Services Provider
N.A.I.C.S.: 523999
Neile Martin (Mgr)
Will J. Murphy (Dir-Ops)
Jeremy Shen (CMO)
Scott Moulden (Mng Partner)

Subsidiaries:

Murray, Jonson, White & Associates, Ltd., P.C. (1)
6402 Arlington Blvd Ste 1130, Falls Church, VA 22042-2333
Tel.: (703) 237-2500
Offices of Certified Public Accountants
N.A.I.C.S.: 541211

Woodcock & Associates, PC (1)
1320 Central Park Blvd Ste 405, Fredericksburg, VA 22401
Tel.: (540) 368-8040
Web Site: http://www.woodcockpc.com
Accounting Services
N.A.I.C.S.: 541211
Jeanette Woodcock (Pres & Mng Partner)

YOUR BUILDING CENTERS, INC.
2607 Beale Ave, Altoona, PA 16601
Tel.: (814) 944-9436   PA
Web Site: http://www.ybconline.com
Year Founded: 1989
Lumber & Building Materials Distr
N.A.I.C.S.: 423310
Tim Leupold (Pres & CEO)
Brent McManigal (CFO)
Caleb Drenning (VP-Pur & Mktg)
Chip Yost (Dir-Safety)
Jeff Tressler (VP-Sls & Ops-West)
Fred Lorson (VP-Sls & Ops-East)
Carol Boland (Mgr-HR)
Rick Ackerman (Mgr-Credit)

Subsidiaries:

Berlin Lumber Company, Inc. (1)
2988 Berlin Plank Rd, Berlin, PA 15530
Tel.: (814) 267-4651
Web Site: http://www.berlinlumber.com
Lumber, Truss & Building Supplies Distr
N.A.I.C.S.: 423310
John Mauger (Mgr--Berlin)
Don Zeigler (Ops Mgr)

Palmerton Lumber Co., Inc. (1)
380 Sand Quarry Rd, Palmerton, PA 18071
Tel.: (610) 826-2327

Web Site: http://www.palmertonlumber.com
Rev.: $3,000,000
Emp.: 20
Lumber, Plywood, Millwork & Wood Panel Merchant Whslr
N.A.I.C.S.: 423310
Andrew Pisulak (Pres)

YOUR HOME PUBLISHING, INC.
3501 Bonita Bay Blvd Ste 300, Bonita Springs, FL 34134
Tel.: (239) 676-7461
Web Site:
  http://www.yourhomepublishing.com
Emp.: 8
Magazine Publisher
N.A.I.C.S.: 513120
Tony Spano (Pres)
Roxanne Hutson (Dir-Ops)
Channing Spano (Dir-Sls & Mktg)
Robert Barsimantov (Acct Mgr)
Kennedy Carroll (Acct Mgr)
Mark Somers (Acct Mgr)

Subsidiaries:

Your Home Magazine (1)
28440 Old 41 Rd Ste 9, Bonita Springs, FL 34134
Tel.: (239) 676-7461
Magazine
N.A.I.C.S.: 513120

YOUR HOME SOLD GUARANTEED REALTY, INC.
8932 Mission Dr Ste 102, Rosemead, CA 91770
Tel.: (626) 789-0159
Web Site:
  http://www.yourhomesoldguaranteedinc.com
Year Founded: 2007
Sales Range: $1-9.9 Million
Emp.: 12
Real Estate Brokerage Services
N.A.I.C.S.: 531210
Rudy Lira Kusuma (Pres & CEO)
Venny The (CFO)
Kristi Ramirez Knowles (Mgr-Bus Dev)

YOUR TRAVEL CENTER, INC.
Loreto Plz 3329 State St, Santa Barbara, CA 93105-2623
Tel.: (805) 683-7611   CA
Web Site: http://www.ytc.com
Year Founded: 1967
Sales Range: $10-24.9 Million
Emp.: 200
Travel Agencies
N.A.I.C.S.: 561510
Robin Sanchez (COO)
Colin Weatherhead (Pres)
Christopher Weatherhead (VP-Hotel Rels)

YOUSENDIT, INC.
1919 S Bascom Ave 3rd Fl, Campbell, CA 95008
Tel.: (408) 879-9118
Web Site: http://www.yousendit.com
Year Founded: 2004
Sales Range: $10-24.9 Million
Emp.: 120
Web-Based Digital Content Delivery
N.A.I.C.S.: 513210
Ranjith Kumaran (Founder & CEO)
Brad Garlinghouse (CEO)

YOUTECH & ASSOCIATES, INC.
1011 Warrenville Rd Ste 255, Lisle, IL 60532
Tel.: (630) 348-9337
Web Site:
  http://www.youtechagency.com
Year Founded: 2012

Sales Range: $1-9.9 Million
Emp.: 50
Marketing & Advertising Services
N.A.I.C.S.: 541810
Wilbur You (CEO)
Lauren Adewole (COO)
Michael Norris (CMO)
Nathin Arthur (VP-Design & Dev)
Eric Siemek (VP-Mktg)

YOUTH CO-OP, INC.
3525 NW 7th St, Miami, FL 33125
Tel.: (305) 643-6730   FL
Web Site: http://www.ycoop.org
Year Founded: 1973
Sales Range: $25-49.9 Million
Emp.: 1,054
Youth Support Services
N.A.I.C.S.: 624110
Alicia Sante (Dir-Programs)
Maria Rodriguez (Pres)
Connie Perez-Borroto (Dir-R&D)
Jorge Pichardo (Dir-Fin)

YOUTH DEVELOPMENT, INC.
6301 Central NW, Albuquerque, NM 87105
Tel.: (505) 831-6038
Web Site: http://www.ydinm.org
Year Founded: 1971
Rev.: $23,180,063
Emp.: 550
Youth Service Organization
N.A.I.C.S.: 813410
Diego Gallegos (Pres)

YOUTH FOR UNDERSTANDING INC.
641 S St NW Ste 200, Washington, DC 20001
Tel.: (240) 235-2100   MI
Web Site: http://www.yfuusa.org
Year Founded: 1963
Sales Range: $10-24.9 Million
Emp.: 142
Provider of Schools & Educational Services
N.A.I.C.S.: 611710
Michael Finnell (Pres)
Elizabeth Dennis (Mgr-Community College Program)
Charles Cadigan (VP-External Affairs)

YOUTH IN NEED, INC.
1815 Boone's Lick Rd, Saint Charles, MO 63301
Tel.: (636) 642-0642   MO
Web Site: http://www.youthinneed.org
Year Founded: 1974
Sales Range: $10-24.9 Million
Emp.: 492
Youth Care Services
N.A.I.C.S.: 624110
Amy Putzler (Chief HR Officer)
Mark Solari (CFO)
Tricia Topalbegovic (Chief Program Officer)
Rob Muschany (Chief Dev Officer)
Michelle Gorman (VP-Youth Programs)
Norma Boozer (Treas)
Fran Ventimiglia (Chm)
Anita Viehmann (Vice Chm)
Pat Holterman-Hommes (Pres & CEO)
Kathleen Hodson (Sec)
Tricia Vineyard (Chief Program Officer)

YOUTHFUL AGING HOME HEALTH, INC.
5602 Marquesas Plz Ste 105, Sarasota, FL 34233
Tel.: (941) 925-9532   FL
Web Site:
  http://www.youthfulaging.net
Year Founded: 1998

Sales Range: $1-9.9 Million
Emp.: 120
Women Healthcare Services
N.A.I.C.S.: 621610
Nicci Kobritz (Founder & Pres)
Laani Brackett (Dir-Nursing)

YTB INTERNATIONAL, INC.
1901 E Edwardsville Rd, Wood River, IL 62095
Tel.: (618) 655-9477 DE
Web Site: http://www.ytbi.com
Sales Range: $25-49.9 Million
Emp.: 120
Travel-Related Internet Services
N.A.I.C.S.: 561599
J. Kim Sorensen (Founder & Sec)

YU BROTHERS, INC.
11077 NW 36th Ave, Miami, FL 33167
Tel.: (305) 688-2228
Web Site:
    http://www.sefoodsupplies.com
Sales Range: $10-24.9 Million
Emp.: 50
Whslr of Groceries Specializing in Chinese Food
N.A.I.C.S.: 424410
Stanley Yu (Pres)
Lawrence Yu (VP)

YUASA BATTERY INC.
2901 Montrose Ave, Reading, PA 19605
Tel.: (610) 929-5781
Web Site:
    http://www.yuasabatteries.com
Year Founded: 1979
Sales Range: $25-49.9 Million
Emp.: 250
Mfr & Sales of Storage Batteries
N.A.I.C.S.: 423610
Jessica Slish (Engr-Product & Process Verification)
Jim Colflesh (VP-Procurement & Logistics)
Karen Fell (Mgr-HR)
Melissa Manara (Sr Acct Mgr)

YUBA COUNTY WATER AGENCY
1220 F St, Marysville, CA 95901
Tel.: (530) 741-6278
Web Site: http://www.ycwa.com
Sales Range: $10-24.9 Million
Emp.: 31
Generation, Electric Power
N.A.I.C.S.: 221118
Curt Aikens (Gen Mgr)
Roger Abe (Vice Chm)
Christina McClung (Mgr-Admin Svcs)
Page Hensley (Mgr-Fin)
Geoff Rabone (Mgr-Projects)
Scott Matyac (Mgr-Water Resources)
Mike Kline (Mgr-Power Sys)
Peter Wade (Sr Engr-Hydro)
Lisa Brown (Office Mgr)

YUBA RIVER MOULDING MILL WORK
3757 Feather River Blvd, Marysville, CA 95901
Tel.: (530) 742-2168
Web Site:
    http://www.yubarivermoulding.com
Sales Range: $10-24.9 Million
Emp.: 120
Wood Moldings
N.A.I.C.S.: 321918
Thomas C. Williams Jr. (Pres)

YUCCA VALLEY CHRYSLER CENTER
57909 29 Palms Hwy, Yucca Valley, CA 92284

Tel.: (760) 228-1818
Web Site:
    http://www.yuccavalleychryslercenter.com
Sales Range: $10-24.9 Million
Emp.: 37
Car Whslr
N.A.I.C.S.: 441110
Carol Smith (Pres)

YUCCA VALLEY FORD CENTER, INC.
57927 29 Palms Hwy, Yucca Valley, CA 92284-2498
Tel.: (760) 365-2353
Web Site:
    http://www.yuccavalleyford.com
Sales Range: $10-24.9 Million
Emp.: 42
Car Whslr
N.A.I.C.S.: 441110
James Scheer (Mgr-Internet)

YUKON DELTA FISHERIES DEVELOPMENT ASSOCIATION
2909 Arctic Blvd, Anchorage, AK 99503
Tel.: (907) 644-0326 AK
Web Site: http://www.ydfda.org
Year Founded: 1992
Sales Range: $10-24.9 Million
Emp.: 19
Fishery Development Services
N.A.I.C.S.: 541715
Jenny Koenig (Controller)
Ragnar Alstrom (Exec Dir)
Robert Andrews (Mgr-Yukon Marine Mfg)

YUKON PARTNERS MANAGEMENT LLC
8500 Normandale Lake Blvd Ste 830, Minneapolis, MN 55437
Tel.: (612) 435-7800
Web Site:
    http://www.yukonpartners.com
Year Founded: 2008
Privater Equity Firm
N.A.I.C.S.: 523999
Michael J. Hall (Mng Partner)
William L. Dietz (Mng Partner)
Corey H. Peters (CFO)
Michael Furey (Partner)
Aaron M. Arnett (Principal)
Anne D. Cattoor (Chief Compliance Officer & Controller)
Mark Edwards (VP)

YUM YUM DONUT SHOPS, INC.
18830 E San Jose Ave, City of Industry, CA 91748
Tel.: (626) 964-1478 CA
Web Site:
    http://www.yumyumdonuts.com
Year Founded: 1971
Sales Range: $50-74.9 Million
Emp.: 100
Doughnut Shops Owner & Operator
N.A.I.C.S.: 722515
Frank W. Watase (Chm & Pres)
Tracy Kitagawa (VP-Fin)
Tony Camolina (VP-Ops)

Subsidiaries:

Quality Naturally Foods, Inc. (1)
18830 E San Jose Ave, City of Industry, CA 91748-1325
Tel.: (626) 854-6363
Web Site: http://www.qnfoods.com
Sales Range: $10-24.9 Million
Emp.: 25
Commercial Baking Ingredient Mfr
N.A.I.C.S.: 311999
Lincoln Watase (Exec VP)

Winchell's Donut Houses Operating Co., LP (1)
3610 Venice Blvd 6th Ave, Los Angeles, CA 90019
Tel.: (626) 964-1478
Web Site: http://www.winchells.com
Sales Range: $125-149.9 Million
Doughnut Franchise Owner & Operator
N.A.I.C.S.: 445291

YURMAN DESIGN, INC.
24 Vestry St, New York, NY 10013
Tel.: (212) 896-1550
Web Site:
    http://www.davidyurman.com
Year Founded: 1979
Sales Range: $10-24.9 Million
Emp.: 200
Mfr of Jewelry & Watches
N.A.I.C.S.: 339910
Sybil Yurman (Pres & CMO)
Carol Pennelli (Pres & Chief Comml Officer)

Z CAPITAL GROUP, LLC
FT Bldg 1330 Ave of the Americas 16th Fl, New York, NY 10019
Tel.: (212) 595-8400
Web Site: http://www.zcapgroup.net
Year Founded: 2006
Privater Equity Firm
N.A.I.C.S.: 523999
Rahul Sawhney (Sr Mng Dir)
Matthew D Kane (Mng Dir, Chief Compliance Officer & Gen Counsel)
Glenn Walsh (Operating Partner)
Ryan Paskin (Dir-Operating)
Andrew C. Curtis (Mng Dir)
Erik Hirschbein (CFO & Mng Dir)
James J Zenni Jr. (Founder, Pres & CEO)

Subsidiaries:

Z Capital Partners, LLC (1)
2 Conway Park 150 Field Dr Ste 300, Lake Forest, IL 60045
Tel.: (847) 235-8100
Web Site: http://www.zcap.net
Privater Equity Firm
N.A.I.C.S.: 523999
James Joseph Zenni Jr. (Pres & CEO)
Thomas P. Wicky (Operating Partner)
Andrew C. Curtis (Mng Dir)
Andrew Coats (Operating Partner)
Stephen Parsons (Operating Partner)
Ashwini Sawhney (Sr Mng Dir)

Holding (Domestic):

Affinity Gaming (2)
3755 Breakthrough Way Ste 300, Las Vegas, NV 89135
Tel.: (702) 341-2400
Web Site: http://www.affinitygaming.com
Sales Range: $400-449.9 Million
Casino & Hotel Operator
N.A.I.C.S.: 721120
James Joseph Zenni Jr. (Chm)
Paige Lion (CIO & VP)
Stana Subaric (Sr VP-HR)
Eric P. Fiocco (COO & Chief Mktg Officer)
Mary Elizabeth Higgins (CEO)

Subsidiary (Domestic):

Primm Valley Casino Resorts (3)
31900 Las Vegas Blvd S, Primm, NV 89019-7002
Tel.: (702) 386-7867
Web Site:
    http://www.primmvalleyresorts.com
Casino Resort Operator
N.A.I.C.S.: 721120
Robin Johnson (Mgr-Convention Sls)
Mark Foley (Mgr-Conventions Sls)
Ralph Marano (Mgr-Convention Catering)

Holding (Domestic):

Autotronic Controls Corporation (2)
1490 Henry Brennan Dr, El Paso, TX 79936
Tel.: (915) 857-5200
Web Site: http://www.msdignition.com
Emp.: 400

Automotive Ignition & Fuel System Mfr
N.A.I.C.S.: 336320
Russell Stephens (Pres)

Subsidiary (Domestic):

Competition Systems, Incorporated (3)
30402 Esperanza, Rancho Santa Margarita, CA 92688
Tel.: (949) 709-5555
Web Site: http://www.racepak.com
Data Acquisition Equipment Design & Mfr for Motorsports Industry
N.A.I.C.S.: 336320

Subsidiary (Domestic):

Racepak, LLC (4)
30402 Esperanza, Rancho Santa Margarita, CA 92688
Tel.: (888) 429-4709
Data Acquisition Equipment Design & Mfr for Motorsports Industry
N.A.I.C.S.: 336320
Chris Vopat (Mgr-Sls & Mktg)

Holding (Domestic):

Daily Racing Form, LLC (2)
708 3rd Ave 12th Fl, New York, NY 10017
Tel.: (212) 366-7600
Web Site: http://www.drf.com
Sales Range: $25-49.9 Million
Horse Racing Information Newspaper
N.A.I.C.S.: 513110
Itay Fisher (CEO)
Phil Trowler (Sr VP)
Irina Platonova (Sr VP-Sls & Mktg)

Techniks, LLC (2)
9930 E 56th St, Indianapolis, IN 46236
Tel.: (317) 803-8000
Web Site: http://www.techniksusa.com
Industrial Tool Holders, Cutting Tools & Accessories Designer & Distr
N.A.I.C.S.: 423710
Chris Schulz (Mgr-Ops)
Chris Deal (Reg Mgr-Sls)

Twin-Star International, Inc. (2)
1690 S Congress Ave - Ste 210, Delray Beach, FL 33445
Tel.: (866) 661-1218
Web Site: http://www.twinstarhome.com
Home Furnishing Mfr & Distr
N.A.I.C.S.: 423220
Marc Sculler (Pres)
Lori Gonzalez (CEO)

Subsidiary (Domestic):

Bell'O International Corp. (3)
711 Ginesi Dr, Morganville, NJ 07752-1235
Tel.: (732) 972-1333
Web Site: http://www.bello.com
Home Theater Furniture Mfr
N.A.I.C.S.: 337126
Marc Sculler (CEO)

Classic Accessories, LLC (3)
26600 72nd Ave S Ste 101, Kent, WA 98032
Tel.: (253) 395-3900
Web Site:
    http://www.classicaccessories.com
Outdoor Product Covers Designer & Distr
N.A.I.C.S.: 314999
Kathryn Pinkney (Mgr-Mktg Svcs)
Shruthi Desai (Mgr-Ecommerce Mktg)

Grand Basket, Inc (3)
5306 Grand Ave, Maspeth, NY 11378
Tel.: (718) 386-6400
Web Site: http://www.grandbasketco.com
Wood Window & Door Mfr
N.A.I.C.S.: 321911
Stephen Hoberman (Mgr-Sls-Natl)

Holding (Domestic):

Universal Pharmaceutical Medical Supply Co, Inc. (2)
27 Sylvaton Terrace, Staten Island, NY 10305
Tel.: (718) 438-4804
Web Site: http://www.ummuk.com
Sales Range: $1-9.9 Million
Emp.: 31
Drugs & Druggists' Sundries Merchant Whslr
N.A.I.C.S.: 424210

Z CAPITAL GROUP, LLC

Z Capital Group, LLC—(Continued)
Julius Nasso (Pres)
Alan Kessman (CEO)

Xperience XRG Restaurant Group (2)
5660 Katella Ave Ste 100, Cypress, CA 90630
Tel.: (562) 346-1200
Web Site: http://www.xperiencerg.com
Mexican Restaurant Operator
N.A.I.C.S.: 722511
Rio Gueli (COO)
Jared Dougherty (Sr VP-Mktg)
Bryan Lockwood (CEO)
Judd Tirnauer (CFO)
Randy Sharpe (CEO)
Ned Algeo (CFO)

Subsidiary (Domestic):

El Torito Restaurants, Inc. (3)
5660 Katella Ave Ste 100, Cypress, CA 90630
Tel.: (562) 346-1200
Web Site: http://www.eltorito.com
Sales Range: $400-449.9 Million
Emp.: 6,000
Restaurant Franchise
N.A.I.C.S.: 722511
Bryan Lockwood (CEO)

Z GALLERIE, LLC
422 N Beverly Dr, Beverly Hills, CA 90210
Tel.: (310) 860-9950 CA
Web Site: http://www.zgallerie.com
Year Founded: 1979
Sales Range: $75-99.9 Million
Emp.: 1,000
Home Furnishings & Accessories
N.A.I.C.S.: 449129
Joseph Zeiden (Pres & CEO)
Michael Zeiden (CFO)
Carole Malfatti (VP-Mdsg)

Z INC.
12 N Main St, Homedale, ID 83628
Tel.: (208) 337-3919 ID
Web Site: http://www.pauls.net
Year Founded: 1956
Sales Range: $50-74.9 Million
Emp.: 400
Grocery Stores
N.A.I.C.S.: 445110
Paul Zatica (Pres)
Stan Zatica (VP)
Terri Pearson (Office Mgr)

Z MICROSYSTEMS INC.
9830 Summers Rdg Rd, San Diego, CA 92122
Tel.: (858) 831-7000
Web Site: http://www.zmicro.com
Sales Range: $25-49.9 Million
Emp.: 58
Computer Peripheral Equipment Mfr
N.A.I.C.S.: 334118
Ted Krupp (Mgr-Sls-Central Reg)
Shaojie Wu (Dir-Sls-Pacific Rim)
Jason Wade (Pres)
Randy Millar (VP-Engrg)

Z SQUARED MEDIA, LLC
17040 Amber Dr, Cleveland, OH 44111
Tel.: (216) 941-5842
Web Site: http://www.zsquaredmedia.com
Year Founded: 2007
Sales Range: $1-9.9 Million
Emp.: 17
Marketing Consulting Services
N.A.I.C.S.: 541613
Joe Pulizzi (Founder)

Z TRANSPORTATION INC.
107 Beaverbrook Rd Ste 2, Lincoln Park, NJ 07035
Tel.: (610) 203-1513
Web Site: http://www.ztransport.net
Year Founded: 2006
Sales Range: $10-24.9 Million
Emp.: 160
Freight Transportation Services
N.A.I.C.S.: 488510
Trajce Ristovski (Owner)

Z-BEST PRODUCTS
980 State Hwy 25, Gilroy, CA 95020
Tel.: (408) 283-4804
Web Site: http://www.bankerrecycling.com
Sales Range: $10-24.9 Million
Emp.: 3
Nonhazardous Waste Disposal Sites
N.A.I.C.S.: 423820
Rich Christina (Gen Partner)

Z-MAR TECHNOLOGY INC.
8541 Crown Crescent Ct, Charlotte, NC 28227
Tel.: (704) 841-8845
Web Site: http://www.z-mar.com
Sales Range: $10-24.9 Million
Emp.: 20
Electronic Parts & Equipment
N.A.I.C.S.: 423690
Michael G. Brisson (Pres)
Robbie Smith (Mgr-Sls)

Z-TEJAS INC.
6909 E Green Way Pkwy, Scottsdale, AZ 85032
Tel.: (480) 612-6380
Web Site: http://www.ztejas.com
Year Founded: 1989
Sales Range: $25-49.9 Million
Emp.: 800
Provider of Restaurant Management Services
N.A.I.C.S.: 722511
Steven Micheletti (CEO)

Z. CAVARICCI INC.
2535 E 12th St Bldg A, Laguna Hills, CA 92653
Tel.: (949) 830-9779
Web Site: http://www.zcavaricci.com
Year Founded: 1976
Sales Range: $75-99.9 Million
Emp.: 100
Mfr of Women's & Girls' Jeans, Slacks, Jackets, Shorts & Skirts
N.A.I.C.S.: 424350

Subsidiaries:

Z. Cavaricci Inc. (1)
350 N Orleans St Ste 1225, Chicago, IL 60654-2123 (100%)
Tel.: (312) 670-7778
N.A.I.C.S.: 315210

Z. Cavaricci Inc. (1)
23161 Mill Creek Dr Ste 320, Laguna Hills, CA 92653
Tel.: (213) 765-0888
Web Site: http://www.zcavaricci.com
Sales Range: $25-49.9 Million
Emp.: 3
Sales of Mens & Womens Fashions
N.A.I.C.S.: 315250

ZABALA ERICKSON, LLC.
1020 8th Ave Ste 5, Naples, FL 34102
Tel.: (239) 692-8245
Web Site: http://www.zellc.us
Sales Range: $1-9.9 Million
Emp.: 2
Architectural Services
N.A.I.C.S.: 541310
Fernando Zabala (Mng Partner & Principal)
Carl E. Erickson (Principal)

ZABIN INDUSTRIES INC.
3957 S Hill St, Los Angeles, CA 90037
Tel.: (213) 749-1215 CA
Web Site: http://www.zabin.com
Year Founded: 1975
Sales Range: $10-24.9 Million
Emp.: 75
Mfr & Wholesaler of Appareal Fasteners
N.A.I.C.S.: 424310
Alan Faiola (CEO)

ZACHARY CONFECTIONS INC.
2130 W State Rd 28, Frankfort, IN 46041
Tel.: (765) 659-4751
Web Site: http://www.zacharyconfections.com
Rev.: $39,000,000
Emp.: 300
Chocolate & Cocoa Products
N.A.I.C.S.: 311351
Patrick Kelley (CFO)
Alan Johnson (Dir-Tech)
Steve Newman (Reg Dir-Sls)
George Anichini (Sr VP-Ops)

ZACHERL MOTOR TRUCK SALES
795 Greenville Pike, Clarion, PA 16214
Tel.: (814) 226-8584
Web Site: http://www.zacherlmotors.com
Sales Range: $25-49.9 Million
Emp.: 30
Trucks, Commercial
N.A.I.C.S.: 423110
Randy Reinsel (Mgr-Parts)
Lou Zacherl (Mgr-Svcs)
Steve Kahle (Mgr-Sls)
Jim Dunsmore (Gen Mgr)
Chris Rhoades (Treas & Sec)
Mike Wile (Asst Mgr-Svc)

ZACHRY HOLDINGS, INC.
527 Logwood Ave, San Antonio, TX 78221
Tel.: (210) 588-5000 DE
Web Site: https://www.zachrygroup.com
Year Founded: 1924
Sales Range: Less than $1 Million
Emp.: 16,500
Offices of Other Holding Companies
N.A.I.C.S.: 551112
John B. Zachry (Chm & CEO)
Keith D. Manning (Exec VP-Enterprise Strategic Dev)
D. Kirk McDonald (Exec VP-Fin)
Ralph J. Biediger (Pres-Projects Grp)
Gerald P. Burke (Grp Pres-Engrg)
Steven K. Brauer (Exec VP-Safety & Quality)
Scott Duffy (Sr VP-Comml Mgmt)
Ray Wenz (Sr VP)
Tammy Mallaise (VP-Employee Rels)
A. J. Rodriguez (VP-External Affairs)

Subsidiaries:

Ambitech Engineering Coproration (1)
1411 Opus Pl Ste 200, Downers Grove, IL 60515
Tel.: (630) 963-6309
Web Site: http://www.ambitech.com
Construction Management Services
N.A.I.C.S.: 813910

Zachry Corporation (1)
2330 N Loop 1604 W, San Antonio, TX 78248-4512
Tel.: (210) 871-2700
Web Site: http://www.zachrycorp.com
Holding Company; General Construction, Project Development, Cement & Aggregates
N.A.I.C.S.: 551112
David S. Zachry (CEO)
Tim Watt (Gen Counsel & Sr VP)

U.S. PRIVATE

Subsidiary (Domestic):

Zachry Construction Corporation (2)
12625 Wetmore Rd Ste 301, San Antonio, TX 78247
Tel.: (210) 871-2700
Web Site: http://www.zachryconstructioncorp.com
General Construction & Infrastructure Maintenance Services
N.A.I.C.S.: 237990
David S. Zachry (CEO)
Bryan Golla (Asst Controller)
Vivian Garza-Steele (VP & Controller)
Kevin McMinniman (Exec VP)
Warren Stokes (CFO & Sr VP)
Cody Webb (Gen Counsel & VP)

Zachry Engineering Corporation (1)
1515 Arapahoe St Ste 800 Twr 1, Denver, CO 80202
Tel.: (303) 928-4400
Web Site: http://www.ue-corp.com
Sales Range: $10-24.9 Million
Emp.: 120
Utility & Engineering Services
N.A.I.C.S.: 541330
John B. Zachry (Chm & CEO)
Michael D. Morris (VP-Bus Dev)
Matthew Czuba (Pres)
Lisa Mayo (VP-Maintenance Svcs)

Unit (Domestic):

Zachry Engineering Corp. - Amarillo (2)
5601 W Interstate 40, Amarillo, TX 79106-4605
Tel.: (806) 359-2400
Web Site: http://www.zhi.com
Engineering, Design, Construction, Supervision & Management Services
N.A.I.C.S.: 541618
Rachel Spence (Coord-Sys)
Joshua Wilburn (Engr-Mechanical)
Heidi Blasingame (Mgr-Mechanical Engrg)
Ralph J. Biediger (Pres-Construction-Grp)
Steven K. Brauer (Pres-Indus Svc-Grp)
Gerald P. Burke (Pres-Engrg-Grp)
Scott Duffy (Sr VP-Enterprise Strategic Dev)
Joe J. Lozano (Exec VP-Acctg & Admin)
Tammy Mallaise (VP-Employee Rels)
Keith D. Manning (Exec VP-Enterprise Strategic Dev)
D. Kirk McDonald (Exec VP-Fin)
David Schwab (Gen Counsel, Sec & Sr VP)

Zachry Nuclear Engineering, Inc. (1)
14 Lords Hill Rd, Stonington, CT 06340-3652
Tel.: (860) 446-9725
Sales Range: $25-49.9 Million
Emp.: 150
Project Engineering & Management Services
N.A.I.C.S.: 541330
Christine Yanelli (Mgr-HR)
Lisa Apicelli (Coord-Mktg Svcs)
Mark Mills (Pres)

Subsidiary (Domestic):

Numerical Applications, Inc. (2)
1955 Jadwin Ave Ste 470, Richland, WA 99354
Tel.: (509) 943-0861
Web Site: http://www.numerical.com
Sales Range: $1-9.9 Million
Emp.: 15
Thermal-Hydraulics Analysis Software & Services
N.A.I.C.S.: 513210
Kevin Wheelwright (Mgr-Quality Assurance)

ZACK BURKETT CO.
105 Burkett Industrial Pkwy, Graham, TX 76450
Tel.: (940) 549-0436
Web Site: http://www.zackburkettco.com
Sales Range: $10-24.9 Million
Emp.: 120

COMPANIES

General Contractor, Highway & Street Construction
N.A.I.C.S.: 237310
James C. Burkett (VP)
Sandra Underwood (Office Mgr)
Margaret Lindley (Controller)
Zack T. Burkett III (Chm & Pres)

ZACK ELECTRONICS, INC.
1075 Hamilton Rd, Duarte, CA 91010-2741
Tel.: (626) 303-0655   CA
Web Site: http://www.zackelectronics.com
Year Founded: 1931
Sales Range: $75-99.9 Million
Emp.: 15
Audio & Video Installation Equipment Distr
N.A.I.C.S.: 423690
Dennis Awad (Pres)

ZACKS INVESTMENT RESEARCH INC.
111 N Canal St Ste 1101, Chicago, IL 60606
Tel.: (312) 630-9880
Web Site: http://www.ziri.com
Sales Range: $25-49.9 Million
Emp.: 200
Investment Research
N.A.I.C.S.: 523940
John Harland (Controller)
Don Ralph (Controller)
Igor Rubchinsky (Project Mgr)
Rick Yeske (VP & Dir-Sls)
Keith Young (Acct Mgr)
Susan Menendez (Mgr-HR)
Richard Hantke (Reg Mng Dir-IR)

ZACKY FARMS, INC.
2020 S East Ave, Fresno, CA 93721
Tel.: (559) 486-2310   CA
Web Site: http://www.zacky.com
Year Founded: 1946
Sales Range: $300-349.9 Million
Emp.: 2,800
Turkeys & Processed Meats
N.A.I.C.S.: 112330
Marcus Curry (CFO)
Ivy Quon (Sr VP-Mktg & Admin)
Lillian Zacky (Dir-Consumer Affairs)
Mark Fisher (VP-Plant Ops)
Mark Duarte (Mgr-Stockton Plant)

Subsidiaries:

Stockton Further Processing   (1)
1111 Navy Dr, Stockton, CA 95206   (100%)
Tel.: (209) 948-0129
Web Site: http://www.zackyfarms.com
Sales Range: $25-49.9 Million
Emp.: 300
Further Processor of Poultry & Other Meats Products
N.A.I.C.S.: 311615
Robert Zacky (Pres)

ZAGAT SURVEY, LLC
424 Broadway 5th Fl, New York, NY 10013
Tel.: (212) 977-6000   NY
Web Site: http://www.zagat.com
Year Founded: 1979
Restaurant Discovery Platform
N.A.I.C.S.: 513199
Chris Tang (CEO)
Nell Potter (Gen Mgr)

ZAHARONI INDUSTRIES, INC.
5400 W Rosecrans Ave, Hawthorne, CA 90250-6609
Tel.: (310) 297-9710   CA
Web Site: http://www.westcosteng.com
Year Founded: 1965
Sales Range: $10-24.9 Million
Emp.: 51
Mfr of Electronic Parts & Equipment
N.A.I.C.S.: 423690
Jerry Velona (Gen Mgr-West Coast Engrg Svcs)

Subsidiaries:

West Coast Engineering Service   (1)
5400 W Rosecrans Ave, Hawthorne, CA 90250-6609   (100%)
Tel.: (310) 297-9710
Web Site: http://www.wcela.com
Sales Range: $10-24.9 Million
Emp.: 25
Provider of Computer Peripherals & Software
N.A.I.C.S.: 423690
Isaac Zaharoni (Pres)

ZAHM & MATSON INC.
1756 Linquist Dr, Falconer, NY 14733
Tel.: (716) 665-3110
Web Site: http://www.zahmandmatson.com
Year Founded: 1958
Sales Range: $50-74.9 Million
Emp.: 27
Farm Equipment & Supplies
N.A.I.C.S.: 459999
Tracy Buck (Owner & Mgr-Store)
Brian Malecki (Mgr-Svc)
Mark Holthouse (Mgr-Parts)
Greg Meeder (Mgr-Parts)
Keith Foster (Mgr-Parts)
Andrew Campbell (Asst Mgr-Woodworking)
Tom Klapper (Asst Mgr-Woodworking)
Tim Black (Mgr-Aftermarket)
Rod Ruttenbur (Mgr-Svc-Columbus)

ZAIS GROUP HOLDINGS, INC.
2 Bridge Ave Ste 322, Red Bank, NJ 07701-1106
Tel.: (732) 978-7518   DE
Web Site: http://www.zaisgroupholdings.com
Year Founded: 2012
Rev.: $30,836,000
Assets: $187,889,000
Liabilities: $59,067,000
Net Worth: $128,822,000
Earnings: ($1,221,000)
Emp.: 59
Fiscal Year-end: 12/31/17
Holding Comapny; Investment & Asset Management Services
N.A.I.C.S.: 551112
Christian Markus Zugel (Founder, Chm & Chief Investment Officer)
Nisha Motani (CFO & Chief Acctg Officer)
Mark Russo (Mng Dir & Gen Counsel)
Denise Crowley (Head-Securitized Credit, Bus Dev, and Client Rels)
Daniel Curry (Pres & CEO)

Subsidiaries:

ZAIS Group (UK) Limited   (1)
20 North Audley Street, London, W1K 6LX, United Kingdom
Tel.: (44) 2036671820
Credit Manager Services
N.A.I.C.S.: 522130

ZAIS Group, LLC   (1)
2 Bridge Ave Ste 322, Red Bank, NJ 07701
Tel.: (732) 530-3610
Web Site: http://www.zaisgroup.com
Rev.: $5,200,000,000
Emp.: 130
Asset Management Services
N.A.I.C.S.: 523940
Christian Markus Zugel (Founder, Chm & Chief Investment Officer)
Lauren Grobelny (VP-Client Rels)
Paul J. McDade III (Mng Dir-Special Projects)

ZAK DESIGNS INC.
1603 S Garfield Rd, Airway Heights, WA 99001
Tel.: (509) 244-0555   WA
Web Site: http://www.zak.com
Year Founded: 1976
Sales Range: $25-49.9 Million
Emp.: 200
Mfr of Children's Dinnerware
N.A.I.C.S.: 423220
Amy Higgins (Mgr-Credit)
Daini Hertel (Mgr-Inventory Procurement)
Ken Long (VP-Sls)
Michael Scott (Sr Mgr-Creative)
Reggy Thomas (VP-Global Licensing & Mktg)
Eric Enger (Reg Mgr-Sls)
Michelle McPherson (Sr Mgr-Licensing)
Nicole Alexander (Mgr-Mktg)
Seth Shepard (Engr-Product-Product Dev)

ZAK PRODUCTS INC.
8333 Royal Ridge Pkwy Ste 100, Irving, TX 75063
Tel.: (972) 739-0300
Web Site: http://www.zakproducts.com
Year Founded: 2003
Sales Range: $10-24.9 Million
Emp.: 20
Automotive Fluid Chemical Maintenance Products
N.A.I.C.S.: 811121
Victor Keller (Gen Partner)

ZAMBEZI
10441 Jefferson Rd Blvd, Culver City, CA 90232
Tel.: (310) 450-6800
Web Site: http://www.zambezi-la.com
Year Founded: 2006
Sales Range: $1-9.9 Million
Emp.: 50
Advetising Agency
N.A.I.C.S.: 541810
Chris Raih (Founder & Pres)
Josh DiMarcantonio (Partner & Exec Dir-Creative)
Kristina Jenkins (Chief Strategy Officer)
Ryan Richards (Grp Dir-Strategy)
Gordon Gray (Acct Dir)
Danielle Pak (Dir-Comm Plng)
Dan Maxwell (Dir-Creative)
Annie Johnston (Assoc Dir-Creative)
Chris Rutkowski (Assoc Dir-Creative)
Jean Freeman (CEO)
Gavin Lester (Chief Creative Officer & Partner-Equity)
Ben George (Dir-Creative)
Nick Rodgers (Dir-Creative)
Erickson Ilog (CFO & COO)
Laura Stayt (Exec Dir-Bus Ops)
Kara Pierce (Dir-Integrated Production)
Tabitha Onofri (Head-Studio-FIN Studios)

ZAMIAS SERVICES INC.
300 Market St, Johnstown, PA 15901-1702
Tel.: (814) 535-3563   PA
Web Site: http://www.zamias.com
Year Founded: 1996
Sales Range: $10-24.9 Million
Emp.: 60
Real Estate Financial & Management Services
N.A.I.C.S.: 531120
George D. Zamias (Founder)
Matt Schaefer (VP-Real Estate)
Monica Peterman (Mgr-Property)
Mark Funyak (Mgr-Construction Property)

ZANIBONI LIGHTING, LLC

Michael Baker (CFO)
Perry D. Russ (Exec VP)
Stephen G. Zamias (Vice Chm)

ZAMPELL REFRACTORIES INC.
3 Stanley Tucker Dr, Newburyport, MA 01950
Tel.: (978) 499-5055   MA
Web Site: http://www.zampell.com
Year Founded: 1966
Refractories Engineering & Construction Services; Insulation, Scaffolding & Facilities Management
N.A.I.C.S.: 238220
James Zampell (CEO)
Jason Murray (Mgr-HR)
John Heffernan (Sr Mgr-Sls & Engrg)
Brian Zampell (Pres)
Jason Heath (Dir-Safety & Loss Control)

ZAMPHR, INC.
898 N 1200 W Ste 100, Orem, UT 84057
Tel.: (801) 377-1190
Web Site: http://www.zamphr.com
Year Founded: 2014
Sales Range: $125-149.9 Million
Emp.: 30
Human Resource Consulting Services
N.A.I.C.S.: 541612
Craig Allred (Pres & CEO)
Cass Joseph (Dir-Agency)
Gulshan Saini (Dir-Web Dev)
Jason Gesullo (Dir-IT)
Jeff Engh (Dir-HR)

ZAMZOWS INC.
1201 Franklin Blvd, Nampa, ID 83687
Tel.: (208) 465-3630
Web Site: http://www.zamzows.com
Sales Range: $10-24.9 Million
Emp.: 200
Garden & Pet Feed
N.A.I.C.S.: 424910
Ken Kirkbride (VP)
Greg Schneider (Mgr-Sls)

ZANDER THERAPEUTICS, INC.
4700 Spring St Ste 304, La Mesa, CA 91942
Tel.: (619) 702-1404   NV
Web Site: http://www.zandertherapeutics.com
Year Founded: 2015
Emp.: 3
Biotechnology Research & Development Services
N.A.I.C.S.: 541714
Todd S. Caven (CFO)
Debbie Dorsee (Dir-Bus Dev)

ZANELLA LTD. INC.
711 5th Ave Fl 12, New York, NY 10022-4308
Tel.: (212) 371-2121   IT
Web Site: http://www.zanella.com
Year Founded: 1950
Sales Range: $10-24.9 Million
Emp.: 31
Whslr of Men's & Women's Wear
N.A.I.C.S.: 424350
Armando Di Natale (Pres & CEO)
Dominick Cicero (Controller)
Carl Sherman (Mgr-Credit)

ZANIBONI LIGHTING, LLC
101 N Garden, Clearwater, FL 33755
Tel.: (727) 213-0410
Web Site: http://www.zanibonilighting.com
Year Founded: 2014
Sales Range: $1-9.9 Million

ZANIBONI LIGHTING, LLC

Zaniboni Lighting, LLC—(Continued)
Emp.: 49
Lighting Product Mfr
N.A.I.C.S.: 335139
Chiara Zaniboni (CEO)

ZANONTIAN & SONS INC.
2499 W Shaw Ave Ste 101, Fresno, CA 93711
Tel.: (559) 248-0151
Web Site: http://www.zanont.com
Sales Range: $10-24.9 Million
Emp.: 5
Developer of Gourmet & Specialty Foods
N.A.I.C.S.: 424490
Samuel Zanontian (Pres)

ZANOTTO MARKET INC.
1970 Naglee Ave, San Jose, CA 95126
Tel.: (408) 293-4594
Web Site: http://www.zanottos.com
Year Founded: 1964
Sales Range: $10-24.9 Million
Emp.: 50
Grocery Stores
N.A.I.C.S.: 445110
Dan Zanotto (Pres)
Fred Zanotto (VP)

ZANTECH IT SERVICES, INC.
1600 Tysons Blvd Ste 1150, McLean, VA 22102
Tel.: (703) 286-1393
Web Site: http://www.zantechit.com
Year Founded: 2007
Sales Range: $10-24.9 Million
Emp.: 55
Information Technology Consulting Services
N.A.I.C.S.: 541512
Zia Islam (Pres & CEO)
Richard J. Roth (CFO & Exec VP)
Missie Knight (VP-HR)
Greg Hanson (COO & Exec VP)

ZANZICO
10115 Kincey Ave Storrs Bldg Ste 150, Huntersville, NC 28078
Tel.: (704) 987-1288
Web Site: http://www.zanzico.com
Year Founded: 2000
Sales Range: Less than $1 Million
Emp.: 7
Advetising Agency
N.A.I.C.S.: 541810
Katie Smith (Pres)
John Maskell (Dir-Creative)
Jim Henderson (Dir-Interactive)

ZAP ENGINEERING & CONSTRUCTION SERVICES, INC.
333 S Allison Pkwy Ste 100, Lakewood, CO 80226-3115
Tel.: (720) 529-4430
Web Site: http://www.zapecs.com
Year Founded: 2001
Sales Range: Less than $1 Million
Emp.: 67
Engineering & Construction Services
N.A.I.C.S.: 541330
Steve Tzap (Project Mgr & Sr Process Engr)
Carl Soderman (Pres)

ZAPATA ENGINEERING
6302 Fairview Rd Ste 600, Charlotte, NC 28210
Tel.: (704) 358-8240
Web Site: http://www.zapatainc.com
Year Founded: 1991
Sales Range: $10-24.9 Million
Emp.: 215
Environmental, Facilities, Infrastructure & Military Munitions Services
N.A.I.C.S.: 541330
Manuel L. Zapata (Pres)
R. Marty Ray (VP-Plng & Strategy)
Samantha Hovis (Engr-Civil)
Subsidiaries:
Zapata Engineering - Blackhawk Division (1)
301 Commercial Rd Ste D, Golden, CO 80401-5646
Tel.: (303) 278-8700
Web Site: http://www.zapatainc.com
Sales Range: $10-24.9 Million
Emp.: 20
Geophysical Contracting & Consulting Services
N.A.I.C.S.: 541611
Jim Hild (Gen Mgr)

ZAPP'S POTATO CHIPS, INC.
307 E Airline Hwy, Gramercy, LA 70052
Tel.: (225) 869-9777
Web Site: http://www.zapps.com
Year Founded: 1985
Sales Range: $75-99.9 Million
Emp.: 100
Mfr of Potato Chips
N.A.I.C.S.: 311919
Tony Dong (Mgr-Quality Assurance)

ZAPTEL CORPORATION
836 S Arlington Heights Rd Ste L, Elk Grove Village, IL 60007
Tel.: (847) 342-2000
Web Site: http://www.zaptel.com
Year Founded: 1996
Sales Range: $1-9.9 Million
Emp.: 8
Online Prepaid Phone Card Retailer & Whslr
N.A.I.C.S.: 517810
Ron Reimann (Pres & CEO)

ZAPWATER COMMUNICATIONS, INC.
118 N Peoria 4th Floor, Chicago, IL 60607
Tel.: (312) 943-0333
Web Site: http://www.zapwater.com
Year Founded: 2004
Public Relations & Communications
N.A.I.C.S.: 541820
David M. Zapata (Founder, CEO & Partner)
Mayra Bacik (Partner & CFO)
Jennifer Lake (Chief Strategy Officer)
Annie Block (VP)
Ileana Perez (VP-Fin)

ZAREMBA GROUP, LLC
14600 Detroit Ave Ste 1500, Lakewood, OH 44107
Tel.: (216) 221-6600
Web Site: http://www.zarembagroup.com
Year Founded: 1920
Sales Range: $75-99.9 Million
Emp.: 100
Real Estate Developer, Contractor & Property Management
N.A.I.C.S.: 237210
Walter Zaremba (Chm, Pres & CEO)
Barbara Von Benken (Sec)
Robert Steadley (CFO)
Subsidiaries:
Zaremba Contractors, LLC (1)
14600 Detroit Ave, Lakewood, OH 44107-4207 (100%)
Tel.: (216) 221-6600
Web Site: http://www.zarembagroup.com
Sales Range: $25-49.9 Million
Emp.: 70
General Contractor, Residential & Retail
N.A.I.C.S.: 236220
Walter Zaremba (Chm & CEO)
Al Soulin (Pres-Retail)

ZARIN FABRICS
314 Grand St, New York, NY 10002
Tel.: (212) 925-6112
Web Site: http://www.zarinfabrics.com
Sales Range: $10-24.9 Million
Emp.: 15
Upholstery & Drapery Fabrics & Venetian Blinds
N.A.I.C.S.: 423220
Bobby Zarin (Chm)
David Zarin (Pres)

ZARTMAN CONSTRUCTION INC.
RR 1 Box 349z, Northumberland, PA 17857
Tel.: (570) 275-4400
Web Site: http://www.zartman.com
Year Founded: 1973
Sales Range: $25-49.9 Million
Emp.: 175
Nonresidential Construction Services
N.A.I.C.S.: 236220
Gene Zartman (Pres)

ZASER & LONGSTON INC.
10518 NE 37th Cir, Kirkland, WA 98033-7920
Tel.: (425) 285-1440
Year Founded: 1956
Sales Range: $25-49.9 Million
Emp.: 20
Television Broadcasting Station
N.A.I.C.S.: 516120

ZATKOFF SEALS & PACKINGS
23230 Industrial Park Dr, Farmington Hills, MI 48335
Tel.: (248) 478-2400
Web Site: http://www.zatkoff.com
Year Founded: 1959
Sales Range: $75-99.9 Million
Emp.: 170
Distr of Seals
N.A.I.C.S.: 339991
Gary A. Zatkoff (Pres)

ZAXBY'S FRANCHISING, INC.
1040 Founders Blvd, Athens, GA 30606
Tel.: (706) 353-8107
Web Site: http://www.zaxbys.com
Year Founded: 1990
Sales Range: $25-49.9 Million
Emp.: 700
Restaurant Franchise
N.A.I.C.S.: 722513
Zach W. McLeroy (Co-Founder & Chm)
Tony D. Townley (Co-Founder)
Robert E. Baxley (COO)
Donny Lau (CFO)
Carl Mount (Chief Supply Chain Officer)
Patrick Schwing (Chief Mktg & Strategy Officer)
Bernard Acoca (CEO)

ZAZZLE, INC.
1900 Seaport Blvd 4, Redwood City, CA 94063
Tel.: (650) 853-0100
Web Site: http://www.zazzle.com
Year Founded: 2005
Sales Range: $1-9.9 Million
Emp.: 99
Online Retail Services
N.A.I.C.S.: 323111
Robert Beaver (Co-Founder & CEO)
Jeff Beaver (Co-Founder & Chief Product Officer)
Bobby Beaver (Co-Founder & & CTO)
Jason Kang (CFO)
Peggy Beaver (Chief People Officer)
Nizzi Karai Renaud (CMO)
Melanie Sherk (Chief Legal Officer & VP-Bus Dev)
Charles Ohiaeri (Chief Fulfillment Officer)
Subsidiaries:
Coveroo, Inc. (1)
1800 Seaport Blvd, Redwood City, CA 94063
Tel.: (415) 240-4886
Web Site: http://www.coveroo.com
Mobile Accessories Mfr & Distr
N.A.I.C.S.: 334210
James Chapman (Pres & Head-Product Mgmt)
Mark Halstead (CTO)
Peter Tomassi (CMO & Head-New Product Dev)

ZCORUM INC.
PO Box 1376, Alpharetta, GA 30009
Tel.: (678) 507-5000
Web Site: http://www.zcorum.com
Year Founded: 1997
Rev.: $19,900,000
Emp.: 230
System Integration Services
N.A.I.C.S.: 517121
Luis Herrera (CFO)
Scott Helms (VP-Tech)
Neal Grillot (VP-Ops)
Julie Compann (Pres & CEO)
Arthur Skinner (VP)
Alex Rivera (Dir-Sls-Latin America)
Peter Olivia (Dir-Sys Engrg)
Dennis Buddy Bertrum (Dir-Tech)
Fonya Frazier (Mgr-Customer Care)
Melissa Amerson (Mgr-Svc-Columbus)
Rick Yuzzi (VP-Mktg)
Jason Young (VP-Support Svcs)

ZEAL CREDIT UNION
29550 5 Mile Rd, Livonia, MI 48154
Tel.: (734) 522-3700
Web Site: http://www.zealcreditunion.org
Year Founded: 1954
Sales Range: $25-49.9 Million
Emp.: 180
Credit Union
N.A.I.C.S.: 522130
Corrina Dee Dye- Hale (Mgr-Mortgage Dept)
Robert Kiidla (Sr VP-Lending)
Margaret Lamb (CFO & Sr VP)
Angela Krogol (Sr VP-Member Svcs)
Julie Kreinbring (Pres & CEO)
Michael O'Hehir (Chm)

ZEALOT NETWORKS, INC.
660 Venice Blvd, Venice, CA 90292
Tel.: (310) 309-0852
Web Site: http://www.zealotnetworks.com
Year Founded: 2014
Sales Range: $25-49.9 Million
Emp.: 100
Holding Company; Digital Media Products & Services
N.A.I.C.S.: 551112
Chad Seymour (Co-Founder & CMO)
Daniel E. Zappin (Co-Founder, Pres & CEO)
Robert W. Vanech (Co-Founder & CFO)
Conn Fishburn (Co-Founder & Chief Strategy Officer)
Subsidiaries:
AudioMicro, Inc. (1)
13351 D Riverside Dr Ste 219, Sherman Oaks, CA 91423
Tel.: (818) 651-6311
Web Site: http://www.audiomicro.com

COMPANIES

Sales Range: $1-9.9 Million
Emp.: 25
Digital Content Licensing Services
N.A.I.C.S.: 533110
Ryan Born (CEO)
Alexander Iovenko (CTO)
Benjamin Barger (VP-Ops)
Noah Becker (VP-Rights Mgmt)
Peter Amloian (VP-Fin)

Subsidiary (Domestic):

DashGo, Inc. (2)
13351-D Riverside Dr Ste 219, Sherman Oaks, CA 91423
Tel.: (818) 651-6311
Web Site: http://www.dashgo.com
Digital Music Content Licensing Services
N.A.I.C.S.: 533110
Ben Patterson (Founder & CEO)

Converge Media Group, LLC (1)
1460 Broadway, New York, NY 10036
Tel.: (212) 849-8228
Web Site: http://www.convergemg.com
Entertainment Talent Management & Video Content Production Services
N.A.I.C.S.: 711410
Rick Dorfman (CEO)
Conan Smith (Founder)
Steven Wettenstein (Mgr)
Mick Perry (Head-Production)
Louis Calderone (COO)

Gotee Records, Inc. (1)
1746 General George Patton Dr, Brentwood, TN 37027-2935
Tel.: (615) 370-2980
Web Site: http://www.gotee.com
Music Publishers
N.A.I.C.S.: 512230
Joey Elwood (Co-Founder & Pres)
Toby Mac (Co-Founder)

Idea Farmer LLC (1)
1685 Beverly Blvd, Los Angeles, CA 90026
Tel.: (323) 207-0880
Web Site: http://www.idea-farmer.com
Advertising Agency; Marketing Video Production Services
N.A.I.C.S.: 541810
Josh Beane (CEO)

Neighbor, Inc. (1)
2114 Narcissus Ct, Venice, CA 90291
Tel.: (310) 633-9311
Web Site: http://www.neighboragency.com
Advertising & Public Relations Agency
N.A.I.C.S.: 541810
Linda Price (Pres)
Carla Byer (Sr VP-Fin & Ops)
Celia Sepulveda (VP-PR)
Jim Wayne (Dir-Digital)
Jessica Zeller (Dir-Social Media)
Amy Meyer (Dir-Strategy)
Michelle Esposito (Grp Acct Dir)
Madeline Grandbois (Grp Dir-Creative)
McKenzie Sixt (Mgr-Digital Acct)

NewMediaRockstars, Inc. (1)
15635 Alton Pkwy Ste 325, Irvine, CA 92618
Tel.: (949) 585-9644
Web Site: http://www.newmediarockstars.com
Sales Range: $1-9.9 Million
Online New Media Trade Magazine Publisher
N.A.I.C.S.: 513120
Filup Molina (Dir-Creative NMR)

Premier Sports & Entertainment, Inc. (1)
16133 Ventura Blvd Ste 500, Encino, CA 91436
Tel.: (310) 584-9474
Web Site: http://www.psemanagement.com
Sports & Entertainment Talent Management & Marketing Services
N.A.I.C.S.: 711410
Gary Uberstine (CEO)
Eric Kaufman (Pres)

Threshold Interactive (1)
8675 Hayden Pl, Culver City, CA 90232
Tel.: (310) 577-9800
Web Site: http://www.thresholdinteractive.com
Sales Range: $1-9.9 Million
Emp.: 28
Advetising Agency

N.A.I.C.S.: 541810
Scott Williamson (CFO & CTO)
John Montgomery (CEO & Chief Innovation Officer)
Renee Westerhout (Dir-Social Media)
Joel Kennedy (Dir-Art)
Arbi Stepanian (Dir-Tech)
Rita Sweeney Benedum (Dir-Acct)
Michael Grgas (Dir-Design)
Laura Schluckebier (Project Mgr)

ZEBRA ENVIRONMENTAL AND INDUSTRIAL SERVICES, INC.
901 E Springfield Rd, High Point, NC 27261
Tel.: (336) 841-5276   NY
Web Site: http://www.zebraenviro.com
Year Founded: 2005
Sales Range: $1-9.9 Million
Emp.: 27
Environmental & Remedial Services
N.A.I.C.S.: 541620
Amy Tedder (Pres)

ZEBRA IMAGING, INC.
9801 Metric Blvd Ste 200, Austin, TX 78758
Tel.: (512) 251-5100
Web Site: http://www.zebraimaging.com
Year Founded: 1996
Rev.: $15,000,000
Emp.: 50
Digital Graphics Printing Services
N.A.I.C.S.: 323111
C. David Perry (Exec VP-Comml Markets & Strategic Partnerships)
Brian G. Hill (VP-Product Dev & Mfg)
James A. Gardner (VP-Federal Sector)
Michael A. Klug (Founder & CTO)
Albert E. Wargo (Chm)
Chuck Scullion (Pres & CEO)
Michael Masters (CMO)
Rudy Guerrero (Dir-Engrg)
Stacey Dannenbrink (Controller)

ZEBULON SOLUTIONS LLC
1822 Skyway Dr Unit A, Longmont, CO 80504
Tel.: (720) 526-2157
Web Site: http://www.zebulonsolutions.com
Year Founded: 2009
Product Design & Supply Chain Services
N.A.I.C.S.: 541490
Chuck Hodges (Pres & CEO)
Jenney Loper (Dir-Ops)

Subsidiaries:

JSL Solutions LLC (1)
1099 W 133rd Way Ste C, Denver, CO 80234-1142
Tel.: (585) 957-2263
All Other Support Services
N.A.I.C.S.: 561990

ZECK FORD
4501 S 4th St, Leavenworth, KS 66048
Tel.: (913) 727-1650
Web Site: http://www.zeckford.com
Year Founded: 1973
Sales Range: $50-74.9 Million
Emp.: 85
Car Whslr
N.A.I.C.S.: 441110
Derek Zeck (Co-Owner)
Dustin Zeck (Co-Owner)
Danny Zeck (Co-Owner)

ZEE AUTOMOTIVE
655 Bridgeport Ave, Milford, CT 06460
Tel.: (203) 882-1971

Web Site: http://www.chevroletofmilford.com
Year Founded: 1982
Sales Range: $10-24.9 Million
Emp.: 45
Car Whslr
N.A.I.C.S.: 441110
Alice Cerwinski (Controller)
Craig Zoufaly (Pres)

ZEELAND FARM SERVICES INC.
2468 84th Ave, Zeeland, MI 49464
Tel.: (616) 772-9042
Web Site: http://www.zfsinc.com
Sales Range: $75-99.9 Million
Emp.: 200
Buyer & Seller of Grains
N.A.I.C.S.: 311224
Cliff Meeuwsen (Pres)
Chris Laarman (Mgr-Parts)
Bentley Kollen (Mgr-Tax)
Bob Stokes (Mgr-Cash & Credit)
Jeremy Trimble (Coord-Food Safety)

ZEELAND LUMBER & SUPPLY CO.
146 E Washington Ave, Zeeland, MI 49464-1226
Tel.: (616) 772-2119
Web Site: http://zeelandlumber.com
Lumber & Building Material Whslr
N.A.I.C.S.: 444110
Mike Dykstra (Pres & CEO)

Subsidiaries:

Maverick Building Systems, LLC (1)
3190 Walnut Lake Ct, Commerce Township, MI 48390-4109
Tel.: (248) 366-9410
Web Site: http://www.mavbldgsys.com
Truss Mfr
N.A.I.C.S.: 321215
Kevin Maguire (Pres)

ZEHNDER COMMUNICATIONS, INC.
650 Poydras St Ste 2450, New Orleans, LA 70130
Tel.: (504) 558-7778
Web Site: http://www.z-comm.com
Year Founded: 1996
Rev.: $25,500,000
Emp.: 32
Advetising Agency
N.A.I.C.S.: 541810
Mike Rainey (Chief Creative Officer & Producer)
Sarah Keiffer (Mgr-Production)
Joann Habisreitinger (Dir-Media)
Craig Schultz (Project Mgr)
Ann Edelman (Dir-PR)
Dave Maher (Chief Digital Officer)
Rob Hudak (Dir-Interactive Creative)
Lauren Gavrelis (Acct Exec)
Blake Killian (Dir-Social Media)
Samantha Brooks (Sr Acct Exec)
Emily Misso (Acct Exec)
Maggie King (Acct Coord)
Geoffrey Fuglaar (Coord-Media)
Sarah Jones (Acct Supvr)

Subsidiaries:

Zehnder Communications (1)
4311 Blue Bonnet Blvd, Baton Rouge, LA 70809
Tel.: (225) 243-5302
Sales Range: $10-24.9 Million
Consumer Marketing
N.A.I.C.S.: 541810
Jeff Zehnder (Owner)
Henry Chassaignac (Pres & Exec Dir-Creative)
Beth Swayne (Assoc Dir-Acct Svcs)
Ann Edelman (VP-PR & Media)

ZEHNDERS OF FRANKENMUTH INC.

ZEKELMAN INDUSTRIES INC.

730 S Main St, Frankenmuth, MI 48734
Tel.: (989) 652-0470   MI
Web Site: http://www.zehnders.com
Year Founded: 1856
Sales Range: $10-24.9 Million
Emp.: 700
Family Restaurant Operator
N.A.I.C.S.: 722511
Albert F. Zehnder (Chm & CEO)
Martha Zehnder Shelton (CFO)
Linda Susan Zehnder (VP-HR)
John Shelton (VP-Sls & Mktg)
William Parlberg (Pres)

ZEIGLER BROS INC.
400 Gardners Station Rd, Gardners, PA 17324
Tel.: (717) 677-6181
Web Site: http://www.zeiglerfeed.com
Sales Range: $10-24.9 Million
Emp.: 80
Animal Feed Mfr
N.A.I.C.S.: 311119
Timothy M. Zeigler (VP-Sls & Mktg)
Matthew P. Zeigler (VP-Ops)
Craig L. Browdy (Dir-R&D)

ZEIGLER CHRYSLER DODGE JEEP OF SCHAUMBURG
208 W Golf Rd, Schaumburg, IL 60195
Tel.: (847) 882-8400
Web Site: http://www.zeiglerchryslerdodgejeep.com
Sales Range: $10-24.9 Million
Emp.: 90
Car Whslr
N.A.I.C.S.: 441110
Greg Sherman (Pres)
Yvonne Sherman (Treas & Sec)
Michael Smalley (Principal)
Joe St. Germain (Gen Mgr)

ZEILER INSURANCE INC.
12159 S Pulaski Rd, Alsip, IL 60803
Tel.: (708) 597-5900
Web Site: http://www.zeiler.com
Sales Range: $10-24.9 Million
Emp.: 20
Insurance Services
N.A.I.C.S.: 524210
Dan Zieler (Pres & Acct Mgr)

ZEISER MOTORS, INC.
1911 E Edwardsville Rd, Wood River, MO 63376-1652
Tel.: (618) 216-8080
Web Site: http://www.woodriverkia.com
Year Founded: 1983
Sales Range: $10-24.9 Million
Emp.: 25
Car Whslr
N.A.I.C.S.: 441110
David Miller (VP)
David Zeiser (Gen Mgr)
Craig Eggert (Office Mgr)

ZEKELMAN INDUSTRIES INC.
227 W Monroe St Ste 2600, Chicago, IL 60606
Tel.: (312) 275-1600   DE
Web Site: http://www.zekelman.com
Year Founded: 2004
Sales Range: $1-4.9 Billion
Emp.: 1,700
Steel Pipe & Tube Mfr
N.A.I.C.S.: 331210
Barry M. Zekelman (Chm & CEO)
Jim Hays (Pres-Electrical, Fence & Mechanical)
Michael E. Mechley (VP-Procurement)
Tom Muth (Pres-HSS & Piling Products Div)

ZEKELMAN INDUSTRIES INC.

U.S. PRIVATE

Zekelman Industries Inc.—(Continued)
Michael J. Graham (CFO)
Ken Pursel (Pres-Sharon Tube)
Kevin Kelly (Pres-Standard Pipe)
Nick Shubat (Pres-Fence & Mechanical)
Randy Boswell (Pres-Energy Tubulars)
Michael P. McNamara Jr. (Pres-Z Modulars, Exec VP & Sec)

Subsidiaries:

Atlas Tube Inc. (1)
200 Clark Street, PO Box 970, Harrow, N0R 1G0, ON, Canada
Tel.: (519) 738-5000
Web Site: http://www.atlastube.com
Sales Range: $10-24.9 Million
Emp.: 120
Hollow Structural Steel Tubing Mfr
N.A.I.C.S.: 331210
Barry M. Zekelman (Chm)

Plant (US):

Atlas Tube Inc. - Chicago (2)
1855 E 122nd St, Chicago, IL 60633-2429
Tel.: (773) 646-4500
Web Site: http://www.atlastube.com
Structural Steel Tubing Mfr
N.A.I.C.S.: 331210

Atlas Tube Inc. - Plymouth (2)
13101 Eckles Rd, Plymouth, MI 48170
Tel.: (734) 738-5600
Web Site: http://www.atlastube.com
Round, Rectangular & Square Structural Steel Tubing Mfr
N.A.I.C.S.: 331210

John Maneely Company (1)
227 W Monroe 26th Fl, Chicago, IL 60606
Tel.: (216) 910-3700
Web Site: http://www.jmcsteelgroup.com
Sales Range: $1-4.9 Billion
Welded Steel Pipes & Tubes Mfr
N.A.I.C.S.: 331210
Barry M. Zekelman (Chm)
David W. Seeger (Pres)
Michael E. Mechley (VP-Procurement)
Jim Hays (Pres-Electrical, Fence & Mechanical)
Tom Muth (Pres-HSS & Piling)
Michael J. Graham (CFO)
Frank A. Riddick III (CEO)
Michael P. McNamara Jr. (Gen Counsel & Exec VP-IT)

Division (Domestic):

Wheatland Tube Company (2)
700 S Dock St, Sharon, PA 16146
Tel.: (724) 347-7771
Web Site: http://www.wheatland.com
Sales Range: $150-199.9 Million
Emp.: 1,000
Steel Pole Mfr
N.A.I.C.S.: 331210
Patrick Walczak (Dir-Credit & Collection)
Bob Bussiere (Gen Mgr-Fire Protection)
Jelani Rucker (VP-Bus Dev)
Kevin Kelly (Pres-Pipe Div)

Subsidiary (Domestic):

Western Tube & Conduit Corporation (3)
2001 E Dominguez St, Long Beach, CA 90810-1088
Tel.: (310) 537-6300
Web Site: http://www.westerntube.com
Rolled Steel Shape Mfr
N.A.I.C.S.: 331221
Steve Gasparro (VP-Sls)
Andy Hardesty (Reg Mgr)
Joe Sheridan (Dir-Sls-Canada & Sr Reg Mgr-USA)
Jennifer Wildhaber (Mgr-Inside Sls)
Kirk Cowan (Mgr-Western Reg)
Hector Saucedo (Mgr-Sls-Fence & Mechanical Div)
Patrick Ongman (Gen Mgr)

Plant (Domestic):

Wheatland Tube Company - Mill Street Plant (3)

134 Mill St, Sharon, PA 16146-2118
Tel.: (724) 981-5200
Web Site: http://www.wheatland.com
Sales Range: $75-99.9 Million
Emp.: 425
Mfr of Pipe & Mechanical Tubing
N.A.I.C.S.: 331210
Ken Pursel (Pres)

ZEKIAH TECHNOLOGIES, INC.
103 Centennial St Ste G, La Plata, MD 20646
Tel.: (301) 392-3788
Web Site: http://www.zekiah.com
Year Founded: 1999
Rev.: $3,700,000
Emp.: 28
Data Processing, Hosting & Related Services
N.A.I.C.S.: 518210
Brianna Bowling (Pres)
Bill Dollins (Sr VP)
Steve Kuiper (Sr VP)
Dan Bowling (Sr VP)

ZEL TECHNOLOGIES, LLC
54 Old Hampton Ln, Hampton, VA 23669
Tel.: (757) 722-5565
Web Site: http://www.zeltech.com
Sales Range: $25-49.9 Million
Emp.: 200
Custom Computer Programming Services
N.A.I.C.S.: 541511
Jim Grant (Pres & COO)
Lynn Taylor (CFO)
W. Scott Arnott (CTO)
Chuck Mitchell (VP-Bus Dev & External Affairs)
Susan Hughes (VP-Contracts & Program Control)
Ralph M. Towell (VP-Ops)
Jack L. Ezzell Jr. (CEO)

Subsidiaries:

ZelTech Training Solutions, LLC (1)
7123 University Blvd, Winter Park, FL 32792
Tel.: (407) 571-9920
Web Site: http://www.zeltechlivetraining.com
Battlefield Simulation & Training
N.A.I.C.S.: 541512

ZELLER MOTOR COMPANY
3021 N Summit St, Arkansas City, KS 67005-8819
Tel.: (620) 442-8650
Web Site: http://www.zellermotors.com
Sales Range: $10-24.9 Million
Emp.: 25
Car Whslr
N.A.I.C.S.: 441110
Linda Ivy (Office Mgr)
Aaron Robbins (Mgr-Sls)
Mark Robbins (Owner & Pres)

ZELLNER CONSTRUCTION COMPANY, INC.
2926 Ridgeway Rd, Memphis, TN 38115
Tel.: (901) 794-1100
Web Site: http://www.zellnerconstruction.com
Sales Range: $10-24.9 Million
Emp.: 30
Civil Engineering Services
N.A.I.C.S.: 237310
Mark Zellner (Pres & Principal)
Jesse Zellner (Principal & VP)
Carey Ward (Dir-Projects)
David Jacobs (Sr Project Mgr)
Jerrell Rucker (Principal)
Renee Ware (Controller)
Ryan Finkle (Project Mgr)
William Welch (Mgr-Field Ops)

ZELNICKMEDIA CORP.
110 E 59th St 24th Fl, New York, NY 10022
Tel.: (212) 223-1383 NY
Web Site: http://www.zmclp.com
Year Founded: 2001
Investment Services
N.A.I.C.S.: 523999
Strauss H. Zelnick (Co-Founder & Mng Partner)
James L. Friedlich (Co-Founder)
Sheila Dharmarajan (Head-IR & Bus Dev)
Morgan Berk (Asst Controller)
Brian D. Motechin (CFO, Chief Compliance Officer & Partner)
Seymour Sammell (Partner)
Jordan Turkewitz (Co-Chief Investment Officer & Mng Partner)
Andrew Vogel (Co-Chief Investment Officer & Mng Partner)
Jason Sporer (VP)
Anastasia Marras (Controller)
Karl Slatoff (Mng Partner)

Subsidiaries:

Defy Media, LLC (1)
498 7th Ave 19th Fl, New York, NY 10018
Tel.: (212) 244-4307
Web Site: http://www.defymedia.com
Digital Media Production & Distribution Services
N.A.I.C.S.: 541870
Barry Blumberg (Chief Content Officer)
Andy Tu (Exec VP-Mktg)
Navid Behzadi (VP-Bus Dev & Distr)
Mark Gall (Chief Revenue Officer)
Christopher Willey (VP-Dev)
Alex Lin (Dir-Dev)
Chris Acquaviva (CFO)
Gina R. DiGioia (Gen Counsel, Sec & Exec VP)
Gina R. DiGioia (Gen Counsel, Sec & Exec VP)

Branch (Domestic):

Defy Media, LLC - Los Angeles (2)
5757 Wilshire Blvd Ste 300, Los Angeles, CA 90036
Tel.: (310) 360-4141
Web Site: http://www.defymedia.com
Digital Entertainment Production Services
N.A.I.C.S.: 512110
Keith Richman (Pres)

Education Networks of America, Inc. (1)
618 Grassmere Park Dr Ste 12, Nashville, TN 37211
Tel.: (615) 312-6000
Web Site: http://www.ena.com
Internet Service Provider
N.A.I.C.S.: 517121
David Pierce (CEO)
Matthew Turner (VP-Ops)
Michael McKerley (CTO & VP)
Rex Miller (Sr VP)
Gayle Nelson (Sr VP-Customer Svcs)
Ruth Braun (Chief People Officer & VP)
Steb Chandor (CFO)
Kitty Ganier (Gen Counsel)
Lillian Kellogg (Sr VP-Client Svcs)
Cory Ayers (Dir-Architecture)
Dana Briggs (Dir-Customer Support)
Brian Dalhover (Dir-Solutions Engrg)
Rod Houpe (Natl Dir-Bus Dev)
Aimee Hull (Dir-People Svcs)
Andrea Krupa (Sr Dir-Customer Svcs)
Mark Smith (Sr Dir-Sls)

Subsidiary (Domestic):

TeleQuality Communications LLC (2)
21202 Gathering Oak, San Antonio, TX 78260
Tel.: (210) 408-0388
Web Site: http://www.telequality.com
Telecommunications Network Products & Services
N.A.I.C.S.: 517810
Natalie Verette (Sr-Sls)
Rex Miller (Gen Mgr)
Ruth Braun (Chief People Officer)
Steb Chandor (CFO)

Kitty Ganier (Gen Counsel)
Michael McKerley (CTO)
Cory Ayers (Dir-Architecture)
Dana Briggs (Dir-Customer Support)
Brian Dalhover (Dir-Solutions Engrg)
Kylie McGee (Dir-Mktg)
Rob Peterson (Dir-Carrier Mgmt)
April Scott (Dir-Funding)
Rand Vincent (Mgr-Client Svcs)
Reid Freeman (Reg Sls Mgr)
Lauren Anderson (Sr Mgr-Fin & Corp Projects)

Naylor Publications Incorporated (1)
5950 NW 1st Pl, Gainesville, FL 32607
Tel.: (352) 332-1252
Web Site: http://www.naylor.com
Publication Printing; Owned by ZelnickMedia Corp. & by Clarity Partners, L.P.
N.A.I.C.S.: 323111
Michael Moss (Vice Chm)

Pure Wafer Inc. (1)
2575 Melville Rd, Prescott, AZ 86301
Tel.: (928) 771-8900
Web Site: http://www.purewafer.com
Silicon Wafer Reclamation
N.A.I.C.S.: 334413
Jerry Winters (Pres & CEO)
Dave Griffeth (CFO)
Ernie Sedillo (VP-Sls)

Simeio Solutions, LLC (1)
55 Ivan Allen Jr Blvd Ste 350, Atlanta, GA 30308
Tel.: (770) 282-4442
Web Site: http://www.simeiosolutions.com
Data Security Services
N.A.I.C.S.: 518210
Hemen Vimadalal (Founder & CEO)
Krishna Prabhu (Pres & COO)
Naynesh Patel (Exec VP)
Shawn Keve (Exec VP)
Elizabeth Shannon (VP-Fin)

Wpromote, LLC (1)
1700 E Walnut Ave 5th Fl, El Segundo, CA 90245
Tel.: (310) 683-0393
Web Site: http://www.wpromote.com
Advertising & Search Engine Optimization
N.A.I.C.S.: 541890
Michael Mothner (Founder & CEO)
Michael Block (COO)
Michael Stone (Chief Relationship Officer)
Andrew McLellan (Gen Mgr-SEO)
Joanne Coghill (Dir-HR)
Andrea Snyder (Mng Dir-Northeast)
Bob Schwartz (Vice Chm)
Eric Reisch (Sr VP-Sls & Customer Success)
Jessica Tauber (Sr VP-Client Svcs)
Kelly Mulvey (CFO)
Marissa Allen (VP-Strategy)
Megan Swisher Fanning (VP-People & Culture)
Paul Rappoport (Pres)
Paul Dumais (CTO)
Rob Phillips (Mng Dir-Soutwest)
Jamie Farrell (Sr Vp- Mktg)
Jeff Harouche (Vp-Strategy & Planning)
Rachel Bucey (VP-Earned Media)
Simon Poulton (VP-Digital Intelligence)
Soso Sazesh (VP-Growth & Innovations)
Tom Hammel (VP-Paid Media)
Jenny Son (Head-Industry)
Armen Baghdasarian (Head-Content Mktg)
David Dweck (Head-Paid Search & Media)
Dexter Rangel (Head-SMB)
Darren D Altorio (Head-Social Media)
Clair Perez (Sr Gp Dir-Strategic Acct Mgmt)
Kevin Kao (Sr Dir-Email Mktg)
Peter Petrou (Sr Dir-Web Svcs)
Steve Comando (Sr Dir-Creative)
Anna Arthur (Gp Dir-Strategic Acct mgmt)
Christine Borg (Gp Dir-Stragetic Acct Mgmt)
Jonathan Gualotuna (Dir-Programmatic)
Kimberlee Raymond (Gp Dir-Strategic Acct Mgmt)
Ryan Neldner (Sr Dir-Engrg)
Steve Blackman (Dir-IT)
Theresa Irving (Dir-Fin Planning & Analysis)
Annamarie Corey (Controller)

Subsidiary (Domestic):

Visiture, LLC (2)
444 King St 2nd Fl, Charleston, SC 29403
Tel.: (843) 790-7286

COMPANIES

Web Site: http://www.visiture.com
Marketing Services
N.A.I.C.S.: 541613
Ronald Dod (Co-Founder & CEO)
Brian Cohen (Co-Founder & CEO)
Ryan Jones (VP-Ops)
Sarah Wilson (Dir-Client Svcs)
Seth Newton (Dir-Paid Search)

Wpromote, Inc. - Dallas (2)
6060 N Central Expy Ste 350, Dallas, TX 75206
Tel.: (214) 696-9600
Web Site: http://www.wpromote.com
Emp.: 65
Internet Marketing Services
N.A.I.C.S.: 541613
Mike Wylie (Mng Dir-Southwest)
Rob Phillips (VP-Client Success)

ZELUCK INC.
5300 Kings Hwy, Brooklyn, NY 11234
Tel.: (718) 251-8060
Web Site: http://www.zeluck.com
Rev.: $10,334,161
Emp.: 78
Window Mfr
N.A.I.C.S.: 321911
Brian Trager (VP)
Demitri Athanasoulis (Project Mgr)
Michael Sincaglia (Project Mgr)
Tao Chen (Dir-IT)
Tommy Morrone (Plant Mgr)
G. Michael Merritt (Pres)

ZEMBA BROS INC
3401 East Pike, Zanesville, OH 43701
Tel.: (740) 455-6468
Web Site: http://www.zembabrosinc.com
Rev.: $2,000,000
Emp.: 100
Site Preparation Contractor
N.A.I.C.S.: 238910
Christopher P. Zemba (VP)
Susan Zemba (Office Mgr)

Subsidiaries:

Geiger Excavating, Inc. (1)
1000 Leavitt Service Rd, Gahanna, 43230, OH
Tel.: (614) 373-7526
Web Site: http://subdomain.geigerexcavatinginc.com
Asphalt Paving Mixture Mfr & Supplier
N.A.I.C.S.: 324121
Dawn Wilson (CFO & VP)

ZEMENICK & WALKER, INC.
8182 Maryland Ave Ste 200, Saint Louis, MO 63105
Tel.: (314) 862-5525
Web Site: http://www.zandw.com
Year Founded: 1987
Sales Range: $1-9.9 Million
Emp.: 10
Financial Consulting Firm
N.A.I.C.S.: 523940
James C. Walker (Co-Founder)
Richard E. Zemenick (Co-Founder)
Chris G. Griesedieck (Chm & Mng Dir)
John M. Johnson (Pres & Mng Dir)
Jonathan A. Best (VP & Portfolio Mgr)
Bryan L. Schulz (VP & Portfolio Mgr)
Krystal Hill (Asst Mgr-Portfolio)
William C. Stude III (Mng Dir & Exec VP)

ZEMPLEO, INC.
1331 N California Blvd Ste 150, Walnut Creek, CA 94596
Tel.: (866) 493-6753
Web Site: http://www.zempleo.com
Year Founded: 2005
Sales Range: $50-74.9 Million
Emp.: 30
Temporary Staffing & Recruitment Services
N.A.I.C.S.: 561311
Ramiro Zeron (CEO & Owner)

ZEN CONTINENTAL CO., INC.
6925 Aragon Cir Ste 6, Buena Park, CA 90620-1166
Tel.: (714) 367-0866   CA
Web Site: http://www.zencon.com
Year Founded: 1984
Sales Range: $10-24.9 Million
Emp.: 20
Freight Transportation Arrangement Services
N.A.I.C.S.: 488510
Cindy Yen-Chen (Pres)

ZENAR CORPORATION
7301 S 6th St, Oak Creek, WI 53154
Tel.: (414) 764-1800
Web Site: http://www.zenarcrane.com
Rev.: $12,800,000
Emp.: 130
Overhead Traveling Crane Hoist & Monorail System Mfr
N.A.I.C.S.: 333923
Richard Simatic (CFO)
Tom Kujath (VP-Parts & Sls)

ZENDEX HOLDINGS, INC.
PO Box 58052, Salt Lake City, UT 84158
Tel.: (801) 904-3855   NV
Year Founded: 1985
Rev.: $83,250
Assets: $850
Liabilities: $112,227
Net Worth: ($111,377)
Earnings: ($11,269)
Fiscal Year-end: 12/31/15
Online Portal Services
N.A.I.C.S.: 551112
Alex Demitriev (Treas & Sec)

ZENITH CUTTER CO.
5200 Zenith Pkwy, Loves Park, IL 61111
Tel.: (815) 282-5200
Web Site: http://www.zenithcutter.com
Sales Range: $10-24.9 Million
Emp.: 230
Manufacture & Distribute Machine Tool Accessories
N.A.I.C.S.: 333515
Steve Kao (Dir-Sls-Asia)
Terry Willis (Mgr-Costing)
Todd Gaines (Mgr-Product)
Romaine Castor Jr. (Supvr-Heat Treat)

ZENITH TECH INC.
N3 W23633 Bluemound Rd, Waukesha, WI 53188-1741
Tel.: (262) 524-1800   WI
Web Site: http://www.zenithtechinc.com
Year Founded: 1982
Sales Range: $10-24.9 Million
Emp.: 70
Provider of Construction Services
N.A.I.C.S.: 237310
Dan Dassow (Mgr-Construction Ops)

ZENO GROUP
140 Broadway 39th Fl, New York, NY 10005
Tel.: (212) 299-8888
Web Site: http://www.zenogroup.com
Year Founded: 1998
Sales Range: $25-49.9 Million
Emp.: 400
Public Relations Agency
N.A.I.C.S.: 541820
Barby K. Siegel (CEO)
Tracey Thiele (Exec VP-Mktg & Integration-Global)
Mark Shadle (Mng Dir)
Ame Wadler (Mng Dir-Health)
Grant Deady (Mng Dir-Chicago & Chief Culture Officer)
Papri Dev (Mng Dir-India)
John Kerr (Chief Digital Officer & Mng Dir-Asia Pacific)
Steve Earl (Mng Dir-Europe)
Todd Irwin (Mng Dir-Tech-California)
Tony Blasco (CFO)
Nancy Ruscheinski (Global COO-Chicago)
Christine Jewell (Mng Dir)
Julie Georgas (Mng Dir-Canada)
Divya Uttam (Head-Digital-India)
Shipra Malik (Acct Dir)
Carol Gronlund (Chief Talent Officer)
David Lian (Mng Dir-Malaysia)
Monica Lourenci (Exec VP-Brazil)
Radityo Prabowo (Mng Dir-Indonesia)
Suresh Raj (Mng Dir-Bus Dev-Global)
Therese Caruso (Mng Dir-Strategy-Global & Insights)
Ruby Fu (Pres-China)
Allanjit Singh (Mng Dir-Singapore)
Kevin Davidson (Exec VP-Healthcare-New York & Washington)
Byron Calamese (Mng Dir-New York & Washington)
Marty Maloney (VP-Consumer)

Subsidiaries:

Zeno Group (1)
130 E Randolph St Ste 3000, Chicago, IL 60601
Tel.: (312) 396-9700
Web Site: http://www.zenogroup.com
Public Relations Agency
N.A.I.C.S.: 541820
Stephanie Tortorici (Exec VP & Dir-Health Care)
Nancy Ruscheinski (COO)

Zeno Group (1)
2850 Ocean park blvd, Santa Monica, CA 90405
Tel.: (310) 566-2290
Web Site: http://www.zenogroup.com
Sales Range: Less than $1 Million
Emp.: 12
Public Relations Agency
N.A.I.C.S.: 541820

Zeno Group (1)
3222 N St NW 5th Fl, Washington, DC 20007
Tel.: (202) 965-7800
Public Relations Agency
N.A.I.C.S.: 541820

ZENO OFFICE SOLUTIONS, INC.
8701 Florida Mining Blvd, Tampa, FL 33634
Tel.: (813) 253-0318
Web Site: http://www.zenosolutions.com
Sales Range: $25-49.9 Million
Emp.: 240
Document, Printer Fleet & Facilities Management; Software Solutions; Office Equipment Distr
N.A.I.C.S.: 561410
Sam Shafir (Mgr-Tech Trng)
Alex Tonus (Mgr-After Market)

ZENOSS, INC.
275 W St, Annapolis, MD 21401
Tel.: (410) 990-0274
Web Site: http://www.zenoss.com
Year Founded: 2005
Sales Range: $1-9.9 Million
Emp.: 62
Custom Computer Programming Services
N.A.I.C.S.: 541511

ZENTRIC, INC.

Greg Stock (Chm & CEO)
Marcus MacNeill (VP-Product Mgmt)
Derek Brown (VP-EMEA)
Megan Lueders (VP-Mktg)
Michael Lovell (CFO-Austin)
Brian Wilson (Chief Customer Officer)
Blair Duncan (CFO)
Trent Fitz (CMO)

ZENOSYS LLC
3084 State Rte 27 Ste 12, Kendall Park, NJ 08824
Tel.: (732) 939-4774
Web Site: http://www.zenosys.com
Year Founded: 2005
Sales Range: $1-9.9 Million
Emp.: 142
It Consulting
N.A.I.C.S.: 541690
Ashok Kumar (VP-HR)

ZENPAYROLL, INC.
425 2nd St Ste 602, San Francisco, CA 94107
Tel.: (800) 936-0383
Web Site: http://www.zenpayroll.com
Sales Range: $1-9.9 Million
Payroll Software
N.A.I.C.S.: 513210
Joshua Reeves (Co-Founder & CEO)
Edward Kim (Co-Founder & CTO)
Tomer London (Co-Founder & Chief Product Officer)
Brett Willms (CMO)

ZENPRINT, LLC
1825 S East Bay Blvd, Provo, UT 84606
Tel.: (800) 373-9844
Web Site: http://www.zenprint.com
Year Founded: 2007
Sales Range: $1-9.9 Million
Software Application Services
N.A.I.C.S.: 513210
J. D. Gardner (Founder & CEO)
J. Nathan Jensen (Co-Founder & CTO)
Justin Biggs (Pres & COO)

ZENSHIN CAPITAL PARTNERS LLC
535 Middlefield Rd Ste 280, Menlo Park, CA 94025
Web Site: http://www.zenshincp.co
Venture Capital Investment Firm
N.A.I.C.S.: 523999
Yoji Kawaguchi (Co-Founder & Mng Dir)
Takeshi Mori (Co-Founder & Mng Dir)

ZENTRA LLC
110 Associates Ln, Indian Trail, NC 28079
Tel.: (704) 708-4027
Web Site: http://www.zentrallc.com
Year Founded: 2012
Sales Range: $10-24.9 Million
Emp.: 14
Online Shopping Services
N.A.I.C.S.: 541614
R. Gary (CEO)
R. Hayden (Founder)
D. Matthew (Ops Mgr)
B. Eugene (Mgr-Warehouse)
P. Jack (Mgr-Key Acct)

ZENTRIC, INC.
28 Schenck Pkwy Ste 200, Asheville, NC 28803
Tel.: (828) 687-9023   NV
Web Site: http://www.zntr.com
Year Founded: 2008
Battery Technology Services
N.A.I.C.S.: 335910
Jeff Mak (CEO)
William Tien (Pres)

ZENZI COMMUNICATIONS

Zenzi Communications—(Continued)

ZENZI COMMUNICATIONS
2235 Encinitas Blvd Suite 212, Encinitas, CA 92024
Tel.: (760) 635-9320
Web Site: http://www.zenzi.com
Year Founded: 2002
Sales Range: $25-49.9 Million
Emp.: 12
Public Relations & Corporate Branding
N.A.I.C.S.: 541820
Hilary McCarthy (VP)
Sarah Znerold Hardwick (Founder & CEO)
Julie Lyons (Pres & COO)

ZEPHYR ALUMINUM INC.
625 2nd St, Lancaster, PA 17603
Tel.: (717) 397-3618
Web Site: http://www.zephyraluminum.com
Sales Range: $10-24.9 Million
Emp.: 80
Architectural Aluminum & Glass Products
N.A.I.C.S.: 331318
Doug Cornell (Pres)

ZEPHYR GRAF-X INC.
1725 Tower Dr W Ste 120, Stillwater, MN 55082
Tel.: (651) 439-9688
Web Site: http://www.zhats.com
Sales Range: $10-24.9 Million
Emp.: 20
Baseball Caps
N.A.I.C.S.: 315990
James R. Seilbach (CFO)
David Gormley (Pres & CEO)

ZEPHYR MANAGEMENT, L.P.
320 Park Ave Fl 28, New York, NY 10022
Tel.: (212) 508-9400   NY
Web Site: http://zephyrmanagement.com
Year Founded: 1994
Sales Range: $1-9.9 Million
Emp.: 18
Privater Equity Firm
N.A.I.C.S.: 523999
Stephen Canter (Mng Dir)

ZEPHYR MEDIA GROUP
990 Grove St Ste 300, Evanston, IL 60201
Tel.: (847) 328-1519
Web Site: http://www.zephyr-media.com
Year Founded: 1991
Sales Range: $25-49.9 Million
Emp.: 20
Direct Marketing; Production; Strategic Planning
N.A.I.C.S.: 541870
Dan Zifkin (Pres & CEO)
Wes Dubin (Dir-Bus Dev)
Carey Chase (Dir-Media)

Subsidiaries:

Zephyr Media Group   (1)
633 3rd Ave 13 Fl, New York, NY 10016
Tel.: (914) 232-0029
Web Site: http://www.zephyr-media.com
Direct Marketing
N.A.I.C.S.: 541830

Zephyr Media Group   (1)
905 W 7th St Ste 225, Frederick, MD 21701
Tel.: (301) 620-1231
Web Site: http://www.zephyr-media.com
Sales Range: $10-24.9 Million
N.A.I.C.S.: 541830

ZEPHYR REAL ESTATE
4200 17th St, San Francisco, CA 94114
Tel.: (415) 552-9500
Web Site: http://www.zephyrsf.com
Year Founded: 1978
Sales Range: $10-24.9 Million
Emp.: 70
Provider of Real Estate Broker Services
N.A.I.C.S.: 531210
William Drypolcher (Founder)
Randall Kostick (Pres & CEO)
Matthew Borland (COO)
Tara Donohue (Partner)
Steve De La Pena (VP-Strategic Svcs)
Noriko Williams (VP-Admin & Relocation Svcs)
Melody Foster (Chief Experience Officer)
Erinn Millar (Mgr-Sls)
Marcia Thomas (Dir-Sls)
Hud Bixler (VP-Tech Svcs)
Kevin Koerner (Mgr-Sls-West Portal)
Jenn Pfeiffer (Sls Mgr-Marin)

ZEPPOS & ASSOCIATES, INC.
400 E Mason St Ste 200, Milwaukee, WI 53202-3703
Tel.: (414) 276-6237   WI
Web Site: http://www.zeppos.com
Year Founded: 1994
Sales Range: $1-9.9 Million
Emp.: 14
Media Relations, Government Affairs, Trade Media Relations & Special Events Planning
N.A.I.C.S.: 541820
Evan N. Zeppos (Pres)
Kris Naidl (Exec VP)
Brenna Kriviskey Sadler (VP)
Brian Knox (VP)
Adina Zeppos (Mgr-Fin)
John Gardner (Sr Acct Exec)
Tiffany Wankowski (Acct Exec)
Mikaela Balfany (Acct Exec)
Laura Krinke (Acct Exec)

ZERO HALLIBURTON, INC.
371 Hoes Ln Ste 201, Piscataway, NJ 08854
Tel.: (732) 393-7400   DE
Web Site: http://www.zerohalliburton.com
Sales Range: $25-49.9 Million
Aluminum & Plastic Protective Cases, Enclosures & Assemblies for the Aerospace, Industrial, Medical, Electronics & Automotive Markets Mfr
N.A.I.C.S.: 331315
Debbie Pawigon (Gen Mgr)

ZERO POINT
1763 Princess Anne Rd Ste 104, Virginia Beach, VA 23456
Tel.: (757) 721-6601
Web Site: http://www.zeropointusa.com
Year Founded: 2006
Sales Range: $1-9.9 Million
Emp.: 21
Defense Security Product Distr
N.A.I.C.S.: 423610
Perry Sasnett (Founder, Pres & CEO)
Mike Farmer (Chief Strategy Officer)
Scott Traurig (CTO)

ZERO TO THREE: NATIONAL CENTER FOR INFANTS, TODDLERS AND FAMILIES
1255 23rd St NW Ste 350, Washington, DC 20037
Tel.: (202) 638-1144   DC
Web Site: http://www.zerotothree.org
Year Founded: 1977
Sales Range: $10-24.9 Million
Emp.: 164
Infant & Toddler Health Development Services
N.A.I.C.S.: 624410
Laura Shiflett (CFO & Chief Admin Officer)
Janice Im (Chief Program Officer)
Tracy Crudup (Dir-HR)
Erica Lurie-Hurvitz (Dir-Pub Policy)
Matthew E. Melmed (Exec Dir)

ZERO ZONE, INC.
110 N Oakridge Dr, North Prairie, WI 53153-9792
Tel.: (262) 392-6400
Web Site: http://www.zero-zone.com
Year Founded: 1961
Sales Range: $75-99.9 Million
Emp.: 200
Freezer & Cooler Display Cases Mfr
N.A.I.C.S.: 333415
David Morrow (Pres & CEO)

Subsidiaries:

Zero Zone, Inc. - Refrigeration Systems Division   (1)
6151 140th Ave NW, Ramsey, MN 55303
Tel.: (763) 398-1996
Refrigerator Equipment Mfr
N.A.I.C.S.: 333415

ZERODESKTOP, INC.
1900 S Norfolk St Ste 245, San Mateo, CA 94403
Tel.: (650) 585-4401
Web Site: http://www.zerodesktop.com
Data Processing, Hosting & Related Services
N.A.I.C.S.: 518210

Subsidiaries:

NComputing, Inc.   (1)
3979 Freedom Cir Ste 600, Santa Clara, CA 95054
Tel.: (408) 380-8400
Web Site: http://www.ncomputing.com
Computer System Design Services
N.A.I.C.S.: 541512
Raj Dhingra (CEO)
Pam Gosal (VP-Global HR)
Peter Downs (CFO)
Sai Allavarpu (Sr VP-Products & Strategy)
Dave Burton (VP-Global Mktg)
Richard Sah (Co-Founder & CTO)
S. Mustafa Canoglu (Co-Founder & CEO)
Stewart Constantine (Mgr-Bus Dev)
Young Song (Co-Founder & CEO)

ZERORZ MINNESOTA
6244 Cedar Ave S, Richfield, MN 55423
Tel.: (651) 779-8888
Web Site: http://www.zerorezminnesota.com
Year Founded: 2006
Sales Range: $1-9.9 Million
Emp.: 117
Carpet Cleaning
N.A.I.C.S.: 561740
Tammy Tonn (Dir-Bus Dev)

ZESKIND'S HARDWARE, INC.
222 S Payson St, Baltimore, MD 21223-2904
Tel.: (410) 233-1919
Web Site: http://www.zeskinds.com
Emp.: 100
Hardware Stores
N.A.I.C.S.: 444140
Deb Zeskind (Owner)

Subsidiaries:

Clement Hardware, Inc.   (1)
500 Ritchie Hwy, Severna Park, MD 21146
Tel.: (410) 647-4611
Web Site: http://www.clementhardware.com
Hardware Merchant Whslr
N.A.I.C.S.: 423710

Tony Gaughan (Gen Mgr)

ZETA COMMUNITIES
951 Mariners Island Blvd Ste 300, San Mateo, CA 94404
Tel.: (415) 946-4084
Web Site: http://zetacommunities.com
Rev.: $10,000,000
Emp.: 3
Produces Net Zero Energy Multifamily Housing & Mixed-Use Structures for Sustainable Communities
N.A.I.C.S.: 236115
Naomi Porat (Pres, CEO & Co-Founder)
Bill Kalff (COO)
Marc Porat (Chm)
Shilpa Sankaran (Co-Founder & VP-Mktg & Comm)
Jodi Clinesmith (Controller)

ZETA EMAIL SOLUTIONS
185 Madison Ave 5th Fl, New York, NY 10016
Tel.: (212) 967-5055
Web Site: http://zetainteractive.com
Email Marketing Services
N.A.I.C.S.: 513140
David A. Steinberg (Founder & CEO)
Steven Gerber (COO)
Anil Unnikrishnan (Sr VP & Gen Mgr)
Marie Aiello (VP-Acct Mgmt)

Subsidiaries:

Zeta Email Solutions   (1)
6-3-679 II-IV Floors Elite Plaza, Somajiguda, Hyderabad, 500 082, India
Tel.: (91) 40 40309000
Email Marketing Solutions
N.A.I.C.S.: 513140

ZETA INTERACTIVE CORPORATION
3 Park Ave 33rd Fl, New York, NY 10016
Tel.: (212) 660-2500   DE
Web Site: http://www.zetaglobal.com
Year Founded: 2007
Digital & Direct Marketing Services
N.A.I.C.S.: 541613
David A. Steinberg (Co-Founder, Chm & CEO)
Steven Gerber (Pres & COO)
Steven Vine (Gen Counsel & Exec VP-Mergers & Acquisitions)
Jermey A. Klein (Pres-Actions Div)
Jeffry Nimeroff (CIO)
Donald Steele (Co-Vice Chm)
John Sculley (Co-Founder & Co-Vice Chm)
Christopher Greiner (CFO)
Will Margiloff (Chief Strategy Officer)
Christian Monberg (CTO)
Neej Gore (Chief Data Officer)
Denise Lang (Asst Gen Counsel & Sr VP-HR)
David Allen (Pres-CRM Div)
Matt Martella (Pres-ZX Div)
Mike Caprio (Pres-Programmatic Div)
Tina McCain (Sr VP-Natl Sls)
Cherryl Valenzuela (Sr VP-IR)
Crystal Eastman (CMO)
Megan Rose (Grp VP-Mktg & Comm)

Subsidiaries:

ClickSquared Inc.   (1)
280 Summer St 6th Fl, Boston, MA 02210
Tel.: (857) 246-7800
Web Site: http://www.clicksquared.com
Sales Range: $10-24.9 Million
Emp.: 125
Direct Marketing Automation & Customization Software
N.A.I.C.S.: 513210
Greg Garnys (Mng Dir-Europe)
Stephen Henkenmeier (CFO)
Robert King (Gen Mgr-Travel & Hospitality)

COMPANIES

Mark Mosholder *(Sr VP-Svcs & Ops)*
Michaela Goodwin *(VP-France)*
Ross Broderson *(VP-Product Mgmt)*
Bob Solat *(VP-Ops)*
Shane Cough *(VP-Bus Dev)*
Kerry Reilly *(VP-Mktg)*
Scott Philips *(VP-IT)*

Subsidiary (Non-US):

ClickSquared Ltd. (2)
3 Startforth Rd Riverside Park, Middlesbrough, TS2 1PJ, United Kingdom **(100%)**
Tel.: (44) 1642 808888
Web Site: http://www.zetainteractive.com
Information Technology Services
N.A.I.C.S.: 519290
Greg Garnys *(Mng Dir)*

Zeta Global Ltd. (2)
WeWork Floor 1 125 Kingsway, London, WC2B 6NH, United Kingdom
Tel.: (44) 2032196200
Web Site: http://www.zetaglobal.com
Software Solutions Provider
N.A.I.C.S.: 513210

Subsidiary (US):

Sizmek DSP, Inc. (3)
401 Park Ave S 5th Fl, New York, NY 10016
Tel.: (650) 595-1300
Artificial Intelligence Advertising Solutions
N.A.I.C.S.: 541890

Subsidiary (Non-US):

Rocket Fuel Ltd. (4)
34 Bow Street, London, WC2E 7AU, United Kingdom
Tel.: (44) 20 3651 1300
Marketing Consulting Services
N.A.I.C.S.: 541613

Collective, Inc. (1)
330 Madison Ave 4th Fl, New York, NY 10017
Tel.: (646) 722-8550
Web Site: http://www.collective.com
Sales Range: $200-249.9 Million
Emp.: 400
Advertising Agencies
N.A.I.C.S.: 541810
Joseph Apprendi *(Founder & Chm)*
John Vandermay *(CTO)*
Eoin Townsend *(Chief Product Officer)*
Giles Ivey *(Mng Dir-UK)*
Jo Carol Robison *(Sr VP-Fin)*
Kerry Bianchi *(Pres & CEO)*

Disqus, Inc. (1)
717 Market St Ste 700, San Francisco, CA 94103
Tel.: (415) 738-8848
Web Site: http://www.disqus.com
Software Publisher
N.A.I.C.S.: 513210
Daniel Ha *(CEO)*
Jason Yan *(CTO)*
Daniel Matteson *(Engr-Backend)*
Ron Sadi *(Dir-Bus Dev)*
Ryan Greaves *(Mgr-Customer Success)*
Steven Stein *(Pres & Gen Mgr)*
Jason Voegele *(VP-Bus Dev)*
Phillip Pham *(Dir-Data Engrg)*
Adi Jain *(VP-Product)*
Harrison Gottlieb *(Engr-Backend)*
Hovsep Lalikian *(Engr-Frontend)*
Taylan Gocmen *(Sr Engr-Frontend)*

ZETTLER COMPONENTS, INC.
75 Columbia, Aliso Viejo, CA 92656
Tel.: (949) 831-5000
Web Site: http://www.zettler-group.com
Sales Range: $75-99.9 Million
Emp.: 500
Holding Company; Electronic Parts & Equipment Whslr
N.A.I.C.S.: 551112

Subsidiaries:

AZ Displays, Inc. (1)
75 Columbia, Aliso Viejo, CA 92656-1498 **(100%)**
Tel.: (949) 360-5830
Web Site: http://www.azdisplays.com
Sales Range: $10-24.9 Million
Emp.: 20
Character & Graphics LCD Modules Distr
N.A.I.C.S.: 334419

American Zettler Incorporated (1)
75 Columbia, Aliso Viejo, CA 92656
Tel.: (949) 831-5000
Web Site: http://www.azettler.com
Sales Range: $25-49.9 Million
Emp.: 135
Electronic Components Distr
N.A.I.C.S.: 423690
Gunther Rueb *(CEO)*
Dave West *(VP-Sls)*

Xiamen Zettler Electronics Co., Ltd. (1)
6-7/F Yinfeng Building No 48-50 Huli Ave, Huli Industrial District, Xiamen, 361006, China
Tel.: (86) 592 2650 988
Electronic Components Distr
N.A.I.C.S.: 423690

Zettler Controls, Inc. (1)
75 Columbia, Aliso Viejo, CA 92656
Tel.: (949) 360-5840
Web Site: http://www.zettlercontrols.com
Emp.: 40
Electronic Components Mfr & Distr
N.A.I.C.S.: 334419
Ryan Magner *(Gen Mgr)*

Zettler Electronics (HK) Ltd. (1)
Unit 2A Wing Tai Centre Front Block 12 Hing Yip Street, Kwun Tong, Kowloon, China (Hong Kong)
Tel.: (852) 23751288
Web Site: http://www.zettlerhk.com
Emp.: 11
Electronic Components Distr
N.A.I.C.S.: 423690
Soren Borg *(Pres)*

Zettler Electronics Belgium B.V.B.A. - S.P.R.L. (1)
Leuvenselaan 172, B 3300, Tienen, Belgium
Tel.: (32) 16 825 183
Web Site: http://www.zettlerelectronics.be
Electronic Components Distr
N.A.I.C.S.: 423690

Zettler Electronics GmbH (1)
Hauptniederlassung Junkersstr 3, 82178, Puchheim, Germany
Tel.: (49) 89800970
Web Site: http://www.zettlerelectronics.com
Emp.: 20
Electronic Components Distr
N.A.I.C.S.: 423690
Stevan Schlosser *(Mng Dir)*

Zettler Electronics Nederland B.V. (1)
Dorpsstraat 51, Zevenhuizen, 2761 AA, Rotterdam, Netherlands
Tel.: (31) 180310663
Web Site: http://www.zettlerelectronics.nl
Electronic Component Mfr & Distr
N.A.I.C.S.: 334419

Zettler Electronics Poland sp.z.o.o. (1)
Osadnikow Wojskowych 40, 68 200, Zary, Poland
Tel.: (48) 684791437
Web Site: http://www.zettlerelectronics.pl
Sales Range: $10-24.9 Million
Emp.: 2
Electronic Components Distr
N.A.I.C.S.: 423690

Zettler Magnetics, Inc. (1)
75 Columbia, Aliso Viejo, CA 92656-1498 **(100%)**
Tel.: (949) 360-5838
Web Site: http://www.zettlermagnetics.com
Sales Range: $25-49.9 Million
Emp.: 20
Transformers Mfr & Distr
N.A.I.C.S.: 335311

ZEUS INDUSTRIAL PRODUCTS INC.
620 Magnolia St, Orangeburg, SC 29115
Tel.: (803) 531-2174
Web Site: http://www.zeusinc.com
Rev.: $23,300,000
Emp.: 1,000
Plastics Product Mfr
N.A.I.C.S.: 326121
John Winarchick *(CEO)*
Xiao Li *(Dir-Sls-Asia-Pacific)*
Alan Andrews *(Sr VP-Global Sls & Mktg)*
Steve Peterson *(Pres)*
Frank P. Tourville Sr. *(Founder & Chm)*

ZEVA INC.
10300 Eaton Pl Ste 305, Fairfax, VA 22030
Tel.: (888) 938-2467
Web Site: http://www.zevainc.com
Custom Computer Programming Services
N.A.I.C.S.: 541511
Jihan Andoni *(Pres)*

Subsidiaries:

NextgenID, Inc. (1)
2810 North Flores St, San Antonio, TX 78212
Tel.: (210) 530-9991
Web Site: http://www.nextgenid.com
Rev.: $1,500,000
Emp.: 10
Other Communications Equipment Mfr
N.A.I.C.S.: 334290
Mohab Murrar *(CEO)*

ZEVOTEK, INC.
19 Sylvan Ave 2nd Fl, Englewood Cliffs, NJ 07632
Tel.: (201) 820-0357　　　　　DE
Web Site: http://www.zevo-tek.com
Year Founded: 2005
Sales Range: Less than $1 Million
Consumer Product Direct Marketer & Distr; Energy Saving Light Bulb Mfr, Marketer & Distr
N.A.I.C.S.: 335139
Jason Ryu *(Chm, CEO, CFO, Treas & Sec)*

ZFERRAL, INC.
333 W 7th St Ste 310, Royal Oak, MI 48067
Tel.: (248) 792-3472　　　　　DE
Web Site: http://www.getambassador.com
Year Founded: 2010
Referral Marketing Software Development Services
N.A.I.C.S.: 541511
Jeff Epstein *(Founder & CEO)*

ZGURA'S CONCRETE SERVICES INC.
4946 Jasper Rd, Emmaus, PA 18049
Tel.: (610) 965-3167
Web Site: http://www.zgurasconcrete.com
Year Founded: 1999
Sales Range: $1-9.9 Million
Emp.: 10
Concrete Contractor
N.A.I.C.S.: 238110
Shelly Zgura *(Pres)*

ZHENA'S GYPSY TEA
205 Bryant St, Ojai, CA 93023
Tel.: (805) 646-1996
Web Site: http://www.gypsytea.com
Year Founded: 2001
Rev.: $3,500,000
Emp.: 11
Tea & Tea Products Distr
N.A.I.C.S.: 424490
Zhena C. Muzyka *(Pres)*
Gerard Linsmeier *(Mgr)*
Ann Leslie *(Mgr)*
Don Gaidano *(VP)*

ZIEGLER BOLT & PARTS CO.

ZHF (USA), INC.
7160 Chagrin Rd, Chagrin Falls, OH 44023
Tel.: (440) 519-9301
Web Site: http://www.zhfilters.com
Year Founded: 2004
Emp.: 20
Air Filter Mfr
N.A.I.C.S.: 333413
Don Wise *(Bus Mgr)*

ZIA ENGINEERING & ENVIRONMENTAL CONSULTANTS, LLC
755 S Telshor Blvd Ste F-201, Las Cruces, NM 88011
Tel.: (505) 532-1526　　　　　NM
Web Site: http://www.ziaeec.com
Year Founded: 2000
Sales Range: $1-9.9 Million
Emp.: 94
Environmental Consulting
N.A.I.C.S.: 541620
Edward H. Martinez *(Pres & CEO)*
Cheryl Cretin *(Mgr-Federal Contracts)*

ZIEBART INTERNATIONAL CORPORATION
1290 E Maple Rd, Troy, MI 48083-2817
Tel.: (248) 588-4100　　　　　MI
Web Site: http://www.ziebart.com
Year Founded: 1959
Sales Range: $125-149.9 Million
Emp.: 200
Franchiser of Automotive Protection Services & Accessory Installations
N.A.I.C.S.: 423120
Thomas E. Wolfe *(Pres & CEO)*
Daniel C. Baker *(Pres-Ziebart Corporation)*
Michael W. Riley *(Sr VP)*
Bruce Weir *(VP-Ops-Intl)*
Sue Spriet *(VP-Admin)*
Rob Harper *(Dir-Retail Ops)*

Subsidiaries:

Tidy Car International, Inc. (1)
1290 E Maple Rd, Troy, MI 48083-2817 **(100%)**
Tel.: (248) 588-4100
Web Site: http://www.ziebart.com
Sales Range: $10-24.9 Million
Emp.: 50
Marketing of Automobile Detailing Services
N.A.I.C.S.: 424690

ZIEBART JAPAN LIMITED (1)
4-23-18 Ukima, Kita-Ku, Tokyo, 115-0051, Japan
Tel.: (81) 3 3558 4388
Sales Range: $10-24.9 Million
Emp.: 48
Automotive Accessory Whslr
N.A.I.C.S.: 423120

ZIEBART OKINAWA CO. LTD (1)
401 Minatogawa, Urasoe, 901-2134, Okinawa, Japan
Tel.: (81) 988 77 4713
Automotive Accessory Whslr
N.A.I.C.S.: 423120

ZIEGER & SONS INC.
6215 Ardleigh St, Philadelphia, PA 19138
Tel.: (215) 438-7060
Web Site: http://www.zieger.com
Sales Range: $10-24.9 Million
Emp.: 50
Flowers, Fresh
N.A.I.C.S.: 424930
Paul Zieger *(Chm)*
Andy Mitchell *(Mgr)*
Mark Zieger *(VP-Sls & Mktg)*
Stephen Zieger *(Pres)*

ZIEGLER BOLT & PARTS CO.

ZIEGLER BOLT & PARTS CO. U.S. PRIVATE

Ziegler Bolt & Parts Co.—(Continued)
4848 Corporate St SW, Canton, OH 44706
Tel.: (330) 478-2542 — OH
Web Site: http://www.zieglerbolt.com
Year Founded: 1968
Sales Range: $10-24.9 Million
Emp.: 85
Provider of Industrial Fasteners, Nuts, Bolts & Screws
N.A.I.C.S.: 423840
Micheal Young (VP)

ZIEGLER CHEMICAL & MINERAL CORPORATION
366 N Broadway Ste 210, Jericho, NY 11753
Tel.: (516) 681-9600 — NY
Web Site: http://www.zieglerchemical.com
Year Founded: 1944
Sales Range: $75-99.9 Million
Emp.: 60
Provider of Gilsonite Mining & Petroleum Refining
N.A.I.C.S.: 324110
William Hyland (VP-Fin)
Chip Ziegler (Exec VP-Sls)
Jacquie Izzo (Controller)

ZIEGLER INC.
901 W 94th St, Minneapolis, MN 55420-4299
Tel.: (952) 888-4121 — MN
Web Site: http://www.ziegler.cat.com
Year Founded: 1914
Sales Range: $450-499.9 Million
Emp.: 1,045
Distr of Road Machinery & Attachments, Tractors, Trailers, Engines, Generators & Asphalt & Aggregate Equipment
N.A.I.C.S.: 423810
William L. Hoeft (Chm & CEO)
Mark R. Allen (CFO & Exec VP)
Diana Pester (Mgr-Product Support Sys)
Tom Russett (Mgr-Sls & Admin)

Subsidiaries:

Ziegler Inc. - Altoona (1)
1500 Ziegler Dr NW, Altoona, IA 50009
Tel.: (515) 957-3828
Web Site: http://www.zieglercat.com
General Construction Machinery & Equipment Whslr, Rental & Repair Services
N.A.I.C.S.: 423810
David Walter (VP-Sls & Mktg)

ZIEGLER LUMBER COMPANY
620 Holland Rd, Spokane, WA 99218-5893
Tel.: (509) 467-4960 — WA
Web Site: http://www.ziggys.com
Year Founded: 1954
Rev.: $43,000,000
Emp.: 130
Supplier of Lumber & Other Building Materials
N.A.I.C.S.: 423310
Vern E. Ziegler (Chm)
Carl Ziegler (Pres)
Vilho Tuomala (Mgr-Ziegler Building Matls)

ZIEGLER TIRE & SUPPLY COMPANY, INC.
7934 Hills & Dales Rd NW, Massillon, OH 44646
Tel.: (330) 833-0500 — OH
Web Site: http://www.zieglertire.com
Year Founded: 1919
Automotive Tires & Tubes; Truck Equipment & Parts Mfr
N.A.I.C.S.: 441340

John Streb (Dir-Ops)
John Ziegler Jr. (VP)

ZIEMS FORD CORNERS, INC.
5700 E Main St, Farmington, NM 87401
Tel.: (505) 325-1961
Web Site: http://www.ziemsfordcorners.com
Year Founded: 1961
Sales Range: $50-74.9 Million
Emp.: 100
New Car Retailer
N.A.I.C.S.: 441110
Matthew Clugston (Mgr-Svc)
Christine Ziems (Owner)
Matt Clugston (Gen Mgr)

ZIETA TECHNOLOGIES LLC
501 Silverside Rd Ste 113, Wilmington, DE 19809
Tel.: (302) 656-2491
Web Site: http://www.zietatech.com
Year Founded: 2002
Rev.: $6,500,000
Emp.: 70
Management Consulting Services
N.A.I.C.S.: 541618
Zieta Tek (Acct Mgr)

ZIFF DAVIS ENTERPRISE, INC.
28 E 28th St, New York, NY 10016
Tel.: (212) 503-5900
Web Site: http://www.ziffdavisenterprise.com
Online Business-to-Business Database & Trade Magazines Publisher
N.A.I.C.S.: 513120
Michael Caruso (CFO)
Jeff Strief (Pres)
Anthony S. Adams (Sr VP-Products)
Josh Heitsenrether (Sr VP-Mktg)
Deirdre Kelly (Dir-HR)
Ben Ronne (Dir-Online Product Mgmt)

Subsidiaries:

Baseline (1)
28 E 28th St 12th Fl, New York, NY 10016
Tel.: (212) 503-5900
Web Site: http://www.baselinemag.com
Trade Magazine Publisher
N.A.I.C.S.: 513120
Ed Cone (Editor-Website)
Eileen Feretic (Editor-Magazine & Mng Editor-Content Svcs)

CIO Insight (1)
28 E 28th St 12th Fl, New York, NY 10016
Tel.: (212) 503-5900
Web Site: http://www.cioinsight.com
Trade Magazine Publisher
N.A.I.C.S.: 513120
Susan Nunziata (Editor-in-Chief)

eWEEK (1)
28 E 28th St, New York, NY 10016
Tel.: (212) 503-5900
Web Site: http://www.eweek.com
Trade Magazine Publisher
N.A.I.C.S.: 513120
Chris Preimesberger (Editor-in-Chief-Features & Analysis)

ZIFTY COM, INC.
1220 Spring St NW, Atlanta, GA 30309
Tel.: (404) 817-3345
Web Site: http://www.zifty.com
Year Founded: 2003
Sales Range: $1-9.9 Million
Emp.: 54
Door to Door Delivery Service
N.A.I.C.S.: 492210
Todd Miller (Pres)

ZIG.MARKETING
4401 Rockside Rd Ste 214, Independence, OH 44131

Tel.: (216) 328-6300
Web Site: http://www.zigmarketing.com
Year Founded: 2001
Sales Range: Less than $1 Million
Emp.: 13
Advetising Agency
N.A.I.C.S.: 541810
Michael Smith (Dir-Creative)
Jennifer Smith (Partner & CFO)
Howard Zoss (Pres)
Lorraine Bivin (Partner & Dir-Art)
Nicole Selzer (Mgr-Production)
Peter Demichele (Dir-Media)

ZIGMAN JOSEPH PR
309 N Water St Ste 315, Milwaukee, WI 53202
Tel.: (414) 273-4680 — WI
Web Site: http://www.zigmanjoseph.com
Year Founded: 1959
Sales Range: $1-9.9 Million
Emp.: 12
Public Relations Agency
N.A.I.C.S.: 541820
Craig J. Peterson (Pres & CEO)

ZIGNEGO COMPANY, INCORPORATED
W 226nd 2940 Duplainville Rd, Waukesha, WI 53186
Tel.: (262) 547-4700
Web Site: http://www.zignego.com
Sales Range: $50-74.9 Million
Emp.: 30
Highway & Street Construction Services
N.A.I.C.S.: 237310
Daniel Zignego (Controller)

ZIGNEGO READY MIX INC.
W 226 N 2940 Duplainville Rd, Waukesha, WI 53186
Tel.: (262) 542-0333
Web Site: http://www.zignego.com
Sales Range: $10-24.9 Million
Emp.: 75
Ready Mixed Concrete
N.A.I.C.S.: 327320
Paul Zignego (Treas & Sec)

ZILBER LTD.
710 N Plankinton Ave, Milwaukee, WI 53203-2417
Tel.: (414) 274-2400 — DE
Web Site: http://www.zilber.com
Year Founded: 1983
Sales Range: $1-4.9 Billion
Emp.: 500
Holding Company; Residential, Commercial & Industrial Real Estate Investment, Development, Construction, Property Management, Sales & Leasing Services
N.A.I.C.S.: 551112
Jim Borris (Pres & CEO)
John Kersey (Exec VP)

Subsidiaries:

Homes by Towne, a Zilber Company, LLC (1)
710 N Plankinton Ave Ste 1200, Milwaukee, WI 53203
Tel.: (414) 274-2400
Web Site: http://www.homesbytowne.com
New Housing Operative Builders
N.A.I.C.S.: 236117

KM Development Corp. (1)
710 N Plankinton Ave, Milwaukee, WI 53203-2417 (100%)
Tel.: (414) 274-2400
Web Site: http://www.zilberltd.com
Sales Range: $50-74.9 Million
Emp.: 100
Residential & Commercial Real Estate Development & Construction

N.A.I.C.S.: 237210
James Theusch (Exec VP)

Subsidiary (Domestic):

Benko Construction Co., Inc. (2)
1600 N Atlantic Ave, Cocoa Beach, FL 32931
Tel.: (321) 784-8093
Web Site: http://www.benkoconstruction.com
New Housing Operative Builders
N.A.I.C.S.: 236117
Jack A. Bennett (Pres)

Towne Development of Hawaii, Inc. (1)
220 S King St Ste 960, Honolulu, HI 96813-4539
Tel.: (808) 537-5976
Web Site: http://www.townehawaii.com
Sales Range: $10-24.9 Million
Emp.: 25
Real Estate
N.A.I.C.S.: 237210
Chris Lau (Pres)

Towne Realty, Inc. (1)
710 N Plankinton Ave, Milwaukee, WI 53203-2417
Tel.: (414) 274-2400
Web Site: http://www.zilberpropertygroup.com
Sales Range: $50-74.9 Million
Emp.: 150
Commercial Real Estate Development, Sales & Leasing Services
N.A.I.C.S.: 531210
Jim Borris (Pres)

ZILIS, LLC
415 US Hwy 377 Ste 2020, Argyle, TX 76226
Tel.: (214) 705-3702
Web Site: http://shopus.zilis.com
Year Founded: 2015
Health, Wellness & Fitness Nutrition Products
N.A.I.C.S.: 456199
Steven Thompson (Founder & CEO)

Subsidiaries:

Zrii, LLC (1)
14183 S Minuteman Dr, Draper, UT 84020
Web Site: http://www.zrii.com
Direct Selling Establishments
N.A.I.C.S.: 424410
William Farley (Founder)

ZILKER TECHNOLOGY LLC
3200 Gracie Kiltz Ln Ste 110, Austin, TX 78758
Tel.: (720) 235-2244
Web Site: http://www.ztech.io
Year Founded: 2014
Sales Range: $10-24.9 Million
Emp.: 211
Information Technology Development Services
N.A.I.C.S.: 541512
Rob Thomas (CEO & Mng Partner)
Matt Clark (Mng Partner & CFO)
Sean Wyrick (Mng Partner & CTO)
David Sayed (Mng Partner & Exec VP-Sls)
Mark Lucente (Mng Partner & Dir-Technical)

ZILLER ELECTRIC INC.
2475 Brown Rd, Orion, MI 48359
Tel.: (248) 340-6000
Web Site: http://www.zillerelectric.com
Year Founded: 1985
Rev.: $8,900,000
Emp.: 26
Electrical Contractor
N.A.I.C.S.: 238210
Lisa Ziulkowski (Treas)
Geoffry Ziulkowski (Owner)

ZILLIANT, INC.

720 Brazos St Ste 600, Austin, TX 78701
Tel.: (512) 531-8500
Web Site: http://www.zilliant.com
Year Founded: 1998
Sales Range: $10-24.9 Million
Emp.: 100
Software Systems Analysis
N.A.I.C.S.: 517810
John O'Connor *(Sr VP-Svcs)*
Greg Howe *(Sr VP-Worldwide Sls)*
Steve Hale *(VP-Worldwide Channel Sls)*
Tom Ward *(VP-Sls-North America)*
Shams Chauthani *(Sr VP-Engrg)*
Maria Carballosa *(CMO)*
Michel Safi *(VP-Europe, MEA & Asia Pacific)*
Pascal Yammine *(CEO)*
John Lewis *(Chm)*
Sofia Simaria *(VP-Science & Applications Delivery)*
Tanya Cunningham *(VP-Pro Svcs)*
Kylie Fuentes *(Chief Product Officer)*

ZILLION TECHNOLOGIES
45189 Research Pl, Falls Church, VA 22043
Tel.: (703) 579-6891
Web Site:
  http://www.zilliontechnologies.com
Year Founded: 2002
Rev.: $3,500,000
Emp.: 50
Computer System Design Services
N.A.I.C.S.: 541512
Anthony Nathan *(CEO)*
Ryan Keener *(Dir-Tech)*

ZIM INDUSTRIES INC.
4545 E Lincoln Ave, Fresno, CA 93725
Tel.: (559) 834-1551
Web Site: http://www.zimwells.com
Sales Range: $10-24.9 Million
Emp.: 100
Water Well Drilling
N.A.I.C.S.: 237110
Curt B. Zimmerer *(Pres)*

ZIMBRICK INC.
1601 W Beltline Hwy, Madison, WI 53713
Tel.: (608) 271-1601
Web Site: http://www.zimbrick.com
Rev.: $182,300,000
Emp.: 240
Automobiles, New & Used
N.A.I.C.S.: 441110
Kendall Dahmen *(Gen Mgr)*
Vikki Brueggeman *(Dir-HR)*
Michael Glover *(Mgr-Sls)*
Ryan Horstmann *(Dir-IT)*
Cathy McTavish *(Controller)*
Monica Winkler *(Sr Mgr-Mktg)*
Amy Wach *(Mgr-Sls)*
Laura Schultz *(Mgr-Mktg)*

ZIMDAR ENTERPRISES
3343 Lousma Dr SE, Wyoming, MI 49548-2251
Tel.: (616) 452-8737   MI
Web Site:
  http://www.framesunlimited.com
Year Founded: 1971
Sales Range: $75-99.9 Million
Emp.: 80
Mfr & Retailer of Picture Frames
N.A.I.C.S.: 423220
Dorothy Zimdar *(Founder & CEO)*
Subsidiaries:

Frames Unlimited Inc.   (1)
3343 Lousma Dr SE, Wyoming, MI 49548-2251
Tel.: (616) 452-8737
Web Site: http://www.framesunlimited.com
Sales Range: $25-49.9 Million
Emp.: 12
Custom Framing & Art Products
N.A.I.C.S.: 238130
Bill Zimdar *(CEO)*
Kyle Zimdar *(Pres)*

ZIMMER GUNSUL FRASCA PARTNERSHIP
1223 SW Washington Ste 200, Portland, OR 97205
Tel.: (503) 224-3860
Web Site: http://www.zgf.com
Year Founded: 1942
Sales Range: $50-74.9 Million
Emp.: 400
Architectural Planning & Interior & Urban Design Services
N.A.I.C.S.: 541310
Robert Frasca *(Partner-Operating)*
Nancy Fishman *(Principal)*

ZIMMER LUCAS CAPITAL LLC.
535 Madison Ave Fl 6, New York, NY 10022
Tel.: (212) 509-1600
Rev.: $11,400,000
Emp.: 30
Financial Services
N.A.I.C.S.: 525990
John Lee *(Dir-Fin)*

ZIMMER MOTORS, INC.
1086 Burlington Pike, Florence, KY 41042
Tel.: (859) 525-1344
Web Site:
  http://www.zimmermotors.com
Year Founded: 1932
Sales Range: $10-24.9 Million
Emp.: 75
Car Whslr
N.A.I.C.S.: 441110
Catherine Zimmer *(Pres & Gen Mgr)*

ZIMMERMAN ARCHITECTURAL STUDIOS, INC.
2122 W Mount Vernon Ave, Milwaukee, WI 53233-2671
Tel.: (414) 476-9500
Web Site: http://www.zastudios.com
Rev.: $14,900,000
Emp.: 100
Architectural Services
N.A.I.C.S.: 541310
Joann Powell *(VP-HR)*
John Sabinash *(VP-Municipal Studio)*
Mark Zimmerman *(VP-Bus Dev)*
Doug Barnes *(VP-Education & Religious Studio)*
David Stroik *(Pres & CEO)*
Gary V. Zimmerman *(Pres)*
Lisa Jansen *(VP-Interior Design Studio)*
Tom DiSalvo *(VP & Dir-Landscape Architecture)*
Curt Baer *(VP-Healthcare Studio)*
Tom Poweleit *(VP-Justice & Corrections)*

ZIMMERMAN ASSOCIATES INC.
10600 Arrowhead Dr Ste 325, Fairfax, VA 22030
Tel.: (703) 883-0506
Web Site: http://www.zai-inc.com
Year Founded: 1979
Rev.: $28,511,421
Emp.: 400
Information Retrieval Services
N.A.I.C.S.: 517810
Mary Blevins *(CEO)*

ZIMMERMAN FORD, INC.
2525 E Main St, Saint Charles, IL 60174
Tel.: (630) 584-1800
Web Site:
  http://www.zimmermanford.com
Year Founded: 1937
Sales Range: $25-49.9 Million
Emp.: 75
New Car Retailer
N.A.I.C.S.: 441110
Chris Krueger *(Mgr-Fin)*
James Smith *(Mgr-Comml Fleet)*
Paulie Rapier *(Mgr-Gen Sls)*

ZIMMERMAN HOLDING COMPANY
1370 Old Freeport Rd, Pittsburgh, PA 15238
Tel.: (412) 963-0949
Web Site:
  http://www.eezimmermanco.com
Sales Range: $10-24.9 Million
Emp.: 50
Holding Company; Paint Thinners, Solvents & Other Chemical Products Mfr & Distr
N.A.I.C.S.: 551112
Elmer E. Zimmerman II *(Pres)*
Subsidiaries:

E.E. Zimmerman Company   (1)
1370 Old Freeport Rd, Pittsburgh, PA 15238
Tel.: (412) 963-0949
Web Site: http://www.eezimmermanco.com
Rev.: $6,600,000
Emp.: 20
Packaged Paint Thinners, Paint Solvents, Paint Removers, Wood Finishes, Fuels & Acids Mfr & Distr
N.A.I.C.S.: 325510

ZIMMERMAN-MCDONALD MACHINERY, INC.
2272 Weldon Pkwy, Saint Louis, MO 63146-3206
Tel.: (314) 291-9360   MO
Web Site:
  http://www.zimmermanmcdonald.com
Year Founded: 1886
Sales Range: $75-99.9 Million
Emp.: 8
Machine Tools Sales
N.A.I.C.S.: 423830
Brad Zimmerman *(Pres)*

ZINK DISTRIBUTING INC
3150 Shelby St, Indianapolis, IN 46227
Tel.: (317) 781-5800
Web Site:
  http://www.zinkdistributing.com
Rev.: $7,500,000
Emp.: 100
Beer & Ale Merchant Whslr
N.A.I.C.S.: 424810
James C. Zink *(Pres)*
Randall Hackworth *(CFO)*
Christopher M. Zink *(VP-Sls)*
James P. Zink Jr. *(VP & Gen Mgr)*
Subsidiaries:

Greenfield Beverage Company Inc   (1)
1763 E Main St, Greenfield, IN 46140
Tel.: (317) 462-2818
Rev.: $1,000,000
Emp.: 10
Other Grocery & Related Products Merchant Whslr
N.A.I.C.S.: 424490
Joseph Duffy *(Pres)*

ZINKAN ENTERPRISES INCORPORATED
1919 Case Pkwy N, Twinsburg, OH 44087
Tel.: (330) 487-1500
Web Site: http://www.zinkan.com
Sales Range: $10-24.9 Million
Emp.: 40
Specialty Chemicals Mfr
N.A.I.C.S.: 325998

ZINNOV LLC
21 Waterway Ave Ste 300, The Woodlands, TX 77380-3099
Tel.: (281) 362-2773   TX
Web Site: http://www.zinnov.com
Year Founded: 2002
Engineering & Digital Practice Consulting Services
N.A.I.C.S.: 541690
Pari Natarajan *(CEO)*
Vamsee Tirukkala *(Co-Founder)*
Vijay Swaminathan *(Co-Founder)*
Praveen Bhadada *(Partner & Head-Digital Transformation Practice)*
Sidhant Rastogi *(Partner & Head-Automotive & Automation Practice)*
Harish Singh *(Partner & Head-Global Tech Practice)*
Nilesh Thakker *(Head-Engrg Excellence Practice-Global)*
Preeti Anand *(Dir & Head-Engrg Excellence Practice)*
Nitika Goel *(Dir-Mktg & Comm)*

ZINPRO CORPORATION
10400 Viking Dr Ste 240, Eden Prairie, MN 55344
Tel.: (952) 944-2736
Web Site: http://www.zinpro.com
Year Founded: 1965
Sales Range: $10-24.9 Million
Emp.: 117
Feed Supplements
N.A.I.C.S.: 311119
Michael D. Anderson *(Chm)*
Terry L. Ward *(Dir-Res & Nutritional Svcs-Global)*
William A. Scrimgeour *(CEO)*
Sou Fei Chin *(VP-Sls-North Asia)*
Carol Lin *(Mgr-Key Acct-China)*
Vladimir Fay da Silva *(Acct Mgr-Argentina, Chile & Brazil)*
Jose Mendes *(Reg Mgr-Bus Unit)*
Lidy Brink *(Mgr-Mktg-Intl)*
Pierre Frumholtz *(Dir-Mktg-Global)*
Corey Carpenter *(Acct Mgr-Swine)*
Tanner Schmidt *(Acct Mgr-Pacific Coast)*
Max Winders *(VP-Sls-Intl)*
Patrick Brunner *(CFO)*
Rob Sheffer *(Pres)*
Russ Wyllie *(VP-Sls-Americas)*
Charles Gay *(Bus Mgr-Manufactured Feed)*
Matt Hutchins *(Acct Mgr-Central Midwest)*
Supunnee Jiarakhun *(VP-Sls-Southeast Asia & India)*

ZIOLKOWSKI CONSTRUCTION INC.
4050 Ralph Jones Dr, South Bend, IN 46628-9408
Tel.: (574) 287-1811
Web Site: http://www.zbuild.com
Year Founded: 1974
Sales Range: $25-49.9 Million
Emp.: 250
Construction Services
N.A.I.C.S.: 236220
Kevin Kampe *(Project Mgr)*
Dan Kidd *(Project Mgr)*
Stacey Shoemaker *(Mgr-Fleet Maintenance)*
Cheryl Hemsworth *(Coord-Mktg)*

ZION & ZION
464 S Farmer Ave Ste 105, Tempe, AZ 85281
Tel.: (480) 751-1007
Web Site:
  http://www.zionandzion.com
Sales Range: $10-24.9 Million

ZION & ZION

Zion & Zion—(Continued)
Emp.: 24
Advertising, Digital/Interactive, Public Relations, Strategic Planning/Research
N.A.I.C.S.: 541810
Aric Zion (CEO)
Jennifer Spangler (Sr Acct Supvr)
Bridgette Zellmann (Dir-Media)
Ashley Oakes (Acct Exec)
Samantha Finnk (Acct Coord-Social Media)
Velvet Elran (Acct Coord-Social Media)
Teri Morris (Sr Acct Exec)
D. D. Kullman (Sr Copywriter)
Sam Fink (Acct Exec)
Brandt Bogdanovich (Sr Mgr-Mktg Automation)
Malory Knutson (Assoc Acct Exec)
Holly Dill (Acct Dir)
Jessica Mattke (Acct Exec)
Anna Bussert (Mgr-Online Mktg)

ZIP MOVING & STORAGE INC.
8705 Grovemont Cir, Gaithersburg, MD 20877
Tel.: (301) 637-8074
Web Site: http://www.zipmoving.us
Year Founded: 2015
Sales Range: $1-9.9 Million
Emp.: 3
Home & Office Moving Services
N.A.I.C.S.: 238990
Dragan Manic (Dir-Ops)
Nash Srdic (Mgr-Dispatch Dept)
Sava Rilak (Reg Mgr)
Igor Stevan (Reg Mgr)
Goran Jelic (Gen Mgr)

ZIPLINE COMMUNICATIONS, INC.
804 S Monroe St Ste 200, Spokane, WA 99204
Tel.: (509) 321-2849
Web Site: http://www.zziplineinteractive.com
Sales Range: $1-9.9 Million
Emp.: 13
Interactive Advertising Services
N.A.I.C.S.: 541810
Shawn Davis (Pres & Dir-Creative)
Ryan Stemkoski (VP & Dir-Interactive)

ZIPLINE LOGISTICS LLC
781 NW Blvd Ste 100, Columbus, OH 43212
Tel.: (614) 458-1144
Web Site: http://www.ziplinelogistics.com
Year Founded: 2007
Sales Range: $1-9.9 Million
Emp.: 50
Freight Transportation Arrangement
N.A.I.C.S.: 488510
Walter Lynch (CEO)
Rick Althoff (Mgr-Natl Ops)
Dustin Verdin (Dir-Innovation)
Todd Tedder (Dir-Ops)
Emily Magill (Dir-HR)
Jessica Newbury (VP-Ops)

ZIPPO MANUFACTURING COMPANY, INC.
33 Barbour St, Bradford, PA 16701-1973
Tel.: (814) 368-2700 PA
Web Site: http://www.zippo.com
Year Founded: 1932
Sales Range: $150-199.9 Million
Emp.: 520
Cigarette Lighters, Knives, Magnifiers, Letter Openers, Pill Boxes & Writing Instruments Mfr
N.A.I.C.S.: 332999
Mark A. Paup (Pres, CEO, VP-Mktg & Sls, Dir-Mktg-Global, Mgr-Sls-National & Mgr-Sls-European)

Subsidiaries:

Northern Lights Enterprises, Inc. (1)
3474 Andover Rd, Wellsville, NY 14895
Tel.: (585) 593-1200
Web Site: http://www.northernlightscandles.com
Sales Range: $1-9.9 Million
Emp.: 120
Luxury Candles & Artisan-Made Accessories Mfr
N.A.I.C.S.: 339999
Mark A. Paup (Pres)
Andrew Glanzman (Pres)

Ronson Consumer Products Corp. (1)
3 Ronson Rd, Woodbridge, NJ 07095
Tel.: (732) 636-2430
Web Site: http://www.ronsoncorp.com
Sales Range: $50-74.9 Million
Emp.: 40
Packaging Services
N.A.I.C.S.: 332999

W.R. Case & Sons Cutlery Company (1)
PO Box 4000 Owens Way, Bradford, PA 16701 (100%)
Tel.: (814) 368-4123
Web Site: http://www.wrcase.com
Rev: $38,000,000
Emp.: 370
Pocket Knives, Hunting & Sporting Knives, Household Cutlery, Shears & Accessories Mfr
N.A.I.C.S.: 332215
Mark A. Paup (Pres & CEO)

Zippo GmbH (1)
Groendahlmscher Weg 87, PO Box 101065, D 46446, Emmerich am Rhein, Germany
Tel.: (49) 2822960275
Web Site: http://www.zippo.de
Sales Range: $75-99.9 Million
Emp.: 17
Personal Lighters Distr; Owned 50% by Zippo Manufacturing Company, Inc. & 50% by Borsumij Wehry N.V.
N.A.I.C.S.: 424990
Guido Heuvelmann (Mng Dir)

Zippo Italia S.R.L. (1)
Via Lagoscuro 5, Vezzano Ligure, 19020, La Spezia, Italy
Tel.: (39) 0187940941
Web Site: http://www.zipposhop.it
Lighter Mfr
N.A.I.C.S.: 339999

Zippo S.A. (1)
AZ Des Petits Carreaux, 7 Ave Du Bouton Dor, 94386, Bonneuil, Cedex, France
Tel.: (33) 143996000
Web Site: http://www.zippo.fr
Sales Range: $10-24.9 Million
Emp.: 20
Mfr of Cigarette Lighters & Accessories, Rules, Knives, Magnifiers & Letter Openers, Pill Boxes & Writing Instruments
N.A.I.C.S.: 339999

Zippo U.K. Ltd. (1)
Barley Mow Centre 10 Barley Mow Passage, Chiswick, London, W44PH, United Kingdom
Tel.: (44) 2089640666
Web Site: http://www.zippo.co.uk
Sales Range: $10-24.9 Million
Emp.: 4
Lighter Mfr
N.A.I.C.S.: 424990
John Sweeney (Gen Mgr)

ZIPPY'S, INC.
1765 S King St 2nd Fl, Honolulu, HI 96826-2134
Tel.: (808) 973-0880 HI
Web Site: http://www.zippys.com
Year Founded: 1966
Sales Range: $50-74.9 Million
Emp.: 2,000
Eating Place
N.A.I.C.S.: 722513
Nolle Ajimine (Sr Dir-Ops)

Subsidiaries:

Germaine's Luau, Inc. (1)
1601 Kapiolani Blvd Ste 940, Honolulu, HI 96814
Tel.: (808) 949-6626
Web Site: http://www.germainesluau.com
Sales Range: $10-24.9 Million
Emp.: 200
Tourist Attraction
N.A.I.C.S.: 711110
Zachary Castro (Dir-Musical)

ZIRCON CORPORATION
1580 Dell Ave, Campbell, CA 95008
Tel.: (408) 963-4550
Web Site: http://www.zircon.com
Year Founded: 1975
Sales Range: $10-24.9 Million
Emp.: 60
Power-Driven Handtools
N.A.I.C.S.: 333991
Barry Wingate (Dir-Design)
Dawn Tapia (Mgr-Inside Sls)
Gregory Heironimus (Engr-Electrical)
Mark Keliihanapule (Mgr-Graphics)

ZIRCON PRECISION PRODUCTS, INC.
818 W 24th St, Tempe, AZ 85282
Tel.: (480) 967-8688 AZ
Web Site: http://www.zirconprecision.com
Year Founded: 1962
Machine Shops
N.A.I.C.S.: 332710
Bruce Treichler (Pres & Gen Mgr)
Gary Miller (Mgr-Quality)
Molly McCoskery (Mgr-Production Control)

ZIRKELBACH CONSTRUCTION, INC.
1415 10th St W, Palmetto, FL 34221
Tel.: (941) 729-0000 FL
Web Site: http://www.zconstruction.com
Year Founded: 1996
Sales Range: $50-74.9 Million
Emp.: 40
Commercial & Institutional Building Construction
N.A.I.C.S.: 236220
Melissa Courtney (Controller)
Allan Zirkelbach (CEO)

ZIZZO GROUP, INC.
648 N Plankinton Ave Ste 270, Milwaukee, WI 53203
Tel.: (414) 319-5700
Web Site: http://www.zizzogroup.com
Advetising Agency
N.A.I.C.S.: 541810
Matt Hensler (Acct Mgr)
Alex Vagelatos (Acct Mgr-PR)
Anne Zizzo (Pres & CEO)
Steve Scholler (Assoc Dir-Creative)
Kristin Settle (Acct Mgr-PR)
Karissa Feller (Acct Exec)
Eric Mickschl (Graphic Designer)
Alyssa Feuerer (Acct Exec)
Mike Stefaniak (Sr VP-Mktg & Acct Svcs)
Lisa Ninmer (VP-Pub Rels)

Subsidiaries:

Celtic, Inc. (1)
316 N Milwaukee St Ste 350, Milwaukee, WI 53202
Tel.: (414) 316-2100
Web Site: https://www.celticinc.com
Sales Range: $10-24.9 Million
Advetising Agency
N.A.I.C.S.: 541810
Kurt Lingel (Co-Owner & Exec VP)
Brian Meehan (Co-Owner & Pres)

U.S. PRIVATE

Cindy Miresse (Dir-Acct Svc)
Jeff Faralli (Dir-Creative)
Kristen Johnson (Dir-Media)
Kristin Paltzer (Mgr-PR)
Peyton Conlin (Coord-PR)
Lori Putchel (Office Mgr)
Jan Topczewski (Mgr-Financial)
Nate Andrews (Dir-Art)

ZL STAR INC.
9341 Baythorne Dr, Houston, TX 77041-7737
Tel.: (713) 690-9055
Web Site: http://www.polytex.com
Year Founded: 1985
Sales Range: $25-49.9 Million
Emp.: 125
Holding Company
N.A.I.C.S.: 551112
Isaac Bazbaz (Pres & CEO)
Denne Smith (Plant Mgr)

Subsidiaries:

Fresh-Pak Corp (1)
16240 Port NW Ste 200, Houston, TX 77041
Tel.: (713) 690-8742
Web Site: http://www.freshpakcorp.com
Sales Range: $10-24.9 Million
Emp.: 50
Plastics, Materials & Basic Shapes
N.A.I.C.S.: 326130
John Bazbaz (Pres)
Jeffrey Chaluh (Exec VP)

Polytex Fibers Corporation (1)
9333 Baythorne Dr, Houston, TX 77041-7737
Tel.: (713) 690-9055
Web Site: http://www.polytex.com
Sales Range: $10-24.9 Million
Emp.: 35
Producer of Woven Polypropylene Bag Mfr
N.A.I.C.S.: 314910

ZLR IGNITION
303 Watson Powell Jr Way Ste 100, Des Moines, IA 50309-1724
Tel.: (515) 244-4456 IA
Web Site: http://www.zlrignition.com
Year Founded: 1987
Sales Range: $10-24.9 Million
Emp.: 25
Advetising Agency
N.A.I.C.S.: 541810
Louis Laurent (Pres)
James B. Anfinson (CFO & VP)
Bob Delsol (Exec Dir-Creative)
Andrea Marinaro (VP & Dir-Media)
William Brewer Jr. (Sr VP)

ZMC HOTELS
2305 W Superior St, Duluth, MN 55806
Tel.: (218) 723-8433
Web Site: http://www.zmchotels.com
Year Founded: 1982
Sales Range: $50-74.9 Million
Emp.: 50
Hotel Management
N.A.I.C.S.: 561110
John Goldfine (Chm)
Kenneth Goldfine (Vice Chm)
Todd Torvinen (Pres & CFO)
Jonathon Driscoll (COO)
Amy Goldfine (VP & Dir-Design)
Marie Ronning (Dir-Revenue Mgmt)
JoAnn Mattson (Dir-HR & Risk Mgmt)
Julie Kowalczak (Dir-Pur)
Ellen Goldfine Troeltzsch (Dir-Reputation Mgmt)
Kelly Dewey (Supvr-Arizona)
Jeannie Hetrick (Supvr-Kansas, Missouri, North Carolina, Florida & Alabama)
Leanne Joynes (VP-Sls & Mktg)

ZMG CONSTRUCTION, INC.

COMPANIES

477 Commerce Way Ste 115, Longwood, FL 32750
Tel.: (407) 865-5771
Web Site:
http://www.zmgconstruction.com
Sales Range: $50-74.9 Million
Emp.: 60
Multi-Family Housing Construction & Restoration
N.A.I.C.S.: 236116
Larry Kiem *(CFO)*
Dee Paonessa *(Exec VP)*

ZNERGY, INC.
808 A S Huntington St, Syracuse, IN 46567
Tel.: (800) 931-5662   NV
Year Founded: 2013
Sales Range: $1-9.9 Million
Emp.: 14
Investment Services
N.A.I.C.S.: 523999
David Baker *(CEO)*

Subsidiaries:

Command Control Center Corp. (1)
1625 VFW Pkwy, Boston, MA 02132   **(100%)**
Tel.: (800) 488-2760
Software Developer
N.A.I.C.S.: 513210
Nissim Shimon Trabelsi *(Pres, CEO & Treas)*

ZNS ENGINEERING, L.C.
201 5th Avenue Dr E, Bradenton, FL 34208
Tel.: (941) 748-8080   FL
Web Site: http://www.znseng.com
Year Founded: 1976
Sales Range: $1-9.9 Million
Emp.: 20
Civil Engineering, Structural Engineering, Planning, Surveying, Landscape Architecture & Environmental Consulting
N.A.I.C.S.: 541330
Diana Hubbard *(Asst Sec & Treas)*
Don Bouchard *(Asst VP)*
Rachel Layton *(Dir-Plng)*

ZNYX NETWORKS, INC.
48421 Milmont Dr, Fremont, CA 94538
Tel.: (510) 249-0800   CA
Web Site: http://www.znyx.com
Rev.: $75,000,000
Emp.: 40
Computer Peripheral Equipment
N.A.I.C.S.: 334118
Connie Austin *(Pres & CEO)*

ZOBMONDO!! ENTERTAINMENT LLC
336 Bon Air Ctr Ste 409, Greenbrae, CA 94904
Tel.: (310) 820-1270
Web Site: http://www.zobmondo.com
Year Founded: 1998
Sales Range: $10-24.9 Million
Emp.: 2
Game, Toy & Children's Vehicle Mfr
N.A.I.C.S.: 339930
Randall Horn *(Pres)*

ZOCDOC, INC.
568 Broadway 9th Fl, New York, NY 10012
Tel.: (855) 962-3621
Web Site: http://www.zocdoc.com
Year Founded: 2007
Sales Range: $25-49.9 Million
Online Doctor Appointment Scheduling Services
N.A.I.C.S.: 541511
Oliver Kharraz *(Co-Founder & CEO)*
Nick Ganju *(Co-Founder)*

Netta Samroengraja *(CFO & CPO)*
Ori Schnaps *(VP-Engrg)*
Joaquim Gamboa *(VP-Legal Affairs)*
Andre Heeg *(VP-Local Sls)*
Anna Elwood *(VP-Ops)*
Colleen Gangl *(VP-People)*
Kate Sigman *(VP-Fin)*
Kevin Kumler *(VP-Health Sys)*
Melissa Esmundo *(VP-Acq & CRM)*
Serkan Kutan *(VP-Engrg & Software Architecture)*
Todd Edebohls *(VP-Bus Dev)*

ZOELLER CO.
3649 Cane Run Rd, Louisville, KY 40211
Tel.: (502) 778-2731   KY
Web Site: http://www.zoeller.com
Year Founded: 1939
Sales Range: $150-199.9 Million
Emp.: 450
Mfr of Sump & Sewage Pumps, Potable Water Pumps & Related Products
N.A.I.C.S.: 333914
John Zoeller *(CEO)*

Subsidiaries:

Flint & Walling Inc. (1)
95 N Oak St, Kendallville, IN 46755-1772   **(100%)**
Tel.: (260) 347-1600
Web Site: http://www.flintandwalling.com
Sales Range: $25-49.9 Million
Emp.: 135
Manufacturers of Potable Water Products (Turbine & Jet Pumps), Tanks & Accessories, Water Purification & Filter Products
N.A.I.C.S.: 333914
Scott Lechner *(Pres)*
Veneda Rose *(Controller)*
Ben Painter *(Mgr-Accts-Wholesale-Natl)*

Lincoln Industries, Inc. (1)
110 W Division St, Boonville, IN 47601-1945   **(100%)**
Tel.: (812) 897-0715
Web Site: http://www.lincolnind.com
Rev.: $2,900,000
Emp.: 69
Mfr of Plastic Injection Molding
N.A.I.C.S.: 326199
Bill Lachowecki *(Mgr-Quality Svcs)*
Sayed Saboohi *(Pres)*

ZOGICS, LLC
309 Pittsfield Rd, Lenox, MA 01240
Tel.: (413) 458-8008
Web Site: http://www.zogics.com
Year Founded: 2007
Sales Range: $10-24.9 Million
Emp.: 15
Gym Wipe Product Mfr
N.A.I.C.S.: 339920
Paul LeBlanc *(Founder & CEO)*
Jeff Stripp *(Dir-Ecommerce, Sls & Svc)*
Misti Mitchell *(Dir-Logistics & Fulfillment)*
Shawnee Tannenbaum *(Office Mgr)*
Justin Mairo *(Mgr-Warehouse)*

ZOGSPORTS LLC
57 W 38th St 12th Fl, New York, NY 10018
Tel.: (212) 694-3600
Web Site: http://www.zogsports.com
Sales Range: $1-9.9 Million
Emp.: 145
Social Sports League Operator
N.A.I.C.S.: 813990
Rob Herzog *(Founder & CEO)*
Mike Mortellaro *(COO)*
Brandon Bitterman *(Gen Mgr-New York)*
Sara Zaremba *(Mgr-Corp & Private Events)*
Jody Zellman *(Mgr-Expansion-Natl)*
Ashley Merdinger *(Mgr-Mktg-NYC)*
Matthew Kemp *(Mgr-Sports Ops & Growth)*

ZOHO CORPORATION
4141 Hacienda Dr, Pleasanton, CA 94588
Tel.: (925) 924-9500
Web Site: http://www.zohocorp.com
Year Founded: 1996
Sales Range: $75-99.9 Million
Emp.: 5,000
Computer Software Publisher
N.A.I.C.S.: 513210
Raj Sabhlok *(Pres)*

Subsidiaries:

Zoho (Beijing) Technology Co., Ltd. (1)
B-1104 11F Horizon International Tower 6 Zhichun Road, Haidian District, Beijing, 100088, China
Tel.: (86) 400 660 8680
Computer Software Publisher
N.A.I.C.S.: 513210

Zoho Corporation Private Limited (1)
DLF IT Park Block 7 Ground Floor 1/124, Mount PH Road, Chennai, 600 089, India
Tel.: (91) 4467447070
Web Site: http://www.Zoho.com
Emp.: 200
Computer Software Publisher
N.A.I.C.S.: 513210

Zoho Japan Corporation (1)
Yokohama Kinkocho Building 6F Kinko-cho 6-3, Kanagawa-ku, Yokohama, 221-0056, Japan
Tel.: (81) 45 444 3880
Computer Software Publisher
N.A.I.C.S.: 513210

ZOLADZ CONSTRUCTION CO., INC.
13600 RailRd St, Alden, NY 14004
Tel.: (716) 937-6575
Web Site: http://www.zoladz.com
Sales Range: $10-24.9 Million
Emp.: 125
Excavation Services
N.A.I.C.S.: 238910
Tom Dougherty *(Owner)*

ZOLFO COOPER, LLC
Grace Bldg 1114 Avenue of the Americas 41st Fl, New York, NY 10036
Tel.: (212) 561-4000   NJ
Web Site:
http://www.zolfocooper.com
Sales Range: $50-74.9 Million
Emp.: 60
Business Advisory, Restructuring & Interim Management Services
N.A.I.C.S.: 541618
John R. Boken *(Sr Mng Dir-Los Angeles)*
Joff A. Mitchell *(Sr Mng Dir-New York)*
Scott W. Winn *(Sr Mng Dir-New York)*
Elizabeth Kardos *(Mng Dir-New York & Gen Counsel)*
David Orlofsky *(Sr Mng Dir)*
Richard Collura *(Sr Mng Dir-New York)*
Rebecca Randall *(Gen Counsel)*

Subsidiaries:

Zolfo Cooper British Virgin Islands (1)
Palm Grove House 2nd Floor Wickhams Cay 1, PO Box 4571, Tortola, Road Town, VG 1110, Virgin Islands (British)
Tel.: (284) 494 9600
Financial Advisory Services
N.A.I.C.S.: 523940
Stuart Mackellar *(Mng Partner)*

Zolfo Cooper Cayman Islands (1)
Suite 776 10 Market Street, Grand Cayman, Camana Bay, KY1 9006, Cayman Islands
Tel.: (345) 946 0081
Web Site:
http://www.caribbean.zolfocooper.com

Emp.: 12
Financial Advisory Services
N.A.I.C.S.: 523940
Gordon MacRae *(Mng Partner)*
Eleanor Fisher *(Co-Partner)*
Tammy Fu *(Co-Partner)*

ZOLON TECH SOLUTIONS INC.
2465 Centreville Rd Ste J17, Herndon, VA 20171-3026
Tel.: (703) 378-6585
Web Site: http://www.zolon.com
Year Founded: 1998
Rev.: $22,000,000
Emp.: 150
Computer Programming Services
N.A.I.C.S.: 541511
Zach Smith *(Exec VP)*
Goutham Amarneni *(Co-Founder & Pres)*
John Dryer *(VP)*
Manish Dadhich *(VP)*
Ram Mattapalli *(Co-Founder & CEO)*
Vish Hiremath *(Dir-MSP & VMS Svcs)*
Kirk Macchiavello *(VP)*
George Kantsios *(VP-IC & DOD)*
Dan Abernathy *(VP/Gen Mgr-Federal Civilian Bus)*

ZOLOTO RESOURCES LTD.
1395 Brickell Ave Ste 800, Miami, FL 33131
Tel.: (305) 357-2010
Year Founded: 2007
Gold & Silver Ore Services
N.A.I.C.S.: 212220
Robert Maddigan *(Pres & CEO)*

ZOM HOLDING, INC.
2001 Summit Park Dr Ste 300, Orlando, FL 32810
Tel.: (407) 644-6300
Web Site: http://www.zomliving.com
Year Founded: 1977
Sales Range: $10-24.9 Million
Holding Company; Multi-Family Housing Construction Services
N.A.I.C.S.: 551112
Joost P. Zyderveld *(Founder)*
Samuel Stephens *(Pres)*

Subsidiaries:

ZOM Florida, Inc. (1)
200 E Broward Blvd Ste 1200, Fort Lauderdale, FL 33301
Tel.: (954) 779-7950
Web Site: http://www.zomusa.com
Emp.: 8
Multifamily Housing Construction
N.A.I.C.S.: 236116
Kyle Clayton *(VP-Dev)*
Gregg West *(Pres)*

ZOMBIE, INC.
420 4th Ave, Seattle, WA 98104
Tel.: (206) 623-9655
Web Site: http://www.zombie.com
Year Founded: 1994
Sales Range: $1-9.9 Million
Emp.: 30
Software & Computer Programming Services
N.A.I.C.S.: 541511
Joanna Alexander *(Co-Founder, Co-CEO & COO)*
Mark Long *(Co-Founder & Co-CEO)*
Hunter Peyron *(Lead Designer)*
Randall Glass *(Designer-Gameplay)*
Terry Hopfenspirger *(Level Designer & 3D Modeler)*
Michael Schorr *(Lead Level Designer)*

ZONAL HOSPITALITY SYSTEMS INC.

ZONAL HOSPITALITY SYSTEMS INC.

U.S. PRIVATE

206 W Sybelia Ave, Maitland, FL
32751-4739
Tel.: (407) 539-0092
Web Site: http://www.zonalusa.com
Office Supplies & Stationery Stores
N.A.I.C.S.: 459410
Richard Hammond (VP)

Subsidiaries:

Comtrex Systems Corporation (1)
520 Fellowship Rd Ste E 508, Mount Laurel, NJ 08054
Tel.: (856) 778-0090
Web Site: http://www.comtrex.com
Computer Technology & Software for Fast-Food & Restaurant Business
N.A.I.C.S.: 541512

ZONE 5

25 Monroe St Ste 300, Albany, NY
12210
Tel.: (518) 242-7000
Web Site: http://www.zone5.com
Year Founded: 1989
Sales Range: $10-24.9 Million
Emp.: 32
Event Planning & Marketing,
Internet/Web Design, Web (Banner Ads, Pop-ups, etc.)
N.A.I.C.S.: 541810
Todd Mosher (Pres & CEO)
Paul Fahey (COO & Dir-Mktg Strategy)
Michelle Lansing (VP-Creative Strategy)
Dave Homsey (Dir-Creative)
Dave Imbarrato (Dir-Creative)
Paul Hook (Dir-Mktg)
Spencer Raggio (Sr Web Designer)
Richard Skiermont (Sr VP & Exec Dir-Creative)
Ray Witkowski (VP)
JoAnne Latham (Dir-Acct Svcs)
Chris Urig (Acct Supvr)
Anthony Palmeri (Supvr-Web Deptq)
Danika Atkins (Acct Exec)
Victoria Barbeisch (Acct Exec)
Brittnay Gilman (Acct Exec)
Brya Emery (Acct Exec)

ZONEPERFECT NUTRITION COMPANY

625 Cleveland Ave, Columbus, OH
43215
Tel.: (614) 624-7485
Web Site:
http://www.zoneperfect.com
Sales Range: $10-24.9 Million
Emp.: 10
Health Food Provider
N.A.I.C.S.: 621399
Christopher P. Baker (CEO)
Julia Stoner (Sr Brand Mgr-ZonePerfect)

ZONES, INC.

1102 15th St SW Ste 102, Auburn,
WA 98001-6509
Tel.: (253) 205-3000   WA
Web Site: https://www.zones.com
Year Founded: 1986
Emp.: 2,300
Other Computer Related Services
N.A.I.C.S.: 541519
Firoz H. Lalji (Founder, Founder, Chm, Chm, CEO & CEO)
Ronald P. McFadden (CFO & Sr VP)
Anwar Jiwani (CIO & Sr VP-Ops)
P. Sean Hobday (Sr VP-Global Sls & Ops)
Derrek Hallock (Sr VP-Partner & Product Mgmt)
Robert McGowen (Sr VP-SMB Sls)
Asif Hudani (Sr VP-Advanced Solutions Grp)
Linda Marbena (Sr VP-Pur & Logistics)
Paul Kerwin (VP-Fin Plng & Analysis)
Mishon Landry (Dir-Supplier Diversity-Central Reg)
Dominic Camden (Sr VP-Enterprise Sls)
Dan Pickett (Pres & Chief Revenue Officer)
Rich Montbriand (Sr VP-Digital Solutions)

Subsidiaries:

E.nfrastructure Technologies, Inc. (1)
5 Enterprise Ave, Clifton Park, NY 12065
Tel.: (518) 664-3899
Web Site: http://www.nfrastructure.com
Information Technology Consulting Services
N.A.I.C.S.: 541512
Firoz H. Lalji (Chm)
Bill Morrissey (Sr VP-Sls)
Chris Pickett (Sr VP-Sls)
Kevin O'Neil (Sr VP-Fin)
Mike Martin (CTO)
Jennifer Perrotta (Sr VP-Svcs)
Gerald Goff (Sr VP-Mission Critical Construction)
Amy Buckley Harlow (Sr VP-HR & Admin)
Suryakant Kale (Sr VP-Tech)
Daniel T. Pickett III (Pres & CEO)

Zones Canada, Inc. (1)
10 Four Seasons Place Suite 701 Burnhamthorpe Square, Toronto, M9B 6H7, ON, Canada
Web Site: http://www.zones.com
Information Technology Products & Services
N.A.I.C.S.: 541519

Zones Europe, Inc. (1)
12-16 Westland Place, London, N1 7LP, United Kingdom
Tel.: (44) 20 7608 7676
Web Site: http://www.zones.com
Information Technology Products & Services
N.A.I.C.S.: 541519

ZONK GROUP INCORPORATED

1505 Precision Dr, Plano, TX 75074
Tel.: (972) 509-7651
Web Site: http://www.zonkgroup.com
Rev.: $50,000,000
Emp.: 10
Packaging Materials
N.A.I.C.S.: 424990
John Lanzillo (Pres)
Shelly Woolwine (Office Mgr)

ZONKO BUILDERS INC.

37116 Lighthouse Rd, Selbyville, DE
19975-3909
Tel.: (302) 436-0222
Web Site:
http://www.zonkobuilders.com
Year Founded: 1973
Sales Range: $10-24.9 Million
Emp.: 2
Residential Construction
N.A.I.C.S.: 236115
Charles A. Zonko (Pres)
Bonnie Zonko (Treas & Sec)

ZONZIA MEDIA, INC.

2580 Anthem Village Dr Ste B-7,
Henderson, NV 89052
Tel.: (646) 560-3227   NV
Year Founded: 1981
Digital Publishing & Broadcasting Services
N.A.I.C.S.: 513199

ZOOLOGICAL SOCIETY OF BUFFALO

300 Parkside Ave, Buffalo, NY 14214
Tel.: (716) 837-3900   NY
Year Founded: 1931
Sales Range: $1-9.9 Million
Emp.: 215
Zoo Conservation Services
N.A.I.C.S.: 712130
Denise Maloney (Dir-Admin)
Amy Habib Rittling (Sec)
Barbara T. Baker (Vice Chm)
David P. Flynn (Chm)
Jonathan Dandes (Vice Chm)
Robert Fox (Vice Chm)
Robert Yalowich (Treas)
Lisa Smith (Interim Pres, Interim CEO & Chief Zoological Officer)

ZOOLOGICAL SOCIETY OF CINCINNATI

3400 Vine St, Cincinnati, OH 45220
Tel.: (513) 281-4700   OH
Web Site: http://cincinnatizoo.org
Year Founded: 1875
Sales Range: $25-49.9 Million
Emp.: 631
Zoo
N.A.I.C.S.: 712130
William T. Maynard (Exec Dir)
Jeff Walton (Dir-HR)
Mark Fisher (Dir-Facilities)
Russel Doyle (Dir-Dev)
Lori Voss (VP-Admin)

ZOOLOGICAL SOCIETY OF PHILADELPHIA

3400 W Girard Ave, Philadelphia, PA
19104
Tel.: (215) 243-1100   PA
Web Site:
http://www.philadelphiazoo.org
Year Founded: 1859
Rev.: $38,182,000
Assets: $121,741,000
Liabilities: $18,403,000
Net Worth: $103,338,000
Emp.: 483
Fiscal Year-end: 02/28/18
Zoo Conservation Services
N.A.I.C.S.: 712130
Amy Shearer (CMO)
Mary R. Burke (Sec)
Vikram H. Dewan (Pres & CEO)
Greg Goldman (VP-Dev)
Joseph T. Steuer (CFO & Treas)

ZOOLOGICAL SOCIETY OF PITTSBURGH

1 Wild Pl, Pittsburgh, PA 15206-1178
Tel.: (412) 665-3639   PA
Year Founded: 1994
Sales Range: $10-24.9 Million
Emp.: 378
Zoo Conservation Services
N.A.I.C.S.: 712130
Frank Cartieri (COO)
Jacqueline Vincunas (CFO)
Barbara Baker (Pres & CEO)

ZOOLOGICAL SOCIETY OF SAN DIEGO

2929 Zoo Dr, San Diego, CA 92112-0551
Tel.: (619) 231-1515   CA
Web Site: http://zoo.sandiegozoo.org
Year Founded: 1916
Sales Range: $250-299.9 Million
Emp.: 1,561
Zoo Owner & Operator
N.A.I.C.S.: 712130
Douglas G. Myers (Pres & CEO)
Robert McClure (Dir-San Diego Zoo Safari Park)
Ted Molter (Chief Mktg Officer)
Paula Brock (CFO)
Richard B. Gulley (Treas)
Robert B. Horsman (Chm)
Steven G. Tappan (Vice Chm)
Mark Stuart (Chief Dev Officer & Chief Membership Officer)
Allison Alberts (Chief Conservation & Res Officer)
Robert J. Wiese (Chief Life Sciences Officer)
Robert Erhardt (CTO)
Linda Lowenstine (Sec)
Dwight Scott (Dir-San Diego Zoo)
Shawn Dixon (COO)
James Lauth (Gen Counsel)

ZOOM ADVERTISING

820 W Jackson Blvd, Chicago, IL
60607
Tel.: (312) 491-8300
Web Site:
http://www.zoomchicago.com
Year Founded: 1993
Rev.: $7,000,000
Emp.: 12
Advetising Agency
N.A.I.C.S.: 541810
Jeffrey J. Halcomb (Pres)
Larry F. Berleman (VP-Creative Svcs)
Martin Frank (Exec Dir-Creative)

ZOOM COMPANIES, INC.

5280 N Ocean Dr Ste 2-F, Riviera
Beach, FL 33404
Tel.: (954) 684-8288   FL
Year Founded: 2009
Sales Range: Less than $1 Million
Emp.: 21
Investment Services
N.A.I.C.S.: 523999
William G. Forhan (Chm & CEO)

ZOOM IMAGING SOLUTIONS, INC.

4603 W Jennifer Ave, Fresno, CA
93722
Tel.: (559) 275-7086
Web Site:
http://www.zoomcopiers.com
Year Founded: 1987
Sales Range: $10-24.9 Million
Emp.: 120
Distr of Photocopy Machines
N.A.I.C.S.: 423420
Gary Johnson (Pres)

ZOOOM PRINTING

2042 Westmoreland St, Richmond,
VA 23230
Tel.: (804) 343-0009
Web Site:
http://www.zooomprinting.com
Sales Range: Less than $1 Million
Emp.: 9
Commercial Printing Services
N.A.I.C.S.: 323111
Jo Ann Rossi (Pres)
Ben Rossi (VP-Ops)
Nora Rossi (VP-Looking Cute)
Tyler Rossi (Dir-Activities)
Nick Phouthakhanty (Mgr-Prepress)

ZOOTS CORPORATION

45 Industrial Blvd, Brockton, MA
02301
Tel.: (508) 584-2659   MA
Web Site: http://www.zoots.com
Year Founded: 1998
Sales Range: $25-49.9 Million
Emp.: 1,000
Dry Cleaning Services
N.A.I.C.S.: 812320
Rick Simoneau (Owner)

ZORIA FARMS INC.

9537 Road 29 1/2, Madera, CA
93637-8501
Tel.: (559) 673-6368
Web Site: http://www.zfoodsinc.com
Sales Range: $10-24.9 Million
Emp.: 150
Processor of Fruits
N.A.I.C.S.: 311423
John Zoria (Pres)

COMPANIES

ZORN COMPRESSOR & EQUIPMENT CO.
1335 E Wisconsin Ave, Pewaukee, WI 53072
Tel.: (262) 695-7000
Web Site: http://www.zorn-air.com
Rev.: $13,500,000
Emp.: 38
Compressor Mfr
N.A.I.C.S.: 423830
John D. Zorn (CEO)
Katie Marks (Treas & Sec)
Matthew D. Zorn (Pres)

ZORREL INTERNATIONAL, INC.
13500 15th St, Grandview, MO 64030
Tel.: (816) 765-5212   NV
Web Site: http://www.zorrel.com
Year Founded: 2005
Emp.: 500
Fabrics & Apparel Mfr & Whlslr
N.A.I.C.S.: 424350
Rob Staudinger (Mgr-Acctg)

ZOTTI GROUP AVIATION, INC.
6323 NW 99th Ave, Miami, FL 33178
Tel.: (305) 592-1753   FL
Year Founded: 1993
Holding Company; Aircraft Parts Whlslr
N.A.I.C.S.: 551112
Roberto F. Zotti (Pres)

Subsidiaries:

ZGA Aircraft Parts, Inc.   (1)
6323 NW 99th Ave, Miami, FL 33166-3336
Tel.: (305) 592-1753
Web Site: http://www.zgasales.com
Sales Range: $1-9.9 Million
Emp.: 9
New & Recertified Aircraft Parts Distr
N.A.I.C.S.: 423860
Roberto F. Zotti (Pres)

ZOUP!
28290 Franklin Rd, Southfield, MI 48034
Tel.: (248) 663-1111
Web Site: http://www.zoup.com
Sales Range: $10-24.9 Million
Emp.: 16
Fresh Soup Retailer
N.A.I.C.S.: 445298
Eric Ersher (Founder & Mng Partner)

ZOUP! SPECIALTY PRODUCTS, LLC
23675 Greenfield Rd, Southfield, MI 48075
Tel.: (248) 395-7000   MI
Web Site: http://www.zoupbroth.com
Year Founded: 2012
Sales Range: $1-9.9 Million
Emp.: 3
Grocery Product Distr
N.A.I.C.S.: 424490
Joe McKernan (Pres)

ZOZZARO BROTHERS INC.
1 Tirrek Mountain Plz 4th Fl, West Paterson, NJ 07424
Tel.: (973) 772-0253
Web Site: http://www.zozzarorecycling.com
Sales Range: $10-24.9 Million
Emp.: 90
Recycling Services
N.A.I.C.S.: 562111
Paul Winkowski (Mgr-Maintenance Dept)
Jim Warin (Mgr-Logistics)
Glenn Wolkovitsch (Asst VP-HR)
Kevin Tinney (VP-Sls)
Joe Triolo (Controller)
Alice Abadiotakis (Asst Controller-Carteret)

ZQUARED LLC
130 Trade Center Dr W, Saint Peters, MO 63376
Tel.: (234) 978-2733
Web Site: http://www.zquared.com
Year Founded: 2010
Sales Range: $25-49.9 Million
Emp.: 15
Software Support Services
N.A.I.C.S.: 541512
Chad Cornett (Co-Founder & Pres)
Zach Cornett (Co-Founder & CEO)
Matt O'Daniel (COO)
Charlie Meyer (Gen Mgr)
Melanie DeMauro (Dir-Content)

ZS ASSOCIATES, INC.
1800 Sherman Ave, Evanston, IL 60201
Tel.: (847) 492-3600
Web Site: http://www.zsassociates.com
Year Founded: 1983
Rev.: $200,000,000
Emp.: 1,000
Management Consulting Services Specializing in Sales & Marketing Consulting
N.A.I.C.S.: 541613
Andris Zoltners (Co-Founder)
Prabhakant Sinha (Co-Founder & Partner)
Jaideep Bajaj (Chm)
Chris Wright (Mng Dir)

Subsidiaries:

Medullan, Inc.   (1)
240 Elm St 2nd Fl, Somerville, MA 02144
Tel.: (617) 547-0273
Web Site: http://www.medullan.com
Sales Range: $1-9.9 Million
Information Technology Services
N.A.I.C.S.: 541512
Ahmed Albaiti (Founder & CEO)

ZS FUND L.P.
340 Madison Ave Fl 19, New York, NY 10173
Tel.: (212) 398-6200
Web Site: http://www.zsfundlp.com
Year Founded: 1985
Sales Range: $25-49.9 Million
Emp.: 8
Privater Equity Firm
N.A.I.C.S.: 523999

Subsidiaries:

Amerijet International Inc.   (1)
4500 NW 36th St, Miami, FL 33166
Tel.: (305) 593-5500
Web Site: http://www.amerijet.com
Multi-Modal Cargo Transportation & Logistics Services
N.A.I.C.S.: 488320
David G. Bassett (Founder)
Christine Richard (Dir-Mktg)
Brian Beach (COO)
Joan Canny (Gen Counsel & Sr VP)
Vicken L. Karjian (Chm & Interim CEO)
John Nash (CFO)
Jon Olin (Sr VP-Corp Strategy & Admin)

Subsidiary (Domestic):

I.T.N. Consolidators   (2)
3401 C NW 72nd Ave, Miami, FL 33122
Tel.: (786) 437-7699
Web Site: http://www.itnworldwide.com
Marine Transportation Services
N.A.I.C.S.: 488390
Diana Abujasen (Mgr-Trade)
Pilar Fadul (Mgr-Trade)

Lily Transportation Corp.   (1)
145 Rosemary St, Needham, MA 02494-3238
Tel.: (781) 449-8811
Web Site: http://www.lily.com
Sales Range: $50-74.9 Million
Emp.: 20
Trucking Transport
N.A.I.C.S.: 541614
Alex Lafaras (CFO & Exec VP)
Gregg Nierenberg (Pres & CEO)
James E. Walker (Exec VP)
Jonathan L. Baldi (VP-Sls & Engrg)
John Simourian II (Pres & CEO)

Transervice Logistics Inc.   (1)
5 Dakota Dr, New Hyde Park, NY 11042-1188
Tel.: (516) 488-3400
Web Site: http://www.transervice.com
Sales Range: $100-124.9 Million
Truck Leasing Services, Transportation Solutions, Contract Maintenance, Full Service Leasing, Dedicated Contract Carriage
N.A.I.C.S.: 484110
Alex Lafaras (CFO)
Gregg Nierenberg (Pres & CEO)
Edward J. Flannigan (Partner)
Pierre Bujold (VP-Canadian Ops)
John Walker (Sr VP-Logistics)
Jim Lavery (Dir-Bus Dev-New England)
William Rodriguez (Dir-Sls-West)
David Wilke (Dir-Sls-Midwest)
Doug Adamson (Sr VP-Sls & Mktg)
Gino Fontana (COO & Exec VP)

Affiliate (Domestic):

Transervice Lease Corp.   (2)
5 Dakota Dr, Lake Success, NY 11042
Tel.: (516) 488-3400
Web Site: http://www.transervice.com
Sales Range: $100-124.9 Million
Construction Transportation Mining & Forestry Machinery & Equipment Rental & Leasing
N.A.I.C.S.: 532412
Eric Sklar (CFO)
Joseph N. Evangelist (Exec VP)
Marie Jansen (Mgr-Mktg)
William G. Doherty (Exec VP)
Pete Hubbard (VP-Fleet Ops & Maintenance)
Wolfgang Marschhauser (VP-Sls)

ZT CORPORATE
1535 West Loop S Ste 410, Houston, TX 77027
Tel.: (713) 627-2000
Web Site: http://www.ztcorporate.com
Year Founded: 1997
Sales Range: $100-124.9 Million
Emp.: 596
Financial Management Services
N.A.I.C.S.: 523999
David Redman (VP)
Shehzad Roopani (VP)
Ali Tariq (VP-Fin)
Taseer A. Badar (Chm & CEO)
Bilal Saeed (Chief Acctg Officer)
Nuruddin Ali (Exec VP)
Fahid Ghaffar (Sr VP-Fin & Banking)
Azhar Hirani (VP)
Robert John Lee (VP)
Mohsin Malik (VP)
Roger Manghnani (Mng Partner)
Farrukh Tariq (Sr VP)
Sheheryar Shah (COO)

Subsidiaries:

ZT Motors Holding, L.P.   (1)
21201 Blair Road The Woodlands, Woodlands, TX 77385
Tel.: (850) 863-2167
Web Site: http://www.ztdealers.com
Pre-Owned & New Vehicle Dealer
N.A.I.C.S.: 441110
Keith Monnin (Pres)
Claire Thompson (CFO)

Subsidiary (Domestic):

Steve Rayman Chevrolet, LLC   (2)
2155 Cobb Pkwy SE, Smyrna, GA 30080-7632
Tel.: (770) 953-0100
Web Site: http://www.steverayman.com
Car Whslr
N.A.I.C.S.: 441110

ZT GROUP INT'L INC.
350 Meadowlands Pkwy, Secaucus, NJ 07094
Tel.: (201) 559-1000
Web Site: http://www.ztsystems.com
Sales Range: $100-124.9 Million
Emp.: 150
Systems Integration, Networking & Storage Solutions
N.A.I.C.S.: 423430
Frank Chang (Pres)
Boh Wen Thian (Acct Exec)
Rosita Ng (Mgr-Sls)
Ruli Shi (Acct Mgr)
Tom Koh (Product Mgr)
William Chan (Engr-Hardware)

ZUBOR BUICK GMC, INC.
14000 Telegraph Rd, Taylor, MI 48180
Tel.: (734) 946-8112
Web Site: http://www.zubor.com
Year Founded: 1994
Sales Range: $10-24.9 Million
Emp.: 54
Car Whslr
N.A.I.C.S.: 441110
John G. Zubor (Pres)

ZUBRA, INC.
717 N Union St #114, Wilmington, DE 19805
Tel.: (302) 918-2382   DE
Year Founded: 2011
Specialty Business Travel Coupon Service
N.A.I.C.S.: 513199
Yitzhak Shtinovitz (Pres, CEO, CFO, Principal Acctg Officer & Treas)

ZUCHELLI & JOHNSON HEALTHCARE COMMUNICATIONS
2873 Ocean Ave, Seaford, NY 11783-3455
Tel.: (516) 783-1400   NY
Web Site: http://www.adwise.com
Year Founded: 1983
Sales Range: $75-99.9 Million
Emp.: 10
N.A.I.C.S.: 541810
Thomas J. Johnson (Pres)
Angela Johnson (VP-Client Services)
Kurt Bickum (Sr Acct Exec)
April Ombres (Sr Dir-Art)

ZUCKERMAN-HONICKMAN INC.
191 S Gulph Rd, King of Prussia, PA 19406
Tel.: (610) 962-0100   PA
Web Site: http://www.zh-inc.com
Year Founded: 1934
Sales Range: $25-49.9 Million
Emp.: 200
Mfr & Retailer of Glass & Plastic Bottles & Containers
N.A.I.C.S.: 423840
Marc Zuckerman (Exec VP)
Benjamin R. Zuckerman (Pres)
Henry Zuckerman (VP-Pur)
Patrick McClafferty (CFO)
Lawrence S. Reichlin (Sec)

Subsidiaries:

Delta Industries   (1)
191 S Gulph Rd, King of Prussia, PA 19406
Tel.: (610) 962-0200
Web Site: http://www.deltasprayers.com
Sales Range: $10-24.9 Million
Emp.: 45
Sell Sprayers
N.A.I.C.S.: 424610

ZUERN BUILDING PRODUCTS INC.

U.S. PRIVATE

Zuern Building Products Inc.—(Continued)

ZUERN BUILDING PRODUCTS INC.
426 Railroad St, Allenton, WI 53002
Tel.: (262) 629-5551
Web Site: http://www.zuerns.com
Rev.: $11,100,000
Emp.: 60
Lumber & Other Building Materials
N.A.I.C.S.: 444110
Kelly Weninger *(Dir-HR)*
Greg Fedorski *(Mgr-Estimating)*
Rick Lettow *(Mgr-IT)*
Brenda Vogt *(Mgr)*
Arleen Mantel *(COO & Controller)*

ZUFALL HEALTH
17 S Warren St, Dover, NJ 07801
Tel.: (973) 328-3344 NJ
Web Site: http://www.zufallhealth.org
Year Founded: 1990
Sales Range: $10-24.9 Million
Emp.: 190
Health Care Srvices
N.A.I.C.S.: 622110
Eva Turbiner *(Pres & CEO)*
Rina Ramirez *(Chief Medical Officer)*
Sam Wakim *(Chief Dental Officer)*
Frances Palm *(COO)*
Peter Bebel *(CFO)*
Paul Nusbaum *(Chm)*
Robert Zufall *(Sec)*
Linda Seeley *(Vice Chm)*
William Shuler Jr. *(Treas)*

ZUGARA INC.
13101 Washington Blvd Ste 225, Los Angeles, CA 90066
Tel.: (310) 566-7431
Web Site: http://www.zugara.com
Sales Range: $1-9.9 Million
Ecommerce Software; Advertising Services
N.A.I.C.S.: 513210
Matthew Szymczyk *(CEO)*
Hans Forsman *(VP-Creative & User Experience)*
Carole Foster *(Dir-HR & Recruitment)*

ZUHNE LLC
8383 Commerce Park Dr Ste 600, Houston, TX 77036 TX
Web Site: http://www.zuhne.com
Year Founded: 2015
Sales Range: $1-9.9 Million
Emp.: 8
Kitchen Accessory Mfr & Distr
N.A.I.C.S.: 337110
Rick Pal *(Sr Partner)*

ZULIE VENTURE INC.
4252 Bluebonnet Dr, Stafford, TX 77477
Tel.: (281) 408-4237 TX
Web Site: http://www.cellpay.us
Year Founded: 2016
Sales Range: $1-9.9 Million
Telecommunication Servicesb
N.A.I.C.S.: 517810
Parvez Jasani *(CEO)*

Subsidiaries:

ZPrepay Inc. (1)
4252 Bluebonnet Dr, Stafford, TX 77477
Tel.: (800) 308-7794
Web Site: http://www.zprepay.com
Payment Processing Services
N.A.I.C.S.: 522320
Parvez Jasani *(Founder & CEO)*
Karam Ali *(Pres)*

ZULU MARKETING, LLC
2912 Executive Pkwy Ste 120, Lehi, UT 84043
Web Site: http://www.zulumarketing.com

Year Founded: 2008
Sales Range: $10-24.9 Million
Emp.: 50
Financial Services
N.A.I.C.S.: 523999
Eddie Stewart *(Founder & Pres)*

ZUMA PRESS, INC.
408 N El Camino Real, San Clemente, CA 92672
Tel.: (949) 494-7704
Web Site: http://www.zumapress.com
Year Founded: 1995
Sales Range: $10-24.9 Million
Emp.: 45
Picture Agency & News Wire Service
N.A.I.C.S.: 541922
Julie Mason *(CFO)*
Ruaridh Stewart *(Mgr-Picture Desk)*

ZUMASYS, INC
9245 Research Dr, Irvine, CA 92618
Tel.: (949) 334-0287
Web Site: http://www.zumasys.com
Year Founded: 2000
Sales Range: $10-24.9 Million
Emp.: 34
Application Software Development Services
N.A.I.C.S.: 541511
Paul Giobbi *(Pres)*
Jennifer McGraw *(COO)*
Tiffaney Giobbi *(Dir-Happiness Program)*
George Dudenhefer *(Dir-Bus Dev)*
Kevin Fitzpatrick *(Dir-Technical Support)*
Randy Joyce *(Dir-Creative)*
Lourdes Ramirez *(Mgr-Acctg)*
Corey Luckow *(VP-Strategic Dev)*
Andy Takacs *(CTO)*
Ananya Ridenour *(Project Mgr)*
Karen Schar *(Dir-Sls)*
Lisa Padilla *(Mgr-Relationship)*
Long Bui *(Engr-Technical Support)*
Maxx Blason *(Project Coord)*
Mike Coelho *(Gen Mgr)*
Mike Street *(Engr-Technical Support)*
Sam Wozniak *(Sr Engr-Sys)*
Saranya Villavankothai *(Project Coord)*
Toby Bierly *(Engr-Technical Support)*

ZUMBIEL PACKAGING CO.
2100 Gateway Blvd, Hebron, KY 41048
Tel.: (531) 531-3600 OH
Web Site: http://www.zumbiel.com
Year Founded: 1843
Sales Range: $150-199.9 Million
Emp.: 500
Paper Box, Carton & Beverage Carrier Mfr
N.A.I.C.S.: 322212
Joseph Yock *(Gen Mgr)*
Charles Mace *(VP-Bus Dev)*
Darren Cottle *(Acct Mgr-Natl)*
Kevin Hawk *(Mgr-Production Control)*
Chuck Brewer *(Mgr-Printing)*
Ron Merkle *(Mgr-Safety & Trng)*

Subsidiaries:

Zumbiel Packaging Co.-Beverage Division (1)
1743 Cleneay Ave, Cincinnati, OH 45212
Tel.: (513) 351-7050
Sales Range: $10-24.9 Million
Emp.: 4
Mfr of Beverage Containers
N.A.I.C.S.: 322212

ZUMOT REAL ESTATE MANAGEMENT, INC.
1356 Beverly Rd Ste 250, McLean, VA 22101
Tel.: (703) 893-7233

Web Site: http://www.zumot.net
Sales Range: $1-9.9 Million
Emp.: 10
Real Estate Management & Investment Services
N.A.I.C.S.: 531390
Richard Enos *(Engr-Building)*

ZUMPANO ENTERPRISES INC.
6354 Warren Dr, Norcross, GA 30093
Tel.: (770) 449-3528
Web Site: http://www.zumpano.com
Sales Range: $10-24.9 Million
Emp.: 70
Tile, Clay & Other Ceramic Products
N.A.I.C.S.: 423320
James J. Zumpano *(CEO)*

ZUPAN ENTERPRISES INC.
7223 NE Hazel Dell Ave, Vancouver, WA 98665
Tel.: (360) 737-2728
Web Site: http://www.zupans.com
Sales Range: $10-24.9 Million
Emp.: 400
Supermarket
N.A.I.C.S.: 445110
Mike Zupan *(Pres)*

ZUPANCICH BROS INC.
303 E Sheridan St, Ely, MN 55731
Tel.: (218) 365-3188
Web Site: http://www.zups.com
Rev.: $19,000,000
Emp.: 50
Grocery Stores, Chain
N.A.I.C.S.: 445110
Brian Zupancich *(Mgr-Silver Bay)*
Rich Huovinen *(Mgr-Babbitt)*
Ed Zupancich *(Mgr-Babbitt)*
Jim Zupancich *(Mgr-Grocery)*
Pat Zupancich *(Mgr-Meat & Delivery)*

ZURPLE, INC.
1935 Camino Vida Roble Ste 120, Carlsbad, CA 92008
Tel.: (800) 520-2312
Web Site: http://www.zurple.com
Year Founded: 2009
Sales Range: $1-9.9 Million
Emp.: 32
Produces SaaS Platform for Online Marketing Real Estate Professionals
N.A.I.C.S.: 531390
Ryan Owen *(Founder)*
Marc Staheli *(VP-Technical Ops)*
Ryan Whitlock *(CEO)*

ZUTANO GLOBAL INC.
686 Belleville Ave, New Bedford, MA 02745
Tel.: (508) 273-2392 DE
Web Site: http://zutano.com
Year Founded: 1989
Children's Clothing Mfr
N.A.I.C.S.: 458110
Uli Belenky *(Co-Founder)*
Michael Belenky *(Co-Founder)*

Subsidiaries:

Morgan & Milo, LLC (1)
46 Waltham St Ste 201, Boston, MA 02118
Tel.: (617) 283-0695
Web Site: http://www.morganandmilo.com
Cildren's Footwear, Apparel & Fashion Mfr
N.A.I.C.S.: 458110

ZV PATE INC.
9120 Morgan St, Laurel Hill, NC 28351
Tel.: (910) 462-2122 NC
Year Founded: 1900
Sales Range: $10-24.9 Million
Emp.: 40
Management Services
N.A.I.C.S.: 561110

David L. Burns *(Pres)*
Samuel H. Fulton *(CEO)*
Allen McLaurin *(Mgr-Farm)*
Carolyn Paul *(Sec)*

Subsidiaries:

Laurinburg KFC Take Home Inc. (1)
452 Atkinson St, Laurinburg, NC 28352-3714
Tel.: (910) 276-6740
Web Site: http://www.scottishfoodsystemsinc.com
Sales Range: $10-24.9 Million
Emp.: 20
Eating Place
N.A.I.C.S.: 722513
Thomas Brrome *(Pres)*

Pizza of Scotland Inc. (1)
452 Atkinson St, Laurinburg, NC 28352-3714
Tel.: (910) 276-6740
Web Site: http://www.scottishfoodsystemsinc.com
Sales Range: $10-24.9 Million
Emp.: 18
Eating Place
N.A.I.C.S.: 722513
Thomas Broome *(Pres)*

Scottish Food Systems Inc. (1)
452 Atkinson St, Laurinburg, NC 28352-3714
Tel.: (910) 276-6740
Web Site: http://www.scottishfoodsystemsinc.com
Sales Range: $10-24.9 Million
Emp.: 18
Management Services For Restaurants
N.A.I.C.S.: 561110
Thomas A. Broome *(Pres)*

Southeast Farm Equipment Co. Inc. (1)
16220 Joy St, Laurinburg, NC 28352
Tel.: (910) 276-8396
Web Site: http://www.southestfarmequipment.com
Sales Range: $10-24.9 Million
Emp.: 25
Farm Equipment Sales
N.A.I.C.S.: 459999
Ann Freeman *(Office Mgr)*

ZVELO, INC.
5445 Dtc Pkwy Ste 500, Greenwood Village, CO 80111
Tel.: (720) 897-8113
Web Site: http://www.zvelo.com
Year Founded: 1984
Network Security Services
N.A.I.C.S.: 541519
Jeff Finn *(Pres & CEO)*

ZWEIGWHITE LLC
38 W Trenton Blvd Ste 101, Fayetteville, AR 72701
Tel.: (479) 287-4016
Web Site: http://www.zweigwhite.com
Year Founded: 1988
Sales Range: $1-9.9 Million
Emp.: 20
Architecture, Engineering & Environmental Consulting
N.A.I.C.S.: 541620
Mark C. Zweig *(Founder & CEO)*
Chad Clinehens *(Exec VP)*
Bill Murphey *(Dir-Education)*
Christy Zweig *(Dir-Res & Mktg)*
Jamie Claire Kiser *(Dir-M&A)*
Richard Massey *(Dir-Newsletters & Special Publ)*
Randy Wilburn *(Dir-Exec Search)*

ZWICKER ELECTRIC CO., INC.
360 Park Ave S 4th Fl, New York, NY 10010-1503
Tel.: (212) 477-8400 NY
Web Site: http://www.zwicker-electric.com
Year Founded: 1947
Sales Range: $25-49.9 Million

Emp.: 250
Contractor of Electrical Work
N.A.I.C.S.: 238210
David B. Pinter *(Pres & CEO)*
Michael D'Auria *(Sr VP-Ops)*
Natasha Vysotskaya *(Project Mgr)*
Nilesh Kadakia *(VP)*
Christian Burke *(Mgr)*
Paul Proctor *(VP-Ops)*
Sabino Pace *(COO)*
Geoffrey Teurfs *(Dir-Engrg)*
Jessica Barreras *(Office Mgr)*

ZYCI LLC
2030 Will Ross Ct, Atlanta, GA 30341
Tel.: (404) 334-7064
Web Site: http://www.zyci.com
Year Founded: 2013
Machine Part Mfr
N.A.I.C.S.: 332710
Mitch Free *(Co-Founder, Chm & CEO)*
Shirene Free *(Co-Founder)*

Subsidiaries:

CNC Machine Group Inc. (1)
2030 Will Ross Ct, Atlanta, GA 30341
Tel.: (404) 334-7064
Web Site: http://www.cncmachinegroup.com
Machine Shops
N.A.I.C.S.: 332710
Mitch Free *(CEO)*

ZYMPHONY TECHNOLOGY SOLUTIONS
4905 W Laurel St Ste 300, Tampa, FL 33607
Tel.: (813) 514-4427
Web Site: http://www.zts.com
Year Founded: 2003
Sales Range: $10-24.9 Million
Emp.: 45
Computer System Design Services
N.A.I.C.S.: 541512
Rick Lott *(Owner)*
Amanda Schilke *(Coord-Mktg)*

ZYNGA INC.
1200 Pk Pl, San Mateo, CA 94403 DE
Web Site: https://www.zynga.com
Year Founded: 2007
ZNGA—(NASDAQ)
Emp.: 3,000
Online Entertainment Application Developer
N.A.I.C.S.: 513210
Frank D. Gibeau *(Pres)*
Scott Koenigsberg *(Chief Product Officer)*
Tanner Logue *(CFO & COO)*
Yaron Leyvand *(Exec VP-Mobile Studios)*
Geoffrey Rowe *(Sr VP & Head-Human Resources)*
Alex Tremblay *(Chief Data Officer & Exec VP)*

Subsidiaries:

NaturalMotion Limited (1)
10 St Ebbe's Street, Oxford, OX1 1PT, United Kingdom
Tel.: (44) 1865250575
Web Site: http://www.naturalmotion.com
Game Software Publishing Services
N.A.I.C.S.: 513210
Jeff Hickman *(Sr VP & Head-Studio)*

Zynga Game Network India Private Limited (1)
No 206 Logos MG Road, Bengaluru, 560001, Karnataka, India
Tel.: (91) 8066699600
Sales Range: $75-99.9 Million
Emp.: 260
Computer Programming Services
N.A.I.C.S.: 541511
Shailesh Cdaxini *(Gen Mgr)*

ZYROBOTICS LLC
3522 Ashford Dunwoody Rd Ste 105, Atlanta, GA 30319
Tel.: (678) 952-9976
Web Site: http://www.zyrobotics.com
Software Development Services
N.A.I.C.S.: 541511
Ayanna M. Howard *(Founder, Pres & CTO)*
Johnetta MaCcalla *(CEO)*
John V. Harding *(COO)*

ZYSCOVICH INC.
100 N Biscayne Blvd 27th Fl, Miami, FL 33132
Tel.: (305) 372-5222
Web Site: http://www.zyscovich.com
Sales Range: $10-24.9 Million
Emp.: 90
Architectural & Interior Design Services
N.A.I.C.S.: 541310
Jose Murguido *(Partner & VP)*
Martha K. O'Hare *(Principal)*
Dawn Hetzer *(Dir-Ops)*

ZYTER, INC.
2600 Tower Oaks Blvd Ste 700, Rockville, MD 20852
Tel.: (301) 355-7760 DE
Web Site: http://www.zyter.com
Year Founded: 2017
Telehealth, Home Health & Remote Patient Monitoring Services
N.A.I.C.S.: 621999
Sanjay Govil *(Founder)*
Joanne Berrios *(Chief Value Officer & VP)*
Kevin Riley *(CEO)*
Natalie Schibell *(VP-Product Mktg)*

Subsidiaries:

Casenet, LLC (1)
36 Crosby Dr, Bedford, MA 01730
Tel.: (781) 357-2700
Web Site: http://www.casenetllc.com
Management Software Solutions Services
N.A.I.C.S.: 449210
Tony Larson *(Sr VP-Strategy & Bus Dev)*
Peter Masanotti *(CEO)*
Samuel DiCapua *(Chief Medical Officer)*
Julie Coviello *(Sr VP-Client Experience & Client Success)*
Tim Rosner *(COO)*

ZYTO TECHNOLOGIES, INC.
1172 W N Ste 300, Lindon, UT 84042
Tel.: (801) 224-7199 NV
Personal Health & Wellness Software & Integrated Computer Hardware Products Mfr
N.A.I.C.S.: 513210
Kami J. Howard *(Pres & COO)*

ZZ PERFORMANCE, LLC
2450 28th St SW, Wyoming, MI 49519
Tel.: (616) 532-5152
Web Site: http://www.zzperformance.com
Year Founded: 2001
Sales Range: $1-9.9 Million
Emp.: 51
Car Parts Retailer
N.A.I.C.S.: 441330
Kyla Stern-Beek *(VP)*